42nd European Photovoltaic Solar Energy Conference and Exhibition (EU PVSEC 2025)

Bilbao, Spain
22-26 September 2025

Volume 1 of 6

ISBN: 979-8-3313-2987-7

Printed from e-media with permission by:

Curran Associates, Inc.
57 Morehouse Lane
Red Hook, NY 12571

CURRAN ASSOCIATES INC. proceedings.com

Some format issues inherent in the e-media version may also appear in this print version.

WIP – Renewable Energies
Sylvensteinstr. 2
81369 Munchen
Germany

Phone: +49 89 72012735
Fax: +49 89 72012791

wip@wip-munich.de

Additional copies of this publication are available from:

Curran Associates, Inc.
57 Morehouse Lane
Red Hook, NY 12571 USA
Phone: 845-758-0400
Fax: 845-758-2633
Email: curran@proceedings.com
Web: www.proceedings.com

42nd European Photovoltaic Solar Energy Conference and Exhibition

Proceedings of the International Conference

22 September – 26 September 2025

Edited by:

C. DEL CAÑIZO
Solar Energy Institute
UPM
Spain

R. KENNY
European Commission
Joint Research Centre
Italy

J. BERGMILLER
WIP Renewable Energies
Germany

J. DE GREGORIO
WIP Renewable Energies
Germany

Edition Team:

B. Yildiz
L. Großhans
A. Michaelsen
U.E. Birgi
WIP Renewable Energies
Germany

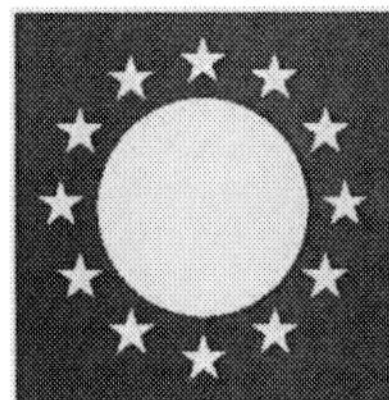

Photos at:

Coordination of the Technical Programme:

European Commission Joint Research Centre
Via E. Fermi 1
21020 Ispra (VA)
Italy

Institutional Support:

European Commission

Institutional PV Industry Cooperation:

SolarPower Europe

ESMC – European Solar Manufacturing Council

Supporting Organisations:

AUSTRALIAN PV INSTITUTE

ASOM – Alliance for Solar Mobility

BASQUE ENERGY CLUSTER

BILBAO CONVENTION BUREAU

EASE – European Association for Storage of Energy

ETIP PV – European Technology & Innovation Platform PV

GÜNDER – Turkish Solar Energy Society

IEA PVPS - IEA Photovoltaic Power Systems Programme

INSTITUTO SOLAR DE ENERGÍA SOLAR

LDES – Long Duration Energy Storage Council

NSEFI – National Solar Energy federation of India

NUS /SERIS – National University of Singapore / Solar Energy Research Institute of Singapore

UPM - Polytechnic University of Madrid

Supporting Associations:

EERA – European Energy Research Aliance

EREF – European Renewable Energies Federation

EUREC – The Association of European Renewable Energy Research Centres

VDMA Photovoltaic Equipment

Local Support:
ENTE VASCO DE LA ENERGÍA
EUH – University of the Basque Country

EU PVSEC 2025 realised by:

WIP Renewable Energies
Sylvensteinstr. 2, 81369 Munich, Germany
Tel: +49 89 720 12 735, Fax: +49 89 720 12 791
Email: pv.conference@wip-munich.de
www.eupvsec.org
www.wip-munich.de

Proceedings produced and published by:

WIP Renewable Energies
Sylvensteinstr. 2, 81369 Munich, Germany
Tel: +49 89 720 12 735, Fax: +49 89 720 12 791
Email: pv.conference@wip-munich.de
www.eupvsec.org
www.wip-munich.de

42nd EUROPEAN PHOTOVOLTAIC SOLAR ENERGY CONFERENCE AND EXHIBITION
22 SEPTEMBER – 26 SEPTEMBER 2025

EU PVSEC 2025 COMMITTEES

INTERNATIONAL SCIENTIFIC ADVISORY COMMITTEE (ISAC)

Chair
P. Szymanski, European Commission Joint Research Centre, Director of Energy, Transport and Climate, Petten, The Netherlands

Committee Members
V. Bermúdez Benito, Founder & Principal Consultant, Berbetin, Antibes, France
G.C. Eder, OFI, Vienna, Austria
P. Frankl, Head of the Renewable Energy Division, International Energy Agency, France
M. Getsiou, European Commission, DG RTD, Brussels, Belgium
S.W. Glunz, Head of Division Photovoltaics - Research, Fraunhofer ISE, Freiburg, Germany
N.M. Haegel, Director of the National Center for Photovoltaics, NREL, Golden, USA
R. Kenny, European Commission Joint Research Centre, Directorate for Energy and Transport and Climate, Ispra, Italy
S. Nowak, Managing Director of NET Nowak Energy & Technology, St. Ursen, Switzerland
R. Schlatmann, Chairman of ETIP PV, Head of the Solar Energy Division at Helmholtz-Zentrum Berlin, Germany
W.C. Sinke, TNO Energy Transition, The Netherlands
M. Topič, Head of Laboratory of Photovoltaics and Optoelectronics of the University of Ljubljana, Slovenia
P. Verlinden, Director at Amrock, Visiting Professor at Sun Yat-Sen University, Guangzhou, China
E. Voroshazi, Head of PV module process laboratory, CEA, Le Bourget-du-Lac, France
J. Bergmiller, Managing Director Events & Knowledge Transfer, WIP Renewable Energies, Munich, Germany
J. de Gregorio, Head of Unit, Scientific Services and Cooperation, WIP Renewable Energies, Munich, Germany

CONFERENCE EXECUTIVE COMMITTEE

Conference General Chair
C. del Cañizo, UPM, Madrid, Spain

Technical Programme Chair
R. Kenny, European Commission Joint Research Centre, Directorate for Energy and Transport and Climate, Ispra, Italy

Committee Members
W.C. Sinke, Program Development Manager, TNO Energy Transition, The Netherlands
S. Nowak, Managing Director of NET Nowak Energy & Technology, St. Ursen, Switzerland
M. Topič, Head of Laboratory of Photovoltaics and Optoelectronics of the University of Ljubljana, Slovenia
V. Bermúdez Benito, BERBETIN, France
E. Voroshazi, Head of PV Module Process Laboratory, CEA, Le Bourget-Du-Lac France
H. Ossenbrink, Former European Commission Joint Research Centre, Germany
J. Bergmiller, Managing Director Events & Knowledge Transfer, WIP Renewable Energies, Munich, Germany
J. de Gregorio, Head of Unit, Scientific Services and Cooperation, WIP Renewable Energies, Munich, Germany

2025 SCIENTIFIC COMMITTEE

Programme Technical Chair
R. Kenny, European Commission, Joint Research Centre, Italy

Topic Chairs

Topic 1: Silicon Materials and Cells
F. Schindler, Fraunhofer ISE, Germany

Topic 2: Thin Films and New Concepts
I. Gordon, imec, Belgium

Topic 3: Photovoltaic Modules and BoS Components
T. Barnes, NREL, USA

Topic 4: PV Systems Engineering, Integrated/Applied PV
A.M. Gracia Amillo, FUNDACION CENER, Spain

Topic 5: PV in the Energy Transition
C. Agraffeil, CEA / INES, France

Topic Organisers and Paper Review Experts

Topic 1: Silicon Materials and Cells
F. Schindler, Fraunhofer ISE, Germany
C. Fischer, Wacker Chemie, Germany
G. Hahn, University of Konstanz, Germany
K. Ding, Forschungszentrum Jülich, Germany
P. Roca i Cabarrocas, CNRS-LPICM, France
A. W. Weeber, TNO Energy Transition, The Netherlands
D. Muñoz, CEA / INES, France
S. W. Glunz, Fraunhofer ISE, Germany
K. Bothe, ISFH, Germany
M. Topic, University of Ljubljana, Slovenia
P. Fath, RCT-Solutions, Germany
S. Peters, Hanwha Q CELLS, Germany

M.P. Bellmann, SINTEF, Norway
A. Ciesla, UNSW, Australia
C. Hagendorf, Freiberg Instruments, Germany
X. Yu, Zhejiang University, China
J.S. Lee, KIER, South Korea
R. Brendel, ISFH, Germany
T. Dullweber, ISFH, Germany
J. Horzel, Fraunhofer ISE, Germany
W. Nemeth, NREL, United States of America
R. Turan, METU, Türkiye
F. Menchini, ENEA, Italy
W. Favre, CEA, France

J. Meier, Meier Technologies, Switzerland
J. Schmidt, ISFH, Germany
M. Wright, University of Oxford, United Kingdom
J. Zhao, CSEM, Switzerland
A. Morisset, CSEM, Switzerland
A. Richter, Fraunhofer ISE, Germany
J. Linke, ISC Konstanz, Germany
B. Geerligs, TNO Energy Transition, The Netherlands
S. Dubois, CEA, France
M. Hermle, Fraunhofer ISE, Germany
B. Terheiden, University of Konstanz, Germany
P. Delli Veneri, ENEA, Italy
T. Matsui, AIST, Japan
Y. Ohshita, Toyota Technological Institute, Japan
E. Bruhat, HOLOSOLIS, France
A. Augusto, Dalarna University, Sweden
F. Ferrazza, ENI S.p.A., Italy
A. Otaegi, UPV/EHU, Spain
M.C. Schubert, Fraunhofer ISE, Germany
H. Duman, KalyonPV, Türkiye
N. Usami, Nagoya University, Japan
Y. Zhu, UNSW, Australia
D. Brunner, RENA Technologies, Germany
A. Danel, CEA, France
C. Gerardi, 3Sun, Italy
H.J. Nonnenmacher, Meyer Burger, Germany
P. Verlinden, AMROCK, Australia
Q. Wang, Wang, Qi, China
W. Zhang, Zhang, Weiming, China
Y. Chen, Trina Solar Energy, China
E. Krassowski, CE Cell Engineering, Germany
M. Foti, 3Sun, Italy
D.L. Bätzner, Meyer Burger Research, Switzerland

Topic 2: Thin Films and New Concepts
I. Gordon, imec, Belgium
J.C. Goldschmidt, Marburg University, Germany
F. Schoofs, Oxford PV, United Kingdom
N. Kyranaki, Hasselt University, Belgium
S. Veenstra, TNO Energy Transition, The Netherlands
T. Aernouts, imec, Belgium
A.N. Tiwari, SOLTIWA, Switzerland
G. Siefer, Fraunhofer ISE, Germany
M. Edoff, Uppsala University, Sweden
A. Martí Vega, UPM, Spain
J. Poortmans, imec, Belgium
I. Ramiro, UPM, Spain
T. Magorian Friedlmeier, ZSW, Germany

S. Albrecht, HZB, Germany
S. Berson, CEA, France
P. Carroy, CEA, France
C. Case, Oxford PV, United Kingdom
G. Coletti, FuturaSun, Italy
S. De Wolf, KAUST, Saudi Arabia
U.W. Paetzold, KIT, Germany
H. Sivaramakrishnan Radhakrisnan, imec, Belgium
P. Schulze, Fraunhofer ISE, Germany
L. Wang, Technology Innovation Institute, United Arab Emirates
Y. Smirnov, Applied Materials, United States of America
B. Stannowski, HZB, Germany
F. Fertig, Hanwha Q CELLS, Germany
L. Lancellotti, ENEA, Italy
S. Cros, CEA, France
S. Hayase, The University of Electro-Communications, Japan
S. Huang, Macquarie University, Australia
M. Khenkin, HZB, Germany
C. Lin, National Taiwan University, Taiwan
M.S.H. Norton, University of Cyprus, Cyprus
P. Pistor, Pablo de Olavide University, Spain
W. Tress, Zurich University of Applied Sciences, Switzerland
A. Aguirre, imec, Belgium
D. Lan, UNSW Sydney, China
M. Saliba, University of Stuttgart, Germany
P. Manshanden, TNO Energy Transition, The Netherlands
L. Vesce, University of Rome II, Italy
I. Dogan, TNO Solliance, The Netherlands
Y. Kuang, imec, Belgium
M. Al Katrib, IPVF, France
M.I. Hossain, QEERI, Qatar
W.H. Chiu, Chang Gung University, Taiwan
C. Chen, Ming Chi University of Technology, Taiwan
C. Fell, CSIRO Energy Technology, Australia
G. Brammertz, imec, Belgium
T. Dalibor, Avancis, Germany
S. Ishizuka, AIST, Japan
A. Redinger, University of Luxembourg, Luxembourg
A. Romeo, University of Verona, Italy
V. Sittinger, Fraunhofer IST, Germany
M. Theelen, TNO/Solliance, The Netherlands
G. Timò, RSE, Italy
A. Kanevce, ZSW, Germany
A. Pérez-Rodríguez, IREC, Spain
R. Gutzler, ZSW, Germany
W. Witte, ZSW, Germany
T. Nishimura, Tokyo Institute of Technology, Japan
C. Qian, University of New South Wales, Australia
J.P. Connolly, CentraleSupelec, France
J.P. Kleider, CNRS/GeePs, France
I. Konovalov, University of Applied Sciences Jena, Germany
Y. Okada, University of Tokyo, Japan
M. Rusu, HZB, Germany
H. Meddeb, DLR, Germany
E. Saucedo, Universitat Politècnica de Catalunya (UPC), Spain
P. Vidal-Fuentes, FUNDACIÓ INSTITUT DE RECERCA EN ENERGIA DE CATALUNYA, Spain
C. Malerba, ENEA, Italy
C. Becker, HZB, Germany
D. Kuciauskas, NREL, United States of America
M. Ochoa, University of Cantabria, Spain
T. Tayagaki, AIST, Japan
S. Wasmer, WAVELABS Solar Metrology Systems, Germany
S. Zandi, UNSW, Australia
C. Messmer, University of Freiburg, Germany
J.B. Puel, Institut Photovoltaïque d'Ile de France (IPVF), France
S. Ternes, University of Rome II, Italy

Topic 3: Photovoltaic Modules and BoS Components
V. Bermúdez Benito, BERBETIN, France
R. Preu, Fraunhofer ISE, Germany
R. Gottschalg, Fraunhofer CSP, Germany
T. Barnes, NREL, United States of America
G. Friesen, SUPSI, Switzerland
G. Bardizza, TÜV Rheinland Solar, Italy

V. Barth, CEA, France
A. Faes, CSEM, Switzerland
A. Lennon, Sundrive Solar, Australia
M. Mittag, Fraunhofer ISE, Germany
M.A. Muñoz-García, UPM, Spain
H. Nagel, Fraunhofer ISE, Germany
S. Pietralunga, CNR, Italy
T. Timofte, ISC Konstanz, Germany

S. Feldbacher, PCCL, Austria
A. Halm, ISC Konstanz, Germany
H. Hanifi, AESOLAR, Germany
E. Warren, NREL, United States of America
S. Zhang, Trina Solar Energy, China
X. Zhen, Canadian Solar, China
G. Beaucarne, Dow Silicones Belgium, Belgium
T. Bejat, CEA, France
C. Camus, LayTec, Germany
U. Jahn, Fraunhofer CSP, Germany
G. Oreski, PCCL, Austria
M. Pander, Fraunhofer CSP, Germany
T. Sample, European Commission JRC, Italy
A. Morlier, imo-imomec, Belgium
C. Barretta, PCCL, Austria
P. Gebhardt, Fraunhofer ISE, Germany
C. Sen, UNSW, Australia
O. Arriaga Arruti, CSEM, Switzerland
X. Gu, NIST, United States of America
C. Xiao, Chinese Academy of Sciences, United States of America
R. Aninat, TNO/Solliance, The Netherlands
S. Mitterhofer, NIST, United States of America
B. Hoex, UNSW, Australia
E. Özkalay, SUPSI, Switzerland
M. Bokalič, University of Ljubljana, Slovenia
S. Bordihn, ISFH, Germany
M. Despeisse, CSEM, Switzerland
J. Govaerts, imec, Belgium
J. Lopez-Garcia, STS-Certified, Spain
M. Pravettoni, Technology Innovation Institute, United Arab Emirates
T. Stoyanova Lyubenova, Joint Research Centre, Italy
C. Ulbrich, HZB, Germany
J. Moereke, Avancis, Germany
Y.S. Long, ITRI, Taiwan
D. Pavanello, European Commission JRC, Italy
A.K. Vidal de Oliveira, UFSC, Brazil
J. Bengoechea, CENER, Spain
M. Ernst, ANU, Australia
H. Ellis, European Commission JRC, Italy
B. Mihaylov, European Commission JRC, Italy
G. Chowdhury, 3E, Belgium
B. Aissa, QEERI - Qatar Environment and Energy Research Institute, Qatar

Topic 4: PV Systems Engineering, Integrated/Applied PV
A. Gracia Amillo, CENER, Spain
W.G.J.H.M. van Sark, Utrecht University, The Netherlands
K. Lappalainen, Tampere University, Finland
J.M. Almeida Serra, University of Lisbon, Portugal
I. Tsanakas, CEA, France
C. Buerhop-Lutz, HI ERN, Germany
D. Moser, Becquerel Institute Italia, Italy
F. Frontini, SUPSI, Switzerland
G.C. Eder, OFI, Austria
A. Scognamiglio, ENEA, Italy
A. Chatzipanagi, European Commission JRC, Italy
I. Antón Hernández, UPM, Spain
R.M.E. Valckenborg, TNO, The Netherlands
T. Reindl, SERIS, Singapore
J.R. Gonzalez, European Space Agency, The Netherlands
G. Mütter, Gerhard Mütter e.U., Austria
T. Merdzhanova, Forschungszentrum Jülich, Germany

V. Lara-Fanego, Solargis, Spain
A. Louwen, Eurac Research, Italy
A. Martinez Fernandez, European Commission JRC, Italy
T. Oozeki, AIST, Japan
J. Remund, Meteotest, Switzerland
M. Sengupta, NREL, United States of America
M. Zehner, Rosenheim Technical University of Applied Sciences, Germany
B. Nouri, German Aerospace Center, Spain
S. Poddar, UNSW, Australia
D. Bachour, HBKU/ Qatar Foundation, Qatar
J. Yang, NREL, United States of America
S. Bouguerra, imo-imomec, Belgium
C. Alonso-Tristán, UBU, Spain
M. Carbone, ENEL Green Power, Italy
M. Dennenmoser, BayWa r.e. Solar Projects GmbH, Germany
C.W. Hansen, Sandia National Laboratories, United States of America
A. Neubert, DNV Maritime Software GmbH, Germany
D. Berrian, Belectric, Germany
M. Oliosi, PVsyst, Switzerland
J. Moschner, KU Leuven / EnergyVille, Belgium
C. Bucher, BUAS, Switzerland
B. Wittmer, PVsyst SA, Switzerland
M. Bolen, SB Energy, United States of America
D. Daßler, Fraunhofer CSP, Germany
R. Einhaus, ZSW, Germany
P. Hacke, NREL, United States of America
A. Heimsath, Fraunhofer ISE, Germany
J. Lin, PV Guider, Taiwan
A. Migan-Dubois, GeePs, France
M. Rinio, University of Karlstad, Sweden
J.S. Stein, Sandia National Laboratories, United States of America
D. Stellbogen, ZSW, Germany
M. Theristis, Sandia National Laboratories, United States of America
A. Virtuani, CSEM, Switzerland
A. Driesse, PV Performance Labs, Germany
M. Øgaard, IFE, Norway
A. Nobre, SERIS, Singapore
T. Trupke, UNSW, Australia
C. Cornaro, University of Rome II, Italy
G. A. dos Reis Benatto, DTU, Denmark
S. Malik, Fraunhofer CSP, Germany
S. Lindig, Univers SAS, France
M.M. Nygård, Institute for Energy Technology, Norway
P. Alonso Gomez, BayWa r.e., Germany
Y. Assoa, CEA, France
P. Bonomo, SUPSI, Switzerland
V. D'Ambrosio, University of Naples Federico II, Italy
E. Román Medina, Tecnalia, Spain
L.H. Slooff, TNO Energy Transition, The Netherlands
S. Villa, TNO, The Netherlands
M. La Rosa, Glass to Power, Italy
T. Del Caño, Onyx Solar Energy, Spain
X. Zhihao, AIST, Japan
P. Sharif, ODTU-GUNAM, Türkiye
K. Umeda, TAISEI CORPORATION, Japan
S. Boddaert, CSTB, France
N. Lysgaard Andersen, DTU, Denmark
K. Meyer, ISFH, Germany
T. Biel, NET Nowak Energy & Technology, Switzerland
F. Colucci, ENEA, Italy
A. Pascaris, NREL, United States of America
C. Dupraz, INRAE, France
C. Alonso-García, CIEMAT, Spain
A. Lefort, BayWa, Germany
H.N. Riise, IFE, Norway
M.A. Schüler, Next2Sun Technology GmbH, Germany
P.J. Pérez-Higueras, University of Jaén, Spain
K. Oda, Agritree,

M. Berwind, Fraunhofer ISE, Germany
M. Dörenkämper, TNO, The Netherlands
M. Heinrich, Fraunhofer ISE, Germany
B. Newman, Lightyear, The Netherlands
A. Reinders, Eindhoven University of Technology, The Netherlands
T. Tanahashi, AIST, Japan
J. Leloux, LuciSun, Belgium
E. Shirazi, University of Twente, The Netherlands
K. Araki, University of Miyazaki, Japan
K. Nishioka, University of Miyazaki, Japan
R. Campesato, CESI, Italy
V. Khorenko, Azur Space, Germany
G. Kakoulaki, European Commission Joint Research Centre, Italy
H. Toyota, JAXA, Japan
P. Garcia-Linares, UPM, Spain
I. Weiss, Weiss, Ingrid, Germany
A. Hensel, Fraunhofer ISE, Germany
J.S. da Fernandes, Hochschule Offenburg, Germany
Y. Ueda, Tokyo University of Science, Japan
J. Braid, Sandia National Laboratories, United States of America

Topic 5: PV in the Energy Transition
J. Stierstorfer, WIP Renewable Energies, Germany
R. Pestana, R&D Nester, Portugal
P.J. Alet, CSEM, Switzerland
C. Agraffeil, CEA, France
K. WAMBACH, Wambach-Consulting, Germany
C. del Cañizo, UPM, Spain
L. Großhans, WIP Renewable Energies, Germany
M. Getsiou, European Commission DG RTD, Belgium
S. Nowak, NET Nowak Energy & Technology, Switzerland
C. Breyer, LUT University, Finland
I. Kaizuka, RTS Corporation, Japan
G. Masson, Becquerel Institute, Belgium
P. Baliozian, VDMA, Germany
L. Großhans, WIP Renewable Energies, Germany
C. Candelise, Bocconi University, Italy
S. Caneva, WIP Renewable Energies, Germany

G. Barchi, Eurac Research, Italy
R. Bründlinger, AIT, Austria
V. Efthymiou, University of Cyprus, Cyprus
M. Centeno Brito, University of Lisbon, Portugal
F. Carigiet, ZHAW, Switzerland
B. Gaiddon, HESPUL, France
F.Z. Ouchani, Green Energy Park, Morocco
M. Rennhofer, AIT, Austria
G. Adinolfi, ENEA, Italy
W. Schaffer, Salzburg Netz, Austria
A. Haber, e-control, Austria
G. Heilscher, Technische Hochschule Ulm, Germany
A. Anctil, Michigan State University, United States of America
S. Arancón, Plug and Play, Spain
S. Capaccioli, ETA - Florence Renewable Energies, Italy
V. Fthenakis, Columbia University, United States of America
G. Heath, NREL, United States of America
K. Komoto, Mizuho Research & Technologies, Ltd., Japan
W. Palitzsch, LuxChemtech, Germany
S. Ovaitt, NREL, United States of America
M. de Wild-Scholten, SmartGreenScans, The Netherlands
S. Herceg, Fraunhofer ISE, Germany
C. Polacchi, Eurac Research, Italy
N. Espinosa, Universidad de Murcia, Spain
E. Drahi, TotalEnergies OneTech, France
S. Guastella, RSE, Italy
H. Ossenbrink, Band Gap, Germany
D. Polverini, European Commission DG GROW, Belgium
N. Taylor, European Commission JRC, Italy
K.A. Weiß, Fraunhofer ISE, Germany
I. Kafedjiska, Helmholtz Zentrum Berlin, Germany
P. Malbranche, Solar Action, France
S. De Iuliis, ENEA, Italy
T. Haarberg, BNW-Energy, Norway
A. Nayfeh, Khalifa University, United Arab Emirates
E. Vartiainen, Fortum Renewables Oy, Finland
E. Veronese, Eurac Research, Italy
P. Sanchez-Friera, Solkeys, Spain
N. Cherradi, Desert Technologies, Saudi Arabia
S. Nold, Fraunhofer ISE, Germany
H.J.J. Yu, CEA, France
M. Beck, U.S. Department of Energy, United States of America
M. Woodhouse, NREL, United States of America
A.B. Cristóbal, UPM, Spain
G. Ruggieri, Insubria University, Italy
S. Tay, NUS, Singapore

Awards Coordinators

Student Awards Coordinator
A.H.M. Smets, Delft University of Technology, The Netherlands

Student Awards Committee
R. Kenny, EU PVSEC Technical Programme Chair, Italy
C. del Canizo, Conference Chair, UPM, Spain
E. Voroshazi, CEA, France
J. Poortmans, imec, Belgium
P.J. Alet, CSEM, Switzerland
S. Caneva, WIP Renewable Energies, Germany
A. Romeo, University of Verona, Italy
G. Friesen, SUPSI, Switzerland
F. Schindler, Fraunhofer ISE, Germany
J.C. Goldchmidt, Marburg University, Germany
D. Moser, Becquerel Institute, Italy
K. Ding, FZJ, Germany
W.C. Sinke, TNO Energy Transition, The Netherlands
M. Topic, University of Ljubljana, Slovenia
R. Schlatman, HZB, Germany
S. Glunz, Fraunhofer ISE, Germany
A.M. Vega, UPM, Spain
I. Kaizuka, RTS, Japan
P.D. Veneri, ENEA, Italy
J. Bengoechea, CENER, Spain

Poster Awards Coordinator
P. Malbranche, Solar Action, France

Poster Awards Committee
R. Kenny, European Commission JRC, Italy
C. del Canizo, UPM, Spain
W. van Sark, Utrecht University, The Netherlands
I. Tsanakas, CEA INES, France
L. Miranda, Oxford PV, United Kingdom
D. Munoz, CEA INES, France
I. Gordon, imec, Belgium
E. Roman, Tecnalia, Spain
G. Eder, OFI, Austria
I. Antón, UPM, Spain
S. Veenstra, TNO, The Netherlands
J.M. Almeida Serra, University of Lisbon, Portugal
T. Magorian Friedlmeier, ZSW, Germany
J. Stierstorfer, WIP Renewable Energies, Germany

G. Kakoulaki, European Commission JRC, Italy
T. Barnes, NREL, USA
T. Merdzhanova, Forschungszentrum Jülich, Germany

Highlights Committee
C. del Cañizo, UPM, Madrid, Spain
R. Kenny, European Commission Joint Research Centre, Directorate for Energy and Transport and Climate, Ispra, Italy
W.C. Sinke, TNO Energy Transition, The Netherlands
S. Nowak, Managing Director of NET Nowak Energy & Technology, St. Ursen, Switzerland
M. Topič, Head of Laboratory of Photovoltaics and Optoelectronics of the University of Ljubljana, Slovenia
V. Bermúdez Benito, BERBETIN, France
E. Voroshazi, Head of PV Module Process Laboratory, CEA, Le Bourget-Du-Lac France
H. Ossenbrink, Band Gap, Germany
J. Bergmiller, Managing Director Events & Knowledge Transfer, WIP Renewable Energies, Munich, Germany
J. de Gregorio, Head of Unit, Scientific Services and Cooperation, WIP Renewable Energies, Munich, Germany
S. Leanza, Marketing and PR Manager, WIP Renewable Energies, Munich, Germany
B. Yildiz, Project Manager Events & Knowledge Transfer, WIP Renewable Energies, Munich, Germany
F. Schindler, Fraunhofer ISE, Freiburg, Germany
I. Gordon, imec, Leuven, Belgium
T. Barnes, NREL, Evergreen, USA
A.M. Gracia Amillo, FUNDACION CENER, Sarriguren, Spain
C. Agraffeil, CEA / INES, Le Bourget-du-Lac, France

SUBJECT INDEX

Silicon Materials and Cells

Sessions 1CP.1, 1EP.3, 1AO.4, 1AO.5, 1AO.6, 1BO.1, 1BO.2, 1BO.3, 1BO.4, 1DO.9, 1BV.5, 1CV.2

Thin Films and New Concepts

Sessions 2CP.2, 2BO.1, 2CO.1, 2CO.2, 2DO.9, 2DO.6, 2DO.7, 2DO.8, 2AO.2, 2AO.3, 2AO.1, 2BO.8, 2BO.9, 2BO.10, 2BV.1, 2BV.2, 2CV.3

Photovoltaic Modules and BoS Components

Sessions 3CP.1, 3CP.3, 3CO.10, 3CO.11, 3DO.12, 3DO.16, 3DO.19, 3DO.20, 3BO.11, 3BO.12, 3BO.14, 3BO.15, 3AV.1, 3AV.2, 3AV.3

PV Systems Engineering, Integrated/Applied PV

Sessions 4AP.1, 4AO.7, 4AO.8, 4AO.9, 4DO.1, 4DO.3, 4BO.6, 4BO.7, 4CO.8, 4CO.9, 4DO.10, 4DO.17, 4BO.5, 4BO.16, 4BO.17, 4DO.2, 4DO.4, 4DO.5, 4CO.3, 4EO.2, 4BV.3, 4BV.4, 4CV.1, 4DV.1, 4DV.4,

PV in the Energy Transition

Sessions 5CP.1, 5CP.2, 5DO.14, 5DO.15, 5CO.4, 5CO.5, 5CO.6, 5DO.18, 5CO.4, 5CO.5, 5CO.6, 5DO.18, 5EO.3, 5EO.1, 5DV.2, 5DV.3,

---

Topic Code	Session Type	Day Codes
1 Silicon Materials and Cells	P = Plenary Session	A = Monday, 22 September 2025
2 Thin-Films and New Concepts	O = Oral Session	B = Tuesday, 23 September 2025
3 Photovoltaic Modules	V = Visual Session	C = Wednesday, 24 September 2025
4 Photovoltaic Systems		D = Thursday, 25 September 2025
5 Photovoltaics in the Energy Transition		E = Friday, 26 September 2025

e.g. 1AO.4 ⇒ 1= Silicon Materials and Cells, A=Monday, O=Oral session, 4=Session 4

FOREWORD

The European Photovoltaic Solar Energy Conference and Exhibition (EU PVSEC) stands as the World's leading and most renowned forum for PV research and development and the biggest conference on PV solar energy. In 2025, celebrating its 42nd edition, the EU PVSEC was the essential meeting and exchanging point for global PV experts from research, development, and industry.

Held from 22–26 September 2025 in Bilbao, Spain, the EU PVSEC 2025 was a resounding success, showcasing a wide range of cutting-edge research results. Bringing together both the Conference and the Exhibition, this edition attracted more than 1600 participants from 61 countries who contributed over 1000 presentations across various fields of science and technology. The event provided an essential platform for the exchange of knowledge and ideas on photovoltaic research, innovations, and applications. In the exhibition area 51 companies from all parts of the world welcomed visitors and presented their products and services.

Conference Highlights

The EU PVSEC covered a broad range of topics with an extensive programme that offers an opportunity for workers from across the entire field of photovoltaics to share their findings, as well as an opportunity for multidisciplinary learning. Rapid advances in materials, designs, and manufacturing processes reflect the accelerating expansion of the global PV market. The programme was arranged into 5 topics as follows:

- Silicon Materials and Cells;
- Thin Films and New Concepts;
- Photovoltaic Modules and Balance of System Components;
- PV Systems Engineering, Integrated/Applied PV;
- PV in the Energy Transition.

Communicating the key messages from the conference, not only to participants, but also to other researchers, key stakeholders, policy makers and the general public was an important added value. We thank the Highlights Committee, composed of selected members of the Scientific Committee, as well as the Session Chairs, for providing a comprehensive summary of the findings and state of the art research that were delivered during this year's event. Some key highlights are listed below, while further details may be found in the dedicated highlights presentation in the annex of these proceedings.

Cross-cutting themes:

- Demonstrated the versatility of solar technologies, spanning traditional and emerging application areas.
- Sustainability and circularity remain central, with research focused on reducing material use, such as replacing silver with copper, and advancing end-of-life management of modules.
- Ensuring long-term stability and predictable energy yield is equally essential, with many examples of studies on degradation mechanisms and efforts to elucidate their root-causes, such as in the case of UVID.
- The role of artificial intelligence across the PV value chain is rapidly expanding, from design to operations and maintenance, including among many others drone applications.

Latest Solar Innovations in Materials, Cells, Modules and PV Systems:

While silicon solar cells remain the cornerstone of PV technology, perovskite solar cells continue to stand out as the leading complementary technology to silicon, both as standalone devices and in tandem configurations. Research efforts are increasingly focused on enhancing stability, understanding degradation mechanisms, improving durability and scalability, and ensuring full industrial compatibility.

Many companies presented impressive results on industrial-size single-junction perovskite modules as well as perovskite-based tandem modules, and several new efficiency records were announced during the event. The rapid pace of innovation in cell and module architecture underscores the need for accelerated and more robust testing and qualification methodologies. Both the industry and the research community are moving swiftly to assess and improve reliability in this fast-evolving PV landscape.

A major focus in module research remains the optimisation of materials and packaging to ensure long lifetimes and predictable energy yields from high-efficiency cells. In parallel, many innovative advances in the operation and maintenance (O&M) of PV systems were presented and discussed.

Applications, Grid Integration and Storage

"PV can be deployed everywhere": from space applications to agrivoltaics, PV noise barriers, building-integrated photovoltaics (BIPV), floating PV systems, and even vehicles. Among these, agrivoltaics is gaining momentum as a promising dual land use approach, offering economic benefits for farmers while increasing resilience to climate change.

Flexibility solutions, particularly through battery storage, were recognised in many technical presentations as essential to accommodate higher PV penetration levels and to reduce energy curtailment. At the same time, strengthening grid infrastructure and enhancing grid management capabilities remain critical to enable the next phase of large-scale PV integration.

Photovoltaics in the Energy Transition

Options for re-establishing competitive module manufacturing in Europe were extensively analysed, including detailed policy recommendations for industrial support and market growth. Currently, a mismatch persists between global PV module installation rates and production rates, resulting in growing inventories and sharply reduced prices.

Finally, inclusiveness, diversity, citizen participation, awareness, education, and social engagement were

underlined as vital dimensions of the sector's long-term sustainability and innovation capacity.

EU PVSEC 2025 Proceedings

Selection for inclusion in the conference was made by the Scientific Committee's paper review experts and topic organisers (see the listing on pages 010002-001-005), to whom we express our sincere gratitude for their comprehensive review work and overall contribution to the success of the conference.

The EU PVSEC 2025 Proceedings contain the full papers covering most of the highlights described above and more. The Proceedings provide a comprehensive overview of the PV solar sector, its current status and future prospects in science, research, innovation, development and deployment extending to 3,750 pages. In addition to the 299 submitted papers, the proceedings include 101 presentations (slides) shown during the plenary and oral presentations as well as 176 poster files of the visual presentations. In total this amounts to 576 publications.

The Conference Proceedings are published as downloadable files and are also fully accessible online. A DOI code (Digital Object Identifier) has been assigned to each paper. This ensures unequivocal and permanent identification and full citability. The EU PVSEC 2025 papers can be viewed and downloaded in a full free open access from the EU PVSEC's Proceedings website https://userarea.eupvsec.org/proceedings.

The proceedings of the EU PVSEC 2025 strengthen the commitment to providing quick and open access to high quality scientific results. This is a powerful source for targeted and quick information search and retrieval, enabling you to search by topic, keywords, paper title, DOI, author, or organization.

We are confident that these Proceedings will play an important role in providing a comprehensive overview of the current actors and activities in the global PV sector and that they will disseminate information on the state-of-the-art of technologies and applications. This can generate further research, add momentum to innovation and promote interest in PV worldwide.

We would like to cordially thank all authors and participants of the EU PVSEC 2025 for their contributions and look forward to welcoming you in Rotterdam, The Netherlands from 14 – 18 September 2026 at the EU PVSEC 2026, the 43rd European Photovoltaic Solar Energy Conference and Exhibition

The Editors

TABLE OF CONTENTS OF EU PVSEC 2025 PROCEEDINGS PAPERS

Visual SESSION 1CV.2 Si Solar Cells | Characterisation & Modelling of Silicon Cells and Their Building Blocks

[1] *Anhalt University of Applied Sciences, Köthen, Germany;* [2] *Fraunhofer CSP, Halle, Germany*

Oral SESSION 2AO.2 Advances in Chalcogenide Devices

2AO.2.3 A New Method for Sb-doped CdSeTe/CdTe Devices with Superior Stability 020057
Elisa Artegiani[1], *Mariyam Mukhtar*[1], *Alessandro Romeo*[1]
[1] *University of Verona, Verona, Italy*

Oral SESSION 2AO.3 III-V Based Devices | Tandem and Perovskite Solar Cells

2AO.3.3 Micro-Crystal GaAs Array Sub-Cells for Si Tandem Solar Cells 020058
James Patrick Connolly[1], *Ahmed Nejim*[2], *Alexandre Jaffré*[1], *José Alvarez*[1], *Jean-Paul Kleider*[1], *Denis Mencaraglia*[1], *Laurie Dentz*[3], *Géraldine Hallais*[3], *Frederic Hamouda*[3], *Laetitia Vincent*[3], *Daniel Bouchier*[3], *Charles Renard*[3]
[1] *CNRS, Gif-sur-Yvette, France;* [2] *SILVACO, St. Ives, United Kingdom;* [3] *CNRS, Palaiseau, France*

2AO.3.5 Multiscale Models for Perovskite Optimisation 020060
Philippe Baranek[1], *James Patrick Connolly*[2], *Antoine Gissler*[1], *Philip Schulz*[3], *Michel Rerat*[4], *Roberto Dovesi*[5]
[1] *EDF R&D, Palaiseau, France;* [2] *CNRS, Gif-sur-Yvette, France;* [3] *IPVF, Palaiseau, France;* [4] *IPREM, Pau, France;* [5] *Academy of Sciences of Turin, Torino, Italy*

2AO.3.6 Modelling Recovery in Perovskite Solar Cells under Light and Dark to Address Stability Challenges 020062
Guillem Álvarez-Pérez[1], *Jean Baptiste Puel*[1], *Jean François Guillemoles* [1]
[1] *IPVF, Palaiseau, France*

Oral SESSION 2BO.10 Advanced Modelling and Characterisation of Perovskite Solar Cells

2BO.10.2 On Perimeter Losses in Perovskite Top- and Poly-Si-Passivated Silicon Bottom Cells – Do Small Area Tandems Reveal the Full Efficiency Potential? 020063
Felix Haase[1], *Lukas Brockmann*[1], *Annika Raugewitz*[1], *Verena Steckenreiter*[1], *Verena Barnscheidt*[1], *Roland Clausing*[1], *Sara Baumann*[1], *Joachim Vollbrecht*[1], *Welmoed Veurman*[1], *Johannes Löhr*[1], *Dongyang Liu*[1], *Mircea Turcu*[1], *Lasse Nasebandt*[1], *Udo Römer*[1], *David Sylla*[1], *Jessica Strey*[1], *Martha Löhning*[1], *Larissa Mettner*[1], *Renate Winter*[1], *Anja Christ*[1], *Heike Kohlenberg*[1], *Cornelia Marquardt*[1], *Emanuel Brueckner*[1], *Hossein Rabiei*[1], *Michael Rienäcker*[1], *Sarah Kajari-Schröder*[1], *Tobias Wietler*[1], *Robby Peibst*[1]
[1] *ISFH, Emmerthal, Germany*

2BO.10.5 In-depth Characterization and Simulation Approach for the Understanding of In- and Outdoor Degradation of Perovskite Solar Cells 020064
Jonathan Parion[1], *Amit Kumar Harit*[1], *Elias Peraticos*[2], *Vasiliki Paraskeva*[2], *Maria Hadjipanayi*[2], *Aranzazu Aguirre*[1], *Filip Duerinckx*[1], *Hariharsudan*

Sivaramakrishnan Radhakrishnan[1], Jef Poortmans[1], Johan Lauwaert[3], Bart Vermang[1]
[1] Hasselt Unversity, Genk, Belgium; [2] University of Cyprus, Nicosia, Cyprus; [3] Ghent University, Ghent, Belgium

Oral SESSION 2BO.8 Advanced Conversion Devices

2BO.8.1 Singlet Fission Route for >30% Efficient Solar Cells: Silicon Cell Requirements 020065
Shona McNab[1], Alex J. Baldacchino[1], Pheobe Pearce[1], Alvin Mo[1], Alison Ciesla[1], Bram Hoex[1], Nicholas J. Ekins-Daukes[1], Murad J. Y. Tayebjee[1], Michael P. Nielsen[1]
[1] UNSW, Sydney, Australia

2BO.8.5 Performance of a 4-Terminals Spectral Splitting Asymmetric Solar Concentrator in Diffuse Sunlight: a Numerical Study 020066
Floriana Morabito[1], Daniela Fontani[2], Paola Sansoni[2], Mehdi Ahmadi[3], Salvatore Lombardo[3], Andrea Farina[1], Silvia Maria Pietralunga[1]
[1] CNR-IFN, Milan, Italy; [2] CNR-INO, Florence, Italy; [3] CNR-IMM, Catania, Italy

2BO.8.6 GaAs for Thermophotonics: From Thin-Film Solar Cells to Highly Efficient LEDs 020067
Natasha Gruginskie[1], Peter Mulder[1], Gerard Bauhuis[1], Jani Oksanen[2], John Schermer[1]
[1] Radboud University, Nijmegen, The Netherlands; [2] Aalto University, Espoo, Finland

Visual SESSION 2BV.1 New Materials, Devices and Conversion Concepts | New Modelling and Characterisation Techniques

2BV.1.4 Low-Energy Electron Multiplication on Nanostructured Solar Cells: a Novel Route to Overcome Si-PV Efficiency Limits 020068
Mikaël Hosatte[1], Brice Rouffie[1], Zbigniew T. Kuznicki[1], Frédéric Milesi[2], Bertrand Paviet-Salomon[3], Audrey Morisset[3], Philippe Wyss[3], Lejo Joseph Koduvelikulathu[4], Lazhar Rachdi[4], Lacramioara Popescu[4], Dominik Rudolph[4], Marek Basta[5], Andrzej Miszczuk[5], Martyna Majak[5], Beata Basta[5], Samuel Queste[6]
[1] SEGTON Advanced Technology, Versailles, France; [2] CEA, Grenoble, France; [3] CSEM, Neuchâtel, Switzerland; [4] ISC Konstanz, Konstanz, Germany; [5] Roltec, Poznań, Poland; [6] Marie and Louis Pasteur University, Besançon, France

2BV.1.5 Tailoring CBTSSe Solar Cells for Indoor Photovoltaic Applications 020069
Hitarth Narsi Patel[1], Bindu Pamula[1], Deepak Joshi[1], Vivek Garg[1]
[1] SVNIT, Surat, India

2BV.1.6 Theoretical Insights through DFT into $AgBiS_2$ Thin Films Absorber for Photovoltaic Applications 020071
Dhruv Singh Thakur[1], Rajesh Kumar Sharma[1], Nithin Chatterji[1], Vivek Garg[1], Shivendra Yadav[1]
[1] SVNIT, Surat, India

Visual SESSION 2BV.2 Compound and Organic Semiconductors

Visual SESSION 2CV.3 Perovskite-based Tandems and Multijunctions

Gerardo Gordillo[1], Oscar Torres[1], Julian Peña-Bermudez[2]
[1] National University of Colombia, Bogotá, Colombia; [2] University of the Caribbean, Santo Domingo, Dominican Republic

2CV.3.71 Comparative Analysis and Efficiency Optimization of Sulfur-based Chalcogenide Perovskites ($MgHfS_3$, $CaZrS_3$, $BaZrS_3$) via Interface Engineering for High-Performance Solar Cells 020111
Anees ur Rehman[1], Kung Ding[1], Jingwei Zhang[1], Xiang Chen[1]
[1] Hohai University, Changzhou, China

2CV.3.72 Development of Inorganic Perovskite $CsPbI_3$ with Heterojunction Engineering at the Buried Interface for Enhanced Stability and Performance 020112
Syed Fawad Ali Shah[1], Hyeonwook Park[1], Muhammad Rehan[2], Donghyeop Shin[2], Kihwan Kim[2], Jae Ho Yun[3]
[1] KENTECH, Naju-Si, South Korea; [2] KIER, Daejeon, South Korea; [3] KENTECH, Naju-si, South Korea

Oral SESSION 2DO.6 Industrially Scalable Processes to Manufacture Perovskite Solar Cells and Modules

2DO.6.2 Eliminating P2 Scribes: A New Interconnection Design for Efficient Perovskite Solar Modules Under Indoor Lighting 020113
Bahri Eren Uzuner[1], Konstantin Tsoi[1], Gorkem Gunbas[1], Selcuk Yerci[1]
[1] ODTÜ-GÜNAM, Ankara, Türkiye

2DO.6.5 Evaporated Self Assembled Monolayer (SAM) Hole Transport Layers for Scalable Perovskite Solar Cells 020114
Joachim Vollbrecht[1], Verena Barnscheidt[1], Roland Clausing[1], Johannes Löhr[1], Larissa Mettner[1], Adam Neuba[2], Annika Raugewitz[1], Jessica Strey[1], Robby Peibst[1]
[1] ISFH, Emmerthal, Germany; [2] Paderborn University, Paderborn, Germany

Oral SESSION 2DO.7 Insights Into the Stability of Perovskite Solar Cells and Modules

2DO.7.1 Outdoor Performance and Degradation Analysis of Inverted Perovskite Solar Cells 020115
Makoto Konagai[1], Hayato Okawa[1], Ryousuke Ishikawa[1], Masatoshi Yanagida[2], Yasuhiro Shirai[2]
[1] Tokyo City University, Setagaya, Japan; [2] NIMS, Tsukuba, Japan

Oral SESSION 2DO.8 Multiple Aspects of Perovskite PV Research

2DO.8.2 Strategies for Quasi-2D Perovskite Integration in p-i-n Solar Cells 020116
Anna Capitaine[1], Hugo Le Bossenec[1], Marion Provost[1], Alexandra Levtchenko[1], Daniel Ory[2], Jean Rousset[2], Iwan Zimmermann[1], Anyssa Derj[1],

Mirella Al Katrib[1]
[1] *IPVF, Palaiseau, France;* [2] *EDF R&D, Palaiseau, France*

2DO.8.3 Innovative Approach to Bismuth-Antimony-Iodide Double Perovskite PV Absorbers via Anion Exchange and Solide-State Reactions 020117
Oleksandr Stroyuk[1], Oleksandra Raievska[1], Sachin Kinge[2], Jens Hauch[1], Christoph J. Brabec[1]
[1] *HI ERN, Erlangen, Germany;* [2] *Toyota Motors Europe, Brussels, Belgium*

Visual SESSION 3AV.1 PV Module Design and Manufacturing

3AV.1.1 Investigating the 3-Dimensional Structure of Metallic Filler Particles in Electrically Conductive Adhesives 020119
Stephan Grosser[1], Alexander Müller[1], Robert Göckeritz[1], Tobias Nitsche[2], Daniel Buckland[2], Giuseppe Galbiati[2], Bengt Jaeckel[1]
[1] *Fraunhofer CSP, Halle, Germany;* [2] *Henkel, Düsseldorf, Germany*

3AV.1.6 Investigation on Different Bypass Diodes for Shade Resistant PV-Modules 020121
Jens Froebel[1], Matthias Pander[1], Bengt Jaeckel[1], Andreas Maixner[2], Pouya Pourshafi[2], Afshin Bakhtiari[2], Hamed Hanifi[2]
[1] *Fraunhofer CSP, Halle, Germany;* [2] *AESOLAR, Koenigsbrunn, Germany*

3AV.1.7 Optimization of Infrared Soldering Process to Reduce the Temperature Inhomogeneity in Silicon Solar Cells Using Finite Element Methods 020123
Daniel Christopher Joseph[1], Angela De Rose[1], Christian Reichel[1], Andreas J. Beinert[1], Holger Neuhaus[1]
[1] *Fraunhofer ISE, Freiburg, Germany*

3AV.1.10 Performance Evaluation of a New Design Photovoltaic Module with Reduced Self-Shading 020125
Pouya Pourshafi[1], Andreas Maixner[1], Hamed Hanifi[1]
[1] *AESOLAR, Königsbrunn, Germany*

3AV.1.11 Materials Assessment for PV-T Modules Thermal Performance Improvement 020127
Lucía Cano[1], Raquel Simón-Allué[1], Raúl Villén[1], Yolanda Lara[1], Isabel Guedea[1]
[1] *ENDEF, Zaragoza, Spain*

3AV.1.12 Evaluating Repair Techiniques for c-Si PV Modules: Spot-Welding 020129
Jorge Rabanal-Arabach[1], Sonia Beltran-Condori[1], Natalia Videla-Magnata[1], Katalina Rojas-Henríquez[1], Andreas Schneider[2], Edward Fuentealba-Vidal[1]
[1] *University of Antofagasta, Antofagasta, Chile;* [2] *University of Applied Sciences Gelsenkirchen, Gelsenkirchen, Germany*

3AV.1.13 Thermally Conductive Filler Particle Mixed Silicone Layer to Provide Heat Dissipation Functionality to c-Si Solar Cell Modules without Encapsulants 020131
Yasushi Sobajima[1], Kouzen Wakazono[1], Keisuke Ohdaira[2]
[1] *Gifu University, Gifu, Japan;* [2] *JAIST, Ishikawa, Japan*

3AV.1.16 Ultrasonic Characterization of Ethylene-Vinyl Acetate in Glass-Glass-Modules 020132
Christopher Bruce Konu[1], Rico Meier[1]
[1] *HTW Berlin, Berlin, Germany*

Visual SESSION 3AV.2 PV Module Durability and Reliability

Nathan Roosloot[1], Harsha Walpita[2], Christoph Seiffert[1], Jean Thomas[3], Maarten Dörenkämper[4], Minne M. de Jong[4], Josefine H. Selj[1], Gaute Otnes[1]
[1] Institute for Energy Technology, Kjeller, Norway; [2] University of Oslo, Kjeller, Norway; [3] Ciel et Terre, Lille, France; [4] TNO, Eindhoven, The Netherlands

Visual SESSION 3AV.3 PV Modules Characterisation and Performances Assessment

3AV.3.1 A New Method for Comprehensive Power Rating and Performance Analysis of PERC Modules based on Half-Cut Cell Technology 020171
Khadija El Ainaoui[1], Mhammed Zaimi[2], Imane Flouchi[1], Said Elhamaoui[1], Yasmine El mrabet[1], Abdellatif Ghennioui[1], El Mahdi Assaid[2]
[1] Green Energy Park, Benguerir, Morocco; [2] University of Chouaib Doukkali, El Jadida, Morocco

3AV.3.2 Energy Rating Analysis of Heterojunction PV Modules 020173
Teodora Stoyanova Lyubenova[1], Ewan D. Dunlop[1]
[1] European Commission JRC, Ispra, Italy

3AV.3.3 Trend of Temperature Coefficients of c-Si Module Technologies from the past 15 Years 020175
Bengt Jaeckel[1], Matthias Pander[1]
[1] Fraunhofer CSP, Halle, Germany

3AV.3.6 Angle of Incidence Measurements on Bifacial PV Modules 020177
Frank Weinrich[1], Stefan Riechelmann[1], Stefan Winter[1]
[1] PTB, Braunschweig, Germany

3AV.3.8 Plug & Play IV Curve Tracer for PV Modules 020179
Adrian Jäggi[1], Christof Bucher[1], Matthias Burri[1]
[1] BFH, Burgdorf, Switzerland

3AV.3.9 Seasonal and Location-Dependent Temperature Coefficients for Thin-Film PV Modules: Enhancing Yield Prediction Accuracy 020180
Thomas Weber[1], Abdullah Abu Sayed[1], Benjamin Lippke[1], Steven Xuereb[1], Marcus Rennhofer[2], Bart E. Pieters[3]
[1] Kiwa PI Berlin, Berlin, Germany; [2] AIT, Vienna, Austria; [3] FZJ, Jülich, Germany

3AV.3.10 Standardisation Methods for Bifacial Energy Yield Estimation and PV Module Long-Term Performance Degradation Estimation: Potential Policy Implications 020181
Jaione Bengoechea[1], Ana María Gracia Amillo[1], Stefan Riechelmann[2], Stefan Winter[2], Giorgio Bardizza[3], Christos Monokroussos[4], Davide Polverini[5], Pablo Vicente-Laiglesia[6], Maria Getsiou[7]
[1] CENER, Sarriguren, Spain; [2] PTB, Braunschweig, Germany; [3] TÜV Rheinland Italia, Milan, Italy; [4] TÜV Rheinland, Shanghai, China; [5] Directorate General for Internal Market, Industry, Entrepreneurship and SMEs, Brussels, Belgium; [6] European Climate, Infrastructure and Environment Executive Agency, Brussels, Belgium; [7] Directorate General for Research and Innovation, Brussels, Belgium

3AV.3.11 Shaalke: Development of a MATLAB Software Tool for Advanced Statistical Outdoor Data Evaluation 020183

Oral SESSION 3BO.11 Imaging Techniques for PV Modules

Cristian Terrados[1], Eva de la Viuda[1], Kabir Paul Sulca[1], Julian Anaya[1], Miguel Ángel González[1], Oscar Martínez[1]
[1] University of Valladolid, Valladolid, Spain

3BO.11.6 Luminescence Measurements of PV Modules with a Cost-Effective and Small-Sized Hood-Based Tool under Daylight Conditions 020206
Marc Köntges[1], Michael Siebert[1], Dieter Lorenz[2], Bernd Kuhrmann[2], Michael Fuß[2]
[1] ISFH, Emmerthal, Germany; [2] MBJ Solutions, Ahrensburg, Germany

Oral SESSION 3BO.12 Characterisation and Energy Rating of PV Modules

3BO.12.1 Developing a New I-V Translation Methodology in Accordance with IEC 60891:2021 Correction Procedure 1 and 2 020208
Wenhao Xu[1], Yating Zhang[1], Mengdi Liu[1], Christos Monokroussos[1], Werner Herrmann[2], Giorgio Bardizza[2], Harald Müllejans[3]
[1] TÜV Rheinland, Shanghai, China; [2] TÜV Rheinland Solar, Cologne, Germany; [3] European Commission JRC, Ispra, Italy

3BO.12.2 Characterization of Vehicle Integrated Photovoltaic Modules 020209
Ricardo Moruno[1], Francisco José Martín[1], Juan Manuel Redondo[1], Javier Malo[1], Luis Javier San José[1], Guido Vallerotto[1], Steve Askins[1], Rubén Núñez[1], César Domínguez[1], Ignacio Antón[1], Rebeca Herrero[1]
[1] UPM, Madrid, Spain

3BO.12.4 Estimating the Energy Yield of Bifacial Photovoltaics with the JRC's Photovoltaic Geographic Information System 020210
Nigel Taylor[1], Teodora Lyubenova[1], Lavanya Malarkannan[2], Nikos Alexandris[1], Alexandros Falangas[3], Robert Kenny[1], Ewan D. Dunlop[1], Blago Mihaylov[1]
[1] European Commission JRC, Ispra, Italy; [2] National Physical Laboratory, Teddington, United Kingdom; [3] TRASIS International, Brussels, Belgium

3BO.12.5 An Update on Energy Rating Amendments – Integration of Bifacial Modules 020211
Stefan Riechelmann[1], Hendrik Sträter[1], Ana María Gracia Amillo[2], Sophie Pelland[3], Anton Driesse[4]
[1] PTB, Braunschweig, Germany; [2] CENER, Pamplona, Spain; [3] Natural Resources Canada, Varennes, Canada; [4] PV Performance Labs, Freiburg, Germany

Oral SESSION 3BO.14 Characterisation and Outdoor Monitoring of Perovskite-based PV Modules

3BO.14.1 Outdoor Measurements of Perovskite Modules 020213
Hanna Ellis[1], Harald Müllejans[1], Ewan D. Dunlop[1], Tony Sample[1]
[1] European Commission JRC, Ispra, Italy

Oral SESSION 3BO.15 Outdoor Performances and Degradation Analysis of PV Modules

3CO.11.5 Indoor Characterization and Analysis of Reverse Breakdown Behavior of Solar Cells with Different Cell Architectures — 020223

Bengt Jaeckel[1], Jens Froebel[1], Matthias Pander[1], Andreas Maixner[2], Hamed Hanifi[2]

[1] Fraunhofer CSP, Halle, Germany; [2] AESOLAR, Koenigsbrunn, Germany

Plenary SESSION 3CP.1 Si PV Manufacturing: Pushing the Limits of Performance

3CP.1.2 IBC4EU: European Back Contact Technology — 020225

Florian Buchholz[1], Daniel Tune[1], Tobias Meßmer[1], Jonathan Linke[1], Manjunath Prasad[1], Valentin D. Mihailetchi[1], Juras Ulbikas[2], Arne Dahle[3], Martijn Meereboer[4], Francesca Fabris[5], Erik Eikelboom[5], Tom Borgers[6], Rik Van Dyck[6], Filip Duerinckx[7], Hariharsudan Sivaramakrishnan Radhakrishnan[7], Timea Bejat[8], Samuel Harrison[8], Ashish Binani[9], Nicolas Guillevin[9], Jan Kroon[9], Yevgeniya Larionova[10], Thorsten Dullweber[10], Ofer Shochet[11], Isaac Rosen [11], Ingo Röver [12], Wolfram Palitzsch[12], Yasmin Zaror[13], Johannes Stierstorfer[14], Aurimas Radzevicius[15], Julius Denafas[16], Tuomas Vanhanen [17], Tuukka Savisalo[17], Maximilian Pospischil [18], Marian Breitenbücher [18], Özlem Coşkun[19], Melodie de l'Epine [20], Philippe Macé[20], Ian Kenchington[20]

[1] ISC Konstanz, Konstanz, Germany; [2] Protechnology, Vilnius, Lithuania; [3] Norsun, Oslo, Norway; [4] Energyra, Westknollendam, The Netherlands; [5] Futurasun, Citadella, Italy; [6] IMEC, Genk, Belgium; [7] Hasselt Unversity, Genk, Belgium; [8] CEA, Le Bourget-du-Lac, France; [9] TNO, Petten, The Netherlands; [10] ISFH, Emmerthal, Germany; [11] Copprint, Jerusalem, Israel; [12] LuxChemTech, Freiberg, Germany; [13] WIP Renewable Energies, Munich, Germany; [14] WIP - Renewable Energies, Munich, Germany; [15] Valoe Cells, Vilnius, Lithuania; [16] Solitek, Vilnius, Lithuania; [17] Valoe, Mikkeli, Finland; [18] Highline Technologies, Freiburg, Germany; [19] Kalyon PV, Ankara, Türkiye; [20] Becquerel Institute, Brussels, Belgium

Plenary SESSION 3CP.3 Perovskite – Silicon Tandems: Towards Commercialisation | PV Stability in the Field

3CP.3.4 Outdoor Performance and Reliability of Perovskite (Pk)-Silicon (Si) Tandems: >1 year of Monitoring in the NEXUS Project — 020226

Atse Louwen[1], Jordi Veirman[1], Alexander Astigarraga[1], Juan José Stivanello[1], David Moser[2], Perrine Carroy[3], Vincent Barth[3], Delfina Muñoz[3], Markus Lenz[4], Anika Sidler[4], Jorge Ferrando[5], Maximiliano Alejandro Senno[5], Henk J. Bolink[5], Talat Özden[6], Hisham Nasser[6], Shuaifeng Hu[7], Xinyi Shen[7], Henry Snaith[7]

[1] Eurac Research, Bolzano, Italy; [2] Becquerel Institute Italy, Trento, Italy; [3] CEA / INES, Le Bourget-du-Lac, France; [4] School of Life Sciences FHNW, Muttenz, Switzerland; [5] University of Valencia, Paterna, Spain; [6] ODTÜ-GÜNAM, Ankara, Türkiye; [7] University of Oxford, Oxford, United Kingdom

Oral SESSION 3DO.12 Innovative Encapsulation Materials

Nikolina Pervan[1], Jutta Geier[1], Christian Veas[1], Gernot Oreski[1]
[1] PCCL, Leoben, Austria

Oral SESSION 4AO.7 Solar Resource Assessment

4AO.7.4 Potential of Decimeter-Resolution Ground Albedo Data for Bifacial Photovoltaics 020235
Niklas Blum[1], Bijan Nouri[1], Yann Fabel[1], Stefan Wilbert[1]
[1] DLR, Almería, Spain

4AO.7.5 Method for the Determination of Spectral Responsivity of Digital Solar Irradiance Sensors 020236
David Hinken[1], Sebastian Denke[1], Karsten Bothe[1], Rolf Brendel[1]
[1] ISFH, Emmerthal, Germany

Oral SESSION 4AO.8 Solar Irradiance Forecasting

4AO.8.2 Cutting-Edge Generative AI for Intra-Hour Solar Forecasting 020237
Yann Fabel[1], Dominik Schnaus[2], Bijan Nouri[1], Stefan Wilbert[1], Niklas Blum[1], Luis F. Zarzalejo[3], Julia Kowalski[4], Robert Pitz-Paal[5]
[1] DLR, Almería, Spain; [2] TUM, Garching, Germany; [3] CIEMAT, Madrid, Spain; [4] RWTH, Aachen, Germany; [5] DLR, Cologne, Germany

4AO.8.4 Integrating Satellite Imagery and GNNs for Improving Day-Ahead Solar Irradiance Forecasting 020238
Baptiste Schubnel[1], Jelena Simeunovic[1], Corentin Tissier[1], Pierre-Jean Alet[1], Rafael E. Carrillo[1]
[1] CSEM, Neuchâtel, Switzerland

4AO.8.5 Enhancing Intra-Hour Solar Irradiance Forecasting for Solar Applications: A Blended Model of Satellite, Sky Imager and Persistence 020239
Bijan Nouri[1], Jorge Lezaca[2], Yann Fabel[1], Annette Hammer[2], Niklas Blum[1], Stefan Wilbert[1]
[1] DLR, Almería, Spain; [2] DLR, Oldenburg, Germany

Oral SESSION 4AO.9 Irradiance for PV Design | Shading and Glare Mitigation

4AO.9.1 Reflective Properties of Urban Materials and Their Impact on PV Yield 020240
Christian Schläger[1], Dennis Bredemeier[1], Arne Dittrich[2], Jan Hendrik Pfau[1], Philip Kühne[1], Rolf Brendel[2]
[1] Leibniz University Hannover, Hannover, Germany; [2] ISFH, Emmerthal, Germany

4AO.9.3 Understanding Short-Term PV Power Variability Based on Solargis Time Series Data and Simulations 020241
Martin Opatovsky[1], Marta Pelfort Ojer[1], Juraj Betak[1], Konstantin Rosina[1]
[1] Solargis, Bratislava, Slovakia

4AO.9.5 Accelerating Photovoltaic System Simulations via Statistical Data Aggregation 020243

Adrián Blanco Aguiar[1], Brais González Rodríguez[2], María Martínez-Barbeito[1], Miguel Sánchez de León Peque[1]
[1] ieco.io, Vigo, Spain; [2] University of Vigo, Vigo, Spain

4AO.9.6 Addressing Glare Problematics for Photovoltaic Projects in the Immediate Proximity of Roads and Railways through the Use of Accurate Digital Surface Models 020244
Christophe Vernay[1], John Coutel[1], Aina Razanajao[1], Sébastien Pitaval[1]
[1] SOLAÏS, Valbonne, France

Plenary SESSION 4AP.1 PV Everywhere

4AP.1.3 Micro-Concentrator Photovoltaics for Deep Space Missions: Overcoming LILT Challenges with High-Specific-Power Solar Arrays 020246
Guido Vallerotto[1], Anderson Bermudez-Garcia[2], Gerald Siefer[3], Maike Wiesenfarth[3], Almudena Garcia-Sanchez[1], Ignacio Antón[1], Carsten Baur[4], Pier Luigi Coz[4], César Domínguez[1]
[1] UPM, Madrid, Spain; [2] Thales Alenia Space, Cannes, France; [3] Fraunhofer ISE, Freiburg, Germany; [4] European Space Agency, Noordwijk, The Netherlands

Oral SESSION 4BO.16 Color in Photovoltaics

4BO.16.1 Experimental Investigation of Colored BIPV/T Systems for Wood-Framed Roofs 020248
Anna-Maria Sigounis[1], Andreas Athienitis[1]
[1] Concordia University, Montreal, Canada

4BO.16.3 How to Perform Accurate Colour Measurements for BIPV Module Glass Covers: an IEA PVPS Task 15 Round-Robin Measurement Campaign 020249
Markus Babin[1], Gabriele C. Eder[2], Thomas Friesen[3], Martina Pelle[4], Gabriella Gonnella[5], Fabrizio Leonforte[6], Yuliya Voronko[2], Helen R. Wilson[7], Sune Thorsteinsson[1], Laura Maturi[4], Niccolò Aste[6], Claudio Del Pero[6], Janne Halme[8], Jun-Tae Kim[9], Susanna Santamaría Fernández[10], Anna-Maria Sigounis[11], Hua Ge[11], Gabi Friesen[12], Francesco Frontini[12]
[1] DTU, Roskilde, Denmark; [2] OFI, Vienna, Austria; [3] Megasol Energie, Deitingen, Switzerland; [4] Eurac Research, Bolzano, Italy; [5] Eurac research, Bolzano, Italy; [6] Polytechnic University of Milan, Milan, Italy; [7] Fraunhofer ISE, Freiburg, Germany; [8] Aalto University, Espoo, Finland; [9] Kongju National University, Chungnam, South Korea; [10] TECNALIA, Derio, Spain; [11] Concordia University, Montreal, Canada; [12] SUPSI, Mendrisio, Switzerland

4BO.16.6 Predicting Light Scatter in Structural Colored BIPV Modules and Textured Glass Using Radiance 020250
Nanna Lysgaard Andersen[1], Markus Babin[1], Jan Svatos[1], Karlis Petersons[2], Leif Yde[2], Jan F. Stensborg[2], Catarina G. Ferreira[3], Ananta Paul[3], Jani Lamminaho[3], Joel D. Cox[3], Morten Madsen[3], Peter B. Poulsen[1], Sune Thorsteinsson[1]
[1] DTU, Roskilde, Denmark; [2] Stensborg, Roskilde, Denmark; [3] SDU Climate Cluster, Odense, Denmark

Oral SESSION 4BO.17 Performance of PV on/in Buildings

4BO.17.1 Modeling Partial Shading at the Cell Level on Photovoltaic Modules 020251

Jean-Paul Calin[1], Jacques Levrat[2], Antonin Faes[2], Fahradin Mujovi[2], Paul Rémondeau[3], Kléber Nicolet-dit-Félix[3], Bénédicte Bonnet-Eymard[2], Didier Dalmazzone[1], Aïcha Hessler-Wyser[3], Christophe Ballif[3]
[1] ENSTA Paris, Palaiseau, France; [2] CSEM, Neuchâtel, Switzerland; [3] EPFL, Neuchâtel, Switzerland

4BO.17.2 Market Potential of Building-Integrated Photovoltaics: a Granular Analysis of the European Building Stock 020252

Juan Ignacio Martinez[1], Julien Van Overstraeten[2], Philippe Macé[2], José Maria Vega de Seoane[1], Elina Bosch[2], Mélodie de l'Epine[3]
[1] Becquerel Institute España, San Sebastian, Spain; [2] Becquerel Institute, Brussels, Belgium; [3] Becquerel Institute France, Lyon, France

4BO.17.3 Photovoltaics in the Built Environment – an Overview of Timely Topics for Research and Development 020253

Francesco Frontini[1], Angele Reinders[2]
[1] SUPSI, Mendrisio, Switzerland; [2] TU Eindhoven, Eindhoven, The Netherlands

4BO.17.5 Advancing BIPV: Shingled HJT Technology for High-Efficiency and Aesthetic Solar Integration 020254

Gabriella Gonnella[1], Alvaro De Gruijter[1], Jordi Veirman[1], Martina Pelle[1], Laura Maturi[1], David Moser[2], Luis Fialho[1]
[1] Eurac Research, Bolzano, Italy; [2] Bequerel Institute Italy, Trento, Italy

4BO.17.6 PV-Planning and Simulation, Daylight Simulation and Energy-Certificate Calculation based on an Open-BIM-Building-Model 020255

Astrid Schneider[1], Karin Stieldorf[1], Christian Schranz[1], Harald Urban[1], Alfred Waschl[2], Markus Feichtner[3], Fedele Rende[4], Andrea Aiello[4], Martin Hauer[5], Kurt Battisti[6], Markus Dörn[6], Jacqueline Scherret[6], Martin Treberspurg[7], Christoph Treberspurg[7]
[1] TU Wien, Vienna, Austria; [2] buildingSMART, Vienna, Austria; [3] Sonnenkraft Energie, St. Veit/Glan, Austria; [4] ACCA Software, Cosenza, Italy; [5] Bartenbach, Vienna, Austria; [6] A-Null Development, Vienna, Austria; [7] Treberspurg und Partner Ziviltechniker, Vienna, Austria

Oral SESSION 4BO.5 PV-Products for Buildings

4BO.5.1 Fabrication of a Novel Semi-Translucent BIPV Module Providing High Power Density and Active Daylight Management 020257

Almudena Garcia-Sanchez[1], Guido Vallerotto[1], Jaime J. Hernández[2], Alejandro García-Cañas[2], Steve Askins[1], Ignacio Antón[1], Isabel Rodríguez[2], César Domínguez[1]
[1] UPM, Madrid, Spain; [2] IMDEA Nanoscience, Madrid, Spain

4BO.5.3 A Comparative Study of Photovoltaic Shading Devices for Net Zero Energy Buildings across French Climates 020259

Visual SESSION 4BV.4 BIPV

Visual SESSION 4CV.1 Advances in Operation, Performance and Maintenance of PV Systems

Oral SESSION 4DO.3 PV System Design and Assessment

Oral SESSION 4DO.4 Agrivoltaics, PV Noise Barriers and Floating PV

Oral SESSION 4DO.5 Modelling and Optimisation of Agrivoltaic Systems

4DO.5.4 Development and Evaluation of Agrivoltaic System in Olive Groves based on a Novel Smart Tracking Algorithm 020392
Ildefonso Muñoz[1], Irati Amatriain[1], Gregorio Olivares[1], Gillen Abrego[2], Eusebio Gainza[2], Iñaki Cornago[1]
[1] CENER, Sarriguren, Spain; [2] ALLOTARRA, Allo, Spain

4DO.5.5 Adoption and Optimisation Analysis of Agrivoltaic Systems for Horticultural Production and Energy Autonomy in Lubumbashi/DR Congo 020393
Eddie Bilitu[1], Shu-Ngwa Asaa[2], Sara Bouguerra[3], Nikoleta Kyranaki[3], Ismail Kaaya[3], Yannick Useni[4], Michael Daenen[3]
[1] Hasselt University, Hasselt, Belgium; [2] imo-imomec, Genk, Belgium; [3] imec, Genk, Belgium; [4] University of Lubumbashi, Lubumbashi, Congo (DRC)

Visual SESSION 4DV.1 Agrivoltaics Approaches, Experiences, Results | Integrated and Innovative PV Applications

4DV.1.5 Maximizing Economic Performance of Agrivoltaic Systems through Module Array Design 020394
Habeel Alam[1], Jenny Nelson[2], Alona Armstrong[1], Duncan Whyatt[1], Nauman Butt[3]
[1] Lancaster University, Lancaster, United Kingdom; [2] Imperial College London, London, United Kingdom; [3] Lahore University of Management Sciences, Lahore, Pakistan

4DV.1.7 Bifacial and Mismatch Factors of Agri-Photovoltaics Systems 020396
Keith R. McIntosh[1], Solomon Freer[1], Bastien J. J. Ardissone[1], S. Ramirez[1], Ben A. Sudbury[1], Malcolm D. Abbott[1]
[1] PV Lighthouse, Coledale, Australia

4DV.1.10 Performance Analysis of Agrivoltaic System Configurations in Nordic Conditions 020398
Magda Szarek[1], Sami Jouttijärvi[1], Lauri Karttunen[1], Samuli Ranta[2], Kati Miettunen[1]
[1] University of Turku, Turku, Finland; [2] TUAS, Turku, Finland

4DV.1.11 Irradiance Management in Agrivoltaic Systems with Varying Designs Across Latitudes: Toward Finland's First Significant Demonstration 020400
Shuo Wang[1], Soroush Moradi Zavie Kord[2], Hugo E. Huerta[1], Antti Lajunen[2], Samuli Ranta[1]
[1] TUAS, Turku, Finland; [2] University of Helsinki, Helsinki, Finland

4DV.1.12 An Innovative Agrivoltaic System for Desert Climates with Anti-Soiling, Irradiance Control, and Water Management 020402
Sagarika Kumar[1], Min Hsian Saw[1], Ahmed Shaaban[1], Kamil Jaworczak[1], Nursulu Kuzhagaliyeva[1], Carlos G. Parrilla[2], Francois M. Tsombou[2], Fouad Lamghari[2], Mauro Pravettoni[1]
[1] Technology Innovation Institute, Abu Dhabi, United Arab Emirates; [2] Fujairah Research Centre, Fujairah, United Arab Emirates

4DV.1.15 Review of Sensor Technologies for Monitoring Agrivoltaic Systems 020403
Sara Pereira[1], José A. Silva[1], Luís Fialho[2], Pedro Horta[1]
[1] University of Évora, Évora, Portugal; [2] Eurac Research, Bolzano, Italy

Visual SESSION 4DV.4 PV System Engineering

[1] Luxembourg Institute of Science and Technology, Esch-sur-Alzette, Luxembourg; [2] University of Lisbon, Lisbon, Portugal

4EO.2.6 Optimizing Angular Performance of Curved VIPV Modules 020459
Francisco José Martín[1], Rebeca Herrero[1], Ignacio Antón[1]
[1] UPM, Madrid, Spain

Oral SESSION 5CO.4 Life Cycle Assessment of Silicon and Perovskite-based Cells and Modules

5CO.4.1 Towards Low-Impact Triple-Junction Perovskite/Silicon Tandem Modules: LCA of Precursor Materials to Describe the Influence of Background Data Sources 020461
Alejandra Galarza[1], Sebastian Nold[2], Lars Oberbeck[3]
[1] IPVF, Palaiseau, France; [2] Fraunhofer ISE, Freiburg, Germany; [3] TotalEnergies OneTech, Paris, France

5CO.4.3 Sustainability Assessment of Perovskite/Silicon Tandem Solar Modules: from Laboratory Scale to Industrial Implementation 020462
Elisabetta Brivio[1], Andrea Danelli[1], Sofia Spagnolo[1], Pierpaolo Girardi[1]
[1] RSE, Milan, Italy

5CO.4.4 LCA Learning Curve for Crystalline Silicon Solar Technologies based on Technology Improvements 020463
Julian Reichle[1], Moritz Fath[1], Sraisth[1], Amish Kumar Sinha[1], Mehul Raval[1], Wolfgang Jooss[1], Peter Fath[1], Gourab Das[1]
[1] RCT Solutions, Konstanz, Germany

Oral SESSION 5CO.5 Life Cycle Assessment of New PV Applications and Recycling

5CO.5.1 Optimizing AgriPV: A Comprehensive Assessment Framework for Sustainable Energy and Agriculture 020464
Ana Patrícia Lopes[1], Bruno Barrionuevo [2], Daniel P. Albuquerque[3], Diogo Cordeiro[4], Cláudia Fernandes[3], Athanasios T. Balafoutis [2], Rui Castro[1]
[1] University of Lisbon, Lisbon, Portugal; [2] CERTH, Athens, Greece; [3] Centre for New Energy Technologies, Sacavém, Portugal; [4] EDP, Lisbon, Portugal

5CO.5.2 Environmental Sustainability Assessment of Agrivoltaic Systems: a Life Cycle Approach 020466
Maria Anna Cusenza[1], Andrea Danelli[1], Pierpaolo Girardi[1], Sofia Spagnolo[1]
[1] RSE, Milan, Italy

5CO.5.4 Closing the Circle: Integrating the Circular Footprint Formula into Photovoltaic System Life Cycle Assessment 020467
Alexis Barrou[1], Selin Kandiyoti-Eskenazi[1], Jacques Levrat[1], Bertrand Paviet-Salomon[1], Christophe Ballif[1]
[1] CSEM, Neuchâtel, Switzerland

5CO.5.6 Environmental Benefits of Silicon Kerf Secondary Products in Pilot Processes over Conventional Production of Equivalent Products with Primary Raw Materials in China and Europe 020468
René Peche[1], Matthias Seitz[1], Markus Schönheits[1], Karsten Wambach[1]
[1] bifa Umweltinstitut, Augsburg, Germany

Oral SESSION 5CO.6 PV Recycling and Circularity

5CO.6.4 Quantification of Technical Recyclability of PV Modules for Different Recycling Scenarios 020470
Matthias Hämmer[1], Kerstin Baumann[1], Karsten Wambach[1], Markus Schönheits[1]
[1] bifa Umweltinstitut, Augsburg, Germany

5CO.6.5 IEC Technical Report 63525 on the Reuse of PV Modules: Final Result 020472
Arvid van der Heide[1], Serge Noels[2], Jan Clyncke[2], Rich Strömberg[3]
[1] imec, Genk, Belgium; [2] PV CYCLE, Brussels, Belgium; [3] University of Alaska, Fairbanks, United States of America

Plenary SESSION 5CP.1 Si PV Manufacturing: Pushing the Limits of Performance

5CP.1.4 Business Model Optimization for European Solar PV: A Study on Costs and Commercial Strategies 020474
Ian Kenchington[1], Philippe Macé[1], Gaëtan Masson[1], Joris Libal[2]
[1] Becquerel Institute, Brussels, Belgium; [2] ISC Konstanz, Konstanz, Germany

Plenary SESSION 5CP.2 Perovskite – Silicon Tandems: Towards Commercialisation | PV Stability in the Field

5CP.2.3 Total Cost of Ownership, LCA and LCOE Analysis of Perovskite-Silicon Tandems Compared to Single Junction Crystalline Silicon PV Technologies 020475
Baljeet Singh Goraya[1], Dilara Maria Subasi[1], Peter Henri Brailovsky[1], Henning Nagel[1], Patricia S.C. Schulze[1], Martin C. Schubert[1], Jochen Rentsch[1], Martin Hermle[1], Ralf Preu[1], Sebastian Nold[1]
[1] Fraunhofer ISE, Freiburg, Germany

Oral SESSION 5DO.11 The Road to Massive PV Deployment

5DO.11.1 Integration of Solar PV in a Norwegian Energy System, Navigating the Trade-offs between Land Use and Solar Power Production 020476
Petry Kristine Nøttum Haaland[1], Ole-Morten Midtgård[1], Magnus Korpås[1]
[1] NTNU, Trondheim, Norway

Oral SESSION 5DO.18 PV Recycling and Material Demand

Visual SESSION 5DV.2 Life Cycle Analysis and PV Recycling | Citizens Participation and Awareness

Visual SESSION 5DV.3 Grid Integration and Flexibility Enablers | Global, Country- and Application-Specific Analysis of PV Deployment Aspects | Costs, Economics, Finance and Markets

Oral SESSION 5EO.1 Citizens Participation and Awareness

42nd European Photovoltaic Solar Energy Conference and Exhibition

This presentation was selected by the Sc. Committee of the EU PVSEC 2025 for submission of a full paper to one of the EU PVSEC's collaborating peer-reviewed journals.

ENHANCING BROADBAND ANTIREFLECTION PERFORMANCE OF SILICON SOLAR CELLS USING GRASS-LIKE ALUMINA VIA ATOMIC LAYER DEPOSITION

Jiahui Xu[1*], Yuxuan Li[2], Wenjing Zhang[1], Geng Zhang[3], Pierre Verlinden[1], Cui Liu[2], Zhenjue Shen[1], Xiao Yuan[1]
[1] Yangtze institute for solar technology (YIST), Jiangyin, Jiangsu, 214400, China
[2] School of Materials Science and Engineering, East China University of Science and Technology, Shanghai, 200237, China
[3] Jolywood (ShanXi) Solar Technology Co., Ltd, Taiyuan, ShanXi, 030000, China

*Corresponding author: telephone: (+86)17621183653, email: xujh@yist.org.cn

ABSTRACT: Nano grass-like alumina structures were fabricated on the front surface of tunnel oxide passivated contact (TOPCon) silicon solar cells to improve broadband antireflection performance. Under the AM1.5G and AM0 spectra from 300 to 1180 nm wavelengths, the nano grass-like alumina structures reduces the weighted reflectance by 0.9%abs and 1.1%abs. The integrated short-circuit current density increases by 0.7 mA/cm^2 and 1 mA/cm^2, respectively. These photocurrent gains are primarily caused by reducing the front-side reflection losses at short wavelengths. Additional benefits arise from reduced front-side escape losses at medium and long wavelengths. No additional surface recombination is observed after nano grass-like alumina structures integration, supported by minority carrier lifetime and IV measurements. The nano grass-like alumina structures also exhibit excellent low optical reflection loss at high incident angles. Finally, post-encapsulation reflectance measurements confirmed that the nano grass-like alumina structures retained superior broadband antireflective properties.
Keywords: antireflection, glass-like alumina, nanostructures, silicon solar cell

1 INTRODUCTION

Recent advances in crystalline silicon (c-Si) solar cells have boosted power efficiency and cut manufacturing costs, accelerating the adoption of photovoltaics [1]. Research is generally focused on new structures and materials to reach the theoretical efficiency limit of c-Si solar cells. Passivated contacts, like amorphous silicon heterojunctions (SHJ) and tunnel oxide passivated contacts (TOPCon), are enabling to reach efficiencies closer theoretical limits and, therefore, are drawing significant attention. A large-area hybrid interdigitated-back-contact (HIBC) solar cell, for instance, has achieved a record efficiency of 27.8% [2]. Regardless of their specific design, a key research goal for c-Si solar cells is to reduce surface recombination and optical absorption losses. These cells typically use micron-scale pyramid textures with antireflection layers. However, front-side short-wavelength reflection losses still accounts for a large portion of power loss and represent a major limitation for further efficiency improvement [3, 4].

Various methods have been developed to minimize front-side optical reflection. One method is using nanostructured silicon textures, also known as black silicon. The sub-wavelength feature sizes of black silicon can scatter light and greatly reduce reflectance across a broadband, with an average reflectance below 2% [5]. But black silicon creates many surface defects, causing severe recombination of photogenerated carriers [6]. The trade-off between optical gains and electrical losses is difficult to resolve within the "coupled surface structures" framework, where light trapping and surface passivation are linked. Another strategy is to engineer multilayer antireflection coatings. This can achieve ultra-low reflection at specific wavelengths by adjusting the refractive index and thickness of the films [7]. However, it is expensive and difficult to achieve broad-spectrum antireflection while maintaining high-quality passivation with this method [8].

To solve this trade-off, decoupled structures have been proposed, where sub-wavelength structure coatings are applied on top of passivation layers. This allows light trapping and surface passivation to be optimized independently. Research on external light-trapping for gallium arsenide (GaAs) solar cells offers insights for c-Si solar cells. GaAs solar cells have high optical absorption, so surface texturing has limited benefits, and their crystal structure is not easily etched. For instance, Liu et al. [9] used SiO_2 nanopillars on GaAs solar cells, which reduced average reflectance to 5.5%, but the constant porosity limited the refractive index gradient and performance. In contrast, Reuna et al. [10] created a grass-like Al_2O_3 layer that lowered average reflectance to 2.8% and preserved electrical performance, showing promise.

In this study, nano grass-like alumina (NGLA) was applied to standard TOPCon solar cells using atomic layer deposition (ALD) for the first time. This reduced the weighted reflectance under the AM1.5G spectrum from 5.38% to 4.52%. Measurements of saturation current density (J_0) and open-circuit voltage (V_{oc}) confirmed that photocurrent was enhanced without harming passivation, leading to a 0.7% absolute increase in efficiency. The process is also compatible with current TOPCon solar cell manufacturing equipment, making it suitable for industrial use.

2 EXPERIMENTAL

2.1 Sample preparation

Industrial bifacial TOPCon solar cells and non-metallized "blue wafers" were cut to 50 mm × 50 mm using a laser to fit the ALD chamber. The TOPCon solar cells were soldered with busbar wires for consistent electrical measurements before and after the NGLA process. The samples were placed in a thermal ALD system with the front surface facing up. Trimethylaluminum (TMA) and deionized (DI) water were used as precursors with nitrogen as a carrier and purge gas. Amorphous ALD Al_2O_3 films were deposited at 150 °C over 400 cycles. The NGLA structures were then formed by immersing the samples in 80 °C DI water for 30 minutes. Finally, a simplified encapsulation with silicone and cover glass was performed to test the stability of the NGLA structures in a module-like environment.

2.2 Characterization

A scanning electron microscope (SEM) with an energy dispersive spectrometer (EDS) was used to analyze the morphology and elemental composition of the NGLA structures. Reflectance and transmittance spectra were measured with a spectrophotometer. Effective minority carrier lifetime (τ_{eff}), implied Voc (iV_{oc}), and J_0 were measured on non-metallized wafers using transient photoconductivity decay. A spectral response system was used for external quantum efficiency (EQE) characterization. Current-voltage (IV) curves and electrical parameters were measured with a class A+A+A+ steady-state AM1.5G & AM0 solar simulator and an IV measurement system.

3 RESULTS AND DISCUSSIONS

3.1 Surface morphology and optical property

Figure 1 shows the SEM images of NGLA morphologies on the TOPCon solar cell front surface. Figures 1a and 1c show top-views of textured and metallized finger regions at 20.0 K magnification, with higher magnification views in Figures 1b and 1d. Cross-section images are shown in Figures 1e and 1f. The NGLA structures are made of randomly stacked Al_2O_3 nano-flakelets, about 10 nm thick and 100 nm high, consistent with other reports [11]. The structure has a graded porosity, decreasing from the air towards the c-Si substrate, which is crucial for creating a smooth refractive index profile. The ALD process ensures uniform coverage, a benefit over other techniques. Figure 1f shows the NGLA layer is about 140 nm thick, roughly three times the original film thickness. The transformation is believed to result from differing dissolution rates of amorphous Al_2O_3 and AlOOH species in DI water, followed by recrystallization into $Al(OH)_3$ during the hydrothermal process [12].

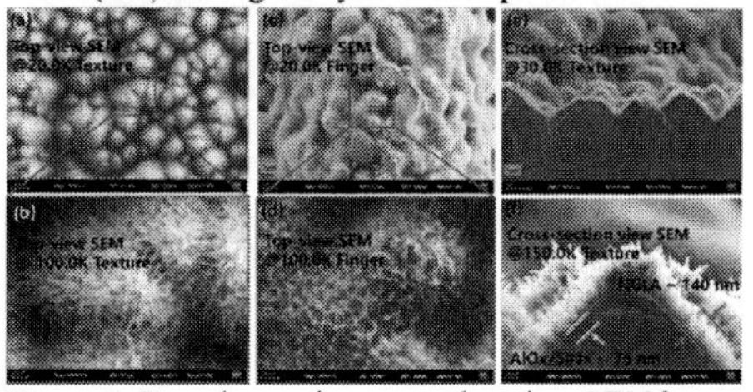

Figure 1: Top-view and cross-section view SEM images of NGLA morphologies.

Figure 2 demonstrates the optical performance of the NGLA structures. Weighted average reflectance (R_{ave}) values were calculated for AM1.5G and AM0 spectra. Figures 2a and 2b show that NGLA structures significantly reduced reflectance at short (300 ~ 535 nm) and medium-long (740 ~ 1050 nm) wavelengths, providing excellent broadband antireflection. This is due to the graded porosity, which creates a gradual refractive index transition from 1.0 (air) to 1.65 (ALD Al_2O_3), reducing Fresnel reflections. The three-dimensional nano-flakelet structure also increases light path length through multiple scattering and refraction, enhancing absorption.

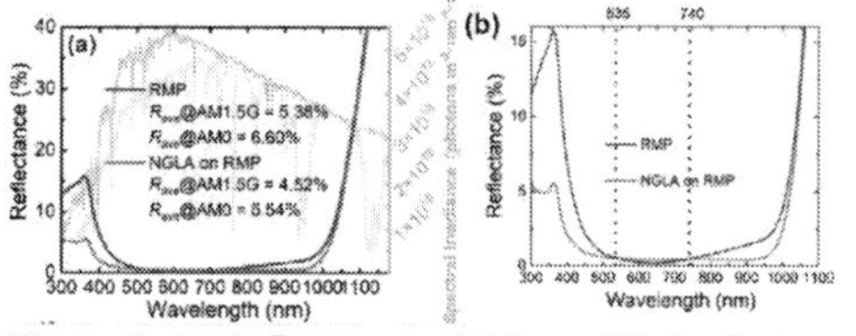

Figure 2: (a) Reflectance and (d) amplified reflectance spectra of conventional RMP TOPCon solar cells and NGLA TOPCon solar cells from 300 to 1180 nm wavelengths.

A slight reflectance increase was seen in the mid-wavelength range (535-740 nm) because the NGLA structures interfere with the original antireflection design. Overall, NGLA integration reduced the R_{ave} from 5.38% to 4.52% under AM1.5G spectrum, and it dropped from 6.60% to 5.54% under AM0 spectrum. This proves NGLA structures improve broadband optical absorption. This characteristic is especially suitable for solar cells designed for space applications that includes a stronger short-wavelength radiation and usually untextured solar cell surface.

3.2 Passivation property

High-quality surface passivation is critical for high efficiency. Unlike black silicon, which results in poor surface passivation [13], NGLA structures do not degrade the quality of passivation. Measurements on non-metallized wafers and soldered solar cells were conducted to evaluate the effect of the NGLA fabrication process on passivation. Figures 3a-3c show that after NGLA formation on non-metallized wafers, the τ_{eff} reached 3196 μs, $iVoc$ was 740 mV, and J_0 was reduced to 8.7 fA/cm^2, indicating no degradation. These results further confirm that the NGLA process does not harm surface recombination parameters, and may even improve passivation quality, possibly by passivating edges damaged by laser cutting. Similar edge passivation effects by ALD Al_2O_3 films have been reported previously [14, 15].

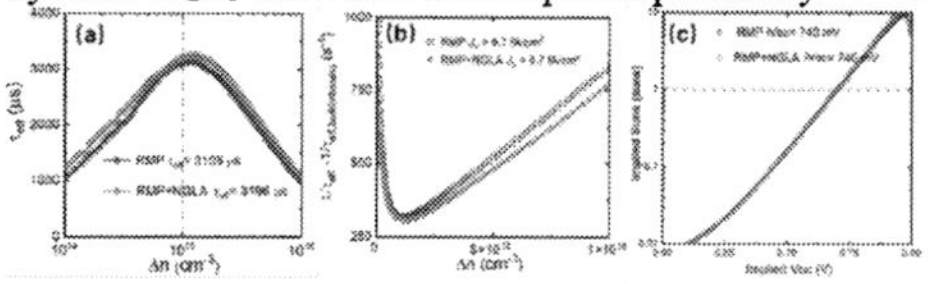

Figure 3: Comparison of passivation properties before and after NGLA structure formation. (a) The τ_{eff} , (b) iV_{oc} and (c) J_0 of non-metallized TOPCon blue wafers with RMP textures and NGLA on top of RMP textures.

3.3 Solar cell performance

The optical improvements from NGLA structures were assessed at the device level. Reflectance and EQE curves were measured on a soldered TOPCon solar cell. As shown in Figure 4, the NGLA TOPCon solar cells had reduced reflectance and improved EQE in the 300 ~ 500 nm range, while the internal quantum efficiency (IQE) remained unchanged. This confirms the EQE improvement is due to enhanced front reflectance, not better carrier collection. In the 500 ~ 750 nm range, reflectance, EQE, and IQE were similar between both structures. In the 750-1000 nm range, NGLA TOPCon solar cells had slightly lower reflectance and higher EQE, while IQE remained high, indicating that the graded refractive index suppresses long-wavelength reflection and improves light trapping. For the 1000 ~ 1180 nm range, NGLA TOPCon solar cells had similar reflectance but higher EQE and IQE. This is likely due to enhanced light trapping and unintentional Al_2O_3 deposition on the rear side. The superior antireflection and slight passivation improvement led to an integrated J_{sc} increase from 41.1 mA/cm² to 42.1 mA/cm², whcih is a 2.4% relative improvement under AM1.5G spectrum. And under the AM0 spectrum, the integrated J_{sc} increase from 50.5 mA/cm² to 51.5 mA/cm², which is a 2% relative improvement.

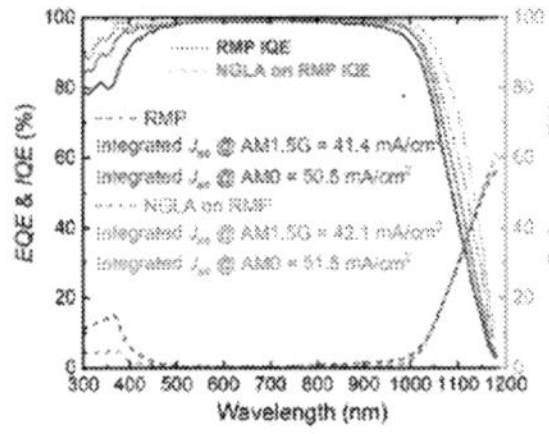

Figure 4: EQE (solid lines), reflectance (dash lines) and IQE (dotted lines) spectra of conventional RMP TOPCon solar cell and one of soldered NGLA TOPCon solar cell.

Table 1 shows the IV data for three soldered solar cells (A1–A3) before and after NGLA process. The V_{oc} of all three solar cells remained stable, with an average improvement of about 1 mV, confirming that passivation quality was not degraded. Significant increases in J_{sc} were observed, confirming the broadband antireflection benefit at the device level. Due to inconsistent fill factor (*FF*) values, efficiency results varied; A1 had a slight drop, while A2 and A3 improved by 0.9% and 0.7%, respectively. Further work with full-size solar cells is planned to get a more accurate evaluation.

Table 1: The IV parameters of three conventional RMP TOPCon solar cells before and after the NGLA process.

Cell Name	V_{oc} (mV)	*FF* (%)	J_{sc} (mA/cm²)	Eff (%)	R_{sh}(Ω)
A1	723	72.0	40. 6	21.1	89
A1@ NGLA	722	70.0	41.5	21.0	22
A2	718	68.6	40.5	19.9	8
A2@ NGLA	719	70.4	41.1	20.8	14
A3	719	77.4	40.8	22.7	527
A3@ NGLA	721	76.8	42.2	23.4	202

Nanostructured textures on c-Si solar cells generally reduce angular sensitivity, which is beneficial for fixed or vertically mounted modules. We measured EQE curves at different incident angles. The EQE of RMP solar cells decreased significantly, especially in short and mid-to-long wavelengths. The NGLA solar cells showed a smaller EQE reduction. At a 60° incidence angle, the integrated J_{sc} of NGLA solar cells was 98.3% of the normal-incidence value, while RMP solar cells only retained 95.6%. This confirms that NGLA structures improve both broadband antireflection and angular stability.

3.4 PV module performance

The optical performance of the NGLA structures was also tested at the module level. Blue wafers with and without NGLA were encapsulated with silicone and glass, and their reflectance was measured. Figure 5a shows that the NGLA structures maintained excellent broadband antireflection after encapsulation, with R_{ave} decreasing by 0.6% under both AM1.5G and AM0 spectra. Cross-section SEM images (Figure 5b) showed that some NGLA structures collapsed or folded during encapsulation. The silicone also infiltrated the porous nano-flakelets, which weakened the graded refractive index profile. These changes account for the slight reduction in antireflective performance observed at the module level.

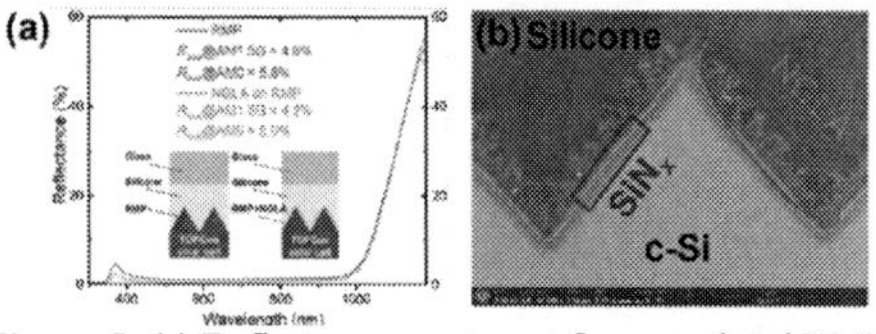

Figure 5: (a) Reflectance spectrum of encapsulated RMP and NGLA TOPCon PV modules. (b) Cross-sectional SEM image of the encapsulated NGLA TOPCon PV modules.

4 CONCLUSIONS

This study presents the direct integration of the NGLA structures based on ALD technique on the front surface of standard textured TOPCon solar cells. The NGLA was fabricated via low-temperature ALD followed by a DI water treatment. This structure composed of Al2O3 nano-flakelets with a graded porosity, establishes a gradual refractive index transition from air to the underlying passivation layer. This significantly reduces broadband reflection. Experimental results indicate that NGLA structure enhances the Jsc of TOPCon solar cells by more than 0.6 mA/cm2. This enhancement occurs without compromising passivation quality, thereby contributing to a notable improvement in efficiency. Additionally, the NGLA TOPCon solar cells exhibit greater stability in light absorption under varying incident angles. Although partial structural collapse was observed after encapsulation, the NGLA structure still maintains superior anti-reflective performance compared to conventional RMP textures. The fabrication process is fully compatible with existing TOPCon production lines, highlighting its strong potential for industrial-scale application.

5 ACKNOWLEDGMENTS

This work was supported by the Yangtze Institute for Solar Technology (Y20240202-RD). We thank Jolywood Solar Technology Co., Ltd for the help of TOPCon solar cell. We thank JITRI Advanced Materials R&D Co. Ltd. for the help with SEM analysis and cross sections.

6 REFERENCE

[1] Li W, Xu Z, Yan Y, Zhou J, Huang Q, Xu S, Zhang X, Zhao Y, Hou G. Advanced Energy Materials 14 (2024)
[2] Green Martin A, Dunlop Ewan D, Yoshita M, Kopidakis N, Bothe K, Siefer G, Hao X, Jiang Jessica Y. Progress in Photovoltaics: Research and Applications 33 (2025) 795-810

[3] Fung T H, Pasanen T P, Zhang Y, Soeriyadi A, Vähänissi V, Scardera G, Payne D, Savin H, Abbott M. Solar Energy Materials and Solar Cells 210 (2020)
[4] Wang G, Su Q, Tang H, Wu H, Lin H, Han C, Wang T, Xue C, Lu J, Fang L, Li Z, Xu X, Gao P. Nature Communications 15 (2024) 8931
[5] Hsu C-H, Liu S-M, Wu W-Y, Cho Y-S, Huang P-H, Huang C-J, Lien S-Y, Zhu W-Z. Arabian Journal of Chemistry 13 (2020) 8239-8274
[6] Otto M, Algasinger M, Branz H, Gesemann B, Gimpel T, Füchsel K, Käsebier T, Kontermann S, Koynov S, Li X, Naumann V, Oh J, Sprafke A N, Ziegler J, Zilk M, Wehrspohn R B. Advanced Optical Materials 3 (2015) 147-164
[7] Selj J H, Mongstad T T, Sondenå R, Marstein E S. Solar Energy Materials and Solar Cells 95 (2011) 2576-2582
[8] Ji C X, Liu W, Bao Y D, Chen X L, Yang G Q, Wei B, Yang F H, Wang X D. Photonics 9 (2022)
[9] Liu S, Qian Y, Lin Y, Sun L, Zhu Y, Li D. Solar Energy Materials and Solar Cells 266 (2024) 112679
[10] Reuna J, Hietalahti A, Aho A, Isoaho R, Aho T, Vuorinen M, Tukiainen A, Anttola E, Guina M. Acs Applied Energy Materials 5 (2022) 5804-5810
[11] An Z, Hao J, Sun S, Su J-a, Yang C, Wang S, Cheng S, Dong B. Langmuir 40 (2024) 21644-21655
[12] Willis S A, McGuinness E K, Li Y, Losego M D. Langmuir 37 (2021) 14509-14519
[13] Özkol E, Procel P, Zhao Y, Mazzarella L, Medlin R, Šutta P, Isabella O, Zeman M. Physica Status Solidi RRL: Rapid Research Letters 14 (2019)
[14] Baliozian P, Al-Akash M, Lohmüller E, Richter A, Fellmeth T, Münzer A, Wöhrle N, Saint-Cast P, Stolzenburg H, Spribille A, Preu R. IEEE Journal of Photovoltaics 10 (2020) 390-397
[15] Lohmüller E, Baliozian P, Gutmann L, Kniffki L, Beladiya V, Geng J, Wang L, Dunbar R, Lepert A, Hofmann M, Richter A, Huyeng J D. Solar Energy Materials and Solar Cells 258 (2023) 112419

長三角太陽能光伏技術創新中心
Yangtze Institute for Solar Technology

YiST

Enhancing Broadband Antireflection Performance of Silicon Solar Cells Using Grass-Like Alumina via Atomic Layer Deposition

Jiahui Xu, Yuxuan Li, Wenjing Zhang, Geng Zhang, Pierre Verlinden, Cui Liu, Xiao Yuan

22.09. 2025 The 42nd European Photovoltaic Solar Energy Conference and Exhibition Bilbao, Spain

1. Introduction

YiST

- Conventional c-Si solar cell

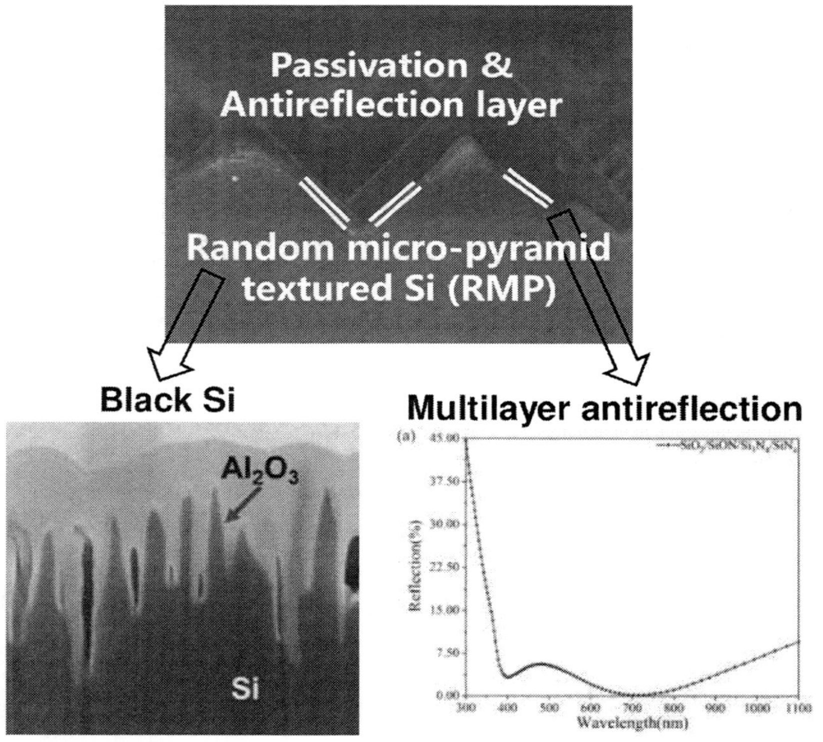

- Objective of this research
- **Developing a decoupling surface offering better antireflection and light-trapping while maintaining low surface recombination and excellent J_0.**
- Decoupling surface

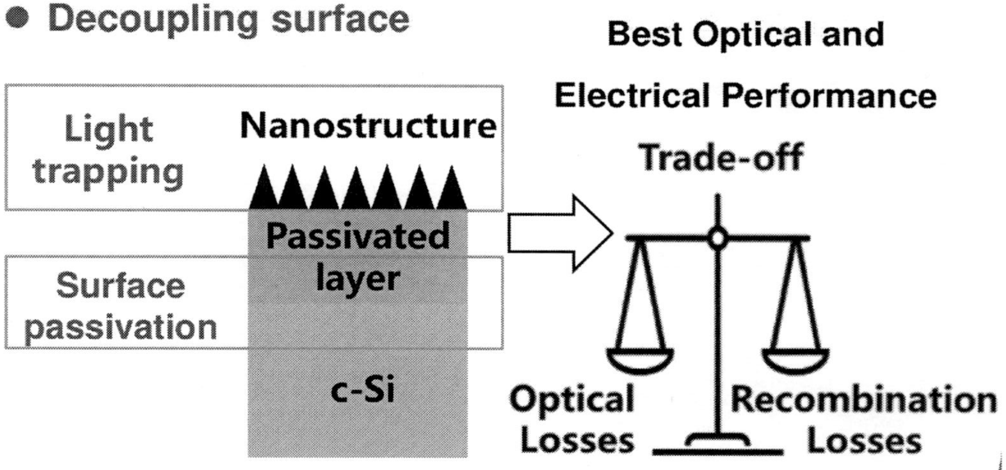

2. Experimental

YiST

■ Nano grass-like Al_2O_3 (NGLA) via (ALD + DIW treatment)

- ✓ Anti-reflectance
- ✓ Passivation
- ✓ Compatibility
- ✓ Cost

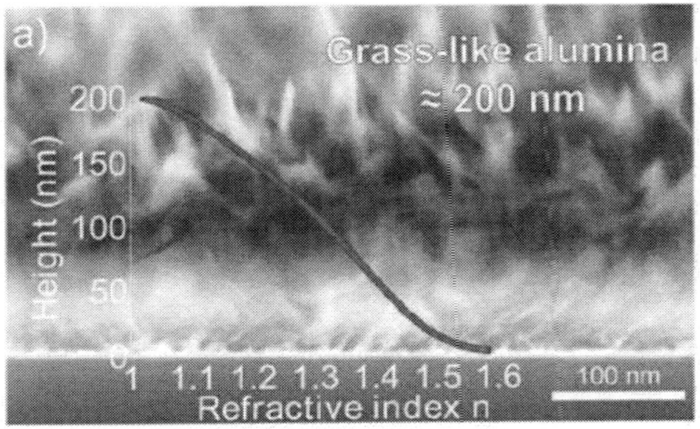

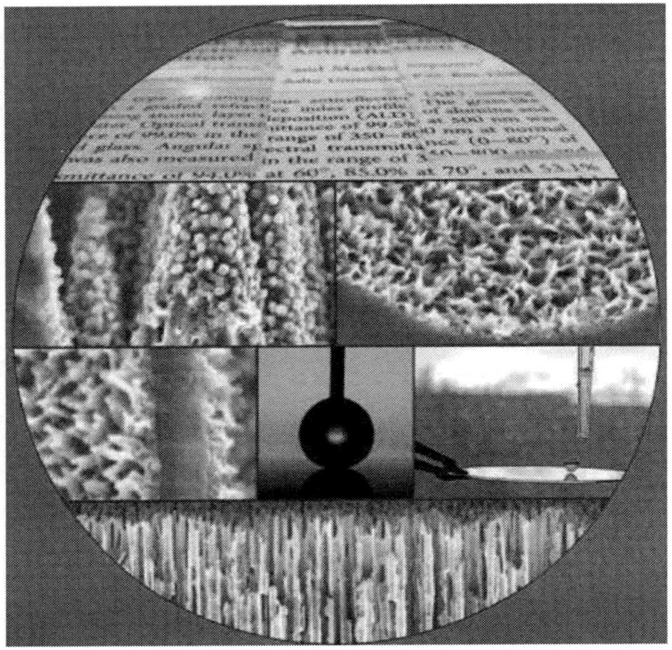

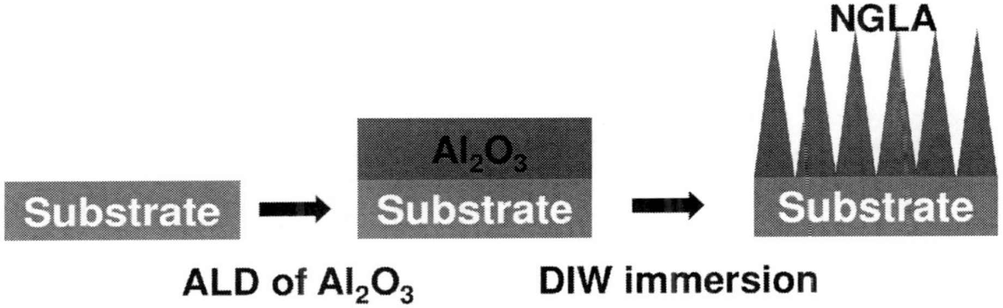

Ref : https://aalto.zoom.us/j/66890081498

2. Experimental

YIST

Process of NGLA solar cell

Bifacial TOPCon solar cell & Non-metallized TOPCon wafer (182 mm *182 mm)

Laser cutting

Bifacial TOPCon solar cell (50 mm * 50 mm)	Non-metallized TOPCon wafer (50 mm * 50 mm)
Soldering	
SEM, *IV*, R_F, *EQE*, *SunsVoc*	τ_{eff}, J_0, iV_{oc}

Thermal ALD Al_2O_3 : TMA + H_2O, 150 °C

DI treatment: 80 °C, 30 min

SEM, *IV*, R_F, *EQE*, *SunsVoc*	τ_{eff}, J_0, iV_{oc}

Encapsulation

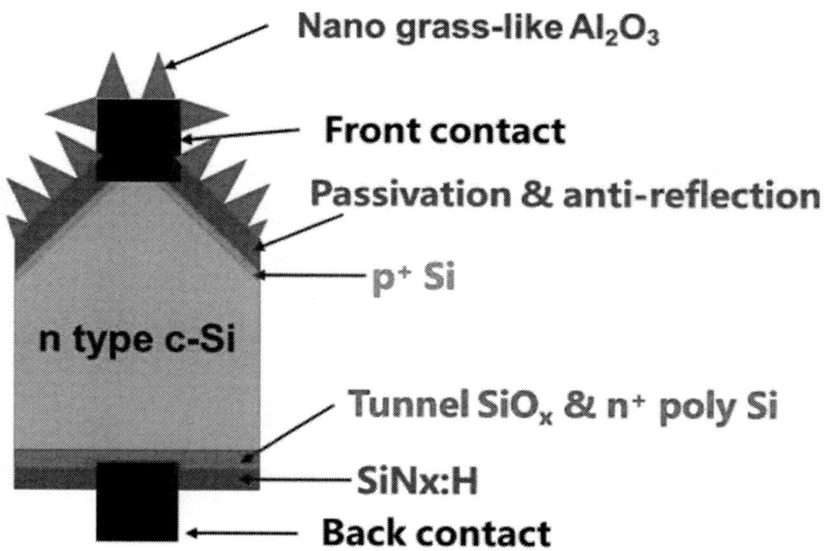

3. Results

YIST

3.1 Surface morphology

NGLA TOPCon solar cell

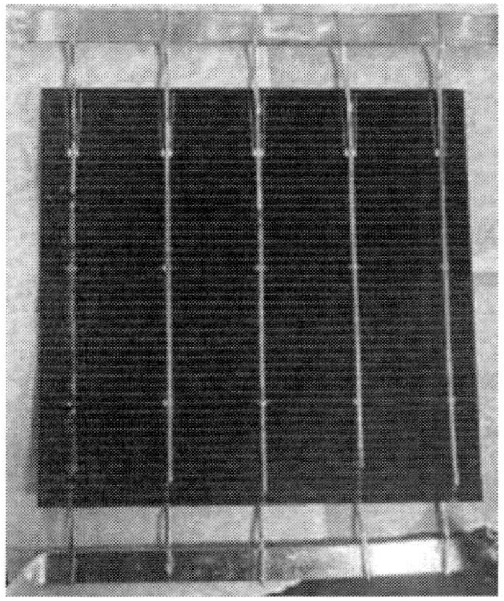

- SEM top-view @ 100.0K

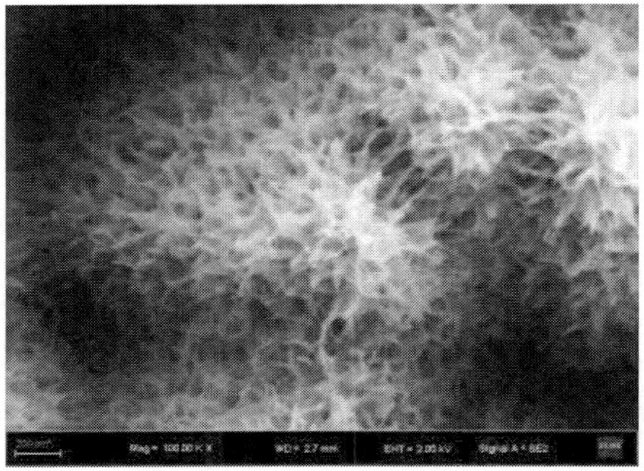

- SEM cross-section view @150.0K

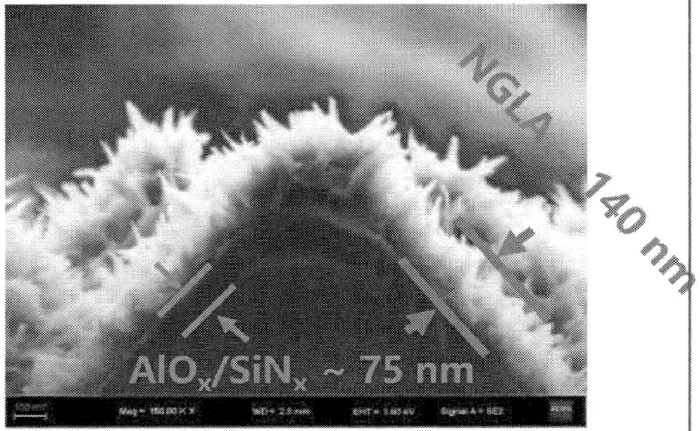

- Disorganized grass-like structure
- Sub-wavelength feature sizes
- Conformal coverage
- Gradually decreasing porosity

www.yist.org.cn

5

3. Results

YiST

3.2 Optical property ■ Reflectance spectra and weighted averaged values

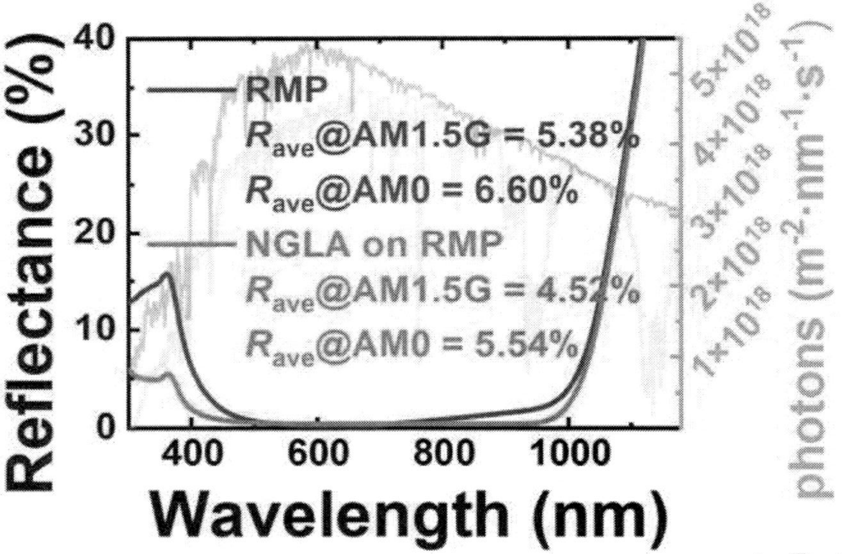

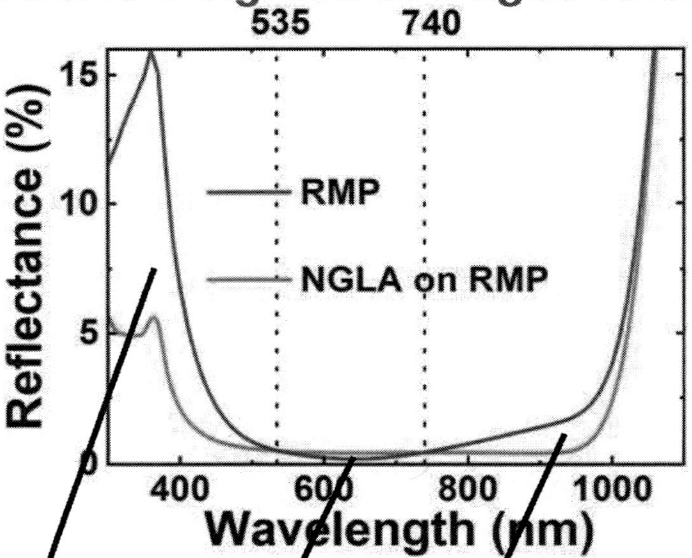

- Better broadband antireflection

① Significantly decrease (300 ~ 535 nm, 5.4×10^{20} photons m^2/s)

② Slight increase (535 ~ 740 nm, 9.3×10^{20} photons m^2/s)

③ Significantly decrease(740 ~ 1050 nm, 10.8×10^{20} photons m^2/s)

① R_{ave} from 5.38% to 4.52% @ AM1.5G

② R_{ave} from 6.60% to 5.54% @ AM0

3. Results

YIST

3.3 Passivation property

■ WCT-120 results

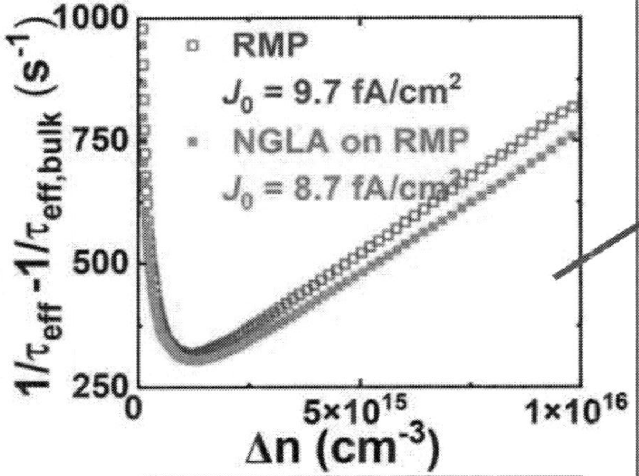

■ SunsVoc results

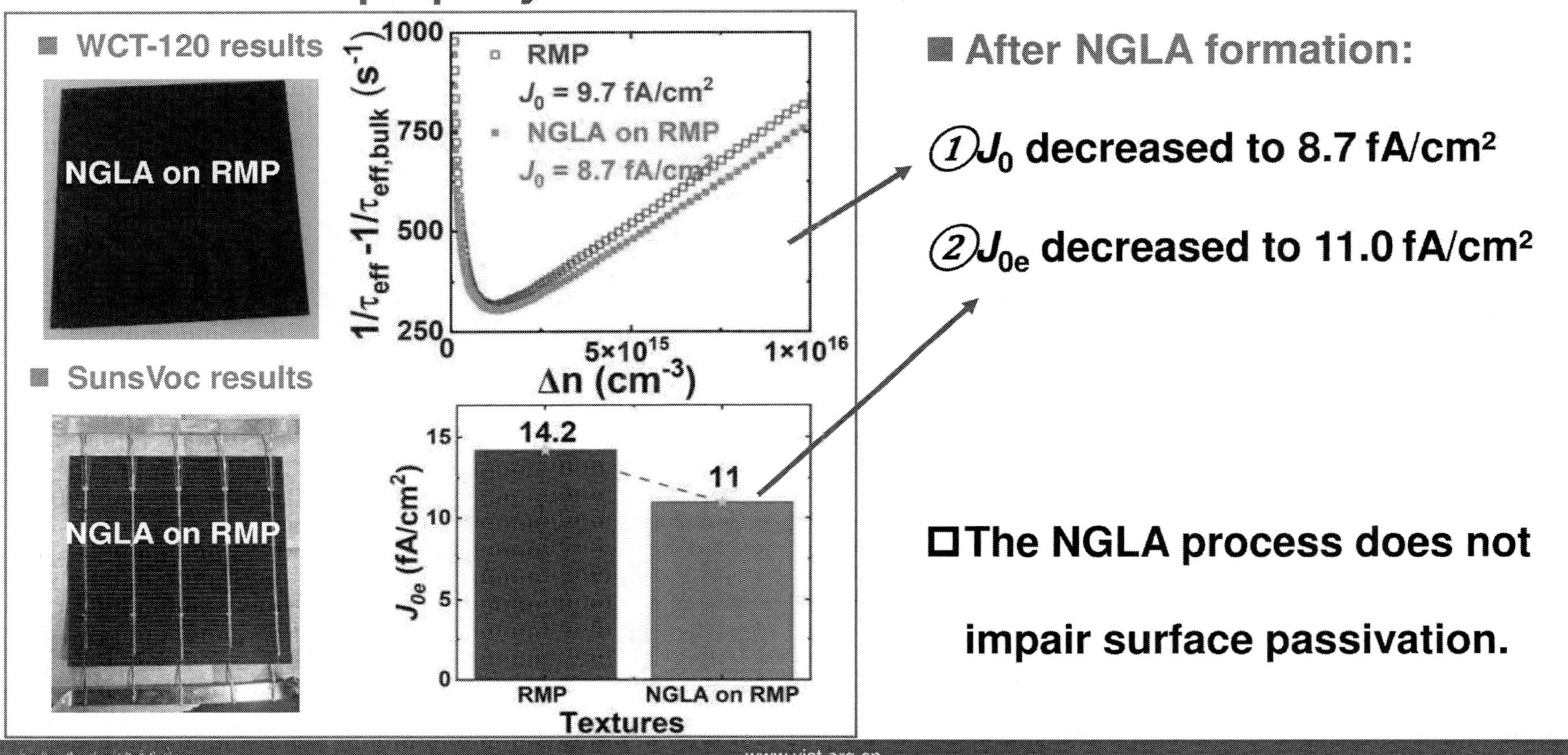

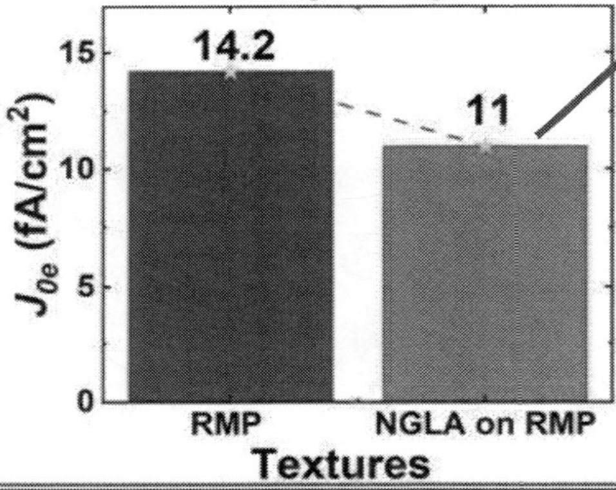

■ After NGLA formation:

① J_0 decreased to 8.7 fA/cm²

② J_{0e} decreased to 11.0 fA/cm²

□ The NGLA process does not impair surface passivation.

3. Results

3.4 EQE & IQE

AM 1.5G	0.1 mA/cm²	0.1 mA/cm²	0.5 mA/cm²
AM 0	0.3 mA/cm²	0.2 mA/cm²	0.5 mA/cm²

YiST

■ EQE measurements

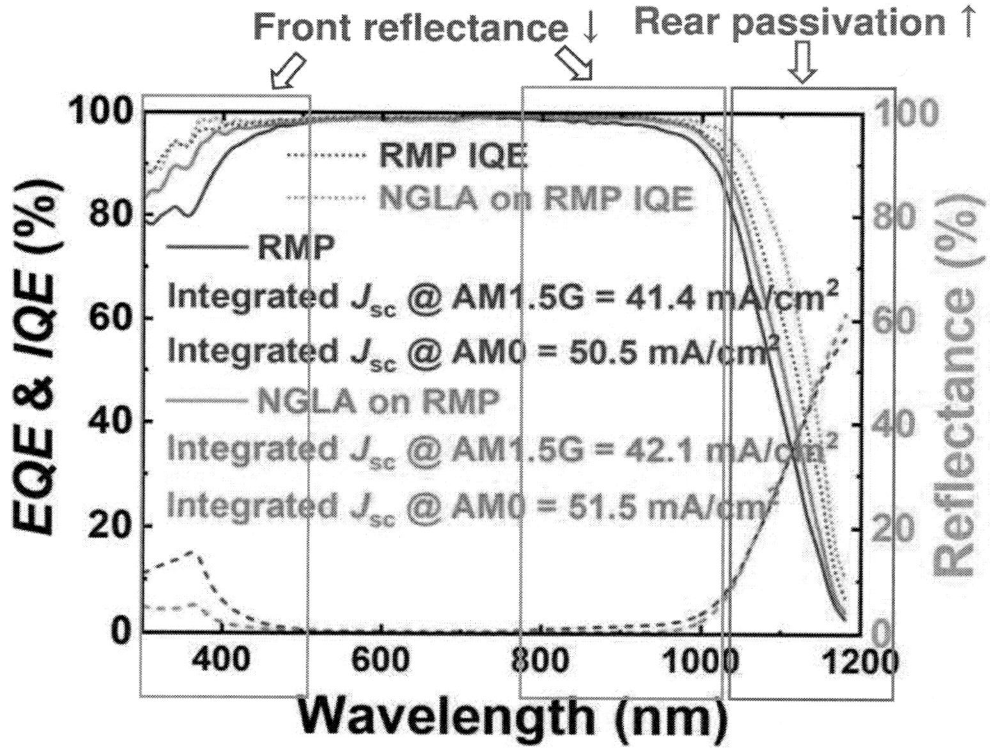

- The integrated J_{sc} increased from 41.4 mA/cm² to 42.1 mA/cm², a 2.4% relative improvement @ AM1.5G
- The integrated J_{sc} increased from 50.5 mA/cm² to 51.5 mA/cm², a 2.0% relative improvement @ AM0

3. Results

YiST

3.5 Solar cell performance

Cell Name	V_{oc} (mV)	Improvement (%)	J_{sc} (mA/cm^2)	Improvement (%)
A1	723	/	40. 6	/
A1@NGLA	722	- 0.1	41.5	+ 2.2
A2	718	/	40.5	/
A2 @ NGLA	719	+ 0.1	41.1	+ 1.5
A3	719	/	40.8	/
A3 @NGLA	721	+ 0.3	42.2	+ 3.4

■ IV measurements:

①The NGLA did not degrade passivation.

②The NGLA enhanced J_{sc} over 1.5% improvement at solar cell level.

➢ Additional full-size solar cells will be fabricated.

3. Results

YiST

3.6 Angular sensitivity in spectral response

■ EQE curves and integrated J_{sc} at different incidence angles

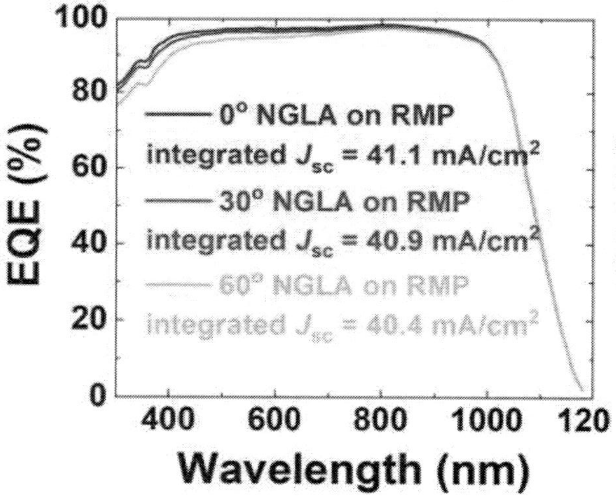

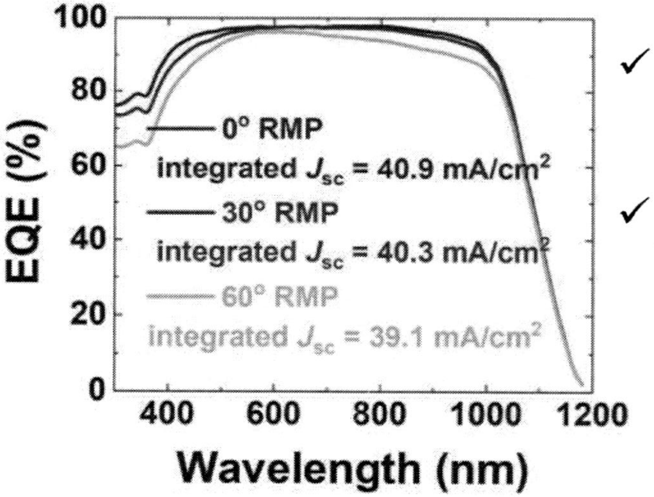

✓ The NGLA shows wide-angle antireflection

✓ Better for fixed angles PV applications

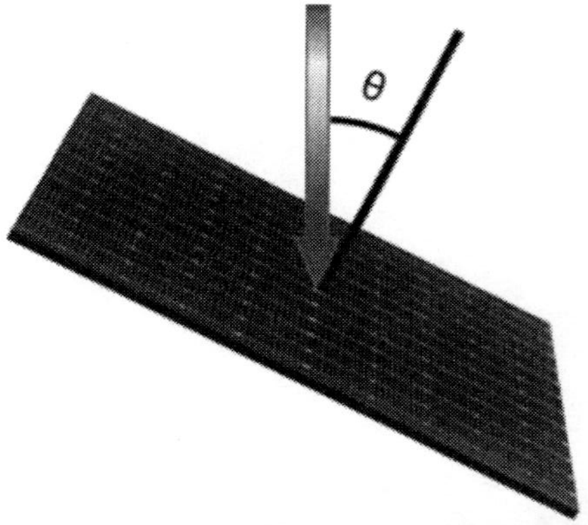

■ J_{sc} (θ) / J_{sc} (θ = 0) (%)

Sample	0°	30°	60°
RMP	100	98.7	95.6
NGLA on RMP	100	99.5	98.3

3. Results

3.7 PV module performance

YiST

- Reflectance spectra, weighted averaged values and SEM cross-section view after encapsulation

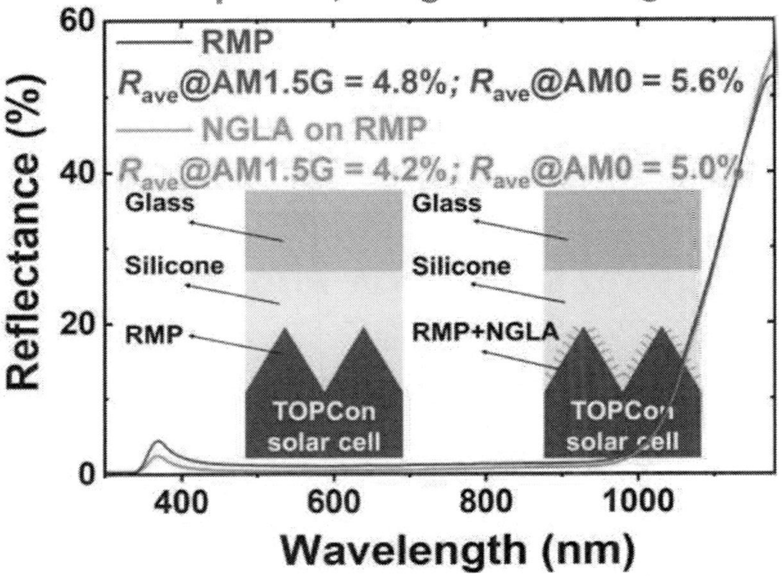

① R_{ave} all decreased by 0.6% @ AM1.5G & AM0 spectrum.

② The NGLA structures collapsed or folded during encapsulation

③ The NGLA retain broadband antireflection after encapsulation.

4. Summary

YiST

- ✓ The NGLA structures show wide-angle broadband antireflection.
- ✓ The NGLA structures enhance the J_{sc} of TOPCon solar cells over 0.6 mA/cm^2, without degrading the surface passivation and the J_0.
- ✓ The open-circuit voltage is preserved.
- ✓ The NGLA structures maintain antireflection and light-trapping performance after encapsulation.

➢ Next steps: Transfer results from small structures to large-size solar cells.

5. Outlook

YIST

■ Potential application : untextured (flat surface) devices with advantage of lowering J_0

- Perovskite/silicon tandem solar cells
- Untextured silicon solar cells
- Multijunction III-V solar cells

Jia, L. *Nature* 644, 2025

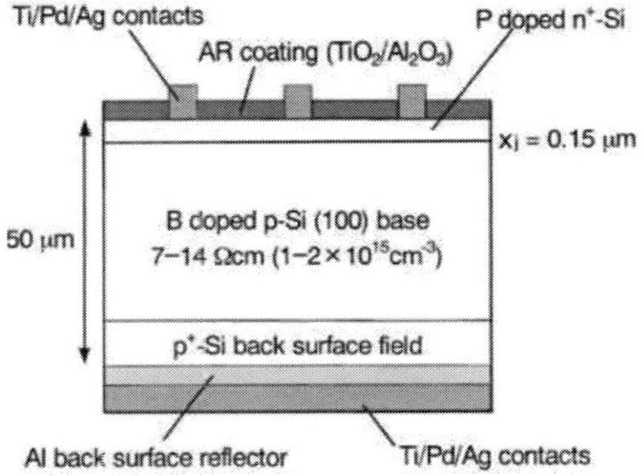

Yamaguchi, M. *Solmat* 68, 2001

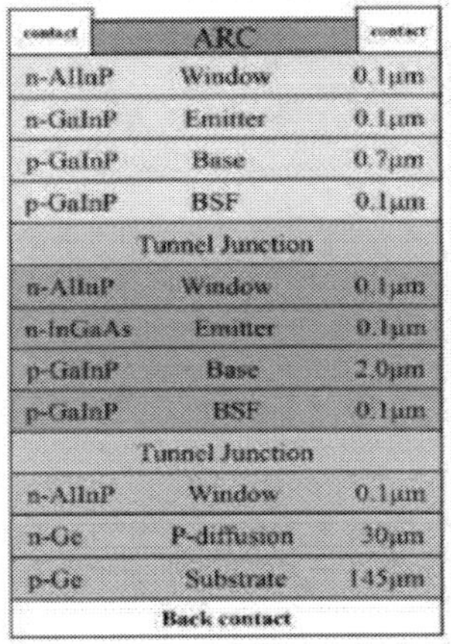

Weinan, Z. *Solener* 217, 2021

長三角太陽能光伏技術創新中心
Yangtze Institute for Solar Technology

YiST

Jiahui Xu

Email: xujh@yist.org.cn

ORCID:

Thank you

https://yist.org.cn

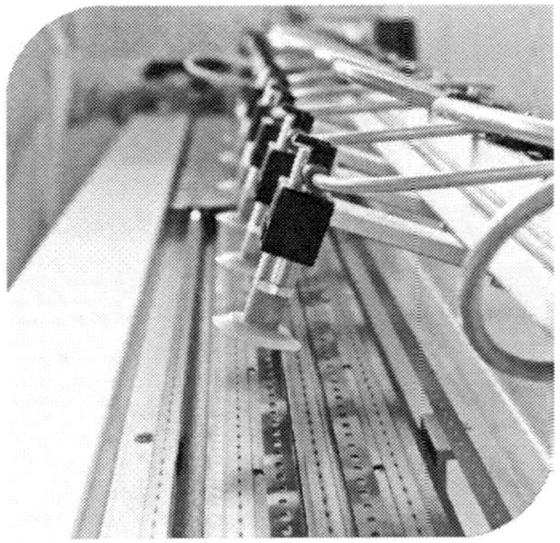

Screen Printed Cu-TOPCon Cells With Reduced Ag Consumption

Jan Lossen, Justus Carstens, Mertcan Comak, Apoorva Gattu,
Dominik Rudolph, Pirmin Preis, Lejo Koduvelikulathu

ISC research for a sunny future

EU-PVSEC Bilbao 2025

22.09.2025

Go for Gold?

NBA star Dennis Schröder (center) was the key man for Germany

Germany came from behind in a tightly contested game to beat **Turkey** 88-83 and win the EuroBasket 2025 final on Sunday in Riga. This comes two years after Germany – with mostly the same players – **won their first FIBA World Cup**.

We were very happy that the German team won the gold medal at EuroBasket.

Comment of my turkish collegue: „You are stupid – investing in silver gives much better returns".

Development of Ag price

From https://www.bullionbypost.eu, downloaded on 21.09.2025

- Silver price has increased 120% in only 3 years.
- The price is now very close to its last record high from 2011
- (but also Gold is on an all-time high)

Ag consumption by PV

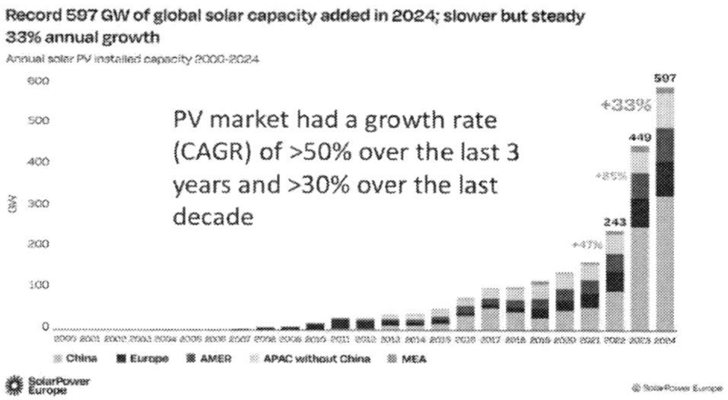

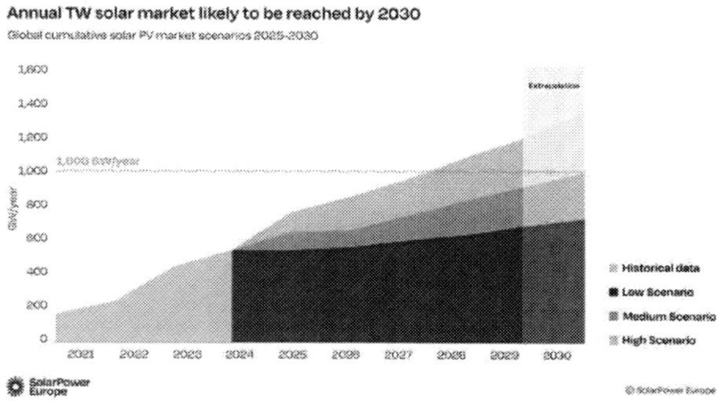

- PV market has increased 14-fold over the past decade [1].
- Even if growth slows down, a production of > 1 TWp/y is likely to be reached in 2030 [2].
- At current Ag consumtion (~12 mg/Wp) 1 TWp of PV would equal to ~41% of world Ag supply [3]

-> **better to reduce dependency on silver!**

[1] IEA PVPS, 2025 Snapshot of Global PV Markets, April 2025
[2] Solar Power Europe, Global Market Outlook for Solar Power 2025-2029, 6 May 2025
[3] The Silver Institute and Metals Focus, Word Silver Survey 2025, April 2025.

Cu-TOPCon Approach

Objective
- Fully screen printed TOPCon solar cell
- Replace as much silver as possible
- Without compromising efficiency

Approach:
- Use Ag paste only for FS fingers and RS contact layer
- Cu- paste for RS conduction layer and BB's

Cu-TOPCon Approach

Objective
- Fully screen printed TOPCon solar cell
- Replace as much silver as possible
- Without compromising efficiency

Approach:
- Use Ag paste only for FS fingers and RS contact layer
- Cu- paste for RS conduction layer and BB's
- Use same number of printers (4x)

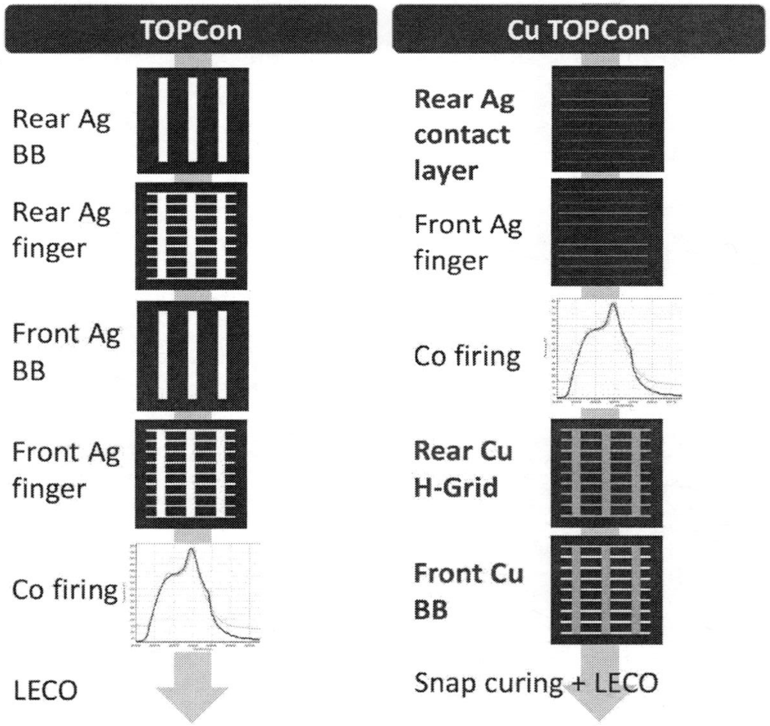

Status technology development

- N. Chen demonstrated ZEBRA IBC cells with Hybrid-Ag-Cu fingers in 2022. [4]
- We demonstrated first Cu-TOPCon cells at SiliconPV2024. [5]
- Yuchao Zhuan from USNW published several papers on TOPCon cells with Ag dash contacts and Cu/Al printed fingers. [6],[7]
- DKEM claims first TOPCon mass production with high-Cu paste (using Ag-coated Cu-particles).[8]

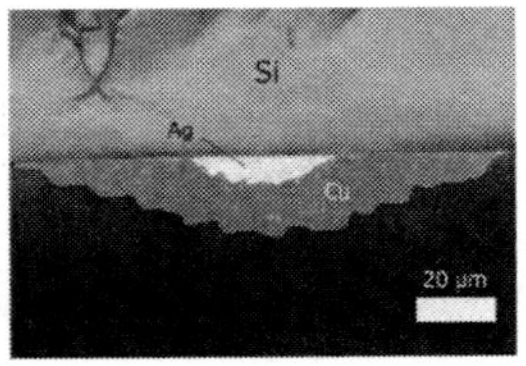

Cross section of Ag-Cu finger on ZEBRA IBC cell [4]

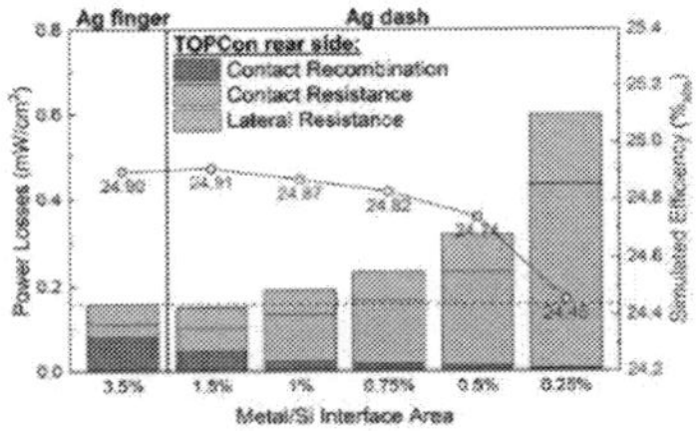

Simulated efficiencies and power losses from contact recombination, contact resistance and lateral resistance in TOPCon solar cells with standard Ag fingers and Ag dashes [7].

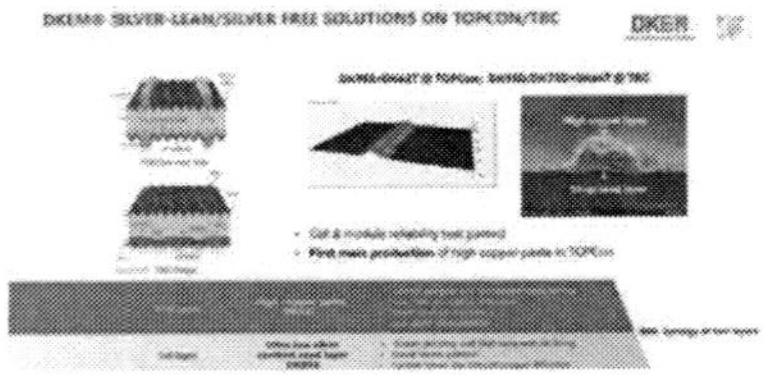

Slide from DKEM talk [8]

[4] N. Chen, et al. Screen printed copper paste for metallization of IBC solar cells, SiliconPV 2022, AIP Conf. Proc. 2023
[5] J. Lossen, et al., Proceedings of Silicon PV 2024, https://doi.org/10.52825/siliconpv.v2i.1316
[6] Y. Zhang, et. al., Ultra-Lean Silver Screen-Printing for Sustainable Terawatt-Scale Photovoltaic. Sol. RRL, 8: 2400478. https://doi.org/10.1002/solr.202400478
[7] Y. Zhang, et al., Silver-lean screen-printing metallisation for industrial TOPCon solar cells: Enabling an 80 % reduction in silver consumption, SOLMAT288, 2025, https://doi.org/10.1016/j.solmat.2025.113654.
[8] F. Guo, TaiyangNews Cell & Module Production Equipment & Processing Materials Conference, Sep. 2, 2025.

Copper paste from Copprint

- Based on a blend of Cu micro and nano particles
- Rapid curing at low temperature (~300°C)
- Sintering agent prevents oxidation

Challenges addressed in this work

- Validate efficiency potential and cost savings
- Confirm feasibility of print-on-print approach
- Optimize curing process towards shorter process time
- Demonstrate solderability

Cell experiment

- Experiment on M10R industrial TOPCon precursor, all printings at ISC
- Ag-Ref-cells vs. Cu-TOPCon cells with 2 different contact layers

	Ag Ref	CuTOPCon Line Contact („Cu Line“)	CuTOPCon Point contact („Cu Point“)
Opening	18 µm	8 µm	8 µm, 50/150
Pr. line width	30 µm	23 µm	19 µm
Cross section	188 µm²	63.6 µm²	12.8 µm²
Ag-Laydown L1	**70.6 mg**	**23.2 mg**	**5 mg**
Cu-Print L2	-	40 µm	40 µm
Total Ag Laydown (with FS and BB)	**194 mg**	**73 mg**	**55 mg**
Ag saving		**-62% (-46%*)**	**-72% (-60%*)**

(* Considering lower Ag-BB laydown in Reference)

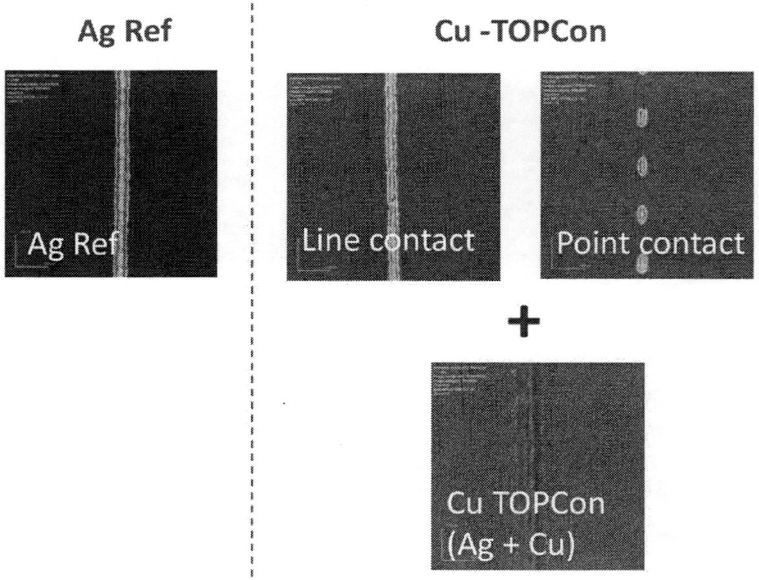

IV parameter of cells

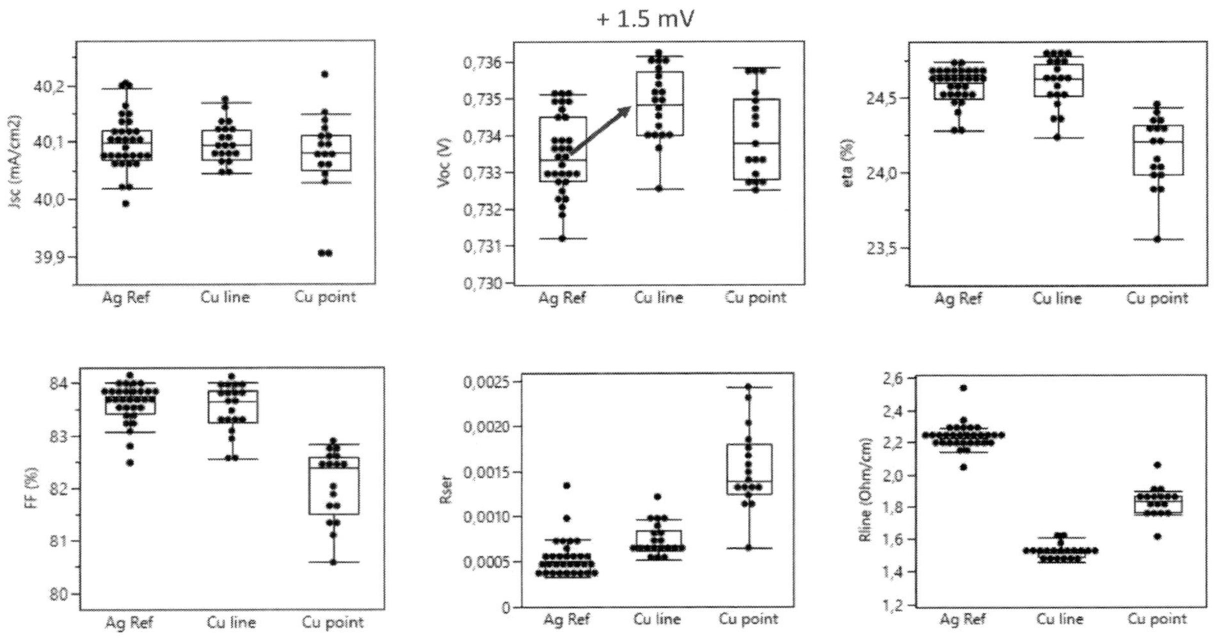

- Best group: Cu line
  - **+1,5 mV gain in Voc**
  - Increased Rser, with marginal effect on FF
- Cu Point group exhibits clearly reduced FF
  - Line resistance is still low
  - Contact area probably too small -> increase of contact resistance loss, in agreement to [7]

[7] Y. Zhang, et al., SOLMAT288, 2025, https://doi.org/10.1016/j.solmat.2025.113654

Cost saving potential

- Lab experiment yielded **equal efficiency** for cells with **46% Ag reduction**
- A demonstration run with an industrial partner showed **similar IV characteristics at efficiency level 25.3%** with lower Ag and Cu laydown
- **Cost saving** calculated for different scenarios based on typical industrial paste laydown[9]
  - With Ag-Price at 1350 USD/kg even most conservative scenario results in savings of **~0.25 USD ct/Wp**

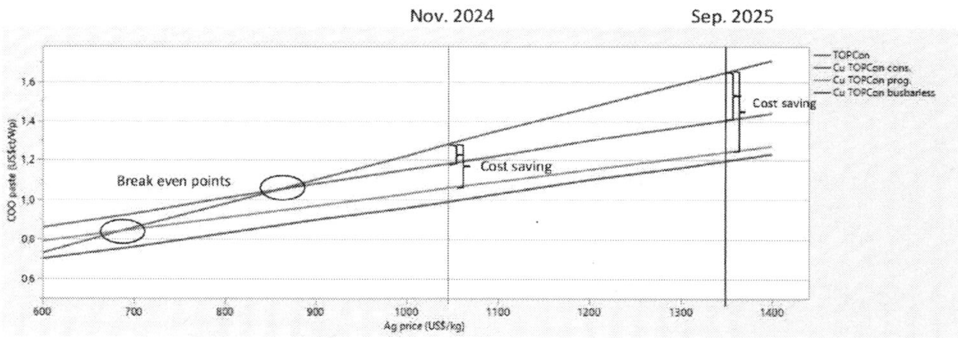

[9] P. Preis et al., Silver paste reduction for TOPCon solar cells using a hybrid Cu and Ag screen printing metallization, PVSEC-35, 2024, Numazu, Japan

Feasibility of print-on-print

First layer with < 10 µm line width need knotless screens

Mertcan Comak investigated the expansion of knotless screens during usage[10]

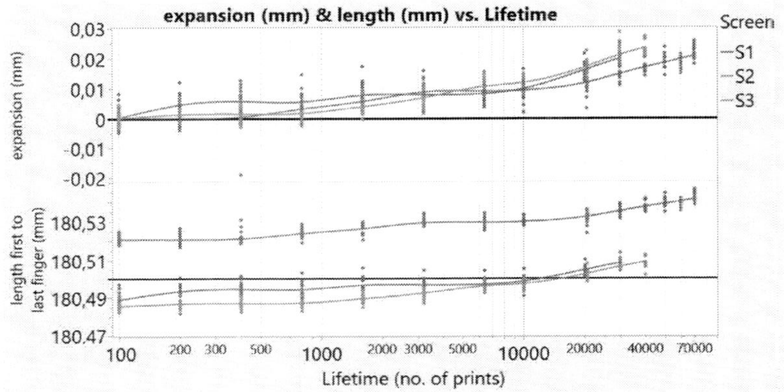

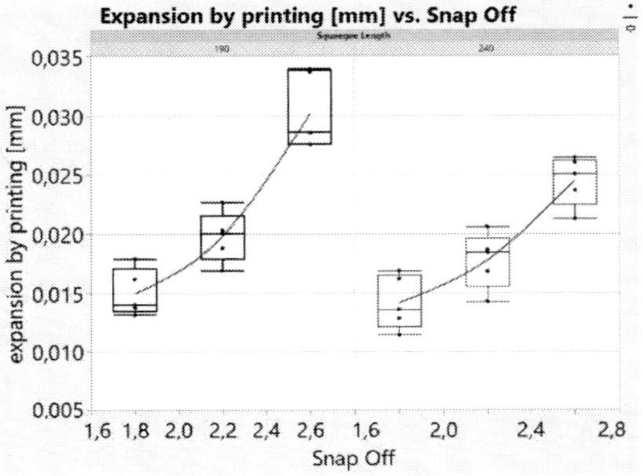

Conclusion: print-on-print of 40 µm Cu line on 10 µm Ag line is feasible!

[10] M. Comak, et al., Distortion of knotless printing screens in solar cell mass-production, SOLMAT 294, 2025, https://doi.org/10.1016/j.solmat.2025.113894.

Optimization of Cu-curing process

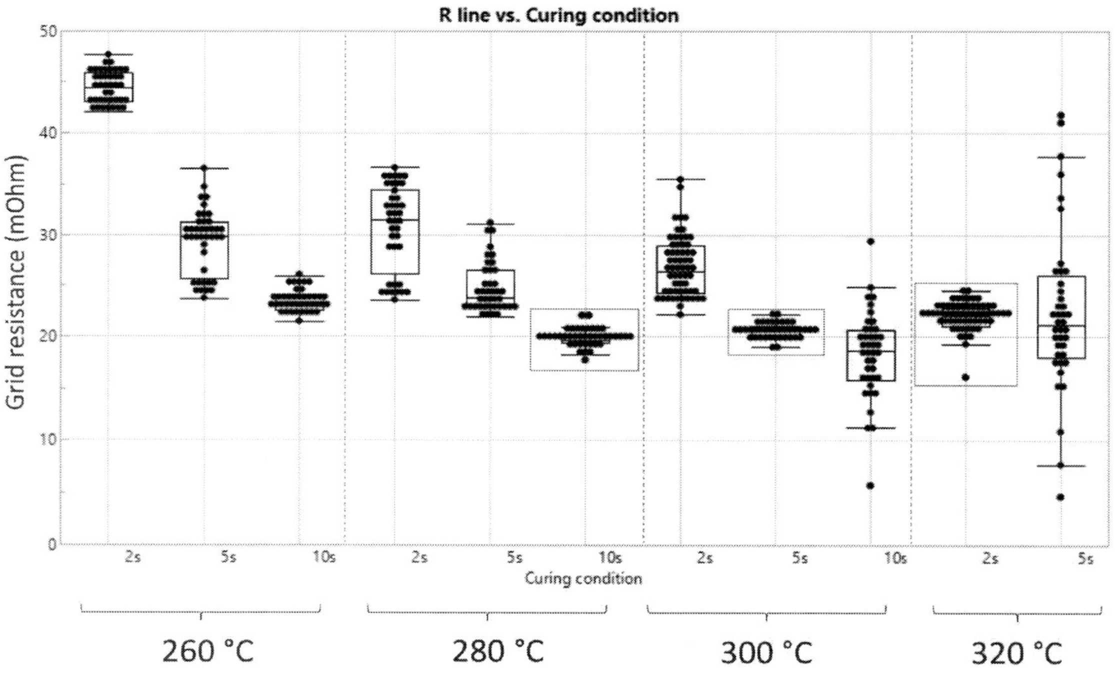

- Cu-Curing is performed as snap curing between two hot plates or rollers
- Lowest grid resistance achieved for:
  - 280°C, 10s
  - 300°C, 5s
  - 320°C, 2s

-> acceleration to process time of 2s is possible

Soldering on Cu BBs

Peel tests after soldering on TT stringer (using Ribbon BS 0.8x0.24 SnPb):

- Peel force initially low (adhesion low on paste surface)
- Modification of paste and introduction of chemical pre-treatment substantially increased peel force,
- Now cohesive breakage

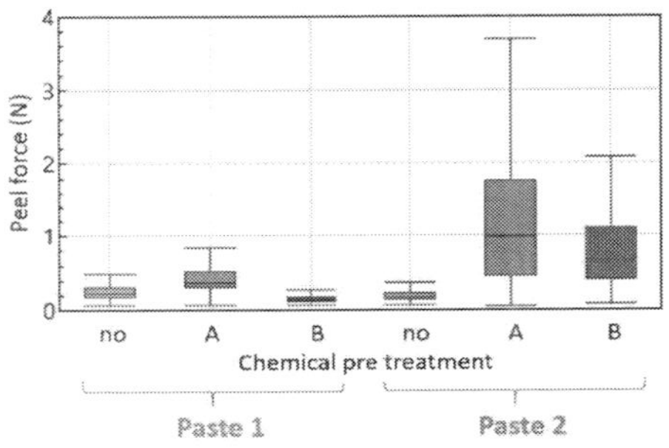

Paste 2, no pre treatment

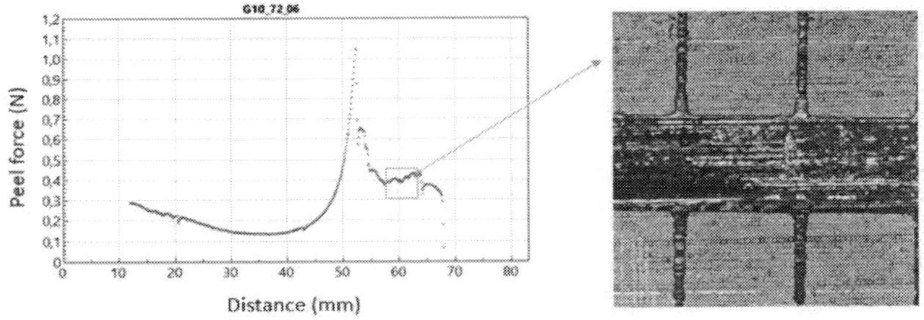

Paste 2, chem. pre treatment A

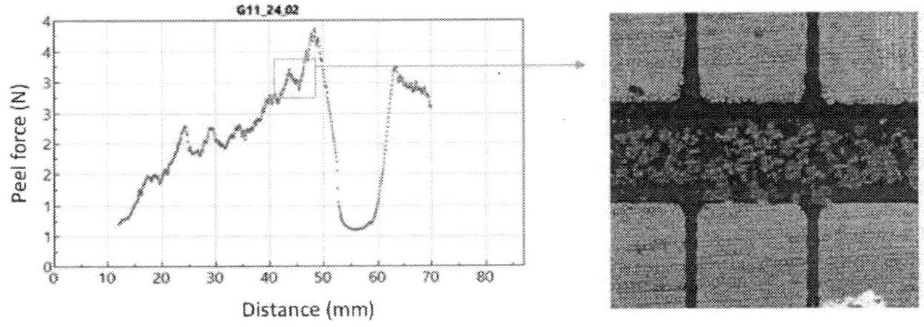

Summary and outlook

- **Same efficiency for Cu-TOPCon**, with headroom for further increase
  - If rhoC can be decreased further, even smaller contact area can be used and Voc improves further.
- Remaining challenges could be adressed successfully
  - Print-on-print on rear side feasible
  - **Fast curing process demonstrated** -> High throughput pilot tool under development with German machine builder
  - **Soldering on Cu-BB with high peel force demonstrated**
- Massive cost savings already for **partially** replacing Ag by Cu
- Let's leave to the gold and silver to the athletes and use more copper on the solar cells

 Lossen et al., Screen Printed Cu-TOPCon Cells With Reduced Ag Consumption, EUPVSEC 2025

ISC research for a sunny future

Thank you

For the attention

Copprint

We thank Copprint for supplying Cu-pastes and discussion of results

Supported by:

Federal Ministry for Economic Affairs and Energy

on the basis of a decision by the German Bundestag

This work has received funding from the German Federal ministry of Economic Affairs and Energy under the project "KONTRAST" with grant agreement 03EE1128A and project "BuKuMu" with grant agreement 03EE1225E

Visit ISC Konstanz 21st – 24th October 2025

Events of ISC K in October 2025 (details: www.isc-konstanz.de)

- MIW Workshop 20th/21st October (in Berlin)
- IBC4EU/EMPOWER workshop 21st /22nd October
- M&M (Module and Material) workshop 23rd /24th October
- 20 years of ISC Konstanz – party! 🎉 23rd October evening from 7pm
- Energy worlds 24th October, afternoon

ISC research for a sunny future

Back-up slides

Cost reduction potential for industrial M10 TOPCon solar cell

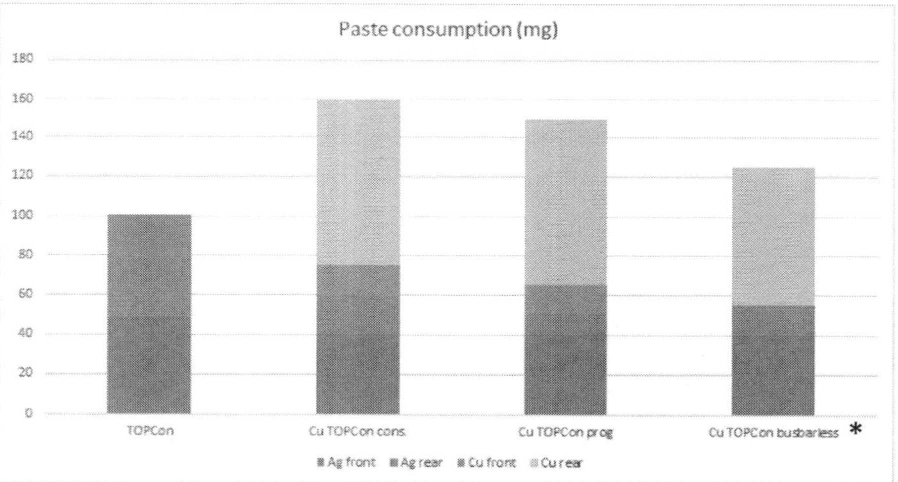

Paste consumption	TOPCon	Cu TOPCon cons.	Cu TOPCOn prog.	Cu TOPCon busbarless
Total Ag paste (mg)	101 mg	60 mg	50 mg	55 mg
Total Cu paste (mg)	-	100 mg	100 mg	70 mg
Ag consumption mg/Wp	12.2	7.3	6.1	6.7

Assumptions:

- 3 different Ag reduction scenarios
- Assumed efficiency 25% / 8.25 Wp
- Price Cu paste 350 US$/kg
- Busbarless cell requires alternative module interconnection with might be attributed with different costs for module manufacturing (f.e. SmartWire or TECC-Wire[14])

*under development

[14] Jonas Marten et al.; 11th Metallization and Interconnection Workshop 2023; TECC Wire: A new technology for interconnecting temperature sensitive solar cells

COO calculation metallization pastes

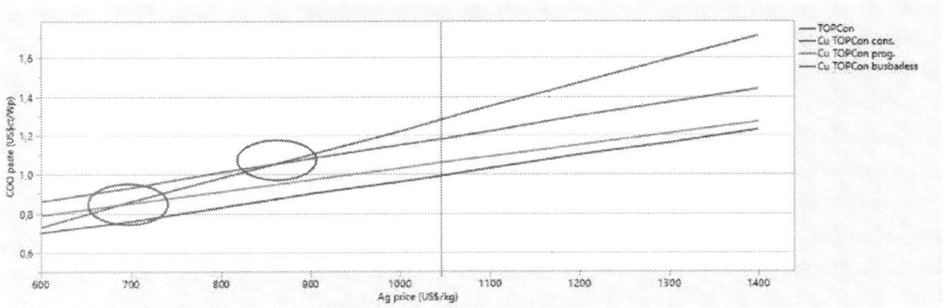

- Break even at silver price of 700 US$/kg or 850 US$/kg, depending on scenario
- Current silver price of 1045 $/kg: cost advantage of **0.1 - 0.22 US$ct/Wp** is possible
- Potential cost saving for 2GW TOPCon factory: **2.0Mio – 4.4 Mio US$/year**
- Even lower metallization costs can be achieved with busbarless approach, but module manufacturing costs will be different

Cell experiment Cu TOPCon

Experiment on M10R industrial TOPCon precursor, all printings at ISC

Ag-Ref-cells vs. Cu-TOPCon cells with 2 different contact layers

	Ag Ref	**CuTOPCon Line Contact**	**CuTOPCon Point contact**
Opening	18 µm	8 µm	8 µm, 50/150
Pr. line width	30 µm	23 µm	19 µm
Cross section	188 µm²	63.6 µm²	12.8 µm²
	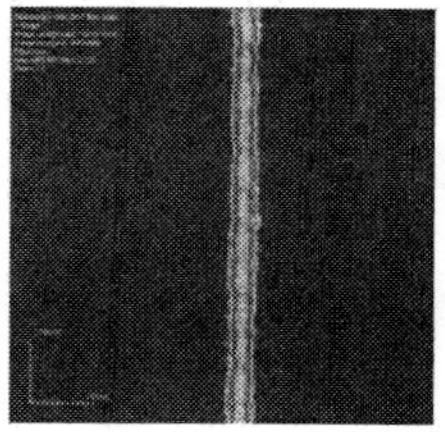	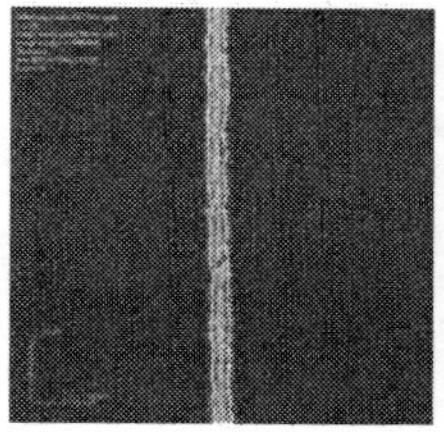	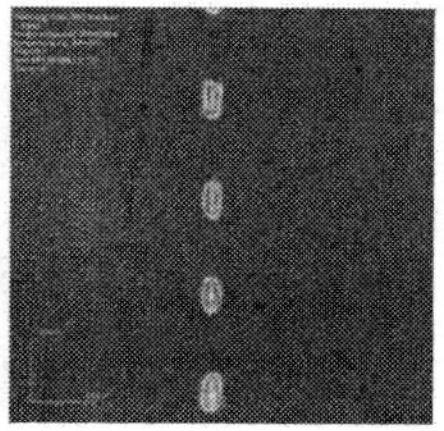

Group	**Ref**	Ref_ Corr	**Cu line**	**Cu point**	**Comment**
	(mg)	(mg)	(mg)	(mg)	comment
FS Finger	49,8	49,8	49,8	49,8	
FS Ag-BB	36,4	**8**			(excessive)
FS Cu-BB			46	46	
RS Finger	**70,6**	70,6	**23,2**	**5**	
RS Cu finger			98	98	
RS BB	37,1	**8**			(excessive)
RS Cu BB			40	40	
Sum Ag	**193,9**	**136,4**	**73**	**54,8**	
Sum Cu			184	184	
mg/Wp		16,4	8,8	6,6	
Ag-Saving			**-46%**	**-60%**	(-

Cell experiment Cu TOPCon

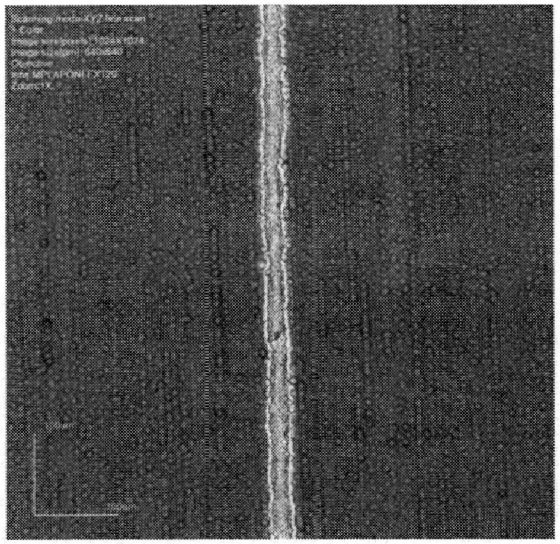

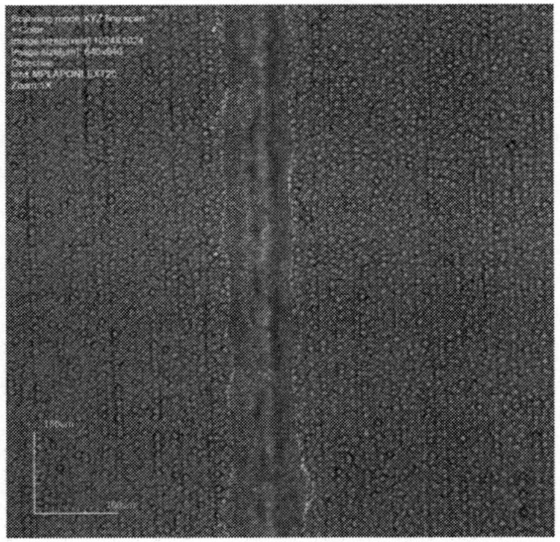

	Line Contact, Ag Layer	Line Contact, Ag + Cu Layer
Opening	8 µm	40 µm (Cu Layer)
Pr. line width	23 µm	66 µm
Cross section	63.6 µm2	238 µm2

ISC research for a sunny future

Fraunhofer CSP

EU-PVSEC 2025

Detecting Local Laser-Doping Variations by (Hyper-)Spectral Imaging and Machine Learning Models

Marko Turek[1], Stefan Eiternick[1], Jonathan Linke[2], Jan Hoß[2]

(1) Fraunhofer Center for Silicon Photovoltaics CSP, Halle, Germany
(2) ISC-Konstanz e.V., Konstanz, Germany

Supported by:
Federal Ministry for Economic Affairs and Climate Action
on the basis of a decision by the German Bundestag

LASER DOPING FOR REAR CONTACT SOLAR CELLS – (HYPER-)SPECTRAL IMAGING

Overview of the presentation

I. Introduction and objective: Alignment assessment of p-/n-contacts

- ISC polyZEBRA cell concept and local laser-activation of (p+) stripe pattern

II. Approach: Optical hyperspectral imaging (HSI)

- Data acquisition: Combining spatial and spectral information
- Data analysis: Pre-processing and classification

III. Result: Separation of (p+) from (p) layers in HSI-data

- Classification of (p+) vs. (p) pixels in image by advanced data processing

IV. Conclusion: Fast imaging of doping patterns possible

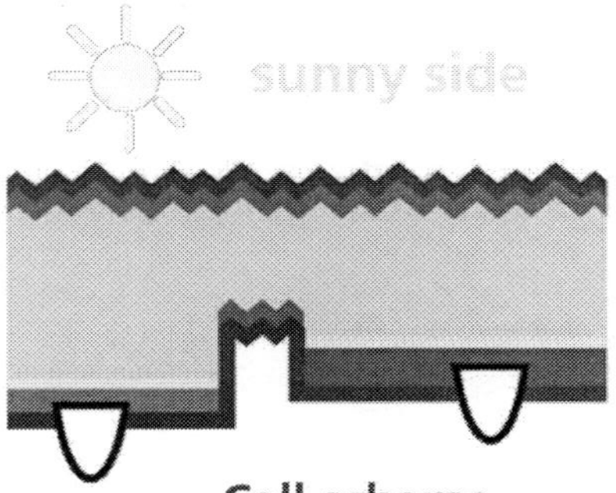

Cell scheme

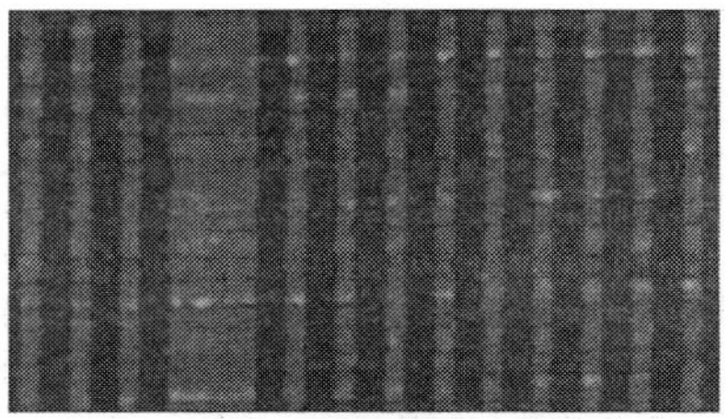

HSI – image (rear side)

Fraunhofer CSP

Introduction

Back-contact solar cells and "polyZEBRA" cell concept

Back-contact solar cells

- Reduced front-side shading → higher cell currents [1]
- TOPCon approach: no polycrystalline silicon (poly-Si) for contact passivation on front side needed [1,2]
- Efficiencies: cell > 27.8% [3] and module > 25%

[1] J. Linke et. al., EPJ PV 16 (2025); [2] R. Kopecek et. al., pv-tech.org/why-tbc-will-follow-shortly-after-topcon/: [3] nrel.gov/pv/cell-efficiency

INTRODUCTION

Back-contact solar cells and "polyZEBRA" cell concept

Back-contact solar cells

- Reduced front-side shading → higher cell currents [1]
- TOPCon approach: no polycrystalline silicon (poly-Si) for contact passivation on front side needed [1,2]
- Efficiencies: cell > 27.8% [3] and module > 25%

ISC "polyZEBRA" cell concept [1]

- IBC patterning via laser processing
- Poly-Si on interfacial oxide (SiO_x) for both contacts
- Processes compatible with industrial technologies

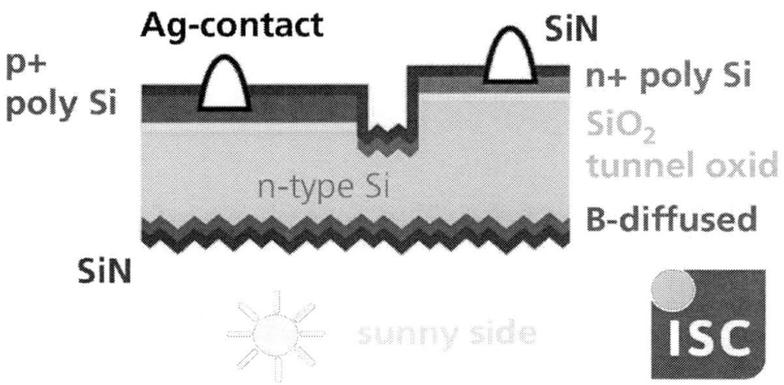

[1] J. Linke et. al., EPJ PV 16 (2025); [2] R. Kopecek et. al., pv-tech.org/why-tbc-will-follow-shortly-after-topcon/: [3] nrel.gov/pv/cell-efficiency

INTRODUCTION

"polyZEBRA" cell concept: Laser activation as major process step

Laser-activation (doping) of p+ poly Si

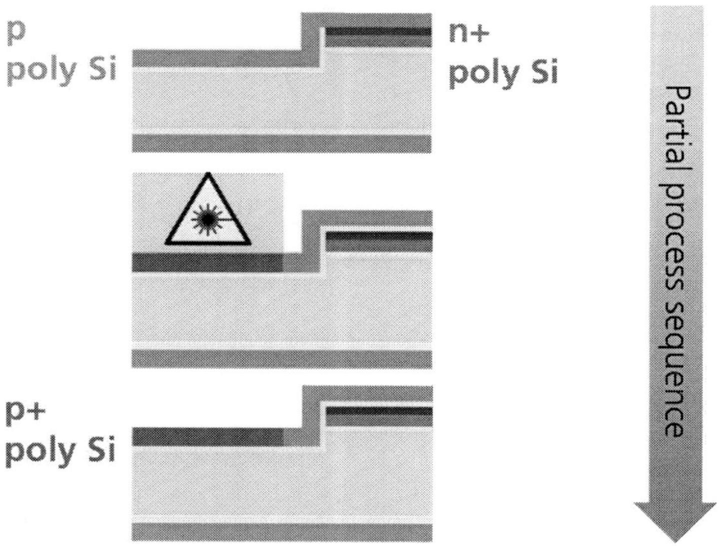

ISC "polyZEBRA" cell concept [1]

- IBC patterning via laser processing
- Poly-Si on interfacial oxide (SiO_x) for both contacts
- Processes compatible with industrial technologies

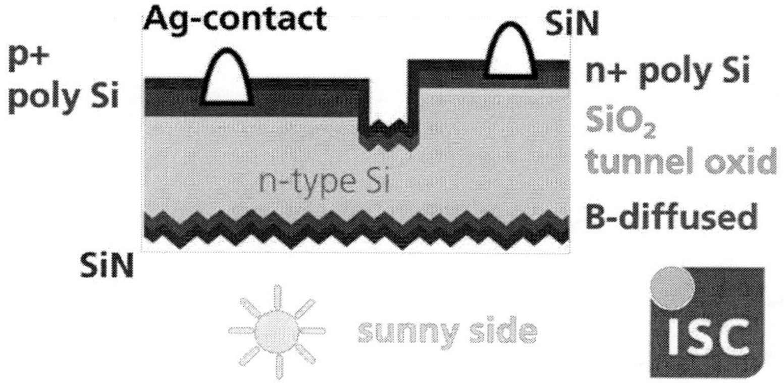

   Fraunhofer CSP

INTRODUCTION

"polyZEBRA" cell concept: Laser activation as major process step

Laser-activation (doping) of p+ poly Si

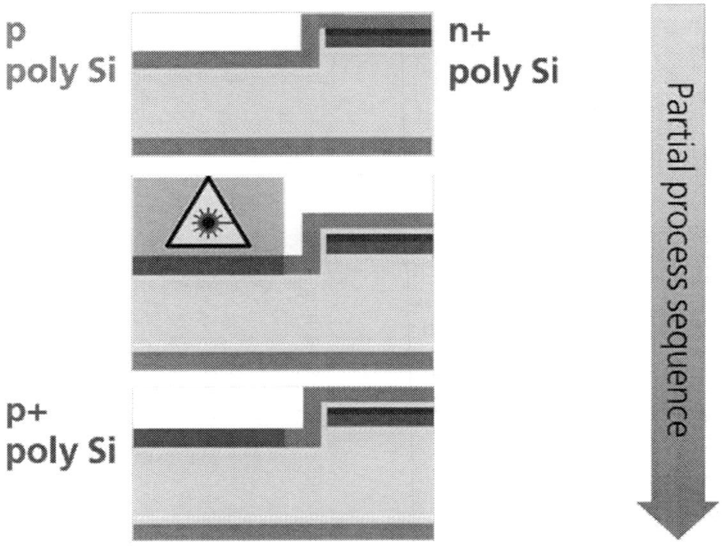

Rear-side pattern with fine structure

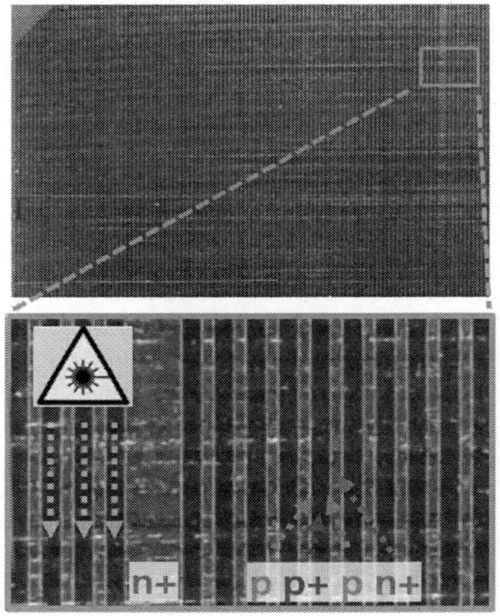

- (p) poly: ~ 500 µm
- (n+) poly: ~250 µm

Major challenge

Identification of laser mis-alignment

INTRODUCTION

"polyZEBRA" cell concept: Laser activation as major process step

Requirements for quality control

- Inspection directly after laser activation
- Method suited for fast inline application
- Contactless, non-destructive

Rear-side pattern with fine structure

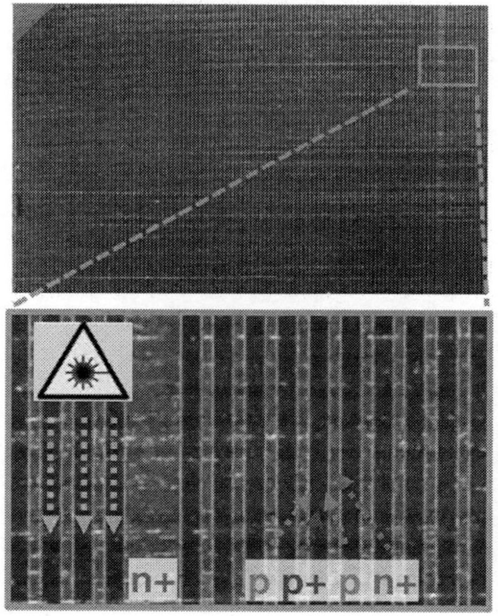

- (p) poly: ~ 500 µm
- (n+) poly: ~250 µm

Major challenge

Identification of laser mis-alignment

INTRODUCTION

"polyZEBRA" cell concept: Quality control of laser-activation step

Requirements for quality control

- Inspection directly after laser activation
- Method suited for fast inline application
- Contactless, non-destructive

Simpler test structure for new approach:

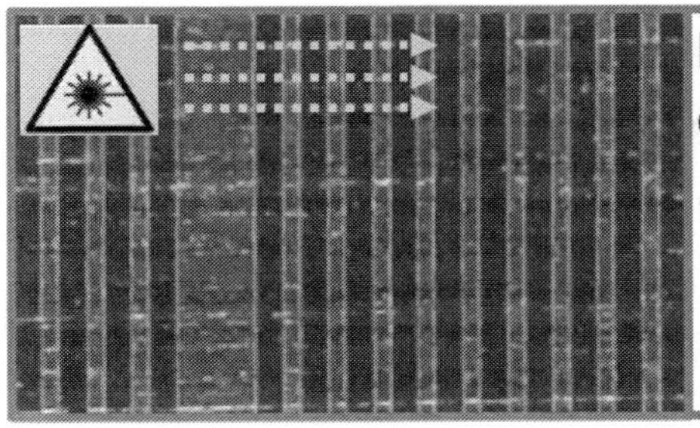

Perpendicular instead of parallel laser-lines:
→ more direct evaluation of inspection method

Rear-side pattern with fine structure

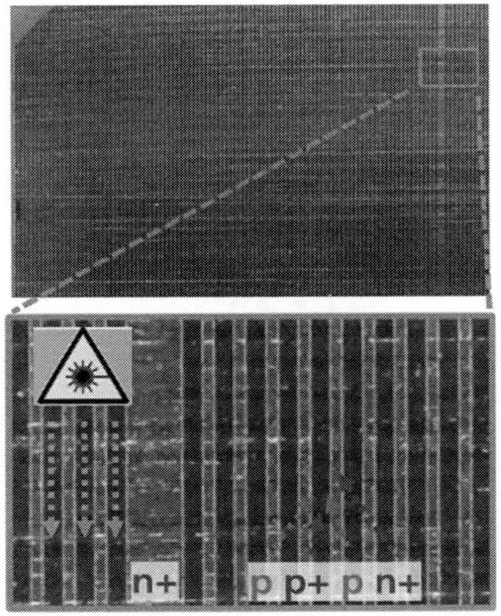

- (p) poly: ~ 500 µm
- (n+) poly: ~250 µm

Major challenge

Identification of laser mis-alignment

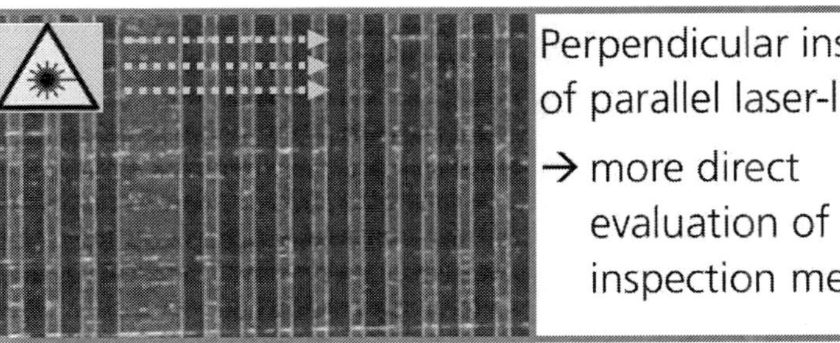

INTRODUCTION

"polyZEBRA" cell concept: Quality control of laser-activation step

Requirements for quality control

- Inspection directly after laser activation
- Method suited for fast inline application
- Contactless, non-destructive

Simpler test structure for new approach:

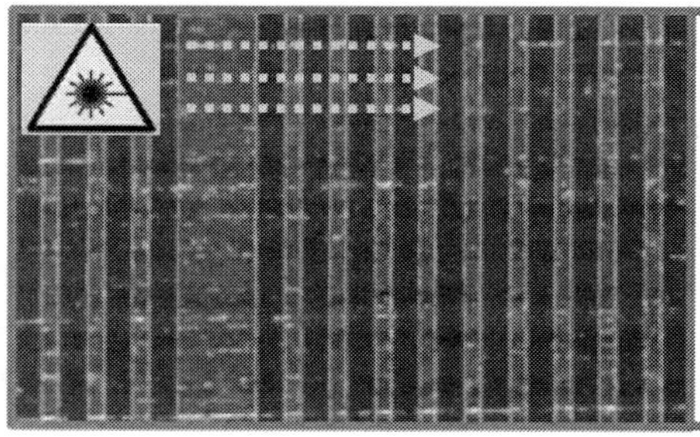

Perpendicular instead of parallel laser-lines:
→ more direct evaluation of inspection method

Identification of laser mis-alignments:

Can laser-activated **(p+)** regions be separated from **(p)** regions by hyperspectral imaging?

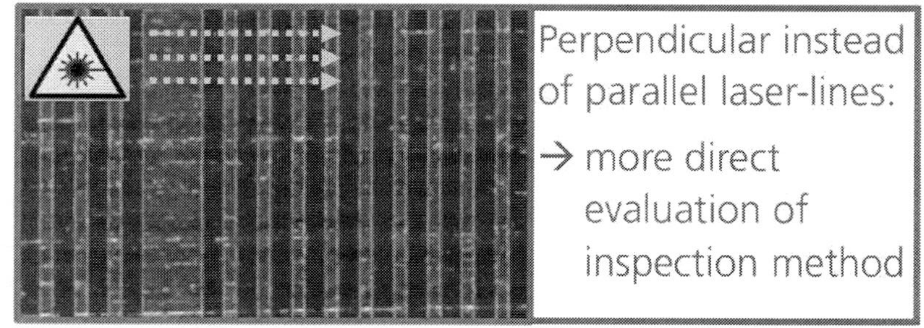

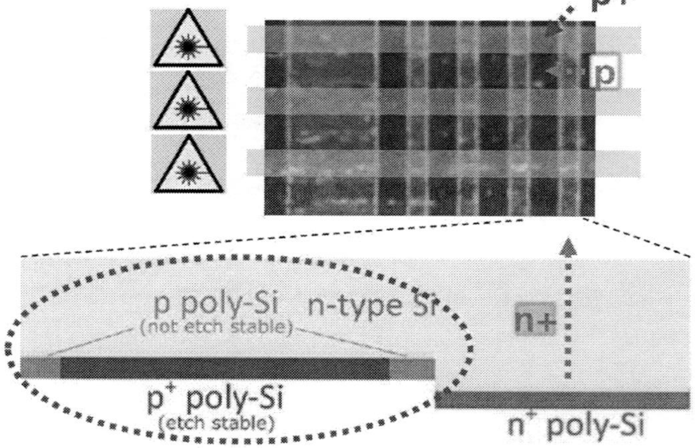

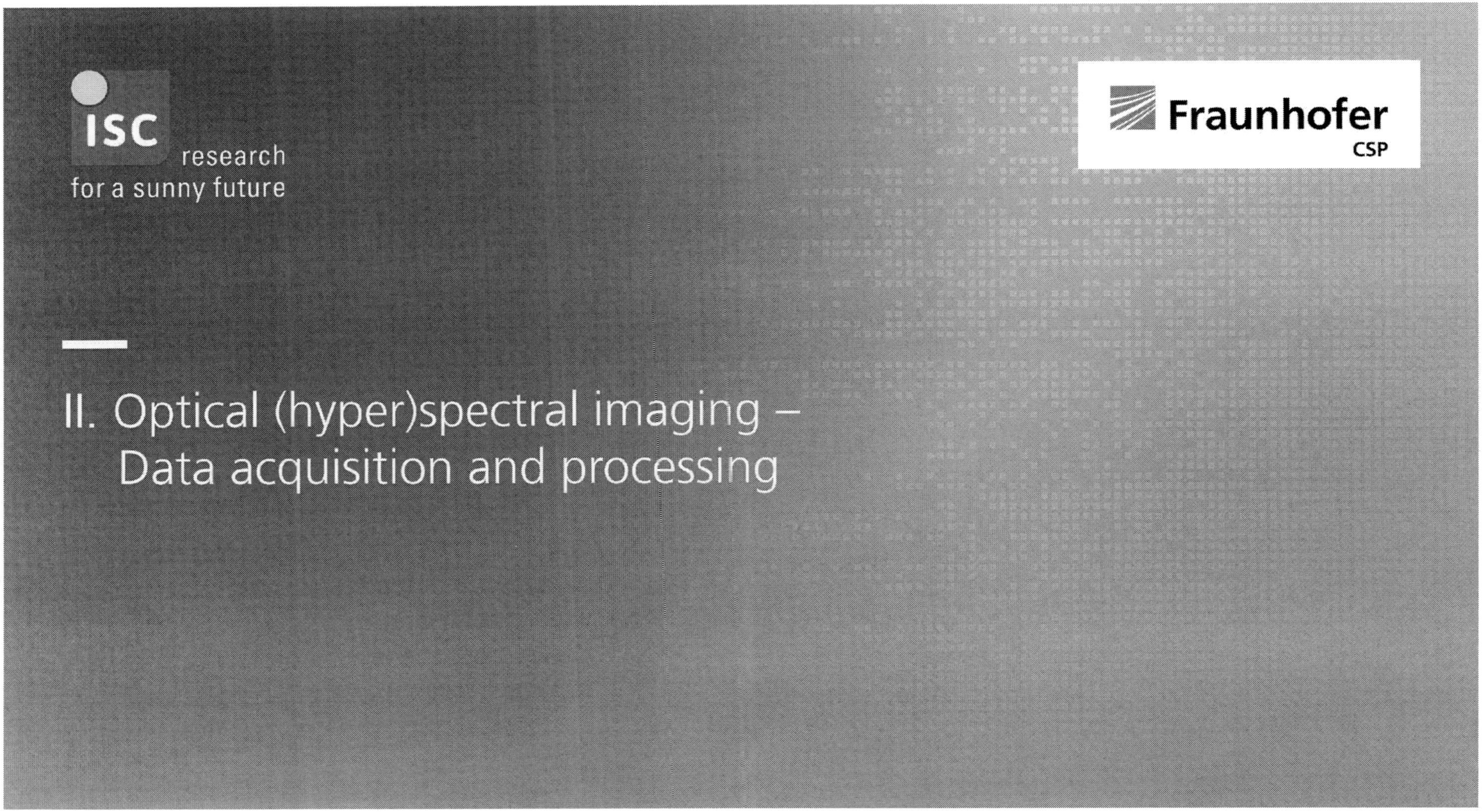
ISC
research
for a sunny future
Fraunhofer
CSP
II. Optical (hyper)spectral imaging –
Data acquisition and processing

APPROACH: HSI – DATA ACQUISITION

Combining spatial imaging with spectral information

HSI camera technology

- Yields spatial and spectral information at the same time
- In general, applicable to inline implementation
- **Many images generated: one image for each wavelength 400 .. 1000 nm**

Test structure – rear side

(horizontal laser pattern!)

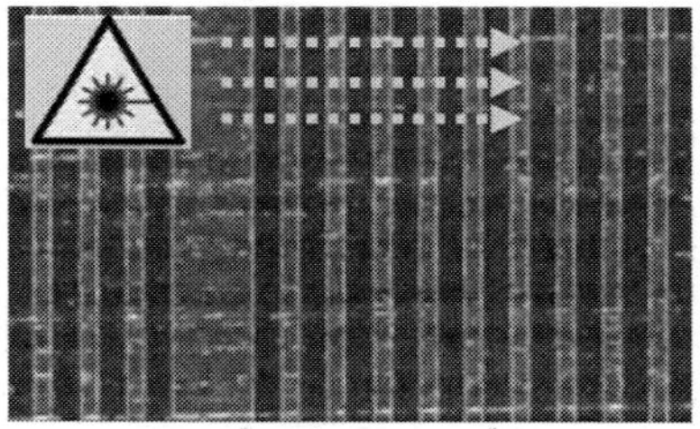

photograph

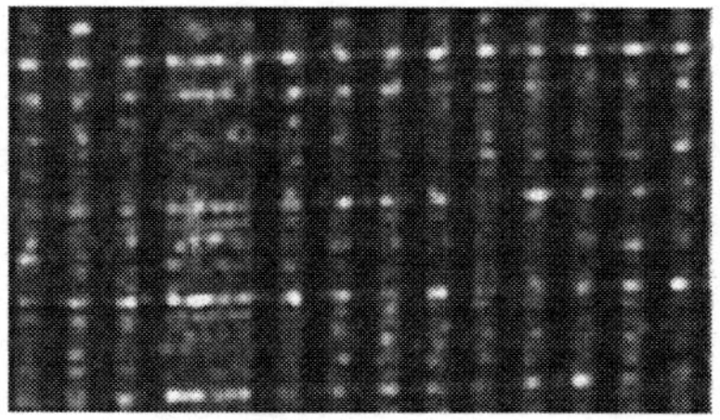

HSI – "RGB" image

Hyperspectral imaging

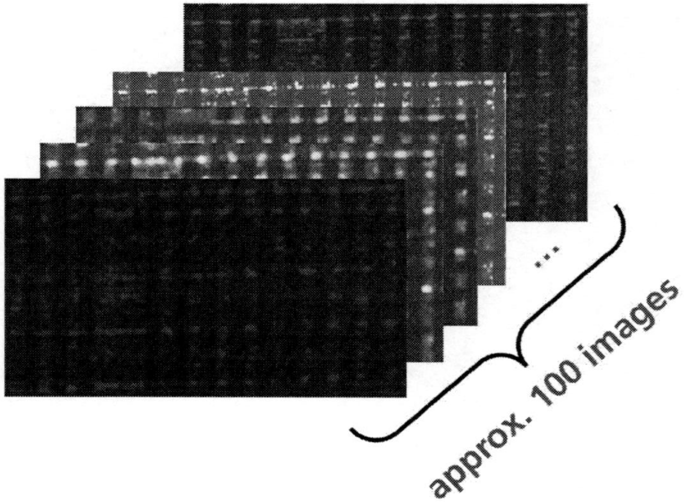

APPROACH: HSI – DATA ACQUISITION

Combining spatial imaging with spectral information

HSI camera technology

- Yields spatial and spectral information at the same time
- In general, applicable to inline implementation
- **Each pixel contains entire optical spectrum**

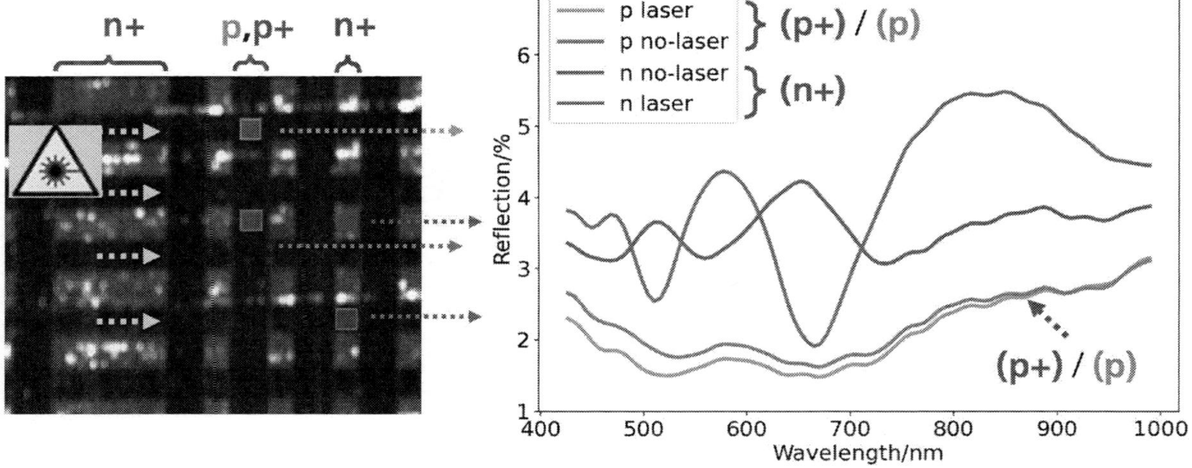

Result:

- Clear spectral difference between (n+) and (p, p+) region
- Very similar spectra for (p) and (p+) region → need to be separated

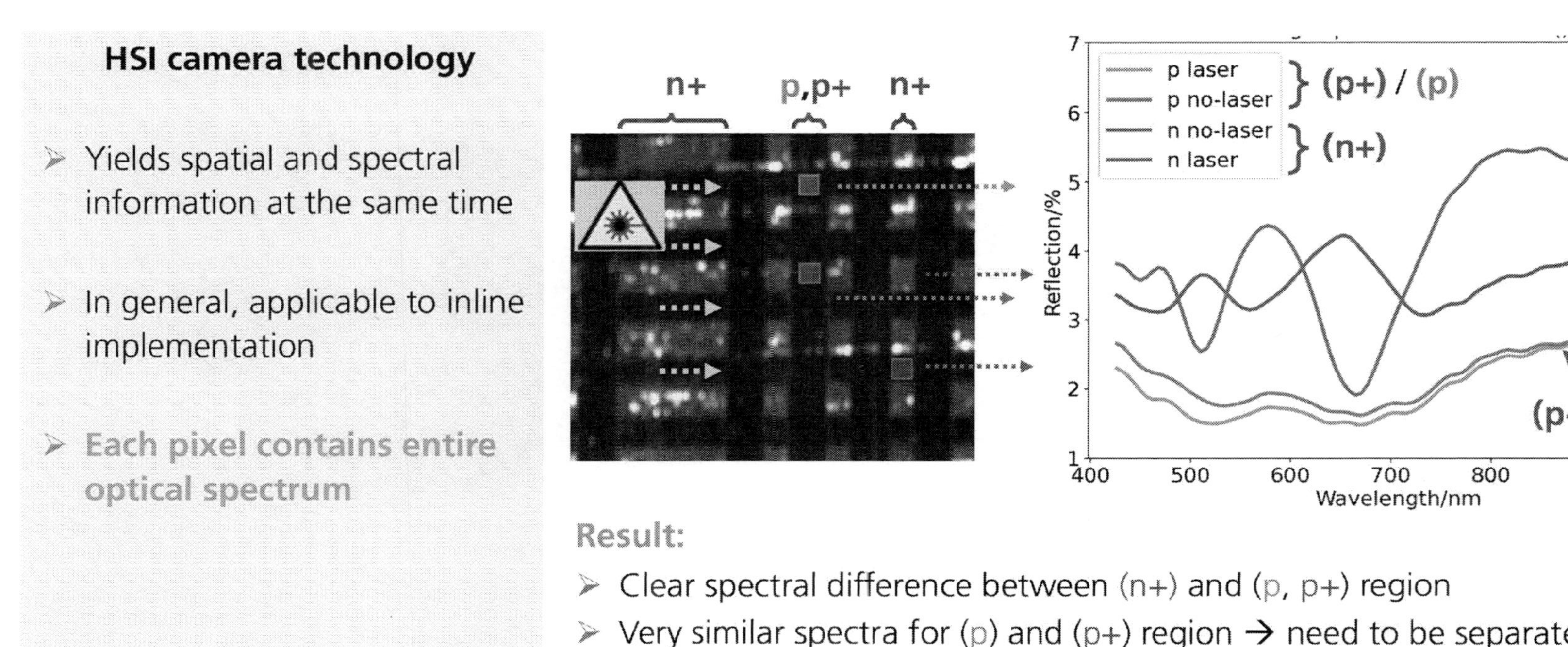

APPROACH: HSI – DATA ACQUISITION

Combining spatial imaging with spectral information

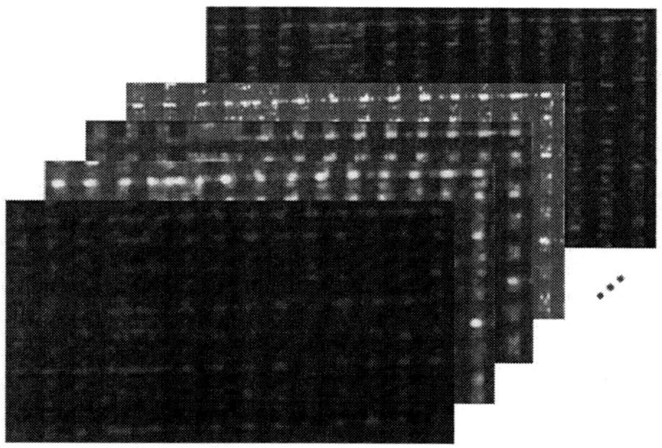

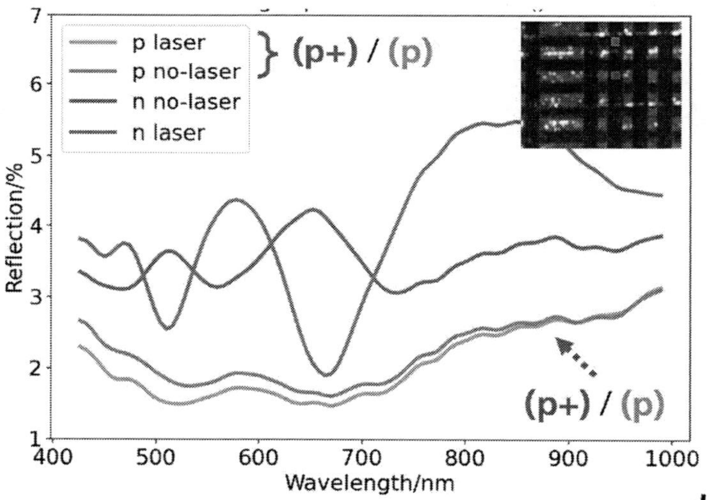

Extensive data set → Automated data-preprocessing and analysis to separate (p+) vs. (p)

APPROACH: HSI – DATA PRE-PROCESSING: "NORMALIZATION"

Material-independent algorithms – extracting relevant spectral finger-prints

Data pre-processing step 1(*): **Correction of local illumination variations** (e.g. sample-to-sample)

HSI raw data → **Pixel-wise intensity correction**

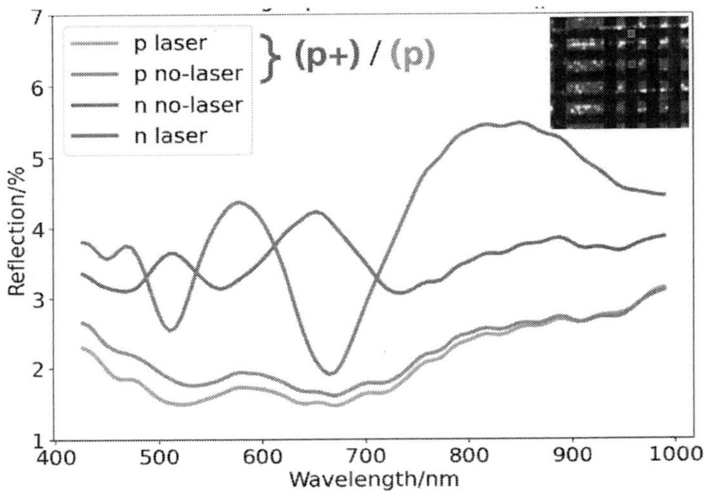

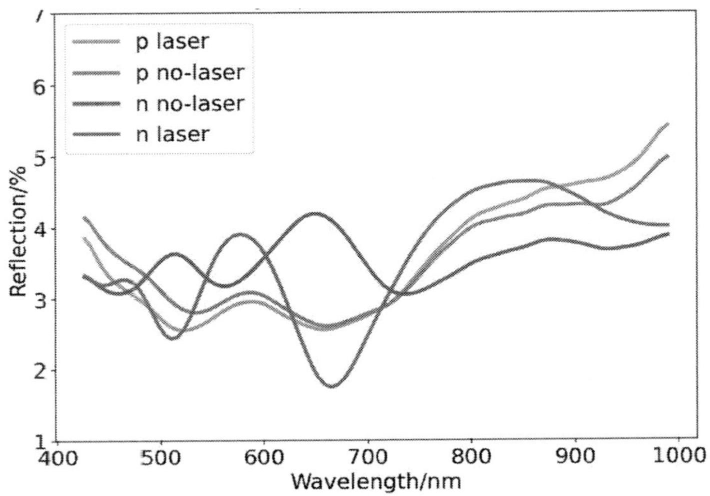

Similar brightness for all ROIs

(*) e.g. A. C. Müller and S. Guido: Introduction to machine learning with Python. O'Reilly Media Inc. (2018)

APPROACH: HSI – DATA PRE-PROCESSING: "FEATURE SCALING"

Material-independent algorithms – extracting relevant spectral finger-prints

Data pre-processing step 2(*): **Correction of local contrast variations**

HSI raw data

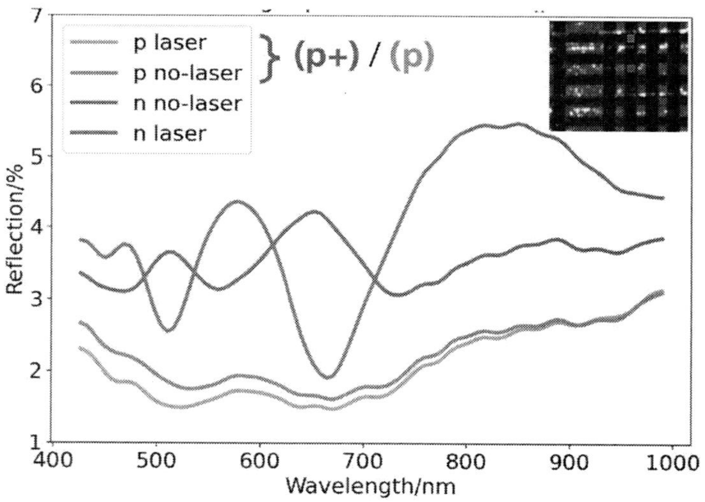

"Feature scaling"

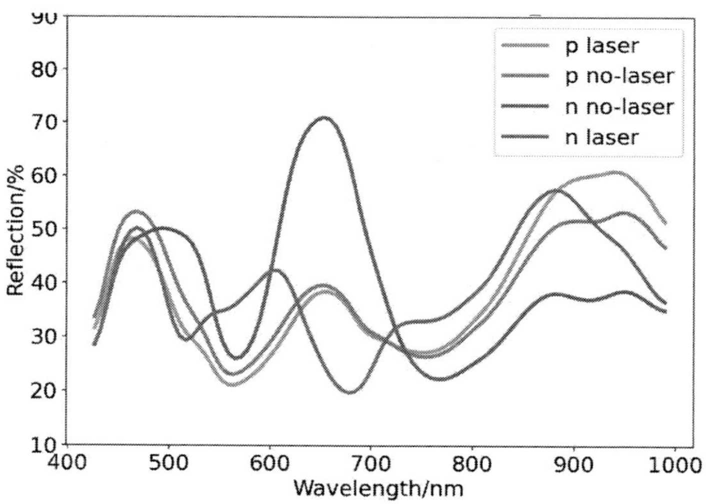

Similar brightness and contrast for all ROIs

(*) e.g. A. C. Müller and S. Guido: Introduction to machine learning with Python. O'Reilly Media Inc. (2018)

APPROACH: HSI – DATA PRE-PROCESSING: "DIMENSIONALITY REDUCTION"

Material-independent algorithms – extracting relevant spectral finger-prints

Data pre-processing step 3(*): **Reducing the data set** to accelerate sub-sequent algorithms

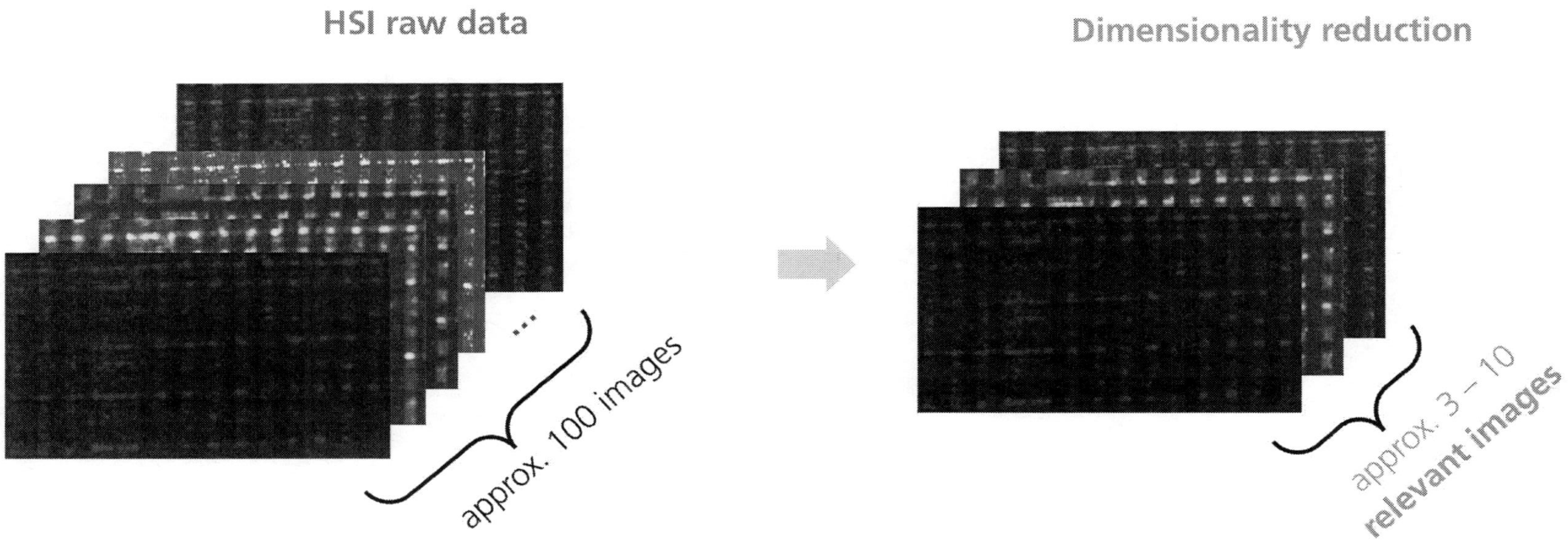

(*) e.g. A. C. Müller and S. Guido: Introduction to machine learning with Python. O'Reilly Media Inc. (2018)

ISC research for a sunny future

Fraunhofer CSP

III. Identification and classification of rear side pattern

RESULTS: HSI – DATA PRE-PROCESSING

Material-independent algorithms – extracting relevant spectral finger-prints

Result of data pre-processing → Drastically reduced data set containing most significant information

HSI raw data

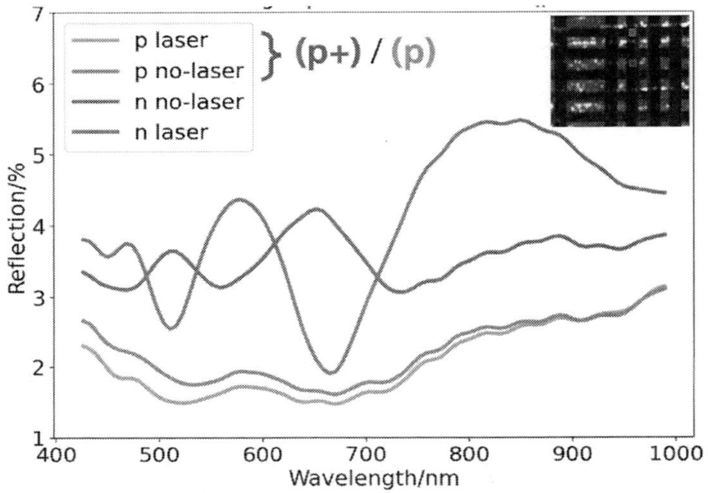

Pre-processed HSI-data: **Local, spectral finger-prints**

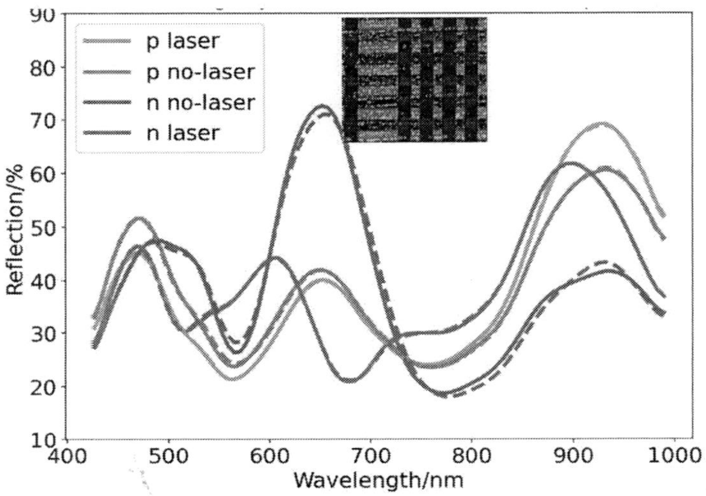

- Similar brightness and contrast for all ROIs
- Low-dimensional data set

   Fraunhofer CSP

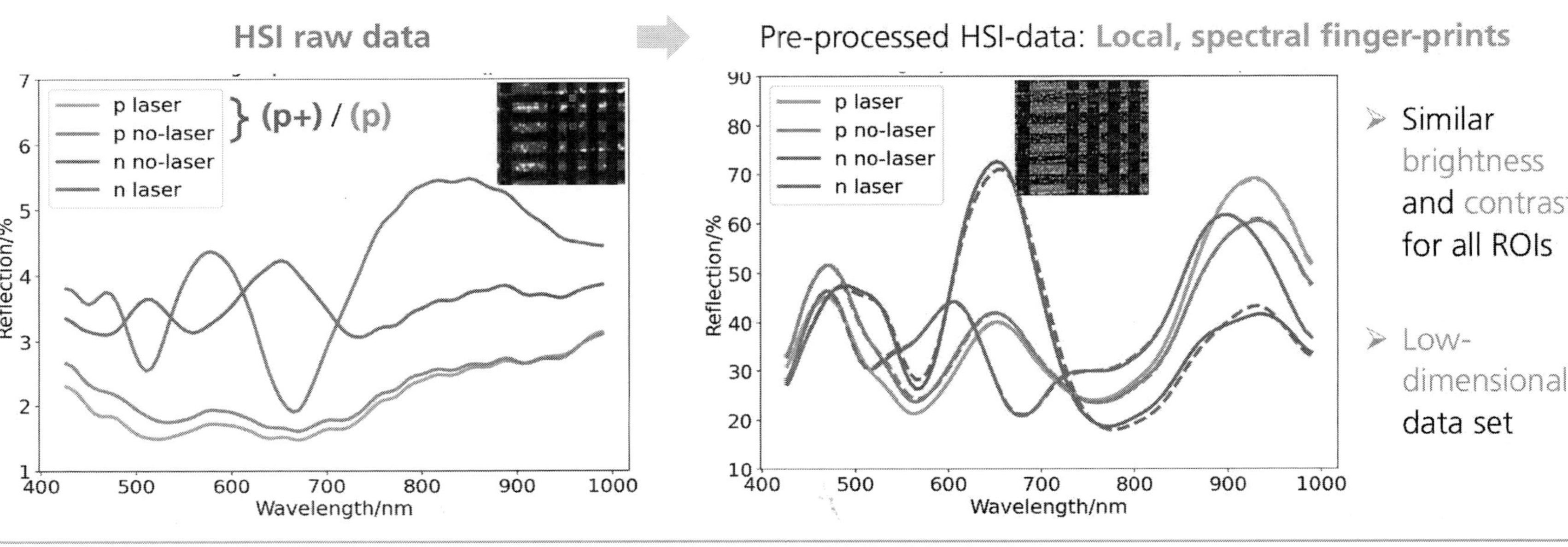

RESULTS: HSI – DATA PRE-PROCESSING

Material-independent algorithms – extracting relevant spectral finger-prints

Result of data pre-processing → Drastically reduced data set containing most significant information

HSI raw data

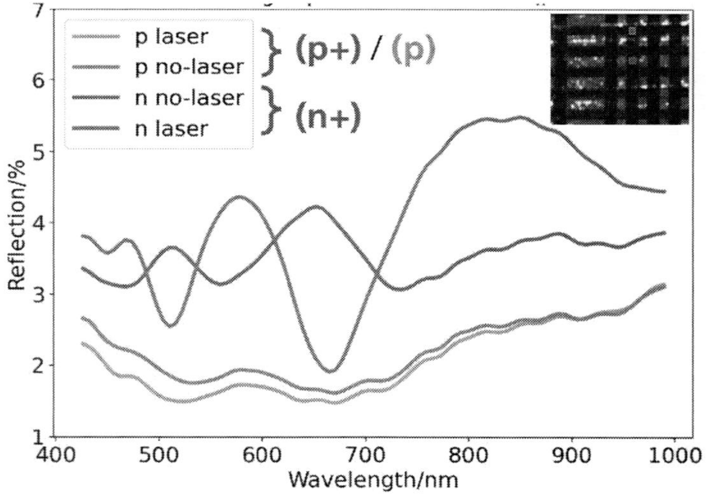

Pre-processed HSI-data: **Local, spectral finger-prints**

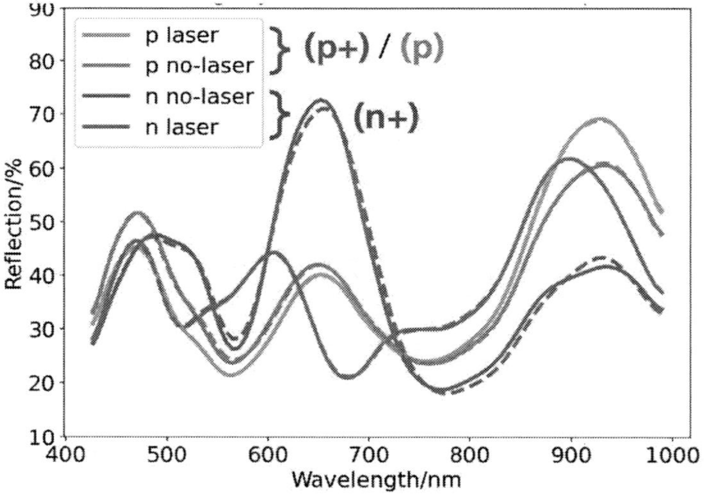

- Difference **(n+)** vs. **(p)** / **(p+)** clearly visible

RESULTS: HSI – DATA PRE-PROCESSING

Material-independent algorithms – extracting relevant spectral finger-prints

Result of data pre-processing → Drastically reduced data set containing most significant information

HSI raw data

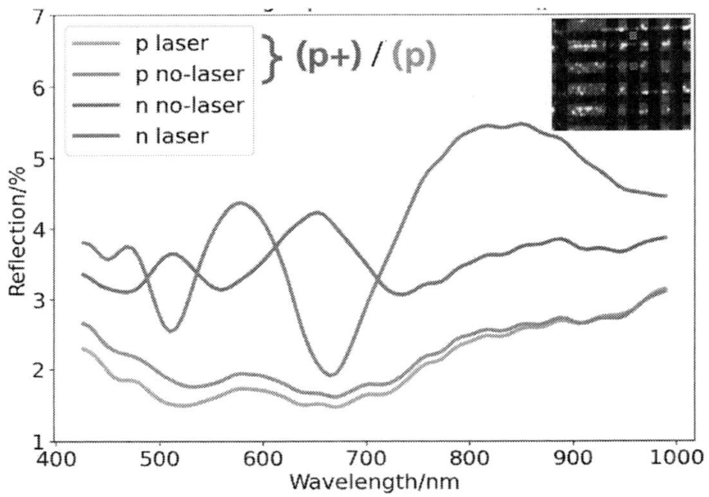

Pre-processed HSI-data: **Local, spectral finger-prints**

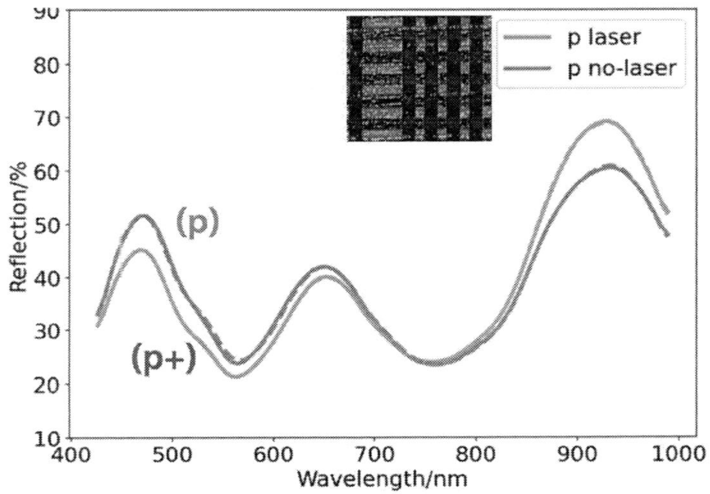

- Difference **(n+)** vs. **(p)** / **(p+)** clearly visible
- Very similar spectra **(p)** vs. **(p+)**

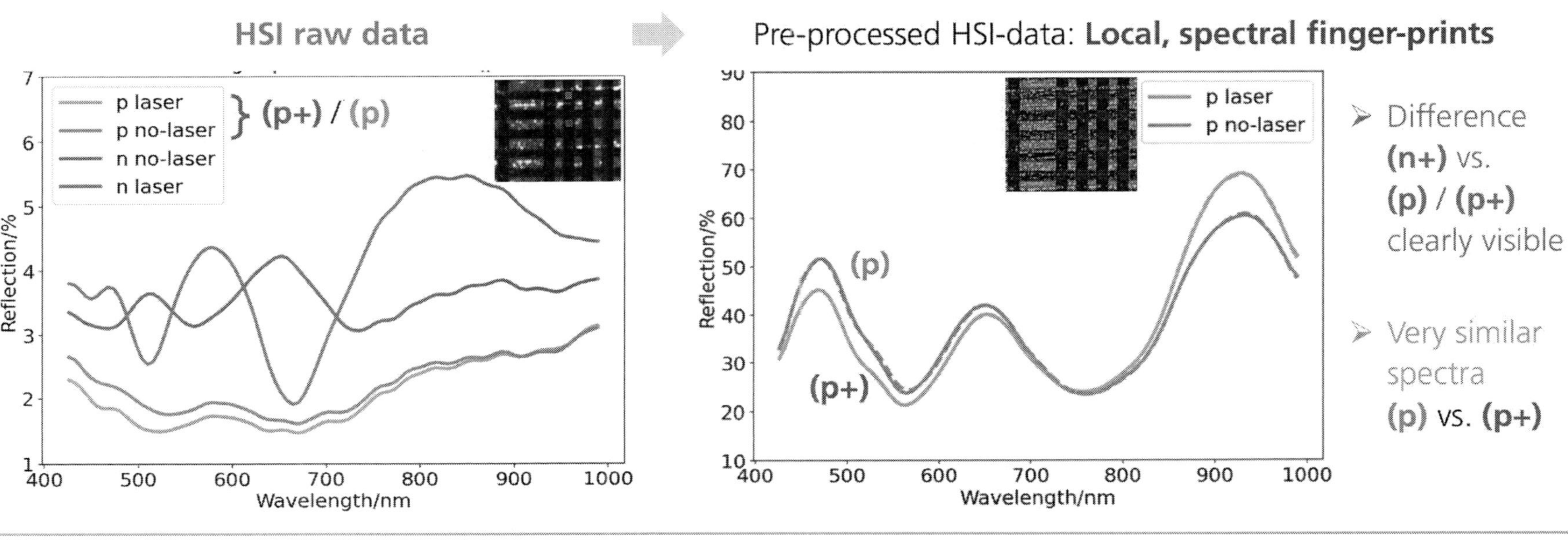

RESULTS: HSI – DATA PREPROCESSING

Material-independent algorithms – classification of pixels requires further data analysis

Identification of laser mis-alignments:

Can laser-activated **(p+)** regions be separated from **(p)** regions by hyperspectral imaging?

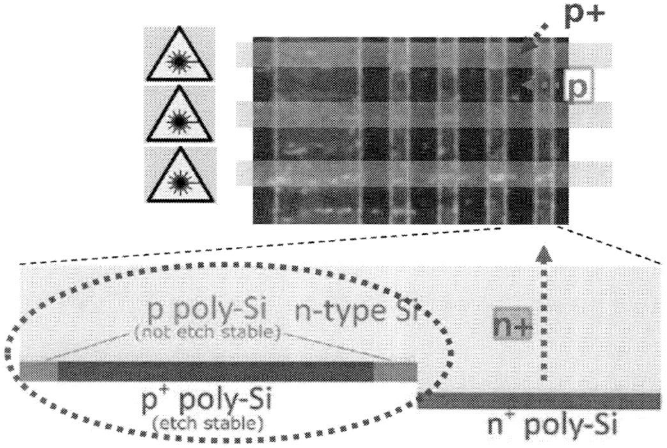

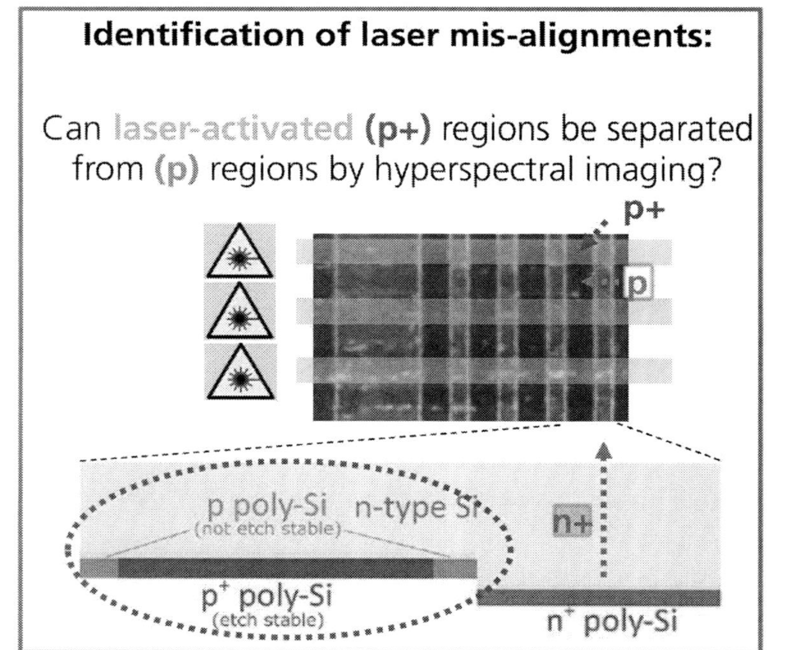

RESULTS: HSI – DATA PREPROCESSING

Material-independent algorithms – classification of pixels requires further data analysis

Identification of laser mis-alignments:

Can laser-activated **(p+)** regions be separated from **(p)** regions by hyperspectral imaging?

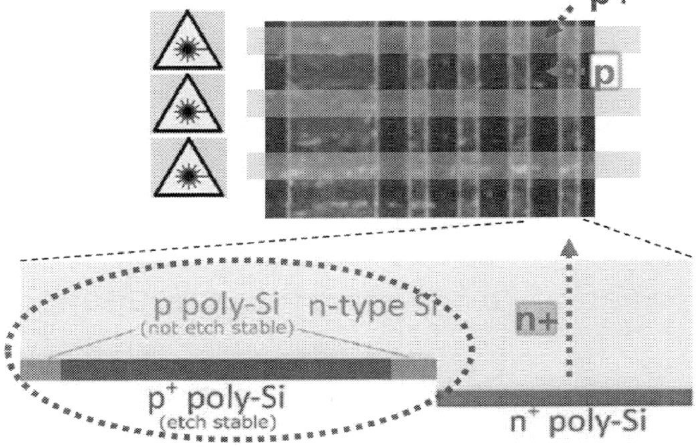

Pre-processed data

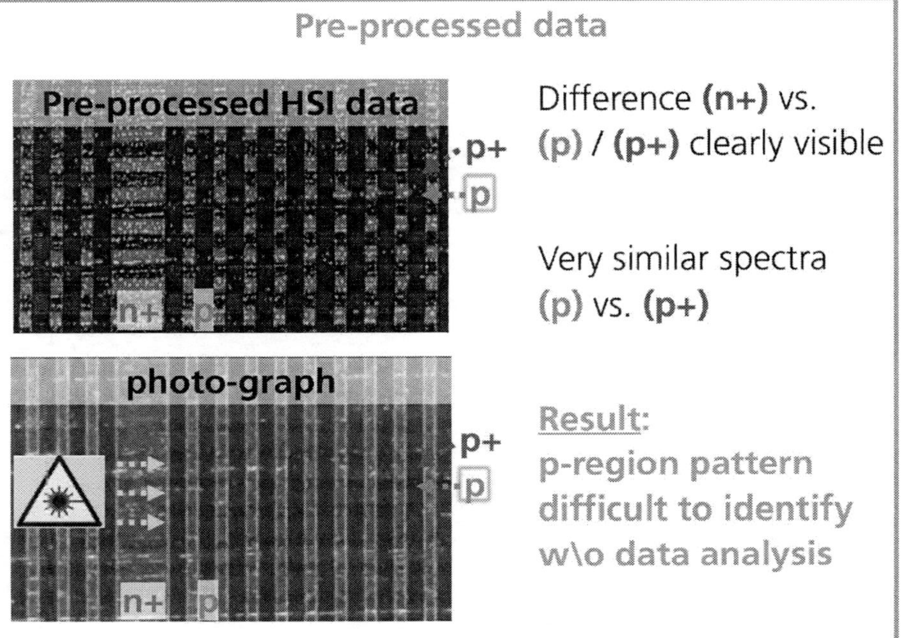

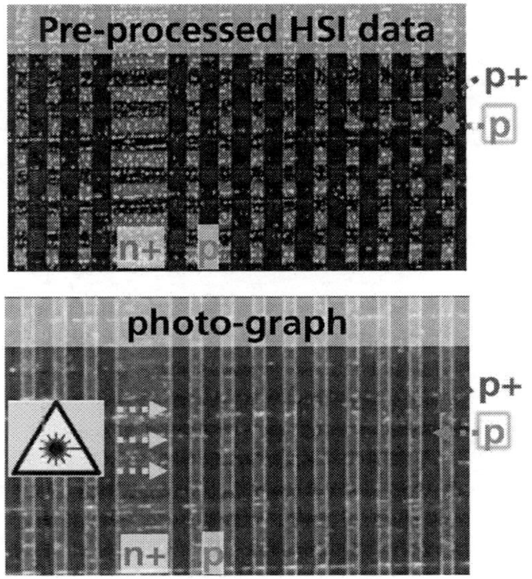

Difference **(n+)** vs. (p) / **(p+)** clearly visible

Very similar spectra (p) vs. **(p+)**

Result:
p-region pattern difficult to identify w\o data analysis

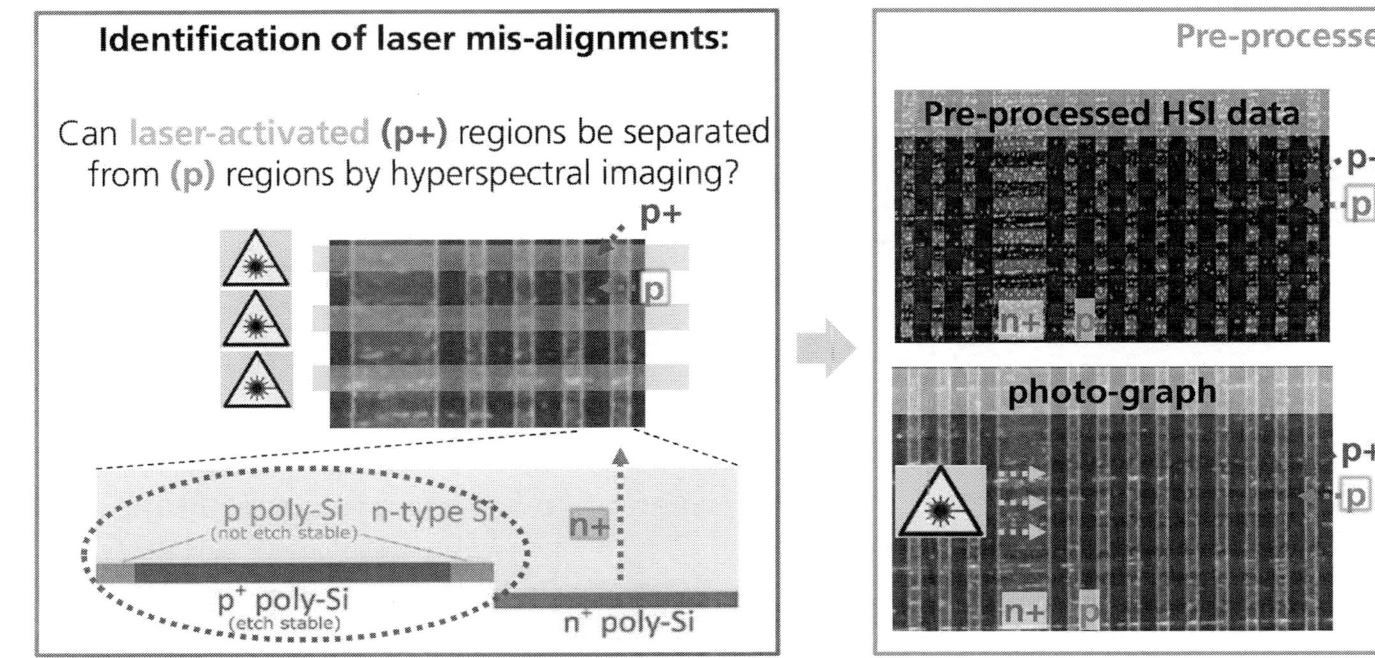

RESULTS: HSI – DATA ANALYSIS

Material-independent algorithms – classification of pixels

Identification of laser mis-alignments:

Can laser-activated **(p+)** regions be separated from **(p)** regions by hyperspectral imaging?

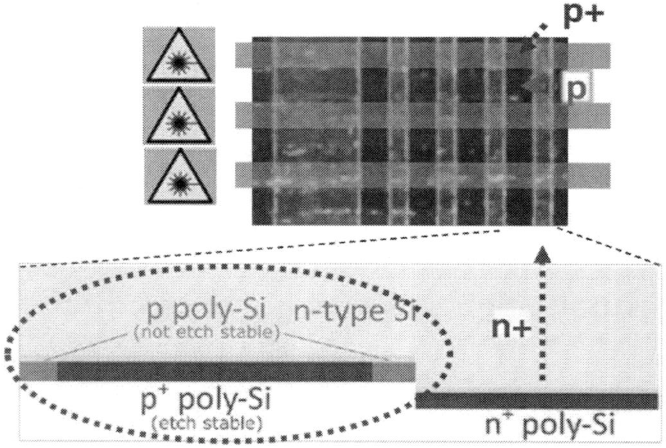

Machine learning – classification of pixels

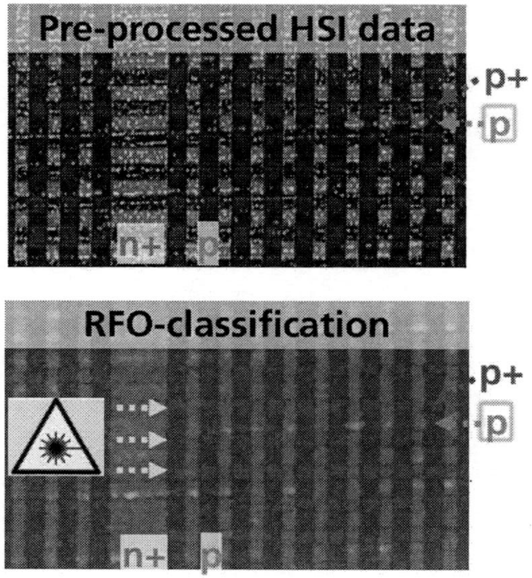

Difference **(n+)** vs. (p) / **(p+)** clearly visible

Very similar spectra (p) vs. **(p+)**

Result:
p-region pattern identified by spectral finger-print

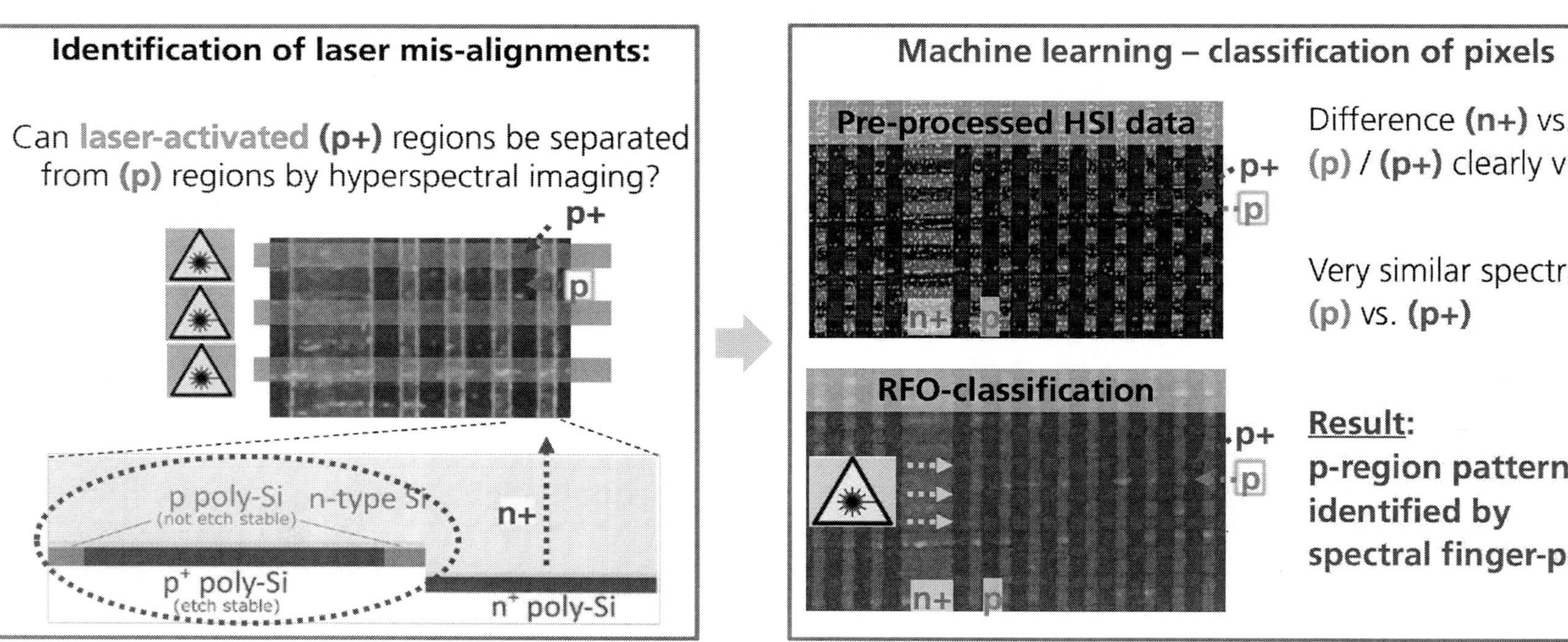

OUTLOOK: SIMPLIFIED APPROACH FOR SPECTRAL IMAGING

LED sun-simulator combined with mono-chrome camera

Identification of laser mis-alignments:

Can laser-activated **(p+)** regions be separated from **(p)** regions by hyperspectral imaging?

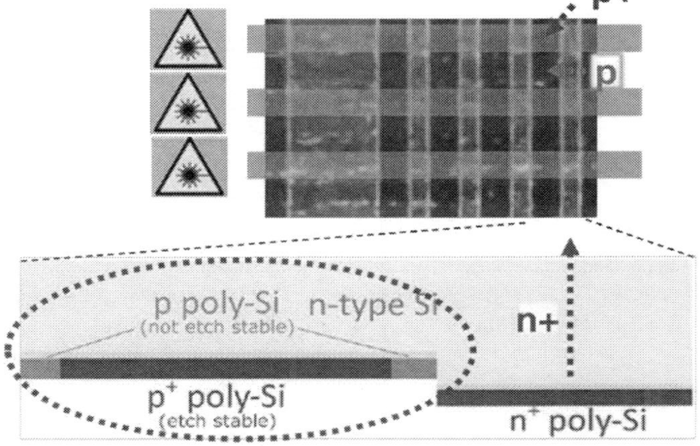

Wavelength-dependent contrasts

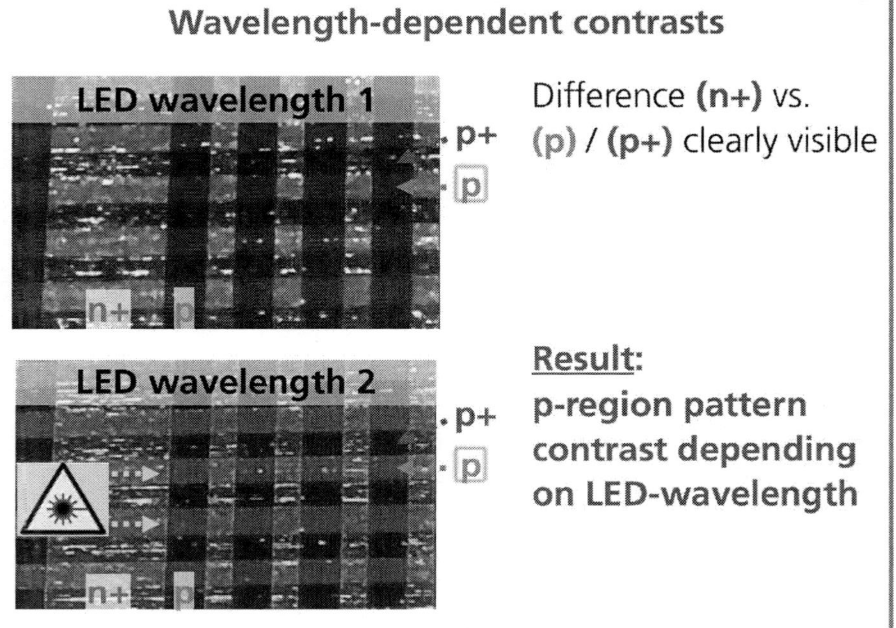

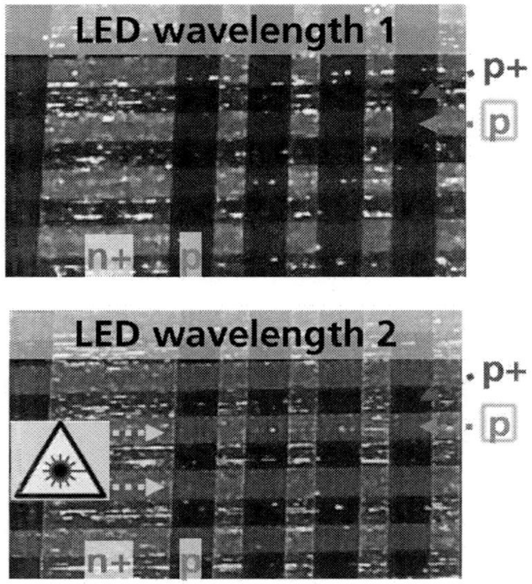

Difference **(n+)** vs. (p) / **(p+)** clearly visible

Result:
p-region pattern contrast depending on LED-wavelength

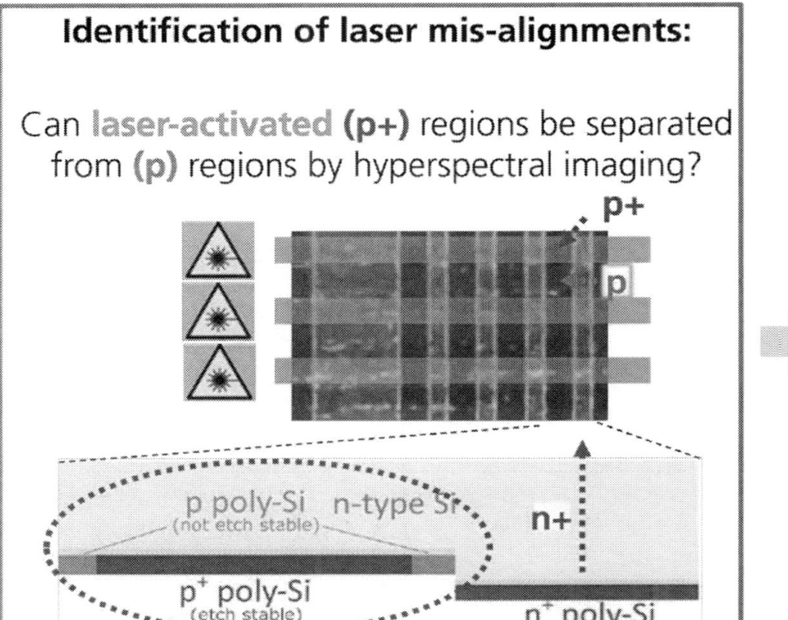

SUMMARY: INLINE QUALITY CONTROL FOR BACK-CONTACT SOLAR CELLS

Rapid imaging of rear side pattern by combining spectral with spatial information

Results of (optical) HSI approach:

1. Test structures with local laser-doped regions investigated by spectral imaging
2. Local spectral finger-prints → only minor differences between (p+) vs. (p)
3. Automated training and classification results in separation of (p+) from (p)

Outlook:

- Simplified "LED-approach" based on identified relevant wavelengths
- Increase of spatial resolution for "real" patterns with dimensions below 20µm

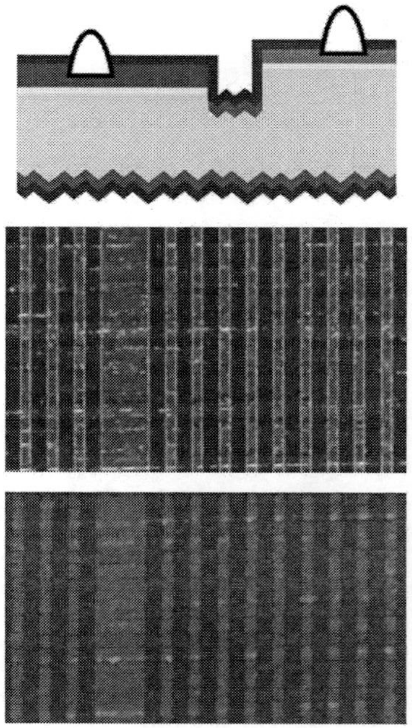

Conclusion: Optical hyperspectral imaging (HSI) can serve as fast and sensitive quality control technique for IBC solar cells

Fraunhofer CSP

ISC research for a sunny future

Fraunhofer CSP

Thank you for your attention!

Marko Turek
Tel. +49 345 5589 5121
marko.turek@csp.fraunhofer.de

Fraunhofer CSP
Otto-Eißfeldt- Straße 12
06120 Halle (Saale)
www.csp.fraunhofer.de

Funded within project "SelFi" (FKZ 03EE1138B)

Supported by:
Federal Ministry for Economic Affairs and Climate Action
on the basis of a decision by the German Bundestag

RCT solutions
Photovoltaic
Services & Technology
Solutions Partner
Pathway to TBC: Process, Design, and Cost Implications for new PERC & TOPCon Lines
Group of companies
RCT solutions
RCT power
RCT hydrogen
Julian Reichle*, Sraisth, Mehul Raval, Gourab Das, Andreas Teppe, Wolfgang Jooss and Peter Fath
RCT Solutions GmbH, Line - Eid - Str. 1, 78467 Konstanz, Germany
With support of Wolfgang Herbst from ViridisIQ GmbH, Germany
*E-mail: julian.reichle@rct-solutions.com

Motivation for TBC Solar Cells
Next phase of production expansion indicates TBC

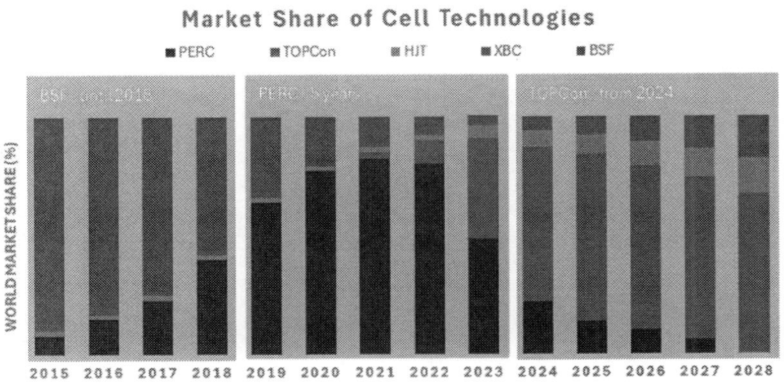

Challenge:
- Advanced technologies like TOPCon and PERC
- Building new factories takes time, while solar cell tech lasts only 5–7 years
- How to future-proof, enable updates, and design adaptable systems?

+ Based on same equipment's as PERC and TOPCon
+ Back contacts – no front side metallization
  - Enhanced light absorption improves cell efficiency [1]. → Higher module yield.
  - Simplifies the metallization process, as only one side needs to be processed [2]
  - Easier to apply low-cost copper metalization
  - TBC structures supports tandem cell configurations, enabling future advancements in solar technology [3]
+ Adopting advanced passivation methods
  - Lowering recombination losses on both polarity surfaces

[1] F. Haase, C. Hollemann, S. Schäfer, M. Merkle, M. Rienäcker, J. Krügener, R. Brendel and R. Peibst, "Laser contact openings for local poly-Si-metal contacts enabling 26.1%-efficient POLO-IBC solar cells.," Sol. Energy Mater. Sol. Cells, p. 186:184-193, 2018;.
[2] M. K. Mat Desa et al., "Silicon back contact solar cell configuration: A pathway towards higher efficiency," Renewable and Sustainable Energy Reviews, vol. Volume 60, pp. 1516-1532, 2016.
[3] Erkan Aydin et al., "Pathways toward commercial perovskite/silicon," Science, no. 383, 2024.

The RCT Group at a Glance

RCT solutions

RCT solutions

2012
Founded, privately owned

≈ 100 GW
Supporting PV manufacturing capacity

26+
Countries

62
Factories worldwide

World's First
Fully integrated giga-scale factory installation

76 GW
Ingot & Wafer integration

RCT power

2015
Founded, privately owned

>15 GWh (5 GWh USA)
Total shipment

20 GWh
production capacity, fully automated

Best Storage
Awarded in Germany

Fully EES manufacturing
Residential, commercial, utility scale (from kWh to MWh)

EU-China-USA Based
Battery production & Operations

RCT hydrogen

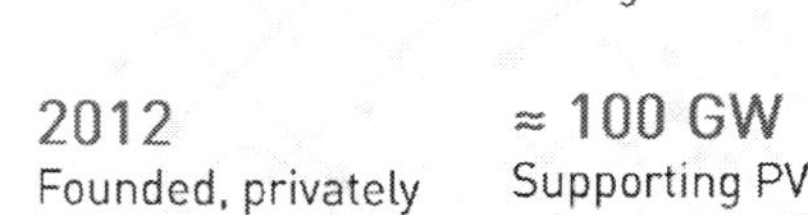

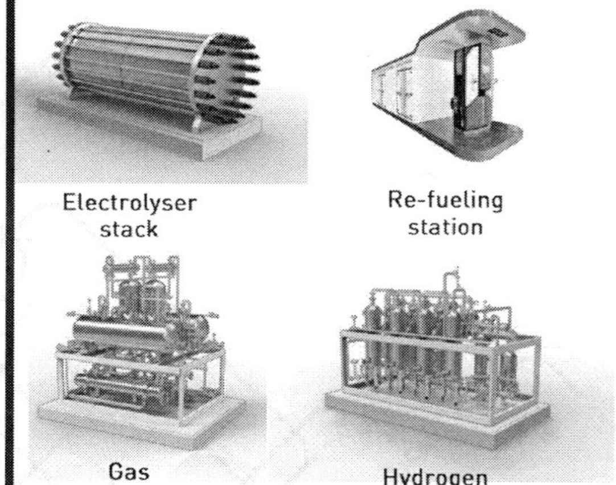

Made/Engineered in Germany
Hydrogen equipment & engineering service

Factory Output
250MW (Target)

Aim and Approach
Application of the conceptional engineering approach

RCT solutions

Technology Selection
- Baseline Technology
- Upgrade Technology

Process Flow Decision
- Process Routes
- Line Balancing

Conceptional Engineering
- Layout & Room book
- Facility Utility Matrix
- Mass & Load Balance
- HR-Plan

Cost of Ownership
- Equipment CAPEX
- Utility, Facility and Building CAPEX
- OPEX
- Sensitivity

Summary and Outlook

Technology Selection
Solar cell efficiency limits & status

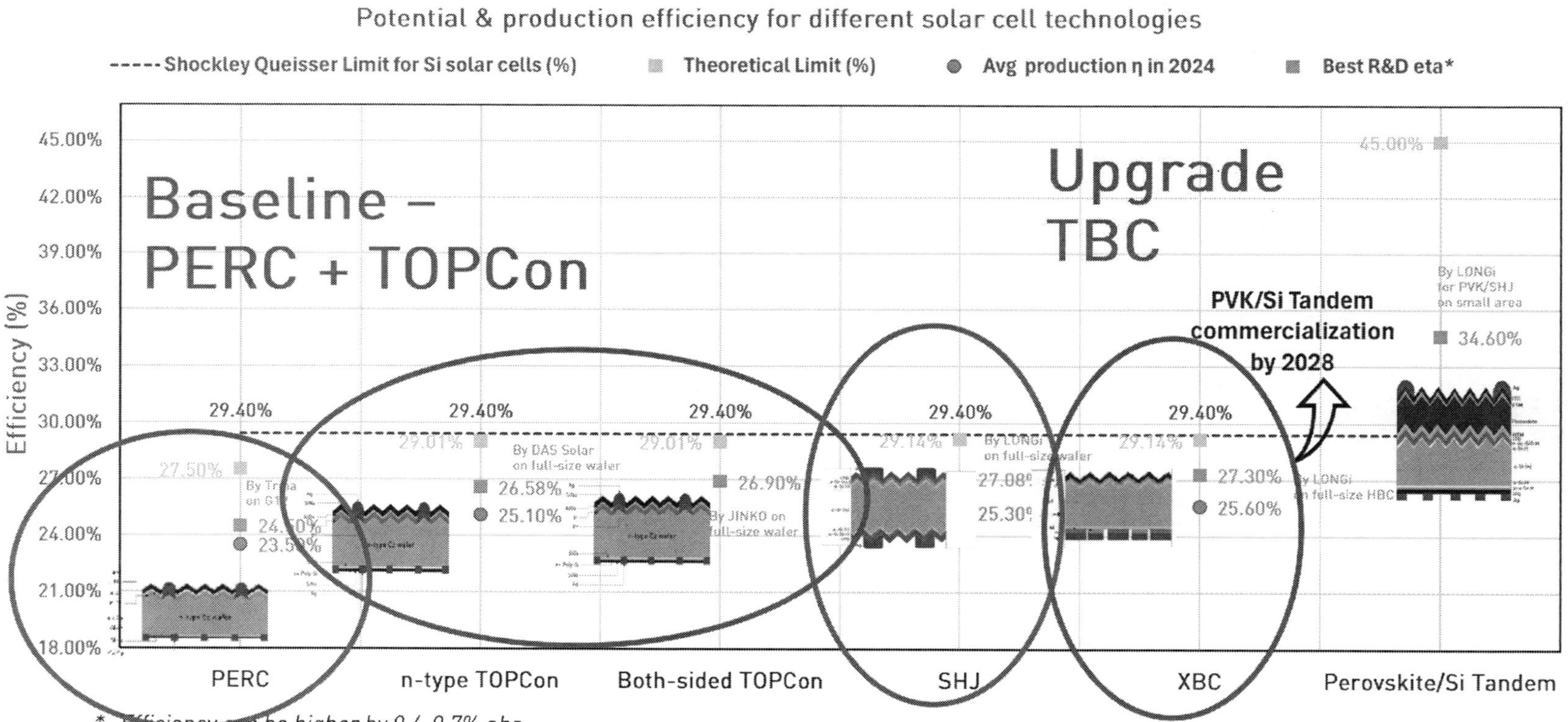

*- Efficiency can be higher by 0.6-0.7% abs

Technology Selection
Scenarios considered for TBC upgrade route

RCT solutions

Case	A-0	A-1	A-2	B-0	B-1	B-2	C-0
Baseline Technology	PERC Reference 5.0 GW	PERC 5.0 GW		TOPCon Reference 5GW	TOPCon 5.5 GW		TBC Reference 5.6 GW
End technology		TBC 5.6 GW	TBC 4.3 GW		TBC 5.6 GW	TBC 4.8GW	
Considerations	N/A	• Space • Utilities	• Utilities	N/A	• Space • Utilities	• Utilities	

- Reference cases for PERC, TOPCon and TBC cell production
- PERC and TOPCon as baseline technology
- PERC was selected, as there are some IP related risks
- Upgrade to TBC from PERC and from TOPCon
- Each upgrade scenario considers complete utility buildout from the beginning
- Two different cases for each technology combination **with and without space provision.**

Process Flow and Cell Design
TOPCon to TOPCon Back Contact (TBC) upgrade

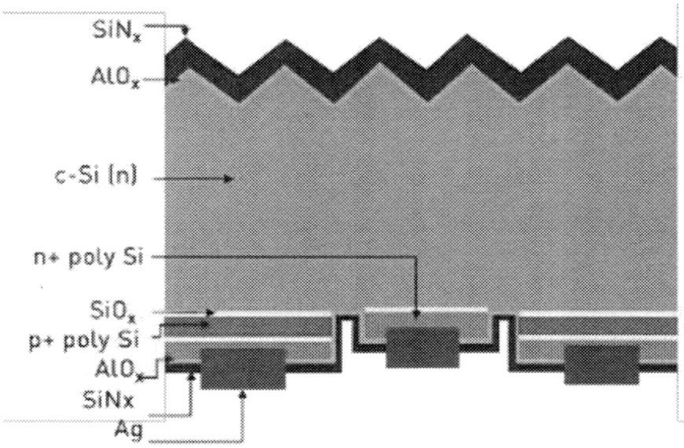

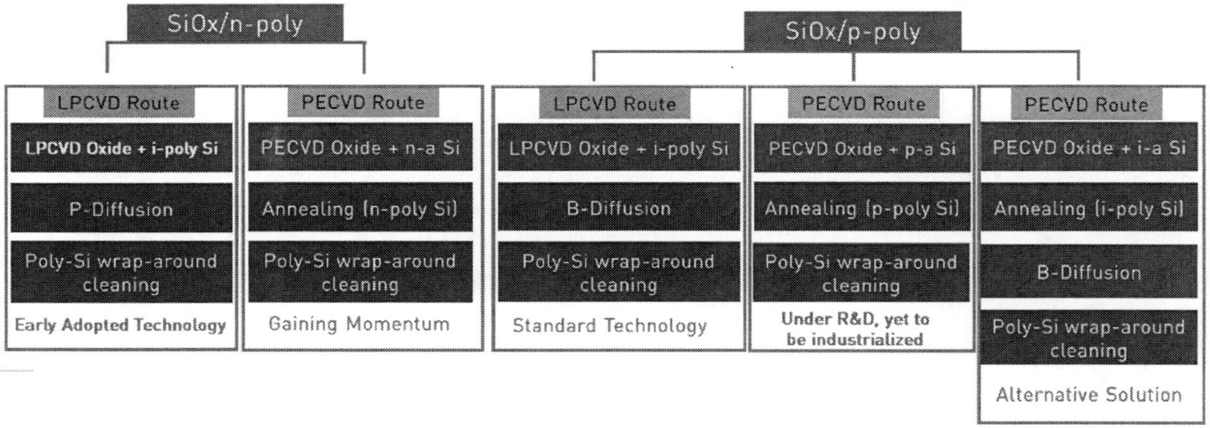

- TBC requires **p-type and n-type poly-Si passivated contacts**
- For in-situ B-doped a-Si, B-atoms migrate easily towards tunnel-oxide upon annealing, creating defects & leads to degradation in the passivating quality
- Thereby LPCVD route adopted for TBC by big players already
- Though in R&D, **p-poly Si (B)** is being developed in **PECVD** process, but the process window is much more narrow as compared to n-poly Si (P)
- PECVD equipment from upgrade available ´→ **Ex-situ diffusion** of PECVD deposited a-Si is an alternative solution

Process Flow and Cell Design
More process steps require more space

RCT solutions

TOPCon Back Contact (TBC) – OPT A

- SDE + Cleaning
- Tunnel Oxide + i-Poly Si Deposition (RS) LPCVD F2F
- B-Diffusion (RS) (F2F Loading)
- Laser Ablation (RS)
- p-poly-Si Etching (Ablated part) + Cleaning
- Tunnel Oxide + i-poly Si Deposition LPCVD F2F
- P-Diffusion (RS) (F2F Loading)
- Laser Isolation (to avoid n-and p-doped shunting)
- Alkaline Texturization (FS)
- AlO_x (Both Side)
- SiN_x ARC (FS) and Capping (RS)
- Printing, Firing & Testing

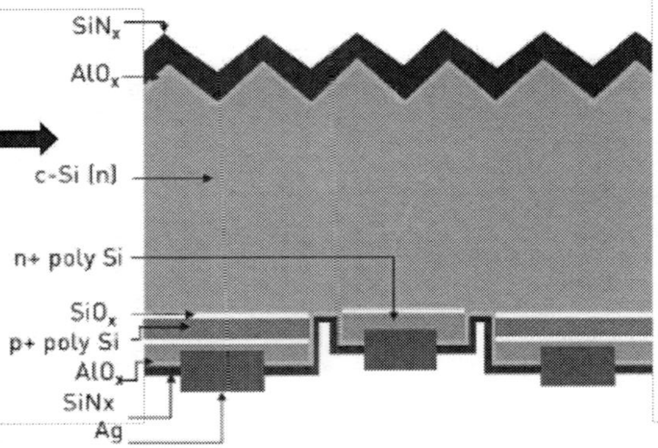

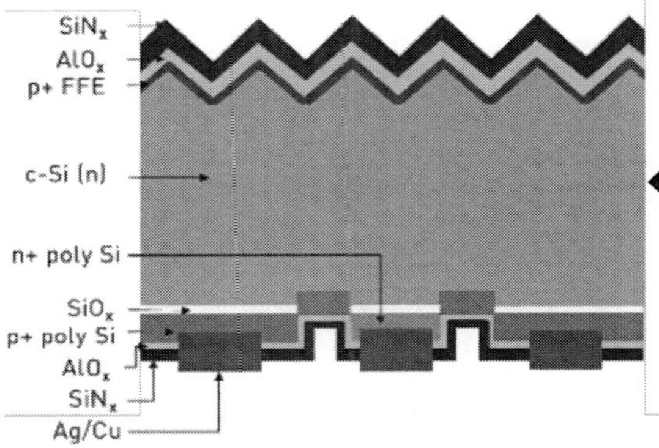

TOPCon Back Contact (TBC) – OPT B

- SDE + Cleaning
- Tunnel Oxide + i-poly Si Deposition (PECVD)
- P-Diffusion
- SiNx Capping layer
- Laser Ablation
- Tunnel Oxide and n-Poly-Si Dtching + Cleaning
- Tunnel Oxide + i-poly Si Deposition (PECVD)
- B-Diffusion (BSG Formation)
- Local Laser Doping
- Alkaline Texturization
- B-Diffusion (Gap & FS)
- AlOx + SiNx Deposition (BS)
- Printing, Firing & Testing

Conceptional Engineering
More process steps required for TBC

RCT solutions

PERC (AX) with Laser Contact Opening +Selective Emitter (SE)	5 GW		TBC (A1,B1,C0) with LECO and HE + Cu Metallization	5.6 GW		(BX) TOPCON with Homogeneous Emitter (HE) and LECO	5.5 GW (G12)
Batch SDE/TEX	6	→	Batch Polish	6	←	Batch SDE/TEX	6
		+14 tools	LPCVD	14	+14 tools		
		+9 tools	BCL3 Diff + Ox. & dr.-in	9	←	BCL3 Diff + Ox. & dr.-in	9
		+12 tools	Laser Patterning	12	+12 tools		
		+6 tools	SSE (BSG)	6	←	SSE (BSG)	6
		+6 tools	Polish and Batch Cleaning	6	←	Batch Polish	6
		+30 tools	LPCVD	30	+14 tools	LPCVD	16
POCL3 Diff	10		POCL3 Diff	20	← +8 tools	POCL3 Diff / or anneal	12
SE-Laser	12	→	Laser Isolation	12	+12 tools		
Oxidation	8						
SSE (PSG)	6	→	SSE (PSG)	6	←	SSE (PSG)	6
Batch Polish	6	→	Batch Texture	6	←	p-Si Wrap-around removal	6
Anneal	8	-6 tools					
		+10 tools	ALD AlOx	10	←	ALD AlOx	10
PECVD AlOx SiNx	20	→	PECVD SiNx	20	←	PECVD SiNx	20
PECVD SiNx	20	→	PECVD SiNx	20	←	PECVD SiNx	20
Laser Contact Opening	10	- 10 tools					
1st Print (RB)	10	→	1st Print (Fine/Dashed Ag Fingers)	10	←	1st Print (RB)	10
			Fast Firing	10			
		+10 tool	LECO	10			
2nd Print (RF)	10	→	2nd Print (Cu Finger)	10	←	2nd Print (RF)	10
3rd Print (FB)	10	→	3rd Print (Isolation Paste)	10	←	3rd Print (FB)	10
4th Print (FF)	10	→	4th Print (Cu BB)	10	←	4th Print (FF)	10
Fast Firing	10					Fast Firing	10
						LECO	10
IV+Sorting+Packing	10	→	IV+Sorting+Packing	10	←	IV+Sorting+Packing	10
Main Tools:	**166**	+ 49%	**Main Tools:**	**247**	+ 32%	**Main Tools:**	**187**

- Upgrade scenario 1 - covers space and utility provision.
- Extra TBC steps raise CAPEX, labor, and complexity.
- Most TOPCon tools are reusable.
- Some minor PERC tools will be removed.
- TBC process flow is still early and expected to evolve.

PERC (AX) with Laser Contact Opening +Selective Emitter (SE) 5 GW			TBC (A1,B1,C0) with LECO and HE + Cu Metallization 5.6 GW			(BX) TOPCON with Homogeneous Emitter (HE) and LECO 5.5 GW (G12)	
Main Tools:	166	+ 49%	**Main Tools:**	247	+ 32%	**Main Tools:**	187
Keep for TBC	150		Keep for TBC	187		Keep for TBC	
Add. required for TBC	97		Add. required for TBC	60		Add. required for TBC	
Not required for TBC	-16		Not required for TBC	0		Not required for TBC	
spez CAPEX [m.USD/GWp]	35 - 48	+ 39%	**spez CAPEX** [m.USD/GWp]	49 - 67	+ 14%	**spez CAPEX** [m.USD/GWp]	43 - 59
Labour Total [FTE]	1100 - 1400	+ 13%	**Labour Total** [FTE]	1300 - 1600	+ 5%	**Labour Total** [FTE]	1200 - 1500
Area [ha]	10 - 14	+ 41%	**Area** [ha]	14 - 19	+ 15%	**Area** [ha]	12 - 17

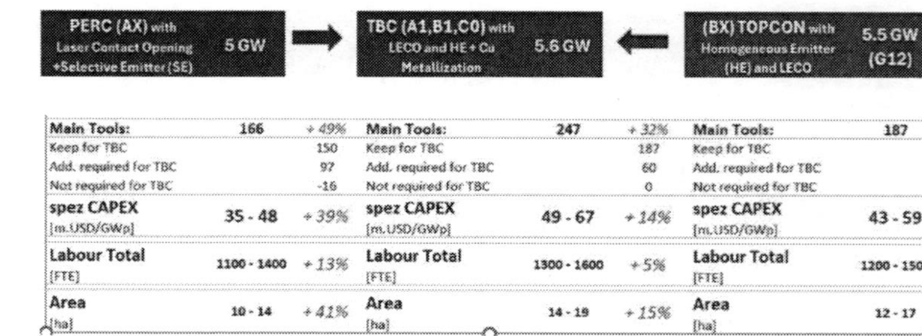

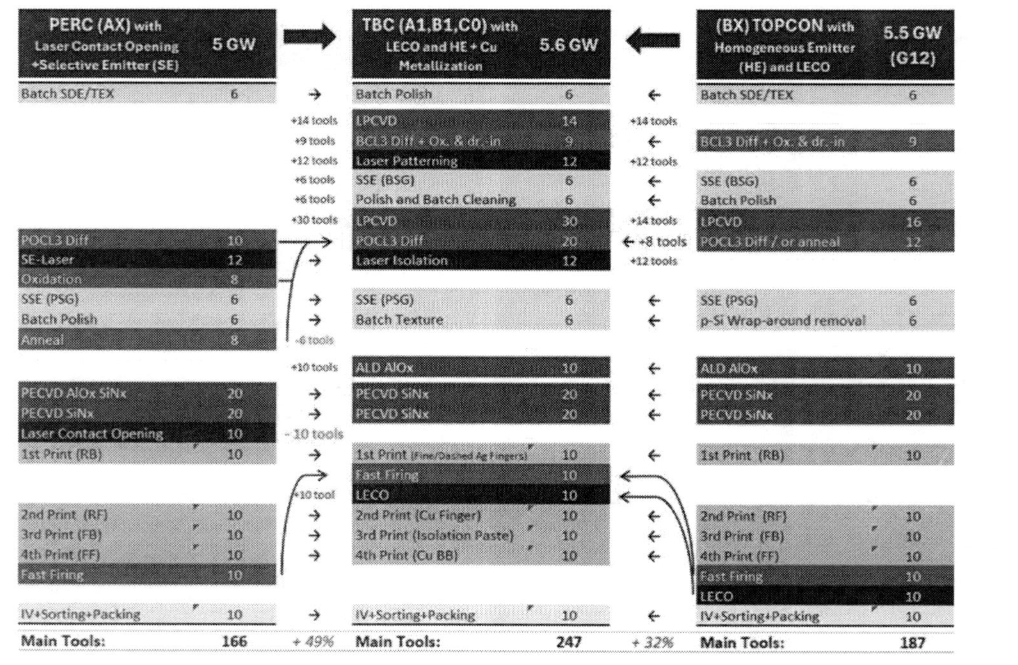

Conceptional Engineering–
Layout – Reserve space within each equipment cluster

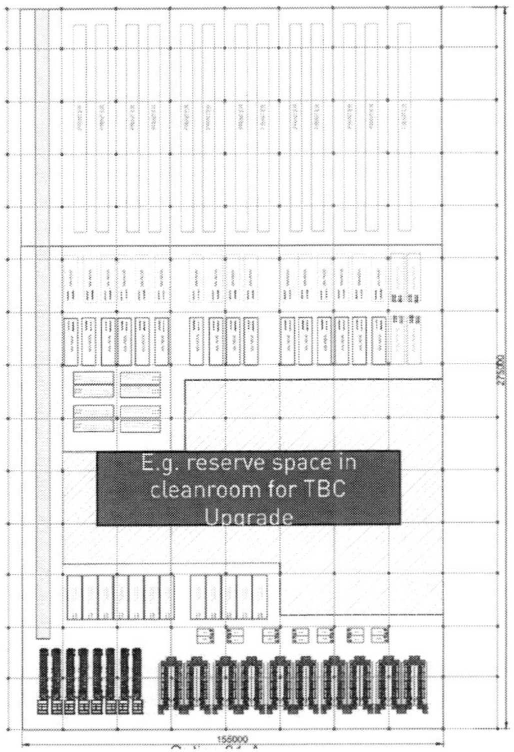

← **Option1 : Separated Reserve Space for Upgrade**

- Easier to temporary close or separate (OPEX reduction of cleanroom or renting out temporarily)

Option 2: Reserve Space Inside the Factory in each Cluster: →

- Piping can be reduced
- Improved material and personnel flow after process or technology upgrade

Option 2 was considered

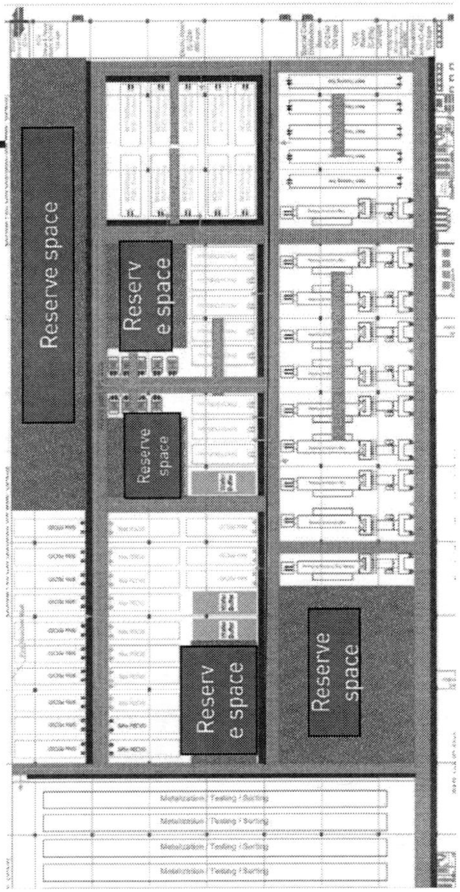

Conceptional Engineering– Often Overseen – Utility, Facility and Building Design

- New technologies → often increased CAPEX
- Utility and facility CAPEX are frequently underestimated.
- E.g. switching gases or liquids, like from Phosphoroxychlorid (POCl3) to Phosphine (PH3), → careful evaluation due to major differences.

Non-Process Packages
Civil
Architectural
Infrastructure
Structural
Rainwater System
General HVAC
Sewage Treatment
LV Power Distribution
MV Power Distribution
Lightning System
Emergency Power System (DG, UPS)

Process Packages
Process Cooling Water
High Side Water Generation/Chilled Water
Waste Water Treatment
Waste Gas Treatment
Bulk Gas Distribution
Process Gas Distribution
Process Chemical Distribution
DI Water
Compressed Dry Air/ Compressed Air
Facility Monitoring & Controlling System
Clean Room Design

Cost of Ownership
Before and after the Upgrade compared to no Upgrade

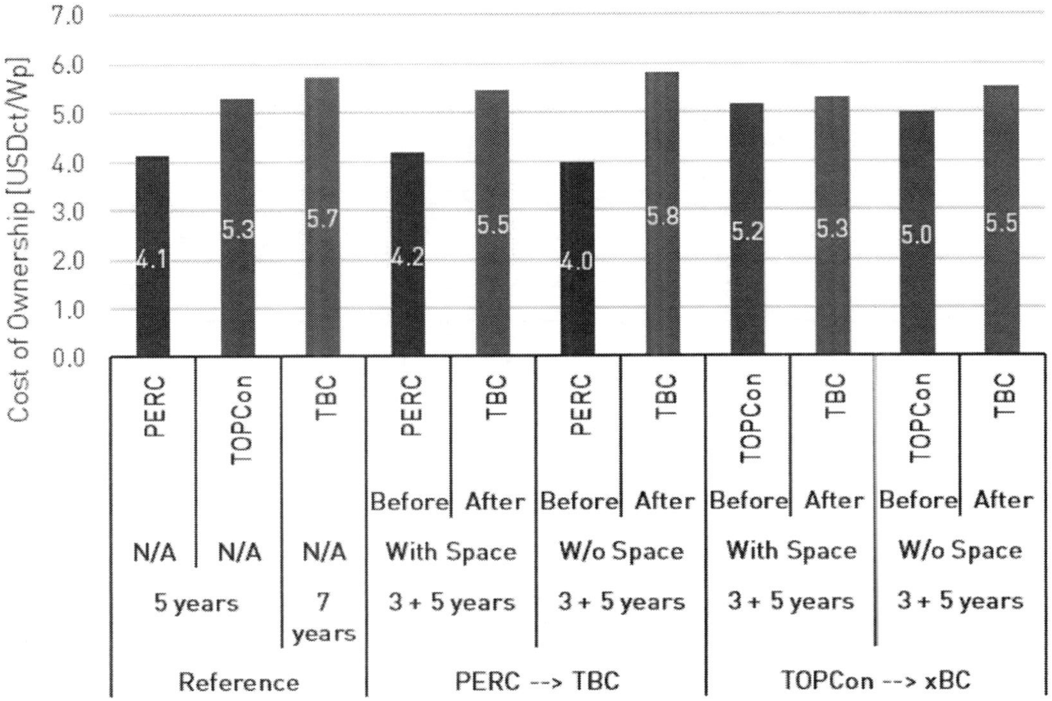

Summary of Ownership Cost Analysis

- Different lifetime assumed.
- Calculate ownership costs before and after upgrade
- References w/o upgrade also included
- Lower initial cost for PERC and TOPCon with utilities only
- Include expansion space increasing upfront cost, but still lower as reference if longer
- TBC Upgrade cost lower, if longer operating can be expected and no equipment needs to be removed or replaced e.g. TOPCon to TBC

* **Key assumptions CoO:** Depreciation: Equipment 5 - 7 years – Utilities 10 years – Building 20 years – Western Location – 2000 USD/sqm building cost reference – Cumulative interest 3.8%

Summary of the Upgrade Scenarios results

RCT solutions

Case	A1	A2	B1	B2
Start Up Technology	PERC 5.0 GW		TOPCon 5.5 GW	
Upgrade Technology	TBC 5.6 GW	TBC 4.3 GW	TBC 5.6 GW	TBC 4.8 GW
Provision	• Space • Utilities	• Utilities	• Space • Utilities	• Utilities
CAPEX [mUSD] Start + Upgrade	723 + 146	587 + 109	795 + 31	723 + 31
CoO [USDct/Wp]	PERC: 4.2 TBC: 5.5	PERC: 4.0 TBC: 5.8	TOPCon: 5.2 TBC: 5.3	TOPCon: 5.0 TBC: 5.5
Removed and added tools for upgrade	-16 tools + 97 tools	-46 tools +72 tools	-0 tools + 60 tools	-12 tools +50
Result	+ Competitive TBC cost + Moderate CAPEX increase	+ Lowest CAPEX Option	+ Simplest Upgrade options (no tool removal) + Most competitive TBC cost	+ Moderate CAPEX + Competitive TOPCon and TBC Cost
Targeted Developer or investor	• Balanced developer • Long-term cost efficiency and stable production output with low TOPCon IP Confidence	• Developers with CAPEX constraints, hesitant adding space for TBC expansion • With low IP Confidence in TOPCon	• Minimal disruptions to existing production lines. • Technological advantage	• New developers seek market-leading technology • Limited confidence in TBC's IP landscape, making them cautious about large-scale investments.

Summary and Outlook

RCT solutions

Key Points:

- **Technology cycles lasts 5–7 years,** so western factories with longer setup times should be upgradeable.
- **TBC** (TOPCon Back Contact) cells are **likely the next evolution**.
- **Various upgrade options** differ in capacity, space, and utility needs.
- Upgrading to TBC requires **more CAPEX and complexity**
- Cost of ownership favors providing utilities only initially (before upgrade) but **allocating extra space reduces future costs (after upgrade)**.

→ RCTs recommendation - reserving space for future upgrades.

Outlook:

Excess space can be also utilized for:

- **Debottlenecking:** Increase line capacity by debottlenecking. Changes in throughput requirements of certain process steps might change.
- **Equipment Upgrade:** Based on existing solar cell concept (comparable to selective emitter in PERC / TOPCon cells, LECO, etc.)
- **Innovation platform** for equipment builders, initial testing of next generation solar cell concepts („pilot line" for next phase extension)

Changes in Module Design to be addressed → Addressed in tomorrows 3CO.11.3 *"Techno-Economic Analysis of Suitable Module BOM for Different Climatic Conditions"* by Sraisth

TBC comes with higher resource demands → addressed in my Sesson tomorrow 5CO.4.4 *"LCA Learning Curve for Crystalline Silicon Solar Technologies based on Technology Improvements"*

Thank you to all RCT Solutions colleagues – Join us at Konstanz

RCT solutions

Gefördert durch:

Bundesministerium
für Wirtschaft
und Energie

aufgrund eines Beschlusses
des Deutschen Bundestages
Project PV Pilot - FKZ 03EE1219

RCT Solutions GmbH
Line-Eid-Strasse 1
D-78467 Konstanz, Germany
Phone +49 7531 58470 12
info@rct-solutions.com
http://www.rct-solutions.com
Regd. HRB 708952,
Executive Board: Dr. Peter Fath
Confidential
Thank you
Group of companies
RCT solutions
RCT power
RCT hydrogen
© 2025 RCT Solutions GmbH All rights reserved

42nd European Photovoltaic Solar Energy Conference and Exhibition

This presentation was selected by the Sc. Committee of the EU PVSEC 2025 for submission of a full paper to one of the EU PVSEC's collaborating peer-reviewed journals.

INDUSTRIAL IMPLEMENTATION OF 24%-EFFICIENT POLO IBC SOLAR CELLS AND FUTURE UPGRADE TO 26%-EFFICIENT POLO2 IBC

Thorsten Dullweber[1,*], Yevgeniya Larionova[1], Philip Jäger[1], Verena Mertens[1], Sabrina Schimanke[1], Melanie Ripke[1], Ulrike Baumann[1], Alaa Osman[1], Udo Römer[1], Robby Peibst[1], Rolf Brendel[1,2], Özlem Coşkun[3], Gamze Çekerek[3], Meriç Çalışkan Arslan[3], Geoffrey Gregory[4], Erik Hoffmann[4], and Massimo Centazzo[4]

[1] Institute for Solar Energy Research Hamelin (ISFH), Am Ohrberg 1, 31860 Emmerthal, Germany
[2] Institute of Solid-State Physics, Leibniz Universität Hannover, Appelstrasse 2, 30167 Hannover, Germany
[3] Kalyon PV, Başkent OSB Şadi Türk Bulvarı 23 Malıköy, Ankara, Türkiye
[4] EnPV GmbH, Durlacher Allee 93, 76131 Karlsruhe, Germany

ABSTRACT: IBC solar cells have gained tremendous interest in the PV industry as next-generation technology. ISFH has developed a lean manufacturing process sequence for POLO IBC solar cells applying p-type Cz wafers, an Al-BSF base contact and local PECVD deposition of the SiO_xN_y/n-type polysilicon emitter through a glass shadow mask. In this paper, we report a new best POLO IBC cell efficiency of 24.3% processed at ISFH on M2 wafer size. In 2024, we started to transfer the POLO IBC process from the ISFH SolarTeC to the Kalyon PV manufacturing line using their M10 sized p-type Ga-doped Cz wafers and cell production tools. With Kalyon PV's wet chemistry and PECVD AlO_x/SiN tools good surface passivation is demonstrated by obtaining an iV_{oc} up to 727 mV using textured, rear side polished AlO_x/SiN passivated test wafers. Kalyon PV targets to process first M10-sized POLO IBC solar cells till end of 2025. However, the POLO IBC efficiency will be limited to below 25.5% by the carrier recombination at the Al-BSF base contact. To overcome this limitation, ISFH is applying a SiO_x/p-type polysilicon layer stack to a novel industrial processing sequence for the POLO² IBC solar cell. We use M2-sized n-type Cz wafers, deposit both polysilicon layers in-situ-doped full-area and laser-structure both polysilicon polarities in a novel and lean IBC trench patterning process. We obtain a measured implied V_{oc} = 735 mV and implied FF = 86.0% of POLO² IBC cell precursors processed without metal contacts. Since the polysilicon contacts minimize carrier recombination at metal contacts, the implied V_{oc} value demonstrates the high V_{oc} potential of this promising new POLO² IBC manufacturing process thereby indicating a conversion efficiency potential above 26%.

Keywords: silicon solar cells, IBC, back contact, passivating contacts, polysilicon

1 INTRODUCTION

In the past years ISFH has developed a lean manufacturing process sequence for POLO IBC solar cells applying p-type wafers, an Al-BSF base contact and a local PECVD deposition of the SiO_xN_y/n-poly-Si emitter through a glass shadow mask [1,2,3]. In this paper, we report a new best POLO IBC cell efficiency of 24.3% processed at ISFH on M2 wafer size using industry-type processing equipment at the ISFH SolarTeC. The POLO IBC process with shadow masks at ISFH is very similar to the typical industrial bifacial PERC+ mass production sequence as e.g. applied by Kalyon PV in their cell production line, allowing to re-use most of the existing PERC+ production tools [2,3]. To convert a PERC+ production line to POLO IBC, only the $POCl_3$ furnace and laser doping tool have to be replaced by a new PECVD tool for local SiO_xN_y/n-poly-Si deposition [2,3]. In 2024, Kalyon PV and ISFH signed a technology licensing agreement and started to transfer the POLO IBC process from the ISFH SolarTeC to the Kalyon PV PERC+ manufacturing line using their M10 sized Ga-doped Cz wafers [4] and their PERC+ cell production tools. In this paper, we publish first promising POLO IBC test wafer results processed at Kalyon PV obtaining implied V_{oc} values up to 727 mV demonstrating a suitable passivation quality of Kalyon PVs wet chemistry and PECVD AlO_x/SiN tools.

However, the POLO IBC efficiency will be limited to below 25.5% by the carrier recombination at the Al-BSF base contact [5]. To overcome this limitation aiming at n-type polysilicon (n-poly-Si) / p-type polysilicon (p-poly-Si) POLO² IBC cell efficiencies beyond 26%, in collaboration with EnPV a carrier selective SiO_x/p-poly-Si layer stack has been developed at ISFH using industrial tools for the wet chemically grown SiO_x and the in-situ doped p-poly-Si deposited by LPCVD. Last year, we have published a best J_0 = 2.3 fA/cm² [6]. ISFH is applying the SiO_x/p-poly-Si layer stack to develop a novel industrial processing sequence for the POLO² IBC solar cell [7]. We deposit both poly layers in-situ-doped full-area on M2-sized n-type Cz wafers and laser-structure both poly-Si polarities in a novel IBC trench layout targeting very cost-effective processes for etch barrier formation and poly-Si etching [7]. In this paper, we present first promising test wafer results demonstrating an implied V_{oc} up to 735 mV for POLO² IBC solar cell precursors without metal contacts processed with industrial tools in the ISFH SolarTeC.

This EUPVSEC conference paper is a shortened version of a corresponding invited full manuscript submitted to EPJ Photovoltaics.

2 24% POLO IBC CELLS BY ISFH AND TECHNOLOGY TRANSFER TO KALYON PV

The POLO IBC process flow is published in detail in previous papers [2,3,8] and yielded a previously best POLO IBC cell efficiency of 23.9% [4]. In this paper, we report a new best POLO IBC cell efficiency of 24.1% independently confirmed by ISFH CalTeC with the current-voltage (IV) parameters summarized in Tab. 1. The high open circuit voltage V_{oc} = 723 mV demonstrates the good surface passivation quality of the AlO_x/SiN and SiO_x/n-poly-Si layers with saturation current densities J_0 around 3 fA/cm² [9]. The efficiency improvement from 23.9% to 24.1% was obtained by applying a 25°C lower n-poly-Si annealing temperature which is now optimized for the wet chemical SiO_x.and which increased the V_{oc} from 720 mV to 723 mV, see Table I. In addition, integrating contact pads in the busbars and applying a new IV test chuck with contact pins ensured a more precise contacting thereby reducing the series resistance from 0.8 to 0.67 mΩcm^2 as shown in Table I. This new IV test chuck was qualified for high-precision IV test at ISFH CalTeC enabling an independent certified efficiency measurement. Subsequently, we optimized the anti-reflection coating applying a triple-layer AlO_x/SiN/SiON stack instead of the AlO_x/SiN layer which reduces the average reflectance from 1.7% to 0.9% thereby increasing the J_{sc} by 0.4 mA/cm^2 leading to a new best POLO IBC efficiency of 24.3% displayed in Table I. As can be seen in Table 1, the POLO IBC series resistance R_s = 0.67 Ωcm^2 is still relatively high thereby limiting the FF to 81.3%. The high R_s is caused by a high Ag to n-poly contact resistance of 25 mΩcm^2 as published in Ref. 8 which is subject to further optimization.

Table I: IV parameters of the best POLO IBC solar cells at ISFH with M2 p-type wafer size. The 23.9% efficient cell is our previously best cell published in [4]. The 24.1% cell was independently confirmed by ISFH CalTeC. The 24.3% cell applies our latest process improvement and is measured in-house while ISFH CalTeC certification is pending.

Efficiency [%]	V_{oc} [mV]	J_{sc} [mA/cm^2]	FF [%]	Rs [mΩcm^2]
23.9	720	41.1	80.5	0.80
24.1	723	40.8	81.5	0.67
24.3	723	41.4	81.3	0.67

Kalyon PV has processed the first M10-sized p-type Ga-doped test wafers to apply and optimize the PERC+ production recipes for alkaline texturing, acidic polishing, wet chemical cleaning, and AlO_x/SiN front and rear passivation for POLO IBC. Double-sided textured and AlO_x/SiN-passivated wafers exhibit iV_{oc} values up to 731 mV. When adding rear polishing after texturing to the test wafer process sequence, first test wafers achieved an iV_{oc} value of only 687 mV. By optimizing the existing cleaning process post polishing and by selecting higher resistivity wafers with higher bulk lifetimes, the median iV_{oc} improves to 717 mV with a best iV_{oc} value of 727 mV as shown in Fig. 1. Hence, the iV_{oc} values obtained with Kalyon PV wet chemistry and AlO_x/SiN production tools are approaching the best POLO IBC iV_{oc} values of 740 mV obtained at ISFH SolarTeC [4,8]. As a next future step, Kalyon PV will process first complete POLO IBC solar cells using their M10 sized Cz wafers and PERC+ processing equipment with support by ISFH and assess the manufacturability via a small-scale pilot production.

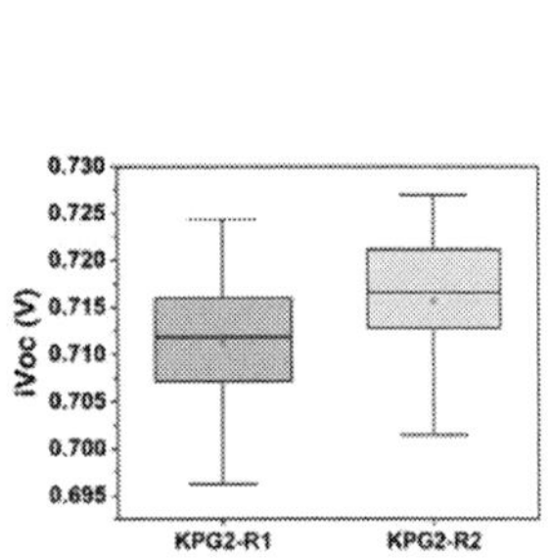

KPG2-R1: Wafer resistivity range is 1.0 Ωcm – 1.09 Ωcm

KPG2-R2: Wafer resistivity range is 1.1 Ωcm – 1.3 Ωcm

Figure 1: QSSPC measurement results of POLO IBC lifetime precursors processed at Kalyon PV using their Ga-doped M10 Cz wafers and their PERC+ mass production tools for wet chemistry, PECVD AlO_x/SiN, and firing. The lifetime samples achieve an implied V_{oc} up to 727 mV demonstrating a suitable surface passivation quality of the industrial process tools.

3 FUTURE UPGRADE TO 26% EFFICIENT POLO2 IBC CELLS

The POLO IBC cell efficiency is limited to below 25.5% by carrier recombination at the alloyed Al-BSF base contact as simulated in [5] and as evident from the large gap between iV_{oc} = 740 mV published in Ref. 4 and V_{oc} = 723 mV in Table 1. Hence, ISFH is developing an industrial POLO^2 IBC design with carrier selective n-poly-Si and p-poly-Si contacts.

ISFH applies the SiO_x/p-poly-Si process of Ref. 6 to develop a novel POLO^2 IBC solar cell processing sequence. Using mostly lab-type tools and p-type float zone silicon wafers, a small-area POLO^2 IBC solar cell with 25.5% efficiency has been developed at ISFH [9]. In this paper, we report for the first time results obtained with a novel industrial POLO^2 IBC process sequence displayed in Fig. 2 [7]. For this industrial approach, we choose M2-sized n-type Cz wafers due to their higher tolerance to Fe contamination and LeTID degradation and use solely industrial processing tools at the ISFH SolarTeC. We grow the SiO_x wet chemically and deposit the p-poly-Si layer in-situ-doped by LPCVD full-area (process steps 1 and 2 in Fig. 2). During the high-temperature poly-anneal in step 3 we use O_2 and hence grow a thin oxide layer on the p-poly-Si. We laser ablate the oxide and apply a KOH etch in steps 4 and 5 to locally remove the p-poly-Si and a few micrometer of the silicon substrate. The final HF dip in step 5 fully removes the barrier oxide. Afterwards we wet chemically grow the second interfacial oxide (step 5) and deposit the n-poly-Si in-situ doped by LPCVD (step 6). In the future, we plan to replace these two steps by an in-situ PECVD SiON/n-poly-Si deposition as published in [3]. In the subsequent high-temperature poly-Si anneal in step 7 we again use O_2 and grow a thin barrier oxide layer on the n-poly-Si. We remove the oxide layer from the front by a single sided etching step 8 and laser ablate the oxide on the rear side at the edges of the p-poly-Si in step 9. Hence, the following texture (step 10) removes the two poly-Si layers and interfacial oxide layers and textures the front side as well as the rear side where the barrier oxide has been removed. Thereby we form a textured trench region on the rear side where all poly layers are fully removed hence insulating the two solar cell polarities.

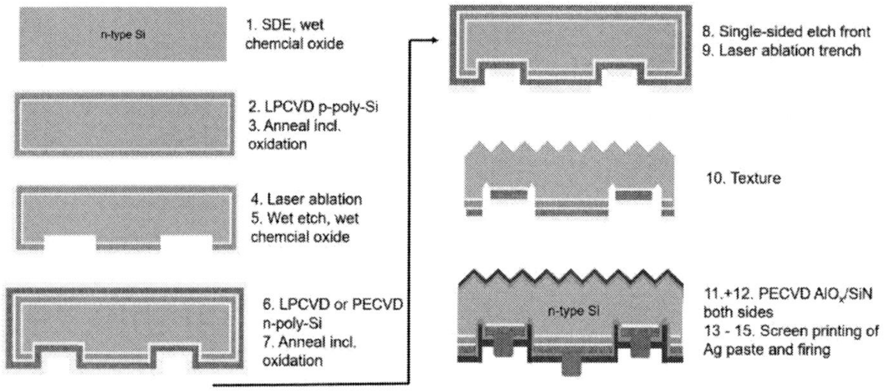

Figure 2: Schematic drawing of the novel industrial POLO² IBC process sequence [7]. We apply an oxide barrier formed in the n-poly-Si anneal, a subsequent laser ablation of the oxide barrier at the p-poly edges followed by a texture etch to remove the poly-Si layers in a narrow trench region in order to insulate the n-poly-Si base contact layer from the p-poly-Si/n-poly-Si emitter tunneling contact.

In the p-poly-Si emitter region the interfacial oxide and n-poly-Si layer form a tunneling contact with the p-poly-Si layer. The final HF dip post texture (step 10) removes the remaining barrier oxide from the rear side. Afterwards, we deposit AlO_x/SiN layer stacks on both sides (steps 11 + 12) and screen print Ag contacts on the rear side and fire the cells at around 800°C set temperature (steps 13 – 15).

We find the POLO² IBC process sequence in Fig. 2 to be a rather short and hence potentially cost-effective process sequences for manufacturing IBC solar cells with n-poly-Si and p-poly-Si passivating contacts. In addition, the trench insulation in steps 9 and 10 requires to laser only about 10% of the rear side wafer area whereas other IBC process sequences e.g. in Refs. 9, 10, 11 have to laser about 50% of the rear side area which is challenging in terms of laser process time and production throughput. Another benefit is that the novel POLO² IBC process sequence in Fig. 2 allows to use UV or alternatively cheaper green or IR lasers where the latter may create silicon defects at the wafer surface which are removed by the texture etch. In contrast, IBC process sequences e.g. in Refs. 9, 10, 11 laser on top of poly-Si layers without etching these layers and hence they have to strictly avoid creating laser damage in the silicon substrate which may limit the choice of suitable laser sources. Finally, both poly-Si polarities in Fig. 2 terminate with an n-poly-Si layer which allows to use the same screen printing paste for both solar cell metal polarities, e.g. an industry-typical TOPCon Ag paste.

To assess the passivation quality and V_{oc} potential of the novel industrial POLO² IBC process flow, we process test wafers as POLO² IBC solar cell precursors with the process sequence in Fig. 2 but without metal contacts using solely industrial processing tools at the ISFH SolarTeC. The test wafers mostly contain the IBC-typical interdigitated finger layout as sketched in Fig. 2. We add two 4 × 4 cm² areas on the wafer where we change the laser patterning processes to obtain a field representing the n-poly-Si base contact (top left) and another field representing the p-poly-Si/n-poly-Si emitter contact (bottom right). Figure 3 shows a photoluminescence (PL) image of the measured carrier lifetime t at an illumination intensity of 0.78 suns of the resulting test wafer with the POLO² IBC finger layout including the vertical busbar regions as well as the n-poly-Si only (top left) and p-poly-Si/n-poly-Si only (bottom right) fields. In these three different areas, we also measure the injection dependent lifetime by QSSPC thereby determining iV_{oc}, iFF and the surface J_0.

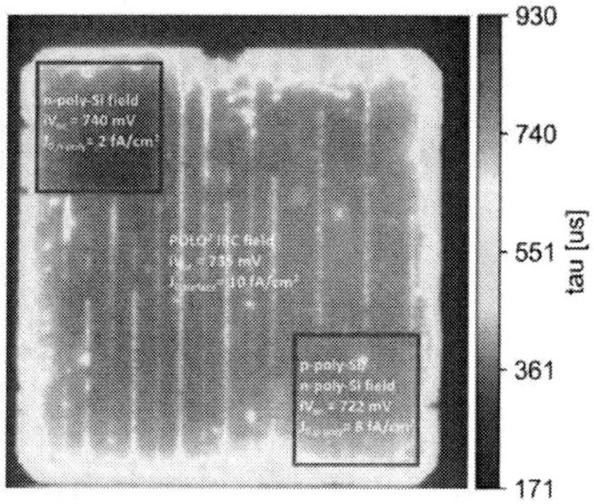

Figure 3: Photoluminescence (PL) mapping of the carrier lifetime τ of a M2-sized n-type Cz test wafer representing a POLO² IBC solar cell without metal contacts applying the novel process sequence in Fig. 2 revealing a promising iV_{oc} = 735 mV. The n-poly-Si field reveals an excellent $J_{0,n\text{-}poly}$ = 2 fA/cm² of the n-poly-Si base area. The p-poly-Si/n-poly-Si field corresponding to the p-poly-Si/n-poly-Si emitter area yields a $J_{0,p\text{-}poly}$ = 8 fA/cm² which is a bit higher than the best values Ref. 6.

As shown in Fig. 3, the POLO² IBC area yields an iV_{oc} up to 735 mV which is in-between the n-poly-Si field with iV_{oc} = 740 mV and the p-poly-Si/n-poly-Si field with 722 mV. The implied fill factor iFF of the POLO² IBC area ranges up to iFF = 86.0%. To estimate the efficiency potential of the novel industrial POLO² IBC process sequence, we calculate the so-called implied efficiency $i\eta$ as follows

$$i\eta = iV_{oc} \times iFF \times J_{sc} / P_{light}$$
$$= 735\ mV \times 86.0\% \times 41.7\ mA/cm^2 / 100\ mW/cm^2$$
$$= 26.4\%$$

Here, we assume a J_{sc} = 41,7 mA/cm² which has been simulated for a POLO² IBC solar cell in Ref. 5. Due to the nature of the passivating poly-Si contacts, we target to maintain the good iV_{oc} value as V_{oc} value in the POLO² IBC cell when including screen-printed metal contacts by stopping the metal contact alloying within the poly-Si keeping the SiO_x passivation intact. However, the fill factor of the POLO² IBC cell including screen-printed metal contacts will be lower than the iFF due to additional resistive losses of the metallization. Nevertheless, we assess the measured iV_{oc} and iFF values in Fig. 3 as promising indication of an POLO² IBC efficiency potential of about 26%.

4 CONCLUSIONS

By optimizing the poly-Si annealing temperature, introducing contact pads for the IV test, and optimizing the anti-reflective coating, we obtained a new best POLO IBC cell efficiency of 24.3% processed at ISFH on M2-sized p-type wafers. With support by ISFH, Kalyon PV is currently transferring and implementing the POLO IBC process to their PERC+ cell manufacturing line using their in-house M10-sized Ga-doped Cz wafers. Textured, rear side polished and AlO_x/SiN passivated test wafers obtain an iV_{oc} up to 727 mV demonstrating a suitable passivation quality of Kalyon PVs wet chemistry and PECVD AlO_x/SiN production tools. Kalyon PV targets to process first M10-sized POLO IBC solar cells till end of 2025.

As a next IBC technology upgrade aiming at 26% efficiency, ISFH is currently developing a novel industrial processing sequence for POLO² IBC solar cells with n-poly-Si and p-poly-Si carrier selective contacts. The novel industrial processing sequence includes in-situ doped and full-area deposited poly-Si layers and laser-structuring of both poly-Si polarities in a novel IBC trench layout. Using solely industrial processing tools in our ISFH SolarTeC, M2 sized n-type Cz wafers, we measured iV_{oc} = 735 mV and iFF = 86.0% of POLO² IBC cell precursors processed without metal contacts. Since the poly-Si contacts minimize carrier recombination at metal contacts, the iV_{oc} value demonstrates the V_{oc} potential and an efficiency potential of up to 26.4% of this promising new POLO² IBC manufacturing process.

Acknowledgments

The authors thank the companies LPKF Laser & Electronics SE, Germany, for manufacturing the glass shadow masks, and TOYO ALUMINIUM K.K., Japan, for providing the aluminum paste. We thank Jan Krügener, Leibniz University Hannover, Germany, for support with LPCVD depositions. We thank our ISFH colleagues Karsten Bothe and Gerrit Lange for support with IV test chuck optimization, Tobias Neubert for laser recipe setup, and Welmoed Veurman for Quokka 3 simulations.

References

[1] T. Dullweber et al., presented at the SNEC Conference, Shanghai, China, 2021.
[2] V. Mertens et al., Proc. 38th Europ. Photovolt. Solar Energy Conf. (2021), pp. 135 - 139
[3] T. Dullweber et al., Proc. 8th World Conference on Photovoltaic Energy Conversion (2022), pp. 35 – 39
[4] T. Dullweber et al., Proc. 41st Europ. Photovolt. Solar Energy Conf. (2024), p. 020008
[5] C. N. Kruse et al., Scientific Reports, **11**, 996 (2021)
[6] E. Hoffmann et al., Proc. 41st Europ. Photovolt. Solar Energy Conf. (2024), p. 020020
[7] ISFH patents pending
[8] V. Mertens et al., Solar RRL **8**, 2300919 (2024)
[9] U. Römer et al, presented at the Silicon PV Conference (2025)
[10] J. Linke et al., Proc. 8th World Conference on Photovoltaic Energy Conversion (2022), pp. 102 – 106
[11] Aiko press release July 2025 available at: https://aikosolar.com/en/the-worlds-most-efficient-solar-technology/

42nd European Photovoltaic Solar Energy Conference and Exhibition

This presentation was selected by the Sc. Committee of the EU PVSEC 2025 for submission of a full paper to one of the EU PVSEC's collaborating peer-reviewed journals.

USING A SHADOW MASK DURING GAS-PHASE ETCHING: A ONE-STEP PATTERNING METHOD FOR POLY-SILICON LAYERS

Laurent F. CLOCHARD[1], Yevgeniya LARIONOVA[2], Thorsten DULLWEBER[2]
[1] Nines Photovoltaics, Synergy Centre, TUD Tallaght Campus, D24A386 DUBLIN, Ireland
[2] ISFH, Institut für Solarenergieforschung GmbH Am Ohrberg 1, D-31860 Emmerthal, Germany

Abstract – This paper presents a convenient poly-silicon layer patterning technique, using a shadow mask during a gas-phase etching process. The etching is carried out at atmospheric pressure and delivers high throughput, single side processing and high selectivity, preserving the mask for multiple use and with potential for industrial application. This work was carried out in the context of the development of solar cell architectures beyond the standard TOPCon, where more sophisticated etching steps are required to accurately pattern poly-silicon layers across the wafer surface, in particular for the application of back contacted cells.
Keywords: silicon, solar cell, etching, manufacturing, patterning, IBC

1 Introduction

There is a strong interest in developing patterning processes for solar cells, enabling new cell architectures and increased efficiency. Passivated contacts have been successfully adopted by the industry in the standard TOPCON (Tunnel Oxide Passivated Contacts) process. In that scheme, the rear contacts are passivated using a tunnel oxide and doped poly-silicon stack across the whole wafer surface. Poly-Si layers lead to parasitic absorption, while the TOPCON stack is only needed under the contacts ; hence the requirement for accurate patterning of the layers. Similarly, IBC cells also require localized interdigitated poly-silicon layers at the rear side. Existing patterning processes can be cumbersome, using multiple steps, typically involving the deposition of a masking layer, that subsequently needs to be removed. This paper explores a simplified, single step patterning process.

We investigate the patterning of poly-Si using a shadow mask within a single sided gas-phase etching process, to locally remove the poly-Si from the unwanted areas. This gaseous etching process, referred as ADE (for Atmospheric Dry Etching) has been used previously for texturing applications of multi-crystalline wafer [1], and for the poly-Si wrap-around removal produced by industrial deposition tools such as LPCVD and PECVD tools [2] and was originally designed to suit the industrial requirements of cell manufacturing (low cost, high throughput). In a recent publication [3], we have shown that this etching process has very high selectivity, and that this characteristic can be leveraged to devise several methods and strategies for patterning. The figure below summaries the various options.

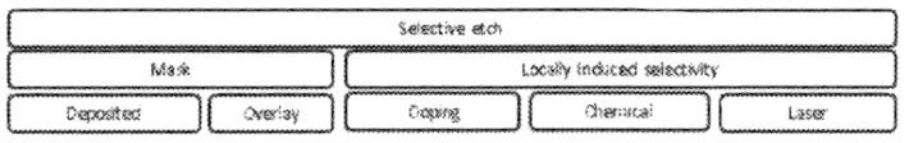

Fig1. Summaries of the various routes toward patterning with gas-phase etch ADE

The process options can be divided in two main strands: schemes using masks, and schemes designed to locally induce etching selectivity. In this work, we will focus on the use of a mask. Our previous publication [3] showed results from a deposited SiOx mask, while this time we will focus on using a physical overlay, commonly referred as "shadow mask", as sometimes used in deposition processes: the mask creates a shadow, protecting specific areas of the substrate from deposition. In our etching application, we will rely on the mask to preserve an existing layer from being etched away. To generate the same patterning outcome, the etch mask design should therefore be the negative version of the deposition mask design (cf fig 2).

Potential advantages of using a shadow mask within an etching process when compared to deposition include : the mask can be used a large number of time (providing the material is selected to provide high etch selectivity), and does not need to be cleaned; for very small narrow area of removal, it might be more efficient to etch ; the inline nature of the process enables easy application/removal of the masks on the wafer, resulting in easier handling and less breakage. The choice of one method or another will depend on the overall impacts of these factors.

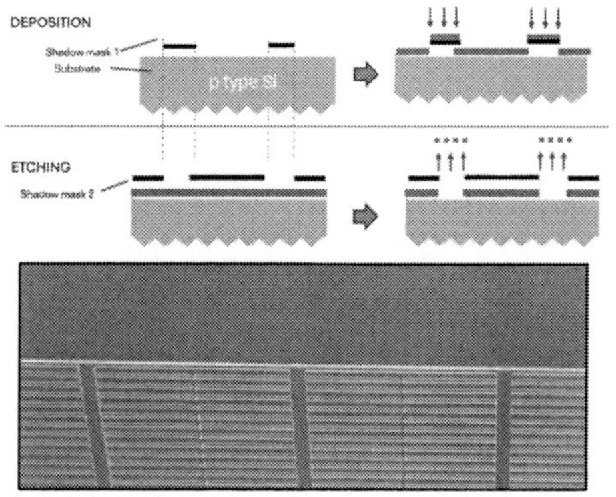

Fig.2 Schematic of shadow mask usage in deposition process (a) and etching process (negative version)(b) and a picture of the mask pattern (c).

2 Materials and method

The shadow mask is made of glass. The mask was provided and used by ISFH in previous publications [4] and originally made by the German company LPKF AG, using their proprietary Laser-Induced Deep Etching glass structuring technology [5]. The thinnest branches of the mask had a 250um width, while the larger branches were in the 950um range. The openings had a width of 750um (fig.2c). Although the mask pattern for etching should be the negative version of a mask designed for deposition, we used the same deposition mask in these experiments.

For this set of experiments, p-type Cz wafers of M2 sizes

were used. After saw damage removal, an 80nm layer of SiNx was deposited (PECVD, Centrotherm) at the front side of the wafer. Then both side were deposited with approximately 150nm of a-Si:H. The presence of the SiNx layer at the front gives the wafer a vivid color, with variations directly proportional to the a-Si:H layer thickness. It can be seen (fig 3.) that the deposition was not fully uniform (color variation from pink to green).

Prior to ADE etching, the wafers are pre-cleaned in a 5%HF solution for 1 minutes, followed by 5 minutes D.I. rinsing, and 10 minutes drying in a 95%Nitrogen gas flow at 80degC, to remove any native oxide or mild contaminations.

The mask was manually positioned directly on top of the wafer, then the ensemble is placed on the conveyor belt of the gas-phase etching tool, held by vacuum suction. The wafer is then conveyed inside the process chamber and etched through the Atmospheric Dry Etching reactor (ADE). The etch rate is directly affected by temperature and gas concentration. We used a low concentration of 2%F2 in N2 carrier gas in order to better control the process, and a reactor temperature of 190 degC while varying the time of etching.

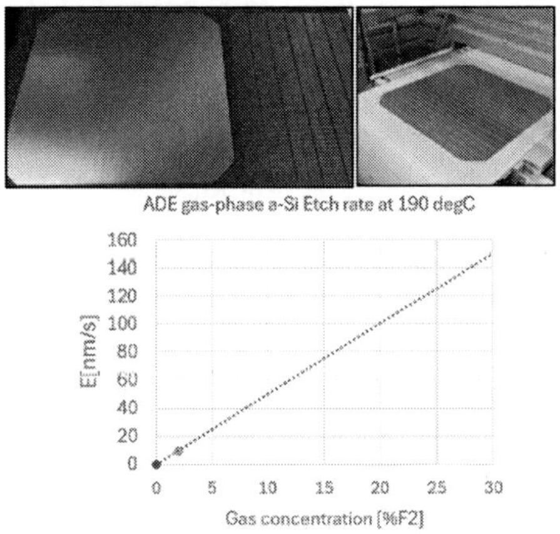

Fig.3 a)Wafer before etching (left), and shadow mask(right) b) ADE process etch rate vs gas concentration c) Wafer + mask positioned on belt before entering the ADE reactor

3 Results

Wafers were initially etched without mask to find the duration required for full removal of the layer. Partially etched wafers were used to highlight the color variation range. After some process tunning adjusting the etch process duration, patterns started to appear. Results below are for etching time of approximately 16 seconds. The SiNx layer underneath the poly layer provides a good contrast and enables straightforward visual inspection of the sample. The area with remaining poly can clearly be seen, and any color variation indicates a variation of the a-Si:H thickness layer. The SiNx layer appears as a dark yellow color.

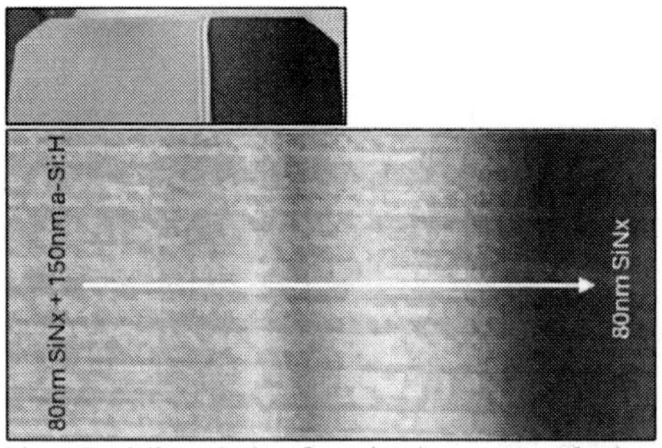

Fig. 4 Partially etched wafers, showing a range of colors related to the a-Si:H layer thickness

The etching time is varied in order to avoid over or under etching, and identify the process window. The wafer was analyzed with optical microscope imaging, and the variation of the remaining a-Si "fingers" width were measured across various areas.

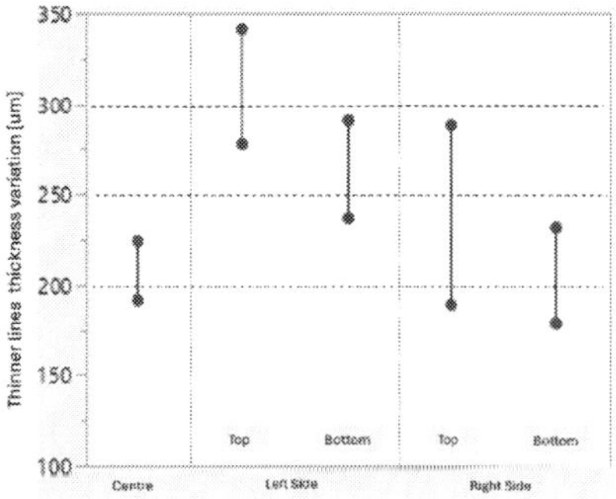

Fig.7 Width variations of the thinner masked section (250um), for the SiNx+a-Si:H stack

Fig.6 optical microscope images of the patterned a-Si:H layer post etching showing larger and thinner masked sections ; Areas on the patterned wafer with 80nm SiNx + 150nm a-Si:H stack

3 Discussion

There are some obvious variations across the wafers that are related to a number of aspects including: homogeneity of the a-Si:H starting layer, homogeneity of the gas flow, flatness of the wafer surface and flatness of the mask (both at the microscopic level and across the wafer width).

One would expect that since the ADE gas-phase process is anisotropic in the conditions used in this experiment, the amount of lateral etching should be comparable to the overall thickness of the a-Si:H layer removed (vertical etching). However, the measured width variation of the thinner masked section is several order of magnitude larger (~50um) compared to the thickness of the a-Si layer being etched (150nm). We also noted that the thinner features disappeared very quickly if the process duration was extended. We therefore look at understanding the impact of the SiNx layer.

Impact of the SiNx under-layer:

The SiNx layer has a much lower etch rate than a-Si:H(~200 times less), and acts as an etch stop. We can divide the process into 2 phases, before and after the etch stop has been reached and analyze the process conditions. In the first phase, there is a large area of a-Si:H exposed through the opening of the mask. During that phase, we can assume both vertical and lateral etch rates are equal (anisotropic), with a given etch rate E1 (fig.9). When the process reaches the SiNx layer, the area that can react with the gas is suddenly dramatically reduced, only the vertical sides of the remaining a-Si located under the glass mask are being etched. Since the incoming etching gas flow has not changed when compared to phase 1, there is now much more unreacted gas molecules available to react with the sidewall area. This directly impact the etch rate. We can therefore argue that in this second phase, the etch rate is higher.

Fig. 9 Schematic describing the two process phases and impact on etch rates and width of features

Taking a single unit of the mask and assuming vertical walls, we calculated a theoretical ratio of more than 2,000 between the exposed area of the two etch phases. If we apply that factor to the overall average etch rate of 10 nm/s measured (based on the a-Si:H layer thickness and the process duration), this would mean that the fingers side walls could be etched at a rate close to 20,000 nm/s during Phase 2 of the etch process. This order of magnitudes tally with the range of finger width variations we have measured.
This artefact from the SiNx layer can therefore have a significant impact on our results. We conclude that although using SiNx as an underlayer is convenient to easily visualize the a-Si:H etch thickness variation, it is not suitable to assess the suitability of the process of delivering consistent feature width. We expect a much wider process window, and lower impact on sidewalls, when the a-Si under-layer has similar etch rates as the poly-Si itself. Additional experiments (fig.10) were conducted on wafers with only a layer of a-Si:H directly on top of c-Si and even though a systematic analysis was not carried out at the time of writing, visual inspection seems to confirm that the finger width is much more consistent in that case, and that the process window can be extended. Visual inspection is less straightforward without the underlying SiNx layer, but the pattern can be observed under low angle light exposure.

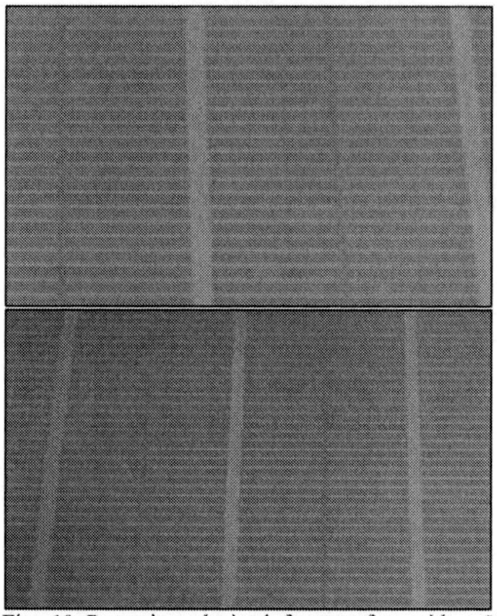

Fig. 10 Patterning obtained from wafers with a-Si:H deposited on c-Si wafers (without SiNx underlayer)

Passivated contacts typically have a thin tunnel oxide layer locate below the poly-Si layer, but this should not in principle be an issue as such layers have pinholes and previous experiments have shown that they can be etched away by the ADE gas-phase process [6]. Follow on experiment will still need to be confirming the impact of such layer in the context of this work however.
Shadowing Efficiency: The etching gas is still reaching across the whole surface of the wafer, since the color is changing when compared to the unetched sample. We can also observe that the wider features of the glass tend to protect better the poly-layer, indicating that there is an edge effect from the glass feature, that is not proportional to the glass width. The chamfer applied to the glass edges might also impact the corner sharpness of the masking.
The surface of the wafer itself would also have an impact on how easily the gas can diffuse below the mask. The wafer used had a typical saw damaged removal surface, presenting large shallow square pits leftover of inverted pyramids created by the KOH wet process. A more polished surface would improve the masking efficiency, but it remains to be seen if it has an impact on the cell device performance.

4 Conclusion

A single side gas-phase etching process was evaluated, using a thin glass mask to pattern a poly-silicon layer for advanced solar cell architecture applications. A pattern could be created in a single process step, in less than 20 seconds. The influence of an underlying 80nm thick SiNx layer on the resulting feature width was analyzed, and found to be detrimental. Further experiments are required to qualify the process at a cell level.

References

[1] B. Kafle, T. Freund, S. Werner, J. Schon, A. Lorenz, A. Wolf, L. Clochard, E. Duffy, P. Saint-Cast, M. Hofmann, J. Rentsch, IEEE J. Photovoltaics. 2017 7, 136, DOI: 10.1109/JPHOTOV.2016.2626921.

[2] Kafle B., Mack S., Teßmann C., Bashardoust S.,

Clochard L., Duffy E., Wolf A., Hofmann M. and Rentsch J. 2022 Sol. RRL 6 2100481
[3] Clochard l. & al, GAS PHASE, SELECTIVE ETCHING OF POLY-SILICON FOR LAYER PATTERNING, Proceedings of the European Photovoltaic Solar Energy Conference and Exhibition, 2024

[4] Verena Mertens & al., LOCAL PECVD SIOXNY/N-POLY-SI DEPOSITION THROUGH A SHADOW MASK FOR POLO IBC SOLAR CELLS, Proceeding of the 38th European Photovoltaic Solar Energy Conference and Exhibition, 2021

[5] M. Stöhr et al., Proc. 37th EUPVSEC, 521-524 (2020).

[6] PATTERNING BY SELECTIVE ETCHING OF POLY-SILICON USING A HIGH ETCH RATE SINGLE SIDED GASEOUS PROCESS, L. Clochard, D. Young, Mingzhe Yu, S. Bonilla, 2024, DOI: 10.52825/siliconpv.v2i.1317

42nd European Photovoltaic Solar Energy Conference and Exhibition

This presentation was selected by the Sc. Committee of the EU PVSEC 2025 for submission of a full paper to one of the EU PVSEC's collaborating peer-reviewed journals.

UV STABLE PASSIVATION STACK WITH PLASMA-ENHANCED ATOMIC LAYER DEPOSITION OF ALUMINIUM OXIDE FROM AN INDUSTRIAL TUBE-TYPE DIRECT PLASMA-ENHANCED CHEMICAL VAPOR DEPOSITION SYSTEM

B. Min[1], C. Hollemann[1], S. Junge[1], V. X. Nguyen[2], T. Pernau[2], D. Seiffert[2], H. Haverkamp[2], T. Dullweber[1], V. Mertens[1], H. Schulte-Huxel[1] and R. Brendel[1, 3]

[1]Institute for Solar Energy Research Hamelin (ISFH), 31860 Emmerthal, Germany
[2]centrotherm international AG, 89143 Blaubeuren, Germany
[3]Dep. Solar Energy, Inst. Solid-State Physics, Leibniz University of Hannover, 30167 Hannover, Germany

ABSTRACT: We implement the plasma-enhanced atomic layer deposition (PEALD) of AlO_x layers in an industrial tube-type plasma-enhanced chemical vapor deposition (PECVD) system with a direct plasma source. Its surface passivation qualities on the boron-diffused textured surface of n-type silicon wafers and on the undiffused textured surface of p-type silicon wafers are investigated by varying the process parameters. The study shows that the number of ALD cycles is one of the essential parameters for achieving high passivation quality on the boron-diffused textured surface of n-type wafers. We achieve a surface recombination current density J_{0s} of 3.6 fA/cm^2, extracted from lifetime measurements with a device simulation by considering a measured electrically active dopant depth profile. In contrast, the number of ALD cycles shows no impact on the surface passivation quality on the undiffused textured surface of p-type wafers. In both cases, we achieve a passivation quality which is on the same level as our reference with a PEALD AlO_x layer, deposited with a lab-scale ALD tool. Our tube-type PEALD AlO_x/PECVD SiN_y passivation stack is integrated at the cell front side of a p-type back junction (BJ) solar cell featuring n$^+$-type passivating polysilicon on oxide (POLO) contacts. Its cell performance is on the same level as the reference group with PECVD AlO_x/SiN_y passivation stack. The UV stability is investigated by exposing cell precursors to ultraviolet light with a dose of 4.5 kWh/m^2. While the PECVD AlO_x/SiN_y passivation stack shows a significant degradation of the measured effective lifetime and the implied open-circuit voltage, the passivation quality of tube-type PEALD AlO_x/PECVD SiN_y passivation stack is stable.
Keywords: PECVD, aluminum oxide, surface passivation, passivating contacts, poly-Si, UV stability, TOPCon

1 INTRODUCTION

The plasma-enhanced atomic layer deposition (PEALD) is currently widely applied for the deposition of aluminum oxide (AlO_x) to passivate the surface of highly efficient industrial solar cells such as TOPCon (tunnel oxide passivated contact) solar cells. Its unique advantages are, in particular, precise thickness control, excellent uniformity and conformity compared to other deposition techniques [1].

On the other hand, the tube-type plasma-enhanced chemical vapor deposition (PECVD) tool is the most used and well-established equipment in PV industry, especially for the deposition of silicon nitride (SiN_y) or also for the deposition of poly-Si layers to fabricate passivating contacts.

The realization of PEALD AlO_x deposition with the tube-type PECVD tool is a very attractive idea for the PV industry, since it will use all the advantages of the ALD technique combined with the benefits of the tube-type PECVD tool such as lower equipment cost and high throughput. Furthermore, no ALD system will be needed in the production line, which reduces the investment cost, maintenance efforts as well as the wafer breakage between different systems. Liao et al. demonstrated the implementation of PEALD AlO_x deposition in an industrial tube-type PECVD tool (LeadMicro, ZR5000), achieving 24.3 % as the best efficiency of their fabricated TOPCon solar cells [1].

In this work, we independently validate the implementation of PEALD AlO_x deposition in an industrial tube-type PECVD system (centrotherm, cPLASMA 2600) from a different equipment manufacturer. Compared to the previous publication of Liao et al., we investigate the impact of the number of ALD cycles on the passivation quality, different surfaces, such as undiffused textured p-type wafer surfaces, and the application of the combination of PEALD AlO_x and PECVD AlO_x to reduce the process duration. Finally, the developed passivation stack is applied in the fabrication of p-type back junction (BJ) solar cells featuring n$^+$-type passivating polysilicon on oxide (POLO) contacts and its UV stability is investigated.

2 EXPERIMENTAL

For the first part of this work, we investigate the passivation quality by fabricating symmetric lifetime samples on phosphorus-doped and gallium-doped Cz-Si wafers featuring boron-diffused and undiffused random-pyramid-textured surfaces, respectively. After a firing step at a set temperature of 800 °C, the samples are characterized using a Sinton lifetime tester (WCT-120). We measure each wafer at five different positions (center and four corners). In the second part of the paper, we fabricate POLO BJ solar cells using gallium-doped p-type Cz-Si wafers to validate the developed tube-type PEALD AlO_x/PECVD SiN_y passivation stack. Its UV stability is investigated by measuring the lifetimes of POLO BJ solar cell precursors (cells without metallization) before and after exposition to UV light.

3 RESULTS

3.1 Passivation quality on n-type Cz-Si wafers with boron-diffused textured surfaces

Figure 1 shows the effective carrier lifetimes (τ_{eff}) at an injection level Δn of 10^{15} cm^{-3} and the emitter

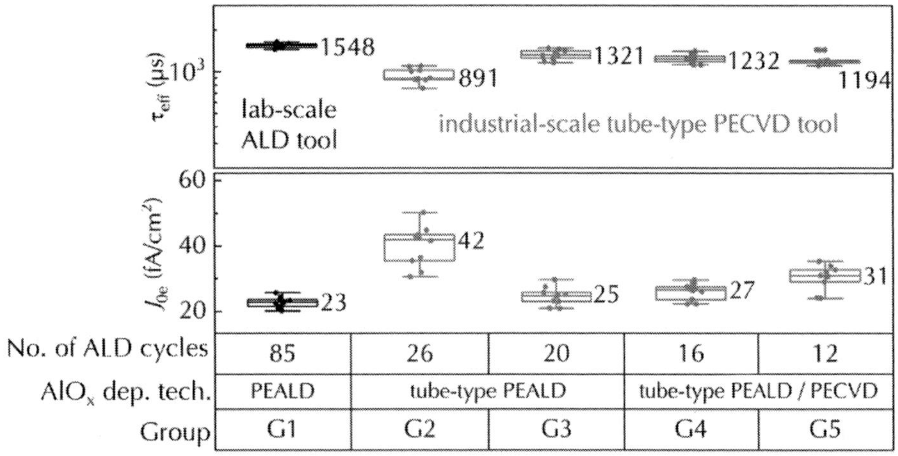

Figure 1 τ_{eff} at the injection level of $\Delta n = 10^{15}$ cm^{-3} and J_{0e} of symmetric n-type Cz-Si samples with boron-diffused random-pyramid-textured surfaces.

recombination current densities (J_{0e}) of symmetric lifetime samples with boron-diffused textured surfaces on n-type wafers. The box height spans from the first to the third quartile (also known as interquartile range [IQR]), and the whiskers indicate the maximum and minimum of 1.5×IQR beyond the box. The numbers next to the boxes give the median values. The colors of boxplots indicate different equipment for the AlO_x deposition. The reference group G1 is passivated with 10-nm-thick PEALD AlO_x layers deposited with a lab-scale ALD tool (FlexAL ALD, Oxford instruments) which is our best-known method with this tool. The groups G2 – G5 receive PEALD AlO_x layer deposited with an industrial tube-type PECVD tool (centrotherm, cPLASMA 2600). The deposition rate is 0.125 nm/cycle, the pulse duration for TMA and O_2 plasma is 4 s. We apply various number of ALD cycles between 12 – 26 as indicated in Figure 1. For the groups G4 and G5 we deposit additionally a 2 nm-thick PECVD AlO_x layer on top of tube-type PEALD AlO_x layer. Finally, we then deposit 75-nm-thick SiN_y layer on all samples using the same PECVD tool. With 20 ALD cycles of tube-type PEALD AlO_x, we achieve 20.9 fA/cm² as the lowest J_{0e} value in the group G3. In order to distinguish the contribution of the emitter bulk and the textured surface to the measured J_{0e} value, we first measure the depth profile of the boron emitter with electrochemical capacitance-voltage profiler (WEP, CVP21) as shown in Figure 2 with a sheet resistance of 140 Ω/□. Subsequently, we apply it in the simulation software EDNA 2 from PV Lighthouse. We then vary the surface recombination current density J_{0s} [2] to reproduce the measured J_{0e} value. The simulation results in a J_{0s} value of 3.6 fA/cm², indicating the excellent surface passivation quality of developed tube-type PEALD AlO_x/PECVD SiN_y passivation stack on boron-diffused textured surfaces.

Based on the simulation analysis, we optimize as the next step our boron diffusion process by adjusting the BBr_3 flow, deposition temperature, temperature and duration of the drive-in and post-oxidation step. Figure 2 shows the measured electrically active boron dopant concentration before and after our optimization of the boron diffusion process with a sheet resistance (R_{sheet}) of 140 Ω/□ and 350 Ω/□, respectively. The peak boron concentration at surface is successfully reduced from 4×10^{19} cm^{-3} to ~10^{19} cm^{-3}. Figure 3 shows the measured τ_{eff} and J_{0e} of symmetric textured n-type Cz-Si samples with optimized boron emitter. Herein, we apply the PEALD AlO_x from the lab-scale ALD tool as a reference and tube-type PEALD AlO_x from the industrial PECVD tool which corresponds the groups G1 and G3 in the previous section.

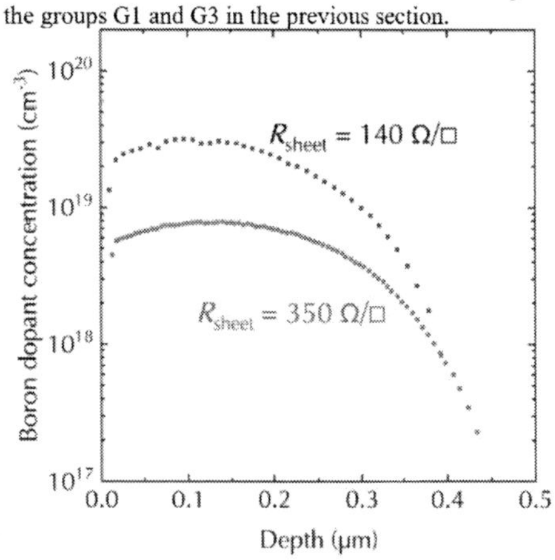

Figure 2: Measured electrically active boron dopant concentrations before and after boron diffusion optimization with a sheet resistance of 140 Ω/□ and 350 Ω/□, respectively.

Compared to our previous results, as depicted as G3 in Figure 1, the surface passivation quality improves by nearly 50 % with the optimized boron emitter. The median J_{0e} value reduces from 25 fA/cm² to 13 fA/cm² and the median τ_{eff} increases from 1321 µs to 2455 µs. Furthermore, the comparison with the reference demonstrates that the passivation quality of the tube-type PEALD AlO_x is on the same level as that of the PEALD AlO_x layer fabricated with a lab-scale tool.

10.4229/EUPVSEC2025/1BO.3.6

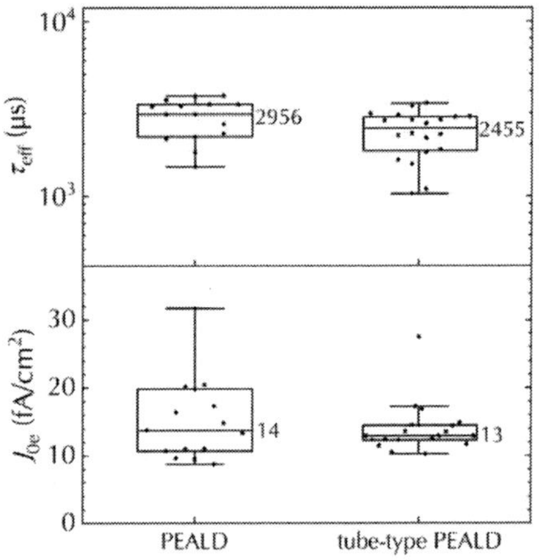

Figure 3: τ_{eff} at the injection level of $\Delta n = 10^{15}$ cm^{-3} and J_{0e} of symmetric textured n-type Cz-Si samples with optimized boron emitter

3.2 Passivation quality on p-type wafers with undiffused textured surfaces

Figure 4**Fehler! Verweisquelle konnte nicht gefunden werden.** shows the measured τ_{eff} at an injection level of 10^{15} cm^{-3} and J_{0s} values of p-type wafers on undiffused textured surfaces. It is to note that J_{0s} is equal to J_{0e} in this case since the samples have no diffused emitter. The resistivity of the Ga-doped p-type Cz-Si wafers is 0.85 Ωcm. Hence, the well-known slope method by Kane and Swanson [3] cannot be applied since the base is in low injection during illumination with the flash lamp from the Sinton lifetime tester. We therefore extract the J_{0s} values by reproducing the measured injection-dependent lifetime curves with the device simulation software Quokka 3. We vary the SRH lifetime parameters in the bulk and the J_{0s} until we achieve an agreement between measured and simulation lifetime curve for an injection level range between 2×10^{14} cm^{-3} and 2×10^{16} cm^{-3}. All groups with tube-type PEALD AlO_x show J_{0s} values on the same level as the reference group G1. The median J_{0s} values corresponds well with J_{0s} values extracted from n-type samples with boron-diffused textured surface in the previous section. However, the τ_{eff} values of the groups with tube-type PEALD AlO_x are slightly lower than that of the reference group. In contrast to the results with n-type samples, the iV_{oc} values are nearly unaffected by different numbers of ALD cycles. Also, the additional PECVD AlO_x layer on top of the tube-type PEALD AlO_x layer seems to have no impact on the passivation quality.

3.3 Cell results

We fabricate POLO back junction (BJ) solar cells as depicted in Figure 5. More details and the advantage of this cell concept were presented in our previous work [4]. The busbarless cells are measured with a LOANA tool from pv-tools applying a contacting scheme that neglects the resistance of the metal grid [5].

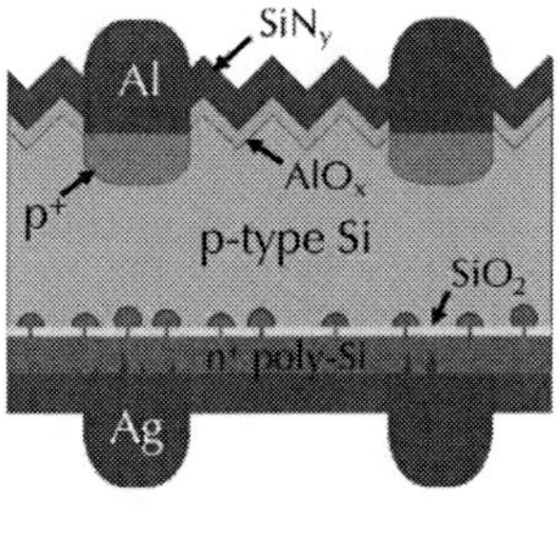

Figure 5: Schematic of a POLO BJ solar cell [3]

Figure 6 shows the IV parameters of POLO BJ solar cells featuring tube-type PEALD AlO_x/PECVD SiN_y passivation stack depicted as black box plot. As a reference, the red box plot shows the IV parameters of POLO BJ solar cells featuring PECVD AlO_x/SiN_y passivation stack. The efficiencies of both groups are on the same level while the group with tube-type PEALD AlO_x/PECVD SiN_y shows slightly higher open-circuit

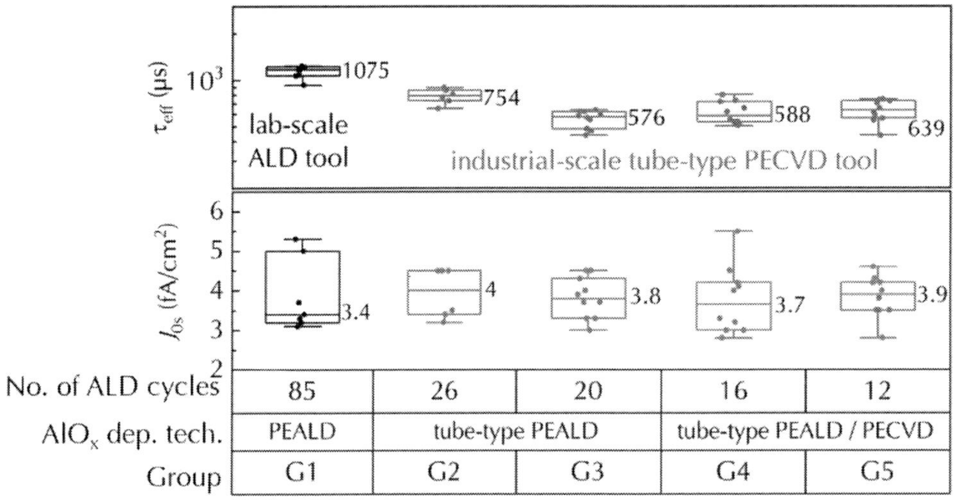

Figure 4 τ_{eff} at the injection level of $\Delta n = 10^{15}$ cm^{-3} and J_{0s} of symmetric p-type samples with undiffused textured surfaces

voltage (V_{oc}) and short-circuit current density (J_{sc}).

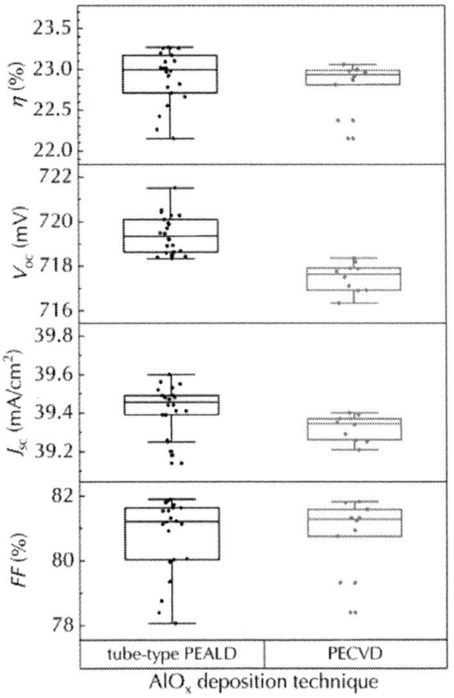

Figure 6: Measured *IV* parameters of POLO BJ solar cells featuring an AlO_x layer deposited with tube-type PEALD and PECVD deposition techniques.

It is worth to note that both groups show excellent surface passivation qualities with a median iV_{oc} of 735 mV and 733 mV, respectively, measured on cell precursors (cells without metallization) using the Sinton lifetime tester as shown in Figure 1. In the finished solar cell, the V_{oc} is about 15 mV lower and hence the efficiencies are also decreased. One reason for the decrease is a strong deterioration of passivating POLO contacts at the rear side due to Ag-spiking, as depicted in the schematic in Figure 5. We are currently working on the avoidance such Ag-spiking by applying different Ag pastes and by adjusting the dielectric layer thickness. This optimization has already been successfully carried out in our previous work with a different Ag paste [6].

3.4 UV stability

The UV stability of the developed passivation stack is investigated by exposing the cell precursors (cells without metallization) to UV light for 24 hours, which corresponds to a UV dose of 4.5 kWh/m². The wavelengths range from 290 nm to 400 nm. The cell precursors are fabricated together with the solar cells presented in Figure 6. The samples were not encapsulated and not covered with any glass pane, hence the UV exposure to the cell is much stronger than the usual standard test with modules. Figure 7 shows the measured τ_{eff} and iV_{oc} values of POLO BJ cell precursors before and after UV exposure. The POLO BJ precursors featuring PECVD AlO_x/SiN_y show a strong degradation in τ_{eff} as well as in iV_{oc}. In contrast, the values of the samples with tube-type PEALD AlO_x/PECVD SiN_y are nearly unchanged, demonstrating their strongly improved UV stability. More detailed studies on the UV stability on the module level will be presented in a separate publication [7].

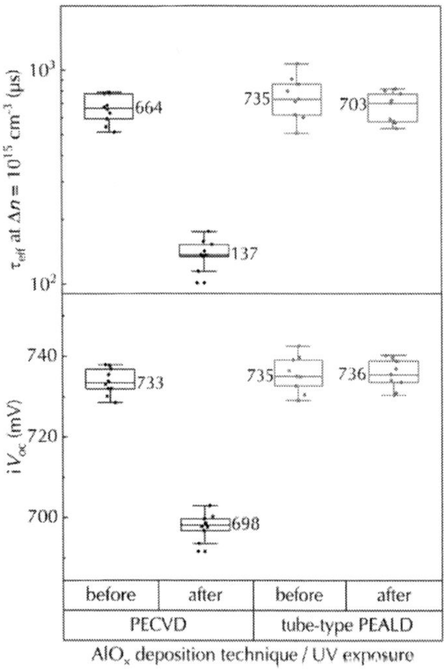

Figure 7: Impact of UV exposure on POLO BJ cell precursors without metallization featuring PECVD AlO_x/PECVD SiN_y and tube-type PEALD AlO_x/PECVD SiN_y front side passivation stack

4 CONCLUSIONS

We have demonstrated the application of tube-type PEALD AlO_x/PECVD SiN_y passivation stacks for the application to high efficiency silicon solar cells. We investigated the impact of the number of ALD cycles on the passivation quality on textured surfaces of n-type and p-type Cz-Si wafers. In addition, we showed that the combination of the tube-type PEALD AlO_x and PECVD AlO_x is an attractive option to reduce the processing time.

On boron-diffused textured surfaces of n-type wafers, the number of ALD cycles is a crucial parameter to achieve a high passivation quality. By applying 20 ALD cycles, we achieve a median J_{0e} value of 13 fA/cm² with an optimized boron emitter featuring a sheet resistance of 350 Ω/□. In contrast to this, the number of ALD cycles shows no impact on the passivation quality on undiffused textured surfaces on p-type silicon wafers, resulting a median J_{0s} values around 4 fA/cm².

The developed tube-type PEALD AlO_x/PECVD SiN_y passivation stack was successfully implemented into POLO BJ solar cells. Our development led to a notable increase in V_{oc} and J_{sc} compared to the PECVD AlO_x/PECVD SiN_y passivation stack.

Finally, the UV exposure of the cell precursors shows that the tube-type PEALD AlO_x layer is UV stable, while the PECVD AlO_x layer degrades strongly under UV exposure.

Our development enables the reduction of cell

fabrication cost as well as the increase of PV module energy yield, since it is more UV stable. This can reduce the fabrication cost of all solar cells with AlO_x layer on the front side (e.g. POLO BJ or TOPCon solar cells).

[1] B. Liao, X. Wu, W. Wu, C. Liu, S. Ma, S. Wang, T. Xie, Q. Wang, Z. Du, W. Shen, X. Li, W. Li, B. Hoex. "Tube-type plasma-enhanced atomic layer deposition of aluminum oxide: Enabling record lab performance for the industry with demonstrated cell efficiencies >24%", Prog. Photovoltaics 31, 52-61 (2023).

[2] K.R. McIntosh, L.E. Black. "On effective surface recombination parameters", J. Appl. Phys. 116, - (2014).

[3] D. Kane, R. Swanson. "Measurement of the emitter saturation current by a contactless photoconductivity decay method", Proc. of the 18th IEEE Photovoltaic Specialist Conference, New York, 1985, pp. 578-583.

[4] B. Min, V. Mertens, Y. Larionova, T. Pernau, H. Haverkamp, T. Dullweber, R. Peibst, B. R. "24.2 %-efficient POLO back junction solar cell with industrial PECVD AlO_x/SiN_y passivation", Proc. of the 40th European Photovoltaic Solar Energy Conference and Exhibition, Lisbon, Portugal, 2023.

[5] K. Bothe, C. Kruse, D. Hinken. "Contacting of busbarless solar cells for accurate I-V measurements", Proc. of the 37th European Photovoltaic Solar Energy Conference and Exhibition, Online event, 2020.

[6] B. Min, N. Wehmeier, T. Brendemuehl, F. Haase, Y. Larionova, L. Nasebandt, H. Schulte-Huxel, R. Peibst, R. Brendel. "716 mV Open-Circuit Voltage with Fully Screen-Printed p-Type Back Junction Solar Cells Featuring an Aluminum Front Grid and a Passivating Polysilicon on Oxide Contact at the Rear Side", Solar RRL 5, 2000703 (2021).

[7] C. Hollemann, B. Min, V.X. Nguyen, T. Pernau, D. Seiffert, H. Haverkamp, R. Brendel, H. Schulte-Huxel. "UV Stability of Aluminum Oxide Fabricated with Tube-Type Plasma-Enhanced Atomic Layer Deposition", Solar RRL n/a, 202500510 (2025).

10.4229/EUPVSEC2025/1BO.3.6

42nd EUPVSEC
Bilbao/Spain, 23rd September 2025, 1BO.3.6

ISFH

UV stable passivation stack with PEALD aluminum oxide from an industrial tube-type PECVD system

B. Min[1], C. Hollemann[1], S. Junge[1], V. X. Nguyen[2], T. Pernau[2], D. Seiffert[2], H. Haverkamp[2], T. Dullweber[1], V. Mertens[1], H. Schulte-Huxel[1] and R. Brendel[1,3]

[1]Institute for Solar Energy Research Hamelin (ISFH), Germany

[2]centrotherm international AG, Germany

[3]Dep. Solar Energy, Inst. Solid-State Physics, Leibniz University Hannover, Germany

Leibniz Universität Hannover

Motivation

ISFH

Plasma-enhanced atomic layer deposition (PEALD) technique

- Widely applied for AlO_x deposition
- Precise thickness control and excellent uniformity and conformity

Tube-type plasma-enhanced chemical vapor deposition (PECVD) equipment

- Most used and well-established equipment in PV industry (SiN_y, poly-Si, …)
- Low equipment cost and high throughput

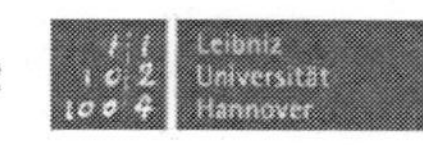

Tube-type PEALD

Plasma-enhanced
atomic layer deposition (**PEALD**) technique

- Widely applied for AlO_x deposition
- Precise thickness control and excellent uniformity and conformity

Tube-type plasma-enhanced
chemical vapor deposition (**PECVD**) equipment

- Most used and well-established equipment in PV industry (SiN_y, poly-Si, …)
- Low equipment cost and high throughput

PEALD AlO_x deposition with the tube-type PECVD tool (**tube-type PEALD**)

- PEALD & PECVD with a same tool → no need for ALD system in the production
- Less investment cost, maintenance efforts as well as the wafer breakage between different systems
- First demonstration by Liao et al. with (LeadMicro, ZR5000), 24.3 %-efficient TOPCon solar cell[1]

B. Min et al., 42nd EU PVSEC, 23rd September 2025, 1BO.3.6 3

[1] B. Liao et al., Prog. Photovoltaics 31, 52-61 (2023)

Aim of this work

ISFH

- **Independent validation** with a system from a different equipment manufacturer (centrotherm, cPLASMA 2600)
- **Impact of the number of ALD cycles** on passivation quality
- **Different surfaces**
  - Boron-diffused textured surface of n-type wafers (TOPCon front side)
  - Undiffused textured surface of p-type wafers
- **Combination of tube-type PEALD AlO_x and PECVD AlO_x** to reduce the process duration
- Investigation on **UV stability**

n-type wafers with boron-diffused textured surfaces

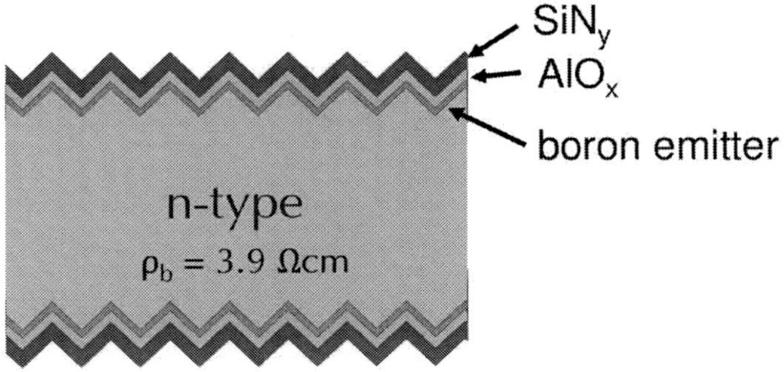

No. of ALD cycles	85	26	20	16	12
AlO_x dep. tech.	PEALD	tube-type PEALD		tube-type PEALD / PECVD	
Group	G1	G2	G3	G4	G5

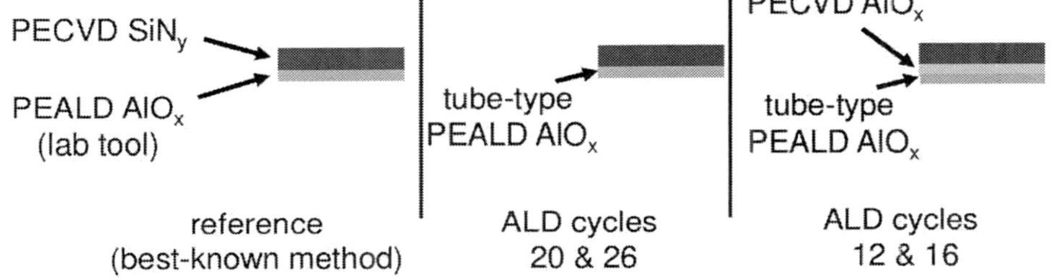

- Equivalent to TOPCon front side
- All samples fired at 800 °C
- Measurement at five wafer positions (center, 4 corners)

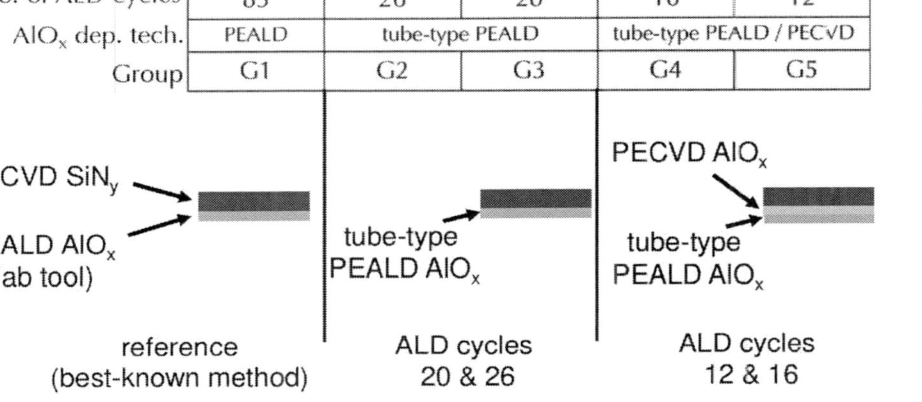

n-type wafers with boron-diffused textured surfaces

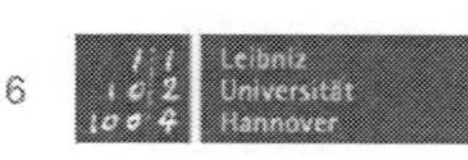

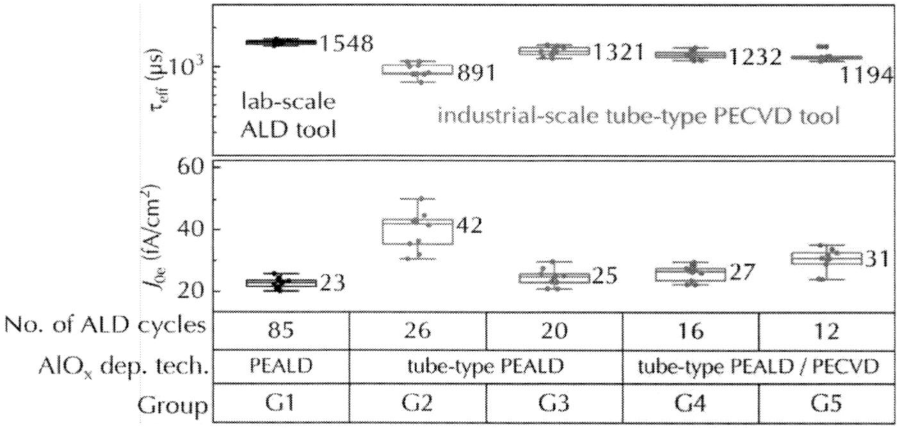

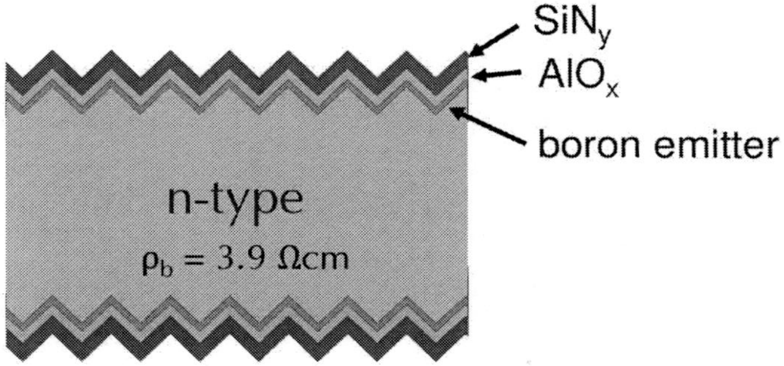

- **Strong impact of number of ALD cycles (G2 vs. G3)**
- 20 ALD cycles leads to the best passivation quality, same level as the reference
- Tube-type PEALD AlO_x / PECVD AlO_x (G4 & G5): promising option with 16 ALD cycles

Separation between J_0 in the emitter bulk & surface

ISFH

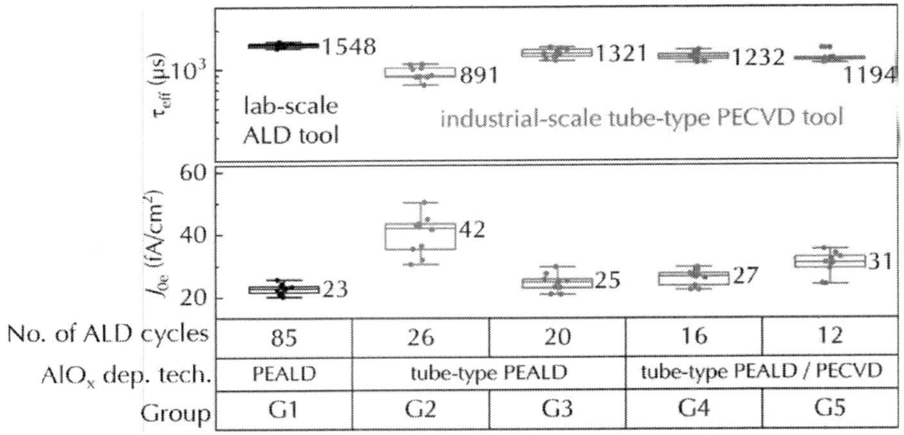

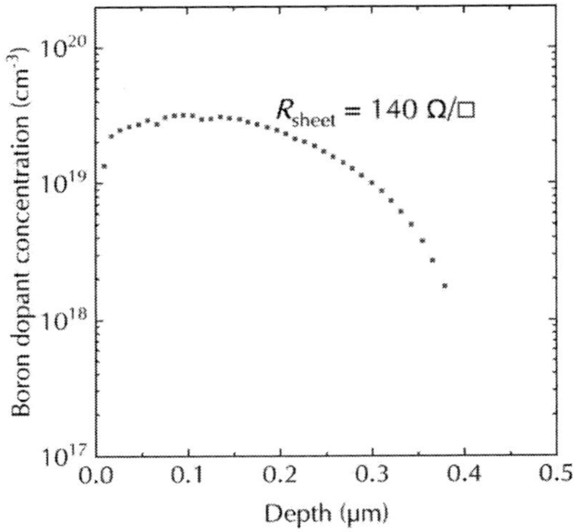

- $J_{0e} = J_{0e,b}$ (Auger in the emitter bulk) + J_{0s} (SRH at surface)
- Separation between $J_{0e,b}$ and J_{0s} with EDNA2[1] & ECV profile as input
- Best result in G3 with tube-type PEALD: J_{0e} = 20.9 fA/cm² = 17.3 fA/cm² + **3.6 fA/cm²** (the 3.6 fA/cm² term is marked J_{0s})

  → Auger in the emitter bulk dominates J_{0e} currently

B. Min et al., 42nd EU PVSEC, 23rd September 2025, 1BO.3.6

7

Leibniz Universität Hannover

[1] K.R. McIntosh and P.P. Altermatt, 35th IEEE PVSEC (2010)

n-type wafers with improved boron emitter

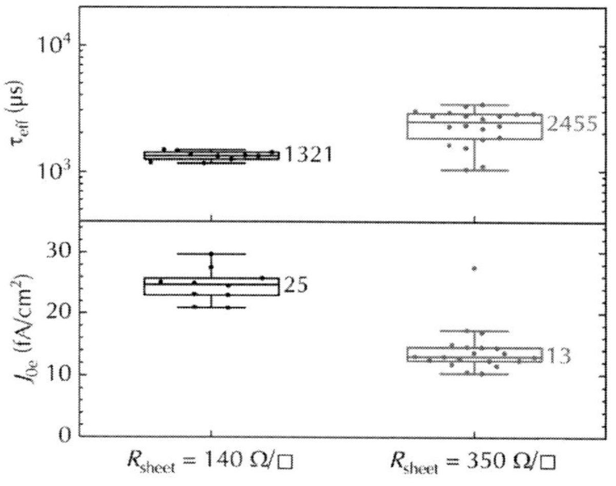

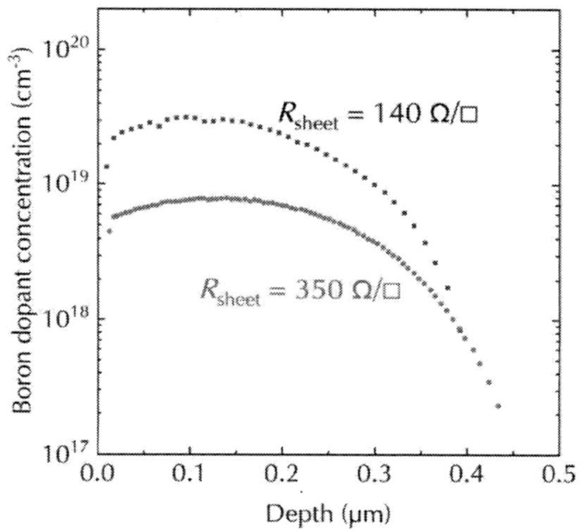

- Improved boron emitter with R_{sheet} = 350 Ω/□
- 20 ALD cycles for tube-type PEALD AlO_x as in G3
- **J_{0e} (median)** decreases from 25 fA/cm² to **13 fA/cm²**

B. Min et al., 42nd EU PVSEC, 23rd September 2025, 1BO.3.6

p-type wafers with undiffused textured surfaces

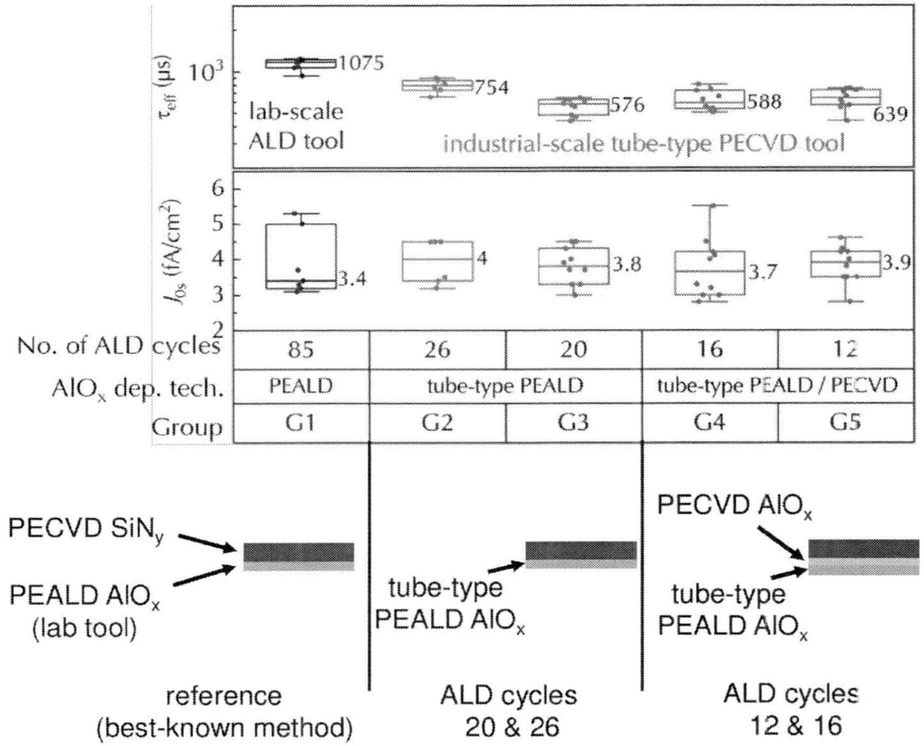

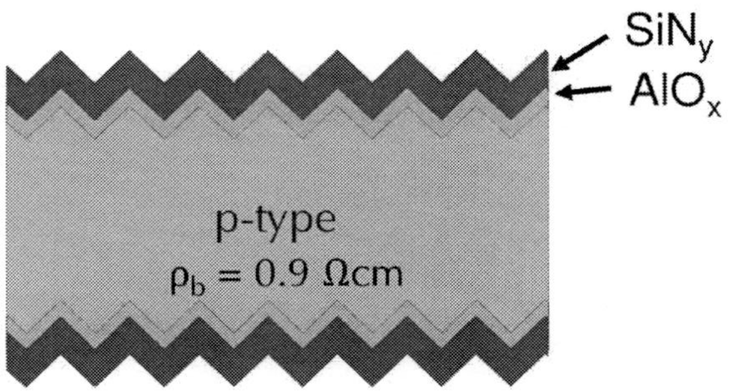

- All samples fired at 800 °C
- Measurement at five wafer positions (center, 4 corners)
- Only J_{0s} since no emitter exists

p-type wafers with undiffused textured surfaces

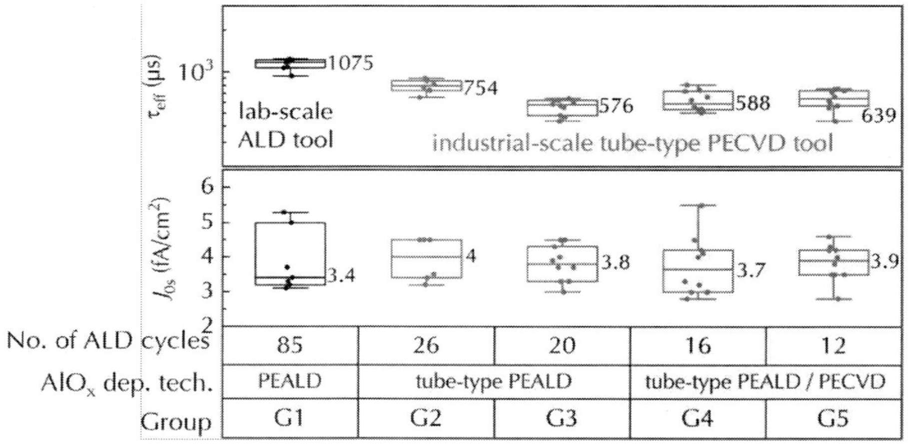

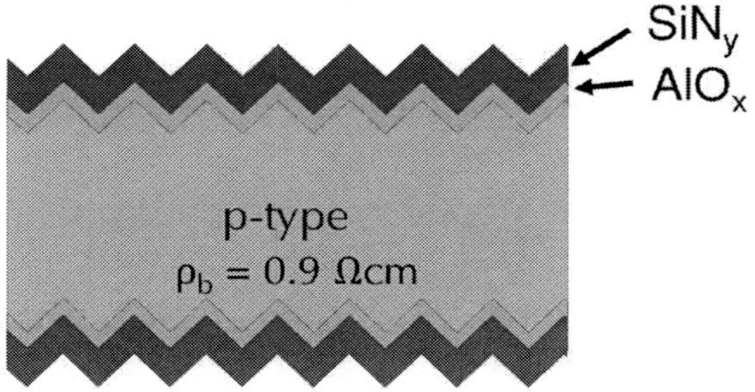

- Notable differences in τ_{eff}, could be also caused by bulk effects
- **No impact of number of ALD cycles on J_{0s}**
- Passivation quality of all groups are on the same level as the reference
- Median J_{0s}: 3.7 – 4 fA/cm², corresponds well with J_{0s} from n-type wafer surface (J_{0s} = 3.6 fA/cm²)

POLO Back Junction (BJ) and its advantages

POLO BJ[1]

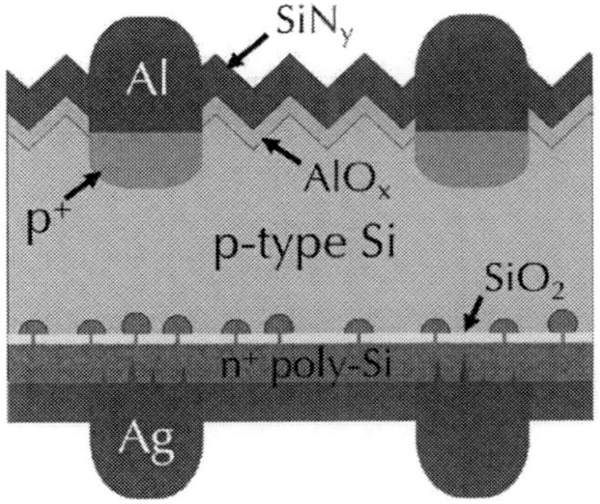

- n$^+$-type passivating poly-Si on oxide (POLO) rear contacts
- **Leaner process flow** compared to TOPCon
  (less process steps, no boron diffusion)
- Up to **50% less Ag consumption** compared to TOPCon & HJT
- Best efficiency so far[2]: 24.2% with a V_{oc} of 725 mV
- Ag-free metallization[3] is also possible
- Ag-free interconnection
  (Brinkmann et al. 3CO.10.1, Wednesday, 3:15 pm)
- Detailed cost analysis of POLO BJ
  (Gomez Trilos et al. 5DO.11.6, Thursday, 8:30 am)

[1] R. Brendel et al., 35th EUPVSEC (2018)
[2] B. Min et al., Prog Photovolt Res Appl., 1-9 (2024)

[3] B. Min et al., 40th EUPVSEC (2023)

Integration of tube-type PEALD AlO_x in solar cells

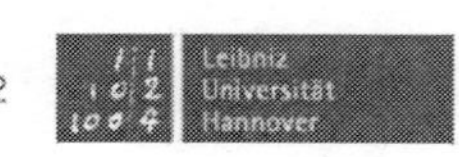

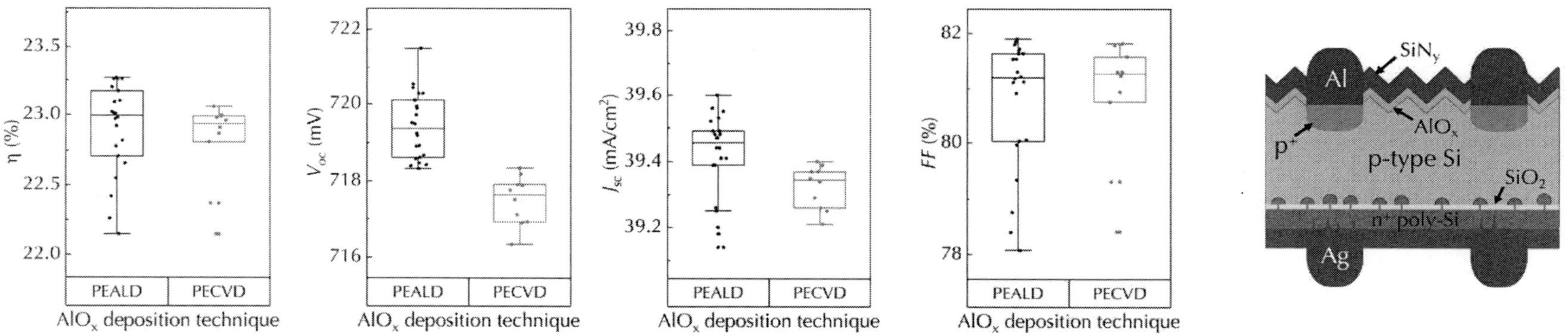

- Reference (red box plot) POLO BJ solar cells featuring PECVD AlO_x/SiN_y passivation stack
- The efficiencies of both groups are on the same level
- **Tube-type PEALD AlO_x/PECVD SiN_y shows notably higher V_{oc} and J_{sc}**

B. Min et al., 42nd EU PVSEC, 23rd September 2025, 1BO.3.6

Leibniz Universität Hannover

Tube-type PEALD AlO_x / PECVD SiN_y is UV stable

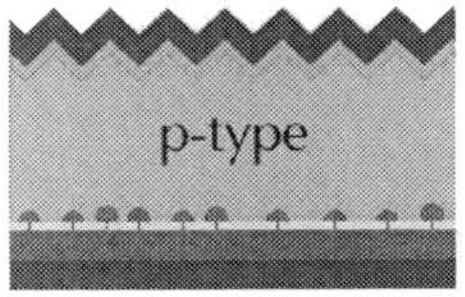

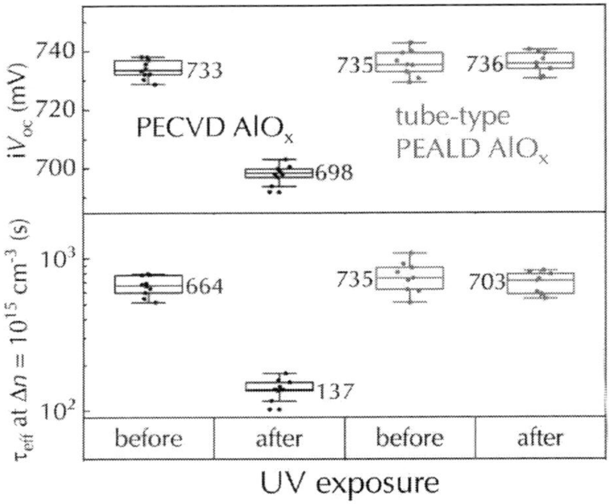

- Undiffused textured surface of p-type wafer
- UV dose of 4.5 kWh/m^2, λ = 290 – 400 nm
- PECVD AlO_x / PECVD SiN_y degrades significantly

More details in C. Hollemann et al., Solar RRL, 2025, https://doi.org/10.1002/solr.202500510

Tube-type PEALD AlO_x / PECVD SiN_y is UV stable

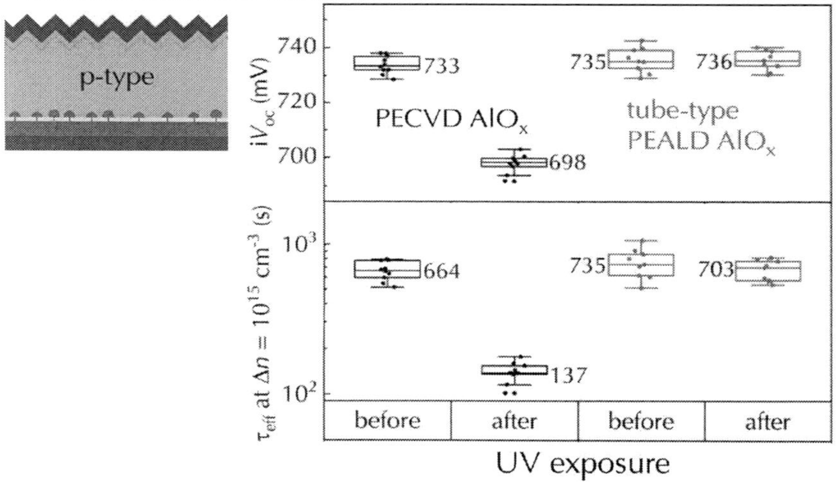

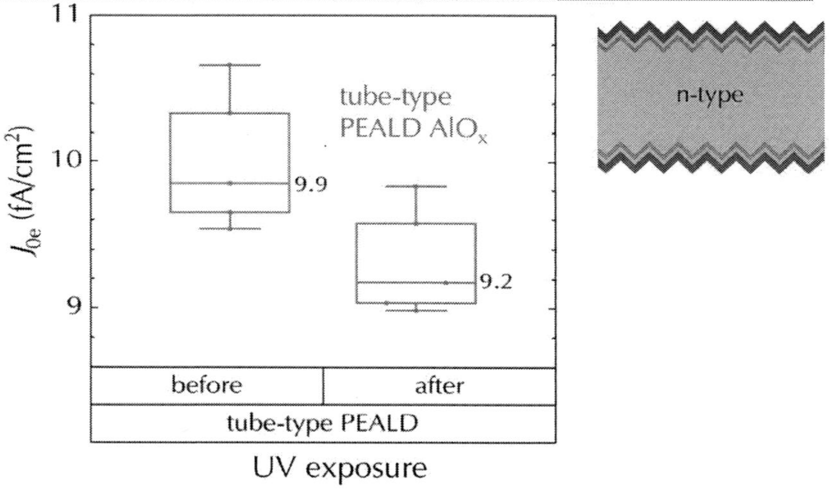

- Undiffused textured surface of p-type wafer
- UV dose of 4.5 kWh/m^2, λ = 290 – 400 nm
- PECVD AlO_x / PECVD SiN_y degrades significantly

- Boron-diffused textured surface of n-type wafer
- UV dose of 9 kWh/m^2, λ = 290 – 400 nm

More details in C. Hollemann et al., Solar RRL, 2025, https://doi.org/10.1002/solr.202500510

B. Min et al., 42nd EU PVSEC, 23rd September 2025, 1BO.3.6

Leibniz Universität Hannover

Summary

ISFH

- Successful validation of tube-type PEALD AlO_x with cPLASMA 2600, centrotherm
- Tube-type PEALD AlO_x shows excellent surface passivation quality
- Number of ALD cycles is crucial for boron-diffused textured surface of n-type wafers
- Combination of the tube-type PEALD AlO_x and PECVD AlO_x is an attractive option
- Tube-type PEALD AlO_x is UV stable, while the PECVD AlO_x degrades strongly under UV exposure.
- Reduction of cell fabrication cost as well as the increase of PV module energy yield of all solar cells with AlO_x on the front side (e.g. POLO BJ or TOPCon solar cells)

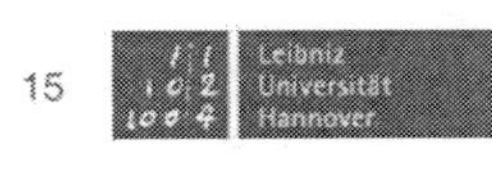

Acknowledgments

ISFH

The authors thank to **M. Pollmann**, **B. Gehring**, **L. Spasówka**, **S. Spätlich**, **T. Brendemühl**, **T. Friedrich**, **T. Neubert** and **D. Sylla** for processing solar cells (all ISFH), **M. Dhamrin** and **K. Tsuji** from Toyo Aluminium K. K. for their supports regarding Al pastes.

This work was financially supported by the German Federal Ministry for Economic Affairs and Energy (BMWE) under contact number 03EE1150A (APOLON) and by the German State of Lower Saxony for the project ARTEMIS through the special assets fund for economic development, ecological sector, chapter 5157.

Supported by:

Federal Ministry for Economic Affairs and Energy

on the basis of a decision by the German Bundestag

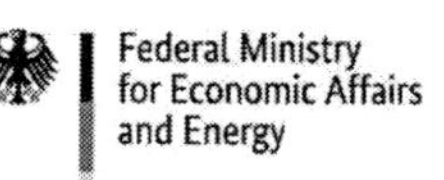

ADVANCEMENTS ON POST-PROCESSING OF HIGH EFFICIENCY CELLS: DATA FROM MASS PRODUCTION AND EXPERIMENTAL ROADMAP

Alessandro Voltan[1], Francesco Dalla Torre[1], Bertrand Hladys[2], Pedro Jeronimo[2], Grazia Litrico[3], Alessandro Furnari[3], Alfredo Di Matteo[3], Marcello Sciuto[3], Jonas De Rose[4]

[1]Applied Materials, Via Postumia Ovest, 244, 31048, Olmi di San Biagio di Callalta, TV, Italy
[2]Univ Grenoble Alpes, CEA, LITEN, DTS, INES, F-38000, Grenoble, France
[3]Enel Green Power, Contrada Blocco Torrazze, Zona Industriale, 95121, Catania, Italy
[4]Fraunhofer Institute for Solar Energy Systems ISE, Heidenhofstr. 2, 79110 Freiburg, Germany

The power output and conversion efficiency of solar cells can change after exposure to illumination, with increases or decreases depending on the cell structure. According to the literature, high-intensity light exposure combined with controlled heating can enhance the performance of amorphous-crystalline silicon heterojunction (HJT) solar cells and modules [1]. This efficiency improvement is attributed to simultaneous defect recovery and reductions in series resistance. In this work, we present a rapid post-treatment process for HJT solar cells, utilizing an LED-based oven jointly designed by Applied Materials (AMAT, Italy) and CEA-INES (France), in collaboration with 3Sun (Enel Group, Italy). The architecture of the developed Fast Light Soaking (LS) solution is described in detail in [2]. Using the Fast Light Soaking process at lab scale, we achieved an efficiency gain of up to +0.6%, with open-circuit voltage (Voc) and fill factor (FF) generally being the main contributors to this improvement [2].
In this paper, we provide an overview of the latest achievements obtained with the Fast Light Soaking process, including: i) data collected in mass production, ii) the effect of the Light Soaking process on cells from different efficiency classes, and iii) a detailed degradation analysis after LS. The impact of Light Soaking on different metallization processes, using various silver- and copper-based pastes, will also be reported.
Preliminary results on the effect of the Light Soaking process on HJT cells with an nc-Si:H n-doped silicon layer, as well as on TOPCon cells, will be presented as part of our experimental roadmap.

Keywords: Heterojunction, Light Soaking, TOPCon, In-line post processing

1 INTRODUCTION

The behavior of HJT cells under Light Soaking and the related defect recovery is still actively investigated in literature. The main requirements for successful post processing are in any case intensive illumination and cell temperature controlled below the cell damage threshold (<250°C) even in localized regions [2].
Based on process requirements, a dedicated Fast Light Soaking oven has been developed using high power LEDs light sources and released in mass production [Fig. 1]. During the R&D testing an efficiency gain up to +0.6%abs has been obtained with 12s exposure time on small batches.
In this work we will focus on deployment of Light Soaking in mass production at 3Sun, including:
1) Effect of Light Soaking process on cells belonging to different efficiency classes;
2) Degradation of HJT cells after Light Soaking process and impacted IV parameters;
3) Light Soaking combined with different metallization processes at lab scale.
Further tests are planned at 3Sun to better quantify the effect of Light Soaking exposure on additional process steps including: i) deposition of an intrinsic amorphous silicon layer on the front side of the cell, using dedicated gases to increase the energy gap, with a benefit in terms of the transparency to the incident light; ii) deposition of a nano-crystalline n-doped silicon layer; iii) deposition of a transparent conductive oxide on the back side of the cell with high mobility, high working function and high transparence values.
To evaluate the applicability of the Light Soaking process to other cell structures, a batch of TOPCon cells was treated after firing using various Light Soaking recipes at high temperature. In all cases, a significant efficiency gain was observed, laying the groundwork for further investigations. These future studies will primarily focus on the combined effects of Light Soaking and LECO (Laser-Enhanced Contact Optimization [3]) on TOPCon cells

a)

b)

Figure 1: Fast Light Soaking design (a) and final installation in mass production at 3Sun-ENEL (b)

10.4229/EUPVSEC2025/1BO.4.2
020010-001

2 RESULTS FROM MASS PRODUCTION

In order to quantify the benefit of Light Soaking process in mass production, a lot of 2k bifacial HJT cells with standard a-Si:H (n) layer has been measured and subdivided in 10 Efficiency classes with a range of +0.2% abs each. The distribution of cells in efficiency classes is reported in Fig. 2. After the measurements, all the cells have been processed and exposed to the same light soaking recipe using the in-line oven reported in Fig 1 and then remeasured. The average efficiency gain for the most representative classes is reported in Table I, where, as expected, the higher gain is obtained on lower classes. An average gain of +0.6%abs is obtained also on the highest classes, confirming the results previously achieved at lab scale. Also in this case (Fig. 3) the efficiency gain is mainly due to the combination of Voc improvement (+6mV average) and FF (+1.5% Average), while the impact on Isc can be considered negligible. The Voc improvements are the results of enhanced passivation properties of the substrate surfaces while the FF gain comes from both series and sheet resistance enhancement.

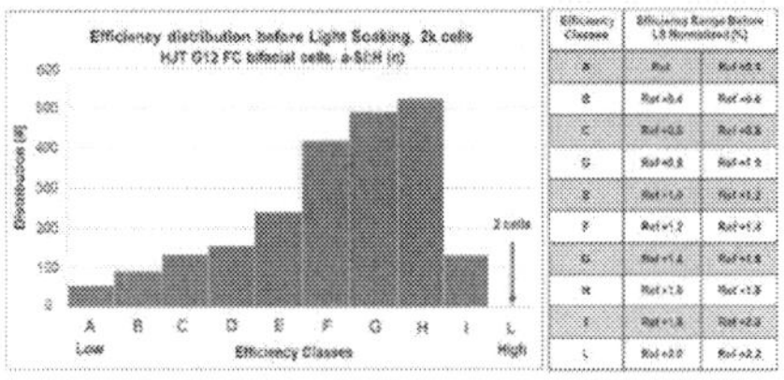

Figure 2: Distribution of Efficiency classes, HJT G12 FC bifacial cells, a-Si:H (n) at 3Sun

Table I: Average Efficiency gain for representative classes

Efficiency gain after Light Soaking [abs]						
Class	A	C	G	H	I	L
Average	+1.12%	+1.01%	+0.61%	+0.60%	+0.59%	+0.56%

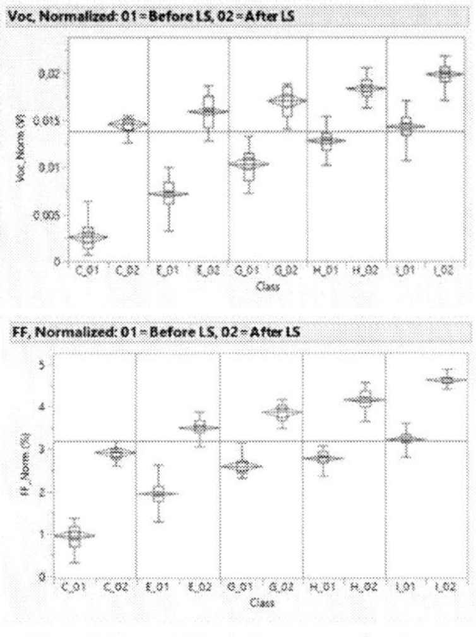

Figure 3: Voc and FF gain for representative classes

Beside the immediate effect on electrical properties due to Light Soaking process on HJT cells, the degradation mechanism during standard dark storage conditions has been investigated. Cells belonging to Class H (Fig. 2) have been selected for this purpose and re-measured multiple times. In Table 2 we report the results of cumulative losses respectively after 11 and 34 days of storages. From Table II it visible that the degradation process in dark condition can be considered stabilized after 11 days with an efficiency loss <0.15%abs starting from an initial gain of +0.64%, with a net stabilized gain of +0.5%abs efficiency, +5mV Voc and +1.3%abs FF. Efficiency losses are partially due to cells handling.

Table II: Cumulative losses during dark storage

CLASS H: weekly monitoring, cumulative losses					
	Voc (mV)	Isc (mA)	Pmax (W)	FF (%)	Eff (%)
Δ (pre/postLS)	+ 6	+ 30	+ 0.28	+ 1.47	+ 0.64
Δ (after 11 Days)	- 1	- 30	- 0.06	- 0.19	- 0.13
Δ (after 34 Days)	- 1	- 39	- 0.06	- 0.19	- 0.15

The Light Soaking process has been fully implemented in mass production and is now running continuously. The process is closely monitored, and the average efficiency gain is periodically checked, consistently confirming the results reported in Table I.

3 EXPERIMENTAL ROADMAP

In order to better understand the Light Soaking mechanics and fully quantify the benefit on high efficiency cells, additional tests have been planned. In this paragraph we report the main results achieved on HJT cells comparing impact of Light Soaking with i) different metallization processes and ii) different layers structure. For what concerning the first point, main results are reported on Fig. 4 where 4 batches of same M2 precursors have been screen printed using 4 different pastes and then exposed at the same Light Soaking process. The four cases represented in Fig. 4 relates respectively to i) Ag-Cu paste provided by Vendor A, ii) Silver paste with Nano particles, iii) Ag-Cu paste provided by Vendor B and iv) Standard Reference Silver paste.

Beside the different starting efficiency, all the batches showed similar results with a clear improvement of data distribution.

Average gain is in good agreement with results reported in previous paragraph and summarized in Table III.

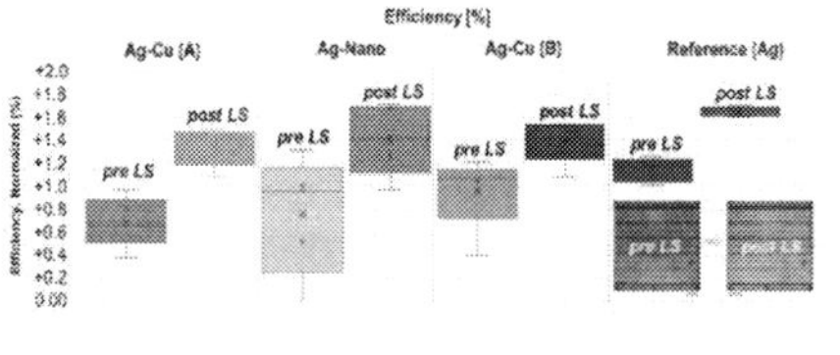

Figure 4: Effect of LS on different metallization processes, HJT cells.

Table III: Average gain after LS using different metallization processes

Δ (pre/postLS)	Isc (mA)	Voc (mV)	Pmax (W)	FF (%)	Eff (%)
AVERAGE	**+40**	**+5.2**	**+0.14**	**+1.14**	**+0.56**

Furthermore, effects of Light Soaking on different HJT structures have been investigated comparing cells with n-doped nc-Si:H layer thickness instead of reference a-Si:H (n) layer. Several tests have been performed with different n-doped nc-Si:H layer thickness (15, 19 and 22nm) showing decreasing efficiency with increasing layer thickness. Best results have been achieved with 15nm n-doped nc-Si:H layer, comparable with Class H a-Si:H (n) reported in previous Fig. 2.
After Light Soaking (Table IV), higher Efficiency gain was achieved on 15nm nc-Si:H cells compared with nc-Si:H HJT cell with same starting efficiency (+0.9%abs vs +0.6%abs). To be noticed the Isc increase in case of nc-Si:H cells probably due to improved nc-Si:H layers crystallinity and better interfaces between amorphous and nc layers after Light Soaking.

Table IV: Gain after LS, comparison between a-Si:H (n) and 15nm nc-Si:H HJT cell with same starting efficiency

	Gain after Light Soaking			
	Voc [mV]	Isc [mA]	FF (%)	Eff (%)
CLASS H, a-Si:H (n)	+6	+30	+1.4	+0.6
DOE2, 15nm nc-Si:H	+12	**+194**	+0.9	+0.9

4 POST FIRING ANNEALING OF TOPCON CELLS

Continuing with the experimental roadmap, the Light Soaking tool has been used for the Post-Firing Anneal (PFA) process on TOPCon solar cells. For this purpose, a dedicated LED-based mock-up oven (FIG. 6) was employed, capable of reaching higher temperatures and maintaining them for longer durations than the standard HJT Light Soaking oven.
Based on existing knowledge, PFA is expected to provide "additional hydrogenation" [4], further passivating remaining defects via hydrogen atoms. By reducing recombination effects, increases in open-circuit voltage (Voc), fill factor (FF), and efficiency (η) are generally observed after PFA on TOPCon cells, while also removing any excess hydrogen that could otherwise lead to further degradation.
For testing purpose, 2 groups of cells (respectively fired at 770°C and 810°C peak Temperature) provided by Fraunhofer ISE, without any additional PFA, have been exposed at 3 different LS processes: i) Recipe_A (400°C for 35s) ii) Recipe_B (400°C for 20s) iii) LSK_STD (Standard Light Soaking Recipe used for HJT cells).
Promising results have been achieved with both Recipe_A and Recipe_B due to increased peak temperature compared with LSK_STD Recipe (Table V). Respect to HJT cells, impact on Voc can be considered negligible.
After Light Soaking, cells have been shipped back to Fraunhofer ISE where they have been exposed to LECO (Laser-enhanced contact optimization, [3]). Results of TOPCon cells processed with Recipe A and reprocessed with LECO are reported in Table VI and Fig. 7. No further improvements after LECO have been obtained on TOPCon cells fired at 810°C, showing equivalence between the two processes. On the other hand, highest Uoc (710mV vs 702mV) and Efficiency (23.3% vs 23.1%) have been obtained adding Light Soaking and LECO on cells fired at 770°C. Additional tests are planned for further process optimization and understanding.

Figure 6: Mock-up Light Soaking Oven used for PFA of TOPCon cells

Table V: PFA on TOPCon cell using different Light Soaking recipes.

Cells fired at (°C)	Average Gain (Recipe A ~35s)		
	Voc [mV]	FF [%]	Eff [abs%]
770	+1.0	+3.0	+0.93
810	+1.5	+1.3	+0.43
Cells fired at (°C)	**Average Gain (Recipe B ~20s)**		
	Voc [mV]	FF [%]	Eff [abs%]
770	+0.5	+3.4	+1.05
810	+1.4	+1.5	+0.48
Cells fired at (°C)	**Average Gain (Recipe LSK_STD ~20s)**		
	Voc [mV]	FF [%]	Eff [abs%]
770	+0.1	+0.04	+0.01
810	+1.4	+0.20	+0.12

Table VI: IV data after Light Soaking and LECO

	IV data: Firing Recipe 770 °C (average)			
	Uoc [mV]	Jsc [mA/cm2]	FF [%]	Eff [%]
After LS, Recipe A	711	40.3	76.9	22.1
After (LS+LECO)	710	40.3	81.3	23.3
	IV data: Firing Recipe 810 °C (average)			
	Uoc [mV]	Jsc [mA/cm2]	FF [%]	Eff [%]
After LS, Recipe A	702	40.2	81.5	23
After (LS+LECO)	702	40.2	81.8	23.1

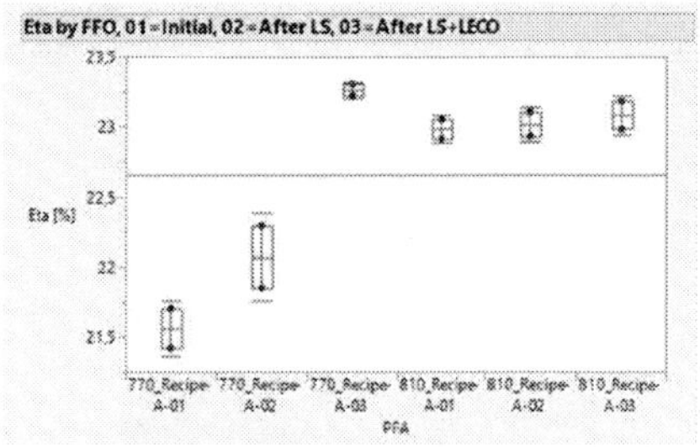

Figure 7: Efficiency results after PFA (Recipe A) and LECO

5 CONCLUSIONS

This work demonstrates the successful industrialization of Fast Light Soaking (LS) for high-efficiency HJT solar cells, confirming lab-scale efficiency gains up to +0.6% can be reliably reproduced in mass production. The process delivers consistent improvements in Voc and FF across different efficiency classes and metallization schemes, with negligible impact on Isc. Degradation studies indicate that the efficiency gain is largely retained after dark storage, supporting the process's robustness. The experimental roadmap further highlights the versatility of LS, showing promising results on HJT cells with nc-Si:H layers and on TOPCon cells, especially when combined with post-firing annealing and LECO treatments. The LED-based oven developed enables both static and dynamic processing, paving the way for flexible integration in industrial lines. Preliminary results suggest that further optimization of LS parameters and cell architectures could unlock additional performance gains. Overall, Fast Light Soaking emerges as a scalable, reliable post-processing step for next-generation silicon solar cells, supporting higher module efficiencies and improved manufacturing yield. Future work will focus on process optimization for advanced cell structures and long-term stability assessment under real-world conditions.

6 ACKNOWLEDGEMENTS

This work was partially supported by the European Union through the Horizon Europe project Shine PV under grant agreement No 101172902

References

[1] M. Wright et al., "High-Intensity Illuminated Annealing of Industrial SHJ Solar Cells: A Pilot Study," in IEEE Journal of Photovoltaics, vol. 12, no. 1, pp. 267-273, Jan. 2022.

[2] A. Voltan et al., "Progress on the design of a tool for the post-treatment of HJT cells : from prototyoe to in-line industrial tool", Proceeding of 40th EUPVSEC conference, 2023, Lisbon

[3] Xie Yi-Bo et al., Influence of Laser-Induced Sintering on Contact Performance of TOPCon Solar Cells, Acta Physica Sinica, 2024

[4] R. Chen et al., "24.58% efficient commercial n-type silicon solar cells with hydrogenation", Progress in Photovoltaics: Research and Applications, https://doi.org/10.1002/pip.3464, 2021

SOLAR PV SILICON RECYCLING VIA CHEMICAL AND VACUUM REFINING TECHNIQUES

Jonas Låstad*, Kai Tang**, Alexander Ulyashin**, Xiang Ma**, Jafar Safarian*
*NTNU, **SINTEF

ABSTRACT: The rapid expansion of global photovoltaic (PV) installations will inevitably result in large quantities of silicon-rich waste as early-generation modules reach their end of life. Recovering this silicon is critical for maintaining a sustainable solar value chain and reducing dependence on high-energy primary production. However, solar-grade silicon requires a purity level of 99.9999 wt% (6N), posing a significant challenge for recycling processes. Within the framework of the Apollo project, a combined chemical and vacuum refining route has been developed to recover and purify silicon from spent PV wafers. The integrated process sequence—acid leaching, alkaline leaching, and vacuum refining—reduces total impurity levels from 33,000 ppm in untreated material to 16 ppm in the final refined silicon. Chemical leaching steps remove adherent glass and metal contaminants, while vacuum refining efficiently eliminates volatile elements such as Ag and Cu. The final material reaches approximately 5N purity, with remaining impurities dominated by Ca and Zn. Minor carbon diffusion from the graphite crucible was detected but not included in the purity assessment. The results demonstrate the complementarity of the processes and suggest that further optimization of refining conditions could enable closed-loop silicon recycling for next-generation PV manufacturing.
Keywords: Solar silicon, PV recycling, Vacuum refining, Alkaline leaching,

1 INTRODUCTION

Global installed photovoltaic capacity has increased exponentially over the past two decades, and projections indicate that solar electricity will constitute a dominant share of renewable power generation within the next ten years. While this represents a major environmental success, it also introduces a new materials challenge: the generation of large volumes of end-of-life PV modules. As most first-generation installations approach the end of their 20–30 year lifetimes, silicon waste streams are expected to exceed several million tons annually.

Recycling these modules is essential for both resource efficiency and environmental stewardship. The silicon contained in solar cells represents more than half of the embodied energy of a module and recovering it could drastically lower the carbon footprint of future PV production. However, the recovery of solar-grade silicon requires achieving purities of 99.9999 wt% (6N) or higher. Such purity is necessary to ensure the low defect densities and long minority-carrier lifetimes that underpin photovoltaic efficiency.

The challenge is compounded by the complex structure of PV wafers, which typically contain doped regions, metallic conductors, and glassy encapsulants. These layers introduce a variety of contaminants—both chemical and structural—that must be eliminated without excessive material loss. Traditional metallurgical refining alone cannot achieve the required purity, while purely chemical processes are often limited by reagent consumption and waste generation.

The Apollo project aims to develop an integrated recycling framework that combines physical separation, chemical purification, and metallurgical refining. This work focuses on the latter stages: the purification of recovered silicon using a combination of acid leaching, alkaline leaching, and vacuum refining. The goal is to demonstrate a viable, scalable route to recover high-purity silicon suitable for reintroduction into the solar manufacturing cycle.

2 EXPERIMENTAL PROCEDURE

2.1 Sample origin and composition

The starting material consisted of mixed silicon fragments obtained from dismantled PV modules. Because these originated from real installations, the feedstock included wafers of different manufacturers, crystal structures, and dopant types. Most of the material was polycrystalline p-type silicon, reflecting the historical dominance of boron-doped cells in commercial production. Small quantities of n-type material were likely present but not separately analyzed. The recovered silicon pieces exhibited surface contamination from encapsulant residues, silver and aluminum metallization, and glass fragments. These features reflect typical characteristics of industrial PV waste, making the samples representative of actual recycling feedstock rather than laboratory-synthesized analogs.

2.2 Acid leaching

The initial chemical purification was performed by Fraunhofer CSP using a multi-step acid leaching process. Their process effectively removed most of the contacts and metallic impurities. The process also aided in removing the antireflective coating and thin glass layers present on the cell surfaces. After leaching, the samples were thoroughly rinsed with deionized water and dried.

2.3 Alkaline leaching

Following acid treatment, an alkaline leaching step was conducted at 25 °C for up to six hours using 1 M NaOH in a stirred beaker reactor. The objective was to dissolve residual glass (SiO_2) and oxide layers that may trap or encapsulate impurities. Sodium hydroxide reacts with SiO_2 to form soluble silicates, effectively etching the wafer surface and exposing cleaner bulk material.

This process also mechanically dislodged metallic inclusions, which were then removed during rinsing. While effective, the use of NaOH introduced trace sodium contamination in the treated samples, which must be carefully managed in future scale-up.

2.4 Vacuum refining

The purified silicon was subsequently refined in a vacuum induction furnace using a graphite crucible at 1500 °C and 5 Pa for 60 minutes. At this temperature, the silicon was fully molten, and volatile impurities such as Na, Mg, P, Zn, Ag, and Cu evaporated preferentially due to their higher vapor pressures relative to silicon. The process was designed to minimize silicon loss while enhancing impurity segregation through vaporization. During refining, carbon diffusion from the graphite crucible into the melt was detected, indicating slight contamination. Although this carbon was not included in the total impurity figures, its presence highlights a design consideration for future furnace materials or coatings to prevent back-diffusion.

2.5 Sample analysis

Elemental analyses were performed by Glow Discharge Mass Spectrometry (GDMS). The results represent surface-layer composition, considered representative of the bulk given the thin samples (~100 μm). Single-sample analyses were used for each process stage. The leachate solution from alkaline leach was also analyzed using Inductively Coupled Plasma Mass spectroscopy. The combined analysis provided insight to the mass flows of the leaching process.

3 RESULTS

3.1 Impurity reduction sequence

The sequential refining route achieved a marked reduction in total impurity concentration. The untreated PV silicon exhibited roughly 33,000 ppm total impurities, dominated by aluminum and copper. After the acid leaching, the impurity concentration dropped to 69 ppm, demonstrating the effectiveness of the nitric-hydrochloric mixture in removing metal-rich surface layers. The alkaline leach provided a further reduction to 24 ppm, primarily by dissolving glass and oxide residues. Despite a minor introduction of sodium from the NaOH reagent, the overall purity improvement confirmed the complementary role of acid and base leaching. Finally, vacuum refining lowered the impurity concentration to 16 ppm, corresponding to approximately 5N purity. This stage efficiently removed volatile elements such as Ag, Cu, and Mn, while also decreasing phosphorus and magnesium levels.

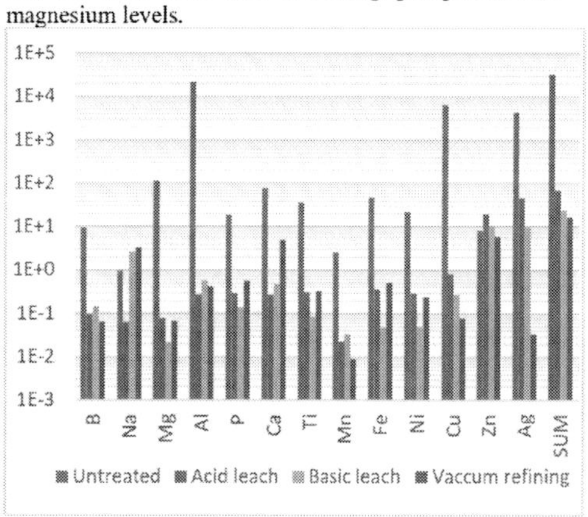

Figure 1: Impurity concentrations for selected elements from GDMS analysis

The trend in total impurities clearly demonstrates the progressive removal of contaminants through each process step. Chemical leaching primarily eliminates external and surface-bound impurities, while vacuum refining targets volatile elements within the silicon bulk. Carbon contamination from the crucible was detected as was expected.

4 DISCUSSION

4.1 Complementarity of chemical and vacuum refining

The experimental results underscore the synergistic interaction between chemical and metallurgical purification. The acid and alkaline leaching stages remove adherent and glassy impurities that would otherwise hinder mass transfer during vacuum refining. Once these layers are removed, the molten silicon surface becomes more active, facilitating impurity evaporation and reducing kinetic barriers.

The vacuum refining stage complements chemical cleaning by removing impurities that cannot be dissolved or dislodged chemically. Its efficiency relies on the difference in vapor pressure between silicon and the impurity elements. This difference allows volatile species to evaporate selectively under low pressure, leading to bulk purification without excessive silicon loss.

4.2 Mechanistic considerations

During the nitric-hydrochloric acid leach, transition metals are oxidized and complexed as soluble chlorides, while the alkaline step promotes the dissolution of silica and disintegration of adherent oxide films. In contrast, vacuum refining depends on mass transfer and vapor–liquid equilibrium, where impurity diffusion from the bulk to the melt surface governs removal efficiency.

The current refining parameters 1500 °C and 5 Pa—represent a balance between impurity volatility and silicon retention. Increasing temperature or reducing pressure further would enhance removal kinetics at the risk of silicon evaporation and contamination from crucible walls. Detailed kinetic modeling is planned to identify the optimal operating window.

4.3 Implications for PV recycling

The near-complete removal of silver and copper confirms the high efficiency of vacuum refining for volatile metals. The persistence of zinc and calcium, which remain as the dominant impurities, indicates their lower volatility and possible formation of stable silicides. Boron remains a key limitation due to its strong affinity for silicon and low vapor pressure; alternative removal methods such as gas-phase slag refining or oxidative treatments could be explored.

4.4 Process integration

The theoretically achieved purity of 5N aligns with reported requirements for feedstock in the Czochralski process for monocrystalline silicon production. This indicates that recycled silicon can feasibly re-enter the production chain without compromising material quality. Importantly, the combined refining route achieves this with moderate process complexity and without resorting to high reagent consumption or multiple refining cycles.

Within the Apollo project, these findings contribute to the broader goal of establishing a closed-loop PV recycling process that integrates mechanical separation, chemical leaching, and metallurgical refining. Such integration could enable recovery of glass, metals, and high-purity silicon from complete modules, supporting both environmental and economic sustainability.

5 FUTURE WORK

Future activities will focus on scaling and optimization. Laboratory-scale experiments will be extended to pilot-scale refining to assess throughput, silicon yield, and impurity removal consistency. Particular attention will be given to refining kinetic models for impurity evaporation, enabling better prediction of removal rates under varying temperature and pressure.

Parallel work will address crucible design and material selection, seeking coatings that prevent carbon diffusion while maintaining thermal conductivity and chemical inertness. Additionally, expanded analytical characterization, including ICP-MS depth profiling and SIMS mapping will verify homogeneity of purity across the silicon bulk.

On the process integration level, the Apollo consortium will explore coupling this refining route with mechanical module disassembly and glass recovery. The aim is to achieve an end-to-end circular recycling pathway where recovered silicon can directly replace virgin feedstock in crystal pulling or wafer casting.

Ultimately, the development of scalable, low-waste refining processes will be key to meeting the material demands of a growing global PV industry while minimizing its environmental footprint.

6 Conclusions

A combined chemical and vacuum refining route were demonstrated for the purification of silicon recovered from spent photovoltaic modules. Sequential treatments reduced impurities from 33,000 ppm in the untreated feedstock to 16 ppm following vacuum refining, corresponding to roughly 5N purity. The chemical leaching steps effectively removed surface contaminants and glass residues, while the vacuum refining stage eliminated volatile metallic elements. Together, these processes act in a complementary manner, addressing both surface and bulk impurities.

Minor carbon contamination from the graphite crucible was observed, suggesting a need for crucible optimization in future testing and upscaling. Besides this, the final material meets the purity criteria for reuse as feedstock in solar-cell manufacturing. The results confirm the feasibility of integrating chemical and metallurgical refining into closed-loop recycling systems, advancing the goal of sustainable, circular photovoltaic production.

REFERENCES

[1] APOLLO Project. (2025). https://www.apolloproject.eu

[2] Gangopadhyay, U. (2012). IOSR Journal of Engineering, 2(8), 41–48.

[3] Safarian, J., & Tangstad, M. (2012). Metallurgical and Materials Transactions B, 43(6), 1427–1445.

[4] Bathey, B. R., & Cretella, M. C. (1982). Journal of Materials Science, 17(11), 3077–3096.

NTNU

Solar PV silicon recycling via chemical and vacuum refining techniques

APOLLO

Jonas Låstad*, Kai Tang**, Alexander Ulyashin**, Xiang Ma**, Jafar Safarian*
*NTNU, **SINTEF

Exponential growth of solar panel deployment, combined with short lifetime, will cause major waste streams, which will require processing. The goal of the Apollo project to achieve complete recycling of solar panels demands solving the problem of Silicon recovery. This problem is difficult because of the high Si purity requirement of 99.9999wt% (6N) or higher. The unique structure and composition of waste poses unique challenges and advantages for recycling. [1]

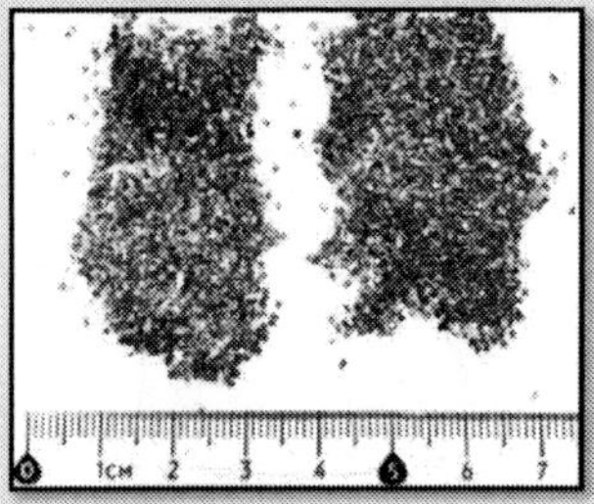

Recovered silicon samples. Left: acid leached, Right: untreated

The Apollo project attempts an improved recycling process, employing additional alkaline-leaching and vacuum refining steps. While the alkaline leach can remove the surface layers and glass impurities, the vacuum refining step is useful for separating volatile elements, such as phosphorus. Other elements suited for vacuum refining are Na, Mg, P, Zn, Ga, Ag, Sn, Sb, Pb, and Bi. The vacuum refining process occurs in 5 distinct steps, where silicon has a low mass transfer rate compared to most associated impurities. The kinetics of vacuum refining needs to be further studied for more development of the previous models about silicon refining. [3]

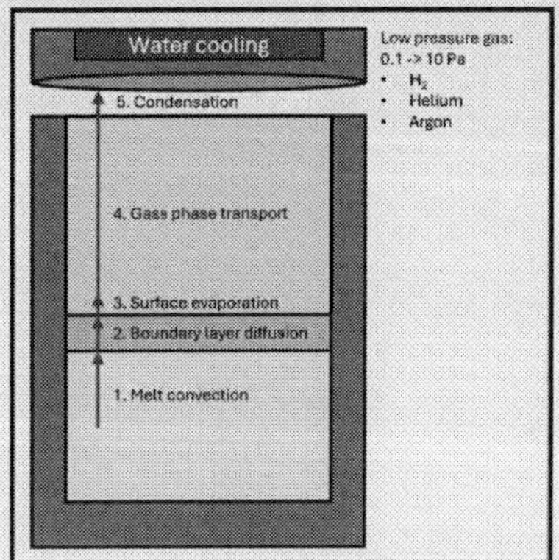

Schematic of NTNU vacuum refining process in lab scale

Surface digestion of the top and bottom wafer surface enables elimination of correlated impurities from the emitter and back surface layers. The structure of PV-wafers allows for this processes. N-type and P-type refer to the positive and negative doping of the different layers. Most impurities can be removed by this process, and selective removal of problematic impurities are possible depending on cell structure.

P-type dopants: **Boron, Aluminum, Gallium**
N-type dopants: **Phosphorous, Arsenic, Antimony**
Conductors: **Silver, Aluminum, Copper**
Emitter and BSF layer:
500 nm thick, 10^{19} cm^{-3} doping density
Bulk silicon layer:
200 µm thick, 10^{16} cm^{-3} doping density [2]

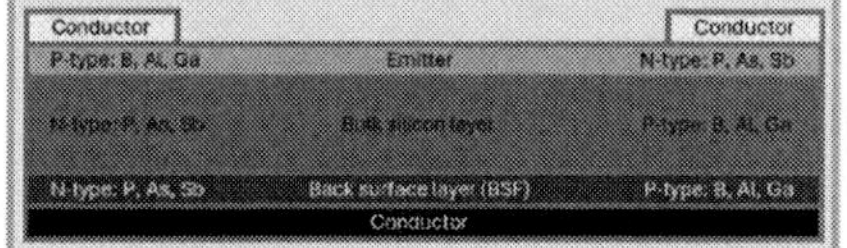

Schematic over PV-cell structure

Vacuum refining proved highly efficient at removing Cu and Ag, while also being promising for Mn. Both techniques yielded improved purity achieving 16 PPM or 5N purity. Alkaline leaching provided a reduction in metallic impurities; these seem to have been dislodged by the alkaline leaching and separated during rinsing. The combined results indicate the refining processeses are complementary. Contamination issues with the final vacuum sample leave the result of the combined process unanswered.

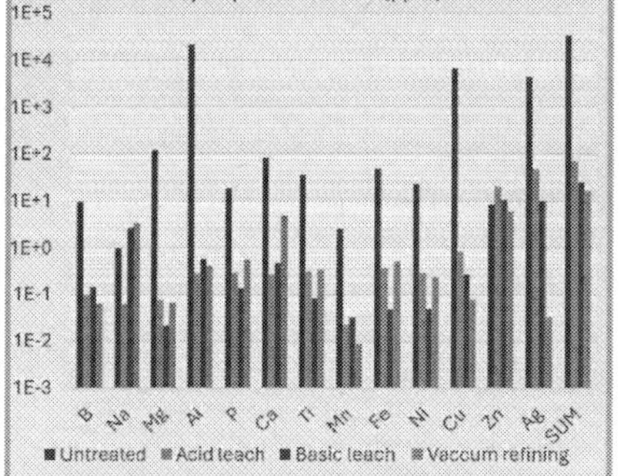

The resulting purity after vacuum refining is within the specifications provided by Bathey and Cretella (1982) [4] and would therefore be applicable for recycling as feedstock in the Czochralski process. The only remaining challenging impurity is B, but expected design changes in the PV-cell structure will eliminate this issue.

Glass and metal particles were observed attached on the surface of the recovered PV-silicon with as seen in the figure below. These contaminants remained after the acid leaching process. An alkaline leaching step was introduced primarily to remove these particles as the glass would be digested, and the metal would dislodged. A secondary benefit was found in the form of surface digestion.

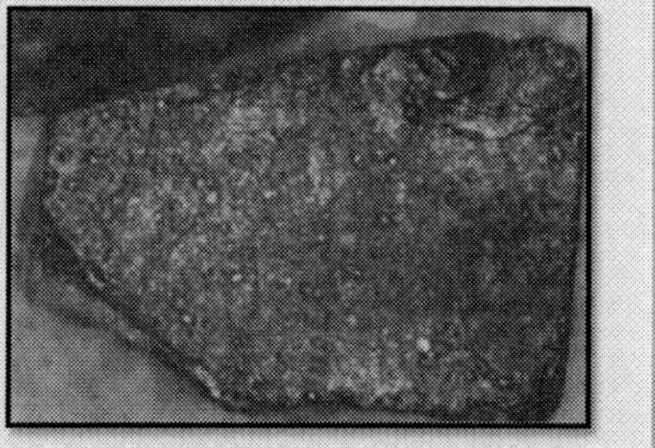

Polarized light image of acid leached PV-Si grain, with impurities

The separation and acidic leaching were initially performed by our partners. The alkaline leaching was performed in a dedicated stirring beaker reactor with 1 M NaOH at 25 °C for up to 6 hours. The vacuum refining was performed at 1500 °C and 5 Pa for 60 minutes. Both using the samples provided by Fraunhofer.

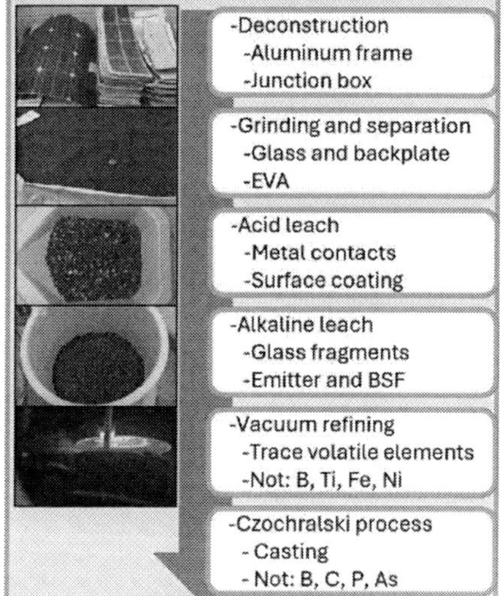

Schematic of Si recycling path, including vacuum refining process

[1] APOLLO. (n.d.). APOLLO. Taken 12. may 2025, from https://www.apolloproject.eu
[2] Gangopadhyay, U. (2012). Comparative simulation study between n- type and p- type Silicon Solar Cells and the variation of efficiency of n- type Solar Cell by the application of passivation layer with different thickness using AFORS HET and PC1D. *IOSR Journal of Engineering, 02*(08), 41–48. https://doi.org/10.9790/3021-02814148
[3] Safarian, J., & Tangstad, M. (2012). Vacuum refining of molten silicon. *Metallurgical and Materials Transactions B, 43*(6), 1427–1445. https://doi.org/10.1007/s11663-012-9728-1
[4] Bathey, B. R., & Cretella, M. C. (1982). Solar-grade silicon. *Journal of Materials Science, 17*(11), 3077–3096. https://doi.org/10.1007/BF01203469

PARTNERS

Fraunhofer CSP, NEW, EPFL, IPN, Swansea University, kalyon PV, MINESPIDER, MGG, ODTÜ GÜNAM, NSG GROUP, FENIX TNT, NTNU, SAULE TECHNOLOGIES, SINTEF, University of Leicester, soleven, University of Glasgow

FUNDING

Innovate UK
Project funded by
Co-funded by the European Union
Co-funded by the European Union under Grant Agreement no 101123277, the State Secretariat for Education, Research and Innovation (SERI) and UK Research and Innovation (UKRI). Views and opinions expressed are however those of the author(s) only and do not necessarily reflect those of the European Union or CINEA. Neither the European Union nor the granting authority can be held responsible for them.

www.apolloproject.eu

@apollo-project-eu

NOVEL PV CONVERSION MECHANISMS IN CRYSTALLINE SILICON FILLED WITH CONDITIONED AMORPHIZED GRAINS

Z.T. KUZNICKI
SEGTON Advanced Technology
Address: 99 Boulevard de la REINE, 78000 VERSAILLES, France
Email: zbig.kuznicki@segton.com

ABSTRACT: Our research reveals a novel mechanism for low-energy generation and multiplication of secondary electrons in silicon nanostructures, specifically triggered by the UV component of the solar spectrum. By harnessing the additional kinetic energy of hot electrons, we introduce a complementary photovoltaic (PV) conversion pathway to surpass the Shockley-Queisser efficiency limit of 30% in silicon solar cells. These experimental findings, along with their theoretical interpretation, were developed within the LEEMONS Project. They directly informed the innovative design and architecture of the hidden tandem demonstrators, which were subsequently fabricated to meet stringent performance requirements.
Keywords: Silicon Solar Cell, High-Efficiency, Interfaces and Nanocomponents, Hot Electrons, Low-energy Secondary Generation and Multiplication.

1 INTRODUCTION

Amorphized grains have been built-in into crystalline silicon lattice by the ion implantation, their controlled amorphization and thermodynamic conditioning. Such an immersion is unfortunately always accompanied by postimplant defects with highly active recombination centers that completely obscures the desired effects of photogeneration.

This work presents the spectacular revelation of a phenomenon triggered by hard UVs in a transformed Si wafer; the secondary generation in highly hostile environment, see Fig. 1.

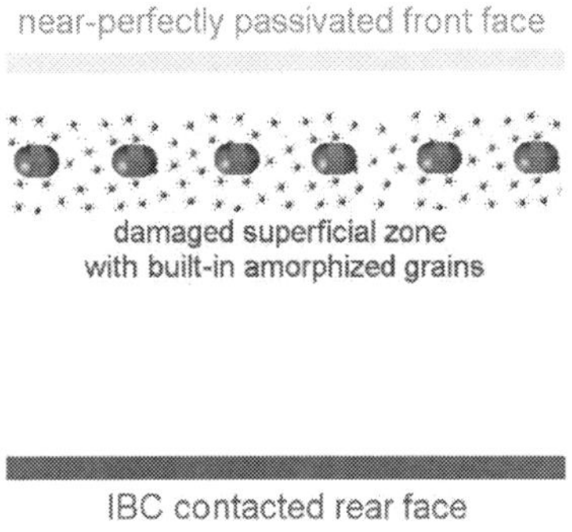

Figure 1: Built-in amorphized nanograins in unifacial silicon test device with a near-perfectly passivated front face (artist's view).

2 EXPERIMENT

FIG. 2 presents an optical view of built-in nanosystem of amorphized grains while FIGs. 3 and 4 show TEM image of amorphized grain cross section and the positions of the two built-in SEG-Matter nanolayers that are well-visualized on the SIMS fluorine profile; upper, at a depth greater than **19.5 nm** and lower, at a depth greater than **28 nm**.

Significant changes in the spectral response measurement conditions enable insight into the generation-recombination (G-R) balance even in the presence of strong recombination activity at well-defined zones.

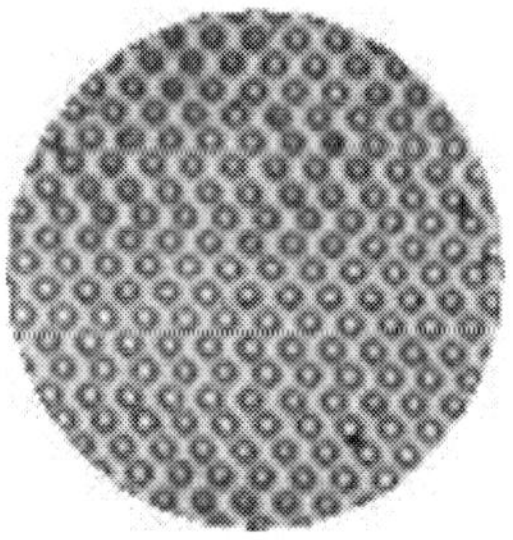

Figure 2: A nanosystem featuring 2 μm amorphized grains built-in into a crystalline silicon wafer, visualized by optical microscopy.

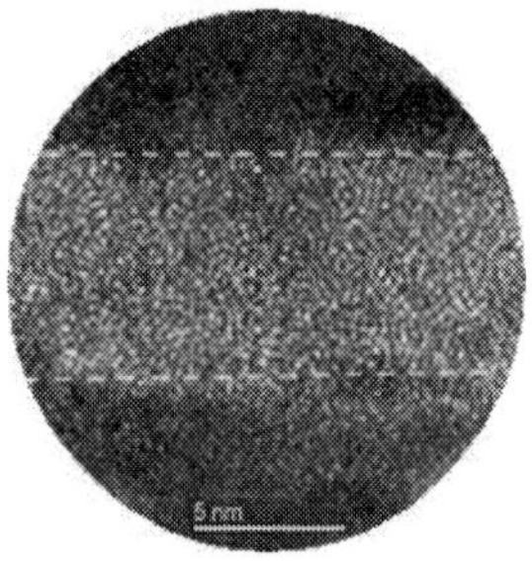

Figure: 3: TEM image of a cross-section illustrating the geometric structure of buried amorphized grains, the layers from top to bottom: upper crystalline, middle amorphous, and lower crystalline.

It should be emphasized that both defects and the secondary generation centers are localized at the superficial zone of the wafer. FIG. 1 illustrates the defected area, in which are plunged the generation centers that are internal to a Si metamaterial, named SEG-Matter.

Indeed, the precise positions of the two built-in SEG-Matter nanolayers appear in SIMS measurements, as shows the related fluorine profile, see FIG. 4.

The active surface coverage of SEG-Matter is limited to that of amorphized grains.

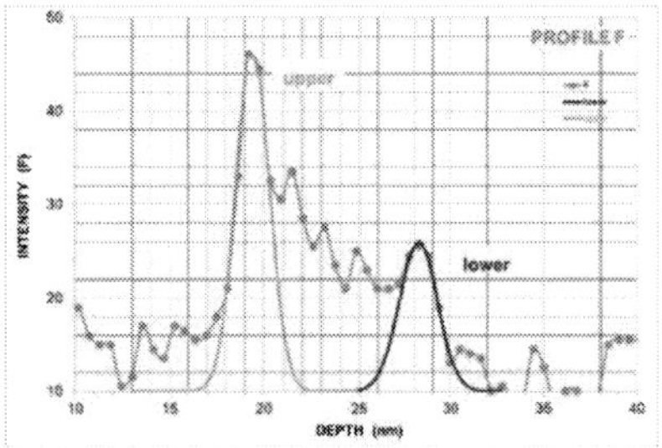

Figure 4: The positions of the two built-in SEG-Matter nanolayer appear clearly on the SIMS fluorine profile: the upper layer at a depth exceeding 19.5 nm and the lower layer at a depth exceeding 28 nm.

2.1 Experimental Protocol and Strategy

An optimized experimental protocol enables direct visualization of light-induced phenomena in silicon-embedded nanostructures. The protocol for our spectral response measurements is designed to deliberately manipulate the G-R balance to achieve defect saturation.

Spectral response measurements, under steady-state and time-resolved excitation, reveal abundant secondary electron generation, even in the presence of strong internal recombination. This secondary generation, localized at the wafer surface, is made observable through near-perfect electron transport and dynamic control of the G-R balance.

2.2 Methods for Achieving Defect Saturation

Saturation of the near-surface recombination centers can be achieved in two ways:

(i) By applying a continuous, broad-spectrum white light optical bias to maintain a steady-state population of free carriers that fill the defect states.

(ii) By increasing the flux of the monochromatic probe beam itself, so that it is intense enough to simultaneously generate collectable free carrier population that is enable to saturate the defects.

2.3 Key Challenges

The main obstacle is isolating the intrinsic optoelectronic activity of SEG-Matter nanostructures, which are integrated into crystalline silicon via ion implantation. The near-surface region, where UV absorption occurs, suffers from high-localized recombination due to surface states and postimplant defect zone, usually masking the useful photogeneration.

2.4 Solution

To observe the specific electronic activity of SEG-Matter under so adverse conditions, it is necessary to suppress or passivate the recombination pathways associated with the postimplant defects localized close to the surface zone.

This is possible to achieve this by employing an **optical bias** technique and different conditions of spectral response measurements.

3 RESULTS

Figure 6 shows the measured spectral response across the entire spectral range, highlighting a distinct feature in the long-wavelength range (800–1100 nm).

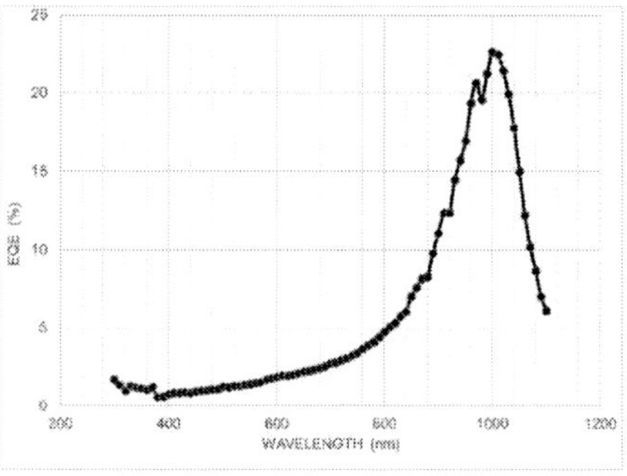

Figure 5: The dark-measured spectral response across the full range highlights a specific long-wavelength region (800–1100 nm), where external circuit collection is observed.

Longer-wavelength light penetrates deeper into the wafer, beyond the defect-rich near-surface region, generating a primary population of electron-hole pairs in the "clean" bulk of the semiconductor. Here, recombination from postimplant defects is negligible. However, a second harmful effect persists: the "sink effect," which causes internal recombination of photocarriers generated in the bulk. These carriers can diffuse back toward the defect-laden near-surface region and be annihilated before collection in the external circuit.

This leakage recombination acts as a powerful sink, ensuring that the overall G-R balance remains dominated by near-surface defects. As a result, the photogenerated carrier population is insufficient to overcome this sink, preventing net current collection in the external circuit at middle wavelengths (400–800 nm).

In general, recombination occurs at front-defects or rear-side contacts. Whereas in the wavelength range between 800 and 1100 nm, useful recombination on contacts predominates. Figure 1 illustrates the device structure, showing how the sink effect drives internal carrier recombination within the surface-damaged zone surrounding amorphized grains.

3.1 Spatial differentiation of photogeneration and recombination areas

Spatial segregation of G-R dynamics, both near the surface and in the bulk, as well as near and far from defects, enables targeted investigation of carrier photogeneration in the short-wavelength range (250–400 nm) via efficient carrier collection, as evidenced by short-circuit current measurements.

At UV, photogeneration remains confined to the shallow depth of light penetration. The "sink effect", where bulk-generated carriers diffuse back and recombine at near-surface defects, is absent, since free carrier generation does not occur in the bulk. Instead, the generation-recombination balance and net current collection are governed exclusively by the superficial zone.

3.2 Carrier collection

Carrier collection was first observed in the long-wavelength range (800–1000 nm), as shown in Fig. 6. This phenomenon arises from the spatial localization of absorption sites and the relative proximity of the collecting contacts, enabling effective collection of electron-hole pairs.

Under the established experimental conditions (detailed experimental protocol), efficient carrier collection should be observed in the short-wavelength UV range. Indeed, the high photogeneration rate saturates defect-related recombination centers, while the near-perfect quality of the wafer ensures excellent carrier transport.

3.3 Time-resolved measurements

Time-resolved photogeneration experiments focused on the surface region reveal critical insights. When the photogeneration intensity exceeds a threshold, internal recombination is dynamically suppressed, as shown in FIG. 6.

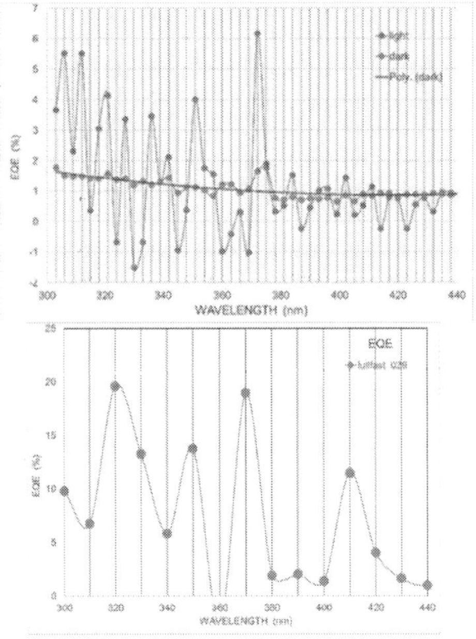

Figure 6: Dynamic EQE in a highly recombinant environment, the G-R balance. Results show in:
upper graph, a shorter 3 nm wavelength spread indicated by thin blue vertical lines. Comparison of curves acquired under two distinct conditions: i) without optical bias (orange) and ii) with optical bias (blue);
lower graph, a larger 10 nm wavelength spread of the measurement points.
Conditions: concentrated spot, acquisition time 1 sec/pt, average over three measurements per point.

The suppression of the recombination activity allows measurements to track the evolution of free electron populations and precisely locate secondary generation centers under UV excitation.

A wavelength-dependent scan further exposes the interplay between beneficial (contact-mediated) and detrimental (defect-driven) recombination processes. Slow-scan UV measurements, highlight dynamic shifts in the G-R balance. This approach enables real-time observation of transient free electron populations in nanostructured silicon wafers, capturing their formation, electron transport and decay.

3.4 Abundant secondary generation

The experimental approach created conditions that allowed observation of abundant secondary carrier generation in the short-wavelength range (250–400 nm), even in the presence of highly active recombination centers, by dynamically modulating the G-R balance.

All observed data result from two recombination mechanisms: beneficial recombination at contacts and detrimental recombination at defects.

Surpassing a certain generation intensity threshold indicated complete dynamic suppression of internal recombination.

Moreover, UV illumination enables precise spatial mapping of these secondary generation sites, see FIG. 7.

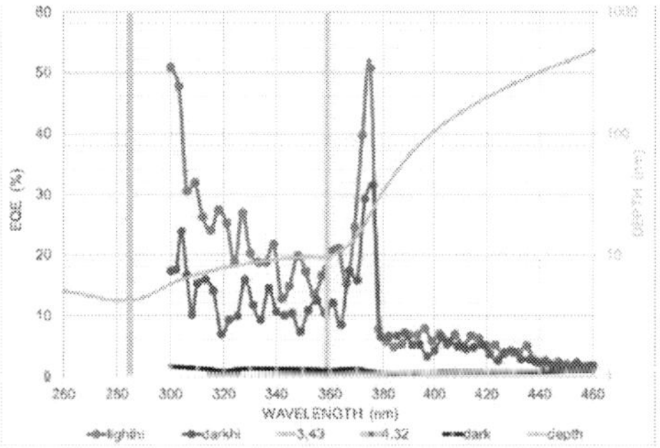

Figure 7: Collection of hard UV conversion in a silicon test device measured in different conditions.

The thresholds of two direct bandgaps are marked by vertical lines: first (green line) at 3.43 eV (358.6 nm) and second (blue line) at 4.32 eV (284.7 nm). The penetration depth of light into crystalline silicon is shown for comparison.

Three spectral responses are shown: dark curve, usual in the dark; blue curve, usual in the dark but with a stronger incident beam; rose curve, measured with optical bias.

4 CONCLUSIONS

Through our experimental approach, we established conditions to improve the detection of secondary generation, even amidst particularly adverse G-R balances. This measurement methodology will be used as part of LEEMONS project to improve solar cell characterization understanding.

A time-resolved equilibrium between generation and recombination was distinctly evident. Elevated photogeneration, driven by well-integrated secondary generation centers, temporarily neutralizes recombination activity under UV excitation.

All observed data are attributable to two recombination mechanisms: beneficial recombination occurring at contacts and detrimental recombination associated with defects.

References

[1] Application of innovations grouped under the name giant photoconversion, Z.T. Kuznicki, P. Meyrueis, M. Hosatte; M. Basta, Proc. SPIE 12150 Photonics for Solar Energy Systems IX, 121500A (24 May 2022; doi:10.1117/12.2620963.

[2] Hidden Tandem Solar Cells, Z.T. Kuźnicki, 8th World Conference on Photovoltaic Energy Conversion (WCPEC-8), September 26-30, 2022, Milan, Italy. M. Smith, A. Miller, Proceedings 17th European Photovoltaic Solar Energy Conference, Vol. I (2022) 903.

Acknowledgements

The author thanks Dr. Mikael Hosatte for experimental support and Mr. Brice Rouffie for coordinating sample production (SEGTON AdT), as well as Dr. Damien Lachenal for providing the experimental platform and Dr. Pierre Papet for the spectral response measurements (Meyer Burger).

Analysis of Cu-Associated Defects in Silicon through Lifetime Spectroscopy

Dasilva-Villanueva N.[1], Fuertes Marrón D.[1], del Cañizo C.[1]

INSTITUTO DE ENERGÍA SOLAR — POLITÉCNICA

Instituto de Energía Solar, ETSI Telecomunicación, Universidad Politécnica de Madrid, Avenida Complutense 40 (28040), Madrid, Spain

Lifetime spectroscopy (LS):

determination of defect parameters from carrier lifetime measurements (Rein, Springer, 2005)

$$\tau_{SRH} = \tau_{n0}\frac{p_0 + p_1 + \Delta n}{n_0 + p_0 + \Delta n} + \tau_{p0}\frac{n_0 + n_1 + \Delta n}{n_0 + p_0 + \Delta n}$$

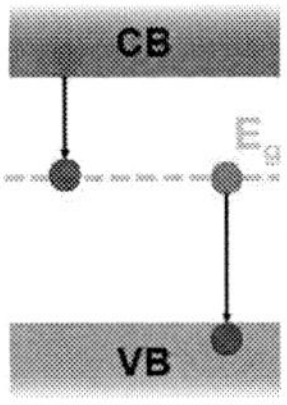

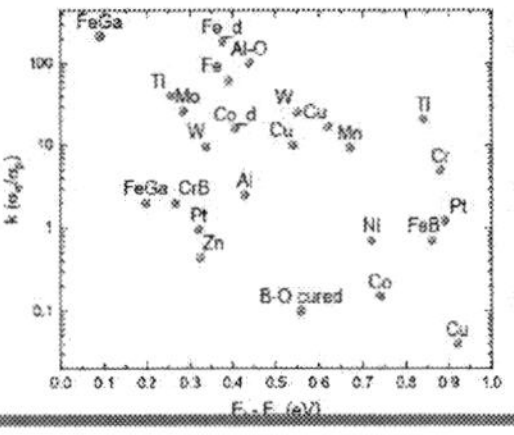

- SRH recombination characterized by defect **energy level** (E_t) and **ratio of capture cross-sections** (σ_n/σ_p, k)
- If SRH recombination **is dominant**: **defect identification through LS**
- Useful for low defect concentration: **undetectable through compositional techniques**

Step 1. Determination of carrier lifetime (LT) contributions:

- LT measurement (PCD)
- Determination of intrinsic and surface contributions
- Determination of SRH contribution

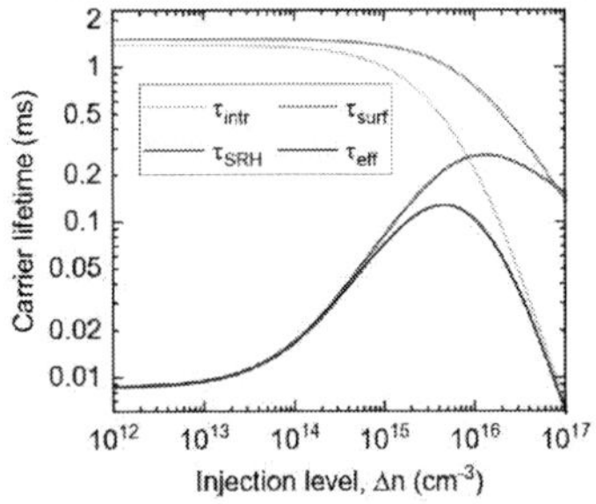

Step 2. Fit of the SRH contribution:

- Change Δn variable to X (n/p) in p-type or Y (p/n) in p-type
- Fit to the harmonic sum of n straight lines, corresponding to n defects
- Extraction of the slope and intercept

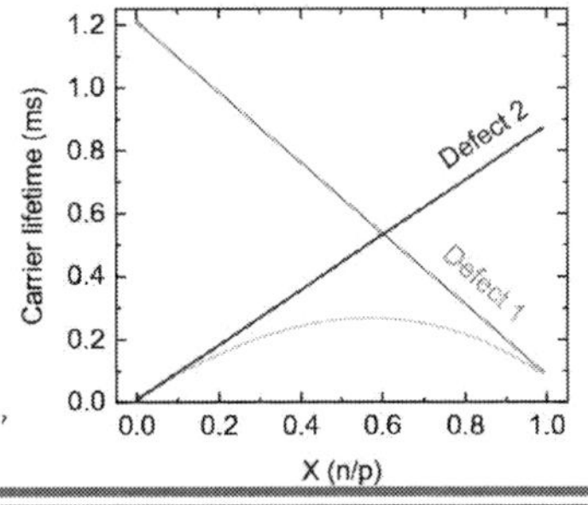

Step 3. Obtain defect parameters:

- Analytical expressions for E_t-k curves from fitting parameters
- Comparison of the curves obtained with the defect map

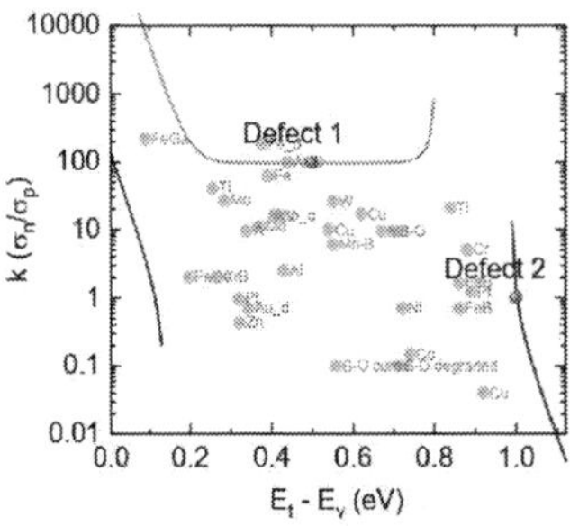

Case study:

- Two p-type mc solar-grade Si wafers, different effective carrier lifetimes, resistivity ~1Ω·cm

LS analysis:

- Difference in carrier lifetime between samples: different nature and/or defect concentration
- Compositional and metaestable analysis: rules out the presence of Fe, Cr and Ni
- LS analysis: two levels associated to Cu precipitates [1, 2]

[1] Inglese et al., Energy Procedia, 2016

[2] Lindroos J., Phd Thesis, 2015

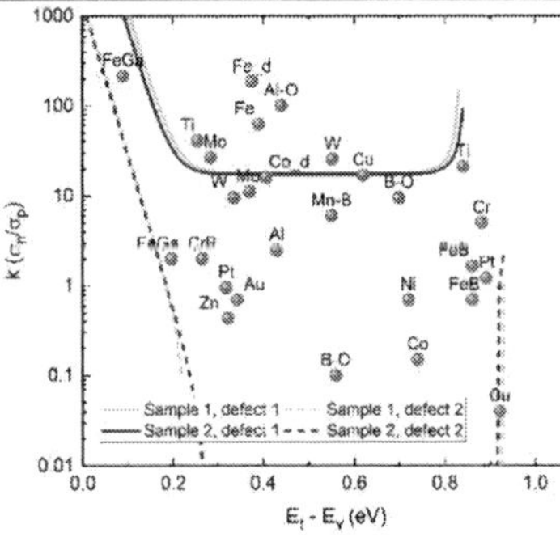

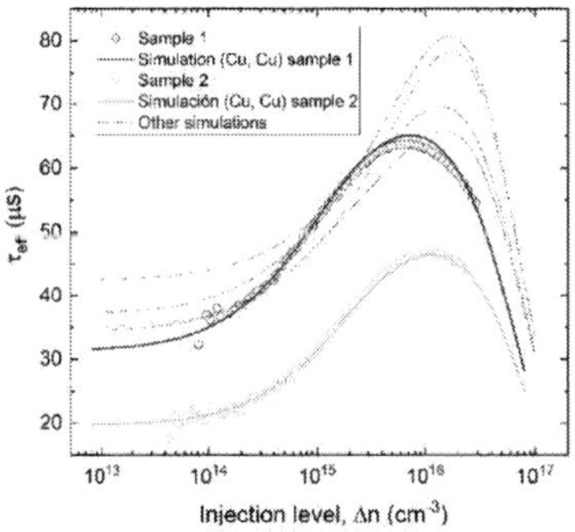

Multi-level defects:

- Some impurities introduce **more than one level**: Cu precipitates reported in literature as a **two-level defect** [2]
- Recombination rate associated to *a two-level defect* **different** from the recombination rate associated to *two defects acting simultaneously*
- **Complex lifetime expression**, 6-variable equation:

$$\tau_{SRH} = \frac{1 + \left(\frac{\sigma_{n1}v_{the}n_1 + \sigma_{p1}v_{thh}p}{\sigma_{p1}v_{thh}p_1 + \sigma_{n1}v_{the}n}\right) + \left(\frac{\sigma_{p2}v_{thh}p_2 + \sigma_{n2}v_{the}n}{\sigma_{n2}v_{the}n_2 + \sigma_{p2}v_{thh}p}\right)}{N_t(n_0 + p_0 + \Delta n)\left[\left(\frac{\sigma_{n1}\sigma_{p1}v_{the}v_{thh}}{\sigma_{p1}v_{thh}p_1 + \sigma_{n1}v_{the}n}\right) + \left(\frac{\sigma_{n2}\sigma_{p2}v_{the}v_{thh}}{\sigma_{n2}v_{the}n_2 + \sigma_{p2}v_{thh}p}\right)\right]}$$

- Fit performed with 4 parameters for each (E_{t1}, E_{t2}) data pair [3]
- **Fitting residuals** shown in contour plot: minimum value indicates **"true" solution**
- Good agreement with reported Cu precipitate states [2]: two-level defect, deep level with E_c - E_t = 0.5 eV and k = 22.4, shallow level with E_c - E_t = 0.96 eV and k = 0.042.

[3] Zhu et al., Solar Energy Materials and Solar Cells, 2020

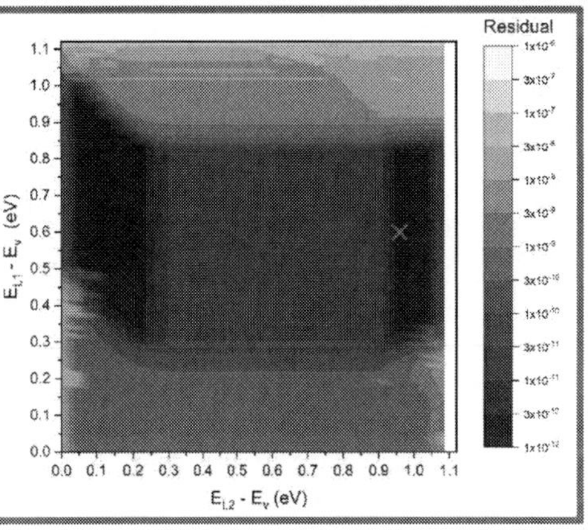

Acknowledgements. This research was funded by CETPartnership, the Clean Energy Transition Partnership under the 2023 joint call for research proposals, co-funded by the European Commission (GA N°101069750) and with the Spanish Research Agency MICIU/AEI/10.13039/501100011033 through the TANDEM Project, (PCI2024-155050-2) Financial support from Grant No. PID2023-148369OB-C41 funded by the Spanish Research Agency is also acknowledged.

Conclusions

- Lifetime spectroscopy analysis **applied to SoG-Si wafers**
- **Computational analysis** for the SRH-equation based on a dual-level defect
- **Solution through fitting residual analysis** shows **good agreement** with reported values for Cu precipitates in literature
- **Identification of the dual-level introduced by Cu precipitates** as dominating SRH recombination in **SoG-Si wafers**

n.dasilva@upm.es

INVESTIGATION OF PROCESS PARAMETERS ON THE DISTRIBUTION OF THE MATERIAL PARAMETERS IN CZ-CRYSTALS DOPED WITH ANTIMONY

F. Mosel[1], N. Schüler[2]
[1] PVA Crystal Growing Sytems GmbH, Im Westpark 10-12, 35435 Wettenberg, Germany
[2] Freiberg Instruments GmbH, Delfter Straße 6, 09599 Freiberg, Germany
e-mail: frank.mosel@pvatepla.com
phone: +49 64168690-125, fax: +49 64168690-822

ABSTRACT: The market share of Cz mono-Si for the industrial mass production of solar cells has grown steadily in recent years. Casted Si has practically disappeared from the market. At the same time, a clear trend from p-type to n-type base material can be observed due to a progressive transition from PERC technology based on p-type cells to TOPCon solar cell structures based on n-type material (Fig.1). Phosphorus (P), arsenic (As), and antimony (Sb) are doping elements for n-type crystals, but until now, P-doped substrate crystals are standard. Here, too, a substitution of phosphorus with antimony as a doping element is emerging, similar to p-type substrate crystals, where the doping element boron was replaced with gallium. The advantage of Sb-doped crystals is the possibility of producing crystals with an almost axial homogeneous distribution of the specific resistivity by selecting appropriate process parameters. We examined the influence of the evaporation behavior of antimony during the crystal growth of Cz mono-Si in the resistivity range of interest for solar cells. We will present our main results in this conference contribution.
Keywords: resistivity distribution, antimony-doping, Czochralski process, evaporation

1 INTRODUCTION

For the c-Si module market the mass production of Si mono-wafers using the Czochralski (Cz) growth technique with recharging is the most economical production method.

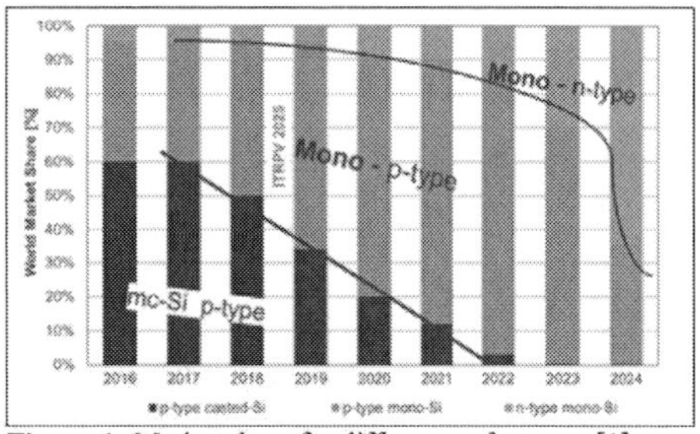

Figure 1: Market share for different wafer types [1]

For technological and economic reasons, the substrate crystals should have homogeneous material properties, both in axial and radial dimensions. The specific resistivity and the minority carrier lifetime are the outstanding material properties for a high solar cell efficiency. All doping elements in silicon have a distribution coefficient $k < 1$. This inevitably leads to a dopant enrichment in the melt during crystal growth, resulting in axial and radial inhomogeneous dopant incorporation. In addition to the segregation effect, some dopants exhibit a noticeable evaporation behavior from the silicon melt. Thus, with these dopants, two physical phenomena occur independently of each other. First, the dopant is incorporated into the growing crystal according to Scheil's law with the distribution coefficient of the dopant used. This means that the melt is continuously enriched with the dopant during the crystal growth process. Second, the dopant evaporates across the free melt surface. This means that the melt volume is permanently depleted of the dopant. Ideally, both effects can be balanced by varying the growth parameters in that way that a nearly constant dopant supply is maintained in the melt volume during the crystal growth process.

Boron was used as dopant for p-type crystals for a long time, but has been replaced by gallium due to its better stability with respect to LID. But also, for n-type crystals there are signs for a transition from phosphorus to antimony as dopant. The reason for this lies in the possibility of controlling the antimony content in the melt to a certain extent by varying the process atmosphere, despite the significantly less favorable distribution coefficient of antimony (k_{Sb}=0.023) compared to phosphorus (k_P=0.35). The effects of dopant enrichment and dopant depletion in the melt during the Cz-process are discussed in this paper.

2 APPROACH

2.1 Crystal growth

The crystal growth experiments presented in this paper were performed in a Cz-puller from PVA Crystal Growing Systems GmbH. Several 8-inch crystals were grown under identical growth conditions, except for the applied process pressure. To ensure comparability of the radial homogeneity of the grown crystals, the same rotation rates of crystal and crucible were applied. All samples examined in this work were grown from solar-grade polysilicon. As dopant antimony of 5N-quality was added as element to the silicon melt during its homogenization phase. Here too, the same time sequence was guaranteed for all crystal growth experiments which were successfully completed in the first attempt, i.e. no remelting due to structure loss was necessary. Six slices were sawn out of each crystal for characterization as shown in Fig.2. Evaporation coefficients were determined in separate experiments in a stagnant silicon melt.

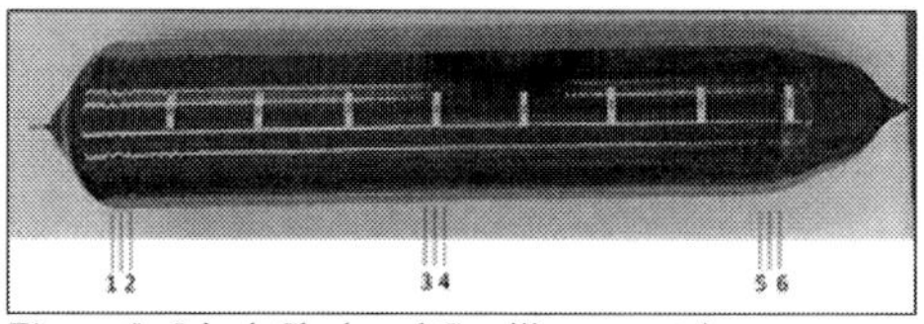

Figure 2: 8-inch Sb-doped Cz-silicon crystal

10.4229/EUPVSEC2025/1BV.5.7

2.2 Axial distribution of the specific resistivity in Sb-doped Si-crystals

Crystal growth experiments were carried out with different initial dopant concentrations (Sb) at different Ar-process pressures. The applied process pressures are given in the legend of Fig.3 and Fig.4. With one exception, the pressures were constant during the growth experiments. In one special case, the process pressure was reduced from 30 mbar to 25 mbar during the body growth. Argon was used as the process gas in all crystal growth experiments at a flow rate of 30 l/min. The axial resistivity distributions were measured on the untreated surface of the grown crystals. Fig.3 shows the axial curves of the specific resistivity fitted to the measured data. For a better comparability of the results, Fig.4 shows the resistivity curves normalized to a starting value of 1 Ωcm at the top of the crystal body. Additionally, the axial resistivity distribution at a pressure of 20 mbar is plotted as a dashed line, as it would be expected theoretically applying a segregation coefficient of Sb (k_{Sb}=0.023), but without evaporation loss of antimony.

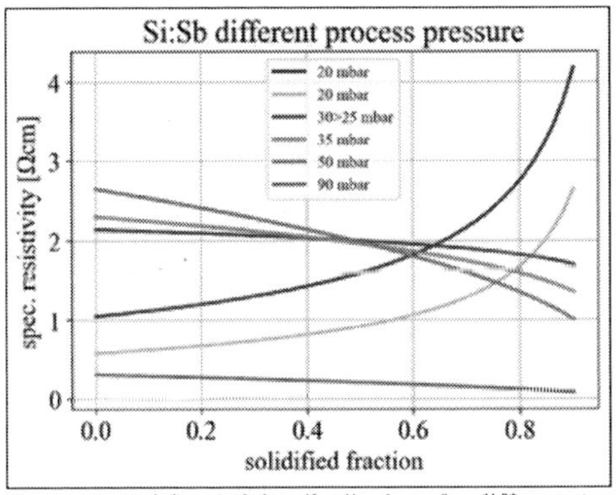

Figure 3: Axial resistivity distributions for different Ar-process pressures

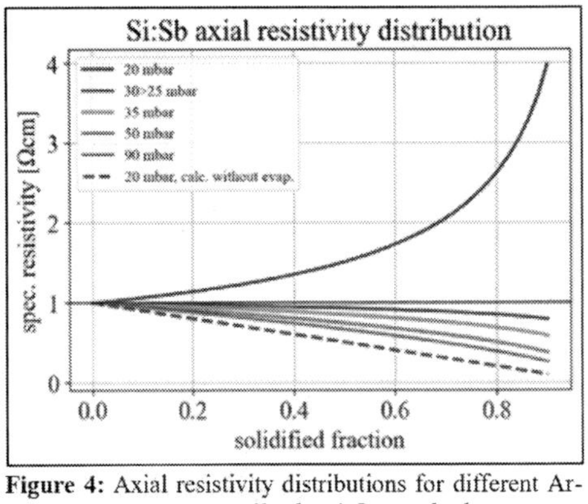

Figure 4: Axial resistivity distributions for different Ar-process pressures, normalized to 1 Ωcm at body start

Fig.4 shows that, under the applied growth parameters, merely an appropriate process gas control should be sufficient to achieve an axial homogeneous resistivity distribution in the Cz-crystal. The extreme sensitivity of the Ar-process pressure in the range between 20 mbar and 30 mbar is evident.

We therefore performed a crystal growth experiment according to Zulehner [2] with a continuously decreasing Ar-pressure from 60 mbar to 18 mbar to investigate the critical pressure range more precisely. Therefore, we previously modeled the limited process data from Fig.4 using a neural network with two hidden layers, as shown in Fig.5.

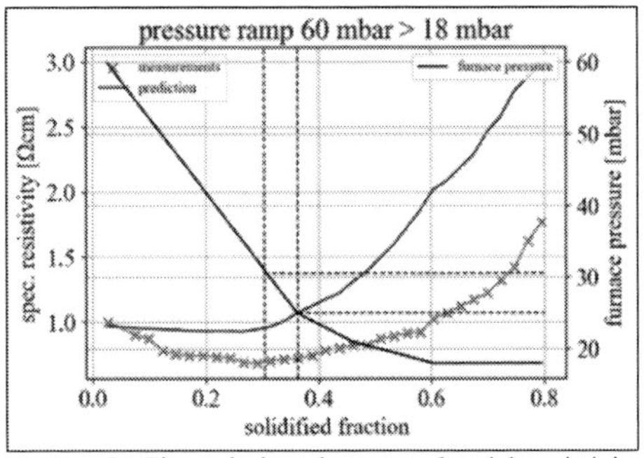

Figure 5: Theoretical and measured axial resistivity distribution of the Si:Sb crystal grown under a descending Ar-pressure of 60 mbar > 18 mbar

The calculated (–prediction) and measured (x) axial resistivity distributions are shown in Fig.5. Although there is a significant discrepancy between the calculated and measured data due to the limited amount of available data, it can be concluded that a control of the Sb evaporation rate under the present crystal growth conditions in the pressure range between 30 mbar and 25 mbar should be applicable to balance the Sb evaporation in the melt with the Sb-enrichment near the crystallization front. Below 25 mbar the Sb-loss by evaporation across the free melt surface outweighs the segregation effect of the Sb-enrichment at the crystallization front causing an increase of the specific resistivity.

2.3 Radial distribution of the specific resistivity and minority carrier lifetime in Sb-doped Si-crystals

All crystal growth experiments shown in Fig.3 and Fig.4 are characterized by means of spatially resolved measurements of the specific resistivity and minority carrier lifetime on the corresponding crystal wafers as sketched in Fig.1. The measurement tool was the MDPpro from Freiberg Instruments GmbH [3] operating with a resolution of 1 mm. The resistivity is measured via an eddy current sensor and the lifetime is determined by means of MDP (Microwave Detected Photoconductivity) technique using a 980 nm laser for excitation with a penetration depth of 500 µm and duration of excitation pulse of 1000 µs. The measurements were performed on the as-sawn surface of the slices. Fig.6 - Fig.9 show the results of the mappings of the two crystal growth experiments, which were grown under a constant process pressure of 20 mbar (ingot A) and a decreasing process pressure of 30 mbar to 25 mbar (ingot B).

A comparison of Fig.7 with Fig.9 shows a drastic optimization in the axial resistivity distribution. In contrast, the process pressure does not appear to have any noticeable influence on the radial resistivity distribution.

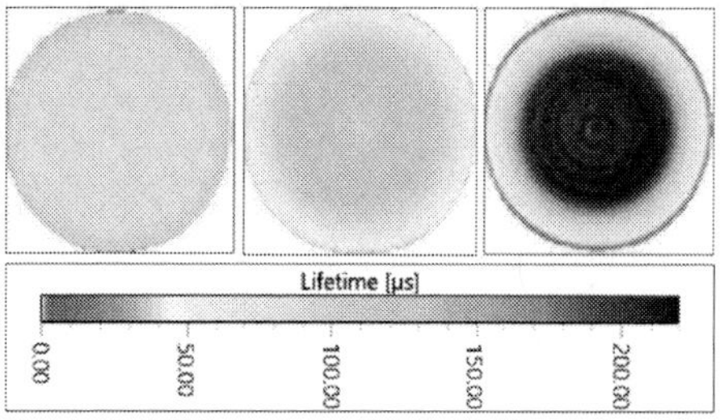

Figure 6: Lifetime maps of top-, middle-, tail-wafer of Ingot A, grown under a constant Ar-pressure of 20 mbar

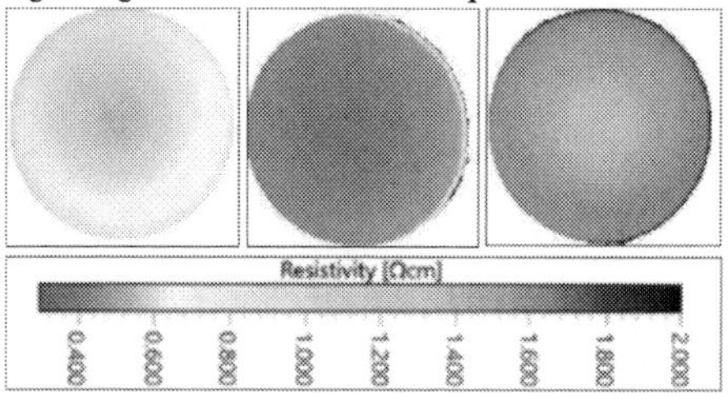

Figure 7: Resistivity maps of top-, middle-, tail-wafer of Ingot A, grown under a constant Ar-pressure of 20 mbar

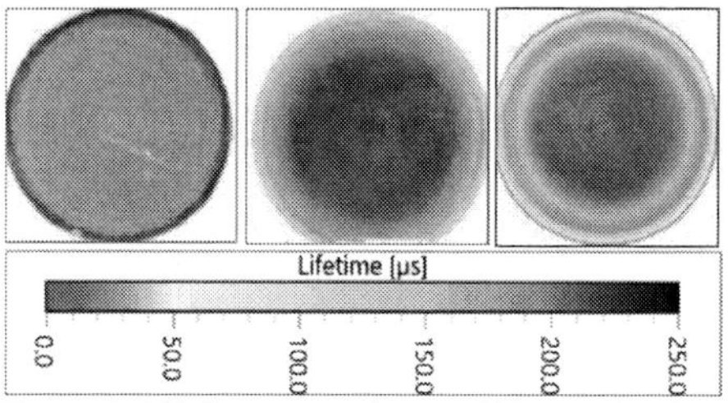

Figure 8: Lifetime maps of top-, middle-, tail-wafer of Ingot B, grown under a descending Ar-pressure of 30 mbar > 25 mbar

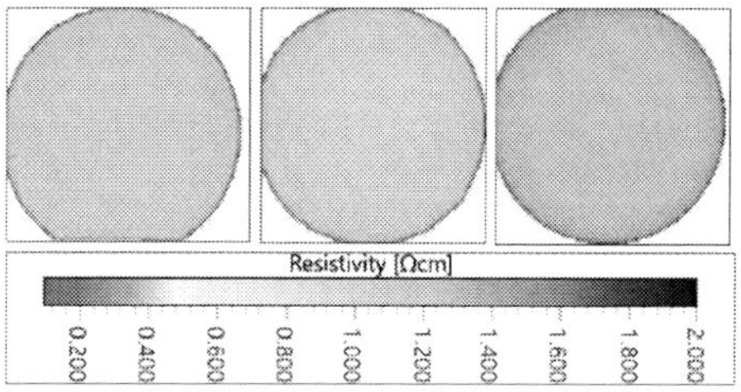

Figure 9: Resistivity maps of top-, middle-, tail-wafer of Ingot B, grown under a descending Ar-pressure of 30 mbar > 25 mbar

2.4 Influence of the growth parameters on the axial and radial Sb-distribution in the grown crystals

The dopant incorporation during the Cz batch process can described by the differential equation [4]:

$$\frac{dC_l}{dt} = \frac{C_l}{m_l}\frac{dm_x}{dt} - \frac{kC_l}{m_l}\frac{dm_x}{dt} - \frac{\gamma A_S}{m_l}C_l \quad (DGL)$$

with: C_l: dopant concentration in the melt, m_l: mass of the melt, m_x: mass of the crystal, k: distribution coefficient, γ: coefficient of evaporation rate, A_S: free melt surface

The following terms in (*DGL*) mean:

$$\frac{C_l}{m_l}\frac{dm_x}{dt} \quad (I)$$

Removal of melt (concentration of dopant) due to crystal growth

$$\frac{kC_l}{m_l}\frac{dm_x}{dt} \quad (II)$$

Removal of dopant due to crystal growth

$$\frac{gA_S}{m_l}C_l \quad (III)$$

Removal of dopant due to evaporation

Solving the *DGL* without considering the dopant reduction in the melt due to evaporation (*III*), applying the corresponding initial conditions, results in the well-known Scheil equation [5]:

$$C_l = C_0\left(1 - {m_x}/{m_0}\right)^{k-1} \quad (Scheil)$$

The two key parameters in the *DGL* that primarily influence the dopant incorporation during the Cz-batch process are the distribution coefficient k and the evaporation rate γ. The possibilities for influencing both parameters are described here:

2.4.1 Evaporation rate γ

The evaporation coefficient γ, also known as the evaporation rate, depends on a variety of factors, which are not all quantitatively accessible [6]. The evaporation rate depends, among other parameters, on the concentration of the evaporating element in the melt, the A/V ratio (A: free melt surface, V: melt volume), the process atmosphere (gas flow, gas pressure, gas type), the design of the hotzone, and the concentration of the elements or molecules which may be also involved in the evaporation process (e.g. oxygen).
Evaporation occurs in four sequential steps as sketched in Fig.10:

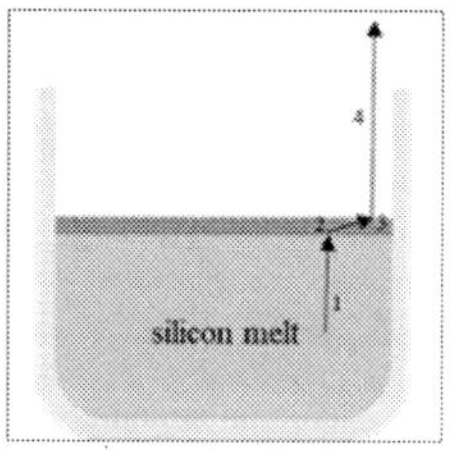

Figure 10: Sketched sequence of evaporation

1) Transport of the doping element or the oxygen compound of the doping element in the melt volume to a boundary layer, 2) Transport through the melt/gas boundary layer, 3) Physical evaporation process, 4) Removal through the gas phase. The time dependence of the evaporation process results from the four sub steps. The transport in the melt volume is dominated by the convection phenomena in the melt volume. The transport in the boundary layer is determined by convection and diffusion of the solute. The physical evaporation process

can be described by the Hertz-Knudsen equation. The transport through the gas phase is essentially influenced by the gas flow, chamber pressure, and nature of the gas (mass of the noble gas).

2.4.2 Determination of the evaporation rate using a 2-point measurement method [7]

For the determination of the evaporation rates at different process pressures, two crystal samples weighing approximately 40 g were taken from a stagnant melt as shown in Fig.11.

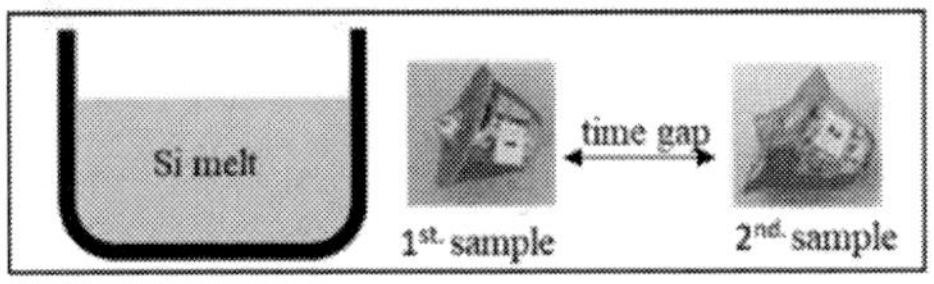

Figure 11: Principle of evaporation experiments

The chemical content of antimony in the samples was measured by means of ICP-MS (Inductively Coupled Plasma Mass Spectrometry). The main process conditions for the different evaporation experiments are given in the legend of Fig.12.

The evaporation of volatile elements can be described by a first-order kinetic reaction [6], i.e. by eq. *(IV)*

$$-\frac{dC}{C} = \gamma\frac{A}{V}dt \quad or \quad ln\left(\frac{C_t}{C_0}\right) = -\gamma\frac{A}{V}t \quad (IV)$$

where C_t, C_0, γ, A, V, t denote the actual doping element concentration [at/cm³], initial doping element concentration [at/cm³], evaporation rate constant [cm/s], free melt surface [cm²], melt volume [cm³], and process time [s], respectively.

The diagram shows the evaporation rates determined for antimony in a stagnant silicon melt without a growing crystal under the applied process conditions plotted versus the initial Sb concentration in the melt.

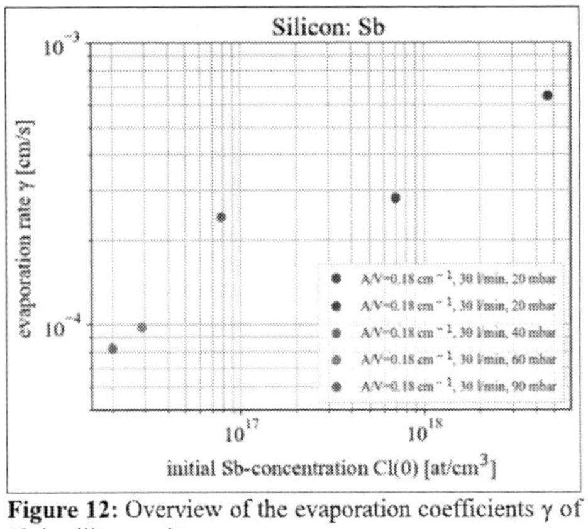

Figure 12: Overview of the evaporation coefficients γ of Sb in silicon melt

The graph illustrates that the evaporation rate γ of antimony in silicon melt is strongly influenced by the pressure of the Ar-process gas.

2.4.3 Segregation coefficient k:

Scheil's model with the segregation coefficient k as material parameter applies to a closed system without material exchange with the environment (evaporation).

$$\frac{C_S}{C_0} = k(1-g)^{k-1} \quad (Scheil)$$

with: C_S: dopant concentration in the crystal at the solidified fraction g, C_0: initial dopant concentration in the melt, k: segregation coefficient, g: solidified fraction

Since directional Cz-solidification is a dynamic process, the segregation coefficient k in Scheil's law is replaced by an effective segregation coefficient k_{eff}.

The dynamics of crystal growth (translation of the phase boundary) are described by the model of Burton, Prim, and Slichter introducing the concept of the effective segregation coefficient k_{eff} [8]:

$$k_{eff} = \frac{k_0}{k_0 + (1-k_0)exp\left(-\frac{f\delta}{D}\right)} \quad (BPS)$$

$$\delta = 1{,}61 D^{1/3} \nu^{1/6} \omega^{-1/2}$$

with: k_0: equilibrium distribution coefficient, f: freezing velocity, δ: extension of a boundary layer, D: diffusion constant of the dopant in the melt, ν: kinematic viscosity of the melt, angular velocity of the crystal

The parameter δ in the BPS-equation is often interpreted as a boundary layer thickness in front of the crystallization interface that is enriched with dopant. The extent of this layer is mainly determined by the convection conditions in the melt. Outside of this fictitious boundary layer, the melt is completely mixed. δ should be understood as a fit parameter that considers the influence of melt convection at the phase boundary. Fig.13 shows the influence of pulling speed and crystal rotation on the effective distribution coefficient of Antimony k_{Sb}.

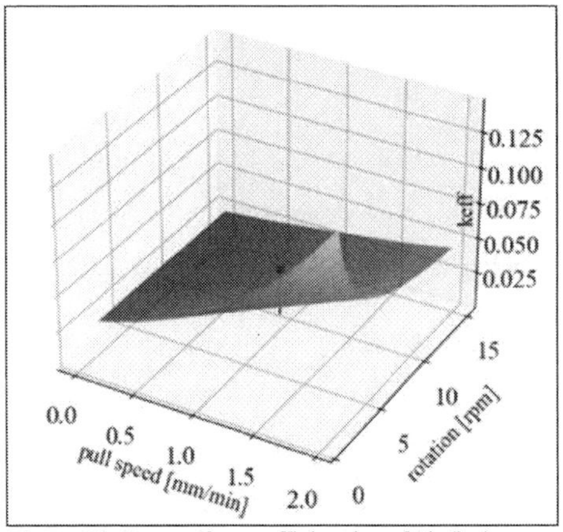

Figure 13: Segregation coefficient k_{eff} of Sb (k_{Sb}) versus average pull speed and crystal rotation. The marker (x) indicates the applied conditions.

Fig.14 illustrates the range of the BPS-parameter (v*δ/D) affecting the effective distribution coefficient of n-type dopants. The black symbols in Fig. 14 indicate the pulling parameters we apply in our 8-inch crystal growth experiments, while the red symbols represent their realistic upper limits.

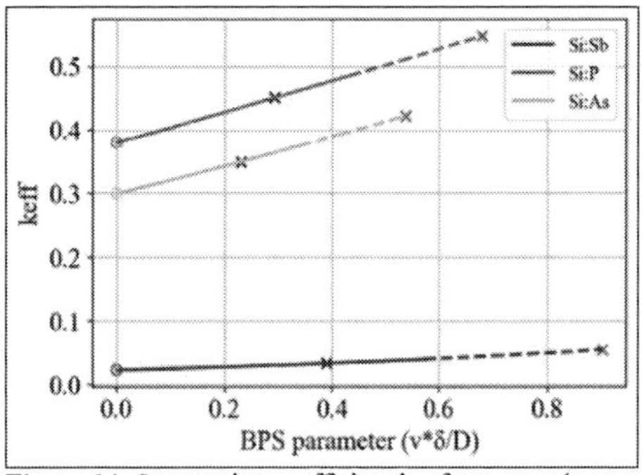

Figure 14: Segregation coefficient k_{eff} for n-type dopants versus BPS parameter. The symbols show the applied conditions (**x**) and a theoretical upper limit (x).

The figures clearly show that adjusting the pulling parameters in a realistic range only have a very limited influence on the distribution coefficient and thus on the dopant incorporation.

2.5 Discussion of the radial resistivity distribution

Whereas the axial Sb-distribution in the crystal can be adjusted by controlling the process pressure during the Cz-process in order to obtain a satisfactory axial resistivity profile, the radial distribution of the resistivity does not seem to be affected and should be discussed more precisely. For that, we prepared line scans from the resistivity maps of Ingot A grown under a constant Ar-pressure of 20 mbar and Ingot B grown under a descending Ar-pressure of 30 mbar > 25 mbar and compared the measured data with theoretical values obtained from an analytical model published by H. Lee [9]. The main root causes of a radially inhomogeneous dopant incorporation are the formation of a curved interphase during crystal growth and a variation in the dopant supply at the crystallization front due to convection phenomena in the melt. The deflection of the solidification front under the applied growth conditions was measured on a crystal slice taken from the middle part of a reference crystal by means of LPS (Lateral Photovoltage Scanning) measurements [10] as shown in Fig.15. The determined deflection of the interface shape is shown in Fig.16.

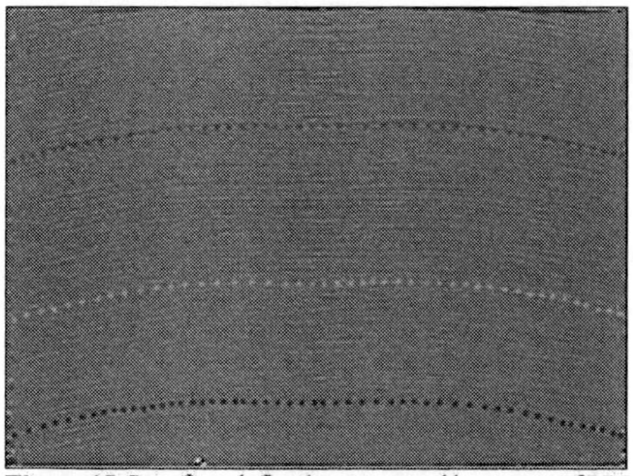

Figure 15: Interface deflection measured by means of LPS on the midlle part of the reference crystal (coloured lines)

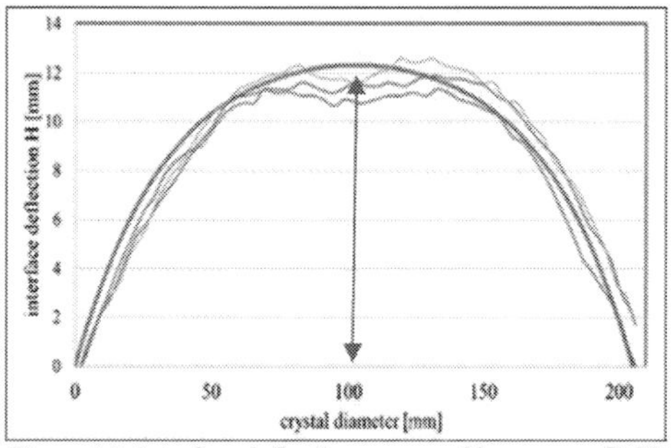

Figure 16: Interface deflection measured by means of LPS on the midlle part of the reference crystal (coloured lines) and the corresponding simulation results obtained by means of FEM simulation (blue line)

According to the model of H. Lee, the radial dopant distribution is approximated by a cubic function that reflects the rotational symmetry of the growth conditions in the Czochralski process. The different flow mechanisms resulting from forced convection (rotation conditions) and buoyancy convection are considered by a radial-dependent dopant concentration at the interface and different segregation coefficients at the center and the rim of the growing crystal. The deflection of the phase boundary is introduced in the model by its deviation from a flat interface in the crystal center (Fig.16). A detailed description of the model can be found in the corresponding literature [9]. In the following figures, the measured resistivity data are marked with blue symbols (x), the colored lines show the calculated curves according to the following theoretical assumptions:

Red curve: inhomogeneous diffusion boundary layer δ, concave interface

Green curve: inhomogeneous diffusion boundary layer δ, flat interface

Magenta curve: homogeneous diffusion boundary layer δ, concave interface

The term "diffusion boundary layer" is established in the BPS theory of the effective segregation coefficient as a descriptive interpretation of the convection conditions at the crystallization front.

10.4229/EUPVSEC2025/1BV.5.7

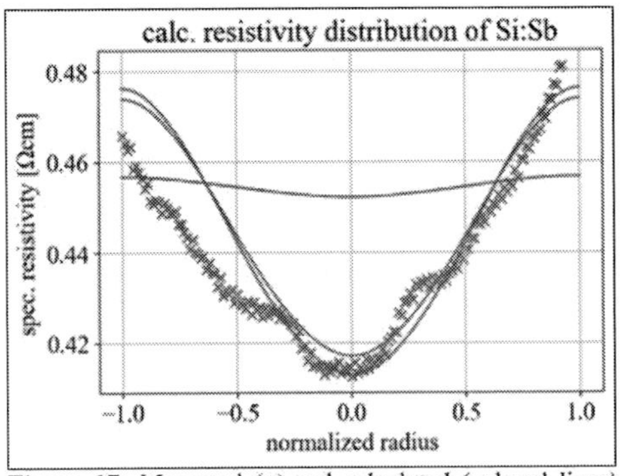

Figure 17: Measured (x) and calculated (colored lines) radial resistivity distribution at the top of ingot A, grown under a constant Ar-pressure of 20 mbar

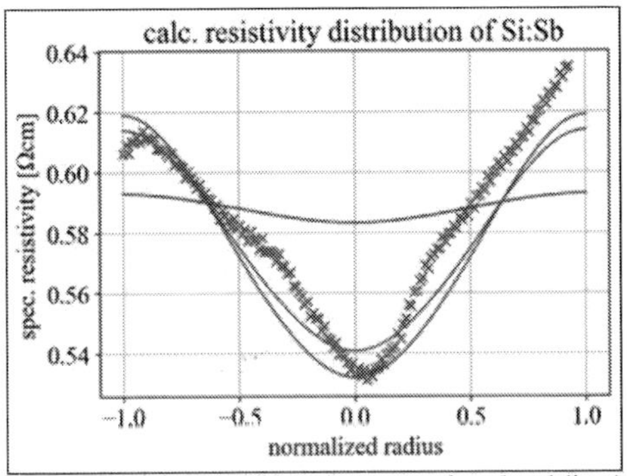

Figure 18: Measured (x) and calculated (colored lines) radial resistivity distribution in the middle of ingot A, grown under a constant Ar-pressure of 20 mbar

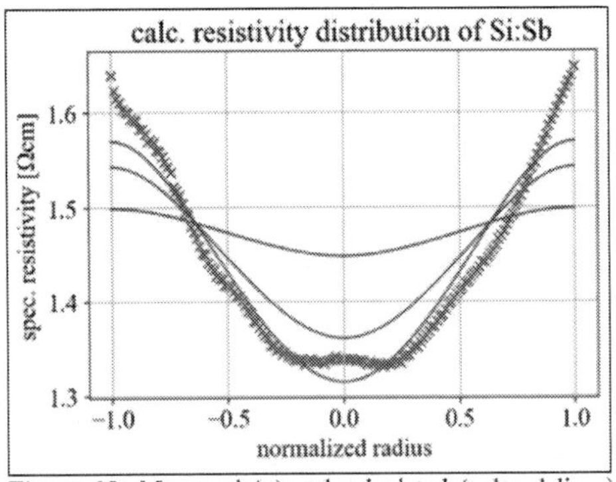

Figure 19: Measured (x) and calculated (colored lines) radial resistivity distribution at the tail of ingot A, grown under a constant Ar-pressure of 20 mbar

A comparison of the radial resistivity distributions of crystal A (Fig.17–Fig.19) with crystal B (Fig.20-Fig.22) shows that the process pressure under the applied crystal growth conditions has no noticeable influence on the resistivity distribution, which is equivalent to the dopant distribution. The factors influencing the radial dopant incorporation are outlined in Fig. 23 according to the model of H. Lee.

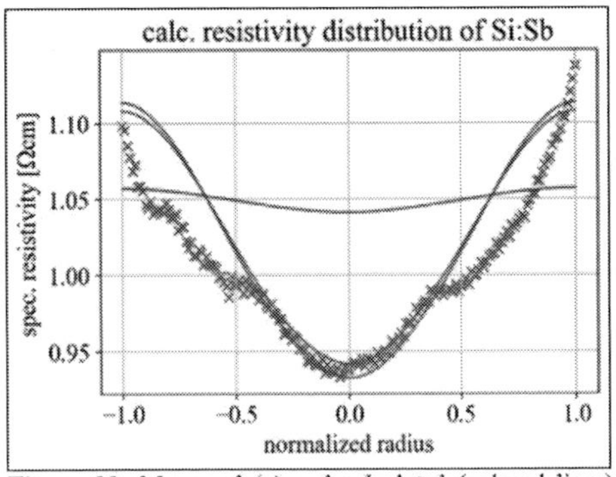

Figure 20: Measured (x) and calculated (colored lines) radial resistivity distribution at the top of ingot B, grown under a descending Ar-pressure of 30 mbar > 25 mbar

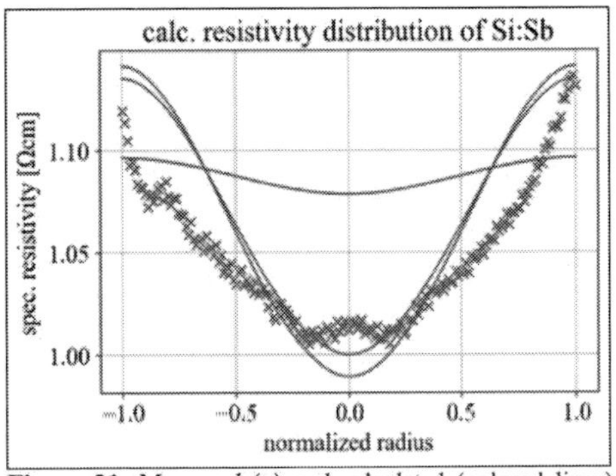

Figure 21: Measured (x) and calculated (colored lines) radial resistivity distribution in the middle of ingot B, grown under a descending Ar-pressure of 30 mbar > 25 mbar

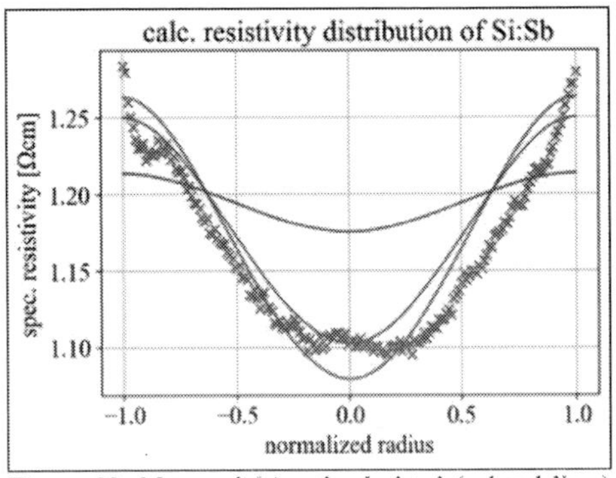

Figure 22: Measured (x) and calculated (colored lines) radial resistivity distribution at the tail of ingot B, grown under a descending Ar-pressure of 30 mbar > 25 mbar

Fig.23 shows the radial Sb-distributions derived from Fig.22 for the theoretical assumptions shown in the legend. The theoretical case of a flat phase boundary with a homogeneous dopant distribution on the melt side of the crystallization front is also plotted as dashed line (curve d). The comparison between the radial homogeneous distribution on a curved interface (curve c) with the conditions of radial inhomogeneous distributions (curve a and curve b) is intended to illustrate the dominant

10.4229/EUPVSEC2025/1BV.5.7

influence of the melt convection pattern on the dopant incorporation at the crystallization front. The influence of the deflection alone is rather low.

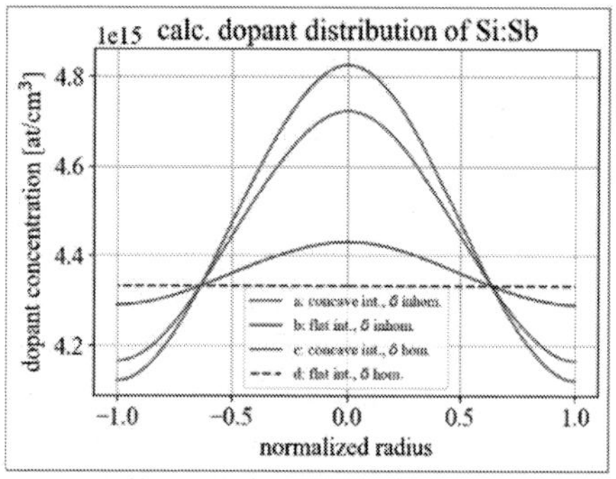

Figure 23: Theoretical Sb-distributions derived from the calculated resistivity distributions in Fig.22

2.6 Remarks on the nature of the volatile species in Sb-doped Cz-mono crystals

Doping elements may react with the oxygen dissolved in the silicon melt to form oxides. In the case of Ga-evaporation from the melt, it is evident that Ga_2O_3 is the dominant volatile species [7]. In the case of antimony evaporating from the melt, the facts are still unclear. Liu and Carlberg show by means of theoretical calculations that the formation of antimony oxide at the melt surface is rather negligible [11]. There are reports in the literature of reduced oxygen incorporation in Sb-doped Cz crystals. This effect is more pronounced in highly Sb-doped Si crystals compared to low Sb-doped Si crystals. The question of whether the oxygen loss is directly correlated with the evaporation process of antimony in the form of Sb_2O_3, or whether antimony evaporates as element and catalyzes the increased oxygen loss, is not clarified [12].

3 SUMMARY

- A precise control of the gas pressure during the Cz-process enables the possibility to grow Sb-doped Cz-mono crystals with an approximately constant axial distribution of the specific resistivity.
- In radial direction, the electronic properties are mainly influenced by an inhomogeneous dopant supply at the crystallization front due to a complex interaction of convection phenomena.

4 ACKNOWLEDGEMENTS

This work was supported by the German Federal Ministry for Economy Affairs and Climate Action under contract number 03EE1126B

5 REFERENCES

[1] M. Fischer, presentation at PV CellTech, Frankfurt am Main, March 11 2025
[2] Zulehner W, Huber D, Crystals, vol. 8, Berlin, Springer 1982 p.36
[3] www.freiberginstruments.com
[4] John P. DeLuca et al., Silicon Single Crystal doped with Gallium, Indium, or Aluminum, Patent Publication No. US 9,051,1659 B2 (2015)
[5] E. Scheil, Bemerkungen zur Schicht-kristallbildung, Z. Metallkunde **34**, (1942), 70-72
[6] Jafar Safarian, Merete Tangstad, Vacuum refining of molten silicon, Metallurgical and Materials Transactions B, Vol. 43B, 2012, 1427-1445
[7] F. Mosel, K. Hess, B. Klipp, M. Trempa, J. Friedrich, Investigation of process parameters on the distribution of the specific resistivity in Ga-doped Cz-crystals; Proceedings 40th European Photovoltaic Solar Energy Conf., Lisbon, (2023), 020024 001-007
[8] J.A. Burton, R.C. Prim, W.P. Slichter, The distribution of solute in crystals grown from the melt. Part I, Theoretical, J.Chem. Phys. **21** (1953), 1987-1991
[9] Hong H. Lee, A "freezing relation" for radial impurity distribution in Czochralski-grown crystakl, J. Cryst. Growth, **83,** (1987), 610-614
[10] F. Mosel, A.V. Denisov, K. Hess, B. Klipp, N. Sennova, C. Kranert, M. Trempa, C. Reimann, J. Friedrich, Influence of an active crystal cooling device on the shape of the phase boundary in mono ingots grown by the Czochralski technique; Proceedings 38th European Photovoltaic Solar Energy Conf., online, (2021), 339-346
[11] Z. Liu and T. Carlberg, On the mechanism of oxygen content reduction by antimony doping of Czochralski silicon melts, J. Electrochem. Soc., Vol.138, 1488-1492, (1991)
[12] K. Izunome et al., Evaluation of evaporated species from silicon melt surface during Sb-doped Czochralski silicon crystal growth, Jpn. J. Appl. Phys.,Vol. 34, (1995), pp L1635-L1637

10.4229/EUPVSEC2025/1BV.5.7

INVESTIGATION OF PROCESS PARAMETERS ON THE DISTRIBUTION OF THE MATERIAL PARAMETERS IN CZ-CRYSTALS DOPED WITH ANTIMONY

F. Mosel[1], N. Schüler[2]
[1] PVA Crystal Growing Sytems GmbH, Im Westpark 10-12, 35435 Wettenberg, Germany
[2] Freiberg Instruments GmbH, Delfter Straße 6, 09599 Freiberg, Germany
e-mail: frank.mosel@pvatepla.com
tel: +49 64168690-125, fax: +49 64168690-822

Introduction

The market share of Cz mono-Si for the mass production of solar cells has grown steadily in recent years. Casted Si has practically disappeared from the market. At the same time, a trend is emerging from p-type to n-type base material due to technology reasons.

Phosphorus (P), arsenic (As), and antimony (Sb) are doping elements for n-type crystals, but until now, P-doped substrate crystals are standard. Here, too, a substitution of phosphorus with antimony as a doping element is emerging, similar to p-type substrate crystals, where the doping element boron was replaced with gallium. The advantage of Sb-doped crystals is the possibility of growing crystals with an almost axial homogeneous distribution of the specific resistivity despite the unfavorable segregation coefficient of antimony (k_{Sb}=0.023) compared to phosphorus (k_P=0.38). The main advantage of Sb doping is the possibility of balancing the permanent enrichment of the melt with Sb due to the distribution coefficient with a controlled evaporation of Sb from the melt due to the evaporation coefficient, in order to get an axial homogenous resistivity distribution. However, this does not significantly affect the radial inhomogenous dopant incorporation.

Axial distribution of the specific resistivity in p-type Cz-ingots (measured on the as-grown surface)

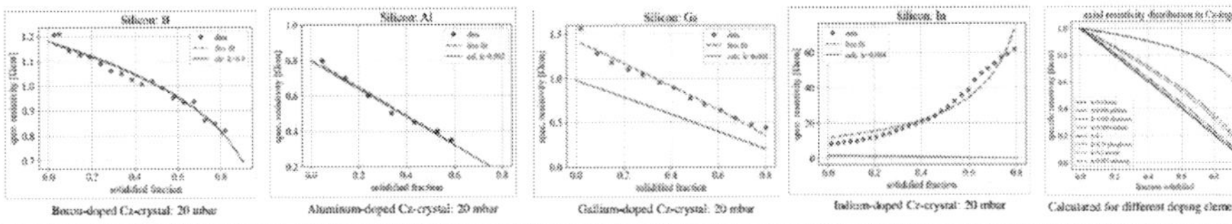

Boron-doped Cz-crystal: 20 mbar | Aluminum-doped Cz-crystal: 20 mbar | Gallium-doped Cz-crystal: 20 mbar | Indium-doped Cz-crystal: 20 mbar | Calculated for different doping elements

The axial resistivity distribution was measured by means of *Semilab RT-1000*

$$\rho = \rho_0(1-g)^{(1-k)} \quad \text{parameter free fit: } \rho_0, k$$

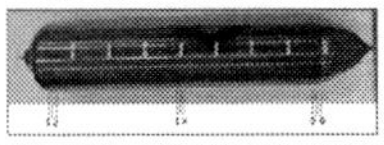

The radial resistivity distribution was measured via an eddy current sensor and the lifetime was determined by means of MDP (Microwave Detected Photoconductivity) technique using the *MDPpro* system from Freiberg Instruments GmbH operating with a resolution of 1 mm.

Axial distribution of the specific resistivity in n-type Cz-ingots (measured on the as-grown surface)

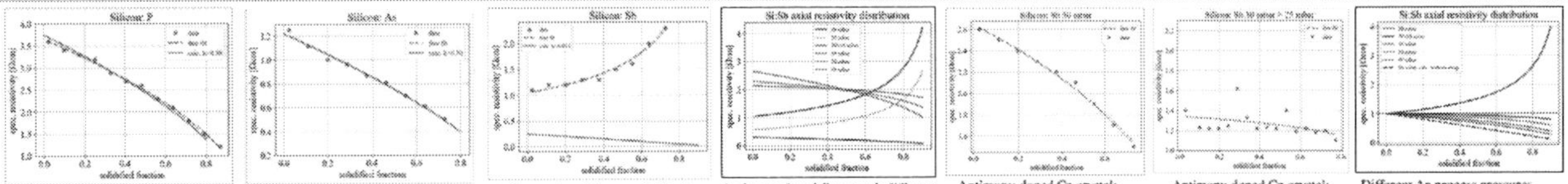

Phosphorus-doped Cz-crystal: 20 mbar | Arsenic-doped Cz-crystal: 20 mbar | Antimony-doped Cz-crystal: 20 mbar | Antimony-doped Cz-crystal: different Ar-process pressures | Antimony-doped Cz-crystal: 50 mbar process pressure | Antimony-doped Cz-crystal: descending process pressure | Different Ar-process pressures, normalized to 1 Ωcm at body start

Radial resistivity and lifetime distribution in Sb-doped Cz-ingots (measured on the as-sawn slices)

Si:Sb-ingot grown under a constant Ar-pressure of 20 mbar | Si:Sb-ingot grown under a constant Ar-pressure of 20 mbar

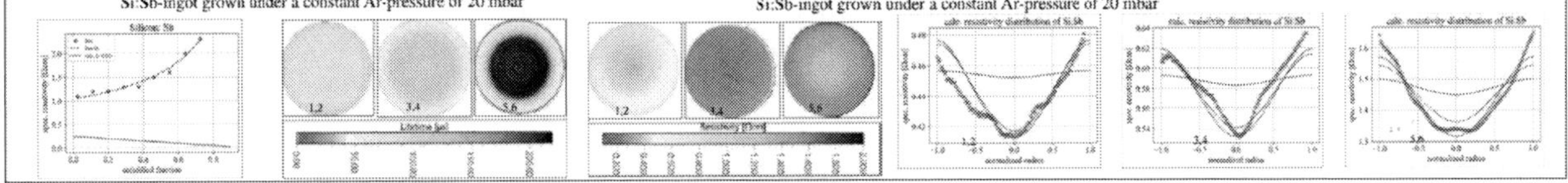

Si:Sb-ingot grown under a descending Ar-pressure of 30 mbar > 25 mbar | Si:Sb-ingot grown under a descending Ar-pressure of 30 mbar > 25 mbar

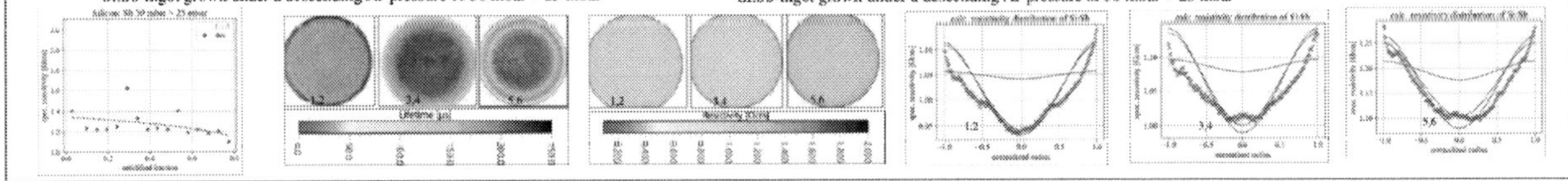

Influence of the growth parameters (k_{eff} and γ) on the axial and radial Sb-distribution in Cz-grown crystals

The dopant incorporation during the Cz batch process can described by the differential equation [4]:

$$\frac{dC_l}{dt} = \frac{C_l}{m_l}\frac{dm_x}{dt} - \frac{kC_l}{m_l}\frac{dm_x}{dt} - \frac{\gamma A_S}{m_l}C_l \quad (DGL)$$

with: C_l: dopant concentration in the melt, m_l: mass of the melt, m_x: mass of the crystal, k: distribution coefficient, γ: coefficient of evaporation rate, A_S: free melt surface

The following terms in (*DGL*) mean:

$$\frac{C_l}{m_l}\frac{dm_x}{dt} \quad (I)$$

Removal of melt (concentration of dopant)

due to crystal growth

$$\frac{kC_l}{m_l}\frac{dm_x}{dt} \quad (II)$$

Removal of dopant due to crystal growth

$$\frac{\gamma A_S}{m_l}C_l \quad (III)$$

Removal of dopant due to evaporation

Solving the *DGL* without considering the dopant reduction in the melt due to evaporation (*III*), results in the well-known Scheil equation [5]:

$$\frac{C_S}{C_0} = k(1-g)^{k-1} \quad (Scheil)$$

The two key parameters in the *DGL* that primarily influence dopant incorporation during the Cz batch process are the distribution coefficient k_{eff} and the evaporation rate γ.

Experimental investigations of the evaporation rate γ

Sketched sequence of evaporation [6]

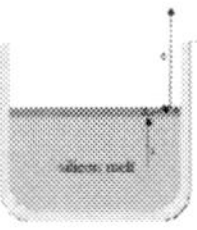

1. Transport of the volatile element in the melt volume to the melt boundary layer (convection)
2. Transport through the boundary layer to the melt/gas interface (convection and diffusion)
3. Physical evaporation process of the volatile element at the free melt surface (Hertz-Langmuir-Knudsen equation)
4. Mass transport of the volatile element by the process gas flow and gas pressure

The evaporation of volatile elements or compounds is represented by a reaction of first order.

$$-\frac{dC}{C} = \gamma\frac{A}{V}dt$$

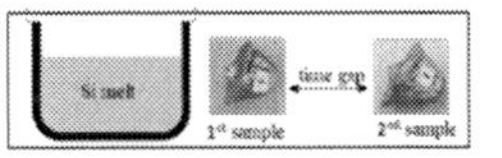

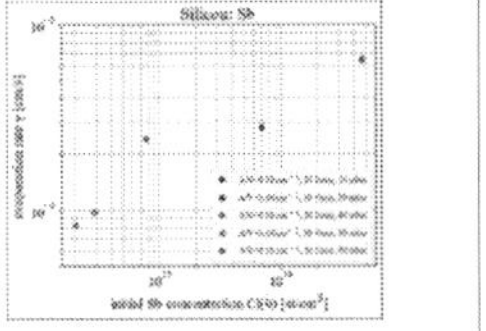

Estimation of the evaporation rate γ for different process conditions by means of 2-point calculation (2-sample estimation, t = time gap)

Original caption of Zulehner [2]:
Axial resistivity variations in antimony-doped Cz Si single-crystals. The initial doping concentration (≈0.018 Ωcm), melt volume and crystal diameter were the same for all curves. Due to the high vapour pressure of Sb, a great variety of axial resistivity profiles can be realized by applying different pressure and gas flow conditions. *Curves A and B*: Same pressure of 11 mbar but different gas flow characteristics. *Curve C*: 67 mbar in region C1, 11 mbar in region C2. *Curve D*: 75 mbar.

Original caption of Zulehner [2]

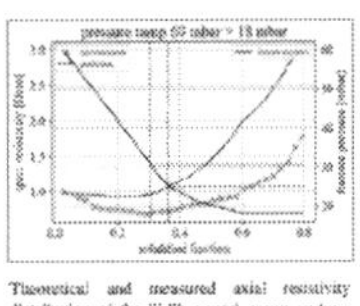

Theoretical and measured axial resistivity distribution of the Si:Sb crystal grown under a descending Ar-pressure of 60 mbar > 18 mbar

According to Zulehner [2] we performed a crystal growth experiment with a continuously decreasing Ar-pressure from 60 mbar to 18 mbar to investigate the critical pressure range more precisely. Therefore we previously modeled the limited process data using a neural network with two hidden layers, as shown. Although there is a significant discrepancy between the calculated (-) and measured (x) data due to the limited amount of available data, it can be concluded that a control of the Sb-evaporation rate under the present crystal growth conditions in the pressure range between 30 mbar and 25 mbar should be applicable to balance the Sb evaporation in the melt with the Sb-enrichment near the crystallization front. Below 25 mbar the Sb-loss by evaporation across the free melt surface outweighs the segregation effect of the Sb enrichment at the crystallization front causing an increase of the specific resistivity.

Theoretical considerations on the segregation coefficient k_{eff}

Model of Burton, Prim and Slichter (radial impurity distribution in Cz-grown crystals [8])

Scheil's model with the segregation coefficient k as material parameter applies to a closed system without material exchange with the environment (evaporation). The model of Burton, Prim, and Slichter describes the dynamics of crystal growth (translation of the phase boundary) introducing the effective segregation coefficient k_{eff} [8]. The parameter δ in the BPS-equation is often interpreted as a boundary layer thickness in front of the crystallization interface that is enriched with dopant, depending on the melt convection

$$k_{eff} = \frac{k_0}{k_0 + (1-k_0)\exp\left(-\frac{f\delta}{D}\right)} \qquad \delta = 1.61D^{1/3}\nu^{1/6}\omega^{-1/2}$$

with: k_0: equilibrium distribution coefficient, f: freezing velocity, δ: extension of a boundary layer, D: diffusion constant of the dopant in the melt, ν: kinematic viscosity of the melt, angular velocity of the crystal

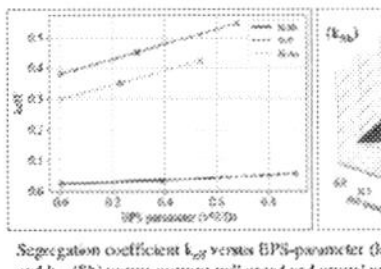

Segregation coefficient k_{eff} versus BPS-parameter (left) and k_{eff} (Sb) versus average pull speed and crystal rotation (right), the marker (x) indicates the applied conditions.

Model of Hong H. Lee (radial impurity distribution in Cz-grown crystals [9])

According to the model of H. Lee, the radial dopant distribution is approximated by a cubic function that reflects the rotational symmetry of the growth conditions during the Czochralski process. The different flow mechanisms resulting from forced convection (rotation conditions) and buoyancy convection are considered by a radial-dependent dopant concentration at the interface and different segregation coefficients at the center and the rim of the growing crystal. The deflection of the phase boundary is introduced in the model by its deviation from a flat interface in the crystal center.

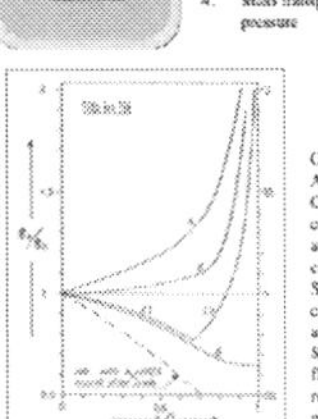

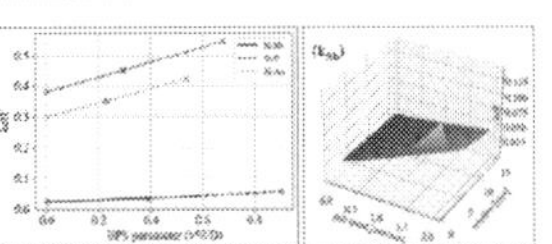

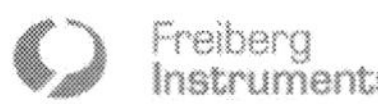

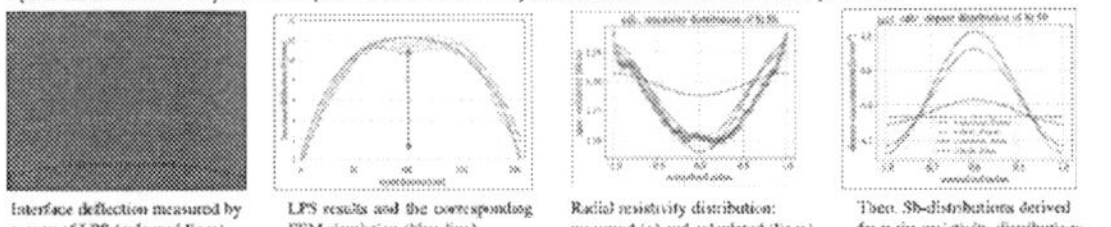

Interface deflection measured by means of LPS (coloured lines) | LPS results and the corresponding FEM simulation (blue line) | Radial resistivity distribution: measured (x) and calculated (lines) | Theo. Sb-distributions derived from the resistivity distributions

Results

references are given in the corresponding conference paper

- A precise control of the gas pressure during the Cz-process enables the possibility to grow Sb-doped Cz-mono crystals with an approximately constant axial resistivity distribution
- In radial direction, the electronic properties are mainly influenced by an inhomogeneous dopant supply at the crystallization front due to a complex interaction of convection phenomena.

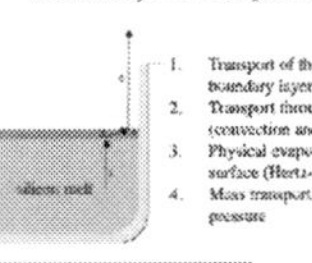

ELLIPSOMETRY CHARACTERIZATION AND MODELLING OF POROUS SILICON LAYERS: UTILIZING DIFFERENT ABSORPTION DEPTHS TO AID MODELLING

Per-Anders Hansen*, Junjie Zhu
Institute for Energy Technology, Norway
*per-anders.hansen@ife.no

Ellipsometry is a powerful and establish characterization tool for porous silicon (PS) and other thin film materials on silicon substrates. PS is often made through electrochemical etching in an HF-containing solution. Etch rates, pore dimensions, porosity level variations in the etch direction etc. depends on the electrical current and the chemistry of the solution among other. In many cases, this leads to interface layers towards the substrate-PS and air-PS interfaces, gradients and even optical anisotropy if the pore dimensions are large enough. In this work, we show that we can utilize the large wavelength-dependent variations in absorption depths to model the different parts of such samples independently, simplifying the modelling process and allows us to solve some aspects of the sample structure without being required to solve the whole structure which can be complex. Ellipsometry data and modelling of one such sample having both porosity gradients, interface layers and a thin and denser layer towards the surface is shown below. Such complexities for PS layers are well-known in literature, but can still be challenging to solve compared to a simple homogeneous film. We show that both the UV-blue and NIR ranges are necessary for a complete solution, but also that these ranges can be used to solve the top and bulk depths independently.

1 INTRODUCTION

Ellipsometry is well established for PS layers, which have been investigated by the PV community both as anti-reflective coatings [1, 2] and production of solar wafers through epitaxial growth [3, 4]. It is well-known in literature that varying electrical parameters and chemical components in the electrolyte solutions can result in porosity profiles that range from simple homogeneous layer to complex structures with interface structures and graded profiles [5, 6]. By utilizing the different probing depths of the shallowly penetrating UV-blue and deep penetrating NIR, the different sections of an overall complex sample structure can be reduced to more simpler components. This can aid modelling of samples with unknown structures, and understanding the different wavelengths ranges penetration depths could also strongly reduce the necessary measurement time. By minimizing the wavelength range and resolution in addition to the number and values of measurement angles, time-consuming measurements such as full-wafer mapping can be done much more efficient with the same or better modelling accuracy.

The aim of this work is to establish a modelling approach that utilizes the large variations in absorption depths in different wavelength ranges to probe different depths into complex sample structures independently. We exemplify our approach with a known and complex porosity profile that show porosity variations in both top, bulk and bottom depths [7, 8]. Without any knowledge of the samples optical structure, it can be challenging to model such samples as all aspects have to be represented well before a good fit can be achieved. In our approach, the different depths can be probed and modelled independently before combining them and establishing the complete sample structure.

2 EXPERIMENTAL

We use a Variable Angle Spectroscopic Ellipsometer (VASE) from J. A. Woollam for data collection and the CompleteEASE software for modelling. Our VASE is equipped with an x-y translation stage for wafer mapping and can be equipped with focusing probes to reduce the measurement spot-size. Measurements cover the 260 – 1700 nm range, and are generally obtained at 70-75 ° incident angle. Full-range and partial-range modelling uses the following parts of the data: Full-range (280 – 1650 nm); UV-blue range (280 – 500 nm); Vis-NIR range (700 – 1650 nm). The wafers and PS layers in this work was provided by NexWafe GmbH in the Horizon-EU project EMPOWER.

3 RESULTS AND DISCUSSIONS

3.1 Absorption depths at different wavelengths

The absorption depths (also called penetration depth) tells us how deep into a material light of a given wavelength can travel before being reduced to 1/e (~37 %) due to absorption. If the light entering the material is I_0, then the intensity I(x) at depth x is defined by Eq.1.

$$I(x) = I_0 e^{-\alpha x} \qquad \text{Eq.1}$$

The absorption depth δ is then defined as Eq. 2.

$$\delta = \alpha^{-1} \qquad \text{Eq.2}$$

Through ellipsometry modelling one obtains the materials wavelength-dependent refractive index an extinction coefficient, n(λ) and k(λ). k(λ) and α(λ) is related through Eq. 3, which allows calculations of δ directly from ellipsometry results.

$$\alpha(\lambda) = \frac{4\pi}{\lambda} k(\lambda) \qquad \text{Eq.3}$$

The absorption depth into silicon at different wavelengths is shown in Figure 1. Note the logarithmic y-scale. Silicon is a indirect bandgap material with the fundamental bandgap at around 1100 nm (1.12 eV). In addition, silicon has two higher direct bandgaps at approximately 265 and 295 nm (3.4 and 4.2 eV). The absorption coefficient near the two direct bandgaps is much higher than in the Vis-NIR range that only experience indirect bandgap absorption. This translates

10.4229/EUPVSEC2025/1BV.5.8

into an absorption depth that is 3-4 orders of magnitude smaller in the UV-blue range than in the Vis-NIR range.

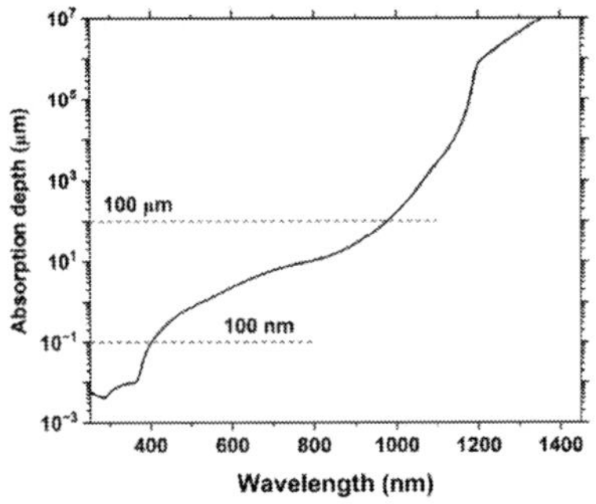

Figure 1: The absorption depth into silicon as a function of probing light wavelength. The very strong absorption in the UV-blue range leads to very shallow absorption depths. Note the logarithmic y-scale.

In ellipsometry, the effective "probing depth", i.e. the sample depth that can contribute significantly to the collected data, is significantly smaller than the absorption depth. This is due to two factors: The light hits the material at an angle, usually 40-80°, which increases the effective optical path. In addition, the light also has to reflect from an interface and travel back up to the surface. If the light intensity that exits the surface this way is insignificant compared to the primary specularly reflected beam, ellipsometry will effectively not "see" this depth. This is illustrated in Figure 2. The short-wavelength UV-blue light will only have significant contributions from structures in the top ~50 nm. On the other hand, the long-wavelength Vis-NIR can probe up to a hundred microns and even further for sub-bandgap light. This light will have contributions from the full sample structure.

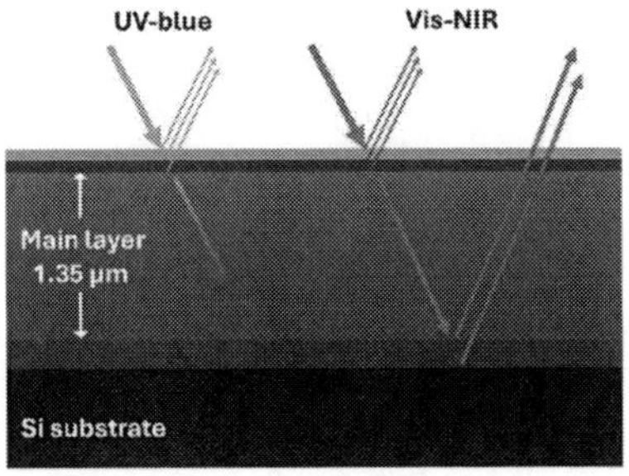

Figure 2: Illustration showing that strongly absorbed light effectively probes exclusively the top sample layers, while poorly absorbed (or not absorbed at all) light contains contributions from the full sample structure.

3.2 ELLIPSOMETRY MODELS

PS layers can be well-represented in ellipsometry through the effective media approximation (EMA) material model, combining crystalline silicon and air [9, 10]. In this model, the percentage of air, i.e. the porosity, is the only material variable. In ellipsometry investigations, material models can also include other elements such as small levels of amorphous silicon [11] or anisotropy [10, 12]. However, in this work, the simple Si/air EMA model was sufficient. In addition to the material model, the data modelling includes sample parameters (number of layers, thicknesses, gradients) and instrument parameters.

Conceptually, the sample consists of a single 1.35 μm porous silicon (PS) layer. However, modelling this as a simple single-layer structure yields a poor fit to the ellipsometry data. To improve the model, two commonly used additions are included: a surface roughness layer and an interface layer between the PS and the silicon substrate (labelled "Si/PS" in Figure 4). These additions significantly enhance the fit, though the result remains only moderately satisfactory. To further refine the model, two additional features are introduced: a gradient in the main PS layers porosity, and a thin low-porosity surface layer. These additions results in a model that fits the data well, as seen in Figure 3.

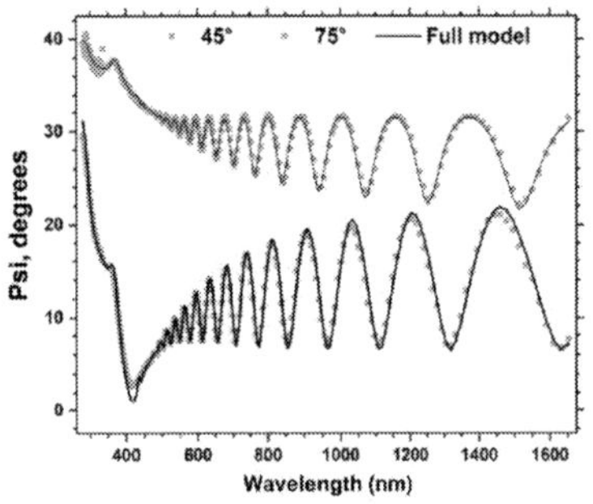

Figure 3: Ellipsometry Psi data and model fit, using the full model and the full data range.

The full ellipsometry model is shown in Figure 4, including the four layer features: Silicon substrate / PS layer interface (Si/PS), a graded-porosity main PS layer, a thin porosity dip layer and finally a surface roughness layers. All these features are known for such samples [7, 8].

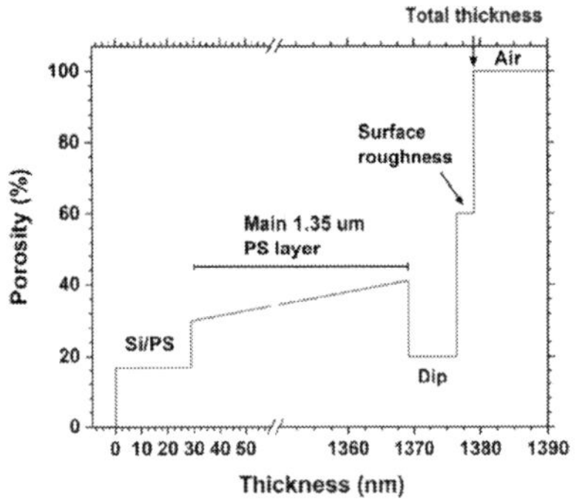

Figure 4: Full ellipsometry model for this PS sample. The model is similar to that reported by Selj et al [7, 8].

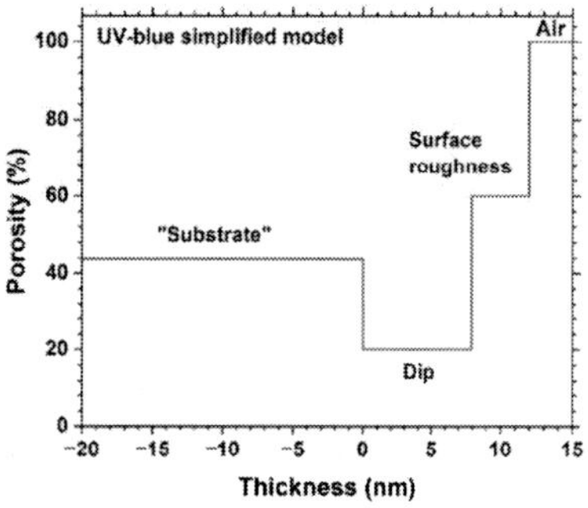

Figure 5: The UV-blue model, treating the top of the main PS layer as a "substrate", as this light cannot probe any deeper than this interface.

3.3 SOLVING THE MODEL STRUCTURE

If we are presented with ellipsometry data from new sample with a (partially) unknown sample structure, constructing the complete model structure can be challenging. In order to solve the full-range data, the complete sample structure must be used and all aspects of the samples must be well-represented before we can obtain a reasonable fit to sample variables such as layer thicknesses and porosities.

Figure 6 shows the mean square error (MSE) of the modelled thickness value for the thin top porosity dip layer as a function of model (full vs UV-blue) and the data range used in the fit. It is seen that the full model (Figure 4) with the full data range (black curve) gives equal thickness value and equal uniqueness ("V" shape) as the simplified UV-blue model (Figure 5) using only the shallow-penetrating (short-wavelength) part of the data (green curve). In the case of an unknown sample structure, the full model would struggle until all aspects of the sample is found and accurately represented. Before that is achieve, it can be challenging to discover these aspects from the ellipsometry data alone, in particular for complex samples. There are many combinations of parameters for the material and sample models that can lead to equally mediocre fits, so freely searching for new aspects to add to improve the fit can lead down a wrong path. On the other hand, there is generally only few-to-one sets of parameters that lead to good fits. The simplified UV-blue model significantly simplifies the number of sample aspects that must be represented to obtain a good fit. This reduces the chance of the model over-compensating with other parameters and the user over-compensating with additional sample aspects that might not be present. Through this approach, we can model the top part individually and accurately, and then add and lock this part into the full model that we are building.

We can also attempt to solve only this top part with the full model using only the shallow-penetration data (yellow curve), as the model for the deeper structures in theory should not affect the fit. However, it is seen that the accuracy is significantly lower (less clear V-shape) and the obtained value is also slightly thicker. The reason for this is that although the deeper-lying structures don't affect the data in this range directly, the porosity immediately below the dip layer (the "substrate" in Figure 5) is part of the deeper-level structure. The full model then still has to fit this parameters as part of the deeper structures which has no correlation with this data range. Effectively, this adds uncertainty and the possibility for unrealistic over-compensation from other parameters. Trying to model the top dip layer with the full model and only the deep-penetrating data results in a nearly flat MSE curve, i.e. this cannot resolve the top structure at all.

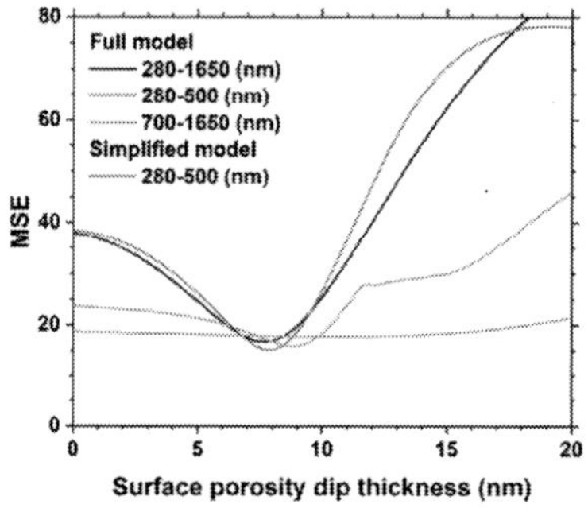

Figure 6: Thickness accuracy of the top porosity dip layer as a function of model and data wavelength range.

Similarly, it is possibly to do simplifications of the deeper structures as well. The Vis-NIR data is of course affected by the top sample structure, but the impact is much smaller. As seen in Figure 2, the contribution to the measured data from the deeper level has very different optical path differences than the contributions from the shallow top layers. The contributions from the deeper structures leads to the short-wavelength oscillations in Figure 3, while the top layer contribution will be very long-wavelength due to the few 10's nm total thickness. This will only contribute as an almost-constant modulation of these short-wavelength oscillations. The top layers can then be approximated as a single "effective" surface layer having the same impact in the Vis-NIR range. We exemplify this through the thickness values of the main 1.35 µm PS layer.

Figure 7 shows the MSE of the thickness of the main PS layer as a function of model and wavelength range. The full model with the full data range (black curve) gives an accurate value for this parameters. In fact, and contrary to the top layers, this parameter can be accurately modelled with the full model and narrowing the data to only the Vis-NIR range (yellow curve). However, this still means that the full model has to be provided. Also, modelling only the Vis-NIR range with the full model results in nearly fully correlated (i.e. inaccurate) values for the top layers (as exemplified in Figure 6). Although an accurate value for the main PS layer thickness can be obtained, it is not good practice to have models with strong correlations among other parameters. What we instead can do is to simplify the top layer structure as a single effective roughness layer. Using this simplified model with only the Vis-NIR range (blue curve, nearly fully overlapping with yellow) yields an accurate fit for the main PS layer thickness, while removing the parameter correlations of the full model.

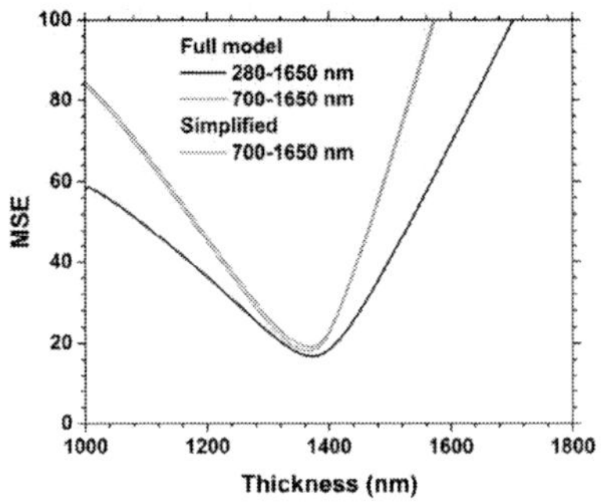

Figure 7: Thickness accuracy of the 1.35 µm main PS-layer as a function of model and data wavelength range.

Through these two simplifications and choice of data range, we can first investigate and establish the top layers and the deeper layers independently, and then afterwards combine them into a full sample model .

4 CONCLUSIONS

In this work, we have showed that by utilizing the large differences in absorption depth in silicon, it is possible to model shallow surface structures and deep bulk layers independently. The NIR range is insignificantly affected by the surface structures details, while the UV-blue range will not have contributions from any of the structures below some tens of nanometers. By approaching these two ranges independently, it is much easier to solve a complex sample structure with multiple interface and grading aspects. This approach is not limited to porous silicon, but rather general for samples that has large differences in absorption depths for different wavelength ranges.

5 ACKNOWLEDGEMENTS

This project has received funding from the European Union's Horizon Europe research and innovation program under grant agreement No 101172767.

6 REFERENCES

[1] Selj, J.H., et al., *Optimization of multilayer porous silicon antireflection coatings for silicon solar cells.* Journal of Applied Physics, 2010. **107**(7).

[2] Ge, D., et al., *Optimization of porous silicon structure as antireflective material.* The European Physical Journal D, 2022. **76**(2): p. 27.

[3] Karim, M., et al., *Tuning of strain and surface roughness of porous silicon layers for higher-quality seeds for epitaxial growth.* Nanoscale Research Letters, 2014. **9**(1): p. 348.

[4] Rittmann, C., et al., *Epitaxially Grown p-type Silicon Wafers Ready for Cell Efficiencies Exceeding 25%.* Solar RRL, 2023. **7**(8): p. 2200698.

[5] Stefan Reber, K.S., US10975490, *Apparatus and method for etching one side of a semiconductor substrate.* 2016

[6] Pettersson, L.A.A., L. Hultman, and H. Arwin, *Porosity depth profiling of thin porous silicon layers by use of variable-angle spectroscopic ellipsometry: a porosity graded-layer model.* Applied Optics, 1998. **37**(19): p. 4130-4136.

[7] Selj, J., et al., *Ellipsometric study of the influence of chemical etching on thin porous silicon structures.* Thin Solid Films, 2011. **519**(9): p. 2998-3001.

[8] Selj, J.H., et al., *Thin Porous Silicon Films Displaying a Near-Surface Dip in Porosity.* ECS Transactions, 2011. **33**(16): p. 181.

[9] Rossow, U., et al., *Influence of the formation conditions on the microstructure of porous silicon layers studied by spectroscopic ellipsometry.* Thin Solid Films, 1995. **255**(1): p. 5-8.

[10] Golovan', L.A., P.K. Kashkarov, and V.Y. Timoshenko, *Form birefringence in porous semiconductors and dielectrics: A review.* Crystallography Reports, 2007. **52**(4): p. 672-685.

[11] Strashnikova, M.I., et al., *Optical properties of porous silicon.* Journal of Experimental and Theoretical Physics, 2001. **93**(2): p. 363-371.

[12] Kovalev, D., et al., *Strong in-plane birefringence of spatially nanostructured silicon.* Applied Physics Letters, 2001. **78**(7): p. 916-918.

IFE

Ellipsometry characterization and modelling of porous silicon layers:
Utilizing different absorption depths to aid modelling

Per-Anders Hansen*, Junjie Zhu
Institute for Energy Technology
Corresponding author: per-anders.hansen@ife.no

INTRODUCTION

Ellipsometry is an excellent tool for porous silicon **(PS)** layers in photovoltaics, explored for anti-reflective coatings and epitaxial wafer growth. By tuning electrolyte conditions, porosities range from uniform to complex structures. This makes ellipsometry modelling challenging. By combining the difference in probing depths of UV-blue and Vis-NIR light, we decompose such structures into simpler components, aiding modelling and interpretation. Samples for this work was provided by NexWafe GmbH in the Horizon-EU project EMPOWER.

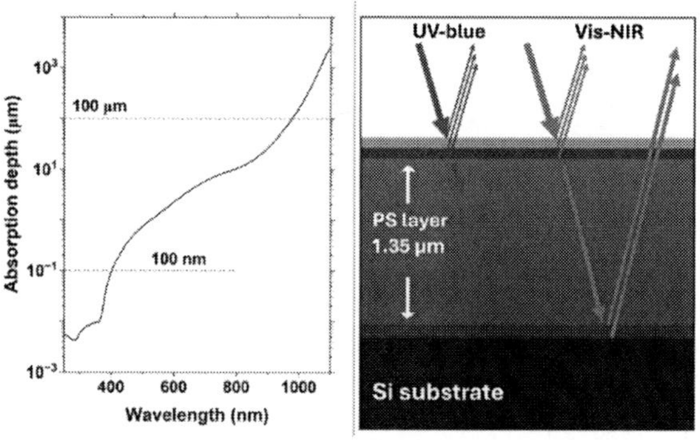

Left: Absorption depth in silicon as a function of wavelength.
Right: An illustration of the different probe depths in ellipsometry.

Ellipsometry model

We demonstrate our approach using a sample with a known porosity profile, featuring a substrate/PS-layer interface, porosity gradient, surface roughness, and a distinct near-surface porosity dip. This structure is documented in literature and by our group [1].

Without prior knowledge of the optical structure, building a complete ellipsometry model is challenging, as all features must be accurately represented for a good fit. Our method uses differing probing depths of UV-blue and Vis-NIR light to model surface layers independently before constructing the full sample structure.

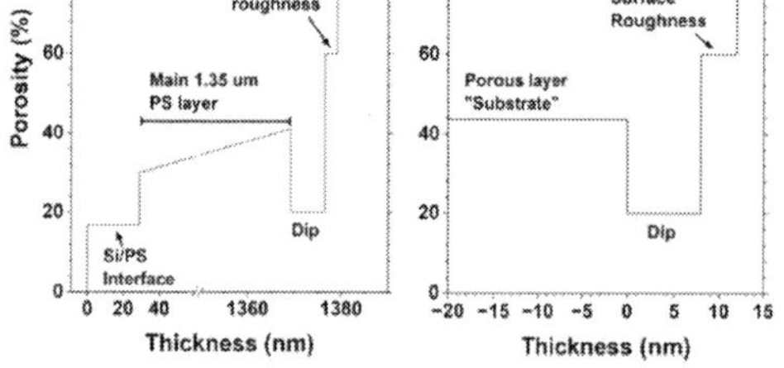

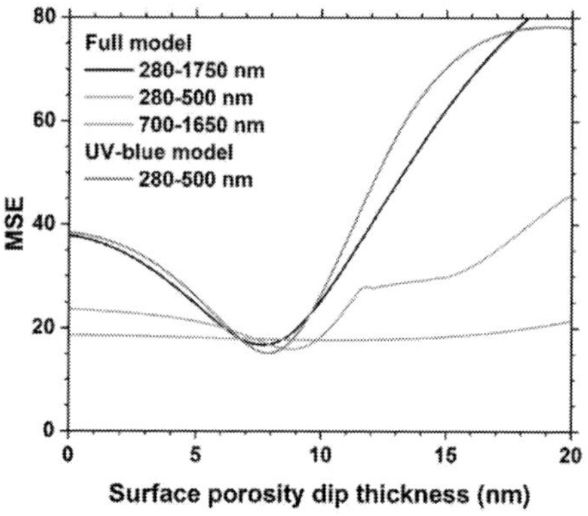

Mean square error (MSE) of the modelled near-surface porosity dip as a function of model complexity and data wavelength range.

Simplifying the modelling

A *parameter uniqueness plot* shows how certain a parameter value is in the model. A sharp V-shape indicates high certainty; a flat curve means other values give equally good fits.

We show that our simplified model **(green)**, using only UV-blue data, achieves similar parameter uniqueness for the near-surface porosity dip as the full-complexity model using the full UV-Vis-NIR range **(black)**.

In contrast, the full-complexity model using only shallow UV-blue data **(yellow)** reduces modelling certainty, over-compensating with many other parameters. Using only deep Vis-NIR data, this model fails to fit the top layer entirely **(blue)**.

A similar simplification is possible for deeper layers. Since Vis-NIR data is nearly unaffected by the top 50 nm, deeper layers can be modelled independently. In this case (not shown), the top multi-layer structure can be simplified to a single "effective surface roughness" layer.

Conclusions

In this work, we present an approach for modelling ellipsometry data of complex layers. By exploiting the large differences in penetration depth across wavelength ranges, surface and bulk structures can be resolved independently. This enables solving parts of the structure sequentially, before assembling the complete model from the simpler components.

REFERENCES

[1] Selj, J.H., *et al.*, Thin Porous Silicon Films Displaying a Near-Surface Dip in Porosity. **ECS Transactions, 2011**. 33(16), p. 181

EMPOWER

This project has received funding from the European Union's Horizon Europe research and innovation program under grant agreement No 101172767 and the Swiss State Secretariat for Education, Research and Innovation (SERI).

Schweizerische Eidgenossenschaft
Confédération suisse
Confederazione Svizzera
Confederaziun svizra
Swiss Confederation

Federal Department of Economic Affairs, Education and Research EAER
State Secretariat for Education, Research and Innovation SERI

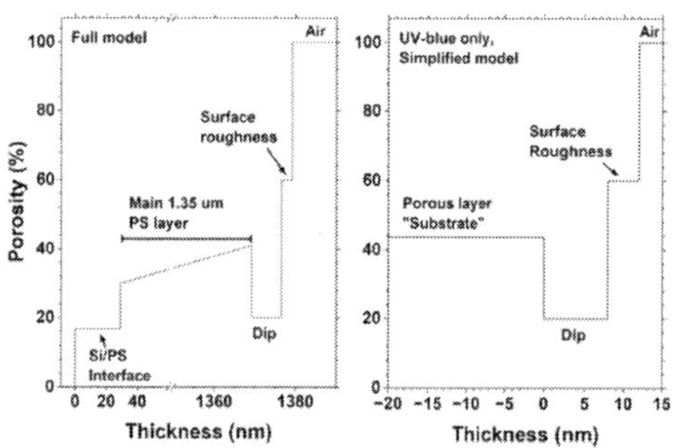

SUSTAINABLE, HIGH-THROUGHPUT, INDUSTRY-READY, NEXT-GENERATION TECHNOLOGY FOR EUROPEAN MANUFACTURING LEADERSHIP IN PHOTOVOLTAICS (SHINE PV)

Nicola Frasson[1], Marco Galiazzo[1], Sven Kluska[2], Vincent Barth[3], Jonathan Govaerts[4], Frank Lenzmann[5], Giovanni Paolo Borzi[6], Betina Debastiani Benato[7] and Victor Acinas[8]

[1]Applied Materials Italia srl,
[2]Fraunhofer ISE - Gesellschaft zur Forderung der Angewandten Forschung EV
[3]CEA-INES- Commissariat a l Energie Atomique et aux Energies Alternatives
[4]IMEC - Interuniversitair Micro-Electronica Centrum
[5]TNO - Nederlandse Organisatie voor toegepast-natuurwetenschappelijk onderzoek
[6]Enginsoft SpA
[7]AMIRES, the Business Innovation Management Institute z.ú.
[8]Applied Materials Ireland Ltd.

ABSTRACT: The SHINE PV project, funded by the European Commission [1], aims to revolutionize the photovoltaic manufacturing landscape in Europe by developing alternative technological routes to mainstream production. This initiative, which started in January 2025 and will last four years, focuses on enhancing the competitiveness of European manufacturers by reducing production costs and simultaneously increasing efficiency.
To drive technological innovation in the photovoltaic (PV) industry, it is essential to explore alternative technological routes for Silicon Heterojunction (SHJ) and Tunnel Oxide Passivated Contact (TOPCon) solar cells. SHINE PV focuses on key steps in back-end manufacturing, such as metallization, post-processing, and interconnection. By introducing high-volume manufacturing (HVM) processes like parallel dispensing and plating, we can replace traditional screen-printing methods. For post processing, the project will develop both edge-repassivation and light soaking processes and equipment, with the aim of recovering or enhancing cell efficiency after laser separation. For the module making step both TWILL interconnection and shingling will be developed, to increase the resilience of the modules in reliability testing and decrease costs. These advancements will not only enhance the efficiency of solar cells and modules but also streamline the manufacturing process, making it more sustainable and economically viable.
In terms of efficiency and cost reduction, the goal is to increase solar cell efficiency by 0.5% absolute compared to the reference process. This improvement, coupled with a 4-10% reduction in the cost of ownership (CoO), can be achieved through reduced material costs and increased equipment productivity. Establishing a robust European PV innovation and production base is crucial for sustainability and competitiveness [2] [3] [4]. Demonstrating complete back-end PV manufacturing lines will reinforce the sustainability of the European PV value chain, enhancing the resilience and diversity of the domestic energy sector industrial base.

1 INTRODUCTION

SHINE PV project will address three manufacturing steps of solar cell production, applied both to TOPCon and SHJ precursors (Figure 1). For each step two different technologies will be evaluated, the process variables will be identified with design of experiments and a dedicated production equipment (TRL7) will be produced.

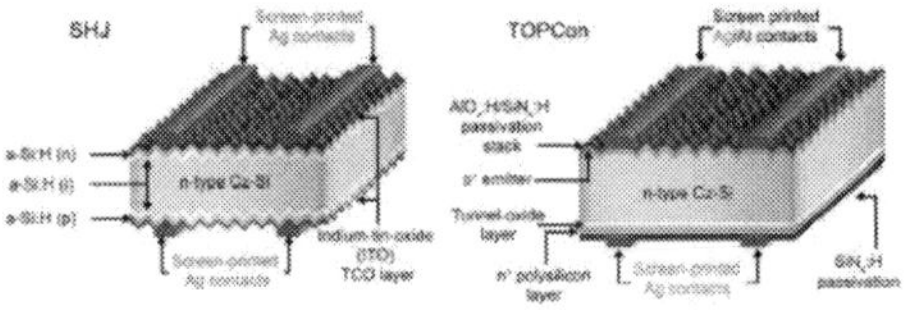

Figure 1 Representation of SHJ (left) and TOPCon (right) cell structures [5].

Parallel dispensing and plating will be evaluated as alternatives to traditional screen printing. These approaches will also enable the partial or complete replacement of silver with copper/silver coated copper materials, which are more cost-effective and abundant.
Post-processing techniques play a crucial role in enhancing the performance and long-term stability of solar cells. The application of Light Soaking (LS) processes in HVM helps to increase the performance of solar cells. Additionally, recovering cutting-induced losses through Edge Re-Passivation (ERP) is essential for maintaining the efficiency of the cells. These processes can restore the electrical properties and overall performance of solar cells after laser cutting or with intrinsic defects which can cause a loss in efficiency.
Innovations in interconnection methods, such as Twill and Shingling processes, are pivotal in optimizing the metallization and post-processing steps. These methods improve the electrical properties, aesthetics, reliability, and compatibility of solar cells with premium module designs. Twill interconnection involves weaving conductive materials in a specific pattern to enhance electrical connectivity and reduce resistance. On the other hand, shingling involves overlapping and gluing solar cells to create a seamless and aesthetically pleasing surface, which also improves the module efficiency by reducing the gaps between cells. By integrating these innovative interconnection techniques, manufacturers can produce solar modules that not only perform better but also meet the aesthetic and reliability demands of the market. More details on the different technologies are discussed later in the paper.

2 PARTNERS

The key metrics of the project are presented in Figure 2 in a matrix structure, where the three key aspects of the manufacturing process are investigated, with several KPIs respectively for efficiency gain, CoO and overall sustainability and exploitation.

10.4229/EUPVSEC2025/1BV.5.24

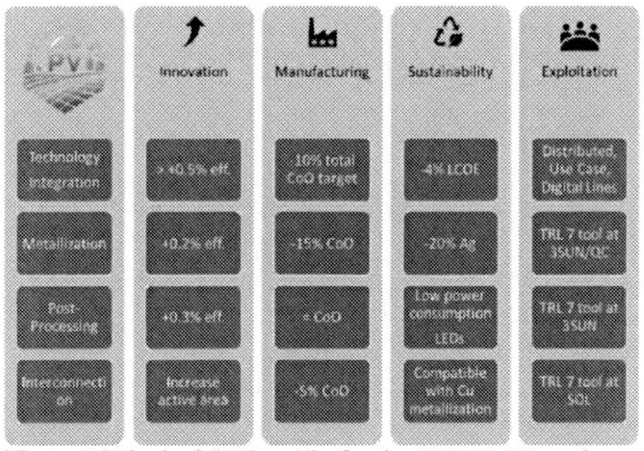

Figure 2 Principal KPI matrix for the SHINE PV project.

Overall project goals are reported in the top row in blue. Regarding the demonstration of the integrated process steps, there will be multiple sites where the equipment modules or the processes will be tested in a manufacturing plant or a research center (Figure 3).

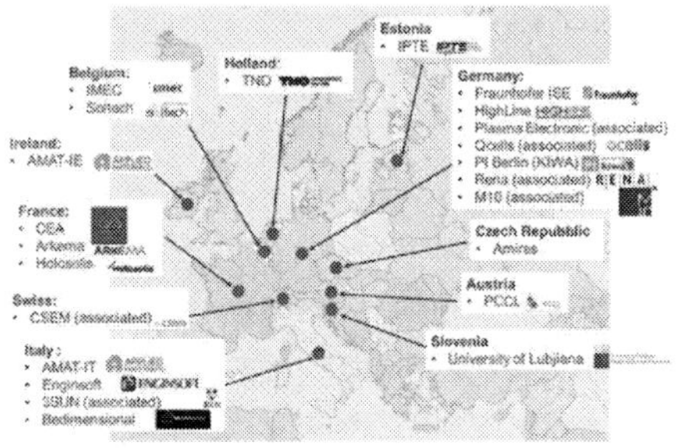

Figure 3 Partners distribution in Europe.

Finally, the process results will be combined by specific experiments and by digital tools that will simulate the production conditions for a full SHINE PV line (Figure 4).

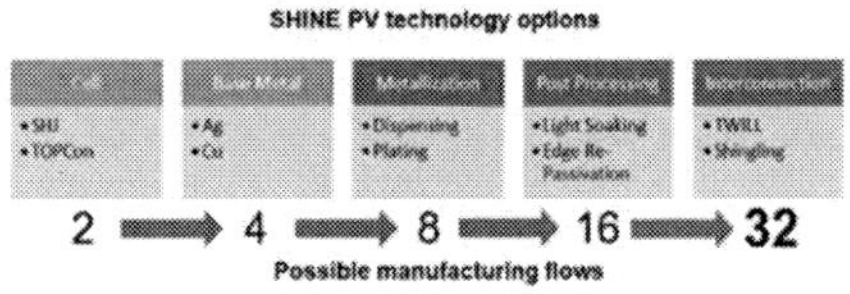

Figure 4 Possible manufacturing sequences generated withing the SHINE PV project.

3 TECHNOLOGICAL INNOVATION

Partners will lead and work on different work-packages (WPs) according to their experience in the different fields (Figure 5) and deliver results to the consortium.

Figure 5 WPs structure and WP leaders.

WP1 focuses on the integration and optimization of dispensing [6] [7] [8] and plating processes [9] [10] for solar cells metallization. Also, a preliminary simulation phase is necessary to establish the best metallization grid pattern over the two cell surfaces, front and back. Dispensing and plating can be further coupled with laser sintering processes to accelerate the curing process and optimize the throughput but also integrate materials like copper which are entering the market and need ad-hoc process conditions. With this purpose, paste developments are also ongoing to find more suitable silver and non-silver pastes that can be compatible with these new metallization technologies, especially on the dispensing side. WP2 aims at developing post-processing technologies that can restore or enhance the cell properties like edge repassivation [11] [12] and light-soaking [13], targeting small defects in the cell that are no longer negligible when pushing the energy efficiency to the physical limit. Part of the work will also include the identification of all potential process-related limitations and provide clear feedback to all equipment providers for hardware or process specific adaptation. WP3 instead focuses on the development of novel interconnection technologies like TWILL [14] [15] and shingling [16] [17] to provide reliable, design flexible and efficient solar modules. Also, the modelling of thermo-mechanical stresses and failure modes for these modules is studied. Finally, the development of an easy-release encapsulant to be used in module manufacturing is studied to permit a more facilitated end-of-life disassembly of module components. In the WP4 the design, development, assembly and validation of different tools is targeted including dispensing, plating, light-soaking, edge-repassivation, shingling and semi-automated foil-making and pick&place for TWILL tools. WP5 aims at creating tools that can simulate and then optimize individual process steps according to Industry 4.0 approaches and technologies and so create a fully digital infrastructure to assess and evaluate the efficiency, compatibility and overall performance of SHINE PV equipment. Furthermore, these tools can be also used to perform reliability and outdoor testing for PV modules produced using SHINE PV processes and equipment, collect data and share it within the consortium and the public. Finally, WP6 and WP7 regard the communication, dissemination, management and coordination of the whole project including the analysis and evaluation of environmental and social impacts of advanced PV manufacturing solutions, new business models and events participation.

4 PRELIMINARY RESULTS

- WP1 (Metallization)

Grid model and simulations studies are initially proposed by University of Ljubljana (UL) to describe cell properties for both SHJ and TOPCon substrates by developing and validating one or more models via Spice, PVMOS, Griddler, COMSOL, Sentaurus T-CAD or a combination thereof. First phase outcomes provided a 7D model that considers the number of shingles, number of fingers on front/back side and the fingers height/width on the two sides in the description of the solar cell. Main issues are related to the description of the cost function (Figure 6) and further discussions are ongoing between partners including Applied Materials (AMAT), CEA-INES and Fraunhofer-ISE (Fh-ISE).

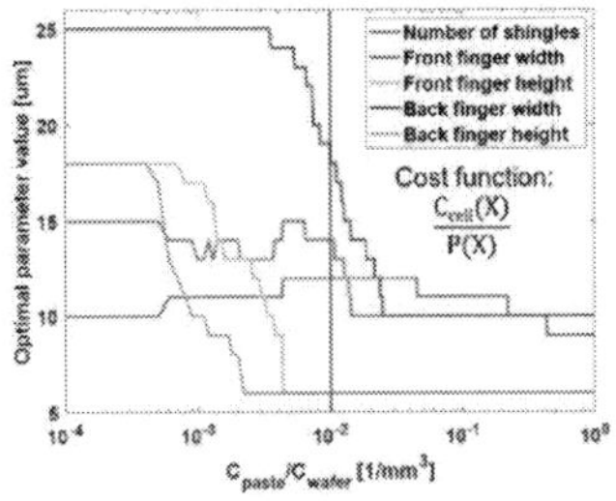

Figure 6 Cost function description.

However, the simulations already reached a good level of accuracy for a given set of parameters (Figure 7).

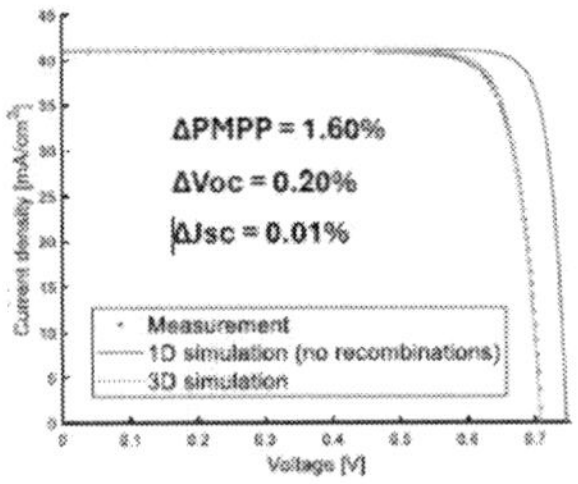

Figure 7 Comparison of simulated and measured IV curves of a TOPCon solar cell.

On the equipment side, the parallel dispensing kit has also been developed by HighLine (HL) and FH-ISE and the integration on a HVM tool (Applied Materials Tempo Presto) is ongoing with main issues solved like head leaks and hardware/software integration of the new printing head (Figure 8). The most crucial point in technology validation is related to the paste sourcing and/or development to match the required properties from a high-performance dispenser.

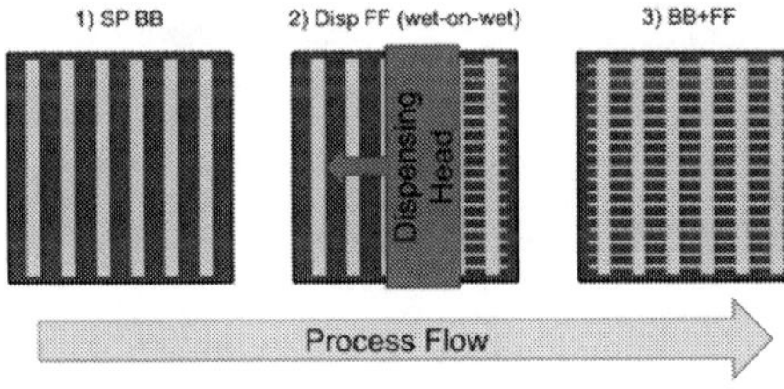

Figure 8 Screen printing and dispensing combined in the cell metallization flow.

Together with BeDimensional (BeD), FH-ISE and HL are working on new stable and compatible formulations for both low and high-temperature processes. On the plating process development and plating for SHJ/TOPCon side, CSEM, FH-ISE and RENA are working on Ni-Cu-Ag or Ni-Cu-Sn processes and a Ni-seed followed by Cu and Ag plating metallization process has already provided promising results. Main discussions include the footprint of the tool, the tool stability and the cost-of-ownership (CoE) of this technology. Also, copper or silver-coated copper particles can be used as seed layers and dispensed to obtain a thin line of around 14 microns (Figure 9).

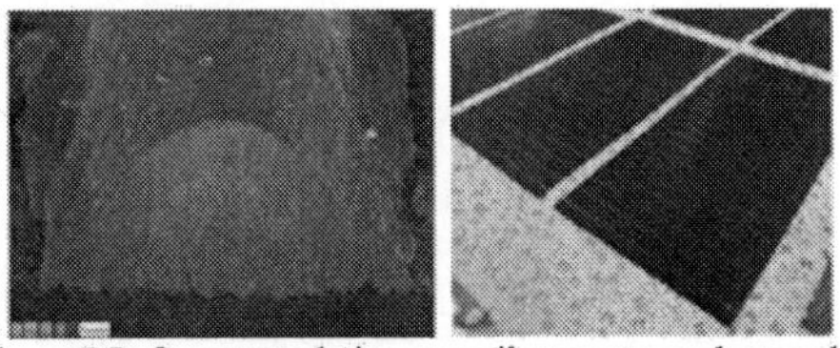

Figure 9 Left, copper plating over silver paste used as seed layer. Right, TOPCon half-cut cells after copper plating.

This last approach has demonstrated the potential to reach the outstanding < 1 mg/watt result.

Also, the development of plated metallization processes for TOPCon solar cells focusses on optimization of laser ablation parameters to achieve a laser contact opening (LCO) and inline plating deposition process scalable for mass production and is mainly driven by FH-ISE/RENA.

To complete the WP1, laser sintering is also introduced as concept, evaluating the use of a laser scan over low temperature curing pastes to accelerate the curing process and permit the curing of copper formulations and so minimizing thermal impact on the a-Si interface in SHJ and preventing Cu in-diffusion into silicon while avoiding degradation of the seed grid-c-Si in TOPCon. This laser process might be compatible with the LS process presented in the WP2 so cross-experiments are planned.

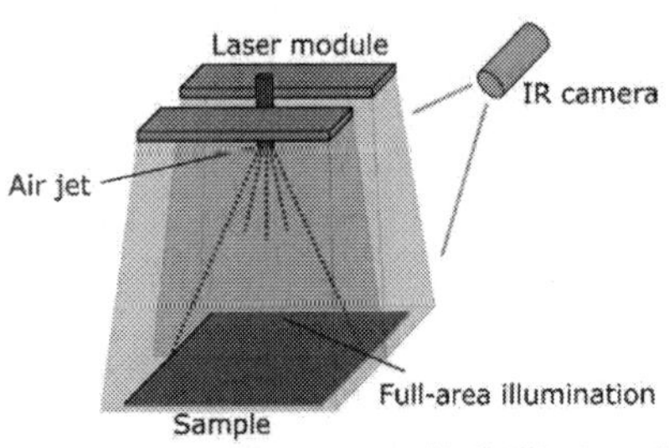

Figure 10 Laser sintering concept with VCSEL laser diode (977nm) and controlled air jet flow for temperature control.

- WP2 (Post Processing)

The LS tool is developed by CEA-INES and AMAT and the procedure consists in the cell exposure to high intensity light source (50 Suns) by using a tool that exposes HJT solar cells to high-intensity, multi-wavelength LED light and controlled heating for rapid post-treatment, enhancing cell performance by reducing defects and improving series resistance. FH-ISE and CSEM will instead focus on light-soaking with TOPCon substrates. The tool is already installed and working at different sites, 2 internal partners and 1 external partner. With this purpose, multiple data can be achieved and analyzed, both from HVM and R&D environments for thermal profiles design and IV characterization (Figure 11, Table 1).

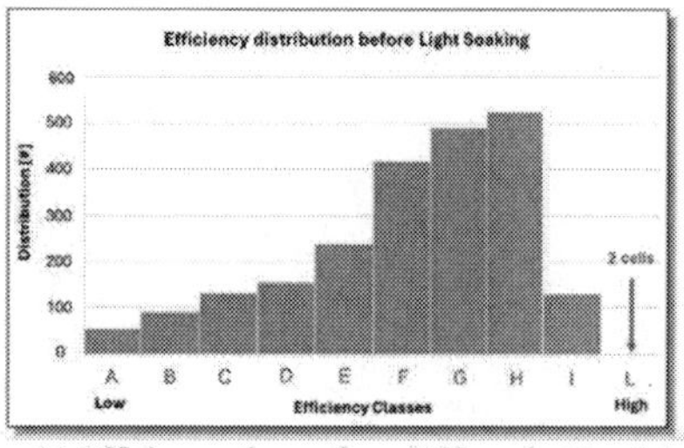

Figure 11 Efficiency classes from SHJ production data.

Efficiency class	Efficiency Gain %
A (low)	+1.12 %
E-F (mid)	+0.60 %
L (high)	+0.56 %

Table 1 LS efficiency gains on SHJ solar cells, HVM data.

Data will be then provided to UL to improve the understanding of LS impact on different depths of the samples via device modelling and to help provide clear guidelines for further process optimization. With the light soaking procedure, an average of +0.5% efficiency gain is recorded and even higher values are measured when exposing low-lifetime and low-grade substrates, meaning that a greater recovery is performed. Further experiments will be done to study the effects of the high-intensity light on the metal grid, contact resistance and line resistance. LS is also compatible with TOPCon solar cells in which an average gain of 0.3% has been already demonstrated (Figure 12).

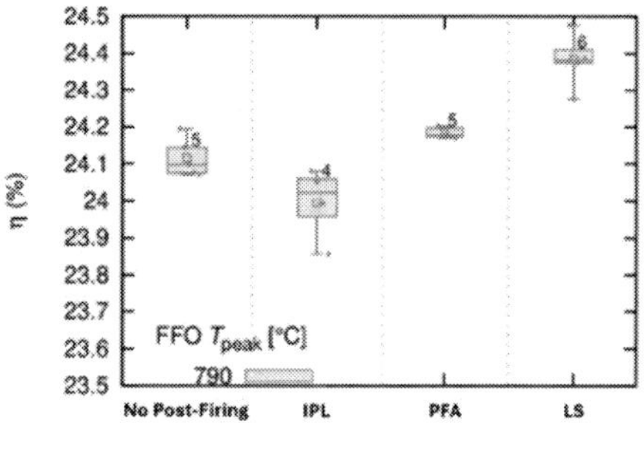

Figure 12 Light Soaking (LS) compared to Intense Pulse Light and Laser Post Firing Anneal post-processes.

On the ERP side, an 80% recovery of the pre-laser cell properties is shown by using AlOx as capping layer on the edge at laboratory scale with SHJ solar cells. The use of ERP has been demonstrated to be valid on both SHJ and TOPCon substrates in which FH-ISE is mostly involved. The process has been validated on shingle configuration (Figure 13).

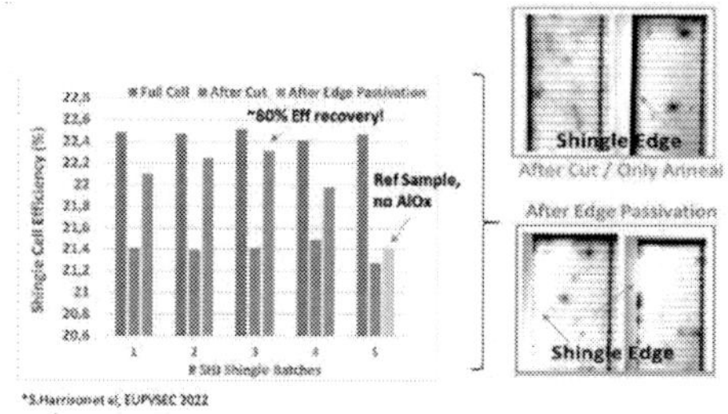

Figure 13 ERP results on SHJ substrates (shingles).

Next steps involving edge-repassivation will include high-throughput tools like plasma-enhanced atomic layer deposition (PE-ALD), study of the best annealing condition and the long-term impact on module (reliability testing) while also evaluating the CAPEX impact of a HVM tool. Also, it will be important to understand if ERP process can impact interconnection quality and/or final module reliability.

- WP3 (Interconnection)

Simulation trials by PCCL and UL and FH-ISE will help in getting insights on the thermomechanical and electrical behaviour of the cells when interconnected and under reliability testing. Also, models have been developed on the encapsulants to be used considering key parameters like thickness and hot-spot resilience. Finite Element Modeling (FEM, Figure 14) of different cell interconnection technologies (shingling and TWILL) has already been started to identify possible fabrication routes and loading related failures but also to compute the temperature distribution, deformation and thermomechanical stress during the shingling.

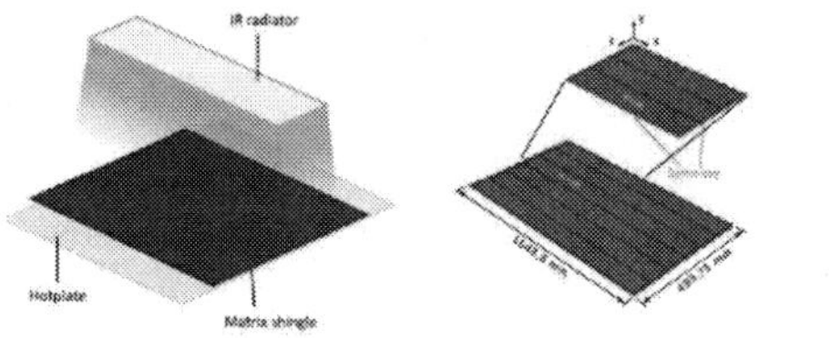

Figure 14 FEM models' principles to study temperature distribution and stress on shingles (let) and develop process and loading failures (right).

About shingling simulations, FH-ISE will focus on the matrix shingling interconnection using COMSOL Multiphysics and determine the minimum encapsulant thickness by a parameter sensitivity study. More data will be provided by partners during the development and scale-up of these alternative interconnection technologies. TWILL consists of a multiple wire interconnection method embedding conductive copper wires in polymeric carrier foils in which the metal interconnection occurs during lamination, eliminating the need of a separate stringing step (Figure 15). This method will be scaled to M10-G12 half-cut by IMEC, IPTE and ARK and reliability testing with different encapsulants and cells is ongoing.

Figure 15 Twill mini module after lamination and curing optimization.

Shingling instead consists of interconnecting solar shingles via electrically conductive adhesives (ECA) to form flexible, any length, ribbon connected solar strings and so provide a certain degree of flexibility in the module design and size. In the shingling process development, partners will focus on shingle overlap reduction, reduction of Ag usage at the ECA level (either by ECA reduction or by usage of low content Ag ECA) and improvement in handling of thin wafers with AMAT/CEA-INES mainly focusing on SHJ and FH-ISE/M10 on TOPCon and matrix shingling. TNO will investigate an easy-release encapsulant to enable the recycling of all constituting materials of the device at end-of-life. This material has been preliminary tested on the front and rear side of solar cells showing that the two surfaces can be separated after material activation. Crucial steps in the development of this material are the lamination step (local delamination points) and the reliability testing according to the IEC61215 standard: single cell glass-glass modules have been made and the reliability testing is ongoing on release encapsulant and release encapsulant combined with TPO samples. Next steps will include the scale up to 4-cell mini-modules. The release encapsulant material properties and consistency will be analyzed in LCA study. The release encapsulant will be also tested for its re-use potential adding information for the LCA study.

- WP4 (Equipment)

WP4 activities are strongly dependent on previous WPs and some of the activities are ongoing in parallel development like the dispensing kit integration as well as the TWILL and ERP tools design. AMAT, HL and FH-ISE will continue to work on the dispensing integration on HVM tool (Figure 16) which in principle will be used for both SHJ and TOPCon.

Figure 16 Dispensing kit mounted on screen-printing tool head

The upscaling potential of the plating process on SHJ and TOPCon will be evaluated on a pilot plating line from RENA installed at FH-ISE to uncover potential limitations and shortcomings. AMAT will also continue to contribute to the development of a light-soaking tool that can demonstrate an efficiency gain entitlement on SHJ cells of 0.3% in industrial cells, with yield of 98% and uptime of 92%. Also, significant efforts will be spent on the upgrade of the shingling tool to scale up to G12 formats and add more flexibility in cell dimension, ribbon shape and string length. Singulus (SING) will develop an equipment platform for the ERP. IPTE will instead first upgrade a semi-automated foil-making tool and a pick-and-place tool and then focus on building a high-TPT, fully automated and flexible roll-to-stack foil-making machine (Figure 17), with a targeted speed of <5s/foil/line, and an availability (>92%) and yield (>97%). This work will be conducted in parallel with IMEC and ARK which will provide encapsulant foils.

Figure 17 Equipment concept for high-volume integrated production with TWILL interconnection concept

- WP5 (Integration and Line Demonstration)

Previous WPs will provide the data and contribute to providing a starting point in the simulation of all the processing steps (Figure 18). As the amount of data will increase, Enginsoft (ENG) will oversee the making of a model that can include all the process variables, individual manufacturing steps performance (e.g. yield, TPT) and process variability that will be used to describe the SHINE PV line and progressively validate it. The final goal will be also creating and making available 2D and 3D models representing the production layout and material flows of a production line. Such models will support the different demonstrators as well as provide a virtual demonstration environment for the project results to assess and evaluate the efficiency, compatibility and overall performance of SHINE PV equipment.

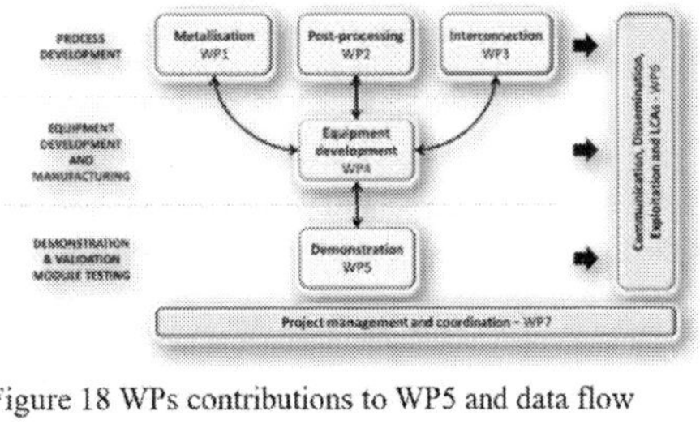

Figure 18 WPs contributions to WP5 and data flow

Also, the assessment and validation of solar modules will be studied via models, providing insights on aggregated raw data from the consortium, periodic metric measurements along long-term testing of installed modules and assessment of performance and seasonality effects.

- WP6-7 (LCA, Exploitation, Management)

Developing new supply chains and business models is crucial when working on alternative technological routes to mainstream advanced photovoltaic production and while trying to be competitive with the Asian market (Figure 19). Diversified EU manufacturing, circular, sustainable materials, job creation & tech leadership and energy security & autonomy are the most important factors to consider while working on a strategy.

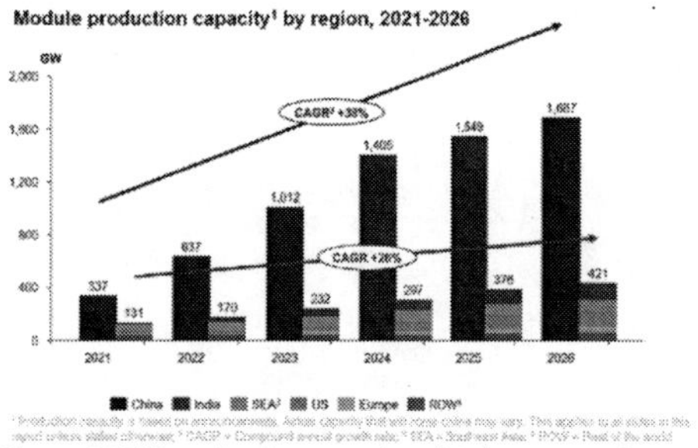

Figure 19 PV production capacity of Asia compared to Europe and rest of the world

SHINE PV supports the EU's goal of strategic autonomy in clean energy, while ensuring sustainable, resilient, and competitive PV production by promoting the adoption of standards (ISO 14044, Semi-35 Standard [18]) and performing circularity assessments like life cycle assessments (LCA, Figure 20).

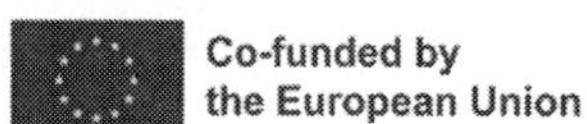

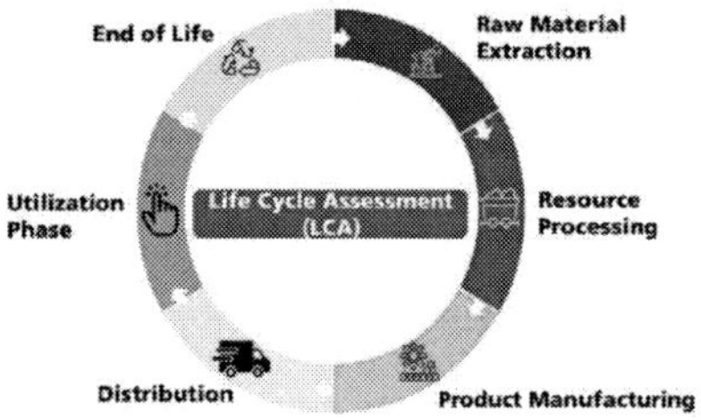

Figure 20 Data requirements for the entire supply chain flow

Some work has already been done on the communication side by introducing the project to the web, social and by creating cloud infrastructure for data sharing and reporting.

5 CONCLUSIONS

Despite the early phase of the project, interesting results have been already achieved especially on the WP2 part in which significant advantages in using the tools developed under the SHINE PV project have been demonstrated at both laboratory and HVM scales. Also, WP3 provided interesting outputs on the use of copper and plating as an alternative to standard silver pastes, providing a more sustainable and efficient route for PV. Some of the WPs are still on hold and will start to contribute to the next months but all the activities, periodic meetings and preliminary test or phases are in place and ready.

The SHINE PV consortium will continue to bring together the key industry expertise in both research and equipment, developing complete solutions for advanced manufacturing and more results will come in the following months.

More on the project and the partners can be found out at the following link: https://shinepv.eu/about/

6 AUTHOR CONTRIBUTIONS

AMAT-Italy for paper writing and submission, all the partners for reviewing and contributing.

7 FUNDING

This project has received funding from the European Union's Horizon Europe research and innovation programme under grant agreement No 101172902.

Co-funded by the European Union

8 ACKNOWLEDGEMENTS

We would like to thank all the partners who have contributed to the making of this paper and the SHINE PV project.

9 REFERENCES

[1] EU-Funding&Tenders, "Sustainable, High-throughput, Industry-ready, Next-generation technology for European manufacturing leadership in PV (SHINE PV)," HORIZON-CL5-2024-D3-01, 01 01 2025. [Online]. Available: https://ec.europa.eu/info/funding-tenders/opportunities/portal/screen/how-to-participate/org-details/897837918/project/101172902/program/43108390/details. [Accessed 01 01 2025].

[2] W. Mackenzie, "How will China's expansion affect global solar module supply chain," Wood Mackenzie, 01 Month 2023. [Online]. Available: https://go.woodmac.com/l/131501/2023-11-10/317ftc/131501/1699609270p9l75YZ9/WOODMA_1.PDF. [Accessed 01 September 2025].

[3] P. J. Verlinden, "Future challenges for photovoltaic manufacturing at the terawatt level," *Journal of Renewable and Sustainable Energy,* vol. 12, no. 2020, p. 053505, 2020.

[4] R. Rossi, "SolarPower Europe," SolarPower Europe, 01 01 2023. [Online]. Available: https://www.solarpowereurope.org/insights/outlooks/eu-market-outlook-for-solar-power-2023-2027. [Accessed 01 01 2025].

[5] Y. Zhang, "Design considerations for multi-terawatt scale manufacturing of existing and future photovoltaic technologies: challenges and opportunities related to silver, indium and bismuth consumption," *Energy & Environmental Science,* vol. 14, no. 11, pp. 5587-5610, 2021.

[6] S. Pordan, "Optimizing solar cell metallization by parallel dispensing," *Solar Energy Materials and Solar Cells,* vol. 266, no. 2024, p. 112685, 2024.

[7] K. Gensowski, "Filament stretching during parallel dispensing – A way to reduce silver consumption in SHJ metallization," *Solar Energy Materials and Solar Cells,* vol. 245, no. 2022, p. 111871, 2022.

[8] K. Gensowski, "Filament stretching during micro-extrusion of silver pastes enables an improved fine-line silicon solar cell metallization," *Scientific Reports,* vol. 12, no. 2022, p. 12318, 2022.

[9] A. Lachowiz, "Aging tests of mini-modules with copper-plated heterojunction solar cells and pattern-transfer-printing of copper paste," *EPJ Photovolt.,* vol. 11, no. 2024, p. 7, 2024.

[10] B. Grubel, "Progress of plated metallization for industrial bifacial TOPCon silicon solar cells," *Progress in Photovoltaics,* vol. 30, no. 6, pp. 615-621, 2022.

[11] S. Harrison, "How to Combine SHJ Cell-Edge Passivation and Module Reliability?," in *SiliconPV Conference Proceedings*, Chambery, 2024.

[12] E. Lohmüller, "Thermal laser separation and high-throughput layer deposition for edge passivation for TOPCon shingle solar cells," *Solar Energy Materials and Solar Cells,* vol. 258, no. 2023, p. 112419, 2023.

[13] A. Voltan, "Advancements on post-processing of high efficiency cells: data from mass production and experimental roadmap," in *Proceeding of 42nd EUPVSEC*, Bilbao, 2025.

[14] J. Govaerts, "Encapsulant-Integrated Interconnection of Bifacial Solar Cells for BIPV Applications: Latest Results in the Twill-BIPV Project," in *Proceedings of the EU PVSEC 2020*, Online, 2020.

[15] J. Govaerts, "Interconnection and lamination technologies towards ubiquitous integration of photovoltaics," *Progress in Photovoltaics,* vol. 31, no. 11, pp. 1114-1129, 2023.

[16] M. Foti, "22% efficiency module combining Silicon Heterojunction Solar and Shingle interconnection," in *49th Photovoltaics Specialists Conference (PVSC)*, Philadelphia, 2022.

[17] N. Klasen, "Performance of shingled solar modules under partial shading," *Progress in Photovoltaics,* vol. 30, no. 4, pp. 325-338, 2021.

[18] SPIE, "SPIE Digital Library," SPIE, 29 08 2017. [Online]. Available: https://www.spiedigitallibrary.org/conference-proceedings-of-spie/10313/1031353/Analyzing-component-manufacturing-costs-using-the-SEMI-E35-standard-for/10.1117/12.2283979.short. [Accessed 01 01 2025].

BEYOND SILVER: COMPARATIVE PERFORMANCE ANALYSIS OF ALTERNATIVE METALLIZATION STRATEGIES IN SILICON SOLAR CELLS

Seda Kilickaya[1], Melisa Korkmaz Arslan[1], Esma Alloji[2], Serdar Akbayrak[3] and Veysel Unsur[1,3,*]

[1] Center for Solar Energy Research and Application (ODTU-GUNAM), Ankara, Turkiye
[2] Nanoscience and Nano-Engineering, Necmettin Erbakan University, Konya, Turkiye
[3] Department of Fundamental Sciences in Engineering, Necmettin Erbakan University, Konya, Turkiye
* veysel.unsur@odtugunam.org

ABSTRACT: The photovoltaic industry's reliance on silver (Ag) for silicon solar cell metallization faces critical challenges due to Ag scarcity, cost volatility, and sustainability concerns. This study systematically evaluates advanced metallization strategies to reduce or eliminate Ag usage while maintaining high-performance solar cell operation. We investigate fine-line printing, hybrid/core-shell architectures, and alternative materials such as copper (Cu), aluminum (Al), and nickel (Ni). Fine-line printing enables Ag finger widths as narrow as 10–15 µm, reducing front-side Ag consumption by up to 25% (9 mg/W) without compromising efficiency. However, sub-10 µm finger widths introduce printability challenges and increased series resistance. Hybrid and core-shell pastes, such as Cu-core/Ag-shell configurations, mitigate Cu's oxidation and diffusion risks at low temperatures but face limitations in high-temperature processes (>750°C) required for TOPCon and IBC cells. To address this, Ag-doped Ni pastes (4% Ag) demonstrate a breakthrough, achieving power conversion efficiencies comparable to traditional Ag contacts while slashing Ag usage to <0.5 mg/Wp. In parallel, Cu-only pastes are explored for their ultra-low cost and high conductivity, yet require advanced barrier layers (e.g., Ni, Ti) to suppress Cu diffusion into silicon during high-temperature firing. Recent optimizations in rapid thermal annealing processes enable Cu paste stability at industrial scales, achieving efficiencies of ~22.5%. Meanwhile, Al-only pastes, while limited by higher contact resistance, show promise for rear-side metallization if used with Al/(boron doped)Si or Al/Ge alloy mixtures.

Keywords: Si solar cells, metallization, alternative materials, Cu contact, Ni contacts

1 INTRODUCTION

The rapid growth of the photovoltaic (PV) industry, driven by global decarbonization efforts, has intensified concerns over the scarcity of silver (Ag), a critical material for silicon solar cell metallization. The limited supply of Ag along with fluctuating cost threatens the sustainability and scalability of PV manufacturing, particularly as screen printing remains the dominant metallization technique.

To address this challenge, significant efforts have been made to optimize screen printing processes, including fine-line printing, narrowing finger widths, and improving screen designs, which reduce Ag consumption while maintaining electrical performance. Additionally, the development of Ag pastes with reduced Ag content or alternative conductive materials is essential.

Copper (Cu) has emerged as the most promising alternative due to its abundance, high conductivity, and cost-effectiveness. However, Cu faces significant challenges, including rapid oxidation and its tendency to diffuse into silicon can lead to the formation of detrimental Cu-related defects, necessitating robust barrier layers such as nickel (Ni) or titanium (Ti) or complete barrier layers underneath the contacts.

Aluminum (Al) and Ni also offer potential as alternative metallization materials, but their lower electrical conductivity and higher contact resistance pose limitations for front-side contacts. Recent advancements in hybrid and core-shell structures such as Cu-core/Ag-shell and Ni-core/Cu-shell configurations seek to leverage the favorable properties of each material while mitigating their individual limitations. These novel approaches aim to enhance performance and durability, although fully functional and industrially scalable implementations remain in development. These innovative approaches aim to balance the cost, performance, and reliability while reducing Ag dependency.

This study critically examines the current state of alternative metallization strategies for silicon solar cells, providing a systematic evaluation of advanced materials (e.g., Cu, Al, Ni) and hybrid/core-shell architectures as sustainable substitutes for Ag.

2 STRATEGIES AND OUTCOMES FOR SILVER REDUCTION and SILVER-FREE SOLAR CELLS

2.1 Ag reduction through fine line printing

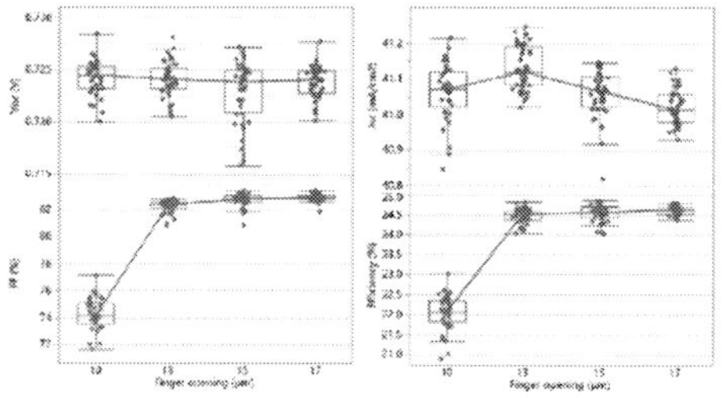

Fig. 1 The change of electrical parameters of a TOPCon solar cells with finger width

Fine-line printing has emerged as a critical strategy to reduce silver (Ag) consumption in silicon solar cells, addressing both cost and sustainability concerns. By narrowing Ag finger widths to 10–15 µm, significant reductions in Ag usage can be achieved without compromising cell efficiency [1]. Recent studies demonstrate that advanced grid designs, can reduce front-side Ag consumption by up to 20% while maintaining power conversion efficiency (PCE) [2], [3], [4]. Similarly, a dual-layer metallization approach, combining fine-line Ag dashes with non-silver fingers, reduced Ag consumption to 9 mg/W, a 25% improvement over

10.4229/EUPVSEC2025/1BV.5.27

standard designs [5]. However, challenges remain, including increased series resistance and printability issues with ultra-fine fingers (below 10μm) as shown in Fig. 1.

2.2 Hybrid and Core-Shell Pastes for Ag Reduction

Hybrid and core-shell structures offer a promising pathway to reduce Ag usage in metallization. These pastes combine the cost-effectiveness of abundant metals, such as Cu or Al, with the superior electrical and interfacial properties of thin Ag or Ni layers [6], [6]. By leveraging the strengths of multiple materials, these designs aim to achieve high performance while minimizing material costs.

In core-shell configurations, a conductive core (Cu) is encapsulated by a thin protective shell (Ag) to mitigate Cu's inherent drawbacks such as oxidation and diffusion into silicon while maintaining high conductivity. This strategy has proven effective for low-temperature applications, as shown in Fig. 2a. However, for solar cell architectures that require high-temperature firing processes (TOPCon and IBC), the protective shell tends to break down at temperatures exceeding 750 °C. When the shell is compromised, the Cu core becomes exposed, increasing the risk of diffusion into the silicon and oxidation, potentially leading to a declined in device performance.

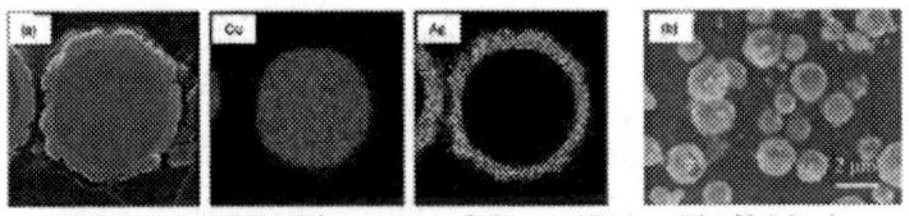

Fig. 2 (a) SEM images of Core (Cu) - Shell (Ag) structure and EDX analysis and (b) core-shell structure after high temperature annealing

One approach to mitigating high-temperature challenges is to incorporate Ag doping into alternative metals such as nickel [7], [8]. Doping Ni particles with a small percentage of Ag not only enhances conductivity but also lowers the metal work function, thereby ensuring optimal ohmic contact with silicon while reducing overall metallization costs (Fig. 3). For example, employing a 4% Ag-doped Ni paste in TOPCon silicon solar cells has demonstrated conversion efficiencies comparable to those of traditional silver contacts, while significantly reducing Ag consumption to below 0.5 mg/Wp [8].

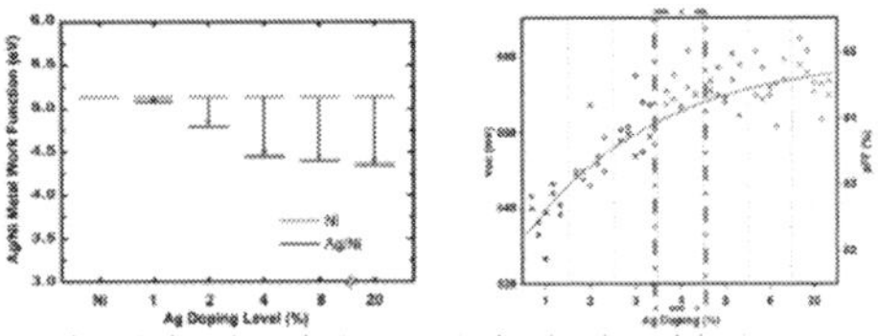

Fig. 3 Dependence of metal work function of Ni on Ag doping levels and the Suns-V_{OC} measurements of iV_{OC} values based on the doping level

2.3 Alternative Conductive Materials

The adoption of Cu metallization requires tailored approaches for low-temperature (SHJ) and high-temperature (e.g., TOPCon) cell architectures, addressing distinct challenges in diffusion control and interfacial engineering. SHJ cells, limited to processing temperatures < 250°C, benefit from Cu pastes cured at 180–220°C. Nanoparticle-based Cu inks with organic stabilizers achieve line resistivities of 0.8–1.2 Ω/cm at 30 μm widths, comparable to Ag references, while maintaining adhesion forces >1 N/mm after lamination [6]. However, resistivity remains ~2× higher than Ag due to oxide formation, necessitating Ag-doped hybrid pastes (4–6 wt% Ag) to reduce contact resistivity to <3 mΩ·cm² [7]. For TOPCon cells requiring firing at 750–850°C, Cu diffusion into n+ poly-Si poses critical risks. Advanced glass frits in screen-printable pastes act as in-situ barriers, limiting Cu mobility while etching SiN_x. However, excessive glass frit content increases recombination (*$J_{0,metal}$*) to 500 fA/cm² and degrades passivation indicated by 45mV drop in open circuit voltage. Incorporating TiN or Al_2O_3 diffusion barriers beneath contacts reduces Cu ingress by 90%,

Aluminum-based pastes, while already common for rear-side metallization, face hurdles on the front side due to their higher resistivity and tendency to form insulating oxides. Recent hybrid approaches, including the incorporation of trace amounts of silver or integrating boron-doped silicon nanoparticles, have improved the performance of aluminum. However, challenges such as thermal expansion mismatch persists and require further investigation. Overall, advancing hybrid architectures and optimizing paste chemistries are crucial steps toward achieving reliable, cost-effective, silver-free metallization in next-generation photovoltaic manufacturing.

Acknowledgment

This conference paper is supported by TÜBITAK BİDEB.

References

[1] Y. Zhang *et al.*, "Ultra-Lean Silver Screen-Printing for Sustainable Terawatt-Scale Photovoltaic," *Solar RRL*, vol. 8, no. 17, p. 2400478, 2024, doi: 10.1002/solr.202400478.

[2] A. Ebong *et al.*, "Innovative front grid design, four-streets and five-busbars (4S-5BB), for high efficiency industrial Al-BSF silicon solar cell," *IEEE Electron Device Letters*, vol. 37, no. 4, pp. 459–462, 2016.

[3] V. Unsur *et al.*, "Rapid thermal processing of cost-effective contacts for silicon solar cells," *Progress in Photovoltaics*, vol. 27, no. 5, pp. 453–459, May 2019, doi: 10.1002/pip.3119.

[4] V. Unsur, "Implementation of nickel and copper as cost-effective alternative contacts in silicon solar cells," *Progress in Photovoltaics*, vol. 32, no. 4, pp. 267–275, Apr. 2024, doi: 10.1002/pip.3792.

[5] T. Schweigstill *et al.*, "Advanced Fine Line Printing With Glass Stencils: Achieving Metal Contact Fingers Below 10 μm," *Progress in Photovoltaics: Research and Applications*, vol. n/a, no. n/a, doi: 10.1002/pip.3885.

[6] D. Du *et al.*, "Low-Cost Metallization Based on Ag/Cu Fingers for Exceeding 25% Efficiency in Industrial Silicon Heterojunction Solar Cells," *Solar RRL*, vol. 8, no. 12, p. 2400052, 2024, doi: 10.1002/solr.202400052.

[7] B. Akgayev *et al.*, "Screen printable fire through nickel contacts for silicon solar cells," *Solar Energy Materials and Solar Cells*, vol. 261, p. 112528, Oct. 2023, doi: 10.1016/j.solmat.2023.112528.

[8] V. Unsur *et al.*, "Screen printed Ag-doped nickel metallization for industrial n-TOPCon silicon solar cells," *Solar Energy Materials and Solar Cells*, vol. 287, p. 113602, 2025.

Impact of doped polysilicon process for mass production TOPCon solar cell

Cheng-Wen Kuo, Ta-Ming Kuan, Yung-Chih Li, Chun-Wei Lee, Wei-Lo Chueh, Li-Guo Wu, Shih-Chieh Lin and Cheng-Yeh Yu
TSEC Corporation, No.85, Gaungfu N. Rd., Hsin-Chu 30351, Taiwan.

ABSTRACT: Tunnel oxide passivated contact solar cells have gradually become a mass-producible solar cell technology due to their excellent performance with cost-effectiveness, and further superimposing other technologies to improve conversion efficiency has become the focus of subsequent research. Heavy doping is usually required to achieve excellent field effect passivation and low contact resistivity in doped polysilicon (poly-Si). In order to increase the throughput, the poly-Si process improvements are needed. During this process, it could be found that as the temperature increases, more nanocrystalline structures will form on the surface of the polysilicon layer. In this study, the electrical properties and reliability of different doped polysilicon films were studied. Finally, industrial-sized (G10-L) TOPCon solar cells were fabricated on a production line with an average efficiency of 25.95%, 0.15% higher than the Baseline solar cells of 25.8%. The above results suggest that nano crystallization may be helpful for passivation, thereby obtaining efficient solar cells.
Keywords: TOPCon, mass production, Poly-Si

1 INTRODUCTION

With the world's growing demand for energy, while coping with human-caused global warming, has become one of the undisputed challenges facing humanity in the near future. This requires the use of clean and environmentally friendly resources to achieve sustainable energy production. Solar photovoltaic (PV) technology is gaining increasing attention, as clearly reflected in the statistics of the total installed capacity of global solar photovoltaic modules. Crystalline silicon (c-Si) has become the market-leading technology since its birth, accounting for nearly 95% of the market share due to its unique characteristics such as non-toxicity, abundant reserves and long-term stability [1]. On the other hand, as the number of solar photovoltaic installations increases and the land available for construction becomes less and less, the demand for high-efficiency solar energy becomes more important.

Using the passivated emitter rear cell (PERC) structure, the mass production efficiency has exceeded 23%, which is close to reaching its theoretical performance [2]. When the efficiency of PERC solar cells approaches 24%, most of the recombination losses are caused by metal contacts [3], making further improvement difficult, especially in the field of industrial manufacturing. Therefore, contact passivation has been a hot research topic in the field of photovoltaics for many years. Among the various materials and compositions studied, TOPCon remains the most interesting in the industry [4]. In the TOPCon design, the metal does not make direct contact with the wafer. Instead, a thin layer of tunnel oxide is applied first, followed by a layer of highly doped n-type or p-type polysilicon, which contacts the metal at the end. The back of the tunnel oxide does not affect the operation of the device because the tunnel oxide blocks one type of carrier. Therefore, these structures are often called passivated contacts. Fraunhofer ISE reported TOPCon cell efficiencies of 25.8% and POLO-IBC cell efficiencies of 26.1% with a specific surface area of 4 cm^2 [5-7]. Inspired by these outstanding research advances, attempts to introduce passive contacts into industrial solar cell manufacturing are fascinating. As a result, TOPCon has gradually gained industry recognition and is considered the next generation cell technology after PERC [8]. The key to achieving high performance of TOPCon lies in the preparation of high-quality nano-SiO_x (T_{ox}) and heavily doped polysilicon. There are many reports on Tox preparation methods, including thermal oxidation [9-12], wet chemical oxidation [12-14], ozone oxidation [12, 13], plasma-assisted oxidation [15-16] and plasma-assisted atomic layer deposition (PEALD) [17], with a composite current density (J_0) of less than 10 fA/cm^2 [18]. However, except for ozone oxidation and plasma-assisted oxidation, most of the above methods cannot be industrialized, which correspond to the following industrial preparation methods of amorphous silicon (α-Si) low-pressure chemical vapor deposition (LPCVD) and plasma-enhanced chemical vapor deposition (PECVD). Compared with ozone oxidation, plasma-assisted oxidation can be integrated with in-situ doping of polycrystalline silicon (n^+poly-Si) in the same tube, thereby reducing process steps and reducing process costs. In addition, PECVD is superior to LPCVD in terms of film deposition rate, wrap-around deposition and equipment-related consumables [30, 31].

In this study, our primary goal was to improve productivity while maintaining a certain level of performance. We modified the doping temperature and time for poly-Si. The results showed that as the temperature increased, the nanostructures became larger and more numerous, which improved the final performance, but the reliability remained similar. This new parameter not only improved productivity but also improved efficiency.

2 EXPERIMENTAL

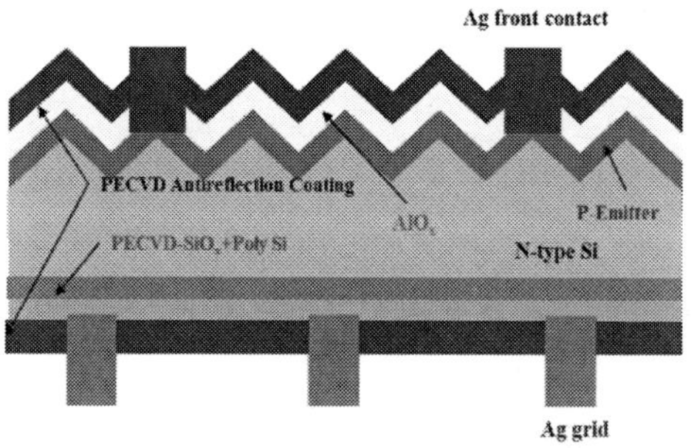

Figure 1: TOPCon structure as investigated in this work.

Figure 1 showed the TOPCon structure in this work. The G10-L size (182.0 mm x 183.75 mm) bifacial TOPCon solar cells were fabricated on 130 μm thick n-type Cz-silicon

10.4229/EUPVSEC2025/1BV.5.32

wafers with a resistivity of 0.4~1.6 Ω-cm..

The process sequence in this work was shown in Figure 2. Chemical wet etching methods were used for saw damage removal and surface texturing, which include alkaline etching for mono-crystalline silicon wafers. The solution composition of alkaline etching was potassium hydroxide (KOH) : deionized water (DI) = 1 : 50 and additives. The diffusion process of this work also improves the temperature curve and its uniformity.

The front side of the solar cells features an alkaline textured (random-pyramids) surface with a boron-doped p+emitter. The emitter was formed by BBr_3 tube furnace diffusion followed by drive-in oxidation, resulting in an emitter with a sheet resistance of R_{sheet} between 400~500 Ω/sq. The borosilicate glass (BSG) was then removed by HF-contained solutions, formed edge isolation in the meantime. Then, the rear surface is polished which removes 5-10 μm silicon in this work, in order to reduce the roughness and its impact on the effective charge carrier lifetime. The emitter was passivated with a 5~10 nm thick Al_2O_3 layer deposited with atomic layer deposition. In order to decrease PID effect and increase efficiency, we optimized the CVD process parameter to improve. An antireflection coating (ARC) layer of silicon nitride (SiN_x:H) and/or $SiO_x/SiO_xN_y/SiN_x$ multi ARC was deposited by plasma enhanced chemical vapor deposition (PECVD) with thickness of 80-120 nm, as shown in Fig 3.

The rear side tunnel oxide layer and doped polysilicon (poly-si) were also deposited using PECVD technology. In order to improve the PECVD equipment's productivity, the polysilicon process parameters was adjusted in our experimental group by increasing the temperature and reducing the time. Figures 4 and 5 show that the back-side thickness was approximately 120-140 nm. The back-side laser aperture ratio was then optimized. The front side and rear side silver metallization layers were formed by screen printing technique and followed by co-firing process. Finally, the current-voltage characteristics of the solar cells were measured under AM 1.5 illumination.

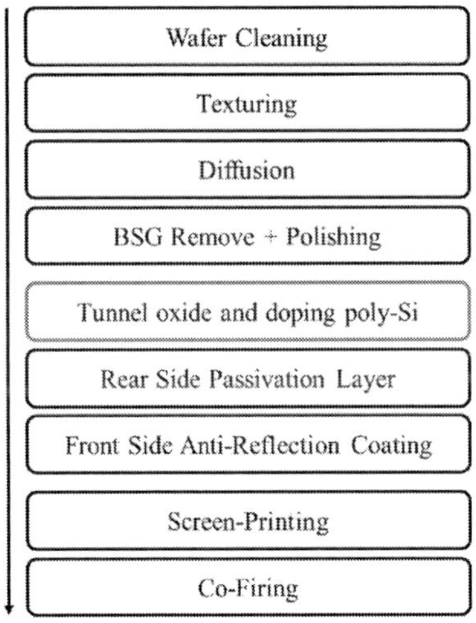

Figure 2: Process flow for the fabrication of PERC solar cell as developed in this work

Figure 3: The scanning electron microscope (SEM) image of front side passivation layer for this work.

Figure 4: The scanning electron microscope (SEM) image of rear side layer for ref sample.

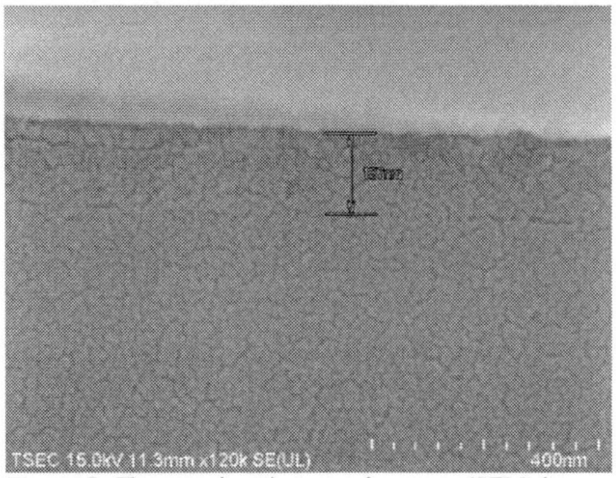

Figure 5: The scanning electron microscope (SEM) image of rear side layer for experiment sample.

3 EXPERIMENTAL RESULTS AND DISCUSSION

The goal of the mass production is to increase production capacity by adjusting the temperature of the PECVD equipment's doping poly-Si process without sacrificing efficiency. Reference 21 explains that as the temperature increases, the thickness of the amorphous silicon deposition increases, indicating that the doping poly-Si thickness can also increase. It implies that this condition can be adjusted to increase production capacity. Table 1 shows that the electrical properties are also better, which is consistent with the iVOC description in reference 21. In addition to the electrical properties, we also conducted top-view SEM analysis on doping poly-Si. From the top-view SEM images (Figs. 6 and 7), it could be observed that the number of poly-Si grains in the polycrystalline silicon layer of the experimental group is significantly larger and the size is larger. The formation of these nanocrystals may be a key factor in enhancing passivation, ultimately improving electrical performance and increasing solar cell efficiency. Besides, we tested the TOPCon tandem process with the research center and found that performance varied with the number of poly grain number.

Table 1: The average electrical results of the TOPCon cells.

	EFF (%)	FF (%)	V_{OC} (V)	I_{SC} (A)
REF TOPCon	25.80	84.64	0.7319	13.940
Experiment	25.95	84.94	0.7347	13.921

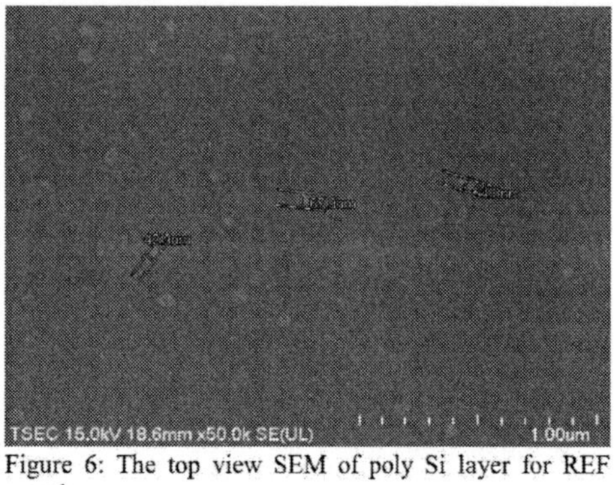

Figure 6: The top view SEM of poly Si layer for REF sample.

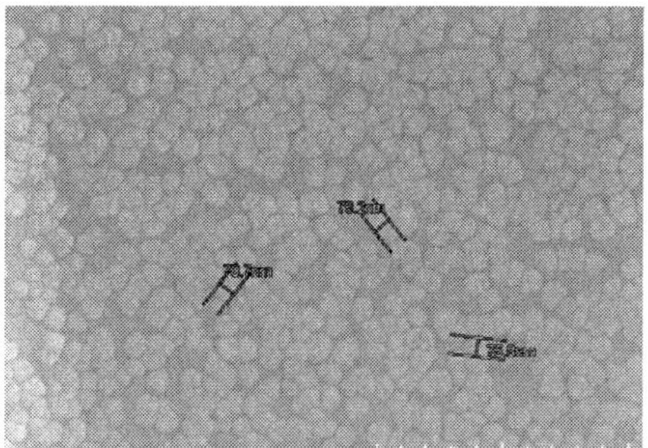

Figure 7: The top view SEM of poly Si layer for experiment sample.

Potential-induced degradation (PID) testing of solar cells also complies with IEC TS 62804-1 and was used in this experiment. Both the REF and experimental solar cells passed PID testing at 85°C and 85% RH, applying -1500 V for 96 hours in a climate chamber, as shown in Figure 7. After PID testing, both the REF and experimental ARC PERC solar cells showed less than 5% power loss and no EL dark regions, demonstrating the effectiveness of the experimental results.

Sample	Pre-Test		Post-Test		EL		Decay Rate(%) (Spec<5%)
Sample	Rsh	Pmpp	Rsh	Pmpp	Pre-PID	Post-PID	•Pmpp
REF-1	489.7	7.7587	554.3	7.6882			0.91%
REF-2	14885.5	7.6565	2426.2	7.5887			0.89%
REF-3	389.1	7.6360	3349.2	7.6301			0.08%
EXP-1	5759.2	7.5293	546.3	7.5004			0.39%
EXP-2	1527.9	7.5367	3915.8	7.4796			0.76%
EXP-3	2421.7	7.6887	496.2	7.5963			1.20%

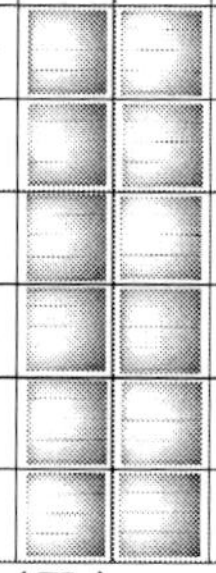

Figure 8: Summary of power loss and EL images of pre-PID and post-PID of REF and experiment TOPCon solar cells. PID test condition is 85 degree Celsius / 85% RH biased -1500V for 96 hours.

4 CONCLUSIONS

In this work, we demonstrate the fabrication of industrial-scale TOPCon solar cells, achieving an average conversion efficiency of 25.95%, a 0.15% improvement over the benchmark efficiency of 25.8%. This achievement is due to optimization of the polycrystalline silicon (poly-Si) process, which is critical for achieving excellent field-effect passivation and low contact resistivity. These findings demonstrate that targeted process improvements can significantly advance the mass production of solar cells. The successful industrialization of this technology provides further improve the efficiency and yield of TOPCon solar cells.

5 REFERENCES

[1] H. Ullah, S. Czapp, S. Szultka, H. Tariq, U. B. Qasim, H. Imran., "Crystalline Silicon (c-Si)-Based Tunnel Oxide Passivated Contact (TOPCon) Solar Cells: A Review," Energies, vol. 16, pp. 715, 2023.

[2] J. Schmidt, R. Peibst, R. Brendel., "Surface passivation of crystalline silicon solar cells: present and future," Sol. Energy Mater. Sol. Cells vol.187, pp.39, 2018.

[3] M. Müller, G. Fischer, B. Bitnar, S. Steckemetz, R. Schiepe, M. Mühlbauer, R. Köhler, P. Richter, C. Kusterer, A. Oehlke, E. Schneiderlöchner, H. Sträter, F. Wolny, M. Wagner, P. Palinginis, and D. H. Neuhaus, "Loss analysis of 22% efficient industrial PERC solar cells," Energy Procedia, vol. 124, pp.131,2017.

[4] H. Yousuf, M. Q. Khokhar, S. Chowdhury, D. P. Pham, Y. Kim, M. Ju, Y. Cho, E. C. Cho, J. Yi, "A Review on TOPCon Solar Cell Technology," Current Photovoltaic Research, vol. 9, pp.9, 2021

[5] A. Richter, J. Benick, F. Feldmann, A. Fell, M. Hermle, S. W. Glunz, "n-Type Si solar cells with passivating electron contact: Identifying sources for efficiency limitations by wafer thickness and resistivity variation," Solar Energy Materials and Solar Cells, Vol. 173, pp. 96-105, 2017.

[6] M. A. Green, Y. Hishikawa, E. D. Dunlop, D. H. Levi, J. HohlEbinger, and A. W. Ho-Baillie, "Solar cell

efficiency tables (version 51)," Progress in Photovoltaics: Research and Applications, vol. 26, pp. 3, 2018.

[7] F. Haase, C. Hollemann, S. Schäfer, A. Merkle, M. Rienäcker, J. Krügener, R. Brendel, and R. Peibst, "Laser contact openings for local poly-Si-metal contacts enabling 26.1%-efficient POLOIBC solar cells," Solar Energy Materials and Solar Cells, vol.186, pp. 184, 2018.

[8] S. Ma, B. Liao,F.Y. Qiao,D. Ding, C. Gao,Z. P. Li, R. Tong, X.Y. Kong, and W.Z. Shen, "24.7% industrial tunnel oxide passivated contact solar cells prepared through tube PECVD integrating with plasma-assisted oxygen oxidation and in-situ doped polysilicon," Solar Energy Materials and Solar Cells, vol, 257, pp.112396, 2023.

[9] U. Römer, R. Peibst, T. Ohrdes, B. Lim, J. Krügener, T. Wietler, and R. Brendel, "Ion Implantation for Poly-Si Passivated Back-Junction Back-Contacted Solar Cells," IEEE Journal of Photovoltaics, vol.5, pp. 507, 2015

[10] D. Yan, A. Cuevas, J. Bullock, Y. Wan, and C. Samundsett, "Phosphorus-diffused polysilicon contacts for solar cells," Sol. Energy Mater. Sol. Cells, vol.142, pp.75, 2015.

[11] M.K. Stodolny, M. Lenes, Y. Wu, G.J.M. Janssen, I.G. Romijn, J.R.M. Luchies, and L.J. Geerligs,"n-Type polysilicon passivating contact for industrial bifacial n-type solar cells," Sol. Energy Mater. Sol. Cells, vol. 158, pp. 24, 2016.

[12] R. Peibst, Y. Larionova, S. Reiter, M. Turcu, R. Brendel, D. Tetzlaff, J. Krügener,T. Wietler, U. Höhne, J.D. Kähler, H. Mehlich, S. Frigge, "Implementation of n+ andp+ POLO junctions on front and rear side of double-side contacted industrial silicon solar cells," 32nd Europ. Photovolt. Sol. Energy Conference, Munich,Germany, pp.323, 2016.

[13]A. Moldovan, F. Feldmann, M. Zimmer, J. Rentsch, J. Benick, and M. Hermle, "Tunnel oxide passivated carrier-selective contacts based on ultra-thin SiO2 layers,"Sol. Energy Mater. Sol. Cells, vol.142, pp.123, 2015.

[14]A. Richter, J. Benick, R. Müller, F. Feldmann, C. Reichel, M. Hermle, S.W. Glunz, "Tunnel oxide passivating electron contacts as full-area rear emitter of high-efficiency p-type silicon solar cells," Prog. Photovolt Res. Appl., vol.26, pp. 579, 2018.

[15]M. Jeon, J. Kang, G. Shim, S. Ahn, N. Balaji, C. Park, Y. Lee, J. Yi, "Passivation effect of tunnel oxide grown by N2O plasma for c-Si solar cell applications," Vacuum, vol.141, pp152, 2017.

[16]Y.Q. Huang, M.D. Liao, Z.X. Wang, X.Q. Guo, C.S. Jiang, Q.Yang, Z.Z. Yuan, D.D. Huang, J. Yan, X.Y. Zhang, Q. Wang, H. Jin, M. Al-Jassim, C.H.Shou, Y.H. Zeng, B.J. Yan, J.C. Ye, "Ultrathin silicon oxide prepared by in-line plasma-assisted N2O oxidation (PANO) and the application for n-type polysilicon passivated contact,"Sol. Energy Mater. Sol. Cells, vol. 208, pp.110389, 2020.

[17] B.C. Liao, W.L. Wu, R.J. Yeo, X.Y. Wu, S. Ma, Q. Wang, Y.M. Wan, X.D. Su, W.Z. Shen, X. Li, W.M. Li, G.Q. Xing, B. Hoex, Atomic scale controlled tunnel oxide enabled by a novel industrial tube-based PEALD technology with demonstrated commercial TOPCon cell efficiencies > 24%, Prog. Photovolt Res. Appl., vol.31, pp.220, 2022.

[18] J. Schmidt, R. Peibst, R. Brendel, Surface passivation of crystalline silicon solar cells: present and future, Sol. Energy Mater. Sol. Cells, vol. 187, pp. 39, 2018.

[19] B. Steinhauser, J.I. Polzin, F. Feldmann, M. Hermle, S.W. Glunz, "Excellent Surface Passivation Quality on Crystalline Silicon Using Industrial-Scale Direct-Plasma TOPCon Deposition Technology," Solar RRL, vol. 2, pp.1800068, 2018.

[20] F. Frank, T. Fellmeth, B. Steinhauser, H. Nagel, D. Ourinson, M. Sebastian, E. Lohmuller, J. Polzin, J. Benick, A. Richter, A. Moldovan, M. Bivour, F. Clement, J. Rentsch, H. Martin, S.W. Glunz, "Large area TOPCon cells realized by a PECVD process," 36th European PV Solar Energy Conference and Exhibition, pp.304, 2019.

[21] W. Chen, T.N. Truong, H.T. Nguyen, C. Samundsett, S.P. Phang, D. MacDonald, A. Cuevas, L. Zhou, Y. Wan, D. Yan, "Influence of PECVD deposition temperature on phosphorus doped poly-silicon passivating contacts," Sol. Energy Mater Sol. Cells, vol. 206, pp.110348, 2020.

Impact of doped polysilicon process for mass production TOPCon solar cell

Speaker : Cheng-Wen Kuo

1BV.5.32

Outline

- Introduction
- Experiment and Result
- Summary

TSEC

Introduction

- To increase the throughput of TOPCon solar cells, we attempted to improve process parameters at key point.
- In the polysilicon process, It could be found that increasing the temperature leads to the formation of more nanocrystalline structures on the surface of the polysilicon layer.

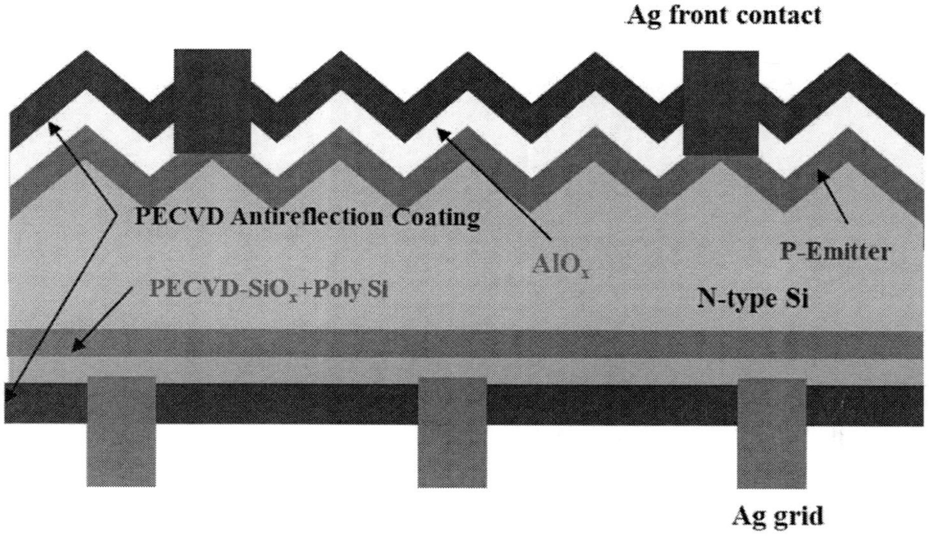

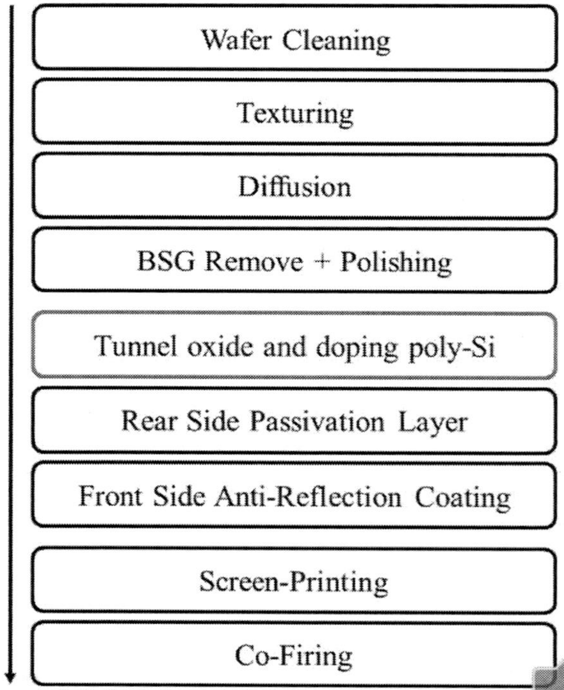

TSEC

Experiment and Result

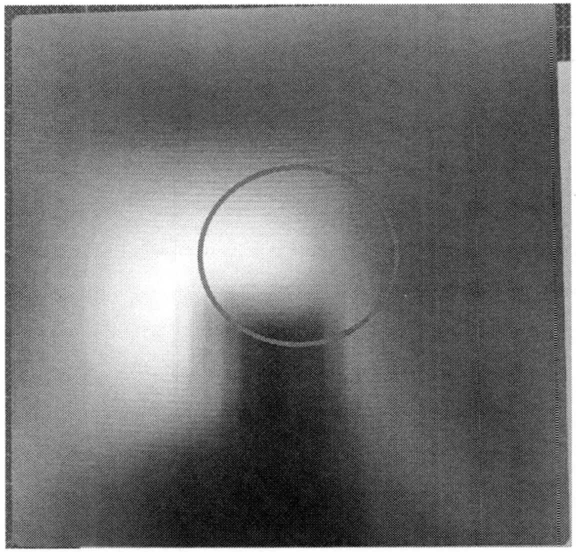

	poly grain size (nm)
REF	42 – 67
Experiment	70 – 76

	REF TOPCon	Experiment
Poly-Si thickness	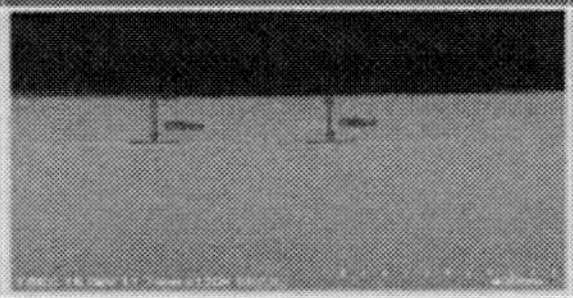	
TOP View SEM 50k		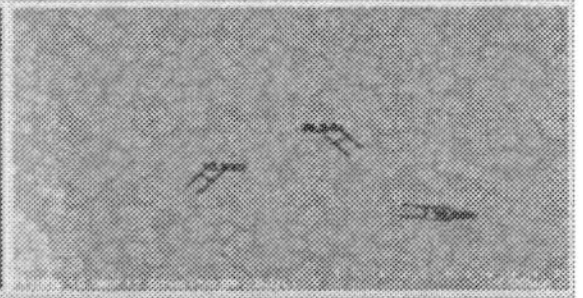
Tilt 55° SEM 10k	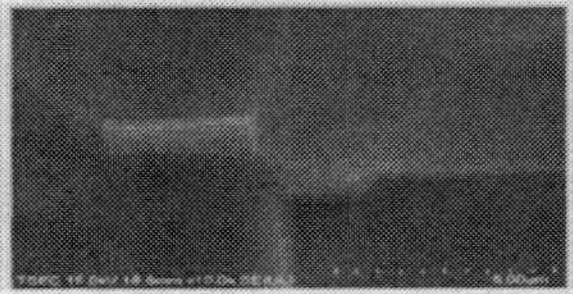	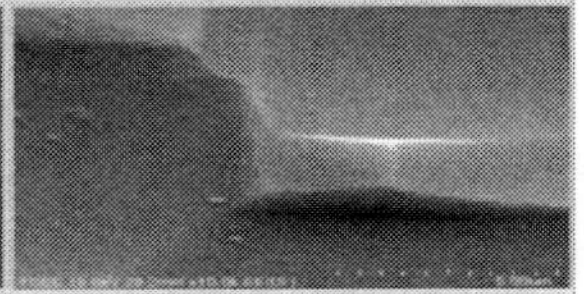
Tilt 55° SEM 50k		
Tilt 55° SEM 150k		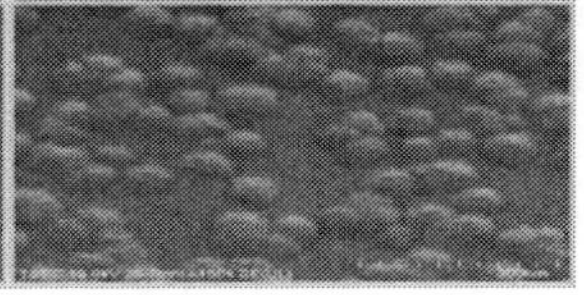

	EFF (%)	FF (%)	V_{OC} (V)	I_{SC} (A)
REF TOPCon	25.80	84.64	0.7319	13.940
Experiment	25.95	84.94	0.7347	13.921

Summary

- We present a process method that improved yield and achieved better performance.
- For the both solar cells, the degradation in PID test is less than 5%.
- Finally, we tested the TOPCon tandem process with the research center and found that performance varied with the number of nanocrystal structures.

ANALYSIS OF TEXTURE ETCHING TO REDUCE LASER-INDUCED DAMAGE IN BORON-DOPED SELECTIVE EMITTERS

Bruno Krever Lopes, Adriano Moehlecke, Moussa Ly, Izete Zanesco, Felipe Chini de Freitas
Solar Energy Technology Nucleus, School of Technology, Pontifical Catholic University of Rio Grande do Sul - PUCRS
Av. Ipiranga, 6681, P.96A, 90619-900, Porto Alegre, RS, Brazil
e-mails: Lopes.bruno@edu.pucrs.br, moehleck@pucrs.br, moussa.ly@pucrs.br, izete@pucrs.br, felipe.freitas@edu.pucrs.br

ABSTRACT: The photovoltaic industry is undergoing a transition from p-type to n-type silicon substrates, with most solar cells incorporating boron-doped emitters. Boron laser-assisted selective emitter is a key area of research in the mass production of high-efficiency devices. However, laser processing can damage silicon wafers and reduce the minority carrier lifetime. This paper presents an analysis of a process developed to obtain boron-doped emitters using laser-assisted doping, combined with texture etching to reduce surface damage. Boron-doped regions exhibit resistance to KOH-based etching, thereby enabling selective material removal and making this approach suitable for the fabrication of selective emitters. Boron was deposited by spin-coating, and diffusion was performed with a Nd-YAG laser. The samples were analysed by SEM images and minority carrier lifetime and sheet resistance measurements. SEM images revealed that, despite the presence of boron in the laser-processed areas, the anisotropic etching produced textured surfaces. The decrease in minority carrier lifetime was smaller in the samples processed using the proposed method compared to those subjected to the reference process. In conclusion, texture etching can be performed after boron diffusion to minimize silicon damage caused by laser processing and to increase the sheet resistance of the doped regions.
Keywords: silicon solar cell, laser processing, texture etching, selective emitter.

1 INTRODUCTION

In the past decade, the passivated emitter and rear solar cell (PERC) has emerged as the industry standard, replacing Al-BSF (aluminum-back surface field) devices. This technology transition occurred because the PERC structure minimizes minority charge carrier recombination on the surfaces and enhances the internal reflectance on the rear face of the device. To further reduce recombination, the tunnel-oxide passivated contact (TOPCon) structure has been introduced in industrial production lines in recent years. The combination of tunnel oxide and polysilicon films reduces recombination at the rear metal contact interface, enabling the fabrication of high-efficiency devices. However, approximately 50% of the recombination occurs at the front side of the devices, in the boron-doped emitter and contacts [1].

In manufacturing lines, PERC and TOPCon devices are typically fabricated using screen-printing to form electrical contacts. The screen-printing has led to significant electrical losses in the emitter, which is a limiting factor for the efficiency of industrial solar cells [2], [3]. These losses stem from the high contact resistance (ρ_c) between the homogeneous emitter and the metal contacts. One solution to this issue is the use of selective emitters, which involves creating a thick and highly doped region beneath the metal finger area, whereas the illuminated region between the fingers maintains a lower dopant concentration and a shallower p-n junction. The selective emitter can reduce ρ_c and Auger and Shockley-Read-Hall (SRH) recombination [4], enhancing solar cell efficiency.

Among the various techniques for selective emitter fabrication, laser-assisted doping is particularly advantageous due to its processing speed, cost-effectiveness, compatibility with industrial production lines, and minimal requirement for additional process steps in solar cell manufacturing [4], [5]. According to the International Technology Roadmap for Photovoltaics (ITRPV) [6], the laser diffusion technique will constitute the mainstream process for obtaining selective emitters in the coming decade. However, notably, the laser diffusion technique introduces defects in the silicon lattice, which are associated primarily with surface melting induced during processing. The recombination centers for minority charge carriers significantly decrease the solar cell efficiency, as evidenced in previous research [7-12]. For example, Gu et al. [12] analyzed the impact of laser pulses on recombination in boron-doped emitters. They reported that the laser irradiation partially destroyed the surface pyramid structure, leading to an increase in surface defects and dangling bonds. A post-oxidation process was proposed to repair laser-induced damage [12].

Moehlecke and Luque [13] proposed an anisotropic surface etching process in a KOH solution to create selective emitters, exploiting the resistance of boron-doped silicon surfaces to anisotropic etching. The strong B-Si bond increases the rigidity of the lattice, increasing the energy required to remove a silicon atom, high enough to stop etching altogether [14]. In the case of KOH solutions, the rate of anisotropic etching can be reduced by approximately twenty times on the surface of silicon with boron concentrations higher than 10^{20} cm^{-3} [14]. In recent years, this concept has been applied to TOPCon and interdigitated back contact (IBC) solar cells [15], [16]. For instance, Hoβ et al. [16] developed TOPCon devices with patterned p-type fingers to obtain local passivating contacts on the front side.

This paper presents an analysis of a process developed to obtain boron-doped emitters using laser-assisted doping, combined with texture etching to reduce surface damage. In the proposed approach, texture etching was performed subsequent to boron diffusion. The results obtained were compared to those from reference processes to evaluate the effectiveness of the method. The use of boron to reduce the etching of selective emitters and laser-induced degradation represents an innovation in solar cell processing. Samples with boron-doped regions were processed and characterized by scanning electron microscopy (SEM) images, the sheet resistance of the boron-doped emitters, and the minority charge carrier lifetime of the silicon wafers.

2 MATERIALS AND METHODS

2.1 Processes

Fig. 1 illustrates the main steps of the proposed process, as well as two reference processes. In the proposed process (A), boron diffusion was performed before texture etching. The reference process B involved anisotropic etching before laser processing, the standard sequence used in industries and labs. The reference process C focused on laser processing of textured silicon wafers without boron doping, aiming to evaluate only the effect of laser on minority carrier lifetime.

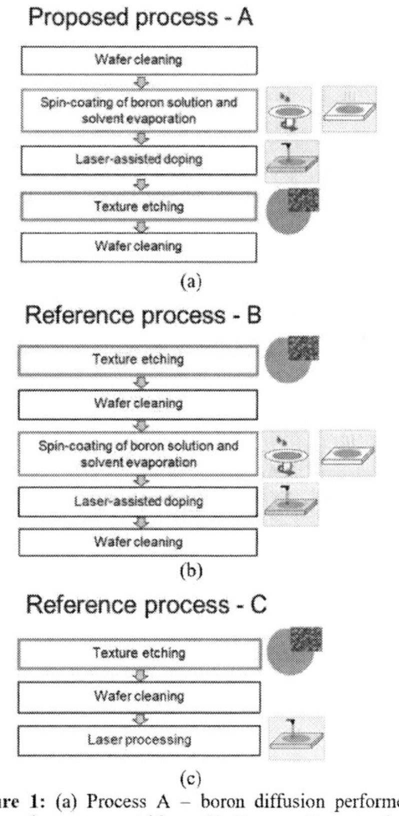

Figure 1: (a) Process A – boron diffusion performed before the texture etching; (b) Process B – standard sequence for boron-doped emitter formation, with texture etching as the initial step; (c) Process C – laser processing of silicon wafers without prior boron deposition by spin-coating.

In the proposed processing sequence (process A), the silicon wafers were cleaned in a CP4 solution, which consists of nitric acid, hydrofluoric acid, and acetic acid. The wafers were subsequently cleaned in a standard RCA2 solution composed of hydrogen peroxide, hydrochloric acid, and deionized water. The boron dopant was PBF20 solution (Filmtronics), which was deposited onto the wafer surface using the spin-coating method. The laser-assisted doping processes were carried out with a Nd:YAG laser equipment (wavelength of 1064 nm), with a nominal power of 18 W. After laser processing, the texture etching was performed in a solution containing potassium hydroxide, isopropyl alcohol, and deionized water at a temperature of approximately 90 °C. The etching times ranged from 20 min to 60 min.

The texture etching was carried out in the first steps in reference processes B and C. The immersion time of the silicon wafers was 60 min, which is a standard time to produce lower reflectance and pyramid heights ranging from 5 µm to 8 µm. After texture etching, the wafers were cleaned in low concentration hydrofluoric acid followed by RCA2 solution. Boron was deposited by spin-coating and diffused by laser irradiation in process B. To assess the damage caused by laser irradiation, no boron-diffused regions were formed in Process C.

2.2 Sample processing

N-type monocrystalline float-zone (FZ) silicon wafers, doped with phosphorus and with resistivity of 1 Ω.cm - 20 Ω.cm, were processed. Six square samples of 4.18 cm^2 with laser diffusion in the "finger areas" and three samples of 4.18 cm^2 with homogeneous laser diffusion were developed in each silicon wafer, as depicted in Fig. 2. The "finger areas" are those that receive the metal contact in solar cells; thus, with boron diffusion only in the finger regions, a selective emitter can be formed.

Three different laser processing configurations were applied, based on processes developed previously [8], [9], namely: 1) Configuration 1, laser produced circular regions (spots) in the "finger areas", without superposition of the spots [8]: laser intensity of 95%, beam scanning speed of 3000 mm/s, and pulse rate frequency of 30 kHz.
2) Configuration 2, circular regions (spots) produced by laser processing were superposed to obtain lines ("fingers") [9]: laser intensity of 95%, beam scanning speed of 500 mm/s, and pulse rate frequency of 60 kHz.
3) Configuration 3: the laser parameters were identical to those of the config. 2, but boron diffusion was performed uniformly over the entire 4.18 cm^2 area. This configuration was used to measure the sheet resistance of the boron doped emitter.

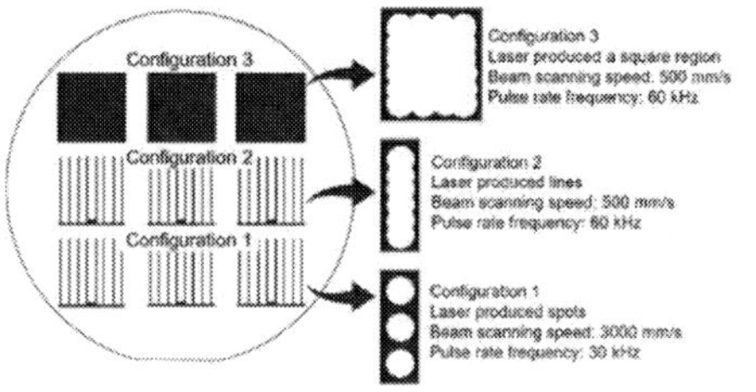

Figure 2: Structure of the samples produced via laser processing. In Configurations 1 and 2, laser processing created "fingers" to form selective emitters, whereas in Configuration 3, the entire surface was laser-processed to enable R_{SH} measurements.

2.3 Characterization techniques

The surface of the silicon wafers was examined by scanning electron microscopy to compare the selective emitters formed in Processes A and B, as well as Laser Configurations 1 and 2.

The minority charge carrier lifetime (τ) was measured using the microwave-photoconductivity decay (µPCD) technique [17]. In this method, the recombination rate of minority charge carriers is measured based on the decay of conductivity, detected by the reflected microwave power [18]. The equipment used was the WT-2000PV, Semilab and the wafers were immersed in an iodine-ethanol solution [19] to reduce surface recombination.

The sheet resistance (R_{SH}) of the boron-doped regions was measured using the four-probe technique [20] in the square areas of the samples (Laser Configuration 3).

3 RESULTS AND ANALYSIS

In Fig. 3, the SEM images of the boron-doped regions formed in process A after four different texture etching times are compared with results obtained in reference process B, both for laser configuration 1. The SEM image of a sample obtained with process B1 (process B and configuration 1) shows an untextured region formed by the laser radiation. In this process, laser radiation melts the silicon wafer near the surface, and in the subsequent re-solidification, the texture is removed. In contrast, the images related to the A1 sample (process A and configuration 1) show the formation of micropyramids in the boron selective emitter region, particularly in the central area of the spot formed by the laser beam. In this process, the hole was shallower than that formed in the process B, independently of etching time. For samples etched during 45 min, the boron doped selective emitter displays a complete texture, with only the edge region of the spot of the laser beam remaining without micropyramids.

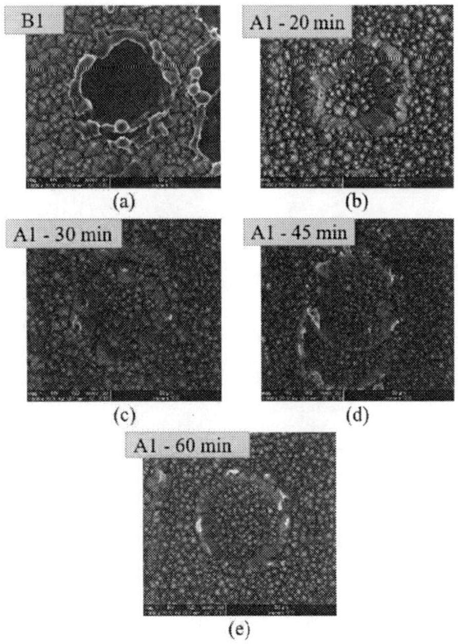

Figure 3: SEM images of silicon wafers submitted to (a) process B – Config. 1, (b) Process A – Config. 1 – texture etching of 20 min, (c) Process A1: texture etching of 30 min, (d) process A1 – 45 min, and (e) process A1 - 60 min. Letter indicates the process and number the laser configuration.

Fig. 4 shows the SEM images of the boron-doped selective emitters formed in process A compared with those produced in process B, for laser configuration 2. The image B2 shows that the texture was removed with laser processing. However, in process A2, the selective emitter region was textured after 20 minutes of etching. According to Garcia [7], the surface boron concentration is approximately of $4x10^{18}$ cm^{-3} after laser processing. As shown in Fig. 3 and Fig. 4, this boron concentration was not sufficient to prevent the formation of micropyramids.

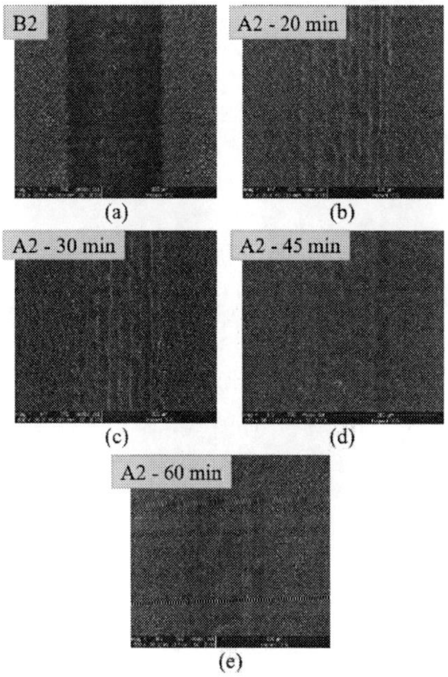

Figure 4: SEM images of silicon wafers submitted to (a) Process B - Config. 2, (b) Process A – Config. 2 – texture etching of 20 min, (c) Process A – Config. 2 – 30 min, (d) Process A – Config. 2 – 45 min, and (e) Process A – Config. 2 – 60 min.

Fig. 5 illustrates the two-dimensional distribution of minority charge carrier lifetime (τ) of samples produced with processes A, B, and C. In the three samples the same behavior was observed: a low minority carrier lifetime in the laser-processed regions. Considering the different initial τ values in the silicon wafers, an analysis of relative data was performed to compare the effect of texture etching on the minority carrier lifetime. Using the software of the WT-2000PV equipment, a pixel line was drawn in the central region of the 4.18 cm^2 sample, as shown in Fig. 6. The τ values from all the pixels in the line were subsequently extracted, and the minority carrier lifetime values as a function of the pixel position was generated. The results are presented in Fig. 7.

The higher values of τ in Fig. 7 were observed in the central regions between the finger areas, where no laser processing occurred. The lower values in Fig. 7 correspond to the central regions of the fingers formed by laser processing. Using these minority carrier lifetime values, the average values τ_{p+} of the regions with laser processing and the average values $\tau_{without\ diffusion}$ for each region between the fingers were calculated. Thus, the percentage difference ($\Delta\tau$) between $\tau_{without\ diffusion}$ and τ_{p+} was determined. This figure of merit was employed to evaluate the degradation of the laser-processed region and the potential improvements introduced by subsequent texturing. Although the reference Process C did not include a p$^+$ (boron-doped) region, the same methodology was applied to compare minority carrier lifetime results. Table I presents the results obtained, and Fig. 8 shows the $\Delta\tau$ of the samples concerning the texture etching times after boron diffusion, for laser configurations 1 and 2. Results from samples of Process B and C (without texture etch after boron diffusion and without boron, respectively) are also depicted.

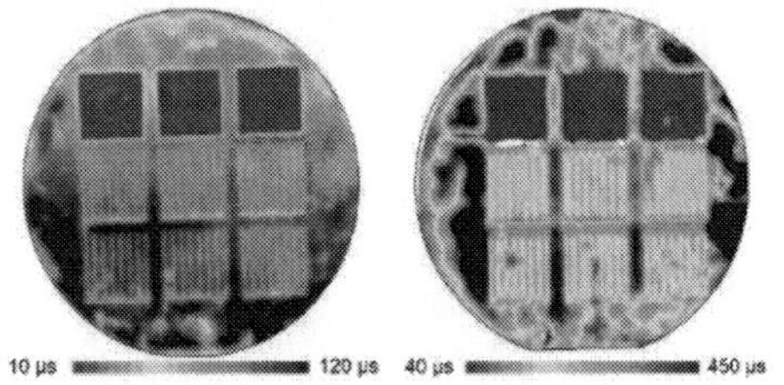

(a) (b)

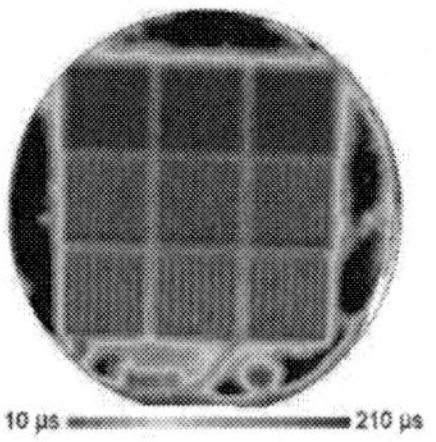

(c)

Figure 5: Two-dimensional distribution of τ measured using the µPCD technique: (a) sample from the proposed process (A), with 45 min of texturing, (b) sample from reference process B and (c) sample from reference process C.

Figure 6: Two-dimensional distribution of τ measured using the µPCD technique for a 4.18 cm² sample, with a selected pixel line (red line). The image was extracted from Fig. 5 (a) (square marked with a red dashed line).

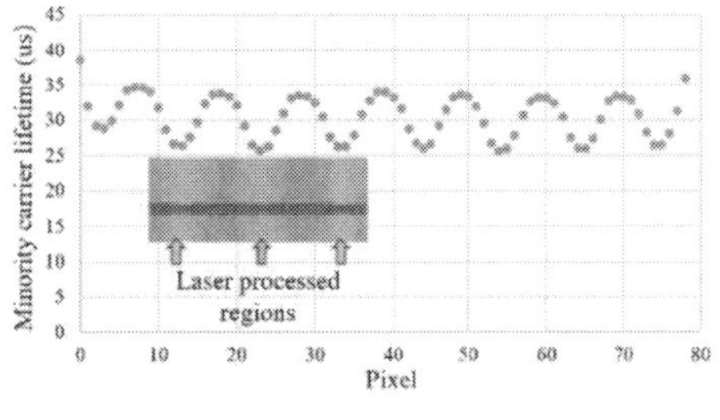

Figure 7: Minority carrier lifetime along the highlighted pixel red line in Fig. 6.

Table I: Average τ_{p+}, $\tau_{without\ diffusion}$, and $\Delta\tau$ (%) of the samples with laser processed regions. The texture time is presented in the first column for samples processed with proposed process (A) and both laser configurations.

Process-Laser configuration	Average τ_{p+} (µs)	Average $\tau_{without\ diffusion}$ (µs)	$\Delta\tau$ (%)
B1	175 ± 18	235 ± 9	34 ± 11
B2	157 ± 5	200 ± 8	28 ± 5
C1	26 ± 1	33 ± 1	29 ± 5
C2	24 ± 2	32 ± 2	33 ± 11
A1 20 min	85 ± 4	100 ± 6	18 ± 7
A2 20 min	78 ± 5	93 ± 7	20 ± 10
A1 30 min	112 ± 7	135 ± 9	24 ± 8
A2 30 min	99 ± 4	117 ± 4	18 ± 5
A1 45 min	91 ± 3	103 ± 4	13 ± 5
A2 45 min	76 ± 5	86 ± 7	13 ± 11
A1 60 min	91 ± 2	100 ± 2	11 ± 3
A2 60 min	80 ± 3	91 ± 3	13 ± 5

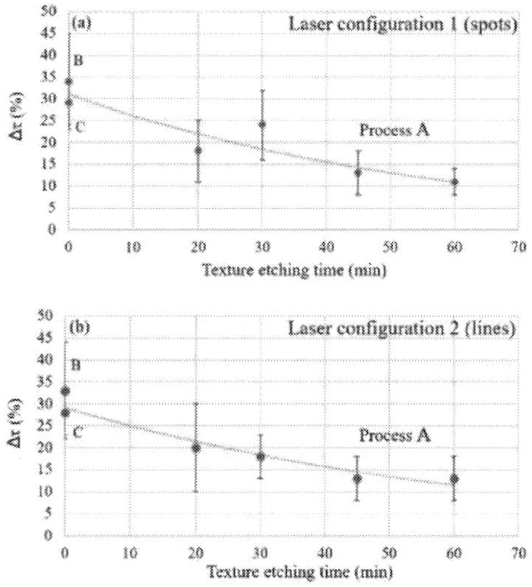

Figure 8: Δτ (%) of samples produced via processes A, B, and C, with laser configurations 1 (a) and 2 (b). The dashed line represents the trend line.

Analysis of the data presented in Table I revealed no significant difference in Δτ (%) between samples processed with laser configuration 1 and those processed with configuration 2. This indicates that, regardless of whether the laser beam overlapped, the damage caused to the wafers during processing was equivalent. When comparing the results from reference processes B and C and laser configurations 1 and 2, the Δτ (%) values are similar. Therefore, the recombination in boron doped regions is not the key factor in reducing minority carrier lifetime in laser processed regions.

A reduction in $\Delta\tau$ is observed in the samples processed with the proposed process (A) compared with those subjected to reference processes B and C. The longer the texture etching period is, the smaller the difference in $\Delta\tau$, as shown in Fig. 8. Therefore, texture etching reduced the damage caused by laser processing, and the minority carrier lifetime values were closer to those in regions without laser processing.

Table II presents the average values and standard deviations of the R_{SH} for the boron-doped emitter obtained using processes A and B. For all samples processed using the proposed method (A), regardless of texturing time, R_{SH} values ranged from 53 to 60 Ω/sq, which are higher than those of the reference process (B), where values ranged from 26 to 28 Ω/sq. The increase in R_{SH} indicated that texture etching reduced the boron concentration and the depth of the p-n junction. However, these values are consistent with the sheet resistances reported in other studies about selective or homogeneous boron emitters [21], [22], [23]. Additionally, according to the ITRPV roadmap [6], the sheet resistance of boron emitters used in industrial solar cells is expected to increase over the next decade, reaching values above 185 Ω/sq. In the proposed method, the increasing of texture etching time can produced high R_{SH}.

Table II: Average sheet resistance of boron-doped samples produced by Processes A and B. The texture time is presented in first column for samples processed with proposed process and both laser configurations.

Process – Laser configuration	Sheet Resistance (Ω/sq)
B-1	28.2 ± 1.5
B-2	26.5 ± 1.4
A-1 - 20 min	60.0 ± 5.6
A-2 - 20 min	60.0 ± 1.9
A-1 - 30 min	55.1 ± 2.5
A-2 - 30 min	53.4 ± 2.9
A-1 - 45 min	60.7 ± 3.9
A-2 - 45 min	60.4 ± 0.8
A-1 - 60 min	59.5 ± 1.8
A-2 - 60 min	60.6 ± 1.6

4 CONCLUSIONS

Boron laser-assisted doping of selective emitters was investigated, with a focus on reducing surface degradation by performing texture etching after boron diffusion.

SEM images of the laser-diffused regions revealed that boron did not inhibit the texture etching. The standard process, which involves laser-assisted boron diffusion after texture etching, produces boron-doped regions with sheet resistances of approximately 27 Ω/sq. However, performing texture etching after boron diffusion increased the sheet resistance, which ranged from 53 to 60 Ω/sq. This result demonstrates that the boron-doped regions were partially etched during the process. Therefore, the boron surface concentration resulting from laser-assisted doping was insufficient to inhibit anisotropic etching.

Regarding the analysis of minority carrier lifetime, no significant difference was observed in the $\Delta\tau$ values of samples processed with laser configurations 1 (spots) and 2 (lines). Furthermore, when comparing processes with pre-laser etching (process B) and those without the presence of the dopant during laser processing (process C), no difference in the $\Delta\tau$ values of the samples was identified. Thereby, the damage caused by laser processing might have a more pronounced effect on the degradation of the minority carrier lifetime than the recombination provided by boron doping.

The proposed process, involving texture etching after boron diffusion via laser, resulted in less damage than the samples from reference process B, which involved pre-laser texture etching. Moreover, the longer the texture etching period is, the smaller the difference in minority carrier lifetime between regions with and without laser processing. Thus, applying an anisotropic KOH-based etch after laser-assisted doping can be an approach to reduce the surface damage induced by the laser process.

5 ACKNOWLEDGMENTS

The authors acknowledge the financial support of the Brazilian funding agencies CNPq (National Council for Scientific and Technological Development), grant numbers 440044/2019-7 and 306916/2017-7, and FINEP (Funding Authority for Studies and Projects), grant number n° 01.22.0194.00 (Ref. 0130/21). BKL is grateful for the grant provided by CAPES (Coordination for the Improvement of Higher Education Personnel) and Hewlett-Packard Brasil Ltda. (with resources from the IT Law Lei nº 8.248, de 1991).

REFERENCES

[1] S. Glunz, F. Feldmann, A. Richter, M. Bivour, C. Reichel, H. Steinkemper, J. Benick, M. Hermle, The irresistible charm of a simple current flow pattern – 25% with a solar cell featuring a full-area back contact, *31st European Photovoltaic Solar Energy Conference and Exhibition (EU PVSEC)*, (2015) 259 - 263. https://doi.org/10.4229/EUPVSEC20152015-2BP.1.1

[2] S. Tepner and A. Lorenz, Printing technologies for silicon solar cell metallization: a comprehensive review, *Progress in Photovoltaics: Research and Applications*, 31 (2023) 557-590. https://doi.org/10.1002/pip.3674

[3] H. Haverkamp, A. Dastgheib-Shirazi, B. Raabe, F. Book, and G. Hahn, Minimizing the electrical losses on the front side: Development of a selective emitter process from a single diffusion, *33rd IEEE Photovoltaic Specialists Conference*, IEEE, (2008) 1–4. https://doi.org/10.1109/PVSC.2008.4922443.

[4] C.W. Kuo, T.-M. Kuan, W.-L. Chueh, L.-G. Wu, C.-C. Huang, and C.-Y. Yu, Impact of laser-doped selective emitters parameter for industrial mono PERC solar cells, *2018 IEEE 7th World Conference on Photovoltaic Energy Conversion (WCPEC)* (A Joint Conference of 45th IEEE PVSC, 28th PVSEC & 34th EU PVSEC), (2018) 1029–1032. https://doi.org/: 10.1109/PVSC.2018.8547466.

[5] U. Jäger, S. Mack, C. Wufka, A. Wolf, D. Biro, and R. Preu, Benefit of selective emitters for p-type silicon solar cells with passivated surfaces, *IEEE Journal of Photovoltaics*, 3(2) (2013) 621–627. https://doi.org/10.1109/JPHOTOV.2012.2230685.

[6] VDMA, *International Technology Roadmap for Photovoltaic (ITRPV) - 2024 Results, 16th Edition*, 2025.

[7] S. Wang, Laser technology in the fabrication of high efficiency solar cells, Doctor Thesis. Sydney, Australia: University of New South Wales (2018). https://doi.org/10.26190/unsworks/20572

[8] V. F. Salvador, Development and analysis of n-base solar cells with selective emitter formed by laser radiation, MSc Dissertation. Porto Alegre, Brazil: Pontifícia Universidade Católica do Rio Grande do Sul, (2019).

https://primo-pmtna01.hosted.exlibrisgroup. com/ permalink/f/164fi7o/puc01000 496600
[9] S. B. Garcia, Development and comparison of p^+nn^+ solar cells with homogeneous and selective emitter. Dr. Thesis. Porto Alegre, Brazil: Pontifícia Universidade Católica do Rio Grande do Sul, (2016). http://tede2.pucrs.br/ tede2/handle/tede/6707
[10] Z. Sun, M.C. Gupta, A study of laser-induced surface defects in silicon and impact on electrical properties, *Journal of Applied Physics*, 124 (2018) 223103. https://doi.org/10.1063/1.5058143
[11] G. Poulain, D. Blanc, A. Focsa, M. De Vita, K. Fraser, Y. Sayad, M. Lemiti, Characterization of laser-induced damage in silicon solar cells during selective ablation processes, *Materials Science and Engineering B*, 178 (2013) 682-685. https://doi.org/ 10.1016/j.mseb. 2012.11.015
[12] S. Gu, L. Yuan, K. Guo, W. Huang, L. Li, Y. Yang, X. Jiang, N. Yuan, Q. Wang, J. Ding, Laser damage and post oxidation repair performance of n-TOPCon solar cells with laser assisted doping boron selective emitter, *Solar Energy Materials and Solar Cells*, 274 (2024) 112988. https://doi.org/10.1016/j.solmat.2024.112988.
[13] A. Moehlecke and A. Luque, New approach to obtain boron selective emitters for Si solar cells, *Proceedings of 1994 IEEE 1st World Conference on Photovoltaic Energy Conversion - WCPEC (A Joint Conference of PVSC, PVSEC and PSEC)*, IEEE, (1994) 1492–1495. https://doi.org/10.1109/WCPEC.1994.520233.
[14] K. E. Petersen, Silicon as a mechanical material, *Proceedings of the IEEE*, 70(5) (1982) 420–457. https://doi.org/10.1109/PROC.1982.12331.
[15] J. Linke, F. Buchholz, C. Peter, J. Hoß, J. Lossen, V.D. Mihailetchi, R. Kopecek, Fully passivating contact IBC solar cells using laser processing, *8th World Conference on Photovoltaic Energy Conversion* (2022). https://doi.org/ 10.4229/WCPEC-82022-1CV.2.11
[16] J. Hoß, S. S. Kalaghichi, M. Comak, P. Preis, J. Lossen, J. Linke, L. J. Koduvelikulathu, F. Buchholz, Advanced TOPCon solar cells with patterned p-type poly-Si fingers on the front side and vanishing metal induced recombination losses, *EPJ Photovoltaics*, 15, 43 (2024). https://doi.org/10.1051/epjpv/2024040
[17] T. Asada, Y. Ichikawa, and M. Kato, Carrier lifetime measurements in semiconductors through the microwave photoconductivity decay method, *Journal of Visualized Experiments*, 146 (2019). https://doi.org/ 10.3791/59007.
[18] D. K. Schroder, *Semiconductor Material and Device Characterization*. Wiley (2005). https://doi.org/10.1002/ 0471749095.
[19] T. S. Horányi, T. Pavelka, and P. Tüttö, In situ bulk lifetime measurement on silicon with a chemically passivated surface, *Applied Surface Science*, 63(1–4) (1983) 306–311. https://doi.org/10.1016/0169-4332(93)90112-O.
[20] D.K. Schroder. *Semiconductor Material and Device Characterization*. Wiley, 2005.
[21] Y. Tomizawa, Y. Ikeda, and T. Shiro, Development of n-type selective emitter silicon solar cells by laser doping using boron doped silicon paste, *Energy Procedia*, 92 (2016) 419–426. https://doi.org/10.1016/ j.egypro.2016.07.122.
[22] W. Lin *et al.*, Green-laser-doped selective emitters with separate BBr_3 diffusion processes for high-efficiency n-type silicon solar cells, *Solar Energy Materials and Solar Cells*, 210 (2020) 110462. https://doi.org/10.1016/j.solmat.2020.110462.
[23] M. Peng, Q. Wang, M. Zhang, X. Xi, G. Liu, L. Wang, L. Chen, Optimization of boron depletion for boron-doped emitter of n-type TOPCon solar cells, *Materials Science in Semiconductor Processing*, 178 (2024) 108424. https://doi.org/ 10.1016/j.mssp.2024.108424

PONTIFICAL CATHOLIC UNIVERSITY OF RIO GRANDE DO SUL – PUCRS
SCHOOL OF TECHNOLOGY
SOLAR ENERGY TECHNOLOGY NUCLEUS – NT SOLAR

PUCRS

NT-Solar Escola Politécnica PUCRS

ANALYSIS OF TEXTURE ETCHING TO REDUCE LASER-INDUCED DAMAGE IN BORON-DOPED SELECTIVE EMITTERS

Bruno Krever Lopes, Adriano Moehlecke, Moussa Ly, Izete Zanesco and Felipe Chini de Freitas

AIM

Analysis of a process to produce boron-doped emitters using laser-assisted doping, combined with texture etching to reduce the surface damage.

Boron-doped regions may reduce or inhibit the silicon etch rate during KOH-based etching, making it a suitable approach for producing selective emitters.

METHODOLOGY

NT-SOLAR / PUCRS / BRAZIL

Research Activities
- Silicon solar cells
- PV modules
- PV systems

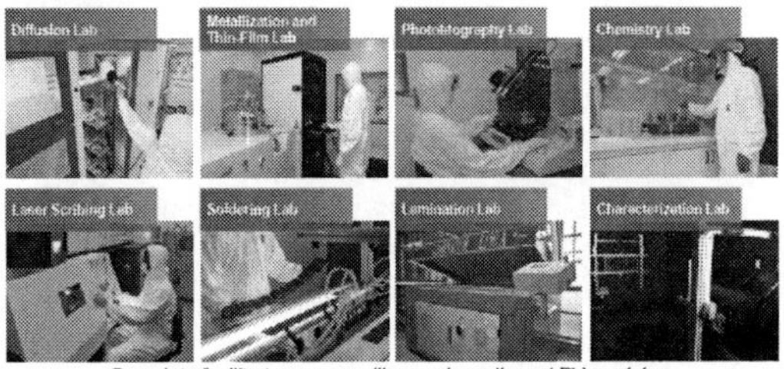

Complete facility to process silicon solar cells and PV modules.

LASER CONFIGURATIONS

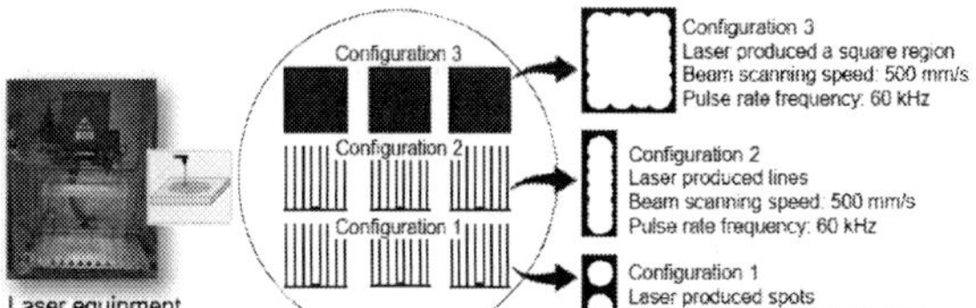

Laser equipment (λ= 1064 nm), 18 W.

PROCESSES

Proposed process - A

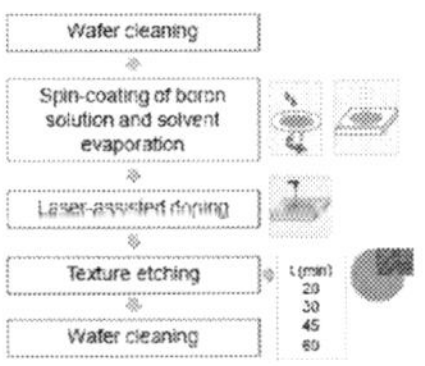

Reference process - B

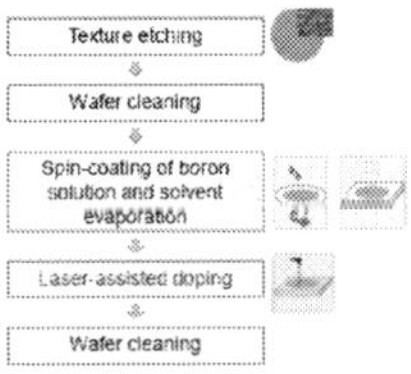

Reference process - C

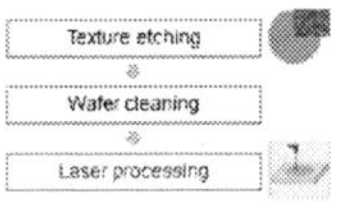

SEM IMAGES / SHEET RESISTANCE / µPCD

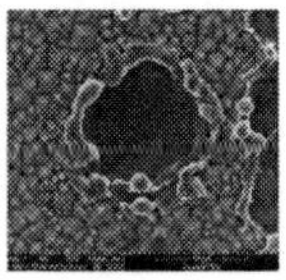

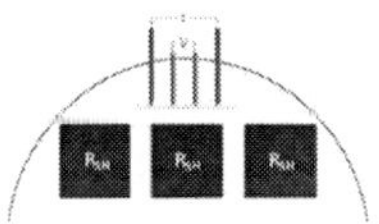

Wafers immersed in iodine–ethanol solution.

RESULTS AND ANALYSIS

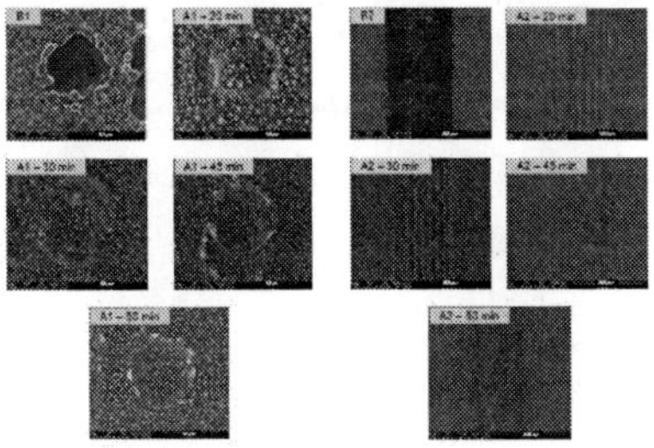

Average R_{SH} of boron-doped emitters.

Process – Laser configuration	Sheet Resistance (Ω/sq)
B-1	28.2 ± 1.5
B-2	26.5 ± 1.4
A-1 - 20 min	60.0 ± 5.6
A-2 - 20 min	60.0 ± 1.9
A-1 - 30 min	55.1 ± 2.5
A-2 - 30 min	53.4 ± 2.9
A-1 - 45 min	60.7 ± 3.9
A-2 - 45 min	60.4 ± 0.8
A-1 - 60 min	59.5 ± 1.8
A-2 - 60 min	60.6 ± 1.6

Process A | Process B | Process C
Texture etch time = 45 min

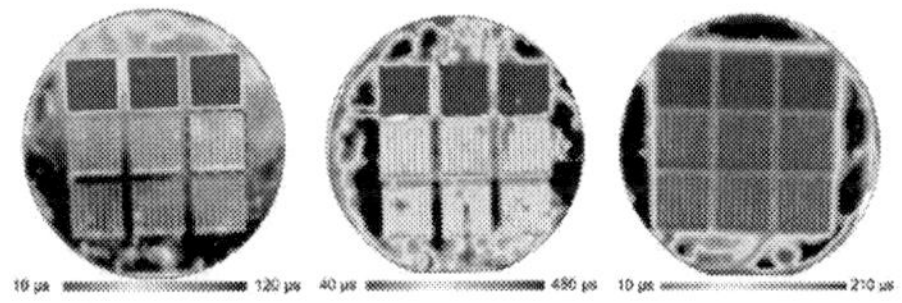

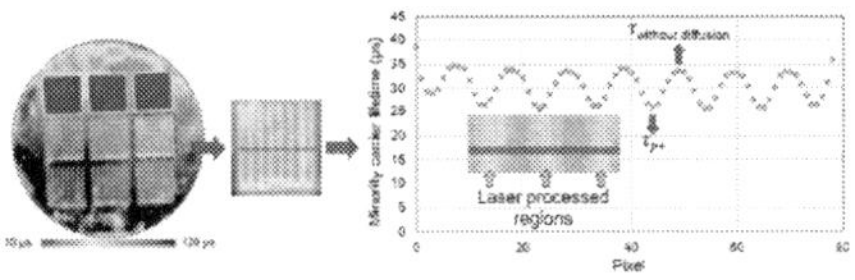

$$\Delta\tau = \frac{\tau_{without\ diffusion} - \tau_{p+}}{\tau_{without\ diffusion}}$$

τ_{p+} - average lifetime in laser processed regions

$\tau_{without\ diffusion}$ - average lifetime in regions between the fingers

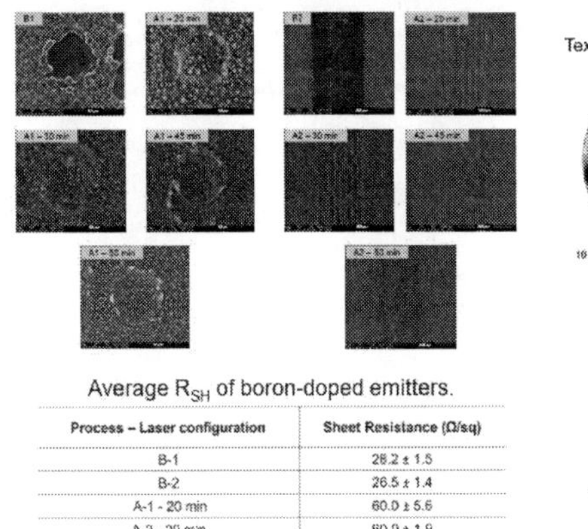

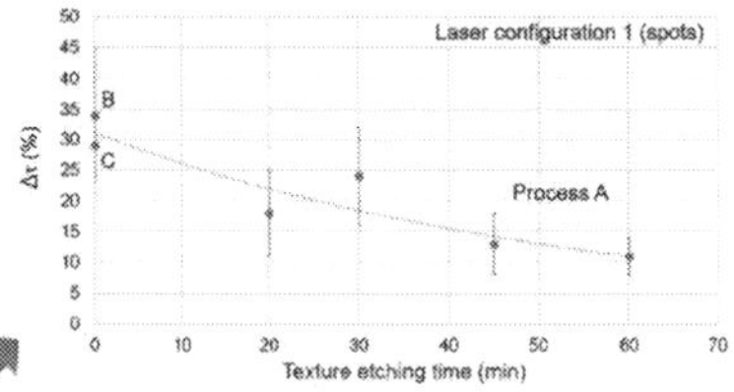

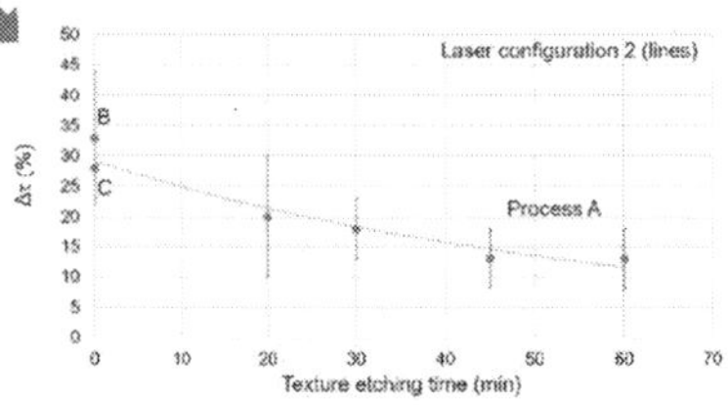

CONCLUSIONS

- **SEM images of laser-diffused regions showed that boron did not inhibit texture etching.**
- **Laser doping after texture etching yielded R_{SH} ~27 Ω/sq; texture etching after doping increased R_{SH} to 53–60 Ω/sq.**
- **Laser configurations 1 (spots) and 2 (lines) showed no significant difference in $\Delta\tau$.**
- **Proposed process A caused less laser damage than process B (pre-laser texture), with longer etching times reducing minority carrier lifetime differences between processed and unprocessed regions.**

Acknowledgments: Brazilian financing agencies FINEP, CNPq and CAPES; HP Brasil Ltda.

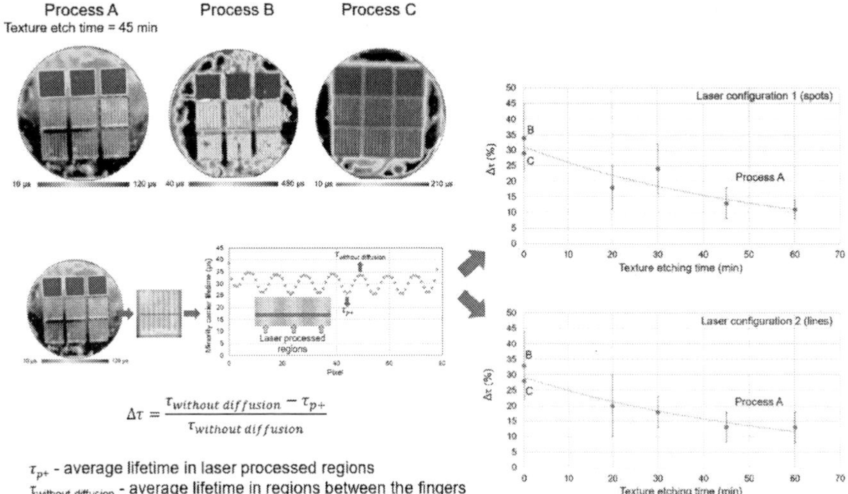

INFLUENCE OF REDUCED GAS FLOW RATES ON THE SHEET RESISTANCE OF BORON-DOPED LAYERS PERFORMED IN A COMPACT FURNACE

Izete Zanesco, Lucas Teixeira Caçapietra Pires da Silva, Adriano Moehlecke, Moussa Ly,
João Victor Zanatta Britto and Vitor Gomes de Venuto
Pontifical Catholic University of Rio Grande do Sul, School of Technology, Solar Energy Technology Nucleus
Av. Ipiranga, 6681, Porto Alegre, RS, Brazil - Corresponding author: izete@pucrs.br

ABSTRACT: Manufacturing processes for bifacial TOPCon and PERC solar cells have been investigated to increase efficiency and reduce costs. Considering that quartz tube furnaces are usually employed to produce doped layers, in this work, we analyse the influence of reduced gas flow rates on the sheet resistance of boron-doped layers formed in a new compact furnace to produce the emitter of TOPCon and the BSF of bifacial PERT solar cells. A compact furnace prototype was developed according to the granted patent BR102012030601-8. The spin-coating method was used to deposit a boron solution on one face of the Si wafer, and diffusion was carried out with reduced and baseline gas flow rates. The average sheet resistance (R_{sh}) of B-BSF produced with oxygen and nitrogen flow rates reduced, respectively, by 50% and 90% ranged from 43.3 to 48.6 Ω/sq, and the standard deviation (SD) was lower than 3.2%. Although the average R_{sh} from 103 to 158 Ω/sq produced with baseline gas flow rates was higher, the SD was 2% - 11%. The emitter formed with reduced gas flow rates presented a R_{sh} from 88 to 118 Ω/sq with a SD between 4% and 7%. Additionally, the boron concentration in the emitter increased slightly at depths greater than 0.45 μm.
Keywords: Boron diffusion, compact furnace, emitter sheet resistance, BSF sheet resistance.

1 INTRODUCTION

Bifacial high efficiency solar cell structures, such as n-type tunnel oxide passivated contact (TOPCon) and p-type passivated emitter and rear (PERC) solar cells, represented 55% and 35%, respectively, of the market share in 2024 [1]. Considering this trend, the dominant technologies in the next decade will remain bifacial high efficiency architectures manufactured with reduced production costs.

TOPCon and PERC solar cells are manufactured using thermal processes for dopant diffusion and silicon oxide growth. Boron is the dopant used to form the p^+ emitter of n-type TOPCon (n-TOPCon) solar cells and the back surface field (BSF) of the p-type passivated emitter and rear totally diffused (p-PERT) solar cells [2], a structure of the PERC family.

Currently, BCl_3 in the vapour phase introduced into a quartz tube furnace is the usual approach to produce a boron-doped layer in homojunction silicon solar cells, although BBr_3 has been the main dopant source used in the last decade [3]. Nevertheless, alternative methods have been investigated to produce boron-doped layers, such as ion implantation, epitaxial growth, deposition of dopant solution by spin coating followed by diffusion using laser or a conventional quartz tube furnace. These alternative methods are usually carried out with nontoxic sources [4].

In p-type TOPCon solar cells, a boron-doped poly-Si/SiO_2 stack is deposited on the rear side to form passivated contacts. Low-pressure chemical vapour deposition (LPCVD) is commonly used to deposit a layer of doped amorphous silicon (a-Si) or polysilicon. However, the deposition of intrinsic a-Si/μ-polysilicon by LPCVD or plasma enhanced chemical vapour deposition (PECVD) and a subsequent doping process has also been investigated [5], [6].

Quartz tube furnaces are widely used for dopant diffusion to manufacture silicon solar cells, and they are often referred to as conventional furnaces. Nevertheless, diffusion methods carried out in different technology furnaces, such as rapid thermal processing furnaces and belt furnaces, have been employed.

With respect to boron diffusion to form a selective emitter of n-type TOPCon solar cells, Wang *et al.* [7] developed p^{++} and p^+ layers formed by 3D printing mask technology and a secondary diffusion using BCl_3 as the dopant source in a quartz tube furnace. The results showed that the drive-in and oxidation processes had more impact than the BCl_3 gas flow rate on the emitter dark saturation current density. The sheet resistance of the boron selective emitter was 75 Ω/sq (p^{++}) and 230 Ω/sq (p^+), and the achieved solar cell efficiency was 24.2%.

To develop n-type TOPCon solar cells, Liu *et al.* [8] presented an alternative method to perform the selective emitter in one step with BCl_3 as the dopant source and a boron-doped silicon paste deposited by screen printing. A diffusion temperature of 950 °C for 20 min was selected based on simulations and experimental results. Boron concentrations of 8.68×10^{18} atoms/cm^3 and 2.35×10^{19} atoms/cm^3 were obtained in the p^+ and p^{++} layers, respectively, with junction depths of 0.53 (p^+) μm and 0.82 μm (p^{++}). The efficiency of TOPCon solar cells achieved in a production line was 25.17%.

An energy-efficient and low-cost approach for boron diffusion was developed by Meßmer *et al.* [9]. A borosilicate glass layer was formed by atmospheric pressure chemical vapour deposition (APCVD) as the boron source, and diffusion was performed in a subsequent thermal step in a quartz tube furnace. With a vertically stacked configuration of silicon wafers, the sheet resistance demonstrated uniform boron diffusion, similar to the results obtained with BBr_3 as the dopant source. The average sheet resistance was (111 ± 4) Ω/sq, and the efficiency of the TOPCon solar cell was 23.1%.

Considering that boron diffusion requires more time than phosphorus diffusion, Lohmüller *et al.* [10] optimized boron diffusion using BBr_3 as the dopant source to form a high-quality emitter with a sheet resistance of approximately 150 Ω/sq and a standard deviation lower than 5%. A reduction in the diffusion process time from 3.5 h to 2 h was achieved by increasing the temperature. The boron profile presented a maximum boron concentration of 1.5×10^{19} atoms/cm^3 and a junction depth of 0.8 μm.

Chu *et al.* [11] optimized the boron doping profile and specific contact resistivity for n-TOPCon solar cells. For a sheet resistance of 150 Ω/sq, a surface dopant concentration of $3.0x10^{19}$ atoms/cm^3 resulted in a minimum saturation current density. Moreover, the authors concluded that the specific contact resistivity was influenced by the ramp-up and cool-down rates during the firing process.

The influence of the boron back surface field (B-BSF) sheet resistance on the electrical parameters of bifacial p-PERT solar cells was investigated [2]. B-BSF and phosphorus-doped emitter were produced in the same thermal step. The average sheet resistance of the B-BSF obtained at a diffusion temperature of 950 °C was 54 Ω/sq, with a standard deviation of 6%. After the diffusion of phosphorus, the B-BSF depth was approximately 1.0 µm, and the boron concentration on the surface of a silicon wafer was $6.4x10^{19}$ atoms/cm^3, with a slight increase in the boron concentration up to a depth of 0.3 µm. The short-circuit current density obtained with incident irradiance on the boron-doped side of bifacial PERT solar cells was the electrical parameter most affected by the B-BSF sheet resistance, influencing both the efficiency and the maximum power bifaciality coefficient.

Considering that boron diffusion is an essential step for producing the emitter of n-TOPCon solar cells and the BSF of bifacial PERT solar cells and that new approaches are being investigated, in this work, we analyse the influence of reduced gas flow rates on the sheet resistance of boron-doped layers formed in a new compact quartz tube furnace to produce the emitter of n-TOPCon solar cells and the BSF of the bifacial p-PERT structure. To reduce production costs, a compact quartz tube furnace prototype to form doped layers in silicon wafers was developed, and the gas flow rates were decreased in relation to a baseline process. The main feature of the developed furnace is that the quartz tube volume is reduced compared with that of a conventional furnace.

2 EXPERIMENTAL METHODS

Fig. 1 shows a prototype of the compact quartz tube furnace developed according to the granted patent BR102012030601-8. The quartz tube length is smaller than that of a conventional furnace to reduce the gas volume used in the processing of silicon wafers. The furnace consists of 1) a thermal heating system with electrical resistance, 2) a compact quartz tube and 3) inlet and outlet gas cabinets. The quartz tube diameter is 300 mm, and the flat zone length is 400 mm. The dimensions of the prototype are depicted in Fig. 1.

Figure 1: Prototype of the compact quartz tube furnace developed to diffuse dopants in silicon wafers according to the granted patent BR102012030601-8.

The methodology adopted is summarized in Fig. 2. The B-BSF of the bifacial PERT solar cell and the boron-doped emitter of the TOPCon device were performed in p-type and n-type Si-Cz wafers, respectively. In the first stage of the investigation, B-BSF was produced with 1) reduced and 2) baseline gas flow rates in the compact furnace and 3) baseline gas flow rates in a conventional quartz tube furnace. In the second stage, the boron-doped emitter was produced in the compact furnace with reduced gas flow rates. The oxygen and nitrogen flow rates were reduced by 50% and 90%, respectively, compared with the gas flow rates used in the baseline process of a conventional furnace. To assess the effect of gas flow reduction in the doped regions, the sheet resistance was measured in all samples, and the boron doping profiles of the emitter and BSF produced with reduced gas flow rates were evaluated.

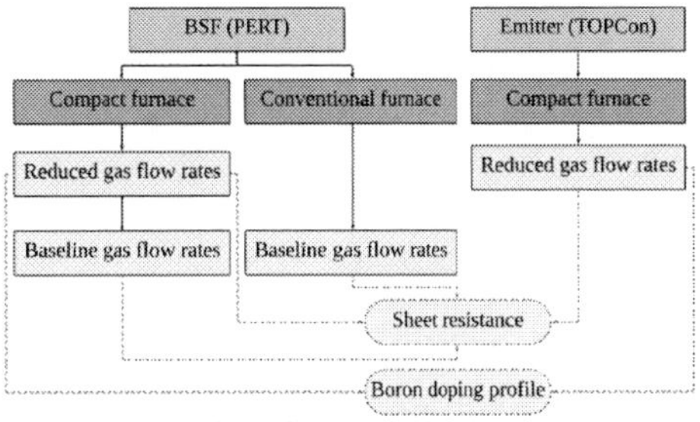

Figure 2: Flow chart of the methodology adopted.

Fig. 3 shows the process sequence for producing samples with a boron-doped emitter and B-BSF in n-type and p-type Si-Cz wafers, respectively, which had a thickness of around 200 µm and resistivity ranging from 1 Ω.cm to 20 Ω.cm. The processing sequence used to produce the samples was as follows: alkaline texture etching in a KOH solution, RCA cleaning, boron diffusion under different conditions and borosilicate glass removal.

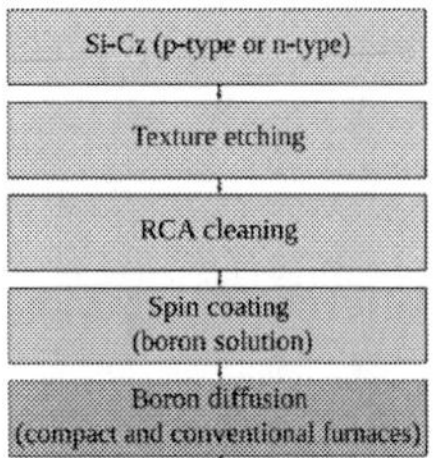

Figure 3: Process sequence to produce samples with the emitter of TOPCon solar cells (n-type Si-Cz wafers) and B-BSF of bifacial PERT solar cells (p-type Si-Cz wafers).

The boron-doped layers were produced using the spin-coating method to deposit a uniform thin layer of boron solution (PBF20, Filmtronics) on one face of the Si wafers. In sequence, the solvents were evaporated, and boron diffusion was performed at a temperature of 950 °C with reduced and baseline gas flow rates. Two samples were introduced at different positions in the flat zone of the compact furnace, as shown in Fig. 4. Position A is located close to the gas flow inlet.

The sheet resistance (R_{sh}) of the boron-doped layers and boron doping profiles were measured to investigate the uniformity of boron diffusion in each silicon wafer and in different positions in the flat zone. The R_{sh} after boron diffusion was measured in 13 regions of each sample.

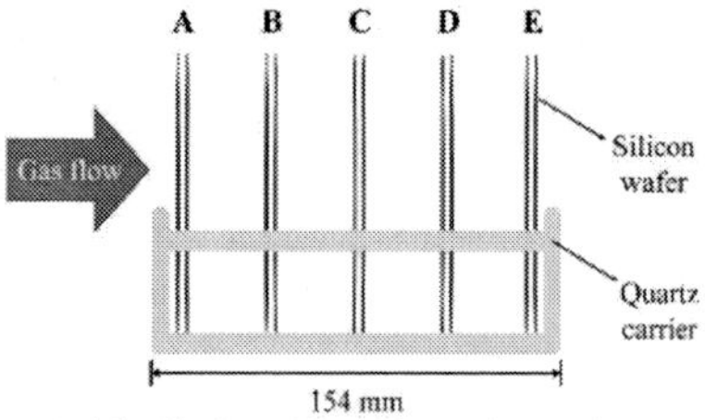

Figure 4: Distribution of samples in the carrier and their respective positions. Position A is located close to the gas flow inlet, and position E is near the gas flow outlet.

3 RESULTS AND DISCUSSION

3.1 Analysis of the boron-doped back surface field of bifacial PERT solar cells

Fig. 5 shows the sheet resistance (R_{sh}) of the B-BSF in samples, which were placed in different positions in the flat zone of the compact furnace and produced with reduced gas flow rates. Excluding a wafer located close to the gas flow outlet (position E – sample Cp15), a typical uniformity in R_{sh} was observed. The results obtained with this sample were not considered in the analysis. To overcome this problem, a Si wafer may be placed in this position as a part of the processing chamber. Table I shows that the standard deviation of the sheet resistance of each silicon wafer was lower than 3.2%, demonstrating the uniformity of boron diffusion in a specific silicon wafer. Considering all the samples and excluding a wafer located close to the gas flow outlet, R_{sh} ranged from 39.0 to 49.8 Ω/sq.

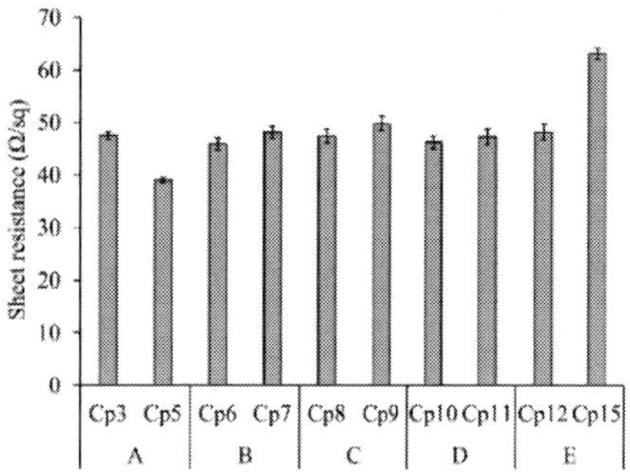

Figure 5: Sheet resistance of the B-BSF produced with reduced gas flow rates in samples located at different positions in the flat zone of the compact furnace. A, B, C, D and E represent five different locations, and Cp# represents a p-type Si wafer.

The average R_{sh} of the B-BSF produced in the compact furnace with reduced gas flow rates, presented in Table II, allows us to analyse the uniformity of boron diffusion in the flat zone. Considering positions A (close to the gas flow inlet) to E, the average sheet resistance at each position ranged from (43.3 ± 0.6) to (48.6 ± 1.4) Ω/sq, with a maximum standard deviation of 3.2%. This standard deviation is lower than that reported in the literature with boron diffusion using BBr_3 as the dopant source [10]. Considering all the Si wafers distributed in the carrier, the average sheet resistance of B-BSF was (46.8 ± 1.2) Ω/sq. Therefore, the sheet resistance of B-BSF of bifacial PERT solar cells can be produced with high uniformity in the compact furnace using reduced gas flow rates.

Table I: Sheet resistance of the B-BSF produced with reduced gas flow rates in samples located at positions A, B, C, D and E in the flat zone of the compact furnace.

Position	Sample	Sheet resistance (Ω/sq)	
A	Cp3	47.5 ± 0.7	47.5 ± 1.4%
	Cp5	39.0 ± 0.5	39.0 ± 1.2%
B	Cp6	45.9 ± 1.1	45.9 ± 2.4%
	Cp7	48.1 ± 1.2	48.1 ± 2.5%
C	Cp8	47.4 ± 1.3	47.4 ± 2.8%
	Cp9	49.8 ± 1.4	49.8 ± 2.8%
D	Cp10	46.2 ± 1.2	46.2 ± 2.5%
	Cp11	47.3 ± 1.5	47.3 ± 3.2%
E	Cp12	48.2 ± 1.5	48.2 ± 3.2%
	Cp15	63.2 ± 1.0	63.2 ± 1.6%

Table II: Average sheet resistance of the B-BSF produced in the flat zone of the compact furnace with reduced gas flow rates.

Position	Sheet resistance (Ω/sq)	
A	43.3 ± 0.6	43.3 ± 1.3%
B	47.0 ± 1.1	47.0 ± 2.4%
C	48.6 ± 1.4	48.6 ± 2.8%
D	46.8 ± 1.4	46.8 ± 2.9%
E	48.2 ± 1.5	48.2 ± 3.2%
Average	46.8 ± 1.2	46.8 ± 2.7%

The dopant concentration profiles of the B-BSF are presented in Fig. 6. In all samples, typical boron depletion is observed near the surface, caused by the borosilicate glass (BSG) formed in the Si wafers in the presence of oxygen in the quartz tube [12], [13]. Boron segregated to the BSG layer, and consequently, the dopant concentration slightly decreased from a depth of approximately 0.1 μm to the surface.

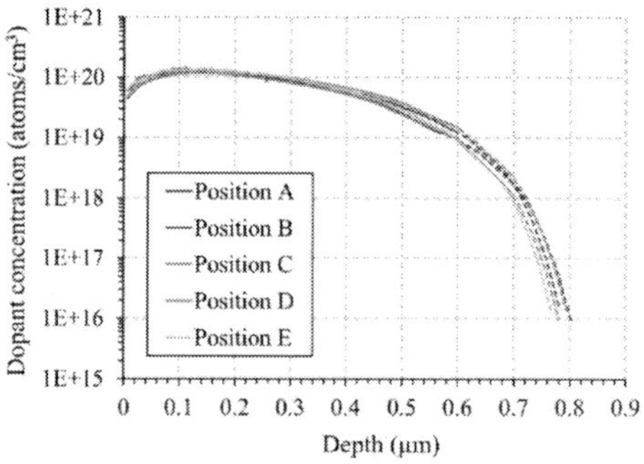

Figure 6: Boron concentration as a function of depth (doping profile) of the B-BSF processed with reduced gas flow rates in the compact furnace and diffusion temperature of 950 °C. The solid lines show the measured doping profiles, whereas the dashed lines indicate the values obtained from fitting the experimental results reported in [14].

The doping concentration on the silicon wafer surface of the BSF produced in the compact furnace with reduced gas flow rates ranged from $4.5x10^{19}$ to $6.0x10^{19}$ atoms/cm^3, and the estimated BSF depth was less than 0.8 µm.

In Fig. 7, the average R_{sh} of the B-BSF processed with reduced gas flow rates in the compact furnace (FR-red) is compared with the results obtained with baseline gas flow rates in the compact (FR-bas) and conventional (FRC-bas) furnaces. A comparison of the results obtained with the reduced gas flow rates to those obtained with the baseline gas flow rates in the compact furnace revealed that the sheet resistance increased with increasing gas volume in the baseline process.

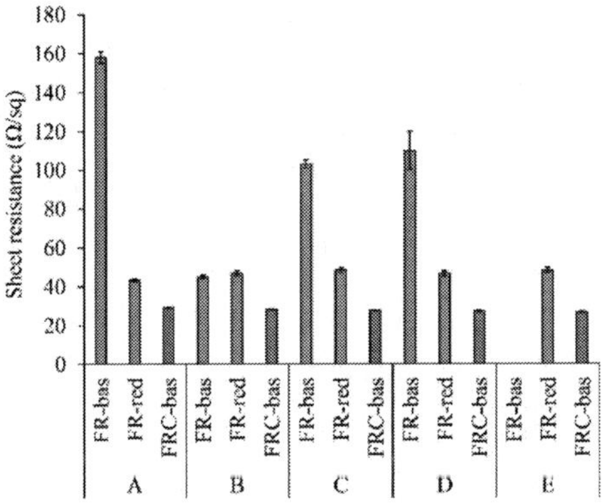

Figure 7: Comparison of the average sheet resistance of B-BSF produced in the 1) compact furnace with baseline gas flow rates (FR-bas), 2) compact furnace with reduced gas flow rates (FR-red), and 3) conventional quartz tube furnace with baseline gas flow rates (FRC-bas).

Table III shows that the sheet resistance obtained with FR-bas ranged from 103 to 158 Ω/sq, with a high value close to the gas flow inlet (position A). The average R_{sh} of the B-BSF was (122 ± 7) Ω/sq, with a standard deviation of 6%, which was higher than the result obtained with reduced gas flow rates.

Table III: Comparison of the average sheet resistance of B-BSF produced in the flat zone of the compact furnace with reduced ($R_{sh\text{-}FR\text{-}red}$) and baseline ($R_{sh\text{-}FR\text{-}bas}$) gas flow rates and in a conventional furnace with baseline gas flow rates ($R_{sh\text{-}FRC\text{-}bas}$).

Position	Compact		Conventional
	$R_{sh\text{-}FR\text{-}red}$ (Ω/sq)	$R_{sh\text{-}FR\text{-}bas}$ (Ω/sq)	$R_{sh\text{-}FRC\text{-}bas}$ (Ω/sq)
A	43.3 ± 0.6	158 ± 3	29.2 ± 0.3
B	47.0 ± 1.1	116 ± 8	28.4 ± 0.3
C	48.6 ± 1.4	103 ± 2	27.8 ± 0.2
D	46.8 ± 1.4	110 ± 12	27.4 ± 0.4
E	48.2 ± 1.5	–	26.7 ± 0.4
Average	46.8 ± 1.2	122 ± 7	27.9 ± 0.3

However, the R_{sh} of B-BSF produced in a conventional furnace was low, ranging from 26.7 to 29.2 Ω/sq. These results indicate high uniformity of boron diffusion in the flat zone of a conventional furnace. The average R_{sh} was (27.9 ± 0.3) Ω/sq, with a standard deviation lower than 1.5%.

3.2 Analysis of the boron-doped emitter of TOPCon solar cell

Fig. 8 shows the R_{sh} of the boron emitter of TOPCon solar cells produced with reduced gas flow rates in the flat zone of the compact furnace. Considering all the samples, the sheet resistance of the emitter, presented in Table IV, ranged from 87 to 120 Ω/sq, and the standard deviation was lower than 8%. These results lead to the conclusion that the sheet resistance and standard deviation of the emitter were higher than those of the B-BSF, as shown in Fig. 9.

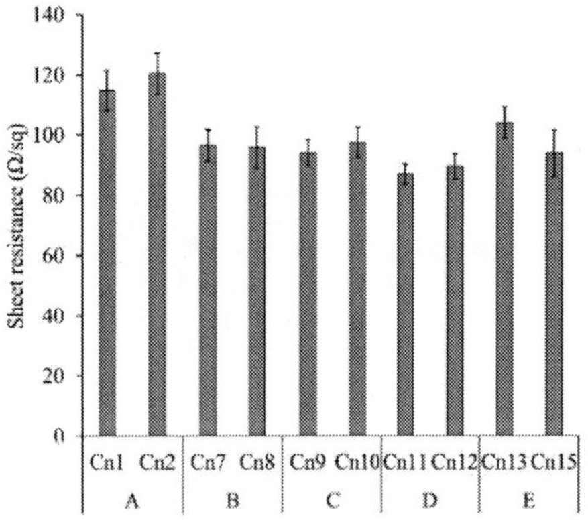

Figure 8: Sheet resistance of the boron-doped emitter of TOPCon solar cells produced with reduced gas flow rates at different positions in the flat zone of the compact furnace. Cn# represents a n-type silicon wafer.

Table IV: Sheet resistance of the boron-doped emitter of TOPCon solar cells formed with reduced gas flow rates in samples located at positions A, B, C, D and E in the compact furnace.

Position	Sample	Sheet resistance (Ω/sq)	
A	Cn1	115 ± 7	115 ± 6%
	Cn2	120 ± 7	120 ± 6%
B	Cn7	96 ± 5	96 ± 5%
	Cn8	96 ± 7	96 ± 7%
C	Cn9	94 ± 4	94 ± 5%
	Cn10	98 ± 5	98 ± 5%
D	Cn11	87 ± 3	87 ± 4%
	Cn12	89 ± 4	89 ± 5%
E	Cn13	104 ± 5	104 ± 5%
	Cn15	94 ± 8	94 ± 8%

Table V shows that the average R_{sh} of the emitter of TOPCon solar cell was (99 ± 6) Ω/sq. The standard deviation of 6% was higher than the value of 2.7% found for R_{sh} of the B-BSF. However, Tables I and IV indicate that samples close to the gas flow inlet or outlet exhibited higher sheet resistance, independent of B-BSF or emitter formation.

The boron doping profiles of the emitter are presented

in Fig. 10. As expected, in the doping profile of a sample at position A, in which the sheet resistance was higher, the boron concentration was lower for depths greater than 0.2 µm. Consequently, in this sample, the estimated depth of the emitter region was slightly lower than the results found in silicon wafers located at other positions.

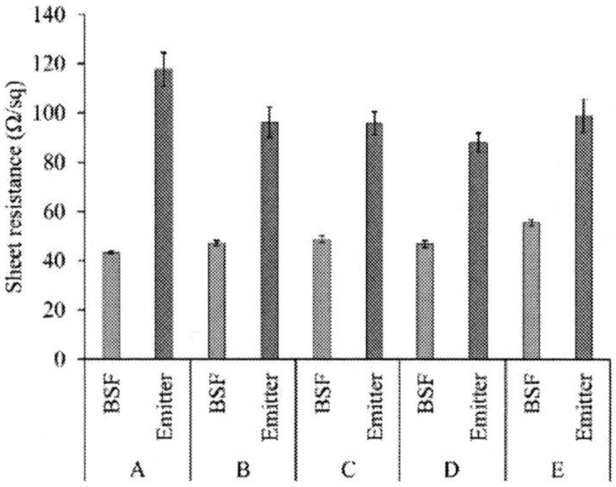

Figure 9: Comparison of the average sheet resistance of the boron-doped emitter with that of B-BSF produced with reduced gas flow rates in the compact furnace.

Table V: Average sheet resistance of the boron-doped emitter produced in the flat zone of the compact furnace with reduced gas flow rates.

Position	Sheet resistance (Ω/sq)	
A	118 ± 7	118 ± 6%
B	96 ± 6	96 ± 6%
C	96 ± 5	96 ± 5%
D	88 ± 4	88 ± 4%
E	99 ± 7	99 ± 7%
Average	99 ± 6	99 ± 6%

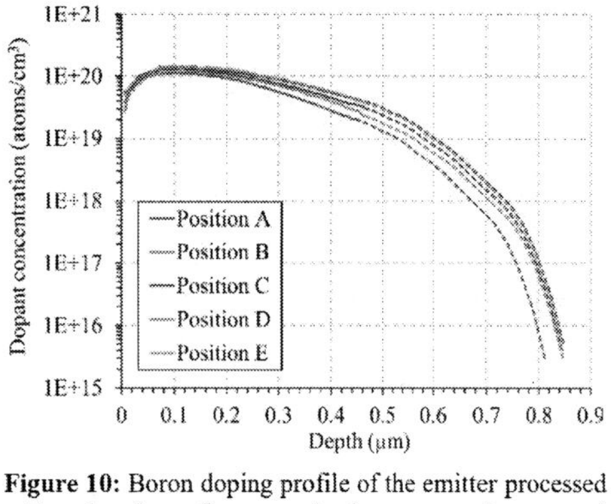

Figure 10: Boron doping profile of the emitter processed with reduced gas flow rates in the compact furnace and diffusion temperature of 950 °C. The solid lines show the measured doping profiles, whereas the dashed lines indicate the values obtained from fitting the experimental results reported in [14].

The boron doping profiles obtained for the samples located at positions B, C, D and E were similar, resulting in an estimated emitter depth of approximately 0.85 µm. However, the surface doping concentration ranged from 2.7×10^{19} to 6.3×10^{19} atoms/cm³, representing a range slightly greater than the results found for B-BSF.

Fig. 11 compares the boron doping profiles of the emitter and BSF, processed with reduced gas flow rates and placed in the center of the flat zone of the compact furnace. The doping profiles were similar up to a depth of approximately 0.45 µm. However, at depths greater than 0.45 µm, the boron concentration of the emitter was slightly higher than that of the BSF. As a result, the boron-doped emitter was deeper than the B-BSF. The estimated junction depth was 0.85 µm, and the BSF depth was 0.78 µm. In the emitter, the surface boron concentration of 5.5×10^{19} atoms/cm³ was slightly higher than the doping concentration of BSF, which was 4.8×10^{19} atoms/cm³.

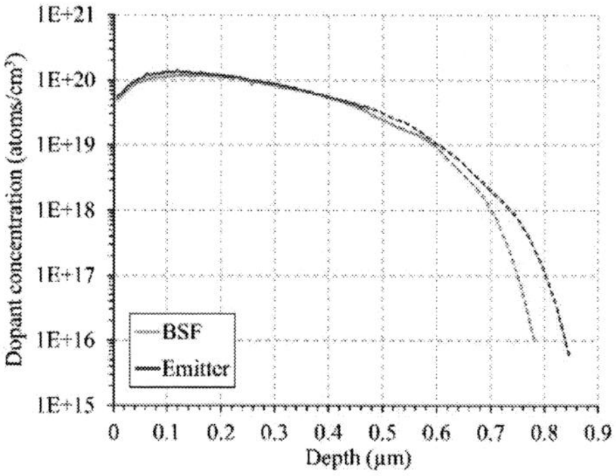

Figure 11. Boron doping profile of emitter and BSF processed with reduced gas flow rates in the compact furnace.

4 CONCLUSIONS

The average R_{sh} of the B-BSF produced with reduced gas flow rates in p-type Cz-Si wafers located at different positions in the flat zone of the compact furnace ranged from 43.3 to 48.6 Ω/sq, and the standard deviation of R_{sh} in each sample was lower than 3.2%. The results obtained with the baseline gas flow rates were higher, ranging from 103 to 158 Ω/sq. In this case, the standard deviation of each sample was greater, from 2% to 11%, demonstrating a lower uniformity of boron diffusion. The average R_{sh} produced in a conventional furnace was (27.9 ± 0.3) Ω/sq, with a low standard deviation of the sheet resistance. The average R_{sh} of the emitter produced with reduced gas flow rates in the compact furnace ranged from 88 to 118 Ω/sq, with a standard deviation of 4 - 7%. This result demonstrates that boron diffusion in n-type Si-Cz wafers was less uniform than that in p-type Si-Cz wafers under the same processing conditions.

The boron doping profile of the emitter, produced with reduced gas flow rates in the compact furnace, was slightly higher than that of B-BSF for depths greater than 0.45 µm. Additionally, the boron-doped emitter was slightly deeper than the B-BSF.

The use of reduced gas flow rates produced an average sheet resistance of (46.8 ± 1.2) Ω/sq and (99 ± 6) Ω/sq for the B-BSF and the boron-doped emitter, respectively. The standard deviation indicated that the boron diffusion was uniform in each Si wafer and in samples located at

10.4229/EUPVSEC2025/1BV.5.35

different positions in the flat zone of the compact furnace, similar to the results reported in the literature. These sheet resistances are compatible with the current technology used to produce the BSF of bifacial p-PERT solar cells and the emitter of the TOPCon structure.

ACKNOLEDGEMENTS

The authors acknowledge the financial support of the Funding Authority for Studies and Projects (FINEP), grant number 01.22.0194.00; Research Support Foundation of Rio Grande do Sul (FAPERGS), grant number 21/2551-0002152-7; and the National Council for Scientific and Technological Development (CNPq), grant numbers 305554/2021-2 and 306916/2017-7.

REFERENCES

[1] VDMA, International Technology Roadmap for Photovoltaic (ITRPV) 2024 Results, Frankfurt am Main, Germany, May 2025.

[2] T. Crestani, I. Zanesco, A. Moehlecke, L. T. C. P. da Silva, and J. V. Z. Britto, Optimization of the boron back surface field produced with reduced thermal steps in bifacial PERT solar cell, *Energies (Basel)*, vol. 18, no. 9, p. 2347, May 2025, doi: 10.3390/en18092347.

[3] Y. Hasnain *et al.*, A Review on TOPCon solar cell technology, *Current Photovoltaic Research*, vol. 9, no. 3, pp. 75–85, 2021, doi: 10.21218/CPR.2021.9.3.075.

[4] A. El Amrani, A. Boucheham, A. Guendouzi, B. Labdelli, C. Nasraoui, and R. Si-Kaddour, Co-diffusion processing of $p^+/n/n^+$ structure for n-type silicon solar cells using boron doped paper sheets, *Silicon*, vol. 14, no. 1, pp. 223–228, Jan. 2022, doi: 10.1007/s12633-020-00809-3.

[5] W. J. Choi *et al.*, Development of 22.5% p-type tunnel oxide passivated contact solar cells through efficiency enhancement by replacing local Al-BSF in PERC cells with (p^+) poly-Si/SiO_2 carrier selective contact, *Solar Energy Materials and Solar Cells*, vol. 283, May 2025, doi: 10.1016/j.solmat.2025.113436.

[6] H. Tong *et al.*, Total-area world-record efficiency of 27.03% for 350.0 cm^2 commercial-sized single-junction silicon solar cells, *Nature Communications*, vol. 16, no. 1, Dec. 2025, doi: 10.1038/s41467-025-61128-y.

[7] Q. Wang *et al.*, Boron tube diffusion process parameters for high-efficiency n-TOPCon solar cells with selective boron emitters, *Solar Energy Materials and Solar Cells*, vol. 253, p. 112231, May 2023, doi: 10.1016/j.solmat.2023.112231.

[8] X. Liu *et al.*, High-efficiency TOPCon solar cell with superior p^+ and p^{++} layer via one-step processing, *Solar Energy*, vol. 271, p. 112448, Mar. 2024, doi: 10.1016/j.solener.2024.112448.

[9] M. Meßmer *et al.*, Stack diffusion process for cost- and energy-efficient boron emitter formation, *IEEE J Photovolt*, vol. 12, no. 6, pp. 1393–1399, 2022, doi: 10.1109/JPHOTOV.2022.3214437.

[10] E. Lohmüller *et al.*, BBr_3 diffusion: Process optimization for high-quality emitters with industrial cycle times, *37th European Photovoltaic Solar Energy Conference and Exhibition*, no. September, pp. 7–11, 2020.

[11] M. Chu *et al.*, Boron doping and specific contact resistivity optimization strategies for high performance n-type TOPCon solar cells, *Inorg Chem Commun*, vol. 180, Oct. 2025, doi: 10.1016/j.inoche.2025.115004.

[12] M. Peng *et al.*, Optimization of boron depletion for boron-doped emitter of n-type TOPCon solar cells, *Mater Sci Semicond Process*, vol. 178, Aug 2024, doi: 10.1016/j.mssp.2024.108424.

[13] Y. Zhou *et al.*, Study of boron diffusion for p^+ emitter of large area n-type TOPCon silicon solar cells, *Applied Physics A*, vol. 126, no. 9, p. 671, Sep. 2020, doi: 10.1007/s00339-020-03851-5.

[14] A. Moehlecke, I. Zanesco, and A. Luque, Practical high efficiency bifacial solar cells, *1st World Conference on Photovoltaic Energy Conversion*, 1994, pp. 1663–1666. doi: 10.1109/WCPEC.1994.520538.

PONTIFICAL CATHOLIC UNIVERSITY OF RIO GRANDE DO SUL – PUCRS
SCHOOL OF TECHNOLOGY
SOLAR ENERGY TECHNOLOGY NUCLEUS – NT SOLAR

INFLUENCE OF REDUCED GAS FLOW RATES ON THE SHEET RESISTANCE OF BORON-DOPED LAYERS PERFORMED IN A COMPACT FURNACE

Izete Zanesco, Lucas Teixeira Caçapietra Pires da Silva, Adriano Moehlecke, Moussa Ly, João Victor Zanatta Britto and Vitor Gomes de Venuto

AIM

Analysis of the influence of reduced gas flow rates on the sheet resistance of boron-doped layers formed in a new compact quartz tube furnace to produce the emitter of n-TOPCon solar cells and the BSF of the bifacial p-PERT structure.

EXPERIMENTAL METHODS

NT-Solar / PUCRS / Brazil

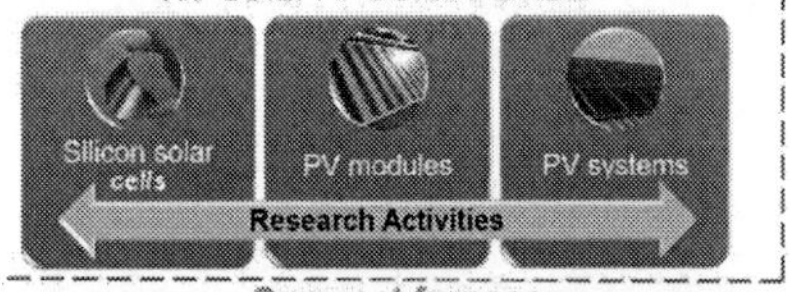

Compact furnace

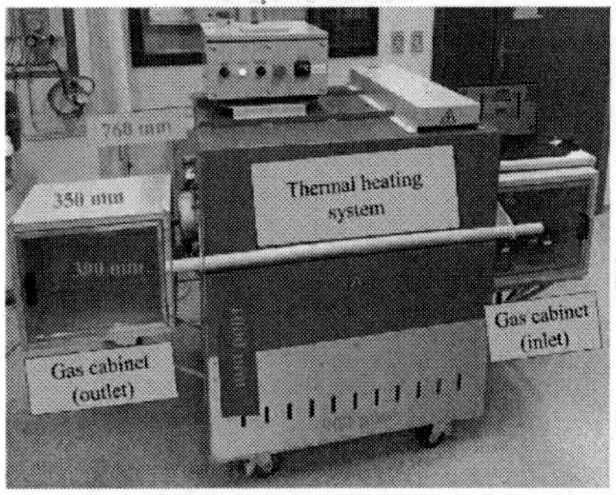

Conventional furnace

Methodology

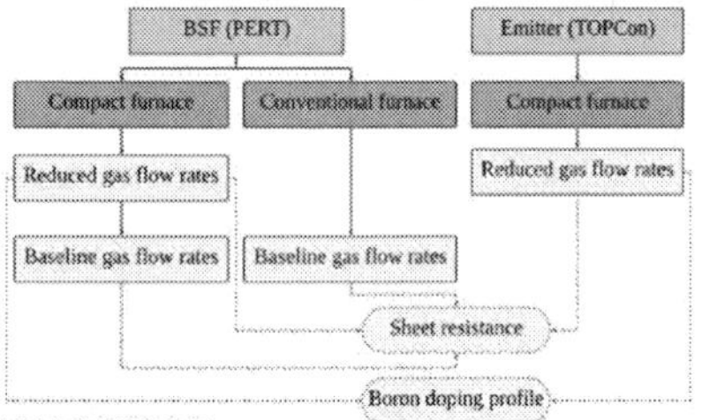

Process sequence

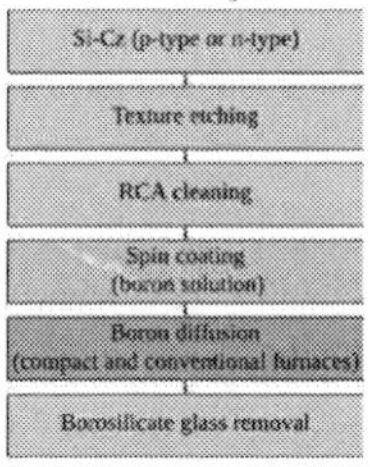

Carrier and samples

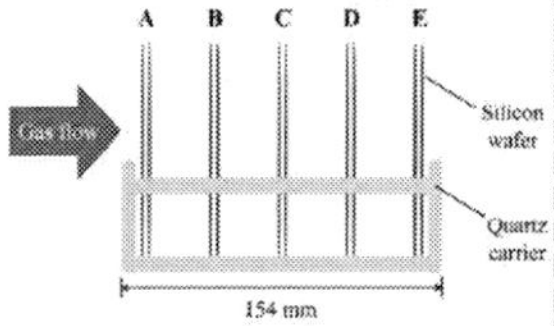

RESULTS AND DISCUSSION

Boron-BSF:

- Compact furnace: reduced gas flow rates (FR-red)
- Compact furnace: baseline gas flow rates (FR-bas)
- Conventional furnace: baseline gas flow rates (FRC-bas)

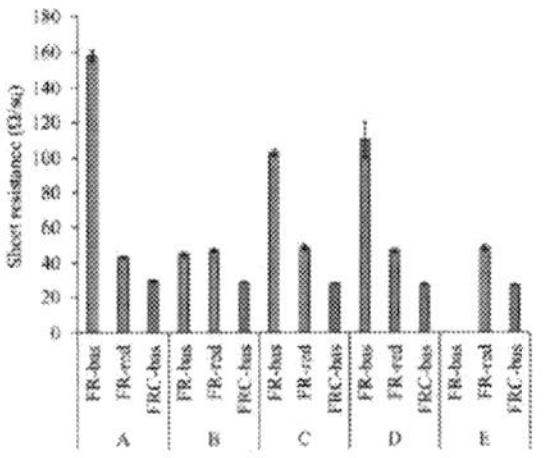

Position	Compact		Conventional
	$R_{sh\text{-}FR\text{-}red}$ (Ω/sq)	$R_{sh\text{-}FR\text{-}bas}$ (Ω/sq)	$R_{sh\text{-}FRC\text{-}bas}$ (Ω/sq)
A	43.3 ± 0.6	158 ± 3	29.2 ± 0.3
B	47.0 ± 1.1	116 ± 8	28.4 ± 0.3
C	48.6 ± 1.4	103 ± 2	27.8 ± 0.2
D	46.8 ± 1.4	110 ± 12	27.4 ± 0.4
E	48.2 ± 1.5	–	26.7 ± 0.4
Average	46.8 ± 1.2	122 ± 7	27.9 ± 0.3

Boron-BSF (p-type Si-Cz)

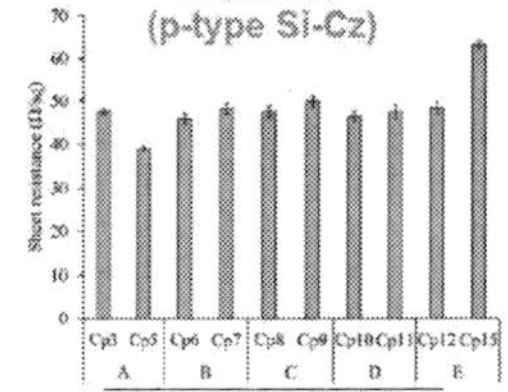

Position	Sheet resistance (Ω/sq)	
A	43.3 ± 0.6	43.3 ± 1.3%
B	47.0 ± 1.1	47.0 ± 2.4%
C	48.6 ± 1.4	48.6 ± 2.8%
D	46.8 ± 1.4	46.8 ± 2.9%
E	48.2 ± 1.5	48.2 ± 3.2%
Average	46.8 ± 1.2	46.8 ± 2.7%

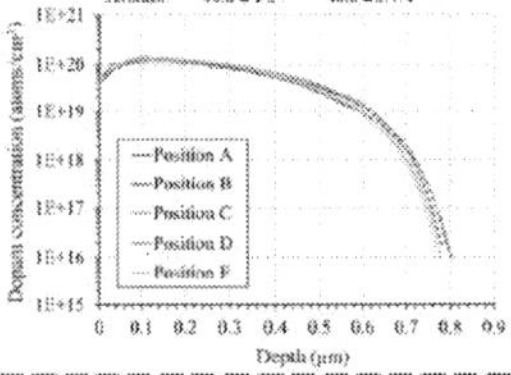

Boron-doped emitter (n-type Si-Cz)

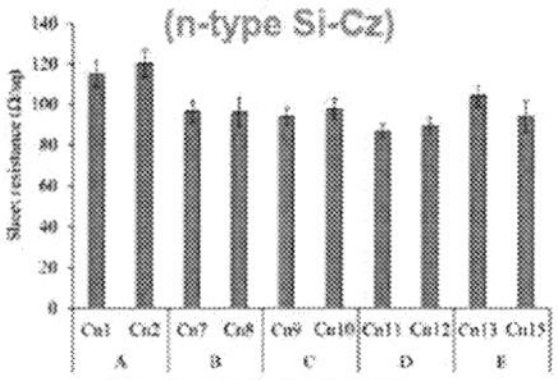

Position	Sheet resistance (Ω/sq)	
A	118 ± 7	118 ± 6%
B	96 ± 6	96 ± 6%
C	96 ± 5	96 ± 5%
D	88 ± 4	88 ± 4%
E	99 ± 7	99 ± 7%
Average	99 ± 6	99 ± 6%

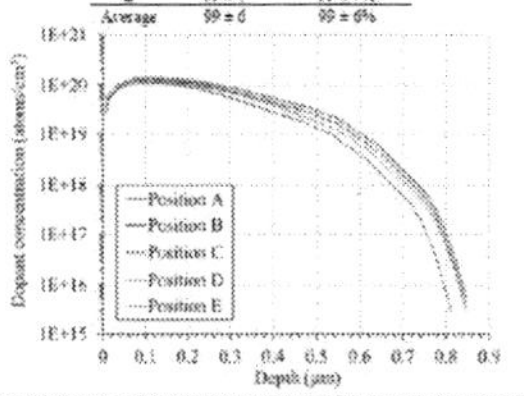

Boron-BSF x Emitter

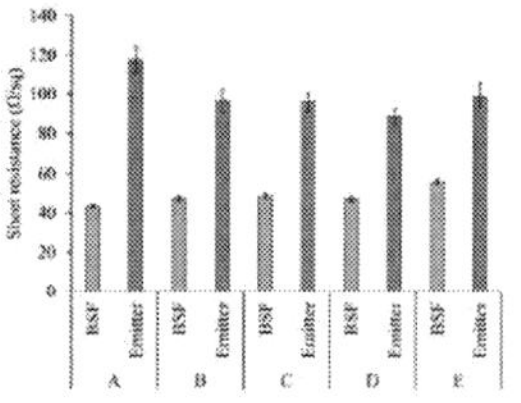

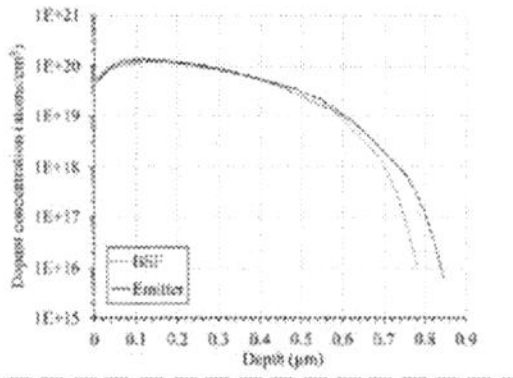

CONCLUSIONS

- **B-BSF of p-PERT solar cells (p-type Si-Cz):**
  - **Compact furnace:** ♦ **reduced gas flow rates → R_{sh} → 43.3 to 48.6 Ω/sq with a standard deviation lower than 3.2%**
    ♦ **baseline gas flow rates → R_{sh} → 103 to 158 Ω/sq with a standard deviation from 2% to 11%**
  - **Conventional furnace:** ♦ **baseline gas flow rates → R_{sh} → 26.7 to 29.2 Ω/sq with a standard deviation lower than 1.5%**
  - **The uniformity of boron diffusion in the compact furnace improved under reduced gas flow rates**
- **Boron-doped emitter of TOPCon solar cells (n-type Si-Cz):**
  - **Compact furnace:** ♦ **reduced gas flow rates → R_{sh} → 88 to 118 Ω/sq with a standard deviation from 4% to 7%**
  - **Average R_{sh} of the emitter of (99 ± 6) Ω/sq was higher than the R_{sh} of the B-BSF of (46.8 ± 1.2) Ω/sq and boron diffusion was less uniform in n-type than in p-type Si-Cz wafers**
- **Boron concentration profile of the emitter was slightly higher than that of B-BSF for depths greater than 0.45 µm and emitter region was slightly deeper**

Acknowledgments: Brazilian financing agencies FINEP, FAPERGS and CNPq

kalyon·PV
R&D

1BV.5.36

INNOVATIONS IN PERC AND TOPCON SOLAR CELL METALLIZATION: REDUCTION OF PROCESS STEPS AND EFFICIENCY IMPROVEMENT

Mert KAHRAMAN[1], Özlem COŞKUN[1], Burcu GÜMÜŞ ÇİFTCİ[1], T.Meriç Yanar[1]

[1] *Kalyon PV Research and Development Center, Kalyon Güneş Teknolojileri Üretim A.Ş., 06909 Ankara, Turkey*

Email: mkahraman@kalyonpv.com

INTRODUCTION & MOTIVATION

- While PERC used to be the most widely adopted mass production technology, it has now been largely replaced by TOPCon. This study covers both technologies.
- According to the NREL best cell efficiency chart, single crystal Si cell highest efficiency is 27.8% and commercial products efficiency values are between 23.0%-26.3% for crystal Si cell technologies[1]. This shows that there is a significant efficiency improvement potential and metallization design is one of the parameter which significantly influences the solar cell efficiency.
- This study aims to reduce the rising screen costs in mass production lines by integrating different screen types into printing equipment, thereby enabling the printing process with a single screen model. Furthermore, potential printing defects occurring during mass production in the metallization process will be monitored and controlled within a single printing step.

EXPERIMENTAL METHODS

- The front busbar and front finger screens used in M10-size PERC and TOPCon technologies have each been combined into a single screen model. The properties of these screens are shown in the table on the side.
- In PERC technology, due to the use of aluminum paste on the rear side during metallization, this project can only be applied to front-side printing. In contrast, in TOPCon technology, it can be implemented for both front and rear-side printing.
- PERC cells were produced on this screen using silver pastes with 92% Ag content.
- Temperatures in the drying and fast-firing furnaces were fine-tuned for optimal performance.
- Trial production of more than 30,000 pieces with trial and baseline groups was carried out.

Table. Specifications of busbar and finger screens.

Screen Specs	Busbar + Finger
Type	Knotless
Mesh	640
Wire Diameter(µm)	5
Tension(N)	14.5±1
Angle	90°
Yarn Thickness	12±1
EOM	5±1
Finger Count	166
Busbar Witdh(µm)	20
Finger Witdh(µm)	12
Mesh Material	Tungsten Steel

Figure. Microscope images of screen.

RESULTS

PRODUCTION LINE SCHEMATIC

- Tests were performed on the PERC metallization line shown below.

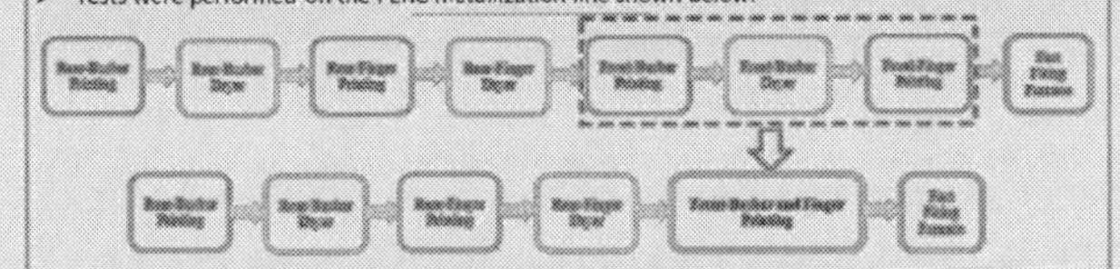

Figure. PERC Metallization Process Flow.

- The metallization production scheme for cell production in TOPCon technology is shown below.

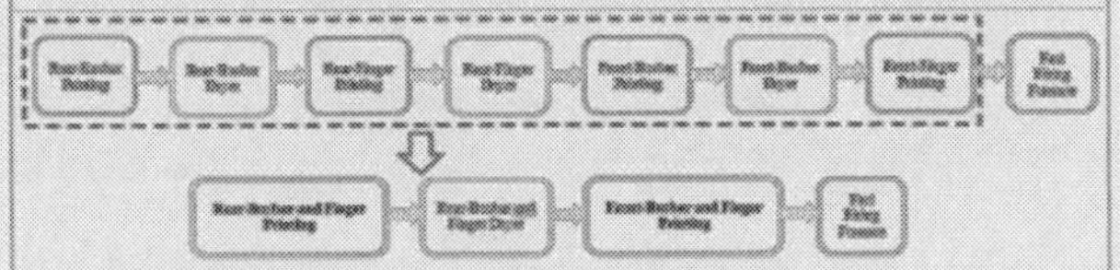

Figure. TOPCon Metallization Process Flow.

- In PERC technology, one dryer and one printing equipment were optimized, while in TOPCon, two dryers and two printing units were optimized, simplifying operations and enabling energy savings.

PASTE COMPARISON

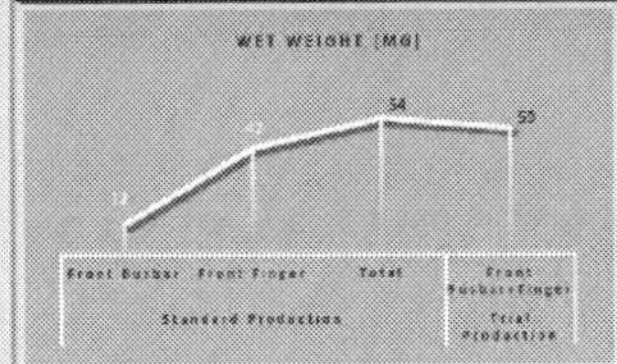

Figure. Silver Paste Wet Weight Comparison

- Comparison of Average Wet Weight of Standard and Trial Cells (shown beside).
- In standard production, 12 mg of silver paste is used for the front busbar and 42 mg for the front fingers, resulting in a total consumption of 54 mg.
- Electrical parameters of A+ class cells from test and standard production are shown in the table below.
- The new screen uses a total of 50 mg silver paste, yielding a paste saving compared to standard production.

EFFICIENCY IMPROVEMENT

- The EL image of the cell produced with the new screen shows increased brightness compared to the standard cell. EL and SEM images of the standard and new-screen cells are shown.

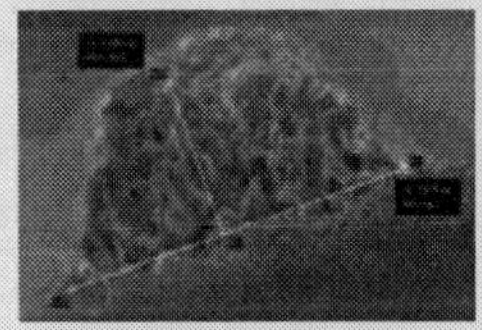

Figure. SEM images of front finger for PERC cell with efficiency of 23,44%.

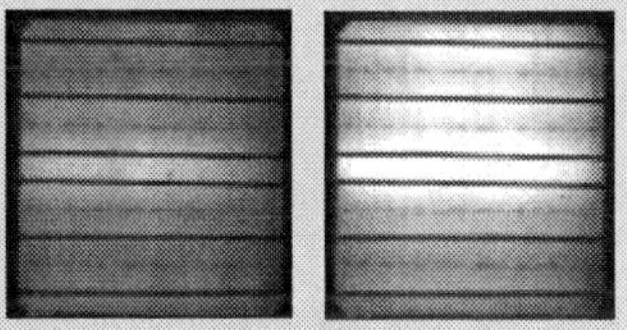

Figure. EL images of standard PERC production cell (L) and cell with PERC new metallization screens (R).

- Comparison of the I-V parameters of both groups is shown in the figure below.
- Comparison of trial and standard Uoc, Fill Factor, and Efficiency is shown below. The new screen design increased the Fill Factor by 0.13, while Rser increased by 0.003 Ω.
- Optimization of the emitter sheet resistance and fast firing in the trial group led to a gain of 3,1 mV compared to the baseline production group.

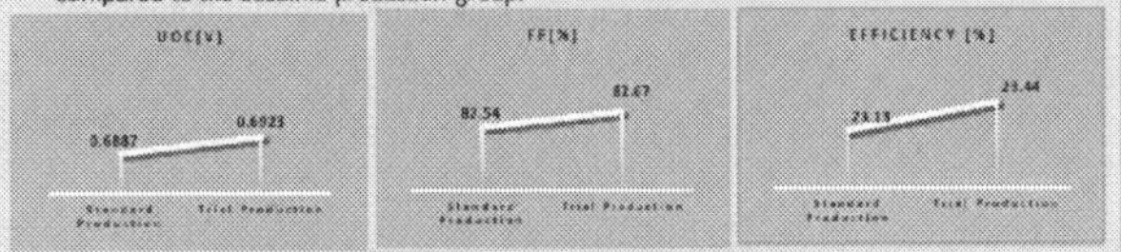

Figure. Comparison of I-V parameters for the standard and trial production groups.

- Comparison of the I-V parameters for the two groups is shown in the table below.
- An absolute gain of 0.31% was observed in the trial group with the newly designed finger and busbar screens combined into a single screen.
- Electrical parameters of A+ class cells from test and standard production are shown in the table below.

Table. Comparison of I-V parameters for the standard and trial production group.

A+ Grade PERC Cell I-V Results						
Groups	Efficiency[%]	Isc[A]	Uoc[V]	FF[%]	Rser[ohm]	Rshunt[ohm]
Standard Production	23,13	13,43	0,6887	82,54	0,0031	374
Trial Production	23,44	13,53	0,6923	82,67	0,0028	298

CONCLUSIONS

- In this study, efficiency improvement studies on PERC solar cell with M10 sizes have been completed carried out.
- In this scope, combining screen designs in PERC cell technology improved FF (%) and Voc (V), leading to higher efficiency. This study serves as a reference for TOPCon cell production, with future trials planned for TOPCon.
- Mass production average efficiency of 23.13% have been achieved with a maximum efficiency of 23.44%.

REFERENCES

[1] NREL Best Research Cell Efficiencies Chart, 2025.

WET ETCHING PATHWAYS FOR TOPCON SOLAR CELL PLATING PREPARATION: ETCHANT EFFECTIVENESS AND PINHOLES FORMATION

Roberto Boccardi[1*], Clara B. Brendstrup Møller[1], Io Mizushima[2], Torben Tang[2], Rasmus S. Davidsen[3], Peter B. Poulsen[1], Gisele A. dos Reis Benatto[1], Sune Thorsteinsson[1]
[1]Technical University of Denmark, Department of Electrical and Photonics Engineering, 4000 Roskilde, Denmark;
[2]IPU P/S, 2830 Virum, Denmark;
[3]Aarhus University, Department of Electrical and Computer Engineering, 8200 Aarhus N, Denmark.
*Corresponding author: robbo@dtu.dk

ABSTRACT: Due to material scarcity, studies are focusing on replacing the Ag metallization of TOPCon with Cu deposited via electroplating, with the outer passivation layers selectively removed to obtain conductive surfaces. Wet etching is being studied as an alternative to the usual laser contact opening (LCO), to reduce the thermal stress on the precursors, and avoid laser damage introduction. Previous tests of photolithography and wet etching with buffered hydrofluoric acid (BHF) showed slower etch rate than expected and formation of pinholes in the poly-Si layer, negatively affecting the cell performance. This work evaluates 10% HF as alternative etchant and aims to determine the mechanism of the pinhole formation. Optical microscope investigation and cross-section SEM images show that 10% HF reduces the etching time for complete passivation removal from 36 to 12 min, when compared to BHF. Moreover, the pinholes originate from pre-existing trenches in the poly-Si, where the passivation is thinner and is completely removed earlier than in the rest of the sample. Additionally, BHF locally over-etches the poly-Si around the exposed trenches, likely due to grain boundary reactivity, while 10% HF leaves the surface intact.
Keywords: Wet etching, Pinholes, TOPCon, Cu plating, Metallization

1 INTRODUCTION

With solar photovoltaic (PV) installations around the world growing significantly (more than 30% total installed capacity increase in 2023 [1]), the silver (Ag) scarcity is an important sustainability bottleneck for solar cells: with the current rate, 85-98% of the currently known Ag reserve will be consumed by the PV industry by 2050, with n-type cells' rapid growth unveiling worse scenarios [2]. Cheaper and more abundant Cu is then being studied as alternative metallization, mainly deposited via electroplating and with Ni as barrier layer to avoid diffusion of copper into the silicon in the metalized areas [3], where it creates recombination traps in the middle of the bandgap.

Electroplating happens on conductive areas, while most of the high efficiency PV cells like the tunnel oxide passivated contact (TOPCon) one present strong surface passivation on both sides. The latter needs then to be selectively removed, and most of the previous studies involved laser contact opening (LCO), exposing the underlying p-doped c-Si and n-doped poly-Si. However, particularly on the front side, laser-induced thermal damage impacts the iV_{OC}, indicating need for further improvement [4].

A valuable alternative to LCO is wet etching: the passivation layers are opened via photolithographic patterning of a mask with busbar and fingers, followed by submersion into etchant chemicals. Compared to LCO, wet etching is expected to cause less or no damage to the PV stack when used for passivation opening of p-type Cz-Si cells [5] or seed layer removal in HJT metallization [6], but previous tests for TOPCon passivation opening in buffered hydrofluoric acid (BHF) showed high etching times and formation of pinholes in the poly-Si [7].

Buffering is the process of mixing an acid with its conjugate base, in this case HF with ammonium fluoride (NH_4F), so that it maintains a constant pH value throughout its use. When buffered, HF provides a stable etch rate, and when used in conjunction with photoresists it doesn't penetrate it through microscopic holes and cracks as much as HF [8].

This work investigates the effectiveness of 10% HF as alternative etchant to BHF and aims to determine the pinholes formation mechanisms to ultimately avoid it, combining optical microscope analysis and Scanning Electron Microscope (SEM) cross-section imaging.

2 EXPERIMENTAL

2.1 TOPCon precursors

The precursors are 135 µm thick M10 industrial TOPCon cells without metallization, with the emitter (or front) side textured as pyramids and the TOPCon (or rear) side chemically polished. The cell stack is shown in Fig. 1, together with some approximate thicknesses.

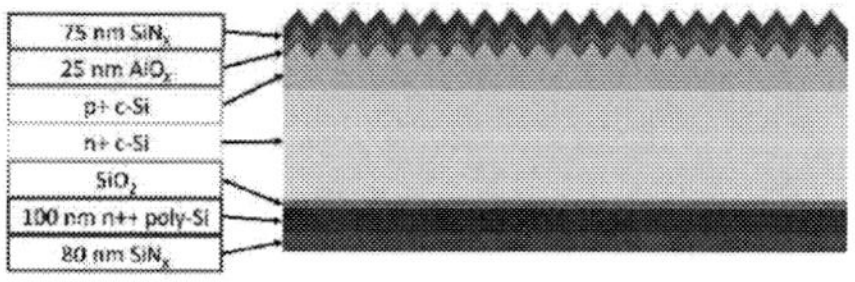

Figure 1: Materials stack of the TOPCon precursors, with approximate thicknesses of the outmost layers.

The cells are scribed with a 1064 nm laser and cleaved into 25x50 mm samples.

2.2 Wet etching

The samples are etched in beaker into two different etchants, Buffered HF (BHF) and 10% HF, which details can be found in Table I.

The samples are etched until the passivation layers are completely removed from both sides, respectively SiN_X and AlO_X from the front and SiN_X from the rear. Intermediate steps are also analysed to compare the etchants effectiveness and study the mechanism of pinholes formation.

10.4229/EUPVSEC2025/1BV.5.38
020028-001

Table I: Chemicals used for wet etching with relative details. The chemical compositions are taken from the manufacturer labels, while the pH is measured with pH test strips.

Etchant	Chemical composition	pH
BHF	10-30% HF 30-50% NH_4F	5
HF	10% HF	2

2.2 Characterization

Samples with different etching times are characterized by optical microscope and Scanning Electron Microscopy (SEM) imaging, with two different goals on front and rear sides.

On the front side, SEM cross-section imaging focuses on studying the etchants effectiveness, determining how and where the residual passivation is located when not completely removed.

On the rear side, SEM cross-section images are backed up by top-view optical microscope analyses, to spot the pinholes and study their development with increasing etching time.

3 RESULTS AND DISCUSSION

3.1 Front side – etchant effectiveness

From cross-section SEM imaging of the front side, the SiN_x and AlO_x layers can't be distinguished but are visible as a single brighter layer on top of the c-Si, as in Fig. 2. Moreover, the pyramids' tips appear rounded, getting sharper when the c-Si is completely exposed (Fig. 3a-b).

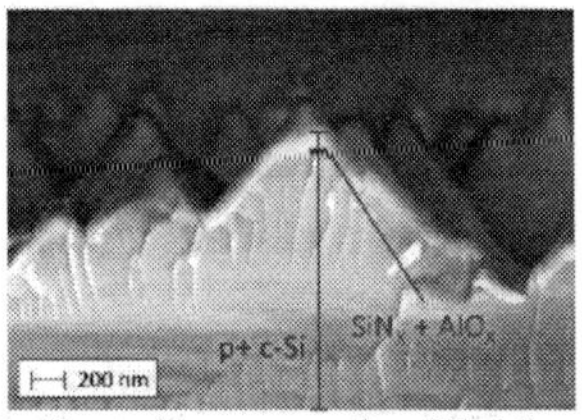

Figure 2: Front side cross-section SEM image of an unetched (Reference) sample. The SiN_x and AlO_x layers can be seen as a single layer above the c-Si, as observed in previous work [7]

Different behavior can be observed for the two etchants when not completely removing the outer layers. After 27 min etching in BHF, the residual passivation can be seen only at the base of the pyramids, suggesting a wetting limitation of the etchant due to the surface texture (Fig. 3a). After 7 min etching in 10% HF, instead, the residual passivation is more uniformly distributed along the sides of the pyramids, suggesting a more isotropic etching and no wetting issues (Fig. 3b).

Etching times necessary to completely remove the passivation are respectively 36 min for BHF and 12 min for 10% HF.

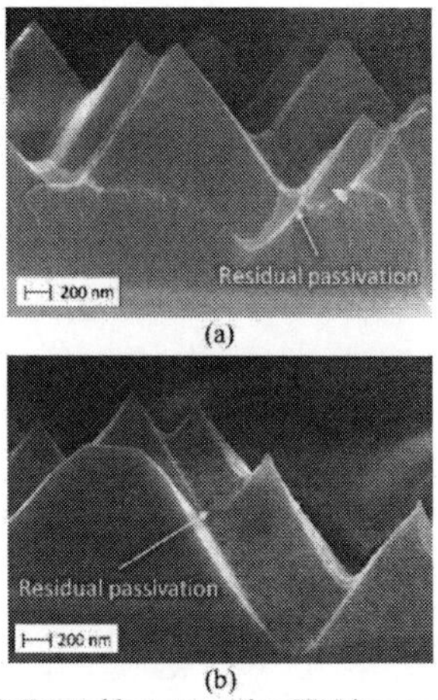

Figure 3: Front side cross-section SEM images after wet etching in BHF for 27 min (b) and 10% HF for 7 min (c). Both cases present residual passivation, concentrated at the base of the pyramids for BHF (likely due to wetting issues) and more uniformly distributed along the pyramids' sides for 10% HF.

3.2 Rear side – pinholes formation

From cross-section SEM imaging of the rear side, the SiN_x layer is clearly visible on top of the poly-Si, the latter being of easy distinction thanks to the typical multi-crystalline aspect [9], as in Fig. 4. Moreover, with the polished texture not perfectly flat, part of the bottom surface is also visible.

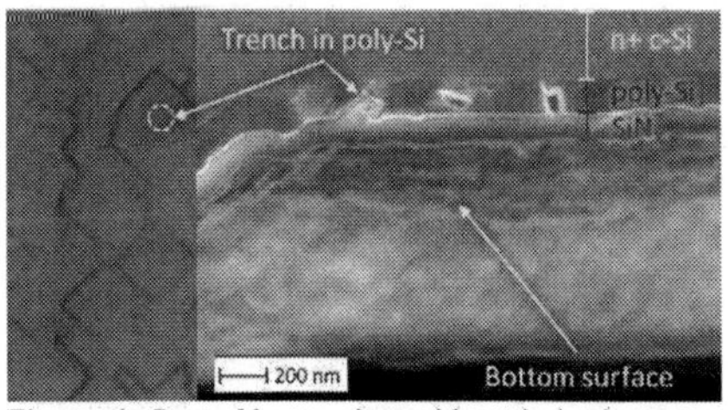

Figure 4: Rear side top-view with optical microscope (left) and cross-section SEM image (right) of an unetched (Reference) sample. Due to the texture not being completely flat, part of the bottom surface is also visible. A trench-defect in the poly-Si is visible in both images, appearing as brownish spots in the optical microscope image.

Fig. 4 contains an important feature for this study: a trench-defect in the poly-Si, filled with air and SiN_x of overall lower thickness and therefore different colour appearance (brownish instead of blue) in the optical microscope view compared to the rest of the passivation. In fact, a visual analysis of the rear side showed that the colour appearance changes significantly with the thickness of SiN_x, as in Fig. 5, ranging from blue for full thickness, through brownish and becoming grey when completely removed.

10.4229/EUPVSEC2025/1BV.5.38

Figure 5: Rear side colour appearance with different thicknesses of SiNx

While etching the samples in BHF and in 10% HF, we observed that the poly-Si in proximity of the trench defects is exposed sooner to the etchant, compared to the rest of the surface, being covered by thinner SiN_X. The latter becomes more exposed as well and is etched more quickly. Therefore, when having residual passivation, the SiN_X appears thinner in the proximity of the trenches, as visible in Fig. 6a-b. This effect is clearly visible both from optical microscope analysis and SEM cross-section imaging, when etching with 10% HF, as in Fig. 6b where the trench-influenced area is visible. When using BHF an additional effect happens, as previous work demonstrated, where the grain boundary reactivity of the poly-Si causes over-etching, expanding the trench to a bigger hole as the exposure to the buffered etchant increases [10], reaching a point where the underlying SiOx is exposed and the TOPCon layer damaged significantly.

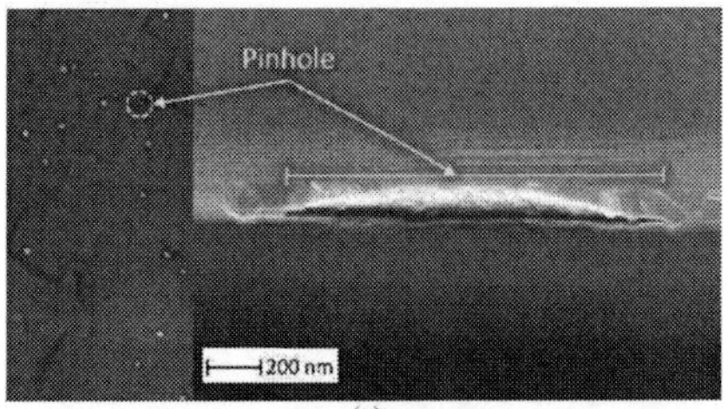

(a)

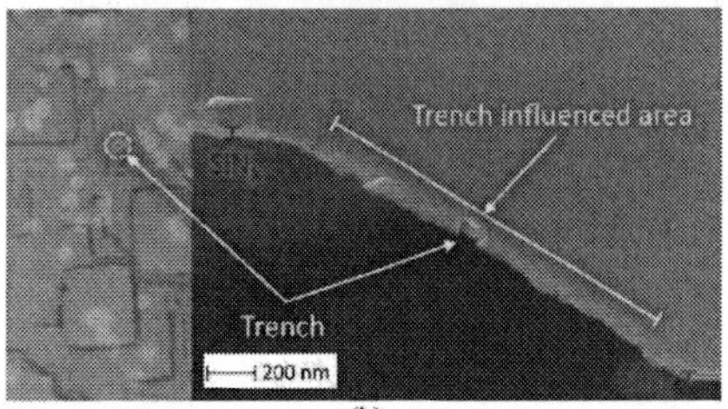

(b)

Figure 6: Rear side top-view with optical microscope (left) and cross-section SEM images (right) after wet etching in BHF for 27 min (a) and in 10% HF for 9 min (b). When etching with 10% HF a trench-influenced area becomes visible (b), with SiNx getting thinner in the proximity of the trench, while with BHF the poly-Si over-etching makes the area look like a crater (a) that we identify as pinhole.

Etching times necessary to completely remove the passivation are respectively 36 min for BHF and 12 min for 10% HF. At this stage, as shown in Fig. 7a, the trench-induced pinholes during BHF etching present dimensions in the order of the micrometers. Much different situation is observed for 10% HF, Fig. 7b, where only the pre-existing trenches are visible, and the rest of the surface is unaffected.

(a)

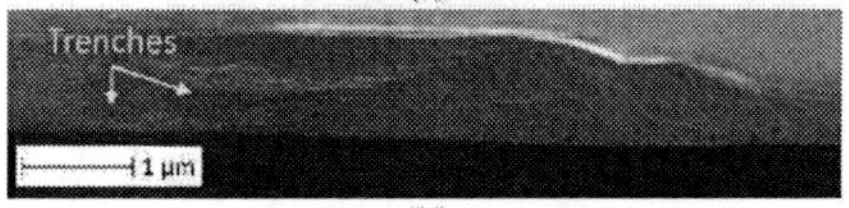

(b)

Figure 7: Rear side cross-section SEM images after complete passivation removal in BHF for 36 min (a) and 10% HF for 12 min (b), with focus on the samples bottom surface. Big pinholes are visible after BHF etching, while only the pre-existing trenches appear as defects after 10% HF passivation removal.

4 CONCLUSIONS AND FUTURE WORK

As concluded in previous work and confirmed in the current one, buffered HF (BHF) damages the poly-Si, due to the combination of pre-existing trench-defects, grain boundary reactivity and long etching time. The cause of the trenches in the poly-Si is yet to be verified, but a valuable hypothesis could be the formation phosphorus silicate glass (PSG) and relative post-crystallization cleaning [11], which might be unavoidable and hardly controllable.

The use of a pure acid like 10% HF seems a promising alternative, as it proved to be faster and not inducing pinholes from the trenches, but a strong photolithography masking is required due to the low pH. In fact, initial tests on a photo-resist masked sample showed critical photoresist durability.

Future tests will include testing hot H_3PO_4 as alternative etchant, where a strong masking is required due to the temperature involved, as well as a combination of BHF and 10%HF in sequential steps.

5 ACKNOWLEDGEMENTS

This research has been funded by Innovation Fund Denmark as part of the "ACES - Advanced Contact Engineering and Surface Passivation for Solar Cells" project under grant 3148-00044B.

6 REFERENCES

[1] G. Masson, E. Bosch, A. Van Rechem and M. de l'Epine, "Task 1 strategic PV analysis and outreach – 2024 snapshot of global PV markets", *Report IEA-PVPS T1-42:2024*, 2024, p.11.

[2] B. Hallam, M. Kim, Y. Zhang, L. Wang, A. Lennon, P. Verlinden, P.P. Altermatt and P.R. Dias, "The silver learning curve for photovoltaics and projected silver demand for net-zero emissions by 2050", in *Progress in Photovoltaics: Research and Applications*, vol. 31, i. 6, pp. 598-606, 2023.

[3] R. Sakakibara, A. Lachowicz, J. Hurni, C. Allebé, B. Paviet-Salomon, F.-J. Haug, C. Ballif, A. Hessler-Wyser and A. Morisset, "Investigating interfacial phenomena in copper-covered, n-type polysilicon-

based contacts by electron microscopy", *EU PVSEC 2024*, 2024.

[4] B. Grübel, G. Cimiotti, C. Schmiga, S. Schellinger, B. Steinhauser, A. A. Brand, M. Kamp, M. Sieber, D. Brunner, S. Fox and S. Kluska, "Progress of plated metallization for industrial bifacial TOPCon silicon solar cells", in *Progress in Photovoltaics: Research and Applications*, vol. 30, i. 6, pp. 615-621, 2022.

[5] M. Aleman, N. Bay, D. Barucha, A. Knorz, D. Biro, R. Preu, S. W. Glunz, "Advances in electroless nickel plating for the metallization of silicon solar cells using different structuring techniques for the ARC", *EU PVSEC 2009*, 2009.

[6] A. Letize, B. Lee and D. Cullen, "Wet chemical metallization of silicon solar cells: status and perspective of industrial application", *EU PVSEC 2016*, 2016.

[7] R. Boccardi, C. B. B. Møller, I. Mizushima, T. Tang, R. S. Davidsen, P. B. Poulsen, G. A. Dos Reis Benatto and S. Thorsteinsson, "Towards simultaneous double-side Ni/Cu plated contacts on wet etch opened TOPCon solar cells", in *Proceedings of 2025 IEEE 53rd Photovoltaic Specialists Conference*, pp. 734-737, 2025.

[8] A. Sarangan, "Nanofabrication: Principles to Laboratory Practice – Chapter 6: Lithography", *CRC Press*, p. 140, 2016.

[9] F. Edelman, A Chack, R. Weil, R Beserman, Yu.L. Khait, P. Werner, B. Rech, T. Roschek, R. Carius, H. Wagner and W. Beyer, "Structure of PECVD Si:H films for solar cell applications", in *Solar Energy Materials and Solar Cells*, vol. 77, i. 2, pp. 125-143, 2003.

[10] S. Tseng, W.-T. Kary Chien and B.-C. Cai, "Improvement of poly-silicon hole induced gate oxide failure by silicon rich oxidation", in *Microelectronics Reliability*, vol. 43, i.5, pp. 713-724, 2003.

[11] Q. Wang, M. Zhang, M. Peng, L. Yu, C. Lin, L. Wang, T. Yan, G. Liu and X. Xi, "Effect of annealing conditions on phosphorus inward diffusion from N+ Poly-Si layer in N-type TOPCon solar cells", in *Materials Science in Semiconductor Processing*, vol. 176, 2024.

Wet Etching Pathways for TOPCon Solar Cell Plating Preparation: Etchant Effectiveness and Pinholes Formation

Roberto Boccardi[1*], Clara B. Brendstrup Møller[1], Io Mizushima[2], Torben Tang[2], Rasmus S. Davidsen[3], Peter B. Poulsen[1], Gisele A. dos Reis Benatto[1], Sune Thorsteinsson[1]

[1]Technical University of Denmark, Department of Electrical and Photonics Engineering, 4000 Roskilde, Denmark;
[2]IPU P/S, 2830 Virum, Denmark; [3]Aarhus University, Department of Electrical and Computer Engineering, 8200 Aarhus N, Denmark.
*robbo@dtu.dk

EU PVSEC 2025

Introduction

- Due to material scarcity, Ag metallization of TOPCon is being replaced by Cu via electroplating. Outer **passivation layers** are selectively **removed** to obtain conductive surfaces.
- **Wet etching** is being studied as an alternative to the usual Laser Contact Opening (LCO), to reduce the thermal stress on the precursors, and avoid laser damage introduction.
- Previous tests [1] of photolithography + wet etching with Buffered HF (BHF) showed **slower etch rate** than expected and **formation of pinholes** in the poly-Si layer, negatively affecting the cell performance.
- This work focuses on the effectiveness of **10% HF as alternative etchant** and on the **mechanism of pinholes formation**.

Methodology

Wet etching | **Characterization**

- 10-20% HF
- 30-50% NH_4F

- 10% HF

Complete passivation removal | **Pinholes formation study**

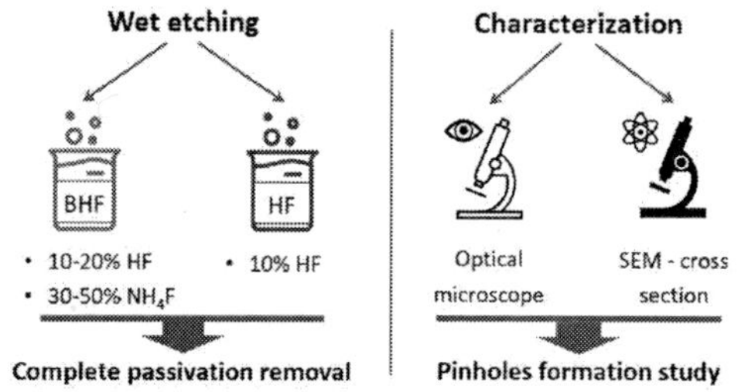

Results and Discussion

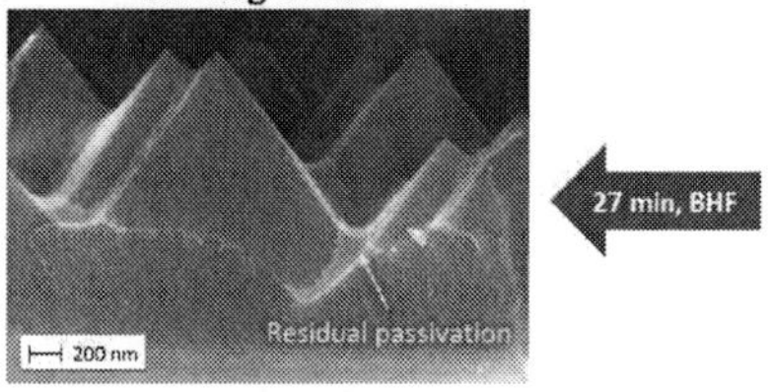

Etching in BHF | Reference | Etching in 10% HF

- Residual passivation at the base of the pyramids
- Complete removal after 36 min

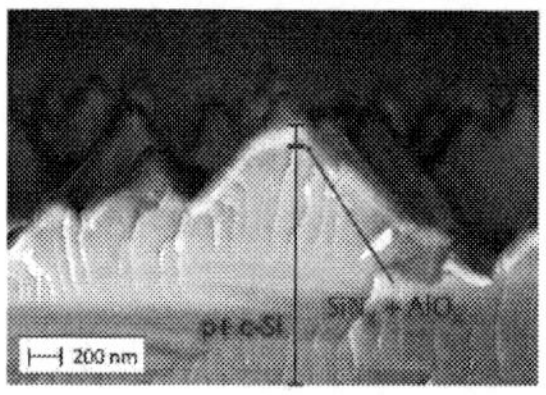

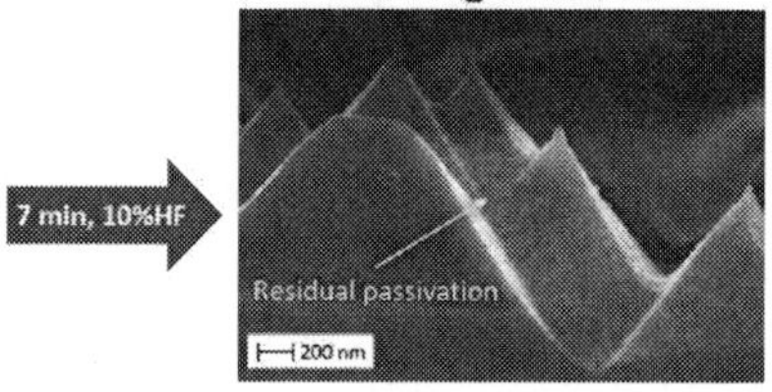

- Residual passivation distributed along the pyramids walls
- Complete removal after 11 min

↑Front side↑

↓ Rear side ↓

Etching in BHF | Reference | Etching in 10% HF

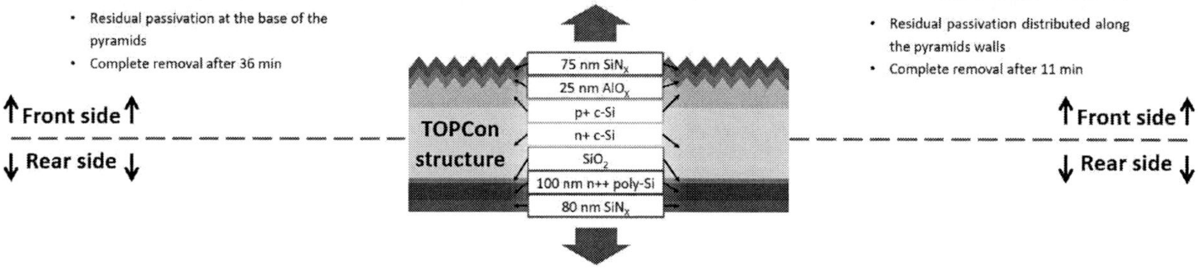

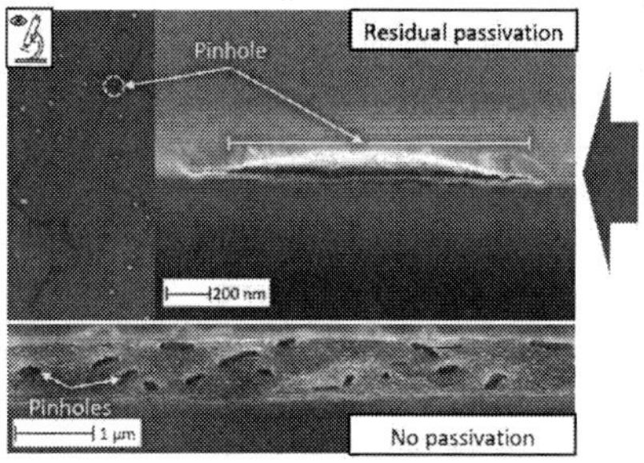

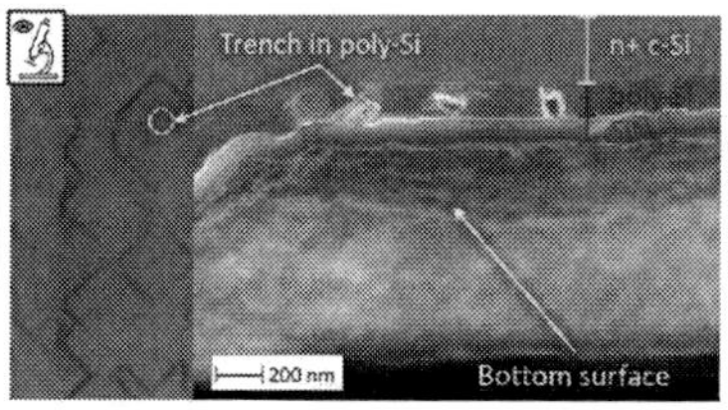

- SiNx changes colour around the trenches, due to different thickness

SiNx colour appearance with thickness: 100 nm | 50 nm | 0 nm

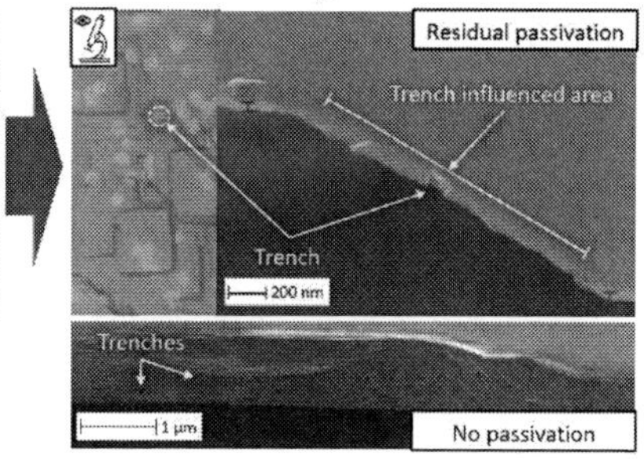

Conclusions and Future work

- Buffered HF damages the poly-Si, due to **long etching time** and **grain boundary reactivity** [2]. Trenches in poly-Si could be caused by post-crystallization cleaning and might be unavoidable.
- Pure acid like **10% HF** seems a promising alternative, being **faster** and **not inducing pinholes**, but a strong photolithography masking is required due to the **low pH**.
- Etching in hot H_3PO_4 will be tested, or a combination of steps with BHF and 10% HF, to evaluate the best etchant.

Etchant	Time
BHF	36 min
10% HF	12 min

Etching time required for complete passivation removal

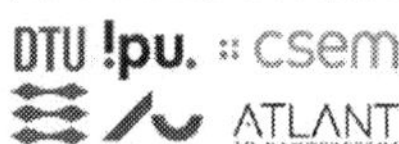

Photoresist delamination after etching in 10% HF – rear side

References

[1] R. Boccardi et al., "Towards simultaneous double-side Ni/Cu plated contacts on wet etch opened TOPCon solar cells",
DOI: 10.1109/PVSC59419.2025.11133113
[2] S. Tseng et al., "Improvement of poly-silicon hole induced gate oxide failure by silicon rich oxidation",
DOI: 10.1016/S0026-2714(03)00059-3

Acknowledgement

This research has been funded by Innovation Fund Denmark as part of the "ACES - Advanced Contact Engineering and Surface Passivation for Solar Cells" project under grant 3148-00044B.

Innovation Fund Denmark DTU !pu. csem ATLANT 3D NANOSYSTEMS

Optimization of Cu metallization in HJT solar cell manufacturing and investigation of possible Cu diffusion

Y. Wu, L.A.G. Okel, E. J. Kossen, E. B. Kucuk, A. Gutjahr, V. Rosca, L. J. Geerligs
Solar Energy Group, Unit of Energy Material Transition, TNO, The Netherlands

Motivation

- To achieve a stable, *silver-free* metallization process for silicon heterojunction (HJT) solar cell manufacturing.
- Reduction of power loss in Cu compared to Ag metallized HJT solar cells.
- Interconnection technology for Cu metallized HJT solar cell

Why screen-printed Cu metallization

Pros:

- Screen printing for drop-in replacement of Ag in the HJT solar cell manufacturing
- Complying to the mainstream metallization process and equipment of PV industry
- Lean process without extra equipment investment

Cons:

- Risk of oxidation during the process
- Risk of Cu diffusion to impact the cell and module performance

Improvement of Cu metallization stability

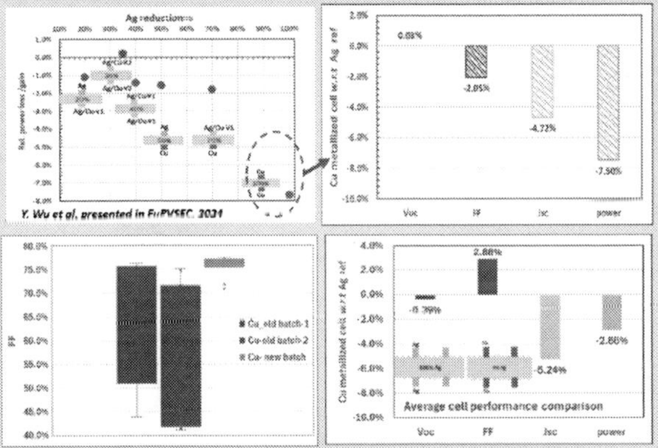

- Optimization of Cu paste printability to improve line definition.
- Refining post-print thermal treatment to enhance metal bulk conductivity and uniformity and prevent oxidation in the process.
- The variation previously noted (e.g., FF) due to unstable Cu metallization has been greatly reduced. However, current loss persists relative to the Ag reference and remains a primary factor in power loss.

Cu fine line printing

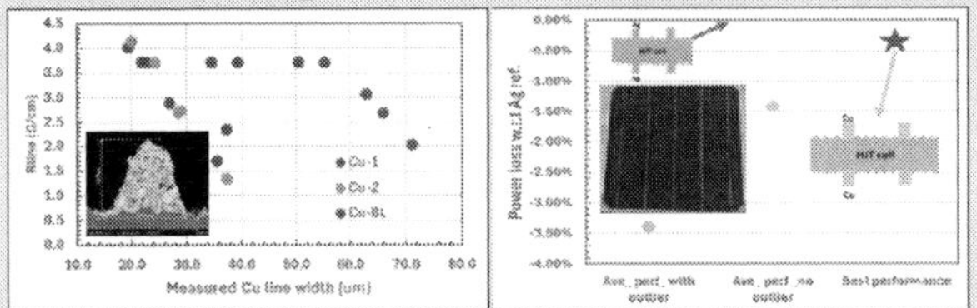

- Cu fine-line printing aims to address current loss issues.
- Cu fine-line printing with finger widths < 20µm has been achieved.
- Pastes 1&2 show lower R_{line} than Cu BL-paste at narrow finger width.
- I_{sc} loss is < 2%. Power loss *w.r.t* Ag reference is down to rel. 0.4% for the best Cu-metallized cell.

Results of interconnection for Cu metallized HJT solar cell

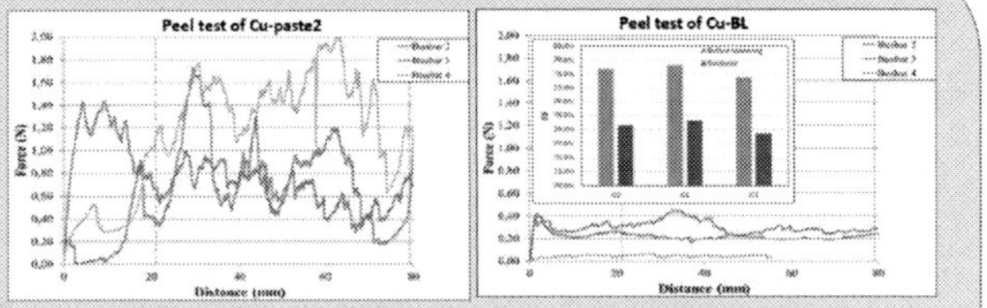

- Low-temperature manual Cu soldering achieves adequate peel force with the new Cu paste (left) but is weaker with the baseline Cu paste (right).
- Soldered Cu metallized HJT cell shows a ~4% FF loss (inset), likely due to a suboptimal manual soldering process that will require further detailed investigation.

Investigation of performance degradation at elevated temperature and damp heat (DH)

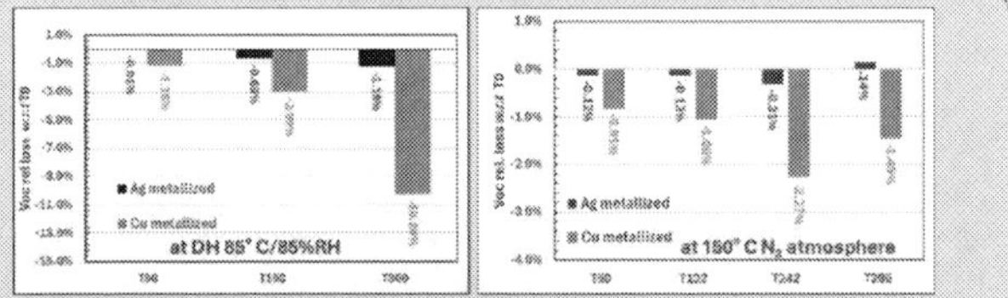

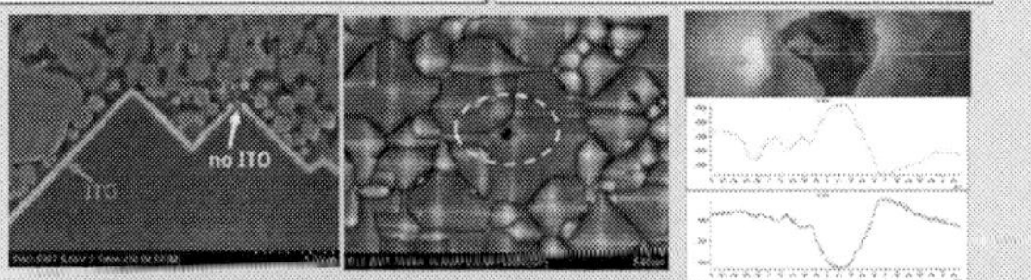

- Ag- and Cu-metallized HJT solar cells with similar starting performance were used.
- The pronounced V_{oc} degradation observed in the Cu-metallized cell during DH testing is likely attributable to Cu diffusion into the silicon bulk via ITO defects (such as pinholes), potentially induced by processing damage. While V_{oc} loss at 150°C in the Cu-metallized cell is less significant, definitive evidence of Cu diffusion has not been identified. Further investigations are currently underway.

Summary & outlook

- ❖ A robust screen-printed Cu metallization process now enables Ag-free HJT solar cells with only ~0.1% lower efficiency than Ag reference, and fine lines under 20µm wide.
- ❖ Cell performance degradation presumably due to Cu diffusion highlights the importance of ITO layers quality.
- ❖ Initial results for Cu contact interconnection are promising, further optimization is necessary to ensure stable, high quality device performance.
- ❖ Efforts to develop compatible cell lamination processes, as well as ongoing module reliability assessment and optimization, are currently underway.

Acknowledgment

Fundings:

SOLARNL

This work was supported by SolarNL, a national research, innovation and industrial development program funded by the Netherlands National Growth Fund

Dutch industrial partner:

MCPV

topsector energie

This work was supported by TKI-Energie from the Toeslag voor Topconsortia voor Kennis en Innovatie (TKI's) of the ministry of Economic Affairs and Climate, project SusCon, project number 2221203.

Dr. M. Bruggeman for sample preparation and SEM measurement

TNO innovation for life

Contact info:
Dr. Y. Wu (yu.wu@tno.nl, 0031-611025105)
Dr. L. J. Geerligs (bart.Geerligs@tno.nl, 0031-650009558)
Address: Westerduinweg 3, 1755LE Petten, the Netherlands

tno.nl

SELECTIVE ETCHING OF DOPED POLYSILICON LAYERS

Sebastian Mack[1], Viola Neuber [1], Marius Meßmer[1], Fabian Geml[2], Joshua Kamphues[2], Barbara Terheiden[2], Laurent Clochard[3], Andreas Wolf[1]
[1]Fraunhofer Institute for Solar Energy Systems, Heidenhofstr. 2, 79110 Freiburg, Germany
[2]University of Konstanz, Universitätsstraße 10, 78464 Konstanz, Germany
[3]Nines Photovoltaics, Synergy Centre, TU Dublin - Tallaght, D24 A386, Dublin, Ireland
sebastian.mack@ise.fraunhofer.de

ABSTRACT: The implementation of p-type passivating contacts is a promising approach to reduce overall recombination in tunnel oxide passivating contact (TOPCon) or back-contact solar cells. Due to the high absorption coefficient in highly doped silicon layers, the polysilicon layer should be confined to the regions near the contact, which requires a structuring process of full area deposited layers. We report on a co-diffusion process using doped phosphosilicate glass layers from APCVD, with a drive-in during BBr_3 diffusion to generate differently doped polysilicon layers in a single thermal process. By exploiting the lower etching rate of highly boron-doped polysilicon layers, we demonstrate the ability to selectively remove n-type polysilicon while only marginally affecting the p-type polysilicon layer, using either alkaline texturing or atmospheric dry etching (ADE) with F_2 gas. This doping-type selective etching is more pronounced in the ADE process. Symmetric samples show a very low level of surface recombination of 5fA/cm² for boron-doped polysilicon layers after passivation.

Keywords: TOPCon, Polysilicon, Structuring, Etching, Mask

1 INTRODUCTION

Over the last decade, tunnel oxide passivating contact (TOPCon) solar cells have evolved from initial publications at research institutes to becoming the dominating solar cell technology in the market [1]. One advantage over its predecessor passivated emitter and rear cell (PERC) is the reduced minority carrier recombination at the rear side, achieved through the introduction of a passivating contact. However, the front side still features a direct contact between metal and the boron-diffused emitter, characterized by a high recombination current density $j_{0,met}$. This value has decreased significantly due to the implementation of current assisted contact formation approaches such as laser-enhanced contact optimization (LECO) [2] in combination with screen-printed Ag pastes that contain low or no Al. Nevertheless, to reduce $j_{0,met}$ below 10 fA/cm², the introduction of a passivating front contact is required, as proposed in this work.

Etching processes play a crucial role in the fabrication of silicon solar cells. Prominent examples of exploiting material-dependent etching rates include diluted HF solutions, which etch silicon oxide (SiO_x) layers while only marginally affecting crystalline silicon. Also, alkaline solutions are used in TOPCon solar cell processing to remove the parasitic Si rear emitter, while the borosilicate glass on the front side acts as an etch stop due to a lower etching rate. Structuring of (sacrificial) dielectric layers such as SiO_x or silicon nitrides (SiN_x) by processes such as laser ablation or mask and etch allows for producing local passivating contacts, which otherwise are difficult to realize. Prominent exceptions are masked deposition of passivating contacts, e.g. by shadow masks made out of thin glass [3] or additive local printing of passivating contacts [4]. Alternatively, local etching of full area polysilicon (poly-Si) layers is being investigated [5] by means of doping type-selective etching. This concept exploits the significantly different etching rates for p- and n-type poly-Si layers, potentially circumventing costly structuring processes. Additionally, the impact of dopant concentration on etching rates is well documented in the literature [6]. This approach has already been successfully used for the fabrication of solar cells with local p-type passivating front contacts (poly-Si fingers), as demonstrated by Hoß et al. [7].

In this work, we present our results for co-diffusion of poly-Si layers with p- and n-dopants in one single thermal process and subsequent doping type-selective etching of poly-Si layers using either wet-chemical etching or atmospheric dry etching (ADE). The results presented here form the basis for the later integration into device fabrication processes, such as local passivating contacts on the front side or interdigitated back contact solar (IBC) cells. However, this technological implementation is beyond the scope of this paper.

2 SAMPLE PREPARATION

Gallium doped and phosphorus doped Cz-Si wafers serve as starting materials. Initially, wet-chemical etching removes the saw damage. Following a wet-chemical cleaning step in ozonized water, a 1.3 nm thick tunnel oxide is grown by thermal oxidation, upon which an intrinsic poly-Si layer with a thickness of 80 nm or 160 nm is deposited by means of low-pressure chemical vapor deposition (LPCVD). Subsequent surface doping is achieved by exposing the samples to either $POCl_3$ or BBr_3 diffusion, resulting in n-type or p-type doping, respectively. As an alternative method for n-type doping, phosphosilicate glass (PSG)/SiO_x layer stacks are deposited using atmospheric pressure chemical vapor deposition (APCVD) at University of Konstanz [8,9], which includes a short HF dip prior deposition. All other processes are performed at Fraunhofer ISE. For the APCVD samples, the drive-in from the PSG dopant source takes place in a BBr_3 diffusion processes, with the PSG/SiO_x layer stack acting as a diffusion source and as a barrier, which prevents boron form the process atmosphere from diffusion into the silicon wafer. Using a single-sided dopant source, this co-diffusion approach enables simultaneous n- and p-type doping of intrinsic poly-Si layers in a single cost-effective high temperature step.

To determine the etch selectivity between n- and p-doped surfaces, two approaches are employed. The first approach uses wet-chemical etching in alkaline solution, while the second one applies atmospheric dry etching in F_2 gas at moderate temperatures of around 200°C. Figure 1 shows a sketch of the experiment process flow for the different sample groups.

10.4229/EUPVSEC2025/1CV.2.3

To evaluate recombination properties, the surfaces are passivated using an Al_2O_3 layer deposited by atomic layer deposition (ALD), an outgassing step in N_2 ambient, and hydrogenated SiN_x layers formed by plasma-enhanced chemical vapor deposition (PECVD). A contact firing process releases hydrogen for effective surface passivation. Photoconductance decay measurements (PCD) performed with a Sinton WCT-120 provide insights into the recombination current densities at the surfaces.

Additional characterization includes weighing of samples before and after etching, sheet resistance measurements, dopant profiling by electrochemical capacitance voltage (ECV) measurement, and transmission measurements at the corresponding stages of processing.

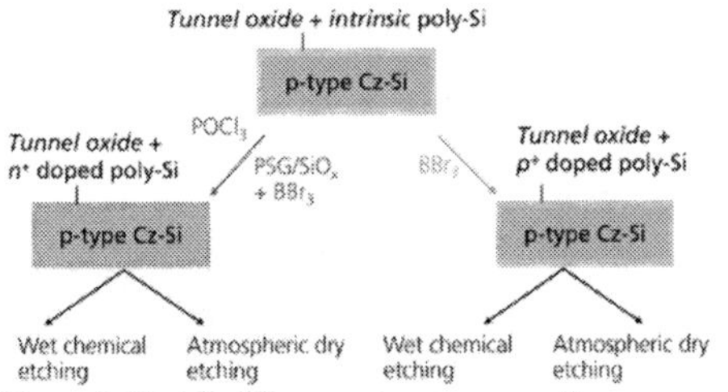

Figure 1: Sketch of the experiment process flow

3 EXPERIMENTAL RESULTS

3.1 Co-diffusion of intrinsic poly-Si layers

Figure 2 shows dopant profiles of p- and n-type poly-Si layers. The black profile represents an 80 nm thick intrinsic poly-Si layer that has been doped in a BBr_3 diffusion process. The diffusion process has been specifically designed to result in a boron dopant profile with a high active dopant concentration, which could show beneficial with respect to contacting and also with respect to etch selectivity, which is a function of dopant concentration [5]. Also shown are n-type poly-Si layers with thicknesses of either 80 nm or 160 nm, doped via a PSG/SiO_x stack containing approximately 4 wt.% or 8 wt.% phosphorus. The P content was calculated from the gas flow rates based on an empirical calibration, and the doping was performed in the same BBr_3 diffusion process as described above. The use of 4 wt.% PSG layers results in a phosphorus dopant concentration of only 10^{19}cm^{-3}. However, for the 8 wt.% PSG layer, both the BBr_3 diffusion and the 8 wt.% PSG layer allow for final dopant concentrations around 10^{20}cm^{-3}, which proofs the successful implementation of a co-diffusion process doping of poly-Si layers. The results show that a wide variety of dopant profiles can be achieved for poly-Si layers of different thickness in one single high temperature step, due to the flexibility in controlling the P content in the PSG layer. PSG layers with phosphorus concentrations higher than 8 wt.% result in even higher dopant concentrations, as has been shown in other results with the same BBr_3 diffusion.

Apart from the local active dopant profiles, also the homogeneity of doped layers is of utmost importance, as it is not only relevant to cell parameters such as contact resistivity and carrier recombination but also might affect the homogeneous etching of those layers for advanced solar cell structures, which require a structuring of those layers.

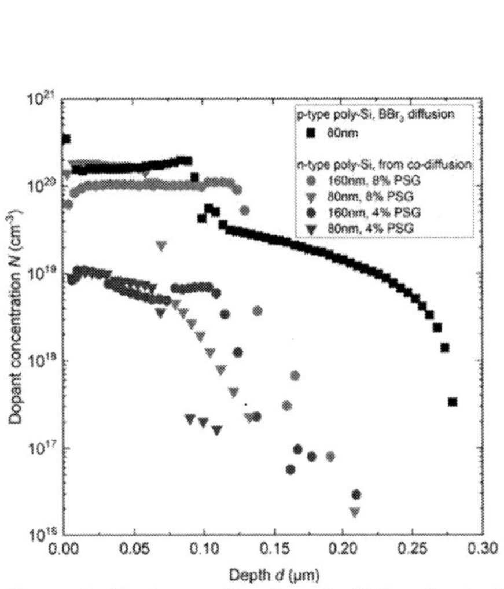

Figure 2: Doping profiles for poly-Si:B and poly-Si:P layers, achieved in one single high temperature step, measured by ECV on planar surface

Figure 3 depicts the 4pp mapping (100 measurement points) of an 80 nm thick poly-Si:P layer, formed on top of a planar p-type Cz-Si wafer. A 4pp measurement on this structure yields the sheet resistance R_{sheet} of the n-doped surface layer, that includes both the poly-Si:P layer as well as the tail of the dopant profile in the c-Si wafer. Here, the poly-Si(i) layer has been doped by an 8 wt.% PSG/SiO_x stack in a BBr_3 diffusion. The ECV profile measured in the center of the wafer has been shown in Figure 2. The low relative standard deviation $\sigma = 6\%$ over the wafer indicates a homogeneous dopant source deposition by APCVD and a homogeneous temperature distribution during BBr_3 diffusion.

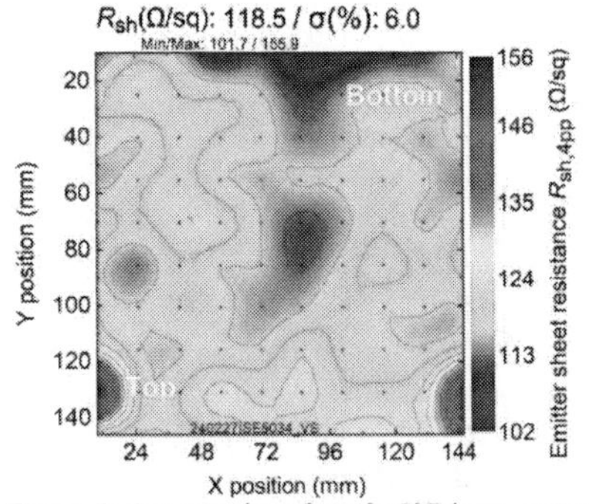

Figure 3: 4pp mapping of a poly-Si:P layer, on top of a p-type Si wafer with planar surface. Also shown are mean sheet resistance R_{sh} and relative standard deviation σ

Figure 4 shows the passivation results of poly-Si:B layers, doped via three different BBr_3 diffusions, after Al_2O_3/SiN_x surface passivation and subsequent contact firing. The three diffusions result in a profile very similar to that shown in Figure 2, but with a shallower dopant tail in c-Si, with B5 having the deepest of the three and B1 the shallowest. The results, which have been achieved on planar surfaces, indicate a high level of surface passivation for the passivating front contact with up to 734 mV implied open circuit voltage iV_{oc}, corresponding to a recombination parameter of 5 fA/cm^2.

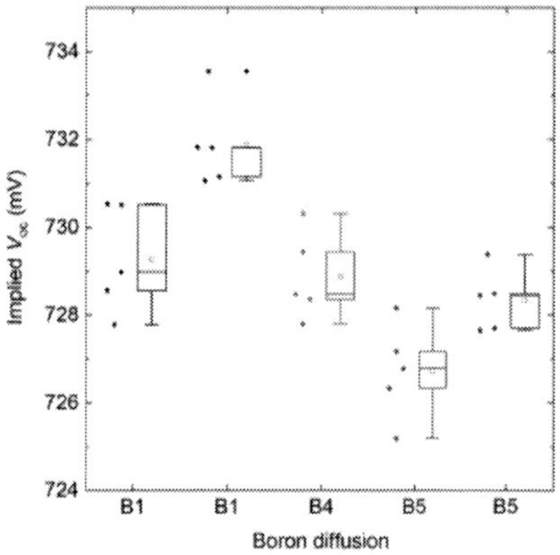

Figure 4: Implied V_{oc} results of symmetric n-type test structures with planar surface and boron doped poly-silicon layers on both sides, measured by PCD after Al_2O_3/SiN_x surface passivation and subsequent contact firing

3.2 Doping type-selective etching of poly-silicon layers

As described above, local passivating contact structures can be formed through doping-type selective etching. To investigate the feasibility of this approach, we conducted an experiment to test the etching rates of p- and n-type poly-Si layers formed by the co-diffusion processes described in section 3.1. For this, we used a wafer with saw damage etched surface, capped with a tunnel oxide and 160 nm thick intrinsic poly-Si. The sample featured a 4 wt.% PSG/SiO_x stack only on the rear side and was doped in a BBr_3 diffusion, leading to poly-Si layers of different polarity on front and rear side of the wafer. Figure 5 shows the results after additional alkaline texturing. The fact that the front side still exhibits a saw-damage etched surface demonstrates that the boron-doped poly-Si layer prevents texturing of the surface, indicating its significantly lower etch rate compared to the phosphorus-doped counterpart. However, a look on the rear side clearly indicates the presence of textured surface with upright random pyramids, thus, the n-doped poly-Si layer has been removed completely, as planned.

Figure 5: Photographs of front and rear side of a M10 wafer after doping type-selective alkaline texturing step. The initial surface before etching was saw-damage etched and capped with a doped poly-Si layer. (left) boron doped poly-Si, still featuring a saw damaged etch surface, indicating a low etching rate, (right) textured surface, indicating the complete removal of n-doped poly-Si in the texturing process

To further investigate the doping type selective etching process, symmetric samples with both sides p- or n-doped poly-silicon layers have been weighed before and after texturing, and from the weight difference, the silicon removal has been calculated, assuming a density of 2.33 g/cm³ for the poly-silicon layer. Table 1 lists the findings. In case of the poly-Si:P sample, characterized by a doping surface concentration of $5*10^{20}cm^{-3}$, as extracted from ECV data, the alkaline texturing step leads to a Si removal of 2.68 µm, averaged over several samples. This is well above the deposited poly-Si layer thickness of 80 nm and further supports the finding of a complete poly-Si layer removal during texturing. In case of the poly-Si:B samples, Table 1 lists results of two diffusion processes, which result in dopant profiles with $7*10^{19}cm^{-3}$ (lightly doped) and $1.3*10^{20}cm^{-3}$. Both surface concentrations are lower than that of the poly-Si:P layer. For the more lightly doped poly-Si:B layer, a Si removal of 0.88 µm is determined after alkaline texturing, whereas only 0.08 µm removal is obtained for the more heavily doped sample. As 0.08 µm corresponds to the thickness of the poly-Si layer before etching it might well be that the poly-Si layer has been removed completely by alkaline etching, but nevertheless the Si removal was too low to lead to the formation of upright pyramids.

Table 1 further depicts the Si removal, when samples of the same groups are subject to ADE instead of alkaline texturing. Here, ADE leads to significantly lower Si removal, which in case of poly-Si:P still exceeds the poly-Si thickness. This changes when going to poly-Si:B layers, where the corresponding Si removals are 0.04 µm and 0.02 µm for the more highly doped layer, respectively. This is below the thickness of the deposited poly-Si layer, and thus, a selective etching of poly-Si:P layers becomes possible by ADE in F_2 gas, even if both polarities are located on the same side of the wafer, which makes the process specifically suited for other advanced cell structures such as back contact cells. The results indicate that selective removal of poly-Si:P layers compared to poly-Si:B is possible.

Table 1: Poly-Si layer and Si removal during alkaline etching or ADE for samples doped with gas phase diffusion. Dopant surface concentration as determined by ECV

Type	**Dopant surface conc. (cm^{-3})**	**Si removal (µm)**	
Etching method	-	Alkaline	ADE
Poly-Si:P	$5*10^{20}$	2.68	0.25
Poly-Si:B	$7*10^{19}$	0.88	0.04
Poly-Si:B	$1.3*10^{20}$	0.08	0.02

To further investigate the impact of the etching processes on the poly-Si:B layers, we also perform ECV measurements. The results are shown in Figure 6. Shown are dopant profiles in the states "initial after diffusion", "after ADE" and, alternatively, "after alkaline texturing". The comparison of the respective profiles after diffusion and after ADE shows a slight shift in the profile along the x-axis, corresponding to very low removal of poly-Si in that process. In contrast to this, the wet-chemical process leads to a complete removal of the poly-Si:B layer, however, the doping-tail in the c-Si wafer is still visible.

This might be explained by the tunnel oxide layer sandwiched between c-Si and poly-Si:B acting as an etch stop during wet-chemical etching. If a complete removal of the dopant profile is needed, a longer etching time is needed to break up the thin interface oxide layer. In both etching cases, a poly-Si:P (n-doped) layer has been removed completely.

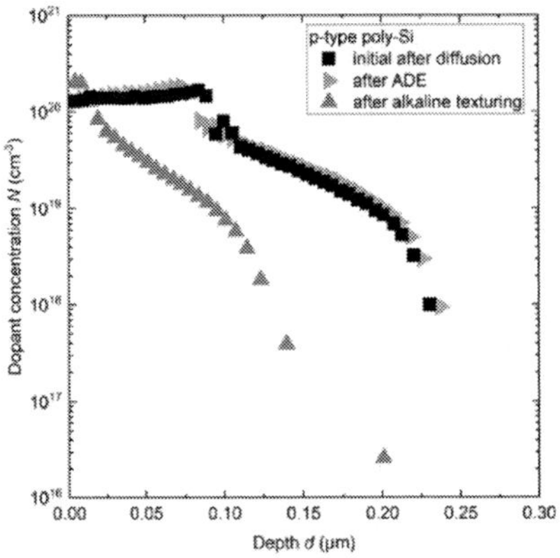

Figure 6: ECV data of poly-Si:B layers after diffusion, as well as after either alkaline etching or ADE

Figure 7 shows results of light transmission measurements before etching and after either alkaline texture or ADE, measured on symmetric samples. The initial thickness of the poly-Si layer before etching is 80 nm. BBr_3 diffusion leads to the formation of boron doped poly-Si, $POCl_3$ diffusion to phosphorous doped poly-Si. As ADE is a single sided process, the corresponding samples are etched once per side, to also yield symmetric samples. An increased transmission within the 1000 to 1200 nm range corresponds to a removal of poly-Si layers. In the first plot in Figure 7 before etching, the transmission T of the sample with n-poly-Si is measured to 23%, in between that of the more highly doped p-poly-Si layer with 22% and the more lightly doped p-poly-Si layer with 29%, all measured at a wavelength $\lambda = 1200$ nm. Wet-chemical etching of the samples in an alkaline texture bath leads to a strong increase of T to over 48% in case of the n-poly-Si layer, which represents the case of full removal of that layer, as explained above. Subjecting samples with p-poly-Si layers in the same texturing step also leads to an increase of T to values between 34 and 45%, indicating a reduce in poly-Si layer thickness, but not yet a complete removal. Here, the more highly doped p-poly-Si layers feature the values in the lower part of that range, slightly differing from sample to sample.

Looking at samples after ADE, the difference in selectivity becomes easily visible. Here, the n-poly-Si layer also gets removed completely, indicated by $T = 44\%$, and slightly less than for the sample after alkaline texturing, which is expected to be mainly a result of the different surface morphology of the sample. However, there are quite large differences with respect to etching of p-poly-Si layers. The more highly doped samples show only a minor increase in T, from $T = 22\%$ before etching to 23-24%, while the lightly doped p-poly-Si layer exhibits a slightly higher increase from $T = 29\%$ before etching to values between 31% and 33% after etching. These results are in accordance with the weighing results in Table 1.

The observed changes in IR transmission strongly support the findings from above, that wet-chemical etching removes both n- and p-poly-Si layers, whereas ADE only leads to a very small removal of Poly-Si:B, while still removing the Poly-Si:P layer completely.

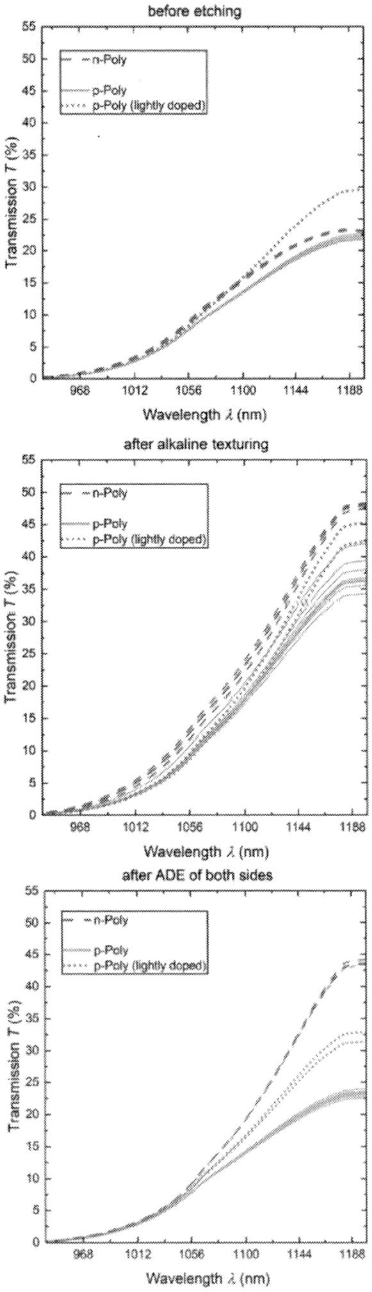

Figure 7: Transmission measurement results of symmetric samples with either n- or p-poly-Si, in different stages of processing: before etching, after wet-chemical etching, after both sides ADE

4 SUMMARY

This paper has focused on the formation of p- and n-type poly-Si layers by either gas-phase diffusion or the combination of APCVD dopant source and drive-in. Further work has been done to selectively etch poly-Si:P layers, thereby exploiting a lower etching rate for poly-Si:B layers in both alkaline texturing solutions and F_2 gas. The results indicate that doping type-selective removal of poly-Si layers is possible.

It has been shown that boron doped poly-Si layers with higher surface concentration feature a lower etching rate than more lightly doped layers. Still, a very high level of surface passivation is achieved for p-type poly-Si layers on planar surface.

The results could help to pave the way for a cost-effective formation of TOPCon solar cells with poly-Si fingers on the front side.

Acknowledgements
The authors want to thank all colleagues at Fraunhofer ISE for the excellent atmosphere and the support of TOPCon activities in general, by means of processing, simulation, discussions or financing.
This work was funded by the German Federal Ministry for Economic Affairs and Energy within the research project "WamTec", Grant Number: Fkz 03EE1193; Funding via the Clean Energy Transition Partnership CETP.

REFERENCES
[1] ITRPV, International Technology Roadmap for Photovoltaics (ITRPV): Results 2024. [Online] Available: https://www.vdma.org/international-technology-roadmap-photovoltaic.
[2] T. Fellmeth, H. Höffler, S. Mack, E. Krassowski, K. Krieg, B. Kafle, and J. Greulich, Prog Photovolt Res Appl., vol. 30, (2022), 1393.
[3] T. Dullweber, V. Mertens, M. Stöhr, J. Langlois, L. Mettner, U. Baumann, F. Haase, R. Brendel, J. Libal, A. Hähnel, A. Müller, V. Naumann, A. Vogt, N. Ambrosius, T. Pernau, H. Haverkamp, Proceedings 8th World Conference on Photovoltaics, 2022, 35.
[4] Z. Kiaee, A. Lösel, C. Reichel, R. Müller, M. Nazarzadeh, M. Jahn, R. Singh, I. Uecker, A. Qazzazie, T. Hanf, A. Terfort, M. C. Holthausen, T. Hanemann, and R. Keding, Proceedings 11th International Conference on Crystalline Silicon Photovoltaics, 2022, 110002.
[5] Clochard L., M. Yu, R. S. Bonilla, P. Tierney, J. Wright, F. Rougieux, and Y. Cai, Proceedings 41st EU-PVSEC, 2024, 020022.
[6] R. Charavel, J.-P. Raskin, Proceedings 16th International Conference on Ion Implantation Technology, 2006, 325.
[7] J. Hoß, S. S. Kalaghichi, M. Comak, P. Preis, J. Lossen, J. Linke, L. J. Koduvelikulathu, and F. Buchholz, EPJ Photovoltaics, 15, 2024, 43.
[8] F. Geml, S. Sanz, D. Wurmbrand, G. Micard, H. Plagwitz, G. Hahn, and B. Terheiden, AIP Conf. Proc. 2826, 2023, 050002.
[9] F. Geml, Dissertation, Universität Konstanz (2024)

42nd European Photovoltaic Solar Energy Conference and Exhibition

Selective Etching of Doped Polysilicon Layers

Sebastian Mack[1], Viola Neuber[1], Marius Meßmer[1], Fabian Geml[2], Joshua Kamphues[2], Barbara Terheiden[2], Laurent Clochard[3], Andreas Wolf[1]
[1]Fraunhofer Institute for Solar Energy Systems ISE, Heidenhofstr. 2, 79110 Freiburg, Germany
[2]University of Konstanz, Universitätsstraße 10, 78464 Konstanz, Germany
[3]Nines Photovoltaics, Synergy Centre, TU Dublin - Tallaght, D24 A386, Dublin, Ireland
Phone +49 761/4588-5048, sebastian.mack@ise.fraunhofer.de

Introduction

- Local poly-Si structures highly relevant for advanced cell processing such as iTOPCon with p-type poly-Si fingers or interdigitated back contact (IBC)
- Doping-type selective etching exploits doping-type [1] and concentration dependent [2] etching rates for selective etching of n-type poly-Si

Sample Preparation

- Symmetric samples
- Tunnel oxide + intrinsic polysilicon by low-pressure chemical vapour deposition (LPCVD)
- Co-diffusion using stack of phosphosilicate glass (PSG) and silicon oxide (SiO_x) from atmospheric pressure chemical vapour deposition (APCVD)
- Alkaline texturing or atmospheric dry etching (ADE) using F_2 gas

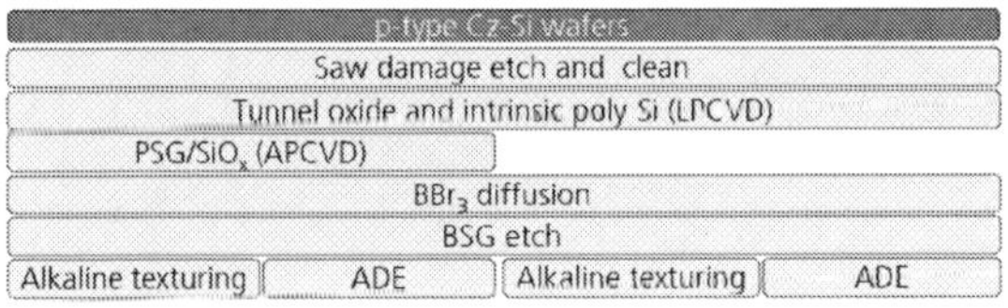

Figure 1: Sketch of the experiment process flow

Dopant Profiles

- Dopant profiles before and after etching
- Wide range of phosphorous dopant profiles realizable in one high temperature step, depending on dopant concentration
- n-type poly-Si and dopant tail removed completely by both etching process, Si removal of 2.7 µm (alk. texturing) and 0.25 µm (ADE)
- p-type poly-Si
  - removed completely by alk. texturing (80 nm removed), but tail in c-Si still present
  - marginally effected by ADE (20 nm removed)

→Selective removal of n-type poly-Si possible

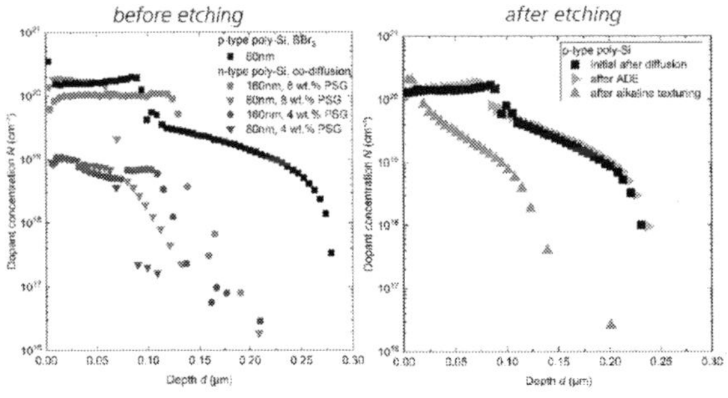

Figure 2: ECV data of before and after etching

Passivation of p-type Poly-Si

- BBr_3 diffused poly-Si samples
- Three diffusions, dopant profiles as above
- Symmetric samples with planar surfaces
- Passivation by Al_2O_3/SiN_x
- Up to 734 mV, average 5 fA/cm²

→High level or surface passivation

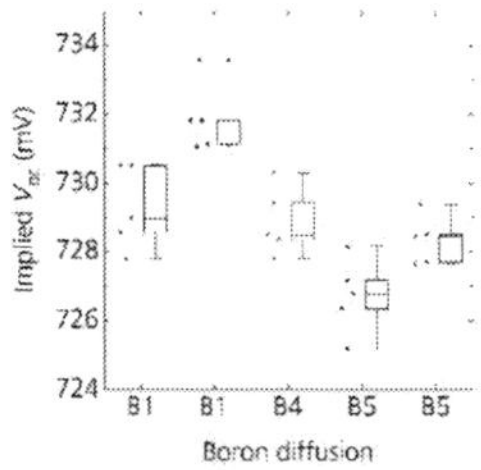

Figure 3: Passivation results after contact firing

Alkaline Texturing of Asymmetric Samples

- Samples with planar surfaces
- p-type poly-Si on front side, n-type poly Si on rear side
- Planar surface still visible for p-type poly-Si (left) after texturing
- Textured surface for n-type poly-Si (right) indicates full poly-Si removal

→ p-type poly-Si lower etch rate

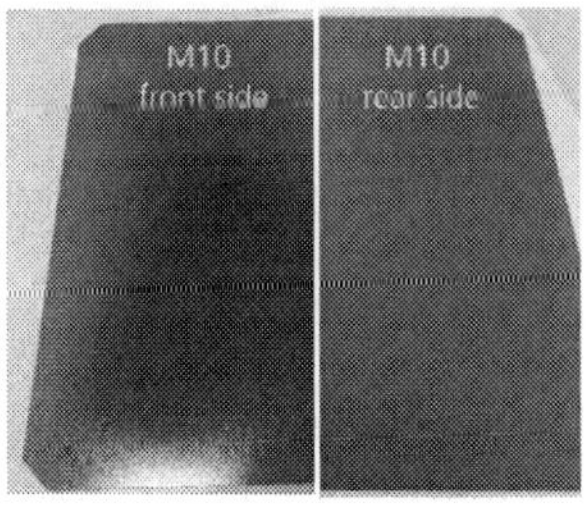

Figure 4: Photographs of front and rear after alkaline texturing process

Transmission

- Alkaline texturing leads to large increase in transmission → poly-Si removed
- ADE removes n-poly, p-poly ($7*10^{19}$ cm^{-3}) partly, p-poly ($1.3*10^{20}$ cm^{-3}) not

→Increased transmission further proof of selective removal of n-type poly-Si

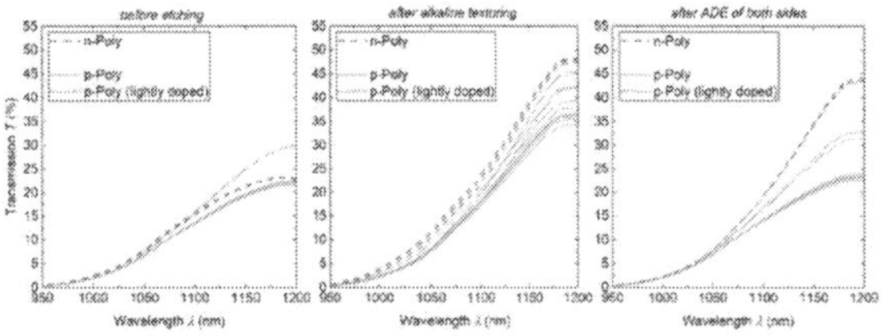

Figure 5: transmission data for symmetric samples

Summary

- Co-diffusion process with APCVD PSG/SiO_x in BBr_3 diffusion developed for simultaneous p- and n-doping of poly-Si layers in one process
- Doping-type selective etching for selective removal of n-type poly-Si demonstrated using ADE and wet chemical texturing
- Selectivity of ADE much higher compared to wet chemical texturing

[1] Clochard L., M. Yu, R. S. Bonilla, P. Tierney, J. Wright, F. Rougieux, and Y. Cai, Proceedings 41st EU-PVSEC, 2024, 020022
[2] R. Charavel, J.-P. Raskin, Proceedings 16th International Conference on Ion Implantation Technology, 2006, 325.

Supported by:
Federal Ministry for Economic Affairs and Energy
on the basis of a decision by the German Bundestag

Funding via the Clean Energy Transition Partnership (CETP) project "WaMTec" (Fkz 03EE1193) from German Federal Ministry for Economic Affairs and Energy (BMWE) is gratefully acknowledged.

42nd European Photovoltaic Solar Energy Conference and Exhibition

ISC research for a sunny future

A TOPCon IBC Solar Cell Architecture with Sputtered Tunnel Oxide and Polysilicon Doped Regions: Design and Process Optimization

Valentin D. Mihailetchi[1], Vaibhav V. Kuruganti[1], Thomas Buck[1], Volker Linß[2], Eric Schneiderlöchner[2]

1. ISC Konstanz e.V., Rudolf-Diesel-Str. 15, 78467 Konstanz, Germany
2. VON ARDENNE GmbH, Am Hahnweg 8, 01328 Dresden, Germany

Background & Aim

- **c-Si solar cells & modules** dominate PV market with record efficiencies:
  - *n*-type bifacial **i-TOPCon cells**[1]: 27.03%
  - **TOPCon IBC modules** (TBC)[2]: 25.2%
  - **Si heterojunction IBC cells** (HIBC)[3]: 27.8%
- **Current challenge**: reduce **LCOE** with simpler, more cost-effective processes
- **Our approach:** Develop a **novel PVD-sputtered route** to fabricate **TBC cells**
  - Inline high-throughput **DC sputtering** of a multilayer stack: TO/a-Si/doped & undoped SiOx
  - **Masking + laser patterning** for selective removal
  - **Ex-situ annealing & doping** for interdigitated regions
- **Advantages of PVD sputter process:**
  - Single-side deposition (no wrap-around)
  - No hazardous gases
  - Precise thickness and doping control
- **Target:** Demonstrate high efficiency with a simplified PVD-based TBC solar cell process

VON ARDENNE inline PVD sputter tool for our pilot line cell development

Fabrication and Characterization Methods

Main process steps[4]

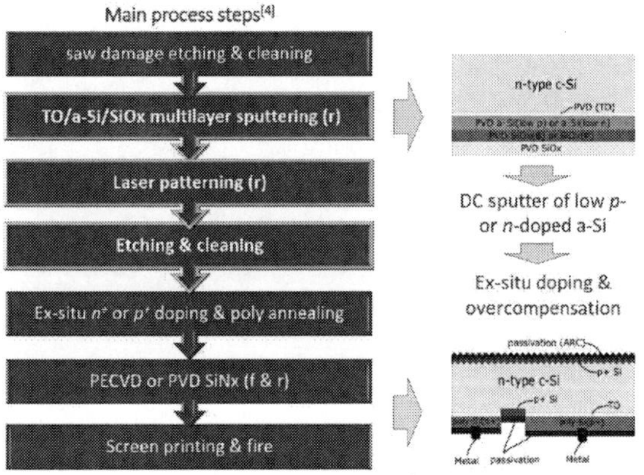

PVD-sputtered low-doped a-Si – overcompensation & passivation:

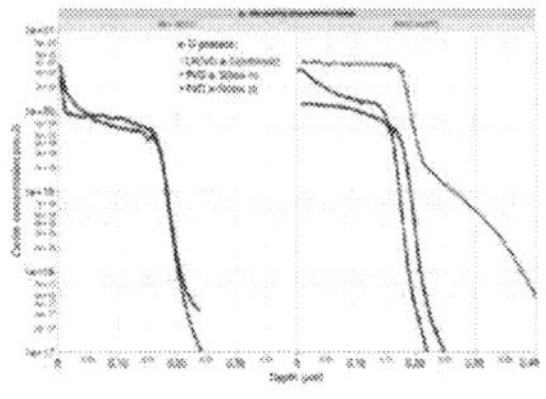

ECV profiles of low *p*- or *n*-doped PVD a-Si after ex-situ doping and 925°C annealing in BBr_3 or $POCl_3$; LPCVD intrinsic poly-Si shown as reference.

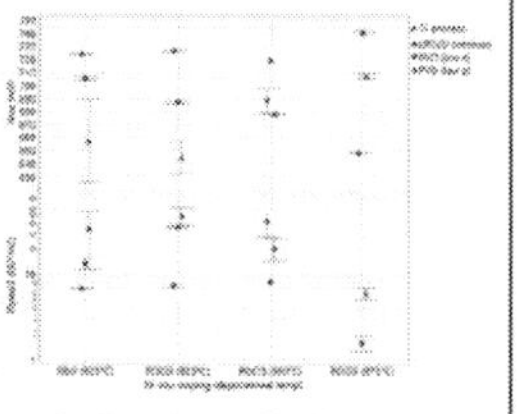

Implied Voc and J_{0pass} after fast firing of DC-sputtered low *p*- or *n*-doped a-Si, as function of ex-situ doping and annealing (925–975°C). A thermally grown TO with a thickness of ≈1.4 nm was used in this study for all samples.

- Both low *p*- and *n*-doped PVD a-Si layers can be ex-situ overcompensated by B or P diffusion, but doping concentration is below LPCVD poly-Si layer.
- n^+ PVD poly-Si achieved iVoc ≈ 740 mV and J_{0pass} ≈ 1.6 fA/cm².

Individual Process Steps Optimization

PVD-sputtered TO layer – preliminary results:

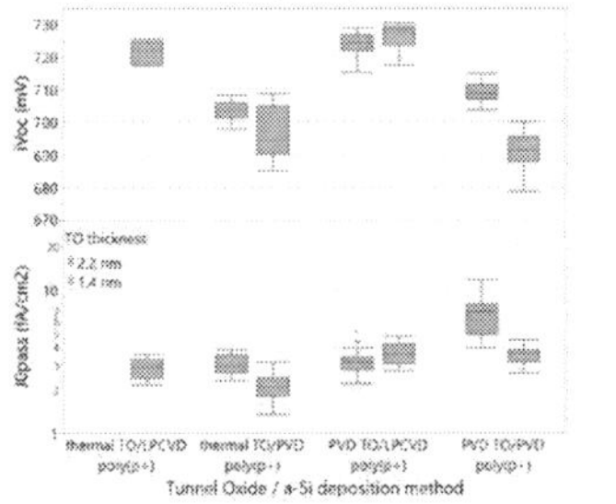

iVoc and J_{0pass} of lifetime test structures with different TO/poly-Si combinations: p^+ poly-Si from PVD (low *p*) or LPCVD (intrinsic) a-Si, B-doped and annealed (TO: 1.4 nm @875°C, 2.2 nm @1025°C).

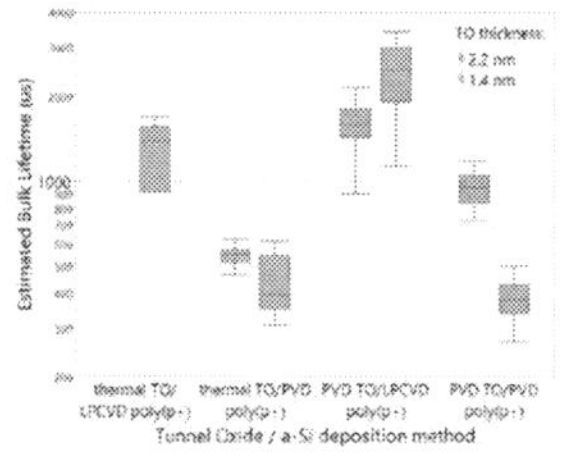

Estimated bulk lifetime from QSSPC for different TO / poly-Si combinations.

- PVD TO + LPCVD poly-Si → highest iVoc (730 mV).
- PVD TO comparable to or better than thermal TO.

Conclusions

- Both low ***p*- and *n*-doped PVD a-Si layers** are suitable for **ex-situ doping** in TBC processes.
- **PVD-based poly-Si layers** can reach **high passivation quality** and compete with **LPCVD benchmarks.**
- Demonstrates strong potential for a **simplified, cost-effective, scalable PVD route** to high-efficiency (>25%) TBC solar cells.

Ongoing work

- Further optimize **PVD-deposited TO layer.**
- Optimize **laser patterning** for process integration.
- Full **TBC solar cells** fabrication.

References

[1] Tong, H., Tan, S., Zhang, Y. et al., Nat. Commun. 16, 5920 (2025)
[2] Aiko, PV Magazine 2024 (https://www.pv-magazine.com/2024/06/19)
[3] Longi, PV Magazine 2025 (https://www.pv-magazine.com/2025/04/14)
[4] ISC-Konstanz patent pending 2024

Acknowledgements

This work is under development within the framework of the BMWE research project "ParIS" (contract No. 020E-100636800).

Supported by:
Federal Ministry for Economic Affairs and Energy

isc-konstanz.de

COMPARISON OF PASSIVATION PROPERTIES OF PHOSPHORUS AND BORON EX-SITU DOPED POLY-SILICON ON OXIDE LAYERS

Raphaël Cabal[1], Clarisse Laurens-Berge[1], Baptiste Marteau[2], Anis Jouini[2], Sebastien Dubois[1]
[1]Univ. Grenoble Alpes, CEA, LITEN, Campus INES, 73375 Le Bourget du Lac, France
[2]ECM Technologies, Grenoble, France
raphael.cabal@cea.fr

ABSTRACT: Passivating the contacts of crystalline silicon (c-Si) solar cells with a polycrystalline silicon layer (poly-Si) on a thin oxide (SiO_x) film is an effective approach to minimize the recombination current at the metal/c-Si interface. Combined with an ex-situ doping step ($POCl_3$ diffusion), this approach has become mainstream in PV market for TOPCon solar cells rear side passivation by poly-Si (P) / SiO_x stacks. Beyond the optimization of n-type poly-Si / SiO_x stacks, this study investigates the use of a BCl_3 diffusion to form poly-Si (B) / SiO_x stacks. Those p-type TOPCon stacks are of high interest both at short term to improve industrial TOPCon front surface passivation and for the development of double side passivated TOPCon bottom-cells for tandem applications. Thereafter are presented the doping profiles and passivation properties of both p and n-type ex-situ doped poly-Si / SiO_x stacks deposited on polished and textured surfaces, as well as their stability toward firing.

1 INTRODUCTION

Current TOPCon industrial structure involves already a poly-Si based passivating contact (n-type) on the rear polished side of the cell. In the future, one probable evolution of this structure should introduce a second poly-Si based passivating contact (p-type) on the front side of the cell, at least locally [1]. Considering that single junction devices feature a textured front surface, the introduction of a boron-doped poly-Si passivating contact remains a challenge: beyond light absorption issues, the passivation properties of p-type poly on textured surface does not reach at the moment the excellent passivation level offered by its phosphorus-doped counterpart [2]. From this sole perspective, there is still a need for improving the poly-Si (B) layers. On the other hand, one key parameter for a successful integration of poly-Si (B) on next generation TOPCon devices is the fact that it should be easy to implement on industrial lines. For this reason, the choice of BCl_3 diffusion (already in use in standard TOPCon lines for diffused emitter formation) seems of great relevance.

2 EXPERIMENTAL

In this work, a first batch of samples was made from Cz n-type wafers with a 3.6 Ohm.cm resistivity (M2 format). The wafers underwent a conventional texturing process (3µm-size pyramids) followed by a SC1/SC2/HF-HCl cleaning sequence, before being submitted to LPCVD growth of an interfacial SiO_x film (~2nm thick) followed by the deposition of an intrinsic poly-Si layer with a thickness of 80nm. Part of these samples were submitted to $POCl_3$ diffusion at temperatures ranging between 830°C and 860°C, while the other part was submitted to BCl_3 diffusion process carried out in the 900-990°C range. Diffused emitter resulting from the 990°C recipe applied directly onto the textured surface (without poly-Si/SiO_x stack) was considered as a reference. 4PP / ECV, and IC-PCD measurements were carried out onto these samples respectively before / after the BSG was removed in HF-HCl, in order to estimate poly-Si / SiO_x stacks sheet resistance (R_{Sheet}), active doping profile and implied V_{oc}. Additional hydrogenation (using single SiN_x layer or an AlO_x / SiN_x passivation stack on poly-Si top surface) and firing (using a peak temperature of 790°C) were applied to the samples in order to assess poly-Si (B) structures performance along TOPCon processing sequence (i-V_{oc} was re-measured after the most relevant step).

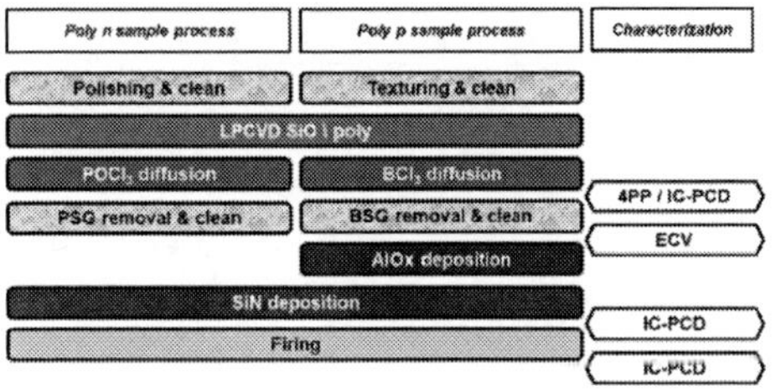

Figure 1: Symmetrical structures process-flow considered in this work.

3 RESULTS

3.1 Poly-Si (P)

Poly-Si (P) doping profiles feature a plateau above $3\times10^{20}cm^{-3}$ and a sharp diffusion tail in the c-Si (depth inferior to 60nm). Figure 2 presents the poly-Si (P) sheet resistances (measured on p-type wafers) for the different $POCl_3$ diffusion processes conducted on poly-Si layers. In this figure are also reported the corresponding active doping profiles measured by ECV. Diffusion temperatures of 830°C, 840°C, 850°C and 860°C were investigated. $POCl_3$ was injected during either 10min (Figure 2b) or 20min (Figure 2c). Similar doping profiles can be obtained for different diffusion temperature conditions, evidencing the robustness of tunnel oxide toward phosphorus dopant migration. Only a combination of high temperature (860°C) and prolonged $POCl_3$ injection permits to slightly increase the final diffusion tail. One can notice the thickness of poly-Si tends to shrink through the doping process leading to a final thickness around 60nm (confirmed by ellipsometry).

The i-V_{oc} measured on SiN_x coated poly-Si (P) structures before firing are also reported in Figure 2, showing values above 740mV for any diffusion temperature (here the $POCl_3$ injection was set to 20min). Passivation properties obtained with the poly-Si (P) reference structures are in good agreement with state-of-the art high levels. Nonetheless, in the present case, the poly-Si (P) samples exhibited poor passivation stability

10.4229/EUPVSEC2025/1CV.2.5

towards firing, significant blistering appearing concomitantly to huge i-V_{oc} losses. For this reason, another batch of devices was fabricated on sister wafers, aiming at investigating different firing conditions (T_{peak} of 750°C, 780°C, 810°C) but also other passivation schemes than SiN_x alone: a stack of AlO_x \ SiN_x including a 8nm-thick layer of alumina was considered.

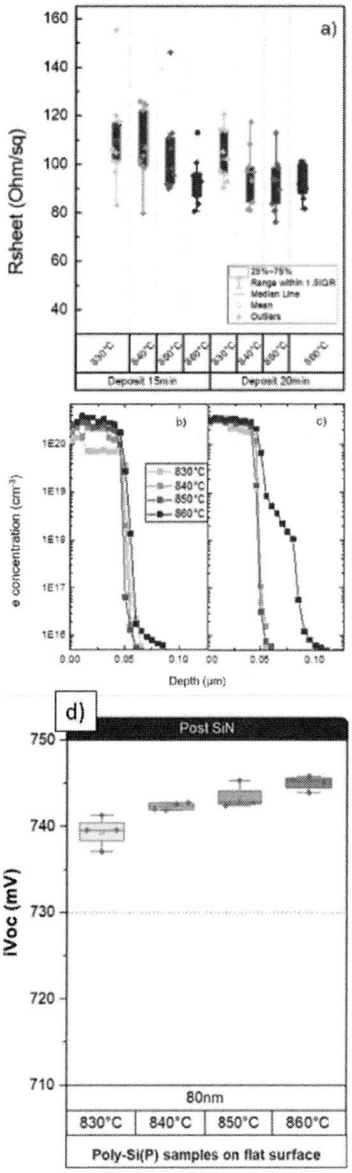

Figure 2: Doping and passivation features of poly-Si (P) structures: (a) R_{sheet} values; and doping profiles (b) for 15min and (c) 20min $POCl_3$ deposit; with (d) i-V_{oc} after SiN_x coating (20min deposit)

As can be noticed from Figure 3, the higher the firing peak temperature, the larger the i-V_{oc} degradation (for both SiN_x and AlO_x\SiN_x passivation schemes). In this context, one can notice that a firing done at low temperature (here 750°C) does not alter passivation, while SiN_x coated samples fired at 810°C features an i-V_{oc} loss of ~70mV, concomitant with a noticeable blistering of SiN_x layer. In addition, i-V_{oc} further drops in time (as observed by measuring the samples after 2 days of storage). This additional passivation degradation is assumed to be caused by an exposition of poly-Si and/or c-Si wafer surface to air, consequently to the aforementioned blistering.

The introduction of the 8nm-thick under layer of AlO_x improves greatly i-V_{oc} stability toward both firing and ageing. When fired at 810°C, AlO_x\SiN_x-coated structures exhibit an i-V_{oc} loss reduced from 70mV to 15mV. Blistering is also visibly mitigated, and time stability is improved accordingly (see Figure 3). Another approach for stabilizing passivation was investigated, focusing on poly-Si layer rather than upper dielectric stacks. A third batch of SiN_x coated poly-Si (P) / c-Si (n) / poly-Si (P) samples was processed integrating thicker poly-Si layer (110nm). This batch exhibits i-V_{oc} drops limited to 15mV after firing, and also a degradation in time reduced to 5mV. The combination of such 110nm-thick poly layer with AlO_x \ SiN_x appears as a good way to completely stabilize passivation properties of this n-type passivating contact.

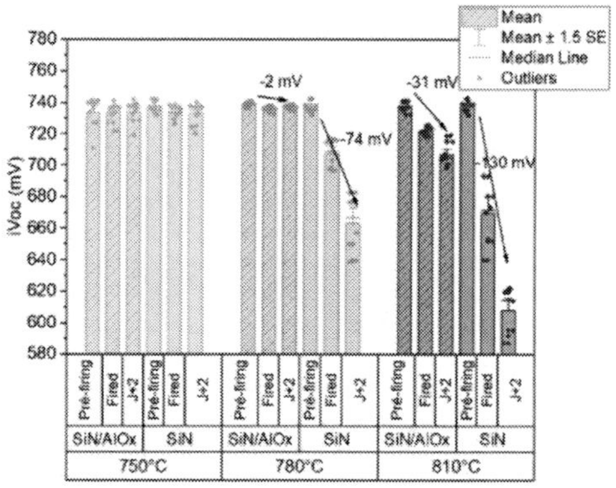

Figure 3: Variation of i-V_{oc} of SiN_x and AlO_x\SiN_x coated poly-Si (P) / c-Si (n) / poly-Si (P) structures through firing temperature and storage (2 days).

3.2 Poly-Si (B) results

We fabricated first reference $p^+/n/p^+$ samples (i.e. without poly-Si) integrating on both sides a 100 Ohm/sq boron emitter with a $2\times10^{19}.cm^{-3}$ surface boron concentration and a 0.8µm depth. Once passivated by AlO_x \ SiN_x and fired at 790°C, these $p^+/n/p^+$ samples reach iV_{oc} of 680mV.

Poly-Si (B) doping profiles obtained from BCl_3 diffusions at 850°C, 900°C, 950°C and 990°C are reported in Figure 4, along with reference (i.e. without poly) 100 Ohm/sq emitter profile. BCl_3 drive-in temperature has a strong effect on the diffusion depth of boron dopants into c-Si underlying substrate, but hardly affects the active doping in the poly layer itself, that stays at approximately $5\times10^{19}cm^{-3}$ whatever the conditions. As expected, lowering the BCl_3 drive-in temperature helps reducing boron diffusion in the c-Si, and sharp optimal diffusion tails are obtained for temperature below 900°C. However, this combination of low active doping in poly-Si layer and sharp diffusion tails in c-Si leads to high sheet resistance values (from ≈400 Ohm/sq to ≈1000 Ohm/sq for respectively 950°C and 850°C boron diffusion) and could potentially cause losses at cell level. A first solution to tackle the issue is the development of specific print technologies for those high sheet resistance structures. A second one would be the use of c-Si (p) bulk materials, as widely published by Fraunhofer ISE with the TOPCoRE solar cells [3].

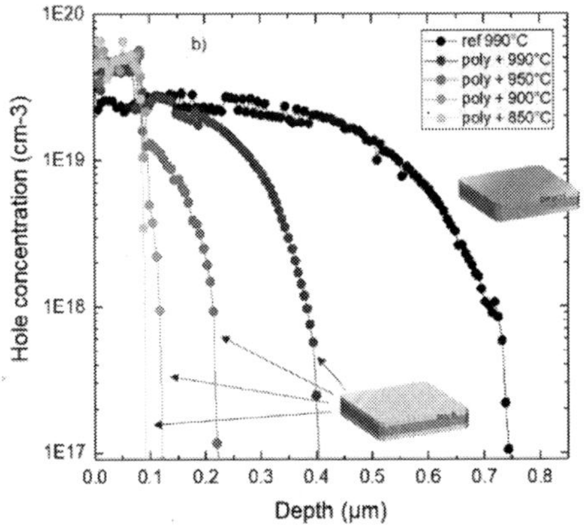

Figure 4: Doping profiles of ex-situ doped poly-Si (B) and reference 100 Ohm/sq diffused emitter (black symbols).

Some good passivation results (not shown here) could be obtained with poly-Si (B) on textured samples (up to 695mV) however reproducibility still need to be improved, some of the samples featuring a peripheral pattern defectivity activated by firing and imaged through PL. By investigating the origin of this pattern, we could evidence that the defect at play was not affecting the wafer bulk since the pattern disappears once poly-Si (B) was chemically etched (after a subsequent re-passivation). Neither the LPCVD nor the BCl_3 diffusion was found to introduce the aforementioned pattern, the latter being more likely the result of an undesired interaction of boron diffusion with the poly-Si / SiO_x stack, presumably causing a disruption / degradation of the underlying tunnel oxide, as evoked in the literature for PECVD poly-Si (B) layers [4]. To check this assumption, and discretize which among boron dopant migration or sole thermal budget is responsible for the supposed SiO_x degradation, another batch of textured samples was fabricated integrating undoped poly-Si / SiO_x on both sides. These samples were either exposed to conventional BCl_3 diffusion (950°C) or exposed to a boron-deprived process featuring the very same thermal budget. The unwanted PL pattern was shown to appear on samples exposed to the boron deprived diffusion cycle, evidencing that temperature alone is already greatly responsible for the tunnel oxide degradation. Two approaches were used with the aim of making tunnel oxide more resistant toward high temperature cycles: the first being an extended oxidation step of 20min-long (against 10min so far); the second consisting in a pre-oxidizing chemistry based on SC2 cleaning. Both approaches provided promising results when applied onto flat surfaces (KOH polished): baseline poly-Si (B) / c-Si (n) / poly-Si (B) structures (with 10min-long oxidation) exhibit i-V_{oc} around 685mV after firing, despite the presence of the PL imaged pattern. Prolonging LPCVD oxidation to 20min did not improve the average i-V_{oc} value but almost suppressed the PL pattern. Eventually, the combination of chemical oxide with 20min-long LPCVD oxidation permits to suppress the pattern too, but also to improve significantly i-V_{oc} values up to 710mV. When applied to textured samples, this best condition still permits to suppress the PL pattern; nonetheless the best resulting i-V_{oc} (660mV, i.e. a +30mV gain compared to baseline 10min long LPCVD oxidized samples) remains too low for a cell integration.

4 CONCLUSION

The combination of ex-situ doping via low pressure diffusion with LPCVD poly-Si is investigated here for both poly-Si (P) and poly-Si (B) structures, using respectively $POCl_3$ and BCl_3 diffusion processes. The passivation levels (740mV or more) reached with poly-Si (P) structures on flat surface evidence the good quality of poly-Si deposition and doping processes. The passivation stability to firing required nonetheless further optimizations: SiN_x-coated samples exhibited important blistering and i-V_{oc} drop (70mV). Thickening poly-Si to 110nm and replacing SiN_x passivation by an AlO_x \ SiN_x stack were found to stabilize passivation properties of the n-type passivating contact through both firing and time.

The evaluation of poly-Si (B) passivation properties on textured surface resulted in i-V_{oc} values up to 695mV, when BCl_3 diffusion was carried out at a temperature of 900°C onto 80 nm-thick poly-Si layers. Nonetheless we found difficulties reproducing this result, due to the appearance of a defectivity pattern activated through firing, and limiting i-V_{oc} to 630-640mV. This pattern is attributed to a degradation of SiO_x tunnel oxide during BCl_3 diffusion process. Strengthening the oxide by prolonging LPCVD oxidation step permitted to suppress the pattern; and combining it with a chemical pre-oxidation, improved i-V_{oc} on both polished and textured samples. While the i-V_{oc} obtained on flat surface are quite good (710mV), the values measured on textured surfaces (660mV) still need to be improved.

References

[1] J. Hoß, S.S. Kalaghichi, M. Comak, P. Preis, J. Lossen, J.Linke, L. Koduvelikulathu, F. Buchholz, Advanced TOPCon solar cells with vanishing metal induced recombination losses, EPJ Photovolt. 15, 43 (2024). https://doi.org/10.1051/epjpv/2024040

[2] F. Feldmann, M. Simon, M. Bivour, C. Reichel, M. Hermle, S.W. Glunz, Efficient carrier-selective p- and n-contacts for Si solar cells, Sol. Energy Mater. Sol. Cells 131 (2014) 100–104, https://doi.org/10.1016/j.solmat.2014.05.039.

[3] A. Richter, R. Müller, J. Benick, et al. Design rules for high-efficiency both-sides-contacted silicon solar cells with balanced charge carrier transport and recombination losses. Nat Energy 6, 429–438 (2021). https://doi.org/10.1038/s41560-021-00805-w

[4] A. Morisset, R. Cabal, V. Giglia, A. Boulineau, E. De Vito, A. Chabli, S. Dubois, J. Alvarez, J-P. Kleider, Evolution of the surface passivation mechanism during the fabrication of ex-situ doped poly-Si(B)/SiOx passivating contacts for high-efficiency c-Si solar cells, Solar Energy

Materials and Solar Cells, Volume 221, 2021, 110899, ISSN 0927-0248, https://doi.org/10.1016/j.solmat.2020.110899.

OVERCOMING PROCESS RELATED LIMITATIONS IN THE CONTEXT OF THE BACK CONTACTED POLYZEBRA SOLAR CELL TECHNOLOGY

Jonathan Linke, Lazhar Rachdi, Sebastian Veerman,
Jan Hoß, Jan Lossen, Lejo Joseph Koduvelikulathu, Florian Buchholz
ISC Konstanz e.V., Rudolf-Diesel-Str. 15, 78467 Konstanz, Germany
Corresponding author: jonathan.linke@isc-konstanz.de

ABSTRACT: TOPCon-based back-contacted silicon solar cells are a bridging technology between current TOPCon industrial standard and future fabrication of high efficient tandem technology. The polyZEBRA concept is such a back-contacted solar cell and promises a lean and cost-effective fabrication. In this contribution, the recent progress in technology optimization is reported, namely the influence of the base resistivity, of an improved screen-printing paste and of the AlO_x deposition technique. The results indicate the usage of high ohmic base material, improved screen-printing paste and of atomic layer deposition for AlO_x passivation. The combined learnings of those aspects lead to a 24.3% efficient champion cell.

Keywords: TBC, polyZEBRA, poly-Si, copper metallization

1 INTRODUCTION

The TOPCon technology is the current mainstream in silicon solar cell production, while many research activities are now focusing on tandem solar cells, which have a significant higher conversion efficiency potential. In the meantime, TOPCon-based back-contacted (TBC) solar cells are an important bridging technology. It has an inherently higher efficiency potential from a higher current due to the absence of optical shading on the front side of the solar cell. However, patterning of the rear side requires advanced technologies and has stronger requirements on process stability.

Successful industrial implementation of TBC solar cells and modules was already achieved by Maxeon SunPower, Aiko and Longi. Naturally, details about their fabrication processes are not available to the public and so the estimation of the actual production costs is difficult. In contrast, the polyZEBRA TBC solar cell production process was published before [1]. It promises a lean and cost-effective process flow that relies on equipment that is already used for industrial mass production such as laser-based patterning of the rear side [2,3] and standard screen-printing technology. Furthermore, it is compatible with screen-printed Cu pastes, which is able to reduce the Ag consumption to <5 mg/W_P [4]. Minimizing the Ag consumption is of high importance as the Ag price is expected to increase in the future as the demand steadily increases with increasing world-wide solar cell production capacity.

This contribution reports about recent progress in optimization of polyZEBRA TBC solar cells since the last publication [5]. In particular, the influence of the base resistivity, of an improved screen-printing paste and of the AlO_x deposition technique is discussed.

2 EXPERIMENTAL

2.1 Cell fabrication and characterization

polyZEBRA solar cells were fabricated according to the process flow reported in [1] and are shown in Figure 1. Cz-grown phosphorous-doped n-type M6 wafers with an initial thickness of 150µm were used. After tunnel oxide growth and LP-CVD poly-Si depositions (Fig. 1, step 1,6), the rear side was patterned by laser ablation of a previously deposited SiN_x mask for the base region (Fig. 1, step 3,4) and laser activation [2,3] of boron-doped poly-Si for the emitter region (Fig. 1, step 8). After texturing of the front side and the gap region, which separates both polarities (Fig. 1, Step 9), a boron diffusion was applied to form a front-floating emitter (Fig. 1, step 10). For surface passivation of both sides, an AlO_x/SiN_y stack was deposited in a conventional PE-CVD tube furnace (Fig. 1, step 11). The solar cells were contacted by simultaneous screen-printing of Ag-based paste on both polarities and a subsequent fast firing step. The busbars were screen-printed either by Ag or Cu paste (Fig. 1, step 12a/b).

The cells were characterized in a conventional cell flasher (Halm elektronik GmbH), simultaneously recording electroluminescence (EL) images. The properties of the individual regions (base, emitter, gap) were monitored on test structures with squares of several centimeters dimensions to enable standard characterization methods like QSSPC.

3 RESULTS

In the following sections 3.1 - 3.3, the three improvements, namely the optimized base resistivity, screen-printing paste and AlO_x deposition technique, are described in detail. In section 3.4 it is described, how the combination of these improvements lead to the best performing polyZEBRA cell batch so far.

3.1 Base Resistivity

The base resistivity of the wafers used for fabrication of back-contacted solar cells has two contradicting effects [6]: First, with higher base resistivity the bulk lifetime and in turn the J_{sc} increases. And second, with higher base resistivity the internal resistivity increases, which in turn decreases the FF. The optimum of this trade-off has to be determined experimentally and depends among others on the cell concept, patterning layout and wafer quality.

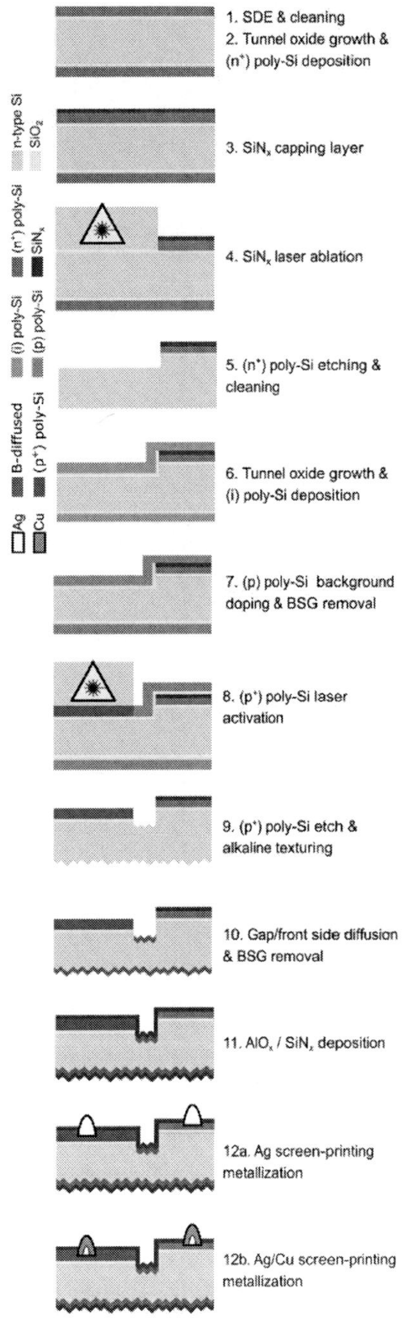

Figure 1: polyZEBRA solar cell fabrication process flow taken from [1].

Figure 2 shows the IV data of polyZEBRA solar cells that were fabricated in the same batch, but on phosphorous-doped Cz wafers with different base resistivities of either 1.25 Ωcm or 5.2 Ωcm. The expected increase in J_{sc} of ~0.5 mA/cm² is clearly visible. However, the FF drops only marginally and so the gain in J_{sc} dominates, which is reflected in the +0.3%$_{abs}$ gain in cell efficiency. It seems that the usage of ~5 Ωcm material is mandatory for high efficiencies.

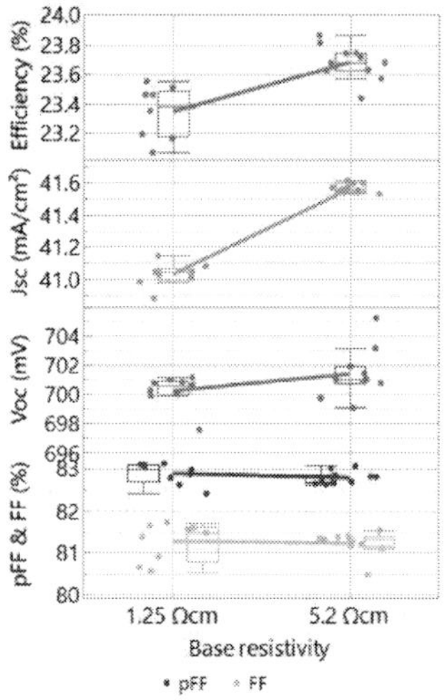

Figure 2: IV measurement data of polyZEBRA solar cells fabricated in the same production batch but on phosphorus-doped n-type M6 wafers with different base resistivity.

3.2 Improved screen-printing paste

For screen-printing of the Ag contacts to the silicon, "paste A" was used for a long time. However, it induced a quite significant metal recombination, visible in the high iV_{oc}-to-V_{oc} loss of 7 mV (Table I, "passivation"). Typical values for TOPCon structures are 1-2 mV. To solve this issue, an improved "paste B" was tested. After optimization of the firing conditions, the iV_{oc}-to-V_{oc} loss was reduced significantly to ~2 mV (Table I, "passivation"), which is a strong indication of vanishing metal recombination. This conclusion of less spiking of the metal through the tunnel oxide is further supported by a higher shunt resistance and +0.4%$_{abs}$ pFF (Table I, "contact").

Table I: Passivation and contact properties of polyZEBRA solar cells fabricated in the same production batch but with different Ag screen-printing pastes for the first layer, which forms the contact to the silicon. Fast-firing conditions were optimized for each paste respectively. The iV_{oc}-to-V_{oc} loss serves as a measure for the metal recombination and the pFF-to-FF loss as a measure for the series resistance.

		Paste A	Paste B
Passivation	PL2V_{oc} cell precursor	716mV	708mV
	V_{oc} cell	709mV	706mV
	iV_{oc}-to-V_{oc} loss	7mV	2mV
Contact	pFF	82.7%	83.1%
	FF	80.3%	81.2%
	pFF-to-FF loss	2.4%	1.9%

At the same time, also the series resistance was reduced, which is reflected in a lower pFF-to-FF loss of 1.9% compared to 2.4% of "paste B" (Table I, "contact"). Since the parameters of all remaining metallization steps were kept the same and these following steps define the grid resistance, the lower series resistance is attributed to a lower contact resistivity. This conclusion is supported by the much smoother EL image of paste B over the whole cell surface (Figure 3).

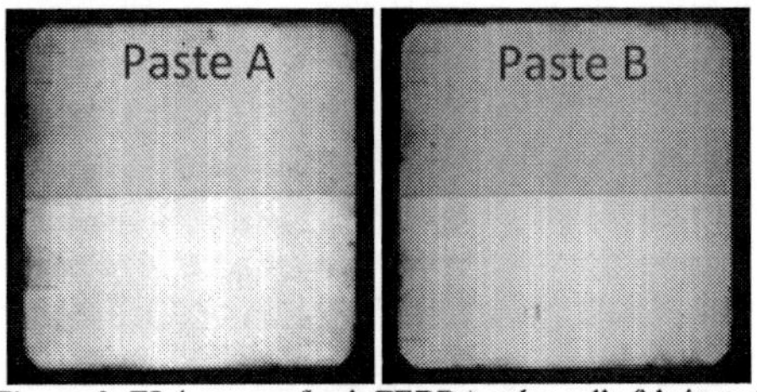

Figure 3: EL images of polyZEBRA solar cells fabricated in the same production batch but with different Ag screen-printing pastes for the first layer, which forms the contact to the silicon. Fast-firing conditions were optimized for each paste respectively.

In this sense, "paste B" is a significant improvement as it decreased the metal recombination and contact resistivity at the same time. However, the potential of this improvement is not fully transferred to the cell efficiency. The firing parameters that were optimized for good electrical performance of paste B, are not optimal for the gap and front side passivation. This is reflected in -8 mV iV_{oc} of not metallized cell precursors compared to precursors that were fired with the parameters optimized for "paste A" (Table I, "passivation"). This effect is even more detrimental than the gain from the lower metal recombination, so that the final V_{oc} of the solar cells is even reduced. However, the +0.9%$_{abs}$ higher FF from lower contact resistivity and higher pFF, overcompensates the loss in V_{oc} and results in an efficiency gain of +0.1%$_{abs}$ (Fig. 4).

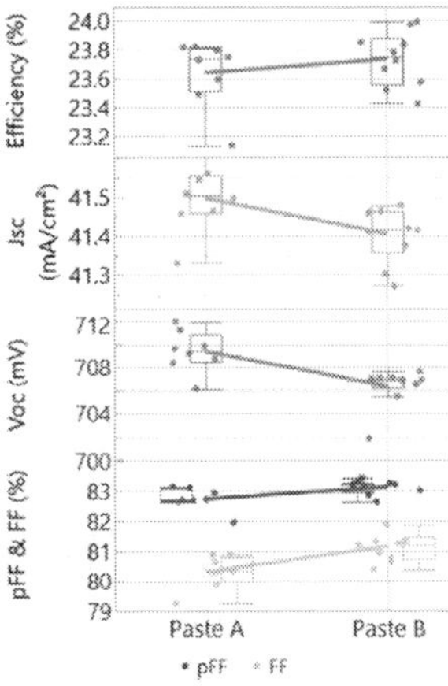

Figure 4: IV measurement data of polyZEBRA solar cells fabricated in the same production batch but with different Ag screen-printing pastes for the first layer, which forms the contact to the silicon. Fast-firing conditions were optimized for each paste respectively.

3.3 AlO_x deposition technique

On the front side of the polyZEBRA solar cells a front floating emitter was formed in a boron diffusion (Fig. 1, step 10), which does also dope the gap region on the rear side. For proper surface passivation, an AlO_x/SiN_y stack was deposited on both sides (Fig. 1, step 11). The properties of the AlO_x layers are key for good cell performance for two reasons. First, excellent surface passivation of the front side is mandatory for high cell voltages [6]. And second, since efficient hydrogenation is important for high quality passivation on the rear side, the AlO_x layer must not hinder hydrogen diffusion towards the poly-Si/SiO_x stacks.

Two AlO_x deposition techniques were compared, namely plasma-enhanced chemical vapor deposition (PE-CVD), which was standard method for polyZEBRA cells in the past, and plasema-enhanced atomic layer deposition (PE-ALD). The recipes of each deposition were previously optimized towards high passivation quality. The IV results are shown in Fig. 5. The cells with PE-ALD deposited AlO_x have a 2 mV higher V_{oc}. Test structures with squares of each region showed that this gain originates from a lower J_0 of the (n) poly-Si region. Considering that the AlO_x properties are influencing the penetration of hydrogen [7], this finding points into the direction of a more efficient hydrogen supply from the SiN_x through the AlO_x layer towards the tunnel oxide. Since also the pFF increases by +0.2%$_{abs}$, it is assumed that the more efficient hydrogen supply through the PE-ALD deposited AlO_x does also improve the bulk lifetime of the wafer.

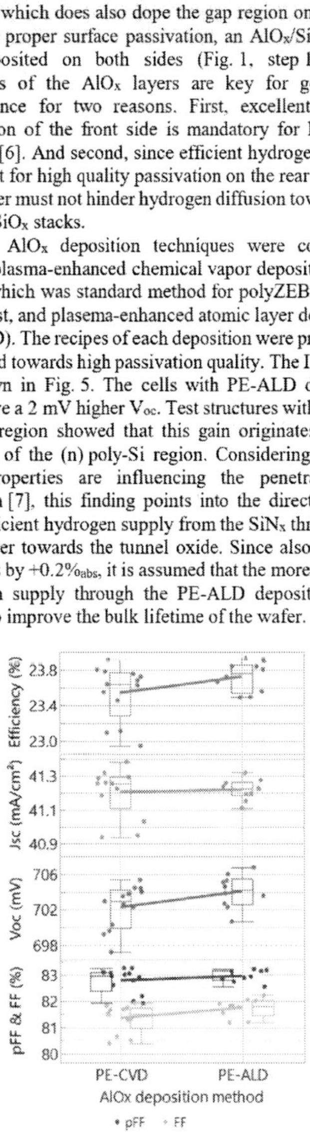

Figure 5: IV measurement data of polyZEBRA solar cells fabricated in the same production batch but with different AlO_x deposition techniques from the same tube furnace.

A second improvement from the PE-ALD deposition compared to the PE-CVD technique is a lower series resistance, which is reflected in a lower pFF-to-FF loss of 1.2%$_{abs}$ compared to 1.4%$_{abs}$ for the PE-CVD deposited AlO_x. One explanation for this behavior could be that the screen-printed Ag paste does solve and penetrate the PE-ALD deposited AlO_x more efficient than the PE-CVD deposited AlO_x. At least for SiO_x layers it is known, that it has a strong influence on paste penetration and can even block it totally [8].

In sum, the increase in V_{oc} as well as FF from lower series resistance and higher pFF leads to an increase of the cell efficiency of +0.2%$_{abs}$. This improvement highlights the limitation of the current toolset in our labs. In particular, AlO_x deposition by thermal ALD is expected to further increase the cell efficiency.

3.4 Combination of all improvements

In Section 3.1 the importance of ~5 Ωcm base resistivity was highlighted as optimum of the trade-off between high J_{sc} and FF. In Section 3.2 and 3.3 significant improvements by an improved screen-printing paste and PE-ALD AlO_x deposition, respectively, were shown. Table I shows the IV results of a cell batch that combined all these learnings. In addition, the cells feature Cu busbars, which were screen-printed and afterwards snap-cured in an industrial tool. Replacing the Ag busbars by Cu busbars saved 44% of the total Ag usage.

Table II: Solar cell parameters of a polyZEBRA production batch, that combined all improvements presented in section 3.1–3.3.

	η	J_{sc} (mA/cm²)	V_{oc} (mV)	FF	pFF
Champion cell	24.3%	41.6	711	82.1%	83.7%
Mean	24.0%	41.5	708	81.6%	83.1%
Stdev	0.3%	0.1	3	0.4%	0.4%

The mean cell efficiency was 24.0% with a champion efficiency of 24.3%. This is an improvement of +0.2%$_{abs}$ efficiency compared to the previously published results [1], [5]. The main improvement is a significant increase of the pFF from vanishing metal recombination, thus spiking through the tunnel oxides, and PE-ALD AlO_x deposition. The highest potential remaining for improvement is the V_{oc} of 708 mV, which is quite low considering that both polarities are passivated with poly-Si/SiO_x stacks. As stated in Section 3.2, this low V_{oc} originates mostly from the firing conditions of the improved paste, which are not aligned with the surface passivation of the front side and gap region. This issue is the current focus of further investigations.

4 CONCLUSION

The polyZEBRA TBC solar cell concept has the potential for a lean and cost-effective production. The importance of high ohmic base material was emphasized. Vanishing metal recombination, which is the main advantage of passivating poly-Si/SiO_x contacts, was achieved with an improved paste and adjusted firing settings. However, the front side and gap surface passivation is not yet aligned with this adjusted firing step. Changing from PE-CVD to PE-ALD boosted the cell efficiency and a combination of those improvements yielded a champion cell efficiency of 24.3% on a cell with Cu busbars, wich saved 44% of the total Ag usage. These results are very promising considering the limitations of our labs in comparison to a future production line that is built from scratch.

5 ACKNOWLEDGEMENTS

This work was partly funded by EU's Horizon Europe programme under the grant agreement No. 101084259 (IBC4EU).

6 REFERENCES

[1] J. Linke *et al.*, ">24% Efficient Tunnel Back Contacted polyZEBRA Solar Cells," in *Proc. of 41th European Photovoltaic Solar Energy Conference and Exhibition EUPVSEC*, 020006, 2024, 10.4229/EUPVSEC2024/1AO.6.5.

[2] F. Buchholz *et al.*, "Local Passivating Contacts from Laser Doped p+ Polysilicon," in *Proc. of 38th European Photovoltaic Solar Energy Conference and Exhibition EUPVSEC*, Online, 140–143, 2021, 10.4229/EUPVSEC20212021-2BO.11.3.

[3] S. SharbafKalaghichi, J. Hoß, R. Zapf-Gottwick, and J. H. Werner, "Laser Activation for Highly Boron-Doped Passivated Contacts," *Solar* 3, 362–381, 2023, 10.3390/solar3030021.

[4] N. Chen *et al.*, "Thermal Stable High-Efficiency Copper Screen Printed Back Contact Solar Cells," *Solar RRL* 7 (2), 2200874, 2022, 10.1002/solr.202200874.

[5] J. Linke *et al.*, "24% Efficient TOPCon-Based Back Contacted polyZEBRA Solar Cells," *EPJ Photovoltaics* 16 (8), 2025, 10.1051/epjpv/2024051

[6] P. Verlinden, "Interdigitated Back Contact Solar Cells," in *Photovoltaic Solar Energy*, A. Reinders, P. Verlinden, W. van Sark, and A. Freundlich, Eds., Chichester, UK: John Wiley & Sons, Ltd, 2017, 92–103, 10.1002/9781118927496.ch10.

[7] A. Schmid *et al.*, "On the Role of AlOx Thickness in AlOx/SiNy:H Layer Stacks Regarding Light- and Elevated Temperature-Induced Degradation and Hydrogen Diffusion in c-Si," *IEEE J. Photovolt.* 11 (4), 967–973, 2021, 10.1109/JPHOTOV.2021.3075850.

[8] R. Glatthaar *et al.*, "Silver Metallization with Controlled Etch Stop Using SiO_x Layers in Passivating Contacts for Improved Silicon Solar Cell Performance," *Solar RRL* 7 (21), 2300491, 2023, 10.1002/solr.202300491.

42nd European Photovoltaic Solar Energy Conference and Exhibition

ISC research for a sunny future

Overcoming Process Related Limitations of the BC polyZEBRA Solar Cell Technology

Jonathan Linke, Lazhar Rachdi, Sebastian Veerman,
Jan Hoß, Jan Lossen, Lejo Joseph Koduvelikulathu, Florian Buchholz

ISC Konstanz e.V., Rudolf-Diesel-Str. 15, 78467 Konstanz, Germany
jonathan.linke@isc-konstanz.de / +49-7531-36183-362

Overview

- Integration of TOPCon technology in IBC cells
- polyZEBRA concept with both polarities TOPCon-structures, patterned by laser processes[1,2]
- Previously reported champion cell efficiency 24.1% and simulated efficiency potential >25%[3]
- Recent improvements presented here

Takeaways

- Vanishing metal recombination with improved paste
- Integration of PE-ALD AlO_x improves V_{oc}/pFF/FF
- High base resistivity ~5Ωcm mandatory for high efficiency
- Combination of all learnings enables 24.3% champion cell efficiency
- Champion cell with screen-printed Cu-BBs
  → Ag consumption reduced by 44%

polyZEBRA fabrication process[3]

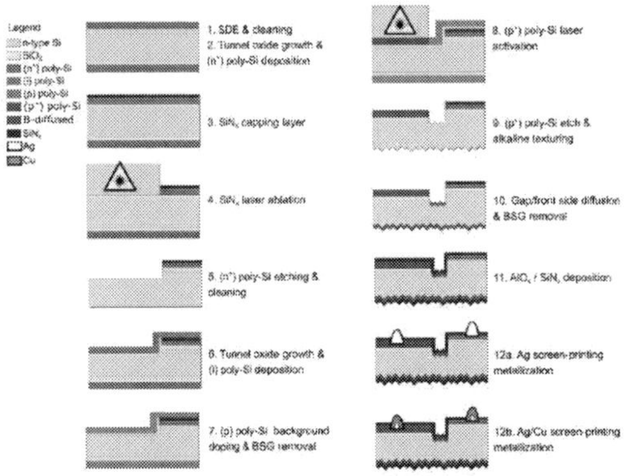

Improved screen-printing paste

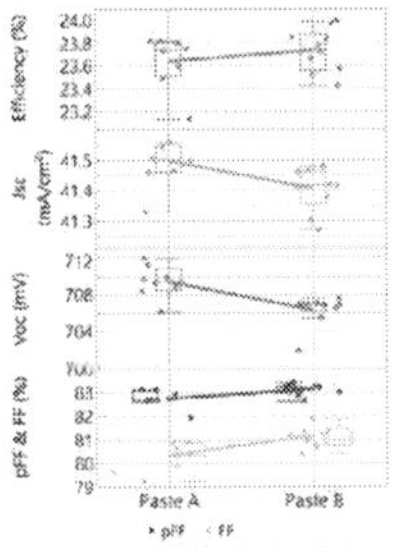

- Vanishing metal recombination with paste B:
  - Barely measurable iV_{oc}-to-V_{oc} loss
  - Higher R_{shunt}, pFF
    (→ less spiking through tunnel oxide)
- Better contact of paste B (lower pFF to FF loss)
  → EL image smoother
- Poor precursors from paste B firing parameters, which degrade front side passivation

		Paste A	Paste B
Passivation	PL2V_{oc} cell precursor	716mV	708mV
Passivation	V_{oc} cell	709mV	706mV
Passivation	iV_{oc}-to-V_{oc} loss	7mV	2mV
Contact	pFF	82.7%	83.1%
Contact	FF	80.3%	81.2%
Contact	pFF-to-FF loss	2.4%	1.9%

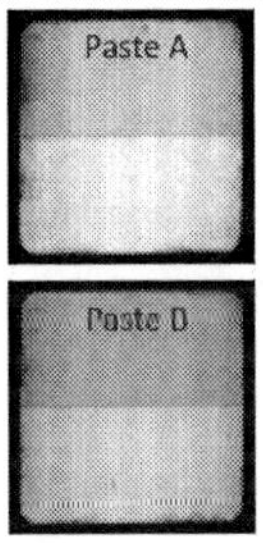

AlO_x deposition technique

- AlO_x deposition techniques from same tube furnace: PE-CVD, PE-ALD
- PE-ALD AlO_x with superior ...
  - ... hydrogenation of (n) poly-Si/SiO_x structures → +2mV V_{oc}
  - ... series resistance, pFF → +0.4% FF
  - ... efficiency +0.2%
- → PE-ALD AlO_x more penetrable for hydrogen and paste

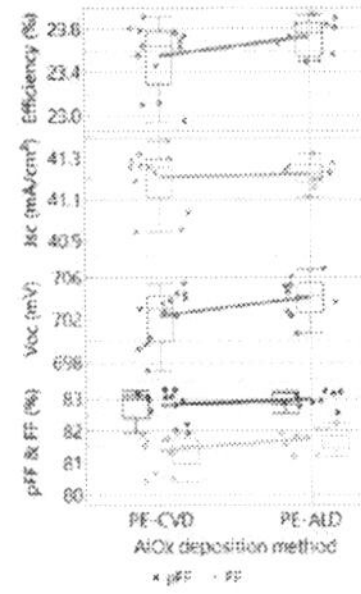

Base resistivity

- Theory:
  Towards higher base resistivity, increasing J_{sc} (higher bulk lifetime), but decreasing FF (higher internal resistivity)[4]
- Experiment:
  Base resistivity 1.25 → 5.2Ωcm
  - J_{sc} +0.5mA/cm²
  - FF only slight decrease
  - → +0.3% efficiency

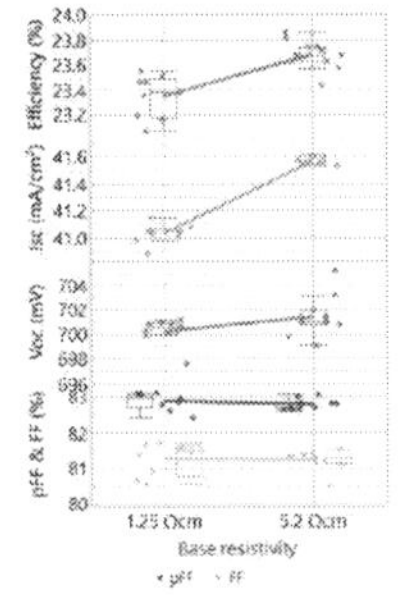

Combination of improvements

	η	J_{sc} (mA/cm²)	V_{oc} (mV)	FF	pFF
Champion cell	24.3%	41.6	711	82.1%	83.7%
Mean ± stdev	24.0 ± 0.3%	41.5 ± 0.1	708 ± 3	81.6 ± 0.4%	83.1 ± 0.4%

- Best polyZEBRA cell batch so far
- Champion cell efficiency +0.2% compared to previous reported data[3]
- Main gain in pFF (thus FF) from improved paste and PE-ALD AlO_x
- With screen-printed Cu-BB, cured on industrial laminator tool
  → Ag consumption reduced by 44%

References

[1] F. Buchholz *et al.*, *Proc. EUPVSEC* 2021, 140-143
[2] J. Linke *et al.*, *Proc. WCPEC 2022*, 102-106
[3] J. Linke *et al.*, *Proc. EUPVSEC 2024*, 020006
[4] P. Verlinden, in *Photovoltaic Solar Energy*, John Wiley & Sons, Ltd, 2017, pp. 92–103.

Acknowledgements

This work was partly funded by EU's Horizon Europe programme under the grant agreement No. 101084259

020036-001

IBC4EU

ADVANCING TOPCON SILICON SOLAR CELLS WITH LASER-GROOVED BURIED CONTACT TECHNOLOGY

Mohammad Hossein Mohammadi [*a], Roberto Boccardi [b], Io Mizushima [c], Irene Tosi [c], Gisele Alves dos Reis Benatto [b], Peter Behrensdorff Poulsen [b], Torben Tang [c], Sune Thorsteinsson [b], Rasmus Schmidt Davidsen [a]
[a] Department of Electrical and Computer Engineering, Aarhus University, 8200, Denmark
[b] DTU Electro, Technical University of Denmark, 2800 Kgs. Lyngby, Denmark
[c] IPU P/S, Virum, Denmark

ABSTRACT: The integration of the TOPCon structure with Cu-plated metallization and laser-grooved BC technology is a new and untested combination in crystalline silicon solar cell design. This approach will likely leverage the excellent passivation and carrier selectivity of TOPCon to minimize recombination losses and enhance power conversion efficiency (PCE). Cu plating, known for its high conductivity and low cost, reduces resistive losses while supporting sustainability due to the well-known Ag scarcity. Laser ablation enables precise and repeatable groove formation, creating a highly efficient top surface with minimal losses. The narrow metal lines of buried contacts potentially reduce shading losses and finger resistance. This innovation addresses key challenges like shading, parasitic resistance, and cost, while being suitable for advanced applications.
Keywords: TOPCon, Cu-plated metallization, buried contact (BC), laser-grooved BC technology

1 INTRODUCTION

Global solar PV installations are expanding rapidly, with total installed capacity rising by over 30% in 2023 [1]. A key sustainability challenge for solar cells lies in the limited availability of silver (Ag): at the current consumption rate, the PV sector could deplete 85–98% of existing Ag reserves by 2050, with even higher demand expected under scenarios of accelerated n-type cell adoption [2]. As a result, copper (Cu), which is more affordable and abundant, is being explored as an alternative for metallization. This is typically achieved through electroplating, with a nickel (Ni) barrier layer applied to prevent Cu diffusion into silicon in the metallized regions [3], since copper can form recombination centers within the bandgap [1-4].

Among high-efficiency PV technologies, tunnel oxide passivated contact (TOPCon) cells have been extensively investigated for copper plating metallization. In most reported approaches, the passivation layers are selectively opened on both sides using laser contact opening (LCO), exposing the underlying p-type crystalline silicon and n-type polycrystalline silicon. Electroplating of Ni/Cu is then carried out on each side sequentially, followed by immersion plating of a silver capping layer [4].

The integration of buried contact (BC) technology, where grooves are precisely formed using laser ablation, further optimizes the solar cell design [5]. Laser processing ensures high precision and repeatability, enabling the creation of well-defined grooves that serve as pathways for plated metal contacts [6, 7]. This technology drastically reduces shading losses and enhances light absorption by confining metal contacts to the grooves [8, 9]. Unlike conventional screen-printed contacts, the BC structure achieves a high metal aspect ratio, allowing for densely spaced fingers with minimal shading loss [10]. This innovation reduces emitter and grid resistance while leveraging Cu low resistivity to improve overall conductivity. Furthermore, the inclusion of a self-aligned, selective emitter in the BC design minimizes contact recombination and supports higher open-circuit voltages. Together, these features enable efficiency improvements compared to traditional screen-printed solar cells, while also reducing parasitic resistance and enabling low-cost electricity generation.

The synergy of the TOPCon structure, Cu-plated metallization, and laser-formed BC technology presents a robust pathway toward high-efficiency and cost-effective solar cells. This integration not only addresses current performance limitations but also offers scalable solutions for advanced photovoltaic systems, paving the way for more sustainable and economical solar energy production.

2 EXPERIMENTAL

Standard TOPCon precurses were received comprising of the standard TOPCon structure as outlined in Fig. 1. The precursors will further be laser processed using a 'microSTRUCT' laser micromachining tool from 3D-Micromac AG. The aim is to produce laser grooves with maximum depth and minimum width for buried contacts. The tool is equipped with a 50 W picosecond laser capable of emitting light at three wavelengths: 355 nm, 532 nm, and 1064 nm, with a pulse repetition rate ranging from 200 kHz to 8000 kHz. Initially, the green laser (λ=532 nm) with a picosecond pulse duration was utilized. The laser source emitted pulses with a duration of 10 ps in TEM00 mode. The scanning speed was set to 300 mm/min, and the laser pulse repetition rate ranged from a single shot to 200 kHz. Additionally, both the laser power and the number of scanning passes were adjustable. To reduce the width of each groove, the laser source was switched from green (532 nm) to red (355 nm) while keeping all other parameters unchanged. The samples are electrically connected to a non-submerged contacting pin at the "electroplating spot" and vertically immersed in the Cu electrolyte solution to approximately 75% of their length for 5–10 minutes. The finalized cells are subsequently characterized using scanning electron microscopy (SEM), optical microscopy, and profilometry.

3 RESULTS AND DISSCUSIONS

First, we examine how the power and repetition in laser can affect the surface properties and groove quality as well as depth during the laser grooving process on TOPCon. The experiments utilized a 532 nm green laser and a 355 nm UV laser on a TOPCon under varying repetition rates. A SEM, optical profilometer, and optical microscopy are employed to assess surface features,

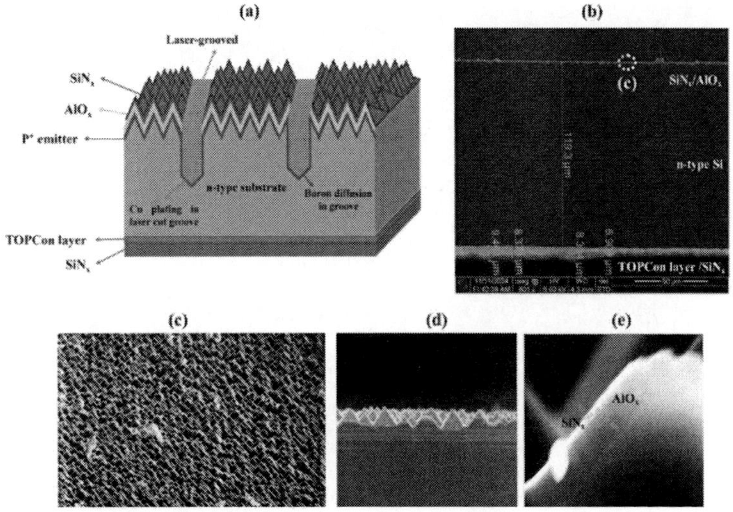

Fig.1. (a) schematic of BC structure with the laser grooved filled out plated Cu. (b), (c), (d) and (e) SEM images of TOPCon surface solar cell before laser scribing.

groove quality, groove profile, and the groove's width and depth. results in more refined and deeper grooves, which is beneficial for improving metallization quality, electrical contact, and ultimately the efficiency of the solar cell. Fig. 2 presents the SEM images of the laser-formed grooves, highlighting the ablation area and visible laser-induced damage. The extent of surface modifications and defects caused by the laser process can be clearly observed. The effect of the number of laser passes on the groove morphology is shown in Fig. 2. With 30 passes, the grooves remain shallow and insufficient to fully penetrate the passivation layer, resulting in incomplete contact opening. At 50 passes, the grooves reach greater depth, but localized damage in the underlying silicon becomes visible, which could negatively affect the electrical performance by introducing defect sites. Increasing the number of passes to 70 and 80 produces grooves with larger depth and width, creating well-defined openings that are more suitable for subsequent metallization steps. However, when the number of passes is further increased to 100, excessive ablation occurs, leading to over-etching and significant structural damage at the groove edges. These observations suggest that while higher numbers of passes improve groove definition, excessive laser exposure compromises surface quality, emphasizing the need to optimize the number of passes to balance sufficient contact opening with minimal substrate damage. Optical microscopy images of the grooves formed with different

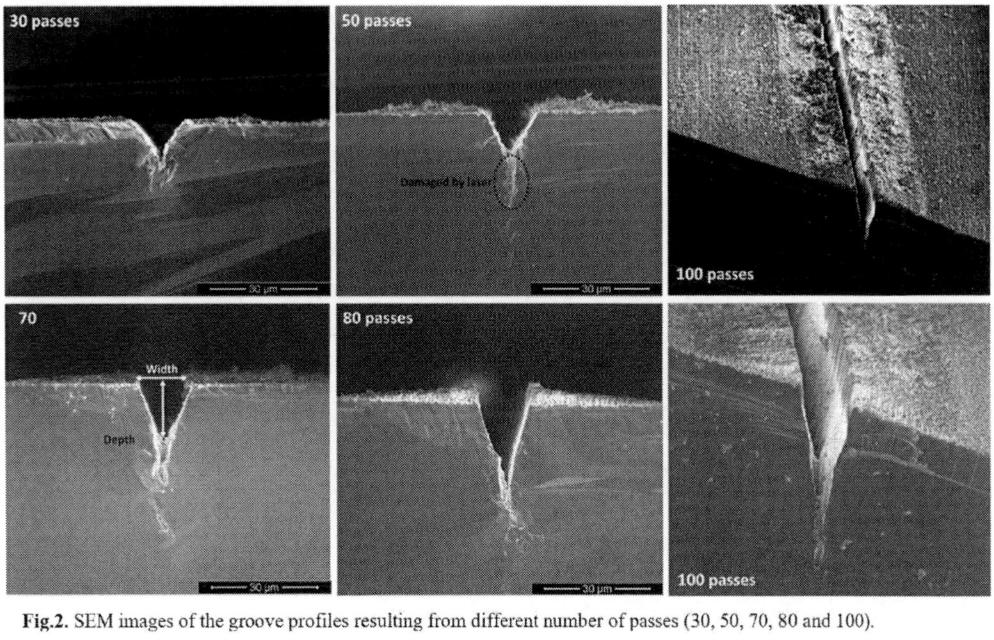

Fig.2. SEM images of the groove profiles resulting from different number of passes (30, 50, 70, 80 and 100).

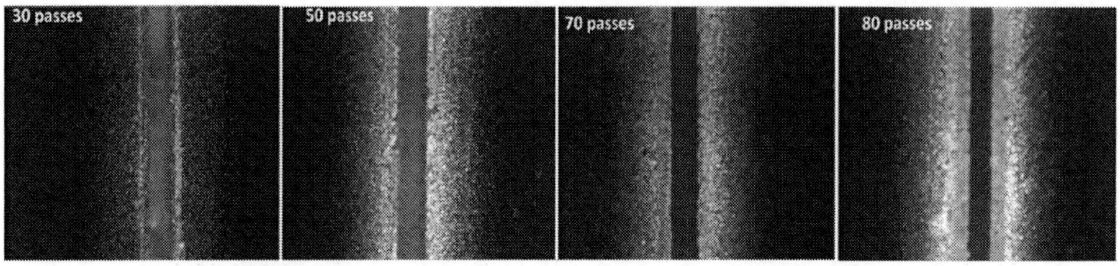

Fig.3. Optical microscope images (top view) of laser-formed grooves on a TOPCon solar cell with varying laser passes (30, 50, 70, 80 and 100 passes).

numbers of laser passes are shown in Fig. 3. At 30 passes, the groove appears narrow and irregular, with incomplete removal of the passivation layer. Increasing to 50 passes results in a more continuous and defined groove, though some surface roughness remains visible along the edges. At 70 passes, the groove becomes wider and cleaner, with more uniform sidewalls compared to lower pass counts. With 80 passes, the groove shows the best definition, exhibiting a well-opened channel with reduced debris accumulation at the edges. These results are consistent with the SEM observations, confirming that higher numbers of passes improve groove opening; however, excessive passes, as previously noted, may also introduce damage. Thus, an intermediate range between 70 and 80 passes appears optimal for achieving clean and well-defined contact openings. Fig. 4 presents the groove depth profiles obtained under different laser conditions. For the 533 nm wavelength at 2.6 W and 200 kHz (left), the groove depth increases with the number of repetitions, ranging from ~3 μm at a single pass to ~8.3 μm at eight repetitions. The profiles also reveal a progressive broadening of the groove with higher repetition numbers, indicating cumulative material removal but also the onset of thermal effects that may degrade edge sharpness. In contrast, for the 355 nm wavelength at 1.3 W and 200 kHz (right), the groove depth is more strongly dependent on the number of passes. Depth increases from ~10 μm at 30 passes to ~35 μm at 100 passes, showing a nearly linear trend up to higher pass counts. Compared to the 533 nm case, the 355 nm laser provides deeper and narrower grooves, reflecting more efficient material ablation at the shorter wavelength. These results suggest that while both laser parameters can achieve selective passivation opening, UV wavelengths offer higher precision and deeper penetration, whereas visible wavelengths provide shallower and wider grooves, potentially more prone to surface damage. The morphology of the grooves after Cu electroplating is presented in Fig. 5. SEM cross-sections reveal that copper successfully deposits along the vertical walls of the laser-etched grooves, forming a relatively uniform layer with thickness values in the range of ~1.18–1.57 μm (Fig. 5c). This indicates effective nucleation and growth of copper within the recessed regions, ensuring electrical continuity along the contact opening. However, in addition to sidewall coverage, significant copper accumulation is observed at the top edges of the grooves (Fig. 5d), with lateral overgrowth reaching thicknesses of ~6–7 μm. Such overplanting may increase series resistance due to uneven current distribution and could interfere with subsequent capping or passivation steps. These results suggest that while electroplating enables conformal filling of grooves, optimization of plating parameters is required to minimize excessive deposition at the groove edges while ensuring sufficient coverage inside the contact region.

4 SUMMERY AND FUTURE WORK

This study investigated the combination of TOPCon structures with BC technology through laser grooving and Cu-based metallization. The results confirmed that groove morphology is highly sensitive to laser wavelength, power, and number of passes. Optical, SEM, and profilometry analyses showed that increasing passes

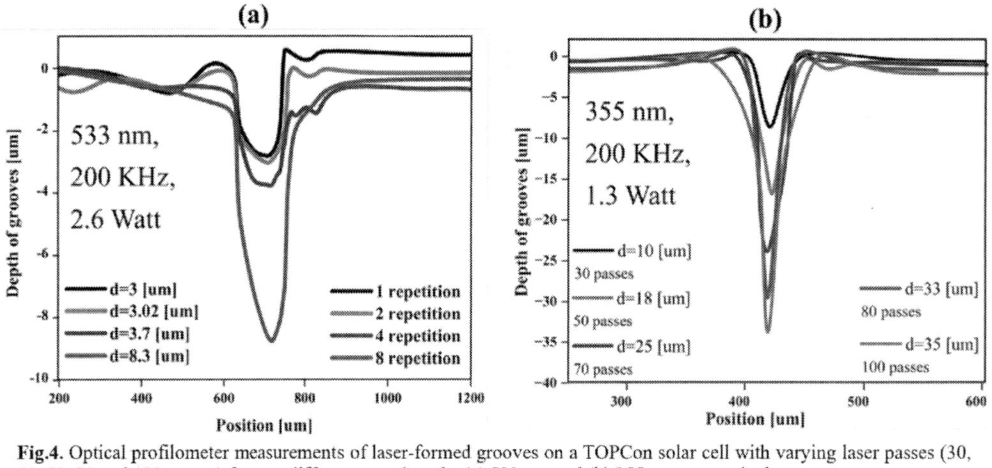

Fig.4. Optical profilometer measurements of laser-formed grooves on a TOPCon solar cell with varying laser passes (30, 50, 70, 80 and 100 passes) for two different wavelengths (a) 533 nm and (b) 355 nm, respectively.

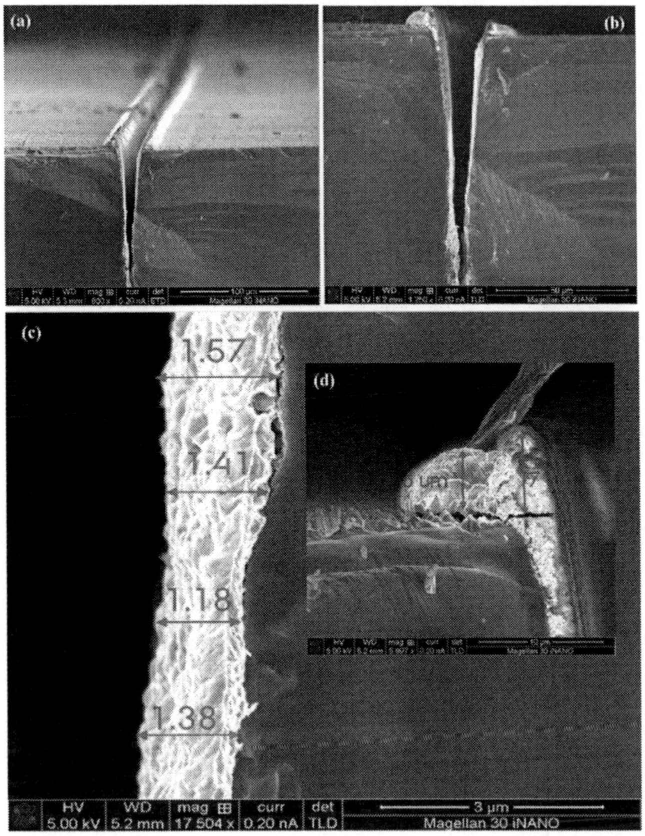

Fig. 5. (a) SEM images of laser-opened grooves after Cu electroplating. (b) Cross-sectional views of the groove showing copper deposition along the walls. (c) Magnified SEM image highlighting Cu coverage inside the groove, with deposited layer thickness ranging from ~1.18 to 1.57 µm. (d) SEM image of copper accumulation on top of the groove, indicating lateral overgrowth with thicknesses of ~6–7 µm.

improves depth and definition, though excessive ablation can introduce surface damage. The 355 nm wavelength produced narrower, deeper grooves than 532 nm, offering better prospects for fine-line contacts. Ni/Cu plating effectively filled the grooves, but challenges such as copper overgrowth at groove edges and uniformity along sidewalls remain.

Future work will concentrate on optimizing laser parameters to balance groove quality with minimal damage, improving plating chemistry to enhance adhesion and conformity, and assessing the electrical performance of complete devices. Long-term stability studies will also be undertaken to evaluate copper diffusion and durability. With these refinements, the BC–TOPCon approach has strong potential to deliver scalable, high-efficiency, and cost-effective crystalline silicon solar cells.

5 SCIENTIFIC INNOVATION AND RELEVANCE

Ni/Cu electroplated metallization, when integrated with laser-grooved buried contacts in TOPCon structures, offers a strong alternative to conventional screen-printed Ag. The laser process enables precise and repeatable formation of narrow, deep grooves that act as conductive pathways for the plated metals. This approach not only minimizes the front metalized area, thereby reducing shading and enhancing light absorption, but also ensures low series resistance due to the high conductivity of Cu. Conducting metallization on both sides further streamlines the process, while maintaining the integrity of the TOPCon stack. Together, the synergy of laser structuring and Ni/Cu plating provides a scalable route toward improving device performance and addressing sustainability challenges linked to silver scarcity.

6 ACKNOLOWDGNENT

This research is financially supported by the CuSun project, funded by the Energy Technology Development and Demonstration Program (EUDP) in Denmark, under grant number 640231-510356.

7 COMPETING INTREST

The authors declare no competing interests.

8 REFERENCES

[1] G. Masson, E. Bosch, A. Van Rechem and M. de l'Epine, "Task 1 strategic PV analysis and outreach–2024 snapshot of global PV markets ", Report IEA-PVPS T1-42:2024, 2024, p. 11.

[2] B. Hallam, M. Kim, Y. Zhang, L. Wang, A. Lennon, P. Verlinden, P.P. Altermatt and P.R. Dias, "The silver learning curve for photovoltaics and projected silver demand for net-zero emissions by 2050 ", in Progress in Photovoltaics: Research and Applications, vol. 31, i. 6, pp. 598–606, 2023.
[3] R. Sakakibara, A. Lachowicz, J. Hurni, C. Allebé, B. Paviet-Salomon, F.-J. Haug, C. Ballif, A. Hessler-Wyser and Y. Xiang, "Investigating interfacial phenomena in copper-covered, n-type polysilicon-based contacts by electron microscopy ", EU PVSEC 2024, 2024.
[4] B. Grübel, S. Kluska, G. Cimiotti, C. Schmiga, V. Arya, B. Steinhauser, B. S. Goraya, S. Nold, M. Hermle, M. Kamp, M. Passig, M. Sieber and D. Brunner, "Plating metallization for bifacial i-TOPCon silicon solar cells ", SiliconPV 2021, 2022.
[5] B. Richards, "Comparison of TiO2 and other dielectric coatings for buried-contact solar cells: a review," Progress in photovoltaics: research and applications, vol. 12, no. 4, pp. 253-281, 2004.
[6] T. Crawford, A. Borowiec, and H. Haugen, "Femtosecond laser micromachining of grooves in silicon with 800 nm pulses," Applied Physics A, vol. 80, pp. 1717-1724, 2005.
[7] T. Ner, P. Rana, and D. Marla, "Pulsed laser grooving of silicon under different ambient media," Lasers in Manufacturing and Materials Processing, vol. 10, no. 4, pp. 626-644, 2023.
[8] Y. H. Cho, A. Ebong, E. Cho, D. Kim, and S. Lee, "Advanced buried contact solar cell structure," Solar energy materials and solar cells, vol. 48, no. 1-4, pp. 173-177, 1997.
[9] J. H. Guo, P. J. Cousins, and J. E. Cotter, "Investigations of parasitic shunt resistance in n-type buried contact solar cells," Progress in Photovoltaics: Research and Applications, vol. 14, no. 2, pp. 95-105, 2006.
[10] S. Wenham, "Buried-contact silicon solar cells," Progress in photovoltaics: research and applications, vol. 1, no. 1, pp. 3-10, 1993.

[291]

Advancing TOPCon Silicon Solar Cells with Laser-Grooved Buried Contact Technology

42nd European Photovoltaic Solar Energy Conference and Exhibition

Mohammad Hossein Mohammadi [*a], Roberto Boccardi [b], Io Mizushima [c], Irene Tosi [c], Gisele Alves dos Reis Benatto [b], Peter Behrensdorff Poulsen [b], Torben Tang [c], Sune Thorsteinsson [b], Rasmus Schmidt Davidsen [a]
[1]Department of Electrical and Computer Engineering, Aarhus University, 8200, Denmark
[2]DTU Electro, Technical University of Denmark, 2800 Kgs. Lyngby, Denmark
[c] IPU P/S, Virum, Denmark

Department of Electrical and Computer Engineering

1CV.2.10-291

Introduction

- TOPCon's thin SiO_x between Si and poly-Si provides strong passivation and carrier selectivity, reducing recombination and raising V_{oc} and efficiency.
- Cu/Ni plated metallization forms fine, low-resistance grids at low temperatures, preserving TOPCon layers while providing high conductivity and enabling scalable, cost-effective manufacturing.
- Laser-grooved buried contacts confine plated metal, reducing shading and boosting absorption, while high-aspect-ratio fingers and a self-aligned selective emitter minimize contact and grid resistance.
- Integrating TOPCon, Cu-plated metallization, and laser-grooved BC reduces recombination, resistive, and optical losses, offering a robust, cost-effective route to next-generation high-efficiency c-Si solar cells.

AIM AND APPROACH

- Advance the efficiency and scalability of crystalline silicon solar cells by integrating the TOPCon, Cu plated metallization, and laser-grooved buried contacts; burying the metal reduces resistive and optical losses.
- Develop and optimize a UV laser scribing process for form narrow, deep grooves for buried front contacts on TOPCon.
- Define robust process grooves (laser power, pulse repetition rate, scan speed, and pass count) that produce groove geometries compatible with Cu plated for metallization, enabling low series resistance and low contact recombination.
- Key challenges are laser-scribing high-aspect-ratio, low-roughness grooves for buried contacts without harming the crystalline silicon and then achieving uniform, void-free Cu plating with a reliable Ni seed/barrier.

Experimental Setup

Sample Preparation

- For front-side preparation, silicon wafers were textured in KOH and the boron emitter was formed by high-temperature BBr_3 diffusion.
- For rear stack formation, the rear surface was polished; 85 nm boron-doped poly-Si was deposited; a silicon oxide film was grown at 1000 °C in ozone; AlO_x was deposited by ALD and activated by a 450 °C anneal.
- For final coatings, SiNx was deposited on both sides by PECVD.

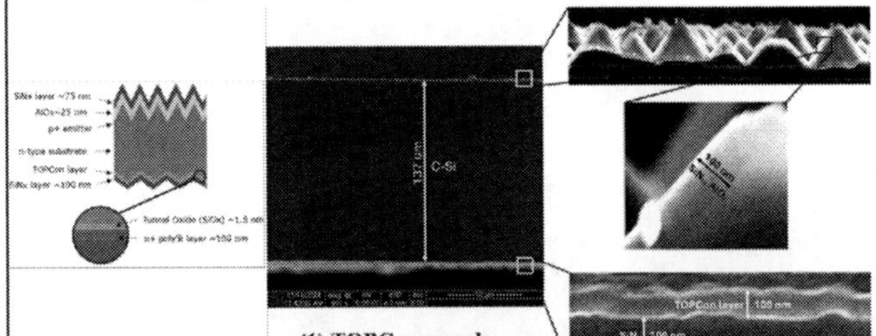

(1) TOPCon sample

Laser Parameters

- Tool / type: 3D-Micromac microSTRUCT picosecond laser micromachining system.
- Output power: 50 W.
- Wavelengths available: 355 nm, 532 nm, 1064 nm (initially used 532 nm; later switched to 355 nm to narrow groove width).
- Pulse duration: 10 ps, pulse repetition rate: 200 kHz and scanning speed: 300 mm/min.
- Adjustable parameters: laser power and number of scanning passes (kept unchanged when switching to 355 nm).

Characterization Tools

- Optical microscopic: Surface morphology
- SEM: cross section morphology, line widths
- Profilometric: measure the roughness and depth

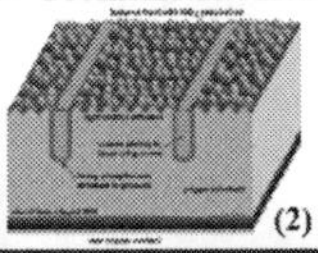

(2) Buried contact structure

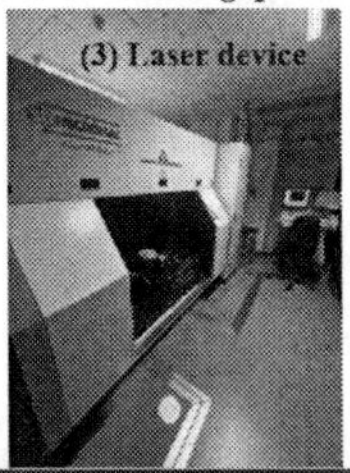

(3) Laser device

Results

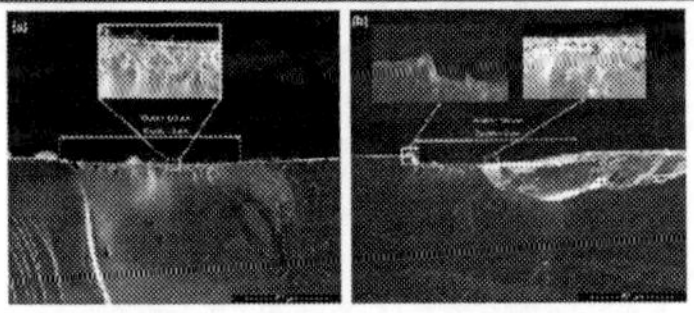

(4) Laser parameters: 532 nm, 200 KHz, 2.6 Watt (a) 1 repetition and (b) 8 repetition

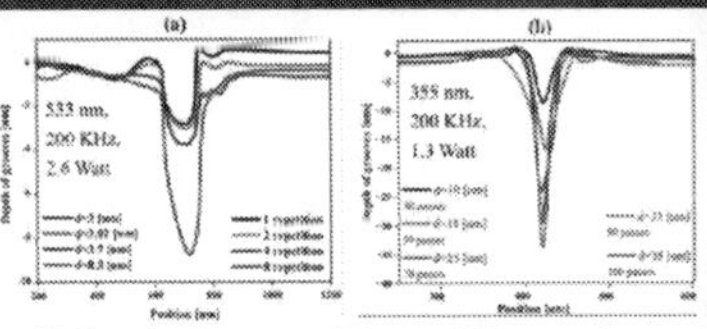

(7) Depth of groove with two difference laser parameters

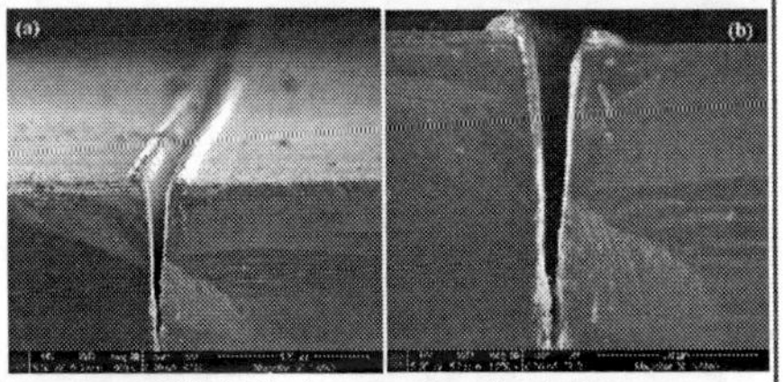

(10) SEM of groove after Cu plating

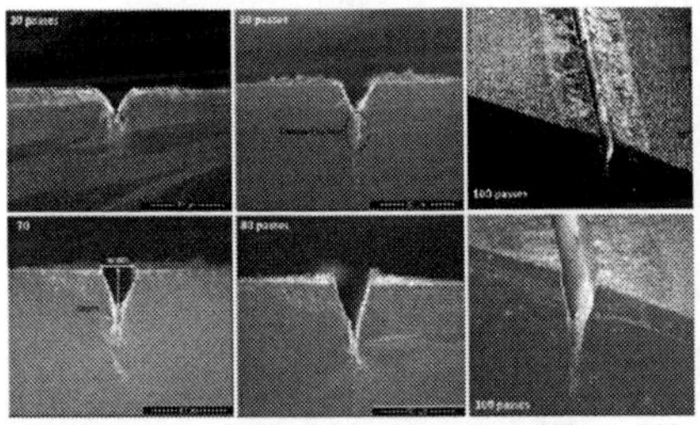

(5) SEM of groove with laser parameters : 355 nm, 200 KHz, 1.3 Watt, (a) 30, 50, 70, 80, 100 repetition

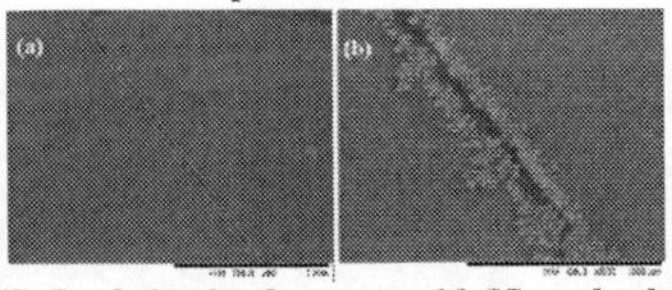

(8) Cu plating for the groove with 35 um depth (a) X80 and (b) X500

(6) Optical microscopy, x50 magnification

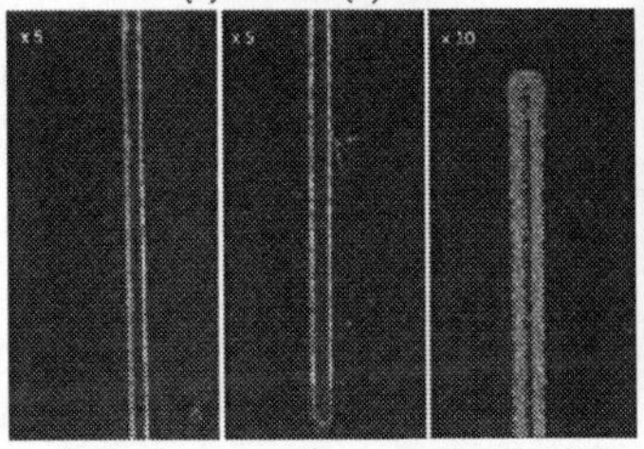

(9) Optical microscopy of groove after Cu plating

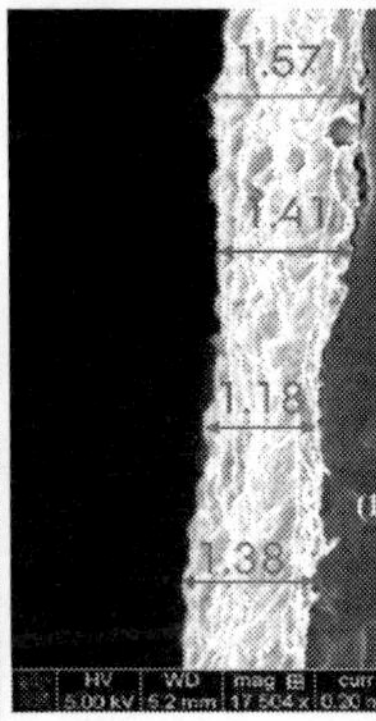

(11) SEM of Cu inside groove plated on the wall of groove

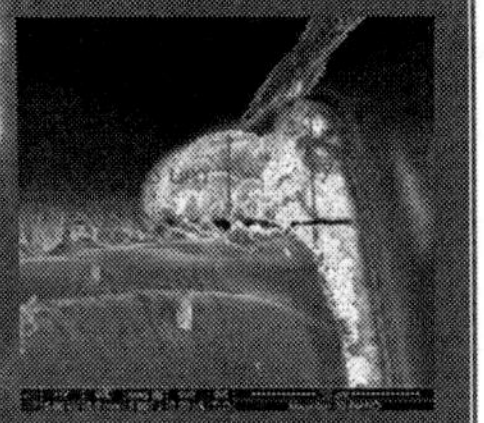

(12) SEM of Cu on top of the groove

Conclusions

- Combining TOPCon, laser-grooved buried contacts (BC), and Ni/Cu-plated metallization shows promising efficiency gains over conventional c-Si cells.
- TOPCon passivation and carrier selectivity suppress recombination at critical interfaces.
- Ni/Cu-plated metallization delivers high conductivity, lowering series resistance and supporting higher fill factor.
- Power, repetition rate, and wavelength set groove depth/width parameters that strongly govern BC performance.
- Narrow buried metal lines minimize front contact area, boosting light absorption and reducing shading losses enabling higher PCE.

Scientific Innovation

- Innovative Integration of TOPCon with Cu-Plated, Laser-Grooved Buried
- Silver-Saving Cu Metallization with TOPCon: Low-Loss, High-PCE c-Si Cells
- Reducing Recombination, Shading, and Resistance via TOPCon & Cu Buried Contacts

Acknowledgements

- Energy Technology Development and Demonstration Program (EUDP) in Denmark (CuSun , No. 640231-510356)

Collaborators: IPU. iNANO DTU Nanolab National Centre for Nano Fabrication and Characterization

Funding: EUDP

AARHUS UNIVERSITY

Contact email: moh@ece.au.dk

020033-001

42nd European Photovoltaic Solar Energy Conference and Exhibition

Local Edge Passivation of Laser Scribed Shingle Cells for Compensating Cut Losses

Dheeraj Sah[1*], Karolis Parfeniukas[2], Roberto Boccardi[3], Narendra Bandaru[1], Agata Lachowicz[4]
Benjamin Borie[2], Mira Baraket[2], Maksym Plakhotnyuk[2], Gisele Benatto[3], Sune Thorsteinsson[3], Peter B. Poulsen[3], Rasmus Schmidt Davidsen[1]

[1]Department of Electrical and Computer Engineering (ECE), Aarhus University, Denmark
[2]ATLANT 3D, Maarkaervej 2B, 2630 Taastrup, Denmark
[3]Technical University of Denmark (DTU), Department of Electrical and Photonics Engineering, Denmark
[4]CSEM, Switzerland
*dsah@ece.au.dk

Aarhus Universitet

EU PVSEC

Introduction

- ❑ Cutting full cell into half or small bits results in lower resistive losses, however, during cutting new defects and recombination centers generated at fresh edges results in lower lifetime and cell parameters[1]
- ❑ Covering the defected edges with dielectric layers helps to lower the losses by minimizing the dangling bond density at these edges[2,3]
- ❑ Combining high efficiency silicon cell architectures like tunnel oxide passivated contact (TOPCon), heterojunction thin film (HJT) with novel edge passivation techniques may help to achieve high module efficiencies with shingling concept

Objectives

❑ Key objective of the present work is **"Local Edge Passivation"**

Local edge passivation i.e. depositing passivation layer in and around the edges only. Here, it is achieved by innovative **"Direct Atomic Layer Processing (DALP)®"** using NANOFABRICATOR® Lite tool developed by ATLANT 3D[4]

❑ Testing of TiO_2 as edge passivating material for TOPCon solar cells

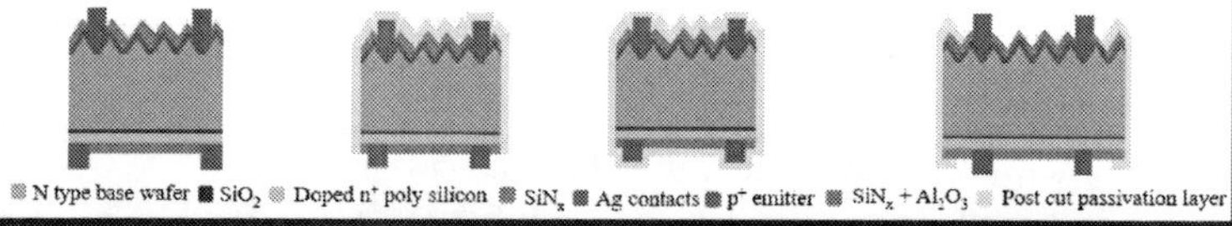

Experiment

- ❖ Non metallized industrial size (182 mm × 184 mm) TOPCon cells cut into small pieces of size 25 mm × 50 mm using laser scribing and mechanical cleaving
- ❖ 50 nm TiO_2 passivating layer at 150°C is deposited using DALP® around the edges only, with TTIP and water as the precursor

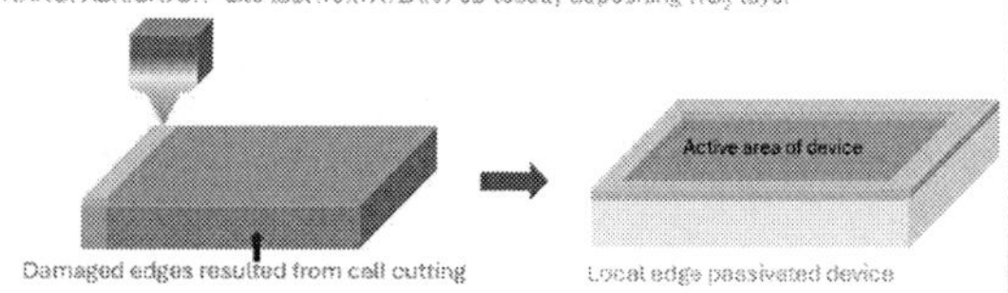

- ❖ Edge passivated samples are then annealed at 180°C, 200 °C,215°C for 10 minutes each
- ❖ 6 non passivated samples are also annealed at various temperature conditions to understand the impact of passivation layer on device lifetime
- ❖ MDP mapping and Sinton lifetime tester WCT-120PL are used to verify the effectiveness of edge passivation on the device lifetime

Results

Optical and SEM-EDS images of the passivation layer

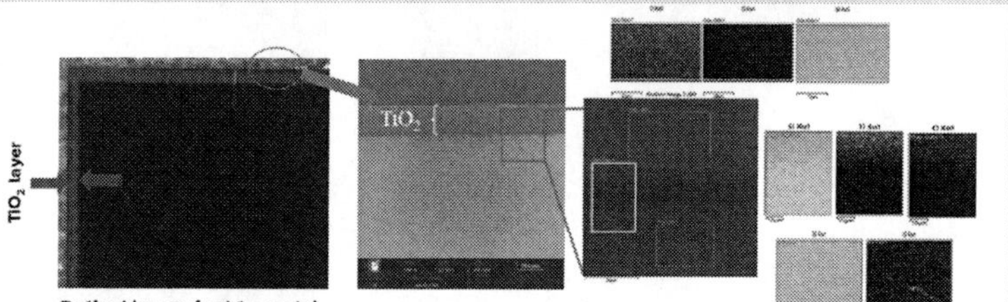

Optical image (not to scale)

Lifetime Mapping Results

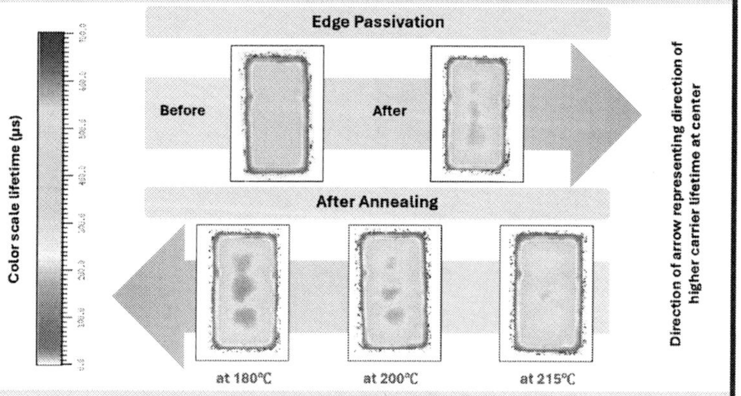

Lifetime results

Edge passivated sample

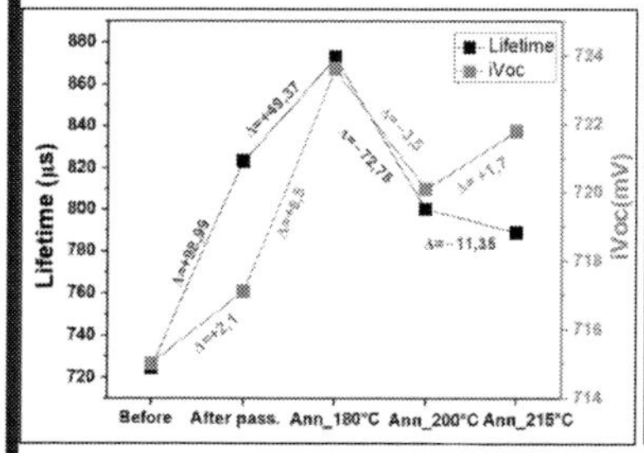

Variation in lifetime (at 1× 10[15]) and iVoc for an edge passivated sample

Non-passivated sample

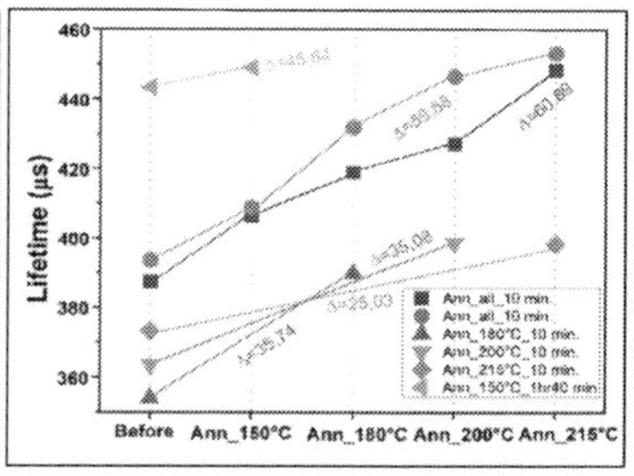

Variation in lifetime (at 1× 10[15]) for only annealed non-passivated samples

Conclusion

- ❑ Successful deposition of TiO_2 as edge passivating layer using DALP®
- ❑ Optical and SEM images confirmed the localized nature of passivating layer with an approximated width of 230-240 µm around the edges
- ❑ Layer deposition followed by annealing at 180°C lead to an improvement of 148.36 µs in lifetime and 8.6 mV in iVoc
- ❑ Further annealing at 200°C, 215°C degraded the device lifetime which may be due to transition from amorphous to crystalline phase of deposited film
- ❑ The lifetime results are further supported by MDP mapper where clear changes in the topogram were observed during the experiment
- ❑ Compared to passivated samples, only annealed non-passivated samples has shown much lower improvements in lifetime effectively highlighting the good passivation offered by TiO_2 film
- ❑ Obtained results suggest that local edge passivation with dielectric films like TiO_2 (tested here), Al_2O_3 (future work) can be a good choice to compensate for the cut losses in shingle cell architectures

References

1. B. Martel et al. (2023). *Solar Energy Materials and Solar Cells, 250*, 112095
2. A. Münzer et al. (2021) *IEEE Journal of Photovoltaics, 11*(6), 1343-1349
3. E. Lohmüller et al. (2023). Solar Energy Materials and Solar Cells, 258, 112419.
4. I. Kundrata et al. (2022) *Small Methods, 6*(5), 2101546.

Acknowledgement

This work is supported by Innovation Fund Denmark under the "ACES- Advanced Contact Engineering and Surface Passivation for Solar Cells with grant number 3148-00044B.

BORON DOPED NANOCRYSTALLINE SILICON AS A REAR-EMITTER IN SILICON HETEROJUNCTION SOLAR CELLS

Amanda Merino[1,2], Tristan Gageot[1], José Alvarez[2], Jean-Paul Kleider[2], Delfina Muñoz[1]
[1]Université Grenoble Alpes CEA, Liten, Campus Ines, Le Bourget du Lac, 73375, France
[2]Laboratoire de Génie Electrique et Electronique de Paris (GeePs), CNRS, CentraleSupélec, Université Paris-Saclay, Sorbonne Université, F- 91190 Gif sur Yvette, France / Institute(s)
Corresponding author: amanda.merinoleiva@cea.fr / +33666394298
tristan.gageot@cea.fr ; jose.alvarez@centralesupelec.fr ; jean-paul.kleider@centralesupelec.fr ; delfina.munoz@cea.fr

ABSTRACT: The best silicon heterojunction (SHJ) solar cells show the potential of hydrogenated nanocrystalline silicon (nc-Si:H) to improve their performance on both the emitter and back surface field (BSF) sides. However, in production, nc-Si:H presents several challenges, particularly in terms of deposition rate, reproducibility and stability of layers and interfaces, as well as substrate selectivity and the amorphising nature of boron for p-type layers. A seed layer, such as (p) a-SiO_x:H, can be introduced to promote nucleation of crystals and protect the passivation layers. In this work, a seed layer was optimized for SHJ integration using (p) nc-Si:H of different thicknesses and doping concentrations. Solar cell integration of (p) nc-Si:H deposited on the doped seed layer shows V_{oc} and FF gains of +2.4 mV and +6.5%$_{abs}$, respectively, compared to those with undoped seed layer. The best solar cells with (p) nc-Si:H as rear-emitter reached 22.2% of power conversion efficiency (PCE), only 0.7%$_{abs}$ lower than the (p) a-Si:H based reference, showing the potential of this material.
Keywords: nanocrystalline silicon, silicon heterojunction, PECVD.

1 INTRODUCTION

Among single-junction photovoltaic technologies, silicon heterojunction (SHJ) solar cells stand out for their ability to achieve high power conversion efficiencies (PCE). In this technology, the buffer and carrier collector layers are typically based on amorphous silicon (a-Si:H) due to its optoelectrical and passivation properties. However, the solar cell performance is limited by the low doping efficiency of a-Si:H, which results in high series resistance and poor contact with the adjacent TCO [1]. Several works [2]-[4] have shown that nanocrystalline silicon (nc-Si:H) is a promising alternative due to its superior electronic and optical properties which are enhanced by crystallinity, allowing higher PCE, with the world record using this type of layers being at 27.3% [5]. However, the deposition of nc-Si:H layers presents several challenges, particularly in terms of deposition rate, reproducibility and layer stability. The properties of nc-Si:H are highly dependent on its crystallinity and evolve during its growth, and its deposition on amorphous substrates results on a thicker incubation layer [6], making its integration in SHJ cells challenging with a relatively thin layer (10-30 nm) [7]. In addition, the growth of boron-doped nc-Si:H films presents an additional challenge, due to the amorphising nature of boron [8]. In order to optimize the properties of (p) nc-Si:H it is important to promote a rapid nucleation, and a suitable seed layer is required. Several optimizations of the seed layers have been reported in the literature, such as oxygen treatment [3], [9] or a thin intrinsic or n-type nc-Si:H film [10]-[12]. More recently, a high performance SHJ with 25.15% of PCE was reported by using a boron-doped a-SiO_x:H buffer layer to promote nucleation on the (p) nc-Si:H emitter [13]. In order to achieve higher SHJ cell performances, it is necessary to evaluate the growth and properties of (p) nc-Si:H both as a material and as a solar cell precursor, and to develop a suitable seed layer.

In this work, we present the characterization of (p) nc-Si:H films grown on a 1 nm boron-doped a-SiO_x:H seed layer with different doping concentrations, in order to subsequently integrate the optimized layer as a rear-emitter for SHJ solar cells grown in an industrial scale equipment.

2 METHODS

For film characterization purposes, seed and (p) nc-Si:H layers were deposited on n-type crystalline silicon (c-Si) and Corning glass using an industrial size plasma enhanced chemical vapour deposition (PECVD) system from Meyerburger Helia. All nc-Si:H films were grown on top of a 9 nm (i) a-Si:H buffer layer to replicate the backside SHJ conditions. Deposition was performed with an RF generator at 13.56 MHz, 200 °C and 175 °C and chamber pressures of 2.5 mbar and 9.5 mbar for amorphous and nanocrystalline layers, respectively. Film precursors and average mass flow are presented in Table I. The diborane mass flow was varied between 1 and 2000 sccm and between 20 and 500 sccm for seed layer ($[B_2H_6]_{seed\ layer}$) and (p) nc-Si:H ($[B_2H_6]_{nc}$) deposition, respectively. The thickness of the films was obtained from spectroscopic ellipsometry (SE) measurements. Crystallinity fraction (φ_c) was obtained from SE and Raman spectra [14]. Conductivity (σ) was measured using the 4-point probe (4PP) technique.

Table I: Average mass flow of film precursors during PECVD deposition

Layer	H_2 (sccm)	SiH_4 (sccm)	CO_2 (sccm)	B_2H_6 (sccm)
(p) a-SiO_x:H	3015	400	500	1-2000
(p) nc-Si:H	10000	30	-	20-500

For SHJ cell integration, (i/n) a-Si:H stacks were deposited on the front side of double-sided textured (n) c-Si wafers. An (i/p) a-Si:H stack was deposited on the rear-side of the wafer for the reference cell (Fig. 1a). To understand the effect of adding a doped seed layer, we integrated (p) nc-Si:H films deposited either directly on the 9 nm thick (i) a-Si:H buffer layer (Fig. 1b) or by adding a 1 nm thick (p) a-SiOx:H film as doped seed layer with $[B_2H_6]_{seed\ layer}$=100 sccm (Fig. 1c). The thickness of the nc-Si:H film was varied from 15 to 45 nm and $[B_2H_6]_{nc}$=30-80 sccm. Indium tin oxide (ITO) layers were subsequently deposited on both sides of the cells by physical vapour deposition (PVD). Silver electrodes were screen-printed and cured at 200 °C for 20 minutes. Minority carrier lifetime of the cell precursors before and after PVD were obtained from photoconductance decay measurements using a Sinton WCT-120, while solar cell parameters were obtained from I-V measurements measured right after screen-printing in the Tempo Preto Line. The I-V measurements were repeated after the cells underwent light-soaking treatment.

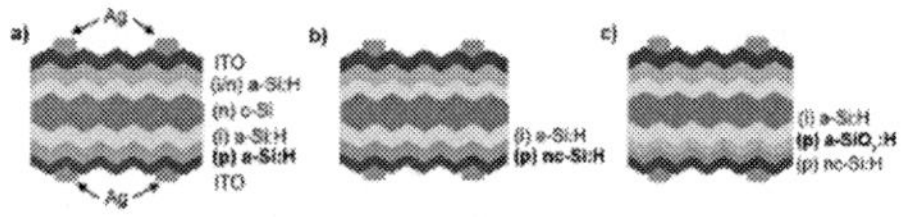

Figure 1: SHJ structures with **a)** (p) a-Si:H (reference) **b)** (p) nc-Si:H and **c)** (p) nc-Si:H deposited on a doped seed layer as rear-emitter used in this work.

3 RESULTS

3.1 Layer characterization

Figure 2 shows the Raman crystallinity and conductivity of 12-120 nm thick (p) nc-Si:H films with $[B_2H_6]_{nc}$=45 sccm grown directly on (i) a-Si:H. By increasing the thickness from 12 to 120 nm the crystallinity increases from 14±2% to 50±2% and conductivity increases from 0.22±0.02 S/cm to 6.7±0.6 S/cm.

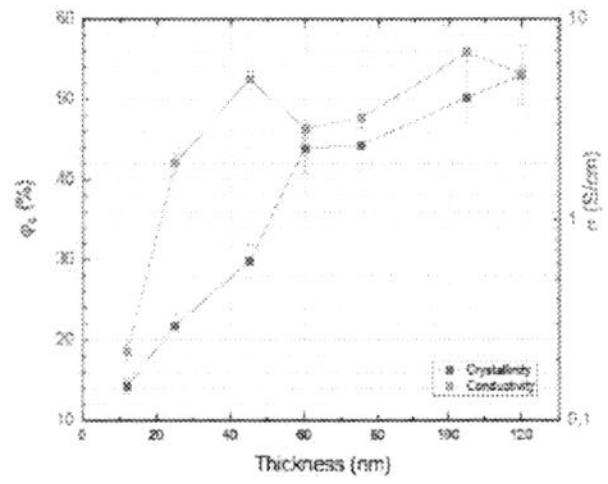

Figure 2: Raman crystallinity and conductivity versus Thickness for (p) nc-Si:H films with no seed layer ($[B_2H_6]_{nc}$=45 sccm).

Fig. 3 shows the SE crystallinity and conductivity of 13 nm thick (p) nc-Si:H films with $[B_2H_6]_{nc}$=45 sccm grown on a doped seed layer with increasing $[B_2H_6]_{seed\ layer}$. Films grown on the undoped seed layer have a crystallinity of 37±2%. The crystallinity of the nc films grown on seed layers with low $[B_2H_6]_{seed\ layer}$ sharply drops when adding 1 sccm of B_2H_6 to the seed layer deposition. When increasing $[B_2H_6]_{seed\ layer}$ from 1 to 30 sccm the crystallinity quickly increases, reaching the level of the nc films grown on undoped seed layer. The crystallinity continues to increase up to $[B_2H_6]_{seed\ layer}$=80 sccm, where it stabilizes around 42%. Similarly, with increasing $[B_2H_6]_{seed\ layer}$, there is an increase in σ of up to three orders of magnitude.

SE crystallinity and conductivity of 13 nm thick (p) nc-Si:H films with $[B_2H_6]_{nc}$=0-100 sccm are shown on Figure 4. At 0 sccm, the SE crystallinity is maximum with 58±2% and it decreases to 35±5% by 100 sccm. Films with 0 and 20 sccm are too resistive. Films with $[B_2H_6]$=30 sccm have a conductivity of 1.5±0.1 mS/cm and it quickly increases two orders of magnitude by 60 sccm. After this point, the conductivity stabilizes around 0.6±0.1 S/cm.

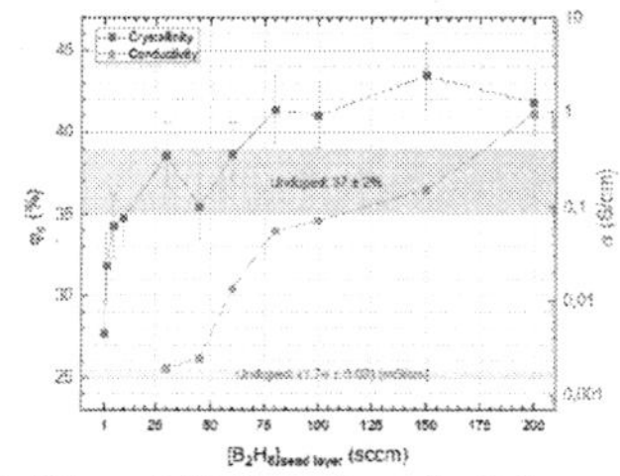

Figure 3: SE crystallinity and conductivity versus B_2H_6 flow during seed layer deposition ($[B_2H_6]_{seed\ layer}$) for 13 nm thick (p) nc-Si:H films ($[B_2H_6]_{nc}$=45 sccm)

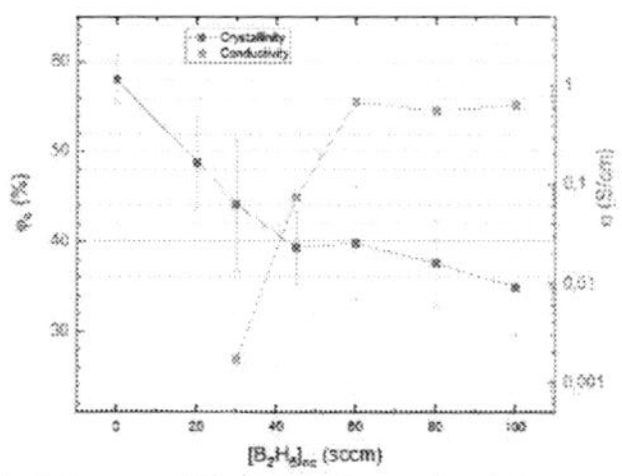

Figure 4: SE crystallinity and conductivity versus B_2H_6 flow on nc layer ($[B_2H_6]_{nc}$) for 13 nm thick (p) nc-Si:H films deposited on doped seed layer ($[B_2H_6]_{seed\ layer}$=100 sccm)

3.2 Solar cell integration

Figure 6 shows the PCE, short-circuit current (J_{sc}), open circuit voltage (V_{oc}) and fill factor (FF) of the integrated solar cells with 15-45 nm thick (p) nc-Si:H films ($[B_2H_6]_{nc}$=45 sccm) grown directly onto the (i) a-Si:H layer and a 20 nm thick (p) nc-Si:H film deposited onto the seed layer ($[B_2H_6]_{seed\ layer}$=100 sccm). There is high dispersion on the performance of the cells in each configuration. Electroluminescence (EL) measurements (Fig. 5) show a clear inhomogeneity of the PECVD deposition on the tray, demonstrating the variability of nc-Si:H growth depending on the substrate position on the chamber. The results shown in the graph are based only on the best 15 cells for each configuration.

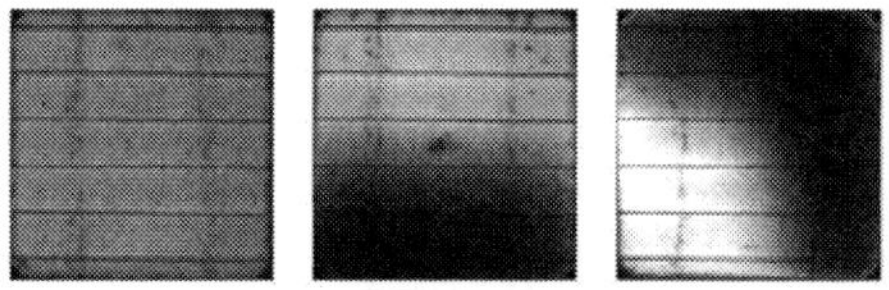

Figure 5: EL images of SHJ devices with (p) nc-Si:H as rear-emitter showing inhomogeneous deposition.

The J_{sc} (Fig. 6b) of all splits is similar to that of the reference (around 38.6 mA/cm²). By comparing the cells with 15-45 nm thick (p) nc-Si:H films deposited directly on (i) a-Si:H, we can see an increase in FF and V_{oc} by increasing the thickness of the (p) nc-Si:H film to 30 nm, which is a result of a higher crystallinity and conductivity of the film. However, by further increasing the thickness, V_{oc} and FF decrease due to higher recombination losses and high series resistance. As shown in Fig. 6a, cells with a doped seed layer have a higher V_{oc}, especially when comparing the 20 nm thickness (+2.4 mV), and are comparable to that of the reference (<1 mV difference). Figures 6c,d show that the limiting factor for the PCE is the FF of the cells. This is due to the high series resistance and low shunt resistance (not shown here). Integration with the seed layer give the best performance among cells with (p) nc-Si:H as emitter, with a mean PCE at 22.22%, only 0.70%$_{abs}$ lower than the a-Si:H reference.

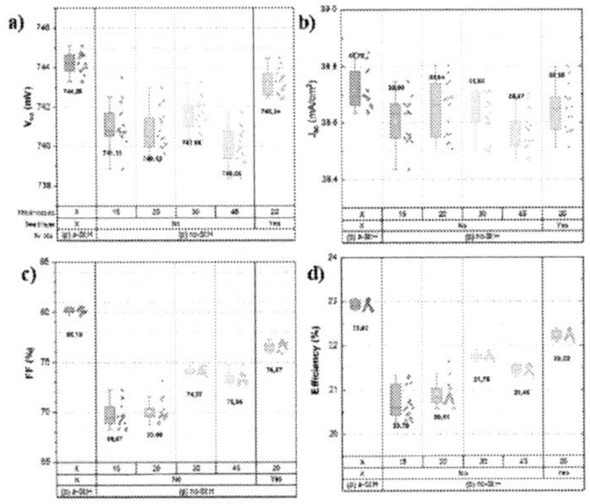

Figure 6. a) V_{oc}, **b)** J_{sc}, **c)** FF and **d)** efficiency of SHJ using (p) nc-Si:H films with different thicknesses with and without seed layer as rear-emitter compared to (p) a-Si:H reference ($[B_2H_6]_{seed\ layer}$=100 sccm, $[B_2H_6]_{nc}$=45 sccm)

Figure 7 shows the V_{oc} and FF before and after light soaking (LS) of the integrated solar cells with 20 and 30 nm thick (p) nc-Si:H films ($[B_2H_6]_{nc}$=30-60 sccm) deposited onto the seed layer ($[B_2H_6]_{seed\ layer}$=100 sccm). Integration with $[B_2H_6]_{nc}$=80 sccm resulted in unmeasurable devices. Both V_{oc} and FF drop when increasing the thickness of the (p) nc-Si:H film with $[B_2H_6]_{nc}$=45 sccm from 20 to 30 nm. Before LS, the best V_{oc} is achieved by the 30 sccm device, reaching 1 mV higher than the reference, due to less dispersion. The V_{oc} (Fig. 7a) of the nc-Si:H devices slightly drops when increasing the doping to 45 and 60 sccm. After LS, the reference V_{oc} is strongly improved (+6.2 mV) while the 20 nm nanocrystalline devices only obtain a slight improvement of around 1 mV. The FF (Fig. 7b) seems to be slightly better (+1%$_{abs}$) when doping with 45 sccm among the 20 nm devices. The LS improves the FF of all devices in at least 2%$_{abs}$. The 20 nm thick (p) nc-Si:H films with 45 sccm devices resulted in the highest PCE among the nanocrystalline configurations, with 21.48% and 22.24% before and after LS, respectively, around 1.3%$_{abs}$ lower than the reference. The FF remains as the limiting factor for the performance of the nanocrystalline devices due to their high series resistance (double than reference) and low shunt resistance (>200 Ω on nc-Si:H devices; 1500 Ω for reference device) (not shown here).

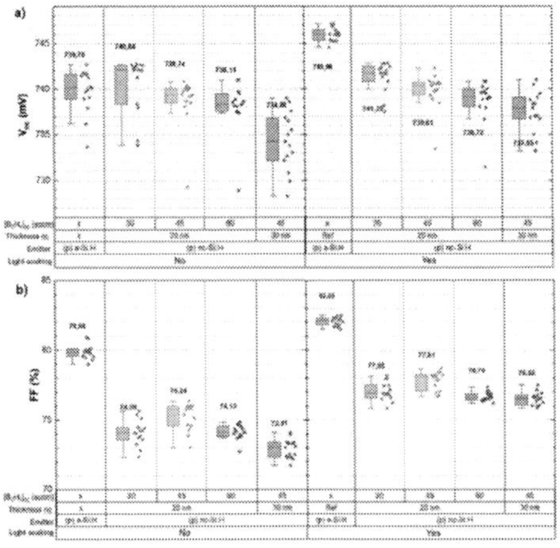

Fig. 7. a) V_{oc} and **b)** FF before and after LS of SHJ using 20 and 30 nm thick (p) nc-Si:H films with different B_2H_6 flow ($[B_2H_6]_{nc}$) deposited on seed layer as rear-emitter compared to (p) a-Si:H reference ($[B_2H_6]_{seed\ layer}$=100 sccm).

4 CONCLUSIONS

Boron-doped nc-Si:H films were deposited in an industrial-scale PECVD equipment for layer optimization as a rear-emitter in SHJ solar cells. Thickness and doping for both the (p) nc-Si:H and the (p) a-SiO_x:H seed layer were assessed from the crystallinity and conductivity of the resulting layers. The layers were later integrated in SHJ solar cells.

The addition of a doped seed layer resulted in a performance improvement with a 2.4 mV and 6.5%$_{abs}$ gain in V_{oc} and FF, respectively, leading to a 1.3%$_{abs}$ PCE gain. The optimum thickness of the (p) nc-Si:H film on devices without seed layer results in 30 nm, while by adding a doped seed layer it shifts to 20 nm. This shows that, due to the substrate selectivity of the layer, parameter optimization cannot be directly translated to films grown on different interfaces. Light soaking on reference cell strongly improves V_{oc} while it remains at the same level on nc-Si:H devices. Light soaking resulted in a 2-4%$_{abs}$ FF gain on nc-Si:H devices.

The FF is the limiting factor for the PCE of the nc-Si:H devices, due to high series resistances and extremely low shunt resistances (>200 Ω). The resistance issues could be caused either by a high contact resistance between the nc-Si:H layers and the TCO or to improper TCO masking. Further studies are ongoing.

5 ACKNOWLEDGEMENTS

Funded by the European Union. Views and opinions expressed are however those of the author(s) only and do not necessarily reflect those of the European Union or RIA. Neither the European Union nor the granting authority can be held responsible for them. NEXUS project has received funding from the European Union's Horizon Europe research and innovation program under grant agreement No. 101075330.

6 REFERENCES

[1] M. Bivour, C. Reichel, M. Hermle, et S. W. Glunz, « Improving the a-Si:H(p) rear emitter contact of n-type silicon solar cells », *Solar Energy Materials and Solar Cells*, vol. 106, p. 11-16, nov. 2012, doi: 10.1016/j.solmat.2012.06.036.

[2] H. Lin *et al.*, « Silicon heterojunction solar cells with up to 26.81% efficiency achieved by electrically optimized nanocrystalline-silicon hole contact layers », *Nat Energy*, vol. 8, n° 8, p. 789-799, 2023, doi: 10.1038/s41560-023-01255-2.

[3] L. Mazzarella, A. Morales-Vilches, L. Korte, R. Schlatmann, et B. Stannowski, « Versatility of Nanocrystalline Silicon Films: from Thin-Film to Perovskite/c-Si Tandem Solar Cell Applications », *Coatings*, vol. 10, n° 8, p. 759, 2020, doi: 10.3390/coatings10080759.

[4] Y. Li *et al.*, « Flexible silicon solar cells with high power-to-weight ratios », *Nature*, vol. 626, n° 7997, Art. n° 7997, 2024, doi: 10.1038/s41586-023-06948-y.

[5] J. Casey, « LONGi unveils heterojunction back-contact cell with record 27.3% conversion efficiency ». visited: 24 june 2024. [Online]. Available on: https://www.pv-tech.org/longi-heterojunction-back-contact-cell-27-3-conversion-efficiency/

[6] P. Roca i Cabarrocas, N. Layadi, T. Heitz, B. Drévillon, et I. Solomon, « Substrate selectivity in the formation of microcrystalline silicon: Mechanisms and technological consequences », *Applied Physics Letters*, vol. 66, n° 26, p. 3609-3611, 1995, doi: 10.1063/1.113803.

[7] L. Mazzarella, S. Kirner, B. Stannowski, L. Korte, B. Rech, et R. Schlatmann, « p-type microcrystalline silicon oxide emitter for silicon heterojunction solar cells allowing current densities above 40 mA/cm2 », *Applied Physics Letters*, vol. 106, n° 2, p. 023902, 2015, doi: 10.1063/1.4905906.

[8] S. Juneja et S. Kumar, « Effect of Power on Crystallinity and Opto-Electronic Properties of Silicon Thin Films Grown Using VHF PECVD Process », *Silicon*, vol. 13, n° 11, p. 3927-3940, 2021, doi: 10.1007/s12633-020-00697-7.

[9] A. N. Fioretti, M. Boccard, R. Monnard, et C. Ballif, « Low-Temperature p-Type Microcrystalline Silicon as Carrier Selective Contact for Silicon Heterojunction Solar Cells », *IEEE J. Photovoltaics*, vol. 9, n° 5, p. 1158-1165, 2019, doi: 10.1109/JPHOTOV.2019.2917550.

[10] O. Vetterl, M. Hülsbeck, J. Wolff, R. Carius, et F. Finger, « Preparation of microcrystalline silicon seed-layers with defined structural properties », *Thin Solid Films*, vol. 427, n° 1-2, p. 46-50, 2003, doi: 10.1016/S0040-6090(02)01237-3.

[11] E. Fathi, Y. Vygranenko, M. Vieira, et A. Sazonov, « Boron-doped nanocrystalline silicon thin films for solar cells », *Applied Surface Science*, vol. 257, n° 21, p. 8901-8905, 2011, doi: 10.1016/j.apsusc.2011.05.052.

[12] G. Nogay *et al.*, « Nanocrystalline Silicon Carrier Collectors for Silicon Heterojunction Solar Cells and Impact on Low-Temperature Device Characteristics », *IEEE J. Photovoltaics*, vol. 6, n° 6, p. 1654-1662, 2016, doi: 10.1109/JPHOTOV.2016.2604574.

[13] L. Wen *et al.*, « Boron-doped amorphous buffer layer for p-type microcrystalline silicon emitter to prepare efficient silicon heterojunction solar cell », *Solar Energy Materials and Solar Cells*, vol. 278, p. 113216, 2024, doi: 10.1016/j.solmat.2024.113216.

[14] C. Droz, E. Vallat-Sauvain, J. Bailat, L. Feitknecht, J. Meier, and A. Shah, "Relationship between Raman crystallinity and open-circuit voltage in microcrystalline silicon solar cells," Solar Energy Materials and Solar Cells, vol. 81, no. 1, pp. 61–71, 2004, doi: 10.1016/j.solmat.2003.07.004.

BORON DOPED NANOCRYSTALLINE SILICON AS A REAR-EMITTER IN SILICON HETEROJUNCTION SOLAR CELLS

Context

The best silicon heterojunction (SHJ) solar cells show the potential of hydrogenated nanocrystalline silicon (nc-Si:H) to improve their performance on both the emitter and back surface field (BSF) sides. However, in production, nc-Si:H presents several challenges, particularly in terms of deposition rate, reproducibility and stability of layers and interfaces, as well as substrate selectivity [1] and the amorphising nature of boron for p-type layers. A seed layer, such as (p) a-SiO_x:H [2], can be introduced to promote nucleation of crystals and protect the passivation layers. In this work, a seed layer was optimized for SHJ integration using (p) nc-Si:H of different thicknesses and doping concentrations.

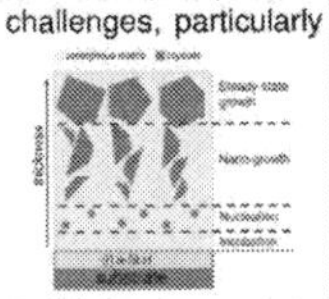

Fig. 1. Schematic representation of nc-Si:H growth on (i) a-Si:H

Methods

- Nanocrystalline silicon films were deposited on both n-type crystalline silicon (c-Si) and Corning glass using a plasma enhanced chemical vapour deposition (PECVD) system at 175 °C with hydrogen (H_2) and silane (SiH_4) as precursor gases. For p-type films, diborane (B_2H_6) was added to the mixture. All nc-Si:H films were grown on top of an (i) a-Si:H buffer layer to replicate the backside SHJ conditions.
- The crystallinity fraction (ϕ_c) was extracted from spectroscopic ellipsometry (SE) and Raman spectra [2] and conductivity was measured using the four-point probe (4PP) technique.
- For SHJ integration, ITO was sputtered by physical vapour deposition (PVD) and silver electrodes were screen-printed for 20 minutes.

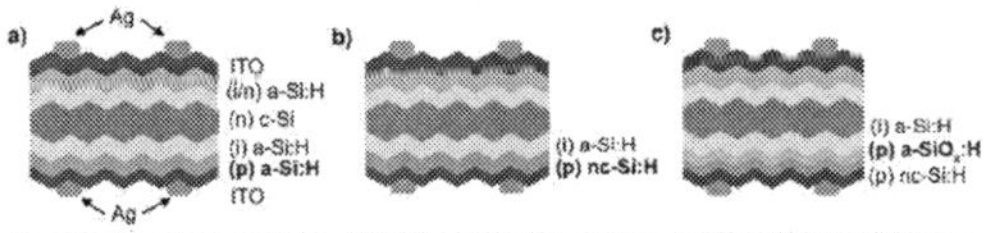

Fig. 2. SHJ structures with a) (p) a-Si:H (reference) b) (p) nc-Si:H and c) (p) nc-Si:H deposited on a doped seed layer as rear-emitter used in this work

Thickness

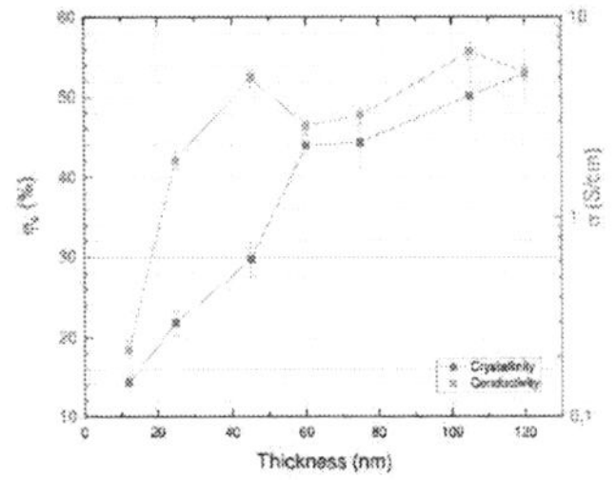

Fig. 3. Raman crystallinity and conductivity versus Thickness for (p) nc-Si:H films with no seed layer ($[B_2H_6]_{nc}$=45 sccm)

Seed Layer

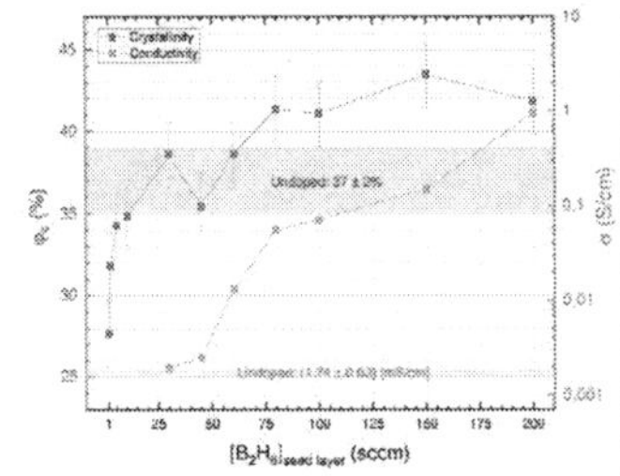

Fig. 4. SE crystallinity and conductivity versus B_2H_6 flow during seed layer deposition ($[B_2H_6]_{seed\ layer}$) for 13 nm thick (p) nc-Si:H films ($[B_2H_6]_{nc}$=45 sccm)

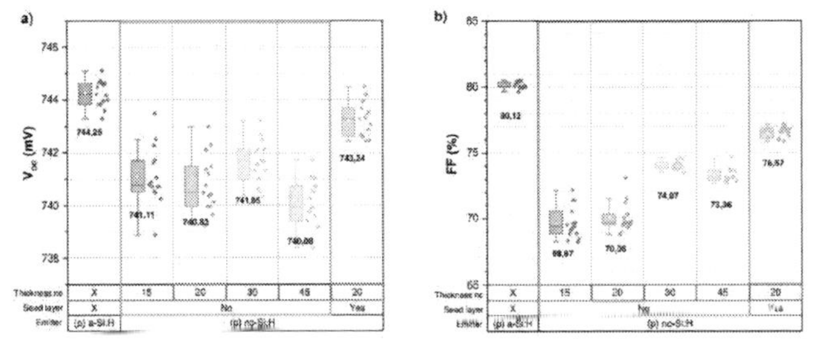

Fig. 5. a) Open-circuit voltage (V_{oc}) and b) Fill factor (FF) of SHJ using (p) nc-Si:H films with different thicknesses with and without seed layer as rear-emitter compared to (p) a-Si:H reference ($[B_2H_6]_{seed\ layer}$=100 sccm, $[B_2H_6]_{nc}$=45 sccm)

- **Optimum (p) nc-Si:H thickness: 30 nm**
- **Adding seed layer increases FF, V_{oc} and PCE** (Fig. 6)
- Power conversion efficiency (PCE) of best cells with (p) nc-Si:H only 0.7%$_{abs}$ lower than amorphous reference

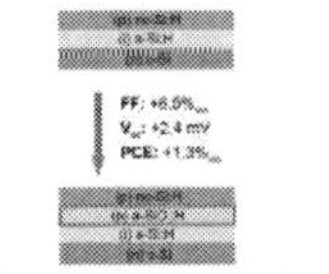

Fig. 6. Effects of adding seed layer

Doping

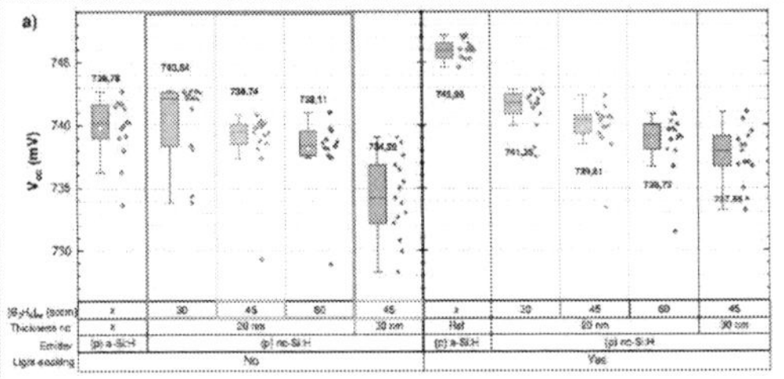

Fig. 8. a) Open-circuit voltage (V_{oc}) and b) Fill factor (FF) before and after light-soaking (LS) of SHJ using 20 and 30 nm thick (p) nc-Si:H films with different B_2H_6 flow ($[B_2H_6]_{nc}$) deposited on seed layer as rear-emitter compared to (p) a-Si:H reference ($[B_2H_6]_{seed\ layer}$=100 sccm)

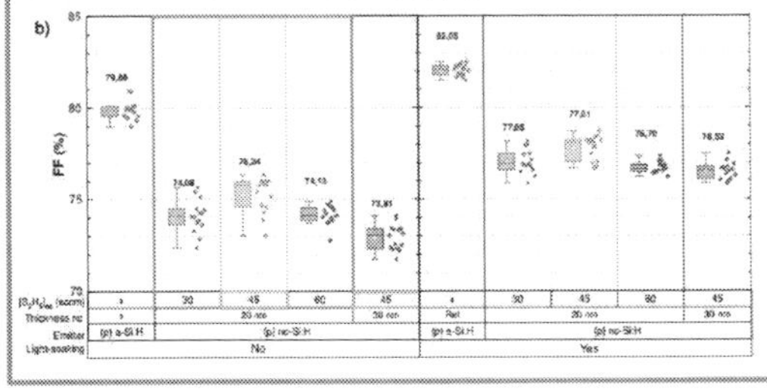

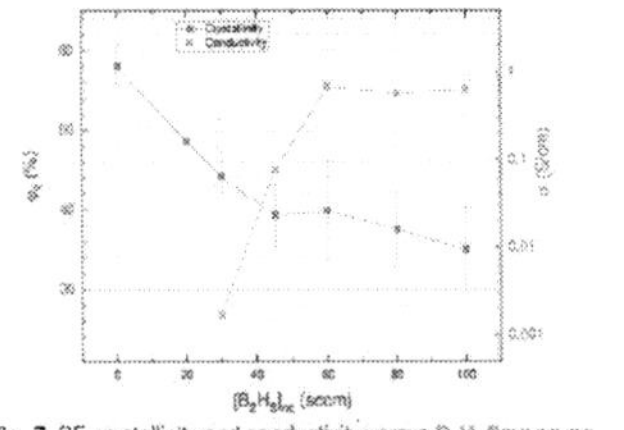

Fig. 7. SE crystallinity and conductivity versus B_2H_6 flow on nc layer ($[B_2H_6]_{nc}$) for 13 nm thick (p) nc-Si:H films deposited on doped seed layer ($[B_2H_6]_{seed\ layer}$=100 sccm)

- **V_{oc} decreases with increasing $[B_2H_6]_{nc}$**
- **After LS:**
  V_{oc} not improved on 20 nm cells
  FF improvement in all nc cells (≥2.5%$_{abs}$)
- **Optimum (p) nc-Si:H doping: 45 sccm**
- Optimum thickness for films deposited on seed layer: 20 nm

Perspectives

Efficiency is limited by FF

- TCO/(p) nc-Si:H contact resistance measurements required.
- SHJ integration with different TCOs.
- TCO/(p) nc-Si:H interface plasma treatment.
- Optimization of the nanocrystalline silicon deposition.

References

[1] P. Roca i Cabarrocas et al., *Applied Physics Letters*, **1995**, vol. 66, no 26, p. 3609-3611.
[2] L. Wen et al., *Solar Energy Materials and Solar Cells*, **2024** vol. 278, p. 113216.
[3] Droz, C et al., *Sol. Energy Mater. Sol. Cells* **2004**, *81*, 61–71.

Acknowledgements

Funded by the European Union. Views and opinions expressed are however those of the author(s) only and do not necessarily reflect those of the European Union or RIA. Neither the European Union nor the granting authority can be held responsible for them.NEXUS project has received funding from the European Union's Horizon Europe research and innovation program under grant agreement No. 101075330.

NEXUS

Commissariat à l'énergie atomique et aux énergies alternatives
INES | 50 avenue du lac Léman | 73375 Le Bourget-du-Lac
www.liten.cea.fr / www.ines-solaire.org

CONTACT :
Amanda Merino Leiva
amanda.merinoleiva@cea.fr

020041-001

ines
INSTITUT NATIONAL DE L'ENERGIE SOLAIRE

ADVANCEMENTS IN AMORPHOUS SILICON HETEROJUNCTION (SHJ) SOLAR CELLS THROUGH THE USE OF PLASMONIC NANOPARTICLES

Brahim Aïssa*, M.I. Hossain and Alessandro Sinopoli
Qatar Environment and Energy Research Institute (QEERI), Hamad Bin Khalifa University (HBKU), Qatar Foundation, Doha, 5825, Qatar
* baissa@hbku.edu.qa

ABSTRACT: This study investigates the incorporation of gold (Au) nanoparticles into indium tin oxide (ITO)/silicon heterojunction (SHJ) solar cells through a drop-casting method, with nanoparticle density finely tuned by varying the number of deposited drops from a 0.05 mg/mL solution. The systematic adjustment of Au-network densities enabled a detailed evaluation of their influence on the photovoltaic response of SHJ devices. The results revealed a maximum short-circuit current (Jsc) enhancement of 11.5% at an optimal nanoparticle density corresponding to six drops, confirming the beneficial role of localized surface plasmon resonance (LSPR) in boosting light absorption and photocurrent generation. However, this improvement in Jsc was accompanied by declines in other photovoltaic parameters, including open-circuit voltage (Voc), fill factor (FF), and overall power conversion efficiency (PCE), particularly at higher nanoparticle densities. These outcomes underscore the delicate balance between plasmonic optical enhancement and electrical performance, emphasizing the need to carefully optimize nanoparticle concentration and distribution depending on the specific requirements of the intended optoelectronic application. To further assess real-world viability, the performance of SHJ solar cells incorporating Au nanoparticles was also evaluated under varying temperature conditions, simulating the hot desert climate of Qatar. The temperature-dependent behavior revealed additional challenges, as elevated temperatures further influenced the photovoltaic parameters, reinforcing the importance of thermal stability in plasmonic device engineering. Overall, these findings provide initial yet valuable insights into the opportunities and trade-offs of integrating plasmonic nanostructures into SHJ solar cells. They highlight both the potential for photocurrent enhancement and the challenges posed by recombination, transport losses, and environmental conditions. This work thus underscores the need for continued research into advanced plasmonic designs, optimized nanoparticle configurations, and hybrid strategies that could fully harness the promise of plasmonics while ensuring robust, efficient, and climate-resilient solar cell performance.

1 INTRODUCTION

The integration of plasmonic nanostructures into solar cells has emerged as a powerful strategy for enhancing optical absorption within the active layer, thereby offering a pathway toward improved power conversion efficiencies [1–3]. Among the different plasmonic designs, ranging from metallic nanogratings and nanoholes to patterned metasurfaces, metallic nanoparticles (NPs) remain the most versatile due to their tunability, straightforward fabrication, and ability to be strategically positioned within the device architecture. Depending on the intended effect, nanoparticles can be deposited directly onto the solar cell surface, embedded at the transparent conductive oxide (TCO)/semiconductor interface, or incorporated into intermediate functional layers. Their presence introduces new optical functionalities into the device, primarily through two well-established mechanisms: near-field light concentration and light scattering.

When metallic nanoparticles interact with incident electromagnetic radiation, their conduction electrons undergo collective oscillations. If the oscillation frequency coincides with that of the incoming photons, the condition of surface plasmon resonance (SPR) is satisfied. At resonance, intense localized electric fields are generated near the nanoparticle surface, amplifying optical absorption in the surrounding semiconductor material [4,5]. This effect is especially pronounced when nanoparticles are positioned within the optical near-field of the p–n junction, typically on the emitter or TCO layer. In such configurations, the enhanced electric fields increase the probability of photon absorption and subsequent electron–hole pair generation, directly contributing to higher photocurrent densities.

In addition to near-field enhancement, metallic nanoparticles play a second crucial role through plasmonic light scattering (PLS). At their SPR frequency, nanoparticles act as highly efficient scattering centers, redirecting incident photons into oblique trajectories that increase the optical path length within the absorber layer. This mechanism effectively "traps" light inside the solar cell, particularly benefiting thin-film devices that suffer from limited absorption thickness. The scattering efficiency strongly depends on nanoparticle size and geometry. Small nanoparticles (<20 nm) tend to absorb more strongly than they scatter, which can result in parasitic absorption losses within the metallic particles themselves. In contrast, larger nanoparticles (>50 nm) exhibit enhanced scattering cross-sections and more effectively redirect light into the absorbing medium. Thus, an optimized balance of nanoparticle size, density, and distribution is essential to maximize scattering benefits while minimizing detrimental absorption. [6,7]

A variety of metallic materials have been explored for plasmonic solar cells, including copper (Cu), aluminum (Al), gold (Au), silver (Ag), and palladium (Pd). Among these, Cu and Al are attractive for their low cost and natural abundance, yet their susceptibility to oxidation undermines the stability of their SPR response, limiting long-term applicability. Noble metals, particularly Au and Ag, have gained more traction due to their chemical inertness and strong, stable plasmon resonances in the visible range. Silver is often considered the most effective plasmonic material for photovoltaics, owing to its high scattering cross-section and relatively low absorption losses. [8,9] However, Ag is prone to forming thin oxide layers on its surface, which can dampen resonance effects and compromise device stability. Gold, by contrast, is resistant to oxidation and maintains

10.4229/EUPVSEC2025/1CV.2.24

long-term stability, but effective scattering requires larger Au nanoparticles compared to Ag [10,11]. Interestingly, larger Au nanoparticles not only enhance scattering efficiency but also preferentially scatter light forward into the active layer, making them particularly suitable for deposition on the top surface of the solar cell. [12-14]

Overall, the careful design of plasmonic nanoparticles, considering factors such as size, distribution, material choice, and placement within the solar architecture, is crucial for harnessing their full potential. By striking the right balance between near-field enhancement and light scattering, plasmonic nanoparticles offer a versatile platform for improving solar cell efficiency, particularly in thin-film and next-generation photovoltaic technologies.

2 METHODOLOGY

Indium tin oxide (ITO) thin films were prepared using a radio frequency (RF) magnetron sputtering technique, a well-established method for fabricating transparent conductive oxides (TCOs) with precise control over film composition and uniformity. A ceramic target composed of 90 wt.% In_2O_3 and 10 wt.% SnO_2 was employed, ensuring optimal stoichiometry for balancing high optical transparency with excellent electrical conductivity. The depositions were carried out at room temperature under an RF power density of 2.5 W/cm^2, conditions chosen to maintain a stable plasma environment while preventing substrate heating that could otherwise induce unwanted structural changes. To regulate film stoichiometry, the oxygen-to-total-gas flow ratio was maintained at 0.5%, a critical parameter for minimizing oxygen vacancies while preserving the degenerately doped, conductive nature of the ITO.

The film thickness was carefully controlled to 60 ± 3 nm, providing sufficient optical transparency in the visible spectrum while maintaining continuous conductivity across the substrate. Depositions were performed on multiple substrates, including cleaned borosilicate glass, (n)a-Si:H/(i)a-Si:H/glass, and (n)μc-Si:H/(i)a-Si:H/glass, in order to examine the influence of underlying layers on film growth, crystallinity, and interfacial properties. Substrates were pre-cleaned using standard ultrasonic treatment in acetone, isopropanol, and deionized (DI) water, followed by nitrogen drying to eliminate surface contaminants.

A comprehensive suite of characterization techniques was applied to probe the structural, electrical, optical, and surface properties of the deposited ITO thin films:

- Structural characterization was carried out using X-ray diffraction (XRD) in standard Bragg–Brentano geometry. This analysis provided insights into crystallinity, grain orientation, and phase composition, distinguishing between amorphous and polycrystalline states and identifying preferential orientations induced by different substrate types.
- Electrical properties, including electrical conductivity (σ), carrier concentration (N_e), and Hall mobility (μ_H), were measured using a four-point probe system integrated with Hall effect measurements at room temperature. These measurements elucidated the balance between doping level, charge carrier mobility, and scattering effects, all of which are central to optimizing the trade-off between transparency and conductivity.
- Optical characterization was performed using a UV–Vis spectrophotometer equipped with an integrating sphere, enabling accurate measurements of transmittance (T) and reflectance (R) over the wavelength range of 300–1100 nm. From these data, the absorptance (A) was calculated using the relation:

$$A(\%)=100-(T+R).$$

This comprehensive optical analysis enabled the assessment of ITO's suitability for photovoltaic applications, where maximizing visible transparency while minimizing parasitic absorption is essential.

- Surface morphology and topography were investigated using atomic force microscopy (AFM) in tapping mode, providing high-resolution three-dimensional images of surface features. Roughness parameters and grain structures were quantified to correlate morphology with optical scattering and charge transport behavior.
- Depth profiling and elemental composition were examined using X-ray photoelectron spectroscopy (XPS) with depth profiling capability. To probe subsurface chemistry, controlled argon ion sputtering at 500 eV was applied, ensuring sufficient resolution to distinguish between the ITO film and the underlying silicon or glass layers. This analysis revealed not only the elemental composition but also the oxidation states of indium and tin, which are closely tied to the electrical and optical functionality of the ITO films.

Finally, to simulate post-deposition thermal treatments commonly employed in device fabrication, all ITO thin films were subjected to thermal annealing at 250 °C for 30 minutes in a nitrogen atmosphere. This annealing step was designed to relax internal stresses, reduce defect densities, and improve grain connectivity, thereby optimizing the ITO's transparent conductive oxide properties. Enhanced conductivity, improved mobility, and reduced scattering following annealing confirmed its importance in tailoring the ITO films for subsequent integration into silicon heterojunction (SHJ) solar cells.

Taken together, this deposition and characterization workflow established a detailed understanding of how sputtering conditions, substrate choice, and post-deposition annealing collectively influence the structure–property relationships of ITO thin films. These insights are crucial for engineering ITO layers that achieve the delicate balance between optical transparency and electrical conductivity required for next-generation photovoltaic and optoelectronic applications.

3 RESULTS AND DISCUSSION

In this study, gold (Au) nanoparticles were incorporated onto the surface of indium tin oxide (ITO)/silicon heterojunction (SHJ) solar cells through a carefully controlled drop-casting technique. The density of the plasmonic Au network was modulated by varying the number of deposited drops from a precursor solution with a concentration of 0.05 mg/mL. This systematic approach allowed for precise adjustment of the surface coverage and nanoparticle distribution, thereby enabling a direct assessment of how varying plasmonic densities influence device performance.

The introduction of Au nanoparticles had a pronounced impact on the photovoltaic characteristics of the SHJ devices. The most notable improvement was observed in the short-circuit current density (Jsc), which exhibited a maximum relative gain of 11.5% when six drops were applied. This enhancement is attributed to the localized surface plasmon resonance (LSPR) effect, whereby Au nanoparticles act as optical antennas, concentrating and scattering incident light into the active layers of the device. This process improves light harvesting efficiency and promotes stronger photocurrent generation, particularly in spectral regions where silicon absorption is weaker.

However, while Jsc improved with increasing nanoparticle density, other critical performance metrics displayed more complex trends. The open-circuit voltage (Voc) initially increased at low Au coverage, reflecting improved interface passivation and light–matter interaction, but subsequently declined at higher densities. This reduction is likely due to enhanced carrier recombination and perturbations in the heterojunction's electrical properties induced by excessive nanoparticle loading. Similarly, the fill factor (FF%) decreased with higher Au densities, suggesting that excessive nanoparticles may introduce resistive losses or act as recombination centers, thereby impeding efficient charge extraction. Consequently, the overall power conversion efficiency (PCE) demonstrated a non-linear response, peaking at intermediate densities before declining at higher coverage levels.

These observations highlight the need for careful optimization of plasmonic nanoparticle density to strike a delicate balance between enhanced optical absorption and the preservation of favorable electrical properties. For practical optoelectronic applications, the ideal nanoparticle concentration will depend on whether the emphasis is on maximizing photocurrent generation, maintaining high Voc and FF stability, or achieving the best compromise for overall PCE.

Beyond density optimization, the study also explored the temperature dependence of SHJ solar cell performance, simulating the harsh operating conditions typical of Qatar's desert climate. The results confirmed that elevated temperatures exacerbate performance degradation, particularly impacting Voc due to increased intrinsic carrier concentration and recombination losses. The interplay between nanoparticle-induced optical enhancement and thermally induced electrical degradation emphasizes the importance of tailoring plasmonic designs not only for spectral control but also for thermal resilience in real-world environments.

These findings are preliminary yet promising, offering a foundation for the development of plasmonically enhanced SHJ solar cells tailored for deployment in challenging climates. Ongoing research is directed toward refining nanoparticle deposition techniques, exploring alternative plasmonic materials, and integrating multilayer designs that combine infrared filtering, self-cleaning, and plasmonic functionalities into a single scalable architecture. Together, these advances aim to pave the way toward next-generation high-efficiency solar technologies capable of delivering reliable performance under the demanding environmental conditions characteristic of the MENA region.

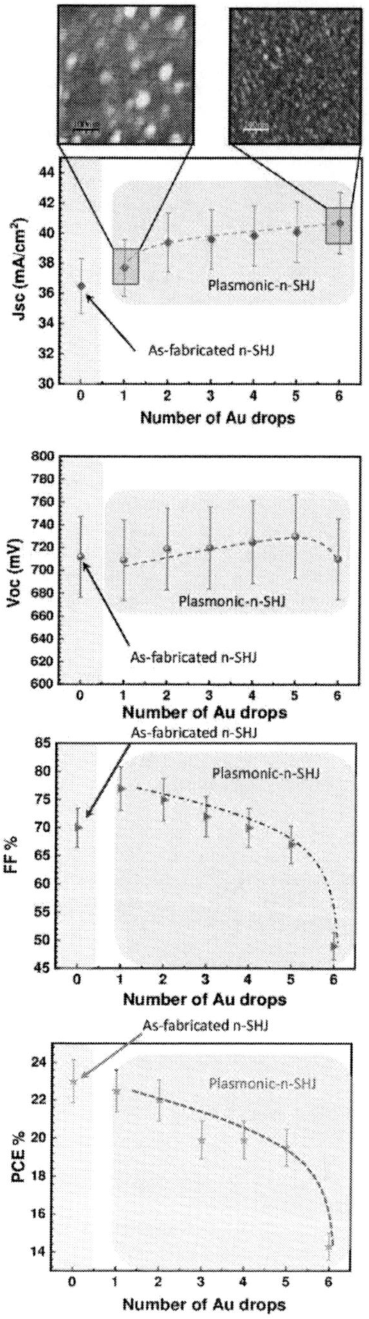

Figure 1: Photovoltaic performance parameters of n-type silicon heterojunction (n-SHJ) solar cells as a function of plasmonic Au nanoparticle network density, controlled by the number of applied drops. The plots illustrate the variation of short-circuit current density (Jsc), open-circuit voltage (Voc), fill factor (FF%), and overall power conversion efficiency (PCE). Increasing Au network density enhances Jsc through improved light absorption, while Voc initially rises before declining at higher densities, indicative of recombination effects.

The FF% decreases with increasing Au content, leading to a non-linear trend in PCE, underscoring the importance of optimizing nanoparticle density to balance plasmonic enhancement with favorable electrical performance.

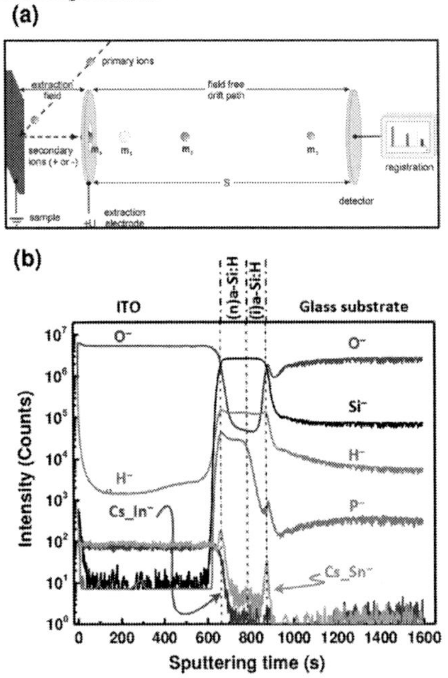

Figure 2: (a) Schematic illustration of the time-of-flight secondary ion mass spectrometry (TOF-SIMS) measurement principle, showing the sputtering of the film surface by a primary ion beam and the subsequent mass analysis of ejected secondary ions. This technique enables high-resolution depth profiling of multilayer thin-film structures. (b) Representative TOF-SIMS depth profile of ITO deposited onto the (n)a-Si:H/(i)a-Si:H/glass stack at an oxygen flow rate of $r(O_2) = 0.01$. The elemental distributions of indium (In) and tin (Sn) are probed using Cs_Sn and Cs_In fragments to avoid spectral overlap with other compounds, ensuring accurate identification. The profiles clearly demonstrate the transition from the ITO layer into the underlying silicon layers, with a decrease in In and Sn signals accompanied by the rise of Si- and H-related signals, thereby confirming distinct compositional gradients across the interfaces. Time-of-flight secondary ion mass spectrometry (TOF-SIMS) was employed to investigate the elemental composition and interfacial characteristics of the deposited thin films, as illustrated in Figure 2. This technique provided detailed depth profiles of the elemental distributions across the multilayer stacks, thereby offering valuable insights into the integrity and sharpness of the interfaces within the heterostructures.

The analysis focused on the detection of key elements, including indium, tin, and oxygen (associated with the ITO layer), and silicon, phosphorus, and hydrogen (associated with the silicon-based layers). Two representative device configurations were examined: ITO/(n)a-Si:H/(i)a-Si:H/glass and ITO/(n)μc-Si:H/(i)a-Si:H/glass.

For both structures, the depth profiles revealed consistent and well-defined trends. Signals corresponding to the ITO layer components (In, Sn, O) gradually diminished as the interface with the n-type silicon layers was approached, while the intensities of silicon, phosphorus, and hydrogen increased accordingly. Within the (n)a-Si:H/(i)a-Si:H and (n)μc-Si:H/(i)a-Si:H regions, a pronounced rise in H, P, and Si signals was observed, reflecting the elemental composition of the doped and intrinsic silicon layers. These signals then exhibited a sharp drop at the glass substrate interface, confirming clear layer termination. Conversely, oxygen, indium, and tin concentrations decreased substantially near the ITO/silicon boundary, in agreement with the expected compositional transition from the transparent conductive oxide to the semiconductor layers.

Although TOF-SIMS does not yield absolute quantitative data, the relative trends clearly demonstrate the existence of distinct compositional gradients at each interface. Such gradients are crucial for understanding the electrical, optical, and recombination properties of the ITO/silicon heterostructures, as even minor interfacial intermixing or diffusion can influence carrier transport, passivation quality, and overall device performance.

These results highlight the capability of TOF-SIMS to provide depth-resolved insights into interfacial chemistry, thereby serving as a powerful diagnostic tool for optimizing multilayer stacks in silicon-based photovoltaics and other thin-film optoelectronic devices.

4 CONCLUSIONS

In conclusion, the integration of Au nanoparticles into ITO/silicon heterojunction solar cells demonstrates a pronounced effect on the key photovoltaic parameters, revealing both the benefits and challenges of plasmonic enhancement. The most consistent improvement was observed in the short-circuit current density (Jsc), which steadily increased with the incorporation of Au nanoparticles. This enhancement can be attributed to localized surface plasmon resonance (LSPR), which promotes stronger light absorption and improved photocurrent generation within the active layer.

The open-circuit voltage (Voc), however, exhibited a more complex behavior. At lower nanoparticle densities, Voc increased, suggesting that moderate plasmonic incorporation can enhance junction properties and reduce recombination pathways. Yet, at higher densities, Voc declined, likely due to increased surface recombination, local field effects, or perturbations at the heterojunction interface caused by excessive nanoparticle loading. Similarly, the fill factor (FF) showed a decreasing trend as Au nanoparticle content increased. This reduction points to negative impacts on charge transport and extraction, possibly linked to increased series resistance or localized recombination centers introduced by the nanoparticles. The combined effects translated into a non-monotonic variation in power conversion efficiency (PCE), where moderate Au incorporation yielded performance gains, but excessive densities compromised device efficiency. These findings highlight the critical importance of optimizing nanoparticle density, size, and spatial distribution to strike a delicate balance between enhanced light harvesting and the preservation of favorable electronic properties. Properly engineered, Au nanoparticle integration offers a powerful route to improving solar cell performance through plasmonic effects. However, without careful control, the benefits of increased photocurrent may be offset by electrical losses. This underscores the necessity of a holistic design approach that couples plasmonic nanostructure engineering with device architecture optimization to achieve sustainable improvements in next-generation plasmonic-enhanced photovoltaic technologies.

5 REFERENCES

[1] B. K. Ghosh, C. N. J. Weoi, A. Islam, and S. K. Ghosh, "Recent progress in Si hetero-junction solar cell: A comprehensive review," Renewable and Sustainable Energy Reviews, vol. 82, pp. 1990–2004, 2018.
[2] Q. Gao, Z. Xu, Y. Yan, W. Li, Y. Song, J. Wang, M. Zhang, et al., "Efficient hole transport layers for silicon heterojunction solar cells by surface plasmonic modification in MoOx/Au NPs/MoOx stacks," Materials Today Energy, vol. 45, p. 101681, 2024.
[3] A. Sharma, D. Pathak, D. P. Sharma, and J. M. Nunzi, "Recent advances in bulk-heterojunction solar cells: a review," The European Physical Journal Applied Physics, vol. 97, p. 81, 2022.
[4] A. K. Dikshit, G. Das, N. Mukherjee, and P. Chakrabarti, "SHJ solar cells on an adequately thin c-Si wafer with dome-like front and double-layer ITO nanoparticles as rear light trapping arrangements," IEEE Transactions on Electron Devices, vol. 69, no. 1, pp. 216–224, 2021.
[5] B. Demaurex, J. P. Seif, S. Smit, B. Macco, W. M. M. Kessels, J. Geissbühler, S. De Wolf, and C. Ballif, "Atomic-layer-deposited transparent electrodes for silicon heterojunction solar cells," IEEE Journal of Photovoltaics, vol. 4, no. 6, pp. 1387–1396, 2014.
[6] L. L. Lebel, B. Aïssa, M. A. El Khakani, and D. Therriault, Composites Science and Technology, vol. 70, no. 3, pp. 518–524, 2010.
[7] W. Julia, C. Luis, R. Federico, et al., Advanced Functional Materials, vol. 23, pp. 5591–5598, 2013.
[8] D. T. H. Dalir, R. D. Farahani, V. Nhim, B. Aïssa, et al., Langmuir, vol. 28, no. 1, pp. 791–803, 2011.
[9] A. Ali, F. El-Mellouhi, A. Mitra, and B. Aïssa, Nanomaterials, vol. 12, no. 5, p. 788, 2022.
[10] R. D. Farahani, D. T. H. Dalir, V. Le Borgne, A. Loick, et al., Composites Science and Technology, vol. 72, no. 12, pp. 1387–1395, 2012.
[11] N. M. H. Gavi, B. D. Ngom, A. C. Beye, A. M. Strydom, B. Aïssa, V. V. Srinivasu, and M. Chaker, Journal of Magnetism and Magnetic Materials, vol. 324, no. 6, pp. 1172–1176, 2012.
[12] B. Aïssa and M. A. El Khakani, Nanotechnology, vol. 20, no. 17, p. 175203, 2009.
[13] M. A. Habib, M. Barkat, B. Aïssa, and T. Denidni, Progress in Electromagnetics Research, vol. 88, pp. 135–148, 2008.
[14] H. Zhao, H. Kimura, Z. Cheng, X. Wang, and T. Nishida, Applied Physics Letters, vol. 95, p. 232904, 2009. https://doi.org/10.1063/1.3271032.

PRECISION UV LASER SCRIBING FOR AMORPHOUS SILICON SOLAR CELLS: LAYER-SPECIFIC ANALYSIS AND OPTIMIZATION

Narendra Bandaru[1]*, Asbjørn Moltke[2], Ole Bang[2], Rasmus Schmidt Davidsen[1]
[1]Department of Electrical and Computer Engineering, Aarhus University, 8200, Denmark
[2]DTU Electro, Technical University of Denmark, 2800 Kgs. Lyngby, Denmark
* Corresponding author: narendra.bandaru@ece.au.dk

ABSTRACT: The demand for efficient and scalable photovoltaic manufacturing necessitates advanced techniques for material processing. This study investigates the use of UV lasers for the scribing process on intrinsic and n-type amorphous silicon layers, focusing on optimizing parameters such as pulse energy (26–30 μJ), repetition rate (1–10 kHz), and environmental conditions. A commercial p-type silicon wafer with intrinsic and n-type layers of 27 nm and 82 nm thickness, respectively, was scribed under precise conditions to minimize thermal effects and material redeposition. The intrinsic layer showed line widths ranging from 16.29 μm to 17.30 μm in SEM analysis, while AFM data revealed widths of 20.27 μm to 24.37 μm, indicating smooth surface morphologies. For the n-type layer, depth values ranged from 13.87 nm to 266.56 nm, with consistent nano-crystalline features observed. Despite challenges such as edge irregularities and surface roughness, the process proved robust, achieving uniform scribing with minimal defects. These findings highlight the adaptability of the laser system for applications in optical and electronic devices and provide valuable insights into improving device efficiency, scalability, and cost-effectiveness. Future work will aim to optimize the scribing process by refining laser parameters to achieve greater precision, uniformity, and scalability in photovoltaic applications.
Keywords: UV laser scribing, amorphous silicon, photovoltaic manufacturing, surface morphology

1 INTRODUCTION

Solar energy continues gaining importance as a clean energy source. Pursuit of higher efficiency, lower cost, and reliable large-area fabrication drives innovation in device architecture and processing methods. Among thin-film solar technologies, hydrogenated amorphous silicon (a-Si:H) retains interest for its flexibility in tuning optical and electrical properties and its compatibility with low-temperature deposition on diverse substrates. To integrate such layers into advanced cell structures (e.g. heterojunction, tandem, or back-contact designs), precise patterning and interconnection become essential. In thin-film and hybrid cell stacks, monolithic series interconnection is typically realized by multi-step laser scribing to remove selected layers in narrow stripes, thereby isolating subcells and enabling current flow through contact zones. Laser scribing offers non-contact precision, minimal mechanical stress, and fine line widths compared to mechanical scribing techniques. The method largely dominates high-throughput manufacturing for thin film photovoltaics [1]. However, laser ablation must be finely controlled to avoid defects such as microcracks, redeposited debris, heat-affected zones, edge roughness, and damage to underlying layers. The quality of scribed grooves and the preservation of electrical continuity in adjacent regions critically influence module efficiency and reliability [1].

Because a-Si:H films (intrinsic or doped) differ in optical absorption, thermal diffusivity, thickness, and adhesion, selective removal (ablation) of these layers demands tailored laser parameters (pulse energy, repetition rate, wavelength, scanning speed). Several works have shown that UV lasers, especially at 355 nm or shorter, help in achieving selective ablation with sharper edges and lower collateral damage [2, 3]. Lauzurica et al. studied selective ablation of a-Si:H thin films using UV lasers (ns and ps pulses at 355 nm), demonstrating that tuning fluence can yield clean removal without significant damage to adjacent regions [2]. García-Ballesteros et al. investigated how laser scribing influences electrical parameters of a-Si:H modules and found that optimized scribing minimally degrades module efficiency [4]. In more recent literature, broader reviews of laser scribing in photovoltaic thin films outline challenges in scaling, defect control, and throughput. Jamaatisomarin et al. provide a comprehensive assessment of laser parameter effects, scribe quality metrics, and guidelines for future improvements [1]. Ishteev et al. examine pulsed laser scribing of transparent conductive oxide / perovskite stacks, contributing to understanding of process limits in mixed-material stacks [3].

Additionally, comparisons between nanosecond and picosecond regimes highlight trade-offs: longer pulses may increase heat diffusion and defect formation, whereas ultrashort pulses reduce thermal damage though require higher peak powers [5, 6]. The formation of crystalline features or defect structures under UV irradiation of a-Si has also been observed, pointing out possible morphological changes even under moderate exposure intensities [7]. Beyond silicon-based systems, laser patterning is being extended to novel absorber stacks (e.g. perovskites) where scribing effects on performance mapping and module integration are actively studied. For example, Schultz et al. analyze P3 patterning in perovskite modules via hyperspectral photoluminescence imaging to correlate fluence to performance losses [8]. Morozov et al. use UV laser scribing to fabricate pixelated perovskite photodiodes, illustrating precision patterning capabilities in thin-film devices [9]. In the realm of advanced silicon architectures, laser-based patterning is also explored as a lithography-free alternative. For instance, Turan et al. propose laser-induced forward transfer (LIFT) for patterning heterojunction full back-contact solar cells without photolithographic steps [10].

This work demonstrates a UV-based scribing route for a-Si:H that is explicitly layer-specific for both intrinsic and n-type films on p-type c-Si. By mapping a robust process window (pulse energy, repetition rate, ambient pressure), we suppress debris, roughness, and depth non-uniformity while preserving underlying wafer quality [11, 12]. The resulting grooves exhibit stable widths and depths across wafers, enabling reliable interconnect formation without collateral damage. These advances translate ultrashort-pulse UV control into manufacturable scribing suitable for modern silicon PV stacks (e.g., SHJ/TOPCon, back-contact), improving scribe quality, reliability, and scalability for high-efficiency module fabrication. Despite extensive prior work, a gap remains in targeted studies of UV laser scribing of intrinsic and n-type a-Si:H layers deposited on p-type crystalline silicon wafers under controlled pulse-energy and repetition-rate regimes optimized for minimal defect formation and strong interconnect integrity. The present work addresses that gap. We systematically vary pulse energy (≈26–30 μJ), repetition frequency (1-10 kHz), and ambient conditions, and we characterize scribe morphology by scanning electron microscopy (SEM) and atomic force microscopy (AFM). The goal is a clearly defined processing window that enables clean, uniform, damage-free scribes suitable for sophisticated layered solar devices.

2 EXPERIMENTAL PROCEDURES

A commercial 4-inch p-type float zone (FZ) double-side polished silicon wafer, supplied by TOPSIL, with a diameter of 100 mm, bulk resistivity of 3 Ω cm, and thickness of 280 ± 25 μm (100 crystal orientation) was used. The wafer underwent cleanroom processing via multi-chamber plasma-enhanced chemical vapor deposition (PECVD) to fabricate intrinsic (a-Si:H:i) and n-type (a-Si:H:n) amorphous silicon layers. To prevent contamination, the i-layer and n-layer were deposited at 230 °C and 200 °C, respectively, in separate chambers, each with a deposition time of 5 minutes.

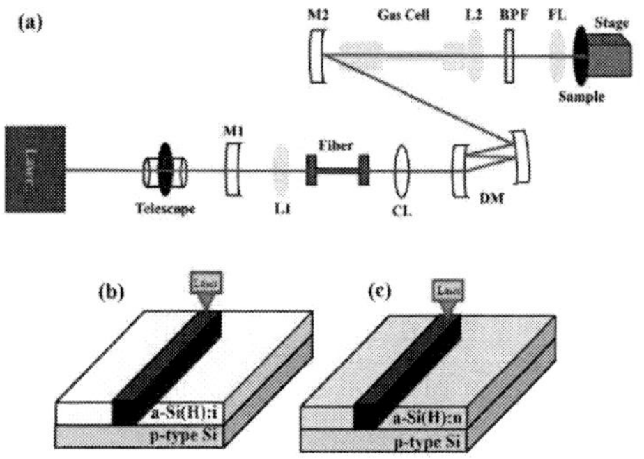

Figure 1. (a) Experimental setup of the UV laser scribing process; Laser Scribing Process Across Different Layers of Silicon: (b) Intrinsic a-Si:H (i-layer) and (c) n-type a-Si:H (n-layer).

The UV laser scribing process is depicted in Figure 1(a). A femto-second Yb-doped laser, operating at 1030 nm with a pulse duration of 300 fs, is initially coupled to a hollow core fiber and subsequently reflected off a set of dispersive mirrors (DM) to temporally compress the pulse to approximately 30 fs. The compressed pulse is then passed through a gas-filled hollow core fiber to generate a UV-supercontinuum. A band-pass filter (BPF) is used to isolate the desired UV wavelength [13]. This setup ensures high precision with minimal groove width and depth variation, critical for uniform scribing performance across samples. The laser scribing process utilized a UV laser operating at a wavelength of 343 nm, generated by1030 nm pulses with pulse energies of 26–30 μJ applied at repetition rates of 1 kHz and 10 kHz, depending on the layer. For the intrinsic (i) layer, at 1 kHz, 6.9 bar argon pressure was used, while the n-type layer (82 nm thick) was processed with the same pulse energy at 10 kHz at 7.3 bar. Laser pulse energy used was 1.6 μJ for the intrinsic layer and 1.0 μJ for the n-type layer, as applied in this study. These parameters ensured precise material removal across the silicon wafer. Ellipsometry measured the intrinsic a-Si:H layer thickness at 27 nm and the n-type a-Si:H layer at approximately 82 nm. SEM analysis examined the laser-treated side morphologies and widths, while AFM measured topography, width, and depth of the laser-processed samples. Figure 1(b-c) illustrates a schematic of the laser scribing on the respective layers.

3 RESULTS AND DISCUSSION

This study examined laser scribing under two scenarios: (i) scribing on the intrinsic (i-layer) of a p-wafer and (ii) scribing on the n-layer of a p-wafer, focusing on the effects of laser parameters on structural integrity, line quality, and surface morphology. Laser scribing on the i-layer of the p-type wafer, analyzed using SEM and AFM, revealed variations in line morphology and measurements across three sets (i.e., 1, 2 and 3) despite consistent laser parameters (refer to Figure 2). SEM images showed differences in line widths and edge quality, while AFM data highlighted variations in surface roughness and depth uniformity. In Set 1, SEM-measured widths ranged from 16.29 μm (L1) to 17.30 μm (L2), with AFM-measured widths increasing from 20.27 μm to 24.37 μm, reflecting increased roughness and edge deformation. Depth measurements indicated symmetrical material removal in L1, with minor asymmetry emerging in L2 and L3, likely due to cumulative thermal effects and material redeposition, as seen in SEM images showing broader lines and debris in L3. Set 2 SEM widths remained relatively consistent for L1 and L2 but increased to 18.05 μm in L3, suggesting heightened thermal effects. AFM measurements showed smaller widths compared to SEM, indicating smoother surface regions while emphasizing laser interaction dynamics. The highest depth asymmetry was observed in L2, where uneven material removal was prominent. SEM images in Set 2 also revealed irregularities and debris accumulation, particularly in L3, attributed to thermal effects and redeposition. Set 3 showed the largest SEM-measured widths, increasing from 22.48 μm (L1) to 26.30 μm (L2), with AFM measurements reflecting similar trends. Pronounced edge deformation and debris were evident in SEM morphology, especially in L2, highlighting the thermal impact. Variations across sets, despite identical parameters, were likely caused by localized surface inhomogeneities, minor laser beam fluctuations, and cumulative thermal effects from repeated passes. AFM consistently indicated increasing roughness and depth variability in later lines, corroborated by SEM images showing edge deformation and material redeposition.

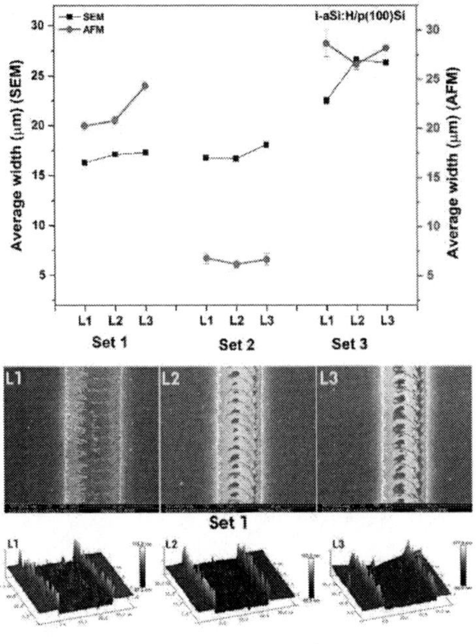

Figure 2: Comparison of SEM and AFM Measurements Across Sets 1, 2, and 3, with SEM and AFM images (L1, L2, L3) for Laser Scribing on Intrinsic a-Si:H Layers in Set 1.

The laser scribing process on the n-layer deposited p-type c-Si wafer was carried out using the same parameters. SEM and AFM analyses revealed distinct surface morphology and topography changes across Sets 1, 2, and 3 (see in figure 3). In Set 1, SEM images displayed smooth surfaces with minimal structural changes, while AFM indicated moderate roughness. Depth values were shallow at L2 (13.87 ± 2.72 nm) and deeper at L3 (266.56 ± 35.52 nm). AFM width measurements variations from 7.12 ± 0.45 μm (L2) to 10.40 ± 0.64 μm (L1), reflecting limited but uniform material modification. Set 2, SEM images showed granular features, indicating localized surface changes. AFM analysis recorded higher roughness at L2, where the depth reached its maximum at 1.86 ± 0.77 nm, while L3 showed a reduction to 1.06 ± 0.05 nm. Widths ranged from 5.55 ± 0.31 μm (L1) to 12.23 ± 0.40 μm (L3), indicating uneven material redistribution with greater interaction at L3. Set 3, SEM revealed well-defined nano-crystalline formations, particularly at L2 and L3, suggesting prominent structural changes due to localized melting and rapid cooling. AFM showed pronounced roughness, with L2 having the highest width (19.06 ± 0.80 μm) and L3 closely following (19.18 ± 1.11 μm). These findings confirm L2 as the region of most effective laser interaction, with enhanced scribing effects. A progression from smooth surfaces in Set 1 to granular structures in Set 2 and nano-crystalline formations in Set 3 was evident. The prominence of L2 across all sets highlights the effectiveness of the central laser zone for consistent material modification. Nano-crystalline formations in Set 3 suggest potential for optical and electronic applications, where precise surface features are critical. Microscopic observations showed localized stress patterns, but no significant degradation like ablation or melting was detected. Despite minor edge irregularities, line widths and continuity were consistent, indicating robust laser control. Further optimization of parameters could improve uniformity and functional properties. Laser scribing on the n-layer highlights the challenges of balancing precision and processing speed. The findings demonstrate that while scribing on the n-layer is feasible, minor edge effects need to be addressed to ensure uniformity and maintain the functional integrity of the n-layer, which plays a critical role in forming the p-n junction. The findings emphasize the importance of optimizing laser parameters to achieve precise, defect-free scribing, enhancing the quality and scalability of thin-film processing.

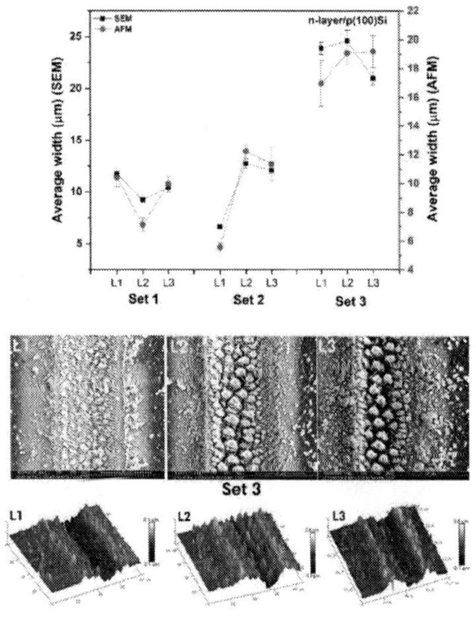

Figure 3: SEM and AFM Width Measurements Across Sets 1, 2, and 3, with SEM and AFM images (L1, L2, L3) for Laser Scribing on n-type a-Si:H Layers in Set 3.

4 CONCLUSIONS

This study establishes the feasibility of UV laser scribing for precise modifications to intrinsic and n-type amorphous silicon layers, demonstrating its potential for achieving smooth and nano-crystalline surface features. While challenges such as edge irregularities and surface roughness remain, the process showed robust and consistent performance. Further optimization of parameters like pulse energy and scan stage stability will enhance uniformity, scalability, and efficiency, paving the way for cost-effective advancements in thin-film manufacturing.

5 ACKNOWLEDGEMENTS

We acknowledge financial support from Innovation Fund Denmark through the project UVSOLAR (project No. 2081-00016A).

6 DECLARATIONS

Conflict of interest: There is no conflict of interest, according to authors.

7 REFERENCES

[1] M. Smith, A. Miller, Proceedings 17th European Photovoltaic Solar Energy Conference, Vol. I (2002) 903.Jamaatisomarin, F., Chen, R., Hosseini-Zavareh, S. and Lei, S., 2023. Laser scribing of photovoltaic solar thin films: A review. Journal of Manufacturing and Materials Processing, 7(3), p.94.

[2] Lauzurica, S., García-Ballesteros, J.J., Colina, M., Sánchez-Aniorte, I. and Molpeceres, C., 2011. Selective ablation with UV lasers of a-Si: H thin film solar cells in direct scribing configuration. Applied Surface Science, 257(12), pp.5230-5236.

[3] Ishteev, R., Gostishchev, P., Tiukhova, M., Sorokin, A., Ishteev, A. and Kondratenko, V., 2024. Technological parameters of thin-film pulsed laser scribing for perovskite photovoltaics. Clean Energy, 8(3), pp.127-135.

[4] García-Ballesteros, J.J., Torres, I., Lauzurica, S., Canteli, D., Gandía, J.J. and Molpeceres, C., 2011. Influence of laser scribing in the electrical properties of a-Si: H thin film photovoltaic modules. Solar Energy Materials and Solar Cells, 95(3), pp.986-991.

[5] Schultz, C., Fenske, M., Dagar, J., Zeiser, A., Bartelt, A., Schlatmann, R., Unger, E. and Stegemann, B., 2020. Ablation mechanisms of nanosecond and picosecond laser scribing for metal halide perovskite module interconnection–An experimental and numerical analysis. Solar Energy, 198, pp.410-418.

[6] Abdul Fattah, T.O., Chen, J., McNab, S., Wilshaw, P.R. and Bonilla, R.S., 2025. Nanosecond vs picosecond: The potential for advanced solar cell processing via pulsed laser technology. Journal of Applied Physics, 138(8).

[7] Persheyev, S.K. and Cairns, J.A., 2016. The formation of well-defined crystalline structures by UV laser irradiation of amorphous silicon films. arXiv preprint arXiv:1606.00181.

[8] Schultz, C., Fenske, M., Otto, N., Dion-Bertrand, L.I., Gélinas, G., Marcet, S., Dagar, J., Schlatmann, R., Unger, E. and Stegemann, B., 2025, April. Loss Analysis of P3 Laser Patterning of Perovskite Solar Cells via Hyperspectral Photoluminescence Imaging. In Solar (Vol. 5, No. 2, p. 13). MDPI.

[9] Morozov, A.P., Gostishchev, P.A., Zharkova, A., Vasilev, A.A., Aleksandrov, A.E., Luchnikov, L.O., Tameev, A.R., Kiselev, D.A., Ilina, T.S., Ishteev, A.R. and Didenko, S.I., 2024. Micro-pixelated halide perovskite photodiodes fabricated with ultraviolet laser scribing. Applied Physics Letters, 124(22).

[10] Turan, B., Ding, K. and Haas, S., 2015. A concept for Lithography-free patterning of silicon heterojunction back-contacted solar cells by laser processing. arXiv preprint arXiv:1506.02879.

[11] Wang, P., Sridharan, R., Ng, X.R., Ho, J.W. and Stangl, R., 2021. Development of TOPCon tunnel-IBC solar cells with screen-printed fire-through contacts by laser patterning. Solar Energy Materials and Solar Cells, 220, p.110834.

[12] Harrison, S., Nos, O., D'Alonzo, G., Denis, C., Coll, A. and Munoz, D., 2016. Back contact heterojunction solar cells patterned by laser ablation. Energy Procedia, 92, pp.730-737.

[13] Smith, C.R., Moltke, A., Adamu, A.I., Michieletto, M., Bowen, P., Moselund, P.M., Markos, C. and Bang, O., 2020. Low-noise tunable deep-ultraviolet supercontinuum laser. Scientific Reports, 10(1), p.18447.

Precision UV Laser Scribing for Amorphous Silicon Solar Cells: Layer-Specific Analysis and Optimization

Department of Electrical and Computer Engineering

Narendra Bandaru[1*], Asbjørn Moltke[2], Ole Bang[2], Rasmus Schmidt Davidsen[1]
[1]Department of Electrical and Computer Engineering, Aarhus University, 8200, Denmark
[2]DTU Electro, Technical University of Denmark, 2800 Kgs. Lyngby, Denmark

1CV.2.25-326

Introduction

- ❖ The global shift toward renewable energy drives demand for efficient photovoltaic manufacturing methods.
- ❖ Ultraviolet (UV) lasers provide advanced capabilities for precise material processing in solar cells.
- ❖ Precision and scalability are critical factors to ensure high-performance and cost-effective device production.
- ❖ Laser-based processing paves the way for next-generation photovoltaic technologies.

Aim

- ❖ Develop and optimize a UV laser scribing process for intrinsic and n-type amorphous silicon layers.
- ❖ The aims is to improve structural integrity, surface precision, and scribing quality.
- ❖ Challenges such as edge irregularities, surface roughness, and material redeposition are specifically addressed.
- ❖ The ultimate goal is to enable scalable and reliable processing for improved photovoltaic device performance.

Experimental Setup

❖ **Sample Preparation**

- ➢ Substrate: 4-inch p-type float-zone (FZ) double-side polished silicon wafer
- ➢ Wafer properties: 100 mm diameter, 3 Ω·cm bulk resistivity, 280 ± 25 μm thickness, (100) orientation
- ➢ Layer deposition: Intrinsic (a-Si:H:i, 27 nm) at 230 °C and n-type (a-Si:H:n, 82 nm) at 200 °C via PECVD in separate chambers.

❖ **Laser Setup**

- ➢ Femtosecond Yb-doped laser, initial wavelength 1030 nm, pulse duration ~300 fs
- ➢ Compressed to ~30 fs through dispersive mirrors and hollow-core fiber
- ➢ UV supercontinuum generated, isolated with band-pass filter (λ = 343 nm)

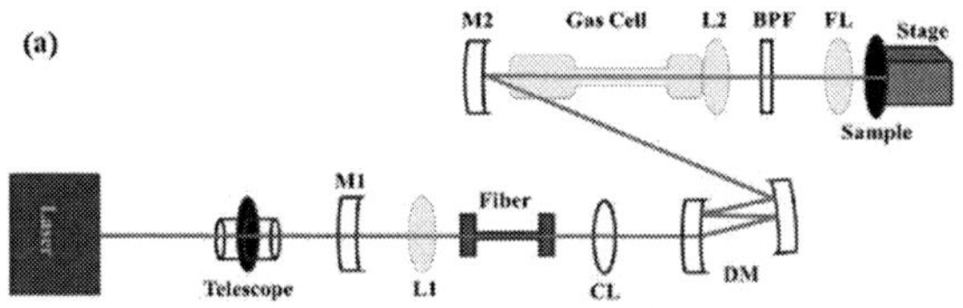

UV Laser scribing process

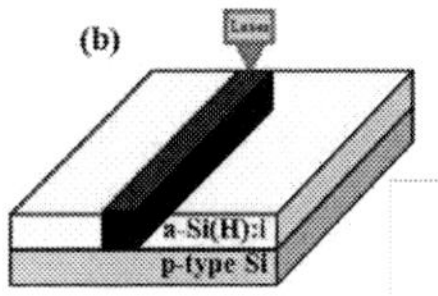

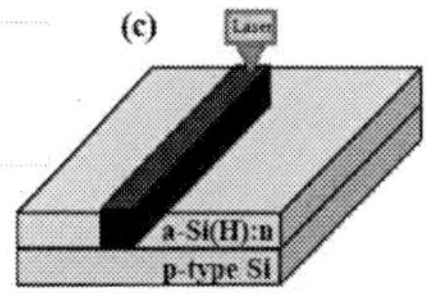

❖ **Scribing Parameters**

- ➢ Pulse energy: 26–30 μJ
- ➢ Repetition rates: 1 kHz (i-layer) and 10 kHz (n-layer)
- ➢ Processing gases: 6.9 bar argon (i-layer), 7.3 bar argon (n-layer)
- ➢ Applied energies: 1.6 μJ (i-layer) and 1.0 μJ (n-layer)

❖ **Characterization Tools**

- ➢ Ellipsometry: Measured layer thickness
- ➢ SEM: Surface morphology, line widths
- ➢ AFM: Topography, roughness, depth

Results

❖ **Intrinsic Layer (i-layer, 27 nm)**

- ➢ Line widths (SEM): ~16–26 μm across sets
- ➢ AFM widths: ~20–24 μm
- ➢ Surface roughness and edge deformation increased in later scans
- ➢ Thermal effects and redeposition observed

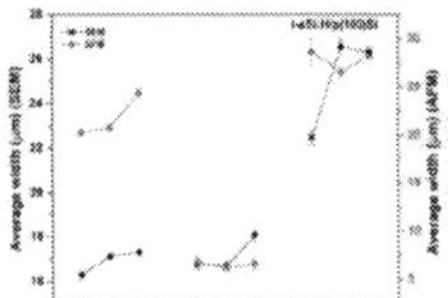

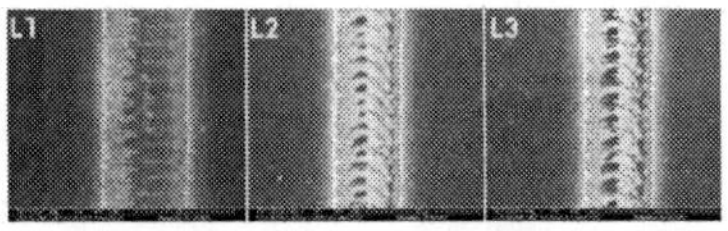

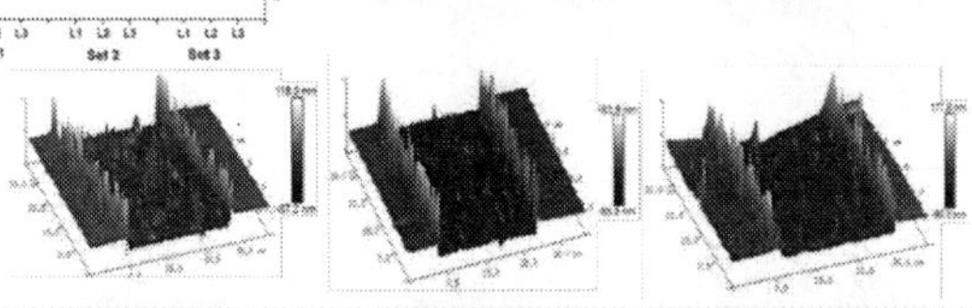

❖ **N-type Layer (n-layer, 82 nm)**

- ➢ Depth range: ~14–267 nm depending on line and set
- ➢ AFM widths: ~7–19 μm
- ➢ Progression from smooth → granular → nano-crystalline features
- ➢ Central laser zone (L2) showed most effective scribing
- ➢ Robust control with minor edge irregularities

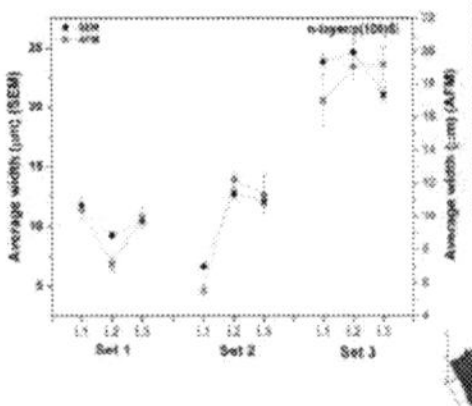

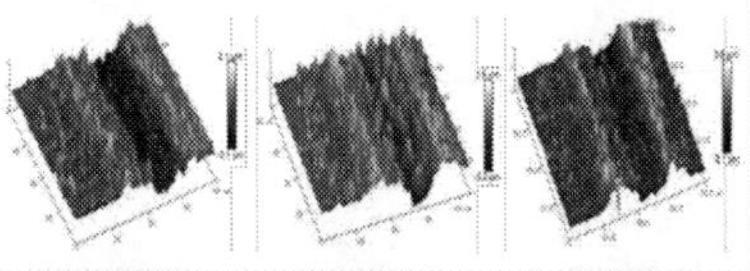

Conclusions

- ❖ UV laser scribing enables precise modifications of intrinsic and n-type amorphous silicon layers
- ❖ Achieved smooth and nano-crystalline surface features with minimal defects
- ❖ Some challenges remain: edge irregularities and surface roughness
- ❖ Process shows robust and consistent performance across layers
- ❖ Further optimization of pulse energy and scan stability will improve uniformity, scalability, and cost-effectiveness

Scientific Innovation

- ➢ First UV laser scribing study with this precision for i- and n-layers
- ➢ Improved control compared to conventional lasers
- ➢ Potential impact on thin-film solar manufacturing

Acknowledgements

➢ Innovation Fund Denmark (UVSOLAR, No. 2081-00016A)

Collaborators: DTU, NKT Photonics, TOPSIL, DFM

Funding: Innovationsfonden

AARHUS UNIVERSITY

Contact email:
narendra.bandaru@ece.au.dk

EU PVSEC 2025

Impact of Pre-Oxidation Treatment on Al_2O_3 Layers for High-Performance Silicon Solar Cells

Kyung Taek Jeong*, Minsoo Jeong, Sang Hee Lee, Yunae Cho, Hee-eun Song , Yong-Jin Kim **

Photovoltaics Research Department, Korea Institute of Energy Research

Motivation

A thermally grown SiO_2 interlayer was introduced between the Si substrate and Al_2O_3 to enhance surface passivation. Unlike conventional Al_2O_3 deposition relying on native SiO_2 formation, the deliberate SiO_2/Al_2O_3 stack yielded improved passivation quality. QSSPC and C–V analyses showed higher iV_{OC}, reduced interface defect density, and more uniform defect distribution compared to single Al_2O_3 layers. SEM and SIMS revealed that the SiO_2 interlayer suppressed hydrogen diffusion and mitigated blister formation during annealing, indicating improved interfacial stability.

Experimental

- Controlled oxide formation prior to Al_2O_3 deposition
  - Group A : Al_2O_3 deposited without an additional oxide layer
  - Group B : Thermally grown SiO_2(~2nm) introduced before Al_2O_3 deposition
- Annealing condition optimization for both groups (fig. 1)
  - Group A : optimum at 425℃
  - Group B : optimum at 500℃
  - Group A showed a larger decrease in iV_{OC} after firing
- Additional analysis performed to investigate the role of the SiO_2 interlayer at the interface (fig.3)

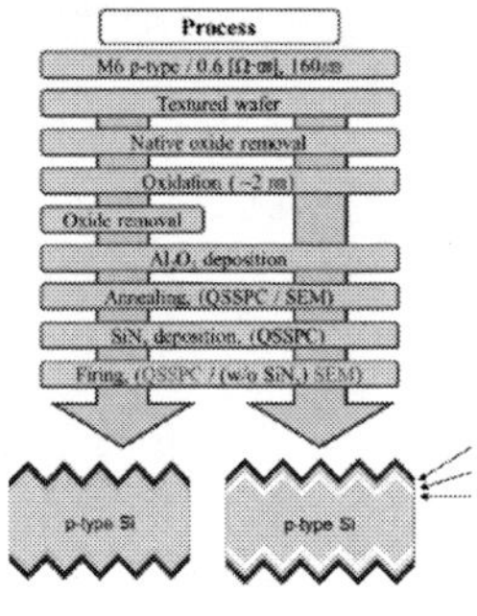

Fig. 1. Process for iV_{OC} optimization and SEM measurements

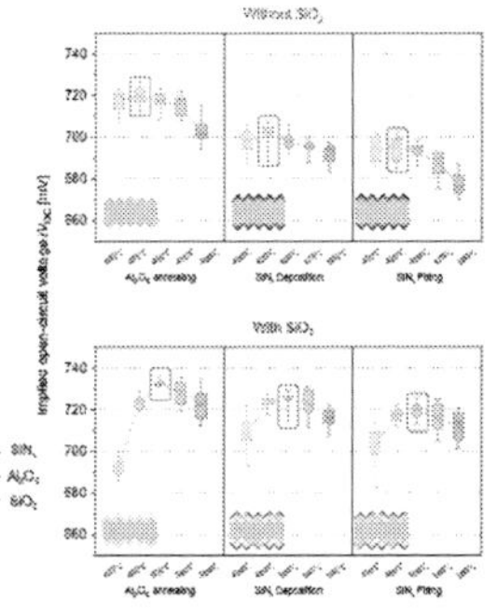

Fig. 2. iV_{OC} measurement results according to firing temperature

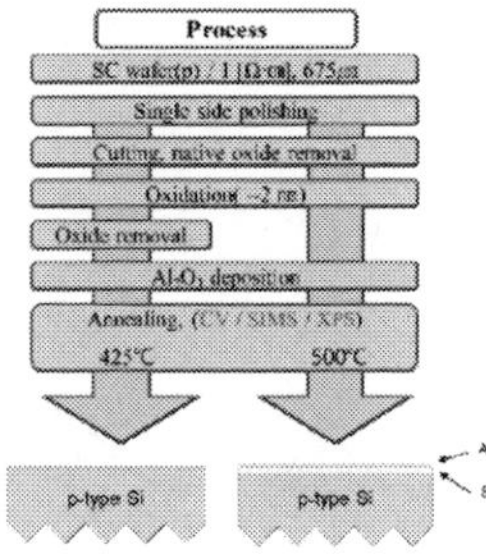

Fig. 3. Process for CV, SIMS, XPS measurements

Results & Analyses

- C–V measurement
  - C–V measurements were carried out to analyze the fixed charge density (Q_f) and interface trap density (D_{it}), with D_{it} calculated by the conductance method.
  - Both Q_f and D_{it} decreased when the SiO_2 growth was deliberately controlled, attributed to the positive fixed charges introduced by SiO_2 and the suppression of dangling bonds on the Si surface.

- SEM measurement
  - SEM clearly revealed structural differences depending on the presence of the SiO_2 layer.
  - Blistering is known to be strongly influenced by hydrogen content.
  - Without SiO_2: blisters were observed, particularly around the valleys of the pyramid texture.
  - With SiO_2: surface remained stable without blister formation.

- SIMS measurement
  - SIMS analysis was performed to examine hydrogen and impurity distributions across the interface.
  - Higher hydrogen concentration at the Al_2O_3/Si interface without SiO_2.
  - Thermally grown SiO_2 effectively blocked hydrogen diffusion from Al_2O_3 into Si.
  - This suppression reduced blister formation and improved interfacial stability.
  - Depth profiles also confirmed more uniform elemental distribution in the stacked structure.

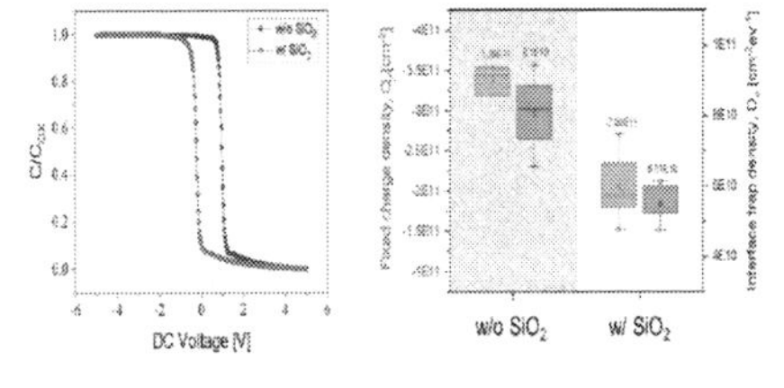

Fig. 4. C-V measurement results according to w/o and w/ SiO_2 layer and calculation results of Q_f and D_{it}

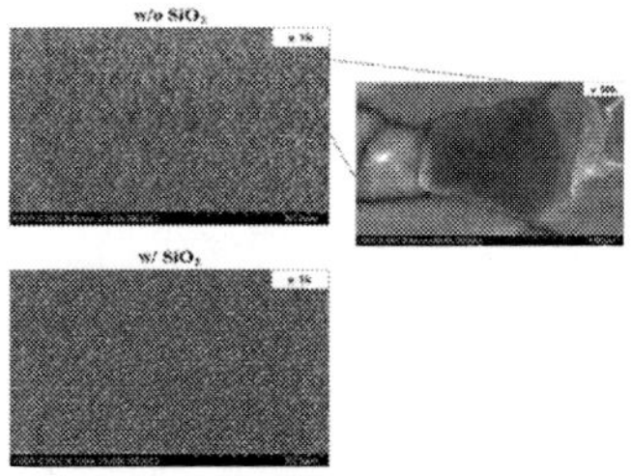

Fig. 5. SEM images according to w/o and w/ SiO_2 layer

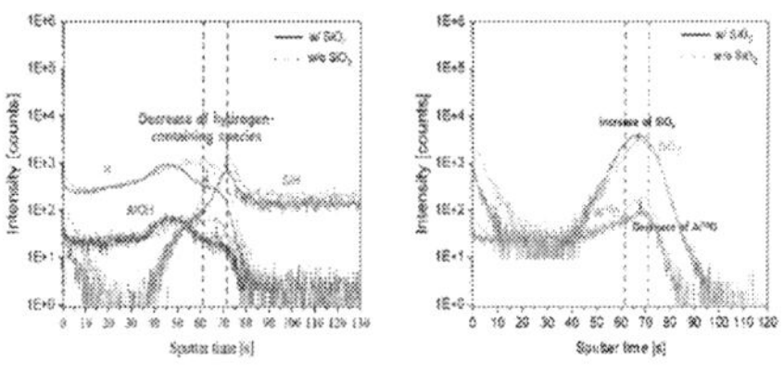

Fig. 6. SIMS profile of w/o and w/ SiO_2

Conclusion

- Introducing a thermally grown SiO_2 interlayer effectively improved interfacial passivation and stability.
- SIMS results indicated that SiO_2 growth reduced hydrogen-related bonding while enhancing oxygen bonding at the Si surface.
- This implies that SiO_2 passivated dangling bonds with oxygen and simultaneously blocked hydrogen incorporation and diffusion.
- Consequently, the SiO_2 interlayer suppressed blister formation during annealing and contributed to more reliable surface passivation.

HIGH EFFICIENCY SHJ SILICON BOTTOM CELL WITH IWO/SIO_2 STACK LAYER FOR III-V/SI TANDEM PHOTOVOLTAICS

Y. Ohshita[1], K. Nakamura[1], H. Lee[2], A. Ogura[2]
[1]Toyota Technological Institute, 2-12-1 Hisakata, Tempaku-ku, Nagoya 468-8511, Japan
[2]Meiji University, 1-1-1 Higashi-mita, Tama-ku, Kawasaki, Kanagawa 214-8571, Japan
Phone: +81-52-809-1876; e-mail: y_ohshita@toyota-ti.ac.jp

ABSTRACT: In this contribution, we demonstrated a route towards high-efficiency SHJ bottom subcells for the fabrication of high-efficiency and low-cost III−V/c-Si tandem solar cells. By optimizing the thickness of front IWO thin films, the reduced reflection loss in the near-infrared region and the contact resistance loss are achieved. This leads to a higher FF and Jsc of optimized SHJ solar cells. It is also shown that, by applying IWO/SiO_2 stack thin films for the fabrication of SHJ solar cells, we can obtain a high Jsc gain as well as high FF gain due to the reduced front reflection and enhanced rear reflection. Finally, we are able to improve the power conversion efficiency of SHJ solar cells from 22.80% to 24.88%, mainly driven by FF and Jsc improvement. Applying TCO/SiO_2 stack thin films for SHJ solar cells is a promising way to enhance both optical and electrical performance of SHJ solar cells for the fabrication of high-efficiency and low-cost III−V/c-Si tandem solar cells.
Keywords: transparent conducting oxide, IWO/SiO_2 stack, silicon heterojunction cell, III−V/c-Si tandem cell

1 INTRODUCTION

Vehicle integrate photovoltaics (VIPV)-powered electric vehicle (VIPV-EV) applications are very attractive for reducing CO_2 emission and creation of new market. In our previous study the Toyota Prius demonstration car powered by III–V three-junction solar cell modules with efficiency of more than 30% has shown actual driving distance of 29.1 km/day at 4.1 kWh/m^2/day irradiation and 36.6 km/day at 6.2 kWh/m^2/day irradiation conditions, respectively [1]. In addition, CO_2 emission reduction of 62 % has been demonstrated [2]. Despite this notable accomplishment, further efficiency improvements of solar cell modules more than 35% and cost reduction of solar cell modules are necessary in order to achieve longer driving distance of VIPV-EV with a daily driving distance of more than 30 km under average solar irradiation of 4 kWh/m^2/day [3]. For the fabrication of such high-efficiency and cost-effective solar cells, III–V solar cells with the highest spectral efficiency among the high-bandgap materials appear as ideal tandem partners for low-cost crystalline silicon (c-Si) solar cells. Meanwhile, it has been reported that c-Si bottom subcells are a key limiting factor in the overall efficiency of III−V/c-Si tandem solar cells. Therefore, enhancing light absorption in the c-Si bottom subcell is crucial for enhancing the overall performance of III−V/c-Si tandem solar cells. In this contribution, we have studied to enhance near-infrared wavelength response of silicon heterojunction bottom subcells by optimizing the light management of silicon heterojunction bottom subcells.

2 EXPERIMENTAL PROCEDURES

Silicon heterojunction (SHJ) solar cells were prepared using n-type Czochralski (CZ) c-Si with 1-5 Ω·cm resistivity. The wafers were cleaned by RCA cleaning. Its surfaces were then textured with KOH and an additive to obtain random pyramids with heights in the range of 1-3 μm with <111> oriented facets and resulting in ~300 μm thick wafers. After RCA cleaning and a dip in a 2.5% diluted hydrofluoric acid solution, nominally 4 nm (i)a-Si:H plus 10 nm (p)a-Si:H layers were deposited at the rear side of the wafer to form the hole contact (rear junction). For the electron contact at the front side a 4 nm (i)a-Si:H and 12 nm (n)a-Si:H stack was deposited. The a-Si depositions were carried out by plasma-enhanced chemical vapor deposition (PECVD). Indium tungsten oxide (IWO) thin films were deposited by reactive plasma deposition (RPD) technique. Silver (Ag) electrodes were formed by photolithography and thermal evaporation of Ag. The fabricated SHJ solar cells were cured at 220 °C for 5 min on a hot-plate under an atmospheric condition. On top of the front and/or rear finished contacts a 110 nm SiO_2 thin film was deposited by sputtering. All SHJ solar cells were light-soaked under 1 sun illumination. To evaluate the SHJ solar cell performance, current–voltage (J-V) characteristics were measured under standard test conditions (AM1.5, 25 °C and 100 mW/cm^2). External quantum efficiency (EQE) and reflectance were measured on a 20 × 20 mm^2 area on the cells with grids inside.

3 RESULTS AND DISCUSSION

3.1 Effects of front IWO thin film thicknesses on the performance of SHJ solar cells

For the investigation of the effects of front IWO thin film thicknesses on the optical and electrical properties of the fabricated SHJ solar cells, the SHJ solar cells with the front IWO thickness of 100, 120, 160, and 250 nm have been fabricated and the reflectance of these SHJ solar cells was measured. As shown in Fig. 1(a), when the IWO thickness increased from 100 nm to 250 nm, the wavelength at which the reflectance approaches zero was shifted to longer wavelength and the reflectance decreased in the near-infrared (NIR) spectral region. In Fig. 1(b), the measured EQE of the SHJ solar cells is shown. The measured EQE in the wavelength range of 300–550 nm decreased as the ITO thickness increased from 100 to 250 nm. However, the measured EQE in the wavelength range of 550–1100 nm increased as the IWO thickness increased. The wavelength range in which the EQE response increases is in line with the range in which the reflection is reduced. In Table 1, the J–V characteristics of the SHJ solar cells are shown. Due to the short-circuit current density (Jsc) and fill factor (FF) increased in the SHJ solar cells with thicker IWO thin films, the power conversion efficiency (PCE) of SHJ solar cells was significantly enhanced. The best SHJ solar cell with 120-nm-thick IWO thin films showed the PCE gain of 1%$_{abs}$, the FF gain of

$0.021\%_{abs}$, and Jsc gain of $0.74\ mA/cm^2_{abs}$ compared to the SHJ solar cell with 100-nm-thick IWO thin films.

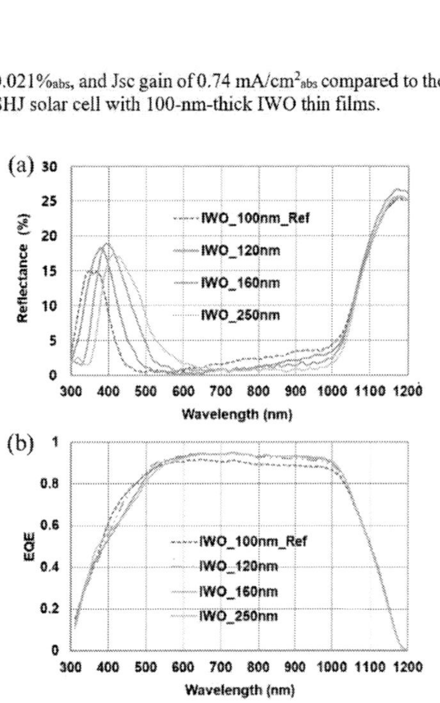

Figure 1: (a) Reflectance and (b) EQE of the SHJ solar cells with different thicknesses of front IWO thin films

Thickness of front IWO thin films	Sample	Isc [A]	Jsc [mA/cm²]	Voc [V]	FF [%]	η [%]
100nm	1-1	0.875	38.00	0.711	0.787	20.72
	1-2	0.896	38.90	0.721	0.804	22.53
	Avg.	0.886	38.45	0.716	0.786	21.63
120nm	2-1	0.903	39.20	0.718	0.802	22.59
	2-2	0.903	39.19	0.718	0.812	22.84
	Avg.	0.903	39.19	0.718	0.807	22.71
160nm	3-1	0.896	38.90	0.717	0.810	22.60
	3-2	0.896	38.90	0.717	0.803	22.40
	Avg.	0.896	38.90	0.717	0.807	22.50
250nm	4-1	0.890	38.61	0.718	0.803	22.27
	4-2	0.894	38.79	0.715	0.796	22.10
	Avg.	0.892	38.70	0.717	0.800	22.18

Table 1: J–V characteristics of the SHJ solar cells with different thicknesses of front IWO thin films

3.2 Effects of IWO/SiO_2 stack thin films on the performance of SHJ solar cells

For the investigation of the effects of IWO/SiO_2 stack thin films on the optical and electrical properties of the fabricated SHJ solar cells, the SHJ solar cells with the front-sided IWO/SiO_2 stack thin film, the rear-sided IWO/SiO_2 stack thin film, or the front/rear-sided IWO/SiO_2 stack thin films. As shown in Fig. 2(a), when the front-sided IWO/SiO_2 stack thin film and the front/rear-sided IWO/SiO_2 stack thin films were fabricated on the SHJ solar cells, the wavelength at which the reflectance approaches zero was shifted to longer wavelength and the reflectance decreased in the whole spectral region except the wavelength range of 420–530 nm. However, the rear-sided IWO/SiO_2 stack thin film demonstrated that the wavelength at which the reflectance approaches zero was shifted to shorter wavelength and the reflectance increased in the wavelength range of 450–1200 nm. In Fig. 2(b), the measured EQE of the SHJ cells is shown. The measured EQE in the whole spectral region increased when the IWO/SiO_2 stack thin films are applied on the SHJ solar cells. For the case of application of the front-sided IWO/SiO_2 stack thin film and the front/rear-sided IWO/SiO_2 stack thin films, the wavelength range in which the EQE response increases is in line with the range in which the reflection is reduced. However, for the case of application of the rear-sided IWO/SiO_2 stack thin film, the wavelength range in which the EQE response increases is in line with the range in which the reflection increases. This confirms the improved spectral response by the rear-sided IWO/SiO_2 stack thin film in the whole spectral region. In Table 2, the J–V characteristics of the SHJ solar cells are shown. Due to the increased Jsc and FF for the SHJ solar cells with IWO/SiO_2 stack thin films, the PCE of SHJ solar cells with IWO/SiO_2 stack thin films was significantly enhanced. The best SHJ solar cell with the front/rear IWO/SiO_2 stack thin films showed the PCE gain of $2.1\%_{abs}$, the FF gain of $0.044\%_{abs}$, and Jsc gain of $1.44\ mA/cm^2_{abs}$ compared to the SHJ solar cell without IWO/SiO_2 stack thin films.

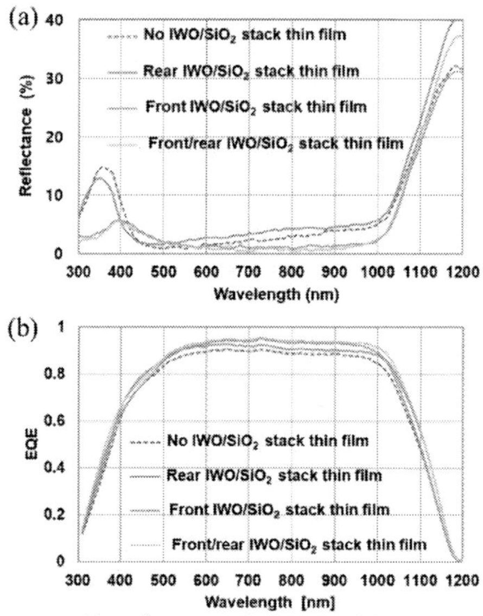

Figure 2: (a) Reflectance and (b) EQE of the SHJ solar cells with front-sided, rear-sided, and front/rear-sided IWO/SiO_2 stack thin films, and without an IWO/SiO_2 stack thin film.

Sample	Isc [A]	Jsc※ [mA/cm²]	Voc [V]	FF [%]	η [%]
No stack	0.919	39.88	0.722	0.792	22.80
Both side stack	0.950	41.22	0.722	0.836	24.88

Table 2: J–V characteristics of the SHJ solar cells with front/rear-sided IWO/SiO_2 stack thin films and without the IWO/SiO_2 stack thin film.

4 SUMMARY AND CONCLUSION

We demonstrated a route towards high-efficiency SHJ bottom subcells. By using an optimized front IWO thin film, reduced reflection and contact resistance losses were achieved. This led to a higher FF and Jsc of SHJ solar cells. It was also shown that, by applying IWO/SiO_2 stack thin films, we could obtain a higher Jsc gain in SHJ solar cells due to the reduced front reflection and enhanced rear reflection. Finally, we were able to improve the PCE of

SHJ solar cells from 22.80% to 24.88%, mainly driven by FF and Jsc improvement. Applying TCO/SiO_2 stack thin films on SHJ solar cells is a promising way to enhance both optical and electrical performance of SHJ solar cells for the fabrication of high-efficiency and cost-effective III−V/c-Si tandem solar cells.

ACKNOWLEDGEMENTS
This study was supported by a grant from the New Energy and Industrial Technology Development Organization (NEDO), Japan.

REFERENCES

[1] M. Yamaguchi, T. Masuda, K. Araki, et al. Prog. Photovolt. 29 (2021) 684-693.
[2] M. Yamaguchi, T. Masuda, T. Nakado, et al. IEEE J. Photovolt. 13 (2023) 343-348.
[3] T. Masuda, M. Yamaguchi, S. Iwasaki, et al. EPJ Photovolt. 16 (2025) 20.

10.4229/EUPVSEC2025/1CV.2.42

Temperature Distribution in c-Si PV Modules Unraveled by Detailed Thermal Modeling

Špela Tomšič, Benjamin Lipovšek, Matevž Bokalič, Marko Topič
University of Ljubljana, Faculty of Electrical Engineering, Ljubljana, Slovenia

UNIVERSITY OF LJUBLJANA
FE Faculty of Electrical Engineering

Abstract

We first investigate the steady-state temperature profile of the entire frameless PV module installed in an open-rack configuration, operating at its maximum power point. We focus on studying the impact of various influencing parameters, such as the optical power density incident on a module, natural convection dependent on the module inclination angle, and forced convection induced by wind. After discerning the temperature distribution across the individual cells of the module, we finally analyze the power loss associated with this temperature inhomogeneity.

Modeling

The PV module studied in this work consists of 60 solar cells arranged in a 6 x 10 layout, with each cell having a surface area of A_{sc} = 16.6 cm × 16.6 cm. The cells are spaced 2 mm apart at a distance of 43 mm and 10 mm from the short and long edge of the module, respectively. COMSOL Multiphysics simulation tool was used to obtain the temperature distribution within the complete PV module.

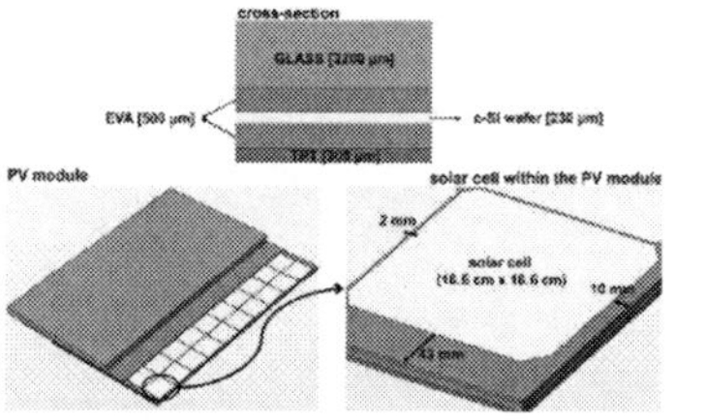

Natural convection vs. forced convection

The influence of natural convection and inclination angle

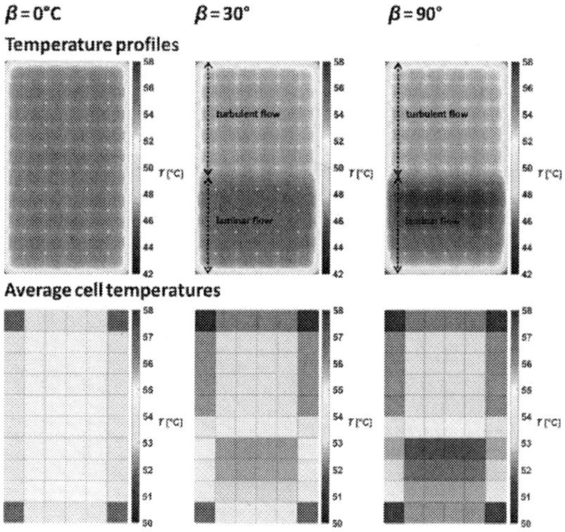

We first analyzed the influence of the inclination angle β on the convection of the PV module installed in portrait orientation. In the case of a horizontally positioned (β = 0°) PV module, we can notice a more homogenous temperature distribution compared to the profiles obtained at the other two β angles. This is because the heated air can travel more easily along the vertical (β = 90°) or tilted (β = 30°) rear surface of the module and may even transform from laminar flow to turbulent flow.

laminar flow can transform to turbulent flow at PV module surface

The influence of forced convection and PV modue orientation

Next, we investigated the impact of the forced convection in the form of wind on the PV module temperature. In both module operation cases, the enhanced cooling effect begins once a sufficiently high wind speed is surpassed.

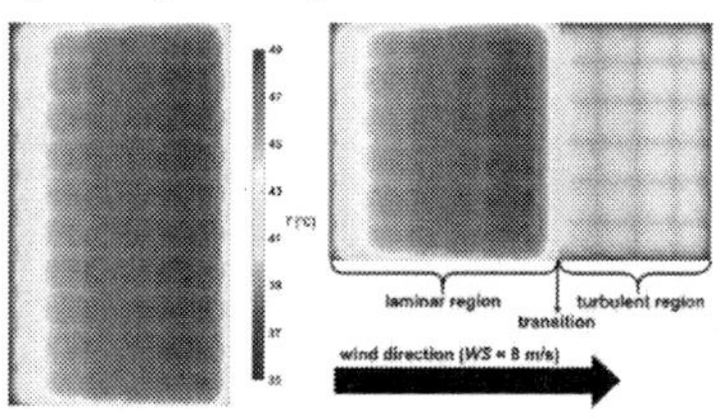

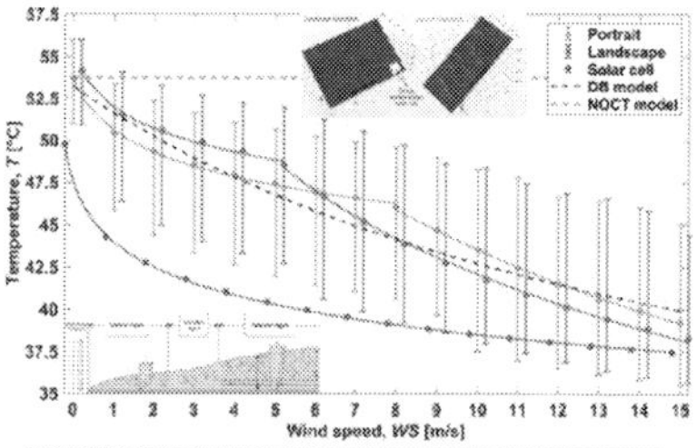

more than a 2 °C drop in average temperature at wind speed of 1 m/s

Power loss analysis

Finally, we investigated to what extent the temperature inhomogeneity within the investigated PV module affects its output power. For this purpose we performed thermal modeling of the entire PV module, installed on the rooftop and calculated:

- the module power by considering the series connection of its cells,
- the power of the module by summing the power of the individual cells, as if they were operating independently from each other, and
- the power of the module as if all cells were operating at the same constant temperature.

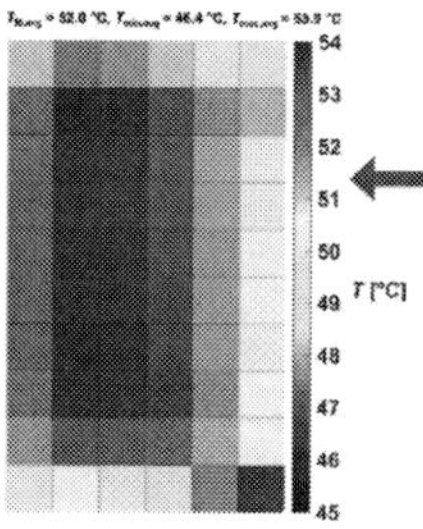

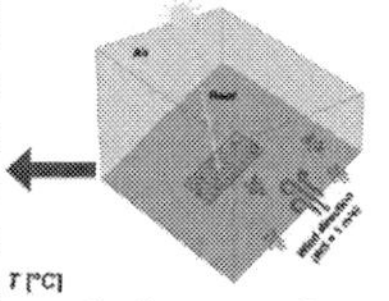

Performance data:

- P_{MPP} = 343.61 W
- P_{sum} = 343.62 W
- $P_{TM,avg}$ = 343.56 W

power loss of the PV module induced by operation of its solar cells at different temperatures is negligible

Further details in ...

Š. Tomšič *et al.*, "Unraveling Temperature Distribution Within Crystalline Silicon PV Modules by Different Finite Element Method-Based Thermal Modeling Approaches," Advanced Theory and Simulations, p. 2401026, Mar 2025, doi: 10.1002/adts.202401026.

Acknowledgements

Slovenian Research and Innovation Agency: research program P2-0415

spela.tomsic@fe.uni-lj.si

REVERSE ANALYSIS OF CONSTITUTIVE PROPERTIES OF SCREEN-PRINTED SILVER OF SILICON HETEROJUNCTION SOLAR CELLS FROM NANOINDENTATIONS

Pei-Chieh Hsiao[1], Jack Colwell[2], Daniel Chen[2], Chris Huang[2], Vince Allen[2], Alison Lennon[1] and Renate Egan[1]
[1] *School of Photovoltaics and Renewable Energy Engineering, UNSW, Sydney, Australia, 2052*
[2] *Sundrive Solar Pty Ltd, Kurnell, NSW, Australia, 2231*

ABSTRACT: The accuracy of long-term module reliability simulations requires the application of high-fidelity constitutive models of materials in the modules. Characterization of the constitutive model of screen-printed Ag contacts is not straightforward since tensile tests are not applicable for their thin-film structure. Although nanoindentation measurements are capable of measuring material hardness and the Young's modulus, the plastic response is not readily available. Reverse analysis through finite element analysis was applied to determine the power law constitutive model of screen-printed Ag contacts of silicon heterojunction solar cells (SHJ).

Keywords: Finite element analysis, screen-printed silver, constitutive model

1 INTRODUCTION

To ensure a 25-year warranty for silicon solar modules, the integrity and reliability of PV modules are routinely examined by a series of durability tests defined in the IEC 61215 standard. Nevertheless, the outdoor performance of PV modules operating in the field may appear differently due to various reasons. As such, reliability is an area of increasing interest and concern in the PV community and at academic institutes. Supplement to the deficiency of IEC tests, finite element modelling provides a systematic analysis in versatile approaches. Pivotal to the accuracy of simulations is applying high fidelity constitutive models of materials in the modules.

Screen printed metal contacts are the dominant method of metallization in silicon solar cells. Owing to their thin film morphologies, measuring the stress-strain curve from tensile tests is not possible, thereby their constitutive models are lacking in literature. The material properties of Ag paste of Al-BSF cells reported in [1] are likely unsuitable for TOPCon or SHJ cells due to the changes in the paste formulation for higher efficiency cells. In this report, the power law model of screen-printed Ag contacts was reverse analyzed using finite element modelling from nanoindentation measurements.

2 EXPERIMENTAL

A G12 screen-printed Ag SHJ cell was laser cleaved into small circles (diameter of 20 mm) and glued onto a hot-mount stub. The sample was ultrasonic cleaned for 1 min and sequentially polished using 1.0 and 0.5 μm abrasive disks to create a smooth surface suitable for nanoindentation performed using a Bruker Hysitron TI 900 TriboIndenter with a 3D Berkovich indenter. The load (P) displacement (h) curves were recorded with varying maximum loads beween 1 and 8 mN and a fixed strain rate of 0.1 s^{-1}. In total 25 measurements were performed with a spacing of 15 μm to avoid interference.

The stress (σ) strain (ε) relationship described in a power law constitutive model is,

$$\begin{cases} \sigma = E\varepsilon & \sigma < \sigma_y \\ \sigma = \sigma_y\left(1+\frac{E}{\sigma_y}\varepsilon_p\right)^n & \sigma \geq \sigma_y \end{cases} \quad (1)$$

Where E is Young's modulus, σ_y is yield strength, ε_p is plastic strain and n is hardening exponent.

Nanoindentations typically report the hardness (H) and E of test materials. To describe the plastic response, a representative stress (σ_r) and a representative strain (ε_r) are used. The $\sigma - \varepsilon$ curves passing a specific point of (σ_r, ε_r) generally generate similar $P - h$ curves in nanoindentations. Therefore, the reverse analysis algorithm was developed in five steps:

- Step 1: use a reference $P - h$ curve of fused quartz to determine the indenter tip radius, r
- Step 2: determine σ_r by matching the loading phase of a $P - h$ curve
- Step 3: determine n by matching the slope of the unloading phase of a $P - h$ curve
- Step 4: determine ε_r by matching the complete $P - h$ curve
- Step 5: calculate σ_y

The finite element simulation applied 2D axisymmetric geometry. The nonideal bluntness of the indenter, which was modelled by a finite radius r, was estimated from the $P - h$ curve of fused quartz used for calibration with a known bilinear elastoplastic model from the literature [see Table 1]. Accurate tip radius is crucial as the tip geometry affects the required load for indentations. For the test material, σ_r was first determined by matching the loading phase of the $P - h$ curve using a bilinear elastic-perfect-plastic model. With an initial ε_r of 0.034 [2], the optimal n was decided by matching the stiffness (S), defined as the slope of the unloading phase of the $P - h$ curve near the maximum load (P_{max}). Subsequently, accurate ε_r was iteratively determined by coinciding the complete $P - h$ curve within a reasonable range around the initial ε_r. Once σ_r, ε_r and n were known, σ_y can be calculated according to Eq. (1).

The finite element simulation was conducted using ANSYS 2023R1 and the material properties listed in Table I. The Poisson ratio of screen-printed Ag is assumed to be 0.38 [2].

Table I: Material properties used in the reverse finite element analysis

Material	Young's modulus E (GPa)	Yield strength σ_y (MPa)	Poisson ratio ν	Isotropic tangent modulus E_T (GPa)
Indenter [3]	1014	-	0.07	-
Fused quartz [4]	71.4	6.0	0.17	13
Si [5]	170	-	0.28	-

3 RESULTS AND DISCUSSIONS

Figure 1 shows the fitted $P-h$ curve of reference fused quartz by varying the tip radius. An indenter tip with a radius of 200 nm resulted in a coinciding loading phase. Although the curves gradually deviated towards the end of the unloading phase due to the densification behavior of fused quartz, the plasticity model was sufficient to estimate the indenter tip radius

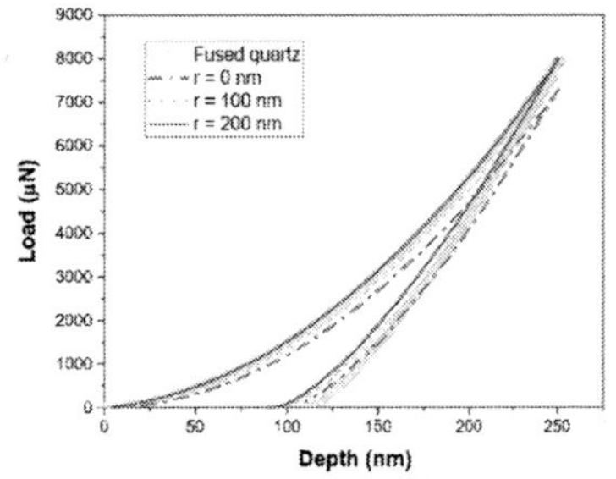

Figure 1: Fitted $P-h$ curves of fused quartz for the determination of indenter tip radius.

For nanoindentation of the test material, as indicated in Figure 2 (a), larger σ_r led to higher load at the same indent depth. The whole loading phase and P_{max} were simultaneously matched with an estimated σ_r of 229 MPa. Figure 2 (b) shows that S was primarily influenced by n. Via interpolation, the optimal n (≈ 0.49) was determined. By dichotomy, ε_r was lastly determined as shown in Figure 2 (c). The best fitted parameters accurately matched most of the loading phase and the unloading phase. The difference at the initial loading phase resulted from indentation size effect [6-8] due to higher density of dislocations generated within the reduced deformation zone when the indentation size decreased. The bottom unloading curve was inconsistent most likely due to the porosity of screen-printed Ag contacts.

(a)

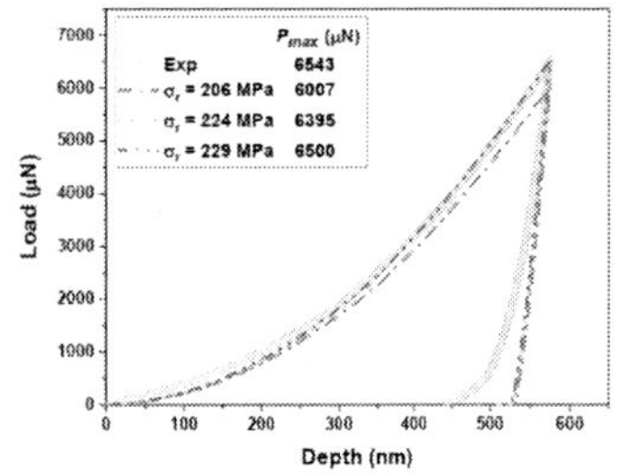

(b)

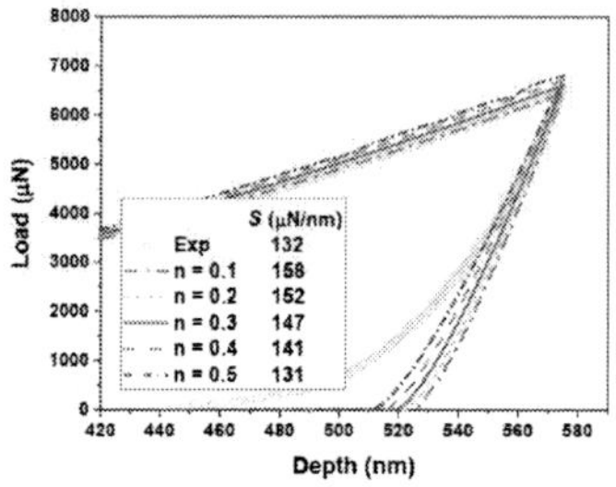

(c)

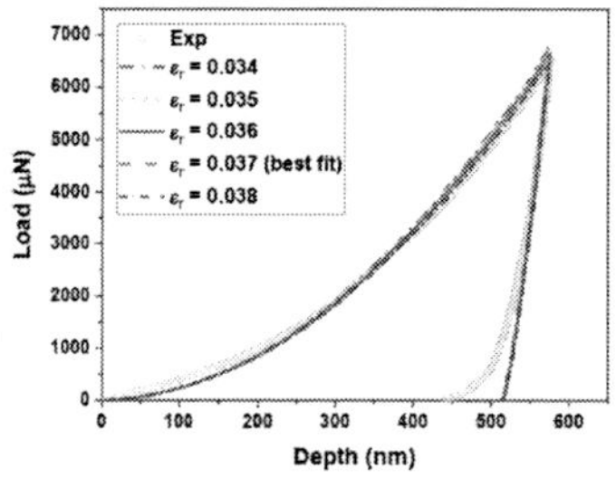

Figure 2: Fitted $P-h$ curves of screen-printed Ag of SHJ cells (a) Step 2 the determination of σ_r; (b) Step 3 the determination of n; and (c) Step 4 the determination of ε_r.

The estimated power law model is graphed in Figure 3. The developed model could assist in finite element simulation of cell and module reliability of emerging technologies, such as zero-busbar interconnection design, which aim to address demands to reduce Ag consumption. Direct bonding of wires to fingers has been demonstrated experimentally to show finger defects near the cell edges in wave-shaped wires soldering [9] and simulated higher stress in the outermost fingers interconnected by SWCT [10]. Consequently, zero-busbar interconnection requires thorough examination for its long-term mechanical stability.

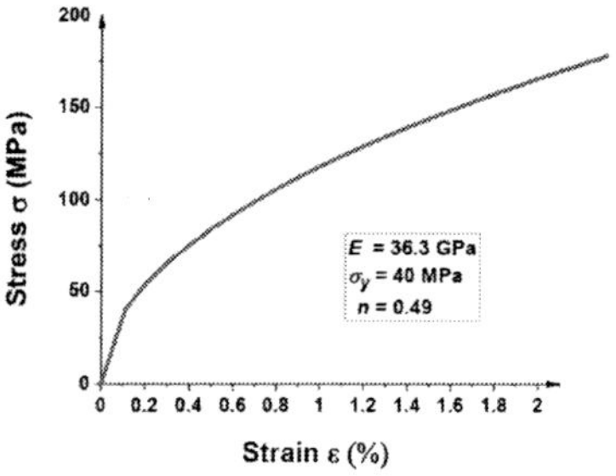

Figure 3: Fitted $P-h$ curves of screen-printed Ag of SHJ cells (a) Step 2 the determination of σ_r; (b) Step 3 the determination of n; and (c) Step 4 the determination of ε_r.

4 CONCLUSIONS

Estimation of power law constitutive model from nanoindentation load-displacement curves was investigated. The finite element reverse analysis consists of sequential determinations of indenter tip radius, representative stress, hardening exponent and representative strain. The extracted E, σ_y and n of screen-printed Ag of silicon heterojunction solar cells were 36.3 GPa, 40 MPa and 0.49, respectively. The developed model could assist in finite element simulation of cell and module reliability, for example direct bonding of wires to fingers in the zero-busbar interconnection.

ACKNOLOGEMENTS

This work has been supported by the Australian government through the Australian Renewable Energy Agency (ARENA), the Australian Centre for Advanced Photovoltaics (ACAP), and the NSW Government through its Environmental Trust. This research includes computations using the computational cluster Katana supported by Research Technology Services at UNSW Sydney. The authors also acknowledge the facilities and the scientific and technical assistance from School of Material Science.

REFERENCES

[1] C. Kohn *et al.*, "Analyses of warpage effects induced by passivation and electrode coatings in silicon solar cells," in *22nd European Photovoltaic Solar Energy Conference and Exhibition*, 2007.
[2] D. Paretkar, N. J. Glassmaker, K. R. Mikeska, G. Blackman, and A. Jagota, "Adhesion of screen-printed silver metallization to crystalline silicon solar cells," *IEEE Journal of Photovoltaics*, vol. 6, no. 5, pp. 1141-1151, 2016.
[3] Y. Li *et al.*, "Constitutive modelling of annealing behavior in through silicon vias-copper," *Materials Characterization*, vol. 179, p. 111359, 2021.
[4] D. Torres-Torres, J. Muñoz-Saldaña, L. Gutierrez-Ladron-de Guevara, A. Hurtado-Macias, and M. Swain, "Geometry and bluntness tip effects on elastic–plastic behaviour during nanoindentation of fused silica: experimental and FE simulation," *Modelling and Simulation in Materials Science and Engineering*, vol. 18, no. 7, p. 075006, 2010.
[5] M. Springer and N. Bosco, "On residual stresses and reference temperatures in thermomechanical simulations of photovoltaic modules using the finite element method," *IEEE Journal of Photovoltaics*, vol. 12, no. 3, pp. 853-859, 2022.
[6] M. S. De Guzman, G. Neubauer, P. Flinn, and W. D. Nix, "The role of indentation depth on the measured hardness of materials," *MRS online proceedings library (OPL)*, vol. 308, p. 613, 1993.
[7] N. Fleck, G. Muller, M. F. Ashby, and J. W. Hutchinson, "Strain gradient plasticity: theory and experiment," *Acta Metallurgica et materialia*, vol. 42, no. 2, pp. 475-487, 1994.
[8] W. D. Nix and H. Gao, "Indentation size effects in crystalline materials: a law for strain gradient plasticity," *Journal of the Mechanics and Physics of Solids*, vol. 46, no. 3, pp. 411-425, 1998.
[9] L. C. Rendler *et al.*, "Wave-shaped wires soldered on the finger grid of solar cells: Solder joint stability under thermal cycling," in *AIP Conference Proceedings*, 2018, vol. 1999, no. 1: AIP Publishing, p. 080001.
[10] P.-C. Hsiao *et al.*, "Comparative Models of Induced Thermomechanical Stress in Silicon Solar Cells Interconnected with Conventional Tabbing and Wire-Based Interconnection Methods," in *2019 IEEE 46th Photovoltaic Specialists Conference (PVSC)*, 2019: IEEE, pp. 0122-0125.

Reverse analysis of constitutive properties of screen-printed silver of silicon heterojunction solar cells from nanoindentations

Pei-Chieh Hsiao[1], Jack Colwell[2], Daniel Chen[2], Chris Huang[2], Alison Lennon[1,2] and Renate Egan[1]
[1] School of Photovoltaics and Renewable Energy Engineering, UNSW, Sydney, Australia, 2052
[2] Sundrive Solar Pty Ltd, Kirrawee, NSW, Australia, 2232

Introduction

- Pivotal to the accuracy of finite element simulations is applying high fidelity constitutive models for a systematic analysis of Si solar cells and modules.
- Screen printed metal contacts are the dominant method of metallization in Si solar cells. Owing to their thin film morphologies, measuring the stress-strain curve by tensile tests is not possible.
- The power law model of screen-printed Ag contacts was reverse analyzed using finite element modelling from nanoindentation measurements.

Experimental

- Silicon heterojunction solar cell samples (2 mm in diameter) were ultrasonic cleaned and polished using 1.0 and 0.5 μm abrasive disks.
- Nanoindentation was performed using a Bruker Hysitron TI 900 TriboIndenter with a 3D Berkovich indenter.
- Load (P) - displacement (h) curves were recorded with varying maximum loads from 1 to 8 mN and a fixed strain rate of 0.1 s^{-1}.

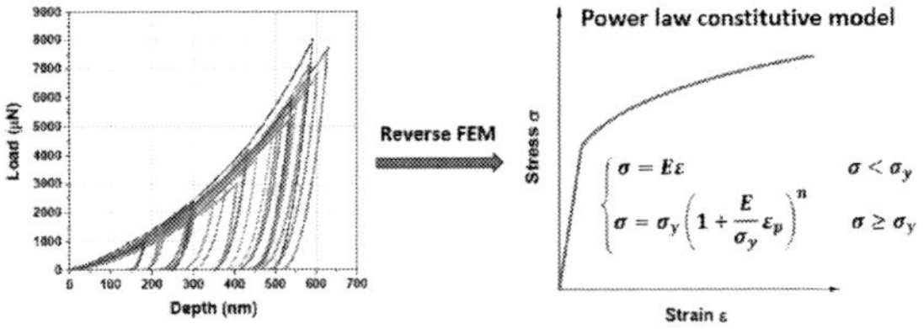

Reverse Finite Element Analysis

- **Material Properties**

Material	Young's modulus E (GPa)	Yield strength σ_y (MPa)	Poisson's ratio, ν	Tangent modulus E_T (GPa)
Indenter [2]	1014	-	0.07	-
Fused quartz [3]	71.4	6.0	0.17	13
Si [4]	170	-	0.28	-
Screen-printed Ag	36.3	TBD	0.38	-

- **The algorithm consists of five steps**

Step 1 – use reference $P-h$ curve (fused quartz) to determine the tip radius of the indenter (r)

Step 2 – find representative stress (σ_r) using elastic-perfectly plastic model to match the loading phase

Step 3 – find stress hardening exponent (n) using power law model to match the slope of the unloading phase

Step 4 – find representative strain (ε_r) using power law model to match the complete $P-h$ curve

Step 5 – calculate σ_y

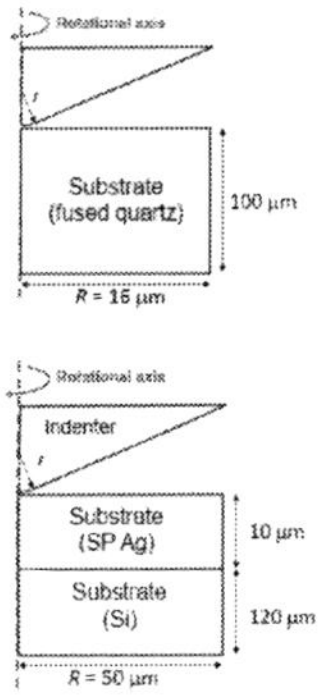

Results and Discussion

Step 1 - Determine tip radius

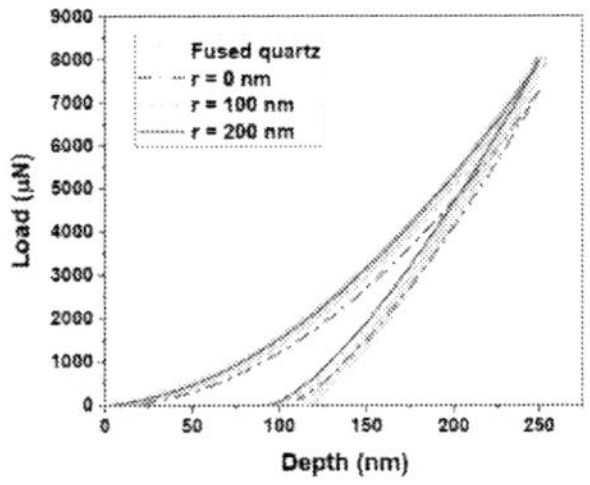

- Simple bilinear elastoplastic model can accurately simulate the loading phase but deviate at the unloading phase.
- The model is sufficient to determine the tip radius (r = 200 nm).

Step 2 - Find representative stress

- The initial σ_r is calculated by:

$$\frac{E_r}{H} = 0.231\frac{E_r}{\sigma_r} + 4.91$$

where H is hardness, E_r is reduced modulus.

- Subsequent σ_r is found by:

$$\sigma_r(i+1) = \sigma_r(i)\frac{P_{max}^{Exp}}{P_{max}^{FEM}}$$

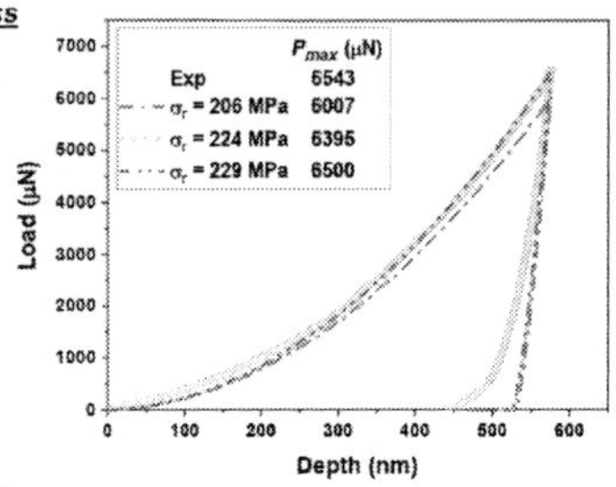

Step 3 - Find hardening exponent

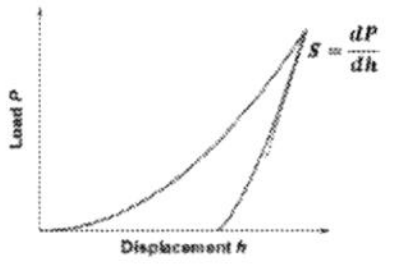

- Use an initial ε_r = 0.034 [1]

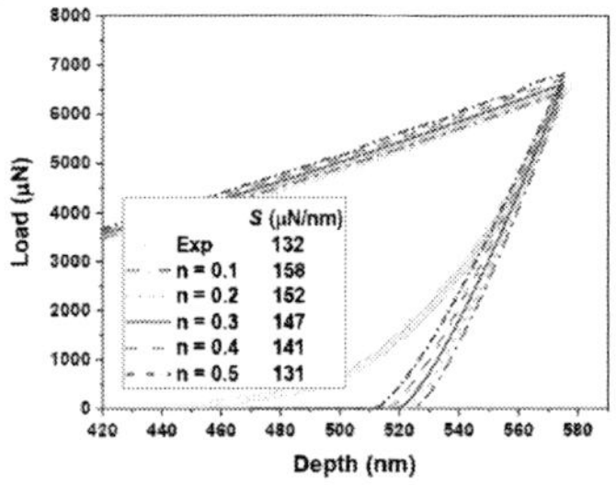

Step 4 - Find representative strain

- Vary ε_r around the initial ε_r.
- The difference at the initial loading phase resulted from indentation side effect.
- The bottom half of the unloading phase was not matched, possibly due to the porosity properties of screen-printed Ag.

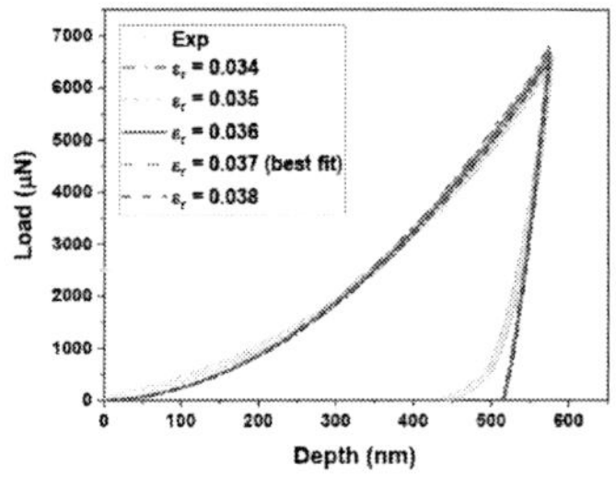

Step 5 – Apply to power law constitutive model

- The extracted E, σ_y and n of screen-printed Ag of silicon heterojunction solar cells were 36.3 GPa, 40 MPa and 0.49, respectively.

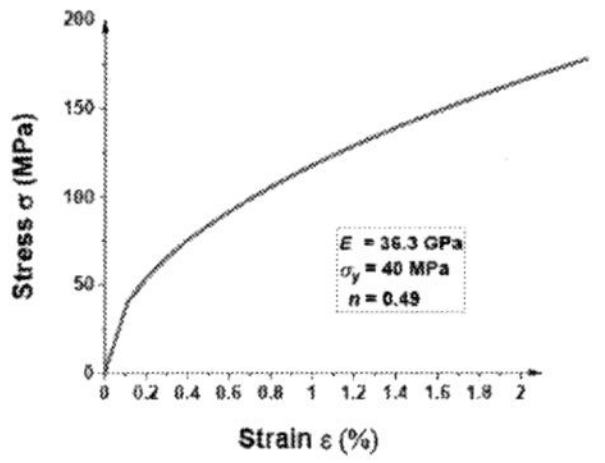

Conclusion

- Estimation of stress strain power law constitutive model from nanoindentation $P-h$ curves was investigated.
- The finite element reverse analysis consists of determining indenter tip radius, representative stress, hardening exponent and representative strain.
- The developed model could assist in finite element simulation in cell and module reliability, for example the zero-busbar interconnection design, which is an emerging technology in the pressing demand of reducing Ag consumption. Direct bonding of wires to fingers requires thorough examination for its long-term mechanical stability.

Acknowledgement

This project has been supported by the Australian government through the Australian Renewable Energy Agency (ARENA), the Australian Centre for Advanced Photovoltaics (ACAP) and the NSW Government through its Environmental Trust.

Reference

[1] J. Antunes, J. Fernandes, L. Menezes, and B. Chaparro, "A new approach for reverse analyses in depth-sensing indentation using numerical simulation," *Acta Materialia*, vol. 55, no. 1, pp. 69-81, 2007.
[2] Y. Li *et al.*, "Constitutive modelling of annealing behavior in through silicon vias-copper," *Materials Characterization*, vol. 179, p. 111359, 2021.
[3] D. Torres-Torres, J. Muñoz-Saldaña, L. Gutierrez-Ladron-de Guevara, A. Hurtado-Macías, and M. Swain, "Geometry and bluntness tip effects on elastic–plastic behaviour during nanoindentation of fused silica: experimental and FE simulation," *Modelling and Simulation in Materials Science and Engineering*, vol. 18, no. 7, p. 075006, 2010.
[4] M. Springer and N. Bosco, "On residual stresses and reference temperatures in thermomechanical simulations of photovoltaic modules using the finite element method," *IEEE Journal of Photovoltaics*, vol. 12, no. 3, pp. 853-859, 2022.

STATUS AND PROSPECTS OF SOLAR CELL CHARACTERIZATION

K. Ramspeck, I. Djeukeu, J. Horn and M. Meixner
halm elektronik gmbh
Friesstraße 20, 60388 Frankfurt

ABSTRACT: This review presents an overview of state-of-the-art solar cell characterization techniques employed in end-of-line testing within high-throughput manufacturing environments. The technologies currently in use are introduced and their relevance to meeting industrial timing constraints is discussed. The effectiveness of established characterization methods is evaluated in the context of quality classification, price determination, and process optimization. Expanding beyond conventional approaches, the review addresses emerging requirements for advanced solar cell architectures - specifically tandem solar cells - and highlights novel techniques such as contactless *IV* measurements. The new requirements and challenges posed by tandem solar cell architectures are described, along with initial strategies developed to address these issues. Finally, a comparative assessment is provided of contactless and traditional contacting *IV* techniques based on their capability to satisfy the comprehensive requirements for solar cell characterization.
Keywords: Characterization, *IV* testing, production

1 INTRODUCTION

Solar cell characterization at the end of the production process is an important step in order to quantify the results of the foregoing process flow. Ever since, it has to serve certain goals. First of all, by measuring the power conversion efficiency solar cell characterization tests effectiveness of production output and determines its value. Furthermore, solar cell characterization shall determine, whether cell quality is good, or whether constraints in usability of the cells in modules are present. This adresses especially questions of security in usage of the cells. Finally, characterization of solar cells serves to understand cell technology. Potential for optimization and origins of efficiency losses have to be found and assigned to process steps in order to find better process settings and to test and compare new process flows. This sums up to the three main tasks of solar cell characterization in modern high speed production, quality sorting, price assignment and process/yield optimization. In order to deliver on these tasks, different approaches are required. Quality sorting requires a binary decision, whether or not a cell can be used in a solar module. Price assignment requires precise, quantitative information on efficiency, to group cells of identical power output and sell them accordingly. Process- and yield optimization opens up the widest field for characterization. Quantitative, spatially resolved and qualitative information is collected and used to identify and quantify defects and potentials, assign them to machines and processes and quickly detect occurrence of defects in order to remove the root cause creating them.

How these manifold and complex tasks are accomplished within the timing constraints of high throughput manufacturing by modern measurement equipment is the topic of our contribution.

2 INSTRUMENTATION

LED-based and Xenon-based flasher systems as the cetisPV-IUCT-LF3.1 or the cetisPV-IUCT-3600BF together with add-on options are capable of providing complete cell analysis within a total measurement time of 350 ms only. A number of versatile characterization techniques are combined in these systems with a typical timing for Si-solar cell characterization shown in Figure 1.

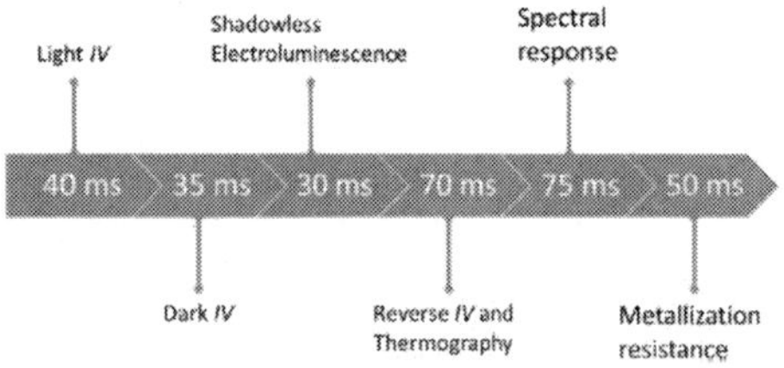

Figure 1. Timing overview for a complete Si-solar cell characterization.

In a first step, the light-*IV* curve is recorded within 40 ms, followed by 35 ms for acquisition of the dark-*IV*. Another 30 ms is reserved for electroluminescence (EL) imaging. Reverse-*IV* and thermography require a stake of approximately 70 ms. About 50 ms need to be reserved for thorough determination of metallization resistances and 75 ms is left over for spectral response (SR) measurements. It is worth noting, that different constraints on timing are set by different sorting machines and other options such as bifacial *IV*-measurements or Suns-V_{OC} may alter the total timing. Therefore, the sequence in Figure 1 gives just one possible example for illustration. Figure 2 displays a cetisPV-celltest5 laboratory setup, which utilizes the same components as the cetisPV-IUCT-LF3.1 production system and is capable of performing the above mentioned measurements within the required timing restrictions. A 28 wavelength LED light engine, cameras for shadowless EL, a pyrometer for temperature measurements, a thermography camera and versatile measurement electronics combined with a channel switching matrix for metallization resistance measurement make up the system.

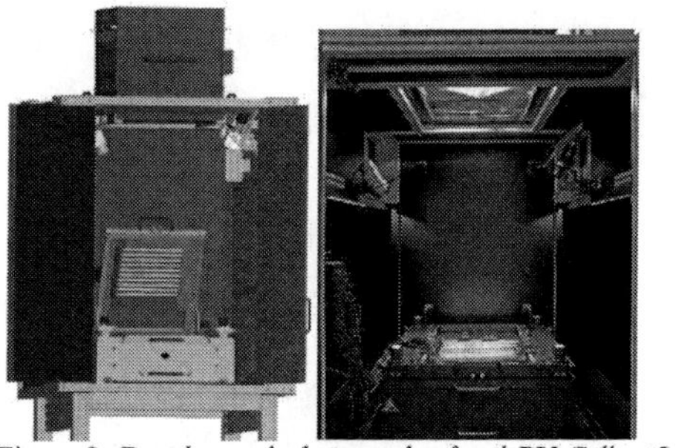

Figure 2: Drawing and photograph of cetisPV-Celltest5 for complete solar cell characterization.

The cell is mounted in a contacting station, positioned in the center of the dark room, which can be equipped with different contacting elements depending on the cell structure to be measured. Figure 3 features its spectrum and intensity map. A close match to AM1.5G and homogeneity of better than +/-1% over a 240 x 240 mm^2 illumination area are reached.

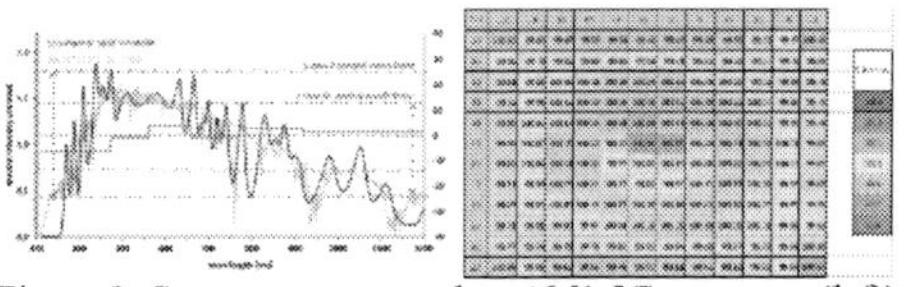

Figure 3: Spectrum compared to AM1.5G spectrum (left) and irradiance map (right) of LF3.1 light source.

3 STATE OF THE ART CHARACTERIZATION OF SI-SOLAR CELLS

The timing diagram in Figure 1 displays an exemplary measurement recipe performed for a complete characterization of solar cells in high throughput production. It comprises the measurement of light- and dark-*IV*, reverse characteristics and thermography, electroluminescence, spectral response and metallization resistances. In order to deliver precise results, the raw data as measured by the system requires sophisticated analysis and refinement. *IV*-curves need to be corrected for cell temperature, light intensity measured synchronized with the *IV*-data points [1], and transient effects caused by high charge carrier lifetimes in the Si-bulk which, for modern high efficiency cells are unavoidable within the timing constraints of production measurements [2]. While these transient effects are an obstacle in the determination of steady-state power output of the solar cell on the one hand, they provide additional information on the solar cell on the other hand and can be used i.e. to determine the cells base doping concentration [3]. Figure 4 gives an example of measured *IV*-curves on a modern high efficiency solar cell (upper left) together with the steady-state *IV*-curves derived from the raw-curves (upper right), the base doping concentration results (lower left) and the series resistance as a function of solar cell voltage (lower right). Noteably, this parameter combines important resistive losses on the solar cell in one parameter of the diode model commonly used to describe the cells. As current flow patterns on the cell are altered when changing the operational state of the cell, the value for this so called „lumped series resistance“ is not one fixed value for a solar cell, but changes as a function of the changes in current flow patterns [4].

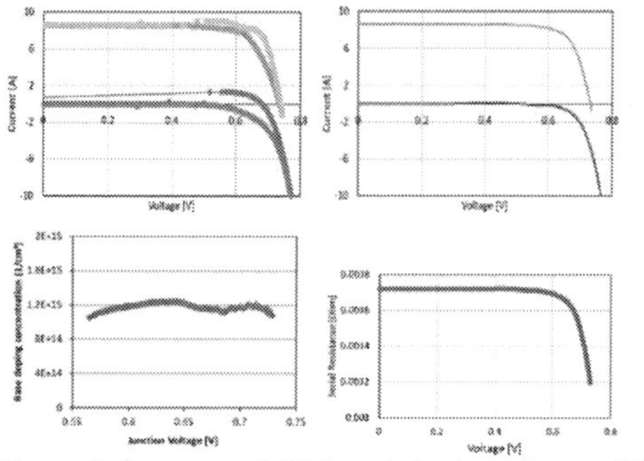

Figure 4: As measured *IV* data, derived steady-state *IV* curves, base doping concentration and series resistance as a function of voltage.

Being one of the main loss mechanisms in solar cells, the series resistance gains a lot of attention and separating origins of increased resistance is important for process and yield optimization. Two additional techniques are mainly utilized to gain further insight into this parameter. Measurements of metallization resistance between the contacts are used to determine the finger resistances and their contribution to the total series resistance and related losses. Making use of cell geometry and current, power losses, series resistance contribution and effect on fill-factor (FF) are calculated from the resistance values as shown in Table 1. One further information gained from these measurements is the minimum required silver or paste consumption to achieve the measured metallization resistance values. This information can be used to judge the effectiveness of the metallization process especially when combined with the paste consumption of the production line.

Table 1: Results from metallization resistance measurements and the derived impact on output power and silver consumption.

Parameter	Front Grid	Rear Grid
Measured Grid Resistance	41.5 - 45 mOhm	17.25 to 23.1 mOhm
Impact on FF	1.17 % - 1.27 %	0.49 % - 0.65%
Rser contribution	0.82 - 0.89 mOhm	0.34 - 0.46 mOhm
Pmpp loss	96 - 104 mW	40 - 53 mW
Min Silver laydown	17 - 18.4 mg	33 - 44 mg
Min cost contribution	0.019 €/cell	0.042 €/cell

Besides the contribution of metallization resistance, sheet resistances, base resistance and contact resistance on both sides of the solar cell contribute to the total series resistance. As sheet resistance is often known with good accuracy, the effect of contact resistance is what remains and dominates series resistance variations not caused by the metallization directly. Thus, knowing the metallization resistance of each cell allows to discriminate the main causes for series resistance variation. Besides this global result, further spatial resolved information on series resistance is derived from electroluminescence imaging [5]. This widespread technique utilizes the intensity of radiative recombination which is suppressed in regions with competing increased nonradiative recombination. It reveals the geometrical distribution of all defects which act to reduce the charge carrier concentration in the solar cell under forward operating conditions in the dark. These defects comprise increased recombination by structural defects, impurities, surface passivation issues as well as series resistance related voltage variations. While commonly parts of the cell under test are shadowed by contacting structures, most recently shadowless EL-technique is introduced to the market, enabling to see the whole cell surface even in contacted state.

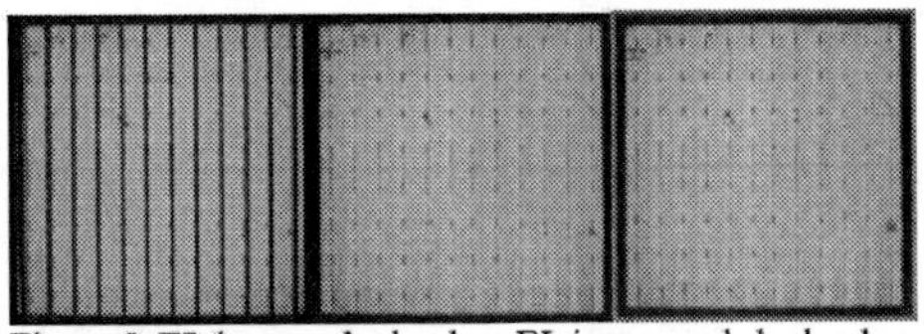

Figure 5: EL image, shadowless EL image and shadowless EL-image with marked defects of a Si-solar cell.

Figure 5 displays a standard EL and a shadowless EL-image of a modern multi-busbar cell, together with results from AI-based defect recognition. Due to different geometrical finger-prints, many different defects and root-causes for their appearance are discriminated from EL images, allowing intense feed-back into the process to optimize yield and cell quality. Given such a wealth of information, EL imaging has become one of the most important characterization techniques for Si-solar cell production and is used to sort out cells with severe local defects, to assign defective cells with less severe defects a quality grade B and to assess root causes for defects in order to optimize and monitor production [6].
One of the most important parameters of Si-solar cells is the short circuit current. It is influenced by the charge carrier diffusion length, metallization shading, reflective properties and light trapping. In order to assign root causes to fluctuations of this parameter, spectral response measurements are used. Spectral response variations show which of the parameters acting on the short circuit current has changed – which in turn can be related to certain process steps in production. Utilizing a large number of LEDs with different wavelengths, LED based flasher systems can directly be used to perform spectral response measurements of every solar cell produced [7]. Figure 6 displays results of an SR-measurement performed using the LED light engine of a cetis-PV Celltest5 system (blue dots).

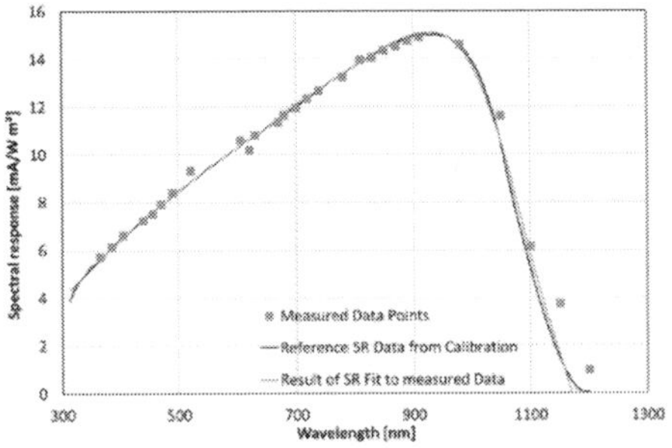

Figure 6: Spectral response data of a Si-solar cell as measured (blue dots) and spectral response curve derived from this data (orange curve) compared to the reference curve measured by an external certification institute (black curve).

The data requires further correction to account for the spectral distribution of each individual LED. The result of this correction is displayed as orange curve. As reference, measurement data from an external certification institute is displayed as black curve. As shown in Figure 1, measurement time available in production is strongly limited and only about 75 ms are available for spectral response measurements. Therefore, not all LED channels can be measured under production conditions. Near neighbours and channels which do not provide additonal information can be omitted to increase the time available per channel for the other channels and still obtain the total SR information of the cell.

Finally, the reverse behaviour of solar cells is important to avoid hot-spots in the field. Reverse *IV* together with thermography measurements are used to cover this topic. As voltages under reverse biasing are much higher then forward operating voltages, power dissipation in local spots can be critical under these conditions while in operating conditions, these spots are completely inconspicious. Therefore, a separate measurement under reverse bias is necessary. Either, a global reverse current criterium is used to sort out critical cells, or, using thermographic imaging, the distribution of reverse currents can be recorded and their impact on module temperature be calculated using a thermal model of the module [8,9]. This characterization technique is required for quality sorting of solar cells, to avoid unwanted hot spots which could cause module degradation and possibly failure under field operating conditions.

All this information on Si-solar cells is gathered and evaluated in about 350 ms time and thus made available in high-throughput manufacturing. It allows effective quality sorting, pricing and process tuning to optimize output and maintain quality of solar cell manufacturing. New solar cell concepts currently being developed add new requirements to characterization.

4 INCORPORATING TANDEMS

With perovskite-silicon tandem solar cells gaining more and more attention and constantly approaching maturity, characterization of such cells is required in laboratory environments as well as in production. However, the additional junction adds additional requirements for the measurements that need to be addressed. Since similar information is generally required for tandem cells as for single junction solar cells, we examine changes in the individual measurements and their impact on required measurement time. Most easily, metallization resistance measurement on two-terminal perovskite-Si tandem cells is not going to experience significant changes.
For the spectral response measurement a larger subsection of the total amount of available wavelengths will be required, as the spectral response curve form for two junctions is much more complex. Moreover, for a spectral response measurement on one subcell, the other subcell must be flooded with charge carriers to keep the cell under test limiting [10]. This means, that several wavelengths in the overlap region will have to be measured for both junctions, further increasing the required measurement time. Assuming a meaningful single junction measurement to be performed in 75 ms, we assume that about 125 ms might be required for a tandem measurement.
A similar consideration holds for reverse *IV* and hot-spot determination. As both junctions are connected in series, hot-spots need to be determined indivdually if spectral non-neutral shadowing is to be taken into consideration for

10.4229/EUPVSEC2025/1CV.2.64

outdoor conditions. This would directly double the required measurement time for reverse characterization from approximately 70 ms to 140 ms. Furthermore, evidence needs to be provided that such quick measurements with the reverse biased junction not being illuminated deliver meaningful results for judging the stability of the perovskite topcell.

For EL imaging, using two differently filtered cameras is a solution to measure the luminescence of both subcells synchronously [11]. Thereby, measurement time is not affected. Figure 7 shows EL images of a perovskite topcell and a silicon bottom cell, recorded with an image integration time of 100 ms each. For further reduction to 30 ms in production, binning of pixels is a commonly utilized technique.

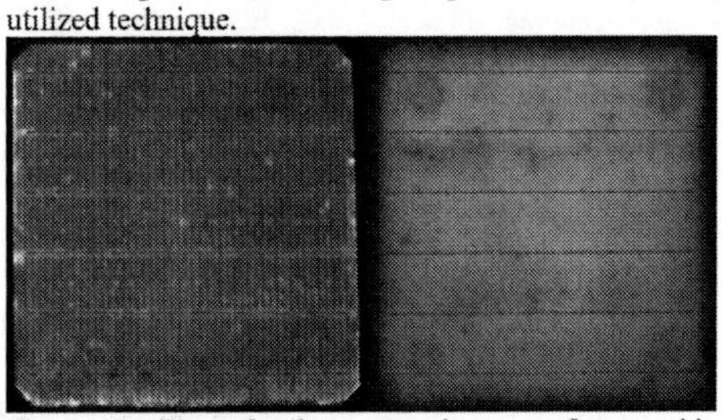

Figure 7: Electroluminescence images of perovskite topcell (left) and silicon bottom cell (right)

Finally, the most basic and relevant characterization technique, measurement of *IV* curve and output power of the solar cells is what is most affected by the evolution from single junction Si solar cells to perovskite-Si tandem cells. Several requirements need to be adressed. First of all, spectral match must be taken into account for both junctions to obtain the correct current generation in both subcells. Even more important, however, are two effects acting on the form of the *IV* curve. The perovskite topcell tends to show metastability and change their recombination behavior depending on the operation condition. This effect may take place on different time scales causing hysteresis in quick *IV* measurements as shown in Figure 8, but as well causing slower effects like wake – up behavior of the cells upon illumination or degradation during the day and recovery over night [12, 13].

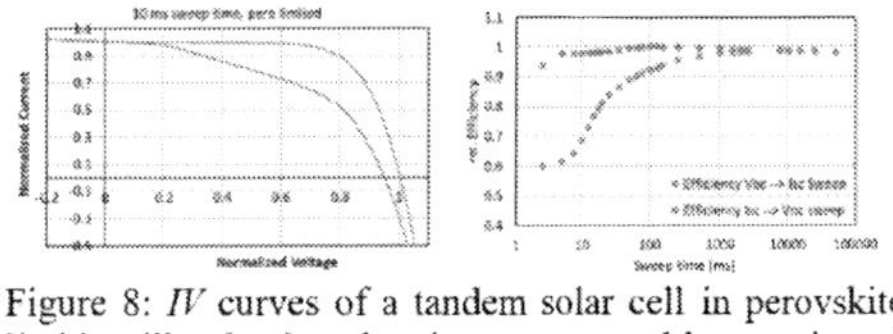

Figure 8: *IV* curves of a tandem solar cell in perovskite limiting illumination showing pronounced hysteresis and hysteresis behavior as a function of sweep time.

Figure 8 displays *IV* curves taken using 10 ms sweep time with a spectrum causing the cell to be limited by the perovskite topcell in current. The hysteresis observed shows a strongly different appearance compared to a standard single junction silicon hysteresis. Observing this behavior as a function of sweep time, pronounced hysteresis is observed even for relatively high sweep times up to about 1 sek in the case displayed in Figure 8.

For measurements with short sweep times, the hysteresis behavior of both subcells interact with each other. As the subcells are connected in series, current flow has to be identical in both cells and hysteresis effects which alter the current flow of one cell shift the voltage of the other cell [14]. This hysteresis interplay complicates evaluation of the curves, which therefore need to be disentangled prior to applying hysteresis compensation methods. Finding suitable procedures for quick and precise *IV* characterization is currently still an active field and standard measurements of tandem cells still employ very slow *IV* sweeps and MPP tracking – often in the range of 5 min [15].

5 COMPARISON OF CONTACTLESS AND CONTACTED IV MEASUREMENTS

Recently, contactless *IV* measurements have been proposed [16, 17] as an alternative for standard *IV* measurements aiming to mitigate the need to develop contacting technologies for solar cell metallizations which are becoming more and more diverse. Such a technique could eventually replace the current *IV* testing systems, potentially reducing costs for production testing. In order to analyze the status of this technology we examine which information of the aforementioned characterization is gained by which measurement in contactless *IV*. Most importantly, the light *IV* parameters need to be measured precisely, i.e. power output, V_{OC}, I_{SC} and FF. V_{OC} can be derived from a calibrated PL measurement. Varying the light intensity, Suns-PL can be used to obtain a Suns-V_{OC} curve of the cell [18]. Parallel and series resistance require contactless EL-measurements effectively realized by two partially shaded PL measurements [19]. From the luminescence spectrum, the external quantum efficiency can be calculated [20] and a measurement of the spectral reflectance is used to complement this in order to determine the I_{SC} value. Aiming at a reduction of these measurements, AI has been proposed to derive *IV* data from Suns-PL and contactless EL alone in [16]. However, this approach requires contacted training data to be used and thus a development of contacting methods for the cell layouts it shall be applied to.

The proposed measurements require many aspects of standard measurement setups (luminescence cameras, sun simulator) and several measurements which might involve more than one light source or very high speed shutters. Moreover, while these approaches should allow to determine the light *IV* parameters no solution was presented for the measurement of reverse characteristics so far. As well, adaptability to new cell concepts and precision of contactless measurements remain to be proven, especially under production conditions. Moreover traceability and measurement uncertainty determination remain unclear especially in the case of the AI based application with reduced measurement effort. Furthermore, the treatment of transient effects that should be present e.g. in Suns-PL measurements as well was not adressed in literature so far. Finally, no operation of the cell at the operating point is possible, as all measurements are performed at open circuit conditions and only the partially shaded measurements allow a lateral current flow on the cell.

5 CONCLUSION

Characterization of single junction Si-solar cells in *IV* testers delivers a wealth of information in a very short period of time out of one single machine. Precise *IV* data, camera based luminescence measurements, reverse-characteristic, spectral response and metallization resistances allow to break-down loss mechanisms, detect and classify defects, sort out cells of minor quality or prone to hot-spots and finally assign a price to the finished device. Work is being done to expand this to tandem cell concepts where similar measurements deliver even more information to be evaluated. Finding solutions to reduce measurement times for methods which need to be applied to both junctions individually and mitigating metastable effects in *IV* measurement still need to be solved. Contactless *IV*, as a newly proposed method for analysis, still falls short in many aspects but provides valuable information and its concepts could be combined with state-of-the-art techniques to deliver even better inside into cell physics for each cell produced in volume manufacturing.

References

[1] IEC 60891:2021, VDE Verlag (2021)

[2] C. Monokroussos, M. Yoshita, K. Yamagoe, H. Müllejans, D. Pavanello, K. Ramspeck, D. Hinken, K. Bothe, Y. Fujita, G. Arnoux, F. Pinto, R. Ambigapathy, Q. Shi, H. Wilterdink, Y. F. Chen and Q. Gao, *Proc. of the 38th EU-PVSEC*, WIP, pp. 594 – 601 (2021)

[3] K. Ramspeck, L. Komp, S. Dauwe, K. Bothe, D. Hinken, M. Wolf and M. Meixner, *AIP Conf. Proc.* 2487, 030008 (2022)

[4] B. Fischer, P. Fath and E. Bucher, *Proc. of the 16th EU-PVSEC*, Glasgow, pp. 1365 – 1368 (2000)

[5] D. Hinken, K. Ramspeck, K. Bothe, B. Fischer and R.Brendel, *Appl. Phys. Lett.* **91**, 182104 (2007)

[6] M. Alt, S. Fischer, S. Schenk, S. Zimmermann, K. Ramspeck and M. Meixner, *Proc. of the IEEE 7th WCPEC*, pp. 3298–3304, (2018)

[7] D. Chojniak, A. Schmid, J. Hohl-Ebinger, S. K. Reichmuth, G. Siefer, D. Kirk, C. Case and S. W. Glunz, *Solar RRL*, **9**, 2400517 (2025)

[8] I. Geisemeyer, F. Fertig, W. Warta, S. Rein and M.C. Schubert, *Sol. En. Mat. & Sol. Cells*, **120**, pp. 259 – 269 (2014)

[9] K. Ramspeck, S. Schenk, D. Duphorn, A. Metz and M. Meixner, *En. Proc.* **55**, pp. 133 – 140 (2014)

[10] Y. Wang, X. Liu, Z. Zhou, P. Ru, H. Chen, X. Yang and L. Han, *Adv. Mater.*, 1803231 (2019)

[11] I. J. Djeukeu, J. Horn, M. Meixner, E. Wagner, S. W. Glunz and K. Ramspeck, *Solar RRL*, **8**, 2400469 (2024)

[12] M. De Bastiani, E. Van Kerschaver, Q. Jeangros, A. U. Rehman, E. Aydin, F. H. Isikgor, A. J. Mirabelli, M. Babics, J. Liu, S. Zhumagali, E. Ugur, G. T. Harrison, T. G. Allen, B. Chen, Y. Hou, S. Shikin, E. H. Sargent, C. Ballif, M. Salvador and S. De Wolf, *ACS En. Lett.*, **6**, pp. 2944 – 2951 (2021)

[13] M. Remec, Š. Tomšič, M. Khenkin, Q. Emery, J. Li, F. Scheler, B. Glažar, M. Jankovec, M. Jošt, E. Unger, S. Albrecht, R. Schlatmann, B. Lipovšek,C. Ulbrich and M. Topič, *Adv. En. Mat.*, **14**, 2304452 (2024)

[14] J. Horn, F. Haas, K. Ramspeck, and M. Meixner, *Tandem PV Workshop*, Amsterdam (2024)

[15] M. Jošt, L. Kegelmann, L. Korte and S. Albrecht, *Adv. En. Mat.* **10**, 1904102 (2020)

[16] J. M. Greulich, W. Wirtz, H. Hoeffler, N. Woehrle, M. K. Juhl, O. Kunz S. Rein and A. W. Bett, *Sol. En. Mat. & Sol. Cells*, **248**, 111931 (2022)

[17] P. Kunze, J. M. Greulich, A. Tummalieh, W. Wirtz, H. Hoeffler, N. Woehrle, S. Glunz, S. Rein and M. Demant, *Solar RRL*, 2200599, 2022

[18] T. Trupke, R. Bardos, M. Abott and J. Cotter, *Appl. Phys. Lett.*, **87**, 093503 (2005)

[19] H. Höffler, W. Wirtz, J.M. Greulich and S. Rein, *Proc. of the 38th EU-PVSEC*, WIP, pp. 233 – 236 (2021)

[20] U. Rau, *Phys. Rev. B*, **76**, 085303 (2007)

Status and prospects of solar cell characterization

halm.

K. Ramspeck, I. Djeukeu, J. Horn and M. Meixner

halm elektronik gmbh, Friesstraße 20, 60388 Frankfurt am Main, Germany,

halm.

Motivation

- Solar cell characterization needs to deliver on three goals – quality control and sorting, value/price assignment, process control and optimization
- In reaching these goals no compromises on throughput are allowed
- We review state of the art characterization for all cell concepts in production and examine new requirement for future cell concepts

End of line characterization methods – state of the art

- cetisPV-IUCT-LF3.1 and cetisPV-IUCT3600-BF: LED and Xenon based sun simulators with add-on options provide complete analysis within 350 ms

Pictures: cetisPV-celltest5 including light source LF3.1

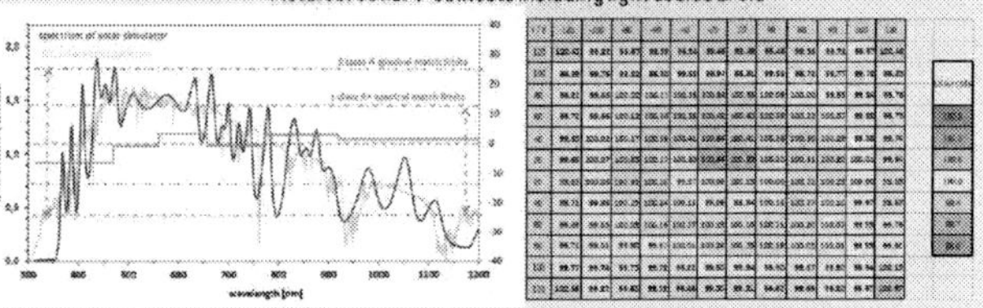

Spectrum and irradiance map of light-source LF3.1

Typical timing of measurements done by the system for inline application – sub selections may alter the time available for individual measurements

Light *IV* 40 ms	Dark *IV* 35 ms	Shadowless Electroluminescence 30 ms	Reverse *IV* and Thermography – 70 ms	Spectral response – 75 ms	Metallization resistance – 50 ms

Data output of measurements and further evaluation

Light and Dark *IV*: Hysteresis evaluation [1] yields Steady-State power output, series resistance, diode-model description, base doping and standard *IV*-parameters

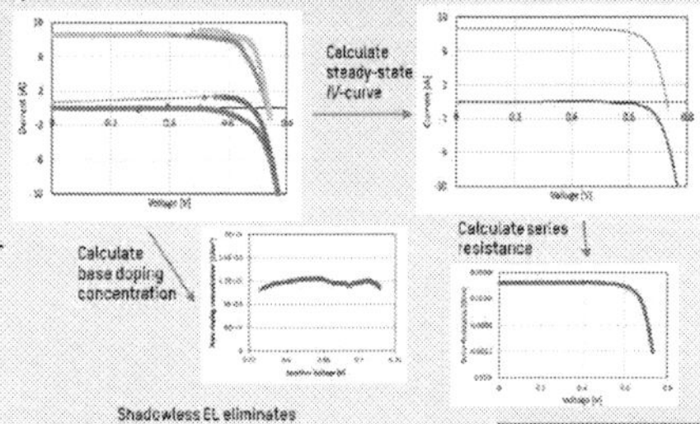

Shadowless EL: Discriminate numerous defects by lateral appearance [2], learn new defect classes, perform cell wide quality decision and process control/optimization

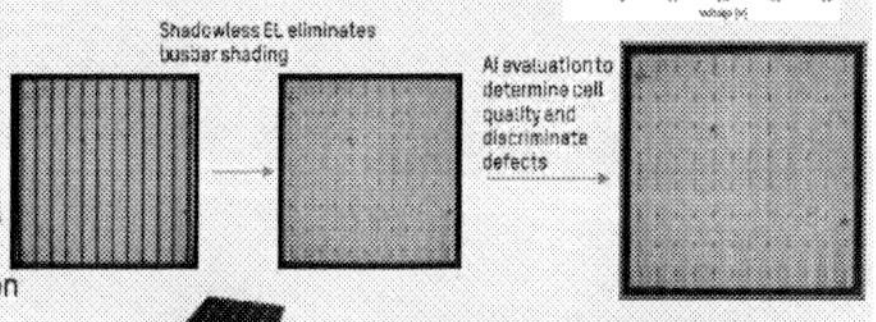

Reverse *IV* and Thermography: Analyze shunt resistance and breakdown behavior [?], sort out cells that pose a security thread in operation – analyze root causes for reverse active defects

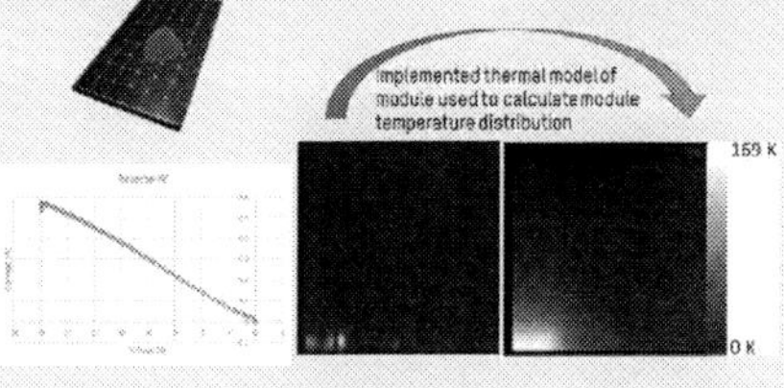

Spectral response: Gain insight into current losses and their origin, correlate with different layers in the cell

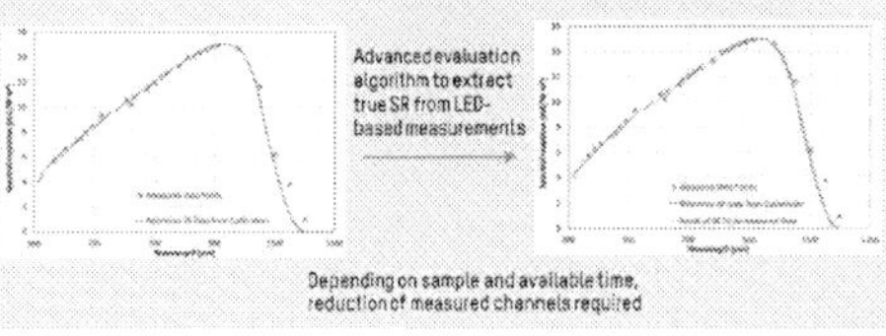

Depending on sample and available time, reduction of measured channels required

Metallization resistance: Examine series resistance contribution of contact grid, calculate minimum silver consumption for resistance

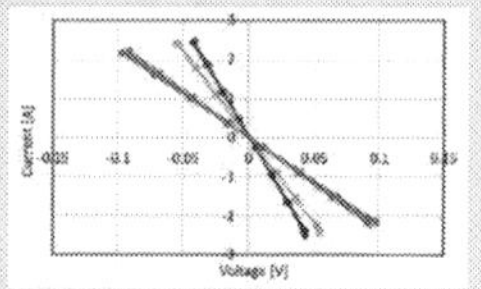

Parameter	Front Grid	Rear Grid
Measured Grid Resistance	41.5 – 45 mOhm	17.25 to 23.1 mOhm
Impact on FF	1.17 % - 1.27 %	0.49 % - 0.85%
Rser contribution	0.82 – 0.89 mOhm	0.34 – 0.46 mOhm
Pmpp loss	96 – 104 mW	40 – 53 mW
Min Silver laydown	17 – 18.4 mg	33 – 44 mg
Min cost contribution	0.019 €/cell	0.042 €/cell

Incorporating Tandems

Another junction adds new requirements - and measurements provide more information

Tandems add requirements for
- Light *IV* evaluation due to metastability [3] and interplay of Si and Pero hysteresis
- EL – due to defect coupling and two wavelength imaging
- Reverse characterization due to series interconnection
- SR – due to requirement to keep one cell limiting [4]
- Metallization resistance and dark *IV* measurement are mainly unchanged
- Pre-Conditioning

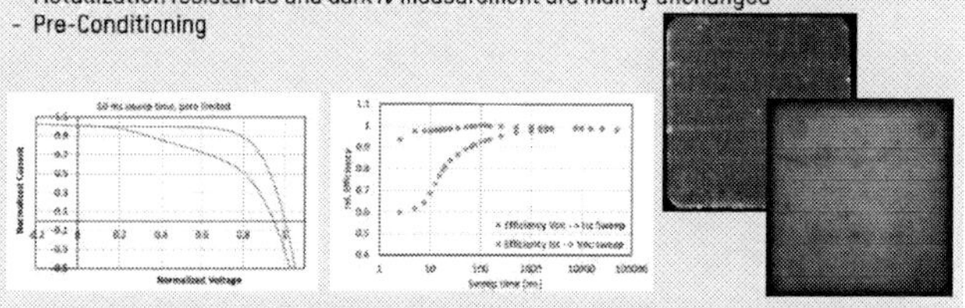

What happens with timing in production?

Light *IV* and Dark *IV* Currently ~ 5min	Shadowless Electroluminescence 30 ms	Reverse *IV* and Thermography - 140 ms	Spectral response – 125 ms	Metallization resistance – 50 ms

Contactless *IV* as a new solution?

Contactless *IV* – recently [5] proposed to mitigate contacting in solar cell characterization

Required measurements:
- Half shaded PL imaging (twice) for series resistance
- Spectral reflection for Shading and front side reflection → models used to get light trapping
- Luminescence Spectrum
- PL for V_{OC}, Suns-PL for Suns-V_{OC} → recombination behavior

I_{SC}:
- Shading by metallization
- Front side reflection
- Light trapping
- IQE
- Parasitic absorption

FF:
- Series Resistance
- SRH recombination
- Higher ideality recombination
- Shunt resistance

Pro Contactless *IV*	Contra Contactless *IV*
Remove contacting	Several PL measurements required
Remove *IV*-measurement and sun simulator	Yet no solution for reverse *IV*
Add-on measurements required anyway	I_{SC} definition from several different measurement methods
	Traceability and measurement uncertainty
	No operation at operating point
	Adaptability for new layouts and cell concepts
	Several additional equipment required
	Transient effects and their mitigation unclear

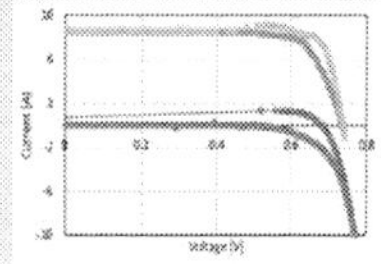

Reverse Characterisitics:
- Required to judge on hot-spot risks

V_{OC}:
- Auger recombination
- SRH Recombination
- Base doping
- Radiative recombination

Conclusion

Characterization of single junction Si-solar cells in *IV*-testers delivers a wealth of information in a very short period of time out of one single machine. Work is being done to expand this to tandem cell concepts where similar measurements deliver even more information to be evaluated. Contactless *IV* as a newly proposed method for analysis still falls short in many aspects but its concepts could be combined with state-of-the art techniques to deliver even better inside into cell physics for each cell produced in volume manufacturing.

References

[1] C. Monokroussos et al., Proc. of the 38th EU-PVSEC, 2021, p. 594 - 601
[2] M. Alt et al., Proc. of the 7th WCPEC, 2018, pp. 3298–330
[3] I. Geisemeyer et al., Sol. En. Mat. & Sol. Cells 120 (2014) 259 - 269
[4] Y. Wang et al., Adv. Mater. 2019, 1803231
[5] T. Song et al., Sol. RRL 2022, 6, 2200800
[6] P. Kunze et al., Sol. RRL 2022, 2200599

Email: k.ramspeck@halm.de

42nd European Photovoltaic Solar Energy Conference and Exhibition

Applicability of Non-Contact Quantum Efficiency Measurements to Various Solar Cell Architectures

Fraunhofer CSP

Fraunhofer Center for SiliconPhotovoltaik CSP

Hedayatullah Karimy, Manuel Meusel, Marko Turek

Motivation and Scope

1. LED sun simulators allow for innovative and fast measurement applications, e.g. rapid-EQE and rapid reflection [1]
2. Non-contact approaches have been developed, e.g. for I-V-measurements [2] and rapid-EQE measurements [3]
3. Industrial implementation of non-contact, non-STC measurements still open

→ Assessment of non-contact EQE (nc-EQE) approach using LED sun simulator

Experimental Approach Contactless rapid-EQE

- **LED sun simulator** SINUS360 with 27 LED-channels
- **Sensor** detecting local electro-luminescence
- **7 cell types** with variations in:
  - **Technology**: HJT vs. PERC / TOPCon
  - **Design**: busbars 9BB…3BB, sizes M6-M2
  - **Material**: mono-Si vs. multi-Si

- **Reference EQE** data:
  LOANA tool → short and long wavelengths with clear variations

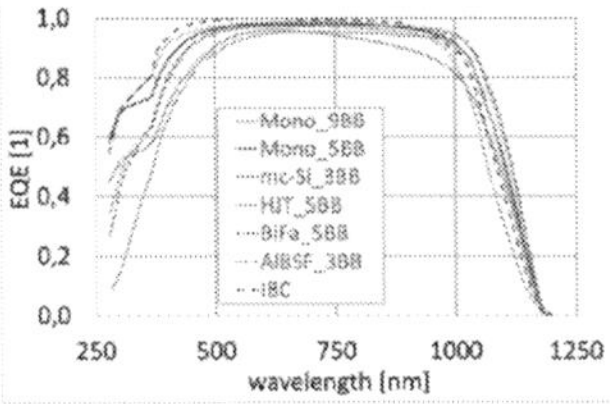

Assessment of measurement setup

- Repeatability for each LED-channel:

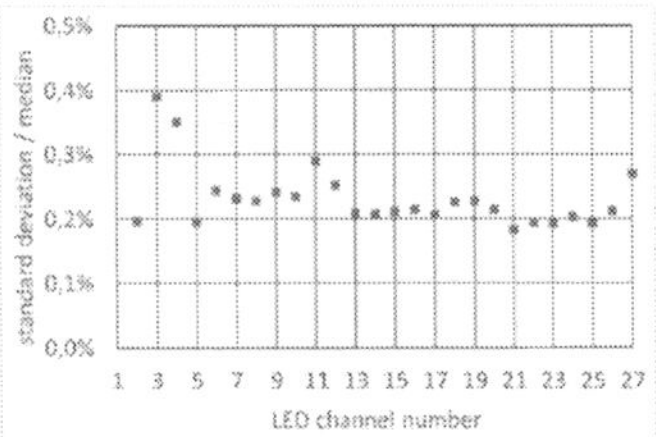

Result:

- LED-channel impacts overall signal → calibration by reference cells
- Low repeatability error of measurement chain »Light-source – EL-sensor«

Result: Example hetero-junction solar cell

- High agreement of nc-EQE with reference data
- Minor deviations at some specific wavelengths observed

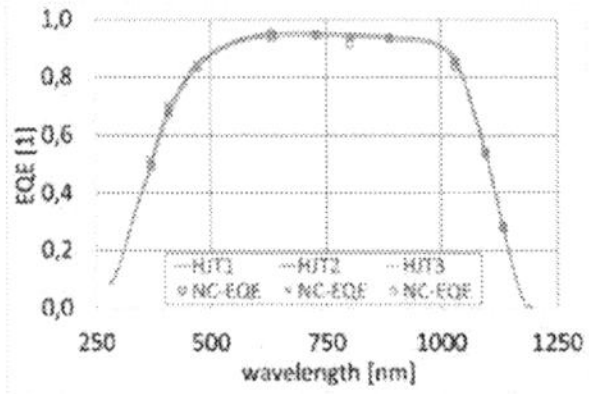

Result: Example mono-crystalline PERC cell

- High agreement of nc-EQE with reference data for some cells
- Few cells show clear deviations at several wavelengths

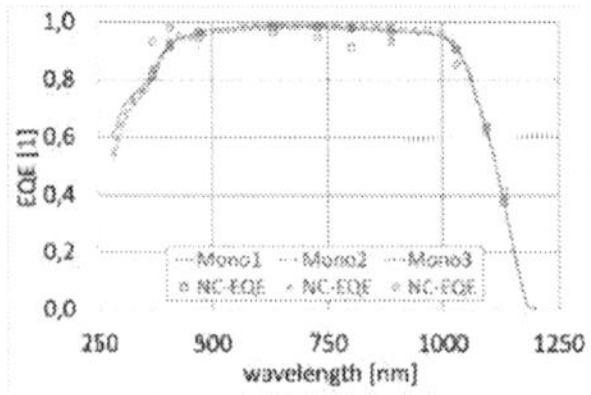

Result: Overview of all investigated cell types

- Overall relative integral errors below 1% can be achieved
- A large spread can be observed for some cells
- Calibration cell of similar technology as test cell required

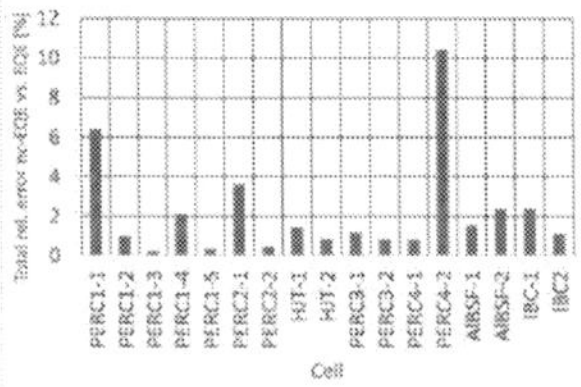

Summary

- Non-contact rapid-EQE using LED sun simulator implemented
- Measurement setup (light-source & sensor cell) with high repeatability
- Selection of suitable reference cell and correction algorithm essential
- Low relative errors <1 % can be achieved
- Large spread in nc-EQE data for individual cells due to local non-uniformities

Supported by the BMWK within the »OptiLearn«- project (FKZ 03EE1108A)

Supported by: Federal Ministry for Economic Affairs and Energy on the basis of a decision by the German Bundestag

Contact

Marko Turek

marko.turek@csp.fraunhofer.de

www.csp.fraunhofer.de

[1] M. Turek, K. Sporlder, T. Luka. Sol. Ener. Mat. & Sol. Cells 194, p 142 (2019).
[2] J. M. Greulich et. al. Sol. Ener. Mat. & Sol. Cells 248, p111931 (2022).
[3] K. S. Chan et al. Solar Energy Vol. 233, p 494 (2022)

STUDY FOR DECAY TREND OF THE SOLAR CELL UNDER VARIED RADIATION DOSE

Yean-San Long[1*], Cheng-Wen Kuo[2], Yung-Tsung Liu[1], Min-An Tsai[1], Ta-Ming Kuan[2], Cheng-Yeh Yu[2]
[1]Center for Measurement Standards, Industrial Technology and Research Institute, Hsinchu 300, Taiwan.
[2]TSEC Corporation, No.85, Gaungfu N. Rd., Hsin-Chu 30351, Taiwan.
Contact information*: mickeylong88@itri.org.tw

ABSTRACT: Any parts and equipment used on satellites, including solar products, need to pass more stringent certification and testing standards than those on the surface. The low temperature and high radiation environment in space are very likely to have an adverse effect on electronic components, so testing the reliability of electronic components under low temperature conditions and their resistance to radiation is an important issue. In addition, the sources of space radiation include cosmic rays, solar flares and radiation belts. These sources contain various high-energy particles such as protons, electrons and heavy ions, which can cause degradation of satellite electronic components and temporary or permanent functional abnormalities. Therefore, before electronic components perform space missions, the impact of radiation needs to be evaluated on the ground. Damage to satellites from space radiation is inevitable, but it can be reduced through mitigation measures. The simplest method is shielding, but this will increase the satellite's payload weight and will not be effective in generating electricity for solar panels. Therefore, in this study, we use different ARC coating materials and consider the design of multi-layer anti-reflection layers to reduce the net charge accumulation at the interface so that it can be used in space environments. In addition, considering the subsequent module packaging method, it is also necessary to design the electrode pattern and the parameters that optimize the resistance to different radiation doses.
Keywords: Space, Solar cell, Dose

1 AIM AND APPROACH

The concept of Passivated Emitter and Rear Cells (PERC) was first proposed by Blakers et al. at the University of New South Wales (UNSW) in Australia in 1989. The main focus is on passivating the back surface of the silicon crystal cell and using local metal electrode contact to reduce the surface carrier recombination rate, increase the reflectivity of light on the back of the cell and the absorption of infrared light. The laboratory prototype cell is a small cell with a size of 2 cm × 2 cm and a P-type FZ silicon wafer. The photoelectric conversion efficiency can reach up to 22.8 %. Its structure is shown in the figure below. A few years later, UNSW developed a high-efficiency cell structure called Passivated Emitter and RearLocally Diffused (PERL) based on the PERC cell concept. Its conversion efficiency can reach 25 %, which remained the world record for quite a long time. The PERC cells in today's solar industry are still based on the PERC and PERL concepts proposed by UNSW. After more than 25 years of technical research and development by international research institutions and cell manufacturers, a low-cost, high-efficiency process has finally been developed, and the PERC prototype concept has been successfully introduced into industrial production. PERC has become the current silicon-based solar cell structure. Any parts and equipment used on satellites, including solar products, need to pass more stringent certification and testing standards than those on the surface. The low temperature and high radiation environment in space are very likely to have an adverse effect on electronic components, so testing the reliability of electronic components under low temperature conditions and their resistance to radiation is an important issue.

In addition, the sources of space radiation include cosmic rays, solar flares and radiation belts. These sources contain various high-energy particles such as protons, electrons and heavy ions, which can cause degradation of satellite electronic components and temporary or permanent functional abnormalities. Therefore, before electronic components perform space missions, the impact of radiation needs to be evaluated on the ground. Damage to satellites from space radiation is inevitable, but it can be reduced through mitigation measures. The simplest method is shielding, but this will increase the satellite's payload weight and will not be effective in generating electricity for solar panels. Therefore, in this study, we use different ARC coating materials and consider the design of multi-layer anti-reflection layers to reduce the net charge accumulation at the interface so that it can be used in space environments. In addition, considering the subsequent module packaging method, it is also necessary to design the electrode pattern and the parameters that optimize the resistance to different radiation doses.

2 SCIENTIFIC INNOVATION AND RELEVANCE

The samples are PERC and TOPCon. All sample size are 1 cm2. In this study, we use different ARC coating materials and consider the design of multi-layer anti-reflection layers to reduce the net charge accumulation at the interface so that it can be used in space environments. In addition, considering the subsequent module packaging method, it is also necessary to design the electrode pattern and the parameters that optimize the resistance to different radiation doses. These I-V curves were carried out by Keithley Source Meter (Model 2651), and 3A solar simulator, meet IEC 60904 requirements. During the I-V measurement under solar simulator, the scan direction was forward and backward, the sample temperature should be stablized at 25 ℃ with a fluctuation of less than 1 ℃ and the irradiance intensity were determined using a reference cell (WPVS), respectively.The bias voltage we applied in the I－V measurement is changed stepwise from Isc to Voc (forward) or in the reverse direction (backward, Voc to Isc). Total Radiation flux： $1x10^{13}$、$2x10^{13}$、$5x10^{13}$、$1x10^{14}$、$2x10^{14}$、$5x10^{14}$、$1x10^{15}$, Testing Process shown in Fig 1

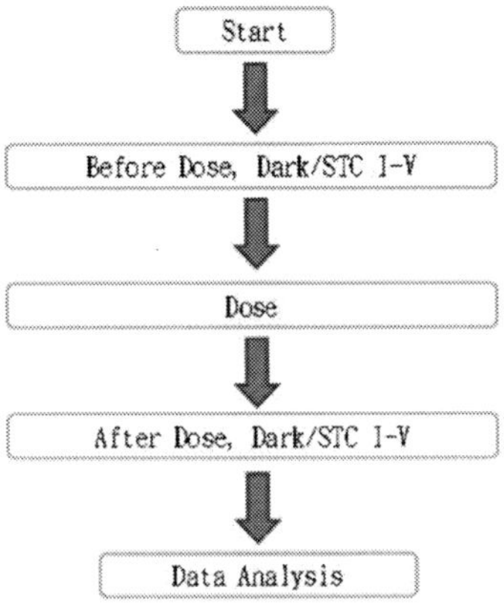

Fig. 1. Test process flow chart

3 RESULTS (OR PRELIMINARY RESULTS) AND CONCLUSIONS

In this work, we use different ARC coating materials and consider the design of multi-layer anti-reflection layers to reduce the net charge accumulation at the interface so that it can be used in space environments. In addition, considering the subsequent module packaging method, it is also necessary to design the electrode pattern and the parameters that optimize the resistance to different radiation doses. there is an irradiated part, and as the amount of irradiation increases, the back glass becomes darker. The Total dose under the irradiation flux is shown Fig. 2

In this work, from the electrical property difference before and after the test, we can get that the Pmax of Ref, S1 and S2 and TOPCon increases with the irradiation dose, ranging from 3 % to 28 % and has a certain balanced radiation resistance level at $1x10^{14}$ to $1x10^{15}$. Therefore, the S2 cell designed this time has certain advantages in 1x1015.

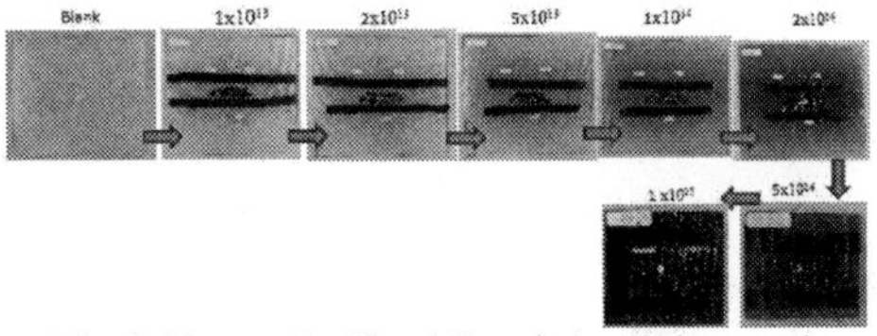

Fig. 2. Pictures for Visual Sample irradiation trend.

4 References

[1] Cory D. Cress et al.,"Radiation Effects in Carbon Nanoelectronics", Electronics, Vol. 1, pp. 23, 2012.
[2] A. W. Blakers, A. Wang, A. M. Milne, J. Zhao and M. A.Green, "22.8% efficient silicon solar cell", Appl. Phys. Lett., vol. 55, pp. 1363-1365, 1989.

42nd European Photovoltaic Solar Energy Conference and Exhibition
42th EU PVSEC
24 Sept. 2025
1CV.2.71

Study for decay trend of the solar cell under varied Radiation dose

Yean-San Long[1*], Cheng-Wen Kuo[2], Yung-Tsung Liu[1], **Min-An Tsai**[1], Ta-Ming Kuan[2], Cheng-Yeh Yu[2]
Industrial Technology Research Institute (ITRI)[1] and TSEC Corporation[2]
*mickeylong88@itri.org.tw

ABSTRACT

Any parts and equipment used on satellites, including solar products, need to pass more stringent certification and testing standards than those on the surface. The low temperature and high radiation environment in space are very likely to have an adverse effect on electronic components, so testing the reliability of electronic components under low temperature conditions and their resistance to radiation is an important issue. In addition, the sources of space radiation include cosmic rays, solar flares and radiation belts. These sources contain various high-energy particles such as protons, electrons and heavy ions, which can cause degradation of satellite electronic components and temporary or permanent functional abnormalities. Therefore, before electronic components perform space missions, the impact of radiation needs to be evaluated on the ground. Damage to satellites from space radiation is inevitable, but it can be reduced through mitigation measures. The simplest method is shielding, but this will increase the satellite's payload weight and will not be effective in generating electricity for solar panels. Therefore, in this study, we use different ARC coating materials and consider the design of multi-layer anti-reflection layers to reduce the net charge accumulation at the interface so that it can be used in space environments. In addition, considering the subsequent module packaging method, it is also necessary to design the electrode pattern and the parameters that optimize the resistance to different radiation doses.

The samples are PERC and TOPCon. All sample size are 1 cm^2. In this study, we use different ARC coating materials and consider the design of multi-layer anti-reflection layers to reduce the net charge accumulation at the interface so that it can be used in space environments. In addition, considering the subsequent module packaging method, it is also necessary to design the electrode pattern and the parameters that optimize the resistance to different radiation doses. These I-V curves were carried out by Keithley Source Meter (Model 2651), and 3A solar simulator, meet IEC 60904 requirements. During the I-V measurement under solar simulator, the scan direction was forward and backward, the sample temperature should be stablized at 25 ℃ with a fluctuation of less than 1 ℃ and the irradiance intensity were determined using a reference cell (WPVS), respectively.The bias voltage we applied in the I–V measurement is changed stepwise from Isc to Voc (forward) or in the reverse direction (backward, Voc to Isc). Total Radiation flux： $1x10^{13}$、$2x10^{13}$、$5x10^{13}$、$1x10^{14}$、$2x10^{14}$、$5x10^{14}$、$1x10^{15}$, Testing Process shown in Fig 1

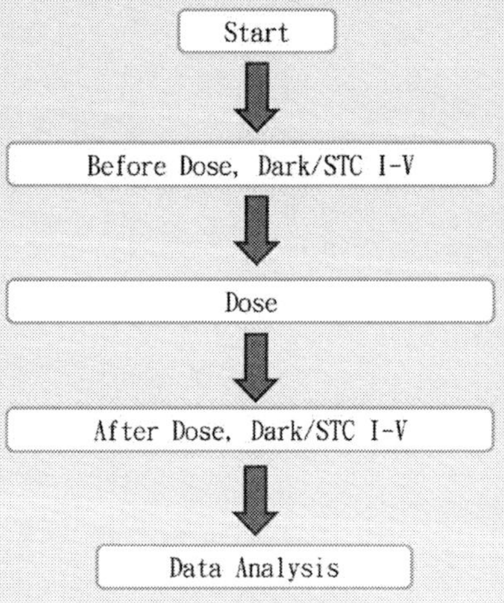

Figure 1: Test process flow chart

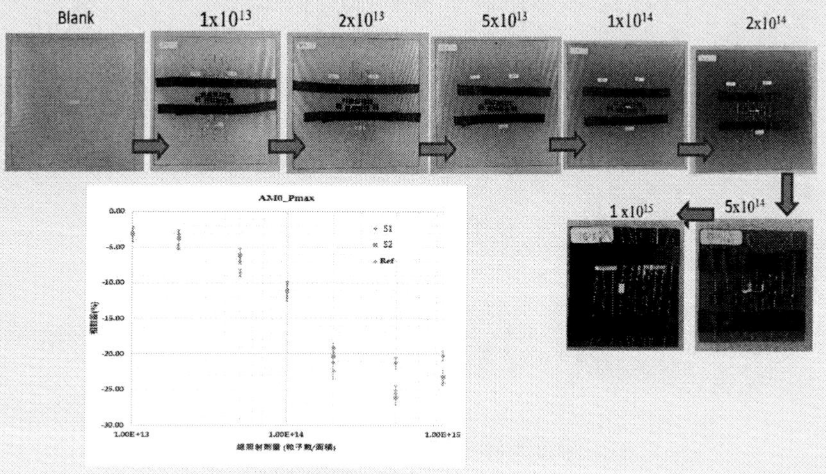

Figure 2: Pictures for Visual Sample irradiation trend

Conclusions

In this work, we use different ARC coating materials and consider the design of multi-layer anti-reflection layers to reduce the net charge accumulation at the interface so that it can be used in space environments. In addition, considering the subsequent module packaging method, it is also necessary to design the electrode pattern and the parameters that optimize the resistance to different radiation doses. there is an irradiated part, and as the amount of irradiation increases, the back glass becomes darker. The Total dose under the irradiation flux is shown Fig. 2

In this work, from the electrical property difference before and after the test, we can get that the Pmax of Ref, S1 and S2 and TOPCon increases with the irradiation dose, ranging from 3 % to 28 % and has a certain balanced radiation resistance level at $1x10^{14}$ to $1x10^{15}$. Therefore, the S2 cell designed this time has certain advantages in $1x10^{15}$.

ANALYSIS OF SERIES RESISTANCE EFFECTS IN CURRENT SOLAR CELL TECHNOLOGIES

Yeray Mateos, Aloña Otaegi, Eneko Cereceda, Vanesa Fano, Nekane Azkona, Eneko Ortega,
José Rubén Gutiérrez and Juan Carlos Jimeno
Institute of Microelectronic Technology, University of the Basque Country, UPV/EHU, Bilbao, Spain
Torres Quevedo ingeniaria plaza 1. 48013, Bilbao, Spain

ABSTRACT: Sunpower's IBC MAXEON III solar cells, composed of three subcells connected in parallel, are studied using a custom-designed PCB prototype adapted for back-contact measurement. The PCB includes metal strips inspired by old 3R12 batteries to ensure solid contact. In addition, the prototype consists of six jumpers, connected just before the cell connection pads allowing selective disconnection to simulate contact faults. EL images are obtained, when injecting 4 A to the cells and two scenarios were tested: in Scenario A, pad 3 (input of subcell) was disconnected, resulting in partially disconnection of subcell; in Scenario B, pads 3 and 4 were disconnected, complete disconnection of one of the subcells leading to minimal leakage current.
Keywords: PCB, IBC, contact-failure

1. INTRODUCTION

The evolution towards back-contact solar cells represents a significant advance in the efficiency of the cell since the incident effective area corresponds to the total geometric area of the front. This happens because, as the name suggests, the front contacts are moved to the back [1-3]. However, characterisation equipments are used to measure Al-BSF or PERC-type solar cells, and if front contacts are moved to the back, basic characterization measurements such as light or dark IV-curves or luminescent measurements become complicated. Furthermore, each manufacturer develops its back contact solar cells based on its own design, and multi-bus or pad-based back contact solar cells can be found in the market [3-4]. Therefore, to summarise this paragraph, it could be said that it is difficult to characterise IBC cells because it is not easy to find equipment adapted to every single design case.

On the other hand, if a prototype for measuring the back contact cells can be manufactured, it is possible to experiment with this prototype and adapt it in turn to characterise certain effects in the cells. If jumpers are added that disconnect certain connections of the solar cell, it would be possible, to go beyond basic characterization and study other effects, i. e. ribbon layer soldering failures, in order to analyse contact failures. Series resistance is the sum of different resistance contributions, including contact resistance. This contact resistance depends on certain factors, one of which is the metal pressure on temporary contacts (in measurements). The effect of a high series resistance is also detected if there is a contact fault or poor soldering, or cracking in the ribbon layer and the effect is a decrease in efficiency [5, 6].

The aim of this work is, on the one hand, to develop a prototype that allows a direct adaptation of characterisation equipment, previously used to measure conventional Al-BSF or PERC cells, in order to be able to measure back contact solar cells such as MAXEON III. On the other hand, it would be interesting to be able to induce contact faults in this prototype in order to detect poor soldering effects and study contact resistance series resistance increase.

2. PROTOTYPE IMPLEMENTATION

Sunpower's IBC MAXEON III are under study. These IBC cells consist of three subcells parallel connected by a thin metallic line in the borders. Fig. 1 shows the rear side of the cell; in this cell the pads have been numbered as if they were pins on an integrated circuit, counterclockwise from the first pad counting from the upper left corner, from 1 to 6. The detail show that pads 1 and 2 are connected by the thin metalic line, as well as pad 5 and 6. The three subcells are then defined by pads 1-6, pads 2-5 and pads 3-4.

Figure 1: Rear side of the cell under study

Our measurement systems must be adapted to measure back contact cells, since until now it measured cells with contacts on both sides. For that, a prototype has been designed and fabricated, based on a printed circuit board (PCB) on which the footprints of the six contact pads of the solar cell have been engraved. A 0,22 ohm resistor has been added to the pad in order to equalize the current and ensure that each cell receives the same amount. The first measurements of IV curves showed high series resistance, indicating that there were contact problems between the pads of the solar cell and the pads of the PCB: our vacuum system caused the cell to bow, lifting it slightly at its perimeter, making poor contact. To ensure good contact, we were inspired by the metal contacting bars in old 3R12 flat 4,5 V batteries, such as shown in Fig. 2 (left). That is why we have soldered metal strips to the engraved pads on the PCB; that will help to make contact when the vacuum in our measuring equipment pulls the solar cell towards the PCB and the pads make contact with the metal strips. This is the detail that is shown in Fig. 2 with the green arrows. In addition, after ensuring good contact, some jumpers have been added to the prototype: by placing jumpers next to each pad we can force one pad to be disconnected from the measurement system by removing the jumper; thereby poor solding contacts, can be induced and the behaviour of the solar cell can be analysed in such condition. Jumpers are also shown in Fig. 2 (right).

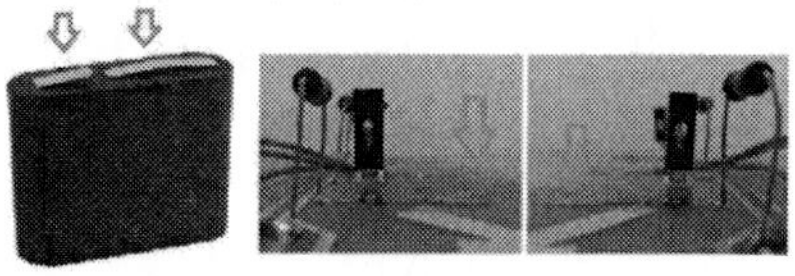

Figure 2: Old flat 4,5-volt battery (left); metal tabs plates to ensure electrical connection (right)

This prototype can be used both in luminescence measurement equipment and in IV curve measurement equipment. Fig. 3 (left) shows a luminescence image in which the brightness is fairly uniform, demonstrating that there are no contact problems. Fig. 3 (right) shows an illuminated IBC cell, ready for measuring its IV curves (which is beyond the scope of this manuscript).

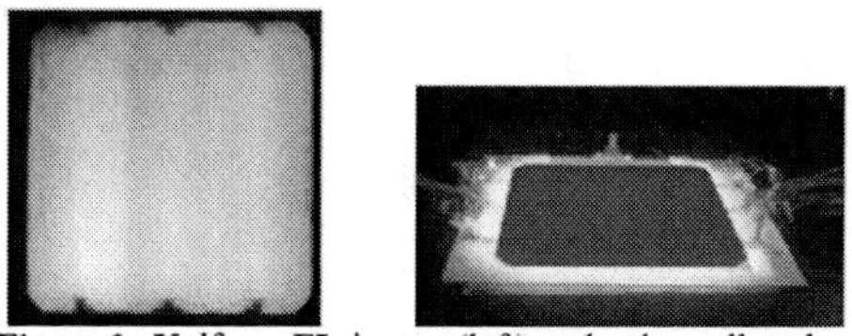

Figure 3: Uniform EL image (left) and solar cell under illumination, ready for IV curves measurement (right)

From here, we would like to see what happens if a cell-contact fails. To do this, the jumpers of the prototype can be disconnected and the cell will react as it is under a bad soldering connection. We can partially disconnect one subcell, or disconnect the subcell completely, depending on which pads are loosened. The cell will behave as if one of its terminals were poorly connected, or as if the contact resistance were very high. According to technical data, the I_{sc} of these cells is around 6 amperes, which means that their operating point (at maximum power) is around 5,8 amperes [7]. Instead, the electroluminescence images to be taken are those corresponding to an injection of 4 amperes. Perhaps the measurements taken were too conservative, and it would be interesting to take measurements closer to 5,8 amperes.

3. PROCEDURE AND MEASUREMENTS

To see what happens if the cell is poorly connected, different disconnections are forced on the measurement platform. This is what the jumpers are for. If one of the current-input jumpers to the circuit is disconnected, the total injected current will enter through the two connected pads, and it will be redistributed throughout the cell and collected at the three output pads. It could also be decided to disconnect an entire subcell by opening the input and output jumpers, all the injected current will also be distributed as much as possible throughout the cell, but it will be collected in the output circuit again through the two output jumpers. In this setup, current will be injected by pads 1, 2 and 3 and the circuit will be closed by recollecting that current through pads 4, 5 and 6 respectively. As said before, in Fig. 1 it was observed that the solar cell consists of three subcells, being pad 1 and 6 the electrical connections for subcell 1, pads 2 and 5 the electrical connections for subcell 2 and pads 3 and 4 for subcell 3.

Again, this study has been quite conservative, as 4 amperes are injected instead of the 5,8 amperes that would replicate the current they would produce on a sunny day under one sun condition and at maximum power point. However, the results obtained are quite representative.

In order to analyse contacting failures, EL-measurements are performed according to two different scenarios, described bellow.

Scenario A: pad 3 is disconnected (corresponding jumper is removed). Subcell 3 is partially disconnected from the circuit by disconnecting its input terminal. However, since pad 4 is connected, the output terminal of the subcell is connected to the rest of the subcells.

Scenario B: pad 3 and pad 4 are disconnected (corresponding jumpers are removed). Subcell 3 is *entirely* disconnected from the circuit by disconnecting its input and output terminals.

In the case of contact failure analysis, the most common scenario would be for one of the soldering pads to fail, in which case simply removing a jumper would suffice, however, the case in which one of the subcells is completely disconnected (i.e. both of its respective solder joints fail) has also been analysed.

Fig. 4 shows the EL-images obtained (left), as well as a 3D representation of the image (right), corresponding to scenario A. If the jumper is not connected to pad 3, the current is injected into the cell only through pads 1 and 2. However, the current reaches the disconnected subcell either through the thin line between pads or through the base. There is a voltage drop in the disconnected area, as can be seen in the 3D representation, but it is not a drastic drop, since the current diverted to the disconnected subcell is collected in the output pad of that subcell. In this scenario, current leakage trough subcell 3 is significant, resulting in a greyish colour.

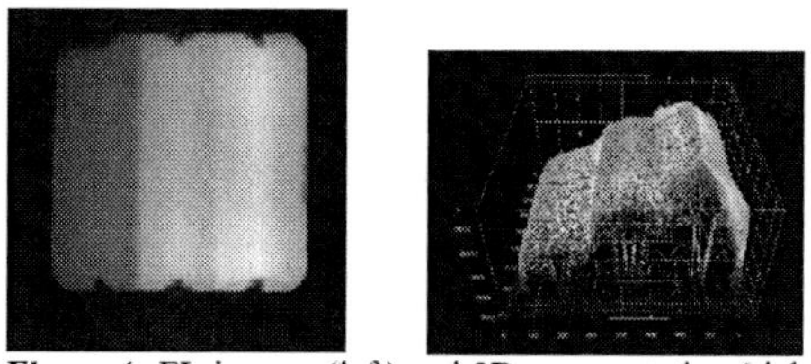

Figure 4: EL images (left) and 3D representation (right) from the solar cell with pad 3 disconneted.

Fig. 5 shows the EL-image obtained (left), as well as a 3D representation of the image (right), corresponding to scenario B. If the jumper is not connected to pad 3, the current is injected into the cell through pads 1 and 2. In this case the current does not reach the disconnected subcell, a little maybe from the thin line between pads or through the base. This is why the voltage drop in the disconnected area, is a drastic drop, which indicates that the subcell is disconnected from the rest. In this scenario, current leakages trough subcell 3 are not significant, resulting in a blackish colour that is considerably darker than in the previous scenario.

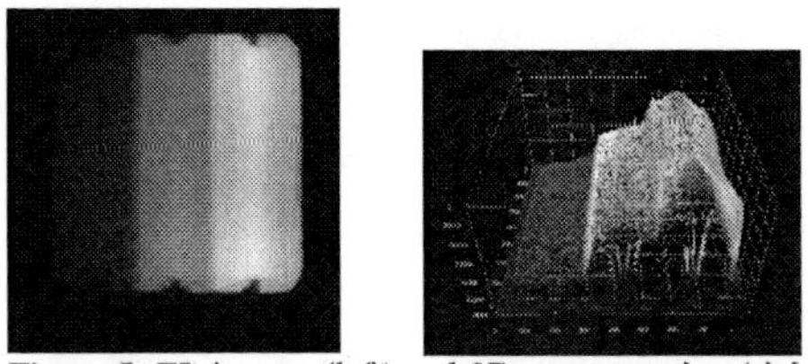

Figure 5: EL images (left) and 3D representation (right) from the solar cell with pads 3 and 4 disconneted.

If the jumper is not connected to pad 3 (Scenario A), the entire 4 A-s are injected into the cell through the two connected pads (1 & 2) and that current is collected up from pads 4, 5 and 6 to close the circuit around the measurement load. However, since there is a thin metal line connecting the three subcells, the current reaches the disconnected subcell either through that thin line between pads or through the base. As a result, the disconnected subcell is partially gray, indicating that photon emission is lower than in the other areas, but not zero, and suggesting that some current is indeed reaching that subcell.

However, it is interesting to observe that in both scenarios, photon emission the three subcells shine differently, indicating that their voltage distribution changes. In both scenarios, the subcell furthest from the failed contacts is the subcell that shines the most, as it is the least affected by current shunting towards the disconnected subcell. The voltage reference has been taken at the central subcell (pads 2 and 5), and the voltage measurements correspond to the values on Table I.

Table I: Voltage measurements in central subcell for the different scenarios

	Current	Voltage
Scenario A	4 A	1003 mV
Scenario B	4 A	1253 mV

The subcells are set to different voltages although the current is injected through two of them in both scenarios. Part of the current injected into the central subcell is diverted to the partially connected subcell in Scenario A. The subcell on the right does not suffer such marked current diversions, i.e., all the injected current is subject to recombination and emits a photon.

In scenario A, the voltage measured in the subcell corresponds to 1003 mV and the voltage map better observed in the 3D distribution, is not so abrupt. In Scenario B, on the one hand, the voltage measurement is higher than that obtained in Scenario A, 1253 mV vs. 1003 mV. It could be said that the effective area of the cell in Scenario B is smaller than in Scenario A, since the subcell 3 is almost disconnected from the rest of the solar cell. This is why the cell is turns to higher voltage, as it is being polarised slightly further away from the conduction knee.

4. CONCLUSIONS

A prototype has been built in which good contact has been achieved thanks to thin metal tabs solded to the pad footprint in the PCB.That prototype allows us to measure Sunpower's back contact cells MAXEON III, both EL-images and IV curves. By means of jumpers strategically placed in the prototype and near the pad connections, failed contacts can be induced and their consequences analysed. Several EL measurements are obtained under two different scenarios by removing jumpers and inducing undesirable situations that could arise if the connection pads are not soldered properly.

A simple PCB made using very basic methods serves as an interface to be added to cell measurement equipments with front and rear contacts, allowing rear contact cells to be measured. We are concerned that each manufacturer has its own IBC design, but the truth is that costs nothing to make a PCB that fits the design in question. However, we believe that to ensure good contact between the cell and the PCB, metal contactin bars such as those we have included are necessary.

2D/3D simulations of the structure to understand current distribution through the base with disconnected pads would be interesting. The metal line connecting the three subcells in parallel should also be characterized to determine the maximum current that can flow through it and to see at what current level it could have conduction problems.

Instead of being conservative, EL tests at around 5,8 A should be performed (better than at 4 A). IV-curves could also be measured at 1 sun condition and forcing contact failures. In that case, temperature measurements could also be taken to detect hotspots in such unexpected situations.

5. ACKNOLEDGEMENTS

This work was funded by the Ministerio de Ciencia, Innovación y Universidades of Spain within the project MCIU-O23/P45 (reference: PID2023-148369OB-C42) under the scheme Proyectos de Generación de Conocimiento 2023.

6. REFERENCES

[1] D.M. DeCeuster et al, Proceedings of 22nd EU PVSEC, 816-819, 2007.

[2] M.A. Green, K. Emery, Y. Hishikawa, W. Warta and E.D. Dunlop, "Solar cell efficiency tables", Prog. Photovolt.: Res. Appl. Vol. 24-1, pp. 3-11, 2016. https://doi.org/10.1002/pip.2728

[3] R. Kopecek et al. "Interdigitated back contact technology as final evolution for industrial crystallinesingle-junction silicon solar cell", Solar, vol. 3, pp. 1-14, 2023. https://doi.org/10.3390/solar3010001

[4] Jonas D et al, "Influence of interconnection concepts for IBC solar cell performance by simulation", AIP Conf. Proc. 1999, 020011. https://doi.org/10.1063/1.5049250 (2018).

[5] J-S. Jeong, N. Park, C. Han, "Field failure mechanism study of solder interconnection for crystalline silicon photovoltaic module", Microelectronics Reliability, vol. 52, pp. 2326-2330, 2012. https://doi.org/10.1016/j.microrel.2012.06.027

[6] S. Kumar, R. Gupta. Thermo-mechanical degradation at finger-solder interface in a crystalline silicon photovoltaic module under thermal fatigue conditions. IEEE 46th PVSC Conf. Proc., pp. 0118–0121, 2019. 10.1109/PVSC40753.2019.8980538
[7] D. D. Smith, P. J. Cousins et al. SunPower's Maxeon Gen III solar cell: High Efficiency and Energy Yield. IEEE 39th PVSC Conf. Proc., pp. 908-913, 2013. 10.1109/PVSC.2013.6744291

42nd European Photovoltaic Solar Energy Conference and Exhibition

This presentation was selected by the Sc. Committee of the EU PVSEC 2025 for submission of a full paper to one of the EU PVSEC's collaborating peer-reviewed journals.

UNDERSTANDING REVERSE I–V CHARACTERISTICS OF SOLAR CELLS USING AN IRRADIANCE-DEPENDENT BISHOP MODEL

Ahmad Hashem[1,2], Hugo Sanchez[1,2], Leila Mortazavifar[1], Bengt Jaeckel [1,2] and Ralph Gottschalg[1,2]
[1]Hochschule Anhalt - Anhalt University of Applied Sciences, Bernburger Str. 55, 06366, Köthen, Germany
[2]Fraunhofer Center for Silicon Photovoltaics CSP, Otto-Eissfeldt-Str. 12, 06120 Halle (Saale), Germany
Email: ahmad.hashem@hs-anhalt.de

ABSTRACT: Mismatch in photovoltaic (PV) modules—arising from shading, soiling, or latent defects—forces individual cells into reverse bias, where their characteristics govern module power loss, hotspot formation, and long-term reliability. Despite substantial changes in cell technology, most system models still adopt Bishop's 1988 reverse-characteristic formulation, originally calibrated for Al-BSF cells. This work reassesses the adequacy of the Bishop model for modern architectures (PERC, TOPCon, HJT) and introduces an adapted formulation that captures the distinct irradiance dependencies observed in modern cells. The model's avalanche and shunt terms are extended with physics-motivated, irradiance-dependent multipliers and provide a stable parameter-extraction framework tailored to reverse-bias data. Model parameters are estimated via particle swarm optimization (PSO). Validation against measured I–V curves under controlled irradiance demonstrates materially improved fits in the reverse quadrant and more accurate prediction of module-level stress indicators, including hotspot onset and severity. The proposed approach supports more reliable system-level simulations under mismatch, enabling better thermal-risk assessment, bypass-diode coordination, and design margins for modern PV modules. Results indicate that updating reverse-bias models is critical to accurately forecasting field performance and mitigating reliability hazards in current and emerging PV technologies.

Keywords: Reverse Bias, Hotspot, Mismatch, Bishop Model, Irradiance Dependency

1 INTRODUCTIION

Reverse bias behavior in crystalline-silicon (c-Si) solar cells governs both reliability and safety at module and array scale. Local reverse conduction can concentrate power dissipation in small regions, triggering hot-spots that degrade encapsulants, activate solder fatigue, and in extreme cases cause thermal runaway. The risk escalates under mismatch—e.g., partial shading or cell defects—where bypass diode turn-on thresholds and the reverse I–V characteristics of shaded cells determine how much heat is localized in a single device versus diverted around it. Accurate reverse-bias models are therefore essential for predicting hot-spot severity and for designing string- and module-level mitigations [1]. Among compact models, the Bishop model [2] has become a practical standard because it augments forward-bias diode physics with an empirical reverse conduction branch that captures avalanche-like breakdown and the characteristic curvature of the reverse I–V. It balances fidelity and parsimony, enabling parameter extraction from laboratory I–V data and integration in circuit-level simulators used for module/array studies. Comparative reviews highlight Bishop's advantages relative to alternatives, while also noting open issues such as parameter identifiability and the sensitivity of hot-spot predictions to the chosen reverse branch [3].

Most prior Bishop-model studies extract the reverse-branch parameters at a single operating condition—typically dark I–V or one sun/STC—and then reuse those parameters across simulations, despite known non-stationarity of the reverse I–V with illumination. Meta-heuristic fits [4-5] likewise target one irradiance snapshot for numerical tractability, reinforcing the "single-G" calibration norm. Yet measurements show that photogeneration and carrier injection under light shift both reverse leakage and breakdown, with a stronger dependence in p-type/PERC than in n-type/TOPCon; using single-irradiance parameters therefore biases hot-spot predictions at real operating conditions [6].

For validation purposes the bishop model was fitted to reverse I–V data from three mainstream c-Si technologies Al-BSF, PERC, and TOPCon measured at 500 W/m²as shown in Figure 1.

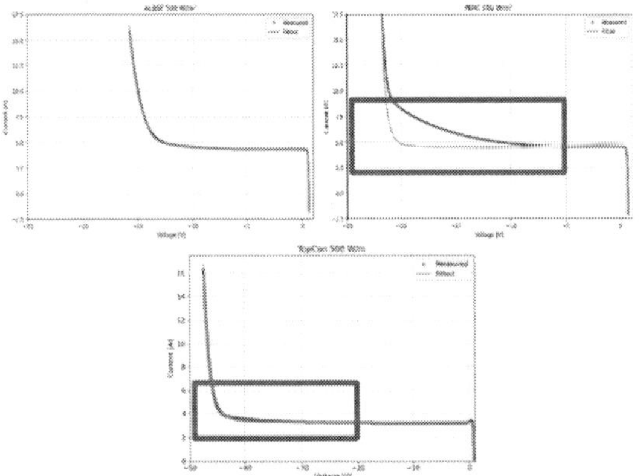

Figure 1: Comparison of Bishop Modelling for Different Cell Technologies

The Bishop model reproduces the Al-BSF reverse I–V very well, capturing both the breakdown knee and the far-tail with low residuals For TOPCon, the fit is serviceable but shows systematic deviations around the knee and in the high-field tail, For PERC, the mismatch is pronounced—the model underestimates leakage at moderate reverse bias and fails to capture the illumination-dependent curvature near breakdown yielding a poor overall fit.

2 METHODOLOGY

The aim of this study is to modify the Bishop reverse branch in equation 1 so it can capture the irradiance-dependent slope observed in modern cells—most notably the stronger light sensitivity of PERC compared with TOPCon and Al-BSF.

An irradiance gain was introduced based on equation 2 that multiplies the Bishop multiplication/curvature term, so the post-knee slope and far-tail increase with G. This form is monotonic, zero-anchored, and saturating: it reverts to the classical Bishop model in the dark ($k(0)=0$), grows approximately as $\propto G^{\gamma}$ at low light (capturing the super-

10.4229/EUPVSEC2025/1CV.2.74
020056-001

linear onset seen in PERC), and remains bounded at high irradiance (k→k0) to avoid non-physical divergence.

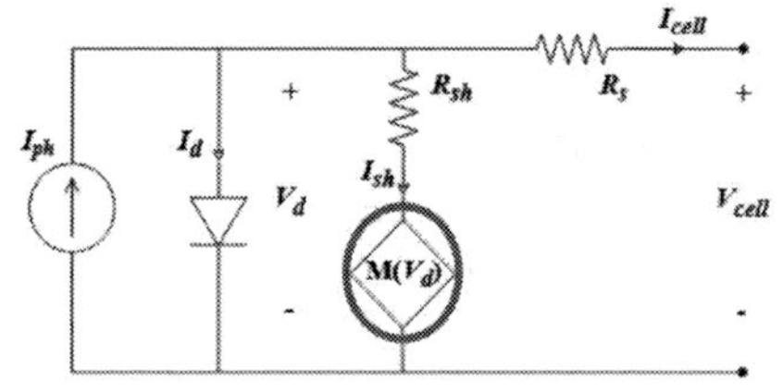

Figure 2 Bishop Model Circuit for PV Cell

$$I_{cell} = I_{ph} - I_o\left(e^{\frac{V_d}{A*Vt}} - 1\right) - \frac{V_d}{R_{sh}}\left(1 + a\left(1 - \frac{V_d}{V_{br}}\right)^{-m}\right) \quad (1)$$

$$K(G) = K_0\left(1 - e^{-K_1\left(\frac{G}{1000}\right)^{\gamma}}\right) \quad (2)$$

PSO is used for the validation of the modified model against PERC & TopCon cells measured at Fraunhofer CSP using Halm A+A+A+ solar simulator with controlled temperature of 25°C and irradiances range between 100 to 1300 W/m2. Here the parameters are extracted with PSO under the hard, physics-based box constraints listed in Table 1.

Table 1: Parameters Boundary Conditions for PSO fitting

Parameter	Lower Bound	Upper Bound
I_{ph}	0	2* Isc
I_o	1e-12	1e-4
R_s	1e-4	0.1
R_s	10	10e6
n	0	3
V_{br}	-60	-5
K_0	1e-3	100
K_1	0	3
m	0	6
γ	0.5	2

3 RESULTS

The modified Bishop model is evaluated by fitting all measured reverse I–V curves across all irradiance range for each technology with a single parameter set per curve representing it. Fits are assessed both by RMSE and by residual maps plotted beneath each I–V curve, which emphasize the knee region and the post-knee tail that dominate hot-spot heating. For clarity, we first discuss PERC and then contrast with TOPCon in the following subsection.

Four irradiance levels are shown in Figure 3 to illustrate the behavior of the modified Bishop model. Relative to the standard Bishop formulation, the new term markedly improves the irradiance-dependent slope in the reverse region: the fits track both the knee and the post-knee tail across G. The residual plots beneath each I–V confirm this—errors are essentially zero in the forward quadrant and along the initial linear segment of reverse bias. At 1300 W m², where the slope enhancement is strongest, residuals remain minimal; at lower irradiance the residuals increase slightly but stay small and largely structure-free, indicating that the model still reproduces the measured curves well with an average root mean square error (RMSE) of 0.26.

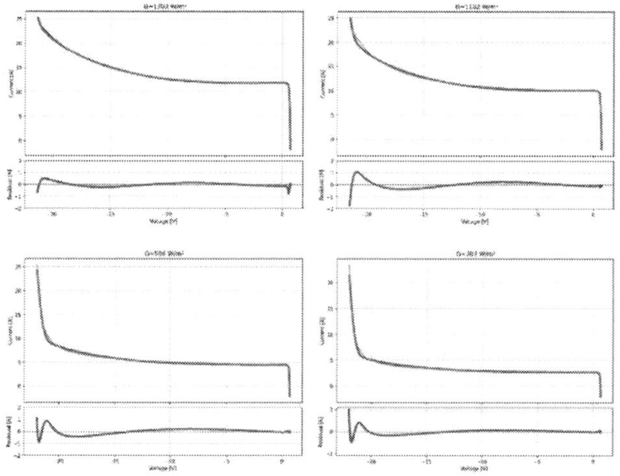

Figure 3: Actual vs Fitted I-V Curves for PERC Cell at varying Irradiances

Unlike PERC, the TOPCon cell exhibits mild hysteresis that appears as a small peak at the onset of reverse bias. To avoid biasing the fit, we used a two-phase procedure: (i) fit the forward quadrant only; (ii) skip a few samples around the peak and fit the reverse branch independently. Figure 4 shows two representative irradiance levels with the two-phase fit, residuals remain close to zero across the long reverse plateau and the knee is reproduced well; only a small, localized error persists near the hysteresis peak we excluded from the fit. Over all TOPCon curves, output an average RMSE of ≈ 0.10

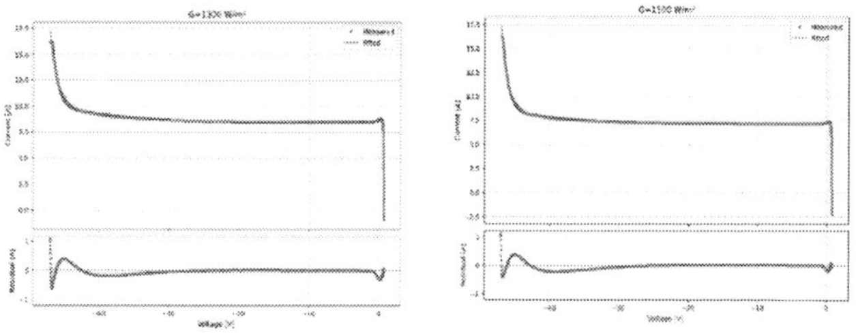

Figure 4: Actual vs Fitted I-V Curves for TopCon Cell at varying Irradiances

The onset of slope change occurs at much higher reverse voltages in TOPCon (≈ –40 V) than in PERC (≈ –10 V), indicating different breakdown initiation mechanisms and field profiles. Moreover, PERC exhibits a markedly steeper irradiance-dependent slope in the reverse region, whereas TOPCon's slope varies only weakly with G; this underscores PERC's higher sensitivity of breakdown behavior to illumination and motivates technology-aware, irradiance-dependent modeling in hot-spot assessments.

4 CONCLUSION

This work is a first-stage formulation. The classical Bishop reverse branch, while convenient, does not capture the illumination-dependent reverse behavior of modern cells. By augmenting Bishop with a bounded, irradiance-dependent multiplier and extracting parameters under physics-based constraints, we achieve stable fits across 100–1300 W m² and materially reduce reverse-quadrant errors (avg. RMSE ≈ 0.26 for PERC and ≈ 0.10 for TOPCon after hysteresis-peak exclusion), while reproducing the technology-specific knee and plateau (onset near −10 V for PERC and ~−40 V for TOPCon).
In the next stage, enhancement to the reverse branch will be done to better capture knee curvature and leakage dispersion, incorporate temperature-coupled breakdown, model minor hysteresis explicitly, and introduce cross-irradiance parameter tying/regularization. These upgrades are aimed at further lowering RMSE and improving prediction fidelity for hot-spot onset and severity in module- and array-level simulations.

5 REFERENCES

[1] Kim, K. A., & Krein, P. T. (2013, June). Photovoltaic hot spot analysis for cells with various reverse-bias characteristics through electrical and thermal simulation. *In 2013 IEEE 14th Workshop on Control and Modeling for Power Electronics (COMPEL)* (pp. 1-8). IEEE.

[2] Bishop, J. W. (1988). Computer simulation of the effects of electrical mismatches in photovoltaic cell interconnection circuits. *Solar cells*, *25*(1), 73-89.

[3] Alonso-García, M. C., & Ruíz, J. M. (2006). Analysis and modelling the characteristic reverse of photovoltaic cells. *Solar Energy Materials and Solar Cells*, *90*(7-8), 1105-1120.

[4] Restrepo-Cuestas, B. J., Montano, J., Ramos-Paja, C. A., Trejos-Grisales, L. A., & Orozco-Gutierrez, M. L. (2022). Parameters estimation of the bishop photovoltaic model using a genetic algorithm. *Applied Sciences*, *12*(6), 2927.

[5] Restrepo-Cuestas, B. J., Durango-Flórez, M., Trejos-Grisales, L. A., & Ramos-Paja, C. A. (2022). Analysis of Electrical Models for Photovoltaic Cells under Uniform and Partial Shading Conditions. *Computation*, *10*(7), 111.

[6] Clement, C. E., Singh, J. P., Birgersson, E., Wang, Y., & Khoo, Y. S. (2021). Illumination dependence of reverse leakage current in silicon solar cells. *IEEE Journal of Photovoltaics*, *11*(5), 1285-1290.

10.4229/EUPVSEC2025/1CV.2.74

A new method for Sb-doped CdSeTe/CdTe devices with superior stability

Elisa Artegiani, Mariyam Mukhtar and Alessandro Romeo

Laboratory for Photovoltaics and Solid State Physics, Department of Computer Science, University of Verona, Ca Vignal 1, Strada le Grazie 15, Verona, Italy.

Abstract - **Currently, one of the primary activities in CdTe solar cell research is to identify an alternative to copper doping. Copper has limited solubility in the CdTe matrix, which restricts the achievement of higher open circuit voltages (Voc). It is also a fast diffuser, making it a major contributor to device degradation. Finding a suitable alternative doping element could enhance Voc, improve cell efficiency, and increase stability. This study introduces a new approach for inserting Sb in CdSeTe/CdTe matrix as a dopant, which will be explained in detail during the conference. This simple and easy method proves to be effective, as Sb-doped cells achieve efficiencies comparable to those of Cu-doped cells. Furthermore, in accelerated stress tests without encapsulation, Sb-doped samples demonstrate much greater stability than Cu-doped cells, comparable to undoped devices.**

I. INTRODUCTION

While research into thin-film technologies continues to expand across various materials, cadmium telluride (CdTe) photovoltaic (PV) modules remain the dominant thin-film product in the global market. The efficiency of CdTe devices has consistently improved over time; in the last two decades, the record efficiency for research-scale cells has increased from 16.5 % to 23.1 %, as recently reported by the U.S. company First Solar. Additionally, module efficiencies have surpassed 19 %, and growing production volumes have enabled CdTe technology to go well below the 1 $/Wp barrier [1].

To further advance the commercial viability of CdTe, it is essential to continue enhancing its efficiency while maintaining low production costs. To date, the primary driver of efficiency improvements has been the introduction of selenium (Se) into the absorber layer, forming a CdSeTe compound near the junction [2], [3]. Current efforts should focus on increasing the open-circuit voltage and improving device stability. Both objectives could potentially be achieved by replacing copper doping with group V elements. Achieving higher voltage requires higher doping levels, which Cu struggles to deliver. Moreover, Cu's high diffusivity in CdTe is widely regarded as the primary contributor to device degradation [4].

Group V elements (N, P, As, Sb, and Bi) present a promising alternative, as they can form acceptor states by substituting tellurium (Te) sites [1].

Although Sb forms deeper acceptor levels than As, it can achieve substantial hole density due to the lower formation energy of Sb_{Te}, attributed to the small atomic radius difference between Te and Sb [5].

We have developed a new approach to dope CdTe with antimony, which will be presented in detail at the conference. This method also reduces the Schottky barrier at the back contact without needing additional etching processes or the introduction of hole transport layers.

II. DEVICES FABRICATION AND ANALYSIS

Our laboratory produces CdSeTe/CdTe devices in a superstrate configuration using a low-temperature substrate deposition process based on thermal evaporation (TE). The substrate and front contact comprise a commercial glass/SnO_2:F (FTO)/SnO_2 (TO) stack, referred to as TEC 12D, provided by NSG Pilkington. A 300 nm-thick CdSe layer is then deposited on TEC 12D, followed by a 300 nm-thick CdTe layer, both at a substrate temperature of 340 °C. This initial stack undergoes vacuum annealing at 450 °C for 30 minutes. Subsequently, an additional 1.4 μm-thick CdTe layer is deposited to complete the absorber, achieving a total thickness of 2 μm. The optimisation of the absorber's growth has been detailed in prior work [6].

Following this, the stack is subjected to a $CdCl_2$ activation treatment using a wet deposition method, followed by air annealing at 400 °C. Afterwards, the stack is immersed in boiling water to remove any $CdCl_2$ residues and to clean the surface.

For copper doping, a 1 nm-thick Cu layer is deposited on the sample by TE. Before this deposition, the sample undergoes a Br-MeOH etching process, which cleans the surface and enriches the absorber surface with Te. This promotes the formation of Cu_xTe compounds at the back contact, enhancing its ohmic properties and long-term stability [7], [8]. The back contact consists of a 30 nm-thick gold layer. Finally, the sample is annealed in air at 200 °C to enable Cu diffusion into the absorber.

For Sb doping, a novel approach is used without the application of the Br-MeOH etching step, the details of which we prefer to disclose directly at the conference.

The current density-voltage (JV) characteristics were recorded using a Keithley Source Meter 2420 under an AM 1.5 spectrum at 100 mW/cm², with a LOT Quantum Design Europe solar simulator (model LS0306). Drive Level Capacitance Profiling (DLCP) and Capacitance-Voltage (CV) measurements were performed using an HP4284A LCR meter.

III. RESULTS

CV-DLCP profiles have been collected for our Cu and Sb-doped samples and our undoped samples (as reference) to prove Sb doping.

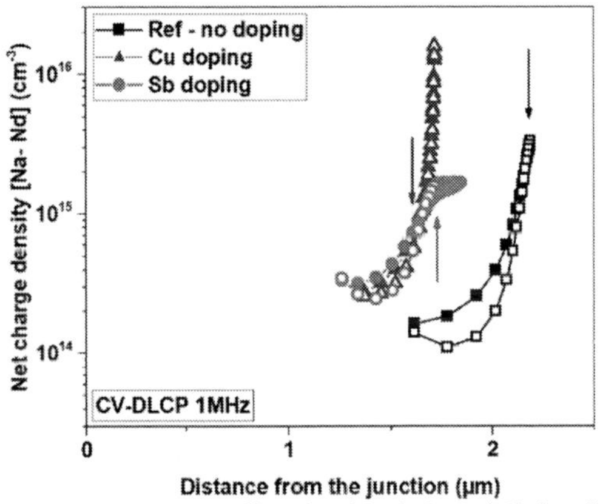

Fig. 1. CV-DLCP profiles of undoped, Cu and Sb-doped cells.

CV profiles reveal contributions from deep and shallow defects, with the deeper states having minimal impact on the DLCP curves [9]. Consequently, the net charge density of the samples is typically derived from the lowest segment of the DLCP curve. The arrows in the graphs indicate measurements at 0 V, which estimate the depletion region width. Fig. 1 shows that Cu and Sb doped cells have similar net charge density, higher than the undoped samples, as expected, demonstrating the successful doping of the devices with antimony.

Table I: efficiency parameters of Cu and Sb-doped cells.

Devices	Voc (mV)	Jsc (mA/cm²)	FF (%)	η (%)
Cu-doped	790	28.7	69	15.7
Sb-doped	797	28.4	68	15.4

Table I compares the Cu- and Sb-doped record devices, which exhibit nearly identical peak efficiencies, with values of 15.7% and 15.4%, respectively. Their efficiency parameters are also comparable, highlighting the potential of our method for doping CdTe.

Figure 2 shows the current-voltage characteristics of these record devices. As indicated by their efficiency parameters, the curves are almost identical. The main difference appears in the first quadrant of the graph: the Cu-doped device exhibits a slight rollover effect, whereas the Sb-doped device shows a more ohmic back contact. This is unexpected, as the Cu-doping process involves a Br-MeOH etching step that enriches the CdTe surface with Te, facilitating the formation of Cu_xTe compounds [7]. These compounds are intentionally formed to enhance the back contact's ohmic behaviour and improve the cells' stability [8], [10].

In contrast, the Sb-doping process does not include any etching process. Further analysis will be presented during the conference to clarify how this can happen.

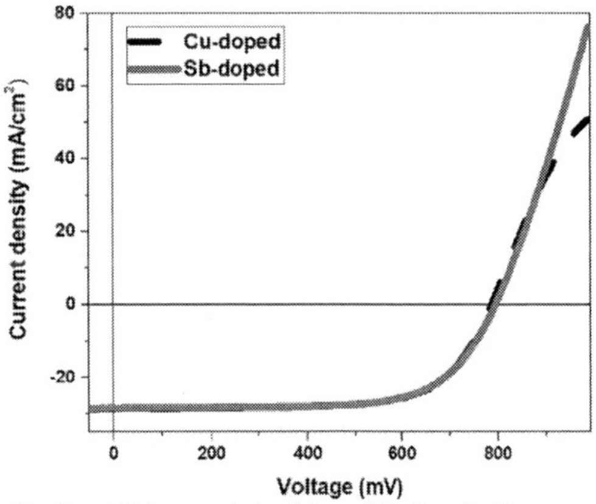

Fig. 2. JV characteristic of Cu and Sb-doped cells.

As previously highlighted, another key objective in exploring alternative doping methods for CdTe devices is to enhance their stability. To evaluate the long-term degradation of the samples, accelerated stress tests (AST) were conducted on both Cu- and Sb-doped devices. For comparison, undoped samples were also included in the tests. Precisely, the cells were placed inside a metal chamber, which provided exposure to 1 sun illumination at a constant temperature of 80 °C. Figure 3 presents the normalized efficiency of the devices relative to their initial values over the course of the AST.

The results of the copper-doped devices align with previous observations of our Cu-doped CdS/CdTe devices [4], [7]. Specifically, their stability is suboptimal, with average efficiency dropping to approximately 80 % of the initial value after about 75 hours and continuing to decline to below 65 % within 250 hours. This degradation is attributed to the diffusion of Cu from the back contact towards the junction and the instability of CuCd acceptor defects [4]. This explanation is supported by the significantly higher stability observed in the undoped samples, which retained about 90 % of their initial efficiency after 250 hours of aging. In these undoped devices, degradation is primarily due to the absence of encapsulation, leaving them vulnerable to moisture and oxygen exposure.

Remarkably, the Sb-doped devices demonstrate exceptional stability. After over 250 hours, they retain, on average, 90 % of their initial efficiency, comparable to the performance of the undoped samples. This indicates no evidence of degradation beyond what is expected from exposure to moisture and oxygen. The results suggest that the acceptor defects introduced [7] by Sb are stable, unlike those associated with Cu, further supporting Sb as a viable alternative dopant for improving device reliability and that our innovative Sb doping method is successful.

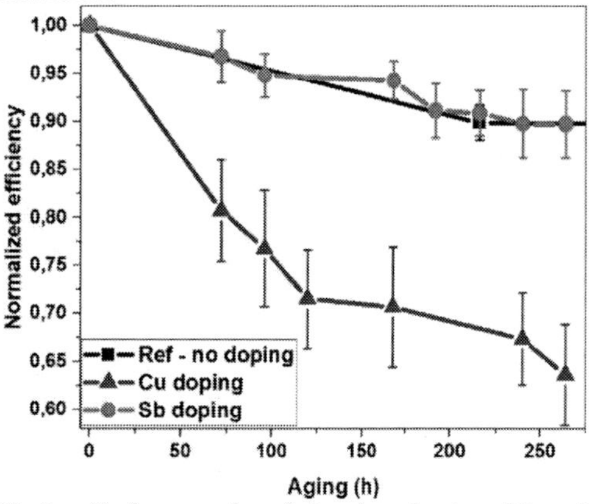

Fig. 3. Performance degradation along the time of Cu and Sb-doped samples and the undoped cells, at different time steps of AST.

IV. CONCLUSIONS

A new method to dope CdSeTe/CdTe devices with Sb has been developed and will be presented in all detail during the conference. This approach effectively dopes CdTe with Sb, as evidenced by CV DLCP measurements, achieving peak efficiencies nearly matching those of Cu doping through the same low-temperature deposition method (15.4 % vs. 15.7 %).

In addition, Sb-doped cells exhibit improved back-contact ohmicity compared to Cu-doped cells, even without the use of etching or a hole transport layer. Accelerated stability tests highlight the superior stability of Sb-doped cells compared to their Cu-doped counterparts. The Sb-doped devices are so stable that their performance matches that of undoped cells, indicating that any observed degradation results solely from the absence of encapsulation in the experiment.

This novel doping technique has demonstrated its effectiveness in producing Sb-doped CdTe devices with efficiencies comparable to Cu-doped cells while offering remarkable stability. However, as this doping method is still in its early stages compared to the well-established Cu doping processes, there remains significant potential for enhancing cell efficiency.

REFERENCES

[1] M. A. Scarpulla *et al.*, "CdTe-based thin film photovoltaics: Recent advances, current challenges and future prospects," 2023. doi: 10.1016/j.solmat.2023.112289.

[2] N. R. Paudel and Y. Yan, "Enhancing the photo-currents of CdTe thin-film solar cells in both short and long wavelength regions," *Appl Phys Lett*, vol. 105, no. 18, pp. 1–6, 2014, doi: 10.1063/1.4901532.

[3] J. Guo *et al.*, "Effect of selenium and chlorine co-passivation in polycrystalline CdSeTe devices," *Appl Phys Lett*, vol. 115, no. 15, 2019, doi: 10.1063/1.5123169.

[4] E. Artegiani, J. D. Major, H. Shiel, V. Dhanak, C. Ferrari, and A. Romeo, "How the amount of copper influences the formation and stability of defects in CdTe solar cells," *Solar Energy Materials and Solar Cells*, vol. 204, p. 110228, Jan. 2020, doi: 10.1016/j.solmat.2019.110228.

[5] B. Dou, Q. Sun, and S. H. Wei, "Optimization of Doping CdTe with Group-V Elements: A First-Principles Study," *Phys Rev Appl*, vol. 15, no. 5, 2021, doi: 10.1103/PhysRevApplied.15.054045.

[6] E. Artegiani, A. Gasparotto, M. Meneghini, G. Meneghesso, and A. Romeo, "How the selenium distribution in CdTe affects the carrier properties of CdSeTe/CdTe solar cells," *Solar Energy*, vol. 260, 2023, doi: 10.1016/j.solener.2023.05.058.

[7] E. Artegiani *et al.*, "Analysis of a novel CuCl2 back contact process for improved stability in CdTe solar cells," *Progress in Photovoltaics: Research and Applications*, vol. 27, no. 8, pp. 706–715, 2019, doi: 10.1002/pip.3148.

[8] X. Wu *et al.*, "Phase control of CuxTe film and its effects on CdS/CdTe solar cell," *Thin Solid Films*, vol. 515, no. 15 SPEC. ISS., pp. 5798–5803, 2007, doi: 10.1016/j.tsf.2006.12.151.

[9] J. T. Heath, J. D. Cohen, and W. N. Shafarman, "Bulk and metastable defects in CuIn1-xGaxSe2 thin films using drive-level capacitance profiling," *J Appl Phys*, vol. 95, no. 3, pp. 1000–1010, 2004, doi: 10.1063/1.1633982.

[10] I. Rimmaudo *et al.*, "Improved stability of CdTe solar cells by absorber surface etching," *Solar Energy Materials and Solar Cells*, vol. 162, 2017, doi: 10.1016/j.solmat.2016.12.044.

42nd European Photovoltaic Solar Energy Conference and Exhibition

This presentation was selected by the Sc. Committee of the EU PVSEC 2025 for submission of a full paper to one of the EU PVSEC's collaborating peer-reviewed journals.

MICRO-CRYSTAL GAAS ARRAY SUB-CELLS FOR SI TANDEM SOLAR CELLS

J.P. Connolly[1*], A. Nejim[3], A. Jaffré[1], J. Alvarez[1], J P. Kleider[1], D. Mencaraglia[1], Laurie Dentz[2], G. Hallais[2], F. Hamouda[2], L. Vincent[2], D. Bouchier[2], C. Renard[2]

[1]GeePs, Group of Electrical Engineering Paris, CNRS, CentraleSupelec, Université Paris-Saclay, Sorbonne Université, 3&11 rue Joliot-Curie, Plateau de Moulon, 91192 Gif-sur-Yvette CEDEX, France

[2]C2N, Centre de Nanosciences et de Nanotechnologies, CNRS, Université Paris-Saclay, 10 Bd Thomas Gobert, 91120, Palaiseau, France

[3]SILVACO Technology Centre, Compass Point, St. Ives, Cambridgeshire PE27 5JL, UK

ABSTRACT: This work reports optical and electronic numerical modelling of a novel emerging structure which is the GaAs nanocrystal on Si tandem solar cell by epitaxial lateral overgrowth, a technique which allows defect free material growth. The techniqueconsists of creating nucleation sites in a silicon surface SiO_2 layer and initiating growth of nanoscalescale seeds, whereby strain energy remains below the Matthews-Blakeslee strain relaxation limit. This leads to Al_xGaAs growth in micro-crystals without generation of material defects. The focus of this presentation is optical and electrical modelling of nanocrystals for applications in the very active field of silicon based multijunction solar cells, and design of a Al_xGaAs/Si two terminal tandem, for compositions ranging from x=0 to x=30% in absorber layers. We present a model of the complete structure in two dimensions, consisting of a Al_xGaAs high bandgap subcell connected with a tunnel junction to the low bandgap Si junction. The elaboration of models is described, with an emphasis on the Al_xGaAs crystal featuring a non-planar pn-junction, and a focus on the optical properties of this lattice of micrometric AlGaAs crystals and in particular their light trapping properties from the resulting surface texture. The question of Al_xGaAs surface coverage is addressed, given that neighbouring Al_xGaAs crystals have different crystal orientations on a (111) Si surface, such that any coalescence of neighbour Al_xGaAs crystals leads to crippling defects at their interface. The result is that some high energy incident light above the Al_xGaAs bandgap is nevertheless transmitted directly to the Si cell, such that the resulting photogenerated carriers thermalise to the Silicon bandgap, and result in a loss of efficiency. The interface between Al_xGaAs and Si subcells is addressed, with an emphasis on current transport efficiency through the nanoseeds and tunnelling currents through appropriately designed SiO_2 buffer layers. This work therefore presents a theoretical framework for evaluating the potential of Al_xGaAs nanocrystal growth on Si for light trapping, for GaAs silicon two terminal tandem cell performance including tunnel junctions, and provides models and design rules for efficient Al_xGaAs microcrystal arrays as high bandgap subcells for tandem solar cells on silicon.

Keywords: III-V, silicon, texturing, epitaxial lateral overgrowth.
Corresponding author : james.connolly@centralesupelec.fr

1 Introduction

The multijunction solar cell is the most successful high efficiency concept. This has led to much work on on this topic based around silicon, for economic and industrial reasons [1].

As part of these efforts, there has been significant effort in integration of III-V semiconductors on Si substrates for photovoltaics and more broadly in opto-electronics. Avenues followed involve a range of techniques [2] which generally need to manage defect densities to lead to usable devices. One technique suggested some decades ago [3] which avoids these issues is the epitaxial lateral overgrowth (ELO) method which presents significant practical growth and fabrication challenges in obtaining high quality III-V films.

We explore the application of these micro-crystal arrays as the high band-gap subcell of III-V / Si two terminal series connected tandem solar cells. We evaluate strategies for optimum tandem designs in light of limiting efficiencies.

We focus on two topics of interest, which are the increased light-matter interaction resulting from light scattering by the micro-crystal array, and the monolithic integration and efficient current transport in the resulting III-V / Si multilayer photovoltaic device. The result is an innovative design which benefits from built-in texturing and light trapping, while developing a promising technological route for III-V integration on Si for wider applications.

2 Experimental context

This paper builds on the recent work [3] which has demonstrated technologically attractive and high quality arrays of single crystal GaAs micro-crystal arrays on Si by epitaxial lateral overgrowth (ELO). As illustrated in figure 1, ELO growth starts with a Si surface on which a 2nm surface SiO_2 layer is fabricated. Nucleation sites of diameter ≈50nm are etched in this oxide. Growth is initiated by epitaxial methods in these nucleation sites.

This technique has allowed the growth of defect free Al_xGaAs crystals on Si despite the mismatched Al_xGaAs/Si atomic lattices because the small contact area and 3D growth mode ensures strain energy never exceeds the Matthews-Blakeslee limit [4], and that no strain relaxation and formation of lattice defects occurs. Current growth methods yield two crystal types. The first is flat rectangular crystals with height to width ratios of 1/4, and of dimensions from 1μm to 2μm wide shown in figure 2(a). The second consists of the same rectangular base with a hexagonal "cap" with facets fixed at 30° from the horizontal, as shown in figure 2(b), which we call "textured".

The materials available are Al_xGaAs with x=0-40% for absorbers and higher x=75 for thin layers including windows or the front emitter.

We note that Al_xGaAs is a complex material. The Al content leads to instabilities in particular with respect to

reaction with oxygen such that Al_xGaAs layers need to be isolated from the atmosphere. This isolation is provided here by contact transparent conducting oxide layers, and anti-reflection coatings.
We note also intrinsic materials problems, in particular the well known DX centre [5] which is associated with Al compositions greater than ≈22% and high doping, which is nevertheless not a critical issue in the Al fractions available, and given the low doping we use in the absorber layer as detailed below.
Finally, GaAs at the lower x=0 composition has long been a nearly ideal solar cell material achieving to date AM1.5G efficiencies of 29% [6], close to the radiative limit of 31% [7].
This concludes the definition of available materials, for which we next present simulations evaluating potential device performance.

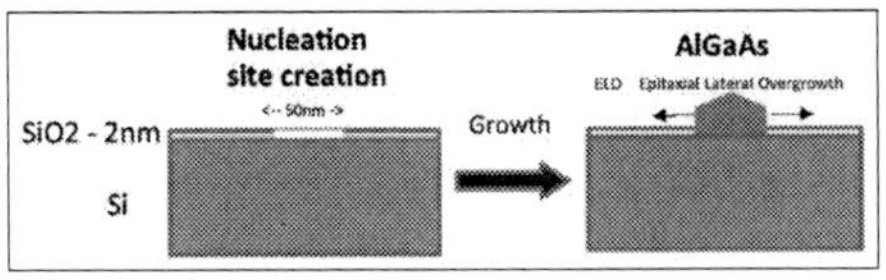

Figure 1 : the epitaxial lateral overgrowth technique, whereby AlGaAs nucleations sites are created by opening holes of some tens of nanometres in a two nanometre thick surface oxide.

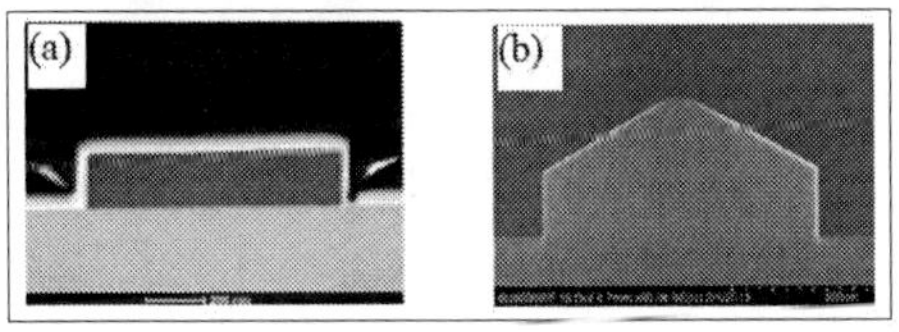

Figure 2 examples of 1μm wide (a) flat and (b) faceted ELO crystals

3 Theoretical limits and device design

It is worth reminding the well-known radiative efficiency limits with familiar efficiency – bandgap contour plots [1] which give an appreciation of potential efficiencies of proposed designs. The fundamental efficiency limit for a silicon based tandem is 41.9% under standard test conditions (STC), for of 1.74eV (top) and and 1.12 (bottom Si).

3.1 Optimum efficiency higher gap top cell

The optimum Si-based tandem upper gap of 1.74eVcorresponds to $Al_{25}Ga_{75}As$. This is a material with sufficienty materials properties for solar cells, as we have seen just above. The material is just above the range where materials issues start to become significant at x≈22% but for highly doped materials. Since we are considering low-doped materials for the absorber region with a large depletion region with field driven transport, this composition is well within the tolerances for efficient photogenerated carrier diffusion and collection.
We can in addition retain higher composition Al_xGaAs for the frontmost emitter layer. This is because the role of this layer is to set up the *pn* junction and internal field. For this role, poor minority carrier transport is not an obstacle and indirect absorption is an advantage since light mainly absorbed in the more efficient absorber region.
We will therefore in further sections evaluate the potential performance of $Al_{25}GaAs$ microcrystals.

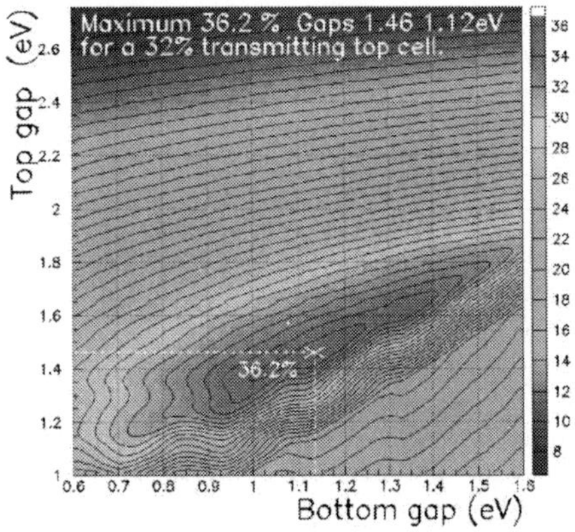

Figure 3 Radiative efficiency limit (STC) of a tandem cell where the top cell is optically thinned across the wavelength range such as to achieve an ideal tandem cell which features Si as the bottom cell at 1.12eV. The efficiency maximum is found a touch above GaAs for $Al_2Ga_{98}As$. This can be simplified by substituting GaAs which barely changes the achievable efficiency which for GaAs is 36%.

3.1 Optimum transport lower gap top cell

While the gap of GaAs is too low for a current-matched tandem cell on Si, with the GaAs cell over-producing, one can optically thin the top cell to achieve current matching.
This is non-ideal and reduces potential efficiency because photons with energies above the GaAs gap are absorbed in the Si. The resulting minority carriers are generated with higher energies than necessary, and lose this energy in thermalising to the Si band-edge. This may however be advantageous for a tandem if the thermalisation loss is small enough to allow high efficiency, and if tandem design is otherwise facilitated, as it is here as we shall see.
The potential efficiency can be evaluated by evaluating limiting radiative efficiency of an non-opaque or optically transmitting top cell which does not absorb all the light above its bandgap.
We tune the transmission of such a top cell such that the optimum bottom bandgap corresponds to Si. This procedure yields an optimum for a non-opaque top cell which transmits 32% of light above its bandgap. This has an achievable efficiency of 36.2% for al $Al_2Ga_{98}As$ cell on Si, which is essentially indistinguishable from a thinned GaAs/Si tandem.
We conclude with an important point which is that this "optical thinning" can be achieved by physically thinning the top cell material, or by depositing the top cell with partial coverage, leaving sections of the bottom Si cell directly exposed to the incident spectrum.

10.4229/EUPVSEC2025/2AO.3.3

This solution is ideally suited to the ELO Al_xGaAs cell growth, since growth proceeds by nucleation of independent crystals. Complete coalescence is in fact a challenge, and while it may be in principle achieved, independent crystals are technologically far easier to fabricate.
For completeness, we mention here work towards complete coverage in similar work by Strömberg *et al.* [8]. This investigates ELO fabrication of GaAsP on Si.

4 Simulations

The simulations first aim to analyse the fabricated devices described in section 2 in order to establish the potential performance of available materials. We start by briefly summarising the modelling strategy, before presenting the properties of the structure assumed in the modelling, before presenting results of electrical and optical modelling.

3.1 Model specification

The simulation in this work is carried out with Silvaco finite element numerical software in the Victory suite, in particular the process, meshing, and device simulation modules which we will not describe and instead refer the reader to manuals and publications which provide these details [9].
The complexity of the multilayer textured structure consisting of two different cells and a range of materials, and the dimensions of the smallest elements in principle require a precise finite difference time domain model (FDTD). This is however computationally expensive. Furthermore the optically relevant layers range from 1μm to hundreds of microns, and the refractive index contrast with the thin Al_xGaAs emitter layer at the front remains small. For these reasons, these studies rely on ray tracing which is sufficient for preliminary investigations, subject to FDTD studies in future work if necessary.

	Dimension (μm)	Material	doping
Transparent conducting oxide	0.1	ITO	-
Top cell			
Crystal facet angle	30° and 0°	-	-
Emitter	0.1	Al_xGaAs, x=0.4-0.7	p 1E18
Base	1 - 2	Al_xGaAs, x=0.3-0.4	n 1E15
Interface oxide			
Oxide	2E-3	SiO_2	-
Seed	0.1	Al_xGaAs, x=0.3-0.4	n 1E15
Silicon bottom cell			
Tunnel 1	0.1	Si	n 1E19
Tunnel 2 / base	0.1	Si	p 1E19
Wafer	2 - 250	Si	n 1E15
Emitter/back contact	0.1	Si	n 1E20

Table 1 model device specification range of materials parameters consistent with current fabrication techniques.

3.2 Device specification

Since we are interested in evaluating the current materials, modelled devices are not optimised from the perspective of layer dimensions, doping, and light interaction (anti-reflection (AR) coatings) in order to match the current experimental achievements.
The modelled device specifications are detailed in table 1. They include both flat and textured geometries with the doping, dimensions indicated, the nucleation site. The chosen compositional parameters are an $Al_{40}Ga_{60}As$ emitter and $Al_{30}Ga_{70}As$ absorber.
Also indicated are preliminary definitions of the tunnel layers and the silicon bottom cell which are however not simulated in this work, again in line with prioritising the experimental status.
Figure 4 shows succinctly the modelled structures, flat and textured, which are analogies to the experimental structures in figure 2. The model structures differ in the presence of a contact transparent conducting oxide and a front surface emitter layer which are in development experimentally.
Figure 5 completes the numerical description of the full cell ranging from the nanometre scale nucleation site to the hundred micron scale silicon substrate. This study concentrates on the top cell and does not consider the tunnel layers and Si performance which are to be implemented experimentally once top cell devices are operational.

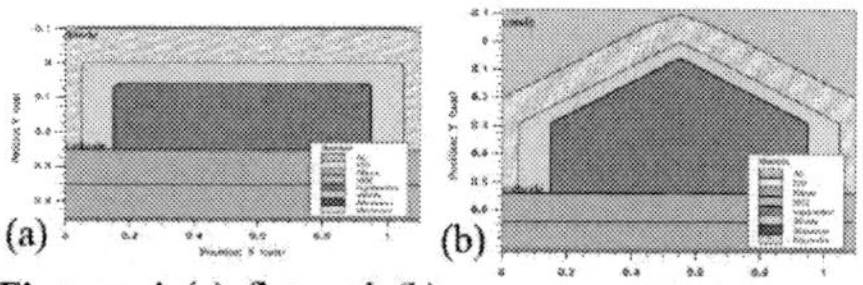

Figures 4 (a) flat and (b) textured GaAs crystals as defined by the process model for the lower 1μm dimension and inter-crystal separatin of 100nm. Also show are the tunnel junction layers for completeness which are not implemented in this study.

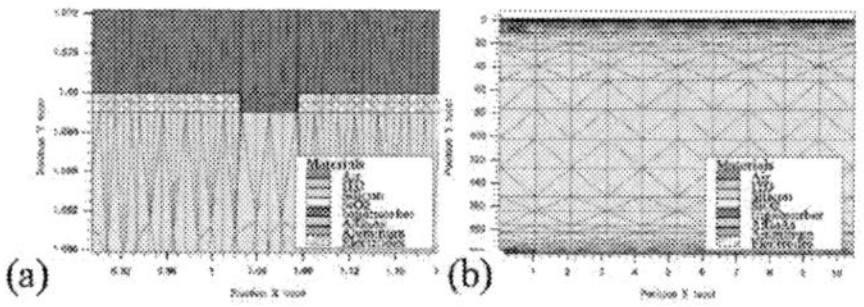

Figure 5 Schematics of the device and numerical Delaunay mesh over the range of scales from (a) the nanometre scale nucleation site to (b) the full device scale which is dominated by the Si substrate at the hundred micron scale.

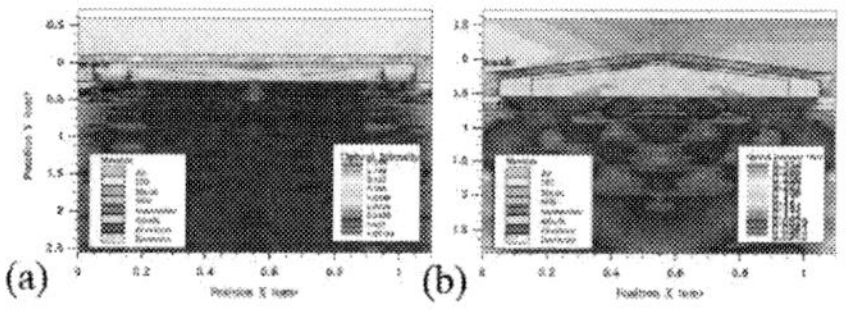

Figure 6 Light intensity map in cross section of (a) a flat 1μm crystal and (b) the textured analogue

3.3 Light management

Figure 6(a) shows light intensity maps in cross section of the flat device model. We note some light diffration at the edges due to the crystal separation. The centre shows an minor artefact corresponding to the nucleation site which however should not be considered reliable given the ray tracing model applied, and the size of this feature well below the incident photon wavelengths. Figure 6(b) shows the analogue for the textured sample.
We note first the difference in light intensity above the cell, with the flat structure reflecting significantly more

light than the textured. This confirms the role of texturing as improving light interaction by reducing surface reflectivity, a well known phenomenon used in textured Si cells as pioneered by Green [10].

Quantification and optimisation of this reduction of reflectivity is at this stage preliminary since we are not considering AR coats at this stage as mentioned previously.

The second effect demonstrated at this state is light refraction within the cell by the surface texture provided by the micro-crystal array. This is evident in the light refraction visible in firure 6b compared to 6a. In the flat case, features in light distribution are visible laterally but as mentioned just above but are due to the presence of spacers.

In the textured case we see enhanced light intensity below the microcrystal which leads to enhanced photogeneration at shorter depths in the Si cell.

This reproduces the same light refraction and light trapping phenomena which are now standard in high efficiency textured Si solar cells[10].

We conclude that the Al_xGaAs ELO crystal array provides the same light management design features which allow a thinning of Si substrates and a higher efficiency due to shorted diffusion scales for carrier collection in the Si. They also provide similar advantages in the Al_xGaAs higher gap subcell.

Both these phenomena will be quantified in future work, including optical coupling between the two. On that point, we note that Al_xGaAs and Si have very similar real refractice indices in the wavelength region below the Al_xGaAs absorber bandgap range [11].

Design	J_{SC} (mA/cm^2)	V_{OC} (V)	FF (%)	Efficency (%)
Flat	61.9	1.38	88	7.58
Textured	91.5	1.39	90	11.5

Table 2 Simulated device performances for material geometries fabricated to date which lacking optimisation feature low efficiencies, but with textured devices close to twice the flat device performance.

3.4 Device performance

We first present in table 2 the performance of current materials with, as noted above, an $Al_{40}Ga_{60}As$ emitter and $Al_{30}Ga_{70}As$ absorber. Lacking optimisation of structure and materials, these are projected to achieve low efficiencies as might be expected.

More important is to note the significant efficiency enhancement in the textured device which at 11.5% is close to twice the efficiency of the flat at 7.6%. This is due for a number of contributing factors.

The difference in absorbing volume is the first. The thin cell, 1μm across and only 0.25μm high, is too thin to absorb the incident spectrum efficiently. In addition, surface reflection is particularly high in the absence of an AR coat. Finally, carrier diffusion lengths are maximised by the 1/4 hight to width geometry and the imposition of current transport through the centred nucleation site.

The textured device, in contrast, benefits first from a greater thickness from the hexagonal cap which raises the maximum thickness by about a third, and increases absorption. This is amplified by the surface refraction by the facets which adds light trapping in the top cell, increasing the absorption of the greater absorbing thickness compared to the flat case. Finally, of course, the surface reflection is reduced by the texturing as we have seen earlier in the light management analysis.

We do not include here the quantum efficiencies and light current characteristics for succinctness but note they are shown in the EUPVSEC2025 presentation available on the conference website.

We conclude by evaluating routes to improvement for the top cell. The first is the modification of the emitter by increasing the Al composition to $Al_{70}Ga_{30}As$, close to the maximum, and reducing the absorber Al composition zero, that is, GaAs.

We also eliminate the spacer which is currently not feasible but which is under investigation by other workers in similar studies [7].

The third and final modification is to increase crystal width to the current achieved of 3μm. This gives a base height of 0.75μm and a cap height of approximately 1.3μm, as shown in figure which is sufficient for complete light absorption above its bandgap of 1.42eV. if slightly above the largest size achieved to date which is 2μm.

The quantum efficiency and power/voltage curve for this device are shown in figures 8a and 8b. This device achieved efficiency f 22%, for a JSC of 216mA/cm2, VOC of 1.15V, and fill factor of 89%.

Extrapolating this to our target 32% transmitting top cell yields a final top cell efficiency in this simple first case of 15.0%.

The achievable tandem efficiency remains low with a Si bottom cell efficiency of just 9.2% based on an optically coupled model for which we show the EQE only for brevity in figure 9. This uses a 200μm Si cell optically coupled to a GaAs surface microcrystal array with 32% transmission. The combined tandem efficiency is of 24.2%, which remains low since as we have already mentioned the intention of this presentation is a preliminary evaluation of potential performance rather than a full optimisation which will follow.

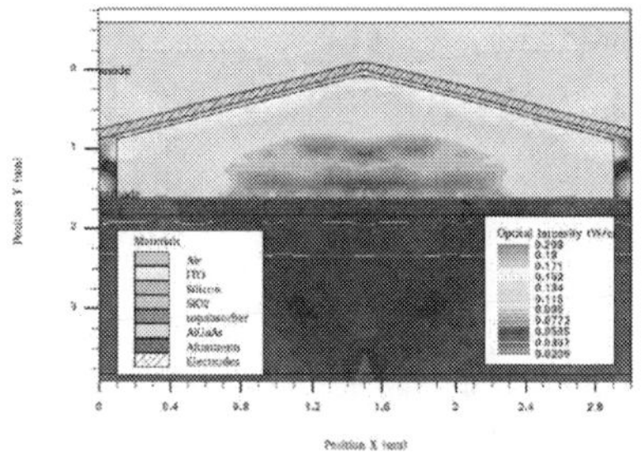

Figure 7 Higher efficiency design consisting of GaAs cell with no spacer, and 3μm width leading to a crystal base height 0.75μm and cap height 1.55μm sufficient for total absorption in the GaAs.

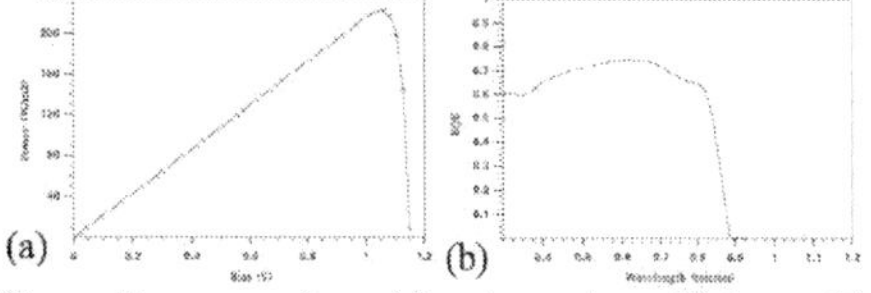

Figure 8 power-voltage (a) and quantum efficiency (b)

10.4229/EUPVSEC2025/2AO.3.3

of idealised device with no spacer and a GaAs top composition

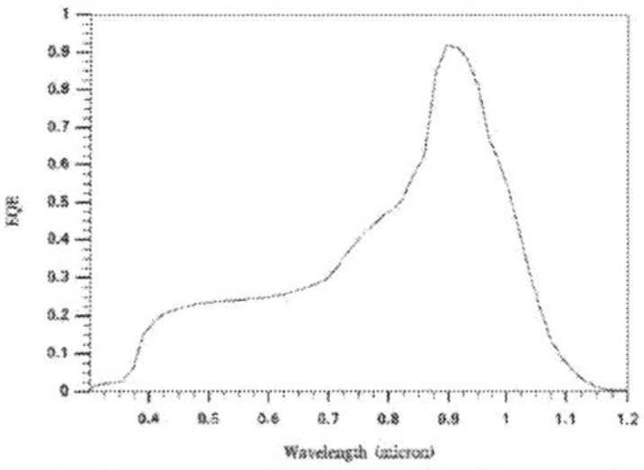

Figure 9 Quantum efficiency of a 200µm think Si bottom cell under 32% optically transmitting GaAs microcrystal array for current matching.

5 Conclusions

We have presented modelling of textured ELO AlGaAs crystals on Si. We find first that these structures allow light scattering of the same type as used in high efficiency standard silicon solar cells. An array of AlGaAs microcrystals is therefore very well suited to provide an effective texturing on a tandem III-V/Si solar cell, with the Si cell consisting of a thinner Si substrate as in high effiicency Si solar cells.

We have evaluated the potential efficiency of the current state of the art ELO crystals. Efficiencies remain low because of a lack of optimisation of optical and structural properties.

We have shown that based on current materials a 32% transmitting top GaAs cell with an efficiency of 15% is achievable, consistent with current matching to a lower gap Si cell.

This is projected to reach efficiencies in tandem structures which reach 24%, which while not impressive for a complex tandem device is nevertheless consistent current materials status and where identified routes to significantly higher performance is clear, and consists of standard solar cell optimisation.

We also note that a higher bandgap design has been identified as an $Al_{20}Ga_{80}As$ providing current matching. While this is currently not achievable since it requires complete coverage, work in the field towards complete top cell coverage makes this an even higher efficiency design to consider in future.

The next steps will be to simulate the top and bottom cell structures and combined tandem performance with experimental developments in the direction of top cell, bottom cell, and complete tandem devices, and thereby evaluate the light management and tandem potential of ELO AlGaAs for photovoltaic and broader applications.

Acknowledgments

The authors acknowledge the support of the French National Research Agency (ANR) financing the project HELLO-PV (ANR22-CE050-0011) which has made this work possible.

References

[1] Connolly J.P., Mencaraglia D., Renard C., Bouchier D., Designing III–V multijunction solar cells on silicon, Prog. in Photovoltaics, vol. 22 (07), p. 810-820, 2014; https://doi.org/10.1002/pip.2463

[2] Masafumi Yamaguchi, Kan-Hua Lee, Kenji Araki and Nobuaki Kojima, 2018 A review of re- cent progress in heterogeneous silicon tandem solar cells J. Phys. D: Appl. Phys. 51 133002; https://doi.org/10.1088/1361-6463/aaaf08

[3] Yoshinori Ujiie and Tatau Nishinaga 198, Epitaxial Lateral Overgrowth of GaAs on a Si Substrate Jpn. J. Appl. Phys. 28 L337; https://doi.org/10.1143/JJAP.28.L337

[3] Charles Renard *et al.*; High current density GaAs/Si rectifying heterojunction by defect free Epitaxial Lateral overgrowth on Tunnel Oxide from nano-seed; Scientific Reports (Nature) 6, 25328, 2016; doi: 10.1038/srep25328, www.nature.com/articles/srep25328

[4] J.W. Matthews, A.E. Blakeslee, Defects in epitaxial multilayers: I. Misfit dislocations, Journal of Crystal Growth, Volume 27, 1974, Pages 118-125, https://doi.org/10.1016/S0022-0248(74)80055-2.

[5] H. Mizuta, K. Yamaguchi, M. Yamane, T. Tanoue and S. Takahashi, "Two-dimensional numerical simulation of Fermi-level pinning phenomena due to DX centers in AlGaAs/GaAs HEMTs," in IEEE Transactions on Electron Devices, vol. 36, no. 10, pp. 2307-2314, Oct. 1989, https://doi.org/10.1109/16.40915

[6] Martin A. Green, Ewan D. Dunlop, Masahiro Yoshita, Nikos Kopidakis, Karsten Bothe, Gerald Siefer, Xiaojing Hao, Jessica Yajie Jiang Solar Cell Efficiency Tables (Version 66) Prog Photovolt Res Appl. 33, 7, https://doi.org/10.1002/pip.3919

[7] Henry CH. Limiting efficiencies of single and multiple energy gap terrestrial solar cells. Journal of Applied Physics 1980; 51(8): 4494. https://doi.org/10.1063/1.328272

[8] Axel Strömberg, Balaji Manavaimaran, Lakshman Srinivasan, Sebastian Lourdudoss, Yan-Ting Sun, (2023). Epitaxial Lateral Overgrowth of GaAsP for III-V/Si-Based Photovoltaics. Physica Status So- lidi (a) Applications and Materials Science, 220(8); https://doi.org/10.1002/pssa.202200623

[9] Silvaco Victory TCAD website contining manuals and webinars websit https://silvaco.com/tcad/interactive-tools/

[10] Green, Martin A, Forty years of photovoltaic research at UNSW., Journal and proceedings of the Royal Society of New South Wales, 148, 1, pp 2-14, https://doi.org/10.5962/p.361724

[11] Refractive index database https://refractiveindex.info/

42nd European Photovoltaic Solar Energy Conference and Exhibition

EUPVSEC 2025

Micro-crystal GaAs array sub-cells for Si tandem solar cells

J.P. Connolly[1], A. Nejim[3], A. Jaffré[1], J. Alvarez[1], J P. Kleider[1], D. Mencaraglia[1], Laurie Dentz[2], G. Hallais[2], F. Hamouda[2], L. Vincent[2], D. Bouchier[2], C. Renard[2]

[1]*GeePs, Group of Electrical Engineering Paris, CNRS, CentraleSupelec, Université Paris-Saclay, Sorbonne Université, 3&11 rue Joliot-Curie, Plateau de Moulon, 91192 Gif-sur-Yvette CEDEX, France*

[2]*C2N, Centre de Nanosciences et de Nanotechnologies, CNRS, Université Paris-Saclay, 10 Bd Thomas Gobert, 91120, Palaiseau, France*

[3]*SILVACO Technology Centre, Compass Point, St. Ives, Cambridgeshire PE27 5JL, UK*

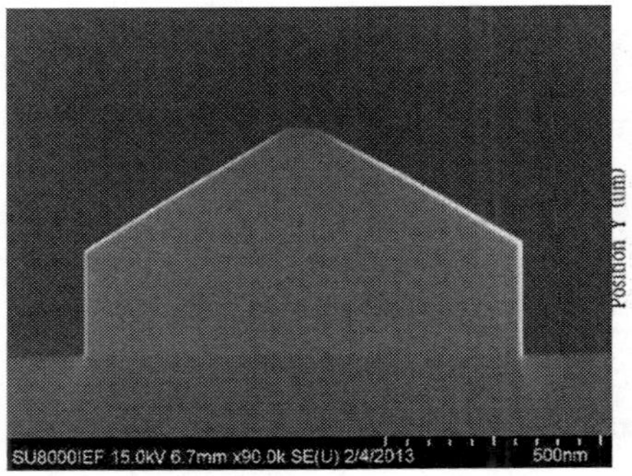

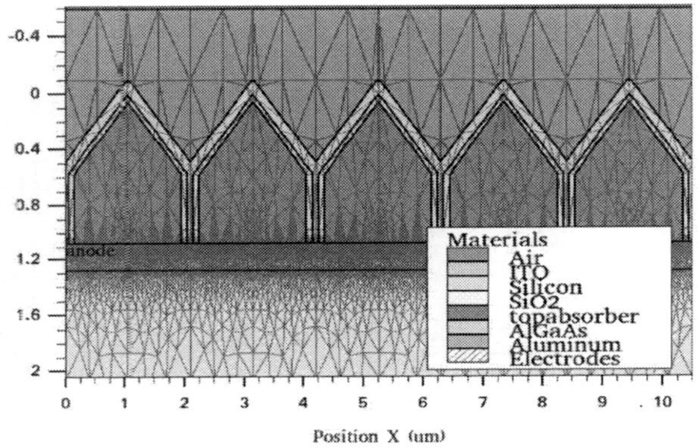

CentraleSupélec GeePs CNRS C2N Université Paris-Saclay EDF anr

020059-001

Overview

- Fabrication : Epitaxial lateral overgrowth (ELO)
- Tandems on silicon : ideal bandgaps
- AlGaAs for high gap tandem subcells
- Current top cell device structure
- Model
- Light management
- Device performance
- Higher efficiency
- Next priorities

Epitaxial lateral overgrowth[1]

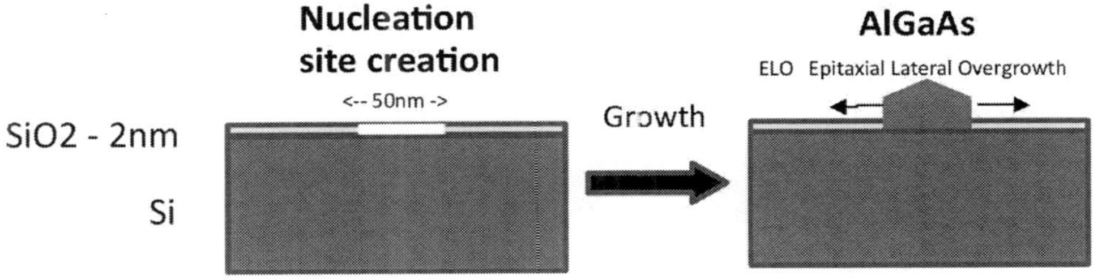

ELO : Epitaxial lateral overgrowth

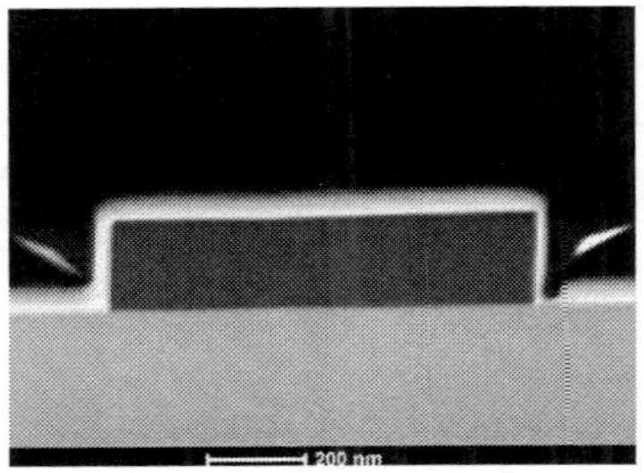

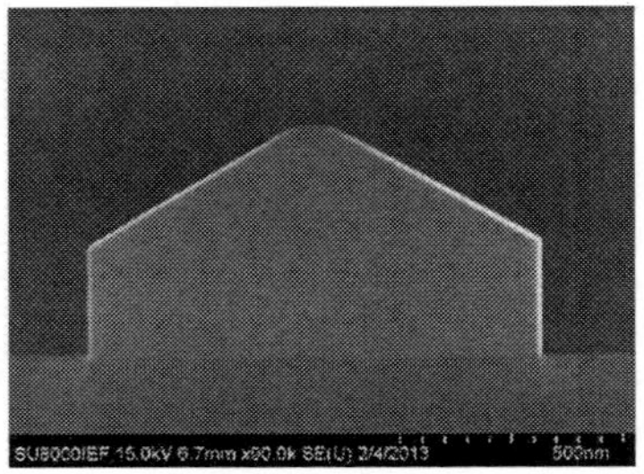

Fabrication : Flat and faceted / "textured" crystals micron scale

Available materials : GaAs -> $Al_{30}GaAs$ (gaps 1.424eV/870nm to 1.8eV/690nm) for absorbers
-> $Al_{75}GaAs$ (to gap 2.3eV/535nm) for thin layers : emitter.

Available geometries: Flat and faceted ("textured") materials
Base aspect fixed : height to width ration 1/4
Cap aspect ratio fixed : 30° angle to the horizontal.

(1) Charles Renard, Timoth´e Moli`ere, Nikolay Cherkashin, Jos´e Alvarez, Laetitia Vincent, Alexandre Jaffr´e, G´eraldine Hallais, James Patrick Connolly, Denis Mencaraglia & Daniel Bouchier , High cur- rent density GaAs/Si rectifying heterojunction by defect free Epitaxial Lateral overgrowth on Tunnel Oxide from nano-seed. Sci. Rep. 6, 25328; https://doi.org/10.1038/srep25328 (2016)

III-V silicon tandem efficiencies[2]

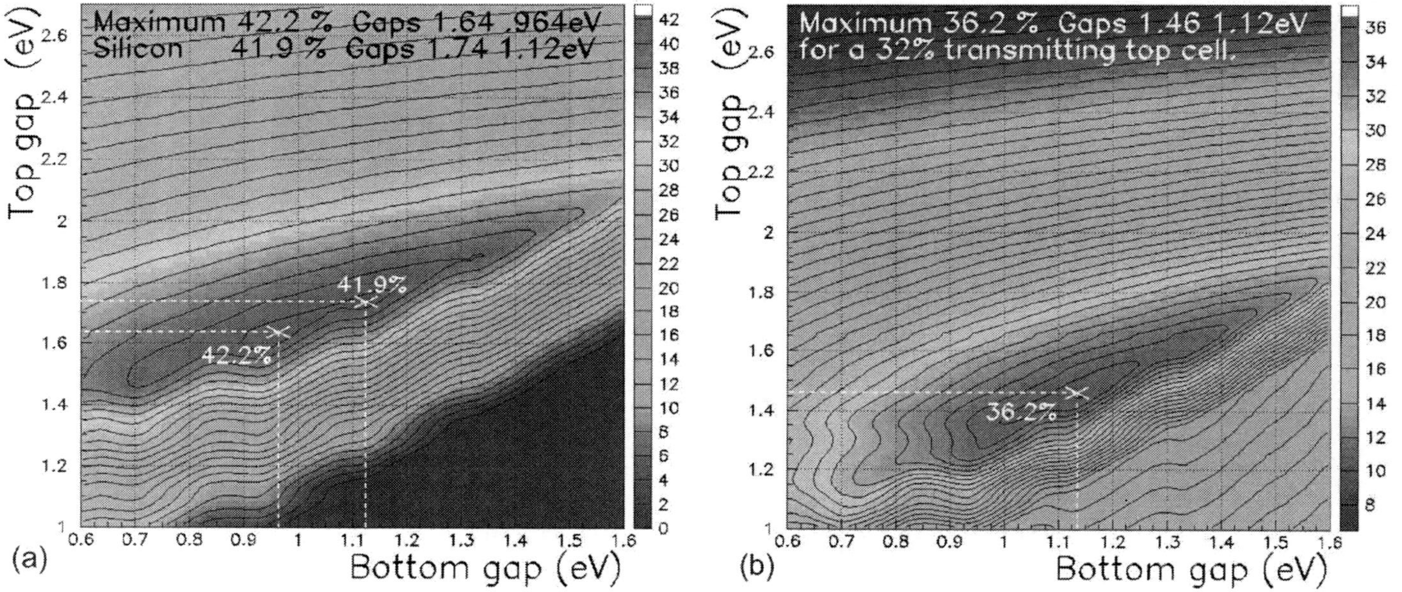

- Al_xGaAs bandgap range : 1.424 -> 2.7eV (1.424+1.247*x)
- GaAs gap too low for tandem application

=> Two solutions :
- Increase gap, add aluminium *but* : material problems
- "Optically thin" the top (AlGaAs) cell : Less ideal, but current matched

=> Highest AlGaAs on Si efficiency : 41.9% Gap 1.74eV is $Al_{25}Ga_{75}As$
Highest GaAs on Si efficiency: 36.2% Gap 1.46eV is $Al_2Ga_{98}As$

Conclusion : Desirable absorber materials 0% - 40% are within fabrication range

[2] J.P. Connolly, D. Mencaraglia, C. Renard, D. Bouchier, Designing III–V multijunction solar cells on silicon, Progress in Photovoltaics, vol. 22 (07), p. 810-820, 2014; https://doi.org//10.1002/pip.2463

Al_xGaAs material notes

Note : AlGaAs material issues for solar cells :

- Close to lattice matched across the range GaAs to AlAs
- Direct / Indirect transition above x≈45%
- Reactive material : oxidation especially ; transport problems
- Doping challenge : tendency to unindentional p doping (Carbon)
- Materials issues at high Al compositions : DX centres, defective – transport problems
- GaAs : Excellent material quality (record cells 29%[3])

Conclusions : Available compositions absorber 0 -30% well suited in principle
High Al composition suitable for window and emitter layers.
Transport issues with increasing Al content a potential problem

Next : Evaluate efficiency of current III-V crystals by ELO

(3) Martin A. Green, Ewan D. Dunlop, Masahiro Yoshita, Nikos Kopidakis, Karsten Bothe, Gerald Siefer, Xiaojing Hao, Jessica Yajie Jiang Solar Cell Efficiency Tables (Version 66) Prog Photovolt Res Appl. 33, 7, https://doi.org/10.1002/pip.3919

Model essentials

Numerical finite element model Silvaco Victory :

- V-Process : composition and deposition of materials (1D - 3D)
- V-mesh : non-linear mesh definition algorithms (Delaunay)
- V-device : Device performance

Note : latest update replacing previous "Atlas", "Athena", "Devedit" models.

Applied here to fabricated devices rather than optimised

Device structure

	Dimension (μm)	Material	doping
Transparent conducting oxide	0.1	ITO	-
Top cell			
Crystal facet angle	30° and 0°	-	-
Emitter	0.1	Al_xGaAs, x=0.4-0.7	p 1E18
Base	1 - 2	Al_xGaAs, x=0.3-0.4	n 1E15
Interface oxide			
Oxide	2E-3	SiO_2	-
Seed	0.1	Al_xGaAs, x=0.3-0.4	n 1E15
Silicon bottom cell			
Tunnel 1	0.1	Si	n 1E19
Tunnel 2 / base	0.1	Si	p 1E19
Wafer	2 - 250	Si	n 1E15
Emitter/back contact	0.1	Si	n 1E20

- Top cell : AlGaAs cell : flat or faceted
- Tunnel junction : Standard Si design (not implemented here)
- Bottom cell : Standard untextured Si cell (not shown in this work).

We focus on the AlGaAs textured cell following fabrication achievements.

Process and mesh steps

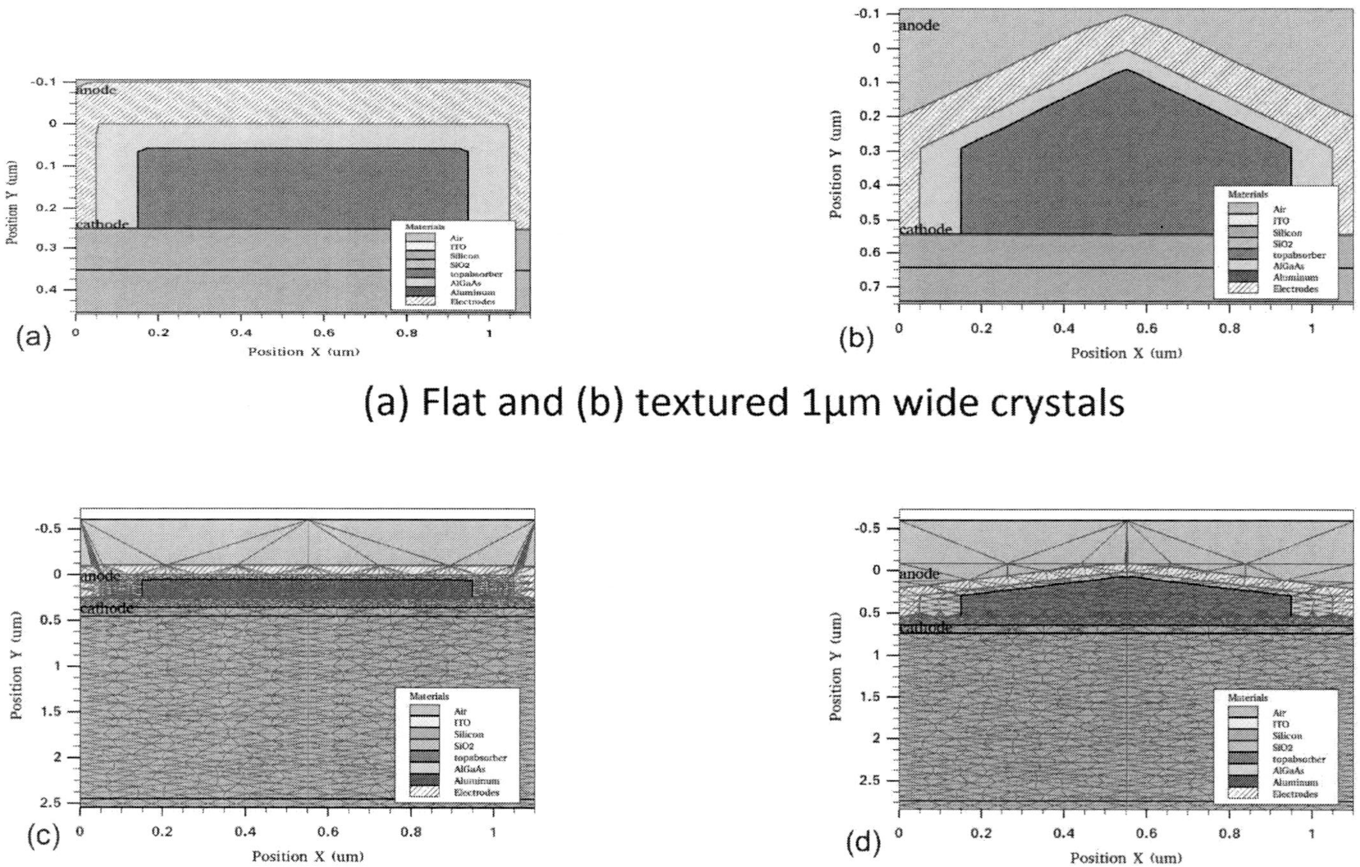

(a) Flat and (b) textured 1µm wide crystals

(c, d) Delaunay non-rectangular mesh in both cases, (thin Si fine mesh)

Flat and single crystal textured structures (with a thin 2µm Si cell for illustrative purposes)

Full structure, five period array

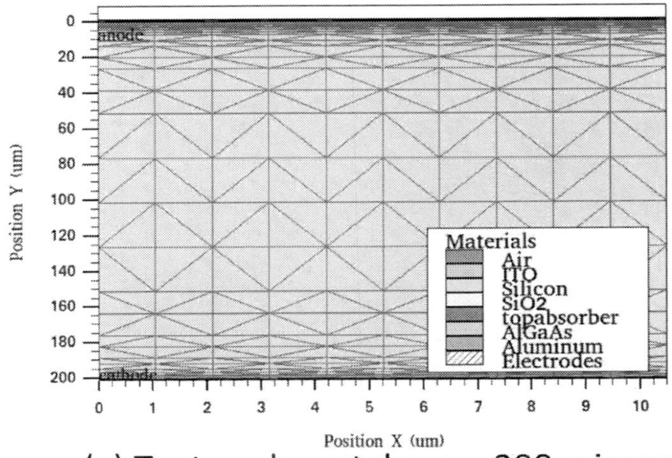

(a) Textured crystal array 200 micron Si cell loose mesh in Si bulk

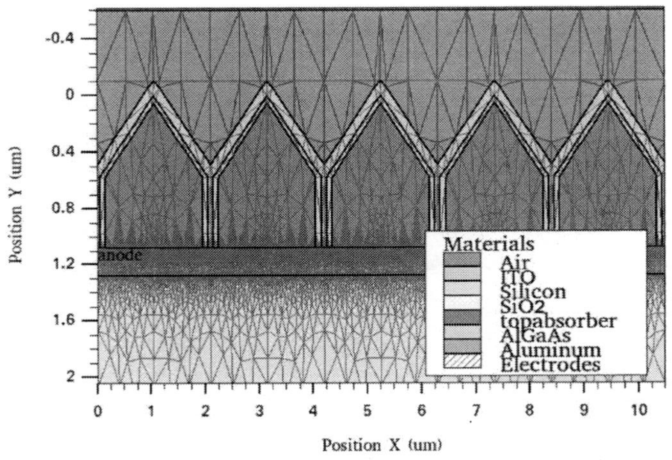

(b) Surface crystal array separation 50nm

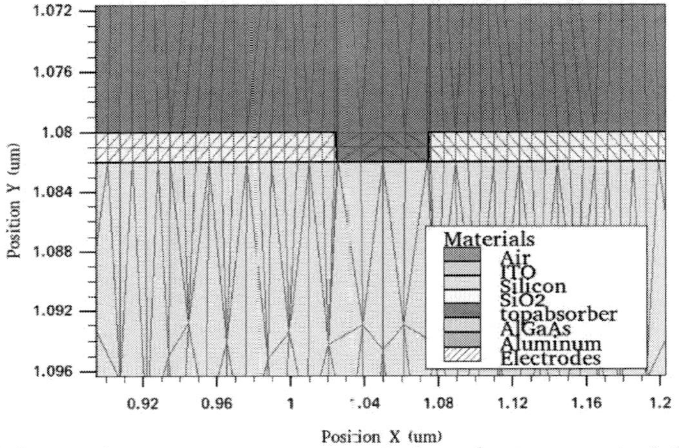

(c) Nucleation site – seed depth 2nm witdth 50nm

Textured five crystal period structure with a thin 200µm Si cell and showing nucleation site

Light management one period

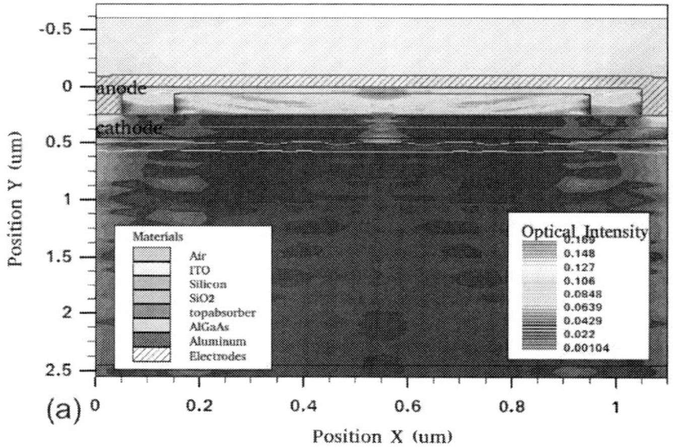

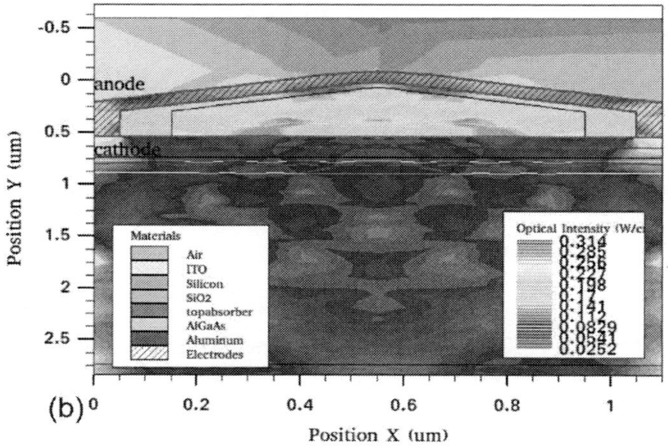

- Intensity maps of (a) flat (b) textured crystals
- Texture reduces reflection
- Texture refracts and traps light : increased absorption

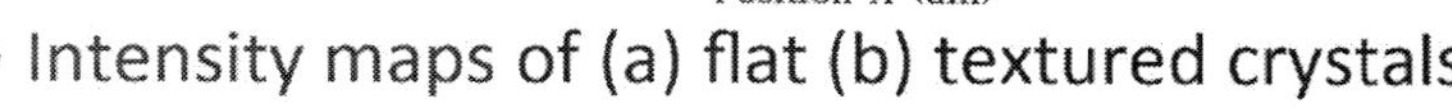

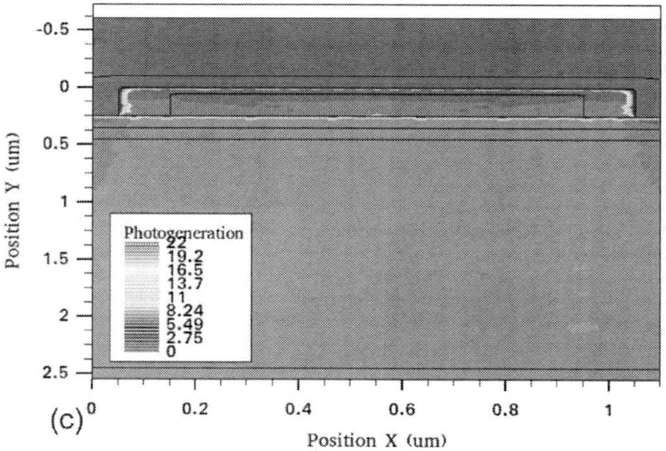

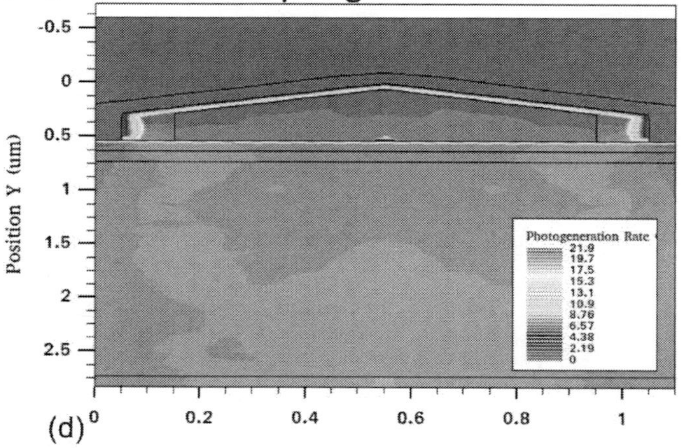

- Corresponding generation maps

Conclusion : Faceted crystal arrays performing the same role as Si cell texturing[4]

(4) Green, Martin A, Forty years of photovoltaic research at UNSW., Journal and proceedings of the Royal Society of New South Wales, 148, 1, pp 2-14, https://doi.org/10.5962/p.361724

Five periods

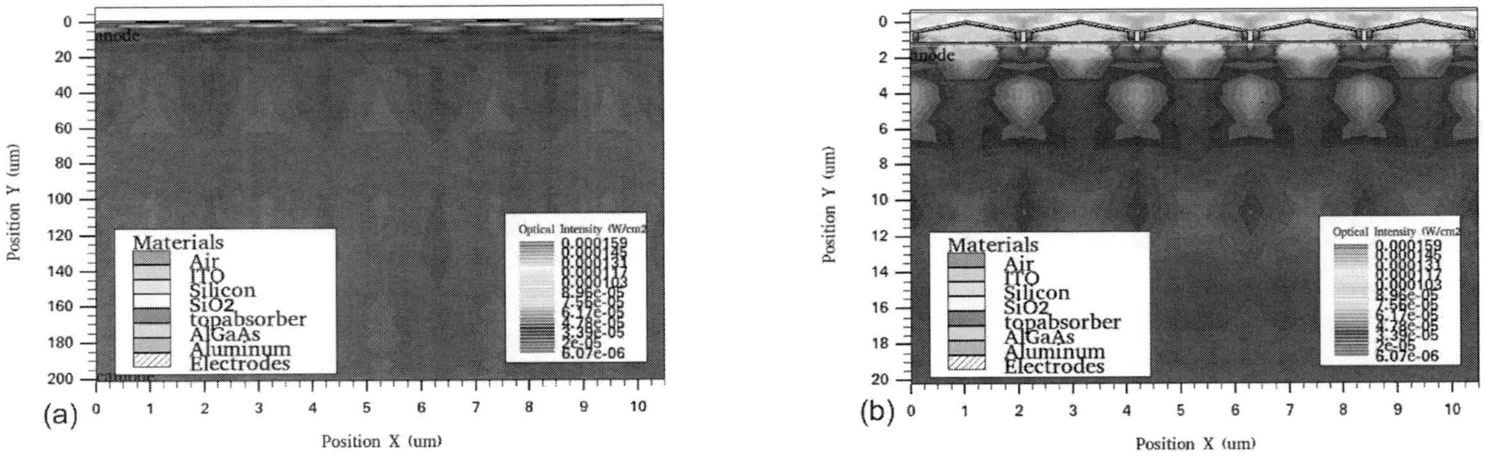

For completeness : Light intensity over (a) whole structure and (b) a zoom over the first 20µm

Device performance

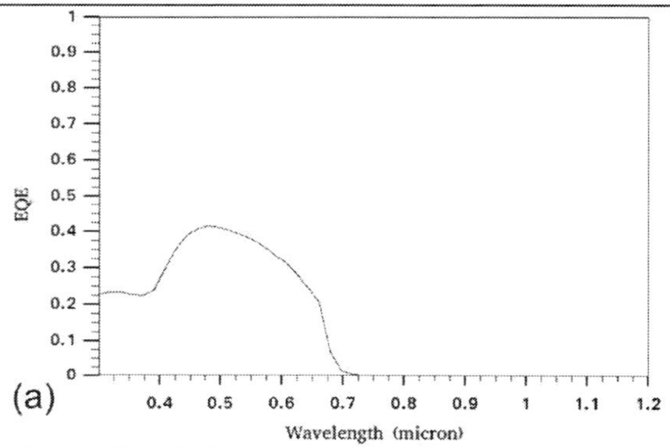

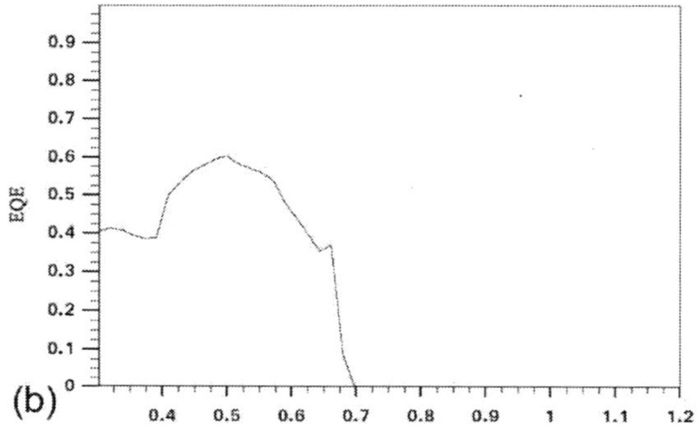

- Plain EQE of (a) flat and (b) textured crystals : no optimisation (AR coat, doping, dimensions0

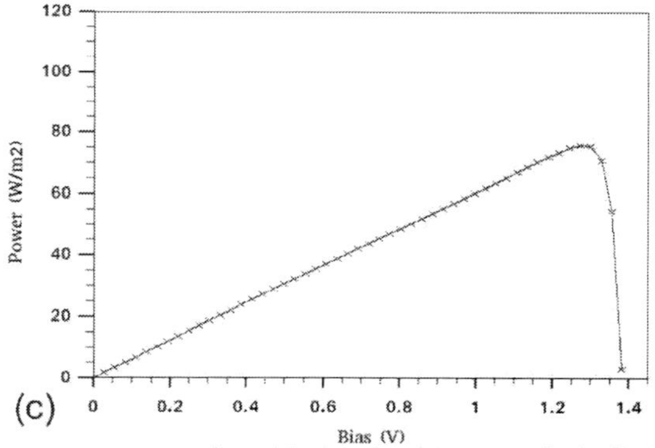

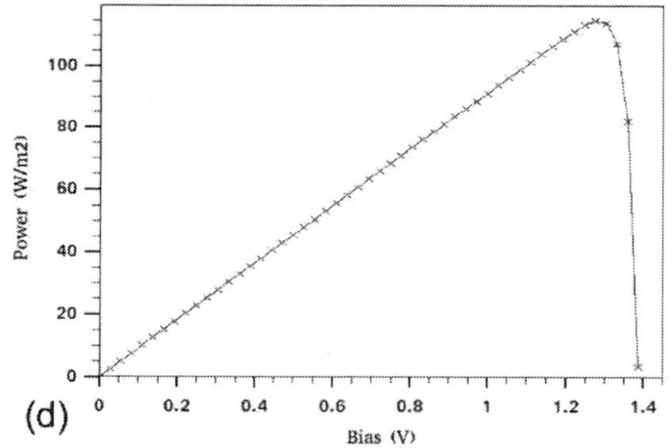

- Power output under STC AM1.5G (a) flat and (b) textured crystals as above

Design	J_{SC} (mA/cm^2)	V_{OC} (V)	FF (%)	Efficency (%)
Flat	61.9	1.38	88	7.58
Textured	91.5	1.39	90	11.5

Performance : Faceted (textured) much better – Efficiencies low, first devices yet to be made

(*nb. Performance independent of number of periods*)

Dimension studies

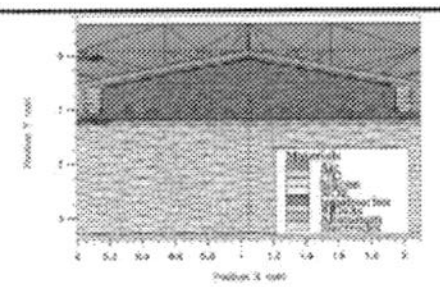

Margin : 0.05μm

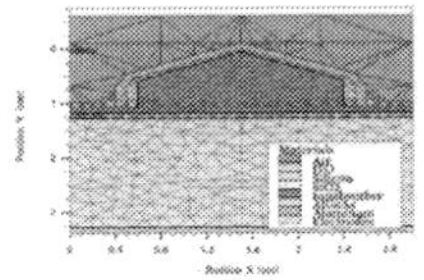

Margin : 0.5μm

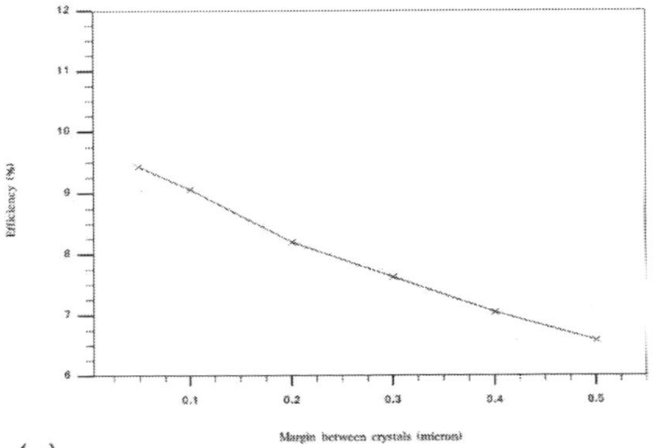

(a)

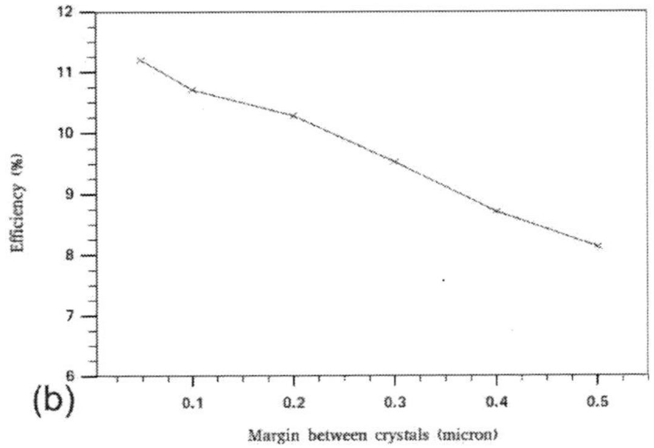

(b)

Impact of crystal spacing : (a) flat (b) textured decrease inter-crystal margin gives linear efficiency decrease (*linear decrease in active area*)

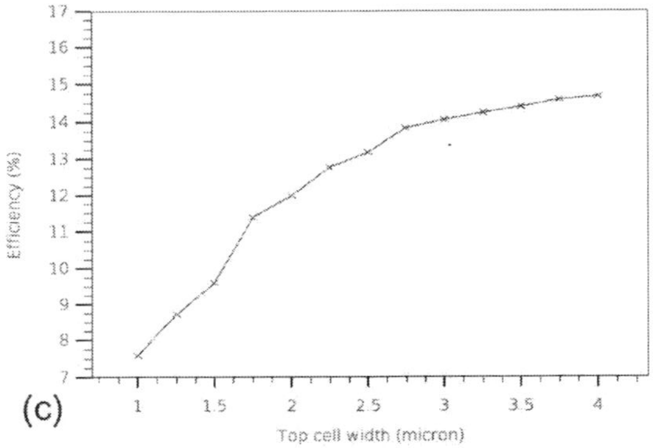

(c)

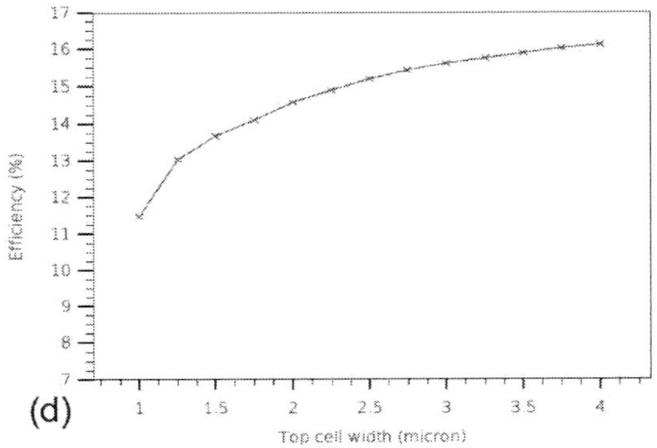

(d)

Impact of crystal size : Log. increase in efficiency – textured (d) higher than flat (c)

Conclusions : Faceted textured crystals are better
Zero crystal separation for highest efficiencies : complete coverage.
Crystal size to be large enough for complete absorption above AlGaAs gap
Proviso : Partly transmitting non-optimal but high efficiency concepts

Higher efficiency GaAs device example

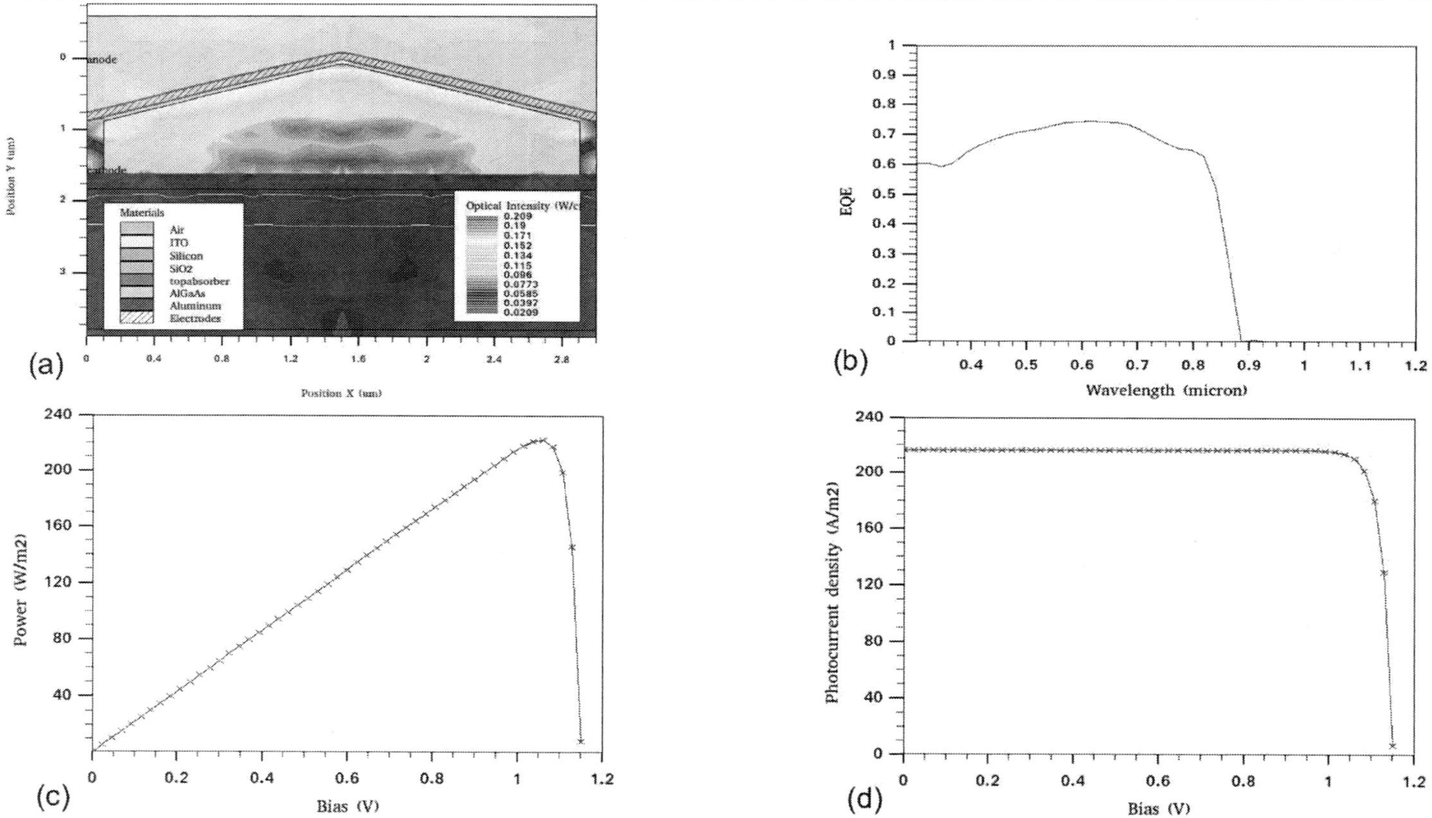

Higher efficiency : No spacer ; Emitters $Al_{0.7}$GaAs 0.1µm highly doped (1E18emitter) ; GaAs absorber

=> STC Efficiency 22% (Jsc=216mA/cm2, Voc=1.15V, FF=89%)

Notes : Far from 29% GaAs record, and not optimised, but an indication of routes to investigate
Not the main route to high efficiency : That is Al_{25}GaAs top array 32% tranmitting to Si.

Conclusions

- Preliminary model : low efficiencies for first devices projected : not optimised
- Light trapping potential demonstrated : equivalent of Si texturing
- We have only touched on incomplete absorption mentioned at the start : Spaced and thinned $Al_{25}Ga_{75}As$ crystals the most promising route
- Optimisation : both light and current transport (AR coats, light transmission ; Doping, material, and structure)
- Much broader III-V on Si applications we have not touched on

=> Next photovoltaic priorities :

- $Al_{25}Ga_{75}As$ surface crystal arrays transmitting 32%
- Si cell optimisation with nanocrystal light trapping

42nd European Photovoltaic Solar Energy Conference and Exhibition

This presentation was selected by the Sc. Committee of the EU PVSEC 2025 for submission of a full paper to one of the EU PVSEC's collaborating peer-reviewed journals.

MULTISCALE MODELS FOR PEROVSKITE OPTIMISATION

Philippe. Baranek[1,2,*], James P. Connolly[3], Antoine Gissler[1,2,4], Philip Schulz[4], Michel Rérat[5] and Roberto Dovesi[6]

[1] EDF R&D, EDF Lab Paris-Saclay, Department SYSTEME, 7 boulevard Gaspard Monge, F-91120 Palaiseau, France
[2] IPVF, Institut Photovoltaïque d'Ile-de-France, 18 boulevard Thomas Gobert, F-91120 Palaiseau, France
[3] [1]GeePs, Group of Electrical Engineering Paris, CNRS, CentraleSupelec, Université Paris-Saclay, Sorbonne Université, 3&11 rue Joliot-Curie, Plateau de Moulon, 91192 Gif-sur-Yvette CEDEX, France
[4] École Polytechnique, IPVF, UMR 9006, CNRS, 18 boulevard Thomas Gobert, F-91120 Palaiseau, France
[5] Université de Pau et des Pays de l'Adour, E2S UPPA, CNRS, IPREM, 2 avenue du Président Pierre Angot, F-64053 Pau, France
[6] Accademia Delle Science di Torino, via Accademia delle Science 6, I-10123 Torino, Italy

ABSTRACT: This paper presents a multiscale approach to evaluate perovskite solar cell performance which determines material properties at the atomistic scale with first-principles calculations, and applies them in macro-scale device models. This work focuses on the $MAPbI_3$ (MA = CH_3NH_3) perovskite and how its phase transitions impact on its optical, electronic, and structural properties which are investigated at the first-principles level. The obtained data are coupled to a numerical drift-diffusion device model enabling evaluation of the performance of corresponding single junction devices. The first-principles simulation applies a hybrid exchange-correlation functional adapted to the studied family of compounds. Validation by available experimental data is presented from materials properties to device performance, justifying the use of the approach for predictive evaluation of existing and novel perovskites. The coupling between atomistic and device models is described in terms of a framework for exchange of optical, vibrational, and electronic parameters between the two scales. The result of this theoretical investigation is a methodology for designing and optimising perovskite materials for both cell performance and stability, the key obstacle in the societal implementation of these record-breaking new materials.

Keywords: Perovskites, optoelectronic properties, cell efficiency, first-principles, drift-diffusion.

1 INTRODUCTION

Perovskite solar cells have progressed extremely rapidly from 3.8% in 2009 to 27.3% in September 2024. Tandem efficiencies have furthermore breached the single-junction Shockley-Queisser efficiency limit, reaching 34.6% in June 2024 (LONGI, certified) [1, 2]. While this rapid efficiency increase is unmatched by any other technology, it remains crippled by stability issues, obstacle for the industrial and societal application of these materials. State of the art perovskite absorber materials still suffer stability issues linked to temperature, to volatile organic cations for the organic case and its reactivity to the air moisture among other issues. Both air moisture and temperature induce phase transitions which degrade the performance and durability of perovskite solar cells (PSCs): the moisture leads to the appearance of a non-perovskite phase (the so-called δ black phase) which is optically inactive, while the temperature can lead to a rich sequence of phase transitions. Their impact concerns mainly the electronic properties and the domains and surface stabilities of the different compounds. A key element is stability implications of the effect of phase transitions on the nonlocal lattice distribution of organic moieties through the lattice

In this work, we focus on the phase transitions impacts on the cell efficiency. They are associated in particular to the existence of soft phonon modes which can locally generate phase instabilities. For both organic and inorganic perovskites, they are linked to the lattice and halide octahedra deformations. However, for the organic case, another factor has to be taken into account which is the nonlocal ordering of the organic moieties inside the lattice through the different phase transitions. Li and co-workers [3, 4] showed that the inorganic-framework deformation depends on the orientation of the organic cation which directly influences the stability of the hybrid perovskites and deserves a multiscale approach to obtain a good description of their properties.

If we consider $CH_3NH_3PbI_3$ as a paradigmatic case from an experimental point of view, the difficulty in obtaining an accurate characterization of its phase transitions comes from the determination of the methalominium ($CH_3NH_3^+$, MA) atomic positions inside the PbX_3 lattice: since the measurements are mainly performed with X-Ray diffraction, the positions of the MA moiety are ill or not defined. Therefore, for the *Pm3m* cubic phase the commonly used assumption is to consider MA as an intrinsic chemical entity which lies in the center of the cubic cell. However, this is not consistent from a crystallographic point of view: For instance, since the MA point group is C_{3v}, the corresponding space groups is C_{3v} *(R3m)* if the C–N bond is along the [1,1,1] direction of the cubic cell. Moreover, with this description $MAPbI_3$ is necessarily in a ferroelectric phase which might lead to a wrong characterization of its optoelectronic properties.

In this paper, using a theoretical multiscale approach, we illustrate how phase transitions can impact the performance of solar cells. This modelling couples atomistic scale first-principles calculations to device scale numerical models. The coupling between atomistic and device models is described in detail by presenting a framework for exchange of optical, and electronic parameters between the two scales.
This approach is based on a crystallographic description of $MAPbI_3$ which allows to take the MA ordering into account. We first describe this crystallographic model. At the first principles level, it is used to determine a

*Corresponding author: philippe.baranek@edf.fr

hybrid exchange-correlation functional adapted to the $MAPbX_3$ (x = Cl, Br and I) family of perovskites. The evolution induced by the phase transitions on the electronic and dielectric properties of $MAPbI_3$ is then systematically investigated. The corresponding band gaps, electron affinities and dielectric responses serve as input data to the device model which integrates these data in the absorber of a standard perovskite solar cell design [5] which we will not detail here. This device model yields the corresponding solar cell performance allowing evaluation of the impact of materials configurations at the atomistic scale on device performance and stability.

2 METHODOLOGICAL ASPECTS

2.1 First-principles approach

We define a crystallographic structure allowing evaluation of the ordering of the MA moities inside the lattice through the different phase transitions (see figure 1).

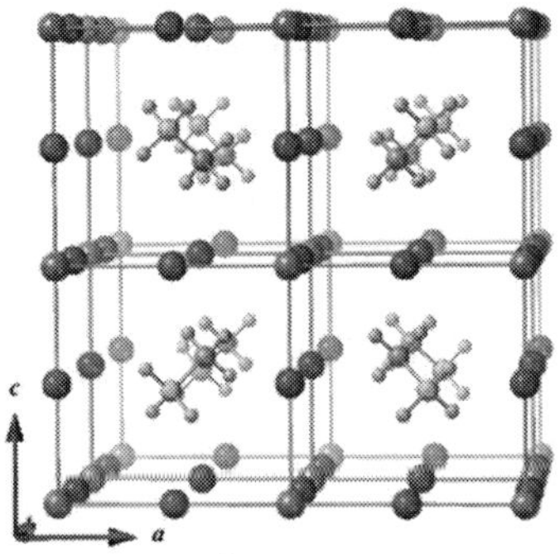

Figure 1: Used crystallographic structure of the *Pm3m* cubic phase of $MAPbI_3$.

First-principles calculations have been performed with the use of the CRYSTAL code [6, 7]. This program enables solution of both the Hartree–Fock (HF) and the Kohn–Sham (KS) systems of equations, combining them within a hybrid scheme. This work uses a hybrid exchange-correlation functional optimized to yield description of the structural, electronic, and dynamic properties of $MAPbX_3$ (X = Cl, Br and I) in good agreement with experiment, and has recently been used efficiently to study the influence of alkali metals on the properties of chalcopyrites, perovskites surface properties and the humidity-induced degradation products of halide perovskites [8-10]. In this work, the Hamiltonian (denoted as **PBEx**) combines 19% of HF exact exchange with the PBE exchange correlation functional [11]. It provides results consistent with a more homogeneous quantitive description of their properties than the most commonly used screened hybrid functional HSE [12] consistent with the most sophisticated methods based on the GW approximation: the obtained mean absolute average errors on the lattice parameters and band gaps of their different phases are 2 and 5 %, respectively, with respect to the available experimental data (as illustrated by the Table II for the cubic phase).

At the first-principles level, the changes induced by the phase transitions of the electronic, vibrational, and dielectric properties of each perovskite is systematically investigated. The resulting band gaps, work functions and dielectric responses serve as input data to the device model which yields the performance of solar cells.

2.2 Device model

The device scale numerical modelling is performed by on SILVACO's ATLAS simulator [13]. This uses the drift diffusion model, solving the current, continuity, and Poisson equations on a one to three dimension mesh. The full list of parameters identified are summarised in table I. The multiscale coupling consists of identifying device level parameters which can be provided by atomistic scale density functional theory materials models.

Table I: Full set of device scale drift-diffusion (DD) model inputs from atomistic scale density functional theory (DFT) level. This study uses a subset which are band parameters and optical functions.

Parameter	Definition
τ_{SRH}	Electron and hole charge neutral and depletion layers Shockley-Read-Hall lifetimes
μ	Carrier mobility, majority and minority, electron and hole
D_N, D_P	Hole and electron diffusion coefficients
C_A	Auger coefficient
ε	Permittivity related to complex refractive index
n, k	Real and imaginary refractive indices
m_e^*	Electron and hole effective masses
χ	Electron affinity
N_C, N_V	Band parameters - conduction and valence band effective densities of states
E_C, E_V, E_g	Band parameters - Conduction and valence band edges and bandgap

In this study, we limit the interaction to optical and band structure parameters since the device model is only weakly dependent on the other parameters listed. The model structure is a simple inverted structure consisting of electron transport layer, perovskite, and hole transport layer with contacts on a glass substrate, simulated with a transfer matrix methodology and diffusive optics to simulate imperfectly planar surfaces of typical structures. The model outputs include all the usual performance figures of merit as presented in the results section.

3 RESULTS AND DISCUSSION

Figure 1 depicts the *Pm3m* cubic unit cell used to perform the calculations and table II gives the results obtained for lattice parameter, band gap and electron affinity, for the cubic $MAPbI_3$: This 96-atoms primitive cell enables us to begin to consider the influence of the distribution of the molecular entity across the lattice on the structural, vibrational and optoelectronic properties of $MAPbI_3$. As noted previously, this unit combined with the optimized Hamiltonian to reproduce the properties of the $MAPbX_3$ perovskites allows the estimation of the lattice parameters and band gaps with an average error of 2. and 5 %, respectively, with respect to the available experimental data. As indicated in the section 2.1, the **PBEx** functional allows us to obtain data

10.4229/EUPVSEC2025/2AO.3.5

of interest in better agreement with experiment than the most commonly used PBE functional (which strongly underestimates the band gap, for instance).

Table II: Calculated lattice parameters (a in Å), band gap (E_g in eV) and electron affinity (χ in eV) for the cubic phase of $MAPbI_3$ at the **PBEx** level. The data obtained at the PBE level (between parenthese) and experimental data are given for comparison.

	Calc.	Exp.
a	6.368 *(6.383)*	6.329[a], 6.308[b]
E_g	1.68 *(0.92)*	1.62 (1.50 – 1.69)[c]
χ	3.79 *(4.06)*	3.45[d], 3.90[e], 4.10[f]

[a]Ref [14]; [b]Ref. [15]; [c]average value of experimental data from Table 2 and between parentheses range of variation of the band gap with different materials formings and measurement techniques cited in Table 1 of Ref. [16], respectively; [d]Ref. [17]; [e]Ref. [18]; [f]Ref. [19].

Table III gives the variation of the band gap and electron affinity for different phases of $MAPbI_3$. For each cell, the systems are fully optimized.

Table III: Calculated band gap (E_g in eV) and electron affinity (χ in eV) for different phases of $MAPbI_3$ at the **PBEx** level. The results on the single cell (12 atoms) are given for comparison.

Phase	E_g	χ.
Cubic *Pm3m*	1.68	3.79
Tetra. *I4/mcm*	2.17	3.49
Ortho. *P222₁*	2.25	3.46
Single cell	2.25	3.45

We note an increase of the band gap and a decrease of the electron affinity with the symmetries lowering of the different phases. As has been noted in the literature (see for instance references 3 and 4), this is due to the combined effects of the octahedra tilting, MA ordering and induced lattice deformations which yields a shift of the top of valence and of the bottom of the conduction bands.

Figure 2 shows the resulting optoelectronic responses for the cubic and tetragonal phase of $MAPbI_3$ compared with experimental data and other DFT calculations at the GW level realized on the single cell [20]. It clearly shows that the proposed method, which takes the MA ordering into account, improves the description of the dielectric responses (notably the peak at 3.5 eV) compared to the local approach based on the single cell or the one obtained at the PBE level. It also illustrates that the phase transitions will directly influence the optical response of the considered perovskites. The corresponding theoretical absorption spectra are in a qualitative agreement with experimental data.

We next evaluated device performance. As mentioned above, the device model simulates standard design consisting of a front ITO surface conductor, MoO_x buffer, PTAA hole transport layer, the perovskite absorber, followed by a SnO_2 electron transport layer, the whole on a glass substrate [5].

Table IV gives the performance of devices for different phases of $MAPbI_3$. We note here important advances, which are comparison of **PBEx** functional results and evaluation of the performance of perovskite phases and their stability, a major question in current PSC development.

a)

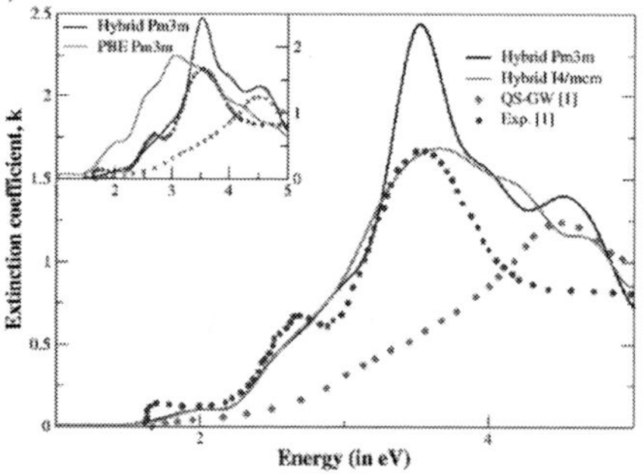

b)

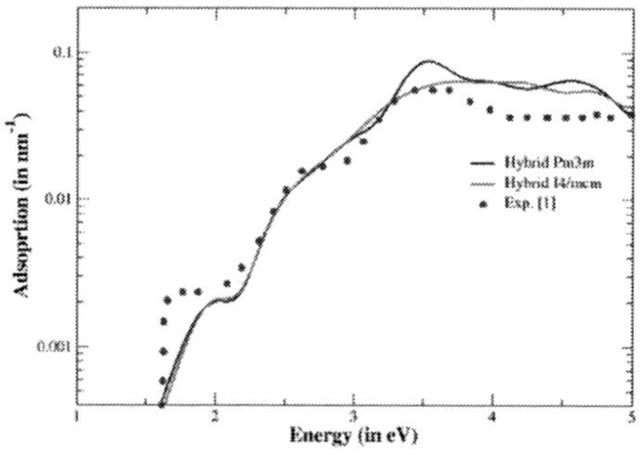

Figure 2: a) Obtained extinction coefficient k and b) absorption for the cubic (*Pm3m*, black) and tetragonal (*I4/mcm*, red) phases of $MAPbI_3$. The blue and green dots present the experimental data obtained via ellipsometry on monocrystal and the theoretical results obtained on the pristine cell at the GW level, respectively [20].

Table IV: Device performance modelling for parameters taken from the experimental data of literature [20], and from successive theoretical **PBEx** calculations ranging from the single cell (12 atoms cell) to tetragonal and cubic phases (96 atoms cell), showing a peak performance for the cubic phase.

Data source	Jsc (A/m^2)	V_{oc} (V)	V_{mp} (V)	FF (%)	η (%)
Single cell	13.4	1.82	1.40	71.9	17.5
Ortho. *P222₁*	11.6	1.80	1.42	73.6	15.5
Tetra. *I4/mcm*	13.4	1.73	1.37	74.6	17.2
Cubic *Pm3m*	18.2	1.25	1.11	84.3	19.2
Exp. [20]	17.5	1.25	1.10	84.3	18.5

Following, the example of the dielectric properties, taking into account the MA ordering in $MAPbI_3$ improves the qualitative description of the device performances with respect to experiment. It shows that the best agreement is obtained for the cubic phase of $MAPbI_3$ which possess the highest efficiency. The efficiency of the device decreases with the increase of the bang gap the lowest one corresponding to the orthorhombic phase.

To explain this trend, figure 3 shows band alignments for **PBEx** data set values of affinities and band parameters of the cubic and orthorhombic phases. We note cliffs in absorber-transport layer band profiles (just below 1.2 µm) which translate as drops in charge carriers potential corresponding to drops in maximum power voltage. The significantly greater cliff in the ortho case leads to greater thermalisation losses for both electrons and holes as visible in the step in the electron quasi-Fermi level. This is in part responsible for the lower efficiency of the ortho material compared to the cubic.

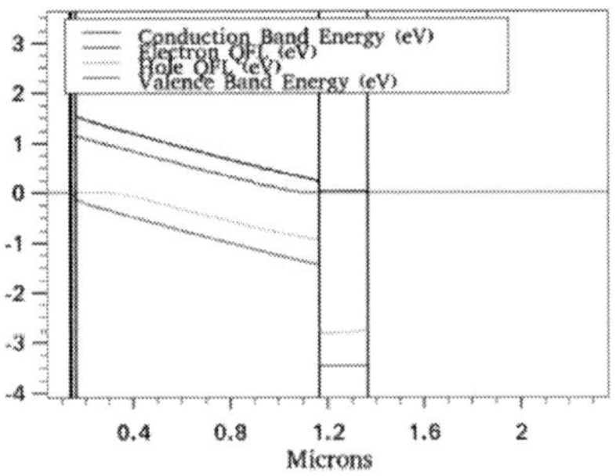

a).

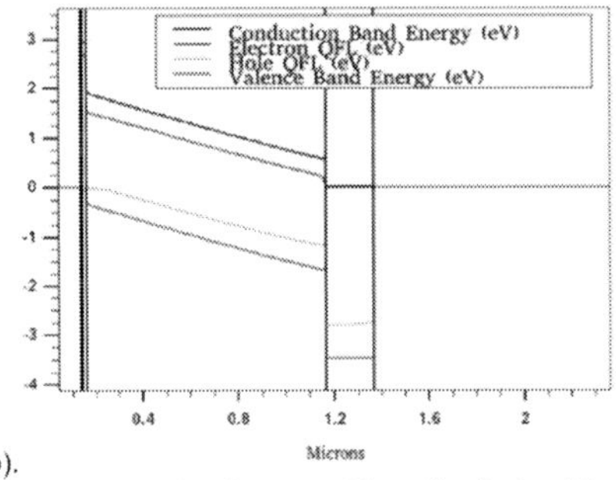

b).

Figure 3: Example of a perovskite cell calculated band profile under illumination at short circuit for experimental parameter input values to the device model for a) the cubic and b) the orthorhombic phases. The **PBEx** input to the device model in this case is the 19.2% efficient cubic dataset .

Figure 4 a) shows the corresponding light current curve for which the figures of merit are given in table III. We note here that the lack of steps and flat IV curve for much of the voltage range which corresponds to a high fill factor is evidence of good band alignments in the device. Figure 4 b) shows the (external) quantum efficiency. This shows a broad tail below the electronic gap which is 1.68eV (wavelength 0.74 µm). This requires further work since there is a significant contribution to the photocurrent which is not reflected in experimental data.

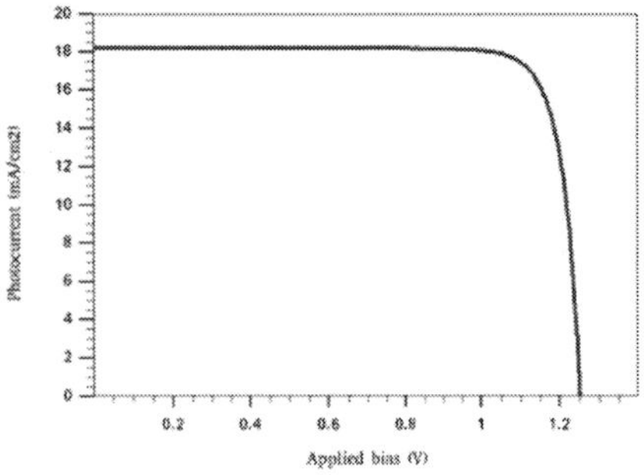

a)

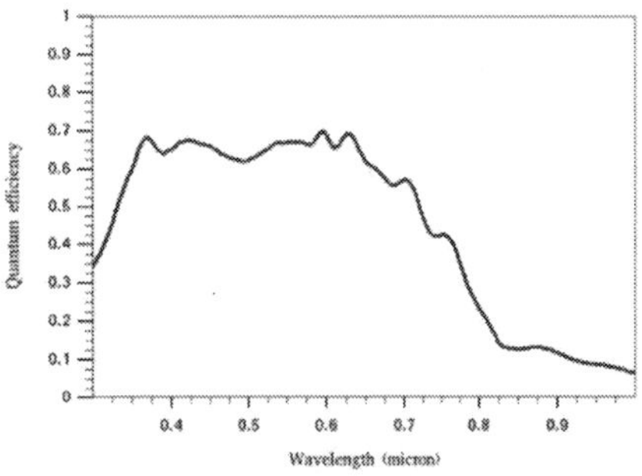

b)

Figure 4: Light current (a) and quantum efficiency (b) showing absorption below the gap at 0.74eV which needs further investigation.

4 CONCLUSIONS

In conclusion, we present the basis of a pragmatic multiscale approach using atomistic scale first-principles calculations coupled to device scale numerical models. At the first-principles level, a hybrid exchange-correlation functional optimized to yield description of their structural, electronic, and phonon properties in good agreement with experiment, has been used. The obtained band gaps, work functions and dielectric responses served as input data to the device model to estimate the performance of solar cells. The preliminary theoretical atomistic and device model results are both in qualitative agreement with experimental data. This methodology has to be proven on a more detailed sets of perovskites, but, if the trends are confirmed, it might allow to provide a set of criteria for optimizing the materials for different PV applications and for suggesting effective complex perovskites. While the main focus of this work is perovskite materials and therefore of single-junction perovskite solar cells, the extension to tandem solar cells is included given the importance of multijunction device exceeding single junction Shockley-Queisser efficiency limits.

Acknowlegments

The authors thank the ANRT (French National Association for Research and Technology) for its financial support within CIFRE agreement 2023/0728 (industrial convention for training through research), and support from the France 2030 programme PEPR-TASE ("Programme et Equipements Prioritaires de Recherche sur les Technologies Avancées des Systèmes Energétiques") specifically within the MINOTAURE project, Grant ANR-22-PETA-0015.

References

[1] M.A. Green *et al.* Prog. Photovolt. Res. Appl. 33 (2025) 795, https://doi.org/10.1002/pip.3919.
[2] https://www.nrel.gov/pv/cell-efficiency
[3] J. Li and P. Rinke, Phys. Rev. B 94 (2016) 045201, https://doi.org/10.1103/PhysRevB.94.045201.
[4] J. Li *et al.*, Phys. Rev. B 96 (2018) 045201, https://doi.org/10.1103/PhysRevB.98.045201.
[5] M.A. Green *et al.* Nature Photonics 8 (2014) 506, https://doi.org/10.1038/nphoton.2014.134.
[6] R. Dovesi *et al.* WIREs Comput. Mol. Sci. 8 (2018) e1360, https://doi.org/10.1002/wcms.1360.
[7] R. Dovesi *et al.* CRYSTAL17 User's Manual (University of Torino, Torino, 2017).
[8] F. Lafond *et al.*, J. Phys. Chem. 124 (2020) 10353, https://doi.org/10.1021/acs.jpcc.0c01767.
[9] A. Mishra *et al.*, Surfaces and Interfaces 25 (2021) 101264, https://doi.org/10.1016/j.surfin.2021.101264.
[10] S. Mejaouri *et al.* Small Methods 8 (2024) 230091, https://doi.org/10.1002/smtd.202300901.
[11] J.P. Perdew et al. Phys. Rev. Lett. 100 (2008) 136406, https://doi.org/10.1103/PhysRevLett.100.136406.
[12] A. Krukau *et al.* J. Chem. Phys. 125 (2006) 224106, https://doi.org/10.1063/1.2404663.
[13] https://silvaco.com.
[14] A. Poglitsch and D. Weber, J. Chem. Phys. 87 (1987) 6373, https://doi.org/10.1063/1.453467.
[15] S.S.H. Dintakurti *et al.* Phys. Chem. Chem. Phys. 24 (2024) 18004, https://doi.org/10.1039/D2CP02131E.
[16] T. Das *et al.* J. Phys. Chem. 126 (2022) 2184, https://doi.org/10.1021/acs.jpcc.1c09594.
[17] M. Caputo *et al.* Sci. Rep. 9 (2019) 15159, https://doi.org/10.1038/s41598-019-50108-0.
[18] J. Ji *et al.* Crystals 9 (2019) 539, https://doi.org/10.3390/cryst9100539.
[19] S. Olthof and K. Meerholz, Sci. Rep. 7 (2016) 40267, https://doi.org/10.1038/srep40267.
[20] A.M.A. Leguy *et al.*, Nanoscale 8 (2016) 6317, https://doi.org/10.1039/C5NR05435D.

EDF IPVF

Multiscale Models for Perovskites Optimization

Ph. Baranek[1,2], J.P. Connolly[3], A. Gissler[1,2], Ph. Schulz[2], M. Rérat[4] and R. Dovesi[5]

[1]EDF R&D, [2]IPVF, [3]GEEPS,

[4]UPPA, [5]Academia delle Scienze di Torino

EUPVSEC 2025, 21 – 26 September 2025

Introduction

***Bottleneck* : Instability of certain perovskites with temperature and moisture.**

- Soft phonon modes which can locally generate phase instabilities [1].
- Moisture-induced degradation important in terms stability issues [2].

Considerable efforts devoted to the understanding of the underlying mechanisms.

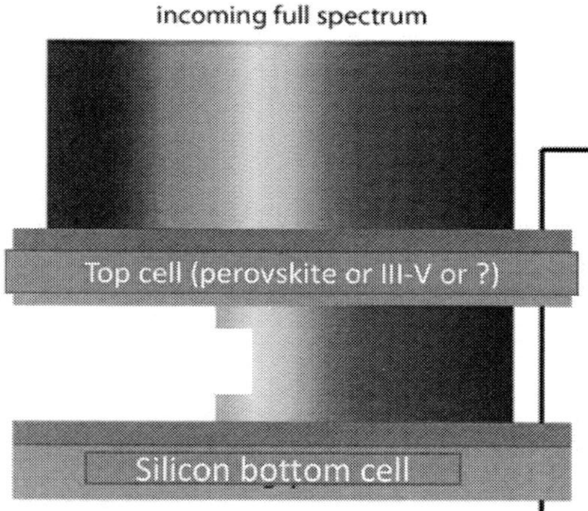

Tandem solar cells

→ **Impact of the chemical composition (phase transition and ordering in $MAPbI_3$) on their optoelectronic properties.**

Atomic modeling interesting alternative to understand their effects [3]

At the atomic level : **Study of the influence of intrinsic/extrinsic defect or substitution on the electrical and optoelectronic properties**

-> **Link to the microscopic properties of compounds and macrosopic data to evaluate performances of devices**

[1] G. Sophia *et al.*, Phys. Chem. Chem. Phys. **24**, 27064 (2022).
[2] S. Mejaouri *et al.*, Small Methods **8**, 2300901 (2024).
[3] Q. Li *et al.*, Applied Surfaces Sciences **538**, 148058 (2021).

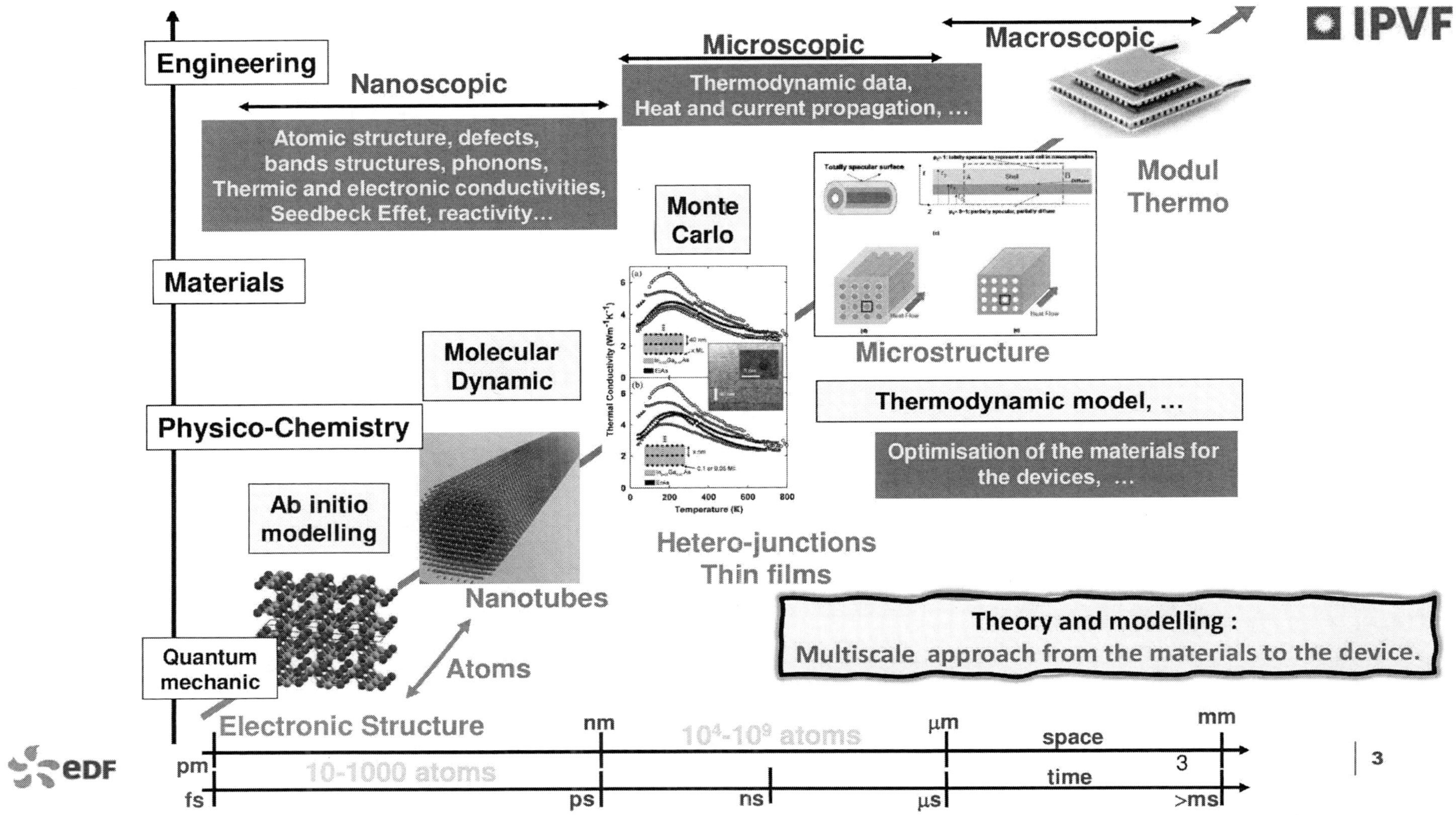
Engineering
Nanoscopic
Microscopic
Macroscopic
IPVF
Thermodynamic data,
Heat and current propagation, ...
Atomic structure, defects,
bands structures, phonons,
Thermic and electronic conductivities,
Seedbeck Effet, reactivity...
Modul
Thermo
Monte
Carlo
Materials
Molecular
Dynamic
Microstructure
Thermodynamic model, ...
Optimisation of the materials for
the devices, ...
Physico-Chemistry
Ab initio
modelling
Hetero-junctions
Thin films
Nanotubes
Theory and modelling :
Multiscale approach from the materials to the device.
Quantum
mechanic
Atoms
Electronic Structure
10-1000 atoms
10^4-10^9 atoms
pm
nm
µm
mm
space
fs
ps
ns
µs
>ms
time
3
eDF

Implement a pragmatic use of the first-principles approaches (DFT)

IPVF

Development of simple models of complex materials

Perovskites

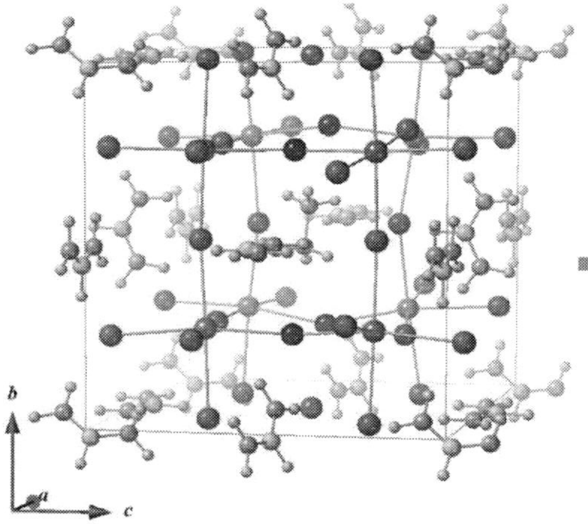

a computational tool for solid state chemistry and physics
CRYSTAL

Study of the electronic and dynamical properties of bulk materials and interfaces

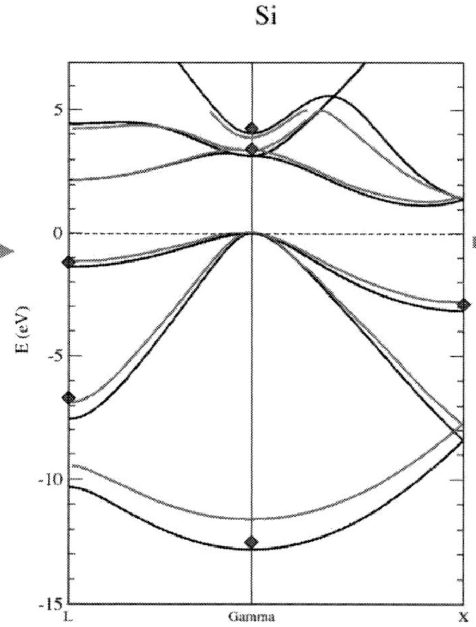

--- Hybrid
--- GW + spin coupling [4]
♦ Exp. [5]

Determination of the properties of interest for photovoltaic

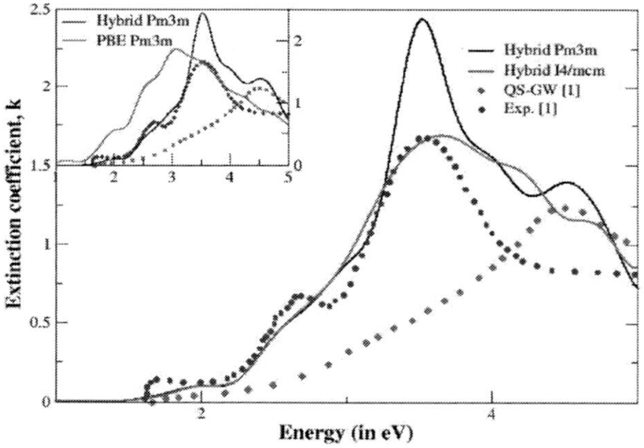

Application to:
- Band alignement at the interfaces
- Electronic affinity
- Surfaces and interfaces stability

edf

[4] Malone et al., J. Phys. Cond. Matt. (2013)
[5] O. Madelung, The Landolt-Bornstein Database, Springer Material (2001).

Study of the ageing of the halide perovskites ABX_3

Ph. Baranek, A. Gissler, A. Mishra, P. Schulz and A. Postnikov

A = Li, K, Na, Rb, Cs, CH_3NH_3
B = Ge, Sn, Pb
X = Cl, Br and I

Bottleneck : Instability of certain perovskites with temperature

Link : Intrinsic properties of materials

- Influence of the phase transitions on the band gap

-> Anharmonicity of the materials

-> Unstable phonon modes

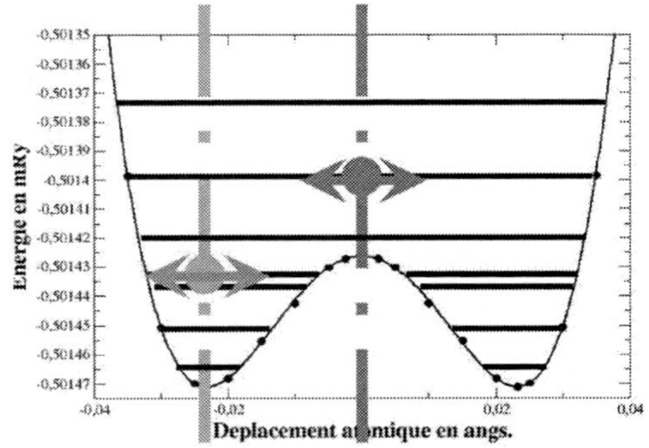

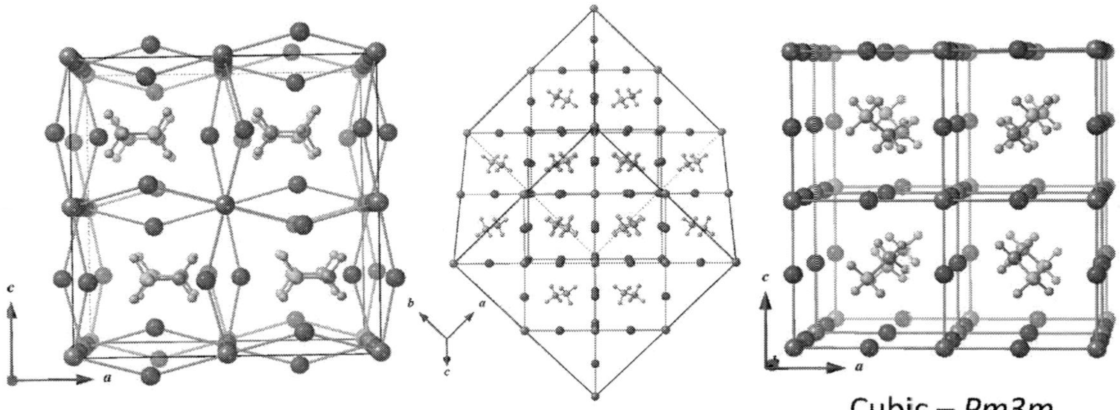

Ortho – *Pna*2_1 Tetra – *I4/mcm* Cubic – *Pm3m*

Increasing temperature

Phase transition driven by unstable phonon mode

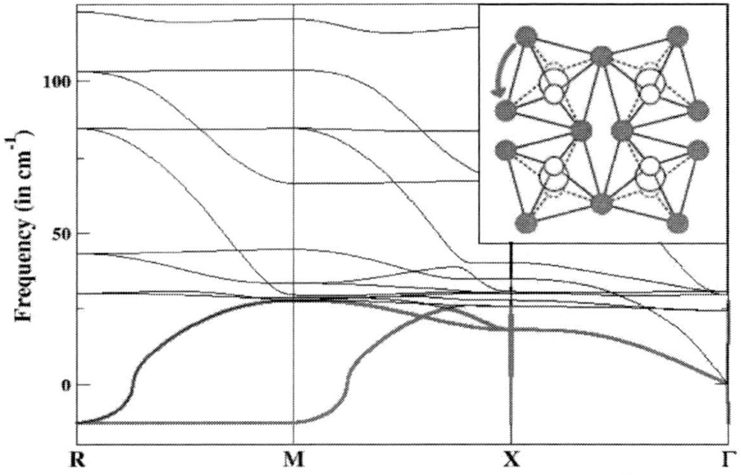

Electronic structure of halides perovskites:

A. Gissler, Ph. Schulz and Ph. Baranek

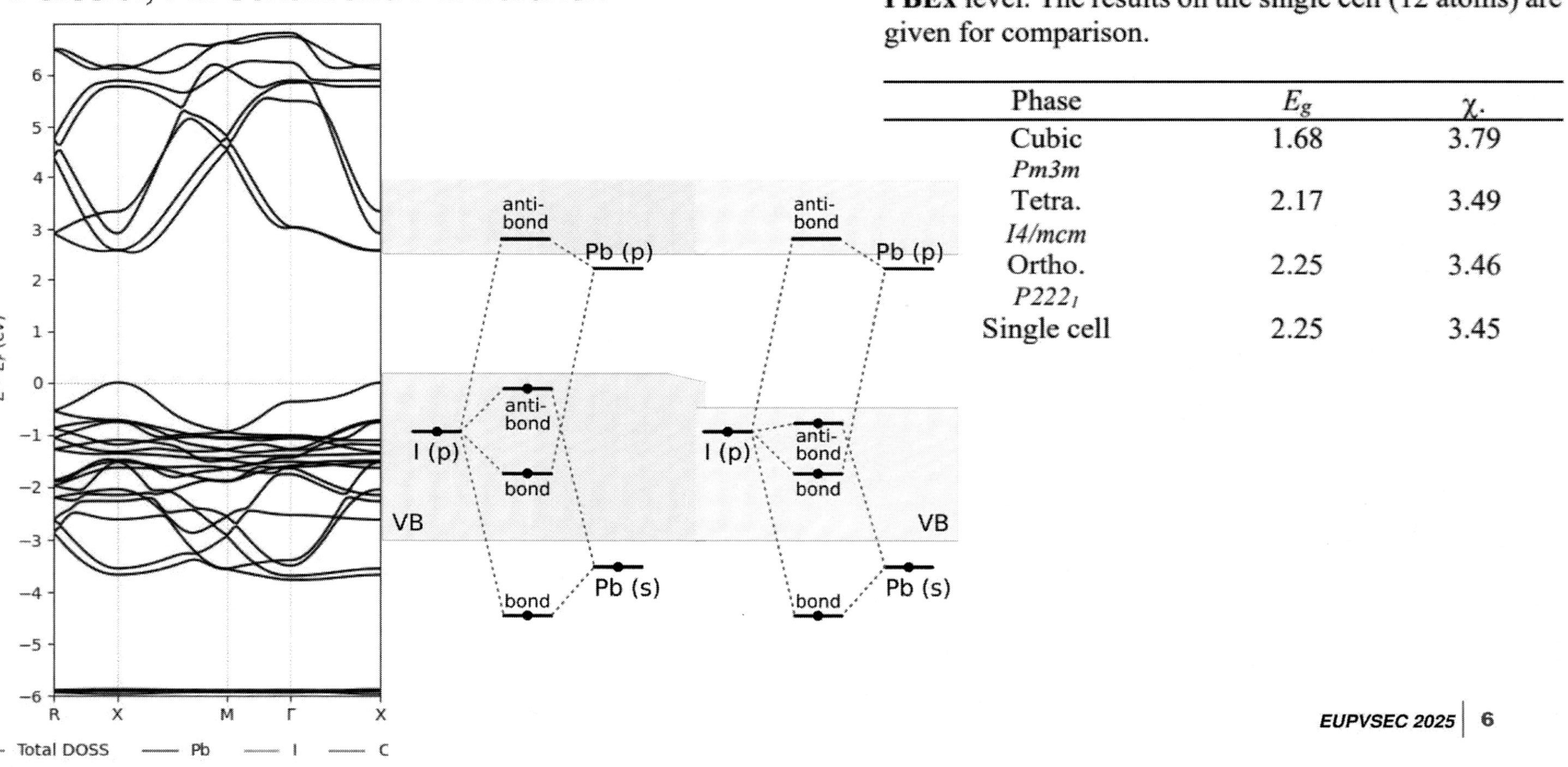

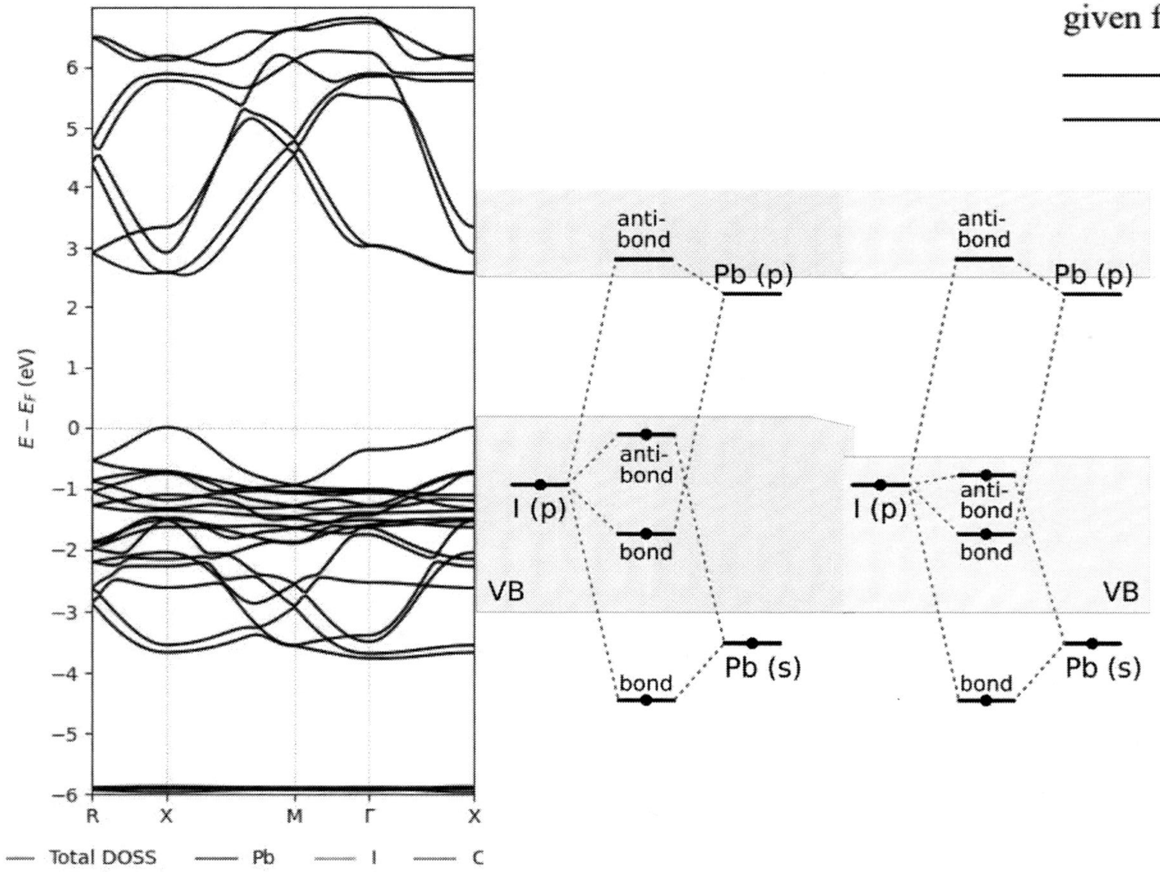

Table III: Calculated band gap (E_g in eV) and electron affinity (χ in eV) for different phases of $MAPbI_3$ at the **PBEx** level. The results on the single cell (12 atoms) are given for comparison.

Phase	E_g	χ.
Cubic *Pm3m*	1.68	3.79
Tetra. *I4/mcm*	2.17	3.49
Ortho. *P222₁*	2.25	3.46
Single cell	2.25	3.45

Dielectric properties: The case of $MAPbI_3$

Ph. Baranek, M. Rérat and R. Dovesi

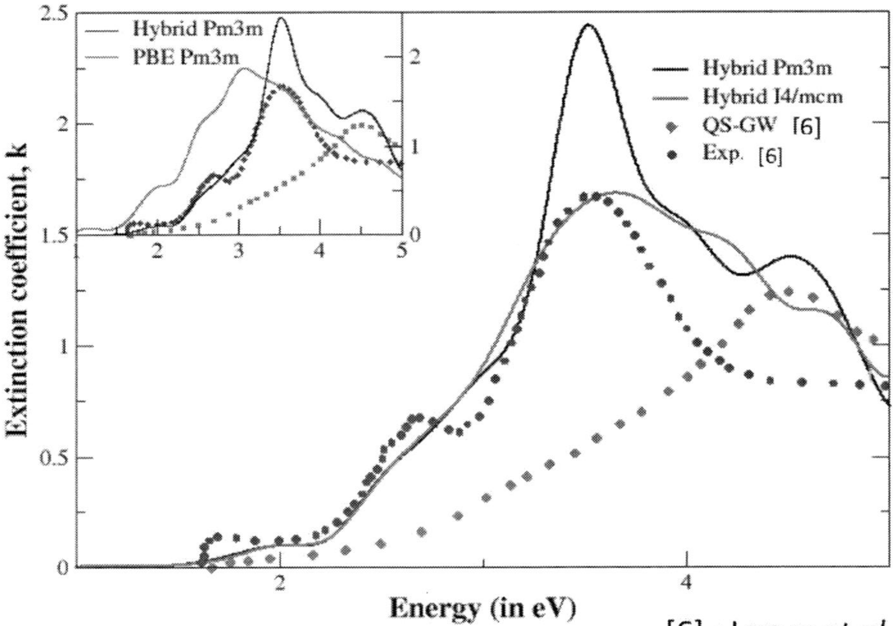

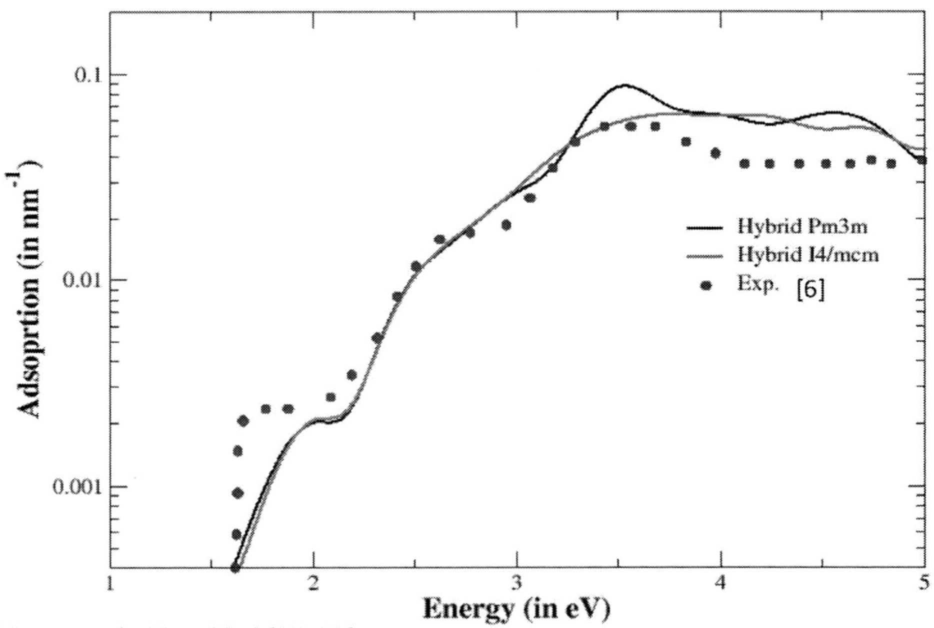

[6] : Leguy *et al.*, Nanoscale **8**, 6317 (2016)

EDF

Ph. Baranek, J.P. Connolly et al. to be submitted

Impact on the cells efficiency: via drift diffusion model

SILVACO IPVF

J.P. Connolly, Ph. Baranek

Parameter	Definition
τ_{SRH}	Electron and hole charge neutral and depletion layers Shockley-Read-Hall lifetimes
μ	Carrier mobility, majority and minority, electron and hole
D_N, D_P	Hole and electron diffusion coefficients
C_A	Auger coefficient
ε	Permittivity related to complex refractive index
n, k	Real and imaginary refractive indices
m_e^*	Electron and hole effective masses
χ	Electron affinity
N_C, N_V	Band parameters - conduction and valence band effective densities of states
E_C, E_V, E_g	Band parameters - Conduction and valence band edges and bandgap

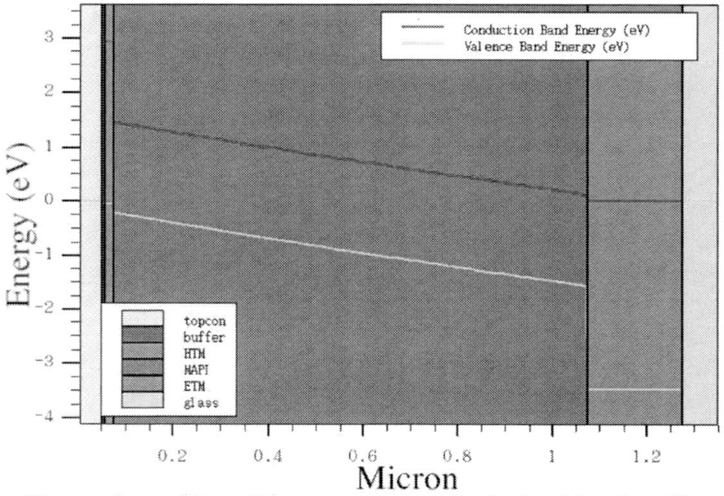

Figure: Perovskite cell layer structure and calculated band profile for experimental parameter input values to device model.

Table IV: Device performance modelling for parameters taken from the experimental data of literature [19], and from successive theoretical **PBEx** calculations ranging from the single cell (12 atoms cell) to tetragonal and cubic phases (96 atoms cell), showing a peak performance for the cubic phase.

Data source	Jsc (A/m^2)	V_{oc} (V)	V_{mp} (V)	FF (%)	η (%)
Single cell	13.4	1.82	1.40	71.9	17.5
Ortho. *P222₁*	11.6	1.80	1.42	73.6	15.5
Tetra. *I4/mcm*	13.4	1.73	1.37	74.6	17.2
Cubic *Pm3m*	18.2	1.25	1.11	84.3	19.2
Exp. [19]	17.5	1.25	1.10	84.3	18.5

Ph. Baranek, J.P. Connolly et al. to be submitted

Impact on the cells efficiency: via drift diffusion model

J.P. Connolly, Ph. Baranek

IPVF

Cubic

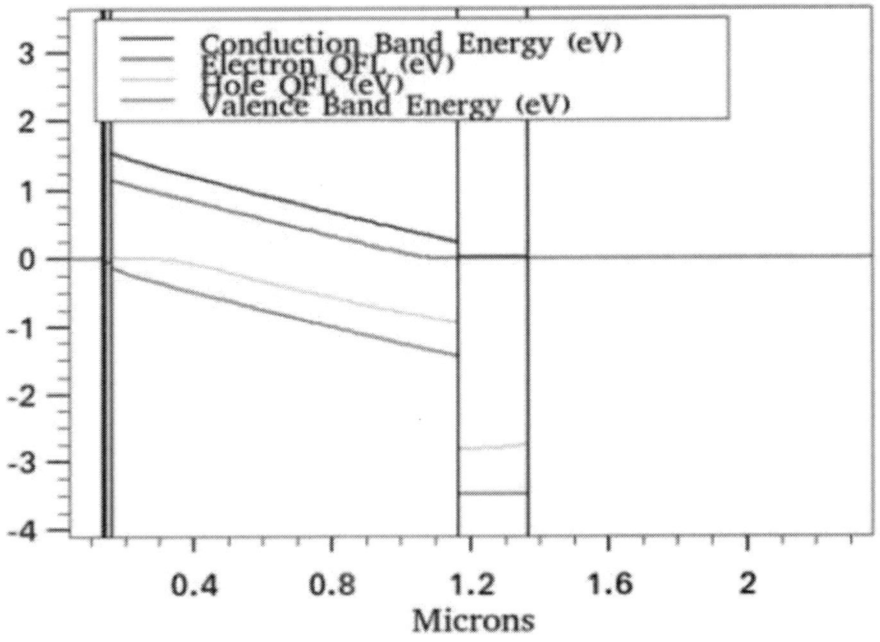

Ortho

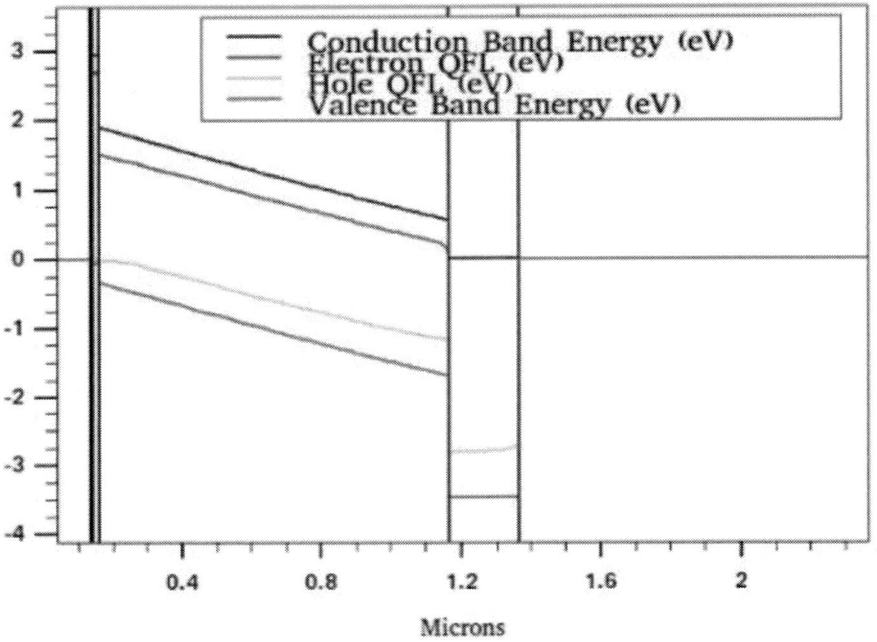

EDF

Impact on the cells efficiency: via drift diffusion model

J.P. Connolly, Ph. Baranek

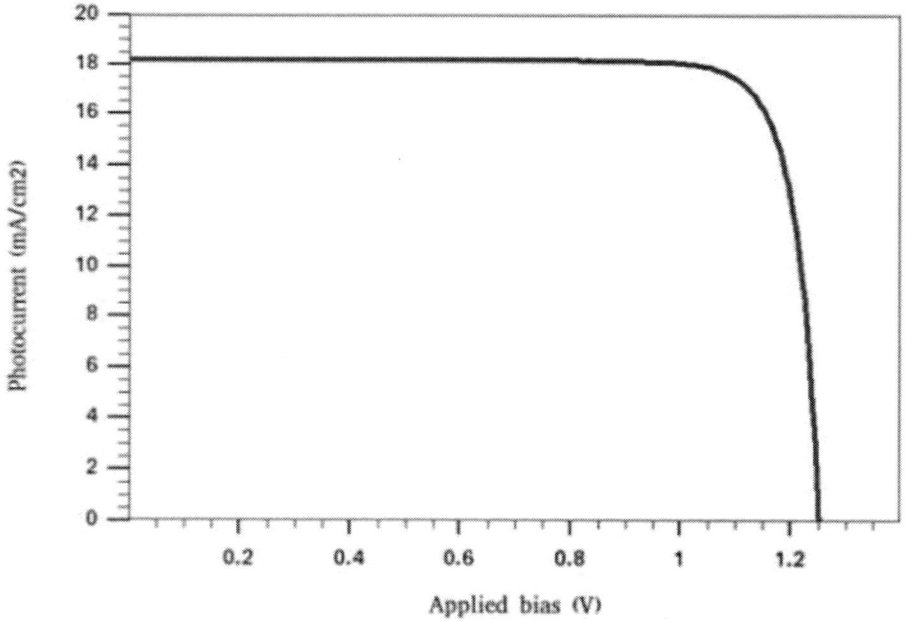

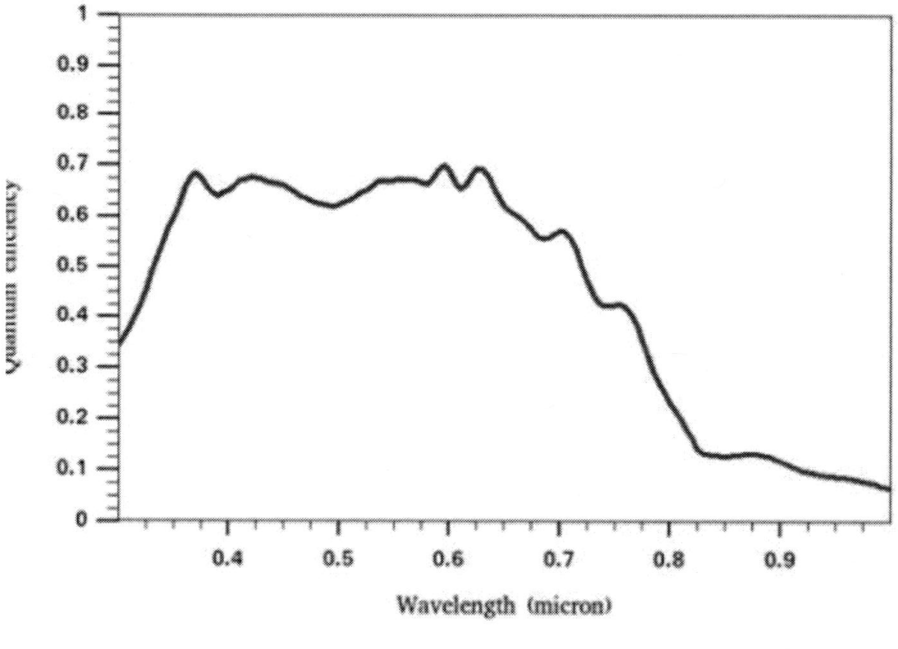

Conclusions

IPVF

- **A pragmatic multiscale approach: atomistic first-principles methods coupled to device numerical model.**
  - **Based on DFT approaches optimized to obtain a good description of a given family of compound.**
  - **➔ Definition of adapted hybrid functional for a given compound.**

  -> Evaluation of the perovskites performances in good agreement with experimental data.

- **Provide a set of criteria for optimizing the materials for different PV applications and for suggesting effective complex perovskites.**

- **Can be used on different materials and types of devices.**

Example of optimisation of inorganic perovskites:

A. Gissler *et al.* "Ab-Initio Approach to Guide the Optimization of Inorganic Halide Perovskites"

Session 2.2 talk 2DO.8 – 25 Sept. 13:30

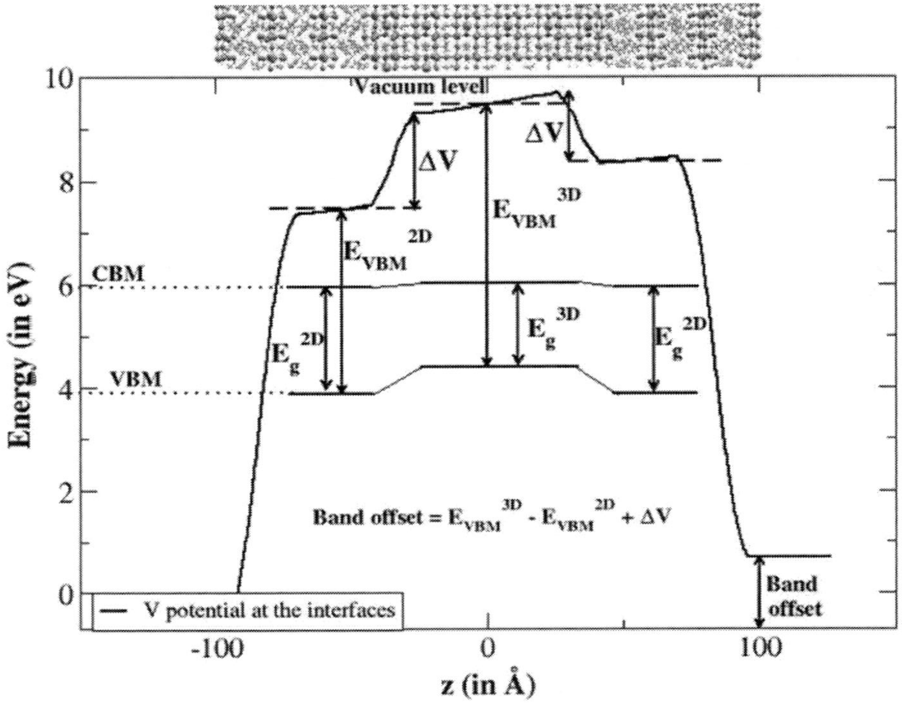

EDF

IPVF

THANK YOU
FOR
YOUR ATTENTION

eDF

12

Modelling Recovery in Perovskite Solar Cells Under Light and Dark to Address Stability Challenges

Session 2AO.3.6
September 22nd, 2025
Bilbao, Spain

Guillem ÁLVAREZ PÉREZ[1,2], Jean Baptiste PUEL[1,3], and Jean François GUILLEMOLES[1,2]

[1]Institut Photovoltaïque d'Île-de-France (IPVF), Palaiseau, 91120, France
[2] InstitutPhotovoltaïque d'Île-de-France (IPVF), UMR 9006, CNRS, École Polytechnique, IP Paris, Chimie Paristech, PSL, Palaiseau, 91120, France
[3]EDF R&D, Palaiseau, 91120, France

IPVF | INSTITUT POLYTECHNIQUE DE PARIS | EU PVSEC

MOTIVATION

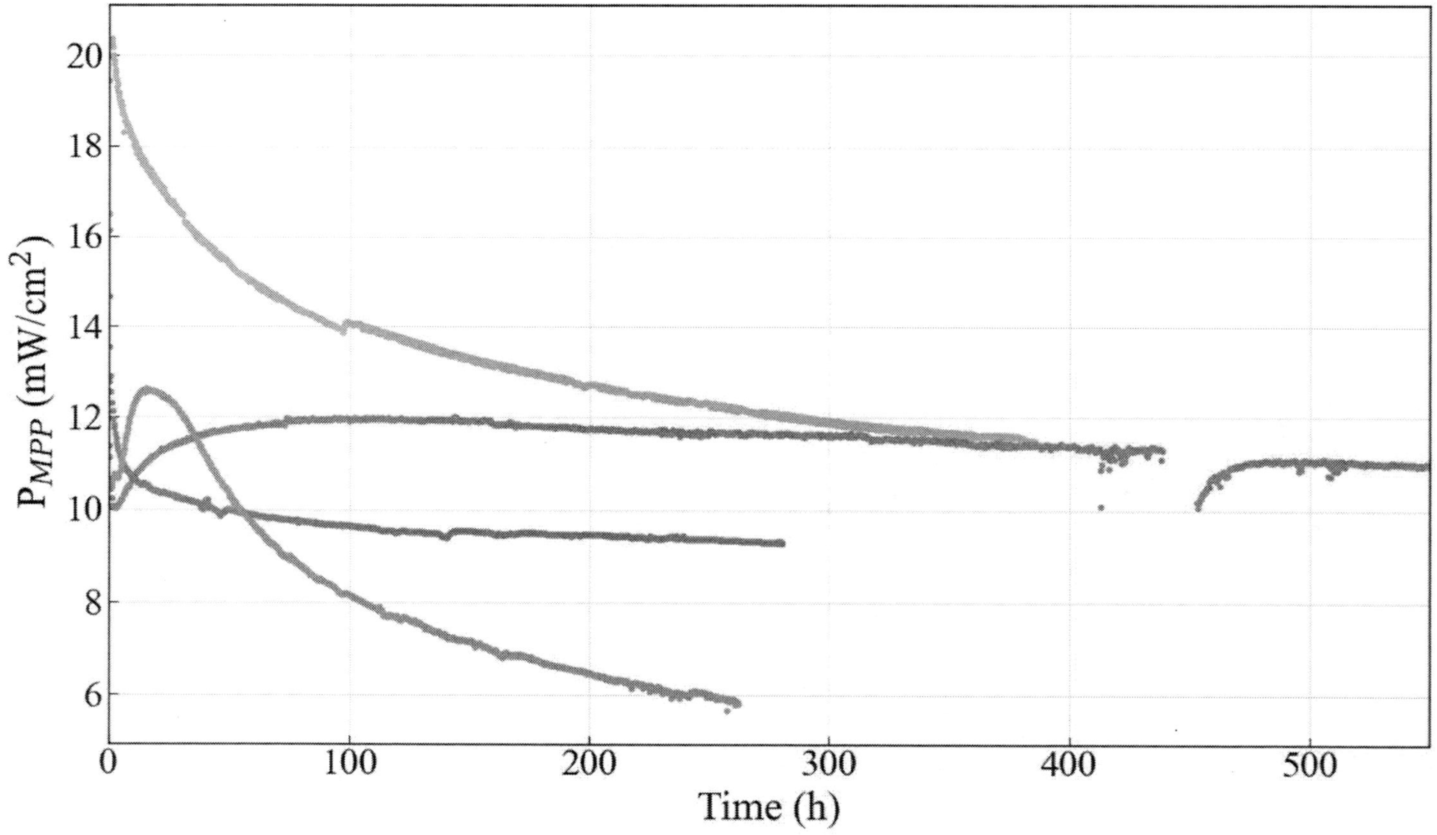

IPVF

STABILITY ISSUES

- Illumination
- Temperature
- Humidity
- Applied Bias
- Oxygen

Boyd, C. et al (2019). Chemical Reviews, 119(5), 3418-3451. doi 10.1021/acs.chemrev.8b00336

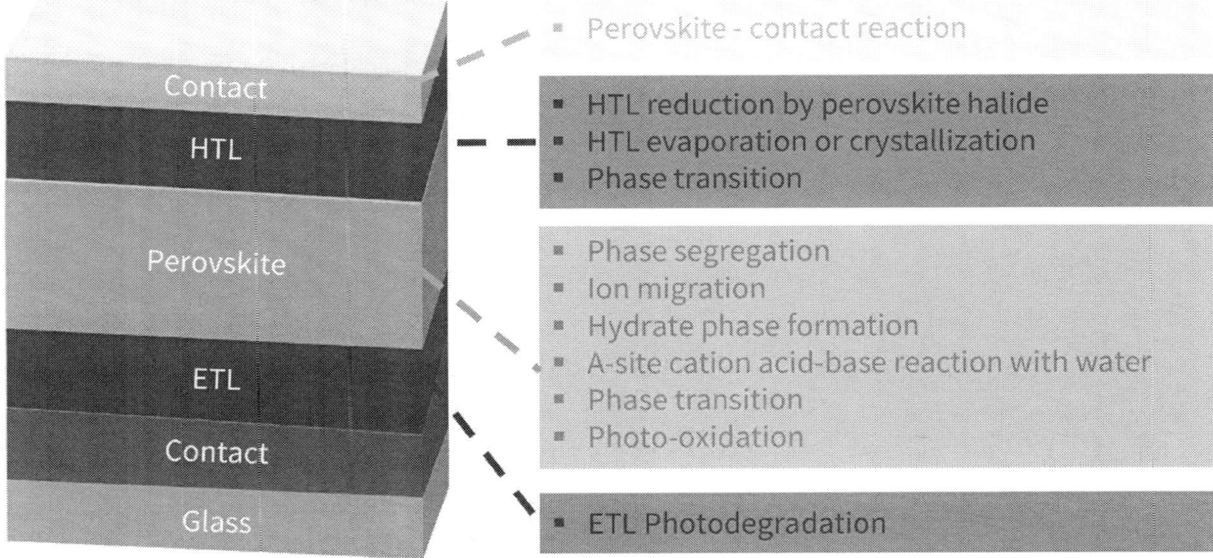

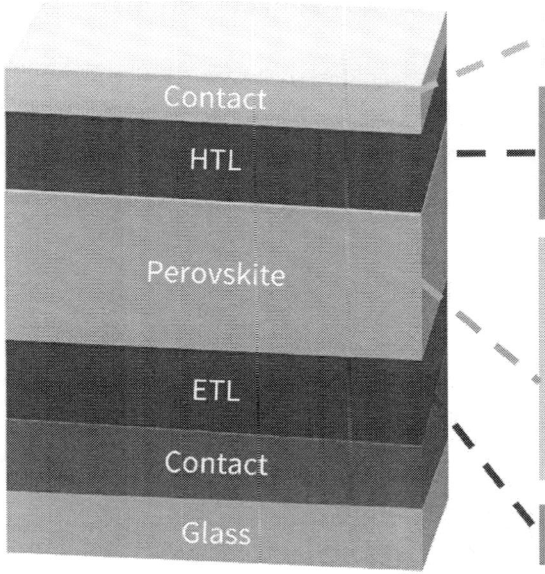

- Perovskite - contact reaction

- HTL reduction by perovskite halide
- HTL evaporation or crystallization
- Phase transition

- Phase segregation
- Ion migration
- Hydrate phase formation
- A-site cation acid-base reaction with water
- Phase transition
- Photo-oxidation

- ETL Photodegradation

nature energy CONSENSUS STATEMENT
https://doi.org/10.1038/s41560-019-0529-5
OPEN

Consensus statement for stability assessment and reporting for perovskite photovoltaics based on ISOS procedures

IPVF

OUR APPROACH

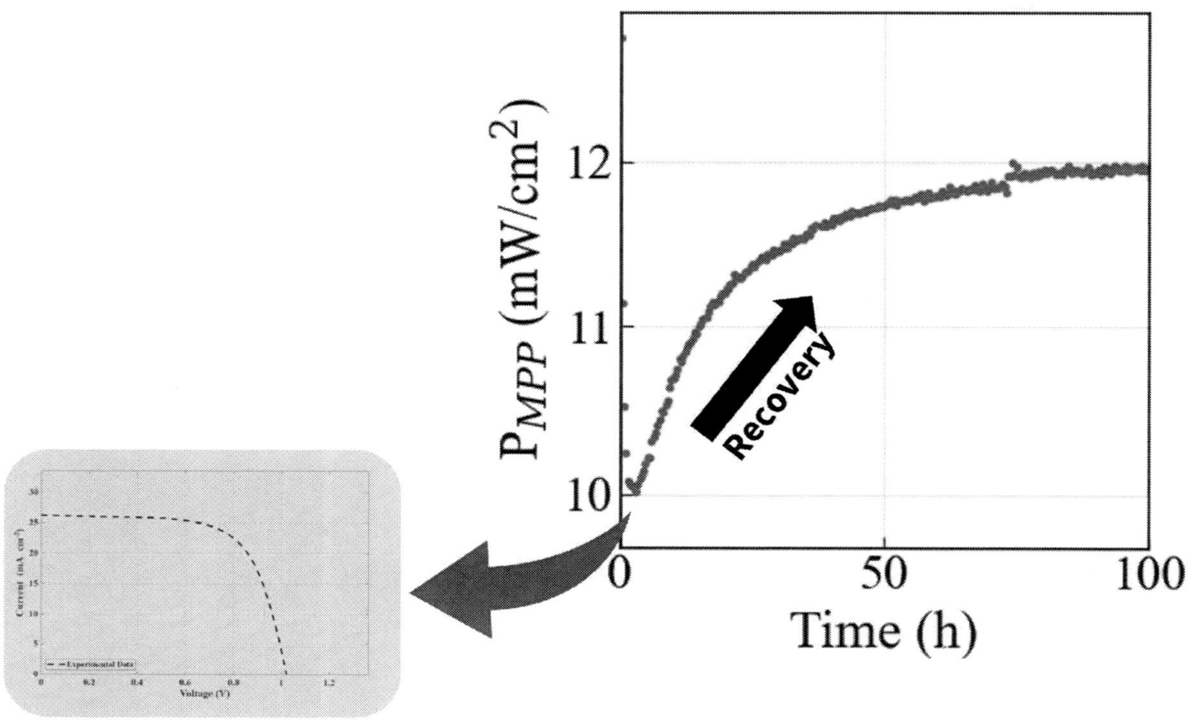

IPVF

OUR APPROACH

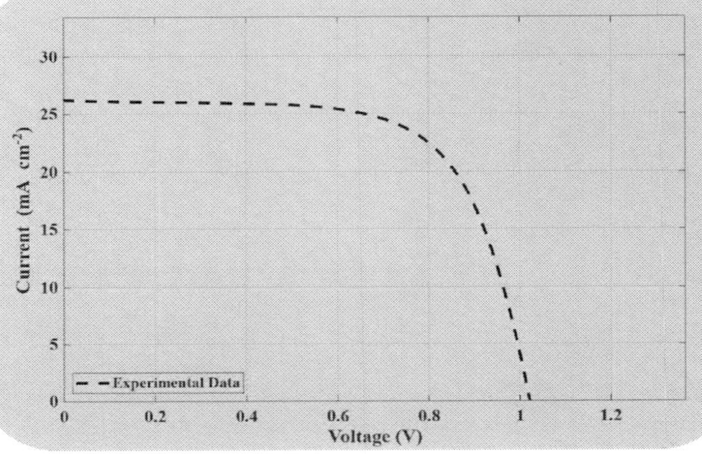

- Optic: Transfer matrix
- Electric: Drift-diffusion

GENETIC ALGORITHM

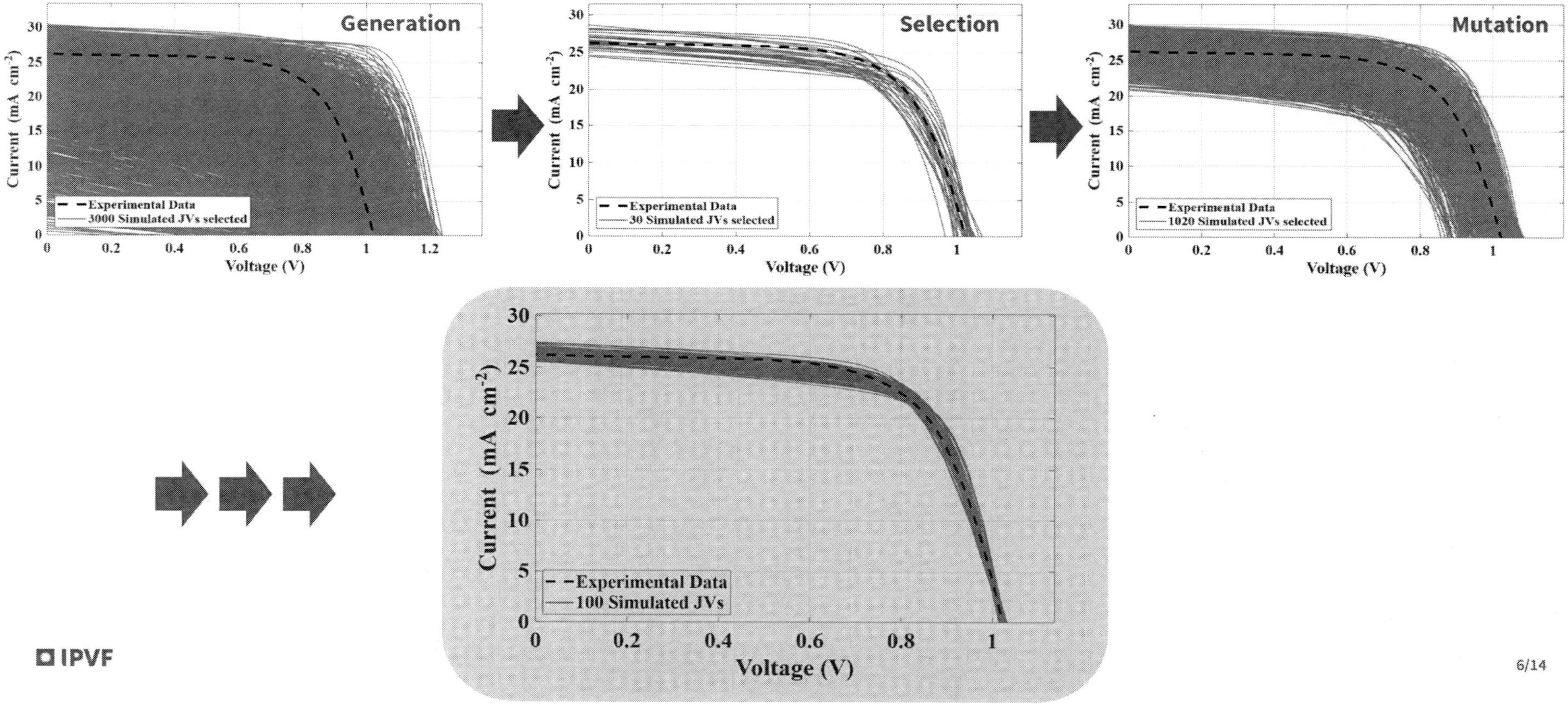

IPVF

GENETIC ALGORITHM

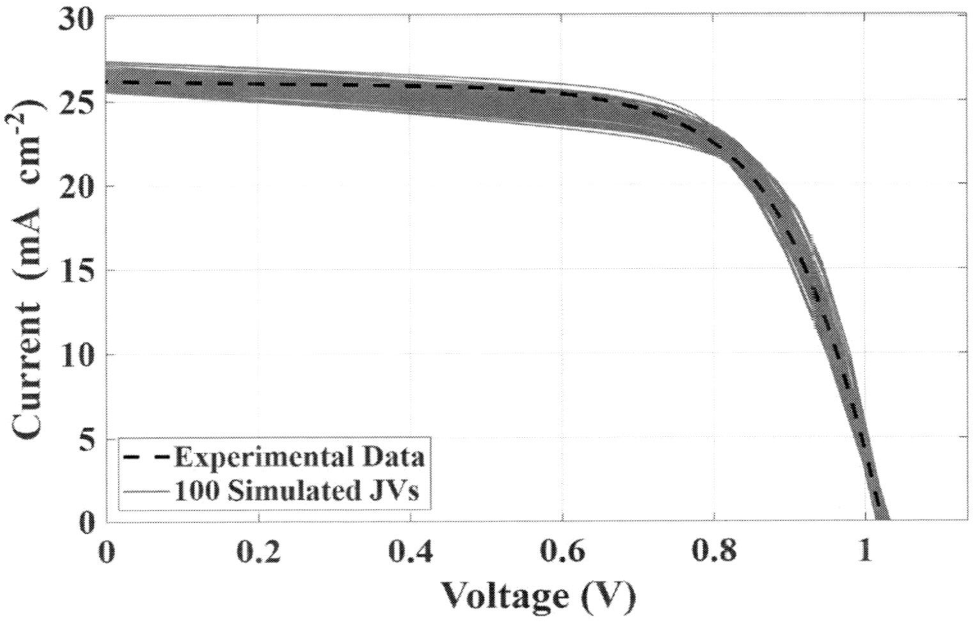

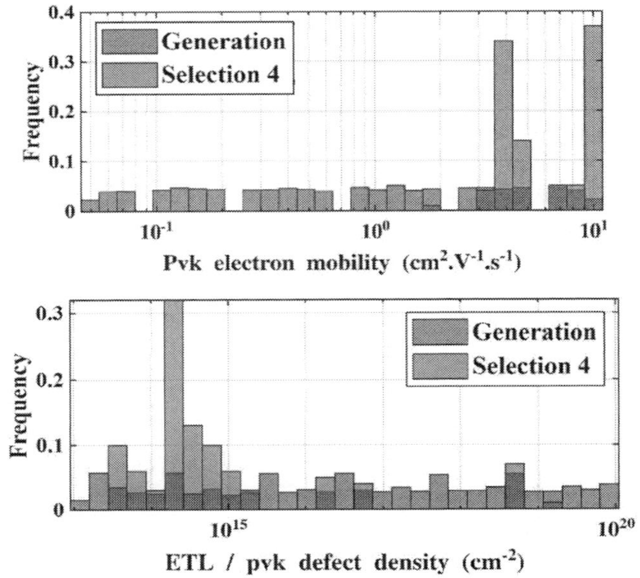

IPVF

SIMULATING RECOVERY

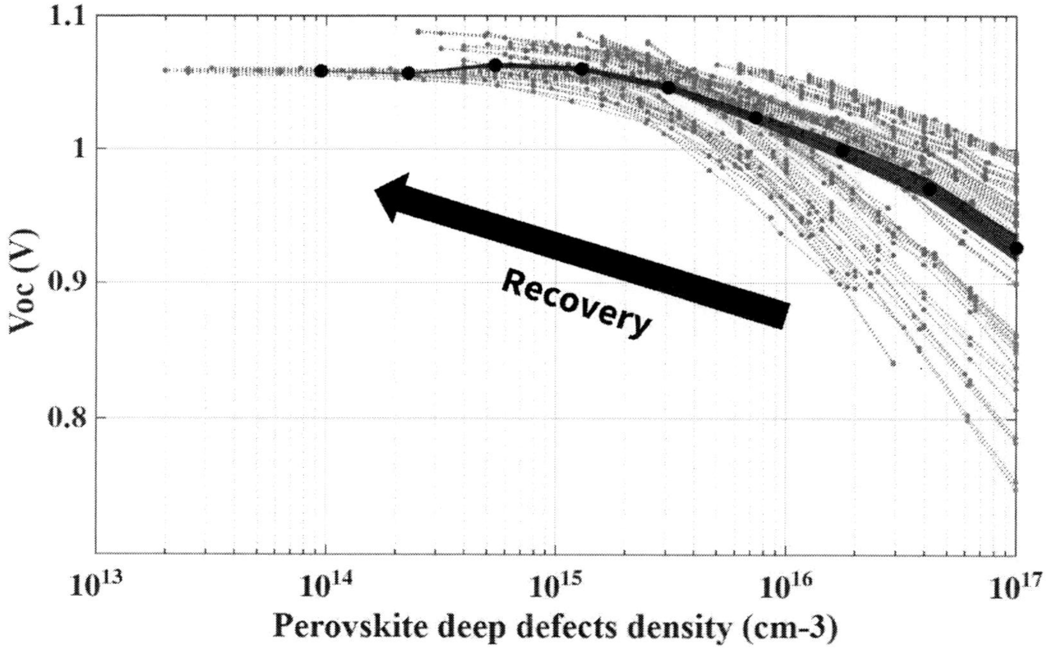

IPVF

CORRELATION PATHWAYS

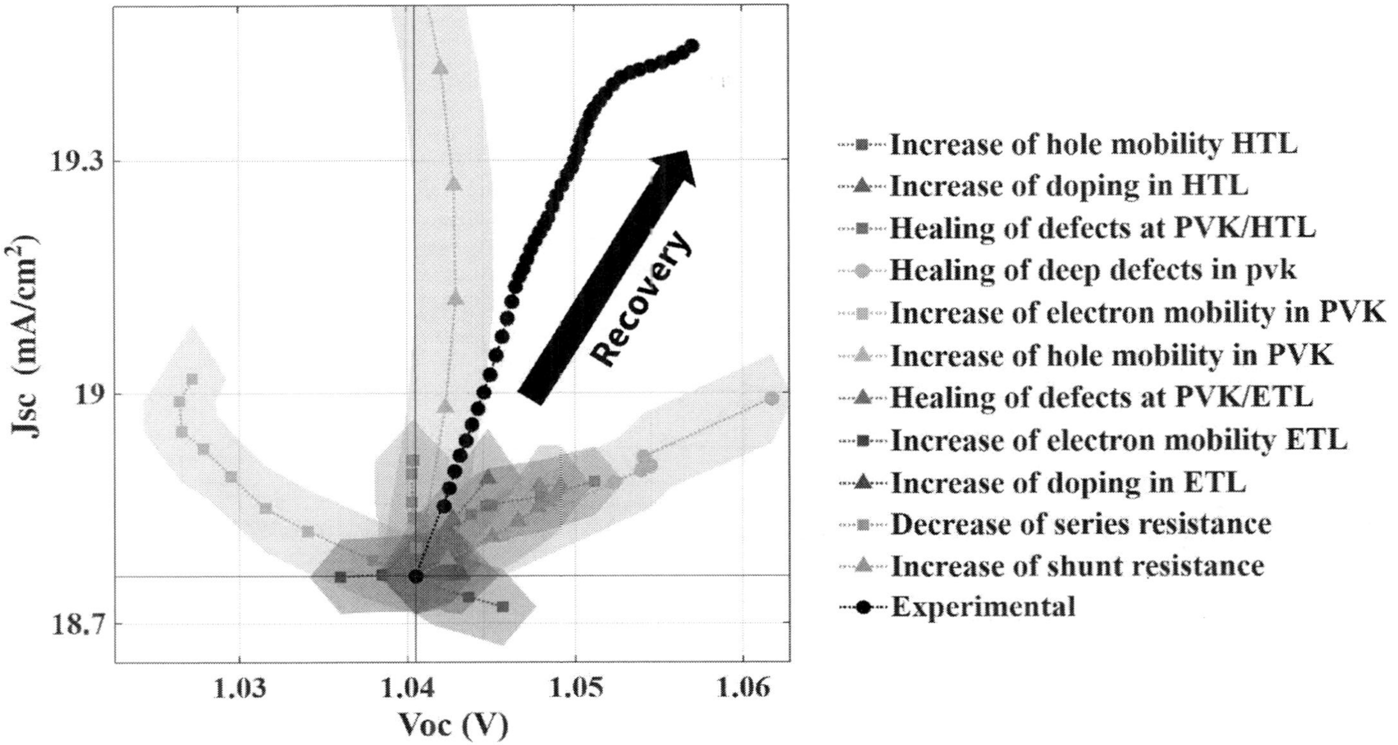

IPVF

(Voc, Jsc, FF, Rs, Rsh)

RESULTS

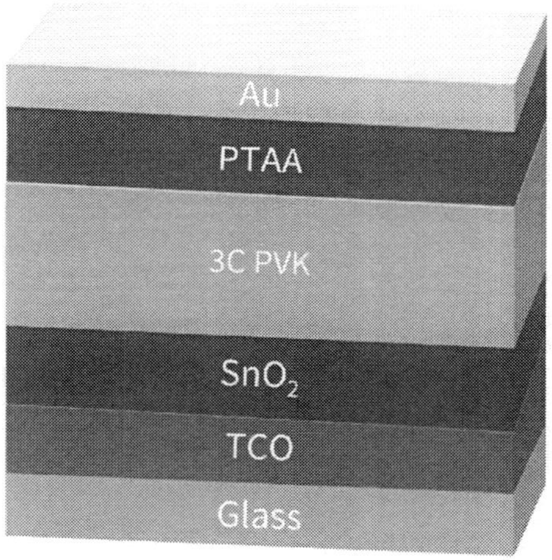

Perovskite Layer Synthesis Conditions	
Sample ID	**Condition**
Cells 1, 2	Solution prepared @ Day 0
Cells 3, 4	Solution prepared @ Day 0 + Heated 70 °C, 1h
Cells 5, 6	Solution prepared @ Day-1
Cells 7, 8	Solution prepared @ Day-1 + Heated 70 °C, 1h

RESULTS
14
12
10
8
6
4
2
0
P_{MPP} (mW/cm²)
0
100
200
300
400
500
600
Time (h)
Cell 2
Cell 5
Cell 6
Cell 7
Cell 8
1.08
1.04
1.00
0.96
J_{SC} (normalized)
0.96
1.00
1.04
V_{OC} (normalized)
Cell 2
Cell 5
Cell 6
Cell 7
Cell 8
1st Recovery
2nd Recovery
Degradation
IPVF
11 /14

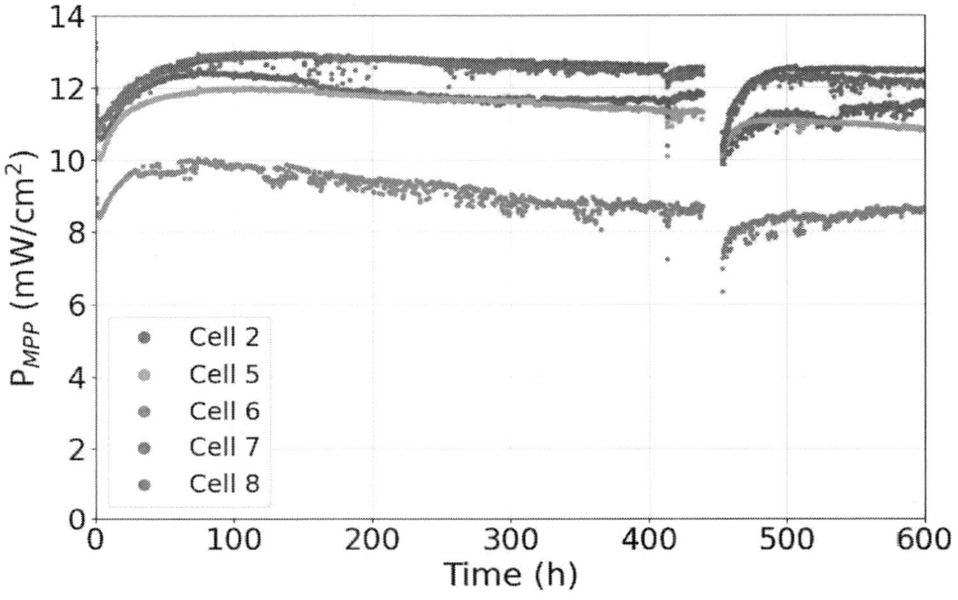

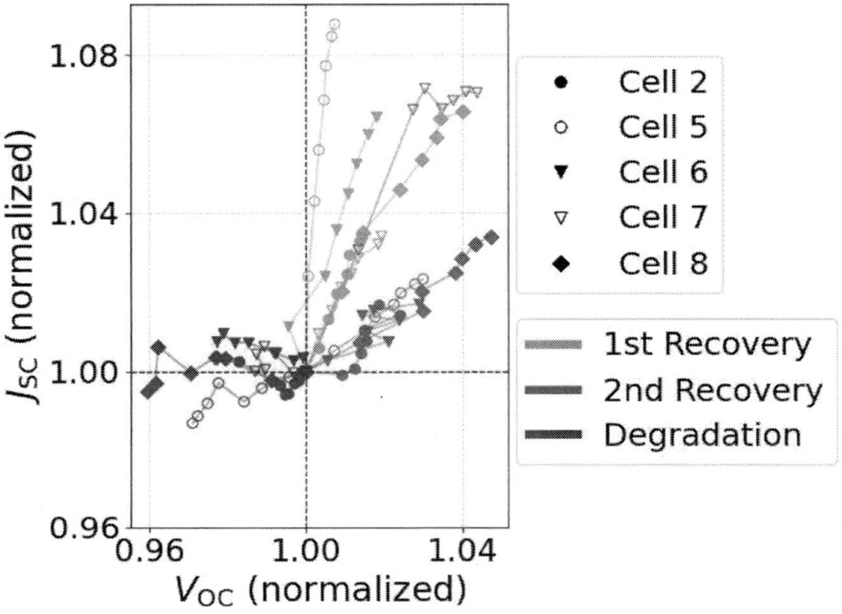

RESULTS

Close to experimental pathways

Far from experimental pathways

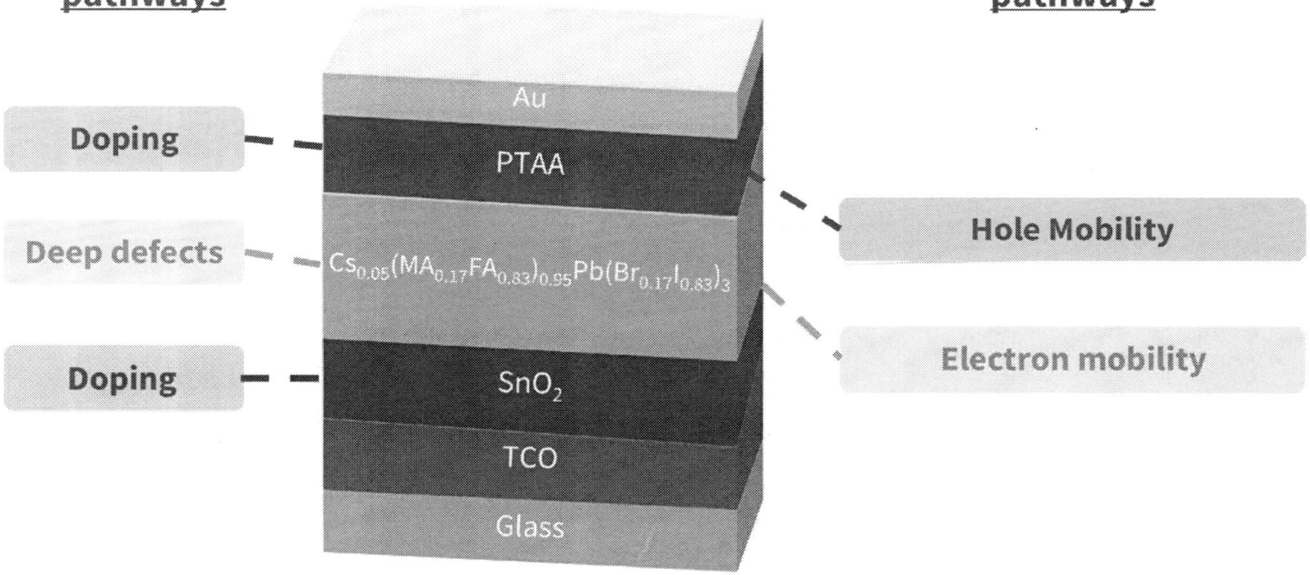

REVERSIBILITY

FABRICATION

IPVF

SUMMARY AND PERSPECTIVES

- Framework to link experiments ↔ simulations in correlation space
- Insights into instabilities under light/dark

Modelling outcomes

Suggest mechanisms causing recovery and degradation

Discard mechanisms that are far from experimental data

Identify Reversible Mechanisms

- Extend number of devices studied
- Apply framework to different ISOS tests

IPVF

THANK YOU

Guillem ÁLVAREZ PÉREZ[1,2], Jean Baptiste PUEL[1,3], and Jean François GUILLEMOLES[1,2]

[1]Institut Photovoltaïque d'Île-de-France (IPVF), Palaiseau, 91120, France
[2]Institut Photovoltaïque d'Île-de-France (IPVF), UMR 9006, CNRS, École Polytechnique, IP Paris, Chimie Paristech, PSL, Palaiseau, 91120, France
[3]EDF R&D, Palaiseau, 91120, France

Contact: guillem.alvarez@ipvf.fr

- EUPVSEC 2025
- Session 2AO.3.6
- September 22nd, 2025
- Bilbao, Spain

INSTITUT POLYTECHNIQUE DE PARIS

IPVF

EU PVSEC

42nd EUPVSEC
Bilbao, 23rd September 2025

On perimeter losses in perovskite top- and poly-Si-passivated silicon bottom cells – do small area tandems reveal the full efficiency potential?

F. Haase[1], L. Brockmann[1], A. Raugewitz[1], V. Steckenreiter[1], V. Barnscheidt[1], R. Clausing[1], S. Baumann[1], J. Vollbrecht[1], W. Veurman[1], J. Löhr[1], D. Liu[1], M. Turcu[1], L. Nasebandt[1], U. Römer[1], D. Sylla[1], J. Strey[1], M. Löhning[1], L. Mettner[1], R. Winter[1], A. Christ[1], H. Kohlenberg[1], C. Marquardt[1], E. Brueckner[1], H. Rabiei[1], M. Rienäcker[1], S. Kajari-Schröder[1], T. Wietler[1,2], R. Peibst[1,3]

[1]Institute for Solar Energy Research Hamelin (ISFH), Germany
[2]Institute of Solid-State Physics, Leibniz University Hannover, Germany
[3]Institute of Electronic Materials and Devices, Leibniz University Hannover, Germany

Influence of shaded perimeter and edge on performance

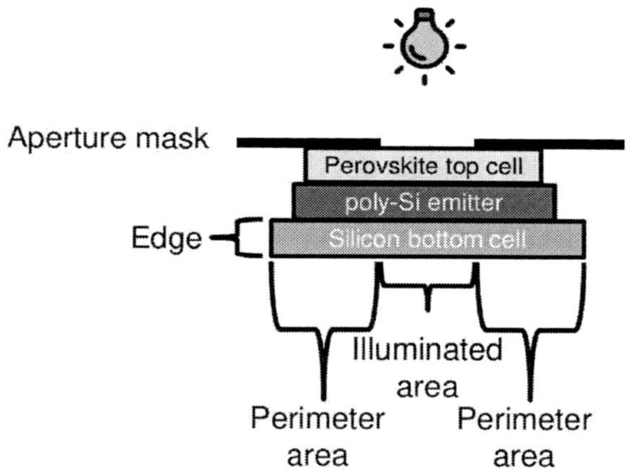

- Record efficiencies of perovskite-silicon tandem cells on 1 cm^2 aperture area
- Influence of different layer perimeter areas? Often not reported
- Reports on single junction cell perimeter losses [1-3]
- **This work: Perimeter losses of different layers in tandem device**

[1] P.P. Altermatt, et al., Prog. Photovolt: Res. Appl., 4 (1996). https://doi.org/10.1002/(SICI)1099-159X(199609/10)4:5<355::AID-PIP145>3.0.CO;2-X
[2] F. Haase et al., IEEE Journal of Photovoltaics, vol. 8, no. 1, (2018). https://doi.org/10.1109/JPHOTOV.2017.2762592
[3] D. Kiermasch et al., Joule 3, (2019). https://doi.org/10.1016/j.joule.2018.10.016

Experimental results: poly-Si passivated c-Si bottom cell

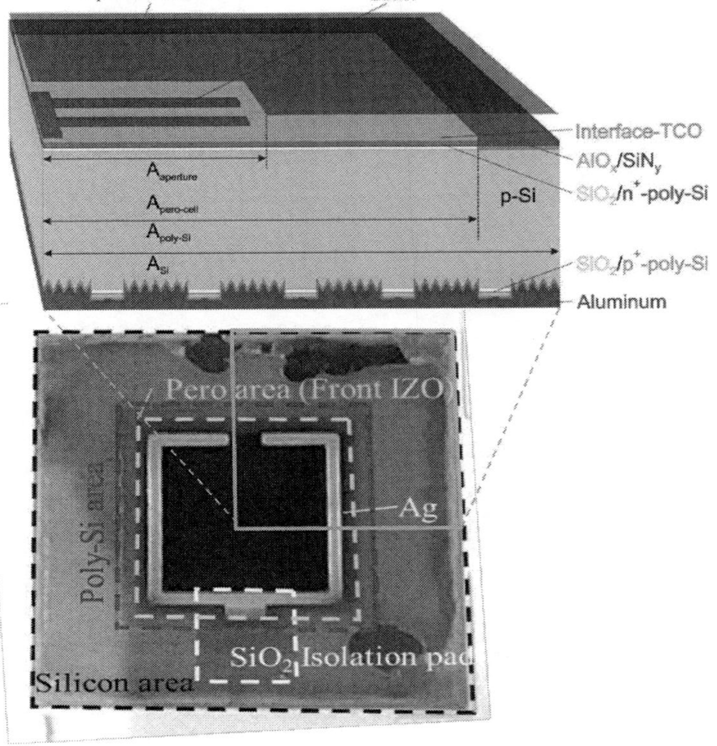

- 25×25 mm² bottom cell with metal front grid on 10×10 mm² area

Experimental results: poly-Si passivated c-Si bottom cell

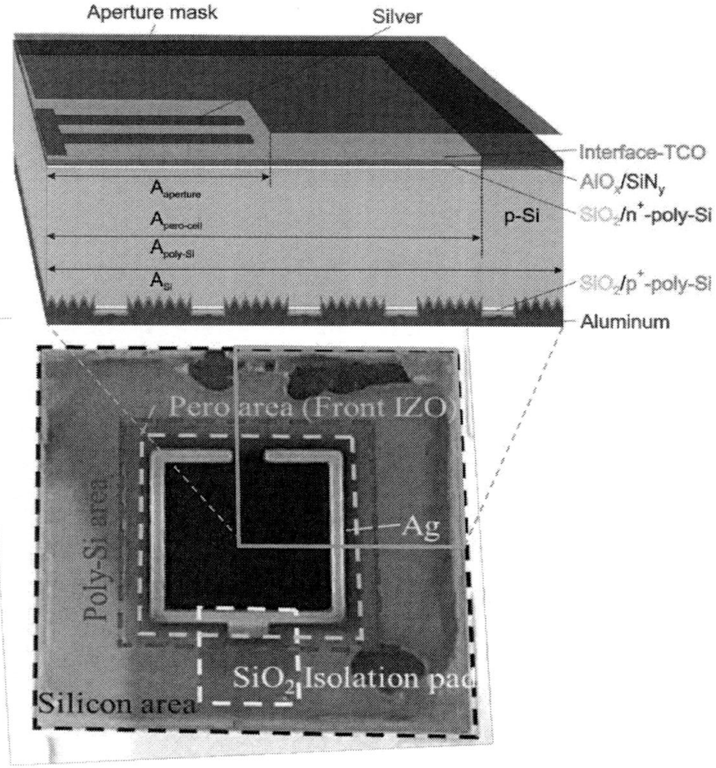

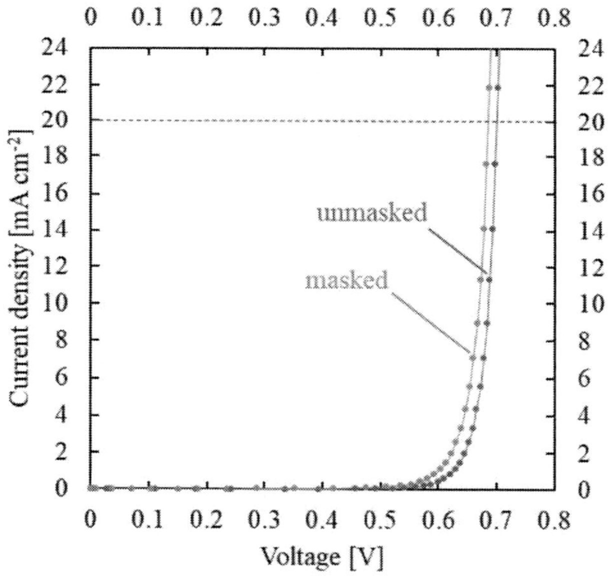

- 25×25 mm^2 bottom cell with metal front grid on 10×10 mm^2 area
- J_{SC}-V_{OC} measurement with and without 10×10 mm^2 aperture area mask
- 19 mV V_{OC} loss
- Best pseudo efficiency of 11.5%

Experimental results: perovskite top cell

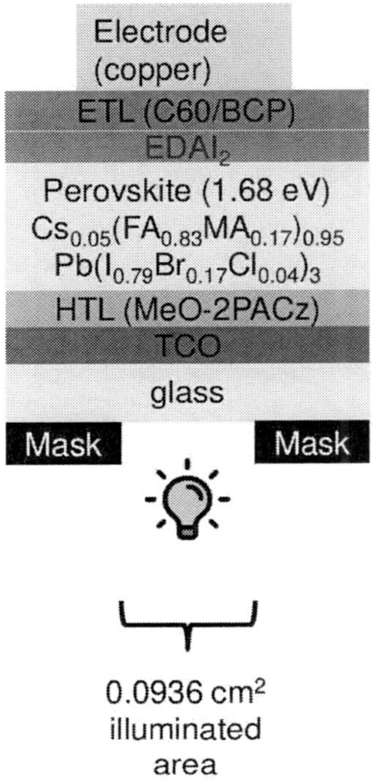

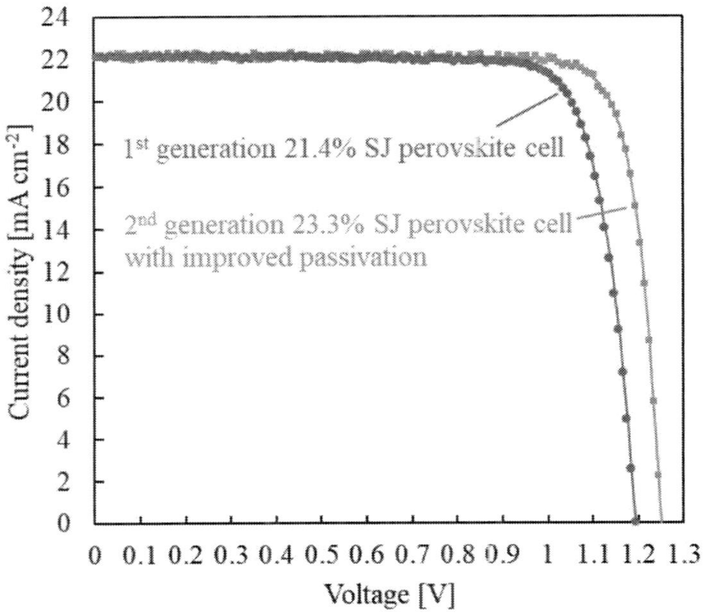

- Wet chemically processed HTL, perovskite and $EDAI_2$
- Evaporated ETL and electrode
- Improvement of $EDAI_2$ passivation layer increases efficiency from 21.4% to 23.3%
- Adding 11.5% from bottom cell gives 32.9% (34.8% with improved $EDAI_2$) tandem efficiency

Experimental results: tandem cell

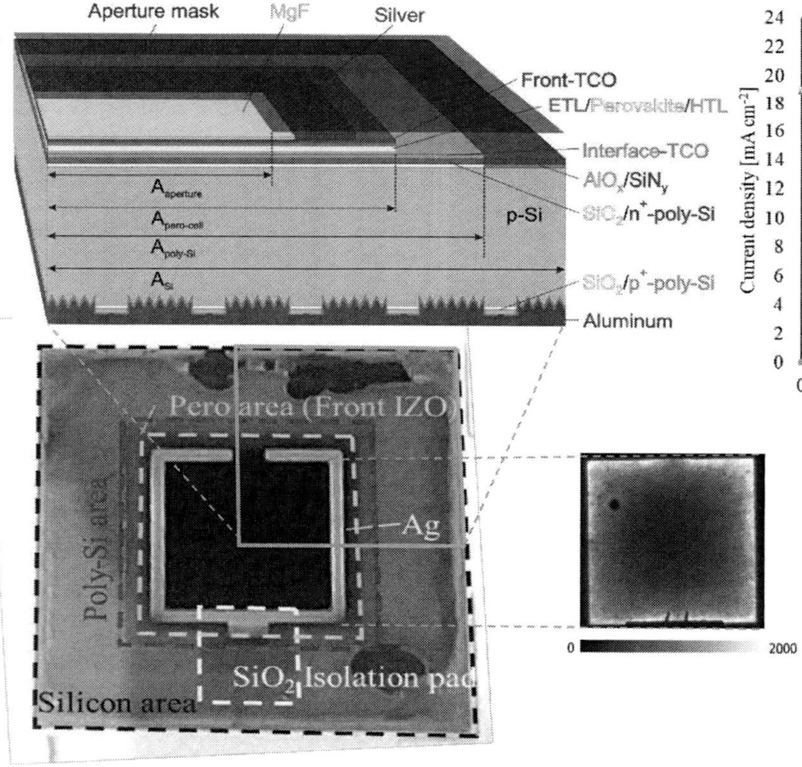

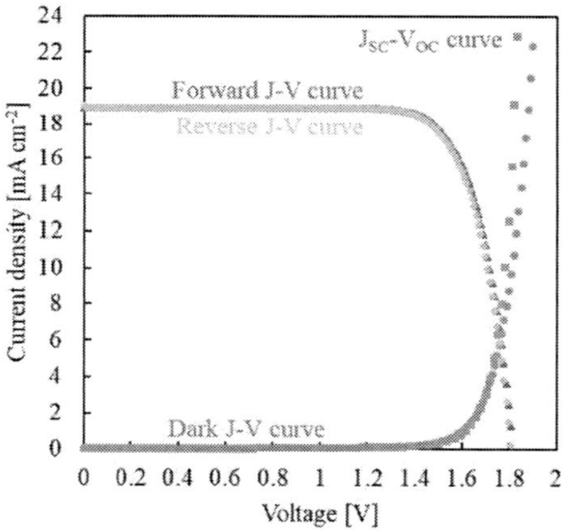

- Measured 26.7% falls behind the theoretical efficiency of 32.9%
- Large series resistance due to low conductive front TCO ($4\%_{abs}$ fill factor loss)
- Current limited to 19 mA/cm^2 by parasitic absorption of
  - Unintended thick poly-Si layer of 115 nm
  - Front C60 layer
- Adapted limit 28%
- **Influence of perimeter region?**

Simulated tandem device

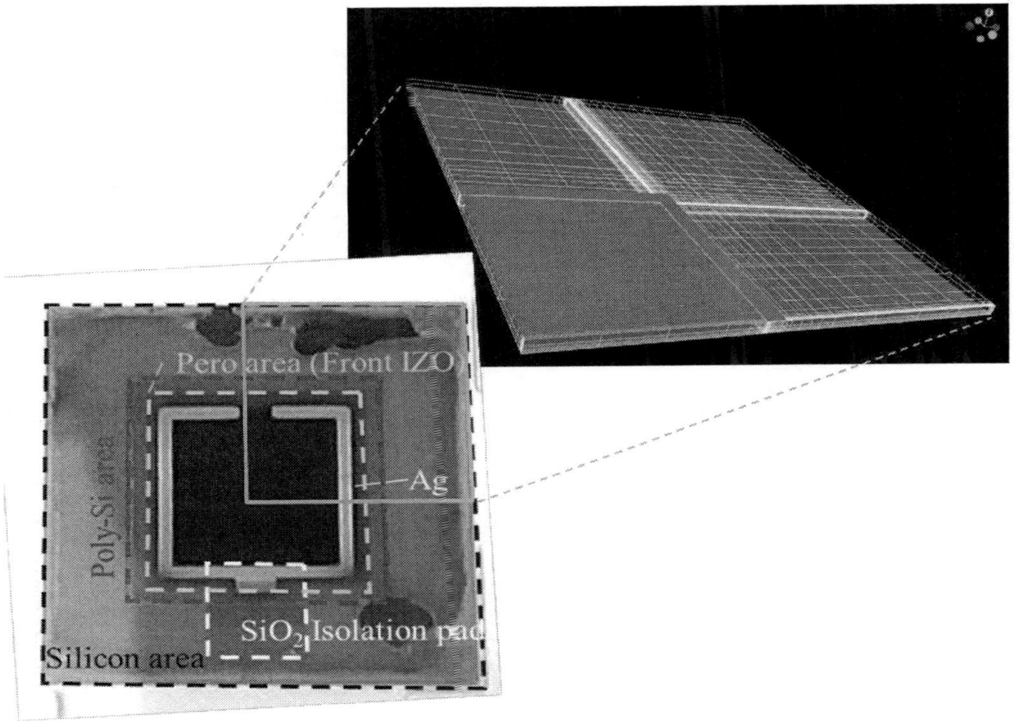

Conductive boundary model [4], Quokka3 [5]:

- Si bottom cell based on measured input parameters
- Perovskite top cell fit to the 1st generation 21.4% measured SJ *J*-*V* curve
- Quarter of the tandem cell simulated

[4] R. Brendel, Progress in Photovoltaics: Research and Applications 20 (1) (2012). https://doi.org/10.1002/pip.954
[5] Quokka3, https://www.quokka3.com/ accessed at 04.09.2025

Simulated variations

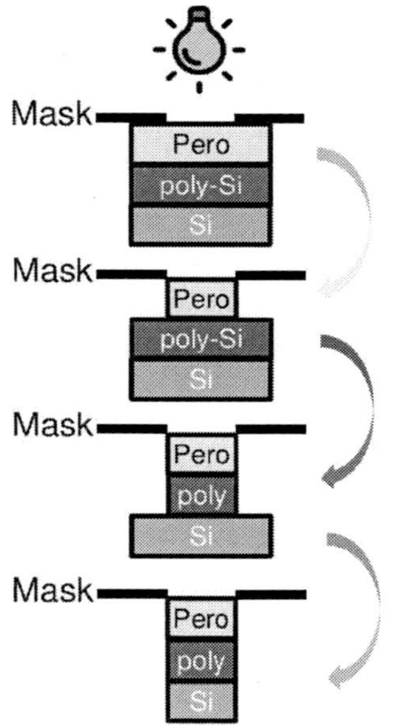

Conductive boundary model [4], Quokka3 [5]:

- Starting with full area of all layers
- Reducing one layer after the other

[4] R. Brendel, Progress in Photovoltaics: Research and Applications 20 (1) (2012). https://doi.org/10.1002/pip.954
[5] Quokka3, https://www.quokka3.com/ accessed at 04.09.2025

V_{OC} gain without perimeter region

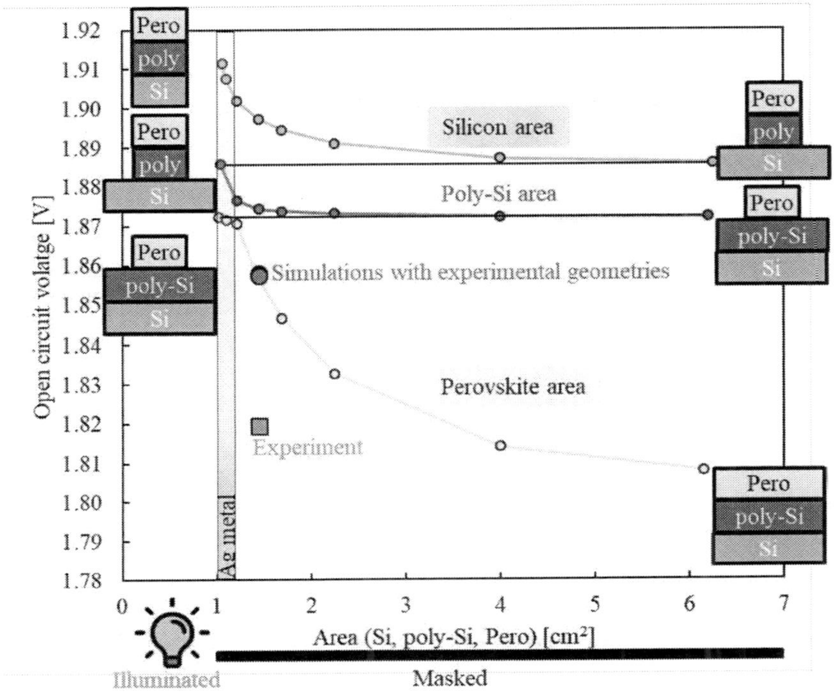

- Perovskite perimeter induces largest loss ($\Delta V_{OC} = 64$ mV)
- 170 Ω-resistant poly-Si layer has minor influence
- Well passivated FZ silicon wafer has induces $\Delta V_{OC} = 26$ mV

V_{OC} loss with high edge recombination

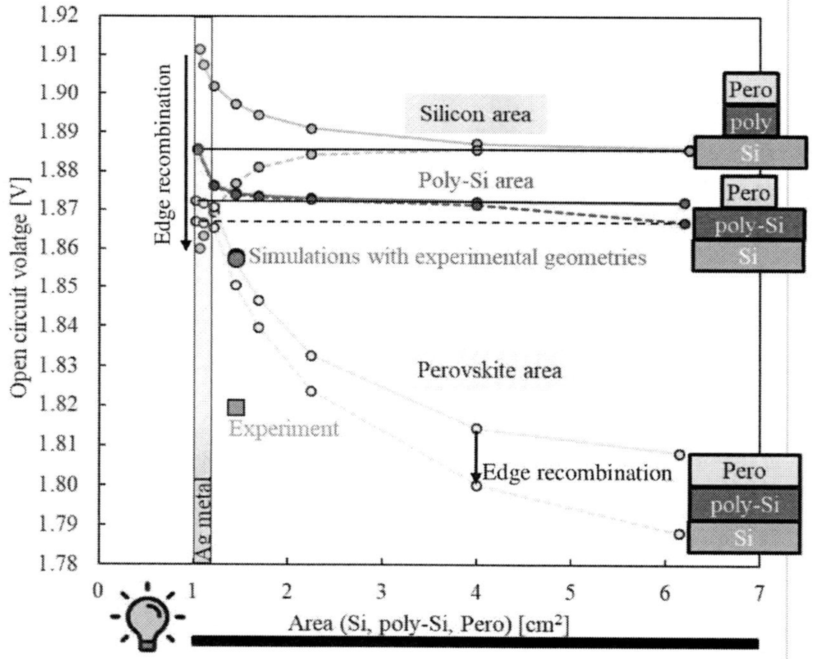

Adding diffusion limited recombination with ideality factor 2 J_{02edge} at silicon outer edge decreases V_{OC} when

- Perovskite area (front TCO) is increasing
- Poly-Si (emitter) extends to silicon edge
- Silicon edge gets closer to illuminated area (up to 52 mV when Si wafer is equal to illuminated area)

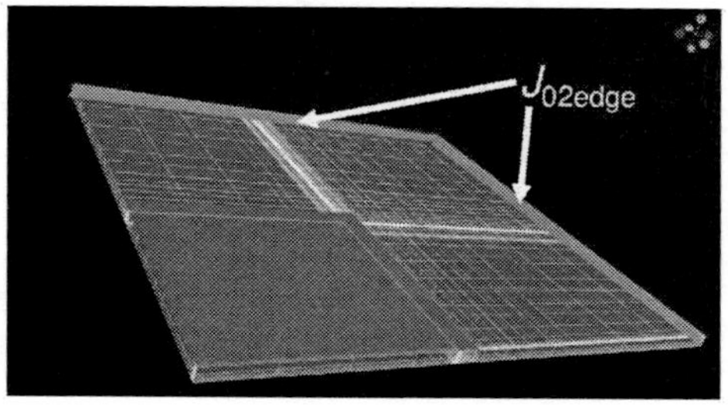

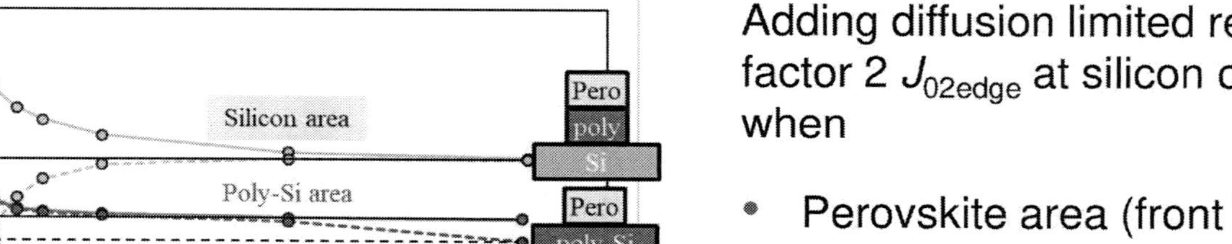

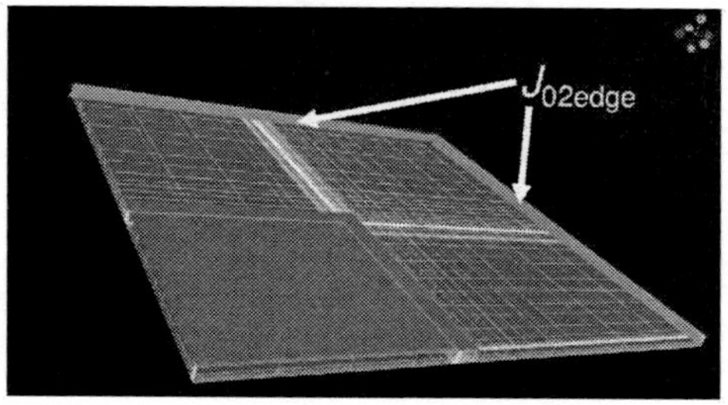

Fill factor loss with high edge recombination

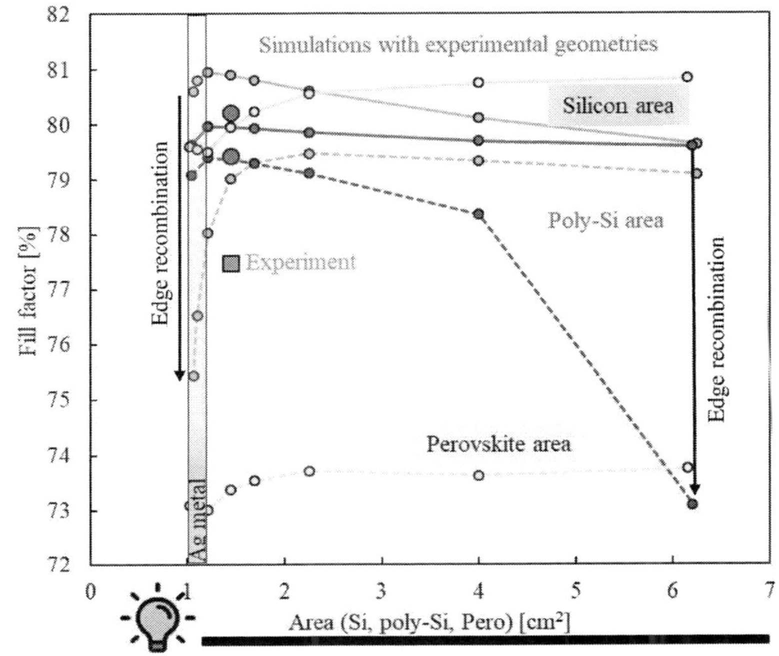

- Without edge recombination fill factor slightly dependent on shaded perimeter
- With edge recombination J_{02edge} the fill factor decreases by
  - $7\%_{abs}$ if poly-Si (emitter) extends to silicon edge
  - $5\%_{abs}$ if Si wafer is equal to illuminated area

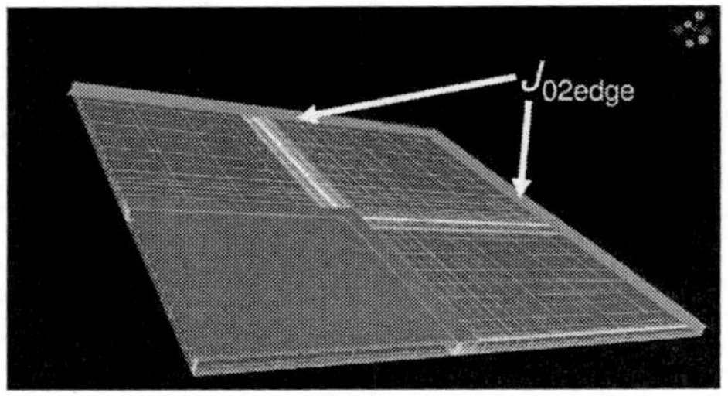

Efficiency gains and losses

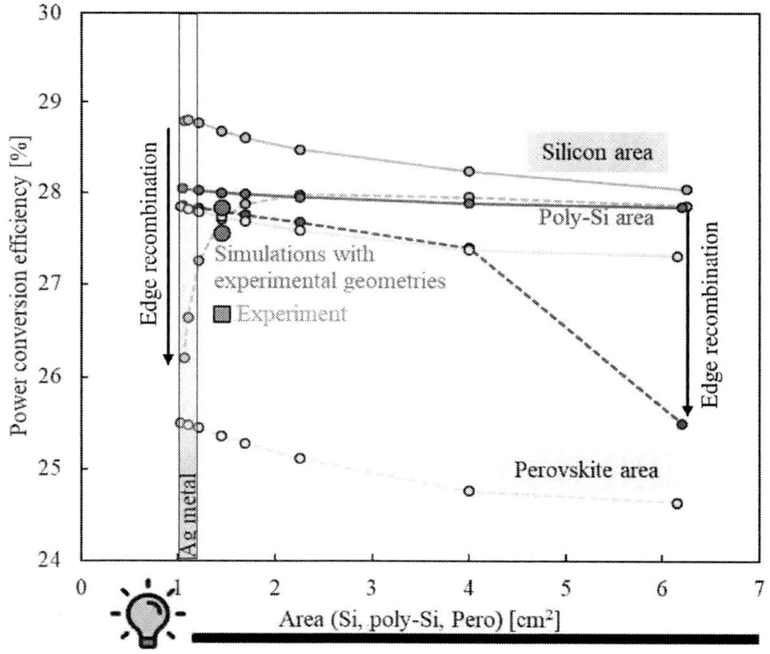

- Short circuit current independent on perimeter losses
- Without edge recombination
  - 28% simulated as sum of both SJ cells
  - Less perimeter increases efficiency by more than 1%$_{abs}$
- With edge recombination
  - 2.8%$_{abs}$ efficiency loss if poly-Si (emitter) extends to silicon edge
  - 2.6%$_{abs}$ efficiency loss if silicon edge gets close to illuminated area

Efficiency gain by 2nd generation perovskite and front fingers

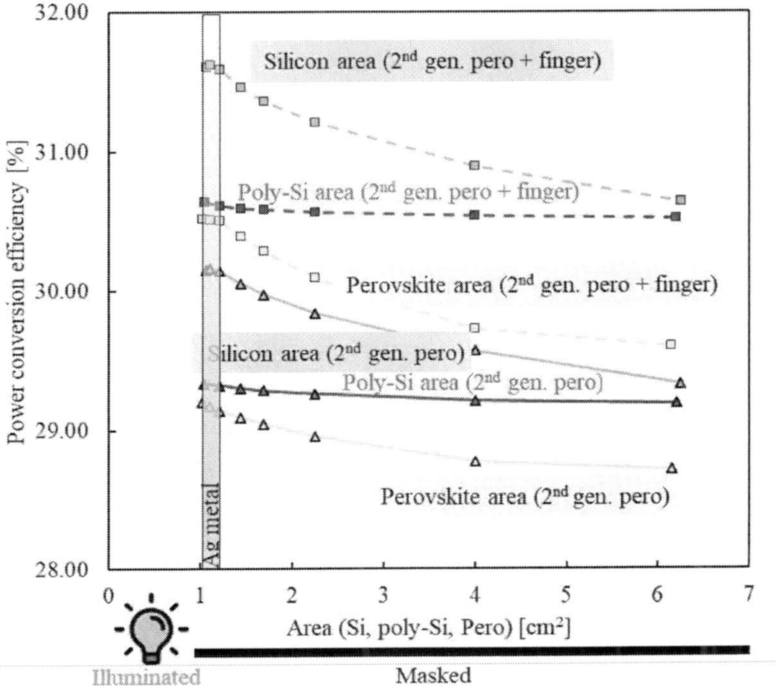

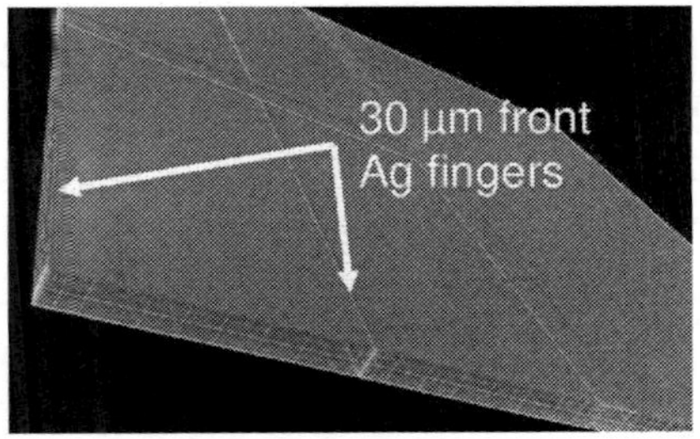

- 2nd generation perovskite cell shows higher fill factors and V_{OC} and thus higher efficiency
- Implementation of front fingers reduces front TCO resistance losses and increases fill factor and efficiency
- Reducing poly-Si and C60 thickness allows >33%

Conclusion

ISFH

Experimental:

- 11.5%-efficient poly-Si passivated bottom cells
- 23.3%-efficient 1.68 eV perovskite single junction cells
- 26.7%-efficient tandem cells

Simulations:

- Efficiency gain by reducing perovskite and poly-Si emitter perimeter area
- Efficiency loss by high edge recombination in combination with small Si area or large poly-Si emitter

Acknowledgments

ISFH

This work was funded by the state of Lower Saxony under grant number ZN4271 (NextGenPV) and the Federal Ministry for Economic Affairs and Energy (BMWE) under grant number 03EE1080C (TOP) and 03EE1113B (APERO).

We thank Ulrich Paetzold, Paul Faßl (both KIT) and Lars Korte (HZB) for fruitful discussions about the perovskite processing.

Supported by:

Federal Ministry for Economic Affairs and Energy

on the basis of a decision by the German Bundestag

zukunft. niedersachsen

IN-DEPTH CHARACTERIZATION AND SIMULATION APPROACH FOR THE UNDERSTANDING OF IN- AND OUTDOOR DEGRADATION OF PEROVSKITE SOLAR CELLS

Jonathan Parion[1,2,3,4], Amit Kumar Harit[1,3,4], Elias Peraticos[5,6], Vasiliki Paraskeva[5,6], Maria Hadjipanayi[5,6], Aranzazu Aguirre[1,3,4], Filip Duerinckx[1,3,4], Hariharsudan Sivaramakrishnan Radhakrishnan[1,3,4], Jef Poortmans[1,3,4,7], Johan Lauwaert[2] and Bart Vermang[1,3,4].

[1] Hasselt University, imo-imomec, Martelarenlaan 42, 3500 Hasselt, Belgium; [2] Ghent University, Department of Electronics and Information Systems, Technology Park 126, 9052 Zwijnaarde, Belgium; [3] Imec, imo-imomec, Thor Park 8320, 3600 Genk, Belgium; [4] EnergyVille, imo-imomec, Thor Park 8320, 3600 Genk, Belgium; [5] PV Technology Laboratory, Department of Electrical and Computer Engineering, University of Cyprus, Nicosia 1678, Cyprus; [6] PHAETHON Centre of Excellence (CoE) for Intelligent, Efficient and Sustainable Energy Solutions, Nicosia 2109, Cyprus; [7] KU Leuven, Department of Electrical Engineering, Kasteelpark Arenberg 10, 3001 Leuven, Belgium

ABSTRACT: Perovskite solar cells (PSCs) have recently shown, on top of their very high power-conversion efficiency (PCE), a remarkable improvement in stability. Despite this, very few studies focus on the long-term testing of these devices. The exact mechanisms governing degradation are yet to be discovered and there is still a lack of a consensus on which accelerated tests can be used to accurately mimic stresses in real-life field deployment. To address these issues, this work uses several of the International Summit on Organic Photovoltaic Stability (ISOS) protocols, combined with an electrical characterization and simulation toolbox, to compare outdoor field testing of PSCs with indoor accelerated tests. The study reveals that long-term outdoor exposure mainly leads to the degradation of the perovskite absorber layer. On the contrary, the very popular dark thermal stress test affects the perovskite/electron transport layer (ETL) interface. It is also shown that testing thermal stability under light and under maximum power point tracking (MPPT) is the closest accelerated test to mimic outdoor exposure, with similar degradation features observed. Overall, this study highlights some of the key degradation modes occurring in PSCs, while showing the importance of diversified testing to better comprehend and improve the stability of these devices.
Keywords: Perovskite degradation, Perovskite outdoor, ISOS protocols, S-shape

1 INTRODUCTION

Perovskite solar cells (PSCs) have recently shown, on top of their very high power-conversion efficiency (PCE), a remarkable improvement in stability [1, 2]. They show the ability to succeed in several indoor accelerated degradation tests, defined by the International Summit on Organic Photovoltaic Stability (ISOS) protocols [3]. Even though this is an important step in the deployment of the perovskite technology, there is still a significant lack of validation of these results in real outdoor conditions. It is moreover unclear which indoor stability tests are the most suited to mimic degradation induced by real-life field exposure. Finally, despite the stability improvements, there is poor understanding as to the exact physical origin of the degradation.

This work aims at addressing these issues, by comparing in- and outdoor degradation of perovskite cells using electrical characterization combined with Devsim TCAD [4] simulations. More specifically, an ISOS-O2 test is performed in Nicosia, Cyprus for a duration of 5 months and compared with a 2000h-long ISOS-D2 test and an 85h-long ISOS-L2 test. The cells that are characterized in this work use a semi-transparent inverted p-i-n architecture and $FAPbI_3$-based perovskite deposited by blade coating. The cell stack is composed of ITO/NiO_x/perovskite/LiF/C_{60}/LiF/ITO/Ag. The NiO_x acts as a p-doped hole transport layer (HTL), and the LiF/C_{60}/LiF stack acts as a n-doped electron transport layer (ETL).

2 OUTDOOR STABILITY TESTING

The outdoor stability of a PSC was tested on the island of Cyprus for a period of 5 months, in between April and August 2025. The evolution of performance is shown in Figure 1. During that period, the cell maintains approximately 80% of its initial performance. The measurements were interrupted for a period of approximately 1 month between May and June and the sample was kept in dark storage at room temperature during that period. Interestingly, this does not seem to have affected the cell performance. The average sample temperature varied between 30°C and 50°C for the entire testing period, getting hotter during the summer months compared to spring.

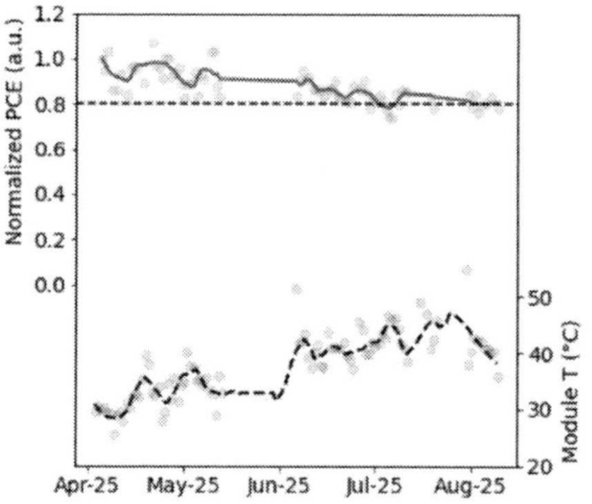

Figure 1: IV measurement of the reference and passivated PSCs, with the main figures of performance given in the table inset. The black arrow shows a slight kink in the reference curve.

In Figure 2a, IV curves taken at different stages of outdoor exposure are depicted. They show that the performance loss was mainly caused by a reduction in short-circuit current density (J_{sc}) and in fill-factor (FF), while the open-circuit voltage (V_{oc}) remained stable

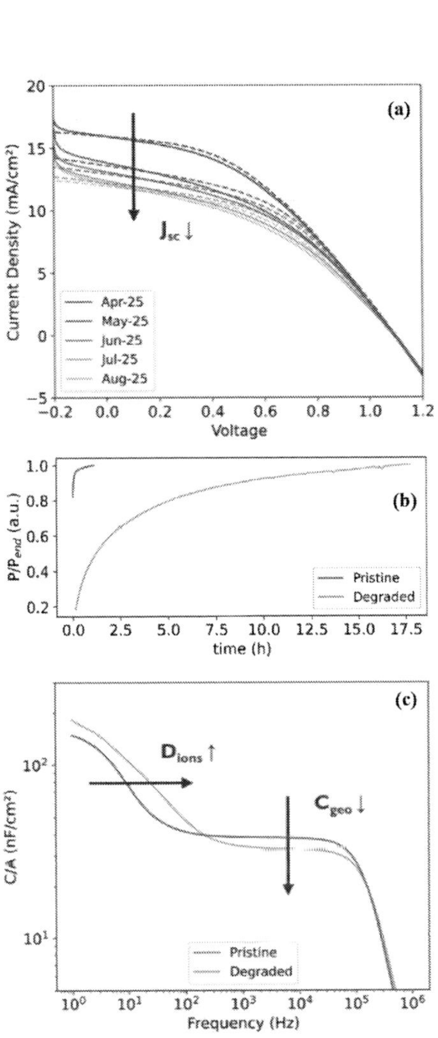

Figure 2: (a) IV curves taken at different dates during outdoor exposure with the solid and dashed curve respectively showing the forward and reverse scans, (b) maximum power point tracking of the device before and after outdoor exposure normalized by the end power value and (c) Capacitance versus frequency (Cf) measurements performed before and after outdoor exposure.

during the testing period. The J_{sc} loss is likely related to a deterioration of the absorber layer, as discussed further. The FF loss seems to be caused by an increased series resistance (R_s). This last one is initially already large, due to the interconnection method used in this specific sample. It is also worth mentioning that the hysteresis of the IV curve increases slightly as the cell degrades, which indicates a change in the behavior of mobile ionic charges. This is confirmed by the data shown in Figure 2(b), where the device MPP was measured for the pristine and degraded sample. Before this measurement, the device is stored in the dark for a few days in order to get to a resting state. Then, MPPT at room temperature and 1 sun irradiance is performed until a stabilized power output is reached. As observed on the Figure, the degraded device takes a significantly longer time to reach a steady-state, while also starting at a much lower value. This highlights the role of degradation as an accelerator for perovskite transient effects: after degradation, the device takes a significantly longer time to reach its maximal power output than before. In Figure 2(c), the capacitance versus frequency (Cf) characteristic is represented before and after the ISOS-O2 test. In the $10^3 - 10^5$ Hz frequency region, where the geometric capacitance C_{geo} dominates, a clear reduction is observed after outdoor exposure. This is a sign of the perovskite layer degradation, in line with the J_{sc} drop and with results from previous works [5-7]. At frequencies below 10^2 Hz, the increase in capacitance is typically related to the movement of mobile ionic charges. These contribute to the total capacitance of the device only when the AC excitation is slow enough. In the present case, the low-frequency region is shifted to the right after outdoor exposure. Typically, such feature indicates an increase in the ionic diffusivity D_{ions}[6]. This is coherent with the larger hysteresis observed with time (Figure 2(a)) as well as with the increased transient effect (Figure 2(b)). Overall, these results indicate that the outdoor exposure of perovskite cells causes degradation of the absorbing layer, while increasing the transient behavior of the cell caused by mobile ions.

3 INDOOR STABILITY TESTING

Despite being fully representative of real-life operation of the cells and modules, outdoor tests are very long and therefore not practical for development and validation of new PSC architectures. For this reason, accelerated tests are often performed, the two most popular being ISOS-D2 (thermal stress in the dark) and ISOS-L2 (thermal stress under light and at MPPT). In this section, these tests are performed, analyzed and compared with the ISOS-O2 outdoor protocol to highlight the differences and similarities in the perovskite cell degradation.

3.1 ISOS-D2

In this test, samples are placed at 85°C and kept in the dark during 2000h. The IV curves taken before and after the test are represented in Figure 3(a). Two main contributors to the reduced performance are identified: a strong reduction of V_{oc} combined with a significant FF loss caused by the appearance of an "S-shape". This kind of feature is often attributed to the formation of an energy barrier at one of the perovskite/transport layer interfaces [8, 9]. To support the understanding of the S-shape origin, a Devsim TCAD [4] simulation model of the perovskite single-junction cell was created. The results obtained from this model are represented in solid lines in Figure 3(a). To obtain a good agreement with the experimental points, two parameters were varied between the pristine and degraded samples:

- The density N_t of the defect at the interface between the perovskite and the ETL layer was increased from $N_t = 10^9 \text{cm}^{-2}$ to $N_t = 3 \cdot 10^{13} \text{cm}^{-2}$
- The mobility of electrons in the ETL layer μ_{ETL} was changed from $\mu_{ETL} = 5 \cdot 10^{-4}\ cm^2V^{-1}s^{-1}$ to $\mu_{ETL} = 4 \cdot 10^{-7}\ cm^2V^{-1}s^{-1}$.

This confirms that the ISOS-D2 test mainly affects the perovskite/ETL interface, while leaving the perovskite bulk unchanged, at least for the blade-coated $FAPbI_3$-based absorber used in this work. It is worth mentioning

10.4229/EUPVSEC2025/2BO.10.5

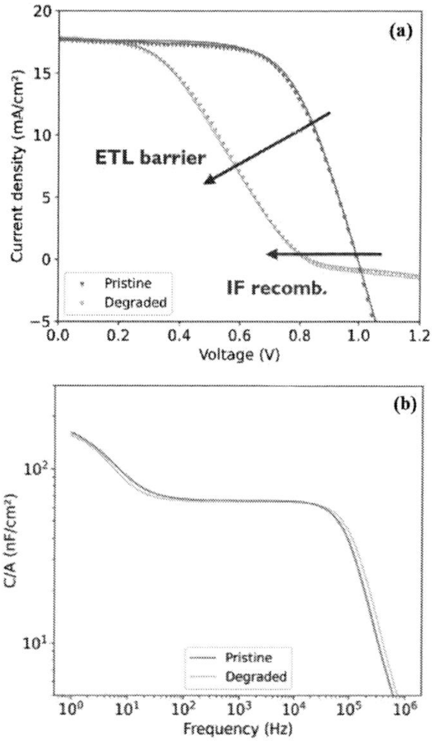

Figure 3: (a) Experimental (triangles) and simulated (solid lines) IV curves before and after ISOS-D2 test and (b) Capacitance versus frequency (Cf) measurements performed before and after ISOS-D2 test.

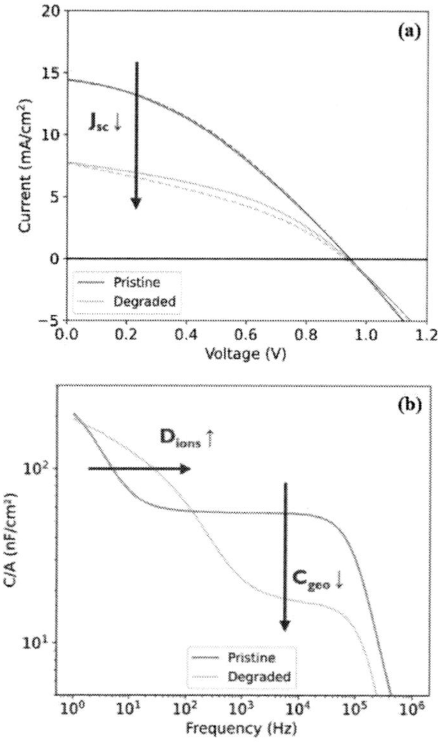

Figure 4: (a) Experimental IV curves before and after ISOS-L2 test. The solid and dashed lines represent respectively the forward and reverse scans. (b) Capacitance versus frequency (Cf) measurements performed before and after ISOS-L2 test.

that changing HTL parameters and inteface defect density instead of the ETL does not yield a similar result as in Figure 3(a). That layer is moreover less likely to deteriorate under thermal stress, as discussed in previous work [9-11]. Turning to Figure 3(b), this last hypothesis is further confirmed by the Cf measurements. They show no change in the intermediary capacitance region, contrarily to what was observed after outdoor exposure. There is also no change in the low frequency region of the capacitance, indicating no modification of the mobile ion transport properties. While the ISOS-D2 stress does not seem to be representative of the cell outdoor degradation for this specific case, it still enables to highlight the instabilities that can occur at the perovskite/ETL interface under thermal stress. Previous work on long-term outdoor exposure of perovskite cells and modules mentions the appearance of such S-shapes for some ETL compositions [9], which motivates the need for accelerated dark thermal stress tests such as ISOS-D2.

3.2 ISOS-L2

In this test, the sample is placed at 60°C under light and its maximum power point is tracked for a duration of 85h. The IV curves before and after the test are given in Figure 4(a). In this case, the effect of degradation on the IV curve is very similar to the ISOS-O2 test shown in Figure 1(a). There is a significant J_{sc} loss, related to the degradation of the perovskite absorber, as well as a FF loss caused by an increased R_s. Increased hysteresis is furthermore also observed after degradation and attributed to an increased D_{ions} after analysis of Figure 4(b). There, the same reduction in the geometric capacitance and increase in the transition of the low frequency capacitance are observed in the degraded sample, similarly to the ISOS-O2 case. It indicates a degradation of the absorber layer as well as an increase in the perovskite transient behavior. From Figure 4, it is very clear that the ISOS-L2 test leads in this case to the same type of degradation as the ISOS-O2 outdoor exposure, while being significantly faster. This is a promising result to support the use of the ISOS-L2 protocol to test the stability of perovskite cells.

4 CONCLUSION

This work investigated the stability behavior of PSCs in different testing conditions, both in- and outdoors. Outdoor exposure (ISOS-O2) of the cells leads to a degradation of the perovskite absorber and to an increase of the perovskite transient behavior. The same degradation is observed during indoor MPP tracking under light and heat conditions (ISOS-L2), though on a much shorter time scale. This poses the ISOS-L2 protocol as a solid candidate to validate PSCs stability in lab conditions. Finally, dark thermal stress (ISOS-D2) leads to the deterioration of the

10.4229/EUPVSEC2025/2BO.10.5

perovskite/ETL interface, while leaving the absorber intact. Overall, this work clearly highlights the importance of diversified testing of PSCs. Indoor accelerated tests are useful for laboratory development and validation but need to be correctly tailored to mimic real outdoor deployment. In future steps, more emphasis should be placed on understanding the intrinsic causes of degradation. Moreover, recovery and seasonality effects are key topics to be investigated in order to further improve the stability of PSCs.

5 ACKNOWLEDGEMENTS

This work was financed by the Fonds voor Wetenschappelijk onderzoek (FWO) with grant number 1S01525N, by the European Union through the TESTARE project (Grant ID: 101079488) and the TRIUMPH project (Grant ID: 101075725) and by the European Regional Development Fund and the Republic of Cyprus through the DegradationLab project (Grant ID: INFRASTRUCTUR ES/1216/0043).

6 REFERENCES

[1] H. Zhu *et al.*, 'Long-term operating stability in perovskite photovoltaics', *Nat. Rev. Mater.*, vol. 8, no. 9, pp. 569–586, Sep. 2023, doi: 10.1038/s41578-023-00582-w.

[2] M. Helal Miah *et al.*, 'Key degradation mechanisms of perovskite solar cells and strategies for enhanced stability: issues and prospects', *RSC Adv.*, vol. 15, no. 1, pp. 628–654, 2025, doi: 10.1039/D4RA07942F.

[3] M. V. Khenkin *et al.*, 'Consensus statement for stability assessment and reporting for perovskite photovoltaics based on ISOS procedures', *Nat. Energy*, vol. 5, no. 1, pp. 35–49, Jan. 2020, doi: 10.1038/s41560-019-0529-5.

[4] J. E. Sanchez, 'DEVSIM: A TCAD Semiconductor Device Simulator', *J. Open Source Softw.*, vol. 7, no. 70, p. 3898, Feb. 2022, doi: 10.21105/joss.03898.

[5] J. Parion *et al.*, 'Multifaceted Characterization Methodology for Understanding Nonidealities in Perovskite Solar Cells: A Passivation Case Study', *Sol. RRL*, vol. 8, no. 21, p. 2400529, 2024, doi: 10.1002/solr.202400529.

[6] C. Messmer *et al.*, 'Understanding Ion-Related Performance Losses in Perovskite-Based Solar Cells by Capacitance Measurements and Simulation', *Sol. RRL*, vol. 8, no. 24, p. 2400630, 2024, doi: 10.1002/solr.202400630.

[7] J. Parion *et al.*, 'In-depth study of degradation in scalable wide bandgap perovskite cells', *Mater. Futur.*, vol. 4, no. 4, p. 045101, Sep. 2025, doi: 10.1088/2752-5724/ae01c1.

[8] R. Saive, 'S-Shaped Current-Voltage Characteristics in Solar Cells: A Review', *IEEE J. Photovolt.*, vol. 9, no. 6, pp. 1477–1484, Nov. 2019, doi: 10.1109/jphotov.2019.2930409.

[9] J. Parion *et al.*, 'A novel way of analyzing perovskite outdoor degradation: the S-Voc', *EES Sol.*, Aug. 2025, doi: 10.1039/D5EL00079C.

[10] U. Erdil *et al.*, 'Delamination of Perovskite Solar Cells in Thermal Cycling and Outdoor Tests', *Energy Technol.*, vol. 13, no. 1, p. 2401280, 2025, doi: 10.1002/ente.202401280.

[11] M. De Bastiani *et al.*, 'Mechanical Reliability of Fullerene/Tin Oxide Interfaces in Monolithic Perovskite/Silicon Tandem Cells', *ACS Energy Lett.*, vol. 7, no. 2, pp. 827–833, Feb. 2022, doi: 10.1021/acsenergylett.1c02148.

Faculty of Engineering
School of Photovoltaic and Renewable Energy Engineering

SINGLET FISSION ROUTE FOR >30% EFFICIENT SOLAR CELLS:
Silicon Cell Requirements

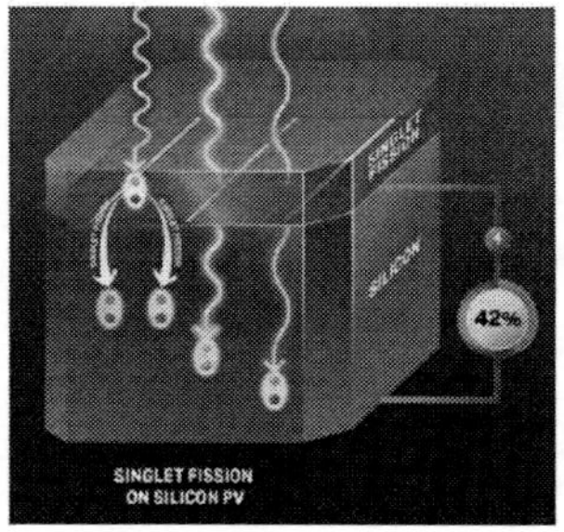

EUPVSEC, Bilbao
23rd September 2025

Dr. Shona McNab

Shona McNab, Alex J. Baldacchino, Pheobe Pearce, Alvin Mo, Alison Ciesla, Bram Hoex, Nicholas J. Ekins-Daukes, Murad J. Y. Tayebjee, Michael P. Nielsen

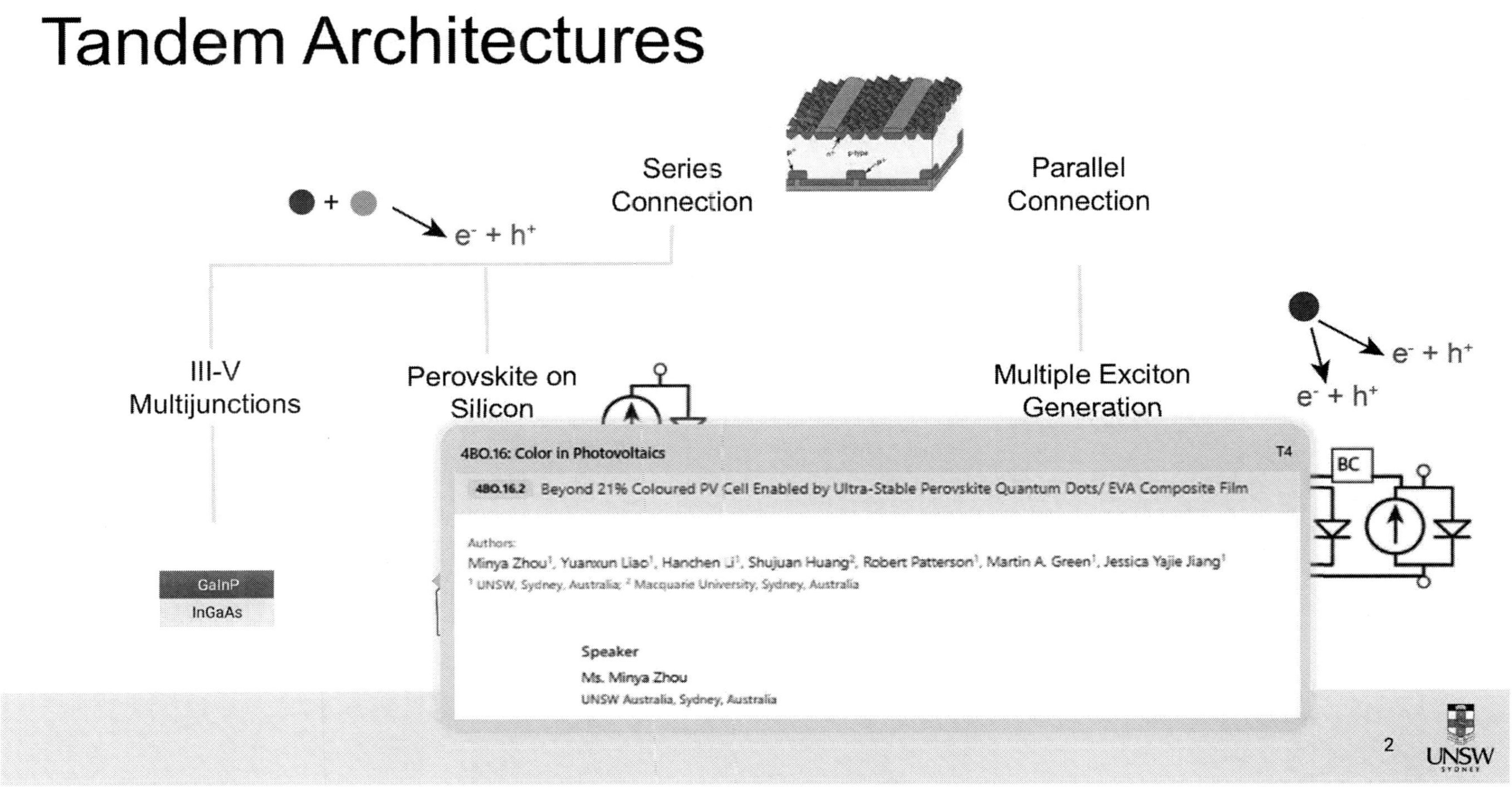
Tandem Architectures
Series Connection
Parallel Connection
e⁻ + h⁺
III-V Multijunctions
Perovskite on Silicon
Multiple Exciton Generation
e⁻ + h⁺
e⁻ + h⁺
GaInP
InGaAs
BC
4BO.16: Color in Photovoltaics
T4
4BO.16.2 Beyond 21% Coloured PV Cell Enabled by Ultra-Stable Perovskite Quantum Dots/ EVA Composite Film
Authors:
Minya Zhou1, Yuanxun Liao1, Hanchen Li1, Shujuan Huang2, Robert Patterson1, Martin A. Green1, Jessica Yajie Jiang1
1 UNSW, Sydney, Australia; 2 Macquarie University, Sydney, Australia
Speaker
Ms. Minya Zhou
UNSW Australia, Sydney, Australia
2
UNSW SYDNEY

Singlet Fission (SF) Down Conversion

- **One** photon yields **two** excitons
- 200% yield of **long-lived** triplet excitons

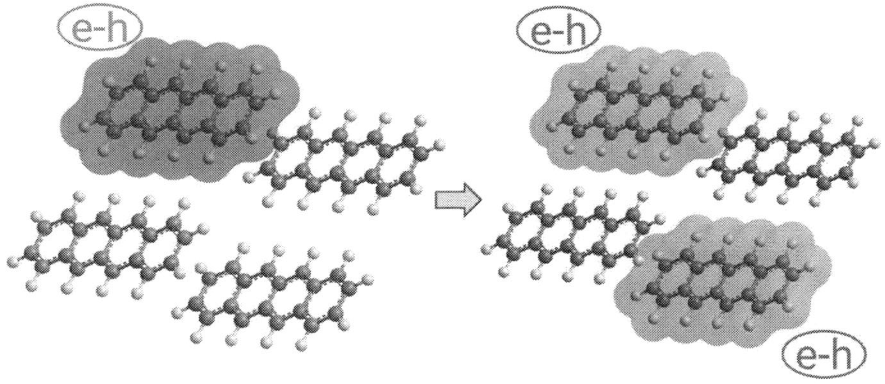

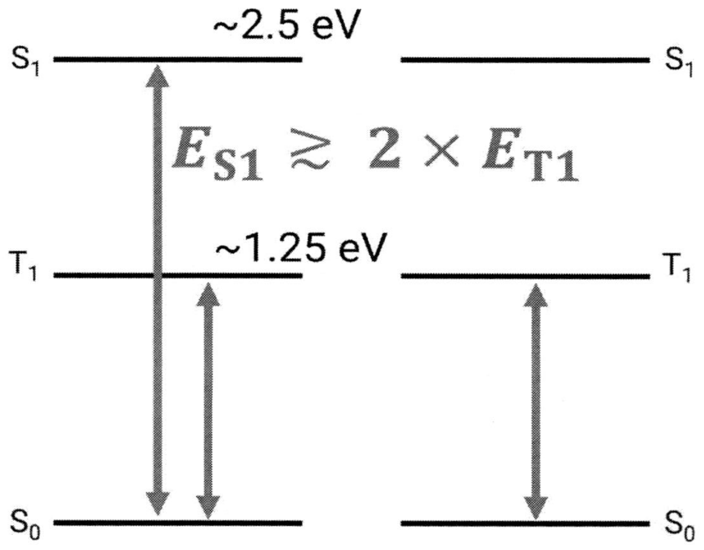

[1] Murad Tayebjee; 2023, *OMEGA Silicon: Toward a singlet fission silicon tandem solar cell,* UNSW SPREE

Direct Energy vs Radiative Transfer

Direct Energy Transfer

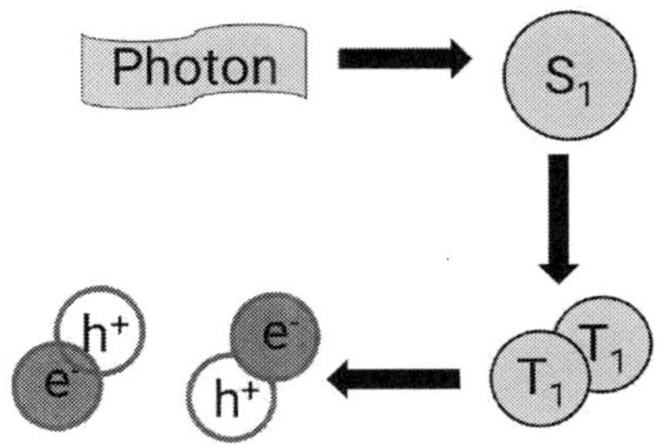

✓ Higher potential efficiency

! Modified Si front surface.

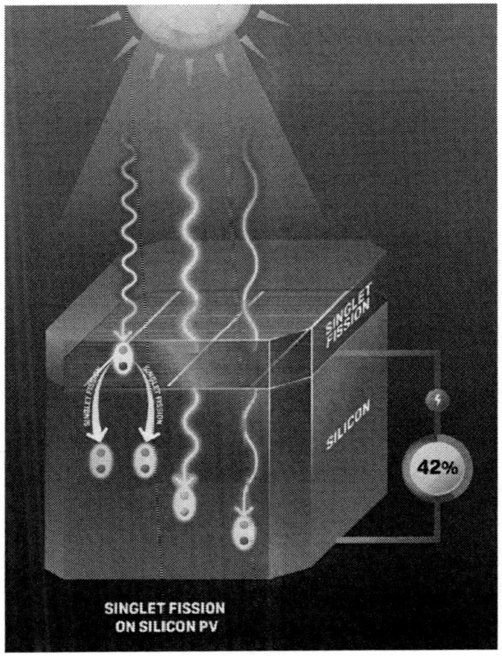

Radiative Transfer

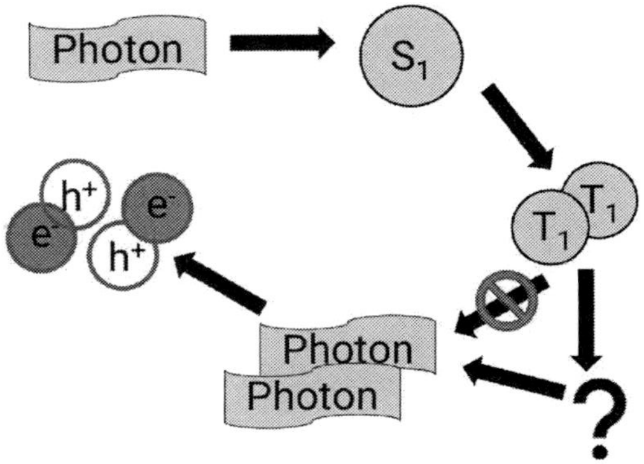

✓ Original silicon cell front surface

! Additional step results in energy loss

! How to get triplets to emit?

✓✓ - Simple device structure – no contact to organic material

UNSW SYDNEY

SF Adjusted Generation Profile

- How much additional current can we get?

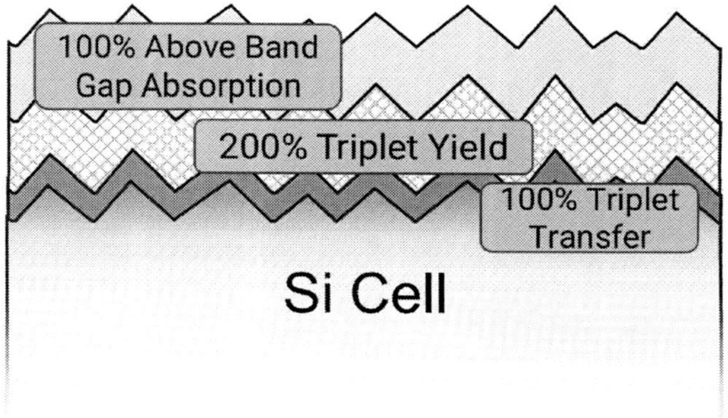

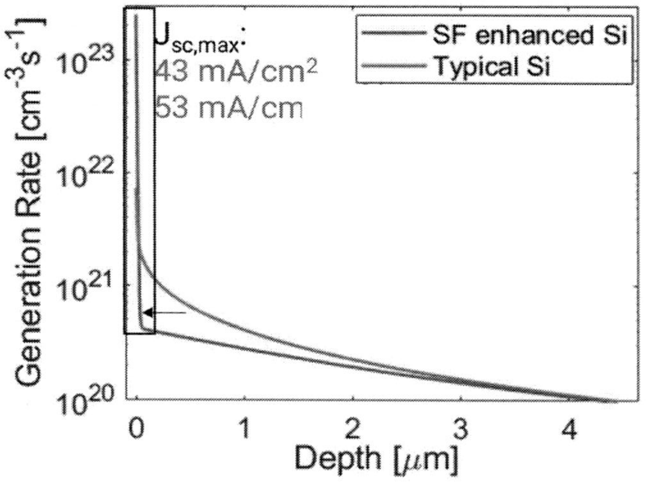

Triplet excitons transferred **very** close to the front surface

Efficiency of the silicon cell will depend on how effectively e-h pairs are collected from the front surface

Calculated using RayFlare: https://rayflare.readthedocs.io

Which Si Cell Architectures

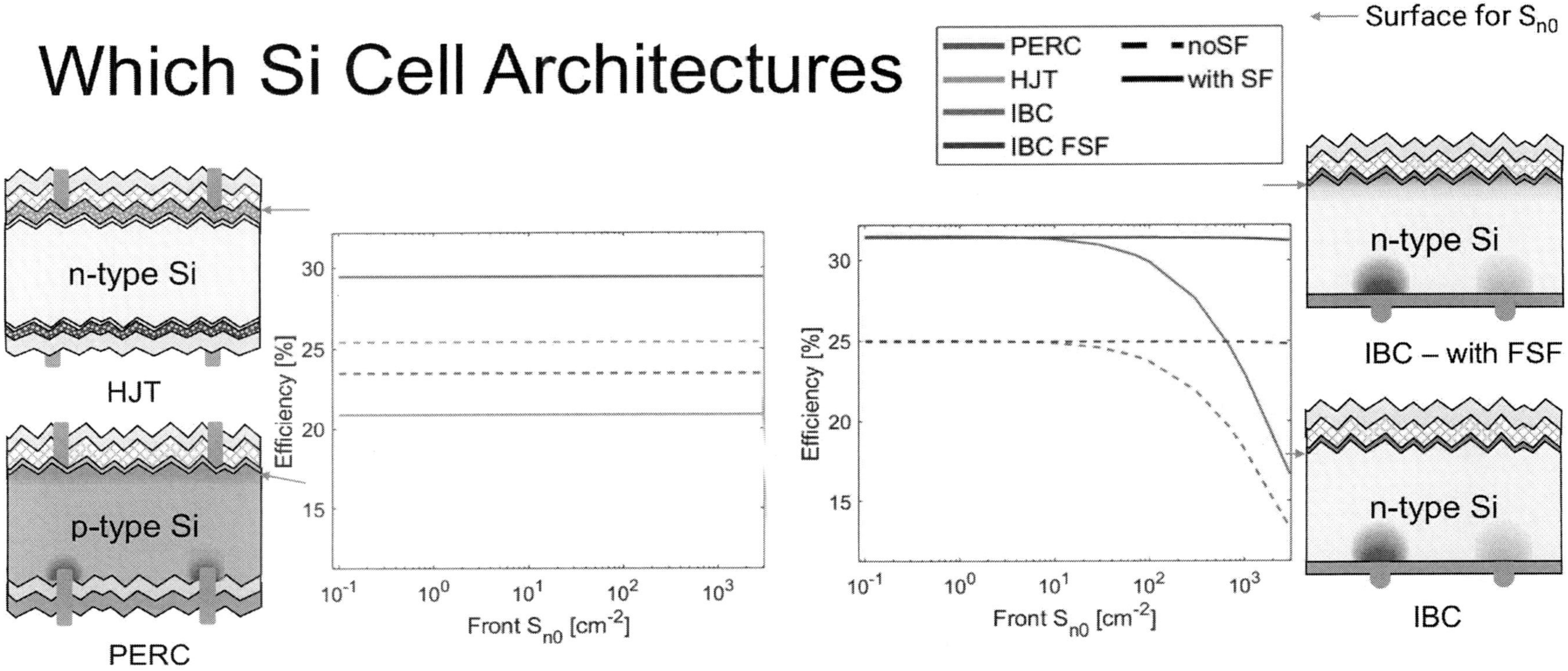

The Importance of Band Alignment for Triplet Transfer

- Both electron and hole must be transferred into silicon

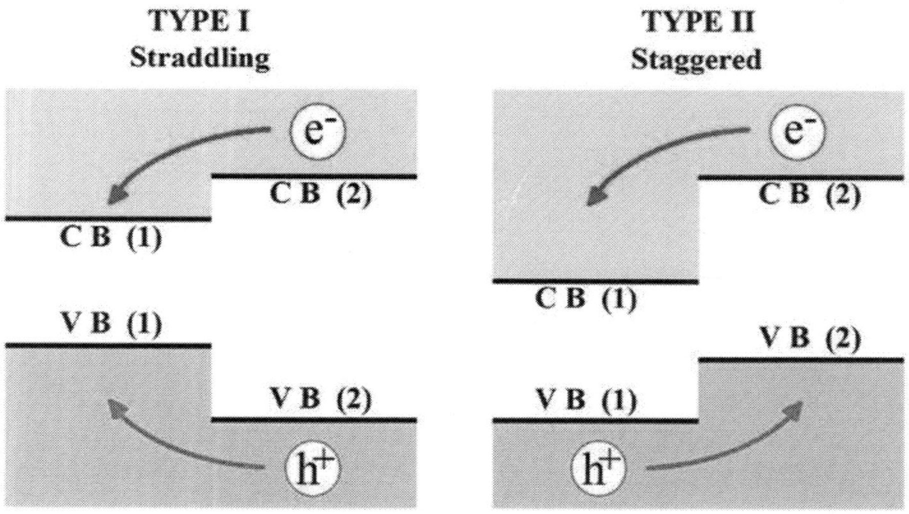

Type I required

A. Giampietri, *Advanced Materials Interfaces*, vol. 4, no. 11, p. 1700144, Jun. 2017.

Mechanisms for Energy transfer

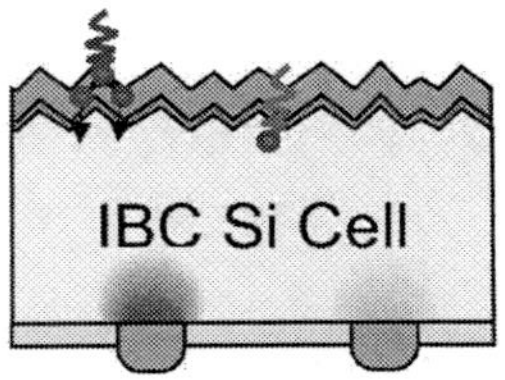

Dexter

- Exciton transfer directly into the silicon
- Limited band alignment required
  - Triplet state can 'float' anywhere in the Tc Singlet energy levels

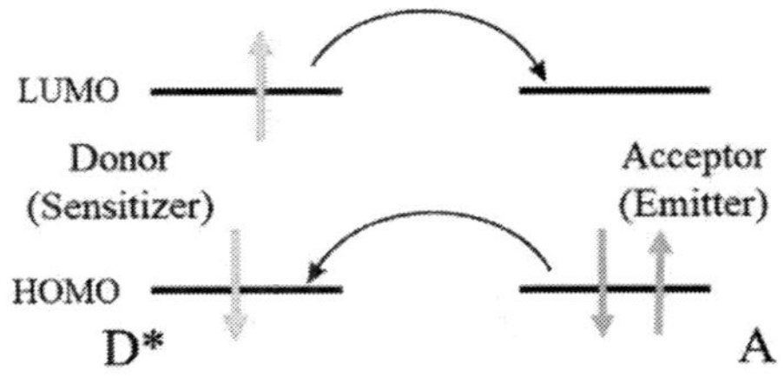

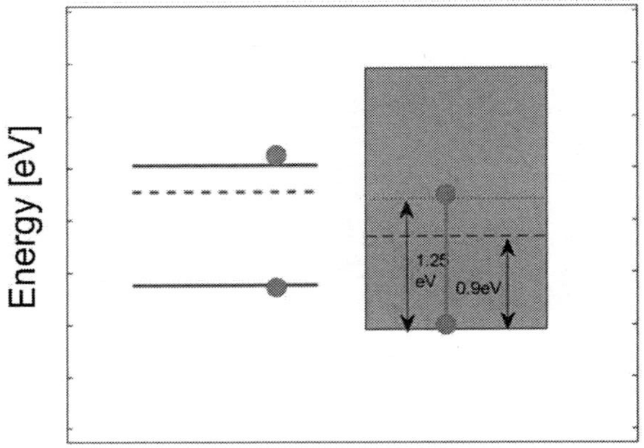

[1]M. Micheva, S. Baluschev; *2022*. "Thermally activated delayed fluorescence in an optically accessed soft matter environment" ***J. Mater. Chem. C***,10, 4533-4545

UNSW SYDNEY

Mechanisms for Energy transfer

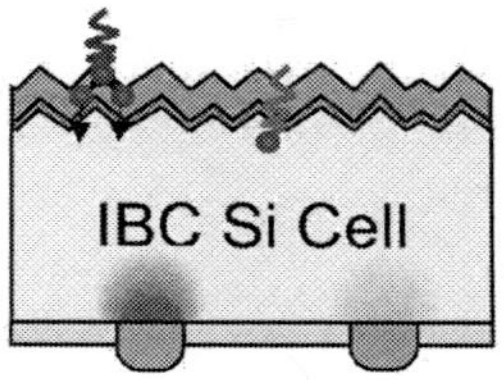

Charge Transfer

- 2 Step Process
- Charge Transfer state
- Band alignment matters to transfer **both** carriers

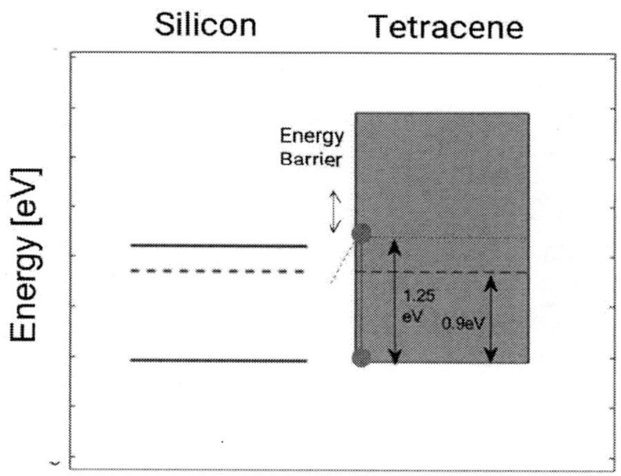

Mechanisms for Energy transfer

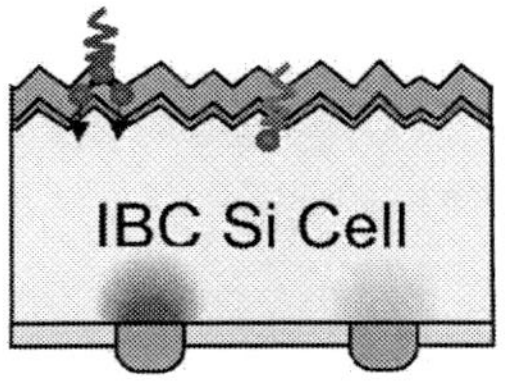

Charge Transfer

- 2 Step Process
- Charge Transfer state
- Band alignment matters to transfer **both** carriers

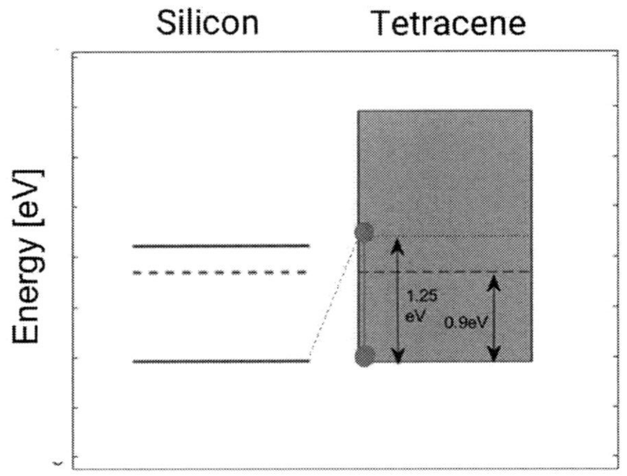

Band Alignment

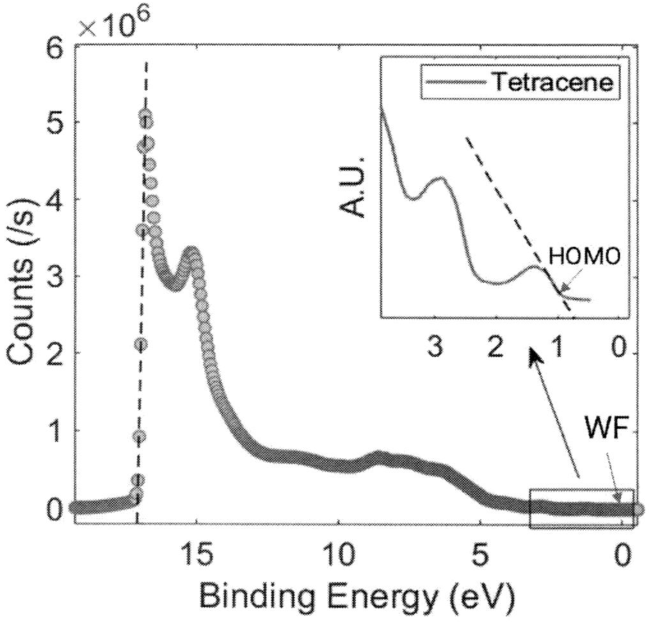

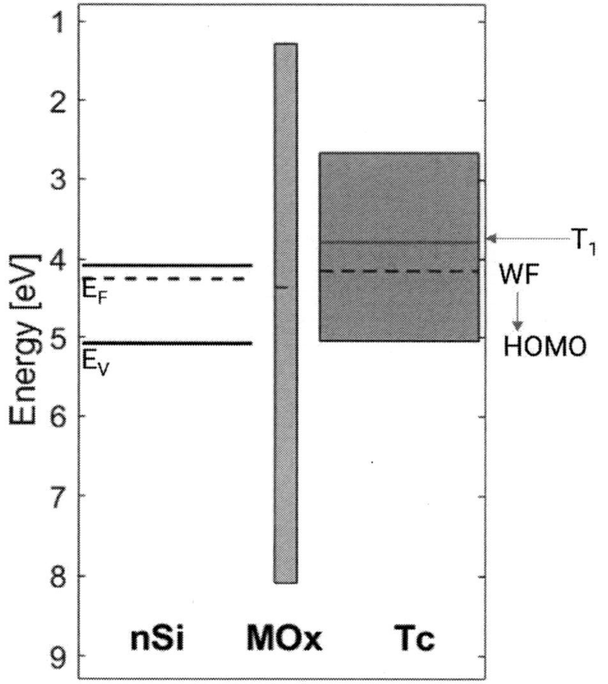

Full Details: N. Nagaya *et al.*, "Exciton fission enhanced silicon solar cell," *Joule*, vol. 0, no. 0, 2025, doi: 10.1016/j.joule.2025.101965. 11

Si/MOx/Tc Band Alignment

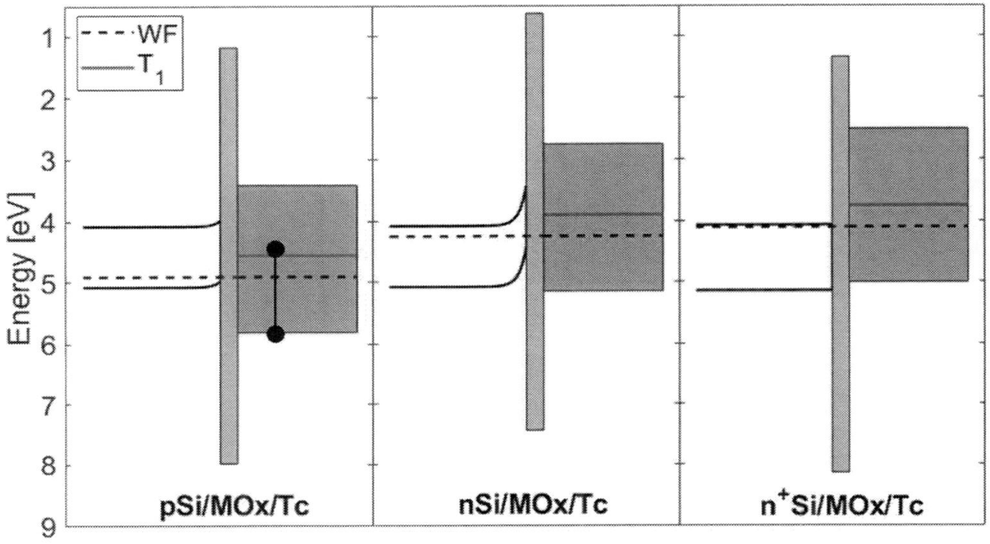

If Band Alignment is important:

- p (or p+) - triplet energy level is in the middle of the Si band gap. **Electrons Blocked**
- n-type – band bending in the Si results in slight barrier to triplets
- n+ removes the Si band bending **improving electron alignment**

UNSW SYDNEY

Characterising SF devices:

- Magnetic Photoluminescence (MPL)

- Triplet generation can be 'turned off' by applying a magnetic field.

At High Field:

- ↑ Singlet Concentration = ↑ PL_{Tc}
- ↓ Fewer Triplets into the Si = ↓ PL_{Si}

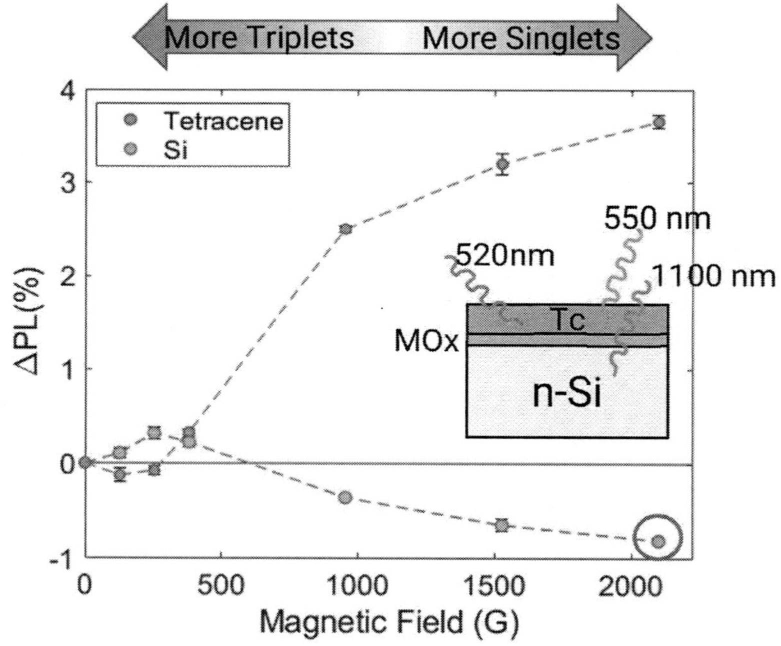

Doping Study Results

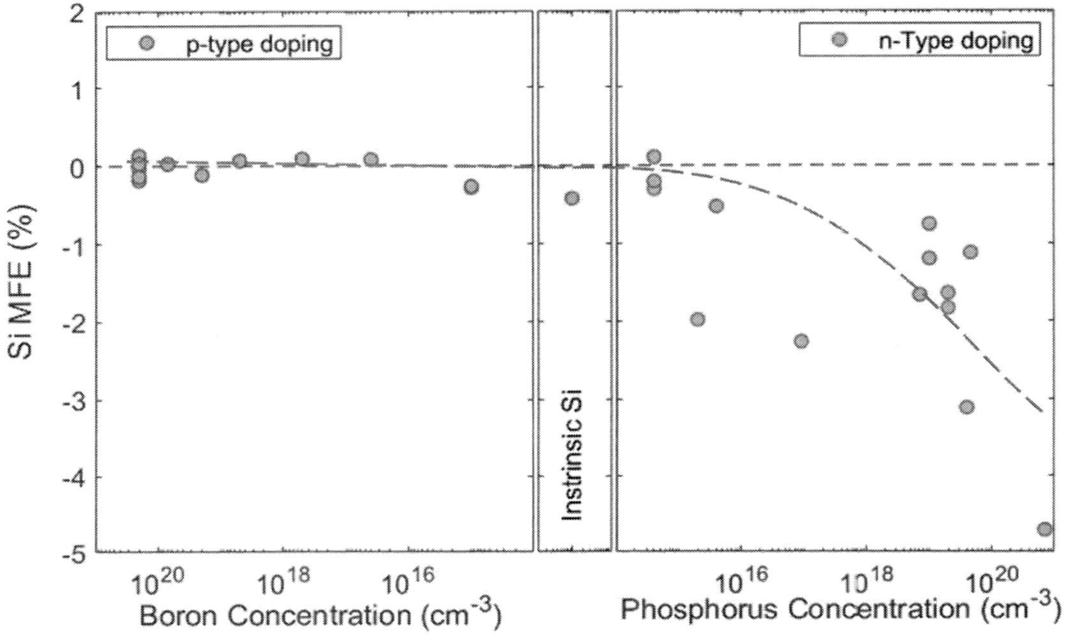

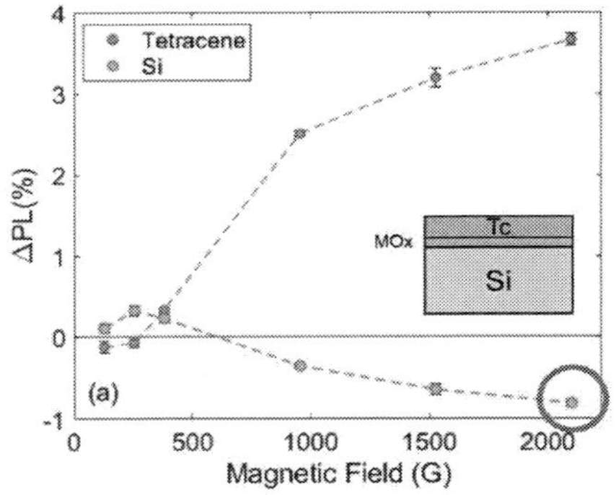

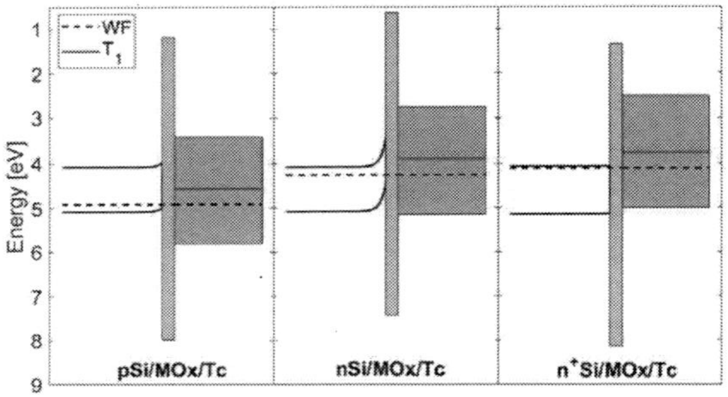

Clear trend with Si doping
In this system, the band alignment is important, suggesting a charge transfer mechanism

14

SF on Si cell device

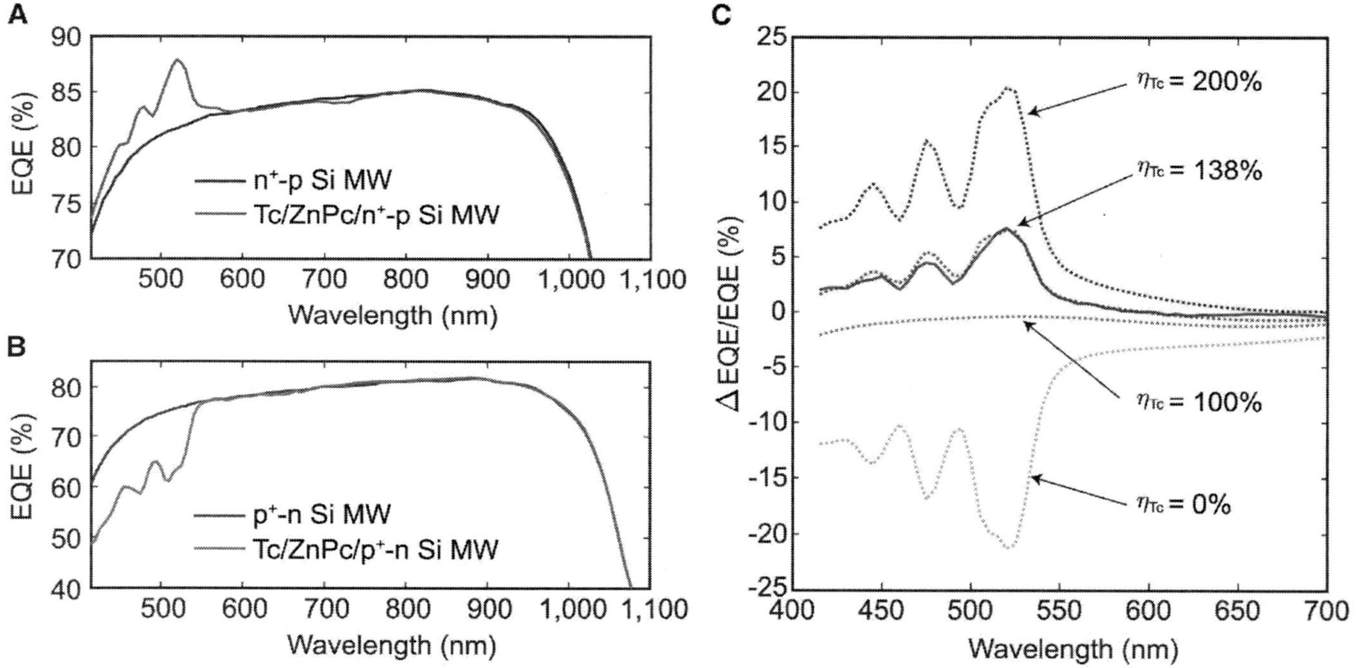

N. Nagaya *et al.*, "Exciton fission enhanced silicon solar cell," *Joule*, vol. 0, no. 0, 2025, doi: 10.1016/j.joule.2025.101965.

15 UNSW SYDNEY

Conclusions

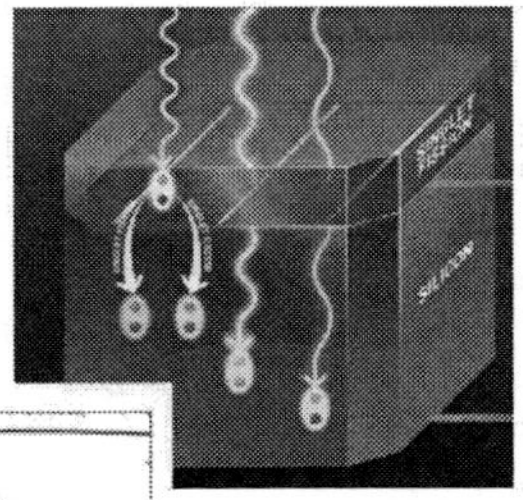

Singlet Fission on Silicon

- SF solar cells offer an alternative approach for **high efficiency** Si tandems
- **Simple** adaption to the industrial silicon technology

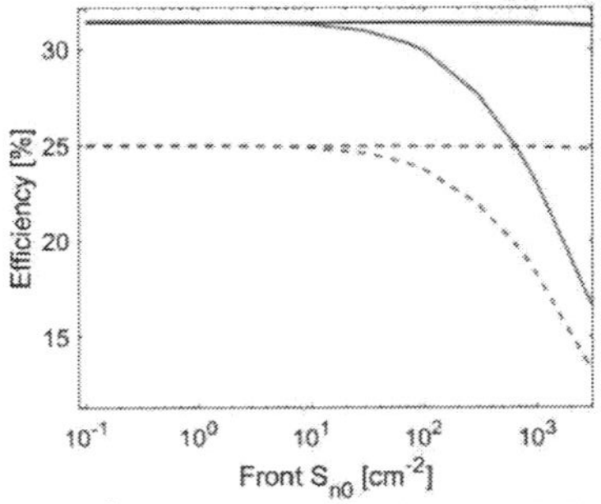

Si Cell Structure

- Certain cell structures will block exciton transfer
- **n+ Si front** surface best for triplet transfer
- PERC cells best for proof of concept

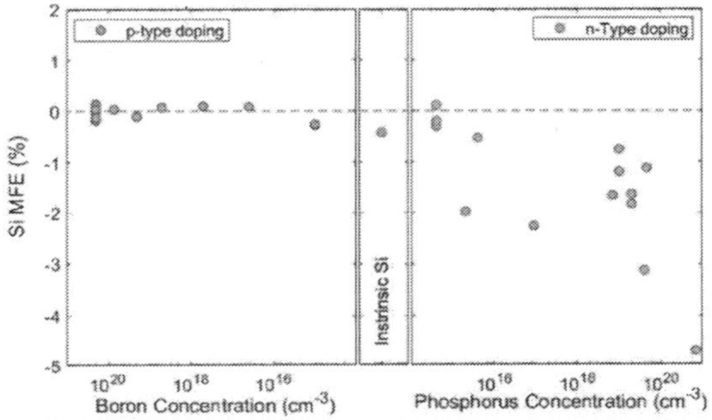

Moving Forward

- Enhancement in EQE has been demonstrated
- Further work to demonstrate on a higher efficiency device

Ω SILICON

Thank you for listening

shona.mcnab@unsw.edu.au

16

UNSW SYDNEY

Mechanisms for Energy transfer

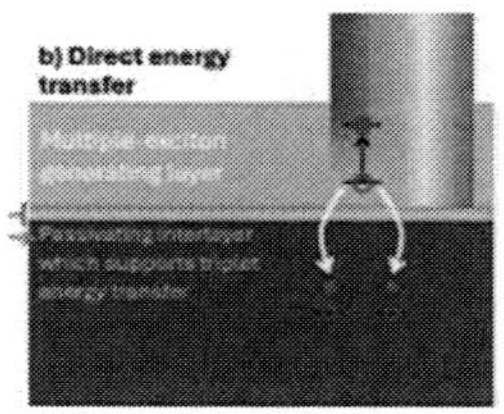

FRET Transfer

- 1/r6 – up to 10nm in organics.
- Donor emission overlaps with acceptor absorption
- ‘matching’ resonances allows excited donor to transfer energy to acceptor.

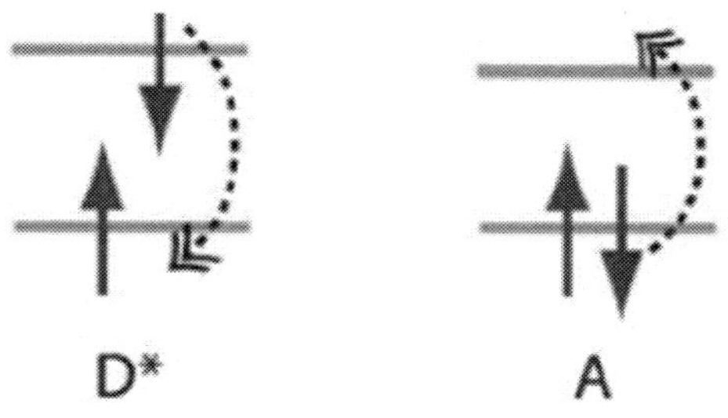

Measuring Band Alignment

1. Si-MOx Alignment
   - Kraut's Method[1]
   - UV-vis

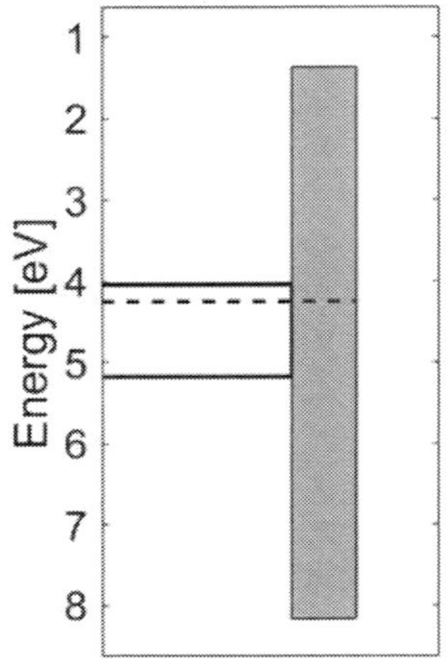

2. Band Bending in Si
   - XPS Si2p Peak Shift[2]

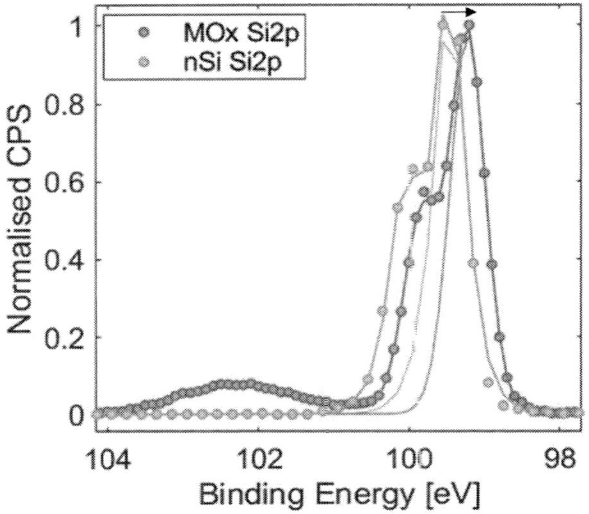

3. Si-Tc Alignment
   - UPS[2]

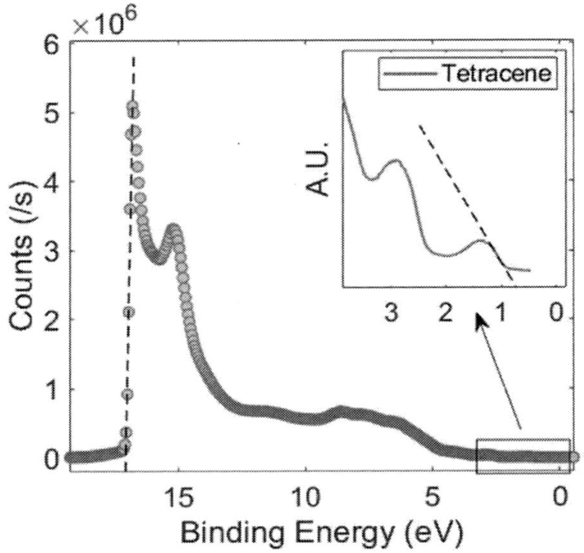

[1]Edris Khorani, Shona McNab; Optoelectronic properties of ultrathin ALD silicon nitride and its potential as a hole-selective nanolayer for high efficiency solar cells. *APL Mater.* 2020; 8 (11): 111106. https://doi.org/10.1063/5.0023336
[2]Baldo

18 UNSW SYDNEY

PERFORMANCE OF A 4-TERMINALS SPECTRAL SPLITTING ASYMMETRIC SOLAR CONCENTRATOR IN DIFFUSE SUNLIGHT: A NUMERICAL STUDY

Floriana Morabito[1], Daniela Fontani[2], Paola Sansoni[2], Mehdi Ahmadi[3], Salvatore Lombardo[3], Andrea Farina[1], Silvia Maria Pietralunga[1*]
[1]CNR-IFN Milano, Piazza L. da Vinci 32 – 20133 Milano, Italy
[2]CNR-INO Largo E. Fermi, 6 – 50125 Firenze, Italy
[3]CNR-IMM Zona Industriale, Ottava Strada, 5 – 95121 Catania, Italy

*Corresponding author: silviamaria.pietralunga@cnr.it

ABSTRACT: We numerically analyze the performance of a spectral splitting low concentrator under diffuse sunlight. The optics is the core of a 4-Terminal (4T) dual-junction PV architecture, with a wedged right-angled prism asymmetric concentrator and NIR and VIS cells respectively coupled to the bottom and the rear sides of the wedge. The spectral splitting approach relaxes the geometrical and technological constraints typical of tandem configurations.
Light guiding is achieved by combining Total Internal Reflection and dichroic reflection, and skew incident rays become fully confined. Perfect optical coupling is supposed. Optical performance depends on the concentration ratio, set by the value of the apex angle of the wedge, on the input spectral content and on the spectral selection performed by the dichroic mirrors. Optical power ratio exceeding 60% can be achieved for diffuse input light. In the case of a HJT silicon cells and a GaAs single junction reference cell, by using license plate data for the electrical parameters of the cells, the Power Conversion Efficiency of the diffuse component in clear sky conditions amounts to around 30%, reaching up to 45% in case of overcast conditions. This geometry also minimizes self-shading and appeals to integrated and bifacial PV applications.
Keywords: photovoltaics, four-terminal, bifacial, diffuse light.

1 INTRODUCTION

The energy sustainability of life and human progress is undoubtedly one of the greatest contemporary challenges. Renewable energy sources are ideally inexhaustible and therefore are strategic resources in which to foster research and innovation. In this perspective, photovoltaic (PV) conversion of solar energy will likely maintain a key role in the global energetic portfolio [1]. However, it is also by economic competitiveness that PV will be able to gain a place of choice among the possible energy supply solutions. When considering the deployment of PV utility-scale plants, competitiveness comes with maximizing power conversion efficiency (PCE) of PV modules and optimization of soil usage, targeting at minimizing the levelized cost of energy. The need to cope with restrictions in terms of the surface available is even stronger in the case of Integrated PV (IPV) on buildings, but also on self-powered vehicles and devices, which face intrinsic limitations in dimensions. To increase the PCE at unitary area is therefore a key request also for the IPV market, where solutions are often customized for specific applications and may be quite diverse in terms of shape, size, optical design, and type of solar cell employed. Also, the stringent constraints in terms of cost that heavily affect the utility-scale market are somewhat relaxed in the IPV context, and the PV module itself becomes a design element of the final product. Functionality and esthetics can then coexist thanks to innovative designs, e.g., as discussed by Borja Block A. and co-authors in [2].

One approach to increase the PCE of PV modules at same occupied area is to use bifacial solar cells that collect backscattered radiation from the ground at their rear side. Silicon solar cells typically improve PCE by around 20%, in dependence on albedo level. Bifaciality may also be an added feature to multijunction PV systems that aim to overcome the Shockley–Queisser limit in PCE [3] by using several solar cells, each of which optimized for a specific spectral range [4]. In the specific case of the four-terminal (4T) dual-junction approach, a classically proposed configuration is made of two stacked cells. The top cell, with a higher bandgap, works in the visible (VIS) spectrum, and the bottom cell works in the near-infrared (NIR) one. Stacked cells have a common shape and are optically, but not electrically, "in series", with no need to integrate them monolithically. An alternative solution to cell stacking is spectral splitting, based on the spectral separation of light and cells [5]. This furtherly relaxes technological constraints, but typically suffers from larger dimensions of the module and poor land usage.

Recently, a solution for a low concentrating dual-junction 4-T PV system, which exploits spectral splitting at minimized footprint and can also profitably embed bifaciality, has been proposed [6,7]. In this paper we recall the design of the PV element, also to be considered as a "solar tile" for IPV solutions, and we specifically numerically analyze its performance in diffuse input light, by numerically evaluation of its PCE for the diffuse portion of input irradiation in selected conditions.

2 DESIGN AND ANALYSIS

2.1 Design of the asymmetric solar concentrator

We make reference to the geometry shown in Figure 1. More details on the conceptual design can be found in [6,7]. The core of the optics is made of a wedged right-angled prism of BK7 glass (refractive index $n = 1.5$) and apex angle φ. The longer cathetus is the input top side. The VIS solar cell is optically coupled to the rear side (short cathetus) and the NIR cell is coupled to the bottom side (hypothenuse). Ideally, we assume perfect optical coupling of all elements (no refractive index mismatches) and anti-reflection treatment at the top input surface. Numerical modelling is developed using a commercial 3D ray-tracing software, (ZEMAX OpticStudio, 22.2 Professional) in non-sequential mode and by performing data post-processing in MATLAB environment, as also detailed in [6]. The solar cells are modeled by detectors in ZEMAX environment. The PEC will be estimated by assuming the cells to be respectively a commercial silicon SHJ bifacial NIR cell ($V_{oc,Si}$ = 0.73V, FF_{Si}= 0.8) and a GaAs reference cell for the VIS-ReRa solutions B.V., ($V_{oc,GaAs}$=1V, FF_{Ga}= 0.82). Spectral splitting is obtained through two dichroic mirrors, one located on the bottom side (high reflection in the VIS) and one at the rear surface of the prism (high reflection in the NIR) and located right in front of the solar cells. Commercially available mirrors have been considered (Thorlabs Inc.) with a cutoff wavelength at 805 nm since it represents the crossing point of the curves of external quantum efficiencies (EQEs) of the two solar cells (from license plate data).

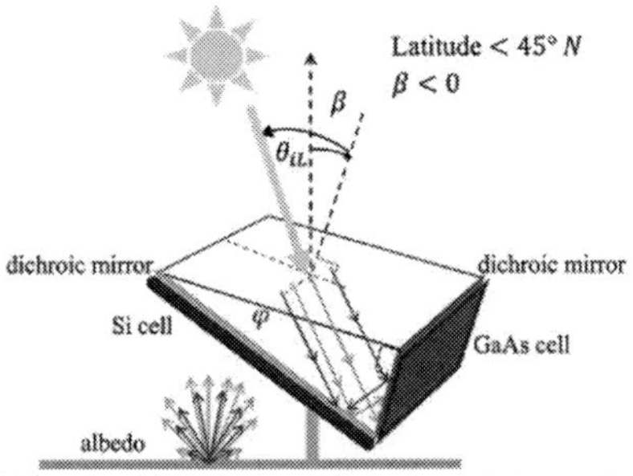

Figure 1: The conceptual design of the 4-T spectral splitting PV concentrator. VIS light (green rays) is absorbed at the VIS cell (here GaAs) and reflected off the NIR cell (here Si). The opposite occurs for the NIR light (dark red rays). Tilt angle β in the N-S direction is marked. At installation latitudes lower than 45° in the northern hemisphere, the top surface is north-side oriented (negative β values). Angle θ_{iL} is the limit incidence angle that guarantees confinement by TIR of direct VIS sunlight. In dependence on the latitude of installation, β may favor albedo collection from ground, also shown.

Low Concentration is obtained for VIS light in the North-South (NS) direction by combining Total Internal Reflection (TIR) at the top glass-air interface and the dichroic reflections. In order to guarantee TIR of light at the top surface, the internal incidence angle must exceed the limit angle for TIR (θ_L). In turn this introduces a limitation on the external incidence angle for light at the top surface, which must exceed a limit angle $\theta_{iL}=\theta_{iL}(n, \varphi)$. Different values for φ were here considered, also including φ = 14.5°, which corresponds to θ_{iL}=21° and to a geometrical concentration C_g = 4, φ = 25° that corresponds to C_g = 2.14 and to θ_{iL}= 0°, and φ = 30° [7]. Starting from $\varphi \geq 25°$ there is full acceptance of direct sunlight under in-field installation conditions; further increase of φ does not bring significant advantages.

It can be demonstrated that, whenever the refractive index of the wedge is n >1.4, TIR condition applies also to input skew rays with a component in the East-West direction, so that they are addressed to either solar cell according to the respective spectral band.

In case 3 < C_g < 5, stationary installation of the module can be considered, with no need for NS tracking. In this configuration, the best tilt angle β obeys the relation: $\beta = \left(90° - (\varphi_s + \theta_{iL})\right)$ where φ_s is the maximum sun elevation at summer solstice (at noon) at the latitude of installation. So installed, the input top surface becomes more north-oriented than for a standard PV module, and this peculiar tilting also brings advantages for bifacial operation, since it reduces self-shading and increases the portion of albedo irradiation that can be collected from the ground. It has been shown that actually, by summing up direct irradiation and albedo contribution, the proposed 4-T geometry may outperform standard bifacial ones, especially at low latitudes [7].

2.2 Numerical method for diffuse light

To simulate input diffuse light, a rectangular light source has been activated in ZEMAX model, immediately outside of the input surface and randomly emitting rays Lambertian distributed in angle (cosine law). Firstly, the optical transfer function for diffuse input light was computed, by admitting a uniform input spectrum in the 410nm-1100nm range. In order to guarantee constant illumination, the area of the top input surface was kept fixed at 77mm x 20mm as the apex angle φ of the wedge varied. Full angular acceptance of input diffuse light leads to a thermodynamical concentration limit C_{MAX} = 1.5 [8]. Secondly, the diffused portion by Rayleigh scattering of a standard solar AM1.5G solar spectrum (clear-sky condition) is considered (www.nrel.gov/grid/solar-resource/spectra-am1.5.html/) and sampled on 175 equally spaced wavelength-points, with spectrally integrated power intensity of 1000 Wm^{-2}. The spectrum sampling was again performed in the wavelength range 410-1100 nm, according to the transparency spectrum of optical material and the operating range of silicon cells. As a third input, the Horizontal Irradiance (DHI) in overcast condition on a selected day was measured (in-field spectrum) at the installation site of Catania town (Sicily, Italy) and sampled.

Normalized input spectra are shown in Fig. 2. The outcast spectrum is richer in blue components and poorer in the VIS and NIR regions.

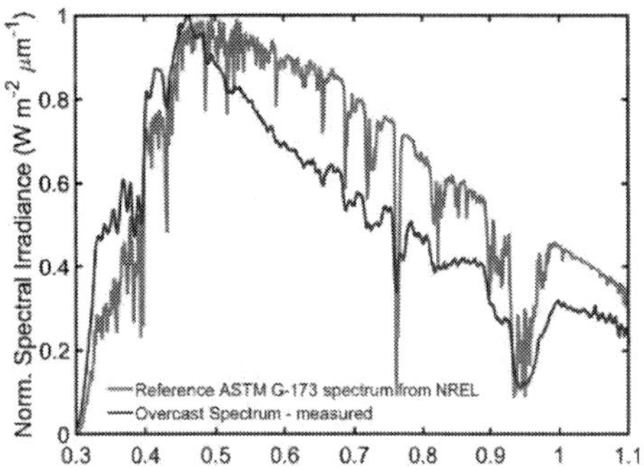

Figure 2: Input spectra used to estimate the PCE.

2.3 Performance evaluation

We rate the performance of the PV concentrator both optically and electrically. We define an optical Power ratio P_{ro} and an optical efficiency η_o as:

$$P_{ro} = \left(P_{out,VIS} + P_{out,NIR}\right)/P_{in} = \left(P_{ro,VIS} + P_{ro,NIR}\right) = \eta_{o-VIS} + \eta_{o-NIR} \quad (1)$$

where $P_{out,VIS/NIR}$ is the spectrally integrated optical power counted at the VIS/NIR detectors (representing the optical power reaching the solar cells), P_{in} is the spectrally integrated optical power at the input surface. The electrical performance is evaluated by computing the PCE as:

$$PCE = \\ = P_{out-Total,el}/P_{in,opt} = \\ = ((I_{sc}V_{oc}FF)_{Si} + (I_{sc}V_{oc}FF)_{GaAs})/P_{in,opt} \quad (2)$$

where the short-circuit current is assumed to be equal to photocurrent at the cell and expressed as:

$$I_{sc} = \int_{selected\ spectrum} PhotonFlux_{cell}(\lambda) \cdot EQE(\lambda) d\lambda. \quad (3)$$

The PhotonFlux at the specific cell in Eq. (3) is computed by dividing the spectral power density at the cell by the photon energy at each selected wavelength (λ).

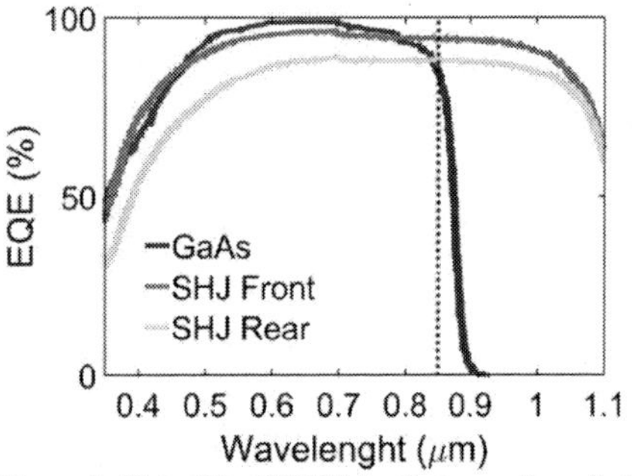

Figure 3: Plot of the EQE(λ) for the two cells and of the transmittance spectra for the dichroic mirrors.

3 RESULTS

The ray-tracing of VIS and IR diffuse light (green and black lines respectively) propagating in the wedged optics is shown in Fig. 4.

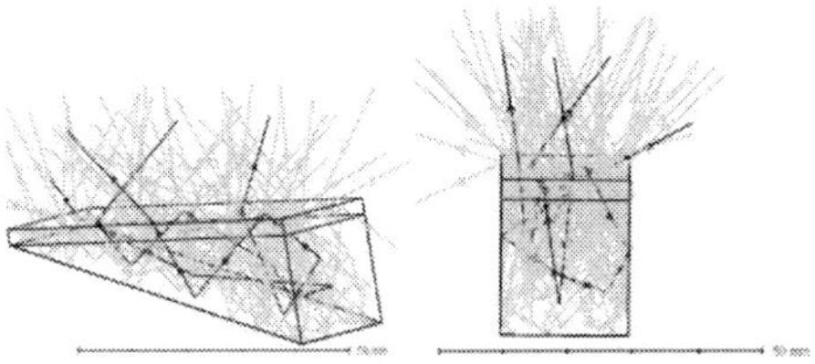

Figure 4: Ray tracing of diffuse light inside the wedged optics. Dichroic mirrors are embedded into the back and bottom sides. The E-W view shows confinement of skew rays.

The East-West view clearly shows how skew rays are confined inside the wedge. Some optical loss occurs at the top surface, due to those rays that do not undergo TIR. Differently from what happens in case of direct irradiation, the performance for diffuse irradiation at top surface is insensitive to sun elevation and to tilt angle. Instead, it still depends on the amplitude of the apex angle of the wedge, φ, which contributes to define θ_{iL} and the rate of input rays confinement by TIR. Depending on the choice of apex angle φ, optical power ratios have been obtained: for $\varphi = 25°$, $P_{ro,VIS}$= 22% and $P_{ro,NIR}$ = 42% which amounts to total collection yield of diffused light equal to P_{ro} = 64%.

The results for PCE are summarized in Tables I and II, when considering both diffuse spectra, clear-sky and overcast, and different values for the apex angle φ (first column on the left). The values of output electrical power $P_{out,el}$ obtained on each solar cell are listed and summed up. In case of clear sky diffuse spectrum, input optical power is set at $P = 169mW$, corresponding to a fraction of 11% of the global irradiation over an illumination area at input equal to 15cm^2; for overcast spectrum the input optical power is estimated in $P = 226mW$, corresponding to a fraction of 35% of a global irradiation estimated in 42 mW/cm^2, over an illumination area at input equal to 15cm^2.

Table I: Computed Power Conversion Efficiency of the PV solution for diffuse irradiation (clear sky conditions)

ASTM G-173 reference spectrum				
φ	$P_{out,el}(mW)$		T-$P_{out,el}(mW)$	PCE_{diff}
	Si	GaAs		
14.5°	16	21	37	22%
25°	15	27	42	25%
30°	16	35	51	30%
35°	15	38	53	31%
40°	15	42	58	34%
45°	15	42	58	34%

Table II: Computed Power Conversion Efficiency of the PV solution for diffuse irradiation (measured overcast spectrum)

Overcast spectrum				
φ	$P_{out,el}(mW)$		T-$P_{out,el}(mW)$	PCE_{dif}
	Si	GaAs		
14.5°	39	35	74	33%
25°	37	45	82	36%
30°	41	59	100	44%
35°	37	64	101	45%
40°	37	72	109	48%
45°	37	72	109	48%

The rightmost columns report the global PCE of the diffuse fraction, respectively for the two input irradiation conditions. We notice that φ = 14.5° corresponds to a C_g≈4 for VIS light, while at φ=45° no concentration occurs. The increase in $P_{out,el}|_{GaAs}$ as the angle φ increases, is motivated by the fact that an increase in φ corresponds to a decrease in $C_g|_{VIS}$ and, correspondingly, to the widening of the angular acceptance of the concentrator. In turn, this increases the photon flux at the cells and $I_{sc}|_{GaAs}$, as can be expressed by Eq. 3. On the contrary, the $P_{out,el}|_{Si}$ in the IR does not substantially change by increasing angle φ. Both input spectra show equivalent behaviors, with a saturation occurring for φ>40°. Under the present conditions the PCE for the diffuse light component of input irradiation amounts up to 34% for blue-sky conditions and up to 48% for the overcast spectrum. If we recall however the fact that the assumptions underlying the choice of the size of the lower leg of the wedge prism, and therefore the size of the angle φ, are the dimensions of the high bandgap solar cell (here made of GaAs) we can set most probable conditions of $\varphi \leq 30°$. This in turn defines PCE values around 30% and 44% for the two spectral inputs. Evidently, the final contribution of PCE for diffuse light to the global PCE has to be rated by the fraction of diffuse irradiation over the total, in the specific weather condition.

4 CONCLUSIONS

A "solar tile" has been designed, also appealing for bifacial operation and that leverages the energy yield of diffuse irradiation component, in dependence on the performance of the VIS solar cell. It is conceived as a spectral-splitting 4-Terminal element, working as a LCPV in the VIS and its performance has been numerically evaluated. As a demonstration case, by assuming a SHJ bifacial cell for the NIR and a commercial GaAs cell for the VIS, in case of $\varphi = 25°$, the conversion efficiency of the diffused portion of input power is PCE_{diff} of 25% in case of clear sky diffused component (mostly Rayleigh scattering) and of 36% in case of typical overcast conditions. The case of $\varphi = 30°$ improves PCE_{diff} to 30% in case of clear sky and to 44% in case of overcast conditions. Further increase of φ might slightly improve PCE_{diff} up to saturation, coping with the thermodynamic limit (as shown in Table 1) but it is considered that the consequent aspect ratio of the PV element would lead to cost inefficiencies in manufacturing.

REFERENCES

[1] International Energy Agency (IEA). NetZeroby2050: A Roadmap for the Global Energy Sector. Paris (2023).
[2] A.B. Block, *et al.*, Energy Build. 314 (2024) 114253.
[3] W. Shockley and H.J.Queisser, J. Appl. Phys. 32 (1961) 510.
[4] M. Yamaguchi, *et al.*, J. Appl. Phys. 129 (2021) 240901.
[5] S. Rühle, *et al.*, J. Renew. Sustain. Energy. 1 (2009) 013106.
[6] A. Farina, *et al.*, Prog. Photovolt. Res. Appl. 31 (2023) 1299.
[7] F. Morabito *et al.*, Energies 18 (2025) 2044.
[8] G. Grasso *et al.*, Solar Energy 86 (2012) 1725.

ACKNOWLEDGMENTS

Present work has been funded by CNR-UVR AMICO2_PoC, through Next Generation EU PoC 2022 - PNRR (MIMIT-UIBM Mission 1 Component 2 Investment 6).

42nd European Photovoltaic Solar Energy Conference and Exhibition

This presentation was selected by the Sc. Committee of the EU PVSEC 2025 for submission of a full paper to one of the EU PVSEC's collaborating peer-reviewed journals.

GAAS FOR THERMOPHOTONICS: FROM THIN-FILM SOLAR CELLS TO HIGHLY EFFICIENT LEDS

N atasha Gruginskie[1], Peter Mulder[1], Gerard Bauhuis[1], Jani Oksanen[2], John Schermer[1]
[1]Radboud University – Nijmegen, The Netherlands; [2]Aalto University – Espoo, Finland
natasha.gruginskie@ru.nl

ABSTRACT: Thermophotonics (TPX) is a technology field that stems from thermophotovoltaics (TPV), in which the hot body of a conventional TPV system is replaced by a hot light-emitting diode (LED). Unlike a TPV system, the radiation from the emitter can be made super-thermal by electrically biasing the hot LED, enabling it to radiate more power than predicted by Planck's law. However, the realization of such a system requires the suppression of most of the non-radiative losses in the LED and extremely efficient light coupling to the photovoltaic absorber (PV). The high quality achieved by GaAs-based devices in the recent years and the advances in the LED industry indicate that this may now be achieved. This study presents the objectives of the *TPX-Power project*, a project that aims to investigate the feasibility of waste thermal energy recovery using TPX devices with the currently available and emerging semiconductor technologies. The experimental challenges associated with applying the well-established fabrication of III-V thin-film solar cells into the modified devices required for the realization of the TPX devices will be explored, and preliminary results will be shown. Finally, an overview of the required steps to fully develop this technology will be discussed.
Keywords: Light emitting diodes; Thermophotonics; III-V semiconductors; Thin-film devices.

1 INTRODUCTION

Light emitting diodes (LEDs) have long been known to convert ambient heat into emitted light [1-3]. This dual contribution to light generation opens up new possibilities for energy harvesting, particularly in the context of thermophotonic (TPX) systems, but yet the practical utilization of this effect has been limited due to the quality of the material and ohmic losses. In recent years, however, improvements in material quality and electronics fabrication suggest that TPX power conversion may now be feasible, and LEDs that convert more energy into light than the supplied electric energy have been recently demonstrated with cooling powers below 50 pW [4].

By combining a heated LED with a photovoltaic cell (PV) kept at a lower temperature, the emitted light can be captured and converted into electricity, as depicted in **Error! Reference source not found.** [5,6]. The project presented in this study aims to extend this concept to high power densities, in the range of 10-100 W/cm^2, and to demonstrate the proof-of-concept for a technology that converts thermal energy into electricity, making it ideal for industrial waste-heat reuse [7, 8]. To achieve this, highly efficient GaAs LEDs and (In)GaAs PV cells are developed. Limited literature exists on the fabrication of highly efficient GaAs LEDs or on the near-field coupling of real-life devices in this manner. This study will, therefore, outline a roadmap and the key technical challenges in developing this groundbreaking energy reuse technology.

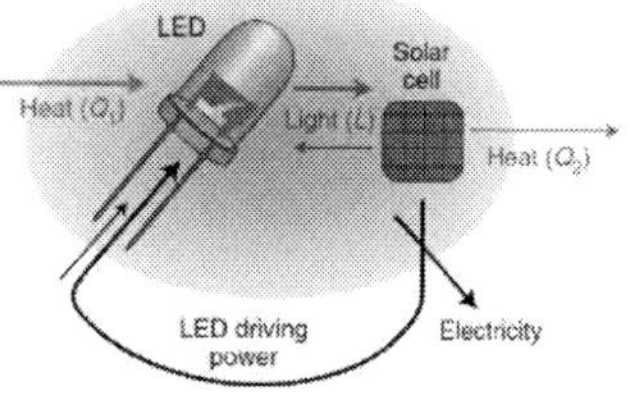

Figure 1: Schematic depiction of the thermophotonic power generation mechanism

2 MATERIALS AND METHODS

To realize these TPX devices, it is necessary to minimize all losses in the LED, as well as to maximize the light extraction and coupling to the PV component. In this context, GaAs LEDs are preferred due to their superior material quality and their high efficiency. The standard LED structure consists of a *p-i-n* junction with intrinsic GaAs as the active layer, sandwiched by two (*p*- and *n*-) InGaP confinement layers, as shown in the schematic depiction in **Error! Reference source not found.**a). During this project, several advances to this structure focused on increasing the devices internal radiative efficiency by reducing non-radiative recombination [9] and series resistance, as well as on increasing light extraction with the application of highly reflective scattering mirrors and current spreading layers [10].

The counterpart to the highly efficient LEDs developed in this project is the PV component (**Error! Reference source not found.**b), tailored to absorb nearly all the emitted light. Since the light absorption will be sub-optimal if the devices are completely symmetrical, i.e. if both the LED and the PV devices are GaAs, in this study we lower the bandgap energy of the PV device by introducing an *In* fraction of 9%. The lattice constant of $In_{0.09}GaAs$, however, differs from the GaAs growth wafer, and in order to fabricate devices with high enough efficiencies, a metamorphic buffer is applied. This entails the development of an inverted metamorphic (IMM) thin-film solar cell structure.

Both the LEDs and the solar cells in this study were fabricated similarly to previously reported techniques [11], and their performance is generally characterized by their dark characteristics and electroluminescence (EL) spectra and images.

10.4229/EUPVSEC2025/2BO.8.6

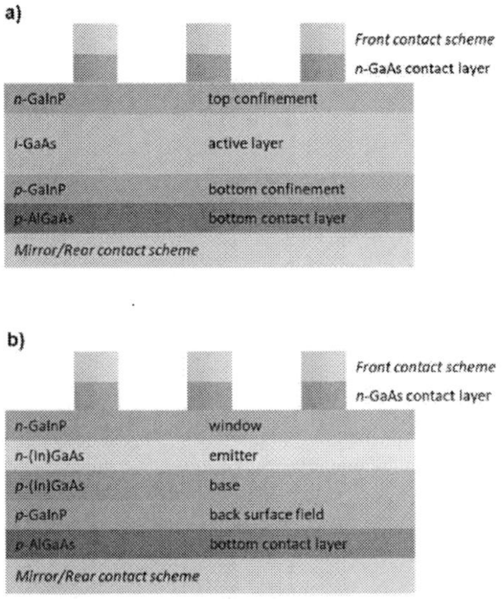

Figure 2: Schematic depiction of a) the basic LED and b) the basic solar cell structure developed in the projects.

3 RESULTS AND DISCUSSION

3.1 LED components

In order to increase light extraction, the application of highly reflective textured mirrors will be necessary, and therefore the rear contact of the LEDs will be patterned [12]. Because the LEDs' active layer is not doped and since the LEDs will be subjected to much higher current densities than solar cells usually operate, current spreading is a limiting mechanism in the LEDs. Several aspects of the front grid characterization and current spreading were discussed van der Krabben et al. [13], and similar considerations must be made to the rear contact when applying a point-contact array.

The dark curves in **Error! Reference source not found.**a) show a large difference in series resistance between the LEDs with planar and patterned rear mirrors, and the EL images show very defined contact points illuminated, indicating that most of the current does not diffuse laterally. A 500 nm highly doped *p*-InGaP layer was then introduced between the p-contact and bottom confinement layers, and the difference in series resistance between the two mirror architectures is significantly reduced. This is also represented in the more uniform illumination observed in the EL images.

3.2 PV cell component

In parallel to the LEDs development, the PV component must be tailored to absorb nearly 100% of the GaAs emission. The need for IMM (In)GaAs PV cells in this context is illustrated in ***Figure 1***, with the external quantum efficiency (EQE) of an inverted lattice matched (ILM) thin-film GaAs solar cell shown together with the EQE of an inverted metamorphic $In_{0.09}GaAs$ cell and the emission spectrum of a standard thin-film GaAs LED at room temperature.

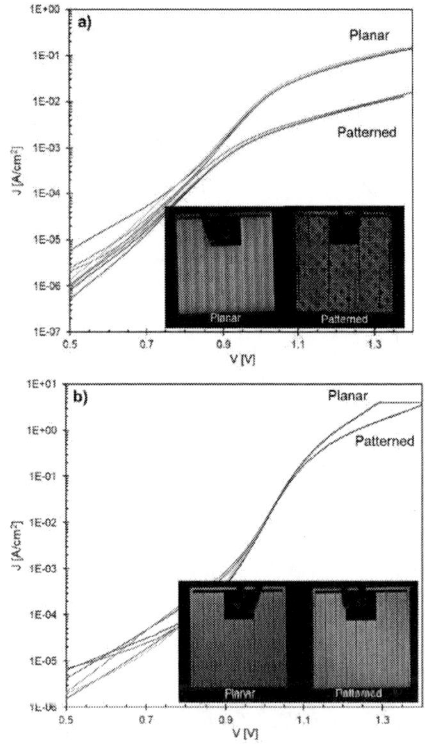

Figure 3: Schematic depiction of a) the basic LED and b) the basic solar cell structure developed in the projects.

The GaAs PV absorption is clearly very low and even zero for a significant portion of the LEDs emission, and this effect increases at higher temperatures, when there is a redshift in the emission peak of LEDs. It is important to note that in the presented curves both PV cells do not have an anti-reflection coating (ARC) applied to the front, and therefore an increase in absorption close to 30% is to be expected. This means that in the wavelength region of interest, the absorption of light by the $In_{0.09}GaAs$ PV with an ARC should be very close to unity.

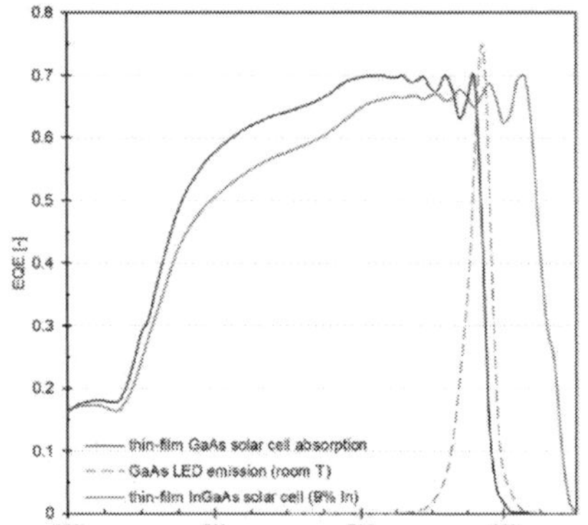

Figure 1: External quantum efficiency (EQE) of a GaAs and an $In_{0.09}GaAs$ solar cells. The emitted spectrum of a standard GaAs LED at room temperature is also depicted.

4 CONCLUSIONS AND OUTLOOK

This study demonstrated the feasibility of adapting thin-film GaAs device technology to thermophotonic applications. The quality of the epitaxial structures has been developed in parallel and pushed close to the limit of non-radiative recombination suppression, an essential step to enable electroluminescence cooling and thermophotonic power generation.

For the LED component, patterned rear mirrors were shown to strongly influence series resistance and current spreading, while the introduction of a *p*-InGaP current-spreading layer significantly reduced resistive losses while improving emission uniformity. For the PV component, inverted metamorphic $In_{0.09}GaAs$ solar cells were developed, providing the required bandgap offset and demonstrating sufficient spectral overlap with GaAs LED emission.

Taken together, these results establish the key design requirements for efficient TPX devices: suppression of resistive and non-radiative losses and maximization of light extraction While several fabrication bottlenecks have been identified, achieving light extraction efficiencies close to unity remains a major challenge and will be the focus of future work.

ACKNOWLEDGEMENTS

This work was supported by the European Research Council under the Horizon 2020 Future and Emerging Technologies program, under the projects OPTAGON (Grant Agreement No. 964698) and TPX-Power (Grant Agreement No. 951976).

REFERENCES

[1] Tauc, J. Czechoslovak Journal of Physics 7. PII: BF01688028, 275–276. issn: 0011-4626 (1957).
[2] Weinstein, M. A. Journal of the Optical Society of America 50, 597 DOI: 10.1364/JOSA.50.000597 (1960).
[3] Dousmanis, G. C. et al. Physical Review 133, A316–A318. DOI:10.1103/PhysRev.133.A316 (1964).
[4] Santhanam, P.et al. Physical review letters 108. 097403. DOI: 10.1103/PhysRevLett.108.097403 (2012).
[5] Chen, K.et al. Journal of Applied Physics 122, 143104. issn: 0021-8979 (2017).
[6] Zhao, B.et al. Nano letters 18, 5224–5230. eprint: 30016115 (2018).
[7] Sadi, et al. Nature Photonics 14. PII: 600, 205–214. issn: 1749-4885 (2020).
[8] *TPX-Power project* page: https://tpx-power-h2020.eu/
[9] Shahahmadi, S.A. et al. Appl. Phys. Lett. 124, 241105 (2024). DOI: 10.1063/5.0206166.
[10] van der Krabben, L.M. et al. Solar Energy Materials and Solar Cells 292 (2025) 113779. DOI: 10.1016/j.solmat.2025.113779
[11] Gruginskie, N. et al. Thin Solid Films 660 (2018) 10-18. DOI: 10.1016/j.tsf.2018.05.042
[12] van Eerden, M. et al. Prog Photovolt Res Appl. 2020;28:200–209. DOI: 10.1002/pip.3220
[13] van der Krabben, L.M. et al. ACS Appl. Electron. Mater. 2024, 6, 1483−1492. DOI: 10.1021/acsaelm.3c01816

LOW-ENERGY ELECTRON MULTIPLICATION ON NANOSTRUCTURED SOLAR CELLS: A NOVEL ROUTE TO OVERCOME SI-PV EFFICIENCY LIMITS

Mikaël Hosatte[1], Brice Rouffie[1], Zbigniew T. Kuznicki[1], Frédéric Milési[2], Bertrand Paviet-Salomon[3], Audrey Morisset[3], Philippe Wyss[3], Lejo J. Koduvelikulathu[4], Lazhar Rachdi[4], Lacramioara Popescu[4], Dominik Rudolph[4], Marek Basta[5], Andrzej Miszczuk[5], Martyna Majak[5], Beata Basta[5], Samuel Queste[6]

Corresponding author: mikael.hosatte@segton.com

[1] Segton Advanced Technology, 99 Boulevard de la Reine, Versailles 78000, France
[2] CEA-Leti, 17 avenue de Martyrs, 38054 Grenoble, France
[3] CSEM, Rue Jaquet-Droz 1, 2002 Neuchâtel, Switzerland
[4] ISC Konstanz e.V., Rudolf-Diesel-Straße 15, 78467 Konstanz, Germany
[5] Roltec, Swiety Marcin 29/8, Poznan 61-806, Poland
[6] Marie and Louis Pasteur University, 1 Rue Claude Goudimel, 25000 Besançon, France

ABSTRACT: Silicon photovoltaics, while dominating global photovoltaic production, are approaching the Shockley–Queisser efficiency limit. The LEEMONS project, funded by Horizon Europe (Grant 101172870), develops a novel nanostructured solar cell concept based on Low-Energy Electron Multiplication (LEEM). This process enables a single high-energy photon to generate multiple low-energy electrons, thereby reducing thermalisation losses and increasing photocurrent. The consortium integrates advanced ion implantation, annealing and metallisation techniques to demonstrate proof-of-concept prototypes using industrially relevant solar technologies such as heterojunction cells. Early results confirm the fabrication of ion-implanted nanostructured layers, validation of implantation masks and low-temperature metallisation alternatives. LEEMONS offers a scalable, industry-compatible pathway to higher Si-PV efficiencies, with strong alignment to EU goals on renewable energy, climate neutrality and technological sovereignty.
Keywords: Photovoltaics, electron multiplication, nanostructures, ion implantation, silicon solar cells

1 INTRODUCTION AND CONCEPT

Silicon photovoltaics have experienced remarkable cost reductions and global expansion over the past two decades. However, conventional Si solar cells remain constrained by the Shockley–Queisser limit [1]. As a result, further efficiency improvements through incremental advances are limited and new physical concepts are needed to sustain both performance gains and continued cost reductions.

The LEEMONS project (Low-Energy Electron Multiplication on Nanostructured Solar Cells) investigates a novel approach to carrier generation in nanostructured silicon. It is based on the concept of Low-Energy Electron Multiplication (LEEM), where high-energy photons generate multiple low-energy electrons instead of dissipating their excess energy through thermalisation. Nanostructuring is achieved through ion implantation, which locally amorphises the silicon, followed by specialised annealing that induces partial recrystallisation and interface flattening. This process reorganises atoms at the amorphous/crystalline (a-Si/c-Si) interfaces, enhancing electron multiplication through modifications of the electronic energy levels. This mechanism reduces thermalisation losses and enhances photocurrent, offering a disruptive pathway for efficiency improvements in silicon photovoltaics (Si-PV).

In contrast to tandem architectures, LEEM does not rely on new absorber materials and remains fully compatible with established silicon technology. Its scalable fabrication relies on industrial processes such as ion implantation, annealing and passivation, which are already widespread in semiconductor manufacturing.

2 ORGANISATION AND OBJECTIVES

LEEMONS (Project 101172870, Horizon Europe) is a 36-month RIA action running from November 2024 to October 2027. The consortium gathers six European partners across the value chain:

- **Segton Advanced Technology (Coordinator)** – development of the LEEM concept, communication and project management
- **CEA-Leti** – development of ion implantation and annealing processes
- **ISC Konstanz** – integration of LEEM layers into c-Si solar cells and optimisation
- **CSEM** – adaptation to back-contact solar cell architectures and characterisation
- **Roltec** – development of metallisation alternatives, lifetime studies, characterisation and simulation
- **Marie and Louis Pasteur University** – fabrication of silicon masks by Deep Reactive Ion Etching (RIE)

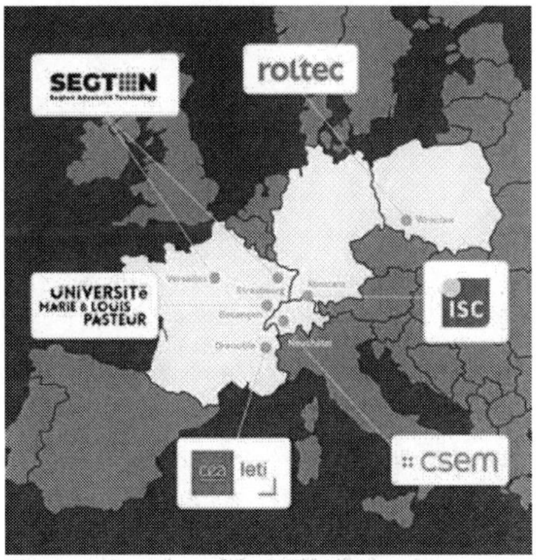

Figure 1: Overview of the LEEMONS partners.

Objectives:

1. Prototype a game-changing photovoltaic innovation through nanotechnology
2. Demonstrate lab-scale proof-of-concept devices on PERC and HJT cells.
3. Ensure high compatibility with industrial Si PV lines (80–95%).
4. Deliver cost-effective, sustainable solutions aligned with EU climate neutrality and strategic autonomy

3 TECHNOLOGY

The LEEMONS technology builds on the principle of LEEM in ion-implanted nanostructures embedded in crystalline silicon. Instead of dissipating the excess energy of above-bandgap photons as heat, impact ionisation generates multiple electron–hole pairs per absorbed photon. This mechanism directly enhances the photocurrent and reduces thermalisation losses, offering a fundamentally new route to surpass the efficiency limits of conventional Si-PV.

In contrast to tandem architectures or external conversion layers (based on photon up- or down-conversion), LEEM is fully compatible with crystalline silicon. It requires no additional absorber materials and relies on established industrial processes such as ion implantation, annealing and low-temperature metallisation. These features position LEEM as a scalable and cost-effective innovation pathway, building on the strengths of mature Si-PV manufacturing.

3.1 Fundamental Principle of Electron Multiplication

Electron multiplication in semiconductors is generally associated with impact ionisation [2], where a high-energy carrier generates a secondary electron–hole pair once its kinetic energy exceeds a threshold. In bulk silicon, the probability of such events is low due to rapid carrier thermalisation. By introducing nanostructured regions with controlled disorder and confinement, the LEEM approach modifies scattering dynamics and increases the probability of secondary pair generation before thermalisation occurs.

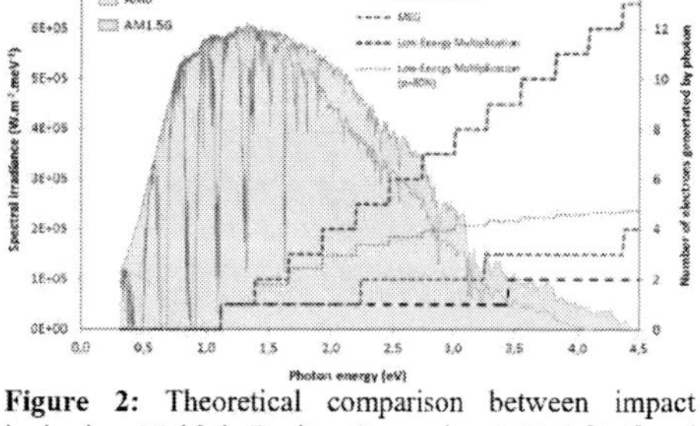

Figure 2: Theoretical comparison between impact ionisation, Multiple Exciton Generation (MEG) [3-5] and the LEEM mechanism. The staircase-like curves represent the stepwise increase in electrons per photon as photon energy rises. In the LEEM scenario, assuming a constant probability of secondary generation of 80%, the average carrier multiplication exceeds that of standard impact ionisation. Standard reference solar spectra AM0 and AM1.5G [6] are indicated in light green and light blue respectively.

3.2 Nanostructuring by Ion Implantation

The enabling step of the LEEM concept is the controlled introduction of amorphised silicon (a-Si) nanolayers within a c-Si matrix. This is achieved by ion implantation at carefully selected energies and doses, followed by annealing. The process generates buried amorphised regions, which may be continuous or spatially modulated, acting as active sites for carrier multiplication. Subsequent annealing partially recrystallises the matrix, stabilising the nanostructures while preserving their electronic functionality.

Transmission electron microscopy (TEM) confirms the structural integration of these buried layers. Preliminary experiments at CEA-Leti have demonstrated discontinuous nanometre-scale layers without compromising the crystalline quality of the surrounding silicon. Such precise nanostructuring within standard wafers represents a key innovation of LEEMONS, leveraging microelectronics-derived implantation tools for photovoltaic applications.

3.3 Precision Implantation Using Hard Masks

Efficient LEEM layers require nanostructuring that supports electronic transport while enabling carrier multiplication. Electrical carriers must be able to cross the amorphised silicon regions through crystalline passages and the feature sizes must remain small since hot electrons in silicon thermalise extremely rapidly, within tens to a few hundred femtoseconds [7]. This ultrafast relaxation imposes strict constraints on the spatial scale of implanted features. To meet these requirements, LEEMONS employs hard masks for ion implantation. Two complementary approaches are being developed:

- Ultra-thin silicon masks, fabricated at UMLP using Deep Reactive Ion Etching (RIE). These masks, with ~10 µm apertures, enable the definition of patterned implantation zones over large wafer areas.

- Metallic mesh masks, consisting of ~7 µm-wide metallic wires assembled into large-area meshes. These masks are robust and compatible with industrial wafer sizes.

Compared to conventional photoresist patterning, hard masks avoid surface contamination and damage while enabling discontinuous implantation at scale. Early results demonstrate that such masks can generate buried amorphised layers with periodicity, enabling reproducible definition of electron multiplication zones.

3.4 Integration into Device Architectures

For LEEM technology to demonstrate its industrial impact, it must be integrated into the mainstream silicon solar cell designs that dominate current and emerging production. The project therefore focuses on three representative architectures:

- PERC (Passivated Emitter Rear Contact): long established as a leading industrial architecture, PERC continues to represent a very large share of global production. Its widespread adoption makes it a relevant platform for demonstrating the compatibility of LEEM layers with mass manufacturing.

- HJT (Heterojunction): offering excellent passivation quality and high open-circuit voltages, HJT is increasingly seen as a pathway to higher efficiency. LEEM layers must be integrated in a way that preserves the low-temperature processing conditions required by this architecture.

- IBC-HJT (Interdigitated Back Contact HJT): combining advanced metallisation with the benefits of heterojunction passivation, IBC-HJT represents one of the most promising high-end cell architectures. Demonstrating LEEM compatibility in this configuration paves the way toward next-generation devices.

Across all these device types, the key challenges are to minimise defect-induced recombination, maintain effective passivation and adapt metallisation strategies.

3.5 Metallisation and Passivation Challenges

Metallisation and passivation are critical bottlenecks for LEEM cell integration. Conventional high-temperature metallisation (>400 °C) risks modifying or erasing the implanted nanostructures. To address this, low-temperature alternatives are developed by ISC and Roltec to preserve the integrity of the LEEM layers while delivering high conductivity.

Passivation within the LEEM framework is approached as a coupled materials and process optimisation problem. Investigations consider alternative dielectric layers, modified deposition conditions and engineered interface treatments to accommodate the presence of ion-implanted nanostructures. Particular attention is given to how implantation, annealing and passivation steps interact, since process sequencing strongly influences both carrier lifetimes and structural stability.

Advances in metallisation and passivation are therefore central to validating the feasibility of LEEM integration. Establishing stable and reproducible processes in these areas will define the boundary conditions under which LEEM can be considered alongside other emerging concepts for high-efficiency silicon photovoltaics.

3.6 Advantages over Tandem and Other Novel Concepts

Several approaches are currently being investigated to overcome the efficiency limitations of single-junction silicon solar cells. Tandem devices combine absorbers with different bandgaps and have demonstrated high laboratory efficiencies, but they require the integration of heterogeneous materials, additional interconnection layers and significant modifications to production infrastructure. Photon conversion layers, which aim to modify the incident spectrum through up- or down-conversion processes, remain limited by incomplete conversion efficiencies and coupling losses. Hot-carrier solar cells represent another direction of research, although their practical implementation is hindered by the lack of absorber materials capable of sustaining slow carrier cooling.

The LEEM concept differs from these strategies by altering the response of silicon itself. Ion implantation and thermal treatments create nanostructured regions that enhance impact ionisation and allow multiple charge carriers to be generated from a single high-energy photon. This approach does not rely on supplementary absorbers or external spectral modification, but instead employs processes already established in the semiconductor and photovoltaic industries.

From a manufacturing perspective, this compatibility with existing equipment and process flows is a central advantage. LEEM offers the possibility of enhancing photocurrent generation while maintaining continuity with established crystalline silicon technology, thereby extending the scope of efficiency improvements within a familiar industrial framework.

4 PROGRESS AND RESULTS

4.1 Nanostructured Layer Fabrication

During the first year of the project, ion implantation experiments at CEA-Leti successfully produced discontinuous amorphised silicon layers embedded in crystalline silicon. However, the preliminary silicon masks used to create these discontinuities were not yet optimised. Their rough geometry generated extensive shadowing effects and limited the formation of buried discontinuous amorphised layers, making detection with standard ellipsometry techniques more challenging.

Therefore, complementary characterisation methods such as Raman spectroscopy, backscattered electron spectroscopy and TEM had to be employed to confirm the structural integration of the amorphised layers.

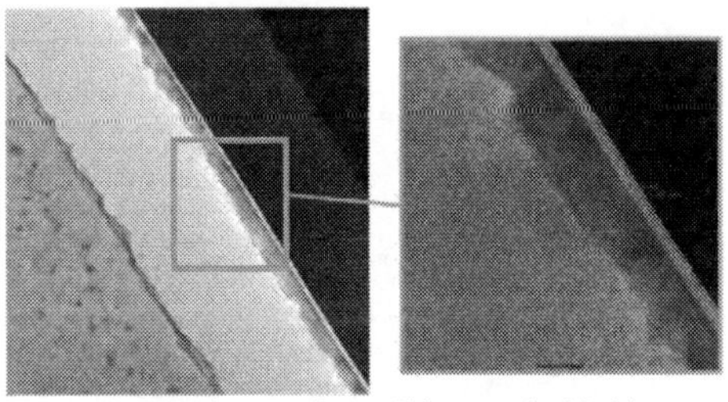

Figure 3: TEM image of an a-Si layer embedded into c-Si by ion implantation for LEEMONS project.

4.2 Hard Mask Development

UMLP developed ultra-thin silicon masks with 10 µm apertures using a deep-RIE process. These masks were successfully tested at CEA-Leti, marking the first validated milestone of the LEEMONS project. Early experiments in Grenoble demonstrated for the first time the feasibility of fabricating discontinuous buried amorphised layers using hard masks with 10 µm apertures.

In parallel, a second masking approach has been designed to enable smaller apertures (up to 7µm) and thinner masks. This method adapts standard metallic stencil printing masks, which are modified and coated to prevent contamination and to operate inside an ion implantation chamber. Production of these metallic mesh masks began in September 2025 in Japan, followed by final assembly in Spain and specialised coating in France.

These hard masks enable discontinuous ion implantation without the need for photoresist deposition and removal, thereby avoiding potential damage to wafers.

Figure 4: Ultra-thin mesh mask (~7µm stainless steel wires) that allows discontinuous ion implantation.

4.3 Low-Temperature Metallisation

At ISC Konstanz, several metallisation alternatives have been investigated to reduce thermal budgets and preserve the integrity of the implanted nanostructures. Initial lab-scale trials included contact resistance measurements across different metallisation pastes and temperature profiles, as well as mini-cell experiments using three test structures with varied diffusions. These experiments provided the first comparative data on how peak firing temperature influences performance.

In parallel, the amorphised nanostructure resistance tests were initiated in September 2025. SEGTON and CEA provided two implanted wafers that were subjected to optimised metallisation temperature curves. Ongoing characterisation will determine the maximum thermal budget that LEEMONS nanostructures can withstand.

Alternative metallisation routes are also under assessment. For example, LECO firing with adapted pastes is planned, although its compatibility with mini-Zebra architectures is still being evaluated due to the back-contact design. These exploratory trials aim to identify metallisation schemes that minimise process temperature while ensuring good electrical contact quality.

Roltec conducted multiple metal contact deposition trials and demonstrated the fabrication of electrodes with ohmic contact on silicon at process temperatures below 100 °C using silver deposition by magnetron sputtering. This approach allows the formation of contacts for Zebra IBC solar cells under low-temperature metallisation conditions, thereby preserving the structural integrity of the LEEMONS nanostructures.

Figure 5: Measuring electrodes on an alternatively metallised sample prepared for LEEMONS.

4.4 Passivation optimisation tests on-going

The first integration steps have combined ion-implanted nanostructured layers with n-type crystalline silicon cells, marking the transition from material-level experiments to device-level validation. Passivation optimisation is currently ongoing at ISC Konstanz and CSEM, with multiple complementary approaches under investigation.

CEA-Leti's July 2025 implantation campaign provided wafers that are now being characterised and prepared for passivation at CSEM. Two diffusion routes are under evaluation: $POCl_3$ diffusion with etch-back and PECVD SiOx:P diffusion, both yielding promising profiles for front surface fields. CSEM has initiated lifetime studies to compare their effectiveness, with first results showing alignment with the LEEMONS concept.

Overall, the passivation optimisation campaign aims to balance effective suppression of recombination with seamless integration into the LEEMONS nanostructuring process, laying the foundation for functional PERC and HJT prototypes in the next phases.

5 IMPACT AND RELEVANCE

The LEEMONS concept addresses critical challenges in the PV industry:

- Sustainability: process relies on recyclable materials and minimises additional steps.
- Industrial compatibility: integration with existing PERC/HJT production lines avoids costly infrastructure changes.
- EU policy alignment: supports strategic autonomy and climate neutrality targets.

If successful, LEEMONS could extend the relevance of Si-PV, enabling higher efficiencies without the complexity of tandems and positioning Europe at the forefront of next-generation solar innovation.

6 CONCLUSIONS

LEEMONS introduces a fundamentally novel PV concept based on low-energy electron multiplication in nanostructured silicon. Initial progress validates ion implantation masks, amorphised layers and metallisation alternatives, laying the groundwork for full device integration. The upcoming project phases will focus on integrating LEEM layers into PERC and HJT prototypes, benchmarking performance and assessing scalability.

By coupling scientific innovation with industrial relevance, LEEMONS aims to deliver a disruptive, cost-effective pathway to higher Si-PV efficiency and long-term sustainability.

7 ACKNOWLEDGEMENTS

This project has received funding from the European Union's Horizon Europe research and innovation programme under grant agreement No. 101172870

8 REFERENCES

[1] W. Shockley, H.J. Queisser, "Detailed Balance Limit of Efficiency of p-n Junction Solar Cells," J. Appl. Phys., 32 (1961), 510–519.
[2] Sabine Kolodinski, Jürgen H. Werner, Thomas Wittchen and Hans J. Queisser, "Quantum efficiencies exceeding unity due to impact ionization in silicon solar cells", Appl. Phys. Lett., Vol. 63, (1993), 2405.
[3] A. J. Nozik, "Spectroscopy and Hot Electron Relaxation Dynamics in Semiconductor Quantum Wells and Quantum Dots", Annu. Rev. Phys. Chem., Vol. 52, (2001), 193–231.
[4] D. Timmerman, J. Valenta, K. Dohnalova, W. D. A. M. de Boer and T. Gregorkiewicz, "Step-like enhancement of luminescence quantum yield of silicon nanocrystals", Nature Nanotechnology, Vol. 6, (2011), 710-713.
[5] N. M. Gabor, Z. Zhong, K. Bosnick, J. Park and P. L. McEuen, "Extremely Efficient Multiple Electron-Hole Pair Generation in Carbon Nanotube Photodiodes", Science, Vol. 325, (2009), 1367-1371.
[6] C. A. Gueymard, "SMARTS2, A Simple Model of the Atmospheric Radiative Transfer of Sunshine: Algorithms and performance assessment", Florida Solar Energy Center Report, (1995).
[7] A Sieradzki, M Basta, P Scharoch and J-Y Bigot, "Ultrafast Optical Properties of Dense Electron Gas in Silicon Nanostructures", Plasmonics, Vol. 9, No. 3, (2014), 545-551.

TAILORING CBTSSE SOLAR CELLS FOR INDOOR PHOTOVOLTAIC APPLICATIONS

Hitarth Narsi Patel*, Bindu Pamula, Deepak Joshi, Vivek Garg
Optoelectronics2Application (O2A) Research Group, Department of Electronics Engineering, S. V. National Institute of Technology Surat-395007, India

ABSTRACT: These Solution-processed $Cu_2BaSn(S,Se)_4$ (CBTSSe) thin films have emerged as promising candidates for next-generation photovoltaics due to their earth-abundant and non-toxic constituents, as well as tunable bandgaps suitable for both outdoor and indoor applications. While significant progress has been made in optimizing CBTSSe-based solar cells for outdoor use, their potential for indoor energy harvesting, particularly for powering IoT devices, remains largely unexplored. This work investigates the performance of a CBTSSe-based device, originally designed for outdoor applications, under indoor light conditions. A baseline simulation model, calibrated against a 6.17% efficient experimental device, was developed using SCAPS. This model incorporates realistic material parameters and interface defect considerations. The absorber layer bandgap was optimized for indoor illumination (1.9 eV) and the impact of absorber thickness and defect density was systematically investigated. Furthermore, the buffer layer was modified by exploring different conduction band offsets and ultimately replacing Zn:CdS with ZnSe to enhance electron transport. Our simulations demonstrate a significant improvement in device performance under indoor WLED illumination (1000K lux), achieving a power conversion efficiency exceeding 30%. This study highlights the potential of CBTSSe as a viable material for high-performance indoor photovoltaics and contributes to the development of self-powered IoT devices
Keywords: CBTS, thin films, indoor photovoltaics, SCAPS

1 INTRODUCTION

Solution processable thin films have attracted significant amount of interest among researchers due to low cost and simple processing techniques. The existing thin film based devices such as CdTe and $CuInGaSe_2$ (CIGS) suffers from toxicity and rare earth element constitutes [1]. Various elemental substitution studies were performed to eliminate the toxic and rare earth elements. It was proposed to replace the rare earth Indium with Zinc and considerable efforts were made to establish a new absorber with Cu_2ZnSnS_4 (CZTS) elemental constituent [2], [3]. Despite tremendous decade long effort to maximize the performance of CZTS devices, the maximum achievable PCE is less than 14% [3]. The performance is effect due to antisite defects which causes band tailing. The effect of antisite defects arises due to similar atomic sizes of elements in CZTS. The elemental substitution of elements with different atomic sizes can mitigate this defect and improve the performance of the devices. Various Density function theory (DFT) studies have been studies to find the potential element to replace Zn in CZTS [4], [5]. It is proposed to replace Zn with Ba which results in an earth abundant and environment friendly material Cu_2BaSnS_4 (CBTS) which has proven in mitigating antisites defects while exhibiting desirable optoelectric properties for photovoltaic application [6], [7], [8]. CBTS has a wide bandgap of 2 eV and by adding selenium to it, the bandgap can be further reduced up to 1.44 eV thus making it suitable for single and multijunction solar cells [9]. $Cu_2BaSn(S,Se)_4$ (CBTSSe) has trigonal structure which deforms to orthorhombic if excess amount of selenium ($X = Se/(Se+S) > 0.75$) is added to it [10]. The CBTSSe devices made using vacuum processing technique had PCE of 2.68% [11]. Various improvements in the device were proposed which boosted the PCE to 5% [12], [13]. The solution processing route was explored and after optimization, the PCE of 5% was achieved which is comparable to vacuum processed devices [14], [15]. Recently by modifying the cell structure, the PCE solution processed devices reach 6.17% [16]. Significant progress has been made in the development of Internet of Things (IoT) devices, many of which require low-power operation. Indoor photovoltaics have emerged as a promising energy harvesting solution for these low-power IoT devices, potentially enabling self-powered operation. Consequently, research efforts have focused on identifying suitable materials for indoor solar cells to replace conventional silicon-based cells, which exhibit suboptimal performance in indoor environments. The low bandgap of silicon hinders its ability to effectively harvest energy from indoor light sources. For optimal performance in these environments, a bandgap of approximately 1.9 eV is desired. Materials possessing this bandgap are expected to exhibit maximum PCE. CBTS offer a tunable bandgap ranging from 1.44 to 2 eV, including the ideal 1.9 eV value. This tunability makes CBTS a promising candidate for indoor photovoltaic applications.

This work investigates the potential of a CBTSSe-based device, originally designed for outdoor applications, as an indoor energy harvesting solution. A baseline simulation model of the cell was developed and calibrated in SCAPS to accurately reproduce the performance of a fabricated counterpart, minimizing discrepancies [17]. This calibrated baseline model was then employed to systematically optimize each layer, exploring variations in thickness and defect density, and evaluating alternative materials. The scarcity of research on CBTS device performance in indoor photovoltaic applications highlights the significance of this work, which aims to contribute to the advancement of CBTS-based indoor energy harvesting technologies. The manuscript is further divided into three sections. Section 2 deals with baseline model development, Section 3 has results and discussions and Section 4 is devoted to conclusion of the work.

2 BASELINE MODEL DEVELOPMENT

The baseline model of 6.17% efficient is designed using Solar Cell Capacitance Simulator (SCAPS)[16]. The tool solves Poisson's equation and continuity equations and accurately predicts the performance of the solar cells. In the baseline model, Mo is used as back contact, CBTSSe is the absorber layer, Zn:CdS (ZCS) is the buffer

10.4229/EUPVSEC2025/2BV.1.5

layer, Mg:ZnO (ZMO) is the window layer, and Al:ZnO (AZO) is the front transparent conductive oxide (TCO) layer (Fig. 1(a)). The performance of the baseline model matches with the experimental device with minimal error. The baseline model is designed with material parameters listed in [18].

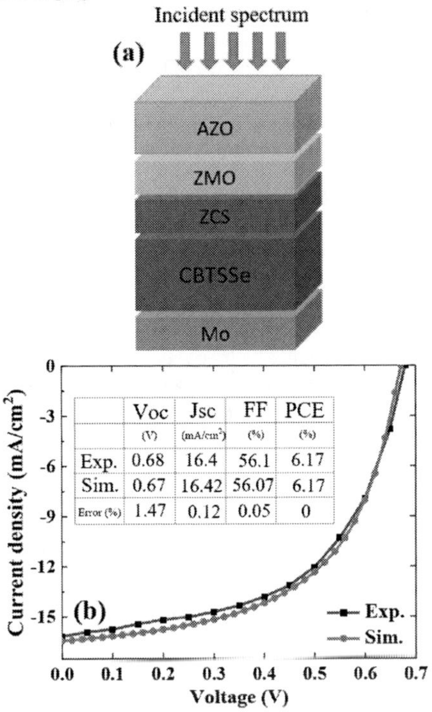

Fig. 1(a): Schematic of CBTSSe cell structure, (b) J-V characteristics of experimental and simulated devices.

The interface defects were added at Absorber – Buffer interface to include the effect of surface recombination of charge carriers at the junction. The effect of reflectance encountered at the TCO is also added in the model [16]. The J-V characteristics of both, experimental and simulated cell, with standard AM 1.5G illumination with 1000 W/m^2 are shown in Fig. 1(b).

3 RESULTS AND DISCUSSION

3.1 Absorber layer optimization

The bandgap of CBTSSe can be tuned from 1.44 to 2 eV by modifying the composition ratio of S and Se (Fig. 2(a)) [18]. The baseline model is subject to indoor illumination of WLED spectrum with 1000K lux. The indoor spectrum has incident power of 53.31 W/m^2. The bandgap of absorber layer is set to 1.9 eV which is the optimum bandgap for indoor photovoltaics applications [19]. The performance of the cell are noted as PCE = 19.85%, Open circuit voltage (Voc) = 0.91 V, Short circuit current density (Jsc) = 1.66 mA/cm^2, and Fill factor (FF) = 69.61%.Optimizing absorber layer thickness and defect density is crucial for high-performance solar cells. High defect densities introduce trap states, increasing charge carrier recombination and consequently degrading device performance.

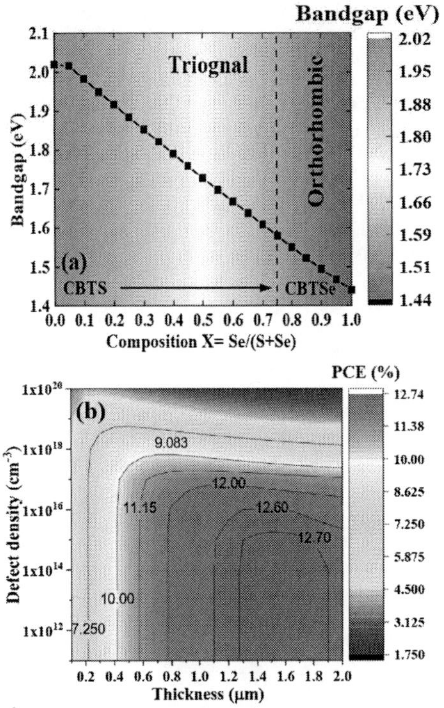

Fig. 2(a) Variation in Eg due to variation in X, (b) Effect on PCE due to variation in defect density and thickness of absorber layer

Defect density is inversely related to both carrier lifetime and diffusion length. While a thicker absorber layer promotes deeper light penetration and higher charge generation, these photo generated carriers must traverse the entire layer without recombining, a process governed by their diffusion length. Excessively thick absorbers can exhibit reduced fill factors due to increased bulk resistance encountered by carriers during transport. Therefore, absorber thickness is fundamentally limited by the carrier diffusion length. Since defect density directly influences diffusion length, it and absorber thickness are interdependent parameters requiring careful co-optimization. Both the parameters, thickness and defect density, are simultaneously varied from 0.1 to 2 μm and 10^{10} to 10^{20} cm^{-3}, and the results are shown as contour plot in Fig. 2(b). From the plot the optimized thickness and defect density are found to be 1.5 μm and 10^{14} cm^{-3} respectively. This optimization balances the benefits of increased light absorption with the detrimental effects of increased recombination, ultimately determining the overall performance of the solar cell. With these modification, the PCE of the cell is boosted to 22.42% with Voc = 0.93 V, Jsc =1.74 mA/cm^2, and FF =73.66%.

3.2 Buffer layer modification

Buffer layer plays an important role in determining the performance of the cell. Buffer layer must ensure smoother movement of electrons and block the holes towards the front junction. The conduction band offset (CBO) analysis is performed to study the effect band alignment on performance of the cell. CBO is defined as the difference between the electron affinity of absorber and buffer layer.

The positive value of CBO exhibits a cliff structure which allows the electrons to flow from absorber layer to buffer layer and block the movement of the holes. Negative value of CBO generates spikes at the absorber-buffer junction which creates a barrier for the electrons to move toward the front contact and encourages their recombination.

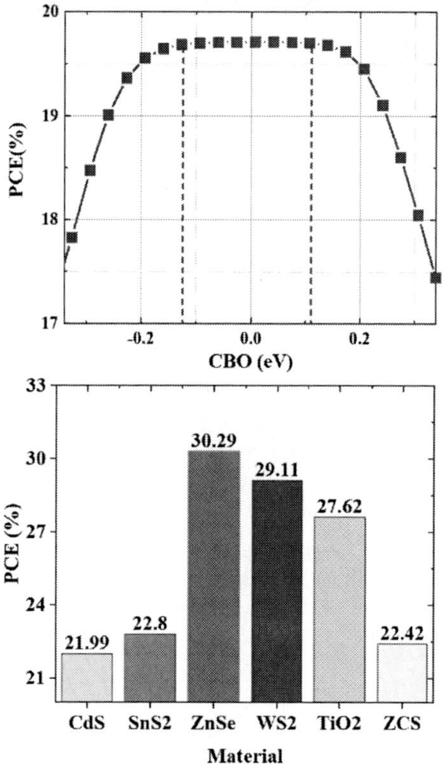

Fig. 3(a) Effect on PCE due to variation in CBO, (b) PCE of cells with various buffer layers

We vary CBO from -0.34 to 0.34 eV and its effect on the PCE of the cell is shown in Fig 3(a). The PCE of the cell shows minimal variation for the range of CBO values allowing an opportunity to replace the existing buffer layer with any alternate material whose electron affinity lies within the range. We investigated several promising electron transport layer (ETL) materials [20], [21] and propose replacing the existing ZCS with ZnSe to enhance the performance of the device (Fig. 3(b)). ZnSe has high doping density in order of 10^{19} cm^{-3} resulting in strong electric field. This field facilitates efficient charge carrier drift across the junction, minimizing recombination losses and enhancing overall device performance. The cell with structure as Mo/CBTSSe/ZnSe/ZMO/AZO has PCE of 30.29% with Voc = 1.12 V, Jsc =1.76 mA/cm^2, and FF =74.55%.

4 CONCLUSION

In this work, we have successfully demonstrated the potential of CBTSSe-based solar cells for high-performance indoor photovoltaic applications. Starting with a calibrated baseline model that accurately reflects the performance of a fabricated device, we systematically optimized the cell structure for indoor light conditions. Our investigations revealed the importance of tuning the absorber layer bandgap to 1.9 eV for optimal indoor performance. Through careful co-optimization of absorber thickness and defect density, we achieved a significant boost in efficiency. Furthermore, the modification of the buffer layer by replacing ZCS with ZnSe, enabled by an analysis of conduction band offset, led to a substantial improvement in charge transport and a further enhancement in device performance. Our simulations demonstrate a remarkable power conversion efficiency exceeding 30% under indoor WLED illumination. This research contributes to the growing field of indoor photovoltaics and paves the way for the development of self-powered devices for a sustainable future.

REFERENCES

[1] A. Wang, M. He, M. A. Green, K. Sun, and X. Hao, "A Critical Review on the Progress of Kesterite Solar Cells: Current Strategies and Insights," *Adv Energy Mater*, p. 2203046, Nov. 2022

[2] W. Wang *et al.*, "Device Characteristics of CZTSSe Thin-Film Solar Cells with 12.6% Efficiency," *Adv Energy Mater*, vol. 4, no. 7, p. 1301465, May 2014.

[3] D. B. Mitzi, O. Gunawan, T. K. Todorov, K. Wang, and S. Guha, "The path towards a high-performance solution-processed kesterite solar cell," *Solar Energy Materials and Solar Cells*, vol. 95, no. 6, pp. 1421–1436, Jun. 2011.

[4] C. Wang *et al.*, "Design of I 2 –II–IV–VI 4 Semiconductors through Element Substitution: The Thermodynamic Stability Limit and Chemical Trend," *Chemistry of Materials*, vol. 26, no. 11, pp. 3411–3417, Jun. 2014.

[5] S. Lie, M. Guc, V. Tunuguntla, V. Izquierdo-Roca, S. Siebentritt, and L. H. Wong, "Comprehensive physicochemical and photovoltaic analysis of different Zn substitutes (Mn, Mg, Fe, Ni, Co, Ba, Sr) in CZTS-inspired thin film solar cells," *J Mater Chem A Mater*, vol. 10, no. 16, pp. 9137–9149, 2022.

[6] F. Hong, *et al.*, "Trigonal Cu 2 -II-Sn-VI 4 (II = Ba, Sr and VI = S, Se) quaternary compounds for earth-abundant photovoltaics," *Physical Chemistry Chemical Physics*, vol. 18, no. 6, pp. 4828–4834, 2016.

[7] B. Teymur *et al.*, "Optoelectronic and material properties of solution-processed Earth-abundant Cu2BaSn(S, Se)4 films for solar cell applications," *Nano Energy*, vol. 80, p. 105556, Feb. 2021.

[8] J. Ge and Y. Yan, "Synthesis and characterization of photoelectrochemical and photovoltaic Cu2BaSnS4 thin films and solar cells," *J Mater Chem C Mater*, vol. 5, no. 26, pp. 6406–6419, Jul. 2017.

[9] J. Ge, Y. Yu, and Y. Yan, "Earth-abundant trigonal BaCu 2 Sn(Se x S 1−x) 4 (x = 0–0.55) thin films with tunable band gaps for solar water splitting," *J. Mater. Chem. A*, vol. 4, no. 48, pp. 18885–18891, 2016.

[10]J. Ge, Y. Yu, and Y. Yan, "Earth-Abundant Orthorhombic BaCu 2 Sn(Se x S 1− x) 4 (x ≈ 0.83) Thin Film for Solar Energy Conversion," *ACS Energy Lett*, vol. 1, no. 3, pp. 583–588, Sep. 2016.

[11]Y. Kim and D. B. Mitzi, "Growth and Photovoltaic Device Application of $Cu_2BaGe_{1-x}Sn_xSe_4$ Films Prepared by Selenization of Deposited Precursors," *ACS Appl Eng Mater*, vol. 4, no.10, pp.11528–11536, Oct. 2021.

[12]D. Shin, E *et al.*, "Synthesis and Characterization of an Earth-Abundant Cu 2 BaSn(S,Se) 4 Chalcogenide for

Photoelectrochemical Cell Application," *J Phys Chem Lett*, vol. 7, no. 22, pp. 4554–4561, Nov. 2016.
[13]D. Shin, *et al.*, "Earth-Abundant Chalcogenide Photovoltaic Devices with over 5% Efficiency Based on a Cu 2 BaSn(S,Se) 4 Absorber," *Advanced Materials*, vol. 29, no. 24, p. 1606945, Jun. 2017.
[14]B. Teymur, *et al.*,"Influence of Copper Composition on $Cu_2BaSn(S,Se)_4$ Solution-Deposited Films and Photovoltaic Devices with Over 5% Efficiency," *ACS Appl Eng Mater*, vol. 5, no. 9, pp. 10645–10656, Sep. 2022.
[15]B. Teymur, *et al.*, "Solution-Processed Earth-Abundant Cu 2 BaSn(S,Se) 4 Solar Absorber Using a Low-Toxicity Solvent," *Chemistry of Materials*, vol. 30, no. 17, pp. 6116–6123, Sep. 2018.
[16]B. Teymur, *et al.*, "Top Stack Optimization for Cu 2 BaSn(S, Se) 4 Photovoltaic Cell Leads to Improved Device Power Conversion Efficiency beyond 6%," *Adv Energy Mater*, p. 2201602, Sep. 2022.
[17]M. Burgelman, *et al.*, "Modeling thin-film PV devices," *Progress in Photovoltaics: Research and Applications*, vol. 12, no. 23, pp. 143–153, Mar. 2004.
[18]H. N. Patel, *et al.*, "Bandgap engineering of earth-abundant Cu2BaSn(S1-xSex)4 for photovoltaic application: A systematic approach to double grading," *Solar Energy Materials and Solar Cells*, vol. 269, p. 112792, Jun. 2024.
[19]S. Mishra *et al.*, "Solution-processed next generation thin film solar cells for indoor light applications," *Energy Advances*, vol. 1, no. 11, pp. 761–792, 2022.
[20]A. Rumberg, *et al.*, "ZnSe buffer prepared by iodine-enhanced chemical vapour deposition for Cu(In,Ga)(Se,S)-based solar cells," *Solar Energy Materials and Solar Cells*, vol. 75, no. 1–2, pp. 1–8, Jan. 2003.
[21]H. N. Patel, *et al.*,, "Elucidating the Potential Strategies for Performance Improvement of CBTSSe-Based Solar Cells: A Pathway Toward 20% Efficiency," *Energy Technology*, vol. 12, no. 4, Apr. 2024.

Tailoring CBTSSe Solar Cells for Indoor Photovoltaic Applications

Hitarth Narsi Patel , Bindu Pamula, Deepak Joshi , Vivek Garg

Optoelectronics2Application (O2A) Research Group, Department of Electronics Engineering, S. V. National Institute of Technology Surat-395007, India

Abstract

This study investigates the application of earth-abundant $Cu_2BaSn(S,Se)_4$ (CBTSSe) films for powering IoT devices through indoor photovoltaics. A calibrated SCAPS simulation model was used to optimize the device's performance. We tuned the absorber layer's bandgap to 1.9 eV and replaced the buffer layer with ZnSe to enhance electron transport. The simulations predict a significant improvement, with the PCE exceeding 30% under indoor WLED illumination. This work highlights CBTSSe as a promising material for indoor energy harvesting.

Device structure and simulation methodology

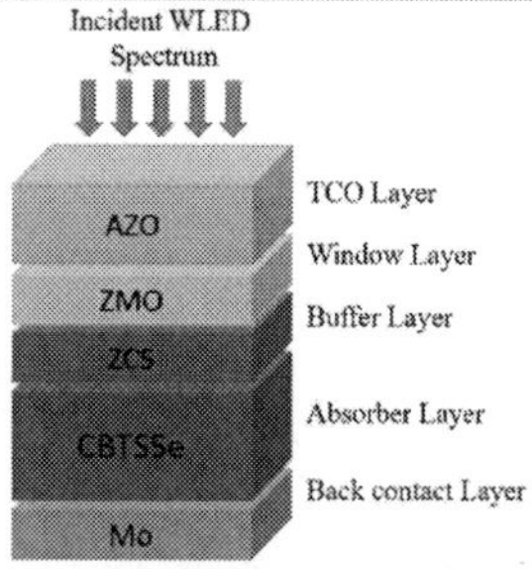

- SCAPS – 1D is used to design the base line model to replicate the behavior of the Simulation device with Experimental cell.
- The baseline model has error less than 1.5%.
- The baseline model is further calibrated to optimize the device.

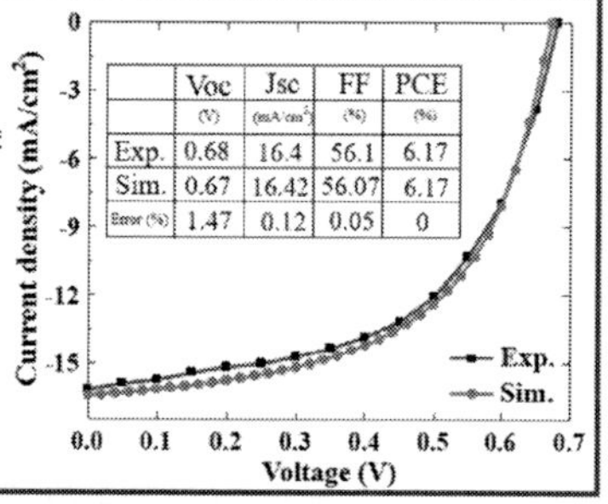

Bandgap optimization

- The Bandgap of CBTSSe is tuned from 1.44 to 2.02 eV by changing composition ratio (X) of S and Se
- CBTSSe shows trigonal structure for X < 0.75 and orthorhombic for X > 0.75.

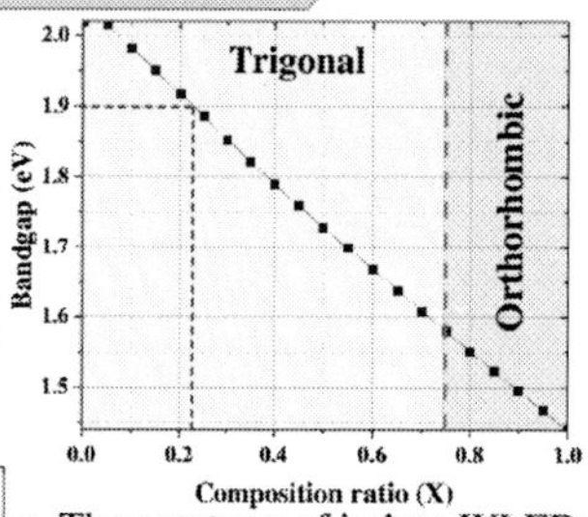

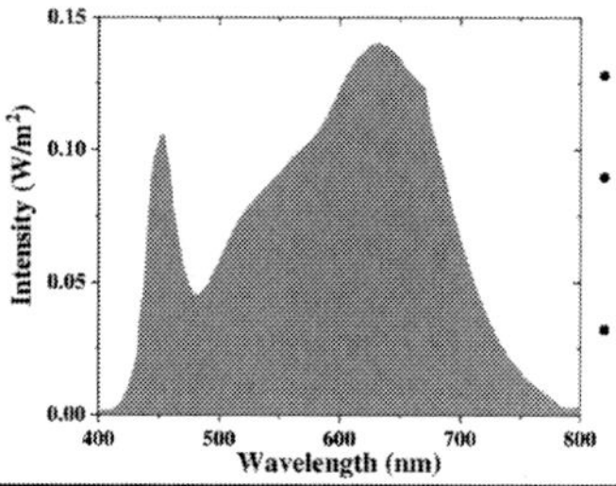

- The spectrum of indoor WLED is different then AM1.5G
- WLED spectrum has strong intensity in Visible - infrared region (600 to 700nm)
- We set the bandgap of CBTSSe to 1.9 eV for optimal spectrum utilization.

Absorber layer optimization

- The Absorber thickness and defect density were simultaneously varied.
- The optimum value of thickness and defect density are found to be 1.5μm and 10^{15} cm^{-3} respectively.

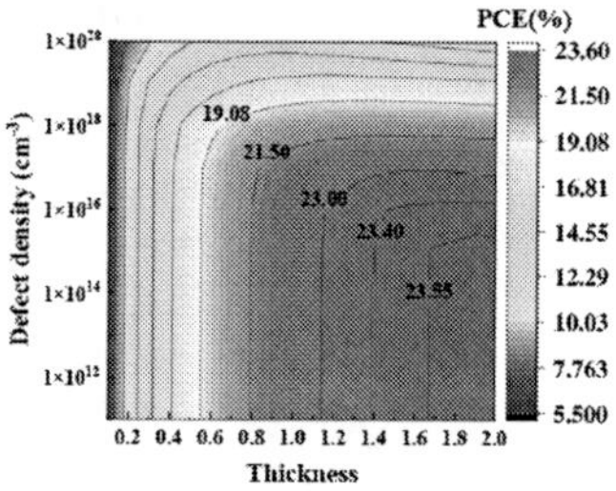

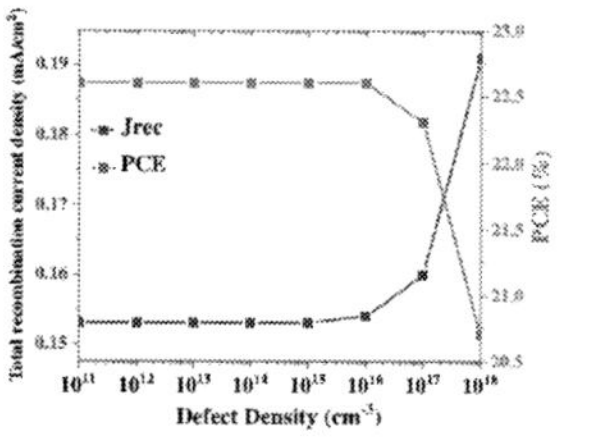

- As the defect density increases, the PCE of the cell reduces and recombination current density increases.

Buffer Layer optimization

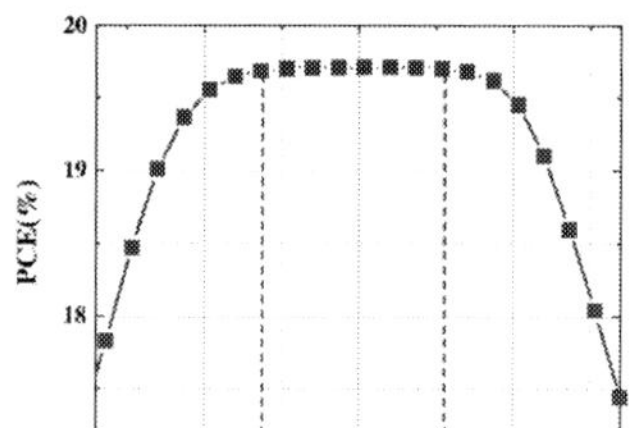

- Conduction band offset (CBO) is the difference in the electron affinity (EA) of absorber and buffer layer.
- The EA of buffer is varied while EA of absorber is kept constant to identify the effect on PCE.
- Materials within CBO range are replaced with existing buffer layer and their performance is analyzed.
- Cell with ZnSe buffer layer exhibits highest PCE of 30.29% Voc = 1.12 V, Jsc =1.76 mA/cm², and FF =74.55%.

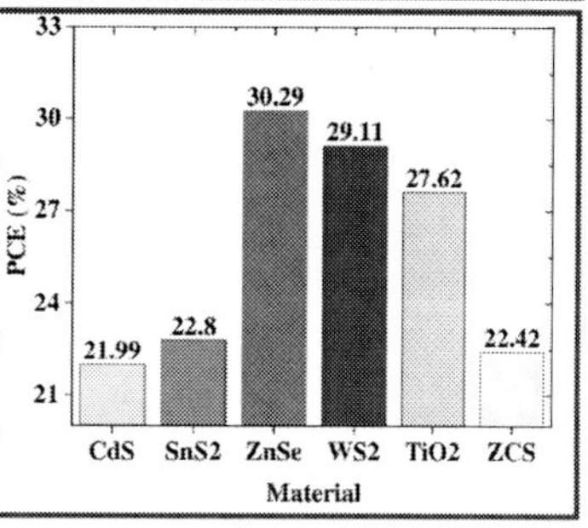

Conclusion

- The bandgap of the absorber layer is tuned to 1.9 eV for efficient utilization of indoor spectrum.
- The Thickness and defect density of the absorber layer is optimized for maximizing performance.
- A suitable replacement of ZCS buffer layer is proposed using CBO analysis.
- The proposed device with cell structure Mo/CBTSSe/ZnSe/ZMO/AZO is 30.29% efficient.

References

- D. Shin, T. Zhu, X. Huang, O. Gunawan, V. Blum, and D. B. Mitzi, Adv. Mater., vol. 29, no. 24, p. 1606945, Jun. 2017.
- B. Teymur, Y. Kim, J. Huang, K. Sun, X. Hao, and D. B. Mitzi, Adv. Energy Mater., vol. 12, no. 40, p. 2201602, Oct. 2022.

Acknowledgement: The authors would like to thank Mr. Marc Burgelman from ELSI at University of Gent, Belgium for providing SCAPS-1D software and acknowledge financial support received from SVNIT - Surat

2BV.1.5

THEORETICAL INSIGHTS THROUGH DFT INTO AGBIS$_2$ THIN FILMS ABSORBER FOR PHOTOVOLTAIC APPLICATIONS

Dhruv Singh Thakur[1], Rajesh Kumar Sharma[2], Nithin Chatterji[3], Vivek Garg[4], Shivendra Yadav[5]
Department of Electronics Engineering, SVNIT, Surat-395007, India
ds22ec001@eced.svnit.ac.in, d21ec011@eced.svnit.ac.in, nithinc@eced.svnit.ac.in, vivekg@eced.svnit.ac.in, shivendra.y@eced.svnit.ac.in

ABSTRACT: $AgBiS_2$ has emerged as a promising absorber material for thin-film solar cell applications due to its earth-abundant, non-toxic composition and tunable optical bandgap (*Eg*) (0.8–1.32 eV), making it suitable for low-cost and scalable production. This study comprehensively investigates the suitability of $AgBiS_2$ absorber for solar cells, emphasizing its structural, optoelectronic, and photovoltaic performance. Using density functional theory (DFT), we explore the electrical and optical properties, including *Eg*, absorption coefficient (α), dielectric constant, and refractive index. The result shows a very high 'α' of the order of ~106, and *Eg* (direct/indirect) calculated by MGGA and HSE method 1.18/0.63, and 1.55/0.99 respectively, which is very close to the experimental value ~1.0 eV. These insights highlight the potential of $AgBiS_2$ as a versatile absorber material, paving the way for advancements in thin film solar cell technologies.
Keywords: $AgBiS_2$, thin film, density functional theory, optoelectrical properties, QuantumATK

1 INTRODUCTION

A promising approach to improving solar cell technology is through the development of thin-film solar cells, which offer a much thinner absorber layer compared to conventional silicon-based solar cells. Ternary and quaternary chalcogenide or Matildite materials have recently attracted considerable research attention for their potential in photovoltaic applications. $AgBiS_2$ stands out as an environmentally friendly, abundant, and non-toxic material with excellent absorption properties, high mobility, and an optimal *Eg* range of 1 1.32 eV [1]. $AgBiS_2$ known as Matildite has two established crystal phases. The two crystal phases are the cubic α-$AgBiS_2$ and hexagonal β-$AgBiS_2$ phases. It belongs to the I–V–VI_2 family of compounds (where I = Cu/Ag/Au; V = As/Sb/Bi and VI = S/Se/Te) [2]. This article investigates the optical and electrical properties of $AgBiS_2$ using DFT simulations. By evaluating its optoelectronic performance, we aim to contribute valuable insights into the potential of $AgBiS_2$ in advancing eco-friendly and high-performance photovoltaic technologies.

2 COMPUTATIONAL METHOD

The linear combination of atomic orbitals (LCAO) calculator is utilized with Meta-generalized gradient approximation (MGGA) and Heyd-Scuseria-Ernzerhof (HSE) exchange-correlation (XC) function in the QuantumATK [3] to calculate the structural and optoelectronic properties of the $AgBiS_2$ compound. Based on DFT, this method is considered the most sophisticated computational technique for determining materials' ground state properties. The interactions of electron-ion are explained by the Vanderbilt-type pseudopotentials (PP). In the process of geometry optimization, the effects of XC interaction are calculated with the MGGA and HSE. We calculated the total energy, unit cell volume, and *Eg* of the AgBiS2 by taking the noncollinear spin, occupational method is Fermi-Dirac and Monkhorst (MP)-Grid k-point density 8×8×2 incorporated for the Brillouin-zone (BZ) sampling as shown in Fig. 1(c) with applying pseudoDojo PP. In the self-consistent iterative process, the criteria of convergence: the total difference in energy found within 1.0×10^{-6} eV/atom, the maximum stress within 0.02 GPa, the maximum atom displacement within 1.0×10^{-4}Å, and the maximum force within 0.01eV/Å.

3 RESULT AND DISCUSSION

3.1 Structural properties of $AgBiS_2$ compound

As shown in Fig.1(a), the β-$AgBiS_2$ crystal belongs to the space group P-3m1, No.164, which is a hexagonally symmetric structure. The placement of the ions is shown in (x, y, z) coordinates: Ag: (0, 0, 0), (0.3333, 0.6667, 0.672), Bi: (0, 0, 0.5), (0.3333, 0.6667, 0.163), S: (0, 0, 0.253), (0.3333, 0.6667, 0.406), (0.3333, 0.6667, 0.926). In this work, for optimization of geometry considering the cost of calculation time and accuracy requirements, we adopted a method to optimize the geometry of β-$AgBiS_2$ crystal, which is the MGGA. The Brillouin Zone is shown in Fig. 1(c) which describes the primitive cell in reciprocal space.

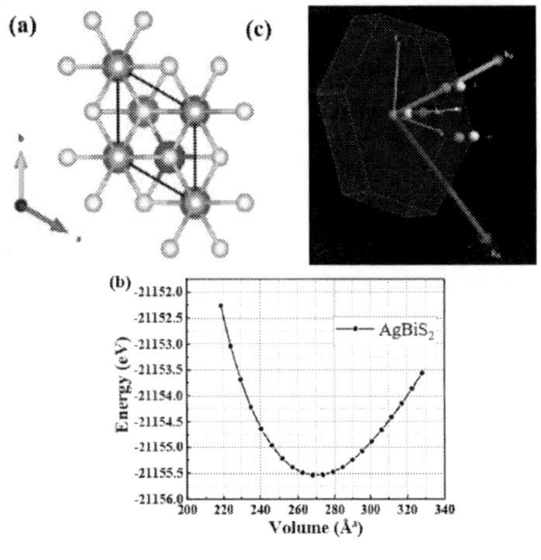

Figure 1: β-$AgBiS_2$ crystal (a) Structure (b) Volume optimization plot (c) Brillouin Zone

Table I reported the calculated lattice constants and other reported experimental and theoretical data for comparison. The calculated lattice constants a and c are 4.043 and 18.93 Å, respectively, with 0.66% and 0.68% deviation from the experimental values, the optimized volume and ground state energy for this compound is 267.97 Å³, -21155.5397 eV as shown in Fig.1(b), a favorable agreement by DFT standards as shown in Table I.

Table I: β-$AgBiS_2$ Crystal lattice constant a(Å), c(Å), and *Eg* (eV) compared to experimental and theoretical data.

Parameter		This study		Other study [1], [2]		Exp. [4], [6], [7]
		MGGA	HSE	PBE	HSE	
Lattice constant (Å)	a	4.043	-	4.0497, 4.02	---	4.07
	c	18.93	-	19.019, 19.05	---	19.06
***Eg* (eV) (Direct/ Indirect)**		1.18/ 0.63	1.55 / 0.99	0.42, 0.46	1.54	0.9, 1.2

3.2 Electronic properties of $AgBiS_2$ compound

To analyze the electronic characteristics of β-$AgBiS_2$ crystal, we have to find out the electronic band structure. Fig. 2 shows the related results, from which we can observe that β-$AgBiS_2$ crystal having *Eg* (direct/indirect) obtained by MGGA and HSE method is 1.18/0.63 eV, and 1.55/0.99 eV respectively, which approximately matches to the experimental value 1.2 eV. The valence band (dashed blue line------) and conduction band (dashed red line------), for the AgBiS2 nanocrystals the *Eg* (~1.0 eV) blue-shifted due to the quantum confinement relative to that of the bulk phase of $AgBiS_2$.

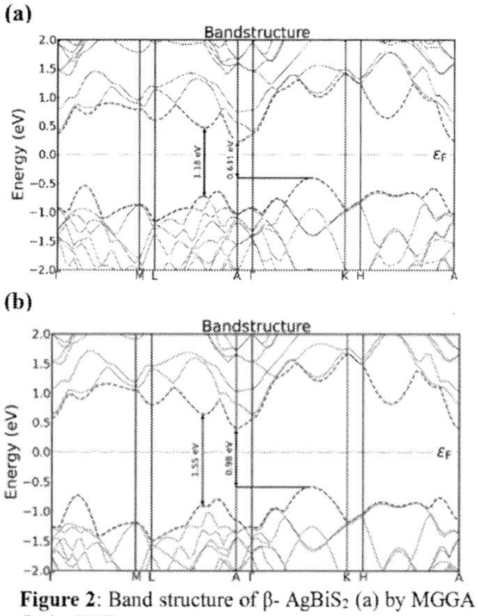

Figure 2: Band structure of β- $AgBiS_2$ (a) by MGGA (b) by HSE

3.3 Optical properties

(a) Absorption coefficient (α)

Optical characteristics are the behavior of materials when exposed to incident light. Optical parameters provide a deep understanding of the selected material and its behavior due to light interaction, highlighting their valuable contribution to the optic, solar technology, and photonic. The absorption coefficient α(ω) is used to quantify the interaction between light and matter. The absorption coefficient α(ω) is expressed by the following equation (1). where "c" is the speed of light.

$$\alpha(\omega) = \frac{\sqrt{2\omega^2}}{c}\left\{\sqrt{\varepsilon_1{}^2(\omega) - \varepsilon_2{}^2(\omega)} - \varepsilon_1(\omega)\right\}^{1/2} \quad (1)$$

Fig. 3(a), displays the α(ω) curve obtained using the complex dielectric function ε(ω). The threshold energy for $AgBiS_2$ is ~1 eV, indicating the point at which these substances begin to absorb electromagnetic radiation. Below the threshold energy, the material is transparent and absorbs no light in this energy range. $AgBiS_2$ compound reveals optical absorption starting in the near-infrared region and extending into the ultraviolet region. With increasing the photon energy, the absorption spectra increase and reaches peak value of 1.1×10^6 at 2.7 eV. The optical absorption as shown in Fig.3(a) starts in the UV region and spreads up to the infrared spectrum of light.

(b) Complex dielectric constant (ε)

The complex dielectric function $\varepsilon(\omega)=\varepsilon_1(\omega)+i\varepsilon_2(\omega)$ describes the complete optical response of a material. $\varepsilon_1(\omega)$ represents the degree of polarization of material under the external electric field, while $\varepsilon_2(\omega)$ is related to their behavior of light absorption. It can be observed from Fig. 3(b) that the first peak of $AgBiS_2$ is located at 1.66 eV, indicating that this material has strong electrical polarization behavior within the visible to near-infrared range. $AgBiS_2$ attains a negative value in $\varepsilon_1(\omega)$ at 2.4 eV to 4 eV, indicating that the materials completely reflect the incident photon. In addition, Fig.3(c) represents $\varepsilon_2(\omega)$, demonstrating the dissipation properties of the material. Incident photon energy of less than 1.0 eV of material shows no response. The point at which the absorption of energy in the material begins is called threshold value which is consistent with the band gap of $AgBiS_2$. $AgBiS_2$ exhibits the maximum value of $\varepsilon_2(\omega)$ = 26.96 at 2.36 eV, and the maximal peak of $\varepsilon_2(\omega)$ is the absorption peak, which shows that $AgBiS_2$ has good absorption capacity in visible light.

(a)

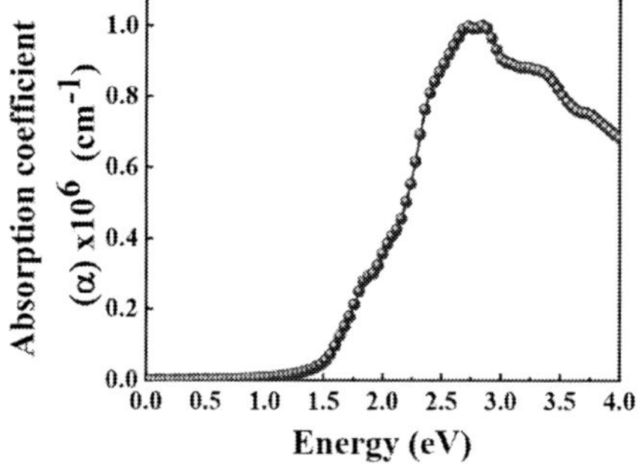

10.4229/EUPVSEC2025/2BV.1.6

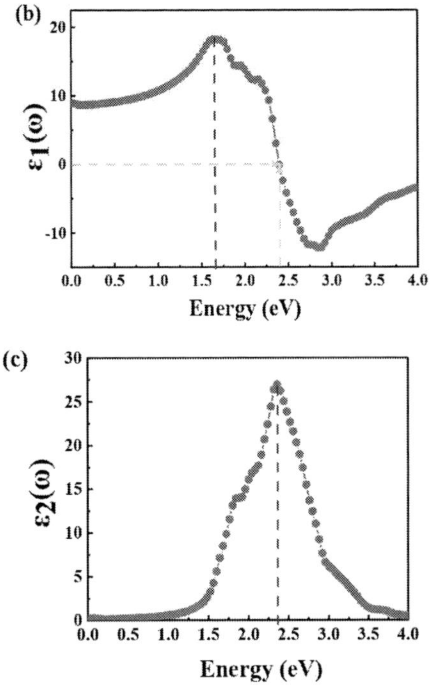

Figure 3: (a) absorption coefficient $\alpha(\omega)$ (b) real part of dielectric function ε_1 (c) imaginary part dielectric function ε_2 of $AgBiS_2$.

(c) Refractive index (n) and extinction coefficient (k)

The refractive index explains how light passes through materials and is influenced by their structure and composition. The refractive index and extinction coefficient of the material can be calculated by equation (2). Fig. 4(a) illustrates the refractive index for the $AgBiS_2$ compound. The static refractive index $n(0)$ is 3. The spectrum of $n(\omega)$ shows the highest peak value of $n(\omega) = 4.42$ around 1.76 eV. The $n(\omega)$ and the static refractive index are valuable for calculating light refraction and for applications in photoelectric devices. A refractive index greater than 1 indicates that photons slow down upon entering the material due to interaction with electrons. Higher values of $n(\omega)$ indicate greater delay in the passage of photons through the material. The peak of refractive index $n(\omega)$ within the visible or near-infrared region suggested that the compound used in devices is working in the visible or near-infrared region.

$$n(\omega) = \left\{\frac{\varepsilon_1(\omega)}{2} + \frac{\sqrt{\varepsilon_1{}^2(\omega) - \varepsilon_2{}^2(\omega)}}{2}\right\}^{1/2} \quad (2)$$

$$k(\omega) = \left\{-\frac{\varepsilon_1(\omega)}{2} + \frac{\sqrt{\varepsilon_1{}^2(\omega) - \varepsilon_2{}^2(\omega)}}{2}\right\}^{1/2} \quad (3)$$

Fig. 4(b) displays the extinction coefficient $k(\omega)$ for $AgBiS_2$ calculated by Equation (3). The extinction coefficient quantifies the light that is absorbed and scattered in the material, characterizing its ability to absorb light. Larger values of $k(\omega)$ indicate stronger absorption and intense scattering of light. The threshold energy for $k(\omega)$ is ~1 eV and the maximum value of the extinction coefficient is 3.967 at 2.68 eV.

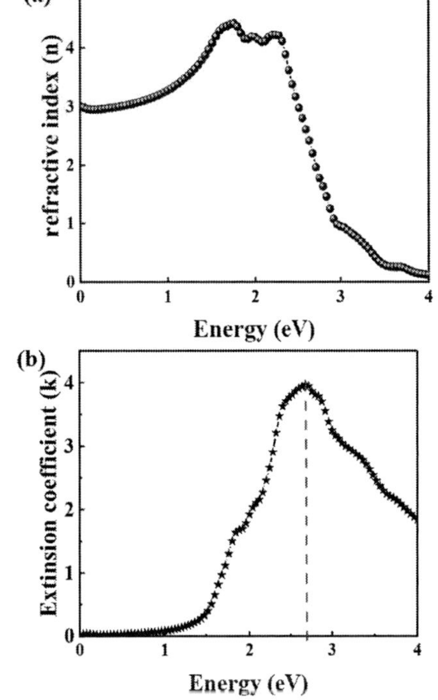

Figure 4: Calculated (a) refractive index $n(\omega)$ (b) extinction coefficient $k(\omega)$

4 CONCLUSION

In conclusion, $AgBiS_2$ demonstrates strong potential as a high-performance, eco-friendly absorber material for thin-film solar cells. Its structural properties, including optimized lattice constants (a = 4.043 Å, c = 18.93 Å), align closely with experimental values, confirming the accuracy of the MGGA method. The electronic band structure calculations match the experimental band gap of 1.2 eV, with values of 1.18/0.63 eV (MGGA) and 1.55/0.99 eV (HSE). The material exhibits excellent optical absorption from near-infrared to ultraviolet regions, peaking at 1.1×106 cm^{-1} at 2.7 eV. The refractive index, with a static value of 3 and a peak of 4.42 at 1.76 eV, indicates significant photon interaction, essential for photoelectric applications. The extinction coefficient shows strong light absorption, with a maximum of 3.967 at 2.68 eV. Overall, these properties make $AgBiS_2$ a promising candidate for efficient, cost-effective photovoltaic technologies.

REFERENCES

[1] M. Bernechea, N. C. Miller, G. Xercavins, D. So, A. Stavrinadis, and G. Konstantatos, "Solution-processed solar cells based on environmentally friendly AgBiS2 nanocrystals," *Nat Photonics*, vol. 10, no. 8, pp. 521–525, Aug. 2016, doi: 10.1038/nphoton.2016.108.

[2] T. Manimozhi, S. Kavirajan, K. Kamala Bharathi, E. Senthil Kumar, and M. Navaneethan, "Ultra-low thermal conductivity of AgBiS2 via Sb

substitution as a scattering center for thermoelectric applications," *Journal of Materials Science: Materials in Electronics*, vol. 33, no. 16, pp. 12615–12628, Jun. 2022, doi: 10.1007/s10854-022-08211-y.

[3] "Manual — | QuantumATK V-2023.12 Documentation." Accessed: Jun. 11, 2024. [Online]. Available: https://docs.quantumatk.com/manual/manual.html

[4] S. Geller and J. H. Wernick, " Ternary semiconducting compounds with sodium chloride-like structure: AgSbSe 2 , AgSbTe 2 , AgBiS 2 , AgBiSe 2 ," *Acta Crystallogr*, vol. 12, no. 1, pp. 46–54, Jan. 1959, doi: 10.1107/S0365110X59000135/FULL.

[5] F. Viñes, M. Bernechea, G. Konstantatos, and F. Illas, "Matildite versus schapbachite: First-principles investigation of the origin of photoactivity in AgBi S2," *Phys Rev B*, no. 23, Dec. 2016, doi: 10.1103/PhysRevB.94.235203.

[6] I. I. Golovach, V. S. Gerasimenko, V. Y. Slivka, N. I. Dovgoshei, M. I. Golovei, and A. V Bogdanova, "VITRIFICATION OF AND OPTICAL AND PHOTOFLI~CTRICAL PROPERTIES OF AgAsS 2, AgSbS2, AND AgBiS 2."

[7] B. Pejova, D. Nesheva, Z. Aneva, and A. Petrova, "Photoconductivity and relaxation dynamics in sonochemically synthesized assemblies of AgBiS2 quantum dots," *Journal of Physical Chemistry C*, vol. 115, no. 1, pp. 37–46, Jan. 2011, doi: 10.1021/jp106605t.

Theoretical insights through DFT into $AgBiS_2$ thin films absorber for photovoltaic applications

Dhruv Singh Thakur, Rajesh Kumar Sharma, Nithin Chatterji, Vivek Garg, Shivendra Yadav
Optoelectronics2Application (O2A) Research Group, Department of Electronics Engineering,
S. V. National Institute of Technology Surat-395007, India

2BV.1.6

Abstract

$AgBiS_2$ is a promising absorber for thin-film solar cells owing to its earth-abundance, non-toxicity, and tunable bandgap (0.8–1.32 eV), enabling low-cost scalable production. This study, based on density functional theory, evaluates its structural, electronic, and optical properties, revealing a high absorption coefficient (~10^6 cm^{-1}) and bandgaps (1.18/0.63 eV by MGGA, 1.55/0.99 eV by HSE) close to the experimental ~1.0 eV. These results establish $AgBiS_2$ as a versatile candidate for efficient photovoltaic applications.

Methodology

Linear combination of atomic orbitals (LCAO) calculator is utilized with Meta-generalized gradient approximation (MGGA) and Heyd-Scuseria-Ernzerhof (HSE) exchange-correlation (XC) function in the QuantumATK to calculate the structural and optoelectronic properties of the $AgBiS_2$ compound.

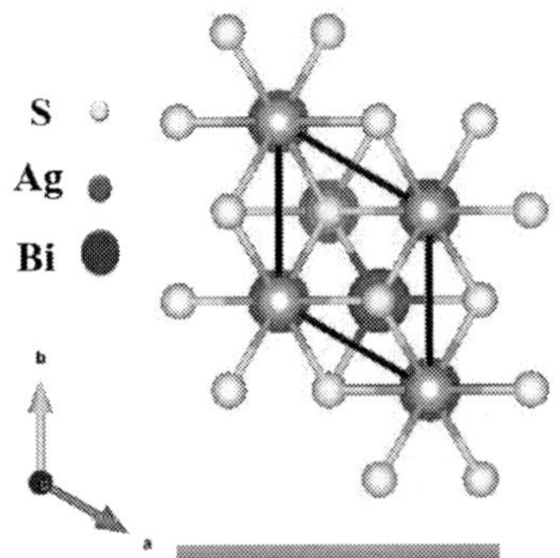

β-$AgBiS_2$ crystal

- It belongs to I–V–VI_2 family of compounds.
- Hexagonal β-$AgBiS_2$ crystal belongs to the space group P-3m1, No.164.

Material Structure Optimization

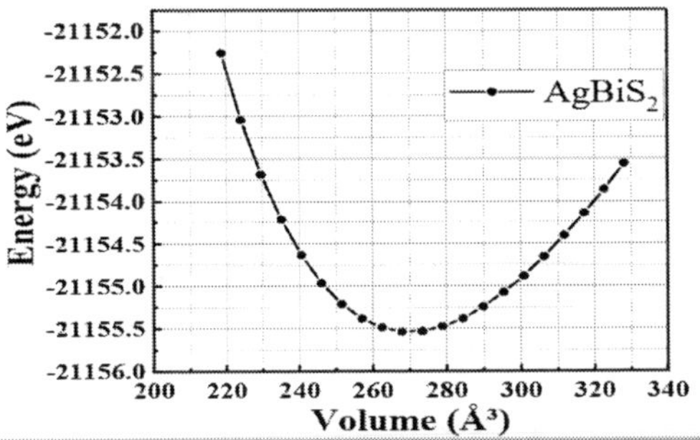

Parameter	This study	Others study	Experimental
	MGGA	PBE	
Lattice constant (Å) a, c	4.043, 18.93	4.0497, 19.019 4.02, 19.05	4.07, 19.06

Electronic properties

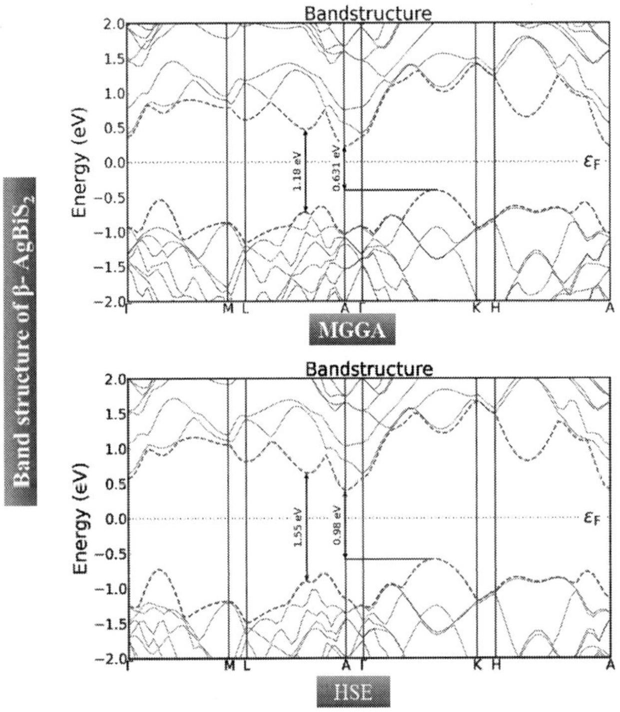

Optical Properties

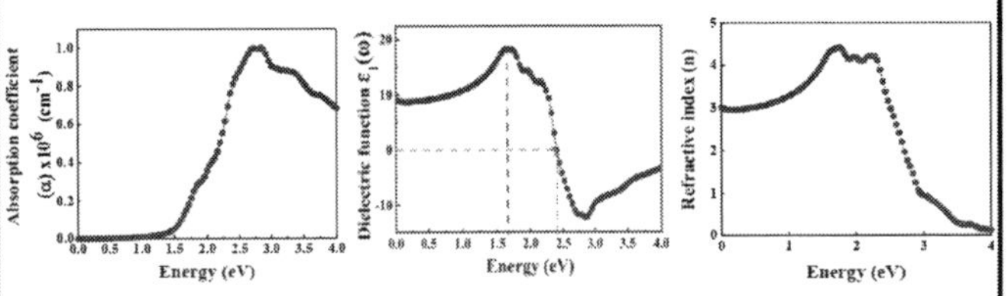

Conclusion

$AgBiS_2$ shows strong promise as an eco-friendly absorber for thin-film solar cells. Its optimized lattice constants (a,c = 4.043, 18.93 Å) closely match experimental values, validating the MGGA method. Electronic band structure results align with the experimental *Eg,* supported by MGGA and HSE calculations. The material exhibits excellent optical absorption (up to 1.1×10^6 cm^{-1}) across a wide spectral range, with high refractive index and extinction coefficient. Hence $AgBiS_2$ emerges as a low-cost, efficient candidate for next-generation photovoltaics.

Acknowledgement

The authors acknowledge the financial support from "SVNIT, Surat" under Grant No. Dean (R&C)/Seed Money/2021-22/10783, and "Divyasampark iHUB Roorkee for the Device Materials and Technology Foundation" under Grant Nos. 4-371 and 4-372.

References

[1] M. Bernechea *et al.*, *Nat Photonics*, vol. 10, no. 8, pp. 521–525, Aug. 2016.
[2] S. Geller *et al.*, Acta Crystallogr, vol. 12, no. 1, pp. 46–54, Jan. 1959.
[3] F. Viñes *et al.*, Phys Rev B, no. 23, Dec. 2016.
[4] B. Pejova *et al.*, Journal of Physical Chemistry C, vol. 115, no. 1, pp. 37–46, Jan. 2011.

Optoelectronics2Application (O2A) Research Group
Contact Person: Dr. Vivek Garg, Assistant Professor,
Department of Electronics Engineering, SVNIT Surat
Phone: -91-9993218492, Email: vivekg@eced.svnit.ac.in

020072-001

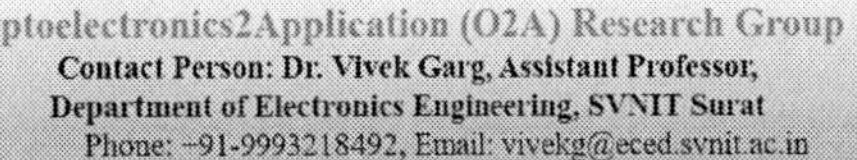

42nd European Photovoltaic Solar Energy Conference and Exhibition

RÉPUBLIQUE FRANÇAISE
Liberté Égalité Fraternité

CLEO Project AZURSPACE SOLAR POWER GMBH esa

ONERA
THE FRENCH AEROSPACE LAB

NOVEL ENCAPSULATION MATERIALS : RADIATION TEST AND RESULTS

D. Lansade, S. Lewandowski, S. Duzellier, H. Gasse

Alternatives to coverglass

Specifications: wide spectral transparency, stable in radiative environment, mechanically flexible

PDMS composite/hybrid (nanoSi)

Embedding of vinyl-functionalized silica nanoparticles photonic crystal

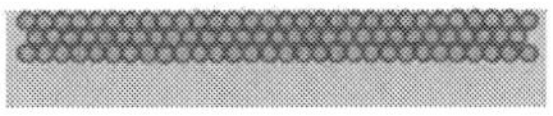

Tunable (short-UV absorbers)
Provide basic shielding
Under scale-up process

Self-healing PDMS (PDMS-UI)

Intrinsic self-healing solution : 50% urea / 50% imine

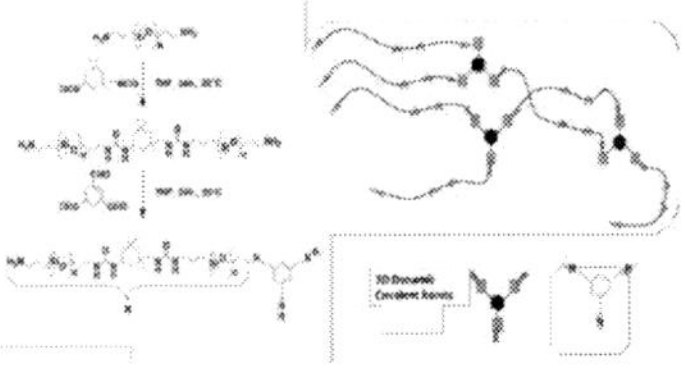

Urea/Tri-Imine:
Home-made 2-step synthesis
Dual crosslinking:
Dynamic covalent & hydrogen-bond

Self-healing theoretically unlimited
Large surface
Sprayable

Blend Polyimide + POSS (CORIN®)

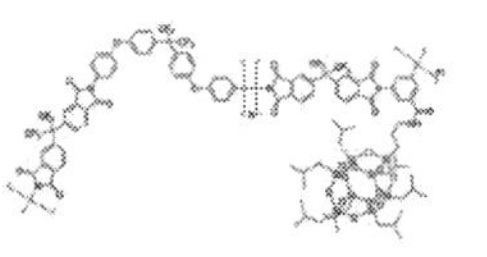

Polyhedral Oligomeric Silsesquioxane
Powder diluted into esters

Commercially available
Solvent-based liquid resin or powder form
Spray, dip or casting applications

PDMS	
composite/ hybrid	Self healing

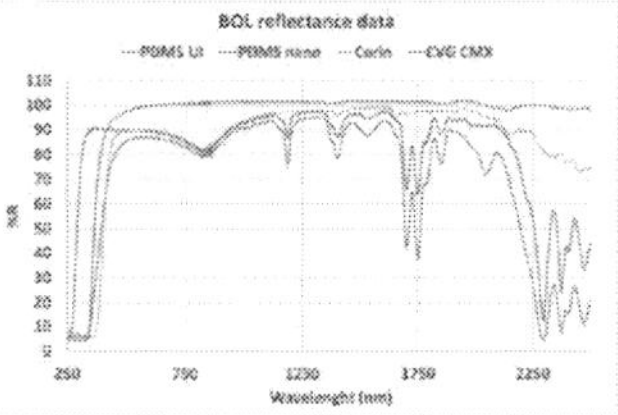

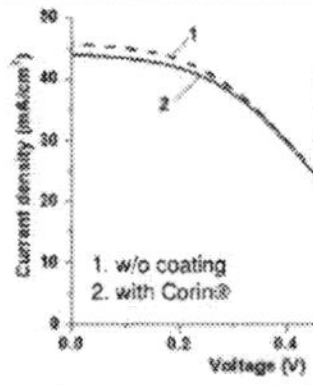

A. Darwish & al. Nanotechnology Reviews (2024).

3.5 10^{15} 600keV e^-/cm^2 (2 years GEO)

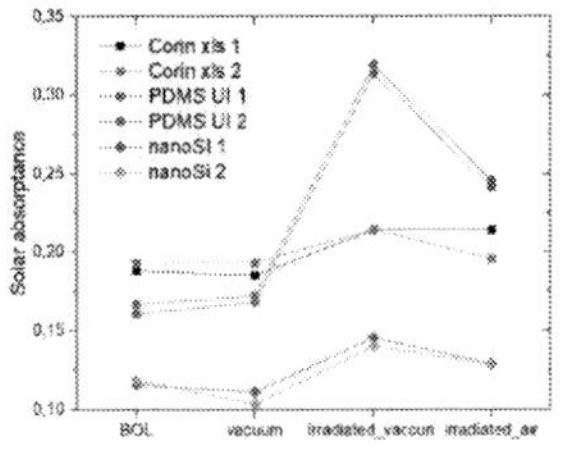

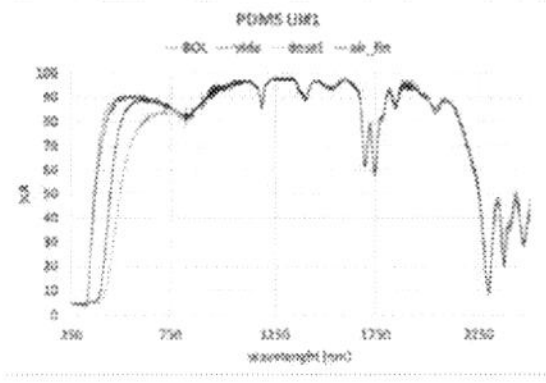

$$\alpha_s = \frac{\int_{250}^{2500} A(\lambda) I_s(\lambda) d\lambda}{\int_{250}^{2500} I_s(\lambda) d\lambda}$$

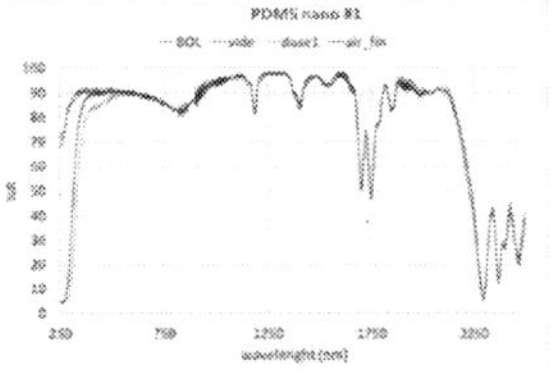

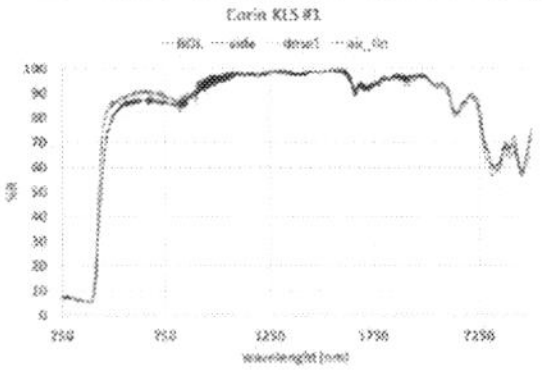

UV (200-400nm) ~1000esh

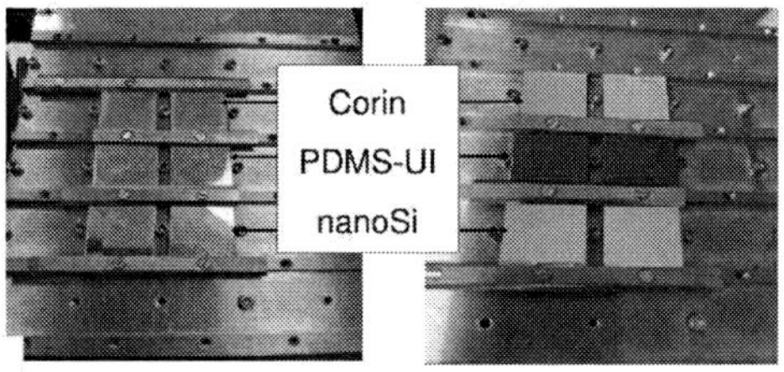

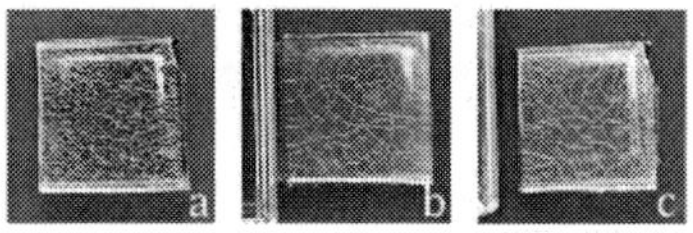

Si-nano 1 year GEO / p+

D. Lansade et al., Polym. Degrad. Stab. 176 (2020)

Conclusions:

- ✓ PDMS composite : high UV/electrons stability. Requires optimisation for proton (avoid cracking). Under industrialisation
- ✓ Self-healing PDMS : sensitive to UV & electrons. Partial recovery of degradation (with protons)

D. Yilmaz, DOI: 10.1021/acsami.4c02431

- ✓ Corin®: high stability to electrons. UV Sensitive. Test with protons shall be carried out

The authors would like to thank : AZUR SPACE Solar Power GmbH and ESA for their financial support in this project, the Organic Polymer Chemistry Laboratory, MAP Space Coatings and CNES for their collaboration in developing the PDMS solutions.

Correlated Disordered Nanostructures for Light Trapping in Ultrathin Solar Cells

L. DE ALMEIDA[1], I. REVOL[1], J-B. DOUCET[1], Mathieu ARRIBAT[1], G.ALMUNEAU[1],S. COLLIN[2]
[1]*LAAS-CNRS, Laboratoire d'analyse et d'architecture des systèmes, 31400 Toulouse, France*
[2]*C2N, Centre de Nanoscience et de Nanotechnologie, 91120 Palaiseau, France*

Nanostructuration and disorder

Light trapping is an important pathway in photovoltaic devices development that aims to **maximize the absorption of light** in a material. Increasing the optical path length of light in a material increases the probability of absorption.

For the past forty years, random texturing has been utilized for light trapping. In recent years, periodic nanostructures have emerged as an alternative. As a further alternative, **disordered correlated** or **amorphous** nanostructures have proven to improve scattering at various angles, to promote light trapping and allow to **reduce production cost** by increasing tolerance to fabrication defects.

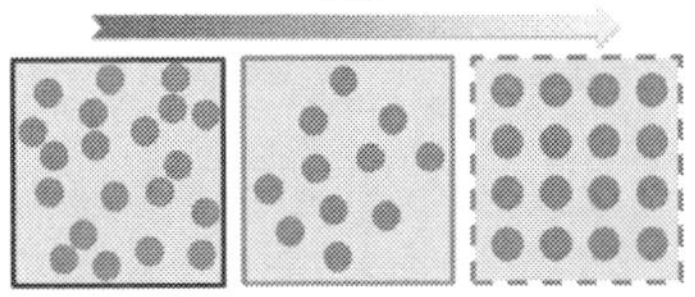

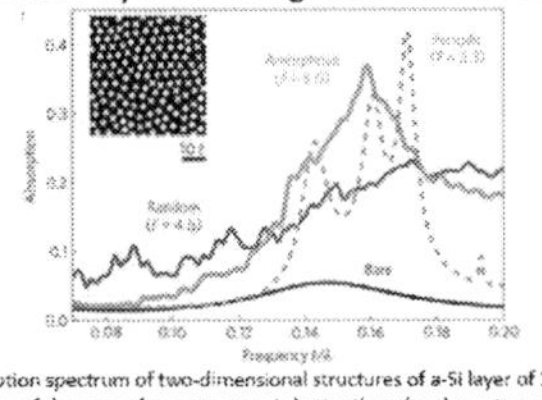

Absorption spectrum of two-dimensional structures of a-Si layer of 100 nm
The absorption of the **amorphous** structure is better than the absorption of the **periodic** and **random** structure at certain wavelengths. (see reference [1])

Objectives

My PhD: Nanostructure Si cell and understand disorder impact on optical and electrical parameters

O1: Low-cost and large surface process
→ Colloidal lithography

O2: Understanding the impact of disorder on optical properties of thin silicon films

O3: Integrating disordered light trapping strategies in silicon thin-film

O1: How to fabricate correlated disorder nanostructures?

Colloidal lithography process

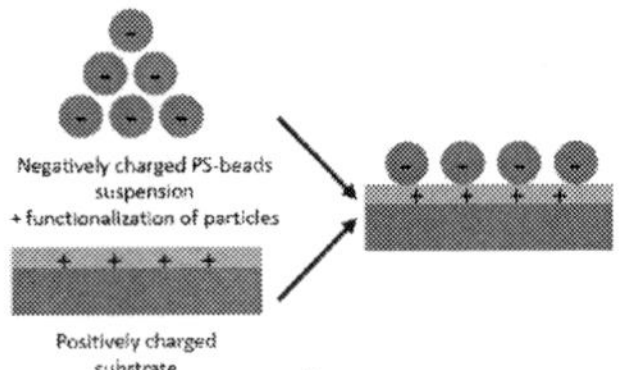

Step 1: Beads deposition

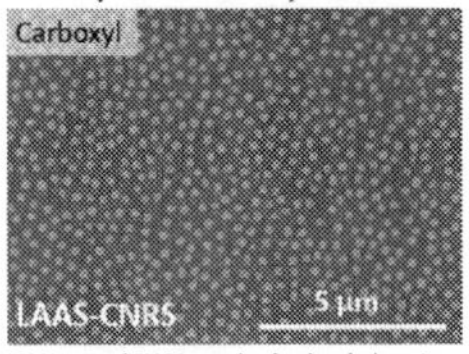

SEM image of CL13B sample after beads deposition

Step 2: Deposition of the etch mask
Mask selection depends on etching, here 50 nm titanium for dry etching

Step 3: Colloidal removal
Adhesive tape and acetone

Step 4: Pattern transfer to substrate by ICP-RIE etching

Isotropic etching
SF_6
$t_{etch} = 15$ sec

Anisotropic etching
SF_6, C_4F_8 and O_2
$t_{etch} = 2\,min\,45\,sec$

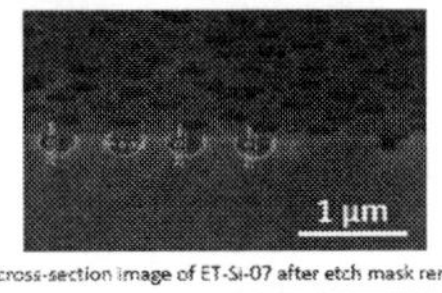

SEM cross-section image of ET-Si-07 after etch mask removal

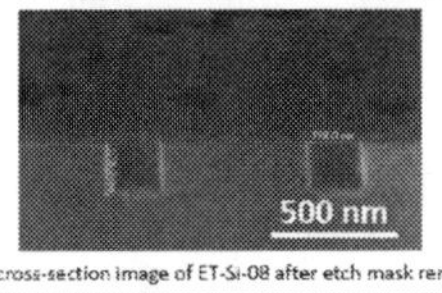

SEM cross-section image of ET-Si-08 after etch mask removal

O2: How do we characterize disorder?

Structure factor

$S(q_x, q_y)$ - CL-TW2-01

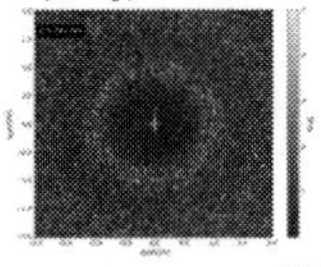

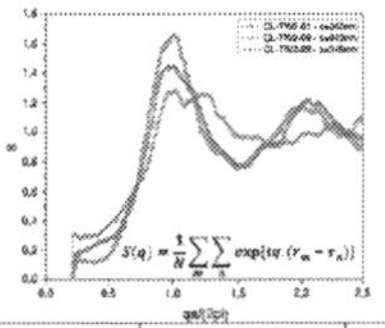

Pair correlation function

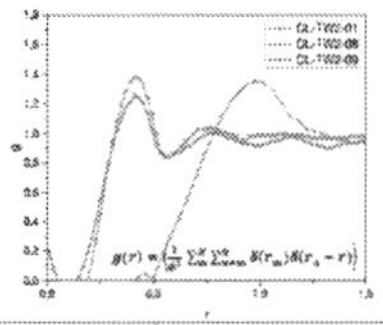

Table: summary of the various parameters used to characterize our arrangements

Sample	Pattern size (nm)	Pseudo-period g(r) (nm)	Pseudo-period S(q) (nm)
CL-TW2-01	210	410	342
CL-TW2-08	500	933	980
CL-TW2-09	210	410	345

O3: How do we characterize disordered light trapping strategies in silicon thin-film?

Objective: Characterization of correlated-disorder nanostructure

Reference: Non-structured samples

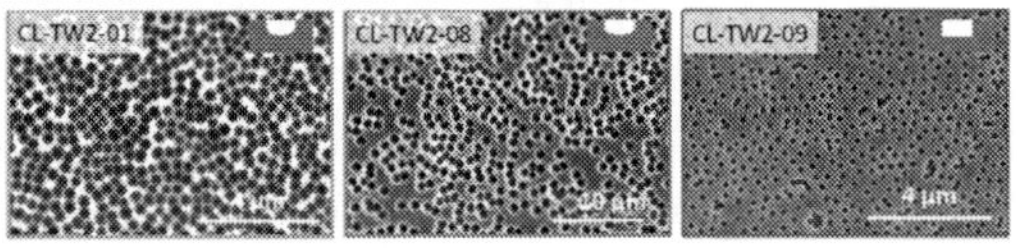

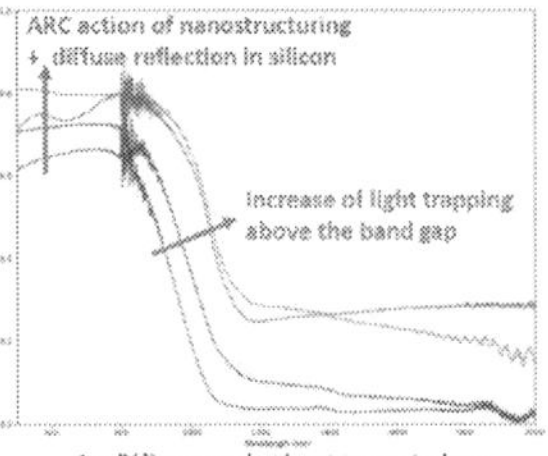

$1 - R(\lambda)$ measured with an integrated sphere

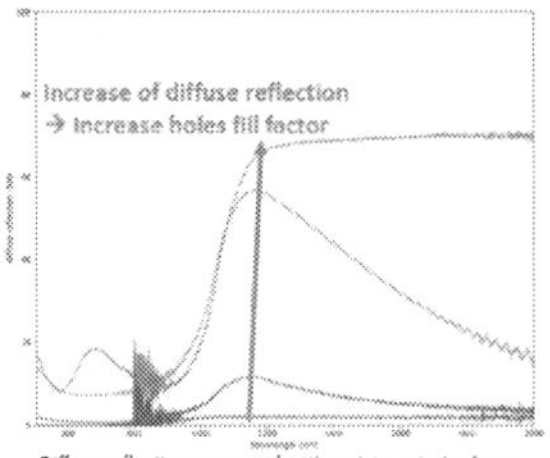

Diffuse reflection measured with an integrated sphere

Conclusion & Outlook

Colloidal lithography

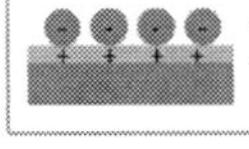

- Development of a repeatable experimental protocol
- Fabricating other geometries of etching profile with wet etching (inverted pyramid)

How does the pattern impact the optical performances?

Integration on silicon thin-film (10, 15, 25 and 50 µm)

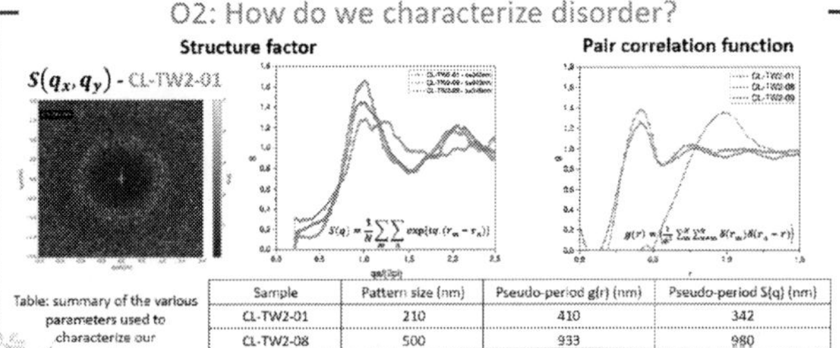

- Preliminary optical measurements
- Observed redshift in transmission for structured samples
- Investigation of long-wavelength absorption mechanisms (ongoing work)

Outlook

- Comparison of the optical performance of these structures with periodic references and correlated disorder fabricated by polymer blend lithography.
- Understanding the impact of disorder on the optical performances

References

[1] Vynck, K., Burresi, M., Riboli, F. et al., Nature Mater 11, 1017–1022 (2012). https://doi.org/10.1038/nmat3442
[2] Massiot, I., Cattoni, A. & Collin, S., *Nat Energy* **5**, 959–972 (2020). https://doi.org/10.1038/s41560-020-00714-4
[3] Terao, T., Nakayama, T., Phys. Rev. E **60**, 7157 (1999). https://doi.org/10.1103/PhysRevE.60.7157

Acknowledgement

The authors acknowledge the support of the French Agence Nationale de la Recherche (ANR), under grant ANR-22-PETA-0005 (PEPR TASE, project IOTA).
This work is also partly supported by LAAS-CNRS micro and nanotechnologies platform, member of the French RENATECH network.

LIGHTWEIGHT PHOTONIC COOLER WITH MULTI-LAYERED THIN FILM IR FILTERS AND ANTI-DUST PROPERTIES FOR PV APPLICATIONS IN DESERT ENVIRONMENTS

Brahim Aïssa*, M.I. Hossain
Qatar Environment and Energy Research Institute (QEERI), Hamad Bin Khalifa University (HBKU), Qatar Foundation, Doha, 5825, Qatar
* baissa@hbku.edu.qa

ABSTRACT: The present research is dedicated to the design and fabrication of advanced multi-stacked thin-film structures composed of alternating metal-oxide and metallic layers. These engineered coatings are conceived as multifunctional photonic coolers, offering a combination of near-infrared (NIR) filtering, anti-dust, and anti-reflective properties that make them highly attractive for deployment in energy-intensive environments. The optimized configuration consists of three key components: titanium oxide (TiOx) as the outermost layer, nickel oxide (NiO) as an intermediate buffer, and silver (Ag) as the reflective hot-mirror layer. Each material in this architecture serves a distinct optical and functional role. The layers were deposited using thermal electron-beam (e-beam) evaporation under a controlled oxygen atmosphere, with a continuous vacuum environment maintained throughout the process to ensure dense, defect-free growth and reproducible film quality. One of the notable characteristics of the TiOx top layer is its inherent super-hydrophilicity. This property imparts both self-cleaning and anti-dust functionalities, critical for outdoor applications in desert climates where soiling can drastically reduce optical efficiency. In parallel, the multi-layer stacking strategy leverages the contrasting refractive indices of constituent oxides to fine-tune the spectral response. Low-refractive-index TiOx, when paired with high-refractive-index oxides such as NiO or molybdenum oxide (MoOx), creates constructive interference effects that enhance visible light transmission while simultaneously suppressing unwanted infrared radiation. Experimental results confirmed that bilayer combinations such as MoOx/TiOx and NiO/TiOx exhibited superior transmittance in the visible spectrum compared to single TiOx films, thereby optimizing light harvesting in photovoltaic and optical applications. The inclusion of a reflective metallic layer (Ag or, alternatively, Al) further enhanced performance, acting as an efficient hot-mirror with a wavelength cutoff beginning at ~800 nm. Beyond this threshold, the structure demonstrated the ability to reflect more than 70% of incident IR radiation, thereby effectively mitigating heat accumulation. This carefully engineered multi-stack thin-film structure not only provides efficient IR filtering but also functions simultaneously as an anti-reflective coating for visible light and as an anti-soiling surface layer. These multifunctional attributes significantly extend its commercial potential, particularly for integration into energy-efficient building envelopes, smart glazing, and large-scale photovoltaic systems operating under harsh and dusty environmental conditions. Furthermore, the reliance on scalable deposition techniques, such as e-beam evaporation, underscores the feasibility of adapting this approach for industrial-scale manufacturing. In sum, the multi-layer metal-oxide/metal-oxide/metal photonic cooler represents a versatile, durable, and scalable solution for managing the solar spectrum, mitigating heat, enhancing light utilization, and resisting environmental degradation. Its multifunctionality positions it as a promising candidate for next-generation energy-saving technologies in desert and other extreme climates.

1 INTRODUCTION

The solar radiation that reaches the Earth's surface is composed of three principal spectral regions: ultraviolet (UV), visible, and infrared (IR) light. Among these, the infrared portion represents the largest share, accounting for approximately 54% of the total incident solar energy. This dominant fraction plays a critical role in heat generation, as the IR wavelengths are efficiently converted into thermal energy upon interaction with materials and surfaces. Consequently, the substantial presence of IR radiation significantly increases the cooling load of buildings, a challenge that is particularly exacerbated in hot and arid desert climates where air conditioning systems already consume vast amounts of energy [1–6].

Given these circumstances, the development of thin-film technologies that can selectively reflect the IR spectrum, while simultaneously ensuring high optical transparency in the visible region, has emerged as a research priority. For applications in the photovoltaic (PV) sector, maintaining maximum transparency in the visible range is not merely desirable but essential, as this spectral region governs the efficiency of light harvesting and, ultimately, the electrical power output of solar devices. To meet this need, metallic layers, such as silver (Ag), aluminum (Al), and gold (Au), have been widely investigated for their potential to act as effective IR filters, owing to their strong capacity to absorb or reflect infrared radiation at resonance frequencies. However, these metallic films are hindered by intrinsic drawbacks, most notably their susceptibility to degradation, which compromises their optical and structural stability over time and thereby limits their long-term performance [7–10]. To mitigate these issues, researchers have proposed the use of composite "sandwich" structures in which the metallic layers are embedded between oxide layers. While such architectures offer improved protection, they remain vulnerable to key reliability challenges. Problems such as oxygen diffusion into the metal layers and the development of internal film stress during deposition can lead to structural cracking and, in turn, reduced optical transparency in the visible spectrum. A comprehensive body of work has identified a range of transition metal oxides, most notably TiOx, SnOx, MoOx, and NiOx, as promising candidates for the fabrication of IR filters, owing to their favorable electronic, optical, and chemical properties, as well as their compatibility with various device architectures [11–15]. These oxides have been successfully deposited using multiple thin-film deposition techniques, including magnetron sputtering, thermal or electron-beam vacuum evaporation, and atomic layer deposition (ALD). Among these, electron-beam (e-beam) evaporation has attracted particular attention for its versatility, scalability, and capacity to achieve high-quality multilayer coatings with controlled stoichiometry.

The overarching objective of the present work is therefore to design and fabricate a cost-effective, multilayered IR filter consisting of a metal-oxide/metal-oxide/metal configuration. The targeted device must simultaneously exhibit high optical transparency within the visible spectrum, thereby enabling adequate solar conversion efficiency in PV applications—and strong reflectivity within the IR region to suppress heat build-up. Furthermore, the filter is specifically conceived for deployment in harsh desert environments, where it must not only withstand elevated temperatures and intense solar flux but also resist dust accumulation. To this end, the multilayer system incorporates anti-soiling surface properties to enhance durability and operational lifetime [16–25].

The research methodology integrates both advanced numerical modeling and experimental validation, enabling systematic optimization of structural design, materials selection, and deposition parameters. A schematic representation of the proposed multilayer stack is provided in Fig. 1. Through this combined approach, the study demonstrates the potential of such engineered IR filters to contribute significantly to energy-efficient building envelopes, photovoltaic modules, and related technologies designed for hot and dusty climates. This work thus represents a critical step toward the broader integration of selective IR-reflecting coatings into sustainable energy systems tailored for some of the world's most challenging environmental conditions.

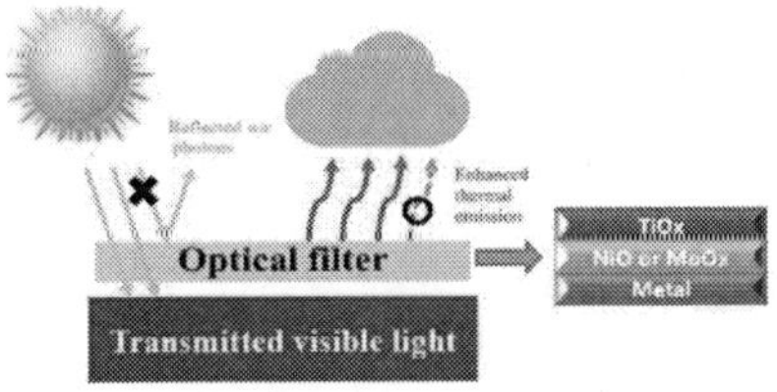

Figure 1: Schematic representation of the multilayered thin-film architecture designed for infrared (IR) filtering applications. The structure consists of sequentially deposited metal oxide and metallic layers, optimized to achieve high transparency in the visible spectrum while reflecting near-infrared (NIR) wavelengths. The inclusion of TiOx as the outermost layer provides anti-reflective and anti-soiling functionalities, NiO serves as a buffer/high-index oxide layer, and Ag (or Al) acts as the reflective hot-mirror layer. This configuration illustrates the functional integration of optical filtering, photonic cooling, and environmental durability within a scalable thin-film design.

2 METHODOLOGY

Metal oxide thin films, with a particular focus on nickel oxide (NiO) and titanium oxide (TiOx), were deposited via electron-beam (e-beam) evaporation under carefully controlled conditions. The depositions were carried out at room temperature while maintaining a constant flow of oxygen to ensure stoichiometric film growth and to minimize oxygen vacancies, which are known to critically influence both optical and electrical properties. In parallel, metallic layers such as aluminum (Al) and silver (Ag) were deposited under vacuum conditions without the introduction of oxygen flow. This deliberate differentiation in process atmospheres allowed for the preservation of metallic conductivity in Al and Ag layers, while simultaneously achieving the desired oxide stoichiometry in NiO and TiOx layers. The films were fabricated on both rigid glass substrates and flexible polyethylene terephthalate (PET) substrates, highlighting the adaptability of the process for applications ranging from conventional photovoltaic modules to lightweight and bendable optoelectronic devices.

A comprehensive suite of characterization techniques was employed to assess the structural, optical, and surface properties of the fabricated films. Ellipsometry and UV–Vis spectrophotometry were used to determine the refractive indices, extinction coefficients, and transmittance spectra of the multilayer structures, thereby enabling direct correlation between deposition parameters and optical performance. Contact angle measurements provided critical insights into the surface wettability and hydrophilicity of the coatings, an essential feature for evaluating anti-soiling and self-cleaning potential under real-world desert conditions. Surface morphology and roughness were investigated using a three-dimensional stylus profilometer (Dektak), which provided quantitative topographical mapping of the films. Complementary nanoscale imaging was performed using field-emission scanning electron microscopy (FESEM) and atomic force microscopy (AFM), offering detailed views of grain structure, uniformity, and surface features that influence scattering and light management within the films. Structural and chemical bonding analyses were conducted via X-ray photoelectron spectroscopy (XPS, Fig. 2), which not only confirmed the oxidation states of Ti and Ni but also provided evidence of stoichiometric stability across the different deposition conditions.

Initial optimization efforts were directed toward fine-tuning the thicknesses of each individual layer, as nanoscale variations strongly affect the interference patterns responsible for visible transmittance and infrared reflectance. By systematically varying thicknesses, it was possible to establish an optimized balance between high visible-light transparency and strong near-infrared rejection, while maintaining robust anti-reflective and anti-soiling characteristics. These optimizations lay the foundation for tailoring multilayered oxide/metal stacks for specific applications, whether as photonic coolers for buildings, protective coatings for photovoltaic panels, or multifunctional surfaces for flexible electronics.

The detailed deposition protocols, characterization results, and structure–property correlations will be presented and discussed extensively in the full version of this study. These findings not only underscore the versatility of e-beam evaporation in producing complex multi-functional thin films but also highlight the potential of such coatings to serve as scalable, durable, and high-performance solutions for next-generation energy and environmental technologies.

3 RESULTS AND DISCUSSIONS

The optical response of the NiO thin films was systematically investigated using UV–Vis spectroscopy over the broad wavelength range of 200–2000 nm. The absorptance (A) of the films was derived using the standard relationship:

$$A(\%) = 100 - (T+R)$$

where T denotes the transmittance and R the reflectance. The results demonstrated a strong dependence of optical behavior on film thickness. Ultra-thin films (~20 nm) exhibited exceptionally high transmittance, reaching values up to 85% for wavelengths above 500 nm, thereby maximizing visible-light penetration. In contrast, thicker films (>100 nm) displayed significantly higher absorptance and reflectance, confirming that careful control of thickness serves as a powerful tool to tailor the optical properties of NiO coatings.

A similar dependence on thickness was observed for metallic layers. For Al and Ag films, reflectance varied markedly between 10 nm and 15 nm, underscoring the critical influence of nanoscale thickness variations on spectral selectivity. Importantly, in hybrid NiO/metal multilayer configurations, such as NiO (100 nm)/Al (10 nm) and NiO (100 nm)/Ag (15 nm), the films simultaneously achieved low reflectance in the visible range, ensuring transparency, while exhibiting strong reflectance in the infrared (IR) region. This dual behavior is highly advantageous for near-infrared (NIR) filtering applications, where blocking thermal IR radiation while preserving visible transmittance is essential for photonic cooling and energy efficiency.

Microstructural characterization provided further insights into film quality and stability. Scanning electron microscopy (SEM) revealed that all evaporated multi-stacked layers were dense, homogenous, and devoid of pinholes or cracks—an essential prerequisite for reliable optoelectronic device performance. Surface roughness was strongly correlated with the thickness of the metallic interlayers. Specifically, NiO/metal (Al or Ag, 20 nm) samples exhibited an average surface roughness of ~17 nm, whereas NiO/metal (Al or Ag, 10 nm) layers displayed smoother surfaces with roughness values closer to ~10 nm. Interestingly, increased roughness was associated with smaller grain sizes, indicating that metallic layers not only determine optical reflectivity but also exert a decisive influence on the surface morphology of subsequent oxide layers. This microstructural control could, in turn, be harnessed to tailor surface wettability.

To further optimize the optical properties, additional experiments were conducted by depositing TiOx on top of NiO/Ag films fabricated on lightweight, flexible PET substrates. These TiOx-capped structures exhibited distinctly modified transmission, reflectance, and absorptance profiles across the measured spectrum. Configurations such as TiOx (50 nm)/NiO (100 nm)/Ag (20 nm) and TiOx (50 nm)/NiO (100 nm)/Ag (25 nm) were particularly promising, achieving enhanced reflectance (~20%) at wavelengths beyond 800 nm. This marked improvement in NIR rejection capability confirmed the effectiveness of the multi-stack approach in producing high-performance hot-mirror coatings.

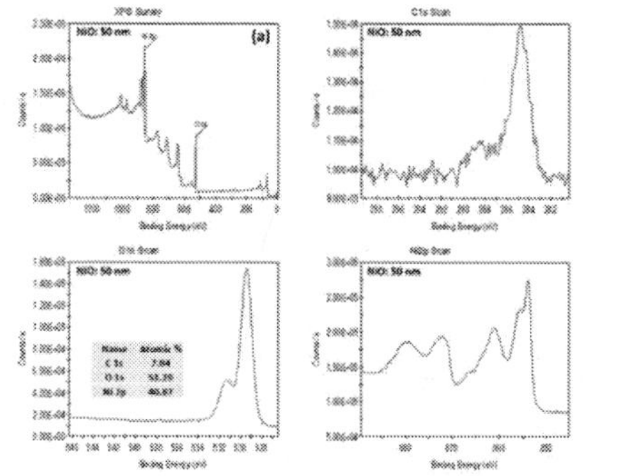

Figure 2: X-ray photoelectron spectroscopy (XPS) survey spectrum of NiO thin films with a thickness of 50 nm. The spectrum confirms the presence of characteristic Ni and O core-level peaks, validating the stoichiometry of the deposited films. The absence of extraneous peaks indicates high purity, while the well-defined Ni 2p and O 1s signals provide evidence of stable oxide bonding states. These results confirm the chemical integrity and quality of the NiO layers fabricated by e-beam evaporation under controlled oxygen flow.

The surface wetting behavior of the thin films was systematically assessed using contact angle (CA) measurements, an important indicator of anti-soiling potential. Films with CA values exceeding 60° were classified as suitable for mitigating dust adhesion in humid environments. Among the tested samples, the TiOx (50 nm)/NiO (300 nm)/Ag (25 nm) configuration displayed the highest degree of hydrophobicity, with a CA of ~104°, reflecting a robust anti-soiling surface. By contrast, the lowest CA (~61.3°) was recorded for the TiOx (50 nm)/NiO (300 nm)/Ag (5 nm) configuration, which was predominantly hydrophilic. These results demonstrated that wettability was intimately linked to surface roughness: higher roughness decreased surface tension, which in turn enabled the possibility of engineering super-hydrophobic surfaces for desert applications.

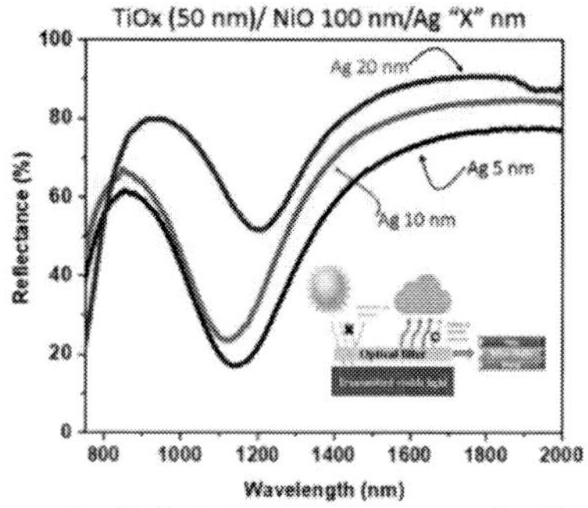

Figure 3: Reflectance spectra as a function of wavelength for multilayer structures incorporating silver (Ag) layers of varying thicknesses. The curves highlight the strong dependence of optical response on Ag thickness, with thinner layers exhibiting lower reflectance across the visible spectrum, while thicker layers enhance reflection in the near-infrared (NIR) region. This tunability demonstrates the critical role of metallic layer thickness in optimizing hot-mirror performance for selective IR filtering applications.

10.4229/EUPVSEC2025/2BV.1.19

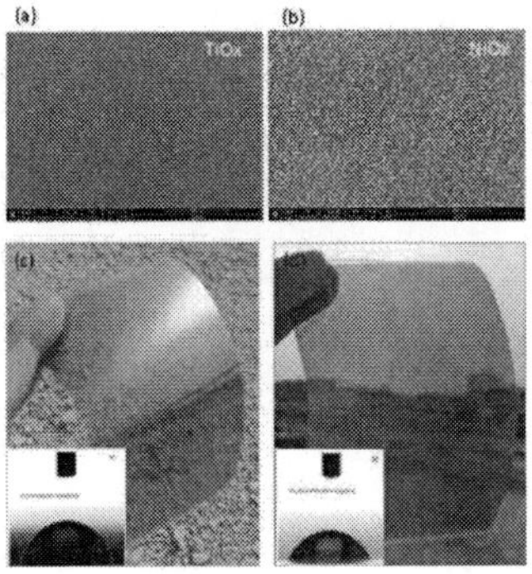

Figure 4: Scanning electron microscopy (SEM) images illustrating the dense, uniform, and pinhole-free morphology of TiOx thin films, alongside high-quality NiOx layers exhibiting smooth and homogeneous surface coverage. The figure also includes optical photographs of flexible multilayer filters deposited on PET substrates, highlighting the visual appearance and transparency of devices with varying silver (Ag) thicknesses. These images collectively confirm the structural integrity, morphological uniformity, and scalability of the fabricated multilayer coatings.

Complementary outdoor field testing over a two-month period provided critical validation of the laboratory findings. Notably, the most hydrophilic configurations showed minimal dust accumulation during real-world exposure, in agreement with the measured CA values. These results emphasize the complex interplay between roughness, wettability, and environmental performance, suggesting that both hydrophilic and hydrophobic strategies may be viable depending on application-specific requirements.

In summary, the study confirms that the optical, morphological, and wetting properties of NiO/metal and TiOx/NiO/metal thin films can be finely tuned through precise control of thickness and material stacking. Such multi-functional coatings combine NIR filtering with anti-soiling behavior, and their scalability on both rigid and flexible substrates highlights their strong potential for integration into energy-efficient photovoltaic systems, smart windows, and other optoelectronic devices designed for operation in harsh desert environments.

The findings of this study clearly demonstrate the promise of optimized NiO/metal/TiOx multilayer configurations as highly effective near-infrared (NIR) filters. By carefully tuning the thickness and sequence of individual layers, these structures exhibit adjustable optical properties across the visible–NIR spectrum, while simultaneously offering controlled surface morphology and tailored wetting behavior. Such multifunctionality not only enhances their performance as hot-mirror coatings but also provides intrinsic anti-soiling characteristics, thereby extending their durability in harsh environmental conditions. Collectively, these attributes highlight the strong potential of the proposed designs for integration into advanced optoelectronic systems, including energy-efficient photovoltaic modules, smart glazing technologies, and photonic cooling applications in desert and other extreme climates.

4 CONCLUSIONS

Infrared (IR) spectrum filters play a critical role in suppressing the transmission of IR wavelengths, which are the dominant contributors to heat generation under solar illumination. By selectively reflecting the IR portion of the spectrum while maintaining acceptable levels of visible transparency, such filters can significantly reduce thermal loading, thereby improving the energy efficiency of photovoltaic (PV) modules and building envelopes, an aspect of particular importance in desert environments where cooling demands are exceptionally high. In this study, we report the successful development of multi-functional stacked thin-film structures that combine *infrared filtering, anti-reflective behavior, and anti-soiling properties* within a single photonic cooler design. The multilayer coatings were fabricated using reactive electron-beam (e-beam) evaporation, a process chosen for its scalability, reproducibility, and ability to precisely control oxide stoichiometry. In this configuration, silver (Ag) was employed as a seed layer with a nominal thickness of 20 nm, providing both reflectivity and a template for the subsequent growth of nickel oxide (NiO) and titanium oxide (TiOx) layers. Optical characterization revealed that the NiO (300 nm)/Ag (20 nm) stack exhibited the strongest IR filtering capability, achieving a pronounced infrared cut-off with more than 75% reflectance for wavelengths exceeding 750 nm. In contrast, the visible-light region maintained a transmittance peak of approximately 45% when the metallic layers were restricted to thicknesses between 5 nm and 20 nm. These results underscore the dual function of the architecture: maintaining sufficient visible transparency while effectively reflecting unwanted IR radiation. To further extend the applicability of the design, the multilayer coatings were also deposited on flexible polymer substrates. These flexible IR filters demonstrated enhanced multifunctionality, combining effective IR blocking with anti-reflective properties and dust-repellent behavior. In particular, the TiOx (50 nm)/NiO (300 nm)/Ag (25 nm) configuration achieved the highest measured hydrophobicity, with a contact angle (CA) of ~104°. This strong water-repellent surface confirmed excellent anti-soiling potential, which is essential for maintaining optical efficiency in arid and dusty outdoor environments.

Collectively, the findings confirm the feasibility of fabricating dense, defect-free, and scalable metal oxide/metal/metal oxide stacks via thermal e-beam evaporation. The resulting coatings simultaneously provide *near-infrared filtering, visible anti-reflection, and self-cleaning capabilities*, thereby addressing three critical challenges of optoelectronic devices deployed in harsh climates. Importantly, the scalability of this approach highlights its suitability for integration into miniaturized PV modules, smart window technologies, and advanced photonic cooling systems.

The detailed mechanism underlying the infrared cut-off, arising from the interplay between interference effects in the oxide layers and plasmonic reflection in the metal seed layer, together with its implications for PV module performance, will be comprehensively discussed in the full version of this paper.

5 REFERENCES

[1] N. Abundiz-Cisneros, R. Sanginés, R. Rodríguez-López, M. Peralta-Arriola, J. Cruz, and R. Machorro, *Energy and Buildings*, vol. 206, p. 109558, 2020.

[2] H. Sahm, C. Charton, and R. Thielsch, *Thin Solid Films*, vol. 455, pp. 819–823, 2004.

10.4229/EUPVSEC2025/2BV.1.19

[3] M. I. Hossain, A. Khandakar, M. E. H. Chowdhury, S. Ahmed, et al., *Journal of Electronic Materials*, pp. 1–11, 2021.
[4] E. Stamate, *Nanomaterials*, vol. 10, no. 1, p. 14, 2020.
[5] W. K. Tan, A. Yokoi, G. Kawamura, A. Matsuda, and H. Muto.
[6] C.-H. Liang, S.-C. Chen, X. Qi, C.-S. Chen, and C.-C. Yang, *Thin Solid Films*, vol. 519, no. 1, pp. 345–350, 2010.
[7] J. T.-W. Wang, J. M. Ball, E. M. Barea, A. Abate, J. A. Alexander-Webber, J. Huang, et al., *Nano Letters*, vol. 14, no. 2, pp. 724–730, 2014.
[8] P. Pinpithak, H.-W. Chen, A. Kulkarni, Y. Sanehira, M. Ikegami, and T. Miyasaka, *Chemistry Letters*, vol. 46, no. 3, pp. 382–384, 2017.
[9] C. Liu, W. Li, J. Chen, J. Fan, Y. Mai, and R. E. Schropp, *Nano Energy*, vol. 41, pp. 75–83, 2017.
[10] K. Cao, Z. Zuo, J. Cui, Y. Shen, T. Moehl, S. M. Zakeeruddin, et al., *Nano Energy*, vol. 17, pp. 171–179, 2015.
[11] P. Baroch, J. Musil, J. Vlcek, K. Nam, and J. Han, *Surface and Coatings Technology*, vol. 193, no. 1–3, pp. 107–111, 2005.
[12] J. Velevska and M. Ristova, *Solar Energy Materials and Solar Cells*, vol. 73, no. 2, pp. 131–139, 2002.
[13] X. Yang, P. Zheng, Q. Bi, and K. Weber, *Solar Energy Materials and Solar Cells*, vol. 150, pp. 32–38, 2016.
[14] I. S. Kim, E.-K. Jeong, D. Y. Kim, M. Kumar, and S.-Y. Choi, *Applied Surface Science*, vol. 255, no. 7, pp. 4011–4014, 2009.
[15] X. J. Feng and L. Jiang, *Advanced Materials*, vol. 18, no. 23, pp. 3063–3078, 2006.
[16] M. I. Hossain, B. Aïssa, A. Samara, S. A. Mansour, C. A. Broussillou, and V. Bermudez Benito, *ACS Omega*, vol. 6, no. 8, pp. 5276–5286, 2021.
[17] L. L. Lebel, B. Aïssa, M. A. El Khakani, and D. Therriault, *Composites Science and Technology*, vol. 70, no. 3, pp. 518–524, 2010.
[18] W. Julia, C. Luis, R. Federico, et al., *Advanced Functional Materials*, vol. 23, pp. 5591–5598, 2013.
[19] D. T. H. Dalir, R. D. Farahani, V. Nhim, B. Aïssa, et al., *Langmuir*, vol. 28, no. 1, pp. 791–803, 2011.
[20] A. Ali, F. El-Mellouhi, A. Mitra, and B. Aïssa, *Nanomaterials*, vol. 12, no. 5, p. 788, 2022.
[21] R. D. Farahani, D. T. H. Dalir, V. Le Borgne, A. Loick, et al., *Composites Science and Technology*, vol. 72, no. 12, pp. 1387–1395, 2012.
[22] N. M. H. Gavi, B. D. Ngom, A. C. Beye, A. M. Strydom, B. Aïssa, V. V. Srinivasu, and M. Chaker, *Journal of Magnetism and Magnetic Materials*, vol. 324, no. 6, pp. 1172–1176, 2012.
[23] B. Aïssa and M. A. El Khakani, *Nanotechnology*, vol. 20, no. 17, p. 175203, 2009.
[24] M. A. Habib, M. Barkat, B. Aïssa, and T. Denidni, *Progress in Electromagnetics Research*, vol. 88, pp. 135–148, 2008.
[25] H. Zhao, H. Kimura, Z. Cheng, X. Wang, and T. Nishida, *Applied Physics Letters*, vol. 95, p. 232904, 2009. https://doi.org/10.1063/1.3271032.

Lightweight Photonic Cooler with Multi-Layered Thin Film IR Filters and Anti-Dust Properties for PV Applications in Desert Environments

Brahim Aissa*, and Mohammad I. Hossain

Qatar Environment and Energy Research Institute (QEERI)- Hamad Bin Khalifa University (HBKU), Doha, P.O. Box 34110, Education City, Doha, Qatar

*Contact: baissa@hbku.edu.qa

QEERI
معهد قطر لبحوث البيئة والطاقة
Qatar Environment & Energy Research Institute
جامعة حمد بن خليفة
HAMAD BIN KHALIFA UNIVERSITY

Abstract

- The overall objective of this work is to develop nano-structured thin films based on cost-effective oxide materials with an integration of very thin metal layer.
- High transmission (T>78%) in the visible light due to low refractive index/high refractive index stacked layer. High reflectance starting (R≈75%) from 800 nm in the IR region. Super hydrophilic TiOx acts as an anti-soiling coating due to photocatalytic behavior and our developed recipe. Scalability, stability. Technology transferable to flexible substrates. Multi-functionalities: IR filtering, anti-reflection coating in the visible range, and anti-soiling coating. Experimental realization and proof-of-concept.

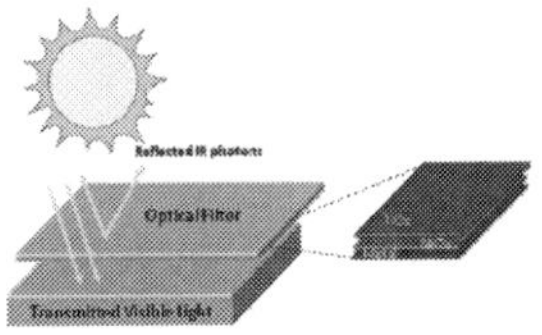

Figure 1: Schematic structure of infrared (IR) photonic filter

We present a novel "metal-oxide/metal-oxide/metal" multi-stack infrared (IR) filter, which incorporates various functionalities.
We use e-beam evaporation process that ensures precise control over the growth parameters.
To meet the desired criteria of achieving a high transmission yield (T%) in the visible spectrum and a high reflection yield (R%) in the IR region, we utilized numerical simulations based on experimental parameters.
Furthermore, we applied these results to perovskite solar cells, demonstrating the enhanced photovoltaic performance achieved through the implementation of IR filtration.

Optical properties:

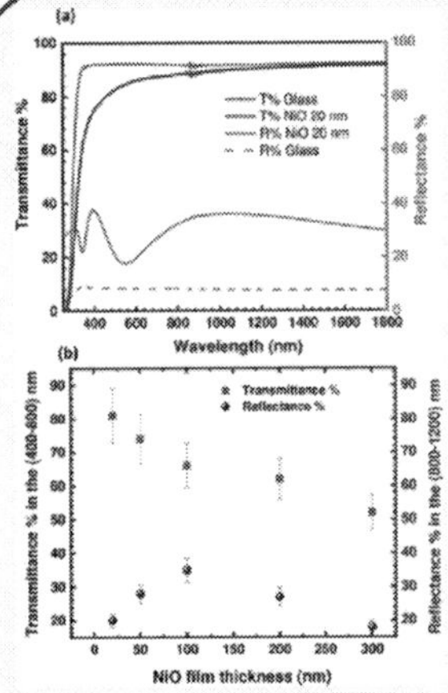

Figure 6. UV–vis of NiO_x layers grown at 2×10^{-4} Torr with different thicknesses: (a) typical example of *T* % and *R* % of NiO_x of 20 nm thickness and (b) summary of *T* % and *R* % of NiO_x films with different thicknesses.

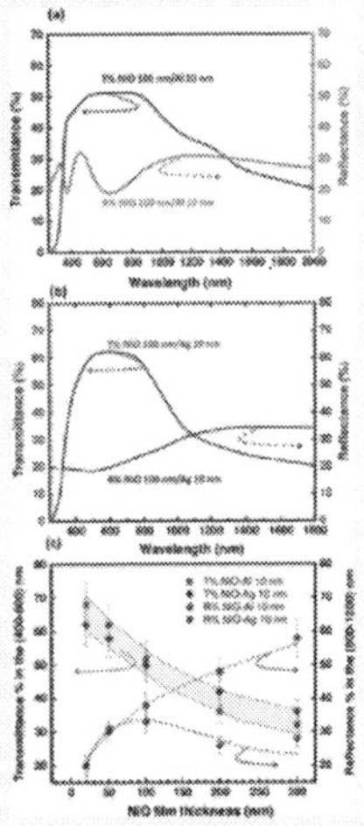

Figure 7: UV–vis results of NiO/metal layers grown with different thicknesses. (a) Transmittance (%) and reflectance (%) of 100 nm thick NiO deposited on (a) 10 nm of Al and (b) 10 nm of Ag layers. (c) Variation of both *T* % and *R* % with respect to the NiO film thicknesses for two metals, namely, Al and Ag.

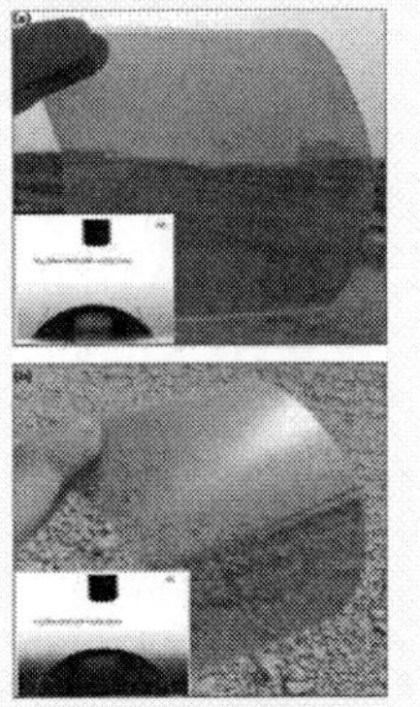

Optical photos of the filters along with the contact angle measurements performed on these flexible coatings.

1. Experimental Setup

NiO and TiOx metal-oxide layers were reactively evaporated at room temperature (RT) with a growth rate of 1 Å/s and a deposition pressure of 2 × 10-4 Torr, under a constant oxygen flow of 20 sccm, using a Denton™ e-beam evaporation. Later, Al and Ag metal layers were evaporated at the same growth rate without any oxygen supply.

specification	our development	ConverLight65 (i)	ConverLight75 (i)	oxide-based multilayer structure (ii)	nitride-based multilayer structure (ii)
fabrication technique	physical vapor deposition	physical vapor deposition	physical vapor deposition	physical vapor deposition	physical vapor deposition
cost	inexpensive due to the simple structure, no process temperature, and available materials	expensive due to the complex structure	expensive due to the complex structure	expensive due to the complex structure	expensive due to the complex structure
applications	broad (building windows to PV)	broad (building windows to PV)	broad (building windows to PV)	PV	PV
functionalities	NIR filter, daylight harvesting, and antisoiling coating	NIR filter	NIR filter	NIR filter	NIR filter
number of stacked layers	3	5	5	8	4

(i) https://chromogenics.com/dynamic-glass/
(ii) Lee, M. et al. Photonic structures in radiative cooling. *Light: Sci. Appl.* **2023**, *12*, 134

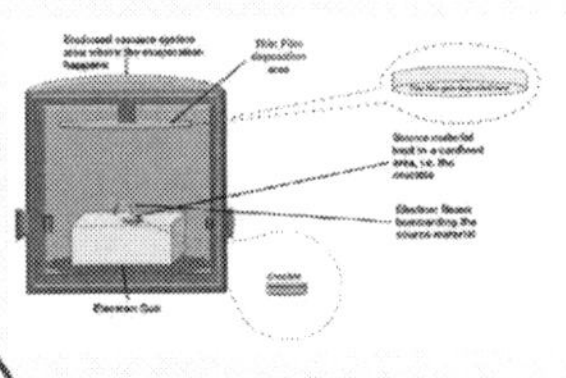

Figure 2: Schematic of the e-beam evaporation process

- The optical measurements were conducted using UV-Vis spectroscopy (PerkinElmer Lambda™) instrument.
- The wetting behavior was assessed through Kruss™ contact angle measurements.
- Surface topology using a Dektak™ 3D stylus.
- Microstructure and morphology using JEOL 7610™ FESEM.
- For structural characterization, XPS analysis was involved with a specific narrow bandwidth analysis at 20 eV with 10 scans for HRXPS.
- The spectral analysis and peak fitting were conducted using the "Avantage" software.

PV Properties :

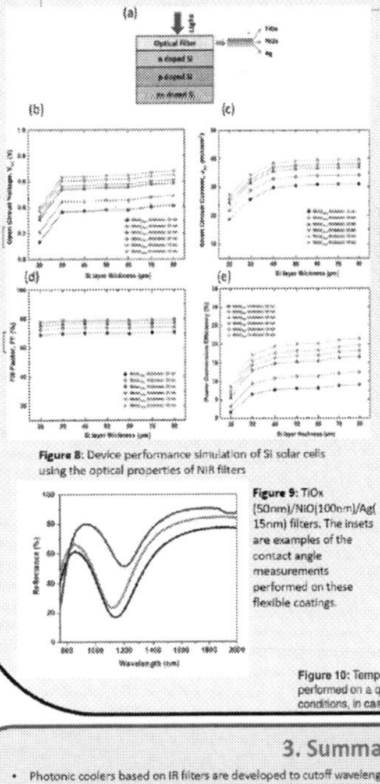

Figure 8: Device performance simulation of Si solar cells using the optical properties of NIR filters

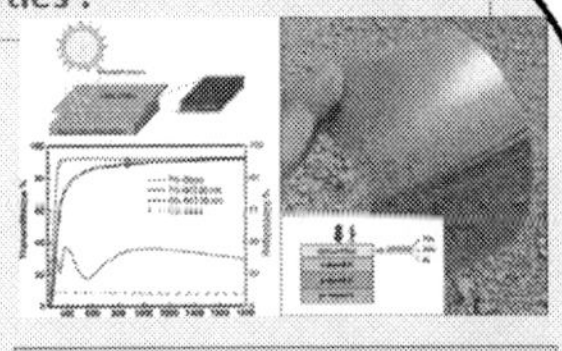

Out of the various configurations and thicknesses that were tested and analyzed, the combinations TiOx(50nm)/NiO(100nm)/Ag(10nm) and TiOx(50 nm)/NiO(100nm)/Ag(15nm) demonstrated the highest infrared (IR) reflection, surpassing 38% in the 750-1200 nm range.

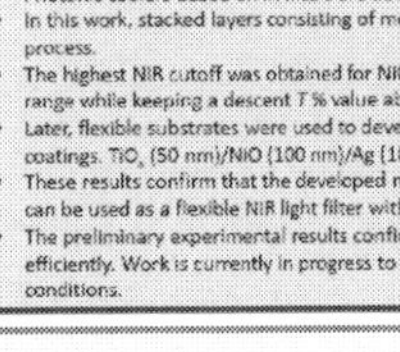

Figure 9: TiOx [50nm)/NiO(100nm)/Ag(15nm) filters. The insets are examples of the contact angle measurements performed on these flexible coatings.

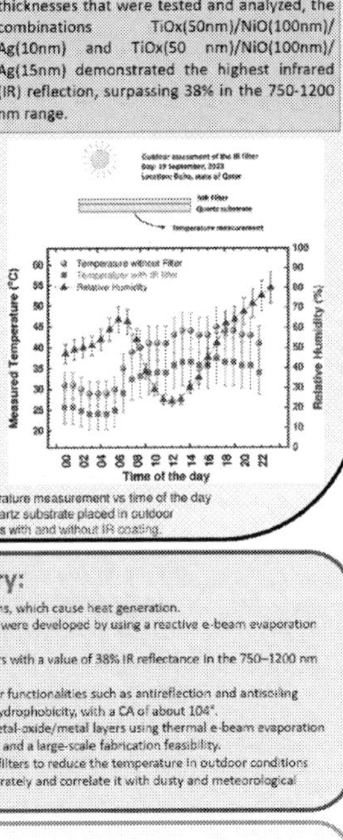

Figure 10: Temperature measurement vs time of the day performed on a quartz substrate placed in outdoor conditions, in cases with and without IR coating.

2. Results

Morphological and Structural properties

Figure 3: Top view SEM images of NiO/metal layers. (a) NiO (300 nm), (b) NiO (100 nm)/Al (10 nm), (c) NiO (300 nm)/Al (20 m), (d) NiO (100 nm)/Ag (10 nm), (e) NiO (300 nm)/Ag (20 nm), and (f) TiOx (50 nm) on NiO (300 nm)..

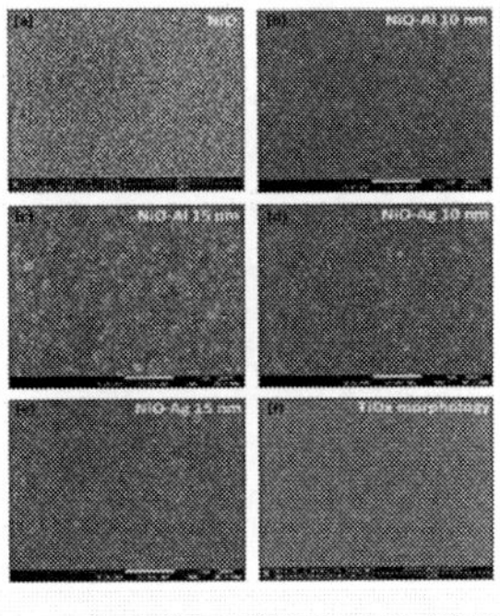

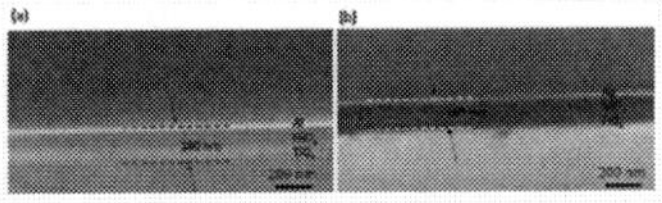

Figure 4: SEM images of NiR-stacked films: (a) TiO_x stacked over NiO_x/Al and (b) TiO_x stacked over NiO_x/Ag.

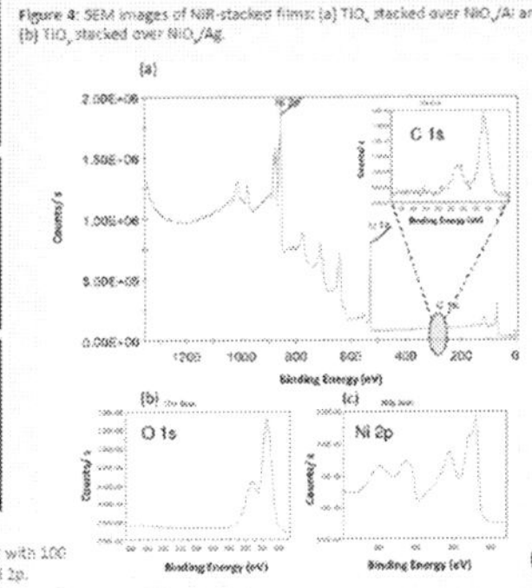

Figure 5: XPS survey of NiO layers grown at 2×10^{-4} Torr with 100 nm thickness. High-resolution XPS for (b) O 1s and (c) Ni 2p.

3. Summary:

- Photonic coolers based on IR filters are developed to cutoff wavelengths, which cause heat generation.
- In this work, stacked layers consisting of metal oxides and metal layers were developed by using a reactive e-beam evaporation process.
- The highest NIR cutoff was obtained for NiO (100 nm)/Ag (10 nm) layers with a value of 38% IR reflectance in the 750–1200 nm range while keeping a descent *T* % value above 50% in the vis range.
- Later, flexible substrates were used to develop such IR filters with other functionalities such as antireflection and antisoiling coatings. TiO_x (50 nm)/NiO (100 nm)/Ag (10 nm) showed the highest hydrophobicity, with a CA of about 104°.
- These results confirm that the developed multistacked metal-oxide/metal-oxide/metal layers using thermal e-beam evaporation can be used as a flexible NIR light filter with a potential antidust ability and a large-scale fabrication feasibility.
- The preliminary experimental results confirmed the capability of such filters to reduce the temperature in outdoor conditions efficiently. Work is currently in progress to quantify this reduction accurately and correlate it with dusty and meteorological conditions.

4. References

1. Abundiz-Cisneros, N., R. Sanginés, R. Rodríguez-López, M. Peralta-Arriola, J. Cruz, and R. Machorro. "Novel Low-E filter for architectural glass pane." Energy and Buildings 206 (2020): 109558.
2. Zhao, Pin, Seohan Kim, Seonghwan Yoon, and Pungkeun Song. "Characteristics of indium zinc oxide/silver/indium zinc oxide multilayer thin layers prepared by magnetron sputtering as flexible transparent film heaters." Thin Solid Layers 665 (2018): 137-142.
3. Loka, Chadrasekhar, Kyoung Ryeol Park, and Kee-Sun Lee. "Multi-functional TiO2/Si/Ag (Cr)/TiNx coatings for low-emissivity and hydrophilic applications." Applied Surface Science 363 (2016): 439-444.
4. Hossain, M. I., A. Khandakar, M. E. H. Chowdhury, S. Ahmed, M. M. Nauman, and B. Aissa. "Numerical and Experimental Investigation [...]ared Optical Filter Based on Metal Oxide Thin Layers for Temperature Mitigation in Photovoltaics." Journal of Electronic Materials (2021): 1-11.

ENHANCING INDOOR PHOTOVOLTAICS: OPTIMIZATION OF DYE-SENSITIZED SOLAR CELLS FOR THE INTERNET OF THINGS

Giorgia Salerno[a] [b], David Roy Bradford [d], Alessio Dessi [c], Daniele Franchi[c] , Alessandro Abbotto[a],Ottavia Bettucci*[a], Marina Freitag* [d].

[a] Department of Materials Science, Solar Energy Research Center MIB-SOLAR and INSTM Milano-Bicocca Research Unit University of Milano-Bicocca,Via Cozzi 55, Milano I-20125, Italy, [b] Department of Information and Electrical Engineering and Applied Mathematics (DIEM) University of Salerno, Invariante 12/B, Via Giovanni Paolo II, 132, Fisciano (SA) I-84084, Italy; [c] National Council of Research – Institute for the Chemistry of Organometallic Compounds (CNR-ICCOM), Via Madonna del Piano 10, Sesto Fiorentino 50019, Italy; [d] School of Natural and Environmental Science, Bedson Building, Newcastle University, NE1 7RU, Newcastle upon Tyne, UK.

giorgia.salerno@unimib.it

ABSTRACT: The rapid expansion of the Internet of Things (IoT) and the increasing reliance on technology in the past decade have intensified the demand for sustainable and efficient energy solutions for powering small indoor devices. Low-light photovoltaics represents an innovative approach to harnessing ambient light in homes and workplaces, and among available technologies, Dye-Sensitized Solar Cells (DSSCs) stand out as a particularly promising option. DSSCs operate by mimicking photosynthesis and typically consist of a photosensitizing dye, a titanium dioxide (TiO_2) photoanode, and a redox couple electrolyte. Unlike conventional silicon-based photovoltaics, they can effectively capture diffuse indoor light, making them highly suited for powering sensors and low-power electronics. Their cost-effectiveness, structural flexibility, and ability to be tailored to specific light sources further enhance their appeal. A key factor in DSSC performance under indoor conditions is the compatibility between the dye's absorption spectrum and the emission spectrum of artificial lighting, such as LEDs and fluorescent lamps. Co-sensitization strategies and the use of dyes with D-π-A (push–pull) structures can significantly improve light harvesting under narrow-spectrum indoor sources. In this study, we focus on optimizing dye selection and co-sensitization to improve DSSC efficiency for indoor applications. Preliminary results show that specific dyes, such as Y123 and TP1, outperform others under particular indoor light sources due to superior spectral matching. Notably, TP1, an affordable and easily synthesized dye, achieved results comparable to the more expensive Y123 under indoor conditions These findings highlight the critical role of dye-lamp matching and device architecture in maximizing DSSC performance. Future work will extend testing to modern LED lamps and refine dye combinations to enhance stability, efficiency, and integration, contributing to the development of sustainable, cost-effective energy solutions for indoor IoT devices.

1 INTRODUCTION

The growing proliferation of the Internet of Things (IoT) and the rising energy demand of low-power indoor devices have driven intensive research into photovoltaic technologies capable of efficiently harvesting ambient light.[1] Among these, dye-sensitized solar cells (DSSCs) have emerged as a promising solution for indoor applications due to their ability to operate efficiently under diffuse and low-light conditions, their structural flexibility, and relatively low production costs. In a DSSC, light is absorbed by a dye anchored to a mesoporous titanium dioxide (TiO_2) layer, promoting electron excitation. The excited electrons are injected into the TiO_2 conduction band and subsequently transported to the fluorine-doped tin oxide (FTO) substrate, from where they flow through an external circuit to generate electricity. The oxidized dye molecules are regenerated by electrons supplied from a redox couple in the electrolyte, thus completing the circuit and enabling continuous energy generation.[2] Dye selection plays a critical role in optimizing DSSC performance under indoor lighting. In this work, we investigate TP1, a dye characterized by advantageous spectroscopic properties and a simpler, more cost-effective synthesis compared to widely used high-performance dyes such as XY1 and Y123.[3] While XY1 and Y123 are typically co-adsorbed with disaggregating agents like chenodeoxycholic acid (CDCA) to prevent dye aggregation on the TiO_2 surface, enhance molecular distribution, strengthen binding to the semiconductor, and improve device stability, recent studies have explored alternative additives such as Bufexamac (BPHA) and its analogue benzohydroxamic acid (BHA). These compounds have been shown to promote an even more orderly dye arrangement on titania. In this study, we examine the performance of TP1 in the presence of BPHA and BHA to assess their impact on the efficiency and stability of DSSCs under indoor illumination.[4]

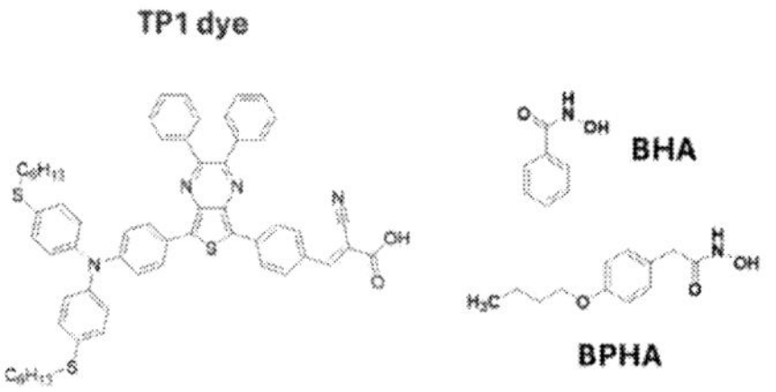

Figure 1: Dye and disaggregating agents used on this project

2 DSSCs DEVICES

2.1 CELL FABRICATION

Conductive glass substrates (Nippon Sheet Glass, Pilkington, 10 Ω sq^{-1} sheet resistance) were sequentially cleaned in Hellmanex solution, deionized water, acetone, and ethanol, followed by UV–ozone treatment to remove residual contaminants. A compact TiO_2 blocking layer was then deposited by spray pyrolysis at 450 °C from a 0.2 M titanium tetraisopropoxide/2 M acetylacetone solution in isopropanol. Mesoporous TiO_2 photoanodes with active areas of 3.2 cm^2 (4 cm × 0.8 cm) or 8 cm^2 (8 cm × 1 cm) were subsequently screen-printed (Seritec Services SA, Corseaux, Switzerland) using DSL 30 NRD-T TiO_2 paste (30 nm, Dyesol/GreatCellSolar) to achieve a 4 μm thick film. For cells tested under AM 1.5G illumination, 18NR-AO Titania (GreatCellSolar) paste was employed. After drying at 120 °C, a 400 nm scattering layer (WER2-0, Dyesol/GreatCellSolar) was screen-printed on top of the mesoporous film and the substrates were gradually heated to 450 °C and sintered for 30 min. The resulting films were treated with 40 mM aqueous $TiCl_4$ at 70 °C for 30 min and sintered again at 450 °C for 30 min. After cooling to room temperature, the titania films were sensitized by immersion in the appropriate dye solution for 12 h. PEDOT counter electrodes were prepared by electro polymerization of 3,4-ethylenedioxythiophene from a 0.01 mM aqueous solution containing 0.1 M sodium dodecyl sulphate.[5] The redox electrolyte for liquid DSSCs consisted of 0.05 M $Cu(tmby)_2TFSI$, 0.02 M $Cu(tmby)_2TFSI_2$, 0.2 M lithium bis(trifluoromethanesulfonyl)imide, and 1.2 M 1-methylbenzimidazole in N-methyl-2-pyrrolidone (MPN).[6] Finally, the photoanode and counter electrode were assembled, and the electrolyte solution was introduced to complete the device.

2.2 PRELIMINARI RESULTS

For reference cells, a 0.1 M TP1 solution with 0.5 M chenodeoxycholic acid (CDCA) was employed, whereas in the alternative approach TiO_2 electrodes were first pretreated with Bufexamac (BPHA) or benzohydroxamic acid (BHA). Specifically, TiO_2 films were immersed in a 3 mM BPHA solution in ethanol for 30 minutes at room temperature, rinsed with ethanol, dried with compressed air, and subsequently sensitized in the TP1 dye solution at room temperature for 12 hours.

Once assembled, the cells were characterized under simulated sunlight using an AM 1.5 solar simulator to ensure comparable conditions. The photovoltaic parameters obtained (Table 1) indicate that the use of alternative co-adsorbents significantly affects device performance. The reference TP1–CDCA cell showed a power conversion efficiency (PCE) of 5.13 %, with Voc = 850 mV, Jsc = 9.23 mA cm^{-2}, and a fill factor (FF) of 0.66. By contrast, TP1–BHA achieved the best performance with a PCE of 6.55 %, Voc = 860 mV, Jsc = 10.6 mA cm^{-2}, and FF = 0.72, demonstrating both higher photocurrent and improved FF compared to the CDCA-based device. TP1–BPHA exhibited a moderate increase in Jsc (9.78 mA cm^{-2}) and FF (0.70), resulting in a PCE of 5.37 %, although a lower Voc (790 mV) was recorded. These results confirm that pretreatment of TiO_2 electrodes with BHA or BPHA can improve dye organization and interfacial properties, leading to enhanced charge collection and higher device efficiency. In particular, BHA appears to be the most promising additive for TP1-based DSSCs, combining a simple procedure with a clear gain in performance.

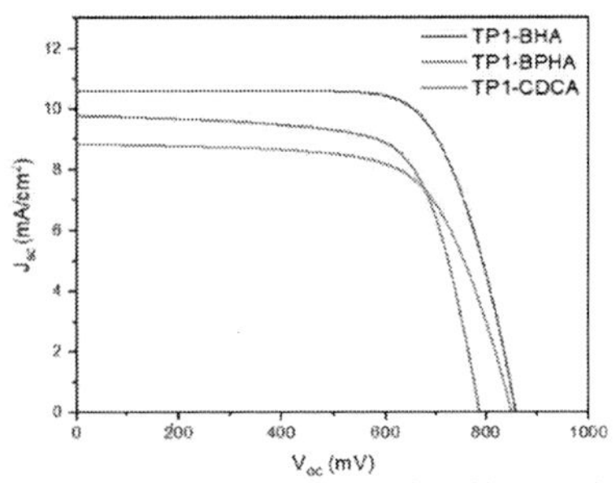

Figure 2: J/V curves of DSSCs sensitized by TP1 dye and the different types of disaggregating agents.

Table 1: J/V characteristics of DSSCs sensitized by TP1 dye and the different types of disaggregating agents.

Cell name	V_{oc} (mV)	J_{sc} (mA/cm²)	FF (%)	η(%)
TP1-CDCA	850 (840±10)	9.23 (8.72±0.7)	0.66 (0.65±0.6)	5.13 (4.87±0.3)
TP1-BHA	860 (830±30)	10.6 (10.5±0.1)	0.72 (0.71±0,1)	6.55 (6.1±0.4)
TPI-BPHA	790 (7700±20)	9.78 (9.16±0.3)	0.70 (0.71±0.4)	5.37 (5.1±0.4)

3 DEVICE CHARACTERIZATION

Current–voltage measurements (J/V) were carried out in ambient air under AM 1.5G illumination using Sinus-70 solar simulator (Wavelabs, Leipzig, Germany), calibrated with reference silicon device (RERA solutions). An X200 source meter (Ossila, Sheffield, UK) was used to assess solar cell performance (scan speed 100 mV s−1). A mask was employed to confine the active solar cell area to 0.196 cm^2.

4 CONCLUSIONS AND FUTURE DEVELOPMENTS

Building on the results obtained so far, the same optimization strategy will be extended to operation under low-light conditions. Once the fabrication protocol is fully optimized, the performance of the cells will be evaluated under artificial indoor illumination using two types of fluorescent lamps commonly employed in domestic and office environments (OSRAM 930 and OSRAM 765), which feature distinct emission spectra but are both largely covered by the absorption profile of the TP1 dye. In addition, a modern LED lamp will be included to reflect the current global trend in indoor lighting technologies. Finally, the pretreatment molecules identified as beneficial for the cost-effective TP1 dye will also be applied to DSSCs employing co-sensitization strategies with TP1 and other dyes, in order to enhance spectral matching between the dyes' absorption and the emission characteristics of indoor light sources.

7 KEYWORDS
DSSC, Indoor application, organic dyes.

8 REFERENCES

[1] H. Michaels, M. Rinderle, I. Benesperi, R. Freitag, A. Gagliardi, M. Freitag, *Chem. Sci.* **2023**, *14*, 5350-5360.
[2] A. B. Muñoz-García, I. Benesperi, G. Boschloo, J. J. Concepcion, J. H. Delcamp, E. A. Gibson, G. J. Meyer, M. Pavone, H. Pettersson, A. Hagfeldt, M. Freitag, *Chem. Soc. Rev.* **2021**, *50*, 12450-12550.
[3] G. Salerno, D. Franchi, A. Dessì, M. Bartolini, N. Manfredi, A. Abbotto, O. Bettucci, *ChemistryOpen*, *n/a*, e202400464.
[4] Y. Ren, D. Zhang, J. Suo, Y. Cao, F. T. Eickemeyer, N. Vlachopoulos, S. M. Zakeeruddin, A. Hagfeldt, M. Grätzel, *Nat.* **2023**, *613*, 60-65.
[5] N. Sakmeche, S. Aeiyach, J.-J. Aaron, M. Jouini, J. C. Lacroix, P.-C. Lacaze, *Langmuir* **1999**, *15*, 2566-2574.
[6] Y. Saygili, M. Söderberg, N. Pellet, F. Giordano, Y. Cao, A. B. Muñoz-García, S. M. Zakeeruddin, N. Vlachopoulos, M. Pavone, G. Boschloo, L. Kavan, J.-E. Moser, M. Grätzel, A. Hagfeldt, M. Freitag, *J. Am. Chem. Soc.* **2016**, *138*, 15087-15096.

EU PVSEC
Bilbao,2025

Enhancing Indoor Photovoltaics: Optimization of Dye-Sensitized Solar Cells for the Internet of Things

Giorgia Salerno[a] [b], David Roy Bradford [d] ,Alessio Dessi [c], Daniele Franchi[c] , Alessandro Abbotto[a],Ottavia Bettucci*[a], Marina Freitag* [d].

[a] Department of Materials Science, Solar Energy Research Center MIB-SOLAR and INSTM Milano-Bicocca Research Unit University of Milano-Bicocca,Via Cozzi 55, Milano I-20125, Italy, [b] Department of Information and Electrical Engineering and Applied Mathematics (DIEM) University of Salerno, Invariante 12/B, Via Giovanni Paolo II, 132, Fisciano (SA) I-84084, Italy; [c] National Council of Research – Institute for the Chemistry of Organometallic Compounds (CNR-ICCOM), Via Madonna del Piano 10, Sesto Fiorentino 50019, Italy, [d] School of Natural and Environmental Science, Bedson Building, Newcastle University, NE1 7RU, Newcastle upon Tyne, UK.

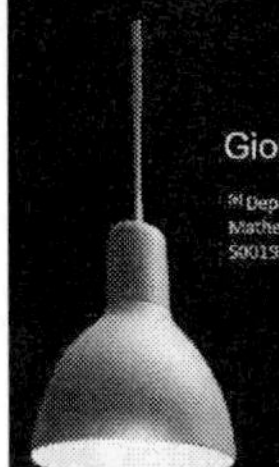

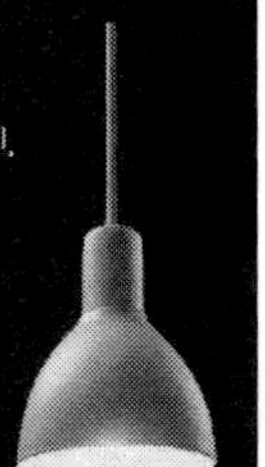

Low light photovoltaics is an innovative strategy to harness light inside homes and power small electronic devices that are part of the Internet of Things (IoT). Among existing photovoltaic devices, Dye Sensitized Solar Cells (DSSCs) are the most promising technology in this field. The core of a DSSC is an organic dye with a D-π-A structure (push-pull) whose absorption must be as compatible as possible with the emission spectrum of indoor lamps.

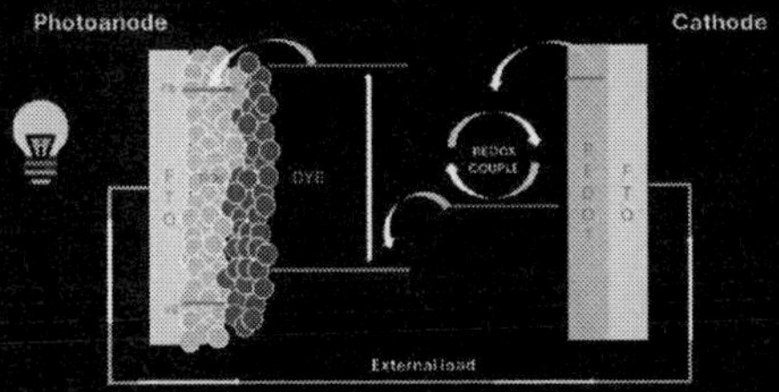

DSSCs DEVICE

In a DSSC the light is caught by a dye anchored on the TiO_2 layer, exciting the electrons. The excited electrons are injected into the TiO_2 conduction band and then transferred to the fluorine-doped tin oxide glass (FTO) and finally flowing through an external circuit, generating electricity. The oxidized dye molecules are regenerated by electrons stemming from an electrolyte containing a redox couple. This step completes the circuit, allowing continuous electron flow and energy generation.

PURPOSE OF THE WORK

The dye selected for this work is the TP1 dye due to its interesting spectroscopic features and its relatively straightforward synthetic process simpler but also significantly more cost-effective compared to other highly efficient dyes such as XY1 and Y123, commonly used in indoor DSSCs studies. XY1 and Y123 are typically used in combination with a disaggregating agent like chenodeoxycholic acid (CDCA), which 1. prevent dye aggregation on the TiO_2 surface, 2. enhance the uniform distribution of dye molecules, 3. promote stronger binding to the semiconductor improving overall cell efficiency, and 4. improve the long-term stability of the solar cell. Recently, various alternative disaggregating molecules such as Bufexamac (BPHA) and its analogue benzohydroxamic acid (BHA) , have been explored in the literature. These compounds fulfill the same role as CDCA, but studies have shown that they facilitate a more orderly arrangement of dye molecules on the titania surface. For these reasons, in this work dye TP1 has been tested in presence of BPHA and BHA to investigate changes in the DSSCs efficiencies. [1-3]

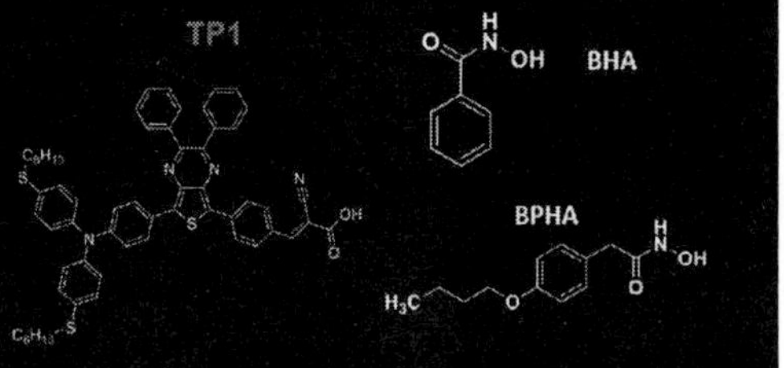

PRELIMINARY RESULTS

The cells were fabricated as described in the literature, using a 0.1 M solution of TP1 with 0.5 M chenodeoxycholic acid for the TP1-type cells. In contrast, for the molecules where pretreatments with BPHA and BHA were applied, TiO_2 electrodes were immersed in an EtOH solution containing 3 mM BPHA at room temperature for 30 minutes. Subsequently, the BPHA-coated TiO_2 electrodes were rinsed with EtOH and dried using compressed air. The BPHA-coated mesoporous TiO_2 films were then sensitized by immersion in the dye solutions at room temperature for 12 hours.

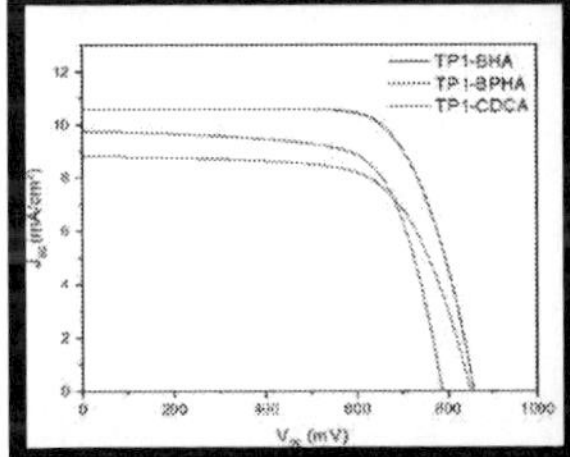

Cell name	V_{oc} (mV)	J_{sc} (mA/cm²)	FF (%)	η(%)
TP1-CDCA	850 (840±10)	9.23 (8.72±0.7)	0.66 (0.65±0.6)	5.13 (4.87±0.3)
TP1-BHA	860 (830±30)	10.6 (10.5±0.1)	0.72 (0.71±0,1)	6.55 (6.1±0.4)
TPI-BPHA	790 (7700±20)	9.78 (9.16±0.3)	0.70 (0.71±0.4)	5.37 (5.1±0.4)

As can be seen from the *J/V* results, TP1 with a 0.5 M concentration of chenodeoxycholic acid produces a lower PCE% compared to the use of BHA and BPHA as pretreatments. The V_{oc} does not show significant differences, except in the case of TP1-BPHA, where it is lower. The current is higher in the case of TP1-BHA, and the fill factor (FF) is also better in the cells that were pretreated with BHA and BPHA.

FUTURE DEVELOPMENTS

Based on the previously described results, the same optimization will also be tested under low-light conditions. Once the fabrication process has been optimized, the cells will be tested using two types of fluorescent lamps commonly used in indoor environments (OSRAM 930 and OSRAM 765), which have different emission spectra but are both well covered by the absorption spectrum of the TP1 dye (see figures on the right). Additionally, a modern LED lamp will be used, reflecting the current global trend in indoor lighting technologies. Finally, the same pretreatment molecules used with the cost-effective TP1 dye could be applied to DSSC cells employing co-sensitization strategies with TP1 and other dyes, in order to enhance the spectral matching between the dyes' absorption and the emission spectra of indoor light sources.

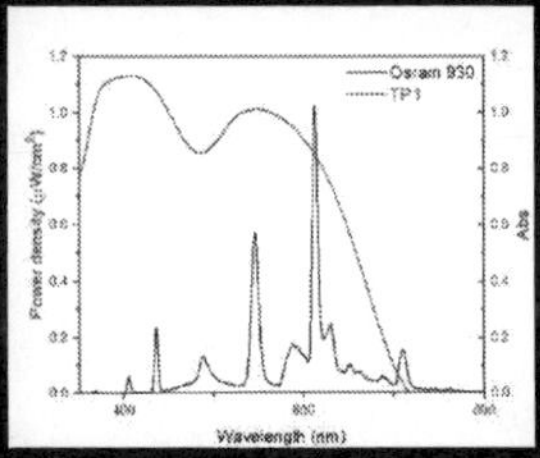

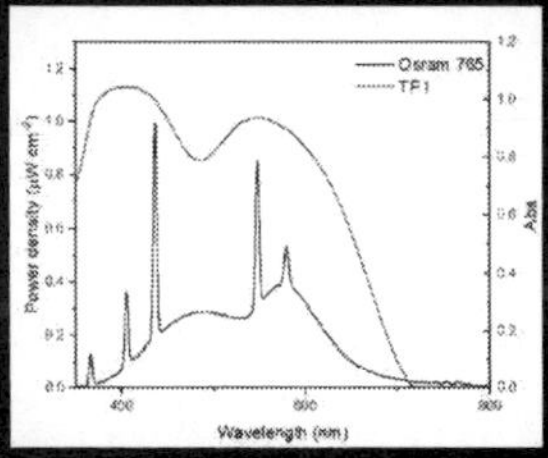

CONCLUSIONS

In conclusion, the TP1 dye had previously been synthesized and studied as a cost-effective alternative to conventional organic dyes such as Y123 and XY1, which are commonly used in DSSCs. Compared to these standard dyes, TP1 was identified as a more economical organic dye option. Moreover, the 1 sun efficiencies of TP1-based cells were improved using alternative co-adsorbents, specifically BHA and BPHA, rather than the commonly employed ones. In particular, BPHA had already been previously studied and demonstrated to enhance performance when used with other organic dyes.

ACKNOWLEDGMENTS

University of Milano-Bicocca, Ministero dellUniversità e della Ricerca (PRIN2022 Mendeleev), and PNRR-Sustainable Mobility Center (CNMS), MOST – Sustainable Mobility Center (funding from the European Union Next-GenerationEU, Piano Nazionale di Ripresa e Resilienza (PNRR) – Missione 4 Componente 2, Investimento 1.4 – D.D. 1033 17/06/2022, CN00000023) for financial support.

REFERENCES

1. Ren, Y. et al. Hydroxamic acid pre-adsorption raises the efficiency of cosensitized solar cells. Nat. 613, 60-65, doi:10.1038/s41586-022-05460-z (2023).
2. Salerno, G. et al. Optimizing DSSCs Performance for Indoor Lighting: Matching Organic Dyes Absorption and Indoor Lamps Emission Profiles to Maximize Efficiency. ChemistryOpen n/a, e202400464. (2024)
3. Muñoz-García, A. B. et al. Dye-sensitized solar cells strike back. Chem. Soc. Rev. 50, 12450-12550, doi:10.1039/D0CS01336F (2021).

CONTACTS

giorgia.salerno@unimib.it
www.linkedin.com/in/giorgia-salerno

SIC RECRYSTALLIZATION BY UV NANOPULSED LASER ANNEALING

Daniele Arduino [a b], Luciano Scaltrito [a], Sergio Ferrero [a], Andrea Ancillao [a]

[a] Department of Applied Science and Technology, Politecnico di Torino, Corso Duca degli Abruzzi 24, 10129 Torino, Italy.

[b] Department of Information Engineering, Electrical Engineering and Applied Mathematics, University of Salerno, Via Giovanni Paolo II 132, 84084 Fisciano, Italy

daniele_arduino@polito.it , luciano.scaltrito@polito.it , sergio.ferrero@polito.it , andrea.ancillao@polito.it

Corresponding Author: Daniele Arduino

ABSTRACT: This work explores the use of nanosecond UV pulsed laser annealing to induce localized recrystallization in amorphous silicon carbide (a-SiC) thin films, a strategic material for power electronics and photovoltaic applications. The experiment was conducted in a vacuum chamber (4.3×10^{-1} mbar) using a 355 nm Q-switched DPSS laser, with a spot size of about 80 μm and power ranging from 1.15 to 3.95 W. The films, 450–500 nm thick and deposited on crystalline 4H-SiC substrates, were irradiated under different combinations of fluence and scan speed. TEM analysis revealed that, under optimal conditions, nanocrystalline domains (5–15 nm) formed up to about 50 nm in depth, while preserving the substrate integrity and avoiding ablation effects. The results demonstrate the feasibility of a compact, selective thermal treatment compatible with fabrication workflows, opening perspectives for advanced devices and novel electronic architectures.

Keywords: Amorphous Silicon Carbide Crystallization, DPSS Q-switched Laser, UV Laser Annealing, Vacuum-Assisted Processing

1. INTRODUCTION

The growing adoption of technologies for sustainable energy and high-performance electronics has driven research toward materials and processes that offer efficiency, miniaturization, and operational robustness. In this context, silicon carbide (SiC) has emerged as one of the most promising semiconductors, thanks to its outstanding properties: wide bandgap, high thermal conductivity, excellent chemical and mechanical stability, and the ability to operate at high temperatures, voltages, and frequencies [1] [2]. These characteristics make SiC an ideal choice for next-generation power devices, particularly in applications such as photovoltaics, electric mobility, and energy conversion systems.

Depending on its crystal structure, SiC can exist in numerous polytypes (over 200), each with slightly different electronic properties [3]. Among them, 4H-SiC is one of the most widely used in microelectronics due to its high carrier mobility. Amorphous SiC (a-SiC) also shows significant potential for optoelectronic and high-frequency applications, thanks to its wider bandgap compared to silicon [1] [4] [5] [6] [7].

However, working with SiC still shows several challenges, particularly in the fabrication of high-quality crystalline layers starting from amorphous films or those damaged by ion implantation [5]. In many cases, a post-deposition thermal treatment is required to restore the crystalline order or to activate dopants [8] [9]. Conventional thermal treatments, typically performed in a furnace, allow for recrystallization and dopant activation, but involve heating the entire device. This can adversely affect already-processed regions, cause unwanted dopant diffusion, or damage existing metal interconnections, making such methods less suitable when localized modification of material properties is required. To overcome these limitations, there has been increasing interest in recent decades in alternative localized annealing techniques, particularly laser annealing. This method allows targeted thermal energy transfer to surface layers while keeping the underlying layers cool [10]. Several studies have explored the use of lasers to process SiC through additive approaches (annealing, doping, surface modification) or subtractive ones (ablation). A wide range of laser sources have been employed: from traditional excimer and Nd:YAG lasers [11] [12] [13] [14] [15] to more recent picosecond and femtosecond lasers [16] [17] [18].

In the context of laser annealing of amorphous SiC films, various studies have demonstrated that optical absorption of laser pulses can induce partial or complete recrystallization of the material through annealing mechanisms. Experiments using UV pulsed lasers (KrF, XeCl) have shown the formation of crystalline phases, with improvements in crystal quality observed via TEM [19] [20]. A KrF laser (248 nm) has been used to induce crystallization in a-SiC films, resulting in the formation of the cubic 3C-SiC phase [21]. At higher fluences, polycrystalline layers have been obtained on ion-implanted films [22]. More recently, visible laser sources such as ruby lasers (694 nm) and Nd:YAG lasers at 532 nm have also been tested with some success, although generally with lower efficiencies [23] [24].

The present study aims to explore a more compact and potentially more sustainable laser-based solution, using a DPSS Q-switched laser at 355 nm operating under controlled vacuum conditions. The use of vacuum helps reduce surface oxidation and improves thermal transfer efficiency, making the process cleaner and more reproducible. The main goal is to evaluate the feasibility of achieving localized and controlled recrystallization of thin amorphous SiC films, allowing selective post-treatment processes for advanced electronic devices and multilayer MEMS structures.

2. STUDY AIM

The main goal of this work was to explore whether it is possible to use localized thermal treatment, specifically laser annealing, to modify thin amorphous silicon carbide (a-SiC) films in a controlled way, aiming to trigger partial or full crystallization of the material. This type of approach could be particularly useful in the electronics field, especially for applications that require selective modifications at the microscale, such as in power devices. A key part of the study focused on testing a DPSS Q-switched laser operating at 355 nm under vacuum conditions, to evaluate whether this system could serve as a valid, and also possibly more compact and cost-effective, alternative to more complex laser technologies commonly used in previous research. Overall, the aim was to assess the feasibility of a selective post-treatment process for SiC, capable of targeting specific areas of the material without exposing the whole device to high thermal stress. If successful, this method could contribute to advancing fabrication techniques for power electronics, especially in scenarios where precision, miniaturization, and material integration are crucial.

3. MATERIALS AND METHODS

3.1 Samples

The experiment was carried out on samples made of amorphous silicon carbide (a-SiC) thin films, about 450 nm thick, deposited by Physical Vapor Deposition (PVD) onto 4H-SiC substrates. The substrates, 100 mm in diameter and 325–375 µm thick, were produced by Dow Corning and supplied by CNRS-SiMaP (Grenoble, France). The deposition was performed with a Si/C ratio of approximately 1.11, at a substrate temperature of 250 °C and a chamber pressure of 0.9 Pa. The plasma power was set to 450 W, and the process lasted 90 minutes, resulting in a growth rate of roughly 300 nm per hour.

3.2 Equipment

The thin films were then locally annealed using a Q-switched DPSS laser (model SOL 4W, 355 nm, Bright Solutions), operating at a wavelength of 355 nm. The repetition rate could be varied between 30 and 120 kHz, with output power ranging from 3.95 W (at 30 kHz) to 1.15 W (at 120 kHz). Depending on the repetition frequency, the pulse duration ranged from 11.9 ns to 31.4 ns. The laser beam had a Gaussian spatial profile, with a spot size of approximately 80 µm. The laser beam was directed onto the samples via a simple optical path that included a UV-enhanced aluminum mirror (Thorlabs PF10-03-F01) and a plano-convex fused silica lens with a 100 mm focal length, AR-coated for the 245–400 nm range (Thorlabs LA4380-UV). Samples were moved under the laser beam using a two-axis motorized stage (Misumi LX26 for X and LX20 for Y), allowing scan speeds between 40 and 100 mm/s. The whole process took place in a custom-built vacuum chamber, kept at a pressure of 4.3 × 10^{-1} mbar using a rotary vane pump (Varian SD90). The laser entered the chamber through a UV-grade fused silica window (Thorlabs WG42012-UV, Ø2", 12 mm thick, AR-coated for 245–400 nm) and was focused directly onto the sample surface.

3.3 Characterization techniques

After processing, the samples were analyzed to assess surface morphology and structural changes induced by the laser treatment. This characterization was performed using optical microscopy (Leitz Wetzlar Ergolux AMC Inspection Microscope) and transmission electron microscopy (TEM) with a Talos F200X system (Thermo Scientific).

3.4 Study protocol

To investigate how the laser treatment affects the material as a function of the irradiation parameters, a calibration table (see Table 1) was first created. This table links the duty cycle (ranging from 10% to 80%) with the laser repetition frequency (30–100 kHz), providing a mapping of the actual average output power for each combination. The resulting power values range from approximately 0.03 W up to a maximum of 2.97 W.

Calibration matrix	10%	20%	30%	40%	50%	60%	70%	80%	duty cycle
30 kHz	0,06	0,25	0,55	0,95	1,39	1,84	2,37	2,97	
40 kHz	0,05	0,18	0,41	0,74	1,12	1,58	2,03	2,5	
50 kHz	0,04	0,14	0,33	0,59	0,93	1,3	1,75	2,2	
60kHz	0,04	0,12	0,27	0,5	0,77	1,12	1,48	1,95	
70kHz	0,04	0,1	0,23	0,42	0,66	0,95	1,3	1,66	
80kHz	0,03	0,09	0,2	0,36	0,58	0,84	1,16	1,47	
90kHz	0,03	0,08	0,18	0,32	0,5	0,74	1,04	1,38	
100kHz	0,03	0,08	0,16	0,28	0,47	0,65	0,92	1,37	
freq									

Table I Calibration table of the laser source

Using this table as a reference, a series of laser scan lines were produced on the a-SiC film, each one characterized by a different combination of power and scan speed. The scan speeds used were within the operational range of the system (40–100 mm/s), allowing the exploration of a wide set of experimental conditions.

After laser processing, all the lines were inspected under an optical microscope to evaluate their surface appearance. The most promising conditions were selected based on two main criteria: the uniformity of the line along its length and its optical appearance, the idea was trying to distinguish between lines that looked burnt or excessively dark (which could indicate damage) and those that showed contrast or reflectivity suggestive of a successful annealing effect.

Following this initial screening, a line was identified as representative of an effective treatment. This was then analysed by transmission electron microscopy (TEM) to investigate possible changes in the film's crystalline structure, in order to assess whether local crystallization of the amorphous SiC had occurred.

During the experiment, numerous sets of irradiation lines were produced, organized into labelled blocks (A–P), each characterized by a specific combination of repetition rate, average delivered power, and scanning speed (see Table 2). These combinations were designed to systematically explore a wide parameter space. The operating conditions were selected based on the laser calibration table obtained experimentally (see Table 1).

Block	Frequency (kHz)	Average Power (W)	Scan Speed (mm/s)	Fluence (J/cm²)
A	40	0,18-0,36	40-50	0,09-0,18
B	40-50	0,74-1,12	50-70	0,37-0,46
C	40	0,05-0,65	40	0,02-0,32
D	80	0,09-0,84	40	0,02-0,21
E	50	0,33-0,84	40-80	0,13-0,33
F	60	0,27-0,77	70-80	0,09-0,26
G	70	0,42-1,66	90-100	0,12-0,47
H	30	0,25-2,47	40-50	0,17-1,77
I	40	1,12-2,03	40-50	0,56-1,01
J	100	0,08-0,92	50	0,02-0,18
K	50-60	0,04-0,33	40	0,01-0,13
L	90	0,08-0,74	40	0,02-0,16
M	60-70	0,10-1,95	40	0,03-0,55
N	80-90	0,82-1,47	40	0,18-0,37
O	50	0,93-1,75	40	0,37-0,70
P	100	0,92-1,37	50	0,18-0,27

Table II The different blocks of sample lines obtained with different combinations of parameters

4. RESULTS

4.1 Optical analysis

A series of laser scan lines were produced on the a-SiC thin film using different combinations of laser power and scan speed. After the treatment, all lines were initially examined via optical microscopy to assess changes in their visual appearance.

The lines obtained in the different blocks were inspected using optical microscopy. In many cases (e.g., blocks A and K), the lines were completely absent or barely perceptible, even at high magnifications, as visible in Figure 1 and Figure 2. This indicates that, under those parameter combinations, the energy delivered to the film was insufficient to trigger a detectable modification.

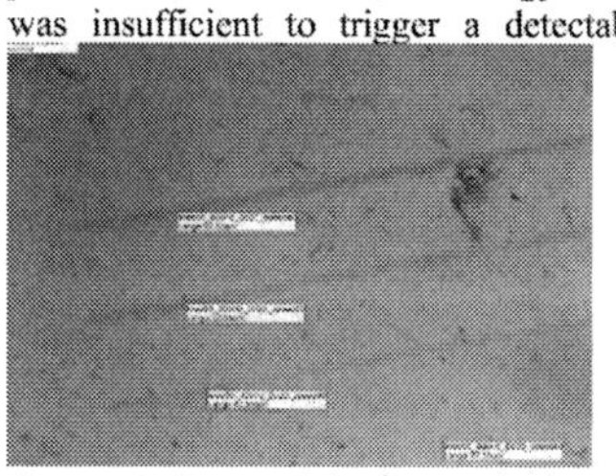

Figure 1 Some of the lines of Block A at the optical microscope: they are barely perceptible

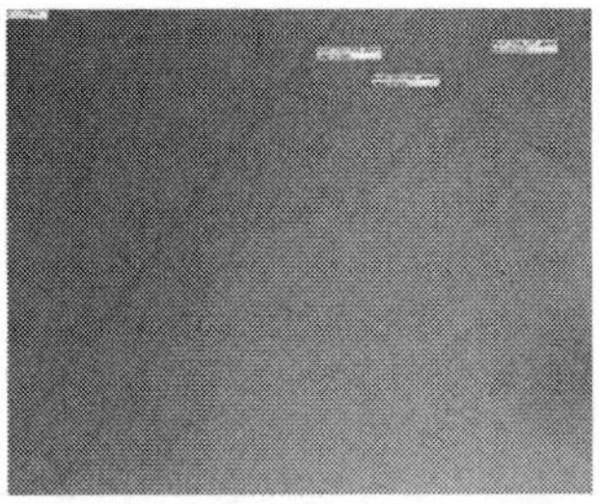

Figure 2 Some of the lines of Block K at the optical microscope: they are barely perceptible

Other blocks (e.g., B, H, I, N, O) showed visible lines, but with clear morphological issues: irregular edges, localized darkening, and discontinuities, potentially related to excessive fluence or thermal instabilities, as visible in the Figures 3-7. These effects suggest that, although sufficient energy was delivered, the irradiation regime was not optimized to ensure an orderly structural transformation.

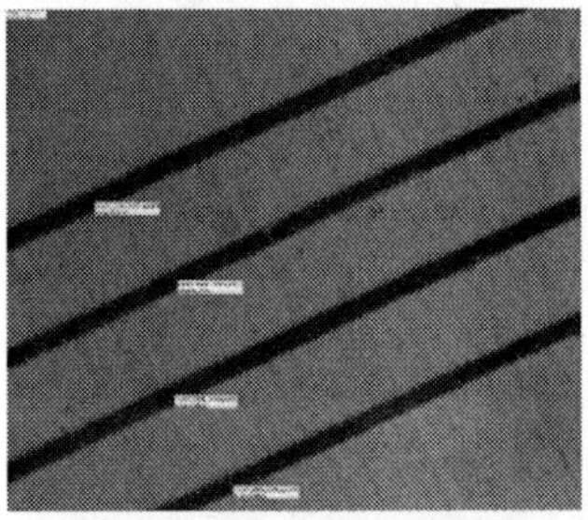

Figure 3 Some of the lines of Block B

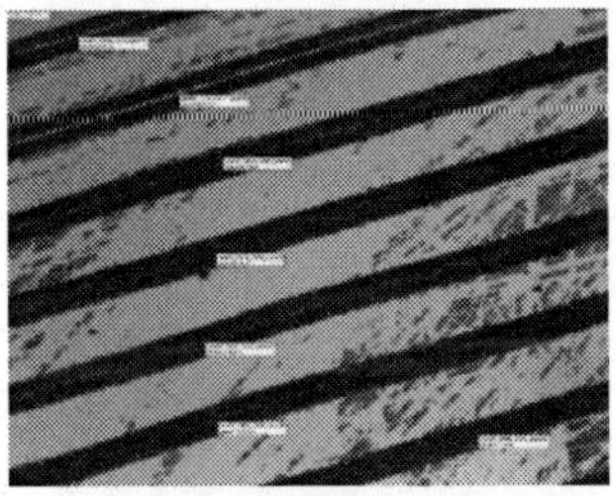

Figure 4 Some of the lines of Block H

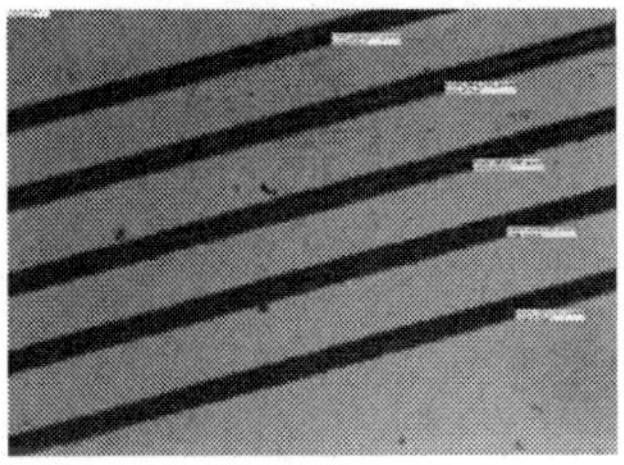

Figure 5 Some of the lines of Block I

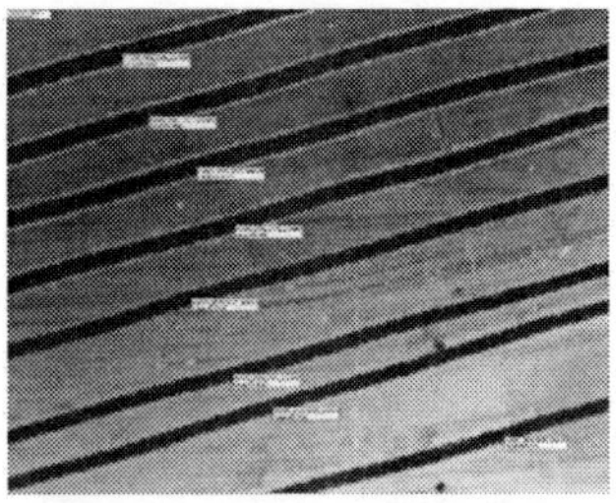

Figure 6 Some of the lines of Block N

Figure 7 Some of the lines of Block O

As visible in Figure 8, in the block G there is a produced line (line β) that appeared significantly better. Line β was produced by using a power of 1,12 W , scan speed of 100 mm/s, frequency of 70 kHz, pulse width of 20,8 ns and fluence of 0,32 J/cm^2. This was characterized by sharp and uniform edges along its entire length, homogeneous visual contrast with respect to the untreated surface, and the absence of cracks, melting, or delamination. These features suggested an optimal balance between fluence and scanning speed, making it particularly promising for controlled material transformation. That line was selected for TEM analysis.

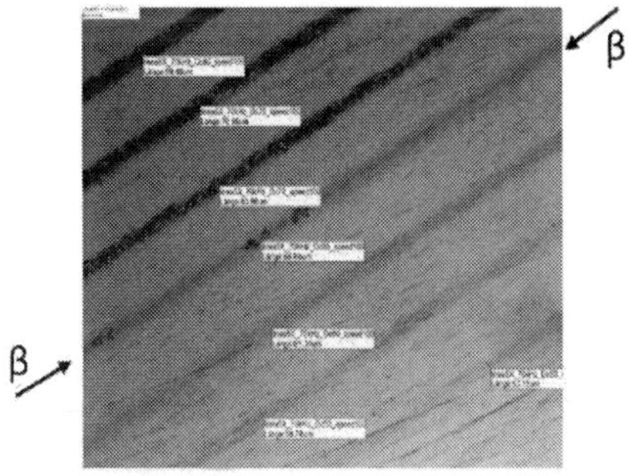

Figure 8 Some of the lines of Block G: line β is indicated by arrows

A part of the lines exhibited either excessive surface darkening or morphological irregularities, indicative of overheating. However, a subset of lines showed uniform width and a consistent surface contrast that suggested successful localized thermal treatment.

Among these, a specific line was selected for further analysis due to its clean edges, uniform contrast, and absence of visual damage such as cracking or melting. This line β was analysed by transmission electron microscopy (TEM) to investigate changes in the structural order of the a-SiC layer induced by laser irradiation.

4.2 TEM analysis

Cross-sectional TEM images revealed significant structural differences between the laser-treated (yellow circle) and untreated areas (blue circle), as visible in Figure 9. In the untreated regions, the a-SiC film appeared as a fully amorphous layer with no discernible lattice fringes. In contrast, the laser-processed zones showed the presence of nanocrystalline domains embedded within the amorphous matrix. These crystalline regions exhibited well-defined lattice fringes and were consistent in size and distribution across the treated area.

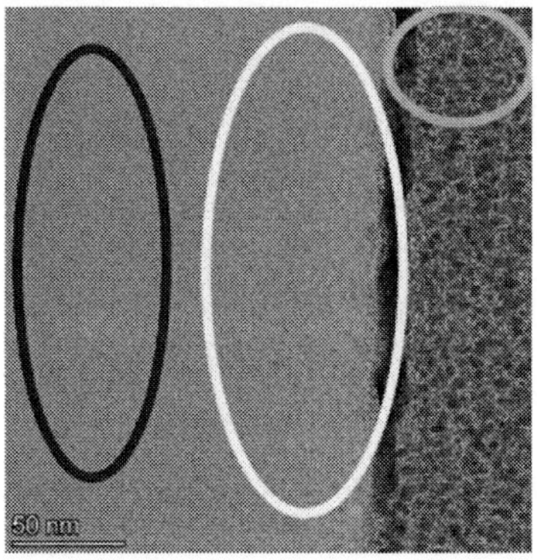

Figure 9 TEM image of the cross-section of line β: the laser-treated area (yellow circle) and untreated area (blue circle) and the protective Platinum layer used during TEM measurements (green circle)

Zoomed TEM images confirmed the presence of crystalline domains of 2–5 nm, indicating the onset of localized polycrystalline crystallization with random orientation. This treated area is from surface of SiC layer to about 50 nm of depth, as visible in Figure 10.

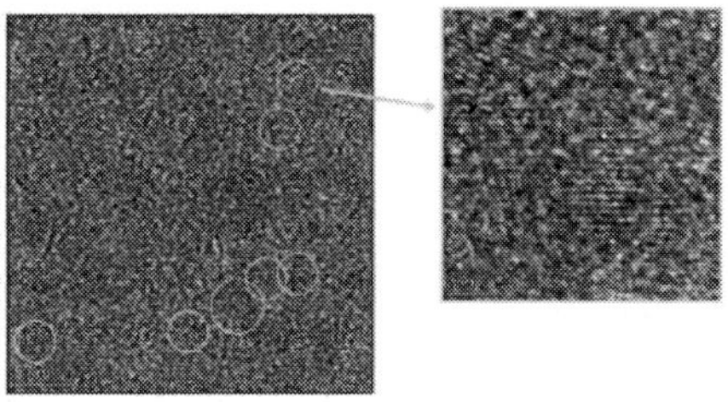

Figure 10 Zoomed TEM images of the treated area of line β

5. DISCUSSION

The results demonstrate that it is possible to induce a localized crystallization process in thin films of a-SiC using a compact DPSS Q-switched laser source at 355 nm, operating under vacuum conditions. The absence of macroscopic melting or visible cracking indicates that the process occurred in a controlled manner, remaining below the material's thermal damage threshold.

The behavior observed in the treated regions suggests a mechanism based on rapid, localized heating that provides sufficient thermal energy to initiate crystal nucleation, but remains limited in depth due to the short pulse duration (11.9–31.4 ns) and small optical spot size (~80 µm). The shallow modification depth (~50 nm) is consistent with a surface-level recrystallization process, which could be particularly useful for applications requiring functional changes in the upper layer without affecting the substrate or underlying layers.

The formation of disordered, nanometric crystalline domains without preferential orientation suggests that, at these fluence levels, the process does not result in complete or epitaxial recrystallization, but rather an initial structural reorganization. This outcome aligns with previous studies using excimer lasers such as KrF and XeCl [21], [22], which reported crystalline phase formation in a-SiC films at comparable fluences. However, the approach presented in this work offers significant advantages in terms of system compactness, optical simplicity, and operational costs, owing to the use of a more accessible commercial DPSS laser compared to excimer sources.

Additionally, the use of a custom vacuum chamber enhanced the energy efficiency of the process by reducing thermal dissipation and preventing surface oxidation or contamination—common issues in treatments performed in ambient air.

The proposed method is distinguished by its high spatial selectivity and by a lower system complexity compared to approaches based on excimer lasers, while at the same time showing significant potential for direct integration into electronic device manufacturing workflows. The results obtained demonstrate that this strategy is not only effective and selective, but also compatible with established technological processes, thereby outlining relevant application prospects in multilayer power electronics, next-generation MEMS, and high-efficiency photovoltaics.

The experimental observations open several directions for future research. A first line of development will focus on the fine optimization of laser parameters, aimed at extending the extent of crystallization and improving the control of the crystallographic orientation of the resulting domains. In this context, the use of shorter wavelengths, particularly in the deep ultraviolet range (<248 nm), could enhance surface absorption and consequently increase process efficiency.

Another research avenue will be the extension of the method to materials with similar structural and functional characteristics, such as SiNx or SiGe alloys, with the aim of assessing its universality and possible limitations. At the same time, it will be necessary to systematically address the challenges related to industrial scalability, including the adaptation of the treatment to larger surface areas or to more complex geometries, such as whole wafers or partially processed devices.

Finally, a strategic objective for technology transfer concerns the integration of the laser treatment into consolidated production lines, with particular reference to photovoltaic technologies and power electronics, where the potential application impact could be especially significant.

6. CONCLUSIONS

In this work, we have shown that it is possible to achieve localized crystallization in thin a-SiC films using a 355 nm UV DPSS Q-switched laser under vacuum conditions. The treatment produced nanocrystalline domains only in the surface layer, without damaging the film's structure or morphology, confirming that the technique can selectively modify the material's surface. Compared to excimer lasers, this approach is more compact, easier to handle, and operationally less complex.

The results also suggest that this strategy could be useful for applications such as power electronics, MEMS, and high-efficiency photovoltaics. Furthermore, the method provides a solid basis for future studies aimed at optimizing the treatment parameters and applying it to different materials and geometries, with potential developments toward integration into existing industrial processes.

Conflict of interest

The authors declare that they have no conflict of interest.

7. REFERENCES

[1] G. Foti, «Silicon carbide: from amorphous to crystalline material», *Appl. Surf. Sci.*, vol. 184, fasc. 1–4, pp. 20–26, dic. 2001, doi: 10.1016/S0169-4332(01)00751-6.

[2] R. Gharbi *et al.*, «Observation of negative capacitance in a-SiC:H/a-Si:H UV photodetectors», *Solid-State Electron.*, vol. 50, fasc. 3, pp. 367–371, mar. 2006, doi: 10.1016/j.sse.2006.02.009.

[3] X.-B. Li, E.-W. Shi, Z.-Z. Chen, e B. Xiao, «Polytype formation in silicon carbide single crystals», *Diam. Relat. Mater.*, vol. 16, fasc. 3, pp. 654–657, mar. 2007, doi: 10.1016/j.diamond.2006.11.078.

[4] J. Homberger, A. B. Lostetter, K. J. Olejniczak, T. McNutt, S. M. Lal, e A. Mantooth, «Silicon-carbide (SiC) semiconductor power electronics for extreme high-temperature environments», in *2004 IEEE Aerospace Conference Proceedings (IEEE Cat. No.04TH8720)*, Big Sky, MT, USA: IEEE, 2004, pp. 2538–2555. doi: 10.1109/AERO.2004.1368048.

[5] J. M. Melzak, «Silicon carbide for RF MEMS», in *IEEE MTT-S International Microwave Symposium Digest, 2003*, Philadelphia, PA, USA: IEEE, 2003, pp. 1629–1632. doi: 10.1109/MWSYM.2003.1210450.

[6] L. Scaltrito *et al.*, «Structural and electrical characterization of epitaxial 4H–SiC layers for power electronic device applications», *Mater. Sci. Eng. B*, vol. 102, fasc. 1–3, pp. 298–303, set. 2003, doi: 10.1016/S0921-5107(02)00726-2.

[7] S. Ferrero *et al.*, «Defect characterization of 4H-SiC wafers for power electronic device applications», *J. Phys. Condens. Matter*, vol. 14, fasc. 48, pp. 13397–13402, dic. 2002, doi: 10.1088/0953-8984/14/48/394.

[8] S. Kühnapfel, D. Amkreutz, C. Klimm, e N. H. Nickel, «Excimer laser crystallization of a-SiC$_x$ on glass», *Can. J. Phys.*, vol. 92, fasc. 7/8, pp. 709–712, lug. 2014, doi: 10.1139/cjp-2013-0571.

[9] U. Coscia *et al.*, «Laser annealing study of PECVD deposited hydrogenated amorphous silicon carbon alloy films», *Appl. Surf. Sci.*, vol. 254, fasc. 4, pp. 984–988, dic. 2007, doi: 10.1016/j.apsusc.2007.08.003.

[10] D. Arduino, S. Stassi, C. Spano, L. Scaltrito, S. Ferrero, e V. Bertana, «Silicon and Silicon Carbide Recrystallization by Laser Annealing: A Review», *Materials*, vol. 16, fasc. 24, p. 7674, dic. 2023, doi: 10.3390/ma16247674.

[11] D. Sciti e A. Bellosi, «Laser Micromachining of Silicon Carbide», *Key Eng. Mater.*, vol. 206–213, pp. 305–308, dic. 2001, doi: 10.4028/www.scientific.net/KEM.206-213.305.

[12] D. H. Lowndes e R. F. Wood, «Studies of pulsed laser melting and rapid solidification using amorphous silicon», *J. Lumin.*, vol. 30, fasc. 1–4, pp. 395–408, feb. 1985, doi: 10.1016/0022-2313(85)90068-7.

[13] M. Vivona *et al.*, «Effects of Excimer Laser Irradiation on the Morphological, Structural, and Electrical Properties of Aluminum-Implanted Silicon Carbide (4H-SiC)», *ACS Appl. Electron. Mater.*, vol. 4, fasc. 9, pp. 4514–4520, set. 2022, doi: 10.1021/acsaelm.2c00748.

[14] C. Calabretta *et al.*, «Laser Annealing of P and Al Implanted 4H-SiC Epitaxial Layers», *Materials*, vol. 12, fasc. 20, p. 3362, ott. 2019, doi: 10.3390/ma12203362.

[15] M. Vivona *et al.*, «Exploring UV-Laser Effects on Al-Implanted 4H-SiC», *Solid State Phenom.*, vol. 342, pp. 85–89, mag. 2023, doi: 10.4028/p-6jg806.

[16] J. Jandeleit, A. Horn, R. Weichenhain, E. W. Kreutz, e R. Poprawe, «Fundamental investigations of micromachining by nano- and picosecond laser radiation», *Appl. Surf. Sci.*, vol. 127–129, pp. 885–891, mag. 1998, doi: 10.1016/S0169-4332(97)00762-9.

[17] M. Farsari, G. Filippidis, S. Zoppel, G. A. Reider, e C. Fotakis, «Efficient femtosecond laser micromachining of bulk 3C-SiC», *J. Micromechanics Microengineering*, vol. 15, fasc. 9, pp. 1786–1789, set. 2005, doi: 10.1088/0960-1317/15/9/022.

[18] Y. Dong e P. Molian, «In-situ formed nanoparticles on 3C–SiC film under femtosecond pulsed laser irradiation», *Phys. Status Solidi A*, vol. 202, fasc. 6, pp. 1066–1072, mag. 2005, doi: 10.1002/pssa.200420015.

[19] Y. Hishida, M. Watanabe, K. Nakashima, e O. Eryu, «Excimer Laser Annealing of Ion-Implanted 6H-Silicon Carbide», *Mater. Sci. Forum*, vol. 338–342, pp. 873–876, mag. 2000, doi: 10.4028/www.scientific.net/MSF.338-342.873.

[20] S. Urban e F. Falk, «Laser crystallization of amorphous SiC thin films on glass», *Appl. Surf. Sci.*,

vol. 184, fasc. 1–4, pp. 356–361, dic. 2001, doi: 10.1016/S0169-4332(01)00517-7.

[21] D. K. Basa, G. Ambrosone, U. Coscia, e A. Setaro, «Crystallization of hydrogenated amorphous silicon carbon films with laser and thermal annealing», *Appl. Surf. Sci.*, vol. 255, fasc. 10, pp. 5528–5531, mar. 2009, doi: 10.1016/j.apsusc.2008.09.042.

[22] A. Hedler, S. Urban, F. Falk, H. Hobert, e W. Wesch, «Excimer laser crystallization of amorphous silicon carbide produced by ion implantation», *Appl. Surf. Sci.*, vol. 205, fasc. 1–4, pp. 240–248, gen. 2003, doi: 10.1016/S0169-4332(02)01071-1.

[23] P. Baeri, C. Spinella, e R. Reitano, «Fast Melting of Amorphous Silicon Carbide Induced by Nanosecond Laser Pulse», *Int. J. Thermophys.*, vol. 20, fasc. 4, pp. 1211–1221, lug. 1999, doi: 10.1023/A:1022623424614.

[24] G. Ambrosone *et al.*, «Crystallization of hydrogenated amorphous silicon–carbon films by means of laser treatments», *Appl. Surf. Sci.*, vol. 247, fasc. 1–4, pp. 471–476, lug. 2005, doi: 10.1016/j.apsusc.2005.01.051.

EU PVSEC
European PV Solar Energy Conference and Exhibition

SiC recrystallization by UV nanopulsed laser annealing

Daniele Arduino

Supervisor: Prof. Luciano Scaltrito, Prof. Sergio Ferrero – Dr. Andrea Ancillao

Research context and motivation

The demand for sustainable energy is driving innovation in power electronics, with SiC as a key material thanks to its wide bandgap, high thermal conductivity and fast switching capabilities, making it ideal for next-gen photovoltaic devices [1]. Since SiC crystals are hard to produce, the crystallization of amorphous SiC by annealing can be an alternative solution [2]. Traditional furnace methods heat the entire device, risking damage to previously fabricated structures, therefore laser annealing was explored because it can heat locally, minimizing such effects [3]. While other studies used effective but costly excimer lasers, this research proposes a more compact, cost-efficient method using a DPSS Q-switched laser in vacuum. By optimizing parameters (frequency, power, pulse duration, scan speed), localized crystallization of amorphous SiC thin films was obtained, improving structural properties and supporting the development of SiC-based devices, especially for photovoltaics.

Adopted methodologies

Used samples

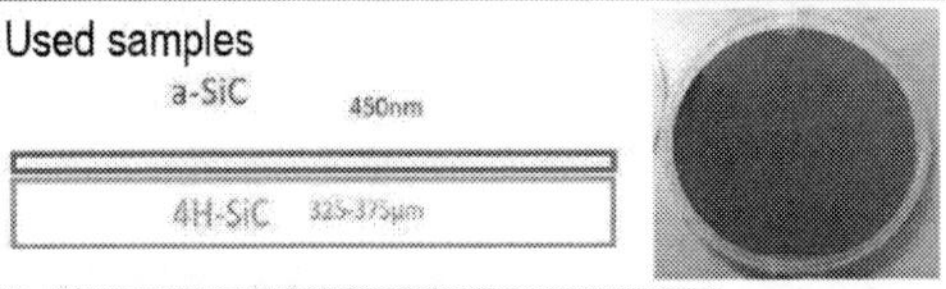

The experimental set up consisted in a **DPSS Q-switched laser (355 nm).** The calibration matrix of frequency and duty cycle was used to control the actual laser power delivered to sample:

Calibration matrix	10%	20%	30%	40%	50%	60%	70%	80% duty cycle
30 kHz	0,06	0,25	0,55	0,95	1,39	1,84	2,37	2,97
40 kHz	0,05	0,18	0,41	0,74	1,12	1,58	2,03	2,5
50 kHz	0,04	0,14	0,33	0,59	0,93	1,3	1,75	2,2
60kHz	0,04	0,12	0,27	0,5	0,77	1,12	1,48	1,95
70kHz	0,04	0,1	0,23	0,42	0,66	0,95	1,3	1,66
80kHz	0,03	0,09	0,2	0,36	0,58	0,84	1,16	1,47
90kHz	0,03	0,08	0,18	0,32	0,5	0,74	1,04	1,38
100kHz	0,03	0,08	0,16	0,28	0,47	0,65	0,92	1,37
freq								

Experimental setup

Annealing was performed under vacuum (~4.3×10^{-1} mbar, granted by a rotary vane vacuum pump) in a custom-designed chamber to ensure clean and controlled conditions. Multiple annealing lines were written by varying frequency, power, and scan speed. They were inspected through an optical microscope. The two most promising conditions were selected for transmission electron microscopy (TEM) analysis to assess crystallinity.

Results

Optical characterization allowed the identification of the best result, obtained with the following settings:

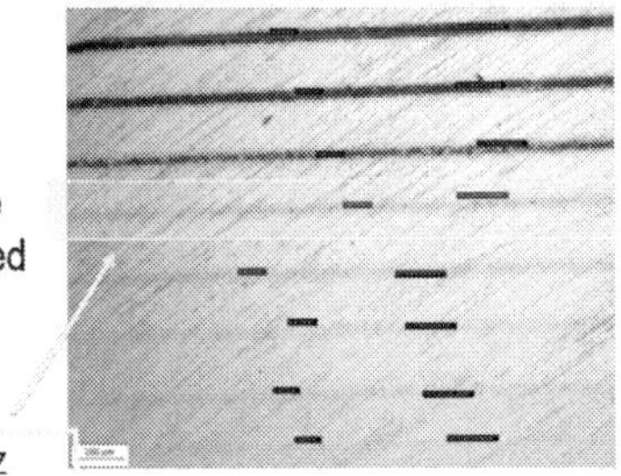

- Frequency: 70 kHz
- Pulse duration: 20,8 ns
- Duty cycle: 65%
- Power: 1.12 W
- Fluence: 0,32 J/cm²
- Scan speed: 100 mm/s

TEM analysis revealed **crystalline domains of 2–5 nm within the top 50 nm** of the film surface, indicating a localized polycrystalline crystallization with **random orientation**.

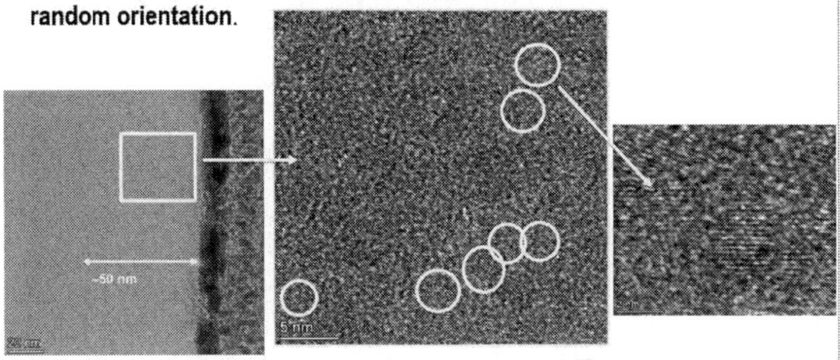

Future work

- Use **shorter-wavelength lasers** to improve annealing and SiC crystallization.
- Test **alternative SiC-like materials** to assess broader applicability
- **Optimize the process for full-wafer annealing**, enabling large-scale industrial use in photovoltaics and power electronics.

References

1. G. Foti, «Silicon carbide: from amorphous to crystalline material», *Appl. Surf. Sci.*, vol. 184, fasc. 1–4, pp. 20–26, dic. 2001, doi: 10.1016/S0169-4332(01)00751-6.
2. U. Coscia *et al.*, «Laser annealing study of PECVD deposited hydrogenated amorphous silicon carbon alloy films», *Appl. Surf. Sci.*, vol. 254, fasc. 4, pp. 984–988, dic. 2007, doi: 10.1016/j.apsusc.2007.08.003.
3. D. Arduino, S.Stassi, C.Spano, L.Scaltrito, S.Ferrero, V.Bertana, «Silicon and Silicon Carbide Recrystallization by Laser Annealing: A Review», *Materials*, vol. 16, fasc. 24, p. 7674, dic. 2023, doi: 10.3390/ma16247674

Politecnico di Torino

UNIVERSITÀ DEGLI STUDI DI SALERNO

PhD program in **Photovoltaics** 39th Cycle

PhD PV

EXPLORING THE CHARACTERISTICS ADDITION METHOD FOR ESTIMATING BIFACIAL EFFICIENCY IN $Cs_3Sb_2I_9$-BASED INDOOR PEROVSKITE SOLAR CELLS

Rajesh Kumar Sharma[1], Dhruv Singh Thakur[2], Deepak Joshi[3], Vivek Garg[4], Shivendra Yadav[5]
Department of Electronics Engineering, SVNIT, Surat, India
d21ec011@eced.svnit.ac.in[1], ds22ec001@eced.svnit.ac.in[2], d.joshi@eced.svnit.ac.in[3], vivekg@eced.svnit.ac.in[4], shivendra.y@eced.svnit.ac.in[5]

The rapid growth of Internet of Things (IoT) devices has increased the demand for efficient indoor photovoltaics (IPV). Lead-free perovskite-inspired materials (PIMs), such as $Cs_3Sb_2I_9$, offer a promising alternative to conventional lead-halide perovskites due to their favourable electronic properties and non-toxic nature. Despite their potential, the bifacial performance of $Cs_3Sb_2I_9$ for indoor light harvesting remains largely unexplored. This study investigates $Cs_3Sb_2I_9$ as an absorber material in a bifacial solar cell with the optimized architecture AZO/TNT/$Cs_3Sb_2I_9$/$SrCu_2O_2$/Ni, designed for a bandgap of 1.95 eV. The monofacial reference device achieves a power conversion efficiency (PCE) of 3.7% under a 1000 lux WLED spectrum. Unlike previous studies that primarily report bifaciality factors, this work focuses on bifacial efficiency estimation. Results indicate that using 'steel' as the rear surface yields the highest PCE of 67.24%, demonstrating the potential of $Cs_3Sb_2I_9$-based bifacial solar cells for high-performance IPV applications.

Keywords: Bifacial efficiency, Characteristics Addition, Sb-Perovskite, SCAPS-1D, UV-Vis spectroscopy.

1 INTRODUCTION

The increasing demand for self-powered wireless devices, particularly in indoor environments with varying light conditions, has driven the development of IPV as a promising energy solution. Indoor light sources, such as fluorescent lamps and white LEDs (WLEDs), provide spectral ranges between 400 and 800 nm [1], [2], with typical illuminance levels of 200 to 1000 lux [3], [4]. However, conventional crystalline silicon solar cells, with their narrow bandgap of 1.12 eV, are not well-suited for indoor applications. While lead-based perovskites offer high efficiency, they pose significant environmental concerns [5], [6], and tin-based alternatives suffer from stability issues [7]. PIMs, particularly those with an $A_3B_2X_9$ structure, present a promising alternative by addressing both toxicity and stability challenges. Among them, $Cs_3Sb_2I_9$, with a bandgap of 1.95 eV, has shown potential for indoor applications. However, its reported PCE remains low at 3.7%, primarily due to poor film morphology and suboptimal device structures. While theoretical studies suggest possible improvements, significant gaps remain in optimizing $Cs_3Sb_2I_9$ for practical IPV applications.

In our previous study, the optimized AZO/TNT/$Cs_3Sb_2I_9$/$SrCu_2O_2$/Ni structure achieved a maximum PCE of 38.77% under front-side illumination (from the AZO side) with WLED light. In this work, for the first time, the optimized device is illuminated from the Ni contact (rear-side), achieving PCE of 38.88% under WLED illumination. Since SCAPS-1D simulations are limited to illuminating light from either side of the device independently, alternative modeling strategies are required to accurately determine bifacial efficiency. This study explores the characteristic addition (CA) method [8], providing deeper insights into the bifacial potential of $Cs_3Sb_2I_9$-based solar cells.

2 AIM AND APPROACH

Figure 1(a) illustrates the baseline device structure, while Figure 1(b) presents the *JV* characteristics of the experimental and simulated models. The baseline model was optimized in SCAPS-1D by adjusting absorber thickness, defect density, doping concentration, and interface properties for improved accuracy [9]. The enhanced AZO/TNT/$Cs_3Sb_2I_9$/$SrCu_2O_2$/Ni device achieves a PCE of 38.77% under front-side (AZO-side) WLED illumination. For the first time, the device is illuminated from the Ni contact (rear-side), yielding PCE of 38.88%. Figure 1(c) presents the *JV* characteristics for both cases, with performance parameters summarized in Table I. As SCAPS-1D only simulates single-sided illumination, alternative modeling is required for bifacial efficiency estimation.

Table I: Performance parameters of the proposed indoor bifacial device under front- and rear-side illumination with 100% incident light intensity.

Illu. side	V_{OC} [V]	J_{SC} [mA cm^{-2}]	FF [%]	η [%]
Front	1.47	1.55	89.08	38.77
Rear	1.47	1.55	89.21	38.88

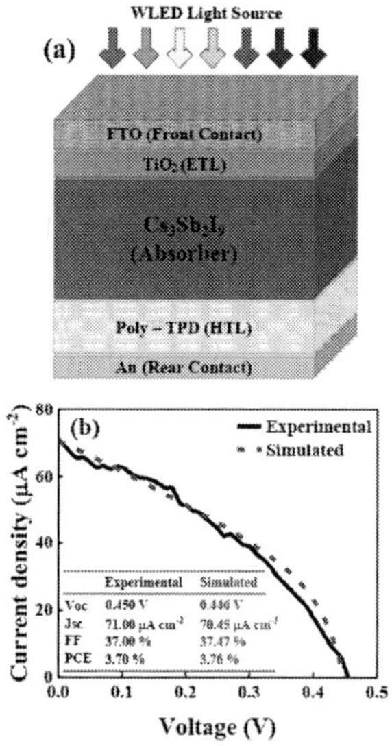

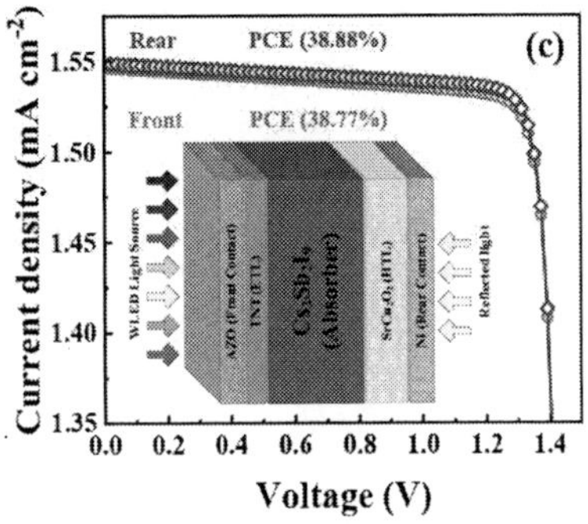

Figure 1: (a) Structure of the indoor monofacial device, (b) *J-V* characteristics of experimental and calibrated model, (c) proposed device with optimized front and rear-side *J-V* characteristics.

3 RESULTS AND DISCUSSION

In practical scenarios, bifacial solar cells are illuminated from both the front and rear sides simultaneously. However, due to SCAPS-1D's limitation to one-sided illumination, the bifacial *JV* characteristics are estimated using the CA method. In this method, the current densities for front and rear illumination, which include both light-generated and dark current components, are combined. To avoid double-counting the dark current, it is subtracted once, as shown by:

$$
\begin{aligned}
J_{bi}(V, P_f, P_r) \\
&= J_D(V) + J_{L,f}(P_f) + J_{L,r}(P_r) \\
&= J_f(V, P_f) + J_r(V, P_r) - J_D(V) \qquad (1)
\end{aligned}
$$

Here, J_{bi} represents the bifacial current density as a function of voltage (V), front illumination intensity (P_f), and rear illumination intensity (P_r), while J_f and J_r represent current densities under front and rear illumination, respectively.

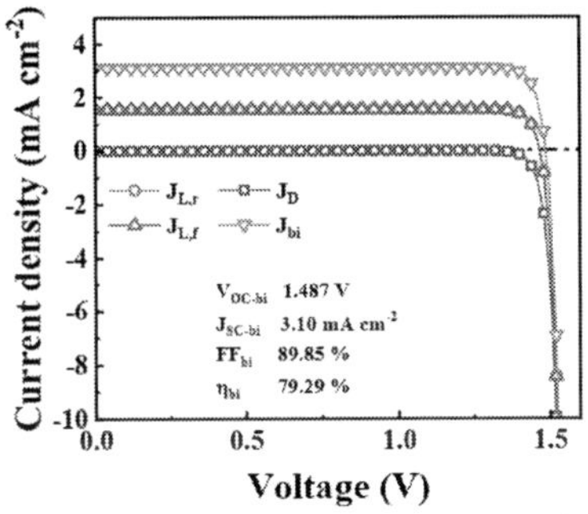

Figure 2: *J-V* characteristics of the proposed indoor bifacial device under dark conditions, rear and front illumination, along with the bifacial *J-V* curve estimated through the CA method.

Figure 2 presents the *JV* characteristics under dark conditions, front illumination, rear illumination, and the bifacial *JV* characteristics derived from the CA method with 100% illumination intensity. Under ideal conditions, with equal 100% illumination from both sides, the proposed bifacial solar cell achieves a PCE of 79.29%. However, since rear-side illumination primarily consists of reflected light, which is not 100% intense, the device's performance was also analyzed under reduced rear-side illumination. The results highlight the significant impact of varying rear-side illumination intensities on bifacial efficiency, underscoring the need to consider realistic operating conditions in bifacial solar cell designs.

The rear-side light intensity is varied from 0% to 50% of the total WLED illumination. Figure 3(a) shows the *JV* curves for different rear-side illumination levels, while Figures 3(b)-(c) display the corresponding performance parameters. The PCE increases from 38.77% with front-side illumination only to 58.93% when the rear-side receives 50% illumination.

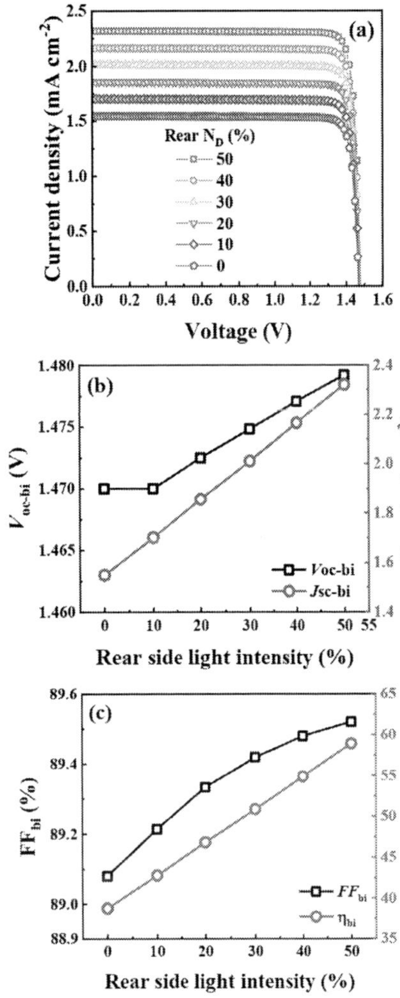

Figure 3: (a) *J-V* characteristics of the proposed bifacial device under varying rear illumination intensities, with N_D ranging from 0% to 50%, to analyze the device's behaviour, (b) $V_{OC\text{-}bi}$ and $J_{SC\text{-}bi}$ and (c) FF_{bi} and η_{bi} of the proposed device with N_D ranging from 0% to 50%.

The rear-side illumination varies with wavelength, influenced by the reflectance of indoor materials, as shown in Figure 4(a)-(b). This reflectance is measured using a UV-Vis fibre-optic spectrometer (Ocean Optics Inc.), as depicted in Figure 4(c). The measured reflectance spectrum acts as an optical filter, modifying the incident WLED light before it reaches the rear side of the device. To account for this effect, SCAPS-1D simulations are performed to extract the *JV* characteristics under rear-side illumination, incorporating the reflectance spectrum as a transmission filter.

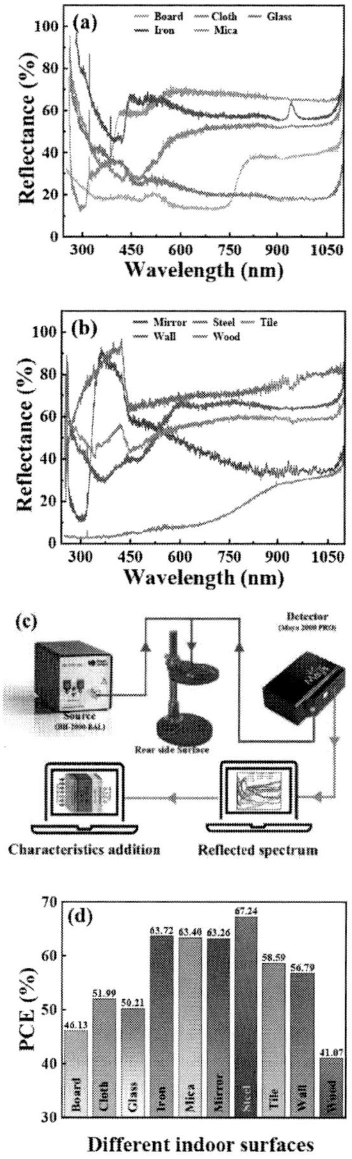

Figure 4: (a)-(b) Reflected spectra of different indoor surfaces, (c) schematic of the setup of bifacial parameter estimation, (d) bifacial PCE of the proposed device for different rear-side surfaces.

These *JV* characteristics are then combined with the front-side illumination *JV* characteristics using the CA method, which ensures accurate estimation of bifacial performance by eliminating redundant dark current components. The resulting bifacial *JV* characteristics are used to determine the efficiency of the proposed bifacial device under varying rear-side surfaces. As shown in Figure 4(d), the highest PCE of 67.24% is achieved when "steel" is used as the rear surface, demonstrating the significant influence of rear-side reflectance on device performance.

4 CONCLUSIONS

In conclusion, the bifacial efficiency of the proposed indoor bifacial device was estimated using the CA method, which combines *JV* characteristics from front and rear illumination while eliminating redundant dark current components. The method enabled precise evaluation of bifacial performance, revealing a maximum PCE of 79.29% under ideal conditions and 67.24% with steel as the rear surface. This study highlights the effectiveness of the CA method in modeling bifacial devices and underscores the importance of rear-side illumination and material reflectance in optimizing real-world performance.

ACKNOWLEDGMENTS

The authors would like to thank Marc Burgelman from ELSI at the University of Gent, Belgium, for providing the SCAPS-1D simulation software. They also acknowledge financial support from "SVNIT Surat" under Grant No. dean(R&C)/seed money/2021-22/10783 and "Divyasampark iHUB Roorkee for the Devices Materials and Technology Foundation" under Grant Nos. 4-371 and 4-372.

REFERENCE

[1] S. Biswas and H. Kim, "Solar Cells for Indoor Applications: Progress and Development," *Polymers 2020, Vol. 12, Page 1338*, vol. 12, no. 6, p. 1338, Jun. 2020, doi: 10.3390/POLYM12061338.

[2] B. P. Lechêne, M. Cowell, A. Pierre, J. W. Evans, P. K. Wright, and A. C. Arias, "Organic solar cells and fully printed super-capacitors optimized for indoor light energy harvesting," *Nano Energy*, vol. 26, pp. 631–640, Aug. 2016, doi: 10.1016/J.NANOEN.2016.06.017.

[3] K. W. Houser, "Something Happened on the Way to a Target Illuminance," *LEUKOS*, vol. 10, no. 1, pp. 1–2, 2014, doi: 10.1080/15502724.2014.841501.

[4] I. Mathews, S. N. Kantareddy, T. Buonassisi, and I. M. Peters, "Technology and Market Perspective for Indoor Photovoltaic Cells," *Joule*, vol. 3, no. 6, pp. 1415–1426, Jun. 2019, doi: 10.1016/J.JOULE.2019.03.026.

[5] F. Di Giacomo, A. Fakharuddin, R. Jose, and T. M. Brown, "Progress, challenges and perspectives in flexible perovskite solar cells," *Energy Environ Sci*, vol. 9, no. 10, pp. 3007–3035, Oct. 2016, doi: 10.1039/C6EE01137C.

[6] P. D. Dissanayake *et al.*, "Environmental impact of metal halide perovskite solar cells and potential mitigation strategies: A critical review," *Environ Res*, vol. 219, p. 115066, Feb. 2023, doi: 10.1016/J.ENVRES.2022.115066.

[7] L. Chen, S. Fu, Y. Li, N. Sun, Y. Yan, and Z. Song, "On the Durability of Tin-Containing Perovskite Solar Cells," *Advanced Science*, vol. 11, no. 1, p. 2304811, Jan. 2024, doi: 10.1002/ADVS.202304811.

[8] R. K. Sharma, H. Narsi Patel, D. Singh Thakur, V. Garg, and S. Yadav, "Investigating ASnI2Br wide bandgap tin perovskite for bifacial solar cells: Modeling of bifacial efficiency with comparative analysis," *Solar Energy*, vol. 283, p. 113017, Nov. 2024, doi: 10.1016/J.SOLENER.2024.113017.

[9] R. K. Sharma, R. Keshri, and S. Yadav, "Computational modeling of Cs3Sb2I9-based novel architecture under WLED illumination for indoor photovoltaic applications," *Optical and Quantum Electronics 2024 56:11*, vol. 56, no. 11, pp. 1–17, Nov. 2024, doi: 10.1007/S11082-024-07708-6.

Exploring the Characteristics Addition Method for Estimating Bifacial Efficiency in $Cs_3Sb_2I_9$-Based Indoor Perovskite Solar Cells

Rajesh Kumar Sharma, Dhruv Singh Thakur, Deepak Joshi, Vivek Garg, Shivendra Yadav

Department of Electronics Engineering, SVNIT, Surat-395007, India

2BV.1.47

Abstract

The rapid expansion of IoT devices has increased the need for efficient indoor photovoltaics (IPV). This study explores lead-free perovskite-inspired $Cs_3Sb_2I_9$ as a non-toxic absorber in a bifacial solar cell with the architecture AZO/TNT/$Cs_3Sb_2I_9$/$SrCu_2O_2$/Ni, optimized for a 1.95 eV bandgap. A monofacial reference device achieves 3.7% PCE under 1000 lux WLED. Unlike prior studies focused on bifaciality factors, we directly estimate bifacial efficiency, finding that a 'steel' rear surface yields a peak PCE of 67.24%, highlighting the strong potential of $Cs_3Sb_2I_9$-based bifacial solar cells for next-generation IPV systems.

Aim and approach

- Bifacial PSCs harvest light from both front and rear sides.
- SCAPS-1D supports only one-sided illumination.
- Adopted the Characteristics Addition (CA) method to model bifacial *J-V*.
- CA method avoids double-counting of dark current.
- *J-V* for front and rear illumination extracted separately under WLED.
- Indoor surface reflectance measured using UV-Vis fibre-optic spectrometer.
- Measured reflectance spectrum used as an optical filter in SCAPS-1D.

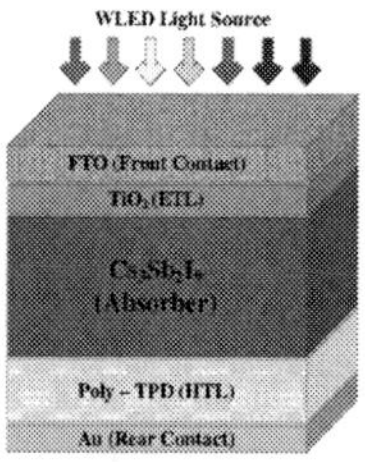

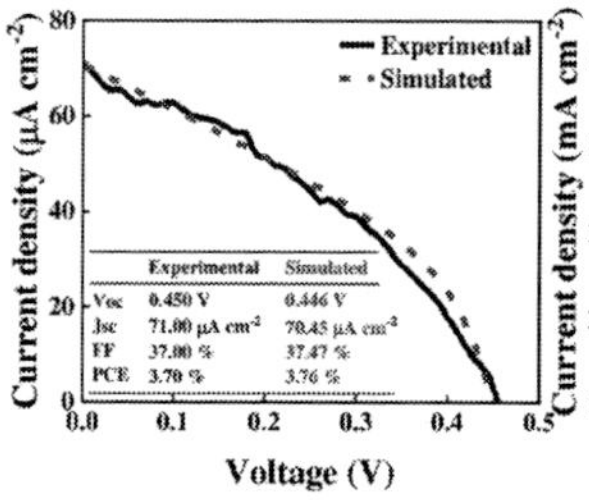

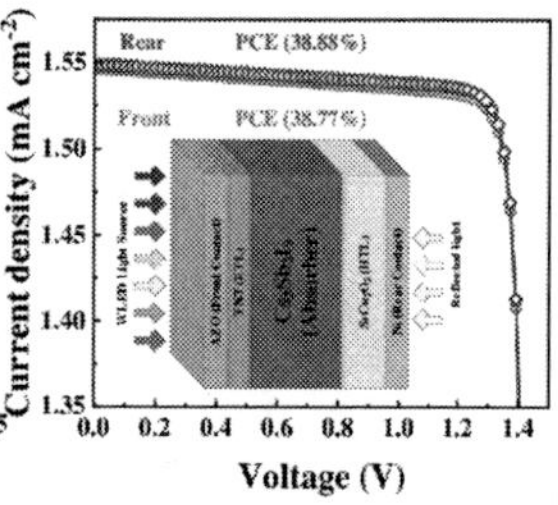

Result and Discussion

- **Ideal case:** With 100% light from both sides → PCE 79.29%.
- **Realistic case:** Rear-side illumination reduced due to reflectance.
- Simulated rear-side illumination from 0% to 50% of WLED.
- **Performance gain:**
  Front only → PCE 38.77% | Rear 50% → PCE 58.93%

Performance Parameters

Illumination side	V_{OC} [V]	J_{SC} [mA cm^{-2}]	FF [%]	η [%]
Front	1.47	1.55	89.08	38.77
Rear	1.47	1.55	89.21	38.88

Characteristics Addition Equation

$$J_{bi}(V, P_f, P_r) = J_D(V) + J_{L,f}(P_f) + J_{L,r}(P_r) = J_f(V, P_f) + J_r(V, P_r) - J_D(V)$$

- Rear illumination strongly boosts efficiency, even at partial levels.
- Reflectance spectrum (tiles, walls, surfaces) filters rear-side light.
- SCAPS simulations capture realistic bifacial behavior with filtered spectra.
- **Key insight:** Indoor bifacial PSC design must account for reflectance.

J-V characteristics at different rear side intensities

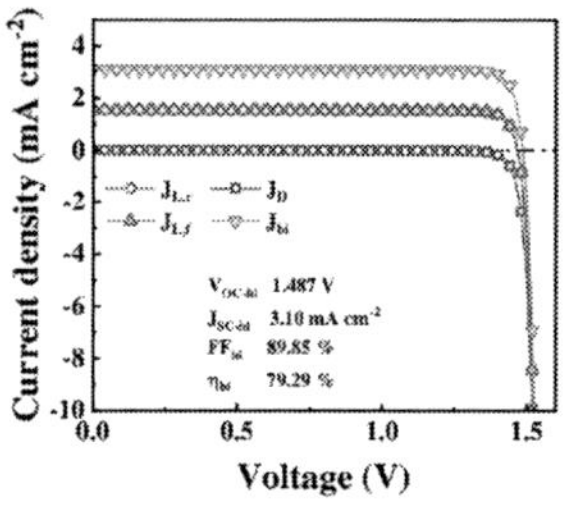

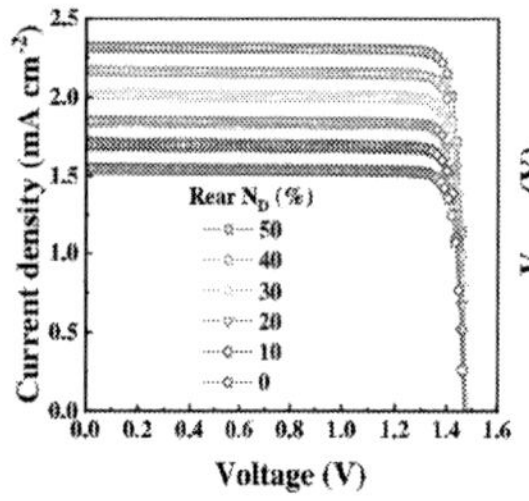

Performance parameters at different rear side intensity

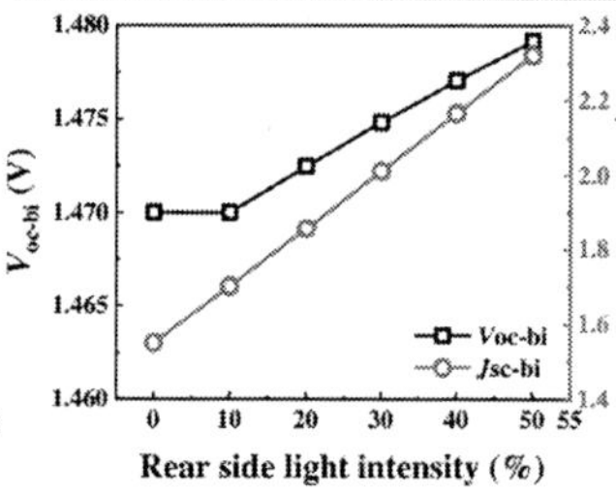

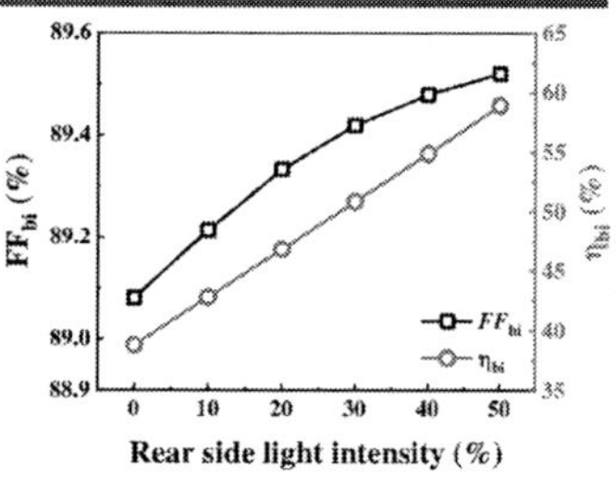

Reflectance extracted from UV-Vis Setup

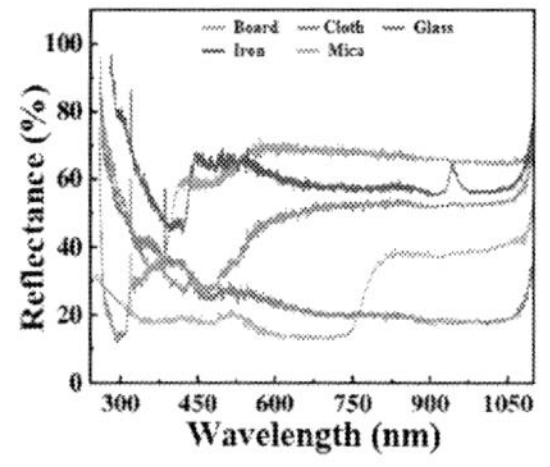

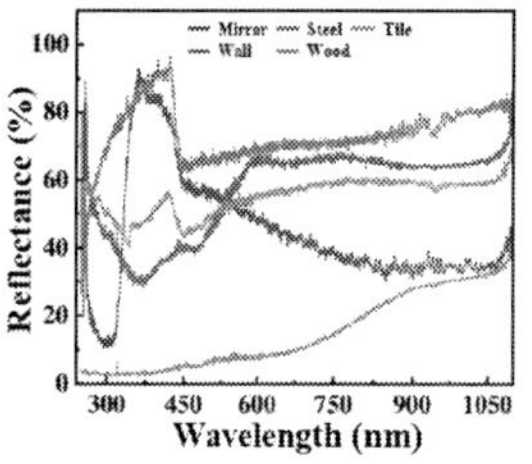

UV-Vis Setup

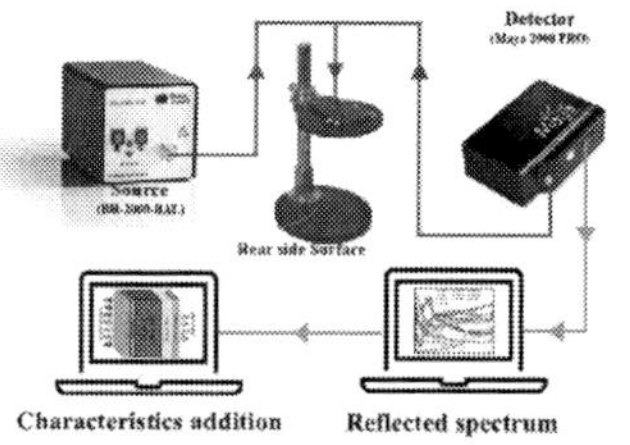

PCE at different rear surfaces

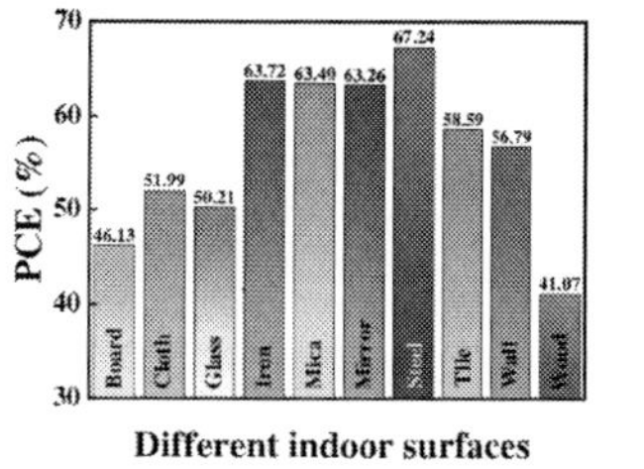

Conclusion

Using the characteristics Addition (CA) method, the bifacial device achieved up to 79.29% PCE (ideal) and 67.24% with a steel rear surface. The study highlights the CA method's accuracy and the critical role of rear-side illumination and reflective materials in enhancing indoor bifacial solar cell performance.

References

[1] R. K. Sharma, H. Narsi Patel, D. Singh Thakur, V. Garg, and S. Yadav, "Investigating ASnI2Br wide bandgap tin perovskite for bifacial solar cells: Modeling of bifacial efficiency with comparative analysis," *Solar Energy*, vol. 283, p. 113017, Nov. 2024, doi: 10.1016/J.SOLENER.2024.113017.

[2] R. K. Sharma, R. Keshri, and S. Yadav, "Computational modeling of Cs3Sb2I9-based novel architecture under WLED illumination for indoor photovoltaic applications," *Optical and Quantum Electronics* 2024 56:11, vol. 56, no. 11, pp. 1–17, Nov. 2024, doi: 10.1007/S11082-024-07708-6.

Acknowledgement

The authors would like to thank Marc Burgelman from ELSI at the University of Gent, Belgium, for providing the SCAPS-1D simulation software. They also acknowledge financial support from "SVNIT Surat" under Grant No. dean(R&C)/seed money/2021-22/10783 and "Divyasampark iHUB Roorkee for the Devices Materials and Technology Foundation" under Grant Nos. 4-371 and 4-372.

Optoelectronics2Application (O2A) Research Group

Contact Person: Dr. Vivek Garg, Assistant Professor,
Department of Electronics Engineering, SVNIT, Surat
Contact: +91 261-220-1707, Email: vivekg@eced.svnit.ac.in

CERTAINLY I-V MEASUREMENT OF THE PEROVSKITE DEVICE UNDER DIM LIGHT INTENSITY

Yean-San Long1*, Yung-Tsung Liu, Min-An Tsai, Cho-Fan Hsieh
Center for Measurement Standards, Industrial Technology and Research Institute, Hsinchu 300, Taiwan.
Contact information*: mickeylong88@itri.org.tw

ABSTRACT: The measured I-V hysteresis is complicated by the vast array of different perovskite solar cell (PSC) device architectures. In our study, we used a dynamic I-V, RTOS method, for I-V then the results showed better accuracy by eliminating in real time the acceptance effect. We also used this method with the testing procedure to compare emerging PV hysteresis behavior under dim light intensity of solar simulator. Therefore, we will compare difference between delay-time and RTOS method under dim light intensity, there are shown RTOS method more certainly I-V measurement of PSC under the dim light intensity.
Keywords: PSC, Solar cell, Intensity

1 AIM AND APPROACH

Emerging PV include organic photovoltaic (OPV), dye-sensitized solar cell (DSSC) and Perovskite solar cell (PSC). The operation principle of OPV/DSSC/PSC is using layers of organic molecules subject to lighting after excitation electronic then pass to the inorganic/organic layer of the wide energy gap nano-layer and voltage. The major differences between OPV/DSSC/PSC and p-n junction solar cells are spectrum, absorption range, photoelectric conversion response time and AM1.5G for standard test condition (STC), etc.

OPV/DSSC/PSC is a high potential product used for energy harvesting, especially in the context of indoor illumination applications. It is important to enhance the quality and reliability of such products, and to overcome the measurement error caused by capacity effect like hysteresis problem. Industry needs a relatively unified international test specifications to make the experimental data are reliable. Therefore, it is necessary to standardize I-V (current – voltage) and SR (spectrum response) and indoor lighting simulator test methods of measurement for OPV/DSSC/PSC.

Therefore, with increasing applications in consumer electronics such as smart phones, laptops and tablet PCs, the need for pervasive computing with a requirement of lower power consumption is increasing every day. This opens the door for energy harvesting that could charge the batteries in these devices to keep them continually functioning in some useful state. There has been a lot of attention on flexible thin film solar cells, such as perovskite solar cell (PSC), given their low-cost and improving efficiency. Performance characterization of PSCs has been investigated, in order to clarify how to determine their performance accurately. Accurate characterization of PSC requires level lighting consideration on each very slow temporal response in the I-V curves of the DSC are clearly dependent on the voltage sweep direction, even when the sweep time is the order of seconds [1][2]. Furthermore, the temporal response is dependent on different level lighting consideration. This analysis showed to improve accuracy, measurement should be real time removing capacitance effect with a Real-Time One-Sweep Method (RTOSM) [3]. Additionally, RTOSM will be useful to measuring cell performance more accurately and rapidly when evaluating solar cell performance..

2 SCIENTIFIC INNOVATION AND RELEVANCE

The samples are perovskite solar cells (PSCs). All sample size are 4 cm2. These I-V curves were carried out by Keithley Source Meter (Model 2651), and 3A solar simulator, meet IEC 60904, SEMI PV57 and SEMI PV69 requirements. Auto-adjustable light intensity (range from Dark to 1,200 W/m2) by homemade-LabVIEW based program, non-uniformity less than 2 % (at 20 cm x 20 cm), and temporal instability less than 2 %. During the I-V measurement in the dark and under solar simulator, the scan direction was forward and backward, the sample temperature should be stablized at 25 ℃ with a fluctuation of less than 1 ℃ and the irradiance intensity were determined using a reference cell (WPVS), respectively.

The bias voltage we applied in the I–V measurement is changed stepwise from Isc to Voc (forward) or in the reverse direction (backward, Voc to Isc). When there is capacitance effect occurs in different level lighting, this measurement process will produce as Fig. 2 of the phenomenon. Its shows the stepwise applied voltage around Voc in a step of 10 mV with 1 point/ms sampling-rate and the transient photocurrent responses of the PSC both in forward and backward scans. I-V measured by RTOS method during the real-time monitoring chart (see Fig. 1) can be removed the capacitance effect of forward/backward under different level lighting. The first advantage can monitor I-V immediately without capacitive effect, available as Fig.1. The other advantage of forward over to backward in I-V curve is very closely to unity, more accurately and rapidly when evaluating sample performance, Ex. Pmax/Isc/Voc/FF (see Fig.1). In Fig. 1, the time constant for equilibrium of PSCs can be estimated by the measurement of the transient photocurrent under the application of a stepwise-changed voltage, an overshot current appears immediately after an abrupt increase of applied voltage, and then the current gradually decreases to an equilibrium state. The response time, which relies on lighting level and property of device, is to decrease while increasing level lighting in the forward and to keep constant in the backward. Because the external biased potential can affect device difference caused by the conversion step like capacitance effect of forward/backward under different level lighting, available as Fig. 1. While using the way of fixed delay time to get the I-V curve, it will cause different set benchmarks, and not enough to achieve complete removal of measurement errors caused by capacitance effect [2, 3]

3 RESULTS (OR PRELIMINARY RESULTS) AND CONCLUSIONS

In this work, we follow the testing flow in [3, 4] in the I-V measure as discussed in reference [1, 2], RTOS method can read simultaneously multi-point forming step after taking the optimization stabilizing test at a point on the I-V curve. The measured performance of sample is highly responsive to the external measurement condition. A reliable evaluation report requires the measurement to be performed under proper condition and the details of the measurement should be clearly described in the report. A list of proposals [2, 4] for the measurement of sample is given below:

In this work, RTOS method can real-time remove the capacity effect from high to low level lighting for I-V successfully (Fig. 5 and Table 1) and proposes the forward/backward schematic reaction mechanism for PSC (Fig. 3). This mean backward scan has a saturation in HUMO and forward scan has a saturation in LUMO, and its response time is shown to increase while decreasing level lighting in the forward and to keep constant in the backward. Thus using the way of fixed delay time to get the I-V curve under high to low level lighting, it is not enough to achieve complete removal of measurement errors caused by capacitance effect [2, 3]. Results also demonstrated the influence from capacitance during the measurement of I-V curves by using a steady-state simulator. Therefore, RTOS method certainly plays the better role than delay time method to get more reasonable characteristics of PSCs (Fig. 5 and Table 1)..

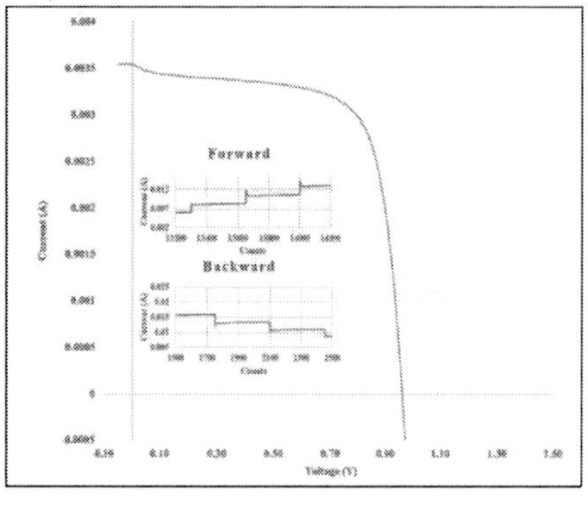

Fig. 1. Step-wised schematic of the RTOS method for I-V.

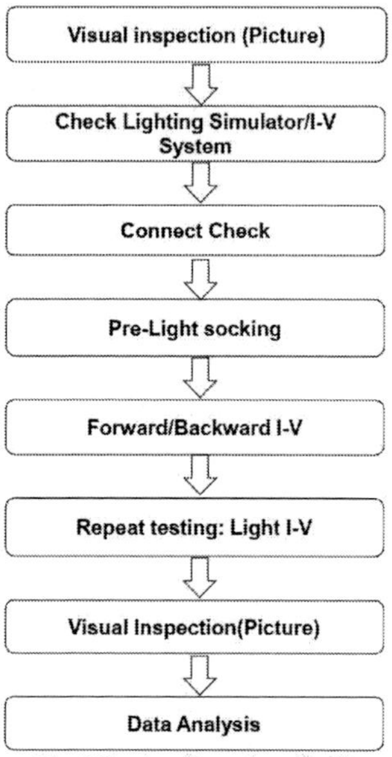

Fig. 2 Testing flow-chart [2, 5].

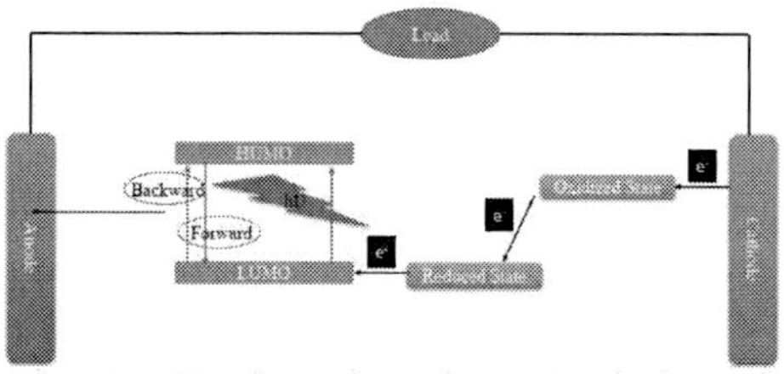

Fig. 3 Principle of operation and energy level scheme of the PSC device in forward/backward

4 References

[1] T. C. Wu, S. T. Hsu and Y. S. Long, "New Set-up Procedures and Integrated Measurement System for Organic Photovoltaic (OPV) Module", International Photovoltaic Science and Engineering Conference (PVSEC23), 2013.

[2] Y. S. Long, S. T. Hsu and T. C. Wu, "Induction of Internal Capacitance Effect in Performance Measurement of OPV (Organic Photovoltaic) Device by RTOSM (Real-Time One-Sweep Method)", Journal of Energy and Power Engineering, Vol 8, pp1059-1066, 2014.

[3] Y. S. Long, S. T. Hsu and T. C. Wu, "A Study of Capacitance Effect in DSC from High to Low Level Lighting by Real-Time One-Sweep Method", OPTIC2014.

[4] SEMI PV57-1214, Test Method for Current-Voltage (I-V) Performance Measurement of Organic Photovoltaic (OPV) and Dye-Sensitized Solar Cell (DSSC).

[5] US PTO. 8224598, Method for forming optimal characteristic curves of solar cell and system thereof.

工業技術研究院 Industrial Technology Research Institute
42nd European Photovoltaic Solar Energy Conference and Exhibition
42nd EU PVSEC
23 Sept. 2025
2BV.1.48
EU PVSEC

Certainly I-V measurement of the perovskite device under dim light intensity

Yean-San Long[1*], Yung-Tsung Liu[1], **Min-An Tsai**[1], Cho-Fan Hsieh
Industrial Technology Research Institute (ITRI)[1]
*mickeylong88@itri.org.tw

ABSTRACT

The measured I-V hysteresis is complicated by the vast array of different perovskite solar cell (PSC) device architectures. In our study, we used a dynamic I-V, RTOS method, for I-V then the results showed better accuracy by eliminating in real time the acceptance effect. We also used this method with the testing procedure to compare emerging PV hysteresis behavior under dim light intensity of solar simulator. Therefore, we will compare difference between delay-time and RTOS method under dim light intensity, there are shown RTOS method more certainly I-V measurement of PSC under the dim light intensity.

The bias voltage we applied in the I–V measurement is changed stepwise from Isc to Voc (forward) or in the reverse direction (backward, Voc to Isc). When there is capacitance effect occurs in different level lighting, this measurement process will produce as Fig. 2 of the phenomenon. Its shows the stepwise applied voltage around Voc in a step of 10 mV with 1 point/ms sampling-rate and the transient photocurrent responses of the PSC both in forward and backward scans. I-V measured by RTOS method during the real-time monitoring chart (see Fig. 1) can be removed the capacitance effect of forward/backward under different level lighting. The first advantage can monitor I-V immediately without capacitive effect, available as Fig.1. The other advantage of forward over to backward in I-V curve is very closely to unity, more accurately and rapidly when evaluating sample performance, Ex. Pmax/Isc/Voc/FF (see Fig.1). In Fig. 1, the time constant for equilibrium of PSCs can be estimated by the measurement of the transient photocurrent under the application of a stepwise-changed voltage, an overshot current appears immediately after an abrupt increase of applied voltage, and then the current gradually decreases to an equilibrium state. The response time, which relies on lighting level and property of device, is to decrease while increasing level lighting in the forward and to keep constant in the backward. Because the external biased potential can affect device difference caused by the conversion step like capacitance effect of forward/backward under different level lighting, available as Fig. 1. While using the way of fixed delay time to get the I-V curve, it will cause different set benchmarks, and not enough to achieve complete removal of measurement errors caused by capacitance effect.

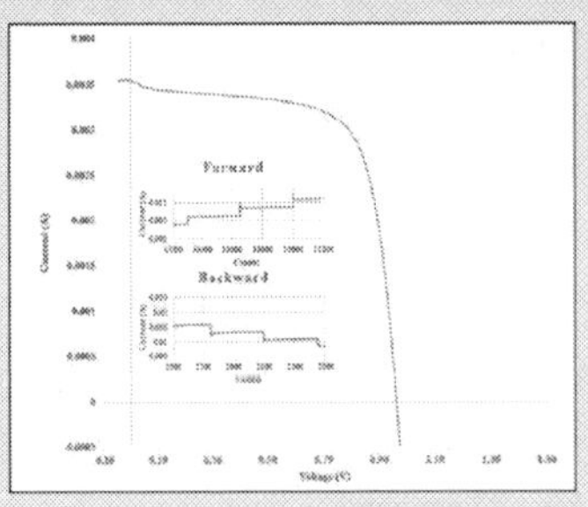

Figure 1: Step-wised schematic of the RTOS method for I-V

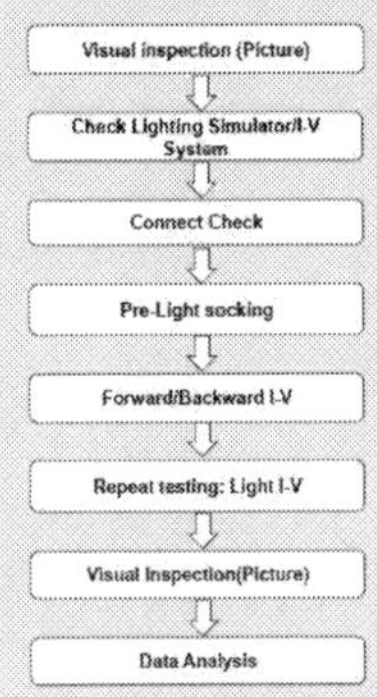

Figure 2: Testing flow-chart

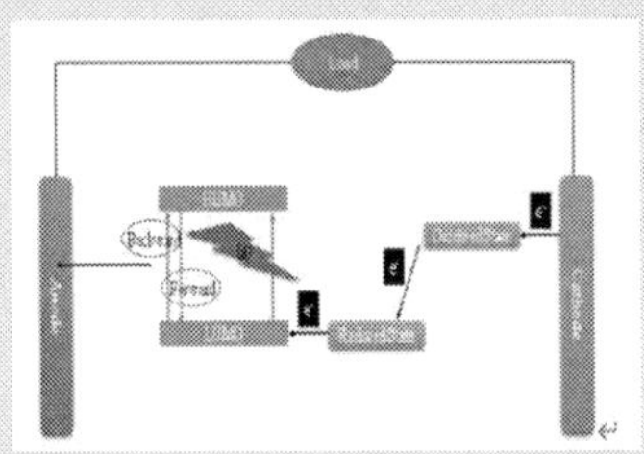

Figure 3: Principle of operation and energy level scheme of the PSC device in forward/backward

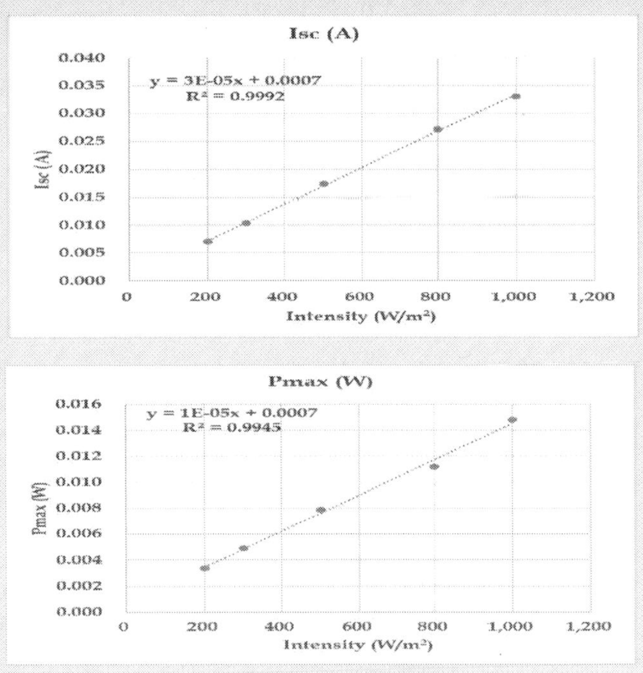

Figure 5: Isc/Pmax under dim lighting.

Conclusions

In this work, RTOS method can real-time remove the capacity effect from high to low level lighting for I-V successfully (Fig. 5) and proposes the forward/backward schematic reaction mechanism for PSC (Fig. 3). This mean backward scan has a saturation in HUMO and forward scan has a saturation in LUMO, and its response time is shown to increase while decreasing level lighting in the forward and to keep constant in the backward. Thus using the way of fixed delay time to get the I-V curve under high to low level lighting, it is not enough to achieve complete removal of measurement errors caused by capacitance effect. Results also demonstrated the influence from capacitance during the measurement of I-V curves by using a steady-state simulator. Therefore, RTOS method certainly plays the better role than delay time method to get more reasonable characteristics of PSCs (Fig. 5).

INVESTIGATION OF CD-FREE SB2SE3 THIN-FILM SOLAR CELLS BY ALD-ZNSNO ELECTRON TRANSPORT LAYER

Luna Lázaro-Castrillón[1], Yudania Sánchez[2], David Payno[3], Umair Razi[2], Victor Bonal[3], Fátima Cabello[1], Beatriz Galiana[4], Alejandro Pérez-Rodríguez[2], José Manuel Merino[3], Raquel Caballero[1,*]
[1]Instituto de Óptica Daza de Valdés-CSIC, C/ Serrano 121, 28006 Madrid, Spain
[2]IREC, Catalonia Institute for Energy Research, C/ Jardins de les Dones de Negre 1, Barcelona 08930, Spain
[3]Universidad Autónoma de Madrid, C/ Francisco Tomás y Valiente 7, 28049 Madrid, Spain
[4]Universidad Carlos III de Madrid, Avda. Universidad 40, 28911 Leganés, Madrid, Spain
*raquel.caballero@csic.es

ABSTRACT: Most of the efficient Sb_2Se_3-based PV devices use CdS as electron transport layer (ETL) or/and an organic hole transport layer. With the objective of fabricating non-toxic and stable solar cells, we investigate substrate Sb_2Se_3 thin-film PV devices by the replacement of CdS by $Zn_{1-x}Sn_xO$ (ZTO) layer without using an organic material in the device structure. In this work, Sb_2Se_3 thin films have been grown by selenization of evaporated Sb layer onto Mo/SLG substrates. ZTO films are fabricated by atomic layer deposition (ALD) to develop Cd-free solar cells, while the reference CdS layer is deposited by chemical bath. The absorber presents an orthorhombic structure with [hk1] preferred orientation, and a compact structure free of pinholes. The different techniques used for the fabrication of the ETLs show the different CdS and ZTO morphologies, with a conformal growth and uniform surface for the ZTO. ITO/ZnO/CdS/Sb_2Se_3/Mo/SLG and ITO/ZnO/ZnSnO/Sb_2Se_3/Mo/SLG solar cells are fabricated. A total efficiency of 4.3 % for the CdS/Sb_2Se_3 solar cell and of 3.0 % for the Cd-free PV device are obtained. It is revealed that ZTO thickness is a critical parameter to optimize the heterojunction. In this work, 40 nm ZTO layer leads to higher device performances.

Keywords: Sb_2Se_3, ZnSnO, thin-film solar cells, chalcogenides

1 INTRODUCTION

Low-dimensional antimony-chalcogenide materials have received an outstanding interest for photovoltaic (PV) devices in the last years. They show high stability, low environmental impact, low cost, low carbon footprint and high technological flexibility. In particular, Sb_2Se_3 shows a high absorption coefficient > 10^5 cm^{-1}, allowing to reduce the film thickness to 50-500 nm, band gap energy E_g of around 1.2 eV, and, a much lower melting point than that of CIGSe, CdTe and CZTSSe, requiring lower processing temperatures. Nowadays, efficiencies above 10% have already been achieved for Sb_2Se_3-based solar cells [1]. However, most of the Sb_2Se_3-based thin-film solar cells use CdS as ETL and/or an organic material as hole transport layer (HTL).

In this work, we fabricate sustainable Sb_2Se_3-based PV devices using only inorganic materials avoiding the use of CdS. ZTO has attracted significant attention for its non-toxic and earth-abundant constituent elements, large and tunable band gap, and good control over the conduction band offset between the active and ETL layer. Here, Sb_2Se_3 thin films are grown by selenization of evaporated Sb layer. ZTO thin films fabricated by ALD are used as non-toxic ETL of the Sb chalcogenide solar cells. Total area efficiencies of 3.0 % are achieved for the Cd-free Sb_2Se_3 solar cells, and, these devices are compared with the standard CdS/Sb_2Se_3.

2 EXPERIMENTAL DETAILS

2.1 Sb_2Se_3 absorber layer growth

Sb_2Se_3 thin films were grown by selenization of Sb evaporated layers onto Mo/SLG substrates. Sb layers with different thicknesses were evaporated, resulting in Sb_2Se_3 films of around 400 and 800 nm after the selenization. The selenization process was carried out in a tubular furnace under Ar atmosphere using elemental Se at temperature of 340 °C for one hour.

2.2 Device fabrication

CdS layer was deposited by chemical bath (CBD) at 70 °C for 40 minutes [2]. The CdS layer presents a band gap energy of 2.4 eV. $Zn_{1-x}Sn_xO$ layer was grown by ALD using TDMASn and DEZ precursors. Varying the number of cycles, ZTO layers with thicknesses of 20, 40 and 60 nm were produced. The composition was slightly varied from x=[Sn]/([Sn]+[Zn]) = 0.25 to 0.33. A window layer composed of i-ZnO (50 nm) and In_2O_3:SnO_2 (ITO) (200 nm) layers was deposited by RF-pulsed sputtering deposition. Neither grids nor an anti-reflection coating were deposited onto the final photovoltaic devices. Moreover, no thermal treatment was performed to the solar cells.

2.5 Characterization techniques

Grazing incidence X-ray diffraction (GIXRD) was performed to study the structural properties of the chalcogenide thin films and to identify the different phases. GIXRD data were collected with a PANAlytical X'Pert Pro MPD diffractometer, using CuK_α radiation and a multilayer mirror to produce a parallel beam. Detector scans with incident angle of 4° were carried out. The morphology of the ETL/Sb_2Se_3/Mo/glass structure was analysed by SEM using a SEM FEI VERIOS 460, operating at 2 kV. EDX depth profile was performed in a Talos F200X field emission TEM/STEM operating at 200 keV with four symmetrical EDX detectors. Spectral reflectance of the completed PV devices was measured in the spectral range from 300 to 1200 nm with wavelength step of 10 nm using a VASE Woollam ellipsometer.

Current-Voltage (*I-V*) characteristics of the photovoltaic devices were measured by using a Sun 3000

10.4229/EUPVSEC2025/2BV.2.1

class solar simulator (Abet Technologies Inc., Milford, Connecticut, USA) under standard test conditions (25°C, AM 1.5, 100 mW/cm^2). External quantum efficiency (*EQE*) of the solar cells was measured using a Bentham PVE300 system (Bentham Instruments Ltd., Berkshire, UK) calibrated with a Si and Ge photodiodes.

3 RESULTS AND DISCUSSION

3.1 Sb_2Se_3 thin films

Fig. 1.a. shows the X-ray diffraction patterns of Sb_2Se_3 thin film using grazing incidence angle of 4°. The absorber or active layer exhibits an orthorrombic crystal structure (JCPDS # 00-015-0861). Mo diffraction peaks are also detected and the formation of $MoSe_2$ phase cannot be ruled out. The texture coefficients (TC) of the main (hk0) and (hk1) planes in the range of 10 ° to 60 ° of the Sb_2Se_3 absorber layer were calculated (see Fig. 1.b.). Sb_2Se_3 thin film presents preferential orientation in the [hk1] direction, which is beneficial for the carrier's transport [3].

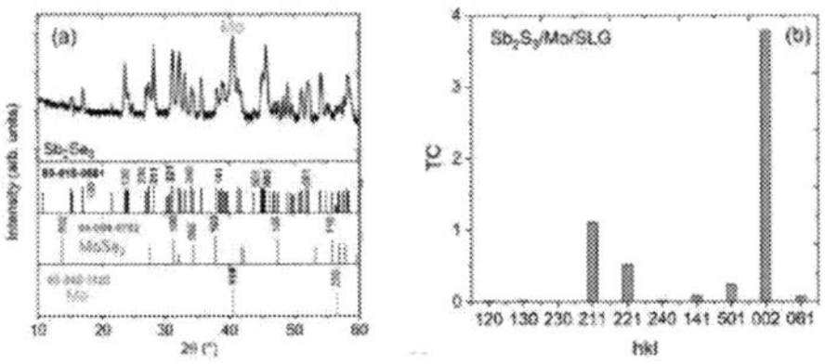

Figure 1: (a) XRD pattern using GI angle of 4° and (b) XRD texture coefficient (TC) of Sb_2Se_3 thin film grown on Mo/SLG.

Fig. 2.a. and 2.b. show the surface of the Sb_2Se_3 and the cross-sectional SEM picture of Sb_2Se_3/Mo structure. A smooth surface and a compact back interface structure free of pinholes is formed. EDX depth profile of Sb, Se and Mo is performed to investigate the elements distribution at the back region (see Fig.2.c.). A thin $MoSe_2$ layer seems to be formed at the Sb_2Se_3/Mo interface, as reported in [3].

Figure 2: (a) Surface of the absorber layer, (b) cross-sectional SEM picture of Sb_2Se_3/Mo structure and (c) EDX depth profile of Mo, Sb and Se elements at the back interface.

3.2 Sb_2Se_3-based PV devices

Fig. 3 shows the surface of both ETLs used in this work, CdS and ZTO, as well as the cross-sectional SEM picture of the ETL/Sb_2Se_3 interfaces. It is clear that the morphology of the ETLs is very different. ZTO layer is characterized by a conformal growth and very uniform surface, related to the ALD technique. In both cases, the Sb_2Se_3 thin films are well covered by the ETLs.

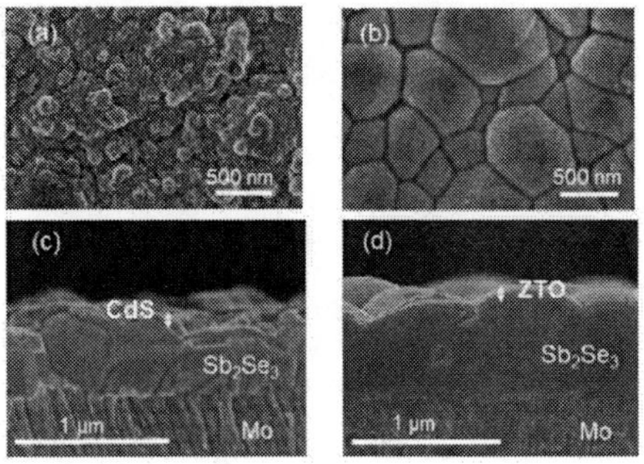

Figure 3: Surface of (a) CdS and (b) ZTO layers, and, (c) and (d) cross-sectional SEM picture of ETL/Sb_2Se_3 interfaces.

Table I shows the PV parameters of the best solar cells fabricated using CdS and ZTO as ETLs and two different thicknesses of Sb_2Se_3 absorber layer. The [Sn]/([Sn]+[Zn]) (TTZ) atomic ratio and thickness of the ZTO layer is also displayed. Open circuit voltage V_{OC} and fill factor FF are much higher for the devices using CdS, leading to higher efficiencies. It is clear that the variation of the ZTO thickness has an important impact on the short circuit current density J_{SC} and the FF of the devices. The increase of the ZTO thickness from 40 to 60 nm leads to a lower J_{SC} and FF, resulting in a lower device performance in the Series of 400 nm Sb_2Se_3. However, in the Series of 800 nm Sb_2Se_3, the reduction from 40 to 20 nm ZTO thickness produced a significant decrease of solar cell efficiency from 3.0 to 1.8 % related to the lower J_{SC} and FF due to a higher series resistance R_s. On the other hand, the slight variation of the TTZ atomic ratio, from 0.25 to 0.33, has not an influence on the PV parameters. Although promising results are achieved, Cd-free PV devices present lower device performances than those produced using CdS as ETL. Luo et al. [4] achieved a device performance of 3.44 % (V_{OC} = 364 mV, J_{SC} = 23.23 mA/cm^2 and FF = 40.63 %) for [Sn]/([Sn]+[Zn]) atomic ratio of 0.43 with the ZTO layer grown by co-sputtering. It is necessary to investigate higher [Sn]/([Sn]+[Zn]) atomic ratios than the used in the present work to optimise the band alignment of the heterointerface and improve device performance [3].

Fig. 4 shows the J-V characteristics of some of the solar cells of Table 1. In any case, a cross-over effect is observed, being clear that the interfaces are not yet fully optimized. As mentioned above, the formation of a thin $MoSe_2$ layer takes place at the back interface, that normally allows for a good ohmic contact and an improved carrier's transport. This is an indication that the heterojunction has to be improved.

Table I: PV parameters of the best solar cells using CdS and ZTO as ETLs, composition and thickness of the ZTO layers.

Sb_2Se_3 (nm)	ETL	[Sn]/([Sn]+[Zn])	ETL (nm)	V_{OC} (mV)	J_{SC} (mA/cm^2)	FF (%)	η (%)	R_s ($\Omega\cdot cm^2$)	R_{sh} ($\Omega\cdot cm^2$)
400	CdS	-	60	373	21.9	50.8	4.2	2.5	96.3
	ZTO	0.33	40	297	20.4	42.7	2.6	3.5	56.2
	ZTO	0.33	60	303	18.2	40.5	2.2	4.5	59.4
800	CdS	-	60	411	20.1	51.6	4.3	5.3	260.0
	ZTO	0.25	20	367	15.2	31.5	1.8	10.6	47.5
	ZTO	0.25	40	344	19.6	45.1	3.0	4.3	117.6
	ZTO	0.33	40	348	20.0	43.7	3.0	4.4	113.9

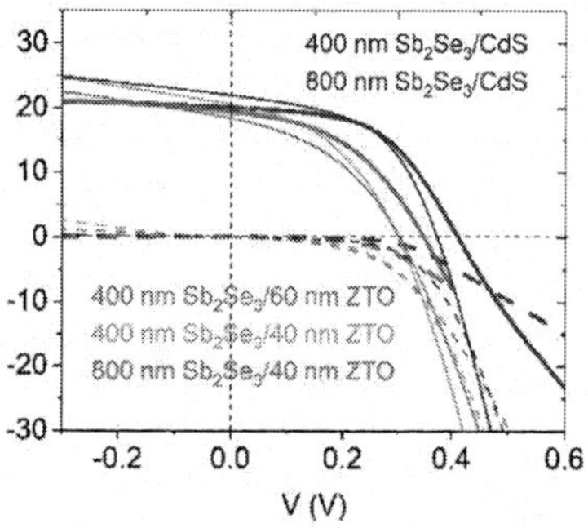

Figure 4: J-V characteristics of PV devices using CdS and ZTO as electron transport layers. All the ZTO layers presented a TTZ atomic ratio of 0.33.

Fig. 5 displays the external quantum efficiency (EQE) of representative Sb_2Se_3-based solar cells. A higher spectral response is measured at short wavelength range for the Cd-free solar cells related to a higher band gap energy of the ZTO layer of around 3.4 eV, while the CdS presents a band gap energy of 2.4 eV. The Cd-free PV devices are characterised by a lower spectral response starting from 550 nm, and a higher EQE is obtained for the case of thinner Sb_2Se_3 layer. Specular reflectance was measured for the PV devices. The Cd-free devices show a higher specular reflectance, being higher when the ZTO layer is thicker, of 60 nm (see inside Fig. 5), which in part is related to a rougher surface. Internal quantum efficiency (IQE) has been also plotted in Fig. 5.

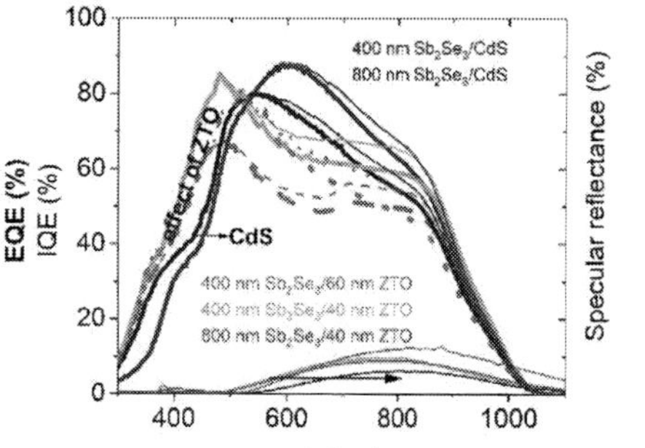

Figure 5: External (thicker line) and internal (thinner line) quantum efficiency measurements of the most representative PV devices. Specular reflectance of the completed devices is also plotted.

4 CONCLUSIONS

Cd-free Sb_2Se_3-based solar cells have been fabricated. Sb_2Se_3 thin films have been grown by a two-stage process, evaporation of Sb layer followed by a selenization process. Sb_2Se_3 single phase orthorhombic crystal structure oriented in the [hk1] is formed on Mo/SLG with a compact structure, free of pinholes. A comparison between Cd-free PV devices and using CdS as ETL is performed. The morphology of both ETLs is very different, outstanding the conformal growth and uniform surface of ZTO deposited by ALD. It is shown that the ZTO thickness is a key parameter to control the heterointerface. In this work, 40 nm of ZTO is the thickness that allows for higher performance. A higher spectral response in the range of the short wavelengths is obtained when using ZTO due to its higher band gap energy of 3.4 eV, and a lower quantum efficiency starting from 500 nm is measured related to the higher reflectance in this range. Although a high performance is achieved when using CdS, first promising results are obtained with ZTO deposited by ALD with a maximum total efficiency of 3.0 %. A further optimization of the composition and optical properties of the ZTO layer and the ZTO/Sb_2Se_3 band alignment will be the objective of a future work to enhance the Cd-free Sb_2Se_3 device performance.

Acknowledgments

This work was supported by SUNLIFE (PCI2024 155033-2) project funded by MICIU/AEI/10.13039/501100011033/UE, ASSESS (TED2021-129666B-C21 and TED2021-129666B-C22) project funded by MCIN/AEI/10.13039/501100011033 and by the "European Union Next Generation EU/PRTR" and InnoPV (PID 2022-140226OB-C3) funded by MICIU/AEI/10.13039/501100011033 and by "FEDER/UE". We also acknowledge the service from the MiNa Laboratory at IMN-CSIC, and funding from CM (project S2018/NMT-4291 TEC2SPACE), MINECO (project CSIC13-4E-1794) and EU (FEDER, FSE).

References

[1] Y. Zhao, S. Wang, Ch. Li, B. Che, X. Chen, H. Chen, R. Tang, X. Wang, G. Chen, T. Wang, J. Gong, T. Chen, X. Xiao, J. Li, Y. Zhao et al., Energy Environ. Sci. 15 (2022) 5118.

[2] M. Neuschitzer, Y, Sánchez, S. López-Marino, H. Xie, A. Fairbrother, M. Placidi, S. Haass, V. Izquierdo-Roca, A. Pérez-Rodríguez, E. Saucedo, Progress in Photovoltaics: Research and Applications 23(11) (2015)1660.

[3] X. Wen, Z. Lu, X. Yang, Ch. Chen, M.A. Washington, G.G. Wang, J. Tang, Q. Zhao, T.M. Lu, ACS Appl. Mater.

Interfaces 15 (2023) 22251.
[4] Y.D. Luo, M. Chen, R. Tang, M. Azam, S. Chen, Z.H. Zheng, Z.H. Su, P. Fan, H.L. Ma, G.X. Liang, X.H. Zhang, Solar Energy Materials and Solar Cells 240 (2022) 111721.

Investigation of Cd-free Sb_2Se_3 thin-film solar cells by ALD-$Zn_{1-x}Sn_xO$ electron transport layer

IO CSIC

Luna Lázaro-Castrillón[1], Yudania Sánchez[2], David Payno[3], Umair Razi[2], Víctor Bonal[3], Fátima Cabello[1], Beatriz Galiana[4], Alejandro Pérez-Rodríguez[2], José Manuel Merino[3], Raquel Caballero[1,*]

[1]Instituto de Óptica-CSIC, Madrid, Spain
[2]IREC, Barcelona, Spain
[3]Universidad Autónoma de Madrid, Madrid, Spain
[4]Universidad Carlos III de Madrid, Madrid, Spain

UAM Universidad Autónoma de Madrid

IREC

uc3m Universidad Carlos III de Madrid

*raquel.caballero@csic.es

Motivation

- Sb_2Se_3 is a promising candidate as an absorber material for thin-film solar cells due to its suitable band gap (1.2 eV), high absorption coefficient (>10^5 cm^{-1}), quasi 1D structure, high stability and low deposition temperature.
- The earth-abundant and non-toxic nature of its elements positions Sb_2Se_3 as a sustainable alternative to conventional photovoltaic materials.
- Sustainable PV devices require the replacement of CdS to avoid its toxicity and the use of inorganic materials to assure its stability.

Objective: Investigation of sustainable Sb_2Se_3-based substrate solar cells, replacing CdS by $Zn_{1-x}Sn_xO$ (ZTO) grown by atomic layer deposition (ALD).

Experimental details

Sb_2Se_3 absorber layer by a two-stage process

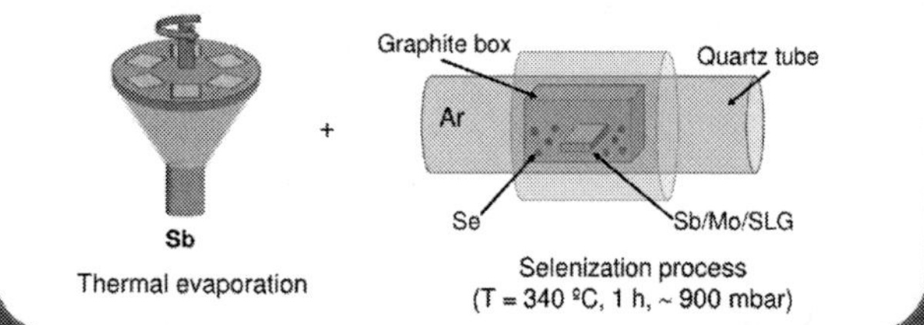

Solar cell devices

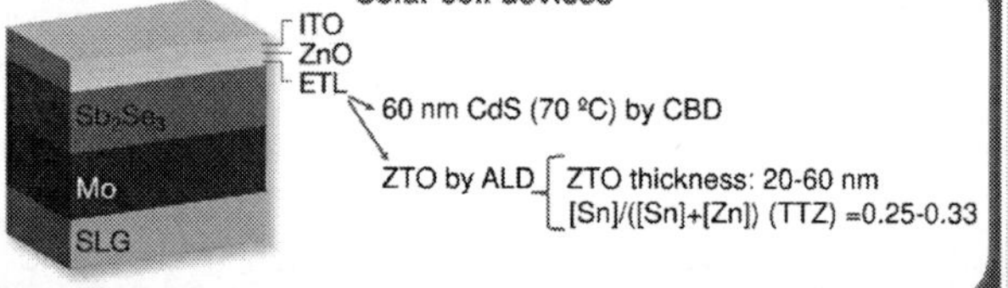

Characterization: XRD, SEM, EDX, Reflectance (R), JV, QE.

Sb_2Se_3 absorber layer

GIXRD

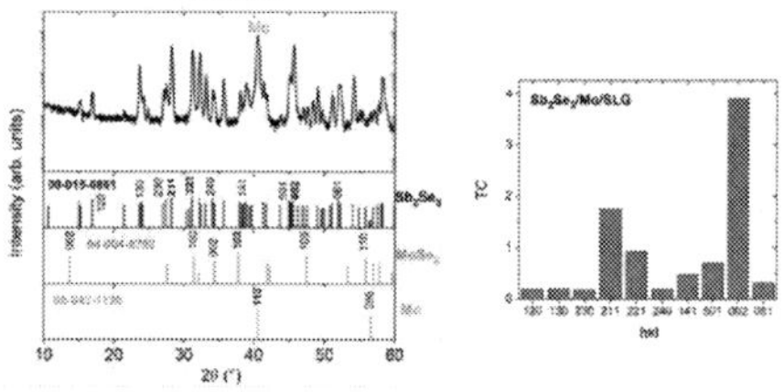

- Sb_2Se_3: Orthorhombic crystal structure with preferential orientation in the [kk1] direction, optimal for the carriers transport.

Surface and cross-sectional SEM

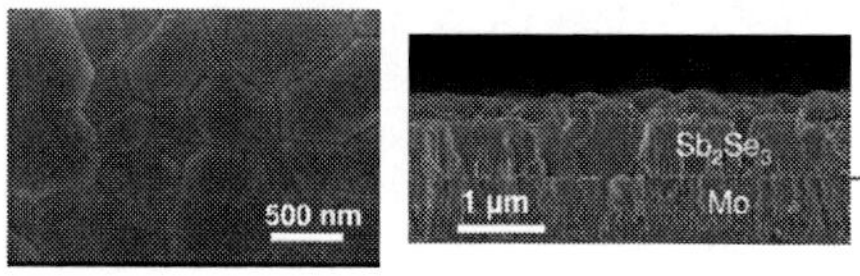

- Compact Sb_2Se_3/Mo structure, free of pinholes.

EDX depth profile

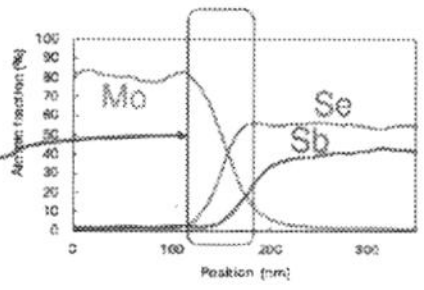

- $MoSe_2$ layer at the back interface.

Sb_2Se_3–based PV devices

Surface and cross-sectional SEM

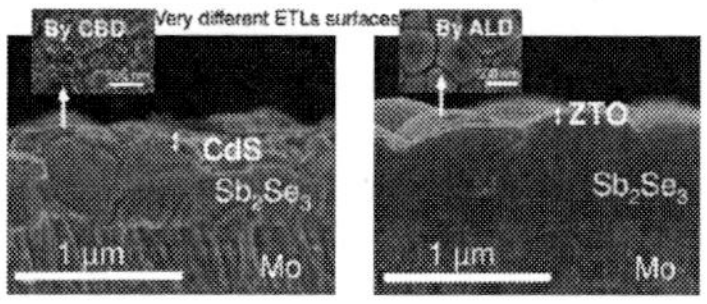

- Sb_2Se_3 thin films are well covered by both ETLs.
- Conformal growth and uniform surface of ZTO.

J-V

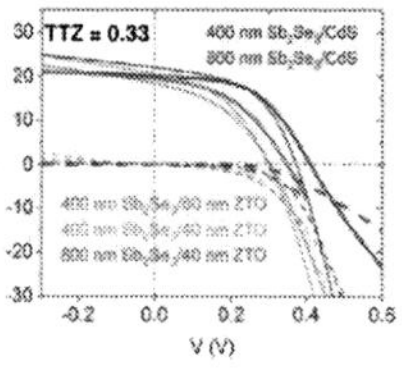

QE

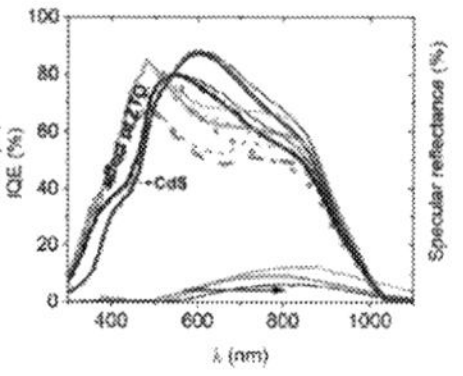

- A higher spectral response (SR) is measured at short λ range related to a higher band gap energy of the ZTO layer of ~ 3.4 eV.
- Lower EQE and higher specular reflectance from 500 nm for ZTO devices.
- Thicker ZTO layer ⇒ ↑ R and roughness.

Effect of Sb_2Se_3 thickness

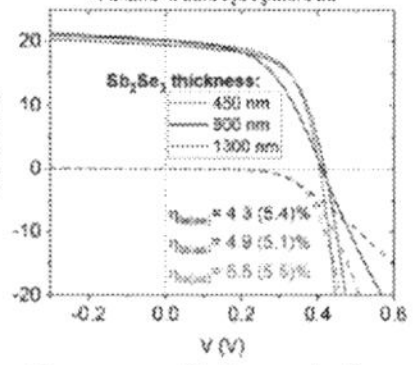

- In all cases, active area efficiency in the range of 5 %.
- Enhanced performance when using thinner absorber.

- ↓ J_{SC} and FF due to ↑ R_s for thinner ZTO (20 nm) ⇒ ↓ η.
- ZTO thickness is the most critical parameter for the range of composition used.
- Cross-over effect in the J-V characteristics ⇒ interfaces are not fully optimized yet.

PV parameters

Sb_2Se_3 (nm)	ETL	[Sn]/([Sn]+[Zn])	ETL (nm)	V_{OC} (mV)	J_{SC} (mA/cm²)	FF (%)	η (%)	R_s (Ω·cm²)	R_{sh} (Ω·cm²)
400	CdS	-	60	373	21.9	50.8	**4.2**	2.5	96.3
	ZTO	0.33	40	297	20.4	42.7	2.6	3.5	56.2
	ZTO	0.33	60	303	18.2	40.5	2.2	4.5	59.4
800	CdS	-	60	411	20.1	51.6	**4.3**	5.3	260.0
	ZTO	0.25	20	367	15.2	31.5	1.8	10.6	47.5
	ZTO	0.25	40	344	19.6	45.1	**3.0**★	4.3	117.6
	ZTO	0.33	40	348	20.0	43.7	**3.0**★	4.4	113.9

Conclusions

- Sb_2Se_3 single phase orthorhombic crystal structure oriented in the [hk1] is formed on Mo/SLG with a compact structure, free of pinholes.
- Sb_2Se_3-based PV devices are fabricated using CdS by CBD and alternative ZTO by ALD as ETLs with efficiencies of 5.5 and 3.0 % respectively.
- Cd-free solar cells are characterized by a higher SR at the short wavelength due to the higher band gap energy of ZTO and a lower SR from 500 nm with a higher specular reflectance.
- The thickness of ZTO is a key parameter to enhance the Sb_2Se_3/ZTO interface. In this work, 40 nm ZTO leads to higher device performance.

This work was supported by ASSESS (TED2021-129666B-C21) project funded by MCIN/AEI/10.13039/501100011033 and by the "European Union Next Generation EU/PRTR", InnoPV (PID 2022-140226OB-C3) project funded by MICIU/AEI/10.13039/501100011033 and by "FEDER/UE" and SUNLIFE (PCI2024-155033-2) project funded by MICIU/AEI /10.13039/501100011033/UE.

INNOPV

NUMERICAL SIMULATION OF CADMIUM-FREE BUFFER LAYERS FOR COPPER-DOPED ANTIMONY SELENIDE SOLAR CELLS

Fabio Butrichi [a, b], Maurizio Acciarri [a], Giorgio Tseberlidis [a, c], Vanira Trifiletti [a], Michele Casappa [d], Stefano Rampino [d], Simona Binetti [a]

[a] Department of Materials Science and Solar Energy Research Center (MIB-SOLAR), University of Milano-Bicocca, Via Roberto Cozzi 55, Milano, Italy

[b] Department of Information and Electrical Engineering and Applied Mathematics, University of Salerno, Via Giovanni Paolo II 132, Fisciano (SA), Italy

[c] Institute of Science, Technology and Sustainability for Development of Ceramic Materials, National Research Council, Via Granarolo 64, Faenza (RA), Italy

[d] Institute of Materials for Electronics and Magnetism, National Research Council, Parco Area delle Scienze 37/A, Parma, Italy

ABSTRACT: Cu-doped Sb_2Se_3 is considered a promising absorber for photovoltaics. The main efficiency bottleneck is related to the n-type buffer layer: the commonly used CdS presents a strong parasitic absorption in the visible light and displays a non-optimal band alignment; moreover, CdS is toxic.

This modelling work presents the simulated performances of alternative buffer layers to overcome these issues: ZnSe, SnS_2 and $In_2(O_x,S_{1-x})_3$.

First, the experimental Cu:Sb_2Se_3/CdS junction reported by some of the authors was simulated to obtain experimental values of Sb_2Se_3 simulation parameters.

ZnSe was found as very promising to substitute CdS; the optimal value of the thickness is dependent on the type of defectivity at the interface. SnS_2 also shows good potential, but strongly dependent on donor doping density, that should be as high as possible, considering the possibility of external doping too. For what concerns $In_2(O_x,S_{1-x})_3$, the outmatch on CdS is possible if the composition is optimized, sticking to the better ratio between oxygen and sulfur. The role of the defectivity at the surface is very important for all the buffer layers object of this work, therefore the selection of an adequate buffer layer and the control of the growth is mandatory to obtain a high-performing device.

Keywords: antimony selenide, buffer layers, Cd-free, thin films, photovoltaics

1 INTRODUCTION

Among absorber materials for thin film solar cells, Sb_2Se_3 has gained great attention in the research, thanks to its optimal direct band gap of about 1.2 eV coupled with an absorption coefficient $>10^5$ cm^{-1} and the abundance and safeness of its constituting elements [1].

The reported record efficiency for Sb_2Se_3-based solar cells is 10.57% [2].

One factor that has limited device efficiencies so far is the low p-type conductivity [3], which can be increased by extrinsic metal doping.

Another issue is related to the V_{oc} loss due to interface recombination. Indeed, the conventionally used buffer layer, CdS, displays a high absorption in the blue range of light and is made by a toxic element such as cadmium; moreover, it presents a high lattice mismatch with Sb_2Se_3 and Cd atoms tend to diffuse into Sb_2Se_3 [4].

Some of the authors of this contribution reported on a 5.25% efficient Cu:Sb_2Se_3 solar cell [5], with a high value of short circuit current but still a loss in the V_{oc}.

This work aims to overcome this issue, simulating the substitution of CdS with various alternative buffer layers, to determine how an increase in transparency and a more proper band-alignment could help to enhance the V_{oc} values of the experimental material, with its properties and defects. The simulated buffer layers will be all Cd-free, to gain also in sustainability.

The approach is based on a numerical simulation using the free simulation software SCAPS-1D [6].

2 SIMULATION METHODS

SCAPS-1D (Solar Cell Capacitance Simulator) free software, version 3.3.11, was used to carry out the J-V simulations reported in this work. The software was developed in the University of Gent by M. Burgelman and co-workers [6].

The continuity equation for holes and electrons and the Poisson equation are the basis for the calculations performed by SCAPS 1-D. J-V curves are therefore produced as output based on the solar cell's architecture.

Each component of the device is characterized by its thickness, band-gap and electronic properties, such as doping density and bulk defects; interfacial defectivity is also considered.

Standard test conditions (STC) are used for simulation performing, choosing a normal to the sample illumination from the top contact, characterized by 1.5 air mass and 100 mW/cm^2 power density.

3 RESULTS AND DISCUSSION

3.1 Experimental Cu:Sb_2Se_3/CdS simulation

The simulations object of this work are not dealing with an optimized absorber but are grounded on experimental data from actual Sb_2Se_3-based solar cells.

Most of the important simulation parameters of Sb_2Se_3, such as the band-gap, the electron affinity (and hence the band position), the density, capture section and energy position of the defects, the density of doping and series and shunt resistance of the whole cell are directly taken from measurements on Sb_2Se_3 solar cell.

First, the experimental junction Sb_2Se_3/CdS already reported by some of the authors [5] has been modelled, to get the most accurate parameters of the absorber material under exam.

The architecture used of the solar cells was FTO/Sb_2Se_3/CdS/i-ZnO/AZO; the parameters for simulating CdS, i-ZnO and AZO have been chosen from literature [7] [8].

Figure 1 reports the simulated and experimental curves, while Table I reports their photovoltaic parameters. It's possible to appreciate how the theoretical and experimental curves are well matching; the photovoltaic parameters of the simulated and of the experimental solar cell are very similar, with a difference lower than 2 %.

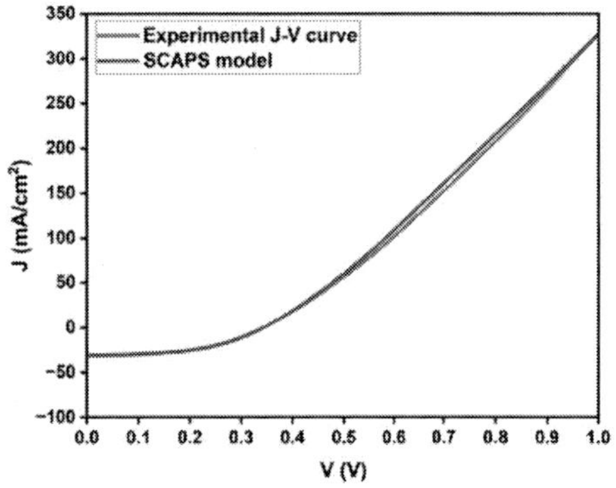

Figure 1: Comparison of simulated and experimental J-V curve of the junction Cu:Sb_2Se_3/CdS.

Table I: Comparison of simulated and experimental PV parameters of the junction Cu:Sb_2Se_3/CdS.

	Experimental	Simulated
V_{OC} (mV)	343.0	344.0
J_{SC} (mA/cm^2)	31.4	31.2
FF (%)	49.0	48.2
η (%)	5.25	5.18

The investigated buffer layers are ZnSe, SnS_2, and $In_2(O_xS_{1-x})_3$. For each of them, three scenarios for the interface modelling have been formulated: no defects (ideal case), a situation of low defectivity starting from the interfacial defectivity energetic level reported in the literature, and a high-defectivity one (the same interface defects of the junction Cu:Sb_2Se_3/CdS).

3.2 Cu:Sb_2Se_3/ZnSe junction

ZnSe simulation optoelectronic parameters and defects have been taken from literature [9] [10] [11]. The energetic levels for the construction of the low defectivity interface were taken from [10].

Figure 2 reports the efficiency calculation as a function of ZnSe thickness. No defect and low defectivity scenarios present their maximum efficiency with buffer layer thickness between 20 and 25 nm, while the high defectivity one between 45 and 50 nm.

ZnSe is effectively able to outmatch CdS performance in the simulation, reaching η = 14.4 % and η = 8.5 % in the low and high defectivity scenario, respectively.

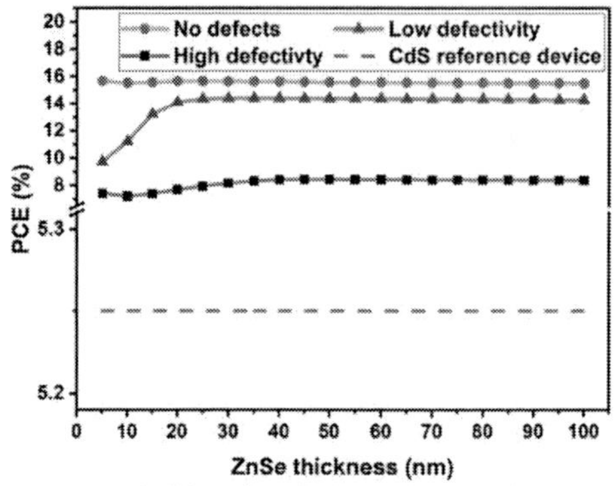

Figure 2: Simulated efficiency of the junction Cu:Sb_2Se_3/ZnSe as a function of ZnSe thickness.

3.3 Cu:Sb_2Se_3/SnS_2 junction

Also, SnS_2 shows very promising results as an alternative buffer layer. Simulation parameters and defects of SnS_2 have been taken from literature [12][13]; the energetic levels for the low-defectivity interface were taken from [13].

In literature, SnS_2 is reported to have the doping acceptor density between 10^{17} [14] and 10^{19} [15] cm^{-3}. Its effect is very impactful and can be appreciated in Table II (with a fixed thickness of 50 nm).

Table II: Simulated efficiency of the junction Cu:Sb_2Se_3/SnS_2 as a function of SnS_2 doping density.

Doping density (cm^{-3})	PCE (%) no defects	PCE (%) low defectivity	PCE (%) high defectivity
$1.0 \cdot 10^{17}$	15.95	9.70	4.55
$5.0 \cdot 10^{17}$	15.59	11.65	5.36
$1.0 \cdot 10^{18}$	15.63	12.05	5.79
$5.0 \cdot 10^{18}$	15.70	12.74	7.77
$1.0 \cdot 10^{19}$	15.72	12.94	9.14
$5.0 \cdot 10^{19}$	15.76	13.29	13.44

The calculated efficiency as a function of the thickness is reported in figure 3 (fixing doping density at the average value of 10^{18} cm^{-3}). In this case also, the optimal point corresponds to a thickness of 10-20 nm for no or low defectivity and to 45-55 nm for high defectivity scenario, confirming the same trend as for ZnSe.

SnS_2 is able to outmatch CdS too, but the delivered efficiency is strongly influenced by the doping density, as described above, and by the level of interface defectivity.

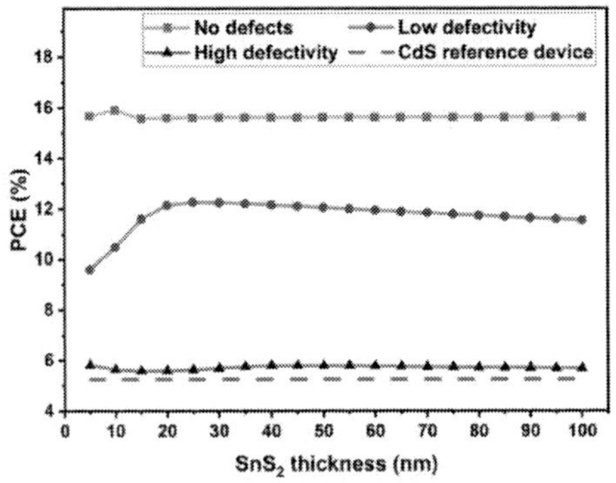

Figure 3: Simulated efficiency of the junction $Cu:Sb_2Se_3/SnS_2$ as a function of SnS_2 and thickness.

3.4 $Cu:Sb_2Se_3/In_2(O_xS_{1-x})_3$ junction

$In_2(O_xS_{1-x})_3$ has also been simulated as an alternative buffer layer, focusing on a low value of x. The value of $In_2(O_xS_{1-x})_3$ simulation parameters as a function of composition and energy levels of interface defects in low-defectivity hypothesis were taken from [16].

Efficiency was simulated as a function of composition (figure 4) finding an optimal value of x=0.107 both for low and high defectivity situations, with the final composition $In_2(O_{0.11}S_{0.89})_3$.

It was not possible to obtain the last two points of the high defectivity curve because the simulation didn't converge for the largest quantities of oxygen.

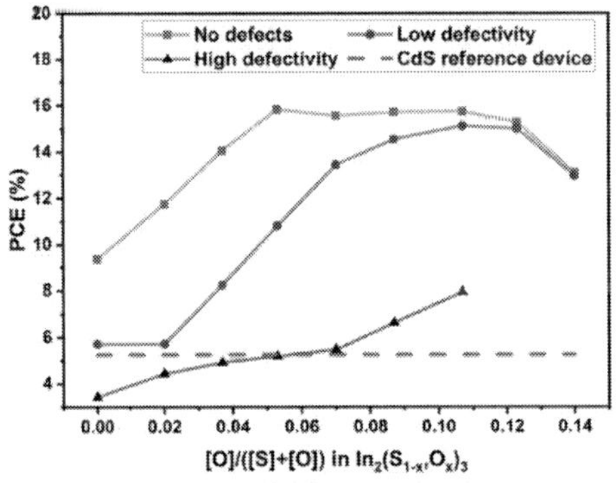

Figure 4: Simulated efficiency of the junction $Cu:Sb_2Se_3/In_2(O_xS_{1-x})_3$ as a function of $In_2(O_xS_{1-x})_3$ composition (A).

The optimal value of x=0.107 was used to simulate the efficiency as a function of the thickness of the buffer layer (figure 5), finding thickness >60 nm optimal for both low and high defectivity hypotheses.

$In_2(O_xS_{1-x})_3$ is the most performing buffer layer reported in this study, reaching η = 15.1 %, in low defectivity scenario

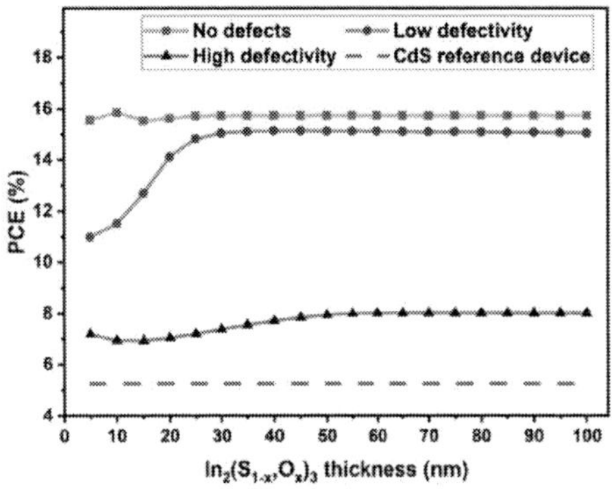

Figure 5: Simulated efficiency of the junction $Cu:Sb_2Se_3/In_2(O_xS_{1-x})_3$ as a function of $In_2(O_xS_{1-x})_3$ thickness.

4 CONCLUSIONS

The intention to find alternative buffer layers with better performances than CdS (experimental η = 5.25%) was fully addressed.

The performance of SnS_2 is strongly related to the doping density, reaching $\eta \approx$ 13% in the best doping density conditions of 10^{19} cm^{-3}: if this layer is to be used, it could be helpful to consider the addition of an external dopant.

ZnSe demonstrated to be able to overcome the CdS standard in all the defectivity scenarios and thicknesses, reaching $\eta \approx$ 8% and $\eta \approx$ 14% in high defectivity and low defectivity scenario, respectively.

$In_2(O_xS_{1-x})_3$ needs to be prepared very carefully, because its better performances are restricted to a very narrow interval of composition; if the stoichiometry requirement is met and the interface defectivity is low, $Cu:Sb_2Se_3/In_2(O_xS_{1-x})_3$ junction could reach η = 15.1%, the highest efficiency value (not in ideal defectivity scenario) reported in this study.

$In_2(O_xS_{1-x})_3$ is able to reach the highest efficiency, ZnSe, whose efficiency is about only 1 % lower, could be considered the most promising alternative buffer layer studied in this work since it is indium-free and hence cheaper and critical raw material free, is easier to prepare (being binary without the anion ratio to tune) and the performances are more robust to the possible interface defectivity.

Finally, the differences between the three scenarios of defectivity show how important the choice of the buffer layer and the control of its growth process are in avoiding or reducing defects at the interface as much as possible.

5 REFERENCES

[1] C. Chen et al., Solar RRL, vol. 6, no. 7, p. 2200094, Jul. 2022.

[2] Y. Zhao et al., Energy Environ Sci, vol. 15, no. 12, pp. 5118–5128, 2022.

[3] Y. B. Kim et al., Energy Environ Sci, vol. 11, no. 9, pp. 2540–2549, 2018.

[4] A. Mavlonov et al., Solar Energy, vol. 201, pp. 227–246, 2020.

[5] R. Jakomin et al., Solar, vol. 4, no. 1, pp. 83–98, Feb. 2024.

[6] M. Burgelman et al., Thin Solid Films, vol. 361–362, pp. 527–532, 2000.

[7] A. Basak et al., Solar Energy Materials and Solar

Cells, vol. 230, p. 111184, 2021.
[8] C. Gobbo et al., Energies (Basel), vol. 16, no. 10, May 2023.
[9] S. H. Zyoud et al., International Review on Modelling and Simulations, vol. 16, no. 3, pp. 120–128, 2023.
[10] R. Kumari et al., ACS Omega, vol. 8, no. 1, pp. 1632–1642, 2022.
[11] A. Rahmoune et al., Optik (Stuttg), vol. 283, p. 170875, 2023.
[12] T. Garmim et al., Mater Today Proc, vol. 66, pp. 146–150, 2022.
[13] B. M. Sakunde et al., ACS Appl Energy Mater, vol. 7, no. 14, pp. 5691–5697, Jul. 2024.
[14] Md. F. Hossain et al., Opt Commun, vol. 559, p. 130410, 2024.
[15] T. Garmim et al., Mater Today Proc, vol. 66, pp. 146–150, 2022.
[16] E. Moradi Haghighi et al., Opt Laser Technol, vol. 169, p. 110107, 2024.

Numerical simulation of cadmium-free buffer layers for copper-doped antimony selenide solar cells

Fabio Butrichi [a,b], Maurizio Acciarri [a], Giorgio Tseberlidis [a,c], Vanira Trifiletti [a], Michele Casappa [d], Stefano Rampino [d], Simona Binetti [a]

[a] *Department of Materials Science and Solar Energy Research Center (MIB-SOLAR), University of Milano-Bicocca, Milano, Italy*

[b] *Department of Information and Electrical Engineering and Applied Mathematics, University of Salerno, Fisciano (SA), Italy*

[c] *Institute of Science, Technology and Sustainability for Development of Ceramic Materials, National Research Council, 48018, Faenza (RA), Italy*

[d] *Institute of Materials for Electronics and Magnetism, National Research Council, 43124, Parma, Italy*

Cu-doped Sb_2Se_3 is considered as a promising p-type semiconductor for photovoltaic applications. The main efficiency bottleneck is related to the choice of n-type buffer layer: the commonly used CdS presents a strong parasitic absorption in the visible range of light and displays a non-optimal band alignment; moreover, CdS is very toxic.

This simulation work presents the possible performances of alternative buffer layers to overcome these issues: ZnSe, SnS_2 and $In_2(O_x,S_{1-x})_3$.

First, the experimental $Cu:Sb_2Se_3/CdS$ junction reported by some of the authors was simulated to obtain experimental values of Sb_2Se_3 parameters.

ZnSe has been found as very promising to substitute CdS; the precise value of the thickness, important for the performance, is dependent on the type of defectivity at the interface. SnS_2 also shows good potential, but strongly dependent on donor doping density, that should be as high as possible, also considering the possibility of an external doping. For what concerns $In_2(O_x,S_{1-x})_3$, the outmatch on CdS is possible if the composition is optimized, sticking to the better ratio between oxygen and sulfur. The role of the defectivity at the surface is very important for all the buffer layers object of this work, therefore the selection of an adequate buffer layer and the control of the growth is mandatory to obtain a high-performing device.

$Cu:Sb_2Se_3/CdS$

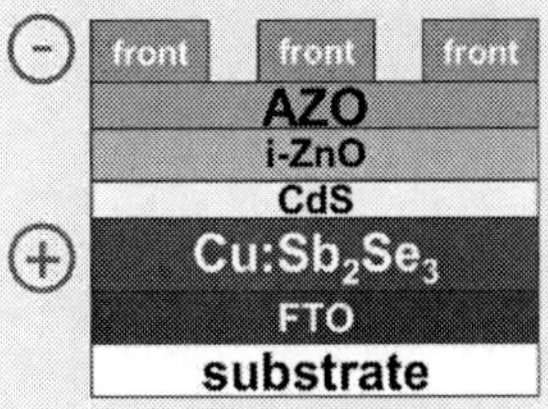

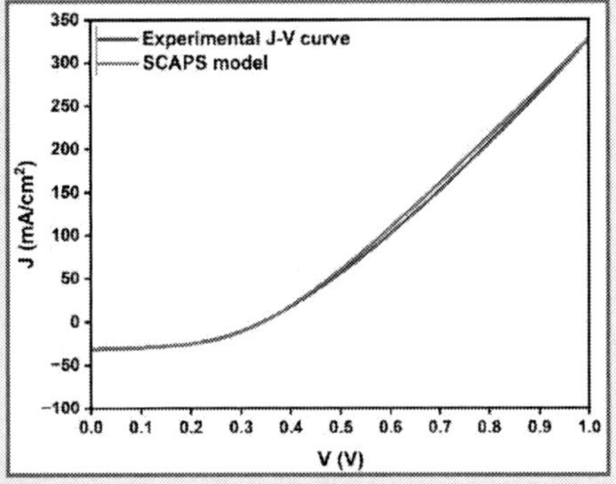

	Experimental	SCAPS model
V_{OC} (mV)	343.0	344.0
J_{SC} (mA/cm^2)	31.4	31.2
FF (%)	49.0	48.2
PCE (%)	5.25	5.18

- Very good agreement between experimental and simulated data
- Reliable $Cu:Sb_2Se_3$ optoelectronic parameters for buffer layer substitution study

$Cu:Sb_2Sc_3/In_2(S_{1-x}O_x)_3$

- Efficiency value strongly dependent on stoichiometry (low oxygen quantity range)
- Best composition considering low defectivity level is: $In_2(S_{0.89}O_{0.11})_3$
- Optimal thickness value dependent on defectivity level
- Increase of series resistance at high thickness underrated in SCAPS modelling

$In_2(S_{1-x}O_x)_3$ stoichiometry

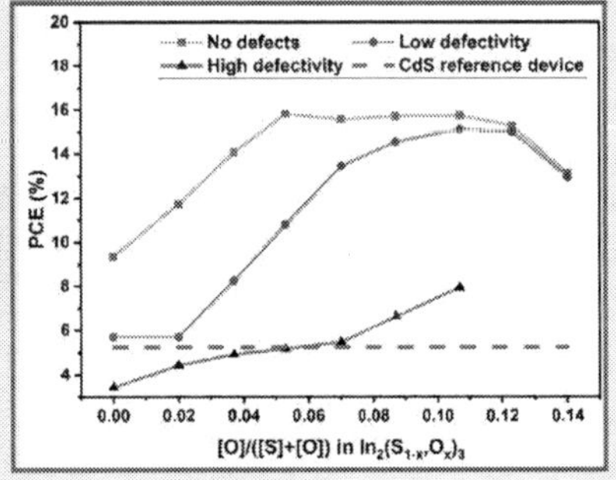

$In_2(S_{1-x}O_x)_3$ thickness

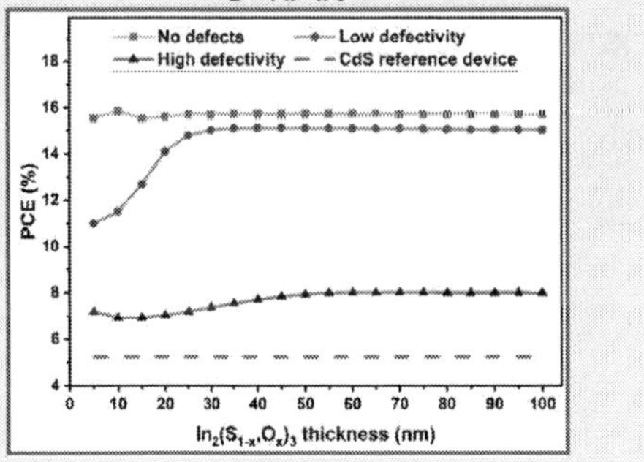

$Cu:Sb_2Se_3/ZnSe$

- Optimal thickness around 30 nm
- Increase of series resistance at high thickness underrated in SCAPS modelling
- The most promising alternative buffer layer, considering also low cost and easy preparation

ZnSe thickness

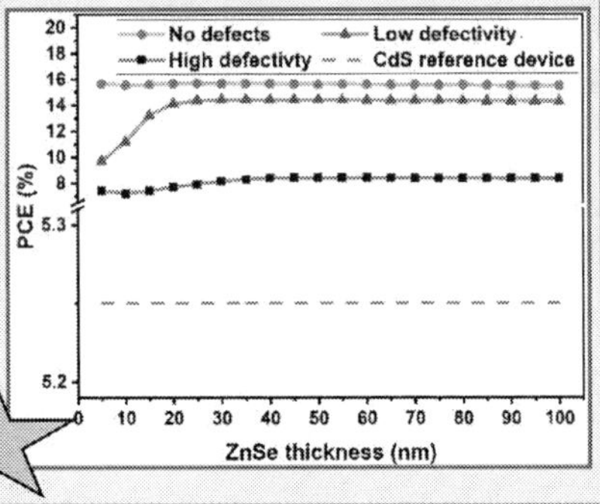

$Cu:Sb_2Se_3/SnS_2$

- Optimal thickness around 30 nm
- Strong **dependence on doping density**

External doping density is suggested

SnS_2 thickness

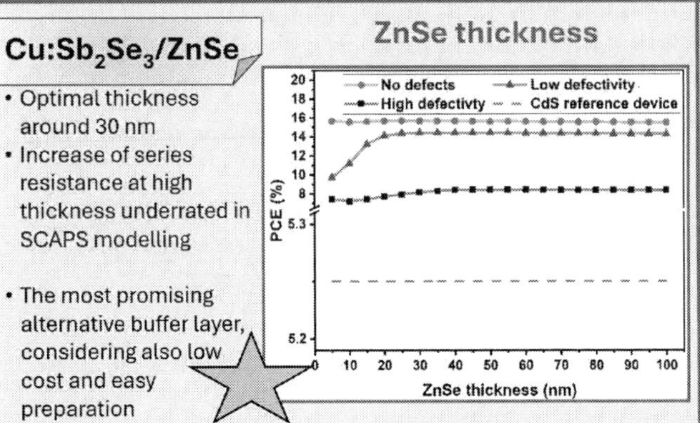

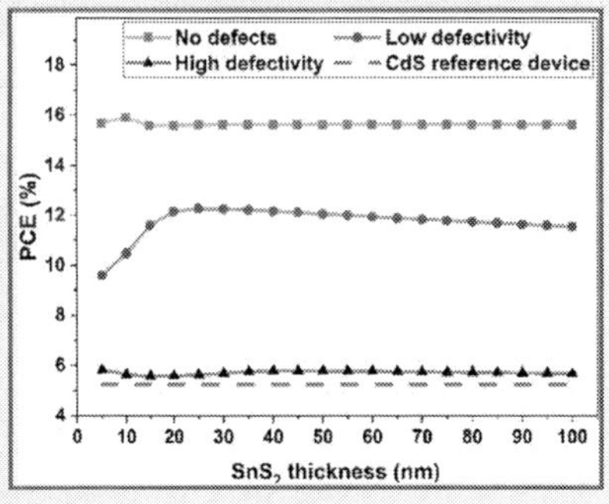

This study is a result of the research project CANVAS, funded by the Italian Ministry of the Environment and the Energy Security, through the Research Fund for the Italian Electrical System (type-A call, published on G.U.R.I. n. 192 on 18-08- 2022) and of the COST Action Research and International Networking project "Emerging Inorganic Chalcogenides for PVs (RENEW-PV)," CA21148. The author F. B. acknowledges the Dottorato di Interesse Nazionale "Photovoltaics".

The effect of thickness on the Sb_2Se_3 superstrate solar cells.

N. Torabi[1], J.M. Delgado-Sanchez[2], E. Artegiani[1], P. Jakuza[3], M. Meneghini[3,4],A. Romeo[1*]

[1] LAPS-Laboratory for Photovoltaics and Solid-State Physics, Department of Computer Science, University of Verona, Ca' Vignal 1, Strada Le Grazie 15, 37134 Verona, Italy.

[2] Department of Applied Physics, University of Seville, Ctra. Utrera km 1, Seville, Spain

[3] University of Padova Department of Information Engineering via Gradenigo 6/B 35131 Padova, Italy

[4] University of Padova, Department of Physics and Astronomy, via Marzolo 8, 35131 Padova, Italy

***Abstract* — In this study, we analyze the impact of different thickness of antimony selenide thin films on the electrical properties of the absorber and on the efficiency of the finished solar cells. Sb_2Se_3 absorbers have been deposited with thickness from 400 nm to 1200 nm, grown by thermal evaporation on CdSe buffer layer in superstrate configuration.**

The highest efficiency has been delivered by the lowest thickness, with a large absorption spectra and higher quantum efficiency response as well as a higher carrier concentration. Moreover, a post-annealing treatment in air at 150 °C, improves the efficiency of the cells with a larger impact on the thinnest absorber, increasing the Voc and correcting the rollover effect observed in the J-V of the thicker absorber layers.

I. Introduction

Antimony selenide (Sb_2Se_3) possesses an optimal band gap of around 1–1.2 eV and has a high absorption coefficient (>10^5cm^{-1}), making it a cost-effective option for thin-film solar cells [1]. It is made of earth-abundant and low-toxic elements but what is more interesting, it is the quasi-one-dimensional (Q-1D) crystal structure, that limits the effects of the grain boundaries [2], [3].

Driven by the high absorption coefficient and by the accurate control of the deposition rate of our thermal evaporation system, both absorbers and finished devices with different Sb2Se3 layer thicknesses have been analyzed and compared. The Sb_2Se_3 films where grown by thermal evaporation with a thickness of 400, 800, and 1200 nm, in a superstrate device structure of glass/SnO_2: F/ SnO_2/CdSe/Sb_2Se_3/Au. Also, a post-annealing treatment (PAT) in air has been applied to the finished device. The optimized annealing temperature and time were defined as respectively 150°C and 20 min.

The best results have been delivered by the thinner absorber that, together with the post deposition annealing, show a higher current density and higher open circuit voltage, which was found to be driven by higher quantum efficiency response and high carrier concentration.

II. Methods

A. Fabrication

Sb_2Se_3 solar cells are fabricated in a superstrate configuration, utilizing a glass/SnO_2:F (FTO)/ SnO_2/CdSe/Sb_2Se_3/Au structure. The commercial coated glasses (NSG TEC 12D) were used as substrates, where 60 nm of the buffer layer, CdSe, is thermally evaporated at 340°C under a pressure of $1*10^{-5}$ bar. Subsequently, Sb_2Se_3 is evaporated from a graphite crucible at 500-600°C, with a pressure of $2*10^{-6}$ mbar and an evaporation rate of 0.15 nm/sec. Annealing in vacuum is applied to enhance the crystallinity by heating the stack in the evaporation chamber at 350°C for 30 minutes. A 30 nm thick gold layer with a cell area of 0.13 cm^2 is thermally evaporated on top of the absorber as back contact. The devices are labeled T400, T800, and T1200 according to their absorber thickness. Finally, one device from each batch undergoes a post-annealing treatment (PAT) in the oven at a temperature of 150 °C for 20 min, resulting in T400-PAT, T800-PAT, and T1200-PAT.

B. Characterization Techniques

Current density–voltage (JV) characteristics are collected with a Keithley Source Meter 2420, under an AM 1.5 spectrum at 100 mW/cm^2, using a LOT Quantum Design Europe solar simulator LS0306.

X-ray diffraction (XRD) and grazing angle x-ray diffraction (GXRD) patterns were obtained on a Bruker D8 Advance instrument equipped with a Cu K_α radiation source operating at 40 kV and 30 mA. The diffractograms were measured in the range of 3-70º 2θ, with step time of 0.1 s and step size of 0.015º.

The morphology and elemental composition of the crystalline phases were analyzed by scanning electron microscopy (SEM/EDX), using a JEOL microscope (JSM 5400 Model) and working 20 kV. This equipment is connected to an energy dispersive system X-ray (EDX) (Oxford Link ISIS) which allows chemical analysis of samples using a detector of Si/Li with a Be window. The external quantum efficiency (EQE) spectra were acquired using a commercial LOANA solar cell analysis system, calibrated with a silicon reference sample with known EQE using an incident spotlight of 1 mm × 2 mm area. An HP4284A LCR, controlled by a specific in-house software, was applied for capacitance-voltage, drive-level capacitance profiling, and admittance spectroscopy.

10.4229/EUPVSEC2025/2BV.2.3

III. Analysis and Results

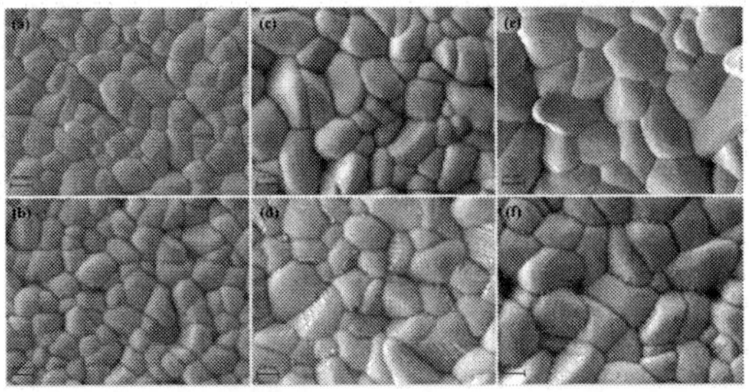

Figure 1: Top-view SEM images of (a) T400, (b) T400-PAT, (c) T800, (d) T800-PAT, (e) T1200, and (f) T1200-PAT Sb_2Se_3 films.

Scanning electron microscope pictures of different thick Sb_2Se_3 films show grain enlargement as the film thickness increases (see figure 1. a, c, and e), with the average grain size developing from 200 to 300 nm. After post-annealing treatment (PAT) (figure 1. b, d, and f), the grain boundaries become more defined, and the average grain size increases slightly. Additionally, some aggregations are present at the grain boundaries in the thicker films. These appear as needle-shaped in the T800-PAT film but as localized particles in the T1200-PAT film. The small size of the aggregations, a few nanometers, make it difficult to detect by EDX (not shown here), XRD. Fleck et al. [4] have reported the formation of α-Sb_2O_3 on the surface through simple air exposure to the samples or annealing in air.

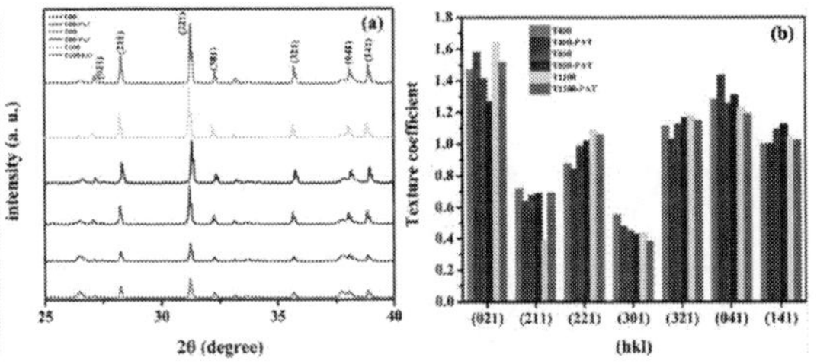

Figure 2: (a) XRD peaks, and (b) texture coefficient of different thick Sb_2Se_3 films before and after PAT.

The X-ray diffraction (XRD) patterns of all the absorber confirm the orthorhombic crystal structure (JCPDS No. 15-0861) of Sb_2Se_3 (Figure 2 (a)). (211) and (221) planes are the preferred orientations due to their large angle to the surface [5].
A TC diffraction value larger than one indicates a preferential orientation of the grains along that direction. Accordingly, our films are orientated along (hkl) planes, but they are textured along (021) and (041) planes, which have a smaller angle to the surface compared to (211) and (221) planes. Increasing the thickness and PAT increase the texturizing along these orientations and has a larger impact on the T400 film.

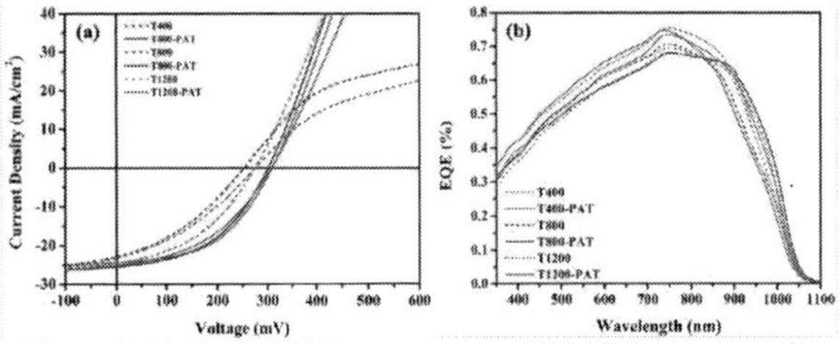

Figure 3: (a) Current-Voltage curves, and (b) EQE response of the various thick Sb_2Se_3 solar cells before and after PAT.

The current-voltage (J-V) characteristics (Figure 3 (a) and Table 1, representing the most efficient solar cells) demonstrate that the T400 cell shows the highest efficiency, while after PAT, the efficiency increases of at least 1% absolute efficiency for all cases. Chen et al. shows that the minimum thickness to capture all photons is 800 nm, however we demonstrate here that 400 nm allows a very efficient absorption of the spectrum [1]. J_{sc} exhibits smaller values for thicker layers of Sb_2Se_3 solar cells, although theoretically, it should increase. This could offer enhancement of defect density in the thicker Sb_2Se_3 films during the growth process. After PAT, J_{sc} has improved except for the T400 cell, where we did not observe the aggregation at the grain boundaries. Although V_{oc} and FF exhibit the highest value in the T400 cell, these parameters have enhanced after PAT in all devices. We can see a similar trend for shunt and series resistances, showing more favorable values of the ultra-thin Sb_2Se_3 solar cells.

Table 1: Photovoltaic parameters of different thick Sb_2Se_3 solar cells before and after PAT.

Sample	J_{sc} (mA/cm^2)	V_{oc} (mV)	FF (%)	η (%)
T400	24.3	279	41.2	2.8
T400-PAT	24.3	314	48.4	3.7
T800	22.6	258	35.2	2
T800-PAT	25.4	307	45.6	3.5
T1200	23	279	34.6	2.2
T1200-PAT	25	314	42.1	3.3

Also, the rollover effect at higher bias voltage in the J-V curves of T800 and T1200 solar cells (Figure 3 (a)) vanishes after PAT. It has been shown that a thin Sb_2O_3 layer on the surface of Sb_2Se_3 acts as a barrier, improving the hole extraction, while a thicker layer would negatively impact increasing series resistance [4]. Similarly, the PAT reduces the rollover effect and decreases the series resistance.

Sb_2Se_3 solar cells, in all cases, exhibit comparable carrier collection in the whole spectrum, as shown in the EQE curves in Figure 3 (b). The lower response of EQE before 600 nm and after 800 nm could be explained by the parasitic absorption of the CdSe and by the recombination due to deep defects, respectively. The broad increase of EQE in the whole spectrum of the T1200-PAT cell supports the higher J_{sc} via an enhanced carrier collection. Although Jsc exhibits similar values after PAT for T400 cells, the EQE drops after 700 nm, which could be associated with a slight reduced absorption of the thinner Sb_2Se_3 layer.

Capacitance-voltage (CV) and deep-level capacitance profiling (DLCP), see Figure 4, identify carrier concentrations of T400, T800, and T1200 cells respectively of $4.6x10^{16}$ cm^{-3}, $2.6x10^{16}$ cm^{-3}, and $2.2x10^{16}$ cm^{-3}. The 400 nm thick Sb_2Se_3 solar cell shows the highest doping density and, consequently, the smallest SCR width.

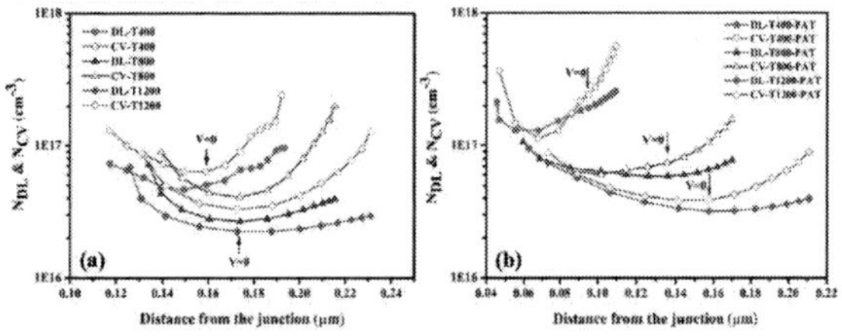

Figure 4: capacitance-voltage (CV) and deep-level capacitance profiling (DLCP) of different thick Sb2Se3 solar cells (a) before and (b) after PAT.

The differences between CV and DLCP profiles are distinct, particularly for thicker absorber layers confirming the presence of deep defects. The carrier concentration of T400-PAT, T800-PAT, and T1200-PAT cells increases to $1.3x10^{17}$ cm^{-3}, $5.8x10^{16}$ cm^{-3}, and $3.1x10^{16}$ cm^{-3}, respectively, resulting in a shrunk SCR width, which is shown at V=0 on the graph. The larger difference between CV and DLCP profiles seen before the annealing, disappears after the annealing and the profiles result almost superposed after PAT. This suggests that the annealing may act as a passivation layer.

IV. Conclusions

This work demonstrates that reducing the Sb_2Se_3 absorber thickness down to 400 nm in a superstrate glass/FTO/SnO_2/CdSe/Sb_2Se_3/Au configuration leads to superior device performance compared to thicker (800 nm and 1200 nm) layers. The thinner absorber delivers the highest efficiency thanks to higher carrier concentration, enhanced quantum efficiency, and improved open-circuit voltage. Post-annealing treatment in air at 150 °C for 20 min further boosts performance across all thicknesses, most notably for the 400 nm films, by increasing carrier density, reducing deep-level defects, and suppressing the J–V rollover effect.

These results indicate that very thin Sb_2Se_3 absorbers, combined with a mild air annealing step, can effectively absorb the solar spectrum while minimizing defect density and series resistance.

V. Acknowledgments

This work has been partially funded by ACT-FAST project, n. CETP22_00039 within CET-partnership program. The Italian Ministry of Research is thankfully acknowledged. Cariverona foundation is thankfully acknowledged for partially funding this project Ref. 2022.0094 – ID 52271 – CUP B33C22001760007.

References

[1] C. Chen *et al.*, "Optical properties of amorphous and polycrystalline Sb2Se3 thin films prepared by thermal evaporation," *Appl Phys Lett*, vol. 107, no. 4, Jul. 2015, doi: 10.1063/1.4927741.

[2] A. Mavlonov *et al.*, "A review of Sb2Se3 photovoltaic absorber materials and thin-film solar cells," May 01, 2020, *Elsevier Ltd.* doi: 10.1016/j.solener.2020.03.009.

[3] Y. Zhou *et al.*, "Thin-film Sb2Se3 photovoltaics with oriented one-dimensional ribbons and benign grain boundaries," *Nat Photonics*, 2015, doi: 10.1038/nphoton.2015.78.

[4] N. Fleck *et al.*, "How Oxygen Exposure Improves the Back Contact and Performance of Antimony Selenide Solar Cells," *ACS Appl Mater Interfaces*, vol. 12, no. 47, pp. 52595–52602, Nov. 2020, doi: 10.1021/acsami.0c14256.

[5] F. Pattini *et al.*, "Role of the substrates in the ribbon orientation of Sb2Se3 films grown by Low-Temperature Pulsed Electron Deposition," *Solar Energy Materials and Solar Cells*, vol. 218, no. June, p. 110724, 2020, doi: 10.1016/j.solmat.2020.110724.

42nd European Photovoltaic Solar Energy Conference and Exhibition

This presentation was selected by the Sc. Committee of the EU PVSEC 2025 for submission of a full paper to one of the EU PVSEC's collaborating peer-reviewed journals.

TRANSFER OF GAAS SOLAR CELLS TO UNPRECEDENTED FLEXIBLE POLYMERIC BASES OF PVC:PMMA:DOP MODIFIED WITH EG

Graciana S. Sousa[1]; Luciana D. Pinto[2]; Fabiele C. Tavares[3]; Guillermo J. N. Soares[4]; Rudy M. S. Kawabata[5]; Rogério Valaski[6]; Maurício P. Pires[7]; Roberto Jakomin[8]; Guilherme M. Torelly[9]; Patrícia L. Souza[10]

[1,2,7,10]Instituto de Física - Universidade Federal do Rio de Janeiro, Rio de Janeiro, Brazil; [3,4,8]Campus Duque de Caxias - Universidade Federal do Rio de Janeiro, Duque de Caxias, Brazil; 5,9Laboratório de Semicondutores (LabSem) - Pontifícia Universidade Católica do Rio de Janeiro, Rio de Janeiro, Brazil; 6Laboratório de Fenômenos de Superfície/DIMAT - Instituto Nacional de Metrologia, Rio de Janeiro, Brazil.

graciana.sousa@ifpa.edu.br; dornnelas@yahoo.com.br; fabieletavares@hotmail.com; guillermo.nog9@gmail.com; rudykawarudykawa@gmail.com; rvalaski@inmetro.gov.br; pires@if.ufrj.br; roberto.jakomin@gmail.com; torelly@puc-rio.br; plsouza@if.ufrj.br

ABSTRACT: Single GaAs solar cells, Produced by Metalorganic Vapor Phase Epitaxy (MOVPE) on a rigid GaAs substrate, were transferred to an unprecedented flexible polymer blend of PVC:PMMA:DOP (1.0:1.0:0.5) modified with exfoliated graphene (EG). The exfoliated graphene was employed to enhance properties such as thermal and mechanical resistance of the polymeric bases. The blend with EG adhered perfectly to the solar cells, providing the necessary mechanical support. The current–voltage measurements on the rigid cells and after their transfer to flexible substrates showed that the cell's efficiency remained unchanged following the transfer. Therefore, we can conclude that PVC:PMMA:DOP blends modified with EG show great potential for use as a flexible base in high-efficiency photovoltaic cells.

Keywords: solar cells, PVC-PMMA blends, flexible substrate, flexible solar cells

1 APPLICABLE TOPIC AND SUB-TOPIC NUMBER

High-efficiency solar cells are commonly produced by Metalorganic Vapor Phase Epitaxy (MOVPE) on rigid monocrystalline Gallium Arsenide (GaAs) substrates, which are responsible for eighty percent of the production cost [1,2]. Solar cells based on these III-V materials hold the current world records for photovoltaic conversion efficiency [3] due to their high photon absorption capability and high crystalline quality. The rigid monocrystalline substrate is indispensable as crystallographic base and mechanical support in the fabrication process of the solar cell structure but it is not active during the photovoltaic operation [4].

Removing the rigid substrate and reusing it for sequential depositions may substantially reduce the overall cost of the solar cells [2,5].There is a growing interest in technologies that allow the commercialization of solar cells on light, flexible, and low-cost substrates, expanding not only the range of applicability but also reducing production, transport, and installation costs [6,7]. The transfer of solar cell structures from GaAs substrates to flexible bases has become a growing focus of interest within the scientific community, as highlighted in various studies [8,12]. In our research group, we developed a methodology for the transfer process of III-V solar cells onto flexible copper substrates obtained through electrodeposition and onto copper adhesive tape [13,14].

Polymeric blends are a cost-effective alternative to be used as flexible bases for III-V photovoltaics. Recentely. we have prepared and characterized polymeric blends using poly(vinyl chloride) (PVC) and poly(methyl methacrylate) (PMMA) with plasticizing agents such as dioctyl adipate (DOA) and dioctyl phthalate (DOP) to be used as unprecedented flexible polymeric bases for III-V photovoltaics [15,16]. The properties of PVC:PMMA polymer blends [17-19], incorporated with these plasticizers [20-22], are being extensively studied. The incorporation of rigid and stiff PMMA into PVC partially plasticized with DOP further improves its flexibility and enhances its mechanical and thermal properties [22]. We successfully performed the transfer of InGaAs/GaAs heterostructures onto two different polymer blend compositions, modified with exfoliated graphene (EG) [16]. Photoluminescence measurements confirmed that the III-V structures were not damaged by the transfer process. The emission peak energy of InGaP, after the transfer process, remained steady at approximately 1.85 eV, corresponding to the bandgap energy of bulk InGaP. The exfoliated graphene (EG) was introduced into the blend with the aim of increasing mechanical and thermal resistance, as well as enhancing the adhesion of the polymers to III-V materials [23]. Blends containing exfoliated graphene are optimal candidates as substrates for solar cells, presenting a new opportunity for reducing the cost of high-efficiency devices and expanding the range of photovoltaic applications. In this work, single GaAs solar cells, produced by MOVPE on a rigid GaAs substrate, were transferred to an unprecedented flexible polymer blend of PVC:PMMA:DOP (1.0:1.0:0.5) modified with exfoliated graphene (EG).

2 EXPERIMENTAL DEVELOPMENT

2.1 Process of preparing polymeric blends

The blend PVC:PMMA:DOP (1.0:1.0:0.5) + EG (Fig. 1) was prepared by solution-casting technique in dimethylformamide (DMF) [15,16]. The preparation consists of the gradual dissolution of the polymers in DMF at 60 °C, under magnetic stirring. After 1 hour the plasticizer DOP is added. After 4 hours under stirring, the solution is poured into a Petri dish. The blends were dried under vacuum at 60 °C for 24 hours.

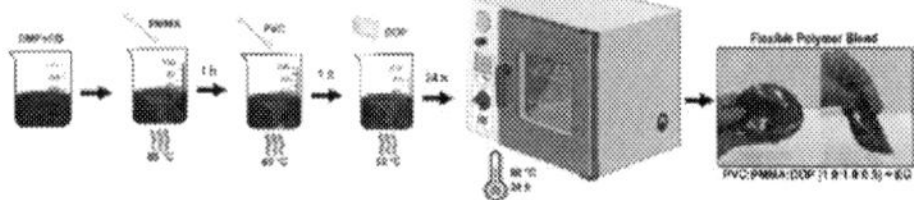

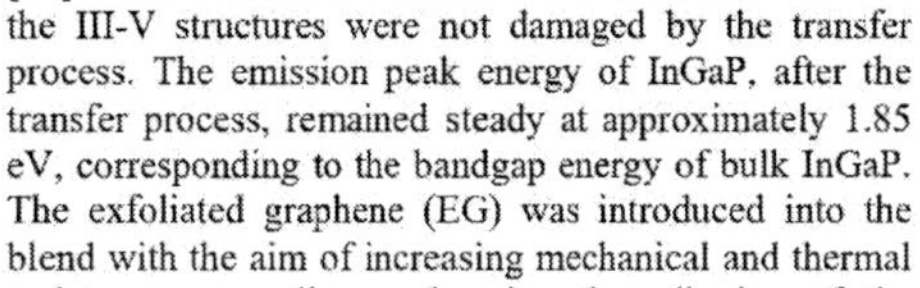

Figure 1: Preparation of the PVC:PMMA:DOP (1.0:1.0:0.5) + EG blend.

2.2 Transfer of GaAs solar cells to polymeric blends

The transfer of solar cell from the GaAs substrates to polymer blends was based on complete etching of the GaAs substrate [13,14], Fig. 2. The process consisted of the following steps: first, a temporary glass substrate was glued over the active layer of the solar cell to ensure mechanical stability. Then, the GaAs substrate was chemically etched using a basic solution of hydrogen peroxide (H_2O_2) and ammonium hydroxide [13,14]. After the etching process, the thin III-V film was ready to be transferred onto the flexible base.

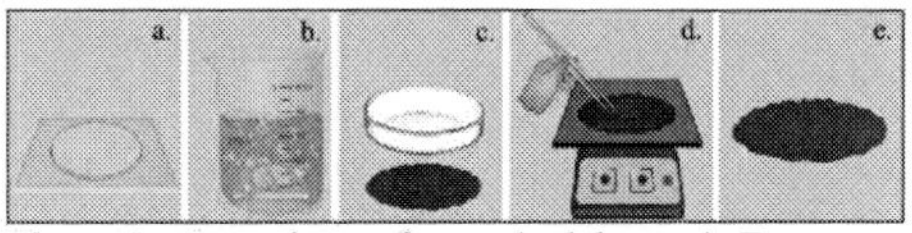

Figure 2: General transfer methodology. a) Temporary substrate bonding (glass); b) complete etching of the GaAs substrate; c) flexible bases adhesion; d) removal of the temporary substrate; e) sample on a flexible substrate [13,14].

GaAs solar cells were transferred to the blend PVC:PMMA:DOP (1.0:1.0:0.5) + EG. The adhesion of the flexible bases to the III-V solar cell occurs during the drying process of the blends, with slow solvent evaporation in a vacuum oven at 60 °C [15,16]. Fig. 3(a) illustrates the structure of a GaAs single-junction solar cell fabricated via MOVPE on a rigid GaAs substrate. Figure 3(b) presents the design of the solar cell mask, while Figure 3(c) shows an image of small solar cells successfully transferred onto the flexible polymer blend. The polymer blend, enriched with EG, adhered seamlessly to the solar cells, providing the required mechanical support. Remarkably, the cells remained intact throughout the entire transfer process.

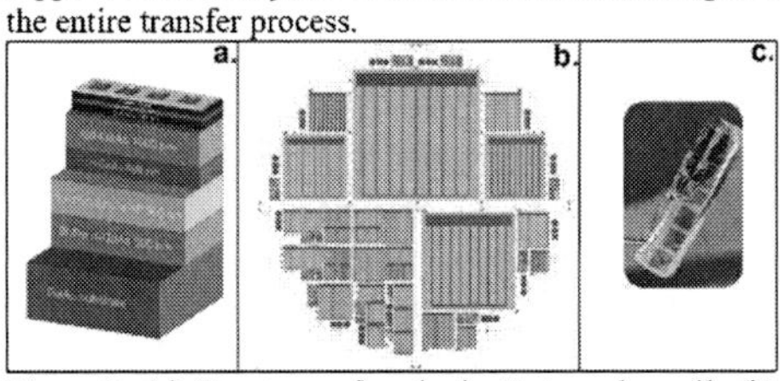

Figure3: (a) Structure of a single GaAs solar cell; (b) Design of a solar cell mask; (c) III-V solar cells transferred onto the blend PVC:PMMA:DOP (1.0:1.0:0.5) + EG.

3 RESULTS AND DISCUSSIONS

The current–voltage measurements were performed using an AM1.5G filter and an incident optical power of 300 W, corresponding to an irradiance of 100 mW/cm², on the rigid cells while still on the GaAs substrate and after their transfer to flexible substrates. The I–V curve measurements in Figure. 4 showed that, after the transfer, the cell's efficiency and other figures of merit, such as open-circuit voltage (Voc), short-circuit current (Isc), and fill factor (FF), showed no significant changes, indicating that the transfer did not compromise the cell's performance.

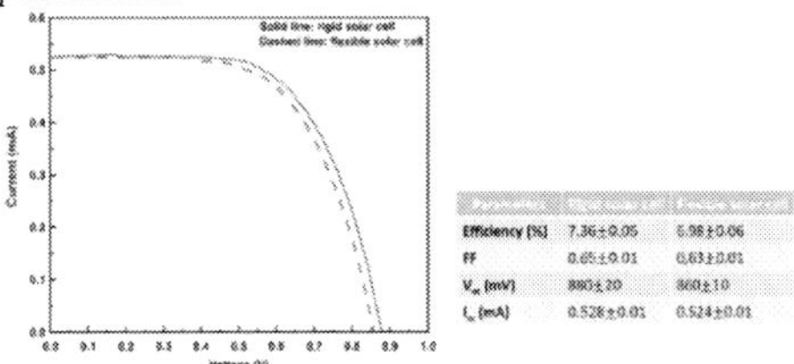

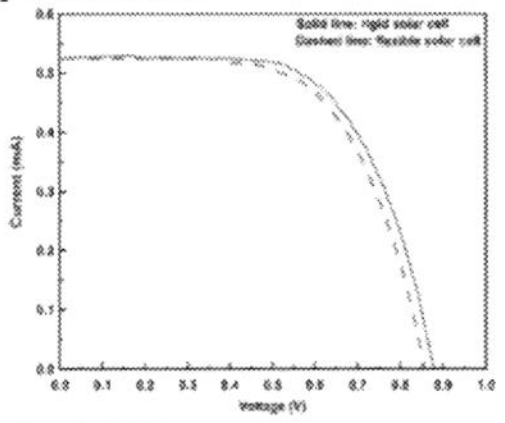

Parameters	Rigid solar cell	Flexible solar cell
Efficiency [%]	7.36±0.05	6.98±0.06
FF	0.65±0.01	0.63±0.01
V_{oc} (mV)	880±20	860±10
I_{sc} (mA)	0.528±0.01	0.524±0.01

Fig 4. I-V measurements at room temperature under the light of the solar simulator with an AM1.5G filter and incident optical power of 300 W.

4 ADDITIONAL COMPONENTS

The GaAs solar cells were successfully transferred onto the flexible PVC:PMMA:DOP (1.0:1.0:0.5) blend modified with exfoliated graphene. The incorporation of graphene into the polymer blend enhanced its thermal resistance and improved its mechanical strength, providing the necessary stability during the transfer process. Current–voltage (I-V) measurements, conducted under AM1.5G solar simulation, showed that the photovoltaic efficiency and other figures of merit were unchanged after the transfer onto flexible substrates. These parameters are essential for assessing the efficiency and overall behavior of solar cells. The fact that all these metrics remained unaltered reinforces the effectiveness of the transfer process and the feasibility of using the graphene-modified flexible blend as a base for high-efficiency solar cells. These results demonstrate that PVC:PMMA:DOP blends modified with exfoliated graphene are promising alternatives for use as flexible substrates in III-V solar cells. The ability to maintain solar cell performance after transferring to flexible substrates marks a significant advancement in making high-efficiency photovoltaic technologies to be used in a wider range of applications. Additionally, we will epitaxially grow new structures for high-efficiency III-V solar cells, and we will explore their transfer onto other polymer blends integrated with with graphene, with the goal of expanding the potential applications of flexible photovoltaic devices.

4.1 References

[1] Lee, Kyusang et al. Reuse of GaAs substrates for epitaxial lift-off by employing protection layers. Journal of Applied Physics, Vol. 111, n. 3, p. 033527, 2012.
[2] Ward, J. Scott et al. Techno-economic analysis of three different substrate removal and reuse strategies for III-V solar cells. Progress in Photovoltaics: Research and Applications, Vol. 24, n. 9, p. 1284-1292, 2016.
[3] NREL.gov, "Best Research-Cell Efficiency Chart," National Renewable Energy Laboratory, 2023, <https://www.nrel.gov/pv/cell-efficiency.html>. Accessed 10 April 2023.J. Clerk Maxwell, A Treatise on Electricity and Magnetism, 3rd ed., vol. 2. Oxford: Clarendon, 1892, pp.68–73.
[4] El-ATab, Nazek; Hussain, Muhammad M. Flexible and stretchable inorganic solar cells: Progress, challenges, and opportunities. MRS Energy & Sustainability, Vol. 7, 2020.
[5] Cheng, Cheng-Wei et al. Epitaxial lift-off process for gallium arsenide substrate reuse and flexible electronics. Nature communications, Vol. 4, n. 1, p. 1-7, 2013.
[6] Schubert, Markus B.; WERNER, Jürgen H. Flexible solar cells for clothing. Materials today, Vol. 9, n. 6, p. 42-50, 2006.
[7] Masuda, Taizo et al. Highly Decorative, Lightweight Flexible Solar Cells for Automotive Applications. SAE Technical Paper, 2019.
[8] Yun, Y., Moon, S., Kim, S., & Lee, J. Flexible fabric-based GaAs thin-film solar cell for wearable energy harvesting applications. *Solar Energy Materials and Solar Cells*, 246, 2022.
[9] Junhua Long, Xuefei Li, Qiangjian Sun, Pan Dai, Yi Zhang, Jingjing Xuan, Feixue Chen, Minghui Song, Shinya Honda, Shiro Uchida, Shulong Lu.. Simple Processing and Analysis of Flexible III–V Multijunction

Solar Cells Using Low-Temperature Transfer Technology. RRL Solar, Volume5, Issue7, 2021.

[10] Bin Zhao, Xian-Sheng Tang, Wen-Xue Huo, Yang Jiang, Zi-Guang Ma, Lu Wang, Wen-Xin Wang, Hong Chen, Hai-Qiang Jia. Characteristics of InGaP/GaAs double junction thin film solar cells on a flexible metallic substrate. Solar Energy, Volume 174, Pages 703-708, 2018.

[11] Moon, S., Kim, K., Kim, Y., Heo, J., & Lee, J. (2016). Highly efficient single-junction GaAs thin-film solar cell on flexible substrate. *Scientific reports*, *6*(1), 1-6, 2016.

[12] Y.H. Lee, K.W. Park, S.J. Kang, C.I. Yeo, J.B. Kim, E.K. Kang, Y.M. Song, Y.T. Lee. Fabrication and analysis of thin-film GaAs solar cell on flexible thermoplastic substrate using a low-pressure cold-welding, Current Applied Physics, Volume 15, Issue 11, Pages 1312-1317, 2015.

[13] B. V. Rocha, M. O. Silva, L. D. Pinto and P. L. Souza, "III-V solar cells transferred to flexible substrates based on Cu," *36th Symposium on Microelectronics Technology (SBMICRO)*, Porto Alegre, Brazil, 2022, pp. 1-4, 2022.

[14] M. O. Silva, "Células de multijunções de alta eficiência: Metodologias para transferência de materiais semicondutores III-V de forma reprodutível para substrato flexível," (master's dissertation). Departamento de Engenharia Elétrica, PUC-Rio, 2021.

[15] G. S. Sousa, L. D. Pinto, F. C. Tavares, P. L. Souza, *et al.*, "Preparation and characterization of PVC-PMMA polymer blends as flexible bases for III–V photovoltaics," *2023 37th Symposium on Microelectronics Technology and Devices (SBMicro)*, Rio de Janeiro, Brazil, 2023, pp. 1-4, 2023.

[16] G. S. Sousa *et al.*, "Transfer of InGaP/GaAs thin-film to unprecedented flexible polymeric bases of PVC:PMMA:DOP modified with EG for solar cell applications," *2024 38th Symposium on Microelectronics Technology and Devices (SBMicro)*, Joao Pessoa, Brazil, 2024, pp. 1-4, 2024.

[17] V. V. Soman, and D. S. Kelkar, "FTIR Studies of Doped PMMA - PVC Blend System". Macromolecular Symposia: POLYCHAR – 16 World Forum on Advanced Materials, vol. 277, pp. 152 – 161, March 2009.

[18] M. S. Khan, R. A. Qazi, and M. S. Wahid, "Miscibility studies of PVC/PMMA and PS/PMMA blends by dilute solution viscometry and FTIR," African Journal of Pure and Applied Chemistry, vol. 2, pp. 41 – 45, April 2008.

[19] S. Ramesh, and CW. Liew, "Development and investigation on PMMA– PVC blend-based solid polymer electrolytes with LiTFSI as dopant salt," Polymer Bulletin, vol.70, pp. 1277–1288, April 2013.

[20] Thamil Selvi Velayutham, Miscibility and immiscibility in PVC-based blends, IPNs, and gels, Editor(s): Sabu Thomas, H. Akhina, Poly(vinyl chloride)-based Blends, Interpenetrating Polymer Networks (IPNs), and Gels, Elsevier, Pages 377-400, 2024.

[21] Hofmann, G.H. (1985). Polymer Blend Modification of PVC. In: Walsh, D.J., Higgins, J.S., Maconnachie, A. (eds) Polymer Blends and Mixtures. NATO ASI Series, vol 89. Springer, Dordrecht.

[22] R. Chakrabarti, M. Das and D. Chakraborty, Physical, mechanical, and thermal properties of PVC/PMMA blends in relation to their morphologies. J. Appl. Polymer Science 93, 2721, 2004.

[23] Razaq, A. *et al.* Review on Graphene-, Graphene Oxide-, Reduced Graphene Oxide-Based Flexible Composites: From Fabrication to Applications. Materials, 15(3), 1012, 2022.

42nd European Photovoltaic Solar Energy Conference and Exhibition

Transfer of GaAs solar cells to unprecedented flexible polymeric bases of PVC:PMMA:DOP modified with EG

Graciana S. Sousa[1]; Luciana D. Pinto[1]; Fabiele C. Tavares[2]; Guillermo J. N. Soares[2]; Rudy M. S. Kawabata[3]; Guilherme M. Torelly[3]; Rogério Valaski[4]; Maurício P. Pires[1]; Roberto Jakomin[2]; Patrícia L. Souza[1]

[1]*Instituto de Física - Universidade Federal do Rio de Janeiro*, Rio de Janeiro, Brazil;

[2]*Campus Duque de Caxias - Universidade Federal do Rio de Janeiro*, Duque de Caxias, Brazil;

[3]*Laboratório de Semicondutores (LabSem) - Pontifícia Universidade Católica do Rio de Janeiro*, Rio de Janeiro, Brazil;

[4]*Laboratório de Fenômenos de Superfície/DIMAT - Instituto Nacional de Metrologia* Rio de Janeiro, Brazil.

I. Introduction

- High-efficiency solar cells based on III-V materials, such as Gallium Arsenide (GaAs) have a high production cost, with the **substrate accounting for 80% of this value.**
- A promising cost-reduction strategy is to transfer the solar cell structure to a **low-cost, flexible base**, which allows for the reuse of the original substrate.
- We developed polymeric blends of poly(vinyl chloride) (**PVC**), poly(methyl methacrylate) (**PMMA**) with a dioctyl phthalate (**DOP**) plasticizer, modified with exfoliated graphene (**EG**).
- Exfoliated graphene enhances mechanical resistance and thermal stability, as well as adhesion of the polymeric blend to the thin film solar cell.

II. Objectives

Transfer GaAs solar cells, produced by Metalorganic Vapor Phase Epitaxy (MOVPE) on a rigid GaAs substrate, to a flexible polymer blend of PVC:PMMA:DOP (1.0:1.0:0.5) modified with exfoliated graphene (EG).

III. Materials and Methods

- **Preparation of polymeric blend**

  The blend PVC:PMMA:DOP (1.0:1.0:0.5) + EG was prepared by solution-casting technique in dimethylformamide (DMF) [1, 2].

  The preparation consists of the gradual dissolution of the polymers in DMF at 60 °C, under magnetic stirring. After 1 hour the plasticizer DOP is added. After 4 hours under stirring, the solution is poured into a Petri dish.

  The blends were dried under vacuum at 60 °C for 24 hours.
- **Preparation of the solar cell for substrate transfer**

  A p-i-n solar cell was grown by MOVPE on a GaAs substrate with an InGaP stop-etch layer. This layer enables selective etching of the substrate without damaging the active region.
- **Substrate transfer**

  Prior to etching, the solar cell's front-side is attached to a temporary glass substrate using a removable glue.

  The substrate is then completely etched under controlled conditions.

  On a petri dish, the liquid blend is poured over the backside of the solar cell. After drying for 24 hours in a vacuum oven at 60°C, the blend is stable and the glass is removed from the solar cell's front side.
- **Solar cell characterization**

  The current–voltage measurements were performed under AM1.5g illumination, before and after flexibilization of the solar cells

IV. Results and Conclusion

- GaAs single-junction cells were successfully transferred onto a flexible blend: PVC:PMMA:DOP + EG (1.0:1.0:0.5).
- The blend adhered perfectly to the III-V semiconductor films, providing the necessary mechanical support.
- I–V measurements on the rigid and flexible cells, indicate preserved optoelectronic and photovoltaic performance after the transfer.
- The PVC:PMMA:DOP blends with EG have great potential to be used as a flexible base for III-V solar cells.

Next steps:

- Transfer III-V cells to novel blends with.
- Fabricate a GaAs solar cell with a selective sacrificial layer for epitaxial lift-off and substrate reuse.

Base solar cell structure

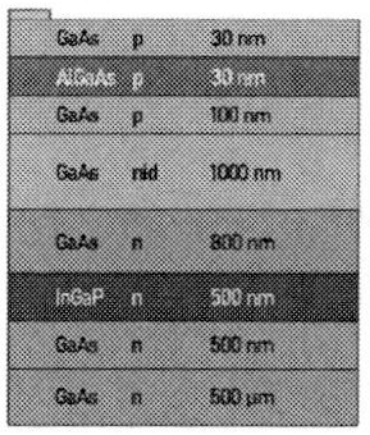

Rigid GaAs solar cell

Structure after substrate etching and polymer casting

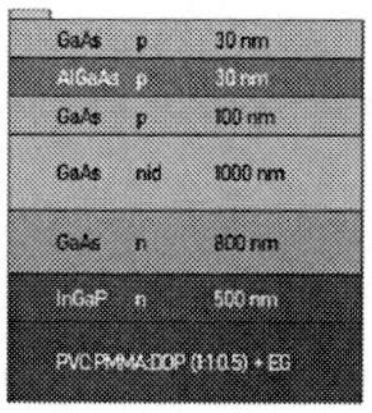

Flexible GaAs solar cell

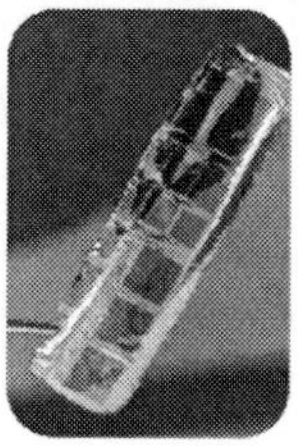

Preparation of the PVC:PMMA:DOP blend with exfoliated graphene

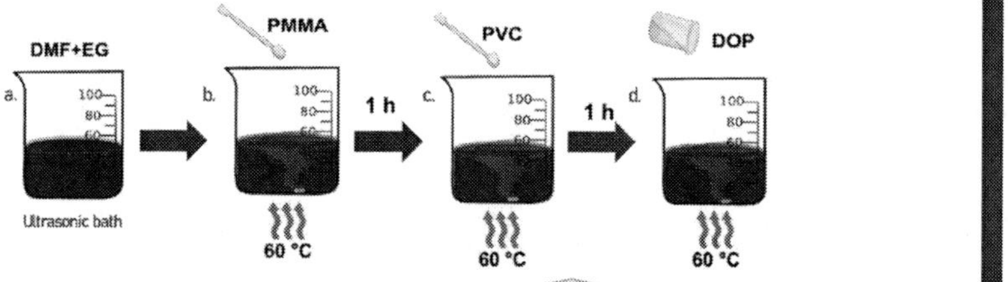

a. Exfoliated graphene is mixed to DMF in an ultrasonic bath;
b. PMMA is added to the solution;
c. PVC is added to the solution;
d. DOP is added to the solution;
e. The blend is dried under vacuum at 60°C for 14 hours;
f. The flexible polymer blend is obtained.

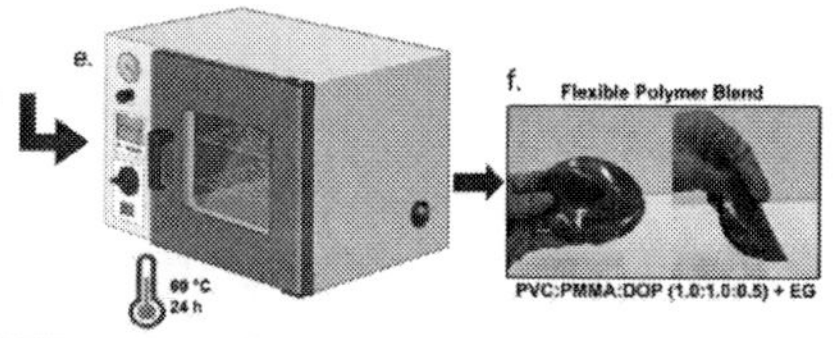

Substrate transfer procedure

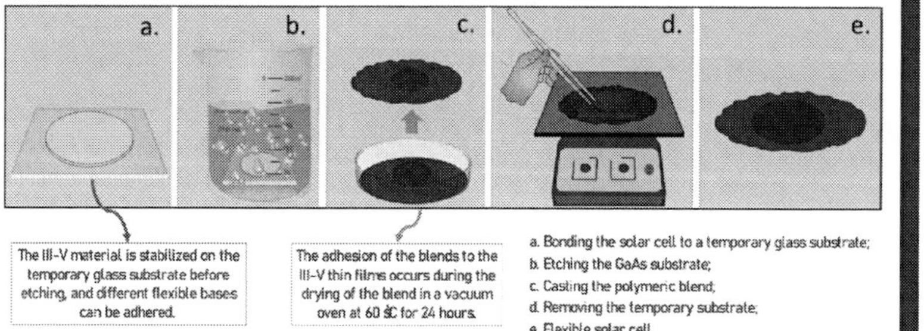

The III-V material is stabilized on the temporary glass substrate before etching, and different flexible bases can be adhered.

The adhesion of the blends to the III-V thin films occurs during the drying of the blend in a vacuum oven at 60 $C for 24 hours.

a. Bonding the solar cell to a temporary glass substrate;
b. Etching the GaAs substrate;
c. Casting the polymeric blend;
d. Removing the temporary substrate;
e. Flexible solar cell.

Photovoltaic parameters of solar cell B before and after transfer to flexible substrates.

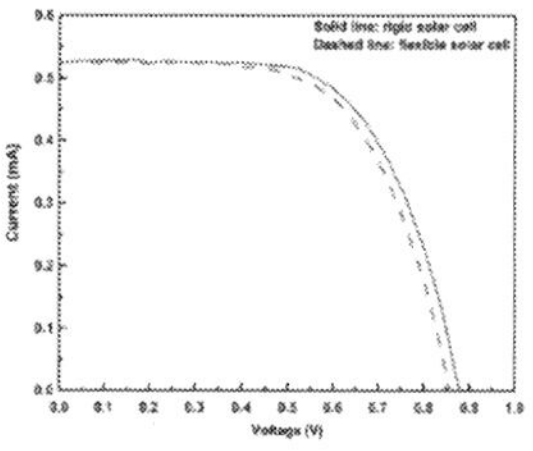

Parameters	Rigid	Flexible
Efficiency (%)	7.36±0.05	6.98±0.06
FF	0.65±0.01	0.63±0.01
V_{oc} (mV)	880±20	860±10
I_{sc} (mA)	0.528±0.01	0.524±0.01

References

[1] G. S. Sousa, L. D. Pinto, F. C. Tavares, P. L. Souza, *et al.*, "Preparation and characterization of PVC-PMMA polymer blends as flexible bases for III–V photovoltaics," *2023 37th Symposium on Microelectronics Technology and Devices (SBMicro)*, Rio de Janeiro, Brazil, 2023, pp. 1-4, 2023.

[2] G. S. Sousa *et al.*, "Transfer of InGaP/GaAs thin-film to unprecedented flexible polymeric bases of PVC:PMMA:DOP modified with EG for solar cell applications," *2024 38th Symposium on Microelectronics Technology and Devices (SBMicro)*, Joao Pessoa, Brazil, 2024, pp. 1-4, 2024.

Acknowledgments

This work was sponsored by the National Council for Scientific and Technological Development – CNPq, via the grant 444979/2024-7.
Financiadora de Estudos e Projetos (FINEP) - Brazil.
Fundação de Amparo à Pesquisa do Estado do Rio de Janeiro (FAPERJ) - Brazil;
Coordenação de Aperfeiçoamento de Pessoal de Nível Superior (CAPES) – Brazil.
The authors would like to thank Daniel N. Micha (Nokia Bell Labs), Braulio S. Arcanjo (UFRJ), Maria Luiza Rocco (UFRJ) and Clara M. Almeida (INMETRO) for their collaboration to the research

UFRJ UNIVERSIDADE FEDERAL DO RIO DE JANEIRO | LabSem LABORATÓRIO DE SEMICONDUTORES DEE/PUC-RIO | PUC RIO | Campus UFRJ Duque de Caxias Prof. Geraldo Cidade | INMETRO

020091-001

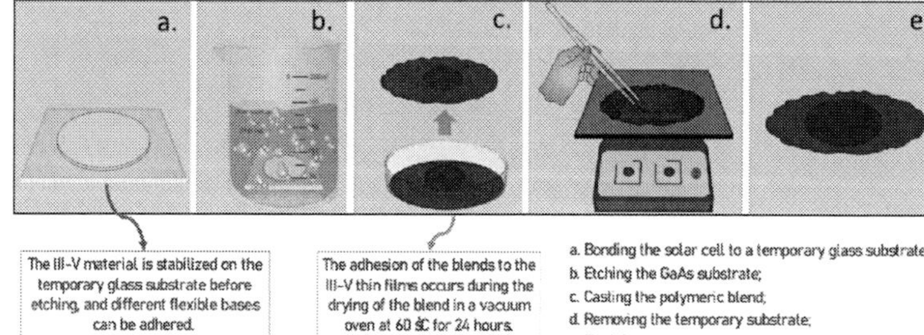

Development and Characterization of a Glued GaAs/Si Tandem Solar Cell in Four-Terminal Configuration

W. M. M. Bazilio[1*], R. M. S. Kawabata[1], L. D. Pinto[2], D. N. Micha[3,1], P. L. Souza[2], G. M. Torelly[1]
[1] Department of Electrical Engineering - PUC-Rio, Rio de Janeiro, RJ, Brazil
[2] Institute of Physics - UFRJ, Rio de Janeiro, RJ, Brazil
[3] Department of Physics - CEFET/RJ, Petrópolis, RJ, Brazil
willian.m.bazilio@aluno.puc-rio.br

ABSTRACT: This work demonstrates a cost-effective fabrication method for a four-terminal (4T) GaAs/Si tandem solar cell using a commercial epoxy for mechanical stacking. The process involves the fabrication of individual cells, removal of the original GaAs substrate, and subsequent bonding. We characterized the electrical and optical properties of both subcells before and after integration.

After bonding, the silicon cell showed a significant performance drop, with an 81% loss in efficiency and an 88% reduction in short-circuit current density. The GaAs cell's performance was less affected, with a 17% decrease in efficiency. The final combined efficiency of the tandem device reached approximately 7%, which is lower than the initial 9.4% efficiency of the standalone Si cell.

The performance degradation is primarily attributed to optical losses from Fabry-Perot interference and increased surface roughness after processing. This initial study validates the bonding approach and identifies clear pathways for improvement, such as implementing anti-reflective coatings and optimizing the GaAs cell structure, to advance III-V/Si integration.

Keywords: Tandem solar cell; Epoxy bonding; III-V/Silicon; Substrate Removal; GaAs/Si

1 INTRODUCTION

The combination of III-V semiconductors with silicon has garnered significant interest in optoelectronic research due to their superior optical properties for photon absorption and versatility in tuning the energy gap. These same semiconductors, on the other hand, are constrained by high production costs and fabrication complexity, in contrast to Si which is abundant, cost-effective, and benefits from advanced technological development and large-scale manufacturing.

The integration of III-V semiconductors with Si for photovoltaic applications was first explored in the 1980s [1, 2], driven by advancements in epitaxial growth techniques that enabled high-efficiency optoelectronic devices. However, the high cost of III-V solar cells limited their use to niche applications, such as space stations and satellites. Currently, approximately 95% of global solar cell production relies on Si [3, 4], and through innovations such as PERC, TOPCon, and HJT technologies, Si solar cell experimental efficiencies have come closer to the theoretical limit of 30% [5]. Meanwhile, III-V solar cells have achieved record efficiencies in the past decades [6]. To overcome the theoretical efficiency limit of single-junction solar cells, tandem structures combining III-V and Si have emerged as a promising solution and have already achieved efficiencies above the 30% barrier [7,8].

Although direct epitaxial growth of III-V materials on silicon has been explored, the results have been limited due to factors such as the mismatch in lattice parameters, which makes it difficult to achieve high crystal quality and induces defects in the structure, thereby affecting device performance. Additionally, the difference in thermal expansion coefficients hinders stability during growth and/or integration, and an optimized structure is required to ensure proper current matching between the different materials [9]. Another approach being studied involves direct bonding of the devices without intermediate adhesives. However, this technique requires specialized equipment for substrate cleaning and polishing, as well as a controlled environment with specific pressure and temperature conditions for the bonding process, which increases the cost of the device [10]. A more viable alternative involves growing III-V solar cells on III-V substrates and transferring the active layers onto silicon solar cells through bonding with glass and epoxy adhesive. This configuration, operating in a four-terminal arrangement, enables optical coupling while maintaining electrical insulation between the devices [11,12].

In 2015, Essig et al. [13] used a transparent epoxy adhesive (TRA-BOND-931-1) to mechanically bond an InGaP cell to a Si cell in a four-terminal configuration, achieving an efficiency of 27%. In 2017, process improvements, including antireflection coatings and the replacement of the original substrate with a glass slide, increased the efficiencies of tandem cells to 32.8% (GaAs/Si) and 35.9% (InGaP/GaAs/Si) [14,15]. More recently, in 2023, Fraunhofer ISE, in collaboration with the AMOLF Institute, set a record efficiency of 36.1% in a tandem solar cell composed of InGaP and InGaAsP layers, featuring a metal-dielectric reflector to enhance light trapping in the bottom cell, as well as a metal/polymer nanocoating. The bottom cell was a state-of-the-art Si (TOPCon) solar cell, integrated through surface-activated wafer bonding [16].

In this study, we fabricated a GaAs/Si tandem solar cell in a four-terminal configuration and performed electrical and optical characterization of the device. We investigated the performance of both the Si and GaAs solar cells prior and after the integration was made to analyze their individual behavior. In this arrangement, the devices operate independently, since the epoxy layer and glass slide ensure electrical insulation post-integration. An advantage to analyzing the system in this approach over a two-terminal configuration is that the currents generated by the individual cells are not constrained to a series connection, enabling optimization of both solar cells independently.

2 AIM AND APPROACH

The Si solar cell was fabricated at the Photovoltaic Solar Energy Laboratory (LB-Solar) at PUC-RS, with dimensions of 2 × 2 cm². It features a PERT (n^+pp^+) structure, a silicon dioxide passivation layer, and a thin

10.4229/EUPVSEC2025/2BV.2.6

titanium dioxide film as an anti-reflective coating. The GaAs solar cell was fabricated at LabSem/PUC-Rio, with dimensions of 2 × 2 cm² and an active area of 1.5 × 1.5 cm². Its layered structure consists of a top contact (GaAs-*p*), a 30 nm thick window layer (AlGaAs-*p*), a 200 nm thick emitter (GaAs-*p*), a 1 µm thick base (GaAs-*nid*), a 800 nm thick back contact (GaAs-*n*), a 500 nm thick sacrificial layer (GaInP-*n*), and a 500 nm buffer layer (GaAs-*n*) grown on a GaAs-n substrate. The structure does not include an anti-reflective coating or a back surface field (BSF) layer.

The photolithographic mask used in processing was designed to allow access to both contacts from the top of the device. The metallic contacts consisted of Ti/Pt/Au : 20/100/200 nm for the front; and Ni/Ge/Au : 25/55/150 nm for the back contact.

We initially performed the electrical and optical characterization of both the Si and GaAs solar cells prior to forming the tandem device. A solar simulator system (SF300A, Sciencetech) was used as the light source, and a semiconductor parameter analyzer (HP 4145B) was employed to measure the *IV*-curve from which we extract the figures of merit J_{SC}, V_{OC}, *FF*, and efficiency (η). The quantum efficiency and the optical properties (in this case, transmittance) were measured using a white light source, a monochromator, and a calibrated Si sensor (SM05PD3A, Thorlabs) as can be seen in Figure 1(c). After bonding the solar cells (Figure 1(a)), we performed electrical characterization in a four-terminal configuration to simulate a real operating condition (Figure 1(b)). For this purpose, a semiconductor parameter analyzer was used to apply a constant voltage of 0.74 V to the GaAs cell, corresponding to its point of maximum extracted power. Subsequently, the parameters of the Si cell were measured using a programmable power supply and a multimeter, both controlled by a Python-based software developed at LabSem-PUC-Rio.

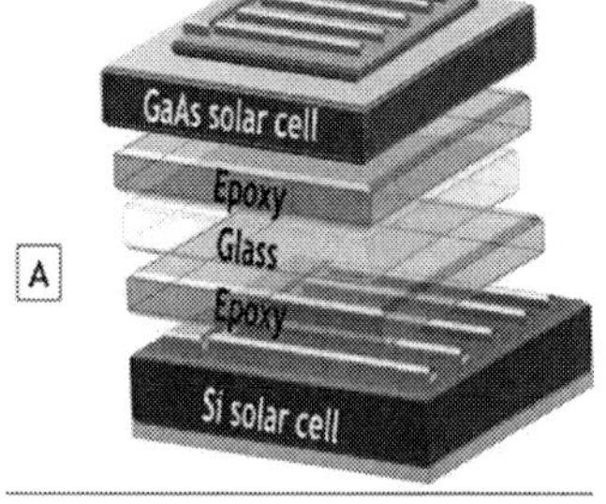

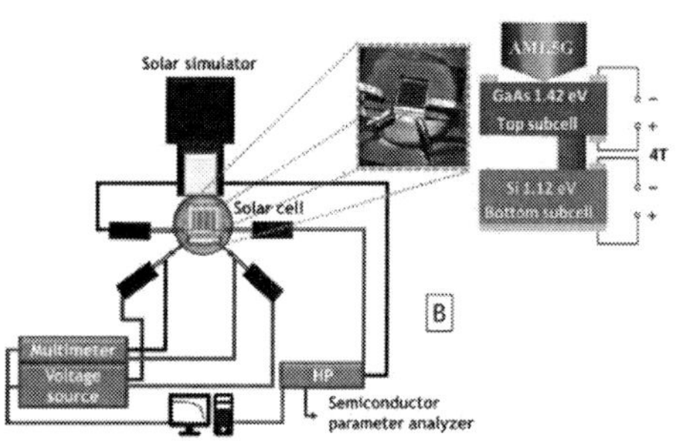

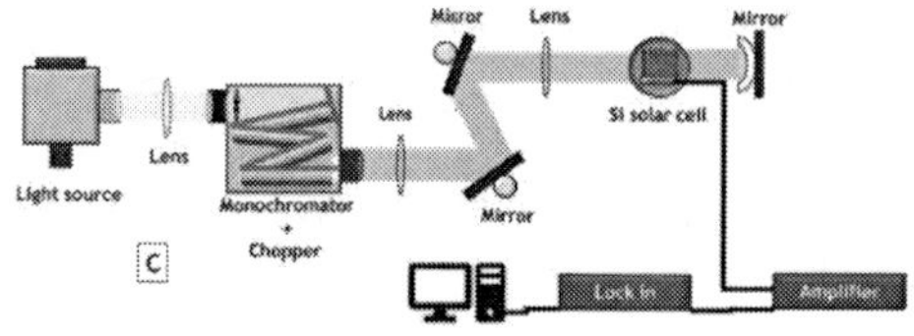

Figure 1: (a) the exploded schematic of the GaAs/Si tandem solar cell, (b) the setup to measure the solar cell's I-V curve, and (c) the setup employed to measure the optical and optoelectronic properties of the solar cells, the epoxy and the glass slide.

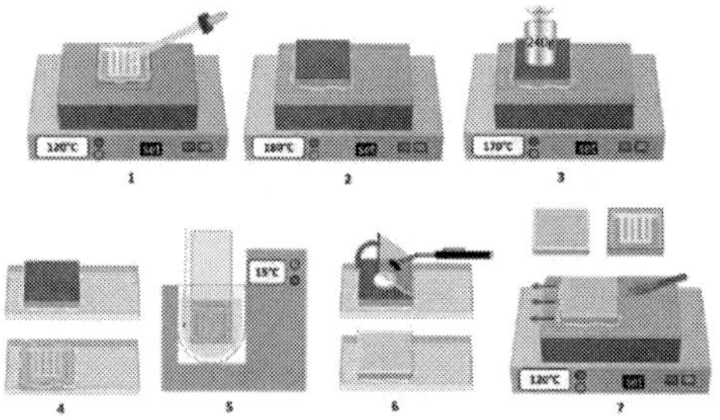

Figure 2: Steps for the processing of the GaAs/Si tandem solar cell.

In this investigation we have analyzed the influence of the GaAs substrate and the impact of its removal, resulting in a 55% increase in J_{SC}, 23% in V_{OC}, 21% in *FF*, and 72% in efficiency of the Si subcell after integration. For the removal of the GaAs substrate, the GaAs solar cell was attached to a glass substrate with the use of a temporary adhesive (WaferBOND HT-10.10).

The aforementioned adhesive was applied using spin coating for uniformity (350 RPM for 30 seconds) and cured under 120, 180 and 170 °C while a 214 g weight was applied (Figure 2(1, 2, 3)). For its removal, the next step was to etch the GaAs substrate down to the InGaP layer using a solution of hydrogen peroxide and ammonium hydroxide. The solution's temperature was maintained constant at 15 °C throughout the procedure using a chiller (Figure 2(5)), and the etching process took 1 hour and 45 minutes.

After the etching procedure, the GaAs solar cell thin film was bonded to a glass slide with epoxy (EPO-TEK 353 ND), and is represented in Figure 2(6). Once the GaAs thin film was stabilized on this glass slide with epoxy, the temporary adhesive and its glass substrate could be removed. A hotplate at 120 °C cured the epoxy in 5 minutes but required an additional 10 minutes to soften the temporary adhesive. The removal of the GaAs solar cell from the glass substrate was performed by mechanically sliding it after the adhesive softened, as illustrated in Figure 2(7). Remaining adhesive residue was removed using a proprietary solvent (HT-10.10). Finally, the GaAs solar cell with epoxy and glass slide was bonded to the Si solar cell with the same epoxy using the same procedure, reaching the final schematic represented in Figure 1(a).

3 RESULTS AND CONCLUSIONS

We probed the performance of the Si and GaAs solar cells individually before and after bonding. We obtained their *I-V* curves and quantum efficiencies shown in Figure 3, from which we extracted the parameters J_{SC}, V_{OC}, FF, and η, as shown in Table 1.

Table I: Parameters of Si and GaAs cells before and after bonding

Si SC	Bonding		Δ (%)
	Before	**After**	
J_{sc} (mA/cm²)	26.0	5.7	-88
V_{oc} (V)	0.50	0.48	-4
FF (%)	72	65	-10
η (%)	9.4	1.8	-81
GaAs SC	**Before**	**After**	**Δ (%)**
J_{sc} (mA/cm²)	9.8	8.7	-11
V_{oc} (V)	0.92	0.96	+4
FF (%)	68	61	-10
η (%)	6.2	5.1	-17

The Si solar cell, whose *I-V* curve is shown in magenta in Figure 3, exhibited initial values of J_{SC} = 26.0 mA/cm², V_{OC} = 0.50 V, FF = 72%, and $\eta \approx$ 9.4%. After coupling, these values dropped to J_{SC} = 5.7 mA/cm², V_{OC} = 0.48 V, FF = 65%, and $\eta \approx$ 1.8% (extracted from the dark yellow curve in Figure 3). This corresponds to a reduction of approximately 88% in J_{SC}, 10% in FF and 4% in V_{OC}, leading to a total loss of 81% in efficiency. The integral quantum efficiency of the silicon solar cell after integration (shown in dark yellow in Figure 4) decreased by approximately 39% in the 870–1100 nm wavelength range with respect to its value before integration (in magenta in Figure 4).

The GaAs solar cell before integration, whose *I-V* curve is shown in blue in Figure 3, presented J_{SC} = 9.8 mA/cm², V_{OC} = 0.92 V, FF = 68%, and η = 6.2%. Its quantum efficiency is far below unity (light blue curve in Figure 4) in the useful spectral range due to a non-optimal design of the structure and the lack of an anti-reflective coating in the front surface. The post-coupling *I-V* curve (orange in Figure 3) shows that the GaAs solar cell experienced reductions of 11% in J_{SC},10% in FF, and 17% in efficiency. Its quantum efficiency curve (light blue in Figure 4) showed that the GaAs solar cell exhibited a 26% reduction compared to the same cell after substrate removal (shown in orange).

The deterioration in performance observed in both solar cells can be attributed to several factors. The largest performance loss occurred in the J_{SC} of the Si solar cell. This drop can be attributed to two factors: the thickness of the GaAs top cell (~2 μm) and the absence of anti-reflective coatings. The lack of coatings leads to destructive Fabry-Perot interference, which compromises the device's overall efficiency. The oscillations observed in the spectral range absorbed by the Si cell, revealed in the dark yellow curve in Figure 4, result from the Fabry-Perot interferences of the light crossing the GaAs solar cell. This effect is one of the main factors responsible for the reduction in the available light for the Si cell. Another critical factor is the roughness of the thinned GaAs cell surface introduced upon removal of the temporary glass substrate. This roughness increases light reflection on the front surface, preventing uniform incidence and further degrading the device's performance. Furthermore, the analysis of the quantum efficiency curve of the Si cell below 870 nm in tandem configuration (tail in the dark yellow curve in Figure 4) reveals that the GaAs cell does not fully absorb the solar spectrum with wavelengths below its bandgap, which reinforces the need for optimization of its structure. Nonetheless, this shows the benefit and the effectiveness of the process used for the top solar cell thinning, as approximately 7% of the useful sunlight was lost to the GaAs substrate prior to the processing and integration.

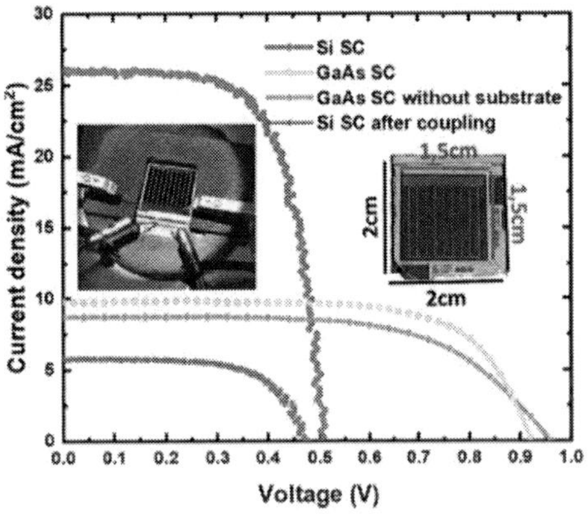

Figure 3: I-V curves of the GaAs and Si solar cells before and after the tandem formation.

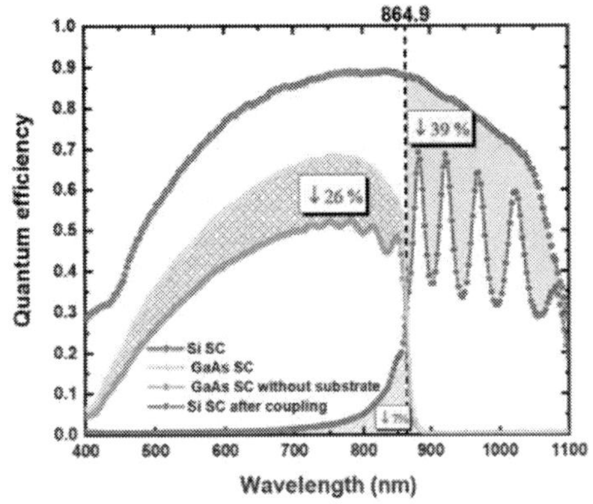

Figure 4: Quantum efficiency of the GaAs and Si solar cells before and after the tandem formation.

This study demonstrated the successful fabrication of a 4T bonded GaAs/Si tandem solar cell using commercially available and low-cost materials, such as epoxy and glass. Despite the 7% combined efficiency, which is lower than that of the standalone silicon cell (9.4%), the results provided valuable insights for future optimizations in the GaAs cell structure and the substrate transfer process. Based on transmittance and quantum efficiency measurements, it will be possible to design optimized anti-reflective coatings for the air/GaAs (front) and GaAs/epoxy+glass (rear) interfaces, reducing optical losses associated with Fabry-Perot destructive interferences. Structural improvements also include optimizing the GaAs active layer thickness for efficient absorption below 870 nm, incorporating a BSF layer to minimize recombination near the back contact, optimizing the layer doping levels and refining the fabrication process of the silicon cells to improve optical and electrical matching, while reducing shading after integration. Another critical aspect to be investigated is the surface roughness observed after the GaAs cell transfer, which affects reflectance and overall device performance.

Implementing these improvements is essential to achieve higher efficiencies in both devices and further establishing the bonding technique as a competitive approach for III-V/Si tandem cell integration. In addition to improving the individual cells' performance in the tandem configuration, we aim to include other techniques to reduce the cost of III-V integrated solar cells, such as epitaxial lift-off and light management techniques to reduce the required volume of materials.

4 References

[1] Gee, J. M. et al. 31%-efficient GaAs/Si mechanically stacked MJ solar cell. *IEEE PVSC*, 1:754–758, 1988.

[2] Jain, N. et al. III–V/Si multijunction integration: Challenges and outlook. *Energy Harvest. Syst.*, 1(3-4):121–145, 2014.

[3] Fraunhofer ISE. *Photovoltaic Report*, 2021.

[4] SolarPower Europe. *Global Market Outlook for Solar Power 2021-2025*, 2021

[5] Shockley, W., Queisser, H. J. Detailed balance limit of pn junction efficiency. *J. Appl. Phys.*, 32(3):510–519, 1961.

[6] NREL. *Cell Efficiency Chart*. Disponível em: https://www.nrel.gov/pv/cell-efficiency.html.

[7] Green, M. A. et al. Solar cell efficiency tables (version 62). *Prog. Photovolt: Res. Appl.*, 29:657, 2021.

[8] Schygulla, P. et al. High-efficiency III-V/Si tandem cells. *Prog. Photovolt: Res. Appl.*, 30:869, 2021.

[9] Green, M. A. et al. Solar cell efficiency tables (version 64). *Prog. Photovolt: Res. Appl.*, 31(7):651–663, 2023.

[10] Tanabe, Katsuaki. "Semiconductor Wafer Bonding for Solar Cell Applications: A Review." Advanced Energy and Sustainability Research 4.11 (2023): 2300073.

[11] Bazilio, W. M. M. et al. Epoxy bonding techniques for III-V/Si tandem cells. *SBMicro*, IEEE, 2024.

[12] Zhang, P. et al. Intermediate connection of subcells in Si-based tandem cells. *Small Methods*, 8:2300432, 2024.

[13] Essig, S. et al. Progress in III-V/Si tandem solar cells. *Energy Procedia*, 77:464, 2015.

[14] Essig, S. et al. Advances in III-V/Si tandem cell fabrication. *IEEE J. Photovolt.*, 6:1012, 2016.

[15] Essig, S. et al. Development of high-efficiencytandem cells. *Nat. Energy*, 2:17144, 2017.

[16] Fraunhofer ISE & AMOLF. Silicon-based MJ cell reaches 36.1% efficiency, 2023. Disponível em:https://www.ise.fraunhofer.de. [Acesso em: 23 jan. 2025].

Comparison of Flexible Molybdenum Foil and Sputtered Molybdenum Back Contacts for CZTSSe Solar Cells.

Ikram Anefnaf, Giorgio Tseberlidis[+], Simona Binetti[+], Alessandro Veneri, Elisa Artegiani, and Alessandro Romeo

LAPS-Laboratory of Photovoltaic and Solid-State Physics, Department of Computer Science, University of Verona, Strada Le Grazie 15, 37134 Verona, Italy

[+]Milano-Bicocca Solar Energy Research Center (MIB-SOLAR), Dipartimento di Scienza dei Materiali, Università degli Studi di Milano-Bicocca

Abstract —
Molybdenum foil (MoF) flexible substrates have attracted significant interest in fabricating kesterite thin-film solar cells, thanks to their potential for lightweight, flexible, and large-scale applications. However, one of the main key challenges with MoF is the absence of sodium, typically introduced from soda-lime glass (SLG) substrates, which is critical in enhancing CZTSSe film quality. To address this, a thin layer of NaF has been deposited on top of the MoF to balance the absence of sodium and thus enable enhanced grain growth and crystallinity. In this paper, the deposition processes were optimized systematically with respect to absorber quality and device performance. Solar cells have been characterized, and their performance has been compared with reference devices processed on sputtered Mo. Preliminary results showed low-performing devices based only on Mo foil. However, upon incorporating the pre-deposited NaF layer, efficiency increased to 2.5%. These preliminary results suggest that Mo foil is a promising substrate for flexible CZTSSe solar cells and, upon optimization, could reach performance comparable to standard devices on sputtered Mo back contacts.

I. INTRODUCTION

The performance of the CZTSSe-based solar cells has been significantly improved by enormous efforts in these years, which therefore stands out as one of the most promising alternatives to traditional silicon-based photovoltaics. Among various influencing factors that determine the performance of CZTSSe solar cells, the quality of the back contact plays a leading role [1], [2], [3].

The back contact is vital in effective charge collection, reducing resistive losses, and ensuring optimal device performance. The molybdenum foil (MF) is emerging as a promising alternative because it offers several advantages, such as low cost, flexibility, ease of fabrication and improved thermal stability [4], [5]. the MF as a back contact material may provide unique opportunities for optimizing the performance of CZTSSe solar cells; however, its impacts on the overall efficiency and performance are still under investigation. Although promising, further research is needed to understand it completely.

The primary objective of the present work is to analyze the performances of the CZTSSe solar cells using different back contact substrates comparatively. By analyzing the resulting device characteristics, we aim to identify the advantages and challenges of using Mo foil as an alternative to the traditionally used sputtered Mo. This study is still ongoing, and several optimizations during the deposition and characterization as well are under active investigation, with extensive characterizations for a better understanding of how changing the back contact affects the overall performance of devices. One of the key focuses of this work was to tackle the back contact defects, one of the major issues that limit the efficiency and performance of CZTSSe-based solar cells.

II. MATERIALS AND DEVICE FABRICATION

A. *CZTS ink preparation*

The CZTS ink is prepared by dissolving zinc acetate dihydrate, copper acetate monohydrate, tin chloride, and thiourea in 2-methoxyethanol at room temperature. The precursor is then deposited on a previously RF-sputtered Mo thin glass by spin coating.

B. *Thin film and device fabrication*

For the fabrication of devices, three batches of samples were prepared. Sputtered Mo was used as the back contact in the first batch, deposited through RF-magnetron sputtering on soda lime glass substrates. The prepared CZTS ink was spin-coated onto the sputtered Mo stack at 2400 rpm for 15 seconds and then dried in the air on a hotplate at 310 °C for 5 minutes. The samples were subsequently annealed in a tubular furnace under a selenium atmosphere to form the CZTSSe absorber. This step was followed by depositing a thin 50 nm CdS layer using chemical bath deposition (CBD) and an i-ZnO/ITO stack via sputtering to complete the solar cell structure.

The second batch followed the same deposition conditions, but molybdenum foil was employed as a flexible substrate. The third batch used the same process as the second batch, with minor differences, incorporating a thin coating of NaF formed by thermal evaporation over an MoF-flexible substrate.

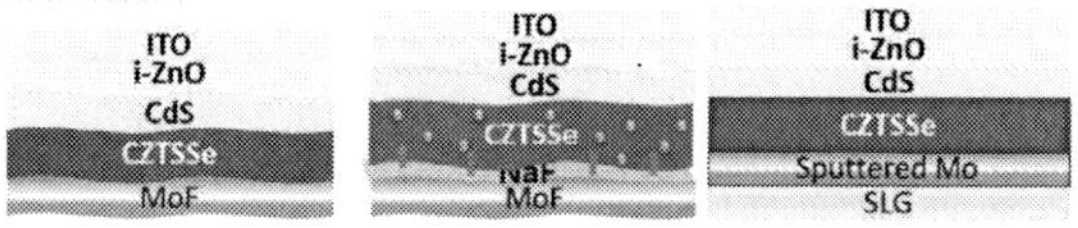

Fig. 1. Schematic illustration of CZTSSe solar cells based on different back contact substrates used in this work.

III. Results and discussions

AFM images of CZTSSe thin films deposited on flexible Mo foil and sputtered Mo substrates are shown in Figure 2: in all cases, homogeneous coverage can be obtained: (a) CZTSSe absorber deposited on MoF, (b) CZTSSe absorber deposited on evaporated Na-coated Mo foil, and (c) CZTSSe absorber deposited on sputtered Mo.

The uniformity of grains on substrates can also be collected from the topography of the surface. In particular, the sputtered Mo and Na-coated MoF samples greatly influence grain size and coverage quality within the substrate. However, the sample using only MoF shows an inhomogeneity of grain distribution. Although this comparative study highlights the effect of the sodium incorporation on the grain size and overall absorber quality.

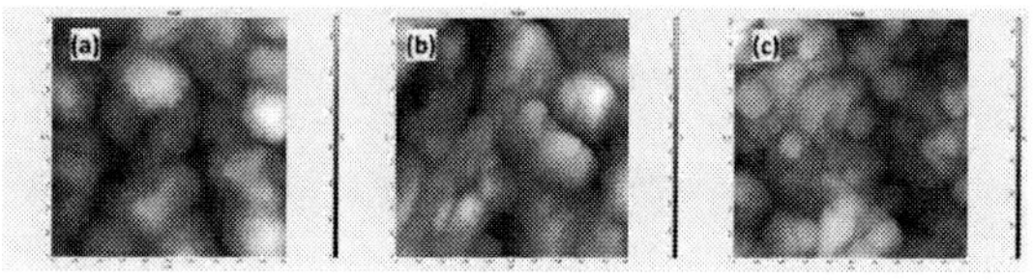

Fig. 2. 2D AFM micrographs of the CZTSSe deposited on different back contact: (a) MoF (b) MoF/Na, and (c) sputtered Mo

The Raman results of CZTSSe absorbers (see figure 3) show the characteristic peaks corresponding to the kesterite phase: the peaks located at 173, 197, and 243 cm^{-1} correspond to the B mode, A mode, and E mode of CZTSSe, respectively. Notably, the Na-coated MF sample shows sharper and more intense peaks than the other back contact samples, indicating increased crystallinity. This enhancement is most possibly due to the sodium ability to passivate grain boundaries and promote crystal formation, as also AFM results support.

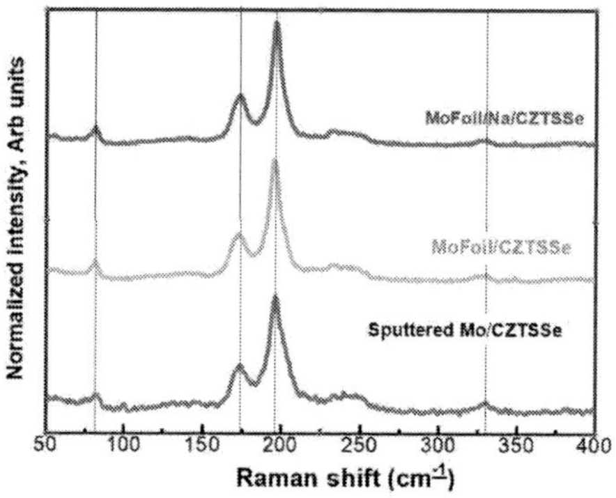

Fig. 3. Raman spectra of the CZTSSe deposited on different back contacts (a) MoF (b) MoF/Na, and (c) sputtered Mo

Figure 4 presents a set of box plots statistics comparing the photovoltaic performance metrics of the efficiency (η), open-circuit voltage (V_{OC}), short-circuit current density (J_{sc}) and fill factor (FF) for CZTSSe devices fabricated on different Mo substrates. The best device performance is achieved with sputtered Mo, as detailed in Table 1.

The devices using an MoF back contact substrate exhibit significantly lower performance, indicating interface defects that limit their performances. However, adding a thin layer of NaF leads to a remarkable enhancement in all optoelectronic parameters. this enhancement is likely due to the sodium role in passivating interface defects and promoting absorber quality, which agrees with AFM and Raman results.

Kee Jeong et al. prove that incorporating a 10 nm layer of NaF on flexible MoF for kesterite solar cells leads to enhanced kesterite-based solar cells' performance [6]. Additionally, several research has demonstrated that MoF flexible MoF substrate-based kesterite solar cells with an additional NaF layer have higher mechanical stability and optoelectronic properties [7], [8].

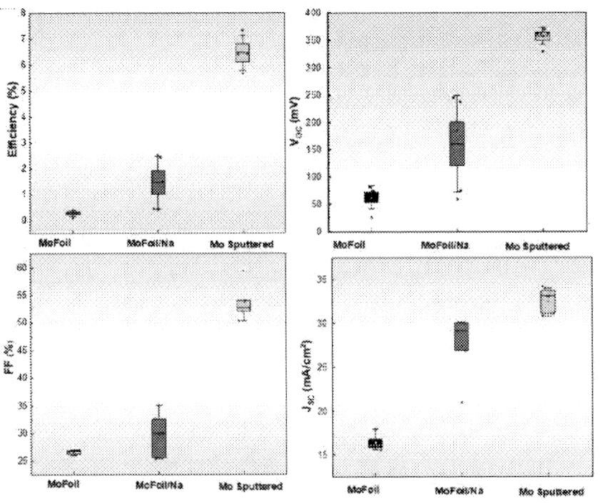

Fig. 4. Device characteristics of CZTSSe thin-film solar cells with various back contact substrates. The parameters given here represent the best of five cells' different substrates.

Table I: Best photovoltaic parameters of CZTSSe solar cells on different substrates.

Sample	V_{oc} (mV)	J_{sc} (mA/cm²)	FF (%)	Eff (%)
Sputtered Mo	375	33.0	58.3	7.2
MF	82.5	16.8	28.6	0.4
MF/Na	279	23.3	41.3	2.6

IV. CONCLUSIONS

In this work, we evaluated the performance of CZTSSe solar cells deposited by spin coating on different back contact substrates: MF, Na-coated MF, and sputtered Mo. The obtained results reveal that the sample with only MF sample shows very poor results related to optoelectronic parameters. This poor performance is primarily related to the absorber quality, with smaller grain sizes and higher defect densities, leading to increased charge carrier recombination and minimize device performance. However, a significant performance enhancement is achieved when the thin Na layer is incorporated on the MoF substrates. This incorporation of Na significantly affected the morphological and structural properties of the absorbers, increasing the grain size and minimizing the grain boundaries.

The best performance achieved devices using sputtered Mo back contacts with PCE around 7.3%. This achievement can be related to the diffusion of Na diffusion from the soda-lime glass substrate in the annealing process.

V. ACKNOWLEDGMENTS

Cariverona foundation is thankfully acknowledged for partially funding this work with INSOBILD project Ref. 2022.0094 – ID 52271 – CUP B33C22001760007. The Italian Ministry of Research through CANVAS project is thankfully acknowledged.

REFERENCES

[1] Nisika, K. Kaur, and M. Kumar, "Progress and prospects of CZTSSe/CdS interface engineering to combat high open-circuit voltage deficit of kesterite photovoltaics: a critical review," *J. Mater. Chem. A*, vol. 8, no. 41, pp. 21547–21584, 2020, doi: 10.1039/d0ta06450e.

[2] V. Karade *et al.*, "Insights into kesterite's back contact interface: A status review," *Sol. Energy Mater. Sol. Cells*, vol. 200, p. 109911, Sep. 2019, doi: 10.1016/j.solmat.2019.04.033.

[3] J. Fu *et al.*, "Defect engineering enabling p-type Mo(S,Se)2:TM (TM = V, Nb, Ta) towards high-efficiency kesterite solar cells," *Chem. Eng. J.*, vol. 457, p. 141348, Feb. 2023, doi: 10.1016/j.cej.2023.141348.

[4] K.-J. Yang *et al.*, "The alterations of carrier separation in kesterite solar cells," *Nano Energy*, vol. 52, pp. 38–53, Oct. 2018, doi: 10.1016/j.nanoen.2018.07.039.

[5] E. Jo, M. G. Gang, H. Shim, M. P. Suryawanshi, U. V. Ghorpade, and J. H. Kim, "8% Efficiency $Cu_2ZnSn(S,Se)_4$ (CZTSSe) Thin Film Solar Cells on Flexible and Lightweight Molybdenum Foil Substrates," *ACS Appl. Mater. Interfaces*, vol. 11, no. 26, pp. 23118–23124, Jul. 2019, doi: 10.1021/acsami.9b03195.

[6] K.-J. Yang *et al.*, "Flexible Cu2ZnSn(S,Se)4 solar cells with over 10% efficiency and methods of enlarging the cell area," *Nat. Commun.*, vol. 10, no. 1, Jul. 2019, doi: 10.1038/s41467-019-10890-x.

[7] H. K. Park *et al.*, "Flexible kesterite thin-film solar cells under stress," *Npj Flex. Electron.*, vol. 6, no. 1, Nov. 2022, doi: 10.1038/s41528-022-00221-4.

[8] N. M. Espinel Pérez, E. Vera López, J. A. Gómez Cuaspud, and J. B. Carda Castelló, "A review of recent advances of kesterite thin films based on magnesium, iron and nickel for photovoltaic application: insights into synthesis, characterization and optoelectronic properties," *Clean Energy*, vol. 8, no. 2, pp. 217–238, Apr. 2024, doi: 10.1093/ce/zkad093.

MONOLITHIC INTERCONNECTION OF THIN FILM MINIMODULE PREPARED BY A CNC MECHANICAL SCRIBING.

David Payno[1], Jacob Andrade-Arvizu[2], Marta Miró-Llorente[2], Pedro Vidal-Fuentes[2], Raquel Caballero[1,3], Victor Izquierdo-Roca[2], Alejandro Perez-Rodriguez[2]

1 - Universidad Autónoma de Madrid, Madrid, Spain. 2 – Institut de Recerca en Energia de Catalunya (IREC), Barcelona, Spain 3 – Instituto de Óptica Daza de Valdés, Consejo Superior de Investigaciones Científicas (CSIC), Madrid, Spain.

ABSTRACT: Monolithic interconnection is a key strategy for thin-film photovoltaic (PV) modules, enabling dense series-connected cell arrays without external wiring. Conventional laser scribing, however, requires complex optimization and can be unsuitable for high-melting-point or highly transparent materials. This work demonstrates a low-cost, flexible alternative based on fully mechanical scribing using a computer numerical control (CNC) system. Kesterite ($Cu_2ZnSnSe_4$) thin-film minimodules with Mo/CZTSe/CdS/ZnO/ITO architecture were fabricated and interconnected into an 8-cell series configuration. By selecting scribing tips of different hardness, specific layers were selectively removed without damaging underlying contacts, achieving effective P1–P2-P3 patterning. The interconnected module delivered a total open-circuit voltage of 2.65 V, consistent with the sum of individual cell voltages, while maintaining comparable current and shunt resistance. Main performance losses arose from increased series resistance and reduced active area, limiting power conversion efficiency to 2% for the module, 3.1% for the module active area, versus a efficiency of 6% for an individual reference cell. These results highlight mechanical scribing as a practical method for early-stage PV technologies and a potential complement to laser scribing in industrial applications.

Keywords: Thin-film, Photovoltaics, Monolithic Interconnection

1 INTRODUCTION

The monolithic interconnection has been the standard adopted technique to interconnect for thin film photovoltaics, since it allows for densely packaged arrays of cells, without the need of wiring and minimising the use of front metallic contacts [1], [2], [3]. However, laser scribing can be inconvenient to use with high melting point materials and/or very transparent materials, like Molybdenum, ZnO or SiO_2. Moreover, the development of a laser monolithic interconnection typically requires a fine-tuning of a set of lasers that must be studied for each material and technology to get a good and reproducible result. For this reason, monolithic interconnection is typically implemented only in mature PV technologies. As a means of accelerating the monolithic integration at earlier stages, we have developed a simple method of mechanically scribed monolithic interconnection as a low-cost, fast and flexible alternative. A mechanically scribed interconnection can be easily applied in the early stages of thin film technology, in a wide variety of materials, and has the potential to expand and complement the laser scribing methods in the late stages of any PV technology.

In this work, a fully mechanical method for monolithic interconnection has been developed, using a computer numerical control (CNC) system, successfully demonstrating a series interconnection of 8 thin-film solar cells based on kesterite. By simply choosing the materials of the scribing tip with an appropriate hardness, the layers to be removed can be easily selected without damaging the bottom layers, and therefore having a minimum impact on the optoelectronic parameters of the cells.

2 EXPERIMENTAL PROCEDURE

Interconnected thin-film solar cells were prepared following a Mo/CZTSe/CdS/ZnO/ITO configuration. The scribing lines were prepared using a CNC machine, following the pattern of **Figure 1a**, and a spring-loaded tool, as shown in **Figures 1b** and **1c**.

2.1 Sample preparation

First, a layer of Molybdenum was deposited by DC sputtering on a clean soda-lime glass substrate. The P1 was then scribed on the molybdenum film, using a hard tungsten carbide tip, to disconnect and delimitate the back contact. Then, $Cu_2ZnSnSe_4$ absorber was prepared by sequentially sputtering Cu, Zn and Sn metals, followed by a selenization treatment in argon on a quartz furnace. A $MoSe_2$ layer is naturally formed during the selenization between the molybdenum and the absorber layers. A CdS buffer layer was prepared by chemical bath deposition, followed by a ZnO window layer prepared by RF sputtering. At this stage, the P2 was scribed using a soft nickel tip, selectively removing the absorber and buffer/window layers without damaging the molybdenum back contact. A conductive and transparent ITO layer was deposited by RF sputtering, acting as the front contact and connecting at the same time the front and the back contacts of consecutive cells. A P3 scribing process was performed to isolate the front contacts, using the nickel tip. A perpendicular P4 is used with the hard WC tip, isolating 8 different rows of cells and preventing shunts in the edges. A complete scheme of the process is shown in **Figure 1d**.

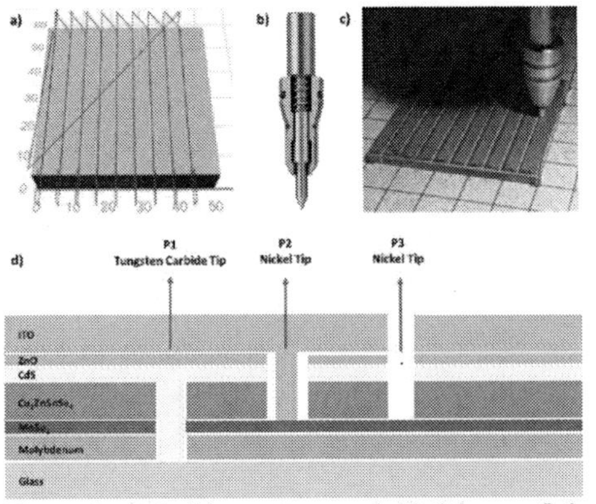

Figure 1. a) Scribing pattern used. b) Scheme of the spring-loaded tool. c) Image of the scribing process. d) Scheme of sample layer stack.

2.2 Characterization

The I-V curves of the cells were characterized under illumination of 1 sun AM1.5, individually and interconnected. Single cells were measured by directly contacting the negative electrode with the ITO of the cell to be measured, while contacting the positive electrode with the ITO of the previous cell. The negative electrode was moved to the subsequent cells to measure all the monolithically interconnected cells between the electrodes.

3 RESULTS AND DISCUSSION

The resulting sample contains 8 rows of 8 monolithically interconnected cells, each cell having a total area of 5x5 mm^2, and an active area of 3.5x4.7 mm^2, as shown in **Figure 2**. The dead area will be the sum of the width of the lines (0.3 mm) and the space between them, adding a total of 8.55 mm^2. Therefore, there is a 34% loss of active area, which counts as the main factor of losses.

First, the optoelectronic parameters of individual cells were measured to observe the inhomogeneities caused by the monolithic interconnection process. As can be observed in Figure 3a and 3b, the process keeps a good homogeneity on the sample, with the parameters of columns A, E and H being slightly affected, likely caused by an incomplete scribing.

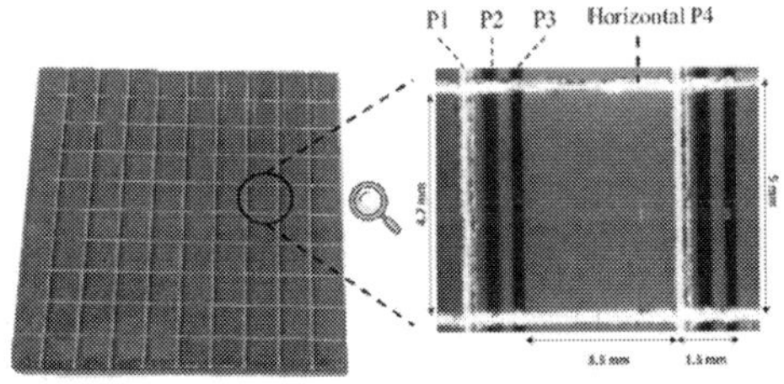

Figure 2. Image of the sample, with a close view of the scribed lines and its dimensions.

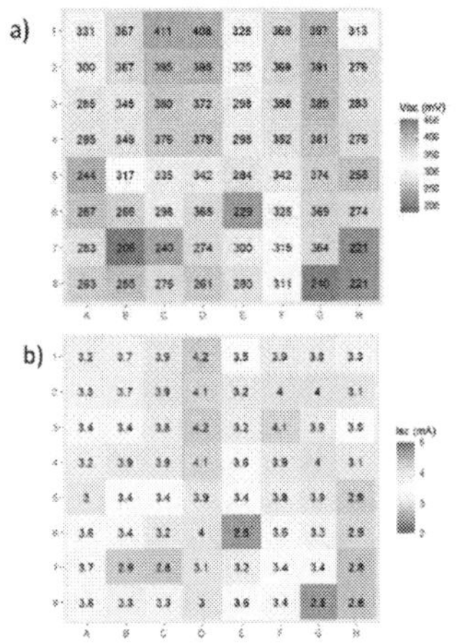

Figure 3. a) Mapping of V_{oc} and b) J_{sc} of individual cells in the sample.

The characteristic IV curves of the interconnected cells were obtained as a function of the number of cells connected, shown in **Figure 4**, from which the optoelectronic parameters were extracted and shown in **Table I**. It can be observed that the V_{oc} increase proportionally to the number of cells connected, with only a loss of 39 mV with respect to the sum of individual cells' V_{oc}, demonstrating a complete and effective interconnection. The small increase in current and R_{sh} suggests that the values obtained are affected by the measurement method, and the losses are mitigated when all the cells connected are measured, reaching values comparable with the reference sample.

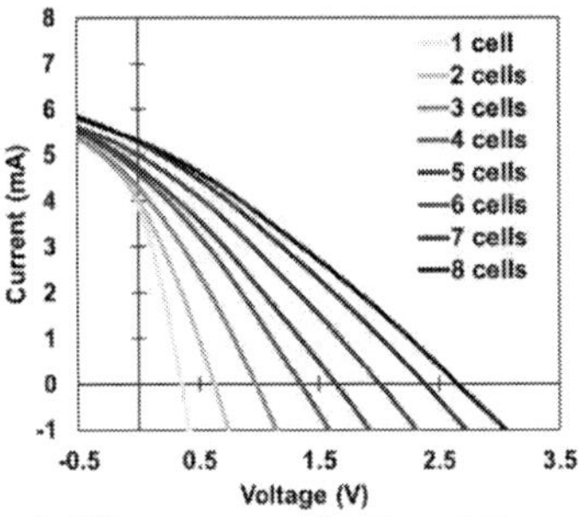

Figure 4. I-V curves as a function of the number of monolithically interconnected cells.

Table I. Parameters measured under AM1.5 of interconnected cells.

	I_{sc} (mA)	V_{oc} (mV)	FF (%)	PCE (%)	R_s (Ω)	R_{sh} eff (Ω cm^2)
Reference	4.11	392	61.0	6.0	10	220
1 cell	3.87	349	30.6	2.5	52	47
2 cells	4.01	621	28.9	2.2	113	73
3 cells	4.29	976	28.9	2.4	167	94
4 cells	4.61	1351	28.9	2.7	214	110
5 cells	4.73	1635	28.5	2.7	274	117
6 cells	5.00	1993	29.2	3.0	306	162
7 cells	5.28	2374	28.9	3.1	353	171
8 cells	5.31	2657	29.0	3.1	388	200

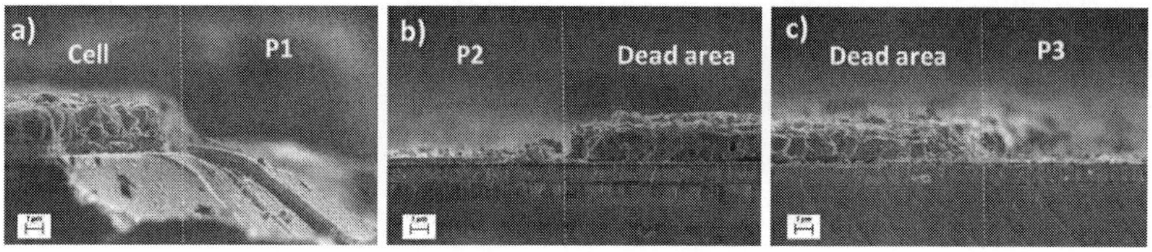

Figure 5. Cross secttional SEM of the area where it can be observed a) the P1 b) P2 and c) P3.

By comparing the mini-module of 8 cells with a reference cell isolated without any interconnection, it can be observed that the main losses come from an increase in the series resistance proportionally with each connected cell, adding 38.5 Ω/cell on average, severely affecting the FF and limiting the power conversion efficiency (PCE).

A close inspection on **Figure 5** of the scribed lines reveals that all layers have been successfully removed in the case of P1, while the molybdenum layer is still intact in the case of P2 and P3, and a smooth deposition of ITO over the Mo can be observed in the P2. Therefore, the observed increase of Rs can be caused by two effects: A non-ohmic contact between the ITO and Mo, due to the $MoSe_2$ interlayer (marked in blue), and a high ITO laminar resistance, both of which are added with each cell connected. These problems can be addressed in future work by the application of better contact material, such as Ag or Cu, in the P2, and the addition of a conductive finger to improve the laminar conductivity. In any case, these problems are independent of the method used to make the scribing. Taking into account the losses of the active area, the total mini-minimodule efficiency drops from 3.1% to 2%, so more efforts are required to reduce the dead area.

4 CONCLUSIONS

We demonstrate that a fully mechanical scribed monolithic interconnection can be prepared without the use of laser scribing, which can be an advantage in certain technologies and a simpler approach for a laboratory and small scale, since it does not require high process optimization. Mechanical scribing can also complement laser scribing with certain types of materials, and be competent for industrial and large-scale. By an appropriate choice of the tip scriber material, a soft nickel tip successfully removed the cell layers, keeping intact the molybdenum back contact, while a hard tungsten carbide tip could easily remove the molybdenum layer as well.

By analyzing both the individual cells and the arrays, we demonstrate that the cells have been successfully connected, reaching a V_{OC} of 2.65 V with 8 cells of 300 - 400 mV individual V_{OC}, maintaining in the array the efficiency of the best individual cell. Other parameters, such as the current and the shunt resistance, are maintained in the array of cells to similar levels as in the reference cell. Main electrical losses come from an increase in the series resistance, affecting the fill factor, due to a high ITO laminar resistance, and non-ohmic TCO/Metal contact in the P2 connection, while a significant loss of active area limits the overall efficiency of the array. Future work will focus on improving and mitigating these losses while reducing and compacting the thickness of the scribed lines.

REFERENCES

[1] K. Li *et al.*, "One-dimensional Sb2Se3 enabling ultra-flexible solar cells and mini-modules for IoT applications," *Nano Energy*, vol. 86, p. 106101, Aug. 2021, doi: 10.1016/J.NANOEN.2021.106101.

[2] G. Heise *et al.*, "Demonstration of the monolithic interconnection on CIS solar cells by picosecond laser structuring on 30 by 30 cm2 modules," *Progress in Photovoltaics: Research and Applications*, vol. 23, no. 10, pp. 1291–1304, Oct. 2015, doi: 10.1002/PIP.2552.

[3] J. Perrenoud, B. Schaffner, S. Buecheler, and A. N. Tiwari, "Fabrication of flexible CdTe solar modules with monolithic cell interconnection," *Solar Energy Materials and Solar Cells*, vol. 95, no. SUPPL. 1, pp. S8–S12, May 2011, doi: 10.1016/J.SOLMAT.2010.11.019.

ACKNOWLEGEMENTS

This project has received funding from the European Union's Horizon 2020 research and innovation programme under grant agreement No 952982 (Custom-Art) and the Project ASSESS (TED2021-129666B-C21) funded by MCIN/AEI/ 10.13039/501100011033

Universidad Autónoma de Madrid
IREC
CSIC

Monolithic interconnection of thin film minimodule prepared by CNC mechanical scribing

David Payno[1], Jacob Andrade-Arvizu[2], Marta Miró-Llorente[2], Pedro Vidal-Fuentes[2], Raquel Caballero[3], Victor Izquierdo-Roca[2], Alejandro Perez-Rodriguez[2]

[1] Universidad Autónoma de Madrid, Madrid, Spain. [2] Institut de Recerca en Energia de Catalunya (IREC), Barcelona, Spain [3] Instituto de Óptica Daza de Valdés, Consejo Superior de Investigaciones Científicas (CSIC), Madrid, Spain.

1 Abstract

The monolithic interconnection is the adopted standard for thin films:

- ✓ Densely packed arrays of cells.
- ✓ Front metal contacts reduced or avoided.

Is it possible?

Is it effective?

Laser is fast and scalable, but:

- x Requires optimization for every layer.
- x Produce heat damage and shunts.
- x Not compatible with some materials.
- x Hazardous vapors.

Mechanical:

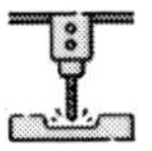

- Easy to adapt.
- Ideal for laboratory scale.
- Scalable to industrial.
- Less hazardous.

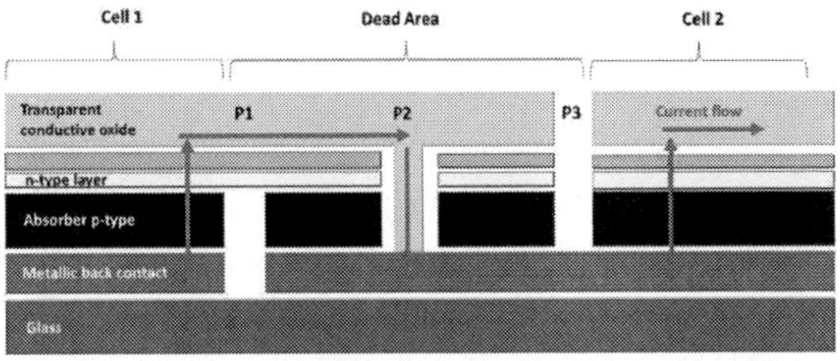

3 Close inspection

8 rows of 8 cells connected in series

P1 P2 P3 Horizontal P4 (Tungsten Carbide tip)

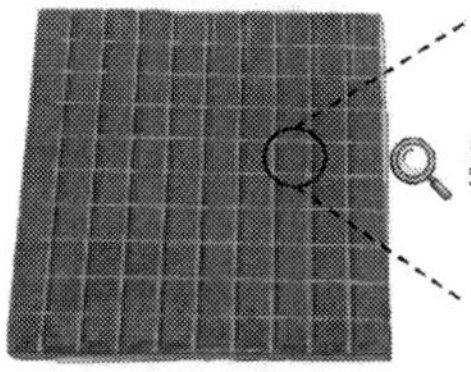

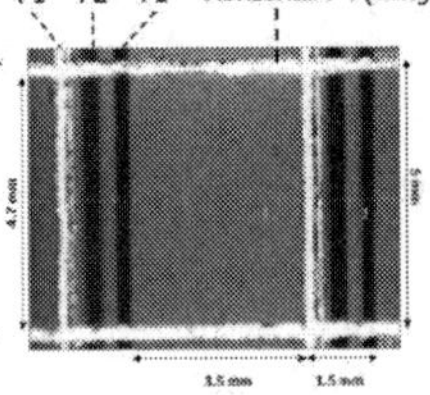

Cross sectional view

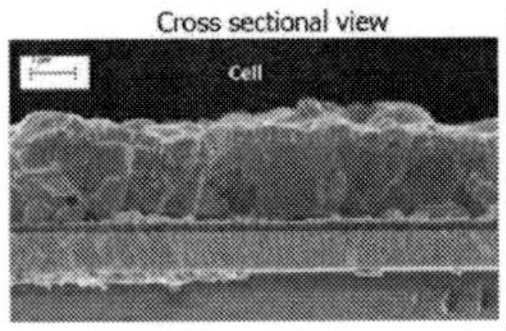

Total Area = 25 mm²

Dead area = 8.55 mm²

Cell active area = 16.45 mm²

Loss of active area = 34 %

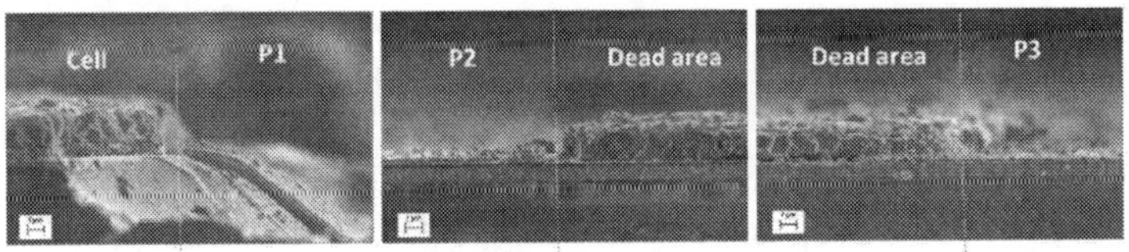

2 Method: Mechanical Scribing

Choose the TIP: **WC** tip to engrave hard layers.

Nickel tip to engrave soft materials without damaging the bottom layers.

Deposit the next layer

Loading pattern on a CNC

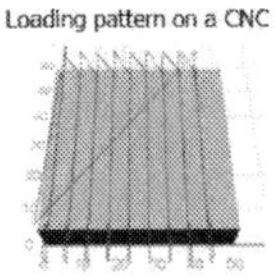

Exchangeable spring-loaded tip

Scribe the pattern

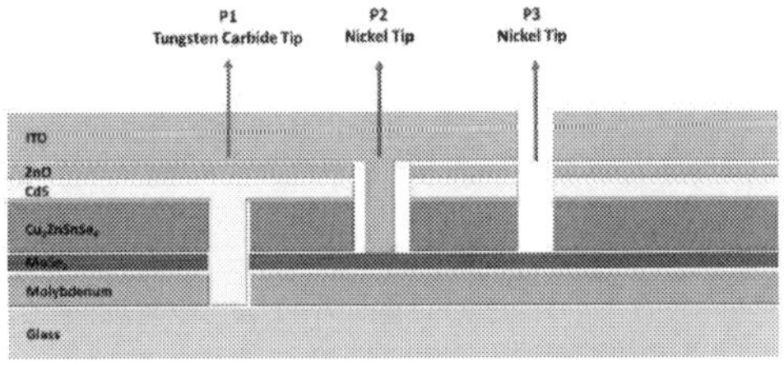

4 PV analysis

Flexible measurements of individual and consecutive connected cells

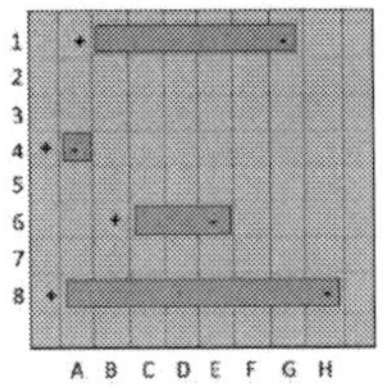

Individual measurements of each cell

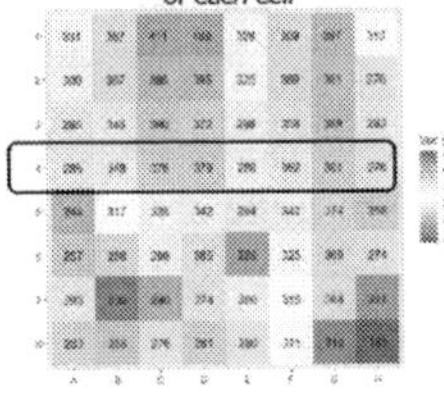

I-V curves under AM 1.5 illumination

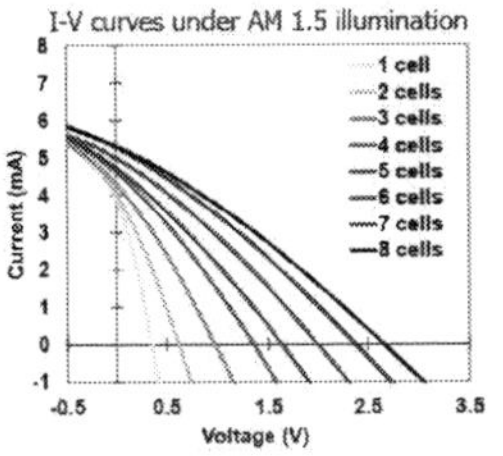

	I_{sc} (mA)	V_{oc} (mV)	FF (%)	Efficiency (%)	R_s (Ω)	R_{sh} effective (Ω cm²)
Reference	4.11	392	61.0	6.0	10	220
1 cell	3.87	349	30.6	2.5	52	47
2 cells	4.01	621	28.9	2.2	113	73
3 cells	4.29	976	28.9	2.4	167	94
4 cells	4.61	1351	28.9	2.7	214	110
5 cells	4.73	1635	28.5	2.7	274	117
6 cells	5.00	1993	29.2	3.0	306	162
7 cells	5.28	2374	28.9	3.1	353	171
8 cells	**5.31**	**2657**	**29.0**	**3.1**	**388**	**200**

Sum of individual 8 cells V_{oc} = 2696 mV

ONLY 39 mV of Voc loss

Average cells adds R_s = 48.5 Ω

Considering the full area of the array efficiency = 2 %

Highly successful:

- V_{oc} minor loss.
- No losses in I_{sc}.
- The effective shunt resistance increases with the connected cells until reference → Minor shunting problems in the array.

Mayor loses:

- Increase of series resistance proportionally to the number of connected cells → Reduction of FF.
- Loss of active area.
- The effect of scribing is slightly inhomogeneous.

5 How to improve

Minimize the dead area:

1. Bring the lines closer together.
2. Sharper tips to reduce the width of the scribed lines.
3. Wider cells.

Improve resistances:

A. Introduce a metal contact in P2.
B. Thin horizontal metal fingers.
C. Isolation and passivation on P1 and P3.

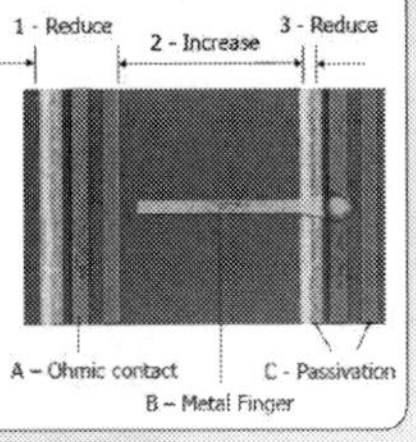

6 Conclusions

- Functional photovoltaic array of series-connected cells prepared by only mechanical scribing.
- Mechanical scribing controlled by CNC is highly precise and can be complementary to laser scribing in industrial processes.
- A soft Nickel tip is used to effectively scribe on soft materials, avoiding damage to the back contact.
- Demonstrated a very low shunt, current and voltage losses.
- Main losses of the process are associated with an increase in the series resistance, due to a high resistance of the TCO, and non-ohmic contact between the top and back contacts.
- Optimization to reduce the dead area is required.

References

1) Heise, G.; Börner, A.; Dickmann, M.; Englmaier, M.; Heiss, A.; Kemnitzer, M.; Konrad, J.; Moser, R.; Palm, J.; Vogt, H.; Huber, H. P. Demonstration of the Monolithic Interconnection on CIS Solar Cells by Picosecond Laser Structuring on 30 by 30 Cm2 Modules. Progress in Photovoltaics: Research and Applications 2015, 23 (10), 1291–1304. https://doi.org/10.1002/PIP.2552.

2) Perrenoud, J.; Schaffner, B.; Buecheler, S.; Tiwari, A. N. Fabrication of Flexible CdTe Solar Modules with Monolithic Cell Interconnection. Solar Energy Materials and Solar Cells 2011, 95 (SUPPL. 1), S8–S12. https://doi.org/10.1016/J.SOLMAT.2010.11.019.

3) qLi, K.; Li, F.; Chen, C.; Jiang, P.; Lu, S.; Wang, S.; Lu, Y.; Tu, G.; Guo, J.; Shui, L.; Liu, Z.; Song, B.; Tang, J. One-Dimensional Sb2Se3 Enabling Ult[illegible] Mini-Modules for IoT Applications. Nano Energy 2021, 86, 106101. https://doi.org/10.1016/J.NANOEN.2021.106101.

Contact

david.payno@uam.es
david.payno@csic.es

Acknowledgments

This project has received funding from the European Union's Horizon 2020 research and innovation programme under grant agreement No 952982 (Custom-Art) and the Project ASSESS (TED2021-129666B-C21) funded by MCIN/AEI/ 10.13039/501100011033

KINETIC MORPHOLOGY EVOLUTION OF NON-FULLERENE BULK HETEROJUNCTION BLENDS: THE ROLE OF SOLVENT ADDITIVES IN THERMAL STABILITY

Tzu-Yen Huang[1*], Anton P. Le Brun[2]
[1]Neutron Group, National Synchrotron Radiation Research Center, Hsinchu 30092, Taiwan
[2]Australian Centre for Neutron Scattering, Australian Nuclear Science and Technology Organization, New South Wales 2234, Australia
*Email: huang.ty@nsrrc.org.tw

ABSTRACT: The thermal stability of bulk heterojunction (BHJ) active layers is a critical factor in determining the long-term performance of non-fullerene organic solar cells (OSCs). In this study, the kinetic morphology of PffBT4T-2OD: ITIC BHJs was systematically investigated under varying annealing temperatures. Pristine PffBT4T-2OD films demonstrated excellent thermal stability, while ITIC thin films exhibited diffusive interfaces and morphological changes when annealed above 120°C. For PffBT4T-2OD: ITIC BHJs, elevated temperatures at 120°C induced the migration of ITIC clusters toward the air interface, accompanied by the formation of a PffBT4T-2OD-rich layer near the substrate. To address this thermal instability, we incorporated the 1,8-diiodooctane (DIO) as a solvent additive into the BHJs. The addition of DIO significantly enhanced the intermixing of donor and acceptor materials, resulting in a uniform morphology of the active layer and improved thermal stability up to 120°C. These findings confirm that solvent additives effectively mitigate thermal-induced phase separation and prolong the stability of BHJs.
Keywords: Organic solar cells, solvent additives, thermal annealing, stability

1 INTRODUCTION

Organic solar cells (OSCs) have emerged as a promising technology owing to their compatibility with solution-process, roll-to-roll production, and potential for low-cost, lightweight, and flexible devices.[1-3] The bulk heterojunction (BHJ) device configuration, in which electron donor and acceptor materials are intimately blended, enables efficient separation of photogenerated excitons and transport of charge carriers through pure phases to the respective electrodes. Strategies such as thermal annealing and the use of solvent additives are widely applied to reorganize the nanoscale morphology, thereby improving exciton dissociation, charge collection, and overall device efficiency.

Poly[(5,6-difluoro-2,1,3-benzothiadiazol-4,7-diyl)-alt-(3,3'''-di(2-octyldodecyl)-2,2';5',2'';5'',2'''-quaterthiophen-5,5'''-diyl)] (PffBT4T-2OD) is a narrow-band-gap polymer (1.65 eV) with high charge-carrier mobility (~10^{-2} $cm^2V^{-1}s^{-1}$) and demonstrated power conversion efficiencies up to 11%.[4] In recent years, non-fullerene acceptors (NFAs) have become an important class of OSC materials due to their strong optical absorption, tunable electronic structures, and ability to synergistically improve device performance when paired with low-band-gap polymers.[5, 6] Among these, 3,9-bis(2-methylene-(3-(1,1-dicyanomethylene)-indanone))-5,5,11,11-tetrakis(4-hexylphenyl)-dithieno[2,3-d:2',3'-d']-s-indaceno[1,2-b:5,6-b']dithiophene (ITIC) is a well-known NFA with energy levels ideally matched to PffBT4T-2OD. In preparing the BHJ thin films, high-boiling-point solvent additives are frequently introduced to promote nanoscale mixing between donor and acceptor phases, facilitating an optimized morphology for enhanced device performance. [7] Our previous studies have shown that in PffBT4T-2OD: ITIC BHJs, thermal annealing can induce aggregation of ITIC molecules within the polymer matrix, resulting in interfacial diffusion and an increase in surface roughness.[8] We propose that limited initial miscibility between donor and acceptor phases creates a thermodynamic driving force for phase separation upon heating. However, the extent to which solvent additives influence vertical phase organization, as well as the kinetics of morphological evolution under different annealing temperatures and durations, remains unclear.

Neutron reflectometry (NR) offers sub-nanometer resolution for probing vertical composition profiles and interfacial structure in thin films.[9-11] In this work, we employ NR to examine PffBT4T-2OD: ITIC BHJ films prepared with and without the solvent additive 1,8-diiodooctane (DIO). By monitoring temperature- and time-dependent morphological changes, we aim to provide new insights into phase behavior in OSCs.

2 EXPERIMENTAL PROCUDUES

2.1 Preparation of PffBT4T-2OD: ITIC Blend Films

The DIO concentrations of 0.25 v/v% were dissolved in a 1,2-dichlorobenzene: chlorobenzene (1:1 v/v%) co-solvent mixture and used to prepare the PffBT4T-2OD: ITIC blend (Solarmer Energy Inc.) solutions at a total concentration of 10 mg/ml. The solutions were stirred at 90°C overnight to ensure complete dissolution. Both the blend solutions and substrates were then maintained at 90°C to prevent severe aggregation during thin-film preparation. The active layer solution was then spin-coated onto the Si wafers under a nitrogen environment (1000 rpm for 60 s). Each sample was subsequently placed in a vacuum chamber and annealed at RT, 90°C, 120°C, and 150°C while NR measurements were performed at the first incident angle.

2.2 Neutron Reflectometry Measurements.

The NR measurements were performed on the Spatz time-of-flight neutron reflectometer at the Australian Nuclear Science and Technology Organization (ANSTO) OPAL reactor (proposal nos. P18686 & P20060).[12] A chopper pairing of choppers 1 and 2 with a separation of 480 mm and a rotation speed of 25 Hz provides a wavelength resolution ($\Delta\lambda/\lambda$) of ~5%. The NR curves were collected at the first incident angles of 0.70° (1 hr) and the second incident angle will be collected at 3.50° (3 hrs) to cover the momentum transfer (Q) range of $0.008 \leq Q \leq 0.24$ Å^{-1}. The momentum transfer is defined as $Q = 4\pi \sin(\theta)/\lambda$, where θ is the incident angle and λ is the neutron wavelength. An illuminated footprint of 18 mm long and 20 mm wide was used. The reduction procedure involves considering detector efficiency, converting the time-of-flight data to wavelength, and then calculating Q range, re-binning the data to instrument resolution, stitching the datasets from the two incident angles at the overlap region to provide a complete reflectivity profile, and scaling the critical edge equal to unity. The NR data were analyzed using the *refnx* software.[13] Parameters defining the properties of the different layers were varied using a differential evolution algorithm until the difference between the experimental and model data was minimized. The fitting parameters for NR mesasurements are summarized in Table 1.

3 RESULTS AND DISCUSSION

The thermal stability and morphological evolution of BHJs are critical factors in improving the performance of OSCs. Our previous work has shown that elevated annealing temperatures promote interfacial diffusion and increase surface roughness due to ITIC aggregation within the polymer matrix.[8] NR was employed to probe the vertical morphology of BHJ thin films during thermal annealing. Based on an assumed bulk density of 0.90 g cm^{-3}, the scattering length density (SLD) values of PffBT4T-2OD and ITIC are calculated to be 0.65 × 10^{-6} $Å^{-2}$ and 1.44 × 10^{-6} $Å^{-2}$, respectively. Our findings indicate that the highly flexible side chains of PffBT4T-2OD do not significantly contribute to vertical morphological changes at temperatures above 90°C, confirming its intrinsic thermal stability under annealing. In contrast, ITIC thin films exhibit the onset of diffusive interface formation at 120°C, suggesting that thermal annealing promotes the formation of ITIC nanocrystal aggregates, thereby altering the vertical morphology. This behavior persists at 150°C. The observed onset temperature for thermal instability is consistent with literature reports on diffusion-limited crystallization, providing further insight into the morphological evolution of ITIC-based BHJs under thermal treatment.[14]

Figures 1(a) and 1(b) present the NR patterns and SLD profiles of pristine PffBT4T-2OD: ITIC (6:4) BHJ films. The NR fringes remained unchanged upon annealing up to 90°C, with the SLD profiles indicating a uniform film of thickness 802 ± 2 Å and surface roughness of 64 ± 9 Å. The fringes are shifted within the Q range of 0.01-0.03 $Å^{-1}$ at 120°C, consistent with the trend observed at 150 °C, indicating similar morphology changes in the film at both temperatures. As shown in Figure 1(b), the SLD profiles reveal the onset of vertical phase segregation above 120°C, forming a two-layer structure. A PffBT4T-2OD-rich layer (235 ± 16 Å, SLD = 0.67 × 10^{-6} $Å^{-2}$) developed adjacent to the substrate, while an ITIC-rich layer (544 ± 19 Å, SLD = 1.45 × 10^{-6} $Å^{-2}$) formed at the air interface, with an accompanying surface roughness of 68 ± 3 Å. This stratification persisted at 150°C, yielding a PffBT4T-2OD-rich layer of 250 ± 13 Å and a ITIC-rich layer of 518 ± 16 Å, with a surface roughness of 63 ± 2 Å. Although the ITIC molecules were reported to have a higher surface energy than PffBT4T-2OD polymers, the observed thermal behavior is consistent with previous findings.[8] Excess thermal energy activates ITIC molecule diffusion toward the air interface rather than accumulation at the substrate.

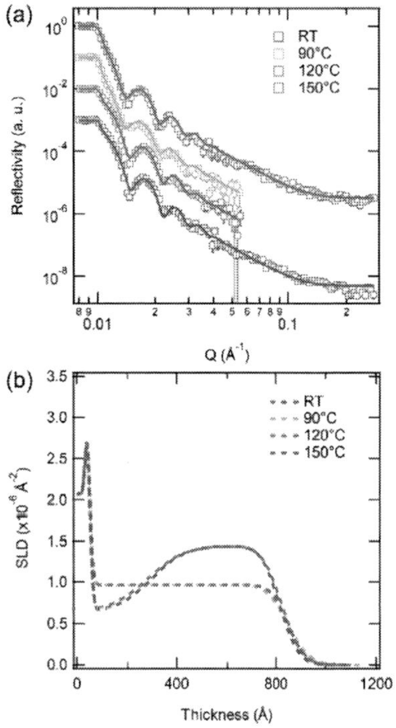

Figure 1. The NR curves and the corresponding SLD profiles for (a, b) pristine PffBT4T-2OD: ITIC (6:4) BHJ films on Si wafers annealed from RT to 150°C. The individual data points and solid lines represent the experimental data and fitting results respectively.

Solvent additives are widely used to promote donor-acceptor intermixing and to achieve a favorable blend morphology for stable device performance. To examine

Table 1. The fitting parameters are summarized from the NR results.

Substrates	Thickness (Å)	SLD ($Å^{-2}$)	Roughness (Å)
BHJ layer (D:A = 6:4) /Si @ RT	802 ± 2	0.97 ± 0.01	57 ± 2
BHJ layer (D:A = 6:4) /Si @ 90°C	802 ± 3	0.97 ± 0.01	70 ± 2
BHJ layer (D:A = 6:4) /Si @ 120°C	544 ± 19	1.45 ± 0.04	68 ± 3
	235 ± 16	0.67 ± 0.02	120 ± 9
BHJ layer (D:A = 6:4) /Si @ 150°C	518 ± 16	1.45 ± 0.04	63 ± 2
	250 ± 13	0.65 ± 0.02	111 ± 8
BHJ layer (D:A = 5:5, 0.25 v/v% DIO) /Si @ RT	739 ± 3	1.05 ± 0.02	52 ± 2
BHJ layer (D:A = 5:5, 0.25 v/v% DIO) /Si @ 90°C	739 ± 2	1.05 ± 0.01	48 ± 2
BHJ layer (D:A = 5:5, 0.25 v/v% DIO) /Si @ 120°C	741 ± 2	1.05 ± 0.01	54 ± 2
BHJ layer (D:A = 5:5, 0.25 v/v% DIO) /Si @ 150°C	337 ± 13	1.19 ± 0.04	92 ± 6
	460 ± 11	0.76 ± 0.02	96 ± 13

whether poor initial mixing contributes to the thermal instability of ITIC molecules upon annealing, 0.25 v/v% DIO was incorporated into PffBT4T-2OD: ITIC (5:5) BHJ films. Figures 2(a) and 2(b) show the corresponding NR curves and SLD profiles. The NR fringes remained well-defined after annealing up to 120°C, indicating enhanced thermal stability with DIO incorporation. The SLD profiles at this stage reveal a uniform donor-acceptor distribution, with a total film thickness of 740 ± 1 Å and surface roughness of 51 ± 3 Å. At 150°C, however, the fringes became less distinct, suggesting morphological changes. Extended annealing induced vertical phase segregation, producing a PffBT4T-2OD-rich bottom layer (460 ± 11 Å, SLD = 0.76 × 10^{-6} Å^{-2}) adjacent to the substrate and a top layer (337 ± 13 Å, SLD = 1.19 × 10^{-6} Å^{-2}) at the air interface. The slightly higher SLD of the top layer compared to the uniform BHJ indicates only modest ITIC enrichment after prolonged annealing. At an annealing temperature of 150°C, the NR fringes of BHJ (6:4) films (*see Figure 1(a)*) remain more pronounced than those of BHJ (5:5) films with 0.25 v/v% DIO, which can be attributed to the higher fraction of thermally stable PffBT4T-2OD in the blends, leading to a more robust vertical morphology. Overall, these results demonstrate that solvent additives promote efficient PffBT4T-2OD: ITIC mixing and significantly improve the thermal stability of BHJ thin films.

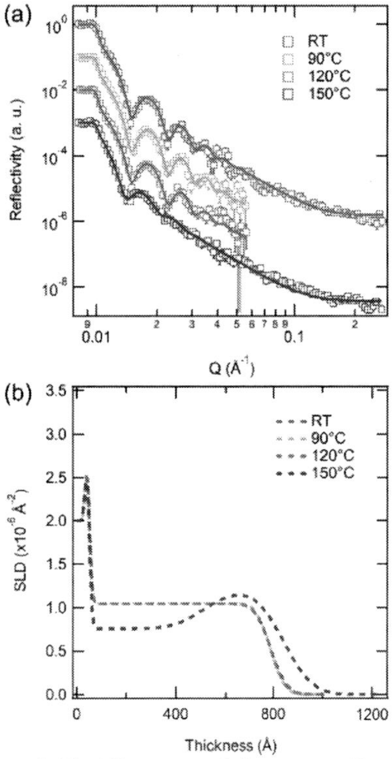

Figure 2. The NR curves and the corresponding SLD profiles for (a, b) PffBT4T-2OD: ITIC (5:5) BHJ films with 0.25% DIO on Si wafers annealed from RT to 150°C. The individual data points and solid lines represent the experimental data and fitting results respectively.

To identify phase stratification after thermal annealing, Figure 3 presents the NR fitting results for PffBT4T-2OD: ITIC (5:5) BHJ films processed with 0.25 v/v% DIO and annealed at 150°C. Pronounced fringes are observed in the Q range of 0.01 - 0.03 Å^{-1}. The one-layer model does not reproduce the experimental data in this range, indicating that the active layer undergoes non-uniform structural changes upon heating. In contrast, a two-layer model provides a better description of the thermal behavior, as further supported by the residual plots, which show improved agreement near Q ~ 0.01 Å^{-1}. These results reveal that thermal annealing promotes the formation of an ITIC-rich layer at the air interface, while the PffBT4T-2OD-rich layer preferentially accumulates adjacent to the substrate.

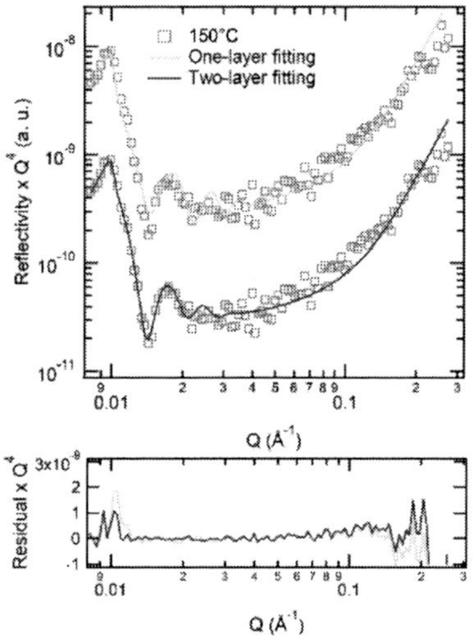

Figure 3. The NR curves and residual plots of PffBT4T-2OD: ITIC (5:5) bulk heterojunction (BHJ) films containing 0.25 v/v% DIO, annealed at 150°C. The solid lines correspond to fits using one-layer and two-layer models, respectively.

4 CONCLUSIONS

We have investigated the vertical morphology of PffBT4T-2OD: ITIC BHJs by varying the annealing temperature. For pristine BHJs, NR analysis revealed that excess thermal energy activates ITIC molecules to diffuse toward the air interface, leading to the formation of an ITIC-rich top layer and a PffBT4T-2OD-rich bottom layer adjacent to the substrate. This vertical phase segregation was evident above 120°C and persisted at 150°C, indicating that the morphology becomes thermally unstable at elevated temperatures. To address this instability, we incorporated the solvent additive, DIO, to enhance donor-acceptor intermixing and achieve a favorable blend morphology. Our results demonstrate that DIO incorporation promotes a more uniform vertical distribution of PffBT4T-2OD and ITIC, as evidenced by stable NR fringes and consistent SLD profiles up to 120°C. This enhanced miscibility delays the onset of phase segregation and significantly improves the thermal stability of the BHJs. These findings confirm our hypothesis that insufficient initial mixing contributes to the thermal instability of ITIC-based blends, and that use of solvent additives can mitigate this effect. Incorporating DIO not only improves the intermixing during film formation but also prolongs the thermal stability of the active layer, offering a viable strategy for enhancing the operational stability of organic solar cell devices.

5 REFERENCES

[1.] M. Kaltenbrunner, M.S. White, E.D. Głowacki, T. Sekitani, T. Someya, N.S. Sariciftci, S. Bauer, Nat. Commun. 3 (2012) 770.
[2.] C. Lungenschmied, G. Dennler, H. Neugebauer, S.N. Sariciftci, M. Glatthaar, T. Meyer, A. Meyer, Sol. Energy Mater. Sol. Cells 91 (2007) 379.
[3.] L.H. Rossander, H.F. Dam, J.E. Carlé, M. Helgesen, I. Rajkovic, M. Corazza, F.C. Krebs, J.W. Andreasen, Energy Environ. Sci. 10 (2017) 2411.
[4.] Y. Liu, J. Zhao, Z. Li, C. Mu, W. Ma, H. Hu, K. Jiang, H. Lin, H. Ade, H. Yan, Nat. Commun. 5 (2014) 5293.
[5.] C. Yan, S. Barlow, Z. Wang, H. Yan, A.K.Y. Jen, S.R. Marder, X. Zhan, Nat. Rev. Mater. 3 (2018) 18003.
[6.] H. Sun, F. Chen, Z.-K. Chen, Mater. Today 24 (2019) 94.
[7.] B. Arredondo, J. Carlos Pérez-Martínez, L. Muñoz-Díaz, M.d.C. López-González, D. Martín-Martín, G. del Pozo, E. Hernández-Balaguera, B. Romero, J. Lamminaho, V. Turkovic, M. Madsen, Sol. Energy 232 (2022) 120.
[8.] T.-Y. Huang, A.P. Le Brun, B. Sochor, C.-M. Wu, Y. Bulut, P. Müller-Buschbaum, S.V. Roth, Y.-L. Yang, ACS Appl. Nano Mater. 7 (2024) 17588.
[9.] B. Morgan, M.D. Dadmun, J. Polym. Sci., Part B: Polym. Phys. 55 (2017) 1142.
[10.] S.J. Rinehart, G. Yuan, M.D. Dadmun, Soft Matter 16 (2020) 1287.
[11.] L.-M. Wang, Q. Li, S. Liu, Z. Cao, Y.-P. Cai, X. Jiao, H. Lai, W. Xie, X. Zhan, T. Zhu, ACS Appl. Mater. Interfaces 12 (2020) 24165.
[12.] A.P. Le Brun, T.-Y. Huang, S. Pullen, A.R.J. Nelson, J. Spedding, S.A. Holt, J. Appl. Crystallogr. 56 (2023) 18.
[13.] A.R.J. Nelson, S.W. Prescott, J. Appl. Crystallogr. 52 (2019) 193.
[14.] L. Yu, D. Qian, S. Marina, F.A.A. Nugroho, A. Sharma, S. Hultmark, A.I. Hofmann, R. Kroon, J. Benduhn, D.-M. Smilgies, K. Vandewal, M.R. Andersson, C. Langhammer, J. Martín, F. Gao, C. Müller, ACS Appl. Mater. Interfaces 11 (2019) 21766.

10.4229/EUPVSEC2025/2BV.2.19

ON THE VIABILITY OF CIGS TECHNOLOGY FOR SILICON BASED TANDEM SOLAR CELLS

Juan C. Jimeno(1), Vanesa Fano(1), Eneko Cereceda(1), Aloña Otaegi(1), Nekane Azkona(1), Rubén Gutiérrez(1), Federico Recart(1), Velia Rodríguez(1), Carlos del Cañizo(2) & David Fuertes(2)
1 Technological Institute of Microelectronics, University of the Basque Country UPV/EHU, 48013, Bilbao, Spain
2 Universidad Politécnica de Madrid, Instituto de Energía Solar,
ETSI Telecomunicación, Ciudad Universitaria, E-28040 Madrid, Spain
jc.jimeno@ehu.eus

ABSTRACT: This work models the efficiency obtainable from tandem structures with a silicon bottom cell and a CIGS top cell. Its results are based on the characteristics obtained by different authors on single CIGS solar cells, modelling their dependence of V_{oc} on E_G and the dependence of V_{oc} on recombination mechanisms with kT or 2kT dependence. Results are modelled for different connection strategies: 4 terminals, with independent bias conditions for top and bottom cells; 3 terminals, with a parallel interconnection of both sub-cells (one top in parallel with a series of two bottoms); 2 terminals as conventional tandem cells with series connection. The work shows the viability of CIGS / Silicon tandem cells for any configuration with different band gap targets for optimum conversion efficiency, upgrading the efficiency of a single high efficiency silicon solar cell.
Keywords: Tandem solar cell, CIGS, Silicon

1 INTRODUCTION

Crystalline silicon cells are currently the workhorse of photovoltaics. However, the efficiency of industrially manufactured cells is approaching its theoretical maximum. It is now widely accepted that solar cells of the future will need to make a more intelligent use of the solar spectrum, perhaps by including two or more pn junctions, each suited to a region of the solar spectrum.

CIGS cells have shown exceptional characteristics in the past, very close to those of the best silicon cells, with the best of them having efficiencies of over 23.3% [1]. In addition, they have other advantages such as being able to be made in thin films, with the savings in material that this entails. Furthermore, their stability and their manufacturability are well demonstrated. However, their efficiency has always been slightly lower than that of silicon cells and the brutal reduction in the cost of the latter has made them a minority option today. The best CIGS cells are made based on materials with E_G close to that of silicon cells, from 1.1 to 1.2 eV, so they do not appear to be a good complement to these in tandem structures. However, their E_G can be modulated in a range of 1 to 2 eV, which has not been sufficiently explored in tandem structures.

In conventional tandem cells connected in series, the useful photons of the solar spectrum must be distributed equally among all the cells composing the tandem structure. This greatly limits the materials to be combined, even more so when one of them, the silicon of the bottom cell, appears today as invariant. Our group presented a three-terminal tandem solar cell structure [2] based on an IBC-type silicon cell whose sensitivity to E_G mismatches between the top and bottom cells is very small, making it useful for structures even with very mismatched E_Gs. This structure was quickly adopted by other groups [3] and today constitutes one of the basic structures in the design of tandem cells, whether based on silicon, perovskites or other materials [4].

This work models the recombination characteristics that appear in the best CIGS cells made so far, trying to establish relationships between the obtainable V_{oc}, their E_G, and the dominant recombination type in the device.

2 THE SOLAR SPECTRUM

Tandem cells have a higher sensitivity to the incident light spectrum than conventional cells. In conventional single-junction solar cells, all collected electrons are extracted at the same voltage, and at most one electron is extracted for each photon. Tandem cells use different materials, each capable of capturing photons only from a certain energy level. For each photon absorbed, a single electron can be extracted, identically to conventional cells, at a voltage directly related to the threshold energy required to capture them, E_G. Screening photons according to their energy allows for better use of the light spectrum. The theoretical limit for converting light to electric current is 68% [5] using a large number of materials. Efficiencies close to 38% [6] have been obtained for three materials, and close to 33% for two junctions [7]. All these record results correspond to cells made of III-V materials, which, due to their high cost, are usually reserved for space applications. For single junction cells the efficiency limit is close to 30% for GaAs cells [8], followed by silicon cells with efficiencies close to 27.5% [9]. Due to their low cost and efficiency close to theoretical limits it seems very likely that silicon cells will continue to dominate the market, but increasing their efficiency requires their combination with other cells in tandem structures.

This work focuses on tandem cells with only two junctions. The study was conducted for the AM1.5G spectrum. The cell with the lowest E_G corresponds to a 1.1 eV silicon cell, assuming a conservative efficiency of 25%. The top cell will be a CIGS cell. The current collected by each cell is a function of the E_G of the top cell (Fig. 1). The voltage it provides is also a function of the band (red to green line) in Fig. 2. The region in which it is located depends on the technology and imperfections of this top cell. The green line corresponds to the maximum obtainable open circuit voltage, V_{oc}, for a solar cell according to our models (the best cell technologies of III-V materials fit well to this green line) and can be roughly expressed as:

$$V_{oc} = \frac{E_G}{q} - 0{,}4$$

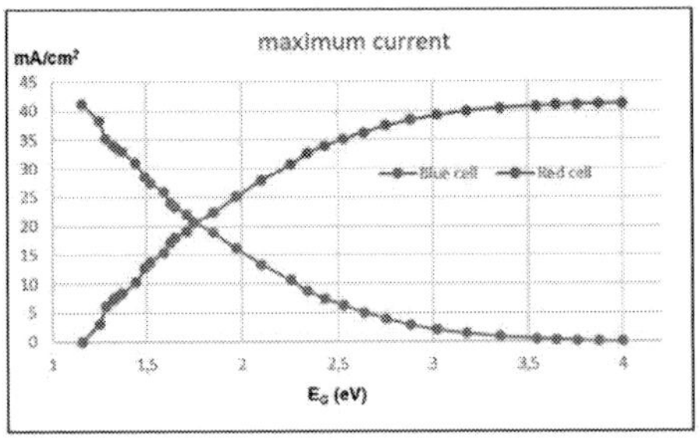

Figure 1: Maximum photocurrents obtainable by the top cell, in blue, and the bottom cell, in red, when the latter is a silicon cell

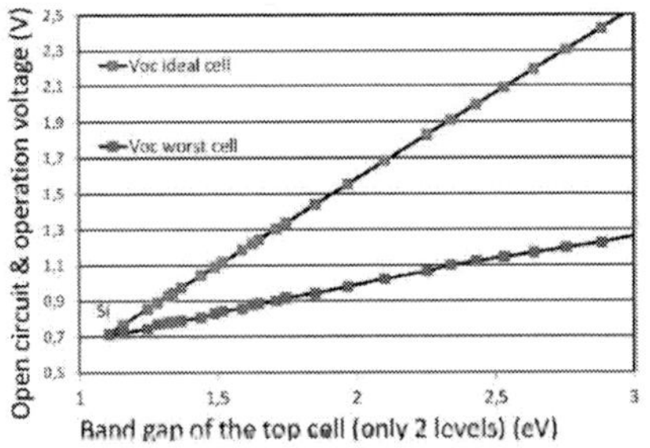

Figure 2: V_{oc} values for the top cell, in green the maximum possible and in red the minimum admissible

The red line represents the minimum V_{oc} voltage required for a top cell, the cell with the highest E_G, to not degrade the performance of a tandem cell based on a silicon bottom cell. In other words, this represents the minimum V_{oc} value required for the bottom cell for the tandem assembly to achieve an efficiency of at least 25%.

3 INTERCONNECTION TOPOLOGIES

In tandem cells, the top cell is used as an optical filter for the bottom cell, so that the most energetic photons are collected in the former, while the lowest-energy ones are collected in the latter. Therefore, the top cell sits above the latter. However, electrical interconnections can vary.

The most common is shown in Fig. 3, in which both cells are connected in series. Its current is limited by the poor cell, which, according to Fig. 1, restricts the E_G range for the top cell from 1.6 to 1.9 eV. Figure 4 shows the maximum efficiency obtainable for a tandem cell as a function of the E_G value of the top cell for the case where the bottom cell is a silicon cell with 25% efficiency.

The 4-terminal connection allows the behavior of each cell to be independent (Fig. 5) and provides the highest efficiencies but requires placing the cells in two different electrical circuits.

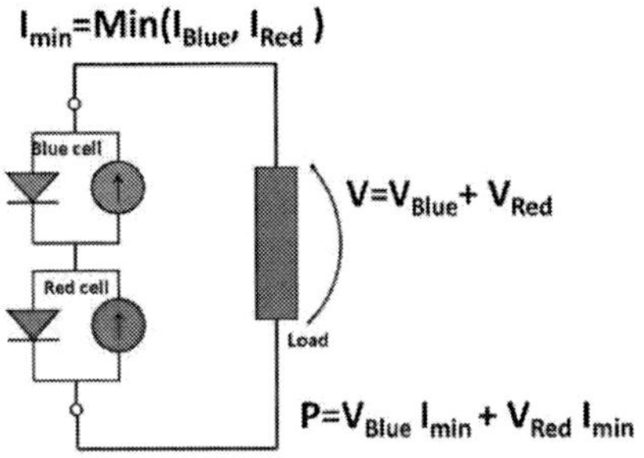

Figure 3: Two-material tandem solar cell with series interconnection

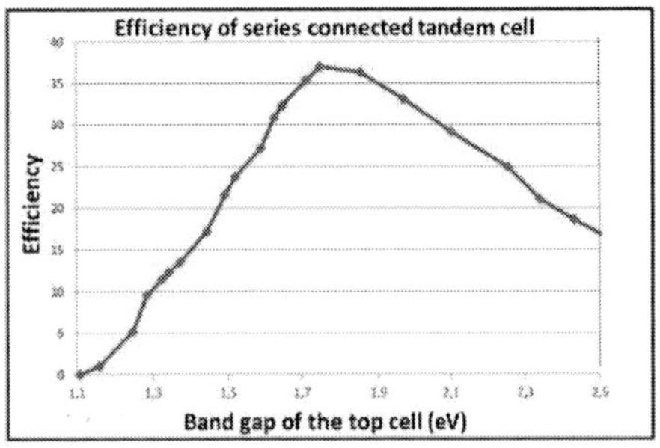

Figure 4: Maximum efficiency is achievable for a series connected tandem cell with a silicon bottom cell and depending on the E_G of the top cell

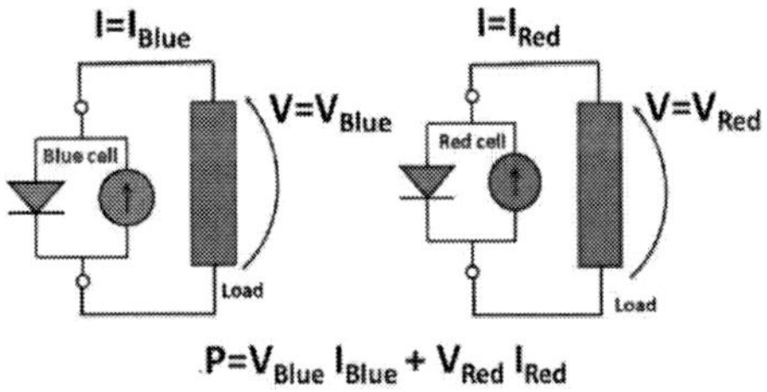

Figure 5: 4-terminal tandem solar cell with two materials without interconnection between them

The parallel connection of the cells (Fig. 6) is limited by the cell voltage. Identically to the case of the series connection, figure 7 shows the maximum efficiency obtainable for a tandem cell as a function of the E_G value of the top cell for the case where the bottom cell is a silicon cell with 25% efficiency. It can be seen that this kind of interconnection offers better adaptability than the series connection. However, it would require implementing 3 pn junctions per cell. A completely equivalent simplification is the 3-terminal cell (Fig. 8), from which modules with tandem cells in parallel can be built.

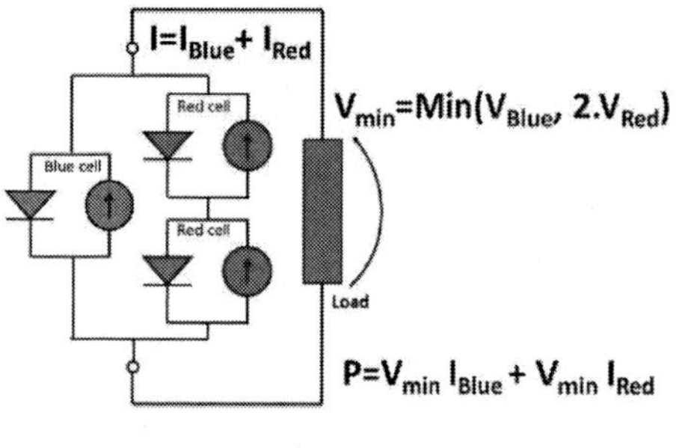

Figure 6: Two-material tandem solar cell with parallel interconnection

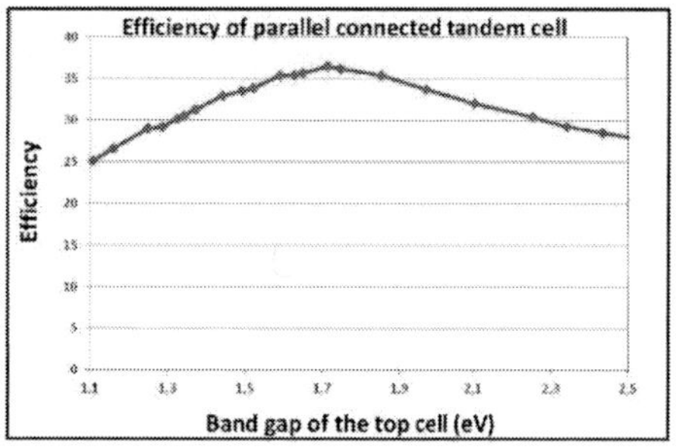

Figure 7: Maximum efficiency achievable for a parallel connected tandem cell with a silicon bottom cell and depending on the E_G of the top cell

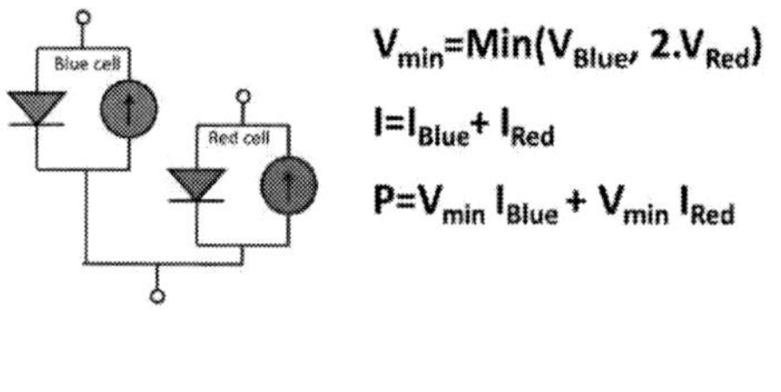

Figure 8: 3-terminal tandem solar cell with two materials and parallel interconnection

4 MODELLING THE CIGS TECHNOLOGY

Currently, there are no models for how CIGS cell characteristics vary depending on E_G. Furthermore, some studies refer to technologies from 10 years ago, and current cells are much better. It is also unknown whether CIGS cells behave with m=1 or 2, which is crucial for the performance of tandem cells.

In order to make a model that covers all possibilities, but always considering the maximum achievable, we have considered the results reported by 3 different authors, Nakamura in 2019 [1] with CIGS cells with record efficiency of 23.35%, Barreau in 2020 [10] and W.N. Shafarman [11]. This last work is the one with the best analysis of CIGS cells in terms of their band-gap, however, as it is almost 25 years old, its results have been clearly surpassed by the other two previously presented.

In order to obtain a valid model for all situations, two extreme behaviors have been considered, depending on whether the V_{oc} was limited by m=1 or m=2 effects. A fit of the best results of the 3 papers presented has been performed. Figure 9 shows the excellent fit of both models to the reported V_{oc} voltages. The recombination models obtained can be expressed as:

$$J = 1.5\ 10^{-4} \exp\left(\frac{-E_G}{2\ V_T}\right).\exp\left(\frac{V}{V_T}\right)\ A/cm^2$$

$$J = 4\ 10^{-4} \exp\left(\frac{-E_G}{4.5\ V_T}\right).\exp\left(\frac{V}{2\ V_T}\right)\ A/cm^2$$

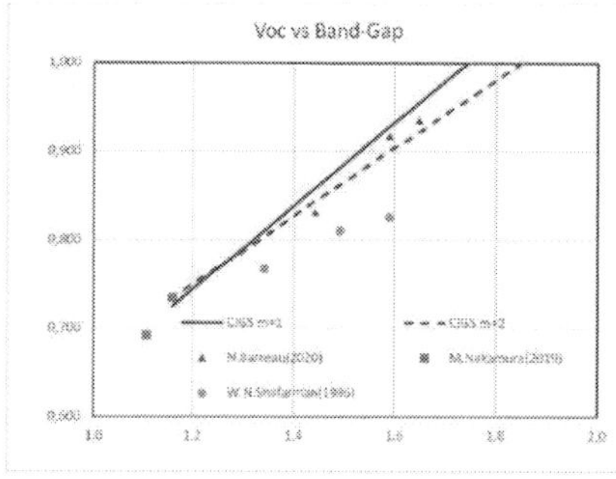

Figure 9: Recombination model for CIGS technology in the cases of m=1 and m=2 vs. experimental data

For the I_{sc} (Fig. 10) small discrepancies are found in the region of high E_G values, above 1.65 eV, which could mean that the optical band gap (obtained as a projection of V_{oc} at T = 0 K) is perhaps larger than this value. In this case the model should be refined a bit more.

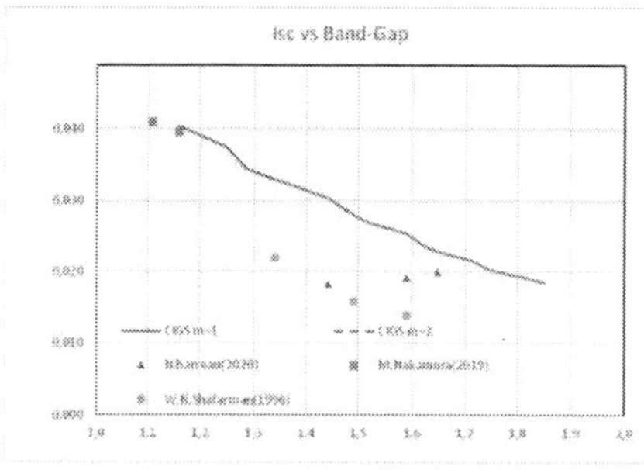

Figure 10: Photogeneration model for CIGS technology vs. experimental data

It should be noted that the fill-factors, shown in figure 11, are highly variable and always depend on parasitic effects. In the fit of the characteristics shown in figure 11 a series resistance, R_s, value of 0.5 $\Omega \cdot cm^2$ has been applied for the case of m=1 and of 3 $\Omega \cdot cm^2$ for the case of m=2. Even if these differences in R_s are not taken into account, the high FF values for the low band-gap cells suggest a behavior close to m=1 and closer to m=2 in the high band-gap cases. Identical conclusions would be obtained from comparison of results from CIGS perovskite technologies. As example for 1.55 eV of E_G the CIGS cell [12] presents a FF of 72,2 % (for a V_{oc} of 0.92 V) compared to 84.0% (for a V_{oc} of 1.19 V) of their equivalent perovskite [13] cell, suggesting that the m=2 behavior of CIGS cells may be the main cause of their low FF and V_{oc} values.

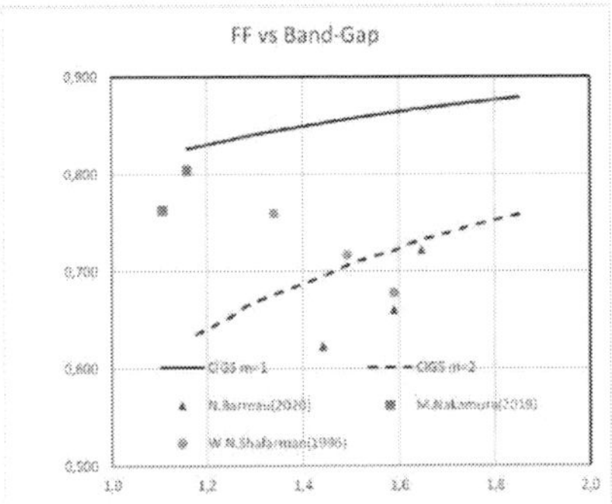

Figure 11: Fill-Factor model for CIGS technology in the cases of m=1 and m=2 vs. experimental data

5 OBTAINED RESULTS

Numerical simulation of tandem cells with a silicon bottom cell and efficiency 25% and a CIGS top cell according to the models in Figure 9 and their corresponding recombination has led to the results in figures 12, 13 and 14 for 4-terminal cells (Fig. 12), 2-terminal cells and series connection (Fig. 13) and 2 or 3-terminal cells and parallel connection (Fig. 14).

The best results are obviously obtained for 4-terminal cells (Fig. 12), where a clear improvement is obtained for tandem structures with CIGS cells. The maximum efficiency obtainable for a tandem structure in these circumstances, on a silicon cell with 25% efficiency and a CIGS top cell behaving like the m=1 model, is 30.3% for band-gaps between 1.85 and 1.95 eV and 28.5% for identical band-gaps under the m=2 model. This indicates that there is a net gain between 3.5 and 5.3 absolute points compared to a silicon cell without a tandem. For an E_G of 1.65 eV the gain is between 2.8 and 4.6 absolute points (efficiencies of 27.8 to 29.6 %).

For cells connected in series (Figure 13), a narrow net gain region appears located between 1.63 and 1.97 eV of E_G, reaching theoretical efficiencies of up to 30.3% for 1.75 eV of E_G, the same as with 4-terminal structures. For the case of m=2, the results are also similar to those obtained for 4 terminals but restricted to the region from 1.65 to 1.9 of E_G. For values outside this range, the CIGS cell causes a deterioration of the results of the tandem cell.

For parallel-connected cells (Fig. 14), there are virtually no restrictions on the window in which the improvement occurs, but it is less spectacular than in series connections, being limited to 2 to 4.5 absolute points of improvement and, for a practical E_G range, perhaps only 1 to 2 points of improvement. We believe this is due to the fact that high-E_G CIGS cells (at least those we studied) have operating voltages that are not as high as they should be.

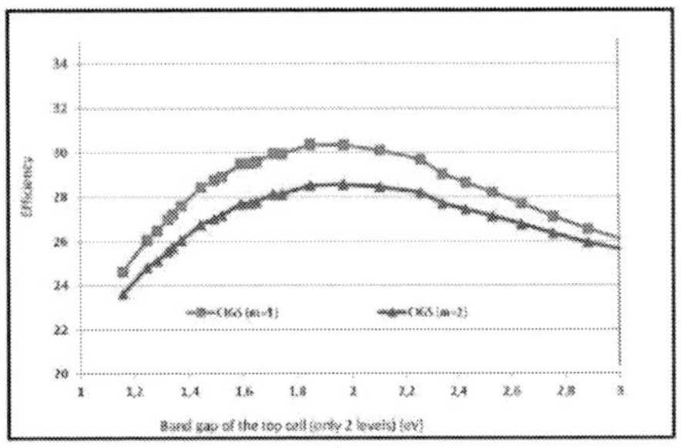

Figure 12: Efficiencies achievable for 4-terminal tandem cells of a silicon bottom cell with 25% efficiency and a CIGS top cell for models m=1 and m=2

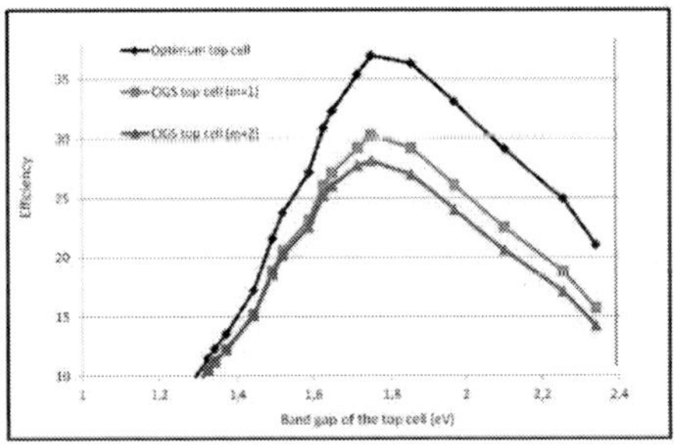

Figure 13: Efficiencies for tandem cells for a silicon bottom cell and 25% efficiency and a top cell according to the CIGS cell model with m=1 and m=2, in cases where cells are interconnected in series

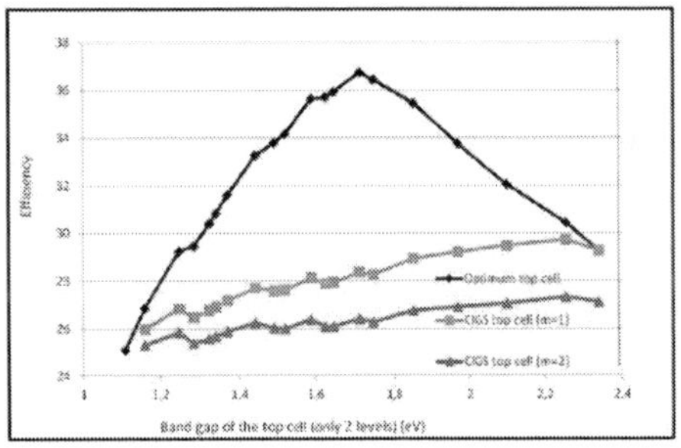

Figure 14: Efficiencies for tandem cells for a silicon bottom cell and 25% efficiency and a top cell according to the CIGS cell model with m=1 and m=2, in cases where cells are interconnected in parallel

10.4229/EUPVSEC2025/2BV.2.22

5 CONCLUSIONS

CIGS solar cells can be a real and easily industrializable alternative for the development of tandem solar cells based on a silicon bottom cell. In conventional series interconnection configurations, they present a narrow region with the potential for more than 5 absolute points of improvement over the silicon cell. For parallel configurations, they are more limited, but the restrictions on the E_G required for the CIGS cell disappear, opening up a significant area for research and ongoing improvement.

Precise characterization of the behavior of CIG cells is essential, and it is necessary to clearly determine in which cases their recombination depends on m=1 or m=2. The results of this work indicate that the final efficiency will largely depend on this factor, which not only determines the device's operating voltage but also its fill factor.

Finally, Figure 15 represents an overview of the regions and magnitudes in which CIGS technology can represent an advance over conventional silicon technologies.

This work has not taken into account the degradation that the joint manufacture of silicon and CIGS cells can produce in the former, which are clearly technological aspects that must be addressed.

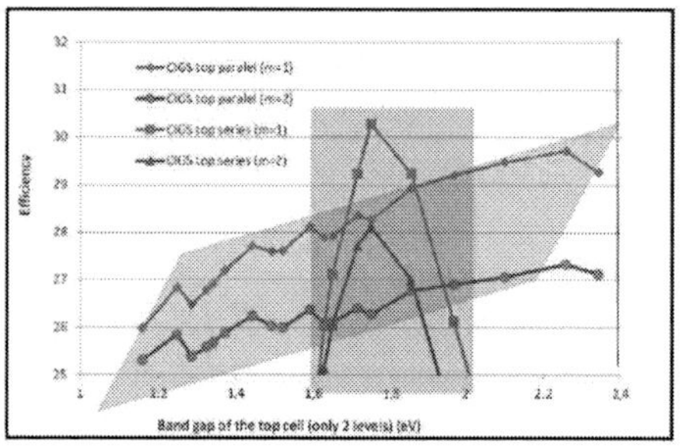

Figure 15: Efficiencies for tandem cells for a silicon bottom cell and 25% efficiency and a top cell according to the CIGS cell model with m=1 and m=2, in cases where cells are interconnected in series or parallel

6 ACKNOWLEDGEMENT

Acknowledgement

This research was supported by the M-ERA.NET Consortium under the 2024 Joint Call, with funding through the PARACELSis Project from the Agencia Vasca de Innovación (Innobasque), the Spanish Research Agency MICIU/AEI/10.13039/501100011033 (PCI2025-16314), the Hazitek ZL-2025/00146 and the European Union.

7 REFERENCES

[1] M. Nakamura, K. Yamaguchi, Y. Kimoto, Y. Yasaki, T. Kato and H. Sugimoto, "Cd-Free Cu(In,Ga)(Se,S)2 Thin-Film Solar Cell With Record Efficiency of 23.35%," in IEEE Journal of Photovoltaics, vol. 9, no. 6, pp. 1863-1867, Nov. 2019, doi: 10.1109/JPHOTOV.2019.2937218.

[2] Juan. C. Jimeno, Rubén Gutierrez, Vanesa Fano, Ahmed Habib, Carlos del Cañizo, Muhammad A. Rasool, Aloña Otaegi, "A 3 Terminal Parallel Connected Silicon Tandem Solar Cell". Energy Procedia, Volume 92, August 2016, Pages 644-65. doi:10.1016/j.egypro.2016.07.031

[3] Emily L. Warren, Michael G. Deceglie, Michael Rienacker, Robby Peibst, Adele C. Tamboli and Paul Stradinsa, "Maximizing tandem solar cell power extraction using a three-terminal design". Sustainable Energy & Fuels, 2018. doi: 10.1039/c8se00133b

[4] Xingliang Li, Qiaojing Xu, Lingling Yan, Chengchao Ren, Biao Shi, Pengyang Wang, Sayantan Mazumdar, Guofu Hou, Ying Zhao and Xiaodan Zhang, "Silicon heterojunction-based tandem solar cells: past, status, and future prospects". Nanophotonics 2021; 10(8): 2001–2022. doi: 10.1515/nanoph-2021-0034

[5] J. F. Geisz, R. M. France, K. L. Schulte, M. A. Steiner, A. G. Norman, H. L. Guthrey, M. R. Young, T. Song, and T. Moriarty, "Six-junction III-V solar cells with 47.1% conversion efficiency under 143 suns concentration," Nat. Energy 5, 326 (2020).

[6] K. Sasaki, T. Agui, K. Nakaido, N. Takahashi, R. Onitsuka, and T. Takamoto, "Development of InGaP/GaAs/InGaAs inverted triple junction concentrator solar cells," AIP Conf. Proc. 1556, 22 (2013).

[7] M. A. Green, E. D. Dunlop, J. Hohl-Ebinger, M. Yoshita, N. Kopiakis, and X. Hao, "Solar cell efficiency tables (version 57)," Prog. Photovoltaics 29, 3 (2021).

[8] Kayes BM, Nie H, Twist R, Spruytte SG, Reinhardt F, Kizilyalli IC, Higashi GS. 27.6% conversion efficiency, a new record for single-junction solar cells under 1 sun illumination. Proceedings of the 37th IEEE Photovoltaic Specialists Conference, 2011.

[9] https://www.longi.com/en/news/

[10]N. Barreau et al., "High efficiency solar cell based on Cu(In,Ga)S2 thin film grown by 3-stage process," 2020 47th IEEE Photovoltaic Specialists Conference (PVSC), Calgary, AB, Canada, 2020, pp. 1715-1718, doi: 10.1109/PVSC45281.2020.9300598.

[11]W. N. Shafarman, R. Klenk and B. E. McCandless, "Characterization of Cu(InGa)Se/sub 2/ solar cells with high Ga content," Conference Record of the Twenty Fifth IEEE Photovoltaic Specialists Conference - 1996, Washington, DC, USA, 1996, pp. 763-768, doi: 10.1109/PVSC.1996.564240.

[12] Hiroi H, Iwata Y, Adachi S, Sugimoto H, Yamada A. New World-record efficiency for pure-sulfide Cu(In,Ga)S2 thin-film solar cell with Cd-free buffer layer via KCN-free process. IEEE Journal of Photovoltaics 2016; 6(3): 760-763.

[13] Jung EH, Jeon NJ, Park EY, et al. Efficient, stable and scalable perovskite solar cells using poly(3-hexylthiophene). Nature. 2019; 567(7749): 511-515.

ON THE VIABILITY OF CIGS TECHNOLOGY FOR SILICON BASED TANDEM SOLAR CELLS

Juan C. Jimeno[1], Vanesa Fano[1], Eneko Cereceda[1], Aloña Otaegi[1], Nekane Azkona[1], Rubén Gutiérrez[1], Federico Recart[1], Velia Rodríguez[1], Carlos del Cañizo[2] & David Fuertes[2]
[1] Technolgical Institute of Microelectronics (TiM), UPV/EHU, Bilbao, Spain. email: jc.jimeno@ehu.eus
[2] Instituto de Energía Solar (UPM), Universidad Politécnica de Madrid, Madrid, Spain

Aim & objectives

- Future increases in solar cell efficiencies will require tandem structures
- Crystalline silicon cells cover 95% of global production; their low cost, high efficiency and stability suggest that they will continue to dominate the market, even in tandem structures.
- CIGS presents an industrial mature technology, with efficiencies of up to 23%, close to silicon and its E_G can be varied from 1 to 2 eV
- The objective of this work is to analyze the feasibility of making CIGS tandems on silicon-based cells

Current and voltages in tandem cells

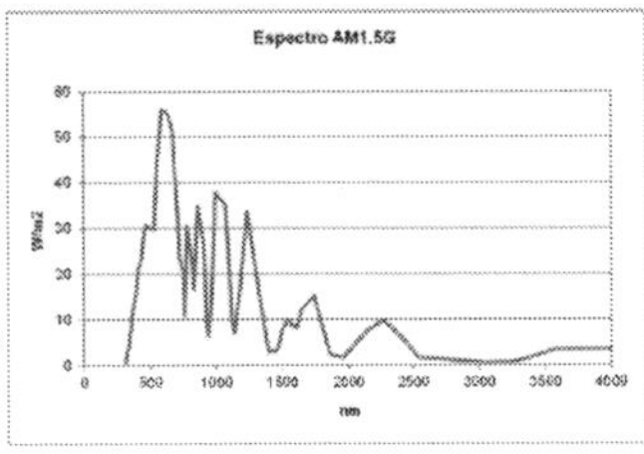

Fig. 1

This work focuses on tandem cells with only two junctions. The study was conducted for the AM1.5 spectrum (**Fig. 1**). The cell with the lowest E_G corresponds to a 1.1 eV silicon cell, assuming an efficiency of 25%. The top cell will be a CIGS cell. The current collected by each cell is a function of the E_G of the top cell (**Fig. 2**). The voltage it provides is also a function of the band (red to green line) in **Fig. 3**. The region in which it is located depends on the technology and imperfections of this top cell.

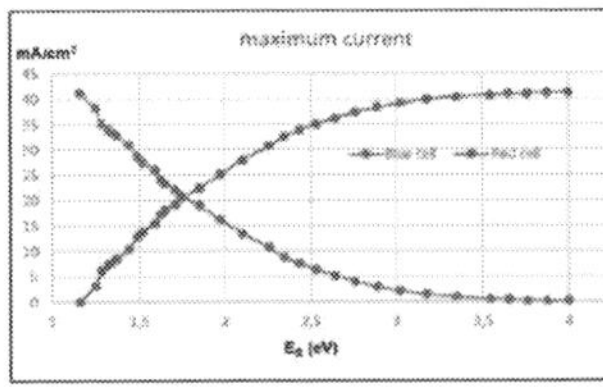

Fig. 2

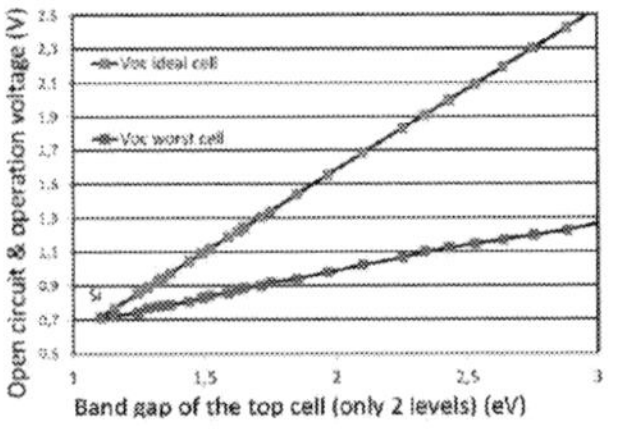

Fig. 3

Tandem cell structures and philosophies

2 terminal series connected tandem cell

$$I_{min}=Min(I_{Blue}, I_{Red})$$
$$V=V_{Blue}+V_{Red}$$
$$P=V_{Blue}I_{min}+V_{Red}I_{min}$$

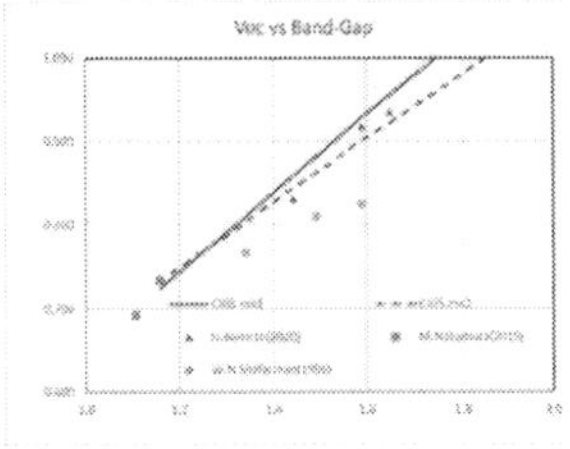

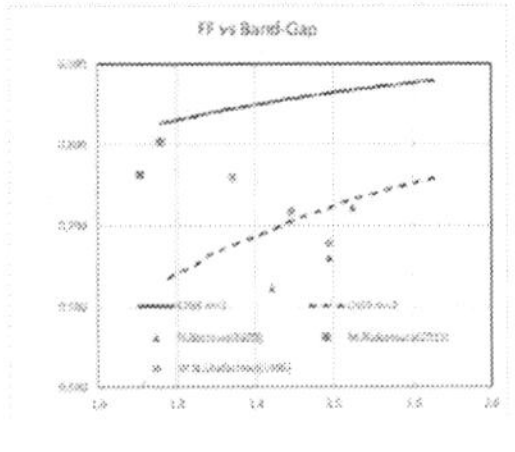

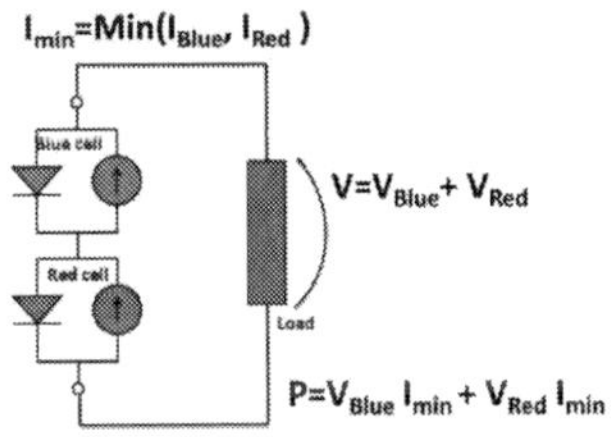

Fig. 4

4 terminal series connected tandem cell

$$I=I_{Blue}$$
$$V=V_{Blue}$$
$$I=I_{Red}$$
$$V=V_{Red}$$
$$P=V_{Blue}I_{Blue}+V_{Red}I_{Red}$$

Fig. 5

In tandem cells are different electrical connection possibilities:
The most common is shown in **Fig. 4**, in which both cells are connected in series. Its current is limited by the poor cell, which, according to **Fig. 2**, restricts the E_G range for the TOP cell from 1.6 to 1.9 eV. The 4-terminal connection allows the behavior of each cell to be independent (**Fig. 5**) and provides the highest efficiencies but requires placing the cells in two different electrical circuits.
The parallel connection of the cells (**Fig. 6**) is limited by the cell voltage, but it offers better adaptability than the series connection. However, it would require implementing 3 pn junctions per cell. A completely equivalent simplification is the 3-terminal cell (**Fig. 7**), from which modules with tandem cells in parallel can be built.

2 terminal parallel connected tandem cell

$$I=I_{Blue}+I_{Red}$$
$$V_{min}=Min(V_{Blue}, 2.V_{Red})$$
$$P=V_{min}I_{Blue}+V_{min}I_{Red}$$

Fig. 6

3 terminal parallel connected tandem cell

$$V_{min}=Min(V_{Blue}, 2.V_{Red})$$
$$I=I_{Blue}+I_{Red}$$
$$P=V_{min}I_{Blue}+V_{min}I_{Red}$$

Fig. 7

Modelling the CIGS Technology

Fig. 8

Fig. 9

Currently, there are no models for how CIGS cell characteristics vary depending on E_G. Furthermore, some studies refer to technologies from 10 years ago, and current cells are much better. It is also unknown whether CIGS cells behave with m=1 or 2, which is crucial for the performance of tandem cells. The solution was to fit the best cells to two models, one with m=1 and the other with m=2. The result can be seen in **Fig. 8** and the following equations.

$$J = 1.5\ 10^{-1} \exp\left(\frac{-E_G}{2\,V_T}\right).\exp\left(\frac{V}{V_T}\right)$$

$$J = 4\ 10^{-4} \exp\left(\frac{-E_G}{4.5\,V_T}\right).\exp\left(\frac{V}{2\,V_T}\right)$$

Comparison of the actual and modelled Fill-Factors (**Fig. 9**) suggests that low E_G cells (<1.3 eV) may have m close to 1, while high E_G cells may be close to 2.

Modelling Results of Tandem Structures

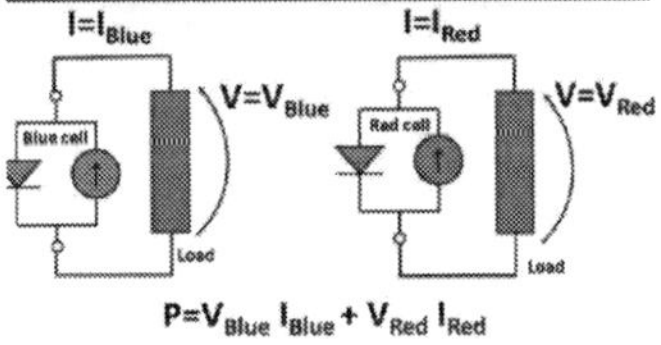

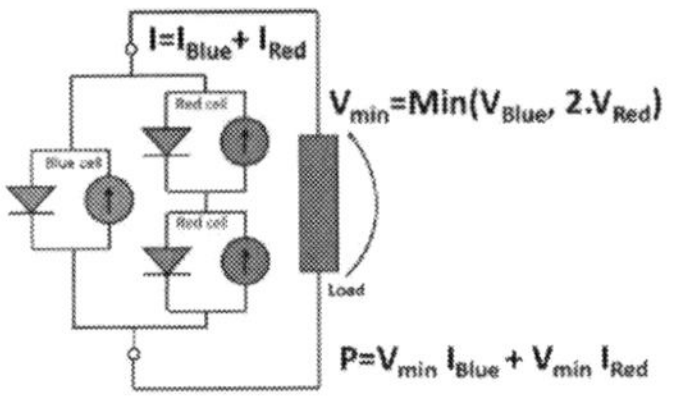

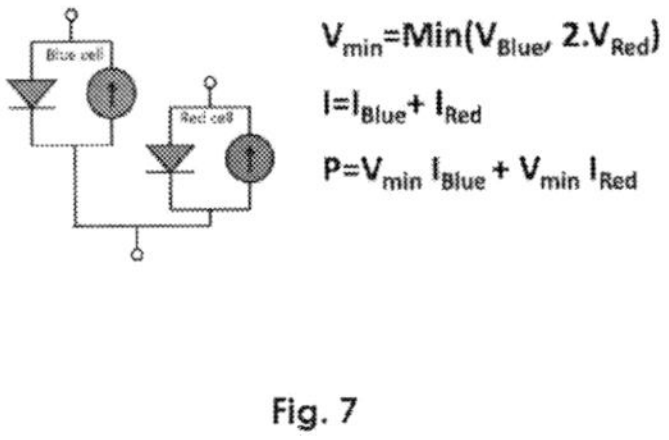

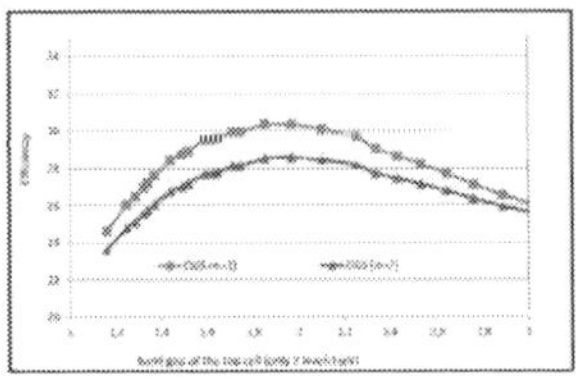

Fig. 10

Numerical simulation of tandem cells with a silicon bottom cell and efficiency 25% and a CIGS top cell according to the models in **Figure 8** and the previous equations, has led to the results in **Figures 10, 11** and **12** for 4-terminal cells (**Fig. 10**), 2-terminal cells and series connection (**Fig. 11**) and 2 or 3-terminal cells and parallel connection (**Fig. 12**).

The best results are obviously obtained for 4-terminal cells (**Fig. 10**), where a clear improvement is obtained for tandem structures with CIGS cells with an E_G greater than 1.4 eV. For the series-connected cells (**Fig. 11**), a narrow window of 1.65 to 1.95 eV is obtained in which the tandem cell with CIGS outperforms a standard silicon cell. For parallel-connected cells (**Fig. 12**), there are virtually no restrictions on the window in which the improvement occurs, but it is less spectacular than in series connections, being limited to 2 to 4.5 absolute points of improvement and, for a practical E_G range, perhaps only 1 to 2 points of improvement. We believe this is due to the fact that high-E_G CIGS cells (at least those we studied) have operating voltages that are not as high as they should be. .

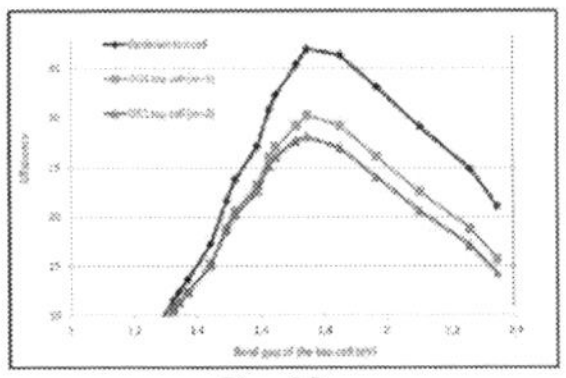

Fig. 11

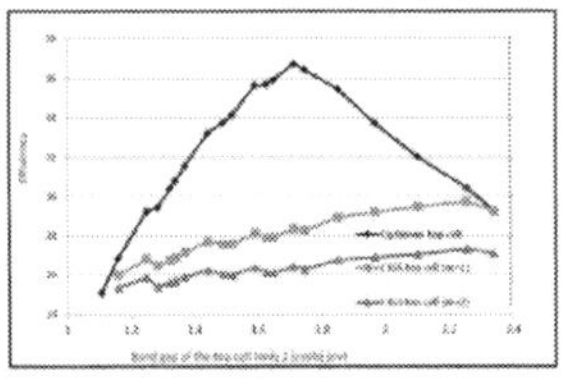

Fig. 12

CONCLUSIONS

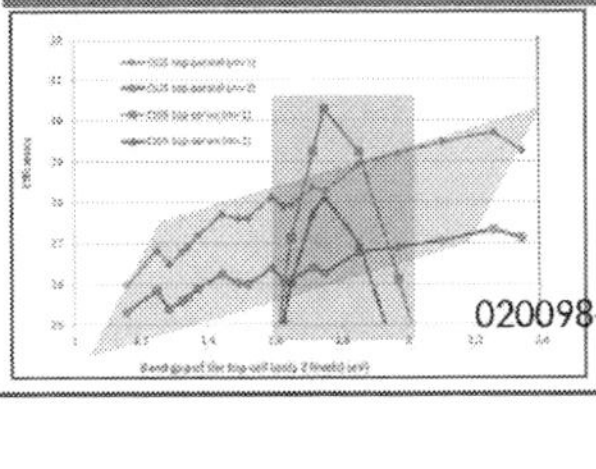

- CIGS technology appears to be a clear opportunity for the development of tandem cells in silicon. It could produce efficiency improvements of up to 5.5 absolute points for 4-terminal structures.
- For 2-terminal structures, the gains range from 3 to 5 points for a very narrow range of E_G values in the case of series connections and are somewhat lower in efficiency but without E_G restrictions for parallel connections. The figure on the left is a summary of what has been discussed here.
- A greater effort must be done in modelling high E_G CIGS cells.

UNIVERSITAT POLITÈCNICA DE VALÈNCIA

Study of the effect of precursor solution aging on Bismuth-based Chalcohalide Thin Films by Solution Method for Photovoltaic Applications

Benjamín Fritz Muñoz, Giulia Longo, Bernabé Marí Soucasé

Instituto de Diseño y Fabricación - Universitat Politècnica de València

Introduction / Objectives

The search for non-toxic and stable alternatives to lead-based perovskites has brought pnictogen-based chalcohalides to the forefront as promising candidates for next-generation photovoltaic absorbers[1]. Among these, **bismuth sulfo-bromide (BiSBr)** stands out as a particularly attractive material due to its earth-abundant composition, intrinsic thermodynamic stability, and suitable optoelectronic properties for single-junction solar cell applications, such as a direct bandgap in the range of ~1.6–1.8 eV and a high absorption coefficient (>10^5 cm^{-1}).[2,3]

In this work, our objectives are :

- Preparation of BiSBr films using a solution-processing method adapted from the synthesis[4] of SbSI.
- Study in the impact of precursor solution aging on the quality of resulting films.

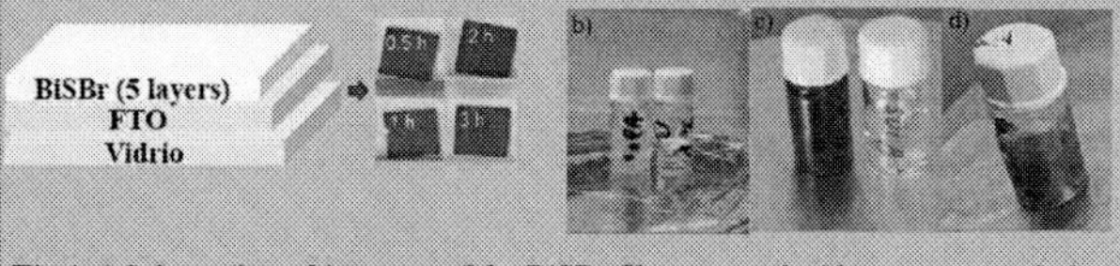

Fig 1 a) Schematic architectures of the BiSBr film prepared with precursors solution aged 0.5, 1, 2 and 3 hours with corresponding pictures.
b) Solutions A and B after 3 hours of stirring. c) Solution A and B after one night.
d) Mixed solution after one day

Methods

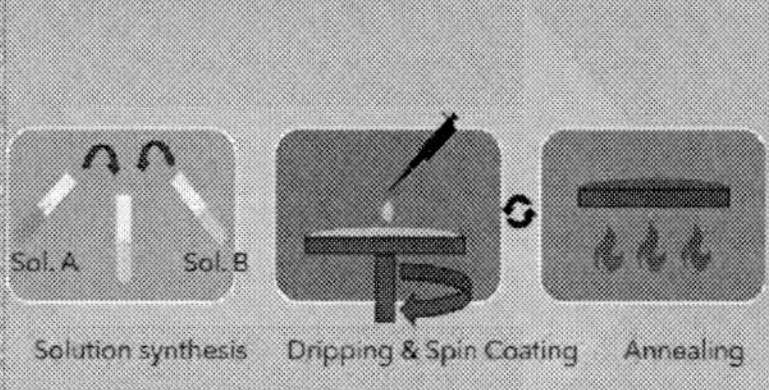

Solution A:

$$\begin{cases} 0,4\ mmol BiCl_3 \\ 0,1\ mmol\ BiBr_3 \\ 1,25\ mmol\ TU \end{cases}$$

in 2 mL DMF for 2 hours at 80ºC

Solution B:

0,5 $mmol\ BiBr_3$ in 1 mL DMSO for 2 hours at 80ºC

Fig 2 Thin film BiSBr preparation

The two solution were mixed in a ratio A:B = 4:1 and then heated at 80ºC for 0.5, 1, 2 and 3 hours, then deposited on FTO by spincoating in air, casting 75 µl at 4000 rpm for 60 sec.
The BiSBr film was then annealed at 160ºC for 15 min each layer.

Results

Effect of aging solution

In the figure 3, The GIXRD diffractograms show increasing crystallinity as the stirring time increases. The samples left 0,5 and 1 hour of stirring show the appearance of the characteristic peaks of BiSBr, even if with very low intensity and with evidence of amorphous phase present. As the time of stirring is increased, the crystallinity of the film is higher, and clear presence of BiSBr can be appreciated. After 1 hour, no evident changes can be appreciated with increasing of stirring time.
The field-emission scanning electron microscopy (FESEM) images reveal a significant change in the surface morphology.

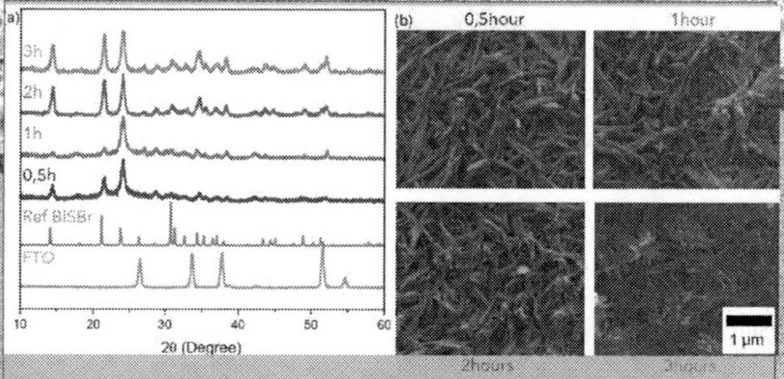

Fig 3 a) GIXRD diffractograms of the BiSBr thin films formed by solution with different aging times
b) FESEM images of the same films

Table 1 a) Distribution of Bi, S and Br taken from EDS of 0,5, 1, 2 and 3 h

Element	0,5 hour	1 hour	2 hours	3 hours
S (%)	40,4	41,9	34,7	30,2
Br (%)	27,6	26,4	34,3	36,3
Bi (%)	32,0	31,7	31,0	33,5

EDS quantifications (table 1) show significant changes in the film composition as stirring time increases. It also reveals that at short stirring times a S-rich phase is preferentially formed. As aging time increases, Br concentration increases, becoming predominant after 3h. Almost stoichiometric composition was found with 2h stirring.

Conclusions

BiSBr shows strong potential as a photovoltaic absorber, it presents several challenges that must be addressed. Our work demonstrates the importance of controlling the aging of the precursor solution as it influences the composition and morphology of the obtained BiSBr films, and contributes to a better understanding of its processing behavior and offers initial solutions for morphological control, paving the way for more effective integration into solar cell devices

Future work

The influence of stoichiometry on the precursor solution is essential, and the aging of precursor solutions with different stoichiometry will be analyzed as follow up work. In particular, variation in Br concentration will be analysed in solution A.

References

1. *J. He, X. Hu, Z. Liu, W. Chen, G. Longo, Prospect for Bismuth/Antimony Chalcohalides-Based Solar Cells. Adv. Funct. Mater. 2023, 33, 2306075.* https://doi.org/10.1002/adfm.202306075
2. *Xiaoyu Guo, Yi-Teng Huang, Hugh Lohan, "Air-Stable Bismuth Sulfobromide (BiSBr) Visible-Light Absorbers: Optoelectronic Properties and Potential for Energy Harvesting" J. Mater. Chem. A, 2023,11, 22775-22785,* https://doi.org/10.1039/D3TA04491B
3. *S. Li, Z. Huang, Y. Ding, C. Zhang, J. Yu, Q. Feng, J. Feng, Growth of BiSBr Microsheet Arrays for Enhanced Photovoltaics Performance. Small 2024, 20, 2306964,* https://doi.org/10.1002/smll.202306964
4. *Choi, Y.C.; Jung, K.-W. One-Step Solution Deposition of Antimony Selenoiodide Films via Precursor Engineering for Lead-Free Solar Cell Applications. Nanomaterials 2021, 11, 3206.* https://doi.org/10.3390/nano11123206

THIN-FILMS CELL FABRICATION: A PRACTICAL APPROACH TO TEACHING PHOTOVOLTAICS FUNDAMENTALS

Alessia Núñez-Osorio[a], María José García-Salinas[b], Manuel Pérez-García[b,c], , Joaquín Alonso-Montesinos[b,c], Antonio M. Puertas-López[b,c] María Jesús Ariza-Camacho[b,c]

Teaching Innovation Group in Photovoltaic Solar Cells, University of Almeria, Spain

[a] Master's Student in Advanced Chemistry Laboratory, Faculty of Experimental Sciences. University of Almería, C/ Sacramento s/n Almería, 04120, Almería, Spain. davidale970@gmail.com

[b] Applied Physics Section; Dept. of Chemistry and Physics, University of Almería, C/ Sacramento s/n Almería, 04120, Almería, Spain. mjariza@ual.es, mjgarcia@ual.es, apuertas@ual.es, mperez@ual.es, joaquin.alonso@ual.es

[c] CIESOL Solar Energy Research Centre. Joint Centre UAL-CIEMAT. University of Almería, C/ Sacramento s/n Almería, 04120, Almeria, Spain

ABSTRACT: Despite being one of the reference renewable energy, photovoltaic solar technology currently faces important challenges. One of them is the potential development of non-silicon-based materials solar cells, which, in addition to the need of tackling operational constrains as durability, introduces the need to adapt the current teaching contents on the fundamentals, fabrication and performance of solar cells taught in science and engineering university programs.

This work outlines a teaching-oriented methodology developed by our research group for the straightforward design, fabrication and performance assessment of dye-sensitized solar cells (DSSCs) using titanium dioxide pastes. We propose a complete manufacturing process and subsequent cell characterization, investigating various methods at each stage: paste preparation, photoelectrode fabrication, counter-electrode fabrication, cell assembly, electrolyte incorporation, and finally, assessment of the efficiency of the obtained cell. The entire methodology was developed to ensure feasibility and reproducibility within academic teaching and research laboratories. Finally, as a complementary resource, practical guides have been developed and interactive simulations implemented, and this material has been organized and consolidated into an web resource. This platform was specifically designed to provide structured access to educational materials, promoting both ease of access and self-learning.

Keywords: Photovoltaic solar energy, dye sensitized solar cells, educational resources, laboratory practices.

1 INTRODUCTION

Producing energy through renewable resources is a key component in achieving some of the most significant targets established by the Sustainable Development Goals (SDGs) concerning the fight against climate change. One of the most widely accepted technologies within solar energy is photovoltaic solar systems. This is constantly progressing and embracing innovations, including the use of solar cells made from alternative materials to silicon that can reduce the environmental impact of their manufacturing. The nature of some of these new materials also offers a highly interesting novelty: cells can be prepared from easily accessible substances through simple, manageable processes in teaching laboratories.

In this context, this paper presents an adaptation of the authors' previous research [1-3] on Dye-Sensitized Solar Cells (DSSCs) [4-6] intended for university-level teaching in undergraduate and specialized master's degrees. The aim of this paper is to provide methods and resources for educational lab-friendly DSSC fabrication and characterization.

2 PROCEDURES

Having in mind this educational aim for university students, we have designed laboratory practices and virtual simulations, written manuals for both, and integrated the whole material comprising a complete didactic unit. This unit has been organized as a set of procedures and guides for laboratory experiences as well as an HTML web-based resource repository including theoretical fundamentals and interactive simulations, called "Plataforma Educativa de Energía Solar" [7]. This platform offers students a global comprehensive learning experience in photovoltaic solar energy.

2.1 Laboratory experience 1: Fabrication of DSSC.

Our simplified method for fabricating a dye-sensitized solar cell begins with the preparation of the working electrode. This involves applying a layer of titanium dioxide (TiO_2) nanoparticle paste onto a fluorine dopped tin oxide (FTO) coated (conductive) glass slide using the "doctor-blade" method [5]. This layer is then sintered at high temperatures (450 °C for 1 hour) to consolidate the nanoparticles structure. Subsequently, the electrode is immersed in a dye solution so that the TiO_2 adsorbs the light-sensitive molecules. In parallel, the counter electrode is prepared by applying a thin layer of graphite onto another FTO glass. Both electrodes are assembled by facing the TiO_2 layer with the graphite one, leaving a gap that is filled with an iodine/iodide-based electrolyte. The active electrode area was around 0.36 cm^2. Further details regarding cell fabrication can be found in [1].

2.2 Laboratory experience 2: Characterizing a DSSC

The freshly assembled cell is then characterized to evaluate its efficiency by measuring the I-V (current vs. voltage) curve under artificial light and/or natural sunlight. The accurate acquisition of I-V curves is one of the key aspects in the characterization and optimization of photovoltaic systems. These curves are obtained through various methodologies; we have used the variable resistance method [1] and the charging capacitor method. The latter uses the energy generated by the cell or photovoltaic module to charge a capacitor and the current and voltage are measured during the charging process [8].

2.3 Web resource repository

A web platform, developed in HTML, compiles educational tools for learning about photovoltaic solar energy. The tools combine theoretical instruction with a rich practical experience gathering the virtual didactic material and the experimental guides. In a first step, the students can access educational materials to study the fundamentals. Next, they will gain practical experience through Virtual Labs (online simulations). Finally, students are prepared to conduct laboratory experiences 1 and 2 in the teaching and research laboratory, where they can fabricate real DSSCs, and analyse the efficiency of their own devices. With this aim, the platform integrates both virtual and physical lab methodologies, an approach that has proven highly effective in engineering and applied sciences.

The Virtual Labs are online simulations that allow students to experiment with photovoltaic systems in a controlled, virtual environment without the need for physical equipment. The Physical Labs are in-person guided sessions using real equipment like multimeters and signal generators to conduct live experiments and take real-time measurements.

2.4 Teaching experience

Laboratory experience 1 and 2 were developed at the University of Almería (Andalusia, Spain) between 2023 and 2025 as part of the University Teaching Innovation Project "Manufacture of a dye-sensitized solar cell (DSSC) and measurement of its characteristic parameters" (UAL PID 24_25_1_43C). Currently there are eight workspaces available for these teaching experiments, and students taking the Photovoltaic Solar Systems course in the Master's Degree in Solar Energy have already carried them out in the 2023-24 and 2024-25 academic years. Prior to conducting these practical experiments, the course's program includes 10 hours of classroom theory to study the basic concepts of solar cell operation and characterization, using silicon cells as a model and also describing the fundamentals of DSSC operation.

In this master's degree program, classes last 2.5 hours. Students manufacture the cell (experience 1) in the first 2.5-hour session. In the next session, they measure the characteristic curves (experience 2) of the cells they have manufactured themselves, as well as those of a commercial silicon cell and a laboratory photovoltaic panel. Students are also encouraged to measure series and parallel combinations of the cells they have manufactured and to use different lighting conditions.

3 RESULTS

After studying the theory and practicing in virtual labs, the real lab experiences follow: 1) Students fabricate the DSSC through a process involving photoelectrode and nanostructure creation, counter-electrode preparation, dye adsorption, and assembly with an electrolyte; 2) the I-V curve is then measured under natural or artificial sunlight using straightforward techniques, such as the variable resistance method and/or the capacitor charging method.

Regarding this practical section, the laboratory work can be completed in multiple sessions. We propose on-site some variations in methodology or materials, encouraging students to critically compare their own results with those obtained by their classmates.

3.1 Laboratory experience 1: Fabrication of DSSC.

A summary of this first part is shown in Fig. 1, with pictures of some of the steps done by the students.

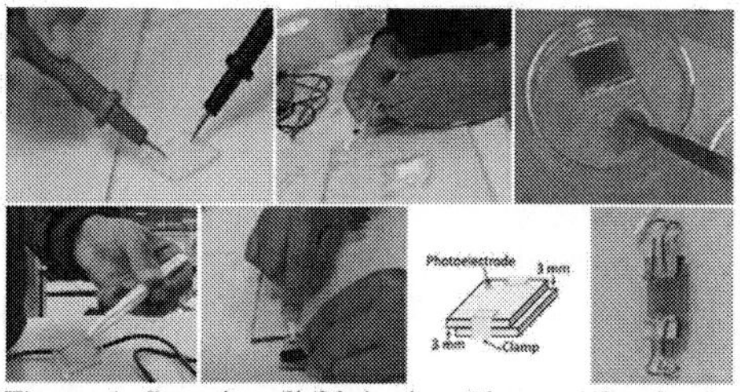

Figure 1: Steps in cell fabrication. Pictures taken by the students during their practical experience.

During lab experience 1), cell fabrication, it is important that students do not simply follow a recipe, systematically adhering to pre-established steps. While these steps should be provided, there should be some freedom to choose options and critically evaluate the consequences afterwards. The initial session is focused on preparing the electrolyte solution, the dye solution, and the nanoparticle paste. Students will gain practical experience in substance extraction, mixture preparation, and solution creation, using appropriate instruments to measure volumes and masses. Furthermore, students will already face a series of decision-making challenges: Which type of semiconducting nanoparticles to use? How to prepare the paste? Which electrolyte to use? Which type of dye, and if natural, what extraction method to employ? Alternatively, these products can be purchased pre-prepared (e.g., Solaronix [11]) which is advisable if time is short. In any case, we recommend providing several options for dyes and/or pastes. This allows students to choose how to fabricate their solar cell and then critically compare the quality obtained with each combination of materials. For example, the titanium dioxide nanoparticle paste can be prepared using high-purity chemicals (nitric acid and ethyl cellulose) or common household products (vinegar and soap).

3.2 Laboratory experience 2: Characterizing a DSSC

In lab experience 2) students apply acquired knowledge to obtain data, plot the I-V curve and calculate the cell characteristic parameters.

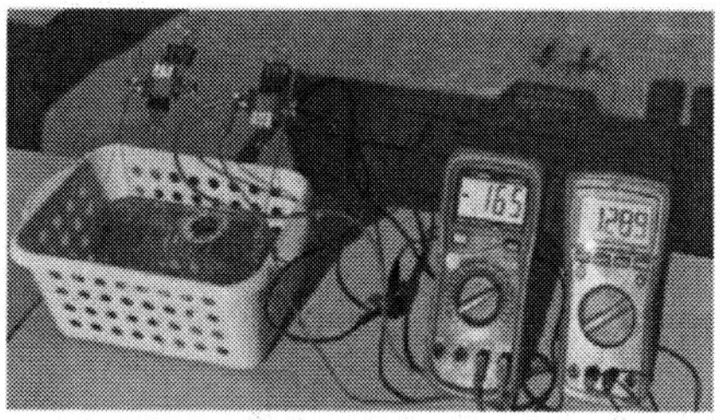

Figure 2: DSSC cell characterization. Method: variable resistance and natural sunlight. Picture taken by the students during their practical experience.

Fig. 2 shows a picture of the I-V data acquisition by using the variable resistance method with natural sunlight, while Fig. 3 shows the I-V curve obtained by a group of students using their own freshly manufactured cell. Analysis of these data leads to critical evaluation of the fabricated cell's performance enabling the determination of its energy conversion efficiency. Furthermore, they can compare different fabrication methods and dye characteristics, providing a comprehensive understanding of DSSC technology.

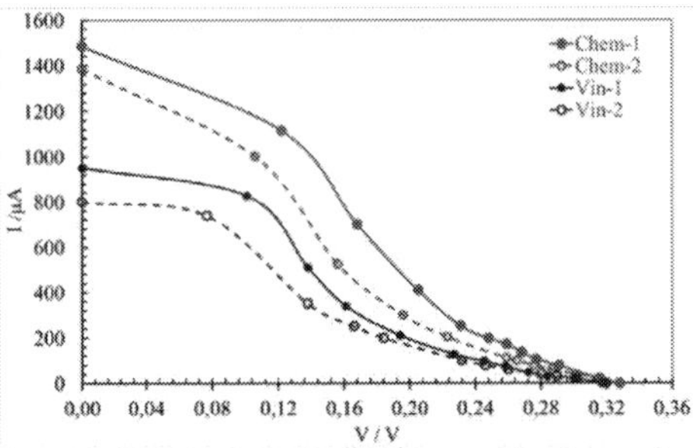

Figure 3: I-V curves obtained by a group of students using their own recently manufactured cell. Method: variable resistance and natural sunlight. Chem-1 and Chem-2: two cells using chemicals in the paste; Vin-1 and Vin-2: other two cells using vinegar and soap.

Alternatively, the I-V curve can be acquired using the capacitor charging method, which presents some challenges. First, the process takes place in a few seconds, so data acquisition devices are needed. Second, due to the low intensity values to be measured in the case of the students DSSC, the current sensors must have high resolution or amplification instruments must be used [12].

The experimental design to obtain measures with this method uses a data logger with voltage and current sensors and a 1100 or 4700 μF capacitor, as illustrated in Fig. 4.

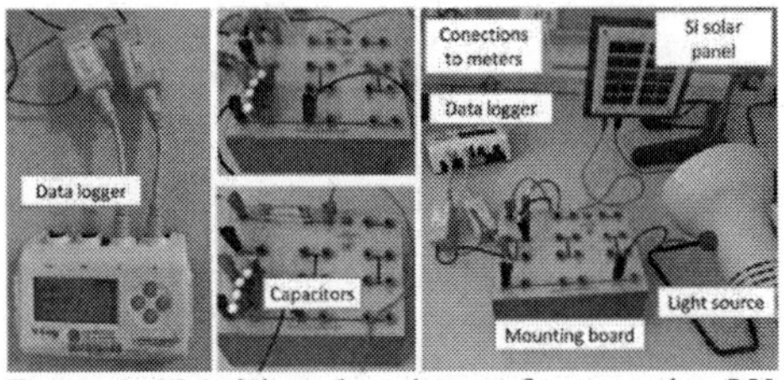

Figure 4: Materials and equipment for measuring I-V curve by the charging capacitor method for a DSSC or photovoltaic Si panel (right). Details of the capacitors (middle) and V-Log meter for data acquisition (left).

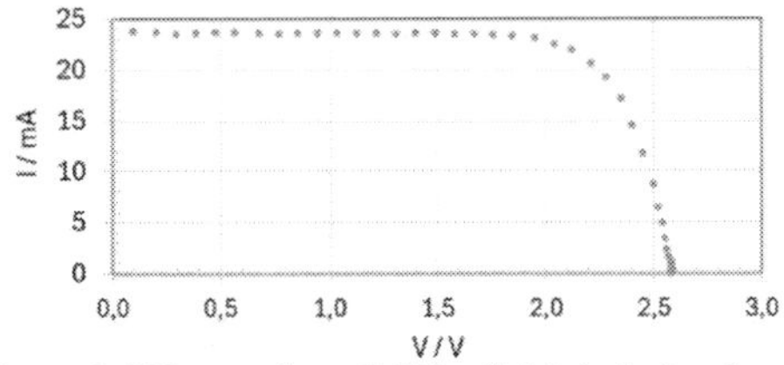

Figure 5: I-V curve for a Si PV cell. Method: charging capacitor with artificial light.

Fig. 5 depicts an example of I-V curve of a silicon panel obtained by the charging capacitor method with the equipment shown in Fig. 4. Moreover, both methods are compared in Fig. 6 for a DSSC. In this case, an instrumental amplifier has been used to measure the intensity of the DSSC using the capacitor method.

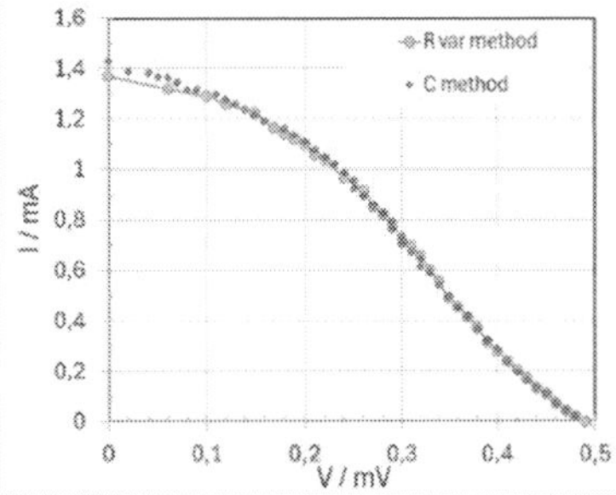

Figure 6: Comparison of the I-V curves of a DSSC measured using the variable resistance method and the charging capacitor method. Natural sunlight, 690 W/m^2.

3.3 Web Resource repository

All the didactic material can be found in a free-access web site [7]. This web platform is organized into a user-friendly interface with drop-down menus for easy navigation. The homepage includes these six main sections:

i) Home: Provides a general introduction to the platform and includes example simulations showing how irradiance and temperature affect I-V curves.

ii) Didactic Units: Contains structured modules with theoretical and practical content, covering everything from basic to advanced concepts.

iii) Virtual Labs: Provides interactive simulations and digital tools for virtual experimentation. Fig.s 7 and 8 show screen captures of some of the virtual labs.

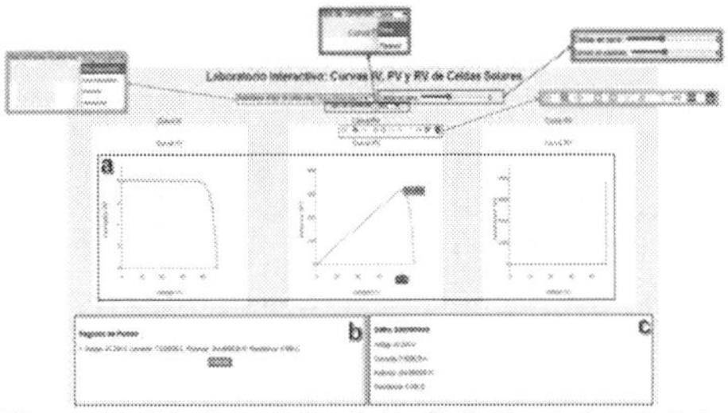

Figure 7: Display of the Solar Cell Simulation Lab in series and parallel – IV, RV, and PV Curves.

iv) In-person Labs: Offers guides for hands-on experiments in physical labs, allowing students to apply concepts in a controlled setting.

v) Videos: Features short, dynamic videos like demonstrations and tutorials to complement theoretical and practical learning.

vi) Simulation Guides: Offers supporting documents and materials to help students understand lab procedures and reinforce learning. Each guide includes a Doc file with instructions and an HTML file with the necessary functions for the simulation.

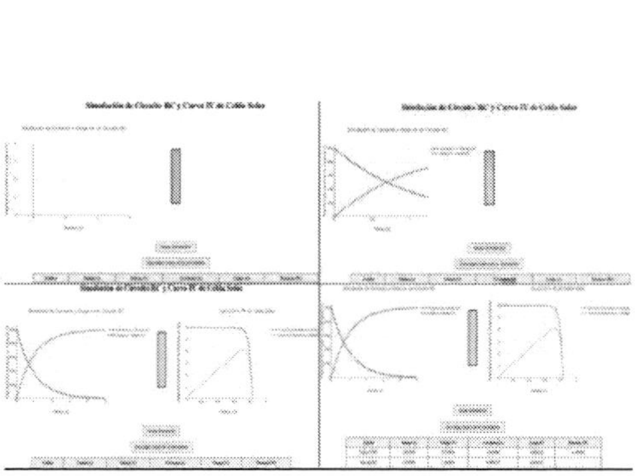

Figure 8: Capacitor Charging Lab with a Photovoltaic Panel - Relationship of the RC Circuit Curve, IV, and PV.

3.4 Teaching experience

So far, 24 students have taken part in the experiment (out of 33 enrolled in the two academic years). Their academic results have been good, with an average grade of 7.4/10 in the assessment of this part of the course. The students' opinion was evaluated through a survey, giving it an overall satisfaction rating of 4.7/5. Sixty percent of them found the cell manufacturing part more interesting, compared to 40% who preferred the cell and module characterization part. As suggestions for improvement, they propose increasing the time allotted to both cell manufacturing and characterization, so that more different cases can be explored in both experiences.

The optimization and adaptation of the DSSC manufacturing process to a 2.5-hour session was carried out in a Trabajo Fin de Carrera (similar to a Bachelor Thesis) for the Degree in Mechanical Engineering at the University of Almeria [9], where basic concepts of photovoltaics are also taught. The method for measuring the characteristic curve of the cell with the charging of a capacitor was developed in a Master's Thesis [10], in which the web resource repository presented above was created. All these teaching tools are available at the Renewable Energy Laboratory of the Department of Chemistry and Physics at the University of Almería.

Future work aims to enable master's students to measure characteristic curves using the capacitor method. To do this, workstations must be equipped with a sufficiently fast data logger and current meters suitable for the characteristic curve of DSSCs. In addition, the number of workstations will be increased in order to schedule these experiments in large classes, such as those in undergraduate programs.

4 CONCLUSIONS

This paper presents practical work for degree or master students consisting in fabricating Dye-Sensitized Solar Cells, DSSC, from the elaboration of pastes to the final use and characterization. TiO_2 thin films are to be prepared using an accurate method to achieve an optimal nanostructure in the photoelectrode. In addition, counter-electrode preparation, dye adsorption, and assembly with an electrolyte are carried out with different procedures to finally obtain the highest possible efficiencies.

Overall, students approach research work: they study, design, and fabricate their own DSSC device, then measure I-V curve for their device and explore, analyse, and compare results.

In addition to the manuals and procedures for DSSC fabrication and characterization by students, the innovation introduced in this work is a complete didactic unit with all the material organized in a HTML web-based resource repository including theoretical fundamentals, practical guidelines and interactive simulations.

The innovative approach of this project lies in empowering students to not only grasp the fundamentals of solar energy but also actively participate in the fabrication and evaluation of solar cells. This methodology promotes deep learning and fosters critical thinking regarding emerging technologies in solar photovoltaics. Students who have already taken the course gained valuable hands-on experience and demonstrated increased motivation and interest in photovoltaic solar energy. They have expressed great satisfaction and achieved good academic results.

The results indicate that this didactic approach can be an excellent tool for teaching about renewable energies and encouraging innovation in solar device design.

Acknowledgements

Financial support from Universidad de Almería, under projects P_LANZ_2024/002 and UAL PID 24_25_1_43C is acknowledged. We thank Prof. Gázquez for his assistance with the charging capacitor method.

References:

[1] A.I. Maldonado-Valdivia, E.G. Galindo, M.J. Ariza, M.J. Garcia-Salinas, Solar Energy 91 (2013) 263-272. DOI: 10.1016/j.solener.2013.02.009

[2] M.J. García-Salinas, M.J. Ariza, Appl. Sci. 9 (2019) 2515. DOI:10.3390/app9122515

[3] M.J. Ariza-Camacho, M.J. García-Salinas, M. Pérez-García M. "Metodología docente para diseño, construcción y caracterización de células solares de colorante". XIX Congreso Ibérico y XV Congreso Iberoamericano de Energía Solar (CIES'2024), 2024.

[4] B. O'Regan, M. Grätzel, Nature 353 (1991), 737–740. DOI: 10.1038/353737a0

[5] S. Ito, T.N. Murakami, P.Comte, P. Liska, C. Grätzel, M.K. Nazeeruddin, M. Grätzel, Thin Solid Films 516 (2008), 4613–4619. DOI:10.1016/j.tsf.2007.05.090

[6] O. Mohiuddin, M. Obaidullah, C. Sabah, Opt. Quant. Electron 50 (2018), 377. DOI: 10.1007/s11082-018-1647-1

[7] https//w3.ual.es/grupodocente/labsolar

[8] Z. Chen, Y. Lin, L. Wu, S. Cheng, P. Lin, Energy Conversion and Management, 226 (2020) 113521. DOI: 10.1016/j.enconman.2020.113521

[9] C. Rodríguez-Martínez, *Experiencia de Fabricación de una célula fotovoltaica para la práctica docente*. Bachelor's Thesis in Mechanical Engineering Degree, Universidad de Almería (Spain), July 2025.

[10] D. A. Núñez-Osorio, *Desarrollo de un banco de recursos didácticos y simulaciones en HTML para la enseñanza y aprendizaje de curvas I-V de células fotovoltaicas obtenidas mediante la carga de un condensador*. Master's Thesis in Solar Energy, Universidad de Almería (Spain), January 2025.

[11] https://www.solaronix.com/materials/kits/ Solaronix. Available on May 2025.

[12] J. A. Gázquez-Parra, M. Fernández-Ros, N. Novas-Castellano, R. M. García-Salvador, IEEE Trans. Instrum. Meas. 64, 10 (2015) 2759-2768. DOI: 10.1109/TIM.2015.2420376

nicolas.otto@htw-berlin.de
nicolas.otto@helmholtz-berlin.de

42nd European Photovoltaic Solar Energy Conference and Exhibition

OPTIMIZING INTERCONNECTION STRATEGIES FOR 2T PEROVSKITE-CIGSE TANDEM SOLAR MODULES: 3-STEP VS. 4-STEP LASER PATTERNING

Nicolas Otto[1,2], Christof Schultz[1], Guillermo Farias-Basulto[2], Wuai Zhang[3,4], Ayman Maqsood[2], Tadeus Ranisch[1], Yoko Schirmer[1], Jonas Preuschoff[1], Stefan Gall[4], Emil List-Kratochvil[3,4], Rutger Schlatmann[1,2], Bert Stegemann[1]

1. HTW Berlin - University of Applied Sciences, D-12459 Berlin, Germany
2. PVcomB, Helmholtz-Zentrum Berlin für Materialien und Energie, D-12489 Berlin, Germany
3. Humboldt-Universität zu Berlin, Institut für Physik, Institut für Chemie und Center for the Science of Materials Berlin, D-12489 Berlin, Germany
4. Helmholtz-Zentrum Berlin für Materialien und Energie GmbH, D-14109 Berlin, Germany

MOTIVATION & BACKGROUND

- Perovskite and CIGSe: adjustable bandgaps → high-efficiency tandem cells
- Low-cost roll-to-roll processing on flexible substrates
- Record efficiencies of perovskite-CIGSe tandems demonstrated (2025) [1]
- Challenge: Simple module fabrication with minimal electrical and dead area losses requires adapted laser patterning [2]
- Key question: Can thin-film tandem modules be realized with only 3 patterning steps, reducing process complexity and costs?

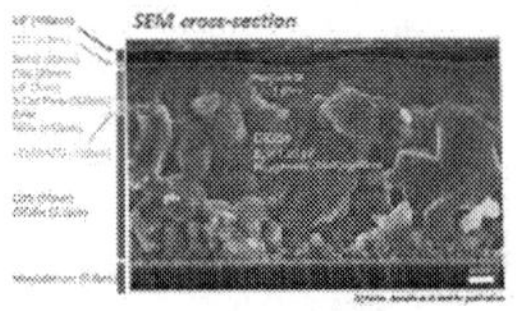

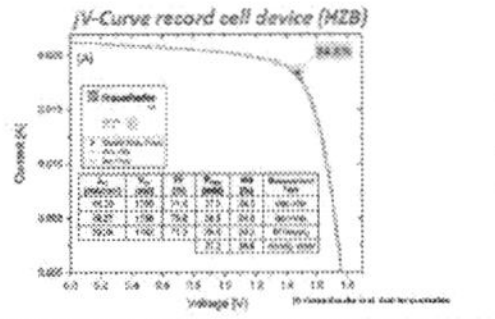

MINI-MODULE LAYOUT

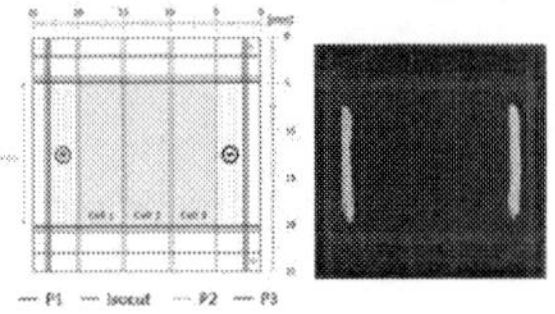

- Substrate size: 25x25 mm²
- Number of interconnected cells: 3
- Cell size: 5 mm x 15 mm
- GFF ~ 90 %

PROCESS DEVELOPMENT

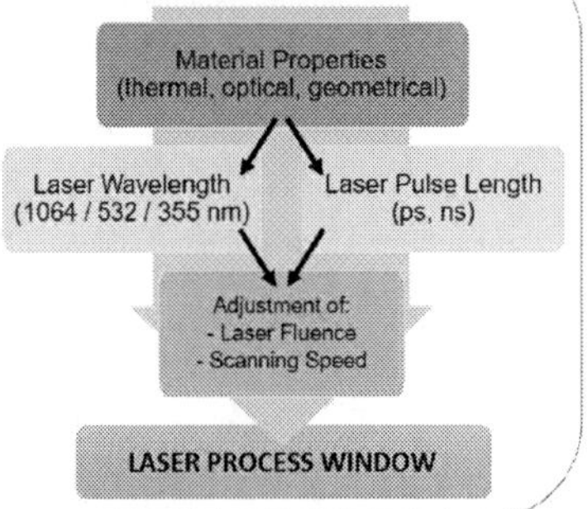

CLASSIC 3-STEP APPROACH

Principle of the 3-step interconnection (P1–P3)

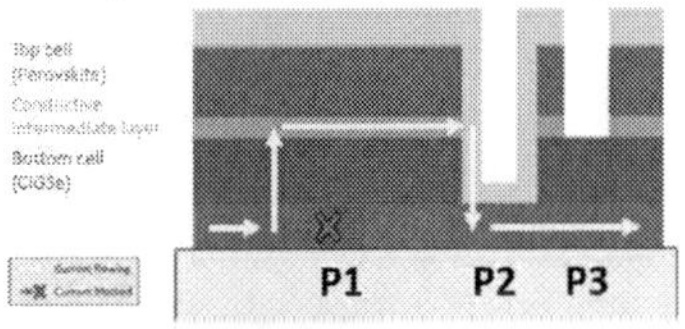

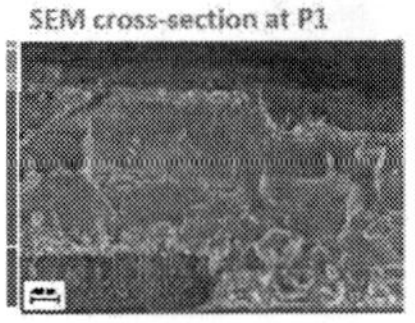

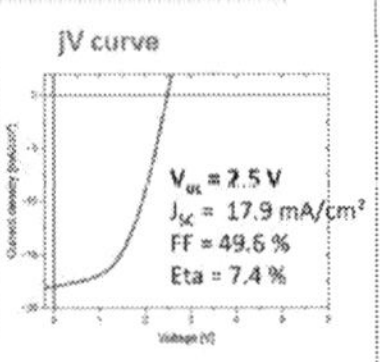

→ physical implementation/ structural details

→ proves voltage losses (reduced V_{oc})

Electroluminescence / Photoluminescence

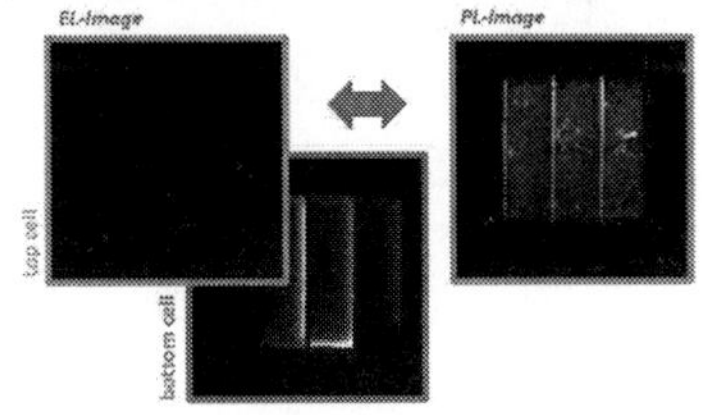

- top cell PL image: clear signal
- top cell EL image: no signal
- bottom cell EL image: clear signal
  → visual evidence of the bypassing effect

→ alternative interconnection approach required

→ electrical separation of conductive inter-connection layer

ADDING THE *ISOCUT*

→ selective removal of the conductive interlayer

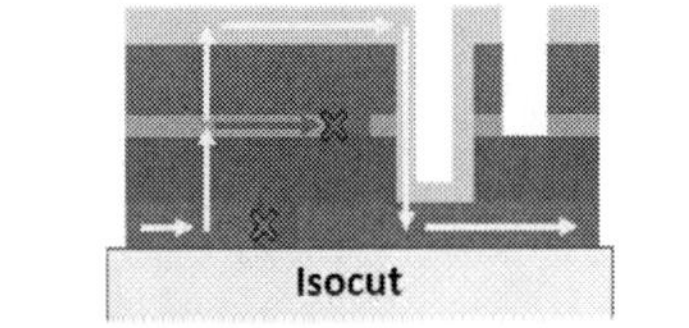

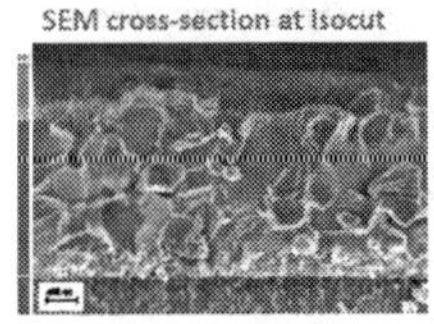

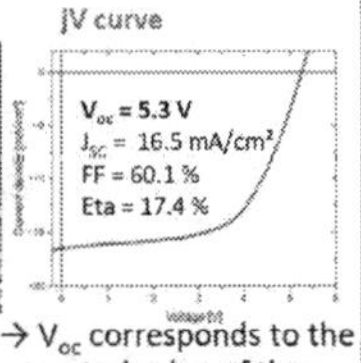

→ visual confirmation of the selective removal

→ V_{oc} corresponds to the expected value of three series-connected cells

Laser Scanning Microscopy / Photoluminescence

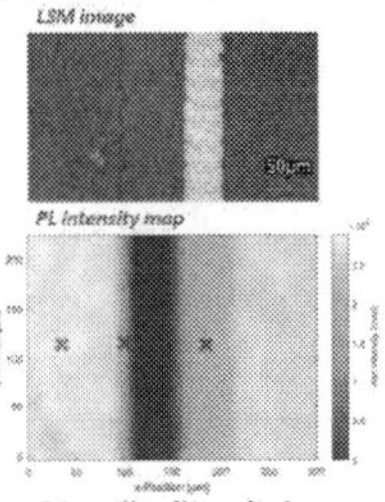

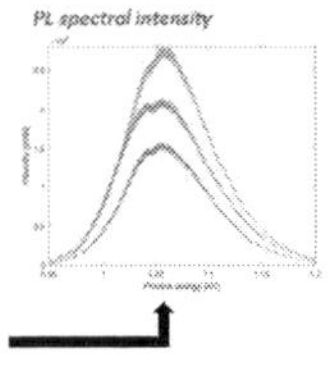

Near P1 scribe line → decrease in intensity, but no change in spectral shape

Within Isocut region→ clear change in spectral profile (blue line) → local alteration of CIGSe absorber

→ Isocut step can overcome the voltage loss issue observed in the 3-step approach

→ increase of overall process complexity

→ inherent risk of unintended material modifications

BACK TO 3 STEPS?

→ combine P1 and Isocut into a single step → **P1Iso**

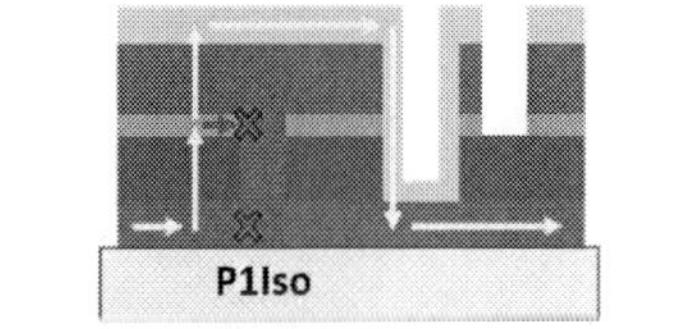

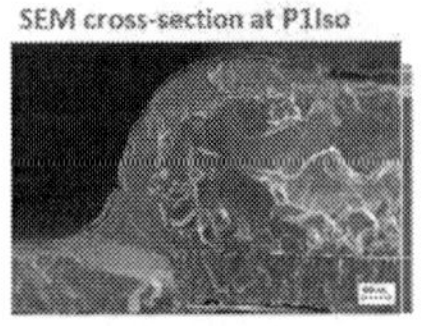

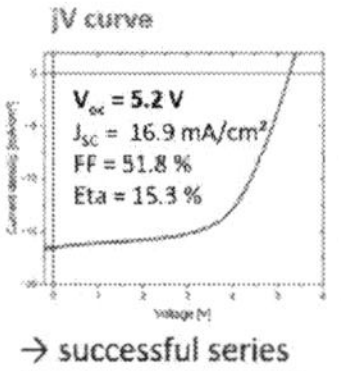

→ steep scribe line edge due to substrate-side patterning

→ successful series interconnection with performance close to the 4-step approach

Laser Scanning Microscopy / Photoluminescence

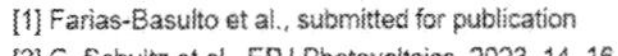

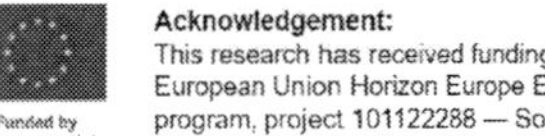

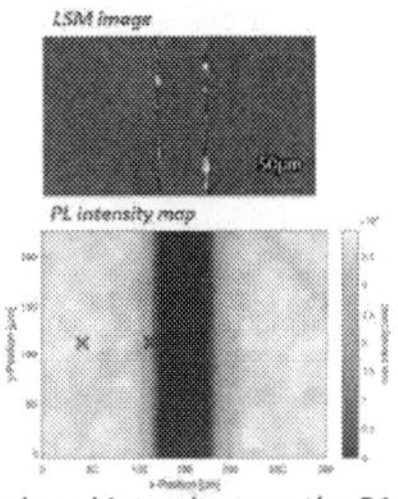

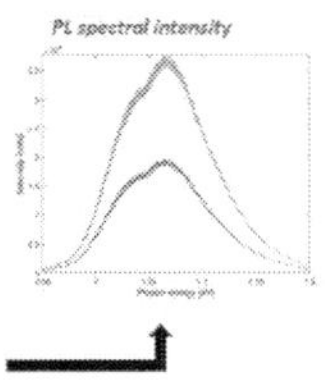

Reduced intensity near the P1 scribe line, but no spectral changes → CIGSe absorber composition remains unaffected by patterning through glass

→ promising compromise:
- simplifies processing
- preserves absorber quality
- ensures efficient series interconnection

SUMMARY & OUTLOOK

- 3-step (P1 - P3): Causes bypassing of the perovskite top cell, leading to reduced V_{oc} and inferior jV characteristics.
- 4-step with Isocut: Prevents bypassing and provides excellent electrical performance. Trade-offs: higher process complexity and larger dead area
- P1Iso (P1 + Isocut combined): Separates the conductive intermediate layer while saving one step, simplifying fabrication and reducing the dead area. Electrical behavior is comparable to the 4-step approach, just slightly behind the best Isocut results.
- **Next step:** Evaluate 3-step patterning approach including the P1Iso on flexible substrates vs. the sequential 4-step process

[1] Farias-Basulto et al., submitted for publication
[2] C. Schultz et al., EPJ Photovoltaics, 2023, 14, 16

Funded by the European Union

Acknowledgement:
This research has received funding from the European Union Horizon Europe Energy program, project 101122288 — SolMates

42nd European Photovoltaic Solar Energy Conference and Exhibition

This presentation was selected by the Sc. Committee of the EU PVSEC 2025 for submission of a full paper to one of the EU PVSEC's collaborating peer-reviewed journals.

ELUCIDATING THE PROCESS OF ACCURATE SPECTRAL CALIBRATION FOR TANDEM I-V MEASUREMENT USING MULTI-LAMP LIGHT SOURCES

Antoine Bourgeois[1,2], Stella Hadiwidjaja[1], Zoltan Nicot-Senneville[1,3], Ye Jiayi[1], Choi Kwan Bum[1], Zhou Qilin[1], Hou Yi[1]
[1]Solar Energy Research Institute of Singapore, National University of Singapore (NUS), [2]Ecole Polytechnique, [3]Centrale Marseille

ABSTRACT: Reproducing the reference spectrum, AM1.5G, using solar simulators is essential for reporting the I-V performance of tandem solar cells. The International Electrotechnical Commission (IEC) presents the classification of solar simulators spectra in IEC 60904-9 and the spectral calibration for tandem devices in IEC 60904-1-1. However, implementation of these standards using multi-lamp light sources can be challenging.

This study presents a process for fulfilling both IEC standards using a multi-lamp light source with 21 tunable intensity channels of different peak wavelengths. A spectrum fitting method based on Gram-Schmidt orthonormalisation is introduced to approximate the AM1.5G spectrum from a known set of LED inputs, enabling forward modelling of the output spectrum. Non-linearity and spectral shift corrections ensure that the modelled spectrum remains accurate. A calibration process is presented to satisfy both solar simulator classification and the IEC-defined spectral mismatch factor and matching factor thresholds.

The method is validated on three perovskite–silicon tandem cells, all of which achieved | 1-M | < 0.05 and |1-Z | < 0.03 and for both sub-cells. This framework enables standard-compliant spectral simulation of AM1.5G for I-V of perovskite-based tandem devices.
Keywords: multi-source solar simulator; IEC 60904; tandem cell characterisation

1 DEADLINES AND DELIVERY

Perovskite-based tandem technologies are expected to become a commercial technology in the next 5-10 years [1][2]. With this momentum comes an increasing demand for accurate and reproducible characterisation of tandem devices. Among all characterisation metrics, the current–voltage (I–V) measurement under Standard Testing Conditions (STC) remains the most critical benchmark.

However, I–V measurements of tandem devices are sensitive to the spectral characteristics of the incident illuminated: the reference spectrum AM1.5G (E_{ref}). Discrepancy between E_{ref} and the laboratory-simulated spectrum (E_{sim}) distorts I-V results, affecting not only short-circuit current (I_{sc}), but also Fill Factor (FF) [3].

For reliable I-V measurements, E_{sim} must: 1) be a close replication of AM1.5G, 2) incite a similar tandem device response. These two conditions were formalised by standards issued by in IEC 60904-9 and 60904-1-1 [4] [5].

Laboratory simulated spectra can be generated by multi-lamp solar simulators, many of which feature 20, or more independently tunable (LED) lamps. The spectral irradiance of each lamp j can be defined as $E_j = \alpha_j e_j(\lambda)$ where α_j is its adjustable intensity and $e_j(\lambda)$ is its emission spectrum at full intensity. The total simulator spectrum is a superposition of all m lamps:

$$E_{\text{sim}}(\lambda) = \sum_{j=1}^{m} \alpha_j e_j(\lambda)$$

Multi-lamp simulators offer significant flexibility, allowing for precise control to fulfill the conditions set out in IEC 60904-1-1 and IEC 60904-0 [6]. However, the procedure delineating how to use multi-lamp light sources to fulfil these conditions is often overlooked [3]. Calibration for tandem devices of a solar simulator with light sources were discussed in several works although non proposed a non-iterative method [7] [8]. This study aims to build a non-iterative spectrum fitting and calibration process to target the requirements both IEC 60904-1-1 and IEC 60904-9 simultaneously, such that the process can be easily replicated by any multi-lamp solar simulator.

2 MATERIALS AND METHODS

2.1 Materials

The essential equipment for the proposed method includes: a multi-lamp solar simulator, a spectrometer and reference cells (RCs) matched to the spectral response of the tandem sub-cells. The required data are: the spectral response (SR) of each sub-cell of the tandem device under test (DUT) (IEC 60904-9) and E_{ref} = AM1.5G spectrum (IEC 60904-3).

2.2 Methods

2.2.1 Accounting for LED Non-Linearity

Lamps have a non-linear relationship between the input intensity command α_{in} and the actual optical output α_{out}, which was characterised. Polynomial functions were fitted to characterised data to model this behavior (Figure 1, $\alpha_{\text{out}} = P(\alpha_{\text{in}})$). This polynomial was inverted and integrated into the spectrum fitting algorithm to apply a correction $\alpha_{in} = P^{-1}(\alpha_{\text{out}})$, ensuring the achieved spectrum matched the intended spectrum based on the input commands.

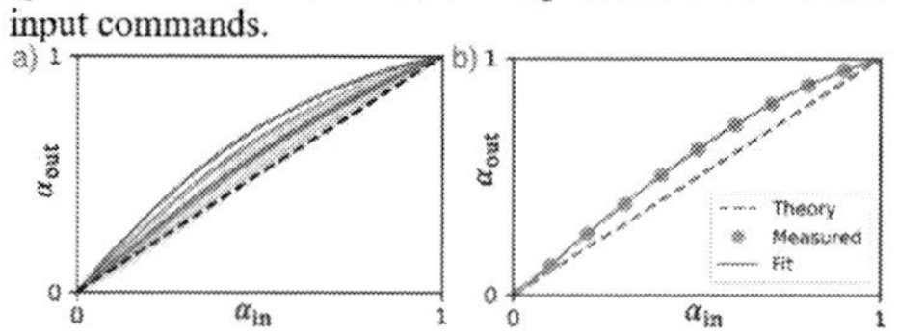

Figure 1: a) $\alpha_{\text{in}} e_{\text{j}} \neq \alpha_{\text{out}}$ for various lamps (shown in different colours). b) Interpolated α_{out} for lamp 19.

2.2.2 Spectrum Fitting using Orthonormal Basis Projection

A non-iterative spectral fitting method was developed to generate E_{sim}. E_{ref} is projected onto an orthonormal basis generated from e_j using the Gram-Schmidt process (Figure 2). This provided a fast, non-iterative estimate for α_j. This method can be used independently or as a stable first-guess for other iterative optimisation routines.

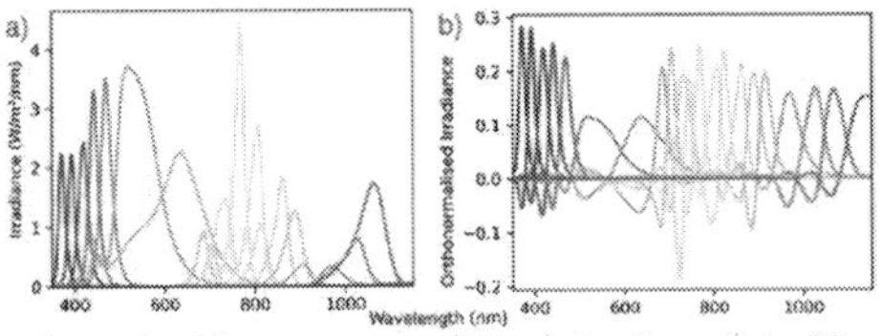

Figure 2: a) lamp spectra e_j b) basis by Gram-Schmidt orthonormalisation.

2.2.3 Calibration for Tandem Device Measurement

The calibration procedure to meet IEC 60904-1-1 requirements for tandem cells follows an adapted version of the calibration method proposed in [9], hereby referred to as Meusel's method. The m lamps are split into two virtual light sources (Figure 3), which are calibrated by Meusel's method. This results in multiple spectra which are then chosen according to the flowchart in Figure 4. The final calibrated spectrum is validated by measuring the I_{sc} of the RCs under E_{sim} to calculate Z. A successful calibration is achieved when $|1 - Z_{top,bot}| < 0.03$.

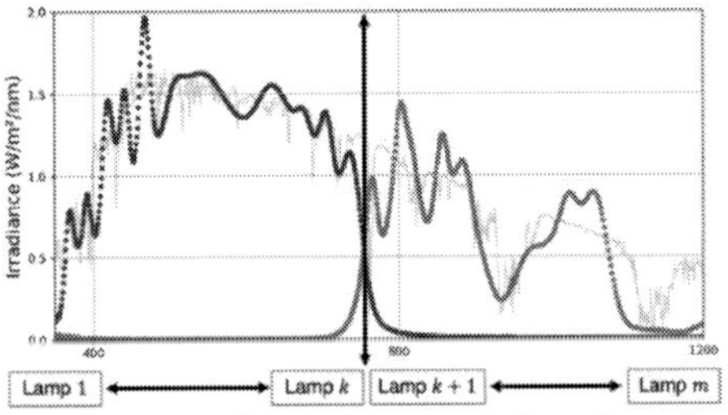

Figure 3. Example of splitting E_{sim} (at lamp $k = 16$).

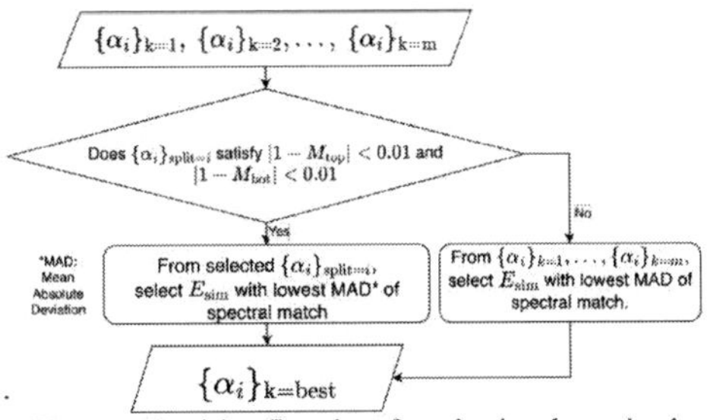

Figure 4. Decision flowchart for selecting the optimal spectrum.

3 RESULTS

The calibration method was tested on three perovskite-silicon tandem solar cells, referred to as Cell A, B and C. The resultant calibrated spectrum of each cell is shown in Figure 5. The uncalibrated calibrated spectra's M and Z are shown in Table 1.

Table I. Calibrated and Uncalibrated Spectra M, Z.

	Cell	$\|1 - Z_{top}\|$	$\|1 - Z_{bot}\|$	$\|1 - M_{bot}\|$	$\|1 - M_{bot}\|$
Uncalibrated	A	0.015	0.032	0.002	0.009
	B	0.016	0.027	0.004	0.004
	C	0.017	0.060	0.004	0.035
Calibrated.	A	0.010	0.001	0.005	0.006
	B	0.006	0.005	0.005	0.004
	C	0.013	0.007	0.005	0.016

For Cell A and B, the SR of the cells and the RCs were well-matched, achieving $|1 - M_{top,bot}| < 0.01$. For Cell C, whilst the top cell was well matched ($|1 - M_{top}| < 0.01$), the bottom cell's SR compared to RC_{bot} differed, resulting in a higher mismatch, but within the $|1 - M_{bot}| < 0.05$ threshold. For each tandem solar cell, a spectrum fulfilling the criterion of $|1 - Z_{top,bot}| < 0.03$ was achieved.

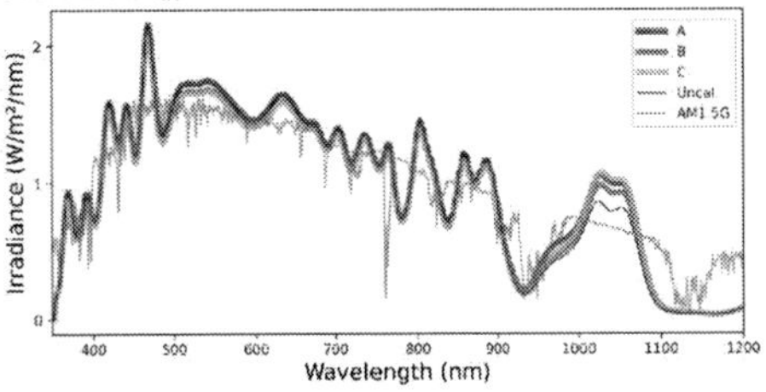

Figure 5. Calibrated spectrum of Tandem Cell A, B, C.

4 CONCLUSION

We developed a method to fit and calibrate the spectrum of a multi-lamp solar simulator for accurate tandem cell measurement. After accounting for lamp non-linearity through polynomial interpolation, we use the Gram-Schmidt orthonormalisation process to provide a stable fit to the AM1.5G spectrum. The calibration procedure then adapts the method from [9] for multi-lamp systems by virtually splitting the lamps into two and choosing the best spectrum from the resultant spectra. Validation on perovskite-silicon tandems achieved M within 1±5% and Z within 1±3%, fulfilling the IEC 60904-1-1 requirements.

5 ACKNOWLEDGEMENTS

SERIS is a research institute at the National University of Singapore (NUS). SERIS is supported by NUS, the National Research Foundation Singapore (NRF), the Energy Market Authority of Singapore (EMA) and the Singapore Economic Development Board (EDB). The author AB acknowledges financial support from EDF in the framework of the research and teaching Chair «Sustainable energies » at Ecole Polytechnique.

6 REFERENCES

[1] ITRPV, "International Technology Roadmap for Photovoltaics (ITRPV)," ITRPV, VDMA, 2024.
[2] H. Li and W. Zhang, Chemical Reviews, vol. 120, no. 18, pp. 9835-9950, 2020.
[3] S. Tao et al., Performance? A Calibration Lab's Perspective," Solar RRL, vol. 6, no. 12, p. 2200800, 2022.
[4] IEC, IEC60904-9: Classification of solar simulator characteristics, 2020.
[5] IEC, IEC60904-1-1: Measurement of current-voltage characteristics of multi-junction photovoltaic (PV) devices, 2020.
[6] M. Turek, et al., Solar Energy Materials and Solar Cells, vol. 194, pp. 142-147, 2019.
[7] D. Chojnak, et al., Silicon PV 2022, Konstanz, Germany, 2023.
[8] S. K. Reichmuth, et al., IEEE 46th Photovoltaic Specialists Conference (PVSC), Chicago, 2019.
[9] M. Meusel, et al., Progress in Photovoltaics: Research and Applications, vol. 10, no. 4, pp. 243-255, 2002.

Elucidating the Process of Accurate Spectral Calibration for Tandem I-V Measurement using Multi-Lamp Solar Simulators

Antoine BOURGEOIS[1,2], Stella HADIWIDJAJA[1], Zoltan NICOT-SENNEVILLE[1,3], YE Jiayi[1], CHOI Kwan Bum[1], ZHOU Qilin[1], HOU Yi[1]
[1]Solar Energy Research Institute of Singapore, National University of Singapore
[2]École Polytechnique, [3]Centrale Méditerranée

NUS National University of Singapore | SERIS Solar Energy Research Institute of Singapore

Motivation & Introduction

- ☐ A 'mismatched' AM1.5G spectrum can mislead the I-V of a 2-terminal tandem solar cell due to current mismatch [1].
- ☐ We propose a non-iterative method to achieve an accurate spectrum using multi-lamp solar simulators.
- ☐ For tandem I-V to be accurate, the AM1.5G spectrum requires:
  - ☐ **Spectrum Fitting** to achieve Spectral Match "A" (IEC 60904-9).
  - ☐ **Calibration** for adequate 'matching factors (Z)' and 'mismatch factors (M)' (IEC 60904-1-1).

Spectrum Fitting

Multi-lamp solar simulators

$$E_{\text{sim}} = \sum_{j=1}^{m} \alpha_j e_j(\lambda)$$

Eq 1: Spectrum of a solar simulator.

- E_{sim} : Spectral irradiance
- α_j : Intensity of Lamp j
- $e_j(\lambda)$: Spectrum of Lamp
- m : Number of lamps

- ☐ Spectrum fitting is done by finding α such that $E_{\text{ref}} = E_{\text{sim}}$.

Accounting for lamp non-linearity

- ☐ Lamps do not scale linearly (Fig. 1a).
- ☐ Polynomial interpolation $\alpha_{\text{out}} = \mathrm{P}(\alpha_{\text{in}})$ accounts for non-linearity (Fig. 1b, Fit) and allows bi-directional control, i.e. $\alpha_{\text{in}} = \mathrm{P}^{-1}(\alpha_{\text{out}})$.

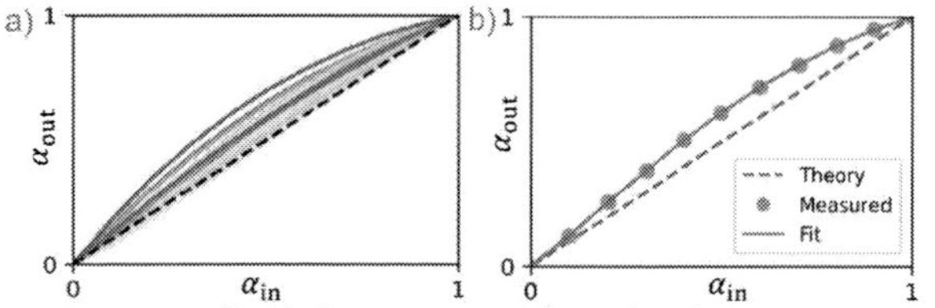

Fig. 1 a) $\alpha_{\text{in}} e_j \neq \alpha_{\text{out}} e_j$ for various lamps
b) Interpolated α_{out} for lamp 19.

Fitting through Gram-Schmidt Orthonormalisation.

- ☐ Using the Gram-Schmidt orthonormalisation algorithm [2], we generate a basis (Fig. 2b) from the measured spectra α (Fig. 2a).
- ☐ Project E_{ref} = AM1.5G on the orthonormal basis to find $\{\alpha\}$.

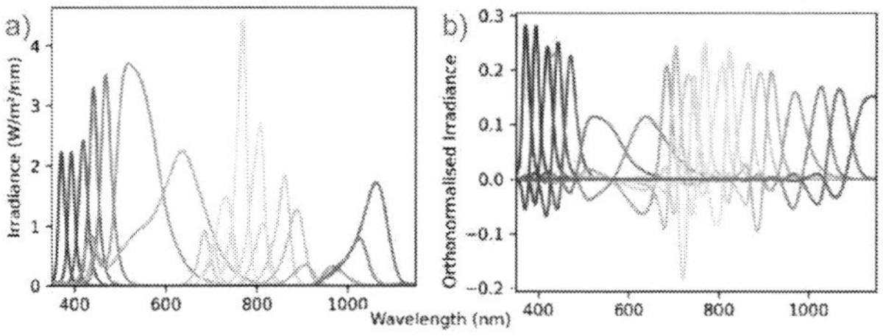

Fig 2. a) lamp spectra b) basis by Gram-Schmidt orthonormalisation.

Calibration

$$\mathrm{M} = \frac{\int_\lambda E_{\text{sim}}\,\mathrm{SR}_{\text{DUT}}\,d\lambda \int_\lambda E_{\text{ref}}\,\mathrm{SR}_{\text{RC}}\,d\lambda}{\int_\lambda E_{\text{ref}}\,\mathrm{SR}_{\text{DUT}}\,d\lambda \int_\lambda E_{\text{sim}}\,\mathrm{SR}_{\text{RC}}\,d\lambda} \qquad \mathrm{Z} = \frac{\mathrm{I}_{\text{RC}}^{\text{sim}}}{\mathrm{I}_{\text{RC}}^{\text{ref}}\mathrm{M}}$$

Eq 2. M considers discrepancies of the spectral response (SR) of the reference cells (RC), SR of the device under test (DUT), E_{ref} and E_{sim}.
Eq 3. Z represents the spectral accuracy of the measurement.

- ☐ *Meusel et al.* [2] calibrates $m = 2$ lamps, solving for $\{\alpha\}$ by the equations of photo-currents of two-junctions.
- ☐ With $m > 2$, but still only two junctions, we 'split' m into 2, and apply Meusel's method (Fig. 3).
- ☐ The best spectrum is chosen by assessing the spectral match and mismatch factor M (Eq. 2, Fig. 4).
- ☐ Z is measured using two reference cells (Eq. 3).

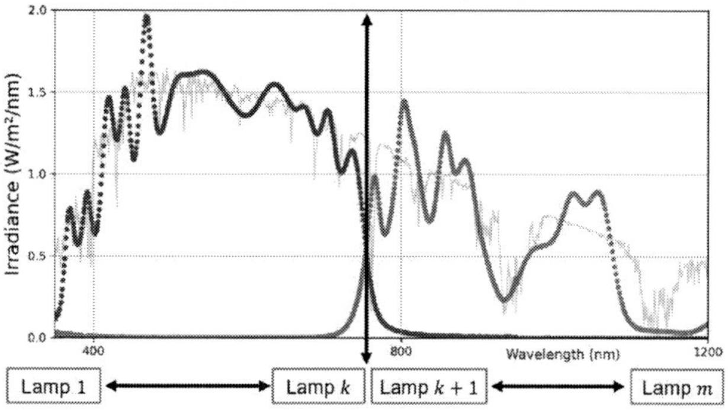

Fig. 3) Example of splitting E_{sim} (at lamp $k = 16$).

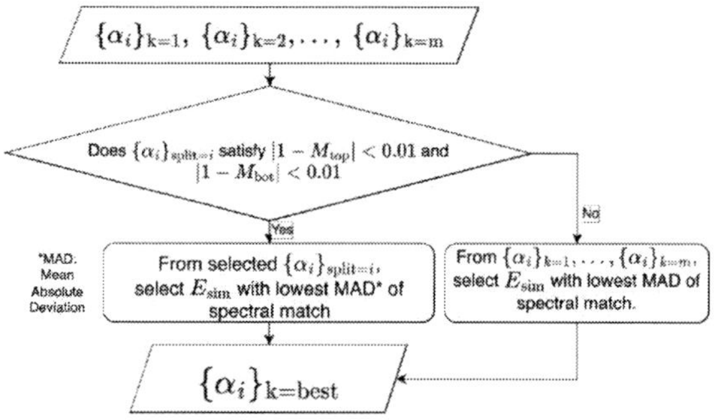

Fig. 4) Decision flowchart for selecting the optimal spectrum.

Results

- ☐ Method validated on 3 tandem solar cells (Cell A,B,C, Fig. 5).

☑ Good spectral match ☑ $|1 - Z| < 0.03$ ☑ $|1 - M| < 0.05$

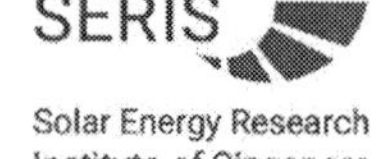

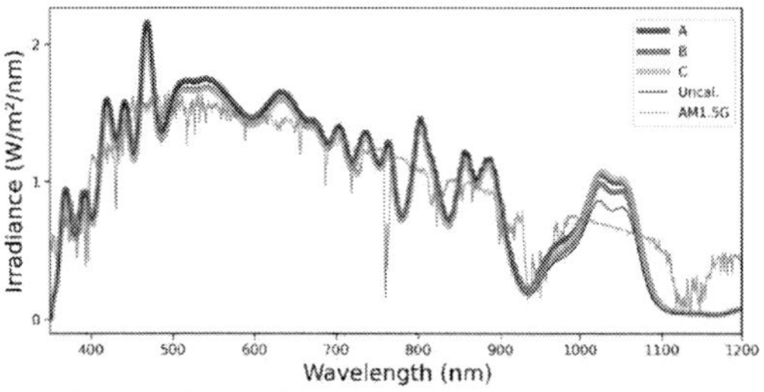

Fig. 5) Calibrated spectrum of Tandem Cell A, B, C.

Conclusion and Discussion

- ☐ IEC-compliant spectrum is achieved through fitting and calibration.
- ☐ Calibration depends on the spectral compatibility of the available reference cells, the number of lamps and their spectra.
- ☐ Method can be extended to multiple junctions.

References

1. Song et al., 2022. Solar RRL, 6(12):2200800
2. Cheney & Kincaid, 2009. Linear Algebra, ISBN 978-0-7637-5020-6.
3. Meusel et al., 2002. Prog Photovolt Res Appl, 10(4):243–255

National Research Foundation Prime Minister's Office Singapore | Energy Market Authority | EDB Singapore | Chaire Énergies Durables École polytechnique - EDF

SERIS is a research institute at the National University of Singapore (NUS). SERIS is supported by NUS, the National Research Foundation Singapore (NRF), the Energy Market Authority of Singapore (EMA) and the Singapore Economic Development Board (EDB).

ACHIEVING IMPROVED LIGHT TRAPPING IN CIGS/PEROVSKITE SOLAR CELLS WITH GRATING-ENHANCED BILAYER HETEROJUNCTIONS: OPTICAL-ELECTRICAL STUDY

Mohammad Hossein Mohammadi*, Narendra Bandaru, Rasmus Schmidt Davidsen
Department of Electrical and Computer Engineering, Aarhus University, Denmark

ABSTRACT: This work investigates a cost-effective and less toxic alternative solar cell design: a CIGS/perovskite bilayer heterojunction integrated with photonic nanostructures. The bilayer structure reduces thermalization losses by combining a high-bandgap perovskite ($CH_3NH_3PbI_3$, 1.55 eV) top cell with a lower-bandgap CIGS (1.2 eV) bottom cell, enabling efficient spectrum utilization. CIGS is selected over silicon due to its direct bandgap, allowing reduced absorber thickness, lower material use, and potentially lower costs. The bilayer achieved a short-circuit current density of 25.98 mA/cm^2 and a power conversion efficiency (PCE) of 22.98%, representing a 15% improvement over single-junction perovskite cells. Further enhancement is achieved with convex grating light-trapping structures, raising the simulated PCE to 25.54%. Device performance was analyzed through coupled optical and electrical modeling using the finite element method in COMSOL Multiphysics, highlighting the potential of bilayer heterojunctions with photonic gratings for high-efficiency, scalable photovoltaics.
Keywords: CIGS/perovskite solar cell, Light trapping (LT), Photonic-nanostructure, Grating structure, COMSOL

1 INTRODUCTION

The rapid decline in the levelized cost of photovoltaics (PV) has driven global installed capacity from less than 50 GW in 2010 to over 2000 GW by 2025 [1]. To sustain this growth, research is increasingly focused on new materials and advanced light-management strategies, addressing the limited absorption of ultra-thin active layers used in flexible, cost-effective devices. Organic–inorganic hybrid perovskite solar cells (PSCs) have reached efficiencies up to 26% [2], owing to their direct bandgap, long carrier diffusion lengths, and high optical absorption [3]. PSCs are fabricated in mesoporous, dye-sensitized, HTL-/ETL-free, and planar (p–i–n, n–i–p) configurations [4], but single-junction devices are limited by the Shockley–Queisser efficiency threshold [5].

Tandem architectures are a promising pathway to surpass this limit by combining wide- and narrow-bandgap absorbers. Notable examples include perovskite/silicon [6], perovskite/CIGS [7], and all-perovskite tandems [8], with reported efficiencies above 30% in advanced configurations [9]. Among these, CIGS/perovskite tandems stand out due to tunable bandgaps, compatibility as thin-film technologies, and suitability for flexible devices. Record efficiencies of 24.6% (2T) and 29.36% (4T) have been reported. However, planar devices still suffer from reflection losses, necessitating optical management strategies.

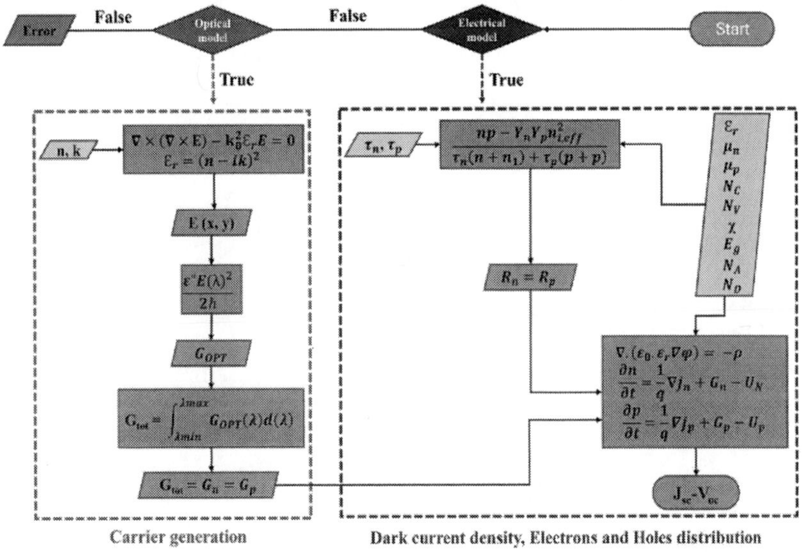

Fig. 1. The algorithm involves solving the electrical and optical models. In the optical part, k_0 denotes the free-space wave number, ε'' represents the imaginary component of the permittivity, and ħ is the reduced Planck constant. Within the electrical part, ρ is the charge density, φ is the electrostatic potential, ε_0 is the vacuum permittivity, Y_p and Y_n correspond to the hole and electron degeneracy factors, respectively.

10.4229/EUPVSEC2025/2CV.3.22

Table 1. Electrical parameters required for PSC.

Parameter	TiO_2	$CH_3NH_3PbI_3$	CIGS	CuSCN
ε_r	9	6.5	13.6	9
N_C (cm^{-3})	1.00×10^{19}	1.66×10^{19}	2.2×10^{18}	2.5×10^{18}
N_V (cm^{-3})	1.00×10^{19}	5.41×10^{19}	1.9×10^{18}	1.8×10^{18}
μ_n/μ_p (cm^2/V)	20/10	50/50	100/25	$2.00\times10^{-4}/2.00\times10^{-4}$
χ (eV)	4.00	3.93	4.5	2.1
E_g (eV)	3.2	1.55	1.2	3.4
N_A (cm^{-3})	-	5.00×10^{13}	1.00×10^{16}	1.00×10^{17}
N_D (cm^{-3})	5.00×10^{18}	-	-	-
τ_n/τ_p (ns)	5/2	8/8	25/25	5/5

Light-trapping (LT) nanostructures—such as nanocones, gratings, and plasmonic nanoparticles—enhance scattering, reduce reflection, and extend the optical path length. These designs mitigate the trade-off between absorption and electrical performance, improve carrier collection, and reduce material consumption, thereby addressing stability and toxicity concerns in perovskite systems. Recent studies combining bilayer heterojunctions with nanophotonic designs, such as nano-prisms or convex gratings, have achieved efficiency gains exceeding 30% compared to planar references [10-12].

In this work, a planar PSC was simulated as a baseline, yielding 19.58% efficiency. Introducing a 500 nm CIGS layer increased PCE to 22.98%. Further enhancement was achieved by implementing patterned convex gratings at all interfaces, which improved light absorption, reduced reflection, and optimized field distribution, leading to significant improvements in device performance.

2 THEORY

In this study, two complementary models were employed to determine the optoelectronic design parameters: an optical model to describe light behavior within the device and an electrical model to evaluate charge transport and collection. The optical model was based on solving the Helmholtz equation (Fig. 1), yielding the electric field (E), from which the absorbed optical power and carrier generation rate were derived. The electron (G_n) and hole (G_p) generation rates were obtained by integrating the optical generation rate (G_{opt}) over a unit volume, using the real and imaginary components of the refractive index (n, k) from established literature sources [50–58]. The electric field distribution and vector field plots were computed using the frequency-domain electromagnetic wave (EWFD) interface in COMSOL Multiphysics. Maxwell's equations were solved in the frequency domain, accounting for the complex refractive indices of each layer. A 2D bilayer heterojunction model, with and without light-trapping (LT) gratings, was analyzed under periodic boundary conditions and perfectly matched layers (PML) to minimize reflection artifacts. Incident plane waves spanning 300–1200 nm (10 nm steps) were simulated to evaluate field behavior across the visible and near-infrared spectrum.

The electrical model solved Poisson's equation together with the electron–hole continuity equations, incorporating recombination rates for electrons (R_n) and holes (R_p). Input parameters included relative permittivity (ε_r), carrier mobilities (μ_n, μ_p), conduction and valence band densities of states, electron affinity (χ), doping concentrations, and Shockley–Read–Hall (SRH) lifetimes (τ_n, τ_p), as listed in Table 1. Breakdown voltage was determined under dark conditions ($G_n = G_p = 0$) using the SRH recombination model. The optical and electrical models were coupled to calculate current density: photons absorbed within the layers generated electron–hole pairs, while increased applied voltage enhanced recombination. Continuity equations including generation and recombination terms were then used to extract the hole and electron current densities (J_p, J_n).

3 RESULTS AND DISSCUSIONS

To optimize spectrum utilization, the bilayer device employs $CH_3NH_3PbI_3$ perovskite (1.55 eV) as the top

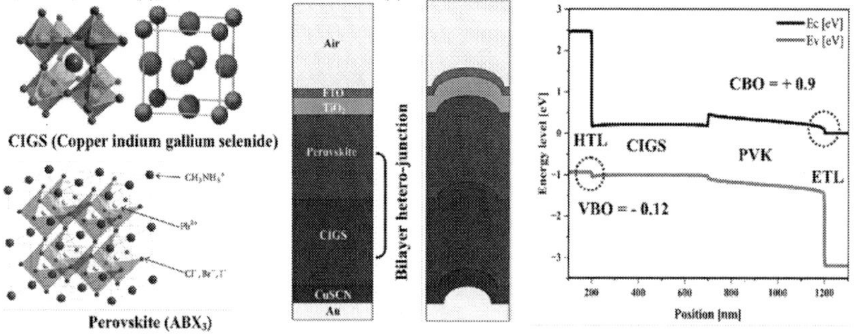

Fig. 2. Schematic representations of: (a) the CIGS crystal structure and the perovskite crystal structure, (b) the bilayer heterojunction configuration (c) the corresponding energy band diagram of the bilayer structure. Crystal structure drawings in (a) are borrowed from [13] with permission.

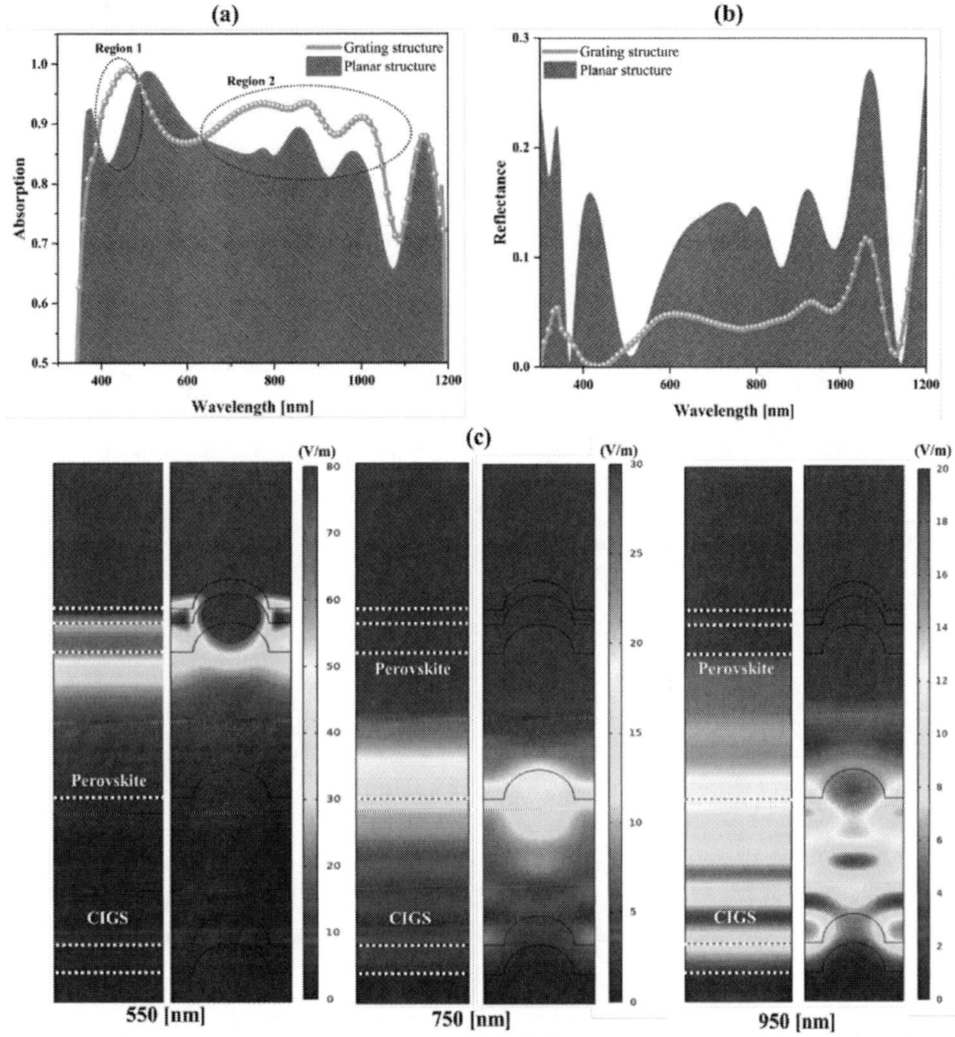

Fig. 3. Diagram showing (a) the absorption spectrum and (b) the reflection rate as functions of wavelength for both planar and LT structures. Electric field distributions across all PSC layers for (c) the planar and LT structure.

absorber for high-energy photons and CIGS (1.2 eV) as the bottom absorber for low-energy photons (Fig. 2a) [68]. An n–i–p configuration was adopted, offering improved V_{oc}, light absorption, and charge separation [13]. The final stack (Fig. 2b) consists of FTO/TiO_2/$CH_3NH_3PbI_3$/CIGS/CuSCN/Au, with energy-band alignment shown in Fig. 2c. A small negative valence-band offset at CuSCN/CIGS ($\approx$ −0.12 eV) promotes hole extraction, while a slightly positive conduction-band offset at TiO_2/perovskite ($\approx$ +0.9 eV) enhances electron collection. FTO serves as the transparent front electrode, and Au as the back contact due to their conductivity and stability.

This section analyzes the simulation results of the light-trapping (LT) structure. Figure 3a shows that converting the planar design into an LT configuration enhances absorption in both active layers, particularly in the 400–500 nm and 650–1100 nm regions. A reduction in absorption between 500–650 nm is observed, caused by strong optical confinement in the TiO_2 layer due to close grating spacing, which limits transmission into the perovskite absorber. Thus, while gratings improve broadband absorption, over-trapping can be counterproductive. Using gratings with a radius and height of 100 nm promoted effective confinement, though further optimization is required to maximize spectral performance.

The LT design also reduces reflection, as shown in Fig. 3b, confirming that light penetrates more efficiently into the active layers and is retained within them. Electric field distributions (Fig. 3c) illustrate this effect: at 550 nm, the LT structure channels more light into the perovskite compared to the planar case; at 750 nm, stronger coupling is observed in both perovskite and CIGS layers; and at 950 nm, field localization deep in the CIGS demonstrates enhanced infrared absorption. These features mitigate parasitic losses while improving confinement on both sides of the grating.

Table 2. Electrical parameters for CIGS/perovskite incorporating LT structure comparing to planar structure.

Structure	J_{sc} (mA/cm^2)	V_{oc} (V)	FF (%)	PCE (%)
Planar	25.98	1.012	87.37	22.98
LT	27.02	1.012	87.18	23.85

Coupling the optical and electrical models confirmed these gains: the higher optical generation (G_{opt}) in the LT design increased J_{sc} from 25.98 to 27.02 mA/cm², improving PCE by ~3.8% relative to the planar device (Table 2). This demonstrates that incorporating LT gratings into CIGS/perovskite bilayer solar cells can significantly enhance performance by reducing reflection and boosting carrier generation. A parametric study was conducted to evaluate the impact of nanostructure dimensions on photovoltaic performance by varying the height (h) and radius (r) of the convex gratings. The heatmaps in Fig. 4b reveal that J_sc and PCE are highly sensitive to grating height, with optimal results obtained for taller features (h > 140 nm) combined with smaller radii (r ≈ 40–60 nm). The best performance was achieved at h = 140 nm and r = 60 nm, yielding J_sc = 28.85 mA/cm², V_oc = 1.011 V, FF = 87.45%, and PCE = 25.54%. This represents a significant enhancement driven by improved light trapping, extended optical path lengths, and more efficient carrier extraction.

Two regimes of optical behavior were identified. Wider gratings (large r) promote initial absorption by allowing more light transmission into the device, while narrower gratings (small r) enhance confinement and internal scattering, leading to longer optical paths and stronger absorption. Table 3 confirms that the optimized geometry provides a ~7% relative increase in PCE compared to the non-optimized grating and a substantial improvement over the planar device. These findings highlight the effectiveness of precision nanostructure tuning for maximizing solar cell efficiency.

4 CONCLUSION

This work presents a performance-enhanced design for CIGS/perovskite solar cells by combining a bilayer heterojunction architecture with grating-assisted light trapping. Finite-element simulations (COMSOL Multiphysics) demonstrated the effectiveness of pairing a high-bandgap perovskite top absorber with a low-bandgap CIGS bottom absorber in a planar n–i–p stack, enabling complementary spectral absorption and improved J_sc and PCE.

Introducing a convex periodic grating further boosted performance by reducing reflection losses and extending optical path lengths through photon confinement and constructive interference. This nanophotonic modification increased PCE from 22.98% (planar bilayer) to 25.54% (optimized grating), representing an ~11% relative gain. Importantly, the nanostructured device maintained its advantage under realistic fabrication constraints, highlighting both robustness and manufacturability.

Overall, this study underscores the promise of light-trapping strategies for advancing thin-film photovoltaics. The proposed design offers a scalable, cost-effective pathway toward high-efficiency, lightweight, and flexible solar cells, providing a strong basis for future experimental validation and commercialization of nanostructured CIGS/perovskite devices.

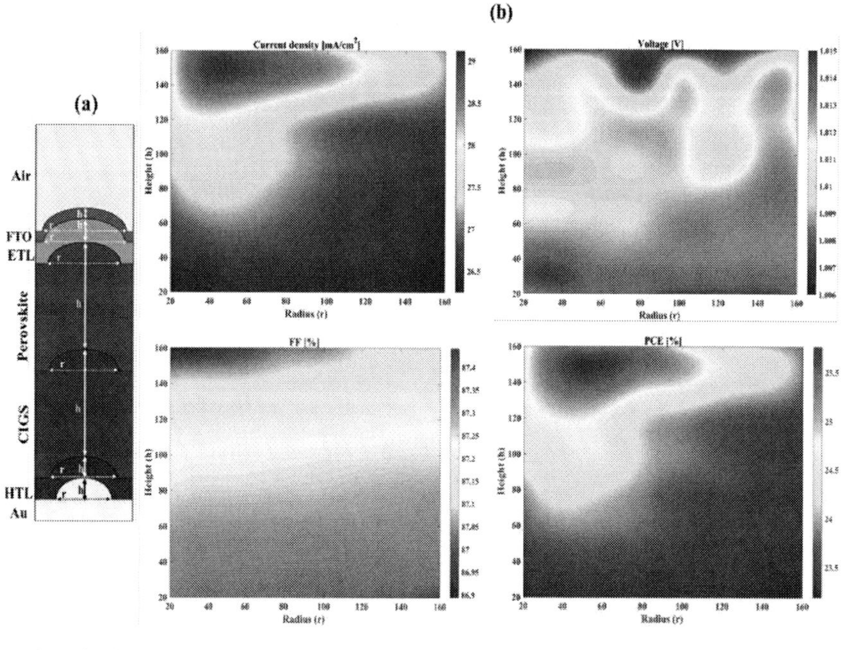

Fig. 4. Schematic (a) cross-section and (b) performance contour maps of a nanostructured CIGS/perovskite solar cell with embedded convex grating structures.

Table 3. Electrical parameters for CIGS/perovskite incorporating optimized grating structure comparing to planar and non-optimized structure.

Structure	J_{sc} (mA/cm^2)	V_{oc} (V)	FF (%)	PCE (%)
Planar	25.98	1.012	87.37	22.98
Non-optimized structure	27.02	1.012	87.18	23.85
Optimized structure	28.85	1.011	87.45	25.54

5 ACKNOLOWDGNENT

This research is financially supported by the CuSun project, funded by the Energy Technology Development and Demonstration Program (EUDP) in Denmark, under grant number 640231-510356.

6 COMPETING INTREST

The authors declare no competing interests.

7 REFERENCES

[1] L. Marroyo and E. L. Pigueiras, "Module Temperature Dispersion Within a Large PV Array: Observations at the Amareleja PV Plant," 2025.

[2] J. Tao *et al.*, "Suppressing non-radiative recombination for efficient and stable perovskite solar cells," *Energy & Environmental Science*, vol. 18, no. 2, pp. 509-544, 2025.

[3] J.-P. Correa-Baena *et al.*, "Promises and challenges of perovskite solar cells," *Science*, vol. 358, no. 6364, pp. 739-744, 2017.

[4] Y. Dai, X. Ge, B. Shi, P. Wang, Y. Zhao, and X. Zhang, "Enhancing Ultraviolet Stability and Performance of Wide Bandgap Perovskite Solar Cells Through Ultraviolet Light-Absorbing Passivator," *Small Methods*, vol. 9, no. 1, p. 2301793, 2025.

[5] J. Li, K. Wang, J. Liu, Y. Ye, and S. Liu, "Union of Perovskite and Silicon: Overcoming Electrical Losses for Surpassing Shockley–Queisser Limit," *Advanced Energy Materials*, p. 2500114.

[6] C. Kan *et al.*, "Efficient and stable perovskite-silicon tandem solar cells with copper thiocyanate-embedded perovskite on textured silicon," *Nature Photonics*, vol. 19, no. 1, pp. 63-70, 2025.

[7] L. Zeng, L. Tang, Z. Luo, J. Gong, J. Li, and X. Xiao, "A review of perovskite/copper indium gallium selenide tandem solar cells," *Solar RRL*, vol. 8, no. 21, p. 2301059, 2024.

[8] Z. Liu *et al.*, "All-perovskite tandem solar cells achieving> 29% efficiency with improved (100) orientation in wide-bandgap perovskites," *Nature Materials*, pp. 1-8, 2025.

[9] A. Abbasiyan and S. Golmohammadi, "Back contact optimization of both sub-cells in bifacial perovskite/silicon tandem solar cell," *Renewable Energy*, vol. 242, p. 122402, 2025.

[10] M. He *et al.*, "Enhancing Flexible Perovskite Photovoltaic Cells and Modules Through Light-Trapping and Light-Shifting Strategies," *Small Methods*, p. 2401954, 2025.

[11] N. Solhtalab, M. H. Mohammadi, M. Eskandari, and D. Fathi, "Efficiency improvement of half-tandem CIGS/perovskite solar cell by designing nano-prism nanostructure as the controllable light trapping," *Energy Reports*, vol. 8, pp. 1298-1308, 2022.

[12] M. H. Mohammadi, M. Eskandari, and D. Fathi, "Design of optimized photonic-structure and analysis of adding a SiO2 layer on the parallel CH3NH3PbI3/CH3NH3SnI3 perovskite solar cells," *Scientific Reports*, vol. 13, no. 1, p. 15905, 2023.

[13] M. W. Bouabdelli, F. Rogti, M. Maache, and A. Rabehi, "Performance enhancement of CIGS thin-film solar cell," *Optik*, vol. 216, p. 164948, 2020.

42nd European Photovoltaic Solar Energy Conference and Exhibition

Achieving Superior Light Trapping in Perovskite/CIGS Solar Cells with Grating-Enhanced Bilayer Heterojunctions

Department of Electrical and Computer Engineering

Mohammad Hossein Mohammadi*, Narendra Bandaru, Rasmus Schmidt Davidsen
Department of Electrical and Computer Engineering, Aarhus University, Denmark

EU PVSEC 2025
2CV.3.22-304

Abstract

- A CIGS/perovskite bilayer heterojunction paired with convex periodic gratings offers a lower-cost, robust, and lower-toxicity route to higher performance than many alternative architectures.
- Complementary bandgaps 1.55 eV perovskite top absorber for shorter wavelengths and 1.2 eV CIGS bottom absorber for near-infrared—expand spectral harvesting, cut thermalization losses, and boost current.
- FEM simulations in COMSOL with coupled optical–electrical models show that grating-assisted light trapping reduces reflection, lengthens optical paths, and improves carrier collection.
- Performance improves from J_{sc}= 25.98 mA cm^{-2}, PCE = 22.98% (bilayer planar) to PCE = 25.54% with gratings, an ≈11% relative gain and ~15% above a single-junction perovskite baseline—supporting scalable, flexible thin-film PV.

Introduction

- Falling PV costs drove global capacity from <50 GW (2010) to >2000 GW (2025), pushing research toward thin, flexible absorbers and advanced light management to overcome limited optical absorption.
- Perovskites combine direct bandgaps, long diffusion lengths, and strong absorption (single-junction PCE ≈ 26%), but are SQ-limited and miss much of the 700–2500 nm irradiance.
- Tandems address this via complementary bandgaps; CIGS/perovskite is attractive for thin-film, flexible devices, with reported records around 24.6% (2T) and 29.36% (4T) and prior studies showing texture-enabled current matching.
- Light-trapping photonic structures (e.g., gratings, textures, nanocones, plasmonic features) reduce reflection and extend optical paths, boosting absorption and often aiding carrier transport—though precise, scalable patterning is a fabrication challenge.

Theory

Modeling Framework

- Optical model: Helmholtz equation solved for light absorption and carrier generation across 300–1200 nm.
- Electrical model: Poisson and continuity equations solved for charge transport and recombination.
- Both integrated in COMSOL Multiphysics using FEM.

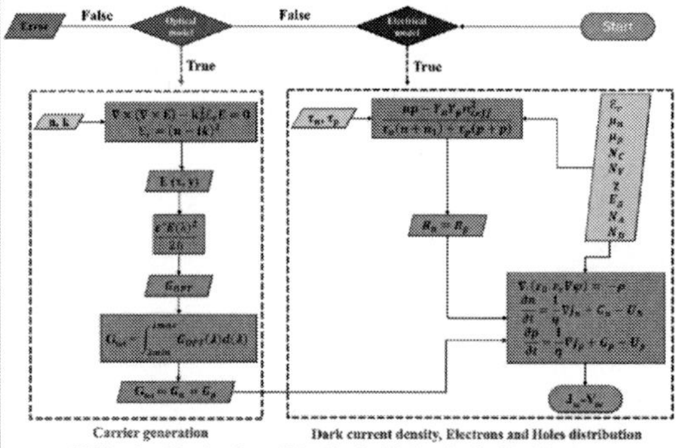

(1) The algorithm involves solving the electrical and optical models.

Device Structure

- n–i–p bilayer heterojunction
- Perovskite (1.55 eV) captures higher-energy photons; CIGS (1.2 eV) captures lower-energy, near-IR photons.
- Convex grating nanostructures added at interfaces for enhanced light trapping.

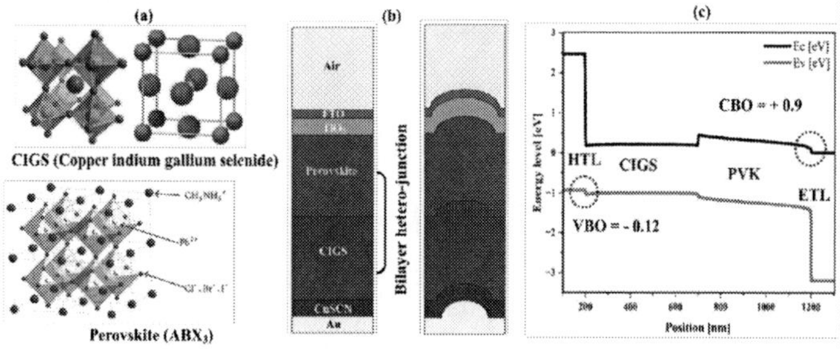

(2) (a) CIGS crystal structure and the perovskite crystal structure (b) the bilayer heterojunction configuration (c) energy band diagram of the bilayer structure.

Results

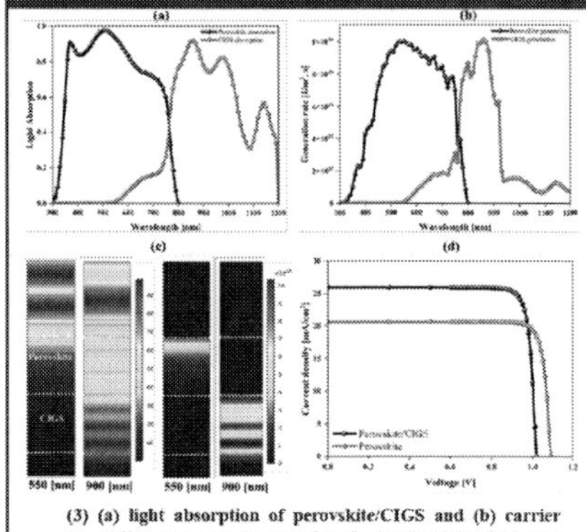

(3) (a) light absorption of perovskite/CIGS and (b) carrier generation rate versus wavelength (c) Electric field and carrier generation rate profiles (d) J–V characteristics.

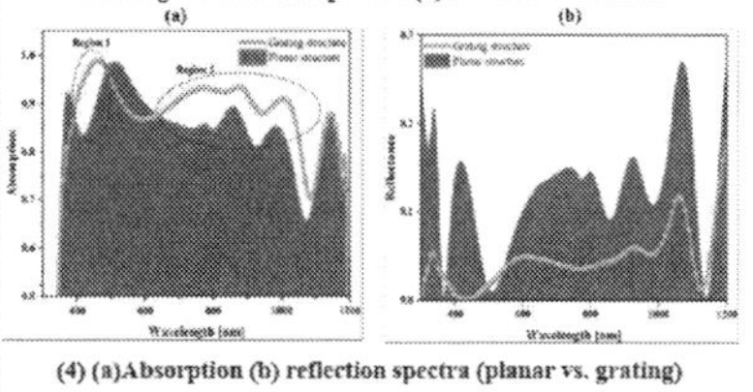

(4) (a)Absorption (b) reflection spectra (planar vs. grating)

Table 1. Electrical parameters for CIGS/perovskite incorporating LT structure comparing to planar structure.

Structure	J_{sc} (mA/cm²)	V_{oc} (V)	FF (%)	PCE (%)
Planar	25.98	1.012	87.37	22.98
LT	27.02	1.012	87.18	23.85

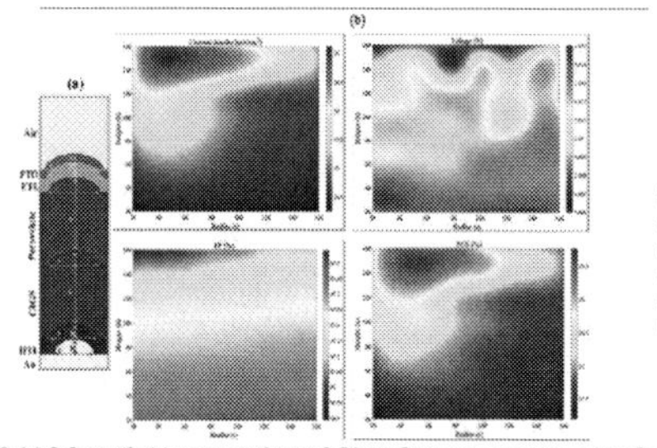

(6) (a) Schematic (a) cross-section and (b) performance contour maps of a nanostructured CIGS/perovskite solar cell with embedded convex grating structures.

Table 2. Electrical parameters for CIGS/perovskite incorporating optimized grating structure comparing to planar and non-optimized structure.

Structure	Jsc (mA/cm2)	Voc (V)	FF (%)	PCE (%)
Planar	25.98	1.012	87.37	22.98
Non-optimized	27.02	1.012	87.18	23.85
Optimized	28.85	1.011	87.45	25.54

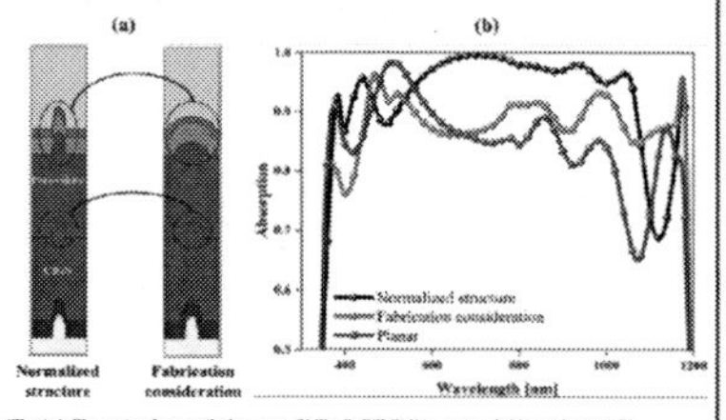

(7) (a) Front view of the modified CIGS/perovskite solar cell structure, illustrating both the sharp-edged and smooth-edged configurations, based on realistic fabrication considerations. (b) Corresponding absorption rate comparison for both the idealized (normalized) and fabrication-aware structures, highlighting the optical impact of edge rounding due to deposition conditions.

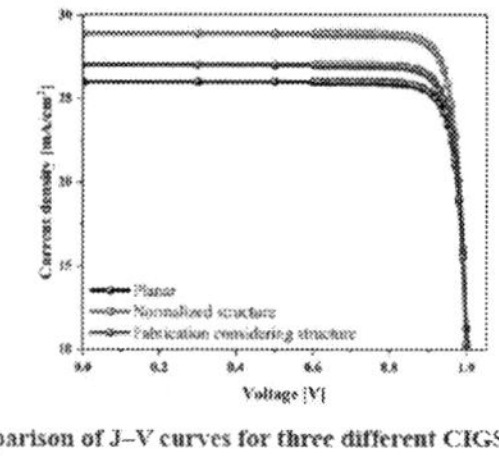

(8) Comparison of J–V curves for three different CIGS/perovskite solar cell configurations: planar structure (baseline), normalized structure (ideal sharp edges) and fabrication considering structure (with realistic smooth edges).

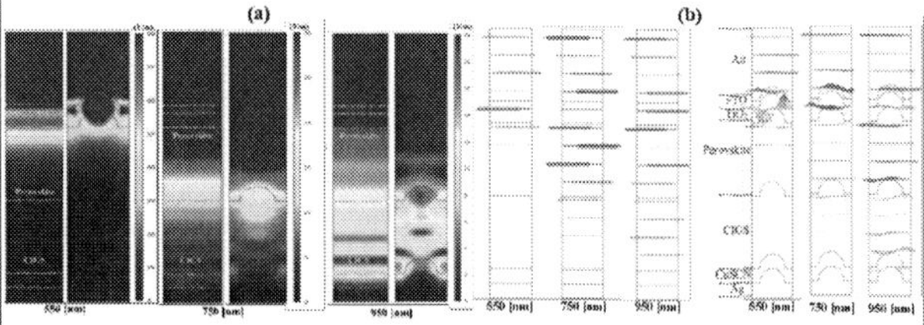

(5) (a) Electric field distributions across all PSC layers for (b) vector field simulations of the electric field intensity

Conclusion

- A bilayer heterojunction stacks a high-bandgap perovskite top absorber over a low-bandgap CIGS bottom absorber in a planar n–i–p layout, enabling complementary spectral absorption and higher J_{sc} and PCE.
- FEM simulations in COMSOL optimize a convex periodic grating that traps light via photon confinement and constructive interference, cutting reflection and extending optical path length.
- PCE rises from 22.98% (bilayer planar) to 25.54% with the optimized grating, an ≈11% relative efficiency while remaining robust under realistic fabrication tolerances.
- The nanostructured, grating-assisted design is cost-effective and scalable, supporting flexible, lightweight thin-film photovoltaics and guiding experimental development toward commercial CIGS/perovskite cells.

Acknowledgements

- This research is financially supported by the CuSun project, funded by the Energy Technology Development and Demonstration Program (EUDP), Denmark, under grant number 640231-510356.

Funding: AARHUS UNIVERSITY EUDP

Contact email : moh@ece.au.dk

FABRICATION OF BENDABLE PEROVSKITE/SILICON HETEROJUNCTION BIFACIAL TANDEM SOLAR CELLS

Kimihiko Saito*, Kanji Takahashi, Hirotaka Shishido, Ryousuke Ishikawa, Makoto Konagai
Tokyo City University, Advanced Research Laboratories
1-28-1 Tamatsutsumi Setagaya-ku Tokyo 158-8557, Japan
Phone +81-3-5707-2769 e-mail: kisaitou@tcu.ac.jp

ABSTRACT: We report the fabrication of a flexible bifacial monolithic perovskite (PVK)/silicon heterojunction (SHJ) tandem solar cell consisting of a $Cs_{0.05}FA_{0.95}PbI_3$ top cell (bandgap ~1.54 eV) and an ~80 μm-thick SHJ bottom cell. External quantum efficiency (EQE) measurements showed a top-cell current of 22.1 mA (1 cm² aperture) and a current mismatch of 8.0 mA between the sub-cells, which can be compensated by rear-side illumination of ~27 mW/cm², as indicated by bifacial SHJ single-cell results. Current–voltage characterization showed a linear increase in short-circuit current up to ~12.3 mW/cm², followed by saturation without achieving current balance with the top cell, accompanied by pronounced hysteresis. Extrapolation of the linear regime yielded a balancing irradiance of ~29 mW/cm², in good agreement with both the EQE-based estimate and reported simulations. In contrast, the four-terminal tandem exhibited no saturation, with the bottom-cell current scaling linearly with rear-side irradiance. These findings indicate that interfacial imperfections at the PVK/hole-transport layer interface may play a critical role in hindering current balancing in monolithic PVK/SHJ tandems.
Keywords: Si heterojunction, perovskite, bifacial, tandem solar cell

1 INTRODUCTION

From the perspective of mitigating greenhouse gas emissions, photovoltaic (PV) technology, as a major renewable energy source, has continued to expand worldwide [1]. In Japan as well, deployment has progressed significantly over the past decade [2]. However, available land for the installation of large-scale PV power plants is becoming increasingly scarce. As a result, policies promoting PV installation on buildings—particularly rooftops and façades in urban areas—are being actively pursued [3]. Perovskite (PVK) solar cells have attracted considerable attention in this context, as they offer advantages such as lightweight design, mechanical flexibility, and high-power conversion efficiency [4]. Furthermore, tandem integration with silicon heterojunction (SHJ) solar cells has achieved efficiencies approaching 35% [5]. It has also been reported that thinning the Si substrate and applying suitable edge treatment can render SHJ solar cells flexible [6]. These developments suggest that lightweight, flexible PVK/SHJ tandem cells employing thin SHJ bottom cells offer strong potential as building-integrated photovoltaics where installation area is limited. Indeed, efficiencies approaching 30% have already been reported [7], and we have also previously demonstrated exceeding 26% efficiency [8,9]. For further efficiency improvement of PVK/SHJ tandem cells, increasing the current density of the SHJ bottom cell—which tends to be lower than that of the PVK top cell—is a critical challenge. This issue becomes even more pronounced in thin SHJ cells. One proposed approach to address this limitation is the use of bifacial PVK/SHJ tandem architectures [10], and such devices have already been demonstrated [11,12]. Simulation studies have further indicated that PVK bandgap narrowing to increase the top cell current, combined with rear-side illumination (albedo) to enhance the SHJ bottom cell current for current matching, can achieve higher efficiencies [13–15]. For example, with an albedo of 30%, the optimal PVK bandgap has been suggested to be ~1.52 eV. In addition, from the viewpoint of long-term stability, which remains a key issue for the practical deployment of PVK solar cells, using a single-halide composition to avoid halide segregation, such as the iodine–bromine phase separation often observed in wide-gap perovskites [16], is a promising strategy [12].

Based on these insights, we fabricated bendable bifacial monolithic (two-terminal) PVK/SHJ tandem cells consisting of an ~80 μm-thick SHJ bottom cell and of a $Cs_{0.05}FA(Formamidine)_{0.95}PbI_3$ PVK top cell with a bandgap of ~1.54 eV. We investigated the dependence of cell performance on rear-side illumination intensity. For comparison, we also examined the bifacial characteristics of a PVK single-junction cell fabricated on glass substrates, a thin SHJ cell with the same structure as that used in the monolithic tandem cells, and a four-terminal PVK/SHJ tandem cell constructed from these cells.

2 EXPERIMENTS

2.1 Fabrication of SHJ cells

A Si substrate was thinned to ~80 μm by KOH etching, after which a micro-texture with a height of <1 μm was formed on the front (top-cell) side and a texture with a height of 2–3 μm was formed on the rear side. A rear-emitter-type SHJ cell with a 1 cm² active area defined by the front and rear indium tin oxide (ITO) electrodes was then fabricated. Details of the fabrication procedures are described in our previous report [17]. To enable bifacial operation, Ag electrodes were patterned into grids on both the front and rear ITO layers.

2.2 Fabrication of PVK cells

For single-junction cells, commercially available ITO-coated glass substrates (~200 nm, ~6 Ω/sq) were used. The ITO surfaces were treated with UV/O_3 cleaning, after which a hole transport layer (HTL) of [2-(3,6-dimethoxy-9H-carbazol-9-yl)ethyl] phosphonic acid (MeO-2PACz) was spin-coated at 3000 rpm and subsequently annealed at 105 °C for 10 min. A perovskite precursor solution was then spin-coated at 5000 rpm using anisole as the antisolvent, followed by a two-step annealing at 105 °C for 45 min and 150 °C for 10 min. Both spin-coating and annealing steps for the HTL and PVK layers were performed in a glovebox filled with nitrogen. A 20 nm-thick C_{60} film was deposited by thermal evaporation as an electron transport layer (ETL), followed by 20 nm-thick SnO_2 deposited by atomic layer deposition (ALD). Subsequently, a transparent electrode was formed to realize a bifacial cell structure, in which a 1 cm^2 ITO layer was sputtered, followed by evaporating Ag grid electrodes and a MgF_2 antireflection layer.

For tandem cells, a 7 nm-thick ITO recombination layer with a size of 1 cm^2 was sputtered onto the n-type a-Si:H layer of the SHJ bottom cell. The PVK top cell was then fabricated using the same procedure as for the single-junction cell, however, due to the surface micro-texture of the SHJ bottom cell, the PVK precursor solution was spin-coated at 3000 rpm.

2.3 Characterization of bifacial cell performance

External quantum efficiency (EQE) measurements were carried out in air at 25 °C using a Bunkoukeiki CEP-25NLT, in which a 1 cm^2 aperture mask was applied to the front side and a black antireflection film (reflectance <1%) was placed behind the rear side of the cell. For tandem cells, appropriate bias light and bias voltage were applied to the top and bottom subcells during EQE measurements. Current–voltage (I-V) characterization was performed in air at room temperature using an EKO MP-180 source measure unit, with 1 cm^2 aperture masks attached to both the front and rear sides of the bifacial single-junction and tandem cells. Standard 1-sun, AM1.5G illumination was applied from both the front and rear sides using an EKO LP-50A and a SAN-EI ELECTRIC XES-40S1 solar simulator, respectively, and the albedo level of rear-side illumination was adjusted by inserting neutral-density (ND) filters with transmittances of 6%, 12%, 25%, and 50% between the simulator and the rear surface of the cell. The actual rear-side irradiance for each ND filter condition was calibrated using an EKO Solar Simulator Spectroradiometer LS-100 in advance. In measurements without rear-side illumination, a black antireflection film was placed behind the cell, as in the EQE measurements. The front illumination intensity for the bifacial I-V measurement was then adjusted to match the EQE current under this dark rear-side condition, which, in the case of a tandem cell, corresponded to the smaller EQE current, namely that of the bottom cell.

3 RESULTS AND DISCUSSIONS

Fig. 1(a) shows the schematic structure of the bifacial PVK single-junction cell fabricated in this study. In this configuration, the transparent electrode consisting of an MgF_2 antireflection layer, an Ag grid electrode, and an ITO layer was placed on the front side, while the glass substrate was located on the rear side. Fig. 1(b) displays its EQE spectrum. From the plot of EQE^2 versus photon energy in this figure, the bandgap of the PVK layer was estimated to be ~1.54 eV, at which the photocurrent of the PVK top cell balances that of the Si bottom cell under an albedo of ~27%, according to the bifacial PVK/Si tandem simulations introduced in the Introduction [13-15]. Figures 1(c) and 1(d) display the I–V curves and cell characteristics under varying rear-side illumination intensities. As the rear illumination intensity increased, the short-circuit current (I_{sc}) rose linearly, and the open-circuit voltage (V_{oc}) also increased with the enhanced photocurrent. In contrast, the fill factor (FF) exhibited a decreasing trend, which can likely be attributed to an

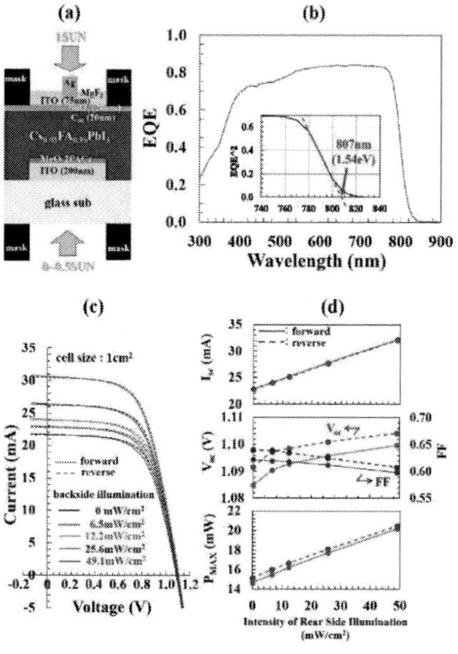

Figure 1: (a) Schematic structure of the bifacial PVK single-junction cell, (b) the EQE spectrum without rear-side illumination, (c) the I–V curves, and (d) cell properties measured under varying rear-side illumination.

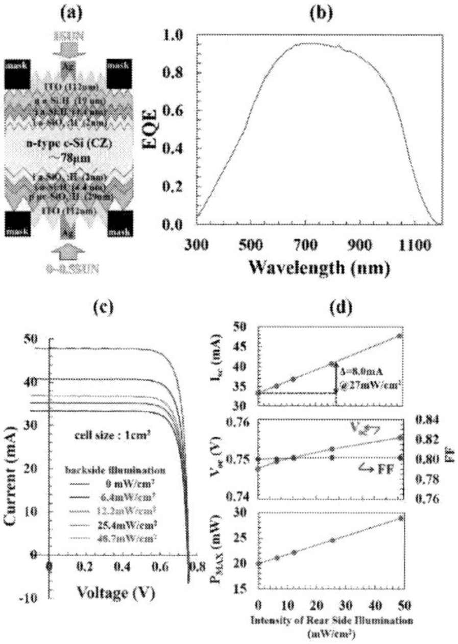

Figure 2: (a) Schematic structure of the bifacial SHJ single-junction cell, (b) the EQE spectrum without rear-side illumination, (c) the I–V curves, and (d) cell properties measured under varying rear-side illumination.

increase in the series resistance with higher photocurrent. Despite a small hysteresis depending on the voltage sweep direction, a power conversion efficiency (PCE) of 15% without rear illumination and maximum output power (P_{MAX}) of 18 mW at 25% albedo was obtained.

Figures 2(a) and 2(b) show the schematic structure and EQE characteristics of the SHJ single-junction cell fabricated in this study, respectively. Due to the use of an a-Si:H n-layer on the front side, the short-wavelength response is low. However, at longer wavelengths above 750 nm, which are meaningful for tandem operation as a bottom cell, high sensitivity was obtained even with a thin substrate with a thickness of 78 μm due to the light-trapping effect enhanced by the front-side micro-texture [17]. Figures 2(c) and 2(d) present the I-V curves and cell characteristics under different rear illumination intensities. Similar to the PVK single-junction cell, I_{sc} increased linearly with rear-side illumination, also causing an increase in V_{oc} due to higher photocurrent. As a result, the P_{MAX} improved from 19.9 mW without rear illumination (corresponding to 19.9% PCE) to 24.6 mW at 25% albedo.

A monolithic PVK/SHJ tandem cell was fabricated based on these PVK and SHJ cells, and its schematic structure together with photographs of the bent state and of the front and rear sides with the measurement attachment are shown in Fig. 3(a). To achieve higher current output from the top cell, not only the bandgap of the PVK material but also its layer thickness is an important factor. In this tandem cell, the PVK layer planarized the underlying micro-texture with a non-uniform thickness, exceeding 1 μm in the valleys and reducing to a few hundred nanometers at the pyramid tips [9,17]. Although the PVK layer exhibited non-uniform thickness, we consider that the coverage is sufficient to ensure reliable current generation in the top cell. This consideration is supported by the top-cell photocurrent of 22.1 mA for a 1 cm² aperture area, which was 8.0 mA higher than that of the bottom cell, as estimated from the EQE spectrum shown in Fig. 3(b). Furthermore, as indicated by the SHJ single-cell results in Fig. 2(d), this current deficit can be compensated by rear-side illumination at an intensity of 27 mW/cm², a value that agrees well with the simulation prediction of the albedo required for current matching between a 1.54 eV PVK top cell and a Si bottom cell [13-15]. Figure 3(c) presents the I–V characteristics of the tandem cell under varying rear illumination intensities. In this study, we did not apply any passivation treatment to the PVK layer [8,18]. The measured V_{oc} of 1.73 V without rear illumination was consistent with the correlation between I_{sc} and V_{oc} observed for the single-junction cells (Figs. 1(d), 2(d)). This indicates that the MeO-2PACz self-assembled monolayer (SAM), which acts as the HTL, is conformally formed on the ITO deposited on the textured surface, resulting in the normal operation of the tandem cell under zero-albedo conditions, as demonstrated in our previous studies [9]. With rear illumination, the output current increased with illumination intensity up to about 12.3 mW/cm². At higher intensities, however, the current did not change and significant hysteresis appeared in the I–V curves. Figure 3(d) summarizes the cell characteristics as a function of rear-side illumination intensity. I_{sc} exhibited saturation beyond ~12.3 mW/cm², and at 25.6 and 49.9 mW/cm²—where I_{sc} had already saturated—pronounced reductions in V_{oc} and FF were observed, particularly during forward (increasing voltage) sweeps. By extrapolating the linear low-intensity region of I_{sc}, the rear-

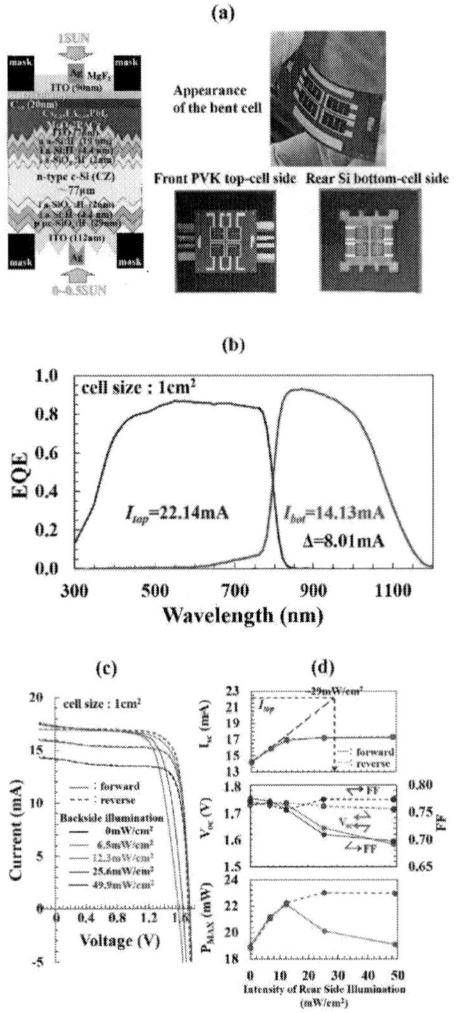

Figure 3: (a) Schematic of the bifacial PVK/SHJ tandem cell and photographs of its bent state and front/rear sides with the measurement attachment, (b) the EQE spectrum without rear-side illumination, (c) the I–V curves, and (d) cell properties measured under varying rear-side illumination.

side illumination required to reach the EQE-derived top-cell current of 22.1 mA was estimated to be ~29 mW/cm², which closely matches the simulated and expected balance point of 27 mW/cm² mentioned above. These results suggest that, although the tandem output should ideally increase up to the top-cell current, some limiting mechanism suppresses the current increase before reaching this value.

To verify this, a four-terminal PVK/SHJ tandem configuration was assembled using the PVK and SHJ single cells characterized in Figs. 1 and 2, as illustrated in Fig. 4(a). In this measurement, the front illumination intensity was adjusted so that the current matched the EQE current of the PVK single-junction top cell. The dependence of each subcell on rear illumination is shown

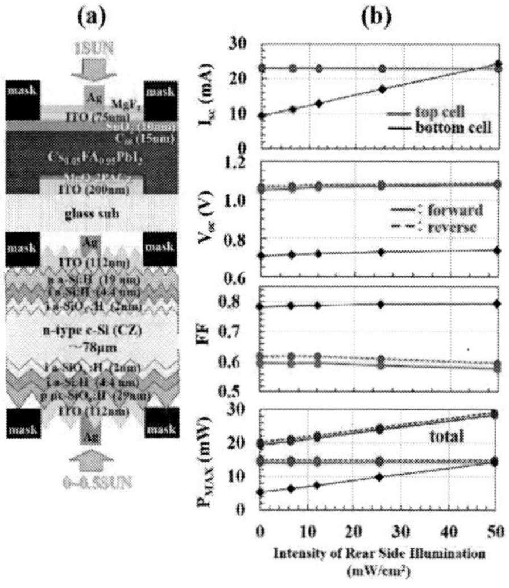

Figure 4: (a) Schematic structure of the four-terminal PVK/SHJ bifacial tandem cell, (b) the top and bottom cell properties measured under varying rear-side illumination.

in Fig. 4(b). The PVK top cell exhibited a constant I_{sc} of 23 mA regardless of rear illumination, indicating that the additional photons incident from the rear side were absorbed almost entirely by the SHJ bottom cell, while the current generated under front illumination remained unchanged. In contrast, without rear illumination, the bottom cell showed an I_{sc} of only 9.4 mA, significantly lower than the monolithic tandem value of 14.1 mA derived from the EQE spectrum. This reduction is attributed to transmission losses, which arise from parasitic absorption in the thick (200 nm) rear ITO electrode of the top cell and reflection at the rear side of the top cell due to the presence of the glass substrate and the air gap in the four-terminal configuration. Nevertheless, the bottom-cell I_{sc} increased linearly with rear illumination, consistent with the behavior observed for the bifacial SHJ single-junction cell, and reached a value comparable to the top-cell current of 24.3 mA at 49.7 mW/cm².

These results suggest that, in the monolithic tandem, the observed saturation of output current before current matching is caused by insufficient recombination of holes from the top cell with electrons from the bottom cell once the bottom-cell current exceeds a certain threshold. Although the HTL-SAM should be conformally formed on the ITO recombination layer as mentioned above, we fabricated tandems employing a thicker ITO recombination layer (20 and 50nm) to rule out concerns about possible inhomogeneity in the quality or thickness of the thin ITO layer (7 nm), which could introduce pinholes. However, even with the thicker ITO recombination layer, the same saturation tendency as that observed in the tandem cell with the 7-nm-thick ITO layer was obtained. This implies that the ITO recombination layer is not the origin of the saturation of output current before current matching. Furthermore, pronounced hysteresis in the I–V characteristics appeared simultaneously, indicating the involvement of ion migration in the PVK layer, which may lead to charge accumulation at the PVK/HTL interface, and/or to charge trapping and delayed release at the same interface [19-22]. Both phenomena can hinder efficient hole supply; therefore, interfacial defects at the PVK/HTL interface may be the root cause of the observed saturation and hysteresis. On the other hand, phenomena such as the saturation of output current before current matching, accompanied by hysteretic I–V curves, were not observed in reports on bifacial PVK/SHJ tandem cells [11,12]. Moreover, monofacial PVK/SHJ tandem cells have achieved I_{sc} values exceeding 20 mA/cm² with well-balanced top and bottom cell currents [5,23-25]. These findings suggest that the limited output power observed in our bifacial cells, which did not increase as expected with higher albedo, is not a problem inherent to the bifacial architecture, but rather arises from imperfections at the PVK/HTL interface due to our unoptimized fabrication process. Therefore, to fully realize the potential of bifacial performance, precise control of both the PVK/ETL and PVK/HTL interfaces in the PVK top cell is likely to be essential.

Based on these considerations, we further explored replacing the HTL with alternative materials, specifically a mixture of MeO-2PACz and [4-(3,6-dimethyl-9H-carbazol-9-yl)butyl]phosphonic acid (Me-4PACz), aiming to achieve fast hole extraction and minimized nonradiative recombination at the PVK/HTL interface [23]. However, the issue persisted, and further studies are underway to clarify the underlying mechanisms and develop effective solutions.

4 SUMMARY

We fabricated a bendable bifacial monolithic tandem solar cell consisting of a $Cs_{0.05}FA_{0.95}PbI_3$ perovskite (PVK) top cell with an estimated bandgap of ~1.54 eV (derived from the EQE spectrum of the single cell) and an ~80 µm-thick SHJ bottom cell. EQE measurements of a 1 cm² tandem device, with the rear side masked by a black anti-reflection film, revealed that the bottom-cell EQE current was 8.0 mA lower than that of the top cell. Based on the dependence of I_{sc} on rear-side illumination intensity in a bifacial SHJ single cell with the same ~80 µm thickness and structure as the bottom cell, this current deficit corresponds to a rear-side irradiance of ~27 mW/cm² under simulated sunlight. In contrast, I–V measurements of the tandem cell under varying rear-side illumination intensities showed that I_{sc} increased linearly with intensity up to 12.3 mW/cm², but saturated at higher intensities, accompanied by pronounced hysteresis in the I–V curves. Extrapolation of the linear regime yielded a balancing irradiance of ~29 mW/cm², which agrees well with both the EQE-based estimate (~27 mW/cm²) and reported simulation values. Furthermore, bifacial characteristics were evaluated in a four-terminal tandem configuration, composed of a bifacial PVK single cell fabricated on a glass substrate and a bifacial SHJ single cell of ~80 µm thickness identical to the bottom cell. In this case, the bottom-cell I_{sc} increased linearly with rear-side illumination intensity without saturation. Overall, these results suggest that, in the monolithic architecture, ion migration in the PVK layer, which may cause charge accumulation, and/or trapping and delayed release at the PVK/HTL interface can hinder the supply of holes needed for recombination with electrons from the bottom cell, and may therefore underlie the observed saturation and hysteresis. While these findings point to the imperfect

PVK/HTL interface as a possible origin of the observed issues, the precise mechanisms remain under investigation.

ACKNOWLEDGEMENT

This work was supported by New Energy and Industrial Technology Development Organization (NEDO) under the project code JPNP20015.

REFERENCES

[1] https://www.iea.org/energy-system/renewables/solar-pv
[2] https://www.fit-portal.go.jp/PublicInfoSummary
[3] https://www.meti.go.jp/shingikai/energy_environment/perovskite_solar_cell/pdf/20241128_1.pdf
[4] Y. Wu, G Xu, Y. Shen, X. Wu, X Tang, C Han, Y Chen, F Yang, H. Chen, Y. Li and Y Li, Adv. Mater. 36 (2024) 2403531
[5] L. Jia, S. Xia, J. Li, Y. Qin, B. Pei, L. Ding, J. Yin, T. Du, Z. Fang, Y. Yin, J. Liu, Y. Yang, F. Zhang, X. Wu, Q. Li, S. Zhao, H. Zhang, Q. Li, Q. Jia, C. Liu, X. Gu, B. Liu, X. Dong, J. Liu, T. Liu, Y. Gao, M. Yang, S. Yin, X. Ru, H. Chen, B. Yang, Z. Zheng, W. Zhou, M. Dou, S. Wang, S. Gao, L. Chen, M. Qu, J. Lu, L. Fang, Y. Wang, H. Deng, J. Yu, X. Zhang, M. Li, X. Lang, C. Xiao, Q. Hi, C. Xue, L. Ning, Y. He, Z. Li, X. Xu and B. He, Nature (2025) https://doi.org/10.1038/s41586-025-09333-z
[6] W. Liu, Y. Liu, Z. Yang, C. Xu, X. Li, S. Huang, J. Shi, J. Du, A. Han, Y. Yang, G. Xu, J. Yu, J. Ling, J. Peng, L. Yu, B. Ding, Y. Gao, K. Jiang, Z. Li, Y. Yang, Z. Li, S. Lan, H. Fu, B. Fan, Y. Fu, W. He, F. Li, X. Song, Y. Zhou, Q. Shi, G. Wang, L. Guo, J. Kang, X. Yang, D. Li, Z. Wang, J. Li, S. Thoroddsen, R. Cai, F. Wei, G. Xing, Y. Xie, X. Liu, L. Zhang, F. Meng, Z. Di and Z. Liu, Nature 617 (2023) 717
[7] Y. Sun, F. Li, H. Zhang, W. Liu, Z. Wang, L. Mao, Q. Li, Y. He, T. Yang, X. Sun, Y. Qian, Y. Ma, L. Zhang, J. Du, J. Shi, G. Wang, A. Han, N. Wang, F. Meng, Z. Liu and M. Liu, Nat. Commun., 16 (2025) 5733
[8] K. Saito, K. Takahashi, H. Shishido and R. Ishikawa, Proceedings in 35th International Photovoltaic Science and Engineering Conference, We2b-Oc1-03 (2024)
[9] H. Shishido, R. Sato, D. Ieki, G. Matsuo, K. Saito, M.Konagai and R. Ishikawa, Sol. RRL, 9 (2025) 2400899
[10] R. Asadpour, R. V. K. Chavali, M. R. Khan and M. A. Alam, Appl. Phys. Lett., 106 (2015) 243902
[11] M. D. Bastiani, A. J. Millabelli, Y. Hou, F. Gota, E. Aydin, T. G. Allen, J. Troughton, A. S. Subbiah, F. H. Isikgor, J. Liu, L. Xu, B. Chen, E. V. Kerschaver, D. Baran, B. Fraboni, M. F. Salvador, U. W. Paetzold, E. H. Sargent and S. D. Wolf, Nat. Energy., 6 (2021) 167
[12] M. R. Golobostanfard, M. Othman, D.Turkay, K. Artuk, X. Y. Chin, M. D. Mensi, D. A. Jacobs, Q. Jeangros, C. M. Wolff, A. Hessler-Wyser and C. Ballif, Nano Energy, 131 (2024) 110269
[13] J. Chantana, Y. Kawano, T. Nishimura, A. Mavlonov and T. Minemoto, Sol. Energy, 220 (2021) 163
[14] M. R. Khan and M. A. Alam, Appl. Phys. Lett., 107 (2015) 223502
[15] A. Onno, N. Rodkey, A. Asgharzadeh, S. Manzoor, Z. J. Yu, F. Toor and Z. C. Holman, Joule, 4 (2020) 580
[16] R. Wang, X. Liu, S. Yan, N. Meng, X. Zhao, Y. Chen, H. Li, S. M. H. Qaid, S. Yang, M. Yuan and T. He, Nat. Commun., 15 (2024) 8899
[17] K. Saito, H. Shishido and R. Ishikawa, Proceedings in 40th European Photovoltaic Solar Energy Conference and Exhibition, 1AO.6.6 (2023) 020009-001
[18] D. B. Khadka, Y. Shirai, M. Yanagida, H. Ota, A. Lyalin, T. Taketsugu and K. Miyano, Nat. Commun., 15 (2024) 882
[19] H. J. Snaith, A. Abate, J. M. Ball, G. E. Eperon, T. Leijtens, N. K. Noel, S. D. Stranks, J. T-W, Wang, K. Wojciechowski and W. Zhang, J. Phys. Chem. Lett., 5 (2014) 1511
[20] B. Chen, M. Yang, S. Priya and K. Zhu, J. Phys. Chem. Lett., 7 (2016) 905
[21] S. Meloni, T. Moehl, W. Tress, M. Franckevicius, M. Saliba, Y. H. Lee, P. Gao, M. K. Nazeeruddin, S. M. Zakeeruddin, U. Rothlisberger and M. Graetzel, Nat. Commun., 7 (2016) 10334
[22] S. A. L. Weber, I. M. Hermes, S-H Turren-Cruz, C. Gort, V. W. Bergmann, L. Gilson, A. Hagfeldt, M. Graetzel, W. Tress and R. Berger, Energy Environ. Sci., 11 (2018) 2404
[23] A. Al-Ashouri, E. Kohnen, B. Li, A. Magomedov, H. Hempel, P. Caprioglio, J. A. Marquez, A. B. M. Vilches, E. Kasparavicius, J. A. Smith, N. Phung, D. Menzel, M. Grischek, L. Kegelmann, D. Skroblin, C. Gollwitzer, T. Malinauskas, M. Jost, G. Matic, B. Rech, R. Schlatmann, M. Topic, L. Korte, A. Abate, B. Stannowski, D. Neher, M. Stolterfoht, T. Unold, V. Getautis and A. Albrecht, Science, 370 (2020) 1300
[24] X. Y. Chin, D. Turkay, J. A. Steele, S. Tabean, S. Eswara, M. Mensi, P. Fiala, C. M. Wolff, A. Paracchino, K. Artuk, D. Jacobs, Q. Guesnay, F. Sahli, G. Andreatta, M. Boccard, Q. Jeangros and C. Ballif, Science, 381 (2023) 59
[25] E. Aydin, E. Ugur, B. K. Yildirim, T. G. Allen, P. Dally, A. Razzaq, F. Cao, L. Xu, B. Vishal, A. Yazmaciyan, A. A. Said, S. Zhumagali, R. Azmi, M. Babics, A. Fell, C. Xiao and S. D. Wolf, Nature, 623 (2023) 732

Department of Physics, Faculty of Science, University of Jaffna

Fyzikální ústav Akademie věd ČR, v. v. i.
Institute of Physics PRAGUE

Czech Technical University in PRAGUE
Faculty of Electrical Engineering

42nd European Photovoltaic Solar Energy Conference and Exhibition [illegible] [bc],
Neda Neykova [bc], Jakub Holovský *[bc]

[a] Department of Physics, Faculty of Science, University of Jaffna, Jaffna 40000, Sri Lanka
[b] SOLar cell MATerial laboratory, Faculty of Electrical Engineering, Czech Technical University in Prague, Technická 2, 166 27 Prague, Czech Republic
[c] Institute of Physics, Czech Academy of Sciences, v. v. i., Cukrovarnická 10, 162 00 Prague, Czech Republic

* Contact: e-mail: amalraj@univ.jfn.ac.lk, stankte3@fel.cvut.cz, jakub.holovsky@fel.cvut.cz,

$FACsPbI_3$ Perovskite Solar Cells:
Ethylammonium Bromide Both as an Additive and Surface Passivation

Why stability matters?
- High efficiency, but poor long-term stability[1]
- $FACsPbI_3$ suffers from defects & degradation[2]

Dual Role of EABr
- Additive in precursor → larger grains
- Surface passivation → defect suppression
- Goal: improve efficiency & stability

Process of fabrication

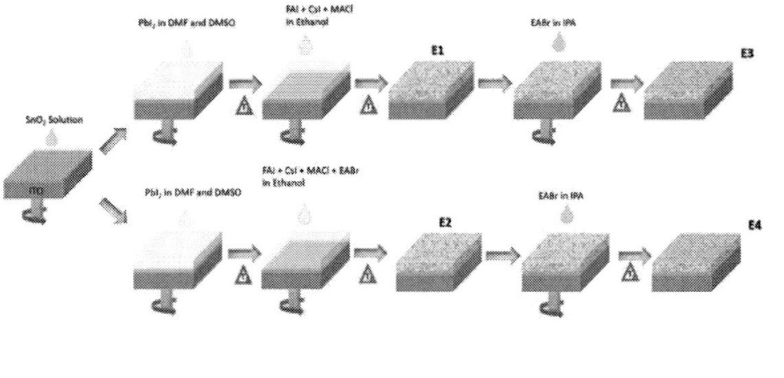

E1 – without an additive and a passivation
E2 – with EABr additive only
E3 – with EABr passivation only
E4 – with EABr both as an additive and a passivation

Grains and defects (SEM, AFM, XRD)

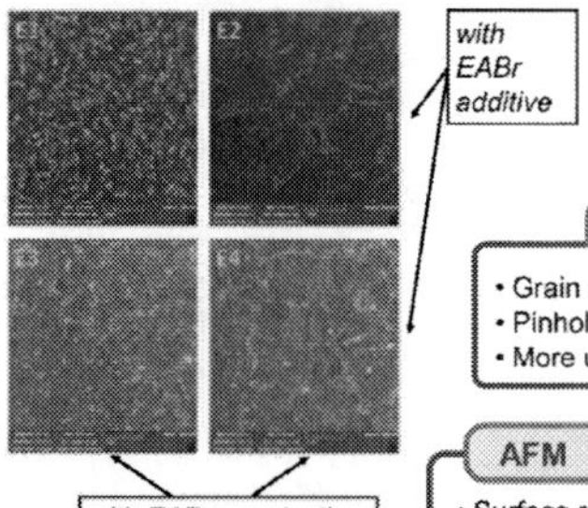

Average crystal size	
E1 ≈ 0.3 µm	E2 ≈ 1.0 µm
E3 ≈ 0.5 µm	E4 ≈ 1.2 µm

SEM
- Grain size ↑
- Pinholes ↓
- More uniform film

AFM
- Surface roughness ↓
- Better interface contact
- Fewer shunt paths

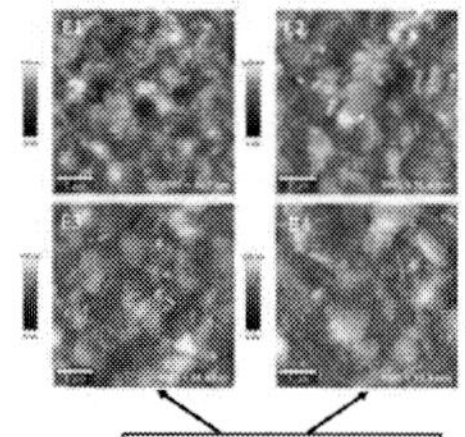

XRD
- Stronger, sharper peaks
- Improved crystallinity
- Enhanced phase purity
- Higher structural stability and reproducibility

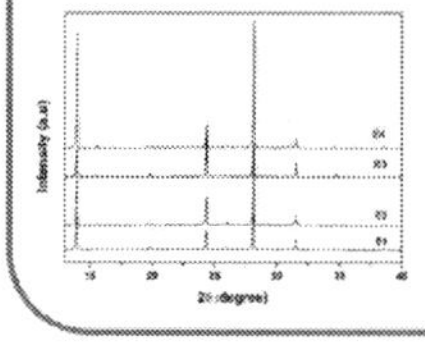

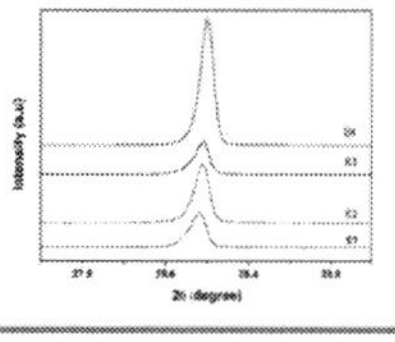

Longer Carrier Lifetime (TRPL)

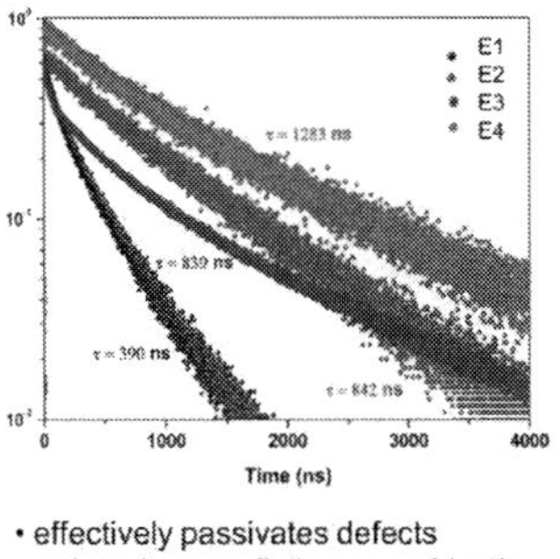

- effectively passivates defects
- reduced non-radiative recombination

Efficiency and stability gains with EABr (J–V Results)

Efficiency

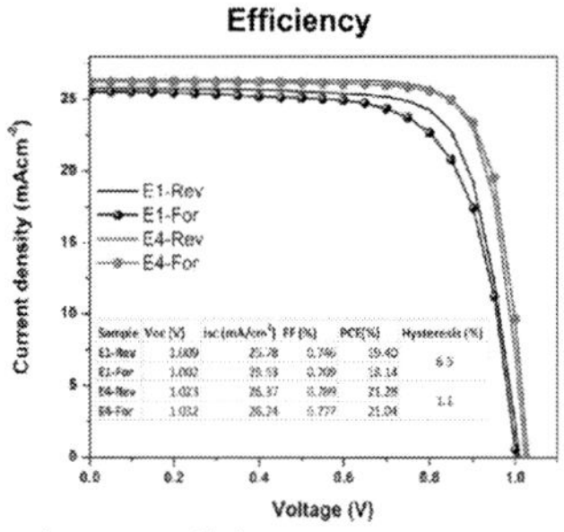

- improves efficiency
- strongly suppresses hysteresis

Stability (1 month test)

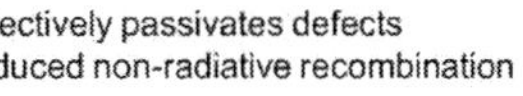

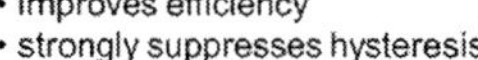

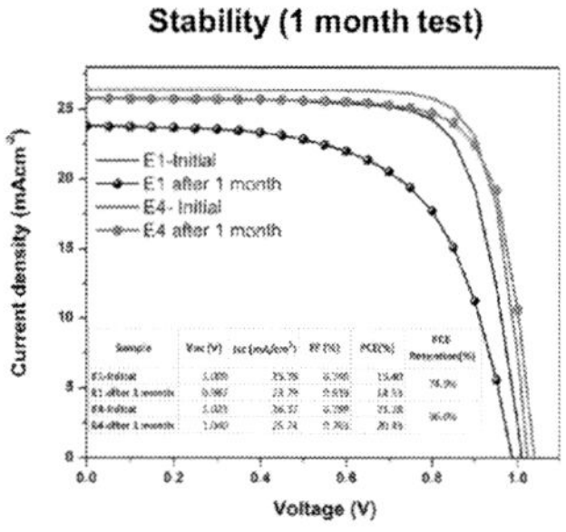

- EABr strongly suppresses long-term degradation

ACKNOWLEDGMENT:
We acknowledge Czech Science Foundation project 23-06543S and CTU student grant SGS24/135/OHK3/3T/13

References:
[1] Yan, Genghua, et al. "Visualizing performances losses of perovskite solar cells and modules: from laboratory to industrial scales." Advanced Energy Materials 15.3 (2025): 2403706.
[2] Guo, Zhendong, et al. "Understanding defects in perovskite solar cells through computation: current knowledge and future challenge." Advanced Science 11.20 (2024): 2305799.

EUPVSEC Bilbao 22.-26. 9. 2025

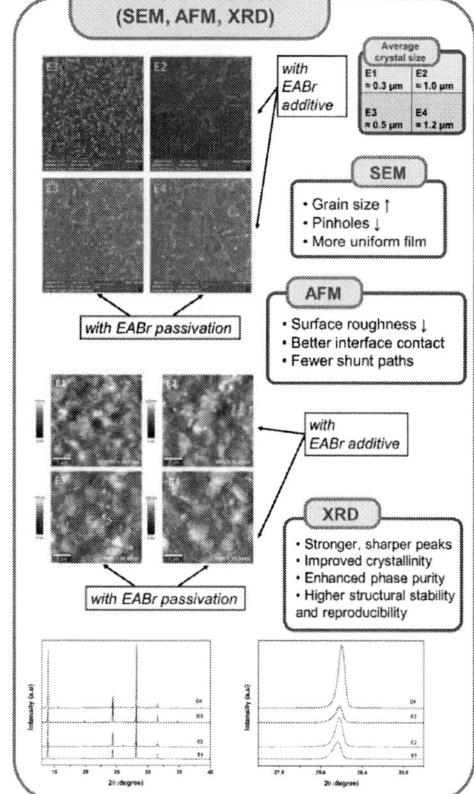

Long-Term Degradation Analysis of Perovskite Solar Cells Over Three Years

Mohammad Istiaque Hossain*, Yongfeng Tong, Brahim Aissa
Qatar Environment and Energy Research Institute (QEERI), Hamad Bin Khalifa University (HBKU), Qatar Foundation, P.O. Box 34110, Doha, Qatar
*E-mail: mhossain@hbku.edu.qa

ABSTRACT: Power-conversion efficiencies (PCEs) in perovskite solar cells (PSCs) have risen to levels that now rival established photovoltaic technologies. Yet translation to market hinges not on peak efficiency alone, but on rigorous demonstrations of operational and long-term stability. The literature remains fragmented: many stability studies are short in duration, poorly harmonized, and therefore difficult to compare or interpret. Because PSCs possess materials properties and degradation pathways distinct from conventional semiconductors, their durability may need to be assessed against adapted, technology-specific criteria rather than by direct analogy. Here we examine the influence of storage on PSC aging over a three-year horizon. Devices with the architecture glass/FTO/compact-TiO_2/mesoporous-TiO_2/perovskite/Spiro-OMeTAD/Au were fabricated and stored in nitrogen gloveboxes under inert atmosphere. Despite the ostensibly benign conditions, ToF-SIMS and XRD analyses reveal progressive layer disintegration that correlates with a decline in PCE from an initial ~17% to ~8% after three years. A salient feature of the aging process is the time-dependent diffusion of lead species toward the metallic back contact, which emerges as a dominant pathway for interfacial degradation. Complementary photoluminescence measurements show pronounced emission quenching in the perovskite layer, consistent with the formation of nonradiative recombination centers associated with ion migration. Taken together, these results underscore the need for stability protocols that capture PSC-specific failure modes, especially interfacial evolution and ion-driven defect formation, even under inert storage. By clarifying how materials transport and interface chemistry govern performance loss over multi-year timescales, this study provides actionable guidance for lifetime engineering and the reliable scale-up of PSC technology toward commercialization.

1 INTRODUCTION

Halide perovskites have emerged as compelling semiconductors for high-performance optoelectronic devices, owing to their exceptional combination of strong light absorption, long carrier diffusion lengths, defect tolerance, and facile, low-temperature processing [1–5]. These attributes have propelled rapid gains in device metrics—most notably the remarkable rise in power-conversion efficiency (PCE) for perovskite solar cells (PSCs) over the past decade—placing the technology squarely in contention with incumbent photovoltaics. Yet, the same soft, ionic nature that enables such impressive optoelectronic behavior also renders perovskites vulnerable to environmental and operational stressors. Oxygen, ambient moisture, and sustained photon flux can trigger phase instabilities and stoichiometric drift, while thermal cycling and built-in fields encourage mobile ionic species to redistribute within the device stack [1–5]. Together, these processes complicate lifetime predictions and impede reliable scale-up.

A central durability concern arises from light-induced redox chemistry and field-assisted ion migration. Even in the absence of an applied bias, continuous illumination generates quasi-steady-state carrier populations and local electrochemical potentials that can drive halide migration, A-site reorganization, and metal/halide interdiffusion. In lead-based compositions, the presence of Pb species further introduces possible pathways for defect formation and interfacial reactions under persistent sunlight and electrical stress, accelerating performance loss [1–5]. Considerable insight has been gained into degradation mechanisms within the perovskite absorber itself, spanning photo-oxidation, halide segregation, and lattice decomposition [6–8], but translating those materials-level findings into robust device-level guidance still demands a systematic account of storage conditions, interfacial chemistry, and the coupled dynamics of ions and carriers across the full stack.

In this work, we focus on a representative $FAMAPbI_3$ perovskite solar cell architecture to disentangle how storage and illumination shape long-term stability in the absence of external electrical bias. By isolating the contributions of dark storage versus controlled light exposure, we delineate the role of non-equilibrium carriers and mobile ions in driving slow, cumulative changes at and near the top surface of the perovskite film[10–12]. Over time, we observe that photo-generated carrier populations and the drift of lead-related ionic species to the illuminated interface foster defect formation, precipitate surface reconstruction, and erode radiative efficiency, degradations that ultimately manifest as declines in open-circuit voltage, fill factor, and PCE [13–15].

Our approach emphasizes a device-centric perspective: storage state (ambient vs. inert, dark vs. illuminated), thermal history, and interfacial energetics are treated as co-equal variables alongside materials composition. By coupling structural and chemical probes with optical and electrical diagnostics, the study maps a coherent pathway from ion-/carrier-driven microstructural evolution to macroscopic performance decay. The resulting framework complements prior absorber-focused mechanistic studies [6–8] and offers practical guidance for stabilizing PSCs: tailoring interfaces to suppress ionic accumulation, engineering barriers to metal/halide interdiffusion, and defining stability protocols that reflect the technology's unique, illumination-activated degradation modes. We anticipate that these insights will aid researchers and engineers in designing storage, encapsulation, and operating regimes that extend device lifetime, thereby smoothing the path from laboratory demonstrations to durable, bankable perovskite photovoltaics.

2 METHODOLOGY

Fluorine-doped tin oxide (FTO)–coated glass substrates were sequentially cleaned three times by ultrasonication in soapy water, deionized (DI) water, and isopropyl alcohol (IPA), 15 min per bath. The rear (non-conductive) sides were masked with adhesive tape. To define the active area, one edge of the FTO was selectively etched using 4 M HCl in the presence of zinc powder, after which the substrates were thoroughly rinsed with DI water and dried under nitrogen. A compact TiO_2 layer was deposited by dip-coating twice from a precursor prepared by mixing 6 mL titanium diisopropoxide bis(acetylacetonate) with 54 mL IPA. The coated substrates were first dried/annealed at 200 °C for 10 min, followed by a high-temperature anneal at 450 °C for 30 min. A mesoporous TiO_2 layer based on ~30 nm particles was applied by spin coating. A dispersion was prepared by mixing 150 mg of TiO_2 paste (Dyesol 30 NR-D) with 1 mL ethanol. The slurry was spin-coated at 4000 rpm for 20 s with an acceleration ramp of 2000 rpm s^{-1}. (Subsequent thermal steps followed the compact-layer schedule above.) The perovskite precursor solution was prepared by dissolving PbI_2 (508 mg mL^{-1}), methylammonium iodide (MAI; 67.1 mg), and formamidinium iodide (FAI; 180.5 mg) in 1.0 mL of solvent (DMF:DMSO = 800:200 µL). Films were deposited using a two-step spin program: 1000 rpm for 10 s, then 4000 rpm for 30 s. During the second step, 300 µL chlorobenzene was dispensed onto the spinning substrate 20 s before the end of the program to promote smooth film formation.Completed devices had the stack: glass/FTO/compact-TiO_2/mesoporous TiO_2/perovskite/Spiro-OMeTAD/Au.

3 RESULTS AND DISCUSSIONS

Devices with the architecture glass/FTO/c-TiO_2/m-TiO_2/perovskite/Spiro-OMeTAD/Au exhibited strong initial performance, with Jsc = 22.26 mA cm^{-2}, Voc = 1.054 V, FF = 71.6%, yielding a PCE = 16.78%. The short-circuit current density integrated from the EQE spectrum agreed with the current–voltage (I–V) measurement (within experimental uncertainty), confirming optical–electrical consistency. Under nominally inert storage (N_2-filled desiccator), devices nevertheless showed a pronounced efficiency loss over time: Jsc fell to 15.10 mA cm^{-2} while Voc remained near 1.054 V at intermediate aging, indicative of transport and collection penalties (and likely FF erosion) preceding any major change in quasi-Fermi-level splitting. After three years, samples measured either in ambient air or in desiccators without continuous nitrogen purge displayed ohmic I–V characteristics, consistent with catastrophic shunting attributed to time-dependent ionic diffusion and interfacial degradation.

Structural and morphological probes tracked this evolution from intact to aged states. XRD patterns collected over three years showed reflections at 14.8°, 20.0°, 28.1°, and 40.1°, assigned to the (110), (200), (220), and (224) planes of the tetragonal perovskite phase, respectively. Notably, PbI_2 signatures intensified most strongly in N_2-stored devices, whereas air-stored films exhibited diminished perovskite crystallinity and the emergence of the δ-$FAPbI_3$ (yellow, non-perovskite) phase, pointing to distinct degradation pathways under dry-inert versus humid/oxygenated conditions. Cross-sectional SEM of pristine devices revealed uniform, dense, and continuous layers; aged cross-sections showed interfacial roughening, local voiding, and film discontinuities consistent with diffusion-driven delamination and phase segregation.

Spectroscopic diagnostics corroborated the microstructural picture. PL spectra exhibited strong quenching with aging, evidencing the growth of nonradiative recombination channels associated with defect formation and interfacial disorder. Depth-resolved chemical analyses by ToF-SIMS and XPS demonstrated elemental redistribution across the stack, implicating halide and metal species transport (including Pb-related ions) through the TiO_2/perovskite/Spiro-OMeTAD interfaces. The chemical gradients and intermixing captured by depth profiling align with the observed transition from diode-like to ohmic behavior, as migrating ions lower interfacial barriers, dope transport layers locally, and eventually form conductive pathways.

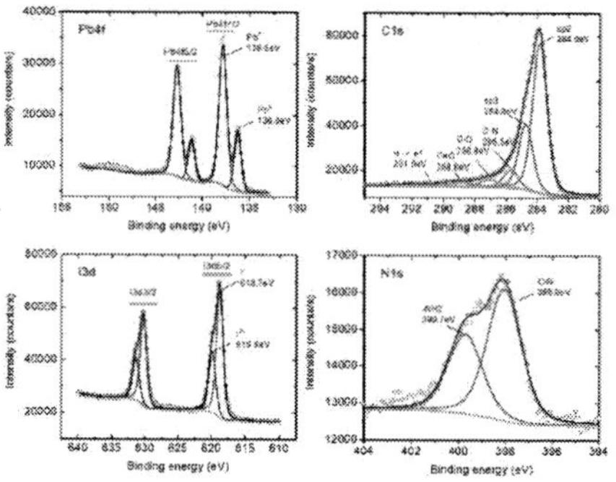

Figure 1: X-ray Photoelectron Spectroscopy (XPS) analysis of the perovskite films. The spectra reveal the characteristic elemental states and interfacial chemical interactions within the device stack. Distinct peaks corresponding to Pb^{2+}, I^{2-}, PbO, and IO_2^- species are observed, evidencing partial oxidation of iodine and the formation of lead oxides. The evolution of these features with increasing depth indicates strong interfacial reactions between the perovskite absorber and the underlying TiO_2 layer, leading to the gradual decomposition of the perovskite lattice and the emergence of metallic Pb at deeper regions. These findings highlight the critical role of interfacial chemistry in governing the stability and degradation pathways of perovskite materials.

10.4229/EUPVSEC2025/2CV.3.47

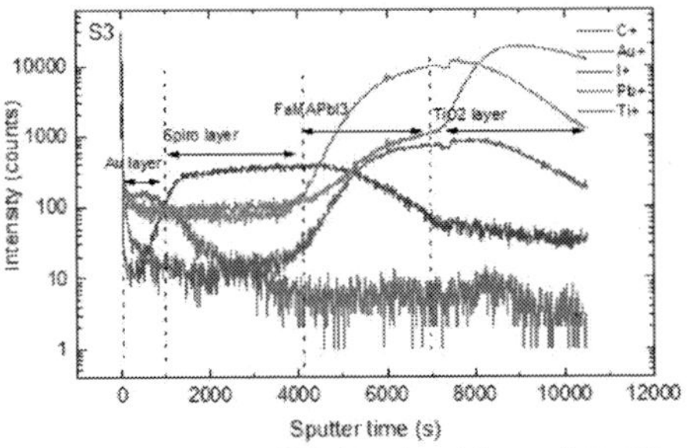

Figure 2: Time-of-Flight Secondary Ion Mass Spectrometry (ToF-SIMS) analysis of the perovskite devices. The depth profiles illustrate the elemental distribution and diffusion behavior across the multilayer device architecture. Noticeable variations in the Pb/I ratio, along with the migration of iodine ions toward the surface and lead diffusion across the interfacial regions, are evident after prolonged operation or environmental exposure. This ionic redistribution disrupts the stoichiometric balance of the perovskite layer, facilitating the formation of secondary non-perovskite phases such as lead iodide hydrates. The observed interdiffusion between layers underscores the dynamic nature of ion transport within the device stack and its pivotal contribution to structural degradation, compositional instability, and the eventual decline in photovoltaic performance.

Photoluminescence (PL) analyses revealed a progressive quenching of emission intensity over time, attributed to an increased density of trap states, accelerated charge-carrier recombination, and the migration of lead and halide ions toward non-radiative recombination centers. Complementary X-ray photoelectron spectroscopy (XPS) depth profiling identified the presence of Pb^{2+}, I^{2-}, PbO, and IO_2^- species, confirming iodine oxidation and strong interfacial interactions with the TiO_2 scaffold at deeper layers. These observations point to the gradual disintegration of the perovskite lattice into metallic lead. Time-of-Flight Secondary Ion Mass Spectrometry (ToF-SIMS) further revealed variations in the Pb/I ratio, extensive elemental interdiffusion across device layers, and pronounced iodine migration toward the surface. This ionic redistribution disrupted the stoichiometry and facilitated the emergence of non-perovskite secondary phases, including lead iodide hydrates. Collectively, these results demonstrate that ion migration, lattice distortion, and environmental stressors act synergistically to degrade the perovskite structure—manifested as a drastic decline in power conversion efficiency (PCE) from 17% to 8% within two years, accompanied by structural decomposition and elevated defect formation. Mitigating ionic migration thus remains pivotal to ensuring the long-term operational stability and performance of perovskite solar cells.

4 CONCLUSIONS

Ion migration in halide perovskites remains a central bottleneck to device reliability. In this study, we present a multi-year degradation analysis of n–i–p perovskite solar cells with the architecture glass/FTO/compact-TiO_2/mesoporous-TiO_2/perovskite/Spiro-OMeTAD/Au. The crystalline structure and surface morphology of the as-fabricated devices were verified by X-ray diffraction (XRD) and scanning electron microscopy (SEM). Over a two-year period, the power-conversion efficiency (PCE) declined from ~17% to ~8%, accompanied by a pronounced quenching of the photoluminescence (PL) emission—signatures consistent with the emergence of nonradiative recombination pathways and an increased defect density in the perovskite absorber. Depth-resolved chemical analyses using time-of-flight secondary ion mass spectrometry (ToF-SIMS) and X-ray photoelectron spectroscopy (XPS) reveal progressive elemental redistribution across the transport and absorber layers, indicating interlayer diffusion consistent with ion migration processes. Taken together, the electrical, optical, structural, and compositional data delineate a coherent degradation pathway driven by slow ionic motion and interfacial evolution. The work provides a rigorous long-term assessment of perovskite material stability at the device level and highlights the need for diffusion-blocking interfaces, robust encapsulation, and stability protocols tailored to the unique ionics of halide perovskites.

5 REFERENCES

[1] F. H. Isikgor, S. Zhumagali, L. V. T. Merino, M. De Bastiani, I. McCulloch, and S. De Wolf, "Molecular engineering of contact interfaces for high-performance perovskite solar cells," *Nature Reviews Materials*, vol. 8, no. 2, pp. 89–108, 2023.

[2] A. S. R. Bati, Y. L. Zhong, P. L. Burn, M. K. Nazeeruddin, P. E. Shaw, and M. Batmunkh, "Next-generation applications for integrated perovskite solar cells," *Communications Materials*, vol. 4, no. 1, p. 2, 2023.

[3] D. Yu, F. Cao, C. Su, and G. Xing, "Exploring, identifying, and removing the efficiency-limiting factor of mixed-dimensional 2D/3D perovskite solar cells," *Accounts of Chemical Research*, 2023, pp. 14558–145.

[4] T. Nie, Z. Fang, X. Ren, Y. Duan, and S. Liu, "Recent advances in wide-bandgap organic–inorganic halide perovskite solar cells and tandem application," *Nano-Micro Letters*, vol. 15, no. 1, p. 70, 2023.

[5] S. Liu, V. P. Biju, Y. Qi, W. Chen, and Z. Liu, "Recent progress in the development of high-efficiency inverted perovskite solar cells," *NPG Asia Materials*, vol. 15, no. 1, p. 27, 2023.

[6] M. I. Hossain, B. Aïssa, A. Samara, S. A. Mansour, C. A. Broussillou, and V. Bermudez Benito, *ACS Omega*, vol. 6, no. 8, pp. 5276–5286, 2021.

[7] L. L. Lebel, B. Aïssa, M. A. El Khakani, and D. Therriault, *Composites Science and Technology*, vol. 70, no. 3, pp. 518–524, 2010.

[8] W. Julia, C. Luis, R. Federico, *et al.*, *Advanced Functional Materials*, vol. 23, pp. 5591–5598, 2013.

[9] D. T. H. Dalir, R. D. Farahani, V. Nhim, and B. Aïssa, *et al.*, *Langmuir*, vol. 28, no. 1, pp. 791–803, 2011.

[10] A. Ali, F. El-Mellouhi, A. Mitra, and B. Aïssa, *Nanomaterials*, vol. 12, no. 5, p. 788, 2022.

[11] R. D. Farahani, D. T. H. Dalir, V. Le Borgne, A. Loick, *et al.*, *Composites Science and Technology*, vol. 72, no. 12, pp. 1387–1395, 2012.

[12] N. M. H. Gavi, B. D. Ngom, A. C. Beye, A. M. Strydom, B. Aïssa, V. V. Srinivasu, and M. Chaker, *Journal of Magnetism and Magnetic Materials*, vol. 324, no. 6, pp. 1172–1176, 2012.
[13] B. Aïssa and M. A. El Khakani, *Nanotechnology*, vol. 20, no. 17, p. 175203, 2009.
[14] M. A. Habib, M. Barkat, B. Aïssa, and T. Denidni, *Progress in Electromagnetics Research*, vol. 88, pp. 135–148, 2008.
[15] H. Zhao, H. Kimura, Z. Cheng, X. Wang, and T. Nishida, *Applied Physics Letters*, vol. 95, p. 232904, 2009. https://doi.org/10.1063/1.3271032.

ENHANCING SEMI-TRANSPARENT PEROVSKITE SOLAR CELL EFFICIENCY IN HARSH ENVIRONMENTS WITH SiO_2/ITO TRANSPARENT CONTACTS AND ANTI-SOILING COATINGS

Mohammad Istiaque Hossain*, Yongfeng Tong, Brahim Aissa
Qatar Environment and Energy Research Institute (QEERI), Hamad Bin Khalifa University (HBKU), Qatar Foundation, P.O. Box 34110, Doha, Qatar
*E-mail: mhossain@hbku.edu.qa

ABSTRACT: Indium tin oxide (ITO) thin films remain the cornerstone among transparent conductive oxides (TCOs) for semi-transparent perovskite solar cells (ST-PSCs), where high optical transparency and electrical conductivity are essential for efficient light harvesting and charge transport. However, conventional ITO processing typically requires high-temperature (>200 °C) annealing to achieve sufficient crystallinity, carrier mobility, and film densification. Such thermal dependence restricts their use on heat-sensitive or flexible substrates, posing a major limitation for scalable device integration and next-generation building-integrated photovoltaics (BIPVs). In this study, we demonstrate a room-temperature RF magnetron sputtering approach to fabricate SiO_2/ITO bilayer transparent electrodes with finely controlled structural, optical, and electronic characteristics. The SiO_2 overlayer functions as both a protective and optical-engineering layer, enhancing light transmission, minimizing surface defects, and imparting hydrophilic, anti-soiling behavior, crucial for maintaining optical clarity and stability under real-world environmental exposure. The underlying ITO film, optimized through precise control of sputtering pressure and RF power, exhibits superior crystallinity and uniform grain morphology even without post-deposition annealing. Comprehensive analyses using Hall effect measurements, X-ray diffraction (XRD), X-ray photoelectron spectroscopy (XPS), transmission electron microscopy (TEM), and atomic force microscopy (AFM) confirm the films' outstanding quality. The optimized SiO_2/ITO structures deliver an average optical transmittance of ~91% in the 400–1000 nm range, a sheet resistance below 45 Ω sq^{-1}, and a surface roughness under 1 nm, underscoring their excellent trade-off between transparency and conductivity. These results establish a scalable, energy-efficient, and substrate-independent route for producing high-performance transparent electrodes suitable for flexible, semi-transparent perovskite solar cells and other optoelectronic devices, enabling the transition toward low-temperature, sustainable photovoltaic manufacturing.

1 INTRODUCTION

Semi-transparent solar cells (ST-SCs) represent a rapidly emerging class of photovoltaic devices that combine light transmission and electrical power generation, enabling their integration into architectural elements such as building façades, smart windows, greenhouses, and tandem photovoltaic modules. Their dual functionality positions them at the forefront of next-generation energy-harvesting and daylight-management systems, where both aesthetic transparency and energy conversion efficiency are paramount.The performance and stability of ST-SCs are critically determined by the quality of their transparent conductive electrodes (TCEs), which must simultaneously exhibit high optical transmittance, low sheet resistance, strong mechanical adhesion, and chemical durability. Among available TCEs, indium tin oxide (ITO) remains the benchmark material owing to its high carrier mobility, wide optical bandgap (~3.5–4.0 eV), and excellent transparency across the visible and near-infrared spectra. However, conventional ITO deposition typically requires high-temperature (>300 °C) annealing, which restricts its application to heat-sensitive substrates such as polymers or hybrid perovskite layers. This thermal limitation has hindered the scalability of flexible and large-area semi-transparent perovskite solar cells (ST-PSCs).

In this study, we report a room-temperature RF magnetron sputtering approach for the fabrication of SiO_2/ITO bilayer transparent electrodes, designed to function as dual-purpose optical and electrical interfaces for ST-PSCs operating under ambient conditions. The SiO_2 capping layer serves multiple critical roles: it acts as an anti-reflective coating, enhances light incoupling, and imparts anti-soiling, self-cleaning, and environmental protection capabilities, thereby improving both optical performance and long-term durability in harsh environments. Furthermore, the SiO_2 overlayer mitigates surface defect density and promotes uniform energy band alignment at the perovskite interface, suppressing charge recombination and enhancing device stability. Meanwhile, the underlying ITO layer, deposited under optimized low-pressure (2 mTorr) and moderate RF power conditions, ensures efficient charge transport and optical transparency exceeding 85%, with a sheet resistance as low as ~45 Ω sq^{-1}. The resulting SiO_2/ITO stacks exhibit smooth, compact morphologies (AFM roughness < 1 nm) and high structural integrity without any post-deposition annealing. This low-temperature process therefore enables scalable, cost-effective fabrication of flexible, lightweight, and high-efficiency ST-PSCs, suitable for deployment in real-world building-integrated photovoltaics and adaptive energy-harvesting systems.

2 METHODOLOGY

At room temperature (RT), metal–oxide thin films were deposited via reactive electron-beam (e-beam) evaporation using a Denton™ system. The deposition was conducted under a base pressure of approximately 2×10^{-4} Torr, with an oxygen flow rate of 20 sccm and a growth rate of 1 Å/s, ensuring uniform layer formation and controlled stoichiometry. The optical properties of the resulting films were characterized using UV–Vis spectrophotometry (PerkinElmer Lambda™), enabling precise assessment of

transmittance and absorption across the visible spectrum. Krüss™ contact angle measurements were employed to evaluate surface wettability and infer the degree of hydrophilicity or hydrophobicity of the coatings. Surface topology and roughness were analyzed using a Dektak™ 3D stylus profilometer, providing quantitative thickness and morphology data.
Microstructural and morphological features were further investigated by field emission scanning electron microscopy (FESEM, JEOL 7610™), revealing surface texture and grain distribution at high resolution. Finally, X-ray photoelectron spectroscopy (XPS) was employed to determine the elemental composition, oxidation states, and chemical bonding environments within the films, offering comprehensive insights into their structural and electronic characteristics.

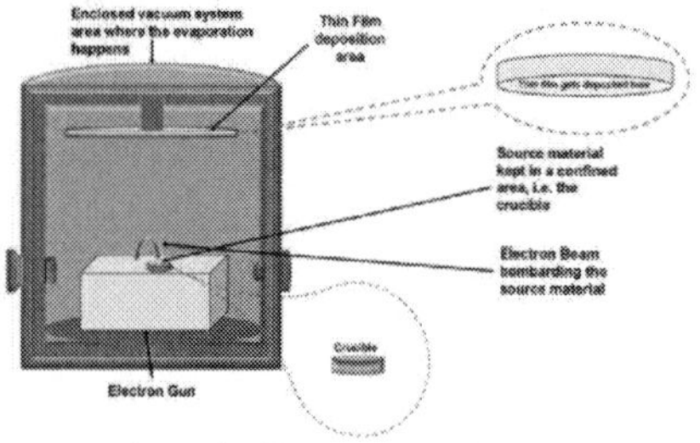

Figure 1: Schematic illustration of the RF magnetron sputtering deposition chamber used for SiO_2/ITO thin-film fabrication. The system comprises independently controlled SiO_2 and ITO targets, a rotating substrate holder to ensure uniform film thickness, and an oxygen–argon reactive gas inlet maintaining a constant flow of 20 sccm. The base pressure was maintained at 2×10^{-4} Torr, and deposition was performed at room temperature with a growth rate of 1 Å s^{-1}. The configuration allows precise control of plasma parameters, enabling low-temperature deposition of highly transparent, conductive oxide layers.

3 RESULTS AND DISCUSSIONS

Room-temperature sputtered indium tin oxide (ITO) films exhibited a dominant (222) diffraction peak centered around 31°, accompanied by secondary reflections consistent with the cubic bixbyite phase of In_2O_3. Depositions conducted under low argon pressure (2 mTorr) and moderate RF power (100–200 W) produced a marked enhancement in the (222) peak intensity, signifying improved crystallinity and enlarged grain domains—key contributors to higher electrical conductivity and optical transparency. X-ray photoelectron spectroscopy (XPS) confirmed the formation of highly pure, stoichiometric oxides with negligible carbon contamination. Both the 2 mTorr and 10 mTorr depositions displayed stable oxygen incorporation ($SiO_{1.91}$ for SiO_2), and the measured work function of ~3.94 eV indicated excellent electronic alignment for optoelectronic interfaces. Deconvolution of the XPS spectra revealed distinct and well-resolved In 3d, Sn 3d, O 1s, and Si 2p peaks, confirming precise stoichiometric control and chemical purity across all compositions. Optical analyses via UV–Vis–NIR spectroscopy demonstrated an average transmittance exceeding 85% for the 2 mTorr films, with lower RF power favoring the highest transparency and minimal absorption losses. A clear thickness-dependent trade-off emerged: thinner layers enhanced visible transparency, whereas thicker ones yielded improved electrical conductivity, reflecting the intrinsic balance between optical and electrical performance. Surface characterization further highlighted the influence of process parameters. Films grown at low pressure (2 mTorr) and low RF power exhibited smaller contact angles and atomic force microscopy (AFM) roughness values below 1 nm, indicating exceptionally smooth, compact, and hydrophilic surfaces—highly advantageous for self-cleaning and anti-fouling functionalities. In contrast, increasing deposition pressure and power led to rougher morphologies, enlarged grains, and higher hydrophobicity, revealing the delicate interplay between plasma energy, adatom mobility, and surface texture.

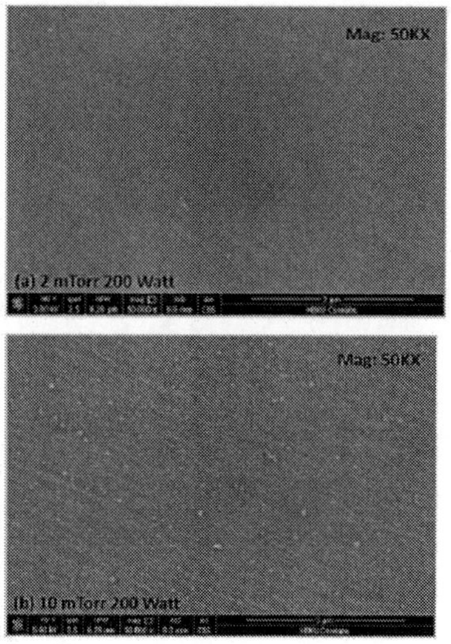

Figure 2: FESEM micrographs of ITO thin films deposited at two different sputtering pressures. At low pressure (2 mTorr), the film exhibits a dense, compact, and uniform granular structure with well-defined boundaries, indicative of enhanced adatom mobility and improved crystallinity. In contrast, deposition at higher pressure (10 mTorr) results in a rougher and less homogeneous surface, characterized by larger, irregular grains and increased porosity due to enhanced scattering and reduced kinetic energy of arriving species. These morphological differences directly influence the films' optical transparency, conductivity, and wetting behavior.

Probing the nanoscale architecture of our films, we found that the room-temperature sputtering process yields a crystalline structure of remarkable integrity. High-resolution TEM analysis revealed dense and sharply defined and ITO layers, with clear lattice fringes throughout the ITO bulk indicating a high-quality crystalline formation. This visual evidence was solidified by SAED patterns, which confirmed the film's structure as the highly conductive cubic bixbyite phase. We discovered that the key to this structural excellence lies in gentle deposition conditions,low pressure and low power—which promote the growth of large, well-aligned grains with minimal defects. This superior microstructure is the very foundation of the exceptional properties achieved, directly linking the atomic arrangement to the film's macroscopic function. Electrically, the films are powerful n-type conductors, boasting a high free carrier concentration on the order of magnitude. By carefully tuning the process to a low pressure of 2 mTorr and a moderate RF power, we optimized the interplay between carrier concentration and mobility, achieving a state-of-the-art resistivity of 2.79 10 Ω·cm and a high carrier mobility of 35.5 $cm^2/V\cdot s$. Deviating from this optimum, for instance by increasing RF power, introduces a critical trade-off: while the creation of more oxygen vacancies boosts the carrier concentration and thus conductivity, it simultaneously degrades mobility due to increased electron scattering at grain boundaries, ultimately hindering overall performance. This deep understanding allows for the deliberate engineering of TCOs with tailored, superior properties for the most demanding applications.

4 CONCLUSIONS

This investigation unveils a facile and scalable RF magnetron sputtering methodology for the fabrication of robust transparent conductive electrodes, specifically designed for next-generation optoelectronics destined for harsh environmental deployment. By forgoing conventional high-temperature annealing, we have successfully synthesized a durable silicon dioxide/indium tin oxide () bilayer at room temperature. The deposition, meticulously controlled at a low pressure of 2 mTorr and a moderate RF power between 100–200 W, yields films possessing an exceptional synergy of properties: a luminous optical transmittance of approximately 90%, a low sheet resistance of ~, and an exquisitely smooth surface topography with an AFM-measured roughness below one nanometer. The strategically deposited overlayer serves as a multifunctional vanguard, imparting anti-reflective, protective, and self-cleaning characteristics. This capping layer demonstrates remarkable resilience against ultraviolet degradation, humidity ingress, and dust accumulation, thereby preserving pristine optical clarity over extended periods. Ultimately, these findings illuminate a pathway toward developing high-performance, mechanically flexible, and environmentally resilient transparent conductive electrodes, poised to significantly enhance the durability and efficiency of devices such as perovskite solar cells operating in challenging outdoor conditions.

5 REFERENCES

[1] Z. Ying, et al., "Sputtered indium-zinc oxide for buffer layer free semitransparent perovskite photovoltaic devices in perovskite/silicon 4T-tandem solar cells," Advanced Materials Interfaces, vol. 8, 2020, Article 2001604.
[2] B. Shi, et al., "Semitransparent perovskite solar cells: From materials and devices to applications," Advanced Materials, vol. 32, 2020, Article 1806474.
[3] S. An, et al., "Cerium-doped indium oxide transparent electrode for semi-transparent perovskite and perovskite/silicon tandem solar cells," Solar Energy, vol. 196, pp. 409–418, 2020.
[4] F. Kurdesau, et al., "Comparative study of ITO layers deposited by DC and RF magnetron sputtering at room temperature," Journal of Non-Crystalline Solids, vol. 352, pp. 1466–1470, 2006.
[5] K. Wang, et al., "ITO films with different preferred orientations prepared by DC magnetron sputtering," Optical Materials, vol. 134, p. 113040, 2022.
[6] M. I. Hossain, B. Aïssa, A. Samara, S. A. Mansour, C. A. Broussillou, and V. Bermudez Benito, ACS Omega, vol. 6, no. 8, pp. 5276–5286, 2021.
[7] L. L. Lebel, B. Aïssa, M. A. El Khakani, and D. Therriault, Composites Science and Technology, vol. 70, no. 3, pp. 518–524, 2010.
[8] W. Julia, C. Luis, R. Federico, et al., Advanced Functional Materials, vol. 23, pp. 5591–5598, 2013.
[9] D. T. H. Dalir, R. D. Farahani, V. Nhim, and B. Aïssa, et al., Langmuir, vol. 28, no. 1, pp. 791–803, 2011.
[10] A. Ali, F. El-Mellouhi, A. Mitra, and B. Aïssa, Nanomaterials, vol. 12, no. 5, p. 788, 2022.
[11] R. D. Farahani, D. T. H. Dalir, V. Le Borgne, A. Loick, et al., Composites Science and Technology, vol. 72, no. 12, pp. 1387–1395, 2012.
[12] N. M. H. Gavi, B. D. Ngom, A. C. Beye, A. M. Strydom, B. Aïssa, V. V. Srinivasu, and M. Chaker, Journal of Magnetism and Magnetic Materials, vol. 324, no. 6, pp. 1172–1176, 2012.
[13] B. Aïssa and M. A. El Khakani, Nanotechnology, vol. 20, no. 17, p. 175203, 2009.
[14] M. A. Habib, M. Barkat, B. Aïssa, and T. Denidni, Progress in Electromagnetics Research, vol. 88, pp. 135–148, 2008.
[15] H. Zhao, H. Kimura, Z. Cheng, X. Wang, and T. Nishida, Applied Physics Letters, vol. 95, p. 232904, 2009. https://doi.org/10.1063/1.3271032.

STUDY OF THE INFLUENCE OF Pb SUBSTITUTION BY Zn^{2+} IONS ON THE PROPERTIES OF $CsPbBr_{3-x}I_x$ THIN FILMS

G. Gordillo[1], O.G. Torres[1] y Julian C. Pena-Bermudez[2],
[1] Departamento de Física, Universidad Nacional, Bogotá, Colombia
[2] Universidad del Caribe (UNICARIBE), Santo Domingo, Dominican Republic

ABSTRACT: In this work is reported results of a study on optical and structural properties of thin films of cesium lead bromide iodide mixed perovskite ($CsPbBr_{3-x}I_x$), synthesized by sequential evaporation of precursors (CsBr, $PbBr_2$, PbI_2). Thin films of $CsPbBr_{3-x}I_x$ with a high degree of reproducibility of both the molar composition and the photovoltaic properties were achieved, using an electronic system with facilities to control the growth of the samples with the help of PID and PWM algorithms. Special emphasis was put in evaluating the effect that the substitution of the Pb cation by Zn^{2+} ions onto its optical, morphological and structural properties through transmittance, photoluminescence, Scanning Electron Microscopy (SEM) and Urbach Energy measurements.

1. INTRODUCTION

Organic-inorganic hybrid perovskite solar cells have been intensively investigated since their discovery, mainly due to their good optical and electronic properties [1], including high absorption coefficients [2], long carrier diffusion lengths [3] and low trap density [4]. A look made to the certified efficiencies reported in the popular NREL photovoltaic chart (Version 64), shows us some interesting trends [5]. The information associated with this chart reveals the following progress made so far [6]. The first single junction $MAPbI_3$ based solar cell, reported by researchers of EPFL, certified in 2013, had an efficiency of 14.1% [7]. This result motivated the researchers worldwide who put their resources into further improving the PCE of PSCs in order to achieve greater efficiency to compete with Si based PV devices. In a period of ten years, the record efficiency of 26.7% was achieved; this record was reported in 2024 by the University of Science and Technology of China (USTC) [8]. Another remarkable development in Perovskite based solar cells research has arisen in recent years. At the 2024 SNEC Expo in Shanghai, LONGi Green Energy Technology Co., Ltd., announced a major breakthrough in the development of its silicon-perovskite tandem solar cells [9]. According to authoritative certification by the European Solar Test Installation (ESTI), this cell's photovoltaic conversion efficiency has reached 34.6%. This achievement once again breaks the world record for silicon-perovskite tandem cell efficiency previously set by the LONGi team. Despite these progress, the presence of Pb is a major limiting to its commercialization [10]. A good candidate for lead replacement is Zn.

In this work, a study was conducted with the purpose of preparing thin films of $CsPbBr_{3-x}I_x$ using a route that includes sequential evaporation of their precursors ($PbBr_2$/PbI_2/CsBr) followed by annealing under normal environmental conditions. Through XRD, SEM, photoluminescence and spectral transmittance measurements carried out on samples prepared by varying the main synthesis variables (ratio of evaporated masses of precursors, precursor deposition rate and annealing temperature) varied in a wide range, conditions were found to grow thin films with composition $CsPbBr_{2.73}I_{0.27}$ that presented good optical, morphological and structural properties. Additionally, a study was conducted to evaluate the effect that the substitution of the Pb cation by Zn^{2+} ions onto its optical, morphological and structural properties through XRD, SEM, transmittance, photoluminescence and Urbach Energy measurements.

2. EXPERIMENTAL DETAILS

Initially thin films of $CsPbBr_{3-x}I_x$ were prepared by sequential evaporation of its precursors ($PbBr_2$, PbI_2,CsBr), where the chemical composition of the resulting compound is adjusted by varying the thickness ratio of precursors, which is determined with the help of a thickness monitor. Sequential evaporation was performed following a routine that includes initial evaporation of PbI_2 followed by evaporation of $PbBr_2$ and CsBr, keeping their respective deposition rates in the range of 4-6 Å/s. The Precursors are evaporated at room temperature from Knudsen cell-type evaporation sources and after the deposition, these are annealed at normal ambient air conditions at temperatures around 250^{0}C, for 20 minutes. Good reproducibility of both the composition and properties of samples with composition $CsPbBr_{2.73}I_{0.27}$ was achieved using equipment with facilities to control electronically the evaporation temperature and deposition rate of precursors, by means of PID and PWM algorithms. Details of equipment used to prepare the $CsPbBr_{2.73}I_{0.27}$ films is described in a previously published paper (see Ref. [11]), where a similar setup was used to deposit thin films of $MAPbI_3$ by sequential evaporation of precursors. After obtaining conditions to grow thin films with composition $CsPbBr_{2.73}I_{0.27}$, a study was carried out to evaluate the influence that the partial substitution of Pb by Zn^{2+} (obtained by additional evaporation of a layer of ZnBr) produces on the optical and structural properties.

The samples prepared were characterized by means of transmittance and reflectance measurements performed using a Varian–Cary 5000 spectrophotometer, as well as by XRD measurements performed with a Philips X'Pert Pro PANalytical diffractometer, using the radiation Cu-Kα (1.540598 Å), an acceleration voltage of 40 KV and a current 40 mA, and the film thickness was determined using a Veeco Dektak 150 surface profiler. The morphological characterization was performed with an electronic scanning microscope TESCAN, model Vega 3.

3. RESULTS AND DISCUSSION

3.1 Optical characterization

The influence that the substitution of Pb by Zn^{2+} ions on the optical properties of a reference $CsPbBr_{2.73}I_{0.27}$ sample was investigated through photoluminescence, and spectral transmittance and reflectance measurements. The samples were prepared using a route based on sequential evaporation of the precursors (PbI_2, $PbBr_2$, ZnBr, CsBr), described previously.

Fig. 1 shows typical transmittance and reflectance spectra of a reference film with composition $CsPbBr_{2.73}I_{0.27}$ in which Pb was replaced by Zn in percentages varying between 0 and 13%, as well as absorption coefficient (α) vs λ and Tauc $(\alpha h\nu)^2$ vs hν curves. The absorption coefficient was estimated using the relation [12]: $\alpha = -(1/d)\ \ln \frac{T(\lambda)}{1-R(\lambda)}$ and the Eg value was obtained from the intercept with the axis hν of the curve of $(\alpha h\nu)^2$ vs hν.

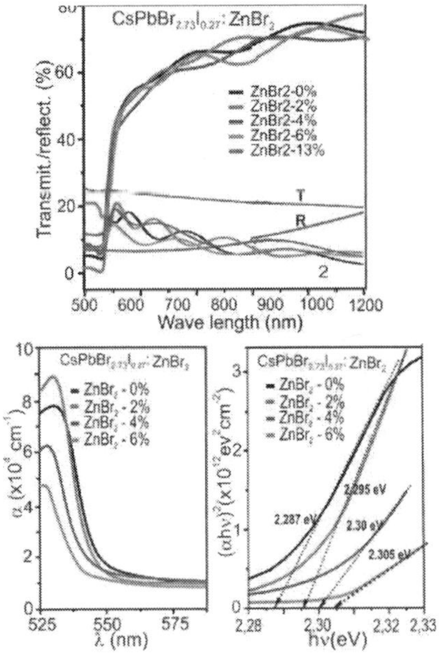

Fig. 1: Transmittance, reflectance, α vs λ and $(\alpha h\nu)^2$ vs hν curves of a reference sample with composition $CsPbBr_{2.73}I_{0.27}$, in which the Pb cation was replaced by Zn in different percentages.

The results in Fig.1 show that the substitution of Pb by Zn at low concentrations has little effect on the energy gap Eg of the $CsPbBr_{2.7}I_{0.27}$ sample, indicating that under these conditions the band structure is not significantly affected; however, when the substitution of Pb by Zn is high (greater than 10%), the transmittance decreases strongly and interference maxima and minima are not observed, indicating that this type of samples present a high degree of crystalline disorder that gives rise to high dispersion of the incident radiation that destroys the coherence of the rays that overlap to generate constructive interference. On the other hand, it is observed that the slope of the transmittance curves is slightly affected when Pb is substituted by Zn; this behavior can be explained by assuming that the substitution of Pb by Zn generates structural defects because the ionic radius of Pb (1.20 Å) is quite larger than that of Zinc (0.74Å); this situation generates band tail states within the gap that cause this decrease in the slope of the transmittance curves.

To evaluate the effect of the percentage of Pb by Zn substitution on the structural disorder in the perovskite films, the Urbach energy E_U, was calculated from the α vs λ curves near the band edge, using the relation $\alpha_U = \alpha_0 exp\left[\frac{h\nu - E_I}{Eu}\right]$ [13]. Where E_U is the Urbach Energy, E_I and α_0 are constant. Thus, a plot of ln(α) vs. hν should be linear and Urbach Energy can be obtained from the slope.

In Fig. 2 is shown , ln(α) vs hν curves (near the band edge) of a perovskite sample with composition $CsPbBr_{2.7}I_{0.27}$ in which Pb was substituted by Zn in a percentage that varied between 0 and 6% are presented; the E_U value calculated from the slopes of the ln(α) vs hν curves is shown in inset of Fig. 2; the E_U value obtained is less than 44 meV for samples in which Pb was substituted by Zn in a percentage ≤ 4%, indicating that they exhibit good crystalline quality; on the contrary, when a high Pb by Zn substitution is made (≥ 6%) the E_U value increases strongly, indicating that this case presents high structural disorder.

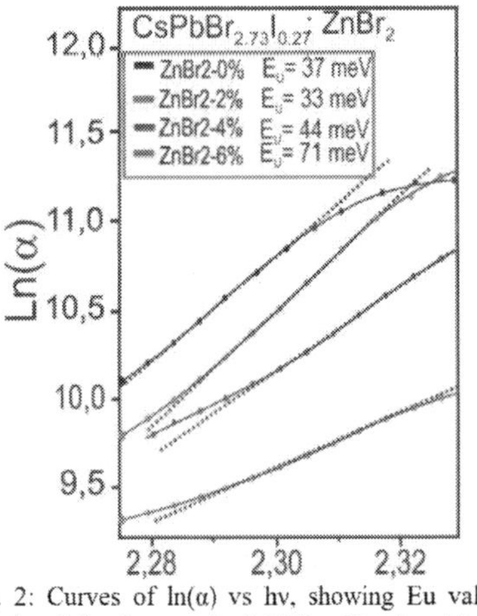

Fig. 2: Curves of ln(α) vs hν, showing Eu values calculated for the sample $CsPbBr_{2.7}I0_{.27}$ in which Pb was replaced by Zn in a percentage that varied between 0 and 6%.

The influence of replacing the Pb cation by Zn on the photoluminescence (FL) emitted by a $CsPbBr_{2.73}I_{0.27}$ sample was also studied in this work. Fig. 3 shows typical FL emission spectra of a $CsPbBr_{2.73}I_{0.27}$ thin film in which Pb was replaced by Zn in percentages ranging from 0 to 6%. These results show that the substitution of Pb by Zn slightly affects the optical gap of the $CsPbBr_{2.73}I_{0.27}$ film, results that agree with those previously obtained from the Tauc curves. It can also be observed that the FL spectrum of films prepared by replacing Pb by Zn in percentages lower than 4% is quite symmetrical, but this symmetry is lost when the substitution of Pb by Zn is increased to percentages higher than 4%. This behavior could be explained by assuming that the emission produced by samples prepared by replacing Pb with Zn in percentages less than 4% is mainly due to fundamental transition between states of the conduction and valence bands, while samples prepared by replacing Pb with Zn in higher percentages emit, in addition to fundamental radiation, radiation induced by transitions via energy levels within the gap associated with native defects and impurities.

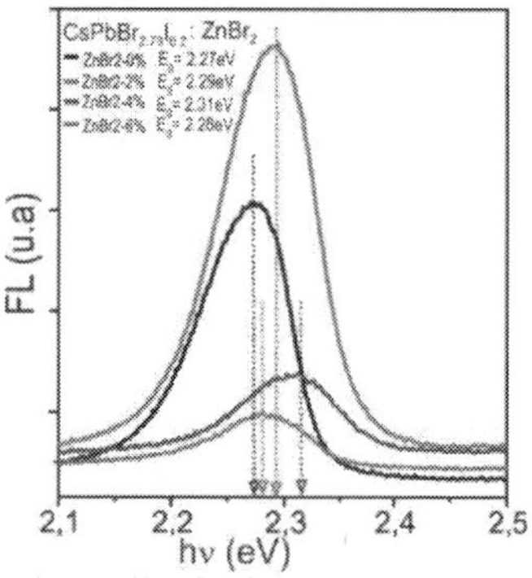

Fig. 3: Photoluminescence spectra of $CsPbBr_{2.7}I_{0.27}$thin films prepared by varying the percentage of Pb substitution by Zn.

It is also observed that $CsPbBr_{2.73}I_{0.27}$ films prepared by replacing Pb with Zn in percentages greater than or equal to 4% exhibit a very low FL intensity; this behavior could be explained by poor crystalline quality and by the generation of non-radiative recombination centers associated with deep emission levels, induced by the excess substitution of Pb with Zn.

3.2 Structural properties

In Fig. 4a is compared the XRD spectrum of the reference $CsPbBr_{2.73}I_{0.27}$ sample with those in which Pb was replaced by Zn in a percentage that varied between 0 and 6%. These results reveals that the $CsPbBr_{2.73}I_{0.27}$ exhibit only reflections corresponding to the cubic-phase (PDF 96-451-0746), and when Zn ions substitute the Pb cation, the crystalline structure does not change; however, the reflections observed in the XRD pattern shift towards larger 2θ values, when the percentage of substitution of Pb by Zn increases. This shift is due to the fact that the ionic radius of Zn^{2+} is smaller than that of Pb^{2+}, which causes a reduction in the size of the unit cell and according to Bragg's law ($n\lambda=2d\sin\theta$) [14] for the relationship to be preserved, the angle θ must increase. Fig. 4b shows the effect that the substitution of Pb by Zn produces on the shift towards larger 2θ values of of the characteristic peak of the phase $CsPbBr_{2.73}I_{0.27}$, observed at $2\theta = 21.5^0$ when the percentage of substitution of Pb by Zn increases. On the other hand, effect of substituting Pb by Zn on the crystallite size was estimated using the Scherrer equation [15]. ($D=k\lambda/(\beta\cos\theta$, where D is the crystallite size, $k = 0.94$, $\lambda_{Cu} = 1.5418$ Å, β is the FWHM and θ is the Bragg angle). It was found that in the range of Pb by Zn substitution studied (% Zn: 0 - 6), the crystallite size is not significantly affected, obtaining a value around 24 nm, which is a typical value for perovskites based on lead halides. The effect of substituting Pb for Zn on the microstrain ϵ of the $CsPbBr_{2.73}I_{0.27}$sample was also estimated using the Williamson-Hall equation given by the relationship $\beta\cdot\cos\theta=Dk/\lambda+4\cdot\epsilon\cdot\sin\theta$ [16]. It was found that in the range of Pb by Zn substitution studied (% Zn: 0 - 6), the microstrain has a value of the order of $\epsilon=3.3\times10^{-4}$

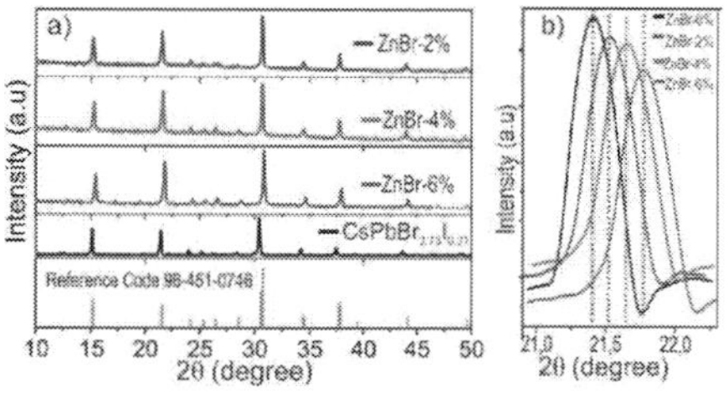

Fig. 4 : Effect that the substitution of Pb by Zn produces on a) the XRD spectra and b) on the shift of the characteristic peak of the phase $CsPbBr_{2.73}I_{0.27}$, observed at $2\theta = 21.5^0$.

3.3 Influence of partial substitution of Pb by Zn^{2+} on morphology of $CsPbBr_{3-x}I_x$ thin films

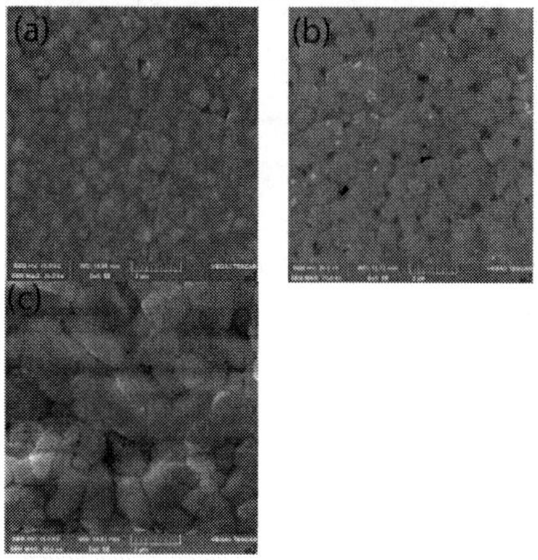

Fig. 5: SEM images of a thin film of $CsP_bBr_{2.73}I_{0.27}$ in which Pb was partially replaced by Zn at concentrations of: a) 0, b) 0.2, c) 0.4 %

The effect of partially replacing the Pb cation with Zn in the structure of a reference sample with composition CsPbBr2.73I0.27 on its morphology was studied through scanning electron microscopy (SEM) measurements. Fig. 5 shows SEM micrographs of the reference sample in which Pb was replaced by Zn at concentrations ranging from 0 to 4%. These results reveal that the sample not doped with Zn presents a morphology consisting of very small grains and the formation of clusters of different sizes; the substitution of Pb by Zn significantly improves its morphology; this type of sample presents a morphology characterized by compact grains whose size increases significantly with increasing percentage of Pb atoms substituted by Zn.

4. CONCLUSIONS

The effect that the substitution of the Pb cation by Zn^{2+} ions on the optical, morphological and structural properties of perovskites thin films with composition $CsPbBr_{2.73}I_{0.27}$ which were synthesized by sequential evaporation of their precursors (PbI2, PbBr2, CsBr), was evaluated through XRD, SEM, spectral transmittance, photoluminescence, and Urbach Energy measurements. From these studies it was found that the substitution of Pb by Zn at low concentrations, does not significantly affect the electronic structure; however, when the substitution of Pb by Zn is greater than 10%, the samples present a high degree of crystalline disorder. On the other hand, it was observed that the substitution of Pb by Zn generates structural defects because the ionic radius of Pb is quite larger than that of Zinc; this situation generates band tail states within the gap that participate in the absorption processes.

XRD characterization revealed that the $CsPbBr_{2.73}I_{0.27}$ exhibit only reflections corresponding to the cubic-phase and when Zn ions substitute the Pb cation, the crystalline structure does not change; however the reflections shift towards larger 2θ values, when Pb is substituted by Zn due to the fact that the ionic radius of Zn^{2+} is smaller than that of Pb_{2+}. On the other hand, photoluminesence measurements indicated that the emission produced by samples prepared by replacing Pb with Zn in percentages less than 4% is mainly due to fundamental transition, while samples prepared by replacing Pb with Zn in higher percentages emit, in addition to fundamental radiation, radiation induced by transitions via energy levels within the gap associated with native defects and impurities.

ACKNOWLEDGEMENTS

This work was funded by the Research and Extension Division (DIEB) of the National University of Colombia - Bogotá Campus, project 59845. GMS & ES Research Group, Faculty of Sciences - Department of Physics - Cra 45 # 26-85, Bogotá, Postal Code 111321 – Colombia

REFERENCES

[1] Ansari, M.I.H.; Qurashi, A.; Nazeeruddin, M.K. Frontiers, Opportunities, and Challenges in Perovskite Solar Cells: A Critical Review. J. Photochem. Photobiol. C Photochem. Rev. 2018, 35, 1–24.

[2] Chen, Z.; Dong, Q.; Liu, Y.; Bao, C.; Fang, Y.; Lin, Y.; Tang, S.; Wang, Q.; Xiao, X.; Bai, Y.; et al. Thin Single Crystal Perovskite SolarCells to Harvest Below-Bandgap Light Absorption. Nat. Commun. 2017, 8, 1890.

[3] Xing, G.; Mathews, N.; Sun, S.; Lim, S. S.; Lam, Y. M.; Grätzel, M.; Mhaisalkar, S.; Sum, T. C., Long-Range Balanced Electronand Hole-Transport Lengths in Organic-Inorganic CH3NH3PbI3, Science 2013, 342, 344-347.

[4]. Juarez-Perez, E.J.; Hawash, Z.; Raga, S.R.; Ono, L.K.; Qi, Y. Thermal Degradation of CH3NH3PbI3 Perovskite into NH3 and CH3I Gases Observed by Coupled Thermogravimetry-Mass Spectrometry Analysis. Energy Environ. Sci. 2016, 9, 3406–3410.

[5] Martin A. Green, Ewan D. Dunlop, Masahiro Yoshita, Nikos Kopidakis, Karsten Bothe,Gerald Siefer, David Hinken, Michael Rauer, Jochen Hohl-Ebinger, Xiaojing Hao, Solar cell efficiency tables (version 64), Prog Photovolt Res Appl. 2024;32:425–441.

[6] NREL, PIP & NREL data, Cell Effiency Data Table, https://www.nrel.gov/pv/assets/docs/cell-effiency-data-table.xlsx (Last accessed: December 10, 2023

[7] Park, N.-G. Organometal Perovskite Light Absorbers Toward a 20% Efficiency Low-Cost Solid-State Mesoscopic Solar Cell. J. Phys.Chem. Lett. 2013, 4, 2423–2429

[8] http://en.ustc.edu.cn/info/1007/4676.htm

[9] https://www.longi.com/en/news/2024-snec-silicon-perovskite-tandem-solar-cells-new-world-efficiency/

[10] Babayigit, A.; Ethirajan, A.; Muller, M.; Conings, B., Toxicity of organometal halide perovskite solar cells. Nat. Mater. 2016, 15, 247-251.

[11] M. A . Reinoso, C. A. Otálora and G. Gordillo, Improvement Properties of Hybrid Halide Perovskite Thin Films Prepared by Sequential Evaporation for Planar Solar Cells, Materials 2019, 12, 1394

[12] J. I. Pankove. Optical Processes in Semiconductors, Dover Inc. New York, 1975.

[13] M.V. Kurik, Review of Urbach's tail. Phys. *Status Solidi A*, vol. 8, No. 9, 1971.

[14] R. Sharma, N. Hooda, A. Hooda, S. Khasa, Physica B : Condensed Matter Structural , dielectric and magnetic study of double perovskite La_2CoMnO_6, Phys. B Condens. Matter 673 (2024) 415473. https://doi.org/10.1016/j.physb.2023.415473.

[15] B.W. Kim, S.H. Im, Supersaturated Antisolvent-Assisted Crystallization for Highly Efficient Inorganic Perovskite Light-Emitting Diodes, ACS Nano 18 (2024) 28691–28699. https://doi.org/10.1021/acsnano.4c06465.

[16] M. Elhamel, Z. Hebboul, M. Elhabib, A. Draoui, A. Benghia, M. Benali, S. Goumri-, L.P. Mat, Journal of Solid State Chemistry Experimental synthesis of double perovskite functional nano-ceramic Eu_2NiMnO_6 : Combining optical characterization and DFT calculations, J. Solid State Chem. 323 (2023) 124022. https://doi.org/10.1016/j.jssc.2023.12402

HOHAI UNIVERSITY

Comparative Analysis and Efficiency Optimization of Sulfur-based Chalcogenide Perovskites ($MgHfS_3$, $CaZrS_3$, $BaZrS_3$) via Interface Engineering for High-Performance Solar Cells

Anees Ur Rehman*, Kung Ding, Jingwei Zhang, Xiang Chen
College of Mechanical and Electrical Engineering, Hohai University, China

Abstract

Chalcogenide perovskites (CP) present a stable and promising alternative to hybrid halide perovskites due to their strong visible-light absorption. This study investigates three sulfur-based chalcogenide absorbers—$MgHfS_3$, $CaZrS_3$, and $BaZrS_3$ —in Perovskite solar cells using SCAPS-1D simulations. $CaZrS_3$ is established as the most efficient absorber. Performance is further enhanced through interface (IF) engineering using 3C–SiC and graphene, achieving a power conversion efficiency of 23.13%.

Scientific Innovation

This study introduces several innovative aspects that contribute to the advancement of stable, high-performance solar cells:

Novel Absorber Focus:

$MgHfS_3$, $CaZrS_3$, and $BaZrS_3$ have seen limited exploration in photovoltaic research. This work provides the first detailed comparative performance analysis and optimization of these three sulfur-based chalcogenide perovskites.

Device Architecture Innovation:

The use of CSTO ($CaSnTiO_3$) as an ETL is unconventional yet effective, offering wide bandgap characteristics and good band alignment with CP.

Interface Engineering Strategy:

We introduce a dual-layer interface engineering approach using 3C–SiC and graphene, which has not been widely applied to CP-based PSCs. These materials help suppress interfacial recombination and enhance charge transport, which are considered critical factors in pushing device efficiency beyond current limits.

ETL	CBO (eV)	VBO (eV)
CSTO/ $CaZrS_3$	0.1	0.9
CSTO/ $MgHfS_3$	0.2	1.27
CSTO/ $BaZrS_3$	0.2	0.8
HTL	**CBO (eV)**	**VBO (eV)**
$CaZrS_3$/nPb	1	-0.5
$MgHfS_3$/nPb	1.1	-0.13
$BaZrS_3$/nPb	1.1	-0.6

$$CBO = X_{PER} - X_{CTL}$$

$$VBO = X_{CTL} - X_{PER} + E_{gCTL} - E_{gPER}$$

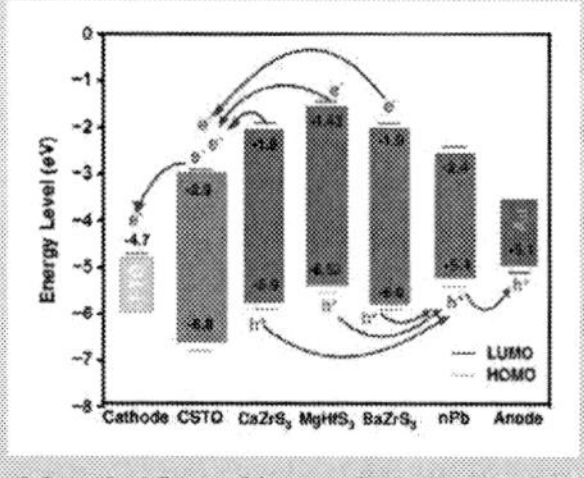

Fig. 1. Energy level diagram of the proposed PSCs without interfacial layers

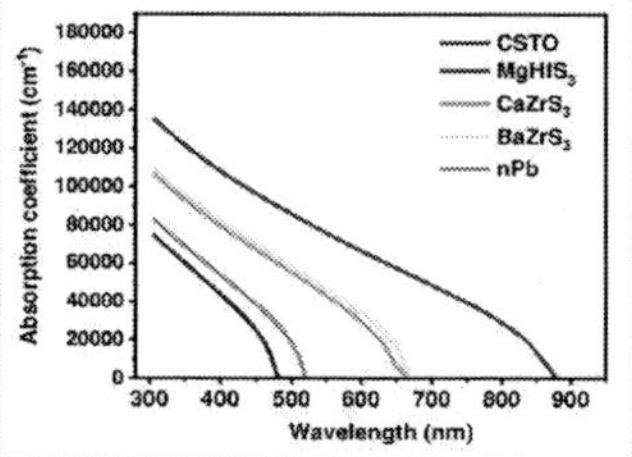

Fig. 2. Optical Absorption of the layers

Table. Power Conversion Efficiency of PSC structures without interface

Structure No.	Configuration	Power Conversion Efficiency
Structure-1	CSTO/ $CaZrS_3$/nPb	21.07%
Structure-2	CSTO/ $MgHfS_3$/nPb	15.30%
Structure-3	CSTO/ $BaZrS_3$/nPb	10.73%

➢ Optimization of layer thickness of proposed PSCs without Interface Layers

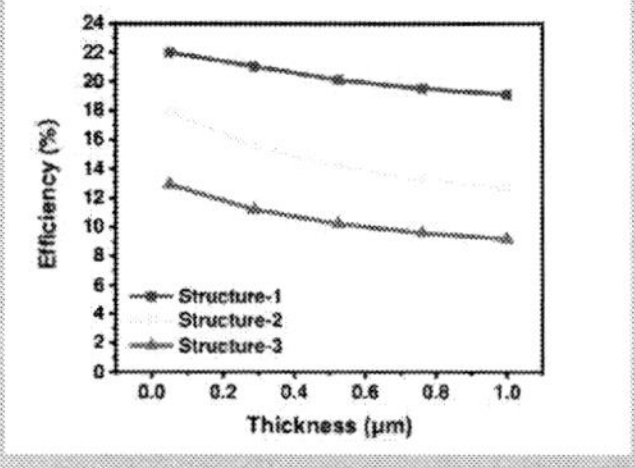

Fig. 3. Effect of Absorber layer thickness on proposed PSCs

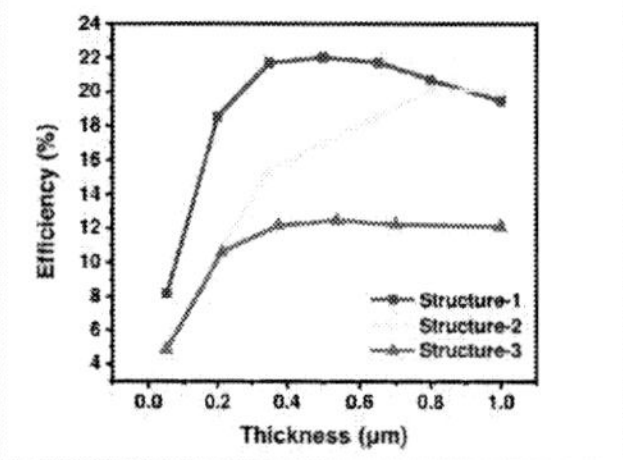

Fig. 4. Effect of ETL layer thickness on proposed PSCs

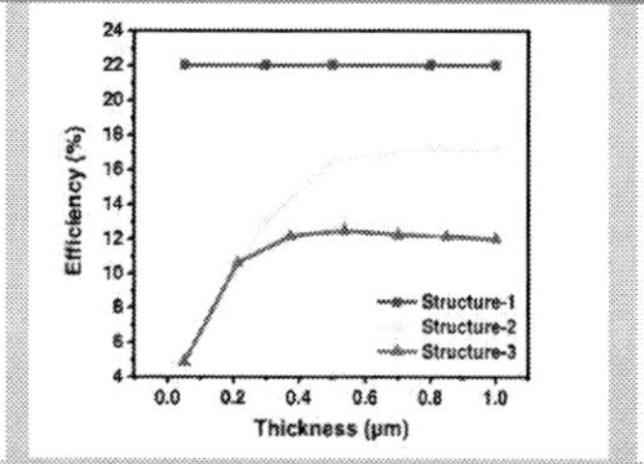

Fig. 5. Effect of HTL layer thickness on $CaZrS_3$-based PSC

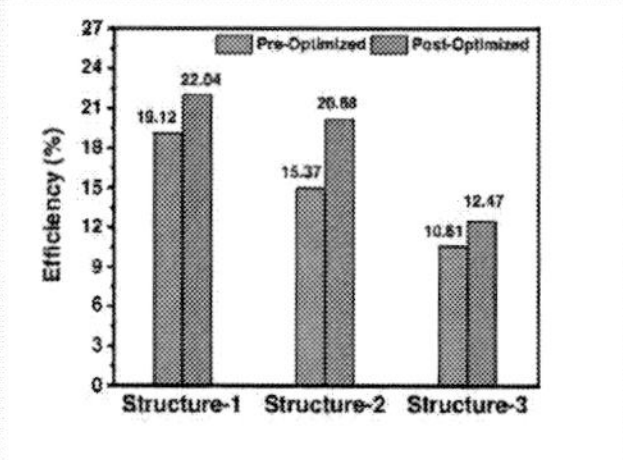

Fig. 6. Efficiency of proposed PSCs before and after optimization

➢ Optimization of $CaZrS_3$-based PSC with Interface Layers

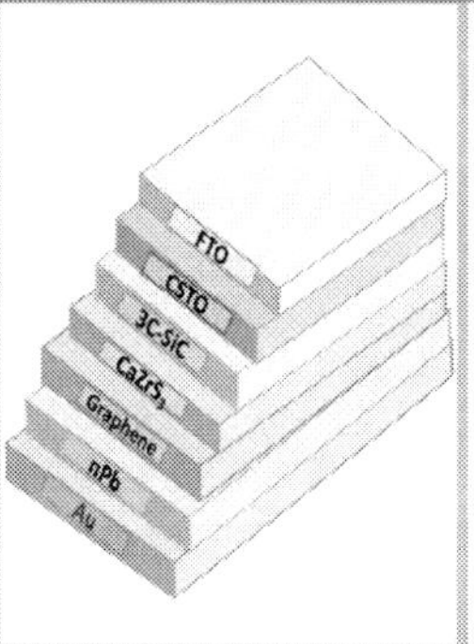

Fig. 7. Layer-by-layer diagram of $CaZrS_3$-based PSC with IF layers.

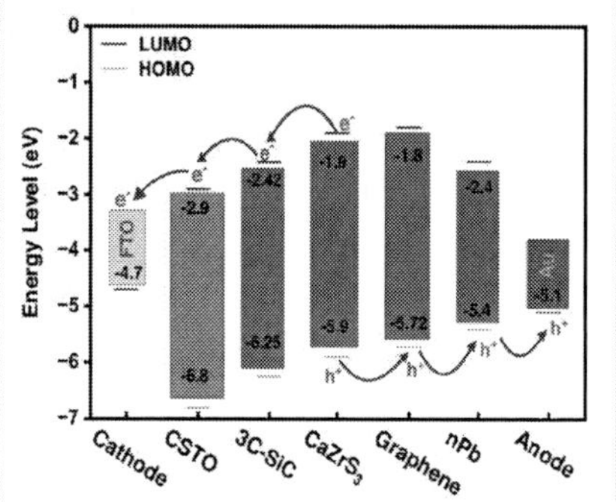

Fig. 8. Energy level diagram of the $CaZrS_3$-based PSC with IF layers

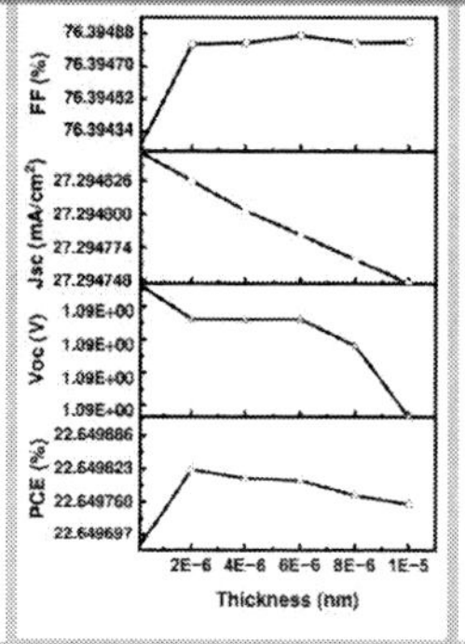

Fig. 9 Effect of varying thickness of 3C-SiC IF layer

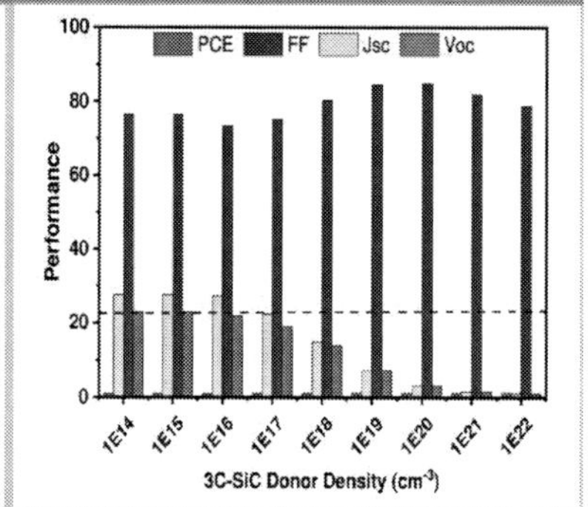

Fig. 10. Effect of varying doping densities of 3C-SiC IF layer

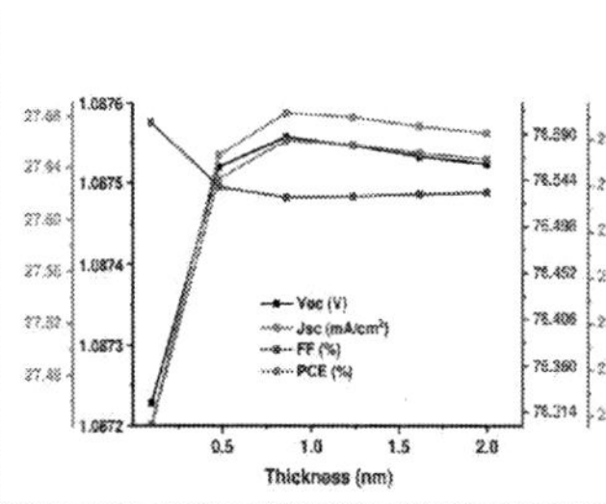

Fig. 11. Effect of varying thickness of graphene IF layer.

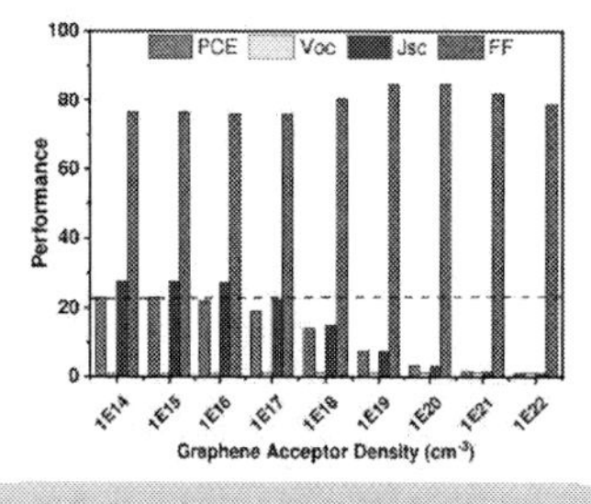

Fig. 12. Effect of varying doping densities of graphene IF layer

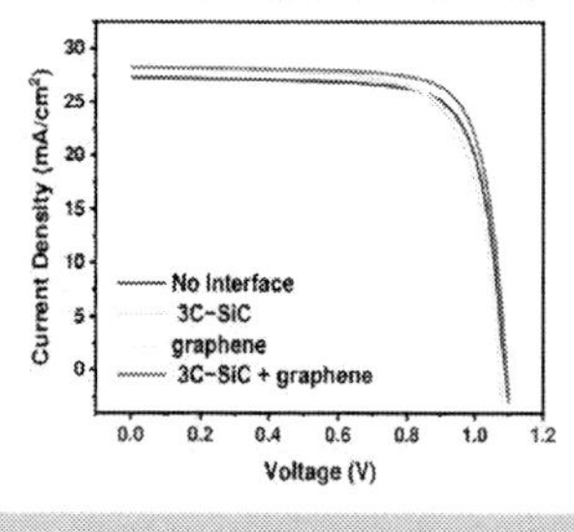

Fig. 13. I-V characteristics of the optimized PSCs structure with various IF layers

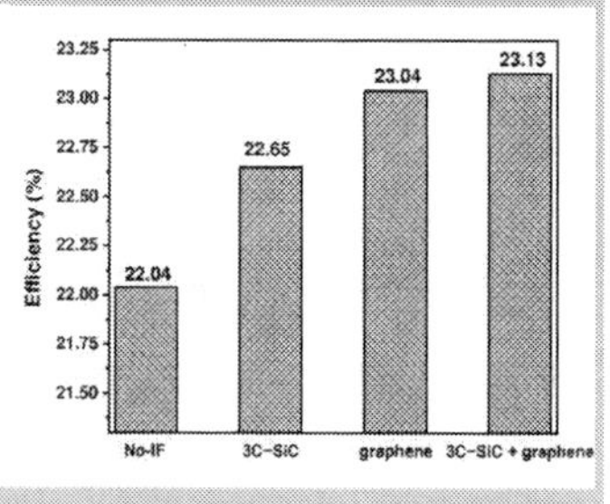

Fig. 14 Efficiency of $CaZrS_3$-based PSCs with & without IF layers

Conclusion

This study establishes $CaZrS_3$ as a promising sulfur-based chalcogenide absorber for efficient and stable PSCs. It also demonstrates the critical role of interface engineering in suppressing recombination losses and enhancing overall performance. These findings provide a scalable and sustainable pathway for future photovoltaic technologies based on environmentally friendly materials.

Funding

This work is supported by the Fundamental Research Funds for the Central Universities, China under grant BC250201180.

Development of Inorganic Perovskite $CsPbI_3$ with Heterojunction Engineering at the Buried Interface for Enhanced Stability and Performance.

KENTECH 2021

Syed Fawad Ali Shah[1*], Hyeonwook Park[1], Muhammad Rehan[2], Donghyeop Shin[2], Kihwan Kim[2*], Jae Ho Yun[1*]

[1] Korea Institute of Energy Technology (KENTECH), Naju-Si, 58277, South Korea

[2] Korea Institute of Energy Research (KIER), Daejeon, 34129, South Korea

Abstract

In recent years, there has been a significant surge in interest in all inorganic cesium lead triiodide ($CsPbI_3$) perovskite, primarily due to its exceptional thermal and light stability, a various range of fabrication methods and an optimal bandgap of 1.71 eV, making it a promising candidate for the development of tandem devices alongside silicon or other low-bandgap perovskite solar cells (PSCs). The reported power conversion efficiency (PCE) of $CsPbI_3$ PSCs has witnessed a remarkable increase, escalating from a mere 2.9% in 2015 to a substantial 21.15% at present, indicating its strong potential for practical application. However, it is essential to acknowledge that $CsPbI_3$ perovskite exhibits multiple phases (α, β, γ) and is prone to converting into the yellow phase (δ) at room temperature, leading to the formation of numerous defects, such as vacancy, interstitial, and antistites defects. The undesired phase transition is often initiated at the buried interface.

Here, we show that the spontaneously formed two-dimensional Ruddlesden Popper phase of $Cs_2PbI_2Cl_2$ at the buried interface improved electron transfer and phase stability of $CsPbI_3$. Perovskite solar cells based on $CsPbI_3/Cs_2PbI_2Cl_2$ light absorbers exhibit a power conversion efficiency of 20.6% under simulated solar illumination. Furthermore, un-encapsulated devices maintained about 90% of their initial efficiency after continuous light exposure during 1000 hrs.

Introduction

Inorganic Perovskite has
- high thermal stability
- lack of halide segregation
- anti-solvent free synthesis process
- high potential possibilities for efficiency improvement

Volatile organic cations MA/FA Unstable at high temperature

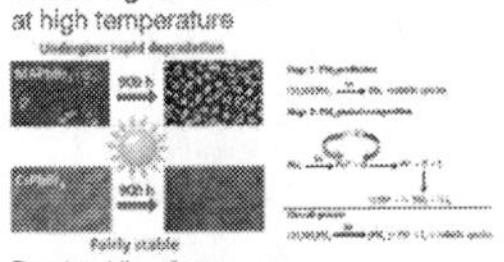

Three degradation pathways.
(1) CH_3NH_2 + HI (identified as the reversible path),
(2) NH_3 + CH_3I (the irreversible or detrimental path),
(3) a reversible Pb(0) + I_2(g) photodecomposition reaction

Experimental Details

→ Crystal structure of the different phases and their relative phase transitions

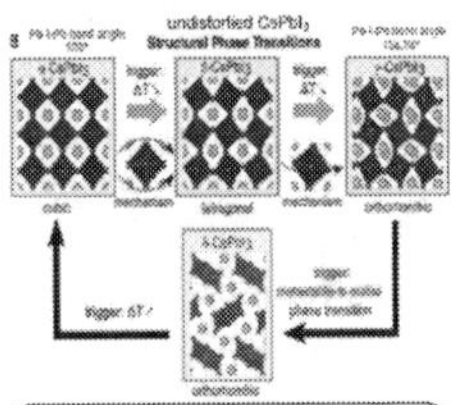

- Phase instability → smaller size of the Cs
- tolerance factor 0.847
- lattice strain induced from the ion size mismatch
- three-dimensional (3D) to one-dimensional (1D) non perovskite phase.

→ **Computational Analysis**

Comparison of properties between existing materials and halogen-mixed materials.

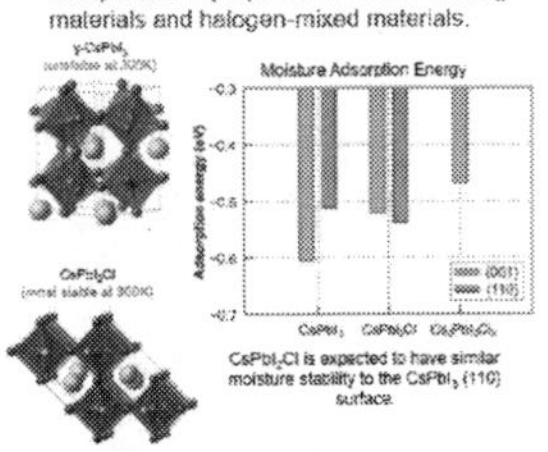

$CsPbI_2Cl$ is expected to have similar moisture stability to the $CsPbI_3$ (110) surface.

$CsPbI_2Cl$ is predicted to exhibit superior properties compared to $CsPbI_3$ in terms of moisture stability.

→ Halides Incorporation in precursor solution

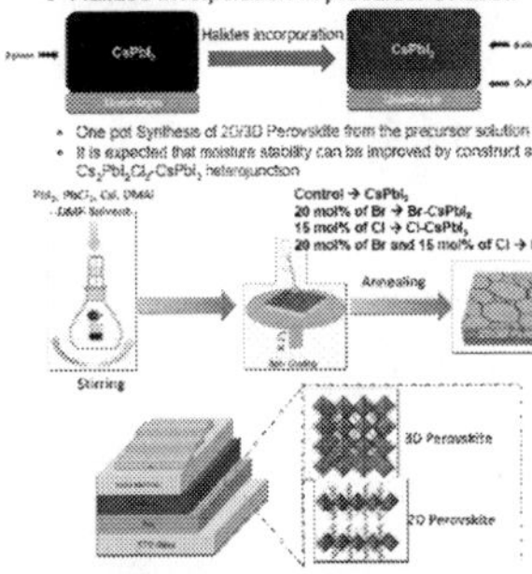

- One pot Synthesis of 2D/3D Perovskite from the precursor solution
- It is expected that moisture stability can be improved by construct a $Cs_2PbI_2Cl_2$-$CsPbI_3$ heterojunction

Control → $CsPbI_3$
20 mol% of Br → Br-$CsPbI_3$
15 mol% of Cl → Cl-$CsPbI_3$
20 mol% of Br and 15 mol% of Cl → Br/Cl-$CsPbI_3$

Results & Discussion

Morphological & Structural Analysis

- SIMS Analysis

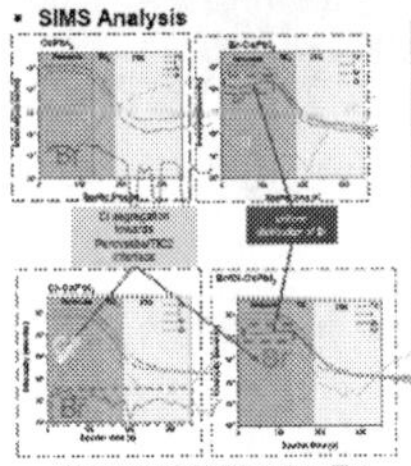

Anion-targeted ToF-SIMS depth profiling

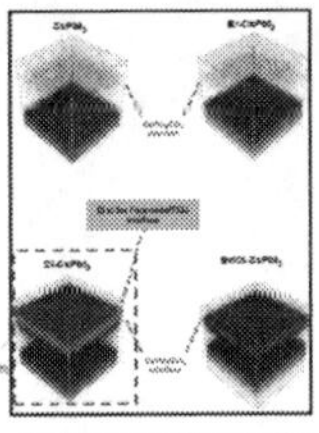

3D redistribution of Cl⁻ obtained by (ToF-SIMS)

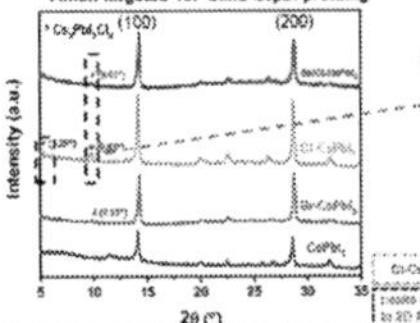

- δ-phase $CsPbI_3$
- stable 2D RP $Cs_2PbI_2Cl_2$ at the buried interface
- enhanced β-phase stability of Cl-$CsPbI_3$

Cl-$CsPbI_3$ showed the highest XRD peak intensity peaks at 5.38° and 9.82° were observed assigned to 2D RP $Cs_2PbI_2Cl_2$

Device Performance

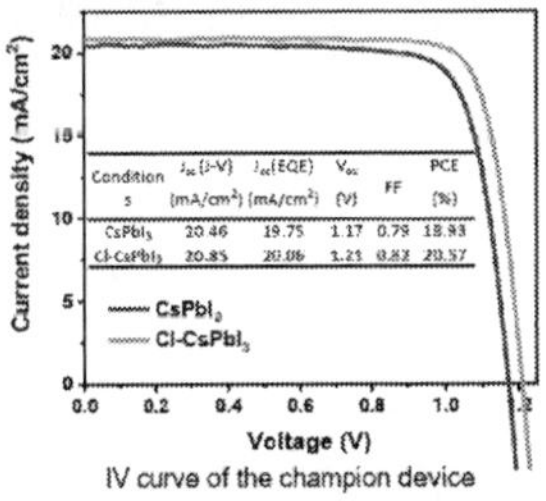

Conditions	J_{sc} (J-V) (mA/cm²)	J_{sc} (EQE) (mA/cm²)	V_{oc} (V)	FF	PCE (%)
$CsPbI_3$	20.46	19.75	1.17	0.79	18.93
Cl-$CsPbI_3$	20.85	20.06	1.21	0.82	20.57

IV curve of the champion device

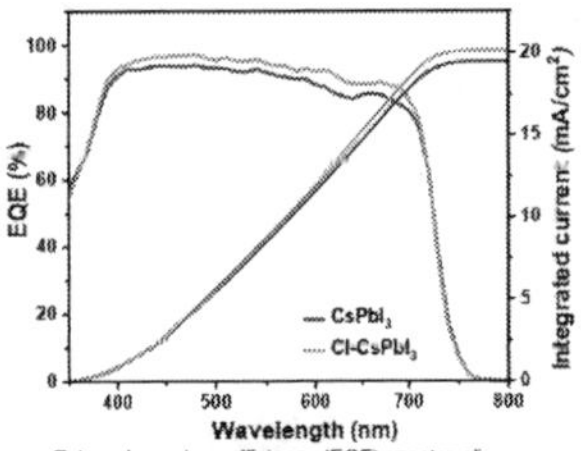

External quantum efficiency (EQE) spectra of the best-performing solar cells

- Steady state power output (SPO)

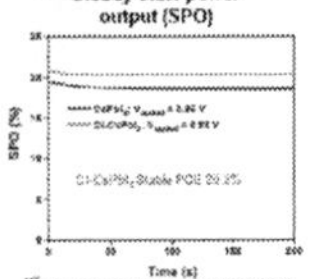

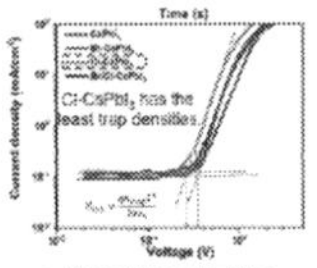

Cl-$CsPbI_3$ has the least trap densities.

- Space Charge Limiting Current (SCLC)

Photovoltaic Performance

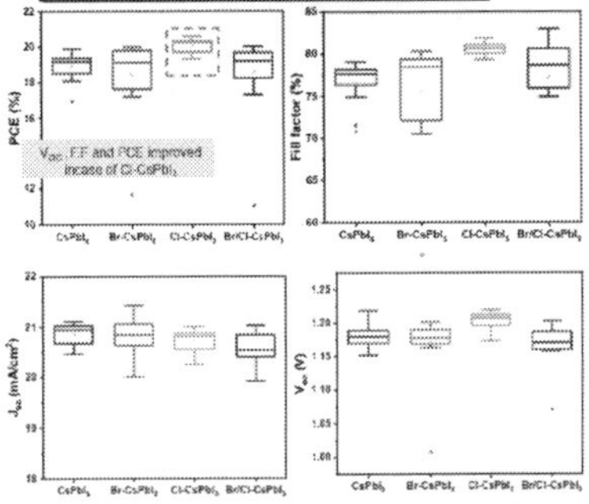

V_{oc}, FF and PCE improved incase of Cl-$CsPbI_3$

Device stability

- Phase Stability at 65% RH

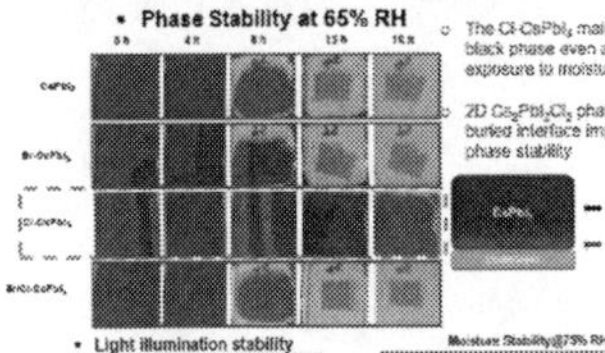

- The Cl-$CsPbI_3$ maintained its black phase even after 16 h of exposure to moisture
- 2D $Cs_2PbI_2Cl_2$ phase at the buried interface improved the phase stability

- Light illumination stability

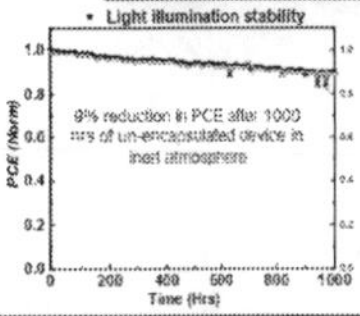

9% reduction in PCE after 1000 hrs of un-encapsulated device in inert atmosphere

Moisture Stability@75% RH

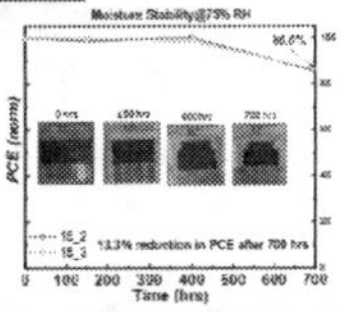

13.3% reduction in PCE after 700 hrs

Optical properties

- UV-Vis Analysis

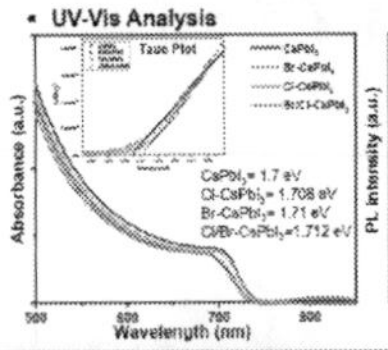

$CsPbI_3$ = 1.7 eV
Cl-$CsPbI_3$ = 1.708 eV
Br-$CsPbI_3$ = 1.71 eV
Cl/Br-$CsPbI_3$ = 1.712 eV

- PL Analysis

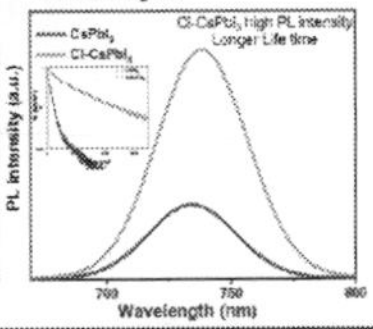

Cl-$CsPbI_3$ high PL intensity Longer Life time

Conclusions

- ☐ Addition of Cl into $CsPbI_3$ induced the spontaneous formation of stable 2D RP $Cs_2PbI_2Cl_2$ at the buried interface.
- ☐ $Cs_2PbI_2Cl_2$ enhanced crystallinity, reduced trap densities, and improved phase stability of $CsPbI_3$
- ☐ Reduced interfacial lattice distortion leading to enhanced charge transfer and improved phase stability.
- ☐ Improved device performances and operational stabilities.
- ☐ These studies highlight the importance of buried interfacial Engineering.

PMDL.
NEXT GENERATION PV MATERIALS AND DEVICES LAB

References

[1] X. Gu, W. Xiang, Q. Tian, S. Liu, *Angewandte Chemie International Edition* **2021**, 60, 23164.

[2] S. S. Mali, J. V. Patil, J.-Y. Shao, Y.-W. Zhong, S. R. Rondiya, N. Y. Dzade, C. K. Hong, *Nature Energy* **2023**, 8, 989.

[3] Y. Cui, J. Shi, F. Meng, B. Yu, S. Tan, S. He, C. Tan, Y. Li, H. Wu, Y. Luo, D. Li, Q. Meng, *Advanced Materials* **2022**, 34, 2205028.

Scan for Lab Introduction

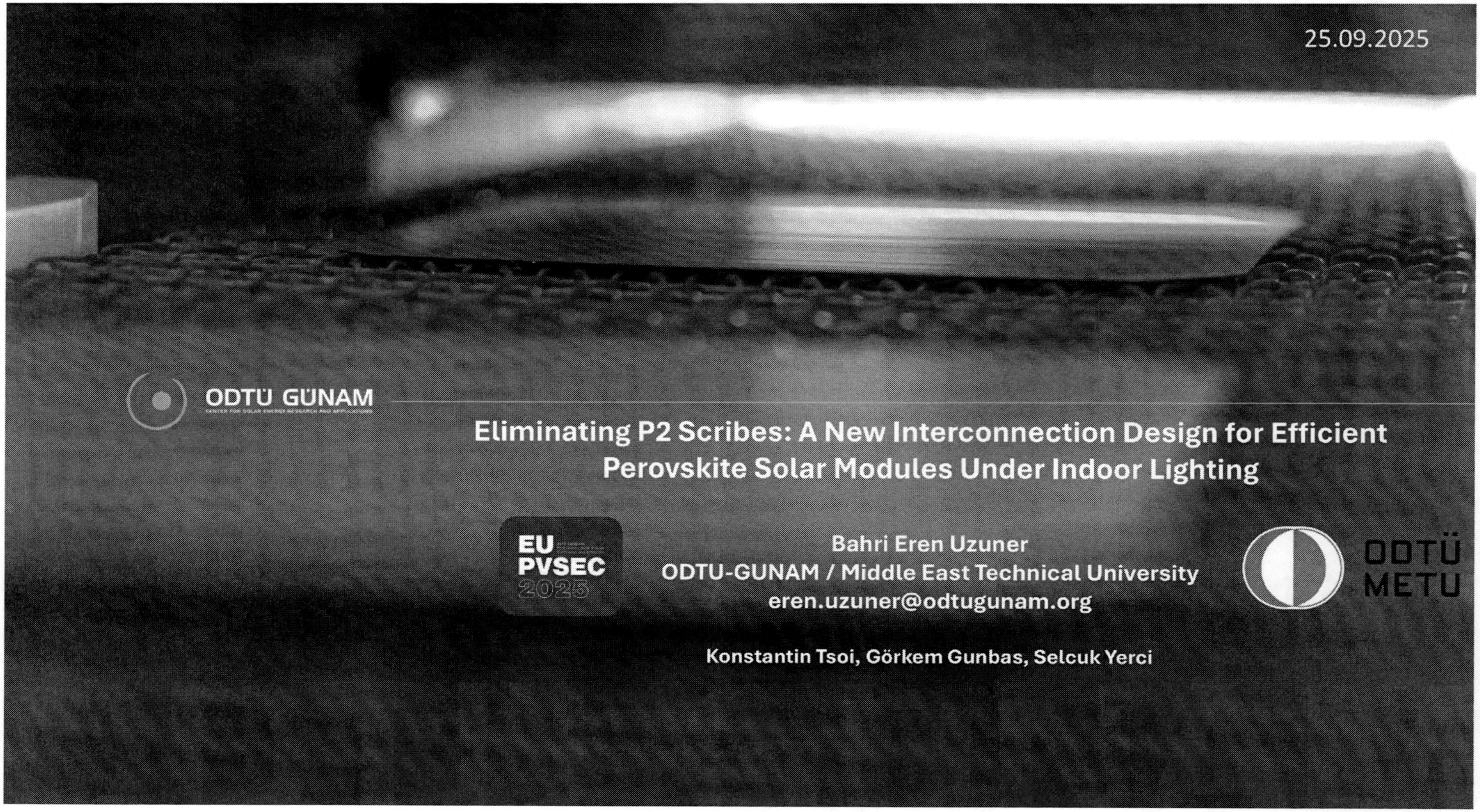
25.09.2025
ODTÜ GÜNAM
Eliminating P2 Scribes: A New Interconnection Design for Efficient Perovskite Solar Modules Under Indoor Lighting
EU PVSEC 2025
Bahri Eren Uzuner
ODTU-GUNAM / Middle East Technical University
eren.uzuner@odtugunam.org
Konstantin Tsoi, Görkem Gunbas, Selcuk Yerci
ODTÜ METU

Introduction

- **Up-scaling** and efficient **interconnection** of perovskite solar cells are essential steps towards their commercial use.

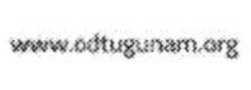

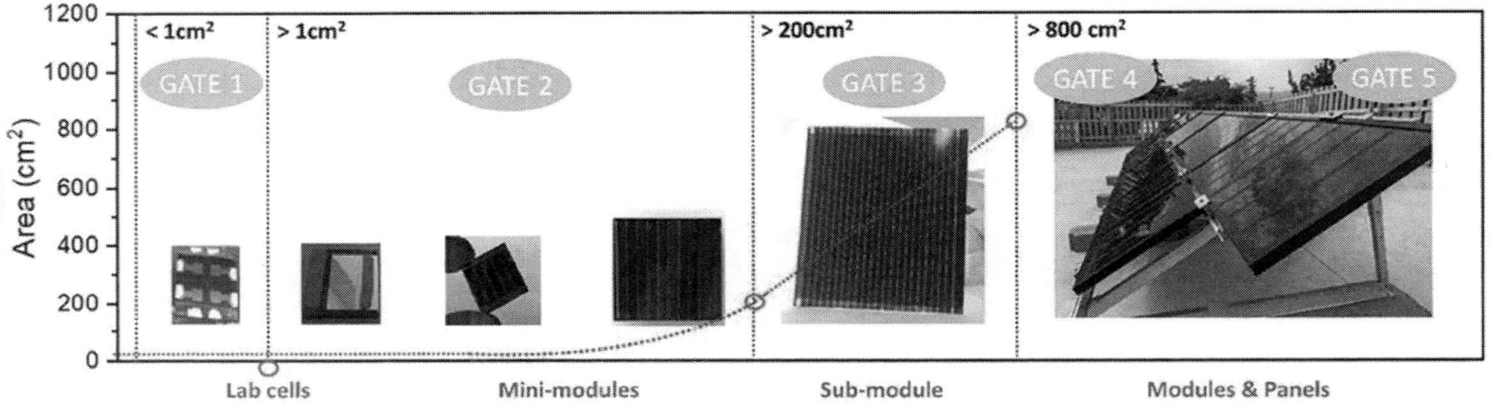

1. Forberich, K. et. al. (2025). Adv. Ene. Mat. 15(13).

Introduction

- **Up-scaling** and efficient **interconnection** of perovskite solar cells are essential steps towards their commercial use.
- **Monolithic series interconnection** holds promise from an **electrical perspective**
  - V_{oc} addition / J_{sc} limitation
  - $P_{loss} = J_{sc,\ module}{}^{2} \times R$

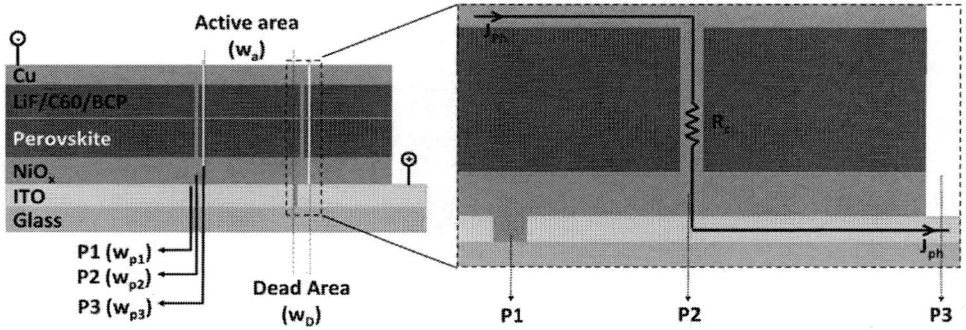

Introduction

- **Up-scaling** and efficient **interconnection** of perovskite solar cells are essential steps towards their commercial use.
- **Monolithic series interconnection** holds promise from an **electrical perspective**
  - V_{oc} addition / J_{sc} limitation
  - $P_{loss} = J_{sc,\ module}{}^2 \times R$
- It is formed by **3 adjacent laser scribes;**
  - Isolation of the front contact (**P1**)
  - Interconnection path of adjacent cells (**P2**)
  - Isolation of the back contact (**P3**)

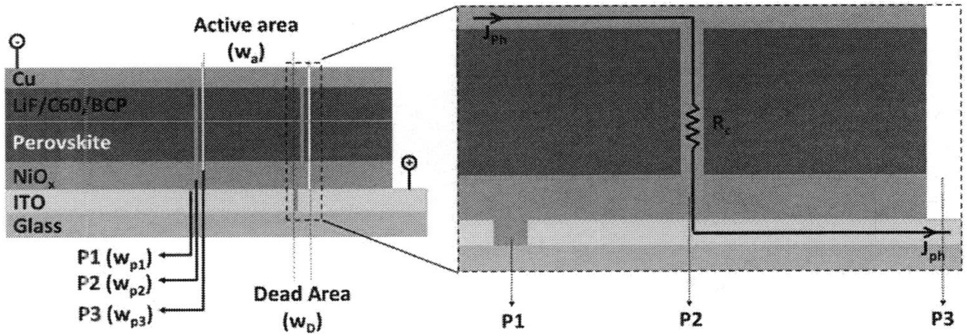

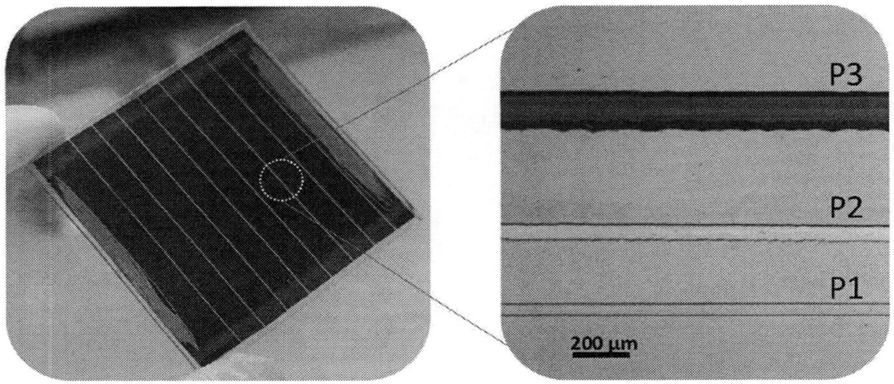

Benchmarks in the interconnection geometries

- **Full-cell-length (FCL) trench scribing**
  - State-of-the-art for the most thin-film module technologies
  - Typically yields >90% geometrical fill factor (GFF)
  - Requires material removal

(A)

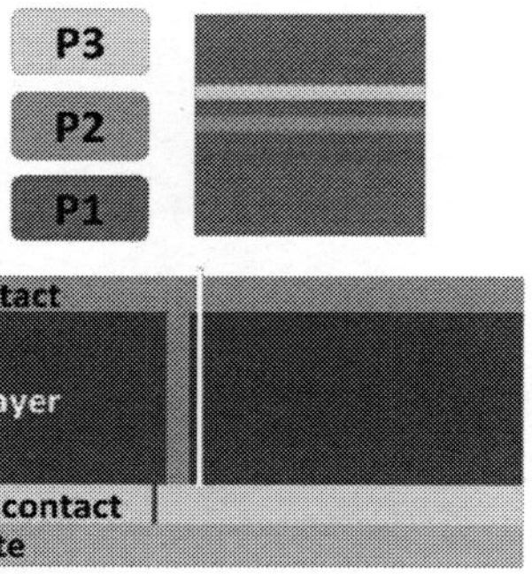

2. Meng, R. *et. al.* (2022). npj Flex. Elect. *6*, 39.
3. Ma, Q. *et. al.* (2023). Device *1*, 100174.
4. Zhang, B. *et. al.* (2024). Ener. Env. Sci *17*, 2935–2944.
5. Feng, E. *et. al.* (2024). ACS Nano *18*, 28026–28037.
6. Uzuner, B.E. *et. al.* (2025). Sol. Ener. Mat. and Sol. Cells *292*, 113793.

Benchmarks in the interconnection geometries

- **Full-cell-length (FCL) trench scribing**
  - State-of-the-art for the most thin-film module technologies
  - Typically yields >90% geometrical fill factor (GFF)
  - Requires material removal
- **Dot or discontinuous line trenches**
  - Very high GFF can be achieved (>99%)
  - Requires material removal

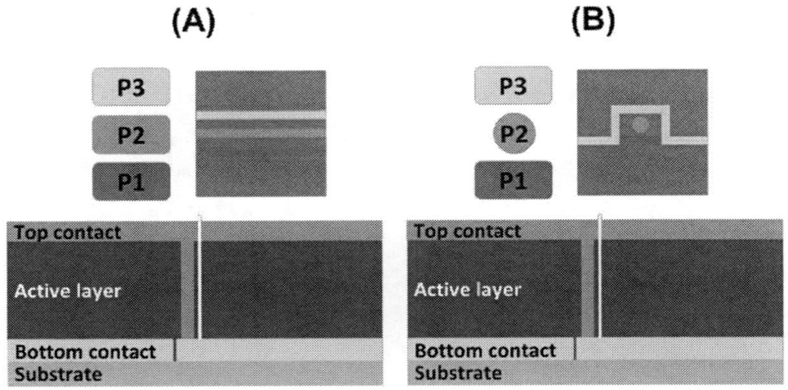

7. Haas, S. *et. al.* (2013). Prog. in Phot. *21*, 972–979.
8. Rakocevic, L. *et. al.* (2020). Prog. in Phot. *28*, 1120–1127.
9. Jiang, E. *et. al.* (2024). Solar RRL *8*.
10. Di Giacomo, F. *et. al.* (2024). Adv Energy Mater *14*.

Benchmarks in the interconnection geometries

- **Full-cell-length (FCL) trench scribing**
  - State-of-the-art for the most thin-film module technologies
  - Typically yields >90% geometrical fill factor (GFF)
  - Requires material removal
- **Dot or discontinuous line trenches**
  - Very high GFF can be achieved (>99%)
  - Requires material removal
- **Chemical or laser-based contact modification**
  - Material removal is not necessary
  - Yields in decent contact resistance and GFF

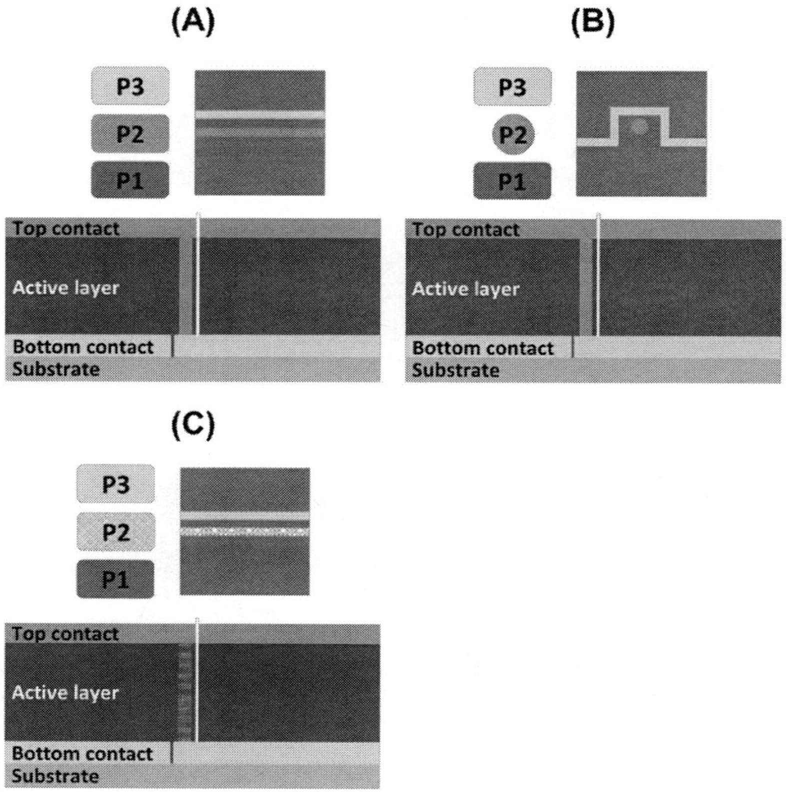

11. Westin, P.-O. *et. al.* (2008). Sol. Ener. Mat. and Sol. Cells 92, 1230–1235.

Circuitry of a standard interconnection (FCL)

- In the standard model, photo-generated current flows **through the P2 contact** to the adjacent cell
    - Parallel resistances of $\mathbf{R_{1-2}}$ and $\mathbf{R_{2-3}}$ are **much higher**.

(A)

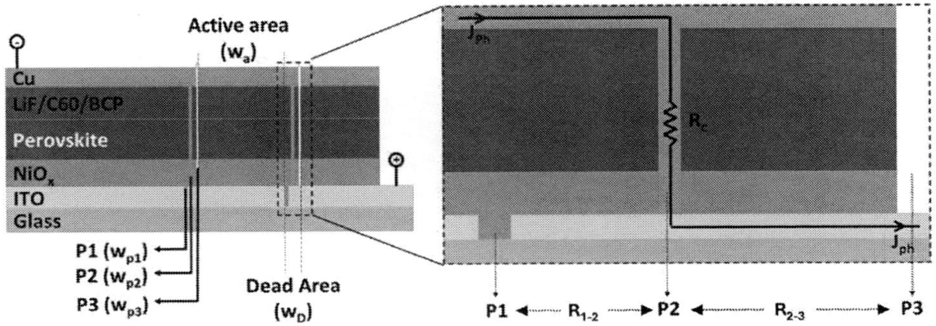

*R_{2-3}: Safe zone between the **P2** and **P3**; R_{1-2}: Safe zone between the **P1** and **P2***

"Missing part" of the circuitry of a standard interconnection

- In the standard model, photo-generated current flows **through the P2 contact** to the adjacent cell
  - Parallel resistances of $\mathbf{R_{1\text{-}2}}$ and $\mathbf{R_{2\text{-}3}}$ are **much higher**.
- The so-called **safe zones** in between the P1-P2 and P2-P3 laser scribes have all layers to form a **"solar cell"**

(B)

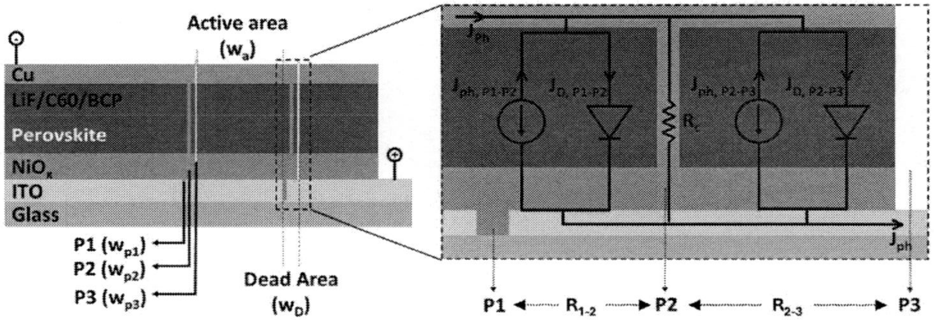

*$R_{2\text{-}3}$: Safe zone between the **P2** and **P3**; $R_{1\text{-}2}$: Safe zone between the **P1** and **P2***

"Missing part" of the circuitry of a standard interconnection

- In the standard model, photo-generated current flows **through the P2 contact** to the adjacent cell
  - Parallel resistances of $\mathbf{R_{1\text{-}2}}$ and $\mathbf{R_{2\text{-}3}}$ are **much higher**.
- The so-called **safe zones** in between the P1-P2 and P2-P3 laser scribes have all layers to form a **"solar cell"**
- Emission detected in the electroluminescence images of the safe zones as the applied bias is **reversed**.
  - Meaning that the PSCs at $\mathbf{R_{1\text{-}2}}$ and $\mathbf{R_{2\text{-}3}}$ are connected reversely to the active areas

(B)

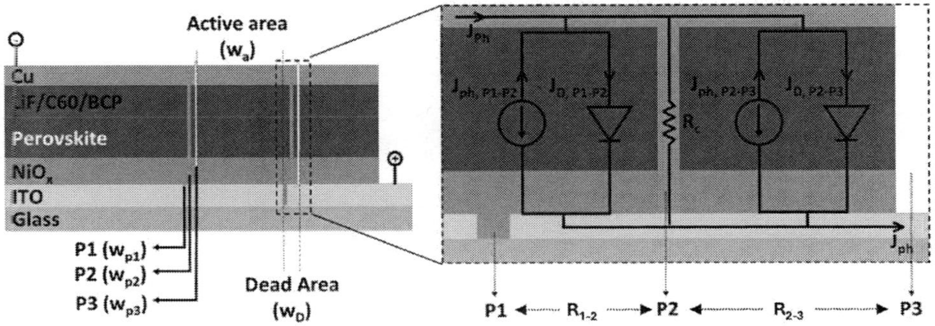

(C)

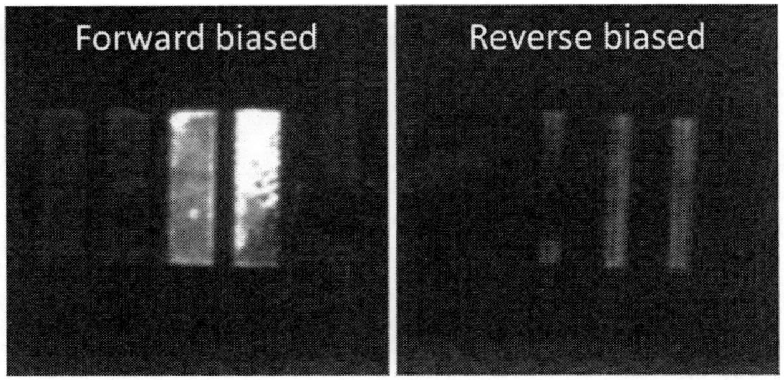

$R_{2\text{-}3}$: *Safe zone between the **P2** and **P3**;* $R_{1\text{-}2}$: *Safe zone between the **P1** and **P2***

Electrical modeling – Silvaco

- Test structure consisting of active area, interconnection, and R_{2-3} was simulated in Silvaco.

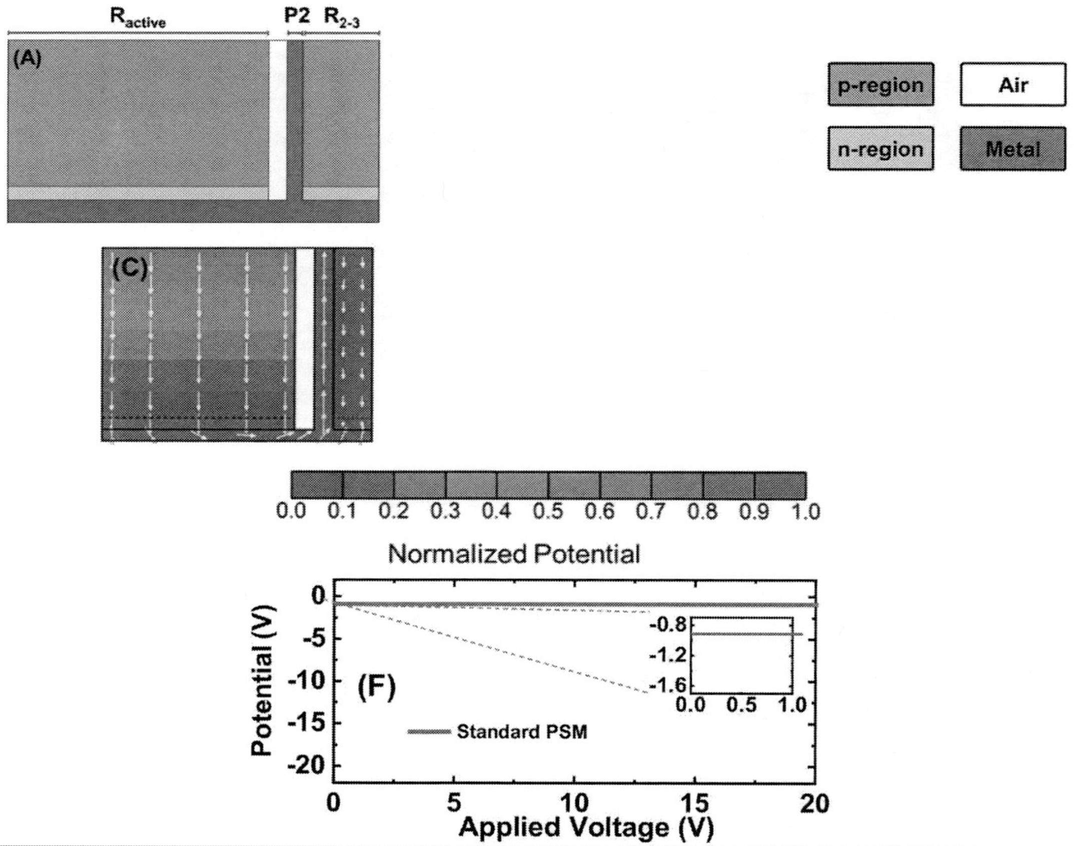

*Silvaco simulations were done by **Konstantin Tsoi***

*R_{2-3}: Safe zone between the **P2** and **P3**; R_{1-2}: Safe zone between the **P1** and **P2***

Electrical modeling – Silvaco

- Test structure consisting of active area, interconnection, and R_{2-3} was simulated in Silvaco.
- Safe-zones experience **reverse-bias** as the standard module is operated under **forward-bias.**

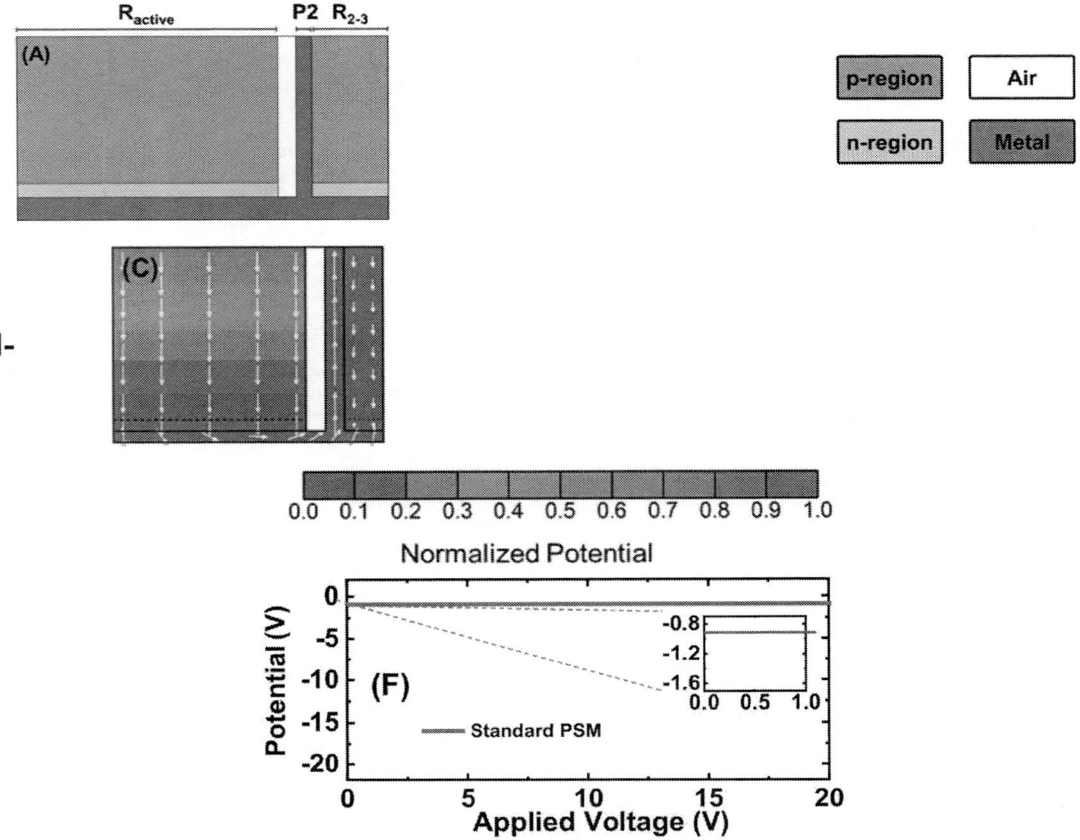

Silvaco simulations were done by ***Konstantin Tsoi***

*R_{2-3}: Safe zone between the **P2** and **P3**; R_{1-2}: Safe zone between the **P1** and **P2***

Electrical modeling – Silvaco

- Test structure consisting of active area, interconnection, and R_{2-3} was simulated in Silvaco.
- Safe-zones experience **reverse-bias** as the standard module is operated under **forward-bias.**
- The existence of a reverse bias in safe zones offers a prospect of achieving a **breakdown** within the dead region (R_{1-3}).
  - In the **absence of the P2 scribe.**

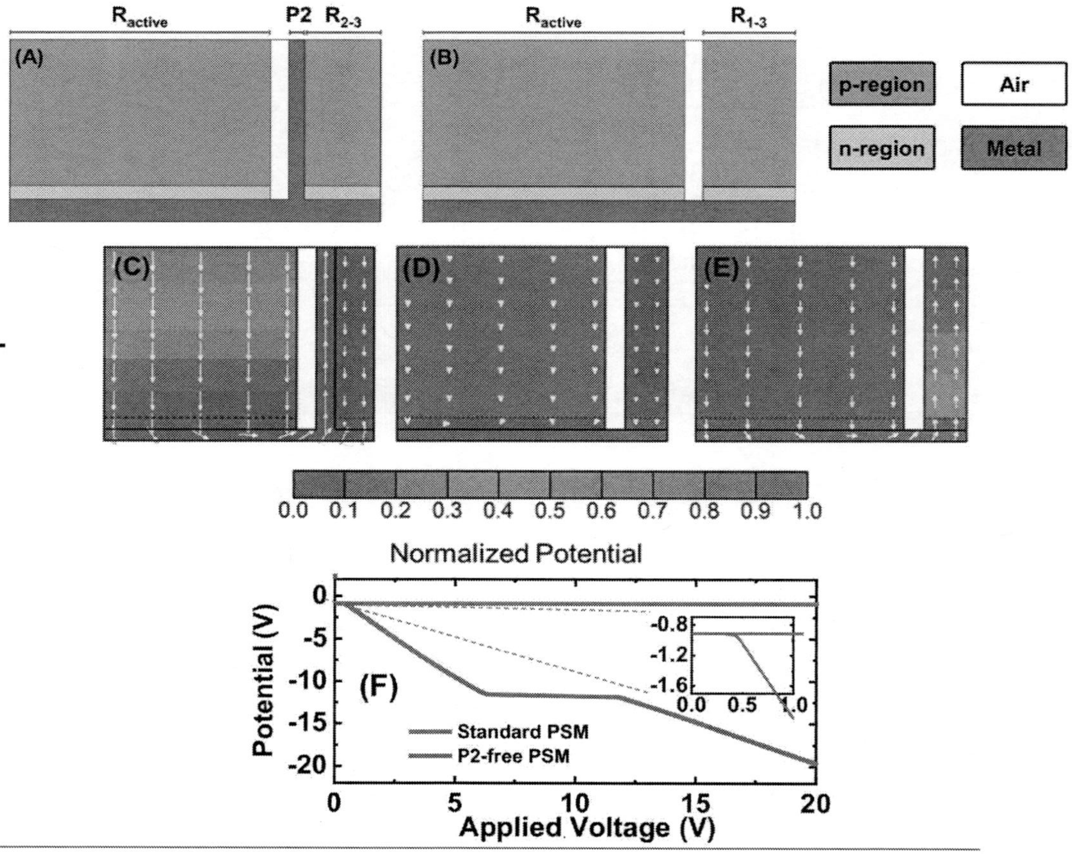

ODTU GUNAM

EU PVSEC 2025

*Silvaco simulations were done by **Konstantin Tsoi***

R_{2-3}**: Safe zone between the **P2** and **P3**; **R_{1-2}**: Safe zone between the **P1** and **P2

ODTÜ METU

www.odtugunam.org

Electrical modeling – Silvaco

- Test structure consisting of active area, interconnection, and R_{2-3} was simulated in Silvaco.
- Safe-zones experience **reverse-bias** as the standard module is operated under **forward-bias.**
- The existence of a reverse bias in safe zones offers a prospect of achieving a **breakdown** within the dead region (R_{1-3}).
  - In the **absence of the P2 scribe**.
- Reverse-broken-down PSC → **Resistor**

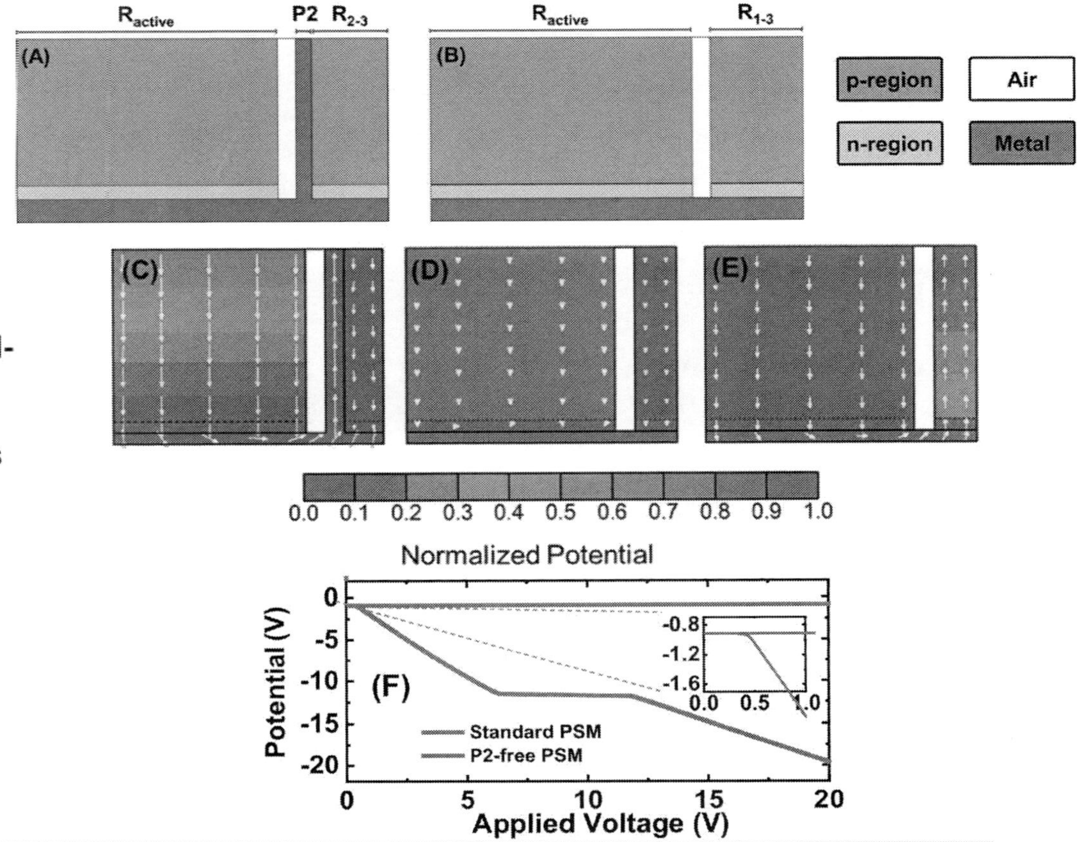

12. Johnson, S. et. al. (2025). Joule, 102102.
13. Jiang, F. et. al. (2024). Nat Energy 9, 1275–1284.

ODTÜ GÜNAM

EU PVSEC 2025

*Silvaco simulations were done by **Konstantin Tsoi***

*R_{2-3}: Safe zone between the **P2** and **P3**; R_{1-2}: Safe zone between the **P1** and **P2***

ODTÜ METU

www.odtugunam.org

Electrical modeling – Reverse breakdown

- Fabricated PSCs possess **ohmic** behavior upon reverse breakdown ~@-3.5V

(A)

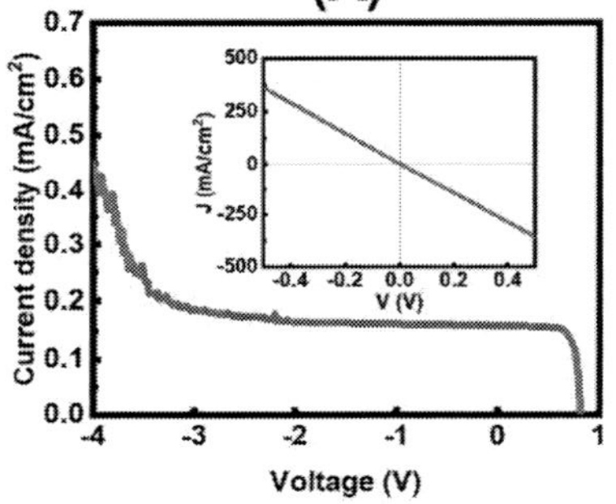

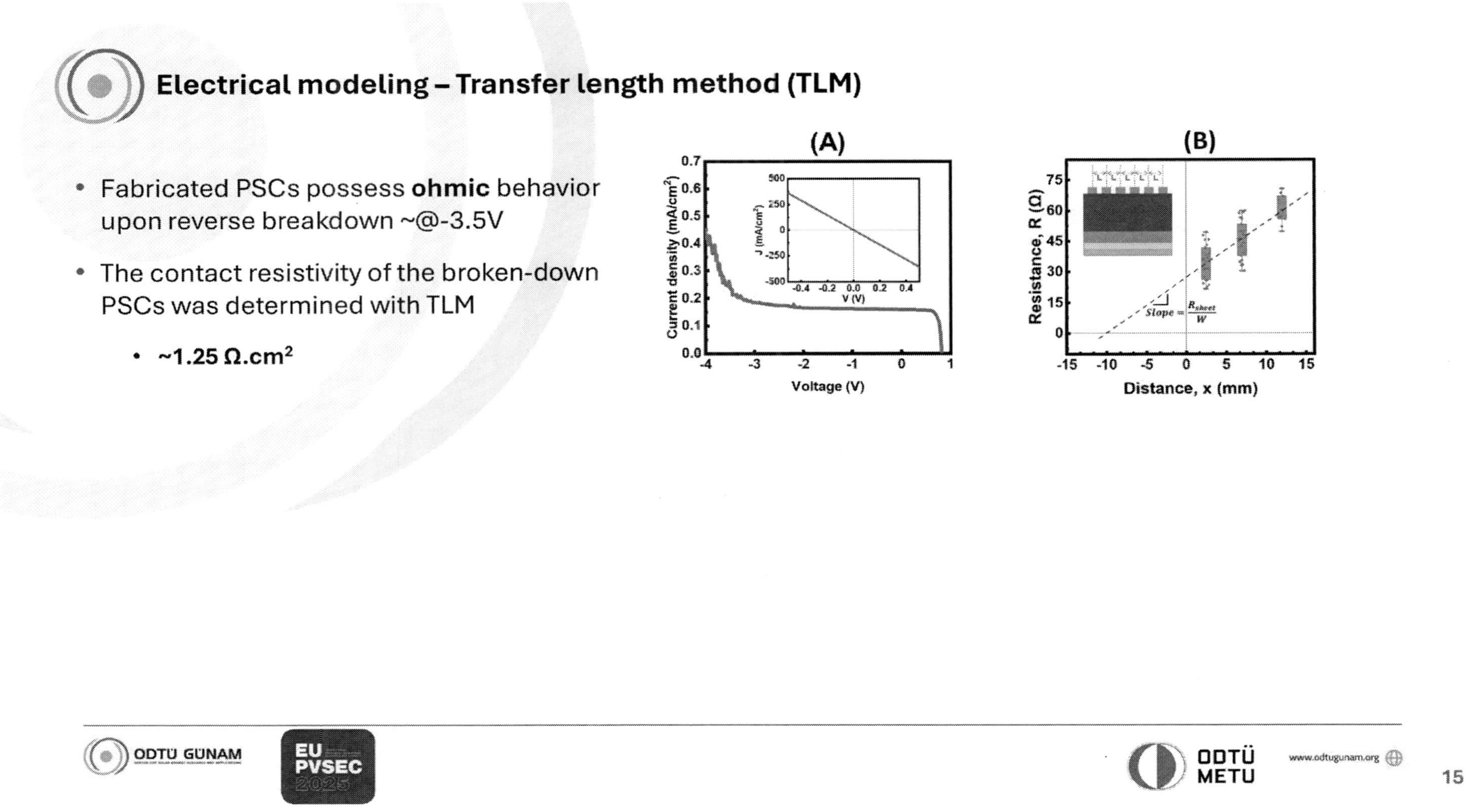

Electrical modeling – Transfer length method (TLM)
• Fabricated PSCs possess ohmic behavior upon reverse breakdown ~@-3.5V
• The contact resistivity of the broken-down PSCs was determined with TLM
• ~1.25 Ω.cm²
(A)
Current density (mA/cm²)
Voltage (V)
J (mA/cm²)
V (V)
(B)
Resistance, R (Ω)
Distance, x (mm)
Slope = R_sheet / W
ODTÜ GÜNAM
EU PVSEC 2025
ODTÜ METU
www.odtugunam.org
15

Electrical modeling – Single diode model

- Fabricated PSCs possess **ohmic** behavior upon reverse breakdown ~@-3.5V
- The contact resistivity of the broken-down PSCs was determined with TLM
  - **~1.25 Ω.cm²**

J_{PH} ~20 mA/cm²

$$I = I_{sc} - I_0 \exp(\frac{q(V + IR_s)}{nkT}) - \frac{V + (IR_s)}{R_{sh}}$$

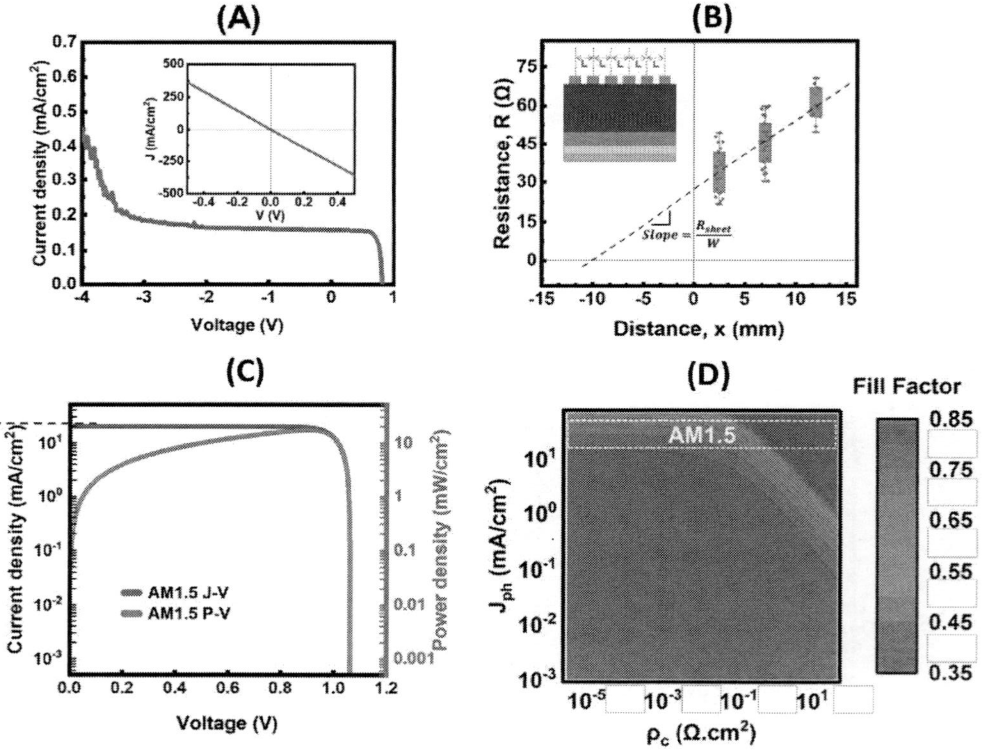

Electrical modeling – Single diode model

- Fabricated PSCs possess **ohmic** behavior upon reverse breakdown ~@-3.5V
- The contact resistivity of the broken-down PSCs was determined with TLM
  - **~1.25 Ω.cm², far lower** than the required interval, based on the single-diode model

J_{PH} ~20 mA/cm²

J_{PH} ~0.1 mA/cm²

Nearly "0"

$$I = I_{sc} - I_0 \exp\left(\frac{q(V + IR_s)}{nkT}\right) - \frac{V + (IR_s)}{R_{sh}}$$

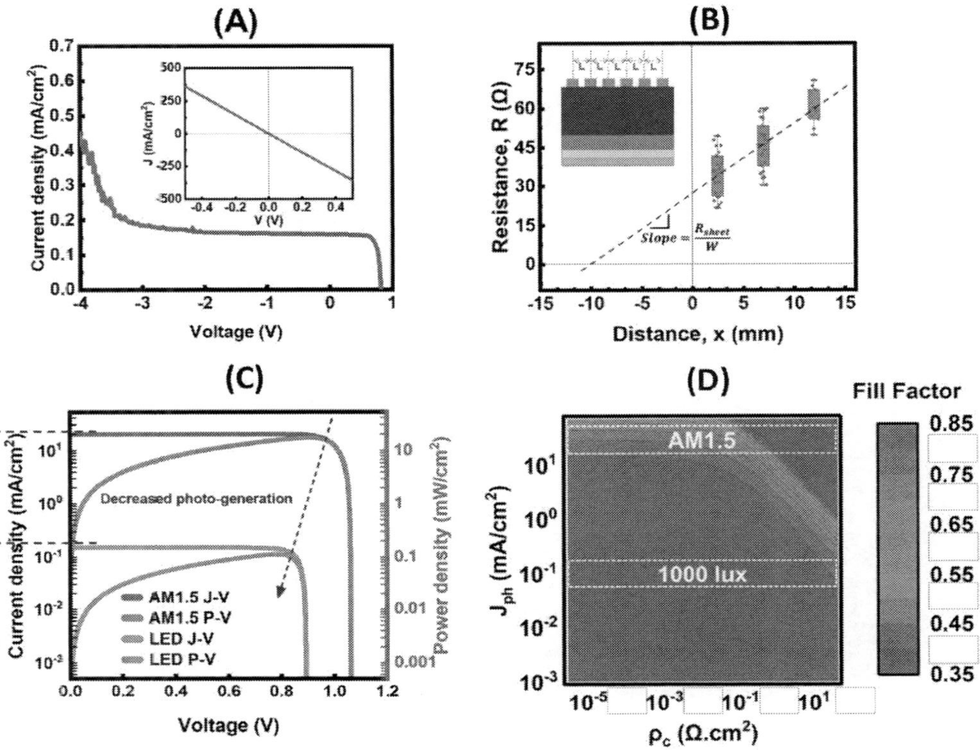

P2-Free Perovskite Solar Modules

- Expectedly the geometrical fill factor (GFF) increase significantly.
  - **90% → 95%**

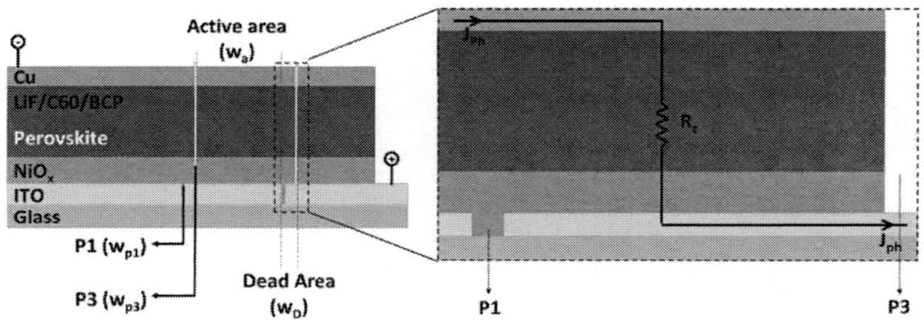

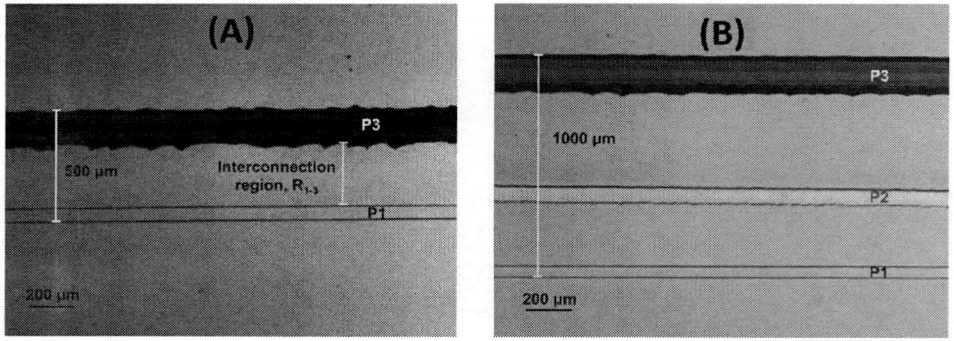

P2-Free Perovskite Solar Modules

- Expectedly the geometrical fill factor (GFF) increase significantly.
  - **90% → 95%**
- P2-free PSMs demonstrated exceptional performance under indoor illumination
  - **>82 % FF** and **>32% PCE.**
  - No electrical loss was observed in compared to the reference cells.

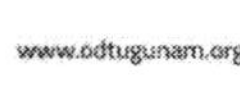

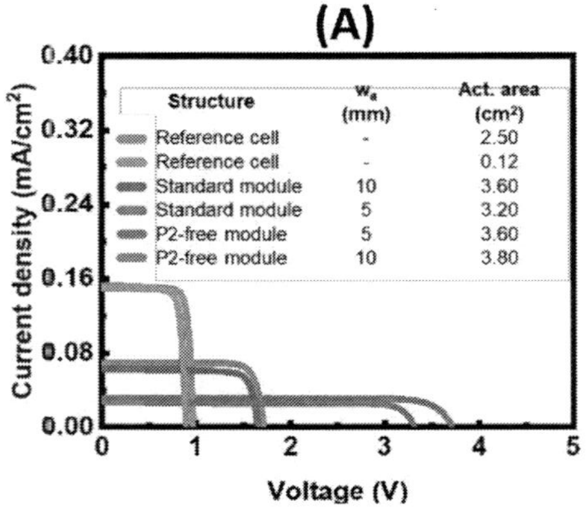

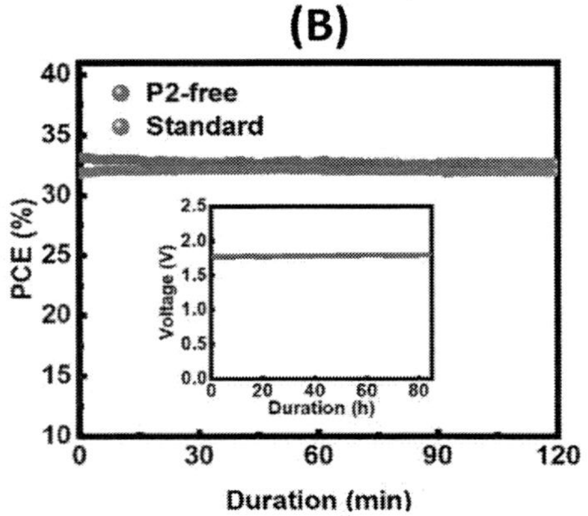

Aperture Area (cm²)	Cell width / Cell number	V_{OC} (V)	Apt. Area J_{SC} (μA/cm²)	FF (%)	Act. Area PCE (%)	GFF (%)
4.00	5 mm / 4	**3.67**	**31.33**	**82.65**	**32.17**	**90**
	5 mm / 4 / Standard	3.31	27.25	81.46	30.65	80
	10 mm / 2	**1.72**	**66.02**	**82.66**	**32.80**	**95**
	10 mm / 2 / Standard	1.65	62.59	80.76	30.05	90
0.12	- / 1	0.97	152.67	82.06	33.60	-
2.50	- / 1	0.89	150.50	80.75	30.01	-

ODTÜ GÜNAM
EU PVSEC 2025
ODTÜ METU
www.odtugunam.org

P2-Free Perovskite Solar Modules

- Expectedly the geometrical fill factor (GFF) increase significantly.
  - **90% → 95%**
- P2-free PSMs demonstrated exceptional performance under indoor illumination
  - **>82 % FF** and **>32% PCE.**
  - No electrical loss was observed in compared to the reference cells
- Air-ambient storage stability of standard and P2-free PSM;
  - **P2-free PSM** kept **~94%** of the initial PCE, whereas **standard PSM** kept **~80%** of the initial PCE

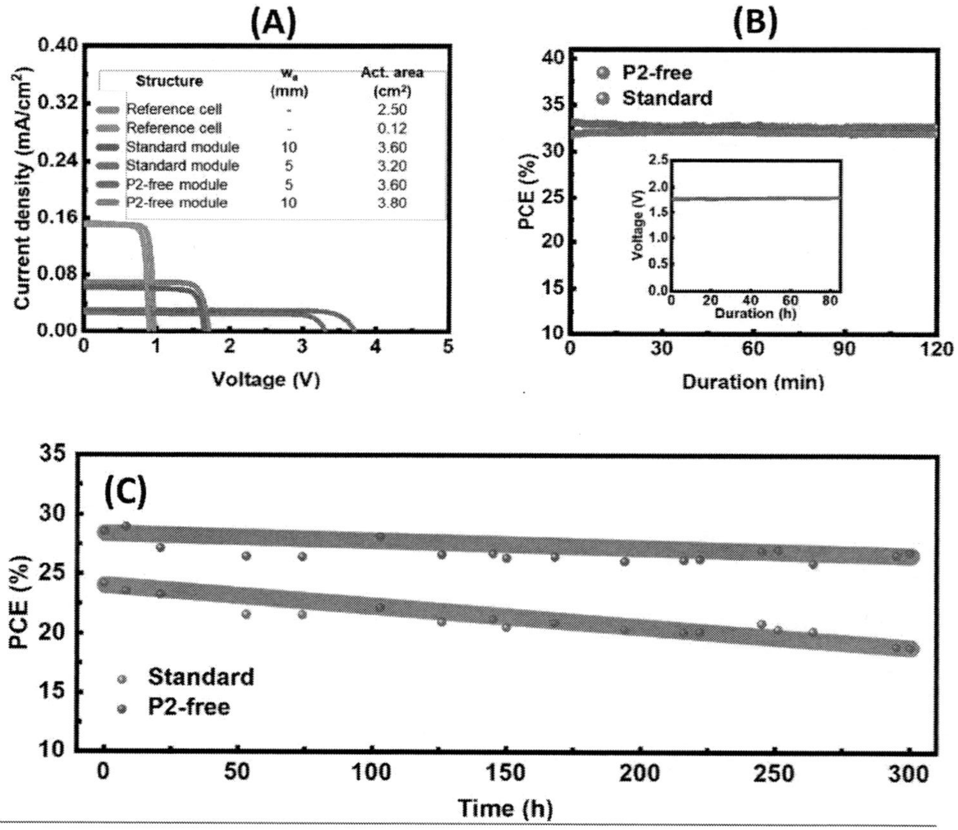

Conclusion

- **P2-free PSMs hold great promise**
  - Reduced fabrication **time**
  - Potentially opens a path for **laser-free** monolithic interconnection
  - Potential use for AM1.5 operations if the contact resistance can be further reduced.

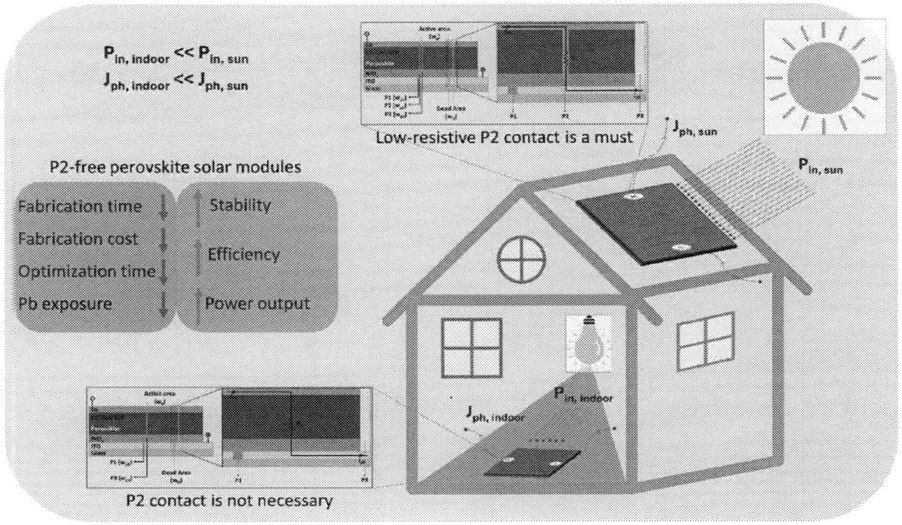

Conclusion

- **P2-free PSMs hold great promise**
  - Reduced fabrication **time**
  - Potentially opens a path for **laser-free** monolithic interconnection
  - Potential use for AM1.5 operations if the contact resistance can be further reduced.
- **>99% GFF could easily be achieved.**
  - Due to the limitations in our nanosecond laser system, GFFs were limited to the presented values.

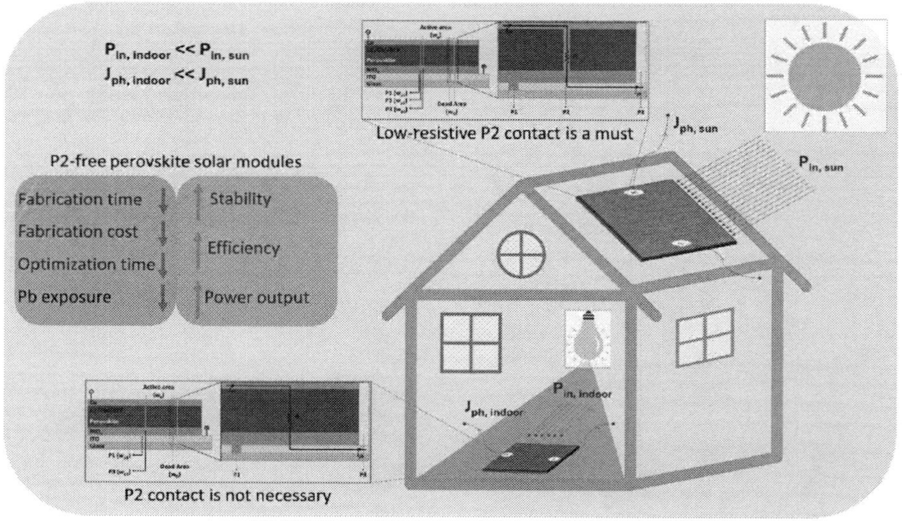

ODTÜ GÜNAM | EU PVSEC 2025 | ODTÜ METU | www.odtugunam.org

Conclusion

- **P2-free PSMs hold great promise**
  - Reduced fabrication **time**
  - Potentially opens a path for **laser-free** monolithic interconnection
  - Potential use for AM1.5 operations if the contact resistance can be further reduced.
- **>99% GFF could easily be achieved.**
  - Due to the limitations in our nanosecond laser system, GFFs were limited to the presented values.
- **Avoiding Pb exposure during P2-scribing**
  - Unlike P1 and P3, ablation of the perovskite is a must during P2.

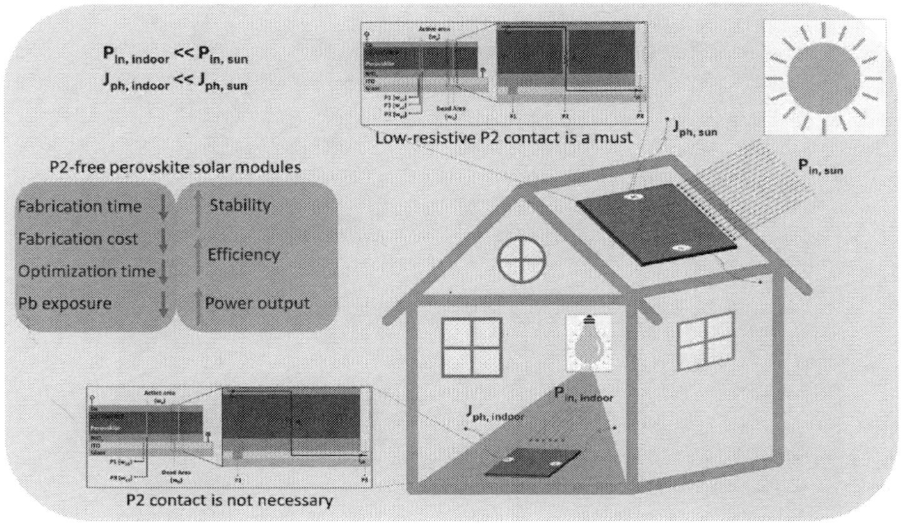

Acknowledgement

Thanks to the attendees, colleagues and co-workers of this study.

Funded by the Scientific and Technological Research Council of Türkiye (**TÜBİTAK**), Grant No. **221M472**, **22AG041**, and **124F194**.

Thanks to the **TÜBİTAK 6550** programme.

ODTÜ METU

ODTÜ GÜNAM CENTER FOR SOLAR ENERGY RESEARCH AND APPLICATIONS

SÜİT

ODTÜ GÜNAM

EU PVSEC 2025

www.odtugunam.org

42nd EU PVSEC
Bilbao, 25.09.2025

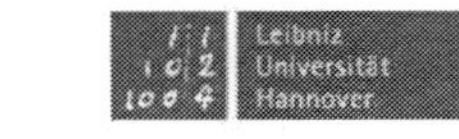

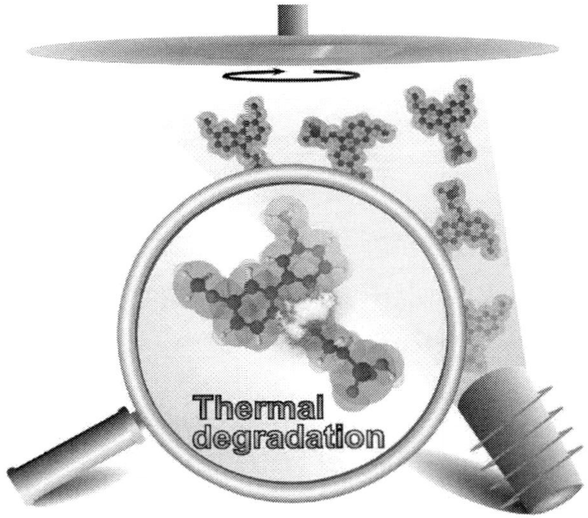

Evaporated self assembled monolayer (SAM) hole transport layers for scalable perovskite solar cells

Joachim Vollbrecht[1], Verena Barnscheidt[1], Roland Clausing[1], Johannes Löhr[1], Larissa Mettner[1], Adam Neuba[2], Annika Raugewitz[1], Jessica Strey[1], Robby Peibst[1,3]

[1] Institute for Solar Energy Research Hamelin (ISFH), Emmerthal, DE
[2] Inorganic Chemistry - Analytics, Dept. of Chemistry, Paderborn University, Paderborn, DE
[3] Leibniz University Hannover, Institute of Electronic Materials and Devices, Hannover, DE

„SAM“ based HTLs – overview

- SAM: **S**elf **A**ssembled **M**onolayer
- Since ca. 2018 used as HTLs in record breaking organic and perovskite (Pk) PV[1]
- Vast amount of organic molecules:[2] structure with head, linker, anchor groups
- Solution based deposition common
- Thickness of „SAM“ HTL[3,4] : $d \approx 3$ nm

→ More than one layer of molecules

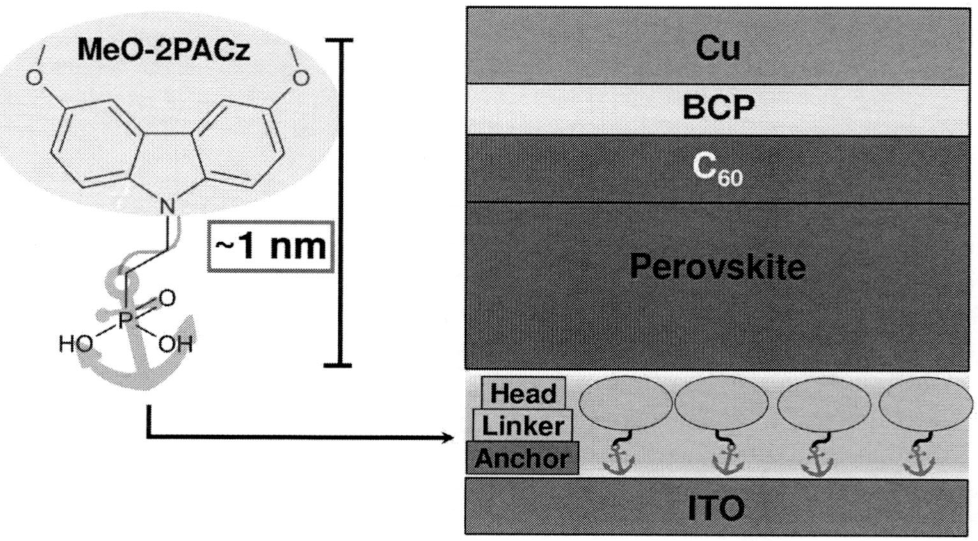

[1] A. Magomedov *et al. Adv. Energy Mater.* 2018, 1801892
[2] D. Yeo *et al. Nanomaterials* 2024, **14**, 175
[3] H. Xu *et al. Adv. Energy Mater.* 2024, 2401262
[4] O. Er-Raji *et al. Small Methods* 2025, 2401758

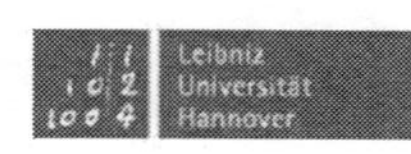

Thermal evaporation of 2PACz, MeO-2PACz, Me-4PACz

- **T**hermal **E**vaporation (TE) possible, but uncommon
- First results for PACz based compounds published with 5 nm thick layers[5]

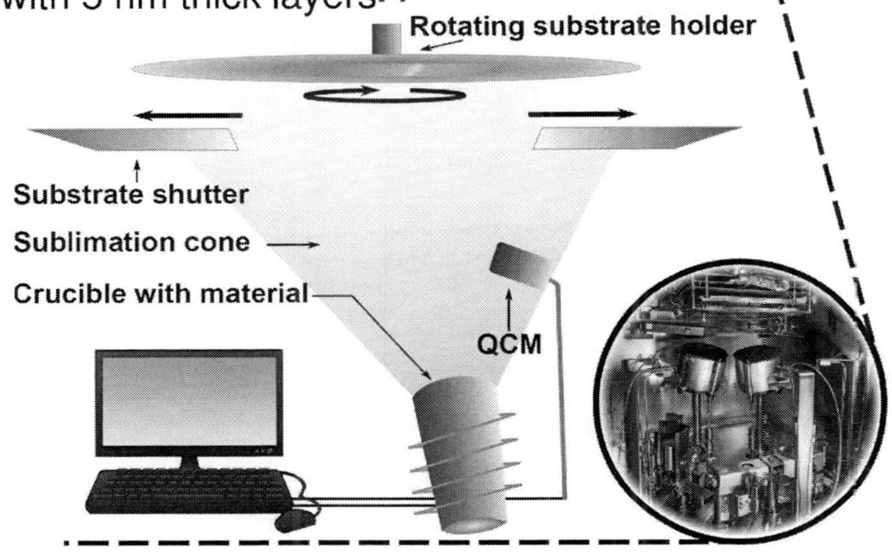

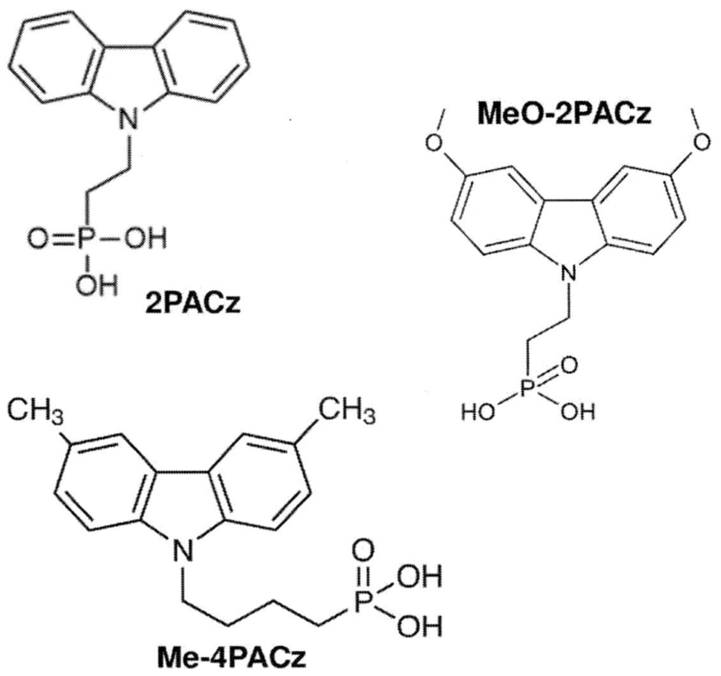

[5] A. Farag *et al. Adv. Energy Mater.* 2023, 2203982

Thermal evaporation of MeO-2PACz – *JV* results

- Spin coated (SC) vs. 5 nm evap. with fresh MeO-2PACz (1st TE) vs. 5 nm evap. with residual MeO-2PACz (2nd TE)
- SJ Pk solar cells: MeO-2PACz variation, $Cs_{0.05}MA_{0.17}FA_{0.78}Pb(I_{0.78}Br_{0.17}Cl_{0.05})_3$ (E_g=1.67eV), ETL, Cu
- Downward trend in efficiency η with each TE

→ Degradation of MeO-2PACz during TE?

Method [a]	V_{OC} (mV)	J_{SC} (mA·cm^{-2})	*FF* (%)	η (%)
SC	**1101** (1161)	**21.3** (21.7)	**66.4** (73.6)	**15.9** (18.1)
1st TE	**1066** (1110)	**20.6** (21.2)	**67.5** (72.8)	**14.9** (16.9)
2nd TE	**1016** (1091)	**20.6** (21.0)	**64.4** (67.6)	**13.5** (15.4)

[a] arithmetic means: **X**; maximum values in brackets

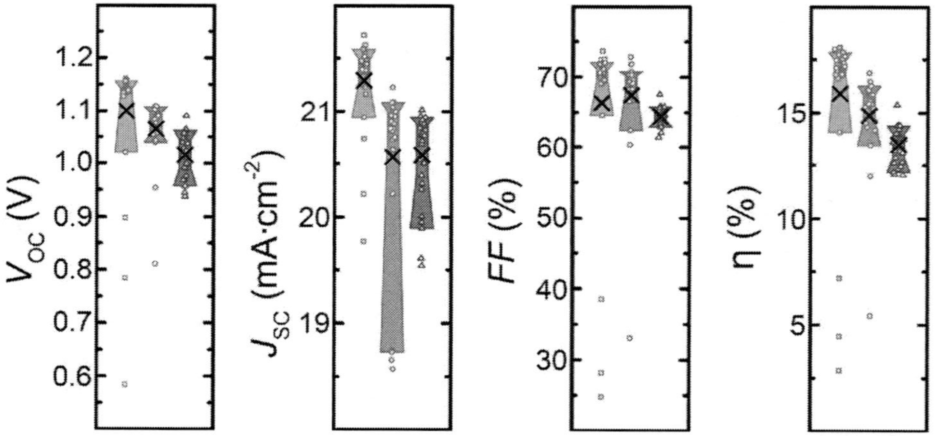

Leibniz Universität Hannover

Thermal evaporation of MeO-2PACz – MS results

ISFH

- Degradation of MeO-2PACz during TE?
- Samples of fresh MeO-2PACz and after 1st TE
- Time-of-flight mass spectrometry with electrospray ionization (TOF MS ES) in methanol
- Fragment of carbazole increased after 1st TE

→ **Adjustment of processing parameters necessary**

fresh

after 1st TE

after 2nd TE

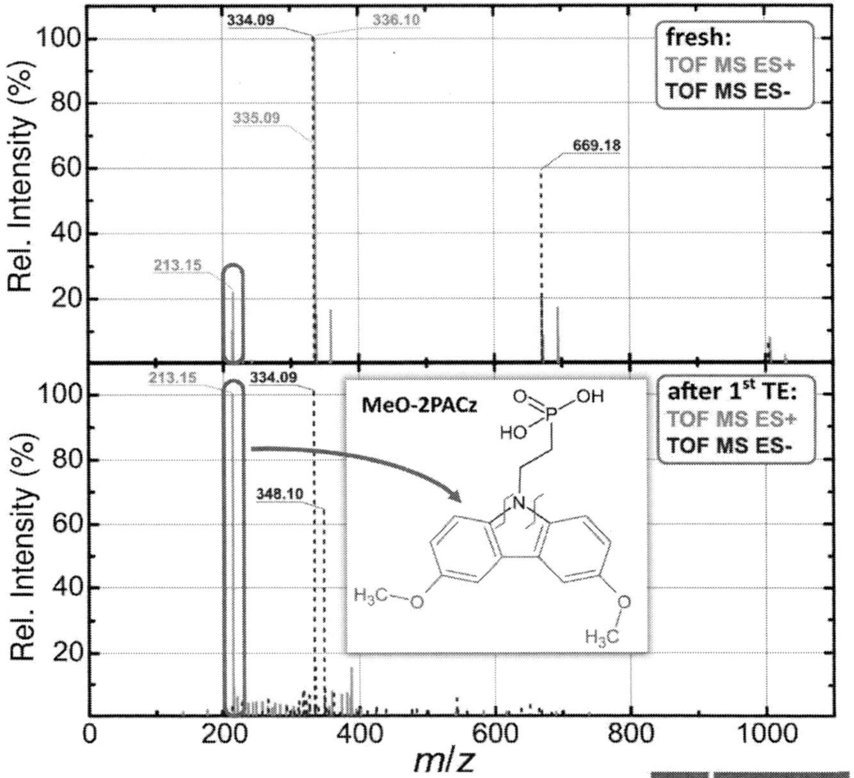

Leibniz Universität Hannover

Thermal evaporation of MeO-2PACz – processing

- Adjustments of processing paramaters: temperature T, rate ν, time t, thickness d

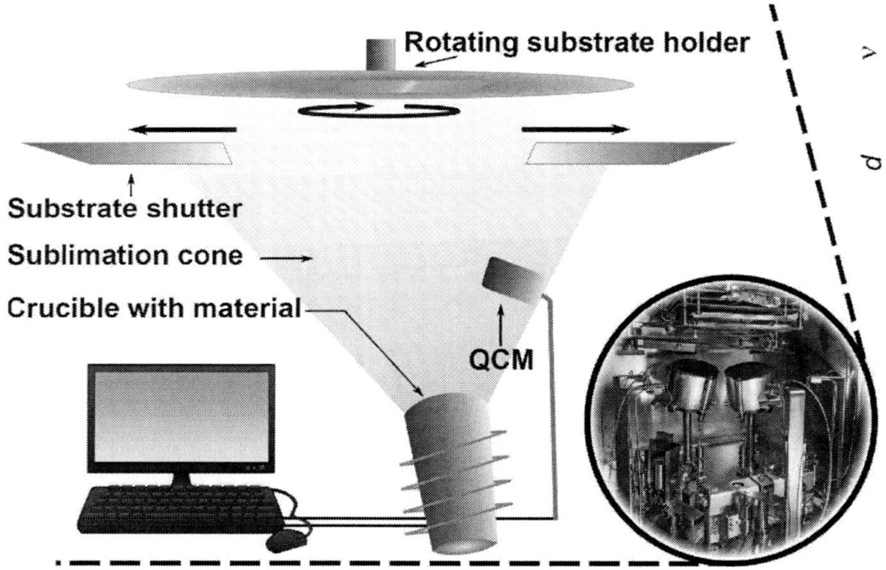

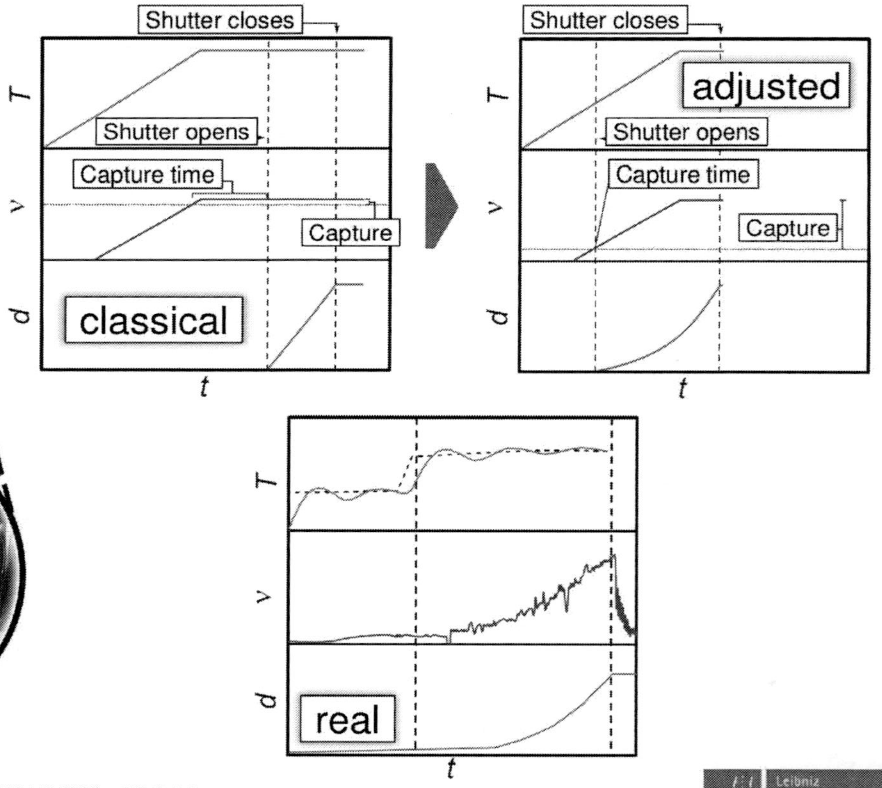

Adjusted TE of MeO-2PACz – *JV* results

- MeO-2PACz via:
  - SC as reference
  - 1 nm TE as „true“ monolayer
  - **3 nm** TE for similar thickness as SC
  - **3.5 nm** TE „complete“ evaporation
- SJ Pk solar cells: MeO-2PACz variation, $Cs_{0.05}MA_{0.17}FA_{0.78}Pb(I_{0.78}Br_{0.17}Cl_{0.05})_3$ (E_g=1.67eV), $EDAI_2$ passivation, ETL, Cu
- SC and 1 nm TE similar efficiency η
- **3 nm** and **3.5 nm** TE higher variation in η

→ MeO-2PACz via TE for evaporated absorber?

Method [a]	V_{OC} (mV)	J_{SC} (mA·cm^{-2})	*FF* (%)	η (%)
SC	**1166** (1214)	**21.3** (21.9)	**75.5** (82.6)	**19.1** (21.5)
1 nm TE	**1196** (1224)	**20.9** (21.7)	**79.6** (82.7)	**19.9** (20.8)
3 nm TE	**1140** (1209)	**19.5** (21.5)	**77.1** (82.7)	**17.2** (20.6)
3.5 nm TE	**1141** (1198)	**20.9** (21.2)	**72.4** (77.4)	**17.7** (20.6)

[a] arithmetic means: **X;** maximum values in brackets

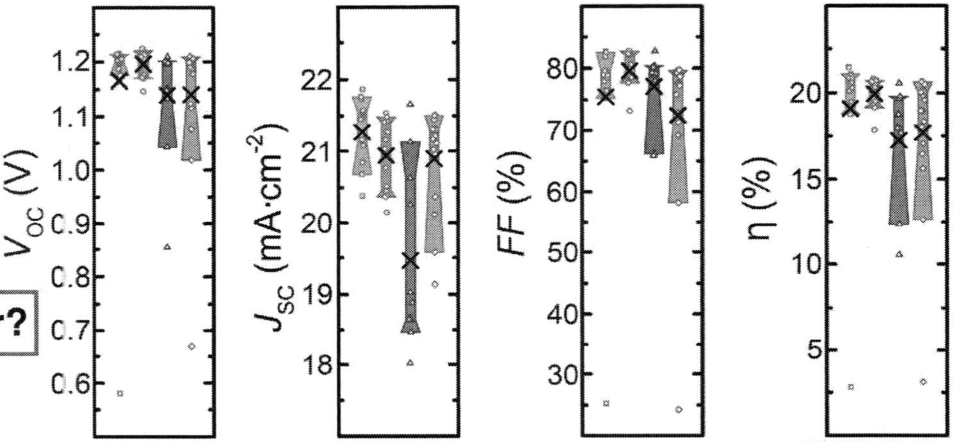

MeO-2PACz for fully solvent free Pk solar cells

- 3 nm MeO-2PACz via adjusted TE
- No washing or annealing of MeO-2PACz layer
- Two different co-evaporated Pk absorbers deposited in dedicated, separate evaporation chamber
- No additional passivation

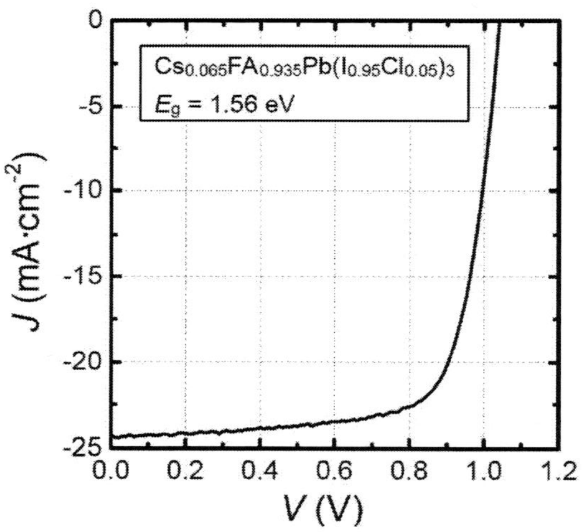

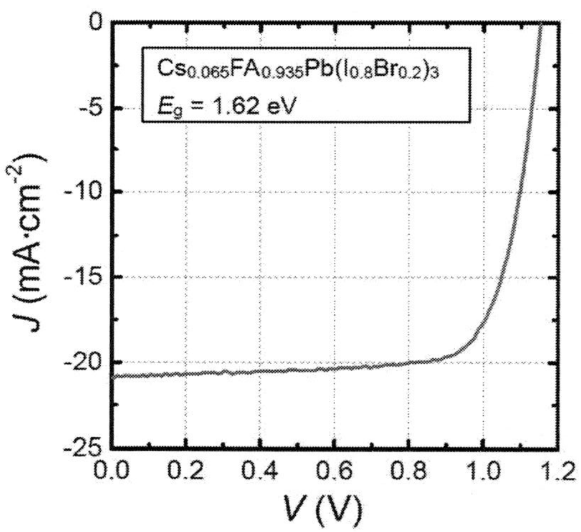

Absorber	E_g (eV)	V_{OC} (mV)	J_{SC} (mA·cm^{-2})	*FF* (%)	η (%)
$Cs_{0.065}FA_{0.935}Pb(I_{0.95}Cl_{0.05})_3$	1.56	1041	24.4	73.6	18.7
$Cs_{0.065}FA_{0.935}Pb(I_{0.8}Br_{0.2})_3$	1.62	1149	20.87	73.5	17.6

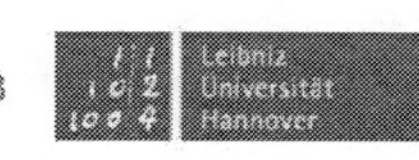

Conclusions

ISFH

- SAM based HTLs can be evaporated, but material degradation a problem
- Adjusted evaporation parameters lead to similar results as solution processing
- Fully solvent free Pk SJ solar cells with SAM based HTLs possible

More Details

Solar RRL

WILEY-VCH Solar RRL

RESEARCH ARTICLE

Less is more: Enabling Solvent-Free Fabrication of Perovskite Solar Cells via Thermal Evaporation of Ultrathin Self-Assembled Monolayers

Joachim Vollbrecht[1] | Verena Barnscheidt[1] | Roland Clausing[1] | Johannes Löhr[1] | Larissa Mettner[1] | Adam Neuba[2] | Annika Raugewitz[1] | Jessica Strey[1] | Robby Peibst[1,3]

[1]Photovoltaics Department, Institute for Solar Energy Research Hamelin (ISFH), Emmerthal, Germany | [2]Inorganic Chemistry - Analytics, Department of Chemistry, Paderborn University, Paderborn, Germany | [3]Institute of Electronic Materials and Devices, Leibniz University Hannover, Hannover, Germany

Acknowledgments

This work was funded by the state of Lower Saxony in the project **NextGenPV** funded by zukunft.niedersachsen, the joint science funding program of the Lower Saxony Ministry of Science and Culture and the Volkswagen Foundation under grant no ZN4271 and the Federal Ministry for Economic Affairs and Energy (BMWE) under grant number FKZ 03EE1098B (**2PowerPero**). The responsibility for the content of this publication lies with the authors.

V. B. thanks the Deutsche Bundesstiftung Umwelt for financial support via a scholarship.

J. V. thanks M. Löhning for the measurements of the SEM cross sections and PD Dr. Hans Egold for fruitful discussion.

Supported by:

Federal Ministry for Economic Affairs and Energy

on the basis of a decision by the German Bundestag

zukunft. niedersachsen

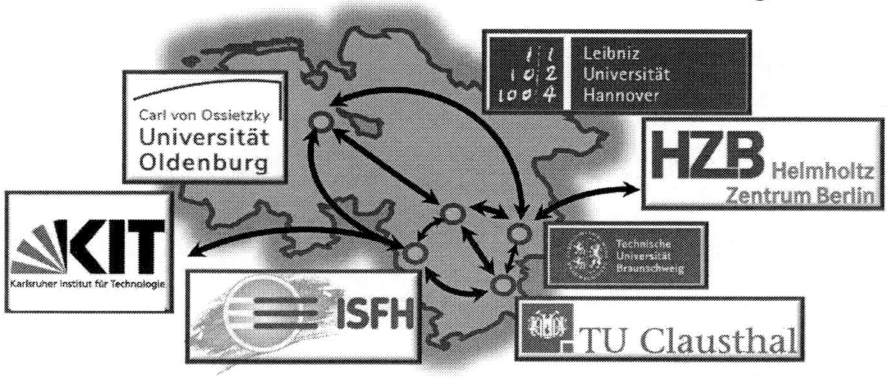

Aging of MeO-2PACz – *JV* curves

ISFH

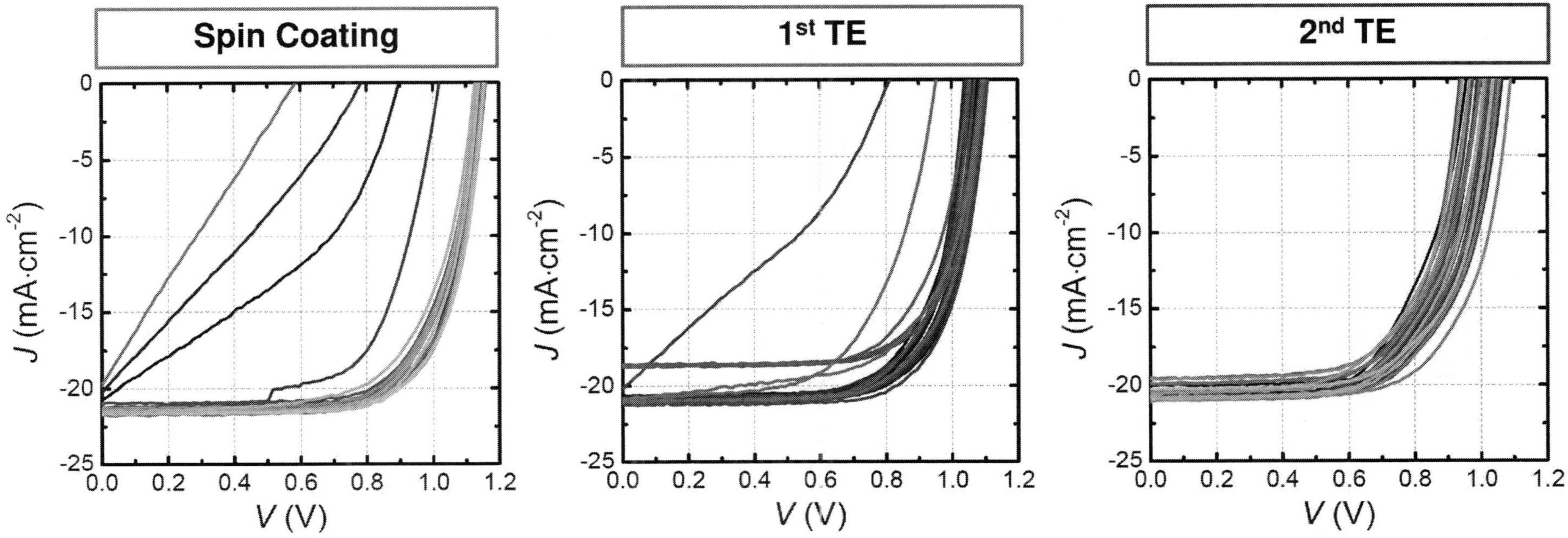

Aging of MeO-2PACz – hysteresis

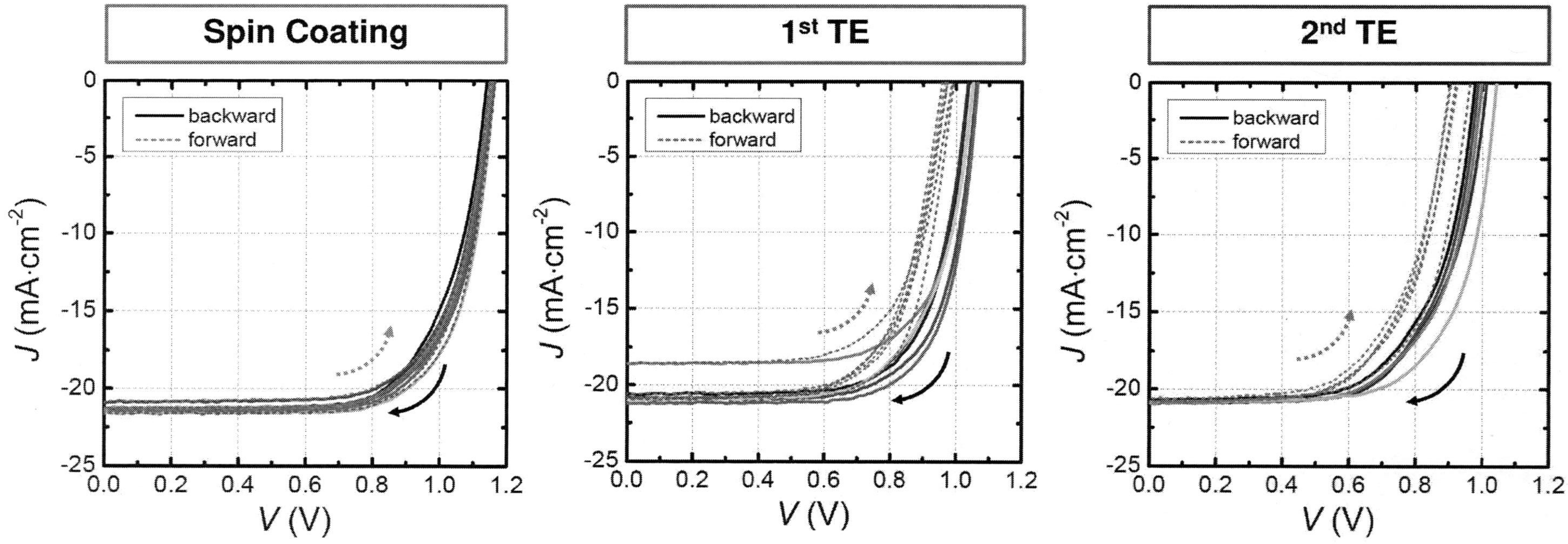

Aging of MeO-2PACz – *JV* results after 306 days

ISFH

- Devices after 306 days of storage under N_2 in the dark
- Only devices that originally worked
- SC devices degraded most

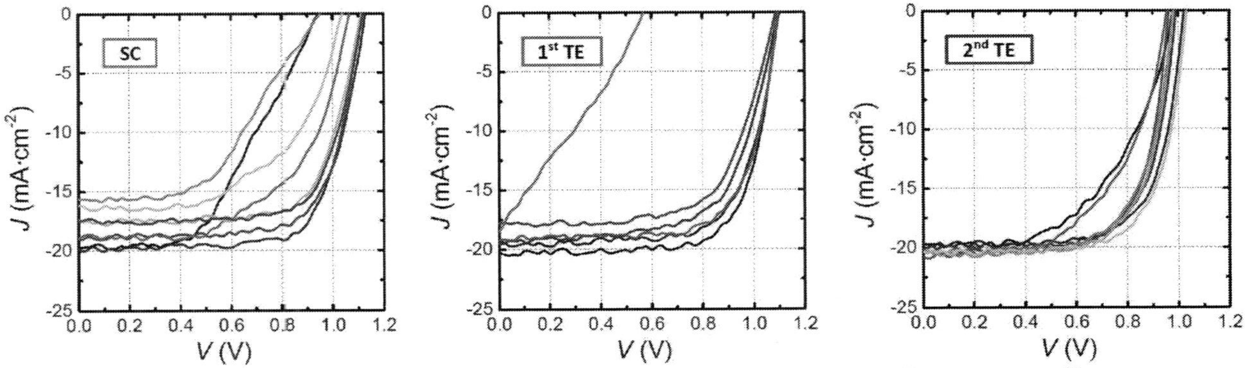

Method a)	V_{OC} (mV)	J_{SC} (mA·cm⁻²)	*FF* (%)	η (%)
SC	1060 (1130)	18.1 (20.0)	61.9 (72.1)	12.0 (16.0)
1st TE	1007 (1099)	19.2 (20.3)	61.6 (71.5)	12.5 (15.9)
2nd TE	989 (1034)	20.2 (20.8)	65.4 (70.2)	12.8 (14.1)

a) arithmetic means shown, maximum values in brackets

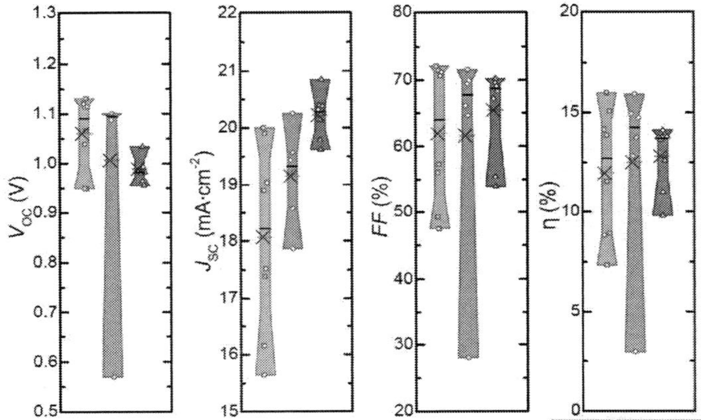

Leibniz Universität Hannover

Thickness variation of MeO-2PACz – *JV* curves

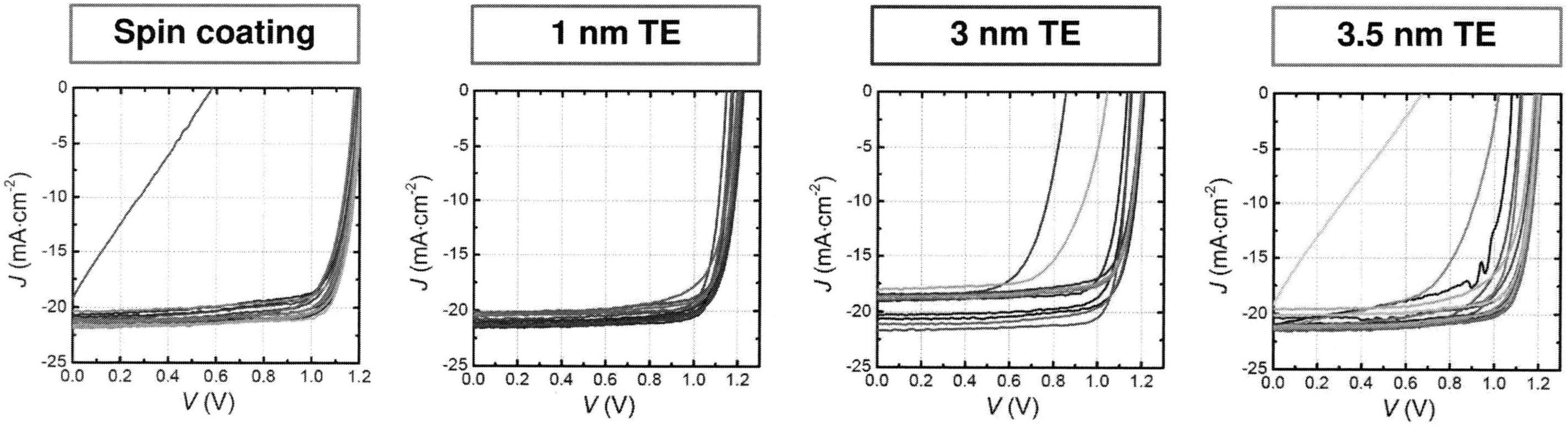

Thickness variation – hysteresis

Spin coating

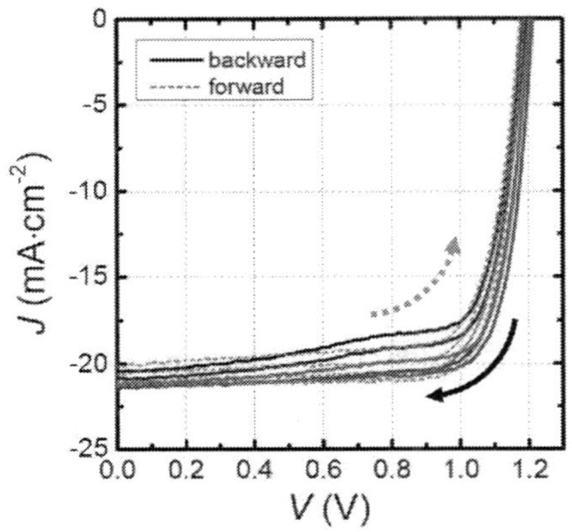

1 nm TE

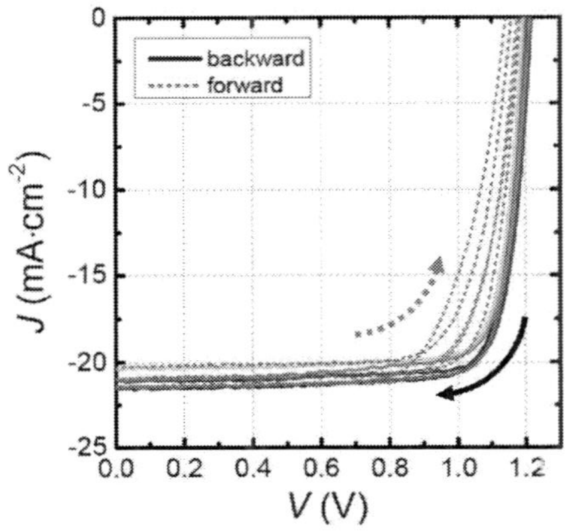

3 nm TE

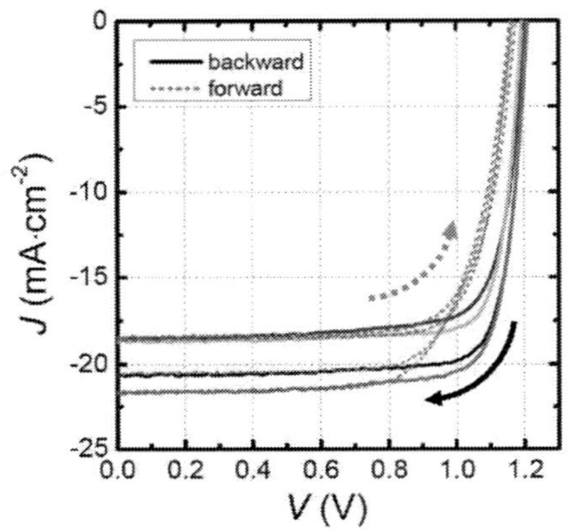

3.5 nm TE

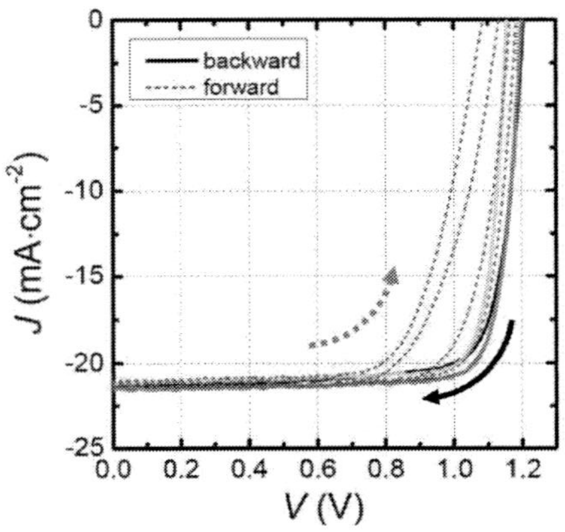

Thickness variation – *JV* results after 257 days

- Devices after 257 days of storage under N_2 in the dark
- Only devices that originally worked
- 1 nm TE least degraded

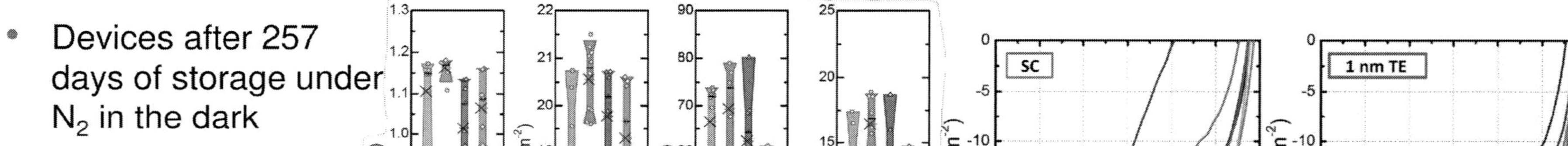

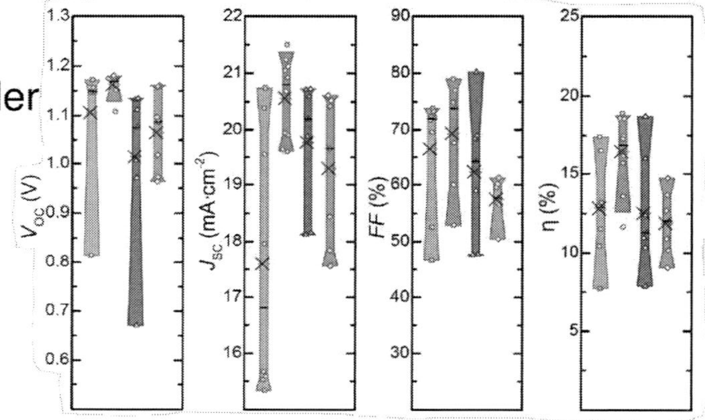

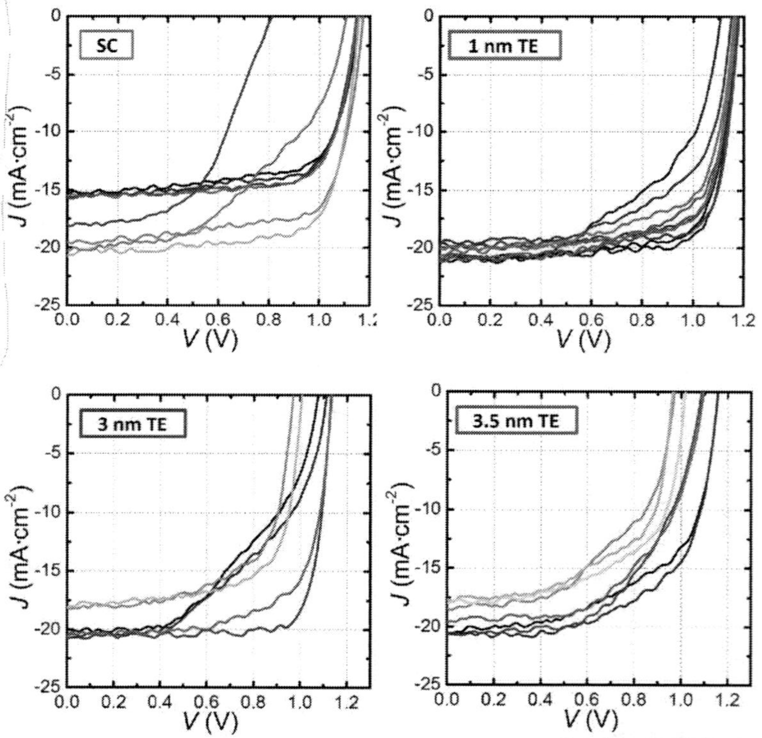

Method [a]	V_{OC} (mV)	J_{SC} (mA·cm^{-2})	*FF* (%)	η (%)
SC	1106 (1172)	17.6 (20.7)	66.5 (73.9)	12.8 (17.4)
1 nm TE	1163 (1181)	20.6 (21.5)	69.3 (79.0)	16.4 (18.9)
3 nm TE	1015 (1135)	19.8 (20.7)	62.3 (80.3)	12.5 (18.7)
3.5 nm TE	1065 (1160)	19.3 (20.6)	57.5 (61.2)	11.9 (14.7)

[a] arithmetic means shown, maximum values in brackets

EQE and absolute PL

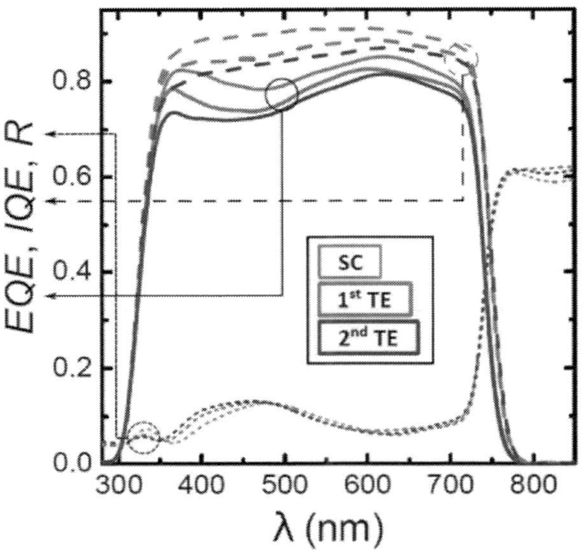

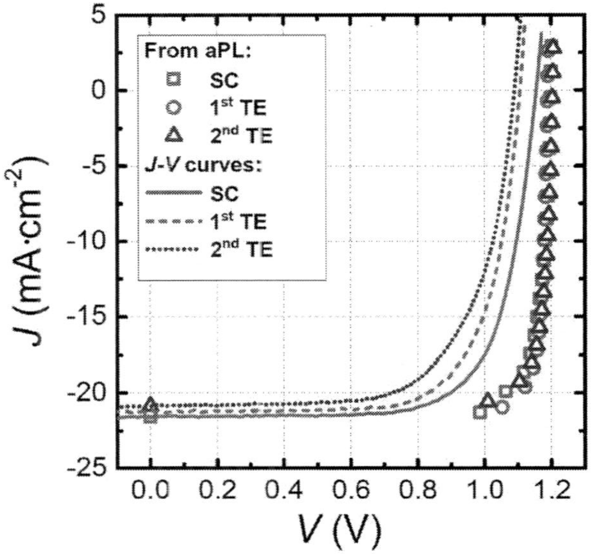

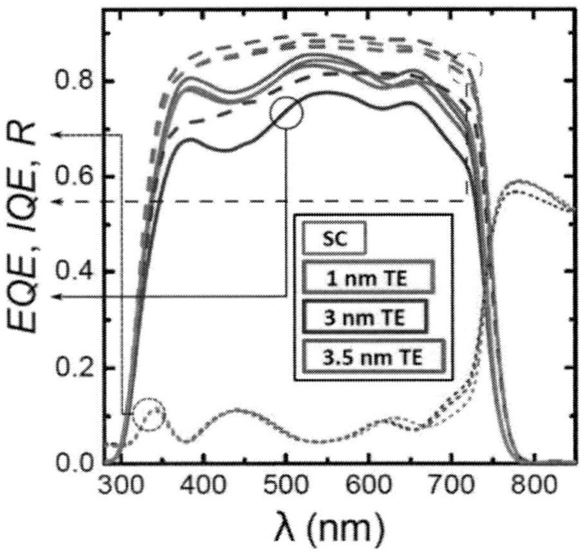

EQE and absolute PL

ISFH

MeO-2PACz aging

Method	$J_{SC,EQE}$ (mA·cm^{-2})	PLQY (%)	E_{loss} (meV)	Shunt rate
SC	18.9	2.06	99.75	31/32 (97%)
1st TE	18.3	1.98	100.77	27/32 (84%)
2nd TE	17.9	2.63	93.47	29/32 (91%)

MeO-2PACz thickness variation

Method	$J_{SC,EQE}$ (mA·cm^{-2})	PLQY (%)	E_{loss} (meV)	Shunt rate
SC	18.5	1.28	112.07	17/20 (85%)
1 nm TE	18.1	0.93	120.25	15/20 (75%)
3 nm TE	16.6	1.19	113.85	11/16 (69%)
3.5 nm TE	18.7	0.93	120.17	17/20 (85%)

SEM cross sections

MeO-2PACz aging

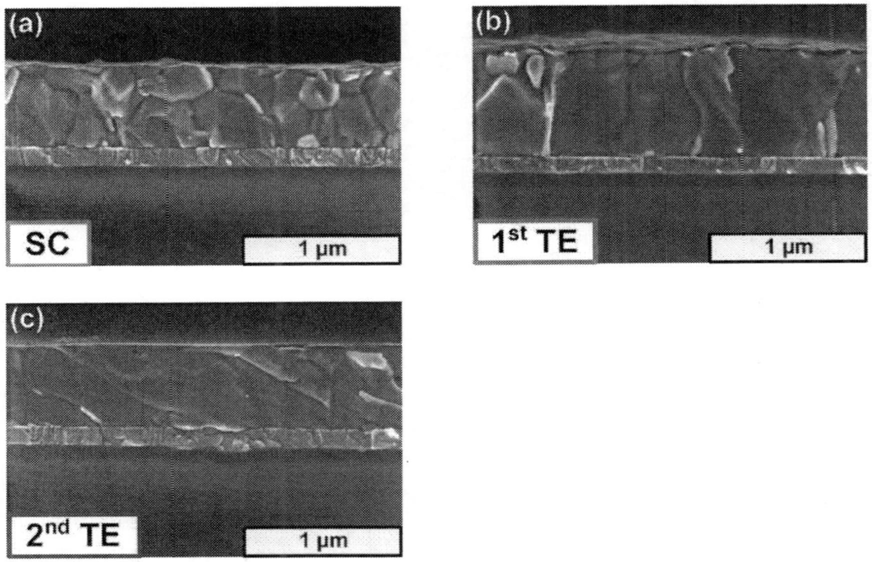

MeO-2PACz thickness variation

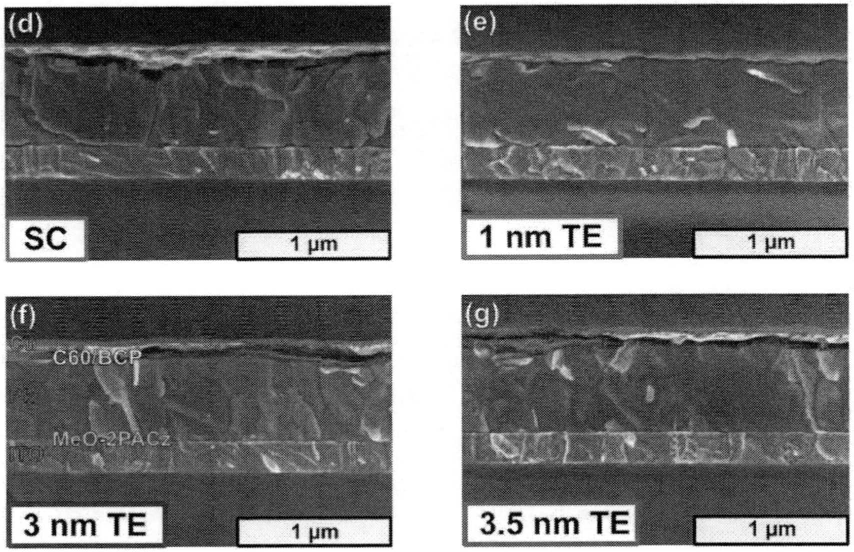

XRD Pk after storage in N_2

MeO-2PACz aging after 306 days

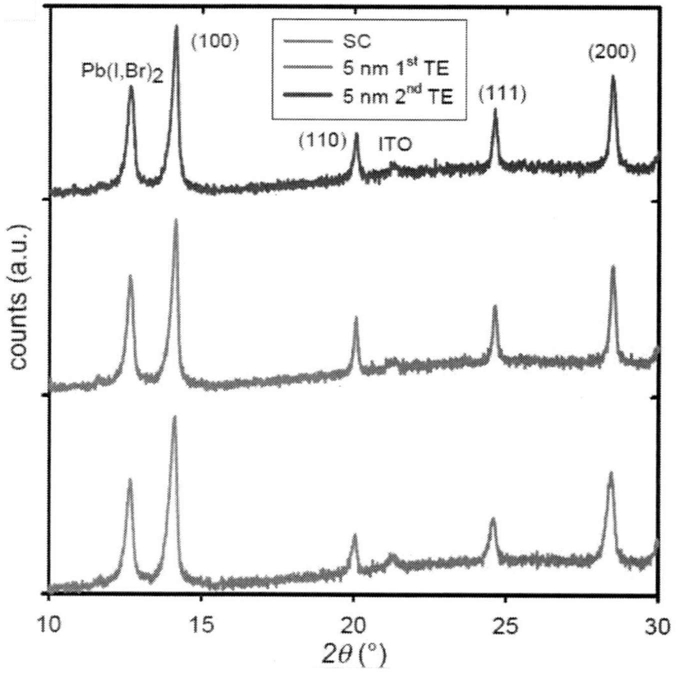

MeO-2PACz thickness var. after 257 days

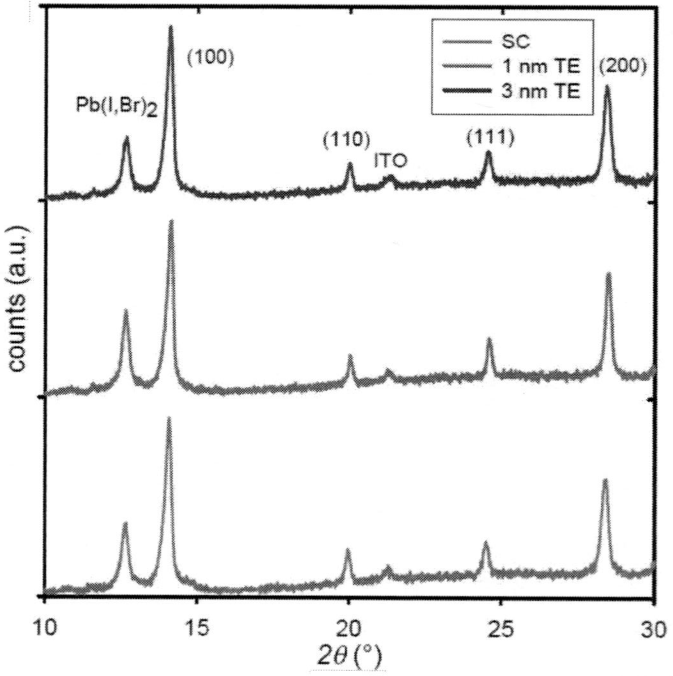

42nd European Photovoltaic Solar Energy Conference and Exhibition

This presentation was selected by the Sc. Committee of the EU PVSEC 2025 for submission of a full paper to one of the EU PVSEC's collaborating peer-reviewed journals.

OUTDOOR PERFORMANCE AND DEGRADATION ANALYSIS OF INVERTED PEROVSKITE SOLAR CELLS

°Makoto Konagai[1], Hayato Okawa [1], Ryousuke Ishikawa[1], Masatoshi Yanagida [2], Yasuhiro Shirai [2]
[1]Advanced Research Laboratories, Tokyo City University, [2]National Institute for Materials Science (NIMS)

ABSTRACT:

Perovskite solar cells were evaluated under two installation conditions: fixed at a south-facing tilt of 35° and mounted on a 2-axis tracking system. Significant performance degradation was observed during the high-temperature periods of July and August, with conversion efficiencies declining from 20–22% to 8–10%. Comparison between fixed-angle and tracking installations indicated that cells on the 2-axis system began to degrade one to two months earlier. Both *J-V* curve tracing and maximum power point tracking (MPPT) methods were employed, and although the sample size was limited, MPPT measurements appeared to induce slightly less degradation than *J-V* tracing. Three years of outdoor measurements revealed that the most critical degradation factor was elevated cell temperature during summer, accompanied by structural changes in the perovskite layer. Post-degradation analyses were conducted using optical microscopy, X-ray diffraction (XRD), and cross-sectional scanning electron microscopy (SEM). Severely degraded cells exhibited high-resistance layers in the cross-sections. Accelerated indoor degradation tests using a solar simulator with heating reproduced similar degradation phenomena, confirming the key role of temperature in device deterioration.

Keywords: Perovskite solar cell, Degradation, Outdoor performance

1 INTRODUCTION

The conversion efficiency of perovskite solar cells has improved remarkably in recent years.[1–3] Moreover, large-area module production has already commenced in several industries. Despite these advances, the widespread deployment of perovskite solar cells for power generation requires a reliable demonstration of long-term stability over 20–30 years. The degradation phenomena of perovskite solar cells have been comprehensively summarized in previous studies.[4–7]

To address this issue, our group has been systematically investigating the outdoor operational stability of perovskite solar cells and elucidating their degradation mechanisms to promote their practical implementation in power generation. This study presents detailed results from outdoor power generation tests conducted over a three-year period, beginning in September 2022, at Tokyo City University. Furthermore, post-degradation evaluations and analyses of the devices are discussed.

For large-area modules, the initial fill factor (FF) is frequently low, which complicates the evaluation of early-stage degradation. To circumvent this, we employed small-area (≈1 cm²) cells with high initial efficiencies of 20–23% and an initial FF of approximately 0.8.

One of the major challenges in the development of perovskite solar cells is the identification of degradation pathways.[8–11] To date, there have been no reports on the observation of degraded perovskite solar cells using optical microscopy, nor on the detection of charge-up phenomena induced by high-resistance layers under high-magnification SEM. In this study, such post-degradation analyses are introduced as they provide essential insights for developing strategies to mitigate thermally induced degradation, particularly under summer operating conditions.[12–15]

2 AIM AND APPROACH

The perovskite solar cells employed for outdoor measurements were fabricated by the National Institute for Materials Science (NIMS) and possessed the following device structure: glass/ITO/NiO_x/perovskite/C60/BCP/Ag (Fig. 1).[16] Each substrate had dimensions of 5 cm × 5 cm and contained four cells, each with an active area of 1.26 cm². The initial power conversion efficiencies (PCEs) were in the range of 20–23%. To enhance durability, the devices were encapsulated with glass on both sides.

Outdoor testing was performed under two installation conditions: (i) fixed mounting with a south-facing tilt angle of 35°, and (ii) installation on a 2-axis solar tracking system. Performance evaluation included comparison of current–voltage (*J-V*) curve tracing and maximum power point tracking (MPPT) methods.[17] Furthermore, efficiencies measured at noon on clear days were compared with the corresponding daily average values. To investigate seasonal degradation effects, particularly during the summer when device deterioration was most pronounced, additional tests were conducted using a UV-cut filter.[18]

The degradation phenomena of perovskite solar cells have been extensively documented in the literature, with multiple degradation pathways identified. In our three-year outdoor stability study, we found that the most critical degradation factor was the rise in cell temperature during summer, which was accompanied by structural changes in the perovskite layer. Notably, cells installed on the 2-axis tracking system exhibited accelerated degradation compared to those fixed at a 35° tilt.

To elucidate the underlying mechanisms, degraded

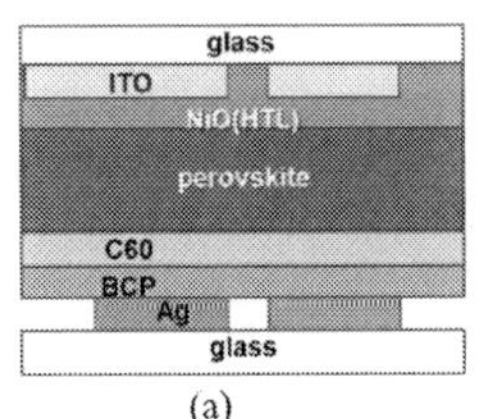

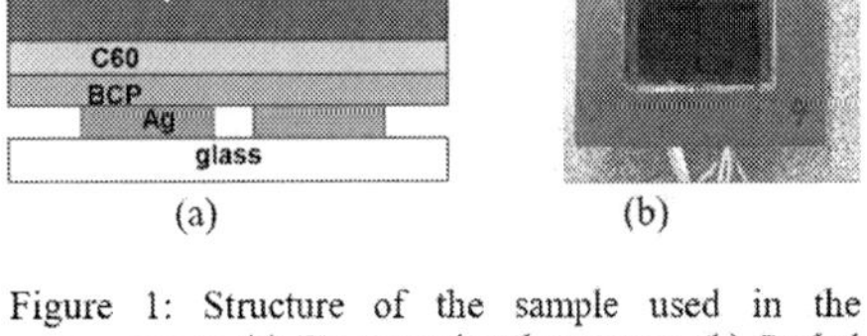

(a) (b)

Figure 1: Structure of the sample used in the measurement. (a) Cross-sectional structure, (b) Sealed cell

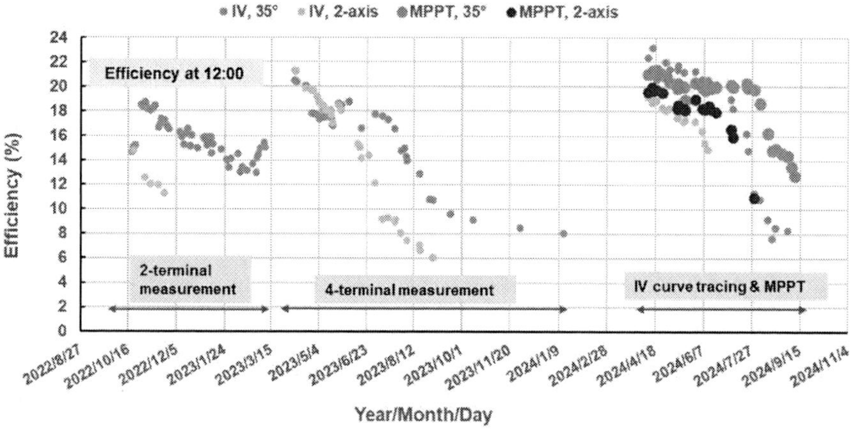

Fig.2 Outdoor power generation characteristics of perovskite solar cells from 2022 to 2024. Conversion efficiency values are based on measurements at 12:00 under solar irradiance conditions of approximately 100 mW/cm². Only reverse scan values are shown

cells were examined using optical microscopy, X-ray diffraction (XRD), and cross-sectional scanning electron microscopy (SEM). In severely degraded devices, high-resistance interfacial layers were clearly identified in the cross-sectional analyses.

To reproduce these phenomena under controlled conditions, accelerated degradation tests were performed indoors using a solar simulator combined with external heating. The results demonstrated that heating the cells to approximately 70 °C induced degradation behaviors analogous to those observed in outdoor environments.

3 EXPERIMETAL RESULTS

3.1 Summary of three-year measurement results

Figure 2 presents the outdoor power generation characteristics measured over a three-year period. All samples exhibited degradation, which was most pronounced during the summer months. In 2023, new devices were introduced in April and evaluated using a four-terminal measurement configuration. These samples exhibited initial efficiencies exceeding 20% with a fill factor of approximately 0.8. However, significant deterioration was observed during the high-temperature periods of July and August. Although a UV-cut filter was installed in July, its effect on suppressing degradation was negligible.

A comparison between fixed-angle (35° tilt) and 2-axis tracking configurations revealed that devices on the tracking system exhibited earlier degradation, typically by one to two months. Beginning in April 2024, MPPT measurements were conducted in parallel with conventional *J-V* curve tracing, owing to concerns that *J-V* curve measurements might contribute to degradation. Nevertheless, despite the limited number of samples, both methods indicated a comparable extent of degradation.

3.2 Comparative evaluation of degradation methods

Although reliability assessments and the identification of degradation mechanisms in perovskite solar cells remain at an early stage, numerous degradation pathways have already been reported. Among them, it has been suggested that *J-V* curve tracing may induce degradation due to the electric field applied across the junction. In this study, both *J-V* curve tracing and MPPT method were employed for performance evaluation, and the results were systematically compared. Under the MPPT protocol, *J-V* curve measurements were limited to three times per day.

Figure 3 compares the outcomes of MPPT and *J-V* measurements. MPPT continuously tracked the maximum power point, whereas *J-V* curves were recorded only at 11:00, 12:00, and 13:00 JST each day. The results demonstrate that both conversion efficiency and fill factor exhibited gradual degradation beginning in April, with accelerated deterioration observed during July and August when cell temperatures exceeded 50 °C. In addition, hysteresis—initially negligible—was found to increase progressively over time.

Although no temperature correction was applied, the conversion efficiency decreased from an initial value of approximately 20% to 10–15% by the end of August. While the sample size was limited, the results suggest that devices evaluated under the MPPT protocol exhibited slightly reduced degradation compared with those measured primarily by *J-V* curve tracing.

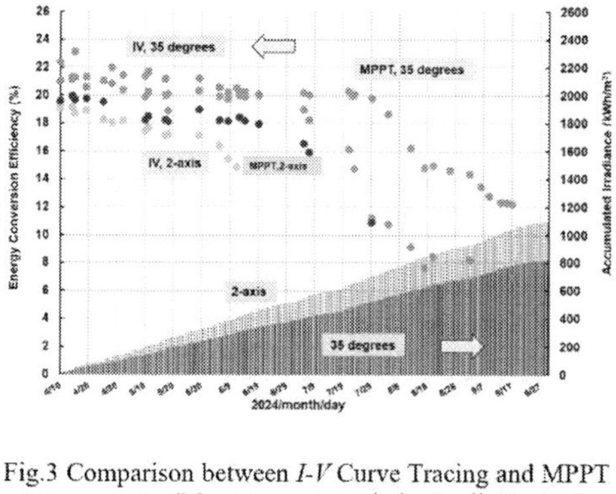

Fig.3 Comparison between *I-V* Curve Tracing and MPPT measurements (Measurement period: April–September 2024)

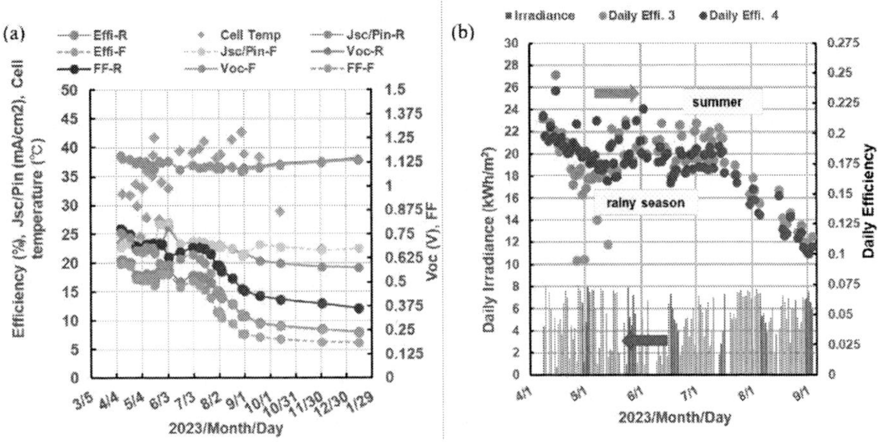

Fig.4 Comparison of (a) 12:00 conversion efficiency trends and (b) daily average efficiency trends.

3.3 Daily average efficiency

Figure 4 compares the conversion efficiency measured at 12:00 by *J-V* curve tracing with the corresponding daily average efficiency. For the 12:00 data, only measurements under an irradiation intensity of approximately 100 mW cm^{-2} were considered, while daily averages were plotted only for days with a total solar irradiance exceeding 5 kWh/m^2. In perovskite solar cells, the fill factor often appears larger under low-irradiance conditions, even after degradation. By restricting the analysis to data collected under sufficiently high irradiance, both measurement methods yielded consistent results.

4 DISCUSSIONS

4.1 Estimating cell temperature during operation

When evaluating the outdoor performance of perovskite solar cells, one of the most critical parameters is the cell operating temperature. However, accurately determining the junction temperature of perovskite solar cells encapsulated between glass plates is challenging, owing to the low thermal conductivity of both glass and the perovskite absorber. Ideally, precise measurement would require encapsulating either a temperature sensor or a calibrated, thin silicon reference cell alongside the device.

In the present study, the measurement system initially employed placed the temperature sensor on the exterior surface of the encapsulated cell, preventing accurate monitoring of the internal cell temperature. To address this limitation, the cell temperature was instead estimated from the I_{sc}–V_{oc} relationship obtained during outdoor measurements (Fig. 5). Although numerous reports on perovskite solar cell degradation exist, relatively few have investigated their temperature characteristics under outdoor operating conditions, as undertaken in this study.

For crystalline Si and GaAs solar cells, the junction temperature during operation can generally be estimated from the I_{sc}–V_{oc} relationship, provided that the temperature dependence of the dark current (I_d–V_d characteristics) is measured indoors. In contrast, for perovskite solar cells, measuring I_d–V_d characteristics at elevated temperatures (70–100 °C) is problematic due to concerns about accelerated degradation under such conditions. Therefore, in this study, the junction temperature during outdoor operation was estimated using the temperature coefficient (within the range of −1.6 to −2.0 mV/K obtained from separate temperature-dependent measurements),[20] this corresponds to a cell temperature rise of ~56 °C. Thus, the cell temperature was estimated to increase from ~14 °C in the early morning to ~70 °C at 14:00. A similar analysis for June 8 yielded a maximum cell temperature of ~78 °C.

For the cell fixed at a 35° tilt, the maximum cell temperature was estimated at ~70 °C. The higher temperature observed in the 2-axis tracking device is attributed to its peak irradiance (~1.1 kW/m^2, ~10% higher than that of the fixed installation) and daily accumulated irradiance (~30% higher).

These results indicate that 2-axis tracking accelerates perovskite solar cell degradation through a combined effect of increased irradiance and elevated operating temperature, compared with fixed-tilt installations.

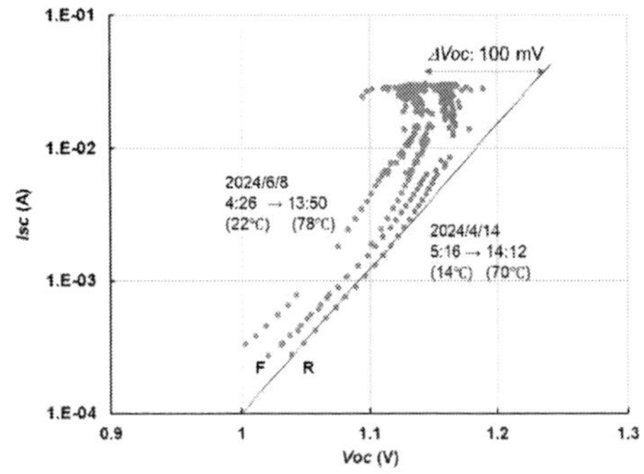

Fig.5 I_{sc}–V_{oc} plot of a perovskite solar cell mounted on a 2-axis tracker. On June 8th, the cell temperature was estimated to have reached a maximum of 78 °C.

4.2 SEM observation after deterioration

The degradation phenomena of perovskite solar cells have been extensively reported in the literature, with causes such as ion migration and elemental diffusion at interfaces identified. Results from the three-year outdoor measurements presented in this study indicate that the most critical factors driving degradation are elevated cell

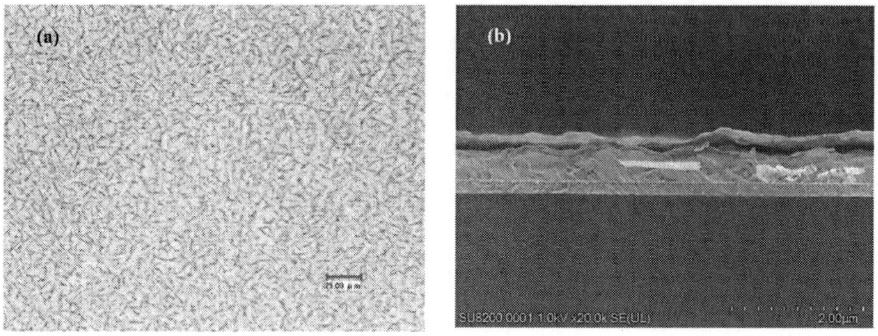

Fig.6 Structural changes in degraded samples:
(a) OM image observed through the glass substrate (contrast adjusted).
(b) Cross-sectional SEM image. White regions indicate high-resistance layers.

temperatures during summer and the resulting structural changes in the perovskite layer.

To further elucidate the underlying mechanisms, surface observations were conducted using optical microscopy (OM), cross-sectional analyses were performed with SEM, and XRD measurements were carried out. Cross-sectional SEM images of severely degraded cells revealed the formation of high-resistance layers (Fig. 6). Although these layers did not produce significant peaks in XRD, they are likely associated with the formation of the δ-phase.

4.3 Indoor Accelerated Degradation Tests

To reproduce these degradation phenomena under controlled conditions, accelerated indoor tests were performed using a solar simulator with external heating. Heating the cells to approximately 70 °C induced degradation behaviors comparable to those observed in outdoor measurements.

5 SUMMARY

In conclusion, although multiple factors contribute to the degradation of contemporary perovskite solar cells, the present study demonstrates for the first time that high-resistance layers emerge at elevated operating temperatures. This phenomenon is likely associated with phase transitions from the α-phase to the δ-phase. Further confirmation through XRD and transmission electron microscopy (TEM) is required to substantiate this interpretation.

ACKNOWLEDGEMENT

This work was supported by the Priority Research Project of Tokyo City University, Japan.

References

[1] T. Miyasaka, A. Kojima, K. Teshima, Y. Shirai, *J Am Chem Soc* 2009, *131*, 6050.
[2] N. G. Park, *Materials Today* 2015, *18*, 65.
[3] M. A. Green, E. D. Dunlop, M. Yoshita, N. Kopidakis, K. Bothe, G. Siefer, X. Hao, J. Y. Jiang, *Progress in Photovoltaics: Research and Applications* 2025, *33*, 3.
[4] T. Matsui, T. Yamamoto, T. Nishihara, R. Morisawa, T. Yokoyama, T. Sekiguchi, T. Negami, *Advanced Materials* 2019, DOI 10.1002/adma.201806823.
[5] J. Zhuang, J. Wang, F. Yan, *Review on Chemical Stability of Lead Halide Perovskite Solar Cells*, Springer Nature Singapore, 2023.
[6] D. B. Khadka, M. Yanagida, Y. Shirai, *Solar Energy Materials and Solar Cells* 2025, *281*, DOI 10.1016/j.solmat.2024.113319.
[7] S. Baumann, G. E. Eperon, A. Virtuani, Q. Jeangros, D. B. Kern, D. Barrit, J. Schall, W. Nie, G. Oreski, M. Khenkin, C. Ulbrich, R. Peibst, J. S. Stein, M. Köntges, *Energy Environ Sci* 2024, *17*, 7566.
[8] M. Jošt, B. Lipovšek, B. Glažar, A. Al-Ashouri, K. Brecl, G. Matič, A. Magomedov, V. Getautis, M. Topič, S. Albrecht, *Adv Energy Mater* 2020, *10*, DOI 10.1002/aenm.202000454.
[9] M. Konagai, H. Okawa, R. Ishikawa, M. Yanagida, Y. Shirai, *Proc. of the 34th International Photovoltaic Science and Engineering Conf. (PVSEC-34)* 2023, 222.
[10] V. Paraskeva, M. Norton, A. Livera, A. Kyprianou, M. Hadjipanayi, E. Peraticos, A. Aguirre, S. Ramesh, T. Merckx, R. Ebner, T. Aernouts, A. Krishna, G. E. Georghiou, *ACS Energy Lett* 2024, 5081.
[11] M. Khenkin, H. Köbler, M. Remec, R. Roy, U. Erdil, J. Li, N. Phung, G. Adwan, G. Paramasivam, Q. Emery, E. Unger, R. Schlatmann, C. Ulbrich, A. Abate, *Energy Environ Sci* 2023, *17*, 602.
[12] G. Hodes, *Science (1979)* 2013, DOI 10.1126/science.1245473.
[13] M. Saliba, T. Matsui, K. Domanski, J.-Y. Seo, A. Ummadisi, M. Saliba, T. Matsui, K. Domanski, J.-Y. Seo, A. Ummadisingu, S. M. Zakeeruddin, J.-P. Correa-Baena, W. R. Tress, A. Abate, M. Grätzel, *Science (1979)* 2016, *354*.
[14] T. Haeger, R. Heiderhoff, T. Riedl, *J Mater Chem C Mater* 2020, *8*, 14289.
[15] M. Nakamura, I. Takenaka, T. Mabuchi, C. Nishiyama, K. Tada, T. Bessho, H. Segawa, *ACS Appl Energy Mater* 2022, *5*, 10409.

[16] M. Yanagida, T. Nakamura, T. Yoshida, D. B. Khadka, Y. Shirai, K. Miyano, *Jpn J Appl Phys* 2023, *62*, SK1054.
[17] L. Cojocaru, S. Uchida, K. Tamaki, P. V. V. Jayaweera, S. Kaneko, J. Nakazaki, T. Kubo, H. Segawa, *Sci Rep* 2017, *7*, 1.
[18] M. B. Islam, M. Yanagida, Y. Shirai, Y. Nabetani, K. Miyano, *ACS Omega* 2017, *2*, 2291.
[19] S. Charan, M. Konagai, K. Takahashi, *J Appl Phys* 1979, *50*, 963.
[20] T. Moot, J. B. Patel, G. McAndrews, E. J. Wolf, D. Morales, I. E. Gould, B. A. Rosales, C. C. Boyd, L. M. Wheeler, P. A. Parilla, S. W. Johnston, L. T. Schelhas, M. D. McGehee, J. M. Luther, *ACS Energy Lett* 2021, *6*, 2038.

IPVF

Strategies for quasi-2D perovskite integration in p-i-n solar cells

Anna Capitaine, Hugo Le Bossenec, Marion Provost, Alexandra Levtchenko, Daniel Ory, Jean Rousset

- EUPVSEC 2025

2D/3D Heterojunctions for increased efficiency and stability

- **Ammonium cations** are the most universal strategy for increasing efficiency

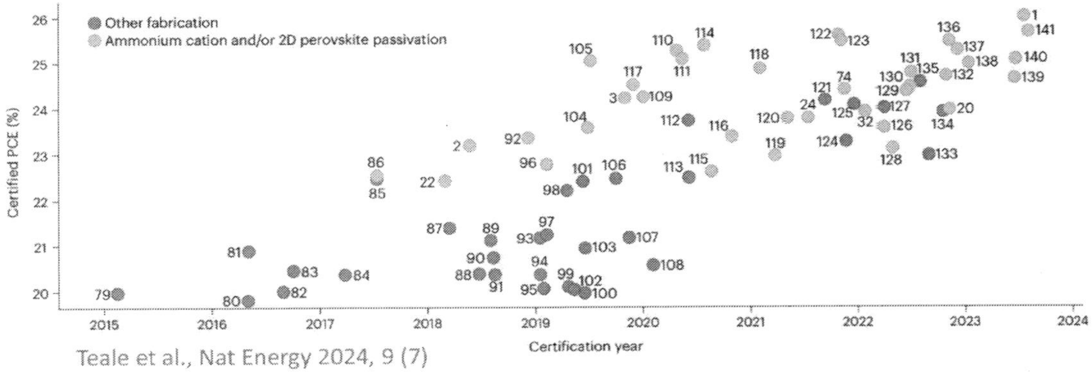

Teale et al., Nat Energy 2024, 9 (7)

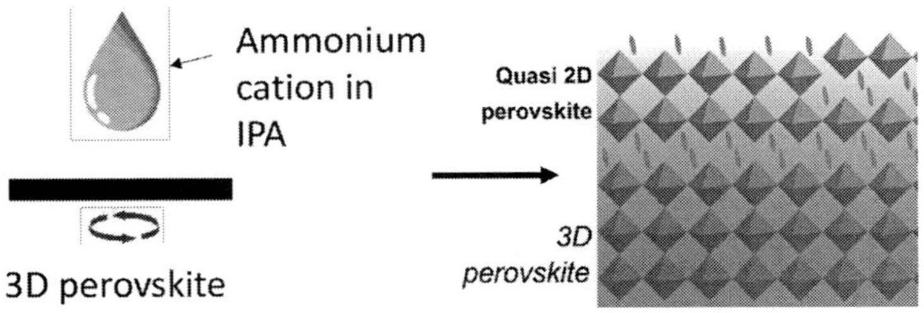

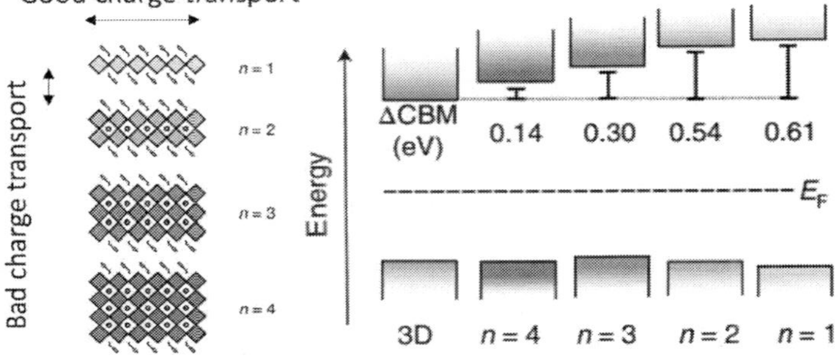

Chen et al., Nature Photonics, 2023

The dimensionality of the quasi-2D layer greatly impacts its properties

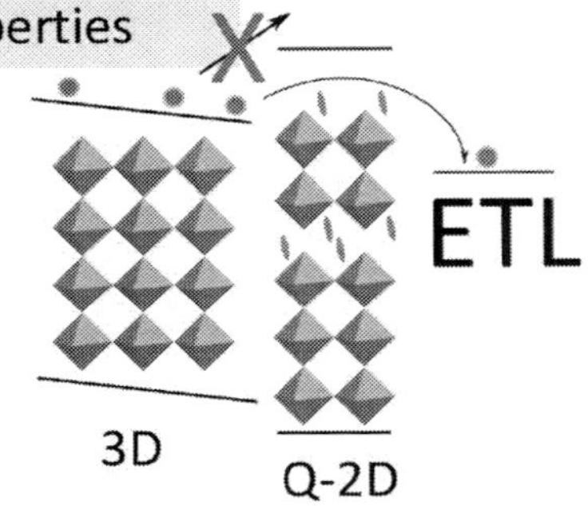

→ The 2D/3D layer can hinder electron extraction

IPVF

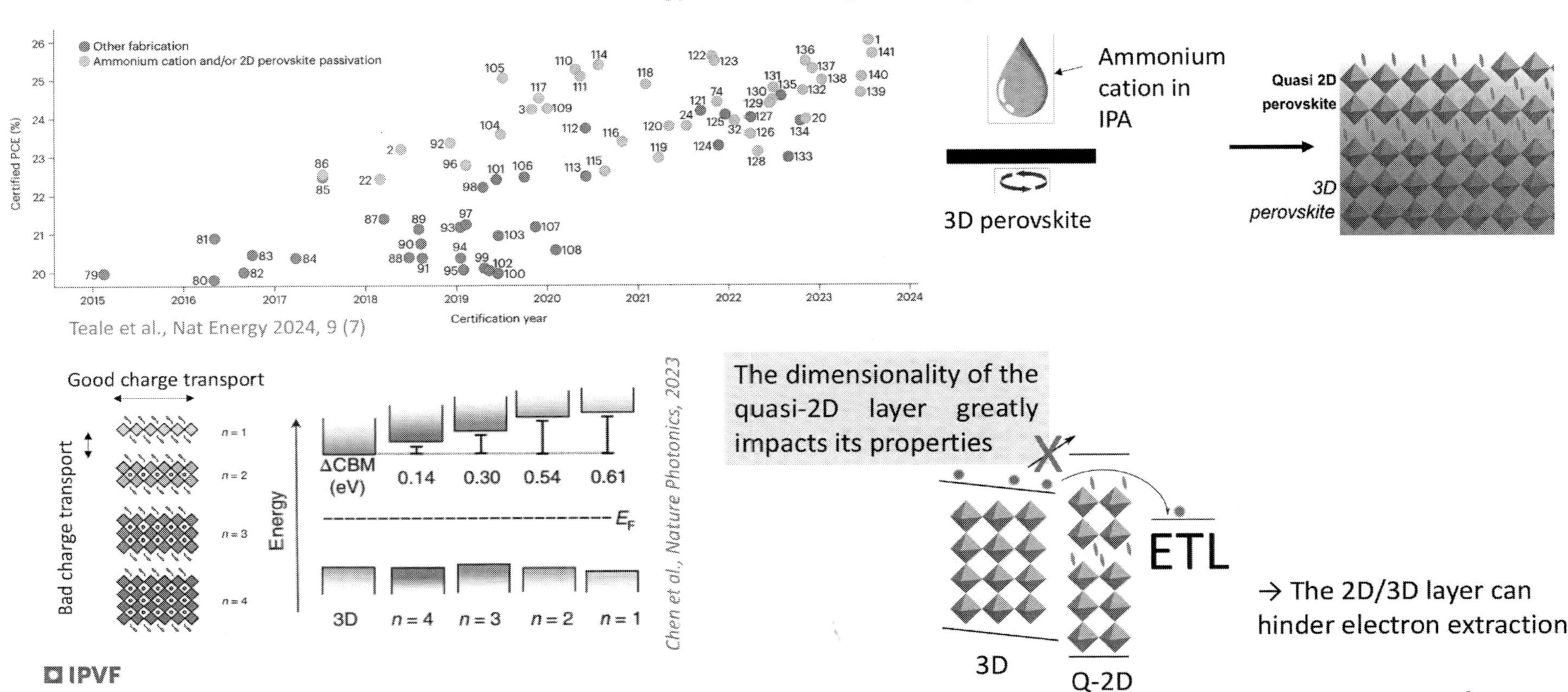

Strategies for quasi-2D perovskite integration in p-i-n solar cells

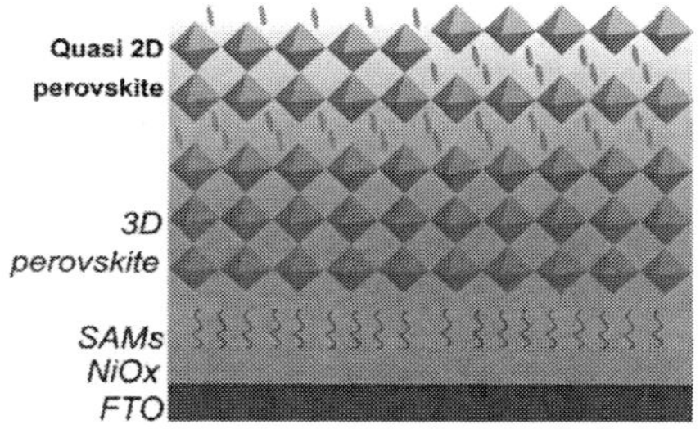

Promising "2D cations"

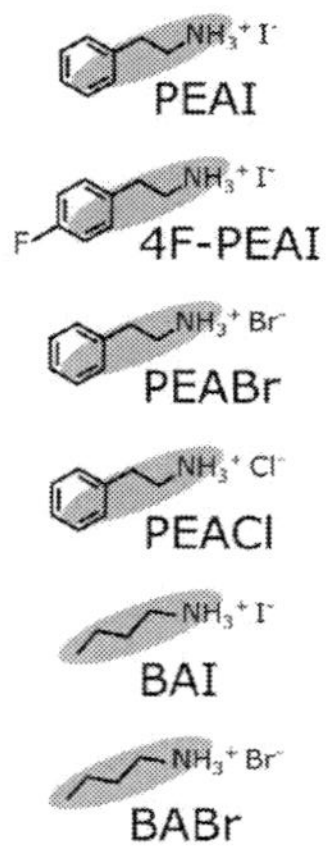

Phenethyl-ammonium derivatives (4F-)PEA^+

Butyl-ammonium derivatives BA^+

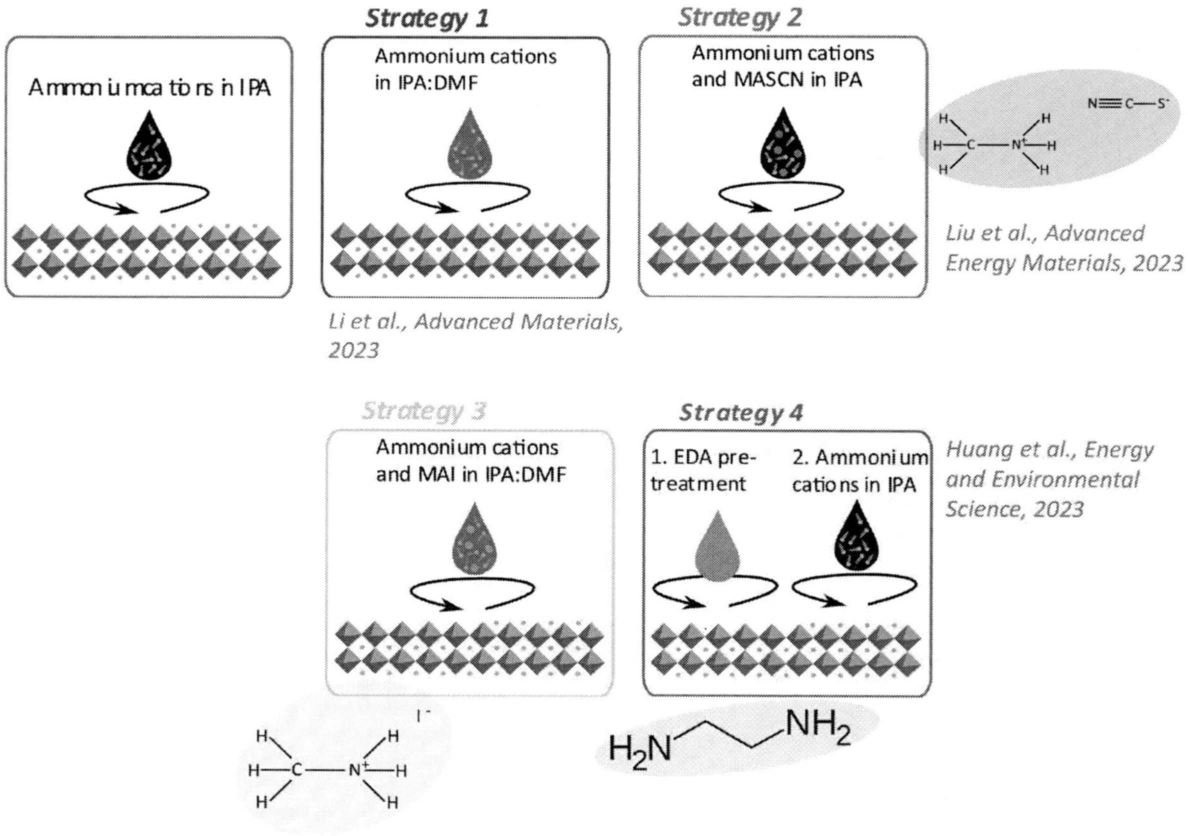

IPVF

3

What is the most promising strategy ?

■ Reference w/o passivation ■ 2D cation in IPA ■ 2D cation in IPA:DMF ■ 2D cation + MASCN in IPA ■ 2D cation + MAI in IPA:DMF ■ EDA pre-treatment + 2D cation in IPA

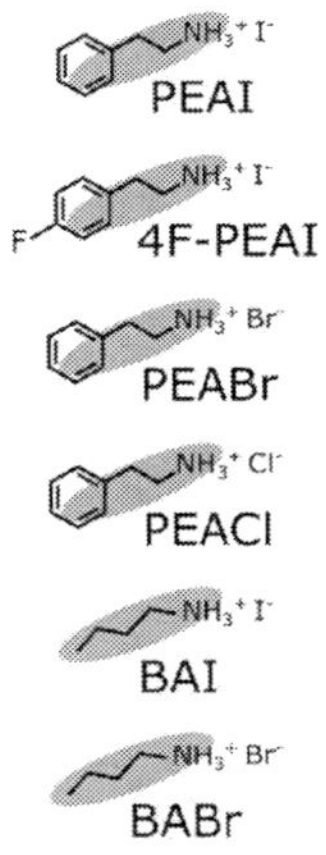

X

Strategies

↓

15 conditions

Half-cells

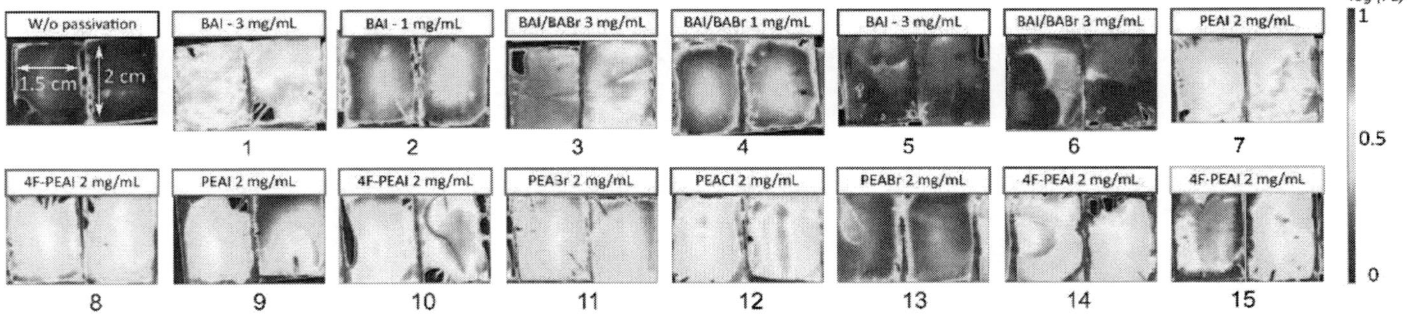

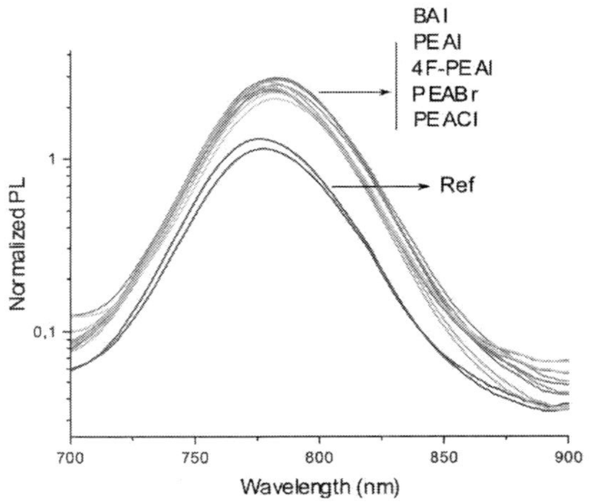

- Different 2D cations have similar effect
- Differences come from the way they are integrated: strategies 1 - 4

IPVF

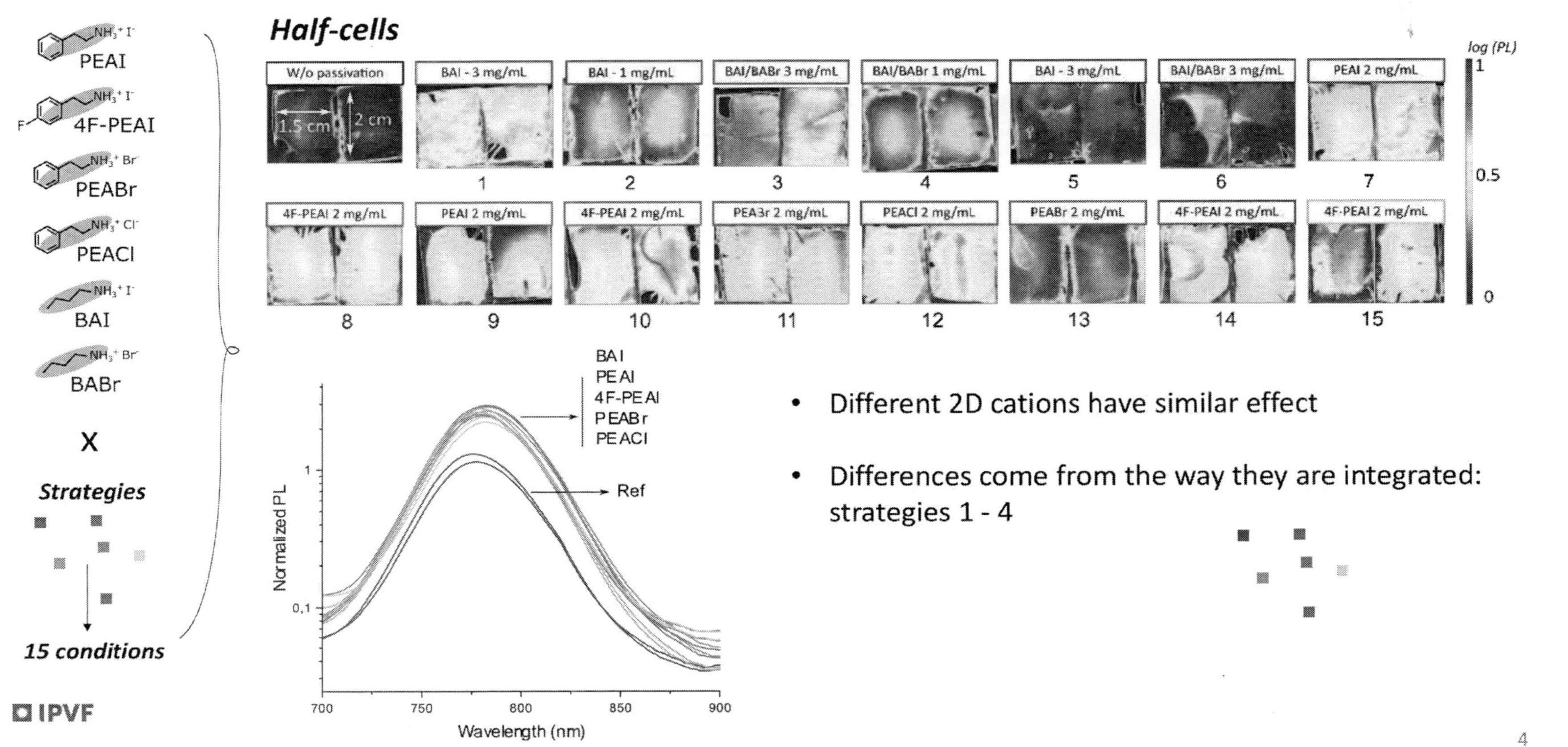

What is the most promising strategy ?

■ Reference w/o passivation ■ 2D cation in IPA ■ 2D cation in IPA:DMF ■ 2D cation + MASCN in IPA ■ 2D cation + MAI in IPA:DMF ■ EDA pre-treatment + 2D cation in IPA

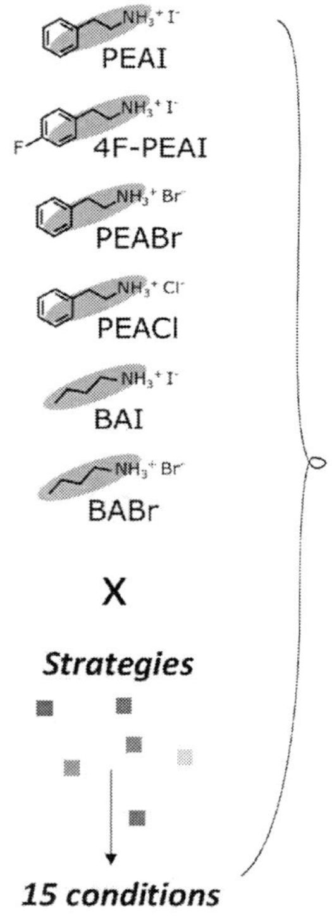

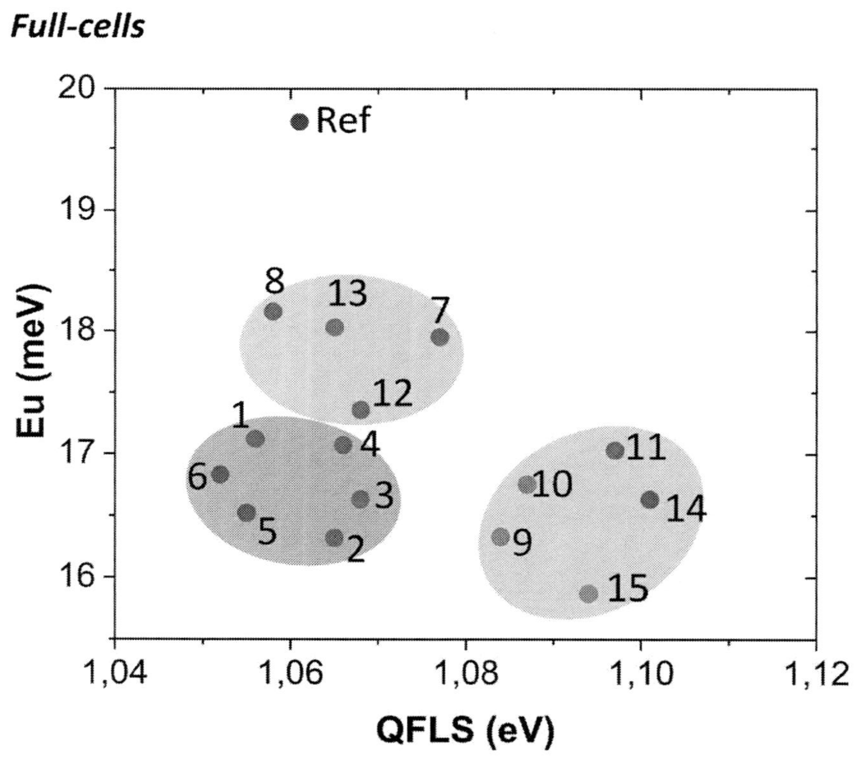

- QFLS up to **+ 40 meV**
- All strategies enable to reduce Urbach Energy (Eu)

IPVF

What is the most promising strategy ?

■ Reference w/o passivation ■ 2D cation in IPA ■ 2D cation in IPA:DMF ■ 2D cation + MASCN in IPA ■ 2D cation + MAI in IPA:DMF ■ EDA pre-treatment + 2D cation in IPA

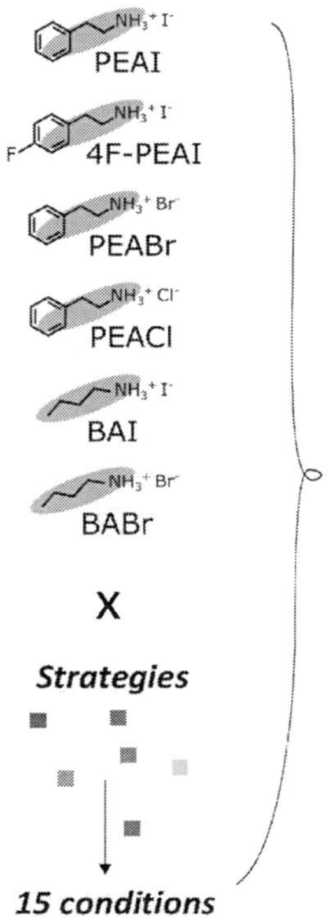

Full-cells

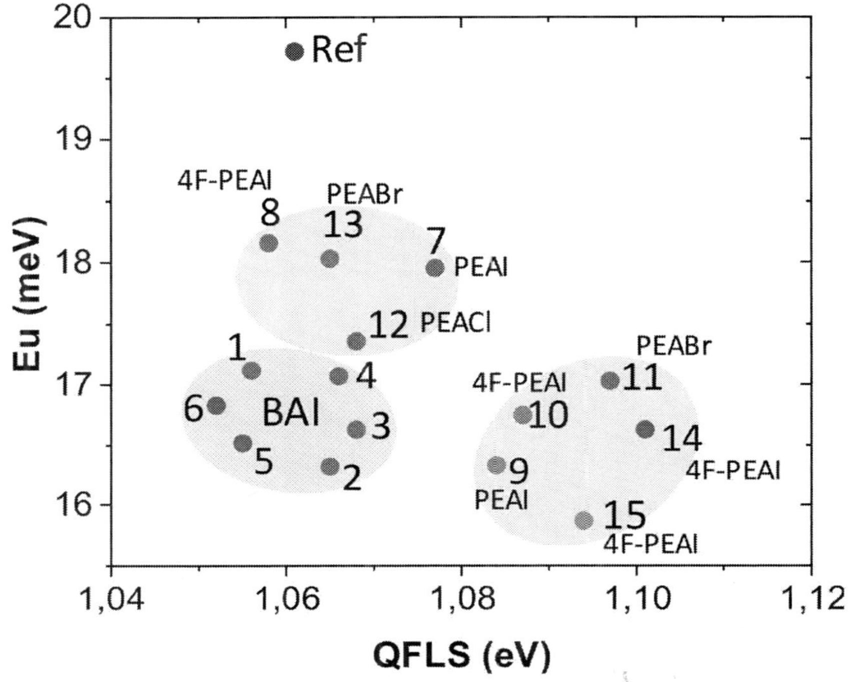

- QFLS up to **+ 40 meV**
- All strategies enable to reduce Urbach Energy (Eu)
- Best passivations – **low Eu and high QFLS** – are achieved with (4F)-PEA⁺ derivatives thanks to solvent engineering solutions or addition of additives

IPVF

Additives and solvent engineering strategies allow for 2D-phases of higher dimensionality

- 10 mg/mL 4F-PEAI for all (concentration x5) to characterize quasi-2D phases

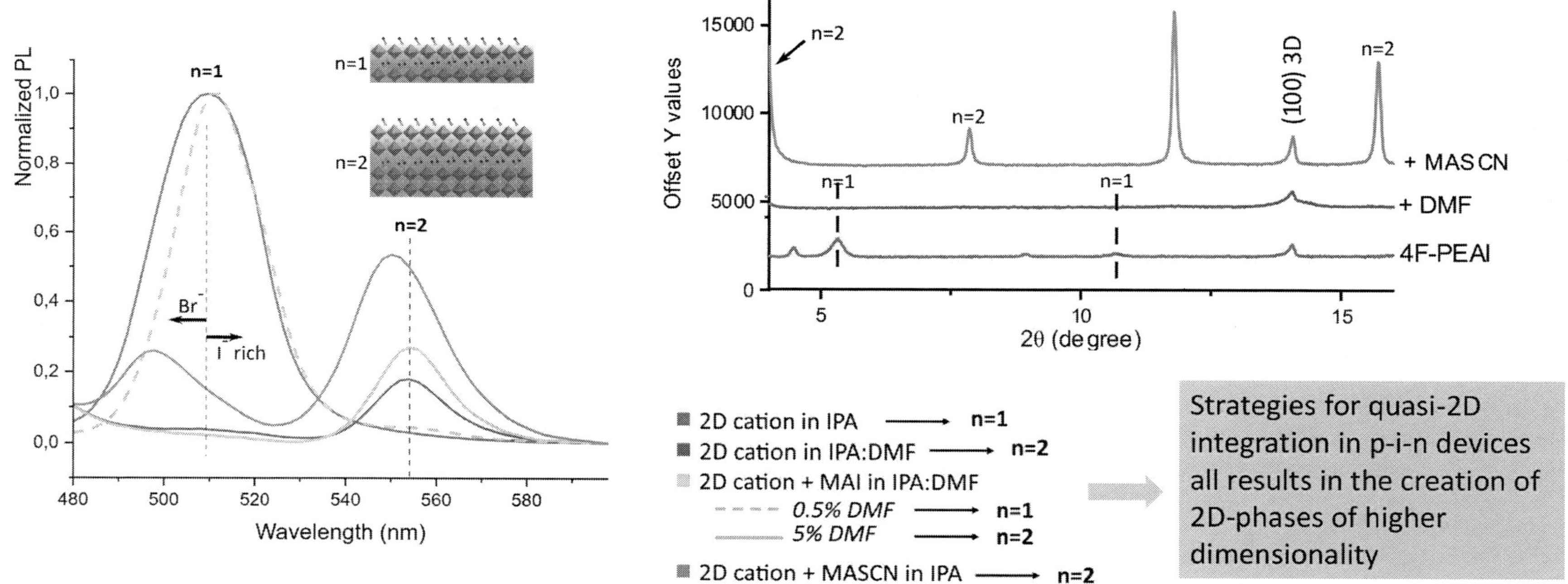

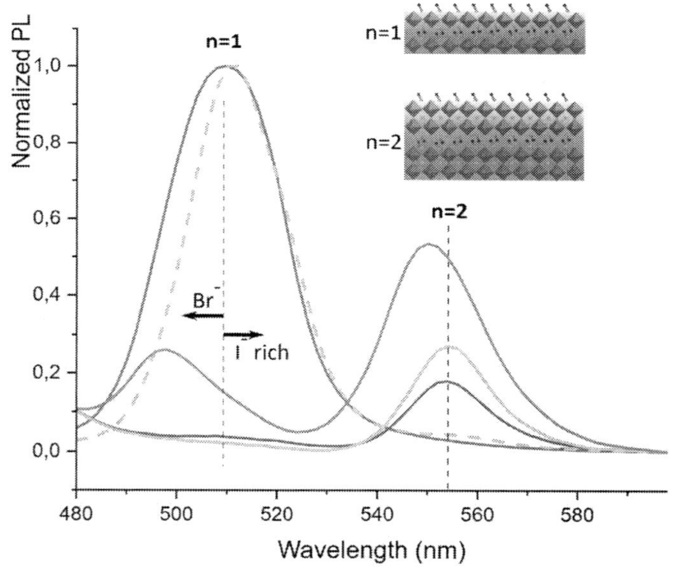

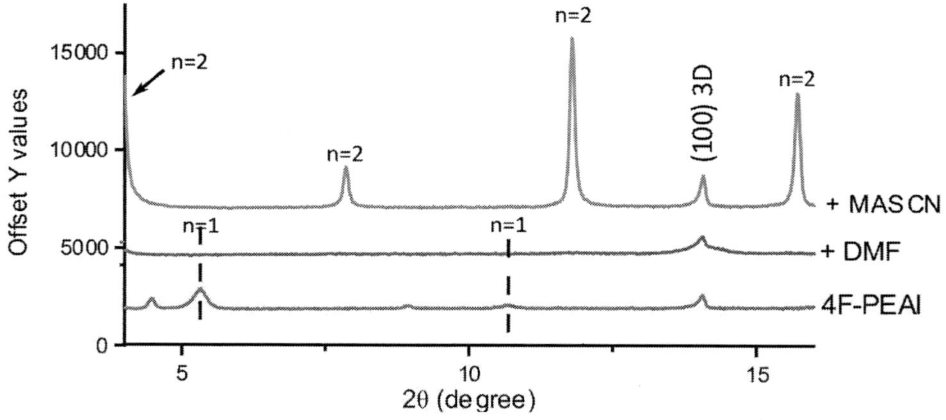

- 2D cation in IPA ⟶ **n=1**
- 2D cation in IPA:DMF ⟶ **n=2**
- 2D cation + MAI in IPA:DMF
  - *0.5% DMF* ⟶ **n=1**
  - *5% DMF* ⟶ **n=2**
- 2D cation + MASCN in IPA ⟶ **n=2**

Strategies for quasi-2D integration in p-i-n devices all results in the creation of 2D-phases of higher dimensionality

IPVF

Increasing performance and stability with quasi-2D phases remains a challenge

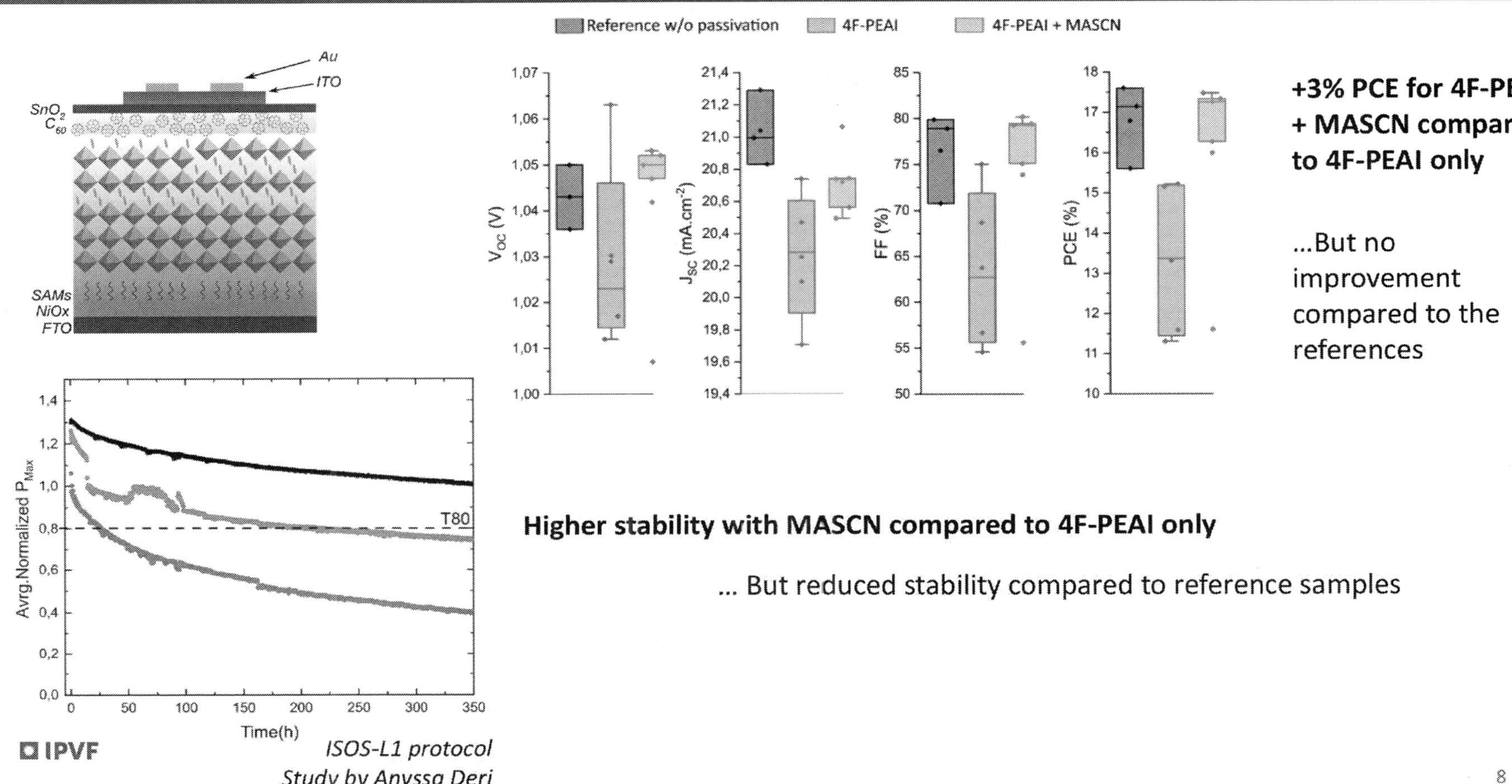

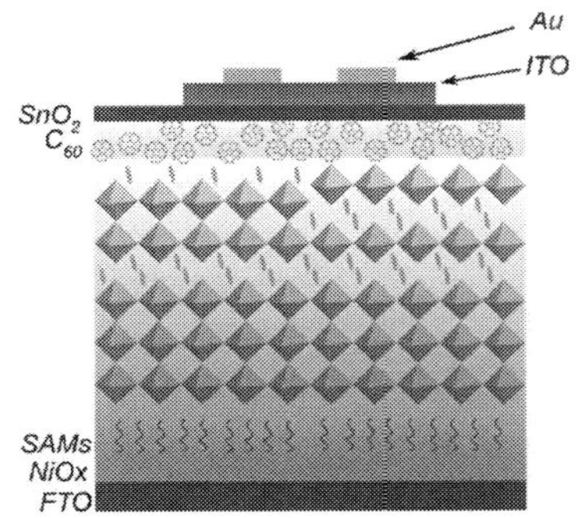

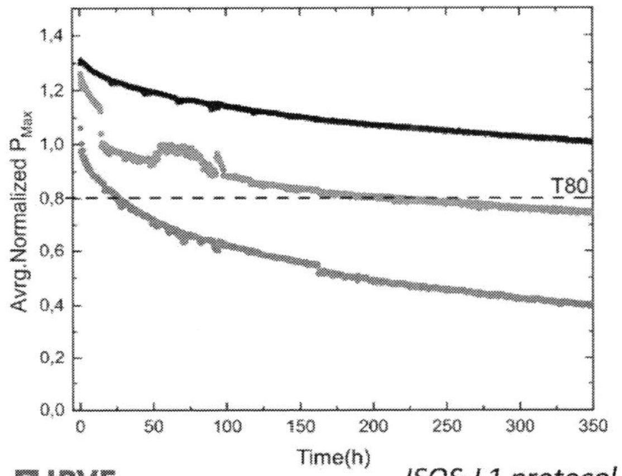

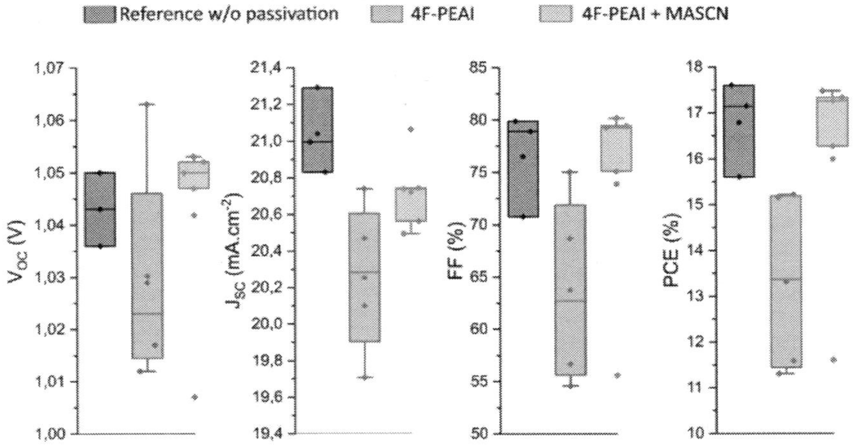

+3% PCE for 4F-PEAI + MASCN compared to 4F-PEAI only

...But no improvement compared to the references

Higher stability with MASCN compared to 4F-PEAI only

... But reduced stability compared to reference samples

IPVF

ISOS-L1 protocol
Study by Anyssa Derj

How to control quasi-2D phases formation for enhanced performance ?

Quasi-2D phases form by intercalation in the 3D perovskite structure

And or by **PbI_2 conversion** → More control

$$2\,(4F\text{-}PEAI) + PbI_2 \rightarrow (4F\text{-}PEA)_2PbI_4 \quad | \; n=1$$

$$2\,(4F\text{-}PEAI) + (n\text{-}1)\,FAI + n\,PbI_2 \rightarrow (4F\text{-}PEA)_2(FA)_{n\text{-}1}Pb_nI_{(3n+1)} \quad | \; n>1$$

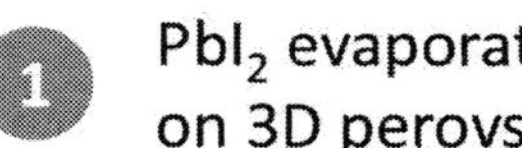

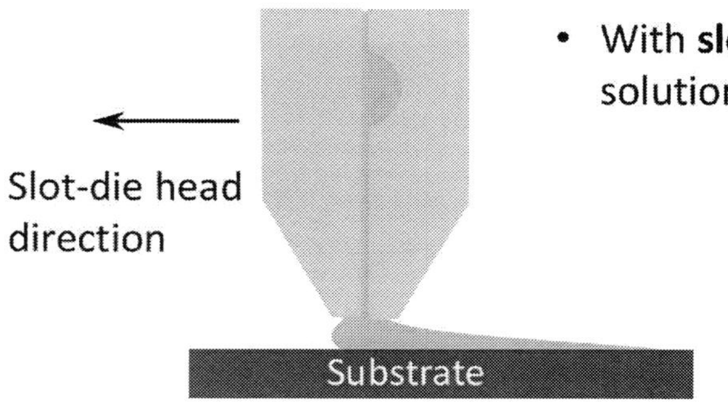

- With **slot-die coating** all the solution remains on the substrate → PbI_2 conversion + Slot-die coating = **Stoichiometric approach**

1. PbI_2 evaporation on 3D perovskite
2. PbI_2 conversion by slot-die coating

IPVF

PbI_2 conversion into quasi-2D perovskite by slot-die coating

Work by Hugo Le Bossenec

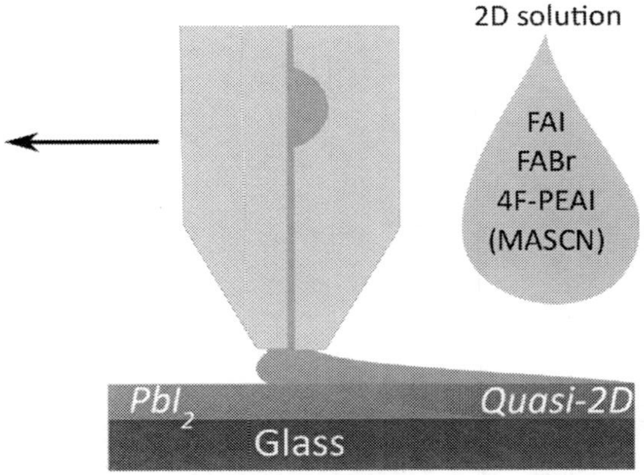

Aiming for n=3

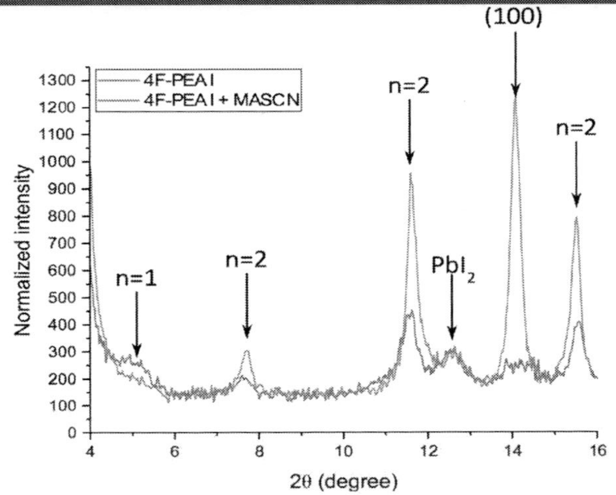

- PbI_2 almost complete conversion
- More n=2 and >2 phases when adding MASCN

IPVF

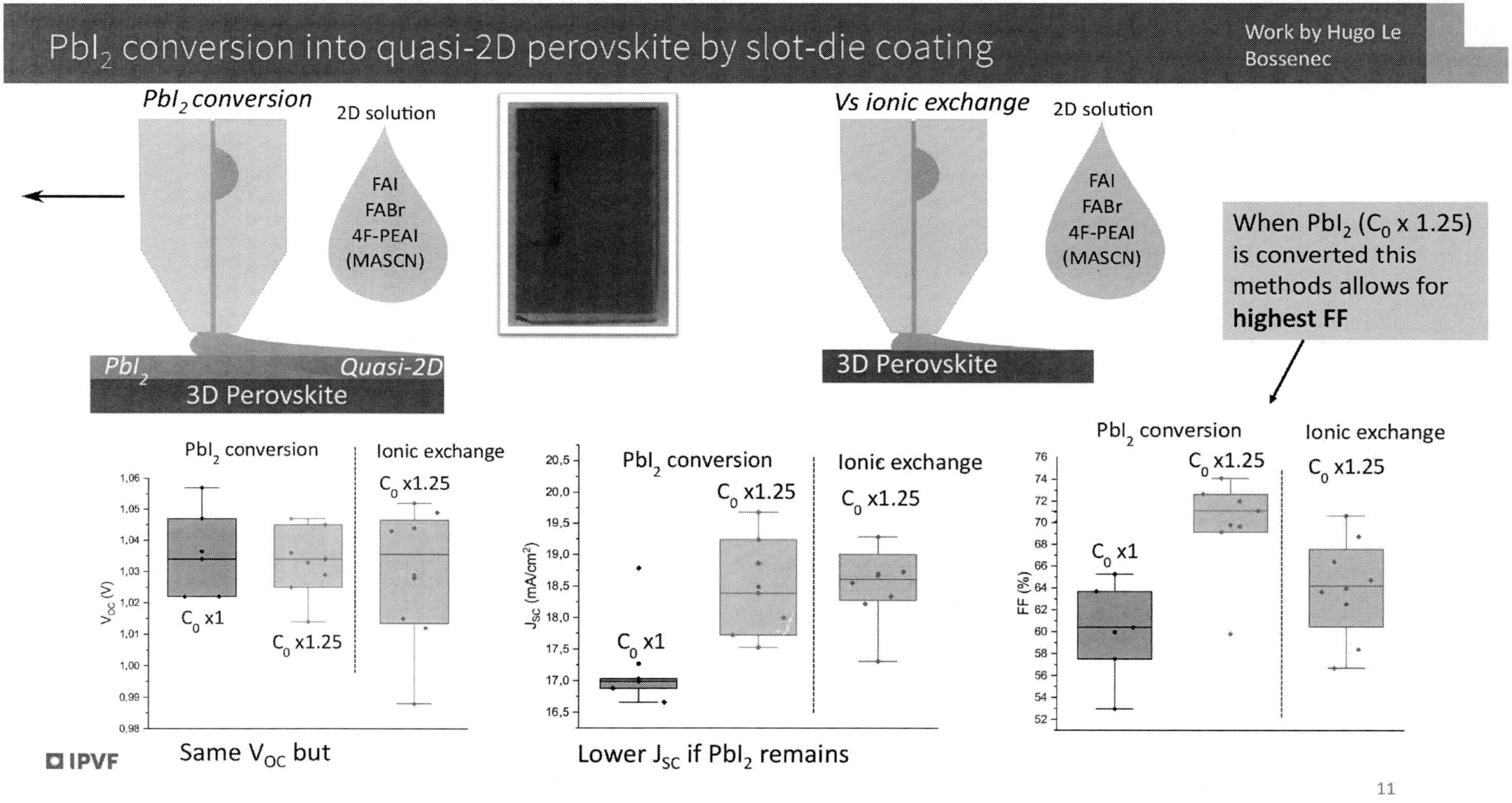

PbI2 conversion into quasi-2D perovskite by slot-die coating
Work by Hugo Le Bossenec
PbI2 conversion
2D solution
FAI
FABr
4F-PEAI
(MASCN)
PbI2
Quasi-2D
3D Perovskite
Vs ionic exchange
2D solution
FAI
FABr
4F-PEAI
(MASCN)
3D Perovskite
When PbI2 (C0 x 1.25) is converted this methods allows for highest FF
PbI2 conversion
Ionic exchange
C0 x1
C0 x1.25
C0 x1.25
VOC (V)
1,06
1,05
1,04
1,03
1,02
1,01
1,00
0,99
0,98
Same VOC but
PbI2 conversion
Ionic exchange
C0 x1
C0 x1.25
C0 x1.25
JSC (mA/cm2)
20,5
20,0
19,5
19,0
18,5
18,0
17,5
17,0
16,5
Lower JSC if PbI2 remains
PbI2 conversion
Ionic exchange
C0 x1
C0 x1.25
C0 x1.25
FF (%)
76
74
72
70
68
66
64
62
60
58
56
54
52
IPVF
11

PbI_2 conversion into quasi-2D perovskite by slot-die coating

Work by Hugo Le Bossenec

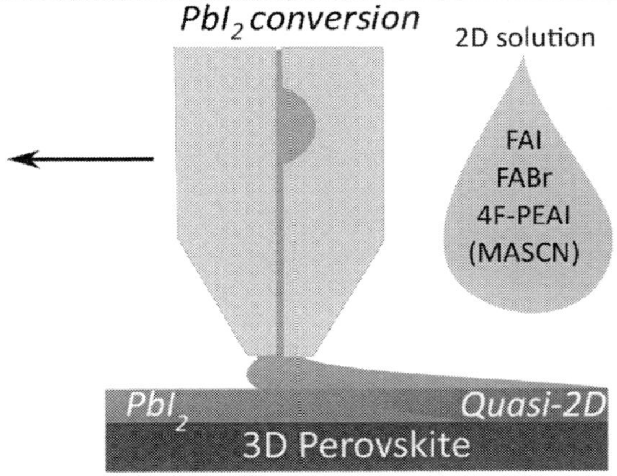

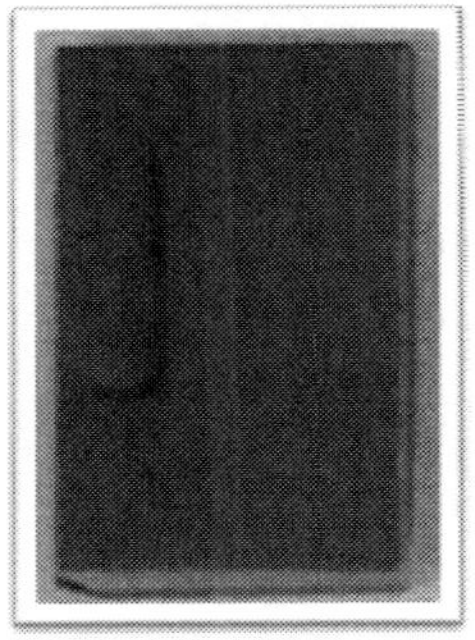

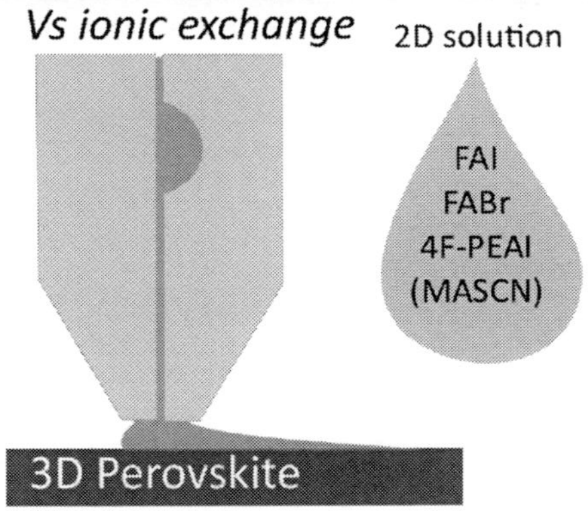

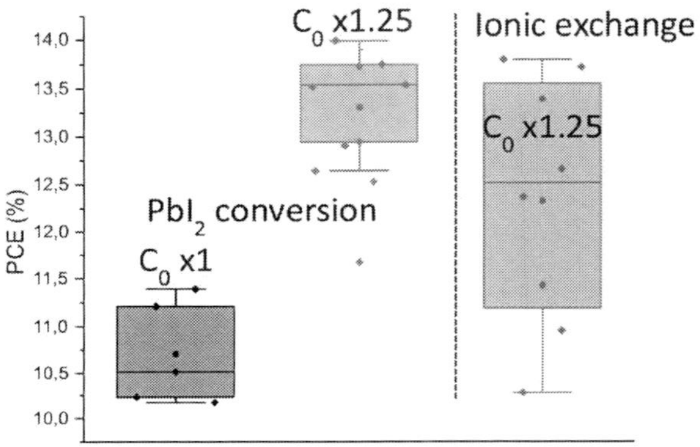

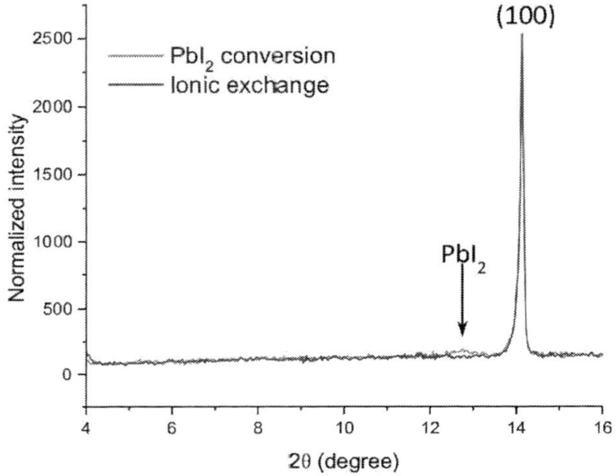

- Almost complete PbI_2 conversion
- **No traces of 2D phases**: penetration of 2D cations deeper than the PbI_2 template

IPVF

12

Conclusion and perspectives

Spin coating

- Strategies developed for 2D cations integration in p-i-n solar cells lead to **n=2 rather than n=1 2D phases**
- Still, improving device performance and stability with a quasi-2D interface **remains a challenge despite their passivation effect** (QFLS, Eu)

PbI_2 evaporation and conversion by slot-die coating

- Quasi-2D perovskite can be formed by PbI_2 conversion by slot-die coating: increased FF
- Stable n>2 quasi-2D phases on top of 3D perovskite remains a challenge even with a stoichiometric reaction

→ Difficult to take advantage of quasi-2D properties with mono-ammoniums

Thank you for your attention

IPVF

42nd European Photovoltaic Solar Energy Conference and Exhibition

This presentation was selected by the Sc. Committee of the EU PVSEC 2025 for submission of a full paper to one of the EU PVSEC's collaborating peer-reviewed journals.

INNOVATIVE APPROACH TO BISMUTH-ANTIMONY-IODIDE DOUBLE PEROVSKITE PV ABSORBERS VIA ANION EXCHANGE AND SOLID-STATE REACTIONS

Oleksandr Stroyuk[1], Oleksandra Raievska[1], Sachin Kinge[2], Jens Hauch[1,3], Christoph J. Brabec[1,3]
[1]Forschungszentrum Jülich GmbH, Helmholtz-Institut Erlangen Nürnberg für Erneuerbare Energien (HI ERN), 91058 Erlangen, Germany, o.stroyuk@fz-juelich.de
[2]Materials Engineering Division, Toyota Motors Europe, sachin.kinge@toyota-europe.com
[3]Friedrich-Alexander-Universität Erlangen-Nürnberg, Materials for Electronics and Energy Technology (i-MEET), Martensstrasse 7, 91058 Erlangen, Germany, christoph.brabec@fau.de

ABSTRACT: This work focuses on the development of advanced synthesis protocols for lead-free $Cs_2AgBi(Sb)Br_6$ perovskites and their conversion into lower-bandgap $Cs_2AgBi(Sb)I_6$ perovskite PV absorbers by using an innovative combination of mild anion exchange with a solid-state reaction between intermediate iodide derivatives. High-throughput robot-assisted experimentation is applied for the optimization of the synthesis conditions, targeting the highest yields of $Cs_2AgBi(Sb)I_6$ perovskites (ca. 90 mass%) with the lowest bandgap (1.78 eV). We provide new insights into the pathways, mechanisms, and dynamics of the formation of iodide double perovskites, reporting stable lead-free double iodide perovskites crystallized in a non-conventional tetragonal symmetry.
Keywords: double perovskites; anion exchange; solid-state reaction; tetragonal perovskites

1 INTRODUCTION

The unprecedentedly successful and fast development of lead-halide-based solar cells stimulates parallel research aimed at the discovery of alternative metal-halide perovskite and perovskite-inspired materials with comparably high photovoltaic (PV) efficiency, but superior to lead-halide absorbers in terms of lower toxicity and higher stability [1,2]. These studies focused on several classes of lead-free perovskites, particularly on stable $Cs_2AgBiBr_6$ (CABB) double perovskite currently showing power conversion efficiencies of ca. 3% [3]. Further progress in this direction is expected from iodide-based analogs with lower bandgaps, such as Cs_2AgBiI_6 (CABI); however, the synthesis of iodide double perovskites is associated with many challenges, including instability of precursors and unreliable structural and compositional control over the products [4].

In the present work, we develop an innovative approach to mixed-halide $Cs_2Ag(Bi,Sb)BrI_5$ (CABSBI) double perovskites from $Cs_2AgBi(Sb)Br_6$ (CABSB) perovskites using a two-stage approach. On the first stage, CABSB is converted into mixtures of $CsAg_2I_3$ and $Cs_3(Bi,Sb)_2(Br,I)_9$ intermediates by mild anion exchanges (AE). The second stage of thermal annealing results in a solid-state reaction and formation of stable tetragonal double CAB(S)BI perovskites. The conditions of the two-stage process are optimized using high-throughput robot-assisted experimentation [5,6], yielding CABSBI perovskites with bandgaps below 1.8 eV, promising for indoor PV and multijunction architectures.

2 SYNTHESES AND CHARACTERIZATIONS

2.1 Syntheses

Microcrystalline $Cs_2AgBi_xSb_{1-x}Br_6$ samples were produced by mixing two precursor solutions at room temperature (RT) in open-atmosphere conditions. Precursor #1 combined x mL of 1.0 M $BiBr_3$ solution in 5.0 M aqueous HBr, ($1-x$) mL of 1.0 M $SbCl_3$ solution in 5.0 M HBr, 1.0 mL of 8.9 M aqueous HBr, and 5.0 mL 2-propanol. Precursor #2 was prepared from 1.0 mL of 1.0 M aqueous $AgNO_3$ solution, 1.2 mL deionized water, 0.25 mL of 25 wt.% aqueous NH_4OH solution, 0.55 mL of 4.0 M aqueous Cs acetate solution, and 5.0 mL of 2-propanol.

The CABSB samples were brought into contact with water/2-propanol solutions of NaI (AE solution). In a typical procedure, 1 mmol of CABSB was mixed with 5.0 mL of 2-propanol in a 25-mL glass vial, capped with a Parafilm layer, subjected to intense magnetic refluxing for 15 min, and an AE solution was added (10 mL of 2-propanol and 2.0 mL of 4.0 M aqueous NaI solution).

All products were subjected to purification. For this aim, as-prepared suspensions were centrifuged at 1500 rpm for 2 min, the supernatant was removed, and 10.0 mL of 2-propanol was added to form a homogeneous suspension, which was subjected to centrifugation, and the purification process was repeated twice.

The as-prepared AE products (AE-CABSBI) were subjected to thermal annealing in air. For this, the microcrystalline AE-CABSBI was distributed as a thin uniform layer on a glass substrate and annealed on an open-air heating plate at varied T for 10 min.

The PV properties of CABB were characterized in planar solar cells with a titania electron transport layer (ETL) and P3HT as a hole transport layer (HTL). A CABB ink (0.5 M) in dimethylsulfoxide (DMSO) was used to form absorber layers. The ETL was formed by spin-coating of Ti(IV) tetraisopropoxide solution in HCl on preliminary cleaned ITO substrates, followed by calcination in air at 460 °C for 30 min. Then, the CABB film was spin-coated and the freshly deposited film was placed under vacuum to evaporate DMSO, then annealed in air at 250 °C for 10 min. Afterwards, a layer of P3HT HTL is spin-coated, and gold back electrodes were deposited by vacuum evaporation through a mask to form six-pixel cells.

2.2 Characterizations

Powder X-Ray diffraction (XRD) patterns were registered using a Panalytical X'pert powder diffractometer with copper K_α radiation. The XRD patterns were subjected to a Rietveld refinement procedure using MAUD software (version 2.99).

Scanning electron microscopic (SEM) imaging and energy-dispersive X-Ray spectroscopic (EDX) analysis were performed using a JEOL JSM-7610F Schottky field emission microscope operating under 15-20 kV and equipped with an X-Max 80 mm2 silicon drift detector

(Oxford Instruments) and AZtec nanoanalysis software.

Reflectance spectra were recorded using a BlackComet spectrometer (StellarNet Inc.) and a 75-W Xenon lamp (Thorlabs) as an excitation source. The spectra were registered with an optical Y-fiber probe in an identical geometry for samples and a scattering reference (ultra-pure $BaSO_4$, Alfa-Aesar). The reflectance spectra were transformed into absorption spectra using the Kubelka-Munk formula and the reference.

The J-V characteristics of CABB-based solar cells were measured using a Botest source measurement unit under AM1.5G illumination provided by an Oriel Sol 1A solar simulator (Newport) under ambient conditions.

3 RESULTS AND DISCUSSION

3.1 Advanced synthesis of bromide perovskites

The conventionally adopted synthesis of CABB double perovskite from a mixture of CsBr, AgBr, and $BiBr_3$ suffers from several drawbacks, including high light sensitivity of AgBr, low solubility of Cs_2AgBr_3 intermediate, and the requirements of using concentrated HBr (48%) and heating at ca. 100 °C. As a more practical alternative, we report a milder and more controlled protocol, where CABB forms at the interaction of two water/2-propanol precursor solutions containing Cs acetate and $AgNO_3$ (precursor 1), and $BiBr_3$ in 5% HBr (precursor 2). The protocol yields single-phase microcrystalline stoichiometric CABB double perovskite (Figure 1a,c,e) at RT with no additional thermal treatments, at the lowest reported HBr concentration. It can be scaled up to multi-gram synthesis and adapted to form other bromide perovskites, in particular, $Cs_2AgBi_xSb_{1-x}Br_6$, $Cs_3Bi_2Br_9$, and Cs_2AgBr_2.

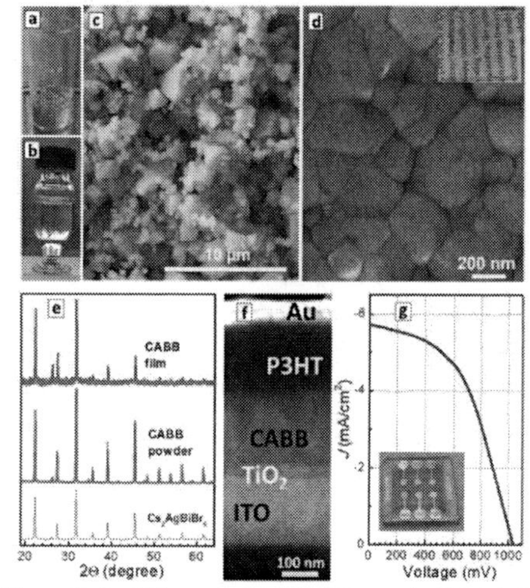

Figure 1: (a-e) Photographs of CABB powder (a), ink (b), and film (insert in (d)). (c-e) SEM images (c,d), and XRD patterns (e) of CABB powder (c) and film (d). In (e), the red line represents Rietveld's refinement. (f,g) Cross-sectional SEM image/scheme (f), J-V curve (g), and photograph (insert in (g)) of a CABB-based solar cell

The CABB powder dissolves spontaneously at RT in DMSO, forming a stable 0.5 M ink (Fig. 1b) that, after the spin-coating and annealing (250 °C), converts into a transparent nanocrystalline CABB film (Fig. 1d,e).

The CABB films were tested as PV absorbers in solar cells with TiO_2 and P3HT as electron- and hole-transport layers, respectively (Fig. 1f), showing a champion power conversion efficiency of 2.89% (Fig. 1g, J_{sc} = 5.73 mA/cm², V_{oc} = 1035 mV, and a fill factor *FF* of 49%).

3.2 Anion-exchange conversion of CAB(S)B

Similar to our recent reports [6, 7], we developed a mild anion-exchange-based approach for converting bromide perovskites into corresponding iodides using NaI as an iodide source. Interaction of CABB with NaI results in a "red" shift of absorption band edge (Figure 2a) and the formation of a bi-phase mixture of $Cs_3Bi_2I_9$ (CBI) double salt and $CsAg_2I_3$ (CAI) perovskite (Fig. 2b,c).

Similarly, AE-driven transformation of $Cs_2AgBi_{0.5}Sb_{0.5}Br_6$ (CABSB) perovskite was found to result in a mixture of $Cs_3(Bi_{0.5}Sb_{0.5})_2I_9$ (CBSI) and CAI phases. In both cases, CAI crystals reveal a distinct morphology, needle-like crystals (AE-driven conversion of CABB) or larger polygons (AE-driven transformation of CABSB), strongly different from the morphology of the CBI (CBSI) phase (Fig. 2d,e).

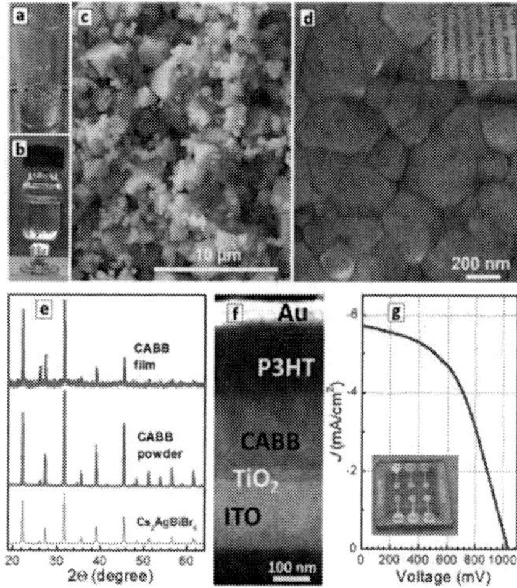

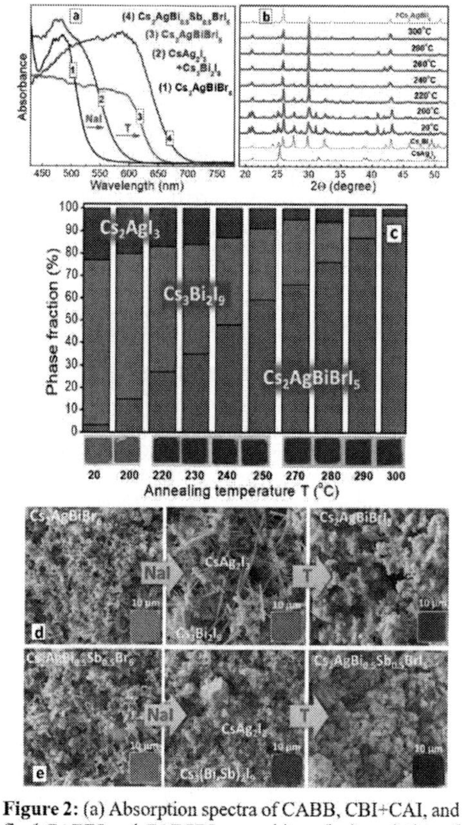

Figure 2: (a) Absorption spectra of CABB, CBI+CAI, and final CABBI and CABSBI perovskites; (b,c) evolution of the powder X-ray diffractogram of CBI+CAI mixture (b) and (c) phases distribution upon annealing at different temperatures; (d,e) SEM images of CABB (d) and CABSB (e) as well as corresponding AE products and final CABBI and CABSBI perovskites

Annealing of the CBI+CAI mixture at 200-300 °C results in the conversion of these intermediates into a new compound that was identified by the Rietveld refinement of XRD patterns and EDX analysis as tetragonal $Cs_2AgBiBrI_5$ (CABBI) double perovskite (symmetry group *I4m*, lattice parameters $a = b = 8.3825$ Å and $c = 11.8451$ Å).

The CABBI phase is present as a minor component even at 20 °C, its content growing with annealing temperature, reaching 85-86% at 290-300 °C (Fig. 2c). The powder XRD and SEM analyses clearly show the annealing-induced disappearance of the CAI phase and formation of tightly aggregated microcrystalline CABBI (CABSBI) products (Fig. 2d,e) of a solid-state reaction that can be presented by a brutto-equation:

$$Cs_3Bi_2I_9 + CsAg_2I_3 = 2Cs_2AgBiI_6$$

with ca. 5-20% of iodide sites still occupied with Br^-.

This reaction results in a considerable red shift of the absorption band edge reaching ca. 650 nm for CABBI and ca. 680 nm for CABSBI (Fig. 2a).

3.3 High-throughput screening of CABSBI perovskites

Considering that $Cs_2AgBi_{0.5}Sb_{0.5}BrI_5$ perovskite showed a much lower bandgap as compared to CABBI, we performed a high-throughput screening of CABSBI perovskites using the previously reported robot-assisted methodology [5, 6]. At that, Bi/Sb and I/Br ratios were varied simultaneously, while conditions of AE and thermal annealing were varied for every composition to achieve the maximal yield of CABBI with the minimal bandgap.

Figure 3a shows exemplary sample arrays produced at varied Sb fractions and NaI content, revealing the low-bandgap domain at excess iodide and mixed Bi-Sb compounds. It is noteworthy that no changes in spectral properties were observed for a similar sample array with $Cs_3(Bi,Sb)_2Br_9$ double salts subjected to the AE with NaI (Fig. 3b). These observations provide additional evidence of the formation of low-bandgap products in a solid reaction between CBI and CAI.

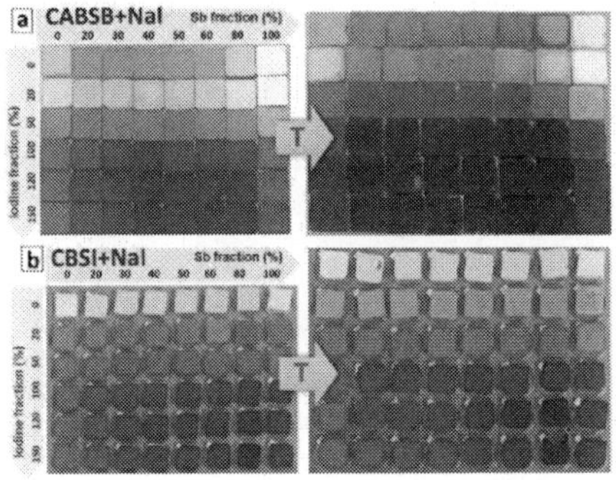

Figure 3: Photographs of sample arrays produced by high-throughput AE of CABSB perovskites (a) and CBSI double salts with varied Sb fraction and relative NaI content before (left panels) and after (right panels) annealing at 290 °C

It was found that the lowest bandgaps of CABSBI perovskites can be reached for AE performed at 133% excess NaI in the reaction mixture with respect to the stoichiometric amount necessary for the complete Br-to-I substitution, the AE duration of 10 min, the annealing T of 290-300 °C, and annealing duration of 10-15 min, for Sb fractions between 45 and 75%.

The evolution of spectral properties of CABSBI perovskites and formation of the lowest bandgap domain can be tracked by comparing the compositional bandgap maps before (Figure 4a) and after the annealing (Fig. 4b).

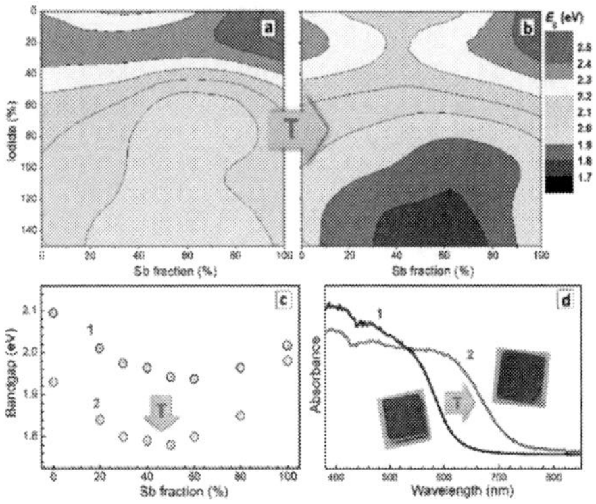

Figure 4: (a,b) Compositional bandgap maps for CABSB+NaI sample array before (c) and after (d) annealing at 290 °C. (c) Bandgap of CABSBI perovskites before (1) and after annealing (1), produced in optimized conditions, versus nominal Sb fraction. (d) Absorption spectra and photographs of the optimal CABSBI sample before (curve 1) and after annealing (curve 2)

Figure 4c additionally illustrates the bandgap dependence on the Sb fraction for the samples produced in optimal conditions. The lowest indirect bandgap of 1.78 eV was observed for CABSBI with 50%Sb, corresponding to the absorption band edge at ca. 730 nm (Fig. 4d). This value falls in the range typically expected for wide-bandgap components of tandem solar cells (ca. 1.8 eV), showing promise for multi-junction and indoor PV applications.

The conversion of optimized microcrystalline CABSBI perovskites into transparent films and their potential as PV absorbers in solar cells are currently being investigated.

4 CONCLUSION

We report an advanced general synthesis of lead-free bromide compounds that yield CABB double perovskite showing ca. 2.9% efficiency as a PV absorber in single-junction solar cells, as well as mixed Bi-Sb double perovskites with controllably varied Bi/Sb ratios.

Anion exchange of CABB (CABSB) with NaI as an iodide source results in bi-phase products composed of CBI (CBSI) double salts and CAI perovskites that can react upon thermal treatment and transform into tetragonal CABBI (CABSBI) double perovskites with ca. 20% of residual bromide. A high-throughput optimization of the conditions of anion exchange and the following thermal solid-state reaction between CBSI and CAI yielded stable CABSBI perovskites with the lowest bandgap of 1.78 eV. The potential of these compounds as PV absorbers is currently under evaluation.

References

[1] I. López-Fernández, D. Valli, C.Y. Wang, S. Samanta, T. Okamoto, Y.T. Huang, K. Sun, Y. Liu, V.S. Chirvony,

A. Patra, et al., Adv. Funct. Mater., 34 (2024) 2307896.
[2] S. Zhang, G. Liu, B. Teng, S. Ji, CrystEngComm, 27 (2025) 3416.
[3] H. Lei, D. Hardy, F. Gao, Adv. Funct. Mater., 31 (2021) 2105898.
[4] K.T. Kluherz, S.T. Mergelsberg, J.J. De Yoreo, and D.R. Gamelin, Chem. Mater., 35 (2023) 5699.
[5] O. Stroyuk, O. Raievska, M. Daum, J. Hauch, C.J. Brabec, J. Mater. Chem. C, 12 (2024) 8705.
[6] O. Stroyuk, O. Raievska, S. Kinge, J. Hauch, and C.J. Brabec, Mater. Adv., 2025, doi: 10.1039/D5MA00479A.
[7] O. Stroyuk, O. Raievska, A. Barabash, R.W. Hooper, V.K. Michaelis, J. Hauch, C.J. Brabec, J. Mater. Chem. C, 12 (2024) 533.

EU PVSEC 2DO.8.3

HI ERN Helmholtz Institute Erlangen-Nürnberg

Innovative Approach to $Cs_2Ag(Bi,Sb)(Br,I)_6$ Double Perovskites via Anion Exchange and Solid-State Reactions

HI ERN Helmholtz Institut Erlangen Nürnberg, D-91058 Erlangen, Immerwahrstraße 2

2025-09-25 ||| **Dr. Oleksandr Stroyuk** ||| Team High Throughput Materials and Devices

part of JÜLICH Forschungszentrum

in cooperation with FAU HZB Helmholtz Zentrum Berlin

Double halide perovskites produced by anion exchange

HI ERN Helmholtz Institute Erlangen-Nürnberg

Regular perovskites

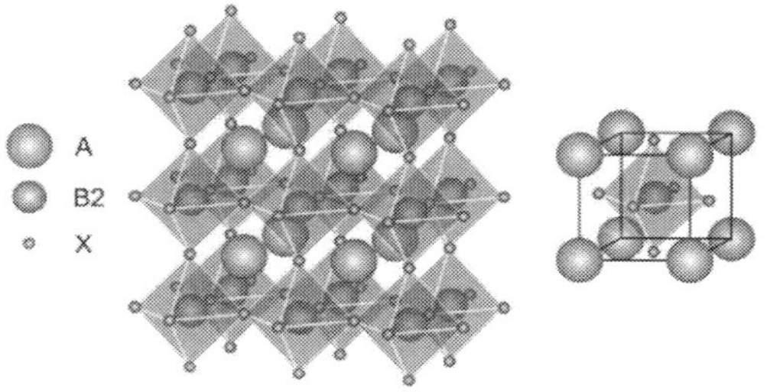

Double perovskites

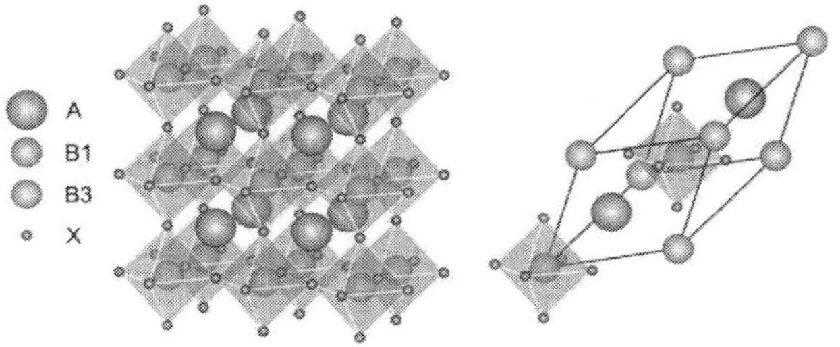

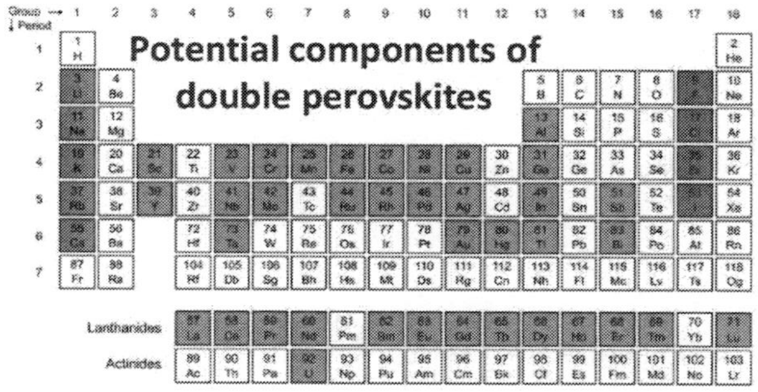

Structure and Stability of the Iodide Elpasolite, Cs_2AgBiI_6

Kyle T. Kluherz, Sebastian T. Mergelsberg, James J. De Yoreo, and Daniel R. Gamelin*

Cite This: *Chem. Mater.* 2023, 35, 5699–5708 Read Online

Nano Lett. 2018, 18, 1118–1123

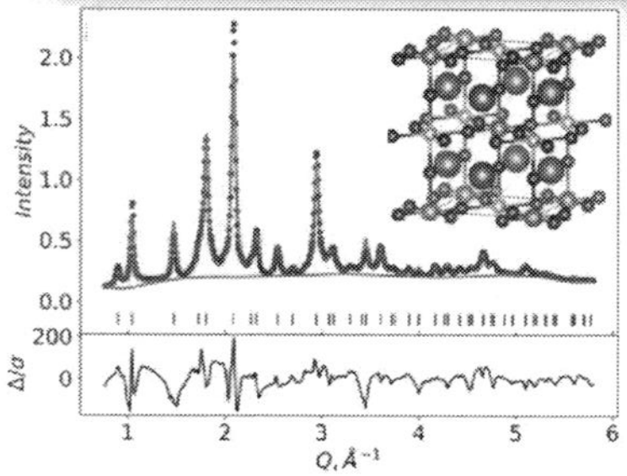

Tetragonal (I4-m)

$$2Cs_2AgBiI_6 \rightarrow Cs_3Bi_2I_9 + 2AgI + CsI$$

Cs_2AgSbI_6 Nanocrystals: a New Air-Stable Iodide Double-Perovskite (Elpasolite) Semiconductor

Faris Horani and Daniel R. Gamelin*

Cite This: *J. Am. Chem. Soc.* 2025, 147, 16552–16559

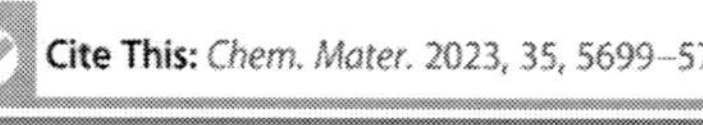

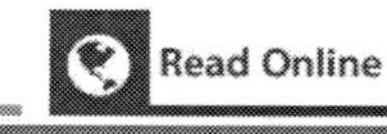

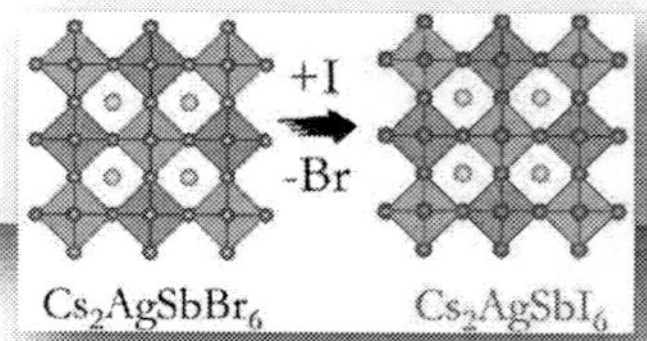

2

High-throughput screening of halide materials

High-throughput workflows

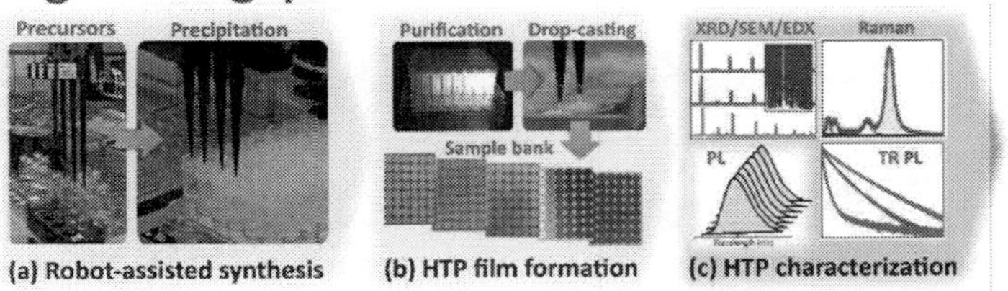

Mater. Res. Bull., 2024, 49, 1284

Lead-free double halide perovskites

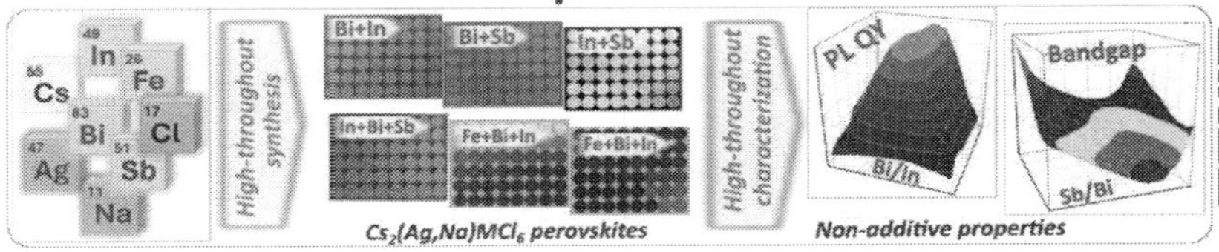

J. Mater. Chem. C, 2024, 12, 8705

Vacancy-ordered perovskites

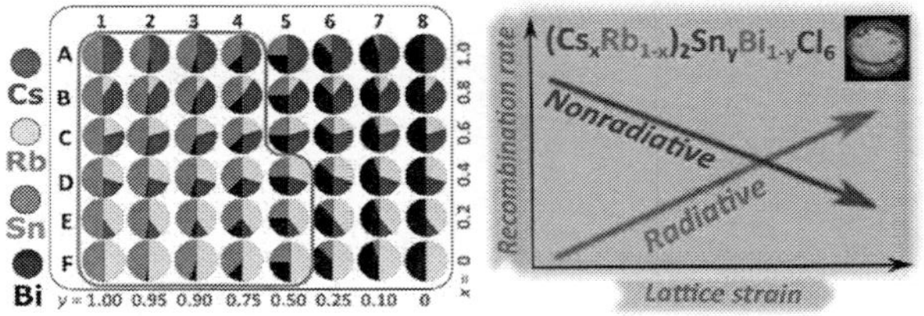

J. Mater. Chem. C, 2025, 13, 2303

Perovskite-like materials

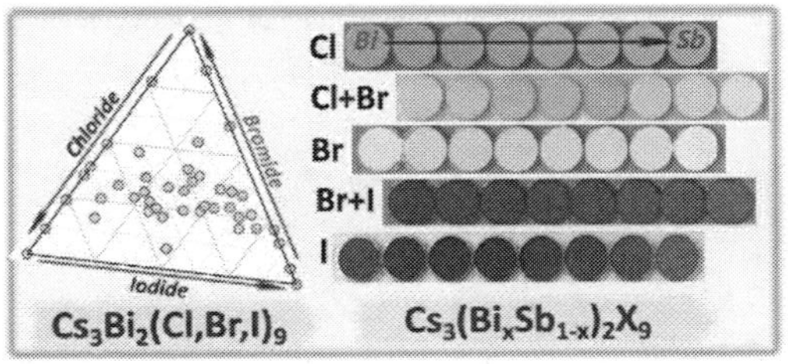

Mater. Adv., 2025, 6, 4847

High-entropy double perovskites

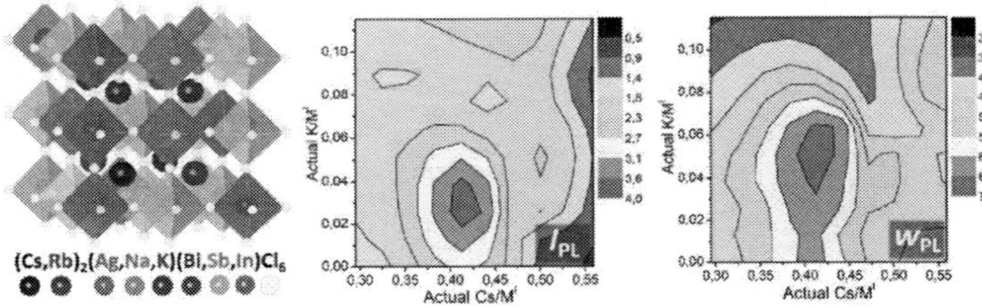

In preparation

3

Starting with $Cs_2AgBiBr_6$ (CABB)

High-Throughput Screening of Environmentally Stable Lead-Free Halide Perovskites for PV

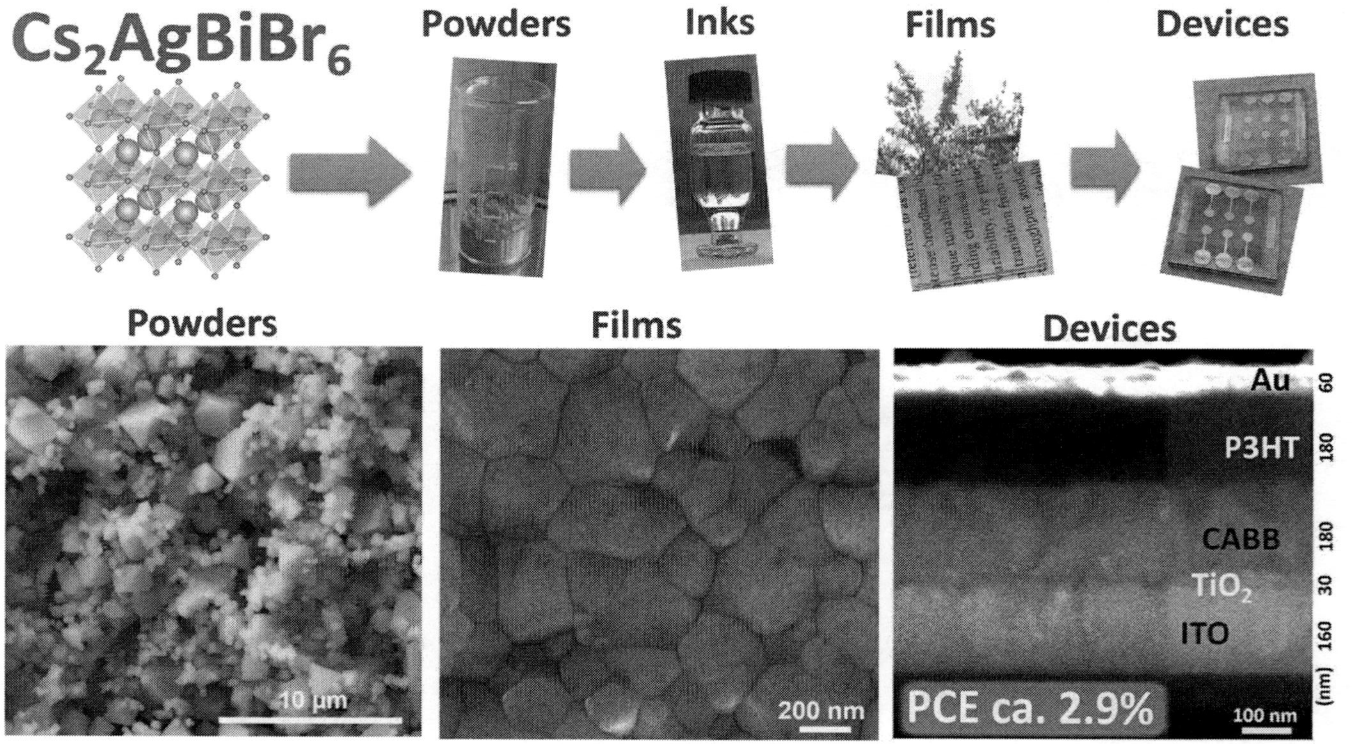

Conversion of cubic $Cs_2AgBiBr_6$ into tetragonal $Cs_2AgBi(Br,I)_6$

HI ERN Helmholtz Institute Erlangen-Nürnberg

SEM images

Cubic $Cs_2AgBiBr_6$

NaI — *anion exchange*

$Cs_3Bi_2(Br,I)_9$ + $CsAg_2I_3$

T — *solid-state reaction*

Tetragonal $Cs_2AgBi(Br,I)_6$

Powder XRD patterns

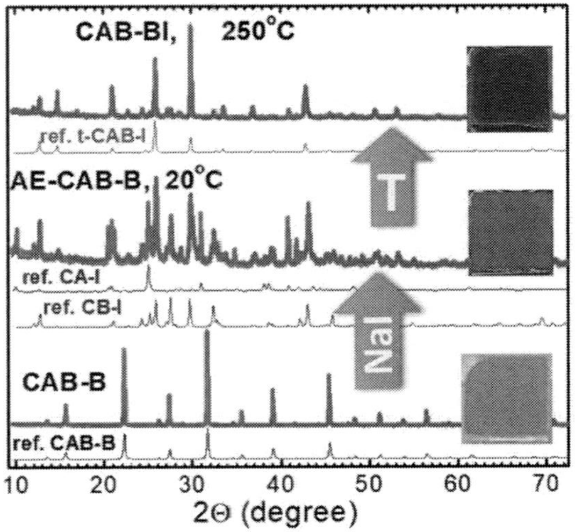

Absorption spectra

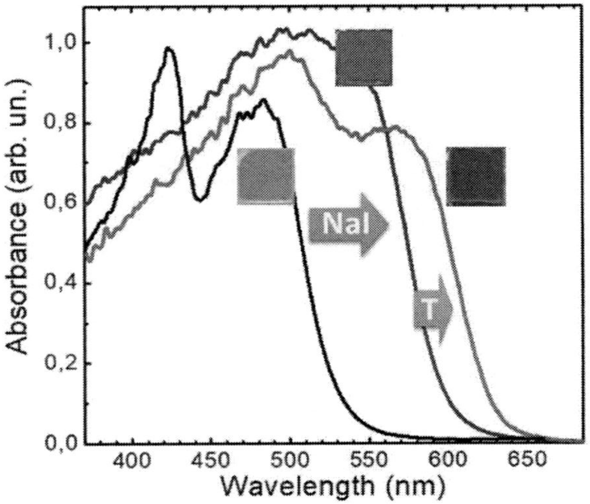

EDX analysis

Sample ID		X = Br+I		X/M^{III}	X/Ag	Cs/M^{III}	Cs/Ag	Formal composition
		Br, %	I, %					
CAB-B		100	0	6.0	6.0	2.2	1.8	$Cs_2AgBiBr_6$
AE of CAB-B	Site #1	20	80	4.6	-	1.5	-	$Cs_3Bi_2(Br_{0.20}I_{0.80})_9$
	Site #2	5	95	-	1.4	-	0.6	$CsAg_2I_3$
CAB-BI, 250 °C		20	80	6.1	6.1	2.0	2.0	$Cs_2AgBi(Br_{0.2}I_{0.8})_6$
CAB-BI, 300 °C		12	88	6.1	5.7	2.1	2.0	$Cs_2AgBi(Br_{0.12}I_{0.88})_6$

Proofs for the solid-state reaction between $Cs_3Bi_2I_9$ and $CsAg_2I_3$

$$Cs_2AgBiBr_6 \xrightarrow{NaI} Cs_3Bi_2I_9 + CsAg_2I_3 \overset{?}{\rightleftarrows} Cs_2AgBiI_6$$

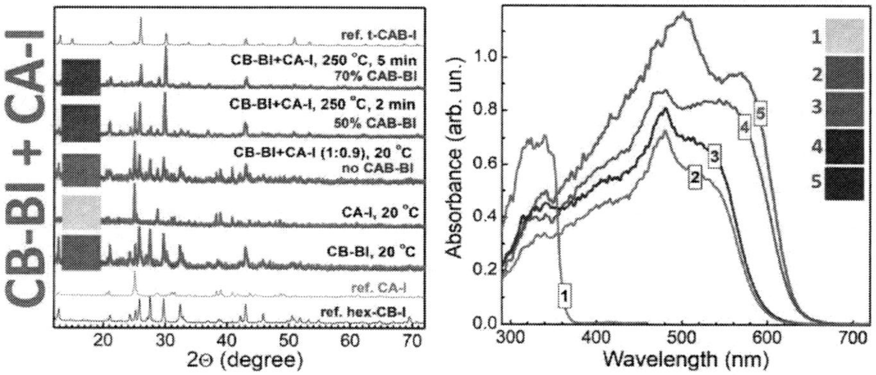

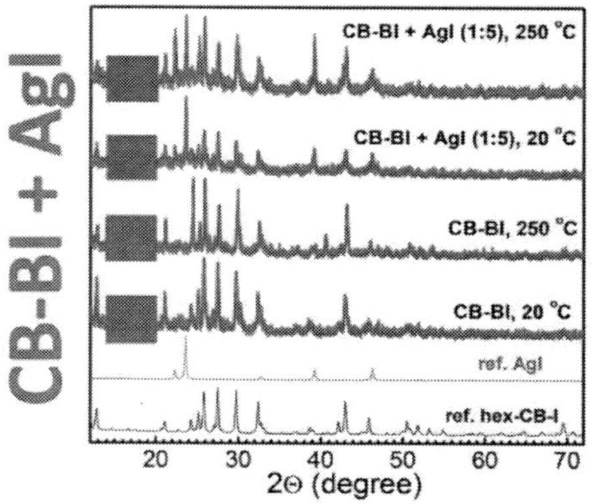

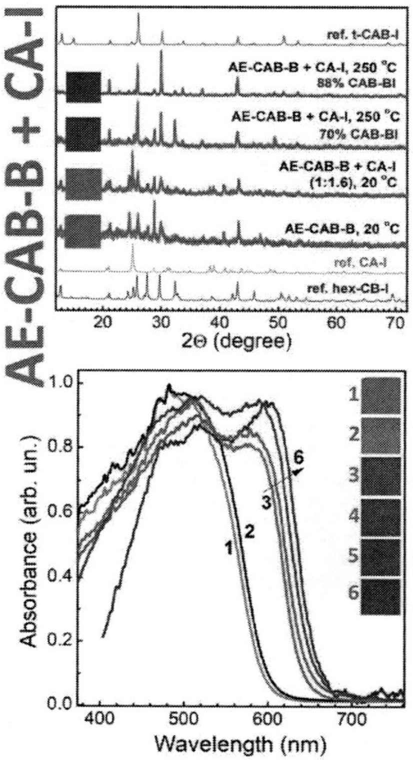

Optimization of the to-stage synthesis of $Cs_2AgBi(Br,I)_6$ perovskites

Optimizing anion exchange...

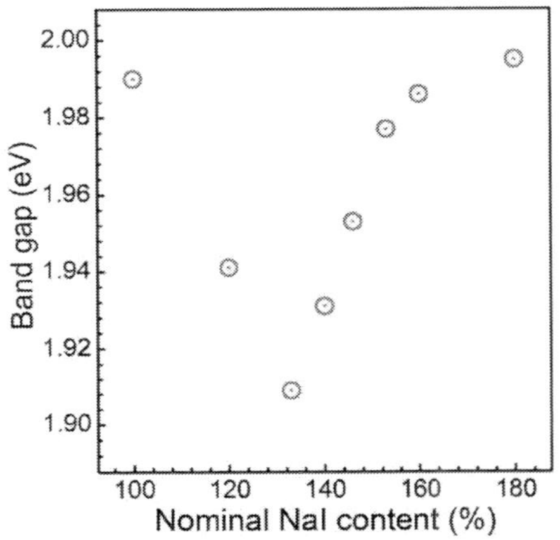

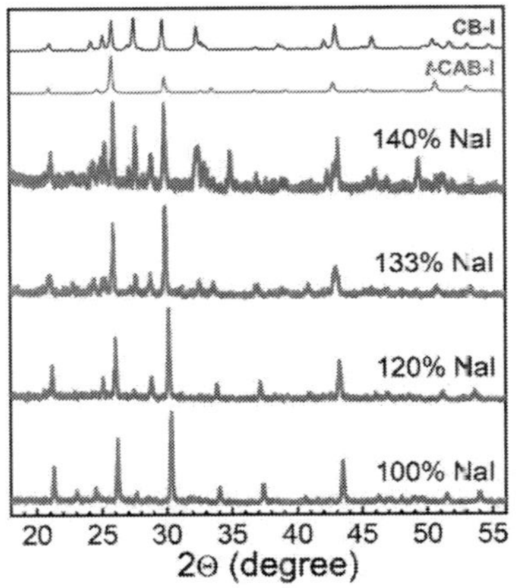

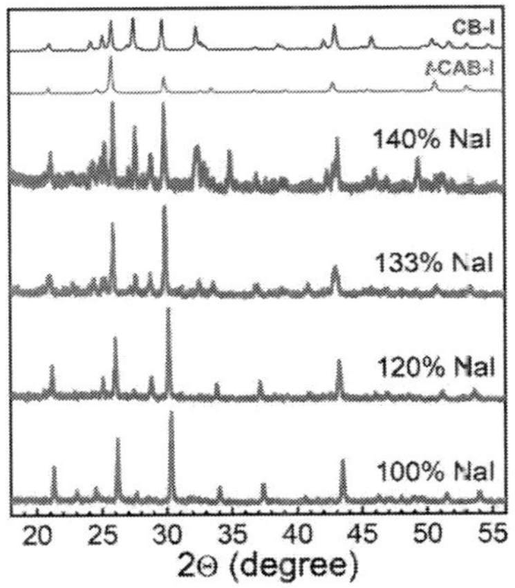

NaI content, %	CAB-BI fraction, wt.%	V_{CAB-BI}, Å^3	Actual iodide fraction in CAB-BI, %
100	95	806	60
120	85	826	70
133	65	845	82
140	15	851	88
150	5	858	92
160	0	-	-

Optimizing solid-state reaction...

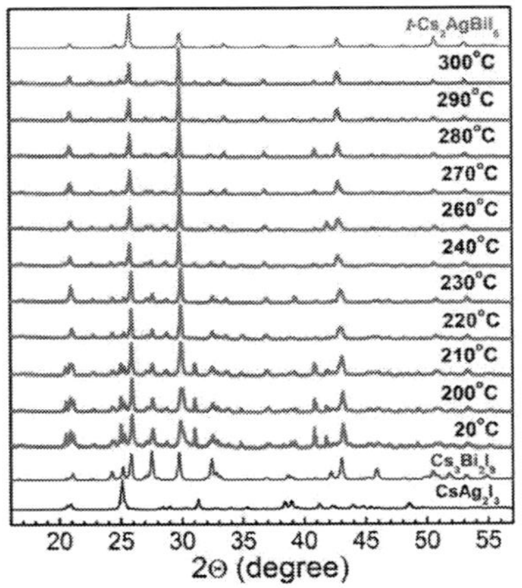

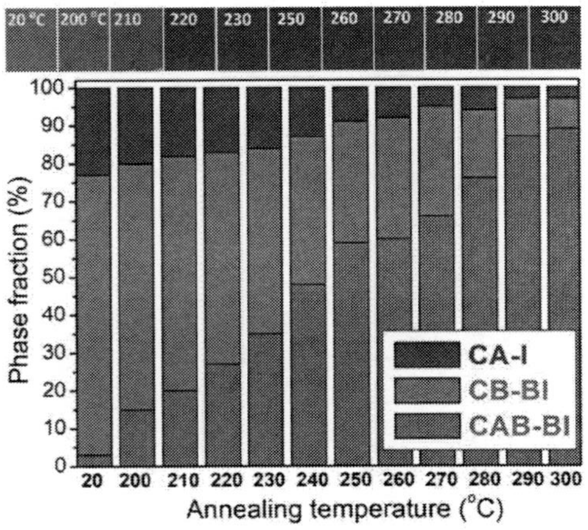

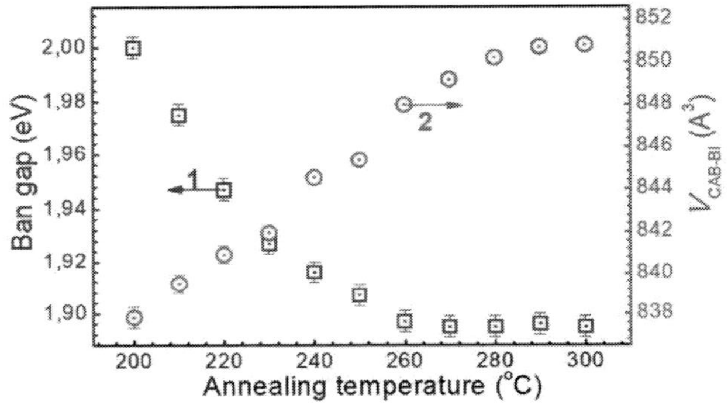

7

Universal character of the two-stage route to iodide perovskites

HI ERN Helmholtz Institute Erlangen-Nürnberg

Combinatorial syntheses

$Cs_2AgBiBr_6 + CsAg_2I_3 + CsAgBr_2$

Anion exchange + T

$Cs_2AgBi(Br_yI_{1-y})_6$

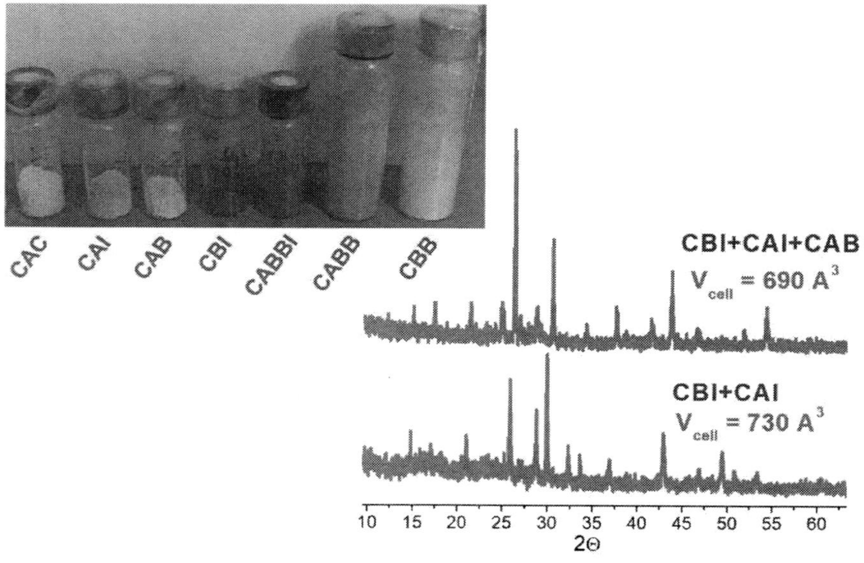

More complex precursors

$Cs_2Ag(Bi_xSb_{1-x})Br_6 + CsAg_2I_3$

Anion exchange + T

$Cs_2Ag(Bi_xSb_{1-x})(Br,I)_6$

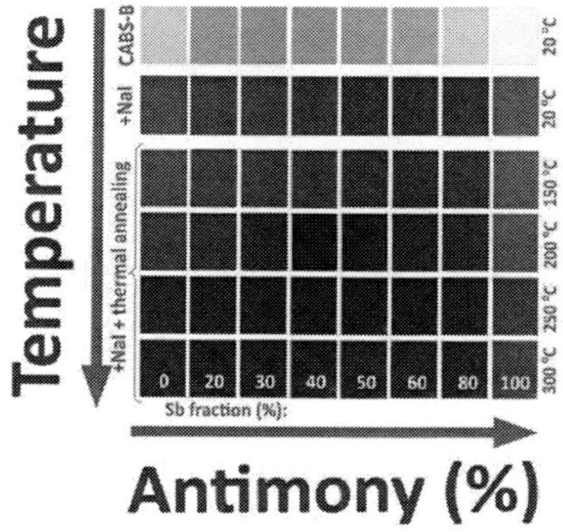

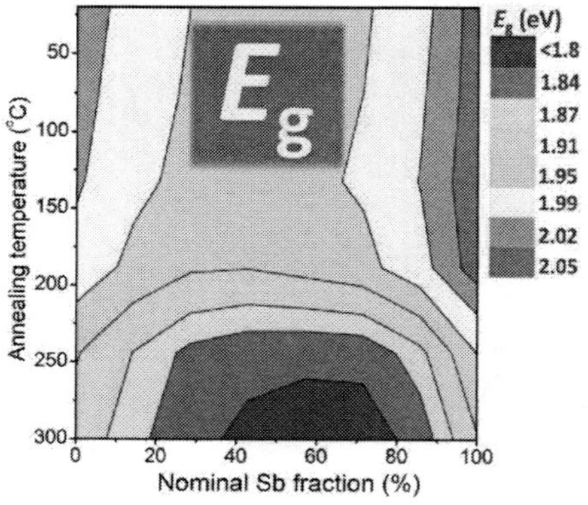

Conversion of $Cs_2Ag(Bi,Sb)Br_6$ into tetragonal $Cs_2Ag(Bi,Sb)(Br,I)_6$

$$Cs_2Ag(Bi_{0.5}Sb_{0.5})Br_6 \xrightarrow[RT]{NaI} Cs_3(Bi_{0.5}Sb_{0.5})_2(Br,I)_9 + CsAg_2I_3 \xrightarrow{T} t\text{-}Cs_2Ag(Bi_{0.5}Sb_{0.5})(Br,I)_6$$

(i) Cs-Ag-(Bi,Sb)-Br (ii) Anion exchange with NaI (iii) Thermal annealing

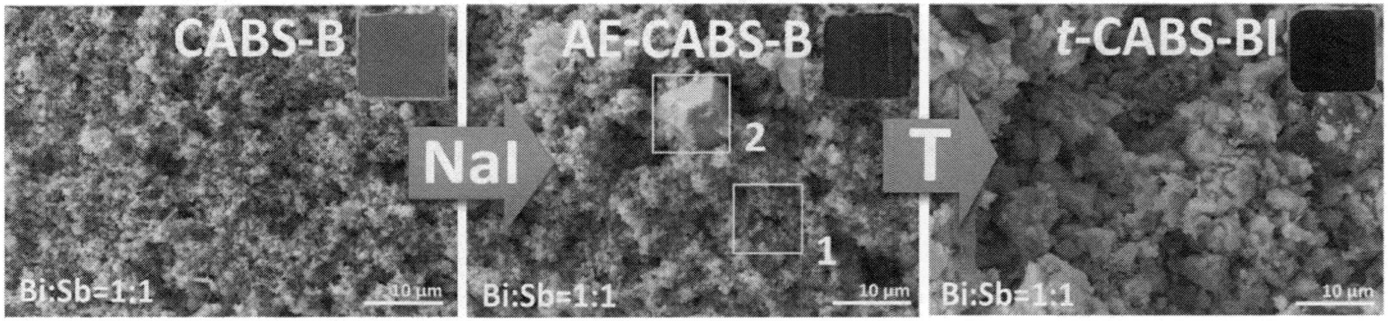

Absorption spectra

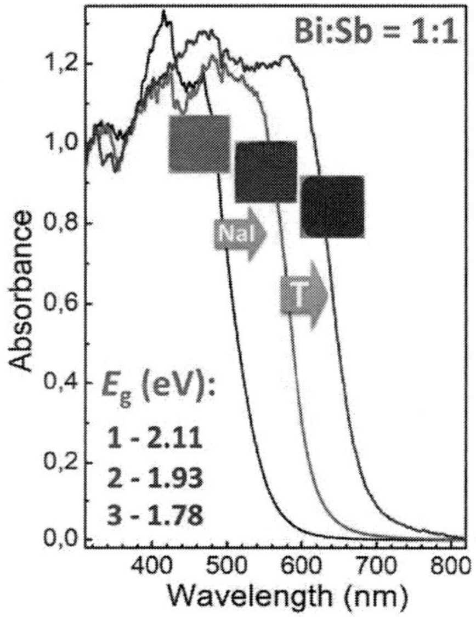

EDX analysis

Sample ID		X = Br+I		X/M^{III}	X/Ag	Cs/M^{III}	Cs/Ag	Bi/M^{III}	Formal composition
		Br, %	I, %						
CABS-B, nom. Bi:Sb=1:1		100	0	5.7	5.6	2.1	2.0	0.48	$Cs_2Ag(Bi_{0.5}Sb_{0.5})Br_6$
AE of CABS-B	Site #1	22	78	4.6	-	1.5	-	0.52	$Cs_3(Bi_{0.5}Sb_{0.5})_2(Br_{0.22}I_{0.78})_9$
	Site #2	3	97	-	1.5	-	0.6	-	$CsAg_2I_3$
CABS-BI, Bi:Sb=1:1, 300 °C		12	88	5.8	0.9	1.6	1.8	0.49	$Cs_2Ag(Bi_{0.5}Sb_{0.5})(Br_{0.12}I_{0.88})_6$

Summary

- A two-stage approach to stable tetragonal $Cs_2AgBi(Br,I)_6$ perovskites (more than 80% I) is developed, based on mild anion-exchange conversion of bromide precursors and open-air annealings
- The solid-state reaction between intermediary products, $Cs_3Bi(Sb)_2I_9$ and $CsAg_2I_3$, is proven and optimized
- The approach is universal and can be applied to (i) more complex mixtures of precursors and (ii) to more complex precursors, in particular, to produce tetragonal $Cs_2AgBi_xSb_{1-x}(Br,I)_6$ perovskites (ca. 90% I) with bandgaps below 1.8 eV
- Developing protocols for the formation of uniform and transparent films of tetragonal iodide double perovskites + PV tests

Thank you

for attention!

Contact info:
Dr. Oleksandr Stroyuk, Forschungszentrum Jülich GmbH,
Helmholtz-Institut Erlangen Nürnberg für Erneuerbare Energien (HI ERN),
Erlangen, Germany, e-mail: o.stroyuk@fz-juelich.de

INVESTIGATING THE 3-DIMENSIONAL STRUCTURE OF METALLIC FILLER PARTICLES IN ELECTRICALLY CONDUCTIVE ADHESIVES

S. Großer[1], A. Müller[1], R. Göckeritz[1], T. Nitsche[2], D. Buckland[2], G. Galbiati[2], B. Jäckel[1]
[1] Fraunhofer CSP, Otto-Eißfeldt-Straße 12, 06120, Halle (Saale), Germany
[2] Henkel AG & Co. KGaA, Henkelstr. 67, 40589, Düsseldorf, Germany

ABSTRACT: Electrically conductive adhesives (ECAs) are emerging interconnection materials whose performance hinges on a continuous three-dimensional metal filler network. Understanding the 3D microstructure is essential for predicting percolation, optimizing filler loading, and ensuring reliable, low-temperature interconnects. 2D analyses miss critical connectivity and distribution details that govern current paths. We present a 3D characterization of the metallic filler network in ECAs using focused ion beam–scanning electron microscopy (FIB-SEM) slice-and-view. The study aims to illuminate the 3D microstructure, enabling prediction of percolation, optimization of filler loading, and assessment of reliable, low-temperature interconnects. A voxel-based reconstruction from aligned 2D slices assigns phase labels (metal vs. resin) and color values to visualize the network and its interfaces, allowing explicit identification of connected and non-connected metal filler particles, which is crucial because macroscopic current conduction relies on a continuous metal network bridging 2 contact interfaces. The metal filler fraction in the resin matrix for 3D (volume) and for 2D (slice) data can be tested and showed a comparable value for the apparent ECA. Variations were found on microscopic scales which average out fast. Segmentation distinguishes connected clusters from isolated fillers, estimate in-plane needed current distances, noting that non-connected particles near sample edges can be artifacts that must be excluded from interpretation.
Keywords: Characterization, 3D microstructure, percolation, ECA, interconnection

1 Introduction

An increasing economic pressure and high silver demand is driving the reduction of silver consumption in PV with remarkable improvements towards the limit for cells and interconnections [1, 2]. Silver-containing interconnection materials are a promising option for temperature-sensitive high-efficiency solar cell modules which require adapted low-temperature interconnection processes in manufacturing [3]. Beside e.g. bismuth-based solder alloys, electrically conductive adhesives (ECAs) are an alternative already used for contact formation in interconnections [4]. Typically, ECAs in PV consists at least in part of expensive silver (Ag). The urgent need to realize material savings and achieving upcoming higher requirements on low-temperature interconnection in ECAs imply a strong demand on material improvement which can only be achieved by an understanding through detailed material analysis. Currently, the experimental access of these conductive networks in ECAs is very limited and based dominantly on 2-dimensional cross-sections. For structural understanding, low-filled ECAs appear to lack a continuous conductive network in two dimensions, yet electrical conduction is sustained by the three-dimensional connectivity of filler particles along the contact material [5]. From the microstructural point of view the metallic filler network forms multiple conduction pathways, each contributing to the total conduction. Consequently, the conductivity of ECAs depends on the arrangement of the metal filler particles.

We tested and applied our approach to data acquisition, processing, and reconstruction to characterize the metallic network of an exemplary ECA in greater detail using modern FIB-SEM, a technique developed more than 40 years ago [6]. The visualization of the metallic network, the metal volume fraction in the contact, the distribution of metal along the contact area, and the identification of low- and high-metal-filled regions, as well as non-contacted metal fillers, can be determined with our approach. The workflow for microstructure elucidation, data reconstruction, and analysis opens up a wide range of applications to improve ECAs and related processes with high relevance. The aim of this work is to enhance the ability to determine the detailed microstructure of ECAs used in photovoltaic applications. Our results show that this approach provides detailed visualization of the metallic network, including the metal volume fraction in the contact, the distribution of metal along the contact area, and the identification of low- and high-metal-filled regions in the ECA, enabling the detection of isolated metal fillers without a conduction path to the metal contact.

2 Experimental

For testing, evaluation and demonstration of the experimental approach the requirements on the sample under test are low. An acrylic-based ECA has been used and manually stencil printed on a $Sn_{60}Pb_{40}$-coated 4 mm wide copper ribbon, usually used in PV for cross connection, offering a wide ECA contact. An equal ribbon has been placed on top and gently pressed down by a sheet of silicone membranes weight. Curing takes place on a hot plate at 150 °C for 30 min, guaranteeing a fully cured ECA. After curing a cross-section has been prepared by a metallographic preparation, shown in Figure 1. The thickness of the cured ECA layer was around 128 µm at the position of investigation.

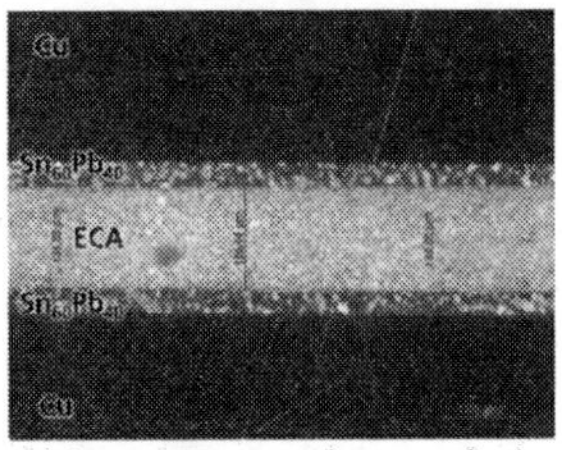

Figure 1: Light microscopy image of the symmetric ribbon/ECA/ribbon sample cross-section.

The workflow for slice and view technique on the material system was tested and evaluated by means of Focused Ion Beam and Scanning Electron Microscopy methodology with different instruments (ZEISS NVision

40 Crossbeam Ga-FIB-SEM and Thermo Scientific Helios 5 Hydra UX Crossbeam multi species plasma FIB). Within the 3-dimensional volume of an ECA (including the interface to the solder contact interface) a sequence of multiple cross-sections was prepared by FIB (using Xe-ion beam at 30 kV) and recorded by SEM which delivered a large dataset from the inspected volume. This dataset has been reconstructed as well as evaluated by means of the Avizo 3D software.

3 Results

From the measured sequence of 2D slices a 3D reconstruction depicts a voxel volume. Each voxel was assigned to a phase label and gray/color value to represent the present material and interface in the three-dimensional structure. This is shown for the dataset in Figure 2 whereas the solder interface is at the bottom and the ECA is on top. By the black arrow in z-direction the direction of the intended current flow direction (to opposite solder contact) is indicated. The resin is set as transparent allowing the unobstructed view on fillers in the near and far background. Metal phases are colored in blue. The 3D volume can be rotated in different arbitrary directions to provide a view on and inspect the metallic network arrangement.

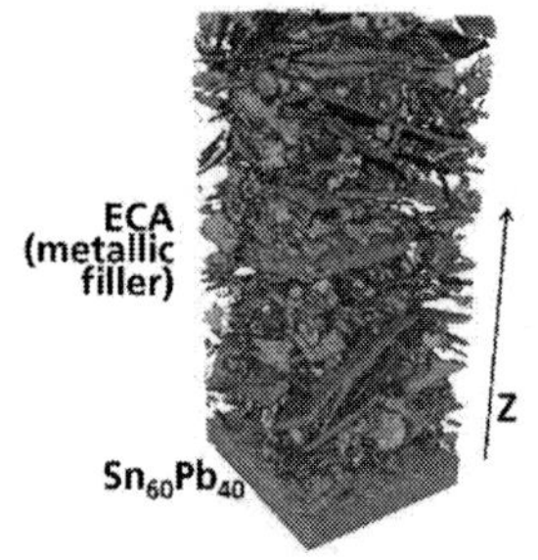

Figure 2: ECA dependent 3D-reconstruction of the metallic filler network (resin transparent).

3.1 From 2D-images to volume phase fraction of metallic filler

In 2D images the image information represents a section through the clusters and particles. By increasing the dimensionality to 3-dimensions the information content increases and results in a complex representation of fillers covering each other (see Figure 2). By using the attributed phase information one can determine absolute and relative volume fractions of metal and resin in an ECA. In the present case the analyzed volume of 10824 µm³ exhibits relative volume fractions of $V_{filler, 3D} = 12$ vol% for the metal and $V_{resin, 3D} = 88$ vol% for the resin.

Due to the massive number of particles in a volume information of position and arrangement of single fillers, filler clusters or filler types are hard to collect. One suitable representation to mitigate self-covering was the sublayer-sectioning of the volume as shown in Figure 3. A layer separation with a layer thickness range (smaller than large particles) allows the screening of different positions in the volume but still give information about the shape of the particles. The benefit can be clearly seen in Figure 3 where on the left-hand side a 2D cross-section image is "connected" to the 3D-sublayer. The sublayer is visually less dense packed and reveals the shape, position and direction of single fillers as well as their arrangement. This information exceeds the limited 2D-representation and enables the screening of the volume. The sample under test exhibited Ag-fillers with different shapes and sizes of flakes and nuggets. Some larger flake-shaped fillers are flat, others are bent. Flakes have a high aspect ratio in contrast to nugget-shaped fillers therefore their orientation is expected crucial to bridge large distances in Z. Extended flakes were found in different direction but empirically seem to be less likely to be aligned with their long axis in Z direction. Nugget-shaped fillers have been found as single particles or as clusters in proximity to flakes. The data representation allows the screening for separated fillers. These fillers or small clusters are surrounded by resin and therefore are electrically isolated with no contribution to the current conduction. The inspected volume exhibited only a neglectable number of isolated fillers but exclusively nugget shaped. Fillers cropped by the edge of the 3D-volume were not considered.

Figure 3: 2D-image (black/gray) and adjacent 3D-layer (blue) of the metallic filler network

The screening of the volume gives valuable access to the present arrangement of the fillers in the sample, expose the filler interconnection, bent and direction in a flexible and qualitative way. Quantifications of arrangement characteristics need different approaches as described in the next passage.

3.2 Testing the metallic filler network on cluster formation

The electrical conductivity in the metal filler network depends on their arrangement to touching or at least very near particles which enable electron transfer. Electron transfer must be feasible from one electrode at the bottom to the other electron on the top. In our representation in Figure 2 it corresponds with the Z-direction. Please note, the upper electrode was not included in the measured volume due to the high ECA thickness. Nevertheless, the investigated Z-range (depth) is representative for typical ECA contact thickness in PV. Clusters are formed in 3-dimensions which infer current flow contribution in in-plane (X-Y plane) to electrode.

The investigated volume of Figure 2 has an in-plane area of 305 µm² (X-Y plane). By means of a segmentation algorithm metal clusters in the volume have been determined. To prove non-connected metal fractions in the volume in $V_{filler, 3D}$ the specific cluster of electrode and electrode touching fillers must be excluded. Figure 4a) demonstrates the result in the volume representation. Different colors represent independent clusters. In contrast to Figure 2 the volume representation is less densely packed notable by strong reduced metal amount. In our calculation, 7 % of the total metal amount is not connected to the lower electrode which corresponds to an absolute value of $V_{non\text{-}connected\ filler,\ 3D} = 0.8$ vol%. However, the approach is lacking in information on the virtual cut of particles at the volume edge. The data gives no information if the edge particles are connected to the electrode through the cropped structure. However, by e.g. visual screening of the data (like shown in Figure 3) clusters can be identified which do not touch the edge, indicating that within the inspected volume only a neglectable amount of filler were not connected to the electrode. Consequently, $V_{non\text{-}connected\ filler,\ 3D}$ must be much lower than 0.8 vol% resulting in the conclusion that for the used ECA an area of 305 µm² is supposed to be sufficient.

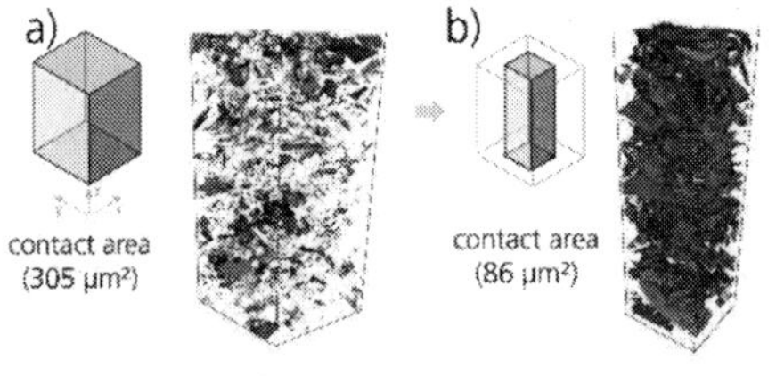

Figure 4: Schematic and reconstructed 3D model of filler and filler clusters, which are non-connected to the solder electrode for 2 different contact areas of the same dataset.

To approximate the minimum requirement of contact area a reduction of the volume under analysis was tested. An inner part of the same volume will be used to perform the cluster analysis whereas the outer part of the structure will be cropped. If cropping of connections between fillers appears then an increase of clusters number will increase, which are not connected to the lower electrode. A reduction of the volume in-plane area by around 73% have been tested representing a contact area of 86 µm² (8.9 µm x 9.7 µm). Figure 4 shows the schematic of the approach as well as the resulting separated cluster representation. One can clearly observe an increase in the non-connected cluster number by comparison with the full area equivalent of 305 µm² (17.2 µm x 17.7 µm). In the particular case we found the massive increase in non-connected metal fraction $V_{non\text{-}connected\ filler,\ 3D}$ from 7 % (305 µm²) to 90 % (86 µm²). By microstructural inspection the root cause has been identified in a low dense volume part near the lower solder electrode, shown in Figure 5 by the red dashed line as a guide to the eye. This gap separates all metal above from the connection. Anyhow the connection is provided on larger length but is limited on smaller length for 3D structured materials. From the investigated position an approximated length for connection in X-Y plane is supposed to be in the range of 10 to 18 µm. It is likely the microstructure sized gap exists on this specific position. Without the gap the length for connection in X-Y plane is expected to be lower for the present sample.

Figure 5: 3D-reconstruction of the metallic filler network of the contact area reduced sub-volume. A depletion of filles is indicated by a dashed-red line as guide for the eye.

3.3 Proofing microstructure relation of 2D to 3D

Interestingly, the found gap in Figure 5 is roughly in plane with the X-Y electrode surface plane. Therefore, an evaluation of metal fraction in the X-Y plane (2D) along the depth Z (1D) would indicate local variations in the (X-Y in plane) filler content. In 2D images the metal fraction $A_{filler,\ slice}$ represents the area fraction of metal on the total image area, at which 0 % is pure resin and 100 % is complete metal. In Figure 6 the volume of Figure 2 (with 305 µm² contact area) has been evaluated and $A_{filler,\ slice}$ plotted in dependence of Z. At 0 µm is the interface to the lower solder electrode located. The values for $A_{filler,\ slice}$ vary from 4 % (minimum at 1.3 µm) to 27 % (maximum at 18 µm). By calculation of the mean value of A_{filler}, taking all points along Z into account, a value of $A_{filler,\ mean} = (11.7 \pm 3.5)$ % results. This statistic value is in consistency with the calculated voxel-based metal fraction of $V_{filler,\ 3D} = 12$ vol%, on the present sample and on the investigated length of Z. On smaller length microstructural variations can take place. Within the inspected volume the minimum in $A_{filler,\ slice}$ correlates with the gap found in Figure 5, as expected. The validity of the interpretation is limited to reduced metal content in respect to the investigated plane and not very meaningful to depletions which are tilted or arbitrary formed in reference to the slice plane.

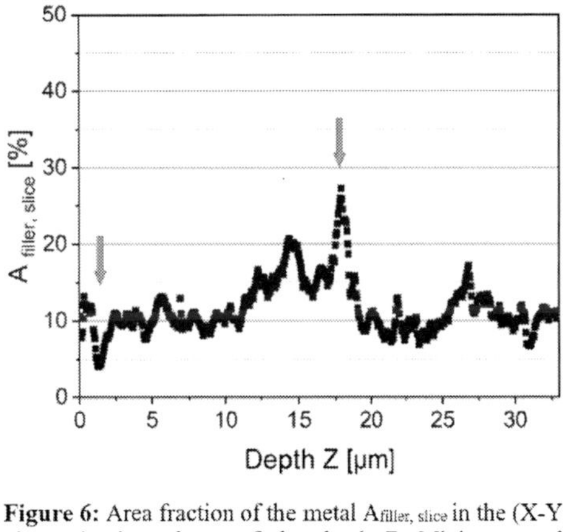

Figure 6: Area fraction of the metal $A_{filler,\ slice}$ in the (X-Y plane) in dependance of the depth Z. Minimum and maximum value are indicated by an arrow.

Nevertheless, the analysis of metal area fractions is an approach to approximate the very local metal volume fraction but needs sufficient data input to draw conclusion of local metal volume fractions.

4 Summary

This study presents a three-dimensional characterization of the metallic filler network in electrically conductive adhesives (ECAs) using focused ion beam - scanning electron microscopy (FIB-SEM) slice-and-view to reveal the continuous metal pathways that govern percolation, filler loading, and interconnect reliability. By reconstructing voxel-based 3D volumes from 2D SEM images and assigning phase labels to metal and resin, the work enables explicit visualization of connected versus isolated metallic filler particles and their interfaces, providing a direct link between microstructure and macroscopic impact to conductivity (qualitatively). In the examined volume, the 3D metal fraction is about 12 vol%, with variations on micron scales that average out. Segmentation distinguishes connected clusters from non-connected fillers, although edge artifacts near sample boundaries must be excluded from interpretation. Fillers that remain non-conductive to the network do not improve conduction and raise material costs. The analysis also demonstrates that local 2D metal fractions, when viewed across the depth of the contact, corroborated by the 3D results but also reveal microstructural metal density variations. The proposed technique and approach offer a practical route to be used for assessing how formulation changes influence network formation and conductance pathways, as well as the reliability of ECA interconnections in photovoltaic applications.

Acknowledgement
The authors like to thank Denise Ulm for supporting the preparation. Financial support from the Federal Ministry for Economic Affairs and Energy within the funded project "IndiFiduell" (FKZ: 03EE1185) is gratefully acknowledged.

References

[1] V. Cattaneo, J. Mast, I. Hackenhaar, S. Nardone, S. Scheerlinck, J. Mertens, J. Dewulf, Resources, Conservation and Recycling, 224 (2025) DOI:10.1016/j.resconrec.2025.108562

[2] M. Kronsbein, L. Böck, K. Dyhr, T. Rößler, N. Willenbacheret, Solar Energy Materials and Solar Cells, 287 (2025) DOI: 10.1016/j.solmat.2025.113603

[4] M. De Bastiani, M. Babics, E. Aydin, A. Subbiah, L. Xu, S. De Wolf, Solar RRL, 6, 3 (2021) DOI: 10.1002/solr.202100493

[4] International Technology Roadmap for Photovoltaics ITRPV) - 2024 Results, VDMA (2025)

[5] I. Devoto Acevedo, R. Wells, S. Großer, K. Wienands, D. Rudolph, A. Halm, R. Gottschalg, D. Tune, Progress in Photovoltaics: Research and Applications. (2024) DOI: 10.1002/pip.3787

[6] J. Melngailis, J., J. Vac. Sci. Technol. B, 5 (1987) 469-495. DOI: 10.1116/1.583937

42nd European Photovoltaic Solar Energy Conference and Exhibition

Investigating the 3-dimensional structure of metallic filler particles in electrically conductive adhesives

Fraunhofer CSP

Fraunhofer Center for Silicon Photovoltaics CSP

S. Großer[1], A. Müller[1], R. Göckeritz[1], T. Nitsche[2], D. Buckland[2], G. Galbiati[2], B. Jäckel[1]

[1] Fraunhofer CSP, Germany

[2] Henkel AG & Co. KGaA, Germany

3AV.1.1

Electrically conductive adhesives (ECA) are emerging interconnection materials [1]. ECA rely on a 3D metal filler network. Understanding the 3D microstructure is key to predict percolation, optimize loading, and ensure reliable, low-temperature interconnects [2,3].

Challenge: 2D analyses miss the 3D arrangement, losing details on metal fraction, connectivity, and filler distribution along the contact.

Task: Use FIB-SEM slice-and-view to reconstruct the 3D microstructure in the ECA contact, creating a dataset to visualize metal fraction, distribution, and isolated fillers to support formulation assessment.

Experimental Approach

- Method evaluation and demonstration on an arbitrary test system: electrically conductive adhesive (with Ag-filler) cured between $Sn_{60}Pb_{40}$ coated Cu ribbon
- Dual-beam Focused Ion Beam (FIB) / Scanning Electron Microscopy (SEM) instrument
- Slice-and-view technique (Sequential polishing and imaging) → sampling of a 3D volume
- Reconstruction of 3D microstructure

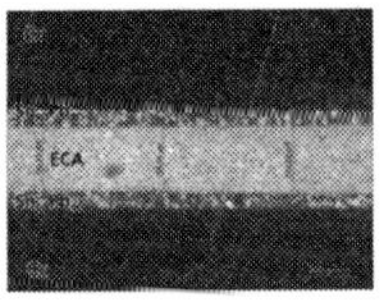

Fig 1: Cross section of ECA test sample (light microscopy)

3D reconstruction of the metallic filler network

From aligned sequence of 2D slices a 3D reconstruction depicts a voxel volume. Each voxel was assigned to a phase label and gray/color value to represent the present material and interface in the three-dimensional structure.

- Phase label to expose metal
  - Metall (set opaque)
  - Resin (set transparent)
- Color
  - Uniform for metallic part
- Visualization
  - Rotation
  - Sectioning

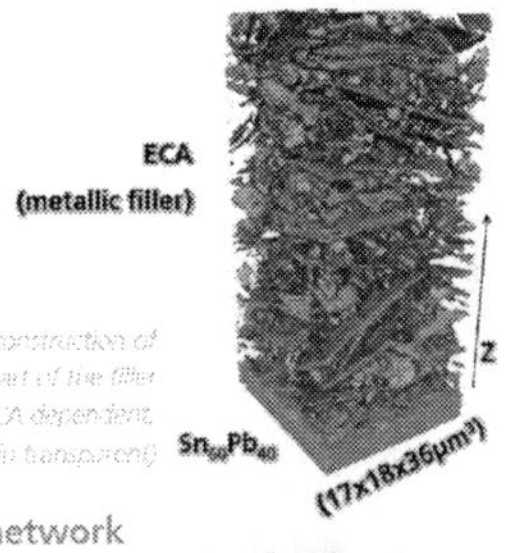

Fig 2: 3D reconstruction of metallic part of the filler network (ECA dependent, resin transparent)

Analysis of the 3-dimensional filler network

From 2D to volume phase fraction of metallic filler

3D cross-section images increase the information depth. From the 3D-microstructure, considering a 2-phase system of metal filler and resin, the volume fraction was calculated (solder-based interface layer excluded).

- Distribution of all fillers in resin matrix
- Metal content in volume
  - $V_{filler,\,3D}$ = 12 vol% (1.781 µm³)
  - $V_{resin,\,3D}$ = 88 vol% (9.043 µm³)

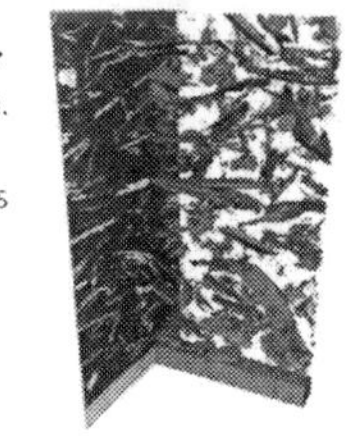

Fig 3: 2D-image and adjacent 3D-layer of the metallic filler network

Approaches to test the metallic filler network on cluster formation

Particle clusters (touching fillers) conduct the current. Segmentation of metallic parts was used to identify clusters. Same local dataset was analyzed.

- Expose of (to $Sn_{60}Pb_{40}$) non-connected filler clusters
  - Metall (opaque if non-connected)
  - Metall (transparent if connected)
  - Color (Cluster dependent)
- Test: Reduction of $Sn_{60}Pb_{40}$ interface area

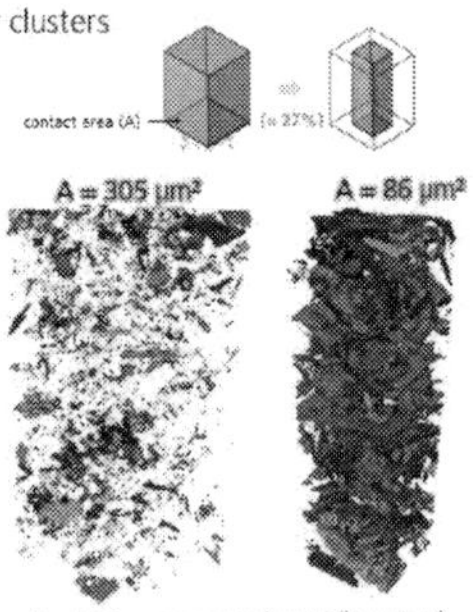

Fig 4: Non-connected metallic part of the same filler network for 2 different contact areas

Non-connected filler fraction (to solder interface)

Contact area	Fraction (relative)
305 µm²	7 %*
86 µm²	90 %

- Tested ECA with negligible* fraction of non-connected fillers
- Reduction of surface area exhibits increase of non-connected fillers → length of in-plane current paths in the network (range of 10 µm – 18 µm) in x and y
- *) Artifacts through edge effect (virtually cropped particles must be considered)

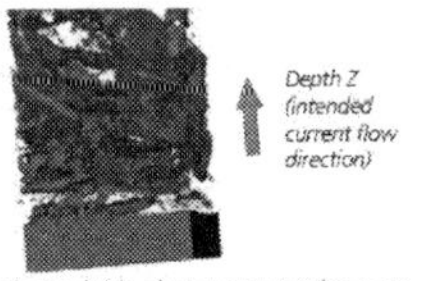

Fig 5: Visible cluster interruption near the interface (at reduced dataset with 86 µm² area)

Validation microstructure relation between 2D to 3D

Determination of the filler area fraction A_{filler} from 2D images along the z-axis (depth).

- Assessment on µm scale (slice) and statistically in dataset (mean)
  - $A_{filler,\,slice}$ = 4 % (min) – 27 % (max)
  - $A_{filler,\,mean}$ = (11.7 ± 3.5) %
- Area and volume filler fraction in same range: $A_{filler,\,mean} \approx V_{filler,\,3D}$

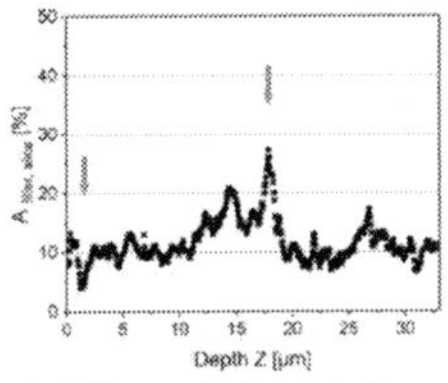

Fig 6: Filler area fraction vs depth (Z-axis)

Summary

- 3D ECA network from FIB-SEM slice-and-view uncovers filler network and depth-dependent metal fraction.
- 3D view outperforms 2D for connectivity and quantitative insights.
- Identifies connected vs. non-connected fillers and rough estimate required in-plane current length.
- Outlook: Application to other ECAs

Contact

Dr. Stephan Großer
Tel. +49 345 5589-5112
stephan.grosser@csp.fraunhofer.de

Otto-Eissfeldt-Strasse 12
06120 Halle (Saale), Germany
www.csp.fraunhofer.de

1 International Technology Roadmap for Photovoltaics (ITRPV) - 2024 Results, VDMA (2025)
2 I. Devoto Acevedo et al., „The effects of increasing filler loading on the contact resistivity of interconnects based on silver–epoxied conductive adhesives and silver metalization pastes" Progress in Photovoltaics: Research and Applications. (2024) DOI: 10.1002/pip.3787
3 M. Kronsbein et al., „Less is more: Enabling low-filled electrically conductive adhesives for shingled solar cell interconnection using the capillary suspension concept" Solar Energy Materials and Solar Cells, 287 (2025) DOI: 10.1016/j.solmat.2025.113603

Financial support by the Federal Ministry for Economic Affairs and Energy funded project »IndiFiduell« (FKZ: 03EE1185B and 03EE1185C) is gratefully acknowledged

Henkel

INVESTIGATION ON DIFFERENT BYPASS DIODES FOR SHADE RESISTANT PV-MODULES

Jens Froebel[1], Matthias Pander[1], Bengt Jaeckel[1], Andreas Maixner[2], Pouya Pourshafi[2], A. Bakhtiari[2], Hamed Hanifi[2]
[(1)]Fraunhofer-Center for Silicon-Photovoltaics (CSP), Halle (Saale), Germany
[2]AESOLAR, Koenigsbrunn, Germany
*Contact: +49 345 5589 5213, jens.froebel@csp.fraunhofer.de

ABSTRACT: The SegmentPV project focuses on developing photovoltaic modules for residential buildings, addressing challenges such as partial and dynamic shading through a collaboration between AESOLAR and the Fraunhofer Center for Silicon Photovoltaics (CSP). The design process encompasses various aspects, including the selection of the bill of materials (BOM), lamination processes, types of photovoltaic (PV) cells, interconnections, and bypass diodes. To understand the electrical, thermal, and structural requirements and challenges, this study investigates a selection of state-of-the-art and alternative bypass diodes. A primary goal is to determine the diode parameters essential for creating a digital twin, specifically a SPICE model, to simulate partial shading effects.

Partial shading of a single PV cell can lead to substantial power losses in the entire substring connected in series. For example, older designs with 60 cells and three substrings may suffer a 33% power loss if one cell is shaded, whereas modern butterfly designs reduce this to one-sixth of the module's power. This research explores various string designs to further minimize losses, requiring a detailed examination of bypass diode requirements, including I-V characteristics, power losses, reverse breakdown voltage, thermal behavior, and form factors for in-laminate designs. Alternatives to conventional Schottky diodes, such as silicon diodes, field-effect diodes, and active bypass diodes, are also evaluated.

Ten different diodes suitable for bypass applications were selected. Four-point measurements using a programmable source meter were conducted to determine I-V characteristics, with temperature-dependent I-V curve tracing performed on a subset. Diode parameters, including saturation current (Is), ideality factor (n), and series resistance (Rs), were extracted, and their temperature dependencies in the Shockley equation were characterized. The results provide insights for robust diode characterization and highlight temperature dependencies critical for accurate simulations.

Keywords: Bypass diodes, Characterization, PV modules

1 INTRODUCTION

Bypass diodes are key protection and performance elements in photovoltaic modules. In standard PV modules they are connected in anti-parallel across cell sub-strings (typically 18–24 cells) and provide an alternative current path in the event of partial shading, soiling or cell mismatch. The aim of the SegmentPV Project is to further subdivide the module to further increase its resistance to shading. One key objective is to identify optimal bypass diodes for residential photovoltaic modules that are resistant to recurring shading. This involves conducting electrical and thermal characterizations of various diode devices. The diodes were measured using a four-point connection setup at high speed to prevent self-heating, and additionally in a climate chamber from -40°C to 125°C to assess temperature behavior. Diode parameters were extracted from the data using a Python-based fitting algorithm, enabling simulations of shading scenarios that account for both partial shading and temperature variations. Standard SPICE simulations are limited because they apply a global temperature to all circuit components, so temperature-dependent modeling requires enhancements.

A measurement protocol was developed to evaluate and characterize potential bypass diodes, focusing on accurately capturing current-voltage behavior as a function of temperature. Measurements spanned a wide range from -40°C to 125°C, covering extreme operational conditions for PV modules. This approach provides a deeper understanding of the temperature-dependent behavior of these semiconductor components.

This paper presents an overview of state-of-the-art and alternative bypass diodes for use in solar modules. A robust measurement setup for diode characterization is described, and temperature-dependent diode parameters for simulations are extracted. The findings contribute to improving shade-resistant PV module designs by minimizing power losses and enhancing reliability.

Different Diode technologies are analyzed. This investigation includes:

Schottky Diodes: Based on a metal-semiconductor junction. They are widely used as BPDs because they offer low losses during forward conduction and enable fast switching. However, they may exhibit higher leakage current at high temperatures or reverse voltages.

Silicon Diodes (PN Junction): Standard silicon diodes with a PN junction. They are robust and have low leakage current but are less commonly used as BPDs due to higher losses.

Super Barrier Diodes (SBR): A hybrid technology that combines Schottky-like properties with PN advantages. They offer a balance of low forward voltage and low leakage current, making them more efficient than pure Schottky diodes.

Smart Diodes (Active Bypass Diodes): Active components, often MOSFET-based, that switch intelligently. They behave like "ideal diodes" with minimal losses and are particularly advantageous in partial shading scenarios due to their dynamic adjustment.

Conventional solar modules utilize junction boxes to house and connect Schottky bypass diodes, which typically have cylindrical or large rectangular form factors. To enhance thermal dissipation, these junction boxes are often filled with a potting compound. For subdivision of the module with the normal concept additional wiring and holes in the backsheet or rear glass would be required. Therefore, direct integration of the bypass diodes in the laminate is desirable. This approach requires diodes with a thin, compact form factor to ensure compatibility with the laminated structure and maintain module efficiency.

2 MATERIALS AND METHODS

2.1 Samples

Twelve solar module bypass diodes were selected, including alternative technologies. For scientific and product development purposes, brands and models were anonymized as P01 to P12, with addendums (e.g., s11) denoting specific samples on boards. Passive diodes included hot spot free, super barrier rectifiers, silicon, and Schottky types; active diodes were smart bypass diodes. Typically, six to eight samples per type were measured to statistically account for variations.

2.2 IV Characterization setup

The emphasis was on examining forward characteristics, including diode voltage and power consumption. The reverse breakdown voltage was verified, and diodes are slated for continuous stress testing in a subsequent work package. Forward characteristic curves were used to derive diode parameters such as saturation current (Is), ideality factor (n), and series resistance (Rs).

Test samples were measured in a climate chamber over a temperature range of -40°C to 125°C (limited from an initial plan of -45°C to 150°C due to technical constraints) to derive temperature-dependent parameters. Determining reverse breakdown voltage proved challenging without specialized equipment, as small currents at high voltages can damage the diodes. For instance, a typical -70 V breakdown at 100 mA equates to 7 W of load. The source meter used was limited to -40 V to +40 V, so only a minimum reverse breakdown of -40 V could be confirmed with our setup. Laboratory power supplies were inadequate for fine current adjustments, and prolonged testing caused heating that altered parameters.

The measurement setup involved soldering all diodes onto carriers designed for four-point measurements. Cross-connectors served as contacts to maximize solder area and minimize series resistance. Typically, six to eight diodes were mounted per test carrier to reduce the statistical impact of defects and errors. A high-accuracy programmable source meter measured IV-curves, with fast sweeps starting at low power to avoid heating.

For measurement of the temperature behavior in a climate chamber, individual carriers per diode were prepared with four-wire connections (Figure 1). Before measurement at a specific temperature the conditions are stabilized for at least 15 min.

Figure 1: Specimen soldered on a PCB to realize a 4-point-measurement inside a climate chamber

2.3 Extraction of diode characteristic parameters

A Python-based fitting algorithm was developed to analyze measurement data and determine Shockley equation parameters. The Shockley equation [1] without series resistance is:

$$I_D = I_0\left(e^{\frac{V_D}{nV_T}} - 1\right) \text{ with } V_T = \frac{kT}{q} \quad (1)$$

Including series resistance (Rs):

$$I_D = I_0\left(e^{\frac{V_D - I_D R_S}{nV_T}} - 1\right) \quad (2)$$

Where I_D represents the diode current, I_0 is the saturation current, V_D is the applied voltage, R_S is the series resistance, n is the ideality factor, and V_T is the thermal voltage.

The saturation current I_0 (also known as reverse saturation current) in Shockley's equation is highly dependent on temperature T. This dependency arises mainly from the temperature dependence of the intrinsic carrier concentration in semiconductors, which is exponentially related to the band gap E_g. A common empirical function used to describe this dependency is:

$$I_0(T) = I_0(T_0)\left(\frac{T}{T_0}\right)^{\frac{m}{n}} \exp\left[\frac{E_g}{nk}\left(\frac{1}{T_0} - \frac{1}{T}\right)\right] \quad (3)$$

In this equation, T represents the current absolute temperature, T_0 is the reference temperature, E_g is the bandgap energy of the semiconductor, k is the Boltzmann constant, and n is the ideality factor, m is a saturation current exponent. [1][2]

3 RESULTS

3.1 Room temperature IV characteristics

At room temperature (25°C), IV characteristics were measured for all diode types. As an overview of all specimen the IV-curve at 25°C is plotted in Figure 2.

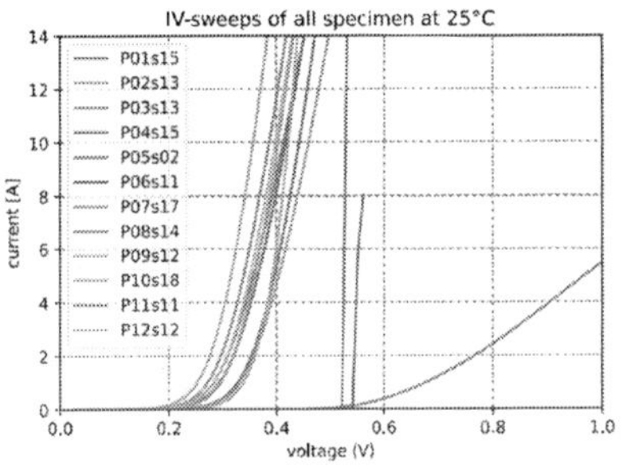

Figure 2: overview of IV-curves for all specimen at 25°C

10.4229/EUPVSEC2025/3AV.1.6
020121-002

Forward voltage drop (VD) aids in estimating power losses during conduction. Schottky Diodes (P07, P08, P09, P10, P12) and Super Barrier Rectifier (P02, P03, P04) show quite similar behaviour with around 0.4 +/- 0.05 V at 8 A, which would result in a power dissipation of 2.8 ... 3.6 W. The silicon based super flat diode (P05) has a much higher Forward Voltage at around 1.2 V at 8.0 A (9.6 W). The active Bypass Diodes (P06, P11) however work like switches – and were not examined here furthermore.

Reverse behavior could not be characterized beyond -40 V, but diodes functioned reliably up to this point.

The extracted parameters, are shown in Table 1. Active BPD (P06 and P11) behaved as switched circuits and were not fitted to the Shockley model at room temperature. Parameters varied across types: forward voltages (VD) ranged from approximately 0.3 V to 0.7 V, saturation currents spanned orders of magnitude, ideality factors were near 1 for Schottky types and higher for silicon, and series resistances were generally low (1.93 mΩ to 56.12 mΩ).

Table 1: extracted diode parameters of the measurement

Sample	Type	Rs[mΩ]	Is(25°C)	n
P01	HS Free*	5.96	1.52E-05	1.15
P02	SBR**	4.3	1.66E-04	1.12
P03	SBR	5.4	7.80E-05	1.11
P04	SBR	6.09	6.36E-05	1.17
P05	Silicon	56.12	1.77E-06	1.82
P06	Active BPD	No measurement		
P07	Schottky	7.05	5.36E-06	1.05
P08	Schottky	7.03	5.35E-05	1.1
P09	Schottky	5.19	7.11E-05	1.14
P10	Schottky	1.93	4.15E-06	1.07
P11	Active BPD	No measurement		
P12	Schottky	4.78	2.36E-05	1.07

*Hot Spot Free
**Super Barrier Rectifier

3.2 Temperature-dependent IV characteristics

Temperature-dependent measurements were performed on a subset, excluding the silicon diode (P05) (anode/cathode not populated) and active BPD (P06, P11) due to setup constraints. IV-curves showed shifts with temperature: higher temperatures reduced forward voltage and increased reverse leakage.

Figure 3 to Figure 7 give an overview of the measured data and specimen size and setup. For example, specimen P01s21 (Hot Spot Free) exhibited decreasing forward voltage with increasing temperature, consistent with semiconductor behavior. Similar patterns were observed across types, with graphs illustrating uniformity.

Figure 3: IV-curves and images of P01 (Hot Spot Free) specimen for multiple temperatures between -40°C and 125°C

P01
Hot Spot Free
Very small size, was soldered onto a wire

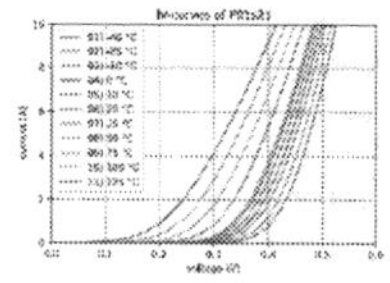

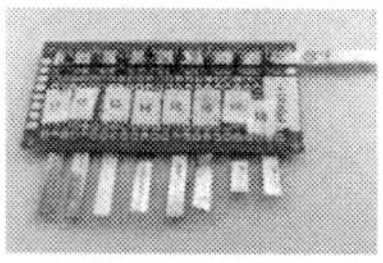

Figure 4: IV-curves and images of P02-P04 (SBR) specimen for multiple temperatures between -40°C and 125°C

P02
Super Barrier Rectifier

TO-277

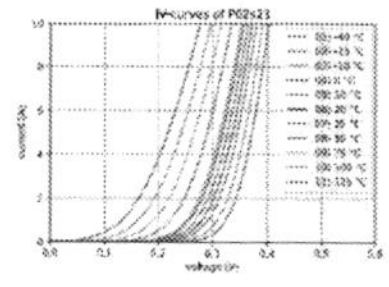

P03
Super Barrier Rectifier

TO-277

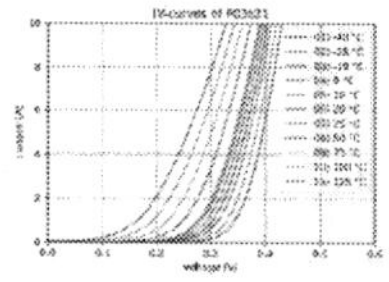

P04
Super Barrier Rectifier

POWERDI5SP

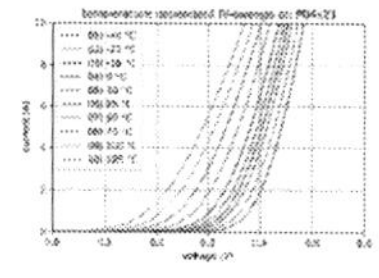

Figure 5: IV-curves and images of P05 (Silicon) specimen for multiple temperatures between -40°C and 125°C

P05
Flat Bypass Diode
Anode/Cathode were not populated

These unpackaged silicon diodes were connected using Electrically conductive adhesive

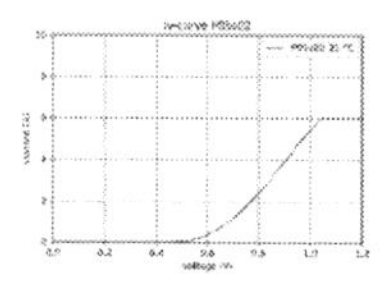

Figure 6: IV-curves and images of P07-P10 (Schottky Rectifier) specimen for multiple temperatures between -40°C and 125°C

P07
Schottky Rectifier

TO-277

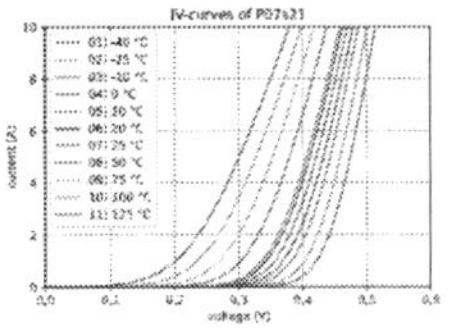

P08
Schottky Rectifier

TO-277

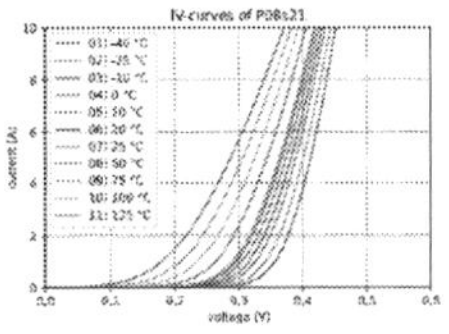

P09
Schottky Rectifier

TO-277

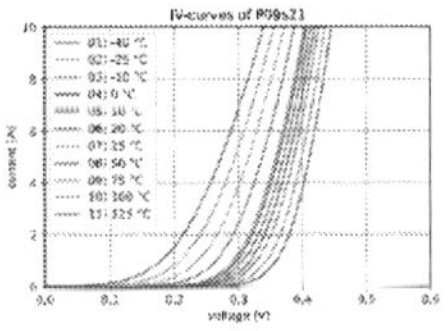

P10
Schottky Rectifier

TO-263

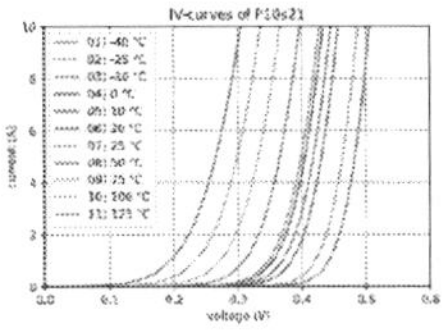

P12
Schottky Rectifier

TO-277

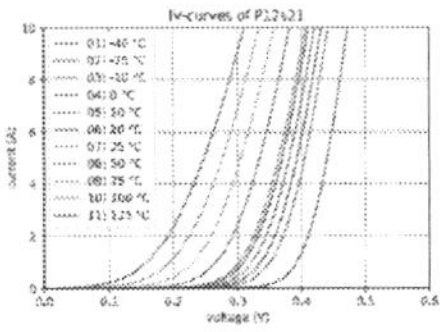

Figure 7: IV-curve at room temperature and images of P06 and P11 (active bypass diodes) specimen

P06
Active BPD (smart Diode)
Was not in temperature test

D^2PAK

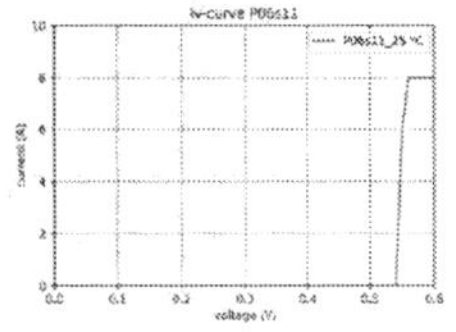

P11
Active BPD
Was not in temperature test

TO-263

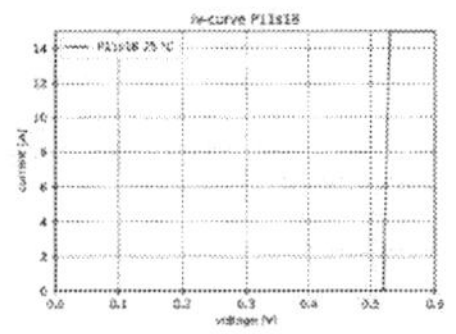

Saturation current (Is) showed exponential temperature dependence, varying by up to five orders of magnitude (log scale). Series resistance (Rs) displayed linear increases, while ideality factor (n) remained constant.

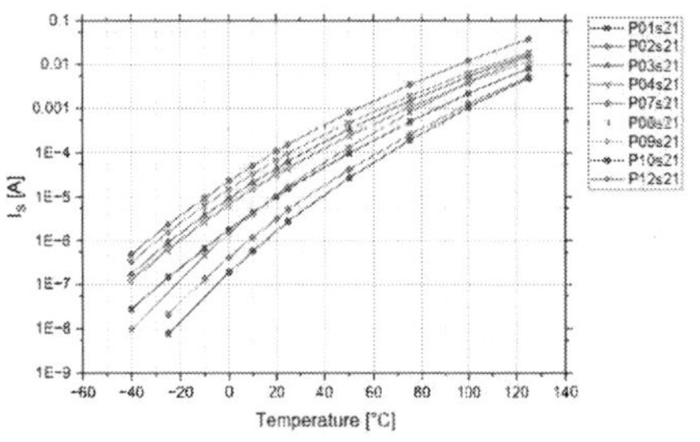

Figure 8: Temperature dependency of saturation current I_S on all Schottky Diodes. (log-axis for current)

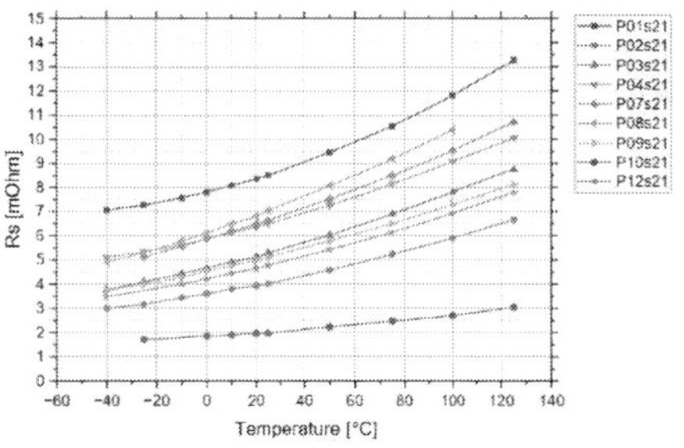

Figure 9: Temperature dependency of series resistance R_S

10.4229/EUPVSEC2025/3AV.1.6

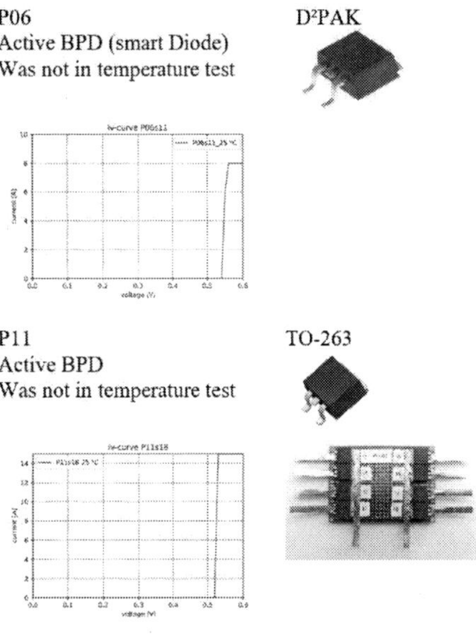

4 SUMMARY AND OUTLOOK

Selection of an appropriate bypass diode for a solar module application is driven by electrical and mechanical criteria: forward voltage at the expected operating current (dictating conduction losses), average and surge current capability under worst-case shading, reverse blocking voltage relative to substring open-circuit voltage, reverse leakage at elevated temperatures, thermal resistance and junction temperature limits, and avalanche robustness. Practical considerations like package form factor, pad layout, soldering/assembly effort, supply availability, and cost also influence the choice.

This study presents a robust test setup and procedure for characterizing bypass diode parameters, stressing the importance of low-resistance contacting and four-wire measurements. Passive diodes align with Shockley equation predictions:

a) Ideality factor n was constant and temperature-independent for each specimen.
b) Series resistance Rs showed linear temperature dependence.
c) Saturation current Is exhibited exponential temperature dependence, as per the formula.

These findings enhance SPICE modeling for temperature-varying conditions, as bypass diodes can reach 90°C or higher in operation if heat dissipation is poor. Passive diodes followed expected Shockley behavior, while active BPD acted as switches turning on at threshold voltages. Active diodes offer low-resistance paths but require careful integration.

Reverse breakdown at ~ -70 V is hard to measure without damage from small currents. Power losses, estimated from IV characteristics, are key for diode selection in PV designs.

Future work includes integrating these parameters into enhanced SPICE models for dynamic shading simulations, stress testing, and evaluating in-laminate designs. This will support SegmentPV's goal of higher-yield, reliable PV modules.

5 REFERENCES

[1] Tietze, U., Schenk, C., & Gamm, E. (2016). *Halbleiter-Schaltungstechnik* (15., überarbeitete und erweiterte Auflage). Berlin: Springer Vieweg. ISBN 978-3-662-48354-1

[2] H. T. Russell, Jr., "The SPICE diode model," in Rectifier Applications: Reference Manual and Handbook, HB214/D Rev. 2, Motorola Inc., Nov. 2001, pp. [page 47 .. 71].

6 ACKNOWLEDGEMENT

This publication was funded by the Federal Ministry for Economic Affairs and Climate Action in the project SegmentPV under grant number 03EE1180B. The findings herein reflect the work, and are solely the responsibility, of the authors.

42nd European Photovoltaic Solar Energy Conference and Exhibition

SEGMENT PV
Segmented photovoltaic module

Fraunhofer CSP

Investigation on Different Bypass Diodes for Shade Resistant PV-Modules

Jens Froebel[1], Matthias Pander[1], Bengt Jaeckel[1], Andreas Maixner[2], Pouya Pourshafi[2], A. Bakhtiari[2], Hamed Hanifi[2]
[1] Fraunhofer-Center for Silicon-Photovoltaics (CSP), Halle (Saale), Germany
[2] AESOLAR, Koenigsbrunn, Germany
Contact: jens.froebel@csp.fraunhofer.de

3AV.1.6

Introduction

This study is part of the project SEGMENT PV: Segmented photovoltaic module to achieve a higher energy yield and reliability with recurring partial shading. Sub-project: Characterization and reliability studies segment PV main components: solar cell and bypass diodes

We investigate a set of bypass diodes (BPD) suitable for solar application and with different technologies, such as Schottky, Silicon, switched Diodes (active BPD). The aim is to compare each properties and extract the diode parameters to create a SPICE simulation model.

Samples and measurement setup

- 12 solar bypass diodes are selected
- All diodes soldered onto a carrier enabling four-point measurements
- Cross-connectors used as contacts to maximize solder area and reduce series resistance
- Typically 6–8 specimens mounted per test carrier to mitigate defects and measurement errors statistically
- For climate chamber tests, one carrier per specimen was prepared with a 4-wire connection.
- A programmable source meter with high accuracy measures the IV-curves

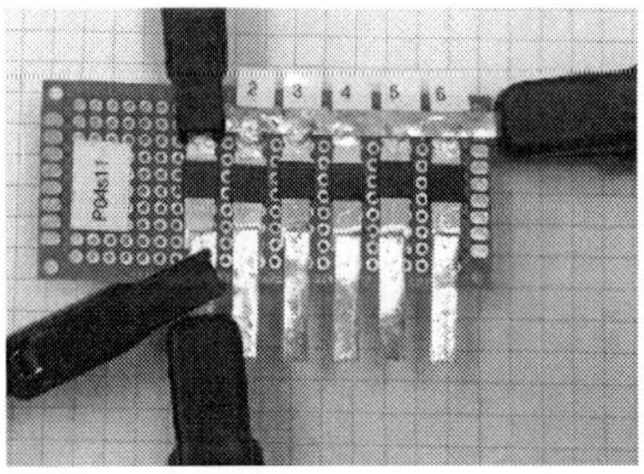

Fig 1.: PCB carrier prepared with 6 diodes. Clamps for voltage and current sensing are in 4-wire connection

Deriving the diode parameters from IV-curves

- P06s11 and P11s11 are active BPD
- P05s02 is a silicon diode
- Fast IV-sweeps starting at low power to avoid heating
- A python script to fit the Shockley Equation was applied

Is Saturation Current, **Rs** Series Resistance, **n** emission coefficient were derived, **Rsh** Shunt Resistance is neglected

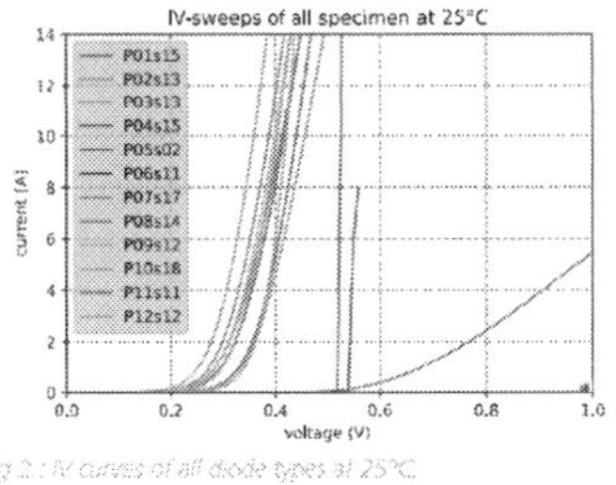

Fig 2.: IV curves of all diode types at 25°C

A set of 12 Solar BPD were investigated, brand and model is anonymized.

Specimen	Type	Rs[mOhm]	Is(25°C)	n
P01	Hot Spot Free	5.96 ± 1.06	1.52E-05 ± 3.7E-06	1.15 ± 0.0153
P02	Super Barrier Rectifier	4.30 ± 0.05	1.66E-04 ± 4.2E-06	1.12 ± 0.0058
P03	Super Barrier Rectifier	5.40 ± 0.09	7.80E-05 ± 2.8E-06	1.11 ± 0.0058
P04	Super Barrier Rectifier	6.09 ± 0.13	6.36E-05 ± 3.9E-06	1.17 ± 0.0100
P05	Flat Bypass Diode (Silicon)	56.12 ± 3.90	1.77E-06 ± 9.2E-07	1.82 ± 0.0985
P06	Active BPD (Smart Diode)		switched circuit	
P07	Schottky Rectifier	7.05 ± 0.04	5.36E-06 ± 1.3E-07	1.05 ± 0.0000
P08	Schottky Rectifier	7.03 ± 0.03	5.35E-05 ± 2.6E-06	1.10 ± 0.0000
P09	Schottky Rectifier	5.19 ± 0.08	7.11E-05 ± 4.5E-06	1.14 ± 0.0058
P10	Schottky Rectifier	1.93 ± 0.08	4.15E-06 ± 4.3E-07	1.07 ± 0.0058
P11	Active BPD (Smart Diode)		switched circuit	
P12	Schottky Rectifier	4.78 ± 0.07	2.36E-05 ± 1.6E-06	1.07 ± 0.0000

Temperature dependent behaviour

- A subset of specimen was IV-traced in a climate chamber at a wide range of temperature steps from -25°C up to 125°C
- Parameters Is, Rs, n were derived for every temperature
- Parameter n is a constant over the temperature

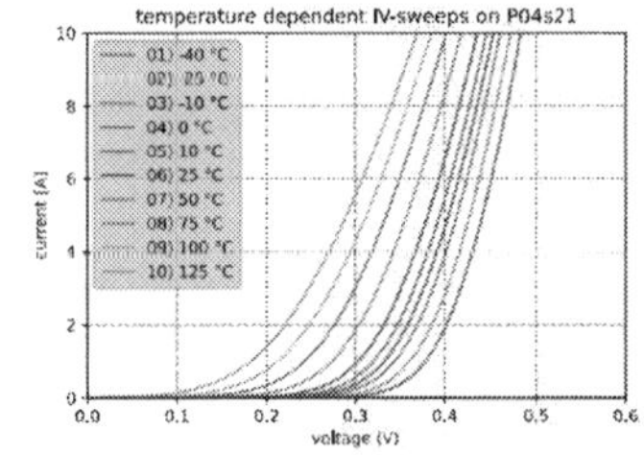

Fig 3.: IV curves of all sweeps over the temperature range from -40°C to 125°C using specimen P04s21 as an example

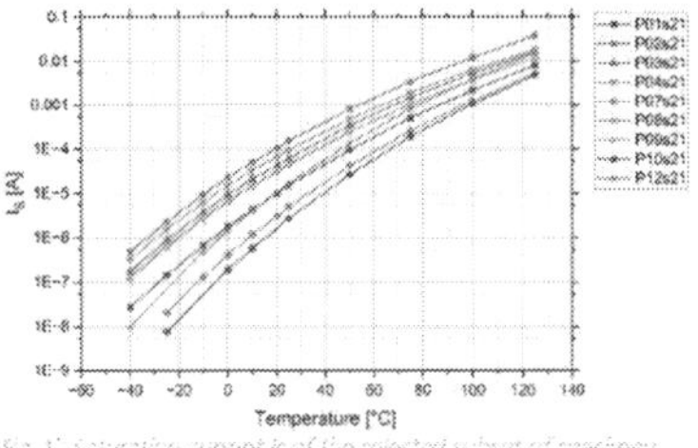

Fig 4.: Saturation current Is of the selected subset of specimen. The values differ in a range of up to 5 orders of magnitude

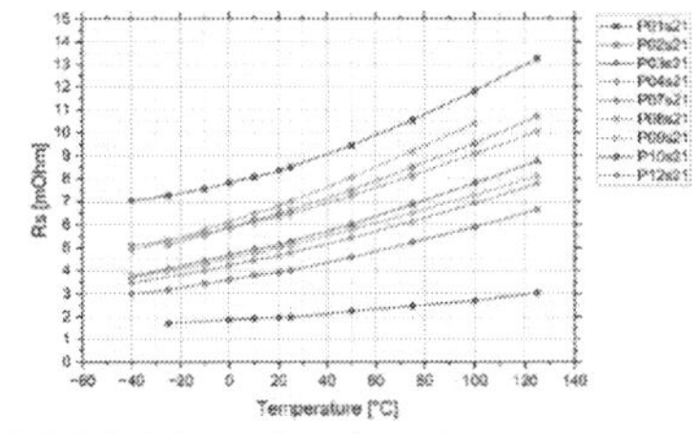

Fig 5.: Series Resistance of the selected subset of specimen

Theory and formulae

- The Shockley Equation describes the characteristic of a diode at a temperature

$$I_D = IS \cdot \left\{\exp\left(\frac{V_D}{N \cdot V_t}\right) - 1\right\} + GMIN \cdot V_D \quad \text{with} \quad V_t = \frac{k \cdot T}{q}$$

ID diode current; **VD** diode voltage; **IS** saturation current; **N** emission coefficient; **Vt** Temperature voltage; **GMIN** reciprocal of series resistance Rs; **K** Boltzmann constant; **T** Temperature; **q** elementary electron charge

- This enhances the simulation parameters under operation conditions because BPD can reach up to 90°C in normal operation and even higher when heat dissipation is insufficient by design of the PV module
- The results demonstrate that especially Is is highly temperature dependent and cannot be used as a constant for calculation or simulation [1]

$$IS(T) = IS(TNOM) \cdot \left(\frac{T}{TNOM}\right)^{XTI1N} \cdot \exp\left\{\left[\frac{q \cdot EG}{N \cdot K}\right] \cdot \left[\frac{1}{TNOM} - \frac{1}{T}\right]\right\}$$

TNOM nominal temperature; **XTI1N** IS temperature coefficient (SPICE); **EG** energy gap

Summary and Conclusion

- Test setup and procedure for robust characterization of characteristic parameters of bypass diodes presented
- It is very important to take good care of low-resistance contacting and 4-wire measurement
- Passives Diodes behave as expected and can be described by Shockley equation
- Active BPD act like switches that turn on at a threshold voltage
- Is is exponentially dependent on temperature
- Reverse breakdown voltage at approx. -70 Volts is hard to measure, a small current may already burn the specimen
- Power losses can be estimated from IV characteristics as part of selection process

Contact

Jens FROEBEL
PV Modules, Components and Manufacturing
jens.froebel@csp.fraunhofer.de
Fraunhofer CSP
Otto-Eißfeldt-Str. 12
06120 Halle
www.csp.fraunhofer.de

In cooperation with our project partner AESolar

AESOLAR

Project funded by the Federal Ministry for Economic Affairs and Energy in the project SegmentPV under grant number 03EE1180B.

Literature: [1] H. T. Russell, Jr., "The SPICE Diode Model," in Rectifier Applications, ON Semiconductor, San Jose, CA, 4 Aug. 1991, ch. 3, pp. 49-71

020122-001

OPTIMIZATION OF INFRARED SOLDERING PROCESS TO REDUCE THE TEMPERATURE INHOMOGENEITY IN SILICON SOLAR CELLS USING FINITE ELEMENT METHODS

Daniel Christopher Joseph*, Angela De Rose, Christian Reichel, Andreas J. Beinert, Holger Neuhaus
Fraunhofer Institute for Solar Energy Systems ISE, Heidenhofstrasse 2, 79110 Freiburg, Germany
*Corresponding author: e-mail to: daniel.christopher.joseph@ise.fraunhofer.de

ABSTRACT: A temperature-controlled infrared soldering process is becoming increasingly crucial for the successful integration of new solar cell technologies, such as silicon heterojunction and perovskite-silicon tandem solar cells. However, optimizing this process remains challenging due to temperature inhomogeneity and difficulties in accurate measurement. In this study, a Finite Element Method model, which can be easily adapted to different solar cell types, sizes and formats, is developed to reduce temperature inhomogeneity by systematically varying key process parameters, including the power supplied to the infrared emitters and the duration of the infrared radiation. A maximum temperature inhomogeneity, $\mathbf{\Delta T_C = 17}$ **K**, is achieved for M6 silicon-heterojunction half solar cell, and $\mathbf{\Delta T_C = 15}$ **K**, is achieved for M10 silicon-heterojunction half solar cell by identifying the optimum process parameters, which is a significant improvement from $\mathbf{\Delta T_C > 40}$ **K** measured from conventional infrared soldering process. Thus, this research improves heating uniformity and minimizes the risk of overheating the solar cells.

Keywords: Finite element method, Infrared soldering, Photovoltaic modules, Radiative heat transfer, Interconnection, Tandem solar cells

1 INTRODUCTION

The emergence of new temperature-sensitive solar cell types, such as silicon heterojunction (SHJ) and perovskite-silicon tandem solar cells, along with new solder alloys, has made precise heating during the industrial infrared (IR) soldering process more critical than ever. In this process, the primary objective is to heat the solar cells above the liquidus temperature of the solder alloy to establish contact between the solder-coated copper wire and the metallization. However, limited control over the maximum temperature reached by the solar cells often results in overheating, particularly in the center of the cells. This overheating can cause damage to sensitive solar cell materials, such as IR radiation-induced degradation in SHJ solar cells [1] and heat-induced degradation in perovskite-based solar cells [2]. In addition to preventing damage, precise heating also offers an opportunity to reduce energy consumption by minimizing unnecessary overheating during the soldering process, thus lowering overall energy costs.

In previous work, a Finite Element Model (FEM) was developed to simulate the temperature distribution across solar cells during the IR soldering process using four IR emitters and two radiation pulses in an industrial stringer. The analysis revealed a temperature inhomogeneity of 27 K for SHJ M6 half-cell. This represents an improvement compared to the typical $\Delta T_C > 40$ K inhomogeneity observed in conventional industrial IR soldering processes. However, this non-uniform heating still resulted in overheating at the cell center, while the edges remained at relatively lower temperatures [3].

The aim of this research is to further optimize the IR soldering process for various solar cell types and sizes, with particular emphasis on minimizing temperature inhomogeneity to $\Delta T_C < 20$ K across the solar cells, using a FEM model. The FEM model has been developed based on an industrial stringer and is designed for direct application in optimizing the IR soldering process within industrial settings.

2 FEM MODEL

The FEM model developed using COMSOL Multiphysics 6.3 employed in this study builds upon our earlier work [3], where a comprehensive description of the material properties [4–6] and physics interfaces is provided. Here, only the key parameters and geometrical modifications are summarized. The tungsten filament temperature (T_F) is defined by the process parameters—input power (P_{IR}) and radiation pulse duration (t_{IR}). Based on T_F, the emitted radiation is calculated and coupled into the heat transfer and surface-to-surface radiation physics to determine the solar cell temperature (T_C). The initial cell temperature (T_0) corresponds to the experimentally measured value prior to IR heating. In the model, the silicon solar cell and the quartz tube are treated as semi-transparent surfaces, the reflector as an opaque surface, and the filament and down-holders as diffuse surfaces.

In our previous work, four IR emitters were used to heat half solar cells, generating two radiation pulses. The first pulse was only partially incident on the cell surface, while the second pulse covered the entire surface. This was primarily due to the smaller dimensions of the solar cell relative to the span of the four emitters, leading to temperature inhomogeneities exceeding 25 K [3]. This caused overheating of the solar cells in the center, in order to heat the edges beyond the liquidus temperature of the solder alloy.

The present work aims on optimizing the IR soldering process to minimize temperature inhomogeneities by identifying suitable process parameters while reducing the number of IR emitters. Through resource optimization, it was determined that three IR emitters are sufficient to heat the solar cells with a single radiation pulse, enabling both the cell and the interconnecting wires with solder alloy to exceed the liquidus temperature. Based on the geometrical model shown in Figure 1 where the half-cells are positioned centrally beneath the three IR emitters, the corresponding process parameters P_{IR} and t_{IR} were determined for M6 and M10 SHJ half-cells, with an emissivity of 0.7 obtained from in-situ measurements. Specifically, an M6 SHJ half solar cell (83 mm × 166 mm) with six busbars (BB), and a down-holder with six metal strips, and an M10 SHJ half solar cell (91 mm × 182 mm) with ten BB and a down-holder with nine metal strips, were modeled for the FEM simulation. To reduce computational complexity, a symmetry plane was applied perpendicular to the longer side of the solar cell. The ribbon consists of a round copper wire attached to the solar cell using solder alloy. The modeled configuration for M6 half-cell with the symmetry plane is illustrated in Figure 2.

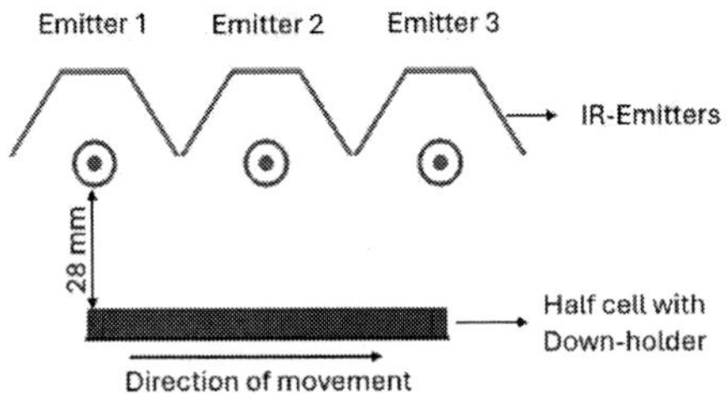

Figure 1: Geometry of the half-cell with down-holder positioned centrally beneath the three IR emitters during IR soldering, not to scale.

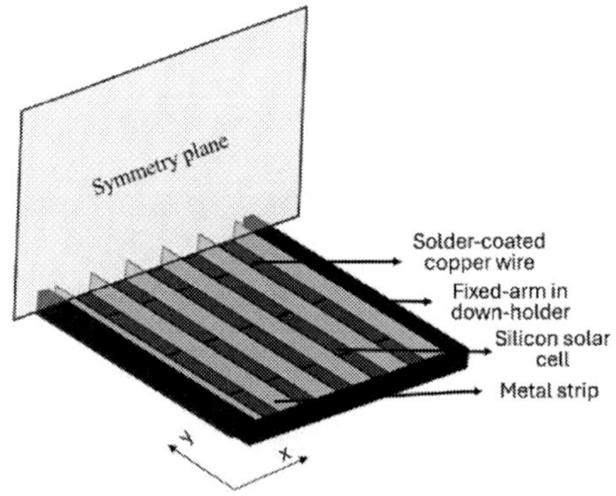

Figure 2: Modelled symmetric geometry of the M6 silicon half solar cell with solder-coated copper wire (ribbon) and the down-holder [3].

3 RESULTS AND DISCUSSION

For the M6 SHJ half-cell, the exposure time to IR radiation (t_{IR}) was initially set to 1.2 s, consistent with our previous study. The input powers of the three IR emitters ($P_{IR1\text{-}3}$) were varied for three different parameter cases, while the temperature of the heat plate below the emitters (T_{HP}) was fixed at 145 °C. The process parameters were chosen to achieve a minimum temperature of at least 190 °C, which is the liquidus temperature of the solder alloy used. These process parameters are summarized in Table I. To mitigate overheating in the central region of the solar cell, as identified in our earlier work, the input power of P_{IR2} was intentionally reduced. The resulting peak-temperature inhomogeneity values are provided in Table II, showing that the inhomogeneity is 20 K for all three cases, representing a good improvement compared to our previous works, which showed an inhomogeneity of more than 25 K [3].

Figure 3 shows the simulated temperature profile for case 3 with both maximum and minimum solar cell temperature. The temperature inhomogeneity (ΔT_C) is larger at the end of the IR-radiation pulse but starts to reduce after the radiation zone ends. The temperature, however, continues to increase for the next 0.8 s after the IR radiation pulse. This behavior arises because the IR lamps continue operating at a threshold power (≈30%) as the solar cell continues to move on the transport belt after the IR radiation pulse, thereby contributing additional heating before the cooling phase begins. The inhomogeneity is thus measured at the maximum peak temperature (Peak $T_{C\_Max.}$), which in this case is at $t = 2$ s. The inhomogeneity is defined as the difference between maximum peak temperature (Peak $T_{C\_Max.}$) and the minimum temperature (Peak $T_{C\_Min.}$) measured at the same time instance of $t = 2$ s. Therefore, the inhomogeneity is measured at the end of the cycle duration of 2 s (divided into a radiation pulse of 1.2 s and the transport duration of 0.8 s)

Table I : Process parameters used in the FEM simulation for M6 SHJ half-cell for a radiation pulse duration t_{IR} = 1.2 s.

	Case 1	Case 2	Case 3
Initial solar cell temperature T_0 (°C)	125	125	125
Hot plate temperature T_{HP} (°C)	145	145	145
Power IR emitter 1 P_{IR1} (%)	85	80	80
Power IR emitter 1 P_{IR2} (%)	30	30	35
Power IR emitter 1 P_{IR3} (%)	85	80	80

Table II: Simulated solar cell temperature T_C for M6 SHJ half-cell for a radiation pulse duration t_{IR} = 1.2 s measured at t = 2 s.

	Case 1	Case 2	Case 3
Peak $T_{C\_Max.}$ (°C)	216	213	215
Peak $T_{C\_Min.}$ (°C)	196	193	195
ΔT_C (K)	**20**	**20**	**20**

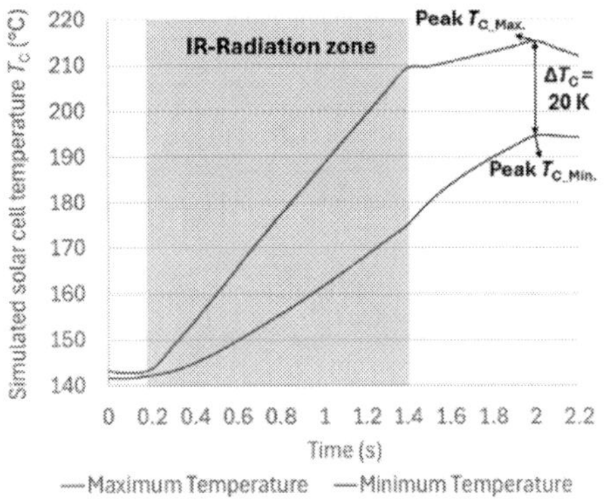

Figure 3: Simulated maximum (red) and minimum (blue) solar cell temperature T_C during IR soldering of SHJ M6 half-cell for case 3.

Based on these findings, and to efficiently use the additional heating after the IR pulse, the IR radiation duration was reduced to 1.0 **s**, while the input powers of P_{IR1} and P_{IR3} were slightly increased to compensate for the shorter pulse. The throughput, however, remains the same, as the transport time after the IR radiation is slightly increased from 0.8 s to 1 s, thus keeping the cycle time constant at 2 s. The corresponding process parameters and the resulting temperature inhomogeneity are listed in Tables III and IV, respectively. In the case 4, 5 and 6 similar inhomogeneity of 17-18 K is obtained. However, case 5 uses less power compared to the other two cases, to achieve ΔT_C = 17 K, maintaining the minimum temperature at a safe limit of at least 5 K above the liquidus temperature of 190 °C. The temperature distribution of the solar cell for case 5 at time t = 2 s, when the maximum temperature is reached, is shown in Figure 4. Further reduction was not possible since the minimum lamp power was constrained by the 30% threshold setting and the other parameter combinations resulted in either higher inhomogeneity or not heating beyond the liquidus temperature of the solder alloy.

Table III: Process parameters used in the FEM simulation for **M6** SHJ half-cell for a radiation pulse duration t_{IR} = 1 s.

	Case 4	Case 5	Case 6
Initial solar cell temperature T_0 (°C)	120	120	120
Hot plate temperature T_{HP} (°C)	145	145	145
Power IR emitter 1 P_{IR1} (%)	90	90	95
Power IR emitter 1 P_{IR2} (%)	35	30	30
Power IR emitter 1 P_{IR3} (%)	90	90	95

Table IV: Simulated solar cell temperature T_C for **M6** half-cell for a radiation pulse duration t_{IR} = 1 s measured at t = 2 s.

	Case 4	Case 5	Case 6
Peak $T_{C\_Max.}$ (°C)	217	215	218
Peak $T_{C\_Min.}$ (°C)	199	198	200
ΔT_C (K)	**18**	**17**	**18**

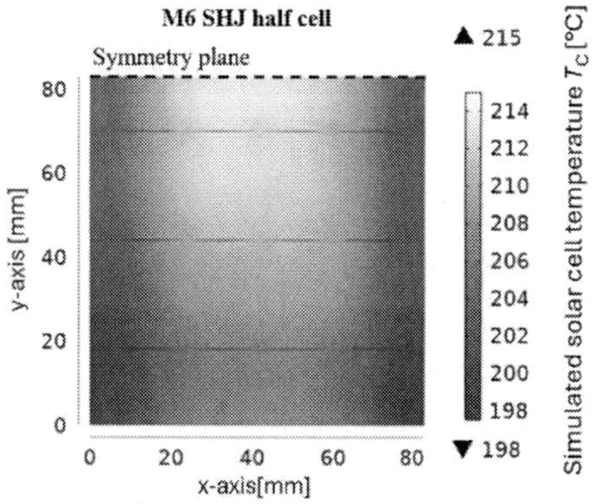

Figure 4: Simulated temperature distribution on the M6 half solar cell at t = 2 s for case 5 process parameters.

A similar set of experiments was conducted for the M10 SHJ half-cell. The investigated process parameters are summarized in Table V, and the corresponding temperature inhomogeneities are reported in Table VI. The temperature distribution of the solar cell for case 8 at time t = 2 s, when the maximum temperature is reached, is shown in Figure 5. Here, a minimum temperature inhomogeneity of ΔT_C = 15 K is achieved as the M10 half-cells have more area under the IR lamps compared to M6 half-cells, resulting in a slightly better temperature distribution. Thus, case 5 and case 8, with the same process parameters, results in minimum temperature inhomogeneity for both M6 and M10 SHJ half solar cells during the IR soldering process.

Table V: Process parameters used in the FEM simulation for **M10** SHJ half-cell for a radiation pulse duration t_{IR} = 1 s.

	Case 7	Case 8	Case 9
Initial solar cell temperature T_0 (°C)	120	120	120
Hot plate temperature T_{HP} (°C)	145	145	145
Power IR emitter 1 P_{IR1} (%)	90	90	95
Power IR emitter 1 P_{IR2} (%)	35	30	30
Power IR emitter 1 P_{IR3} (%)	90	90	95

Table VI: Simulated solar cell temperature T_C for **M10** half-cell for a radiation pulse duration t_{IR} = 1 s measured at t = 2 s.

	Case 7	Case 8	Case 9
Peak $T_{C\_Max.}$ (°C)	218	214	217
Peak $T_{C\_Min.}$ (°C)	202	199	201
ΔT_C (K)	**16**	**15**	**16**

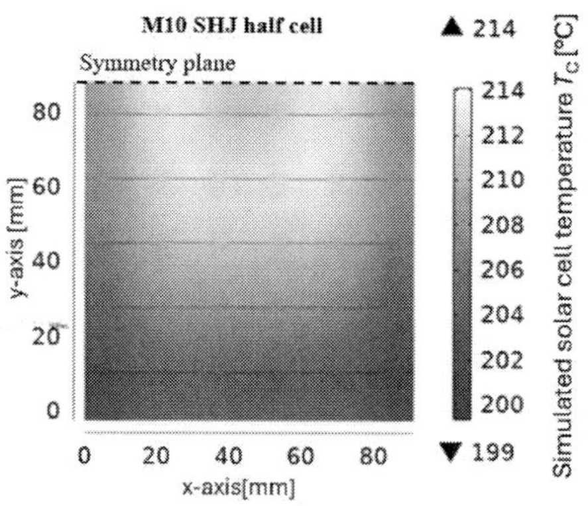

Figure 5: Simulated temperature distribution on the M10 half solar cell at t = 2 s for case 8 process parameters.

4 CONCLUSION

In summary, this research uses an FEM model to optimize the IR soldering process and minimize temperature inhomogeneity to $\Delta T_C < 20$ K . The study not only focuses on reducing temperature inhomogeneities but also helps in determining the maximum temperature reached during the IR soldering process, which is crucial for adapting the process to new solar cell technologies and sizes. A major adaption is to use only three IR emitters instead of four, which helps achieve the required heating with fewer resources. The second adaption is a variation of the process parameters - such as the power of the IR emitters P_{IR} and the duration of radiation t_{IR}, to determine the optimal values for the M6 and M10 SHJ half solar cell, achieving a temperature inhomogeneity of 17 K and 15 K respectively. Thus, the robust FEM model has been effectively used to determine the optimal process parameter that helps reduce inhomogeneity during the IR soldering process for M6 and M10 SHJ half solar cell. The model can be easily adapted to other solar cell types and sizes. Additionally, the FEM model will also be applied to compute thermomechanical stress during the cooling phase following the IR soldering process, providing a comprehensive framework for optimizing the interconnection process.

5 ACKNOWLEDGEMENT

The authors would like to thank the German Federal Ministry for Economic Affairs and Climate Action for the financial support within the project "Quelle" (Grant number 03EE1172E). The authors would further like to thank Teamtechnik Industrieausrüstung GmbH and Ceramicx ltd. for supporting with the infrared emitter characteristics.

6 REFERENCES

[1] A. De Rose, C. Rosado Alberdi, and A. Kraft, "Influence of IR Soldering Profile on Industrial Silicon Heterojunction Solar Cells," p. 536-540, 2022, doi: 10.4229/WCPEC-82022-3CO.4.3.

[2] G. Divitini, S. Cacovich, F. Matteocci, L. Cinà, A. Di Carlo, and C. Ducati, "In situ observation of heat-induced degradation of perovskite solar cells," *Nat Energy*, vol. 1, no. 2, 2016, doi: 10.1038/nenergy.2015.12.

[3] D. C. Joseph, A. De Rose, D. Eberlein, O. Parlayan, B. Grübel, A. J. Beinert, H. Neuhaus, "Investigation of temperature homogeneity during infrared soldering of silicon solar cells using the finite element method," *EPJ Photovolt.*, vol. 16, p. 9, 2025, doi: 10.1051/epjpv/2024052.

[4] Y. S. Touloukian and D. P. DeWitt, *Thermophysical Properties of Matter - The TPRC Data Series. Volume 7. Thermal Radiative Properties - Metallic Elements and Alloys*, 1970. Accessed: July 2025.

[5] M. Zhao, Z. Zhou, M. Zhong, J. Tan, Y. Lian, and X. Liu, "Thermal shock behavior of fine grained W–Y 2 O 3 materials fabricated via two different manufacturing technologies," *Journal of Nuclear Materials*, vol. 470, pp. 236–243, 2016, doi: 10.1016/j.jnucmat.2015.12.042.

[6] F. Hu and S. Lucyszyn, "Modelling Miniature Incandescent Light Bulbs for Thermal Infrared 'THz Torch' Applications," *J Infrared Milli Terahz Waves*, vol. 36, no. 4, pp. 350–367, 2015, doi: 10.1007/s10762-014-0130-8.

42nd European Photovoltaic Solar Energy Conference and Exhibition

Optimization of Infrared Soldering Process to Reduce the Temperature Inhomogeneity in Silicon Solar Cells using Finite Element Methods

Fraunhofer ISE

D. C. Joseph , A. De Rose, C. Reichel, A. J. Beinert and H. Neuhaus
Fraunhofer Institute for Solar Energy Systems ISE, Heidenhofstr. 2, 79110 Freiburg, Germany
daniel.christopher.joseph@ise.fraunhofer.de | www.ise.fraunhofer.de/module-fem

Link to Fraunhofer ISE contributions of the 42nd EU PVSEC

Motivation

- Precise heating of solar cells during the industrial infrared (IR) soldering process is critical for new solar cell technologies to prevent overheating and cell damage [1,2,3]
- Experimentally measured temperature inhomogeneity for an industrial IR soldering process exceeds 40 K for Silicon Heterojunction (SHJ) solar cells
- Previous simulation work reduced the temperature inhomogeneity to 27 K for SHJ half-cells using two radiation pulses from the four pre-heating IR emitters in an industrial stringer [4]
- **Aim of this work:** Optimize the infrared soldering process to minimize the temperature distribution inhomogeneity to $T_C < 20$ K on the half solar cell with optimum resources using a finite element method (FEM) model

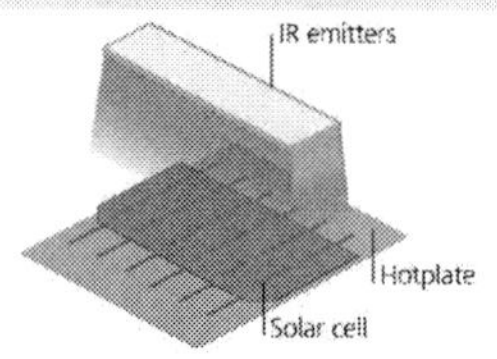

Fig. 1: IR emitters heating the solar cell during the IR soldering process.

Method

- Experimentally validated FEM model adapted from our previous work that computes the radiative heat transfer for entire IR soldering process including the influence of hotplate [4]
- Single radiation pulse from three IR emitters is sufficient to achieve the required temperature on a half-cell
- Radiation pulse duration (t_{IR}) and the power of the IR emitter (P_{IR}) are systematically varied to determine the temperature inhomogeneity
- Two different sizes of Silicon Heterojunction (SHJ) half solar cells are used: M6 with six busbars and M10 with ten busbars

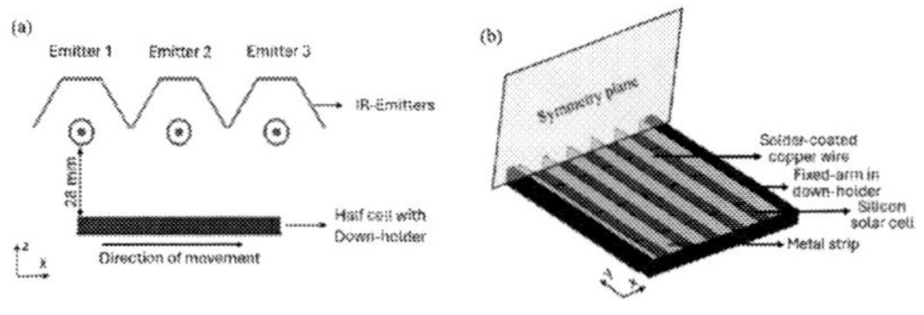

Fig. 2: (a) Half-cell with down-holder positioned centrally beneath the three IR emitters during IR soldering, not to scale. (b) Modelled symmetric geometry used in the FEM simulation [4].

- Industrial IR soldering process heats the solar cells with a radiation pulse duration of 1.2 to 1.3 seconds

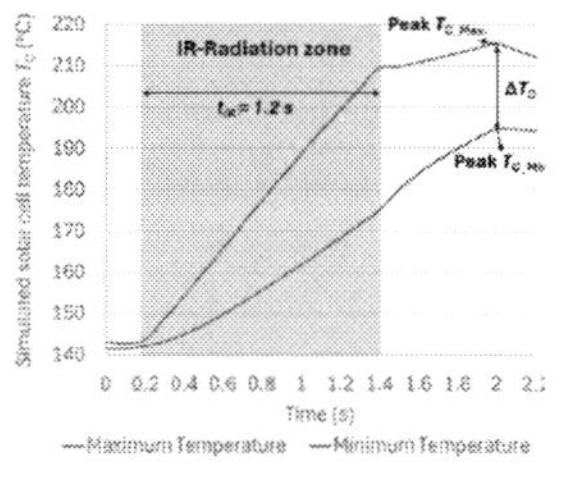

Fig. 3: Simulated maximum (red) and minimum (blue) solar cell temperature T_C of SHJ M6 half-cell with the industrial process radiation pulse duration $t_{IR} = 1.2$ s.

- Temperature slightly increases after the IR radiation pulse as IR emitters continue to emit radiation at threshold power (≈ 30%)
- Inhomogeneity is measured at the peak maximum temperature ($t = 2$ s), as shown in the figure

Results

- Shorter radiation pulse duration helps in decreasing the inhomogeneity
- Radiation pulse duration $t_{IR} = 1$ s is determined to be sufficient to heat the solar cells
- Optimized power of the IR emitters 1, 2 and 3 for both M6 and M10 SHJ half-cells to achieve low inhomogeneity:

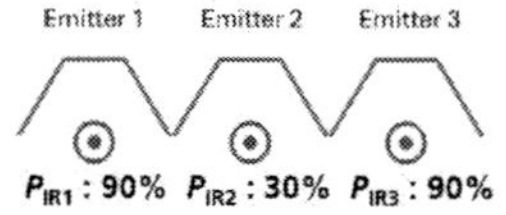

Table 1: Simulated temperature T_C for SHJ half-cell for a radiation pulse duration $t_{IR} = 1$ s measured at peak $T_{C,Max.}$ ($t = 2$ s).

Solar cell size	Peak $T_{C\ Max.}$ (°C)	Peak $T_{C\ Min.}$ (°C)	ΔT_C (K)
M6 half-cell	215	198	17
M10 half-cell	214	199	15

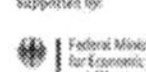

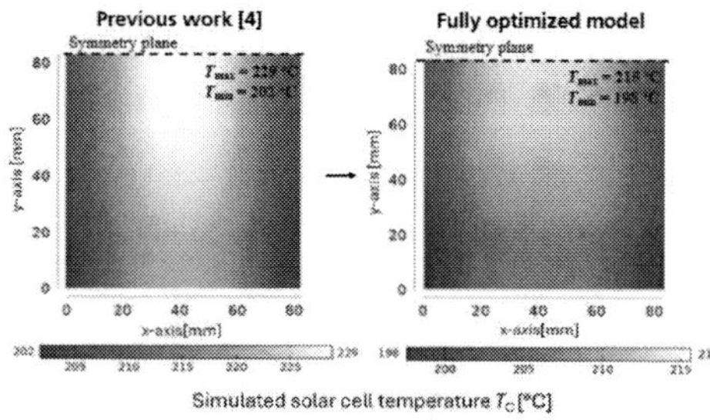

Fig. 4: M6 SHJ half-cell simulated temperature distribution T_C on: (left) partially optimized with 27 K inhomogeneity from previous work [4], (right) fully optimized M6 SHJ half-cell with 17 K inhomogeneity.

- **Reasons for inhomogeneity on the edges**: (a) shading of radiation because of the down-holder (b) inhomogeneity of IR emitters in y direction

Summary

- FEM model is precisely developed using the influential process parameters: radiation pulse duration (t_{IR}) and the power of the IR emitter (P_{IR})
- Optimum process parameters have been identified to reduce the inhomogeneity on M6 and M10 SHJ half solar cells
- Inhomogeneity has been reduced from more than 40 K (measured for industrial IR soldering process) to 17 K and 15 K on M6 and M10 SHJ half cells, respectively
- Easy to adapt to new solar cell sizes and technologies

Contact information

Daniel C. Joseph
Finite Element Methods – Module Technology
daniel.christopher.joseph@ise.fraunhofer.de
Fraunhofer Institute for Solar Energy Systems ISE
www.fraunhofer.de

1. A. J. Beinert, P. Romer, M. Heinrich, J. Aktaa, and H. Neuhaus, "Thermomechanical design rules for photovoltaic modules," *Progress in Photovoltaics*, vol. 31, no. 12, pp. 1181–1193, 2023, DOI: 10.1002/pip.3624.
2. M. Hertl, D. Weidmann, and J.-C. Lecomte, *Microelectronics and Packaging Conference, 2009. EMPC 2009. European*, 2009.
3. A. De Rose, C. Rosado Alberdi, A. Kraft, "Influence of IR Soldering Profile on Industrial Silicon Heterojunction Solar Cells", 8th World Conference on Photovoltaics, p. 536-540, 2022, DOI: 10.4229/WCPEC-82022-3CO.4.3.
4. D. C. Joseph, A. De Rose, D. Eberlein, O. Parlayan, B. Grübel, A. J. Beinert, H. Neuhaus, "Investigation of temperature homogeneity during infrared soldering of silicon solar cells using the finite element method," EPJ Photovolt., vol. 16, p. 9, 2025, doi: 10.1051/epjpv/2024052.

020124-001

Supported by: Federal Ministry for Economic Affairs and Climate Action, on the basis of a decision by the German Bundestag

This research was funded by German Federal Ministry for Economic Affairs and Climate Action under the project "Quelle" (Grant number 03EE1172E).

PERFORMANCE EVALUATION OF A NEW DESIGN PHOTOVOLTAIC MODULE WITH REDUCED SELF-SHADING.

Pouya Pourshafi[1], Andreas Maixner[1], Hamed Hanifi[1*]
[1] AESOLAR, Messerschmittring 54, Koenigsbrunn, Germany
*Corresponding Author: h.hanifi@ae-solar.com

ABSTRACT: Photovoltaic (PV) systems are a key component of renewable energy, yet their extensive land requirements can limit deployment, particularly in agricultural regions. With decreasing module costs and rising land prices, combining energy generation with farming activities has become increasingly attractive. Vertical bifacial PV modules enable dual land use by allowing crop cultivation and machinery access. However, such vertical setups of bifacial modules often suffer from self-shading caused by junction boxes, frames, and cabling, which diminishes energy output. AESOLAR has addressed this challenge by redesigning module interconnections and relocating junction boxes and cables to the edges, while an optimized frame minimizes rear-side shading. This study evaluates the performance of the redesigned module against a standard half-cell module using a Python-SPICE simulation that incorporates shading from junction boxes, frames, and cables. Results indicate that mitigating self-shading can boost energy yield by up to 3.21%, lowering the levelized cost of electricity. Additionally, simulations across various geographic locations show that regions with higher solar irradiation benefit most from the improvements. These findings improve the practicality of vertical bifacial PV systems, enabling efficient solar energy production with agricultural activities.

1 INTRODUCTION

The role of photovoltaic (PV) energy in the global energy mix has expanded considerably in recent years. In 2023, PV represented 74% of newly installed renewable capacity worldwide [1]. With a levelized cost of energy (LCOE) at 0.044 USD/kW, which is significantly lower than fossil fuels, PV has become an economically viable and environmentally sustainable energy source [2]

Extensive land use is a major limitation that PV faces. Meanwhile, a surging global population heightens food production demands, requiring more farmland and intensifying land competition, particularly in fertile regions like Europe [3], [4]. According to German market data, PV module prices have fallen 97% over the past 24 years, while land prices have more than tripled [5].

The increasing gap between the declining cost of photovoltaic technology and the rising price of agricultural land accentuates the importance of dual-use land strategies. Agrivoltaics integrate agriculture and photovoltaic energy on shared land, resulting in enhanced land efficiency [6], [7]. To accelerate the deployment of agrivoltaics, it is essential to minimize structural costs to enhance accessibility and reduce the LCOE [8]. One effective strategy for achieving this is through vertical mounting, which helps to lower initial investments and, consequently, the LCOE in agrivoltaics [9]. Bifacial modules, which can capture energy from both sides, are particularly well-suited for vertical installations [10]. Research has highlighted the advantages of East-West oriented bifacial modules in various conditions, including elevated latitudes [11], [12] and desert regions facing soiling issues [13], [14].

Bifacial solar modules face rear-side shading challenges. According to [15], [16], junction box positioning can block up to 45% of light on impacted cells, thereby diminishing module energy yield.

In 2023, AESOLAR company unveiled the "TERRA" PV module, engineered for agrivoltaic applications to minimize self-shading from the junction box and frame, enhancing overall yield. This article aims to precisely evaluate the performance of this PV module compared to standard modules.

2 METHODOLOGY

2.1 New module design

The TERRA module utilizes half-cell TOPCon technology, providing high resistance to wind and snow and enhanced bifaciality by minimizing rear-side shading. Redesigned for durability, it improves performance in vertical installations, ensuring it withstands over 20 years of environmental stress [17]. Conventional PV modules experience rear-side shading from frames, junction boxes, and cables (**Figure 1a**), which decreases energy gain. TERRA overcomes these limitations through an innovative interconnection layout and optimized junction box placement (**Figure 1b**), thereby reducing self-shading and improving overall energy yield.

This paper presents a summarized version of our recent study. A more detailed and extended version of this work has been published in Renewable Energy [18], where comprehensive analyses and additional results are provided.

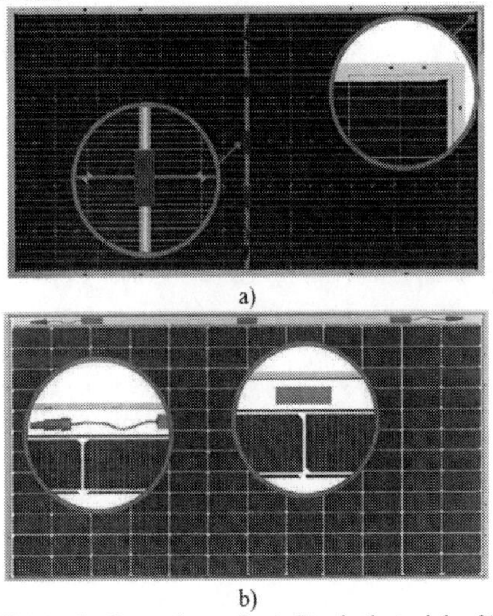

a)

b)

Figure 1: Rear view of: a) Standard module, b) TERRA with new design and reduced self-shading

10.4229/EUPVSEC2025/3AV.1.10

2.2 SPICE MODEL

Accurate models are essential for comparing the energy yield of TERRA to that of standard modules. While traditional simulation tools are useful for system-level analysis, they often fail to accurately capture the effects of shading and performance at the cell level. In this study, we employ a SPICE-based model to simulate photovoltaic (PV) modules, allowing for a detailed evaluation of thermal and electrical losses. The model has been developed and thoroughly tested by Hanifi et al. [19].

Both modules, rated at 420 W with 108 cells, are modeled in SPICE. Each bifacial cell is represented by two parallel cells, and the one-diode approach ensures a balance between simplicity and accuracy. The key parameters and their assumed values are listed in **Table 1.**

Table 1: List of key parameters used in the model

Parameter		Value
Nominal power of modules	P [W]	420W
Number of cells	n	108
Cell size	S [mm^2]	16562
Series resistance	R_S [Ω]	0.00436
Shunt resistance	R_{Sh} [Ω]	1000
Bifaciality	B_f [%]	85

2.3 Shading area

In standard modules, 12 cells are shaded by junction boxes, and one cell per side is shaded by cables during vertical installation. As shown in **Figure 1**, all cells around the rear side of the module are impacted by frame shading. All shading elements are measured and imported to the model. By contrast, TERRA's updated design—with optimized junction box placement and slightly wider glass—eliminates self-shading, ensuring uniform irradiance across all 108 cells.

Relocating the junction box to the edge of the module presented some manufacturing challenges, especially with the gluing process at the top corner and the framing. These issues were addressed by adjusting the module dimensions and incorporating an inactive area. Since customers prioritize energy yield (kWh) over efficiency, we optimized the edge distances for better performance. This resulted in a slightly larger module area and a minor reduction in efficiency.

2.4 Python script

While SPICE provides detailed analysis, it processes only one input step at a time, defined as front irradiance, rear irradiance, and temperature. Each iteration produces an output file with parameters such as maximum power. Calculating annual energy yield requires hourly inputs for all 8760 hours. Consequently, performing simulations across multiple locations and conditions is time-consuming.

To overcome SPICE's computational limits, a Python-based framework was developed to automate simulations and calculate energy yield. The workflow includes three steps: 1) preparing input data in an Excel file containing 8,760 hourly values of front irradiance, rear irradiance, and temperature. 2) A SPICE model defining circuit parameters and shading assumptions simulates I-V characteristics in steady-state. 3) A Python script updates the netlist for each hour, executes SPICE, and generates output files containing I–V curves and key parameters. The script extracts maximum power (P_max) from all outputs, compiles results into Excel, and sums hourly values to determine annual energy yield. This integration enables efficient comparison of TERRA and standard modules. The overall simulation workflow is illustrated in the flowchart shown in **Figure 2**.

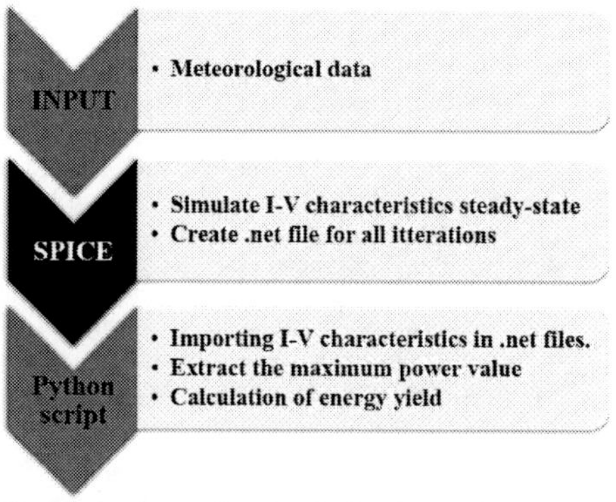
INPUT
• Meteorological data
SPICE
• Simulate I-V characteristics steady-state
• Create .net file for all itterations
Python script
• Importing I-V characteristics in .net files.
• Extract the maximum power value
• Calculation of energy yield

Figure 2: A step-by-step Python-based framework integrating SPICE simulations for hourly energy yield calculation

3 **RESULTS**

3.1 South-faced vs. vertical East-West

Figure 3 illustrates the difference in the energy production patterns of the TERRA module in vertical east–west and south-facing installations, based on meteorological data from Athens. In the east–west configuration, the module receives more irradiance during the morning and late afternoon hours, leading to higher energy production in these periods compared to the south-facing installation. However, around noon, the south-facing module benefits from stronger vertical radiation, resulting in greater energy generation. A detailed comparison of the two configurations shows annual energy yields of 752 kWh for the vertical east–west installation and 785 kWh for the south-facing installation. Although the east–west orientation results in approximately 4–5% lower total yield, it provides a broader daily generation profile.

3.2 Terra vs. Standard

Both TERRA modules and standard modules (with 108 cells and a power output of 420 W) were modeled, differing only in rear-side self-shading. **Figure 4** illustrates the hourly energy output for both types of modules over the course of a year. In the morning, the output is similar for both, as the front side primarily captures irradiation. However, in the afternoon, the rear side becomes more significant. In this period, self-shading negatively impacts the performance of the standard module, while TERRA achieves up to 7% higher output in the evening.

Figure 5 presents a month-by-month comparison of the energy production of the TERRA module versus that of the standard module in Athens. The primary axis illustrates the absolute monthly energy output for both modules, while the secondary axis quantifies the relative difference in energy production between the TERRA and standard modules for each month. The results show that the TERRA module consistently outperforms the standard module, achieving an energy gain ranging from 3.07% to 3.56%. This variation shows how the impact of self-shading mitigation changes with the seasons.

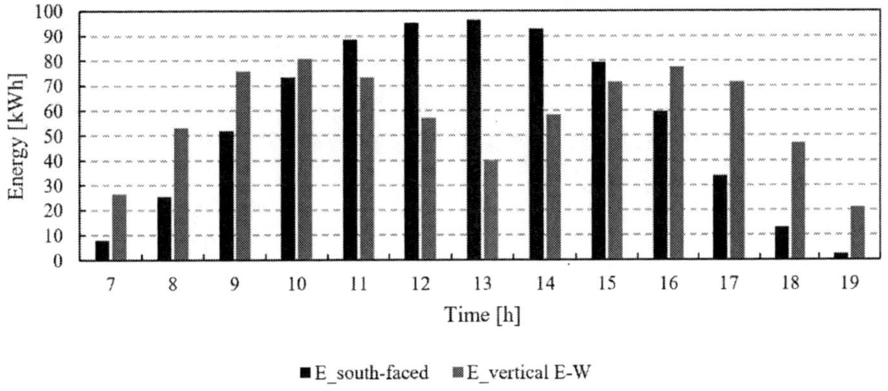

Figure 3: Annual energy production per hour of vertical E-W and south-faced (tilt=30°) installation of TERRA in Athens, For both installations, ground albedo = 0.2, height from ground = 1 meter, bifaciality factor = 85%, and the temperature is equal to the hourly temperature of Athens.

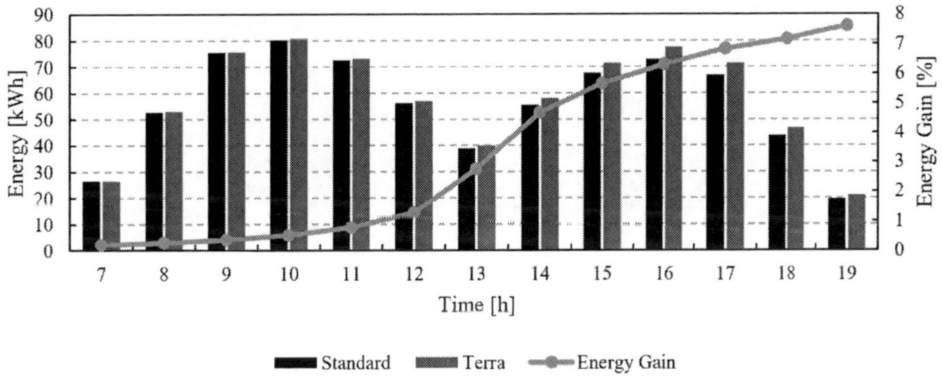

Figure 4: Annual hourly energy production of TERRA and standard modules with vertical E–W installation in Athens, The secondary axis represents TERRA's hourly energy gain relative to the standard module.

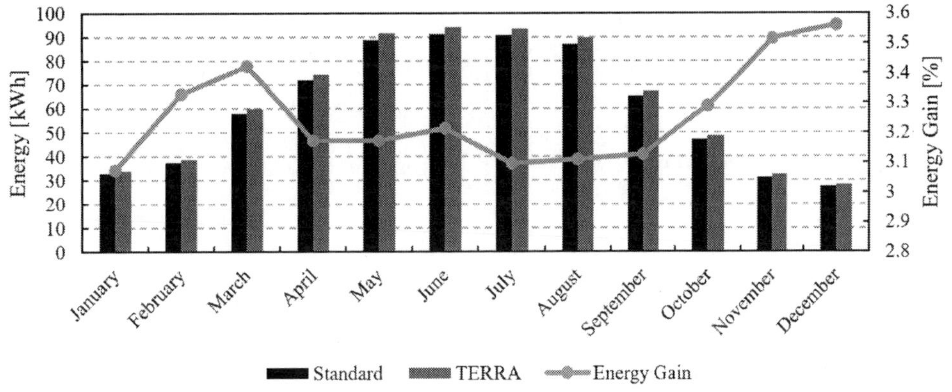

Figure 5: Monthly comparison of energy production between TERRA and the Standard module in Athens. The secondary axis indicates the difference in energy production for each month, showing that TERRA provides an energy gain ranging from 3.07% to 3.56%.

3.3 Global investigation

The model results indicate that the TERRA module delivers superior performance in sunny locations such as Athens. To validate these findings, the analysis was extended to additional cities with diverse meteorological conditions. By incorporating variations in solar radiation, temperature, and atmospheric effects, the robustness of the model predictions was thoroughly evaluated. The detailed results for each location are presented in **Figure 6**, while the overall workflow is shown in **Figure 2**. Meteorological data from each city, combined with the base SPICE model, served as inputs for the simulations. Following the procedure described in Section 2.4, a Python script was used to compute the annual energy output of both modules for each city. Finally, the difference in yearly energy production between TERRA and the standard module was determined for several locations.

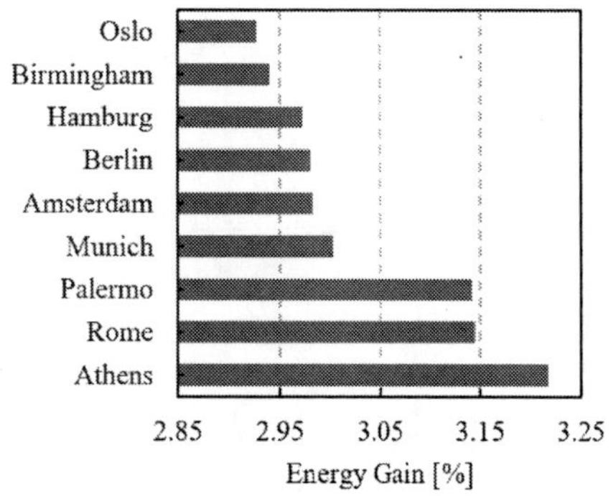

Figure 6: Energy yield differences between TERRA and standard modules across European cities. TERRA demonstrates an energy gain of 2.94% to 3.22%. Higher gains were observed in locations with greater solar irradiance.

4 CONCLUSIONS

The results of this study highlight the advantages of the TERRA module in vertical installations. To examine these benefits, both TERRA and standard modules were modeled using SPICE, with each design comprising 108 cells and a total power output of 420 W. The main difference between the two modules is the rear-side self-shading present in the standard module. While the SPICE model generates output for a single operating point, assessing annual energy production requires consideration of 8,760 operating points. To tackle this challenge, a Python script was developed to automate the SPICE simulations and calculate energy output with hourly resolution. This framework processes the hourly irradiance incident on the module surfaces and the cell temperature as inputs, enabling an accurate estimation of the energy yield.

Based on meteorological data for Athens, the TERRA module achieves approximately 3.217% higher energy yield in vertical installations compared to the standard module. This demonstrates the potential of the new design to enhance performance under real conditions. Extending the analysis to additional cities offers valuable insights for both researchers and investors, supporting more informed decision-making. As represented in **Figure 6**, the results consistently confirm the superior performance of the TERRA module across multiple locations. Its design makes it particularly effective for applications such as solar-powered fencing, photovoltaic noise barriers, agrivoltaics, and urban environments with limited space.

5 REFERENCES

[1] R. Alfaro-Pelico, "IRENA (2024), World Energy Transitions Outlook 2024: 1.5°C Pathway, International Renewable Energy Agency," 2024. [Online]. Available: www.irena.org

[2] Technology Collaboration Programme by International Energy Agency Photovoltaic Power Systems Programme PVPS Task 1 Strategic PV Analysis and Outreach. 2024. [Online]. Available: www.iea-pvps.org

[3] M. Trommsdorff, M. Hopf, O. Hörnle, M. Berwind, S. Schindele, and K. Wydra, "Can synergies in agriculture through an integration of solar energy reduce the cost of agrivoltaics? An economic analysis in apple farming," Appl Energy, vol. 350, p. 121619, Nov. 2023, doi: 10.1016/j.apenergy.2023.121619.

[4] M. Barragán Sánchez-Lanuza, I. Lillo-Bravo, G. Egea, and J. M. Delgado-Sanchez, "Spectral irradiance, ground and crop dynamic reflectance: Key determinants in predicting photocurrent for agrovoltaic systems," Energy Convers Manag, vol. 312, p. 118572, Jul. 2024, doi: 10.1016/j.enconman.2024.118572.

[5] Fraunhofer Ise, "Agrivoltaics: Opportunities for Agriculture and the Energy Transition." [Online]. Available: www.ise.fraunhofer.de

[6] S. Amaducci, X. Yin, and M. Colauzzi, "Agrivoltaic systems to optimise land use for electric energy production," Appl Energy, vol. 220, pp. 545–561, Jun. 2018, doi: 10.1016/j.apenergy.2018.03.081.

[7] A. Garrod, S. N. Hussain, and A. Ghosh, "The technical and economic potential for crop based agrivoltaics in the United Kingdom," Solar Energy, vol. 277, p. 112744, Jul. 2024, doi: 10.1016/j.solener.2024.112744.

[8] M. Trommsdorff et al., "Combining food and energy production: Design of an agrivoltaic system applied in arable and vegetable farming in Germany," Renewable and Sustainable Energy Reviews, vol. 140, p. 110694, Apr. 2021, doi: 10.1016/j.rser.2020.110694.

[9] K.-W. Hwang and C.-Y. Lee, "Estimating the Deterministic and Stochastic Levelized Cost of the Energy of Fence-Type Agrivoltaics," Energies (Basel), vol. 17, no. 8, p. 1932, Apr. 2024, doi: 10.3390/en17081932.

[10] T. M. Mahim, A. H. M. A. Rahim, and M. M. Rahman, "Review of Mono- and Bifacial Photovoltaic Technologies: A Comparative Study," IEEE J Photovolt, vol. 14, no. 3, pp. 375–396, May 2024, doi: 10.1109/JPHOTOV.2024.3366698.

[11] S. Guo, T. M. Walsh, and M. Peters, "Vertically mounted bifacial photovoltaic modules: A global analysis," Energy, vol. 61, pp. 447–454, Nov. 2013, doi: 10.1016/j.energy.2013.08.040.

[12] M. R. Khan, A. Hanna, X. Sun, and M. A. Alam, "Vertical bifacial solar farms: Physics, design, and global optimization," Appl Energy, vol. 206, pp. 240–248, Nov. 2017, doi: 10.1016/j.apenergy.2017.08.042.

[13] M. Kivambe, A. Abdallah, B. Figgis, G. Scabbia, M. Abdelrahim, and J. Lopez-Garcia, "Assessing vertical east-west bifacial photovoltaic systems in desert environments: Energy yield and soiling

mitigation," Sep. 01, 2024, Elsevier Ltd. doi: 10.1016/j.solener.2024.112835.

[14] U. Bin Qasim, M. H. Riaz, and H. Imran, "Investigation of soiling effects for east/west vertical bifacial and north/south tilted monofacial photovoltaic farms," Energy & Environment, vol. 35, no. 6, pp. 2991–3009, Sep. 2024, doi: 10.1177/0958305X221143410.

[15] A. González-Moreno, D. Mazzeo, A. Dolara, E. Ogliari, and S. Leva, "Outdoor Performance Comparison of Bifacial and Monofacial Photovoltaic Modules in Temperate Climate and Industrial-like Rooftops," Applied Sciences, vol. 14, no. 13, p. 5714, Jun. 2024, doi: 10.3390/app14135714.

[16] R. O. Yakubu, L. D. Mensah, D. A. Quansah, and M. S. Adaramola, "A systematic literature review of the bifacial photovoltaic module and its applications," The Journal of Engineering, vol. 2024, no. 8, Aug. 2024, doi: 10.1049/tje2.12421.

[17] H. Hanifi et al., "Optimum PV module interconnection layout and mounting orientation to reduce inhomogeneous soiling losses in desert environments," Solar Energy, vol. 203, pp. 267–274, Jun. 2020, doi: 10.1016/j.solener.2020.04.025.

[18] P. Pourshafi, A. Maixner, A. Bakhtiari, and H. Hanifi, "Performance analysis of a novel photovoltaic module design for vertical applications: Mitigate self-shading of bifacial modules," Renew Energy, vol. 256, p. 124186, Jan. 2026, doi: 10.1016/j.renene.2025.124186.

[19] H. Hanifi, C. Pfau, M. Turek, and J. Schneider, "A practical optical and electrical model to estimate the power losses and quantification of different heat sources in silicon based PV modules," Renew Energy, vol. 127, pp. 602–612, Nov. 2018, doi: 10.1016/j.renene.2018.04.060.

10.4229/EUPVSEC2025/3AV.1.10
020125-005

AESOLAR 42nd European Photovoltaic Solar Energy Conference and Exhibition

PERFORMANCE EVALUATION OF A NEW DESIGN PHOTOVOLTAIC MODULE WITH REDUCED SELF-SHADING

Pouya Pourshafi[1*], Andreas Maixner[1], Hamed Hanifi[1]

1 AESOLAR, Messerschmittring 54, 86343 Koenigsbrunn, Germany
*Corresponding author: p.pourshafi@ae-solar.com

MOTIVATION

- Photovoltaics' key challenge: substantial land usage.
- As PV costs drop, optimal installation becomes less critical.
- Smart choice: Vertical agrivoltaics.
- Major challenge:
  - Self-shading on the rear side.
- TERRA, a new module designed by AESOLAR.

PV PRICE ↓ + LAND PRICE ↑ › DUAL LAND USAGE › AGRIVOLTICS

SUMMARY

- A new PV design with no self-shading from junction boxes, frame, or cables on the rear side is developed to maximize the bifaciality at the module level.
- The new module(TERRA) achieves an energy gain of 2.94–3.22% over a standard module across European cities, with higher gain in energy yield in regions of higher solar irradiance.
- The new design with elimination of self-shading achieves a higher energy yield in all locations, which can be a factor in reducing the Levelized cost of electricity.

TERRA shows up to 3.21% higher energy yield compared to standard butterfly design modules when vertically mounted.

METHODOLOGY

Module designs

Standard module

- Self-shading:
  - junction box
  - Frame
  - cabling

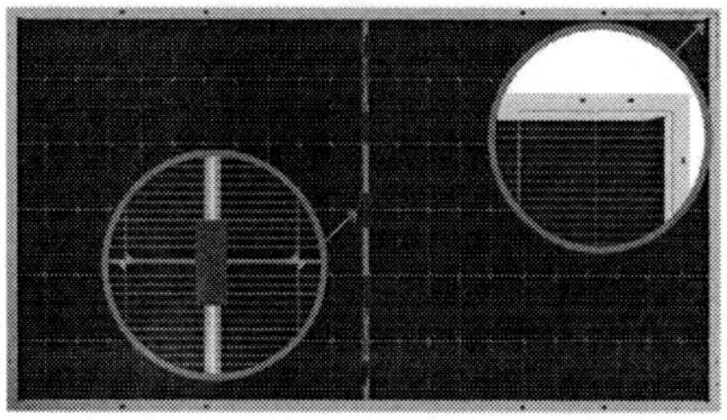

Figure 1: Rear view of a standard module, highlighting the self-shading elements.

TERRA module

- TERRA removes self-shading on the rear-side by redesigning the circuit:
  - No self-shading from junction boxes cables, and frame.

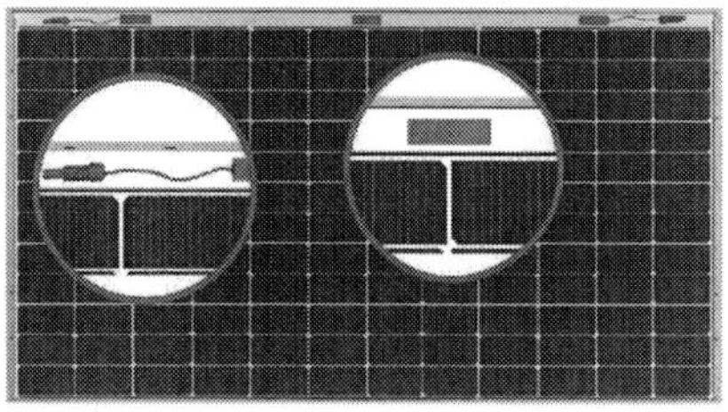

Figure 2: Rear view of a TERRA, highlighting the modifications made to eliminate self-shading.

PERFORMANCE ANALYSIS:

- Model:
  - IV characteristics: SPICE model based on Hanifi et al.[1]
  - Energy yield: Developed an hourly-scale Python model.
- Modules:
  - 108 cells, 420W
  - Same electrical characteristics
- Self-shading of standard module is included.

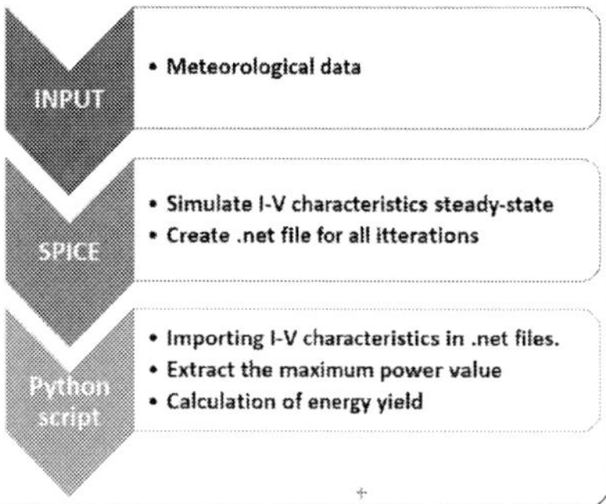

RESULTS

- Average hourly energy yield over the year shows: In the afternoon, direct rear-side illumination accentuates the effect of removing self-shading. Afternoon hours: TERRA shows an energy yield gain of up to 7.6% higher than the standard module.

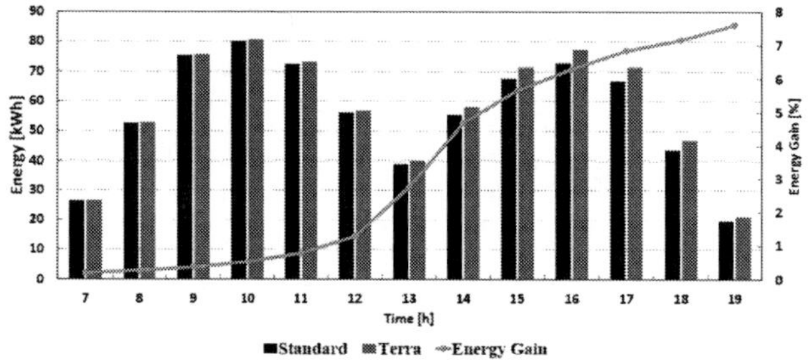

Figure 3: Annual average hourly energy production based on meteorological data from Athens. The secondary axis shows TERRA's energy gain relative to the standard module.

- Figure 4 shows that the TERRA module produces 3.07–3.56% more energy than the standard module across different months.

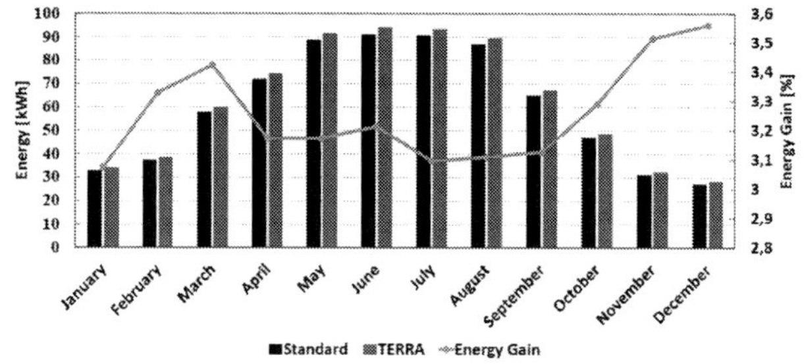

Figure 4: Monthly average annual energy production using meteorological data from Athens. The secondary axis indicates TERRA's energy gain compared to the standard module.

- Investigation in various cities demonstrates that TERRA offers enhanced yield performance by effectively mitigating self-shading.

Figure 5: Energy yield differences between TERRA and standard modules across European cities. TERRA demonstrates an energy gain of 2.94% to 3.22%, with higher gains observed in locations with greater solar irradiance.

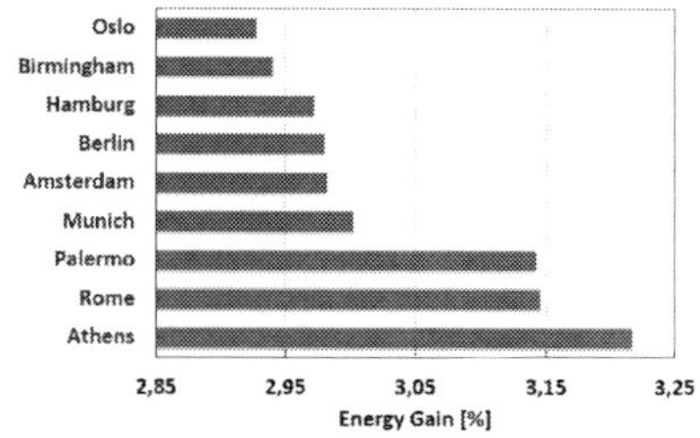

[1] H. Hanifi et al. "Reduced Shading Effect of Half-Cell Modules - Measurement and Simulations," EUPVSEC, Hamburg, 2015

MATERIALS ASSESSMENT FOR PV-T MODULES THERMAL PERFORMANCE IMPROVEMENT

Author(s): L. Cano[1]*, R. Simón-Allué[1], R. Villén[1], Y. Lara[1], I. Guedea[1]
Company / Institute(s): [1]ENDEF
Address(es): *lucia.cano@endef.com

ABSTRACT: Photovoltaic-thermal (PV-T) collectors integrate solar thermal and photovoltaic technologies into a single system, enabling simultaneous production of electricity and heat. The efficiency of PV-T collectors is directly linked to effective heat transfer through the system layers, which impacts overall thermal and electrical performance. This study evaluates the role of adhesives, the attachment media between the photovoltaic (PV) panel and the heat exchanger (HX); and insulating materials, which constitute the back-side of the PV-T panel, in optimizing heat transfer and improving the efficiency of PV-T collectors. Two small-scale prototypes were developed to test selected adhesives and insulations under real-world conditions. The investigation considers not only thermal performance but also economic feasibility, durability, and ease of manufacture. Final conclusions integrate experimental data with a one-dimensional Python simulation, identifying the most conductive adhesive and the most effective insulating material. The findings contribute to the development of a more efficient and cost-effective new PV-T collector design.
Keywords: Hybrid photovoltaic-thermal (PV-T) collector, adhesives, insulations, experimental testing, heat transfer modelling.

1 INTRODUCTION

Photovoltaic-thermal (PV-T) collectors combine solar thermal and photovoltaic technologies in a single panel, producing electricity and heat simultaneously. This hybrid technology may be used for diverse applications, such as pool heating, domestic hot water production, and heat production at low temperature for industrial processes (Herrando et al., 2014; Kalogirou & Tripanagnostopoulos, 2006). However, the temperature requirements of the final application also determine the most suitable PV-T collector type for each case (Herrando et al., 2014; Ramos et al., 2017). PV-T collectors usually have a photovoltaic (PV) laminate and an absorber or heat exchanger (HX), through which thermal energy is extracted.

This work aims to study the influence of different materials on the heat transfer along the PV-T collector, focusing on the impact of the attachment media between the PV panel and the absorber, as well as the back insulation of the PV-T modules.

PVT collector materials have direct impact on heat transfer through layers and, therefore, are related to the energy performance of the PV-T collector (Abdelrazik et al., 2018; Michael et al., 2015; Zhang et al., 2012). Thermal performance is conditioned by the heat transfer between the PV and the HX, as well as by keeping the PV-T panel isolated to avoid ambient losses (Herrando et al., 2019; Joshi & Dhoble, 2018). Moreover, PV panels reduce its performance ratio operating at high temperatures. Extracting heat to the heat exchanger also raises the electrical performance (Dubey et al., 2013; Rawat et al., 2017).

The final objective of the study is to assess the most adequate materials for a new PV-T collector design, in order to maximize the heat transfer through all the layers and, in consequence, its thermal and electrical efficiency. Economic and durability aspects will be additionally considered in the assessment, as well as each material's handling, especially for adhesives, in order to facilitate the PV-T collector manufacturing as much as possible.

2 EXPERIMENTAL SETUP DESCRIPTION

2.1 Prototypes

Two small-scale prototypes are prepared and evaluated in order to determine the suitability of the materials in terms of heat transfer and insulation performance.

A range of materials (both adhesives and insulations) have been reviewed and two sets have been selected for the testing. Apart from the costs, which have been used for both; application modes, ease of handling during manufacturing and thermal conductivity (ranged between 0.18 to 3.40 W/m·K) have been used as criteria for choosing adhesives, while insulations have been selected based on the thermal insulation properties (from 0.025 to 0.037 W/m·K), their physical characteristics and handling. **Table I** describes each prototype and its tested materials.

Each prototype consists of a PV panel with four test probes made of the material to be tested along with the absorber, each one sized 30x30 cm. Each prototype has the same layer structure (PV panel, adhesive, absorber, insulation and backsheet). **Figure 1** shows Prototype 1 disposition in detail.

Prototype 1 tests four back insulations, with the PV attached to the HX with the same adhesive, while Prototype 2 tests four adhesives, maintaining the same insulation. Both prototypes contain a glass-glass PV panel (unglazed PV with a laminated glass in place of the tedlar backsheet). The PV panel incorporates N-type and TOPCon cell technology, with 600 Wp of maximum power and a 22.21% of efficiency at STC.

Table I: Prototypes 1 and 2 description

Prototype 1 - Insulations		
Probe	Thickness (m)	Thermal conductivity (W/m·K)
1	0.025	0.037
2	0.025	0.032
3	0.025	0.025
4	0.030	0.025
Prototype 2 - Adhesives		
Probe	Thickness (m)	Thermal conductivity (W/m·K)
5	0.00013	0.16
6	0.00013	0.18
7	0.0002	1.5
8	0.002	3.4

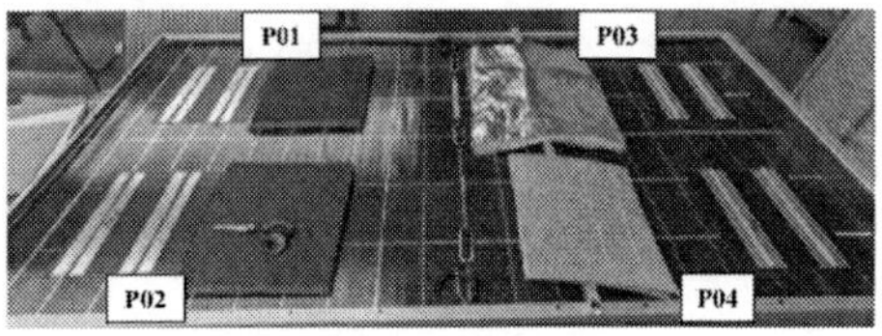

Figure 1: Prototype 1 design and assembly

2.2 Test procedure

In order to measure and analyse heat transfer performance, temperature sensors are placed in each prototype. Only heat transfer due to solar radiation is being taken into account; thus, thermal and electrical circuits are disconnected. Experimental tests are performed in Zaragoza, Spain (latitude 41.716), during winter months. Prototypes are tested under natural conditions, exposed to a quasi-constant solar in-plane irradiance between 300-420 W/m^2 (horizontal). Panels are placed in horizontal 120 cm height benches.

Pt100 temperature sensors are distributed in each layer to measure every prototype: two under the PV laminate, two between the absorber and the insulation for each probe, one in the back side of the insulation for each probe. Therefore, each prototype counts with 15 precision probes (described in **Figure 2**). An additional methacrylate layer is added to the probes to fasten the assembly of all the materials and ensure a proper contact between components.

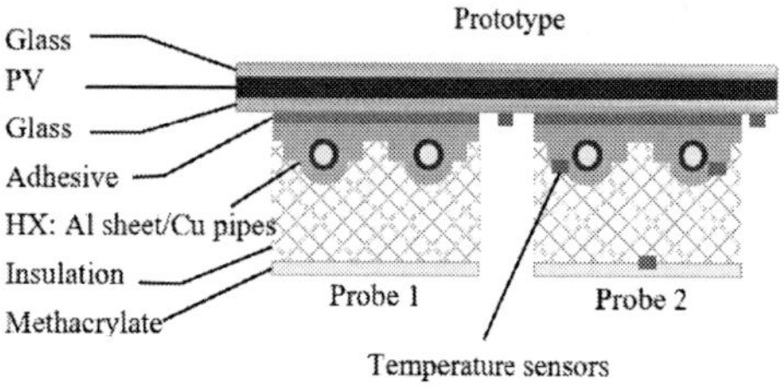

Figure 2: Prototype layers and temperature sensors distribution

Environmental data (irradiance, ambient temperature and wind speed) are also measured (see **Table II**) and registered with a frequency of 1 min in a PLC Modicon 241. Each test is performed at least for 2 days with similar weather conditions and 4 days in total. The test starts when the panel is exposed to sun and lasts at least one hour. The first 30-40 minutes of exposure are intended to allow the prototypes to acclimatize until they become stable. All temperature sensors measured the same value before exposing the panel to the sun.

Table II: Instrumentation and sensors

Physical property	Sensor model	Range	Precision
Temperature	Pt100	-50-400 °C	± 0.05 °C
Irradiance	Pyranometer, LP-PYRA-03 AC	0-2000 W/m^2	± 0.025 W/m^2
Wind velocity	4.3303.22.007, Thies Clima	0-50 m/s	± 0.3 m/s

2.3 One-dimensional simulation

One-dimensional model is developed using Python for simulating temperatures in each layer of the PV-T collector and prototypes. This simulation is intended to be validated with the experimental data, in order to implement it in a more complex model for estimating PV-T panel efficiency and both electrical and thermal productions.

Figure 3 shows the PV-T layer configuration and the energy flows considered.

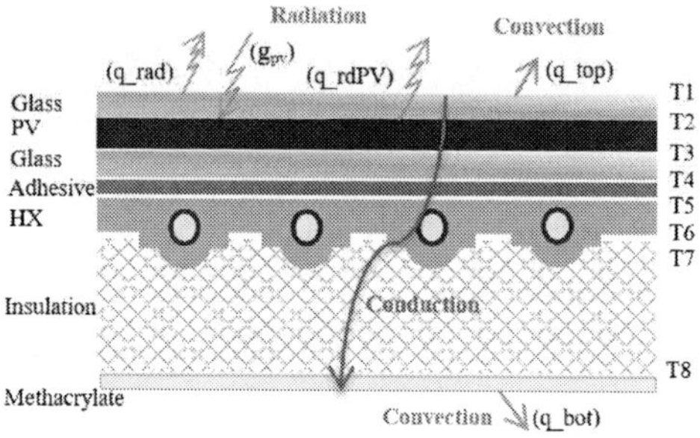

Figure 3: PV-T collector layers and energy flows

The PV-T collector model is developed under the following assumptions:

- radiation absorption in the glass layer and the collector frame is negligible; (Agarwal & Garg, 1994; Herrando et al., 2019)
- the ambient temperature is uniform around the collector and heat losses from the PV panel frame and the borders of each probe are negligible (Cristofari et al., 2009; Notton et al., 2005);
- the PV cells and the thermal absorber are in perfect thermal contact; (Herrando et al., 2019)
- solar irradiance and wind speed are uniform over the collector surface area. (Herrando et al., 2019)

The model is run under steady-state conditions (Herrando et al., 2019; Zondag et al., 2003). Energy conservation equation is used for defining heat transfer through layers. In addition, there is no fluid running into the copper tubes so there is no thermal energy generated and the electric circuit of the PV panel is disconnected, so there is no electricity production. Above all these assumptions, boundary conditions for these equations are detailed below:

Top Layer. The main losses on the top of the PV-T collector are due to forced convection caused by wind (q_{top}, see eq. (2)) and radiation from the glass to the sky (q_{rad}, see eq. (3)). The convective heat transfer coefficient depends on wind velocity (v_{wind}) and various expressions are given in bibliography for its estimation. In previous works (Bhattarai et al., 2012; Notton et al., 2005; Rejeb et al., 2015) for similar applications, validated with experimental data, expression showed in eq. (1) provided accurate values. Initially, the model is based on this experimentally obtained h_{wind} approximation, but has been adjusted according to the results of the tests. Hence:

$$h_{wind} = 4{,}2 + 2{,}9 \cdot v_{wind} \qquad (1)$$

$$q_{top} = h_{wind} \cdot \left(T_{glass} - T_{amb}\right) \qquad (2)$$

$$q_{rad} = \varepsilon_{glass,long\lambda} \cdot \sigma \cdot \left({T_{glass}}^4 - {T_{sky}}^4\right) \qquad (3)$$

where T_{glass} is the glass temperature in the above surface, T_{sky} is the sky temperature, which is calculated as $T_{sky} = 0.0552 \cdot T_{amb}^{1.5}$, with the ambient temperature (T_{amb}) in Kelvin, $\varepsilon_{glass,long\lambda}$ is the glass emissivity at long wavelengths and σ is the Stefan-Boltzmann constant ($\sigma = 5.67 \cdot 10^{-8}$ W/(m^2·K^4)) (Cristofari et al., 2009; Notton et al., 2005).

PV layer. The PV layer absorbs the fraction of the total solar irradiance (G_{inc}) that is not reflected by the glass (g_{PV}), calculated as:

$$g_{PV} = G_{inc} \cdot \tau_{g,short\lambda} \cdot \alpha_{PV,short\lambda} \qquad (4)$$

10.4229/EUPVSEC2025/3AV.1.11

where $\tau_{g,short\lambda}$ is the transmittance of the glass while $\alpha_{PV,short\lambda}$ is the absorptivity of the PV panel, both at short wavelengths (Tiwari & Sodha, 2006; Zondag et al., 2003).

The radiative heat flux emitted by the PV layer at long wavelengths, which is not absorbed by the glass, is lost to the environment. This radiative heat loss (q_{rdPV}) can be estimated as follows:

$$q_{rdPV} = \varepsilon_{PV,long\lambda} \cdot \tau_{g,long\lambda} \cdot \sigma \cdot \left(T_{PV}{}^{4} - T_{sky}{}^{4}\right) \quad (5)$$

where T_{PV} is the temperature of the PV layer, $\tau_{g,long\lambda}$ is the transmittance of the glass and $\varepsilon_{PV,long\lambda}$ is the emissivity of the PV layer, both for long wavelengths (Tiwari & Sodha, 2006; Zondag et al., 2003).

Back insulation layer. The main loss in the back layer of the PVT collector is due to forced convection caused by wind (q_{bot}, see eq. (6)), calculated similarly to q_{top}:

$$q_{bot} = h_{wind} \cdot (T_{metha} - T_{amb}) \quad (6)$$

where T_{metha} is the temperature in the bottom side of the methacrylate layer.

Heat conduction. For every layer, it is considered perfect thermal contact, which allows a heat flow from the hottest layers to the coolest, in contact with the ambient. For every layer, heat conduction equation is defined as:

$$q_{layer,a} = \frac{k_a}{\delta_a} \cdot (T_{a\_in} - T_{a\_out}) \quad (7)$$

where k_a is the thermal conductivity coefficient of the layer, δ_a corresponds to the thickness of each layer and T_{a_in} and T_{a_out} relay to the temperatures in the top and the bottom of each layer. The top temperature of each layer is the bottom of the one above, due to the assumptions made previously.

Introducing environmental data (wind velocity, irradiance and ambient temperature) in the one-dimensional model, temperatures in each layer and heat fluxes between them are obtained. Conduction, convection and radiation can be studied as well as the heat and energy losses to the ambient. For comparing both experimental and simulated temperatures, only results from the moment the system has stabilized onwards are considered.

The model also included T_{cell}, the theorical temperature of the PV cells (Hajji et al., 2014; Santos et al., 2022), calculated as:

$$T_{cell} = ((T_{NOCT} - 20) / 800) \cdot G_{inc} + T_{amb} \quad (8)$$

where T_{NOCT} is the nominal operating cell temperature, characteristic of each PV panel.

A statistics analysis is additionally performed in order to evaluate the numerical goodness of the simulation. The Percentage Error is calculated for the period in which panel temperature is already stabilized.

$$Percentage\ Error = \frac{|y_{exp} - y_{sim}|}{y_{exp}} \cdot 100 \quad (9)$$

Table III: Properties of the PVT collector layers

Layer	Parameter		Wavelengths	Value
Top layer	$\varepsilon_{g,short\lambda}$	Emissivity (-)	Short	0.05
	$\tau_{g,short\lambda}$	Transmittance (-)	Short	0.94
	$\varepsilon_{g,long\lambda}$	Emissivity (-)	Long	0.86
	$\tau_{g,long\lambda}$	Transmittance (-)	Long	0.06
PV layer	$\alpha_{PV,short\lambda}$	Solar absorption coefficient (-)	Short	0.95
	$\varepsilon_{PV,long\lambda}$	Emissivity (-)	Long	0.89

3 RESULTS AND DISCUSSION

Experimental tests have been conducted for **Prototype 1 and Prototype 2** to analyse the influence of the four insulations and four adhesive materials on heat transfer with a glass-glass PV. The results obtained provide qualitative information on the performance of each test sample. Figures containing the results are discussed below. Temperatures of the probes are represented in Celsius. Each Figure contains the collector absorber temperatures of each probe, simulated (solid lines) and experimental (dashed lines), as well as environmental (T_{amb}) and cell (T_{cell}) temperatures.

3.1 PV temperatures comparison

Both experimental and simulated results have been analysed firstly considering only the PV layers, taking temperatures from the free PV area where there are no heat exchanger nor material probes. **Figure 4** and **Figure 5** show experimental and simulated PV panel temperatures, as well as ambient temperature and theoretical PV cell temperature.

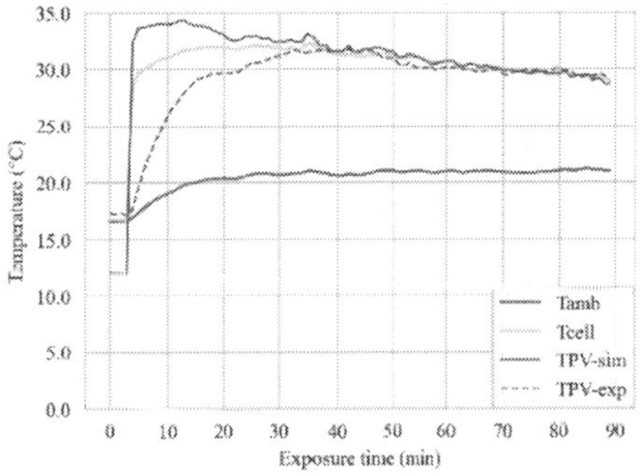

Figure 4: PV panel temperatures. Windless day

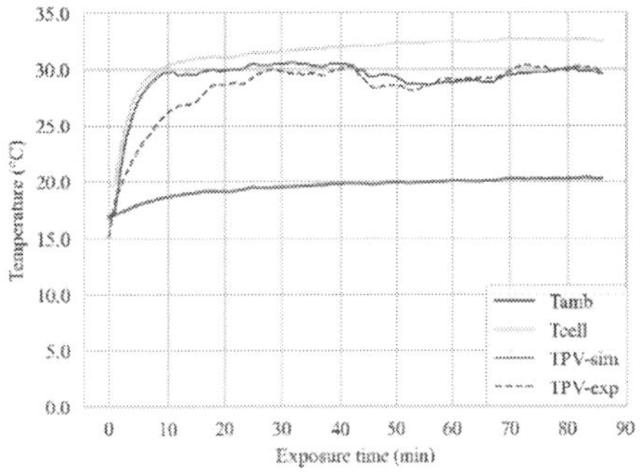

Figure 5: PV panel temperatures. Windy day

In these figures, simulated values do match experimental data, which means the one-dimensional simulation can reproduce experimental temperatures and heat transfer fluxes through the PV panel layers. However, it can be noticed that the simulated results do not match the first few minutes of the experimental tests, in which the panels are still acclimatizing. This is explained because the one-dimensional model has no inertia, unlike the experimental data, as it is performed under steady-state conditions.

It is significant to notice differences in the theoretical

temperature of the PV cells between windy and windless days. During windless or very low wind days T_{cell} matches both experimental and simulated PV temperatures once they are stabilized; however, this matching does not exist in windy days, where the T_{cell} is higher, due to the fact that T_{cell} definition does not take into account wind effect.

3.2 Insulating materials comparison

Small-scale tests were conducted for Prototype 1 in order to determine which insulation kept more heat inside the absorber.

Temperatures of the heat exchanger are represented for the four insulating materials (**Table I**). $T_{1\text{-}exp}$-$T_{4\text{-}exp}$ correspond with the mean of both temperature sensors placed inside the **heat absorber** (see **Figure 2**) for each probe. **Figure 6** shows results for a test performed with windless weather conditions while **Figure 7** shows results obtained during a windy day.

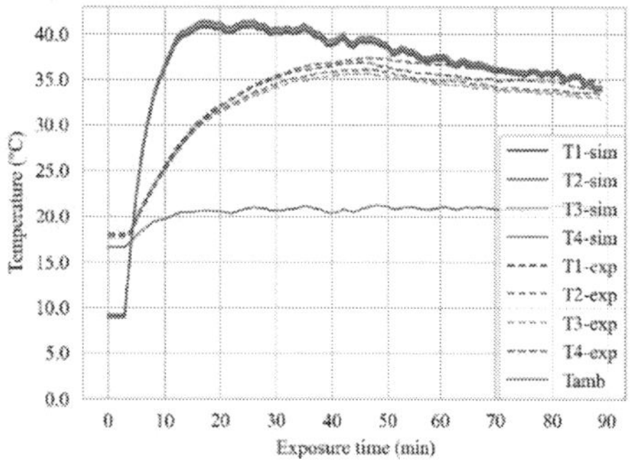

Figure 6: Prototype 1 heat absorber temperatures for each probe. Windless day

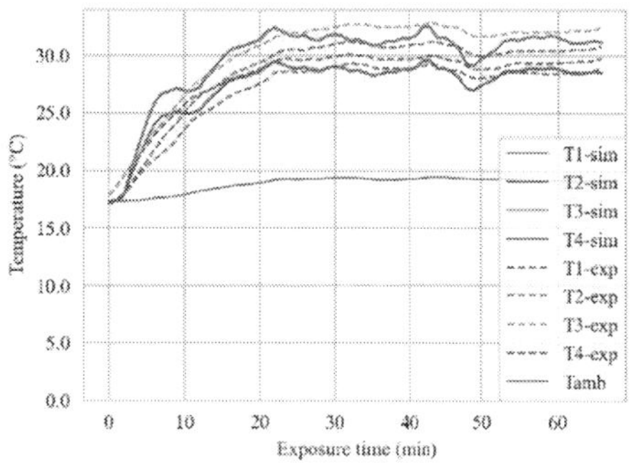

Figure 7: Prototype 1 heat absorber temperatures for each probe. Windy day

Experimental results reveal higher temperatures during windless days in probes 1 and 2, with a difference of 2,5 °C with probes 3 and 4; while this difference between probes is barely noticeable for simulated results.

On the contrary, on windy days (more than 4 m/s) probes 3 and 4 are the ones reaching higher temperatures during experimental tests. Moreover, temperature differences between probes are bigger (~ 5 °C). This can be explained because wind affects to the results and alters heat transfer depending not only on wind speed, but also direction and prototype orientation. Probes 1 and 2 are being penalized due to their orientation and location in the panel. Observing results from different windy days based on wind direction and the location of the probes in the panel, it is conclusive that the assumption of wind speed being uniform over the collector surface area is not valid. A new model for wind speed over a flat-plate surface has been designed for recalculate the convective heat losses due to the wind in the entire surface of the PV-T collector, considering probes distribution and prevailing wind. This new convective heat transfer coefficient has been included as an enhancement of the first simulation approach. The results of this new model show two distinct curves for the probes facing the wind directly (1 and 2, more affected by the wind) and indirectly (3 and 4, less affected) (**Figure 7**). This differentiation fits better with the experimental data.

As in the PV temperatures, the one-dimensional simulation can predict quantitatively thermal changes, heat fluxes and layer temperatures, although simulated data do not reproduce the first minutes of experimental data, in which real temperature sensors have inertia and a period of acclimatation. Moreover, the simulation is considerably sensitive to radiation and wind, whose changes are straight reflected on simulated results.

Overall, insulating materials contained in probes 1 and 2 have better heat performance, reaching higher temperatures during windless days.

3.3 Adhesive materials comparison

The following **Figure 8** and **Figure 9** show results obtained from adhesives small-scale tests (Prototype 2) for low and high wind speed respectively. Temperatures ($T_{5\text{-}exp}$-$T_{8\text{-}exp}$) represent the mean temperature inside the **heat absorber**, for each material (Probes 5-8, **Table I**).

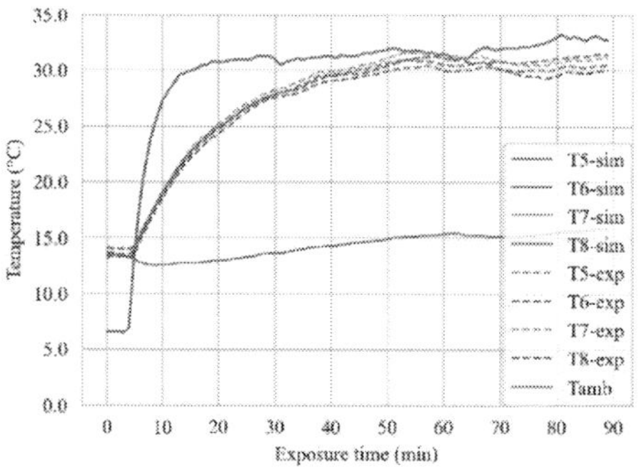

Figure 8: Prototype 2 heat absorber temperatures for each probe. Windless day

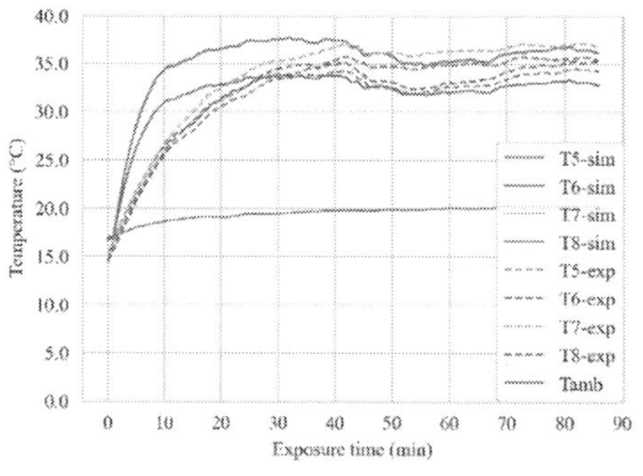

Figure 9: Prototype 2 heat absorber temperatures for each probe. Windy day

Figure 8 shows differences of less than 2 °C between probes during a windless day test, while for a windy day test in **Figure 9**, the differences of temperature between probes are higher, around 5 °C. As it happened with insulating material tests, temperature results on windy days are more affected by the wind depending on probe location, regarding the wind direction, in the adhesive's comparison tests.

Probe 7 and probe 8 reach higher temperatures in both tests. Probe 8 attaching media is a thermal paste with higher conductivity; however, its handling and applicability were a disadvantage against the double-face adhesive of probe 7.

As in the previous sections, the one-dimensional simulation can predict quantitatively layer temperatures and heat transfer, although simulated data do not reproduce the inertia of the temperature sensors. The simulation remains sensitive to radiation and wind, with the improvements included.

Overall, differences between adhesives during windless days, when results are not affected by probe location regarding
wind distribution above flat-plate, are not as significant as in the insulating material tests. Heat transfer depends on the thickness and thermal conductivity of materials, in particular for adhesives, where the thicknesses are very low, no appreciable differences are measured in the experimental tests. Other criteria, as ease of handling, prices, sustainability and lifetime are taken into account for choosing the ideal adhesive for the PV-T design.

3.4 Numerical assessment of 1D simulation

Percentage Error has been calculated in order to evaluate numerically the assessment of the one-dimensional model, comparing simulated results with the experimental values measured.

Table IV shows this indicator obtained for each scenario. In all the comparison tests, a Percentage Error of less than 8.0 % is obtained, so it can be concluded that the one-dimensional simulation is capable of predict reliable numerical data within that measurement range.

Table IV: Average Percentage Error values for each comparison test.

	Windless days	Windy days
PV	1.5 %	1.3 %
Prototype 1		
Probe 1	2.9 %	2.5 %
Probe 2	1.4 %	1.3 %
Probe 3	7.3 %	2.6 %
Probe 4	6.6 %	3.4 %
Prototype 2		
Probe 5	6.1 %	4.1 %
Probe 6	6.6 %	2.3 %
Probe 7	3.6 %	2.4 %
Probe 8	4.2 %	1.8 %

4 CONCLUSIONS

Following conclusion can be resumed from this work:

- The experimental study shows no significant differences between adhesives, but does show between insulations.
- Insulations in probe 1 and 2 are chosen because of the experimental results during windless days and its ease of installation and handling.
- Experimental results are highly dependent of the wind direction and the location of the probe in the panel. Forced heat convection in flat plate should be studied and taken into account in future studies or experiments.
- The one-dimensional simulation can reproduce experimental temperatures and heat transfer fluxes through the PV-T panel layers.
- The Percentage Error between simulated and experimental data remains under 8.0% in every comparison test.

5 ACKNOWLEDGEMENTS

This work was undertaken in the framework of CRETE VALLEY project, funded by the European Union's *Horizon Europe* research and innovation program through grant agreement No 101136139.

6 REFERENCES

Abdelrazik, A. S., Al-Sulaiman, F. A., Saidur, R., & Ben-Mansour, R. (2018). A review on recent development for the design and packaging of hybrid photovoltaic/thermal (PV/T) solar systems. *Renewable and Sustainable Energy Reviews*, *95*(December 2017), 110–129. https://doi.org/10.1016/j.rser.2018.07.013

Agarwal, R. K., & Garg, H. P. (1994). Study of a Photovoltaic-Thermal system - Thermosyphonic solar water heater combined with solar cells. *Energy Conversion and Management*, *35*(7), 605–620.

Bhattarai, S., Oh, J., Euh, S., Krishna, G., & Hyun, D. (2012). Simulation and model validation of sheet and tube type photovoltaic thermal solar system and conventional solar collecting system in transient states. *Solar Energy Materials and Solar Cells*, *103*, 184–193. https://doi.org/10.1016/j.solmat.2012.04.017

Cristofari, C., Notton, G., & Canaletti, J. L. (2009). Thermal behavior of a copolymer PV/Th solar system in low flow rate conditions. *Solar Energy*, *83*(8), 1123–1138. https://doi.org/10.1016/j.solener.2009.01.008

Dubey, S., Sarvaiya, J. N., & Seshadri, B. (2013). Temperature dependent photovoltaic (PV) efficiency and its effect on PV production in the world - A review. *Energy Procedia*, *33*, 311–321. https://doi.org/10.1016/j.egypro.2013.05.072

Hajji, M., Naimi, S. E., Hajji, B., & El Hafyani, M. L. (2014). A comparative study between two structures of hybrid photovoltaic/thermal (PV/T) collectors for water pumping systems. *Proceedings of 2014 International Renewable and Sustainable Energy Conference, IRSEC 2014*, 235–240. https://doi.org/10.1109/IRSEC.2014.7059745

Herrando, M., Markides, C. N., & Hellgardt, K. (2014). A UK-based assessment of hybrid PV and solar-thermal systems for domestic heating and power: System performance. *Applied Energy*, *122*, 288–309.

Herrando, M., Ramos, A., Zabalza, I., & Markides, C. N. (2019). A comprehensive assessment of alternative absorber-exchanger designs for hybrid PVT-water collectors. *Applied Energy*, *235*(July 2018), 1583–

1602. https://doi.org/10.1016/j.apenergy.2018.11.024

Herrando, M., Wang, K., Huang, G., Otanicar, T., Mousa, O. B., Agathokleous, R. A., Ding, Y., Kalogirou, S., Ekins-Daukes, N., Taylor, R. A., & Markides, C. N. (2023). A review of solar hybrid photovoltaic-thermal (PV-T) collectors and systems. In *Progress in Energy and Combustion Science* (Vol. 97). Elsevier Ltd. https://doi.org/10.1016/j.pecs.2023.101072

Joshi, S. S., & Dhoble, A. S. (2018). Photovoltaic - Thermal systems (PVT): Technology review and future trends. *Renewable and Sustainable Energy Reviews*, *92*(September 2017), 848–882. https://doi.org/10.1016/j.rser.2018.04.067

Kalogirou, S. A., & Tripanagnostopoulos, Y. (2006). Hybrid PV/T solar systems for domestic hot water and electricity production. *Energy Conversion and Management*, *47*(18–19), 3368–3382. https://doi.org/10.1016/j.enconman.2006.01.012

Michael, J. J., Iniyan, S., & Goic, R. (2015). Flat plate solar photovoltaic-thermal (PV/T) systems: A reference guide. *Renewable and Sustainable Energy Reviews*, *51*, 62–88. https://doi.org/10.1016/j.rser.2015.06.022

Notton, G., Cristofari, C., Mattei, M., & Poggi, P. (2005). Modelling of a double-glass photovoltaic module using finite differences. *Applied Thermal Engineering*, *25*(17–18), 2854–2877. https://doi.org/10.1016/j.applthermaleng.2005.02.008

Ramos, A., Guarracino, I., Mellor, A., Alonso-Álvarez, D., Childs, P., Ekins-Daukes, N. J., & Markides, C. N. (2017). Solar-Thermal and Hybrid Photovoltaic-Thermal Systems for Renewable Heating. In *Grantham Institute* (Issue 22). www.imperial.ac.uk/grantham/publications

Rawat, R., Lamba, R., & Kaushik, S. C. (2017). Thermodynamic study of solar photovoltaic energy conversion: An overview. *Renewable and Sustainable Energy Reviews*, *71*(October 2015), 630–638. https://doi.org/10.1016/j.rser.2016.12.089

Rejeb, O., Dhaou, H., & Jemni, A. (2015). Parameters effect analysis of a photovoltaic thermal collector: Case study for climatic conditions of Monastir, Tunisia. *Energy Conversion and Management*, *89*, 409–419. https://doi.org/10.1016/j.enconman.2014.10.018

Santos, L. D. O., De Carvalho, P. C. M., & Filho, C. D. O. C. (2022). Photovoltaic Cell Operating Temperature Models: A Review of Correlations and Parameters. *IEEE Journal of Photovoltaics*, *12*(1), 179–190. https://doi.org/10.1109/JPHOTOV.2021.3113156

Tiwari, A., & Sodha, M. S. (2006). Performance evaluation of hybrid PV/thermal water/air heating system: A parametric study. *Renewable Energy*, *31*(15), 2460–2474. https://doi.org/10.1016/j.renene.2005.12.002

Zhang, X., Zhao, X., Smith, S., Xu, J., & Yu, X. (2012). Review of R&D progress and practical application of the solar photovoltaic/thermal (PV/T) technologies. *Renewable and Sustainable Energy Reviews*, *16*(1), 599–617. https://doi.org/10.1016/j.rser.2011.08.026

Zondag, H. A., de Vries, D. W., van Helden, W. G. J., van Zolingen, R. J. C., & van Steenhoven, A. A. (2003). The yield of different combined PV-thermal collector designs. *Solar Energy*, *74*(3), 253–269. https://doi.org/10.1016/S0038-092X(03)00121-X

42nd European Photovoltaic Solar Energy Conference and Exhibition

EU PVSEC 2025

Materials assessment for PV-T modules thermal performance improvement

Author(s): L. Cano[1*], R. Simón-Allué[1], R. Villén[1], Y. Lara[1], I. Guedea[1]
[1]ENDEF

*Corresponding author: lucia.cano@endef.com

The efficiency of PV-T collectors is directly linked to effective heat transfer through the system layers, which impacts overall thermal and electrical performance. This study evaluates the role of adhesives, the attachment media between the photovoltaic (PV) panel and the heat exchanger (HX); and insulant materials, which constitute the back-side of the PV-T panel. Two small-scale prototypes were developed to test selected adhesives and insulants under real-world conditions.

Approach

Prototypes

Two sets of four adhesives **and four** insulating materials were selected for the testing. Two prototypes were assembled.

Prototype 1 - Insulations			Prototype 2 - Adhesives		
Probe	Thickness (m)	Thermal conductivity (W/m·K)	Probe	Thickness (m)	Thermal conductivity (W/m·K)
1	0.025	0.037	5	0.00013	0.16
2	0.025	0.032	6	0.00013	0.18
3	0.025	0.025	7	0.0002	1.5
4	0.030	0.025	8	0.002	3.4

Figure 1. Prototype 1 design and assembly

Experimental setup

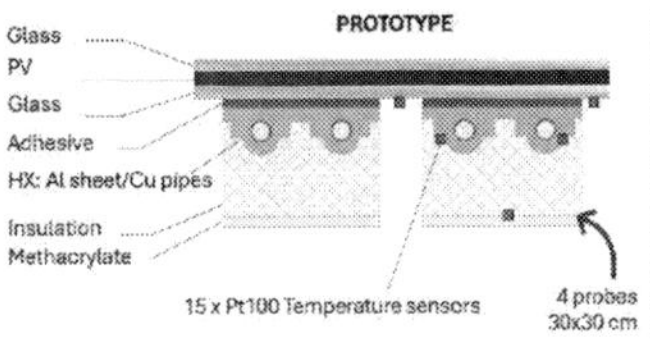

Figure 2. Prototype layers and temperature sensors distribution

Experimental tests were performed in **Zaragoza**, Spain, during winter months. Panels were placed in horizontal.

Objective of the study: **measuring temperatures in the heat exchanger to compare materials.**

Simulation

One-dimensional model was developed for simulating temperatures in each layer of the PV-T collector and prototypes.

$$q_{layer\,a} = \frac{k_a}{\delta_a} \cdot (T_{a\_in} - T_{a\_out})$$

$$q_{top} = h_{wind} \cdot (T_{glass} - T_{amb})$$
$$q_{bot} = h_{wind} \cdot (T_{metha} - T_{amb})$$

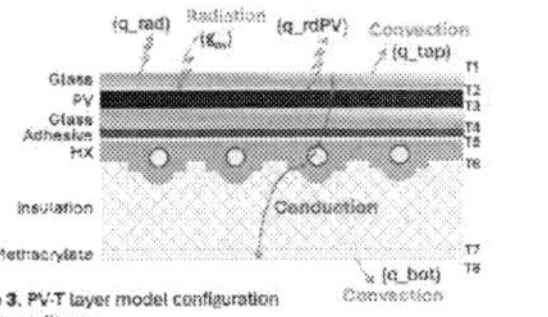

Figure 3. PV-T layer model configuration and energy flows

$$q_{rad} = \varepsilon_{glass,long\lambda} \cdot \sigma \cdot (T_{glass}^4 - T_{sky}^4)$$
$$q_{rdPV} = \varepsilon_{PV,long\lambda} \cdot \tau_{g,long\lambda} \cdot \sigma \cdot (T_{PV}^4 - T_{sky}^4)$$
$$g_{PV} = G_{inc} \cdot \tau_{g,short\lambda} \cdot \alpha_{PV,short\lambda}$$

Results and discussion

PV panel

The first approach of the one-dimensional model only considers the PV panel, excluding the heat exchanger and the material probes.

Windless/very low wind day

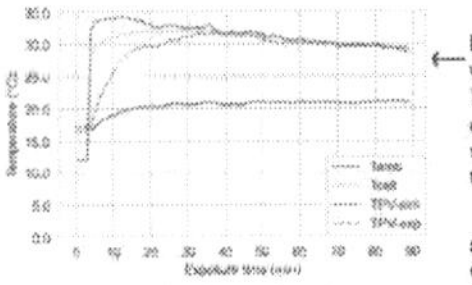

During **windless** or very low wind days Tcell matches both experimental and simulated PV temperatures.

Simulated values do match experimental data.

Figure 4. PV panel temperatures. Windless day

Windy day

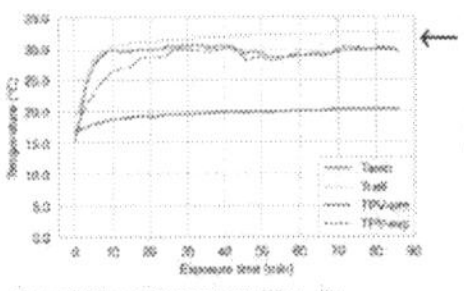

In **windy** days the Tcell is higher, due to the fact that Tcell definition does not take into account wind effect.

Figure 5. PV panel temperatures. Windy day

Insulating materials

Windless/very low wind day

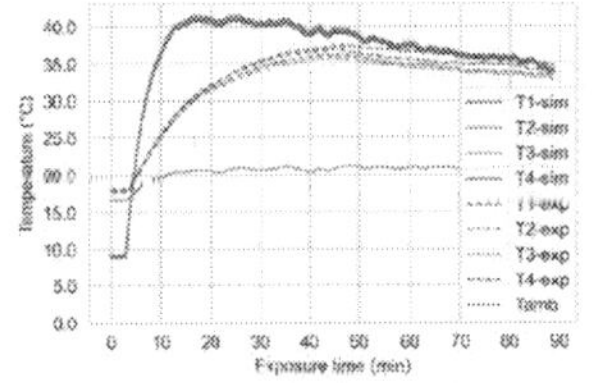

Figure 6. Prototype 1 heat exchanger temperatures. Windless day

Experimental results reveal higher temperatures in **probes 1 and 2**.

Windy day

New wind speed model implemented*

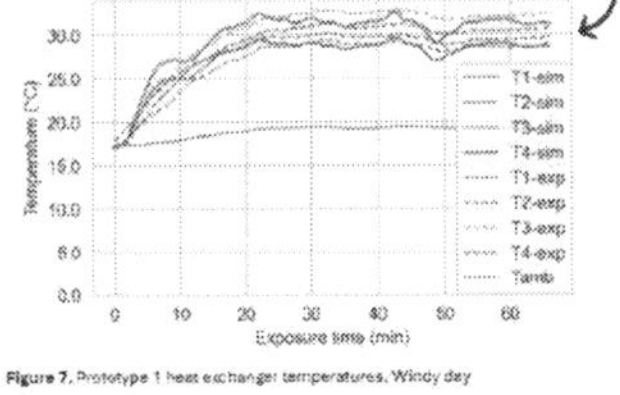

Figure 7. Prototype 1 heat exchanger temperatures. Windy day

Wind affects to the results and **alters heat transfer** depending not only on wind speed, but also direction and prototype orientation. Probes 1 and 2 are being penalized. A **new model** for wind speed over a **flat-plate surface** has been designed for recalculate the convective heat losses of the PV-T collector*.

Adhesives

Windless/very low wind day

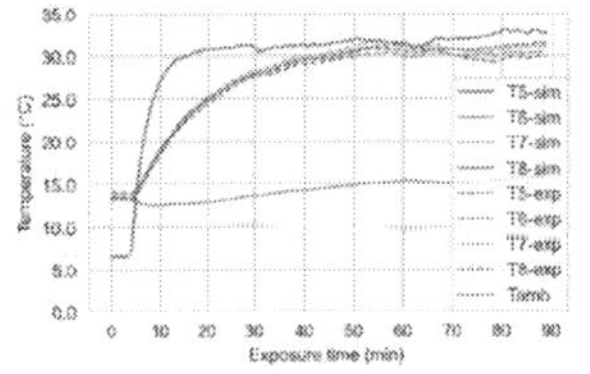

Figure 8. Prototype 2 heat exchanger temperatures. Windless day

Probes 7 and 8 reach higher temperatures in experimental tests, but the **differences are not as significant as in the insulating material tests.** No appreciable differences are shown by the 1D model for adhesives, where the thicknesses are very low.

Windy day

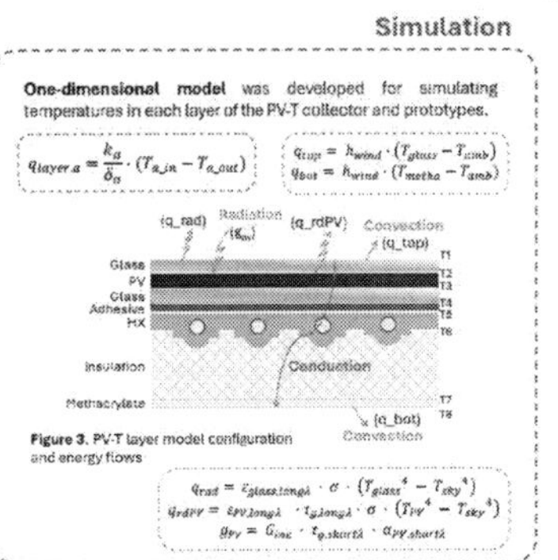

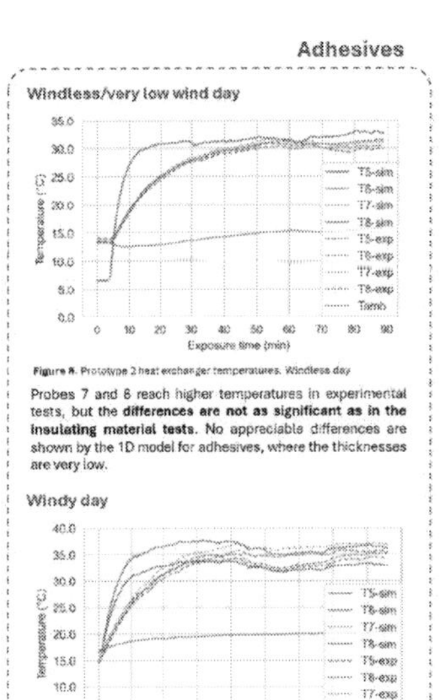

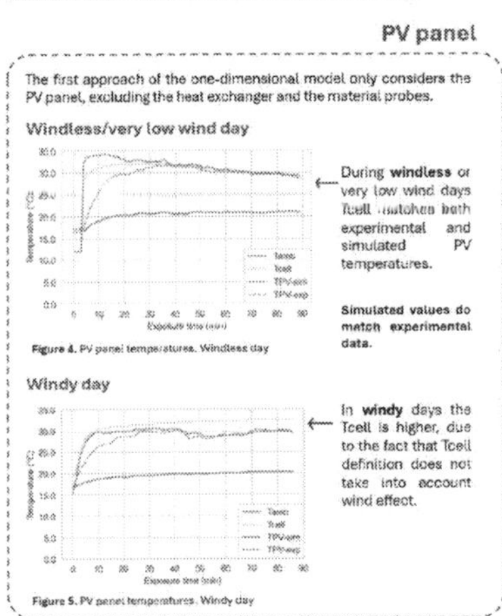

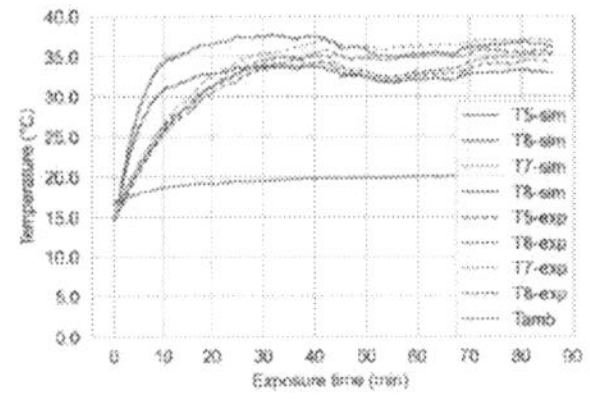

Figure 9. Prototype 2 heat exchanger temperatures. Windy day

The simulation remains sensitive to radiation and wind, with the improvements included.

Simulation numerical assessment

	Windless days	Windy days
PV	1.5 %	1.3 %
Prototype 1		
Probe 1	2.9 %	2.5 %
Probe 2	1.4 %	1.3 %
Probe 3	7.3 %	2.8 %
Probe 4	6.6 %	3.4 %
Prototype 2		
Probe 5	8.1 %	4.1 %
Probe 6	6.6 %	2.3 %
Probe 7	3.6 %	2.4 %
Probe 8	4.2 %	1.8 %

$$\%Error = \frac{|y_{exp} - y_{sim}|}{y_{exp}} \cdot 100$$

Percentage Error of less than 8.0 % is obtained in every test.

The 1D model is capable of predict reliable numerical data within that measurement range

Conclusions

1. The experimental study shows **no significant differences** between adhesives, but does show between insulations.
2. Insulations in **probe 1 and 2** are chosen because of the experimental results during windless days and its ease of installation and handling.
3. Experimental results are highly dependent of the wind direction and the location of the probe in the panel. **Forced heat convection in flat plate** should be studied and taken into account in future studies or experiments.
4. The one-dimensional simulation can **reproduce** experimental temperatures and heat transfer fluxes through the PV-T panel layers.
5. The **Percentage Error** between simulated and experimental data remains under 8.0% in every comparison test.

ENDEF website

CRETE VALLEY website

020128-001

This work was undertaken in the framework of the CRETE VALLEY project, funded by the European Union's Horizon Europe research and innovation program through grant agreement Nº 101136139.

EVALUATING REPAIR TECHNIQUES FOR C-SI PV MODULES: SPOT-WELDING

Jorge Rabanal-Arabach [1,3*], Sonia Beltran-Condori [1*], Natalia Videla-Magnata[1,3], Katalina Rojas-Henríquez [1], Andreas Schneider [2], Edward Fuentealba-Vidal [1,3]

[1] University of Antofagasta, Av Angamos 601, 1270300 Antofagasta, Chile.
[2] University of Applied Sciences Gelsenkirchen, Germany.
[3] Solar Energy Research Center, Tupper 2007, 8370451 Santiago, Chile.
[*] email: jorge.rabanal@uantof.cl, sonia.beltran.condori@ua.cl

ABSTRACT: Extending the operational life of photovoltaic (PV) modules is essential for sustainable energy transitions and waste reduction and repairing them is one option to achieve this aim. This study focuses on crystalline silicon (c-Si) modules affected by failures inside the junction box (jbox), where overheated solder joints often interrupt current flow. We explored spot-welding with nickel plates as an alternative to traditional soldering. Three welding strategies are considered through digital simulations to evaluate ease of application and reliability, and the most promising is applied experimentally: horizontal placement with a double-folded plate. The PV modules are assessed before and after repair using current–voltage curves, series resistance measurement, and thermal imaging under direct current injection. The intervention of the jbox successfully restored conductivity and power output, with no evidence of hot-spot formation. Post-repair performance is within ±5% of reference modules in terms of power output, without a significant change in the series resistance of the modules under test, supporting second-life use. The findings confirm spot-welding as a robust and lead-free repair method that contributes to circular economy practices in the PV sector.
Keywords: Photovoltaics, modules, junction box, repair, bussing, ribbons, spot-welding

1 INTRODUCTION

The rapid global expansion of photovoltaic technologies highlights the need for effective strategies to extend module lifetimes [1, 2]. With the increasing number of PV systems reaching their mid-life stage, repair and refurbishment provide cost-efficient alternatives to premature disposal [3, 4, 5, 6, 7, 8]. In particular, second-life applications are gaining traction as a sustainable approach that aligns with circular economy principles. However, to date most of the related standards focus on the quality qualification for fabrication or for recycling of this type of solar devices, and only few research publications focus on its repair.

Fault diagnosis frameworks, often guided by international standards such as IEC 60904, IEC 61215, and IEC 62446, along with IEA PVPS methodologies, allow classification of modules by the type and severity of degradation. Previous large-scale studies on crystalline silicon (c-Si) modules have shown that failures are not uniformly distributed but frequently localized in components such as the junction box (jbox), frame, connectors, or backsheet.

A recurrent issue inside the jbox is the deterioration of tin solder joints that connect bussing ribbons to the main electrical busbar. Overheating can cause melting, leading to disconnections and reduced power output. To overcome these limitations, alternative interconnection strategies are needed. Spot-welding using nickel plates has emerged as a potential solution due to nickel's mechanical resilience, corrosion resistance, and stable electrical properties.

This work investigates the feasibility of spot-welding as a repair method for bussing ribbon disconnections. Our study evaluates three welding layouts, compares their practicality, and experimentally validates the most effective technique. Electrical and thermal assessments before and after repair provide insight into the reliability of the restored modules and their suitability for continued service.

2 METHODOLOGY

The study develops and applies an experimental repair strategy for PV modules, targeting damaged bussing ribbons inside the jbox through spot-welding with nickel plates. Nickel is selected as the interconnection material due to its high conductivity and resistance to corrosion. Figure 1 provides a schematic view of a typical jbox, indicating key components such as diodes, busbars, and bussing ribbons.

To identify the most practical configuration, three welding approaches are digitally simulated: (1) vertical placement of two nickel plates covering the busbar, (2) horizontal folding of the ribbon secured by a single plate, and (3) a variation of the second approach using a double-folded plate to strengthen the weld and increase the contact area. The experimental methodology consisted of three main steps. First, modules with faulty junction boxes (devices under test, DUTs) are identified and characterized through baseline testing by measurements of I–V curves and electrical resistance. Second, the spot-welding repair is performed. Finally, post-repair evaluation included repeat I–V and resistance testing, complemented by hot-spot detection using infrared thermography.

2.1 Baseline Testing

The objective of this step is to assess the pre-repair condition of the bussing ribbons and depict the exiting faults: I-V curves and electrical resistance. The latter is determined using the four-wire Kelvin method under dark conditions to ensure accurate detection of conductivity anomalies. Probes are placed at points A (common), B, C, and D according to Figure 1, corresponding to measurements across one substring (1/3), two substrings (2/3), and the full cell matrix (3/3). A test voltage of (2.00 ± 0.02) V_{DC} is applied and the current and voltage recorded to later calculate the series resistance.

Current–voltage curves are obtained with a portable tracer under natural sunlight, following IEC 60904-1 guidelines. All measurements are performed directly on the bussing ribbons inside the jbox, as the external cables are disconnected from the DUT circuit.

10.4229/EUPVSEC2025/3AV.1.12

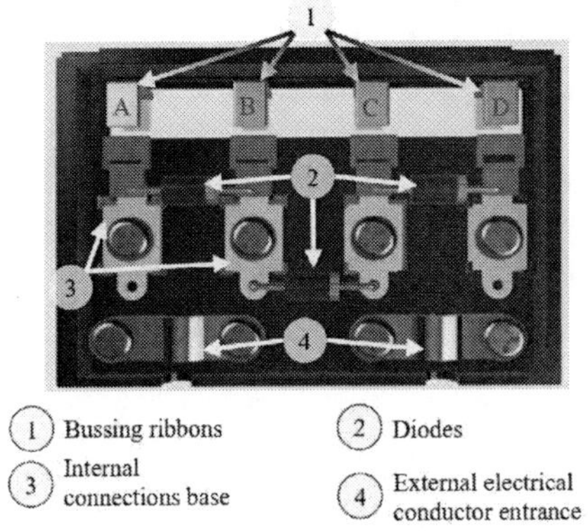

Figure 1: Scheme of a jbox from the DUTs.

2.2 Repair Implementation

To restore electrical continuity, the bussing ribbons are repaired using spot-welding with nickel plates. Nickel alloys are chosen because they combine resistance to electrical and thermal stress with ease of welding [3]. The repair protocol involved four sequential steps, from opening and preparing the junction box to completing the final welds, as shown in Figure 2. While three possible welding approaches are considered, only the "horizontal welding reinforced with a double-folded plate" is implemented across all modules, as it offered the most reliable and straightforward solution.

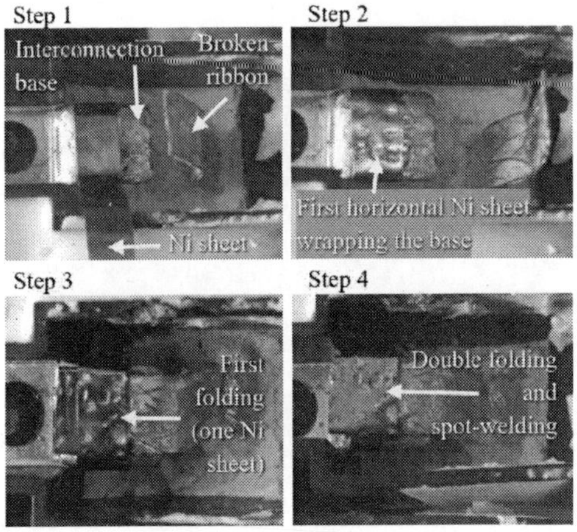

Figure 2: Implementation of broken outgoing ribbon refurbishment into a jbox.

2.3 Post-repair Evaluation

After repair, modules are re-characterized but this time measures are taken at their outer connections (MC4 terminals). Electrical recovery is validated by comparing I–V and resistance values before and after welding. Additionally, infrared thermography, as shown in Figure 3, is used to monitor local heating during direct current injection at near-nominal operating conditions. Images are recorded at 15 s and 60 s to track short-term thermal evolution.

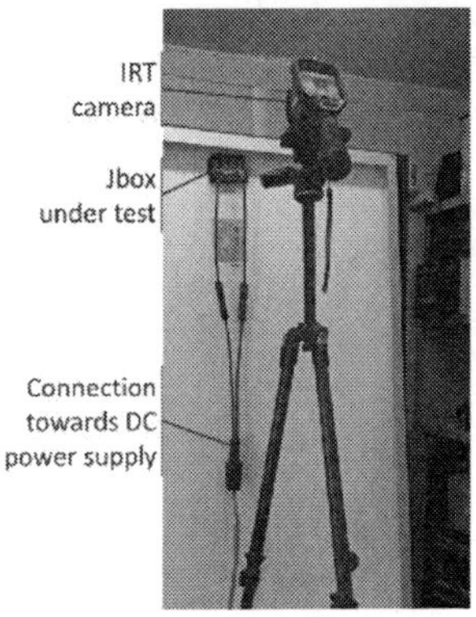

Figure 3: Experimental setup for hot-spot assessment.

3 RESULTS AND DISCUSSION

Post-repair analysis reveals that electrical resistance remained essentially unchanged across all DUTs, indicating that the spot-welding process does not introduce additional series resistance. Instead, the repair enhances electrical continuity, with improvements evident at both the substring scale and across the full module. Figure 4 presents the average electrical resistance measured across the devices under test (DUTs), alongside a reference group of 11 healthy PV modules (R_ref), whose mean value and associated error bars are shown for comparison (full module only). Pre-repair measurements are represented by circles, while post-repair results are indicated by triangles. The labels "1/3," "2/3," and "3/3" correspond to the fraction of the cell matrix evaluated: "1/3" refers to measurements between points B and A in Figure 1, "2/3" between points C and A, and "3/3" between points D and A.

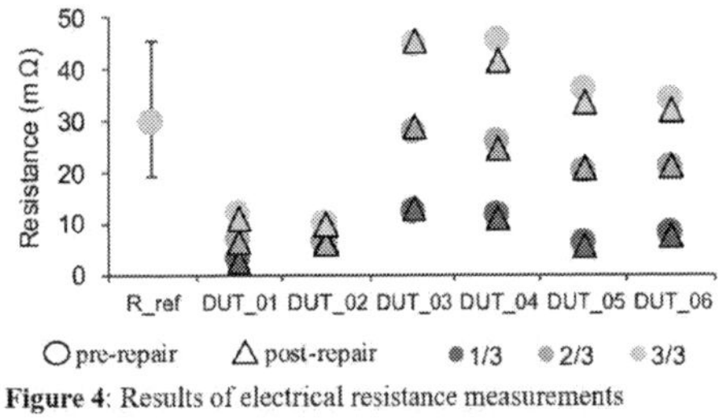

Figure 4: Results of electrical resistance measurements

No hot-spot formation is detected in any of the repaired modules. Under controlled ambient conditions of (20 ± 2) °C, junction box temperatures ranged between 24 °C and 26 °C, with a maximum rise of 2 K. These variations fall well within the safe operational range for PV modules.

Module power output is assessed before and after refurbishment in accordance with IEC 60904-1, using natural sunlight under clear-sky conditions. Pre-repair measurements are obtained by directly contacting the bussing ribbons inside the junction box, as no current is available at the external MC4 terminals due to the fault. After repair, power is measured conventionally through the outer MC4 connectors. The results, summarized in Table I, show that the repair process successfully restores module functionality. It should be noted that pre-repair power values could only be acquired internally from the jbox, highlighting the loss of output through the external connectors prior to restoration.

Table I: Comparison of Power Output before and after repair.

DUT	Pre-repair Power (W)	Post-repair Power (W)	Rel. Dif. (%)
P_ref	290 ± 15	--	--
DUT_01	294	280	−5
DUT_02	276	271	−2
DUT_03	279	265	−5
DUT_04	279	268	−4
DUT_05	282	286	1
DUT_06	287	289	1

4 CONCLUSION

The results of this study confirm that spot-welding with a double-folded nickel plate is a practical and effective method for repairing localized bussing ribbon failures in PV module junction boxes. This approach restores electrical functionality and power output while avoiding the use of toxic materials such as lead. Compared with conventional tin soldering, spot-welding offers improved reliability by minimizing the risk of future disconnections caused by solder melting under thermal stress.

Although the restored power output did not fully reach the original pre-failure values, the deviation is within 5%, which remains acceptable for second-life applications where minor performance losses are tolerable.

By offering a lead-free and mechanically stable alternative to soldering, spot-welding supports sustainable module management and contributes to the circular economy. Expanding the sample size in future work will further validate its reliability for large-scale refurbishment.

5 ACKNOWLEDGEMENTS

This work was supported by the Solar Circular fase2 project (CORFO 23BP-251214), the ANID/FONDEF/IDEA project ID24I10478, and the Chilean Solar Energy Research Center (SERC Chile) under Grant ANID/FONDAP/1523A0006. The authors gratefully acknowledge the support provided by the Master's Program in Solar Energy at the University of Antofagasta.

6 REFERENCES

[1] H. Mirletz, S. Ovaitt, S. Sridhar and T. Barnes, "Circular economy priorities for photovoltaics in the energy transition," *PLoS ONE,* vol. 17, no. 9, p. e0274351, 2022.

[2] J. Rabanal-Arabach, E. Fuentealba-Vidal, J. Astudillo-Ledezma, S. Beltran-Condori, A. Taquichiri, J. Tapia-Jelcic, D. Muñoz, A. Schneider, M. Riquelme-Zambrano and I. Jamett-Aranda, "Procedure Proposal to Determine PV Module Status for Its Second Life Application," in *EU PVSEC 2023,* 2023.

[3] G. Beaucarne, G. Eder, E. Jadot, Y. Voronko and W. Mühleisen, "Repair and preventive maintenance of photovoltaic modules with degrading backsheets using flowable silicone sealant," *Progress in Photovoltaics,* vol. 30, no. 8, pp. 1045-1053, 2021.

[4] Y. Voronko, G. Eder, C. Breitwieser, W. Mühleisen, L. Neumaier, S. Feldbacher, G. Oreski and N. Lenck, "Repair options for PV modules with cracked backsheets," *Energy Science and Engineering,* vol. 9, no. 9, pp. 1583-1595, 2021.

[5] Y. Kawano, J. Chantana, Y. Kuroda, K. Hirose and T. Minemoto, "Development of repairing technique for interconnection of silicon photovoltaic modules using an induction heating system," *Solar Energy,* vol. 261, pp. 55-62, 2023.

[6] M. Tas and W. van Shark, "Experimental repair technique for glass defects of glass-glass photovoltaic modules – A techno-economic analysis," *Solar Energy Materials and Solar Cells,* vol. 257, p. 112397, 2023.

[7] F. Rosillo, M. Nieto-Morone, J. Benavides Esteva, F. Soriano, S. Temprano, C. González and M. d. C. Alonso-García, "Repairing ribbon bus bar interruptions in photovoltaic modules using non-intrusive interruption location," *Renewable Energy,* vol. 223, p. 120012, 2024.

[8] M. B. Nieto-Morone, F. Rosillo, M. Muñoz-García and M. d. C. Alonso-García, "Enhancing photovoltaic module sustainability: Defect analysis on partially repaired modules from Spanish PV plants," *Journal of Cleaner Production,* vol. 461, p. 142575, 2024.

EVALUATING REPAIR TECHNIQUES FOR C-SI PV MODULES: SPOT-WELDING

Jorge Rabanal-Arabach[1,3], Sonia Beltrán-Condori[1], Natalia Videla-Magnata[1,3], Katalina Rojas-Henriquez[1], Andreas Schneider[2], and Edward Fuentealba-Vidal[1,3]
[1]Universidad de Antofagasta, Av. Angamos 601, 1270300 Antofagasta, Chile.
[2]University of Applied Sciences Gelsenkirchen, , Neidenburger Str. 43, 45897 Gelsenkirchen, Germany.
[3]Solar Energy Research Center, Tupper 2007, 8370451 Santiago, Chile.

EU PVSEC 2025

INTRODUCTION

The diagnosis of PV modules health status and the repair of its anomalies are mandatory to enable a second life of such devices. However, to date most of the related standards focus on the quality qualification for fabrication or for recycling of this type of solar devices, and only few research publications focus on its repair [1-5]. This study assess the repair of broken soldering in jboxes due to overheating. To address this, spot-welding using nickel plates was proposed for bussing ribbons. DC current was injected into repaired modules to evaluate thermal behavior and detect hot spots.

RESULTS

Post-repair resistance measurements (△) show a slight but consistent decrease compared to pre-repair values (○) at all substring positions (1/3=B-A, 2/3=C-A, 3/3=D-A), with reference values from 11 undamaged modules confirming the trend (Fig. 1).

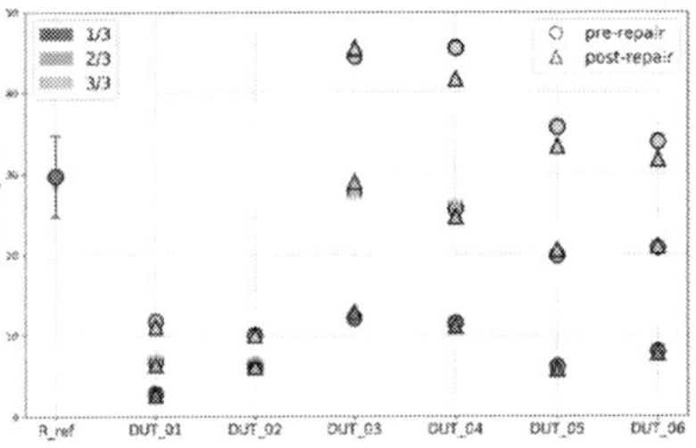

Zero hot-spots post-repair.
Jbox temps stable (24–26)°C, Δ≤2K) under (20±2)°C ambient temp.
IRT shows in average minimal ΔT: +0.9K after 15s and +0.5K after 60s. All within safe limits.

Power measurement (IEC 60904-1) confirms the effectiveness of the repair, showing pre-repair characterization limited to bus ribbon access (no MC4 output) and restored functionality after repair (Fig. 2).

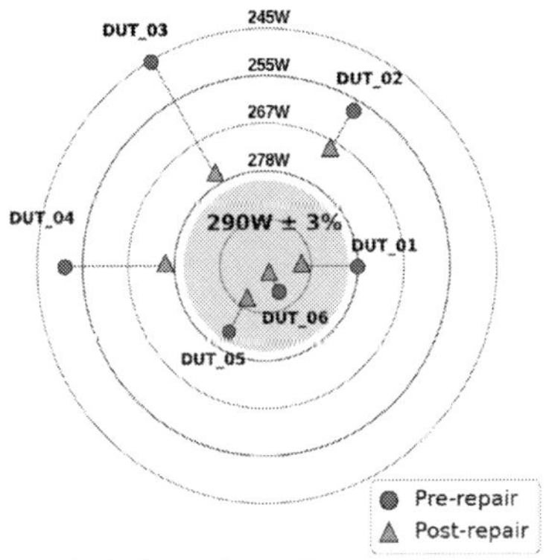

Fig. 2. Comparisson of power output before and after repair.

METHODOLOGY

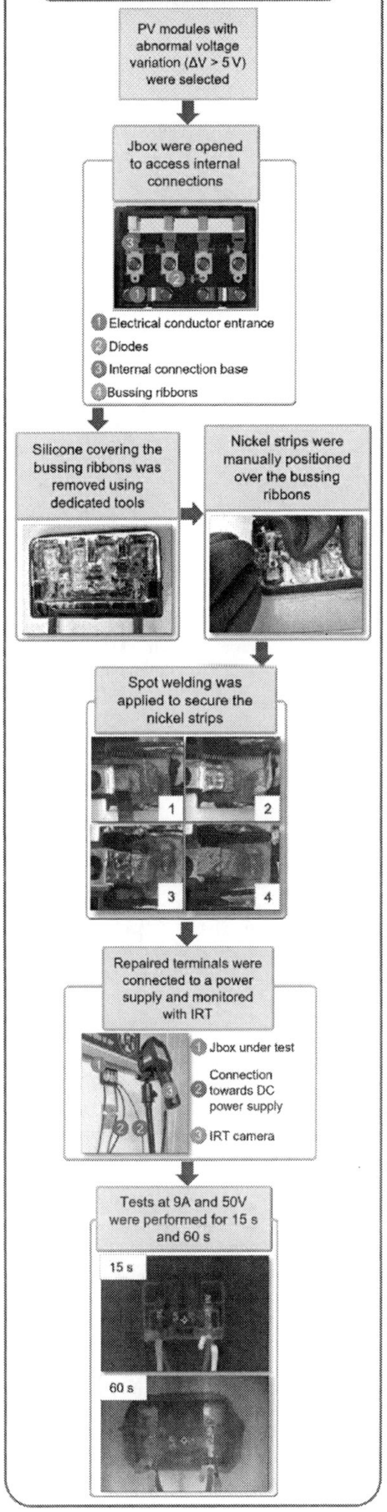

CONCLUSION

The double-folded nickel plate spot-welding technique provides an effective, lead-free solution for repairing bussing ribbons in PV modules, restoring electrical performance with only a ~5% deviation in power output. The method offers a safer alternative to tin soldering, supports second-life applications, and contributes to circular economy strategies in the PV sector. While further validation with larger sample sets is needed, the results confirm spot-welding as a practical approach to refurbishing damaged junction box connections.

REFERENCES

[1] R. Avery and G. Moe, Guidelines for the welded fabrication of nickel alloys, The Nickel Institute, 2018.
[2] G. Beaucarne et al., Prog. Photovolt., 30(8), pp. 1045-1053, 2021.
[3] Y. Voronko et al., Energy Sci. Eng., 9(9), 1583-1595, 2021.
[4] H. Mirletz et al., PLoS ONE, 17(9), pp. e0274351, 2022.
[5] J. Rabanal-Arabach et al., EU PVSEC, 2023.
[6] Y. Kawano et al., Solar Energy, 261, pp. 55–62, 2023.
[7] M. Tas and W. van Shark, Sol. Energy Mater. Sol. Cells, 257, pp. 112397, 2023.
[8] F. Rosillo et al., Renew. Energy, 223, pp. 120012, 2024.
[9] M. B. Nieto-Morone et al., J. Clean. Prod., 461, pp. 142575, 2024.

This work was supported by Solar Circular fase2 project under Grant CORFO 23BP-251214, by the project ANID/FONDEF/IDEA ID24I10478, and by the Chilean Solar Energy Research Center (SERC Chile) under Grant ANID/FONDAP/1523A0006.

CDEA Centro Desarrollo Energético Antofagasta · SERC CHILE Solar Energy Research Center · Westfälische Hochschule · CORFO

THERMALLY CONDUCTIVE FILLER PARTICLE MIXED SILICONE LAYER TO PROVIDE HEAT DISSIPATION FUNCTIONALITY TO C-SI SOLAR CELL MODULES WITHOUT ENCAPSULANTS

Yasushi Sobajima[1], Kouzen Wakazono[1], Keisuke Ohdaira[2]
[1]Gifu Univ., [2]JAIST
*Y. Sobajima, sobajima.yasushi.b2@f.gifu-u.ac.jp

ABSTRACT: To ensure stable photovoltaic conversion performance, reducing the operating temperature of encapsulant-free solar cell modules (novel solar cell module). We have developed a method to improve heat dissipation in this novel solar cell module structure by using a high-density mixture of highly thermally conductive filler material in silicone, arranged in sheet form at the bottom substrate of the cell. In this study, we explored ways to improve heat dissipation: incorporating AlN particles, creating through-holes in the substrate, and filling these holes with silicone material. Additionally, an AlN/silicone layer was applied to curved modules with increased cell area, demonstrating the effectiveness of this approach.
KEYWORDS: c-Si cell, novel module structure, thermally conductive filler, AlN, MgO, Heat dissipation effect

1 INTRODUCTION

The adoption of crystalline silicon (c-Si) solar cell modules continues to increase each year. Solar cell modules must withstand weather conditions and mechanical stress, which is why structures using encapsulants are now commonly employed. [1-3] However, this design makes recycling difficult due to the strong adhesion of the encapsulant. To support the ongoing large-scale adoption of next-generation solar cell modules, there is a clear need for significantly improved recyclability. S. Shimpo et al. have proposed a novel structure that does not use encapsulants [4]. This novel structure, through eliminating encapsulants, this structure can enhance the recyclability of solar modules. The novel module is formed by enclosing it within a lower substrate, installing the cells, and covering the top with a transparent material, with the substrate or cover providing mechanical strength. It is hypothesized that this will improve traditional solar module designs by reducing potential induced degradation (PID) phenomena [4].

However, novel structure still faces challenges such as component selection, achieving mechanical strength in large-area modules, increasing incident light intensity, and maintaining long-term performance stability. One key issue is suppressing internal temperature rise during the photoelectric conversion process. Since the band gap of c-Si is small, a decrease in cell efficiency due to a decrease in V_{OC} caused by temperature rise can occur during operation [5, 6].

We have demonstrated that SiO_X containing high thermal conductivity filler particles is effective for heat dissipation in encapsulated c-Si modules [7]. Recently, we transitioned from using SiO_X to silicone, which enables the formation of a strong sheet structure. This change has helped establish a more durable, robust sheet. Additionally, replacing MgO thermal conductive filler with AlN was considered, since white AlN provides higher thermal conductivity.

In this study, we applied silicone mixed with highly thermally conductive AlN particles (AlN/silicone) to a novel solar cell module structure to investigate improvements in heat dissipation performance. We also examined substrate enhancements, specifically the effect on heat dissipation when vertical through-holes were added to the substrate.

2 EXPERIMENTAL DETAILS

2.1 Method for preparing silicone material with thermally conductive filler

The silicone used in this study is a commercially available product with a proven track record as an encapsulant for c-Si solar cell modules. The raw material for this silicone is liquid, and mixing the two components begins curing through a chemical reaction. Like other encapsulants, silicone has low thermal conductivity. In this study, particles of a thermally conductive filler were mixed into this liquid silicone and cured, resulting in a material with improved thermal dissipation in both vertical and horizontal directions. Figure 1 shows how thermal conduction paths form in silicone by adding AlN thermally conductive particles. When heat is generated from the bottom during device operation, it spreads through the highly conductive material toward cooler areas. If AlN particle is present in enough quantity to create a continuous chain, the high temperature can easily spread throughout the entire material. Naturally, this efficiency in thermal conduction is expected to change depending on the amount of filler material, the formation of chains, and the adhesion strength.

In this study, a mixture of MgO or AlN particles, ranging from 250 to 500 mg, was used per 1 ml of silicone, which was blended from two liquids in a 1:1 ratio. The particle-mixed silicone was allowed to diffuse for 30 minutes before being applied over the entire substrate surface. The silicone thickness could be adjusted by varying the volume of liquid applied. The desired thickness was achieved by changing the number of application passes. After applying a single coat of silicone solution, the substrate was cured by drying at 80°C for 1 hour in air. To evaluate the thickness per application and the transverse thermal conductivity of the fabricated silicone material, cross-sectional scanning electron microscope (SEM) images and surface thermography

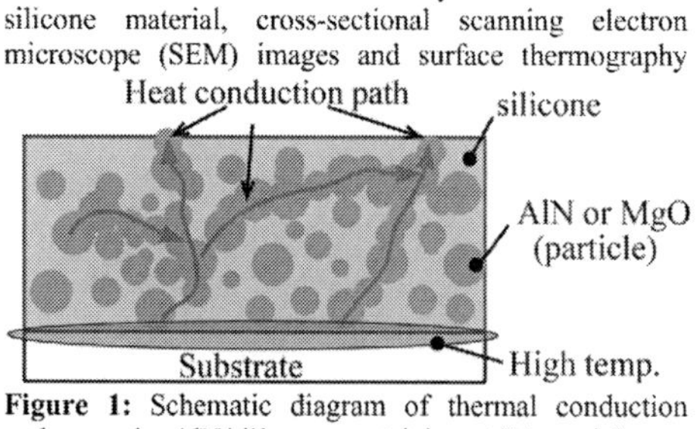

Figure 1: Schematic diagram of thermal conduction pathways in AlN/silicone containing AlN particles as highly thermally conductive fillers

Figure 2: Novel module structure using small area c-Si cells (15 x 15 mm^2)

2.2 Structure and fabrication method of novel c-Si solar cell modules

The structure of the novel solar cell module in this study is shown in Figure 2. The module size is 50 mm square, and the upper transparent cover material uses EagleXG glass (0.7 mm thick). The substrate is made of gray PVC and was manufactured using the laboratory's 3D printer. The c-Si cells installed in the module were commercially available cells cut into 15 mm squares using a diamond cutter. The backside of these cells contains silicone (MgO/silicone or AlN/silicone) combined with thermally conductive filler particles. To improve thermal conductivity between the c-Si cell, a commercially available thermal conductive film that covers the cell area is applied. The structure with through holes on the substrate was designed on a PC and manufactured using a 3D printer. To accurately measure this module's heat dissipation performance, the interior must be sealed. When measuring temperature rise caused by light irradiation, the substrate and glass were bonded with quick-drying silicone putty and measured in a tightly sealed environment. Moreover, when using through-holes, heat dissipation occurs through these holes. Therefore, the holes were filled with AlN/silicone material before use. During this filling process, trapped air bubbles could reduce the module's heat dissipation ability. To prevent this, the filling was performed multiple times to thoroughly remove all air bubbles.

2.3 Continuous light irradiation experiment

The change in J-V characteristics of c-Si solar cell modules with AlN/silicone was measured as a function of continuous light irradiation (AM 1.5, 100 mW/cm^2) time up to 3 hours. Since directly measuring the temperature inside the solar module during continuous operation is difficult, the temperature in the novel module was estimated based on the temperature characteristics of the c-Si solar cell [6]. This study estimated the module's internal temperature rise caused by light irradiation by measuring the change in V_{OC} (ΔV) from immediately after the start to 180 minutes of continuous light exposure. The ΔV of the conventional structure without AlN/silicone (ΔV_S) was used as a reference, and the ΔV of the measured samples (ΔV_F), along with the temperature characteristics of c-Si solar cells in Ref. [6], were used to calculate the estimated temperature difference (ΔT), which indicates the heat dissipation effect of AlN/silicone, using the following formula.

$$\Delta T = \frac{\Delta V_S - \Delta V_F}{\alpha}$$

ΔT(^{O}C): Estimated temperature difference
ΔV_F(V): The V_{OC} change values from immediately after light irradiation starts to 180 min later when AlN/silicone-coated module is applied
ΔV_S(V): The ΔV_F of the silicone-uncoated module
α (V/^{O}C): The temperature coefficient of V_{OC} in c-Si cells (α is calculated from data in Ref. [6])

The magnitude of ΔT was used to evaluate the heat dissipation performance under each condition. Measurements were taken indoors under light irradiation at room temperature, with no cooling fan used to regulate the module's internal temperature. Additionally, materials with low thermal conductivity were used at the module installation points to suppress heat transfer from the substrate to the outside.

3 RESULTS AND DISCUSSION

3.1 Thermally conductive material AlN/silicone and MgO/silicone

Using thermography images, the surface heat dissipation of a glass substrate coated with MgO/silicone was observed. The glass used was flat and measured 20 × 20 mm² (EagleXG). As shown in Figure 3(a), since the glass itself has low thermal conductivity, almost no heat diffusion was observed even when a heat source was placed at one end of the glass. However, when MgO/silicone (Figure 3(b)) or AlN/silicone (Figure 3(c)) was applied to the glass surface, uniform thermal conductivity spread laterally from the heat source. This shows that silicone materials exhibit lateral thermal diffusion characteristics when they contain an appropriate amount of thermally conductive filler particles.

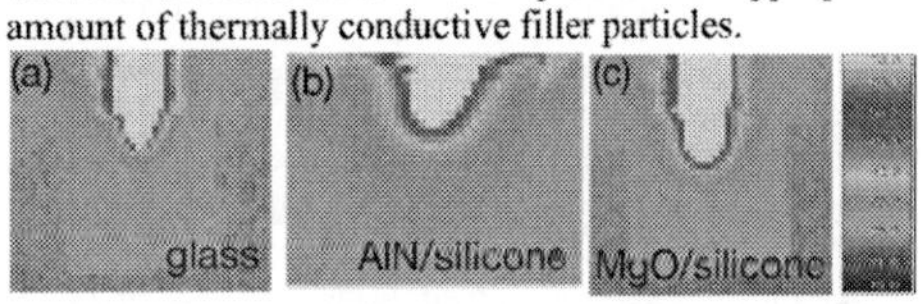

Figure 3: Surface thermographic images of samples without (EagleXG flat glass) (a), 5 times layer applications of AlN/silicone (b), and MgO/silicone (c).

3.2 Evaluation of surface thermal conductivity

Samples with varying numbers of layers were fabricated on flat glass substrates, and their thickness was evaluated using cross-sectional SEM images. Figure 4 shows the change in thickness with the number of layers. The figure indicates that, for all materials, thickness steadily increases as the number of layers grows. The solution used to make the materials contained 250 to 500 mg of thermally conductive filler per 1 ml of silicone solvent. The figure shows that each layer of the fabricated silicone material was about 60 μm thick, regardless of the type of particles added. This thickness is significantly greater than in the SiO_X case shown in the

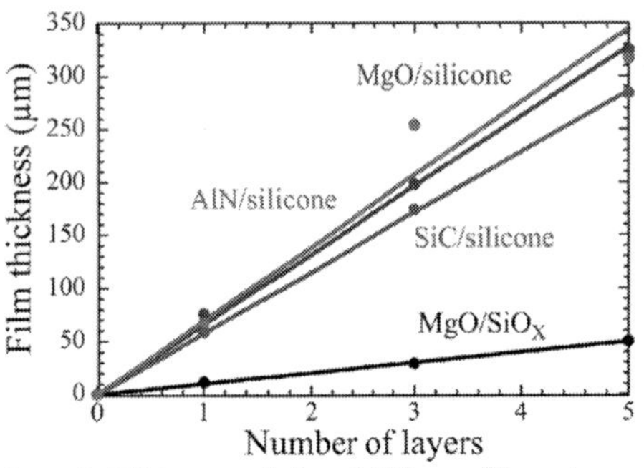

Figure 4: Thickness variation of different silicone layers with the number of coatings

figure. The difference in thickness is likely due to variations in the solute's viscosity and volatility.

3.3 Heat dissipation effect of different solutions

Figure 5 shows the estimated internal temperature rise within the module for different types of heat-conductive filler materials. In these heat dissipation experiments, the same c-Si material was used for all tests. First, when using the novel module alone, the decrease in V_{OC} after light exposure began was significantly larger compared to c-Si modules made with conventional vacuum lamination and EVA encapsulants (not shown in the Figure). As indicated by the temperature characteristics of c-Si solar cells discussed earlier, assuming the entire V_{OC} decrease is due to an internal temperature rise, this suggests that the novel module heats up more easily than the conventional design. In all cases, the reduction in V_{OC} levels reaches equilibrium after 180 minutes of light exposure. This study focused on the values at the start of light irradiation and after 180 minutes of continuous exposure. Furthermore, in case (a) without coating and case (b) without transparent silicone (i.e., without incorporating the heat-conductive filler material), no change was observed, including any variation over the course of light exposure. This demonstrates that silicone alone does not contribute to improving heat dissipation performance.

Furthermore, in cases (c) and (d), where the entire substrate is coated with silicone containing thermally conductive filler material, the reduction in V_{OC} after 180 minutes of light irradiation is smaller compared to cases (a) and (b). Additionally, when using AlN particles with high thermal conductivity, the reduction in V_{OC} due to light irradiation is further suppressed compared to using MgO particles. Calculating the estimated temperature difference DT for cases (c) and (d) based on case (a) yields values of 8.9°C and 11.5°C, respectively, indicating high heat dissipation performance regardless of the particle type used.

Note that the heat dissipation capacity of each silicone material depends on the concentration of the thermally conductive filler and the material's thickness. This trend remains consistent whether MgO/SiO_X is used in a general module structure with encapsulants [7] or MgO/silicone is applied to a novel module structure. However, no significant change was observed in small-area c-Si modules at various AlN densities for AlN/silicone. The latent heat dissipation ability of AlN particles is expected to be very high. Based on the reasons mentioned above, the conditions used in this study for MgO/silicone and AlN/silicone involve applying three coats (approximately 200 μm thick) over the entire substrate surface and using at least 250 mg of particles per 1 ml of silicone to ensure

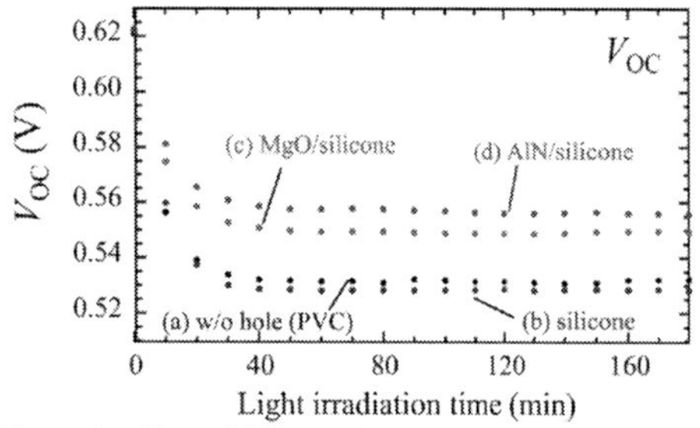

Figure 5: Effect of different thermally conductive filler materials in silicone layers on V_{OC} changes

Table I: The estimated temperature difference (ΔT) between conditions without AlN/silicone coating (Fig. 7(a)) and those with surface coating (b) or filling of the through hole by AlN/silicone (diameter 2.0 mmφ ((c) in the Figure, 4.0 mmφ (d) and 10 mmφ ((e), respectively).

	ΔT (°C)
(b) Fully covered by AlN/silicone (3 layers)	9.78
(c) Fill the 2.0 mm diameter through-hole with AlN/silicone	12.0
(d) In the case of 4.0 mm diameter	12.5
(e) In the case of 10 mm diameter	12.2

proper heat dissipation. These conditions are crucial to effectively facilitate heat dissipation from the thermally conductive filler particles.

3.4 Application of through-holes on substrates and investigation into improved heat dissipation performance

In our previous research, we confirmed that applying heat dissipation materials across the entire surface while ensuring lateral heat dissipation performance achieves sufficient thermal results. However, for modules larger than 1m², this approach is inefficient for dissipating heat generated at the cell center. Furthermore, in novel modules designed for airtightness, it remains uncertain whether heat dissipation mechanisms can be incorporated at the module edges or sides.

This section analyzed the improvement of performance by adding through-holes in the substrate and filling these areas with heat dissipation material as a solution to the problems. Complex structures immediately increase costs, so it is preferable to use through-holes with the lowest possible density and simplest structure in actual modules. As a first step to assess the maximum heat dissipation performance achievable with this structure, a through-hole was drilled across the entire substrate.

The diameter of the through-holes used throughout the module substrate for 15mm² cells was varied during fabrication, and all holes and the entire surface were filled with AlN/silicone (250 mg/ml). Figure 6 shows the change in V_{OC} over continuous light exposure time when using these substrates. Furthermore, Table 1 presents the results obtained by deriving ΔT using a function derived from the data in Fig. 6. As a result, using through holes enhances heat dissipation performance by approximately 2°C or more compared to covering the entire heat dissipation material. Additionally, the heat dissipation performance does not improve significantly even when varying the through-hole diameter. Therefore, while using through

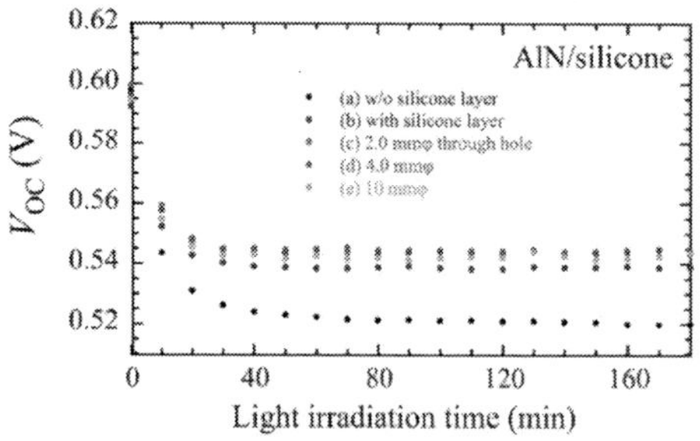

Figure 6: Reduction of V_{OC} through a novel c-Si module structure under continuous light irradiation

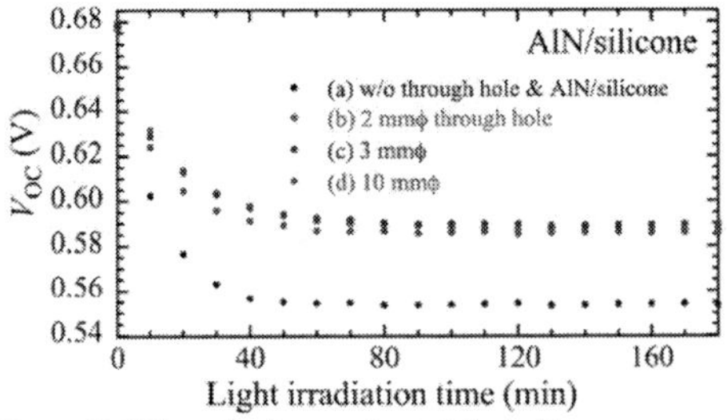

Figure 7: Effect of substrate through-hole diameter on heat dissipation effect in curved-surface modules using large-area cells (52 x 28mm²)

holes provide some improvement in heat dissipation, the extent of this improvement is not greatly affected by the size of the through holes. These results demonstrate the high heat dissipation performance of AlN particles, indicating that sufficient heat dissipation can be achieved without applying through-holes across the entire surface, at least for this particle size. The substrate thickness used in this study was 5.0 mm, and the raw material PVA has low thermal conductivity, similar to PC. Further improvement in heat dissipation performance is expected by reducing the substrate thickness within the range that ensures mechanical strength.

3.5 Evaluation of applicability to curved surface shapes with expanded cell area

AlN/silicone has demonstrated sufficient heat dissipation in small-area cells of 15 mm². For large-area novel module structures, switching the cover material from traditional glass to transparent PC is being considered to realize curved-shaped modules. To assess the usefulness of this silicone in such applications, a curved prototype was made after increasing the cell size to 28 x 52 mm². Through-holes of different diameters were drilled in each substrate, filled with AlN/silicone (250 mg/ml), and the surface was also coated with this silicone. The top cover is 2.0 mm thick PC material. After sealing the components with silicone putty, thermal performance was tested. The results, shown in Figure 8, indicate that effective heat dissipation was achieved regardless of through-hole diameter when filled with AlN/silicone. This silicone material demonstrates good heat dissipation across different cell areas and module shapes. However, increasing the area relative to smaller modules causes the ΔT values in Table 2 to tend to rise, indicating that the module's internal temperature increases as the area expands. This may be due to the internal structure of the module being in early development, possibly providing more space than small-area modules, which suggests room for improvement through design modifications. Even in these cases, the new through-hole AlN/silicone-filled structure shows significant heat dissipation benefits, and further enhancements could be made by integrating it into module design.

Table II: Estimated temperature difference (ΔT) between conditions without AlN/silicone coating (a) and various through-hole diameters in the substrate in the case of Fig. 7 with increasing cell area (52 x 28 mm²).

	ΔT (°C)
(b) Fill the 2.0 mm diameter through-hole with AlN/silicone	16.7
(c) In the case of 3.0 mm diameter	18.0
(d) In the case of 10 mm diameter	17.4

4 CONCLUSIONS

This study examined the adoption of AlN/silicone and a method for creating through-holes in the entire substrate to fill them with AlN/silicone, aiming to enhance the heat dissipation performance of innovative solar cell modules. AlN/silicone shows higher thermal conductivity than MgO/silicone because it contains AlN particles with superior thermal properties. The through-hole AlN/silicone filling structure showed better heat dissipation compared to simply covering the substrate surface. Furthermore, this method remained effective even when the area was expanded. By ensuring thermal conductivity in the vertical direction, it significantly improved heat dissipation performance, overcoming the decline observed with previous structures that relied only on lateral conduction as the area increased.

5 ACKNOWLEDGEMENT

This research was commissioned by NEDO and funded by the General Incorporated Foundation International Club.

6 REFERENCES

[1] A.W. Czanderna, F. J Pern, Solar Energy Materials and Solar Cells (1996) 101-181.
[2] Oliveira MCC, Cardosa ASA, Viana MM, Lins VTC, Solar Energy Materials and Solar Cells 81 (2018) 2299-2317.
[3] G. Oreski, G.M. Wallner, Solar Energy 79 (2005) 612-617.
[4] S. Shimpo, H. T. C. Tu, K. Ohdaira, Jpn. J. Appl. Phys. 62, SK1039 (2023).
[5] E. Radziemska, E. Klugmann, Energy Conversion and Management 43 (2002) 1889-1900.
[6] E. Radziemska, Renewable Energy 28 (2003) 1-12.
[7] E. Shimokata, Y. Sobajima, K. Ohdaira, A. Masuda, Proc. of EUPVSEC 2024 (2024) 3AV.1.15, 020148-001-004.

ULTRASONIC CHARACTERIZATION OF ETHYLENE-VINYL ACETATE IN GLASS-GLASS-MODULES

Christopher Bruce Konu, Rico Meier
HTW Berlin - University of Applied Sciences, Wilhelminenhofstr. 75a Berlin, 12459, Germany
Christopher.Konu@HTW-Berlin.de

ABSTRACT: The encapsulant properties, particularly in modules with passivated emitter and rear cells (PERC) and silicon heterojunction (SHJ) configurations, are increasingly pivotal for long-term reliability. Optimal processing conditions for the encapsulant are therefore essential; however, manufacturers often prioritize reduced lamination times to increase throughput, which can lead to incomplete cross-linking and unconsumed reaction starters, potentially resulting in degradation modes such as accelerated aging, cell breakage, delamination, corrosion, and local inhomogeneities. Traditional destructive characterization methods, such as differential scanning calorimetry, Soxhlet extraction, or Shear testing, yield limited insights into the local material properties across the module. Since glass-glass (G–G) modules are gaining a large market share, also due to their bifacial capabilities, preparing samples for traditional characterization techniques has become even more cumbersome and costly. This study proposes a novel non-destructive ultrasonic approach to characterize EVA in G-G modules, extending techniques previously developed for the glass-backsheet configuration. By analyzing frequency-dependent time-of-flight measurements through the samples during lamination, we established a quantitative correlation with the lamination progression. A comparison with results from mechanical shear tests showed the potential of the method for non-destructive evaluation of adhesion strength. Furthermore, the method revealed new insights into the lamination process, including the time-of-flight dynamics during the different stages of lamination. This research, therefore, offers a pathway for in-situ lamination process surveillance and optimization to enhance production yields and reliability, ultimately reducing the levelized cost of energy.

Key Words: Ultrasonic Characterization, Lamination Monitoring, Glass-Glass Modules, In-situ Process Control

1 INTRODUCTION

1.1 The Critical Role of the Encapsulant for Photovoltaic Module Reliability

The long-term reliability and performance of photovoltaic (PV) modules are intrinsically linked to the quality of the lamination process. Within this process, the degree of cross-linking in the encapsulants (in this case, Ethylene-Vinyl Acetate (EVA)) is a paramount factor, governing critical module properties such as adhesion strength, resistance to moisture ingress, and resilience against thermomechanical stress.

Suboptimal lamination conditions resulting in incomplete or non-uniform EVA cross-linking initiate a cascade of degradation modes. While often electrically undetectable in initial performance tests, these deficiencies manifest severely in the field, leading to premature power degradation and an increased Levelized Cost of Energy (LCOE) [1]. This issue is crucial as manufacturers are trying to shorten lamination times to boost output, but cannot risk producing modules that will not last for their required 25-year lifespan [2], [3].

1.2 Degradation Modes from Cross-linking Deficiencies

The failure mechanisms stemming from inadequate cross-linking are well-documented:

Delamination: Reduced adhesion at critical interfaces (glass-EVA, EVA-cell) promotes layer separation, facilitating moisture ingress and increasing optical losses. This is a primary failure mode repeatedly observed in field-aged modules [4].

Corrosion: A not fully-crosslinked EVA layer provides an insufficient barrier against humidity, accelerating corrosion of cell metallization and busbars, which are observable as snail trails, discoloration, and increased series resistance [2]. Moisture ingress, often through degraded encapsulant or backsheets, is a key initiator of these secondary processes [5], [6].

Cell Fractures: Inhomogeneous curing can create localized stress concentrations, enhancing the propagation of microcracks into cell breakage, especially under thermomechanical load [7].

Potential-Induced Degradation (PID): PID occurs when voltage stress drives leakage currents through the encapsulant. Lower cross-linking density reduces EVA volume resistivity, increasing PID susceptibility and causing power loss and potential hot spots [8].

1.3 The Industrial Challenge: Limitations of Current Quality Control

The PV industry predominantly relies on destructive, offline techniques for quality assurance of the lamination process. The standardized Soxhlet extraction method, while considered a reference for determining gel content, is laborious and time-consuming, not suited for a production environment where quick quality management decisions are necessary [9]. Similarly, Differential Scanning Calorimetry (DSC) provides precise measurements of the cross-linking progress (the DSC degree of cross-linking), but is inherently unsuitable for in-line module inspection due to its destructive nature [10]. Shear tests, while indicative of adhesion strength, are also destructive and localized. Consequently, a critical technological gap exists for a non-destructive evaluation (NDE) method capable of quantifying EVA quality in situ and in real-time to enable closed-loop process control.

1.4 Potential of Ultrasonic Methods

Ultrasound has emerged as a promising NDE technique for polymers, leveraging the fact that during the cross-linking process, the material's viscoelastic properties are altered, which in turn affect acoustic wave propagation parameters such as velocity and attenuation [11].

Ultrasonic wave propagation depends on the mechanical properties of the material. A change in storage modulus during cross-linking can be observed as a change in longitudinal sound velocity [12]. The longitudinal sound velocity c_L can (when boundary effects can be neglected, such as in an infinite medium) be described by the equation

$$c_L = \sqrt{\frac{C_{ij}}{\rho}}, \quad (1)$$

where C_{ij} represents the elastic tensor of the sound-transmitting material. In isotropic materials, it corresponds to the elastic modulus (Young's modulus) Y and ρ is the density of that material.
Previous studies have demonstrated correlations between ultrasonic parameters and the cross-linking state of EVA [9]. This work continues the ultrasonic approach and transfers the previously developed methodology to glass-glass modules.

2 EXPERIMENTAL APPROACH

2.1 High-Temperature Ultrasound Transducer Design

Standard ultrasonic transducers are unsuitable for the elevated temperatures encountered in the PV lamination process, which mostly exceeds 140°C. Furthermore, their typical dimensions limit their integration potential in standard laminators. To overcome these limitations, custom transducers were designed and fabricated in-house. A high-temperature piezoceramic disc element served as the active component. Electrical contact was established by bonding insulated, high-temperature coaxial cables to the disc's electrodes using a thermally stable conductive epoxy. This assembly was then encased and sealed within a custom-machined aluminum housing. The aluminum housing acts as mechanical support and can also be heated by electric heating pads glued to its backside.

2.2 Sample Preparation

To imitate the structure of a commercial photovoltaic module, a simplified glass-encapsulant-glass configuration was utilized. Square float glass plates measuring 40 mm x 40 mm x 2 mm were thoroughly cleaned and dried before lamination. Sheets of EVA encapsulant foil from Vista Solar were cut to dimensions matching the glass.
The laminate stack (glass-EVA-EVA-glass) was assembled in a clean, dry environment and represents the core layered structure of a glass-glass PV module around the solar cells.

2.3 In-Situ Ultrasonic Monitoring of the Lamination Process

The setup was designed to perform non-destructive, in-situ ultrasonic transmission measurements throughout the entire lamination cycle. The prepared glass-EVA-glass sample was placed between two custom-made ultrasonic transducers and coupled to them via high-temperature ultrasonic gel. This complete assembly, as shown in Figure 1, was then housed within a temperature-controlled vacuum chamber. Before initiating the thermal cycle, the chamber was evacuated to a vacuum pressure of 0.003 mbar absolute (stated limit of the pump) to eliminate air gaps and prevent the formation of bubbles.

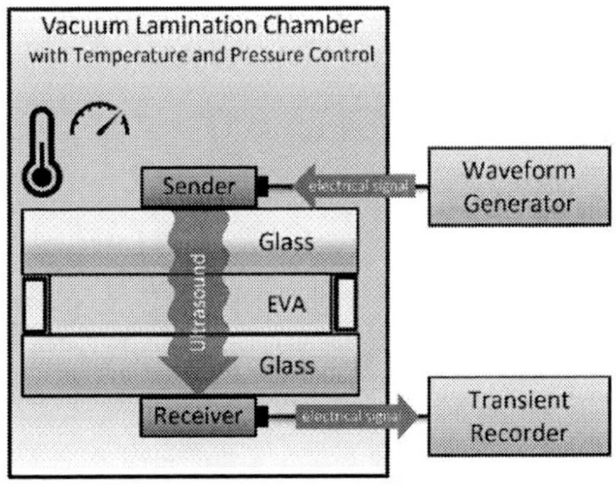

Figure 1. Ultrasound transmission setup for real-time monitoring of the lamination process.

A representative lamination cycle was then executed: The sample was heated from room temperature to a temperature of 140°C. This temperature was maintained for an hour, a duration expected to be sufficient for completing the cross-linking reaction, and then cooled to 60°C. Throughout the entire thermal cycle, encompassing the ramp-up, dwell, and cool-down phases, a high-frequency ultrasonic chirp was continuously transmitted through the sample as indicated in Figure 1. The receiving transducer captured the transmitted ultrasonic signal and converted it to an electric signal, which was recorded by a transient recorder at regular two-second intervals.

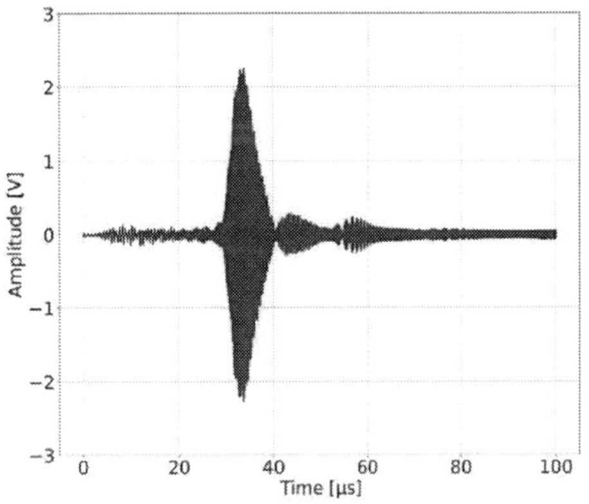

Figure 2. Typical ultrasonic waveform (time-signal) recorded during lamination.

A second lamination cycle was applied afterwards on the same sample to distinguish the effects of permanent changes, e.g., cross-linking or rearrangement of the polymer fibers (which should only occur once), and heating.
Additionally, a thermal cycling experiment was conducted on a separate, identically prepared sample, by repeatedly running cooling-heating cycles between 140 °C and 80°C. Ultrasonic time-of-flight (ToF) was again continuously measured throughout these cycles.

2.4 Frequency Selection of the Ultrasonic Excitation Signal

The excitation signal was optimized by selecting an appropriate thickness for the piezoelectric disk and exciting it with an electric chirp. Higher frequencies demonstrated an increased sensitivity to variations in the thin EVA layer; however, they also exhibited greater absorption, which consequently limited the signal-to-noise ratio. To achieve a balance between sensitivity and detectability, we employed a $100\,\mu s$ linear chirp that spanned from 1 to 20 MHz for excitation. Spectral analysis (Fast Fourier Transform (FFT)) revealed a prominent spectral peak at 6.5 MHz (see Fig. 2 and Fig. 3), upon which our evaluation was focused.

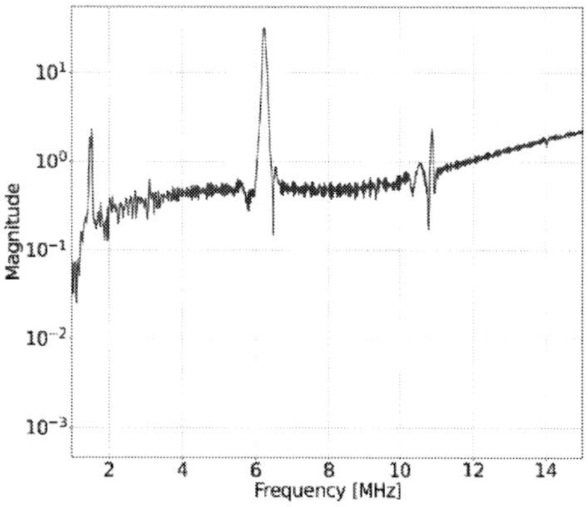

Figure 3. Amplitude spectrum of the recorded time signal (Fig. 2).

2.5 Determination of Changes in Time-of-Flight

A precise determination of the changes in Time-of-Flight (ToF) was crucial for tracking small changes in sound velocity during lamination. The signal processing methodology, outlined in Figure 4, consists of the following steps:

First, the recorded waveform $V(t, t_{rec})$, called the time signal, was captured by a transient recorder. The recorded time signal has a length of 100 µs, and was recorded every 2 s. The corresponding time of the recording is denoted as t_{rec} in Figure 4.
The waveform before lamination was used as a reference signal $R(t)$ at a well-known temperature. The time shift $dToF$ will later be calculated with respect to that reference signal (Figure 4, top-left).

To enhance the signal-to-noise ratio and select a specific acoustic mode, both the raw signal $V(t, t_{rec})$ (Fig. 4a) and the reference signal $R(t)$ (Fig. 4b) were filtered using identical bandpass filters (here from 5.6 MHz to 6.6 MHz), resulting in the filtered signals $V'(t, t\,rec)$ (Fig. 4c) and $R'(t)$ (Fig. 4d). The core of the $dToF$ calculation relied on a cross-correlation analysis. The cross-correlation function $M_{VR}(dt, t_{rec})$ was computed for each recorded time signal by shifting the filtered reference signal $R'(t + dt)$ by a constant dt and multiplying it by the filtered signal $V'(t, t_{rec})$.

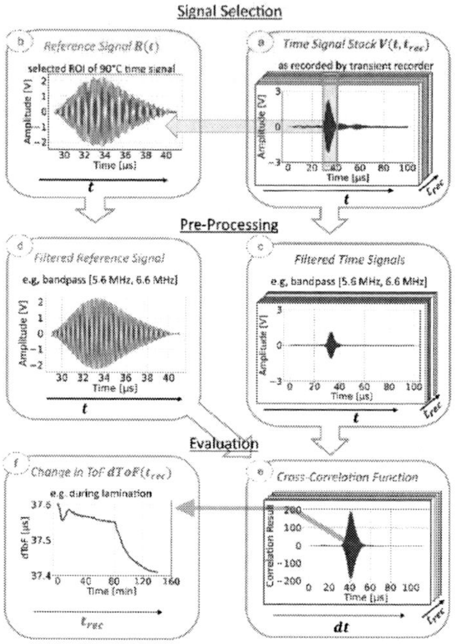

Figure 4. Overview of the $dToF$ determination method.

This product is then summed up over each datapoint of the complete signal by

$$M_{VR}(dt,\, t_{rec}) := \sum V^{*}(t,\, t_{rec}) R^{*}(t + dt) \qquad (2)$$

This procedure is repeated for all dt in an interval from 0 to 100 µs. The plot of all those sums (correlation result) vs. dt is represented in Fig. 4e. The time shift dt that maximizes the cross-correlation result corresponds to the Change in Time-of-Flight $dToF(t_{rec})$, for that specific recording time t_{rec} relative to the reference signal. Figure 4f shows all the evaluated dToFs during the lamination process.

2.5 Shear Testing for Evaluation of the Adhesion Strength

To compare the acoustic properties to adhesion parameters, shear tests were performed using a specially designed shear wedge, illustrated in Figure 5.
Multiple glass/EVA/glass laminates were prepared under different lamination conditions: at 80°C, 100°C, 120°C, and 140°C (with peak-temperature holding times of 1, 5, 20, 40, and 60 minutes).
The laminates were arranged within the shear wedges, with one glass sheet securely clamped in the lower wedge and the other in the upper wedge. A universal testing machine applied a compressive force on the assembly, pressing the upper wedge downward. Due to the geometry of the wedges, the lower wedge was displaced horizontally, thereby subjecting the EVA layer between the two glass sheets to shear loading. A load cell measured the applied force, and force-displacement curves were recorded for each sample. To ensure statistical relevance, three samples were tested for each lamination condition.

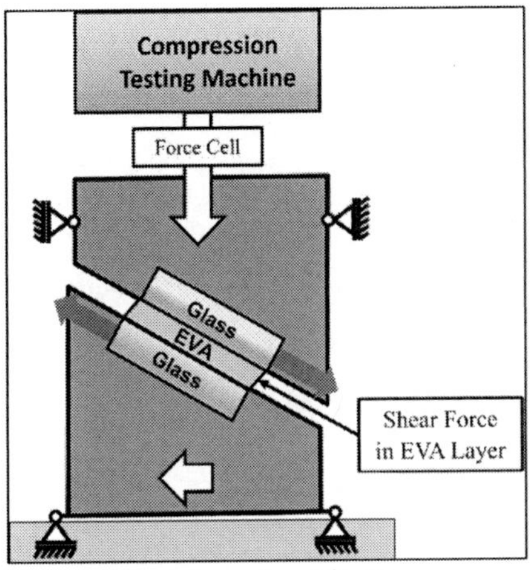

Figure 5. Shear test experimental setup

The shear strength of the EVA interface was then calculated from the maximum recorded force using the standard relation:

$$\tau_{shear} = \frac{F_{Max}}{A}, \quad (3)$$

where τ_{shear} denotes the shear strength, F_{Max} the maximum force when failure occurred, and A the area of the sheared EVA layer. The shear strength was then compared to the acoustic measurements.

3 RESULTS AND DISCUSSION

3.1 In-Situ Ultrasonic Characterization of EVA Lamination and Our Interpretation

With our custom setup, we were able to monitor the lamination process of the previously mentioned Glass-EVA-Glass samples with ultrasound in real-time. The ToF of the 6.5 MHz acoustic longitudinal wave mode was utilized as the primary metric to track the structural and chemical transformations within the polymer. The recorded ToF data over the entire process, spanning two full thermal cycles, is presented in Figure 6. The process can be distinctly segmented into five key phases, each correlating to a specific physical or chemical phenomenon.

Phase I: Initial Compression and Air Expulsion (0 min - 6 min)
The process begins with an immediate and sharp decrease in ToF. This initial drop corresponds directly to the application of pressure and the onset of heating.
Mechanically, the applied vacuum pressure leads to an outgas of entrapped air from the interstitial spaces between the EVA and the adjacent glasses. The rising temperature softens the EVA, allowing it to conform and compress under the applied load. This compaction reduces the effective acoustic path length and increases the material density, both of which contribute to a decrease in Time-of-Flight.

Phase II: Melting and Structural Transformation (6 min - 16 min)
As the temperature approaches and surpasses the melting point of the EVA (around 70 to 80°C) [13], a pronounced reversal in the ToF trend is observed, characterized by a significant increase. This critical phase is governed by two primary mechanisms:
1. Polymer Melting and Softening: The crystalline regions within the EVA melt, and the polymer transitions into a low-viscosity molten state. Hence, the modulus of elasticity drops drastically, as well as the speed of sound (see eqn. 1), which can be seen as an increase in ToF.
2. Moisture Evaporation: The heat out-gases residual moisture and solvents within the polymer. The presence of these small, scattered gas pockets significantly scatters and attenuates the ultrasonic signal and further delays the observed peak in ToF [14].

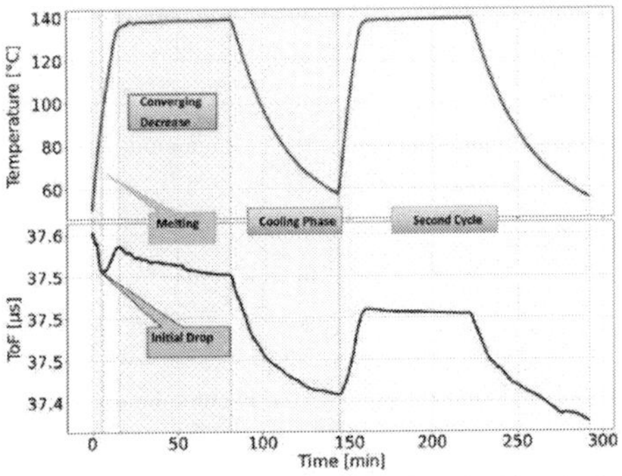

Figure 6. Evaluated Time-of-Flight (ToF) of the ultrasonic waves travelling through the sample during the lamination process. The data reveals five distinct phases: (I) Initial Drop, (II) Melting, (III) Cross-Linking and Stabilization, (IV) Cooling Phase, and (V) Second Cycle.

Phase III: Realignment, Cross-Linking and Network Formation (16 min – 121 min)
Following the melting phase, the ToF begins a steady, converging decrease throughout the remainder of the high-temperature plateau. This trend signifies a gradual and sustained increase in sound velocity. This phenomenon is directly attributed to structural changes such as the realignment of the polymer fibers and/or the peroxide-initiated cross-linking reaction. As covalent bonds form between adjacent polymer chains, a three-dimensional network structure is created. This network drastically increases the rigidity and structural integrity of the polymer melt [9]. The growing cross-link density progressively raises the elastic modulus, which in turn increases the sound velocity, resulting in a stable, reduced ToF. The convergence of the signal indicates the fiber realignment and reaction approaching completion.

Phase IV: Cooling Phase (121 min - 222 min)
Upon initiation of the cooling cycle by floating the chamber with room-temperature air, a further sharp decrease in ToF was recorded. As the temperature drops below the EVA melting regime (about 80 °C), molecular mobility of the polymer chains is reduced as crystallites reform. The material transitions from a rubbery melt to a semi-crystalline solid, leading to stiffening of the encapsulant, accompanied by a significant increase in its elastic modulus [15]. This thermo-physical stiffening during cooling leads to a continuous increase in sound velocity, observed as a decrease in ToF, consistent with previous ultrasound measurements of EVA cure and cooling behavior [9].

Phase V: Second Cycle and Structural Stability (222 min - 42 min)
A second thermal cycle was applied afterwards to the laminated sample. The ToF profile in this cycle is significantly different. It is a rather flat function at peak temperature without the pronounced, decreasing slope indicating the realignment/cross-linking progression, showing only reversible changes in ToF that mirror the temperature-induced changes in the elastic properties. A slight offset before and after the cycle is attributed to a slight displacement of the transducer when floating the setup with air.
The absence of the initial drop and realignment/cross-linking slope provides critical insight. The lamination process is almost complete after the first cycle. The reorientation of the fibers, the chemical (cross-linking) and physical (air expulsion) transformations are irreversible and permanent. The polymer network formed is stable and does not further cross-link or degrade upon re-heating. The small, almost reversible change confirms that the ultrasonic response is now fully dominated by the temperature dependence of the elastic constant of the solidified, cross-linked polymer.

3.2 Ultrasonic Monitoring of Thermal Cycling

For further confirmation of our interpretation, thermal cycling tests were carried out on unlaminated samples in order to stepwise laminate the samples during the process. The simultaneous ultrasonic and temperature measurements recorded over 250 minutes are presented in Figure 7. The sample was repeatedly cycled between 80 °C and 140 °C. The change in time-of-flight closely tracks each temperature cycle, increasing during heating and decreasing during cooling due to the thermoelastic softening and stiffening of the polymer.

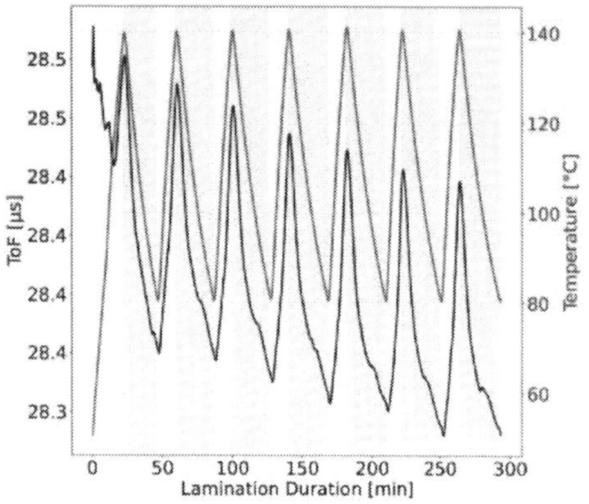

Figure 7. Time-of-Flight (ToF) evolution during successive EVA lamination cycles at temperatures between 80°C and 140°C, with the cooling phases marked blue.

As seen in our previous measurement (Figure 6), the ToF exhibits an indication of the different phases of the lamination process: A sharp initial drop in ToF during the first minutes of the first cycle aligns with the previously observed effects of compression, air expulsion, and early heating, reflecting densification of the EVA layer (Phase I). In the following temperature cycles between 80°C and 140°C, despite the temperature-induced softening and hardening of the polymer during temperature change, an overall reduction in ToF can be observed. The decrease progressively continues with each cycle until it converges. This trend indicates ongoing material evolution, primarily attributed to realignment and cross-linking of the EVA fibers. Each cycle drives further network formation, increasing rigidity and sound velocity, consistent with the converging ToF reduction observed in the earlier monitoring experiment in Figure 6 (Phase III). The lamination experiment confirms that even under repeated thermal cycling, irreversible changes in the acoustic properties of the polymer continue to accumulate, providing a quantitative measure of progressive realignment/cross-linking and densification across cycles.

Furthermore, we evaluated the slope of the change in ToF with respect to temperature in each cooling phase (Figure 7). This quotient $dTof/T$ is a material-dependent parameter dependent on the structure and composition of the sample. In Figure 8, we can identify a similar behavior as we have previously seen for the ToF in Phase III (of Figures 6) and Figure 7, with a general downward trend and a convergence at the later cycles. Even though it is a different parameter, the observation can be attributed to the same origin. The continuing reduction is a result of the ongoing reorientation and cross-linking of the EVA fibers in each temperature cycle. The convergence in the later cycles indicates that the material changes are almost completed at this point, and the curing process is cumulative and irreversible.

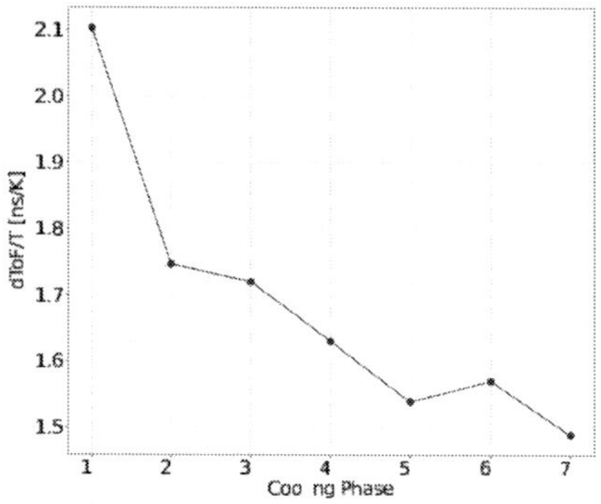

Figure 8. During the cooling phases (blue areas in Fig. 7) the ToF is proportional to temperature. The proportionality constant of each cycle is plotted here for each cooling phase.

3.3 Adhesion Testing

For comparison, mechanical shear tests were performed on laminates prepared with lamination durations capturing the critical phases of the process, as defined by the ToF and temperature profiles in Figure 6.
Samples from the early stages of the process (Phase I, Phase II) exhibited consistently low shear strength. Conversely, as the ToF decreases in Phase III, which we attributed to advancing fiber reorientation, cross-linking, and polymer network formation, achieved significantly higher shear strength, which increases as the cross-linking progresses. After the test, all samples showed a delamination of the EVA from the glass, and never a rupture within the EVA layer. This clearly shows that the dominant failure mode was driven by adhesion failure.

10.4229/EUPVSEC2025/3AV.1.16

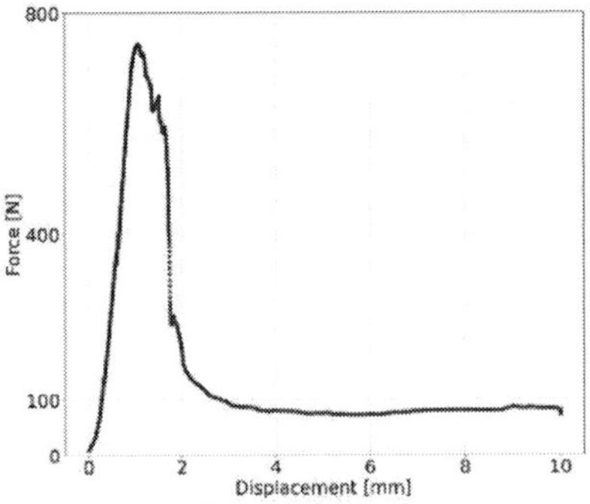

Figure 9. The measured force in dependence on the vertical displacement of the upper wedge recorded by a universal testing machine while performing the shear test (on an 80-minute laminated sample).

There is some statistical scatter in the shear strength data in Figure 10, which can be attributed to small variations during sample preparation and interfacial defects.
The samples were small (1 cm x 1 cm) and manually prepared. Small shifts of the glass during lamination could not be completely avoided and affected the shear strength. Larger samples would decrease the influence of those small variations but would also require higher shear forces, which would increase the probability of glass failure. So instead, to address that scatter, we decided on a more statistical analysis. The overarching trend is unambiguous: the development of mechanical adhesion strength closely follows the irreversible downward drift of the ToF baseline and thus the cross-linking progression. This indicates that the in-situ and non-destructively evaluated ultrasonic time-of-flight could be used as a promising and reliable indicator for the evolution of the adhesion state.

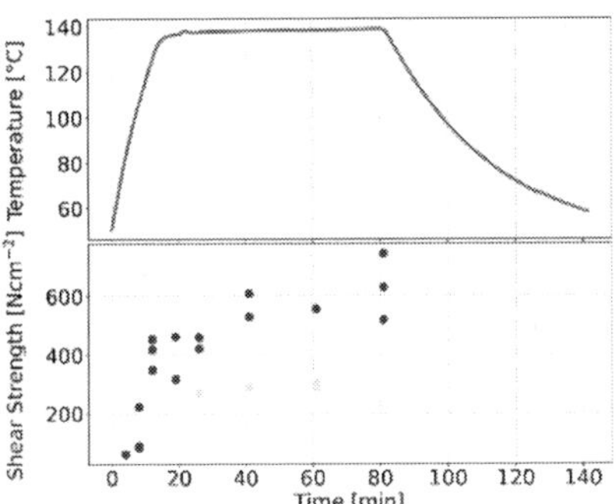

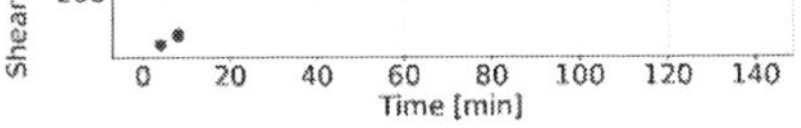

Figure 10. Shear tests show an increase in shear strength with lamination duration.

4 CONCLUSIONS

This study demonstrates that high-frequency longitudinal ultrasound can be utilized as a powerful tool for in-situ monitoring of the lamination process of glass-glass photovoltaic modules. The time-of-flight (ToF) of ultrasonic signals provides a real-time, non-destructive metric, sensitive to structural and chemical changes in the EVA encapsulant, successfully capturing five distinct lamination process phases: initial compression and air expulsion, melting and moisture evaporation, fiber realignment/cross-linking and network formation, cooling and solidification.
The irreversible decrease in ToF during the high temperature phase of the lamination process was identified as a key indicator of polymer network formation, showing strong correlation with adhesion as validated through shear tests, which confirmed increasing adhesion strength with extended lamination time. Thermal cycling experiments on unlaminated samples revealed that the ultrasonic response comprises reversible thermoelastic variations during heating and cooling, superimposed on a progressive, irreversible decrease in ToF caused by permanent material changes, including cross-linking and densification of the EVA layer.
The consistent correlation between ultrasonic and mechanical adhesion measurements shows the robustness and reliability of this technique and the potential for non-destructive, real-time quantification of the lamination progression. This paper provides a strong foundation for the successful industrial implementation of an in-line ultrasonic monitoring tool, ensuring reliable quality control of the lamination process in PV manufacturing.

5. ACKNOWLEDGEMENTS

This work was generously supported by Franz-W. Aumund-Stiftung. We also thank Michael Wendt and his colleagues from Fraunhofer CSP for fruitful discussions and for providing EVA material. Finally, we thank Finn Ole Peterson and Leon Necat from HTW Berlin for sample preparation and setup optimization.

6. REFERENCES

[1] D. C. Jordan, S. R. Kurtz, K. VanSant, and J. Newmiller, "Compendium of photovoltaic degradation rates," *Progress in Photovoltaics: Research and Applications*, vol. 24, no. 7, pp. 978–989, Jul. 2016, doi: 10.1002/pip.2744.
[2] D. Wu *et al.*, "Influence of Lamination Conditions of EVA Encapsulation on Photovoltaic Module Durability," *Materials*, vol. 16, no. 21, Nov. 2023, doi: 10.3390/ma16216945.
[3] M. C. C. de Oliveira, A. S. A. Diniz Cardoso, M. M. Viana, and V. de F. C. Lins, "The causes and effects of degradation of encapsulant ethylene vinyl acetate copolymer (EVA) in crystalline silicon photovoltaic modules: A review," Jan. 01, 2018, *Elsevier Ltd.* doi: 10.1016/j.rser.2017.06.039.
[4] A. Kaan Öz, C. Herzog, C. Wellens, D. E. Mansour, M. Heinrich, and A. Kraft, "The Impact of the Lamination Process on the Adhesion Properties at the Glass-Encapsulant Interface and Damp Heat Stability of PV Modules," *38th European PV Solar Energy Conference and Exhibition, 6-10 September 2021*.
[5] O. K. Segbefia, A. G. Imenes, and T. O. Sætre, "Moisture ingress in photovoltaic modules: A review," Aug. 01, 2021, *Elsevier Ltd.* doi: 10.1016/j.solener.2021.06.055.
[6] M. Baiamonte, C. Colletti, A. Ragonesi, C. Gerardi, and N. T. Dintcheva, "Durability and Performance of Encapsulant Films for Bifacial Heterojunction Photovoltaic Modules," *Polymers (Basel)*, vol. 14, no. 5, Mar. 2022, doi: 10.3390/polym14051052.

[7] M. Sander, S. Dietrich, M. Pander, M. Ebert, and J. Bagdahn, "Systematic investigation of cracks in encapsulated solar cells after mechanical loading," 2013. doi: 10.1016/j.solmat.2012.12.031.

[8] M. Aghaei *et al.*, "Review of degradation and failure phenomena in photovoltaic modules," May 01, 2022, *Elsevier Ltd.* doi: 10.1016/j.rser.2022.112160.

[9] W. Stark and M. Jaunich, "Investigation of Ethylene/Vinyl Acetate Copolymer (EVA) by thermal analysis DSC and DMA," *Polym Test*, vol. 30, no. 2, pp. 236–242, Apr. 2011, doi: 10.1016/j.polymertesting.2010.12.003.

[10] C. Hirschl *et al.*, "Determining the degree of crosslinking of ethylene vinyl acetate photovoltaic module encapsulants - A comparative study," *Solar Energy Materials and Solar Cells*, vol. 116, pp. 203–218, 2013, doi: 10.1016/j.solmat.2013.04.022.

[11] R. Meier, I. M. Slauch, and M. I. Bertoni, "Ultrasonic Characterization of Ethylene Vinyl Acetate (EVA) Crosslinking for Quality Assurance and Lamination Process Control," *Proc. of the 50th IEEE Photovoltaic Specialists Conference (PVSC)*, pp. 1–5, 2023.

[12] M. Jaunich and W. Stark, "Monitoring the vulcanization of rubber with ultrasound: Influence of material thickness and temperature," *Polym Test*, vol. 28, no. 8, pp. 901–906, Dec. 2009, doi: 10.1016/j.polymertesting.2009.08.006.

[13] R. Kuwahara *et al.*, "Crystallization and hardening of poly(ethylene-co-vinyl acetate) mouthguards during routine use," *Sci Rep*, vol. 7, Mar. 2017, doi: 10.1038/srep44672.

[14] K. Ono, "A comprehensive report on ultrasonic attenuation of engineering materials, including metals, ceramics, polymers, fiber-reinforced composites, wood, and rocks," Apr. 01, 2020, *MDPI AG.* doi: 10.3390/app10072230.

[15] J. Dutta and K. Naskar, "Investigation of morphology, mechanical, dynamic mechanical and thermal behaviour of blends based on ethylene vinyl acetate (EVA) and thermoplastic polyurethane (TPU)," *RSC Adv*, vol. 4, no. 105, pp. 60831–60841, 2014, doi: 10.1039/c4ra07823c.

42nd European Photovoltaic Solar Energy Conference and Exhibition

Contact

Hochschule für Technik und Wirtschaft Berlin

University of Applied Sciences

Ultrasonic Characterization of Ethylene-Vinyl Acetate in Glass-Glass-Modules

Christopher Bruce Konu[1], Rico Meier[1]

[1] University of Applied Sciences – HTW Berlin, Wilhelminenhofstr. 75a, D-12459 Berlin, Germany

60°C 70°C 80°C 90°C 100°C 110°C 120°C 130°C 140°C

MOTIVATION

Optimal processing of the EVA encapsulant during lamination is crucial to ensuring long-term photovoltaic (PV) module reliability and performance, preventing failures such as:

- Delamination compromising structural integrity.
- Humidity ingress leading to metallization corrosion.
- Local inhomogeneities causing property variations and failures [1].

Challenges

Traditional methods for evaluating EVA quality (Differential Scanning Calorimetry, Dynamic Mechanical Analysis, Peel Tests) are:

- Destructive, time-consuming, and costly.
- Limited to small selected samples and unable to monitor the lamination process of all modules in real time.

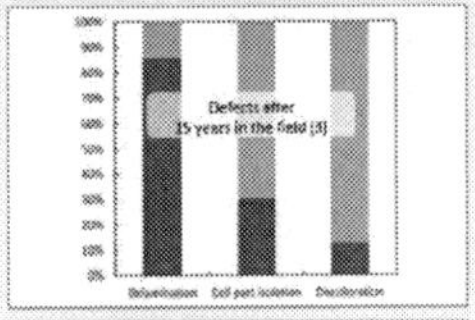

Goals

This study aims to:

- Develop a real-time ultrasonic method for EVA quality monitoring in glass-glass modules during lamination.
- Understand how polymer networks and additives influence ultrasound propagation during lamination.
- Adapt the method for various module designs and encapsulants.

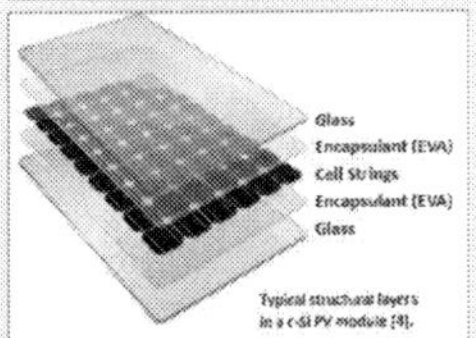

Typical structural layers in a c-Si PV module [4].

THEORETICAL BACKGROUND

Speed of Sound in Solid Materials

The longitudinal speed of sound c_L depends on elastic modulus C_{ii} and density ρ.

$$c_L = \sqrt{\frac{C_{ii}}{\rho}}$$

The Impact of Crosslinking on Sound Velocity

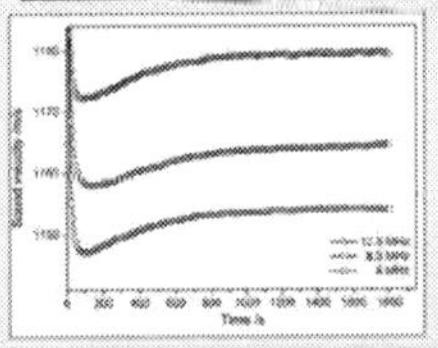

- Sound velocity decreases as a result of initial melting or initial internal moisture evaporating during heating.
- Sound velocity increases with lamination time due to increasing stiffness from polymer network formation, then converges once the network is fully formed.
- Higher frequencies result in higher sound velocities without affecting the overall shape of the graph [5].

RESEARCH METHODOLOGY

Ultrasonic Characterization

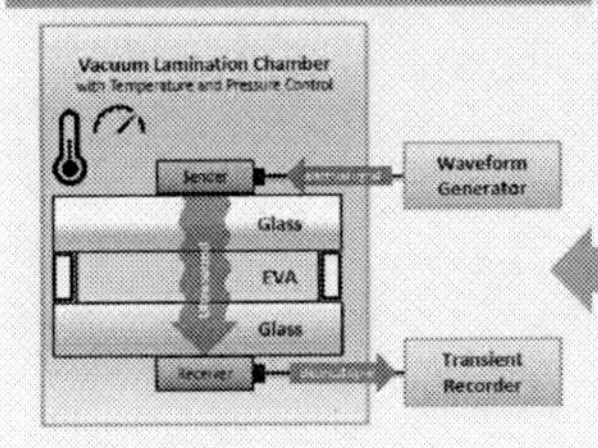

Ultrasound waves are transmitted through the sample, received by a transducer on the opposite side, then amplified and recorded.

Adhesion Testing

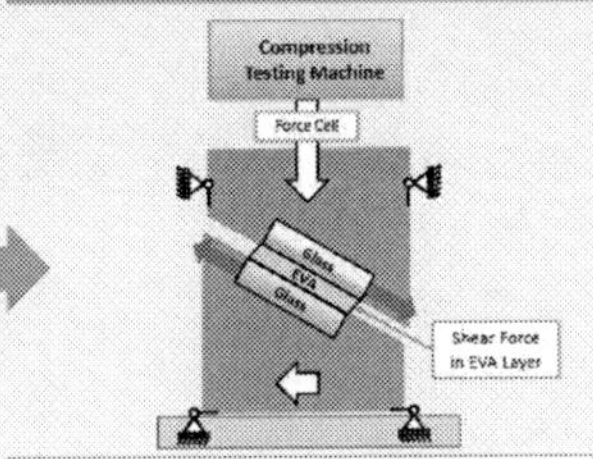

Laminated samples are shear tested in a 45° fixture. The force required for adhesion failure is recorded for each sample.

Change in Time-of-Flight Determination

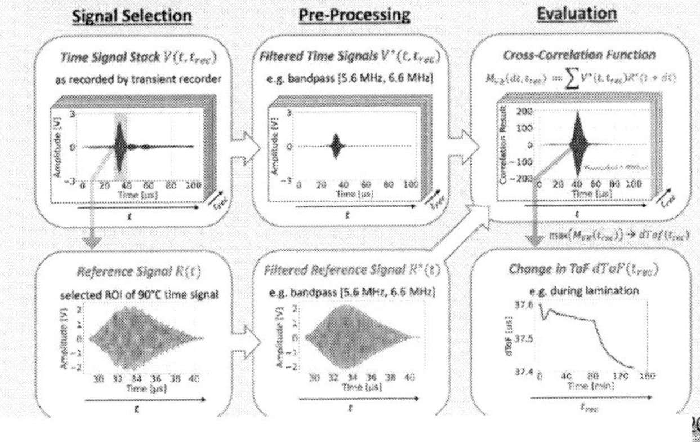

RESULTS

Samples were laminated at 140°C and 0.3 Pa absolute pressure for one hour and then cooled by room temperature air at atmospheric pressure. This cycle was repeated. Ultrasound transmission data was recorded in real-time. Samples at different stages of lamination were removed and shear tested.

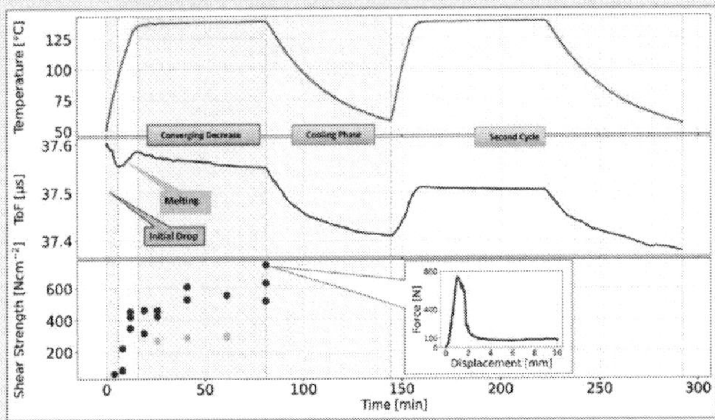

Ultrasound-Characterization:

- **Initial drop in ToF (0...6 min):** corresponds to thickness reduction as air is expelled and sample compresses under pressure and heat while softening.
- **Melting onset (6...16 min):** ToF increases as a result of EVA softening, melting and moisture evaporation during heating. Sound velocity drops due to the lower moduli of elasticity at higher temperatures.
- **Converging Decrease (16...121 min):** ToF decreases and stabilizes, indicating increased sound velocity from crosslinking due to the growth of a stiffened polymer network.
- **Cooling Phase (121...222 min):** Decrease in ToF due to the increase in elastic moduli at lower temperatures
- **Second cycle (222...429 min):** Shows only minor irreversible changes, indicating that structural changes in first cycle were almost completed.

Adhesion Testing:

- High differences in delamination shear strength between the samples due to sample variations, local properties and occasional glass breakage → statistical analysis required
- Overall, the critical shear stress for delamination (shear strength) increased with lamination time.

CONCLUSSION AND OUTLOOK

The evaluation of high-frequency longitudinal ultrasound transmitted through the thickness of solar glass-glass modules allowed for the identification of irreversible changes in the encapsulant's properties during lamination. This is a promising step towards the industrial realization of an ultrasonic technique for in-line polymer characterization during PV module manufacturing. Shear tests, while statistically scattered, confirmed the expected increase in shear strength with longer lamination durations.

Next Steps

Comparing Ultrasonic Results to In-depth Polymer Analysis:

- **Dynamic Mechanical Analysis (DMA):** Mechanical characterization of the temperature-dependent elastic-viscoplastic material properties
- **Differential Scanning Calorimetry (DSC):** Precise identification of melting points, crosslinking temperatures and progress.
- **Soxhlet Extraction (SE):** Determination of gel content and crosslinking progress

Polymer Variation

- Characterization of the influence of different additives (adhesion promoters, crosslinking agents). Decoupling of adhesion and crosslinking behavior and their ultrasonic fingerprint.
- Transfer of the method to new polymers e.g. Polyolefin Elastomers (POE) or polymer coatings

Polymer Ageing

- Characterization of the ultrasonic properties during polymer ageing under different environmental stressors (UV, heat, humidity)

ACKNOWLEDGEMENTS

This work was generously supported by *Franz-W. Aumund-Stiftung*. We also thank Michael Wendt and his colleagues from Fraunhofer CSP for fruitful discussions and for providing EVA material. Finally, we thank Finn Ole Peterson and Leon Necat from HTW Berlin for sample preparation and setup optimization.

REFERENCES

1. Meier, R., Slauch, I. M., Bertoni, M. I. (2023). *Ultrasonic Characterization of Ethylene Vinyl Acetate (EVA) Crosslinking for Quality Assurance and Lamination Process Control.* Proc. of the 50th IEEE Photovoltaic Specialists Conference (PVSC), 1-5.
2. Wohlgemuth, J., Silverman, T., Miller, D. C., McNutt, P., Kempe, M., Deceglie, M.,(2015). *Evaluation of PV module field performance.* IEEE 42nd Photovoltaic Specialist Conference. PVSC 2015. Institute of Electrical and Electronics Engineers Inc., Dec. 2015.
3. Polverini, D., Alfieri, F., Spiliotopoulos, C., and Arcipowska, A. (2024). *Towards a recyclability index for photovoltaic modules: Methodology, challenges and policy implications.* Progress in Photovoltaics: Research and Applications, 10.1002/pip.3781.
4. Dodd, N., Espinosa Martinez, M.D.L.N., Van Tichelen, P., Peeters, K. and Soares, A. (2020). *Preparatory study for solar photovoltaic modules, inverters and systems,* EUR 30468 EN, Publications Office of the European Union, Luxembourg, 2020, JRC122431.
5. Stark, W., Jaunich, M., Bohmeyer, W., Lange, K. (2012). *Investigation of the crosslinking behavior of ethylene vinyl acetate (EVA) for solar cell encapsulation by rheology and ultrasound.* Polymer Testing, 31(7), 904-908.

20133-001

42nd European Photovoltaic Solar Energy Conference and Exhibition

COMPARISON OF DIFFERENT ECAs APPLIED TO PK/SI TANDEM SOLAR CELLS IN A MINI-MODULE CONFIGURATION

F. Mouhoubi [1], V. Barth[1], S. Berson[1]
[1] Univ. Grenoble Alpes, CEA Liten, Campus INES, Le Bourget du Lac, France.
Contact: felicia.mouhoubi@cea.fr

Context and motivations

- High efficiency: perovskite-silicon tandem cells outperform conventional cells
- Key limitation: degradation under humidity, oxygen and temperature exposure
- Current progress in the field:

→ **Qcells**: Record 28 ± 1.5% (M10 commercial module, 330 cm^2).
→ **Fraunhofer & Oxford PV**: Certified module, 25% efficiency.
→ **Trina Solar**: Large-area module (3.1 m^2), 808 W output, TÜV SÜD certified [a,b,c]

Objectives

- **Apply ECAs** as an interconnection solution
- **Assess compatibility** with PK–Si tandem solar cells
- **Evaluate electrical & mechanical properties**
- **Assess stability** during dark aging and thermal cycling

Goal → Enable stable and reliable interconnection of perovskite-silicon tandem solar cell by mitigating degradation during this step and beyond

Materials & Methods

•**Mini-modules:** Perovskite–silicon tandem solar cells (two architectures) + Silicon solar cells with tandem FS materials
•**Active area:** 8.5 cm^2
•**Metallization:** Silver screen-printed, cured at ultra-low-temperature

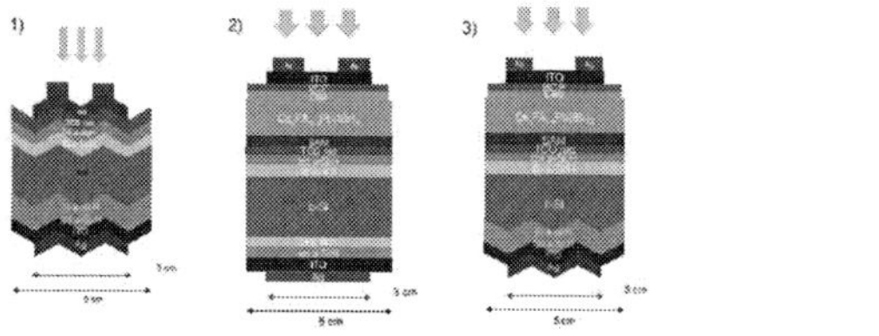

Fig 1. *cell schematics used for interconnection and encapsulation*

•**Encapsulation:** TPO with edge sealant
•**Architecture:** Glass–glass

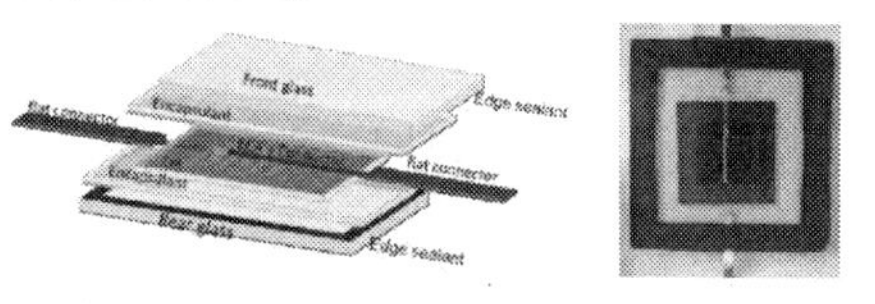

Fig 2. *Schematic view and an image of a tandem mini-module*

•**Approach:** Test ultra-low-temperature ECAs (<150 °C) for interconnection

ECA	Matrix	% Ag
A1 ref	Acrylate	~55
A2	Acrylate	~90
A3	Acrylate	~46
E1	Epoxy	~48
[illegible]	[illegible]	[illegible]

A1 reference: single junction & tandem

•**Evaluation:**
- Compare behavior of cells interconnected with different ECAs
- Evaluate **electrical** properties and **stability**
  - ➢ **Environmental stability testing:**
    - •Dark storage over several days
    - •Thermal cycling (TC)

Results

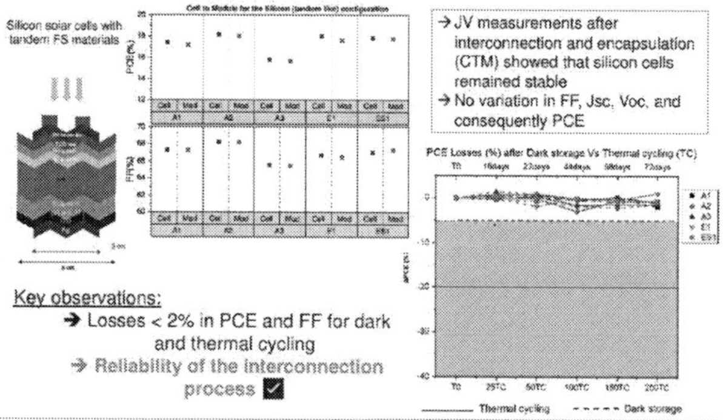

→ JV measurements after interconnection and encapsulation (CTM) showed that silicon cells remained stable
→ No variation in FF, Jsc, Voc, and consequently PCE

Key observations:
→ Losses < 2% in PCE and FF for dark and thermal cycling
→ Reliability of the interconnection process ☑

ECA	FF (%)	Jsc (%)	PCE (%)	Voc (%)
A1-ref	-10,76	10,96	0,52	1,54
A2	-4,84	8,99	4,53	0,87
A3	-14,95	9,45	-5,80	1,17
E1	-3,82	10,02	7,17	1,23
ES1	-0,47	6,24	5,90	0,06

CTM mainly reduces FF, while increasing Jsc and keeping Voc nearly unchanged

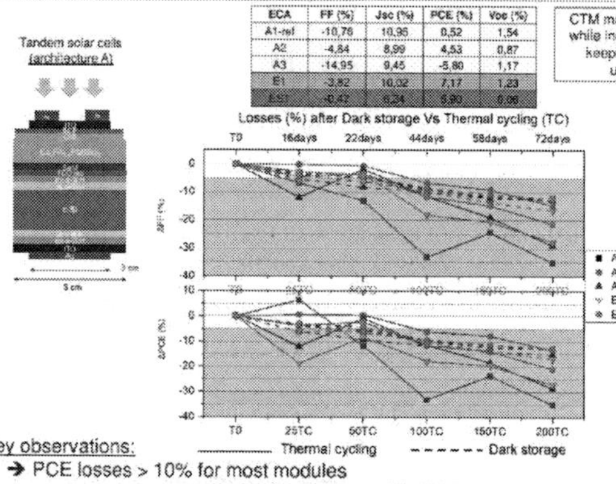

Key observations:
→ PCE losses > 10% for most modules
- « *A1 ref* » loses 35% of PCE & FF after 200 TC cycles
- « A2 » loses less than 15% of PCE and FF after 200 TC cycles and dark storage

→ **Degradation of the top cell** under both dark storage and thermal aging
→ Interconnection affects the cell, reducing its performance

ECA	FF (%)	Jsc (%)	PCE (%)	Voc (%)
A1-ref	-6,94	7,59	-0,93	-1,28
A2	-16,75	7,18	-13,69	-0,39
E1	-6,36	6,94	-2,78	-1,33

CTM mainly reduces FF (severely for A2), increases Jsc (~7%), and Voc remains nearly affected

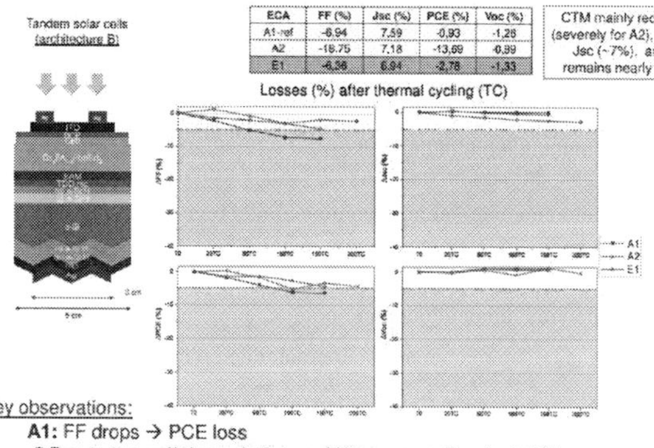

Key observations:
A1: FF drops → PCE loss
→Due to **top cell degradation** and **interconnection instability**
A2: Jsc & FF losses
→ Caused by **partial top cell degradation** and **current mismatch in tandem**
E1: FF loss only → PCE loss < 5%
→ Most suitable ECA at this stage

Conclusion

- ➢ Ultra-low-temperature ECA interconnection ensures reliable and stable module assembly.
- ➢ **Tandem modules** show that top cell degradation **and interconnection quality** strongly affect performance.
- ➢ Some modules remain stable with minimal PCE loss (<5%) under thermal cycling.
- ➢ Correlation between ECA properties and module performance is under investigation, highlighting the importance of formulation and module architecture for long-term stability and performance.

a) Bhambhani, A. *Fraunhofer ISE & Oxford PV Achieve 25% Tandem Module Efficiency*. TaiyangNews. https://taiyangnews.info/fraunhofer-ise-oxford-pv-achieve-25-tandem-module-efficiency
b) *US/Trinasolar Develops World's First 800W+ Tandem Module. Ushering in a New Era.* Trinasolar. https://static.trinasolar.com/us/resources/newsroom/Worlds-First-800W-Tandem-Module
c) *Qcells Achieves World Record Efficiency for Commercially Scalable Perovskite-Silicon Tandem Solar Cell - Qcells North America.* https://us.qcells.com/blog/qcells-tandem-cell-world-record-efficiency

EUPVSEC
22 — 26
September
BEC —
Bilbao Exhibition Centre
Bilbao —
Spain
EU
PVSEC
2025
42nd European
Photovoltaic Solar Energy
Conference and Exhibition

Conference Highlights

Robert Kenny

European Commission Joint Research Centre

EU PVSEC Technical Programme Chair

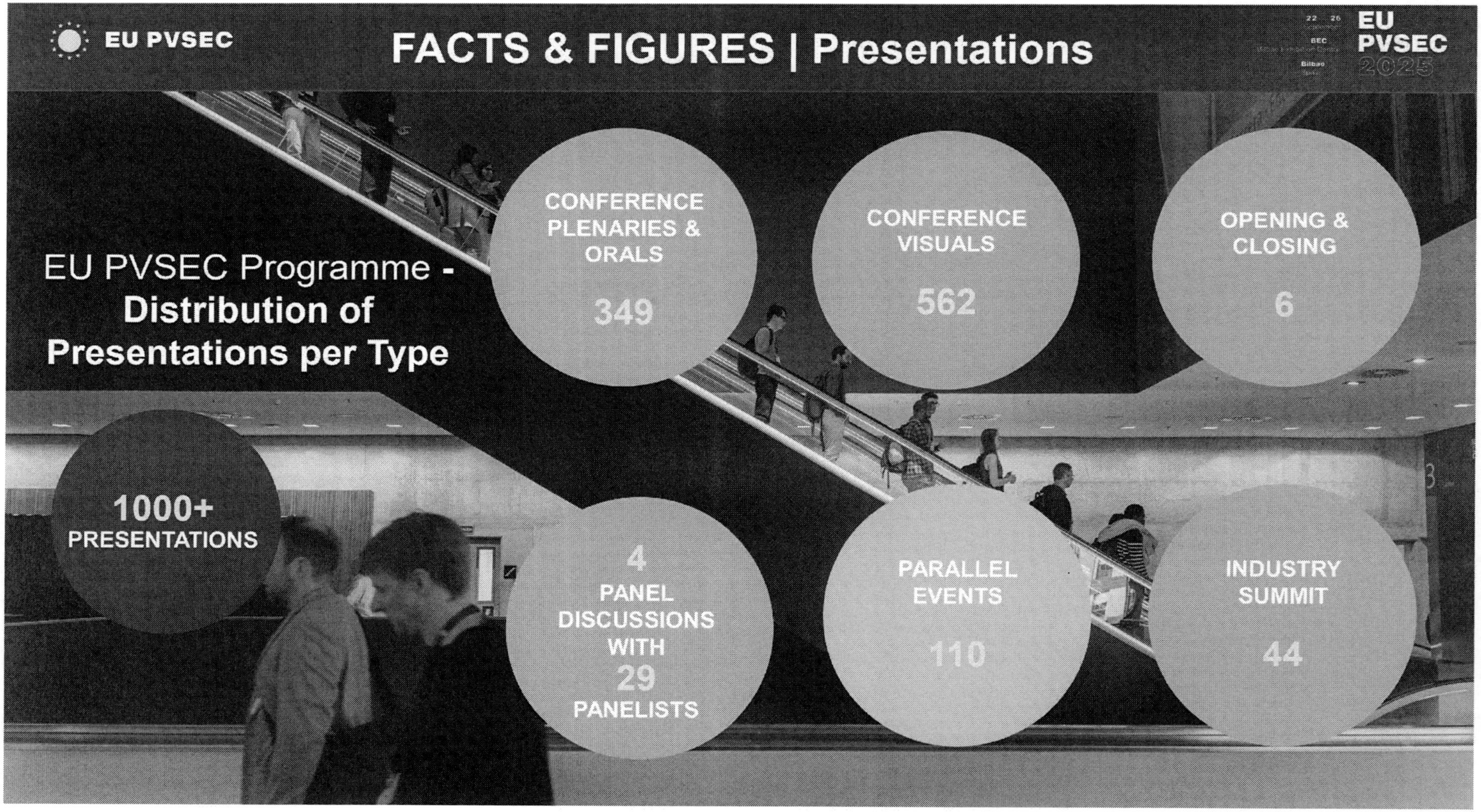
EU PVSEC
FACTS & FIGURES | Presentations
EU PVSEC 2025
Bilbao
EU PVSEC Programme - Distribution of Presentations per Type
CONFERENCE PLENARIES & ORALS
349
CONFERENCE VISUALS
562
OPENING & CLOSING
6
1000+ PRESENTATIONS
4 PANEL DISCUSSIONS WITH 29 PANELISTS
PARALLEL EVENTS
110
INDUSTRY SUMMIT
44

030001-004

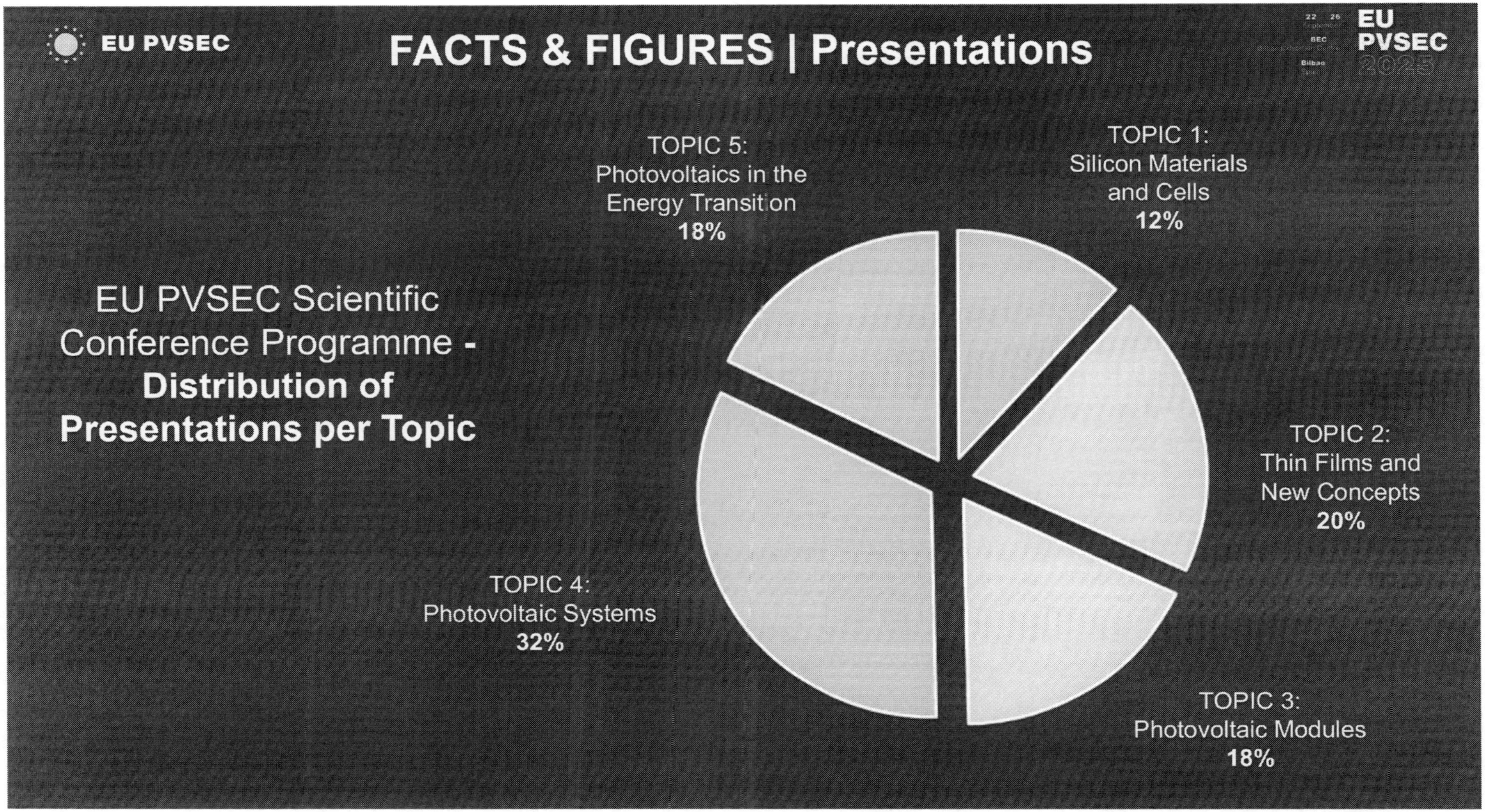
EU PVSEC
FACTS & FIGURES | Presentations
22 26 September
BEC
Bilbao
EU PVSEC 2025
EU PVSEC Scientific Conference Programme - Distribution of Presentations per Topic
TOPIC 1: Silicon Materials and Cells 12%
TOPIC 2: Thin Films and New Concepts 20%
TOPIC 3: Photovoltaic Modules 18%
TOPIC 4: Photovoltaic Systems 32%
TOPIC 5: Photovoltaics in the Energy Transition 18%

030001-005

FACTS & FIGURES | Participants

Participants by Countries
Top 10

No	Country	Participants
1	Germany	310
2	Spain	270
3	France	108
4	Italy	90
5	The Netherlands	76
6	South Korea	67
7	Switzerland	62
8	Japan	55
9	Belgium	44
10	Norway	35

TOTAL PARTICIPANTS
1600+
FROM 61
COUNTRIES

Plenary Session
"PV Everywhere"
Welcome Messages
Key Note Speech
"The Dual Face of Global Solar Growth"
OPENING
Monday, 22 Sept. 2025
Moderated Panel Discussion
"Solar in Turbulent Times: Global Dynamics and the Way Forward"
Becquerel Prize Ceremony
Jon DE GREGORIO
EU PVSEC 2025
www.eupvsec.org

EU PVSEC
PANEL DISCUSSIONS
22 26
BEC
Bilbao
EU PVSEC 2025
BO.13 Reliability and Bankability in PV
"The rapid developments of PV technology require increased attention to be paid to reliability testing."
CO.7 Challenges and Opportunities of PV up to 2030
"PV Technology is already reliable and cost effective, and even though improvements are welcome, key blockages are storage and grid strengthening. AI and robotics are essential to meet the scale of developments needed."
DO.13 Scalability and Manufacturability Prospects in Europe for New Technologies
"The prospects for reaching the 30GW target for PV module manufacturing in Europe were discussed and policy measures proposed."

EU PVSEC

22 26 September
BEC
Bilbao
EU PVSEC 2025

CONFERENCE

KEY MESSAGES

Cross-cutting themes emerged throughout the programme, showcasing how solar technologies can be applied everywhere, from traditional to emerging fields.

- Sustainability and circularity remain central, with research focused on reducing material use, such as replacing silver with copper, and advancing end-of-life management of modules.
- Ensuring long-term stability and predictable energy yield is equally essential, with studies of degradation mechanisms such as UVID carried out.
- The role of AI across the PV value chain is rapidly expanding, from design to operations and maintenance, including drone applications.

EU PVSEC

EU PVSEC 2025

CONFERENCE

TOPIC 1: SILICON MATERIALS AND CELLS

Enhancements in IV measurement procedures

- Michael Rauer, Fraunhofer ISE: 1AO.4.5 *Universal Contacting Approaches for the Characterization of Solar Cells*
- Shuai Nie, UNSW: 1AO.4.6 *Contact-Free J-V: a Simple Technique for Universal State-of-the-Art Solar Cells*

Replacement of critical by sustainable materials:

- Reduced Ag consumpion e.g. by replacing by Cu (plating)
- In-free SHJ solar cells and Pero-Si tandems

EU PVSEC

EU PVSEC 2025

Bilbao

CONFERENCE

TOPIC 1: SILICON MATERIALS AND CELLS

Great advance in understanding of UV induced degradation and Hydrogen related degradation

- Excellent PLENARY by Bram Hoex (presenting for Muhammad Umair Khan), UNSW: 1CP.3.5 *Understanding the Root Cause of UV-Induced Degradation in TOPCon and PERC Solar Cells*

Further high quality orals:

- Christina Hollemann, ISFH: 1AO.4.2 *Mitigating UV-Induced Degradation: Impact of PECVD and PEALD AlOx Layers Deposited in a Tube-Type Direct Plasma-Enhanced Chemical Vapor Deposition System*
- Hugo Lajoie, CEA: 1AO.4.3 *New Insights on UV-Induced Degradation of SHJ Solar Cells*
- Byungsul Min, ISFH: 1BO.3.6 *UV Stable Passivation Stack with Plasma-Enhanced Atomic Layer Deposition of Aluminum Oxide from an Industrial Tube-Type Direct Plasma-Enhanced Chemical Vapor Deposition System*
- Wolfram Kwapil, Fraunhofer ISE: 1AO.5.6 *Impact of Illumination on Solar Cell Properties: Insights into Atomic Hydrogen Release*

EU PVSEC

EU PVSEC 2025

CONFERENCE

TOPIC 1: SILICON MATERIALS AND CELLS

Advances in TOPCon and SHJ technology → Pushing the Limits of Performance

- Fantastic keynote lecture (PLENARY) on heterojunction solar cells by Dr. Guangtao Yang, Trina: 1CP.1.1 *Silicon Surface and Interface Study for >27% Efficient SHJ Solar Cell*
  - Deep insight into technological aspects eg. influence of rear side polishing on cell performance
  - Very high efficiencies for both-sides contacted HJT > 27%
  - Issues with CAPEX, sustainibility (Ag, In)
  - Pero-Si tandem cells on large area and modules

Late News Presentation on 27.8% efficient back contact silicon solar cells by Hua Wu, Longhi: 1DO.9.1 *Hybrid Interdigitated Back Contact Silicon Solar Cells with Superior Efficiency*

Late News Presentation as TOPCon for Bottom Solar Cells in Pero-Si Tandem devices by Jana Polzin-Isabelle Polzin, Fraunhofer ISE: 1DO.9.3 *Silicon Solar Cells – From High Efficiency Single-junction to Bottom Cells in Two-Terminal Perovskite-Silicon Tandem Devices*

EU PVSEC

22–26 September, BEC, Bilbao — EU PVSEC 2025

CONFERENCE

TOPIC 1: SILICON MATERIALS AND CELLS

Further high quality orals:

- Hua Wu, Longhi: 1DO.9.1 *Hybrid Interdigitated Back Contact Silicon Solar Cells with Superior Efficiency*
- Daming Chen, Trina: 1AO.5.1 *Large Area i-TOPCon Solar Cells with 25.9% Record Efficiency*
- Maysa Sarsour, UNSW: 1AO.6.1 *Evaluating Silicon Heterojunction Solar Cell Stability under Industrial Illuminated Hydrogenation Conditions*

Bottom cell optimization for Pero-Si tandems

EU PVSEC

22 26 September BEC Bilbao EU PVSEC 2025

CONFERENCE

TOPIC 2: THIN FILMS AND NEW CONCEPTS

A lot of focus on the long-term stability improvement and upscaling of tandem devices based on a variety of materials (hence not only pero-Si).

Many companies (e.g. Hanwha Q-cells, Oxford PV, Microquanta Seminconductor, Jinko Solar, Longi, etc. non-exhaustive list) presented impressive results on industrial size single-junction pero modules and pero-based tandem modules. A highlight here was the plenary talk from Hanwha Q-cells showing a record large area (M10) pilot-scale Pk/Si tandem cell of 28.6% efficiency.

CONFERENCE

TOPIC 2: THIN FILMS AND NEW CONCEPTS

In the field of pero-Si tandems, there is clearly more focus on improving the stability of the tandem devices than before with many contributions doing in-depth investigations into the different degradation mechanisms that can occur in pero-Si tandems.

In this respect, 2DO9.5 presented a consensus statement about reliability testing of perovskite-based tandems that is endorsed by specialists worldwide from both industry and research and presents a kind of minimum that should be done in terms of testing and reporting concerning the stability and lifetime of perovskite-based tandem devices.

More and more advanced characterization methods for perovskite and perovskite - silicon tandem solar cells are being used, hyperspectral imaging methods identify non-uniformities by layer for processing development.

EU PVSEC

EU PVSEC 2025

22 26 September

BEC

Bilbao

CONFERENCE

TOPIC 2: THIN FILMS AND NEW CONCEPTS

Another clear trend is that pero-TOPCon cells are nearing the same record efficiencies as pero-Heterojunction cells. A highlight talk here was the certified 34.22% efficiency perovskite/ topcon tandem solar cell(1cm2) by Jinko Solar 2CO2.1

Another highlight was the 30.5% triple junction pero/pero/silicon cell by EPFL (2CO2.3)

In the field of perovskite single junction devices, 2DO.7.3 showed perovskite devices with remarkable reliability, withstanding 4 years of outdoor exposure. The degradation mechanism is attributed to the diurnal behaviour, also verified and replicated with indoor experiments.

2AO3.6 investigated experimental degradation and recovery of perovskite solar cells, improving the comprehension of instability's dynamics, to extend the lifetime of devices.

EU PVSEC

EU PVSEC 2025

CONFERENCE

TOPIC 2: THIN FILMS AND NEW CONCEPTS

In the field of compound semiconductors, there were many presentations on alternative materials for perovskite in tandems. In this way, first monolithic (AgCu)(InGa)Se2 on Si tandem cells were demonstrated as well as 16.1% semitransparent Ag doped Cu(InGa)S2 sulfide top cells.

An exciting highlight in this field was 2BO8.2 in which UPC Barcelona achieved 18% efficiency under indoor lighting for kesterite solar cells with alkali doping

EU PVSEC

22 26 September BEC Bilbao EU PVSEC 2025

CONFERENCE

TOPIC 3: PHOTOVOLTAIC MODULES

“Reliable packaging to Maximize the energy yield from high efficiency cells”

big theme: Optimizing module materials and packaging for long lifetime and predictable energy yield from high efficiency cells. The industry and research community are moving quickly to assess and improve reliability.

- Understanding, accelerated testing, and mitigating UV-ID in n-type cells and modules
- How do you develop accelerated tests for constantly changing BOMs - new encapsulants, new metallization, thinner glass, and high efficiency cells

EU PVSEC

22 – 26 September
BEC
Bilbao
EU PVSEC 2025

CONFERENCE

TOPIC 3: PHOTOVOLTAIC MODULES

- Degradation and metastability in packaged perovskite tandems - understanding energy yield and realistic degradation rates
- Characterization out of the lab and into the field and factory - accurate outdoor performance, online quality control measurements for encapsulant cross linking
- Reducing silver content and metallization temperatures - reliability of low temperature and low silver metallization
- Developing glass qualification requirements to minimize breakage

EU PVSEC

EU PVSEC 2025

CONFERENCE

TOPIC 4: PHOTOVOLTAIC SYSTEMS

Advances in O&M of PV systems

(4CV.1) focuses on fault detection, cleaning optimization, soiling (and snow 4CO.8), UAV for autonomous monitoring and digital twin.

Data driven and AI based O&M (4CO.9) including a medicine-like workflow in Autonomous multi-AI agent system for health monitoring: a fully automated O&M pipeline with field robotics (4CO.9.4 D. Moser, EURAC)

PV Everywhere from space to agricultural applications like integration in vineyards (Mo, Opening plenary) and many other **integrated options** as we have seen throughout the week. On Thursday (4DO.4) agriPV, noise barriers and floating integrated systems. AgriPV technologies (4DO.2), BIPV

PV needs solar energy. **Solar resource and forecasting** (Mo, 4AO.7-9 & Tu 4BV.3). Shortly IEA PVPS T16 will publish minute irradiance data, some including GT over 220 stations worldwide with. Same format and quality controlled. (*Worldwide solar radiation measurement database with quality-control added value*, Anne Forstinger CSP Services, 4AO.7.1)

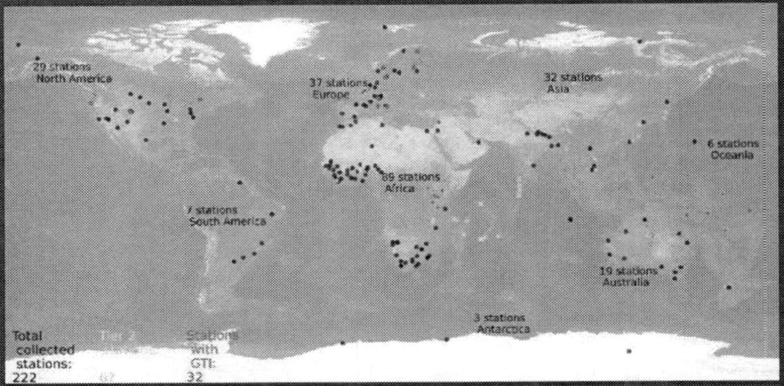

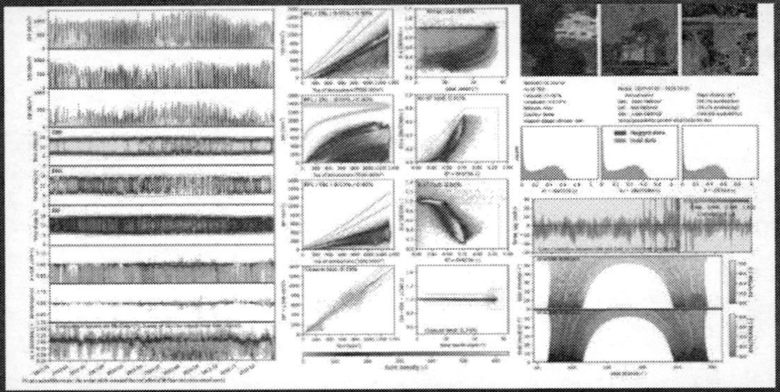

(4BV.3). Poster winner 4BV.3.12 *Advancing Very Short-Term Solar Irradiance Forecasting in Africa: A Low-Cost Sky Imaging and Machine Learning-Based Approach*, implications for PV deployment and grid integration (Martin Ansong, KIT). Runner-up 4BV.3.25 *Evaluating the Suitability of Köppen-Geiger Climate Classifications for Photovoltaic Systems: Micro-climate Analysis and Risk Assessment Maps*, with worldwide distribution of humidity related risk assessment for PV performance (Pavan Kumar Panda, Anhalt University of Applied Sciences).

TOPIC 4: PHOTOVOLTAIC SYSTEMS

Integrated PV

BIPV (4BO.16) examples of coloured modules (which was main topic of the poster session along with fire concerns of BIPV, 4BV.4), lightweight solutions (4BO.5) and modelling partial shading effects 4BO.17.1, *Modelling partial shading at the cell level on PV modules,* Jean-Paul Calin, ENSTA) and 4BO.17.3, *Comparing the energy yield and degradation rates of smart PV modules compared to conventional PV system designs in shaded urban scenario's,* Youri Blom, TU DELF.

AgriPV 4DO.2 the room was fully packed showing the interest in the topic. 5 talks were on new ways of sharing light (2 spectral splitting before the PV conversion, 2 semitransparent PV modules both c-Si and CdTe, 1 on downshifting encapsulate) + 1 new AgrivPV like application with Algae instead of crops.

4DO.4 also included AgriPV and **Others types of integration like noise barriers and floating.** In addition to performance other aspects like (*Hydrological and ecological effects on floating PV,* Konstantin Ilgen, FHO ISe) have been highlighted this week

4DO4.2

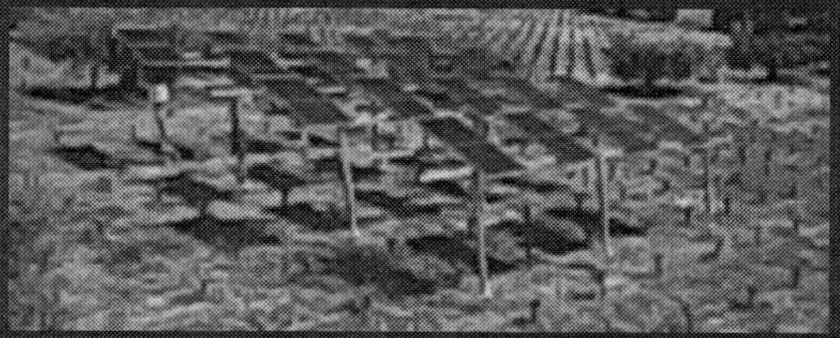

BOS and tracking systems (4DO.1) focused on backtracking strategies and terrains with complex topography.

4DO.1.4

EU PVSEC

22 – 26 September
BEC
Bilbao

EU PVSEC 2025

CONFERENCE

TOPIC 4: PHOTOVOLTAIC SYSTEMS

Reliability of PV systems

Several presentations focused long-term monitored degradation, failure modes and degradation modes identification techniques (non-destructive, aerial images, AI-based)

4BO.6.1 *Three decades, three climates: insights and lessons on PV reliability*. Good BOM offer very high reliability in power production, with 30-35 years old modules showing 0.24% degradation rate per year.

4BO.6.3 *Non-destructive detection of water ingress in solar modules using NIR spectroscopy* (Oleksandr Mashkow HI ERN) proved near-infrared absorption (NIRA) technique to detect water ingress in modules in the field, which correlated with the module degradation.

4BO.7.2 *Robust PV performance loss rate calculation for high latitudes* (Lauri Karttunen, Meteo Inst Helsinki) and 4BO.7. 3 *Detailed analysis of degradation rates of operating PV assets in tropical climate conditions* (Xioaqi Xu, Seris Singapore) Performance loss rates reported for high latitudes and tropics based on solid data sets. PLR in the tropics -1.4%/year

4DO.3.6 PV system design and assessment highlighted how inverter safety issues are extremely important and how more research about inverter safety and reliability is needed.

EU PVSEC

EU PVSEC 2025

CONFERENCE

TOPIC 5: PHOTOVOLTAICS IN THE ENERGY TRANSITION

Main topics of interest :

- Flexibility
- Artificial intelligence
- EoL management

EU PVSEC

EU PVSEC 2025

CONFERENCE

TOPIC 5: PHOTOVOLTAICS IN THE ENERGY TRANSITION

5.1 Grid Integration and Flexibility Enablers (2 sessions)

- Smoothing effect related to different orientations of PV systems in a given area allows 10 to 15% additional hosting capacity of the distribution grid compared to the conservative calculation that consists in summing the AC power. Such accurate calculation enabled by high resolution large area images and LIDAR and induces therefore very low costs.

5.2 Sustainability of PV (4 sessions)

- New inventories LCI and LCA for emerging technologies even though lack of data for perovskites, LCA showing a way for low environmental Impacts with technology improvement and localisation. / Technological improvements will contribute to the reduction of environmental Impact / Grid Efficiency has an Impact on the environmental Footprint.
- Manufacturing optimization / Reuse & recycling: results from the perspective of economic performance – would it convince manufacturer to consider it if economic benefit ?
- EoL Management /recycling -> emerging field attracting lots of activities / mainly EU projects (EVERPV / ICARUS / QASAR) – highlight on polymer, interesting question came up and to be debated for the next decade: is it worth it to consider polymer (EVA/ backsheet) recycling ?
- Major progress in methodology and indicators to assess sustainable design & circularity and improve transparency recyclability index, technical recyclability, digital passport)

EU PVSEC

EU PVSEC 2025

CONFERENCE

TOPIC 5: PHOTOVOLTAICS IN THE ENERGY TRANSITION

5.3 Scenarios for Renewables, Policy, Global Challenges (1 session)

- wide scope of contributions on the way to massive, medium- to long-term PV deployment -> should not be taken for granted despite positive projections since there can be limiting factors such as public acceptance / regulatory restrictions and effect of climate change

5.4 Costs, Economics, Finance and Markets (1 session)

- Annual installed capacity over 400 GWp / total cumulative installed capacity worldwide over 2.1 TWp / Clear mismatch between PV module installations rate worldwide and PV module production rate leading to bunch of inventories and drastically reduced prices.

5.6 Societal Challenges; Citizens' Participation, Awareness (1 session)

- data and analysis in gender aspects are emerging in PV! (poster session) + Highlight on innovation in education! On example that targets students & skilled workers -> mobile Lab for advanced experimental training PV-related to bring skills and characterization tools everywhere.

PARALLEL EVENTS
Collaborat° Network
Diversity
PREJUDICE
JUSTIFICAT°
CHANGE
NEEDS — PROFILE MATCH
AVOID BLIND SPOTS
JOB LOSS?
INTEGRATION
LACK OF ATTRACTIVENESS
RESILIENCE (PEOPLE + COMPANY)
CREATIVITY
DIFFERENT COMMUNICAT°
INTERNAL FRICTION
MORE EFFORT

030001-027

EU PVSEC

EU PVSEC 2025

PARALLEL EVENTS

- Perovskite Innovation Roundtable: Driving EU Leadership in Perovskite Innovation
- Women in PV presents: Leading with Inclusion – Embracing the 6 Traits of Inclusive Leadership
- Unlocking the Potential of Integrated Photovoltaic Systems - European R&D Approach
- Why Do PV Plants Perform Lower than Expected? (Estimating losses by backtracking algorithms in undulating terrain & Analysis of the loss chain and identification of deviations from initial expectations)
- PV Made in the EU: How Do Companies Die and How Can They Thrive?

22 — 26
September
BEC —
ilbao Exhibition Centre
Bilbao — Spain
EU
PVSEC
2025
42nd European Photovoltaic Solar Energy Conference and Exhibition
GEOPOLITICS & PV MANUFACTURING CHALLENGES
EXHIBITION
FORUM
INDUSTRY
SUMMIT

The road to a

EU PVSEC

EU PVSEC 2025

22 26 BEC Bilbao

INDUSTRY SUMMIT

Industry Summit Opening (session I)

Session Title: Solar PV production in Europe - the way forward

Moderators: Begoña Molinete, Walburga Hemetsberger

Key Takeaway:

This session discussed the state of play of European manufacturing projects and whether there is enough European support. It was clear that political support is further lacking – only 3 Member States have developed schemes to support European manufacturing. While the Net Zero Industry Act is helpful to diversify supplies, it will not particularly support European manufacturing.

All panellists agreed that apart from further policy support (financing, derisking) collaboration is the way forward.

EU PVSEC

EU PVSEC 2025

INDUSTRY SUMMIT

Session II
Session Title: International corporations in the light of changing geopolitics
Moderators: Radovan Kopecek, Puzant Baliozian

Key takeaway:
EU machine builders are still supporting mostly Indian but also US and EU projects with their technology and expertise. The major arguments for choosing EU tech are quality, training, support and low OPEX.

Session III
Session Title: PV Systems: How do we get the produced electricity in Europe into the grid?
Moderators: Catarina Augusto, Peter Fath

Key Takeaway:
Hybrid PV + storage systems (co-located or distributed) are essential for integrating PV into electricity grids. Storage adds flexibility and stabilizes the grid, making it a cornerstone of resilient energy systems; while the technology is mature, scalable and bankable revenue models remain the key gap for widespread deployment.

LIST OF EXHIBITORS
(in alphabetical order)

Company name	Country
2nd Cycle FlexCo	Austria
9-Tech	Italy
Avalon ST / Pasan	Switzerland
BASQUENERGY Cluster	Spain
Becquerel Institute	Belgium
ECOPROGETTI	Italy
EKIENERGY	Spain
ESMC Pavilion	Belgium
Eternal Sun I WAVELABS	The Netherlands
EU PVSEC Startup Pavilion	
European Commission JRC	Italy
exateq	Germany
FLUXiM AG	Switzerland
G2V Optics	Canada
GALEA	Spain
halm elektronik	Germany
HighLine Technology	Germany
IEA PVPS	
Innovations in Optics, Inc.	United States of America
ISC Konstanz	Germany
LAB14	Germany
MBJ Solutions	Germany
Mondragon Assembly	Spain
Nagase Chemtex America	United States of America
NEO Messtechnik Holding	Austria
ODTÜ GÜNAM	Türkiye
Phoenixolar	China
PSE Instruments	Germany
PVsyst	Switzerland
RCT Future	Germany
RCT Solutions	Germany
RENA	Germany
ReNewPV-CA21148 / 5GSOLAR	Estonia
SALD B.V.	The Netherlands

SCIPRIOS	Germany
SEMILAB	Hungary
SINGULUS TECHNOLOGIES	Germany
Sinton Instruments	United States of America
SOLAR MATERIALS	Germany
SolarNL	The Netherlands
Soli Tek R&D	Lithuania
TAMURA ELSOLD	Germany
TECNALIA	Spain
The Netherlands Pavilion	The Netherlands
TNO	The Netherlands
University of the Basque Country	Spain
Vector Energy	Spain
VON ARDENNE	Germany
WCPEC-9	South Korea
WIP Renewable Energies	Germany
ZSW	Germany

We thank the EU PVSEC 2025 Sponsors

Platinum

MONDRAGON ASSEMBLY

Gold

ENERGIAREN EUSKAL ERAKUNDEA
ENTE VASCO DE LA ENERGÍA

G2V

halm.

RCT solutions

Silver

Sinton instruments

Bronze

AESOLAR

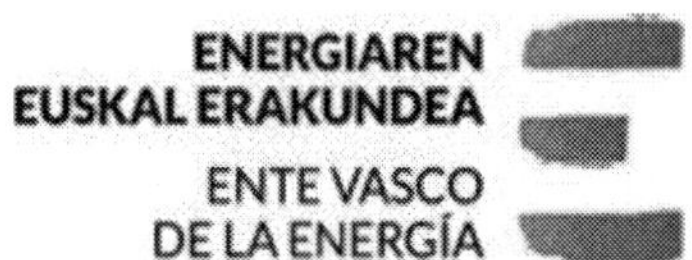

AUTHORS OF EU PVSEC 2025 PROCEEDINGS PAPERS

A. dos Reis Benatto, Gisele DTU, Roskilde, Denmark	020028, 020037, 020039, 020191, 020265, 020376, 020477
Aaltonen, Lauri Tampere University, Tampere, Finland	020537
Abad Alcaraz, Verónica University of Almería, La Cañada de San Urbano, Spain	020336
Abbott, Malcolm D. PV Lighthouse, Coledale, Australia	020396
Abbotto, Alessandro University of Milano-Bicocca, Milan, Italy	020077
Abdallah, Amir A. QEERI, Doha, Qatar	020146, 020166
Abdel Nour, Christine EDF R&D, Moret Loing Orvanne, France	020188
Abdelrahim, Mohamed QEERI, Doha, Qatar	020166
Abdou-Tankari, Mahamadou Paris-East Créteil University, Créteil, France	020562
Abrego, Gillen ALLOTARRA, Allo, Spain	020392
Acciarri, Maurizio University of Milano-Bicocca, Milan, Italy	020087
Acevedo Devoto, M. Ignacia ISC Konstanz, Konstanz, Germany	020220
Achenbach, Jannik University of Applied Science Cologne, Cologne, Germany	020522
Acinas, Victor Applied Materials, Dublin, Ireland	020019
Adachi, Satoru NIED, Shinjo, Japan	020436
Aden, Samira HZB, Berlin, Germany	020513
Adinolfi Borea, Riccardo University of Bologna, Bologna, Italy	020314
Adnan Hameed, Mohammed Martin-Luther-University Halle-Wittenberg, Halle, Germany	020156
Adothu, Baloji DEWA, Dubai, United Arab Emirates	020229
Aghaei, Mohammadreza NTNU, Aalesund, Norway	020335, 020356
Aghaei, Mohammadreza NTNU, Ålesund, Norway	020374, 020375

Aghamohammadi, Amirhossain 020356
Amirkabir University of Technology, Tehran, Iran

Aguirre, Aranzazu 020064
Hasselt Unversity, Genk, Belgium

Ahmadi, Mehdi 020066
CNR-IMM, Catania, Italy

Aiello, Andrea 020255
ACCA Software, Cosenza, Italy

Aimé, Jérémie 020217, 020311
CEA / INES, Le Bourget-du-Lac, France

Aissa, Brahim 020042, 020075, 020108, 020109, 020146, 020147
QEERI, Doha, Qatar

Aizpurua, Jon 020139
Tecnalia, Donostia - San Sebastián, Spain

Akbayrak, Serdar 020020
Necmettin Erbakan University, Konya, Türkiye

Akram, M. Waqar 020164
Hohai University, Changzhou, China

Al Katrib, Mirella 020116
IPVF, Palaiseau, France

Alam, Habeel 020394
Lancaster University, Lancaster, United Kingdom

Alberts, Vivian 020229
DEWA, Dubai, United Arab Emirates

Albuquerque, Daniel P. 020464
Centre for New Energy Technologies, Sacavém, Portugal

Alet, Pierre-Jean 020238, 020544
CSEM, Neuchâtel, Switzerland

Alexandris, Nikos 020210
European Commission JRC, Ispra, Italy

Alfieri, Felice 020497
Viegand Maagøe, Copenhagen, Denmark

Ali, Adnan 020147
QEERI, Doha, Qatar

Allen, Vince 020048
SunDrive Solar, Kurnell, Australia

Alloji, Esma 020020
Necmettin Erbakan University, Konya, Türkiye

Almeida Silva, José 020565
University of Évora, Évora, Portugal

Almuneau, Guilhem 020074
LAAS-CNRS, Toulouse, France

Alonso, Ricardo 020197, 020198, 020353, 020358
TECNALIA, Derio, Spain

Alonso-Montesinos, Joaquín 020100
University of Almeria, Almeria, Spain

Alonso-Montesinos, Joaquín — 020336
University of Almería, La Cañada de San Urbano, Spain

Álvarez Hervás, José Domingo — 020336
University of Almería, La Cañada de San Urbano, Spain

Alvarez, José — 020040, 020058
CNRS, Gif-sur-Yvette, France

Álvarez, Marta — 020300
CENER, Sarriguren, Spain

Álvarez-Pérez, Guillem — 020062
IPVF, Palaiseau, France

Alvaro Høye, Ingar — 020443
Solkraft Sør, Øyslebø, Norway

Alves e Silva, Kiane — 020439, 020535, 020567, 020575
UPM, Madrid, Spain

Amaro e Silva, Rodrigo — 020490
University of Lisbon, Lisbon, Portugal

Amatriain, Irati — 020392
CENER, Sarriguren, Spain

Anamiati, Gaetana — 020448, 020481
GreenPowerMonitor a DNV company, Barcelona, Spain

Anaya, Julian — 020191, 020205
University of Valladolid, Valladolid, Spain

Ancillao, Andrea — 020079
Polytechnic University of Turin, Turin, Italy

Anderlini, Alessandro — 020155
Coveme, Gorizia, Italy

Andersen, Nanna L. — 020250
DTU, Roskilde, Denmark

Andersen, Nanna Lysgaard — 020306
DTU, Roskilde, Denmark

Andrade-Arvizu, Jacob — 020094
IREC, Barcelona, Spain

Andreozzi, Federico — 020494
University of Rome Tor Vergata, Rome, Italy

Anefnaf, Ikram — 020093
University of Verona, Verona, Italy

Ansong, Martin — 020272
KIT, Eggenstein-Leopoldshafen, Germany

Antognini, Luca — 020196
PVsyst, Geneva, Switzerland

Antoine, C. — 020508
IMDEA Nanoscience Institute, Madrid, Spain

Antón, Ignacio — 020209, 020246, 020257, 020453, 020459
UPM, Madrid, Spain

Antonucci, Daniele — 020551
Eurac Research, Bolzano, Italy

Apostoleris, Harry 020487
EPRI, Dubai, United Arab Emirates

Arakawa, Hayato 020436
NIED, Shinjo, Japan

Aranguren, Gerardo 020289, 020353
UPV/EHU, Bilbao, Spain

Arbaretaz, Sebastien 020317
CEA INES, Le Bourget-du-Lac, France

Ardissone, Bastien J. J. 020396
PV Lighthouse, Coledale, Australia

Arduino, Daniele 020079
Polytechnic University of Turin, Turin, Italy

Ariolli, Daniela Maria Godinho 020325
BayWa r.e, Rome, Italy

Ariza Camacho, Maria Jesus 020100
University of Almeria, Almería, Spain

Armstrong, Alona 020394
Lancaster University, Lancaster, United Kingdom

Arribat, Mathieu 020074
LAAS-CNRS, Toulouse, France

Arrizabalaga, Igor 020139
Tecnalia, Donostia - San Sebastián, Spain

Artegiani, Elisa 020057, 020089, 020093
University of Verona, Verona, Italy

Arumughan, Jayaprasad 020569
ISC Konstanz, Konstanz, Germany

Asaa, Shu-Ngwa 020393
imo-imomec, Genk, Belgium

Ascencio-Vásquez, Julián 020371
Univers, Courbevoie, France

Askins, Steve 020209, 020257
UPM, Madrid, Spain

Assaid, El Mahdi 020171
University of Chouaib Doukkali, El Jadida, Morocco

Aste, Niccolò 020249
Polytechnic University of Milan, Milan, Italy

Astigarraga, Alexander 020226
Eurac Research, Bolzano, Italy

Athienitis, Andreas 020248
Concordia University, Montreal, Canada

Aurrekoetxea, Olaia 020302
TECNALIA, Saint Sebastian, Spain

Awadallah, Carlos 020536
Wattkraft, Madrid, Spain

Azkona, Nekane 020055, 020097, 020153, 020287
UPV/EHU, Bilbao, Spain

Azzopardi, Brian 020318, 020334, 020520
FIR, Birkirkara, Malta

Azzopardi, Carmel 020334
FIR, Birkirkara, Malta

Babich, Francesco 020551
Eurac Research, Bolzano, Italy

Babics, Maxime 020217
CEA / INES, Le Bourget-du-Lac, France

Babin, Markus 020249, 020250, 020306, 020477
DTU, Roskilde, Denmark

Bachour, Dunia A. 020275, 020278
QEERI, Doha, Qatar

Bachour, Dunia 020291
QEERI, Doha, Qatar

Baderiya, Naman 020390
MARIN, Wageningen, The Netherlands

Badosa Franch, Jordi 020214
Polytechnic Institute of Paris, Palaiseau, France

Baeck, Pieter-Jan 020511
Flemish Institute for Technological Research (VITO), Genk, Belgium

Bai, Jianbo 020164
Hohai University, Changzhou, China

Bailache, Simon 020303
CSTB, Marne-la-Vallée, France

Bakhtiari, Afshin 020121
AESOLAR, Koenigsbrunn, Germany

Balafoutis, Athanasios T. 020464
CERTH, Athens, Greece

Bald, Juan 020514
AZTI, PASAIA, Spain

Baldacchino, Alex J. 020065
UNSW, Sydney, Australia

Baležentienė, Skirmantė 020380
The Applied Research Institute for Prospective Technologies, Vilnius, Lithuania

Baležentis, Algirdas 020380
The Applied Research Institute for Prospective Technologies, Vilnius, Lithuania

Ballif, Christophe 020467
CSEM, Neuchâtel, Switzerland

Ballif, Christophe 020251
EPFL, Neuchâtel, Switzerland

Bandaru, Narendra 020039, 020043, 020104
Aarhus University, Aarhus, Denmark

Bang, Ole 020043
Technical University of Denmark, Copenhagen, Denmark

Barakel, Damien 020188
Toulon University, Marseille, France

Baraket, Mira 020039
ATLANT 3D, Taastrup, Denmark

Baranek, Philippe 020060
EDF R&D, Palaiseau, France

Barchi, Grazia 020485, 020489, 020544
Eurac Research, Bolzano, Italy

Bardizza, Giorgio 020181
TÜV Rheinland Italia, Milan, Italy

Bardizza, Giorgio 020208
TÜV Rheinland Solar, Cologne, Germany

Bardizza, Giorgio 020144
TÜV Rheinland, Cologne, Germany

Barguès, Anna 020505
Becquerel Institute France, Lyon, France

Barguès, Anna 020558
Becquerel Institute, Brussels, Belgium

Barnscheidt, Verena 020063, 020114
ISFH, Emmerthal, Germany

Barretta, Chiara 020325
PCCL, Leoben, Austria

Barrionuevo, Bruno 020464
CERTH, Athens, Greece

Barroso, João 020565
University of Évora, Évora, Portugal

Barrou, Alexis 020467
CSEM, Neuchâtel, Switzerland

Barrutia, Laura 020446, 020536
UPM, Madrid, Spain

Barth, Vincent 020134
CEA / INES, Le Bourget-du-Lac, France

Barth, Vincent 020019
CEA, Le Bourget-du-Lac, France

Barth, Vincent 020226
CEA/ INES, Le Bourget-du-Lac, France

Bartholomäus, Martin 020346
DTU, Roskilde, Denmark

Bartolo, Brian 020334
FIR, Birkirkara, Malta

Basta, Beata 020068
Roltec, Poznań, Poland

Basta, Marek 020068
Roltec, Poznań, Poland

Battisti, Kurt 020255
A-Null Development, Vienna, Austria

Bauhuis, Gerard 020067
Radboud University, Nijmegen, The Netherlands

Baumann, Kerstin 020470
bifa Umweltinstitut, Augsburg, Germany

Baumann, Sara 020063
ISFH, Emmerthal, Germany

Baumann, Ulrike 020006
ISFH, Emmerthal, Germany

Baur, Carsten 020246
European Space Agency, Noordwijk, The Netherlands

Beaucarne, Guy 020384
Dow Silicones Belgium, Seneffe, Belgium

Becker, Carl 020331
DLR, Almería, Spain

Behrensdorff Poulsen, Peter 020037
DTU, Lyngby, Denmark

Beinert, Andreas J. 020123
Fraunhofer ISE, Freiburg, Germany

Bejat, Timea 020225, 020500
CEA, Le Bourget-du-Lac, France

Belawadi, Aditya Girish 020231
Fraunhofer ISE, Freiburg, Germany

Belferkous, Brahim Anis 020325
PCCL, Leoben, Austria

Bellmann, Martin 020495, 020510
SINTEF, Trondheim, Norway

Bellvert, Eduard 020139
Tecnalia, Donostia - San Sebastián, Spain

Beltran-Condori, Sonia 020129, 020417
University of Antofagasta, Antofagasta, Chile

Belzunce, María Jesús 020514
AZTI, PASAIA, Spain

Bendix, Peter 020388
Next2Sun Technology, Dillingen, Germany

Bengoechea, Jaione 020181, 020300
CENER, Sarriguren, Spain

Bermudez Benito, Veronica 020146
QEERI, Doha, Qatar

Bermudez-Garcia, Anderson 020246
Thales Alenia Space, Cannes, France

Berrian, Djaber 020492
Belectric, Kolitzheim, Germany

Berson, Solenn 020134
CEA / INES, Le Bourget-du-Lac, France

Besson, Pierre 020373
INES, Le Bourget-du-Lac, France

Betak, Juraj 020241
Solargis, Bratislava, Slovakia

Bettucci, Ottavia 020077
University of Milano-Bicocca, Milan, Italy

Bhardwaj, Shashank 020515
TU Delft, Delft, The Netherlands

Bhatnagar, Shrey 020367
Nextracker, Fremont, United States of America

Biard, Yves 020303
SemperStyl, Eragny, France

Bieber, Lisa-Marie 020195
Fraunhofer ISE, Freiburg, Germany

Bilitu, Eddie 020393
Hasselt University, Hasselt, Belgium

Binani, Ashish 020225
TNO, Petten, The Netherlands

Binetti, Simona 020093
University of Milano Bicocca, Milan, Italy

Binetti, Simona 020087
University of Milano-Bicocca, Milan, Italy

Blakesley, James 020293
National Physical Laboratory, Teddington, United Kingdom

Blanc, Philippe 020291
MINES Paris, Nice, France

Blanco Aguiar, Adrián 020243
ieco.io, Vigo, Spain

Blieske, Ulf 020141
University of Applied Science Cologne, Cologne, Germany

Blieske, Ulf 020140
University of Applied Sciences Cologne, Cologne, Germany

Blstak Catlosova, Katarina 020274
Solargis, Bratislava, Slovakia

Blum, Niklas 020235, 020237, 020239
DLR, Almeria, Spain

Boccardi, Roberto 020039
DTU, Copenhagen, Denmark

Boccardi, Roberto 020037
DTU, Lyngby, Denmark

Boccardi, Roberto 020028
DTU, Roskilde, Denmark

Boddaert, Simon 020302, 020303
CSTB, Marne-la-Vallée, France

Bokalič, Matevž 020047, 020319
University of Ljubljana, Ljubljana, Slovenia

Bolink, Henk J. 020226
University of Valencia, Paterna, Spain

Bonal, Victor 020085
UAM, Madrid, Spain

Bonnet, Martin 020141
University of Applied Science Cologne, Cologne, Germany

Bonnet-Eymard, Bénédicte 020251
CSEM, Neuchâtel, Switzerland

Borgers, Tom 020225
IMEC, Genk, Belgium

Borgna, Luciano 020369
BFH, Burgdorf, Switzerland

Borie, Benjamin 020039
ATLANT 3D, Taastrup, Denmark

Borowski, Peter 020307
Avancis, Munich, Germany

Borriello, Aniello 020378
ENEA, Portici, Italy

Borzi, Giovanni 020019
Enginsoft, Padua, Italy

Bosch, Elina 020252, 020543, 020564, 020573
Becquerel Institute, Brussels, Belgium

Bosma, Theo 020571
DNV, Arnhem, The Netherlands

Bothe, Karsten 020236
ISFH, Emmerthal, Germany

Bou-Nassif, Liliane 020338
CETHIL, Villeurbanne, France

Bouchier, Daniel 020058
CNRS, Palaiseau, France

Bouguerra, Sara 020156, 020294, 020389, 020393
imec, Genk, Belgium

Bourdin, Vincent 020406
CNRS, Paris, France

Bourgeois, Antoine 020102
SERIS, Singapore, Singapore

Bovesecchi, Gianluigi 020494
University of Rome Tor Vergata, Rome, Italy

Brabec, Christoph J. 020117
HI ERN, Erlangen, Germany

Bradford, David Roy 020077
Newcastle University, Newcastle upon Tyne, United Kingdom

Brailovsky, Peter Henri 020475
Fraunhofer ISE, Freiburg, Germany

Braña, Alejandro F. 020508
Autonomous University of Madrid, Madrid, Spain

Brandstätter, Andreas Lenzing Plastics, Lenzing, Austria	020227
Braun, Christian Luxembourg Institute of Science and Technology, Esch-sur-Alzette, Luxembourg	020457
Brecl, Kristijan University of Ljubljana, Ljubljana, Slovenia	020269, 020319
Bredemeier, Dennis Leibniz University Hannover, Hannover, Germany	020240
Breitenbücher, Marian Highline Technologies, Freiburg, Germany	020225
Brendel, Rolf ISFH, Emmerthal, Germany	020006, 020008, 020236, 020240, 020260, 020482
Brendstrup Møller, Clara Bolette DTU, Roskilde, Denmark	020028
Bretzel, Tamara Fraunhofer ISE, Freiburg, Germany	020195
Breyer, Christian LUT University, Lappeenranta, Finland	020479
Brito, Miguel University of Lisbon, Lisbon, Portugal	020457
Brivio, Elisabetta RSE, Milan, Italy	020462
Brockmann, Lukas ISFH, Emmerthal, Germany	020063
Brodnicke, Linda ETH, Zurich, Switzerland	020296
Brueckner, Emanuel ISFH, Emmerthal, Germany	020063
Bründlinger, Roland AIT, Vienna, Austria	020369
Brun, Gonzalo ENDEF, Zaragoza, Spain	020414, 020517
Bruno, Maddalena Fraunhofer ISE, Freiburg, Germany	020452
Buceta, Alicia CENER, Sarriguren, Spain	020300
Bucher, Christof BFH, Burgdorf, Switzerland	020179, 020322, 020359, 020369, 020386
Buchholz, Florian ISC Konstanz, Konstanz, Germany	020035, 020225, 020569
Buchmann, Johanna Berlin University of Applied Sciences, Berlin, Germany	020309
Buck, Thomas ISC Konstanz, Konstanz, Germany	020033

Buckland, Daniel — 020119, 020218
Henkel, Düsseldorf, Germany

Buddana, Viswa Harinath — 020482
DLR, Oldenburg, Germany

Bühlmann, Gian-Luca — 020385
ZHAW, Winterthur, Switzerland

Buerhop, Claudia — 020149, 020150, 020377
HI ERN, Erlangen, Germany

Buerhop-Lutz, Claudia — 020185, 020230
HI ERN, Erlangen, Germany

Burgers, Antonius R. — 020405
TNO, Petten, The Netherlands

Burri, Matthias — 020179
BFH, Burgdorf, Switzerland

Busto, Chiara — 020521
Eni, Novara, Italy

Butrichi, Fabio — 020087
University of Milano-Bicocca, Milan, Italy

Butt, Nauman — 020394
Lahore University of Management Sciences, Lahore, Pakistan

C. Tavares, Fabiele — 020090
Federal University of Rio de Janeiro, Duque de Caxias, Brazil

Cabal, Raphael — 020034
University Grenoble Alpes, Le Bourget-du-Lac, France

Caballero, Luis Jaime — 020501, 020508
UPM, Madrid, Spain

Caballero, Raquel — 020094
CSIC, Madrid, Spain

Caballero, Raquel — 020085
IO-CSIC, Madrid, Spain

Cabecinha, Vasco — 020565
Nova University Lisbon, Lisbon, Portugal

Cabello, Fatima — 020085
IO-CSIC, Madrid, Spain

Caçapietra Pires da Silva, Lucas Teixeira — 020025
PUCRS, Porto Alegre, Brazil

Caccavelli, Dominique — 020551
CSTB, Bussy-Saint Georges, France

Caccivio, Mauro — 020204, 020574
SUPSI, Mendrisio, Switzerland

Caffari, Francesca — 020551
ENEA, Ispra, Italy

Calabrese, Nicolandrea — 020551
ENEA, Ispra, Italy

Calin, Jean-Paul 020251
ENSTA Paris, Palaiseau, France

Çalışkan Arslan, Meriç 020006, 020135
Kalyon PV, Ankara, Türkiye

Caluori, Philip 020455
Virtual Vehicle, Graz, Austria

Camara, Assa 020274
Solargis, Bratislava, Slovakia

Cambarau, Werther 020139
Tecnalia, Donostia-San Sebastián, Spain

Campana, Pietro Elia 020381
Mälardalen University, Västerås, Sweden

Campos Guzman, Laura 020331
DLR, Almería, Spain

Cancro, Carmine 020378
ENEA, Naples, Italy

Canesse, Auriane 020196
PVsyst, Geneva, Switzerland

Cañizo, Carlos 020097
IES-UPM, Madrid, Spain

Cano, Francisco J. 020139
Tecnalia, Donostia - San Sebastián, Spain

Cano, Lucía 020127
ENDEF, Zaragoza, Spain

Cánovas, Enrique 020508
IMDEA Nanoscience Institute, Madrid, Spain

Cao, Han 020263
SERIS, Singapore, Singapore

Capitaine, Anna 020116
IPVF, Palaiseau, France

Cappelle, Jan 020329, 020351
KU Leuven, Ghent, Belgium

Capron, Guillaume 020217
CEA / INES, Le Bourget-du-Lac, France

Carballo López, José Antonio 020336
University of Almería, La Cañada de San Urbano, Spain

Cardenas, Luis Alejandro 020339, 020546
National University of Colombia, Bogotá, Colombia

Carmo, Paulo 020304, 020420
University of Évora, Évora, Portugal

Carrasco, Luis Miguel 020439, 020535, 020567
UPM, Madrid, Spain

Carrillo Mejía, Luis 020279
District University of Bogotá, Bogotá, Colombia

Carrillo, Rafael E. 020238
CSEM, Neuchâtel, Switzerland

Carroy, Perrine 020226
CEA/ INES, Le Bourget-du-Lac, France

Carstens, Justus 020003
ISC Konstanz, Konstanz, Germany

Cartenì, Fabrizio 020378
University of Naples Federico II, Naples, Italy

Casappa, Michele 020087
National Research Council, Parma, Italy

Casasola Paesa, Marta 020389
Hasselt University, Diepenbeek, Belgium

Castilla Nieto, María del Mar 020336
University of Almería, La Cañada de San Urbano, Spain

Castillo Patton, Daniel Jason 020326
Enertis Applus+, Madrid, Spain

Castro, Luis Guilherme 020530
Casa dos Ventos, Fortaleza, Brazil

Castro, Rui 020464
University of Lisbon, Lisbon, Portugal

Castro-Gallardo, Fernando 020417, 020422
University of Antofagasta, Antofagasta, Chile

Cavaco, Afonso 020304, 020565
University of Évora, Évora, Portugal

Cebecauer, Tomas 020274
Solargis, Bratislava, Slovakia

Çekerek, Gamze 020006
Kalyon PV, Ankara, Türkiye

Celik, Duygu 020551
WIP Renewable Energies, Munich, Germany

Çeliktaş, Melih Soner 020559
Ege University, İzmir, Türkiye

Centazzo, Massimo 020006
EnPV, Karlsruhe, Germany

Centeno Brito, Miguel 020421, 020490
University of Lisbon, Lisbon, Portugal

Cereceda, Eneko 020055, 020097, 020153, 020287
UPV/EHU, Bilbao, Spain

Ceretti, Mattia 020204
SUPSI, Mendrisio, Switzerland

Cesar, I. 020405
TNO, Petten, The Netherlands

Ceuppens, Ignas 020302
BUILD'UP, Aarschot, Belgium

Chatterji, Nithin 020071
SVNIT, Surat, India

Chen, Daniel 020048
SunDrive Solar, Kurnell, Australia

Chen, Syh-Homg 020161
ITRI, Hsinchu, Taiwan

Chen, Xiang 020111
Hohai University, Changzhou, China

Cheung, Kak Pong 020313
Kiel University of Applied Sciences, Kiel, Germany

Chhapia, Gaurang 020492
Belectric, Kolitzheim, Germany

Chiba, Takahiro 020436
Hokkaido University of Science, Sapporo, Japan

Chichignoud, Guy 020495
13Institut Polytechnique De Grenoble, Grenoble, France

Chicote, Beatriz 020289
Mondragon University, Arrasate-Mondragon, Spain

Chiesa, Matteo 020487
Khalifa University, Abu Dhabi, United Arab Emirates

Chini de Freitas, Felipe 020023
PUCRS, Porto Alegre, Brazil

Cho, Yunae 020045
KIER, Daejeon, South Korea

Choi, Kwan Bum 020102
SERIS, Singapore, Singapore

Chouder, Aissa 020301
University of M'sila, M'sila, Algeria

Chowdhury, Gofran 020276, 020544
3E, Brussels, Belgium

Christ, Anja 020063
ISFH, Emmerthal, Germany

Chrkavy, Daniel 020262
Solargis, Bratislava, Slovakia

Chueh, Wei-Lo 020021
TSEC, Hsinchu, Taiwan

Ciesla, Alison 020065
UNSW, Sydney, Australia

Cirimele, Vincenzo 020314
University of Bologna, Bologna, Italy

Clausing, Roland 020063, 020114
ISFH, Emmerthal, Germany

Clochard, Laurent 020031
Nines Photovoltaics, Dublin, Germany

Clochard, Laurent 020007
Nines Photovoltaics, Dublin, Ireland

Clyncke, Jan 020472, 020513
PV CYCLE, Brussels, Belgium

Coşkun, Özlem 020006, 020027, 020225
Kalyon PV, Ankara, Türkiye

Colberts, Fallon 020389
Zuyd University, Heerlen, The Netherlands
Colin, Hervé 020217, 020262
CEA / INES, Le Bourget-du-Lac, France
Collin, Stéphane 020074
C2N, Palaiseau, France
Colwell, Jack 020048
SunDrive Solar, Kurnell, Australia
Comak, Mertcan 020003
ISC Konstanz, Konstanz, Germany
Connolly, James Patrick 020058, 020060
CNRS, Gif-sur-Yvette, France
Cordeiro, Diogo 020464
EDP, Lisbon, Portugal
Cornago, Iñaki 020392
CENER, Sarriguren, Spain
Cornaro, Cristina 020494
University of Rome Tor Vergata, Rome, Italy
Correa, Guillermo 020412
Gonvarri MS R&D, Corvera - Asturias, Spain
Correia, Joana 020565
University of Évora, Évora, Portugal
Couderc, Romain 020217, 020311, 020546
CEA / INES, Le Bourget-du-Lac, France
Coutel, John 020244
SOLAÏS, Valbonne, France
Cowan, Don 020230
Kiwa PI Berlin, Hudson, United States of America
Cox, Joel D. 020250
SDU Climate Cluster, Odense, Denmark
Cox, Joel D 020306
SDU Climate Cluster, Odense, Denmark
Coz, Pier Luigi 020246
European Space Agency, Noordwijk, The Netherlands
Crespo, Carolina 020490
University of Lisbon, Lisbon, Portugal
Cristiane Pan, Aline 020548
UFRGS, Tramandaí, Brazil
Cristóbal, Ana Belén 020491, 020535, 020575
UPM, Madrid, Spain
Crozier McCleland, Jacqueline 020185, 020344
Nelson Mandela University, Port Elizabeth, South Africa
Cuadra, Juan Manuel 020318
CENER, Sarigurren, Spain
Cui, Jindan 020320, 020525
Tokyo University of Science, Tokyo, Japan

Culot, Dominique 020384
Dow Silicones Belgium, Seneffe, Belgium
Curon, Jonathan 020384
Dow Silicones Belgium, Seneffe, Belgium
Cusenza, Maria Anna 020466
RSE, Milan, Italy

D. Pinto, Luciana 020090
Federal University of Rio de Janeiro, Rio de Janeiro, Brazil
Daenen, Michael 020156, 020389, 020393
imec, Genk, Belgium
Dagla, Anastasia 020276
3E, Brussels, Belgium
Dahle, Arne 020225, 020495
Norsun, Oslo, Norway
Dahlioui, Dounia 020443
University of Agder, Grimstad, Norway
Dalibor, Thomas 020307
Avancis, Munich, Germany
Dalla Maria, Enrico 020485
Eurac Research, Bolzano, Italy
Dalla Torre, Francesco 020010
Applied Materials, Treviso, Italy
Dalmazzone, Didier 020251
ENSTA Paris, Palaiseau, France
Damon, Keanu 020382
7SecondSolar, Cape Town, South Africa
Danelli, Andrea 020462, 020466
RSE, Milan, Italy
Darsene Dimd, Berhane 020270
SINTEF, Trondheim, Norway
Das, Gourab 020005, 020222, 020463
RCT Solutions, Konstanz, Germany
Dasilva-Villanueva, Nerea 020014, 020501, 020508
UPM, Madrid, Spain
Daßler, David 020313
Fraunhofer CSP, Halle, Germany
Daßler, David 020355
Fraunhofer IMWS, Halle, Germany
Daume, Darwin 020361
pvnode, Rosenheim, Germany
Davidsen, Rasmus Schmidt 020028, 020039, 020043
Aarhus University, Aarhus, Denmark
De Almeida, Laura 020074
LAAS-CNRS, Toulouse, France

De Biasio, Martin 020504
Silicon Austria Labs, Villach, Austria
De Blasi, Mariam 020378
Enel Green Power, Pisa, Italy
de Graaf, Gertjan J. 020405
TNO, Petten, The Netherlands
de Groot, Koen M. 020405
TNO, Petten, The Netherlands
De Gruijter, Alvaro 020254
Eurac Research, Bolzano, Italy
de Jong, Minne M. 020169, 020425
TNO, Eindhoven, The Netherlands
De Jong, Richard 020156, 020294, 020389
imec, Genk, Belgium
de l`Epine, Mélodie 020252, 020505, 020543, 020564
Becquerel Institute France, Lyon, France
de l`Epine, Melodie 020225, 020334, 020520, 020558
Becquerel Institute, Brussels, Belgium
de l`Epine, Melodie 020570
IEA PVPS Task 1, Lyon, France
de la Casa Higueras, Juan 020269
University of Jaén, Jaén, Spain
de la Viuda, Eva 020205
University of Valladolid, Valladolid, Spain
de Meatza, Iratxe 020495
CIDETEC, San Sebastián, Spain
De Rose, Angela 020123
Fraunhofer ISE, Freiburg, Germany
De Rose, Jonas 020010
Fraunhofer ISE, Freiburg, Germany
Debastiani Benato, Betina 020019
AMIRES, Prague, Czech Republic
Deepti, 020563
SRM University, Sonipat, India
Del Campo, Valeria 020311
Federico Santa María Technical University, Valparaiso, Chile
del Cañizo, Carlos 020014, 020501, 020507, 020508
UPM, Madrid, Spain
Del Pero, Claudio 020249
Polytechnic University of Milan, Milan, Italy
Del Pozo, Alberto 020197, 020198
TECNALIA, Derio, Spain
del Prado Santamaria, Rodrigo 020191, 020376
DTU, Roskilde, Denmark
del Ser, Javier 020358
UPV/EHU, Bilbao, Spain

Delgado-Sanchez, Jose Maria 020089
University of Seville, Seville, Spain

Delli Veneri, Paola 020378
ENEA, Naples, Italy

Denafas, Julius 020225, 020353
Solitek, Vilnius, Lithuania

Deniz, Engin 020559
Ege University, İzmir, Türkiye

Denke, Sebastian 020236
ISFH, Emmerthal, Germany

Dentz, Laurie 020058
CNRS, Palaiseau, France

Derin Gure, Pinar 020513, 020521, 020556
ODTU GUNAM, Ankara, Türkiye

Derj, Anyssa 020116
IPVF, Palaiseau, France

Dessì, Alessio 020077
CNR-ICCOM, Sesto Fiorentino, Italy

Devenson, Jan 020157
Center for Physical Sciences and Technology (FTMC), Vilnius, Lithuania

Dhimish, Mahmoud 020346, 020376
DTU, Roskilde, Denmark

Di Matteo, Alfredo 020010
Enel Green Power, Catania, Italy

Diab, Mohanad 020203
Eurac Research, Bolzano, Italy

Diano, Marcello 020378
M2M Engineering, Naples, Italy

Diaz, Roberto 020300
Notio Association, Toledo, Spain

Díaz, Sara 020365, 020366
CENER, Sarriguren, Spain

Dietrich, Andreas 020355
DiSUN Deutsche Solarservice, Werder, Germany

Díez Alcántara, Eduardo 020501
UCM, Madrid, Spain

Díez, Eduardo 020508
UCM, Madrid, Spain

Dimd, Berhane Darsene 020495, 020510
SINTEF, Trondheim, Norway

Ding, Kaining 020233
FZJ, Jülich, Germany

Ding, Kung 020111
Hohai University, Changzhou, China

Dittmann, Sebastian 020318
Anhalt University of Applied Sciences, Köthen, Germany

Dittrich, Arne 020240
ISFH, Emmerthal, Germany
Dizier, Antoine 020373
INES, Le Bourget-du-Lac, France
Djeukeu, Ivanol Jaurece 020050
halm elektronik, Frankfurt am Main, Germany
Dobreva, Petja 020193
University of Namibia, Windhoek, Namibia
Dörenkämper, Maarten 020169
TNO, Eindhoven, The Netherlands
Dörn, Markus 020255
A-Null Development, Vienna, Austria
Doi, Minh Thong 020317
CEA INES, Le Bourget-du-Lac, France
Domínguez, César 020209, 020246, 020257
UPM, Madrid, Spain
Donadello, Alessandro 020485, 020489
Edyna, Bolzano, Italy
Donėlienė, Jolanta 020157
Applied Research Institute for Prospective Technologies, Vilnius, Lithuania
Donoso, José 020570
UNEF, Madrid, Spain
Doppler, Christian 020455
Virtual Vehicle, Graz, Austria
dos Reis, Givaldo 020348
University of São Paulo, São Paulo, Brazil
dos Santos, Jeremias 020409
University of Évora, Évora, Portugal
Doucet, Jean-Baptiste 020074
LAAS-CNRS, Toulouse, France
Dovesi, Roberto 020060
Academy of Sciences of Turin, Torino, Italy
Driesse, Anton 020211, 020293, 020452
PV Performance Labs, Freiburg, Germany
Duarte, Dorivaldo 020418, 020565
University of Evora, Évora, Portugal
Dubois, Sebastien 020034
University Grenoble Alpes, Le Bourget-du-Lac, France
Dubravskij, Piotr 020157
Applied Research Institute for Prospective Technologies, Vilnius, Lithuania
Dubravskij, Piotr 020380
Modern E-Technologies, Vilnius, Lithuania
Duerinckx, Filip 020064, 020225
Hasselt Unversity, Genk, Belgium

Düz, Cansel 020135
Kalyon PV, Ankara, Türkiye

Dullweber, Thorsten 020006, 020007, 020008, 020225
ISFH, Emmerthal, Germany

Dunlop, Ewan D. 020173, 020210, 020213
European Commission JRC, Ispra, Italy

Dupon, Olivier 020294
imec, Genk, Belgium

Dupuis, Julien 020188
EDF R&D, Moret Loing Orvanne, France

Dutykh, Denys 020338
Khalifa University, Abu Dhabi, United Arab Emirates

Duzellier, Sophie 020073
University of Toulouse, Toulouse, France

Dypvik Sødahl, Elin 020340
IFE, Kjeller, Norway

Ebert, Matthias 020426
Fraunhofer CSP, Halle, Germany

Ebert, Matthias 020355
Fraunhofer IMWS, Halle, Germany

Ebner, Rita 020318, 020334, 020521
AIT, Vienna, Austria

Echeverria, Oihane 020139
Tecnalia, Donostia - San Sebastián, Spain

Eder, Gabriele C. 020160, 020162, 020249, 020500, 020504
OFI, Vienna, Austria

Eelma, Tonis 020302
IBS, Tartu, Estonia

Efthymiou, Venizelos 020544
EPL Technology Frontiers, Dhali, Cyprus

Egan, Renate 020048
UNSW, Sydney, Australia

Egido, Miguel-Ángel 020407
UPM, Madrid, Spain

Eidtmann, Maximilian 020385
ZHAW, Winterthur, Switzerland

Eijgelaar, Marcel 020571
DNV, Arnhem, The Netherlands

Eikelboom, Erik 020225
Futurasun, Citadella, Italy

Einhaus, Roland 020312
ZSW, Stuttgart, Germany

Eisenacher, Matthias 020141
University of Applied Science Cologne, Cologne, Germany

Eiternick, Stefan — 020004, 020052
Fraunhofer CSP, Halle (Saale), Germany

Ekins-Daukes, Nicholas J. — 020065
UNSW, Sydney, Australia

El Ainaoui, Khadija — 020171
Green Energy Park, Benguerir, Morocco

El mrabet, Yasmine — 020171
Green Energy Park, Benguerir, Morocco

Elgaili, Mohamed — 020166
QEERI, Doha, Qatar

Elhamaoui, Said — 020171
Green Energy Park, Benguerir, Morocco

Ellis, Hanna — 020213
European Commission JRC, Ispra, Italy

Engelen, Tine — 020389
Hasselt University, Diepenbeek, Belgium

Erber, Alexander — 020386
BFH, Burgdorf, Switzerland

Eryılmaz, Hande — 020521
ODTÜ-GÜNAM, Ankara, Türkiye

Escudero, Ana — 020414
IaSol, Zaragoza, Spain

Esmailifar, Seyyed Majid — 020335, 020356, 020374, 020375
Amirkabir University of Technology, Tehran, Iran

Espinosa, Nieves — 020497, 020506
University of Murcia, Murcia, Spain

Essam T. Mohammed, Sarah — 020546
EU SOLARIS, Almeria, Spain

Esteras, Miguel — 020358
TECNALIA, Derio, Spain

Eyhorn, Steffen — 020369
Fraunhofer ISE, Freiburg, Germany

Fabel, Yann — 020235, 020237, 020239
DLR, Almeria, Spain

Fabris, Francesca — 020225
Futurasun, Citadella, Italy

Faes, Antonin — 020251
CSEM, Neuchâtel, Switzerland

Falangas, Alexandros — 020210
TRASIS International, Brussels, Belgium

Fang, Xue — 020525
Tokyo University of Science, Tokyo, Japan

Fano, Vanesa — 020055, 020097, 020153, 020287
UPV/EHU, Bilbao, Spain

Farhat, Mohammad Australian University, Kuwait City, Kuwait	020428
Farina, Andrea CNR-IFN, Milan, Italy	020066
Farrias-Basulto, Guillermo HZB, Berlin, Germany	020101
Fath, Moritz RCT Solutions, Konstanz, Germany	020463
Fath, Peter RCT Solutions, Konstanz, Germany	020005, 020463
Fava, Henrique University of Évora, Évora, Portugal	020565
Feichtner, Markus Sonnenkraft Energie, St. Veit/Glan, Austria	020255
Feichtner, Markus Sonnenkraft Energy, St. Veit/Glan, Austria	020160
Feldbacher, Sonja PCCL, Leoben, Austria	020136, 020500
Feldhof, Anne Maren University of Applied Science Cologne, Cologne, Germany	020522
Fernandes, Cláudia Centre for New Energy Technologies, Sacavém, Portugal	020464
Fernández Solas, Álvaro DLR, Almería, Spain	020331
Ferrando, Jorge University of Valencia, Paterna, Spain	020226
Ferreira, Catarina G. SDU Climate Cluster, Odense, Denmark	020250
Ferreira, Catarina SDU Climate Cluster, Odense, Denmark	020306
Ferrero, Sergio Polytechnic University of Turin, Turin, Italy	020079
Feuerherdt, Niels Berlin University of Applied Sciences, Berlin, Germany	020309
Fialho, Luis Eurac Research, Bolzano, Italy	020203, 020254, 020261, 020304, 020403, 020409, 020418, 020420, 020565
Figueroa, Andrés National University of Colombia, Bogotá, Colombia	020339
Fischer, Stefan SGL Carbon, Meitingen, Germany	020495
Fleischanderl, Martin voestalpine Stahl, Linz, Austria	020136
Fleury, Perine Biosphere Solar, Delft, The Netherlands	020513, 020521
Flouchi, Imane Green Energy Park, Benguerir, Morocco	020171

Fodor, Nikoletta 020521
SolarPower Europe, Brussels, Belgium

Fontani, Daniela 020066
CNR-INO, Florence, Italy

Forster, Jacob 020135
Fraunhofer ISE, Freiburg, Germany

Forstinger, Anne 020331
CSP Services, Cologne, Germany

Franch, Jordi Badosa 020406
Ecole Polytechnique, Palaiseau, France

Franchi, Daniele 020077
CNR-ICCOM, Sesto Fiorentino, Italy

Franquet, Erwin 020259, 020428
Côte d'Azur University, Nice, France

Frasson, Nicola 020019
Applied Materials, San Biagio di Callalta, Italy

Freer, Solomon 020396
PV Lighthouse, Coledale, Australia

Freitag, Marina 020077
Newcastle University, Newcastle upon Tyne, United Kingdom

Freund, Timo 020312
EnBW, Karlsruhe, Germany

Friansyah, Rizal 020376
DTU, Roskilde, Denmark

Friesen, Gabi 020160, 020249, 020574
SUPSI, Mendrisio, Switzerland

Friesen, Thomas 020249
Megasol Energie, Deitingen, Switzerland

Fritz Muñoz, Benjamín 020099
UPV, Valencia, Spain

Froebel, Jens 020121, 020142, 020192, 020223
Fraunhofer CSP, Halle, Germany

Frontini, Francesco 020249, 020253
SUPSI, Mendrisio, Switzerland

Fuentealba-Vidal, Edward 020129, 020311, 020342, 020417, 020422
University of Antofagasta, Antofagasta, Chile

Füreder-Kitzmüller, Friedrich 020136
voestalpine Stahl, Linz, Austria

Fuertes Marrón, David 020014, 020501, 020507, 020508
UPM, Madrid, Spain

Fuertes, David 020097
IES-UPM, Madrid, Spain

Furnari, Alessandro 020010
Enel Green Power, Catania, Italy

Fuß, Michael 020206
MBJ Solutions, Ahrensburg, Germany

Gabor, Andrew M. BrightSpot Automation, Boulder, United States of America	020166
Gaete, Martin University of Antofagasta, Antofagasta, Chile	020311
Gafert, Michael AIT, Vienna, Austria	020369
Gageot, Tristan CEA / INES, Le Bourget-du-Lac, France	020040
Gainza, Eusebio ALLOTARRA, Allo, Spain	020392
Galarza, Alejandra IPVF, Palaiseau, France	020461
Galbiati, Giuseppe Henkel, Düsseldorf, Germany	020119, 020218
Galdikas, Algirdas Applied Research Institute for Prospective Technologies, Vilnius, Lithuania	020157
Galiana, Beatriz Charles III University of Madrid, Madrid, Spain	020085
Galiazzo, Marco Applied Materials, San Biagio di Callalta, Italy	020019
Gall, Stefan HZB, Berlin, Germany	020101
Gallmetzer, Sandra Eurac Research, Bolzano, Italy	020261, 020509
Galparsoro, Ibon AZTI, PASAIA, Spain	020514
Gamarra, Ana Rosa CIEMAT, Madrid, Spain	020502
Ganter, Alissa ETH, Zurich, Switzerland	020296
Gaona García, Elvis Eduardo District University of Bogotá, Bogotá, Colombia	020279
Garabetian, Thomas SolarPower Europe, Brussels, Belgium	020551
García Campos, Enrique University of Almeria, La Cañada de San Urbano, Spain	020336
García, Fernando UC3M, Madrid, Spain	020326
García, Sonia Tecnalia, Donostia - San Sebastián, Spain	020139
García-Cañas, Alejandro IMDEA Nanoscience, Madrid, Spain	020257
García-Salinas, María José University of Almeria, Almería, Spain	020100

Garcia-Sanchez, Almudena 020246, 020257
UPM, Madrid, Spain

Garg, Vivek 020069, 020071, 020081
SVNIT, Surat, India

Garraín, Daniel 020502
CIEMAT, Madrid, Spain

Gasse, Hugues 020073
University of Toulouse, Toulouse, France

Gassner, Anika 020160, 020162, 020500, 020504
OFI, Vienna, Austria

Gatti, Cesare 020541
PedersoliGattai, Milan, Italy

Gattu, Apoorva 020003
ISC Konstanz, Konstanz, Germany

Gautier, Damien 020505
Becquerel Institute, Brussels, Belgium

Gauvin, Xavier 020302
Bouygues Construction, Saint-Quentin-en-Yvelines, France

Ge, Hua 020249
Concordia University, Montreal, Canada

Gebhardt, Paul 020195
Fraunhofer ISE, Freiburg, Germany

Geerligs, L. J. 020030
TNO, Petten, The Netherlands

Gehrlein, Janek 020522
University of Applied Science Cologne, Cologne, Germany

Geier, Jutta 020234
PCCL, Leoben, Austria

Geml, Fabian 020031
University of Konstanz, Constance, Germany

Genovese, Maria 020378
Enel Green Power, Pisa, Italy

Georghiou, George E. 020534
University of Cyprus, Nicosia, Cyprus

Germani, Simone 020302
CEI, Milan, Italy

Getsiou, Maria 020181
Directorate General for Research and Innovation, Brussels, Belgium

Geymayer, Lukas 020136
voestalpine Stahl, Linz, Austria

Ghahremani, Amirreza 020335, 020374
Amirkabir University of Technology, Tehran, Iran

Ghennioui, Abdellatif 020171
Green Energy Park, Benguerir, Morocco

Ghosh, Saptak 020519
CSTEP, Bengaluru, India

Girardi, Pierpaolo 020462, 020466
RSE, Milan, Italy

Giroux-Julien, Stephanie 020338
CNRS, Villeurbanne, France

Gissler, Antoine 020060
EDF R&D, Palaiseau, France

Göckeritz, Robert 020119
Fraunhofer CSP, Halle, Germany

Gohil, Hardik 020222
RCT Solutions, Konstanz, Germany

Gomes de Venuto, Vitor 020025
PUCRS, Porto Alegre, Brazil

Gomez Trillos, Juan Camilo 020482
DLR, Oldenburg, Germany

Gomez-Lazaro, Emilio 020562
University of Castilla-La Mancha, Albacete, Spain

Gonnella, Gabriella 020249, 020254
Eurac research, Bolzano, Italy

González Pérez, Sara 020151
ULL, San Cristóbal de La Laguna, Spain

González Rodríguez, Brais 020243
University of Vigo, Vigo, Spain

González, Miguel Ángel 020205
University of Valladolid, Valladolid, Spain

González-Díaz, Benjamín 020151
ULL, San Cristóbal de La Laguna, Spain

Goraya, Baljeet Singh 020475
Fraunhofer ISE, Freiburg, Germany

Gordillo, Gerardo 020110
National University of Colombia, Bogotá, Colombia

Gordon, Ivan 020521
imec, Genk, Belgium

Gottschalg, Ralph 020158
Anhalt University of Applied Sciences, Köthen, Germany

Gottschalg, Ralph 020056, 020201, 020229, 020233, 020284, 020574
Fraunhofer CSP, Halle, Germany

Govaerts, Jonathan 020019
imec, Genk, Belgium

Gracia Amillo, Ana María 020211
CENER, Pamplona, Spain

Gracia Amillo, Ana María 020318
CENER, Sarigurren, Spain

Gracia Amillo, Ana María 020181, 020365, 020366, 020497
CENER, Sarriguren, Spain

Gregory, Geoffrey 020006
EnPV, Karlsruhe, Germany

Greslou, Olivier 020551
CSTB, Bussy-Saint Georges, France

Grommes, Eva-Maria 020522, 020523
University of Applied Science Cologne, Cologne, Germany

Grosser, Stephan 020119, 020142, 020218
Fraunhofer CSP, Halle, Germany

Grünsteidl, Stefan 020307
Avancis, Munich, Germany

Gruginskie, Natasha 020067
Radboud University, Nijmegen, The Netherlands

Guedea, Isabel 020127, 020517
ENDEF, Zaragoza, Spain

Gülsoy, Eren Cihan 020521
METU, Ankara, Türkiye

Gümüs Çiftci, Burcu 020027
Kalyon PV, Ankara, Türkiye

Guerra, Gerardo 020448, 020481
GreenPowerMonitor a DNV company, Barcelona, Spain

Guidetti, Giulia 020541
Green Horse Advisory, Milan, Italy

Guillemoles, Jean François 020062
IPVF, Palaiseau, France

Guillevin, Nicolas 020225
TNO, Petten, The Netherlands

Gunbas, Gorkem 020113
ODTÜ-GÜNAM, Ankara, Türkiye

Gupta, Akshit 020551
Eurac Research, Bolzano, Italy

Gutierrez, Jose Ruben 020055, 020097, 020153, 020287
UPV/EHU, Bilbao, Spain

Gutjahr, Astrid 020030
TNO, Petten, The Netherlands

Haaland, Petry Kristine Nøttum 020476
NTNU, Trondheim, Norway

Haase, Felix 020063
ISFH, Emmerthal, Germany

Hadiwidjaja, Stella 020102
SERIS, Singapore, Singapore

Hadjipanayi, Maria 020064
University of Cyprus, Nicosia, Cyprus

Haedrich, Ingrid 020195, 020231
Fraunhofer ISE, Freiburg, Germany

Hämmer, Matthias 020470
bifa Umweltinstitut, Augsburg, Germany

Hafidi, Elias 020511
Inflights BV, Brussels, Belgium

Hagemann, Elizabeth M. 020416
Nelson Mandela University, Port Elizabeth, South Africa

Hallais, Géraldine 020058
CNRS, Palaiseau, France

Halle, Lasse 020359
BFH, Burgdorf, Switzerland

Hallensleben, Carina 020220
TAMURA-ELSOLD, Ilsenburg, Germany

Halm, Andreas 020218, 020220, 020221
ISC Konstanz, Konstanz, Germany

Halme, Janne 020249
Aalto University, Espoo, Finland

Hamada, Toshiyuki 020190
Osaka Electro-Communication University, Osaka, Japan

Hammer, Annette 020239
DLR, Oldenburg, Germany

Hamouda, Frederic 020058
CNRS, Palaiseau, France

Hanifi, Hamed 020121, 020125, 020137, 020223
AESOLAR, Koenigsbrunn, Germany

Hansen, Per-Anders 020017, 020503
Institute for Energy Technology, Kjeller, Norway

Harit, Amit Kumar 020064
Hasselt Unversity, Genk, Belgium

Harrison, Samuel 020225
CEA, Le Bourget-du-Lac, France

Hashem, Ahmad 020056, 020201
Anhalt University of Applied Sciences, Köthen, Germany

Hategan, Sergiu Mihai 020283
West University of Timisoara, Timisoara, Romania

Hauch, Jens 020117, 020149, 020150
HI ERN, Erlangen, Germany

Hauer, Martin 020255
Bartenbach, Vienna, Austria

Haverkamp, Helge 020008
centrotherm international, Blaubeuren, Germany

Hee Lee, Sang 020045
KIER, Daejeon, South Korea

Heidrich, Robert 020233
Fraunhofer CSP, Halle, Germany

Heikkinen, Kyösti 020423
VTT Technical Research Centre of Finland, Oulu, Finland

Heiser, Moritz 020230
Kiwa PI Berlin, Berlin, Germany

Helbig, Matthias 020220
ISC Konstanz, Konstanz, Germany

Helten, David 020331
CSP Services, Cologne, Germany

Hennig, Carsten 020313, 020355
saferay holding, Berlin, Germany

Hennig, Patrick 020313
Kiel University of Applied Sciences, Kiel, Germany

Heras, Jesús 020536
Wattkraft, Madrid, Spain

Hermle, Martin 020475
Fraunhofer ISE, Freiburg, Germany

Hernández Mora, Johann Alexander 020279, 020441
District University of Bogotá, Bogotá, Colombia

Hernández, Jaime J. 020257
IMDEA Nanoscience, Madrid, Spain

Hernández, Johann 020526
Francisco José de Caldas District University, Bogota, Colombia

Herodotou, Panayiotis 020534
University of Cyprus, Nicosia, Cyprus

Herrera Leon, Fernando Augusto 020339, 020546
National University of Colombia, Bogotá, Colombia

Herrero, Leire 020139
Tecnalia, Donostia - San Sebastián, Spain

Herrero, Rebeca 020209, 020453, 020459
UPM, Madrid, Spain

Herrmann, Werner 020208
TÜV Rheinland Solar, Cologne, Germany

Herteleer, Bert 020329, 020351
KU Leuven, Ghent, Belgium

Herteleer, Bert 020574
SUPSI, Mendrisio, Switzerland

Hessler-Wyser, Aïcha 020251
EPFL, Neuchâtel, Switzerland

Heydari, Azim 020485
Eurac Research, Bolzano, Italy

Hinken, David 020236
ISFH, Emmerthal, Germany

Hladys, Bertrand 020010
CEA, Grenoble, France

Hoex, Bram 020065
UNSW, Sydney, Australia

Hofer, Leo 020322
BFH, Burgdorf, Switzerland

Hoffmann, Erik 020006
EnPV, Karlsruhe, Germany

Hogan Almeida, Rita UPM, Madrid, Spain	020535, 020567
Hollemann, Christina ISFH, Emmerthal, Germany	020008
Holovský, Jakub Czech Technical University, Prague, Czech Republic	020107
Honrubia-Escribano, Andrés University of Castilla-La Mancha, Albacete, Spain	020562
Hopp, Tobias Sunman Energy, Frankfurt, Germany	020384
Horn, Jonas halm elektronik, Frankfurt am Main, Germany	020050
Horta, Pedro University of Évora, Évora, Portugal	020304, 020403, 020409, 020418, 020420, 020565
Hosatte, Mikaël SEGTON Advanced Technology, Versailles, France	020068
Hoß, Jan ISC Konstanz, Konstanz, Germany	020004, 020035
Hossain, Mohammad Istiaque QEERI, Doha, Qatar	020042, 020075, 020108, 020109, 020146, 020147
Hou, Yi SERIS, Singapore, Singapore	020102
Hsiao, Pei-Chieh UNSW, Sydney, Australia	020048
Hsieh, Cho Fan ITRI, Hsinchu, Taiwan	020083, 020161, 020163
Hu, Shuaifeng University of Oxford, Oxford, United Kingdom	020226
Huang, Chris SunDrive Solar, Kurnell, Australia	020048
Huang, Gan KIT, Eggenstein-Leopoldshafen, Germany	020272
Huang, Lu-Jan TNO, Leiden, The Netherlands	020425
Huang, Tzu-Yen National Synchrotron Radiation Research Center, Hsinchu, Taiwan	020096
Hügi, Matthias BFH, Burgdorf, Switzerland	020322
Huemer, Martin University of Linz, Linz, Austria	020227
Huerta, Hugo E. TUAS, Turku, Finland	020286, 020400
Hüttl, Bernd Coburg University of Applied Sciences, Coburg, Germany	020361

Hulik Jansova, Marketa 020274
Solargis, Bratislava, Slovakia

Hung, Tzu Han 020552
ITRI, Taipei City, Taiwan

Hutterer-Tik, Thomas 020347
Watt Analytics, Vienna, Austria

Hwang, Hye-Mi 020324, 020357, 020561
KIER, Daejeon, South Korea

Iglesias, Unai 020139
Tecnalia, Donostia - San Sebastián, Spain

Ikeda, Kazuaki 020436
AIST, Koriyama, Japan

Infante, Paulo 020420
University of Évora, Évora, Portugal

Isabella, Olindo 020515
TU Delft, Delft, The Netherlands

Ishikawa, Ryousuke 020106, 020115
Tokyo City University, Setagaya, Japan

Iwaszko, Victorien 020495
ROSI Solar, Saint-Martin-d'Hères, France

Izquierdo-Roca, Victor 020094
IREC, Barcelona, Spain

J. N. Soares, Guillermo 020090
Federal University of Rio de Janeiro, Duque de Caxias, Brazil

Jacob, Julieu 020302
METABUILD, Berlin, Germany

Jacobs, Ayesha 020382
Zutari, Cape Town, South Africa

Jaeckel, Bengt 020056, 020119, 020121, 020140, 020142, 020175, 020192, 020201, 020223, 020229
Fraunhofer CSP, Halle, Germany

Jäger Waldau, Arnulf 020570
European Commission, Rome, Italy

Jäger, Philip 020006
ISFH, Emmerthal, Germany

Jäggi, Adrian 020179
BFH, Burgdorf, Switzerland

Järventausta, Pertti 020445
Tampere University, Tampere, Finland

Jaffré, Alexandre 020058
CNRS, Gif-sur-Yvette, France

Jahn, Ulrike 020521, 020574
Fraunhofer CSP, Halle, Germany

Jahn, Ulrike 020355
Fraunhofer IMWS, Halle, Germany

Jahreis, Sophia 020142, 020192
Fraunhofer CSP, Halle, Germany

Jakomin, Roberto 020090
Federal University of Rio de Janeiro, Duque de Caxias, Brazil

Jakubik, Martin 020274
Solargis, Bratislava, Slovakia

Jakuza, Paola 020089
University of Padova, Padova, Italy

Jalkh, Judy 020455
Virtual Vehicle, Graz, Austria

Jandl, Ralf 020204
FFHS, Zurich, Switzerland

Jankovec, Marko 020197
University of Ljubljana, Ljubljana, Slovenia

Jaworczak, Kamil 020402
Technology Innovation Institute, Abu Dhabi, United Arab Emirates

Jensen, Adam R. 020267
DTU, Kongens Lyngby, Denmark

Jeong, Jungi 020323
K-water, Daejeon, South Korea

Jeong, Kyung Taek 020045
KIER, Daejeon, South Korea

Jeong, Minsoo 020045
KIER, Daejeon, South Korea

Jeronimo, Pedro 020010
CEA, Grenoble, France

Jiang, Zonghan 020158, 020201
Anhalt University of Applied Sciences, Köthen, Germany

Jimenez, Maria 020302
Onyx Solar, Avila, Spain

Jimeno, Juan Carlos 020055, 020097, 020153, 020287, 020289, 020353
UPV/EHU, Bilbao, Spain

Jo, Hyunsik 020323
K-water, Daejeon, South Korea

Job, Enzo 020231
Fraunhofer ISE, Freiburg, Germany

Johnson, Mark Robert 020546
Institut Laue-Langevin (ILL), Grenoble, France

Joo, Dongmyoung 020449
KETI, Wonmi-gu, South Korea

Jooss, Wolfgang 020005, 020222, 020463
RCT Solutions, Konstanz, Germany

Joseph, Daniel Christopher 020123
Fraunhofer ISE, Freiburg, Germany

Joshi, Deepak 020069, 020081
SVNIT, Surat, India

Joss, David 020359, 020369, 020386
BFH, Burgdorf, Switzerland

Jouini, Anis 020034
ECM Technologies, Grenoble, France

Jouttijärvi, Sami 020286, 020298, 020398
University of Turku, Turku, Finland

Joziak, Roman 020230
Kiwa PI Berlin, Berlin, Germany

Ju, Young-Chul 020324, 020357, 020561
KIER, Daejeon, South Korea

Jugo, Josu 020437
UPV/EHU, Leioa, Spain

Junge, Sebastian 020008, 020482
ISFH, Emmerthal, Germany

Kaaya, Ismail 020156, 020294, 020389, 020393
imec, Genk, Belgium

Kähler, Jan-Dirk 020482
Centrotherm International, Blaubeuren, Germany

Kahraman, Mert 020027
Kalyon PV, Ankara, Türkiye

Kainz, Konrad 020430
AIT, Vienna, Austria

Kaiser, Martin 020215
Fraunhofer ISE, Freiburg, Germany

Kaizuka, Izumi 020570
RTS Corporation, Tokyo, Japan

Kajari-Schröder, Sarah 020063
ISFH, Emmerthal, Germany

Kallioharju, Kari 020444, 020445
TUAS, Tampere, Finland

Kalliojärvi, Heidi 020194
Tampere University, Tampere, Finland

Kalshetty, Mahesh 020519
CSTEP, Bengaluru, India

Kaltenbach, Thomas 020195
Fraunhofer ISE, Freiburg, Germany

Kamphues, Joshua 020031
University of Konstanz, Constance, Germany

Kandiyoti-Eskenazi, Selin 020467
CSEM, Neuchâtel, Switzerland

Kang, Min Gu 020045
KIER, Daejeon, South Korea

Kapetanovic, Viktor 020367
Nextracker, Fremont, United States of America

Karhu, Juha 020286
Finnish Meteorological Institute, Helsinki, Finland

Kari, Thøger 020191, 020376
DTU, Roskilde, Denmark

Karimy, Hedayatullah 020052
Fraunhofer CSP, Halle (Saale), Germany

Karttunen, Lauri 020298, 020398
University of Turku, Turku, Finland

Kasper, Ruth 020167, 020232
University of Applied Sciences Cologne, Cologne, Germany

Katouli, Tannaz 020195
Fraunhofer ISE, Freiburg, Germany

Kaufmann, Kai 020355
DENKweit, Halle, Germany

Kawabata, Rudy 020092
PUC-Rio, Rio de Janeiro, Brazil

Kemp, Linda 020390
MARIN, Wageningen, The Netherlands

Kenchington, Ian 020225, 020474, 020558
Becquerel Institute, Brussels, Belgium

Kenny, Robert 020210
European Commission JRC, Ispra, Italy

Khan, Abeer Ali 020513
First Solar, Mainz, Germany

Khosravi, Arash 020381
Mälardalen University, Västerås, Sweden

Kikkert, Benjamin W. J. 020405
TNO, Petten, The Netherlands

Kilickaya, Seda 020020
ODTÜ-GÜNAM, Ankara, Türkiye

Kim, Jin-Hong 020449
KETI, Wonmi-gu, South Korea

Kim, Jun-Tae 020249
Kongju National University, Chungnam, South Korea

Kim, Kihwan 020112
KIER, Daejeon, South Korea

Kim, Seok Won 020449
KETI, Wonmi-gu, South Korea

Kim, Yong-Jin 020045
KIER, Daejeon, South Korea

Kinge, Sachin 020117
Toyota Motors Europe, Brussels, Belgium

Kuczyńska-Łażewska, Anna 020498, 020499
Gdansk University of Technology, Gdansk, Poland

Kühne, Philip 020240
Leibniz University Hannover, Hannover, Germany

Kuhrmann, Bernd 020206
MBJ Solutions, Ahrensburg, Germany

Kujansivu, Eino 020554
Solarigo Systems, Pirkkala, Finland

Kumar, Gaurav 020563
MERI College of Engineering and Technology, Bahadurgarh, India

Kumar, Sagarika 020402
Technology Innovation Institute, Abu Dhabi, United Arab Emirates

Kumar, Saurabh 020563
PTB, Braunshweig, Germany

Kuo, Cheng-Wen 020021, 020053
TSEC, Hsinchu, Taiwan

Kurtulus, Gunes 020556
ODTU GUNAM, Ankara, Türkiye

Kuruganti, Vaibhav V. 020033
ISC Konstanz, Konstanz, Germany

Kurz, Hannes 020136
voestalpine Stahl, Linz, Austria

Kusch, Alexander 020361
Coburg University of Applied Sciences, Coburg, Germany

Kuzhagaliyeva, Nursulu 020402
Technology Innovation Institute, Abu Dhabi, United Arab Emirates

Kuznicki, Zbigniew T. 020013, 020068
SEGTON Advanced Technology, Versailles, France

Kwiatkowski, Jerzy 020551
NAPE, Warsaw, Poland

Kyranaki, Nikoleta 020156
Hasselt University, Genk, Belgium

Kyranaki, Nikoleta 020393
Hasselt University, Hasselt, Belgium

Kyranaki, Nikoleta 020294
imec, Genk, Belgium

Kyratsi, Theodora 020495
University of Cyprus, Nicosia, Cyprus

L. Andersen, Nanna 020477
DTU, Roskilde, Denmark

L. Souza, Patrícia 020090
Federal University of Rio de Janeiro, Rio de Janeiro, Brazil

Lachowicz, Agata CSEM, Neuchâtel, Switzerland	020039
Lahr, Simon Next2Sun Technology, Dillingen, Germany	020388
Lahr, Simon Next2Sun, Dillingen, Germany	020411
Lajunen, Antti University of Helsinki, Helsinki, Finland	020400
Lambertz, Andreas FZJ, Jülich, Germany	020233
Lamblot, Hervé Sunstyle, Paris, France	020302
Lamghari, Fouad Fujairah Research Centre, Fujairah, United Arab Emirates	020402
Lamminaho, Jani SDU Climate Cluster, Odense, Denmark	020250, 020306
Landaas, Christian Northern Silicon, Meråker, Norway	020495
Landberg, Lars DNV Denmark, Hellerup, Denmark	020448
Landberg, Lars DNV Denmark, Hellerup, Spain	020481
Landes, Dieter Coburg University of Applied Sciences, Coburg, Germany	020361
Landová, Lucie Czech Technical University, Prague, Czech Republic	020107
Lansade, David University of Toulouse, Toulouse, France	020073
Lappalainen, Kari Tampere University, Tampere, Finland	020194, 020528, 020537
Lara, Yolanda ENDEF, Zaragoza, Spain	020127, 020414, 020517
Larionova, Yevgeniya ISFH, Emmerthal, Germany	020006, 020007, 020225
Låstad, Jonas NTNU, Trondheim, Norway	020011
Laurens-Berge, Clarisse University Grenoble Alpes, Le Bourget-du-Lac, France	020034
Laurikėnas, Paulius Solitek, Vilnius, Lithuania	020353
Lauwaert, Johan Ghent University, Ghent, Belgium	020064
Lazaro-Castrillon, Luna IO-CSIC, Madrid, Spain	020085
Le Bossenec, Hugo IPVF, Palaiseau, France	020116

Le Brun, Anton 020096
Australian Nuclear Science and Technology Organisation, Lucas Heights, Australia

Lechón, Yolanda 020502
CIEMAT, Madrid, Spain

Ledesma, Javier R. 020337
UPM, Madrid, Spain

Ledesma, Javier 020446
UPM, Madrid, Spain

Lee, Chun-Wei 020021
TSEC, Hsinchu, Taiwan

Lee, Hyunju 020046
Meiji University, Kanagawa, Japan

Lee, Jieun 020323
K-water, Daejeon, South Korea

Lee, Jin-Seok 020324, 020357, 020561
KIER, Daejeon, South Korea

Legarrea, Aritz 020365
CENER, Sarriguren, Spain

Lelievre, Jean-Francois 020373
INES, Le Bourget-du-Lac, France

Lelong, Benoit 020373
Cythelia Energy, La Motte-Servolex, France

Leloux, Jonathan 020262
LuciSun, Villers-la-Ville, Belgium

Lenain, Philippe 020495
benkei, Lyon, France

Lennon, Alison 020048
UNSW, Sydney, Australia

Lenz, Markus 020226
School of Life Sciences FHNW, Muttenz, Switzerland

Lenzmann, Frank 020019
TNO Energy Transition, Petten, The Netherlands

Leone, Sander 020405
Novar, Rotterdam, The Netherlands

Leonforte, Fabrizio 020249
Polytechnic University of Milan, Milan, Italy

Leopold, Ulrich 020457
Luxembourg Institute of Science and Technology, Esch-sur-Alzette, Luxembourg

Levrat, Jacques 020251, 020467
CSEM, Neuchâtel, Switzerland

Levtchenko, Alexandra 020116
IPVF, Palaiseau, France

Lewandowski, Simon 020073
University of Toulouse, Toulouse, France

Leza, Baurin 020412
Gonvarri MS R&D, Corvera - Asturias, Spain

Lezaca, Jorge 020239
DLR, Oldenburg, Germany

Li, Xinyang 020222
RCT Solutions, Konstanz, Germany

Li, Yung-Chih 020021
TSEC, Hsinchu, Taiwan

Li, Yuxuan 020001
East China University of Science and Technology, Shanghai, China

Libal, Joris 020218, 020474
ISC Konstanz, Konstanz, Germany

Lichtenberger, Janine 020430
AIT, Vienna, Austria

Lițiu, Andrei Vladimir 020551
EPB Center, Rotterdam, The Netherlands

Lin, Shih-Chieh 020021
TSEC, Hsinchu, Taiwan

Lindahl, Johan 020486, 020532
Becquerel Sweden, Knivsta, Sweden

Linder, Johannes 020492
Belectric, Kolitzheim, Germany

Lindfors, Anders 020286
Finnish Meteorological Institute, Helsinki, Finland

Lindig, Sascha 020371
Univers, Courbevoie, France

Linke, Jonathan 020004, 020035, 020225
ISC Konstanz, Konstanz, Germany

Linß, Volker 020033
VON ARDENNE, Dresden, Germany

Lipovšek, Benjamin 020047
University of Ljubljana, Ljubljana, Slovenia

Lippke, Benjamin 020180, 020230
Kiwa PI Berlin, Berlin, Germany

List-Kratochvil, Emil 020101
HZB, Berlin, Germany

Litrico, Grazia 020010
Enel Green Power, Catania, Italy

Liu, Cui 020001
East China University of Science and Technology, Shanghai, China

Liu, Dongyang 020063
ISFH, Emmerthal, Germany

Liu, Han-Chang 020350
ITRI, Tainan, Taiwan

Liu, Huiping 020495
GRÄNGES, Finspång, Sweden

Liu, Mengdi 020144, 020208
TÜV Rheinland, Shanghai, China

Liu, Yung-Tsung 020053, 020083
ITRI, Hsinchu, Taiwan

Livera, Andreas 020534
University of Cyprus, Nicosia, Cyprus

Lizin, Sebastien 020513, 020521
UHasselt, Hasselt, Belgium

Llarena, María Elena 020151
ITER, Granadilla de Abona, Spain

Loeckenhoff, Ruediger F. 020416
AZUR SPACE Solar Power, Heilbronn, Germany

Löhning, Martha 020063
ISFH, Emmerthal, Germany

Löhr, Johannes 020063, 020114
ISFH, Emmerthal, Germany

Lokhat, Ismaël 020262
Cythelia Energy, La Motte-Servolex, France

Lokhat, Ismael 020373
Trace Software, Saint-Romain-de-Colbosc, France

Lombardo, Salvatore 020066
CNR-IMM, Catania, Italy

Long, Yean-San 020053, 020083
ITRI, Hsinchu, Taiwan

Longo, Giulia 020099
UPV, Valencia, Spain

Lopes Gomes, Carlos Javier 020432, 020434
Sunveon, Madrid, Spain

Lopes, Ana Patrícia 020464
University of Lisbon, Lisbon, Portugal

López Cuéllar, Juan Manuel 020501
UCM, Madrid, Spain

López Dalmau, Daniel 020432, 020434
Sunveon, Madrid, Spain

López, Nuria 020451
DTU, Roskilde, Denmark

Lorenz, Dieter 020206
MBJ Solutions, Ahrensburg, Germany

Lorenzo Pigueiras, Eduardo 020363
UPM, Madrid, Spain

Lorenzo, Celena 020337, 020536
UPM, Madrid, Spain

Lorenzo, Eduardo 020439, 020446
UPM, Madrid, Spain

Lossen, Jan ISC Konstanz, Konstanz, Germany	020003, 020035
Louwen, Atse Eurac Research, Bolzano, Italy	020203, 020226, 020261, 020509, 020546
Louwen, Atse RISE, Boras, Sweden	020316
Lu, Huan-Wu ITRI, Hsinchu, Taiwan	020161
Lu, Matthew Kiwa PI Berlin, Shanghai, China	020230
Lucea, Aingeru TECNALIA, Derio, Spain	020197, 020198
Lüdemann, Marius Fraunhofer CSP, Halle, Germany	020233
Luís, Margarida University of Lisbon, Lisbon, Portugal	020421
Lustoza de Souza, Patricia UFRJ, Rio de Janeiro, Brazil	020092
Ly, Moussa PUCRS, Porto Alegre, Brazil	020023, 020025
Lyubenova, Teodora European Commission JRC, Ispra, Italy	020210
M. Bazilio, Willian PUC-Rio, Rio de Janeiro, Brazil	020092
M. S. Kawabata, Rudy Pontifical Catholic University of Rio de Janeiro, Rio de Janeiro, Brazil	020090
M. Torelly, Guilherme Pontifical Catholic University of Rio de Janeiro, Rio de Janeiro, Brazil	020090
Ma Lu, Silvia Mälardalen University, Västerås, Sweden	020381
Ma, Xiang SINTEF, Oslo, Norway	020011
Macé, Philippe Becquerel Institute, Brussels, Belgium	020225, 020252, 020474, 020505, 020543, 020558, 020573
Mack, Sebastian Fraunhofer ISE, Freiburg, Germany	020031
Madsen, Morten SDU Climate Cluster, Odense, Denmark	020250, 020306
Mahmood, Aysha DTU, Roskilde, Denmark	020265, 020376
Maixner, Andreas AESOLAR, Koenigsbrunn, Germany	020121, 020125, 020137, 020223

Miró-Llorente, Marta 020094
IREC, Barcelona, Spain

Misra, Prashant 020429
NISE, Gurugram, India

Miszczuk, Andrzej 020068
Roltec, Poznań, Poland

Mittag, Max 020137
Fraunhofer ISE, Freiburg, Germany

Mittal, Ankit 020318
AIT, Vienna, Austria

Mittelman, Gur 020379
Afeka Tel-Aviv Academic College of Engineering, Tel Aviv, Israel

Mizushima, Io 020028
IPU P/S, Virum, Denmark

Mizushima, Io 020037
IPU, Virum, Denmark

Mngomezulu, Ndumiso 020344
PVinsight, Port Elizabeth, South Africa

Mo, Alvin 020065
UNSW, Sydney, Australia

Mockeviciute-Azzopardi, Austeja 020334
FIR, Birkirkara, Malta

Moe Nygård, Magnus 020340
IFE, Kjeller, Norway

Moehlecke, Adriano 020023, 020025
PUCRS, Porto Alegre, Brazil

Mohammadi, Mohammad Hossein 020037, 020104
Aarhus University, Aarhus, Denmark

Mollier, Stéphane 020262
CEA / INES, Le Bourget-du-Lac, France

Moltke, Asbjørn 020043
Technical University of Denmark, Copenhagen, Denmark

Mondaca-Cuevas, Gino 020422
University of Antofagasta, Antofagasta, Chile

Monokroussos, Christos 020181
TÜV Rheinland Shanghai, Shanghai, China

Monokroussos, Christos 020144, 020208
TÜV Rheinland, Shanghai, China

Monteiro Martins, Filipa 020317
Galp Energia, Lisbon, Portugal

Montes, Carlos 020151
ITER, Granadilla de Abona, Spain

Montoya, Josefa 020311
University of Antofagasta, Antofagasta, Chile

Morabito, Floriana 020066
CNR-IFN, Milan, Italy

Moradi Sizkouhi, Amirmohammad 020356, 020375
Concordia University, Montreal, Canada

Moradi Zavie Kord, Soroush 020400
University of Helsinki, Helsinki, Finland

Morales, Sergio 020491
UPM, Madrid, Spain

Morantes Quintana, Giobertti Raul 020551
Eurac Research, Bolzano, Italy

Mordvinkin, Anton 020233
Fraunhofer CSP, Halle, Germany

Moreda, Guillermo P. 020407
UPM, Madrid, Spain

Morin, Claire 020551
SolarPower Europe, Brussels, Belgium

Morisset, Audrey 020068
CSEM, Neuchâtel, Switzerland

Morlier, Arnaud 020156
Hasselt University, Genk, Belgium

Morlier, Arnaud 020294, 020389
imec, Genk, Belgium

Mortazavifar, Leila 020056, 020158, 020201, 020284
Anhalt University of Applied Sciences, Köthen, Germany

Moruno, Ricardo 020209, 020453
UPM, Madrid, Spain

Mosel, Frank 020015
PVA TePla, Wettenberg, Germany

Moser, David 020573
Becquerel Institute Italy, Trento, Italy

Moser, David 020316
Becquerel Institute, Bolzano, Italy

Moser, David 020254
Bequerel Institute, Trento, Italy

Moser, David 020203, 020226, 020261, 020325, 020485, 020489, 020546
Eurac Research, Bolzano, Italy

Mouhoubi, Felicia 020134
CEA / INES, Le Bourget-du-Lac, France

Müllejans, Harald 020208, 020213
European Commission JRC, Ispra, Italy

Müller, Alexander 020119
Fraunhofer CSP, Halle, Germany

Müller, Larissa 020523
University of Applied Sciences Cologne, Cologne, Germany

Mugica, Maikel 020139
Tecnalia, Donostia - San Sebastián, Spain

Mujovi, Fahradin 020251
CSEM, Neuchâtel, Switzerland

Mukherjee, Srijani 020338
CEA / INES, Le Bourget-du-Lac, France

Mukhtar, Mariyam 020057
University of Verona, Verona, Italy

Mulder, Peter 020067
Radboud University, Nijmegen, The Netherlands

Muller, Matthew 020314
NREL, Denver, United States of America

Munkhammar, Joakim 020532
Uppsala University, Uppsala, Sweden

Muñoz Cerón, Emilio 020269
University of Jaén, Jaén, Spain

Muñoz, Delfina 020040, 020311, 020546
CEA / INES, Le Bourget-du-Lac, France

Muñoz, Delfina 020521
CEA, Le Bourget-du-Lac, France

Muñoz, Delfina 020226
CEA/ INES, Le Bourget-du-Lac, France

Muñoz, Ildefonso 020365, 020366, 020392
CENER, Sarriguren, Spain

Muñoz, Jesús Ángel 020508
UCM, Madrid, Spain

Muñoz-García, Miguel-Ángel 020407
UPM, Madrid, Spain

Murano, Giovanni 020551
ENEA, Ispra, Italy

Murillo, Asier 020497
CENER, Sarriguren, Spain

Musembi, Robinson J. 020272
University of Nairobi, Nairobi, Kenya

Nabipouor, Mohammad 020426
Anhalt University of Applied Sciences, Köthen, Germany

Nagel, Henning 020475
Fraunhofer ISE, Freiburg, Germany

Nakamura, Kyotaro 020046
Toyota Technological Institute, Nagoya, Japan

Nanno, Ikuo 020190
Nanno Energy Research Center, Yamaguchi, Japan

Nargelienė, Viktorija 020157
Center for Physical Sciences and Technology (FTMC), Vilnius, Lithuania

Narsi Patel, Hitarth 020069
SVNIT, Surat, India

Narvarte, Luis 020337, 020446, 020491, 020535, 020536, 020567, 020575
UPM, Madrid, Spain

Nascimento, Lucas 020377
Solar Energy Research Laboratory Fotovoltaica/ UFSC, Florianópolis, Brazil

Nasebandt, Lasse 020063
ISFH, Emmerthal, Germany

Nasser, Hisham 020226
ODTÜ-GÜNAM, Ankara, Türkiye

Naveiro, José Manuel 020414
ENDEF, Zaragoza, Spain

Nazififard, Mohammad 020259, 020428
Côte d`Azur University, Nice, France

Nejim, Ahmed 020058
SILVACO, St. Ives, United Kingdom

Nel, Paul 020382
7SecondSolar, Cape Town, South Africa

Nelson, Jenny 020394
Imperial College London, London, United Kingdom

Neuba, Adam 020114
Paderborn University, Paderborn, Germany

Neuber, Viola 020031
Fraunhofer ISE, Freiburg, Germany

Neuhaus, Holger 020123, 020140
Fraunhofer ISE, Freiburg, Germany

Neumaier, Lukas 020504
Silicon Austria Labs, Villach, Austria

Neussl, Vassilissa 020318, 020430
AIT, Vienna, Austria

Neykova, Neda 020107
Czech Technical University, Prague, Czech Republic

Nezhad, Mahyar 020230
Kiwa PI Berlin, Hudson, United States of America

Nguyen, Viet Xuan 020008
centrotherm international, Blaubeuren, Germany

Nicolet-dit-Félix, Kléber 020251
EPFL, Neuchâtel, Switzerland

Nicot-Senneville, Zoltan 020102
SERIS, Singapore, Singapore

Nielsen, Michael P. 020065
UNSW, Sydney, Australia

Nissen, Hauke 020313
Wattmanufactur, Galmsbüll, Germany

Nitsche, Tobias 020119, 020218
Henkel, Düsseldorf, Germany

Nobre, André M. 020263
PV Doctor, Singapore, Singapore

Noels, Serge 020472
PV CYCLE, Brussels, Belgium

Noh, Yong-Su 020449
KETI, Wonmi-gu, South Korea

Nold, Sebastian 020461
Fraunhofer ISE, Freiburg, France

Nold, Sebastian 020475
Fraunhofer ISE, Freiburg, Germany

Nordboe, Eirik 020495
Fiven Norge, Lillesand, Norway

Norde Santos, Fernanda 020331
DLR, Almería, Spain

Nouri, Bijan 020235, 020237, 020239
DLR, Almería, Spain

Nova, David 020339
National University of Colombia, Bogotá, Colombia

Núñez, Rubén 020209, 020453
UPM, Madrid, Spain

Núñez-Osorio, Alessia 020100
University of Almeria, Almeria, Spain

Nurmesjärvi, Antti 020423
VTT Technical Research Centre of Finland, Oulu, Finland

Nussbaumer, Hartmut 020385
ZHAW, Winterthur, Switzerland

Nyang'onda, Thomas N. 020272
University of Nairobi, Nairobi, Kenya

Obeidavi, Sahereh 020361
Coburg University of Applied Sciences, Coburg, Germany

Oberbeck, Lars 020461
TotalEnergies OneTech, Paris, France

Oberegger Filippi, Ulrich 020551
Eurac Research, Bolzano, Italy

Ocaña, Luis Manuel 020151
ITER, Granadilla de Abona, Spain

Ockert, Ajka 020312
EnBW, Karlsruhe, Germany

Odilio dos Santos, Daniel 020548
UFSC, Florianopolis, Brazil

Öhgren, Gustav 020532
Becquerel Sweden, Knivsta, Sweden

Öttl, Christian 020347
Watt Analytics, Vienna, Austria

Öz, Aksel Kaan 020135
Fraunhofer ISE, Freiburg, Germany

Özden, Talat 020226
ODTÜ-GÜNAM, Ankara, Türkiye

Özkalay, Ebrar 020160, 020204
SUPSI, Mendrisio, Switzerland

Ogura, Atsushi 020046
Meiji University, Kanagawa, Japan

Ohdaira, Keisuke 020131
JAIST, Ishikawa, Japan

Ohshita, Yoshio 020046
Toyota Technological Institute, Nagoya, Japan

Ojala, Aleksi 020554
Solarigo Systems, Pirkkala, Finland

Okawa, Hayato 020115
Tokyo City University, Setagaya, Japan

Okel, Lars A. G. 020030
TNO, Petten, The Netherlands

Oksanen, Jani 020067
Aalto University, Espoo, Finland

Oliosi, Michele 020196
PVsyst, Geneva, Switzerland

Olivares, Douglas 020311
University of Antofagasta, Antofagasta, Chile

Olivares, Gregorio 020365, 020366, 020392
CENER, Sarriguren, Spain

Oliveira Santos, João Victor 020188
EDF R&D, Moret Loing Orvanne, France

Oliveira, Helena 020420
University of Évora, Évora, Portugal

Oller Westerberg, Amelia 020570
Becquerel Sweden, Knivsta, Sweden

Ollo, Olatz 020139
Tecnalia, Donostia - San Sebastián, Spain

Oozeki, Takashi 020436, 020525
AIST, Koriyama, Japan

Opatovsky, Martin 020241, 020262
Solargis, Bratislava, Slovakia

Oreski, Gernot 020136, 020234, 020325, 020500, 020574
PCCL, Leoben, Austria

Ortega, Eneko 020055, 020153, 020287, 020353
UPV/EHU, Bilbao, Spain

Ortega, Eneko 020289, 020437
UPV/EHU, Leioa, Spain

Ortega, Pascal 020214
University of French Polynesia, Faa'a, French Polynesia

Ortiz-Pena, Aaron 020562
University of Castilla-La Mancha, Albacete, Spain

Ory, Daniel 020188
EDF R&D, Palaiseau, France

Ory, Daniel — 020116
EDF, Palaiseau, France

Osman, Alaa — 020006
ISFH, Emmerthal, Germany

Osuna, Jose Antonio — 020358
MAGTEL, Córdoba, Spain

Osvald, Oliver — 020274
Solargis, Bratislava, Slovakia

Otaegi, Aloña — 020055, 020097, 020153, 020287
UPV/EHU, Bilbao, Spain

Otnes, Gaute — 020169
Institute for Energy Technology, Kjeller, Norway

Otto, Nicolas — 020101
HTW, Berlin, Germany

Otto, William — 020390
MARIN, Wageningen, The Netherlands

Ou, Chao-Wei — 020350
National Chin-Yi University of Technology, Taichung, Taiwan

Ovaitt, Silvana — 020314
NREL, Denver, United States of America

Ovaitt, Silvana — 020574
NREL, Golden, United States of America

Oviedo Hernandez, Guillermo — 020325
BayWa r.e, Rome, Italy

Ozer, Shay — 020379
Agricultural Research Organization, Rishon LeZion, Israel

P. Pires, Maurício — 020090
Federal University of Rio de Janeiro, Rio de Janeiro, Brazil

Pabiou, Herve — 020338
CETHIL, Villeurbanne, France

Pabst, Elena — 020312
ZSW, Stuttgart, Germany

Paiva, Lúcio — 020530
Casa dos Ventos, Fortaleza, Brazil

Palais, Olivier — 020188
Toulon University, Marseille, France

Palitzsch, Wolfram — 020225, 020495
LuxChemTech, Freiberg, Germany

Palomino, Laura — 020491, 020535
UPM, Madrid, Spain

Pamir Aly, Shahzada — 020229
DEWA, Dubai, United Arab Emirates

Pamula, Bindu — 020069
SVNIT, Surat, India

Panda, Pavan Kumar Anhalt University of Applied Sciences, Köthen, Germany	020284
Pandar, Matthias Fraunhofer CSP, Halle, Germany	020229
Pander, Matthias Fraunhofer CSP, Halle, Germany	020121, 020142, 020175, 020192, 020218, 020223, 020232
Panduri, Fabio BFH, Burgdorf, Switzerland	020322
Pantoja, Jaime Francisco José de Caldas District University, Bogota, Colombia	020526
Papantoni, Veatriki DLR, Oldenburg, Germany	020482
Paraficz, Danuta FFHS, Zurich, Switzerland	020204
Paraskeva, Vasiliki University of Cyprus, Nicosia, Cyprus	020064
Pardo, Eduardo Tecnova, Almeira, Spain	020414
Parfeniukas, Karolis ATLANT 3D, Taastrup, Denmark	020039
Parion, Jonathan Hasselt Unversity, Genk, Belgium	020064
Park, Hyeonwook KENTECH, Naju-Si, South Korea	020112
Parmar, Richa NISE, Gurugram, India	020429
Parra, Johan Ecole Polytechnique, Palaiseau, France	020406
Parra, Johan Polytechnic Institute of Paris, Palaiseau, France	020214
Parrilla, Carlos G. Fujairah Research Centre, Fujairah, United Arab Emirates	020402
Pascual Gallego, Valero UPM, Madrid, Spain	020407
Pasquier, Mathis DTU, Roskilde, Denmark	020451
Passaro, Marcello Sunzest Solar, Rotterdam, The Netherlands	020513
Patel, Dharm Fraunhofer IMWS, Halle, Germany	020355
Paul, Ananta SDU Climate Cluster, Odense, Denmark	020250, 020306
Paulescu, Marius West University of Timisoara, Timisoara, Romania	020283

Paviet-Salomon, Bertrand CSEM, Neuchâtel, Switzerland	020068, 020467
Payno, David UAM, Madrid, Spain	020085, 020094
Pearce, Pheobe UNSW, Sydney, Australia	020065
Peche, René bifa Umweltinstitut, Augsburg, Germany	020468, 020495
Pehlivanli, Ezgi METU, Ankara, Türkiye	020521
Peibst, Robby ISFH, Emmerthal, Germany	020006, 020063, 020114
Pelfort Ojer, Marta Solargis, Bratislava, Slovakia	020241
Pelland, Sophie Natural Resources Canada, Varennes, Canada	020211
Pelle, Martina Eurac Research, Bolzano, Italy	020249, 020254
Peña-Bermudez, Julian University of the Caribbean, Santo Domingo, Dominican Republic	020110
Peng, Cheng-Yu National Chin-Yi University of Technology, Taichung, Taiwan	020350
Pera, David Luxembourg Institute of Science and Technology, Esch-sur-Alzette, Luxembourg	020457
Perani, Martina FFHS, Zurich, Switzerland	020204
Peraticos, Elias University of Cyprus, Nicosia, Cyprus	020064
Pereda, Ainhoa TECNALIA, Derio, Spain	020198, 020358
Pereira Fialho, Luis Andre Eurac Research, Bolzano, Italy	020509
Pereira, Sara University of Évora, Évora, Portugal	020403, 020418, 020565
Pérez García, Manuel University of Almería, La Cañada de San Urbano, Spain	020336
Pérez, Ernesto National University of Colombia, Bogotá, Colombia	020339
Pérez, Jairo Gonvarri AgroTech, Corvera - Asturias, Spain	020412
Pérez, Jorge Gonvarri AgroTech, Corvera - Asturias, Spain	020412
Pérez, Luis Gonvarri MS R&D, Corvera - Asturias, Spain	020412

Perez, Richard University at Albany, Albany, United States of America	020494
Perez-Astudillo, Daniel QEERI, Doha, Qatar	020275, 020278, 020291
Pérez-García, Manuel University of Almeria, Almería, Spain	020100
Pérez-Rodríguez, Alejandro IREC, Barcelona, Spain	020085, 020094
Pernas, Tomás Gonvarri AgroTech, Corvera - Asturias, Spain	020412
Pernau, Thomas centrotherm international, Blaubeuren, Germany	020008
Perrin, Marion Energy Pool, Le Bourget-du-Lac, France	020544
Pervan, Nikolina PCCL, Leoben, Austria	020136, 020234
Peter Amalathas, Amalraj University of Jaffna, Jaffna, Sri Lanka	020107
Peter, Kristian ISC Konstanz, Konstanz, Germany	020569
Peters, Ian Marius Forschungszentrum Jülich, Erlangen, Germany	020230, 020263
Peters, Ian Marius HI ERN, Erlangen, Germany	020149, 020150, 020377, 020574
Petersons, Karlis Stensborg, Roskilde, Denmark	020250, 020306
Petkovski, Emil DNV, Arnhem, The Netherlands	020571
Petzschmann, Jonas ZSW, Stuttgart, Germany	020312
Pfau, Jan Hendrik Leibniz University Hannover, Hannover, Germany	020240
Pfeiffer, Oliver University of Applied Science Cologne, Cologne, Germany	020141
Pfeiffer, Oliver University of Applied Sciences Cologne, Cologne, Germany	020140
Philipp, Daniel Fraunhofer ISE, Freiburg, Germany	020215, 020231
Pierro, Marco Eurac Research, Bolzano, Italy	020489, 020494
Pieters, Bart E. FZJ, Jülich, Germany	020180
Pieterse, Marco Chemconserve, Bussum, The Netherlands	020495
Pietralunga, Silvia Maria CNR-IFN, Milan, Italy	020066

Pietsch, Veith 020331
Aquila Capital, Hamburg, Germany
Pilat, Eric 020311
CEA / INES, Le Bourget-du-Lac, France
Pilat, Eric 020317
CEA INES, Le Bourget-du-Lac, France
Pillai, Akhildev 020558
Becquerel Institute, Brussels, Belgium
Pinheiro, Philippe 020457
Luxembourg Institute of Science and Technology, Esch-sur-Alzette, Luxembourg
Pinho Almeida, Marcelo 020348
University of São Paulo, São Paulo, Brazil
Pinto, Cristina Leyre 020497
CENER, Sarriguren, Spain
Pinto, Luciana 020092
UFRJ, Rio de Janeiro, Brazil
Pitaval, Sébastien 020244
SOLAÏS, Valbonne, France
Pitz-Paal, Robert 020237, 020331
DLR, Cologne, Germany
Plakhotnyuk, Maksym 020039
ATLANT 3D, Taastrup, Denmark
Platero Gaona, Carlos A. 020332
UPM, Madrid, Spain
Plaza, Caroline 020543, 020564, 020573
Becquerel Institute France, Lyon, France
Polacchi, Cristina 020509, 020513
Eurac Research, Bolzano, Italy
Polo, Jaime 020300
CENER, Sarriguren, Spain
Polo, Jesús 020297
CIEMAT, Madrid, Spain
Polverini, Davide 020181
Directorate General for Internal Market, Industry, Entrepreneurship and SMEs, Brussels, Belgium
Polverini, Davide 020497
European Comission, Brussels, Belgium
Pongthanacharoenkul, Nattapark 020230
Kiwa PI Berlin, Berlin, Germany
Poortmans, Jef 020064
Hasselt Unversity, Genk, Belgium
Popescu, Lacramioara 020068
ISC Konstanz, Konstanz, Germany
Pospischil, Maximilian 020225
Highline Technologies, Freiburg, Germany

Poulsen, Peter B. DTU, Copenhagen, Denmark	020039
Poulsen, Peter B. DTU, Roskilde, Denmark	020250, 020265, 020267, 020376, 020451
Poulsen, Peter Behrensdorff DTU, Roskilde, Denmark	020028, 020306, 020346
Pourshafi, Pouya AESOLAR, Koenigsbrunn, Germany	020121, 020125, 020137
Pozza, Cristian Eurac Research, Bolzano, Italy	020551
Prakash, Jai NISE, Gurugram, India	020429
Prando, Davide Edyna, Bolzano, Italy	020485, 020489
Prasad, Manjunath ISC Konstanz, Konstanz, Germany	020225
Pravettoni, Mauro Technology Innovation Institute, Abu Dhabi, United Arab Emirates	020402
Preis, Pirmin ISC Konstanz, Konstanz, Germany	020003
Preu, Ralf Fraunhofer ISE, Freiburg, Germany	020475
Preuschoff, Jonas HTW, Berlin, Germany	020101
Protti, Alexander Aguilar Fraunhofer ISE, Freiburg, Germany	020140
Protti, Alexander Fraunhofer ISE, Freiburg, Germany	020137
Provost, Marion IPVF, Palaiseau, France	020116
Puel, Jean Baptiste IPVF, Palaiseau, France	020062
Puertas López, Antonio Manuel University of Almeria, Almeria, Spain	020100
Puttock, Claire Nextracker, Fremont, United States of America	020367
Queste, Samuel Marie and Louis Pasteur University, Besançon, France	020068
Quiroz, Mónica Qualifying Photovoltaics, Madrid, Spain	020328
R. Ledesma, Javier UPM, Madrid, Spain	020363

Rabanal Arabach, Jorge 020183
University of Antofagasta, Antofagasta, Chile

Rabanal-Arabach, Jorge 020129, 020342, 020417, 020422
University of Antofagasta, Antofagasta, Chile

Rabiei, Hossein 020063
ISFH, Emmerthal, Germany

Rachdi, Lazhar 020035, 020068
ISC Konstanz, Konstanz, Germany

Radzevicius, Aurimas 020225
Valoe Cells, Vilnius, Lithuania

Rafiee, Hossein 020539
Frankfurt University of Applied Sciences, Frankfurt am Main, Germany

Raginskis, Justinas 020380
Kaunas University of Technology, Kaunas, Lithuania

Raievska, Oleksandra 020117, 020149
HI ERN, Erlangen, Germany

Rajan, S. Prithivi 020262
LuciSun, Villers-la-Ville, Belgium

Rajkiewicz, Katarzyna 020551
NAPE, Warsaw, Poland

Rakotoniaina, Jean Patrice 020311
CEA / INES, Le Bourget-du-Lac, France

Ramachandran Nair, Jishnu 020233
Fraunhofer CSP, Halle, Germany

Ramesh, Santhosh 020389
imec, Genk, Belgium

Ramírez Ledesma, Javier 020535
UPM, Madrid, Spain

Ramirez, S. 020396
PV Lighthouse, Coledale, Australia

Rampino, Stefano 020087
National Research Council, Parma, Italy

Ramspeck, Klaus 020050
halm elektronik, Frankfurt am Main, Germany

Ranisch, Tadeus 020101
HTW, Berlin, Germany

Ranta, Samuli 020286, 020400
TUAS, Turku, Finland

Ranta, Samuli 020298, 020398
Turku University of Applied Sciences, Turku, Finland

Raposo, Mauro 020565
University of Évora, Évora, Portugal

Ratnagiri, Abhinav 020367
Nextracker, Fremont, United States of America

Raugewitz, Annika 020063, 020114
ISFH, Emmerthal, Germany

Raval, Mehul 020005, 020222, 020463
RCT Solutions, Konstanz, Germany

Razanajao, Aina 020244
SOLAÏS, Valbonne, France

Razi, Umair 020085
IREC, Barcelona, Spain

Recart, Federico 020097
UPV/EHU, Bilbao, Spain

Redondo Cuevas, Marta 020332
UPM, Madrid, Spain

Redondo, Juan Manuel 020209
UPM, Madrid, Spain

Rehan, Muhammad 020112
KIER, Daejeon, South Korea

Rehman, Anees ur 020111, 020164
Hohai University, Changzhou, China

Reichart, Hannah 020167, 020232
University of Applied Sciences Cologne, Cologne, Germany

Reichel, Christian 020123, 020137, 020140
Fraunhofer ISE, Freiburg, Germany

Reichle, Julian 020005, 020222, 020463
RCT Solutions, Konstanz, Germany

Reinders, Angele 020253
TU Eindhoven, Eindhoven, The Netherlands

Reindl, Thomas 020263
SERIS, Singapore, Singapore

Reis, Luiz Filipe 020530
Casa dos Ventos, Fortaleza, Brazil

Rémondeau, Paul 020251
EPFL, Neuchâtel, Switzerland

Renard, Charles 020058
CNRS, Palaiseau, France

Rende, Fedele 020255
ACCA Software, Cosenza, Italy

Rennhofer, Marcus 020180, 020281, 020318, 020334, 020347, 020430
AIT, Vienna, Austria

Rentsch, Jochen 020475
Fraunhofer ISE, Freiburg, Germany

Rerat, Michel 020060
IPREM, Pau, France

Reshef, Liad 020379
Agricultural Research Organization, Rishon LeZion, Israel

Revol, Inès 020074
LAAS-CNRS, Toulouse, France

Reyal, Jean-Pierre 020303
SemperStyl, Eragny, France

Riaño, Sandra 020197, 020358
TECNALIA, Derio, Spain

Richards, Bryce S. 020272
KIT, Karlsruhe, Germany

Riechelman, Stefan 020181
PTB, Braunschweig, Germany

Riechelmann, Stefan 020177, 020199, 020211
PTB, Braunschweig, Germany

Riedel-Lyngskær, Nicholas 020451
DTU, Roskilde, Denmark

Rienäcker, Michael 020063
ISFH, Emmerthal, Germany

Rindert, Sören 020230
Kiwa PI Berlin, Berlin, Germany

Ríos Moral, Lucía 020501
UCM, Madrid, Spain

Ríos-Ledesma, Felipe 020446
UPM, Madrid, Spain

Ripke, Melanie 020006
ISFH, Emmerthal, Germany

Riva, Roland 020495
CEA, Le Bourget-du-Lac, France

Rivas Rodríguez, José Manuel 020326
Enertis Applus+, Madrid, Spain

Robledo, Jesús 020262
LuciSun, Villers-la-Ville, Belgium

Rodríguez Lucas, Delia 020407
EkiLabs, Boston, United States of America

Rodríguez Plaza, José Luis 020508
Autonomous University of Madrid, Madrid, Spain

Rodríguez Rodríguez, Araceli 020501
UCM, Madrid, Spain

Rodríguez Salazar, David Leonardo 020441
District University of Bogotá, Bogotá, Colombia

Rodríguez, Araceli 020508
UCM, Madrid, Spain

Rodríguez, Diego Julián 020526
Francisco José de Caldas District University, Bogota, Colombia

Rodríguez, Isabel 020257
IMDEA Nanoscience, Madrid, Spain

Rodriguez, Sonia Maria 020289
UPV/EHU, Leioa, Spain

Rodríguez, Velia 020097
UPV/EHU, Bilbao, Spain

Rodríguez-Conde, Sofía 020326
Enertis Applus+, Madrid, Spain

Rodríguez-Gallegos, Carlos D. 020149, 020150
SERIS, Singapore, Singapore
Rodríguez-Romero, Sebastián 020342, 020417, 020422
University of Antofagasta, Antofagasta, Chile
Rodziewicz, Hanna 020498
Gdansk University of Technology, Gdansk, Poland
Römer, Udo 020006, 020063
ISFH, Emmerthal, Germany
Röver, Ingo 020225
LuxChemTech, Freiberg, Germany
Rojas, Christian A. 020422
Federico Santa María Technical University, Valparaíso, Chile
Rojas-Henríquez, Katalina 020129
University of Antofagasta, Antofagasta, Chile
Román, Eduardo 020139
Tecnalia, Donostia - San Sebastián, Spain
Romeo, Alessandro 020057, 020089, 020093
University of Verona, Verona, Italy
Romer, Pascal 020231
Fraunhofer ISE, Freiburg, Germany
Roodt, Roelof 020185
Nelson Mandela University, Port Elizabeth, South Africa
Roosloot, Nathan 020169
Institute for Energy Technology, Kjeller, Norway
Rosca, Victor 020030
TNO, Petten, The Netherlands
Rosen, Isaac 020225
Copprint, Jerusalem, Israel
Rosenfeld, Lavi 020379
Agricultural Research Organization, Rishon LeZion, Israel
Rosina, Konstantin 020241
Solargis, Bratislava, Slovakia
Rossa, Carlos 020432, 020434
Sunveon, Madrid, Spain
Rouffie, Brice 020068
SEGTON Advanced Technology, Versailles, France
Roulleau, Lea 020303
CSTB, Marne-la-Vallée, France
Rousset, Jean 020116
EDF, Palaiseau, France
Roy, Shantanu 020519
CSTEP, Bengaluru, India
Rudolph, Dominik 020003, 020068
ISC Konstanz, Konstanz, Germany

Sayed, Abdullah Abu 020180, 020230
Kiwa PI Berlin, Berlin, Germany

Scaltrito, Luciano 020079
Polytechnic University of Turin, Turin, Italy

Scerri, Kenneth 020334
University of Malta, Msida, Malta

Schading, Steve 020443
University of Agder, Grimstad, Norway

Schäfer, Aysim 020388
Next2Sun Technology, Dillingen, Germany

Schäfer, Sebastian 020539
Frankfurt University of Applied Sciences, Frankfurt am Main, Germany

Schenk, Paul 020192
Fraunhofer CSP, Halle, Germany

Schermer, John 020067
Radboud University, Nijmegen, The Netherlands

Scherret, Jacqueline 020255
A-Null Development, Vienna, Austria

Schifferegger, Raffael 020162
OFI, Vienna, Austria

Schimanke, Sabrina 020006
ISFH, Emmerthal, Germany

Schirmer, Yoko 020101
HTW, Berlin, Germany

Schläger, Christian 020240
Leibniz University Hannover, Hannover, Germany

Schlatmann, Rutger 020101
HTW, Berlin, Germany

Schmidt Davidsen, Rasmus 020037, 020104
Aarhus University, Aarhus, Denmark

Schnaus, Dominik 020237
TUM, Garching, Germany

Schneider, Andreas 020129, 020183
University of Applied Sciences Gelsenkirchen, Gelsenkirchen, Germany

Schneider, Astrid 020255
TU Wien, Vienna, Austria

Schneider, Friedrich 020482
LPKF SolarQuipment, Suhl, Germany

Schneider, Marc Gabriel 020522
University of Applied Science Cologne, Cologne, Germany

Schneiderlöchner, Eric 020033
VON ARDENNE, Dresden, Germany

Schnierer, Branislav 020262
Solargis, Bratislava, Slovakia

Schönau, Maximilian Coburg University of Applied Sciences, Coburg, Germany	020361
Schönau, Maximilian smartblue, Munich, Germany	020544
Schönheits, Markus bifa Umweltinstitut, Augsburg, Germany	020468, 020470
Schranz, Christian TU Wien, Vienna, Austria	020255
Schrempf, Michael PTB, Braunschweig, Germany	020199
Schrijvers, Patrick MARIN, Wageningen, The Netherlands	020390
Schröter, Nick Fraunhofer CSP, Halle, Germany	020142
Schubert, Martin C. Fraunhofer ISE, Freiburg, Germany	020475
Schubnel, Baptiste CSEM, Neuchâtel, Switzerland	020238
Schüler, Marc Andre Next2Sun Technology, Dillingen, Germany	020388
Schüler, Marc Andre Next2Sun, Dillingen, Germany	020411
Schueler, Nadine Freiberger Instruments, Freiberg, Germany	020015
Schulte-Huxel, Henning ISFH, Emmerthal, Germany	020008, 020260
Schultz, Christof HTW, Berlin, Germany	020101
Schulz, Philip IPVF, Palaiseau, France	020060
Schulze, Achim Rosenheim Technical University of Applied Sciences, Rosenheim, Germany	020361
Schulze, Patricia S.C. Fraunhofer ISE, Freiburg, Germany	020475
Schwenke, Almut SGL Battery Solutions, Meitingen, Germany	020495
Sciuto, Marcello Enel Green Power, Catania, Italy	020010
Scognamiglio, Alessandra ENEA, Naples, Italy	020541
Scognamiglio, Alessandra ENEA, Portici, Italy	020378
Sedaghat, Ahmad Australian University, Kuwait City, Kuwait	020428
Seiffert, Christoph Institute for Energy Technology, Kjeller, Norway	020169

Seiffert, Daniela 020008
centrotherm international, Blaubeuren, Germany

Seitz, Matthias 020468
bifa Umweltinstitut, Augsburg, Germany

Selj, Josefine H. 020169
Institute for Energy Technology, Kjeller, Norway

Senno, Maximiliano Alejandro 020226
University of Valencia, Paterna, Spain

Senturk, Bilge 020556
ODTU GUNAM, Ankara, Türkiye

Setien, Eneko 020198
TECNALIA, Derio, Spain

Šetkus, Arūnas 020157
Center for Physical Sciences and Technology (FTMC), Vilnius, Lithuania

Shaaban, Ahmed 020402
Technology Innovation Institute, Abu Dhabi, United Arab Emirates

Shah, Syed Fawad Ali 020112
KENTECH, Naju-Si, South Korea

Shanmugam, Raphael 020218, 020220
ISC Konstanz, Konstanz, Germany

Sharma, Rajesh Kumar 020071, 020081
SVNIT, Surat, India

Sharma, Sushma 020563
SRM University, Sonipat, India

Shen, Xinyi 020226
University of Oxford, Oxford, United Kingdom

Shen, Zhenjue 020001
YIST, Jiangyin, China

Shin, Donghyeop 020112
KIER, Daejeon, South Korea

Shin, Woo Gyun 020324, 020357
KIER, Daejeon, South Korea

Shin, Woo-gyun 020561
KIER, Daejeon, South Korea

Shirai, Yasuhiro 020115
NIMS, Tsukuba, Japan

Shirazi, Elham 020544
University of Twente, Enschede, The Netherlands

Shishavan, Amir Asgharzadeh 020367
Nextracker, Fremont, United States of America

Shishido, Hirotaka 020106
Tokyo City University, Setagaya, Japan

Shochet, Ofer 020225
Copprint, Jerusalem, Israel

Shyong, Yung-Jen 020163
ITRI, Hsinchu, Taiwan

Sicot, Lionel 020217
CEA / INES, Le Bourget-du-Lac, France

Sidler, Anika 020226
School of Life Sciences FHNW, Muttenz, Switzerland

Siebert, Michael 020206
ISFH, Emmerthal, Germany

Siefer, Gerald 020246
Fraunhofer ISE, Freiburg, Germany

Sierra, Daniel 020491
UPM, Madrid, Spain

Sigounis, Anna-Maria 020248, 020249
Concordia University, Montreal, Canada

Søiland, Anne-Karin 020495
ReSiTec, Kristiansand, Norway

Silva, José A. 020304, 020409, 020420
University of Évora, Évora, Portugal

Silva, José 020403
University of Évora, Évora, Portugal

Silvestre, Santiago 020301
UPC, Barcelona, Spain

Simeunovic, Jelena 020238
CSEM, Neuchâtel, Switzerland

Simón-Allué, Raquel 020127, 020414, 020517
ENDEF, Zaragoza, Spain

Singh, Ravi 020571
DNV, Arnhem, The Netherlands

Sinha, Amish Kumar 020463
RCT Solutions, Konstanz, Germany

Sinopoli, Alessandro 020042
QEERI, Doha, Qatar

Sivaramakrishnan Radhakrishnan, Hariharsudan 020064
Hasselt Unversity, Genk, Belgium

Sivaramakrishnan, Hariharsudan 020225
IMEC, Genk, Belgium

Snaith, Henry 020226
University of Oxford, Oxford, United Kingdom

Søndenå, Rune 020503
Institute for Energy Technology, Kjeller, Norway

Sobajima, Yasushi 020131
Gifu University, Gifu, Japan

Soler Toledo, Denet 020509
University of Antofagasta, Antofagasta, Chile

Solomon, Asfaw A. 020479
LUT University, Lappeenranta, Finland

Solórzano, Jorge 020328
Qualifying Photovoltaics, Madrid, Spain

Sondoqah, Mousa 020316
Becquerel Institute, Bolzano, Italy

Sondoqah, Mousa 020261
Eurac Research, Bolzano, Italy

Song, Hee-eun 020045
KIER, Daejeon, South Korea

Spagnolo, Sofia 020462, 020466
RSE, Milan, Italy

Spataru, Sergiu V. 020265, 020267, 020283, 020376, 020451
DTU, Roskilde, Denmark

Spataru, Sergiu Viorel 020346
DTU, Roskilde, Denmark

Spera, Fabian 020411
Next2Sun, Dillingen, Germany

Spihola, Jan 020355
DiSUN Deutsche Solarservice, Werder, Germany

Sraisth, 020005, 020222
RCT Solutions, Konstanz, Germany

Sraisth, Sraisth 020463
RCT Solutions, Konstanz, Germany

Staňková, Tereza 020107
Czech Technical University, Prague, Czech Republic

Steckenreiter, Verena 020063
ISFH, Emmerthal, Germany

Stegemann, Bert 020309
Berlin University of Applied Sciences, Berlin, Germany

Stegemann, Bert 020101
HTW, Berlin, Germany

Stellbogen, Dirk 020312
ZSW, Stuttgart, Germany

Stensborg, Jan F. 020250
Stensborg, Roskilde, Denmark

Stensborg, Jan 020306
Stensborg, Roskilde, Denmark

Stieldorf, Karin 020255
TU Wien, Vienna, Austria

Stierstorfer, Johannes 020225
WIP - Renewable Energies, Munich, Germany

Stierstorfer, Johannes 020551
WIP Renewable Energies, Munich, Germany

Stivanello, Juan José 020226
Eurac Research, Bolzano, Italy

Stoicescu, Liviu 020198
Solarzentrum Stuttgart, Stuttgart, Germany

Stowhas-Villa, Alejandro Federico Santa María Technical University, Valparaiso, Chile	020422
Stoyanova Lyubenova, Teodora European Commission JRC, Ispra, Italy	020173
Sträter, Hendrik PTB, Braunschweig, Germany	020211
Strey, Jessica ISFH, Emmerthal, Germany	020063, 020114
Strömberg, Rich University of Alaska, Fairbanks, United States of America	020472
Stroyuk, Oleksander HI ERN, Erlangen, Germany	020185
Stroyuk, Oleksandr HI ERN, Erlangen, Germany	020117, 020149, 020150
Suárez Sánchez, Sergio Enertis Applus+, Madrid, Spain	020326
Subasi, Dilara Maria Fraunhofer ISE, Freiburg, Germany	020475
Sudbury, Ben A. PV Lighthouse, Coledale, Australia	020396
Suemitsu, Issei Hitachi, Kokubunji, Japan	020484
Suhonen, Riikka VTT Technical Research Centre of Finland, Oulu, Finland	020423
Sulca, Kabir Paúl University of Valladolid, Valladolid, Spain	020191, 020205
Svatos, Jan DTU, Roskilde, Denmark	020250
Sylla, David ISFH, Emmerthal, Germany	020063
Syre Wiig, Marie IFE, Kjeller, Norway	020340
Szarek, Magda University of Turku, Turku, Finland	020298, 020398
Taghipour Kani, Ghaem Amirkabir University of Technology, Tehran, Iran	020335, 020374
Takahashi, Kanji Tokyo City University, Setagaya, Japan	020106
Talvi, Micke Tampere University, Tampere, Finland	020528
Tanahashi, Tadanori AIST, Koriyama, Japan	020436
Tang, Kai SINTEF, Trondheim, Norway	020011

Tang, Torben 020028
IPU P/S, Virum, Denmark

Tang, Torben 020037
IPU, Virum, Denmark

Tayebjee, Murad J. Y. 020065
UNSW, Sydney, Australia

Taylor, Nigel 020210
European Commission JRC, Ispra, Italy

Tellez Rodriguez, Eduardo 020230
Kiwa PI Berlin, Berlin, Germany

Teppe, Andreas 020005
RCT Solutions, Konstanz, Germany

Terheiden, Barbara 020031
University of Konstanz, Constance, Germany

Terrados, Cristian 020205
University of Valladolid, Valladolid, Spain

Thakur, Dhruv Singh 020071, 020081
SVNIT, Surat, India

Theocharides, Spyros 020371
Univers, Courbevoie, France

Thomas, Jean 020169
Ciel et Terre, Lille, France

Thorning, Jacob K. 020267, 020283
DTU, Roskilde, Denmark

Thorsteinsson, Sune 020039
DTU, Copenhagen, Denmark

Thorsteinsson, Sune 020037
DTU, Lyngby, Denmark

Thorsteinsson, Sune 020028, 020249, 020250, 020265, 020306, 020477
DTU, Roskilde, Denmark

Timofte, Tudor 020218, 020221
ISC Konstanz, Konstanz, Germany

Ting, San-Yu 020161, 020163
ITRI, Hsinchu, Taiwan

Tissier, Corentin 020238
CSEM, Neuchâtel, Switzerland

Tönies, Alexandra 020523
University of Applied Sciences Cologne, Cologne, Germany

Tomšič, Špela 020047
University of Ljubljana, Ljubljana, Slovenia

Tong, Yongfeng 020108, 020109
QEERI, Doha, Qatar

Topič, Marko 020047, 020269, 020319
University of Ljubljana, Ljubljana, Slovenia

Torabi, Narges 020089
University of Verona, Verona, Italy

Torelly, Guilherme 020092
PUC-Rio, Rio de Janeiro, Brazil

Torre, Gorka 020437
UPV/EHU, Leioa, Spain

Torres Aguilar, Moira Itzel 020214
CentraleSupélec, Gif-sur-Yvette, France

Torres Aguilar, Moira Itzel 020406
CNRS, Gif-sur-Yvette, France

Torres Silva, Nicole 020546
ATAMOSTEC, Santiago, Chile

Torres, Oscar 020110
National University of Colombia, Bogotá, Colombia

Tosi, Irene 020037
IPU, Virum, Denmark

Tran Caliste, Thu Nhi 020546
European Synchrotron Radiation Facility (ESRF), Grenoble, France

Treberspurg, Christoph 020255
Treberspurg und Partner Ziviltechniker, Vienna, Austria

Treberspurg, Martin 020255
Treberspurg und Partner Ziviltechniker, Vienna, Austria

Trefzer, Aaron 020135
Fraunhofer ISE, Freiburg, Germany

Trifiletti, Vanira 020087
University of Milano-Bicocca, Milan, Italy

Trigo-Gonzalez, Mauricio 020342, 020422
University of Antofagasta, Antofagasta, Chile

Tsai, Min-An 020053, 020083, 020161, 020163
ITRI, Hsinchu, Taiwan

Tsanakas, Ioannis (John) A. 020262
CEA / INES, Le Bourget-du-Lac, France

Tsanakas, Ioannis (John) A. 020544
CEA, Le Bourget-du-Lac, France

Tsanakas, Ioannis (John) 020546
CEA / INES, Le Bourget-du-Lac, France

Tsanakas, Ioannis (John) 020317
CEA INES, Le Bourget-du-Lac, France

Tsanakas, Ioannis (John) 020513, 020521
CEA, Le Bourget-du-Lac, France

Tsanakas, Ioannis 020217, 020338
CEA / INES, Le Bourget-du-Lac, France

Tsanakas, Ioannis 020500
CEA, Le Bourget-du-Lac, France

Tsanakas, John A. 020311
CEA / INES, Le Bourget-du-Lac, France

Tseberlidis, Giorgio 020093
University of Milano Bicocca, Milan, Italy

Tseberlidis, Giorgio 020087
University of Milano-Bicocca, Milan, Italy

Tsoi, Konstantin 020113
ODTÜ-GÜNAM, Ankara, Türkiye

Tsombou, Francois M. 020402
Fujairah Research Centre, Fujairah, United Arab Emirates

Tsuno, Yuki 020436
AIST, Koriyama, Japan

Tsunoda, Jun 020484
Hitachi, Kokubunji, Japan

Tsunoda, Jun 020186
Hitachi, Tokyo, Japan

Tulinski, Lona 020385
ZHAW, Winterthur, Switzerland

Tune, Daniel 020220, 020221, 020225
ISC Konstanz, Konstanz, Germany

Turcu, Mircea 020063
ISFH, Emmerthal, Germany

Turek, Marko 020004, 020052
Fraunhofer CSP, Halle (Saale), Germany

Ueda, Yuzuru 020320, 020525
Tokyo University of Science, Tokyo, Japan

Ujvari, Gusztav 020318, 020430
AIT, Vienna, Austria

Ulbikaitė, Vaidvilė 020157
Applied Research Institute for Prospective Technologies, Vilnius, Lithuania

Ulbikas, Juras 020225
Protechnology, Vilnius, Lithuania

Ulyashin, Alexander G. 020011
SINTEF, Oslo, Norway

Unsur, Veysel 020020
ODTÜ-GÜNAM, Ankara, Türkiye

Urban, Harald 020255
TU Wien, Vienna, Austria

Useni, Yannick 020393
University of Lubumbashi, Lubumbashi, Congo (DRC)

Uzuner, Bahri Eren 020113
ODTÜ-GÜNAM, Ankara, Türkiye

Väisänen, Kaisa-Leena 020423
VTT Technical Research Centre of Finland, Oulu, Finland

Vaicikauskas, Viktoras 020157
Center for Physical Sciences and Technology (FTMC), Vilnius, Lithuania

Valaski, Rogério 020090
National Institute of Metrology Quality and Technology, Rio de Janeiro, Brazil

Valencia, Felipe 020342, 020546
AtamosTec, Santiago, Chile

Vallerotto, Guido 020209, 020246, 020257
UPM, Madrid, Spain

van Aken, Bas B. 020405
TNO, Petten, The Netherlands

van der Heide, Arvid 020472
imec, Genk, Belgium

van der Zee, Friso F. 020405
Wageningen University and Research, Wageningen, The Netherlands

Van Dyck, Rik 020225
IMEC, Genk, Belgium

van Dyk, E. Ernest 020193, 020416
Nelson Mandela University, Port Elizabeth, South Africa

van Dyk, Ernest E. 020344
Nelson Mandela University, Port Elizabeth, South Africa

Van Overstraeten, Julien 020543
Becquerel Institute France, Lyon, France

Van Overstraeten, Julien 020252
Becquerel Institute, Brussels, Belgium

vanBaal, Rene 020492
Belectric, Kolitzheim, Germany

Vanhanen, Tuomas 020225
Valoe, Mikkeli, Finland

Vargas, Renzo 020348
University of São Paulo, São Paulo, Brazil

Varney, Valérie 020522
University of Applied Science Cologne, Cologne, Germany

Varney, Valérie 020523
University of Applied Sciences Cologne, Cologne, Germany

vas Dyk, Ernest 020185
Nelson Mandela University, Port Elizabeth, South Africa

Vasconcelos, Letícia 020530
Casa dos Ventos, Fortaleza, Brazil

Vavilkin, Tatjana 020302
Soltech, Genk, Belgium

Vázquez Adán, Alejandra 020501
UCM, Madrid, Spain

Vázquez, A. 020508
UCM, Madrid, Spain

Veas, Christian 020136, 020234
PCCL, Leoben, Austria

Vecino, Fernando Román 020346
DTU, Roskilde, Denmark

Veerman, Sebastian 020035
ISC Konstanz, Konstanz, Germany

Vega de Seoane, José Maria 020252
Becquerel Institute Spain, San Sebastian, Spain

Vega de Seoane, Jose 020546
Becquerel Institute, Brussels, Belgium

Vega-Herrera, Jorge 020342
University of Antofagasta, Antofagasta, Chile

Vehus, Tore Sandnes 020443
University of Agder, Grimstad, Norway

Veirman, Jordi 020203, 020226, 020254
Eurac Research, Bolzano, Italy

Velasco, Angel 020367
Nextracker, Fremont, United States of America

Veludo, Jorge 020317
Galp Energia, Lisbon, Portugal

Veneri, Alessandro 020093
University of Verona, Verona, Italy

Vergura, Silvano 020301
Polytechnic University of Bari, Bari, Italy

Verlinden, Pierre 020001
YIST, Jiangyin, China

Vermang, Bart 020064
Hasselt Unversity, Genk, Belgium

Vernay, Christophe 020244
SOLAÏS, Valbonne, France

Vero, Giuseppe 020301
Polytechnic University of Bari, Bari, Italy

Veronese, Elisa 020513
Eurac Research, Bolzano, Italy

Veurman, Welmoed 020063
ISFH, Emmerthal, Germany

Viani, Lucas 020326
Enertis Applus+, Madrid, Spain

Vicente-Laiglesia, Pablo 020181
European Climate, Infrastructure and Environment
Executive Agency, Brussels, Belgium

Vidal de Oliveira, Aline 020377
Solar Energy Research Laboratory Fotovoltaica/ UFSC,
Florianópolis, Brazil

Vidal, Beatriz Muñoz 020414
IaSol, Zaragoza, Spain

Vidal-Fuentes, Pedro 020094
IREC, Barcelona, Spain

Videla-Magnata, Natalia 020129
Universidad de Antofagasta, Antofagasta, Chile

Videla-Magnata, Natalia 020417
University of Antofagasta, Antofagasta, Chile

Vilches, Anna Morales 020388
Next2Sun Technology, Dillingen, Germany

Villalonga Palou, Joan Tomás 020432, 020434
Sunveon, Madrid, Spain

Villén, Raúl 020127, 020414, 020517
ENDEF, Zaragoza, Spain

Villodas, Aritz 020198
TECNALIA, Derio, Spain

Vincent, Laetitia 020058
CNRS, Palaiseau, France

Vincent, Robin 020196
PVsyst, Geneva, Switzerland

Viorel Spataru, Sergiu 020191
DTU, Roskilde, Denmark

Viriyaroj, Bergpob 020298
Aalto University, Espoo, Finland

Viti, Valeria 020541
Legance, Milan, Italy

Vitoshkin, Helena 020379
Agricultural Research Organization, Rishon LeZion, Israel

Vögeli, Pascal 020385
ZHAW, Winterthur, Switzerland

Vogt, Malte R. 020515
TU Delft, Delft, The Netherlands

Vogt, Thomas 020482
DLR, Oldenburg, Germany

Vollbrecht, Joachim 020063, 020114
ISFH, Emmerthal, Germany

Voltan, Alessandro 020010
Applied Materials, Treviso, Italy

von Friedeburg, Christoph 020557
CF Energy Research-Consulting-Operation, Berlin, Germany

Voronko, Yuliya 020162, 020249
OFI, Vienna, Austria

Vorster, Frederik J. 020193, 020344, 020416
Nelson Mandela University, Port Elizabeth, South Africa

Vorster, Frederik 020185
Nelson Mandela University, Port Elizabeth, South Africa

Vuillon, Laurent 020338
CNRS, Chambery, France

Vulic, Natasa 020296
Univesity of Applied Arts and Sciences Northwestern Switzerland, Muttenz, Switzerland

Vumbugwa, Monphias 020185, 020193, 020344
Nelson Mandela University, Port Elizabeth, South Africa

Waibel, Christoph 020511
Flemish Institute for Technological Research (VITO), Genk, Belgium

Wakabayashi, Ryo 020484
Hitachi, Kokubunji, Japan

Wakazono, Kouzen 020131
Gifu University, Gifu, Japan

Wallner, Gernot M. 020227
University of Linz, Linz, Austria

Walpita, Harsha 020169
University of Oslo, Kjeller, Norway

Walsh, Yoselyn 020520
Costa Rica Institute of Technology, Cartago, Costa Rica

Wambach, Karsten 020468, 020470
bifa Umweltinstitut, Augsburg, Germany

Wang, Chia-Chen 020549
ITRI, Hsinchu, Taiwan

Wang, Shuo 020286, 020400
TUAS, Turku, Finland

Wang, Tzuya 020549
ITRI, Hsinchu, Taiwan

Wang, Xiaolin 020381
Mälardalen University, Västerås, Sweden

Wannenwetsch, Jann 020312
EnBW, Karlsruhe, Germany

Wargocki, Pawel 020551
DTU, Roskilde, Denmark

Waschl, Alfred 020255
buildingSMART, Vienna, Austria

Weber, Thomas 020180, 020230
Kiwa PI Berlin, Berlin, Germany

Weeber, Arthur W. 020515
TU Delft, Delft, The Netherlands

Wei, Wenpeng 020484
Hitachi, Kokubunji, Japan

Weihs, Philipp 020281
BOKU, Vienna, Austria

Weinrich, Frank 020177
PTB, Braunschweig, Germany

Weiß, Marius 020361
Coburg University of Applied Sciences, Coburg, Germany

Wellens, Christine 020135
Fraunhofer ISE, Freiburg, Germany

Whyatt, Duncan 020394
Lancaster University, Lancaster, United Kingdom

Wienands, Karl 020218, 020220, 020221
ISC Konstanz, Konstanz, Germany

Wiesenfarth, Maike 020246
Fraunhofer ISE, Freiburg, Germany

Wietler, Tobias 020063
ISFH, Emmerthal, Germany

Wilbert, Stefan 020235, 020237, 020239, 020331
DLR, Almería, Spain

Willers, Guido 020201
Fraunhofer CSP, Halle, Germany

Wilson, Helen R. 020249
Fraunhofer ISE, Freiburg, Germany

Winter, Renate 020063
ISFH, Emmerthal, Germany

Winter, Stefan 020177, 020181
PTB, Braunschweig, Germany

Wirtz, Wiebke 020260
ISFH, Emmerthal, Germany

Witkowska, Agnieszka 020498
Gdansk University of Technology, Gdansk, Poland

Wittmer, Bruno 020196
PVsyst, Geneva, Switzerland

Wolf, Andreas 020031
Fraunhofer ISE, Freiburg, Germany

Wong, Craig 020230
Kiwa PI Berlin, Berlin, Germany

Wu, Li-Guo 020021
TSEC, Hsinchu, Taiwan

Wu, Yu 020030
TNO, Petten, The Netherlands

Wyss, Philippe 020068
CSEM, Neuchâtel, Switzerland

Xiong, Weizhen 020320
Tokyo University of Science, Tokyo, Japan

Xu, Jiahui 020001
YIST, Jiangyin, China

Xu, Wenhao 020144, 020208
TÜV Rheinland, Shanghai, China

Xu, Xiaoqi 020263
SERIS, Singapore, Singapore

Maiz, Alexander 020437
UPV/EHU, Vitoria-Gasteiz, Spain

Majak, Martyna 020068
Roltec, Poznań, Poland

Makrides, George 020534
University of Cyprus, Nicosia, Cyprus

Malarkannan, Lavanya 020210
National Physical Laboratory, Teddington, United Kingdom

Malcorps, Philippe 020276
3E, Brussels, Belgium

Malik, Stephanie 020313
Fraunhofer CSP, Halle, Germany

Malik, Stephanie 020355
Fraunhofer IMWS, Halle, Germany

Maliutina, Kristina 020141
University of Applied Science Cologne, Cologne, Germany

Malo, Javier 020209
UPM, Madrid, Spain

Mancini, Simone 020425
TNO, Eindhoven, The Netherlands

Mandiola, Gotzon 020514
AZTI, PASAIA, Spain

Manganiello, Patrizio 020389
Hasselt University, Diepenbeek, Belgium

Manganiello, Patrizio 020294
imec, Genk, Belgium

Manito, Alex 020348
University of São Paulo, São Paulo, Brazil

Manochehrian, Rasoul 020539
Frankfurt University of Applied Sciences, Frankfurt am Main, Germany

Manzolini, Giampaolo 020261
Polytechnic University of Milan, Milan, Italy

Maqsood, Ayman 020101
HZB, Berlin, Germany

Marangis, Demetris 020534
University of Cyprus, Nicosia, Cyprus

Marcos-Castro, Ana 020297
CIEMAT, Madrid, Spain

Marechal, Philippe 020217
CEA / INES, Le Bourget-du-Lac, France

Marí Soucase, Bernabé 020099
UPV, Valencia, Spain

Markert, Jochen 020231
Fraunhofer ISE, Freiburg, Germany

Marquardt, Cornelia 020063
ISFH, Emmerthal, Germany

Marteau, Baptiste ECM Technologies, Grenoble, France	020034
Martín Rueda, Javier UPM, Madrid, Spain	020535
Martín, Francisco José UPM, Madrid, Spain	020459
Martín, Francisco UPM, Madrid, Spain	020209
Martín-Chivelet, Nuria CIEMAT, Madrid, Spain	020297
Martín-Rueda, Javier UPM, Madrid, Spain	020337, 020363
Martínez González, Mario Enertis Applus+, Madrid, Spain	020326
Martinez, Juan Ignacio Becquerel Institute Spain, San Sebastian, Spain	020252
Martinez, Oscar University of Valladolid, Valladolid, Spain	020191, 020205
Martínez-Barbeito, María ieco.io, Vigo, Spain	020243
Maruyama, Rodrigo P. University of São Paulo, São Paulo, Brazil	020154, 020348
Marzo, Aitor University of Granada, Granada, Spain	020311, 020546
Mashkov, Oleksandr HI ERN, Erlangen, Germany	020149, 020150, 020377
Massaro, Lorenzo PedersoliGattai, Milan, Italy	020541
Masson, Gaëtan Becquerel Institute, Brussels, Belgium	020474, 020558, 020564, 020573
Masson, Gaëtan IEA PVPS Task 1, Brussels, Belgium	020570
Mateos, Yeray UPV/EHU, Bilbao, Spain	020055, 020153
Maturi, Laura Eurac Research, Bolzano, Italy	020249, 020254, 020551
Mayer-Ullmann, Philipp AIT, Vienna, Austria	020430
Mazzoleni, Stefano University of Naples Federico II, Naples, Italy	020378
McIntosh, Keith R. PV Lighthouse, Coledale, Australia	020396
McNab, Shona UNSW, Sydney, Australia	020065
Meereboer, Martijn Energyra, Westknollendam, The Netherlands	020225

Meier, Rico 020132
HTW Berlin, Berlin, Germany

Meixner, Michael 020050
halm elektronik, Frankfurt am Main, Germany

Mekhaldi, Bouchra 020406
Ecole Polytechnique, Palaiseau, France

Melges de Andrade, Adnei 020154
University of São Paulo, São Paulo, Brazil

Melino, Francesco 020314
University of Bologna, Bologna, Italy

Mellone, Celeste 020541
Green Horse Advisory, Rome, Italy

Menard, Lionel 020291
MINES Paris, Nice, France

Mencaraglia, Denis 020058
CNRS, Gif-sur-Yvette, France

Menchaca, Iratxe 020514
AZTI, PASAIA, Spain

Mendes Ferreira Gomes, Amanda 020548
UFSC, Florianopolis, Brazil

Mendikoa, Iñigo 020514
Tecnalia, BRTA, Derio, Spain

Meneghini, Matteo 020089
University of Padova, Padova, Italy

Ménézo, Christophe 020317
LOCIE, Le Bourget-du-Lac, France

Menghini, Mariela 020508
IMDEA Nanoscience Institute, Madrid, Spain

Mercade Ruiz, Pau 020448, 020481
GreenPowerMonitor a DNV company, Barcelona, Spain

Merino, Amanda 020040
CEA / INES, Le Bourget-du-Lac, France

Merino, José Manuel 020085
UAM, Madrid, Spain

Mermoud, André 020196
PVsyst, Geneva, Switzerland

Merodio, Pablo 020337
UPM, Madrid, Spain

Mertens, Jan 020389
imec, Genk, Belgium

Mertens, Verena 020006, 020008
ISFH, Emmerthal, Germany

Meßmer, Marius 020031
Fraunhofer ISE, Freiburg, Germany

Messmer, Tobias 020218, 020221, 020225
ISC Konstanz, Konstanz, Germany

Messner, Christian 020369
AIT, Vienna, Austria
Mettner, Larissa 020063, 020114
ISFH, Emmerthal, Germany
Meusel, Manuel 020052
Fraunhofer CSP, Halle (Saale), Germany
Meyer, Kevin 020260
ISFH, Emmerthal, Germany
Meza, Carlos 020318, 020334, 020426, 020520
Anhalt University of Applied Sciences, Köthen, Germany
Mezzasalma, Frédéric 020217
CEA / INES, Le Bourget-du-Lac, France
Micha, Daniel 020092
CEFET/RJ, Petrópolis, Brazil
Michael, Poland 020193
Nelson Mandela University, Port Elizabeth, South Africa
Miclea, Paul-Tiberiu 020233
Fraunhofer CSP, Halle, Germany
Midtgård, Ole-Morten 020476
NTNU, Trondheim, Norway
Miettunen, Kati 020286, 020298, 020398
University of Turku, Turku, Finland
Migan-Dubois, Anne 020406
CNRS, Gif-sur-Yvette, France
Mignonac, Alexandre 020217
CEA / INES, Le Bourget-du-Lac, France
Mignonac, Alexandre 020334
CEA, Cadarache, France
Mignonac, Alexandre 020318
CEA, Saint-Paul-Lez-Durance, France
Miguel Laborda, María 020414
IaSol, Zaragoza, Spain
Mihailetchi, Valentin Dan 020033
ISC Konstanz, Konstanz, Germany
Mihailetchi, Valentin 020225
ISC Konstanz, Konstanz, Germany
Mihaylov, Blago 020210
European Commission JRC, Ispra, Italy
Milani, Emanuele 020495
Marelli Europe, Venaria Reala, Italy
Milesi, Frédéric 020068
CEA, Grenoble, France
Min, Byungsul 020008, 020482
ISFH, Emmerthal, Germany
Mirandona López, Haritz 020432, 020434
Sunveon, Madrid, Spain

Kitamura, Ibuki 020190
Osaka Electro-Communication University, Osaka, Japan

Kitzberger, Gregor 020136
voestalpine Stahl, Linz, Austria

Kivambe, Maulid 020166
QEERI, Doha, Qatar

Kizukuri, Rihoko 020220
TAMURA-ELSOLD, Ilsenburg, Germany

Kladas, Anastasios 020329, 020351
KU Leuven, Ghent, Belgium

Kleider, Jean-Paul 020040, 020058
CNRS, Gif-sur-Yvette, France

Kleissl, Jan 020528
University of California, San Diego, United States of America

Klengel, Robert 020355
Fraunhofer IMWS, Halle, Germany

Klenk, Markus 020385
ZHAW, Winterthur, Switzerland

Klos, Christine 020510
Buhck Re.Energy, Hamburg, Norway

Kluska, Sven 020019
Fraunhofer ISE, Freiburg, Germany

Klute, Carola 020355
Fraunhofer IMWS, Halle, Germany

Knausdorf, Christian 020361
Coburg University of Applied Sciences, Coburg, Germany

Ko, Seok-whan 020561
KIER, Daejeon, South Korea

Ko, Suk Whan 020324, 020357
KIER, Daejeon, South Korea

Koc, Timurhan 020376
DTU, Roskilde, Denmark

Koduvelikulathu, Lejo Joseph 020035, 020068
ISC Konstanz, Konstanz, Germany

Koduvelikulathu, Lejo 020003
ISC Konstanz, Konstanz, Germany

Köntges, Marc 020206
ISFH, Emmerthal, Germany

Koepge, Ringo 020142, 020192
Fraunhofer CSP, Halle, Germany

Koester, Lukas 020203, 020261, 020325
Eurac Research, Bolzano, Italy

Kohlenberg, Heike 020063
ISFH, Emmerthal, Germany

Kohno, Tohru 020186
Hitachi, Tokyo, Japan

Kolahi, Mohammad 020356, 020375
University of Isfahan, Isfahan, Iran
Konagai, Makoto 020106, 020115
Tokyo City University, Setagaya, Japan
Kono, Toru 020484
Hitachi, Kokubunji, Japan
Konu, Christopher Bruce 020132
HTW Berlin, Berlin, Germany
Kopecek, Radovan 020569
ISC Konstanz, Konstanz, Germany
Kopp, Nils 020220
TAMURA-ELSOLD, Ilsenburg, Germany
Korkmaz Arslan, Melisa 020020
ODTÜ-GÜNAM, Ankara, Türkiye
Korpås, Magnus 020476
NTNU, Trondheim, Norway
Kortetmäki, Aki 020444, 020445
TUAS, Tampere, Finland
Koskela, Juha 020444, 020445, 020554
Tampere University, Tampere, Finland
Kossen, Eric J. 020030
TNO, Petten, The Netherlands
Kowalski, Julia 020237
RWTH, Aachen, Germany
Kräling, Ulli 020215
Fraunhofer ISE, Freiburg, Germany
Kraft, Thomas M. 020423
VTT Technical Research Centre of Finland, Oulu, Finland
Krainer, Diana Maria 020430
AIT, Vienna, Austria
Krasilnikov, Inga 020379
Tel Aviv University, Tel Aviv, Israel
Krever Lopes, Bruno 020023
PUCRS, Porto Alegre, Brazil
Kribus, Abraham 020379
Tel Aviv University, Tel Aviv, Israel
Krishnan, Sasikumar 020361
Coburg University of Applied Sciences, Coburg, Germany
Kroon, Jan 020225
TNO, Petten, The Netherlands
Kuan, Ta-Ming 020021, 020053
TSEC, Hsinchu, Taiwan
Kubicek, Bernhard 020281, 020318, 020334, 020347, 020430
AIT, Vienna, Austria
Kucuk, E. Busra 020030
TNO, Petten, The Netherlands

Sanchez, Laura — 020437
UPV/EHU, Leioa, Spain

Sánchez, Yudania — 020085
IREC, Barcelona, Spain

Sanchez-Friera, Paula — 020412, 020513, 020521
Solkeys, Gijón, Spain

Sanchez-Ruiz, Alain — 020437
UPV/EHU, Vitoria-Gasteiz, Spain

Sansavini, Giovanni — 020296
ETH, Zurich, Switzerland

Sansoni, Paola — 020066
CNR-INO, Florence, Italy

Santamaría Fernández, Susanna — 020249
TECNALIA, Derio, Spain

Santamaría-Sancho, Juan — 020363
UPM, Madrid, Spain

Santos, Jose Domingo — 020197, 020198, 020358
TECNALIA, Derio, Spain

Santos, Rodrigo — 020530
Casa dos Ventos, Fortaleza, Brazil

Sanz Martinez, Asier — 020546
Tecnalia, Bilbao, Spain

Sanz, Asier — 020514
Tecnalia, BRTA, Derio, Spain

Sanz, Asier — 020197
TECNALIA, Derio, Spain

Sanz-Cuadrado, Cristina — 020575
UPM, Madrid, Spain

Sanz-Saiz, Carlos — 020297
CIEMAT, Madrid, Spain

Sarafijanovic-Djukic, Natasa — 020204
FFHS, Regensdorf, Switzerland

Saretti, Angelica — 020301
Polytechnic University of Bari, Bari, Italy

Sarkadi, Monika — 020569
ISC Konstanz, Konstanz, Germany

Sauer, Thomas — 020140
EXXERGY, Gräfelfing, Germany

Saura, Juan Antonio — 020506
University of Murcia, Murcia, Spain

Savisalo, Tuukka — 020225
Valoe, Mikkeli, Finland

Saw, Min Hsian — 020402
Technology Innovation Institute, Abu Dhabi, United Arab Emirates

Saxena, Anmol Ratan — 020429
NIT, Delhi, India

Rudzikas, Matas 020380
The Applied Research Institute for Prospective Technologies, Vilnius, Lithuania

Rüther, Ricardo 020377
Solar Energy Research Laboratory Fotovoltaica/ UFSC, Florianópolis, Brazil

Rüther, Ricardo 020548
UFSC, Florianopolis, Brazil

Ruf, Manuel 020455
Robert Bosch, Stuttgart, Germany

Ruiz Donoso, Elena 020331
DLR, Almería, Spain

S. Sousa, Graciana 020090
Federal University of Rio de Janeiro, Rio de Janeiro, Brazil

Safarian, Jafar 020011
NTNU, Trondheim, Norway

Sah, Dheeraj 020039
Aarhus University, Aarhus, Denmark

Sahin, Hasret 020479
LUT University, Lappeenranta, Finland

Saito, Kimihiko 020106
Tokyo City University, Setagaya, Japan

Salem, Mohammad 020428
Australian University, Kuwait City, Kuwait

Salerno, Giorgia 020077
University of Milano-Bicocca, Milan, Italy

Salis, Fabio 020541
Iberdrola, Rome, Italy

Salvador, Antonio 020358
MAGTEL, Córdoba, Spain

Sample, Tony 020213
European Commission JRC, Ispra, Italy

Samuolienė, Giedrė 020380
The Lithuanian Research Centre for Agriculture and Forestry, Kaunas, Lithuania

San José, Luis Javier 020209, 020453
UPM, Madrid, Spain

Sánchez de León Peque, Miguel 020243
ieco.io, Vigo, Spain

Sanchez Garcia, Alfredo 020270
SINTEF, Trondheim, Norway

Sanchez, Hugo 020056, 020158, 020284
Anhalt University of Applied Sciences, Köthen, Germany

Sanchez, Jesus 020437
UPV/EHU, Vitoria-Gasteiz, Spain

Xu, Yu 020263
SERIS, Singapore, Singapore

Xuereb, Steven 020180, 020230
Kiwa PI Berlin, Berlin, Germany

Yadav, Shivendra 020071, 020081
SVNIT, Surat, India

Yamaguchi, Yosuke 020484
Hitachi, Kokubunji, Japan

Yanagida, Masatoshi 020115
NIMS, Tsukuba, Japan

Yanar, T. Meriç 020027
Kalyon PV, Ankara, Türkiye

Yang, Donggeon 020323
K-water, Daejeon, South Korea

Yang, Hyoung-Kyu 020449
KETI, Wonmi-gu, South Korea

Yde, Leif 020250, 020306
Stensborg, Roskilde, Denmark

Ye, JiaYi 020102
SERIS, Singapore, Singapore

Yerci, Selcuk 020113
ODTÜ-GÜNAM, Ankara, Türkiye

Ylikunnari, Mari 020423
VTT Technical Research Centre of Finland, Oulu, Finland

Ylinen, Marko 020444
Satakunta University of Applied Sciences, Pori, Finland

Ylipaino, Juho 020444, 020445, 020554
TUAS, Tampere, Finland

Yılmaz, Büşra 020521
Kameleon Solar, Roosendaal, The Netherlands

Yordadov, Georgi 020389
imec, Diepenbeek, Belgium

Younes, Kareem 020487
Khalifa University, Abu Dhabi, United Arab Emirates

Yu, Cheng-Yeh 020021, 020053
TSEC, Hsinchu, Taiwan

Yu, Shusen 020406
Ecole Polytechnique, Palaiseau, France

Yuan, Xiao 020001
YIST, Jiangyin, China

Yun, Jae Ho 020112
KENTECH, Naju-si, South Korea

Zaimi, Mhammed 020171
University of Chouaib Doukkali, El Jadida, Morocco

Zanatta Britto, João Victor 020025
PUCRS, Porto Alegre, Brazil

Zanesco, Izete 020023, 020025
PUCRS, Porto Alegre, Brazil

Zaror, Yasmin 020225
WIP - Renewable Energies, Munich, Germany

Zarzalejo, Luis F. 020237, 020331
CIEMAT, Madrid, Spain

Zekri, Atef 020146
QEERI, Doha, Qatar

Zerafa, Steve 020334
PIXAM, Msida, Malta

Zhang, Geng 020001
Jolywood (ShanXi) Solar Technology, Taiyuan, China

Zhang, Jingwei 020111
Hohai University, Changzhou, China

Zhang, Kai 020233
FZJ, Jülich, Germany

Zhang, Wenjing 020001
YIST, Jiangyin, China

Zhang, Wuai 020101
HZB, Berlin, Germany

Zhang, Yating 020144, 020208
TÜV Rheinland, Shanghai, China

Zhou, Qilin 020102
SERIS, Singapore, Singapore

Zhu, Junjie 020017
Institute for Energy Technology, Kjeller, Norway

Ziaullah, Abdul Wahab 020278, 020291
QEERI, Doha, Qatar

Zilles, Roberto 020154, 020348
University of São Paulo, São Paulo, Brazil

Zimmermann, Iwan 020116
IPVF, Palaiseau, France

Zubillaga, Oihana 020139
Tecnalia, Donostia - San Sebastián, Spain

Zugasti, Eugenia 020334
CENER, Pamplona, Spain

Zugasti, Eugenia 020300
CENER, Sarriguren, Spain

Zwahlen, Theo 020369
BFH, Burgdorf, Switzerland

KEYWORDS OF EU PVSEC 2025 PROCEEDINGS PAPERS

42nd European Photovoltaic Solar Energy Conference and Exhibition (EU PVSEC 2025)

Bilbao, Spain
22-26 September 2025

Volume 2 of 6

ISBN: 979-8-3313-2987-7

Printed from e-media with permission by:

Curran Associates, Inc.
57 Morehouse Lane
Red Hook, NY 12571

WIP – Renewable Energies
Sylvensteinstr. 2
81369 Munchen
Germany

Phone: +49 89 72012735
Fax: +49 89 72012791

wip@wip-munich.de

Additional copies of this publication are available from:

Curran Associates, Inc.
57 Morehouse Lane
Red Hook, NY 12571 USA
Phone: 845-758-0400
Fax: 845-758-2633
Email: curran@proceedings.com
Web: www.proceedings.com

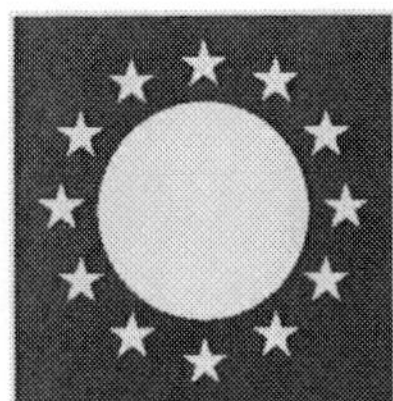

42nd European Photovoltaic Solar Energy Conference and Exhibition

---

Proceedings of the International Conference

22 September – 26 September 2025

Edited by:

C. DEL CAÑIZO
Solar Energy Institute
UPM
Spain

R. KENNY
European Commission
Joint Research Centre
Italy

J. BERGMILLER
WIP Renewable Energies
Germany

J. DE GREGORIO
WIP Renewable Energies
Germany

Edition Team:

B. Yildiz
L. Großhans
A. Michaelsen
U.E. Birgi
WIP Renewable Energies
Germany

Photos at:

Coordination of the Technical Programme:

European Commission Joint Research Centre
Via E. Fermi 1
21020 Ispra (VA)
Italy

Institutional Support:

European Commission

Institutional PV Industry Cooperation:

SolarPower Europe

ESMC – European Solar Manufacturing Council

Supporting Organisations:

AUSTRALIAN PV INSTITUTE

ASOM – Alliance for Solar Mobility

BASQUE ENERGY CLUSTER

BILBAO CONVENTION BUREAU

EASE – European Association for Storage of Energy

ETIP PV – European Technology & Innovation Platform PV

GÜNDER – Turkish Solar Energy Society

IEA PVPS - IEA Photovoltaic Power Systems Programme

INSTITUTO SOLAR DE ENERGÍA SOLAR

LDES – Long Duration Energy Storage Council

NSEFI – National Solar Energy federation of India

NUS /SERIS – National University of Singapore / Solar Energy Research Institute of Singapore

UPM - Polytechnic University of Madrid

Supporting Associations:

EERA – European Energy Research Aliance

EREF – European Renewable Energies Federation

EUREC – The Association of European Renewable Energy Research Centres

VDMA Photovoltaic Equipment

Local Support:
ENTE VASCO DE LA ENERGÍA
EUH – University of the Basque Country

EU PVSEC 2025 realised by:

WIP Renewable Energies
Sylvensteinstr. 2, 81369 Munich, Germany
Tel: +49 89 720 12 735, Fax: +49 89 720 12 791
Email: pv.conference@wip-munich.de
www.eupvsec.org
www.wip-munich.de

Proceedings produced and published by:

WIP Renewable Energies
Sylvensteinstr. 2, 81369 Munich, Germany
Tel: +49 89 720 12 735, Fax: +49 89 720 12 791
Email: pv.conference@wip-munich.de
www.eupvsec.org
www.wip-munich.de

42nd EUROPEAN PHOTOVOLTAIC SOLAR ENERGY CONFERENCE AND EXHIBITION
22 SEPTEMBER – 26 SEPTEMBER 2025

EU PVSEC 2025 COMMITTEES

INTERNATIONAL SCIENTIFIC ADVISORY COMMITTEE (ISAC)

Chair

P. Szymanski, European Commission Joint Research Centre, Director of Energy, Transport and Climate, Petten, The Netherlands

Committee Members

V. Bermúdez Benito, Founder & Principal Consultant, Berbetin, Antibes, France
G.C. Eder, OFI, Vienna, Austria
P. Frankl, Head of the Renewable Energy Division, International Energy Agency, France
M. Getsiou, European Commission, DG RTD, Brussels, Belgium
S.W. Glunz, Head of Division Photovoltaics - Research, Fraunhofer ISE, Freiburg, Germany
N.M. Haegel, Director of the National Center for Photovoltaics, NREL, Golden, USA
R. Kenny, European Commission Joint Research Centre, Directorate for Energy and Transport and Climate, Ispra, Italy
S. Nowak, Managing Director of NET Nowak Energy & Technology, St. Ursen, Switzerland
R. Schlatmann, Chairman of ETIP PV, Head of the Solar Energy Division at Helmholtz-Zentrum Berlin, Germany
W.C. Sinke, TNO Energy Transition, The Netherlands
M. Topič, Head of Laboratory of Photovoltaics and Optoelectronics of the University of Ljubljana, Slovenia
P. Verlinden, Director at Amrock, Visiting Professor at Sun Yat-Sen University, Guangzhou, China
E. Voroshazi, Head of PV module process laboratory, CEA, Le Bourget-du-Lac, France
J. Bergmiller, Managing Director Events & Knowledge Transfer, WIP Renewable Energies, Munich, Germany
J. de Gregorio, Head of Unit, Scientific Services and Cooperation, WIP Renewable Energies, Munich, Germany

CONFERENCE EXECUTIVE COMMITTEE

Conference General Chair

C. del Cañizo, UPM, Madrid, Spain

Technical Programme Chair

R. Kenny, European Commission Joint Research Centre, Directorate for Energy and Transport and Climate, Ispra, Italy

Committee Members

W.C. Sinke, Program Development Manager, TNO Energy Transition, The Netherlands
S. Nowak, Managing Director of NET Nowak Energy & Technology, St. Ursen, Switzerland
M. Topič, Head of Laboratory of Photovoltaics and Optoelectronics of the University of Ljubljana, Slovenia
V. Bermúdez Benito, BERBETIN, France
E. Voroshazi, Head of PV Module Process Laboratory, CEA, Le Bourget-Du-Lac France
H. Ossenbrink, Former European Commission Joint Research Centre, Germany
J. Bergmiller, Managing Director Events & Knowledge Transfer, WIP Renewable Energies, Munich, Germany
J. de Gregorio, Head of Unit, Scientific Services and Cooperation, WIP Renewable Energies, Munich, Germany

2025 SCIENTIFIC COMMITTEE

Programme Technical Chair

R. Kenny, European Commission, Joint Research Centre, Italy

Topic Chairs

Topic 1: Silicon Materials and Cells
F. Schindler, Fraunhofer ISE, Germany

Topic 2: Thin Films and New Concepts
I. Gordon, imec, Belgium

Topic 3: Photovoltaic Modules and BoS Components
T. Barnes, NREL, USA

Topic 4: PV Systems Engineering, Integrated/Applied PV
A.M. Gracia Amillo, FUNDACION CENER, Spain

Topic 5: PV in the Energy Transition
C. Agraffeil, CEA / INES, France

Topic Organisers and Paper Review Experts

Topic 1: Silicon Materials and Cells
F. Schindler, Fraunhofer ISE, Germany
C. Fischer, Wacker Chemie, Germany
G. Hahn, University of Konstanz, Germany
K. Ding, Forschungszentrum Jülich, Germany
P. Roca i Cabarrocas, CNRS-LPICM, France
A. W. Weeber, TNO Energy Transition, The Netherlands
D. Muñoz, CEA / INES, France
S. W. Glunz, Fraunhofer ISE, Germany
K. Bothe, ISFH, Germany
M. Topic, University of Ljubljana, Slovenia
P. Fath, RCT-Solutions, Germany
S. Peters, Hanwha Q CELLS, Germany

M.P. Bellmann, SINTEF, Norway
A. Ciesla, UNSW, Australia
C. Hagendorf, Freiberg Instruments, Germany
X. Yu, Zhejiang University, China
J.S. Lee, KIER, South Korea
R. Brendel, ISFH, Germany
T. Dullweber, ISFH, Germany
J. Horzel, Fraunhofer ISE, Germany
W. Nemeth, NREL, United States of America
R. Turan, METU, Türkiye
F. Menchini, ENEA, Italy
W. Favre, CEA, France

J. Meier, Meier Technologies, Switzerland
J. Schmidt, ISFH, Germany
M. Wright, University of Oxford, United Kingdom
J. Zhao, CSEM, Switzerland
A. Morisset, CSEM, Switzerland
A. Richter, Fraunhofer ISE, Germany
J. Linke, ISC Konstanz, Germany
B. Geerligs, TNO Energy Transition, The Netherlands
S. Dubois, CEA, France
M. Hermle, Fraunhofer ISE, Germany
B. Terheiden, University of Konstanz, Germany
P. Delli Veneri, ENEA, Italy
T. Matsui, AIST, Japan
Y. Ohshita, Toyota Technological Institute, Japan
E. Bruhat, HOLOSOLIS, France
A. Augusto, Dalarna University, Sweden
F. Ferrazza, ENI S.p.A., Italy
A. Otaegi, UPV/EHU, Spain
M.C. Schubert, Fraunhofer ISE, Germany
H. Duman, KalyonPV, Türkiye
N. Usami, Nagoya University, Japan
Y. Zhu, UNSW, Australia
D. Brunner, RENA Technologies, Germany
A. Danel, CEA, France
C. Gerardi, 3Sun, Italy
H.J. Nonnenmacher, Meyer Burger, Germany
P. Verlinden, AMROCK, Australia
Q. Wang, Wang, Qi, China
W. Zhang, Zhang, Weiming, China
Y. Chen, Trina Solar Energy, China
E. Krassowski, CE Cell Engineering, Germany
M. Foti, 3Sun, Italy
D.L. Bätzner, Meyer Burger Research, Switzerland

Topic 2: Thin Films and New Concepts
I. Gordon, imec, Belgium
J.C. Goldschmidt, Marburg University, Germany
F. Schoofs, Oxford PV, United Kingdom
N. Kyranaki, Hasselt University, Belgium
S. Veenstra, TNO Energy Transition, The Netherlands
T. Aernouts, imec, Belgium
A.N. Tiwari, SOLTIWA, Switzerland
G. Siefer, Fraunhofer ISE, Germany
M. Edoff, Uppsala University, Sweden
A. Martí Vega, UPM, Spain
J. Poortmans, imec, Belgium
I. Ramiro, UPM, Spain
T. Magorian Friedlmeier, ZSW, Germany

S. Albrecht, HZB, Germany
S. Berson, CEA, France
P. Carroy, CEA, France
C. Case, Oxford PV, United Kingdom
G. Coletti, FuturaSun, Italy
S. De Wolf, KAUST, Saudi Arabia
U.W. Paetzold, KIT, Germany
H. Sivaramakrishnan Radhakrisnan, imec, Belgium
P. Schulze, Fraunhofer ISE, Germany
L. Wang, Technology Innovation Institute, United Arab Emirates
Y. Smirnov, Applied Materials, United States of America
B. Stannowski, HZB, Germany
F. Fertig, Hanwha Q CELLS, Germany
L. Lancellotti, ENEA, Italy
S. Cros, CEA, France
S. Hayase, The University of Electro-Communications, Japan
S. Huang, Macquarie University, Australia
M. Khenkin, HZB, Germany
C. Lin, National Taiwan University, Taiwan
M.S.H. Norton, University of Cyprus, Cyprus
P. Pistor, Pablo de Olavide University, Spain
W. Tress, Zurich University of Applied Sciences, Switzerland
A. Aguirre, imec, Belgium
D. Lan, UNSW Sydney, China
M. Saliba, University of Stuttgart, Germany
P. Manshanden, TNO Energy Transition, The Netherlands
L. Vesce, University of Rome II, Italy
I. Dogan, TNO Solliance, The Netherlands
Y. Kuang, imec, Belgium
M. Al Katrib, IPVF, France
M.I. Hossain, QEERI, Qatar
W.H. Chiu, Chang Gung University, Taiwan
C. Chen, Ming Chi University of Technology, Taiwan
C. Fell, CSIRO Energy Technology, Australia
G. Brammertz, imec, Belgium
T. Dalibor, Avancis, Germany
S. Ishizuka, AIST, Japan
A. Redinger, University of Luxembourg, Luxembourg
A. Romeo, University of Verona, Italy
V. Sittinger, Fraunhofer IST, Germany
M. Theelen, TNO/Solliance, The Netherlands
G. Timò, RSE, Italy
A. Kanevce, ZSW, Germany
A. Pérez-Rodríguez, IREC, Spain
R. Gutzler, ZSW, Germany
W. Witte, ZSW, Germany
T. Nishimura, Tokyo Institute of Technology, Japan
C. Qian, University of New South Wales, Australia
J.P. Connolly, CentraleSupelec, France
J.P. Kleider, CNRS/GeePs, France
I. Konovalov, University of Applied Sciences Jena, Germany
Y. Okada, University of Tokyo, Japan
M. Rusu, HZB, Germany
H. Meddeb, DLR, Germany
E. Saucedo, Universitat Politècnica de Catalunya (UPC), Spain
P. Vidal-Fuentes, FUNDACIÓ INSTITUT DE RECERCA EN ENERGIA DE CATALUNYA, Spain
C. Malerba, ENEA, Italy
C. Becker, HZB, Germany
D. Kuciauskas, NREL, United States of America
M. Ochoa, University of Cantabria, Spain
T. Tayagaki, AIST, Japan
S. Wasmer, WAVELABS Solar Metrology Systems, Germany
S. Zandi, UNSW, Australia
C. Messmer, University of Freiburg, Germany
J.B. Puel, Institut Photovoltaïque d'Ile de France (IPVF), France
S. Ternes, University of Rome II, Italy

Topic 3: Photovoltaic Modules and BoS Components
V. Bermúdez Benito, BERBETIN, France
R. Preu, Fraunhofer ISE, Germany
R. Gottschalg, Fraunhofer CSP, Germany
T. Barnes, NREL, United States of America
G. Friesen, SUPSI, Switzerland
G. Bardizza, TÜV Rheinland Solar, Italy

V. Barth, CEA, France
A. Faes, CSEM, Switzerland
A. Lennon, Sundrive Solar, Australia
M. Mittag, Fraunhofer ISE, Germany
M.A. Muñoz-García, UPM, Spain
H. Nagel, Fraunhofer ISE, Germany
S. Pietralunga, CNR, Italy
T. Timofte, ISC Konstanz, Germany

S. Feldbacher, PCCL, Austria
A. Halm, ISC Konstanz, Germany
H. Hanifi, AESOLAR, Germany
E. Warren, NREL, United States of America
S. Zhang, Trina Solar Energy, China
X. Zhen, Canadian Solar, China
G. Beaucarne, Dow Silicones Belgium, Belgium
T. Bejat, CEA, France
C. Camus, LayTec, Germany
U. Jahn, Fraunhofer CSP, Germany
G. Oreski, PCCL, Austria
M. Pander, Fraunhofer CSP, Germany
T. Sample, European Commission JRC, Italy
A. Morlier, imo-imomec, Belgium
C. Barretta, PCCL, Austria
P. Gebhardt, Fraunhofer ISE, Germany
C. Sen, UNSW, Australia
O. Arriaga Arruti, CSEM, Switzerland
X. Gu, NIST, United States of America
C. Xiao, Chinese Academy of Sciences, United States of America
R. Aninat, TNO/Solliance, The Netherlands
S. Mitterhofer, NIST, United States of America
B. Hoex, UNSW, Australia
E. Özkalay, SUPSI, Switzerland
M. Bokalič, University of Ljubljana, Slovenia
S. Bordihn, ISFH, Germany
M. Despeisse, CSEM, Switzerland
J. Govaerts, imec, Belgium
J. Lopez-Garcia, STS-Certified, Spain
M. Pravettoni, Technology Innovation Institute, United Arab Emirates
T. Stoyanova Lyubenova, Joint Research Centre, Italy
C. Ulbrich, HZB, Germany
J. Moereke, Avancis, Germany
Y.S. Long, ITRI, Taiwan
D. Pavanello, European Commission JRC, Italy
A.K. Vidal de Oliveira, UFSC, Brazil
J. Bengoechea, CENER, Spain
M. Ernst, ANU, Australia
H. Ellis, European Commission JRC, Italy
B. Mihaylov, European Commission JRC, Italy
G. Chowdhury, 3E, Belgium
B. Aissa, QEERI - Qatar Environment and Energy Research Institute, Qatar

Topic 4: PV Systems Engineering, Integrated/Applied PV
A. Gracia Amillo, CENER, Spain
W.G.J.H.M. van Sark, Utrecht University, The Netherlands
K. Lappalainen, Tampere University, Finland
J.M. Almeida Serra, University of Lisbon, Portugal
I. Tsanakas, CEA, France
C. Buerhop-Lutz, HI ERN, Germany
D. Moser, Becquerel Institute Italia, Italy
F. Frontini, SUPSI, Switzerland
G.C. Eder, OFI, Austria
A. Scognamiglio, ENEA, Italy
A. Chatzipanagi, European Commission JRC, Italy
I. Antón Hernández, UPM, Spain
R.M.E. Valckenborg, TNO, The Netherlands
T. Reindl, SERIS, Singapore
J.R. Gonzalez, European Space Agency, The Netherlands
G. Mütter, Gerhard Mütter e.U., Austria
T. Merdzhanova, Forschungszentrum Jülich, Germany

V. Lara-Fanego, Solargis, Spain
A. Louwen, Eurac Research, Italy
A. Martinez Fernandez, European Commission JRC, Italy
T. Oozeki, AIST, Japan
J. Remund, Meteotest, Switzerland
M. Sengupta, NREL, United States of America
M. Zehner, Rosenheim Technical University of Applied Sciences, Germany
B. Nouri, German Aerospace Center, Spain
S. Poddar, UNSW, Australia
D. Bachour, HBKU/ Qatar Foundation, Qatar
J. Yang, NREL, United States of America
S. Bouguerra, imo-imomec, Belgium
C. Alonso-Tristán, UBU, Spain
M. Carbone, ENEL Green Power, Italy
M. Dennenmoser, BayWa r.e. Solar Projects GmbH, Germany
C.W. Hansen, Sandia National Laboratories, United States of America
A. Neubert, DNV Maritime Software GmbH, Germany
D. Berrian, Belectric, Germany
M. Oliosi, PVsyst, Switzerland
J. Moschner, KU Leuven / EnergyVille, Belgium
C. Bucher, BUAS, Switzerland
B. Wittmer, PVsyst SA, Switzerland
M. Bolen, SB Energy, United States of America
D. Daßler, Fraunhofer CSP, Germany
R. Einhaus, ZSW, Germany
P. Hacke, NREL, United States of America
A. Heimsath, Fraunhofer ISE, Germany
J. Lin, PV Guider, Taiwan
A. Migan-Dubois, GeePs, France
M. Rinio, University of Karlstad, Sweden
J.S. Stein, Sandia National Laboratories, United States of America
D. Stellbogen, ZSW, Germany
M. Theristis, Sandia National Laboratories, United States of America
A. Virtuani, CSEM, Switzerland
A. Driesse, PV Performance Labs, Germany
M. Øgaard, IFE, Norway
A. Nobre, SERIS, Singapore
T. Trupke, UNSW, Australia
C. Cornaro, University of Rome II, Italy
G. A. dos Reis Benatto, DTU, Denmark
S. Malik, Fraunhofer CSP, Germany
S. Lindig, Univers SAS, France
M.M. Nygård, Institute for Energy Technology, Norway
P. Alonso Gomez, BayWa r.e., Germany
Y. Assoa, CEA, France
P. Bonomo, SUPSI, Switzerland
V. D'Ambrosio, University of Naples Federico II, Italy
E. Román Medina, Tecnalia, Spain
L.H. Slooff, TNO Energy Transition, The Netherlands
S. Villa, TNO, The Netherlands
M. La Rosa, Glass to Power, Italy
T. Del Caño, Onyx Solar Energy, Spain
X. Zhihao, AIST, Japan
P. Sharif, ODTU-GUNAM, Türkiye
K. Umeda, TAISEI CORPORATION, Japan
S. Boddaert, CSTB, France
N. Lysgaard Andersen, DTU, Denmark
K. Meyer, ISFH, Germany
T. Biel, NET Nowak Energy & Technology, Switzerland
F. Colucci, ENEA, Italy
A. Pascaris, NREL, United States of America
C. Dupraz, INRAE, France
C. Alonso-García, CIEMAT, Spain
A. Lefort, BayWa, Germany
H.N. Riise, IFE, Norway
M.A. Schüler, Next2Sun Technology GmbH, Germany
P.J. Pérez-Higueras, University of Jaén, Spain
K. Oda, Agritree,

M. Berwind, Fraunhofer ISE, Germany
M. Dörenkämper, TNO, The Netherlands
M. Heinrich, Fraunhofer ISE, Germany
B. Newman, Lightyear, The Netherlands
A. Reinders, Eindhoven University of Technology, The Netherlands
T. Tanahashi, AIST, Japan
J. Leloux, LuciSun, Belgium
E. Shirazi, University of Twente, The Netherlands
K. Araki, University of Miyazaki, Japan
K. Nishioka, University of Miyazaki, Japan
R. Campesato, CESI, Italy
V. Khorenko, Azur Space, Germany
G. Kakoulaki, European Commission Joint Research Centre, Italy
H. Toyota, JAXA, Japan
P. Garcia-Linares, UPM, Spain
I. Weiss, Weiss, Ingrid, Germany
A. Hensel, Fraunhofer ISE, Germany
J.S. da Fernandes, Hochschule Offenburg, Germany
Y. Ueda, Tokyo University of Science, Japan
J. Braid, Sandia National Laboratories, United States of America

Topic 5: PV in the Energy Transition
J. Stierstorfer, WIP Renewable Energies, Germany
R. Pestana, R&D Nester, Portugal
P.J. Alet, CSEM, Switzerland
C. Agraffeil, CEA, France
K. WAMBACH, Wambach-Consulting, Germany
C. del Cañizo, UPM, Spain
L. Großhans, WIP Renewable Energies, Germany
M. Getsiou, European Commission DG RTD, Belgium
S. Nowak, NET Nowak Energy & Technology, Switzerland
C. Breyer, LUT University, Finland
I. Kaizuka, RTS Corporation, Japan
G. Masson, Becquerel Institute, Belgium
P. Baliozian, VDMA, Germany
L. Großhans, WIP Renewable Energies, Germany
C. Candelise, Bocconi University, Italy
S. Caneva, WIP Renewable Energies, Germany

G. Barchi, Eurac Research, Italy
R. Bründlinger, AIT, Austria
V. Efthymiou, University of Cyprus, Cyprus
M. Centeno Brito, University of Lisbon, Portugal
F. Carigiet, ZHAW, Switzerland
B. Gaiddon, HESPUL, France
F.Z. Ouchani, Green Energy Park, Morocco
M. Rennhofer, AIT, Austria
G. Adinolfi, ENEA, Italy
W. Schaffer, Salzburg Netz, Austria
A. Haber, e-control, Austria
G. Heilscher, Technische Hochschule Ulm, Germany
A. Anctil, Michigan State University, United States of America
S. Arancón, Plug and Play, Spain
S. Capaccioli, ETA - Florence Renewable Energies, Italy
V. Fthenakis, Columbia University, United States of America
G. Heath, NREL, United States of America
K. Komoto, Mizuho Research & Technologies, Ltd., Japan
W. Palitzsch, LuxChemtech, Germany
S. Ovaitt, NREL, United States of America
M. de Wild-Scholten, SmartGreenScans, The Netherlands
S. Herceg, Fraunhofer ISE, Germany
C. Polacchi, Eurac Research, Italy
N. Espinosa, Universidad de Murcia, Spain
E. Drahi, TotalEnergies OneTech, France
S. Guastella, RSE, Italy
H. Ossenbrink, Band Gap, Germany
D. Polverini, European Commission DG GROW, Belgium
N. Taylor, European Commission JRC, Italy
K.A. Weiß, Fraunhofer ISE, Germany
I. Kafedjiska, Helmholtz Zentrum Berlin, Germany
P. Malbranche, Solar Action, France
S. De Iuliis, ENEA, Italy
T. Haarberg, BNW-Energy, Norway
A. Nayfeh, Khalifa University, United Arab Emirates
E. Vartiainen, Fortum Renewables Oy, Finland
E. Veronese, Eurac Research, Italy
P. Sanchez-Friera, Solkeys, Spain
N. Cherradi, Desert Technologies, Saudi Arabia
S. Nold, Fraunhofer ISE, Germany
H.J.J. Yu, CEA, France
M. Beck, U.S. Department of Energy, United States of America
M. Woodhouse, NREL, United States of America
A.B. Cristóbal, UPM, Spain
G. Ruggieri, Insubria University, Italy
S. Tay, NUS, Singapore

Awards Coordinators

Student Awards Coordinator
A.H.M. Smets, Delft University of Technology, The Netherlands

Student Awards Committee
R. Kenny, EU PVSEC Technical Programme Chair, Italy
C. del Canizo, Conference Chair, UPM, Spain
E. Voroshazi, CEA, France
J. Poortmans, imec, Belgium
P.J. Alet, CSEM, Switzerland
S. Caneva, WIP Renewable Energies, Germany
A. Romeo, University of Verona, Italy
G. Friesen, SUPSI, Switzerland
F. Schindler, Fraunhofer ISE, Germany
J.C. Goldchmidt, Marburg University, Germany
D. Moser, Becquerel Institute, Italy
K. Ding, FZJ, Germany
W.C. Sinke, TNO Energy Transition, The Netherlands
M. Topic, University of Ljubljana, Slovenia
R. Schlatman, HZB, Germany
S. Glunz, Fraunhofer ISE, Germany
A.M. Vega, UPM, Spain
I. Kaizuka, RTS, Japan
P.D. Veneri, ENEA, Italy
J. Bengoechea, CENER, Spain

Poster Awards Coordinator
P. Malbranche, Solar Action, France

Poster Awards Committee
R. Kenny, European Commission JRC, Italy
C. del Canizo, UPM, Spain
W. van Sark, Utrecht University, The Netherlands
I. Tsanakas, CEA INES, France
L. Miranda, Oxford PV, United Kingdom
D. Munoz, CEA INES, France
I. Gordon, imec, Belgium
E. Roman, Tecnalia, Spain
G. Eder, OFI, Austria
I. Antón, UPM, Spain
S. Veenstra, TNO, The Netherlands
J.M. Almeida Serra, University of Lisbon, Portugal
T. Magorian Friedlmeier, ZSW, Germany
J. Stierstorfer, WIP Renewable Energies, Germany

G. Kakoulaki, European Commission JRC, Italy
T. Barnes, NREL, USA
T. Merdzhanova, Forschungszentrum Jülich, Germany

Highlights Committee
C. del Cañizo, UPM, Madrid, Spain
R. Kenny, European Commission Joint Research Centre, Directorate for Energy and Transport and Climate, Ispra, Italy
W.C. Sinke, TNO Energy Transition, The Netherlands
S. Nowak, Managing Director of NET Nowak Energy & Technology, St. Ursen, Switzerland
M. Topič, Head of Laboratory of Photovoltaics and Optoelectronics of the University of Ljubljana, Slovenia
V. Bermúdez Benito, BERBETIN, France
E. Voroshazi, Head of PV Module Process Laboratory, CEA, Le Bourget-Du-Lac France
H. Ossenbrink, Band Gap, Germany
J. Bergmiller, Managing Director Events & Knowledge Transfer, WIP Renewable Energies, Munich, Germany
J. de Gregorio, Head of Unit, Scientific Services and Cooperation, WIP Renewable Energies, Munich, Germany
S. Leanza, Marketing and PR Manager, WIP Renewable Energies, Munich, Germany
B. Yildiz, Project Manager Events & Knowledge Transfer, WIP Renewable Energies, Munich, Germany
F. Schindler, Fraunhofer ISE, Freiburg, Germany
I. Gordon, imec, Leuven, Belgium
T. Barnes, NREL, Evergreen, USA
A.M. Gracia Amillo, FUNDACION CENER, Sarriguren, Spain
C. Agraffeil, CEA / INES, Le Bourget-du-Lac, France

SUBJECT INDEX

Silicon Materials and Cells

Sessions 1CP.1, 1EP.3, 1AO.4, 1AO.5, 1AO.6, 1BO.1, 1BO.2, 1BO.3, 1BO.4, 1DO.9, 1BV.5, 1CV.2

Thin Films and New Concepts

Sessions 2CP.2, 2BO.1, 2CO.1, 2CO.2, 2DO.9, 2DO.6, 2DO.7, 2DO.8, 2AO.2, 2AO.3, 2AO.1, 2BO.8, 2BO.9, 2BO.10, 2BV.1, 2BV.2, 2CV.3

Photovoltaic Modules and BoS Components

Sessions 3CP.1, 3CP.3, 3CO.10, 3CO.11, 3DO.12, 3DO.16, 3DO.19, 3DO.20, 3BO.11, 3BO.12, 3BO.14, 3BO.15, 3AV.1, 3AV.2, 3AV.3

PV Systems Engineering, Integrated/Applied PV

Sessions 4AP.1, 4AO.7, 4AO.8, 4AO.9, 4DO.1, 4DO.3, 4BO.6, 4BO.7, 4CO.8, 4CO.9, 4DO.10, 4DO.17, 4BO.5, 4BO.16, 4BO.17, 4DO.2, 4DO.4, 4DO.5, 4CO.3, 4EO.2, 4BV.3, 4BV.4, 4CV.1, 4DV.1, 4DV.4,

PV in the Energy Transition

Sessions 5CP.1, 5CP.2, 5DO.14, 5DO.15, 5CO.4, 5CO.5, 5CO.6, 5DO.18, 5CO.4, 5CO.5, 5CO.6, 5DO.18, 5EO.3, 5EO.1, 5DV.2, 5DV.3,

Topic Code

1 Silicon Materials and Cells
2 Thin-Films and New Concepts
3 Photovoltaic Modules
4 Photovoltaic Systems
5 Photovoltaics in the Energy Transition

Session Type

P = Plenary Session
O = Oral Session
V = Visual Session

Day Codes

A = Monday, 22 September 2025
B = Tuesday, 23 September 2025
C = Wednesday, 24 September 2025
D = Thursday, 25 September 2025
E = Friday, 26 September 2025

e.g. 1AO.4 ⇒ 1= Silicon Materials and Cells, A=Monday, O=Oral session, 4=Session 4

FOREWORD

The European Photovoltaic Solar Energy Conference and Exhibition (EU PVSEC) stands as the World's leading and most renowned forum for PV research and development and the biggest conference on PV solar energy. In 2025, celebrating its 42nd edition, the EU PVSEC was the essential meeting and exchanging point for global PV experts from research, development, and industry.

Held from 22–26 September 2025 in Bilbao, Spain, the EU PVSEC 2025 was a resounding success, showcasing a wide range of cutting-edge research results. Bringing together both the Conference and the Exhibition, this edition attracted more than 1600 participants from 61 countries who contributed over 1000 presentations across various fields of science and technology. The event provided an essential platform for the exchange of knowledge and ideas on photovoltaic research, innovations, and applications. In the exhibition area 51 companies from all parts of the world welcomed visitors and presented their products and services.

Conference Highlights

The EU PVSEC covered a broad range of topics with an extensive programme that offers an opportunity for workers from across the entire field of photovoltaics to share their findings, as well as an opportunity for multidisciplinary learning. Rapid advances in materials, designs, and manufacturing processes reflect the accelerating expansion of the global PV market. The programme was arranged into 5 topics as follows:

- Silicon Materials and Cells;
- Thin Films and New Concepts;
- Photovoltaic Modules and Balance of System Components;
- PV Systems Engineering, Integrated/Applied PV;
- PV in the Energy Transition.

Communicating the key messages from the conference, not only to participants, but also to other researchers, key stakeholders, policy makers and the general public was an important added value. We thank the Highlights Committee, composed of selected members of the Scientific Committee, as well as the Session Chairs, for providing a comprehensive summary of the findings and state of the art research that were delivered during this year's event. Some key highlights are listed below, while further details may be found in the dedicated highlights presentation in the annex of these proceedings.

Cross-cutting themes:

- Demonstrated the versatility of solar technologies, spanning traditional and emerging application areas.
- Sustainability and circularity remain central, with research focused on reducing material use, such as replacing silver with copper, and advancing end-of-life management of modules.
- Ensuring long-term stability and predictable energy yield is equally essential, with many examples of studies on degradation mechanisms and efforts to elucidate their root-causes, such as in the case of UVID.
- The role of artificial intelligence across the PV value chain is rapidly expanding, from design to operations and maintenance, including among many others drone applications.

Latest Solar Innovations in Materials, Cells, Modules and PV Systems:

While silicon solar cells remain the cornerstone of PV technology, perovskite solar cells continue to stand out as the leading complementary technology to silicon, both as standalone devices and in tandem configurations. Research efforts are increasingly focused on enhancing stability, understanding degradation mechanisms, improving durability and scalability, and ensuring full industrial compatibility.

Many companies presented impressive results on industrial-size single-junction perovskite modules as well as perovskite-based tandem modules, and several new efficiency records were announced during the event. The rapid pace of innovation in cell and module architecture underscores the need for accelerated and more robust testing and qualification methodologies. Both the industry and the research community are moving swiftly to assess and improve reliability in this fast-evolving PV landscape.

A major focus in module research remains the optimisation of materials and packaging to ensure long lifetimes and predictable energy yields from high-efficiency cells. In parallel, many innovative advances in the operation and maintenance (O&M) of PV systems were presented and discussed.

Applications, Grid Integration and Storage

"PV can be deployed everywhere": from space applications to agrivoltaics, PV noise barriers, building-integrated photovoltaics (BIPV), floating PV systems, and even vehicles. Among these, agrivoltaics is gaining momentum as a promising dual land use approach, offering economic benefits for farmers while increasing resilience to climate change.

Flexibility solutions, particularly through battery storage, were recognised in many technical presentations as essential to accommodate higher PV penetration levels and to reduce energy curtailment. At the same time, strengthening grid infrastructure and enhancing grid management capabilities remain critical to enable the next phase of large-scale PV integration.

Photovoltaics in the Energy Transition

Options for re-establishing competitive module manufacturing in Europe were extensively analysed, including detailed policy recommendations for industrial support and market growth. Currently, a mismatch persists between global PV module installation rates and production rates, resulting in growing inventories and sharply reduced prices.

Finally, inclusiveness, diversity, citizen participation, awareness, education, and social engagement were

underlined as vital dimensions of the sector's long-term sustainability and innovation capacity.

EU PVSEC 2025 Proceedings

Selection for inclusion in the conference was made by the Scientific Committee's paper review experts and topic organisers (see the listing on pages 010002-001-005), to whom we express our sincere gratitude for their comprehensive review work and overall contribution to the success of the conference.

The EU PVSEC 2025 Proceedings contain the full papers covering most of the highlights described above and more. The Proceedings provide a comprehensive overview of the PV solar sector, its current status and future prospects in science, research, innovation, development and deployment extending to 3,750 pages. In addition to the 299 submitted papers, the proceedings include 101 presentations (slides) shown during the plenary and oral presentations as well as 176 poster files of the visual presentations. In total this amounts to 576 publications.

The Conference Proceedings are published as downloadable files and are also fully accessible online. A DOI code (Digital Object Identifier) has been assigned to each paper. This ensures unequivocal and permanent identification and full citability. The EU PVSEC 2025 papers can be viewed and downloaded in a full free open access from the EU PVSEC's Proceedings website https://userarea.eupvsec.org/proceedings.

The proceedings of the EU PVSEC 2025 strengthen the commitment to providing quick and open access to high quality scientific results. This is a powerful source for targeted and quick information search and retrieval, enabling you to search by topic, keywords, paper title, DOI, author, or organization.

We are confident that these Proceedings will play an important role in providing a comprehensive overview of the current actors and activities in the global PV sector and that they will disseminate information on the state-of-the-art of technologies and applications. This can generate further research, add momentum to innovation and promote interest in PV worldwide.

We would like to cordially thank all authors and participants of the EU PVSEC 2025 for their contributions and look forward to welcoming you in Rotterdam, The Netherlands from 14 – 18 September 2026 at the EU PVSEC 2026, the 43rd European Photovoltaic Solar Energy Conference and Exhibition

The Editors

TABLE OF CONTENTS OF EU PVSEC 2025 PROCEEDINGS PAPERS

Visual SESSION 1CV.2 Si Solar Cells | Characterisation & Modelling of Silicon Cells and Their Building Blocks

[1] Anhalt University of Applied Sciences, Köthen, Germany; [2] Fraunhofer CSP, Halle, Germany

Oral SESSION 2AO.2 Advances in Chalcogenide Devices

2AO.2.3 A New Method for Sb-doped CdSeTe/CdTe Devices with Superior Stability 020057
Elisa Artegiani[1], Mariyam Mukhtar[1], Alessandro Romeo[1]
[1] *University of Verona, Verona, Italy*

Oral SESSION 2AO.3 III-V Based Devices | Tandem and Perovskite Solar Cells

2AO.3.3 Micro-Crystal GaAs Array Sub-Cells for Si Tandem Solar Cells 020058
James Patrick Connolly[1], Ahmed Nejim[2], Alexandre Jaffré[1], José Alvarez[1], Jean-Paul Kleider[1], Denis Mencaraglia[1], Laurie Dentz[3], Géraldine Hallais[3], Frederic Hamouda[3], Laetitia Vincent[3], Daniel Bouchier[3], Charles Renard[3]
[1] *CNRS, Gif-sur-Yvette, France;* [2] *SILVACO, St. Ives, United Kingdom;* [3] *CNRS, Palaiseau, France*

2AO.3.5 Multiscale Models for Perovskite Optimisation 020060
Philippe Baranek[1], James Patrick Connolly[2], Antoine Gissler[1], Philip Schulz[3], Michel Rerat[4], Roberto Dovesi[5]
[1] *EDF R&D, Palaiseau, France;* [2] *CNRS, Gif-sur-Yvette, France;* [3] *IPVF, Palaiseau, France;* [4] *IPREM, Pau, France;* [5] *Academy of Sciences of Turin, Torino, Italy*

2AO.3.6 Modelling Recovery in Perovskite Solar Cells under Light and Dark to Address Stability Challenges 020062
Guillem Álvarez-Pérez[1], Jean Baptiste Puel[1], Jean François Guillemoles [1]
[1] *IPVF, Palaiseau, France*

Oral SESSION 2BO.10 Advanced Modelling and Characterisation of Perovskite Solar Cells

2BO.10.2 On Perimeter Losses in Perovskite Top- and Poly-Si-Passivated Silicon Bottom Cells – Do Small Area Tandems Reveal the Full Efficiency Potential? 020063
Felix Haase[1], Lukas Brockmann[1], Annika Raugewitz[1], Verena Steckenreiter[1], Verena Barnscheidt[1], Roland Clausing[1], Sara Baumann[1], Joachim Vollbrecht[1], Welmoed Veurman[1], Johannes Löhr[1], Dongyang Liu[1], Mircea Turcu[1], Lasse Nasebandt[1], Udo Römer[1], David Sylla[1], Jessica Strey[1], Martha Löhning[1], Larissa Mettner[1], Renate Winter[1], Anja Christ[1], Heike Kohlenberg[1], Cornelia Marquardt[1], Emanuel Brueckner[1], Hossein Rabiei[1], Michael Rienäcker[1], Sarah Kajari-Schröder[1], Tobias Wietler[1], Robby Peibst[1]
[1] *ISFH, Emmerthal, Germany*

2BO.10.5 In-depth Characterization and Simulation Approach for the Understanding of In- and Outdoor Degradation of Perovskite Solar Cells 020064
Jonathan Parion[1], Amit Kumar Harit[1], Elias Peraticos[2], Vasiliki Paraskeva[2], Maria Hadjipanayi[2], Aranzazu Aguirre[1], Filip Duerinckx[1], Hariharsudan

Sivaramakrishnan Radhakrishnan[1], Jef Poortmans[1], Johan Lauwaert[3], Bart Vermang[1]
[1] Hasselt Unversity, Genk, Belgium; [2] University of Cyprus, Nicosia, Cyprus; [3] Ghent University, Ghent, Belgium

Oral SESSION 2BO.8 Advanced Conversion Devices

2BO.8.1 Singlet Fission Route for >30% Efficient Solar Cells: Silicon Cell Requirements 020065
Shona McNab[1], Alex J. Baldacchino[1], Pheobe Pearce[1], Alvin Mo[1], Alison Ciesla[1], Bram Hoex[1], Nicholas J. Ekins-Daukes[1], Murad J. Y. Tayebjee[1], Michael P. Nielsen[1]
[1] UNSW, Sydney, Australia

2BO.8.5 Performance of a 4-Terminals Spectral Splitting Asymmetric Solar Concentrator in Diffuse Sunlight: a Numerical Study 020066
Floriana Morabito[1], Daniela Fontani[2], Paola Sansoni[2], Mehdi Ahmadi[3], Salvatore Lombardo[3], Andrea Farina[1], Silvia Maria Pietralunga[1]
[1] CNR-IFN, Milan, Italy; [2] CNR-INO, Florence, Italy; [3] CNR-IMM, Catania, Italy

2BO.8.6 GaAs for Thermophotonics: From Thin-Film Solar Cells to Highly Efficient LEDs 020067
Natasha Gruginskie[1], Peter Mulder[1], Gerard Bauhuis[1], Jani Oksanen[2], John Schermer[1]
[1] Radboud University, Nijmegen, The Netherlands; [2] Aalto University, Espoo, Finland

Visual SESSION 2BV.1 New Materials, Devices and Conversion Concepts | New Modelling and Characterisation Techniques

2BV.1.4 Low-Energy Electron Multiplication on Nanostructured Solar Cells: a Novel Route to Overcome Si-PV Efficiency Limits 020068
Mikaël Hosatte[1], Brice Rouffie[1], Zbigniew T. Kuznicki[1], Frédéric Milesi[2], Bertrand Paviet-Salomon[3], Audrey Morisset[3], Philippe Wyss[3], Lejo Joseph Koduvelikulathu[4], Lazhar Rachdi[4], Lacramioara Popescu[4], Dominik Rudolph[4], Marek Basta[5], Andrzej Miszczuk[5], Martyna Majak[5], Beata Basta[5], Samuel Queste[6]
[1] SEGTON Advanced Technology, Versailles, France; [2] CEA, Grenoble, France; [3] CSEM, Neuchâtel, Switzerland; [4] ISC Konstanz, Konstanz, Germany; [5] Roltec, Poznań, Poland; [6] Marie and Louis Pasteur University, Besançon, France

2BV.1.5 Tailoring CBTSSe Solar Cells for Indoor Photovoltaic Applications 020069
Hitarth Narsi Patel[1], Bindu Pamula[1], Deepak Joshi[1], Vivek Garg[1]
[1] SVNIT, Surat, India

2BV.1.6 Theoretical Insights through DFT into $AgBiS_2$ Thin Films Absorber for Photovoltaic Applications 020071
Dhruv Singh Thakur[1], Rajesh Kumar Sharma[1], Nithin Chatterji[1], Vivek Garg[1], Shivendra Yadav[1]
[1] SVNIT, Surat, India

Visual SESSION 2BV.2 Compound and Organic Semiconductors

Gerardo Gordillo[1], Oscar Torres[1], Julian Peña-Bermudez[2]
[1] *National University of Colombia, Bogotá, Colombia;* [2] *University of the Caribbean, Santo Domingo, Dominican Republic*

2CV.3.71 Comparative Analysis and Efficiency Optimization of Sulfur-based Chalcogenide Perovskites ($MgHfS_3$, $CaZrS_3$, $BaZrS_3$) via Interface Engineering for High-Performance Solar Cells 020111
Anees ur Rehman[1], Kung Ding[1], Jingwei Zhang[1], Xiang Chen[1]
[1] *Hohai University, Changzhou, China*

2CV.3.72 Development of Inorganic Perovskite $CsPbI_3$ with Heterojunction Engineering at the Buried Interface for Enhanced Stability and Performance 020112
Syed Fawad Ali Shah[1], Hyeonwook Park[1], Muhammad Rehan[2], Donghyeop Shin[2], Kihwan Kim[2], Jae Ho Yun[3]
[1] *KENTECH, Naju-Si, South Korea;* [2] *KIER, Daejeon, South Korea;* [3] *KENTECH, Naju-si, South Korea*

Oral SESSION 2DO.6 Industrially Scalable Processes to Manufacture Perovskite Solar Cells and Modules

2DO.6.2 Eliminating P2 Scribes: A New Interconnection Design for Efficient Perovskite Solar Modules Under Indoor Lighting 020113
Bahri Eren Uzuner[1], Konstantin Tsoi[1], Gorkem Gunbas[1], Selcuk Yerci[1]
[1] *ODTÜ-GÜNAM, Ankara, Türkiye*

2DO.6.5 Evaporated Self Assembled Monolayer (SAM) Hole Transport Layers for Scalable Perovskite Solar Cells 020114
Joachim Vollbrecht[1], Verena Barnscheidt[1], Roland Clausing[1], Johannes Löhr[1], Larissa Mettner[1], Adam Neuba[2], Annika Raugewitz[1], Jessica Strey[1], Robby Peibst[1]
[1] *ISFH, Emmerthal, Germany;* [2] *Paderborn University, Paderborn, Germany*

Oral SESSION 2DO.7 Insights Into the Stability of Perovskite Solar Cells and Modules

2DO.7.1 Outdoor Performance and Degradation Analysis of Inverted Perovskite Solar Cells 020115
Makoto Konagai[1], Hayato Okawa[1], Ryousuke Ishikawa[1], Masatoshi Yanagida[2], Yasuhiro Shirai[2]
[1] *Tokyo City University, Setagaya, Japan;* [2] *NIMS, Tsukuba, Japan*

Oral SESSION 2DO.8 Multiple Aspects of Perovskite PV Research

2DO.8.2 Strategies for Quasi-2D Perovskite Integration in p-i-n Solar Cells 020116
Anna Capitaine[1], Hugo Le Bossenec[1], Marion Provost[1], Alexandra Levtchenko[1], Daniel Ory[2], Jean Rousset[2], Iwan Zimmermann[1], Anyssa Derj[1],

Mirella Al Katrib[1]
[1] *IPVF, Palaiseau, France;* [2] *EDF R&D, Palaiseau, France*

2DO.8.3 Innovative Approach to Bismuth-Antimony-Iodide Double Perovskite PV Absorbers via Anion Exchange and Solide-State Reactions 020117
Oleksandr Stroyuk[1]*, Oleksandra Raievska*[1]*, Sachin Kinge*[2]*, Jens Hauch*[1]*, Christoph J. Brabec*[1]
[1] *HI ERN, Erlangen, Germany;* [2] *Toyota Motors Europe, Brussels, Belgium*

Visual SESSION 3AV.1 PV Module Design and Manufacturing

3AV.1.1 Investigating the 3-Dimensional Structure of Metallic Filler Particles in Electrically Conductive Adhesives 020119
Stephan Grosser[1]*, Alexander Müller*[1]*, Robert Göckeritz*[1]*, Tobias Nitsche*[2]*, Daniel Buckland*[2]*, Giuseppe Galbiati*[2]*, Bengt Jaeckel*[1]
[1] *Fraunhofer CSP, Halle, Germany;* [2] *Henkel, Düsseldorf, Germany*

3AV.1.6 Investigation on Different Bypass Diodes for Shade Resistant PV-Modules 020121
Jens Froebel[1]*, Matthias Pander*[1]*, Bengt Jaeckel*[1]*, Andreas Maixner*[2]*, Pouya Pourshafi*[2]*, Afshin Bakhtiari*[2]*, Hamed Hanifi*[2]
[1] *Fraunhofer CSP, Halle, Germany;* [2] *AESOLAR, Koenigsbrunn, Germany*

3AV.1.7 Optimization of Infrared Soldering Process to Reduce the Temperature Inhomogeneity in Silicon Solar Cells Using Finite Element Methods 020123
Daniel Christopher Joseph[1]*, Angela De Rose*[1]*, Christian Reichel*[1]*, Andreas J. Beinert*[1]*, Holger Neuhaus*[1]
[1] *Fraunhofer ISE, Freiburg, Germany*

3AV.1.10 Performance Evaluation of a New Design Photovoltaic Module with Reduced Self-Shading 020125
Pouya Pourshafi[1]*, Andreas Maixner*[1]*, Hamed Hanifi*[1]
[1] *AESOLAR, Königsbrunn, Germany*

3AV.1.11 Materials Assessment for PV-T Modules Thermal Performance Improvement 020127
Lucía Cano[1]*, Raquel Simón-Allué*[1]*, Raúl Villén*[1]*, Yolanda Lara*[1]*, Isabel Guedea*[1]
[1] *ENDEF, Zaragoza, Spain*

3AV.1.12 Evaluating Repair Techiniques for c-Si PV Modules: Spot-Welding 020129
Jorge Rabanal-Arabach[1]*, Sonia Beltran-Condori*[1]*, Natalia Videla-Magnata*[1]*, Katalina Rojas-Henriquez*[1]*, Andreas Schneider*[2]*, Edward Fuentealba-Vidal*[1]
[1] *University of Antofagasta, Antofagasta, Chile;* [2] *University of Applied Sciences Gelsenkirchen, Gelsenkirchen, Germany*

3AV.1.13 Thermally Conductive Filler Particle Mixed Silicone Layer to Provide Heat Dissipation Functionality to c-Si Solar Cell Modules without Encapsulants 020131
Yasushi Sobajima[1]*, Kouzen Wakazono*[1]*, Keisuke Ohdaira*[2]
[1] *Gifu University, Gifu, Japan;* [2] *JAIST, Ishikawa, Japan*

3AV.1.16 Ultrasonic Characterization of Ethylene-Vinyl Acetate in Glass-Glass-Modules 020132
Christopher Bruce Konu[1]*, Rico Meier*[1]
[1] *HTW Berlin, Berlin, Germany*

Visual SESSION 3AV.2 PV Module Durability and Reliability

Nathan Roosloot[1], Harsha Walpita[2], Christoph Seiffert[1], Jean Thomas[3], Maarten Dörenkämper[4], Minne M. de Jong[4], Josefine H. Selj[1], Gaute Otnes[1]
[1] Institute for Energy Technology, Kjeller, Norway; [2] University of Oslo, Kjeller, Norway; [3] Ciel et Terre, Lille, France; [4] TNO, Eindhoven, The Netherlands

Visual SESSION 3AV.3 PV Modules Characterisation and Performances Assessment

3AV.3.1 A New Method for Comprehensive Power Rating and Performance Analysis of PERC Modules based on Half-Cut Cell Technology 020171
Khadija El Ainaoui[1], Mhammed Zaimi[2], Imane Flouchi[1], Said Elhamaoui[1], Yasmine El mrabet[1], Abdellatif Ghennioui[1], El Mahdi Assaid[2]
[1] Green Energy Park, Benguerir, Morocco; [2] University of Chouaib Doukkali, El Jadida, Morocco

3AV.3.2 Energy Rating Analysis of Heterojunction PV Modules 020173
Teodora Stoyanova Lyubenova[1], Ewan D. Dunlop[1]
[1] European Commission JRC, Ispra, Italy

3AV.3.3 Trend of Temperature Coefficients of c-Si Module Technologies from the past 15 Years 020175
Bengt Jaeckel[1], Matthias Pander[1]
[1] Fraunhofer CSP, Halle, Germany

3AV.3.6 Angle of Incidence Measurements on Bifacial PV Modules 020177
Frank Weinrich[1], Stefan Riechelmann[1], Stefan Winter[1]
[1] PTB, Braunschweig, Germany

3AV.3.8 Plug & Play IV Curve Tracer for PV Modules 020179
Adrian Jäggi[1], Christof Bucher[1], Matthias Burri[1]
[1] BFH, Burgdorf, Switzerland

3AV.3.9 Seasonal and Location-Dependent Temperature Coefficients for Thin-Film PV Modules: Enhancing Yield Prediction Accuracy 020180
Thomas Weber[1], Abdullah Abu Sayed[1], Benjamin Lippke[1], Steven Xuereb[1], Marcus Rennhofer[2], Bart E. Pieters[3]
[1] Kiwa PI Berlin, Berlin, Germany; [2] AIT, Vienna, Austria; [3] FZJ, Jülich, Germany

3AV.3.10 Standardisation Methods for Bifacial Energy Yield Estimation and PV Module Long-Term Performance Degradation Estimation: Potential Policy Implications 020181
Jaione Bengoechea[1], Ana Maria Gracia Amillo[1], Stefan Riechelmann[2], Stefan Winter[2], Giorgio Bardizza[3], Christos Monokroussos[4], Davide Polverini[5], Pablo Vicente-Laiglesia[6], Maria Getsiou[7]
[1] CENER, Sarriguren, Spain; [2] PTB, Braunschweig, Germany; [3] TÜV Rheinland Italia, Milan, Italy; [4] TÜV Rheinland, Shanghai, China; [5] Directorate General for Internal Market, Industry, Entrepreneurship and SMEs, Brussels, Belgium; [6] European Climate, Infrastructure and Environment Executive Agency, Brussels, Belgium; [7] Directorate General for Research and Innovation, Brussels, Belgium

3AV.3.11 Shaalke: Development of a MATLAB Software Tool for Advanced Statistical Outdoor Data Evaluation 020183

Oral SESSION 3BO.11 Imaging Techniques for PV Modules

Cristian Terrados[1], Eva de la Viuda[1], Kabir Paul Sulca[1], Julian Anaya[1], Miguel Ángel González[1], Oscar Martínez[1]
[1] University of Valladolid, Valladolid, Spain

3BO.11.6 Luminescence Measurements of PV Modules with a Cost-Effective and Small-Sized Hood-Based Tool under Daylight Conditions 020206
Marc Köntges[1], Michael Siebert[1], Dieter Lorenz[2], Bernd Kuhrmann[2], Michael Fuß[2]
[1] ISFH, Emmerthal, Germany; [2] MBJ Solutions, Ahrensburg, Germany

Oral SESSION 3BO.12 Characterisation and Energy Rating of PV Modules

3BO.12.1 Developing a New I-V Translation Methodology in Accordance with IEC 60891:2021 Correction Procedure 1 and 2 020208
Wenhao Xu[1], Yating Zhang[1], Mengdi Liu[1], Christos Monokroussos[1], Werner Herrmann[2], Giorgio Bardizza[2], Harald Müllejans[3]
[1] TÜV Rheinland, Shanghai, China; [2] TÜV Rheinland Solar, Cologne, Germany; [3] European Commission JRC, Ispra, Italy

3BO.12.2 Characterization of Vehicle Integrated Photovoltaic Modules 020209
Ricardo Moruno[1], Francisco José Martín[1], Juan Manuel Redondo[1], Javier Malo[1], Luis Javier San José[1], Guido Vallerotto[1], Steve Askins[1], Rubén Núñez[1], César Domínguez[1], Ignacio Antón[1], Rebeca Herrero[1]
[1] UPM, Madrid, Spain

3BO.12.4 Estimating the Energy Yield of Bifacial Photovoltaics with the JRC's Photovoltaic Geographic Information System 020210
Nigel Taylor[1], Teodora Lyubenova[1], Lavanya Malarkannan[2], Nikos Alexandris[1], Alexandros Falangas[3], Robert Kenny[1], Ewan D. Dunlop[1], Blago Mihaylov[1]
[1] European Commission JRC, Ispra, Italy; [2] National Physical Laboratory, Teddington, United Kingdom; [3] TRASIS International, Brussels, Belgium

3BO.12.5 An Update on Energy Rating Amendments – Integration of Bifacial Modules 020211
Stefan Riechelmann[1], Hendrik Sträter[1], Ana Maria Gracia Amillo[2], Sophie Pelland[3], Anton Driesse[4]
[1] PTB, Braunschweig, Germany; [2] CENER, Pamplona, Spain; [3] Natural Resources Canada, Varennes, Canada; [4] PV Performance Labs, Freiburg, Germany

Oral SESSION 3BO.14 Characterisation and Outdoor Monitoring of Perovskite-based PV Modules

3BO.14.1 Outdoor Measurements of Perovskite Modules 020213
Hanna Ellis[1], Harald Müllejans[1], Ewan D. Dunlop[1], Tony Sample[1]
[1] European Commission JRC, Ispra, Italy

Oral SESSION 3BO.15 Outdoor Performances and Degradation Analysis of PV Modules

3BO.15.2 Performance Characterization of Monofacial and Bifacial Modules in French Polynesia: Case Study of Tahiti 020214

Moira Itzel Torres Aguilar[1], Pascal Ortega[2], Jordi Badosa Franch[3], Johan Parra[3]

[1] *CentraleSupélec, Gif-sur-Yvette, France;* [2] *University of French Polynesia, Faa'a, French Polynesia;* [3] *Ecole Polytechnique, Palaiseau, France*

3BO.15.4 Statistical Trends in Nominal vs. Measured Performance of PV Modules and the Impact of Metastability 020215

Ulli Kräling[1], Daniel Philipp[1], Martin Kaiser[1]

[1] *Fraunhofer ISE, Freiburg, Germany*

3BO.15.6 Fifteen Years Under the Sun: Real-Field Degradation Analysis of Veteran PV Modules 020217

Ioannis (John) A. Tsanakas[1], Frédéric Mezzasalma[1], Maxime Babics[1], Alexandre Mignonac[1], Hervé Colin[1], Romain Couderc[1], Lionel Sicot[1], Philippe Marechal[1], Guillaume Capron[1], Jérémie Aimé[1]

[1] *CEA / INES, Le Bourget-du-Lac, France*

Oral SESSION 3CO.10 Advanced Interconnection Technology

3CO.10.4 Towards Enhanced Reliability of Busbar-Free IBC Solar Cell Interconnections by Non-Conductive Adhesive Reinforcement 020218

Tudor Timofte[1], Tobias Messmer[1], Karl Wienands[1], Joris Libal[1], Stephan Grosser[2], Matthias Pander[2], Giuseppe Galbiati[3], Tobias Nitsche[3], Daniel Buckland[3], Andreas Halm[1], Raphael Shanmugam[1]

[1] *ISC Konstanz, Konstanz, Germany;* [2] *Fraunhofer CSP, Halle, Germany;* [3] *Henkel, Duesseldorf, Germany*

3CO.10.6 Contact Resistance Limitations in Conductive Adhesive and Solder Paste Modules 020220

Daniel Tune[1], M. Ignacia Acevedo Devoto[1], Raphael Shanmugam[1], Karl Wienands[1], Nils Kopp[2], Carina Hallensleben[2], Rihoko Kizukuri[2], Matthias Helbig[1], Andreas Halm[1]

[1] *ISC Konstanz, Konstanz, Germany;* [2] *TAMURA-ELSOLD, Ilsenburg, Germany*

Oral SESSION 3CO.11 Innovative Module Design and Characterisation

3CO.11.2 Process and Design Freedom Enabled by Back-Contact Solar Cells Minimizing the Inactive Module Area 020221

Andreas Halm[1], Daniel Tune[1], Karl Wienands[1], Tudor Timofte[1], Tobias Messmer[1]

[1] *ISC Konstanz, Konstanz, Germany*

3CO.11.3 Techno-economic Analysis of Suitable Module BOM for Different Climatic Conditions 020222

Sraisth[1], Julian Reichle[1], Mehul Raval[1], Gourab Das[1], Xinyang Li[1], Hardik Gohil[1], Wolfgang Jooß[1]

[1] *RCT Solutions, Konstanz, Germany*

3CO.11.5 Indoor Characterization and Analysis of Reverse Breakdown Behavior of Solar Cells with Different Cell Architectures 020223

Bengt Jaeckel[1], Jens Froebel[1], Matthias Pander[1], Andreas Maixner[2], Hamed Hanifi[2]

[1] Fraunhofer CSP, Halle, Germany; [2] AESOLAR, Koenigsbrunn, Germany

Plenary SESSION 3CP.1 Si PV Manufacturing: Pushing the Limits of Performance

3CP.1.2 IBC4EU: European Back Contact Technology 020225

Florian Buchholz[1], Daniel Tune[1], Tobias Meßmer[1], Jonathan Linke[1], Manjunath Prasad[1], Valentin D. Mihailetchi[1], Juras Ulbikas[2], Arne Dahle[3], Martijn Meereboer[4], Francesca Fabris[5], Erik Eikelboom[5], Tom Borgers[6], Rik Van Dyck[6], Filip Duerinckx[7], Hariharsudan Sivaramakrishnan Radhakrishnan[7], Timea Bejat[8], Samuel Harrison[8], Ashish Binani[9], Nicolas Guillevin[9], Jan Kroon[9], Yevgeniya Larionova[10], Thorsten Dullweber[10], Ofer Shochet[11], Isaac Rosen [11], Ingo Röver [12], Wolfram Palitzsch[12], Yasmin Zaror[13], Johannes Stierstorfer[14], Aurimas Radzevicius[15], Julius Denafas[16], Tuomas Vanhanen [17], Tuukka Savisalo[17], Maximilian Pospischil [18], Marian Breitenbücher [18], Özlem Coşkun[19], Melodie de l'Epine [20], Philippe Macé[20], Ian Kenchington[20]

[1] ISC Konstanz, Konstanz, Germany; [2] Protechnology, Vilnius, Lithuania; [3] Norsun, Oslo, Norway; [4] Energyra, Westknollendam, The Netherlands; [5] Futurasun, Citadella, Italy; [6] IMEC, Genk, Belgium; [7] Hasselt Unversity, Genk, Belgium; [8] CEA, Le Bourget-du-Lac, France; [9] TNO, Petten, The Netherlands; [10] ISFH, Emmerthal, Germany; [11] Copprint, Jerusalem, Israel; [12] LuxChemTech, Freiberg, Germany; [13] WIP Renewable Energies, Munich, Germany; [14] WIP - Renewable Energies, Munich, Germany; [15] Valoe Cells, Vilnius, Lithuania; [16] Solitek, Vilnius, Lithuania; [17] Valoe, Mikkeli, Finland; [18] Highline Technologies, Freiburg, Germany; [19] Kalyon PV, Ankara, Türkiye; [20] Becquerel Institute, Brussels, Belgium

Plenary SESSION 3CP.3 Perovskite – Silicon Tandems: Towards Commercialisation | PV Stability in the Field

3CP.3.4 Outdoor Performance and Reliability of Perovskite (Pk)-Silicon (Si) Tandems: >1 year of Monitoring in the NEXUS Project 020226

Atse Louwen[1], Jordi Veirman[1], Alexander Astigarraga[1], Juan José Stivanello[1], David Moser[2], Perrine Carroy[3], Vincent Barth[3], Delfina Muñoz[3], Markus Lenz[4], Anika Sidler[4], Jorge Ferrando[5], Maximiliano Alejandro Senno[5], Henk J. Bolink[5], Talat Özden[6], Hisham Nasser[6], Shuaifeng Hu[7], Xinyi Shen[7], Henry Snaith[7]

[1] Eurac Research, Bolzano, Italy; [2] Becquerel Institute Italy, Trento, Italy; [3] CEA / INES, Le Bourget-du-Lac, France; [4] School of Life Sciences FHNW, Muttenz, Switzerland; [5] University of Valencia, Paterna, Spain; [6] ODTÜ-GÜNAM, Ankara, Türkiye; [7] University of Oxford, Oxford, United Kingdom

Oral SESSION 3DO.12 Innovative Encapsulation Materials

Nikolina Pervan[1], Jutta Geier[1], Christian Veas[1], Gernot Oreski[1]
[1] PCCL, Leoben, Austria

Oral SESSION 4AO.7 Solar Resource Assessment

4AO.7.4 Potential of Decimeter-Resolution Ground Albedo Data for Bifacial Photovoltaics 020235
Niklas Blum[1], Bijan Nouri[1], Yann Fabel[1], Stefan Wilbert[1]
[1] DLR, Almería, Spain

4AO.7.5 Method for the Determination of Spectral Responsivity of Digital Solar Irradiance Sensors 020236
David Hinken[1], Sebastian Denke[1], Karsten Bothe[1], Rolf Brendel[1]
[1] ISFH, Emmerthal, Germany

Oral SESSION 4AO.8 Solar Irradiance Forecasting

4AO.8.2 Cutting-Edge Generative AI for Intra-Hour Solar Forecasting 020237
Yann Fabel[1], Dominik Schnaus[2], Bijan Nouri[1], Stefan Wilbert[1], Niklas Blum[1], Luis F. Zarzalejo[3], Julia Kowalski[4], Robert Pitz-Paal[5]
[1] DLR, Almería, Spain; [2] TUM, Garching, Germany; [3] CIEMAT, Madrid, Spain; [4] RWTH, Aachen, Germany; [5] DLR, Cologne, Germany

4AO.8.4 Integrating Satellite Imagery and GNNs for Improving Day-Ahead Solar Irradiance Forecasting 020238
Baptiste Schubnel[1], Jelena Simeunovic[1], Corentin Tissier[1], Pierre-Jean Alet[1], Rafael E. Carrillo[1]
[1] CSEM, Neuchâtel, Switzerland

4AO.8.5 Enhancing Intra-Hour Solar Irradiance Forecasting for Solar Applications: A Blended Model of Satellite, Sky Imager and Persistence 020239
Bijan Nouri[1], Jorge Lezaca[2], Yann Fabel[1], Annette Hammer[2], Niklas Blum[1], Stefan Wilbert[1]
[1] DLR, Almería, Spain; [2] DLR, Oldenburg, Germany

Oral SESSION 4AO.9 Irradiance for PV Design | Shading and Glare Mitigation

4AO.9.1 Reflective Properties of Urban Materials and Their Impact on PV Yield 020240
Christian Schläger[1], Dennis Bredemeier[1], Arne Dittrich[2], Jan Hendrik Pfau[1], Philip Kühne[1], Rolf Brendel[2]
[1] Leibniz University Hannover, Hannover, Germany; [2] ISFH, Emmerthal, Germany

4AO.9.3 Understanding Short-Term PV Power Variability Based on Solargis Time Series Data and Simulations 020241
Martin Opatovsky[1], Marta Pelfort Ojer[1], Juraj Betak[1], Konstantin Rosina[1]
[1] Solargis, Bratislava, Slovakia

4AO.9.5 Accelerating Photovoltaic System Simulations via Statistical Data Aggregation 020243

Adrián Blanco Aguiar[1], Brais González Rodríguez[2], María Martínez-Barbeito[1], Miguel Sánchez de León Peque[1]
[1] ieco.io, Vigo, Spain; [2] University of Vigo, Vigo, Spain

4AO.9.6 Addressing Glare Problematics for Photovoltaic Projects in the Immediate Proximity of Roads and Railways through the Use of Accurate Digital Surface Models 020244
Christophe Vernay[1], John Coutel[1], Aina Razanajao[1], Sébastien Pitaval[1]
[1] SOLAÏS, Valbonne, France

Plenary SESSION 4AP.1 PV Everywhere

4AP.1.3 Micro-Concentrator Photovoltaics for Deep Space Missions: Overcoming LILT Challenges with High-Specific-Power Solar Arrays 020246
Guido Vallerotto[1], Anderson Bermudez-Garcia[2], Gerald Siefer[3], Maike Wiesenfarth[3], Almudena Garcia-Sanchez[1], Ignacio Antón[1], Carsten Baur[4], Pier Luigi Coz[4], César Domínguez[1]
[1] UPM, Madrid, Spain; [2] Thales Alenia Space, Cannes, France; [3] Fraunhofer ISE, Freiburg, Germany; [4] European Space Agency, Noordwijk, The Netherlands

Oral SESSION 4BO.16 Color in Photovoltaics

4BO.16.1 Experimental Investigation of Colored BIPV/T Systems for Wood-Framed Roofs 020248
Anna-Maria Sigounis[1], Andreas Athienitis[1]
[1] Concordia University, Montreal, Canada

4BO.16.3 How to Perform Accurate Colour Measurements for BIPV Module Glass Covers: an IEA PVPS Task 15 Round-Robin Measurement Campaign 020249
Markus Babin[1], Gabriele C. Eder[2], Thomas Friesen[3], Martina Pelle[4], Gabriella Gonnella[5], Fabrizio Leonforte[6], Yuliya Voronko[2], Helen R. Wilson[7], Sune Thorsteinsson[1], Laura Maturi[4], Niccolò Aste[6], Claudio Del Pero[6], Janne Halme[8], Jun-Tae Kim[9], Susanna Santamaria Fernández[10], Anna-Maria Sigounis[11], Hua Ge[11], Gabi Friesen[12], Francesco Frontini[12]
[1] DTU, Roskilde, Denmark; [2] OFI, Vienna, Austria; [3] Megasol Energie, Deitingen, Switzerland; [4] Eurac Research, Bolzano, Italy; [5] Eurac research, Bolzano, Italy; [6] Polytechnic University of Milan, Milan, Italy; [7] Fraunhofer ISE, Freiburg, Germany; [8] Aalto University, Espoo, Finland; [9] Kongju National University, Chungnam, South Korea; [10] TECNALIA, Derio, Spain; [11] Concordia University, Montreal, Canada; [12] SUPSI, Mendrisio, Switzerland

4BO.16.6 Predicting Light Scatter in Structural Colored BIPV Modules and Textured Glass Using Radiance 020250
Nanna Lysgaard Andersen[1], Markus Babin[1], Jan Svatos[1], Karlis Petersons[2], Leif Yde[2], Jan F. Stensborg[2], Catarina G. Ferreira[3], Ananta Paul[3], Jani Lamminaho[3], Joel D. Cox[3], Morten Madsen[3], Peter B. Poulsen[1], Sune Thorsteinsson[1]
[1] DTU, Roskilde, Denmark; [2] Stensborg, Roskilde, Denmark; [3] SDU Climate Cluster, Odense, Denmark

Oral SESSION 4BO.17 Performance of PV on/in Buildings

4BO.17.1 Modeling Partial Shading at the Cell Level on Photovoltaic Modules 020251

Jean-Paul Calin[1], Jacques Levrat[2], Antonin Faes[2], Fahradin Mujovi[2], Paul Rémondeau[3], Kléber Nicolet-dit-Félix[3], Bénédicte Bonnet-Eymard[2], Didier Dalmazzone[1], Aïcha Hessler-Wyser[3], Christophe Ballif[3]

[1] ENSTA Paris, Palaiseau, France; [2] CSEM, Neuchâtel, Switzerland; [3] EPFL, Neuchâtel, Switzerland

4BO.17.2 Market Potential of Building-Integrated Photovoltaics: a Granular Analysis of the European Building Stock 020252

Juan Ignacio Martinez[1], Julien Van Overstraeten[2], Philippe Macé[2], José Maria Vega de Seoane[1], Elina Bosch[2], Mélodie de l'Epine[3]

[1] Becquerel Institute España, San Sebastian, Spain; [2] Becquerel Institute, Brussels, Belgium; [3] Becquerel Institute France, Lyon, France

4BO.17.3 Photovoltaics in the Built Environment – an Overview of Timely Topics for Research and Development 020253

Francesco Frontini[1], Angele Reinders[2]

[1] SUPSI, Mendrisio, Switzerland; [2] TU Eindhoven, Eindhoven, The Netherlands

4BO.17.5 Advancing BIPV: Shingled HJT Technology for High-Efficiency and Aesthetic Solar Integration 020254

Gabriella Gonnella[1], Alvaro De Gruijter[1], Jordi Veirman[1], Martina Pelle[1], Laura Maturi[1], David Moser[2], Luis Fialho[1]

[1] Eurac Research, Bolzano, Italy; [2] Bequerel Institute Italy, Trento, Italy

4BO.17.6 PV-Planning and Simulation, Daylight Simulation and Energy-Certificate Calculation based on an Open-BIM-Building-Model 020255

Astrid Schneider[1], Karin Stieldorf[1], Christian Schranz[1], Harald Urban[1], Alfred Waschl[2], Markus Feichtner[3], Fedele Rende[4], Andrea Aiello[4], Martin Hauer[5], Kurt Battisti[6], Markus Dörn[6], Jacqueline Scherret[6], Martin Treberspurg[7], Christoph Treberspurg[7]

[1] TU Wien, Vienna, Austria; [2] buildingSMART, Vienna, Austria; [3] Sonnenkraft Energie, St. Veit/Glan, Austria; [4] ACCA Software, Cosenza, Italy; [5] Bartenbach, Vienna, Austria; [6] A-Null Development, Vienna, Austria; [7] Treberspurg und Partner Ziviltechniker, Vienna, Austria

Oral SESSION 4BO.5 PV-Products for Buildings

4BO.5.1 Fabrication of a Novel Semi-Translucent BIPV Module Providing High Power Density and Active Daylight Management 020257

Almudena Garcia-Sanchez[1], Guido Vallerotto[1], Jaime J. Hernández[2], Alejandro García-Cañas[2], Steve Askins[1], Ignacio Antón[1], Isabel Rodríguez[2], César Domínguez[1]

[1] UPM, Madrid, Spain; [2] IMDEA Nanoscience, Madrid, Spain

4BO.5.3 A Comparative Study of Photovoltaic Shading Devices for Net Zero Energy Buildings across French Climates 020259

Oral SESSION 4BO.6 Assessing the Reliability of PV Systems

Oral SESSION 4BO.7 Field Insights, Performance and Modelling of PV Systems

Visual SESSION 4BV.3 Solar Resource and Forecasting

Visual SESSION 4BV.4 BIPV

Visual SESSION 4CV.1 Advances in Operation, Performance and Maintenance of PV Systems

Oral SESSION 4DO.1 PV Tracking and Simulation

Oral SESSION 4DO.3 PV System Design and Assessment

Oral SESSION 4DO.4 Agrivoltaics, PV Noise Barriers and Floating PV

Oral SESSION 4DO.5 Modelling and Optimisation of Agrivoltaic Systems

4DO.5.4 Development and Evaluation of Agrivoltaic System in Olive Groves based on a Novel Smart Tracking Algorithm 020392

Ildefonso Muñoz[1], Irati Amatriain[1], Gregorio Olivares[1], Gillen Abrego[2], Eusebio Gainza[2], Iñaki Cornago[1]
[1] CENER, Sarriguren, Spain; [2] ALLOTARRA, Allo, Spain

4DO.5.5 Adoption and Optimisation Analysis of Agrivoltaic Systems for Horticultural Production and Energy Autonomy in Lubumbashi/DR Congo 020393

Eddie Bilitu[1], Shu-Ngwa Asaa[2], Sara Bouguerra[3], Nikoleta Kyranaki[3], Ismail Kaaya[3], Yannick Useni[4], Michael Daenen[3]
[1] Hasselt University, Hasselt, Belgium; [2] imo-imomec, Genk, Belgium; [3] imec, Genk, Belgium; [4] University of Lubumbashi, Lubumbashi, Congo (DRC)

Visual SESSION 4DV.1 Agrivoltaics Approaches, Experiences, Results | Integrated and Innovative PV Applications

4DV.1.5 Maximizing Economic Performance of Agrivoltaic Systems through Module Array Design 020394

Habeel Alam[1], Jenny Nelson[2], Alona Armstrong[1], Duncan Whyatt[1], Nauman Butt[3]
[1] Lancaster University, Lancaster, United Kingdom; [2] Imperial College London, London, United Kingdom; [3] Lahore University of Management Sciences, Lahore, Pakistan

4DV.1.7 Bifacial and Mismatch Factors of Agri-Photovoltaics Systems 020396

Keith R. McIntosh[1], Solomon Freer[1], Bastien J. J. Ardissone[1], S. Ramirez[1], Ben A. Sudbury[1], Malcolm D. Abbott[1]
[1] PV Lighthouse, Coledale, Australia

4DV.1.10 Performance Analysis of Agrivoltaic System Configurations in Nordic Conditions 020398

Magda Szarek[1], Sami Jouttijärvi[1], Lauri Karttunen[1], Samuli Ranta[2], Kati Miettunen[1]
[1] University of Turku, Turku, Finland; [2] TUAS, Turku, Finland

4DV.1.11 Irradiance Management in Agrivoltaic Systems with Varying Designs Across Latitudes: Toward Finland's First Significant Demonstration 020400

Shuo Wang[1], Soroush Moradi Zavie Kord[2], Hugo E. Huerta[1], Antti Lajunen[2], Samuli Ranta[1]
[1] TUAS, Turku, Finland; [2] University of Helsinki, Helsinki, Finland

4DV.1.12 An Innovative Agrivoltaic System for Desert Climates with Anti-Soiling, Irradiance Control, and Water Management 020402

Sagarika Kumar[1], Min Hsian Saw[1], Ahmed Shaaban[1], Kamil Jaworczak[1], Nursulu Kuzhagaliyeva[1], Carlos G. Parrilla[2], Francois M. Tsombou[2], Fouad Lamghari[2], Mauro Pravettoni[1]
[1] Technology Innovation Institute, Abu Dhabi, United Arab Emirates; [2] Fujairah Research Centre, Fujairah, United Arab Emirates

4DV.1.15 Review of Sensor Technologies for Monitoring Agrivoltaic Systems 020403

Sara Pereira[1], José A. Silva[1], Luís Fialho[2], Pedro Horta[1]
[1] University of Évora, Évora, Portugal; [2] Eurac Research, Bolzano, Italy

Visual SESSION 4DV.4 PV System Engineering

Oral SESSION 4EO.2 Vehicle Integrated PV

[1] Luxembourg Institute of Science and Technology, Esch-sur-Alzette, Luxembourg; [2] University of Lisbon, Lisbon, Portugal

4EO.2.6 Optimizing Angular Performance of Curved VIPV Modules 020459
Francisco José Martín[1], Rebeca Herrero[1], Ignacio Antón[1]
[1] UPM, Madrid, Spain

Oral SESSION 5CO.4 Life Cycle Assessment of Silicon and Perovskite-based Cells and Modules

5CO.4.1 Towards Low-Impact Triple-Junction Perovskite/Silicon Tandem Modules: LCA of Precursor Materials to Describe the Influence of Background Data Sources 020461
Alejandra Galarza[1], Sebastian Nold[2], Lars Oberbeck[3]
[1] IPVF, Palaiseau, France; [2] Fraunhofer ISE, Freiburg, Germany; [3] TotalEnergies OneTech, Paris, France

5CO.4.3 Sustainability Assessment of Perovskite/Silicon Tandem Solar Modules: from Laboratory Scale to Industrial Implementation 020462
Elisabetta Brivio[1], Andrea Danelli[1], Sofia Spagnolo[1], Pierpaolo Girardi[1]
[1] RSE, Milan, Italy

5CO.4.4 LCA Learning Curve for Crystalline Silicon Solar Technologies based on Technology Improvements 020463
Julian Reichle[1], Moritz Fath[1], Sraisth[1], Amish Kumar Sinha[1], Mehul Raval[1], Wolfgang Jooss[1], Peter Fath[1], Gourab Das[1]
[1] RCT Solutions, Konstanz, Germany

Oral SESSION 5CO.5 Life Cycle Assessment of New PV Applications and Recycling

5CO.5.1 Optimizing AgriPV: A Comprehensive Assessment Framework for Sustainable Energy and Agriculture 020464
Ana Patrícia Lopes[1], Bruno Barrionuevo [2], Daniel P. Albuquerque[3], Diogo Cordeiro[4], Cláudia Fernandes[3], Athanasios T. Balafoutis [2], Rui Castro[1]
[1] University of Lisbon, Lisbon, Portugal; [2] CERTH, Athens, Greece; [3] Centre for New Energy Technologies, Sacavém, Portugal; [4] EDP, Lisbon, Portugal

5CO.5.2 Environmental Sustainability Assessment of Agrivoltaic Systems: a Life Cycle Approach 020466
Maria Anna Cusenza[1], Andrea Danelli[1], Pierpaolo Girardi[1], Sofia Spagnolo[1]
[1] RSE, Milan, Italy

5CO.5.4 Closing the Circle: Integrating the Circular Footprint Formula into Photovoltaic System Life Cycle Assessment 020467
Alexis Barrou[1], Selin Kandiyoti-Eskenazi[1], Jacques Levrat[1], Bertrand Paviet-Salomon[1], Christophe Ballif[1]
[1] CSEM, Neuchâtel, Switzerland

5CO.5.6 Environmental Benefits of Silicon Kerf Secondary Products in Pilot Processes over Conventional Production of Equivalent Products with Primary Raw Materials in China and Europe 020468
René Peche[1], Matthias Seitz[1], Markus Schönheits[1], Karsten Wambach[1]
[1] bifa Umweltinstitut, Augsburg, Germany

Oral SESSION 5CO.6 PV Recycling and Circularity

5CO.6.4 Quantification of Technical Recyclability of PV Modules for Different Recycling Scenarios 020470
Matthias Hämmer[1], Kerstin Baumann[1], Karsten Wambach[1], Markus Schönheits[1]
[1] bifa Umweltinstitut, Augsburg, Germany

5CO.6.5 IEC Technical Report 63525 on the Reuse of PV Modules: Final Result 020472
Arvid van der Heide[1], Serge Noels[2], Jan Clyncke[2], Rich Strömberg[3]
[1] imec, Genk, Belgium; [2] PV CYCLE, Brussels, Belgium; [3] University of Alaska, Fairbanks, United States of America

Plenary SESSION 5CP.1 Si PV Manufacturing: Pushing the Limits of Performance

5CP.1.4 Business Model Optimization for European Solar PV: A Study on Costs and Commercial Strategies 020474
Ian Kenchington[1], Philippe Macé[1], Gaëtan Masson[1], Joris Libal[2]
[1] Becquerel Institute, Brussels, Belgium; [2] ISC Konstanz, Konstanz, Germany

Plenary SESSION 5CP.2 Perovskite – Silicon Tandems: Towards Commercialisation | PV Stability in the Field

5CP.2.3 Total Cost of Ownership, LCA and LCOE Analysis of Perovskite-Silicon Tandems Compared to Single Junction Crystalline Silicon PV Technologies 020475
Baljeet Singh Goraya[1], Dilara Maria Subasi[1], Peter Henri Brailovsky[1], Henning Nagel[1], Patricia S.C. Schulze[1], Martin C. Schubert[1], Jochen Rentsch[1], Martin Hermle[1], Ralf Preu[1], Sebastian Nold[1]
[1] Fraunhofer ISE, Freiburg, Germany

Oral SESSION 5DO.11 The Road to Massive PV Deployment

5DO.11.1 Integration of Solar PV in a Norwegian Energy System, Navigating the Trade-offs between Land Use and Solar Power Production 020476
Petry Kristine Nøttum Haaland[1], Ole-Morten Midtgård[1], Magnus Korpås[1]
[1] NTNU, Trondheim, Norway

Oral SESSION 5DO.18 PV Recycling and Material Demand

Visual SESSION 5DV.2 Life Cycle Analysis and PV Recycling | Citizens Participation and Awareness

Visual SESSION 5DV.3 Grid Integration and Flexibility Enablers | Global, Country- and Application-Specific Analysis of PV Deployment Aspects | Costs, Economics, Finance and Markets

Oral SESSION 5EO.1 Citizens Participation and Awareness

Sponsors

Author Index

Keyword Index

OPTIMIZATION OF SOXHLET EXTRACTION PARAMETERS FOR GEL CONTENT DETERMINATION OF CO-EXTRUDED EPE

A. Trefzer[1], A.K. Öz[1], J. Forster[1], C. Wellens[1], M. Çalişkan[2], C. Düz[2]
[1]Fraunhofer Institute for Solar Energy Systems ISE, Heidenhofstraße 2, 79110 Freiburg, Germany
[2]Kalyon PV Solar Technologies Factory, Başkent Osb, Şaditürk Blv., 06909 Malıköy, Sincan, Ankara / Türkiye
Corresponding Author: Aksel Kaan Öz | +49 (0) 761 4588-2556 | e-mail: aksel.kaan.oez@ise.fraunhofer.de

ABSTRACT: With the transition to TOPCon technology raising several challenges regarding reliability and long-term stability of PV modules, tailored encapsulant solutions like EPE (EVA+POE+EVA) are more commonly used in PV module production due to their advantageous properties. The optimization and adaptation of precise quality control is hereby most important. While the measurement of Gel Content (GC) with DMA, DSC and FTIR are relative methods, Soxhlet offers a more accurate and reliable quantitative alternative. This study focuses on optimizing Soxhlet extraction parameters for GC measurements of co-extruded EPE encapsulants. The influence of various extraction cycle times as well as number of cycles and resting time in cooling solvent on GC values is investigated. Furthermore a sweep of extraction time from 8-24 h is performed for two different EPE and POE encapsulants to identify the point at which the change in GC saturates. At this point any further increase in extraction time will not lead to significant changes in GC values. With EPE this point of saturation was found at 22-24 h while POE exhibits this saturation behavior at 20-26 h minimum extraction time highly depending on the specific material.

Keywords: Soxhlet extraction, degree of cross-linking, gel content, co-extruded EPE, quality control

1 INTRODUCTION

With the progressive transition from PERC (Passivated Emitter and Rear Cell) to TOPCon (Tunnel Oxide Passivated Contact) several challenges regarding reliability, long-term stability and failure modes of TOPCon came to light [1]. TOPCon is much more susceptible to high humidity, contamination and PID (potential-induced degradation) than PERC as *C. Sen et al.* have shown [1]. According to forecasts from the International Technology Roadmap for Photovoltaic (ITRPV 2025), the market share of TOPCon technology is expected to rise to up to almost 70 % by 2029, thereby replacing PERC as the dominant cell technology [2]. The development of tailored encapsulants and corresponding BOMs is therefore most important [1].

S.K. Chunduri and *M. Schmela* also reached a similar conclusion in the TaiyangNews Market Survey 2022-2023 suggesting the usage of co-extruded EPE consisting of a multilayer system of EVA+POE+EVA [3]. This material combines the advantageous mechanical properties of EVA (ethylene-vinyl acetate) with the low water vapor permeability of POE (polyolefin elastomer) and is priced between these two [4–6].

Due to this combination of properties, the market share of co-extruded EPE encapsulants is expected to rise to up to about 45 % by 2035 according to forecasts from the ITRPV 2025, thus replacing EVA as the dominant encapsulant material [2]. Therefore EPE will be the alternative encapsulant for bifacial products in GG (glass-glass) combinations [2].

For quality control of laminated PV modules DMA (Dynamic Mechanical Analysis), DSC (Differential Scanning Calorimetry) and FTIR (Fourier Transform Infrared Spectroscopy) are commonly used methods for determining GC (Gel Content) of cross-linked encapsulant material [7]. In comparison to these methods, Soxhlet extraction is based on washing out non-cross-linked monomers using a suitable solvent [8]. On the one hand this process is significantly more time-consuming, on the other hand it is a quantitative method and more precise and reliable [8]. In case of EVA a Soxhlet extraction time of up to 16 hours can be expected while POE needs up to 24 hours highly depending on the specific material [8]. Since there is no recommendation for determining the GC of co-extruded encapsulants, the optimization of Soxhlet extraction parameters for GC determination is essential to reliably assess the quality of laminated PV modules using these encapsulant solutions.

The goal of this study is to find suitable process parameters for determining the GC using Soxhlet extraction for co-extruded EPE. For this, the total extraction time as well as cycle time and number of extraction cycles are varied in case of POE and EPE with a high degree of cross-linking. The extraction time is varied from 8-24 h in 1 h increments. The recommended extraction time is determined at which the change in the measured GC saturates. At this point a complete extraction is ensured and any further increase in extraction time no longer has a significant effect on the measured GC.

2 MATERIALS AND METHODS

To compare the GC behavior of POE and EPE using Soxhlet extraction, the materials *POE-A* and *EPE-A* of a Turkish solar encapsulant film manufacturer were used, as well as *POE-B* and *EPE-C* from two different Chinese solar encapsulant film manufacturers. For producing samples for the Soxhlet extraction with a high degree of cross-linking, the POE and EPE materials were laminated according to their longest recommended datasheet processes using a *Ypsator* PV-module laminator from *Robert Bürkle GmbH*. The used materials are listed in Table 1 along with their respective thicknesses.

To be able to extract the double layer of cross-linked encapsulant from the mini – GBS (glass-backsheet) laminates (280x250 mm) for Soxhlet measurements, Teflon sheets are added in between the different layers as seen in Figure 1.

Table 1: List of used materials and their specifications.

Layer	Material	Thickness [mm]
POE-A	POE	0.740
POE-B	POE	0.500
EPE-A	EPE	0.650
EPE-C	EPE	0.550
Glass	Solar glass	3.000
Backsheet	PET/Primer	0.218
Teflon sheet	Polytetrafluoroethylene (PTFE)	0.080

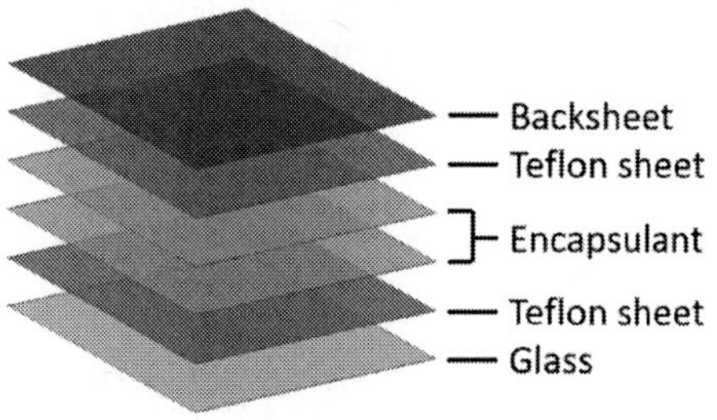

Figure 1: Module lay-up without cells for Soxhlet sample preparation.

In addition to the gel content determination by Soxhlet extraction, the performance of mini-modules with *EPE-A* and *POE-A* encapsulants was evaluated after reliability tests. *Damp Heat* (DH), *Thermal Cycling* (TC) and *Ultraviolet* (UV) aging tests were conducted in accordance with *IEC 61215-2* using the parameters stated in Table 2.

Table 2: Reliability test parameters for mini-modules with *EPE-A* and *POE-A*.

Test	Parameters
***Damp Heat* (DH)**	1000 h at 85 °C / 85 % RH
***Thermal Cycling* (TC)**	200 cycles from -40 °C to 85 °C
DH200 + UV60	200 h DH + 60 kWh/m² UV

2.1 Soxhlet Extraction

For Gel Content determination via Soxhlet extraction a *Behrotest* Soxhlet extraction unit was used in accordance with *IEC 62788-1-6*. Each sample was measured 3 separate times. Each datapoint of the results represents the mean value of these separate measurements. Unless stated otherwise a cycle time of 3.5 min is used resulting in about 17 extraction cycles per hour implemented by an integrated siphon-system to continuously cycle fresh solvent. The Gel Content was calculated by the following formular [9,10]:

$$GC\,[\%] = \left(\frac{M_2 - M_0}{M_1 - M_0}\right) * 100,\ M_2 \leq M_1 \qquad [9,10]$$

Each sample was weighed in to 1±0.05 g and placed in a cylindrical stainless steel mesh tube. M_0 represents the pre-determined weight of the tube with M_2 representing the total weight of the sample including the tube before the extraction process. M_1 represents the total weight of sample and tube after extraction and subsequent drying in a vacuum oven at 100 °C for 7 h.

3 RESULTS AND DISCUSSION

3.1 Influence of Soxhlet cycle time and number of cycles

The influence of Soxhlet cycle time on the measured GC was tested by varying the cycle time from 2-5 min (30-12 cycles/hour) with intervals of 1.5 min. The results are shown in Table 3 for EPE-C after a constant extraction time of 6 h therefore effectively varying the total amount of extraction cycles.

Decreasing the cycle time from 5 to 2 min leads to a change of only -0.43 % in measured GC. The influence of varying the Soxhlet cycle time on the measured GC with a constant extraction time is therefore not significant.

Table 3: GC values of EPE-C after 6 h extraction with different cycle times.

Cycle time [min]	No. of extraction cycles [ ]	Gel Content [%]
2	180	91.57
3.5	~100	91.67
5	72	92.00

To further test the influence on the measured GC a Soxhlet extraction was carried out with a constant number of 100 cycles while varying the cycle time from 2-5 min with intervals of 1.5 min therefore varying the total extraction time from 200-500 min as shown in Table 4.

Decreasing the number of cycles from 500 to 350 and to 200 leads to significant changes of +1,23 % and +2,68 % in measured GC respectively. Since the number of cycles was held constant, this change in GC can be explained by the total extraction time. A longer extraction time necessarily leads to more non-cross-linked monomers and/or low molecular weight polymer chains being washed out therefore resulting in a decrease in measured GC.

Table 4: GC values of EPE-C after 100 extraction cycles with different cycle times.

Cycle time [min]	Total extraction time [min]	Gel Content [%]
2	200	94.42
3.5	350	92.97
5	500	91.74

3.2 Influence of resting time in cooling Soxhlet solvent

To investigate the influence of additional resting time in the cooling solvent after a finished Soxhlet extraction a 6 h extraction of *EPE-C* was performed. After the finished extraction the samples were taken out of the Soxhlet apparatus and dried in a vacuum oven after different resting times. The first sample was taken out after 0.75 h (45 min) while the second sample rested in the solvent for 3 h (180 min). The third sample was taken out on the following day after a total amount of 18 h (1080 min) of resting time in the solvent. In Table 5 the measured GC values are shown. Due to the heating plates of the *Behrotest* Soxhlet apparatus needing to cool down, the usual amount of resting time is about 20-30 min before being able to take out samples.

After 45 min a GC of 91.78 % was measured. After a resting time of +3 h a decrease of 1.39 % could be measured compared to the initial GC value of 91.78 %.

When comparing the measured GC values after +3 h and +18 h of resting time this initial decrease of GC is no longer visible. In this case no significant change on GC can be measured.

This behavior can be explained by the remaining temperature of the solvent. Until it cools down non-cross-linked monomers and/or low molecular weight polymer chains are still being extracted from the sample since the diffusion coefficient is still high enough for effectively washing out compounds. With a decrease in temperature this diffusion process slows down heavily resulting in no more significant changes in GC after +18 h resting time at room temperature.

Table 5: GC values of EPE-C after additional resting time in cooling solvent after a finished 6 h extraction.

Resting time [h]	Gel Content [%]
+ 0.75	91.78
+ 3	90.39
+ 18	90.47

Lust et. al. encountered a similar effect in their study [11]. In their case a 5 h extraction was conducted with additional heating/cooling steps with 15 h of overnight resting time resulting in a significant decrease of 8.1 % compared to a 5 h extraction without resting time [11]. This highlights the importance of a set amount of time until taking out the samples. Otherwise, the results can become highly distorted and will no longer be reproducible.

3.3 Variation of Soxhlet extraction time

To determine suitable process parameters for GC measurement of co-extruded EPE using Soxhlet the extraction time was varied from 8-24 h in 1 h increments. To ensure a complete extraction another set of samples was measured after 32 h extraction. An EVA encapsulation film of a Chinese solar encapsulant film manufacturer is used as reference and is therefore listed as *EVA ref* in the following diagrams. The results of this extraction time sweep from 8-24 h can be seen in Figure 2 for both *EPE-A* and *EPE-C*. The material *EPE-A* was laminated at 155°C for 20 min while *EPE-C* was laminated at 150°C for 18 min. These lamination parameters represent the longest recommended datasheet processes.

Both EPE encapsulants exhibit considerably higher GC values than the *EVA ref* material. At the lowest extraction time of 8 h *EPE-A* and *EPE-C* reach GC values of 93.8 % and 92.51 % respectively while *EVA ref* reaches 86.51 %. At the highest extraction time of 24 h 90.57 % and 86.03 % are reached. Over the period of the 8-24 h extraction time sweep *EPE-A* therefore shows a decrease of 3.23 % while *EPE-C* shows a decrease of 6.48 % which is twice as high. After 32 h extraction time a decrease of 0.15 % in case of *EPE-A* and 0.3 % in case of *EPE-C* can be seen in comparison with the GC values after 24 h. Since 8 h more extraction time leads to an insignificant decrease in GC for both EPE encapsulants a complete extraction can be assured.

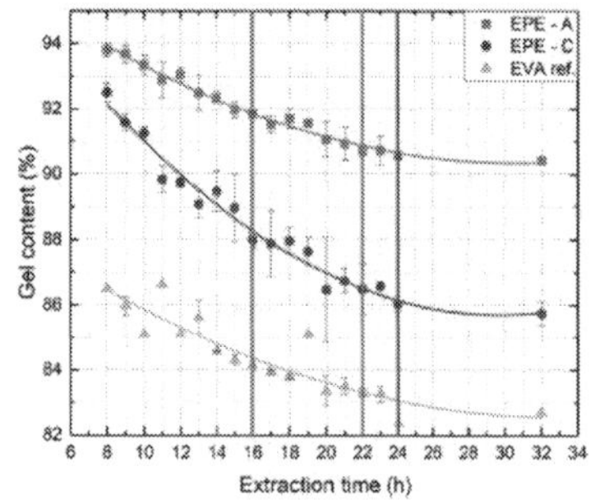

Figure 2: Measured gel content of EPE encapsulants as function of extraction time (3 samples per data point) with fitted curves and calculated minimum extraction time (green & blue line) in comparison with recommended extraction time for POE [12] (red line).

The changes in GC values of both EPE encapsulants are shown in Figure 3. The measured data exhibits volatile jumps in GC values above and below the 0 %-line due to unavoidable measurement inaccuracies. This is exceptionally true for *EPE-C* which shows several jumps above the line at high extraction times as seen in Figure 3. To be able to graphically determine the extraction time where the GC saturates, the curves of both EPE encapsulants were individually fitted as shown in Figure 4 in case of EPE-A.

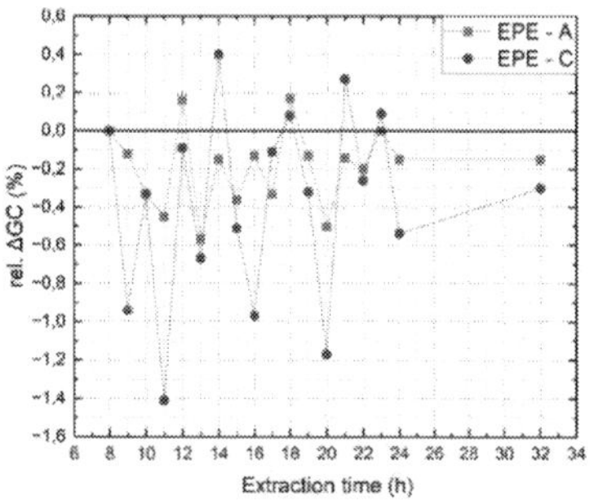

Figure 3: Relative change in measured gel content of co-extruded EPE encapsulants as function of extraction time (3 samples per data point).

The data of these individually fitted curves was then used to calculate the change in GC values of both EPE encapsulants as seen in Figure 5. To determine the gel content at the saturation point the change of GC was analyzed at the intersection with the 0 %-line.

In case of *EPE-A* this saturation is reached at 31 h of calculated extraction time with a GC value of 90.34±0.52 % which is well above the recommended extraction time for POE of 16 h [12]. Taking the calculated standard deviation of 0.52 % into account the minimum extraction time to reach the measured GC value of 90.34 % is 22 h.

10.4229/EUPVSEC2025/3AV.1.18

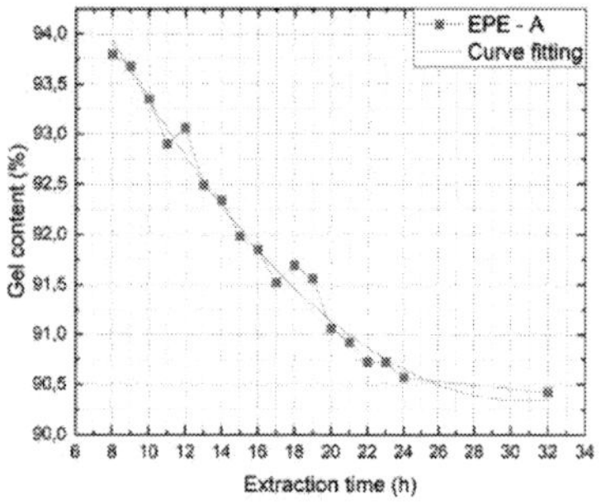

Figure 4: Measured gel content of co-extruded *EPE-A* as function of extraction time (3 samples per data point) with fitted curve.

In case of *EPE-C* the point of saturation is reached at 30 h of calculated extraction time with a GC value of 85.70±0.52 % as seen in Figure 5. With the standard deviation of 0.52 % the GC value of 85.70 % can already be reached at 24 h of Soxhlet extraction. This coincides with the recommended 24 h for certain POE encapsulant materials [8]. It should be noted that this might not be the case for badly cross-linked material. Since the recommended extraction time for EVA encapsulants with a low degree of cross-linking is 12 h compared to samples with high degree of cross-linking with 8 h, the GC values of badly cross-linked EPE encapsulants are expected to saturate at higher extraction times than shown here [13].

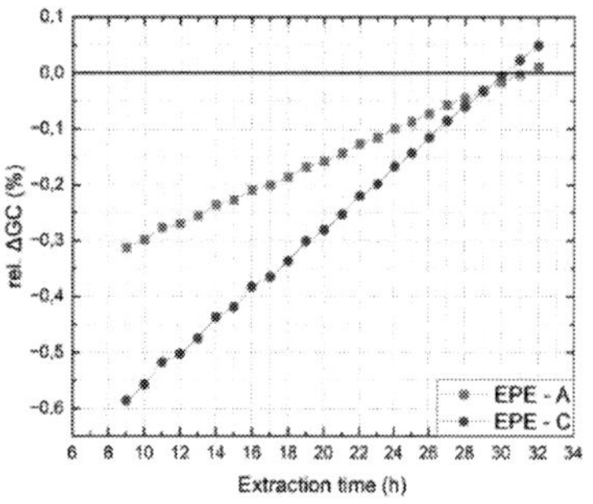

Figure 5: Calculated relative change in gel content of co-extruded EPE encapsulants as function of extraction time (3 samples per data point) using individually fitted curve data.

To further determine suitable process parameters for GC measurement of *POE-A* and *POE-B* using Soxhlet extraction the extraction time was varied similarly to both EPE encapsulants. The results of this extraction time sweep from 8-24 h can be seen in Figure 6 for both *POE-A* and *POE-B*. Both POE materials were laminated at 155°C for 20 min. These lamination parameters represent the longest recommended datasheet process.

POE-A exhibits high GC values starting at 87.35 % after 8 h extraction and decreasing to 82.48 % after 24 h with a total decrease of 4.87 % showing a similar behavior in GC changes compared to *EVA ref.* After 8 h extraction *POE-B* exhibits a measured GC value of 80.35 % decreasing to 73.16 % after 24 h with a total decrease in GC of 7.19 %. After 32 h extraction a change in GC of 0.1 % in case of *POE-A* and 0.02 % in case of *POE-B* can be measured in comparison to 24 h extraction. Since 8 h more extraction time leads to an insignificant change in GC for both POE encapsulants a complete extraction can be assured similar to the extraction time sweep for both EPE encapsulants.

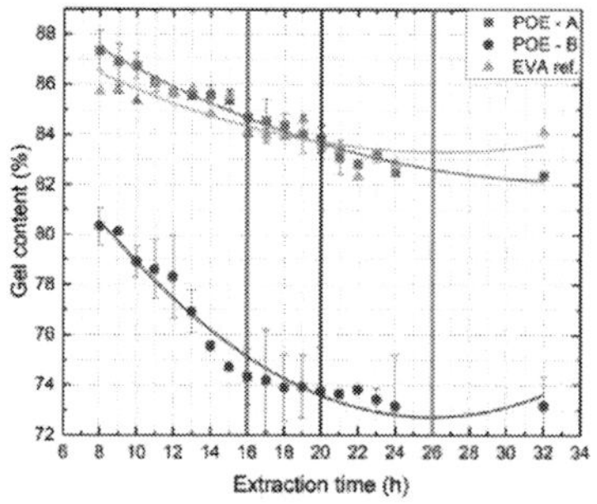

Figure 6: Measured gel content of POE encapsulants as function of extraction time (3 samples per data point) with fitted curves and calculated minimum extraction time (green & blue line) in comparison with recommended extraction time for POE [12] (red line).

The changes in GC values of both POE encapsulants are shown in Figure 7. Similar to the measured data of both EPE encapsulants in Figure 3 volatile jumps in GC values can be seen in case of both POE encapsulants. For graphical determination of the saturation point both POE encapsulants are individually fitted as shown in Figure 8 in case of *POE-B*.

The data of these individually fitted curves was then used to calculate the change in GC values of both POE encapsulants as seen in Figure 9. When analyzing for intersection with the 0 %-line *POE-A* exhibited saturation at 32 h of calculated extraction time with a GC value of 82.16±0.52 %, leading to a minimum extraction time of 26 h when considering standard deviation.

As seen in Figure 9 *POE-B* shows saturation at 26 h of calculated extraction time with a GC value of 73.17±0.52 % which corresponds to a minimum extraction time of 20 h. It should be noted that the influence of specific material on the minimum extraction time is more noticeable in case of POE with a difference of 6 h between *POE-A* and *POE-B* compared to a difference of 2 h with *EPE-A* and *EPE-C* as shown in Figure 2 and Figure 6 with vertical lines. This dependance on the specific POE encapsulation material was already mentioned by *Öz et al* [12].

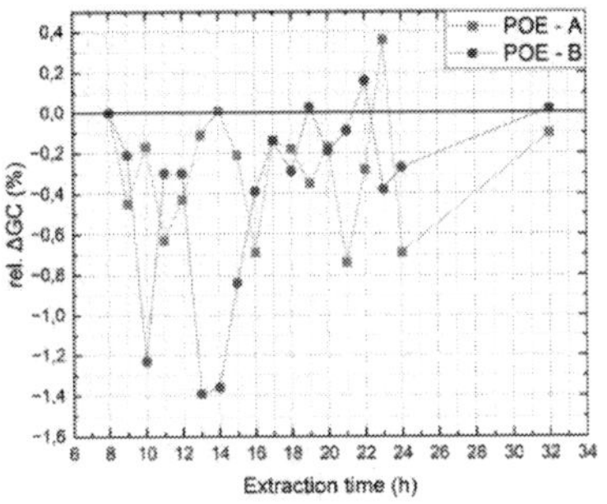

Figure 7: Relative change in measured gel content of POE encapsulants as function of extraction time (3 samples per data point).

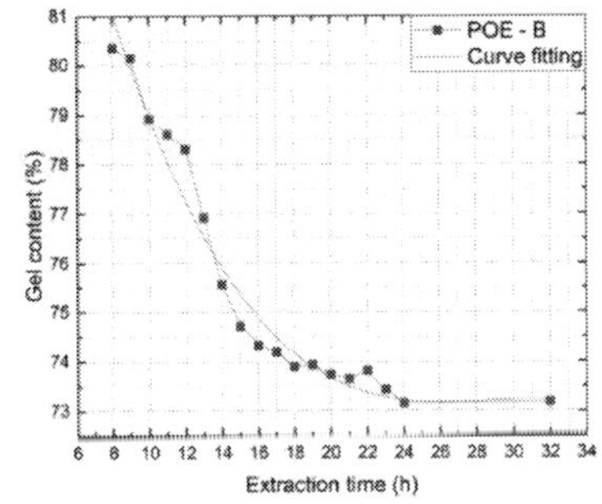

Figure 8: Measured gel content of *POE-B* as function of extraction time (3 samples per data point) with fitted curve.

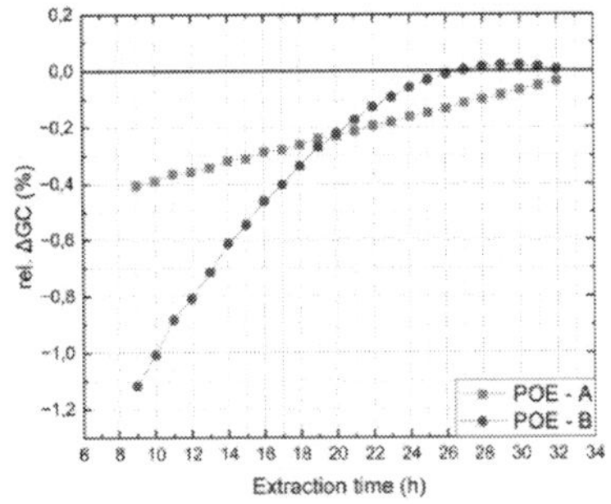

Figure 9: Calculated relative change in gel content of POE encapsulants as function of extraction time (3 samples per data point) using individually fitted curve data.

3.4 Mini-module reliability (*EPE-A & POE-A*)

In Figure 10 the power losses of mini-modules comprised of *EPE-A* and *POE-A* after different reliability tests are shown. DH1000 and TC200 tests resulted in average below -1.15 % power loss at MPP (*Maximum Power Point*) with the highest loss of -1.73 % in case of *DH1000_2*. After UV exposure the modules initially show power losses of up to -10 % in case of *UV60_1*. After stabilization (*stab_1*/stab_2, see Figure 10) by light soaking the modules show an average of -3 % in P_{mpp}. This so called *dark storage effect* is known for TOPCon modules and can be recovered by a light soaking process just prior to the power measurement as reported by *Gebhardt et al.* [14].

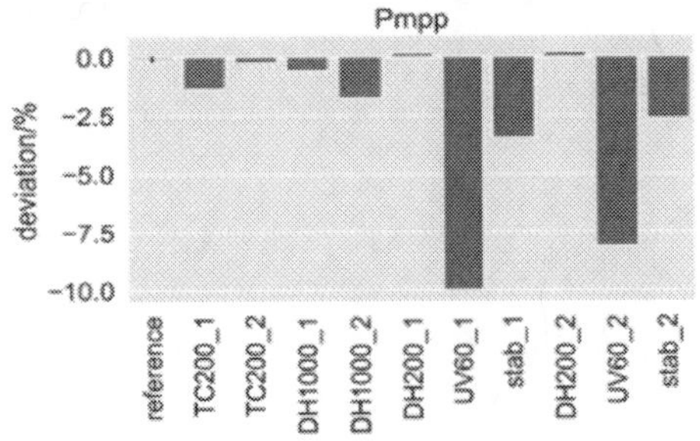

Figure 10: Power loss (ΔPmpp) of mini-modules (A-series encapsulants) after reliability tests.

In Figure 11 the captured EL images before and after DH1000 are shown. No significant visible damage can be observed which is consistent with the low power loss of -1.15 % in average.

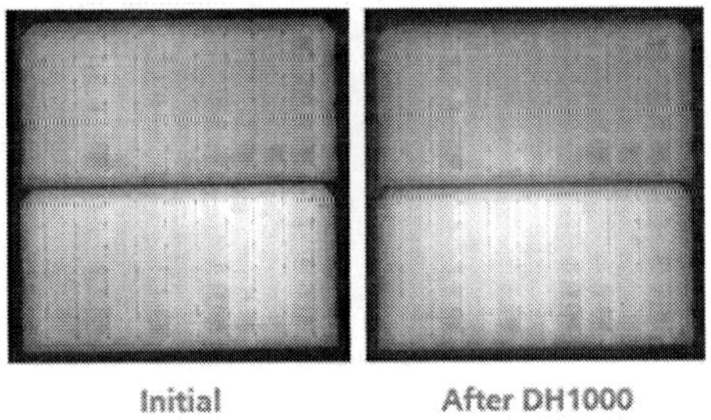

Figure 11: EL images of mini-module (A-series encapsulants) before and after DH1000.

4 CONCLUSION AND OUTLOOK

This study recommends suitable process parameters for Gel Content determination using Soxhlet extraction for co-extruded EPE. By systematically varying process parameters like extraction cycle time, number of extraction cycles and total extraction time a recommendation can be given for complete extraction of EPE and POE encapsulant films with a high degree of cross-linking. The point of complete extraction is determined as the extraction time at which the change in measured GC saturates. At this point an increase in extraction time will no longer have significant effects on the measured GC of the cross-linked encapsulant.

By variation of cycle time from 2-5 min in 1.5 min intervals the measured GC of *EPE-C* was analyzed regarding changes in GC values. Since decreasing the cycle time from 5 min to 2 min resulted in only - 0.43 % change in measured GC it can be concluded that the variation of cycle time in the tested range has no significant influence on the measured GC. Further testing showed that an increased number of extraction cycles and therefore a higher total amount of extraction time led to lower GC values. Due to this increase in extraction time more non-cross-linked compounds are being washed out resulting in a decrease in measured GC.

For testing the influence of resting time in the cooling solvent samples of *EPE-C* were taken out of the Soxhlet apparatus after different amounts of resting time after a finished extraction. Between the samples taken out after + 45 min and + 3 h of resting time a decrease of 1.39 % in GC was measured. Comparing the samples taken out after + 3 h and + 18 h of resting time no more significant changes in GC could be measured. This is explained by the remaining high temperature of the solvent and therefore higher diffusion coefficient allowing non-cross-linked compounds to diffuse out until the solvent cools down. After cooling down the diffusion process slows down heavily resulting in no more significant changes in measured GC. Due to this effect the resting time in the cooling solvent is highly important to accurately measure GC values. When being inconsistent with this parameter the results can become highly distorted and will no longer be reproducible.

To determine the minimum extraction time for EPE and POE with a high degree of cross-linking a sweep from 8-24 h extraction time was performed to analyze the change in GC for the point of saturation where a further increase in extraction time no longer significantly affects the measured GC. For *EPE-A* this point of saturation was found at 31 h (GC of 90.34±0.52 %) while *EPE-C* saturates at 30 h (GC of 85.70±0.52 %). Taking the standard deviation of 0.52 % into account yields a minimum extraction time of 22 h and 24 h for *EPE-A* and *EPE-C* respectively. The necessary extraction time needed for EPE samples with a low degree of cross-linking are expected to saturate at higher extraction times due to a higher percentage of non-cross-linked compounds needed to be washed out. Analyzing the POE samples, it was found that *POE-A* reaches saturation at 32 h (GC of 82.16±0.52 %) with a minimum extraction time of 26 h. *POE-B* exhibits saturation at 26 h (GC of 73.17±0.52 %) with a minimum extraction time of 20 h.

The tested mini-modules with *EPE-A* and *POE-A* encapsulants exhibited high stability with power losses of -1.15 % in average after DH1000 and TC200 tests and no visible damage in EL images. Initial UV-induced losses recovered after light soaking, stabilizing at around -3 % in average.

In further experiments the GC measurements for both POEs and EPEs conducted in this study will be analyzed in case of low degree of cross-linking. Since the recommended extraction time for EVA encapsulants differs from 8-12 h depending on the degree of cross-linking according to *IEC 62788-1-6* the GC values of EPE encapsulants with a low degree of cross-linking are expected to exhibit a similar behavior due to the multilayer EPE encapsulant being comprised partly of EVA encapsulant films [13]. With this a better understanding of the correlation between GC and necessary extraction time can be achieved.

5 ACKNOWLEDGEMENTS

We would like to thank *Kalyon PV* for their collaboration and support in this study.

6 REFERENCES

[1] C. Sen, H. Wang, M. U. Khan et al., "Buyer aware: Three new failure modes in TOPCon modules absent from PERC technology," *Solar Energy Materials and Solar Cells*, vol. 272, p. 112877, 2024.

[2] M. Fischer, M. Woodhouse, P. Baliozian et al., "International Technology Roadmap for Photovoltaics (ITRPV): 2024 Results," 16. Edition, May 2025.

[3] S. K. Chunduri and M. Schmela, "Market Survey on Backsheets and Encapsulation 2022-2023," 2023.

[4] G. Cattaneo, A. Faes, H.-Y. Li et al., "Lamination process and encapsulation materials for glass–glass PV module design," *Photovoltaics International*, 2015.

[5] N. T. Dintcheva, E. Morici, and C. Colletti, "Encapsulant Materials and Their Adoption in Photovoltaic Modules: A Brief Review," *Sustainability*, vol. 15, no. 12, p. 9453, 2023.

[6] S. K. Chunduri and M. Schmela, "Market Survey on Backsheets and Encapsulation 2024-2025," 2025.

[7] M. L. Pliquet, T. Béjat, M. Sérasset et al., "Standardized cross-linking determination methods applied to POE encapsulants in lamination recipe development," *40th European Photovoltaic Solar Energy Conference and Exhibition*, 2023.

[8] S. Lust, N. Schnitzler, A. Brendler et al., "Challenges for Quality Control Posed by New PV Encapsulation Materials," *40th European Photovoltaic Solar Energy Conference and Exhibition*, 2023.

[9] C. Hirschl, L. Neumaier, S. Puchberger et al., "Determination of the degree of ethylene vinyl acetate crosslinking via Soxhlet extraction: Gold standard or pitfall?," *Solar Energy Materials and Solar Cells*, vol. 143, pp. 494–502, 2015.

[10] A. K. Öz, J. Vasani, C. Reichel et al., "Temperature Distribution during the Lamination Process of PV Modules and its Influence on the Degree of Crosslinking for EVA-Simulation vs Test Results," *40th European Photovoltaic Solar Energy Conference and Exhibition*, 2023.

[11] S. Lust, T. Weber, S. R. Kuntamukkula et al., "Update of quality control tests for new PV encapsulation materials," *EPJ Photovoltaics*, vol. 15, p. 5, 2024.

[12] A. K. Öz, J. Vasani, C. Reichel et al., "Simulation and Experimental Analysis of Temperature Profiles and Crosslinking in PV Module Lamination," *IEEE Journal of Photovoltaics*, vol. 14, no. 5, pp. 777–784, 2024.

[13] VDE Verlag GmbH, "Measurement procedures for materials used in photovoltaic modules - Part 1-6: Encapsulants: Test methods for determining the degree of cure in Ethylene-Vinyl Acetate," IEC 62788-1-6.

[14] P. Gebhardt, U. Kräling, E. Fokuhl et al., "Reliability of Commercial TOPCon PV Modules—An Extensive Comparative Study," *Progress in Photovoltaics: Research and Applications*, 2024.

Transforming Industrial Façades with Integrated Photovoltaics

N. Pervan[1,2], C. Veas[1,2], S. Feldbacher[1], L. Geymayer[3], G. Kitzberger[3], M. Fleischanderl[3], H. Kurz[3], F. Füreder-Kitzmüller[3], G. Oreski[1,2]

[1] Polymer Competence Center Leoben GmbH (PCCL), Leoben, Austria – nikolina.pervan@pccl.at
[2] Chair of Materials Science and Testing of Polymers, Montanuniversität Leoben, Leoben, Austria
[3] voestalpine Stahl GmbH, 4020 Linz, Austria

PCCL
Polymer Competence Center Leoben

INTRODUCTION AND OBJECTIVES

- The **integration of photovoltaics** (PV) into infrastructures, especially in buildings, is an important factor for achieving the targets for the expansion of **renewable energies** without the additional use of green spaces.
- **Building integrated photovoltaic (BIPV)** modules serve as both **building element** and an **energy generation source**.[1]
- In addition to the **efficiency** of the PV modules, BIPV modules must meet the architectural and structural requirements of buildings, including **mechanical stability**, **thermal insulation** and **fire retardancy**. The final product must have a service life of more than 30 years, and standardization should align with both building and electrical norms.[2]
- The **objectives** of the project "**PV- Industrial Façade**" are:
  - to develop a glass - free PV module concept for integration into **large-scale steel façade elements**
  - to identify, modify and qualify solutions for the **polymeric frontsheet (FS)**, **encapsulant** and **backsheet (BS) foil**.

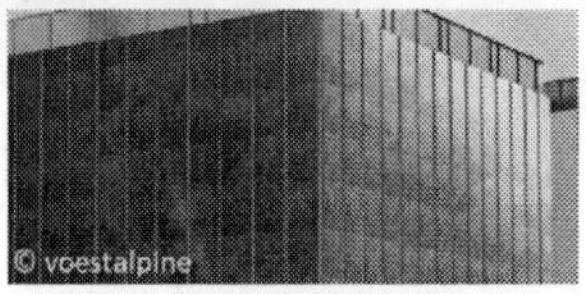

Figure 1. Rendering of PV steel façade.

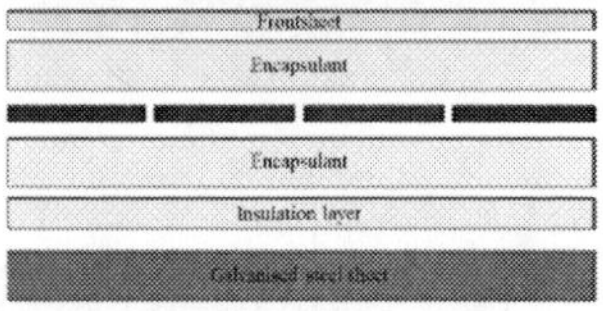

Figure 2. Material lay-up of BIPV module structure.

EXPERIMENTAL PART

POLYMER MATERIAL CHARACTERISATION

Melting temperature (DSC)

Thermal stability (TGA)

Coefficient of thermal expansion (CTE)

ADHESION OF BACKSHEET TO GALVANIZED STEEL (GS) + DAMP HEAT (DH) AGING

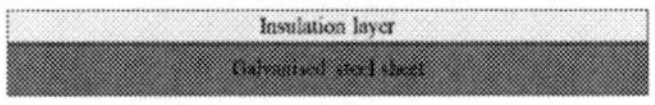

ASTM D3330 standard

ADHESION AND INTERACTION OF *FS – ENCAPSULANT (POE and TPO) - BS*

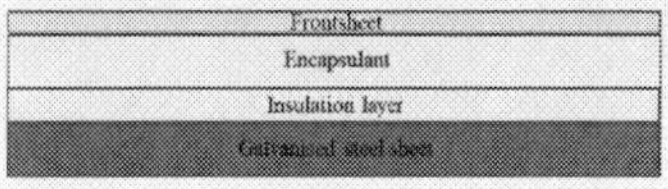

ASTM D3330 standard

PV MODULE ASSEMBLY [3]

RESULTS AND DISCUSSION

BACKSHEET (BS) FOIL THERMAL PROPERTIES

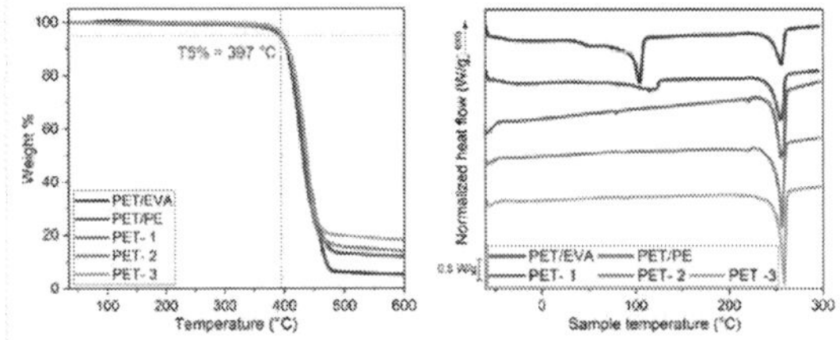

Figure 3. TGA (T5% - on the left) and DSC 1st heating curves (melting peaks – on the right) of BS foils.

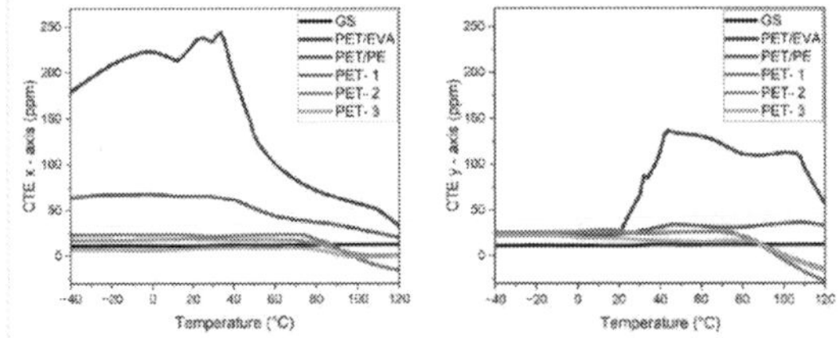

Figure 4. CTE curves in x- and y- direction of galvanized steel (GS) and BS foils.

BS/GS – PEEL MECHANISM

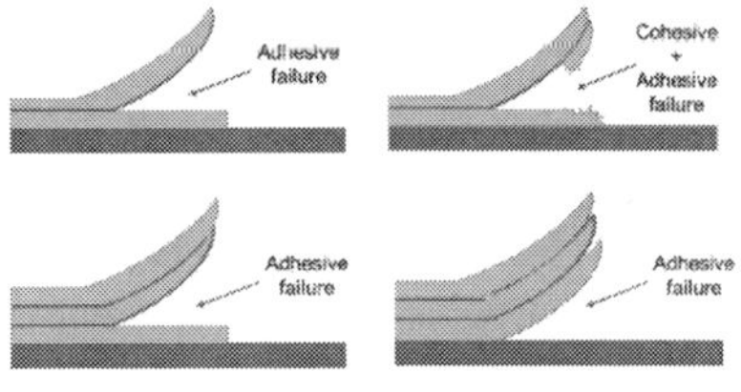

Figure 5. Peel test - delamination mechanisms between BS foil (blue) and GS substrate (grey).

INTERLAYER - PEEL STRENGTH

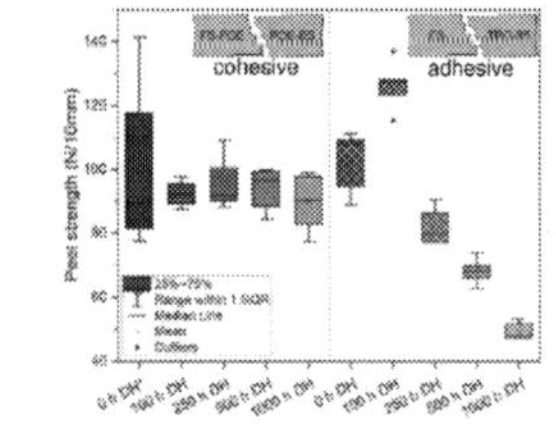

Figure 6. Peel test – peel strength between FS-encapsulant-BS + DH exposure.

- All backsheets - **thermally stable** up to 397 °C – **fit in the production process** of steel sheets.
- Best match in the **CTE values** between **GS and BS** is with **PET 1-3 BS**. Presence of EVA and PE in the BS results in higher CTE values.
- **Delamination** mechanism between GS and BS – for all, but PET/EVA BS was cohesive **within the BS layer**. For PET/EVA BS galvanized steel developed corrosion in the interface layer and this resulted in reduced adhesion.
- Interlayer adhesion tests shown **good adhesion between POE and BS** since delamination was mostly in the encapsulant layer – cohesive failure type.
- Coupons with **POE maintain** the same **adhesion strength** even after 1000 h in the DH, while the adhesion of coupons with **TPO** is **decreased gradually**.

CONCLUSIONS AND OUTLOOK

PET backsheets have good thermal properties and fit in the **production process** of the **steel sheets**.

Polymeric foils with **EVA** component are **not suitable** for the PV modules on top of the galvanized steel plate due to the **corrosion development**.

POE maintains same **adhesion strength** even after 1000 h in the damp heat, while **TPO** is being **affected by** the **humidity**.

Mini and **full size PV modules** have been prepared for aging and performance tests – results by the end of the year.

REFERENCES

1. IEA-PVPS T15-04: 2018, International definitions of "BIPV", https://iea-pvps.org/wp content/uploads/2020/02/IEAPVPS_Task_15_Report_C0_International_definitions_of_BIPV_hrw_180823.pdf
2. http://dx.doi.org/10.3390/buildings14061510
3. Copilot AI image creation – August 2025.

ACKNOWLEDGMENT

This work was conducted as part of the Austrian "eMISSION.at – Energy Mission Austria" project "PV Industriefassade" (FFG No. FO999915082) funded by the Austrian Climate and Energy Fund and the Austrian Research Promotion Agency (FFG).

ORCID

FFG Promoting Innovation · voestalpine ONE STEP AHEAD · KUNSTSTOFF TECHNIK LEOBEN · MONTAN UNIVERSITÄT LEOBEN

42nd European Photovoltaic Solar Energy Conference and Exhibition

This presentation was selected by the Sc. Committee of the EU PVSEC 2025 for submission of a full paper to one of the EU PVSEC's collaborating peer-reviewed journals.

Indoor Characterization and CTM Evaluation of Photovoltaic Modules with Colored Backsheets and Rear-Side Glazed Glasses

Pouya Pourshafi[1*], Alexander Protti[2], Max Mittag[2], Christian Reichel[2], Andreas Maixner[1], Hamed Hanifi[1]
[1] AESOLAR, Messerschmittring 54, Koenigsbrunn, Germany
[2] Fraunhofer Institute for Solar Energy Systems (ISE), Freiburg, Germany
*Corresponding Author: p.pourshafi@ae-solar.com

ABSTRACT: The photovoltaic (PV) industry operates in a highly price-sensitive market, necessitating continuous advancements and optimizations to enhance module efficiency and power output. Traditionally, the primary approach to increasing the power output of PV modules has been the incorporation of high-efficiency solar cells. However, alternative strategies exist that focus on minimizing energy losses and optimizing other module components to improve overall performance. After integrating solar cells into a module stack, several loss mechanisms occur, typically resulting in a lower output power compared to the theoretical sum of the individual cell powers. These losses are generally classified into two categories: optical losses and electrical losses. As a result, photovoltaic (PV) manufacturers experience financial challenges due to cell-to-module (CTM) losses. By adopting strategies to improve optical gains and reduce electrical losses, the CTM ratio can be significantly enhanced. In this study, we systematically evaluate the impact of different back cover materials on CTM gains and the overall power output of PV modules. Methodology of this work involves the characterization and assessment of the transmission and reflection properties of polymer-based backsheets in white, black, and transparent variants. Additionally, transparent, black, and white-colored rear-side glass configurations are investigated. These materials are analyzed in terms of their influence on CTM gains and their overall contribution to the module's power output. The raw measurement data obtained from these characterizations were processed using SmartCalc.Module, an analytical software tool for CTM analysis. This study offers valuable insights into the optimization of back cover materials for enhanced PV module performance.

1 INTRODUCTION

In recent years, declining production costs and the maturation of the photovoltaic supply chain have positioned photovoltaic technology as a major contributor to global energy supply. By 2024, photovoltaic systems accounted for 81% of newly installed renewable capacity [1]. Along with the expansion of photovoltaic systems, their efficiency is also continuously increasing. Over the past decade, the efficiency of commercial solar modules has increased from approximately 16% to over 22% [2]. In the laboratory test, silicon cells achieved a record efficiency of 27.8%, while the efficiency of silicon modules has reached 26% [3]. Although efficiency continues to improve, physical, electrical, and optical factors cause Cell-to-Module (CTM) losses. Identifying these losses is essential for enhancing performance under both standard and real operating conditions. To this end, detailed models incorporating optical, electrical, thermal, and environmental effects were developed, enabling precise assessment of module performance in practice [4], [5].

Researchers have concentrated on various aspects of CTM losses in their studies. Guo et al. [6] and Jung et al. [7] have investigated the mechanisms behind CTM losses, with a particular focus on resistive and mismatch effects—meanwhile, Dasary et al. [8] have focused on optimizing the number and width of busbars to reduce CTM resistive losses. Hanifi et al. [9] developed a practical optical–electrical model that enables a detailed quantification of losses and highlights the potential for achieving optical gain at the module level. Another work by Haedrich et al. [10] introduced a unified methodology for determining CTM ratios, providing a systematic approach to predict module power by analyzing optical, electrical, and geometrical loss and gain mechanisms. This methodology has become a cornerstone for subsequent research and practical applications in PV module design. Haedrich et al. [11] enhanced the framework to estimate annual yield losses and gains due to solar module design and materials in real-world conditions, moving from predictions under STC to actual field exposure. A similar approach was followed by Shen et al. [12], [13] who adopted a more comprehensive perspective, analyzing electrical and thermal performance as well as loss mechanisms under real environmental conditions. Additional refinements to Haedrich's methodology have been proposed, incorporating new loss factors, additional components such as junction boxes and ribbon geometries, and extensions tailored to specific module concepts such as shingled and overlapping cells [14]-[17].

The CTM methodology is widely used in the analysis of different module concepts and has been applied to different cell designs, module concepts, applications, and even historical analysis of module development [18]-[24].

Based on the reviewed literature in the evolving landscape of photovoltaic technology, one of the main challenges is maximizing the energy conversion efficiency from individual solar cells to fully assembled solar modules. Recent studies have highlighted important strategies to reduce CTM losses by implementing innovative modeling and optimization techniques. From a different perspective, this study aims to improve module efficiency by enhancing optical gain and reducing the performance gap between the cell and the module.

2 METHODOLOGY

This work aims to characterize, evaluate, and analyze the effect of the backsheet color on the CTM gains and total power of PV modules. For this purpose, in the first place, all module components are characterized optically and electrically with a spectrometer and a sun simulator. The characterization includes interconnecting tabs, solar cells, encapsulation materials, front side glasses, and three standard backsheets with black, white, and transparent colors. In the second step, the measurement data are evaluated with SmartCalc.Module, a CTM analysis software developed by Fraunhofer ISE [25], is used to determine the CTM losses and gains for each module. In the final step, the losses and gains for modules with each back cover type are compared.

The experimental methodology is focused on characterizing and assessing the transmission and reflection properties of glass-based and polymer-based backsheets available in white, black, and transparent variants. The influence of these materials on CTM gains and their overall contribution to module power output is analyzed. Furthermore, a thorough evaluation is conducted on other critical components of photovoltaic (PV) modules—including solar cells, encapsulation materials, interconnection tabs, and front-side glass—from both electrical and optical perspectives. The analyses performed focus on the reflection of the rear cover and the subsequent power gain from increased irradiance on the solar cell. The gain mechanism is called "k11" following the nomenclature by Haedrich et al. **Figure 1**.

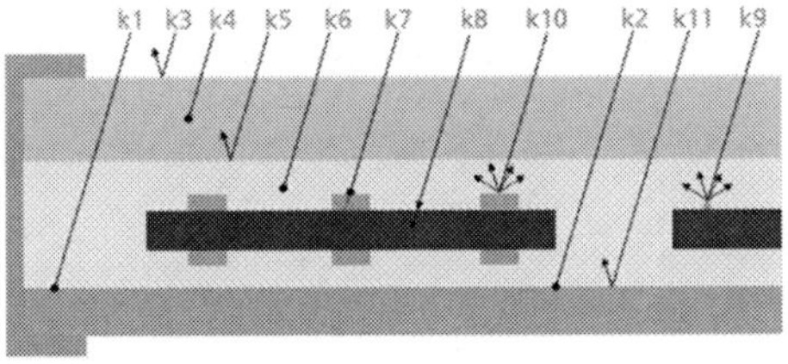

Figure 1: Detailed analysis of gain and loss mechanisms, k11 represents the optical gain obtained from the module back cover.

2.1 Materials

In this study, three glass-glass PV modules with white and black glazing, as well as without glazing, were examined (**Figure 2**).

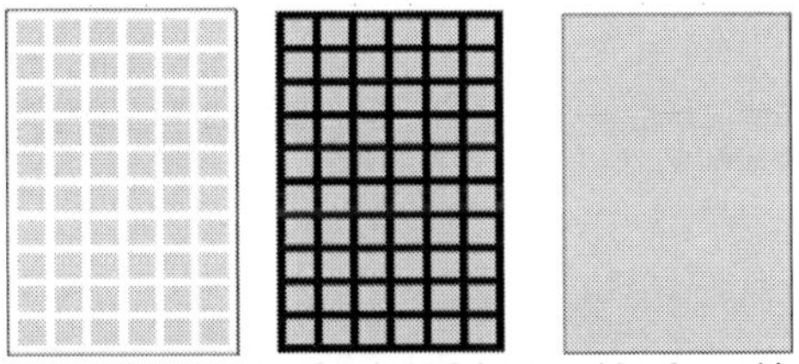

Figure 2: Schematic drawing of the rear side glass with (left) white-glazed, (middle) black-glazed, and (right) transparent glasses on the rear side of the PV module.

In addition, three modules with white, black, and transparent backsheets were examined (**Figure 3**).

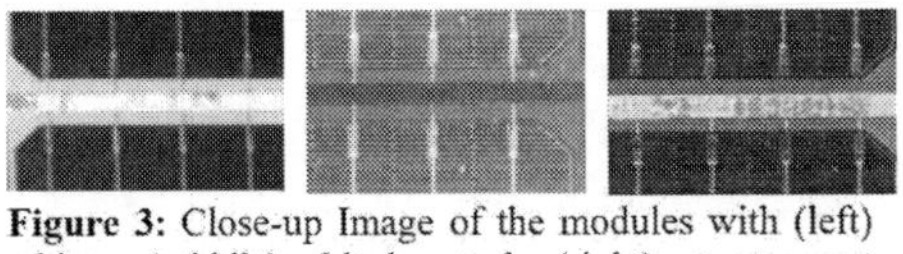

Figure 3: Close-up Image of the modules with (left) white, (middle) black, and (right) transparent backsheet.

2.2 Modelling

In 2016, Mittag et al. [26] developed CTM software, offering the photovoltaic community a precise, user-friendly, and standardized tool for CTM analysis. This software has been developed based on a comprehensive methodology for CTM analysis provided by Haedrich et al. in 2014 [10]. Important input parameters for the modelling are listed in **Table 1**.

Table 1: Characteristics of the analyzed module

Layout	Module area = 2.856 m²
Cell	Cell type: half-cut 182x91 mm, Pseudo-square diameter: 247 mm Efficiency = 23.7% Bifaciality = 75% Number of busbars: 10
Cover	Front: 2.0 mm clear glass with ARC Rear: 2.0 mm clear glass
Encapsulant	Front: UV blocking POE Rear: UV blocking EVA
Cell interconnectors	Resistivity = 1.8 μΩ-cm Diameter = 250 μm
String interconnectors	Resistivity = 1.8 μΩ-cm Width = 5.072 mm Thickness = 0.472 mm
Junction box	Number: 2 Internal resistance = 0.5 mΩ
Cables	Length = 0.5 m Cross section = 4 mm² Specific resistance = 0.02 Ω-mm²/m Contact resistance plug/jack=0.3mΩ

3 RESULTS

3.1 Characterization

Initially, all components of the photovoltaic module both electrically and optically were characterized using a spectrometer and a solar simulator. These components include solar cells, front side glasses, encapsulation materials, interconnecting tabs, and three standard backsheets with black, white, and transparent colors and three rear glasses in white glazed, black glazed and transparent. Since the number of resulting graphs from this characterization is considerable, only one representative example is presented here. Specifically, **Figure 4** illustrates the reflectance of backsheets with different colors, serving as a demonstration of the obtained results. **Figure 4** indicates that the white backsheet exhibits higher reflectance compared to the black and transparent variants, suggesting a stronger contribution to the optical gain of the module.

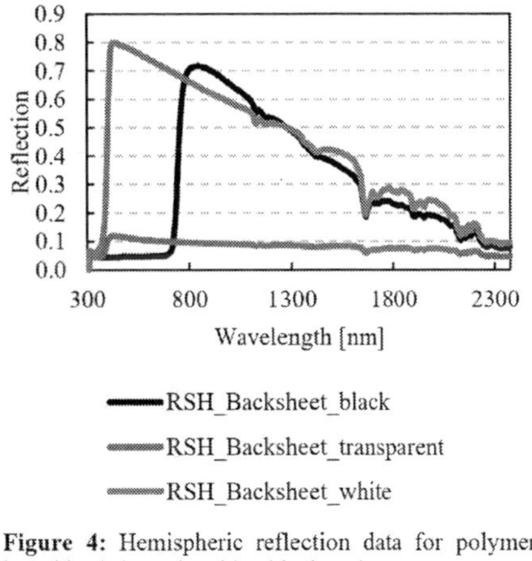

Figure 4: Hemispheric reflection data for polymer based backsheets in white, black and transparent

3.2 CTM analysis

All backsheets show very different optical properties in the visible and the infra-red spectrum (**Figure 4**). Worth noting is also the difference between the reflection of the inner side and the outer side of the white backsheet. While the inside is highly reflective, the outside has a low reflection reducing energy input into the module and lowering module temperature.

Figure 5 illustrates the results of CTM simulations conducted for polymeric backsheets in white, black, and transparent configurations. The findings reveal that the primary distinction among these variants is associated with differences in optical gain, which are quantified by the k11 coefficient. This coefficient serves as an indicator of the backsheet's positive contribution to enhancing optical gain at the module level.

The white backsheet provides the highest contribution, with a positive effect of 0.59%, increasing the overall optical gain to 1.67%. This is followed by the black backsheet, which enhances the optical gain by 0.33%, reaching a total of 1.41%. As shown in the results, the use of a transparent backsheet yields no significant impact on the optical gain.

Figure 6 illustrates the CTM simulation results obtained for three types of rear glass configurations: white-glazed, black-glazed, and transparent. The comparison highlights how different rear-glass glazing influence the optical behavior of the module and, consequently, its overall performance.

The results for the black glazing and no glazing modules are the same, because black glazing does not significantly contribute to the rear-cover coupling gains, as does the very low reflection of the transparent rear glass. It is worth noticing that an analysis with more decimals would show a difference because the black layer is not a perfect absorber. Here, the efficiency and power gains caused by the rear cover of 0.03% absorption is due to the reflection of light that passes through the cell and is reflected.

Regarding the white glazing, it caused an increment of 0.10% abs. in the simulated module efficiency. These gains are mostly due to the scattered reflection of light in the inactive module area between the cells and strings (k1 and k2, **Figure 1**).

These CTM gains are lower than the benefits from having a fully white backsheet instead of white glazing, which increases the reflected light not only from the inactive module area, but also from the transmitted light in the cell module area. But the module would be monofacial with a fully white backsheet, while the glazing allows for bifaciality. This will significantly affect the energy yield depending on the installation site, as well as the tilt and orientation of the module.

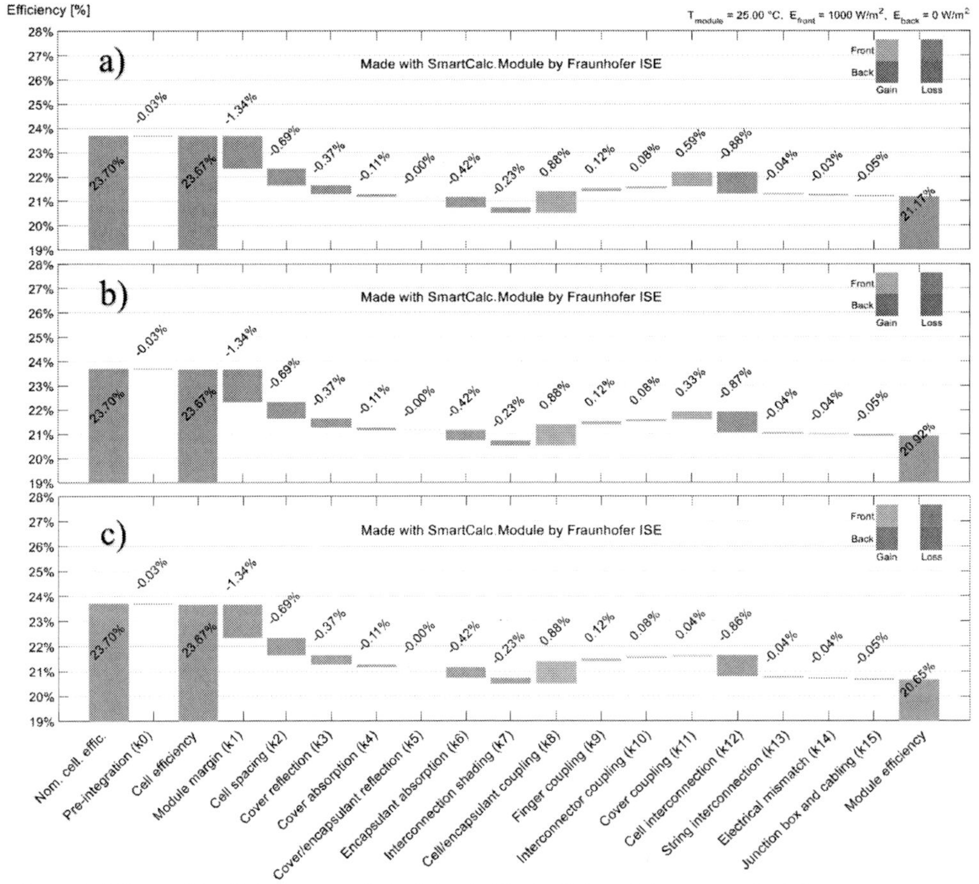

Figure 5: Cell to module efficiency loss analysis of the: a) white, b) black, and c) transparent backsheet

Efficiency loss analysis shows no significant loss for the black backsheet compared to the white backsheet. The high IR-reflection of the black backsheet compensates for losses in the visible spectrum. The transparent backsheet shows significant losses in the range of 0.2%abs but allows for a bifacial module. A further assessment on the yield of the modules in operation is necessary to quantify benefits.

Figure 7 provides a comprehensive summary of the effect of different backsheet types on the optical gain of the module. In both cases, whether using glass or polymeric materials, the incorporation of a white-colored backsheet consistently results in an increased optical gain. This highlights the significance of backsheet color selection in enhancing module performance, particularly through its contribution to the optical gain component.

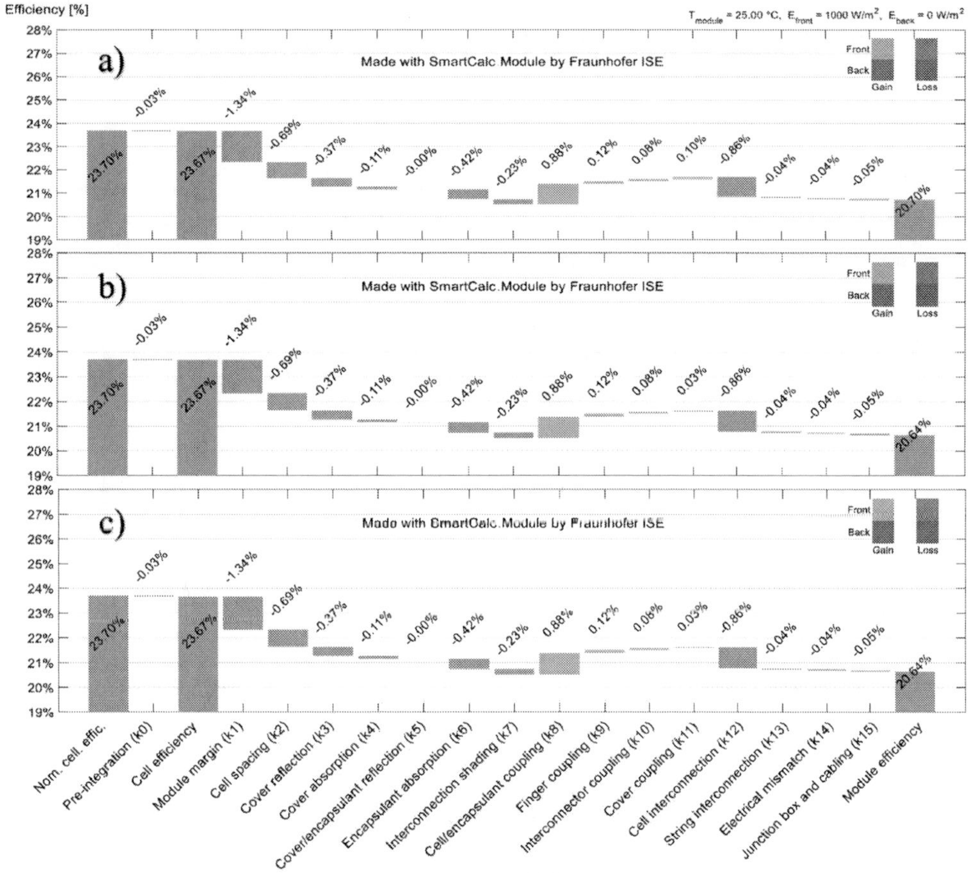

Figure 6: Cell to module efficiency loss analysis of the: a) white, b) black, and c) transparent backsheet

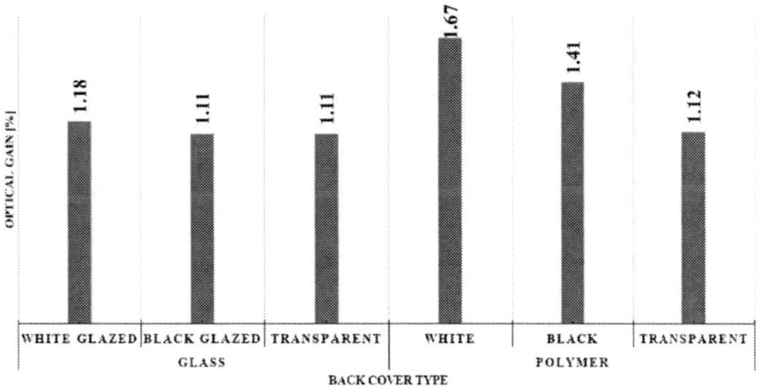

Figure 7: Calculated optical gain for different types of back cover materials, white colored back covers perform better in both polymer and glass.

4 DISCUSSION

Photovoltaic (PV) modules are subject to significant cell-to-module (CTM) losses arising from optical, electrical, and thermal mechanisms. Accurate modeling of these losses is therefore essential for predicting real-world module performance. While previous studies have primarily focused on quantifying and mitigating various CTM loss mechanisms, the present study shifts the focus toward the positive contribution of optical gain. In particular, the effects of different backsheet and rear-glass materials—including polymeric and glass variants with varying colors—on module optical gain were investigated.

Based on the results shown in **Figures 5–7**, backsheet and rear-glass selection strongly influence the optical gain of PV modules. White backsheets, whether polymeric or glass, provide the largest enhancement, increasing optical gain by 0.55% absolute over transparent and 0.26% over black backsheets. In comparison, white-glazed rear glass offers a smaller improvement of 0.07% absolute. These findings indicate that backsheet color has a greater impact on module optical gain than rear-glass glazing, highlighting the importance of reflective backsheets for maximizing monofacial performance. However, while backsheets enhance optical gain, they limit bifacial operation. Conversely, color-glazed rear glass, although contributing less to CTM gains, allows bifacial modules to capture additional irradiance from the rear, potentially increasing overall energy yield under real-world conditions.

Future work will focus on developing a more detailed CTM model for glazed glass, incorporating additional optical, electrical, and geometrical factors to better predict module performance under real operating conditions.

5 CONCLUSION

This study examines rear glass with different glazes (white, black, and transparent) and backsheets of corresponding colors. Their influence on cell-to-module (CTM) efficiency and the overall power output of photovoltaic (PV) modules is evaluated. Using spectroscopic analysis and CTM modeling via the SmartCalc.Module software, the study evaluates the contributions of these materials to CTM gains.

The study demonstrates that the choice of rear-side glazing material significantly influences the CTM efficiency and power output of PV modules. While white backsheet offers the highest CTM gains due to enhanced light scattering, modules become monofacial. High infrared reflection of black backsheets shows significant benefits but also results in monofacial modules. Glazed glass yields in lower CTM gains but provides module bifaciality which results in higher energy production in operation.

These findings underline the need for tailored material selection to optimize PV module performance based on application and environmental factors. Future work should focus on real-world operational assessments to quantify long-term energy yield benefits.

Acknowledgment

The authors thank the German Federal Ministry of Economics and Energy, BMWE, for the project MiMoRisk with the contract number 03EE1149A.

6 References

[1] REN21.2025, "Renewables 2025 Global Status Report Collection, Global Overview (Paris: REN21 Secretariat)."

[2] S. W. W. Philipps, "Photovoltaics Report," May 2025. Accessed: Aug. 26, 2025. [Online]. Available: https://www.ise.fraunhofer.de/content/dam/ise/de/documents/publications/studies/Photovoltaics-Report.pdf

[3] M. A. Green et al., "Solar Cell Efficiency Tables (Version 66)," Progress in Photovoltaics: Research and Applications, vol. 33, no. 7, pp. 795–810, Jul. 2025, doi: 10.1002/pip.3919.

[4] L. Shen, Z. Li, and T. Ma, "Analysis of the power loss and quantification of the energy distribution in PV module," Appl Energy, vol. 260, Feb. 2020, doi: 10.1016/j.apenergy.2019.114333.

[5] T. Ma et al., "Performance modelling of photovoltaic modules under actual operating conditions considering loss mechanism and energy distribution," Appl Energy, vol. 298, Sep. 2021, doi: 10.1016/j.apenergy.2021.117205.

[6] S. Guo, J. P. Singh, M. Peters, A. G. Aberle, and J. Wong, "Two-dimensional current flow in stringed PV cells and its influence on the cell-to-module resistive losses," Solar Energy, vol. 130, pp. 224–231, Jun. 2016, doi: 10.1016/j.solener.2016.02.012.

[7] T. hee Jung, H. eun Song, H. keun Ahn, and G. hwan Kang, "A mathematical model for cell-to-module conversion considering mismatching solar cells and the resistance of the interconnection ribbon," Solar Energy, vol. 103, pp. 253–262, May 2014, doi: 10.1016/j.solener.2014.01.032.

[8] S. M. Dasari, P. Srivastav, R. Shaw, S. Saravanan, and P. Suratkar, "Optimization of cell to module conversion loss by reducing the resistive losses," Renew Energy, vol. 50, pp. 82–85, Feb. 2013, doi: 10.1016/j.renene.2012.05.022.

[9] H. Hanifi, C. Pfau, M. Turek, and J. Schneider, "A practical optical and electrical model to estimate the power losses and quantification of different heat sources in silicon based PV modules," Renew Energy, vol. 127, pp. 602–612, Nov. 2018, doi: 10.1016/j.renene.2018.04.060.

[10] I. Haedrich, U. Eitner, M. Wiese, and H. Wirth, "Unified methodology for determining CTM ratios: Systematic prediction of module power," Solar Energy Materials and Solar Cells, vol. 131, pp. 14–23, 2014, doi: 10.1016/j.solmat.2014.06.025.

[11] I. Haedrich, D. C. Jordan, and M. Ernst, "Methodology to predict annual yield losses and gains caused by solar module design and materials under field exposure," Solar Energy Materials and Solar Cells, vol. 202, Nov. 2019, doi: 10.1016/j.solmat.2019.110069.

[12] T. Ma et al., "Performance modelling of photovoltaic modules under actual operating conditions considering loss mechanism and energy distribution," Appl Energy, vol. 298, Sep. 2021, doi: 10.1016/j.apenergy.2021.117205.

[13] L. Shen, Z. Li, and T. Ma, "Analysis of the power loss and quantification of the energy distribution

in PV module," Appl Energy, vol. 260, Feb. 2020, doi: 10.1016/j.apenergy.2019.114333.

[14] J. Shahid and A. Ö. Karabacak, "Presented at the 30th PV Solar Energy Conference, 08 th-13 th," 2020.

[15] M. Mittag, T. Zech, M. Wiese, D. Bläsi, M. Ebert, and H. Wirth, "Cell-to-Module (CTM) Analysis for Photovoltaic Modules with Shingled Solar Cells."

[16] M. Mittag, C. Kutter, S. Hoffmann, P. Romer, A. J. Beinert, and T. Zech, "ELECTRICAL AND THERMAL MODELING OF JUNCTION BOXES."

[17] M. Mittag, A. J. Beinert, L. C. Rendler, M. Ebert, and U. Eitner, "TRIANGULAR RIBBONS FOR IMPROVED MODULE EFFICIENCY."

[18] H. Hanifi, D. Dassler, J. Schneider, M. Turek, S. Schindler, and J. Bagdahn, "Optimized Tab Width in Half-cell Modules," Energy Procedia, vol. 92, pp. 52–59, Aug. 2016, doi: 10.1016/j.egypro.2016.07.009.

[19] H. Hanifi, C. Pfau, M. Turek, and J. Schneider, "A practical optical and electrical model to estimate the power losses and quantification of different heat sources in silicon based PV modules," Renew Energy, vol. 127, pp. 602–612, Nov. 2018, doi: 10.1016/j.renene.2018.04.060.

[20] J. Schneider, J. Bagdahn, H. Hanifi, and J. Bagdahn, "REDUCED SHADING EFFECT ON HALF-CELL MODULES-MEASUREMENT AND SIMULATION," 2015. [Online]. Available: https://www.researchgate.net/publication/283488492

[21] I. Haedrich et al., "How cell textures impact angular cell-to-module ratios and the annual yield of crystalline solar modules," Solar Energy Materials and Solar Cells, vol. 183, pp. 181–192, Aug. 2018, doi: 10.1016/j.solmat.2018.04.006.

[22] A. Tummalieh and A. Pfreundt, "TREND TRACKING OF EFFICIENCY AND CTM RATIO OF PV MODULES."

[23] M. Mittag, A. Pfreundt, and J. Shahid, "Presented at the 30th PV Solar Energy Conference, 08 th-13 th," 2020.

[24] M. Mittag, A. Pfreundt, J. Shahid, N. Wöhrle, and D. H. Neuhaus, "TECHNO-ECONOMIC ANALYSIS OF HALF CELL MODULES-THE IMPACT OF HALF CELLS ON MODULE POWER AND COSTS."

[25] "Fraunhofer Institute for Solar Energy Systems ISE, SmartCalc.Module." Accessed: Sep. 01, 2023. [Online]. Available: http://www.cell-to-module.com

[26] M. Mittag, "Systematic PV module optimization with the cell-to-module (CTM) analysis software," vol. 5, pp. 97–105, 2017. [Online]. Available: www.ise.fraunhofer.de

AESOLAR

Fraunhofer ISE

Indoor Characterization and CTM Evaluation of Photovoltaic Modules with Colored Backsheets and Rear-Side Glazed Glasses

Pouya Pourshafi[1*], Alexander Aguilar Protti[2], Max Mittag[2], Christian Reichel[2], Andreas Maixner[1], Hamed Hanifi[1]

1 AESOLAR, Messerschmittring 54, 86343 Königsbrunn, Germany
2 Fraunhofer Institute for Solar Energy Systems (ISE), Heidenhofstraße 2, 79110 Freiburg, Germany
*Corresponding author: p.pourshafi@ae-solar.com

Bundesministerium für Wirtschaft und Energie

MOTIVATION

- PV modules experience significant **cell-to-module (CTM) losses** due to optical, electrical, and thermal mechanisms.
- Accurate CTM modeling is essential for predicting real-world PV module performance.
- Previous studies have focused on various loss mechanisms.
- This study shifts focus from losses to optical gain using different back cover materials including polymer and glass with different coloring on the cell side.

METHODOLOGY

- Back cover materials:
  - Glass: White-glazed, black-glazed, transparent

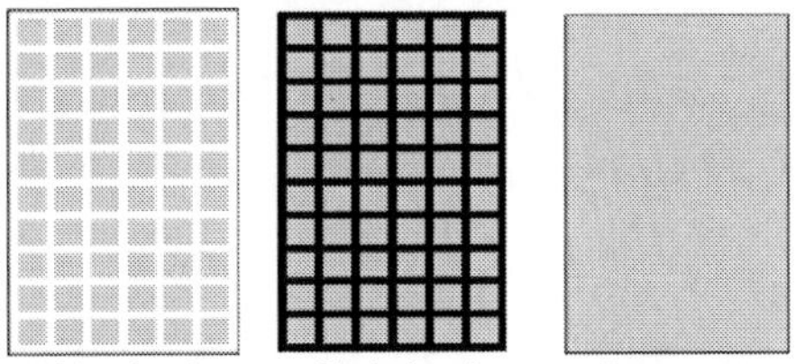

White-glazed | Black-glazed | Transparent

  - Polymer Backsheet: white, black, transparent

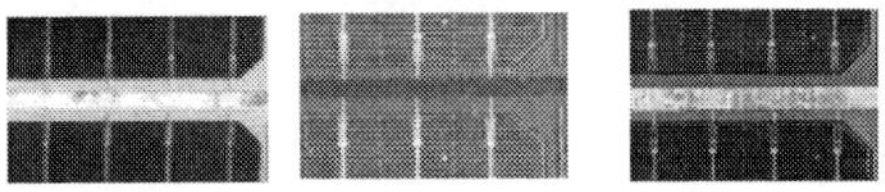

White | Black | Transparent

- Optical and electrical Characterization:
  - Optical characterization of module components with a focus on back cover
  - Assessment of electrical and optical contributions
- Comparative analysis:
  - Processing with SmartCalc.Module[1]
  - Comparison of CTM ratios & power output across materials variations

SUMMARY

- **CTM Loss Challenge:** PV modules deliver less power than the sum of the power of their solar cells due to optical and electrical losses ➡ Financial loss for producers
- **Optical gains:**
  - White backsheet: 0.55% abs. and 0.26% abs. extra optical gain compared to transparent and black backsheets
  - White-glazed glass: 0.07% abs. extra gain compared to other glass types
- **Key Insight:**
  - White back cover materials (polymer or glass) increase optical gain compared to black or transparent counterparts.
  - Backsheets outperform the color-glazed glasses in optical gains. However, the module will be limited to monofacial design and the bifaciality is compromised
  - Color-glazed glasses contribute less to CTM gains compared to the backsheets but the module can produce more yield because of bifaciality
- The bifacial design ultimately leads to a higher annual energy yield, which in turn improves the economic performance of the PV system.

Outlook: The CTM model for glazed glass with more details will be developed.

[1] Fraunhofer ISE, www.cell-to-module.com

The authors thank the German Federal Ministry of Economics and Energy, BMWE, for the project MiMoRisk with the contract number 03EE1149A

RESULTS

- CTM analysis of the modules with different back cover is shown as following:

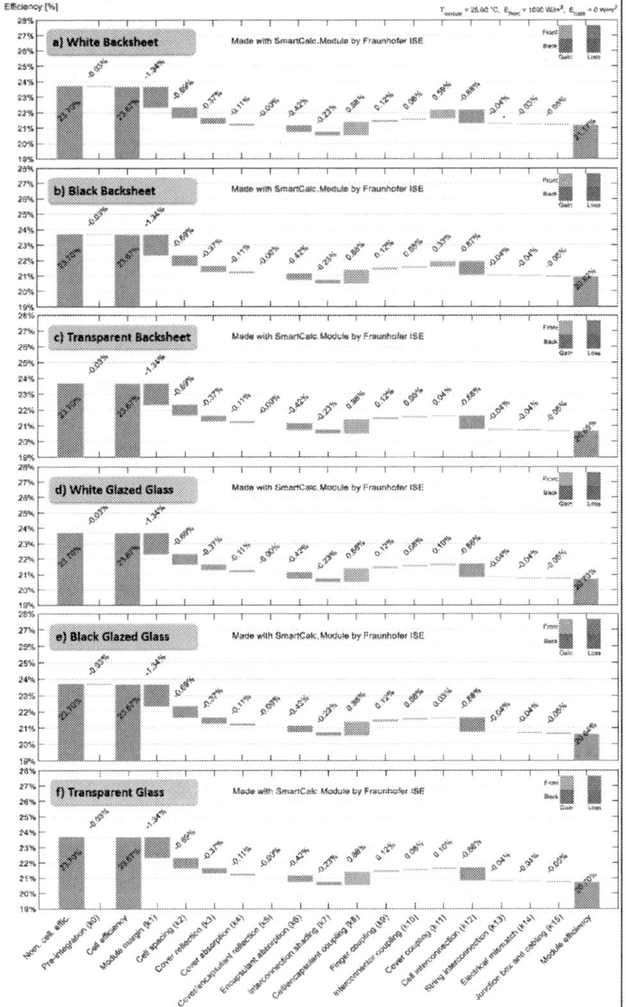

- Optical Gain with polymer backsheet:

White backsheet= +1.67 %	Black backsheet= +1.41 %	Transparent backsheet= +1.12 %

- White Polymer backsheets boosts CTM power by 0.59% .
- Optical gain with rear side glass:

White Glazed= +1.18 %	Black Glazed= +1.11 %	Transparent Glass= +1.11 %

- White-glazed glass boosts CTM power by 0.10% vs. black/transparent only 0.03%.

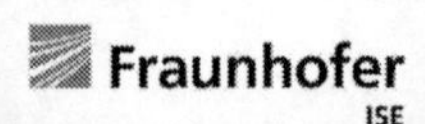

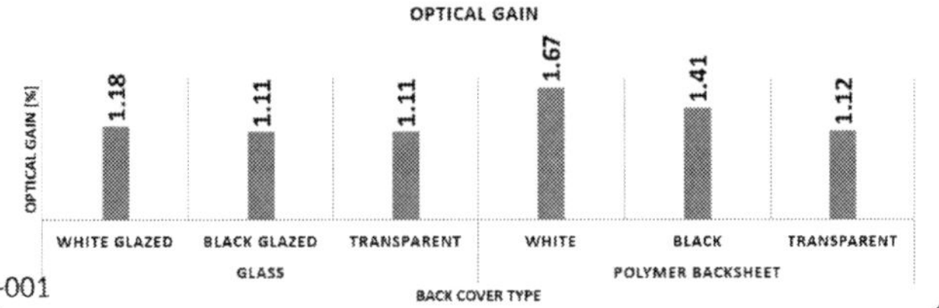

020138-001

FIBER REINFORCED COMPOSITE PHOTOVOLTAIC MODULES BY HP-RTM MANUFACTURING PROCESS

Jon Aizpurua, Igor Arrizabalaga, Leire Herrero, Unai Iglesias, Oihane Echeverria, Eduard Bellvert, Sonia Garcia, Olatz Ollo, Maikel Mugica, Werther Cambarau, Francisco J. Cano, Eduardo Roman, Oihana Zubillaga*
TECNALIA, Basque Research and Technology Alliance (BRTA); *oihana.zubillaga@tecnalia.com

ABSTRACT: Lightweight photovoltaic (PV) modules made of continuous fiber reinforced transparent composite are promising for BIPV, VIPV and other urban applications. The present work compiles the recent results obtained for composite module manufacturing through high-pressure resin transfer moulding (HP-RTM), regarding process quality and durability of corresponding modules. Minimodules were manufactured with successful mould filling and demoulding step, while maintaining the integrity of the cells and module quality. Regarding reliability of the modules, after 200 thermal cycles, a power and short-circuit current loss of 2.3% and 2.8% were observed respectively, with a colour change of 27% in b* chromatic coordinate. The power and short-circuit losses were more pronounced after 1000 hours in damp-heat exposure, reaching values of 3.0 and 4.0% respectively. The colour change was also higher in this last case, with a 123% increase in b*, suggesting that optical losses may be affecting the electrical performance. With power losses detected due to aging below 5%, the modules would meet the PV standard requirements. The study concluded that the HP-RTM is a promising approach to advance towards a composite PV module manufacturing process with higher automation level, repeatability and precision, leading finally to an increased throughput and cost reduction.
Keywords: Composite encapsulant, HP-RTM process, PV module, performance stability, PV integration

1 INTRODUCTION

Photovoltaic modules made of continuous fiber composite have been developed for BIPV, VIPV and other urban applications using vacuum assisted resin infusion (VARI) as manufacturing process [1,2].

An approach to a process of higher automation level comprises module manufacturing by high-pressure resin transfer moulding (HP-RTM).

The inherent challenges of HP-RTM include tackling with fast-curing resins and the interaction between PV cells and process parameters. Advancing in the automation of composite PV module manufacturing will allow not only increasing throughput and reducing costs, but also improving repeatability and precision.

Recent advances carried out on back-contact silicon cell encapsulation by HP-RTM and stability performance of resulting PV modules are presented.

2 EXPERIMENTAL

2.1 Materials and module manufacturing

PV modules were manufactured with back-contact silicon solar cells using as encapsulant continuous E-type glass fiber fabric and fast-curing clear bisphenol-A epoxy resin. Research on process parameters and module configuration was carried out until complete mould filling was reached while maintaining the integrity of cells and electrical connections.

2.2 Module characterization

The modules were characterized by current-voltage (I-V) curves carried out by solar simulator and electroluminescence (EL) images.

The reliability of the modules was studied in accelerated aging tests comprising exposure to damp-heat and thermal cycling, under conditions indicated in IEC 61215 standard. The damp-heat test was performed in a climatic chamber and the modules were exposed to 85°C and 85% relative humidity for 1000 hours. The thermal cycling test covered 200 cycles between -40°C and 85°C. The weathering progress was evaluated by I-V curves carried out by solar simulator, EL images and colour analysis under CIE system. For colour analysis, b* chromatic coordinate in the blue-yellow axis was measured. A higher b* value corresponds to yellower composite and may indicate potential power decrease due to optical losses.

3 RESULTS AND DISCUSSION

3.1 Module manufacturing and characterization

Minimodules consisting of four, six and nine crystalline silicon cells were manufactured with successful mould filling and demoulding step, while maintaining the integrity of the cells and module quality. A picture of a module and corresponding EL image are presented in figure 1. Suitable process parameters and module configuration were identified to avoid cell breakage.

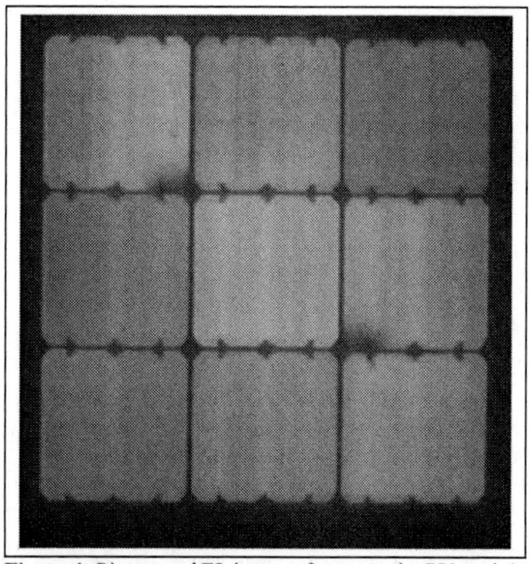

Figure 1: Picture and EL image of a composite PV module with 9 cells manufactured by HP-RTM.

3.2 Accelerated aging test results

After 200 thermal cycles, a power and short-circuit current loss of 2.3% and 2.8% were observed respectively, with a colour change of 27% in b* CIE parameter, showing a slightly yellowish appearance at naked-eye (figure 2). The power and short-circuit losses were more pronounced after 1000 hours in damp-heat exposure, reaching values of 3.0 and 4.0% respectively (figure 3). The colour change was also higher in this case, with a 123% increase in b* and more accused yellow appearance of the samples, suggesting that optical losses may be affecting the electrical performance (figure 2). No significant damage was observed in EL analysis after thermal cyclaing or damp-heat exposure. With power losses due to aging below 5%, the modules would meet the IEC standard requirements.

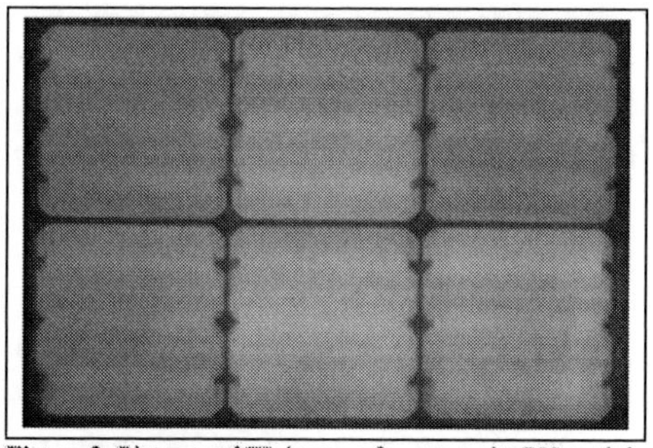

Figure 2: Picture and EL image of a composite PV module after exposure to 200 thermal cycles.

4 CONCLUSIONS

Suitable process parameters and module configuration were found to manufacture minimodules of 4, 6 and 9 cells, with successful mould filling while maintaining cell integrity. The manufactured modules showed good performance stability in damp-heat and thermal cycling exposure. Further accelerated aging tests are on going under PV standards and regulatory framework of PV integrated applications.

The study concluded that the HP-RTM process is a promising approach to advance towards a composite PV module manufacturing with higher automation level. This process may allow tackling particular cases requiring tailored designs usually found in integrated photovoltaics, while target throughput and cost values are achieved.

Figure 3: Picture and EL image of a composite PV module after 1000 hours damp-heat exposure.

5 ACKNOWLEDGEMENTS

This work was supported by the European Union's Horizon Europe research and innovation programme under SEAMLESS project [grant agreement number 101096126].

6 REFERENCES

[1] N. Yurrita, J. Aizpurua, W. Cambarau, G. Imbuluzqueta, J.M. Hernández, F.J. Cano, O. Zubillaga, Photovoltaic modules encapsulated in composite material modified with ultraviolet additives, Solar Energy Materials and Solar Cells 230 (2021) 111250.

[2] E. Rico, I. Huerta, T. del Caño, L. Villada, Á. Gallego, V. Velasco, O. Zubillaga, J.M. Vega de Seoane, I. Arrizabalaga, N. Yurrita, J. Aizpurua, G. Imbuluzketa, F.J. Cano, "PVCOM Project: Manufacture of PV Modules Encapsulated in Composite Materials for Integration in Urban Environments", Communications in computer and information science 978 (2019), 38-52.

OPTICAL CHARACTERISATION OF PV GLASSES WITH VARYING ANTIMONY CONTENTS

Oliver Pfeiffer[1], Alexander Aguilar Protti[2], Christian Reichel[2], Bengt Jaeckel[3], Thomas Sauer[4], Holger Neuhaus[2], Ulf Blieske[1]
[1]University of Applied Sciences Cologne, [2]Fraunhofer ISE, [3]Fraunhofer CSP, [4]EXXERGY
alexander.aguilar.protti@ise.fraunhofer.de, christian.reichel@ise.fraunhofer.de, bengt.jaeckel@csp.fraunhofer.de, tcs@exxergy.com, holger.neuhaus@ise.fraunhofer.de, ulf.blieske@th-koeln.de
*oliver.pfeiffer@th-koeln.de (Tel: 0049 221 8275 4993), Betzdorfer Str. 2, 50679 Cologne

ABSTRACT: Antimony pentoxide is often added during the production of rolled solar glass to reduce light absorption in the near-infrared spectrum. However, this compound is toxic, poses environmental risks, and restricts the recycling of antimony-containing solar glass. This study examines the optical properties of solar glasses with varying antimony concentrations to determine how much the content can be reduced without compromising the optical performance of PV glass. An antimony-free float glass was compared with four rolled (textured) glass samples containing antimony levels from 10 ppm to 1240 ppm. Optical quality was assessed through transmittance, reflectance, and IAM measurements. These results were then used to calculate the linear absorption coefficient and to simulate PV module performance with SmartCalc.Module. The rolled glass samples showed better transmittance than the float glass, but no advantage in reflectance. IAM performance was slightly higher for the rolled glasses, though this was due to the textured surface rather than the antimony content. When normalized for thickness using the linear absorption coefficient, the rolled glasses showed lower absorption than the float glass. Surprisingly, no clear correlation was found between antimony concentration and absorption behaviour. Overall, the superior optical properties of the rolled glasses translated into a rated energy yield about 1% higher than that of the float glass. It is important, that it is difficult to generalise these results without knowing the exact chemical composition or the production process of the glasses. However, a key finding is, that high-quality rolled solar glass can be produced without the need of adding antimony.
Keywords: Antimony, solar glass, optical characterisation, rated energy yield

1 INTRODUCTION

High optical transmission is a key requirement for PV module front covers to maximise the amount of light available to the solar cells. The most common front cover material is soda-lime glass because of its low cost. Since the raw material (sand) is gained in natural mining, it can contain a significant amount of iron in the form of FeO. The not fully oxidized iron has the disadvantage of absorbing light in the near infrared band, critically decreasing a PV module's efficiency. Therefore, the solar glass industry hasdeveloped two strategies for reducing iron-induced absorption of light: The usage of low iron natural materials, and further, the oxidation of FeO into Fe_2O_3 which only insignificantly absorbs light in the near UV and blue range. The oxidation of FeO is performed by adding antimony pentoxide (Sb_5O_5) during the glass melting process.

$$Sb_2O_5 + 4FeO \rightarrow Sb_2O_3 + 2Fe_2O_3 \qquad (1)$$

Using Sb_5O_5 as an additive is, however, only common in the production of patterned solar glass, since it is suspected to react with the tin bath during float glass production causing a poor glass surface. In the float glass production, molten (low iron) glass flows onto a molten tin bath, resulting in advantages related to production yield and process stability, producing a glass with a mirror-like surface. However, it is challenging to use Sb_5O_5 in float glass since the molten glass can possibly interact with the liquid tin bath. In the patterned glass production, molten glass is formed between two rollers into a flat sheet. The rollers imprint a texture onto the glass defined by the roller structure; the texture can create a light trapping function. Since adding Sb_5O_5 does not lead to interactions and since there is no tin layer on the glass surface, patterned glass usually has a higher transmission than float glass. [1]
Nonetheless, antimony is toxic for humans [2] and can potentially contaminate soil and groundwater if not disposed properly [3]. When melted, toxic emissions impose the risk of negative respiratory, skin and gastrointestinal effects for industry workers and furthermore, its reaction with tin bath limits the use of recycled glass cullet in the float glass production [4].
Therefore, in the context of the EU Ecodesign Directive, limiting the content of antimony could be an interesting option for improving the sustainability ratings of PV modules, since disclosing the content of materials is a key recommendation of leading institutions for a future ecolabel [5]. Thus, it is expected that the market share of antimony-free glass in PV modules may increase from ~5% to ~18% between 2025 and 2035 [6].
This work builds on the study by Glaubitz et al. [7], who concluded that the positive optical effects are not linear to the antimony content of the glass. However, it further analyses how the antimony content affects the optical properties of glass samples, in particular the hemispherical spectral transmittance, reflectance and absorbance, as well as the angular behaviour of the transmittance, by means of the incidence angle modifier (IAM). Furthermore, the impact of these properties on the rated energy yield [8] is determined.

2 MATERIAL AND METHODS

2.1 Glass samples

Five glass types with varying antimony content and from two European producers were tested. Table I summarizes the main properties of the samples. It is important to mention that the samples are hand-made specimen without thermal curing and without anti-reflective coating. Besides the thickness and the antimony content, the glass surface roughness differs due to the different hot-forming process.

Table I: Glass sample characteristics

Producer	Thickness [mm]	Sb_2O_5 content [ppm]	Glass type
1	3.2	0	Float (low iron)
2	4	10	Rolled
2	4	290	Rolled
2	4	660	Rolled
2	2	1240	Rolled

The glass roughness was measured, using a "hommel etamic w10" device as summarized in Table II. While the float glass has an average roughness value of R_a=0,008-0.009 µm, the roughness of front and rear side from the rolled glasses is higher and differs since usually, the counter-rotating rollers have a different texture. For the optical characterisation of the samples, the textured front side is directed to the light source.

Table II: Average roughness value of front and rear side of the glass samples

Sample	R_a – front [µm]	R_a – rear [µm]
Float 3.2mm	0.008	0.009
Rolled 4mm	1.614	3.126
Rolled_2mm	1.153	1.579

2.2 Transmittance measurements

Transmittance measurements were carried out at TH Köln in accordance with DIN EN 62805-2 [9]. This comprises a xenon arc lamp as the light source, small-band optical filters (monochromator) and an integrating sphere in which a C-Si sensor measures the light intensity, as displayed in Figure 1 a). Further information about the measurement system are given in [7]. During a measurement, the light intensity in the sphere is measured at each wavelength interval when a glass sample is placed in front of the sphere's entrance (allowing light to pass through the glass) and when there is no glass present. Transmission $\tau_i(\lambda)$ is obtained by dividing the light intensity in the sphere with glass, $I_i(\lambda)$, by the light intensity in the sphere without glass, $I_0(\lambda)$. In total, 40 wavelength intervals between 300 nm and 1200 nm are measured. Ten measurements are taken and averaged for each glass sample.

$$\tau_i(\lambda) = \frac{I_i(\lambda)}{I_0(\lambda)} \quad (2)$$

2.3 Reflectance measurement

The reflectance measurement was also carried out at TH Köln in accordance with DIN EN 62805-2 [9] with a similar setup as for the transmittance measurements, as seen in Figure 1 b). However, this time the samples are placed inside the integrating sphere on a sample holder that has a high absorbing surface. The reflected part of the light is measured by the sensor. Light that is transmitted through the glass sample is absorbed by the absorber. Reflectance $\varrho_i(\lambda)$ is obtained by dividing the light intensity in the sphere with glass and absorber, $I_i(\lambda)$, by the light intensity in the sphere without glass and without absorber, $I_0(\lambda)$.

$$\varrho_i(\lambda) = \frac{I_i(\lambda)}{I_0(\lambda)} \quad (3)$$

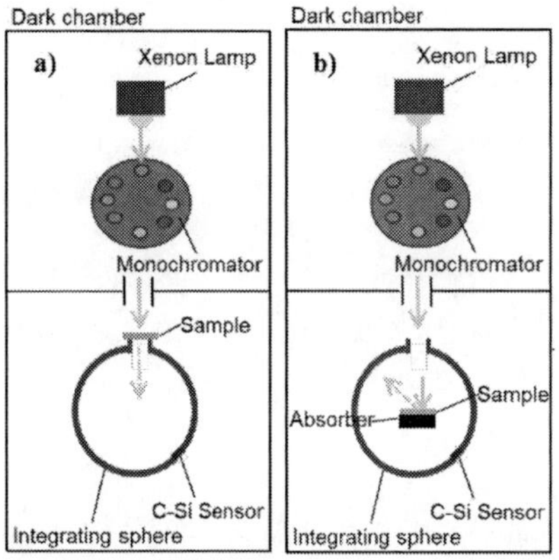

Figure 1: Schematic representations of the measurement setup at TH Köln for: a) the transmittance measurement and b) the reflectance measurement

2.4 Absorption coefficient

The absorbance characteristics of the glass samples were analysed using the spectral absorption coefficient, enabling a comparison independent of glass thickness. The spectral absorption coefficient α describes the loss of light intensity which is transmitted through a thin layer of homogeneous medium and can be derived from the Beer-Lambertian law. [10]

$$I(d) = I_0 * e^{-\alpha d} \quad (4)$$

In this Equation (4), I_0 refers to the initial light intensity, $I(d)$ to the light intensity after traveling the distance d through the medium, and α is the absorption coefficient, which is occasionally referred to as linear attenuation coefficient or extinction coefficient in other contexts [11]. To calculate the spectral absorption coefficient for a glass sample $\alpha_i(\lambda)$, the following equation is used.

$$\alpha_i(\lambda) = -\ln\left(\frac{\tau_i(\lambda)}{1 - \varrho_i(\lambda)}\right) * d_i^{-1} \quad (5)$$

In this Equation (5), $\tau_i(\lambda)$ corresponds to the light intensity $I(d)$ in the Beer-Lambertian law. The term $1 - \varrho_i(\lambda)$ is analogous to to I_0, as the light that passes through the glass sample consists of the incident light from the light source that is reduced by reflection losses. The parameter d_i corresponds to the thickness of the glass sample in centimetre.

2.5 IAM measurement

IAM measurements were carried out in accordance with IEC 61853-2 [12] at the TH Köln laboratories. The setup included a xenon arc lamp as the light source, an aperture to adjust the size of the light spot, and an automatically angle-adjustable sample holder, and is displayed in Figure 2. Mini-modules were built for measuring the IAM. For this, two glass/glass mini-modules were manufactured using M6 PERC half cells and EVA as the encapsulant. To assess whether the antimony content influences the IAM, the sample with the lowest content was compared to the sample with the highest content. Consequently, measurements were taken on a mini-module with low-iron float glass containing 0 ppm of antimony and a mini-module with 2 mm rolled glass containing 1240 ppm of antimony. The short-circuit current was measured using a "Keithley 2700" data logger. Fifteen measurements were taken per angle and averaged. The mini-module was underexposed during the measurement, as can be seen in the following figure.

Figure 2: IAM measurement setup at TH Köln

2.6 Module performance

This study evaluates the impact of antimony content in glass on the performance of photovoltaic (PV) modules, specifically in terms of rated module power and rated energy yield. The rated power at Standard Test Conditions (STC) was determined using CTM simulations, while the rated energy yield was assessed through the Virtual Energy Rating method, both implemented in the SmartCalc.Module software [13]. For this analysis, an exemplary module with a total cell power of 644.63 Wp was selected. Additional specifications are provided in Figure 3 and Table III. To account for the fact that the glasses have different thicknesses, the refractive and extinction coefficients are extracted from the optical measurements as specified in [14] and the thickness is then normalized to 2 mm for all simulations.

For the energy yield calculations, the angular loss coefficient (a_r) of the Martin-Ruiz model [15] is extracted from the IAM measurements by applying a least-squares fitting. Since only one sample with antimony (rolled glass) is measured, the same a_r value is assumed for all the simulations with rolled glass (10, 290, 660 and 1290 ppm).

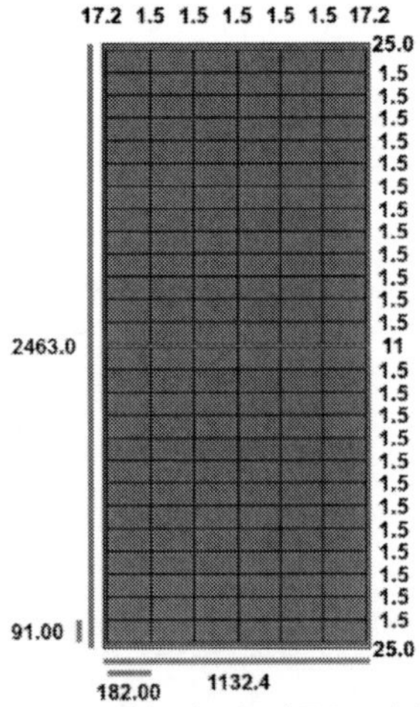

Figure 3: Layout of the simulated PV module

Table III: Characteristics of the simulated module

Layout	Cell spacing: 1.5 mm String spacing: 1.5 mm Top and bottom margins: 25 mm Side margins: 17.2 mm Number of cells: 156 Module length = 2.46 m Module width = 1.13 m Module area = 2.789 m²
Cell	Cell type: half-cut M10 HJT Efficiency = 25.0% Bifaciality = 90% Number of fingers = 78/90 (front/bottom) Number of busbars = 16
Cover	Front: 2.0 mm clear glass with ARC Rear: 2.0 mm clear glass with ARC
Encapsulant	Front: UV transmitting POE Rear: UV blocking POE Thickness = 600 µm
Cell connectors	Resistivity = 1.8 µΩ-cm Diameter: 0.25 mm
String connectors	Resistivity = 1.8 µΩ-cm Width = 5.072 mm Thickness = 0.472 mm
Junction box	Quantity = 2 Internal resistance = 0.03 mΩ
Cables	Length = 1.3 m Cross section = 4 mm² Specific resistance = 0.02 Ω-mm²/m Contact resistance plug/jack = 2mΩ

3 RESULTS

3.1 Transmittance

The results of the transmittance measurements are displayed in Figure 4. While low iron glass without antimony showed the lowest overall transmittance, decreasing from 92% at wavelength of 600 nm to 90.6% at 1100 nm, the transmittance of the 2 mm rolled glass with the highest antimony stayed constant over 92% for all wavelengths down to approx. 500 nm. The transmittance of all 4mm rolled glass was very similar, decreasing around 0.5 percent points from 92% at 600 nm to 91.5% at 1100 nm. It should be mentioned that the results at wavelengths below 400 nm and above 1150 nm were highly uncertain which is due to the low sensitivity of the c-Si optical sensor. They were therefore not included in the diagram. However, the trend of decreasing transmittance below 400 nm is generally established for soda-lime glass. The same is true for the reflectance measurement results and therefore also for the calculated absorption coefficient.

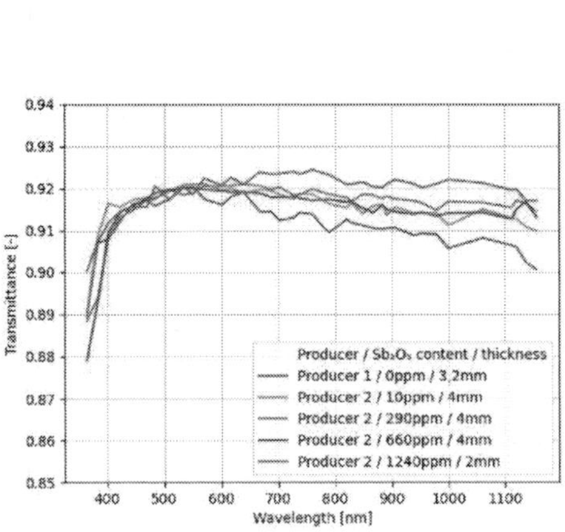

Figure 4: Transmittance results

3.2 Reflectance

The reflectance measurements in Figure 5 show no significant differences between the different glass samples. At small wavelengths between 400nm and 500nm, the reflection is between 8-8.5% and decreases steadily to 6.5-7% at 1100 nm.

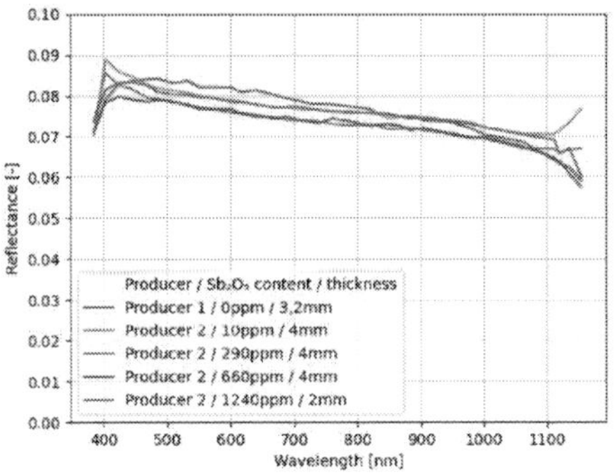

Figure 5: Reflectance results

3.3 Absorption coefficient

When calculating the absorption coefficient with equation 3, results can be displayed as in Figure 6. For all glasses an absorption coefficient between 0-0.01 cm^{-1} can be seen at wavelengths to around 650 nm. Then, it steadily increases over the whole wavelength range. While the rolled glass results show high coherence regardless of the antimony content, absorbing between 4-6% of the light per centimetre at 1100 nm, the low iron float glass has a significantly higher absorbance of 9.8% per centimetre. This result can mainly be attributed the lower transmittance of this glass in the corresponding wavelength range.

It should be noted that the calculated absorption coefficients in a range between 400-650 nm and for the 2 mm rolled glass additionally between 650-780 nm, was at some points slightly below zero. Since these results are not valid and can be explained by uncertainties in the transmittance and reflectance measurements, they were artificially changed to zero.

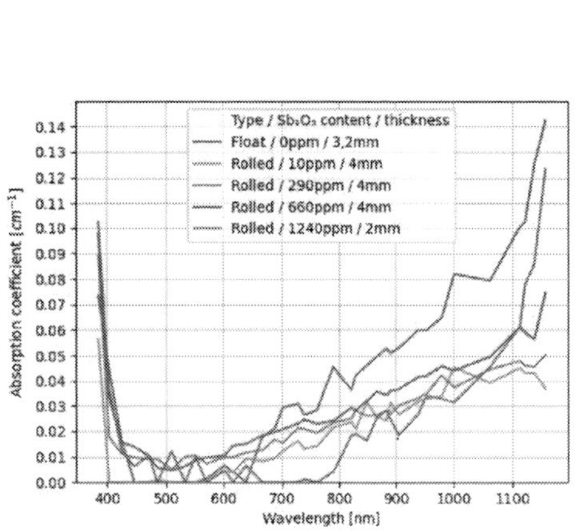

Figure 6: Absorption coefficient results

3.4 IAM

The IAM measurements revealed a slight difference between the low iron float and the high antimony rolled glass at high angles, as illustrated Figure 7. The discrepancy can be attributed to the different surface textures of float and rolled solar glass that are detailed in section 2.1. To confirm this, the results from the float glass were compared to a synthetic IAM curve resembling pure Fresnel reflections. As the graphs are coherent, it can be concluded that the higher reflections at higher angles are due to the low surface roughness of the float glass. The slightly rougher texture of the rolled glass decreases reflections at high angles, meaning that the IAM is higher for higher angles compared to the float-glass.

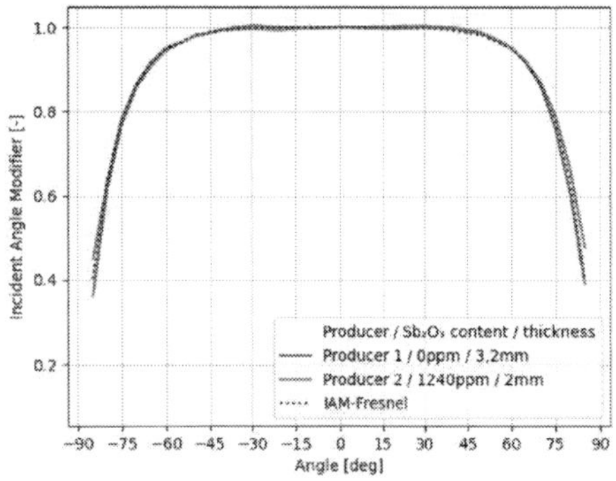

Figure 7: IAM results

The angular loss coefficients that minimize the difference between the measurements and the Martin-Ruiz model are $a_r = 0.1812$ for the 0 ppm (float) glass and $a_r = 0.1685$, for the rolled glass.

3.5 Module performance

The impact of antimony content in glass on module rated power is illustrated in Figure 8. For rolled glasses, no discernible trend is observed between antimony content and rated power, with an average module power of 589.98 Wp. This value is 3.32 Wp (0.4%) higher than the 587.58 Wp recorded for float glass, primarily attributable to increased glass absorption.

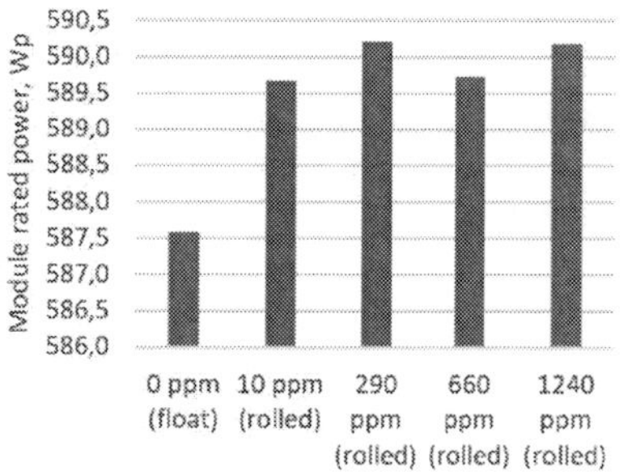

Figure 8: Impact of the antimony content on the rated power of a 156 M10 half-cell module

Figure 9 depicts the effect of glass antimony content on average rated energy yield. Similarly, no trend is evident between antimony content in rolled glass and energy yield. The rolled glass demonstrates an average yield of 341.58 kWh/m²/yr, which is 1% higher than the 338.26 kWh/m²/yr achieved with float glass. The improved incident angle modulation (IAM) of the rolled glass, owing to its textured surface, is the primary factor contributing to this difference compared to the results at Standard Test Conditions (STC).

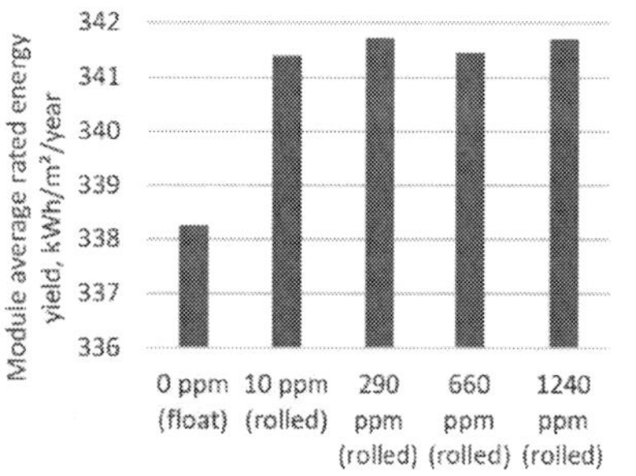

Figure 9: Rated energy yield of an exemplary PV module (average of 6 climatic regions)

4 DISCUSSION

The results are validated by comparing the measurements presented in this study with literature values.

Regarding the transmission, Babin et al. measured transmissions of around 91.5% - 92% over a similar wavelength range for low-iron glass with a slight texture [16]. This result is coherent with the measurement conducted on the rolled glass samples. Blieske and Stollwerck also report that a transmission of 91.5% can be expected for antimony containing glasses [1].

In terms of the reflectance, slightly lower values were published by Starowicz et al. [17]. However, these were measured on laminated mini-modules and not on glass sheets, as in this study. Since a glass/EVA junction will alter the reflection behaviour compared to a glass/air junction, different results can be expected.

Comparable absorbances were published by Allsopp et al. [18], who experimented with different glass recipes and glass dopants such as Fe_2O_3 and Bi_2O_3. Since the exact chemical composition of the samples used in this study is not known, the applicability of these results remains uncertain.

Regarding the IAM, the measured values are of high certainty, especially those for the flat mirror-like surface glass, who were coherent with a synthetical curve for Fresnel reflections.

The energy yield simulations are based on measured data, so the results are consistent with the findings presented earlier. The rated energy yield was approximately 1% higher for textured glass than for flat glass. This finding is comparable to the results of a real-world study which compared textured and flat glass modules over a six-month period, finding that textured glass had a 1.4% higher optical gain than flat glass [19].

Surprisingly, the antimony content of the glass does not seem to influence the absorption. An earlier study conducted on different glass samples using a different method observed such an effect [7]. As there are no other studies that have conducted a similar analysis to quantify the effect of distinct antimony contents (to the best of the authors' knowledge), the results cannot be directly compared. As outlined, aside of the known Sb_2O_5 content, the glass chemistry is unknown. This might explain why the antimony did not affect the absorption as expected. Another possible explanation is that the effect of the surface texture, which increases transmission, outweighs the optical effect caused by antimony. This would mean that reducing the antimony content would not compromise the optical quality of solar glass, paving the way for more eco-friendly solar modules.

5 CONCLUSION

This study involved the optical characterisation of glass samples with different antimony contents. Five samples were compared in total: a float glass without antimony and four rolled glasses with antimony contents ranging from 10 ppm to 1,240 ppm. The samples were characterised using total transmission and reflection measurements, which were then used to calculate absorption. IAM measurements were also performed, and these results were then used alongside the others to calculate the energy annual yield of a module containing these glasses using the SmartCalc.Module software.

While the rolled, antimony-containing glasses outperformed the float glass (with transmission values of 91.5% to slightly over 92% compared to 90% at 1100 nm), reflectance was unaffected. Similarly, the IAM was not influenced by the antimony content but rather by the texture of the glass surface, resulting in lower IAM values at high angles for textured glass.

The energy yield simulations were also found to be influenced mainly by the glass texture rather than the antimony content, leading to a 1% higher rated energy yield of the textured glasses compared to the flat glass.

To the authors' surprise, the antimony content in the rolled glasses did not affect the absorption when normalised for glass thickness. As this result is novel and unlikely to be due to a measurement error, it suggests that high-quality solar glass can be produced without the need for antimony. However, without knowing the exact chemical glass composition of the glass substrates used in this study, this conclusion may deserve further investigation.

ACKNOWLEDGEMENTS
This work is part of the Green Solar Modules Project (ID: 03EE1161B) which is funded by the Federal Ministry for Economic Affairs and Energy (BMWE) and managed by Projektträger Jülich (PtJ).

6 REFERENCES

[1] U. Blieske and G. Stollwerck, Eds., *Advances in photovoltaics: Chapter Four: Glass and other Encapsulation Materials,* 1st ed. Amsterdam: Elsevier, 2013.

[2] S. Sundar and J. Chakravarty, "Antimony toxicity," (eng), *International journal of environmental research and public health*, vol. 7, no. 12, pp. 4267–4277, 2010.

[3] P. A. Nishad and A. Bhaskarapillai, "Antimony, a pollutant of emerging concern: A review on industrial sources and remediation technologies," (eng), *Chemosphere*, vol. 277, p. 130252, 2021.

[4] EUROPEAN SOLAR PV INDUSTRY ALLIANCE, "Addressing uncertain antimony content in solar glass for recycling," [Online] Available: https://solaralliance.eu/wp-content/uploads/2023/10/Recommendation-on-Addressing-uncertain-antimony-content-in-solar-glass-for-recycling.pdf. Accessed on: Jun. 30 2025.

[5] "Expert Input Paper – Eco Design and Energy Labelling for Photovoltaic Modules, Inverter and Systems in the EU, ETIP PV, SolarPower Europe, PVthin, European Solar Manufacturing Council, IECR," 2021. [Online] Available: https://pvthin.org/wp-content/uploads/2021-02-ETIP-PV-Report-expert-input-paper.pdf. Accessed on: Jun. 30 2025.

[6] VDMA, "International Technology Roadmap for Photovoltaics (ITRPV) 16th. Edition," May. 2025.

[7] A. Glaubitz, S. Grüttner, S. Yagci, O. Pfeiffer, and U. Blieske, "Optimizing Sustainability: Balancing Antimony Content for Enhanced Optical Properties and Environmental Impact in Solar Glass," in 2024.

[8] International Electrotechnical Commission, "Photovoltaic (PV) module performance testing and energy rating," Geneva, International standard / International Electrotechnical Commission IEC 61853-3, 2018.

[9] *Method for measuring photovoltaic (PV) glass – Part 2: Measurement of transmittance and reflectance (IEC 62805-2:2017)*, DIN EN 62805-2, 2018.

[10] T. G. Mayerhöfer, S. Pahlow, and J. Popp, "The Bouguer-Beer-Lambert Law: Shining Light on the Obscure," (eng), *Chemphyschem : a European journal of chemical physics and physical chemistry*, vol. 21, no. 18, pp. 2029–2046, 2020.

[11] J. D. Jackson, *Classical electrodynamics,* 2nd ed. New York: Wiley, 1975.

[12] *Photovoltaic (PV) module performance testing and energy rating – Part 2: Spectral responsivity, incidence angle and module operating temperature measurements (IEC 61853-2:2016)*, DIN EN 61853-2 (VDE 0126-34-2), 2017.

[13] A. Protti, J. Shahid, M. Mittag, D. H. Neuhaus, U. Kräling, and M. Kaiser, "Virtual Energy Rating: a Method for Optimizing Module Performance Through Cell-To-Module Analysis," (eng), 2022.

[14] I. Haedrich, U. Eitner, M. Wiese, and H. Wirth, "Unified methodology for determining CTM ratios: Systematic prediction of module power," *Solar Energy Materials and Solar Cells*, vol. 131, pp. 14–23, 2014.

[15] N. Martín and J. M. Ruiz, "A new model for PV modules angular losses under field conditions," *International Journal of Solar Energy*, vol. 22, no. 1, pp. 19–31, 2002.

[16] M. Babin, A. Bertomeu i Baldé, S. V. Spataru, M. L. Jakobsen, and S. Thorsteinsson, "Study of Optical Transmission Losses of Satinated PV Glass," (eng), 2022.

[17] Z. M. Starowicz, K. Drabczyk, K. Gawlińska, and P. Zięba, "METROLOGICAL ASPECTS OF EVALUATION OF GLASS TYPES USED IN PHOTOVOLTAIC MODULES IN LABORATORY SCALE," *Metrology and Measurement Systems*, 2018.

[18] B. L. Allsopp, R. Orman, S. R. Johnson, I. Baistow, G. Sanderson, P. Sundberg, C. Stålhandske, L. Grund, A. Andersson, J. Booth, P. A. Bingham, and S. Karlsson, "Towards improved cover glasses for photovoltaic devices," *Progress in Photovoltaics*, vol. 28, no. 11, pp. 1187–1206, 2020.

[19] Y. S. Khoo, J. P. Singh, T. M. Walsh, and A. G. Aberle, "Comparison of Angular Reflectance Losses Between PV Modules With Planar and Textured Glass Under Singapore Outdoor Conditions," *IEEE J. Photovoltaics*, vol. 4, no. 1, pp. 362–367, 2014.

TOWARDS CIRCULAR SOLAR TECHNOLOGIES: NOVEL BIO-BASED POLYMERS AS NEXT-GENERATION ENCAPSULANTS

Kristina Maliutina[1], Oliver Pfeiffer[1], Matthias Eisenacher[1], Martin Bonnet[1], Ulf Blieske[1]
[1]Cologne Institute for Renewable Energy (CIRE), University of Applied Science Cologne, Betzdorfer Straße 2, 50679 Cologne, Germany
Email: kristina.maliutina@th-koeln.de

ABSTRACT: Conventional photovoltaic (PV) encapsulants such as ethylene-vinyl acetate (EVA) suffer from yellowing, delamination, irreversible crosslinking, and poor recyclability, limiting module lifetimes and sustainability. To enable a circular economy (CE) for PV modules, new encapsulants must combine long-term stability with programmed end-of-life (EoL) pathways. This review critically evaluates recent progress in bio-based polymers synthesized via ring-opening metathesis polymerization (ROMP) and alternating ROMP (AROMP) as candidates for next-generation encapsulants. Compared to EVA, these systems offer modular design flexibility, renewable feedstock origins, and recyclability potential. Key challenges remain, including long-term UV and moisture stability, lack of standardized testing, and limited scalability. Future work should prioritize in situ aging, quantitative benchmarking of barriers and optical properties, and module-level validation. Building on these insights, we outline design principles for circular encapsulants: thermomechanical tuning via modular monomers, incorporation of aromatic blocks for UV stability, and degradable motifs as "molecular fuses" to reconcile durability with recyclability. This study emphasizes catalyst footprint minimization, continuous-flow synthesis for scalability, and standardized durability testing. By integrating renewable precursors (aromatics, furans, saccharides) with precision polymerization, a pathway toward closed-loop PV encapsulants that combine reliable performance with sustainable EoL recovery is presented.

Keywords: bio-based polymers, ROMP, AROMP, circular economy, photovoltaic encapsulation

1. INTRODUCTION

Durability challenges of conventional encapsulants are central to PV module degradation. Sunlight, humidity, and chemically aggressive environments induce glass corrosion, backsheet photo-oxidation, encapsulant yellowing as well as delamination, leading to power losses [1]. Long-term stability therefore remains the primary bottleneck, demanding new materials with improved UV and hydrolytic resistance. From a life-cycle perspective, Abian et al. showed that although PV systems reduce emissions compared to fossil energy, manufacturing and end-of-life stages still contribute significantly to the overall footprint. Energy payback time (EPBT) and global warming potential (GWP) vary strongly across technologies: crystalline silicon PV panels have high burdens, while perovskite and organic PV modules offer shorter EPBT but suffer from insufficient stability [2]. Extending service lifetimes and developing scalable recycling solutions are thus critical strategies for sustainability.

EVA remains the benchmark encapsulant due to its low cost and adequate performance, but it suffers from irreversible crosslinking, poor recyclability, and degradation pathways such as yellowing and delamination that limit module lifetime [1, 3]. To align with CE strategies, novel non-crosslinking and recyclable encapsulants are needed. Renewable polymers synthesized via precision polymerization, ring-opening metathesis polymerization (ROMP) and alternating ROMP (AROMP) attract interest of researchers nowadays [4–7]. These materials offer tunable structure–property relationships and inherent recyclability, making them prospective candidates to compete with EVA in both durability and CE compatibility.

Recent progress in continuous-flow ROMP further strengthens this direction. Flow setups enable faster polymerizations, improved molecular weight control, higher reproducibility, and easier scale-up compared to batch systems [8, 9]. These features are particularly relevant for translating bio-based ROMP/AROMP polymers from laboratory concepts to industrial encapsulants. By connecting advances in polymer design with requirements for PV reliability and circularity, this review highlights both the opportunities and the outstanding challenges for next generation encapsulant development. The urgent demand for systematic and comprehensive evaluation drives interest of researchers and represents the biggest interdisciplinary gap between materials, synthetic approaches and practical applications within CE goals.

2. METHODOLOGY

This multidisciplinary review follows four steps:

1. The study is based on an extensive literature synthesis of polymer chemistry and encapsulant requirements for the potential application in PV.
2. Benchmarking of current advances of ROMP/AROMP polymers derived from bioresources and their precursors against EVA with respect to transparency, glass transition temperature (Tg), thermal stability, recyclability, and UV resistance.
3. CE assessment prospectives, including degradability pathways and recycling strategies.
4. The study is finalized by a gap analysis and discussion to identify limitations and define future research opportunities.

3. RESULTS AND DISCUSSION

3.1 State of the art of ROMP/AROMP Polymers

The development of bio-based ROMP and AROMP polymers has expanded rapidly in recent 5 years, driven by the need for sustainable functional materials in various fields of applications [10]. It can be associated with unique features, such as:

1. **Versatility of monomers**. This enables integration of renewable feedstocks directly into high-performance polymers [11].
2. **Precision in structure–property control.** Advanced strategies such as AROMP or living ROMP enable sequence control and

10.4229/EUPVSEC2025/3AV.1.39

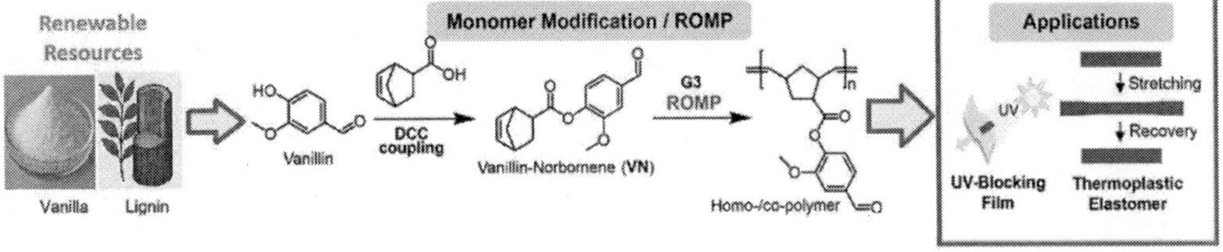

Figure 1: Overview of B. Koo's study [16]. These materials were evaluated for use in UV-blocking films and TPEs [16].

programmed degradability [12–14].

3. **Compatibility with CE goals and needs.** ROMP polymers can be designed for chemical recyclability (via acid-triggered depolymerization or mechanochemical scission) [10].
4. **Demonstrated performance in functional materials.** ROMP-based systems already exhibited UV resistance, optical clarity, and tunable mechanical strength across different studies [5, 13, 15]. Therefore, their properties are directly transferable to PV encapsulant requirements. Although comprehensive datasets on long-term durability, moisture ingress, and standardized PV qualification testing are still limited, the reported results clearly demonstrate the potential of these materials to meet encapsulant performance demands.

The comparison of benchmarking EVA, vanillin-derived ROMP and furan/maleic anhydride-derived AROMP polymers is represented in Tab 1. Vanillin, derived from lignin biomass, has been functionalized as a ROMP monomer [16]. It can be seen from Tab.1, that the resulting polymer exhibited glass transition temperatures (Tg) up to 95 °C, high optical transparency, and mechanical flexibility [16]. In addition, vanillin-derived polymers have been processed into UV-blocking films with enhanced thermal and mechanical properties compared to conventional thermoplastic elastomers (TPEs) [16]. It can be seen in Fig 1, that lignin-derived vanillin, was chemically modified via DCC coupling to attach a norbornene group, forming the monomer VN. This VN was polymerized using a G3 catalyst to create pVN and block copolymers. These findings highlight the potential of lignin-derived feedstocks to combine sustainability with performance in PV encapsulants (Fig. 1).

Sun et al. introduced an elegant strategy to access degradable polymers by AROMP of biomass-derived exo-oxanorbornenes and cyclic enol ethers (Fig. 2) [17]. Exo-oxanorbornenes were synthesized from furan and maleic anhydride via a Diels–Alder reaction, followed by acyl substitution, providing thermodynamically stable monomers resistant to retro-Diels–Alder processes [17]. The resulting copolymers showed >94% alternation, tunable molecular weights, and Tg values from 11 to 98 °C, with imide-containing monomers yielding the highest stability [17]. Crucially, the alternating architecture enabled acid-triggered depolymerization into low-molecular-weight fragments (<1000 Da), while homopolymers remained stable, proving that degradability originates from enol ether units [17]. This work highlights how renewable monomers and precision polymerization can deliver programmed chemical recycling while maintaining versatile thermal and mechanical properties, aligning with CE goals.

themselves are critical for circular encapsulant design. Aydonat et al. demonstrated that mechanochemistry using mechanical force to trigger chemical reactions, can induce controlled bond scission and depolymerization in otherwise robust polymer networks [18]. This approach offers an attractive route for prospective PV encapsulants, as it provides energy-efficient recycling pathways that avoid harsh solvents or extreme processing conditions. Integrating mechanochemical recycling into the life cycle of ROMP/AROMP materials could therefore further enhance their alignment with CE principles.

3.2 Molecular design strategies in ROMP

Molecular design in ROMP and alternating ROMP enables a wide range of strategies to balance in-use stability with programmed EoL degradation.

An entirely different class of monomers was recently introduced by Jiang et al., who developed monosaccharide-derived cyclic ketene acetals (CKAs) from glucose, mannose, and galactose [19]. These CKAs undergo fully quantitative, regiospecific, and stereoselective radical ring-opening polymerization (rROP), yielding degradable polyesters with high glass transition temperatures (Tg = 104 °C for P(Glu-CKA); 102 °C for P(Man-CKA); 72 °C for P(Gal-CKA)) and decomposition temperatures up to 228 °C [19]. Degradation studies confirmed complete hydrolytic cleavage to lactones under acidic or basic conditions [19]. Moreover, copolymerization with methacrylates and maleimides enabled uniform incorporation of Glu-CKA, producing degradable terpolymers that fully depolymerized upon alkaline hydrolysis [19]. This sugar-based approach opens a new dimension for bio-based encapsulants, combining high Tg, service stability, and programmed degradability.

ROMP-derived polymers have demonstrated high versatility in biomedical contexts, including drug release, sensing, and cellular uptake. As summarized by Gandra et al., ROMP enables precise functionalization with hydrophilic, hydrophobic, and bioactive groups; self-assembly into stable nanostructures; and incorporation of cleavable units for programmable degradation [20]. These attributes, such as functional tunability, self-assembly, stability, and controlled degradability are promising transfer to PV encapsulation. In principle, such design strategies could be exploited to introduce UV stabilizers or adhesion promoters, build nanoscale barriers against

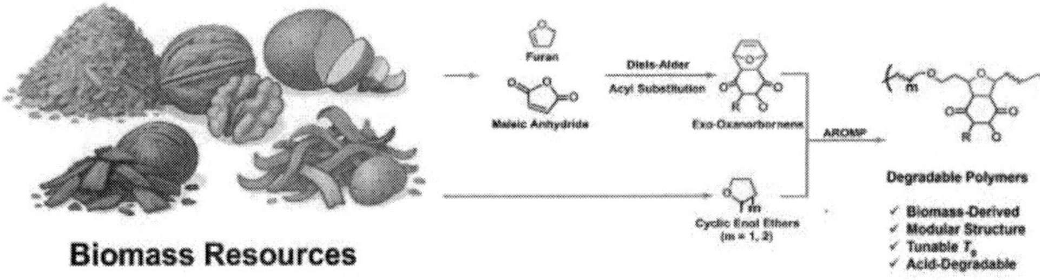

Figure 2: Degradable polymers were synthesized via AROMP using biomass-derived exo-oxanorbornenes and cyclic enol ethers [17]. Two enol ethers: 2,3-dihydrofuran and 3,4-dihydropyran were explored to tune the polymer properties such as thermal stability and degradability [17].

moisture ingress, and encode EoL into encapsulant architectures. Recent progress in living ROMP has shown that it is possible to precisely control polymer architecture at the monomer-sequence level. Elling et al., demonstrated that single monomer units can be placed at defined positions within ROMP chains [21]. This opens opportunities to embed functional units, for instance, UV stabilizers or cleavable linkers directly in situ into the backbone. Such precision design could be exploited to tailor encapsulants for both long-term stability and controlled EoL degradation, bridging performance requirements with recyclability.

Microstructural engineering has recently emerged as a powerful strategy to tune polymer performance for energy and environmental applications. Starvaggi et al., extended this concept by incorporating dihydrofuran (DHF) into ROMP of cyclooctadiene (COD) and cyclooctene (COE). The resulting alternating copolymers featured regularly distributed acetal linkages in the backbone, which acted as programmed weak points [22]. Such design illustrates how degradability can be encoded directly into otherwise robust polyolefin-like materials, advancing the vision of recyclable encapsulants for PV modules. Xue et al., demonstrated that controlling chain length distribution, stereo- and regioregularity, and sequence architecture enables tailoring of crystallinity, Tg, permeability, and degradation kinetics without altering overall chemical composition [23]. These insights are highly relevant for engineering of PV encapsulants: microstructural control in ROMP and AROMP systems could be exploited to balance optical transparency, mechanical stability, and durability, while encoding programmed EoL degradation.

In addition to degradable systems, reversible alternating copolymerizations represent another path towards sustainable materials. Zhang et al. (2023) reported aldehyde–anhydride alternating copolymers that are chemically recyclable back to monomers under acidic conditions [24]. A recent comprehensive review by Purohit et al., synthesizes the state of the art in degradable and chemically recyclable polymers enabled by ROMP and AROMP for CE [25]. Two pillars emerge: (i) backbone-degradable ROMP via monomer design that embeds acid/base-labile motifs (acetal/ketal, orthoester, silyl ether, phosphoramidate, enol ether), and (ii) chemically recyclable POs analogues engineered through ring-strain energy (RSE) and ceiling-temperature (Tc) control [25].

However, current limitations include bench-scale demonstrations, multistep monomer synthesis, energy-intensive conditions, the cost and toxicity of Ruthenium-based (Ru) catalysts. Authors emphasized the need for organocatalytic or non-toxic alternatives and for systematic durability assessments, including hydrolytic and photostability tests directly relevant to PV encapsulants [25].

Collectively, these strategies show that ROMP/AROMP can integrate renewable feedstocks, functional tunability, precision sequence control, degradable linkages, and reversible thermodynamics to deliver bio-derived that are transparent, mechanically stable, UV-resistant and recyclable at EoL of PV modules.

4. CRITICAL PERSPECTIVES: DESIGN STRATEGY FOR CIRCULAR PV ENCAPSULANTS

The transition from EVA to truly circular bio-based encapsulants requires balancing in-use reliability (optical clarity, UV/moisture stability, adhesion, Tg) with EoL pathways (chemical recycling, hydrolytic or acid/base degradation, and even upcycling). Recently overviewed studies demonstrate that such balance is achievable through molecular design in ROMP and AROMP systems [11, 16, 17, 26, 27].

Lessons from POs, and TPOs degradation underline the need for multi-parameter optimization [3]. Future bio-based encapsulants must integrate:

(i) Thermomechanical tuning: AROMP copolymers and vanillin-based ROMP segments provide Tg ranges from 11 to 98 °C, enabling design of multiphase systems for adhesion and service stability.

(ii) Optical/UV control: lignin biomass derived ROMP forms UV-blocking films, while alternating architectures enable precise integration of stabilizers without sacrificing transparency.

(iii) Programmed degradation: acetal- or ester-rich AROMP backbones undergo predictable acid/base cleavage, with sequence-defined placement of labile units ensuring recyclability without premature hydrolysis .

(iv) Renewable sourcing and scalable synthesis: oxanorbornene monomers from furans and itaconic anhydride demonstrate solvent-free, atom-economic routes, aligning material innovation with supply sustainability.

10.4229/EUPVSEC2025/3AV.1.39

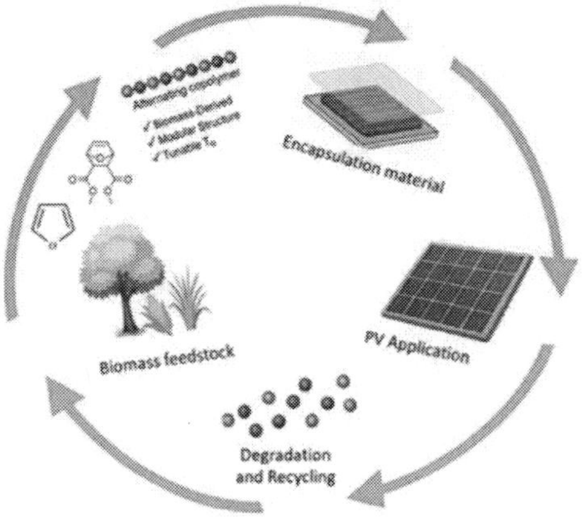

Figure 3: A schematic diagram of the proposed closed-loop model for novel bio-based PV encapsulation materials.

Yet, vulnerabilities remain. As Oladele et al. emphasized, environmental factors (UV radiation, humidity, chemical exposure) continue to challenge durability, requiring stabilizer chemistry and surface modifications [5]. Moreover, high density of degradable motifs may compromise service stability, demanding careful spatial distribution of cleavable units.

Looking forward, the rational design of circular encapsulants will hinge on the choice of precursors and functional groups. Biomass-derived aromatics such as vanillin offer rigid, conjugated structures that enhance UV resistance, transparency, and thermal stability, while hydroxyl and methoxy groups provide handles for functionalization and adhesion to glass. Furan- and itaconic-derived oxanorbornenes contribute to ROMP reactivity and enable incorporation of acetal or enol-ether motifs, which act as acid/base-labile linkages for programmed degradation. Cyclic enol ethers such as 2,3-dihydrofuran provide enthalpy-driven ROMP pathways with tuneable depolymerization kinetics, critical for chemical recycling. Sugar-derived cyclic ketene acetals add another dimension: they combine high Tg with ester backbones that undergo hydrolytic cleavage, ensuring service stability and recyclability.

By combining these biomass-derived precursors, i.e. aromatics for stability and optical clarity, enol ethers and acetals for degradability, and saccharide-derived esters for high-Tg tunability, a new bunch of engineered encapsulants can be tailored to satisfy the stringent demands of photovoltaics.

Fig. 3 illustrates the proposed closed-loop concept for bio-based PV encapsulants. Renewable feedstocks such as lignin, furans, oils and saccharides are converted into ROMP/AROMP monomers, enabling precision polymerization into encapsulants with tailored stability and recyclability. After service, programmed degradation pathways (acid/base cleavage, mechanochemical scission, reversible depolymerization) allow recovery of monomers or value-added fragments, which can be reintegrated into the material cycle. This model highlights how molecular design strategies translate into a practical CE framework for PV encapsulation.

5. CONCLUSIONS AND OUTLOOK

Bio-based ROMP and AROMP polymers offer a credible route to circular PV encapsulants by combining durability with programmed recyclability. Vanillin-derived systems provided high transparency, UV resistance, flexibility, and Tg up to 95 °, while AROMP copolymers from furan/enol ethers show tunable Tg (11–98 °C) and complete acid-triggered degradability. Mechanochemistry enables solvent-free recycling, precision ROMP/AROMP allows embedding stabilizers or cleavable units, and reversible copolymerizations demonstrate true closed-loop pathways.

To transfer these concepts into PV encapsulation practice, several priorities emerge:

1. Catalyst footprint minimization: residual Ru (from Grubbs catalyst systems) must be reduced to sub-ppm levels via short-residence synthesis, scavenging, and post-polymerization deactivation.
2. Flow manufacturing: continuous-flow ROMP/ROP offers faster kinetics, narrower dispersities, safer operation, and better scalability.
3. Architectural strategies: low-density cleavable motifs (acetal, enol-ether) act as "molecular fuses" maintaining in-service stability but enabling mild depolymerization at EoL
4. Benign catalysis: development of organocatalytic or non-toxic metal pathways is critical to overcome cost and toxicity concerns.

Remaining challenges include lack of long-term durability data under UV, humidity, and thermal cycling; absence of standardized encapsulant testing protocols; limited module-level demonstrations; and uncertainties in scalability and economy.

In conclusion, ROMP/AROMP bio-polymers establish a materials design toolbox for circular PV encapsulation. By integrating thermomechanical tuning, UV/moisture resistance, and programmed degradation, these systems can merge operational reliability with CE goals.

ACKNOWLEDGMENTS

This contribution has been developed in the project PLan_CV. Within the funding programme FH-Personal, the project PLan_CV (reference number 03FHP109) which is funded by the Federal Ministry for Economic Affairs and Energy (BMWE) and Joint Science Conference (GWK).

6. REFERENCES

1 A. I. Abian, S. Azam, D. Ompong, D. Mathur, *Solar Energy* 2025, *301*, 113927.

2 A. Mdallal, A. Yasin, M. Mahmoud, M. A. Abdelkareem, A. H. Alami, A. G. Olabi (2025), *Sustainable Horizons*, 13, Elsevier B.V.

3 A. K. Schnatmann, F. Schoden, E. Schwenzfeier-Hellkamp (2022), *Sustainability (Switzerland)*, 14, MDPI.

4 Francis O. Boadi, Jingling Zhang, Xiaoxi Yu, Surita R. Bhatia, Nicole S. Sampson, *Macromolecules* 2020, *53* (14), 5857–5868.

5 I. O. Oladele, V. O. Oki, T. F. Omotosho, M. B. Adebanjo, O. T. Ayanleye, S. A. Adekola (2025) , *Next Materials*, 8, Elsevier B.V.

6 Benjamin R. Elling and Yan Xia, *Journal of the American Chemical Society* 2015, *137* (31), 9922–9926.

7 U. R. Gandra, S. K. Podiyanachari, H. S. Bazzi, M. Al-Hashimi (2022), *ACS Omega*, 8, American Chemical Society.

8 Y. Liu, S. Ou, J. Wu, R. Zhao, R. Hou, X. Li, Y. Sun, Y. Li, X. Hu, N. Zhu, K. Guo, *European Polymer Journal* 2024, *216*, 113288.

9 M. G. Banwell, X. Liu, L. A. Connal, M. G. Gardiner, *Macromolecules* 2020, *53* (13), 5308–5314.

10 V. B. Purohit, M. Pięta, J. Pietrasik, C. M. Plummer (2024), *European Polymer Journal*, 208, Elsevier Ltd.

11 T. Ibrahim and H. Sun, *ACS Applied Polymer Materials* 2024, *6* (23), 14076–14083.

12 Na Chuan Jiang, Zefeng Zhou, Jia Niu, *Journal of the American Chemical Society* 2024, *146* (8), 5056–5062.

13 S. Aydonat, Adrian H. Hergesell, Claire L. Seitzinger, R. Lennarz, G. Chang, C. Sievers, J. Meisner, I. Vollmer, R. Göstl (2024), *Polymer Journal*, 56, Springer Nature.

14 K. A. Parker and N. S. Sampson (2016), *Accounts of Chemical Research*, 49, American Chemical Society.

15 Y. Xue, M. Cao, C. Chen, M. Zhong (2023), *JACS Au*, 3, American Chemical Society.

16 Byungjin Koo, *ACS Applied Polymer Materials* 2024, *6* (3), 1653–1661.

17 H. Sun, T. Ibrahim, A. Ritacco, K. Durkee, *ACS Macro Letters* 2023, *12* (12), 1642–1647.

18 S. Aydonat, A. H. Hergesell, C. L. Seitzinger, R. Lennarz, G. Chang, C. Sievers, J. Meisner, I. Vollmer, R. Göstl, *Polymer Journal* 2024, *56* (4), 249–268.

19 N.-C. Jiang, Z. Zhou, J. Niu, *Journal of the American Chemical Society* 2024, *146* (8), 5056–5062.

20 U. R. Gandra, S. K. Podiyanachari, H. S. Bazzi, M. Al-Hashimi, *ACS Omega* 2023, *8* (2), 1724–1738.

21 B. R. Elling, J. K. Su, J. D. Feist, Y. Xia, *Chem* 2019, *5* (10), 2691–2701.

22 F. A. Starvaggi, B. A. Suslick, Y. Xia, *ACS Macro Letters* 2024, *13* (3), 296–301.

23 Y. Xue, M. Cao, C. Chen, M. Zhong, *JACS Au* 2023, *3* (5), 1284–1300.

24 X. Zhang, W. Guo, C. Zhang, X. Zhang, *Nature Communications* 2023, *14* (1), 5423.

25 V. B. Purohit, M. Pięta, J. Pietrasik, C. M. Plummer, *European Polymer Journal* 2024, *208*, 112847.

26 Kelly A.E. Amorim, Virgínia C.A. Martins, Benedito S. Lima-Neto, *Polymer* 2025, *317*.

27 Benjamin R. Elling, Jessica K. Su, John D. Feist, Yan Xia, *Chem* 2019, *5* (10), 2691–2701.

10.4229/EUPVSEC2025/3AV.1.39

RELIABILITY OF ELECTRICALLY CONDUCTIVE ADHESIVE JOINTS FOR PERC AND HJT-BASED BUILDING-INTEGRATED PHOTOVOLTAIC FACADE ELEMENTS

R. Koepge, S. Jahreis, J. Froebel, N. Schröter, M. Pander, S. Großer, B. Jaeckel
Fraunhofer Center for Silicon Photovoltaics CSP
Otto-Eissfeldt-Strasse 12, 06120 Halle, Germany
ringo.koepge@csp.fraunhofer.de

ABSTRACT: Integrating photovoltaic solutions directly into building facades presents a crucial strategy for achieving Europe's goal of climate neutrality by 2050. A widespread adoption of building-integrated photovoltaics (BIPV) can bolster energy security, diversify the energy mix, and create new green jobs. By seamlessly integrating renewable energy generation into our cities, BIPV becomes a cornerstone of a sustainable future for Europe and keeping aesthetic and functional benefits, such as providing shade, mitigating heat gain, and enhancing the overall building envelope performance. To achieve such goals, especially the building and construction sectors needs to be facilitated to adapt photovoltaic technologies into their production and value chains. With the results of the AluPV project, we will demonstrate how PV production processes and material combination can be adapted to realize PV-integrated aluminum facades as building-integrated photovoltaics elements. One main objective is to adapt the manufacturing process to handle redesigned photovoltaics modules, in terms of electrical adaptation due to other dimensional and architecture constraints and mechanical structures due to direct incorporation with Al-façade elements. Therefore, suitable material combinations and process parameters were studied, with particular attention to reducing mechanical stress and utilizing cost-effective standard PV production equipment. Within the paper, we demonstrate our findings to successfully use commercially available aluminum façade elements as backside encapsulation and solar cell string material layer. Standard industrial lamination equipment was demonstrated to be suitable for cost-efficient production and rapid implementation of the prototype into the production line. A material study will show an optimum of material types and layers for reliable façade modules. Test sequences according to IEC are performed and performance measurements as well as electroluminescence (EL) images were applied to quantify our findings. In summary, multiple challenges related to manufacturing and material selection were addressed, especially the differences in the thermal expansion of the materials. Modules with an aluminum back sheet show less moisture ingress than those with a polymer back sheet, because moisture can only enter through the edges. This effect is independent of cell technology; there is no observed difference between PERC cells and HJT cells. This investigation will give significant feedback regarding reliability of façade solar modules to improve manufacturing processes. and increase the acceptance of building integrated PV on the market.

1 INTRODUCTION

The EU has set itself the binding target of achieving climate neutrality by 2050 - emissions are to be reduced by at least 55% by 2030 [1]. Globally, it is important to align development, economic, financial, energy and transport policies with climate protection goals. Energy generation from photovoltaic systems plays a decisive role in achieving the desired goals. A current draft of the European Commission has targeted a 90% share of EU electricity from renewables by 2040 – mostly solar and wind – and complemented by nuclear energy. BIPV market is still rising, and the potential is currently hardly used. The current market share is less than 3% [2]. Challenging is the requirement of reliable and in shape integration into existing architectural elements [3]. One aspect is the development of BIPV facade elements. The evaluation of suitable material combinations and economic manufacturing process parameters plays an important role in the implementation of prototypes for industrial series production.

Within this work PV solar cell strings and encapsulation were integrated into commercially available aluminum façade elements. Suitable material combinations and processes have been studied. Approaches for mechanical stress reduction and the use of economic standard PV production equipment were successfully evaluated [4]. We implemented different electrically conductive adhesive (ECA) strings and different solar cell technology (PERC and HJT) strings and performed a material variation to identify suitable and reliable façade modules.

Current investigations address the reliability of façade modules that were manufactured by direct lamination. The production of PV integrated aluminum façades places high demands on the material composite. Due to the different coefficients of thermal expansion, internal stresses are introduced into the façade solar module. Cracks can occur in the cell connectors joints, in the glass and delamination of the encapsulation can take place. A manufacturing process will be presented that shows a defective free aluminum façade element ready for application in BIPV. Delamination issues as well as module bending caused by different thermal expansions during the manufacturing are not detected. Smart pressure distribution during the lamination process is the key for flawless manufacturing. Electroluminescence (EL) images give evidence for properly working solar cell strings without cell breakage. Magnetic field imaging (MFI) was also used for investigation, which provided evidence of properly functioning solar cell strings without interconnector failures [5]. It is shown that standard industrial lamination equipment can be used to ensure cost-efficient production and rapid implementation of the prototype into the production line. To overcome the high different coefficients of thermal expansion two major paths are followed. On the one hand a variation of materials was performed. On the other hand, two different types of electrically conductive adhesive were used to see the influence of reliability. In addition, HJT cells strings are compared to reliability of PERC cell strings in façade modules.

2 MATERIALS & METHODS

2.1 Manufacturing

Different material combinations were used to investigate the influence of thermal cycling on the reliability of the solar modules. The Table 1 shows the bill of material (BOM) for each module batch. Batch B0 was the reference batch, a glass back sheet module with a standard solder cell connection. The batches from B1 to B6 are facade solar modules with an aluminum facade as back sheet. Material component substitutions take place. Thus, a change from solder to ECA connection (B2), a change of the encapsulant from POE to EVA (B6), the electrical isolation was changed from polyester foil (modified polyester - MPE) to a polymer fiber mesh (B7), a change of cell type from PERC to HJT (B8) and finally the acrylic based ECA instead of epoxy bases ECA was used (B9). The material stack is illustrated in Figure 1.

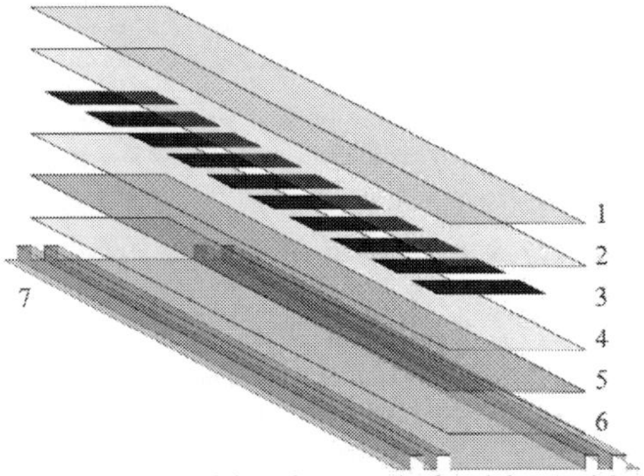

Figure 1 BIPV module, a) layup stack of module materials (1 – Front Glass, 2 – Encapsulant, 5 – Insulation Layer, 4 – Encapsulant, 3 – Cell String, 6 - Encapsulant, 7 - Facade)

The cell connectors are not shown as well as the back sheet at layer position seven, the figure shows the aluminum facade at layer number seven. On the top of the Solar panel an Opti-White glass with a thickness of 3 mm was used, without any anti reflection coating. The encapsulants (EVA and POE) were commercial materials from the market. The cell strings were manufactured with 9BB PERC and 0BB HJT cells with Team Technik TT Lab i8 ECA stringer. The solder string batch B1 was manufactured with a Komax Solar's Xcell X3 Stringer with 5BB PERC. The aluminum facade sheet was provided by project partner MN Metall. Finally, the layup was made manually before the material stack runs into the lamination process. The Lamination takes place at a vacuum laminator ICOLAM 28/26 from SM Inno Tech GmbH & Co. KG. The following Figure 2 shows a aluminum facade with a PV activation after lamination process.

Figure 2 BIPV module, a PV activated aluminum facade after lamination process.

2.2 Treatment

After manufacturing the modules are tested by accelerated ageing test according to the IEC standard [6, 7]. The major focus is on the thermal cycling (sequence E) of the modules. Caused by the huge thermal deformation of the aluminum facade at the back side of the module, a connector fail between the cells is assumed. In addition, a multiple stressor test (sequence B) was performed for all batches, and a damp heat test (sequence D) was performed on a selection of samples. The following Table 2 shows an overview of the batch treatment.

Table 1 Sample Overview for reliability testing (POE – Polyolefin Elastomer, PERC - Passivated Emitter and Rear Cell, MPE – Modified Polyester, PF – Polymer Fiber, EVA - Ethylenvinylacetat, HJT - Heterojunction Solar Cell, SnPb – Tin Lead, ECA – Electrically Conductive Adhesive)

Batch		B1	B2	B3	B4	B5	B6	B7	B8	B9
Material layer	1	Glass	Glass	Glass	Glass	Glass	Glass	Glass	Glass	Glass
	2	POE	EVA	POE	POE	POE	EVA	POE	POE	POE
	3	M3-10HC PERC	M6-6HC PERC	M6-6HC PERC	M6-10HC PERC	M6-6HC PERC	M6-10HC PERC	M6-10HC PERC	M6-6HC HJT	M6-10HC PERC
	4	POE	EVA	POE	POE	POE	EVA	POE	POE	POE
	5	MPE	-	BS	MPE	MPE	MPE	PF	MPE	MPE
	6	POE	-	Adhesive	POE	POE	EVA	POE	POE	POE
	7	Facade	BS	Facade	Facade	Facade	Facade	Facade	Facade	Facade
Connection		SnPb Solder	ECA1 Epoxy based							ECA2 Acrylic-based

2.3 Characterization

Module characterization was done using a HALM Cetis PV-Moduletest 4 A+A+A+ Solar simulator. The repeatability of the system is usually better than 0.15 % for maximum power determination. Flash measurements were done at STC conditions and 200 W/m². For the HJT cells hysteresis compensation is performed by incorporating a forward and backward measurement. Electroluminescence images were taken in a commercial EL system from Halm with a cooled CCD camera. The injection current was set close to ISC (5 A) and at 10 % ISC (500 mA). Since there were no issues related to shunting that are more pronounced under low irradiance and low current injection, we limit the presented results to the STC characterization. In addition, magnetic field imaging (MFI) was performed at sample with an abnormal performance drop. Magnetic field imaging visualizes the current flow in photovoltaic modules in a non-invasive manner by measuring triaxial magnetic fields above the glass during a constant current injection (e.g., ISC = 5 A). Using a DENKWEIT B-LAB with a 160 mm magnetically sensitive line sensor on a motorized x-y-z table scans are created at a constant distance spatial maps of B_x, B_y, B_z in micro tesla.

Table 2 Overview of applied test sequences according to IEC 61730 and IEC 61215 standards

	Sequence B Multiple Tests	Sequence D Damp Heat	Sequence E Thermal Cycling
B1	2 Samples	2 Samples	2 Samples
B2	0 Samples	2 Samples	2 Samples
B3	0 Samples	2 Samples	2 Samples
B4	2 Samples	2 Samples	2 Samples
B5	0 Samples	2 Samples	2 Samples
B6	2 Samples	0 Samples	2 Samples
B7	1 Samples	0 Samples	2 Samples
B8	0 Samples	2 Samples	2 Samples
B9	2 Samples	0 Samples	2 Samples

After offset/background correction and filtering, false-color maps of the field components (often B_y) co-registered with EL images qualitatively show the current paths without requiring a full inversion. Defects such as desoldering, misalignments, or broken connections disturb the otherwise uniform field and create local inhomogeneities, enabling rapid, non-contact diagnosis, with the resolution determined by the sensor spacing and distance.

3 RESULTS

The following chapter contains the relative power loss of solar modules after damp heat (Seq. D), thermal cycling (Seq. E) and multiple stressor testing (Seq. B). In addition, electroluminescence images were made of all modules and abnormal modules with increased power loss are presented in the following chapter. Magnetic field measurements were performed on abnormal modules, which are also shown.

3.1 Performance Loss

Damp Heat | The duration of each test of this study is not equal, caused by delays in manufacturing. The results of the damp heat treatment are shown in Figure 3. We can see the time of duration versus the relative power loss. Batches B1 (Solder) and B5 (ECA1) have the highest duration time of 3000 hours. Both batches pass the IEC 5% limit at 1000 hours.

With an increase in damp heat duration time, we see an increase of the power loss up to almost minus 3 and minus 7 percent for the ECA batch B4. In comparison the solder batch shows less power loss. This is attributed to cell batch and metallization paste which is more stable for the older M3 cells of B1. Further it can be correlated to a smaller cell size, that means a bigger distance from the facade edges to the solar cells. Diffusion of water from the outside to the cells is impeded. The other batches are still pending. Currently Batches B5 and B8 show equally stable behavior with less than 1.2 % power loss after 1000 h. The B3 batch is on the faster degradation path with 2.2 and 2.8 % after 1000 h. B2 shows the strongest degradation with 2.6 and 3.4 % already after 1000 h and more than 15 % after 2000 h. The test was stopped after 2250 h with a power loss of more than 20 %. This demonstrates the susceptibility of these cells to humidity related degradation.

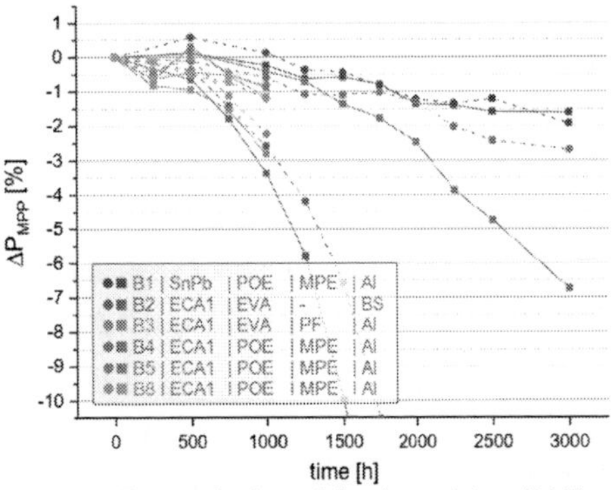

Figure 3 Characterization of facade module reliability. Damp Heat results, Reference Batches of solder connection (B1) and ECA connection (B4) finished at 3000 hours. B2 is finished after 2250 hours because of too high degradation

Thermal Cycling | The highest mechanical stress was caused by the thermal cycling test. Again, non-equal number of cycles are caused by different finishing times in manufacturing. Differences in thermal expansion of the aluminum facade at the backside and the rest of solar module materials stress the cell connectors. The power loss after thermal cycling is shown in Figure 4.

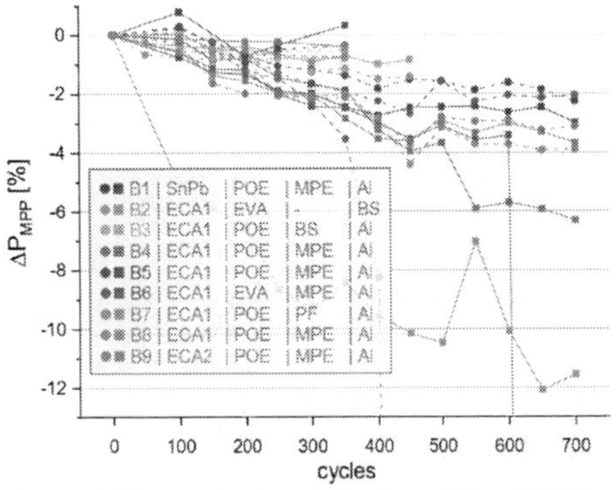

Figure 4 Characterization of facade module reliability. Results of thermal cycling tests after 350 and 700 cycle treatment.

All batches pass the IEC standard of 200 cycles with a power loss of less than 5 percent. The most abnormal facade module behavior until 700 cycles was observed for batch B7 (polymer fiber mesh) and batch B4 (ECA1 facade reference). A drop of 4 to 12 percent was detected for batch B7 and a drop of 6 percent to total failure was observed for batch B4. All the other batches show almost equal behavior. The batches finishing the 700 cycles show a drop of maximum 4 percent apart from the abnormal module batches. The batches of 350 cycles are still pending till reaching the 700 cycles but, the current drop in power loss is lower in comparison to the finished batches (B1, B4, B6, B7, B9).

Multiple Stressor | The last aging test was a multiple stressor sequence. Only five batches were tested. Figure 5 shows the results. For efficiency reasons, no UV60 treatment was carried out on the reverse side, as irradiating aluminum from behind in the desired application is not necessary. Almost all samples with the exception Batch B7 shows a power loss of less than 1.5%, which is an excellent result. The highest power loss is recorded in sample B7. The cause of the 2.5% is unclear. Approximately 1% is attributable to a loss in I_{sc} and 1% to a lower FF. The following Table 3 shows an overview of the final performance drop of each facade module after treatment.

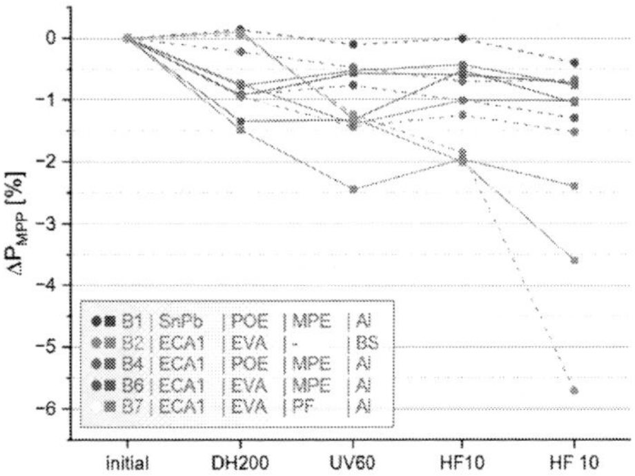

Figure 5 Characterization of facade module reliability. Results of multiple stressor tests after Damp Heat, UV60 and humidity Freeze treatment.

Table 3 Overview of relative module degradation at the end of testing

	Damp Heat	Thermal Cycling	Multiple Stressor
B1	-1.6 | -1.9	-2.2 | -3.0*	-0.4 | -0.7
B2	-21.2 | -32.7	-1.0 | -1.8*	-3.6 | -5.7
B3	-1.1 | -1.5*	-0.5 | -0.8*	not tested
B4	-2.7 | -6.7	-6.3 | fail	-0.7 | -0.8
B5	-0.5 | -0.5	-0.3 | -0.4	not tested
B6	not tested	-2.0 | fail	not tested
B7	not tested	-3.9 | -11.5	-2.4
B8	-0.5 | -0.7*	-0.4 | -0.8*	not tested
B9	not tested	-3.1 | -3.7	-1.0 | -1.5
*Treatment not finished			

3.2 Module Fails

The aluminum facade modules do not show a clear trend of degradation regarding the bill of materials. The Table 3 shows an overview of facade module degradation. The modules with the highest degradation are investigated in more detail by EL and MFI.

Damp Heat | There is a problem with the cross connection at solder joint in Batch B1, which is unusual for DH and could indicate a cold solder joint. The existing cracks remain stable, see Figure 6. Otherwise, there are hardly any anomalies. A performance change of around 1.5% seems plausible. It is noteworthy that another cross-connection failed after approximately 4,250 operating hours (not shown in the graph), indicating a potential systematic problem with the connections.

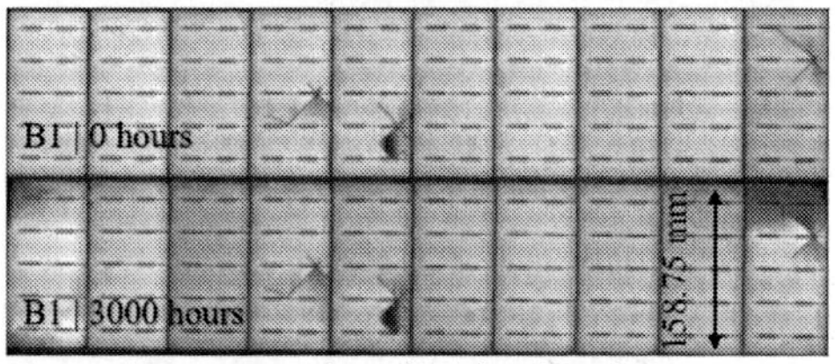

Figure 6 EL Images of one Module of Batch B1

With Charge B2, the power loss for the DH1000 remains below 5%, but a negative trend is already apparent. In the following stages, the loss increases disproportionately. With the DH2000, the power reduction is already more than 15%. EL images correlate to the power loss, see Figure 7. In batch B4 (ECA1 facade reference) see Figure 8, the cracks remain stable. There are slight anomalies at the connection ends, and a performance change of approximately 1.5% appears plausible.

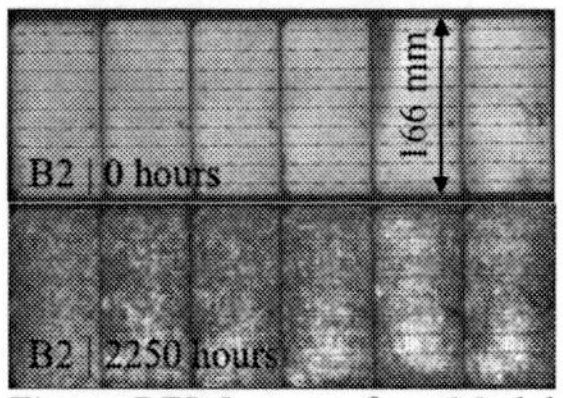

Figure 7 EL Images of one Module of Batch B2

The edges of the bottom and top cells are affected by corrosion. After 1,000 operating hours, moisture-induced degradation, which begins at the edges, is clearly visible and continues to spread, indicating that these cells are more susceptible than soldered cells. The sample is significantly more affected than the parallel sample. After 4,500 hours (not shown here), the sample looks worse than the comparison sample, although the power loss is still moderate at around 3.7%. The areas with connection problems have increased slightly. Once corrosion has set in, the degradation of the cells progresses steadily.

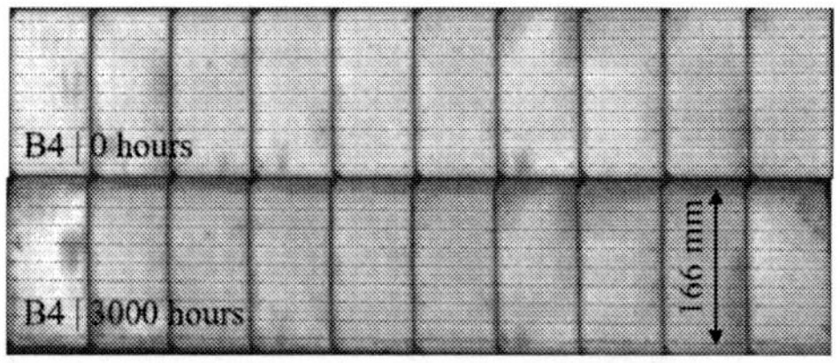

Figure 8 EL Images of one module of Batch B4

Thermal Cycling | We consider 3 times IEC (600 cycles) to be completely sufficient for reliable applications in central Europe. The most important points are that the solder connection is not optimal in all samples and even the soldered samples exhibit problems. Smaller M3 cells may have an advantage over M6 in terms of fatigue, so it should be checked whether 5 mm instead of 10 mm distance between the cell and the cross connection offers an advantage. worse the batches, B7 clearly performs worst, and B4 is scorched at the cross connection equal to a Module of Batch B6, see Figure 9.

Figure 9 Cross connection fail by thermal cycling and current flow

The changes to the BOM have not made much difference so far, and an important lever for noticeable improvements is missing. The modules of batch B9 also shows initial problems, but the dark areas remain stable. Significant anomalies in the lower cross connection. The upper and lower cross connections are also conspicuous in EL and MFI, see Figure 10. A higher magnetic flux density correlates with a higher current density, caused by intact connections covering the defective ones. Thus, not all cell connectors show a proper connection to the cross connector (marked in red), the current flow is strongly inhomogeneous. Two cell connectors have detached from a solar cell and no longer make electrical contact (marked in blue).

a)

b)

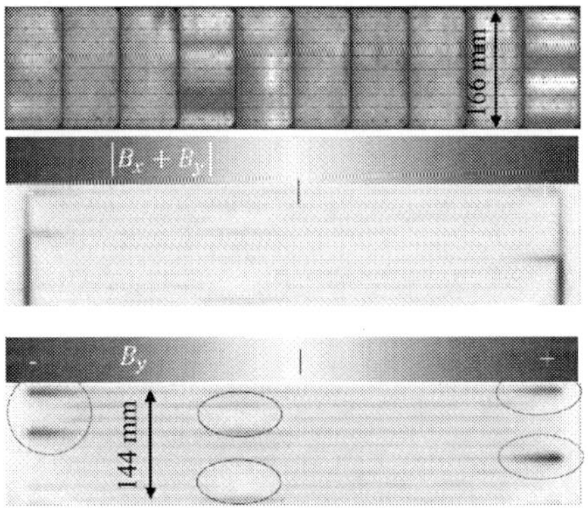

Figure 10 Comparison of EL (a) and Magnetic Field (b) image with failed cross connections of Batch B9

Multiple Stressor | The EL images show no abnormal modules apart from batch B2. The maximum power loss was detected for batch B2 and the EL images correlate to them, see Figure 11.

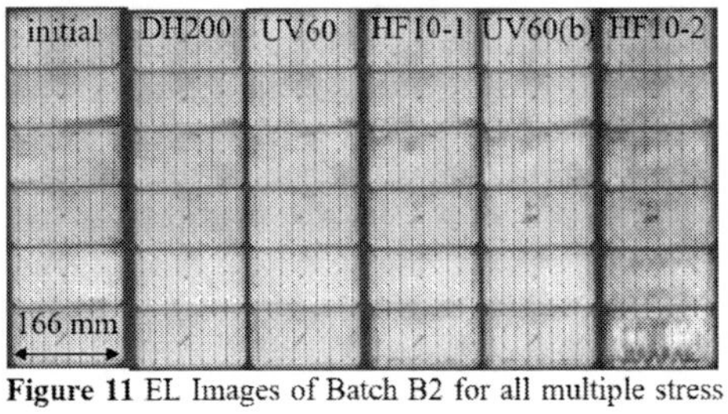

Figure 11 EL Images of Batch B2 for all multiple stress sequences

Crack and Surface artifacts stay stable. A degradation of the entire cells takes place by multiple stressor testing.

4 SUMMARIZE

The evidence was given that aluminum facade modules are ready to use in BIPV application. Less moisture penetration for aluminum facade modules in comparison to back sheet modules was detected. Moisture, and the degradation associated with it, can only enter through the module edge and the junction box. The Facade module degradation of HJT cells and PERC cells are equal and almost independent from material selection, apart from back sheet batch and polymer fiber mesh batch. Magnetic field imaging was used to confirm the cross-connector failure that has been seen in EL imaging and to get more information about current flow.

5 ACKNOWLEDGEMENTS

Financial support by the Federal Ministry for Economic Affairs and Energy funded project "AluPV" (FKZ: 03EN1069B) is gratefully acknowledged.

6 REFERENCES

[1] Document 32021R1119, Regulation (EU) 2021/1119 of the European Parliament and of the Council of 30 June 2021 establishing the framework for achieving climate neutrality and amending Regulations (EC) No 401/2009 and (EU) 2018/1999 ('European Climate Law'), http://data.europa.eu/eli/reg/2021/1119/oj

[2] International Technology Roadmap for Photovoltaics (ITRPV) 2024, Results 16. Edition, May 2025

[3] Wiebke Wirtz, Kevin Meyer, Rolf Brendel, Henning Schulte-Huxel, "Improved robustness against thermal stress for building-integrated PV modules built on aluminum façade elements", Progress in Photovoltaics: Research and Applications, 2025, Vol. 33, Page 717–725, https://doi.org/10.1002/pip.3915

[4] Ringo Koepge, Matthias Pander, Stephan Großer, Bengt Jaeckel, "Process Development and Material Evaluation of Photovoltaic Aluminum Facade Element for BIPV Application", Proceedings, 41st EU PVSEC, 2024

[5] Dominik Lausch, Marcus Patzold, Maik Rudolph, Chia-Mei Lin, Jens Froebel, Kai Kaufmann, "Magnetic Field Imaging (MFI) of Solar Modules", Proceedings, 35th EU PVSEC, 2018

[6] IEC 61215-2:2021, Terrestrial photovoltaic (PV) modules – Design qualification and type approval – Part 2: Test procedures

[7] IEC 61730-2:2023, Photovoltaic (PV) module safety qualification - Part 2: Requirements for testing

Reliability of Electrically Conductive Adhesive Joints for PERC and HJT-based Building-integrated Photovoltaic Facade Elements

Fraunhofer CSP

Fraunhofer Center
for Silizium Photovoltaik CSP

R. Koepge, S. Jahreis, J. Froebel, N. Schröter, M. Pander, S. Großer, B. Jaeckel

3AV.2.1

Motivation

- The **potential of building integrated PV is currently hardly used,** less than 3% market share[1]
- **Building facades have high potential to increase the share of** PV application **beside the standard PV module** applications on roof tops.
- **Evaluation of suitable material combinations** plays an important role in the implementation of facade modules
- **Prevent material-induced module** failures to secure long-term reliability

Scope of this Study

- Accelerated climate stress testing of different material combinations to demonstrate high reliability of facade solar modules and identify weaknesses

		Reference module	Variation encapsulant (2,4,6) | cell type (3) | electrical insulation layer (5) | back sheet / plate (7) and cell connection type (8)							
Batch		**B1**	**B2**	**B3**	**B4**	**B5**	**B6**	**B7**	**B8**	**B9**
Material layer	1	Glass	Glass	Glass	Glass	Glass	Glass	Glass	Glass	Glass
	2	POE	EVA	POE	POE	POE	EVA	POE	POE	POE
	3	M3-10HC PERC	M6-6HC PERC	M6-6HC PERC	M6-10HC PERC	M6-6HC PERC	M6-10HC PERC	M6-10HC PERC	M6-6HC HJT	M6-10HC PERC
	4	POE	EVA	POE	POE	POE	EVA	POE	POE	POE
	5	MPE	-	BS	MPE	MPE	MPE	PFM	MPE	MPE
	6	POE	-	Adhesive	POE	POE	EVA	POE	POE	POE
	7	Facade	BS	Facade	Facade	Facade	Facade	Facade	Facade	Facade
Connection	8	SnPb Solder	Epoxy ECA1							Acrylic ECA2

Table 1 Overview of manufactured facade modules (POE – Polyolefin Elastomer, PERC – Passivated Emitter and Rear Cell, MPE – Modified Polyester, PF – Polymer Fiber Mesh, EVA - Ethylenvinylacetat, HJT - Heterojunction Solar Cell, SnPb – Tin Lead, ECA – Electrically Conductive Adhesive)

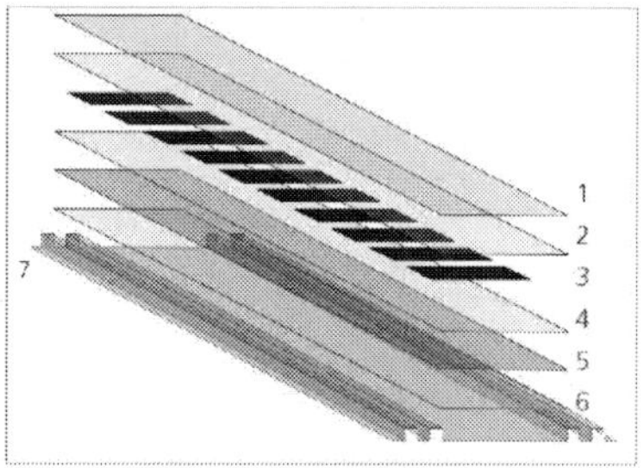

Figure 1 Material stack of facade modules

Results

Damp Heat

- All material are within the IEC pass criteria, less than 5 percent power loss[2]
- All aluminum facades demonstrate better moisture barrier compared to polymer BS
- Higher distance between cell-module edge, B1 compared to B4, increase moisture barrier

Thermal Cycling

- Almost all materials combinations pass the IEC TC200[2]
- Apart from B7 all facade modules pass the TC600 with a power loss of 2 to 4 %[2]
- BS module slightly better than façade module[2]

Manufacturing

- Successful manufacturing of photovoltaic activated building facades
- Optimized manufacturing processes by Fraunhofer CSP
- Ready to hand over to industry

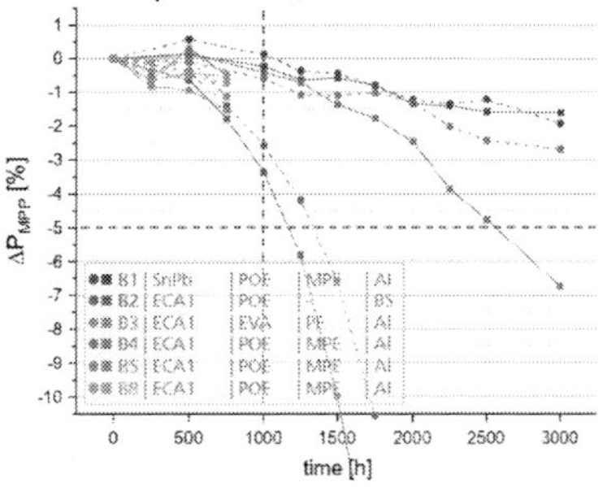

Figure 2 Power loss of each facade module after damp heat treatment

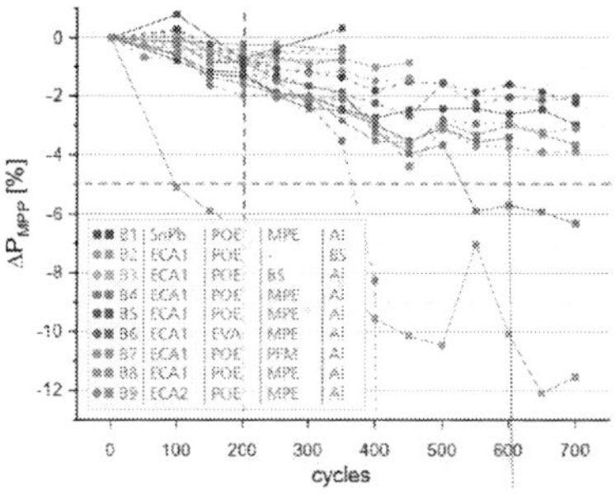

Figure 3 Power loss of each facade module after thermal cycling treatment

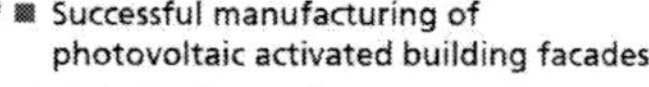

Figure 4 Aluminum facade solar module

Summary

- Evidence was given that **aluminum facade modules are ready to use in BIPV** application
- **Less moisture penetration** for aluminum facade modules in comparison to back sheet modules
- Facade module **degradation of HJT cells and PERC cells are equal and almost independent from material selection**, apart from back sheet batch and polymer fiber mesh batch

[1] International Technology Roadmap for Photovoltaics (ITRPV) 2024, Results 16. Edition, May 2025 [2] Tests have not yet been completed

Ringo Koepge
PV Modules, Components and Manufacturing
Tel. +49 345 5589-5311
Ringo.Koepge@csp.fraunhofer.de
Fraunhofer Center für Silicon Photovoltaics CSP
Otto-Eissfeldt-Strasse 12
06120 Halle
www.csp.fraunhofer.de

Financial support by the Federal Ministry for Economic Affairs and Energy funded project » AluPV « (grant no.: 03EN1069B) is gratefully acknowledged.

Bundesministerium für Wirtschaft und Energie · PtJ · MN METALL & NEUE IDEEN

DURABILITY AND RELIABILITY: A CROSS-TECHNOLOGICAL STABILITY ANALYSIS OF SILICON PHOTOVOLTAICS

Mengdi Liu[1], Wenhao Xu[1], Yating Zhang[1], Giorgio Bardizza[2], Christos Monokroussos[1]

[1]TÜV Rheinland (Shanghai) Co., Ltd., No.177, Lane 777, West Guangzhong, 200072, Shanghai, P.R. China

[2]TÜV Rheinland Solar GmbH, Am Grauen Stein, 51105, Cologne, Germany

ABSTRACT: Due to environmental concerns and the depletion of fossil fuels, photovoltaics (PV) is set to play a significant role in meeting future energy demands. For PV technology to be economically feasible, maintaining high efficiency over the typical 25-year lifespan of PV modules is critical. This study examines the reliability of advanced solar cell technologies, namely Passivated Emitter Rear Cell (PERC), Tunnel Oxide Passivated Contact (TOPCon), Heterojunction with Intrinsic Thin layer (HJT), and Back-Contact (BC). Additionally, it compares the durability of different module structures like Glass/Backsheet (G/BS) and Glass/Glass (G/G) under extensive standardized reliability tests according to IEC standards, covering thermal cycling (TC), damp heat (DH), potential induced degradation (PID), light- and elevated temperature-induced degradation (LETID), and ultraviolet-induced degradation (UVID).

The results show that PERC cells exhibit degradation, with a median decrease of approximately 2.0% and 2.3%, after TC600 and DH1000 stress tests, respectively. BC and HJT cells demonstrate low degradation levels, approximately 1.0%, following post-TC200 conditions. BC technology shows the lowest median degradation, around 1.2%, following DH1000 exposure. TOPCon cells exhibit lower degradation rate under thermal cycling and PID. It is particularly notable that in TC600 a mean degradation of 0.3% was observed, while after 96h of PID test the mean degradation stayed below 0.5%. However, they experience higher degradation under UVID, with a median rate of 1.5%. Regarding LETID, both technologies, TOPCon and BC, exhibit low sensitivity, with median degradation levels of 0.3% and 0.1%, respectively. Overall, these results highlight the performance differences between cell technologies and the importance of comprehensive stress testing for informed selection and implementation to enhance the longevity and performance of photovoltaic systems.

Keywords: Reliability, Silicon Photovoltaics,

1 Introduction

As environmental concerns grow and fossil fuel reserves continue to deplete, the generation of electricity via renewable energy sources becomes essential for fulfilling future energy requirements. While a diverse mix of renewable resources will likely satisfy our energy needs, photovoltaic (PV) technology is expected to play a pivotal role. For PV to be commercially viable and sustainable, it is imperative that modules sustain high efficiency over operational durations exceeding 25 years. Therefore, enhancing module reliability is paramount for reducing the Levelized Cost of Energy (LCOE) and ensuring the long-term success of solar energy.

A critical pathway to improving reliability lies in understanding degradation mechanisms. Accelerated stress tests, standardized by the International Electrotechnical Commission (IEC), are indispensable for this purpose, as they simulate years of field exposure in a condensed timeframe. For instance, Thermal Cycling (TC) can identify thermo-mechanical fatigue issues such as cell soldering defects and interconnect failures, while Damp Heat (DH) exposes susceptibility to corrosion and delamination. The continuous evolution of cell technologies—from the industry-dominant Passivated Emitter and Rear Cell (PERC) to advanced designs like Tunnel Oxide Passivated Contact (TOPCon), Heterojunction (HJT), and Back-Contact (BC)—introduces new materials and structures whose long-term behavior must be rigorously compared. Furthermore, module construction elements, such as the choice between Glass/Backsheet (G/BS) and Glass/Glass (G/G) configurations and advanced encapsulants like Polyolefin Elastomer (POE), are increasingly recognized as critical factors influencing longevity.

This study conducts a direct comparison of the degradation behavior of leading commercial cell technologies (PERC, TOPCon, HJT, and BC) and module structures under a comprehensive suite of IEC-standardized tests, including TC, DH, Potential Induced Degradation (PID), and Light- and Elevated Temperature-Induced Degradation (LETID). The findings provide valuable insights into the relative resilience of these technologies. By linking specific degradation signatures to cell technology and module architecture, this work provides critical data to guide the development of more reliable and durable PV modules for the future.

2 Methodology

2.1. Sample Description and Preparation

A set of commercial photovoltaic (PV) modules representing leading cell technologies was selected for this accelerated lifetime testing study. The sample cohort included modules fabricated using PERC, TOPCon, HJT, and BC technologies. To investigate the role of module construction, samples with different structural configurations—specifically G/G and G/BS—and encapsulants (Ethylene-Vinyl Acetate (EVA) and POE) were incorporated.

It is important to note that the sample sizes for certain technologies, particularly PERC and BC, were limited. While sufficient for identifying dominant degradation trends, this limitation precludes definitive statistical conclusions for these groups and indicates a need for further investigation with a larger dataset. All modules underwent initial flash testing (I-V curve measurement) under Standard Test Conditions (STC: 1000 W/m², 25°C, AM1.5G spectrum) to establish a baseline maximum power (Pmax).

2.2. Stress Testing Protocols

The modules were subjected to a sequence of accelerated stress tests, following relevant portions of the IEC standards [1, 2], to simulate long-term field degradation. The specific tests conducted were:

- Thermal Cycling (TC): Modules underwent 200, 400, and 600 cycles. This test evaluates the resistance to thermo-mechanical stress by cycling the chamber temperature between -40°C and 85°C.
- Damp Heat (DH): Modules were exposed to 1000 hours of damp heat conditions at 85°C and 85% relative humidity to assess the susceptibility to moisture ingress and corrosion.
- Potential Induced Degradation (PID) Testing: PID sensitivity was evaluated under both positive and negative polarities at a voltage of ±1500V, applied for a defined period at 85°C. This test identifies vulnerabilities to ion migration driven by high system voltages.
- Ultraviolet Irradiation and Light- and Elevated Temperature-Induced Degradation (UVID & LETID): Modules were subjected to a prescribed dose of ultraviolet (UV) irradiation. Subsequently, LETID testing was performed by exposing the modules to light at an elevated temperature to activate and monitor this specific degradation mechanism.

Following each stress test sequence (post-TC200, post-TC400, etc.), the modules were removed from the environmental chambers, and their maximum power output (Pmax) was re-measured under STC.

2.3. Measurement and Data Analysis

The power degradation for each module was calculated as the percentage change in Pmax from its initial baseline value. The results are presented using box plots to show the median degradation, variance, and potential outliers for each technology group and test condition. To ensure the reported degradation signals were not artifacts of measurement variance, the uncertainty of the flash tester was rigorously characterized. The expanded measurement uncertainty (k=2) for Pmax was determined to be ±2.0%, with a reproducibility (k=2) of ±0.6%. This high level of reproducibility confirms that the observed degradation trends are indicative of actual module performance changes rather than measurement noise.

3 Results

This section presents the key findings from a series of accelerated stress tests designed to evaluate the reliability and degradation behavior of various PV cell technologies and module configurations. The results highlight significant differences in degradation rates between PERC, TOPCon, HJT, and BC technologies, and further demonstrate the critical influence of module construction, such as glass-glass configuration and POE encapsulant, in mitigating certain stress-induced losses.

3.1 Thermal Cycling

Figure 1 presents the results of power degradation under post-TC at 200, 400, and 600 cycles. In the results, PERC technology showed a more pronounced reduction in power output with a degradation of ~1.5% after 200 and 400 cycles, and up to ~2.0% after 600 cycles. This is an improvement to the degradation rates that PV modules sustained after TC200; on average 4.0% 10 years ago [3, 4]. This is primarily attributed to the novel metallization concepts, which have been implemented [5]. On the other hand, both BC and HJT technologies exhibited a moderate median degradation of about 1.0%, but the larger variance seen in BC could imply a need for enhanced manufacturing consistency to mitigate the risk of performance outliers. Notably, TOPCon PV-modules emerged with the least degradation after TC600 with a median degradation of 0.4%. It is important to note that the sample sizes for PERC and BC technologies were not sufficient to draw definitive conclusions, indicating a need for further investigation with a larger dataset.

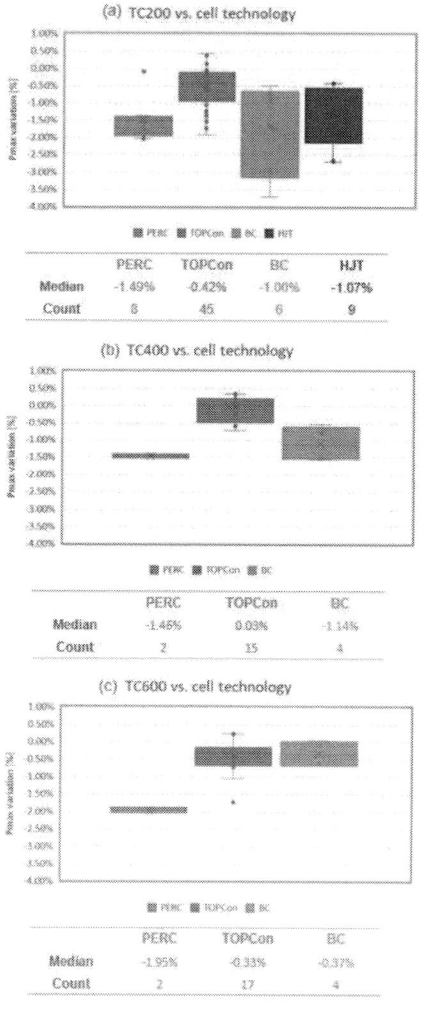

Figure 1: power variation of different cell technologies under post-TC at 200 (a), 400 (b), and 600 (c) cycles

3.2 Damp Heat

The impact of damp heat (DH) on maximum power

output of different cell technologies is depicted in Figure 2 (a). On average, PERC technology exhibited a median degradation of approximately 2.3%, compared to TOPCon and BC technologies, which showed median degradations of roughly 1.3% and 1.2%, respectively. Additionally, modules with G/G configurations demonstrated enhanced resistance to DH-induced power degradation, with performance losses approximately 50% lower than those noted in G/BS structures shown in Figure 2 (b). This suggests that while choice of technology is critical, module configuration plays a significant role in the longevity and reliability of solar cells under DH conditions. Particularly noteworthy is the shift from EVA to POE as the preferred encapsulant in newer PV module designs. This change mitigates the tendency of EVA to release acetic acid, which contributes to the degradation process. Modern modules that employ POE, especially combined with the improved moisture sealing of G/G configurations, could result in the reduced susceptibility to these detrimental effects, thereby enhancing the overall reliability of the modules.

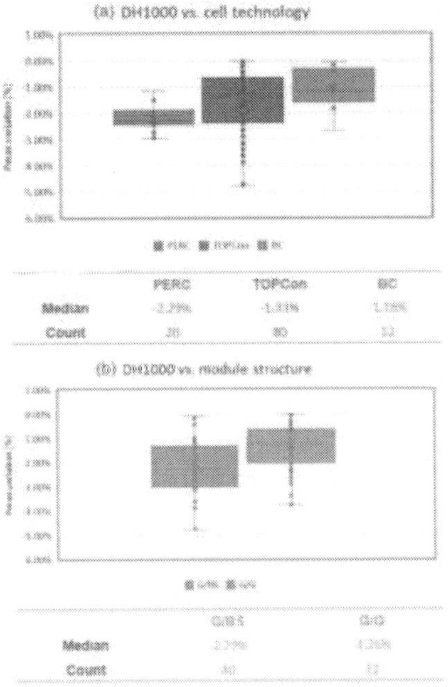
(a) DH1000 vs. cell technology
PERC
TOPCon
BC
Median
Count
(b) DH1000 vs. module structure
G/BS
G/G
Median
Count

Figure 2: power variation under post-DH1000 condition for different cell technologies (a) and different module structures (b).

3.3 Potential Induced Degradation

Figure 3 illustrates the variations in power degradation across different cell technologies under post-PID conditions. From the results, BC showed greater resilience against both positive and negative PID stress in comparison to TOPCon and PERC, with a median degradation rate of approximately 0.5% at +1500V and around 0.8% at -1500V. Conversely, PERC cells exhibited higher degradation, trailing BC by an estimated 0.6% under both polarity stress conditions. Generally, there are several PID phenomena such PID-s and PID-p and the magnitude of degradation appears to be particularly sensitive to module type than cell technology. These findings highlight the critical need to factor in PID effects during the selection and implementation of solar cells to ensure sustained long-term performance.

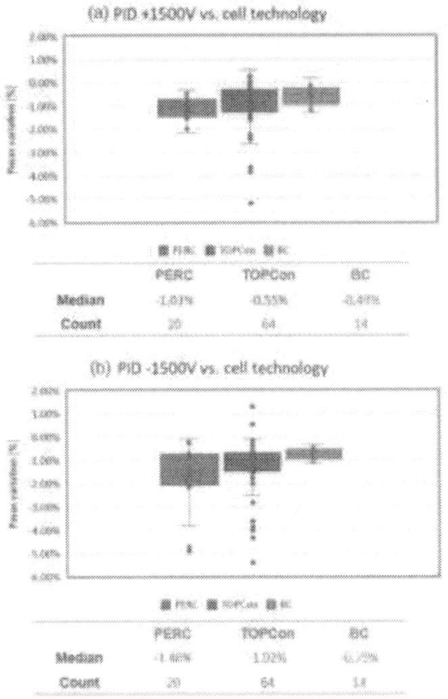
(a) PID +1500V vs. cell technology
PERC
TOPCon
BC
Median
Count
(b) PID -1500V vs. cell technology
PERC
TOPCon
BC
Median
Count

Figure 3: power variation of different cell technologies under post-PID at +1500 V (a), and -1500 V (b)

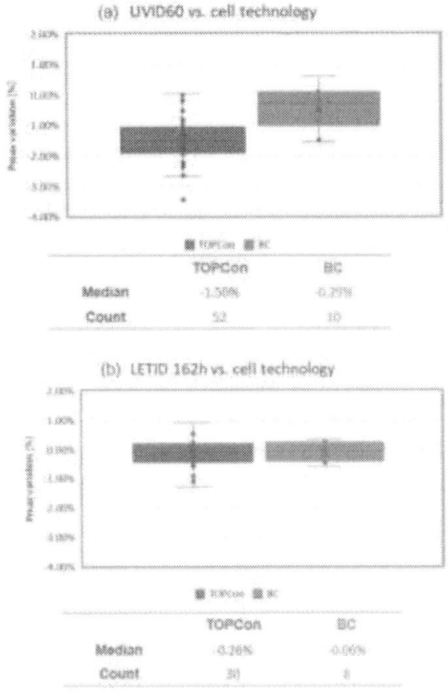
(a) UVID60 vs. cell technology
TOPCon
BC
Median
Count
(b) LETID 162h vs. cell technology
TOPCon
BC
Median
Count

Figure 4: power variation of different cell technologies under post-UVID (a), and post-LETID (b)

3.4 Ultraviolet-induced Degradation and Light- and Elevated Temperature-Induced Degradation

Figure 4 provides evidence of the differentiated impact that post-UVID (a) and LETID (b) conditions have on TOPCon and BC cell technologies. TOPCon cells exhibit significantly greater degradation under UVID, with an estimated decrease of around 1.5%, which is notably five times higher than that observed in BC. In contrast, both cell types demonstrate less sensitivity to LETID, with TOPCon and BC showing median degradations of approximately 0.3% and 0.1%, respectively. These findings underscore the necessity of considering encapsulation material performance in harsh environmental conditions to ensure the longevity and efficiency of solar cell technologies.

Notably, degradation rates have been observed to be small, and as such, it becomes imperative to differentiate the effects of measurement uncertainty from the actual degradation phenomena. We have determined that the measurement uncertainty associated with our testing is ±2.0%, k=2 and the reproducibility ±0.6%, k=2 This emphasis on reproducibility serves to corroborate that the degradation signals we report are not artifacts of measurement variance but are indeed indicative of the modules' performance over time.

4 ConclusionThis study provides a comparative analysis of the reliability of leading PV cell technologies—PERC, TOPCon, HJT, and BC—under a comprehensive set of accelerated stress tests. The results clearly demonstrate that the degradation behavior is highly dependent on both the cell technology and the module's construction, with no single technology exhibiting superiority across all conditions.

PERC cells exhibit considerable degradation, with recorded losses of approximately 2.0% and 2.3% after TC600 and DH1000 stress tests, respectively, which lower the confidence of the suitability for long-term application. Conversely, BC and HJT cells demonstrate markedly less degradation, around 1.0%, following TC600 testing. Specifically, BC technology shows low degradation of approximately 1.2% at post-DH1000 condition. Notably though, the BC cells display a relatively broad distribution of degradation rates. This variability may suggest that while certain manufacturers have optimized their production processes for BC cells, yielding high reliability, others may benefit from further refinement in their manufacturing techniques to achieve consistent quality and reduce variability across the board. TOPCon cells are distinguished by their exceptional thermal stability and lower degradation rates, particularly during TC (~0.3%), DH (~1.3%) and PID (~0.5% positive stress) assessments, yet they exhibit increased sensitivity to UVID, with an average degradation of 1.5%. Regarding LETID results, both TOPCon and BC technologies tested show limited impact, with median degradations of 0.3% and 0.1%, respectively.

Overall, these findings indicate that while there is no one-size-fits-all solution, the selection of solar cell technology and module design must be tailored to specific environmental conditions to ensure the maximum efficiency and longevity of solar power systems. Applying these insights can guide manufacturers, designers, and consumers in making informed decisions for sustainable and reliable solar energy solutions.

References

[1] IEC61215, "Crystalline Silicon terrestrial photovoltaic (PV) modules- design qualification and type approval," The International Electrotechnical Commission (IEC), 2021.

[2] IECTS63202-4, "Photovoltaic cells - Part 4: Measurement of light and elevated temperature induced degradation of crystalline silicon photovoltaic cells," The International Electrotechnical Commission (IEC), 2022.

[3] K. Morita, P. Sochor, Y. Tsuno, Y. Yasuda, S. Kera, T. Kohno and M. Fujimori, "Correlation between Thermal Cycling Test and Outdoor Exposure for Major Degradation Modes of PV modules," in WCPEC6, Kyoto, Japan, 2014.

[4] P. Hacke, K. Terwilliger, S. Glick, R. Smith, G. Perrin and S. Kurtz, "Application of the terrestrial photovoltaic module accelerated test-to-failure protocol," in 2014 IEEE 40th Photovoltaic Specialist Conference (PVSC), Denver, CO, USA, 2014.

[5] N. C. A Ebong, "Metallization of crystalline silicon solar cells: A review," High capacity optical networks and emerging/enabling technologies, pp. 102-109, 2012.

Durability and Reliability: A Cross-Technological Stability Analysis of Silicon PV

Mengdi Liu[1], Wenhao Xu[1], Yating Zhang[1], Giorgio Bardizza[2], Christos Monokroussos[1]
[1] TÜV Rheinland (Shanghai) Co., Ltd., No.177, Lane 777, West Guangzhong, 200072, Shanghai, P.R. China
[2] TÜV Rheinland (Italy), Via E. Mattei, 3 - 20005, Pogliano Milanese, Italy

Why Reliability Matters in PV Technology

- Maximizing Energy Performance
- Energy Independence
- Withstanding Extreme Conditions
- Cost Savings
- Protecting Investments
- Sustainability

PID Performance of Cost-effective Material

EPE (EVA/POE/EVA) sandwich structure may not have sufficient diffusion resistance with power loss >10% after PID 96 exposure.

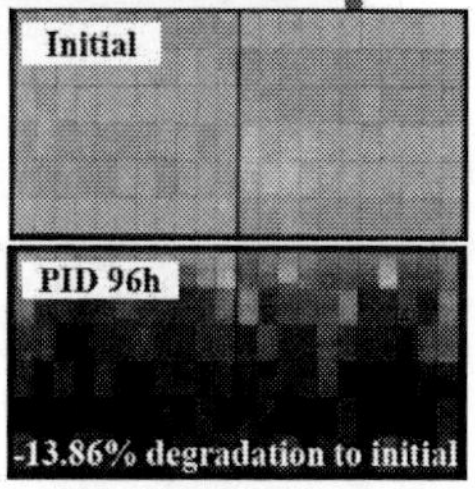

Reliability Analysis

Sequence 1: Thermal Cycling	Sequence 2: Damp Heat	Sequence 3: Potential Induced Degradation	Sequence 4: UV-Induced Degradation	Sequence 5: Light- and elevated Temperature-Induced Degradation
TC 200 -40°C to +85°C for 200 temperature cycles	**DH 1000** 85°C and 85% RH for 1000 h	**PID 96** 85°C, 85% RH, V_{sys} [(+) and (-)] for 96 h	**UVID 60** 60kWh/m², 60°C	**LeTID 162** 1000W/m², 162h, 75°C

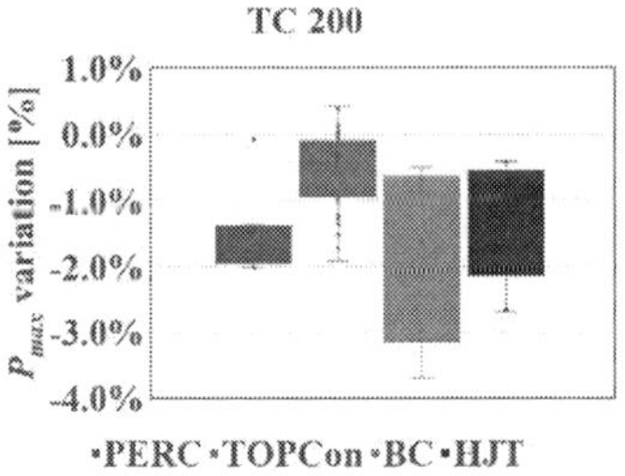

	PERC	TOPCon	BC	HJT
Median	-1.49%	-0.42%	-1.00%	-1.07%
Count	8	45	6	9

Measurement Reproducibility: ±0.6 %, k=2

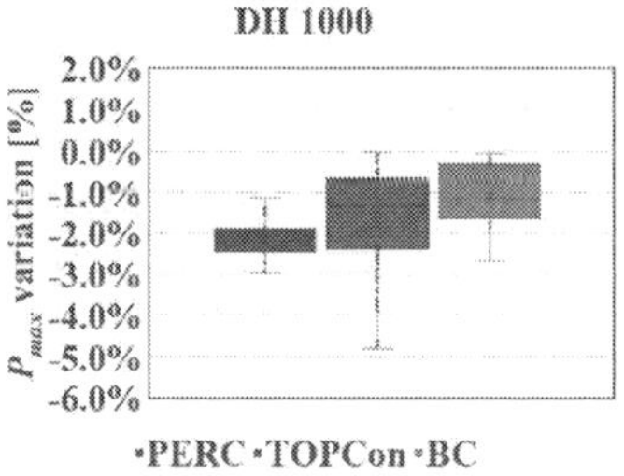

	PERC	TOPCon	BC
Median	-2.29%	-1.33%	-1.16%
Count	20	80	12

Measurement Reproducibility: ±0.6 %, k=2

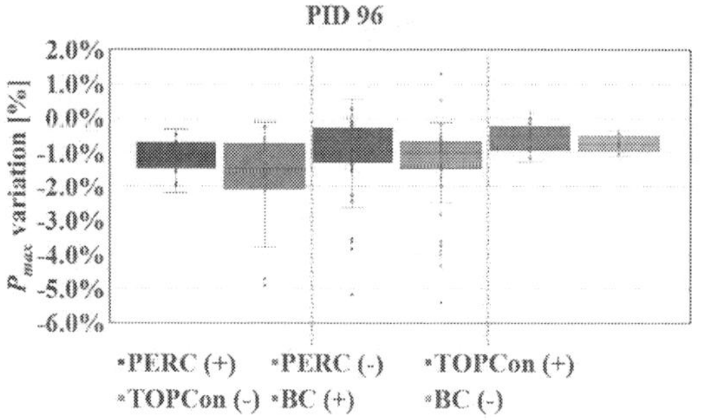

	PERC		TOPCon		BC	
	+	-	+	-	+	-
Median	-1.03%	-1.46%	-0.55%	-1.02%	-0.49%	-0.75%
Count	20		64		14	

Measurement Reproducibility: ±0.6 %, k=2

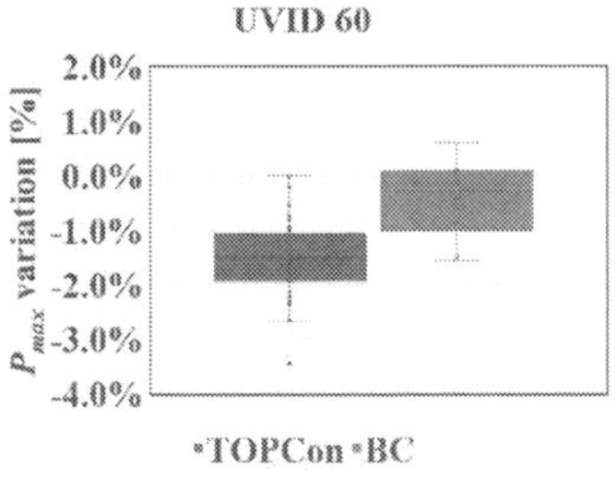

	TOPCon	BC
Median	-1.50%	-0.29%
Count	52	10

Measurement Reproducibility: ±0.6 %, k=2

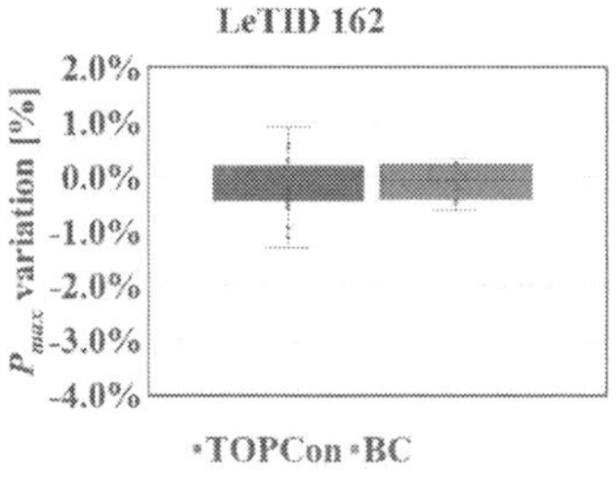

	TOPCon	BC
Median	-0.26%	-0.06%
Count	30	8

Measurement Reproducibility: ±0.6 %, k=2

Key Points

- TOPCon modules displayed excellent reliability with particular low degradation in the TC 200 test.
- BC modules exhibited strong resistance to DH, PID, LeTID and UVID.
- Today's modules exhibit significantly less degradation than those Al-BSF modules a decade ago.
- Individual module types need to be analyzed case-by-case.

Corresponding author: Dr. Mengdi Liu
Email: mengdi.liu@tuv.com

TÜVRheinland®
Genau. Richtig.

SILICA COATING WITH OPTIMIZED OPTICAL AND MECHANICAL PROPERTIES FOR ANTI-REFLECTION AND DUST RESISTANCE IN HARSH DESERT ENVIRONMENTS

Brahim Aïssa*, Mohammad I. Hossain, Atef Zekri, Amir Abdallah, Veronica Bermudez Benito
Qatar Environment and Energy Research Institute (QEERI), Hamad Bin Khalifa University (HBKU), Qatar Foundation, Doha, 5825, Qatar
* baissa@hbku.edu.qa

ABSTRACT: This research directly addresses the persistent challenges encountered in desert environments, where solar energy systems, optical devices, and building surfaces are continuously exposed to two harsh stressors: intense ultraviolet (UV) radiation and heavy dust deposition. Both factors significantly degrade performance, leading to efficiency losses, higher maintenance requirements, and reduced operational lifetimes. To mitigate these environmental impacts, a specialized silica-based coating was developed, designed not only to enhance optical performance but also to provide long-term durability under extreme conditions. The coating, produced via reactive RF magnetron sputtering using high-purity SiO_2 targets, was fabricated under carefully controlled conditions. By varying the oxygen-to-argon flow ratios during deposition, researchers were able to finely tune the microstructural and surface properties of the films. Systematic testing revealed that higher oxygen content during sputtering resulted in coatings with improved smoothness and enhanced hydrophilicity (water-attracting behavior). This property plays a key role in the coating's self-cleaning functionality, as it facilitates water spreading and the removal of dust particles from the surface. Beyond optical and wetting properties, the mechanical robustness of the coatings was rigorously assessed. Mechanical tests demonstrated that the films remained structurally stable and mechanically strong even after 24 months of continuous outdoor exposure to desert conditions. Furthermore, the hardness of the coatings could be effectively tailored by adjusting oxygen content, offering a pathway for optimizing both strength and resilience. Notably, coatings deposited at higher oxygen flow ratios exhibited a reduced tendency for dust accumulation, confirming their dual role as both anti-reflective and anti-soiling layers. Collectively, these findings highlight the promise of silica coatings engineered for desert environments as a durable, eco-friendly, and multifunctional solution. By simultaneously reducing sunlight reflection, improving light absorption, resisting mechanical degradation, and suppressing dust buildup, such coatings extend the performance and operational lifetime of solar panels, optical devices, and building-integrated surfaces. This approach not only supports the deployment of renewable energy technologies in harsh climates but also aligns with the broader vision of sustainable and low-maintenance materials for energy and environmental applications.

1 INTRODUCTION

Significant advancements have been achieved in the design and fabrication of anti-reflection (AR) and anti-soiling (AS) coatings, given their broad impact across industries such as photovoltaic (PV) solar energy, laser optics, automotive components, architectural glass, and high-performance optical devices. These coatings play a pivotal role in enhancing efficiency and durability, particularly in PV systems where environmental dust accumulation can lead to severe performance losses. For instance, dust storms can reduce module efficiency by up to 22%, while even a thin, ~1 μm layer of dust deposited on crystalline silicon (c-Si) modules can cause a 25% efficiency drop [1–3]. Such statistics underline the urgency of developing advanced thin-film coatings that combine both AR and AS functionalities in order to mitigate performance degradation and reduce maintenance demands.

Self-cleaning AR–AS coatings have emerged as one of the most promising approaches to address these dual challenges. Achieving optimal AR performance typically requires destructive interference of reflected light at the glass/coating and coating/air interfaces, which is usually obtained by tailoring the film thickness to approximately one-quarter of the wavelength of incident light. Conventional approaches employ porous coatings to lower the refractive index and minimize reflection, or stacked SiO_2/TiO_2 bilayers to enhance transmission. However, these designs often face practical limitations: stacked systems, while optically efficient, may suffer from scalability issues, reduced self-cleaning performance, higher refractive indices, and elevated fabrication costs [4,5]. Thus, the challenge lies in striking a balance between durability, optical efficiency, surface functionality, and cost-effectiveness. Among available materials, silicon dioxide (SiO_2) stands out for its exceptional optical transparency, low refractive index, mechanical strength, and chemical stability. Its high transmission across the near-ultraviolet to near-infrared spectrum makes it an ideal candidate for AR–AS coatings. Beyond photovoltaics, SiO_2 thin films are widely employed in flexible displays, protective coatings, bioengineering, and ophthalmic applications, owing to their robustness and optical clarity. A wide range of deposition techniques has been explored for SiO_2 thin films, including electron-beam evaporation, ion-assisted deposition, magnetron sputtering, sol–gel processing, and atomic layer deposition. Among these, RF magnetron sputtering is often considered the most suitable for industrial-scale applications due to its excellent reproducibility, precise control over microstructural properties, and low defect rates. In particular, reactive sputtering has been extensively adopted in the PV industry for fabricating SiO_2-based AR coatings, though further work is still required to establish a comprehensive correlation between deposition parameters, film microstructure, and functional performance.

In the present study, 100 nm-thick SiO_2 thin films were deposited via RF sputtering under varying oxygen flow rates (0–50 sccm) at a controlled substrate temperature of 200 °C. The influence of the oxygen-to-argon flow ratio [$r(O_2) = O_2/Ar$] on the structural, optical, and surface properties of the films was systematically investigated. The coatings were characterized using a suite of techniques:

- Ellipsometry and UV–Vis spectroscopy to evaluate refractive index, extinction coefficient, and optical transmittance,
- Contact angle measurements to probe wettability and self-cleaning potential,
- 3D stylus profilometry for surface roughness quantification, and
- Field-emission scanning electron microscopy (FESEM) to assess surface morphology and microstructural features.

The findings demonstrated that oxygen flow is a critical tuning parameter in controlling film performance. Higher oxygen content during sputtering resulted in smoother, more uniform films with enhanced hydrophilicity, which in turn promoted self-cleaning behavior by reducing dust accumulation. Interestingly, the coatings also exhibited hydrophobic contributions under certain oxygen flow conditions, further improving resistance to particulate adhesion. Together, these properties enabled the SiO_2 films to significantly improve the optical and environmental stability of PV modules, particularly in dust-prone desert climates.

This work underscores the immense potential of SiO_2 coatings to combine AR and AS functionalities into a single, scalable thin-film solution. By enhancing light transmission, suppressing dust buildup, and maintaining long-term mechanical integrity, such coatings represent a durable and eco-friendly pathway to boost both the performance and lifespan of solar modules and other optoelectronic devices in harsh environments.

Looking ahead, future research should aim to refine deposition techniques, optimize oxygen-to-argon ratios, and explore the interplay between film microstructure, surface chemistry, and functional response. A deeper understanding of these relationships will be crucial for pushing the boundaries of next-generation AR–AS coatings, ultimately enabling self-sustaining, high-performance solar energy systems that thrive even under the most demanding environmental conditions.

2 METHODOLOGY

Silica thin films were deposited onto soda lime glass (SLG) substrates (dimensions: 1″ × 3″) using a Torr Magnetron Sputtering Tool™ under carefully controlled conditions to ensure high-quality coatings with tunable properties. The sputtering chamber was evacuated to a base pressure of 5×10^{-5} Torr prior to deposition, minimizing contamination and ensuring reproducibility. A reactive sputtering configuration was employed, utilizing high-purity (99.995%) argon and oxygen gases. Substrate rotation was continuously applied during deposition to guarantee uniform film coverage across the glass surface. The sputtering target consisted of a high-purity SiO_2 source (99.995%, Kurt J. Lesker), ensuring consistent stoichiometry and purity in the deposited films. All depositions were performed at a constant substrate temperature of 200 °C and a stable deposition rate of 0.5 Å/s, providing controlled growth conditions for uniform thin films. The argon flow rate was fixed at 200 sccm to sustain plasma ignition and stabilize sputtering, while the oxygen flow rate was systematically varied between 0 and 50 sccm. This adjustment enabled oxygen-to-total gas flow ratios ranging from 0% to 25%, allowing precise tuning of the thin film's optical and surface characteristics as a function of deposition chemistry. Following deposition, the silica-coated samples were transferred to the Outdoor Testing Facility (OTF) for real-world environmental evaluation. To examine the role of surface orientation on dust accumulation and self-cleaning behavior, the samples were mounted at five different tilt angles (0°, 22°, 45°, 60°, and 90°). All samples were exposed simultaneously to identical desert outdoor conditions, ensuring a fair comparison of soiling dynamics across the tested geometries. This experimental design provided critical insights into the influence of tilt angle on dust deposition, removal, and overall performance stability, directly relevant to optimizing photovoltaic (PV) module performance in dust-prone environments.

3 RESULTS AND DISCUSSION

Fig. 1. X-ray Photoelectron Spectroscopy (XPS) survey spectra of silica thin films deposited with varying oxygen flow ratios (0%–25%) at a substrate temperature of 200 °C. The survey includes the Si 2p and O 1s core-level peaks acquired after monatomic etching, complemented by oxygen depth profiling across the films. To ensure accurate quantification, oxygen bound to carbon-related contaminants was subtracted, and the remaining oxygen signal was attributed to oxide-related bonds such as oxygen–metal linkages. The dominant peaks corresponding to silicon and oxygen confirmed the formation of SiOx chemical states. Notably, the Si 2p peak consistently appeared at ~103 eV, indicative of stable silicon–oxygen bonding. The calculated stoichiometry of the films ranged from $SiO_{1.85}$ to $SiO_{1.91}$, depending on the oxygen flow ratio. Both cluster ion and monatomic ion etching were employed to cross-validate results, ensuring reliable assessment of the films' chemical composition.

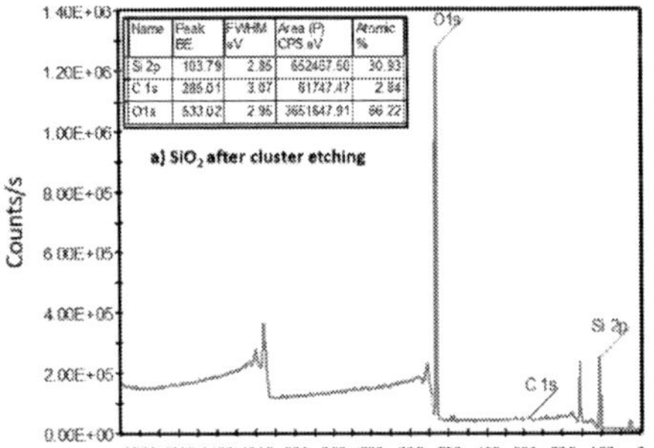

Figure 1: X-ray Photoelectron Spectroscopy (XPS) survey spectrum of silica thin films deposited at an oxygen flow ratio of $r(O_2) = 0\%$ and a substrate temperature of 200 °C. The survey highlights the elemental composition of the as-deposited films, with clear signals corresponding to silicon (Si 2p) and oxygen (O 1s), confirming the presence of SiOx-related chemical states. Minor carbon peaks are also observed, attributed to surface contamination during sample handling. The analysis establishes a baseline for subsequent comparisons with oxygen-enriched films, providing insight into the evolution of chemical bonding

10.4229/EUPVSEC2025/3AV.2.4

and stoichiometry as a function of deposition parameters.

Fig. 2. Correlation between the refractive index and the wettability properties (hydrophobic/hydrophilic behavior) of the silica thin films as a function of oxygen flow ratio ($r(O_2)$). The results demonstrate that higher oxygen content enhances film transparency while simultaneously modifying surface morphology and wetting properties. Surfaces with increased oxygen content exhibited greater hydrophilicity, supporting water spreading and potential self-cleaning behavior. Conversely, lower oxygen ratios yielded more hydrophobic surfaces, where water droplets resisted spreading and remained pinned to the surface. These trends suggest that silica films with optimized oxygen incorporation not only enhance optical transmission but also display functional wetting characteristics suited to dust mitigation. The interplay between chemical composition and surface roughness was evident: hydrophilicity was linked to hydroxyl (–OH) group formation and three-dimensional capillary action within rougher surfaces, whereas hydrophobicity arose from reduced substrate effects and lower surface energy. Further surface roughness characterization is recommended to validate the strong influence of morphology on wettability transitions.

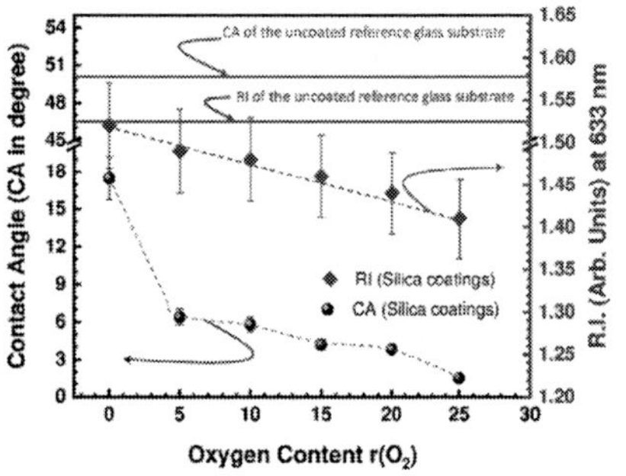

Figure 2: Summary of contact angle (CA) measurements for sputtered silica thin films deposited at varying oxygen flow ratios ($r(O_2)$), with a reference uncoated glass sample included for comparison. Dashed lines are provided as visual guides to highlight the observed trends. The results reveal a clear dependence of wettability on oxygen incorporation: as the oxygen content increases, the coatings exhibit progressively lower contact angles, indicating enhanced hydrophilicity. This transition reflects changes in surface chemistry (e.g., hydroxyl group formation) and morphology, which play a crucial role in enabling self-cleaning and anti-soiling properties for applications such as PV modules in desert environments.

Fig. 3a. Comparative micromechanical hardness of uncoated soda-lime glass and silica-coated samples fabricated under different oxygen concentrations, measured using the Vickers indentation method. Results confirmed that silica coatings maintained substantial hardness, approximately 10% lower than bare glass, demonstrating their structural robustness. Increasing oxygen content correlated with a slight reduction in hardness, consistent with enhanced porosity and surface hydroxylation.

Fig. 3b. Mechanical degradation of silica films over time, plotted as hardness reduction as a function of oxygen flow ratio ($r(O_2)$). After two months of outdoor exposure, no measurable hardness loss was observed, while after 24 months, only a ~5% reduction was recorded, confirming the films' exceptional long-term durability and stability. These findings highlight that oxygen-rich silica coatings can combine mechanical integrity with functional hydrophilicity, making them well-suited for durable AR–AS applications in harsh desert conditions.

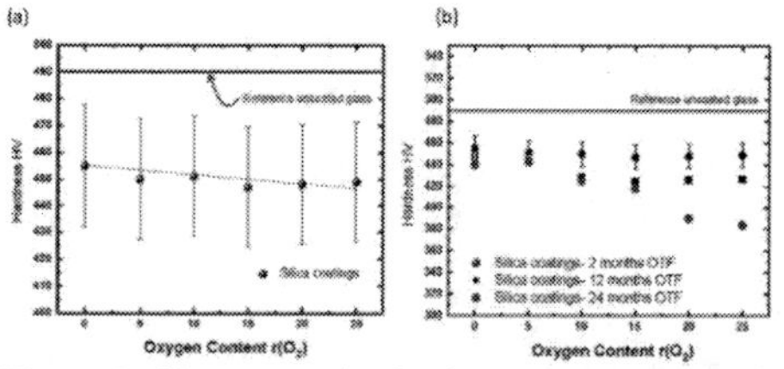

Figure 3: (a) Comparative hardness measurements of reference uncoated glass and silica thin films deposited with varying oxygen flow ratios ($r(O_2)$). The results highlight the influence of oxygen incorporation on the micromechanical properties of the coatings, with increased oxygen content generally leading to slightly reduced hardness values relative to bare glass. (b) Long-term assessment of mechanical stability, showing the evolution of hardness as a function of exposure time under outdoor conditions for different $r(O_2)$. The data demonstrate the excellent durability of silica coatings, with only marginal degradation observed after extended exposure. Even after 24 months, hardness reduction remained within ~5%, underscoring the coatings' ability to retain their mechanical integrity while simultaneously delivering optical and anti-soiling functionalities.

Fig. 4. Scanning Electron Microscopy (SEM) images of the front surfaces of silica-coated glass coupons after two months of outdoor exposure at the Outdoor Test Facility (OTF). Dust accumulation was quantified by calculating the surface coverage (SC) of particles, enabling direct comparisons across different oxygen flow ratios ($r(O_2)$) and tilt angles. The results showed a clear angular dependence: higher tilt angles reduced dust deposition, with soiling behavior scaling proportionally to the cosine of the tilt angle (θ). Moreover, coatings deposited with higher oxygen content exhibited superior hydrophilicity, which substantially reduced dust retention without the need for manual cleaning. In contrast, coatings fabricated at lower oxygen flow rates accumulated significantly more dust, highlighting the importance of optimized oxygen incorporation. Collectively, these results demonstrate that hydrophilic silica films not only enhance transparency but also offer self-cleaning functionality by resisting dust buildup, thereby mitigating one of the most critical performance losses for PV modules and optical devices in desert climates.

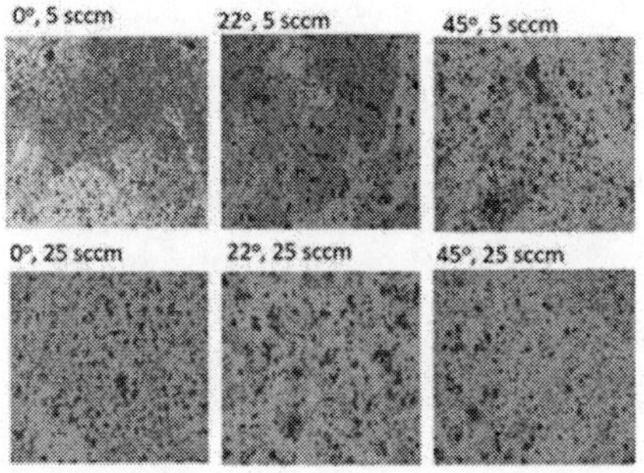

Figure 4: Representative optical microscope images of the front surfaces of silica-coated glass coupons after two months of outdoor exposure at the Outdoor Test Facility (OTF). The images illustrate characteristic soiling patterns and dust accumulation on the coatings, enabling qualitative comparison of surface coverage across different oxygen flow ratios and tilt angles. Distinct differences in particle adhesion and distribution are observed, reflecting the role of oxygen content in governing the films' hydrophilicity and self-cleaning performance. These visual observations support quantitative analyses of dust coverage, confirming that oxygen-rich silica coatings exhibit reduced dust retention and enhanced resistance to environmental soiling.

4 CONCLUSIONS

This research provides a comprehensive investigation into the optical and morphological properties of silica thin films fabricated via reactive RF magnetron sputtering using high-purity SiO_2 targets. By systematically varying the oxygen-to-total-flow ratios between 0% and 25%, the deposition process enabled precise tailoring of film properties to achieve multifunctional performance. The resulting silica coatings demonstrated exceptional optical clarity, with transmittance values exceeding 90% across the visible spectrum, confirming their suitability for transparent applications such as protective and anti-reflective (AR) layers. Ellipsometric analysis revealed refractive index values in the range of 1.4–1.5, closely matching those of high-quality AR coatings, thereby validating the films' potential to minimize reflection losses and enhance light harvesting in photovoltaic and optical devices. Surface analyses provided further insights into the influence of oxygen incorporation. Contact angle measurements showed that films deposited with higher oxygen flow ratios displayed markedly improved hydrophilicity, while surface roughness characterization indicated subtle morphological adjustments that promoted self-cleaning behavior. These surface properties directly translated into enhanced anti-soiling performance during real-time outdoor exposure tests. Indeed, a clear correlation was observed between oxygen content and dust resistance: films fabricated under oxygen-rich conditions exhibited significantly reduced dust accumulation, whereas oxygen-deficient films were more prone to particulate deposition. Collectively, these findings underscore the dual functionality of silica thin films as both anti-reflective and anti-soiling coatings. Their ability to combine high optical transmission, tunable refractive indices, hydrophilic surface properties, and environmental durability highlights their value for solar modules deployed in harsh desert environments, where dust accumulation and reflection losses remain critical challenges. Beyond photovoltaics, such coatings hold promise for broader applications in lasers, optical sensors, architectural glass, and automotive systems. By bridging fundamental material characterization with real-world outdoor testing, this study establishes silica-based coatings as a scalable, robust, and eco-friendly solution for next-generation energy and optical technologies. Future work should focus on refining deposition parameters, exploring multi-layer or doped silica architectures, and investigating the long-term stability of AR–AS properties under prolonged desert exposure to further enhance their practical viability.

5 REFERENCES

[1] I. Arabatzis, N. Todorova, I. Fasaki, C. Tsesmeli, A. Peppas, W. X. Li, and Z. Zhao, "Photocatalytic and self-cleaning coatings for solar applications," Solar Energy, vol. 159, pp. 251–259, 2018.

[2] K. Nishioka, S. P. Moe, and Y. Ota, "Performance evaluation of photovoltaic modules with anti-reflection coatings," Coatings, vol. 9, no. 1, p. 49, 2019.

[3] T. Shao, F. Tang, L. Sun, X. Ye, J. He, L. Yang, and W. Zheng, "Nanostructured coatings for enhanced optical and surface properties," Nanomaterials, vol. 9, no. 2, p. 180, 2019.

[4] T.-C. Chen, T.-W. Kuo, Y.-L. Lin, C.-H. Ku, Z.-P. Yang, and I.-S. Yu, "High-transmittance hydrophobic coatings for photovoltaic protection," Coatings, vol. 8, no. 12, p. 418, 2018.

[5] L. L. Lebel, B. Aïssa, M. A. El Khakani, and D. Therriault, Composites Science and Technology, vol. 70, no. 3, pp. 518–524, 2010.

[6] W. Julia, C. Luis, R. Federico, et al., Advanced Functional Materials, vol. 23, pp. 5591–5598, 2013.

[7] D. T. H. Dalir, R. D. Farahani, V. Nhim, and B. Aïssa, et al., Langmuir, vol. 28, no. 1, pp. 791–803, 2011.

[8] A. Ali, F. El-Mellouhi, A. Mitra, and B. Aïssa, Nanomaterials, vol. 12, no. 5, p. 788, 2022.

[9] R. D. Farahani, D. T. H. Dalir, V. Le Borgne, A. Loick, et al., Composites Science and Technology, vol. 72, no. 12, pp. 1387–1395, 2012.

[10] N. M. H. Gavi, B. D. Ngom, A. C. Beye, A. M. Strydom, B. Aïssa, V. V. Srinivasu, and M. Chaker, Journal of Magnetism and Magnetic Materials, vol. 324, no. 6, pp. 1172–1176, 2012.

[11] B. Aïssa and M. A. El Khakani, Nanotechnology, vol. 20, no. 17, p. 175203, 2009.

[12] M. A. Habib, M. Barkat, B. Aïssa, and T. Denidni, Progress in Electromagnetics Research, vol. 88, pp. 135–148, 2008.

[13] H. Zhao, H. Kimura, Z. Cheng, X. Wang, and T. Nishida, Applied Physics Letters, vol. 95, p. 232904, 2009. https://doi.org/10.1063/1.3271032.

PLASMONIC-DECORATED TiO_2 THIN FILMS AS PHOTOCATALYTIC ANTI-SOILING COATINGS

Brahim Aïssa*, M.I. Hossain and Adnan Ali
Qatar Environment and Energy Research Institute (QEERI), Hamad Bin Khalifa University (HBKU), Qatar Foundation, Doha, 5825, Qatar
* baissa@hbku.edu.qa

ABSTRACT: Soiling of solar collectors represents one of the most pressing challenges for the reliability and efficiency of solar energy systems, particularly in arid and semi-arid regions such as the Middle East and North Africa (MENA). The accumulation of dust, sand, and organic residues on solar surfaces leads to substantial reductions in power output and escalates operational and maintenance (O&M) costs, often making soiling the single largest contributor to performance losses in photovoltaic (PV) plants. Soiling on PV modules is broadly categorized into inorganic and organic components, each posing distinct challenges. Inorganic soiling, typically derived from mineral-rich sources such as desert sand, sea salt, and suspended mineral particles, tends to be less adhesive and can often be removed through routine cleaning or wind action. In contrast, organic soiling, originating from airborne dust mixed with pollen, microbial deposits, and biological residues such as bird droppings, exhibits strong adhesion to surfaces. Organic matter is particularly problematic as it not only resists removal but can also serve as a substrate for microbial growth, leading to corrosive byproducts that degrade encapsulants, coatings, and even glass surfaces over time. To address this critical issue, the present study investigates the use of plasmonic metal nanoparticles (NPs) as a strategy for mitigating the impact of organic dust deposition on solar surfaces. Specifically, the work evaluates the role of localized surface plasmon resonance (LSPR) in enhancing photocatalytic degradation of organic contaminants. Gold (Au) nanoparticles were deposited onto plain glass and TiO_2-coated glass substrates via the solid-state dewetting (SSD) process, which enables the formation of uniformly distributed nanoscale particles with strong plasmonic activity. The SSD approach also maximizes the nanoparticle–substrate interface, thereby promoting efficient charge transfer and improved catalytic reactivity under solar illumination. The experimental results demonstrated that the incorporation of Au nanoparticles significantly enhances the photocatalytic activity of TiO_2, leading to a pronounced reduction in the organic fraction of deposited dust. This effect is attributed to the excitation of LSPR in Au NPs, which increases light absorption and generates hot electrons that actively participate in photocatalytic reactions at the surface. As a result, organic contaminants decompose more efficiently, reducing adhesion and facilitating easier removal. These findings highlight the potential of plasmonic nanostructures to serve as the foundation for next-generation anti-soiling coatings, combining optical transparency with self-cleaning functionality. By targeting the persistent problem of organic soiling, often the most difficult to mitigate in real-world PV deployments, this approach provides a promising pathway toward reducing cleaning frequency, lowering O&M costs, and ensuring higher long-term energy yields in desert and coastal environments.

1 INTRODUCTION

A phenomenon known as localized surface plasmon resonance (LSPR) emerges when incident electromagnetic radiation interacts with metallic nanoparticles confined on a surface. This interaction arises because the oscillating electric field of light induces a collective motion of mobile charge carriers within the nanoparticles, driving coherent electron oscillations relative to the fixed ionic lattice. The displacement of these electrons generates restoring Coulomb forces, and under the right conditions, resonance is established between the external electromagnetic field and the natural oscillation frequency of the conduction electrons [1,2]. This resonant interaction gives rise to strongly enhanced optical absorption and scattering, along with intensified near-field effects, which are the hallmarks of plasmonic nanostructures.

The LSPR effect is highly sensitive to multiple factors, including the size, distribution, morphology, and dielectric environment of the nanoparticles [1,3,4]. By carefully tuning these parameters, the plasmonic response can be engineered across a wide spectral range. Gold (Au) and silver (Ag) nanoparticles are among the most widely employed materials due to their superior plasmonic efficiency in the visible range and their chemical stability, although other metals can also exhibit plasmonic activity [3]. While LSPR is most commonly observed in the visible spectrum, it can be deliberately extended into the ultraviolet (UV) and infrared (IR) regions through appropriate material choices and nanostructuring. For example, aluminum nanoparticles have been shown to support UV plasmonics, while compound semiconductors such as GaAs and InP, or transparent conducting oxides like indium-doped tin oxide (ITO), enable plasmonic resonances that extend well into the near-infrared (NIR) [5]. The resonance frequency of LSPR is governed by several key parameters. Nanoparticle size is particularly influential: as particle diameter increases, the resonance intensity is amplified, often accompanied by red-shifts in the spectral response [7]. Similarly, inter-particle spacing and arrangement critically affect resonance conditions. When the distance between nanoparticles increases, the plasmon resonance typically shifts toward shorter wavelengths (blue-shift), whereas strong electromagnetic coupling between closely spaced particles may induce energy splitting or hybridization effects, producing multiple resonance modes [6]. Geometrical factors such as nanoparticle aspect ratio, shape (spheres, rods, triangles), and orientation relative to the incident field further expand the tunability of LSPR, making it a versatile platform for tailoring optical functionalities. [7-11]

One practical route to fabricating plasmonic nanoparticles is the solid-state dewetting process, which transforms thin continuous films into discrete nanoscale islands upon thermal treatment. Dewetting typically progresses through three stages: (i) the initial formation

of voids in the nanofilm, (ii) the lateral growth and coalescence of these voids, and (iii) the eventual breakup of the film into nanoparticles driven by Rayleigh instability. These self-assembled nanoparticles naturally exhibit size distributions and inter-particle spacings determined by the initial film thickness, annealing temperature, and substrate properties. [12-15]
In the present work, we systematically investigate the dewetting behavior of thermally evaporated Au nanofilms deposited on TiO_2 thin films supported by quartz glass substrates. A series of experiments were conducted by varying both the annealing temperature and the initial thickness of the Au layers, enabling us to study their influence on nanoparticle evolution. The properties of the underlying TiO_2 films—including crystallinity, surface energy, and morphology, also played a significant role in guiding nanoparticle nucleation and growth. The resulting Au nanostructures were characterized in terms of their average particle size, surface density, and inter-particle distance, providing a quantitative understanding of how processing parameters dictate LSPR-active nanostructures. [16-21]
Beyond fundamental insights into nanoparticle formation, this study explores the functional application of plasmonic metal nanoparticles for mitigating the effects of soiling on solar energy devices. Specifically, Au nanoparticles supported on both glass and TiO_2-coated substrates were evaluated for their ability to reduce organic dust deposition through a photocatalytic mechanism. By leveraging the enhanced light absorption and hot-electron generation associated with LSPR, the Au/TiO_2 nanocomposites facilitate more efficient decomposition of organic matter, thereby reducing adhesion and promoting self-cleaning behavior under solar illumination [22].
Taken together, this investigation not only deepens the understanding of LSPR tuning via dewetting processes but also highlights its potential as a practical tool for developing next-generation anti-soiling coatings for photovoltaic and optoelectronic systems operating in challenging desert environments.

2 METHODOLOGY

Thin films of titanium oxide (TiOx) were deposited using electron beam (e-beam) evaporation under carefully optimized conditions to ensure high-quality growth. The depositions were performed at room temperature with a meticulously controlled deposition rate of 1 Å/s. To achieve stoichiometric oxide formation, a constant oxygen flow was introduced, maintaining a stable deposition pressure of 2×10^{-4} Torr throughout the process. For comparison, thin metallic layers of gold (Au) were also deposited under identical conditions using the same e-beam evaporation system and deposition rate. In this case, however, oxygen flow was excluded to preserve the metallic state and avoid unwanted oxidation.
To prevent electrical arcing caused by excess free charge carriers in the presence of oxygen, the oxygen flow rate was capped at 20 standard cubic centimeters per minute (sccm). This limit ensured stable plasma conditions and uninterrupted deposition. The use of a Denton Vacuum Explorer™ evaporator allowed sequential deposition of multilayer stacks without breaking vacuum, thereby minimizing interfacial contamination and preserving the structural and chemical integrity of the layers.
Prior to deposition, substrates (glass slides, 1 inch × 1 inch) were prepared by ultrasonic cleaning in successive baths of deionized (DI) water, acetone, and isopropanol, followed by drying under an inert nitrogen stream to eliminate residual contaminants and moisture. For multilayer configurations, TiOx and Au were alternately deposited in stacked sequences, with individual layer thicknesses systematically adjusted to tune the resulting optical and structural properties.
The deposited thin films were subjected to post-deposition annealing in a programmable muffle furnace. Annealing was carried out at temperatures ranging from 300 °C to 900 °C for one hour in ambient air. This thermal treatment was employed to enhance film crystallinity, stabilize the stoichiometry, and improve overall film quality, with particular attention to tailoring grain structure and optical performance.
A comprehensive suite of characterization techniques was used to evaluate the deposited films:

- Optical properties were investigated using UV–Vis spectroscopy to extract transmittance, reflectance, and absorption spectra over the 200–2000 nm wavelength range.
- Wetting behavior was assessed by static contact angle measurements, providing insights into hydrophilicity and potential anti-soiling performance.
- Surface topology was examined with both a 3D stylus profilometer (Dektak) and atomic force microscopy (AFM) to quantify surface roughness and morphological features.
- Microstructural analysis was conducted using field-emission scanning electron microscopy (FESEM), enabling visualization of film density, uniformity, and nanoscale features.
- Chemical composition and bonding states were determined using X-ray photoelectron spectroscopy (XPS), which confirmed the oxidation state of Ti in TiOx films and the purity of Au layers.

High-purity precursors (99.9995% Ti and Au pellets, Kurt J. Lesker) were employed to minimize impurities and ensure reproducibility. The combination of controlled deposition, in-situ vacuum stacking, and systematic annealing produced thin films with tunable optical and structural properties suitable for integration into infrared-filtering, anti-soiling, and plasmonic optoelectronic applications.

3 RESULTS AND DISCUSSION

Figure 1 presents the grazing-incidence X-ray diffraction (GIXRD) patterns of Au–TiOx thin films annealed at temperatures ranging from 300 °C to 900 °C, measured within the 2θ range of 20°–80°. The as-deposited TiOx films exhibited an amorphous nature, showing no discernible diffraction peaks, which is typical for films grown at room temperature without post-deposition treatment. Upon thermal annealing, however, distinct phase transformations were observed. The emergence of the anatase phase of TiOx was confirmed by characteristic diffraction peaks at 25° (101) and 47° (200), while the rutile phase appeared at higher temperatures, with reflections identified at 65° (310) and 70.1° (301). The coexistence of anatase and rutile phases at elevated annealing temperatures indicates a temperature-driven structural transition, consistent with the known polymorphic behavior of TiO_2. In the case of gold, the GIXRD patterns revealed well-defined crystalline features across all samples, confirming the formation of a face-centered cubic (FCC) lattice structure. Four prominent Bragg reflections were identified at 38.1° (111), 44.3° (200), 64.5° (220), and 77.7° (311). Among these, the sharp and intense (111) peak at 38.1° suggests a preferred orientation along the (111) plane, which is commonly reported for thin Au films due to its lowest surface energy configuration.

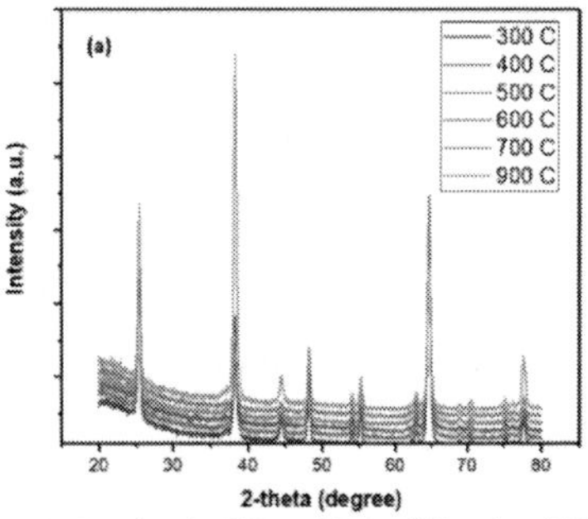

Figure 1: Grazing-incidence X-ray diffraction (GIXRD) patterns of Au/TiOx thin films annealed at temperatures ranging from 300 °C to 900 °C. The as-deposited TiOx films exhibit an amorphous structure, while post-annealing treatments induce crystallization into the anatase phase with characteristic peaks at 25° (101) and 47° (200), and the rutile phase with reflections at 65° (310) and 70.1° (301). The Au layers display a face-centered cubic (FCC) structure with prominent Bragg reflections at 38.1° (111), 44.3° (200), 64.5° (220), and 77.7° (311), with the (111) peak indicating preferential orientation. Increasing annealing temperature enhances the crystallinity of both TiOx and Au, as evidenced by sharper and more intense diffraction peaks, consistent with grain growth and improved structural ordering.

A clear correlation between annealing temperature and crystallinity was observed: with increasing temperature, the intensity and sharpness of the diffraction peaks for both TiOx and Au became more pronounced, indicative of enhanced crystallite size and improved structural ordering. This trend is in strong agreement with complementary morphological studies, which showed that higher annealing temperatures facilitate the formation of larger crystallites through grain coalescence. Overall, the XRD results confirm that annealing serves as a key parameter in tailoring the phase composition, crystallinity, and preferential orientation of Au–TiOx thin films.

Figure 2 presents the surface morphology of evaporated Au/TiOx thin films subjected to post-deposition annealing at six different temperatures, ranging from 300 °C to 900 °C, with TiOx serving as the seed layer. The microstructural evolution clearly reveals that with increasing annealing temperature, the TiOx films deposited on quartz substrates undergo grain growth, leading to the formation of progressively larger crystallites. This coarsening behavior is consistent with thermally driven diffusion processes, which promote atomic rearrangement and grain boundary migration. Correspondingly, the Au thin films exhibit enhanced crystallinity, as evidenced by the development of larger grains and more pronounced grain boundaries.

In general, seed layers characterized by smaller grains possess a greater density of grain boundaries, which act as energetically favorable sites for diffusion and nucleation. At the highest annealing temperature of 900 °C, a marked increase in particle density along grain boundaries was observed. This phenomenon is attributed to the migration of atoms from grain edges toward surface pits, resulting in localized nanoparticle formation and surface texturing. Importantly, despite these morphological changes, the analysis confirmed that all evaporated layers remained dense, uniform, and free from pinholes, thereby ensuring excellent structural integrity. The TiOx films provided complete and uniform surface coverage, a feature that is indispensable for advanced optoelectronic devices, where defects such as cracks or voids can severely compromise both optical and electronic performance.

Beyond structural quality, the study also highlights the functional significance of incorporating noble metal nanoparticles, particularly gold (Au), into oxide thin films. Gold nanoparticles are well known for their unique optical and photocatalytic properties, which arise from the phenomenon of localized surface plasmon resonance (LSPR). When illuminated, the oscillating electromagnetic field of incident light couples with the collective oscillations of free electrons in the nanoparticles, generating localized electromagnetic "hotspots." These hotspots create highly reactive sites that can degrade organic matter deposited on surfaces while simultaneously loosening dust particles.

When Au nanoparticles are integrated into TiO_2 thin films, the intrinsic photocatalytic activity of TiO_2 is significantly amplified under both UV and visible illumination, owing to synergistic charge transfer effects between the semiconductor and the plasmonic metal. This dual mechanism, LSPR-induced plasmonic enhancement coupled with TiO_2 photocatalysis, results in surfaces with powerful anti-dust and self-cleaning functionalities. Such plasmonic coatings not only mitigate the accumulation of both organic and inorganic dust but also ensure the breakdown of adherent contaminants over time, maintaining surface transparency and performance.

These characteristics are especially valuable for solar energy systems deployed in arid and dust-prone environments, where soiling is a major contributor to power loss. By leveraging LSPR and photocatalytic mechanisms, plasmonic coatings provide a sustainable and energy-efficient approach to dust mitigation, thereby improving both the efficiency and the operational lifetime of solar panels and other optoelectronic devices exposed to harsh outdoor conditions.

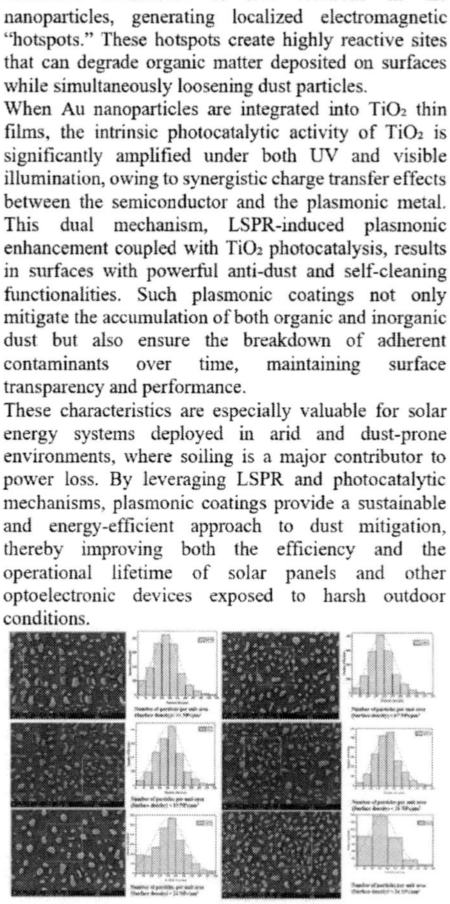

10.4229/EUPVSEC2025/3AV.2.5

Figure 2: Morphological characterization of Au/TiOx thin films annealed at six different temperatures ranging from 300 °C to 900 °C. The images illustrate the progressive grain growth and surface evolution of both TiOx seed layers and Au films with increasing annealing temperature. At higher temperatures, Au crystallites become larger and more defined, with pronounced grain boundaries and increased particle density along these regions, attributed to thermally driven diffusion. The TiOx films provide uniform surface coverage, ensuring dense and pinhole-free layers, which is critical for maintaining structural integrity. These results confirm that annealing temperature strongly influences nanoparticle size, surface density, and grain separation, thereby enabling precise control of film morphology for applications in plasmonic and optoelectronic devices.

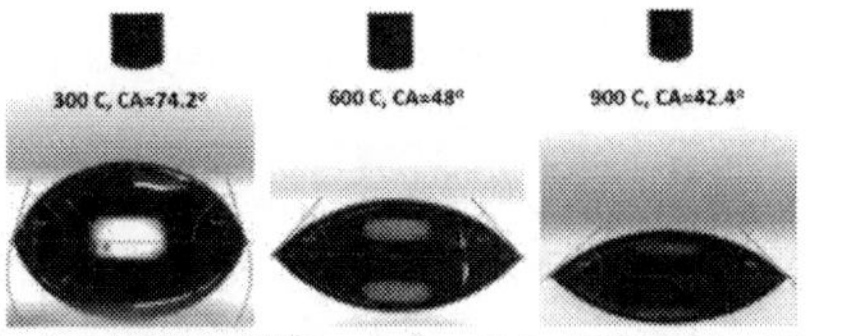

Figure 3: Wettability study of Au/TiOx thin films obtained by e-beam evaporation and subsequent annealing. Static contact angle measurements reveal the evolution of surface hydrophilicity with increasing annealing temperature, showing a decrease in contact angle from 74.2° to 42.4°. This change is attributed to the dewetting-driven transformation of Au into nanoparticle islands, which alters surface roughness and interfacial energy. The results demonstrate the strong correlation between annealing-induced morphological changes and surface wettability, underscoring the potential of Au/TiOx films for applications requiring tailored wetting behavior, such as self-cleaning and anti-soiling coatings.

The surface tension dynamics of Au thin films are strongly governed by the surface energy of the underlying TiO_2 seed layers, which dictates the nucleation and growth behavior of Au during thermal treatment. This interplay leads to the formation of Au particles with systematically varying sizes, surface densities, and grain separations, depending on the annealing conditions. The wettability of the resulting films was evaluated through static contact angle measurements, as illustrated in Figure 3, which revealed a pronounced evolution in surface properties as a function of annealing temperature.
Specifically, the contact angle decreased from 74.2° to 42.4° with increasing annealing temperature, signifying a substantial transition from moderately hydrophobic to more hydrophilic behavior. This shift in wettability can be directly correlated with the nanostructural transformation of the Au layers: the continuous Au films progressively evolve into discrete nanoparticle islands through solid-state dewetting, thereby increasing surface roughness and altering the surface energy landscape. The emergence of well-separated Au nanoparticle domains enhances the interaction of water molecules with the substrate, effectively reducing the interfacial tension between the liquid droplet and the film surface.
These observations highlight the critical role of annealing in modulating both surface morphology and wettability, offering a versatile pathway for tailoring thin-film properties. By controlling annealing temperature and thereby tuning particle formation dynamics, it is possible to engineer films with customized surface energies suited to specific functionalities. Such tunability is particularly relevant for applications where precisely controlled wettability is essential, including anti-soiling coatings, photocatalytic self-cleaning surfaces, and biointerface engineering.

4 CONCLUSIONS

In conclusion, this study underscores the critical challenge that soiling poses to the long-term performance and reliability of solar collectors, particularly in the Middle East and North Africa (MENA) region where high dust loads and frequent deposition events are prevalent. The accumulation of dust and particulate matter on photovoltaic (PV) modules and solar thermal collectors not only reduces power generation efficiency but also drives up operational and maintenance (O&M) costs, often becoming one of the most significant barriers to the widespread deployment of solar energy technologies in desert climates. Importantly, this work highlights the necessity of distinguishing between inorganic and organic soiling mechanisms: while inorganic particles such as sand and mineral dust tend to be less adhesive and easier to remove, organic soiling—comprising pollen, microbial residues, and biological contaminants—presents a more persistent and damaging challenge due to its strong adhesion and potential to catalyze corrosive processes through microbial activity.
To address this challenge, the study investigated the integration of plasmonic metal nanoparticles, with a focus on gold (Au), onto both bare glass and TiO_2-coated glass substrates. By leveraging the phenomenon of localized surface plasmon resonance (LSPR), it was demonstrated that Au nanoparticles can significantly enhance the photocatalytic activity of the underlying TiO_2 layer. The use of the solid-state dewetting (SSD) technique to deposit and self-assemble Au nanoparticles proved particularly effective, as this method maximizes the nanoparticle–substrate interface and ensures well-distributed nanostructures capable of resonant optical excitation. Under illumination, the resulting plasmonic substrates exhibited superior performance in degrading and mitigating the organic fraction of dust, thereby reducing adhesion and facilitating self-cleaning behavior.
The findings presented here contribute to the advancement of next-generation anti-soiling coatings that combine optical transparency, plasmonic activity, and photocatalytic self-cleaning capabilities. By effectively targeting the more problematic organic component of dust deposition, these coatings offer a pathway to significantly improve solar energy yield, reduce cleaning frequency, and lower O&M costs for solar plants deployed in harsh desert and coastal environments. Beyond their immediate application in PV modules and solar collectors, the concepts demonstrated here open avenues for multifunctional surface coatings in broader optoelectronic and environmental applications, positioning plasmonic nanostructures as a versatile tool for sustainable energy technologies in dust-prone regions.

5 REFERENCES

[1] E. Petryayeva, U.J. Krull, Anal. Chim. Acta 706 (1) (2011) 8–24, https://doi.org/10.1016/j.aca.2011.08.020.
[2] K.L. Kelly, E. Coronado, L.L. Zhao, G.C. Schatz, et al., J. Phys. Chem. B 107 (3) (2003) 668–677, https://doi.org/10.1021/jp026731y.
[3] J.N. Anker, W.P. Hall, O. Lyandres, N.C. Shah, J. Zhao, R.P. Van Duyne, et al., Nat. Mater. 7 (6) (2008) 442–453, https://doi.org/10.1038/nmat2162.
[4] T. Chung, Y. Lee, M.S. Ahn, W. Lee, S.I. Bae, C.S.H. Hwang, K.H. Jeong, et al., Nanoscale 11 (18) (2019) 8651–8664, https://doi.org/10.1039/c8nr10539a.
[5] G.V. Naik, V.M. Shalaev, A. Boltasseva, Alternative Plasmonic Materials: Beyond Gold and Silver (2013). URL www.MaterialsViews.com. https://doi.org/10.1002/adma.201205076.
[6] M.M. Jiang, H.Y. Chen, B.H. Li, K.W. Liu, C.X. Shan, S. De Zhen, et al., J. Mater. Chem. C 2 (1) (2014) 56–63, https://doi.org/10.1039/c3tc31910e.
[7] M.B. Ross, J.C. Ku, M.G. Blaber, C.A. Mirkin, G.C. Schatz, et al., Proc. Natl. Acad. Sci. U.S.A. 112 (33) (2015) 10292–10297, https://doi.org/10.1073/pnas.1513058112.
[8] L.L. Lebel, B. Aïssa, M.A. El Khakani, D. Therriault, Compos. Sci. Technol. 70 (3) (2010) 518–524.
[9] W. Julia, C. Luis, R. Federico, et al., Adv. Funct. Mater. 23 (2013) 5591–5598.
[10] D.T.H. Dalir, R.D. Farahani, V. Nhim, B. Aïssa, et al., Langmuir 28 (1) (2011) 791–803.
[11] A. Ali, F. El-Mellouhi, A. Mitra, B. Aïssa, Nanomaterials 12 (5) (2022) 788.
[12] R.D. Farahani, D.T.H. Dalir, V. Le Borgne, A. Loick, et al., Compos. Sci. Technol. 72 (12) (2012) 1387–1395.
[13] N.M.H. Gavi, B.D. Ngom, A.C. Beye, A.M. Strydom, B. Aïssa, V.V. Srinivasu, M. Chaker, J. Magn. Magn. Mater. 324 (6) (2012) 1172–1176.
[14] B. Aïssa, M.A. El Khakani, Nanotechnology 20 (17) (2009) 175203.
[15] M.A. Habib, M. Barkat, B. Aïssa, T. Denidni, Prog. Electromagn. Res. 88 (2008) 135–148.
[16] M.I. Hossain, B. Aïssa, A. Samara, S.A. Mansour, C.A. Broussillou, V. Bermudez Benito, ACS Omega 6 (8) (2021) 5276–5286.
[17] L.L. Lebel, B. Aïssa, M.A. El Khakani, D. Therriault, Compos. Sci. Technol. 70 (3) (2010) 518–524.
[18] W. Julia, C. Luis, R. Federico, et al., Adv. Funct. Mater. 23 (2013) 5591–5598.
[19] D.T.H. Dalir, R.D. Farahani, V. Nhim, B. Aïssa, et al., Langmuir 28 (1) (2011) 791–803.
[20] A. Ali, F. El-Mellouhi, A. Mitra, B. Aïssa, Nanomaterials 12 (5) (2022) 788.
[21] R.D. Farahani, D.T.H. Dalir, V. Le Borgne, A. Loick, et al., Compos. Sci. Technol. 72 (12) (2012) 1387–1395.
[22] H. Zhao, H. Kimura, Z. Cheng, X. Wang, T. Nishida, Appl. Phys. Lett. 95 (2009) 232904, https://doi.org/10.1063/1.3271032.

Plasmonic-Decorated TiO2 Thin Films as Photocatalytic Anti-Soiling Coatings

Brahim Aissa*, Mohammad I. Hossain, Adnan Ali and
Qatar Environment and Energy Research Institute (QEERI)- Hamad Bin Khalifa University (HBKU), Doha, 34110, Qatar

*Contact: baissa@hbku.edu.qa

QEERI
معهد قطر لبحوث البيئة والطاقة
Qatar Environment & Energy Research Institute
جامعة حمد بن خليفة
HAMAD BIN KHALIFA UNIVERSITY
IEEE
ELECTRON DEVICES SOCIETY

Abstract

The overall objective of this work is to fabrication plasmonics Au nanostructures on the surfaces of TiO2 thin films by a solid state thermal dewetting for solar cells applications.

More specifically:

- Developing efficient and cheap designs to optimize light management in optoelectronic devices.
- Considering the utilization of abundant and cheap materials to ensure cost-effectiveness.
- Developing multi-physics tool for solar cell design considering comprehensive and interactive optical, thermal, and electrical analyses.
- Experimental realization and proof-of-concept.

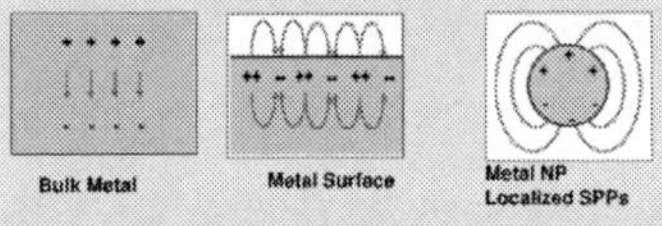

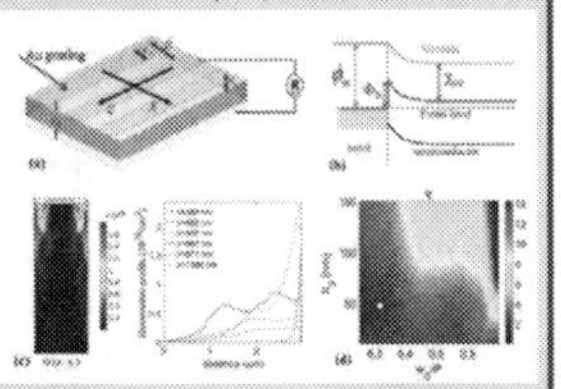

Figure 1: Illustration of a Plasmonically enhanced Schottku Solar cell. (a) Structure, (b) energy bands, (c) generation rate, and (d) PCE of the Schottky solar cell.

We report here on the nucleation of Au nanostructures onto TiOx thin films surfaces which occurred in consecutive steps.

Firstly, TiOx thin films were grown on quartz substrates reactively by e-beam evaporator and then thermally annealed at different temperatures, starting from 300 to 900 °C.

Subsequently, a nano-film of Au was deposited on the top of these TiOx surfaces.

The stacked Au/TiOx samples were post-annealed using muffle furnace at a temperature of 600°C for 1 hour, to study the thermal dewetting properties and the controlled growth of the different TiOx morphologies on the formation of Au nanoparticles and their plasmonic response.

The average surface roughness also increased significantly with respect to the TiOx annealing temperature, which is mainly attributed to the porosity of the films.

Finally, the absorption peak for Au nanostructures has shown a localized surface plasmon resonance close to 520 nm, along with a broad shoulder peak with a strong tail thereby reflecting the wide distribution of the formed Au nanoparticles sizes.

1. Experimental Setup

Metal oxide thin films (TiO_x) were grown using e-beam evaporation of Ti pellet at room temperature under a constant oxygen flow rate to maintain a deposition pressure of 2×10^{-4} Torr. Metal layers (Au) were also grown on quartz substrates using the same e-beam evaporation, at room temperature(Denton Vacuum Explorer™ evaporator). Pristine TiO_x films were annealed at different temperatures ranging from 300 °C to 900 °C, using muffle furnace for 1 hour, whereas annealing temperature for Au/TiO_2 films was kept at 600 °C.

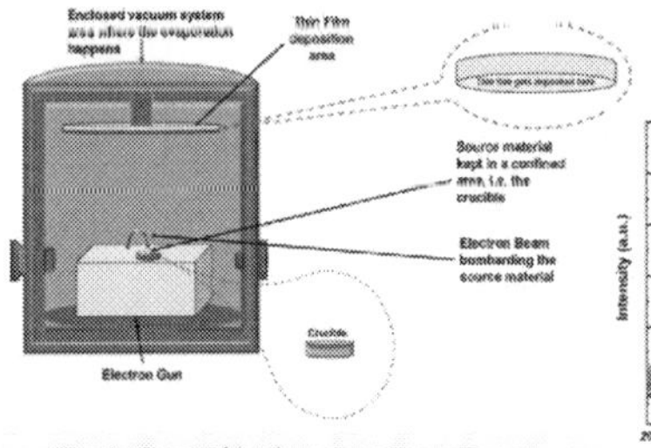

Figure 1: Schematic of the e-beam evaporation process

Figure 2: (a) XRD patterns of the Au/TiO_x thin films with 300°C–900 °C annealing temperature of TiO_x films.

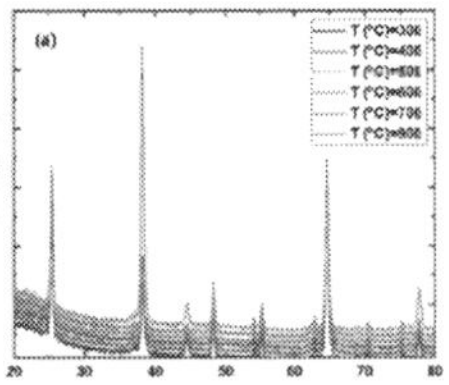

Samples were optically measured using ultraviolet–visible (UV–Vis) spectroscopy. The wetting behavior was characterized using contact angle measurements. Dektak™ 3D stylus and BrukerTM atomic force microscopy (AFM, Fig. 6) were used to characterize surface topology. JEOL 7610™ field-emission scanning electron microscopy (FESEM) was engaged to study the microstructure of the films. Structural characterization of the grown films was carried out using x-ray photoelectron spectroscopy (XPS) and Bruker™ X-ray diffraction (XRD).

2. Results. Morphological and Surface properties:

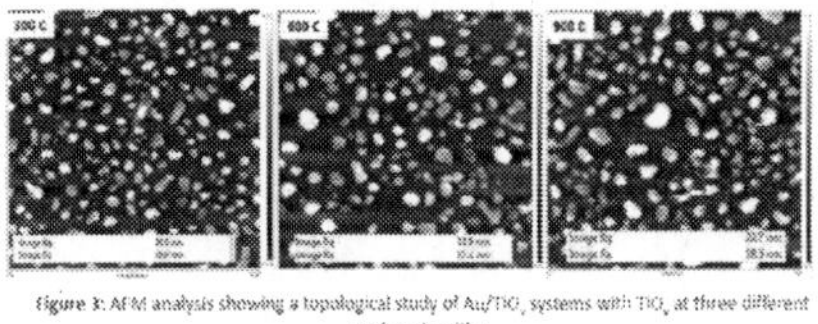

The surface tension dynamics of gold (Au) films significantly depends on the surface kinetics of TiOx films, which leads to the formation of Au particles with various shapes and sizes, different densities, and different grain distances.

Figure 3: AFM analysis showing a topological study of Au/TiO_x systems with TiO_x at three different surface densities.

Figure 4: Wettability study of Au/TiOx structures

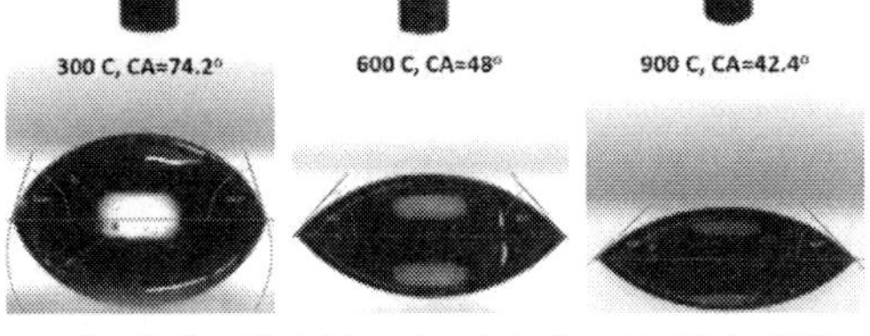

As confirmed by the wetting technique using contact angle measurement shown in Figure 4, surface wettability has changed significantly, and the CA has decreased from 74.2° to 42.4° with respect to the annealing temperature. The samples became more hydrophilic.

4. SEM and XPS analyses:

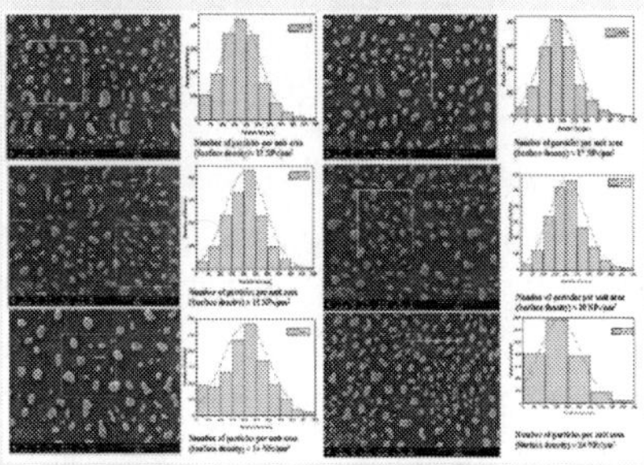

Figure 5:
SEM morphological results of Au/TiO_x systems with TiO_x films annealed at six different temperatures, from 300 C to 900 °C. The size distribution and surface density of the Au NPs is associated with their respective histograms. Figure 5. AFM analysis showing a topological study of Au/TiOx systems with TiOx annealed at three different temperatures, namely 300, 600 and 900 °C.

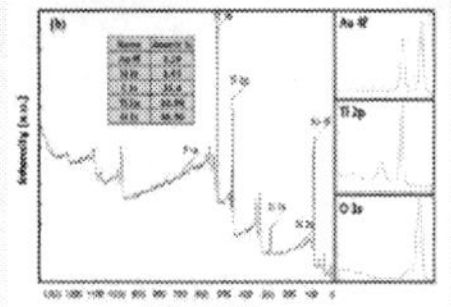

Figure 6: XPS survey of the Au/TiO_x system (TiO_x annealed at 900 °C, Au/TiO_x annealed at 600 °C) along with Au 4f, Ti 2p and O 1s spectra.

5. Optical properties and plasmonic responses:

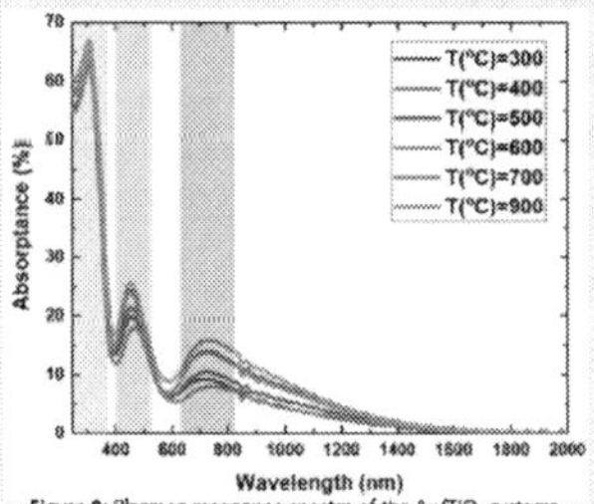

Figure 8: Plasmon resonance spectra of the Au/TiO_x systems.

The absorption peak for Au nanostructures has shown a localized surface plasmon resonance close to 520 nm, along with a broad shoulder peak with a strong tail thereby reflecting the wide distribution of the formed Au nanoparticles sizes, highlighting the evidence of a thermal dewetting efficiency for large scale and high-throughput fabrication.

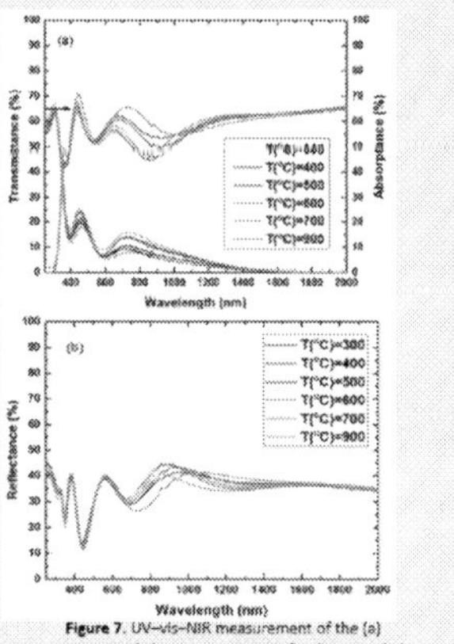

Figure 7. UV–vis–NIR measurement of the (a) transmittance and absorptance spectra for the annealed samples and (b) reflectance spectra of the annealed samples.

6. Conclusions

- ✓ The correlations between soldi state thermal dewetting temperatures and Au/TiOx systems properties have been established in this work.
- ✓ Sharp peak intensity has been observed of all the films with the highest dewetting temperature and attributed to the crystallinity of the films.
- ✓ It was found that crystallinity of Au NPs depended significantly on the TiOx seed layer surface properties.
- ✓ The optical measurements showed that transmission shifts to a higher range with > 65%, while reflectance ranges below < 40% in the visible range as the dewetting temperature increased, confirming thereby that the Au/TiOx systems become more transparent.
- ✓ Finally, the absorption peak for Au nanostructures has shown a localized surface plasmon resonance close to 520 nm, along with a broad shoulder peak with a strong tail thereby reflecting the wide distribution of the formed Au nanoparticles sizes, highlighting the evidence of a thermal dewetting efficiency for large scale and high-throughput fabrication.

References:

1. Naik, Gururaj, Jongbum Kim, Nathaniel Kinsey, and Alexandra Boltasseva. "Alternative plasmonic materials." In Handbook of Surface Science, vol. 4, pp. 189-221. North-Holland, 2014.
2. Khurana, Kanika, and Neena Jaggi. "Localized surface plasmonic properties of Au and Ag nanoparticles for sensors: A review." Plasmonics 16, no. 4 (2021): 981-999.
3. Kotni, Tirumala Rao, Jayati Sarkar, and Rajesh Khanna. "Dewetting of thin wetting film supported by different solid substrates: a review." Phase Transitions 95, no. 8-9 (2022): 551-566.
4. Rudakova, Aida V., Alexei V. Emeline, Andrey I. Romanychev, and Detlef W. Bahnemann. "Photoinduced hydrophilic behavior of TiO2 thin film on Si substrate." Journal of Alloys and Compounds 872 (2021): 159746.

Acknowledgments

This publication was made possible by NPRP grant # NPRP11S-0117-180330 from the Qatar National Research Fund (QNRF), a member of Qatar Foundation. The findings herein reflect the work and are solely the responsibility of the authors. The authors acknowledge the technical support from colleagues who exchanged constructive discussions about the topic of this research. The authors are also grateful for the support from QEERI CORE Labs and Thin Films Lab for material deposition and characterization.

42nd European Photovoltaic Solar Energy Conference and Exhibition

This presentation was selected by the Sc. Committee of the EU PVSEC 2025 for submission of a full paper to one of the EU PVSEC's collaborating peer-reviewed journals.

EVALUATING CLIMATE-SPECIFIC DEGRADATION OF PV MODULES BY SPECTRAL UV-FLUORESCENCE MAPPING

Oleksandr Stroyuk[1], Oleksandra Raievska[1], Oleksandr Mashkov[1], Carlos D. Rodríguez-Gallegos[2], Claudia Buerhop[1], Jens Hauch[1], Ian Marius Peters[1]
[1]Forschungszentrum Jülich GmbH, Helmholtz-Institut Erlangen Nürnberg für Erneuerbare Energien (HI ERN), 91058 Erlangen, Germany, o.stroyuk@fz-juelich.de
[2]Solar Energy Research Institute of Singapore, National University of Singapore, Singapore 117574, cardarod88@gmail.com

ABSTRACT: Spectral mapping of the UV-excited fluorescence (UVF) band maximum is introduced as a universal approachto evaluate the degradation status of PV modules exposed to different climatic conditions and aging periods. The UVF band maximum maps are independent of the excitation conditions, enabling direct comparisons of the degradation state of PV modules exposed to different environments. A distinct correlation between the UVF band position and oxidative degradation of EVA encapsulants,of PV modules revealed by near-infrared absorption spectroscopy allows spectral UVF mapping to be applied for very fast comparative field evaluation of the degradation of PV polymers in different climates.
Keywords: fluorescence; spectral mapping; polymer degradation; near-infrared absorption spectroscopy

1 INTRODUCTION

Degradation of encapsulants and backsheets is a major cause of premature PV module failures. The evaluation of the degradation status of polymer packaging requires the development of new non-invasive characterization methods that are upscalable for high-throughput deployment and allow the comparability of the data collected in different climates. UV-excited fluorescence (UVF) imaging of aged encapsulants has emerged as an informative and fast diagnostic tool, providing new insights into polymer degradation depending on the bill-of-materials (BOM) and climate [1, 2]. At the same time, the potential of using spectral parameters of UVF emission, such as UVF band position or emission lifetime, to provide additional meaningful information on polymer degradation, remains largely unexplored and under-appreciated.

Here, we introduce spectral mapping of the UVF band maximum as a universal approach for evaluating polymer degradation in PV modules. In a case study of PV modules exposed to a tropical climate, a distinct correlation between the UVF band position and oxidative degradation of ethylene vinyl acetate (EVA) copolymer encapsulants of PV modules was found, the latter expressed as a carbonyl index (CI) determined by near-infrared absorption (NIRA) spectroscopy [3]. This correlation is assumed to reflect a competition between primary EVA photodegradation, generating emissive species, and secondary oxidative degradation resulting in UVF quenching and an increase of CI. The interrelation between spectral UVF parameters and CI allows spectral UVF mapping to be introduced together with NIRA as a fast tool for field evaluation of the degradation of PV polymers [1, 2, 4], even at very early stages [5]. The feasibility of such comparison was exemplified by spectral datasets collected for PV modules with the same BOM and age but exposed to different climates, moderate European and tropical in Singapore.

2 SAMPLES AND METHODS

2.1 Samples

The spectral measurements were performed on a set of 34 coupon samples and extracted from 15-year-old PV modules installed as a rooftop system in a tropical climate of Singapore. The coupons were 8 per 7 cm in size, cut between four adjacent cells (Figure 1) from laminates detached from the frontal glass.

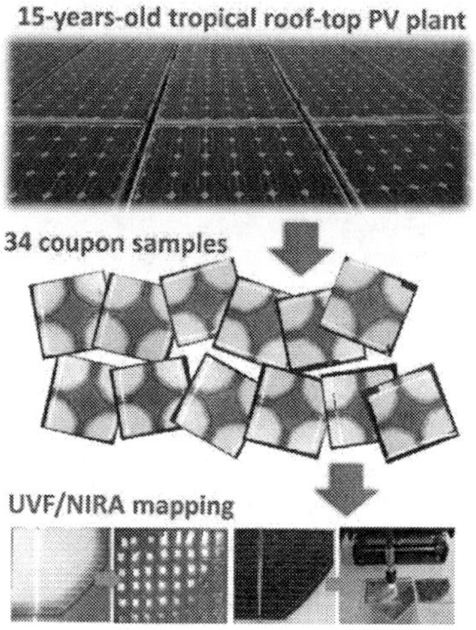

Figure 1: Illustration of the tested samples and workflow (photos of coupons were taken under UV illumination, 350-370 nm)

A cross-sectional Raman study (reported in detail in 3AV.2.10) of coupons showed them to contain a Tedlar-like BSh with symmetrical air- and inner-side 30-mkm layers of rutile-filled polyvinyl fluoride (PVF) and a 280-mkm core layer of polyethylene terephthalate (PET). The coupons also included two layers of EVA encapsulant and residuals of Si cells.

2.2 Methods

Carbonyl indices were measured in two modes.

Single-point CI measurements were performed for a set of PV modules (in the lower left corner of each module [3]) and for coupons (in the center between the cell fragments). For a selected sample, the frontal EVA layer was detached from the rest of the coupon (see Fig. 1), mounted on an Al mirror, and subjected to point-wise NIRA measurements using a Y-shaped optical fiber (Fig. 1) with a step of 5 mm along both X and Y axes. The point-wise measurements resulted in a set of 64 NIRA spectra, used to calculate CI and WI for each point and map them as a function of the coordinates. NIRA measurements were performed with a fiber-coupled FT-NIR Rocket 2.6 spectrometer (Arcoptix) in a spectral range of 900-2600 nm (3800-11000 cm^{-1}) with a resolution of 8 cm^{-1}. The samples were excited by a stabilized fiber-coupled SLS201/M NIR lamp (Thorlabs). Typically, 20 reflectance spectra were averaged for noise reduction. Carbonyl index was calculated as a ratio of integral intensities of a C=O-related band at 2140 nm and a reference C-H first-overtone vibrational band at 1730 nm [3]. Similarly, the water index WI was calculated as a ratio of integral intensities of the water-related O-H vibrational band at 1910 nm and the reference band at 1730 nm [6].

Fluorescence spectra were collected point-wise for the detached frontal layer of EVA of a selected sample, similar to the point-wise NIRA measurements, with steps of 5 mm along the X and Y axes. The sample was excited by a fiber-coupled 365-nm LED (Thorlabs), and the emission was detected by a Black Comet diode-array-based UV-Vis spectrometer (StellarNet) in the range of 400-800 nm with a resolution of ca. 1 nm. Afterwards, the detached EVA sample was cut into a set of 8 by 8 pieces and arranged as a rectangular array (see Fig. 1). The array was used to collect a set of fluorescence and fluorescence excitation spectra using a plate-reading monochromator-based Tecan spectrometer with an excitation wavelength of 370 nm.

3 RESULTS AND DISCUSSION

Spectral measurements were performed on a series of 34 samples, provided by the Solar Energy Research Institute of Singapore (SERIS), extracted from silicon PV modules exposed to the tropical climate of Singapore in a rooftop installation for 15 years starting in 2008. The samples were produced by delaminating the stack of backsheet and cells sandwiched between two encapsulant layers from the front glass and cutting to have an intercell void and corner fragments of four neighboring cells in each sample. A cross-sectional Raman analysis (see more details in 3AV.2.10) showed the samples to be composed of Tedlar-like tri-layer PVF-PET-PVF backsheet and EVA co-polymer encapsulant.

Under UV excitation (360–370 nm), samples showed strong fluorescence (UVF), with intensity highest over Si cells, quenched between cells, and intermediate at cell corners. (Figure 2a). Spectral measurements in different points showed that UVF band center (UVF_{max}) shifts from ca. 550 nm for the sample center to 570-580 nm for the cell corner to 600-610 nm for the brightest areas over cells (Fig. 2b). To quantify the distribution of UVF_{max}, the UVF spectra were measured grid-wise for the sample shown in Fig. 1a, taking 5 mm steps along X and Y axes, resulting in a UVF_{max} distribution map (Fig. 2c).

The UVF measurements were performed using two types of UV-Vis spectrometers, diode-array-based and monochromator-based, yielding identical UVF spectra. The attempt to collect fluorescence excitation spectra yielded no meaningful results due to the dominance of artifacts in the UVF excitation spectra, most probably due to the antireflective geometry of the tested EVA samples.

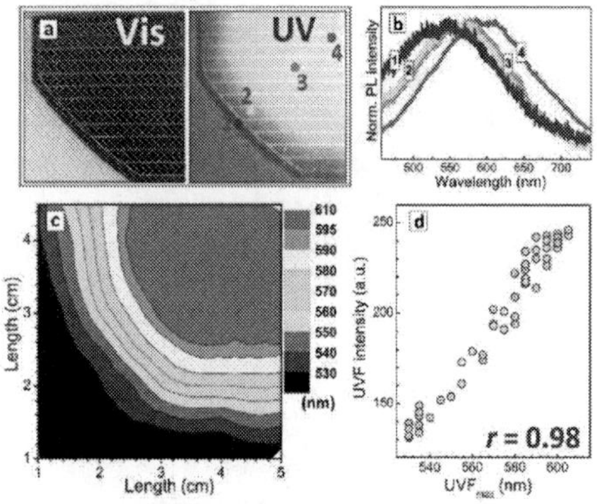

Figure 2: (a) Photographs of the mapped sample fragment made under visible (Vis) and UV illumination. (b) Normalized UVF spectra registered at the points numbered in (a, UV). (c,d) UVF_{max} band mapping and correlation between the UVF intensity and UVF_{max} (d) for a 5×5 cm sample fragment in (a). *R* is Pearson's correlation coefficient

The UV_{max} distribution was found to mimic the emission intensity distribution observed in the UVF images, showing a positive correlation between the UVF_{max} position and emission intensity (Fig. 2d). In this view, the UVF_{max} mapping can be used as an alternative to conventional UVF imaging, allowing direct comparison between different samples, while UVF imaging is dependent on the excitation intensity and angle, requiring additional measurements of emissive reference to enable comparisons between different sites and/or climates.

Along with the spectral UVF_{max} mapping, the samples were subjected to NIRA mapping performed similarly to our recent reports [2, 6] with the same spatial resolution. The NIRA mapping produces spatial maps of CI and WI distributions (Figure 3a,b), both parameters serving as degradation markers in EVA encapsulants. The distributions of CI and WI were found to be negative reflections of the corresponding UVF_{max} distribution and UVF image, with higher UVF_{max} wavelengths and emission intensities corresponding to lower CI/WI values, that is, to a lower depth of oxidative degradation.

Overall, CI values collected over the entire sample surface showed a clear inverse correlation to the UVF band maxima collected from the same spots (Fig. 3c). This correlation reflects a competition between primary photochemical and secondary oxidative degradation modes. The photodegradation of EVA generates emissive species with longer UVF_{max} wavelengths corresponding to deeper degradation, while the secondary degradation by air oxygen results in gradual UVF quenching and oxidation of EVA with shorter UVF_{max} wavelengths and higher CIs corresponding to deeper degradation. These observations indicate that more deeply oxidized sections of the sample located on cell edges and between the cells are characterized by strongly quenched UVF and UVF band maxima at shorter wavelengths, with an almost linear relationship between CI and UVF_{max} determined by two different spectroscopic approaches. Considering this correlation, the UVF spectroscopy of EVA encapsulant emerges as a feasible method for field evaluation of oxidative degradation in PV modules, providing the same level of detail and confidence as NIRA spectroscopy.

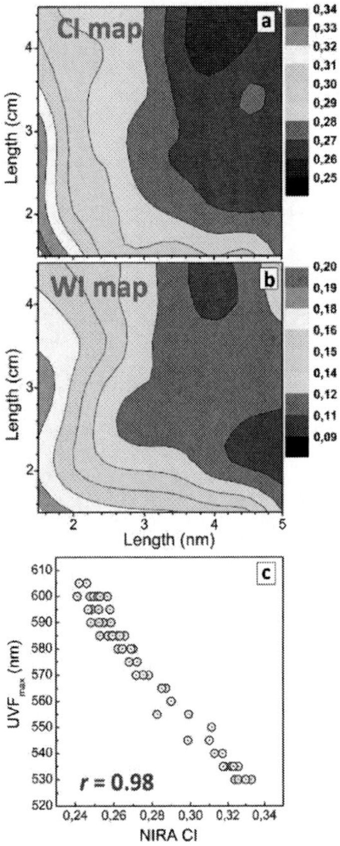

Figure 3: (a) Carbonyl index CI (a) and water index WI (b) mapping by NIRA and correlation between the CI values and UVF_{max} (d) for a 5×5 cm sample fragment in Fig. 1a

As reported in [2], the CI values measured in the inter-cell spots of field-aged PV modules, where the oxidative degradation of EVA is maximal, are inversely proportional to the "wet" leakage resistance R_{iso}, with higher CIs corresponding to lower R_{iso}. This correlation allows the CI distributions measured in the field for a statistically significant number of modules (more than 20 per field) to be used to evaluate the isolation integrity and degradation of the tested modules and compare different fields without making actual electrical measurements.

Here, we further extend this approach by replacing NIRA measurements of CI for multiple modules with the measurements of UVF_{max} that can be done for a single representative module. The evaluation of the feasibility of this approach was performed for a set of samples with the same PVF-type backsheet type and age, but installed in two different climatic zones, in Germany (PVF-G) and Singapore (PVF-S).

Spectral UVF_{max} measurements made for several representative areas of both module types showed a strong difference in the position and shape of UVF_{max} distribution (Figure 4a, left column), the PVF-G modules showing a narrow UVF_{max} group centered at ca. 500 nm, while the PVF-S samples revealed a broadened bi-modal distribution with two apparent peaks at ca. 540 nm and 590 nm. These data show that despite the very similar BOM and age, UVF_{max} distributions of PVF-G and PVF-S samples do not even overlap, indicating an advanced degradation state of PVF-S modules subjected to harsher climatic conditions and stronger irradiation.

To provide additional emphasis on the difference in spectral UVF properties between the two climates, we collected UVF_{max} distribution from a historic module with a PET-type backsheet and EVA encapsulant exposed to field aging in Germany (PET-G) for more than 30 years, showing the highest UVF emission of all samples available in our lab. Figure 4 shows that the UVF_{max} distribution for this module type only partially overlaps with the UVF_{max} distribution of PVF-S, showing the advanced degradation state of the latter samples.

The right column in Fig. 4 shows distributions of CI values measured in the most oxidized inter-cell spots for multiple modules of PVF-G (59 modules), PET-G (22), and PVF-S (34) types. These distributions follow the same trend as UVF_{max} distributions (left column), centering at CI ca. 0.20 for PVF-G, ca. 0.24 for PET-G, and extending from 0.28 to 0.32 for the most degraded PVF-S.

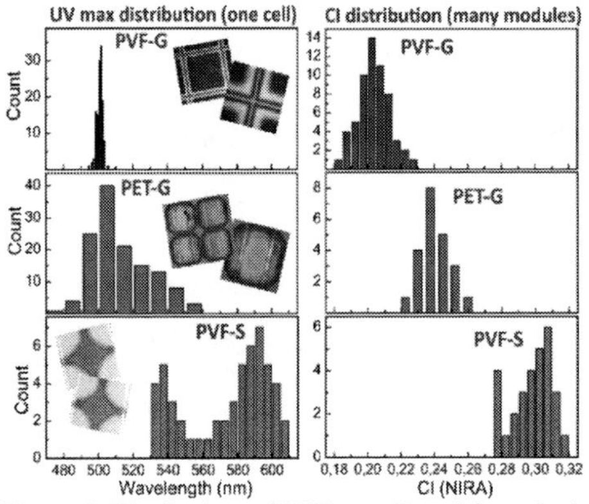

Figure 4: Distributions of UVF_{max} collected for a single particular cell area (left column) and distributions of CI measured between the cells from numerous module samples (right column) for samples with PVF-type backsheet aged in the field for 10 years in Germany (PVF-G) and in Singapore (PVF-S), as well as for the samples with PET-based backsheet aged for more than 30 years in Germany (PET-G). Insets in the left column show photographs of the samples under UV illumination

Similar evolution of the relative positions of UVF_{max} and CI distributions stems from the inherent relationship between the depth of primary photochemical degradation of EVA (expressed in terms of UVF_{max}) and the secondary oxidative degradation (expressed in terms of CI). While both parameters can be used to compare the degradation state of PV modules of different ages and in different climatic conditions, the UVF measurements can be collected from a single module and require a shorter time.

4 CONCLUSION

The feasibility of using spectral mapping of UVF emission band maximum for the evaluation of the degradation status of encapsulants in field-aged PV modules is shown. Based on a set of strongly degraded samples from a tropical climate of Singapore, we found a distinct positive correlation between the UVF emission intensity and UVF maximum wavelength, as well as an inverse correlation between the CI and UVF max values. PV modules exposed to different climates, moderate European and tropical in Singapore, showed distinctly different UVF band maximum distributions, illustrating the potential of the spectral UVF imaging for the comparative evaluation of the degradation progress in different climatic zones.

This work was funded by the German Federal Ministry for Economic Affairs and Climate Action (BMWK) by the project "dig4morE" (FKZ: 03EE1090B) and by the WIPANO project "PolymAERA" (FKZ: 03TN0053E). The samples were collected in the frame of the international PV Camper initiative.

References

[1] C. Buerhop, O. Stroyuk, O. Mashkov, J. Hauch, I.M. Peters, Sol. RRL, 8 (2024) 2400566.
[2] C. Buerhop, O. Stroyuk, O. Mashkov, A. Barabash, J.A. Hauch, I.M. Peters, Sol. Energy Mater. Sol. Cells, 277 (2024) 113111.
[3] O. Stroyuk, C. Buerhop, E. Wittman, O. Mashkov, P. Stephan, J.L. Crozier McCleland, M. Vumbugwa, F.J. Vorster, E.E. van Dyk, J. Hauch, C.J. Brabec, I.M. Peters, Sol. RRL, 8 (2024) 2301022.
[4] C. Buerhop, E. van Dyk, F.J. Vorster, O. Stroyuk, O. Mashkov, J.L. Crozier McCleland, M. Vumbugwa, J. Hauch, I.M. Peters, IEEE J. Photovoltaics, 15 (2024) 30.
[5] A.A. Abdallah, M. Kivambe, M. Abdelrahim, M. Elgaili, A. Ahmed, K. Mroue, O. Stroyuk, O. Mashkov, I.M. Peters, C. Buerhop-Lutz, Sol. Energy Mater. Sol. Cells, 294 (2026) 113899.
[6] O. Mashkov, O. Stroyuk, C. Buerhop, S. Bind, D. Clark, J. Hauch, I.M. Peters, Sol. RRL, 2025, 202500499.

IDENTIFICATION OF SPECTRAL INDICATORS OF DEGRADATION IN TEDLAR-TYPE BACKSHEETS: A CASE STUDY OF PV MODULES AGED IN TROPICAL CLIMATE

Oleksandr Stroyuk[1], Oleksandr Mashkov[1], Carlos D. Rodríguez-Gallegos[2],
Claudia Buerhop[1], Jens Hauch[1], Ian Marius Peters[1]
[1]Forschungszentrum Jülich GmbH, Helmholtz-Institut Erlangen Nürnberg für Erneuerbare Energien
(HI ERN), 91058 Erlangen, Germany, o.stroyuk@fz-juelich.de
[2]Solar Energy Research Institute of Singapore, National University of Singapore, Singapore 117574,
cardarod88@gmail.com

ABSTRACT: Degradation of backsheets and encapsulants induces significantlosses in insulation resistance, often decreasing it below the allowed threshold and inducing inverter shut-offs. The deterioration of polymer packaging can be reliably detected by measurements of the insulation resistance, which, however, are resource-demanding and limited to wet periods. In this connection, alternative non-invasive and resource-efficient methodologies are highly demanded. Recently, we showed that insulation resistance can be indirectly evaluated by near-infrared absorption spectroscopy, using an inverse correlation between the insulation resistance and spectrally identified carbonyl index, which indicates the depth of oxidative degradation of ethylene vinyl acetate copolymer encapsulation. In the present contribution, we extend this spectral approach by applying Raman spectroscopy to identify spectral features of the polymer degradation in Tedlar-type backsheet components of PV modules aged in a tropical climate. We report several spectral parameters that correlate with the carbonyl index of the encapsulant and can be used as substitute for the measurements of the insulation resistance, including the ratio of C=O- and C=C-related vibrational bands in polyethylene terephthalate core layer, the ratio of polyvinyl fluoride- and rutile-related bands in Raman spectra of the air layer, as well as the integral photoluminescence of the air layer. The relevance of the selected spectral parameters as descriptors of degradation events in Tedlar-like backsheets was further confirmed by artificial UV aging tests. This demonstrates Raman-based field diagnostics as a practical complement to insulation resistance and NIRA methods.
Keywords: polymer degradation; backsheets; encapsulants; climate-dependent degradation; Raman spectroscopy

1 INTRODUCTION

Degradation of backsheets and encapsulants can induce severe losses in insulation resistance of PV modules, compromising operational safety and inducing inverter shut-offs. The deterioration of polymer packaging can be reliably detected by measurements of the insulation resistance R_{iso} on the module level. However, such measurements are resource-demanding and weather-dependent. For these reasons, alternative, non-invasive approaches for reliable field evaluation are urgently needed.

Recently, we showed that the insulation resistance of PV modules can be evaluated indirectly and contactless by near-infrared absorption (NIRA) spectroscopy, using an inverse correlation between R_{iso} and spectrally identified carbonyl index (CI). The later indicates the depth of oxidative degradation of ethylene vinyl acetate (EVA) copolymer encapsulants and, in general, the extent of PV module degradation [1]. This correlation was confirmed for several backsheet (BSh) types, highlighting CI as a viable "proxy" indicator of the quality of polymer PV packaging [2-4].

Here, we further extend this spectral approach by identifying new spectral features of BSh components that correlate with the CI of EVA encapsulant and can be used as additional "proxies" proportional to R_{iso}, measurable by field-ready Raman spectroscopy from the air side of PV modules. These spectral indicators can provide additional insights into the degradation status of PV modules, complementing other approaches, such as electrical R_{iso} measurements, spectral evaluations by NIRA, and UV-excited fluorescence imaging [1, 5, 6]. The relevance of the selected spectral parameters as descriptors of degradation events in Tedlar-like (PVF/PET/PVF) backsheets was further confirmed by artificial UV aging tests.

2 SAMPLES AND METHODS

2.1 Samples

The spectral measurements were performed on a set of 34 coupon samples, provided by SERIS and extracted from 15-year-old PV modules installed as a rooftop system in a tropical climate of Singapore. The coupons were 8 per 7 cm in size, cut between four adjacent cells (Figure 1) from laminates detached from the frontal glass. The coupons contained the whole stack of backsheet, inner EVA encapsulant, silicon cell fragment, and external EVA encapsulant layers.

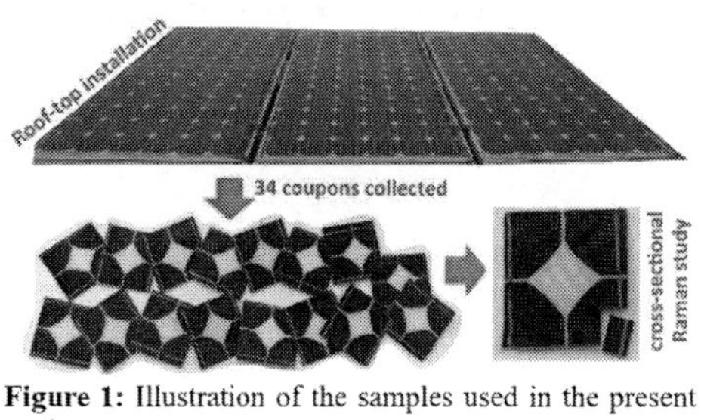

Figure 1: Illustration of the samples used in the present study

2.2 Methods

Carbonyl indices were measured by NIRA spectroscopy in the center of every coupon, that is, on the silicon-free BSh/encapsulant spots between the four adjacent cell fragments. NIRA spectra were collected in a reflectance mode and converted into absorption spectra using the spectrum of lamp irradiation reflected from an Al mirror. Measurements were performed with a fiber-coupled FT-NIR Rocket 2.6 spectrometer (Arcoptix) in a spectral range of 900-2600 nm (3800-11000 cm^{-1}) with a resolution of 8 cm^{-1}. The samples were excited by a

10.4229/EUPVSEC2025/3AV.2.10

stabilized fiber-coupled SLS201/M NIR lamp (Thorlabs). Typically, 20 reflectance spectra were collected consecutively and averaged for noise reduction. Carbonyl index was calculated as a ratio of integral intensities of a C=O-related band at 2140 nm and a reference C-H first-overtone vibrational band at 1730 nm [1, 7].

Raman measurements were performed pointwise on cross-sections of the coupons produced by cutting 1 per 2 cm corner fragments from each of the coupons. Raman spectra were detected on a WITec alpha700 confocal Raman microscope equipped with a UHTS 300 spectrometer in a spectral range of 130-3700 cm^{-1} and a resolution of 3 cm^{-1}. The samples were excited by a 532-nm laser with the maximum power of 50 mW [7].

Artificial UV ageing tests were carried out using a commercial Atlas UVTest weathering setup (Ametek) equipped with UVA-340 fluorescent lamps. The coupons of BShs (PVF/PET/PVF) and BSh components (PET) were supplied by Sunset company (Germany) and subjected to 4000 h of UV weathering at ambient relative humidity (50-60%) and 40-42 °C.

3 RESULTS AND DISCUSSION

The identification of spectral degradation markers was performed on a series of 34 coupon samples, provided by SERIS and extracted from 15-year-old PV modules installed as a rooftop system in a tropical climate of Singapore and showing an advanced state of degradation. A cross-sectional Raman study showed that the samples have a Tedlar-like BSh (Figure 2a) with identical air-side and inner 30-mkm layers of rutile-filled polyvinyl fluoride (PVF) and a 280-mkm core layer of polyethylene terephthalate (PET), as well as EVA encapsulant. The degradation state of the samples was evaluated by measuring the carbonyl index (CI) by NIRA of the frontal EVA layer [1] in the central spots between four neighboring Si cells.

The samples showed a rather broad distribution of CI values as well as Raman features indicative of a broad variation of the degradation depth among the tested samples. Distributions of various spectral Raman parameters collected for both PVF layers and PET cores, with the CI distribution among the tested samples, were compared, with the aim of finding Raman indicators correlating with CI and, therefore, with R_{iso} [2-4].

3.1 Degradation markers for the PET layer

Cross-sectional Raman spectra of the PET core layer reveal "fingerprint" vibrational bands at ca. 1620 and 1740 cm^{-1} assigned to C=C and C=O bonds in PET, respectively (Fig. 2b) [7]. The oxidation state of PET evaluated as a ratio of integral intensities, $R_{C=O/C=C}$, showed a distribution of values among the tested samples, indicating a variation of oxidative degradation depth of the PET core layer. A comparison of $R_{C=O/C=C}$ values with corresponding CIs of EVA measured by NIRA (NIRA CI) [1] revealed a positive correlation between both datasets (Fig. 2c). This correlation indicates that $R_{C=O/C=C}$ measured by Raman spectroscopy is a meaningful descriptor of PET degradation, proportional to EVA CI and R_{iso} [2-4].

3.2 Degradation markers for the PVF layers

Cross-sectional Raman spectra of PVF layers of non-aged BSh show a characteristic PVF C-H vibration band at 2800-2900 cm^{-1} and strong signals of rutile titania (R) pigment at 200-700 cm^{-1} (Figure 3a) [7]. The air layers of field-aged samples were strongly degraded, showing only a photoluminescence (PL) background with no detectable PVF-related features (Fig. 3b).

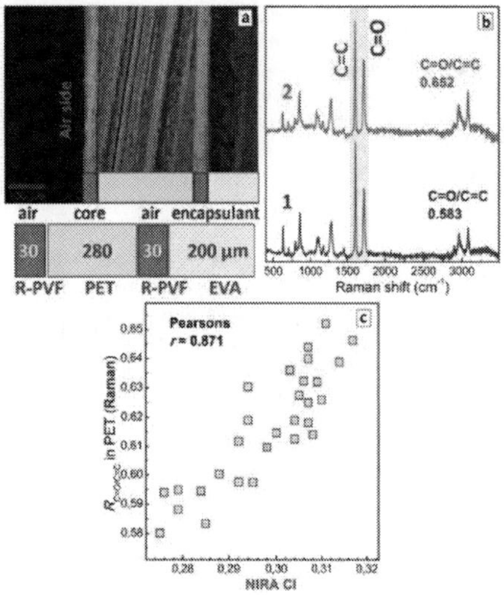

Figure 2: (a) Cross-sectional photograph and schematic of BSh structure; (b) Exemplary Raman spectra of PET layers with lower (1) and higher (2) depth of oxidation; (c) correlation between $R_{C=O/C=C}$ and NIRA CI

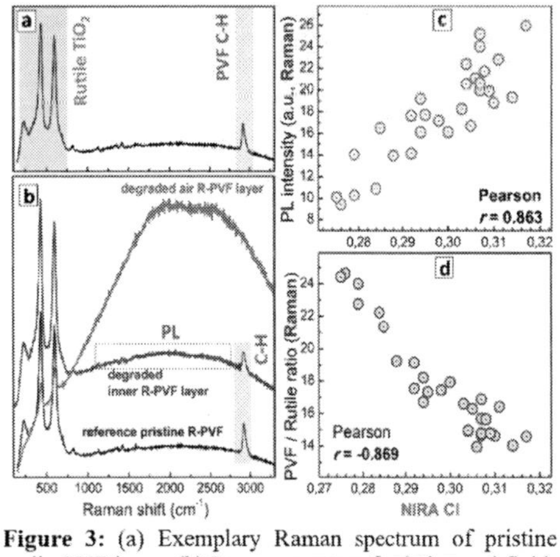

Figure 3: (a) Exemplary Raman spectrum of pristine rutile-PVF layer; (b) Raman spectra of pristine and field-aged inner and air layers of rutile-PVF; (c,d) Correlations between NIRA CI and the integral PL intensity of air rutile-PVF layers (c) and PVF/Rutile peak intensity in the inner rutile-PVF layers (d) of field-aged samples

The degradation depth of the inner rutile-PVF layer is lower, allowing both rutile and PVF-related features to be observed, along with a moderate PL background. At that, the ratio of integral intensities of PVF C-H peak to rutile-related peaks is lower for field-aged inner layers as compared to the pristine one, indicating partial decomposition of the PVF component. Considering these observations, both the integral intensity of the PL background and PVF/Rutile peak intensity ratio can be used to evaluate the degradation state of PVF layers. Indeed, both PL intensity and PVF/Rutile peak ratio were found to correlate with the NIRA CI values.

Higher PL intensities of air rutile-PVF layers correspond to higher NIRA CI values of EVA encapsulant with Pearson's correlation coefficient of 0.863 (Fig. 3c). Lower PVF/Rutile ratios in the inner PVF layers correspond to higher NIRA CI, in line with the expectedly higher degradation depth of such samples (Fig. 3d). These data show the relevance of both PL intensity and PVF/Rutile ratio in PVF layers as spectral descriptors of the degradation.

3.3 Artificial UV degradation

The relevance of the above-discussed spectral markers for assessments of the field degradation of polymer packaging was supported by the outcomes of artificial UV degradation of selected pristine samples, including pure PET film and a Tedlar-like R-PVF/PET/R-PVF BSh. The samples were characterized by cross-sectional Raman and FTIR spectroscopies before and after the test, while a combination of NIRA, Raman, and PL spectroscopies was applied to monitor the UV aging continuously.

The UV aging of PET film was found to result in distinct evolutions in the Raman spectrum, including an increase in $R_{C=O/C=C}$ and a rise of a PL background (Figure 4a, upper part). The integral PL intensity increases with exposure, showing some acceleration at the initial stage (Fig. 4b, scatter 1), most probably due to the photoinduced formation of new chromophores capable of absorbing additional UV light and accelerating UV degradation.

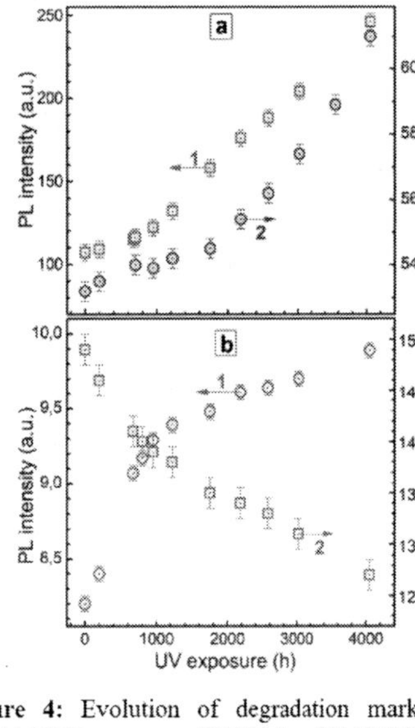

Figure 4: Evolution of degradation markers during artificial UV exposure of PET (a) and R-PVF/PET/R-PVF (b) samples. In (b) scatter 1 – PL intensity, 2 – $R_{C=O/C=C}$; in (c) scatter 1 – PL intensity, 2 – PVF/Rutile ratio

The increase of $R_{C=O/C=C}$ with UV exposure also shows an auto-catalytic character (Fig. 4b, scatter 2), indicating the participation of the photodecomposition products in light absorption and further photodegradation. Summarizing, the UV degradation of PET results in the decomposition and oxidation of the polymer, with the integral PL intensity and $R_{C=O/C=C}$ ratio proportional to the UV exposure, showing both spectral parameters to be adequate descriptors for the degradation processes in PET.

Similar to the case of PET, the UV degradation of R-PVF/PET/R-PVF BSh results in noticeable changes in the Raman spectra of the illuminated air layer, in particular, in a decrease of the ratio of PVF/Rutile peak intensities and a rise of a PL background (Fig. 3a, lower part). The integral PL intensity showed a gradual increase with UV exposure, slowing down at longer illumination times (Fig. 4c, scatter 1), most probably due to the gradual depletion of the surface layer with PVF and the UV light filtering effect of rutile deposits. The assumption of the surface polymer decomposition is also supported by a decrease in the PVF/Rutile ratio with exposure (Fig. 4c, scatter 2). Both observations, the growth of PL intensity and the decrease of the PVF/Rutile ratio, indicate that these spectral descriptors are relevant for tracking the degradation of PVF-based BSh layers.

4 CONCLUSIONS

Several new spectral indicators measurable by Raman spectroscopy from the BSh surface that can be used to evaluate the degradation of PV modules with Tedlar-type BShs are reported. In particular, the ratios of PVF/Rutile Raman peaks, integral PL intensity of the PVF layer, and C=O/C=C signal ratio in the underlying PET layer were found to correlate with CI values measured by NIRA spectroscopy for EVA encapsulant, which, in turn, correlates with insulationresistance of tested PV modules. These spectral indicators are readily measurable in the field with portable Raman and UV-Vis spectrometers and can provide additional insights into the degradation status of PV modules, complementing spectral evaluations by NIRA, R_{iso} measurements, and UV-fluorescence imaging [1, 5, 6]. Artificial UV aging reproduced the same spectral trends as field samples, confirming the robustness of these Raman markers as general descriptors of polymer degradation.

This work was funded by the German Federal Ministry for Economic Affairs and Climate Action (BMWK) by the project "dig4morE" (FKZ: 03EE1090B) and by the WIPANO project "PolymAERA" (FKZ: 03TN0053E). The samples were collected in the frame of the international PV Camper initiative.

References

[1]. O. Stroyuk, C. Buerhop, E. Wittman, O. Mashkov, P. Stephan, J.L. Crozier McCleland, M. Vumbugwa, F.J. Vorster, E.E. van Dyk, J. Hauch, C.J. Brabec, I.M. Peters, Solar RRL, 8 (2024) 2301022.

[2]. C. Buerhop-Lutz, O. Stroyuk, J. Zöcklein, T. Pickel, J. Hauch, I.M. Peters, Progr. in Photovolt., 30 (2022) 938.

[3]. C. Buerhop, L. Lüer, O. Stroyuk, J. Hauch, I.M. Peters, Sol. Energy Mater. Sol. Cells, 257 (2023) 112398.

[4]. C. Buerhop-Lutz, T. Pickel, O. Stroyuk, J. Hauch, I.M. Peters, Sol. Energy Mater. Sol. Cells, 246 (2022), 111913.

[5] C. Buerhop, O. Stroyuk, O. Mashkov, J. Hauch, I.M. Peters, Solar RRL, 8 (2024), 2400566.

[6]. C. Buerhop, O. Stroyuk, O. Mashkov, A. Barabash, J.A. Hauch, I.M. Peters, Sol. Energy Mater. Sol. Cells, 277 (2024) 113111.

[7]. O. Stroyuk, C. Buerhop-Lutz, A. Vetter, J. Hauch, C.J. Brabec, Sol. Energy Mater. Sol. Cells, 216 (2020) 110702.

PVDF-BASED SOLUTION FOR USE AS A DIELECTRIC LAYER IN BACKSHEET CRACKINGS

C. Montes[1], L. Ocaña[1], B. González-Díaz[2], S. González-Pérez[3], E. Llarena[1].
[1]Instituto Tecnológico y de Energías Renovables, S. A. (ITER)
Pol. Industrial de Granadilla, s/n, E 38600 Granadilla de Abona, Spain.
Ph. +34 922 747 700 / Fax +34 922 747 701 / E-mail cmontes@iter.es
[2]Departamento de Ingeniería Industrial. Universidad de La Laguna.
Camino San Francisco de Paula, s/n, 38206 San Cristóbal de La Laguna. S/C de Tenerife. Spain.
[3]Departamento de Didácticas Específicas. Universidad de La Laguna.
c/ Pedro Zerolo, s/n, Edificio Central Planta 2. Apartado 456, 38200 San Cristóbal de La Laguna. S/C de Tenerife. Spain.

ABSTRACT: Backsheet cracking is a critical reliability issue in photovoltaic (PV) modules, often leading to leakage currents and module failure. This study presents the development and characterization of a PVDF-based fluoropolymer solution designed to act as a dielectric repair layer for damaged backsheets.
Various formulations using N-Methyl-2-pyrrolidone (NMP) as the main solvent and acetone or diethyl ether as co-solvents were prepared and evaluated. The most promising formulation (PVDF:NMP:Ac = 21.5:48.7:29.7 wt%) demonstrated good stability, adhesion, and ease of application. Morphological analysis revealed a porous structure with embedded air bubbles and gaps ranging from 20 μm up to several millimeters.
Initial electrical insulation tests showed resistance values exceeding 100 MΩ. However, due to the material's porosity, localized dielectric breakdown occurred under high-voltage stress tests.
To enhance performance, several strategies are proposed, such as multilayer deposition, the incorporation of hydrophobic additives, and the application of superhydrophobic protective topcoats.
This approach offers a practical, field-deployable method for extending the service life of PV modules affected by backsheet degradation.
Keywords: PV module reliability, backsheet,cracking, fluoropolymer materials, characterization.

1 INTRODUCTION

As of November 2024, the global installed photovoltaic (PV) capacity has surpassed 2 terawatts (TW) [1], with the majority of systems utilizing photovoltaic modules encapsulated with backsheet layers composed of polymer films such as Polyethylene Terephthalate (PET), Polyvinyl Fluoride (PVF), Polyvinylidene Fluoride (PVDF), and Polyamide (PA) [2], [3]. Backsheet cracking is a significant reliability concern in PV modules. A 2019 study by DuPont revealed that 14% of examined modules exhibited backsheet defects, with cracking accounting for 66% of these issues [4], [5]. Further research analyzing 26 power plants found that 67% of polyamide-based backsheets developed cracks, particularly in cell gap areas [6]. These findings underscore the prevalence of backsheet cracking, especially in certain material types, highlighting the need for ongoing monitoring and maintenance, as well as finding ways to address this kind of issues, to ensure long-term PV module performance [7].

The photovoltaic cell laboratory at the Instituto Tecnológico y de Energías Renovables (ITER, SA, Tenerife, Spain), with the support of the University of La Laguna (ULL, Tenerife, Spain), has been working for years on the development of thin-film perovskite photovoltaic cells. In one iteration of this research, solutions with high concentrations of PVDF were developed and used as a binding agent [8].

Although various solutions have been proposed to address backsheet cracking in PV modules [9], [10], to the best of our knowledge, the development of a PVDF-based compound for this purpose is a novel approach. If proven effective, this compound could restore functionality to modules typically deemed unusable due to backsheet cracking. Notably, it would enable on-site repairs without requiring the removal of the affected modules, significantly simplifying maintenance procedures.

This article presents the development of a PVDF-based solution designed to cover damaged areas in the backsheet of photovoltaic modules. In the specific case studied, the damage observed in the backsheet is not primarily due to material aging or typical cracking phenomena. Instead, it results from poor handling during the "string soldering" stage of module manufacturing. This type of defect manifests as a perforation in the backsheet, typically near the aluminum frame, which creates an unintended electrical bridge that leads to leakage currents.

Figure 1: Images of modules with damaged backsheet (left) and close-up of the damaged areas (right).

2 METHODOLOGY

The following table shows the most relevant physical properties of the substances considered for our purposes:

Table I: Physical properties of the materials used. ρ = density (g/ml), Bp = boiling point (ºC), ε = dielectric contact.

	ρ	Bp	ε	Origin
PVDF [11]	1.77–1.79	173 140	10	KF Polymer W#1700 by KUREHA
NMP [12]	1.028	202-204	33	Sigma-Aldrich 328634
Acetone [13]	0.7845	55–57	20.7	Honeywell 32201
Diethyl Ether [14]	0.7134	34.6	4.3 [15]	Merck 1.00921

The study was divided into two parts.

First, using PVDF powders and based on the studies by A. Bottino et al. [15], that investigates the solubility of PVDF in 50 different solvents, as well as the work by Mengyuan Li et al. [16], in which PVDF is dissolved in DMF at a specific temperature, we have established a course of action to create PVDF solutions based on the following principles:

- Use a single polar solvent, in our case NMP.
- Perform the mixing process at 200 ºC, which is close to the boiling point of NMP (and well above the melting point of PVDF).
- Stir the mixture 200 rpm to ensure homogeneity. A speed that is too low can lead to the mixture splitting into two phases, while excessive stirring can introduce turbulence and drag the solution.
- Test two co-solvents of different natures:
  - Acetone (Ac): The relatively high dielectric constant of acetone should help NMP dissolve the PVDF. Its low boiling point also promotes agitation of the material during mixing and facilitates faster drying of the solution.
  - Diethyl Ether (DE): Having a very low dielectric constant, it should not contribute much as a solvent. However, its very low boiling point should make its contribution during both stirring and drying considerably better than that of acetone.

Once the best solution candidate was obtained—that is, the one that accommodates the largest amount of PVDF while remaining in a liquid state for a long time—the second part of the study consisted of putting it to the test:

- Drying and adhesion on samples of backsheet material from photovoltaic modules (typically Tedlar-Polyester-Tedlar or TPT type laminates [17]).
- Performing layer thickness measurements on conductive material.
- Taking images with a microscope (looking for porosity).
- Performing electrical measurements on conductive material: Continuity tests, estimation of volume resistance, and electrical insulation tests.

3 PVDF solutions in NMP with Ac and DE as Co-solvents

Table II shows the relevant information of the different solutions prepared by mixing PVDF with NMP and Ac, while Table III is for the ones made with PVDF, NMP and DE:

Table II: Solutions of PVDF in NMP and Ac.

	PVDF		NMP				+Ac			
Vial	Wt%	g	Wt%	ml	g	V%	Wt%	ml	g	V%
1	11.2%	1.3	61.9%	7	7.196	63.6%	27.0%			36.4%
3	15.0%	1.64	56.3%	6	6.168	60.0%	28.7%			40.0%
5	18.5%	1.88	50.6%				30.9%			
7	19.5%	2	50.0%				30.5%	4	3.138	
8	20.5%	2.14	49.3%	5	5.140	55.6%	30.1%			44.4%
9	21.5%	2.27	48.7%				29.7%			
10	22.5%	2.4	48.1%				29.4%			

Table III: Solutions of PVDF in NMP and DE.

	PVDF		NMP				+DE			
Vial	Wt%	g	Wt%	ml	g	V%	Wt%	ml	g	V%
2	11.2%	1.011	57.1%				31.7%			
4	15.0%	1.41	54.7%	5	5.140	55.6%	30.3%	4	2.854	44.4%
6	18.5%	1.81	52.4%				29.1%			

Where:

- Wt% refers to the weight percentage of each element.
- V% refers to the volume percentage of the solvents.

Figure 2 shows the weight percentage (Wt%) of PVDF relative to the mass of the material used, as a function of the solvent combination.

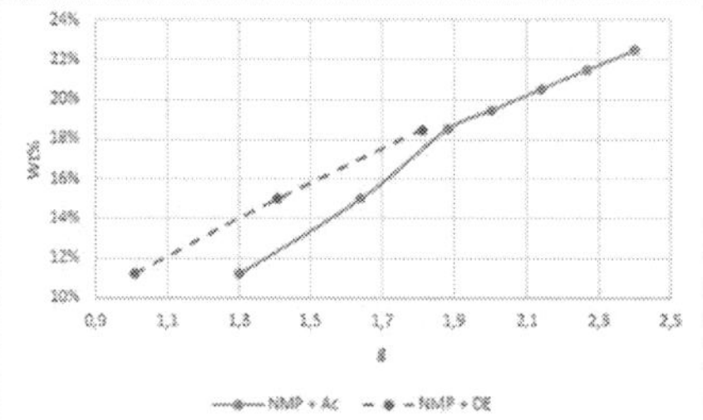

Figure 2: Weight percentage (Wt%) of PVDF relative to the total mass of this material, when using NMP+Ac (blue line) or NMP+DE (green dashed line).

All solutions were liquid when freshly made. A month later, however, their condition had changed, and the results can be seen in Figure 3.

Figure 3: Appearance of the solution vials one month after fabrication, in normal orientation (top) and inverted (bottom).

As it can be seen in Figure 3:

- Vials 1, 2, and 3 contained perfectly liquid solutions.
- The solutions in vials 4, 6, and 10 were almost completely gelled.
- The solutions in vials 5, 7, 8, and 9 were mostly liquid but contained gel agglomerations. The proportion of these agglomerations increased with the amount of PVDF added to the mixture.

Based on these results, the solution from Vial 9, with a PVDF:NMP:Ac mixture of 21.5:48.7:29.7%, was selected for morphological characterization and electrical performance studies.

3 MORPHOLOGICAL AND ELECTRICAL ANALYSIS

The initial deposition of the solution was carried out via a spatula. This method was later deemed impractical for subsequent field trials, leading to the adoption of a brush for application.

3.1 Drying and Adhesion with spatula deposition

Using a spatula, a small amount of the solution from Vial 9 was deposited onto a TPT sheet to estimate the drying time and degree of adhesion. It was also poured onto a copper tape to estimate the deposited layer thickness.

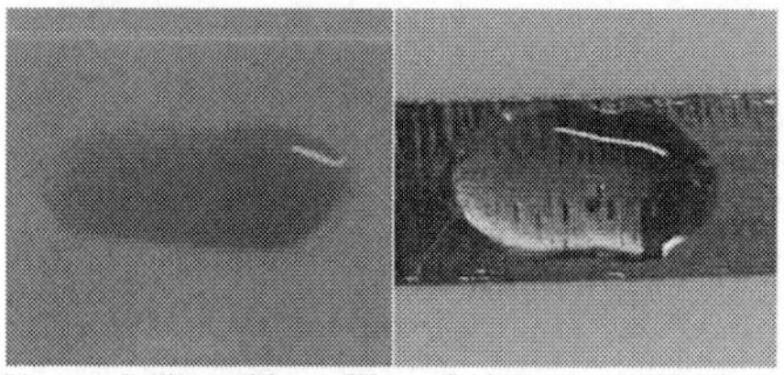

Figure 4: Deposition of the solution onto a TPT sheet (left) and a TPT sheet with copper tape (right) for subsequent analysis.

Two days later, the substance was observed to have dried, though it retained a faint yellowish color. Furthermore, it showed strong adhesion to the TPT when scraped with a spatula, but weaker adhesion to the copper tape, as shown in Figure 5.

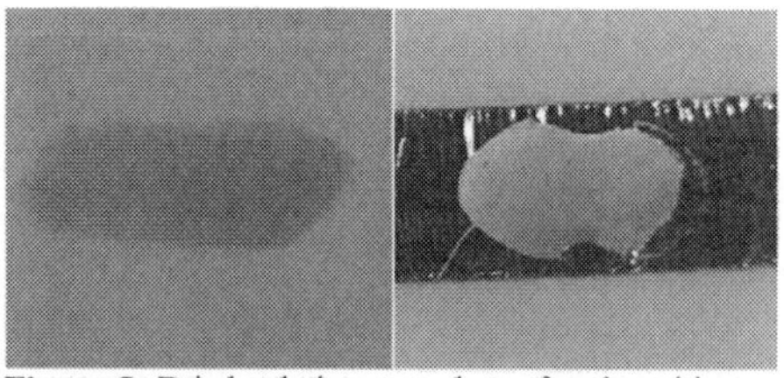

Figure 5: Dried solution, two days after deposition, showing good adhesion to the TPT substrate (left) and poor adhesion to the copper tape (right).

3.2 Thickness measurement with spatula deposition

Using a PCE-CT 28 thickness gauge, a measurement of the deposited layer thickness was taken on the copper tape. As shown in the following illustration, the layer thickness was estimated to be around 640 μm.

3.3 Drying and adhesion with brush deposition

In order to obtain better statistical data on thickness measurements and to have enough substrates for the electric tests, a small amount of the Vial 9 solution was deposited with a brush onto a set of six copper tapes adhered to a glass slide, as it can be seen in Figure 6.

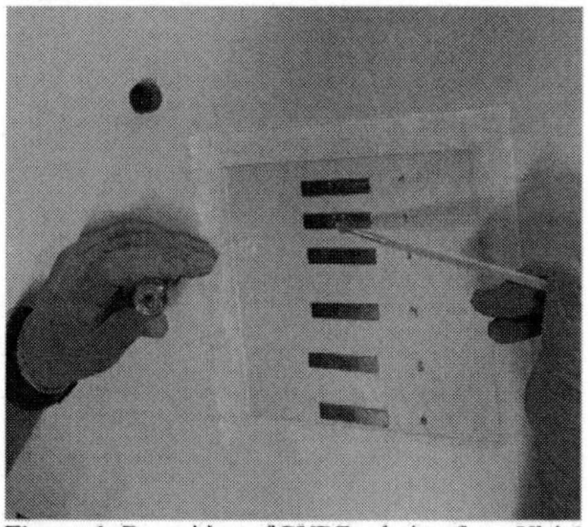

Figure 6: Deposition of PVDF solution from Vial 9 onto pieces of copper tape adhered to glass, using a brush.

Upon deposition of the solution onto the copper tapes, the samples were imaged using a recently acquired electronic microscope with the following specifications:

- Objective Magnification (and C-Mount) with a manual optical zoom ranging from 0.7X to 4.5X.
- Camera Sensor: The microscope is equipped with a Sony IMX224, a 1/3-inch color CMOS sensor. The diagonal of this sensor is approximately 6 mm (0.236 inches). This is a crucial detail for calculating the system's theoretical magnification, which, when paired with a 24" monitor, ranges from 71.2X to 457.7X [16].

To avoid the "empty magnification" effect inherent to this type of microscopy imaging technique [17], we limited the optical zoom up to 3.5X, which corresponds to a theoretical magnification of 350X. Figure 7 shows images taken with the microscope, displaying their appearance immediately after deposition.

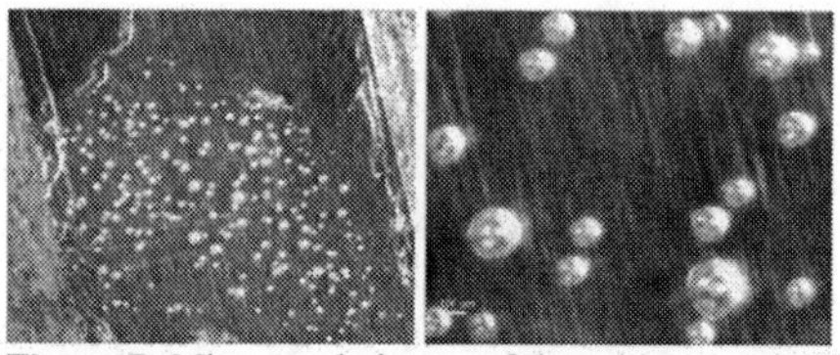

Figure 7: Microscopic image of deposition 5 at 0.7X (left) and at 3.5X optical zoom (right).

As seen in Figure 7, the chosen deposition method (brush) leaves a large number of spherules, between 100 and 200 μm in size, embedded within the material. These spherules appear to be air or solvent vapor bubbles. Five days later, the PVDF solution depositions from Vial 9 were observed to be perfectly dry. The images obtained with the microscope confirm the porous appearance of the deposited material and that the observed spherules were, in fact, bubbles of air trapped in the solution, as it can be seen in Figure 8.

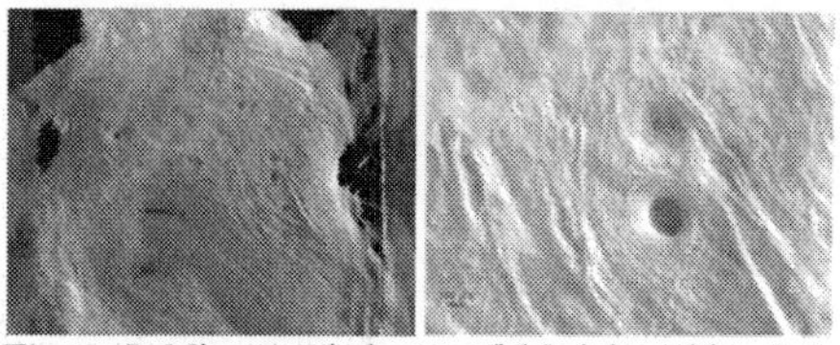

Figure 8: Microscopic image of dried deposition 5 at 0.7X (left) and at 3.5X optical zoom (right).

To ensure the reliability of our results, we prepared a new solution with a PVDF concentration identical to that of Vial 9, which was 30 days old and had begun to semi-gel. This fresh solution, labeled Vial 11, allowed us to replicate the experiment and ensure accurate data for the subsequent thickness measurements and electrical tests. Figure 9 provides a visual comparison of the two solutions.

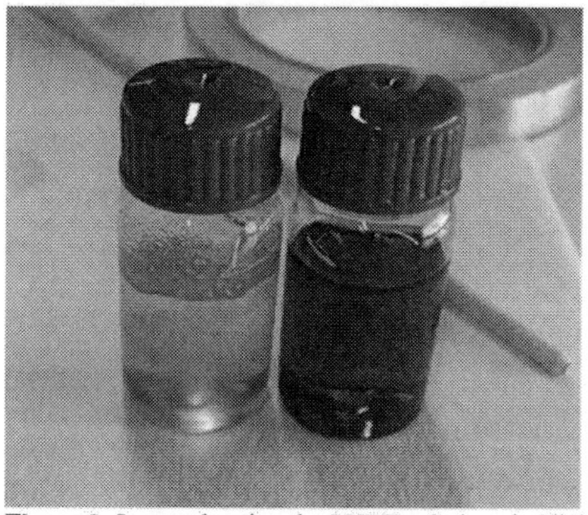

Figure 9: Image showing the PVDF solutions in Vial 9 (left) and Vial 11 (right).

Next, we repeated the PVDF deposition process on six copper tapes adhered to glass. The new samples were labeled sequentially, continuing from the last Vial 9 sample, starting with numbers 7, 8, up to 12. Microscopic images of these freshly prepared depositions were then taken, as shown in Figure 10.

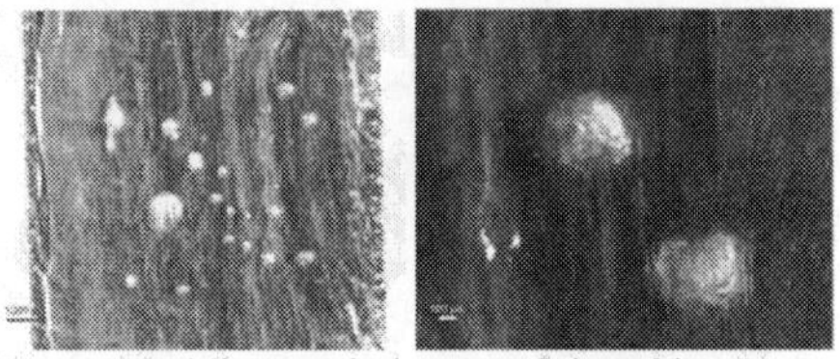

Figure 10: Microscopic images of deposition 10 at 0.7X (left) and at 3.5X optical zoom (right).

A comparison of the brush-deposited samples shows that the freshly prepared solution also produced air bubbles, with some reaching up to 1 mm in diameter. After two days, the PVDF samples were visibly dry but had a more distinct yellow hue than the earlier samples (deposited with the aged solution).

As it can be seen in Figure 11, the microscope images confirm the porous nature of the deposited material, which was also observed in previous depositions. With the current optical system's resolution, the overall granularity is deemed to be below 20 µm. Additionally, we can see fractures over 100 µm thick, which in some cases extend across most of the sample in the direction of the brush application. This is a critical factor for the material's intended application, as porosity affects absorption, liquid diffusion, and mechanical strength [18].

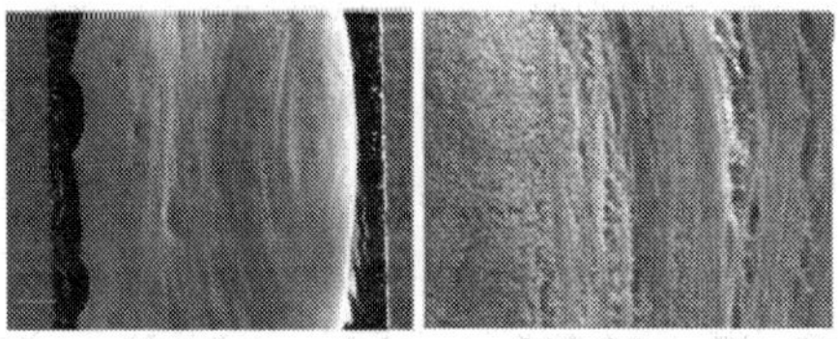

Figure 11: Microscopic images of dried deposition 10 at 0.7X (left) and at 3.5X optical zoom (right).

The obtained images reveal that the deposited material has a rough surface morphology, characteristic of a layered polymer network. The formation of this irregular topography is a common phenomenon in thin polymer films, resulting from the kinetics of deposition, the solvent's evaporation rate, or the interaction between polymer chains during the drying process [19]. These morphological features are critical as they directly influence the material's properties, including adhesion, optical properties, and conductivity [20], [21], [22].

For a more precise characterization of the distribution, size, and interconnectivity of these pores, a higher-resolution microscope is required. Alternatively, we propose the use of techniques such as scanning electron microscopy (SEM), which is a standard tool for this type of analysis in polymer materials science [23], [24].

3.4 Thickness measurement with brush deposition

Table IV shows the thickness measurements of the deposited layers, which were obtained using a PCE-CT 28 thickness gauge.

Table IV: Measured thicknesses of the deposited samples. All values are in µm.

	Vial 9						Vial 11					
Sample	1	2	3	4	5	6	7	8	9	10	11	12
10/09/2025	93.5	89.1	134.0	193.0	213.0	136.0	-	-	-	-	-	-
12/09/2025	116.0	65.4	72.4	176.0	100.0	123.0	290.0	305.0	341.0	253.0	350.0	448.0
16/09/2025	115.0	60.5	117.0	201.0	189.0	123.0	288.0	320.0	280.0	250.0	356.0	420.0
Avg. value per sample	108.2	71.7	107.8	190.0	167.3	127.3	289.0	312.5	310.5	251.5	353.0	434.0
Avg. value	128.7						325.1					

As it can be seen, there is a clear difference in the average thickness of the deposited layers. Samples prepared with the Vial 9 solution had an average thickness of 129 µm, whereas those from the fresh Vial 11 solution averaged 325 µm. This last value is also approximately half the thickness of the sample deposited with a spatula, indicating that brush application results in a thinner coating. Also, when comparing only the brush-deposited samples, those from Vial 11 were 2.5 times thicker than those from Vial 9. This finding, along with the visible non-uniformity of the Vial 9 solution, leads us to hypothesize that the PVDF within the solutions undergoes progressive gelation over time. As a result, less solute remains in the effectively dissolved liquid phase, which is the main component transferred by the brush during application.

3.5 Electrical studies

Using a TENMA 72-2600 multimeter, we first performed continuity tests and estimated the bulk resistance. For all deposited samples, the multimeter was unable to detect continuity, with measured bulk resistances exceeding 20MΩ.

Next, using the HT PV-ISOTEST multifunction instrument in its insulation resistance measurement configuration, insulation resistance tests were conducted on the deposited samples. The tests were performed in accordance with IEC/EN 62446-1 and IEC/EN 61557 standards. Due to the material's porosity, we took special care to position the electrode as horizontally as possible on the surface, as shown in Figure 12.

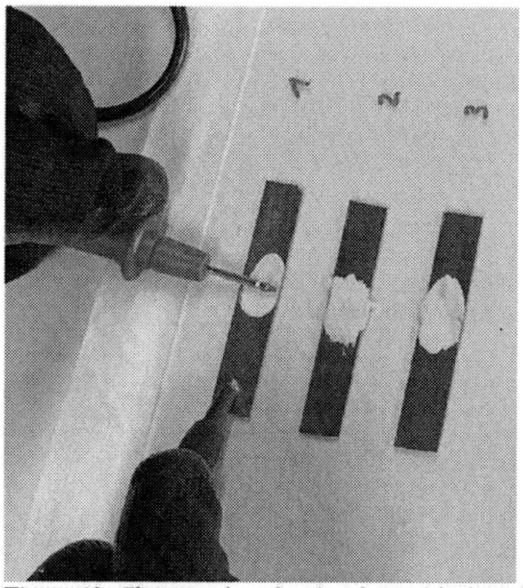

Figure 12: Close-up view showing the positioning of the electrodes for the electrical insulation test.

The tests were conducted at 250V (with a max of 260V), 500V (with a max of 520V), and 1000V (with a max of 1039V). In all cases, the results were positive ("OK"), and the volume resistance (Ri) was estimated to be greater than 100 MΩ.

Finally, in order to evaluate the worst-case scenario, the insulation test was repeated, this time pressing the electrode point first onto the coating's surface and applying the highest voltage setting (1000V). This time the test resulted in an insulation failure. An electrical arc was generated, which carbonized the area surrounding the point of contact, as shown Figure 13. This outcome is highly significant, as it underscores the critical need to implement strategies to reduce the material's porosity to enhance its electrical robustness.

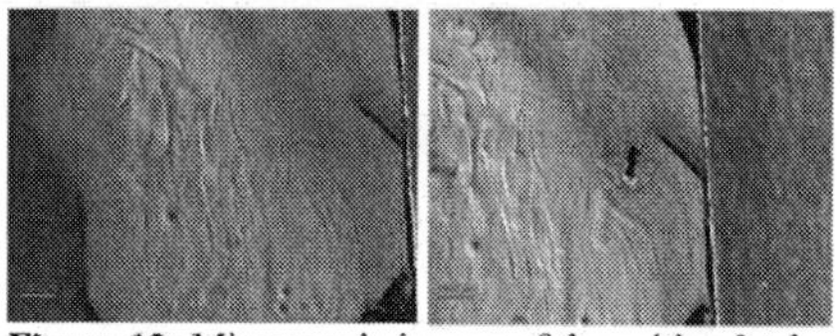

Figure 13: Microscopic images of deposition 3 taken at 0.7X optical zoom before (left) and after the stress test (right).

4 CONCLUSIONS AND DISCUSSION

This study successfully developed and characterized various PVDF solutions with NMP and co-solvents such as acetone and diethyl ether, intended for use as insulating coatings on the backsheets of solar modules damaged by bypass diodes. Through systematic testing of preparation, deposition, drying, morphology, and electrical insulation, we identified that the porosity of the deposited material—estimated to be below 20 μm, though with fractures up to several millimeters in some areas—is a critical factor that compromises its effectiveness as a dielectric barrier.

Insulation tests showed that while the samples exhibit high bulk resistance (>100 MΩ), the presence of pores and shear fractures can induce insulation failure under high voltage.

A practical solution could be to simply apply multiple deposition layers, with sufficient time between each application to allow the previous layer to dry completely. This technique has been shown to improve the structural integrity and dielectric properties of porous polymer films [25].

Additionally, incorporating hydrophobic materials, such as nanocomposites of silicon dioxide (SiO_2) [26], [27], [28], into the PVDF solution could be a promising approach.

Finally, adding hybrid coatings of titanium dioxide and silicon dioxide (TiO_2–SiO_2) have demonstrated superhydrophobic properties, high mechanical strength, and excellent adhesion [29], [30]. These characteristics would make them suitable for application on top of our PVDF layers, acting as a protective topcoat.

The proposed strategies will be a focus of future work. Should they prove successful in laboratory trials, the resulting material will undergo field testing directly on damaged photovoltaic modules to validate its performance and durability under realistic operating conditions.

5 ACKNOWLEDGMENTS

This study was conducted within the SIROCO project (code CPP2023-010858), and is co-funded by the Ministerio de Ciencia e Innovación and the Agencia Estatal de Investigación (under code /10.13039/501100011033), and by the European Union within the framework of the EU NextGenerationEU Recovery Plan and the Plan de Recuperación, Transformación y Resiliencia de España (PRTR).

6 REFERENCES

[1] "Global installed PV capacity tops 2 TW – pv magazine International." Accessed: Sep. 17, 2025. [Online]. Available: https://www.pv-magazine.com/2024/11/13/global-installed-pv-capacity-tops-2-tw/

[2] "International Technology Roadmap for Photovoltaic (ITRPV) - vdma.eu - VDMA." Accessed: Sep. 17, 2025. [Online]. Available: https://www.vdma.eu/en-GB/international-technology-roadmap-photovoltaic

[3] "Solar Backsheets & Encapsulants Market Survey 2022/23." Accessed: Sep. 17, 2025. [Online]. Available: https://taiyangnews.info/reports/solar-

backsheets-encapsulants-market-survey-2022-23

[4] "DuPont module reliability study finds that backsheet defects are increasing." Accessed: Sep. 17, 2025. [Online]. Available: https://www.solarpowerworldonline.com/2019/06/dupont-module-reliability-study-finds-that-backsheet-defects-are-increasing/

[5] M. Kempe, D. Miller, A. Zielnik, D. Montiel-Chicharro, J. Zhu, and R. Gottschalg, "Survey of Mechanical Durability of PV Backsheets," *2017 IEEE 44th Photovoltaic Specialist Conference, PVSC 2017*, pp. 3208–3213, 2018, doi: 10.1109/PVSC.2017.8366198.

[6] J. Markert, S. Kotterer, D. E. Mansour, D. Philipp, and P. Gebhardt, "Advanced analysis of backsheet failures from 26 power plants," *EPJ Photovoltaics*, vol. 12, p. 7, 2021, doi: 10.1051/EPJPV/2021006.

[7] M. Waqar Akram, G. Li, Y. Jin, and X. Chen, "Failures of Photovoltaic modules and their Detection: A Review," *Appl Energy*, vol. 313, p. 118822, May 2022, doi: 10.1016/J.APENERGY.2022.118822.

[8] E. Llarena. C. Montes, L. Ocaña, B. González-Díaz, S. González-Pérez, "REVIEW OF A RESEARCH CARRIED OUT TO PRODUCE CONDUCTIVE INKS AND AGGLOMERATES THAT MAKE USE OF NON-PRECIOUS MATERIALS TOGETHER WITH VEHICLES COMPATIBLE WITH THIN LAYERS OF PEROVSKITE," in *40th European Photovoltaic Solar Energy Conference and Exhibition*, 2023, pp. 020105-001-020105–006. doi: 10.4229/EUPVSEC2023/2BV.2.12.

[9] W. M. Guy Beaucarne, Gabriele Eder, Emmanuel Jadot, Yuliya Voronko, "REPAIR AND PREVENTIVE MAINTENANCE OF PV MODULES WITH DEGRADING BACKSHEETS USING FLOWABLE SILICONE SEALANT," in *38th European Photovoltaic Solar Energy Conference and Exhibition*, 2021, pp. 1051–1053. doi: 10.4229/EUPVSEC20212021-5DO.2.6.

[10] Y. Voronko *et al.*, "Repair options for PV modules with cracked backsheets," *Energy Sci Eng*, vol. 9, no. 9, pp. 1583–1595, 2021, doi: 10.1002/ese3.936.

[11] Kureha Co, "KF POLYMER Poly(vinylidene fluoride) (PVDF)", Accessed: Sep. 17, 2025. [Online]. Available: https://www.kureha.co.jp/

[12] "N-Methyl-2-pyrrolidone - Wikipedia." Accessed: Sep. 17, 2025. [Online]. Available: https://en.wikipedia.org/wiki/N-Methyl-2-pyrrolidone

[13] "Acetone | 32201 | Honeywell Research Chemicals." Accessed: Sep. 17, 2025. [Online]. Available: https://lab.honeywell.com/shop/acetone-32201

[14] "Diethyl ether - Wikipedia." Accessed: Sep. 17, 2025. [Online]. Available: https://en.wikipedia.org/wiki/Diethyl_ether

[15] "Liquids - Dielectric Constants." Accessed: Sep. 17, 2025. [Online]. Available: https://www.engineeringtoolbox.com/liquid-dielectric-constants-d_1263.html

[16] I. Rasnik, T. French, K. Jacobson, and K. Berland, "Electronic Cameras for Low-Light Microscopy," *Methods Cell Biol*, vol. 114, pp. 211–241, Jan. 2013, doi: 10.1016/B978-0-12-407761-4.00010-5.

[17] Greenfield. Sluder and D. E. . Wolf, "Digital microscopy," p. 697, 2013.

[18] P. Colombo, D. C. Dunand, and V. Kumar, "ADVANCES IN THE SYNTHESIS, CHARACTERIZATION, AND PROPERTIES OF BULK POROUS MATERIALS," 2017, doi: 10.1557/jmr.2013.232.

[19] S. Suprapto, G. S, S. R, and J. Jubaidah, "Fabrication and Characterization of PVDF Thin Film," no. II, pp. 2–9, 2022, doi: 10.4108/eai.11-10-2022.2325314.

[20] M. Sharma, P. Chauhan, R. Sharma, and D. Kumar, "Materials and Chemistries of Polymers," *Specialty Polymers*, pp. 15–28, Dec. 2022, doi: 10.1201/9781003278269-2/MATERIALS-CHEMISTRIES-POLYMERS-MANSI-SHARMA-PRAGATI-CHAUHAN-REKHA-SHARMA-DINESH-KUMAR.

[21] R. K. Gupta, "Specialty Polymers," *Specialty Polymers*, Dec. 2022, doi: 10.1201/9781003278269/SPECIALTY-POLYMERS-RAM-GUPTA.

[22] R. O. Ebewele, *Polymer science and technology*. 2000. doi: 10.1016/0261-3069(95)90127-2.

[23] "Introduction to the Scanning Electron Microscope," 1997.

[24] P. M. V Raja and A. R. Barron, "Physical methods in chemistry," *Nature*, vol. 134, no. 3384, pp. 366–367, 1934, doi: 10.1002/jctb.5000533702.

[25] B. Qiu, Y. Gao, P. Gorgojo, and X. Fan, "Membranes of Polymer of Intrinsic Microporosity PIM-1 for Gas Separation: Modification Strategies and Meta-Analysis," *Nanomicro Lett*, vol. 17, no. 1, pp. 1–33, Dec. 2025, doi: 10.1007/S40820-024-01610-2/FIGURES/5.

[26] X. Tan *et al.*, "A simple fabrication of superhydrophobic PVDF/SiO2 coatings and their anti-icing properties," *J Mater Res*, vol. 36, no. 3, pp. 637–645, Feb. 2021, doi: 10.1557/S43578-020-00034-Z/FIGURES/8.

[27] Q. Wu *et al.*, "Dual hydrophilic/hydrophobic SiO2 transparent super-hydrophobic coating with good interfacial adhesion and high mechanical robustness," *J Mater Sci*, vol. 59, no. 46, pp. 21294–21309, Dec. 2024, doi: 10.1007/S10853-024-10470-5/FIGURES/8.

[28] X. Gong and S. He, "Highly Durable Superhydrophobic Polydimethylsiloxane/Silica Nanocomposite Surfaces with Good Self-Cleaning Ability," *ACS Omega*, vol. 5, no. 8, pp. 4100–4108, Mar. 2020, doi: 10.1021/ACSOMEGA.9B03775.

[29] Q. Li, F. Qian, K. Yuan, W. Dong, Y. Han, and J. Lu, "Properties of superhydrophobic filter media prepared by TiO2–SiO2@PDMS coating," *J Solgel Sci Technol*, vol. 107, no. 1, pp. 178–189, Jul. 2023, doi: 10.1007/S10971-022-05871-4/METRICS.

[30] Z. Jin *et al.*, "Preparation and characterization of Superhydrophilic TiO2-SiO2 films for double-layer broadband antireflective coating," *Journal of Porous Materials*, vol. 31, no. 6, pp. 1955–1964, Dec. 2024, doi: 10.1007/S10934-024-01648-Y/FIGURES/12.

PVDF-BASED SOLUTION FOR USE AS A DIELECTRIC LAYER IN BACKSHEET CRACKINGS

INTRODUCTION

From the Lab to the Field: Building on our expertise in thin-film perovskite cells, we've adapted our high-concentration PVDF solutions for a new purpose: repairing damaged PV module backsheets.

Addressing a Manufacturing Flaw: The focus is on a unique problem: perforations caused by faulty soldering. This defect creates an electrical bridge, leading to harmful leakage currents.

A Simple, Practical Repair: Develop a PVDF-based solution to be painted directly onto the damaged areas using a simple brush-based method, making it a practical and accessible fix for on-site repairs.

Reliability focus: Through detailed characterization and rigorous testing, investigate how this coating performs. Such analysis will determine if and how the solution seals defects, prevents further damage, and contributes to the module's electrical integrity.

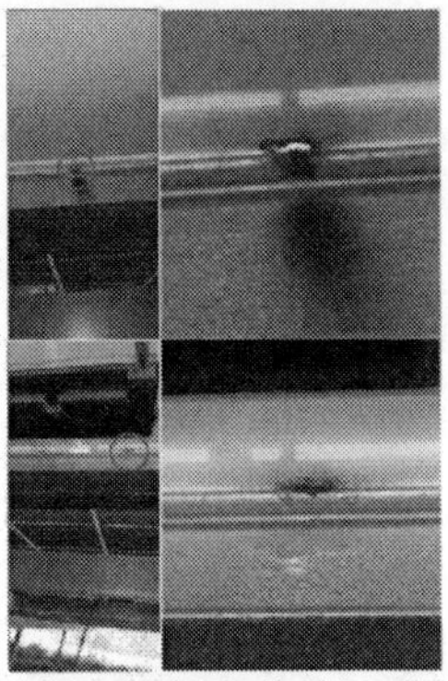

Modules with damaged backsheet (left) and close-up of the damaged areas (right).

Authors:

C. Montes[1], L. Ocaña[1], B. González-Díaz[2], S. González-Pérez[3], E. Llarena[1].
[1]Instituto Tecnológico y de Energías Renovables, S. A. (ITER)
Pol. Industrial de Granadilla, s/n, cp. 38600 Granadilla de Abona, Spain.
Ph. +34 922 747 700 / Fax +34 922 747 701
E-mail cmontes@iter.es
[2]Departamento de Ingeniería Industrial. Universidad de La Laguna.
Camino San Francisco de Paula, s/n, cp. 38206, S/C de Tenerife, Spain
[3]Departamento de Didácticas Específicas. Universidad de La Laguna.
C/ Heraclio Sánchez, s/n. Apartado 456. cp. 38200, San Cristóbal de La Laguna. S/C de Tenerife. Spain.

METHODOLOGY

Solution Preparation

- PVDF dissolved in NMP as a single polar solvent.
- Mixing performed at 200 °C (near NMP boiling point).
- Stirring speed set to 200 rpm for optimal dissolution.
- Two co-solvents tested:
  - Acetone (Ac): High dielectric constant, promotes dissolution and fast drying.
  - Diethyl Ether (DE): Low dielectric constant, enhances agitation and drying due to low boiling point.

Solution Selection Criteria

- Chosen solution must:
  - Dissolve maximum PVDF.
  - Remain liquid for extended periods.

Characterization and Testing

- Applied solution to photovoltaic backsheet samples (TPT laminates) and copper tape, via *brush deposition*.
- Measured:
  - Drying and adhesion.
  - Layer thickness on conductive material.
  - Porosity via microscopy.
  - Electrical properties: continuity, volume resistance, insulation.

EXPERIMENTAL

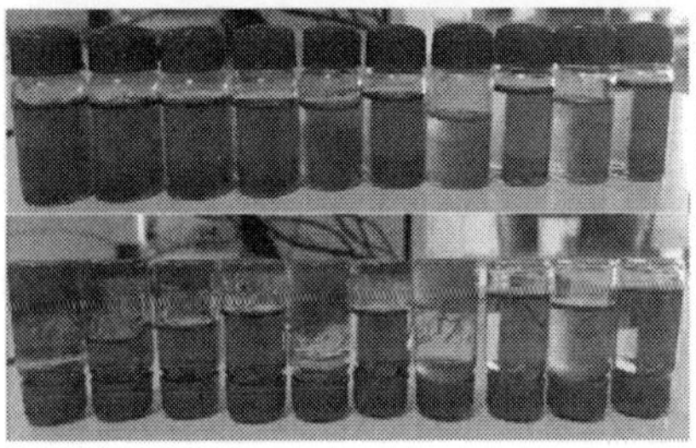

Appearance of the solution vials one month after fabrication, in normal orientation (top) and inverted (bottom).

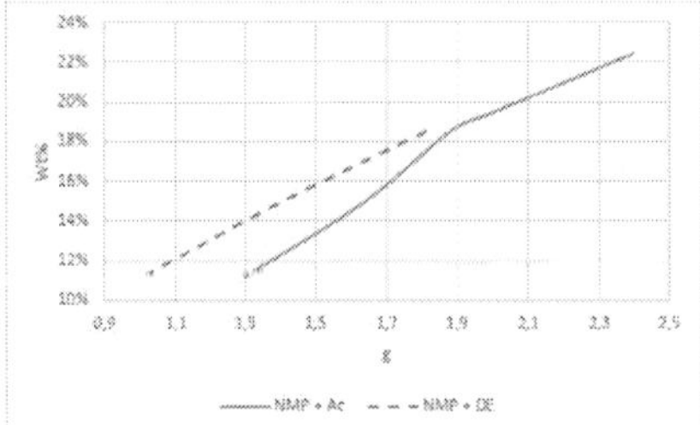

Weight percentage (Wt%) of PVDF relative to the total mass of this material, when using NMP+Ac (blue line) or NMP+DE (green dashed line).

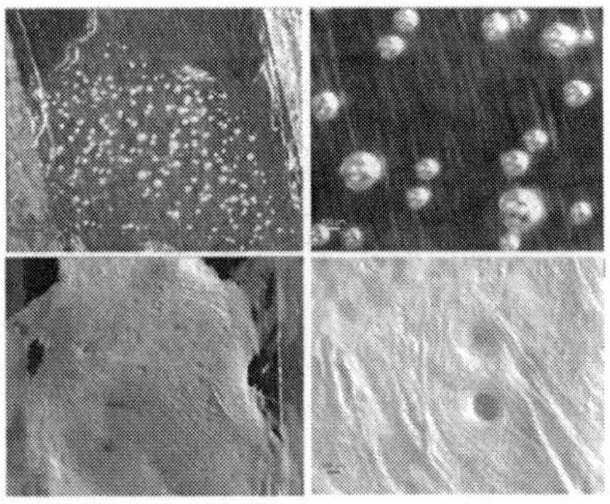

Microscopic image of fresh (above) and dried (below) deposition #5 at 0.7X (left) and at 3.5X optical zoom (right).

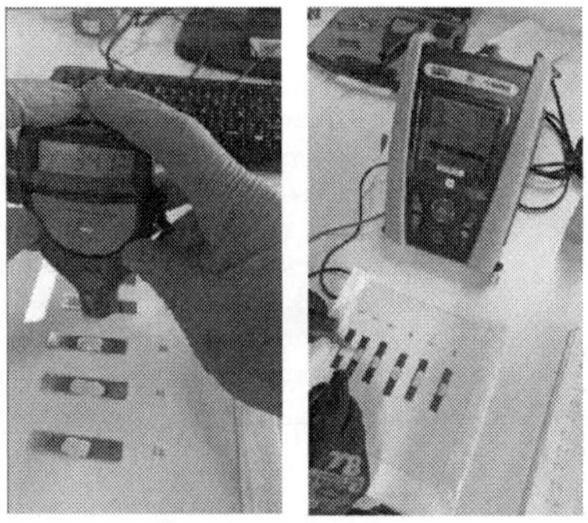

Thickness measurement (left) and insulation test (right).

RESULTS

- **Optimal Formulation:** A 21.5:48.7:29.7 wt% PVDF:NMP:Ac ratio proved most stable.
- **Progressive Gelation:** Brush-deposited layers were **325 µm** thick, while aged solutions created a thinner **129 µm** layer.
- **Porous Structure:** Coatings showed embedded air bubbles and fractures (**>100 µm**), with higher porosity in aged samples.
- **Electrical Performance:** While exhibiting high bulk resistance (**>100 MΩ**), the coatings suffered dielectric breakdown under high-voltage stress, highlighting porosity as a key issue.
- **Conclusion:** PVDF-based coatings show promise for PV module repair, with future work focused on multilayer deposition and hydrophobic topcoats.

CRITICAL ANALYSIS OF THE PROTECTION OFFERED BY BYPASS DIODES IN CURRENT MODULES

Eneko Cereceda [1], Nekane Azkona [1], Yeray Mateos, Alona Otaegi [1], Vanesa Fano [1], Eneko Ortega [1], Jose Ruben Gutierrez [1] and Juan Carlos Jimeno [1]
1 Technological Institute of Microelectronics, University of the Basque Country UPV/EHU, 48013, Bilbao, Spain
nekane.azkona@ehu.eus

ABSTRACT: Bypass diodes are integral components of photovoltaic (PV) modules. Their function is to protect these modules from the adverse effects of partial shading by providing an alternative path for the current. This allows shaded or defective cells to be bypassed, thus maintaining the performance and longevity of the module. In the photovoltaic industry, it is common practice to incorporate three bypass diodes per module, regardless of the number and type of solar cells that comprise it. As a result, the module is divided into three substrings, which prevents a single shaded cell from causing the loss of energy from the entire module. Numerous studies have explored various configurations and quantities of bypass diodes within photovoltaic modules, seeking to optimise energy production under different shading conditions. However, there is a notable lack of research dedicated to evaluating the protective function of bypass diodes in relation to the physical integrity of solar cells in shaded situations. This article aims to address this gap with the objective of verifying whether this three-diode configuration offers sufficient protection to new cell models.

Keywords: bypass diodes, partial shading, thermal stress

1 INTRODUCTION

Installed photovoltaic capacity has increased significantly in recent years, and is expected to continue to do so in the future [1], as it offers the best alternative for generating clean energy, at least for the time being, in line with policies such as the European Green Deal [2]. The cost per kWh of solar photovoltaic energy has shown an exponential downward trend [3], due in part to improvements in cell efficiency. A longer module lifespan also influences the Levelized Cost of Electricity (LCOE). In this regard, there are many studies on the different types of failures in solar modules, depending on the type of cell or the environment in which the modules are installed, among others [4].

One of the components that protect the module from degradation is the bypass diode. Although the cells in a module will have virtually identical characteristics when they leave the factory, some shading is inevitable, causing an imbalance between cells in the same module. If the module is located in a place where it is shaded by nearby buildings, for example, the repetitive module's operation under thermal stress will eventually degrade the shaded cells. Even in an open-air location, vegetation can cast shadows or release leaves or pollen that stain the module. This is why bypass diodes are necessary.

Bypass diodes play a key role in photovoltaic (PV) modules, as they provide alternative current paths that bypass shaded or damaged cells. This alternative current path has a dual advantage: on the one hand, it prevents the loss of the entire module's generation. On the other hand, when a cell enters reverse bias due to shading or mismatch, bypass diodes limit the voltage in the cell, reducing power dissipation and the risk of overheating and localised failures.

The effect of these diodes has been extensively analyzed, especially with regard to the number of diodes used and the different connection configurations with the module [5]. In most of these studies, the objective is to maximize output power [6], [7]. In some cases, the failure of the bypass diode itself and its effect on the module have been studied [8].

Although less common, there are also studies that characterize the temperature increase generated by partial shades and its distribution in the module [9], and relate the area of the shaded with the risk hot spot generation [10]. However, despite the studies on this subject, it seems that the use of three bypass diodes is common practice in the photovoltaic market.

Given that improved cell efficiency is linked to higher photocurrent, it is worth asking whether the configuration of three bypass diodes per module continues to offer the necessary protection against thermal stress in cases of partial shading. This paper aims to offer some thoughts on this issue.

2 HOMOGENEOUS SHADING SIMULATIONS

We carried out simulations using Matlab. We created a module by connecting several cells in series. One of the cells simulated the shaded cell, so different percentages of irradiance were applied to it: from 100% for an unshaded cell, decreasing to 0% when the cell was completely shaded.

Next, we connected three bypass diodes, each in parallel with a set of cells in series, dividing the module into three substrings. The measurements were repeated for the different percentages of shading.

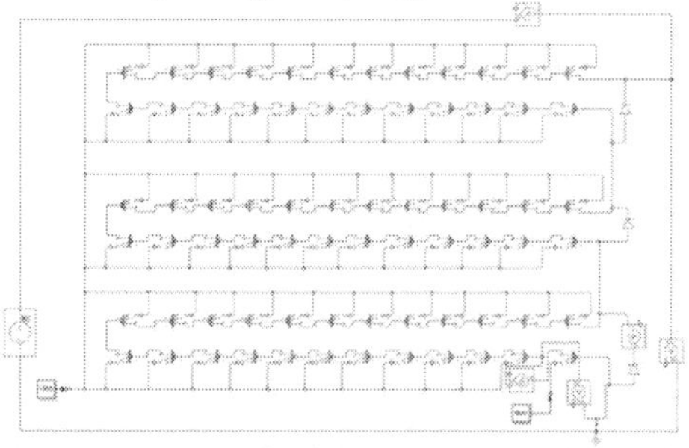

Figure 1: Simulation in Matlab of a module with 72 cells in series, with 3 bypass diodes and a shaded cell.

10.4229/EUPVSEC2025/3AV.2.17

Figure 1 shows the resulting circuit with the cells in the substring protected by the bypass diodes. As expected, when a cell is shaded, the current through this cell limits the current through the entire module until at a given point the bypass diode is activated. This means that, although the generation of the string in which the shaded cell is located is lost, at least that of the other two strings is not.

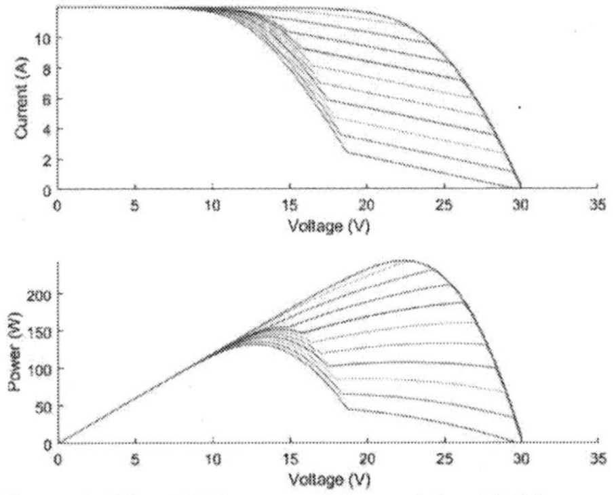

Figure 2: IV and PV curves of the module with 3 bypass diodes and a cell homogeneously shaded to different percentages (0% to 100% in 10% increments).

To see the degree of stress to which the shaded cell is subjected, we look at the power dissipated in it for different percentages of shading. Figure 3 shows the module current (blue), the current through the bypass diode (green) and the power dissipated in the shaded cell (red, right axis) for four different shading conditions, including no shade. It can be seen that for a small amount of shading, the overall generated power loss is small, but the power that the shaded cell must dissipate is high. The worst-case scenario corresponds to shading values between 5% and 25%. The exact value will depend on the design of the module, such as the number of cells in each string or the value of their parallel resistance.

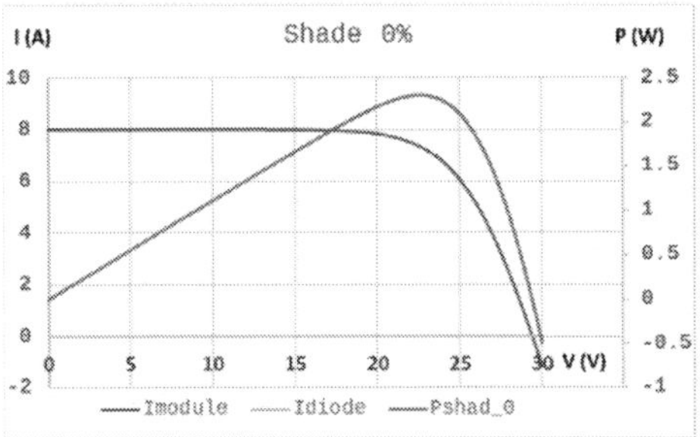

Figure 3: Photocurrent in the module (blue), current in the BPD (green) and power in the shaded cell (red), for 0% shade situation.

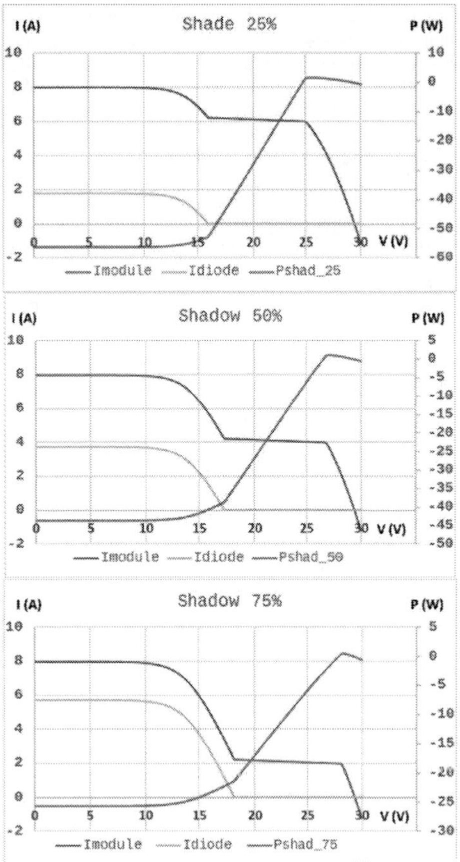

Figure 4: Photocurrent in the module (blue), current in the BPD (green) and power in the shaded cell (red), for a module with 3 bypass diodes and shade of 25% (up), 50% (middle) and 75% (down).

These results seem to indicate that tiny debris, such as a flower petal or a bird dropping, could be the more harmful than a leaf or a building shadow, and lead to increased temperatures in the shaded cell. However, these simulations, although common, are unrealistic, since reducing the irradiance by 5% across the entire area of a cell or reducing the irradiance by 100% in 5% of the cell area are totally different situations. In fact, the former is highly unrealistic, as it would be equivalent to having a cloud the exact size of the cell that attenuates the irradiance it receives.

3 INHOMOGENEOUS SHADING SIMULATIONS

To simulate the effect of partial shading more realistically, a photovoltaic module with three strings of 20 cells in series was simulated using LTSpice. Each string had a bypass diode in parallel. These cells are small blocks containing the equivalent circuit of the cells. The equivalent circuit of a diode was used for this purpose.

In one of the strings, one of these cells was replaced by a set of 20 small subcells in parallel, representing the shaded cell. This allows different portions of a cell to be completely shaded, with a resolution of 5%. More cells could be placed in parallel if greater precision were considered necessary. We are aware that this diagram greatly simplifies the physical behaviour of a partially shaded cell, but we believe it is a good approximation for better understanding the most compromising situation.

Figure 5 shows the circuit representing the entire module, with three strings each with a BPD in parallel and a cell that can be partially shaded.

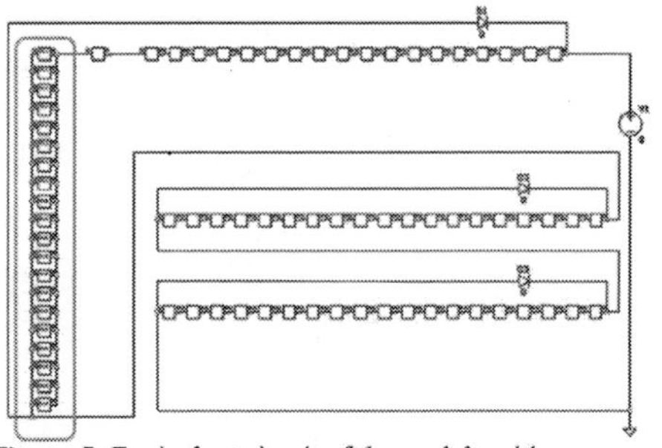

Figure 5: Equivalent circuit of the module with a partially shaded cell (in the orange box) in LTspice.

We have used for our model a general cell with I=6A, Rs=0.01Ω, and Rp=100Ω. For the subcells that compose the shaded cell, the values have been scaled according to the divisions. In this first case, they have been calculated for an area 20 times smaller. Assuming that the conclusions regarding the current and power generated by the module obtained with the homogeneous shadow simulation are valid, we now focus on analysing what happens in the shaded cell. In this regard, figure 6 shows the IV and PV curves for the entire shaded cell (including the 20 subcells in parallel). In contrast, figures 7 and 8 analyse the effect of shading on different parts of that same cell. Shading percentages corresponding to 5%, 25%, 50% and 75% have been selected for comparison.

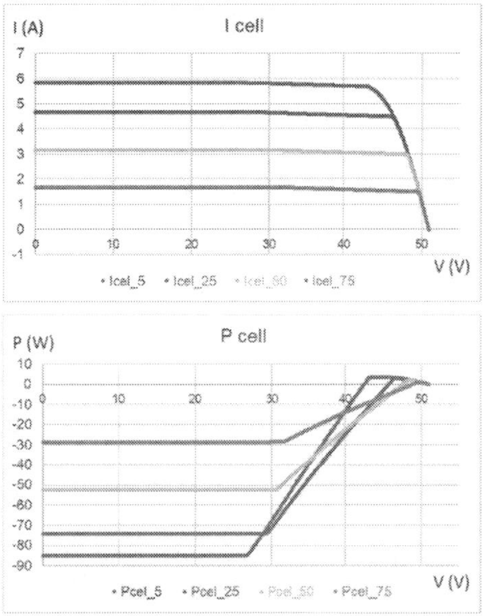

Figure 6: IV and PV curves in the shaded cell as a whole for shading percentages of 5%, 25%, 50% and 75%.

Figures 7 shows the same IV and PV curves but for an illuminated subcell, i.e. one portion of the partially shaded cell that fells into illumination. Finally, fiigure 8 shows the same curves in a shaded subcell.

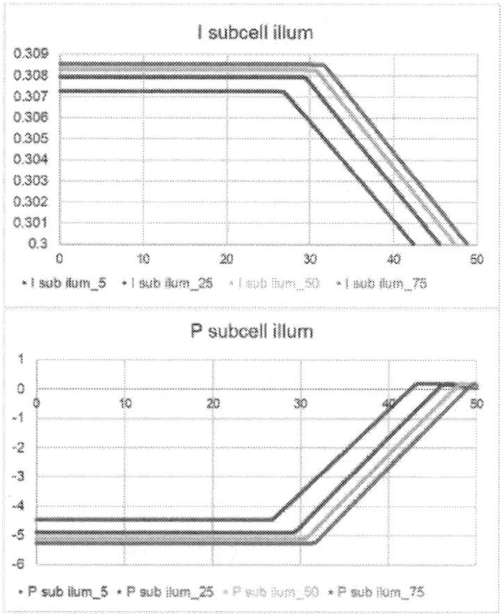

Figure 7: IV and PV curves in an illuminated subcell unit of the shaded cell for shading percentages of 5%, 25%, 50% and 75%.

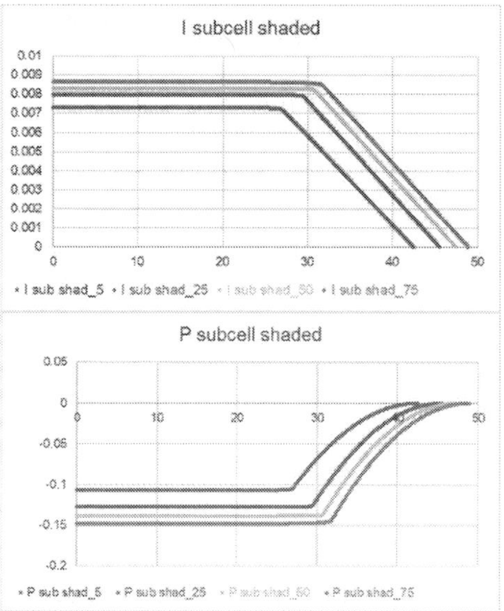

Figure 8: IV and PV curves in a shaded subcell unit of the shaded cell for shading percentages of 5%, 25%, 50% and 75%.

From the simulations with the subdivided cell, it can be concluded that:

- For values close to V_{OC}, the shaded cell also contributes to generation. The lower the percentage of shading, the longer it takes to start consuming.

- If we look at the values for the entire cell (Figure 6), the smaller the shadow, the greater the power dissipated in that cell.

However, if we observe the behaviour in the illuminated and shaded areas of a partially shaded cell, we see that:

- In both the shaded and illuminated areas, the greater the shade, the more power is dissipated. It should also be noted that the difference is quite small.
- Based on the dissipated power values obtained, it can be deduced that it is the illuminated part of the partially shaded cell that is suffering, and not the shaded part. The difference in power here is considerable (about forty times greater).

Considering that a shaded subcell and an illuminated subcell are two parts of the same size of the cell, the values obtained will be proportional to current and power densities, so greater heating is to be expected in the areas under illumination of the cells with most of their area shaded.

4 CONCLUSIONS AND DISCUSION

Simulations of partial shading have been performed in two ways: shadow of the total area of the cell with partial irradiance, and total shadow of only a part of the cell. From the first simulations, the conclusion that the worst-case scenario happens for a small percentage of shading is derived. From the second simulations on the contrary, the conclusion is that the worst-case scenario occurs when almost all the cell is covered, and the part that handles the thermal stress is the illuminated part of the shaded cell.

These simulations have considered a short-circuit current of 6A, so it can be said that we have been quite conservative. In conclusion, we would say that, although bypass diodes prevent total loss of generation, they do not seem to offer an adequate protection to the cells from excessive heating in a realistic case of partial shading.

We believe that in order to determine the relationship with cell heating, the parameter to be taken into consideration is not the total power consumed by the shaded cell, but rather the current and power density, which will be distributed unevenly across the cell area.

ACKNOWLEDGEMENTS

This work was funded by the *Ministerio de Ciencia, Innovación y Universidades* of Spain within the project MCIU-O23/P45 (reference: PID2023-148369OB-C42) under the scheme *Proyectos de Generación de Conocimiento 2023*.

REFERENCES

[1] International Energy Agency (IEA) *Task 1 Strategic PV Analysis and Outreach – 2025 Snapshot of Global PV Markets* https://iea-pvps.org/wp-content/uploads/2025/04/Snapshot-of-Global-PV-Markets_2025.pdf

[2] European Commission *The European Green Deal. Striving to be the first climate-neutral continent* https://commission.europa.eu/strategy-and-policy/priorities-2019-2024/european-green-deal_en

[3] Our Worl in Data *Solar panel prices have fallen by around 20% every time global capacity doubled* https://ourworldindata.org/data-insights/solar-panel-prices-have-fallen-by-around-20-every-time-global-capacity-doubled

[4] Al Mahdi, H., Leahy, P. G., Alghoul, M., & Morrison, A. P. (2024, January). A review of photovoltaic module failure and degradation mechanisms: Causes and detection techniques. In *Solar* (Vol. 4, No. 1, pp. 43-82). MDPI.

[5] Vieira, R. G., de Araújo, F. M., Dhimish, M., & Guerra, M. I. (2020). A comprehensive review on bypass diode application on photovoltaic modules. *Energies*, *13*(10), 2472.

[6] Silvestre, S., Boronat, A., & Chouder, A. (2009). Study of bypass diodes configuration on PV modules. *applied energy*, *86*(9), 1632-1640.

[7] Pannebakker, B. B., de Waal, A. C., & van Sark, W. G. (2017). Photovoltaics in the shade: one bypass diode per solar cell revisited. *Progress in photovoltaics: Research and Applications*, *25*(10), 836-849.

[8] Lee, C. G., Shin, W. G., Lim, J. R., Kang, G. H., Ju, Y. C., Hwang, H. M., ... & Ko, S. W. (2021). Analysis of electrical and thermal characteristics of PV array under mismatching conditions caused by partial shading and short circuit failure of bypass diodes. *Energy*, *218*, 119480.

[9] Mohammed, H., Kumar, M., & Gupta, R. (2020). Bypass diode effect on temperature distribution in crystalline silicon photovoltaic module under partial shading. *Solar Energy*, *208*, 182-194.

[10] Gao, C., Liang, P., Ren, H., & Han, P. (2018). Experimental research on the relationship between bypass diode configuration of photovoltaic module and hot spot generation. *Journal of Semiconductors*, *39*(12), 124014.

BREAKAGE IN BIFACIAL PV MODULES

Rodrigo P. Maruyama, Adnei Melges de Andrade, Roberto Zilles
Institute of Energy and Environment, University of São Paulo
Av. Prof. Luciano Gualberto, 1289 - 05516-050 - São Paulo - Brazil

ABSTRACT: This work presents the occurrence of glass cracking in bifacial photovoltaic modules installed at the São Paulo campus of University of São Paulo. One of the systems consists of 78 bifacial modules (545 Wp) arranged in six strings connected to a 35 kW inverter with a single-axis tracker. Within the first month of operation, two modules exhibited cracks in the rear glass. Over the following months the number of PV modules with cracks increased to 20 (25.6%) in 14 months. To gain understanding of the reasons for the glass cracking events, after discussions with the supplier and manufacturer, a second system with 30 modules (545 Wp) of the same maker and model was installed on a fixed-tilt structure. In the fixed-tilt system cracks were observed in nine modules after 10 months of installation (30%). This study documents the cracking patterns in both systems and compares their occurrence to better understand the underlying causes.
Keywords: bifacial PV modules, glass cracking, solar panel reliability, module design.

1 INTRODUCTION

The global solar photovoltaic (PV) market has grown rapidly over the past decade, driven by cost reductions and a variety of technological changes. In Brazil, PV has become one of the most dynamic energy sources, supported by abundant solar resources and favorable policies that enabled fast deployment of distributed generation, strengthening the diversification of the national energy mix.

While the Brazilian electric capacity remains dominated by hydropower, renewable sources account for about 90% of the national electricity mix. Within this context, solar PV participation has already reached nearly 23,5%. This rapid growth of solar PV capacity, however, also raises the need to ensure the reliability, performance, and safety of PV systems.

Reports of spontaneous glass breakage in photovoltaic modules, often referred to as "spontaneous cracking," have been increasingly reported worldwide. Recent studies highlight that thinner glass, evolving module designs, and inadequate adaptation of qualification standards have created a scenario in which thin glass used in large-area bifacial modules is particularly vulnerable. Field observations show that modules can crack prematurely, sometimes even before commissioning, raising significant concerns about long-term reliability and the adequacy of current testing protocols.

Several research groups [1,2,9-12] have reported glass failures in bifacial modules tested under local weather conditions and some large power plants. The study carried on by Nascimento e Silva et al. [1] investigated premature glass cracking in large-area bifacial glass/glass photovoltaic modules (2 mm thick) installed at a 100 kWp test plant in Florianópolis, Brazil, where approximately 50% of the modules exhibited cracks within nine months of operation. Using scanning electron microscopy (SEM), the research analyzed both the glass thickness and the glass–frame interface, identifying regions with thickness below the manufacturer's specifications (up to 8% reduction) and defects such as voids or improper polyurethane filling along the aluminum frame interface.

A study from NREL [2] highlights broader interacting factors, including reduced surface compression, edge flaws, lamination "edge pinch," frame contact, and stresses from larger module sizes. Both studies point to the vulnerability of 2 mm thick glass.

Together, they show that premature breakage arises from combined mechanical and manufacturing issues rather than a single cause.

2 PV SYSTEMS DESCRIPTION

The studied systems are installed on the University of São Paulo campus, in the city of São Paulo, Brazil. According to the Köppen–Geiger classification [8], the site is characterized as a humid subtropical climate (Cfa). The single-axis tracker PV system and the fixed-tilt PV system are shown in Figures 1 and 2, respectively.

Figure 1: Single tracker PV system. Cracked modules marked yellow (adapted from Google Earth).

Figure 2: Fixed-tilt PV system. Cracked modules marked yellow (adapted from Google Earth).

The single axis tracking system consists of three sets, each comprising two strings of 13 modules arranged sequentially from right to left and connected to a 35 kW inverter. The tracker operates based on solar time at the site's geographic location, with an angular range of +55° (east) to −55° (west). It is equipped with a wind protection mechanism that is automatically activated after sustained wind speeds exceeding 60 km/h for more than one minute.

The fixed-tilt system consists of a single set with two rows of 13 modules each, along with four additional non-connected modules mounted on the same racking structure in the front row. The array is installed at a tilt angle of 24° and oriented toward geographic north.

The photovoltaic modules employed in the systems under study are bifacial silicon monocrystalline n-type PERC devices, each composed of 144 half-cut cells. Their main electrical parameters include a maximum power (P_{MAX}) of 545 W, an open-circuit voltage (V_{OC}) of 49.75 V, a short-circuit current (I_{SC}) of 13.93 A, and a temperature coefficient of power (γ) of $-0.35\%/°C$. Furthermore, the modules exhibit a bifaciality factor of 70% ±10%.

Figure 3 shows the mounting position of the PV modules and in the images in Figures 5 and 6 these positions are identified by blue dots.

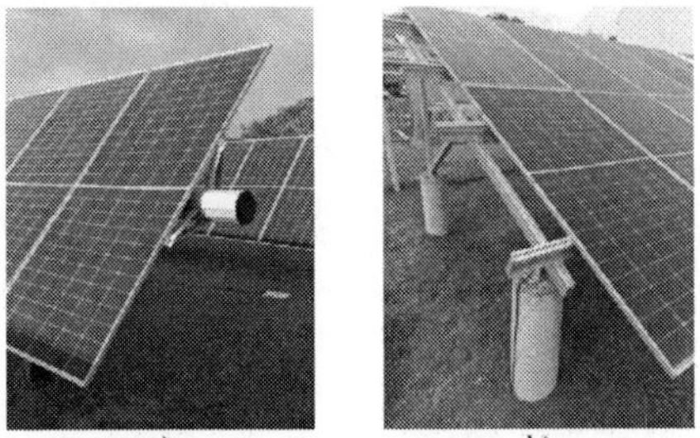

a) b)

Figure 3: PV module mounting position. a) Tracker PV system and b) Fixed-tilt PV system.

The module's dimensions are 2,278 × 1,134 × 30 mm (L×W×H), a total mass of 31.8 kg, and a double-glass structure composed of 2.0 mm glass on both the front and rear sides. They are designed to withstand static mechanical loads, with maximum tolerances of 5,400 Pa (112 lb/ft^2) applied on the front surface and 2,400 Pa (50 lb/ft^2) on the rear surface.

In terms of reliability assurances, the manufacturer provides a product warranty of 12 years and a linear performance warranty of 30 years. According to this guarantee, the modules are warranted to deliver at least 85% of their initial nominal power output by the 30th year of operation, corresponding to an average annual degradation rate of approximately 0.45%.

In addition to the mechanical parameters described above, the glass layers play a central role in the structural integrity of photovoltaic modules. Commercial PV modules typically employ one of two glass types: rolled (patterned) glass or float glass. Rolled glass is produced by drawing molten glass through water-cooled rollers, which imprint a dimpled inner surface and leave a relatively smooth outer surface; it is frequently used on the front and rear sides of c-Si modules. Float glass, on the other hand, is manufactured on a molten tin bath, resulting in very smooth surfaces free of dimples.

Although both technologies are widely adopted, rolled glass has not demonstrated consistent optical or adhesion advantages, and the dimples introduced during manufacturing may act as stress concentrators that slightly reduce mechanical strength compared to float glass [4]. The manufacturer's datasheet of the studied module does not indicate all the characteristics of the employed glass, introducing an additional layer of uncertainty to the failure analysis.

3 CRACK OBSERVATION

In the tracker system, installed in November 2023, the first cracks were observed in two modules as early as 10 days after installation (2.56% of the modules). The number of affected modules continued to grow, reaching 20 cracked units after 14 months, corresponding to 25.64% of the modules.

In the Fixed-tilt system, where less cracking was expected, the first glass crack was recorded after three months of installation. After six months of operation, 30% of the modules had cracks.

The comparative analysis showed that both systems had similar failure rates: 20/78 modules (25.64%) in the tracker system and 9/30 modules (30%) in the fixed system. Different crack patterns, however, were observed; in the fixed system, cracks displayed periodic-like waviness, while in the tracker system no periodic-like waviness was observed.

Crack formation was recorded over time in order to understand its dynamics, as shown in Figure 4. In this example the cracks in three modules are illustrated.

In Figure 4a the cracking evolution is recorded at two different moments. The first record, shown in red, corresponds to the initial observation, while the yellow markings indicate the cracking evolution pattern after approximately 100 days. Figures 4b and 4c show the cracks in modules 01 and 02 of the bottom string and were observed 8 months and 9 months after installation startup, respectively. The red line marks the initial crack observation, while the yellow line indicates the second observation.

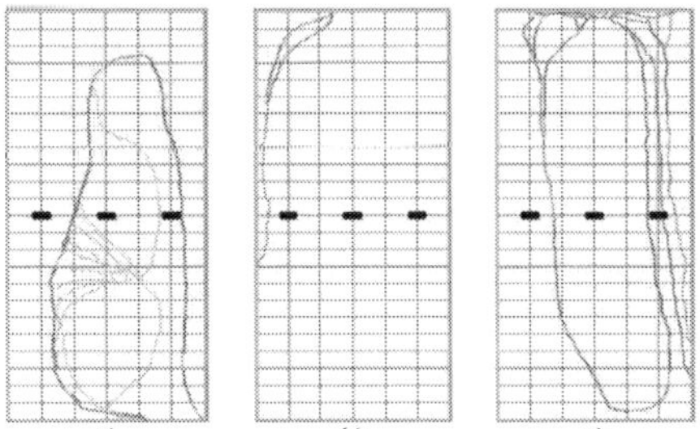

a) b) c)

Figure 4: Example of recorded cracking patterns. a) Top String module 01, b) Bottom string module 01 and c) Bottom string module 02.

Data registration was performed for all 29 cracked modules, 20 of them located in the single-axis tracking PV system and 9 in the fixed-tilt PV system. For each cracked module, the cracking records were mapped into a matrix of 24 rows by 6 columns, corresponding to the physical position of each half-cell within the module. Initially, the matrices were filled with zeros, and whenever a glass crack was identified, the value at the corresponding position was set to 1. This procedure was repeated for every cracked module, and the resulting matrices were subsequently combined to generate the aggregated crack distributions presented in Figure 5. The color scale represents the frequency of cracks at each cell position. Darker shades indicate a higher concentration of cracks in that specific location.

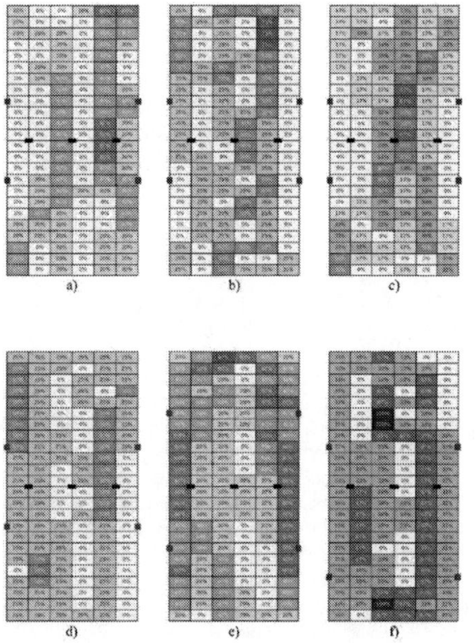

Figure 5: Matrix combination for strings in both PV systems. a) String 1, b) String 02, c) String 03, d) String 05, e) Bottom string and f) Top string.

To get a broader view of each system analyzed, the matrices were summed for all modules in each system. The results can be seen in Figure 6.

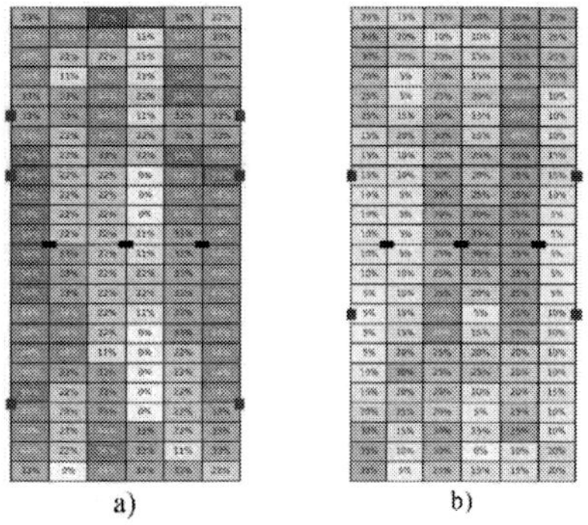

Figure 6: Matrix sum of all cracked modules, a) Fixed-tilt and b) Tracker PV system.

The observation of crack initiation and growth shows a clear difference between the single-axis tracker PV system and the fixed-tilt PV system. In the tracker system, cracks occur more often in the middle of the module, whereas in the fixed-tilt system they tend to form close to the edges. It is also important to highlight that in the tracker system, cracks are rarely found close to the clamps in the mounting, which rules out the assembly clamps as a possible cracking initiation cause.

The observed mechanical behavior of the module frame under static load can be explained by its boundary conditions and structural constraints. When the module is fixed at the 400 mm mounting position, the frame in the immediate vicinity of the mounting point remains largely prevented from torsional deformation. However, as the distance from the mounting point increases, the frame exhibits a tendency to twist. This torsional movement propagates along the frame until it approaches the corner region. At this point, the corner geometry and the rigidity of the frame prevent further torsional displacement, leading instead to localized stress concentration. These concentrated stresses at the corners provide a plausible explanation for the high frequency of cracks observed in Figure 6b.

A graphic of the local ambient temperature is shown in Figure 7. To seek the understanding of crack evolution, the dates of the observation were plotted on the graph. It should be noted that the recording dates may not correspond to the exact day of the crack's initiation or growth.

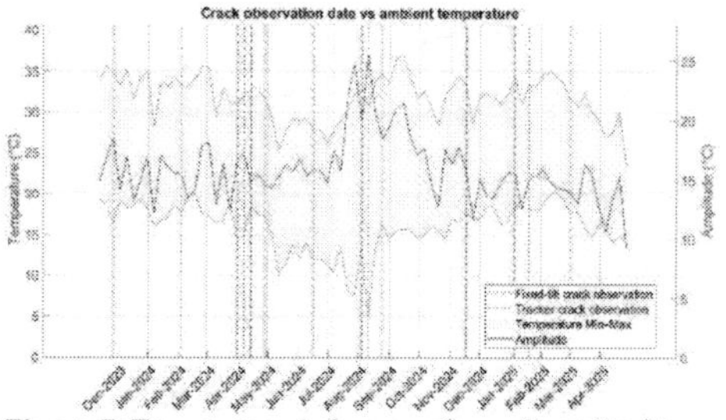

Figure 7: Temperature (min, max, thermal amplitude) and timestamps of new cracks.

4 EVALUATION TECHNIQUES

In addition to recording and organizing the collected data, technical analyses were carried out, namely electroluminescence (IEC 60904-13), IV Curve (IEC 60904-1), dry (IEC 61215 - MQT 03) and wet (IEC 61215 - MQT 15) insulation resistance, and measurements of module deflection (sagging).

The tests were performed in our laboratory, which is signatory of the ILAC Mutual Recognition Arrangement (ILAC-MRA), ensuring that the results are internationally recognized for their technical competence, impartiality, and compliance with ISO/IEC 17025 requirements.

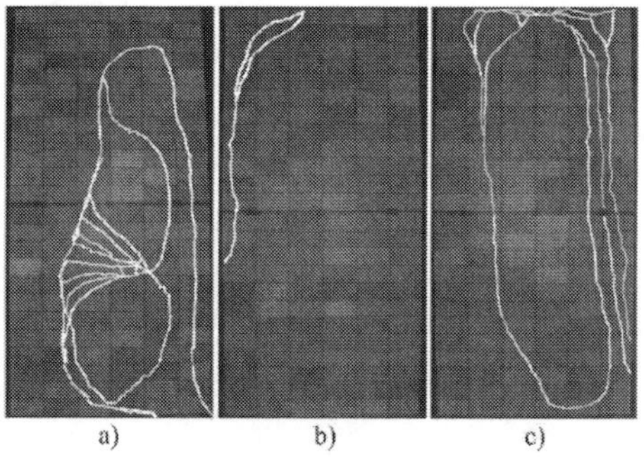

Figure 8: Electroluminescence in the modules seen in Figure 4. a) Top String module 01, b) Bottom string module 01 and c) Bottom string module 02.

4.1 Electroluminescence evaluation

Test was carried out following IEC TS 60904-13. Figure 8 shows the electroluminescence generated by the cracked modules previously seen in Figure 4.

4.2 IV Curve

Modules in Figure 9 are coded by their exposure history and mounting scheme: **UNExp** (unexposed) is a reference module that has never been exposed to real-world sunlight and is kept stored as a testimonial sample; **Exp** denotes a module that has been field-exposed but was not electrically connected; **Conn** indicates a module in normal operation with no cracks; and **ConnCrack** designates a module in operation that exhibits glass cracks.

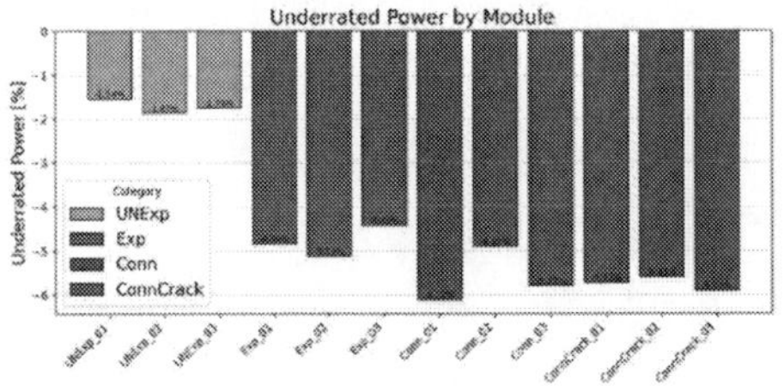

Figure 9: Underrated power by module.

Average power loss from the 545 W nameplate is: **UNExp** 1.72% (9.4 W), **Exp** 4.80% (26.2 W), **Conn** 5.61% (30.6 W), **ConnCrack** 5.75% (31.3 W). Loss increases from unexposed to exposed to operating modules. The solar simulator has an uncertainty of ±2%, so **Exp**, **Conn**, and **ConnCrack** are statistically indistinguishable from each other in these tests. The observed power losses, ranging from 5.61% to 5.75%, significantly exceed the degradation rate outlined in the manufacturer's datasheet. For the 16-month period of use, the manufacturer specifies a linear degradation rate of 0.45% per year, which would result in an expected loss of 2.6%.

4.3 IEC 61215:2021 MQT 03 and MQT 15

The tests were carried out following IEC 61215:2021 [7] with calibrated equipment with traceable calibration certificates linked to national and international standards.

The MQT 03 test verifies the insulation resistance of the photovoltaic module under dry conditions. It ensures that the insulation between the active electrical circuits and the metallic frame can withstand the system's maximum voltage without excessive leakage current. The result is expressed in GΩ and normalized by the module area ($G\Omega \cdot m^2$). The results are shown in Table I.

The MQT 15 test verifies the insulation resistance of the photovoltaic module under wet conditions as specified in this standard. The results are shown in Table I.

Three tests were conducted: one for MQT 03; two for MQT 15 in two different moments. Test 3 was conducted 2 hours after test 2. The results are shown in Table I.

The module showed very high insulation resistance under dry conditions (7.13 $G\Omega \cdot m^2$), well above the minimum limit of 40 $M\Omega \cdot m^2$ required by IEC 61215:2021. In the two wet leakage current tests, the insulation resistance showed to be between 2.78 $G\Omega \cdot m^2$ and 3.09 $G\Omega \cdot m^2$, demonstrating stability and electrical safety under humidity. The module was considered PASSED in the Insulation Resistance (MQT 03) and Wet Leakage Current (MQT 15) tests, according to IEC 61215:2021.

Table I: MQT 03 and MQT 15 test results.

Parameter	Test 1 – MQT 03	Test 2 – MQT 15	Test 3 – MQT 15
Ambient temperature	26.2 °C	16.1 °C	16.1 °C
Relative humidity	35 %	NA*	NA*
Water temperature	NA*	14.9 °C	15.4 °C
Applied voltage	1544 V (2 min)	1544 V (2 min)	1544 V (2 min)
Insulation resistance	18.4 GΩ	7.17 GΩ	7.99 GΩ
Module area	2.58 m^2	2.58 m^2	2.58 m^2
Normalized insulation value	7.13 $G\Omega \cdot m^2$	2.78 $G\Omega \cdot m^2$	3.09 $G\Omega \cdot m^2$
Conclusion	PASSED	PASSED	PASSED

*Not applicable.

4.4 Deflection measurement

Shortly after the tracking system installation was completed, module deflection was observed, caused by the combined effects of gravity and temperature variations.

Figure 10 illustrates how the span progressively bends under varying environmental and operational conditions. The reference values d', d'' and d''' are not measured data but schematic indicators, highlighting the relative increase in mid-span deflection as the day advances and external factors such as temperature, irradiance, and wind loading change.

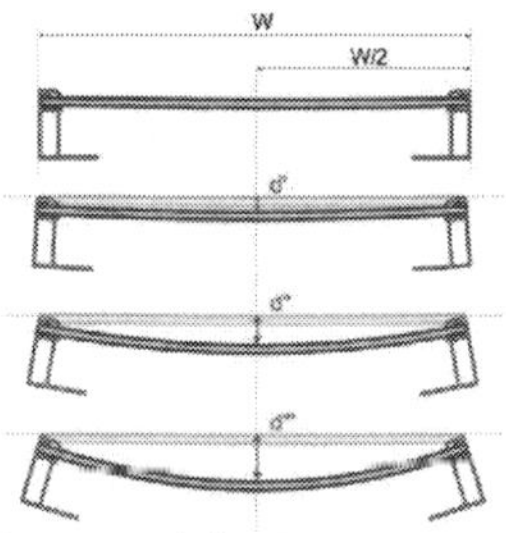

Figure 10: Transverse deflection.

Considering this information extremely relevant to investigation the cause of the cracks in the rear glass, measurements of this deflection were conducted throughout the day on four modules. Two modules in the single-axis tracker PV system and another two in the fixed-tilt PV system. The results of these measurements are presented in the graph shown in Figures 11 and 12.

The collected results demonstrate that deflection varies throughout the day. In Figure 11 the deflection is shown for modules 1 and 5 on string 01 in the single-axis tracker PV system. Glass deflection is higher in the early morning and late afternoon. Although deflection decreases during the day, a slight increase is observed around solar noon, likely due to the combination of tilt position at 0° with thermal and irradiance stress at that time. Deflection likely begins at a higher value because the tracker "sleeps" at an almost horizontal 9°, which is almost horizontal.

In the fixed-tilt PV system, deflection varies less during the day but is still influenced by temperature. Since the tilt angle remains constant, the gravitational effect contribution to sagging does not change. This behavior may be different in modules installed in different geographical locations.

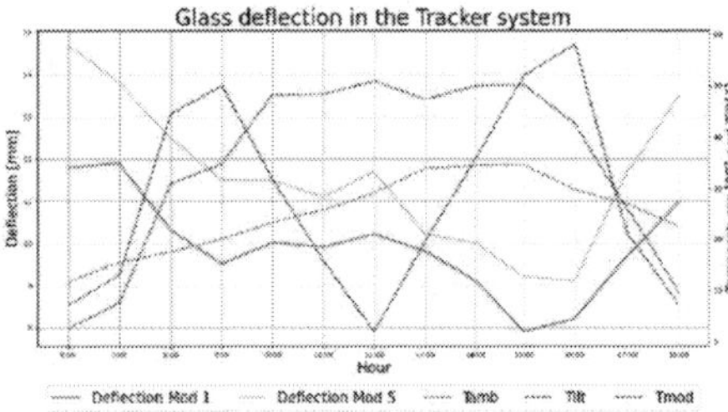

Figure 11: Tracker PV module deflection. Deflection of Modules 1 and 5 measured in mm. Tamb is the ambient temperature, Tilt is the module angle with respect to the ground plane, and Tmod is the module temperature.

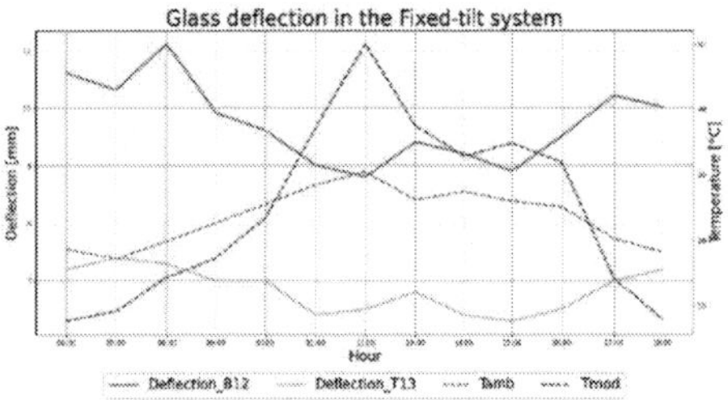

Figure 12: Fixed-tilt PV module deflection. Deflection of Modules B12 and T13 measured in mm. Tamb is the ambient temperature, and Tmod is the module temperature.

5 RESULTS AND DISCUSSION

The comparative monitoring of the two systems, fixed-tilt and tracker, revealed that glass cracking in bifacial modules is not limited to a specific mounting configuration, although different crack distribution patterns were observed. In the tracker system, 20 out of 78 modules (25.64%) exhibited cracks within 14 months of operation, whereas the fixed-tilt system showed 9 failures among 30 modules (30%) in just over one year. Although the absolute numbers differ, both systems converged toward similar failure rates, suggesting that glass laminate fragility is intrinsic rather than driven by the mounting scheme.

In the fixed system, cracks exhibited a periodic-like waviness, a feature often attributed in the literature [3] to the crack propagation speed: when propagation occurs rapidly, the crack tends to deviate upon encountering local resistance, producing a wavy-like track. Conversely, tracker-mounted modules developed cracks without a clear periodic pattern, possibly reflecting the continuous movement and the dynamic stresses imposed by daily sun-tracking.

Although many cracks were initially observed after periods of high thermal stress, timely crack observations in relation to ambient temperature indicate that their occurrence cannot be attributed solely to thermal conditions.

Complementary laboratory tests indicated that individual cracked modules continued to meet IEC 61215:2021 requirements. Both MQT 03 and MQT 15 insulation tests yielded values well above the minimum thresholds.

IV Curve results show that the average power loss relative to the 545 W nameplate ranged from 1.72% in testimonial sample modules and from 5.61% to 5.75% in modules exposed to sunlight but not electrically connected and operating. Since simulator uncertainty (±2%) makes exposed, connected, and cracked connected modules statistically similar, their actual losses, well above the expected 2.6% after 16 months (0.45%/year), indicate significantly faster degradation than specified by the manufacturer.

Electroluminescence imaging shows cells mismatch that can explain the power loss verified in IV curve tests results.

Although the highest deflection is expected to occur around solar noon, when irradiance can reach its maximum and the module is positioned almost horizontally, so that the gravity vector acts fully normal to the glass surface, the collected data reveal a different behavior. At the start of the monitoring period (~6:00 AM), Module 1 in the tracker system already shows its largest deflection, 11.8 mm, while Module 5 starts even higher, at 14.7 mm.

This discrepancy underscores the importance of integrating field-representative mechanical stress scenarios, such as catenary deflection, dynamic wind loading, and thermal cycling with constrained edges, into bifacial module reliability protocols and highlights the necessity of updating normative testing procedures and criteria.

6 CONCLUSIONS

This study documented extensive rear-glass cracking in bifacial PV modules under both tracker and fixed-tilt installations at the University of São Paulo, São Paulo, Brazil. In less than 14 months, over one-quarter of the modules in both systems exhibited cracking, despite passing the IEC 61215:2021 tests.

The convergence of crack incidence across mounting configurations suggests that the problem is systemic to module design and manufacture rather than module mounting schemes. The distinct crack morphologies point to interactions between structural boundary conditions and environmental stresses.

The IV curve test clearly shows that the measured modules exhibit electrical behavior that deviates more strongly and rapidly than predicted on the manufacturer's datasheet. The lack of significant difference between intact and cracked operating modules suggests that performance deviations are more closely related to exposure and operation than to cracking itself. Further tests will be performed to evaluate the evolution and condition of the electrical characteristics of these modules.

These findings demonstrate the urgent need to refine existing qualification standards to better reflect real-world operating conditions of bifacial modules. Future work should focus on (i) improved mechanical testing protocols that account for bifacial modules, (ii) correlation of crack initiation with structural deflection and thermal cycles, (iii) long-term monitoring of power degradation in cracked modules, and (iv) accelerated degradation studies such as MQT 16 and MQT 20 of IEC 61215:2021 to verify whether cracks contribute to faster degradation than guaranteed by the manufacturer. By bridging the gap between laboratory tests and field reality, more reliable evaluation frameworks can be established, ultimately supporting the secure deployment of bifacial PV at scale.

7 ACKNOWLEDGMENTS

This research was supported by the National Council for Scientific and Technological Development (CNPq/MCTI/Brazil), which funding the project "Real-World Characterization of Bifacial Photovoltaic Modules and Generators.", through process No. 406711/2022-5. We also thank the Photovoltaic Systems Laboratory (LSF-IEE/USP) for technical analysis and support.

8 REFERENCES

[1] Nascimento e Silva, B., Matos, M. F. A., Lira, A. L. O., Alves, C. G. L., Ferreira, D. A., de Sousa, A. R., & Emiliavaca, S. A. S. (2024). Análise da espessura dos vidros e da interface moldura-vidro em módulos fotovoltaicos bifaciais com uso de microscopia eletrônica de varredura. Revista Brasileira de Energia Solar, 15(1), 46–53.

[2] Silverman, T. J., Palmiotti, E. C., Springer, M., Bosco, N., Deceglie, M., Repins, I., & Gaulding, A. (2024). Tough break: Many factors make glass breakage more likely (NREL/TP-5K00-91695). National Renewable Energy Laboratory.

[3] Quinn, G. D. (2020). Fractography of ceramics and glasses (Special Publication 960-16e3). National Institute of Standards and Technology. https://doi.org/10.6028/NIST.SP.960-16e3

[4] E. C. Palmiotti, M. Springer, J. Zuboy, T. J. Silverman, J. L. Braid, D. C. Jordan, S. Rabade, and T. M. Barnes. Growing Panes: Investigating the PV Technology Trends Behind Frequent Early Failures in Modern Glass–Glass Modules. IEEE Journal of Photovoltaics, vol. 15, no. 2, pp. 297–306, Mar. 2025.

[5] J. Markert, A. G. Belawadi, E. Job, I. Hädrich, and D. Philipp. What Can We Learn from the Comparison of Glass Breakage between Lab and Field?. in Proc. SOPHIA Workshop 2025, DTU Risø Campus, Denmark, Apr. 29, 2025.

[6] D. Wang, A. Hermawan, and E. Woolard. Wind Speed and Rear Glass Breakage on Bifacial PV Modules Mounted on Trackers. DNV White Paper, Utrecht, The Netherlands, 2024.

[7] IEC 61215-1:2021 – Terrestrial Photovoltaic (PV) Modules – Design Qualification and Type Approval – Part 1: Test Requirements, International Electrotechnical Commission, Geneva, Switzerland, Apr. 2021.

[8] KOTTEK, Markus; GRIESER, Jürgen; BECK, Christoph; RUDOLF, Bruno; RUBEL, Franz. World Map of the Köppen-Geiger climate classification updated. Meteorologische Zeitschrift, v. 15, n. 3, p. 259-263, 2006.

[9] M. Braga, G. X. A. Pinto, A. M. Pires, A. H. Zamboni, L. R. Nascimento, and R. Rüther. Investigating the causes and consequences of glass cracks on double-glass large area bifacial PV modules. Poster presented at PV Research Workshop, Florianópolis, Brazil, Mar. 2023. [Online].

[10] Barnes, T. (ed.). DuraMAT FY 2023 Annual Report: Toward Reliability Forecasting. Durable Module Materials Consortium (DuraMAT), National Renewable Energy Laboratory (NREL), Sandia National Laboratories, Lawrence Berkeley National Laboratory, 2023.

[11] Wang, D.; Hermawan, A.; Woolard, E. Wind Speed and Rear Glass Breakage on Bifacial PV Modules Mounted on Trackers. Whitepaper, DNV Netherlands B.V., Arnhem, 2024.

[12] Pilliod, M. Central Tension – Glass Durability and Breakage. Presented at the NREL Photovoltaic Reliability Workshop (PVRW 2024), Glass Durability and Breakage session, February 28, 2024, Golden, CO, USA.

DAMP HEAT TEST ON TOPCON MODULES MADE WITH GLASS/BACKSHEET

Author(s): Alessandro Anderlini
Company / Institute(s): Coveme Spa
Address(es): Via Emilia 288, 40068 -San Lazzaro di Savena (BO)- Italy, aanderlini@coveme.com

ABSTRACT:
Given the rising market share of TOPCon cell technologies, where the typical PV module configuration is Glass/Glass, there is a need to prove that also Glass/Backsheet can be considered as a valid alternative in terms of performance and reliability.
On the one hand these backsheets need to have a high resistance towards water ingress; a factor which gains increasing importance with latest developments in cell technologies like TOPCon which are assumed to be more sensitive to humidity.[1] On the other hand, the combination of different BOM and different production processes, suggests to investigate the reliability of backsheets, combined with different encapsulants and running through different production process, towards environmental stresses with a common test procedure following the existing standards.
In order to test for the general backsheet durability, 8 modules have been tested in a standardized (IEC61215, MQT13) damp heat test (1000 h) in the TestLab PV Modules at Fraunhofer Institute for Solar Energy Systems ISE. The modules were built by two third-party module manufacturers. The module compositions are depicted in Table 01 and Table 02. The test consisted of a total of 1000 h damp heat exposure, The difference between the modules was the encapsulant supplier both being POE based. The aim was to understand differences in PV modules performance that might arise from various material combinations and different production process.
At the end of the test all PV modules except one passed the test, remaining below the 5% power loss limit according to IEC 61215. The Glass/Glass module obtained the best result with only 1.68% power loss. The Glass/Backsheet modules power loss was between 3.0 % and 4.3% for all PV modules except one. In addition the backsheets employed remained clear and free of cracks. Only one module lost more then 5% but it is likely that the higher degradation of this module was not due to the backsheet, but rather associated with the difference in encapsulant. Another possibility could be a variation in module manufacturing quality.

1 AIM AND APPROACH

The major aim of his work is to understand more about the reliability of PV modules with TOPCon cell technologies in Glass/Backsheet configuration compare to Glass / Glass and specifically the behaviour of different moisture barrier backsheet types, combined with 2 types of encapsulants in different production process towards environmental stresses with a common test procedure following the existing standards.

The 1000h damp heat test was conducted with full size PV modules produced by known PV module producers from their standard production process.

All modules were exposed to the following test sequence:

- Power measurement at STC acc. to IEC 61215, MQT02
- EL imaging
- Damp Heat test acc. to IEC 61215, MQT13
- Power measurement at STC acc. to IEC 61215, MQT02
- EL imaging

Manufacturer	Module ID	front side	cells	Encapsulant front/back	Backside	Pmpp_[W] %	stress test
A	M06	Glass	16BB TOPCon	Brand A - POE/POE	Glass	-1,68	DH 1000h
A	M07	Glass	16BB TOPCon	Brand A - POE/POE	COVEME dyMat HDPYE SPV L (370 µm / white)	-3,26	DH 1000h
A	M08	Glass	16BB TOPCon	Brand A - POE/POE	COVEME dyMat HDPYE SPV LDO (420 µm / white)	-3,17	DH 1000h
A	M09	Glass	16BB TOPCon	Brand A - POE/POE	COVEME dyMat HDPYE SPV C (314 µm / white)	-4,26	DH 1000h
Manufacturer	Module ID	front side	cells	Encapsulant front/back	Backside	Pmpp_[W] %	stress test
B	M02	Glass	16BB TOPCon	Brand B - POE/POE	COVEME dyMat HDPYE SPV L (370 µm / white)	-3,22	DH 1000h
B	M03	Glass	16BB TOPCon	Brand B - POE/POE	COVEME dyMat Clr HDPYE F (320 µm / Clear)	-5,87	DH 1000h
B	M04	Glass	16BB TOPCon	Brand A - POE/POE	COVEME dyMat Clr HDPYE F (320 µm / Clear)	-3,39	DH 1000h
B	M05	Glass	16BB TOPCon	Brand A - POE/POE	COVEME dyMat HDPYE SPV L (370 µm / white)	-3,72	DH 1000h

Table I: List of tested modules

10.4229/EUPVSEC2025/3AV.2.19

2 RESULTS (OR PRELIMINARY RESULTS) AND CONCLUSIONS

2.1 Manufacturer A

All modules passed the DH1000 test according to the pass/fail criteria of less than 5 % power loss. In the electroluminescence images the GBS modules revealed dark features after DH1000 located on the cell edges. The origin of the features is likely related to tapes used for string fixing.

FIGURE 01 - DEVIATION IN POWER OUTPUT FROM INITIAL VALUES

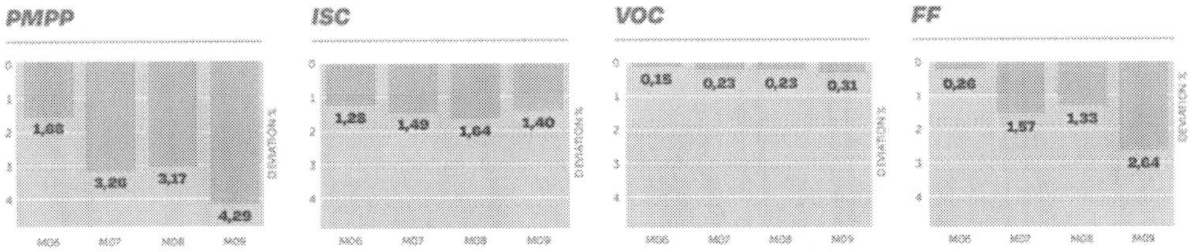

2.2 Electroluminescence Imaging

The GBS modules revealed dark features on the cell edges after damp heat exposure. A possible explanation is that they result from tapes that are often used to fix the module strings. M08 and M09 additionally reveal darker areas on some cells after DH1000. M08 exhibits a vertical darker strip after the damp heat exposure. The origin is unknown. It is not visible on the module with the bare eye.

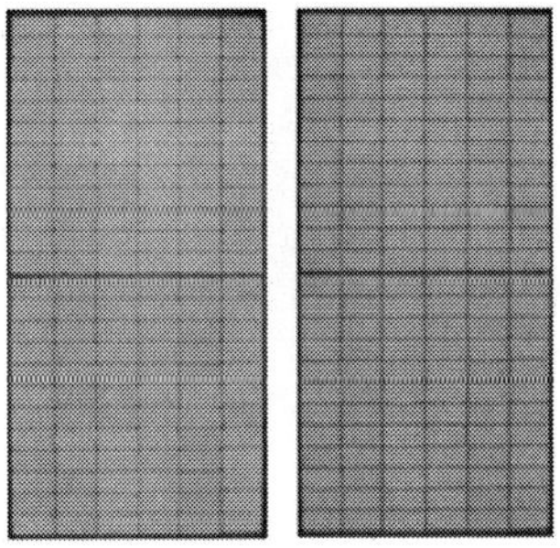

Left: M06 before DH1000 exposure.

Right: M06 after DH1000 exposure.

2.3 Manufacturer B

With exception of M03 all modules passed the DH test. M03 has the same BS as M04, which passed the test, but is constructed with a different encapsulant. Therefore, it is likely that the higher degradation of M03 is not due to the backsheet, but rather associated with the difference in encapsulant. Another possibility could be a variation in module manufacturing quality. The electroluminescence images revealed slightly impaired solder connections of the grid fingers around the cell edges. This issue is particularly pronounced in M03 after DH1000. This suggests that the module manufacturing quality may be a contributing factor to the higher power loss observed in M03.

10.4229/EUPVSEC2025/3AV.2.19
020155-002

FIGURE 02 - DEVIATION IN POWER OUTPUT FROM INITIAL VALUES

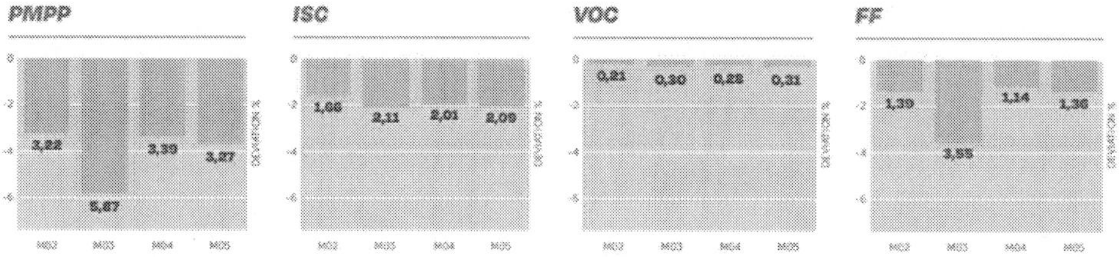

2.4 Electroluminescence Imaging

The electroluminescence (EL) images in the initial condition exhibit some darker areas around the cell edges, which are likely associated with an impaired solder connection of the fingers. After DH1000 more such dark areas are developed in particular in M03. This is an indication that the module quality is the major reason for the relatively higher power loss of M03.

After damp heat exposure in particular M05 exhibits dark features on the cell edges, which most likely stem from tapes used for string fixing.

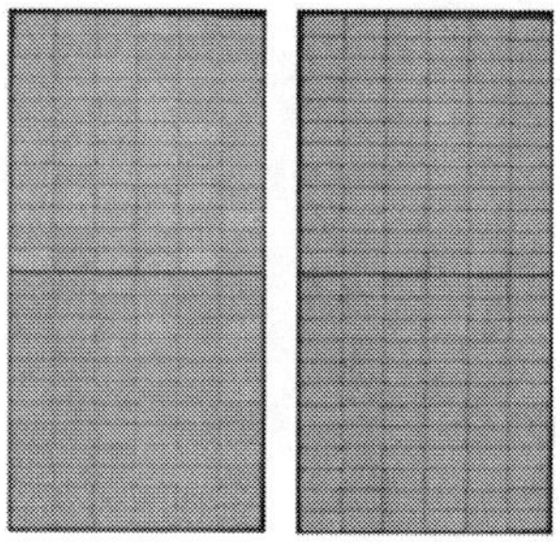

Left: M02 before DH1000 exposure.

Right: M02 after DH1000 exposure.

3 COMPARATIVE AGING TEST FROM FRAUNHOFER ISE

Coveme backsheets have also been tested at 1000 h damp heat in a comparative analysis of 20 TOPCon PV module types in the Test- Lab PV Modules at Fraunhofer Institute for Solar Energy Systems ISE, showing a superior performance compared to all other backsheets tested [2]

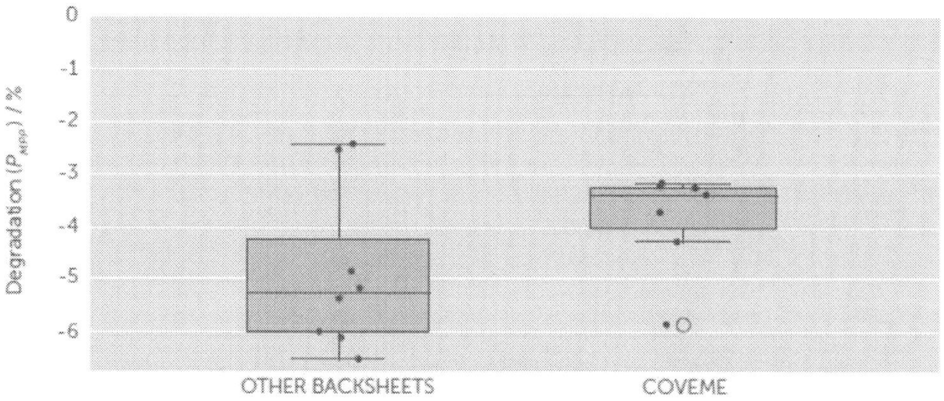

10.4229/EUPVSEC2025/3AV.2.19
020155-003

4 SCIENTIFIC INNOVATION AND RELEVANCE

At the end of the test all PV modules except one passed the test, remaining below the 5% power loss limit according to IEC 61215. The Glass/Glass module obtained the best result with only 1.68 % power loss. The Glass/Backsheet modules power loss was between 3.0 % and 4.3% for all PV modules except one. In addition the backsheets employed remained clear and free of cracks. Only one module lost more then 5% but it is likely that the higher degradation of this module was not due to the backsheet, but rather associated with the difference in encapsulant. Another possibility could be a variation in module manufacturing quality.

The Glass/Glass module performed quite well with minimum power loss. Also the Glass/backsheet modules passed the aging test, except one which shows that encapsulant material choice and production process are key factors to reach optimum performance. In addition, a comparative analysis of 20 TOPCon PV module types demonstrated that COVEME backsheets perform better than other backsheets. Finally Glass/backsheet configuration can be considered a valid alternative to Glass/Glass for specific installations where light module weight, lower cost and high resistance to hail are considered winning factors.

References

[1] O. Arriaga Arruti, A. Virtuani, C. Ballif, Long-term performance and reliability of silicon heterojunction solar modules, Prog. Photovolt: Res. Appl. 31 (2023) 664–677.

[2] Paul Gebhardt, Ulli Kräling, Esther Fokuhl, Ingrid Hädrich, Daniel Philipp Reliability of Commercial TOPCon PV Modules—An Extensive Comparative Study, Progress in Photovoltaics: Research and Applications, 2024; 0:1–9

IMO-IMOMEC ▸▸ UHASSELT imec EnergyVille

The influence of angle of incidence on the reliability of photovoltaic modules: Lessons Learned

N. Kyranaki [1,2,3], I. Kaaya [1,2,3], M. Adnan Hameed [4,5,6], R. de Jong [1,2,3], S. Bouguerra [1,2,3], A. Morlier [1,2,3], M. Daenen [1,2,3]

[1] Hasselt University, Institute for Materials Research (imo-imomec), Hasselt, Belgium, [2] imec, imo-imomec, Thor Park, Genk, Belgium, [3] EnergyVille, imo-imomec, Thor Park, Genk, Belgium, [4] Martin-Luther-University Halle-Wittenberg, Halle, Germany, [5] Ministry of Oil -SCOP, Baghdad, Iraq, [6] Fraunhofer Center for Silicon Photovoltaics CSP, Halle, Germany

Motivation

- Photovoltaic (PV) system designers optimize parameters that **enhance plane-of-array irradiance**, to **maximize energy yield**.
- **However, higher irradiation raises UV levels and operating temperatures**, leading to accelerated PV module degradation.
- An **indoor accelerated aging test** is presented, replicating variations in UV exposure linked to tilt angle.

Methodology

imec framework

Ageing procedure

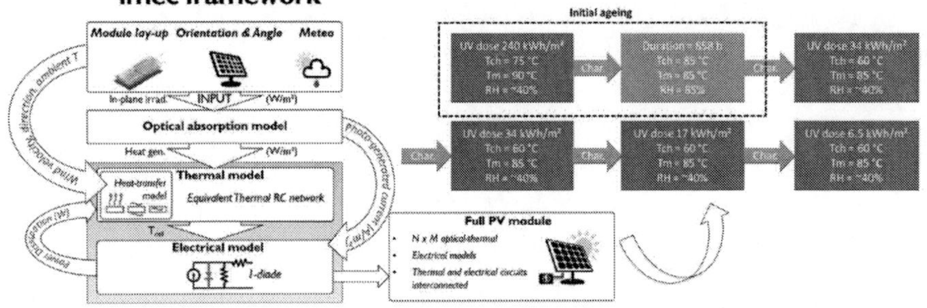

- Estimating variation in climate stressors with tilt angle using the imec PV simulation framework [1]
- Modelling acceleration factor of degradation for different tilt angles according to:

$$AF = \left(\frac{UV_A}{UV_F}\right)^{\gamma} \cdot \left(\frac{1+RH_A^n}{1+RH_F^n}\right) \cdot \exp\left(\frac{-E_{gF}}{k_B}\left(\frac{1}{T_A}-\frac{1}{T_F}\right)\right)$$

- Designing a relevant ageing sequence accounting for varied tilt angle, including electrical (I-V measurements) and optical (EL, visual inspection) characterization (Char.). Tch and Tm were the chamber and module temperature, respectively.

Results

- **First UV ageing 240 kWh/m²** (Fig. 1): P_{max} **↓ 0.79%** (mainly V_{OC} ↓ 0.97%); I_{SC} ↑ 0.11%
- **Damp-heat** (DH, Fig. 1): P_{max} **loss;** all electrical parameters↓
- **2nd UV** (Fig. 1): Full recovery after initial (34 kWh/m²) → degradation resumes after further 34 kWh/m²
- **Trend:** Cyclic degradation–regeneration ↔ BO-LID/LeTID; + encapsulant discoloration & photobleaching (Fig. 2)
- **Activation energy** (Fig. 3): ~0.54 eV ≈ BO-LID [2] (LeTID cannot be excluded)
- **UV dose sensitivity** (Fig. 3): Strongly module-quality (or activation energy) dependent

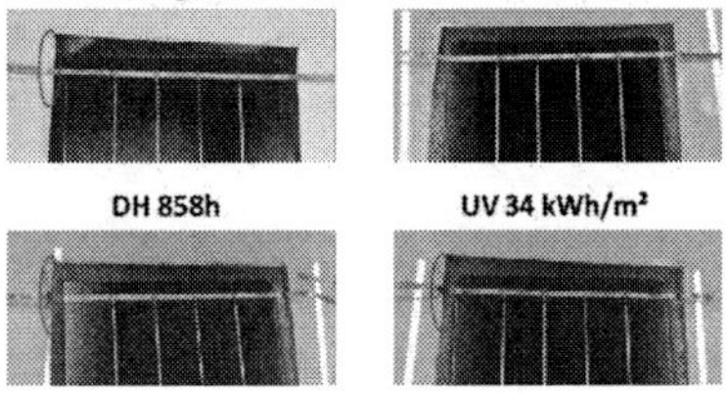

Fig. 2: Encapsulant discoloration

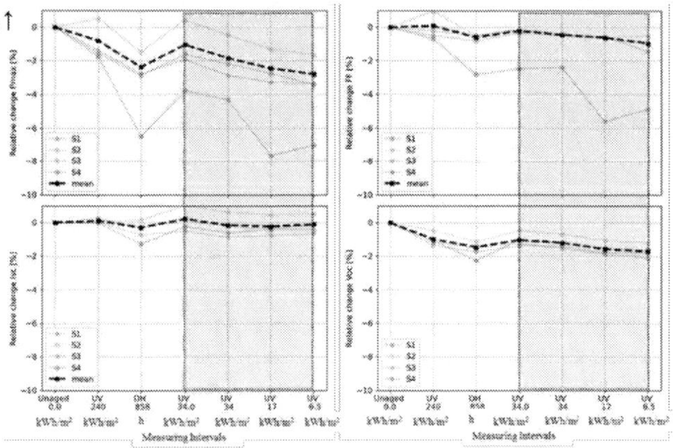

Fig. 1: Electrical performance parameters from I-V measurements

LESSONS LEARNED!!!

Exposure	34 kWh/m²	17 kWh/m²	6.5 kWh/m²
P_{max} drop	0.79%	0.61%	0.35%

- **Correlation of accelerated aging to tilt & outdoor effects:** further study needed ⚠. No BO-LID stabilization was performed so the impact of the various degradation mechanisms (LeTID and encapsulant discoloration/photobleaching) could not be distinguished
- **BO-LID/LeTID behavior**: PERC c-Si PV → requires further investigation and outdoor validation ☑

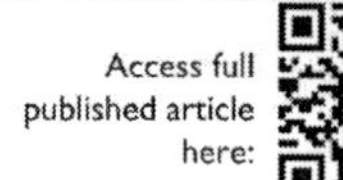

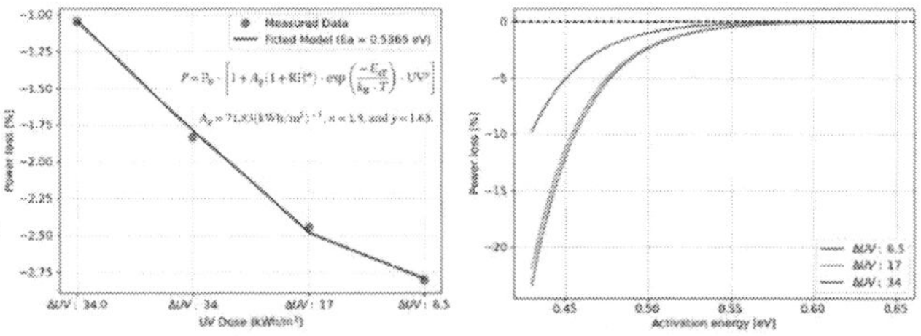

Fig. 3: Fitted model to experimental data (left) and simulated dose sensitivity for different activation energies

References

[1] SIMULATION OF PHOTOVOLTAIC MODULES, *https://data.epo.org/publication-server/rest/v1.0/publication-dates/20170705/patents/EP2998756NWB1/document.html*, accessed December 15, **2023**

[2] Woodhouse et. al, https://www.nrel.gov/docs/fy21osti/78629.pdf

Access full published article here:

DETECTION OF TRANSFORMATIONS IN ENCAPSULANTS AFTER MODULE LAMINATION PROCESS

V. Ulbikaitė[1], J. Donėlienė[1], P. Dubravskij[1], A. Galdikas[1], J. Devenson[2], V. Vaičikauskas[2], V. Nargelienė[2], A. Šetkus[2]
[1] Applied Research Institute for Prospective Technologies, Vilnius, Lithuania
[2] Center for Physical Sciences and Technology (FTMC), Vilnius, Lithuania
<vaidvile.ulbikaite@protechnology.lt>, <arunas.setkus@ftmc.lt>

ABSTRACT: Lamination of the PV-modules based on the thermal treatment of the encapsulants is primarily accepted to enhance the stability and durability of the module functioning. However, the encapsulants are modified due to transformations in polymers during the lamination process. In spite of the optimized conditions of the process, there is a lack in clear understanding about these modifications even if there were reliable proofs about a significant influence of the quality of the encapsulant on the characteristics of the PV-modules especially in the long-term exploitation. There is no reliable description of the parameters acceptable to characterize the polymer transformations in correlation with the lamination process conditions. In addition, an absence of informative parameters significantly diminishes possibilities to identify the encapsulation related problems in the long-term functioning of the PV-modules.
Keywords: solar modules, encapsulant defects, polymer properties, modules testing

1 AIM AND APPROACH

The module lamination process is worthy to investigate aiming to enhance the reliability and long-term stability of the PV-modules that directly makes significant impact on sustainability and recyclability [1]. Improvements of PV module durability and reliability include diverse aspects and depends on series of the technological processes and materials. Lamination of the PV modules is supposed to protect the functional parts from the surrounding influence. The transformations in the encapsulant determines the quality of the protection [2] and, therefore, this aspect is worthy to study in more details filling in the gaps in existing knowledge.

The characteristics acceptable to identify the transformations in the encapsulant during the lamination process have to be studied in details aiming to combine the most informative parameters into a model description of a relationship between the conditions of the lamination process and the properties of the encapsulant.

In this work, a novel approach was introduced acceptable to combine the infrared spectroscopy characteristics with the information extracted from the polarized light-based experiments. For this, the lamination process was reproduced by manufacturing double-side glass polymer models. The ethylene vinyl acetate (EVA) and polyolefin elastomer (POE) films were used in these models. The reflectance and transmittance spectra were measured, and the absorbance bands were analyzed in the near- and mid-infrared (NIR and MIR) intervals. Large area images were produced for the models in a polarized light (wight) illumination with a polarizing filter (analyzer) and a camera. In addition, the rotation of the light polarization plane was quantitatively measured along selected areas of the double-side glass polymer models.

2 METHODS AND TESTS

2.1 Sample modules

The EVA and POE films were purchased from three diverse companies that were not disclosed in this text. For the experiments, the samples of the films were produced as the square shape pieces with the dimensions about 10 x 10 cm^2. The PV-module lamination process were simulated by producing the double-side glass polymer samples. The lamination process for the EVA and POE was conducted using a standardized approach with the laboratory laminator ICOLAM 18/11 (Germany). EVA and POE films were used for this.

The gel content was obtained by the Soxhlet method [3] as the marker of the process. Two specimens (~ 1 g each) were cut from two diverse areas in each of the EVA or POE test square samples with dimensions 10 x 10 cm^2. All specimens were weighed by precision balance before (the initial weight W_{ini}) and after (the final weight W_F) the extraction. Each specimen was cut into 1×1 cm^2 pieces and put into a sample flask with organic solvent. To determine the gel content of cured EVA film specimens were used ~100 ml toluene (p.a., Chempur, Poland) with 10% of butylated hydroxytoluene – BHT (≥99.7%, Carl Roth GmbH+Co. KG, Germany) antioxidant. Flasks with the contents/substance were kept in the oven at 60±1 °C for 24 h. The solvent was then decanted and all specimens were dried in an oven at 105±1 °C temperature for 4 hours. Xylene (Reag.Ph.Eur., CARLO ERBA Reagents S.A.S., France) solvent extractions were performed for the determination of the gel content of the cured polymer films.

2.2 Methods and tests

The NIR absorbance spectra were obtained from the transmittance and reflectance measurements. The spectra of optical absorbance were obtained from the measurements using a Bruker Vertex 80 spectrometer in three modes: Attenuated Total Reflectance (ATR), specular Reflectance (R), and Transmittance (T). The aluminum-coated mirror optics of the spectrometer was used for the measurements in the interval of the wavelengths from 400 nm to 60 μm. Depending on the task of the experiment, individual sets of the beam splitters and the detectors were included into the active configuration of the spectrometer.

The model samples were also analyzed in the polarized white light illumination. Large area photographs were obtained by placing the sample module between the light source and a camera with a standard polarizing filter. Before the experiments the analyzer (polarizing filter) was rotated around the central axis until the polarized light was completely quenched. In addition, the module samples were scanned point-by-point with a laser beam. The scanning was performed along the top of the sample surface and perpendicular to the sample boundaries. In these tests, the polarization plane rotation angle was measured quantitatively for the light laser light beam.

3 RESULTS AND DISCUSSIONS

3.1 Polarized light images

Large area images of the model samples visually displayed large scale deformations. Typical large area images were illustrated in Fig.1 for the model samples.

The clear and transparent image in the day light transformed into non-homogeneous picture of the combined dark-shadow-bright zones images if the deformations were presented in the polymer film. The brightness of the zones depended on the strengths of the deformations. Novel aspects about a relationship between the lamination conditions and the polymer transformations were described by combining the results of the polarized light tests and the absorbance band analysis.

The intensity of the transmitted polarized light in Fig. 1 was dependent on the rotation of the light polarization plane in the polymer film. Deep dark (even black) areas corresponded to the completely quenched illumination zone that represented the preparatory state of the experimental setup. The arrangement of the polarized light source, polarizing filter (analyzer) and camera was fixed so that the light was completely quenched after the polarizing filter and a black screen was seen without the model sample. After the sample was placed between the source and the analyzer, the bright zones appeared.

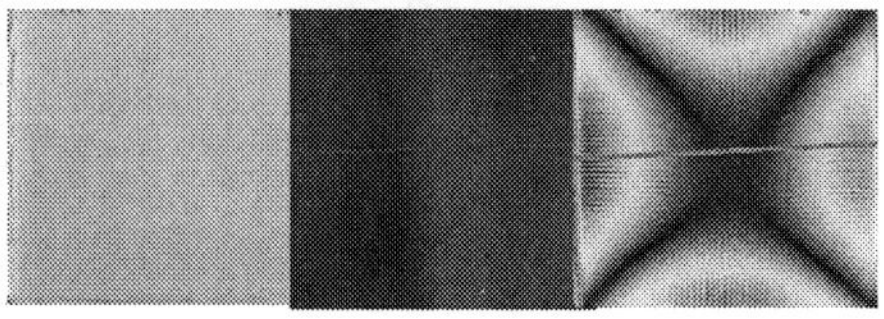

Figure 1: Model samples 10x10 cm2. Photos: in non-polarized day-light illumination (left), polarized white light (center and right)

3.2 Rotation of the polarization plane

The rotation of the polarization plane was measured using a laser beam. A profile of the rotation angle was measured by scanning the sample surface along a straight line. A sample line of such scans corresponded with the red and green lines in Fig. 1.

In these tests the laser beam was focused on the sample. Reflected beam passed through the polarizing filter (analyzer) and was pointed to the photodetector. The starting arrangement of the setup was accepted being with the analyzer position when the signal of the detector was negligible. In this case, rotation of the analyzer wit the sample fixed in the setup was equal to the polarization rotation angle produced by the sample module. Typical profiles were illustrated in Fig. 2.

It followed from the rotation angle profiles, that the deep dark zones in the polarized light images corresponded to the negligible rotation of the polarization plane by the polymer. These zones were represented by $U_{detector} = 0$ V in Fig. 2 whereas the bright areas corresponded to high the detector responses. The rotation of the polarization plane angle was higher for the higher detected signal.

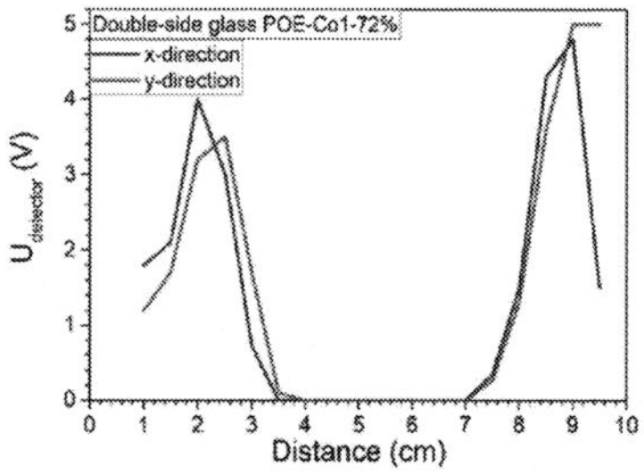

Figure 2: Signal proportional to rotation of the light polarization angle vs. distance: x-direction is along green line (right-to-left) in Fig. 1; y-direction is perpendicular to the green line

3.3 Spectra of optical absorbance

The spectra of optical absorbance were obtained from the measurements using a Bruker Vertex 80 spectrometer. During the measurements in mid-infrared interval, the setup included a Bruker A225/Q Platinum ATR single reflection diamond ATR accessory with a crystal of 2.35 mm × 2.35 mm surface area. A high-pressure clamp was employed to ensure the contact between the ATR crystal and the polymer films. The spectra were measured in the range of the wavenumbers from 8000 cm^{-1} to 650 cm^{-1} with the scanning step 2 cm^{-1}. A KBr beam splitter and a Globar light source were included in the setup.

It must be noted here, that 6-8 spectra were measured for each of the samples in diverse freely selected spots on the surface of an individual sample. For the spots with practically the same polarization rotation angle, the scattering of the experimental spectra obtained at the diverse spots of the same sample was lower than the differences between the samples with individual gel content. It was not applicable to the results obtained in the spots with obvious polarization angle rotation. Typical experimental results were illustrated by the NIR absorbance bands in Fig. 3.

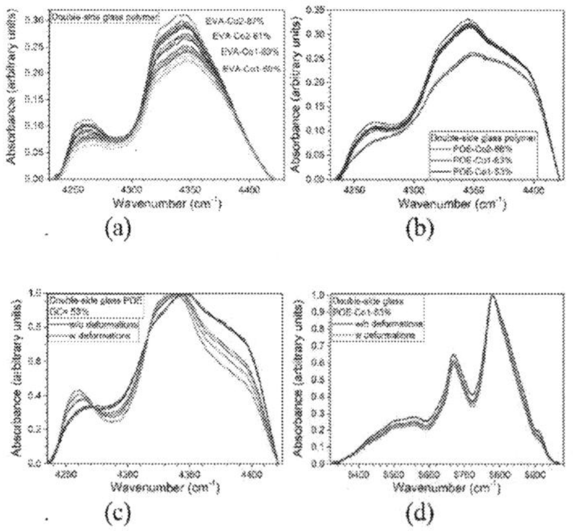

10.4229/EUPVSEC2025/3AV.2.23

Figure 3: Near-infrared absorbance bands for (a, b) the double-side glass polymer films ((a) EVA and (b) POE) without deformations with individual gel (%) content from diverse producers (Co1 and Co2); (c, d) POE films with (w) and without (w/o) deformations.

The absorbance bands in Figs. 3(a) and 3(b) demonstrated few important aspects of the polymer transformations in the homogeneous non-deformed film zones. First, the absorbance band only slightly depended on the position across the dark area. The lines of the absorbance spectra that were quite close one to another for the same model sample. Second, the absorbance band shape was sensitive to the gel content. Third, the absorbance band shape was individual for the polymer films produced by separated companies. Fourth, the band shape was individual for EVA and POE films.

The bright zone absorbance bands proved the fact that the film deformations produced significant distortions in the band shape. The distortions were larger than the differences attributed to the properties of the polymer films.

3.4 Point defects

In addition to the large area deformations, small area defects were also detected. We used microscope with polarized light source for imaging of the pont defects in the encapsulants after the lamination.

Typical results of more precise study of the dark areas were illustrated in Fig. 4.

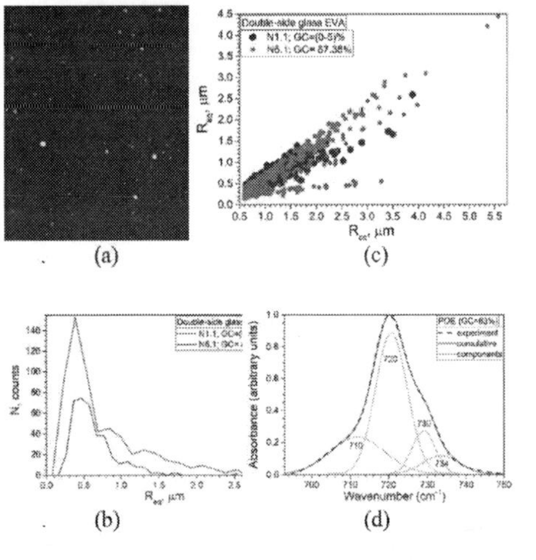

Figure 4: (a) Polarized light double-side glass EVA image in 90x90 μm^2 area. (b) Distribution of equivalent disc radius R_{eq} of the bright spots for two EVA model samples with individual gel content. (c) Correlation between the radius R_{eq} and minimum circumcircle radius R_{cc} of the bright spots for the EVA films. (d) Deconvolution of the absorbance band 720 cm^{-1} with the 730 cm^{-1} component as the crystallinity marker.

The small area images under the polarized light illumination (Fig. 4(a)) visualized the polymer crystallites as the bright spots. The distribution of the dimensions (Fig. 4(c)) proved that the density and the diameter of the crystallite increased with an increase n the gel content after the lamination process. In addition, appearance of specific groups were detected by analysis of the correlation Req vs. Rcc in Fig. 4(c). The deconvolution of the 720 cm-1 absorbance band (Fig. 4(d)) proved an increase in the density of the polymer crystallites in the films after the lamination process.

4 SUMMARY AND CONCLUSIONS

The combinations of the characteristics extracted from the polarized light images and the absorbance bands were acceptable to identify mechanical deformations and the related mechanisms in the encapsulants after the lamination process. The detailed analysis of the properties can be carried out using the optical reflection mode. The combined description can be acceptable for control of lamination process as well as to analyze the drifts and degradation in the long term periods by non-destructive trials of the PV-modules.

It was proved that the crystallinity of the polymers increased with an increase in the gel content that depended on the lamination conditions. The crystallinity was detected from the component analysis of the absorbance band at the wavenumber 720 cm-1. The density and dimensions of the polymer crystals were evaluated from the analysis of the large area images. In these images, the polymer deformation zones were also visualized. The degree and the extent of the deformations were quantitatively described by the dependences of the polarization angle on the coordinate of the probing spot on the model surface. The MIR absorbance bands were highly dependent on the deformation suggesting a non-homogeneous transformations in the polymer encapsulants during the lamination process.

5 REFERENCES

[1] V. Fiandra, L. Sannino, C. Andreozzi, G. Flaminio, M. Pellegrino, Polymer Degradation and Stability 220 (2024) 110643.

[2] M. Landa-Pliquet, T. Bejat, M. Serasset, A. Descormes, E. Mofakhami, E. Voroshazi, Solar Energy Materials & Solar Cells, 267 (2024) 112725

[3] Ch. Hirschl et al. Solar Energy Materials & Solar Cells, 116 (2013) 203.

6 ACKNOWLEDGMENTS

This work has been co-funded under Horizon Europe project IBC4EU (GA: 101084259). Views and opinions expressed are however those of the author(s) only and do not necessarily reflect those of the European Union or CINEA. Neither the European Union nor the granting authority can be held responsible for them.

IMPROVING ULTRAVIOLET FLUORESCENCE ANALYSIS FOR PHOTOVOLTAIC ENCAPSULANT ASSESSMENT

Zonghan Jiang[1], Hugo Sanchez[1,2], Leila Mortazavifar[1,2], Ralph Gottschalg[1,2]
[1]Hochschule Anhalt University of Applied Sciences
[2]Fraunhofer Center for Crystalline Silicon Photovoltaics CSP
zonghan.jiang@hs-anhalt.de

ABSTRACT: Fluorescence spectroscopy could be used for lamination control of the PV module, but the mapping is time-consuming. Camera-based ultraviolet fluorescence (UVF) imaging has potential for rapid crosslinking degree mapping but is unreliable due to the lack of uncertainty control. Temporal instability and spatial non-uniformity of UV excitation, camera nonlinearity and noise, keep current UVF largely qualitative and limit reliable per-location quantification of lamination quality from fluorescence intensity. To address these issues, an improved methodology is presented: multi-frame acquisition and averaging reduce camera-noise uncertainty by approximately 10 times; an automated saturation-avoidance algorithms prevents the sensor from entering nonlinear response; 1 hour pre-operation of the UV excitation reduced a maximum of 18.4% fluorescence change during measurement. Furthermore, with the per-location linear response model and uniform-field simulation, errors driven by excitation-field non-uniformity are reduced from up to 60.72% (worst-case responsivity) to near zero. These combined improvements provide a reliable foundation for mapping local encapsulant crosslinking using camera-based UVF.

Keywords: Ultraviolet fluorescence, Non-uniform UV illumination, semi-quantitative UVF, Crosslinking

1 INTRODUCTION

Ultraviolet fluorescence (UVF) technology has been widely applied in the photovoltaic (PV) industry. Camera-based UVF systems with UV LEDs excitation are widely used as rapid and non-destructive tools for defect inspection [1–4], whereas UV laser excitation coupled with spectrometric detection enables more detailed monitoring of lamination quality in PV modules [5, 6]. Morlier et al. demonstrated the potential of camera-based UVF for rapid assessment of lamination quality [7], and showed that in-line monitoring in production environments is feasible.

However, current camera-based UVF systems remain predominantly qualitative and are still not able to achieve the mapping of the crosslinking degree. The previous study demonstrated that the detected fluorescence intensity is strongly dependent on local UV excitation irradiance [8]. Due to the non-uniformity of the UV illumination field, differences in fluorescence signals may arise from variations in excitation rather than intrinsic material properties. This limitation has been the primary obstacle preventing camera-based UVF from mapping the crosslinking degree of the PV module.

In addition, the limited linear range of camera sensors can cause signal saturation when fluorescence intensity exceeds the upper end of the linear range, making accurate measurement impossible [8], while the intrinsic noise of the camera leads to fluctuations in the acquired signal and leads to the wrong prediction of the crosslinking degree. Morlier et al. and Jiang et al. further reported that temperature significantly affects UVF results, introducing reproducibility issues under varying testing conditions [8, 9]. Collectively, these limitations hinder the quantitative determination of the pointwise crosslinking degree of PV module encapsulants using UVF.

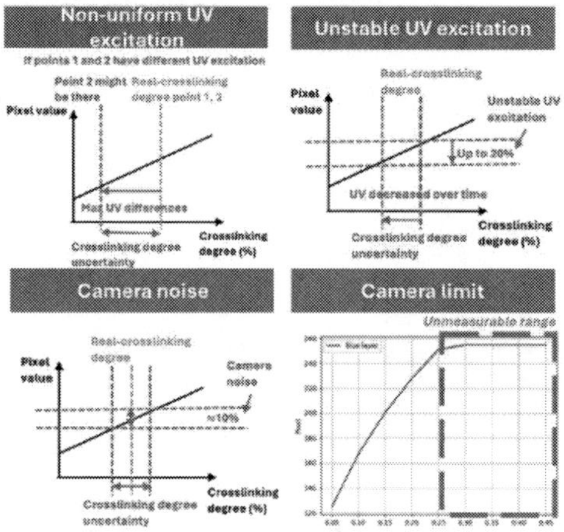

Figure 1: Uncertainty-driven variations in crosslinking degree

This work presents a comprehensive methodology to enhance the accuracy and reliability of camera-based UVF for PV encapsulant analysis. An excitation-fluorescence response model was established by capturing images under varying UV excitation levels. This mitigates the effects of spatial non-uniformity in the UV illumination field without requiring uniform illumination. Furthermore, an automated threshold-detection system was developed to prevent sensor saturation, temperature control was implemented to minimize thermally induced variations, and multi-frame averaging was employed to reduce camera noise fluctuations. These improvements enable the camera-based UVF for the crosslinking mapping, providing a foundation for inline monitoring of lamination quality and uniformity in PV module manufacturing.

2 EXPERIMENTAL SETUPS

A camera-based ultraviolet fluorescence (UVF) measurement system was developed for the experiments. The system was equipped with a 365 nm LED array combined with a bandpass filter (Peak 360nm) as the excitation light source and a Basler ace 2 a2A3840-45ucBAS camera for image acquisition. To prevent ambient light interference, the entire setup is enclosed with black blackout cloth to ensure light isolation (detailed configuration can be found in [8]). The camera operated in Bayer RG10 mode with 10-bit pixel values (0–1023). To obtain raw image data, automatic gain control, automatic white balance, and automatic exposure adjustment were all disabled, and demosaicing/color space processing was turned off. Color channel gains were set to unity (R = G = B = 1) to avoid white balance bias.

The experimental samples consist of mini-PV modules exhibiting ring-shaped UVF patterns that had undergone damp heat (DH) and UV aging to simulate encapsulant degradation.

To characterize the uniformity and stability of the illumination field, a spectrometer coupled with an XY scanning stage covering an effective area of 500 mm × 500 mm was employed to measure the light intensity distribution across the field. Additionally, a fixed UV sensor read out via an Arduino microcontroller was integrated into the UVF system to monitor illumination stability in real time.

Three temperature sensors were installed to monitor the internal environment temperature of the UVF setup as well as the sample temperature, thereby addressing temperature-induced measurement variations. The laboratory ambient temperature was strictly controlled within 20–22 °C (Sample temperature 20 – 24°C) to ensure stable experimental conditions.

The output intensity of the UV-LEDs array was regulated by an adjustable converter to allow flexible excitation control. The measurement and data acquisition process was automated via Python scripts, improving experimental efficiency and repeatability.

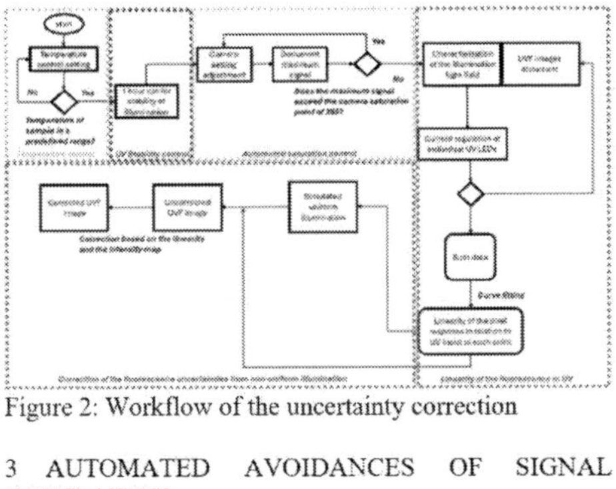

Figure 2: Workflow of the uncertainty correction

3 AUTOMATED AVOIDANCES OF SIGNAL SATURATION

Previous work established the camera's linear response range [8]; when fluorescence signals exceed this range, pixel values saturate and enter a nonlinear, non-measurable regime. To prevent such saturation, an automated exposure-control algorithm was implemented. For each acquisition, the frame-maximum pixel value is computed; if this maximum exceeds a predefined threshold (set inside the camera's linear operating region), the exposure time is iteratively reduced to another predefined value until all pixel values fall within the linear range, and the corresponding fluorescence-crosslinking model will be selected. This procedure ensures that fluorescence measurements remain within the sensor's linear response range, preserving quantitative integrity and preventing bias introduced by nonlinear sensor behaviour.

4 CHARACTERIZATIONS OF CAMERA NOISE AND STABILITY

Camera fluctuations originate from the combined effects of various noise sources, including shot noise due to the random arrival of photons, readout noise, and dark current noise, etc, which will cause the uncertainties of the crosslinking prediction. In this study, all noise contributions are aggregated into a single total-noise term for analysis. To emulate a near worst-case noise scenario while avoiding saturation, the exposure time was set to the maximum allowable value (1s) under constant illumination and stable temperature conditions.

The camera noise level was characterized by acquiring 100 consecutive images under the constant illumination and controlled temperature, using the maximum exposure time of 1 s.

The standard deviation of pixel values was calculated according to Eq. (1), yielding σ = 169.23 DN. The average noise-signal percentage is approximately 10%.

$$s = \sqrt{\frac{1}{N-1}\sum_{i=1}^{N}(r_i - \bar{r})^2} \qquad (1)$$

If 100 images are captured and averaged per measurement, the standard error of the mean (SEM) can be estimated σ/√N (with N = 100), according to Eq. (2) [10]:

$$u = \frac{\sigma}{\sqrt{N}} \qquad (2)$$

where σ is the standard deviation (169.23 DN), and N=100 is the number of images averaged. Thus, the standard error standard error of the mean is 16.92 DN, indicating a significant reduction in measurement uncertainty through averaging.

5 UNCERTAINTIES DUE TO EXCITATION INSTABILITY AND NON-UNIFORMITY

In camera-based UVF measurement systems, the instability and non-uniformity of the UV illumination are the main reasons that make the mapping of crosslinking impossible. As a result of the mutual interactions among the intrinsic characteristics of LEDs, variations in operating temperature, and the temperature-dependent behaviour of the bandpass filter, the intensity of the UV excitation source gradually decreases during operation, thereby affecting the stability of the detected fluorescence signal and bringing uncertainty to the crosslinking degree detection.

In addition to this temporal instability, the spatial non-uniformity of the excitation field introduces another critical limitation. While the fluorescence intensity is approximately proportional to the excitation irradiance, achieving a perfectly uniform excitation field is nearly impossible in practice. Consequently, two regions with identical inherent material properties may exhibit significantly different fluorescence intensities solely due to variations in local UV excitation. Because the signal intensities at different positions cannot be reliably compared, this limitation has constrained the camera-based UVF measurements to the mapping of the crosslinking degree.

To address this issue, we propose a correction method based on the relationship between local excitation irradiance and the measured fluorescence signal. Specifically, for each spatial location, the actual excitation irradiance is measured under multiple illumination levels, while the corresponding UVF images are acquired. A linear fit between the fluorescence pixel values and the measured excitation intensity is then performed for each location. The resulting fit parameters will be used to simulate the fluorescence results for each point in the UVF images under uniform illumination conditions. The adjustable uniform illumination range defined as the maximum excitation in the weakest field to the minimum excitation in the strongest field.

5.1 Stability of the illumination field

Since the temporal stability of the excitation source is a prerequisite for reliable spatial characterization, the stability of the illumination field was first evaluated over time. A spectrometer and a fixed-position UV sensor read out via an Arduino unit were employed to continuously monitor the UV irradiance. The measurements indicated that the UV irradiance decayed by a maximum of 20% (see Fig. 3) in the 1-hour run (which could cause a maximum of 18.4% fluorescence change at the most responsive location, a 1% change in UV excitation produces a 0.92% change in fluorescence per channel pixel values), and the excitation UV source required ≈1 h after activation to reach a stable output. Consequently, all subsequent experiments were performed following a warm-up period of one hour. During data acquisition, the fixed-position UV sensor remained active to ensure consistency of the illumination field throughout the measurements.

Figure 3: Stability of the illumination field over time at three points within the field

5.2 Non-uniformity of the illumination field

To quantify the impact of excitation-field non-uniformity on fluorescence measurements, spatial mapping of the UV irradiance distribution was performed. Before mapping, the UV source was preheated for one hour, and measurements were initiated only after the UV sensor confirmed irradiance stability. The spectrometer was positioned at the same height used during UVF image acquisition to ensure consistency between fluorescence detection and excitation measurements. The UVF image resolution (3840 × 1920 pixels) was divided into a 32 × 16 measurement grid, yielding 120 × 120 pixels per cell, which is sufficient for mapping. At each grid position, the excitation intensity was recorded with the spectrometer. Since the LED spectral profile remained invariant across different output levels, the peak spectral value was taken as the representative UV excitation intensity. To suppress measurement noise, five repeated measurements were conducted at each position, and the across-repeats value was used for analysis.

The excitation-field intensity was varied by adjusting the driving current of the UV-LED source (1 A, 1.3 A, 1.5 A, 1.7 A, and 2 A). For each illumination level, 100 UVF images were acquired and averaged to determine the mean fluorescence pixel value. To ensure repeatability, a fixed-position UV sensor continuously monitored overall field stability during data acquisition.

The resulting intensity map was scaled by the same factor (i.e., 120 per axis) to match the UVF image resolution.

By multiple UV illumination level and the corresponding UVF images, a per-location linear response model (pixel value vs. excitation irradiance) is first established (see Fig. 4). Using the determined linear calibration parameters, the fluorescence images are subsequently corrected for spatial non-uniformity, thereby enabling direct and quantitative comparison of fluorescence signals across the entire field of view.

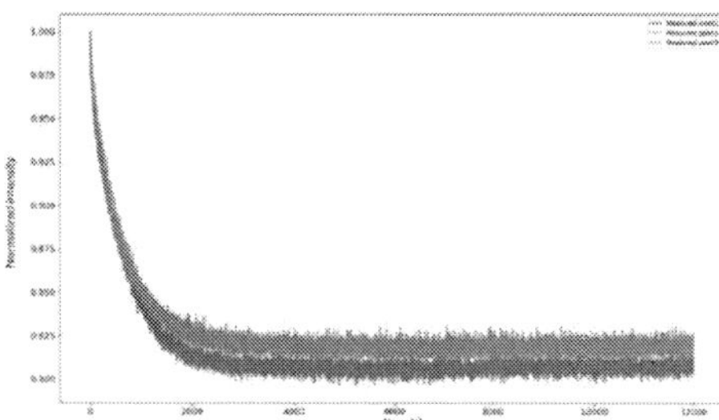

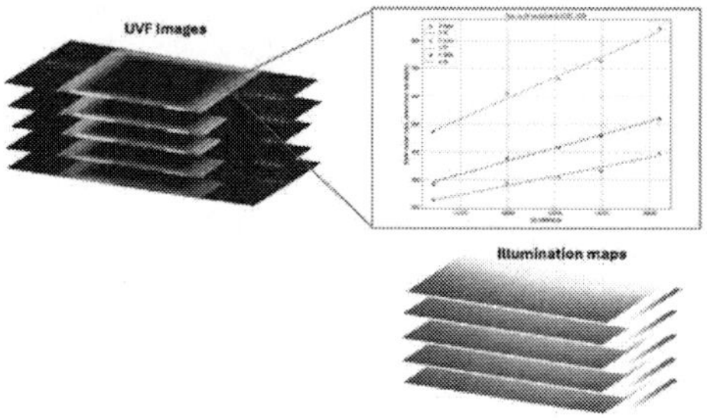

Figure 4: Per-location linear response model of fluorescence versus excitation based on multi-image UVF data and excitation-field measurements

The test results reveal pronounced non-uniformity in the UV excitation field, with the maximum-to-minimum illumination ratio reaching ≈ 166% Because the fluorescence–excitation responsivity varies across spatial locations, we adopt the maximum measured responsivity for a conservative assessment. At the most responsive location, a 1% change in UV excitation produces a 0.92% change in fluorescence per channel pixel values. Under this worst-case responsivity, the observed illumination non-uniformity can propagate to pixel-level deviations of up to 60.72% in the final image, posing a substantial risk to quantitative interpretation. This upper bound (60.72%) follows from ((Maximum-to-minimum illumination ratio − 1) * maximum local slope), using maximum-to-minimum illumination ratio R = 166% and the maximum local slope S = 0.92% (0.92%-pixel variation per 1% change in UV intensity).

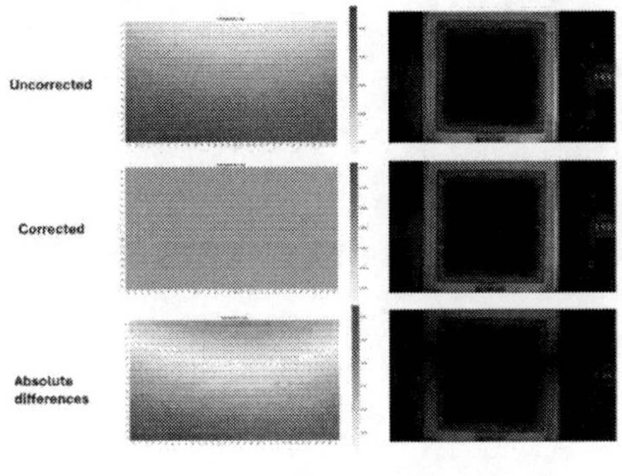

Figure 5: UV excitation irradiance maps (left) and UVF images (right), shown uncorrected, corrected, and as absolute-difference images; the absolute-difference row is displayed at 2× brightness for visibility

Figure 5 shows the uncorrected UVF image, the corrected UVF image, and the absolute-difference map between them. The correction is based on a pixel-wise linear model that captures the local dependence of fluorescence intensity on UV excitation. As evidenced by the substantial reduction in absolute differences, this approach effectively compensates for fluorescence pixel deviations arising from non-uniform excitation, producing a UVF image that is functionally equivalent to one acquired under spatially uniform UV illumination, which was achieved without physical homogenization of the UV field and provides a foundation for the mapping of the crosslinking degree of encapsulant via camera-based UVF.

6 SUMMARY

This work presents a methodology to enable camera-based UV fluorescence used for the mapping of the crosslinking degree.

The approach couples automated saturation prevention, multi-image averaging noise reduction, pre-operation of the UV excitation light source and the per-location linear response model and uniform-field simulation.

The multi-image averaging yielding ≈10× camera-noise reduction, 1 hour pre-operation of the UV excitation reduced a maximum of 18.4% fluorescence change during measurement, furthermore, with the per-location linear response model and uniform-field simulation, errors driven by excitation-field non-uniformity are reduced from up to 60.72% (worst-case responsivity) to near zero, substantially mitigating spatial bias. These combined improvements provide a reliable foundation for mapping local encapsulant crosslinking using camera-based UVF.

7 ACKNOWLEDGEMENTS

This work is supported by the Deutsche Forschungsgemeinschaft (DFG, German Research Foundation) – 467133067.

8 REFERENCES

[1] M. Kontges, A. Morlier, G. Eder, E. Fleis, B. Kubicek, and J. Lin, "Review: Ultraviolet Fluorescence as Assessment Tool for Photovoltaic Modules," *IEEE J. Photovoltaics*, vol. 10, no. 2, pp. 616–633, 2020, doi: 10.1109/JPHOTOV.2019.2961781.

[2] A. Morlier, M. Siebert, I. Kunze, G. Mathiak, and M. Kontges, "Detecting Photovoltaic Module Failures in the Field During Daytime With Ultraviolet Fluorescence Module Inspection," *IEEE J. Photovoltaics*, vol. 7, no. 6, pp. 1710–1716, 2017, doi: 10.1109/JPHOTOV.2017.2756452.

[3] C. Buerhop, O. Stroyuk, T. Pickel, J. Hauch, and I. M. Peters, "Identification of solar module behavior originating from backsheet failure - from lab studies to field tests," in *2021 IEEE 48th Photovoltaic Specialists Conference (PVSC)*, Fort Lauderdale, FL, USA, 2021, pp. 831–834.

[4] M. Köntges, S. Kajari-Schröder, and I. Kunze, "Crack Statistic for Wafer-Based Silicon Solar Cell Modules in the Field Measured by UV Fluorescence," *IEEE J. Photovoltaics*, vol. 3, no. 1, pp. 95–101, 2013, doi: 10.1109/JPHOTOV.2012.2208941.

[5] J. C. Schlothauer, C. Peter, C. Hirschl, G. Oreski, and B. Röder, "Non-destructive monitoring of ethylene vinyl acetate crosslinking in PV-modules by luminescence spectroscopy," *J Polym Res*, vol. 24, no. 12, 2017, doi: 10.1007/s10965-017-1409-y.

[6] J. C. Schlothauer, R. M. Ralaiarisoa, A. Morlier, M. Köntges, and B. Röder, "Determination of the cross-linking degree of commercial ethylene-vinyl-acetate polymer by luminescence spectroscopy," *J Polym Res*, vol. 21, no. 5, 2014, doi: 10.1007/s10965-014-0457-9.

[7] A. Morlier, M. Köntges, S. Blankemeyer, and I. Kunze, "Contact-free Determination of Ethylene Vinyl Acetate Crosslinking in PV Modules with Fluorescence Emission," *Energy Procedia*, vol. 55, pp. 348–355, 2014, doi: 10.1016/j.egypro.2014.08.101.

[8] Z. Jiang, C. Meza, H. Sanchez, and R. Gottschalg, "Evaluation of the Impact of the UV Excitation Intensity on the Ultraviolet Fluorescence Measurement System for Photovoltaics," *41st European Photovoltaic Solar Energy Conference and Exhibition*, 2024, doi: 10.4229/EUPVSEC2024/3AV.2.35.

[9] A. Morlier, M. Siebert, I. Kunze, S. Blankemeyer, and M. Kontges, "Influence of environmental conditions on UV fluorescence imaging in the field," in *2018 IEEE 7th World Conference on Photovoltaic Energy Conversion (WCPEC) (A Joint Conference of 45th IEEE PVSC, 28th PVSEC & 34th EU PVSEC)*, Waikoloa Village, HI, 2018, pp. 1309–1312.

[10] J. Lisiecki and S. Kłysz, "Estimation of Measurement Uncertainty," *Research Works of Air Force Institute of Technology*, vol. 22, no. 1, 2007, doi: 10.2478/v10041-008-0004-4

HOCHSCHULE ANHALT University of Applied Sciences

IMPROVING ULTRAVIOLET FLUORESCENCE ANALYSIS FOR PHOTOVOLTAIC ENCAPSULANT ASSESSMENT

Zonghan Jiang[1], Hugo Sanchez[1,2], Leila Mortazavifar[1,2], Ralph Gottschalg[1,2]
E-Mail: zonghan.jiang@hs-anhalt.de
[1]Hochschule Anhalt University of Applied Sciences, Bernburger Str. 55, 06366, Köthen, Germany
[2] Fraunhofer-Center for Silicon Photovoltaics CSP, Halle (Saale), Germany

Motivations

Challenge:

- **Fluorescence intensity via fluorescence spectroscopy could be used for lamination control of the PV module, but the mapping is time-consuming [1].**
- **Camera-based UVF has potential for rapid crosslinking degree mapping, but is not yet reliable due to the lack of uncertainty control. [2].**

Goal:

- **Develop a methodology to enable reliable mapping of local crosslinking degree via camera-based UV fluorescence.**

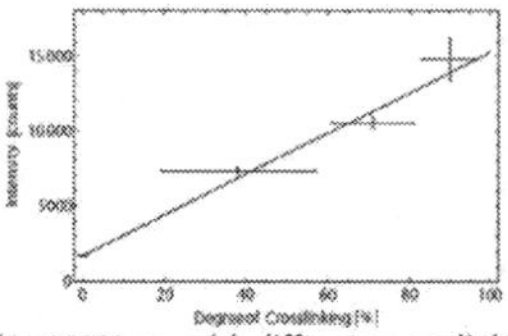

Fig. 1: Fluorescence intensity at 450 nm with different crosslinking degree and linear fit [1]

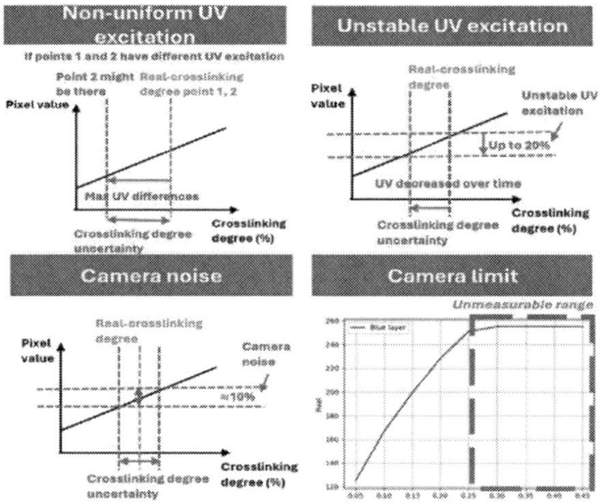

Fig. 2: Uncertainty-Driven Variations in Crosslinking Degree

Camera-related uncertainties

Solution

- **Automated saturation-avoidance algorithms.**
- **Multi-frame acquisition (e.g., 100 frames) with averaging reduce camera-noise uncertainty by approximately a factor of 10.**

UV illumination-related uncertainties

Solution for the instability of the UV illumination caused uncertainties

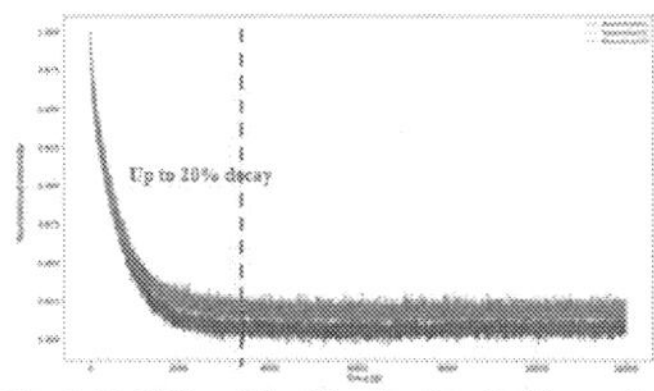

Fig. 3: Stability of the illumination field over time at three points within the field of view

- **The UV light source should be operated until the LED output stabilizes (typically ~1 hour).**
- **Control sensor to monitor the UV illumination stability during the measurement.**

Solution for non-uniform illumination caused uncertainties

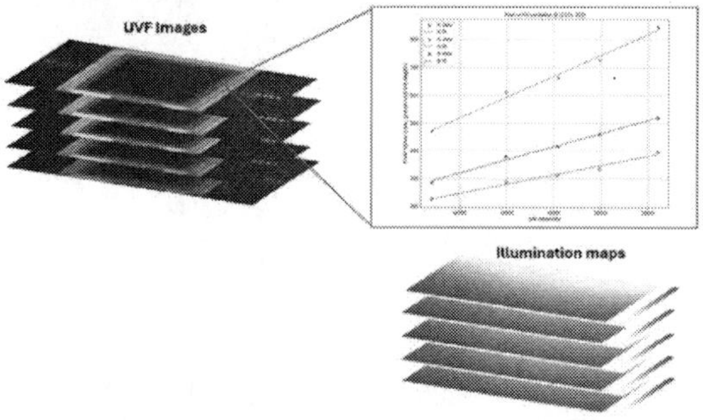

Fig. 4: Per-location linear response model of fluorescence versus excitation based on multi-image UVF data and excitation-field measurements

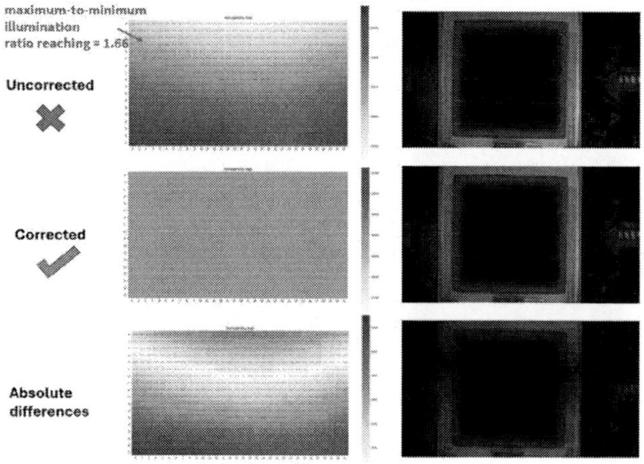

Fig. 5: UVF images and UV excitation fields before correction, after correction, and their absolute differences (Absolute-difference image displayed with brightness scaled by 2× for visualization.)

Conclusions / Key findings

- **Noise reduction:** *Multi-frame averaging decreased camera noise by 10x.*
- **UV stability:** *Pre-operating the UV source ensured stable illumination.*
- **Spatial correction:** *The per-location linear response model and uniform-field simulation corrected the uncertainties caused by non-uniform UV illumination. Enable the mapping of the crosslinking degree.*
- ***Implication for crosslinking:*** *These combined improvements provide a reliable foundation for mapping local encapsulant crosslinking using camera-based UVF.*

References

[1] J. C. Schlothauer, R. M. Ralaiarisoa, A. Morlier, M. Köntges, and B. Röder, "Determination of the cross-linking degree of commercial ethylene-vinyl-acetate polymer by luminescence spectroscopy," J Polym Res, vol. 21, no. 5, 2014, doi: 10.1007/s10965-014-0457-9

[2] Z. Jiang, C. Meza, H. Sanchez, and R. Gottschalg, "Evaluation of the impact of the UV Excitation Intensity on the Ultraviolet Fluorescence Measurement System for Photovoltaics," 41st European Photovoltaic Solar Energy Conference and Exhibition, 2024, doi: 10.4229/EUPVSEC2024/3AV.2.35.

ACKNOWLEDGEMENT

This work is supported by the Deutsche Forschungsgemeinschaft (DFG, German Research Foundation) – 467133067.

University of Applied Sciences and Arts of Southern Switzerland

SUPSI

Institute for Applied Sustainability to the Built Environment

Evaluating Hot-Spot Stress in PV Modules under Shading: from PV System and Laboratory Data

Ebrar Özkalay[1]*, Anika Gassner[2,3], Gabriele C. Eder[2], Gabi Friesen[1], Markus Feichtner[4]

1 – SUPSI, University of Applied Sciences and Arts of Southern Switzerland, Mendrisio, Switzerland; 2 – OFI, Austrian Research Institute for Chemistry and Technology, Vienna, Austria; 3 – TU Wien, Institute for Material Science and Technology, Vienna, Austria; 4 – Sonnenkraft Energy GmbH, St.Veit a.d. Glan, Austria

Corresponding author: ebracoezkalay@supsi.ch

Motivation

- **Shading in the built environment** exposes PV modules to frequent and localized hot-spot stress, unlike open-field systems—raising reliability concerns beyond energy yield loss.
- **Current standard hot-spot endurance testing** (IEC 61512-2, MQT09) may underestimate real-world stress (especially in residential PV): long-term repetitive shading can cause more severe material degradation than observed in standard 1-hour to maximum 5-hour lab tests.

Indoor Hot-Spot Endurance Test

- **Hot-Spot (HS) test** performed at **standard (55 ± 15 °C)** and **extended (75 ± 15 °C)** temperature conditions
- Each module tested **3× for 5 hours → 15 hours total HS test**

Module Technology	Indoor – Hot-spot endurance		Outdoor (3 years)
	55°C; 3 x 5h	75°C; 3 x 5h	BIPV & shadow mask
G/PERC/BS-1	1	1	1 (Insulated)
G/IBC/BS	1	1	1 (Insulated)
G/HJT/BS	1	1	1 (Insulated)
G/PERC/G	1	1	-
G/PERC/BS-2	1	1	-
G/TOPCon/G	1	1	-

Outdoor Accelerated Ageing using Shadow Mask

- **Outdoor accelerated ageing** using a **36% transmittance shadow mask**
- Shadowing adjusted to achieve **10 ± 5% difference** between global maximum power (low V) and local maximum power (high V) → **diode activation**

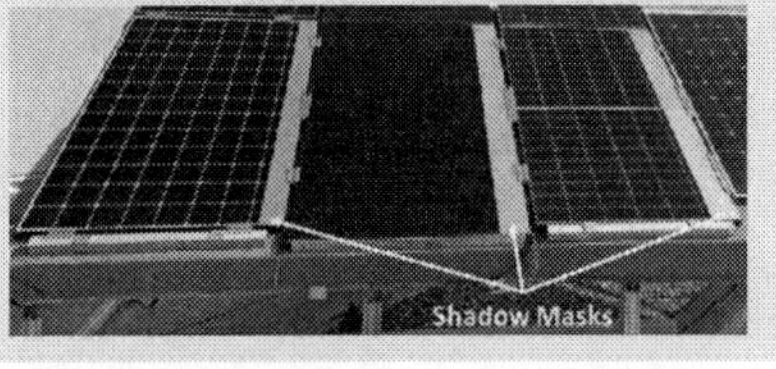

PV System—Field Experience

- **G/EVA/BS Al-BSF modules** after **11 years** of rooftop operation in Cfb Köppen-Geiger climate (warm, humid, warm summer)
- **Regular partial shading** on some modules due to rooftop signage

Temperature Analysis of Indoor Hot Spot Endurance Test

- **HJT & TOPCon:** Highest hot spot temperatures → higher power dissipation in reverse
- **IBC:** Lowest hot spot temperature → low breakdown voltage (V_{BR}) limits dissipation [1]
- **PERC:** Hot spot-to-module ΔT increases with temperature → V_{BR} becomes more negative (see the I-V curves below)

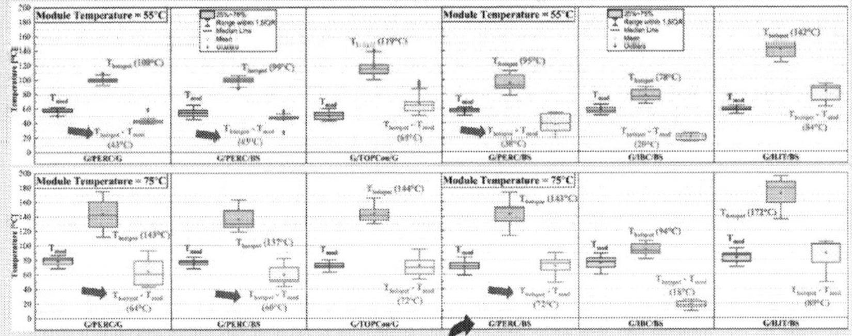

Degradation Analysis:

- **EVA Discolouration:** Significant yellowing observed in the shaded module (ΔE = 4, Δb > 3) compared to the non-shaded module (ΔE < 1).
- **Chemical Analysis:** Acetate compounds detected in the shaded area via thermal desoprtion (TC GC/MS), indicates higher operating temperatures.
- **Front Metallization Corrosion:** Corrosion visible in the shaded region, confirmed by EL imaging.
- **Backsheet Degradation:** PVDF outer layer shows more pronounced degradation in the shaded area (not shown).

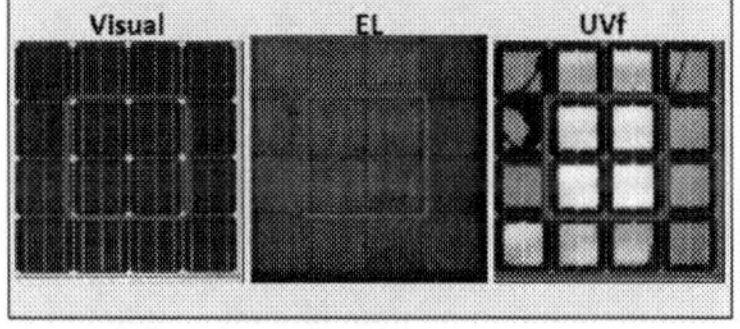

I–V curves of individual cells measured under shadow mask conditions used in the hot spot test:

Temperature increase cause more negative V_{BR}

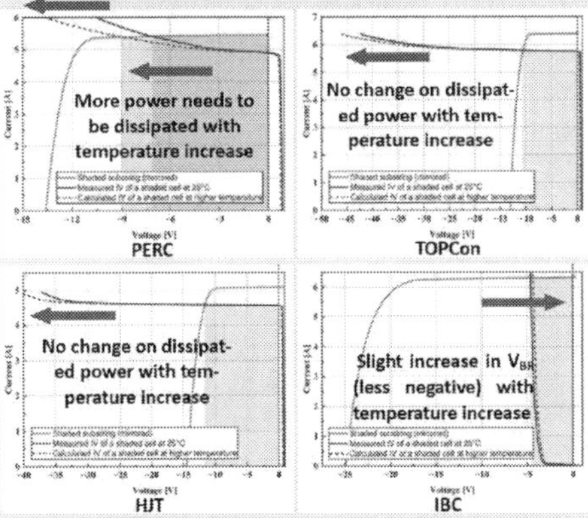

- **Avalanche breakdown (PERC, TOPCon and HJT):** V_{BR}↓ with ↑ **temperature** (positive temp. coefficient) [2]
- **Zener breakdown (IBC):** V_{BR}↑ with ↑ **temperature** (negative temp. coefficient) [1]

G/PERC/BS-1 Module

- **Discolourationl n outdoor shadow-masked module:**
  - **EVA:** ΔE = 7.7, Δa > 2.3 (red)
  - **PVDF/PET/PE backsheet:** ΔE = 12.5, Δb > 11.5 (yellowing)
  - ΔE < 1 in non-shaded and indoor HS-tested modules
- **PET layer:** Thermal degradation of the PET core layer can be detected after outdoor shadow mask and, to lower extent, for the HS test 143°C (see PET core layer spectra)
- **Adhesive degradation:** The adhesive layer between PVDF and PET is degrading in parallel to the thermal stress applied leading to delamination after outdoor shadow mask for 3 years [3, 4] (see ATR, attenuated total reflectance images)

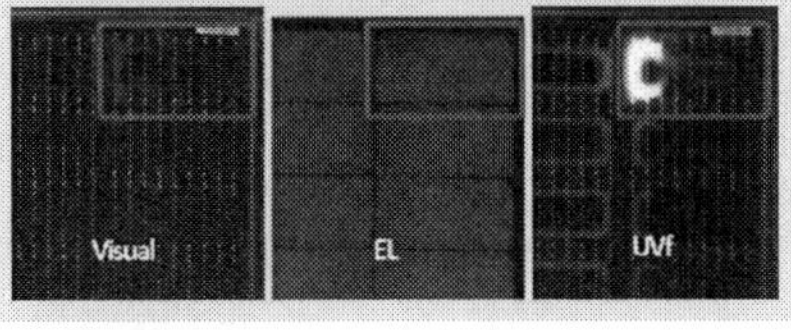

PET Core Layer Spectra

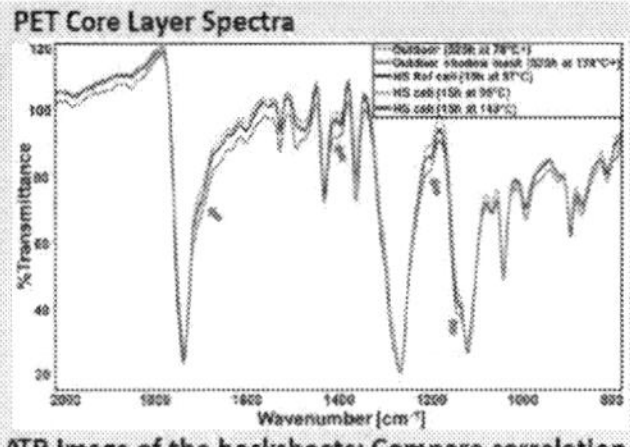

ATR Image of the backsheets: Compare correlation with adhesive spectra

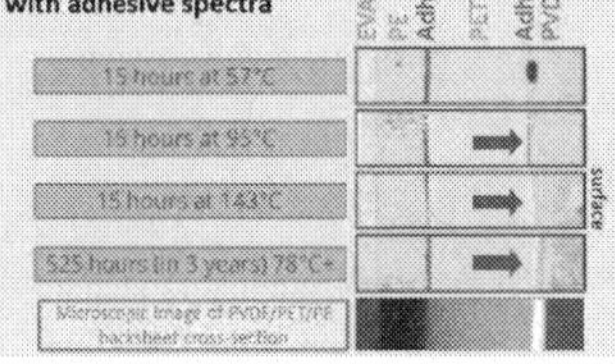

Summary

- **Persistent shading** leads to **gradual degradation** of encapsulant and backsheet materials, increasing long-term **reliability risks** in PV modules.
- **Indoor HS tests**, even at **75°C for 15 hours, fail to replicate** the degradation observed in real-world or outdoor accelerated ageing — **except for backsheet adhesive degradation** after 15 hours at 75°C.
- **PERC modules** may reach **higher hot spot temperatures** with increasing operating temperatures if their breakdown voltage falls within the series-connected substring voltage range.
- **Ongoing analysis focusses on** identifying a **reliable degradation indicator** aligned with observed **outdoor module behavior.**

References:
[1] H. Chu et al (2015), 10.1016/j.egypro.2015.07.006
[2] F. Fertig et al. (2013), 10.1016/j.egypro.2013.07.246
[3] Y. Voronko et al. (2014), 10.1366/13-07291
[4] Y. Voronko et al. (2015), 10.1002/pip.2580

42nd European Photovoltaic Solar Energy Conference and Exhibition

SALT SPRAY CORROSION RESISTANCE TESTING AND RELIABILITY EVALUATION OF LARGE-SIZE SOLAR MODULES AND METAL COMPONENTS

工業技術研究院
Industrial Technology Research Institute

EU PVSEC 2025

3AV.2

San-Yu Ting, Huan-Wu Lu, Syh-Homg Chen, Min-An Tsai, Cho-Fan Hsieh
Center for Measurement Standards, Industrial Technology Research Institute, Hsinchu 310, Taiwan
jackting@itri.org.tw; kuanwu@itri.org.tw; shuhing@itri.org.tw, MATsai@itri.org.tw; hsiehchofan@itri.org.tw

This study evaluates salt spray resistance of large PV modules (M6, M10, BIPV) and fasteners under IEC 60068-2-52. M10 showed higher power loss, while BIPV performed better. Stainless steel resisted corrosion best but caused galvanic effects; galvanized steels sacrificed protection but corroded faster; zinc-tin alloy was moderate. Improving encapsulation, sealing, and using coated or insulated fasteners can enhance durability in coastal environments.

Keywords: Large-Size PV Modules, Salt Spray Corrosion, Durability Enhancement.

Aim and Approach

This study evaluates the corrosion resistance and reliability of large-size PV modules and metal fasteners in salt spray environments, offering insights into long-term stability in high-salinity regions. Test samples include M6, M10 (single/dual glass), and BIPV corrugated modules, along with electro-galvanized, hot-dip galvanized, zinc-tin alloy, and stainless steel fasteners. Following IEC 60068-2-52, a platform was developed for modules over 2.1 m, simulating cyclic salt spray, drying, and humidity.

The testing process—from sample installation (Figure 1) to reliability evaluation (Figure 2)—assesses power degradation, insulation resistance, and structural integrity. Corrosion analysis of fasteners includes weight loss and surface deterioration. Findings highlight the importance of optimizing encapsulation, improving sealing, and selecting durable materials to enhance long-term reliability of PV systems in coastal environments.

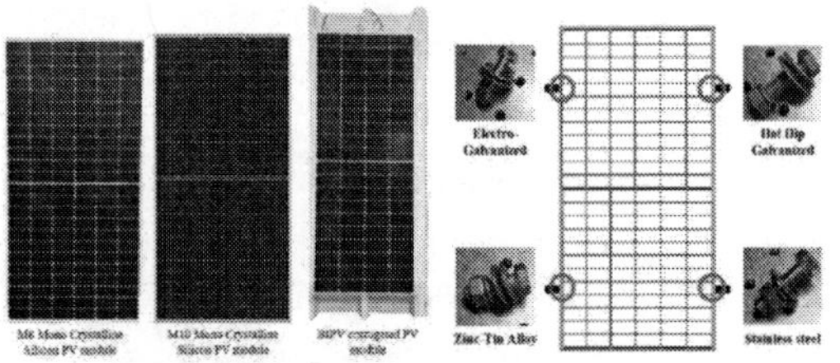

Figure 1: Large size PV module and metal component erection

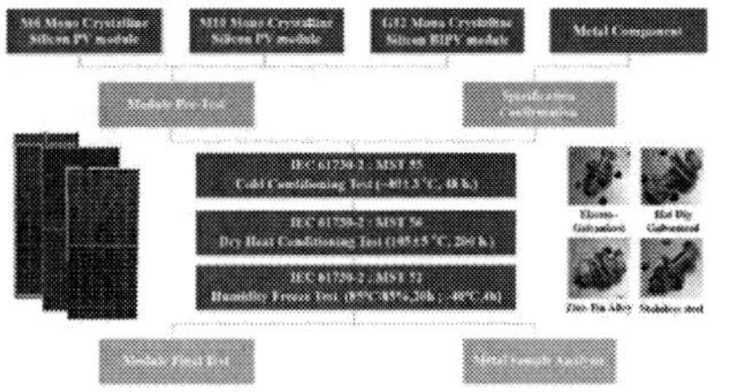

Figure 2: Flowchart of large size PV module and component reliability evaluation testing

Research Results

Preliminary results show that large-size PV modules degrade in salt spray environments, with durability strongly influenced by module type and encapsulation materials. As shown in Figure 3, M10 modules suffered greater power loss than M6 due to encapsulant deterioration and chloride infiltration, while BIPV modules maintained better stability, underscoring the value of optimized encapsulation.

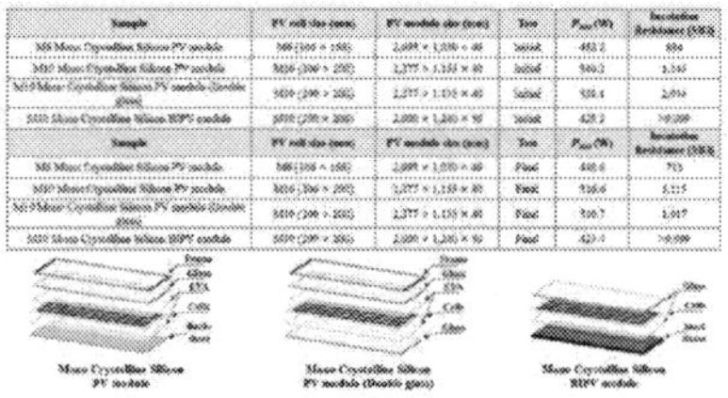

Figure 3: Power measurement results before and after testing for large-size modules

For fasteners, four common metals were tested. As shown in Figure 4, hot-dip and electro-galvanized fasteners provided sacrificial protection but corroded heavily, stainless steel offered the best resistance yet caused localized galvanic corrosion, and zinc-tin alloy demonstrated relatively stable performance, making it a suitable option for high-salinity environments.

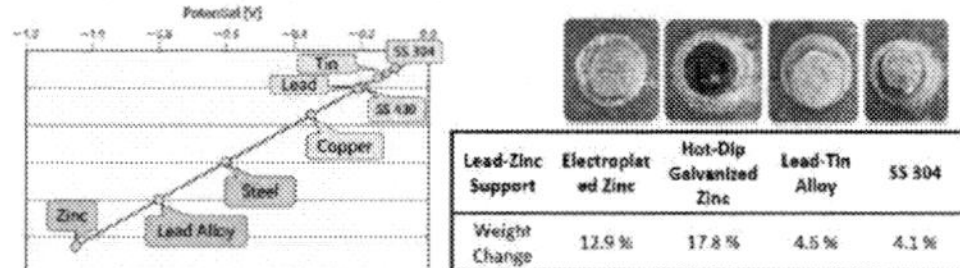

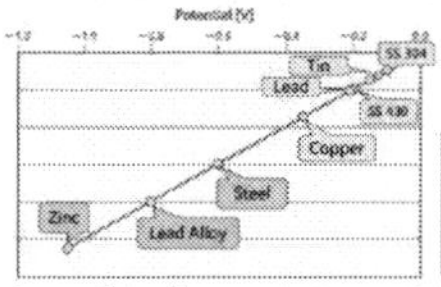

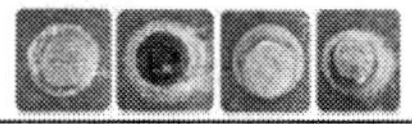

Lead-Zinc Support	Electroplated Zinc	Hot-Dip Galvanized Zinc	Lead-Tin Alloy	SS 304
Weight Change	12.9 %	17.8 %	4.5 %	4.1 %

Figure 4: Before and after weight comparison of commonly used metal fasteners in testing

Acknowledgments

This study was successfully conducted with the support of Energy Administration, Ministry of Economic Affairs, R.O.C., for which we express our sincere gratitude.

References

1. IEC 61730-2:2023, Photovoltaic (PV) module safety qualification – Part 2: Requirements for testing.
2. IEC 61215-2:2021, Terrestrial photovoltaic (PV) modules - Design qualification and type approval - Part 2: Test procedures.
3. CNS 14122, Corrosion of metals and alloys-Removal of corrosion products from corrosion test specimens
4. CNS 15753, Corrosion of metals and alloys-Corrosivity of atmospheres-Classification, determination and estimation

Conclusion

Power stability of large-size PV modules in salt spray conditions depends on encapsulation quality and frame sealing, while fastener durability relies on material and surface protection. Optimizing encapsulation, enhancing sealing, and selecting corrosion-resistant fasteners such as stainless steel or zinc-tin alloy with protective coatings can effectively extend service life and ensure reliable operation in high-salinity environments.

Analysis of Performance Loss in PV Systems due to Cracked Backsheets and Insulation Problems

Raffael Schifferegger [1,2], Yuliya Voronko [1], Anika Gassner [1,3], Gabriele C. Eder [1]
[1] OFI, Austrian Research Institute for Chemistry and Technology, Vienna, Austria;
[2] TU Wien, Institute of Applied Physics, Vienna, Austria;
Corresponding author: gabriele.eder@ofi.at

See also Poster 3.AV2.14 on „Restoring the Functionality of Damaged PV-Backsheets"

Motivation

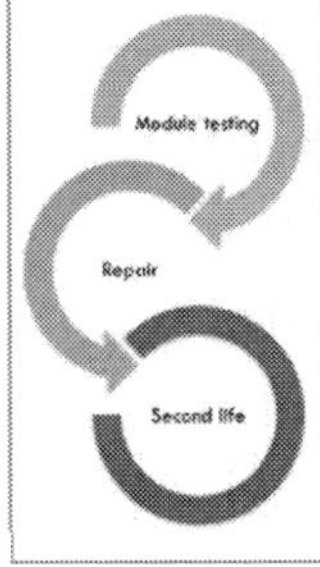

While PV systems generate clean energy throughout their operational lifetime, their sustainability across the full lifecycle requires further attention. Manufacturing remains resource-intensive, but todays modules with m-cry Si-technology installed and manufactured in Europe can achieve a energy payback time of round one year. However, dealing with early-failing modules, potential repair and reuse as second-life modules, and end-of-life (EOL) management are becoming increasingly challenging—especially as PV waste volumes are expected to rise sharply in the coming decades.

Addressing module failures through repair strategies can extend module lifetimes, reduce waste, and decrease the need for premature replacements.

One major failure type of PV modules is the degradation of the backsheet, which serves as an electrical insulator and protective layer of a PV module laminate. Cracks in the backsheet can lead to reduced insulation resistance ($R_{iso\ wet}$), triggering inverter shutdowns to prevent electrical hazards on the one hand but resulting in reduced energy production on the other hand.

Thus, a study was performed investigating the occurrence of insulation-related inverter failures and quantifies their impact on energy production.

A	As good as new, only small scratches etc.
B	Encapsulant and/or backsheet discoloration, minor delamination
C	Snail trails with < 10% module power loss
D	Cracked cells with < 10% module power loss
E	Failed bypass diode(s) that can be replaced (no potting)
F	Damaged junction boxes and/or cabling that should be replaced
G	Modules with severe power loss caused by PID
H	Cracked back sheet/severe scratches in back sheet that could be repaired
I	Unacceptable module damage that cannot be repaired: broken glass, hot spots / burn marks, excessive delamination, broken interconnects or poor soldering, corrosion, cracked cells with > 10% module power loss.

Table 1: Classification matrix for PV modules triage and eligibility for repair/reuse.
Toward Reuse-Ready PV: A Perspective on Recent Advances, Practices, and Future Challenges Wiley; Adv Energy and Sustain Res, 2024, DOI: 10.1002/aesr.202400237

Approach

The polymeric backsheet of a PV-module protects the internal components from environmental stresses and provides electrical insulation. Over time, environmental stressors such as UV radiation, temperature fluctuations, and mechanical loads can degrade the backsheet (dependent of the materials used), leading to delaminations, discolouration, cracks and insulation failures. Some failures impact the systems safety leading to inverter shutdowns and - on the long run – to underperformance.

→ A more detailed understanding of these inverter failures/shutdowns can help estimate the potential power loss and costs (financial impact of downtime) associated with not repairing defective modules and provides a clear economic rationale for repair strategies.

Repairing backsheets presents a viable solution to extend module lifetimes and reduce environmental impact by delaying the need for new materials and energy-intensive replacements.

Figure 1: PV-System in Koper/Slovenia with cracked backsheets; Monitoring data for the period 2016-2024; BAPV system

Analysis of Monitoring Data / Inverter Failures

Insulation resistance ($R_{iso\ wet}$) measures the ability of the module's encapsulation and backsheet to prevent leakage currents between the active electrical components and the grounded frame. Cracks in the backsheet reduce insulation resistance, especially in high humidity, and increase the likelihood of leakage currents that trigger the inverter's safety shutdown.

Safety-related inverter shutdown due to too low insulation resistance leads to power outages

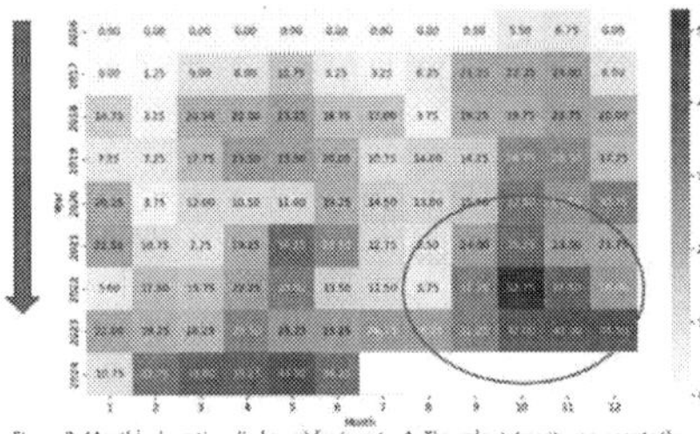

Figure 2: Monthly downtime (in hours) for inverter 1. The color intensity represents the magnitude of downtime, with darker colors indicating longer durations.

Downtime caused by inverter shutdown (Error 41)

Measurement period: 01.2016 - 07.2024 :

- increasing frequency of inverter failure E41
- Increased occurrence from 2020 (5-6 y of operation)
- Seasonality: more downtime in spring and especially fall

Comparison of humidity before the occurrence of the inverter error

- Humidity significantly higher on downtime days
- downtime days vs. reference days H: 83% vs. 65%

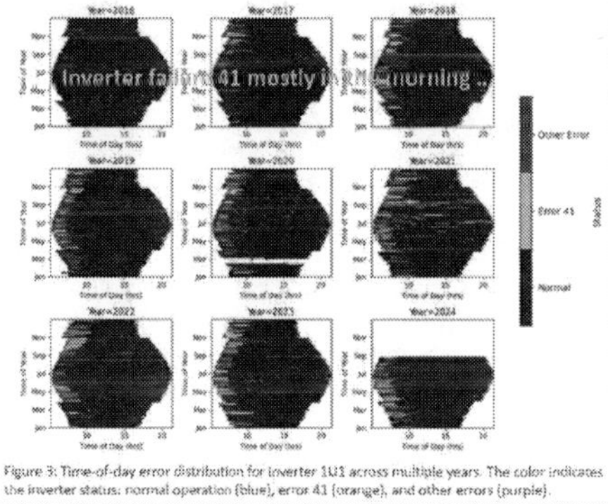

Figure 3: Time-of-day error distribution for inverter 1U1 across multiple years. The color indicates the inverter status: normal operation (blue), error 41 (orange), and other errors (purple).

Calculated Energy loss → Underperformance

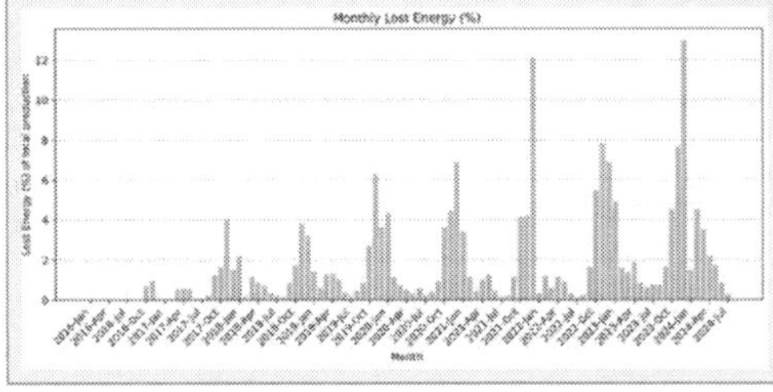

Figure 4: Calculated energy loss due to inverter shutdown; data available 2016 - 07.2024, Error 41 = invertor shutdown

Underperformance not very high (1,7% / year)
BUT: safety issues !

Figure 5: Yearly energy production and lost energy due to the inverter shutdown under low insulation resistance. Percentage values indicate lost energy as a fraction of total production.

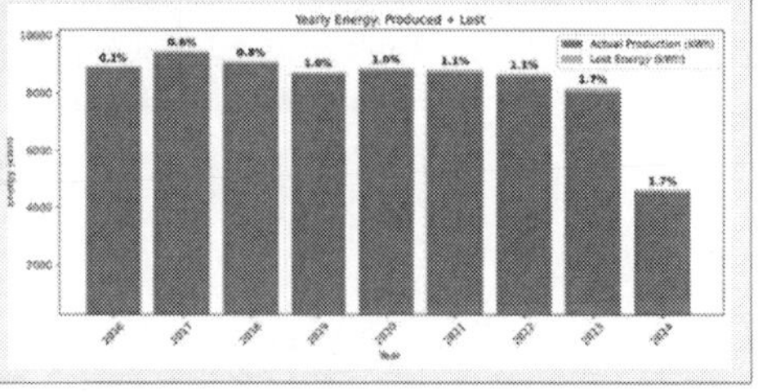

Conclusions

Serious defects (deep cracking) in the polymer backsheet of a PV module can

- pose a serious safety risk (loss of insulation strength; $R_{iso\ wet}$ breakdown),
- reduce the electrical performance of a PV module (penetration of water vapor and oxygen into the encapsulation -> solar cell -> corrosion of cell; degradation of encapsulant),
- lead to financial losses (increased inverter downtime) – especially under humid/wet conditions

Thus, the effected modules have to be replaced (and sent as EoL module to recycling) or can be repaired.

A specific repair technology or approach that can offer backsheet repair without compromising the module's performance, can be a game-changer for the PV industry. Repair coatings and tapes/foils have been developed and tested for their long-term stability:

- Repair options for PV modules with cracked polyamide backsheets: Yuliya Voronko, et al.; Energy Science & Engineering 2021 DOI: 10.1002/ese3.936; and IEEE PVSC 48 2021.
- Repair and Preventive Maintenance of PV Modules with Degrading Backsheets Using Flowable Silicone Sealant; Guy Beaucarne, et al., EU PVSEC 2021 5.DO.2.6. and PIP3492; DOI: 10.1002/pip.3492
- Towards reuse-ready PV: A perspective on recent advances, practices and future challenges; I.A. Tsanakas, et al., Adv. Energy Sustainability Res. 2024; doi.org/10.1002/aesr.202400237

PCCL   ofi   SONNENKRAFT   2nd cycle   ATB BECKER

The project ReNewPV is funded by the Austrian Federal Ministry for Climate Action, Environment, Energy, Mobility, Innovation and Technology represented by the Austrian Research Promotion Agency (FFG)
Projectnr.: FO999912440

42nd European Photovoltaic Solar Energy Conference and Exhibition

RESEARCH ON THE IMPACT OF OUTDOOR DUST ACCUMULATION AND COPPER-ACCELERATED ACETIC ACID SALT SPRAY ON SOLAR PHOTOVOLTAIC MODULES

工業技術研究院
Industrial Technology Research Institute

EU PVSEC 2025

3AV.2

San-Yu Ting, Yung-Jen Shyong, Min-An Tsai, Cho-Fan Hsieh
Center for Measurement Standards, Industrial Technology Research Institute, Hsinchu 310, Taiwan
jackting@itri.org.tw; ryanshyong@itri.org.tw, MATsai@itri.org.tw; hsiehchofan@itri.org.tw

With limited land, Taiwan increasingly adopts water-based PV. The 100 MW Changbin plant faces humidity, salt, and coastal dust, causing faster efficiency loss than inland sites. This study establishes an outdoor platform to evaluate dust and humidity effects, verify cleaning methods, and reduce costs. CASS accelerated corrosion tests further reveal dust–material interactions. Results on power loss, corrosion, and insulation aim to guide durable PV design for offshore use and provide industry strategies for cleaning and maintenance.

Keywords: Dust Accumulation, Corrosion Resistance, PV Reliability.

Aim and Approach

The primary objective of this research is to assess the impact of environmental stressors, such as dust accumulation and salt corrosion, on the long-term reliability of PV modules deployed in high-risk coastal areas. The study aims to:

a. Evaluate power loss and efficiency degradation caused by prolonged outdoor dust exposure and re-accumulation cycles.
b. Investigate corrosion mechanisms of different metallic components through accelerated CASS testing under simulated harsh conditions.
c. Identify effective mitigation and cleaning strategies to enhance module durability, reduce maintenance frequency, and optimize lifecycle costs.

To achieve these objectives, an experimental platform was established, combining long-term outdoor exposure testing with laboratory-based CASS testing. PV modules were systematically exposed to coastal environments characterized by high humidity, salt-laden air, and dust-laden winds, followed by corrosion resistance evaluation under controlled CASS testing conditions (Refer to Figure 1). The study integrates power performance measurements, electroluminescence (EL) imaging, insulation resistance evaluation, and structural integrity analysis to provide comprehensive insights into degradation pathways. These results are expected to support the development of more resilient PV designs and inform industry stakeholders in formulating practical maintenance and reliability strategies.

Figure 1: Experimental Procedure of this Study (Left), Outdoor Dust Test (Center), CASS Test Records (Right)

Research Results

The experimental results indicate that outdoor dust accumulation leads to a measurable decline in power generation efficiency. Manufacturer A's modules exhibited a 3% power loss, while Manufacturer B's modules showed a 1.5% loss after one month of exposure (Refer to Figure 2). This suggests that dust accumulation affects different module designs to varying extents, potentially due to differences in surface coatings, frame materials, or encapsulation methods. Post-CASS testing, no significant electrical degradation was observed; however, visual inspections revealed varying degrees of corrosion on metal frames and module surfaces, particularly in areas where dust had accumulated before exposure to the corrosive environment (Refer to Figure 3). The presence of fine dust particles may have enhanced the retention of moisture and corrosive agents, accelerating material degradation.

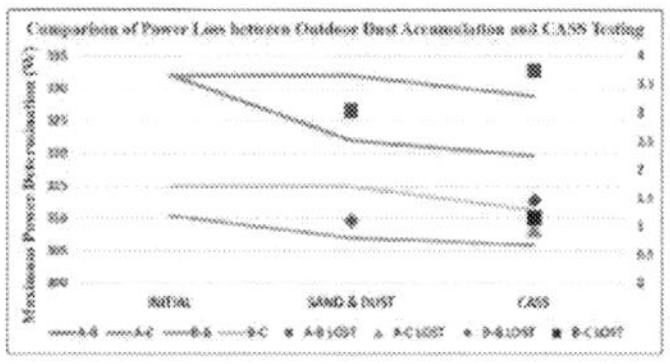

Figure 2: Power measurement results before and after testing for large-size modules

Figure 3: From Left to Right: (1) A Manufacturer Dust + CASS, (2) A Manufacturer CASS Only, (3) B Manufacturer Dust + CASS, (4) B Manufacturer CASS Only

Acknowledgments

This study was successfully conducted with the support of Energy Administration, Ministry of Economic Affairs, R.O.C., for which we express our sincere gratitude.

References

1. IEC 60068-2-68:1994, Environmental testing - Part 2-68: Tests - Test L: Dust and sand.
2. ISO 9227:2022, Corrosion tests in artificial atmospheres Salt spray tests
3. Hussain, Athar, Ankit Batra, and Rupendra Pachauri. "An experimental study on effect of dust on power loss in solar photovoltaic module." Renewables: Wind, Water, and Solar 4.1 (2017): 9.

Conclusion

This study demonstrates that while dust alone has limited short-term effects, its interaction with salt-laden environments significantly accelerates corrosion, particularly in aluminum frames, and contributes to insulation decline. These findings highlight the need for periodic cleaning, protective measures, and alternative materials to ensure durability in coastal PV systems. Future work will refine predictive models and explore advanced anti-corrosion treatments to further enhance long-term reliability.

TEXT-TO-IMAGE AND IMAGE-TO-IMAGE AUGMENTATION AND CLASSIFICATION OF DEFECTS IN PHOTOVOLTAIC MODULES

M. Waqar Akram[a,b*], Jianbo Bai[a*], Anees Ur Rehman[c]
[a]School of Renewable Energy, Hohai University, Changzhou, Jiangsu, China
[b]School of Electrical and Power Engineering, Hohai University, Nanjing, Jiangsu, China
[c]College of Mechanical and Electrical Engineering, Hohai University, Changzhou, Jiangsu, China
*Correspondence: waqarakramuaf@gmail.com, (M. W. Akram), bai_jianbo@hhu.edu.cn (J. Bai)

ABSTRACT: The autonomous photovoltaic (PV) monitoring is an emerging field with potential application in large-scale PV farms to maximize their output and reliability. However, it experiences several critical challenges like limited data constraints, intricate data collection and insufficient performance on unseen data in unknown working conditions. Addressing these challenges, the present study explores text-to-image and image-to-image synthetic data generation methods. The synthetic electroluminescence (EL) images are generated using Stable Diffusion (text-to-image) and Style Generative adversarial Networks, StyleGAN (image-to-image) variants. The real and synthetic data combinations are then used for solo and mixed training experiments that demonstrated enhanced (highest) classification performance with text-to-image data augmentation followed by image-to-image augmentation and real data. Moreover, a hybrid classification architecture based on MobileNetv3 small and YOLOv11 is proposed that achieved enhanced precision, recall and accuracy of 94.3 %, 87.3 % and 91.3 % respectively compared to baseline and other models. The introduction of inverse and effective sampling along with class weighting is also studied to handle class imbalance. This study explored synthetic data generation methods and proposed a classification architecture to improve the performance of autonomous PV monitoring as well as addresses limited volume and diverse data constraints, simplifying the data acquisition process.
Keywords: Photovoltaic (PV) modules, Defect detection, Generative AI, Text-to-image generation, Electroluminescence (EL) images

1 INTRODUCTION

With the exponential global expansion of Photovoltaic (PV) technology and ongoing development of large-scale PV farms, the autonomous and intelligent monitoring has become an integral aspect of PV systems to optimize their operation, performance and reliability [1,2]. The PV systems require continuous and fast monitoring as they are exposed to several environmental and climatic stresses and factors throughout their entire life. Regarding this, PV systems intelligence has caught significant attention of researchers globally and has been studied widely using classical computer vision and deep learning based methods [3]. The classical computer vision usually includes image processing and feature engineering based methods, that were mainly studied for classification of defects [4]. They can also be adapted for detection or localization and segmentation of defects [5]. However, they offered limited and multi-stage (fragmented) applications. These methods lack generalization, wide defects coverage, large-scale application, and real-time inference [6].

In recent years, deep learning based methods demonstrated broad prospects and achieved remarkable progress in PV systems intelligence [7]. They overcome many existing limitations and widely applied for classification [8,9], detection [10,11] and segmentation [12,13] tasks of defects as well as studied for real-time application and deployment on edge devices [14,15]. As a fundamental component of these systems, the robustness and generalization of models trained for these systems has a direct and significant impact on their practical and in-field applications. In practical and outdoor environments, PV cells and modules often experience multiple degradation stages, multi-scale defects, susceptibility to interference with examination background, complex lighting conditions, unseen rare data and other detection challenges [16]. Moreover, there are different types and designs of cells, modules and other components that make detection more challenging.

One of the factors behind these challenges is volume and diversity limited data available for training these models, as these methods are data-driven and heavily relies on data size, diversity and other characteristics for their robust and generalized application. Data collection is an intricate and costly process requiring expertise, specific conditions, and instrumentation, particularly for Electroluminescence (EL) imaging, which is considered as one the most-effective methods. These factors, in turn, leads to limiting the diversity and size of data, which has a significant impact on training, robustness and generalization of detection systems. They particularly suffer with performance constraints upon application on unseen data in unknown working conditions, limiting their application in the field.

Consequently, these data and practical limitations have become a critical issue in this field. In recent years, synthetic data generation through integration of language (textual descriptions) with images (visual) data marked several advancements and achieved highly realistic generation, simplifying data acquisition and related constraints [17,18]. These advancements are associated with capturing long-range dependencies through introduction of self-attention mechanism and transformer model [19], which has enabled to manage the generation and understanding in Large Language Models (LLMs) and Natural Language Processing (NLP). These developments lead to highly realistic images generation by text-to-image models like Recraft, DALL-E, Ideogram, Midjourney, Flux, and Stable Diffusion, that have learnt millions and billions of text-image pairs [20]. These models are widely used in many domains for data creation and performance augmentation including Agriculture, Remote sensing, Digital Media, Medical, and others. Similarly, there are wide prospects for text-to-image models application in PV intelligence, but they need to be explored yet. On the other hand, image-to-image models also have potential application for synthetic PV data creation. Image-to-image models like Generative adversarial network (GAN) based methods were developed in few studies and demonstrated performance gains in PV monitoring intelligence [21–23]. Both these text-to-image and image-to-image models uses deep learning for generating images and their difference lies in the architectures, algorithms and inputs. They offered different output quality, source replication, resemblance, variability, object coverage, customization, control, usability, and resource efficiency in different contexts of real data like image complexity, presence of multiple objects and backgrounds, data size, and others [24,25]. These factors, in turn demand the exploration of their application in PV domain and evaluation of generated data to assess their representation of real environment.

In this light, this study aims to explore text-to-image and image-to-image synthetic data generation methods for their application in autonomous PV monitoring. It explores Stable Diffusion and StyleGAN variants for text-to-image and image-to-image generation of EL images of PV modules respectively. The generated and real data is then used for mixed and solo training experiments. Moreover, a hybrid classification architecture based on MobileNetv3 and YOLOv11 is proposed that achieved enhanced accuracy of 91.3 %. The proposed architecture is compared with baseline and several other models i.e. MobileNetv3, YOLOv11, EfficientNet, ConvNext, Vision Transformer, Swin Transformer, ResNet, YOLOv8, and YOLOv12. The introduction of inverse and effective sampling along with class weighting is also studied to handle class imbalance.

2 METHODOLOGY

2.1 Text-to-image generation

For text-to-image generation, Stable Diffusion models [17,18] from study [26] are used for generation of images including stable diffusion iterations v1, 2, and XL. These models are based on forward diffusion and reverse diffusion i.e. denoising processes which are carried out in latent space, and guided by text prompt-to-image conditioning. The supervised real data in text-image pairs form i.e. textual descriptions along with corresponding images is used to train these networks. Seed, guidance scale, inference steps, mixed/blended prompts, and negative prompts are used for generating diverse data. For instance, the seed, guidance scale, and inference steps are varied between 0 to 200, 5 to 15, and 20 to 60 respectively. Additionally, mixed prompts mentioning multiple defects with variations in numbers and severities of defects, and negative prompts mentioning low quality, unclear, blurriness, and other undesired guiding words are used.

2.2 Image-to-image generation

For text-to-image generation, StyleGAN [27] iterations from study [23] including StyleGAN2, and StyleGAN3-T (Translation equiv.), and StyleGAN3-R (Rotation and Translation equiv.) are used for generation of images. These models are based on generator and discriminator networks. They are trained from unsupervised real EL images data of normal operating and defective PV modules. Truncation and seeds are varied between 0.3 to 1.7 and 0 to 999 respectively to generate large number of images by these models.

2.3 Classification

2.3.1 Training data

This study used real data, text-to-image generated data (section 2.1) and image-to-image generated data (section 2.2) for training experiments. The real data used in this study consists of total 964 images including 472 defective and 492 normal operating modules. 836 images are taken from a from a public dataset [28] and remaining 128 images are collected from EL imaging experiments. The complete data is openly shared on Kaggle data hub [See data availability statement]. These modules are of different brands having different designs of cells, modules and other components. The defective modules cover multiple defects including cracks, black edges, low cells, finger or grid interruptions, dark cells, breaks, contamination, and backsheet scratches.

Each text-to-image and image-to-image generated data consists of total 600 images of normal and defective modules. The incremental augmentation (training with incremental data proportions from 100 to 600 in steps of 100) for both synthetic datasets lead to selection of only defective images (300 for each case). The text-to-image generated module images have cracks, black edges, low cells, black cells and breaks. The image-to-image generated module images have black edges, low cells, contamination, black cells, and breaks.

The synthetic datasets are then used to augment real data. The real and synthetic images are used for solo and mixed training experiments in following solo and mixed formations i.e. (1) real data (2) real+text-to-image synthetic mix, and (3) real+image-to-image synthetic mix. The details of each data category or combination are given in table I.

Table I: Data combinations used for solo and mixed training experiments

Module/ Data category	Real image data (solo)	Text-to-image data	Image-to-image data	Real+ Text-to-image	Real+ Image-to-image
Total	964	300	300	1264	1264
Normal	492	0	0	492	492
Defec-tive	472	300	300	772	772

2.3.2 Proposed classification architecture

Initially, we studied YOLOv11 variants for classification of PV modules, which results in higher efficiency by YOLOv11 Nano variant when trained from pre-trained ImageNet weights. Focusing further on improved feature extraction, subtle defects, light-weight application, and better generalization, we studied different architectural backbones i.e. ConvNeXt, EfficientNetV2, Swin Transformer, Vision Transfomer, MobileNetV3, ShuffleNetV2, and ResNet. Moreover, we also carried out experimentation with other YOLO family models whose classification pipelines are available. Based on the above models training, error analysis from the misclassifications by the models and limitation by the data size, we proposed a hybrid architecture based on MobileNetv3 [29] and YOLOv11 [30], which is shown in figure 1.

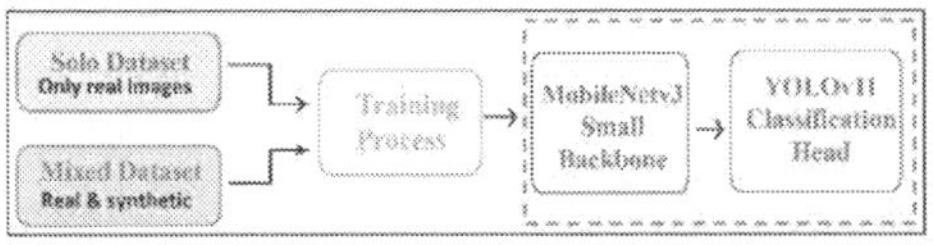

Figure 1: Overall methodology of this study and proposed architecture

This proposed architecture employs a MobileNetv3-Small backbone which makes it efficient as well as light weight. Originally the MobileNet introduced a depth-wise separable convolution technique consisting of depth-wise and point-wise convolution layers for filtering the input channels and combining their output to create a new feature respectively, which results in reduced computation and model size compared to conventional convolution operation. Later the MobileNetv2 introduced inverted residuals blocks and linear bottlenecks that further improve the efficiency as well as reduce the complexity. The inverted residuals block starts with a bottleneck having a smaller number of channels followed by expansion to larger number of channels instead of direct connection with layers having large number of channels. The MobileNetv3 combines the existing versions and uses Platform-aware NAS, NetAdapt, Squeeze-and-Excite (SE) modules, and H-Swish activation for developing an enhanced network. It has two large and small versions and we used MobileNetV3-Small in our proposed architecture as it provides excellent results with low resources compared to MobileNetV3-Large.

The platform-aware neural architecture search (NAS) helps in optimization of the architecture complimented with NetAdapt to fine-tune the layers. The Squeeze-and-Excite (SE) modules improves feature learning and network accuracy with a small increase in number of parameters. The nonlinearity H-Swish activation, a harder version of swish function improves the model efficiency as the original Swish function is computationally expensive for edge or embedded environments.

We used TorchVision library to load the MobileNetV3-Small model with pretrained ImageNet weights. The classifier layers of MobileNetV3 are truncated, which is handled by YOLO head as discussed later. During loading, the feature width of MobileNet is aligned with YOLO head.

The MobileNetV3-Small backbone is then followed by YOLOv11 classification head. YOLOv11 is designed to handle diverse computer vision challenges of classification in addition to detection, segmentation, and other tasks. It has different classification variants which are trained on ImageNet data with 1000 classes. The architectural changes in these variants lies in depth, width and maximum channels having different number of layers, parameters, gradients and GFLOPs.

The YOLOv11 classification head used in proposed architecture takes the input channels from backbone and reduces the final layer to number of classes n_c. It adds an extra 1x1 convolution layer prior to final classification and includes global average pooling. Global average pooling computes the average of every value in entire feature map and give a single output for each channel. This reduces the dimensionality as well as maintain classification efficiency. The YOLOv11 used SiLU activation instead of H-Swish used by MobileNetv3 as mentioned earlier. Moreover, it does not used dropout for regularization as used by MobileNetv3, it uses other regularization methods instead. The final layer is followed by softmax activation to produce probability distribution.

For handling data imbalance, a data-level approach of class-balanced sampling is used in this study. A weighted random sampling strategy based on class weights w for n_c number of sample images in class c is used, which helps to create approximately class-balanced mini batches in an epoch during training. While, natural data distribution is used during validation to prevent biasness. For class weighting, inverse-frequency and effective-number rules are studied and inverse frequency class weighting is found as more robust and it is also simple, therefore, used in final architecture.

The model is trained for 100 epochs with a batch size of 4 and image size of 640x640. The initial and final learning rates are 0.01 with a momentum of 0.937.

3 RESULTS AND DISCUSSION

3.1 Text-to-image data

These images are generated using different text-prompts, seeds, guidance scales. negative prompts, and inference steps, as shown in figure 1. It can be observed that the generated images have diverse characteristics with different cell and module designs and have multiple defect types. There are multiple instances and severities of the defects appeared in many of the images, leading to robust model development. The text-to-image synthetic data includes cracks, low cells, dark cells, black edges and breaks. The contamination and finger interruptions are not well preserved in the generated images.

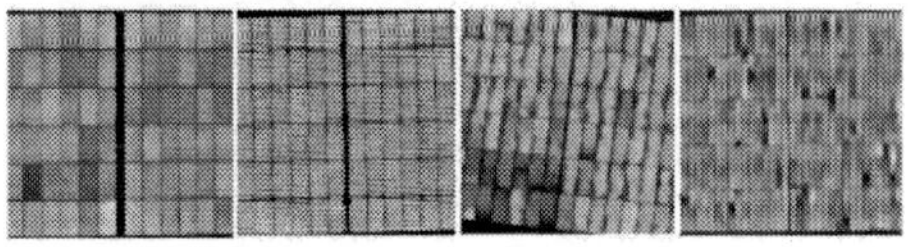

Figure 2: Text-to-image synthetic data generated by different iterations and variants of stable diffusion

3.2 Image-to-image data

These images are generated using different truncation and seed variations. The images generated by different iterations and variants of StyleGAN are shown in figure 2. Similar to above, the generated images have diverse characteristics with different cell and module designs and have multiple defect types. However, the variation is less compared to stable diffusion based models. There are multiple instances and severities of the defects appeared in many of the images. The image-to-image synthetic data includes low cells, dark cells, black edges, breaks, and contamination. The cracks and finger interruptions are not well preserved in the generated images.

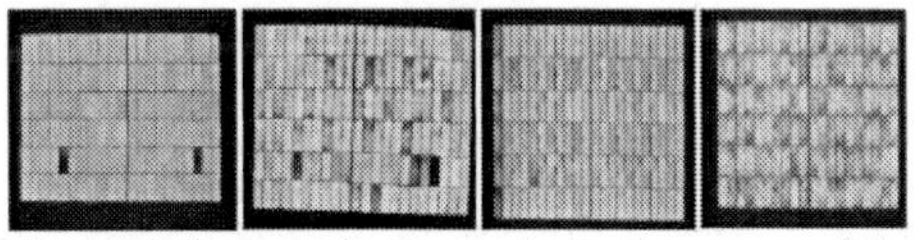

Figure 3: Image-to-image synthetic data generated by different StyleGAN iterations

3.3 Classification results

In present study, we studied different architectures and training strategies tailored for enhanced performance, real-time speed and data imbalance. Firstly, YOLOv11-n classification network is trained on solo and real-synthetic data combinations from pre-trained weights. The training experiments demonstrates highest results for real+text-to-image synthetic data mix followed by real+image-to-image mix and real data. These results are given in table II.

Table II: Classification results with different data combinations

Training Data	Precision	Recall	Accuracy
Real data	0.919	0.842	0.887
Real+Image-to-image	0.895	0.905	0.902
Real+Text-to-image	0.913	0.894	0.908

Following above results, the remaining experiments are carried out with real+text-to-image synthetic data mix. These include training of proposed network, baselines and other models. The proposed architecture obtained Precision, Recall and Accuracy of 94.3 %, 87.3 % and 91.3 % respectively. It shows that 94.3% of modules predicted as defective were actually defective. However, the recall value is a bit low that shows 87.3 % correct predictions for defective modules.

The proposed method is compared with baseline and several state-of-the-art and widely used architectures as discussed earlier. This also includes training with YOLOv11-s, and YOLOv11-m models that shows similar results as by YOLOv11-n at higher computational cost. Therefore, we continue to choose YOLOv11-n for further architectural and training changes tailored for enhanced performance, real-time speed and data imbalance; which results in proposed architecture and training methods. The comparison is given in table III.

Table III: Results of different architectures trained on real+text-to-image data mix

Networks	Precision	Recall	Accuracy
YOLOv11-s	0.918	0.831	0.882
YOLOv8-n	0.903	0.884	0.897
YOLOv12-n	0.862	0.926	0.892
ResNet-18	0.919	0.843	0.887
EfficientNetv2-s	0.881	0.928	0.907
Convnext tiny	0.836	0.805	0.820
Vision Vit-l-16	0.767	0.484	0.676
YOLOv11-n	0.913	0.894	0.908
MobileNetV3-s	0.897	0.897	0.897
Proposed Architecture	0.943	0.873	**0.913**

It can be seen from table 3 that the proposed architecture demonstrates enhanced performance compared to baseline and other models. However, the recall value is found higher for other models. The EfficientNetv2-s achieved highest recall value of 0.928 with an overall accuracy of 0.907 indicating highest correct prediction rate for defective modules followed by YOLOv12-n with recall value of 0.926. Here, the baseline models are trained with original heads and architectures using different training formations like training of head with frozen base, training of n base layers and training entire model.

The training and validation losses for the proposed model are shown in figure 4. Their curves show a steady decline that indicates effective model learning. The validation loss value was initially around 0.6 which first decreases rapidly to value around 0.5, followed by progressive decrease to value around 0.3. Similar pattern is observed for training loss. Both the losses eventually remained between a small range with slight fluctuations, indicating training stability.

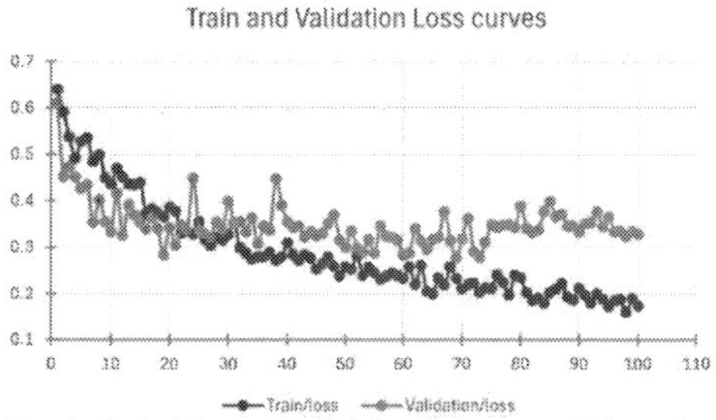

Figure 4: Training and validations losses over 100 epochs.

The confusion matrix analysis shows that the model is hardly classifying the defective class comparatively. Few defective images are misclassified as normal which is further analyzed with inference results. The inference results of proposed network are shown in figure 5. There was misclassification problem mainly observed for the module images having low cell defects with low contrast. Their color and texture are very similar to normal cells creating confusion for the model. This problem can be further analyzed with global or local/selective contrast adjustment.

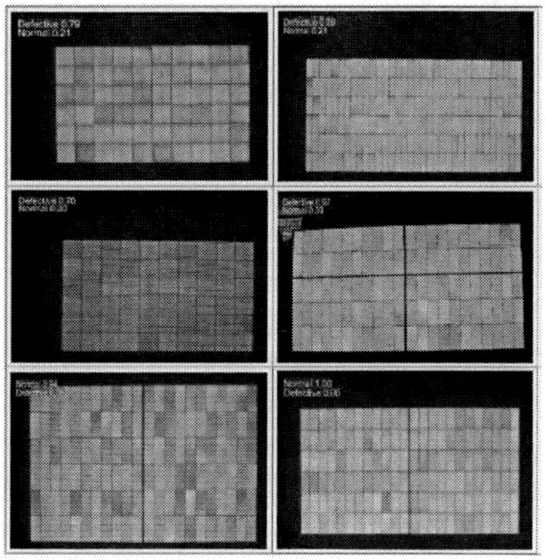

Figure 5: Inference results of proposed method (Last row shows incorrect predictions)

4 CONCLUSIONS

This study proposed a hybrid architecture integrating MobileNetv3 small backbone and YOLOv11 classification head for enhanced classification of normal and defective PV modules. The proposed architecture outperforms baseline and other architectures in terms of precision and accuracy. This study also investigated text-to-image and image-to-image synthetic data generation and the mixed data training results demonstrates highest

10.4229/EUPVSEC2025/3AV.2.37

results for real+text-to-image synthetic data mix followed by real+image-to-image mix and real data. Furthermore, the inverse weighted sampling is found robust in handling class imbalance.

The integration of MobileNet and YOLO head is easy and consistent with Ultralytics YOLO framework and training pipeline, and the experiments demonstrates the adaptability and robustness of YOLOv11 classification head. This is an easy-to-use and end-to-end pipeline in which Ultralytics framework deals with all steps.

ACKNOWLEDGEMENTS

This research work was supported by "The Fundamental Research Funds for the Central Universities Program, China Project Number B250201205".

REFERENCES

[1] Solar Farm Automation Market: Global Forecast From 2025 To 2033 - Dataintelo Report (2024).
[2] Databridge. Global Solar Farm Automation Market - Industry Trends and Forecast to 2029. DATA BRIDGE (2021).
[3] Buratti Y, Javier GMN, Abdullah-Vetter Z, Dwivedi P, Hameiri Z. Machine learning for advanced characterisation of silicon photovoltaics: A comprehensive review of techniques and applications. Renewable and Sustainable Energy Reviews 202 (2024) 114617.
[4] Mahdavipour Z. Defect inspection of photovoltaic solar modules using aerial electroluminescence (EL): A review. Solar Energy Materials and Solar Cells 278 (2024) 1-28.
[5] Akram MW, Li G, Jin Y, Chen X, Zhu C, Ahmad A. Automatic detection of photovoltaic module defects in infrared images with isolated and develop-model transfer deep learning. Solar Energy 198 (2020). https://doi.org/10.1016/j.solener.2020.01.055.
[6] Waqar Akram M, Li G, Jin Y, Chen X. Failures of photovoltaic modules and their detection: A Review. Applied Energy 313 (2022) 118822. https://doi.org/10.1016/j.apenergy.2022.118822.
[7] Masita K, Hasan A, Shongwe T, Hilal HA. Deep learning in defects detection of PV modules: A review. Solar Energy Advances 5 (2025).
[8] Akram MW, Li G, Jin Y, Chen X, Zhu C, Zhao X. CNN based automatic detection of photovoltaic cell defects in electroluminescence images. Energy (2019) 116319. https://doi.org/10.1016/j.energy.2019.116319.
[9] Zhang J, Chen X, Wei H, Zhang K. A lightweight network for photovoltaic cell defect detection in electroluminescence images based on neural architecture search and knowledge distillation. Applied Energy 355 (2024).
[10] Ramadan EA, Moawad NM, Abouzalm BA, Sakr AA, Abouzaid WF, El-Banby GM. An innovative transformer neural network for fault detection and classification for photovoltaic modules. Energy Conversion and Management 314 (2024).
[11] Liu Q, Liu M, Wu QMJ, Shen W. A novel few-shot detector for rare defect localization in photovoltaic cells using electroluminescence images. Solar Energy 296 (2025).
[12] Zhou P, Wang R, Wang C, Chen H, Liu K. SIIF: Semantic information interactive fusion network for photovoltaic defect segmentation. Applied Energy 371 (2024) 123643.
[13] Mahboob Z, Khan MA, Lodhi E, Nawaz T, Khan US. Using SegFormer for Effective Semantic Cell Segmentation for Fault Detection in Photovoltaic Arrays. IEEE Journal of Photovoltaics (2024)1-12.
[14] Tang W, Yang Q, Hu X, Yan W. Deep learning-based linear defects detection system for large-scale photovoltaic plants based on an edge-cloud computing infrastructure. Solar Energy 231 (2022) 527–35.
[15] Di Renzo AB, de Morais HRF, Lazzaretti AE, de Arruda LVR, Lopes HS, Martelli C, et al. Edge Device for the Classification of Photovoltaic Faults Using Deep Neural Networks. Journal of Control, Automation and Electrical Systems 35 (2024) 861-9.
[16] Waqar Akram M, Bai J, Xuan C, Xiaotuo X, Hu J, Wu S. Advancing photovoltaic cells defect detection in electroluminescence images through exploring multiple object detectors. Solar Energy Materials and Solar Cells 292 (2025) 113777. https://doi.org/https://doi.org/10.1016/j.solmat.2025.113777.
[17] Ho J, Jain A, Abbeel P. Denoising diffusion probabilistic models. Adv Neural Inf Process Syst (2020).
[18] Podell D, English Z, Lacey K, Blattmann A, Dockhorn T, Müller J, et al. Sdxl: Improving Latent Diffusion Models for High-Resolution Image Synthesis. 12th International Conference on Learning Representations, ICLR (2024).
[19] Vaswani A, Shazeer N, Parmar N, Uszkoreit J, Jones L, Gomez AN, et al. Attention is all you need. Advances in Neural Information Processing Systems (2017).
[20] Schuhmann C, Beaumont R, Vencu R, Gordon C, Wightman R, Cherti M, et al. LAION-5B: An open large-scale dataset for training next generation image-text models. Advances in Neural Information Processing Systems 35 (2022) 1-50.
[21] Luo Z, Cheng SY, Zheng QY. GAN-based augmentation for improving CNN performance of classification of defective photovoltaic module cells in electroluminescence images. IOP Conference Series: Earth and Environmental Science 354 (2019).
[22] Lu F, Niu R, Zhang Z, Guo L, Chen J. A Generative Adversarial Network-Based Fault Detection Approach for Photovoltaic Panel. Applied Sciences 12 (2022).
[23] Akram MW, Bai J. Defect detection in photovoltaic modules based on image-to-image generation and deep learning. Sustainable Energy Technologies and Assessments 82 (2025).
[24] Wang H. Comparative Analysis of GANs and Diffusion Models in Image Generation. Highlights in Science, Engineering and Technology 120 (2024) 59-66.
[25] Peng Y. A Comparative Analysis Between GAN and Diffusion Models in Image Generation. 2nd International Conference on Artificial Intelligence, Database and Machine Learning (AIDML), Vol. V (2024) 189–95.
[26] M. Waqar Akram. PVEL-Text-to-image-Generator. Hugging Face Model Hub (2025). https://huggingface.co/mwaqarakram/PVEL-Text-to-image-Generator-1 or https://huggingface.co/mwaqarakram/PVEL-Text-to-image-Generator-2
[27] Karras T, Laine S, Aila T. A Style-Based

Generator Architecture for Generative Adversarial Networks. IEEE Transactions on Pattern Analysis and Machine Intelligence 43 (2021).
[28] M. Waqar Akram. Solar PVMEL-Solar PV module-level EL images data (2025). https://kaggle.com/datasets/b6ebe1ef566cc298a4173b697c121f1a49234762d24910982a530d73bd30a8ca or https://www.kaggle.com/datasets/waqarakram/solar-pvmel-solar-pv-module-level-el-images-data
[29] Howard A, Sandler M, Chu G, Chen L-C, Chen B, Tan M, et al. Searching for MobileNetV3. ArXiv ID 190502244 (2019).
[30] Khanam R, Hussain M. YOLOv11: An Overview of the Key Architectural Enhancements. ArXiv ID 241017725 (2024).

Text-to-Image and Image-to-Image Augmentation and Classification of Defects in Photovoltaic Modules

M. Waqar Akram, Jianbo Bai, Anees Ur Rehman
School of Renewable Energy, Hohai University, Changzhou, Jiangsu, China

Introduction

The autonomous and intelligent monitoring has become an integral aspect of photovoltaic (PV) systems to optimize their operation, performance and reliability. Deep learning demonstrated broad prospects and achieved remarkable progress in PV systems intelligence. However, the detection systems face different detection challenges in outdoor and practical applications concerning appearance of multiple degradation stages, multi-scale defects, susceptibility to interference with examination background, complex lighting conditions, unseen diverse cell and module designs, and others. One of the factors behind these challenges is volume and diversity limited data available for training these data-driven and data-reliant models, as data collection is an intricate and costly process. This study explored text-to-image and image-to-image synthetic data generation methods for their application in autonomous PV monitoring. Moreover, it proposes a hybrid classification architecture based on MobileNetv3 and YOLOv11 for enhanced performance.

Text-to-Image Generation

It used stable diffusion models based on forward diffusion and reverse diffusion processes in latent space, and guided by text prompt-to-image conditioning. The text-image pairs i.e. textual descriptions along with corresponding images are used for training these networks. Seed, guidance scale, inference steps, mixed/blended prompts, and negative prompts are varied to generate diverse data.

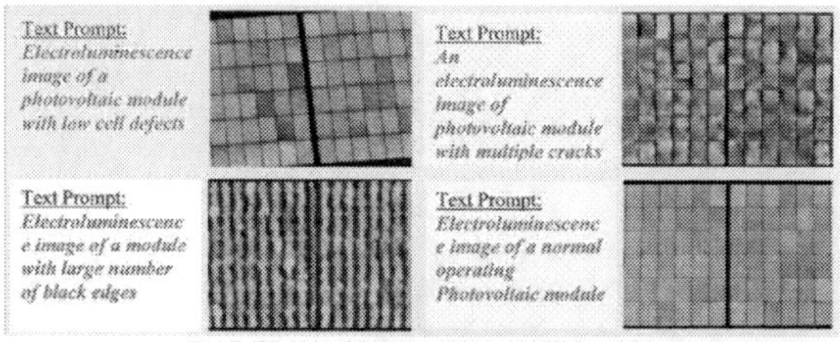

Fig 1. Text-to-Image generated images

Image-to-Image Generation

It used StyleGAN3 variants i.e. Translation and Rotation-Translation equivalent based on generator and discriminator networks. The unsupervised images data of normal operating and defective PV modules is used for training these StyleGAN3 variants .

Table 1. Data combinations used for solo and mixed training experiments

Modules / Data category	Real images data (solo)	Text-to-image data	Image-to-image data	Real+Text-to-image (mixed)	Real+Image-to-image (mixed)
Total	964	300	300	1264	1264
Normal operating	492	000	000	492	492
Defective modules	472	300	300	772	772

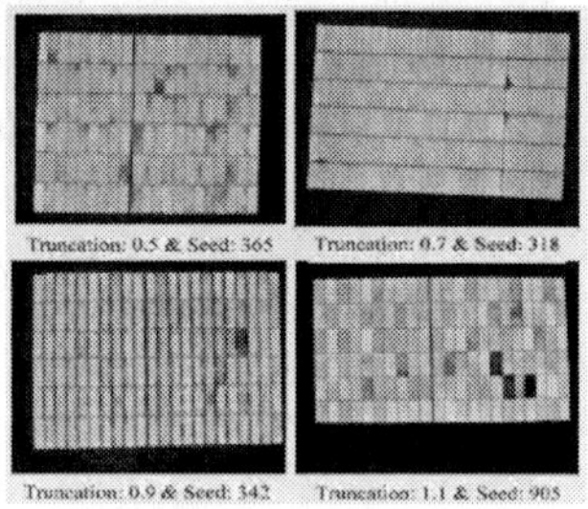

Fig 2. Image-to-Image generation

Classification

The real data used in this study is collected from the electroluminescence imaging of PV modules having diverse designs and characteristics exposed to accelerated ageing. The synthetic datasets are used to augment real data, and solo and mixed training experiments are performed, with data combinations shown in table 1. A hybrid classification architecture based on MobileNetv3 and YOLOv11 is proposed that employs a MobileNetv3-Small backbone followed by YOLOv11 classification head, as shown in figure 3.

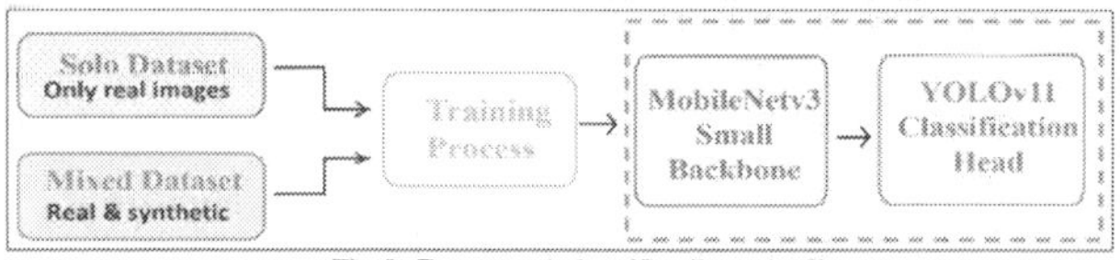

Fig 3. Proposed classification pipeline

Table 2. Classification results with different data combinations

Training Data	Precision	Recall	Accuracy
Real data	0.919	0.842	0.887
Real+Image-to-image	0.895	0.905	0.902
Real+Text-to-image	0.913	0.894	0.908

Results

Firstly, YOLOv11-s classification network is trained on the data combinations of solo and synthetic data from pre-trained weights. The training results showed best results for real+text-to-image synthetic data mix followed by real+image-to-image mix and real data, given in table 2. Following above results, several architectures including the proposed network and baselines models are trained on real+text-to-image data mix. The proposed architecture obtained Precision, Recall and Accuracy of 94.3 %, 87.3 % and 91.3 % respectively. The results of proposed method is compared with baseline models and other networks as shown in figure 4. The inference results of proposed architecture are shown in figure 5.

Conclusions

Mixed training with text-to-image synthetic augmentation demonstrates enhanced (highest) performance followed by image-to-image augmented training compared to solo data training.

The proposed hybrid architecture integrating MobileNetv3 and YOLOv11 demonstrates highest classification accuracy compared to baseline and other networks. This integration is an end-to-end pipeline, which is easy-to-use and consistent with Ultralytics framework and training script.

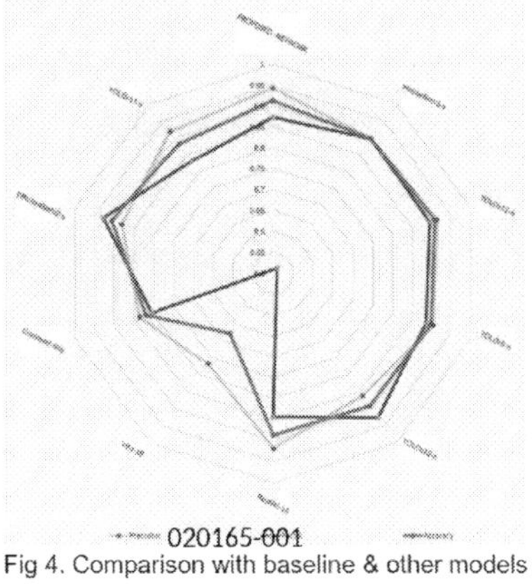

Fig 4. Comparison with baseline & other models

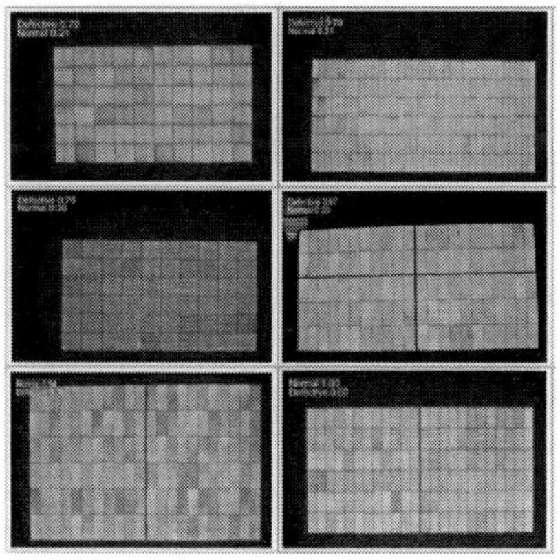

Fig 5. Inference by proposed architecture trained on real+synthetic mix data (Last row: misclassification)

UV FLUORESCENCE IMAGING OF DEFECTS AND BILL OF MATERIALS VARIATIONS IN BIFACIAL SOLAR PANELS

Andrew M. Gabor[1], Maulid Kivambe[2], Mohamed Abdelrahim[2], Mohamed Elgaili[2], Amir A. Abdallah[2]

[1] BrightSpot Automation, Boulder Colorado, USA; gabor@brightspotautomation.com
[2]Qatar Environment & Energy Research Institute (QEERI), Hamad Bin Khalifa University (HBKU), Doha, Qatar

ABSTRACT: UV Fluorescence (UVF) is a high-throughput, non-contact method of imaging defects and bill of material variations in solar panels. Cracks in silicon solar cells are easily seen by this technique since oxygen can diffuse through polymer backsheets, through the cracks in the cells, and then quench the fluorescence in the front encapsulant above the crack lines. Most of the reported data on UVF imaging in the literature shows images of panels with polymeric backsheets, but bifacial panels with rear glass layers are steadily taking market share, and oxygen cannot penetrate the rear glass in such panels except through the junction box penetrations and the perimeter edges. We therefore ask the question, "Does UVF have a useful role in imaging glass/glass panels?" Here we present data from several different glass/glass bifacial panels installed in desert climate (Qatar), showing effective UVF imaging of varying levels of oxygen ingress from the frame edges, varying oxygen ingress from the junction box penetrations, encapsulant bill of materials variations, hot spots, and cell cracks. We therefore conclude that a use case does exist for UVF in at least certain glass/glass solar panel models.

Keywords: UV Fluorescence, Characterization, Defects

1 INTRODUCTION

UV Fluorescence (UVF) is a powerful imaging technology for revealing defects and bill of materials variations in solar panels [1-5]. In this technique, the panels are illuminated with UV light in the dark, and the encapsulant and/or polymer backsheet fluoresce in the visible spectrum. The longer the field exposure or environmental chamber exposure, the stronger the encapsulant will fluoresce. The benefits of the technique include its non-contact and high throughput nature, adaptability to drone imaging, and ability to see a wide range of defects. Such defects include 1) solar cell cracks, 2) edge and junction box sealing failures, 3) hot spots (regions that had run hot during the panel lifetime), 4) cracked glass, and 5) gridline corrosion. Bill of materials (BOM) variations in the panel construction that can be seen directly or indirectly include: 1) encapsulant, 2) polymer backsheet, and 3) metallization paste. An important mechanism for seeing some of these defects involves the diffusion of oxygen into the panel to quench the fluorescence of the encapsulant. In panels with polymer backsheets, the oxygen can diffuse into the panel continuously over the entire back surface. In the case of detecting cracked solar cells, the oxygen can diffuse through the cracks and then spread laterally a few mm's to either side of the crack lines to create a vivid image of the crack locations as dark lines against a brighter background.

Over the last several years, the market share of bifacial panels has steadily grown due to the importance of gains in energy delivery. A majority of these bifacial panels use rear glass layers rather than transparent polymer backsheets. Oxygen cannot penetrate the rear glass in such panels except through the junction box penetrations and the perimeter edges, and thus any defect imaging that relies on oxygen quenching may be less effective with such panels as compared to polymer backsheet panels. We therefore ask the question, "Does UVF have a useful role in imaging glass/glass panels?"

The literature mentions only a few examples of glass/glass UVF imaging. Koentges showed an example of ring pattern fluorescence in a panel that incorporated a metal foil oxygen barrier on the rear side, and showed an example of a cell crack which fluoresced brightly due to fluorophores diffusing through the crack from the back encapsulant [2]. Although this panel did not use rear glass, the use of a similar oxygen barrier suggests that bright crack lines might be visible in glass/glass panels for certain bill of material combinations. Sinha showed ring pattern fluorescence in glass/glass modules indicating that fluorophores could migrate though the gaps between cells from a rear encapsulant rich in fluorophores to the front encapsulant with a low fluorophore concentration, but no defects were found in this case [3]. Gilleland showed the quenching of fluorescence near the short edges of a glass/glass panel as is shown below in Figure 1, which may indicate greater diffusion of oxygen through the edge seals on the short edges of that panel type than the long edges [4]. Although not explicitly mentioned in their paper, there is observable darkening near several interconnect wires which could be due to quenching from oxygen diffusing through cell cracks commonly found by the interconnect wires. Most recently, Buerhop showed small bright spots in UVF images over interconnect wire locations where intense resistive heating was taking place in panels with cracked glass [5].

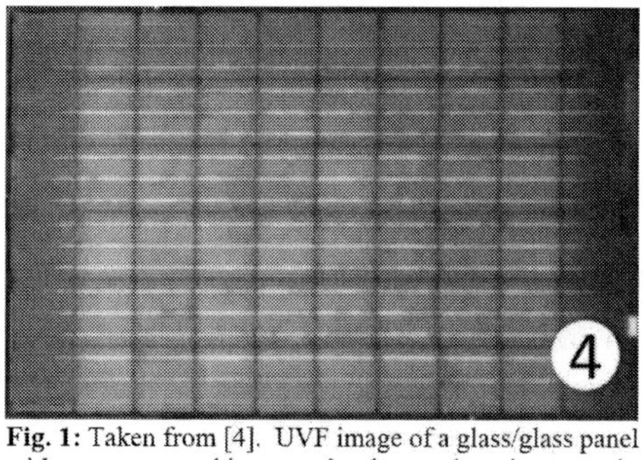

Fig. 1: Taken from [4]. UVF image of a glass/glass panel with oxygen quenching near the short ends and apparently by some interconnect wires.

10.4229/EUPVSEC2025/3AV.2.41
020166-001

In order to add to the body of literature on UVF imaging of glass/glass panels, we imaged several different glass/glass panel models installed at the QEERI outdoor test facility in Qatar.

2 UVF IMAGING METHOD

The panels imaged were installed outside for varying amounts of time at the Qatar Environment and Energy Research Institute (QEERI) OTF Outdoor Testing Facility at GPS coordinates 25.326661, 51.432340. Most panels were installed on single axis trackers.

The hardware used for imaging was a **UVF-Spot**™ system from BrightSpot Automation [6]. The system components included a broadband flash head with filters to allow only the UV light to be transmitted, a full-frame sensor consumer camera with a UV cut filter and a 28mm lens, a tall monopod to elevate the camera and flash above the panels for frontside imaging, a remote eyelevel display to see the captured UVF images or the field of view of the camera prior to imaging, and a remote trigger to focus and capture images.

For panels that were imaged outdoors, the images were all taken at least 45 minutes after sundown to reduce noise light effects. An initial image was captured for each panel type, and then the camera gain was adjusted to give good brightness for that panel type. The f-stop of the camera was kept constant at 2.0. The field of view of the camera varied but was generally at least as wide as the panel under test. The monopod pole was employed for imaging the front side of some panels, but in a few cases, the camera was removed from the pole for rear-side imaging underneath the racking.

No post processing was performed for any of the images presented here, but in general, post processing can be valuable to allow certain defects to appear more clearly or to remove perspective distortion. Images shown below are cropped to show the regions of interest.

In addition to the UVF data, in some cases the Performance Ratio (PR) of the panels was measured where PR is defined as the Pmax measured indoors with an IV flash tester divided by the nameplate Pmax value.

3 UVF IMAGES AND COMPLEMENTARY DATA

Panels displaying different types of UVF signatures are grouped into the following subsections.

3.1 Bill of Materials Variations

Figure 2 shows UVF images of two Heterojunction (HJT) panels with identical model numbers but which show the incorporation of a different front encapsulant layer. The panel on the left has a front encapsulant which fluoresces strongly and where oxygen is apparently diffusing inward both from the panel edges as well as from the gaps between the cells to produce a darker ring around each cell where the fluorophores are partially quenched. It is unclear why oxygen diffuses so uniformly through these gap regions when the source of the oxygen is presumably only from the perimeter of the panels. In contrast, the panel on the right displays ring pattern fluorescence, where the front encapsulant did not incorporate UV absorbing additives, but where fluorophores from the rear encapsulant are diffusing through the gaps and across the surface of the cells. In both cases, oxygen has diffused in from each long edge up to the first interconnect wire to produce a dark band along each long edge. It is unclear whether the abrupt ending of oxygen quenching at the first interconnect wire is a coincidence, or whether perhaps the thinner region of encapsulant between the glass and wire reduces the inward diffusion of the oxygen. If the kinetics of oxygen diffusion can indeed be affected in this manner, perhaps this effect could be intentionally designed into oxygen and moisture sensitive panels.

Fig. 2: UVF images showing BOM variations in the front encapsulant layer for the same model number of HJT panels installed in 2020. PR = 92.7%.

3.2 Sealing Failures

Figure 3a shows a UVF image taken from the back side a different HJT panel type where oxygen is diffusing inward from both the edge perimeter regions as well as through the 3 junction box penetrations. It is interesting to note that the diffusion front from each long edge shows that oxygen appears to have diffused inward faster over the middle regions of the cells. In contrast, the UVF image taken from the front side in Figure 3b shows the oxygen diffusing inward more strongly from the gaps between cells, but overall that the quenched regions reach less far inward than on the backside, perhaps due to the differences in UV additives within the encapsulant layers or the different UV aging doses experienced on the front and back sides. Also, there are some scattered dark spots seen on the rear side that are unexplained. It is possible that these correspond to cell crack locations, but it is not clear why enhanced oxygen diffusion would take place from the front side.

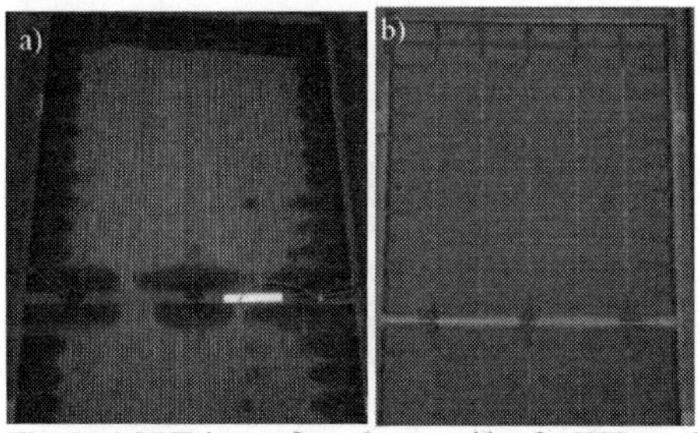

Fig. 3: a) UVF image from the rear side of a HJT panel showing oxygen diffusing through holes in the glass for junction box penetrations, varying degrees of oxygen diffusion from the perimeter, and a few unexplained dark spots; b) UVF image from the front side of a panel of the same model. Panels installed in 2020. PR = 94.7%

Fig. 4 shows another example of strong rear side fluorescence where oxygen is seen diffusing inward from the perimeter in a PERC panel. In contrast with the panel shown in Figure 3, there the diffusion appears to be occurring more rapidly in the gaps between cells. Also, here the sealing around the junction box penetrations appears to be more effective.

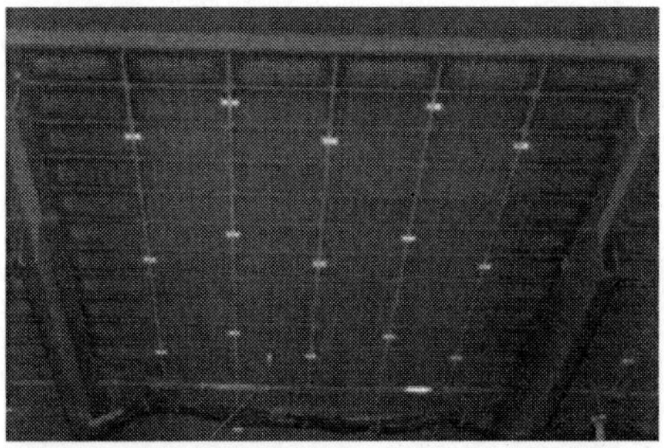

Fig. 4: UVF image from the rear side of a PERC panel showing oxygen diffusing inward from the perimeter. Panels installed in 2018.

We also collected UVF images from thin-film CIGS panels. Although these panels were not of a bifacial design, these data points have high importance in evaluating the potential for UVF in imaging thin-film panel defects. Figure 5 shows the UVF image of panels where the CIGS is deposited on the rear glass in a substrate type configuration and the encapsulant between the CIGS and the top glass is fluorescing brightly. Each panel displays some degree of sealing problems on the edges, but in 3 of the panels, there are large dark regions emanating from an edge which incur deeply into the panel central regions. In some cases narrow dark lines extend down the length of the scribed cells. It is not clear why oxygen can diffuse down the length of a cell, but perhaps the scribing process in some cases leaves channels that are not fully filled with encapsulant or where delamination is occurring. These correspond to white regions by eye. Each panel also displays some large brighter regions that can be seen by eye as light brown spots where perhaps hot spot heating has occurred.

Fig. 5: UVF image of CIGS panels showing likely sealing failures and possible delamination (dark spots) and bright regions where possible hot spot heating has occured. Panels installed in 2015.

3.3 Cracked Cells

Figure 6 shows a UVF image of a TOPCon panel with ring pattern fluorescence where variations in the ring pattern likely correlate to cell crack locations. Most cracks appear to be near interconnect wire locations where the oxygen quenching leads to dips in the outer perimeter of the rings near the wire locations. In a few examples, diagonal cracks show bright lines in the center of the cells where fluorophores are diffusing through the cracks from the rear encapsulant and where oxygen has not diffused in from the cell perimeter to quench that fluorescence.

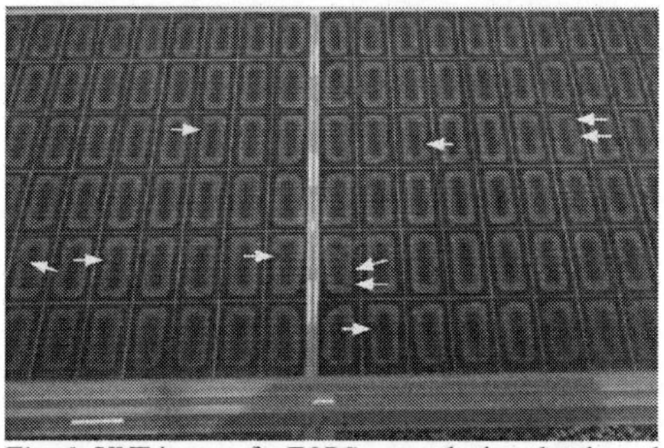

Fig. 6: UVF image of a TOPCon panel where breaks and variations in the ring patterns likely correspond to cell cracks. Yellow arrows show cracks that may lie underneath busbars, while red arrows show cracks that propagate between busbars. Panels installed in 2022 at a fixed tilt southward of 22 degrees. PR = 96.0%.

3.4 Hot Spots

Figure 7 shows a UVF image of a PERC panel with no visible fluorescence anywhere except near the junction boxes and the perimeter frame. We assume the fluorescence has evolved preferentially in these locations due to resistive heating in the junction boxes and due to regions near the frame running hotter than elsewhere. The competing kinetics of fluorescence activation from heat and fluorescence quenching from oxygen diffusion through glass penetrations and edges give rise to complex patterns.

Fig. 7: UVF image showing the effect of hotter regions near the junction boxes and the perimeter of a PERC solar panel. The competing kinetics of fluorescence activation from heat and fluorescence quenching from oxygen diffusion through glass penetrations and edges give rise to complex patterns. Panels installed in 2018.

Figure 8a shows frameless PERT panels where some clamping positions where shifted after some years of operation and where there may be local heating near the clamp positions. The regions around both the old and new clamping positions shows visible browning above the white regions at the perimeter of the panels. The glass surface was manually scrubbed to verify that the discoloration was not due to residue on the top surface of the glass. Possible causes of the discoloration are due to hotter internal panel temperature under the clamp positions or diffusion of some chemical species from the polymer used in the clamps. Figures 8b and 8c show UVF images of the panels where the browned regions fluoresce strongly but where there is little other fluorescence in the panel. The fluorescence appears quite strong over the cell regions close to the clamps, and it is possible that the strong fluorescence correlates to hot spot regions.

Fig. 8: a) RGB image of frameless PERT panels where some clamp positions had been shifted after some years of field operation; b) a UVF image of the same panels, and c) a closeup UVF image near a clamp position. Panels were installed in 2020.

Finally, we show in Figure 9 a UVF image of the rear side of a Series 4, First Solar CdTe panel installed for >10 years in Ohio. Strong fluorescence is seen along both edges of the bussing wire near the edge of panel. We assume that some local heating had occurred in this location, but do not understand the origin of the heating or the reliability/performance impacts.

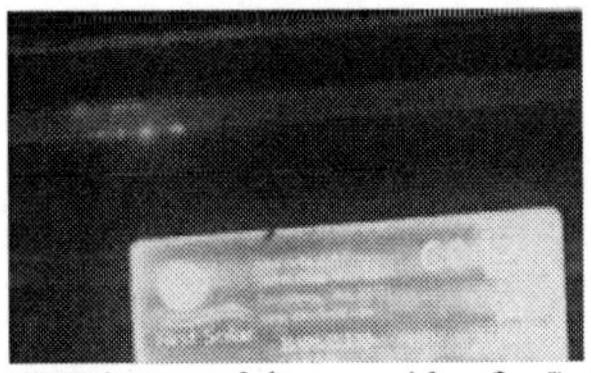

Fig. 9: a) UVF image of the rear side of a Series 4 First Solar panel showing strong fluorescence along a bussing wire, potentially due to local heating (poor TCO connection?).

4 DISCUSSION

As a field testing technique, UVF suffers from its high dependency on bill of materials, panel design, installation location, and panel history. Encapsulants that have no UV absorbing additives do not fluoresce unless fluorophores diffuse from other layers. When fluorophores are present, it can take years of field exposure for sufficiently strong fluorescence to evolve. Oxygen diffusion barriers such as rear glass can reduce the effectiveness of seeing cracked cells. However, the strengths of UVF lie in its high throughput, non-contact nature, and ability to image problems not otherwise seen by EL and thermal IR imaging. The data presented above demonstrate that even for the most challenging cases of relatively new glass/glass panels, useful defect imaging can occur.

Despite the rear glass acting as an oxygen diffusion barrier, the diffusion of oxygen from panel edges and junction box penetration still occurs in glass/glass panels, as does the diffusion of oxygen from the rear encapsulant layer to the front encapsulant layer both in the gaps between cells as well as through cracks in the cells. For most silicon based panels, such sealing failures may not represent a significant durability problem, and in the context of UVF imaging, may present an opportunity for more informative imaging of other defect types where oxygen ingress has occurred. However, in more sensitive thin-film panels such as those based on Perovskites, such sealing failures may be catastrophic, and their detection critical. Our observation here of oxygen possibly diffusing preferentially down the scribe lines of the monolithically integrated thin film cells points to a potential problem deserving attention.

While the successful imaging here of the superstrate type CIGS thin-film panels is promising for UVF imaging of thin-film panels, we note that the vast majority of monolithically integrated thin-film panel produced to date (CdTe panels from First Solar) are of the superstrate variety with no encapsulant to image from the front side except in the narrow regions between scribe lines. The emerging field of Perovskite PV is of varied designs with most monolithically integrated panels having a superstrate front cell, while the Perovskite on Si-wafer designs are more promising for front-side UVF imaging with encapsulant between the cells and the front glass. Our finding here of successful UVF imaging from the rear side may find application in superstrate type thin-film panels depending on their bill of materials. While high throughput UVF imaging by pole-mounted or drone mounted camera imaging may not obviously be applicable to rear-side imaging, such rear side imaging may still be conveniently performed by systems that are hand held or mounted to vehicles, robots, and even drones, especially for tracker systems that could be tilted to nearly vertical for better access to the rear side.

The overall trend over the last decade for glass/glass panels of using encapsulants with no UV absorbers bodes poorly for universal application of UVF to such panels, but our findings here give promise that for some significant number of GWs of panels, UVF will find useful applications. In particular, based on our finding here in Figures 7, 8, and 9 and in Buerhop's investigations [5], the imaging of hot spots may be effectively performed even in panels with no fluorescence elsewhere in the panel. Operations and Maintenance groups and field testing companies can use UV flashlights to assess any site for UVF imaging potential, and then where applicable follow up with high throughput imaging tools [6].

A summary of the different panel problems that may be visible with UVF imaging in glass/glass panels is shown in Table I with very rough estimates of the probability that UVF can see the problem and amount of field exposure time needed for the fluorescence to be strong enough to image the problem.

Table I. UVF effectiveness for defects in glass/glass panels

Problem	UVF Imaging Probability	Field exposure time needed
Encapsulant BoM variation	High	0-3 yrs
Local heating	High	0-1 yrs
Sealing failures	Med	2-5 yrs
Cracked Cells	Low	2-5 yrs

10.4229/EUPVSEC2025/3AV.2.41

5 CONCLUSIONS

Despite the relatively few examples in the literature of UVF being used to characterize glass/glass solar panels, we have found multiple examples of useful applications over a range of different PV technologies in panels fielded for 5-10 years. We demonstrated detection of 1) front encapsulant bill of material variation between panels of the same model number, 2) sealing failure at the panel perimeter edges and at the junction box penetrations, 3) possible hot spot heating near junction boxes, frames, clamping positions, and 4) cell cracking. We also demonstrated useful imaging of the rear side for three panel types.

The emerging technology of Perovskite solar cells is particularly sensitive to sealing failures, and the ability of UVF to image such failures from either the front or rear sides could be helpful for both product development after chamber testing and for field testing.

6 REFERENCES

[1] D. J. Colvin *et al.*, "Ultraviolet Fluorescence Imaging for Photovoltaic Module Metrology: Best Practices and Survey of Features Observed in Fielded Modules," in *IEEE Journal of Photovoltaics*, vol. 15, no. 3, pp. 465-477, May 2025, doi: 10.1109/JPHOTOV.2025.3545825.

[2] M. Kontges, A. Morlier, G. Eder, E. Fleis, B. Kubicek, and J. Lin, "Review: Ultraviolet fluorescence as assessment tool for photovoltaic modules," *IEEE J. of Photovolt.*, vol. 10, no. 2, pp. 616–633, 2020.

[3] A. Sinha, D. B. Sulas-Kern, M. Owen-Bellini, L. Spinella, S. Ulicná, S. Ayala Pelaez, S. Johnston, and L. T. Schelhas, "Glass/glass photovoltaic module reliability and degradation: a review," *J. Phys. D: Appl. Phys.*, vol. 54, no. 41, p. 413002, 2021.

[4] B. Gilleland, W. B. Hobbs, and J. B. Richardson, "High throughput detection of cracks and other faults in solar PV modules using a high-power ultraviolet fluorescence imaging system." IEEE, 2019, pp. 2575–2582.

[5] C. Buerhop et al., "Combined Non-Destructive Techniques for On-Site Failure Analysis -Showcase of Glass Cracks with Burn Marks in a PV Power Station," 2025 IEEE 53rd Photovoltaic Specialists Conference (PVSC), Montreal, QC, Canada, 2025, pp. 0526-0529, doi: 10.1109/PVSC59419.2025.11132595.

[6] UVF-Spot. Available: brightspotautomation.com/products/ultraviolet-fluorescence/uvf-spot/. [Accessed: Sep. 12, 2025].

DETERMINATION THE RELIABLITY OF SOLAR MODULES IN ANALOGY TO GLASS IN BUILDINGS

Ruth Kasper*, Hannah Reichart
University of Applied Sciences Cologne (TH Köln)
Betzdorfer Str. 2, 50679 Köln, Germany
*Contact: ruth.kasper@th-koeln.de, +49 221-8275-2791

ABSTRACT: In recent years, photovoltaic (PV) module designs have doubled in size, introducing XXL modules, with approximately 3 m². Meanwhile, the single glass height of glass-glass modules has decreased from 3.2 mm to 2 mm or less. This reduction, coupled with decreased frame stiffness, raises concerns about load-bearing capacity and modules increasingly show damage like glass and frame breakage in the field.

PV module load bearing capacity is determined via MQT 16, a static mechanical load test in accordance with IEC 61215. This test inadequately represents real damage scenarios as it does not consider material strength variability and time-temperature behavior of the interlayer.

Instead, the design method from the construction industry can be used to determine the static reliability of solar modules. Regardless of the material, the partial safety concept is used, which considers variations in loading and material. Components or structures can then be dimensioned using a suitable mechanical model. For many years, glass has been used in façades and roof structures without frequent breakage due to static overloading.

This paper describes the current problems related to unexpected solar module damage, illustrates load-bearing behavior of glass-glass modules considering material, mounting, and mechanics, and presents the construction industry design method.

Keywords: PV-module reliability, partial safety concept, mechanical load test, glass stress, Eurocode

1 INTRODUCTION

The design of photovoltaic (PV) modules has undergone continuous development in recent years. In addition to improvements in cell structure, designs are trending toward larger modules. Over the last 10 years, these modules have grown on average, to twice their original size, and new XXL modules (approximately 3 m²) are reaching significantly larger dimensions [1]. Additionally, the application of glass-glass modules is reaching a new high, with an expected market share of over 50% in 2024 and a continued upward trend [2]. However, this has resulted in a significant increase in weight. To counteract this, there has been a reduction in height decreased from 3.2 mm to 2 mm [1]. For small module dimensions, glass heights up to 1.6 mm are also found [3]. This results in a significant reduction in stiffness and load-bearing capacity, leading to the moniker "big, floppy modules" [1].

The load-bearing capacity of PV modules is determined by the static mechanical load test (MQT 16) according to IEC 61215 [4]. However, while modules had high load-bearing reserves in the past, many modern PV modules have difficulty passing the minimum load requirement of 2.4 kN/m² according to the standard [1]. Concurrently, there has been an increase in glass breakage in PV modules despite prior type testing in accordance with IEC 61215. In some cases, this can be attributed to extreme weather events such as hail or storms, but spontaneous glass breakage is also frequently observed, mainly in the first few years after installation [5].

This has a significant impact not only on the economic efficiency of solar parks but also on their safety standard.

This paper examines how to ensure the load resistance of PV modules. In this regard, the current state of the art in the PV industry is explained in greater detail in Chapter 2. Sample calculations are used to illustrate the mechanical principles of load transfer and the impact of changes in glass height, frame stiffness, and support conditions (see Chapter 3). Additionally, the design concept in construction is presented in Chapter 4. The Eurocode 10 [10] is available in draft form as a European harmonized standard for designing and dimensioning structural glass components. As with building materials such as steel, reinforced concrete, or wood, the partial safety concept is applied here as well, covering variations on the impact and material sides. For many years, glass has been used in façades and roof structures without an increase in breakage due to static overload due to a proper design based on the Eurocode safety concept [11].

2 STATE OF THE ART IN THE PV INDUSTRY

2.1 Static mechanical load test according to IEC 61215

In the PV industry, the load bearing capacity of PV modules is ensured by mechanical load testing MQT 16, which is conducted in accordance with the International Electrotechnical Commission (IEC) standard 61215. This process involves simulating wind and snow loads using a constant load structure. The load is typically generated with sandbags or pneumatic cylinders. The manufacturer may determine the design situation. The load consists of a design load and a safety factor of 1.5:

$$Test\ load = \gamma_M \cdot design\ load = 1.5 \cdot design\ load$$

According to the standard, the minimum test load is 2.4 kN/m². Usual pressure levels are 2.4 kN/m² for wind loads (suction) and up to 5.4 kN/m² for snow loads

10.4229/EUPVSEC2025/3AV.2.42

(pressure). Each level is maintained for one hour. The module is mounted on a rigid test frame in the most unfavorable support situation and is subjected to alternating positive (pressure) and negative (suction) loads. Three load cycles are performed. After each cycle, the module undergoes a visual inspection for damage and electrical tests to detect breaks or performance losses. To pass type approval, one module must be tested according to MQT 16. There are no specifications for maximum deflection or plastic deformation of the frame to pass the load test. [4]

2.2 Criticism of the testing procedure

The test procedure according to IEC 61215 has been the subject of criticism for several years. A significant point of criticism is the inadequate consideration of the diverse real-world conditions under which photovoltaic modules are operated. The test conditions are considerably simplified, and thus, they are unable to fully reflect the complex environmental interactions to which modules are exposed. This encompasses, among other considerations, the selection of an appropriate load level. The modules are frequently found to be significantly overloaded at an external load of 5.4 kN/m², a condition that invariably results in a change to the static system. The large deformations that result from this force cause the glass pane to rest on the substructure, thereby fundamentally altering the static system [13]. The load paths that occur - in some cases also via unspecified load-bearing elements under the solar module - correspond to an overloaded system and do not reflect the realistic load and bearing situation in the installed state. Only in the event of an once-in-a-century storm or exceptional snowfall under special installation conditions due to characteristic loads of up to 5.4 kN/m² and the associated deformations occur. Therefore, it is not advisable to determine the "design load" by means of testing.

The assumption of a uniform load also results in simplifications that do not accurately reflect the complexity of the situation. The typical mounting of PV modules at a defined angle results in inhomogeneous snow and wind loads. Studies have demonstrated that greater stresses emerge from an asymmetric distribution of loads in comparison to a uniform distribution. These assumptions entirely exhaust the safety factor of 1.5 [14], [15].

However, the failure to consider material dispersion has a particularly significant effect. In modules with larger dimensions, the primary load transfer occurs through the glass pane. Consequently, the load-bearing capacity of the module is determined by the strength of the used glass. The theoretical strength of glass is very high; however, due to its brittle behavior and material variability, the actual strength of glass depends heavily on the condition of the surface and any irregularities present. Consequently, the strength of glass is subject to a very high degree of variation. In the field of construction, the characteristic strength of glass is evaluated by the 5th percentile value, with a 95% probability [16], [17]. It is generally accepted that a minimum of 30 samples, which must be identical and undamaged, are required to ensure the production of representative results for the characteristic strength. The MQT 16 load test does not consider this material variation. According to IEC 61215, the successful completion of a single module's load test is sufficient for the attainment of type approval. In conjunction with this phenomenon, the process of tempering thin glass is notably more challenging than that of thicker panes. This discrepancy may lead to the occurrence of irregular tempering values across the surface of the pane [1]. Consequently, the load test does not yield any information regarding the general load-bearing capacity of the modules; it provides a single, non-representative spot value.

Moreover, end users are frequently confronted with a lack of congruent information. The data sheet for photovoltaic (PV) modules typically provides insufficient information regarding their load-bearing capacity. If a statement is made regarding the load-bearing capacity, the maximum tested load situation is specified without any information about the mechanical system [3]. Information about the mounting arrangement or support can only be found in the user manual. It is evident that the specified maximum load depends on the mounting situation, and the design situation mentioned in the data sheet is only applicable to specific, optimal mounting conditions [20]. This phenomenon is especially evident in conjunction with a tracking system. Large solar parks primarily utilize single-axis trackers, which facilitate the optimal alignment of the PV modules with the sun's position throughout the day [21]. In this case, a combination of substructure and modules is subjected to rigorous testing. However, it was observed that none of the combinations were able to achieve the maximum load specified in the data sheet. The actual load levels are significantly lower [20].

3 MECHANICAL AND GEOMETRICAL FACTORS INFLUENCING THE STRESS STATE

3.1 Load bearing elements of a PV-System

A PV-System consists of three different main parts. First, the PV-modul composed of the PV-laminate containing the glass and the interlayer in connection with the frame. For the determination of the load bearing capacity, the cells themselves can be neglected. Second, the clamping system and third, the tracing system.

Starting with the behavior of glass-glass-laminate, the main influences on the stress state in the glass are demonstrated in the following.

3.2 Load-bearing behavior of a glass plate

3.2.1 Influence of the glass height and the span

The load-bearing behavior of a component is largely determined by a variety of influencing parameters [25]. In addition to material-related factors such as the modulus of elasticity E, the geometric influences play a decisive role. These include in particular:

- the mechanical system with its load transfer and
- the geometry of the cross-sections and the resulting moments of resistance.

A glass pane with a height h linearly supported on two sides can be described mechanically using linear beam theory (see Figure 1). Here, the static system is defined by its support conditions and external loads, which result in internal forces such as normal force, shear force and moment (N, V and M) (see Figure 2). The glass in solar modules is mainly subjects to bending, so only the internal moment M is relevant.

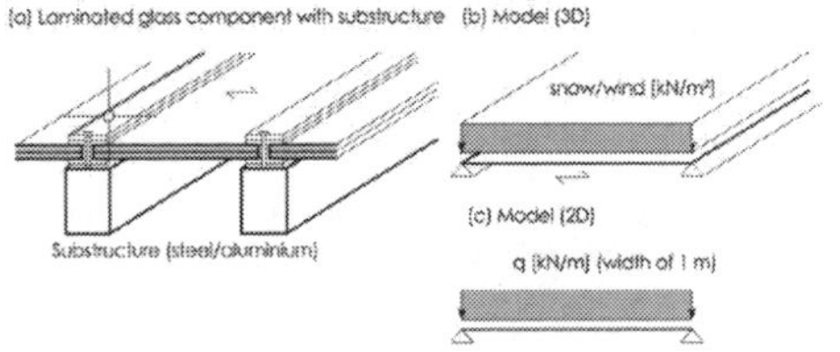

Figure 1: 2-sided linear supported glass plate

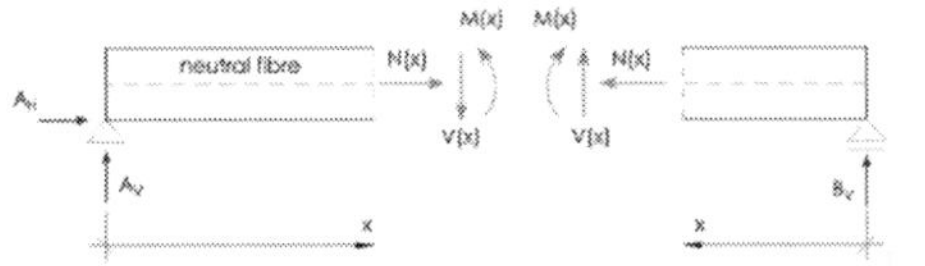

Figure 2: Section forces in a beam (general mechanical definition)

There are three basic types of bearings in the two-dimensional plane: roller bearings, fixed bearings and clamping bearings, which differ in terms of their degree of retention. While a roller bearing absorbs only vertical forces, a fixed bearing is capable of bearing vertical and horizontal forces. A clamp can also absorb a moment. The arrangement of the supports and the type of loading have a significant influence on the resulting internal forces. The simplest static system is the single-span beam under a constant load, which can be used to describe the load-bearing behavior of a glass plate supported on both sides by linear bearings. Given a line load q [kN/m] and a span L, the internal moment M [kNm] for a beam with free rotation at the supports is calculated as follows

$$M = q \cdot L^2 / 8 \qquad (1)$$

with

q line load

L span

Figure 3 shows the shear force and moment distribution for a simple beam under line load for two different kinds of bearing arrangements. In these cases, the internal normal forces N are zero.

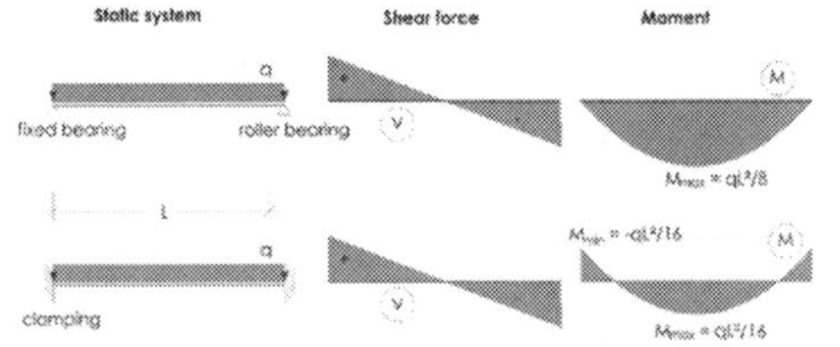

Figure 3: Shear force and Moment for a single beam

The internal forces are for such simple case independent from the type of material. Glass components usually fail when a critical normal stress level is reached on the glass surface. The normal stress on the glass surface is influenced by the internal force M as well as by the geometry of the cross-section. For a rectangular cross-section, the maximum normal stresses (surface) can be calculated by (see Figure 4):

$$\sigma = \frac{M}{W} = \frac{M}{\frac{1}{6} b \cdot h^2} \qquad (2)$$

with

M Internal bending moment

h height of the section (here: plate thickness)

b width of the section (we assume a glass component with a width of 1000 mm equal to the supported length)

The main factor influencing the determination of normal stresses is therefore the height of the component.

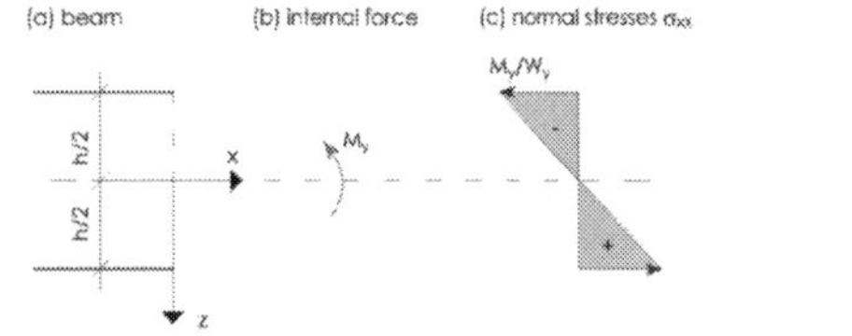

Figure 4: Relation between internal force M and normal stresses

With the moment of resistance W for the glass heights 3.2 mm and 2 mm

$$W_{(3.2\,mm)} = \frac{(3.2\,mm)^2 \cdot 1000\,mm}{6} = 1.71 \cdot 10^3\ mm^3 \quad (3)$$

$$W_{(2\,mm)} = \frac{(2\,mm)^2 \cdot 1000\,mm}{6} = 0.67 \cdot 10^3\ mm^3 \quad (4)$$

and the corresponding stresses in [N/mm²]

$$\sigma_{(3.2\,mm)} = M / W_{(3.2\,mm)} \qquad (5)$$

$$\sigma_{(2\,mm)} = M / W_{(2\,mm)} \qquad (6)$$

the increase in normal stress can be determined for an identical span L and the load q when the glass height changes from 3.2 to 2 mm:

$$\sigma_{(2\,mm)} / \sigma_{(3.2\,mm)} = 1.71 / 0.67 = 2.55 \quad (7)$$

A reduction in glass height of 37.5 %, therefore results in 2.55 times the normal stress on the glass surface.

This calculation only applies to a monolithic glass panel, but the effect is the same for any type of bearing.

In addition to normal stress, the deformation of a component also plays a central role in load-bearing capacity considerations. An additional factor for the deformation is the stiffness of the material. It is defined by the product $(E \cdot I)$, which is composed of the modulus of elasticity E and the second-degree moment of inertia I. For the example described above of a glass component linearly supported on two sides under uniform load respectively line load, the following deformations result:

$$w = \frac{q \cdot L^4}{76{,}8 \cdot E \cdot I} \qquad (8)$$

with

q line load

L span

E modulus of elasticity

I second-degree moment of inertia

The second-degree moment of inertia I for a glass plate with a width of 1 m and the glass heights of 3.2 mm or 2 mm is equal to:

$$I_{(3.2\,mm)} = \frac{(3.2\,mm)^3 \cdot 1000\,mm}{12} = 2.73 \cdot 10^3\ mm^4 \quad (9)$$

10.4229/EUPVSEC2025/3AV.2.42

$$I_{(2\,mm)} = \frac{(2\,mm)^3 \cdot 1000\,mm}{12} = 0.67 \cdot 10^3\ mm^4 \quad (10)$$

By changing the glass height from 3.2 to 2 mm, the deformation increases by a factor of

$$w_{(2\,mm)}/w_{(3{,}2\,mm)} = 2.73/0.667 \approx 4.1 \quad (11)$$

The example illustrates the influence on the normal stresses due to bending because of material reduction.

3.2.2 Stiffness of the composite material

The normal stress distribution in glass-glass modules depends on the stiffness of the composite material and equation (2) is no longer valid here. The normal stress distribution in the cross-section lies between the boundary cases 'with and without full shear connection'.

For a structure consisting of two glass layers with height h, the normal stresses on the surface in [N/mm²] for the boundary case 'with connection' are equal to:

$$\sigma_{(2\,x\,h)} = \frac{M}{W_{(2\,x\,h)}} = \frac{M}{(\frac{2}{3}h^2 \cdot b)} \quad (12)$$

with

$$W_{(2\,x\,h)} = (2\,h)^2 \cdot b/\,6 = 2/3\,h^2 \cdot b \quad (13)$$

or 'without shear coupling' (the load q is divided equally between the individual glass layers):

$$M_{(h)} = \frac{(\frac{q}{2})\,L^2}{8} = \frac{q\,L^2}{16} = \frac{M}{2} \quad (14)$$

$$W_{(h)} = (h)^2\,/\,6 = 1/6\,h^2 \quad (15)$$

$$\sigma_{(h)} = \frac{M_{(h)}}{W_{(h)}} = \frac{M/2}{1/6\,h^2} = 3\,M/h^2 \quad (16)$$

The normal stress ratio is equal to:

$$\sigma_{(h)}\,/\,\sigma_{(2h)} = 2 \quad (17)$$

This simple mechanical derivation shows that without shear effect, the normal stresses in the glass are twice as high as with full lamination. The truth lies somewhere between these two extremes and is determined by the stiffness of the composite material, the temperature and the duration of the loading (see Figure 5). In structural glass construction in Germany, for example, the shear composite approach is only permitted if the shear composite properties of the intermediate material data have been evaluated by testing.

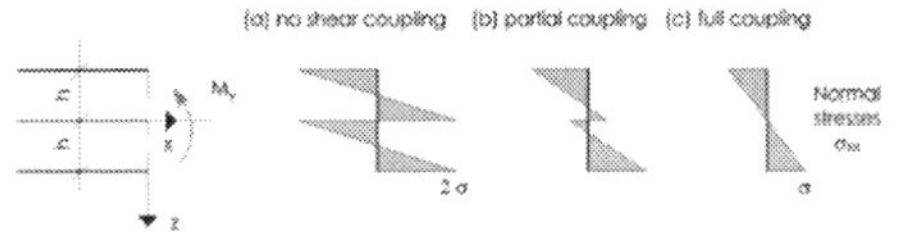

Figure 5: Normal stress distribution due to bending for the limits "no shear coupling", "partial shear coupling" and "full coupling"

Additionally, to the parameters "system span" and "glass height" (exponent 2), the coupling effect of the interlayer may influence the normal stresses in the glass in the factor equal to 2.

3.2.3 Four-sides linearly supported plate

The module frame changes the load transfer of the laminated glass from a single-axis to a two-axis load transfer. Assuming that the module frame is sufficiently rigid, the bearing is assumed to be a stiff roller bearing. The effect of multi-axial load transfer is present up to an aspect ratio of the edge lengths of 1:3. After that, single-axis load transfer resumes.

For small deformations, the load-bearing behavior of the glass plate can be described by *Kirchhoff's* linear plate theory. Linear plate theory loses its validity as soon as the deformations w of the glass pane exceed the glass height h. This case occurs with the glass heights used in the PV industry even under very low loads and is therefore always be applicable. A membrane load-bearing behavior then occurs, comparable to the load transfer in a rope. The center of the glass pane 'hangs' in the rigid glass plate edge and causes a load transfer via a combination of normal stresses due to bending and membrane effects (see Figure 6). This significantly reduces the stresses and deformations in the glass pane. Another effect is that the relationship between the load q and the stresses and deformation is not directly proportional. Stresses and deformation increase more slowly than the external load q. Neglecting this favorable membrane load-bearing behavior, glass panes in construction often cannot be dimensioned economically.

The membrane effect generally depends on:

- the height of the pane: the thinner, the greater.
- the aspect ratio: the greater, the lower.
- the loading: the higher the loading q, the stronger the effect.

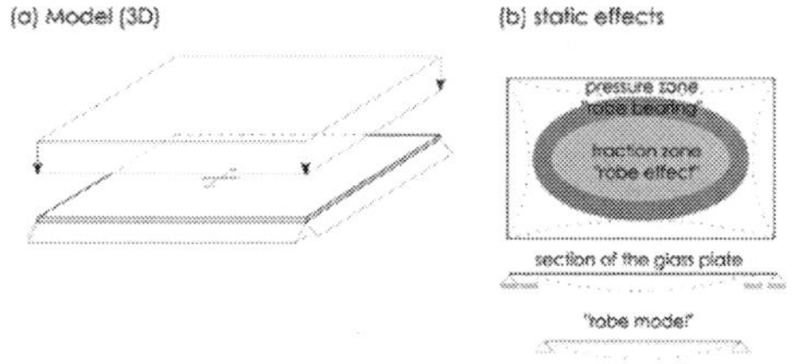

Figure 6: Membrane effect of a four-sides supported plate

Taking into consideration the linear plate theory, the maximum principal (normal) stresses occur at the middle of the plate. In contrast, when the membrane theory is considered the maximum principal (normal) stresses shift to the corners of the plate. Figure 7 compares the distribution and values of the maximum principal stresses for a rectangular 4-sided linear supported plate.

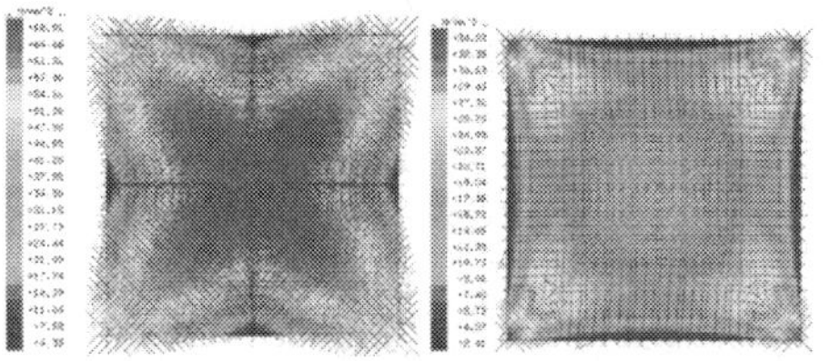

Figure 7: Maximum principal stresses with vector plots indicating the direction (left side: linear plate theory, right side: membrane theory), dimension 1000 mm x 1000 mm, glass height 2 mm, 4-sides linear supported, q = 1 kN/m²

3.3 Variation of support conditions

The influence of the support conditions has been analyzed for the following parameters:

- Dimension 1000 mm x 1000 mm
- Laminated glass of 2 x 1.6 mm, no shear coupling
- Constant distributed loading of 1 kN/m²

In glass in building, a prerequisite for accepting a linearly supported plate is a deformation restriction of the support. The supports (equal to the frame of a PV-module) may only deflect by L/200 (L = span) [30]. After that, the deflection of the substructure must be included in the design model. Figure 8 shows the influence on stress and deformation depending on the frame stiffness EI (E-modulus · area moment of inertia I). The span of the plate is equal to 1000 mm, so the deflection limit might be L/200 = 1000 mm / 200 = 5 mm.

The diagrams show that this deformation limit marks the transition between a single-axis to a two-axis load transfer. The results shown in Figure 8 are calculated with the finite element program SJ MEPLA PRO [26]. This tool includes a shell laminate element to examine the stresses of a laminate depending on the shear stiffness of the interlayer. The module frame can be modelled with an edge beam. A disadvantage of SJ MEPLA PRO is that the edge beam does not include torsional stiffness so that an analyzation of restraint effects at the frame support is not possible.

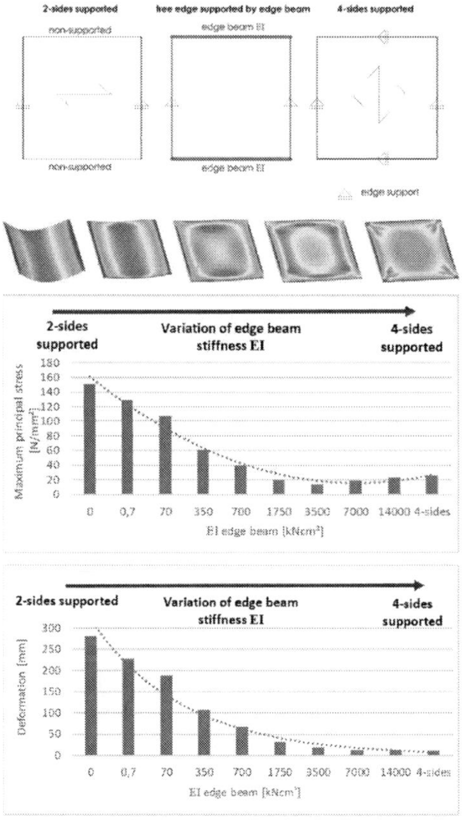

Figure 8: Maximum principal stresses and deformation depending on the bending stiffness EI of the frame (dimension 1000 mm x 1000 mm, laminate of 2 x 1.6 mm, no shear coupling, q = 1 kN/m²)

In the next step the linear support is replaced by four springs acting vertical to the plate simplifying the effect of four edge clamping's (see results in Figure 9). The change of the maximum principal stresses (top and bottom side) and deflections are shown in Figure 9 depending on bending stiffness EI of the edge beam (= module frame). Caused by the local springs, stress concentrations occur next to the springs. With increasing edge beam stiffness, the maximum principal stresses occur at the edge.

Considered that the characteristic bending strength of solar glass is about 70 N/mm², the edge stiffness of the frame has a significant influence on the load carrying capacity of a solar module. Having in mind that the presented values are calculated for the parameters mentioned above.

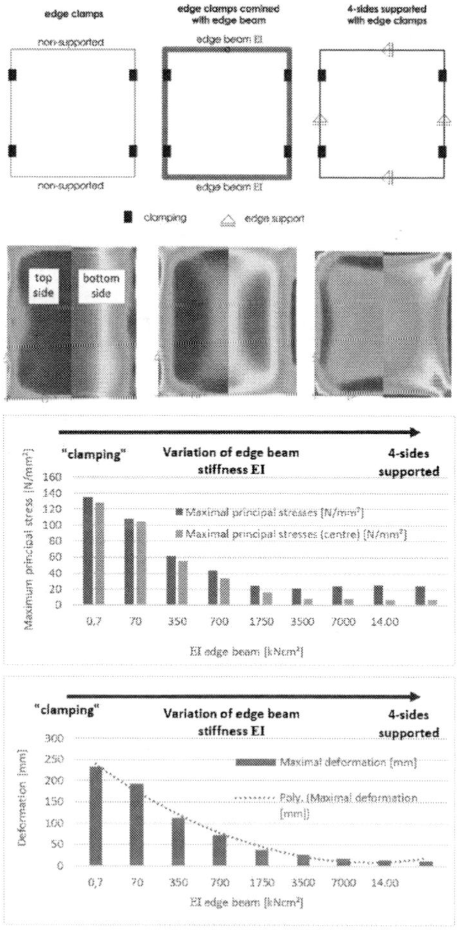

Figure 9: Maximum principal stresses and deformation depending on the bending stiffness EI of the frame (dimension 1000 mm x 1000 mm, laminate of 2 x 1.6 mm, no shear coupling, q = 1 kN/m²)

Using the FEM-program ANSYS the edge beam can be modelled with volume elements according to the real geometry of the module frame.

Figure 10 shows the results for the dimension of 1000 mm x 1000 mm, monolithic pane of 2.5 mm with a constant distributed load of 2 kN/m². The results are influenced by the chosen boundary conditions between the glass and the module frame. In glass in building restraints from the edge cover of a façade plate is generally neglected, due to thicker glass plates (height ≥ 3 mm) the influence of the edge cover on the stress distribution is low. However, in case of a PV-element, the edge cover has in combination with the bending and torsional stiffness of the frame a significant influence on the stress distribution in the glass (see Figure 10).

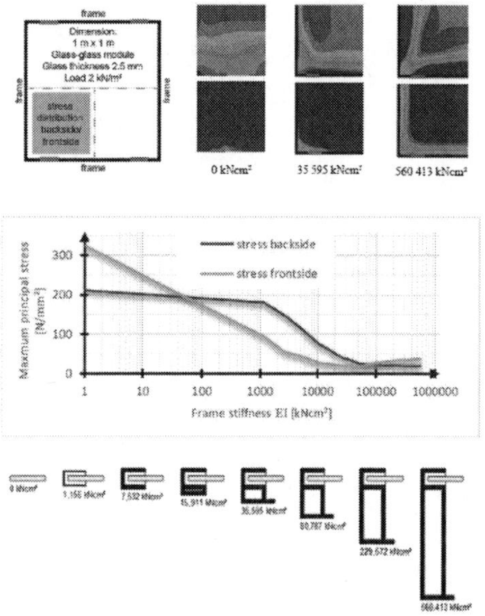

Figure 10: Maximum principal stresses depending on the bending stiffness EI of the frame (dimension 1000 mm x 1000 mm, monolithic pane of 2 mm, q = 2 kN/m²) [29]

3.4 Influence of frame stiffness and module mounting

The results shown in Chapter 3.3 are related to a module fixed with four clamps at two opposite edges. These results cannot be transferred to arbitrary mounting situation. For example, stress and deformation for a mounting situation with an overhang (mechanically equal to a cantilever) are shown in Figure 11. For the mounting situation and dimension analyzed in Chapter 3.3, a beam bending stiffness of EI = 14000 kNcm² gives a stress distribution similar to a 4-sided-suppported pane. Here, the determined span is the length of the cantilever: maximum deformation of the frame L/200 = 700 mm/200 = 3.5 m. The value of the maximum deformation of the cantilever is with 50 mm a multiple of this value, so that the deformation of the substructure (here the frame) has influence on the stress distribution which is approximately 30% higher compared to a stiff support.

3.5 Conclusions

The parameters demonstrated above have a large impact on the load bearing capacity of a PV module. The parameters are:

- glass height and span,
- stiffness of the interlayer (material, load duration, temperature),
- span,
- bending and torsional stiffness of the module frame and
- support conditions of the PV-module,

For example, the stiffness of the interlayer is a major factor which cannot be evaluated by a single load test. The question is how to define the "load bearing capacity" of a PV-module. The target is to find a method to give a design load or module properties which can be the basis for a reliability evaluation to ensure solar systems with a minimal breakage risk.

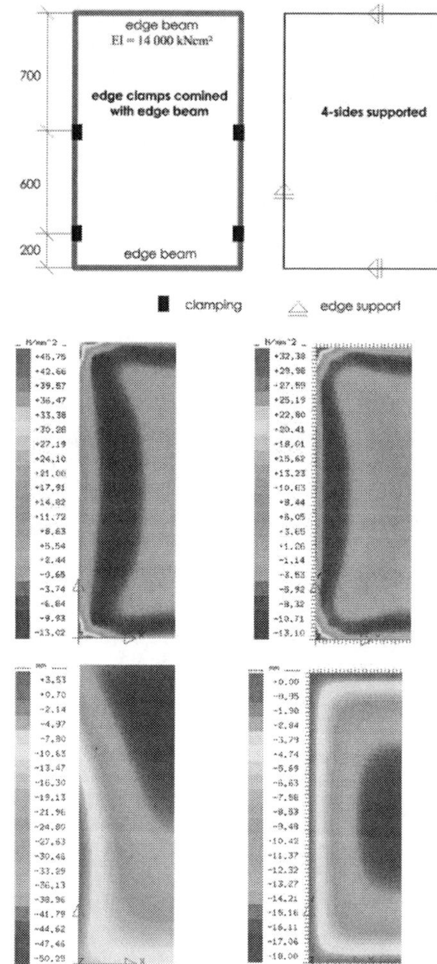

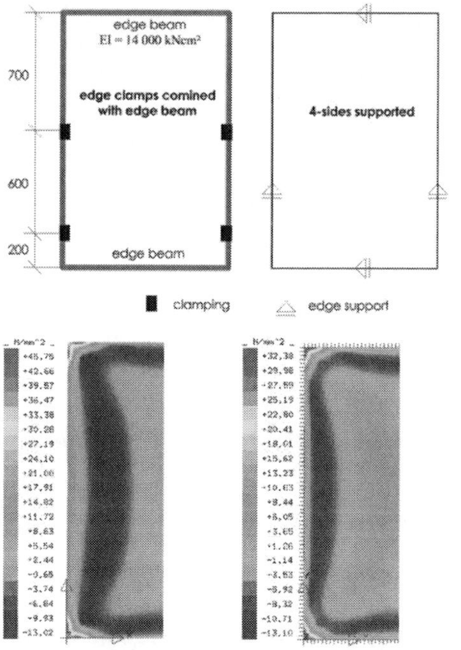

Figure 11: Maximum principal stresses and deformation (dimension 1000 mm x 1500 mm, laminate of 2 x 1.6 mm, no shear coupling, q = 1 kN/m², EI = 14,000 kNcm²)

4 SAFETY CONCEPT ACCORDING TO EUROCODE

4.1 General verification concept

The development of harmonized European design standards began 50 years ago [11]. For the past 20 years, Eurocodes (EC) have formed the basis for designing structures and their associated components, such as façades and glass components.

EC 0 describes the fundamentals of structural design by the partial safety concept [27]. This concept aims to ensure the safety and serviceability of structures by using differently weighted safety factors. This concept separates effects (loads, "E") and resistances (material properties, "R") for safety assessments. Rather than using a uniform global safety factor, a differentiated approach is employed, wherein separate safety factors are defined for actions (γ_F) and material resistances (γ_M). These factors account for uncertainties in actions that can affect a structure. Actions can be permanent or variable and include loads such as dead loads, live loads, wind loads, snow loads, and others. The magnitude of the safety factor reflects the variability and uncertainty of these loads. Material safety factors account for uncertainties in material properties and manufacturing processes. These factors vary depending on the material, for example, steel, aluminum or glass, and address variations in material strength due to manufacturing tolerances or natural variability. The basic idea behind the partial safety concept is to convert characteristic values into design values. For design purposes, the characteristic value of an action is multiplied by the corresponding safety factor, while the characteristic resistance value is divided by its safety factor. The design formula is generally written to:

$$E_k \cdot \gamma_F \geq \frac{R_k}{\gamma_M} \quad (18)$$

with

E_k characteristic effects (stresses)

γ_F partial safety factor on the load side (F = "forces")

R_k characteristic resistance

γ_M material partial safety factor

The global safety of the structures is equal to:

$$\gamma_{global} = \gamma_F \cdot \gamma_M \quad (19)$$

and respect a variation of external loading and variation of material data.

Considering the variation of the effects and the variation of the loading in a load test, it leads to an overloaded system with unrealistic deformation and mechanical conditions (e.g. unwanted load paths or similar). It is more appropriate to carry out a calculation with characteristic load combination and multiplying the result with the corresponding partial safety factor. The result is then compared with the characteristic strength divided by the material partial factor γ_M.

4.2 Wind and snow loading and design load combination

Wind and snow loading are regulated by the National Annexes of the Eurocode. Clearly, the climatic conditions at building sites differ depending on climate in the northern Europe, next to the sea, or in the Mediterranean. For this reason, every nation defined wind and snow zones.

For example, a gust speed pressure (mean value over gust period of 2-4 seconds, annual probability of occurrence of 2%) is assigned to the wind zones depending on the wind speed. The acting wind pressure is calculated depending on the geometry and the height of the building, the installation position (façade or roof) and the size of an element. Due to the small dimension of a solar element (2-3 m²), the mean wind value is higher than the mean value for a dimension larger than 10 m².

In analogy snow zone maps localize the characteristic snow loads (98% fractal value with an annual exceedance probability of 0.02 and a return period of 50 years). The geometry of the roof must be respected to consider slipping or drifting effects.

Clearly, the worst snow event and the worst storm will not occur simultaneously. The combination factors Ψ_i take this effect into account: $\Psi_{1,wind} = 0.6$ and $\Psi_{1,snow} = 0.5$.

The design load according to Eurocode is written to:

$$q_d = max \begin{vmatrix} 1{,}35\ g + 1{,}5\ (w_{pressure} + 0.5\ s) \\ 1{,}35\ g + 1{,}5\ (s + 0.6\ w_{pressure}) \\ g + 1{,}5\ w_{suction} \end{vmatrix} \quad (20)$$

with

g self weight

s snow

g wind

Conversely, for standardized elements the maximum design load q_d can be defined.

Table 1 exemplary shows how the requirements vary considerably depending on the construction site. Important for a better understanding is that the design load $q_{d,max}$ does not correspond to a test load.

Table 1 Examples: Design load due to wind and snow loading for two different construction sites in Germany

	Cologne (snow zone and wind zone 1)	Sylt (snow zone 2 and wind zone 4)
s_k *	0,65 kN/m²	0,85 kN/m²
$w_{k,suction}$ **	-1,0 kN/m²	-2,8 kN/m²
$w_{k,pressure}$ **	0,55 kN/m²	1,7 kN/m²
$q_{d,max}$	1,5 kN/m²	4,2 kN/m²
* characteristic snow load on the ground without snow accumulation		
** Assumptions: building height < 10 m, flow conditions of the wind comparable to canopies		

4.3 Calculation of the effects

After evaluation of the design load q_d, the effects due to the loading E_d can be calculated. In case of a thin glass plate with favorable membrane effects, the partial safety factor should be applied after the calculation of the stresses in the system. Because of the small ratio g/q_d the characteristic stresses may be multiplied on the safe side with the partial factor $\gamma_F = 1.5$.

As shown in Chapter 3, multiple parameters are influencing the value and distribution of the maximum principal stresses, which are the determined fracture criterion for glass.

4.4 Design value

The expression

$$R_d = \frac{R_k}{\gamma_M} \qquad (21)$$

with

R_d design value

γ_M material partial factor

is a general definition for all type of construction materials and it is defined in the material codes (e.g. EC3 for steel or EC9 aluminum). Because of the small variation in strength the material partial factor of steel is equal to $\gamma_M = 1.0$ the material partial factor for aluminum is equal to $\gamma_M = 1.1$.

The design value for pre-stressed glass is more sophisticated because of the influence of the pre-stress. Furthermore, the material partial safety factor is higher compared to aluminum because of the large variation in strength:

$$R_d = f_{gd} =$$

$$k_e \cdot k_{mod} \cdot \frac{k_{sp} \cdot f_{g,k}}{\gamma_M} + k_p \cdot k_{e,p} \cdot \frac{f_{b,k} - f_{g,k}}{k_i \cdot \gamma_p} \qquad (22)$$

with

k_e edge or hole finishing factor

k_{mod} modification factor on load duration

k_{sp} surface treatment factor

$f_{g,k}$ characteristic value of bending strength of annealed glass

γ_M material partial factor

k_p coefficient accounting for the reduction of the process-induced prestress

$k_{e,p}$ edge or hole prestress factor

$f_{b,k}$ characteristic value of bending strength of annealed glass

k_i interference factor

γ_p partial safety factor for prestress on the surface

Clearly, proofed material data are necessary to determine a design value.

Since glass has a very wide range of strengths due to its material properties, the characteristic strength is described using the 5% quantile with a confidence level of 95%. Figure 12 shows the frequency distribution of 2 mm thick solar glass from Glasmanufaktur Brandenburg (GMB) [28]. The strength range shown there (119 N/mm² - 198 N/mm²) is typical for glass as a material and clearly illustrates the large variations.

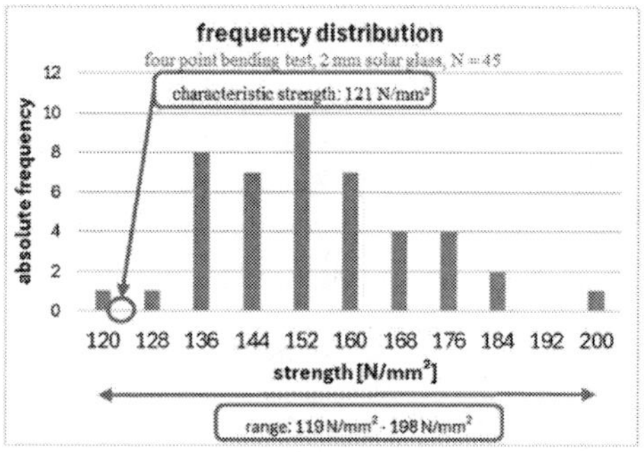

Figure 12: frequency distribution of solar glass by GMB [28]

Considering material data from test of solar glass (GMB), the design value is written according to EC10 to:

$$R_d = f_{gd} =$$

$$0.8 \cdot 1.0 \cdot \frac{0.75 \cdot 45}{1.8} + 1.0 \cdot 1.0 \cdot \frac{120 - 45}{1.0 \cdot 1.2} = 77{,}5 \ N/mm^2 \qquad (23)$$

The effects E_d in the glass due to the design load q_d must be smaller than the design value R_d.

5 COMPARISON AND GUIDELINE

Finally, the procedures of Eurocode and IEC 61215 are illustrated and compared in Figure 13. The design method of the Eurocode from material and the loading side is based on statistical basis and proofed values are available for the load (EC1) and the material side (e.g. EC10 for glass in building). For a reliable design of solar modules, strength values for PV modules are always necessary. In comparison, the informativeness of the test method of IEC is limited due to the small number of tests and the unknown breakage stress and therefore unknown breakage strength. Additionally, there is no informativeness about the input data which have to be compared with the design load according to Chapter 4.2.

In first instance, the procedure according to Eurocode seems not appropriate for "systems". But inversely, by a calculative optimization a maximum design load can be given in combination with the system data and support conditions. Finally, the usability of a solar system can be checked depending on the construction site and if necessary, targeted reinforcement of the system can be developed to avoid cost intensive replacement of modules and waste of resources after damage.

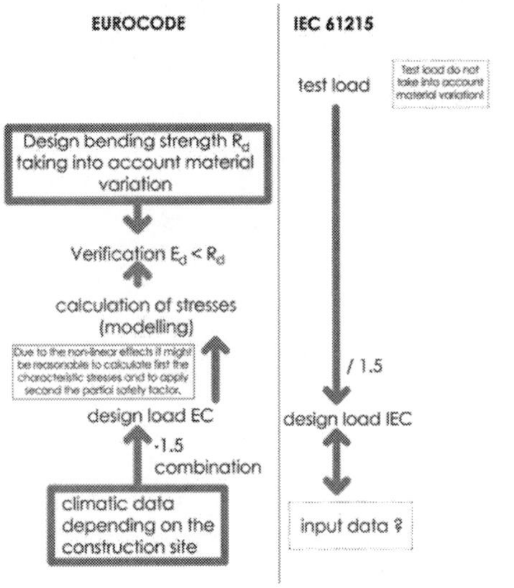

Figure 13: Comparison of Eurocode and test method of IEC 61215

6 OUTLOOK

The application of the Eurocode method might be appropriate to avoid cost intensive damage cases. The given values of the Eurocode e.g. concerning the safety level, the building geometries for the determination of the wind load etc. have to be analyzed to adapt the given rules for the special need of the solar industry.

The paper has the aim to raise awareness in the solar industry to change the planning process and the product quality control.

ACKNOLEDGEMENTS

This publication was funded by the Federal Ministry for Economic Affairs and Energy in the project Green Solar Modules under grant number **00EE1161A** and **03EE1161B**. The findings herein reflect the work, and are solely the responsibility, of the authors.

REFERENCEE

[1] Palmiotti, E. C., Springer, M., Zuboy, J., Silverman, T. J., Braid, J. L., et al., "Growing Panes: Investigating the PV Technology Trends Behind Frequent Early Failures in Modern Glass–Glass Modules," IEEE Journal of Photovoltaics, Vol. 15, No. 2, 1 Jan. 2025, pp. 297–308. doi: 10.1109/JPHOTOV.2025.3526170.

[2] International Technology Roadmap for Photovoltaic (ITRPV), 15th Edition, 1 Jan. 2024.

[3] JinkoSolar, "JinkoSolar module datasheet JKM420-440N-54HL4-BDV-D1-EN," URL: https://jinkosolar.eu/wp-content/uploads/JKM420-440N-54HL4R-BDV-F1.2-EN-4.pdf [retrieved 3 June 2025].

[4] International Electrotechnical Commission, "Terrestrial photovoltaic (PV) modules - Design qualification and type approval: Part 2: Test procedures," IEC 61215-2, Feb. 2022.

[5] PV magazine USA, "Spontaneous glass breakage on solar panels on the rise," URL: https://www.pv-magazine.com/2024/06/24/spontaneous-glass-breakage-on-solar-panels-on-the-rise/ [retrieved 14 July 2025].

[6] Silverman, T., Palmiotti, E., Springer, M., Bosco, N., Deceglie, M., et al., "Tough Break: Many Factors Make Glass Breakage More Likely," National Renewable Energy Laboratory, Jan. 2024, URL: https://www.nrel.gov/docs/fy25osti/91695.pdf

[7] T. Weber et al., Glass breakage: A growing phenomenon in largescale PV, PV magazine webinar, 20th Jan. 2023

[8] Solar Builder, "Solar module glass is 'spontaneously breaking' in the field," URL: https://solarbuildermag.com/featured/solar-module-glass-is-spontaneously-breaking-in-the-field/ [retrieved 3 June 2025].

[9] The American Ceramic Society, "Solar panel breakage on the rise as glass thickness decreases and hail severity increases - The American Ceramic Society," URL: https://ceramics.org/ceramic-tech-today/solar-panel-breakage-on-the-rise-as-glass-thickness-decreases-and-hail-severity-increases/ [retrieved 3 June 2025].

[10] "Eurocode 10 – Design of glass structures," prEN 19100 (all parts), Jan. 2024.

[11] https://eurocodes.jrc.ec.europa.eu/ [retrieved 19 September 2025].

[12] International Electrotechnical Commission, "Terrestrial photovoltaic (PV) modules - Design qualification and type approval: Part 1: Test requirements," IEC 61215-1, Feb. 2022.

[13] Matthias Pander, The increasing importance of the substructure for PV modules under high mechanical loads, 40. PV- Symposium 2025, Bad Staffelstein, March 2025. DOI: https://doi.org/10.52825/pv-symposium.v2i

[14] Romer, P., Pethani, K. B., and Beinert, A. J., "Effect of inhomogeneous loads on the mechanics of PV modules," Progress in Photovoltaics: Research and Applications, Vol. 32, No. 2, 1 Jan. 2024, pp. 84–101. doi: 10.1002/pip.3738.

[15] Dietrich, S., Zeller, U., Pander, M., and Ebert, M., "Evaluation of non-uniform mechanical loads on solar modules," 2013 IEEE 39th Photovoltaic Specialists Conference (PVSC), IEEE, 16 Jun. 2013, pp. 2998–3003.

[16] "Glass in Buildings - Design and construction rules: Part 1: Termes and general bases," DIN 18008-1, 1 May 2020.

[17] "Eurocode: Basis of structural design," EN 1990 (all parts), 1 Jan. 2021.

[18] Markert, J., Ensslen, F., Rist, T., Beinert, A. J., Job, E., et al., "Mechanical Stability of PV Modules," PV-Symposium Proceedings, Vol. 1, 1 Jan. 2024. doi: 10.52825/pv-symposium.v1i.1237.

[19] CSI Solar Co. Ltd., "CS-Datasheet-TOPBiHiKu7(Topcon)_CS7N-TB-AG_Bifacial

High efficiency," URL: https://static.csisolar.com/wp-content/uploads/2025/05/14135820/CS-Datasheet-TOPBiHiKu7_CS7N-TB-AG_v1.9_EN.pdf [retrieved 4 August 2025].
[20] JinkoSolar, "JinkoSolar Photovoltaic Modules Installation Manual," URL: https://jinkosolarcdn.shwebspace.com/uploads/JinkoSolar%20Global%20Installation%20Manual_202506_A1.5.pdf [retrieved 31 July 2025].
[21] Valentín, D., Valero, C., Egusquiza, M., and Presas, A., "Failure investigation of a solar tracker due to wind-induced torsional galloping," *Engineering Failure Analysis*, Vol. 135, Jan. 2022, p. 106137. doi: 10.1016/j.engfailanal.2022.106137.
[22] CSI Solar Co. Ltd., "Installation Manual of Photovoltaic Module v3.0" URL: https://static.csisolar.com/wp-content/uploads/sites/9/2025/08/04091415/CS_Installation-Manual_PV-Modules_EN-v3.0-EN.pdf
[23] Feldmann, M. et al. (2023): The New CEN/TS 19100: Design of Glass Structures. In: Glass Structures and Engineering.
[24] Vrouwenvelder, T. et al. (2024): Reliabilty background of the Eurocodes – Support to the implementation and further development of the Eurocodes. JRC139110
[25] Leicher, G.; Kasper, R. , Kasper, J. (2022): Tragwerkslehre in Beispielen und Zeichnungen. 5. Auflage. Reguvis Verlag
[26] https://www.mepla.net/
[27] EN 1990 (all parts) (2021) Eurocode: Basis of structural design.
[28] Reichart, H., Pander, M., Kasper, R., „Determining the strength of solar glass – test and evaluation methods" Progress in Photovoltaics: Research and Applications, in review process
[29] Jan Spelthahn (2025) Parametrische Betrachtung des Tragverhaltens von Solarmodulen in Abhängigkeit der Glaslagerung (unpublished). TH Köln.
[30] DIN 18008-2 (2020) Glass in Building – Design and construction rules - Part 2: Linearly supported glazings

42nd European Photovoltaic Solar Energy Conference and Exhibition

3AV.2.42

Determination the reliability of solar modules in analogy to glass in buildings

R. Kasper, H. Reichart
TH Köln-University of Applied Sciences
IKI Institut für konstruktiver Ingenieurbau
Contact: ruth.kasper@th-koeln.de

Technology Arts Sciences TH Köln

MOTIVATION

In recent years, photovoltaic (PV) modules have doubled in size, introducing XXL modules around 3 m² that challenge mechanical load management. Simultaneously, glass thickness in glass-glass modules has reduced to below 2 mm, along with decreased frame stiffness, leading to increased breakage and earning them the moniker "big floppy modules". The current MQT 16 static load test according to IEC 61215 inadequately represents real-world damage scenarios as it doesn't take into account material strength variability, time and temperature depending behavior of the interlayer. Adopting the construction industry's design methods (EUROCODE), which use a partial safety concept accounting for load and material variations, could better ensure PV module structural reliability. Since decades, façade and roof elements made of the brittle material glass with individual shapes, boundary conditions and varying loading conditions are effectively used with a minimal breakage risk designed exclusively by calculation. First, this poster examines the load-bearing interaction of materials, mounting, and mechanics in glass-glass modules. Second, the established reliability methods of the construction industry is explained.

Material and geometrical factors influencing the stress state

GLASS AND INTERLAYER INTERACTION

The stress distribution across the thickness in a glass-glass-laminate is – besides the glass thickness - hardly influenced by the shear stiffness G of the encapsulation material. The shear stiffness itself depends on the load duration and the temperature. The real stress state lies in between of "no shear coupling" and "full coupling".

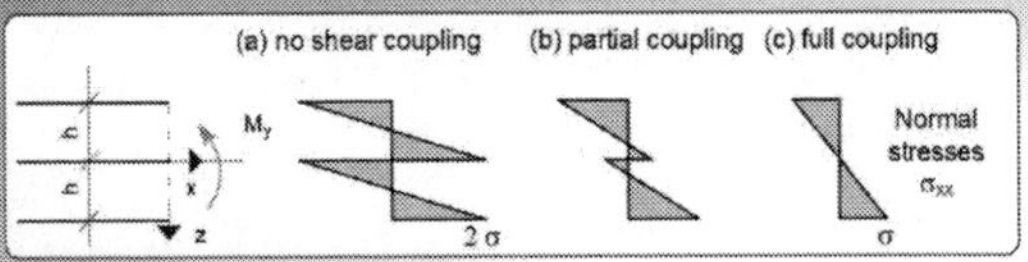

FRAMING AND CLAMPING

Frame stiffness EI (= E-Modulus · Area moment of inertia) hardly influences the stress distribution and the resulting maximal principal stresses in the glass. Stiffer frames induce clamping effects at the edges and lower stresses in the center.

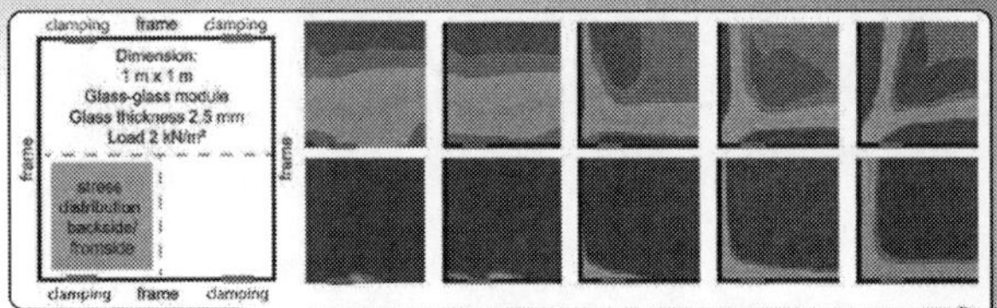

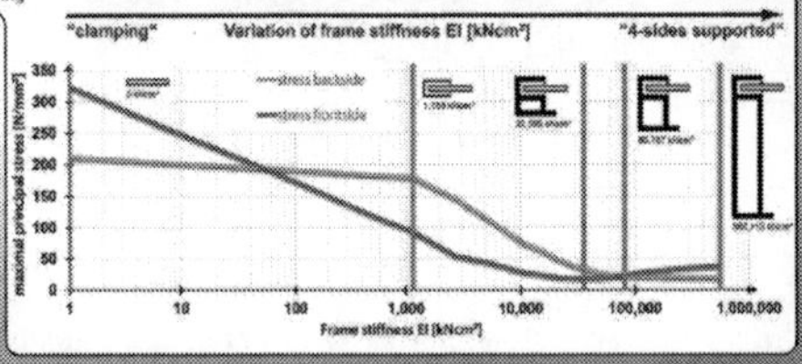

MECHANICAL SYSTEM, LOAD TRANSFER AND MECHANICAL CALCULATION THEORY

Stress distribution and deflection in the glass laminate depends highly on the load transfer and the calculation theory (linear plate theory or membrane theory).

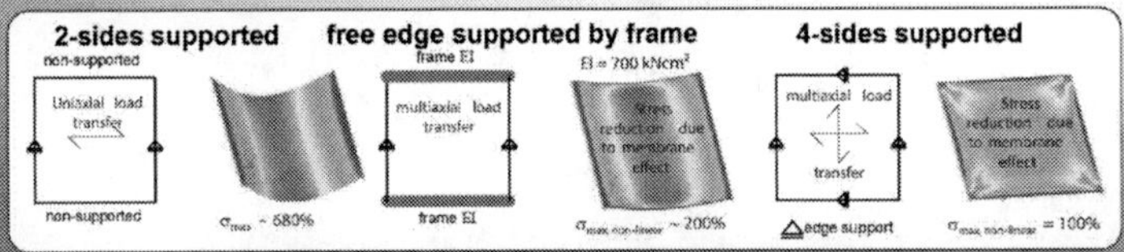

CONCLUSION The stress distribution in a PV element due to external loading must be evaluated to estimate the stress state.

Material Strength Data

Test and material standards are the basis for a reliable structural design

EUROPEAN GLASS PRODUCT STANDARDS BASED ON EN 1288-3

Characteristic strength f_k = 5% quantile value at a 95% confidence level (glass thickness ≥ 3 mm)

Float glass (EN 572-1) fk = 45 N/mm²	Heat strengthened glass (EN 1863-1) fk = 70 N/mm²	Thermally toughened glass (EN 12150-1) fk = 120 N/mm²

FRAME MATERIAL

For all constructive materials (steel or aluminum) reliable material data and product standards are available.

SOLAR GLASS

Experimental tests and evaluation for solar glass shows material strength range from 119 to 198 N/mm² which results in a characteristic bending strength of 121 N/mm² (Glass producer GMB Germany). The large scattering is typical for the material glass.

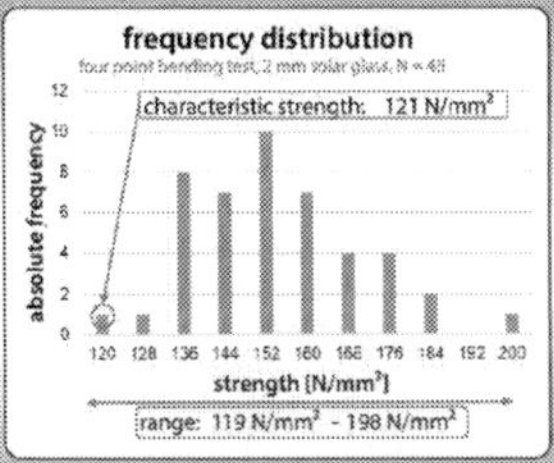

CONCLUSION A static load test according to IEC 61215 can not determine the strength scattering of the load bearing elements, so that the load bearing capacity of a PV element can not be evaluated by testing.

Safety concept according to EUROCODE

$E_d < R_d$

DESIGN VALUE OF EFFECTS

1. Wind and snow loads (EUROCODE 1) with climatic zones according to the national annex

2. Calculation of maximum stresses σ_{max} (characteristic effect) using a suitable calculation model

3. $E_d = \gamma_F \cdot \sigma_{max}$

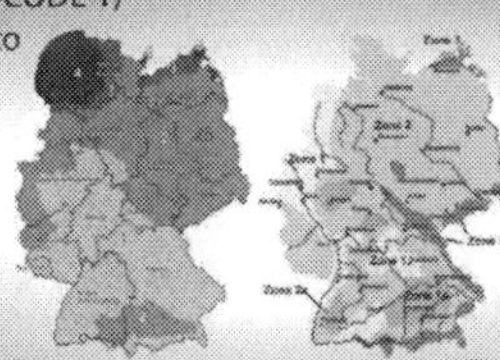

wind zones *snow zones*

DESIGN VALUE OF RESISTANCE

1. Reduction of the characteristic material strength f_k by individual material safety factor depending on the frequency distribution: e.g. $\gamma_{M,Glass} = 1.5$, $\gamma_{M,Aluminum} = 1.1$ (Design according to e.g. EC9 for aluminum, EC10 for glass or EC3 for steel)

2. $R_d = f_k / \gamma_M$

CONCLUSION The global safety factor is the product of the partial safety factors $\gamma_{global} = \gamma_F \cdot \gamma_M$ and considers the variation of effects and material. Vice versa, a maximal design load respecting the variation of the material strength and of the effects can be determined.

Outlook

In combination with the load test according to IEC 61215 a theoretical assessment for the evaluation of the load bearing capacity is absolutely necessary. A roll model can be the safety concept according to the EUROCODES which has been used successfully in the construction industry to minimize the failure risk. The basis are proofed material data. Further research is necessary to evaluate the boundary effects with regard to the stress state (= "effects").

References

References, detailed information and further explanations can be found in the additional paper published in the Conference Proceeding.

Federal Ministry for Economic Affairs and Energy

This publication was funded by the Federal Ministry for Economic Affairs and Energy in the project Green Solar Modules under grant number 00EE1161A and 03EE1161B. The findings herein reflect the work, and are solely the responsibility, of the authors.

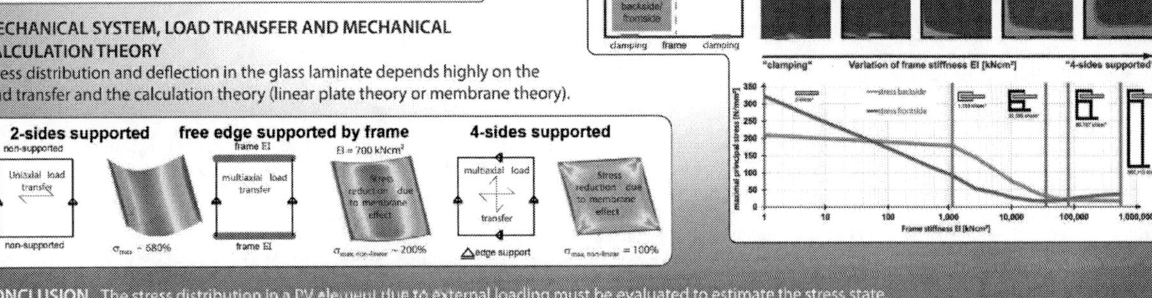

A VISUAL INSPECTION DATA COLLECTION TOOL FOR FLOATING PHOTOVOLTAIC SYSTEMS

Nathan Roosloot[1,2*], Harsha Walpita[2,1], Christoph Seiffert[1], Jean Thomas[3], Maarten Dörenkämper[4], Minne de Jong[4], Josefine H. Selj[1], Gaute Otnes[1]
[1]Institute for Energy Technology, Kjeller, Norway
[2]University of Oslo, Oslo, Norway
[3]Ciel et Terre, Lille, France
[4]TNO, Eindhoven, The Netherlands
*email: nathan.roosloot@ife.no

ABSTRACT: Floating photovoltaic (FPV) system reliability depends on the reliable performance of all system components, with degradation and/or failure of even a single element potentially leading to more extensive failure. Yet, most FPV reliability research to date has focused on the PV modules, leaving other components underexplored. To help address this gap, we here present a data collection tool for visual inspection of FPV systems. The tool complements existing tools for PV modules and enables the quantifiable assessment of visual defects on all non-module components in any FPV system. As such, it facilitates the evaluation of (long-term) visually observable degradation and/or failure in FPV systems and enables correlational analysis with system design and site-specific stressors, informing targeted system improvements and operations & maintenance (O&M) strategies. Lastly, if outputs are openly shared, large-scale use of the tool can provide statistics on FPV system degradation that can help derisk the sector as a whole.

KEYWORDS: Floating photovoltaics, reliability, visual inspection

1 INTRODUCTION

The floating photovoltaic (FPV) sector, where PV modules are mounted on floating structures on top of water bodies, is a relatively young but rapidly growing segment of the PV market. The global installed FPV capacity more than quadrupled between 2020 and 2024, reaching over 9 GW [1], with a further 20 GW of installations forecasted until 2030 [2]. The main driver behind the growth of FPV is the use of water bodies for electricity generation in cases where land area is unsuitable or too expensive for PV deployment. In addition, FPV can have several other benefits, such as installation close to areas of high electricity demand, dual use of water bodies, potential reduced evaporation of water and lower module operating temperatures [3], [4]. However, forecasted installations are still far from the global technical potential of FPV, which can for example be up to 7.6 TW for FPV systems on hydropower reservoirs alone, assuming a reservoir coverage of 20% [5].

The FPV market faces several obstacles to reaching its full technical potential, including legislative barriers, cost competitiveness with ground mounted PV (GPV), and uncertainties regarding environmental impacts, energy yield and reliability. Uncertainties regarding FPV system reliability primarily stem from expectations that these systems will be subjected to significantly different stress levels than GPV installations, while publicly available data on observed degradation or failures of FPV installations, which can be used as a basis for evaluating these expectations, are scarce. This is mainly caused by the fact that observations of degradation and/or failure on operational FPV systems are rarely openly shared. This can be attributed to fierce competition between the large number of FPV system suppliers [6], leading to confidentiality and limited data sharing. This ultimately reduces bankability as the sector lacks statistics on expected degradation rates, while research and development to improve system reliability, if needed, is slowed down. However, even if data were openly shared, mid- to end-of-life degradation and/or failure modes can typically not be evaluated, as most FPV systems are too young to have encountered these, with more than 75% of the global installed FPV capacity being less than 5 years old at the end of 2024 [1].

In addition to potential stress level differences, variations in system design can also affect FPV reliability compared to GPV. A FPV system, of which an example is sketched in Figure 1, typically consists of more components than a GPV one of similar size, with modules mounted on (interconnected) floats, which are held in place by mooring and anchoring systems, rather than on mounting systems that go straight into the ground. In addition, much of the electrical infrastructure might be placed on water too, requiring more floating parts. A comprehensive overview of FPV system components can be found in [7], [8].

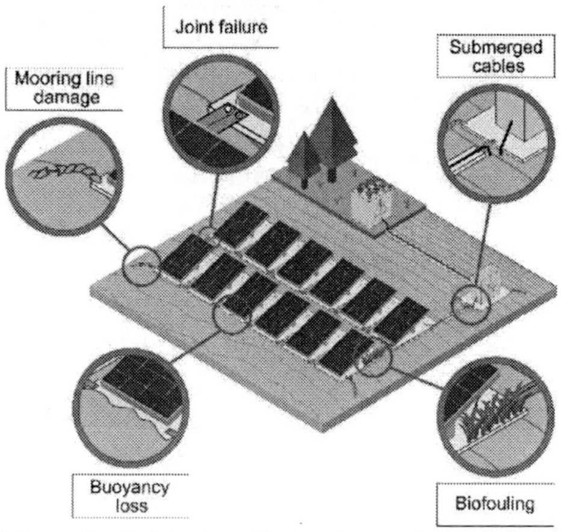

Figure 1: Sketch of an FPV system with examples of potential visually observable non-module defects.

In addition to having more components, the dynamic behavior of the FPV system on the water can increase the chance of parts failing, while the failure of even a single element, of which some examples are given in Figure 1, can potentially lead to wider system issues (for example due to sinking), something that is more rare for GPV cases. All in all, FPV system reliability is thus highly dependent on the reliable performance of all system components. In fact, several examples of FPV component and sometimes

10.4229/EUPVSEC2025/3AV.2.43

subsequent system degradation and/or failure have been observed in the field [7]. Yet, in FPV reliability literature, focus is typically on the module only.
A common way in which module health in the field is assessed is by visual inspection, which can be performed without the use of specialized equipment or in-depth PV knowledge. While visual inspection can give insights into the visually observable effects of degradation and/or failure, it does not necessarily reveal the underlying causes. However, it is complementary to more in-depth characterization techniques where the opposite might be true. As a result, visual inspection is typically a standard part of module health assessments.
When performing visual inspection, it is crucial that outputs are recorded in a consistent, user-independent and quantifiable manner, so that inspections of different systems or the same system over time can quantitatively be compared. For this reason, a standardized data collection tool for visual inspection of PV modules has been created at NREL [9], and adopted by Task 13 of the International Energy Agency's Photovoltaic Power Systems Programme (IEA PVPS) [10], with recommendations for use as an international standard for visual inspection in the field.
Due to the dependence of FPV system reliability on other components than the module, as mentioned before, a similar tool for the visual inspection of these components could be of great use, and is hence presented in this work. For individual FPV systems, the tool allows system conditions to be tracked over time, and visual observations of degradation and/or failure to be linked to system design and site-specific conditions, allowing for targeted system improvements and operations & maintenance (O&M) actions where necessary. Larger scale data collection allows for the statistical analysis of relationships between system degradation and/or failure and FPV system type, water body type and climate conditions. Additionally, large-scale statistics of FPV system degradation would give investors and insurers greater confidence in long-term performance, thereby facilitating financing and wider deployment.
In the next section, the tool and explanations for its use are given.

2 FPV VISUAL INSPECTION DATA COLLECTION TOOL

The FPV visual inspection data collection tool can be used to collect data on any component on the DC side of any FPV system except for the PV modules themselves, for which the tool from [10] can be used. The FPV tool was made in the same format as the tool from [10] to ensure complimentary between the two. The tool is based on a combination of published literature on FPV system reliability and first-hand experience from visual inspections of a wide range of FPV installations. In addition, it has been reviewed by international FPV experts from both industry and academia. To balance detail, ease of use, and the time required to complete, the tool combines multiple-choice items with open questions, the latter allowing respondents to provide additional information not captured by the fixed options. The tool is meant to be filled out once for an entire system and thus benefits from access to the full system for visual inspection. If this is not the case, relevant information can still be gained from filling out the tool for the accessible parts only. It is then recommended to indicate what parts of the system were assessed in the tool.
In total, the tool focuses on four parts of the FPV system, each of which have their own section: (1) the floating system, (2) mooring and anchoring, (3) cables and inverters and (4) other relevant technologies. Due to the multitude of different FPV technologies in the market, the tool does not only include a description of damage to these parts, but also a more general description of the system components themselves. The description of the components are in part A of each section, while the damage description are in part B. An accurate description of the system can greatly aid in understanding what type of damage is seen and how it relates to the FPV design. However, such a description is not always necessary when the inspection is done on a known system with no plans to share the results beyond those that are familiar with it. In such cases, parts A of the checklist can be omitted for quicker inspection.
Section 1 of the tool focuses on the float technology. This includes all buoyant components and their interconnections, such as floats and float-to-float connectors, as well as the module mounting structures attached to them. The tool requires assessment of the entire floating system, which can be divided into two lower levels: interconnected floating islands/arrays and individual floats that make up the islands. An example of a floating system with two floating islands is given in Figure 2, while a single floating island with individually interconnected floats are shown in Figure 1. Note that this division does not apply to all FPV systems.

Figure 2: Example of a floating PV system that consists of two floating islands. Image courtesy of Ciel et Terre.

Section 2 of the tool looks at the mooring and anchoring system. Terminology for mooring and anchoring types are derived from [8].
Section 3 covers cables and inverters. As damage to module cables and interconnectors are already covered in [10], these are not included here. Instead, the tool considers placement and attachment of the cables and related components to the floating system. To keep the tool comprehensive, the AC side of the electrical system is not included.
Lastly, section 4 focuses on other technologies that might be present on FPV systems, including cooling and/or anti-soiling technologies and tracking systems. The questions in this section can also be used to provide information of other, rarer, technologies not included here, such as concentrator systems.
When filling out the inspection tool, the use of a measurement device and a camera are recommended to take measurements and images of relevant components

and defects. To have images and the filled out inspection tool in the same location, digitalization of this tool can be of aid. The authors of this work also use a digitalized version of this tool for personal use. However, because of limitations in how easily this could be shared, this paper version is shared instead. In case of interest in use of the digital tool, please reach out to the corresponding author.

FPV system visual inspection data collection tool

Documentation of FPV system condition for field exposed systems

Date ________________ Name of recorder ______________________________

System name ____

Latitude ______________ Longitude ______________ Altitude ________________

1. Float technology

Floating system here refers to the entire FPV plant (of the same technology). The system can consist of several floating islands/arrays, which each can consist of several individually connected floats

1A – System description

1A.1 Floating system technology provider (Original Equipment Manufacturer) _______

____

1A.2 Floating system product name/model ___________________________

1A.3 Is the system deployed? **Jump to question 1A.5 if answering 'Yes, on water' or 'No'* ☐ Yes, on water ☐ Yes, on land ☐ No (explain where system was surveyed): ________________

1A.4 Why is the system deployed on land? ☐ Intended amphibious operation ☐ Drought ☐ System not yet deployed on water ☐ Unknown ☐ Other ______________

1A.5 Approximate size of floating system **Either in m^2 or length x width (m x m)* ___________

1A.6 Number of modules on floating system **Capacity can be given also. Specify unit* _________

1A.7 Does the floating system consist of several floating islands/arrays? **Jump to question 1A.9 if answering 'No' or 'Unclear/Unknown'* ☐ Yes ☐ No ☐ Unclear/Unknown

1A.8 Number of floating islands/arrays on system ___________________

1A.9 Does the floating system consist of individually connected floats? **Jump to question 1A.15 if answering 'No' or 'Unclear/Unknown'* ☐ Yes ☐ No ☐ Unclear/Unknown

1A.10 Number of individual floats on system ___________________

1A.11 Do all individual floats contain modules? **Jump to question 1A.13 if answering 'Yes'* ☐ Yes ☐ No

1A.12 Describe location and rough fraction of all floats that do not contain modules **Add reason why no modules are present on these floats, if known* ______________________________

____

1A.13 Amount of modules per individual float **Only for floats that contain modules* _________

1A.14 Are all individual floats of the same type? **Jump to question 1A.16 if answering 'Yes'* ☐ Yes ☐ No

1A.15 Describe how the individual floats differ and what part of the system consists of what float type **It is recommended to fill in the full tool once per float type* _______________

____

1A.16 Describe how the individual floats are connected **E.g. directly to each other, or by material in between (e.g. hinges). Describe connection points including location, number, dimensions and type of material if possible.* ____

____

1A.17 Float material(s) **Mark all that apply* ☐ Aluminium ☐ Steel ☐ Plastics (specify under 'other' if type is known) ☐ Cement ☐ Unknown ☐ Other ______________

1A.18 PV module mounting system materials **Mark all that apply* ☐ Same as float materials ☐ Aluminium ☐ Steel ☐ Plastics (specify under 'other' if type is known) ☐ Cement ☐ Unknown ☐ Other ________________

1A.19 Type of attachment of module to mounting system **Mark all that apply* ☐ Clamps ☐ Adhesive (glue/silicone/etc) ☐ Bolting ☐ Other ________________

1A.20 Location of attachment of module to mounting system **Mark all that apply* ☐ At edges ☐ In corners ☐ Across part of backside ☐ Across full backside ☐ Along full frame ☐ In middle ☐ Other ________________

1A.21 How does one move on the floating system? **Mark all that apply* ☐ Pathways to walk between modules ☐ Walking over modules ☐ Not possible to move ☐ Other

____

1A.22 Are all modules accessible for visual inspection? **Jump to question 1A.24 if answering 'Yes' or 'Unknown/unclear'* ☐ Yes ☐ No ☐ Unknown/unclear

1A.23 If not all modules are accessible for visual inspection, explain why ____________

____

1A.24 Approximate inclination of the panels **0° = flat on water, 90° = vertical* ____________

1A.25 Direction panels are facing **Mark all that apply* ☐ North ☐ North-East ☐ East ☐ South-East ☐ South ☐ South-West ☐ West ☐ North-West ☐ Varying ☐ Single-axis zenith East-West tracking ☐ Single-axis zenith North-South tracking ☐ Single axis azimuth tracking ☐ Dual-axis tracking ☐ Directly up (0° tilt) ☐ Unknown

1A.26 If not all panels are facing in the same direction, describe what modules face in what direction ____

1A.27 Approximate height of panels above water (cm) **Use lowest panel-water distance according to design (in case of no damage)* ______________________

1A.28 Does the floating system cover the water surface directly underneath the modules? **Jump to question 1A.30 if answering 'Yes'. Answer 'No' or 'Partly' if theoretically possible to touch the water at any location directly underneath the module.* ☐ Yes ☐ No ☐ Partly

1A.29 Describe the space and size of the floating system underneath the module, focusing on water coverage **E.g. 'rectangular gap in float approximately half the length of the module' or '30 cm wide beam across middle of module backside'. Add measurements if possible.* ________________

____

1A.30 Other relevant information for float description **Only focus on description of the floating system that is not covered by the questions above. Description of other components (mooring lines, anchors, cables) will come in the following sections.* ________________________________

____

1B - System damage

The questions in this section refer to damage to the entire floating system, not of a single individual float.

1B.1 Float and/or PV supporting system damage **Jump to question 1B.6 if answering 'Not present/visible'. Damage of mooring lines, anchors and cables are discussed in coming sections and should not be included here* ☐ Not present/visible ☐ Small, localized ☐ Extensive

1B.2 Float damage type **Mark all that apply* ☐ Corrosion ☐ Parts fallen/broken off/disconnected ☐ Scratches/cracks ☐ Holes ☐ Fire/burn marks or damage ☐ Other

____

1B.3 Float damage location (1) **Mark all that apply* ☐ Walkways ☐ Underneath modules ☐ Between modules ☐ Attachment between module and supporting system ☐ Attachment between smaller floats ☐ Underneath float ☐ Float edges ☐ Float corners ☐ Other

____

10.4229/EUPVSEC2025/3AV.2.43
020169-004

1B.4 Float damage location (2) **If relevant, explain where on the overall system the damage is (e.g. towards N/E/S/W, incoming waves, land, etc)* ______________________________

____

1B.5 Fraction of floating system affected by damage **If multiple types of damage exist, specify what accounts for what percentage in question 1B.16* ☐ <5% ☐ 5 - 25% ☐ 25 - 75% ☐ 75 - 100% (uniform)

1B.6 Float and/or PV supporting system soiling **Jump to question 1B.11 if answering 'Not present/visible* ☐ Not present/visible ☐ Small, localized ☐ Extensive

1B.7 Float soiling type **Mark all that apply* ☐ Biofouling ☐ Bird soiling ☐ Dust/dirt ☐ Pollen ☐ Bird nests ☐ Other ______________

1B.8 Float soiling location **Mark all that apply* ☐ Walkways ☐ Underneath modules ☐ Between modules ☐ Attachment between module and supporting system ☐ Attachment between smaller floats ☐ Underneath float ☐ Float edges ☐ Float corners ☐ Other ______________

1B.9 Float soiling location **If relevant, explain where on the overall system the soiling is (e.g. towards N/E/S/W, incoming waves, land, etc)* ______________________________

____

1B.10 Fraction of floating system affected by soiling **If multiple types of soiling exist, specify what accounts for what percentage in question 1B.16* ☐ <5% ☐ 5 - 25% ☐ 25 - 75% ☐ 75 - 100% (uniform)

1B.11 Floating system buoyancy **Jump to question 1B.15 if answering 'Buoyant'* ☐ Buoyant ☐ Partially non-buoyant ☐ Completely non-buoyant

1B.12 Fraction of floating system under water ☐ <5% ☐ 5 - 25% ☐ 25 - 75% ☐ 75 - 100% (uniform)

1B.13 Locations of floating system that is under water **Mark all that apply* ☐ Edges ☐ Corners ☐ Walkways between modules ☐ Around/at modules ☐ Random/no pattern ☐ Complete system ☐ Other ______________

1B.14 Suspected cause of loss of buoyancy ______________________________

1B.15 Describe damage to attachment points **Can be module supporting system to floats and floats to floats.* ______________________________

____

1B.16 Other relevant information on float damage **Only focus on description of damage to the floating system that is not covered by the other questions in Section 1B* ______________________________

____

2. Mooring and anchoring

2A - System description

System description of the full mooring and anchoring system

2A.1 Mooring lines **Jump to question 2A.6 if answering 'Not present/visible'* ☐ Present and visible ☐ Not present/visible

2A.2 Amount of mooring lines **If uncertain, write how many are visible* ______________________________

2A.3 Type of mooring lines **Mark all that apply* ☐ Compliant mooring ☐ Taut mooring ☐ Catenary mooring ☐ Rigid piles ☐ Unknown ☐ Other ______________

2A.4 Mooring line materials **Mark all that apply* ☐ Steel ☐ Fiber (specify type under 'other' if known) ☐ Other ______________

2A.5 Mooring line attachment **Describe attachment of mooring lines to the floating system and anchoring (including but not limited to used materials, location on system, attachment type)* ______________

10.4229/EUPVSEC2025/3AV.2.43
020169-005

2A.6 Anchors **Jump to section 2A.9 if answering 'Not present/visible'* ☐ Present and visible ☐ Not present/visible

2A.7 Location of anchoring **Mark all that apply* ☐ Under water ☐ On land ☐ Unknown ☐ Other ________________

2A.8 Type of anchoring **Mark all that apply* ☐ Gravity anchor ☐ Pile/helical anchor ☐ Plate anchor ☐ Drag anchor ☐ Unknown ☐ Other ________________

2A.9 Other relevant information on mooring and anchoring **Only focus on description of mooring and anchoring that is not covered by the questions above.* ____________________________

2B – System damage

Damage description of the full mooring and anchoring system

2B.1 Mooring lines physical state **Jump to question 2B.5 if answering 'No visible issues'* ☐ No visible issues ☐ Damaged ☐ Missing

2B.2 Mooring lines damage type **Mark all that apply* ☐ Corrosion ☐ Biofouling ☐ Breakage ☐ Soiling ☐ Abrasion ☐ Entangled lines ☐ Other ________________

2B.3 Location of mooring line damage **Mark all that apply* ☐ Attachment with floats ☐ Middle of line (above water) ☐ Middle of line (under water) ☐ Attachment with anchors ☐ Other ________________

2B.4 Fraction of mooring lines affected **Fraction of all observable mooring lines. Specify how damage is distributed (e.g. even across all lines, one line with all damage) in question 2B.8 if relevant.* ☐ <5 % ☐ 5 - 25% ☐ 25 - 75% ☐ 75 - 100% (uniform)

2B.5 Anchoring physical state **Jump to question 2B.8 if answering 'No visible issues'* ☐ No visible issues ☐ Damaged ☐ Missing ☐ Not observable

2B.6 Anchoring damage type **Mark all that apply* ☐ Corrosion ☐ Biofouling ☐ Breakage ☐ Soiling ☐ Other ________________

2B.7 Fraction of anchors affected **Fraction of all observable anchors. Specify how damage is distributed (e.g. even across all anchors, one anchor with all damage) in last question of section if relevant.* ☐ <5 % ☐ 5 - 25% ☐ 25 - 75% ☐ 75 - 100% (uniform)

2B.8 Other relevant information on mooring and anchoring damage **Only focus on description of mooring and anchoring damage that is not covered by the questions above.* ______________

---

3. Cables and inverters

Only covers DC side of the system. For questions regarding wire and connector damage on module level, use the PV module visual inspection data collection tool

3A – System description

Description of the DC cabling and inverters

3A.1 Cables between modules in string **Jump to question 3A.3 if answering 'Not present/visible'* ☐ Present and visible ☐ Not present/visible

3A.2 Placement of cables between modules **Mark all that apply* ☐ Above water, and no contact with water ☐ Above water, but in contact with water ☐ Under water ☐ Other ________________

3A.3 Cable combiner boxes **These combine string cables into larger DC cables. Jump to question 3A.5 if answering 'Not present/visible'* ☐ Present and visible ☐ Not present/visible

3A.4 Placement of cable combiner boxes **Mark all that apply* ☐ Above water, and no contact with water ☐ Above water, but in contact with water ☐ Under water ☐ Other ________________

3A.5 Cables from strings to inverter **Jump to question 3A.7 if answering 'Not present/visible'* ☐ Present and visible ☐ Not present/visible

3A.6 Placement of cables to inverter **Mark all that apply* ☐ Above water, and no contact with water ☐ Above water, but in contact with water ☐ Under water ☐ Other ________________

3A.7 Inverters **Jump to section 3A.10 if answering 'Not present/visible'* ☐ Present and visible ☐ Not present/visible

3A.8 Number of inverters ______________________

3A.9 Inverter locations **Mark all that apply* ☐ On land ☐ On water ☐ Unknown

3A.10 Other relevant information on cables and inverters **Only focus on description of cables and inverters that is not covered by the questions above.* ____________________________________

3B - System damage

Damage description of the DC cabling and inverters

3B.1 Cable combiner box damage **Mark all that apply* ☐ No visible issues ☐ Burn marks/heat discoloration ☐ Damages/loose glands or cable entries ☐ Water ingress/condensation ☐ Corrosion/rust ☐ Other ________________

3B.2 Cables to inverter damage **Mark all that apply* ☐ No visible issues ☐ Pliable, but degraded ☐ Embrittled ☐ Cracked/disintegrated insulation ☐ Burnt ☐ Corroded ☐ Animal bites/marks ☐ Other ________________

3B.3 Attachment of cables/combiner boxes to floats ☐ No attachments ☐ No visible issues ☐ Damaged ☐ Missing in some locations ☐ Unknown

3B.4 Inverter physical state **Jump to question 3B.6 if answering 'No visible issues'* ☐ No visible issues ☐ Damaged

3B.5 Inverter damage **Mark all that apply* ☐ Cracks/dents/holes (impact damage) ☐ Burn marks/heat discoloration ☐ Damages/loose glands or cable entries ☐ Water ingress/condensation ☐ Corrosion/rust ☐ Labels/markings missing or illegible ☐ Other

3B.6 Other relevant information on cables and inverters damage **Only focus on description of cable and/or inverter damage that is not covered by the questions above.* ____________________________

4. Additional technologies

Potential additional technologies present on FPV systems: cooling/anti-soiling, tracking or others

4A – System description

Description of additional technologies

4A.1 Is a cooling and/or anti-soiling technology used? **Jump to question 4A.3 if answering 'No' or 'Unknown'* ☐ Yes ☐ No ☐ Unknown

4A.2 Describe the cooling and/or anti-soiling technology ____________________________

4A.3 Is a tracking technology used? **Jump to question 4A.7 if answering 'No' or 'Unknown'* ☐ Yes ☐ No ☐ Unknown

4A.4 Type of tracking technology **Jump to question 4A.6 if answering 'Dual-axis' or 'Unknown'* ☐ Single-axis ☐ Dual-axis ☐ Unknown

4A.5 What axis is tracked? ☐ Azimuth ☐ Zenith ☐ Other ________________

4A.6 Is the tracking technology functioning? ☐ Yes ☐ No ☐ Unknown
4A.7 Other relevant information on damage of other technologies **Only focus on description of cooling/anti-soiling, tracking or other relevant technologies that is not covered by the questions above.*
____
____

4B - System damage

Description of damage to additional technologies
4B.1 Cooling/anti-soiling technology damage **Jump to question 4B.4 if answering 'No damage'* ☐ No damage ☐ Small, localized ☐ Extensive
4B.2 Cooling/anti-soiling damage type **Mark all that apply. If cooling and anti-soiling are not the same system, specify which of the two is damaged in question 4B.7.* ☐ Corrosion ☐ Cracks/breakage ☐ Biofouling ☐ Soiling ☐ Other electrical failure (specify in question 4B.7) ☐ Other ________________
4B.3 Cooling/anti-soiling damage location **Mark all that apply* ☐ Connection with floater ☐ Connection with modules ☐ On technology itself ☐ Other ________________
4B.4 Tracker damage **Jump to question 4B.7 if answering 'Not present/visible' or 'Unknown'* ☐ Not present/visible ☐ Small, localized ☐ Extensive
4B.5 Tracker damage type **Mark all that apply* ☐ Corrosion ☐ Cracks/breakage ☐ Biofouling ☐ Soiling ☐ Electrical failure ☐ Abrasion ☐ Entangled lines ☐ Damage to propulsion system ☐ Other ________________
4B.6 Tracker damage location **Mark all that apply* ☐ Connection with floater ☐ Connection with module support ☐ On tracker itself ☐ Other ________________
4B.7 Other relevant information on tracker technology and damage **Only focus on description of damage to cooling/anti-soiling, tracking or other relevant technologies that is not covered by the questions above.* ________________________________
____

5. Other remarks

5.1 Other remarks **Further clarification or additional information not covered above. Include location/ID wherever relevant.* ________________________________
____
____
____

ACKNOWLEDGMENTS

This work was supported by the European Union's Horizon Europe research and innovation program through the project SuRE (grant agreement 101135567).

REFERENCES

[1] T. Reindl, "Overview, Status and Outlook of Floating PV," in *4th International Integrated PV Workshop*, 2025.
[2] International Energy Agency, "Trends In Photovoltaic Applications 2024," 2024.
[3] International Energy Agency, "Trends In Photovoltaic Applications 2023," 2023.
[4] SolarPower Europe, "Floating PV Best Practice Guidelines Version 1.0," 2023.
[5] N. Lee, U. Grunwald, E. Rosenlieb, H. Mirletz, A. Aznar, R. Spencer, and S. Cox, "Hybrid floating solar photovoltaics-hydropower systems: Benefits and global assessment of technical potential," *Renew Energy*, vol. 162, pp. 1415–1427, Dec. 2020, doi: 10.1016/j.renene.2020.08.080.
[6] C. D. Rodríguez-Gallegos, O. Gandhi, H. Sun, C. Paton, J. Zhang, J. Moideen Yacob Ali, M. S. Alvarez-Alvarado, W. Zhang, C. A. Rodríguez-Gallegos, L. H. C. Chua, and T. Reindl, "Global floating PV status and potential," *Progress in Energy*, vol. 7, no. 1, p. 015001, Jan. 2025, doi: 10.1088/2516-1083/ad9074.
[7] IEA PVPS Task 13, "Floating Photovoltaic Power Plants: A Review of Energy Yield, Reliability, and Maintenance," 2025.
[8] H. L. Walpita, N. Roosloot, G. Otnes, B. L. Aarseth, J. Selj, V. S. Nysted, and E. S. Marstein, "Operation and Maintenance of Floating PV Systems: A Review," *IEEE J Photovolt*, vol. 15, no. 3, pp. 400–415, May 2025, doi: 10.1109/JPHOTOV.2025.3548322.

[9] C. E. Packard, J. H. Wohlgemuth, and S. R. Kurtz, "Development of a Visual Inspection Data Collection Tool for Evaluation of Fielded PV Module Condition," in *PV Module Reliability Workshop*, 2012.
[10] M. Kontges *et al.*, "Review of failures of photovoltaic modules," 2014.

SURE

A visual inspection data collection tool for floating PV systems

Nathan Roosloot[1,2*]
Harsha Walpita[1,2]
Christoph Seiffert[1]
Jean Thomas[3]
Maarten Dörenkämper[4]
Minne de Jong[4]
Josefine Helene Selj[1]
Gaute Otnes[1]

[1]Institute for Energy Technology, Kjeller, Norway
[2]University of Oslo, Oslo, Norway
[3]Ciel et Terre, Lille, France
[4]TNO, Eindhoven, The Netherlands
*nathan.roosloot@ife.no

IFE · CIEL & TERRE THE FLOATING SOLAR COMPANY · TNO

Visual inspection is a key tool for identification and assessment of field failures and degradation in PV systems. By using a standardized data collection tool, system conditions can be assessed consistently, allowing for longitudinal analysis and meaningful comparison of system conditions across sites. Due to these benefits, a harmonized collection tool has been developed for PV modules [1], [2]. For floating PV (FPV) systems, module reliability can be strongly affected by degradation and/or failure of other system components. Therefore, this work complements the existing PV module inspection tool with a similar tool to quantify the condition of all other components of an FPV system except for the PV modules. The tool has been developed based on reported (potential) system component degradation in FPV literature and on experience with visual inspections performed on different FPV systems. It has been reviewed by FPV experts both from industry and academia. The tool is shared with the aim of standardizing visual inspection outputs in the FPV sector, thereby contributing to improved system reliability.

Below are examples of potential FPV system component issues that are covered in the visual inspection tool. The full tool is published in the conference proceedings. In addition, it can be found using the QR-code on the right or the link below:
https://docs.google.com/document/d/14kV1Vl6dzO_1TiVqEx11RC1HVFZk9eXej1XA3Zvii8Q/edit

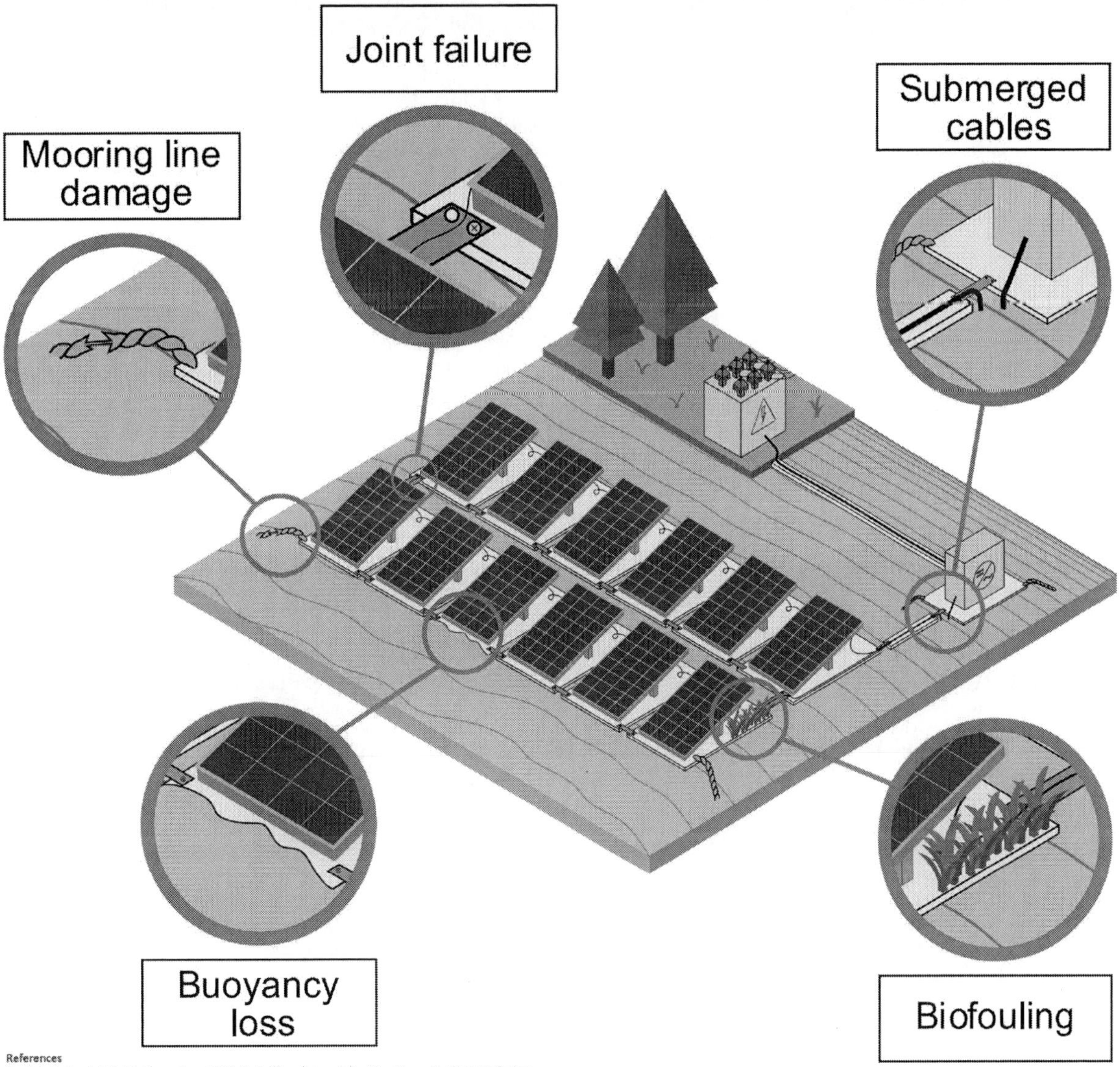

References
1. C. E. Packard, J. H. Wohlgemuth, and S. R. Kurtz, "Development of a Visual Inspection Data Collection Tool for Evaluation of Fielded PV Module Condition," in *PV Module Reliability Workshop*, 2012.
2. M. Kontges *et al.*, "Review of failures of photovoltaic modules," 2014.

SUSTAINABLE, RELIABLE AND EFFICIENT FLOATING PHOTOVOLTAIC POWER PLANTS

SuRE project has received funding from the European Union's Horizon Europe research and innovation program under grant agreement No 101135567.

Schweizerische Eidgenossenschaft
Confédération suisse
Confederazione Svizzera
Confederaziun svizra
Swiss Confederation

Federal Department of Economic Affairs, Education and Research EAER
State Secretariat for Education, Research and Innovation SERI

A NEW METHOD FOR COMPREHENSIVE POWER RATING AND PERFORMANCE ANALYSIS OF PERC MODULES BASED ON HALF-CUT CELL TECHNOLOGY

Khadija El Ainaoui[a, b*], Mhammed Zaimi[a], Imane Flouchi[b], Said Elhamaoui[b], Yasmine El mrabet[b],

Abdellatif Ghennioui[b], El Mahdi Assaid[a]

[a]*Electronics and Optics of Semiconductor Nanostructures and Sustainable Energy Team, Laboratory of Instrumentation of Measure and Control, Department of Physics, Faculty of Sciences, Chouaïb Doukkali University, El Jadida, Morocco*

[b]*Electrical Systems and Photovoltaics Department, Green Energy Park, Benguerir, Morocco*

**Corresponding author: elainaoui@greenenergypark.ma; elainaoui.k@ucd.ac.ma*

ABSTRACT: Photovoltaic (PV) Solar energy plays a vital role in the transition to sustainable and renewable energy sources. The performance and durability of PV cells are significantly influenced by their operating conditions, particularly temperature and irradiance. Understanding these variables and their combined effects is critical for optimizing PV technology. In this context, this work evaluates the effect of temperature and irradiance on the performance of PERC (Passivated Emitter and Rear Cell) modules with half-cut cell technology using novel approach based on an analytical model. The model includes three shape parameters (A , M and N) and two PV metrics: open-circuit voltage (V_{OC}) and short-circuit current (I_{SC}). By developing explicit formulas for A and M in terms of PV metrics and employing an iterative method to determine N , the model accurately describe the module behavior under controlled power rating tests across a range of irradiances (100 to 1100 W/m²) and temperatures (15 to 75°C), as specified by IEC 61853-1, as well as real weather variations. The findings indicate that irradiance has a significant effect on PERC performance. As irradiance increases, the generation rate of electron-hole pairs rises significantly, leading to a substantial increase in I_{SC} and output power. On the other hand, temperature predominantly affects V_{OC} , with higher temperatures reducing it due to increased electron-hole recombination, leading to a decline in output power. In contrast, I_{SC} shows a slight increase as temperature rises, driven by enhanced material conductivity and a broader absorption spectrum. The reliability and accuracy of the approach are evidenced by an average Root Mean Square Error (RMSE) of under 0.053 A and a normalized Root Mean Square Error (NRMSE) of less than 1.76 %. These outcomes highlight the method's precision in modeling PV performance across different temperature and irradiance conditions.

Keywords: Photovoltaic; PERC; Effects of temperature and irradiance; Energy testing; IEC 61853-1.

1 INTRODUCTION

PERC technology has become a dominant choice due to its high efficiency and cost-effectiveness [1]. PERC leverages monocrystalline silicon cells with a rear surface passivation layer [2,3], enabling reduced surface recombination, enhanced light reflection, and improved energy conversion efficiency compared to conventional aluminum back surface field (Al-BSF) modules [4]. The integration of half-cut cells further minimizes resistive losses, improving output energy even under partial shading conditions [5]. Despite these advantages, the performance of PERC modules based on half-cut cells, like other PV technologies, is highly influenced by environmental factors, particularly solar irradiance and temperature [6,7]. The simultaneous variation of these factors introduces dynamics that necessitate a deeper understanding of their combined effects on module performance. To address this, the study proposes a novel approach to assess the impact of temperature and irradiance on the performance of PERC modules with half-cut cell technology. The approach is based on the analytical model that incorporates two PV metrics (V_{OC} and I_{SC}), along with three shape parameters (A , M and N). By developing explicit formulas for A and M in terms of PV metrics and using an iterative method to determine N , the module's behavior under controlled power rating tests across a range of irradiance values (100 to 1100 W/m²) and temperature values (15 to 75°C), as specified by the IEC 61853-1 standard, as well as under real-world environmental variations, is investigated.

2 METHODOLOGY

2.1 PV modeling

Miceli et al. [8] introduced an analytical model to characterize the behavior of thin-film PV modules:

$$I = I_{SC}\frac{1-\left(V/V_{OC}\right)^{M}}{1+A\left(V/V_{OC}\right)+\left(V/V_{OC}\right)^{N}} \qquad (1)$$

Where A , M and N are model parameters. To determine these parameters, we introduce novel formulas in terms of key PV metrics. The model is then applied to mimic the behavior of PERC module based on half-cut cell technology.

At Maximum Power Point (MPP) (V_{MPP}, I_{MPP}) , Eq. (1) becomes:

$$I_{MPP} = I_{SC}\frac{1-\left(V_{MPP}/V_{OC}\right)^{M}}{1+A\left(V_{MPP}/V_{OC}\right)+\left(V_{MPP}/V_{OC}\right)^{N}} \qquad (2)$$

The MPP condition is expressed as:

$$\frac{d}{dV}\left(V\frac{I_{SC}\left(1-\left(V/V_{OC}\right)^{M}\right)}{1+A\left(V/V_{OC}\right)+\left(V/V_{OC}\right)^{N}}\right)=0 \qquad (3)$$

At $V = V_{MPP}$, the condition for MPP is satisfied.

New formulas of A and M are derived by solving Eqs. (2) and (3):

$$A = -V_{OC}\frac{I_{MPP}\left(e^{\alpha N}\left(\beta+\alpha\left(1-N\right)\right)+\beta+\alpha\right)-I_{SC}\beta}{\beta I_{MPP}V_{MPP}} \qquad (4)$$

$$M = \frac{\beta}{\alpha} \qquad (5)$$

Where:

$$\alpha = \ln\left(\frac{V_{MPP}}{V_{OC}}\right) \qquad (6)$$

$$\beta = LambertW\left(-\frac{\alpha I_{MPP}}{I_{SC}}\left(e^{\alpha N}\left(N-1\right)-1\right)\right) \qquad (7)$$

To determine the parameter N , an iterative method is used, as illustrated in the flowchart below.

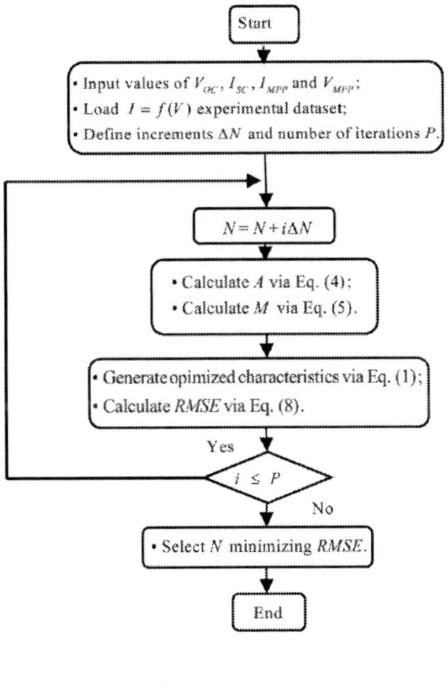

Fig. 1. Flowchart of the iterative method for determining the suitable value of parameter N .

2.2 Assessment of the method

The reliability of the proposed method, aiming to produce numerical values of PV metrics and analyze PV performance data, is evaluated using the RMSE and NRMSE statistical indicators [9]:

$$RMSE = \sqrt{\frac{1}{K}\sum_{i=1}^{K}\left(I_{Measured}^{i}-I_{Produced}^{i}\right)^{2}} \qquad (8)$$

$$NRMSE = \frac{\sqrt{\frac{1}{K}\sum_{i=1}^{K}\left(I_{Measured}^{i}-I_{Produced}^{i}\right)^{2}}}{\frac{1}{K}\sum_{i=1}^{K}I_{Measured}^{i}} \qquad (9)$$

3 RESULTS AND DISCUSSION

In order to validate the proposed method for analyzing the influence of temperature and irradiance on PV module performance, we selected a PERC module based on half-cut cell technology, recognized for its high efficiency and applicability across various PV systems. The module experienced a series of power rating tests designed to examine how solar irradiance and temperature affect its performance. Additionally, real weather testing was conducted to observe the module's behavior under natural environmental conditions.

3.1 Indoor testing

Indoor testing was conducted using an Eternal Sun pulse solar simulator, classified as class AAA and compliant with IEC 60904-9. Irradiance across the module plane was measured using a Fraunhofer WPVS-type reference cell and module temperature was monitored at six points using RTD sensors with measurements recorded across a temperature range from 15°C to 75°C. The irradiance levels were controlled to range between 200 and 1100 W/m², covering most of the required points specified by the IEC 61853-1 standard. However, the test at an irradiance level of 100 W/m² could not be performed due to equipment limitations.

Table 1. Test points for the performance matrix measurements required by IEC 61853-1.

Irradiance (W/m²)	**Solar spectrum**	**Temperature (°C)**			
		15	25	50	75
1100	AM1.5	⊠	1	2	3
1000	AM1.5	4	5	6	7
800	AM1.5	8	9	10	11
600	AM1.5	12	13	14	15
400	AM1.5	16	17	18	⊠
200	AM1.5	19	20	21	⊠
100	AM1.5	22	23	⊠	⊠

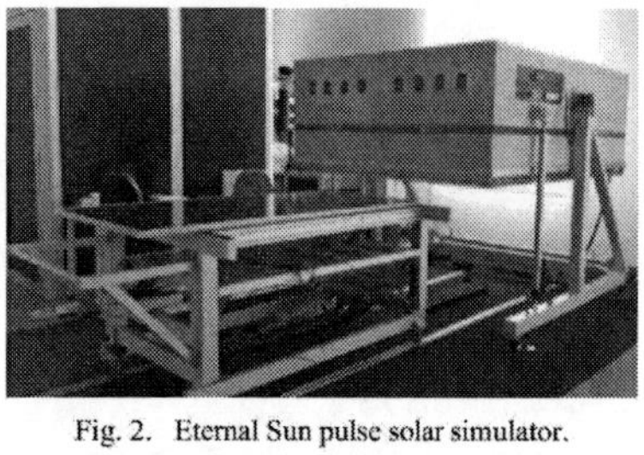

Fig. 2. Eternal Sun pulse solar simulator.

3.1.1 Irradiance effects

Table 2 summarizes the module's performance metrics across the irradiance range at a constant temperature of 25°C.

Table 2. Module performance across the irradiance range.

I_{POA} (W/m^2)	I_{SC} (A)	V_{OC} (V)	I_{MPP} (A)	V_{MPP} (V)	P_{MPP} (W)
1100	13,12	53,3	12,40	42,3	524,86
1000	11,70	53,0	11,06	42,6	471,45
800	9,57	53,2	9,10	43,8	398,72
600	7,38	52,0	7,06	43,3	305,69
400	4,96	51,6	4,76	43,7	208,13
200	2,51	50,1	2,35	43,1	101,31

As depicted in Figs. 3 and 4, I-V and P-V curves measured across the irradiance range from 200 to 1100 W/m² at a constant temperature of 25°C closely match those produced by the proposed method. The results reveal that as irradiance increases, the absorption of photons intensifies, leading to a higher generation rate of electron-hole pairs within the material. This causes a substantial rise in output current and power, while voltage remains relatively stable due to the logarithmic relationship between voltage and irradiance, as dictated by the PN junction characteristics. The upward shift in MPP with increased irradiance highlights its direct impact on carrier generation and collection efficiency. The effects of irradiance are enhanced in PERC cells by rear surface passivation and dielectric layer displacing rear metal reflector, which reduces electron-hole recombination, improves photon absorption and reduces heat absorption, further enhancing performance.

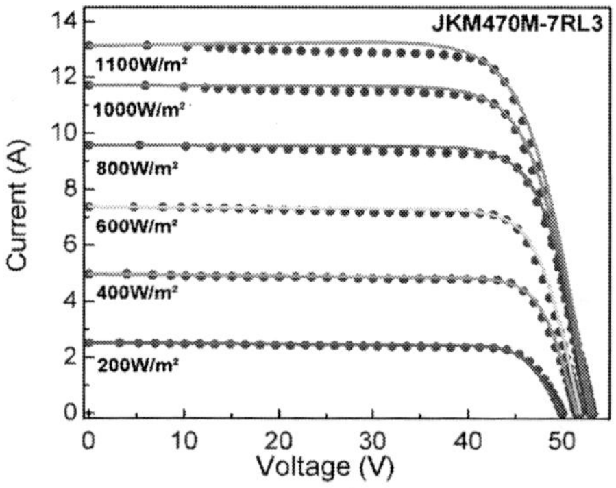

Fig. 3. Measured (garnet dots) and produced (colored lines) I-V curves at 25°C, for irradiance values ranging from 200 to 1100 W/m².

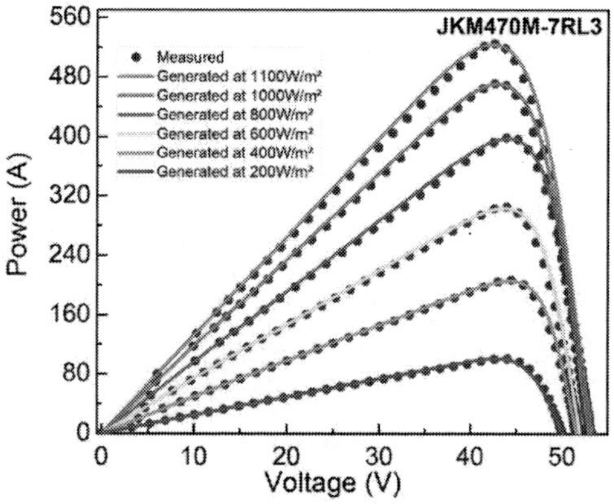

Fig. 4. Measured (garnet dots) and produced (colored lines) P-V curves at 25°C, for irradiance values ranging from 200 to 1100 W/m².

3.1.2 Temperature effects

Table 3 summarizes the module's performance metrics across the temperature range at a constant irradiance of 1000 W/m².

Table 3. Module performance across the temperature range.

T_{MBS} (°C)	I_{SC} (A)	V_{OC} (V)	I_{MPP} (A)	V_{MPP} (V)	P_{MPP} (W)
15	11,22	54,4	10,70	44,7	478,4
25	11,70	53,0	11,06	42,6	471,4
50	11,70	48,3	11,06	37,3	412,9
75	11,85	46,8	11,21	36,0	404,1

Figs. 5 and 6 present I-V and P-V curves measured over a temperature range from 15°C to 75°C, under a constant irradiance of 1000 W/m². The experimental results align closely with the produced ones. As temperature rises, significant changes occur in the module's performance. The increase in temperature reduces the bandgap energy of PERC cells, causing a notable drop in open-circuit voltage, which contributes to the decrease in overall output power. While the current slightly increases due to enhanced material conductivity and a broader absorption spectrum with higher temperatures, this gain is insufficient to offset the voltage-related losses, resulting in a net reduction in output power.

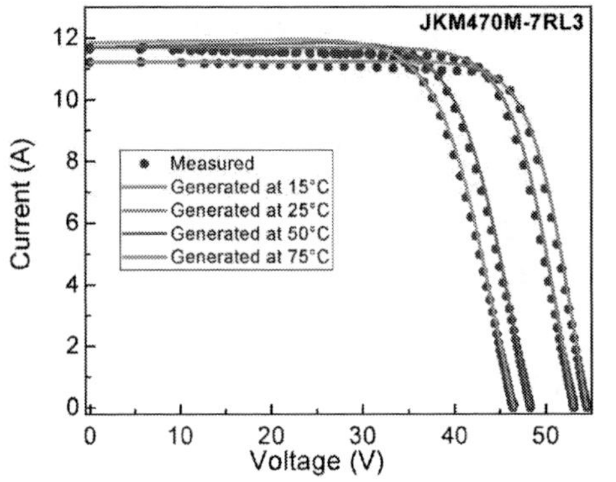

Fig. 5. Measured (garnet dots) and produced (colored lines) I-V curves at 1000 W/m², for temperature values ranging from 15 to 75 °C.

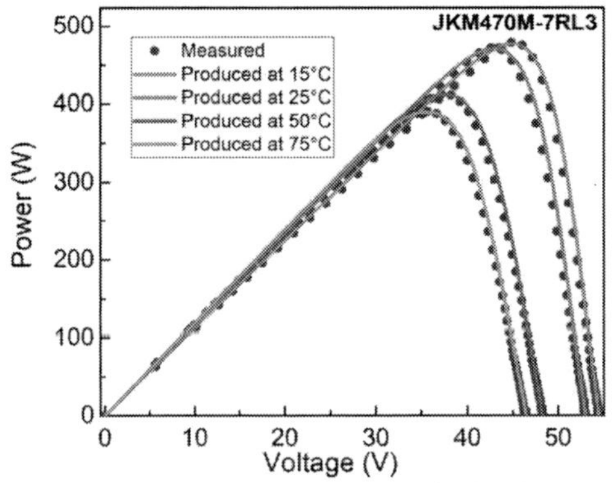

Fig. 6. Measured (garnet dots) and produced (colored lines) P-V curves at 1000 W/m², for temperature values ranging from 15 to 75 °C.

3.2 Outdoor testing

The module, initially subjected to performance matrix testing indoors, was then installed outdoors on a cloudy day to investigate the effects of real world irradiance and temperature. Data were collected using the PVPM1000X I-V curve tracer, along with its accessories: the PT1000 thermal sensor to monitor the module's back surface temperature and a reference cell to measure solar irradiance. Fig. 7 shows the PV module (a), reference cell (b), PT1000 sensor (c), and PVPM1000X I-V curve tracer (d).

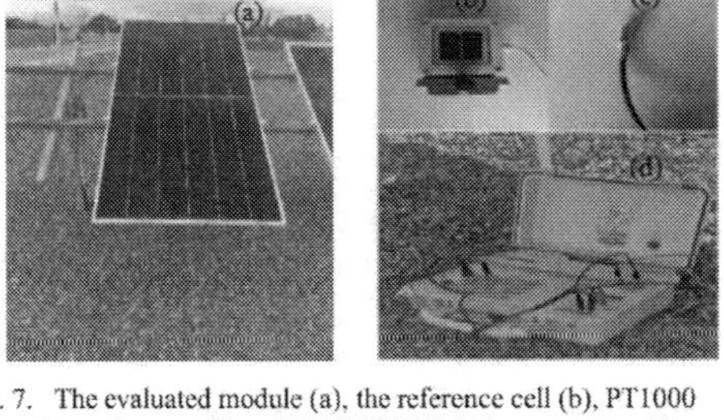

Fig. 7. The evaluated module (a), the reference cell (b), PT1000 thermal sensor (c) and PVPM1000X I-V curve tracer (d).

Figs. 8 to 10 show the measured and produced curves (I-V, P-V and peak power) for the evaluated module serving in Benguerir, Morocco, on May 8, 2024, under varying levels of temperature and irradiance. The produced curves, shown in colored lines show high agreement with the measured curves, represented by garnet dots, reflecting the precision of the method in generating performance data in real world conditions. The observed curves reveal how the combined effects of irradiance and temperature influence module performance. While increasing irradiance boosts current and power, higher temperatures lead to voltage reduction, which limits output power.

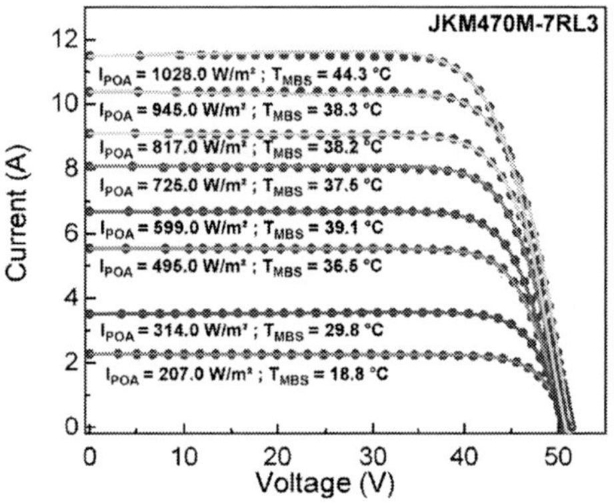

Fig. 8. Measured (garnet dots) and produced (colored lines) I-V curves under real weather conditions.

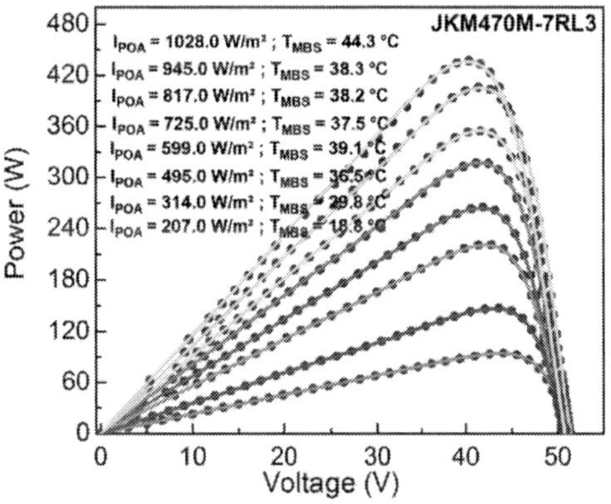

Fig. 9. Measured (garnet dots) and produced (colored lines) P-V curves under real weather conditions.

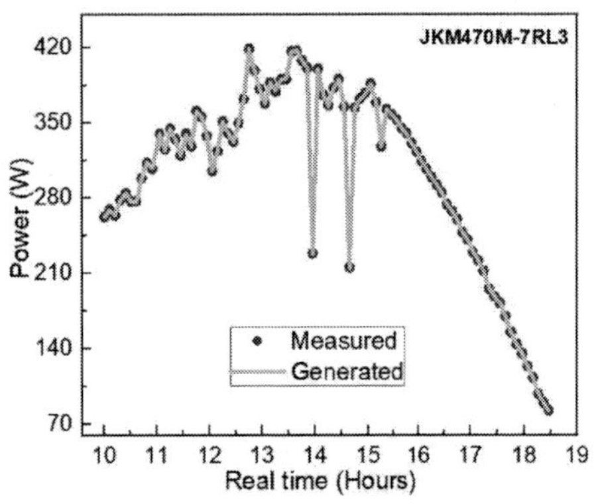

Fig. 10. Measured and produced peak power curves under real weather conditions.

The curves in Figs. 11 and 12 provide a clear visualization of the method's performance over time, as measured by RMSE and NRMSE. The RMSE curve (Fig. 11) exhibits fluctuations throughout the day due to varying conditions caused by cloud cover. However, the average RMSE remains low at 0.053 A.

Similarly, the NRMSE curve (Fig. 12) reflects these fluctuations, with the average normalized error remaining within 1.76 % over the entire observation period. This relatively low percentage of error compared to actual measurements underscores the method's accuracy and reliability, even under dynamically changing environmental conditions.

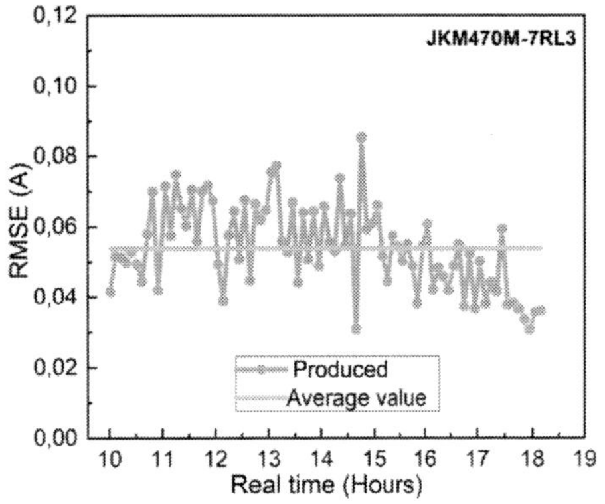

Fig. 11. RMSE for produced current corresponding to evaluated module operating under real weather conditions.

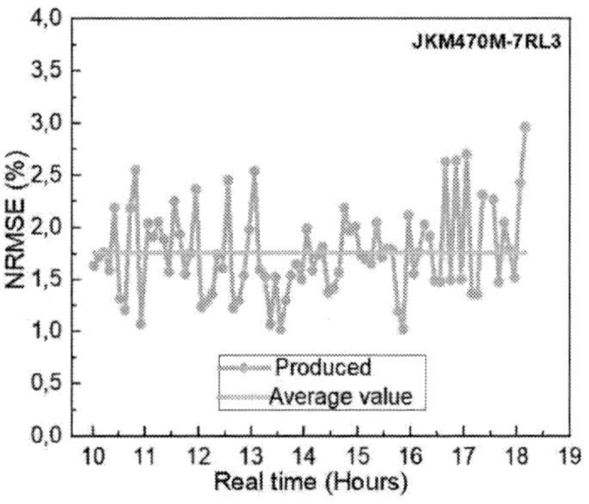

Fig. 12. NRMSE for produced current corresponding to evaluated module operating under real weather conditions.

4 Conclusion

This study highlights the significant effects of temperature and irradiance on the performance of PERC modules with half-cut cell technology. The results show that higher irradiance enhances the output power, while elevated temperatures lead to a reduction in voltage and power. The analytical model based method successfully captures these effects, providing an accurate representation of module performance under varying environmental conditions, with an average NRMSE of less than 1.76 %. This method offers a valuable tool for optimizing the design and power rating of PV systems, ensuring better performance forecasting and more reliable operation in diverse climatic settings.

Acknowledgment

The authors express their gratitude to Chouaib Doukkali University and Green Energy Park for their support.

References

[1] Fazal MA, Rubaiee S. Progress of PV cell technology: Feasibility of building materials, cost, performance, and stability. Solar Energy 2023;258:203–19. https://doi.org/10.1016/j.solener.2023.04.066.

[2] Green MA. The Passivated Emitter and Rear Cell (PERC): From conception to mass production. Solar Energy Materials and Solar Cells 2015;143:190–7. https://doi.org/10.1016/j.solmat.2015.06.055.

[3] Blakers AW, Wang A, Milne AM, Zhao J, Green MA. 22.8% efficient silicon solar cell. Applied Physics Letters 1989;55:1363–5. https://doi.org/10.1063/1.101596.

[4] Danelli A, Brivio E, Girardi P, Baggio N, Libal J. Environmental Life Cycle Assessment of Passivated Emitter and Rear Contact (PERC) Photovoltaic Module Technology 2024.

[5] Cabrera-Tobar A, Dolara A, Leva S, Mazzeo D, Ogliari E. Comparative analysis of half-cell and full-cell PV commercial modules for sustainable mobility applications: Outdoor performance evaluation under partial shading conditions. Sustainable Energy Technologies and Assessments 2024;71:103981. https://doi.org/10.1016/j.seta.2024.103981.

[6] Zaimi M, El Achouby H, Ibral A, Assaid EM. Determining combined effects of solar radiation and panel junction temperature on all model-parameters to forecast peak power and photovoltaic yield of solar panel under non-standard conditions. Solar Energy 2019;191:341–59. https://doi.org/10.1016/j.solener.2019.09.007.

[7] El Ainaoui K, Zaimi M, Flouchi I, Elhamaoui S, El mrabet Y, Ibaararen K, et al. Novel optimized models to enhance

performance forecasting of grid-connected PERC PV string operating under semi-arid climate conditions. Solar Energy 2024;282:112976. https://doi.org/10.1016/j.solener.2024.112976.
[8] Miceli R, Orioli A, Di Gangi A. A procedure to calculate the I – V characteristics of thin-film photovoltaic modules using an explicit rational form. Applied Energy 2015;155:613–28. https://doi.org/10.1016/j.apenergy.2015.06.037.
[9] El Ainaoui K, Zaimi M, Assaid EM. Innovative approaches to extract double-diode model physical parameters of a PV module serving outdoors under real-world conditions. Energy Conversion and Management 2023;292:117365. https://doi.org/10.1016/j.enconman.2023.117365.

Université Chouaïb Doukkali

جامعة شعيب الدكالي

EU PVSEC

A new method for comprehensive power-rating and performance analysis of PERC modules based on half-cut cell technology

K. El Ainaoui, M. Zaimi, I. Flouchi, S. Elhamaoui, Y. El mrabet, A. Ghennioui, E. M. Assaid

Laboratory of Instrumentation of Measure and Control, Chouaïb Doukkali University, El Jadida, Morocco

Electrical Systems and Photovoltaics Department, Green Energy Park, Benguerir, Morocco

green energy IRESEN UM6P University Mohammed VI Polytechnic

How do temperature and irradiance affect the performance of PERC modules with half-cut cells?

Key contributions

- Proposes a practical method to evaluate PERC module performance using key PV metrics;
- Performance assessed under controlled power rating tests conducted according to IEC 61853-1;
- Validated with real outdoor operational data, demonstrating accuracy and reliability;
- Quantifies and models the effects of irradiance and temperature on current, voltage, and power.

Methodology

Miceli et al. analytical model [1] :

$$I = I_{SC}\frac{1-\left(V/V_{OC}\right)^{M}}{1+A\left(V/V_{OC}\right)+\left(V/V_{OC}\right)^{N}} \quad (1)$$

At Maximum Power Point (MPP) :

$$I_{MPP} = I_{SC}\frac{1-\left(V_{MPP}/V_{OC}\right)^{M}}{1+A\left(V_{MPP}/V_{OC}\right)+\left(V_{MPP}/V_{OC}\right)^{N}} \quad (2)$$

$$\frac{d}{dV}\left(V\frac{I_{SC}\left(1-\left(V/V_{OC}\right)^{M}\right)}{1+A\left(V/V_{OC}\right)+\left(V/V_{OC}\right)^{N}}\right)=0 \quad (3)$$

New formulas of A and M are derived by solving Eqs. (2) and (3):

$$A = -V_{OC}\frac{I_{MPP}\left(e^{\alpha N}\left(\beta+\alpha\left(1-N\right)\right)+\beta+\alpha\right)-I_{SC}\beta}{\beta I_{MPP}V_{MPP}} \quad (4)$$

$$M = \frac{LambertW\left(-\alpha I_{MPP}/I_{SC}\left(e^{\alpha N}\left(N-1\right)-1\right)\right)}{\alpha = \ln\left(V_{MPP}/V_{OC}\right)} \quad (5)$$

Flowchart for Parameter N Determination :

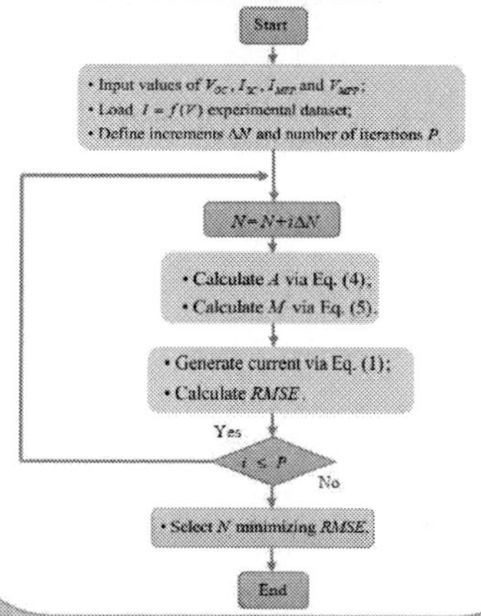

Results

Table 1: Test points for the performance matrix measurements required by IEC 61853-1 [2]

Irradiance (W/m²)	Solar spectrum	Temperature (°C)			
		15	25	50	75
1100	AM1.5	⊠	1	2	3
1000	AM1.5	4	5	6	7
800	AM1.5	8	9	10	11
600	AM1.5	12	13	14	15
400	AM1.5	16	17	18	⊠
200	AM1.5	19	20	21	⊠
100	AM1.5	22	23	⊠	⊠

Table 2: Module performance across the irradiance range

I_{POA} (W/m²)	I_{SC} [A]	V_{OC} [V]	I_{MPP} [A]	V_{MPP} [V]	P_{MPP} [W]
1100	13,12	53,3	12,40	42,3	524,86
1000	11,70	53.0	11,06	42,6	471,45
800	9,57	53,2	9,10	43,8	398,72
600	7,38	52,0	7,06	43,3	305,69
400	4,96	51,6	4,76	43,7	208,13
200	2,51	50,1	2,35	43,1	101,31

Table 3: Module performance across the temperature range

T_{MBS} (°C)	I_{SC} [A]	V_{OC} [V]	I_{MPP} [A]	V_{MPP} [V]	P_{MPP} [W]
15	11,22	54,4	10,70	44,7	478,4
25	11,70	53,0	11,06	42,6	471,4
50	11,70	48,3	11,06	37,3	412,9
75	11,85	46,8	11,21	36,0	404,1

Fig. 1: Measured (garnet dots) and produced (colored lines) I-V curves at 25° C, for irradiance values ranging from 200 to 1100 W/m²

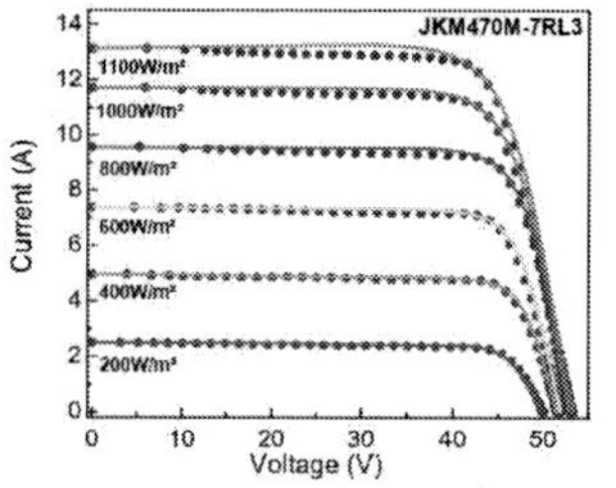

Fig. 2: Measured (garnet dots) and produced (colored lines) P-V curves at 25° C, for irradiance values ranging from 200 to 1100 W/m²

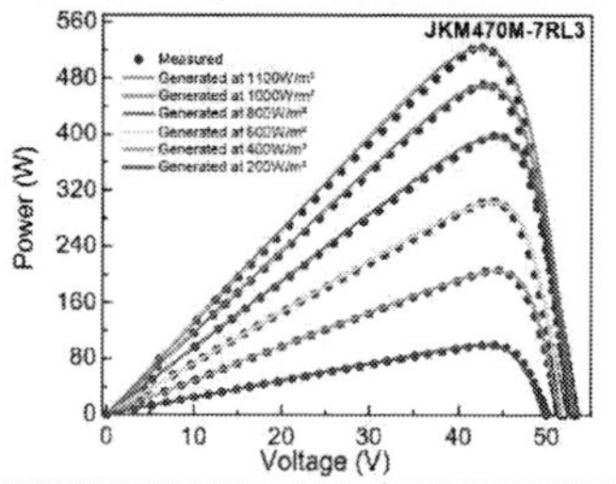

Fig. 3: Measured (garnet dots) and produced (colored lines) I-V curves at 1000 W/m², for temperature values ranging from 15 to 75 ° C

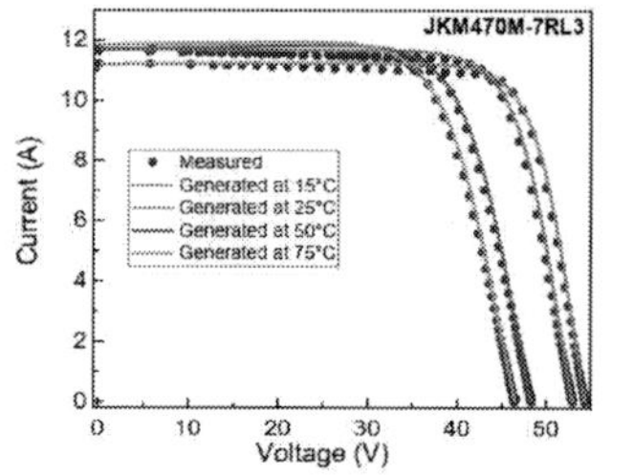

Fig. 4: Measured (garnet dots) and produced (colored lines) P-V curves at 1000 W/m², for temperature values ranging from 15 to 75 ° C

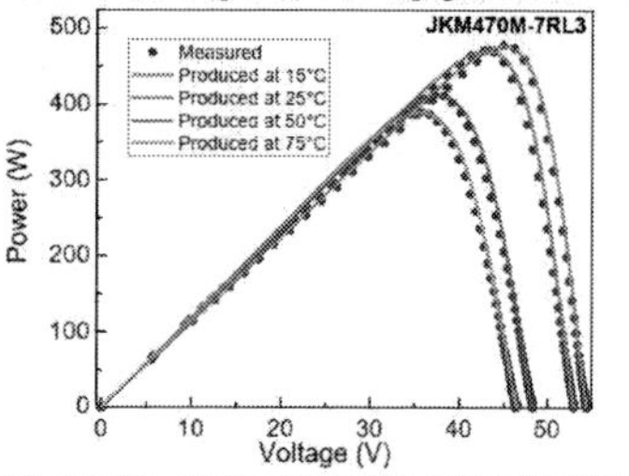

Fig. 5: Measured (garnet dots) and produced (colored lines) I-V curves (a), P-V curves (b) and peak power curve (c) under real weather conditions

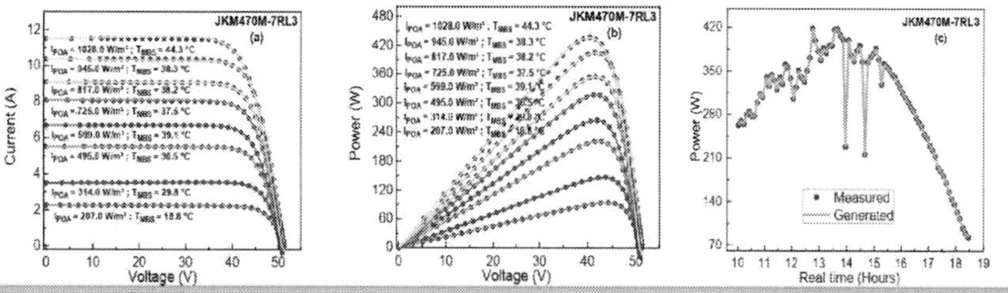

JKM470M-7RL3 PERC module

Green Energy Park, Benguerir (Morocco)

Fig. 6: RMSE for produced current corresponding to evaluated module operating under real weather conditions

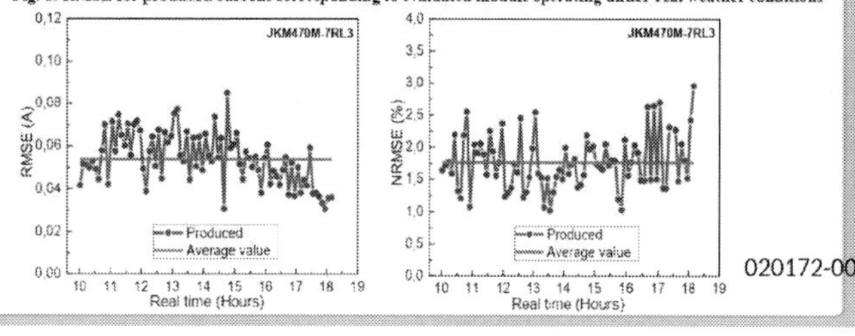

Conclusions

- The method accurately describes PERC module behavior under controlled power rating tests and real outdoor conditions;
- Irradiance strongly impacts performance: higher irradiance increases electron-hole pair generation, boosting current and output power;
- Temperature mainly reduces V_{OC}, decreasing output power, while I_{SC} slightly increases with temperature;
- The approach demonstrates high accuracy and reliability: RMSE < **0.053 A**, NRMSE < **1.76 %**.

References

[1] Miceli R, Orioli A, Di Gangi A. A procedure to calculate the I – V characteristics of thin-film photovoltaic modules using an explicit rational form. Applied Energy 2015;155:613–28. https://doi.org/10.1016/j.apenergy.2015.06.037

[2] Photovoltaic (PV) module performance testing and energy rating - Part 1: Irradiance and temperature performance measurements and power rating https://webstore.iec.ch/en/publication/6035

ENERGY RATING ANALYSIS OF HETEROJUNCTION PV MODULES

Teodora S. Lyubenova, Ewan D. Dunlop
European Commission, Joint Research Centre (JRC), Ispra (VA), Italy
e-mail: Teodora.LYUBENOVA@ec.europa.eu

ABSTRACT: This work analyses the Climate Specific Energy Rating (CSER) of three heterojunction (HJT) PV devices from the same production batch, following the methodology outlined in IEC 61853-1 [1]. The objective is to assess the reliability and repeatability of the performance analysis and to determine if testing three modules is necessary, or whether fewer tests could provide equally reliable results, thus reducing measurement time and costs. This study is focused on HJT technology as one of the solar PV that has gained huge industrial popularity over the last decade. However, it presents challenges during characterization due to capacitive effects and temporal metastability, known as "dark ageing". Such effects require the use of non-routine instrumentation like steady-state solar simulators and complex measurement protocols. This study also investigates the influence of irradiance and temperature on module performance, as well as the electrical response of modules under different climatic profiles (IEC 61853-4 [2]), with a particular focus on CSER and annual energy yield.
Keywords: Energy rating; IEC 61853 standard; heterojunction PV modules

1 INTRODUCTION

Silicon heterojunction technology (HJT) has been gaining popularity over the last decade due to its rapid technological developments and cost-effectiveness. It is currently the solar industry's most effective process for increasing efficiency (>20%) and power output (720W) [3]. In terms of market outlook, the global HJT solar cell market is expected to reach $4.6 billion by 2031, rising at a market growth of 17.3% during the forecast period 2024-2031 [4]. The advanced manufacturing processes, premium raw materials, and specific cell design of these PV modules make them highly appealing to consumers, commercials and academic field, establishing HJT devices as a compelling option in the industry. However, this technology presents challenges for accurate characterization. The HJT cell architectures, made by passivating a-Si layers, exhibit high open circuit voltages (Voc) that requires longer sweeps (>250ms) for accurate I-V measurements to avoid under or overestimated power output (P_{max}). Depending on the sweep time and sweep direction, the P_{max} could be inaccurately measured by over 20% [5] [6]. This technical requirement of sweep duration puts severe constraints for the flash simulators commonly used in industry to test PV devices. For these purposes, continuous or long-pulse solar simulators are recommended. However, these simulators are not universally adopted, nor routinely used by manufacturers or testing labs. Their temperature control can be problematic, although temperature correction can be applied with good results in terms of accuracy.

Additionally, the HJT devices suffer from "dark ageing" i.e. degradation during extended storage in low light or dark conditions and pre-conditioning treatments are needed to ensure that the performance measurements are representative of those in normal operation [5].

While a single I-V measurement at STC can be a challenging task for the HJT modules, energy rating analysis according to standard series IEC 61853 [1], [7], [8], [2] adds an extra layer of complexity, requiring multiple testing under specific conditions and algorithms that are time-consuming to implement. The IEC 61853-1 (point 3) outline, as a sampling requirement, the testing of three modules from a production batch. The goal of this investigation is to assess the reliability and repeatability of performance analysis and to determine whether testing three modules is strictly necessary or if the number of tests can be reduced to simplify the procedure. The study investigates the impact of irradiance (G) and temperature (T) on module performance parameters, including open-circuit voltage (V_{oc}), short-circuit current (I_{sc}) and power output (P_{max}). Furthermore, we analyze the behavior of the devices under test (DUTs) for each climate profile, discussing the influence of ambient (T_{amb}), module temperature (T_{mod}) and irradiance (G) on maximum power (P_{max}), CSER and yearly energy yield (EY).

The present work is of relevance to the PV community and to manufacturers that may be required to estimate and provide the CSER values in their information sheets due the future Ecodesign [9] and Energy label [10] legislation. In addition, the PV experts involved in the revision of IEC 61853 standard series can be assisted of the results from this work as well.

2 RESUTLS AND DISCUSSION

The devices under test (DUTs) were pre-conditioned (light soaked) and characterized using a pulsed solar simulator with a multiflash approach (~300 ms). Extended power matrices with 28 operating points (irradiance: 100–1100 W/m^2; module temperature: 15–75°C) were experimentally determined. The results show linear dependence of P_{max} and I_{sc} with irradiance (G) and temperature (T) and logarithmic growth of V_{oc}. All tested modules exhibit highly consistent electrical behavior, as expected from devices originated from the same production batch and class.

CSER values were calculated using an in-house developed algorithm in accordance with the requirements of IEC 61853. The behavior of the DUTs was analyzed under different standard climatic profiles, focusing on the effects of ambient temperature (T_{amb}), module temperature (T_{mod}), and irradiance (G) on P_{max}, CSER, and annual energy yield (EY). Notable differences were observed across climatic zones, particularly due to temperature and irradiance variations in the reference datasets. Consequently, the annual energy yield shows significant variation between climates.

These results highlight the added value of CSER

analysis, which provides more realistic performance predictions for specific climatic zones compared to the conventional power rating at Standard Test Conditions.

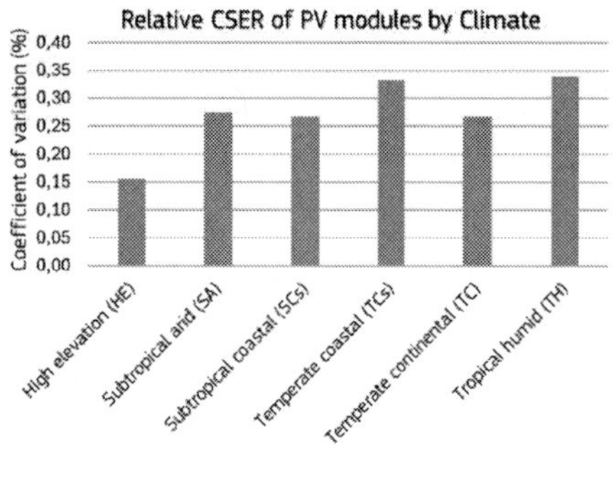

Figure.1: Coefficient of variation of for all modules and climates (CSER spread in % relative to the mean value).

The CSER values of the modules were close, though not identical. The coefficient of variation (CV) in Fig.1, defined as the ratio of standard deviation to the mean vales, ranged from ~0.15% (High elevation) to ~0.34% (Tropical humid). The values fall within the estimated measurement uncertainty of 2–4% and are therefore statistically insignificant. This indicates highly consistent PV behavior.

The findings suggest that fewer test samples may be sufficient for reliable CSER determination, and that reducing the number of devices tested would not compromise accuracy.

3 CONCLUSIONS

The analysis shows that CSER values of the three HJT devices are highly consistent across all climatic profiles, with coefficients of variation below 0.4%, well within measurement uncertainty. Repeating tests on three modules provides only marginal additional insight and could be reduced without significantly affecting reliability. Furthermore, the study confirms the effectiveness of CSER analysis in providing more accurate estimates of PV module energy yield in specific climates, revealing significant regional differences due to environmental conditions.

4 REFERENCES

[1] IEC61853-1: PV module performance testing and energy rating - Part 1: Irradiance and temperature performance measurements and power rating, 2011.

[2] IEC61853-4: PV module performance testing and energy rating - Part 4: Standard reference climatic profiles, 2018.

[3] T. S. M. TaiylanNews, "www.taiyangnews.info." TaiylanNews, January 2025. [Online]. Available: https://taiyangnews.info/topmodules. [Accessed 28/01/2025 January 2025].

[4] K. Research, "Heterojunction (HJT) Solar Cell Market," KBV Research, KBV-23512, 2024.

[5] N.Taylor, "Guidelines for PV Power Measurment in Idustry," Luxemburg, 2010.

[6] Mauro Pravettoni, Daren Poh, Jai Prakash Singh, Jian Wei Ho and Kenta Nakayashiki, "The effect of capacitance on high-efficiency photovoltaic modules: a review of testing methods and related uncertainties," Journal of Physics D: Applied Physics , vol. 54, p. 193001, 2021.

[7] IEC61853-2: PV module performance testing and energy rating - Part 2: Spectral responsivity, incidence angle and module operating temperature measurements, 2016.

[8] IEC61853-3: PV module performance testing and energy rating - Part 3: Energy rating of PV modules, 2018.

[9] "Directive 2009/125/EC of the European Parliament and of the Council establishing a framework for the setting of ecodesign requirements for energy-related products, OJ L285, 31.10.2009, p.10-35," 2009.

[10] "Regulation (EU)2017/1369 of the European Parliament and of the Council of 4 July 2017 setting a framework for energy labelling and repealing Directive 2010/30/EU, OJ L198, 28.7.2017, p.1–23," 2017.

Topic 3
3AV.3.2

42nd European Photovoltaic Solar Energy Conference and Exhibition

European Commission

EU PVSEC 2025

ENERGY RATING ANALYSIS OF HETEROJUNCTION PV MODULES

Teodora S. Lyubenova, Ewan D. Dunlop
European Commission, Joint Research Centre, Ispra, Italy

This study evaluates the Climate Specific Energy Rating (CSER) of silicon heterojunction (HJT) photovoltaic modules, focusing on whether the IEC 61853-1 requirement of testing three devices is essential or if fewer measurements can ensure reliable results. The analysis examines the influence of irradiance and temperature on P_{max}, I_{sc}, and V_{oc}, and assesses device performance under IEC 61853-4 climatic profiles. The findings provide guidance for PV manufacturers in CSER reporting and for testing laboratories seeking to improve measurement protocols.

Climatic Specific Energy Rating (CSER)

Tool for accurate comparison of PV module performance under real operating conditions worldwide (IEC 61853 series)

$$CSER = \frac{E_{year}/P_{STC}}{G_{year}/1000}$$

Irradiance-Temperature (G-T) power matrix (IEC 61853-1)

Angular response, NMOT, Spectral responsivity (IEC 61853-2)

Climatic Specific Energy Rating (CSER) (IEC 61853-3)

Standard reference climatic profiles (IEC 61853-4)

HJT annual energy yield

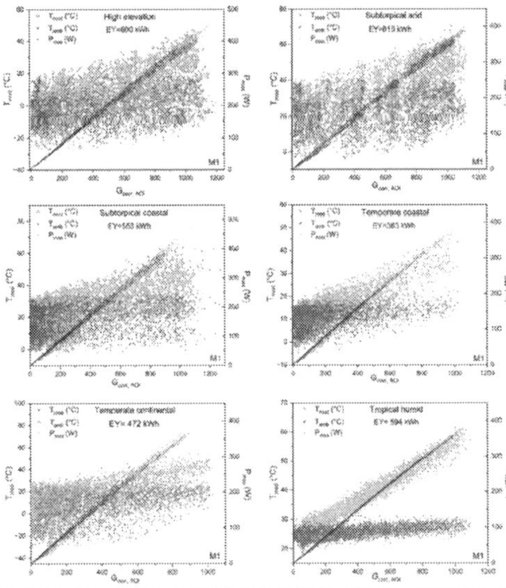

Scatter plots display an ambient (T_{amb}), module temperature (T_{mod}) and P_{max} dependence of the angle of incidence (AOI) corrected irradiance for each reference climatic profile. Inset, the estimated annual energy yield (EY, kWh) is shown. Difference PV module behavior is expected, driven by variations in irradiance and temperature profiles within the representative environmental dataset.

HJT module characterization

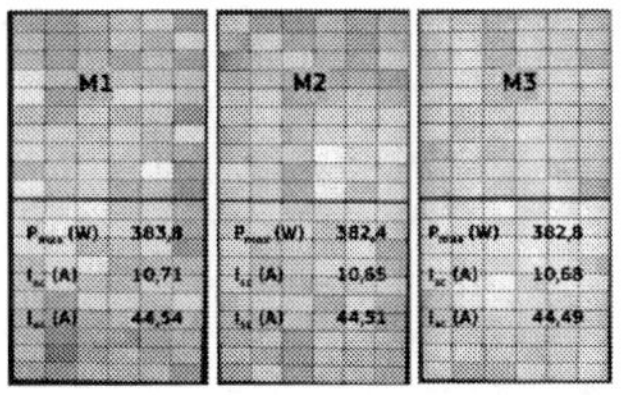

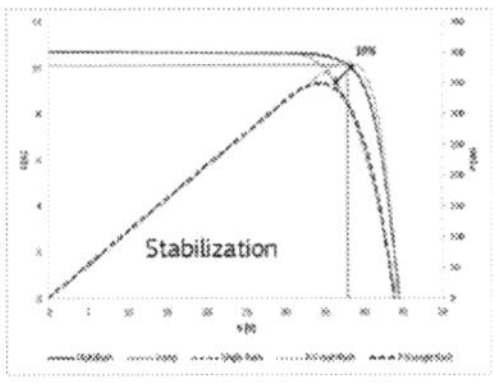

HJT electrical performance

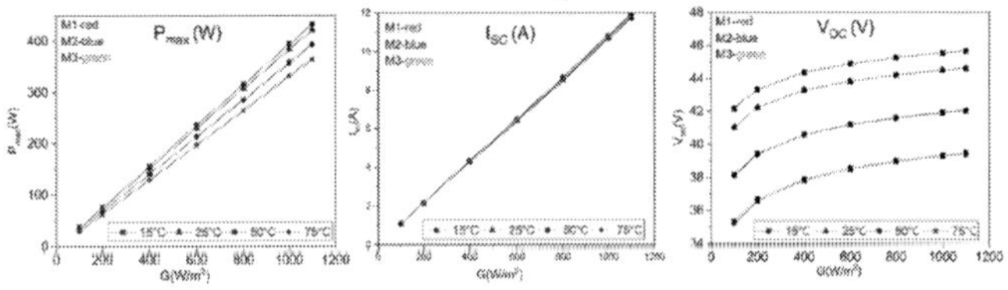

Extended power matrices with 28 data points were experimentally determined indoors. The results illustrate that P_{max} and I_{sc} exhibit linear dependence, with both irradiance (G) and temperature (T), while V_{oc} increases logarithmically. All tested modules are from the same production batch, which is reflected in their highly consistent electrical behavior.

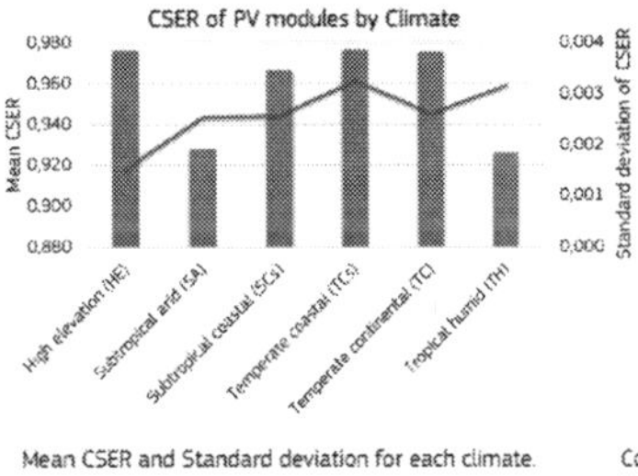

Mean CSER and Standard deviation for each climate.

- The lowest STD variation is in High elevation (HE).
- The highest SDV is in Temperate coastal (TCs) and Tropical humid (TH).

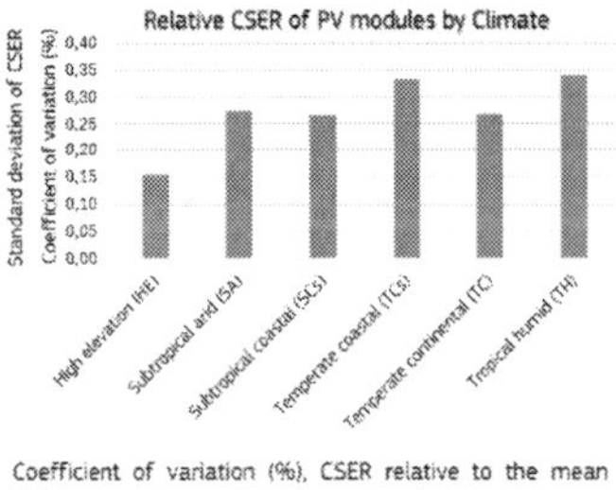

Coefficient of variation (%), CSER relative to the mean value.

- The lowest variation is in High elevation (HE) (~0.15%).
- The highest variation is in Tropical humid (TH) (~0.34%).

CSER values across the modules are close, but not identical. The lower standard deviation and coefficient variation values reveal consistent PV behaviour. The results suggest that fewer tests might be enough for reliable CSER determination. The results highlight the value of Climatic Specific Energy Rating analysis (CSER), as it enables realistic real-world performance energy generation prediction.

Climate		High elevation (HE)	Subtropical arid (SA)	Subtropical coastal (SCs)	Temperate coastal (TCs)	Temperate continental (TC)	Tropical humid (TH)
	M1	799,8	815,3	553,5	363,2	472,4	594,3
EY (kWh)	M2	798,6	812,9	552,6	363,4	472,1	593,2
	M3	800,1	817,4	555	364,7	473,7	596,7
Mean_EY		799,5	815,2	553,7	363,8	472,7	594,7
STD_EY		0,79	2,25	1,21	0,81	0,85	1,79
CV_EY (%)*		0,10	0,28	0,22	0,22	0,18	0,30

* coefficient of variation CV = SD/mean x 100%

Climate	High elevation (HE)	Subtropical arid (SA)	Subtropical coastal (SCs)	Temperate coastal (TCs)	Temperate continental (TC)	Tropical humid (TH)
M1_CSER	0,974	0,926	0,964	0,973	0,972	0,923
M2_CSER	0,976	0,926	0,966	0,977	0,975	0,925
M3_CSER	0,977	0,930	0,969	0,979	0,978	0,929
Mean_CSER	0,9759	0,9273	0,9660	0,9763	0,9750	0,9256
STD_CSER	0,00151	0,00254	0,00257	0,00324	0,00261	0,00315
CV_CSER (%)*	0,1551	0,2735	0,2660	0,3321	0,2673	0,3401

CONCLUSIONS

The analysis shows that the CSER values of the three HJT devices are highly consistent between climates, with coefficients of variation below 0.4% in all cases. The lowest variation occurs in High elevation (HE) (~0.15%), while the highest is observed in Tropical humid (TH) (~0.34%). These results, together with the highly consistent electrical behavior of the devices suggest that repeating tests on three modules may give only marginal additional insight. Moreover, the uncertainty estimation (UC) of the energy yield and CSER are in the order of 2 to 4% so such module to module variation is statistically insignificant. The study suggest that testing laboratories could potentially optimize their measurement protocols by reducing the number of devices tested without significantly affecting reliability. The CSER give a more consistent estimate of the energy yield of a PV module installed in a specific climatic region.

Joint Research Centre
020174-001

Teodora Stoyanova Lyubenova
Email: Teodora.LYUBENOVA@ec.europa.eu

ESTI

Trend of temperature coefficients of c-Si Module technologies from the past 15 years

Bengt Jaeckel, Matthias Pander

Fraunhofer Center for Silicon Photovoltaics CSP, Otto-Eißfeldt-Str. 12, 06120 Halle (Saale), Germany
*Corresponding author: bengt.jaeckel@csp.fraunhofer.de

ABSTRACT: The temperature dependence of PV module power is a key parameter for energy yield calculations, especially for hot climates. Project yield assessments typically rely on datasheet values where temperature coefficients (TCs) are often reported optimistically and seldom verified. A representative selection of crystalline silicon (c-Si) modules with various cell technologies produced over the past 15 years was screened. The dataset covers Al-BSF, PERC, TOPCon, HJT and back contact (BC) designs with varying cell sizes (5", M0, M3, M6, M10), module circuitries (60 cells in series, 144 cells with 2x72cells as series-parallel interconnection) and module sizes (168x97cm² vs 228x114cm²).

A long-pulse flash method to determine TCs consistently across three irradiance levels was applied. A clear trend towards lower TCs for maximum power γ with newer cell technologies was observed. Additionally, module design and cell cutting quality can impact absolute values. The TC irradiance dependence for Isc α, Voc β and Pmpp γ showed similar patterns across all technologies. The presented data support industry trends and helps to further improve energy rating according to IEC 61853-series. The presented results can also serve as base for benchmarks where new concepts are checked versus older modules where long term field experience exists.

Keywords: temperature coefficient, PV module, crystalline silicon, irradiance dependence, energy yield

1 INTRODUCTION

Accurate temperature coefficients (TCs) for Isc α, Voc β and Pmpp γ are essential inputs for energy yield prediction and bankability for a PV project. While STC power is routinely verified, low-light behavior and temperature dependence are typically taken from manufacturer datasheets and not systematically checked. Recent datasheet trends suggest improving (less negative) TCs for Pmpp γ and Voc β Resulting in higher yields especially in hot climates. This work evaluates whether such improvements are observed in practice across c-Si module generations and architectures, and quantifies the influence of irradiance, cell cutting and module circuitry. The data collection presented is essentially reproducing the module temperatures and irradiance matrix (*G–T* matrix) which is the major contribution to the yield prediction.
The results can be integrated in energy yield calculations and energy rating per IEC 61853 and can support to overall improve climate-specific energy yield modelling [1–4].

2 EXPERIMENTAL

2.1 Test setup and procedure

Modules were characterized using a long-pulse A+A+A+ xenon flash tester (halm electronics cetis PV-Moduletest 4) with an extended pulse to mitigate capacitive effects, particularly for HJT and TOPCon cell technologies. The flash was set to three irradiance levels, namely 1000, 500, and 200 W/m² in a single very long flash. This approach was taken to measure all three intensities at exact the same PV module temperature during the cooling phase. The temperature range covered measurements from 30 to 75°C. Each individual measurement took approximately two hours and is in line with IEC 61215 best practice for 1000 W/m² TC measurements [1–4].

Pre- and post-tests with electroluminescence (EL) were performed to exclude any cell damage during heating and cooling of the PV module while determining the TCs. For HJT, TOPCon and BC a hysteresis check was conducted to qualify the extent of hysteresis and its temperature dependence. Based on test runs with a long pulse, approx. 140ms, 1000 W/m² with hysteresis measurement (Isc → Voc, Voc → Isc) it was determined that the impact on TC is negligible. Therefore, the measurements for such technologies were performed only in Isc → Voc direction, accepting a lower FF/Pmpp compared to hysteresis corrected values.
Temperature coefficients for Isc, Voc, and Pmpp were extracted by linear regression of each parameter versus temperature at each irradiance level.

2.2 Samples

We measured commercially produced modules and laboratory demonstrator's representative of the last 15 years, focusing on c-Si. The modules included:

- Aluminum back surface field (Al-BSF), Passivated Emitter and Rear Cell (PERC), Tunnel Oxide Passivated Contact (TOPCon), Heterojunction (HJT) and (interdigitated) Back contact ((I)BC)
- Cell formats: 5″, 6″ full cells and various half-cut generations (e.g., M3, M6, M10)
- Module circuitries: from smaller early-generation designs with 60 full cells in series to utility modules with 144 half-cut cells
- Module formats: from 168x97cm² (60 cell Al-BSF) to 228x114cm² PERC/TOPCon.
- (~2.28 × 1.14 m²).

This diversity enables technology- and design-dependent TC comparisons while maintaining a uniform measurement methodology.

The analysis focused on technology- and design-related trends using a single, repeatable indoor setup; developing detailed uncertainty budgets (e.g., per [12]) was not a primary objective. While indoor flash testing offers high repeatability, complementary outdoor validation remains valuable for capturing site-specific effects. This cross-validation between indoor and outdoor data enables further improvements.

3 EXPERIMENTAL RESULTS

All modules were measured with the procedure described in section 2. Exemplarily a suite of IV-curves is given in Figure 1.
From such curves the temperature coefficients for Isc α, Uoc β and Pmpp γ were determined. Exemplarily the three intensities (1000, 500, and 200 W/m²) for Pmpp are given in Figure 2. A linear regression was applied to determine the slope for each suite of measurements.

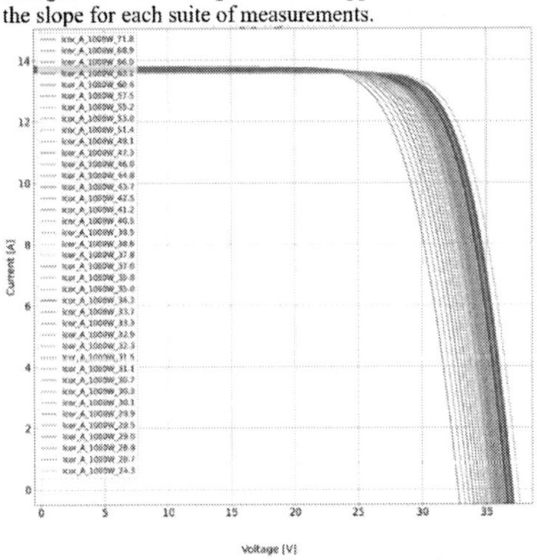

Figure 1: Selected set of IV-curves from a PERC PV module measured at 1000W/m² in the temperature range of ~25°C to 71°C.

The results from all measurements with respect to irradiance and sorted by cell type and number of cells is shown in Figure 3.

4 DISCUSSION

4.1 Overall trends

A trend towards lower absolute values of temperature coefficients for Pmpp is observed from Al-BSF, PERC to TOPCon, HJT and (I)BC cell types, meaning the cells are less temperature sensitive. This is consistent with manufacturers' more favorable TC claims and attributable to improvements in device physics and reduced series resistance.
Module level implementation is, however, critical. Cell cutting quality, interconnection layout, and number of cells influence TC. This is highlighted with the circle in Figure 3 for a 108-half cell (HZ) module. Here the same cells were used as for the 54-full cell (VZ) module showing clear impact on the cutting process.

4.2 Irradiance dependence

Across cell technologies, TC β (Voc) and TC γ (Pmpp) become less negative as irradiance decreases, while TC α (Isc) shows a slight reduction in magnitude. These shifts are consistent with the differing irradiance sensitivities of recombination and resistive losses reported in indoor and outdoor studies [5–11]. The persistence of these trends across multiple module generations and the relatively small magnitude supports the use of simplified irradiance-dependent matrices within IEC 61853-1 energy rating workflows [3] CSER assessments, and supports tool enhancements (e.g., SmartCalc) within the GSM project.

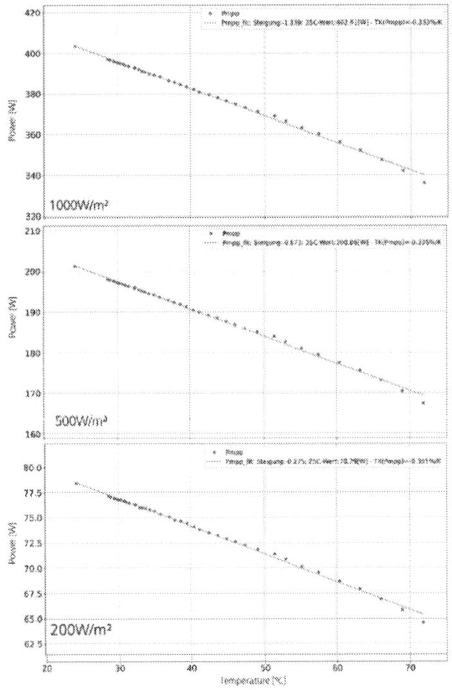

Figure 2: Pmpp results from a PERC module, measured at 1000, 500, and 200 W/m².

4.3 Implications for energy yield and rating

Using (too) optimistic datasheet temperature coefficients (TCs) can significantly bias energy-yield predictions, particularly in hot climates [4]. The measured and presented technology- and design-specific TC distributions enable more realistic project modeling and de-risk key assumptions.

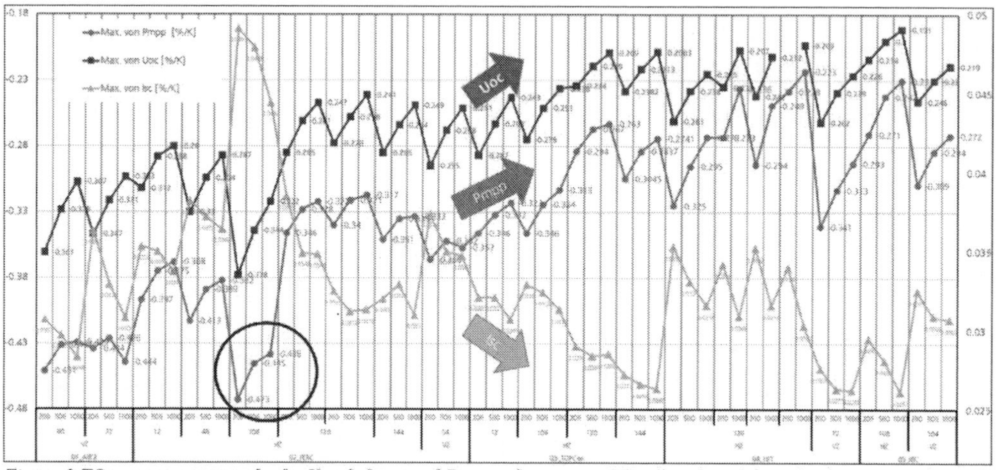

Figure 3 TC measurement results for Voc β, Isc α and Pmpp γ for various PV cell and module technologies, sorted by cell architecture and number of cells for intensities of 1000, 500, 200W/m². Each triple of numbers shows basically same trend to either higher (Uoc, Pmpp) or lower (Isc) TCs as a function of intensity. The PERC with 108 cells had bad cell cutting process impacting the TC negatively.

5 CONCLUSIONS AND OUTLOOK

We measured temperature coefficients for a broad set of c-Si modules spanning over the past 15 years. Multiple cell architectures under three irradiance levels using a long-pulse flash method were studied.

A pronounced improvement (reduction of temperature impact /lower number) in TC γ (Pmpp) with newer technologies was observed, while module design and cell cutting quality can offset intrinsic gains. Irradiance dependence shows consistent patterns across technologies, supporting standardized energy rating praxis.

Future work will include results from accelerated-aged and field-aged modules to quantify TC shifts over lifetime and their impact on climate-specific energy yield.

6 ACKNOWLEDGMENT

This publication was funded by the Federal Ministry for Economic Affairs and Climate Action in the project GreenSolarModules (GSM) under grant number 03EE1161A. The findings herein are solely the responsibility of the authors.

7 REFERENCES

[1] IEC 61215 series: Design qualification and type approval.

[2] IEC 61730 series: Photovoltaic (PV) module safety qualification.

[3] IEC 61853-1: Photovoltaic (PV) module performance testing and energy rating – Part 1: Irradiance and temperature performance measurements and power rating.

[4] W. Herrmann, "Uncertainty of Climate Specific Energy Rating (CSER) of PV Modules in Accordance With IEC 61853", Progress in Photovoltaics: Research and Applications (2025): 1–15, https://doi.org/10.1002/pip.70007

[5] D. Philipp, "Nominal Module Power vs. Measured Power," PV Symposium, Bad Staffelstein, 2024.

[6] K. Emery, "Temperature dependence of photovoltaic cells, modules and systems," Proc. 25th IEEE PVSC, 1996. https://doi.org/10.1109/PVSC.1996.564365

[7] D. L. King, "Temperature Coefficients for PV Modules and Arrays: Measurement Methods, Difficulties, and Results," 26th IEEE PVSC, 1997. [7] A. Virtuani, "Overview of Temperature Coefficients of Different Thin Film Photovoltaic Technologies," 25th EU PVSEC/5th WCPEC, 2010. [8] R. Dubey, "Measurement of Temperature Coefficient of Photovoltaic Modules in Field and Comparison with Laboratory Measurements," 41st IEEE PVSC, 2015. https://doi.org/10.1109/PVSC.2015.7355852

[8] H. Ibrahim, "Variations of PV module parameters with irradiance and temperature," Energy Procedia 134, 276–285, 2017. https://doi.org/10.1016/j.egypro.2017.09.617

[9] M. Piliougine, "Temperature coefficients of degraded crystalline silicon photovoltaic modules at outdoor conditions," Prog. Photovolt: Res. Appl. 25(5), 556–570, 2020. https://doi.org/10.1002/pip.3396

[10] B. R. Paudyal, "Investigation of temperature coefficients of PV modules through field measured data," Solar Energy 224, 425–439, 2021. https://doi.org/10.1016/j.solener.2021.06.013

[11] P. Kamkird, "Investigation on Temperature Coefficients of Three Types Photovoltaic Module Technologies under Thailand Operating Condition," Procedia Engineering 32, 376–383, 2012. https://doi.org/10.1016/j.proeng.2012.01.1282

[12] B. Mihaylov, "Uncertainty Estimation of Temperature Coefficient Measurements of PV Modules," 43rd IEEE PVSC, 2016.

42nd European Photovoltaic Solar Energy Conference and Exhibition

Trend of Temperature Coefficients of c-Si Module Technologies from the past 15 Years

Fraunhofer CSP

Fraunhofer Center for Silicon Photovoltaics CSP

Bengt Jaeckel, Matthias Pander

3AV.3.3

Motivation

- Longevity and predictability are key parameters for the operation of PV assets. All projects start with a financial forecast.
- Energy production calculations typically are based on datasheet values and fixed numbers, assuming the given linear degradation rate
- Only maximum power and e.g. gel content are evaluated in quality assessment campaigns – temperature coefficients are taken for granted
- Irradiance dependence is normally not given
- Some older studies presented some irradiance dependence [1-6]
- PV module power increased in recent years while temperature coefficients decrease to enable higher energy yields – at least in the calculations
- Aim of the study: validate this trend and to check for outliers.
- Check for influence of cell cutting, solar cell dimensions and PV module circuitry and number of cells

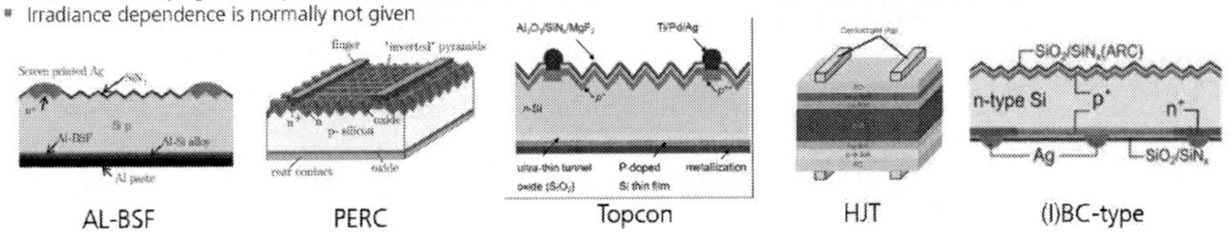

Figure 1: typical c-Si cell structures from the past 15+ years (Images: Fhg ISE)

Test setup, procedure and samples

- Halm A+A+A+ solar simulator used for IV characterization
- Approach utilized a multi-intensity flash (1000 [7], 500 and 200W/m²) to simultaneously measure the IV curves at specific temperature (see Figure 2).
- heat-up and cool down procedure used to measure within temperature of ~75°C to ~30°C → time per module approx. 2h
- Dependent on cell technology, a hysteresis check was made.
- Modules are from all common cell technologies (Al-BSF, PERC, TOPCon, HJT, (I)BC) from the past 15 years
- Prior measurement modules were checked for major cell damages by EL
- Isc, Voc, Pmpp evaluation via linear regression (see Figure 3)

Figure 2: PERC 108 half cell module: No critical findings in EL, set of IV curves taken at 1000W/m². Corresponding power vs temperature plots for 1000, 500, and 200 W/m² to determine temperature coefficients for Pmpp.

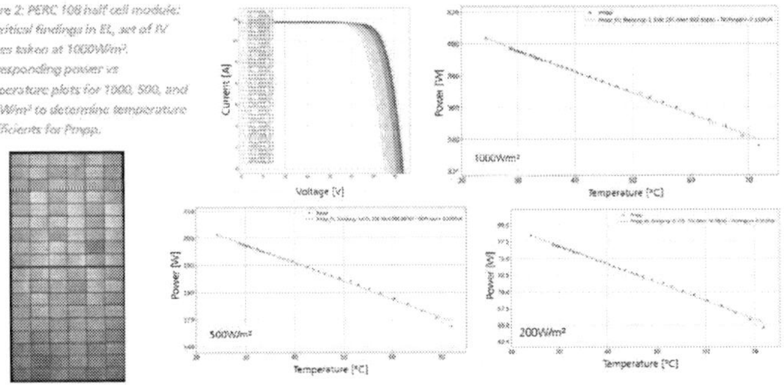

Temperature coefficients (TC) overview

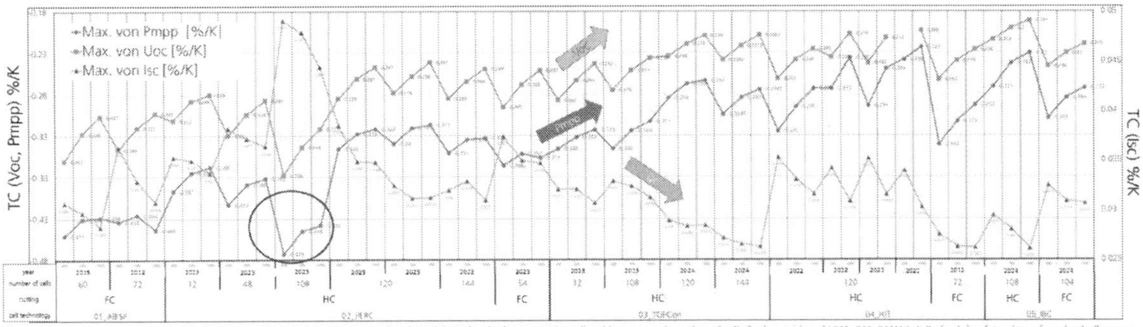

Figure 3: TC measurement results for Voc β, Isc α and Pmpp γ for various PV cell and module technologies, sorted by cell architecture and number of cells for intensities of 1000, 500, 200W/m². Each triple of numbers show basically same trend to either higher (Voc, Pmpp) or lower (Isc) TCs as a function of intensity. The PERC with 108 cells had bad cell cutting process impacting the TC negatively.

Take aways

- A trend to lower TC for Pmpps is clearly visible as a function of cell technology from Al-BSF to TOPCon/BC → agrees with "better" TC statements made by manufactures
- Module design and cell cutting play a role in the absolute number of PV-module TC
- The "old" 72 cell HJT-module (2012) is quite impressive keeping its age in mind showing how advanced the technology was compared to Al-BSF almost 15 years ago
- All measurements show a very similar trend of the TC change by irradiance. TC of Pmpp (γ) and Voc (β) increase with decreasing irradiance, vice versa does TC of Isc (α)
- Outlook: Not only does cell technology has an impact on the TC, but also module design and cell cutting. The data herein is the basis for a comparison between new and accelerated/field aged modules.

Contact

Dr. Bengt Jaeckel
PV Modules, Components and Manufacturing
Tel. +49 345 5589-5135
bengt.jaeckel@csp.fraunhofer.de

Fraunhofer CSP
Otto-Eißfeldt-Straße 12
06120 Halle (Saale)

[1] A. Virtuani, "Overview of Temperature Coefficients of Different Thin Film Photovoltaic Technologies", 25th EuPVSEC
[2] R. Dubey, "Measurement of Temperature Coefficient of Photovoltaic Modules in Field and comparison with Laboratory Measurements," 41st PVSC, 2015
[3] H. Ibrahim, "Variations of PV module parameters with irradiance and temperature", Energy Procedia, 134, 276-285, 2017
[4] M. Piliougine, "Temperature coefficients of degraded crystalline silicon photovoltaic modules at outdoor conditions", PiP, 25, 5, 556-570, 2020
[5] B. R. Paudyal, "Investigation of temperature coefficients of PV modules through field measured data", Solar Energy 224 (2021) 425–439
[6] P. Kamkird, "Investigation on Temperature Coefficients of Three Types Photovoltaic Module Technologies under Thailand Operating Condition", Procedia Engineering 32 (2012) 376-383
[7] IEC 61215 series: Design qualification and type approval

020176-001

This publication was funded by the Federal Ministry for Economic Affairs and Energy in the project GreenSolarModules GSM under grant number 03EE1161A.

Federal Ministry for Economic Affairs and Energy

ANGLE OF INCIDENCE MEASUREMENTS ON BIFACIAL PV MODULES

Frank Weinrich[1*], Stefan Riechelmann[1] and Stefan Winter[1]

[1]*Physikalisch-Technische Bundesanstalt* (PTB), Braunschweig, Germany

*Corresponding author: frank.weinrich@ptb.de

ABSTRACT: The current international standard EN IEC 61853-2 presents an outdoor and an indoor measurement method for the determination of angular losses [1]. Both methods determine the short circuit current $I_{sc}(\theta)$ of the PV device in the angular range from -90° to +90° with a maximum step size of 10°. The results are used to calculate the incident angle modifier $IAM(\theta)$ and the angular response curve $AR(\theta)$ with fitting parameter a_r. Angle of Incidence (AOI) measurements are usually carried out with indoor solar simulators which lead to certain problems for commercial sized modules due to light field non-uniformity when tilting the PV devices. To overcome these problems the standard allows for testing smaller-size and optically equivalent modules, to isolate electrically one cell within the module (destructive method) or to partially shade one cell in the module (non-destructive method). We show measurement results conducted with an outdoor method, utilizing direct sunlight for AOI measurements while most of the diffuse light is shaded. The advantage of this outdoor measuring method is that full-sized modules can be measured without limiting them to a particular cell, getting the most realistic values for the full module. We performed measurements on the front and rear side of seven bifacial modules of different product designs and cell technology. During rear side-measurements we observed partial cell row shading from the module frame. Although this shading effect has no influence on the output of the short-circuit current $I_{sc}(\theta)$ it does have an influence on the output of the maximum power point $P_{mpp}(\theta)$. The fitting parameters a_r from our rear side measurements show a factor of approximately 2 to 3 between $a_{r\ rear\ Isc}$ and $a_{r\ rear\ Pmpp}$ resulting in significantly different energy yield calculations for the rear side. The traditionally used $a_{r\ rear\ Isc}$ gives the wrong result. This effect cannot be characterized by the methods given by the current standard EN IEC 61853-2, since all methods rely on I_{sc} for the calculation of $IAM(\theta)$ and using just a particular cell for those measurements only produces correct values if there is no self-shading of the module apparent. Our results lead to the conclusion that for rear side AOI measurements on bifacial modules with a frame, the self-shading effect must also be considered.

Keywords: PV Module, Energy Rating, Incidence Angle Modifier, Direct Sunlight Method (DSM)

1 INTRODUCTION

The angular losses of PV modules during non-optimal irradiance incident angles play an increasingly important role for yield prediction and energy rating. Our working group focuses on reducing measurement uncertainty along the photovoltaic value chain. For this purpose, we also participate in standardization work, including revising the current international standard, EN IEC 61853-2. For our current study, we conduct AOI measurements for seven bifacial PV modules based on the described outdoor measurement method in the standard. The device used for this is our outdoor test stand, the so-called solar module tube (SMT), an in-house construction by PTB whose concept was already presented in 2022 [2]. The SMT allows us to measure full-sized modules without limiting measurements to a particular cell. This way, we can see the influence of angular effects on the whole PV module and not only on a particular cell. In addition, we obtain the whole IV curve including I_{sc} and P_{mpp} and not only I_{sc}. In 2024 the SMT took part in an interlaboratory comparison of conducting frontside AOI-measurements for commercial-size modules. Therefore, we performed outdoor method 1 (absolute method). The results showed a very good agreement between the different measurement methods, which also prove the capabilities of our outdoor test stand [3]. Despite these conclusions, our current paper aims to show that certain limitations in other AOI measurement methods, such as limiting measurements to a particular cell, can lead to inaccurate rear side IAM results for bifacial PV modules.

2 SETUP

To conduct our AOI measurements, we are using the direct sunlight method on our outdoor test stand (SMT). Inside the SMT the module is mounted on an adjustable module holder while most of the diffuse light is shaded by the tube. A pyrheliometer, which monitors the direct component of the irradiance, is mounted on a separate two-axis solar tracker near the SMT. Five temperature sensors attached to the rear of the tested module are used to record the temperature. The measurements were taken on days with clear sky in August 2024 and March 2025 in the region of Northern Germany.

2.1 Modules

We decided to measure seven different bifacial full-sized PV-modules, which are listed in Table 1. They are built by different manufacturers and show a representative selection of product designs and technologies as well as a wide range of bifaciality factors. The factors shown for each module were previously determined by our LED-based solar simulator (SINUS-3000, Wavelabs). The modules M1 to M4, M6 and M7 are framed, while M5 is frameless. M5 will be used to cross-check our measurement results and verify the influence of rear side cell row shading caused by a module frame.

10.4229/EUPVSEC2025/3AV.3.6

Table 1: List of measured bifacial PV modules with their technology and bifaciality factors.

Module	Technology	$\varphi_{Pmax, measured}$
M1	Heterojunction, n-Type	88 %
M2	TOPCon white	76 %
M3	TOPCon transparent	80 %
M4	TOPCon black	73 %
M5	PERC frameless	70 %
M6	IBC	41 %
M7	TOPCon transparent	77 %

2.2 Outdoor test stand

All seven PV modules were measured using the direct sunlight method on our outdoor test. The SMT, as shown in Figure 1, is a large rectangular tube with a size of 4.0 m x 4.0 m x 7.2 m capable of tracking the sun and limiting the field of view of a mounted PV module under test. The tube is lined with optical black fabric and equipped with a shutter to allow a well-defined start/end of the module's light exposure. The module under test is mounted on an adjustable module holder inside the tube. All seven bifacial PV modules were measured front and rear side with an angular range from -95° to +95° and a step size of 5°. At each step an IV curve is measured. The results were used to calculate the incident angle modifier $IAM(\theta)$ and the angular response curve $AR(\theta)$ with the fitting parameter a_r.

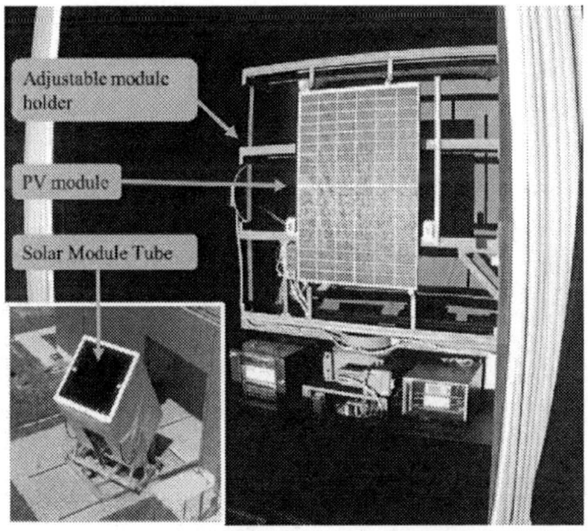

Figure 1: Photograph of the solar module tube during AOI measurements with a mounted PV module inside.

3 RESULTS

We perform AOI measurements for front and rear side of the PV modules shown in Table 1. The $I_{sc}(\theta)$ and $P_{mpp}(\theta)$ are derived from IV curves that are measured at every angle between -95° and +95° and calculated the $IAM(\theta)$ from both $I_{sc}(\theta)$ and $P_{mpp}(\theta)$ to check whether there is any difference when following an energy-based approach. Figure 2 shows all seven of these IAM curves for each module. For the front side IAM measurements, the difference between I_{sc} -based and P_{mpp} -based IAM is small for all examined modules. In case of the rear side measurements, we observe a substantial drop between I_{sc}-based and P_{mpp}-based IAM results for the framed modules, but as expected not for frameless module M5.

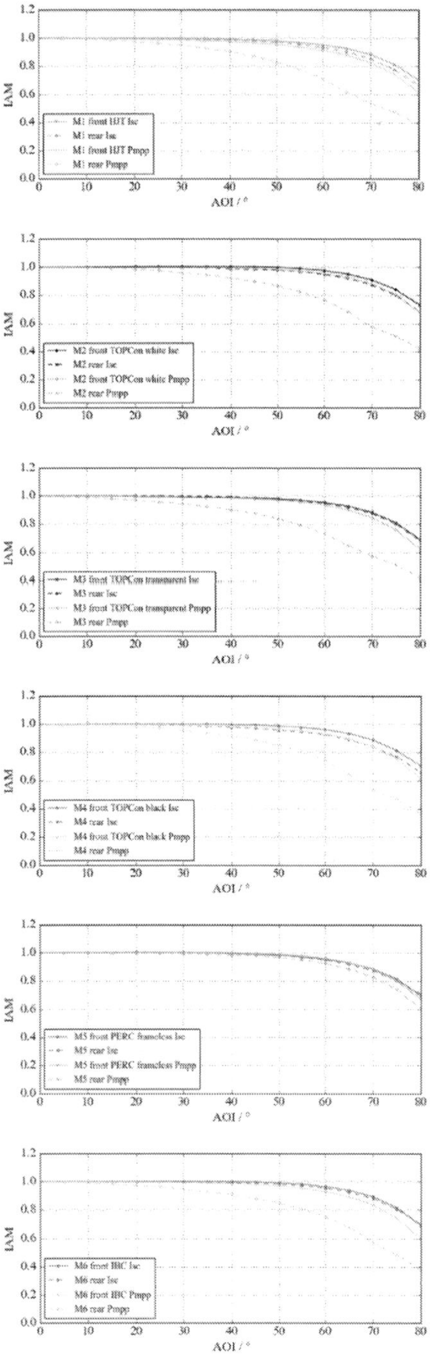

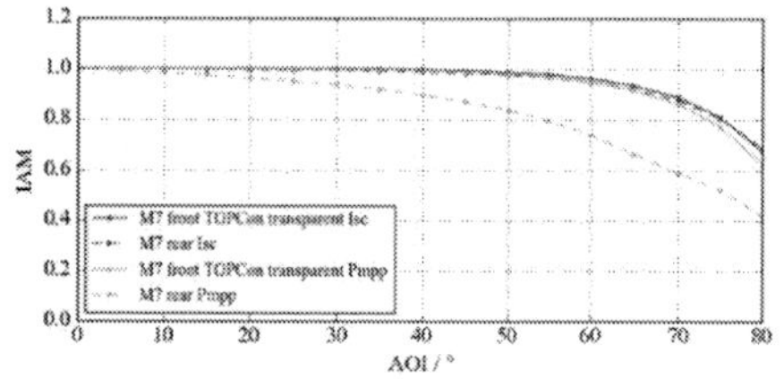

Figure 2: IAM curves based on I_{sc} and P_{mpp} for all seven examined bifacial PV modules.

The deviation of the rear side P_{mpp} -based IAM can be explained by a cell row shading effect as shown in Figure 3 and 4. This causes a reduced current flow in the shaded cells, which can also lead to a bypass of the entire string. This can only be seen by additionally determining the angle-dependent power output of the entire module. The results from the frameless module M5 also confirm this assessment, as the previously observed effects do not occur. Rather, all measured values are close to each other without the P_{mpp} -based IAM on the rear side deviating significantly.

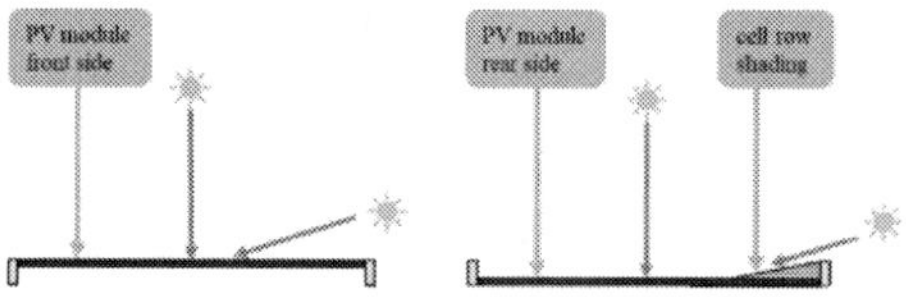

Figure 3: Picture of rear side cell row shading, caused by a PV module frame depending on the angle of irradiation.

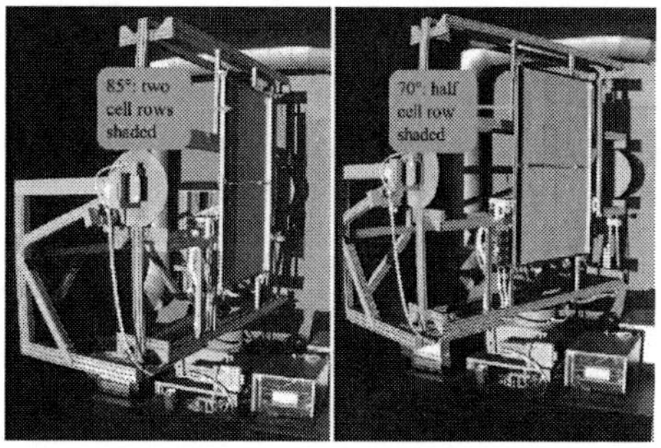

Figure 4: Photograph of cell row shading from PV module M2 at angle 85° (left) and 70° (right).

In addition, we calculate the fitting parameter a_r of the angular response curve for the I_{sc} -based front and rear side measurements and the P_{mpp} -based rear side measurements. The results can be seen in Table 2. The greater the a_r value, the higher the angular loss. The I_{sc} -based a_r range for PV modules is typically between 0.13 and 0.18, which was confirmed by our measurements. On the other hand, the P_{mpp} -based rear side a_r shows a much larger range due to the previously observed cell row shading effect caused by the module frame. The last column shows the difference between $a_{r\ rear\ Isc}$ and $a_{r\ rear\ Pmpp}$ as well as the mean value difference for all six framed PV modules. Module M1 has the largest difference with a value of 0.353 while the mean value difference for all six framed modules is 0.309. The difference between $a_{r\ rear\ Isc}$ and $a_{r\ rear\ Pmpp}$ for the frameless M5 module is much smaller (0.031), due to the absence of cell row shading from the module frame. However, even if a frameless module does not cause self-shading on the rear side, the standard module mountings will instead cause shading in the application. For the frameless modules to benefit from their improved angle dependence, an appropriate module holder would need to be used or even developed.

Table 2: Calculated fitting parameter a_r of the angular response curve based on front side $I_{sc}(\theta)$, rear side $I_{sc}(\theta)$ and rear side $P_{mpp}(\theta)$.

Module	$a_{r\ front}$ I_{sc}	$a_{r\ rear}$ I_{sc}	$a_{r\ rear}$ P_{mpp}	Difference
M1 (HJT)	0.153	0.169	0.522	0.353
M2 (TOPCon white)	0.152	0.163	0.445	0.282
M3 (TOPCon transparent)	0.157	0.163	0.468	0.305
M4 (TOPCon black)	0.152	0.177	0.491	0.314
M6 (IBC)	0.153	0.154	0.466	0.312
M7 (TOPCon transparent)	0.154	0.154	0.443	0.289
Mean value:				**0.309**
M5 (PERC frameless)	0.155	0.159	0.190	0.031

4 CONCLUSION

The previously described shading effect cannot be characterized by the methods given by the current standard EN IEC 61853-2, since all methods are based on I_{sc} for the calculation of $IAM(\theta)$ or perform measurements on a particular cell of the PV module which also does not take P_{mpp} losses into account. Our results lead to the conclusion that for rear side AOI measurements on bifacial modules with a frame, the self-shading effect must also be considered. Since most laboratories use indoor methods to conduct AOI measurements, the determination of the $P_{mpp}(\theta)$ for a full-sized PV module cannot be realized due to light field non-uniformity of indoor solar simulators when a module is tilted. However, if the effect is to be considered, a constant offset could be added to $a_{r,rear}$ if a frame is present, according to the results of these measurements on a wide variety of bifacial PV modules. Based on our current research, we would suggest an offset within the range of 0.3 to 0.35 (see Table 2).

5 ACKNOWLEDGEMENT

This work is partly developed within the project „ MetroKomPV ", which is funded by the Federal Ministry for Economic Affairs and Energy (BMWE), Germany (funding reference number 03EE1024) and within ECOSTANPV.

6 REFERENCES

[1] IEC 61853-2, "Photovoltaic (PV) module performance testing and energy rating – Part 2: Spectral responsivity,

incidence angle and module operating temperature measurements" (2016).

[2] Riechelmann S, Friedrich D, Müller M et al. (2022) Primary Calibration of Solar Modules With Direct Sunlight. 39th European Photovoltaic Solar Energy Conference and Exhibition; 474 - 476

[3] Pravettoni M, Saw M, Bardizza G, Bellenda G, Couderc R, Friesen G, Herrmann W, Leow S, Riechelmann S, Valoti F, van der Heide A, Weinrich F, Winter S. (2024) Incidence Angle Effect: Results of an Interlaboratory Comparison of Measurements on Commercial-Size Modules. 41st European Photovoltaic Solar Energy Conference and Exhibition.

42nd European Photovoltaic Solar Energy Conference and Exhibition

PTB
Physikalisch-Technische Bundesanstalt
National Metrology Institute

Frank Weinrich, Stefan Riechelmann, Stefan Winter

Angle of Incidence Measurements on Bifacial PV Modules

Are AOI measurements based on I_{sc} values representative of actual module performance?

- We conduct AOI measurements for seven different bifacial PV modules, built by various manufacturers who show a representative selection of product designs and technologies as well as a wide range of bifaciality factors. The modules were not purchased directly from the manufacturers.
- The modules are measured based on the described outdoor measurement method in the current international standard EN IEC 61853-2, utilizing direct sunlight. Therefore, we are using our outdoor test stand the so-called solar module tube (SMT).
- Inside the SMT an adjustable module holder is located that allows us to measure full-size modules with an angular range from -95° to +95° and a step size of 5°. At each step we obtain the IV curve of the module without limiting the measurements to a particular cell.
- All AOI measurements have been conducted for the front and rear side of all bifacial modules.

Solar Module Tube (SMT)

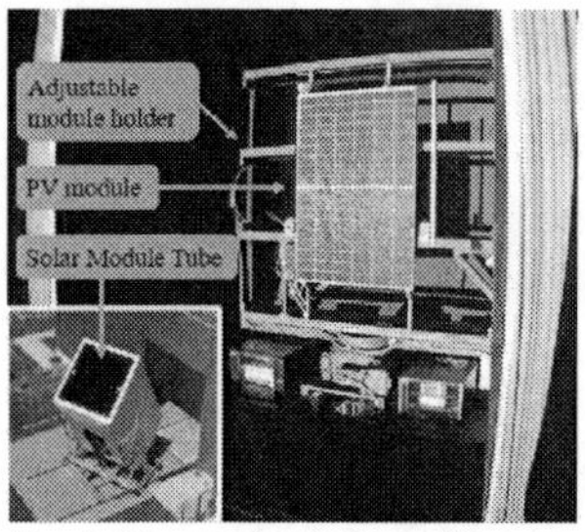

Fig. 1: Solar module tube (SMT) during AOI measurements with a mounted PV module inside.

Examined Bifacial PV Modules

Module	Technology	φ_{Pmax} measured
M1	Heterojunction	88 %
M2	TOPCon white	76 %
M3	TOPCon transparent	80 %
M4	TOPCon black	73 %
M5	PERC frameless	70 %
M6	IBC	41 %
M7	TOPCon transparent	77 %

Tab. 1: List of measured bifacial PV modules with their technology and bifaciality factors.

Angular Measurement Results

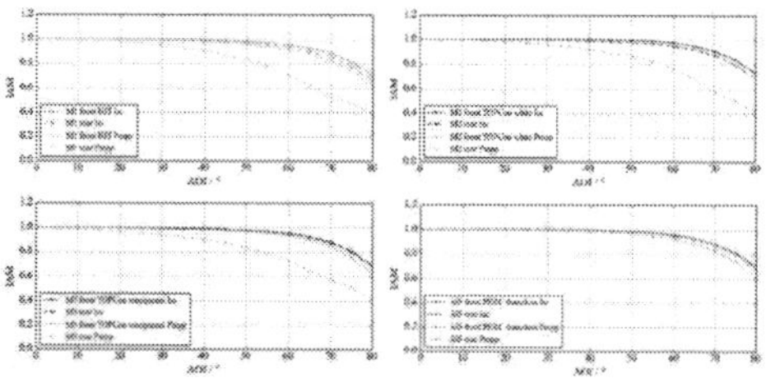

Fig. 2: IAM curves based on I_{sc} and P_{mpp} for four of the bifacial PV modules examined. While the front and rear side IAM is nearly identical when using I_{sc} as a measure, there is a substantial drop in Pmpp for higher angles on modules with frames. Calculating rear-side IAM based on Pmpp results in significantly worse performance.

Module Frame Shading Effect

- During rear-side measurements we observed partial cell row shading from the module frame which causes a reduced current flow in the shaded cells.
- While I_{sc} is unaffected, P_{mpp} of the module is significantly reduced by the shade.

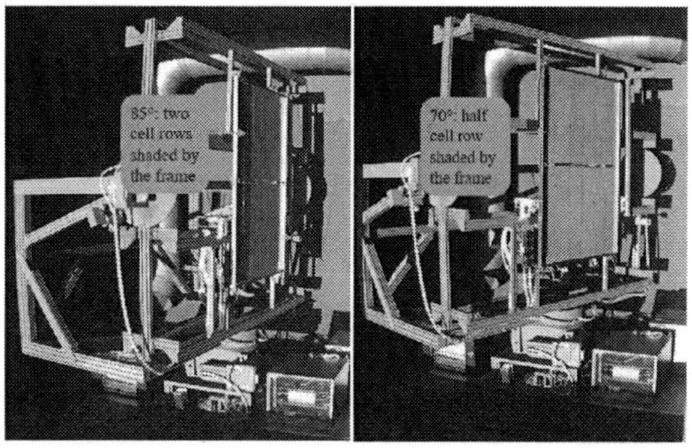

Fig. 3: Photograph of cell row shading from PV module M2 at angle 85° (left) and 70° (right).

Calculation of the Fitting Parameter a_r

- We calculate the front and rear side fitting parameter a_r of the angular response curve both on I_{sc} and P_{mpp}. The results can be seen in Table 2.
- The last column shows the difference between ar rear I_{sc} and a_r rear P_{mpp} as well as the mean value difference of 0.309 for all six framed PV modules, while the difference for the frameless M5 module is much smaller (0.031), due to the absence of cell row shading.

Module	$a_{r\ front\ Isc}$	$a_{r\ rear\ Isc}$	$a_{r\ rear\ Pmpp}$	Rear-side Difference
M1 (HJT)	0.153	0.169	0.522	0.353
M2 (TOPCon white)	0.152	0.163	0.445	0.282
M3 (TOPCon transparent)	0.157	0.163	0.468	0.305
M4 (TOPCon black)	0.152	0.177	0.491	0.314
M6 (IBC)	0.153	0.154	0.466	0.312
M7 (TOPCon transparent)	0.154	0.154	0.443	0.289
Mean value:				<u>0.309</u>
M5 (PERC frameless)	0.155	0.159	0.190	0.031

Tab. 2: Calculated fitting parameter a_r of the angular response curve based on front side $I_{sc}(\theta)$, rear side $I_{sc}(\theta)$ and rear side $P_{mpp}(\theta)$.

Conclusion: For rear-side AOI measurements on bifacial modules with a frame, I_{sc}-based IAM results might not be representative for the actual loss in performance due to steep incidence angles.

European Commission
The study is supported by the European Climate, Infrastructure and Environment Executive Agency (CINEA)

Frank Weinrich
4.53 | Solar Modules
+49 531 592 4536
frank.weinrich@ptb.de

Physikalisch-Technische Bundesanstalt
Bundesallee 100, 38116 Braunschweig, Germany
www.ptb.de

42nd European Photovoltaic Solar Energy Conference and Exhibition

Plug & Play IV Curve Tracer for PV Modules

EU PVSEC 2025, 22.-26. September 2025 Bilbao (Spain)
Adrian Jäggi[1], Christof Bucher[1], Matthias Burri[1]
[1]Bern University of Applied Sciences (BFH), School of Engineering and Computer Science (TI), Institute for Energy and Mobility Research (IEM), Laboratory for Photovoltaic Systems (PV-Lab), Burgdorf (Switzerland) christof.bucher@bfh.ch

A newly developed current-voltage characteristic curve measuring device (IV Curve Tracer) for photovoltaic modules enables novel measurements. It can briefly disconnect photovoltaic modules from the inverter during operation and measure the current-voltage characteristic curve, including bypass diodes. It is small, lightweight and universally applicable thanks to wireless communication. The IV Curve Tracer has numerous connections for various external sensors, which can measure the module temperature or irradiation. Several IV Curve Tracers can be used in a measurement network with temporal synchronization and central data processing.

Concept

The IVCT is designed to automatically measure photovoltaic modules (PV modules) on a regular basis during operation. It measures the characteristic curve from no-load to short circuit, including bypass diode on request. The IVCT also records the module and ambient temperature, irradiation and other parameters from external sensors. Several IVCTs can be operated in a measurement network, which is controlled by a central host. This also processes and stores all measurement data. The user interface consists of a website that can be accessed via any device.

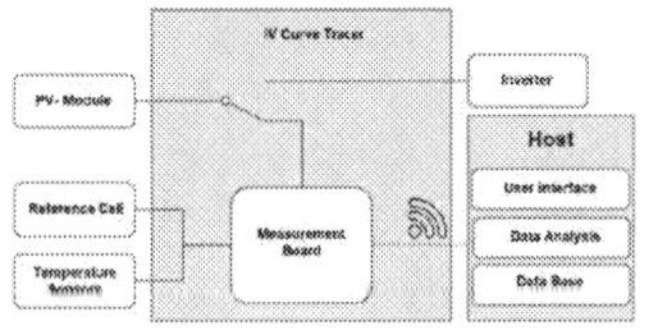

Figure 1: Concept of IV Curve Tracer

Measures

- The IVCT can record the following measurands:
- Current-voltage characteristic curve (IV curve) and power-voltage characteristic curve (PV curve)
- Current and voltage values during operation
- Irradiation on a reference cell
- Module backside and ambient temperature
- Irradiation by external pyranometer via Modbus
- Weather data by external weather station via Modbus

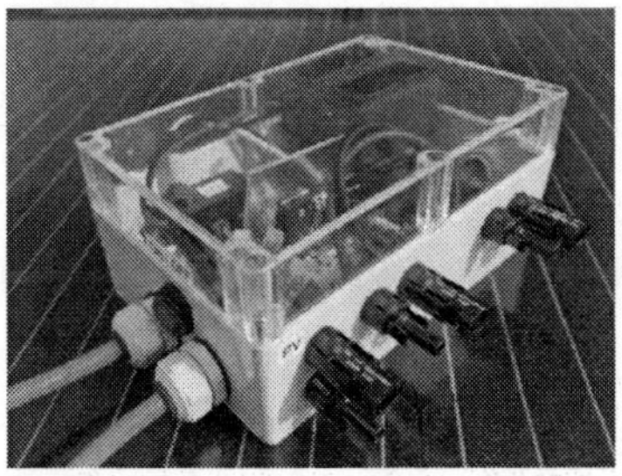

Figure 2: The characteristic curve measuring device IVCT developed in this work.

Evaluation and Data Export

In the user interface, the IV curve with various characteristic parameters is printed after the measurement. In addition, current, voltage and power are displayed in the point of maximum power (MPP), short-circuit current, open-circuit voltage, temperatures and irradiance values. All measurements are is stored in a database, which can be exported for further analysis. Additional parameters are calculated (e.g. the number of local maxima, fill factor, shunt and series resistance.

Measurements

Figure 3 shows an measurement of a TOPCon module in the solar simulator. Two different measurement time durations show an overshoot and undershoot of the characteristic curve in the capacitive module if the measurement is too fast. Thanks to the individually adjustable measurement time duration and support point distribution, characteristic curve measurements can be individually adapted to the PV module to be measured with the new IVCT.

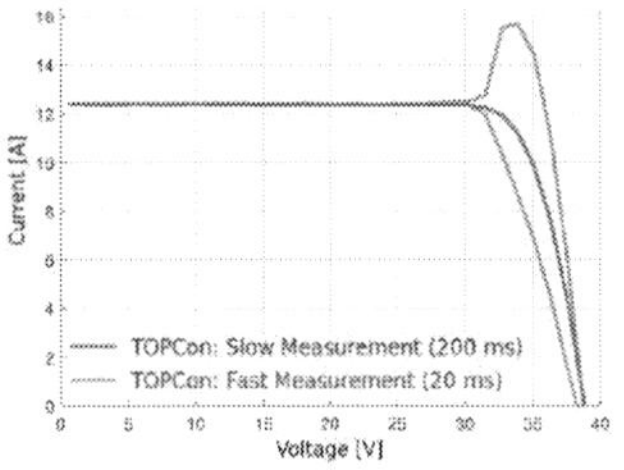

Figure 3: Measured IV curve of a TOPCon module. Measurement too fast (orange), slower, correct measurement (blue)

Validation

The measurement accuracy of the IVCT is validated in a defined environment in the laboratory. The temperature dependence of the measured variables is determined by tests in a climatic chamber. The results of the validation are presented in Table 1. The IVCT is tested for the applications in an installation of several PV modules and an inverter, as well as for different module technologies. Several IVCTs in a measurement network can measure in time synchronously, so that productive operation is not disrupted.

Table 1: Measurement accuracy and temperature dependence of the IVCT

Measurement	Measurement accuracy absolute	Measurement accuracy relative	Temperature dependence
Voltage	+/- 400 mV	+/- 0.4 %	- 0.02 % / K
Current	+/- 90 mA	+/- 0.6 %	+ 0.02 % / K

User interface

The IVCT is operated via the web browser of any device. In the user interface shown in Figure 4, the direction and duration of the characteristic curve measurement can be set, the measurement of the bypass diodes can be activated, and other configurations can be made. Furthermore, measurements can be started and the measurement database can be exported. Measurements of characteristic curves can be carried out individually or automatically at regular intervals. The IVCT can be calibrated and updated via the user interface.

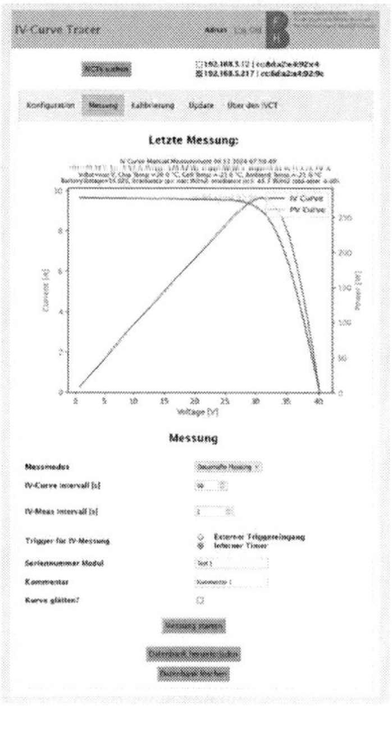

Figure 4: User interface of the IVCT in the web browser

References

[1] M. Müller, IV-Curve-Tracer, Bachelorarbeit, BFH, 2021
[2] J. Keta, D. Villiger, Firmware und Bedienungssoftware für ein Photovoltaik-Kennlinienmessgerät, Bachelorarbeit, BFH, 2023

42nd European Photovoltaic Solar Energy Conference and Exhibition

Kiwa PI Berlin

3AV.3.9 | SEASONAL AND LOCATION-DEPENDENT TEMPERATURE COEFFICIENTS FOR THIN-FILM PV MODULES: ENHANCING YIELD PREDICTION ACCURACY

Thomas Weber[1], Abdullah Abu Sayed[1,2], Benjamin Lippke[1], Steven Xuereb[1], Marcus Rennhofer[3], Bart E. Pieters[4]

[1]Kiwa PI Berlin AG
Wrangelstr. 100, 10997 Berlin, Germany
thomas.weber@kiwa.com, +49 30 314 52 64 -111

[2]Carl von Ossietzky University of Oldenburg, Germany
[3]AIT Austrian Institute of Technology GmbH, Austria
[4]IMD-3 Photovoltaics Forschungszentrum Jülich GmbH, Germany

Incorporate stabilization-dependent Tcoeff variations for a-Si/µc-Si & CdTe PV modules in laboratory testing, yield predictions, and warranty claims

Supported by:
Federal Ministry for Economic Affairs and Climate Action
on the basis of a decision by the German Bundestag

This research work has been carried out under the ReliaREN-Pro-D Project 03EI4052A (6202266) supported by the Federal Ministry for Economic Affairs and Climate Action.

Introduction

Background

- Thin-Film (TF) PV modules show often metastability behavior.
- Nominal power varies in TF equipped PV plants depending on the locations.
- Seasonal fluctuation are not considered when predicting the yield of a TF module, as datasheets provide only a constant (nominal, stabilized) power.
- Current warranties, testing standards and industry practice are insufficient to cover these TF-specific deviation properties.

Aim

Improve yield prediction by determining variable temperature coefficients (Tcoeff).

- Based on different stabilization states:
  - high power = summer and
  - low power = winter
- Considering the location impact on this new variable Tcoeff.

Methodology

Reference conventional scenario: One fixed Tcoeff (datasheet)
New: Tcoeff as a function of location and season

Stabilization a) Field exposure b) High & low power → **Experimental** Determination of Tcoeff → **Monte Carlo** Environmental Simulation of Tcoeff → **Yield analysis** Simulation

- Stabilization: See Table 1, investigated thin-film technologies: a) a-Si/µc-Si (2010) b) CdTe (2015, Serie 4)
- Experimental: Following MQT 04 by IEC 61215:2021
- Monte Carlo: In: Varying weather conditions and locations. Out: Random variable range of monthly possible Tcoeff
- Yield analysis: Capacity: 5 MW; Type: FS-4110A-3; Tilt: 30°; Yearly degradation: 0.4 %; New average Tcoeff values

Validation of Nominal Module Power / Tcoeff

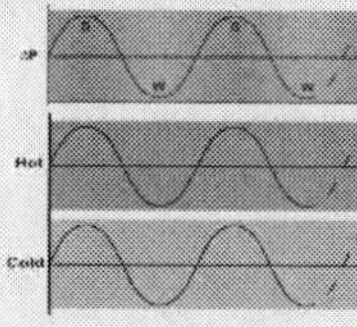

Figure 1: The mean temperature level of a specific site sets the 0-level. Therefore, power is a function of climate and location of the site. A climate dependent datasheet should be included in standard warranty procedures or contracts [1].

Figure 2: Experimental determination of Tcoeff following IEC 61215:2021, MQT 04. The Tcoeff values were determined on a module heated to 70°C during the cooling process of the solar simulator. The cooling process was delayed by insulation material.

Locations of the 4 Studied PV Plants

Figure 3: Four PV plant places have been selected: Berlin – DEU, Sicily – ITA, Cairo – EGY, Kuala Lumpur – MYS.

Climate Data Sets

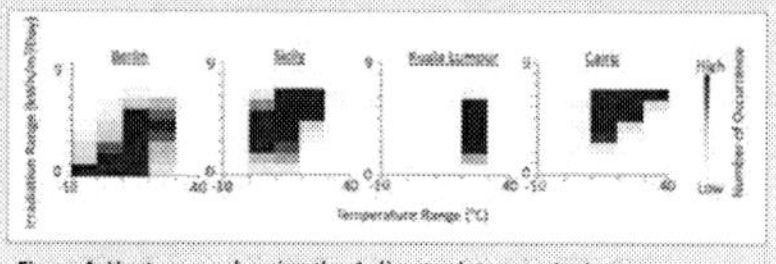

Figure 4: Heat-maps showing the 4 climate data sets. It shows a statistical analysis of the frequency distribution for the ranges of irradiation and temperature.

Precondition of Thin-Film Module

Technology	High power stabilization		Low power stabilization	
	Method	Parameter	Method	Parameter
a-Si/µc-Si (Sharp) [2]	Annealing	85°C, 2 days	Light soaking	86 kWh/m² (2 * 43)
CdTe [3]	Annealing	65°C, 24 h, 70 V	Dark storage	(25 ± 3)°C, two weeks

Table 1: Used methods for stabilization of a-Si/µc-Si and CdTe modules according to IEC standard, module manufacturer prescribed preconditioning, and dark storage. Field exposure (mpp) was stopped in Berlin after long-term exposure in January 2025 in order to determine the Tcoeff.

Results

Laboratory: P@STC & Tcoeff = f(stabilization)

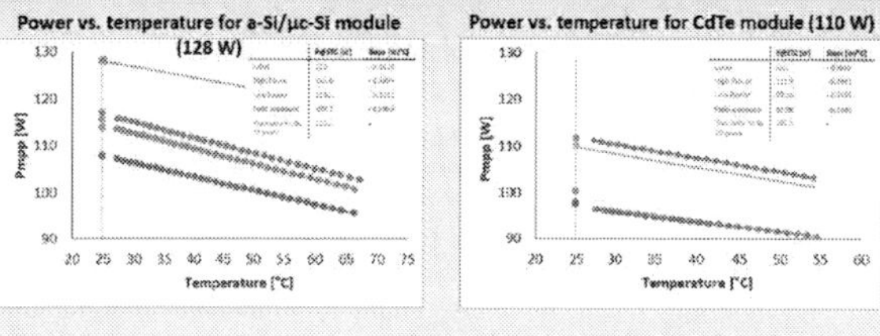

Figure 5: Measured power as function of temperature for a a-Si/µc-Si (left) and a CdTe (right) module (n = 1) for different stabilization scenarios. The datasheet provided Tcoeff and the nameplate power are marked in purple.
P@STC and Tcoeff deviate under the different stabilization from nameplate values. The field exposure (red) shows the lowest slope, the low-power stabilization (blue) shows a mid-slope, and the high-power stabilization (grey) shows the highest slope. A delta of 14 W is observed for both technologies at 25 °C, comparing low power to label. For CdTe, the high-power stabilization Tcoeff is even higher compared to nominal power.

Monte Carlo Simulation (CdTe): Monthly Tcoeff

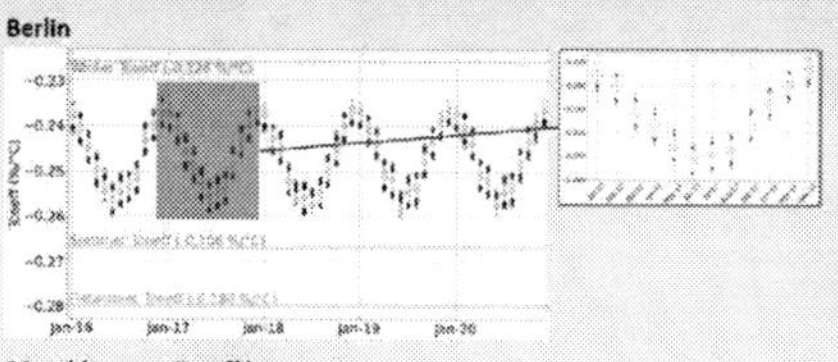

Figure 6: The graph show 5 years sinusoidal behavior in Berlin with the new simulated Tcoeff of the CdTe module. All the values are fluctuating in between the high-power stabilization Tcoeff and low-power stabilization Tcoeff determined in the laboratory (dashed lines). In summer, Tcoeff values reach to high-power stabilization Tcoeff value. In winter, Tcoeff values reach to low-power stabilization Tcoeff value.

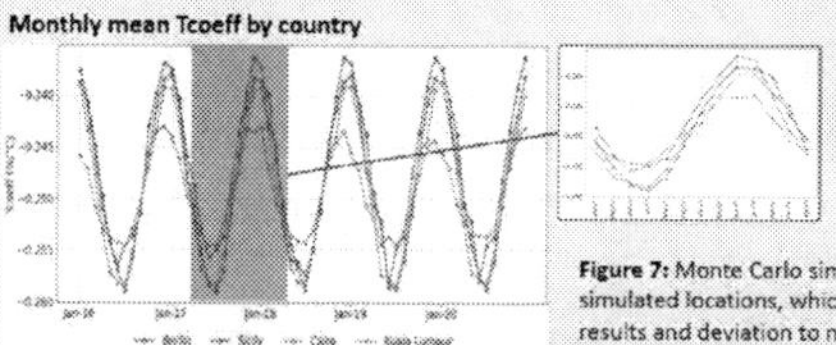

Figure 7: Monte Carlo simulated monthly Tcoeff for all simulated locations, which reveal significant different results and deviation to nameplate.

Yield Analysis Comparison (CdTe)

Yield deviation comparison: new vs. conventional

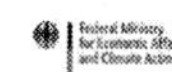

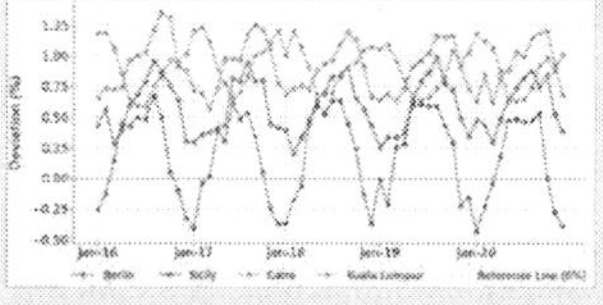

Location	New / conventional deviation (%)			
	Summer mean ± sd	Winter mean ± sd	Min.	Max.
Berlin	(0.5 ± 0.1)	(-0.1 ± 0.2)	-0.4	0.7
Sicily	(0.7 ± 0.2)	(0.5 ± 0.2)	0.2	1.0
Cairo	(1.0 ± 0.2)	(0.8 ± 0.2)	0.6	1.4
Kuala Lumpur	(0.8 ± 0.1)	(1.1 ± 0.1)	0.6	1.2

Figure 8: Simulation results are shown in 4 places over 5 years. The new simulation uses the modified set of Tcoeffs and the conventional simulation uses the datasheet Tcoeff. First, all monthly absolute yields were determined. **Left:** The graph shows the percentage deviation of yield compared to the conventional datasheet value-based approach (reference line). **Right:** Statistics showing summer (April to September) and winter (October to March) mean ± sd, minimum and maximum value.
Cairo shows the highest yield deviation (in max. value), which is 1.4 % higher and Berlin the lowest -0.4 % than the conventional approach. For a-Si/µc-Si the effects are much more pronounced but not shown here.

Conclusion

Results

- Tcoeff is not constant through the year.
- Tcoeffs change depending on module stabilization status, leading to
  - Seasonal variation of Tcoeff,
  - Location dependency of Tcoeff.
- Module manufactures should provide a set of high- and low-power Tcoeff, and the corresponding stabilization procedures.
- PVsyst and other simulation tools should allow at least two temperature coefficients for better output prediction.
- For CdTe, an installation closer to the equator is leading to higher module power and yields. In other words: the current industry standard for yield prediction leads to significant underestimations, especially in regions close to the equator.

Discussion

- Laboratory determined IV-curves on fielded modules are likely not able to determine the last actual field-stabilized power value. This make the current approach of warranty claims not working anymore.
- Will field-stabilized power determinations become the standard for warranty claims on all metastable technologies?
- IEC 61215 needs an update or creation of a new technical specification to cover variable Tcoeffs.
- Seasonal and location influence should be checked for all technologies. Different stabilizations influence the Tcoeff, if necessary, the stabilization procedures need to reflect that.

REFERENCES
[1] Thomas Weber, Marcus Rennhofer, Benjamin Lippke, ... "Do we correctly determine the power of thin-film modules?", ... European Photovoltaic Solar Energy Conference and Exhibition
[2] Sharp CORPORATION, "Maximum Power Measurement Guideline for thin-film PV module"
[3] First Solar, "First Solar Module Preconditioning for CdTe Modules," Reliability Group, 2015-07

STANDARDISATION METHODS FOR BIFACIAL ENERGY YIELD ESTIMATION AND PV MODULE LONG-TERM PERFORMANCE DEGRADATION ESTIMATION: POTENTIAL POLICY IMPLICATIONS

Jaione Bengoechea[1], Ana Maria Gracia[1]; Stefan Riechelmann[2], Stefan Winter[2]; Giorgio Bardizza[3]; Christos Monokroussos[4]; Davide Polverini[5]; Pablo Vicente-Laiglesia[6]; Maria Getsiou[7]
Spanish National Renewable Energy Center[1]; German National Metrology Institute[2]; TÜV Rheinland Italia SRL[3]; TÜV Rheinland Shanghai SRL[4]; Directorate General for Internal Market, Industry, Entrepreneurship and SMEs[5]; European Climate, Infrastructure and Environment Executive Agency[6]; Directorate General for Research and Innovation[7]
jbapezteguia@cener.com[1], agracia@cener.com[1]; stefan.riechelmann@ptb.de[2], stefan.winter@ptb.de[2]; giorgio.bardizza@tuv.com[3]; christos.monokroussos@tuv.com[4], davide.polverini@ec.europa.eu[5]; pablo.vicente-laiglesia@ec.europa.eu[6]; maria.getsiou@ec.europa.eu[7]

ABSTRACT: European policies like the Ecodesign Directive [1], the Energy Labelling Regulation [2] or the recently implemented Ecodesign for Sustainable Products Regulation [3] have improved the efficiency and sustainability of energy related products in the European market. In recent years, measures to incorporate PV products (modules and inverters) within the scope of these policies are being prepared [4]. In this regard, the EC's European Climate, Infrastructure and Environment Executive Agency (CINEA) is managing a three-year project aimed at developing standardized methods relevant for the implementation of the aforementioned policy measures to PV modules. The project has two distinctive objectives. Define a methodology to estimate the energy yield of bifacial PV modules, and develop a method and testing sequence to estimate the long-term degradation rate of the PV module´s performance. The project is carried out by the consortium formed by the German National Metrology Institute (PTB), TÜV Rheinland Italia SRL and the Spanish National Renewable Energy Centre (CENER), and it is supported by the EC's Directorate General for Internal Market, Industry, Entrepreneurship and SMEs (DG GROW) and the Directorate General for Research and Innovation (DG RTD).
Keywords: energy yield, bifacial modules, long-term degradation rate.

1 INTRODUCTION

The European Commission (EC), through policies like the Ecodesign Directive [1], the Energy Labelling Regulation [2] or the recently implemented Ecodesign for Sustainable Products Regulation [3] has improved the efficiency and sustainability of the energy related products in the European market, providing consumers information and tools to make better informed decisions about the products available. Likewise, manufacturers have received means by which improve the characteristics of their products in terms of efficiency and sustainability, which in turn advances their position in the EU market and upgrades the overall quality of the products therein available.

Photovoltaic (PV) energy is one of the key players to achieve the EU's ambitious objectives for energy transition and security, which is reflected in the pace at which the installed PV capacity in the EU has grown in recent years. However, the deployment of this technology should not pose new burdens on the environment. With the aim of reducing and minimizing this impact, in recent years, measures to incorporate PV products (modules and inverters) within the scope of the aforementioned policies are being prepared [4].

In this regard, the EC's European Climate, Infrastructure and Environment Executive Agency (CINEA) is managing a project aimed at developing standardized methodologies relevant for the potential implementation of Ecodesign and Energy Label policy measures for PV modules. The project, which has a duration of three years starting in December 2023, has a twofold objective. On the one hand, define a methodology to estimate the energy yield of bifacial PV modules. And, on the other hand, develop a method and testing sequence to estimate the long-term degradation rate of the PV module´s performance. The project is being developed by the contractor formed by the German National Metrology Institute (PTB), TÜV Rheinland Italia SRL and the Spanish National Renewable Energy Centre (CENER). Furthermore, it is supported by the active participation of the EC's Directorate General for Internal Market, Industry, Entrepreneurship and SMEs (DG GROW) and the Directorate General for Research and Innovation (DG RTD).

This paper presents the current status of the project detailing the methodologies and testing sequences proposed to determine both parameters: the energy yield of bifacial PV modules and the long-term performance degradation rate. The project is divided in two tasks, each dedicated to one objective. Similarly, each objective has a dedicated section in the current paper, where information about the PV modules tested and results obtained so far are presented as well. For the project's development, the involvement of stakeholders is highly valuable and Section 4 is dedicated to the consultation activities performed to date. The paper finalizes with the conclusions drawn thus far, presented in Section 5.

More information about this project can be found at: https://ecodesign-pv-testing.eu/ or requested to the contractor at info@ecodesign-pv-testing.eu.

2 ENERGY YIELD OF BIFACIAL PV DEVICES

2.1 Introductory remarks

The first objective of this CINEA project is the development of a standardisation method for the calculation and testing of the energy yield of bifacial PV modules. The method should take into consideration the effect of the in-plane irradiance, the albedo, the module's temperature and the impact on the performance of the mounting configurations considering, primarily, those normally applied in bifacial PV modules installations in Europe.

Based on the potential implementation of this model in energy label measures to bifacial modules, the aim of the requested method is not a detailed energy yield assessment model but an estimation model for an energy rating application.

2.2 Methodology

The EC's proposal for an energy label for PV modules is based on the IEC 61853 Standard series which defines a method to estimate the energy yield from a monofacial device (Part 3) [5] based on input data retrieved from analysing the module under test (Part 1 [6] and 2 [7]) and predefined working conditions described as yearly datasets of hourly values of irradiance and climatological variables (Part 4) [8]. The thus estimated yield from monofacial devices is extended to bifacial ones assuming a fixed gain based on the device's bifaciality factor.

In opposition to this simplified approach, the method developed in this CINEA project follows the IEC's approach for monofacial devices based on hourly simulations. The new method estimates the rear side's contribution to the estimated energy yield in the hourly calculations by means of the effective irradiance received by the bifacial device (front side irradiance plus rear side irradiance multiplied by the bifaciality factor) and the temperature reached by the module, estimated from the received irradiance, ambient temperature and wind speed. Besides, the effective irradiance considers as well the spectral response of the device and the angle of incidence effects, like in [5], but in this case analysing both front and rear side of the bifacial device.

The IEC 61853 Standard series defined for monofacial devices, does not take into consideration the effect of albedo. However, in this project, in order to consider the effect of the ground-reflected irradiance on the estimated energy yield, different values of albedo will be analysed. These could be possibly linked to the three reference climates in [8] relevant for Europe, denoted Subtropical arid, Temperate coastal and Temperate continental.

Furthermore, different mounting configurations representative of bifacial installations will be considered. The current IEC 61853 Standard series assumes the monofacial module installed in an open-rack ground mounted configuration with a tilt angle of 20° and facing the Equator. In the proposed methodology three additional configurations will be analysed for bifacial devices, as shown in Fig. 1. In addition to the standard configuration (Top left), an equator facing building attached system (Top right), a vertical east/west oriented configuration (Bottom left), and a one-axis horizontal tacking system (Bottom right) will be studied.

For every mounting configuration, both the front and the rear side in-plane irradiance values have to be defined, for every reference climate in the form of new hourly values like in [8] to extend these reference climatic datasets.

Figure 1: Proposed new mounting configurations for bifacial PV modules.

2.3 Testing sequence

The testing activities described in IEC 61853 Part 1 [6] and 2 [7] for monofacial devices have been adapted where necessary for bifacial devices. For example, the performance matrix defined in [6] has been extended with more data points to complete a regular grid and reach higher irradiance values, up to 1300 W/m^2. While tests defined in [7] have been applied to both sides of the bifacial device to obtain the spectral responsivity (*SR*) and the angle of incidence parameter (a_r) or incidence angle modifier (AIM) for both sides. The thermal coefficients of the bifacial module (u_0 and u_1) used to estimate the temperature under working conditions have been obtained with a testing procedure equivalent to that applied to monofacial devices, following the method defined in the ongoing amendment to Part 2. However, further indoor testing is being carried out in this project to validate this approach for bifacial PV devices.

All the testing activities are being carried out by PTB.

2.4 Selected bifacial PV modules for the energy yield estimation task

Based on the project's specifications, the current European PV market and future market share projections, the stakeholders' opinions and the availability of bifacial PV modules in small quantities in the German PV retail market six different bifacial PV modules were selected from different manufacturers, who have been duly informed. As shown in Table I there are devices from the main PV technologies, with diverse characteristics and configurations (for example, spacing between cells) to analyse the effect on the performance. The selection contains one heterojunction (HJT) device, three TOPCon modules, one PERC module and one Interdigitated back contact (IBC) device. Glass/glass IBC modules could be considered bifacial devices since the rear side of the cell receive irradiance contributing to the performance of the module. All modules have frame except the PERC device.

Table I: Selection of bifacial PV devices for the energy yield estimation task.

	Technology	Bifaciality φ_{Pmax} (%)
1	HTJ	90 ± 5
2	TOPCon, white	80 ± 10
3	TOPCon, transparent	80 ± 5
4	TOPCon, black	80 ± 10
5	PERC	Not declared
6	IBC	Not applicable

2.5 Interim results

All bifacial PV devices have been characterized already and the parameters used as input for the energy yield method have been determined. One module of every PV module type has been used to obtain the performance matrix modifying the measurement conditions from 15°C to 75°C for the module's temperature and from 100 W/m² to 1300 W/m² for the in-plane irradiance. As an example, the results, in terms of efficiency, obtained for the HJT module and the IBC are shown in Fig. 2. From the selected devices, the IBC module shows higher efficiency values than the HJT device.

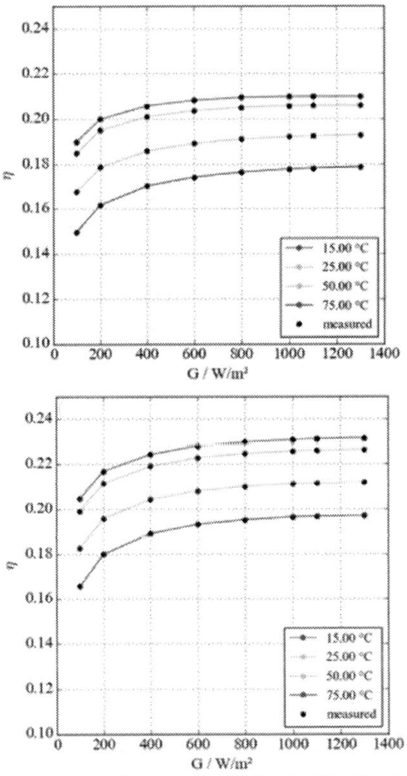

Figure 2: Performance matrix for the HJT (Top) and IBC (Bottom) selected PV bifacial devices.

The same PV module was then used to retrieve the *SR* and the *AIM* parameter for each side of the bifacial module, and the bifaciality factor, which is always within the declared tolerance. The bifaciality factor of the IBC module was determined as 41%.

In general, the rear side performs worse than the front side in relation to the *SR* (Fig. 3) and the *AIM* (Fig. 4) parameters.

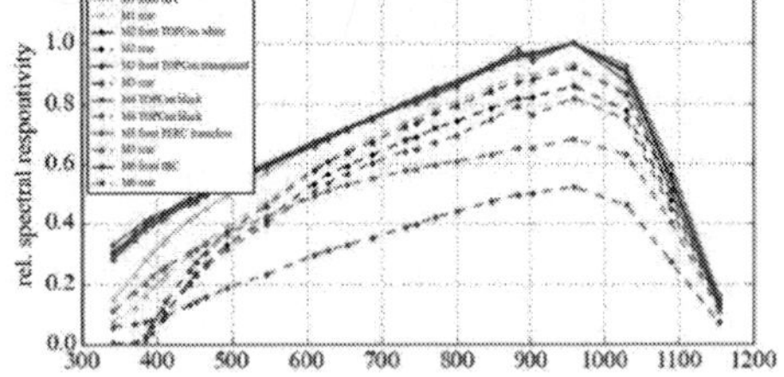

Figure 3: Relative spectral responsivity measured for the front and rear side of the selected bifacial devices.

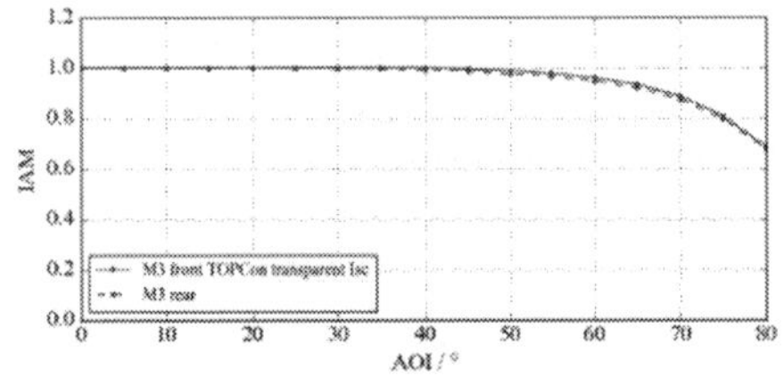

Figure 4: Relative internal angular transmittance values for one of the selected TOPCon device.

Considering the duration of the outdoor monitoring campaign to obtain the thermal coefficients (u_0 and u_1), a different PV module was used for this test. The monitoring campaign will be completed in forthcoming weeks.

3 LONG-TERM PV PERFORMANCE DEGRADATION

3.1 Introductory remarks

The second objective of the ongoing CINEA project is the development of a standardisation method for the measurement and testing of the long-term degradation of the PV modules' performance, including both monofacial and bifacial devices. The method shall take into consideration the effect of environmental stress factors like irradiance and temperature, and internal stress factors such as presence of non-suitable materials.

Based on the potential implementation of this model in ecodesign and energy label measures to PV modules, the complexity of the proposed method will be carefully assessed to balance duration and reliability of the results, since it should be easily implemented by Market Surveillance Authorities and PV testing laboratories.

3.2 Methodology

Due to the implications on the profitability of any PV installation on an underestimated degradation factor, the scientific community has tried with remarkable efforts to define this parameter. Furthermore, while there is significant evidence that PV installations perform mostly as expected, there are also cases of product recalls and observations of new (unexpected) failures. Therefore, the topic of degradation of the PV modules is still under open debate within the PV community and all the standardisation bodies.

Well-known performance (IEC 61215 series [9]-[14]) and safety (IEC 61730 [15]-[16]) qualification Standards are valuable for rapidly uncovering well-known early field failures, but they are insufficient to assess long-term degradation and its risk/impact. Recently, testing approaches for the long-term durability of PV modules are being explored within the preparatory work for the second edition of IEC TS 63209-1 Photovoltaic modules - Extended-stress testing - Part 1.

The proposed methodology focuses on the most common and impactful degradation mechanisms affecting the most representative PV technologies in the PV market, and includes a series of tests trying to trigger them on the devices analysed. These tests are based on others available in standardized protocols in order to minimize, when possible, the number of new tests assuming PV modules in the EU market comply with these standardized protocols.

The main degradation mechanisms considered include potential induced degradation (PID), moisture diffusion processes and UV induced degradation. These will be studied submitting the PV modules to severe conditions of temperature, humidity and UV irradiation. The results on the observed performance loss will be used in an extrapolation method, based on Arrhenius kinetics, to estimate the long-term degradation rate.

3.3 Testing sequence

The proposed testing sequence contains four main sections:

- PID testing sequence. Three temperatures of 65°C, 75°C and 85°C are applied with 85% relative humidity for 96 hours. Three separate PV modules are used, one per temperature. The applied voltage depends on the modules' specifications in terms of range and polarity.
- Damp heat testing sequence. Same conditions of temperatures and relative humidity as for the PID tests, no applied voltage and increased duration of 2000 hours per temperature. Three separate PV modules are used, one per temperature.
- UVID testing sequence. The main aim of this test is the analysis of the susceptibility of the PV material to the UV irradiation. Based on renown characterization protocols of various PV laboratories (TÜV and PVEL) which already include an independent UVID testing sequence and the lack of an standardized approach in this regard, the proposed UVID testing sequence includes a UV dose of 200 kWh/m^2 on the front side only of the device under test. One PV module is required for this test, whose temperature throughout the test shall be 60°C±5°C.
- Outdoor exposure. One year of outdoor exposure of one PV module which shall be electrically polarized at its maximum power point using an individual MPP tracker.

These testing activities will be performed by TÜV and CENER. While the damp heat and the UVID testing sequences are to be performed by both laboratories, the PID testing sequence and the outdoor exposure will be carried out by CENER.

The proposed testing sequence is completed by an initial characterization of the PV devices by means of IV curves at Standard Test Conditions (STC) and electroluminescence images, followed by outdoor exposure or Light Induced Degradation test (LID). Additionally, insulation test and wet leakage test are to be applied before the actual testing sequence. Similarly, at the end of every testing sequence, this characterization is to be performed again.

3.4 Selected PV modules for the long-term degradation rate estimation task

For this task a total of eight different module types have been selected based on the project's requirements, the current and projected European PV market share, the stakeholders' collaboration and the availability of PV modules in small quantities in the Spanish PV retail market.

The final selection, shown in Table II, includes two PERC devices, four TOPCon devices (two monofacial and two bifacial), one heterojunction (HJT) device and one Interdigitated Back Contact (IBC) device. They all belong to different manufacturers who have been informed about their products being used in this study. The power under STC, the efficiency and the layout are also indicated. This latter parameter indicates whether it is a monofacial (M) or bifacial (B) device, and the configuration glass/glass (G/G) or glass/backsheet (G/BS). Due to the characteristics of the climatic chambers used in this project, the size of the modules was limited to 2 m.

Table II: Selection of PV modules for the long-term degradation rate estimation task.

	Technology	P_{max} $_{STC}$ (W)	Eff (%)	Layout
A	TOPCon, n-Type	450	22.5	M, G/BS
B	PERC, p-Type	450	20.8	M, G/BS
C	HJT, n-Type	450	21.6	M, G/BS
D	TOPCon, n-Type	475	21.9	B, G/G
E	TOPCon, n-Type	440	22.5	B, G/G
F	IBC, p-Type	460	22.5	M, G/BS
G	TOPCon, n-Type	500	22.2	M, G/BS
H	PERC, p-Type	460	21.2	M, G/BS

3.5 Interim results

The testing activities in this second task are not as advanced as in the energy yield estimation task. First results show significant deviations of the power output compared to nominal values. Figure 5 shows the differences, compared to the *Pmax* under STC declared by the manufacturer, of the obtained values in the initial characterization upon reception of the PV modules and after LID test.

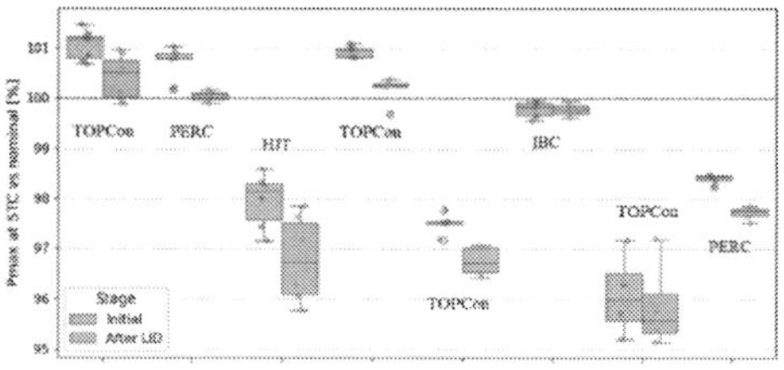

Figure 5: Comparison of *Pmax* at STC in the initial characterization and after LID test with regard to nominal values.

Two PV devices have already reached 100 kWh/m^2 of UV dose (half of the complete test) showing already 0.7% and 1.8% power loss respectively. Other results from PID testing are being analysed while testing continues.

4 STAKEHOLDERS CONSULTATION

Throughout the duration of the project, the consortium in charge of the project is committed to ensure that relevant stakeholders can provide input on the

10.4229/EUPVSEC2025/3AV.3.10

methodologies being developed. To that aim a dedicated website (https://ecodesign-pv-testing.eu/) was created were documentation and updates as well as invitations to consultation activities are announced. Furthermore, a functional mailbox was created to communicate directly with registered stakeholders (info@ecodesign-pv-testing.eu).

At present, more than 130 people have registered to the project including academia, research institutes and PV manufacturers. Two general stakeholder meeting have been organized so far, in months 3 and 19 to update stakeholders on the status of the project's development. Presentation and minutes are shortly after available on the website. After every meeting a period of various weeks is granted to provide feedback. Furthermore, an specific online questionnaire was launched after the first stakeholder meeting to get detailed feedback about the first approach to develop both standardized methodologies.

In addition, various meetings with experts have been organized for both tasks, particularly with the group of experts of IEC TC82 WG2 involved in the amendment of IEC 61853 Standard series and experts on the field of PV performance degradation.

So far, the project has benefited from the active participation and collaboration of stakeholders.

A third and last stakeholder meeting is planned for Autumn 2026 before the end of the project (November 2026). In this meeting the final methodologies and results will be presented.

5 CONCLUSIONS

In policy terms, the expected outcome from this study, which consists in the development of standardised (pre-normative) methods, could be highly relevant, inter alia, for environmental policies such as the potential implementation ecodesign and energy labelling measures to PV modules. This possibility implies that both methods and the corresponding testing activities should be easily implemented and validated by Market Surveillance Authorities. Furthermore, they should not become an excessive burden for manufacturers who shall comply with these testing requirements.

To facilitate the implementation of the proposed methodologies, the tests required are based on standardized ones, which are already applied by the PV industry. Furthermore, in the next stages of the project, a sensitivity analysis will be performed to study the impact of simplified testing and estimation methods in the final parameters' estimation. For example, by reducing the number of measurement points in the performance matrix, the new bifacial mounting configurations or the temperatures or UV dose applied in the testing activities for the degradation rate determination. If these simplifications were validated, the proposed testing activities could be also simplified.

With regard to the results obtained so far from the bifacial PV modules task, front and rear sides show significant differences. Therefore, it does not seem reasonable to assume the parameters of one side only for the estimation of the performance of both.

Despite the early stages in the testing activities of the long-term degradation rate task, it is important to highlight the value of the first initial characterization and stabilization (LID test) where significant differences between the modules of the same module type and between module types have been observed already. The final conclusions from the completed testing activities will be presented at the final stakeholder meeting. To register, please fill in the form in https://ecodesign-pv-testing.eu/meetings/.

6 REFERENCES

[1] Directive 2009/125/EC of the European Parliament and of the Council of 21 October 2009 Establishing a Framework for the Setting of Ecodesign Requirements for Energy-Related Products, OJ L285, 31.10.2009, p. 10–35, https://webstore.iec.ch/home.

[2] Regulation (EU) 2017/1369 of the European Parliament and of the Council of 4 July 2017 Setting a Framework for Energy Labelling and Repealing Directive 2010/30/EU, OJ L198, 28.7.2017, p. 1–23, https://webstore.iec.ch/home.

[3] Regulation (EU) 2024/1781 of the European Parliament and of the Council of 13 June 2024 establishing a Framework for the setting of ecodesign requirements for sustainable products, amending Directive (EU) 2020/1828 and Regulation (EU) 2023/1542 and repealing Directive 2009/125/EC Text with EEA relevance.

[4] Dodd N, Espinosa N et al. Preparatory study for solar photovoltaic modules, inverters and systems. https://publications.jrc.ec.europa.eu/repository/handle/JRC122431

[5] IEC 61853-3. Photovoltaic (PV) module performance testing and energy rating – Part 3: Energy rating of PV modules. Edition 1.0 International Electrotechnical Commission (2018).

[6] IEC 61853-1. Photovoltaic (PV) module performance testing and energy rating – Part 1: Irradiance and temperature performance measurements and power rating. Edition 1.0 International Electrotechnical Commission (2011).

[7] IEC 61853-2. Photovoltaic (PV) module performance testing and energy rating – Part 2: Spectral responsivity, incidence angle and module operating temperature measurements. Edition 1.0 International Electrotechnical Commission (2016).

[8] IEC 61853-4. Photovoltaic (PV) module performance testing and energy rating – Part 4: Standard reference climatic profiles. Edition 1.0 International Electrotechnical Commission (2018).

[9] IEC 61215-1 ED2. Terrestrial photovoltaic (PV) modules - Design qualification and type approval - Part 1: Test requirements. Edition 2.0 International Electrotechnical Commission (2021).

[10] IEC 61215-1-1 ED2 Terrestrial photovoltaic (PV) modules - Design qualification and type approval - Part 1-1: Special requirements for testing of crystalline silicon photovoltaic (PV) modules. Edition 2.0 International Electrotechnical Commission (2021).

[11] IEC 61215-1-2 ED2 - Terrestrial photovoltaic (PV) modules - Design qualification and type approval - Part 1-2: Special requirements for testing of thin-film Cadmium Telluride (CdTe) based photovoltaic (PV) modules. Edition 2.0 International Electrotechnical Commission (2022).

[12] IEC 61215-1-3 ED2 Terrestrial photovoltaic (PV) modules - Design qualification and type approval - Part 1-3: Special requirements for testing

of thin-film amorphous silicon based photovoltaic (PV) modules. Edition 2.0 International Electrotechnical Commission (2021).
[13] IEC 61215-1-4 ED2 Terrestrial photovoltaic (PV) modules - Design qualification and type approval - Part 1-4: Special requirements for testing of thin-film Cu(In,Ga)(S,Se)2 based photovoltaic (PV) modules. Edition 2.0 International Electrotechnical Commission (2021).
[14] IEC 61215-2 ED2 Terrestrial photovoltaic (PV) modules - Design qualification and type approval - Part 2: Test procedures. Edition 2.0 International Electrotechnical Commission (2021).
[15] IEC 61730-1 ED3 Photovoltaic (PV) module safety qualification – Part 1: Requirements for construction. Edition 3.0 International Electrotechnical Commission (2023).
[16] IEC 61730-2:2023/COR1:2024 ED3 Corrigendum 1 - Photovoltaic (PV) module safety qualification – Part 2: Requirements for testing. Edition 3.0 International Electrotechnical Commission (2023).

STANDARDISATION METHODS FOR BIFACIAL ENERGY YIELD ESTIMATION AND PV MODULE LONG-TERM PERFORMANCE DEGRADATION ESTIMATION: POTENTIAL POLICY IMPLICATIONS

Jaione Bengoechea[1], Ana María Gracia[1]; Stefan Riechelmann[2], Stefan Winter[2]; Giorgio Bardizza[3]; Christos Monokroussos[4]; Davide Polverini[5]; Pablo Vicente-Laiglesia[6]; Maria Getsiou[7]

Spanish National Renewable Energy Center[1]; German National Metrology Institute[2]; TÜV Rheinland Italia SRL[3]; TÜV Rheinland Shanghai SRL[4]; Directorate General for Internal Market, Industry, Entrepreneurship and SMEs[5]; European Climate, Infrastructure and Environment Executive Agency[6]; Directorate General for Research and Innovation[7]

jbapezteguia@cener.com[1], agracia@cener.com[1]; stefan.riechelmann@ptb.de[2], stefan.winter@ptb.de[2]; giorgio.bardizza@tuv.com[3]; christos.monokroussos@tuv.com[4], davide.polverini@ec.europa.eu[5]; pablo.vicente-laiglesia@ec.europa.eu[6]; maria.getsiou@ec.europa.eu[7]

3AV.3.10

EU PVSEC 2025

ABSTRACT:

European policies like the **Energy Labelling Regulation**, the **Ecodesign Directive** and the recently implemented **Ecodesign for Sustainable Products Regulation** have successfully improved the efficiency and sustainability of energy related products in the European market. In recent years, measures to incorporate **photovoltaic (PV) modules** within the scope of these policy tools are being prepared. In this regard, the European Commission's European Climate, Infrastructure and Environment Executive Agency (CINEA) is managing the **ECODESIGN-PV-TESTING project** aimed at developing two standardized methodologies relevant for the implementation of these policy measures to PV modules. The project is supported by the EC's Directorate General for Internal Market, Industry, Entrepreneurship and SMEs (DG GROW) and the Directorate General for Research and Innovation (DG RTD).

Keywords: energy yield, bifacial PV modules, long-term degradation rate.

1. INTRODUCTION

The three-year project (December 2023 to November 2026) developed by the German National Metrology Institute (PTB), TÜV Rheinland Italia SRL and the Spanish National Renewable Energy Centre (CENER) has a twofold objective:

- Define a methodology to estimate the **energy yield of bifacial PV modules**.
- Develop a method and testing sequence to estimate the **long-term degradation rate of the PV module's performance**.

These standardised methods shall be easily implemented by **Market Surveillance Authorities**, PV laboratories and manufacturers.

2. ENERGY YIELD OF BIFACIAL PV MODULES

Methodology

- Energy yield method to **account for various effects** including:
  - Irradiance
  - Albedo
  - Mounting configuration
  - Temperature
  - PV module design
- Based on IEC 61853 Standard series approach and extended for bifacial devices analysing in detail the **contribution from the rear side**.

IEC 61853 configuration (top left) and three relevant configurations for bifacial PV systems.

Testing activities and First results

- Bifacial PV module characterization:
  - Spectral responsivity *(SR)* } Front & Rear side
  - Incidence angle modifier (IAM) } Front & Rear side
  - Performance matrix (G-T)
  - Thermal coefficients (u_0 & u_1)
  - Bifaciality (φ_{Pmax})
- Six bifacial PV module types from different manufacturers
  - 1 HJT
  - 3 TOPCon
  - 1 PERC
  - 1 IBC

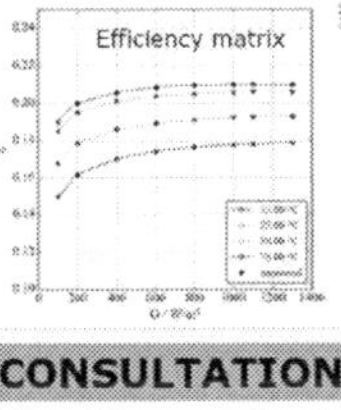

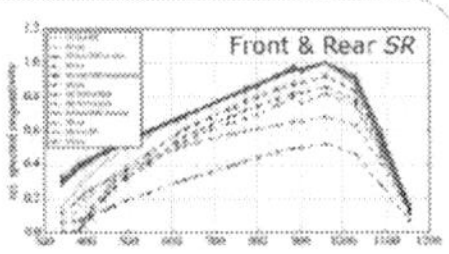

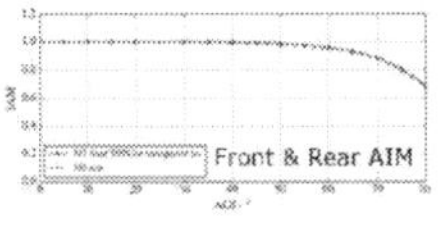

- Declared φ_{Pmax} between 80% and 90%.

3. LONG-TERM PV PERFORMANCE DEGRADATION

Methodology

- **Accelerated stress tests**, based on standardised sequences, to activate the most severe and common degradation mechanisms.
- **Extrapolation model** to relate testing results to long-term evolution of the degradation modes based on Arrhenius kinetics.

Testing activities and First results

- Eight PV module types from different manufacturers
  - 1 HJT
  - 2 PERC
  - 4 TOPCon
  - 1 IBC
- 6 monofacial and 2 bifacial devices (TOPCon)

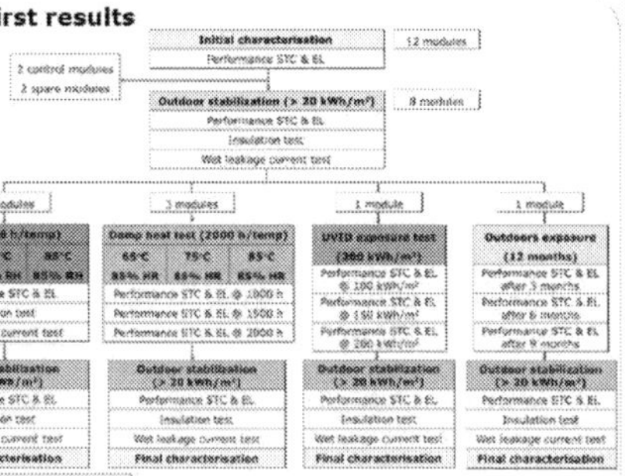

- 96 PV devices to be tested

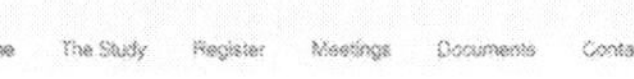

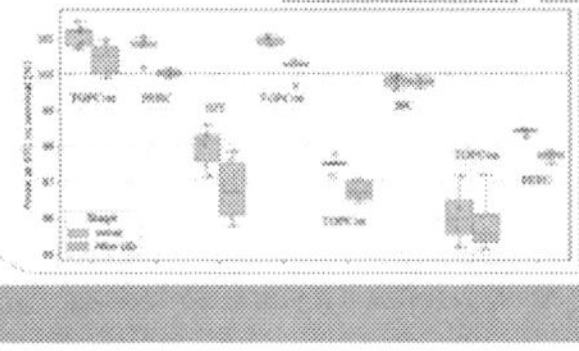

Comparison of *Pmax* at STC in the initial characterization and after LID test with regard to nominal values.

4. STAKEHOLDERS CONSULTATION

- More than 130 people registered from **academia, research institutes and PV manufacturers**.
- **Two general stakeholder meetings** organized so far, in months 3 and 19 to update stakeholders on the status of the project's development. Feedback received at info@ecodesign-pv-testing.eu.
- **Presentation and minutes** are available on the website https://ecodesign-pv-testing.eu/.
- **Last stakeholder meeting in autumn 2026**. To register visit https://ecodesign-pv-testing.eu/meetings/.

Development of standardisation methods for eco-design and energy labelling of photovoltaic products

Home The Study Register Meetings Documents Contact

5. CONCLUSIONS

- Both standardised methods, could be highly relevant for the **potential implementation ecodesign and energy labelling measures to PV modules**.
- **Duration and complexity** will be carefully assessed to guarantee an easy implementation by Market Surveillance Authorities, PV laboratories and manufacturers.
- Proposed testing activities are **based on available standard methods** already implemented by the PV industry.
- **First results show significant differences** between the tested PV devices.
- Final standardised methods and results will be presented in the **last stakeholder meeting** at the end of 2026.

SHAALKE: DEVELOPMENT OF A MATLAB SOFTWARE TOOL FOR ADVANCED STATISTICAL OUTDOOR DATA EVALUATION

Andreas Schneider[1] and Jorge Rabanal Arabach[2]
[1]University of Applied Sciences Gelsenkirchen, Neidenburger Str. 43,
45897 Gelsenkirchen, Germany
[2]Universidad de Antofagasta, Angamos Avenue 601, 1270300 Antofagasta, Chile

ABSTRACT: This paper introduces Shaalke, a novel analytical software tool developed for the high-accuracy evaluation of long-term photovoltaic module measurement data. Addressing the critical need for robust parameter extraction from field data, Shaalke integrates advanced filtering, linear regression, and algorithmic processing to overcome limitations of traditional evaluation methods. We demonstrate Shaalke's capability to accurately determine STC parameters and both static and dynamic temperature coefficients, showing excellent agreement with manufacturer specifications and independent laboratory measurements. A key finding is Shaalke's precise mapping of the irradiance dependence of module efficiency, filling a significant gap left by typical datasheet values which often only provide data at 1000 and 200 W/m². Furthermore, the tool enables reliable power degradation analysis, identifying modules that exceed manufacturer-tolerated limits. Shaalke provides a comprehensive, data-driven platform for understanding real-world module performance, offering invaluable insights for system design, operation, and quality assurance, thereby bridging the gap between laboratory specifications and field performance.
Keywords: Photovoltaic modules, Software tool, Data Evaluation, Field performance, STC parameters, Temperature coefficients, Power degradation

1 INTRODUCTION

Accurate determination of key performance parameters of photovoltaic (PV) modules - such as power at standard test conditions (STC), temperature coefficients, irradiance response, and long-term degradation behavior - is essential for both, scientific analysis and operational decision making in solar energy systems. While laboratory characterization provides controlled measurements, real-world performance often deviates due to environmental variability, non-standard operating conditions, and measurement noise. Over the past two decades, several approaches have been proposed to extract module parameters from field data, including linear regression methods, filtering of irradiance and temperature fluctuations, and statistical degradation analyses [1–3]. These studies highlight the value of long-term monitoring but also demonstrate the challenges of reducing uncertainty and ensuring reproducibility.

Despite these advances, the gap remains wide between raw monitoring data and actionable, accurate module parameters, particularly when effects of degradation and dynamic thermal behavior are to be captured simultaneously. Traditional evaluation pipelines often rely on restrictive filtering or simplified regression, potentially overlooking subtle but relevant effects in large datasets. There is, therefore, a strong need for analytical software that can process long-term high-resolution data efficiently, while integrating advanced signal processing and modeling algorithms for parameter extraction [4].

In response to this need, we introduce Shaalke, a dedicated software tool designed for analytical long-term evaluation of PV module performance. The program combines advanced filtering techniques, robust linear regression, and algorithmic post-processing to reliably determine STC performance, degradation rates, and static as well as dynamic temperature coefficients. This approach provides improved reproducibility and higher accuracy compared with standard methodologies, as shown by the initial analyses presented here.

In this paper, we first outline the methodological framework of Shaalke, followed by a demonstration of its application to long-term measurement datasets from solar modules under realistic outdoor conditions. We then present initial results highlighting the accuracy of extracted STC parameters and module temperature coefficients. The study concludes with a discussion of Shaalke's value for both research and industry practice, as well as its potential for enabling standardized, high-fidelity evaluation of long-term PV data.

2 SOFTWARE DEVELOPMENT

For the systematic evaluation of long-term field measurements, a dedicated software tool named Shaalke (Software for Harvested and at Ambient Acquired and Logged Key data for Evaluation) has been developed at the University of Applied Sciences, Gelsenkirchen. The program was implemented in the MATLAB environment, a platform well-suited for handling large numerical datasets and performing statistical analysis of time-series measurement data.

Shaalke is specifically designed to process data from PV module measurements collected in outdoor test facilities. It provides an intuitive graphical user interface (GUI) and supports the direct import of I–V parameters (current, voltage, operating power) and module rear-side temperature (T_{module}) on a one-minute timescale. These electrical and thermal data are automatically synchronized with local weather station records, including irradiance (G_{POA}), ambient temperature, relative humidity, and wind vectors. This design ensures that all relevant environmental and electrical parameters can be evaluated in a temporally consistent manner. With input capabilities for up to several years, the software can process datasets exceeding 500,000 rows (>5 million data points).

The main functions of Shaalke are (i) advanced filtering, allowing automated removal of outliers and erroneous entries caused by sensor drift or failures, and (ii) statistical parameter extraction by means of linear regression and correlation analysis. The software facilitates the determination of characteristic module coefficients such as temperature dependence of power,

10.4229/EUPVSEC2025/3AV.3.11

voltage, and current. In addition, Shaalke contains modules for yield simulation, enabling direct estimation of energy output under both, measured and synthetic climatic conditions. For synthetic inputs, the software provides seamless integration of Meteonorm datasets and other climate models, supporting comparative studies of climate variability and its influence on PV performance.

A distinctive feature of Shaalke is its ability to predict module operating temperature from purely meteorological inputs (irradiance, wind, ambient temperature) in combination with static module-specific parameters. This function enables two independent approaches for assessing electrical performance: one directly based on measured operating conditions, and another derived from reconstructed thermal behaviour. Such redundancy enhances model reliability and provides additional robustness in long-term degradation and climate impact studies.

By combining flexible data import, robust statistical analysis, and predictive functions, Shaalke establishes a unified platform for bridging experimental field measurements with theoretical yield simulations. The modular design allows further extension to additional performance metrics or future integration with machine-learning approaches for long-term PV performance prediction. Figure 1 shows exemplarily the temperature coefficient determination part of the GUI: Determination of the temperature coefficient of open circuit voltage close to 1000 W/m^2.

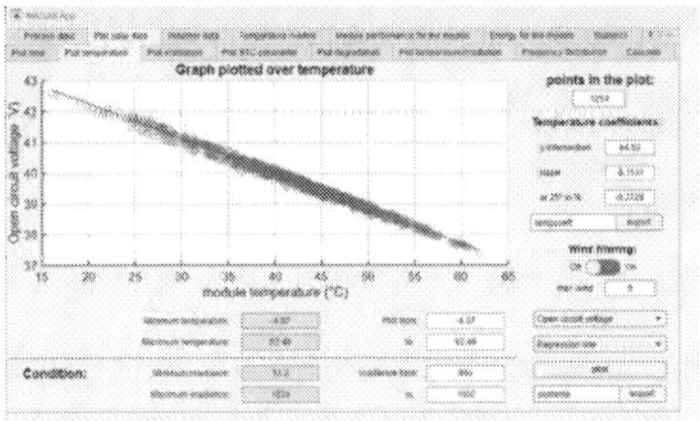

Figure 1: Example plot showing part of Shaalkes GUI

3 RESULTS AND DISCUSSION

3.1 Metrological and specimen information

A long-term outdoor monitoring campaign of photovoltaic (PV) modules was initiated in 2020 and is currently ongoing. The study focuses on commercially available crystalline silicon modules, the relevant datasheet specifications are provided in Table I. The modules are mounted under fixed-tilt conditions (module no 1-6), on a 2-axes tracker (module no 7) and on a single axis tracker (module 8 and 9) and continuously operated at their maximum power point (P_{mpp}), ensuring realistic field exposure and degradation assessment.

Current-voltage (I–V) characteristics are recorded at one-minute resolution using a calibrated Papendorf SOL.Connect® device. The system reports an accuracy better than 1% for I–V tracing, consistent with metrological standards. Module operating temperature is determined at the rear side with a Pt1000 resistance thermometer, while in-plane global irradiance is measured by an ISET sensor. Complementary environmental data, including ambient temperature, relative humidity, wind speed, wind direction, and both, global horizontal and tilted plane irradiance, are obtained from a nearby Thies weather station at five-minute intervals.

Table I: Type of solar modules including specific data from the datasheets

Module type	No	Cell /module technology	P (W)
Panasonic VBHN 340 SJ53	1	HIT	340
Sunpower P3 325 BLK	2	PERC shingled	325
REC Alpha-Series	3	HJT SmartWire	365
Heckert NeMo 4.1 80M	4	PERC	400
Hyundai DG-Series, HiE-S420DG	5	G12 PERC shingled	420
Solarwatt Vision AM4	6	PERC	405
Trina-TSM-440NEG9R.25	7	N-Typ i-TOPCon	420
Aiko Neostar Series-A445-MAH54Mb Nebular 2P Serie	8	N-Type ABC	445
Aiko A-MCE54Db Neostar 3S+54	9	N-Type ABC	470

The measurement schedule is illustrated in Figure 2, showing the individual PV modules included in the campaign, their start times, and whether they are still under evaluation or have completed testing. This long-term dataset allows the temporal evolution of module performance to be correlated with environmental stress factors such as temperature fluctuations, irradiance dose, and seasonal variations. To validate field measurements, modules are periodically dismounted and characterized under STC using an A+A+A+ mbj solar simulator (solar flasher), following IEC 60904-9 guidelines.

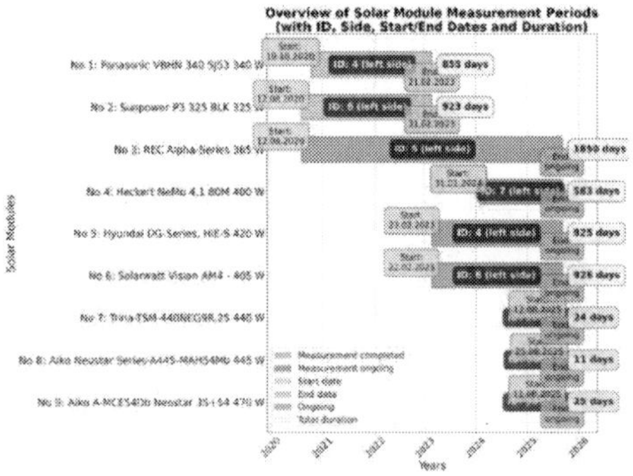

Figure 2: Measurement campaign schedule

Such continuous outdoor-to-laboratory correlation ensures that observed degradations are reliably attributed to environmental exposure rather than measurement artifacts. The combination of high temporal resolution, redundant temperature and irradiance sensing, and independent cross-validation through flasher tests provides a robust metrological framework. Similar approaches to long-term field monitoring have been described in literature on PV reliability studies [5].

3.2 Determination of STC parameters

Measurement data of the first six operation months were imported and subsequently filtered within the irradiance range of 1000 ± 50 W/m² (except for modules 7–9, which were just installed in August 2025 and hence less measurement data was available). Linear regression was then applied to the filtered dataset. Due to the large volume of available data points, sufficient coverage exists to accurately calculate I_{sc}, V_{oc}, and P_{mpp} at a reference temperature of 25°C ± 0.5°C. Table II lists the STC data for I_{sc}, V_{oc}, and P_{mpp} as specified by the supplier.

Table II: STC data given by the supplier (datasheet)

No	Datasheet (supplier)		
	I_{sc} (A)	**V_{oc} (V)**	**P_{mpp} (W)**
1	6.1	71.3	340
2	9.7	43.6	325
3	10.3	44.3	365
4	18.2	28.3	400
5	12.9	41.6	420
6	13.7	37.2	405
7	10.7	52.2	440
8	14.0	40.6	445
9	14.7	40.6	470

For reference, the modules had also been characterized using a calibrated mbj LED flasher immediately before the start of the measurement campaign. This provides an independent benchmark to which the results of Shaalke can be compared. Table III summarizes the corresponding results obtained through the mbj flasher (using a calibrated reference module) and through the Shaalke analysis tool.

Table III: STC results as obtained by the mbj LED flasher using a calibrated reference module and Shaalke

No	Flasher Data			Outdoor results (fitting)		
	I_{sc} (A)	V_{oc} (V)	P_{mpp} (W)	I_{sc} (A)	V_{oc} (V)	P_{mpp} (W)
1	6	70.9	320	6.1	70.1	326
2	9.4	43.5	321.1	9.6	43.1	322
3	10.1	43.6	337.1	10.2	43.3	335.3
4	17.9	27.8	390.5	17.9	27.3	385
5	12.5	42.2	407.6	12.7	41.4	394.1
6	13.6	37.5	400.9	13.8	36.7	400.9
7	10.7	52.8	445.4	10.5	52.9	431.3
8	13.3	40	425	13.6	39.7	435.0
9	15	40.3	479.7	14.9	40.1	477.9

The comparison clearly illustrates that Shaalke yields results in excellent agreement with the independent flasher measurements. Minor deviations can be attributed to differences in calibration schemes and slight module aging between flasher characterization and the onset of long-term data collection or any degradation occurring during the first 6 months of operation. Also, the regression-based evaluation confirms the high validity of Shaalke for automated STC determination under field conditions. These findings underline the robustness of combining long-term datasets with advanced filtering and regression techniques, providing a reliable complement and potential alternative to laboratory-based STC verification.

Figure 3 shows a box plot of the differences of P_{mpp}, V_{oc} and I_{sc} determined by Shaalke and the calibrated flasher measurement.

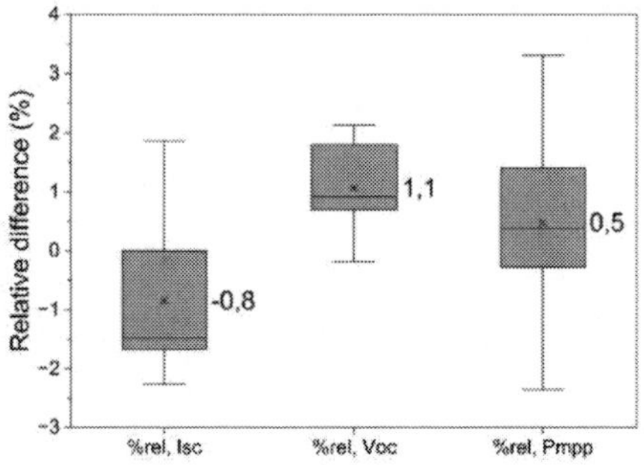

Figure 3: Relative difference of P_{mpp}, V_{oc} and I_{sc}

3.3 Determination of temperature coefficients

In the next step, the temperature coefficients for voltage, current, and power were determined for the same PV modules. As in the STC evaluation, the key requirement for extracting meaningful coefficients is to restrict the irradiance band as closely as possible to 1000 W/m², while still maintaining a sufficient number of datapoints after filtering to allow a stable linear regression fit. This ensures that variations in irradiance do not bias the slope determination and that the regression reflects only the temperature dependence of the electrical parameters.

Among the parameters considered, the temperature coefficient of voltage is typically the most straightforward to determine, as module voltage is measured with the highest accuracy and exhibits a clear and strong linear dependence on temperature. In contrast, the determination of the current coefficient is more difficult and is often affected by a higher degree of noise. This difficulty originates partly from the small intrinsic magnitude of the current-temperature dependence and partly from the nature of current measurement itself, which introduces larger measurement deviations compared with voltage.

Even under controlled laboratory environments, extracting reliable temperature coefficients of current is challenging because the small change of current with temperature is often comparable to the measurement uncertainty. As a result, significant scatter is commonly observed, and researchers typically mitigate this by employing wide temperature intervals, repeated measurements, and averaging procedures. In the present study, considerable improvement was achieved through the combination of long-term outdoor datasets and Shaalke's filtering and regression algorithms, which reduce noise levels and stabilize the regression slope. Figure 4 illustrates the filtered short-circuit current data used for determining the current temperature coefficient for one module. When compared to the supplier information, the values obtained through Shaalke show excellent agreement.

10.4229/EUPVSEC2025/3AV.3.11

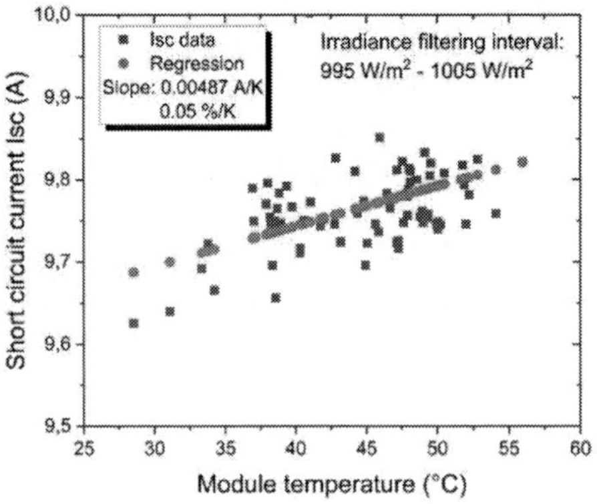

Figure 4: Example of filtered data for short circuit current to determine its temperature coefficient

Table IV lists the temperature coefficients provided by the manufacturer alongside results determined by Shaalke. The close match highlights the effectiveness of the method, particularly considering that values were obtained from field data under naturally varying conditions.

Table IV: Temperature coefficients as given by the module maker and determined by Shaalke

No	Datasheet			Outdoor results (fitting)		
	T_K for P_{mpp} (%/K)	T_K for V_{oc} (%/K)	T_K for I_{sc} (%/K)	T_K for P_{mpp} (%/K)	T_K for V_{oc} (%/K)	T_K for I_{sc} (%/K)
1	-0.26	-0.24	0.06	-0.30	-0.24	0.02
2	-0.36	-0.29	0.05	-0.37	-0.29	0.05
3	-0.26	-0.24	0.04	-0.35	-0.24	0.05
4	-0.34	-0.26	0.03	-0.36	-0.27	0.04
5	-0.34	-0.27	0.04	-0.34	-0.27	0.02
6	-0.33	-0.26	0.05	-0.39	-0.27	0.04
7	-0.29	-0.24	0.04	-0.31	-0.23	0.05
8	-0.26	-0.22	0.05	-0.25	-0.22	-
9	-0.26	-0.22	0.05	-0.24	-0.22	-

Small deviations are within typical uncertainty margins and can be attributed to measurement errors, environmental noise, and minor module variability. Importantly, Shaalke not only reproduces the voltage and power coefficients with good reliability but also yields a consistent estimate of the current coefficient—despite the known difficulties associated with its determination. This demonstrates that long-term outdoor monitoring, when combined with filtering and regression approaches, can yield results comparable to controlled laboratory testing.

Overall, these findings validate Shaalke as a powerful tool for automated determination of temperature coefficients directly from field data. Beyond the practical advantages of avoiding repeated laboratory flash tests, the methodology also reflects real operating conditions, which are highly relevant for long-term energy yield prediction and reliability assessment. The demonstrated accuracy of the results illustrates the potential for standardized, field-based module evaluation and quality assurance.

3.4 Irradiance dependence of efficiency

The dependence of module efficiency on irradiance was analyzed in detail for module 3 and compared with the reference data provided in the manufacturer's datasheet. Under standard test conditions (STC), both Shaalke and the datasheet predict the almost same efficiency value, confirming the consistency of the initial calibration. When moving away from STC and assessing performance in lower or higher irradiance ranges, however, deviations in the efficiency curve become apparent. Specifically, Shaalke results reveal a relative deviation of approximately 2–3% compared with the supplier's curve.

Although this deviation may appear numerically large at first glance, it is important to emphasize that the value is a relative percentage difference. In terms of absolute efficiency, the divergence is comparatively small and does not significantly affect overall energy yield estimations. Still, such irradiance-dependent effects are technologically relevant, as they impact performance particularly under real operating conditions with frequent low-light levels (e.g., mornings, evenings, or cloudy conditions).

A critical problem is that most suppliers usually specify efficiency values only at 1000 W/m² and, in some cases, at 200 W/m² for so-called "low light" behavior. This leaves the important irradiance range between 200–1000 W/m² largely undocumented in datasheets, even though this interval is where modules spend a significant portion of their operating lifetime.

Figure 5 illustrates the irradiance dependence of module 3, plotting both the supplier's reported curve and the results derived with Shaalke.

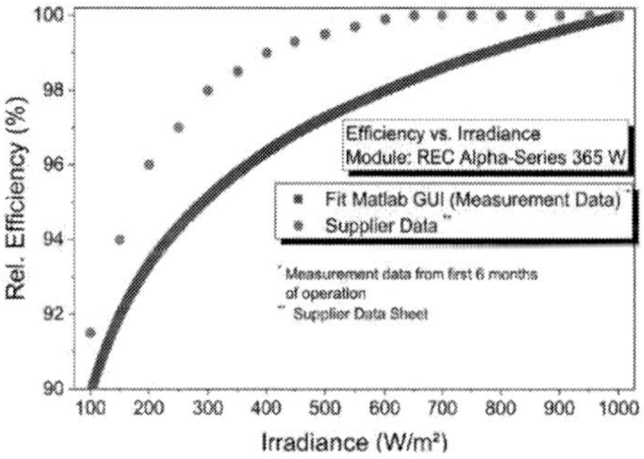

Figure 5: Irradiance dependence of module 3 as given by the supplier and determined by Shaalke

It can be observed that while the general shape and trend are in agreement, Shaalke provides a more data-driven representation that reflects actual long-term outdoor operation. This highlights the value of long-term datasets in capturing subtle performance deviations that are not always apparent from laboratory tests alone.

The observed difference may be attributed to several factors, including natural module degradation, variations in spectral distribution under real conditions, or the simplifications in measurement protocols used by the supplier. Importantly, the small but consistent deviations illustrate that Shaalke can serve not only as a validation tool for datasheet claims but also as a means to uncover real-world performance characteristics that are highly relevant for system energy yield predictions.

In summary, the assessment demonstrates that Shaalke reliably reproduces manufacturer-given efficiency curves while also capturing subtle irradiance-dependent effects that stem from outdoor operation. This ability to quantify low-light behavior and irradiance effects helps bridge the gap between laboratory specifications and field performance, thereby providing valuable input for module comparison, system modelling, and bankability assessments.

10.4229/EUPVSEC2025/3AV.3.11

3.5 Determination of the power degradation

As shown in the measurement data set, many of the investigated modules have been in continuous operation at the location for several years, with some still active today. This provides an extensive long-term data pool that can be leveraged to assess the power degradation of the modules under real outdoor conditions. Since suppliers typically report only limited degradation values - such as the performance loss in the first year and a subsequent annual linear degradation rate, or, in some cases, only the total guaranteed degradation after 25 or 30 years, our evaluation focuses on the actual years of operation available for the tested modules.

This necessarily introduces some uncertainty because the degradation trajectory during the first years may not be perfectly linear, and measurement intervals differ from the assumptions underlying the datasheet values. On the other hand, the supplier's values are provided as maximum guaranteed limits, which means our results can be directly compared against them to verify whether observed degradation remains within the specified tolerance.

The Shaalke analysis, based on regression of long-term monitoring data, reveals that most modules remain within the acceptable limits of the manufacturer's degradation specifications. However, in the case of modules 3 and 4, significantly larger degradation rates were identified compared to the values tolerated by the datasheet. This suggests either early-onset degradation mechanisms (e.g., encapsulant browning, interconnect fatigue, or light-induced degradation) or module-specific issues related to production variability. Importantly, Shaalke's long-term analysis makes such deviations from expected performance visible at an early stage, supporting proactive quality control.

Table V summarizes the degradation results determined with Shaalke after several years of operation and compares them directly to the manufacturer's maximum degradation claims. The comparison demonstrates that while most modules are well within specification, individual modules exceed supplier guarantees, underscoring the importance of continuous monitoring with advanced analysis tools rather than relying solely on datasheet projections.

Table V: Degradation after several years of operation as determined by Shaalke and compared to the max. value as calculated by the supplier datasheet

No	Operation	Max. degradation Datasheet (supplier)	Determined Degrad-ation (fitting)
	Years	%	%
1	2	3.5	1.2
2	3	3	0.2
3	6	4.5	7.3
4	2	2	2.8
5	3	3.1	0.4
6	3	1.3	0.6

These findings highlight both, the practical relevance and the reliability of Shaalke for degradation monitoring. In contrast to manufacturer warranties, which often use conservative or averaged values, our approach provides real data tailored to module-specific conditions. This information is highly valuable for system operators, investors, and researchers alike, as it enables more accurate predictions of long-term energy yield, early detection of underperforming modules, and validation of warranty claims.

3.6 Dynamic temperature coefficient determination

If long-term measurement data are available, Shaalke enables straightforward determination of dynamic temperature coefficients, which describe the irradiance dependence of the individual temperature coefficients. In contrast to static values taken at nominal conditions, dynamic coefficients provide deeper insight into how voltage, current, and power responses evolve under varying irradiance and temperature combinations [6, 7].

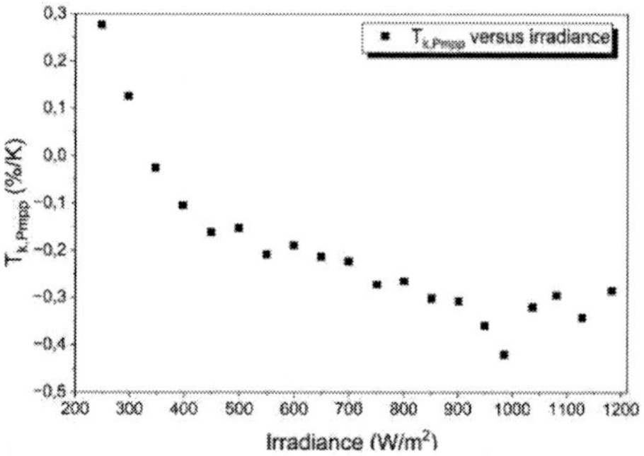

Figure 6: Dynamic P_{mpp} temperature coefficient

Shaalke incorporates a built-in function that automatically extracts these parameters once the dataset is imported, cleaned and filtered. This greatly simplifies the analysis, reducing a complex evaluation to a user-friendly process while retaining high accuracy. Figure 6 illustrates the determination of the dynamic P_{mpp} temperature coefficient as obtained with Shaalke.

The ability to derive dynamic coefficients from real, long-term data provides valuable information for modelling real-world module behavior, enabling more precise yield simulations and more reliable system design.

4 CONCLUSION

This paper presents Shaalke, an advanced analytical software tool designed for the high-accuracy evaluation of long-term PV module measurement data. Addressing the critical need for robust parameter extraction from field data, Shaalke integrates sophisticated filtering techniques, linear regression, and algorithmic processing to overcome the limitations of traditional evaluation methods and datasheet-only information.

Our results demonstrate Shaalke's capability to accurately determine key module parameters under real-world operating conditions. The analysis of STC parameters (I_{sc}, V_{oc}, P_{mpp}) showed excellent agreement with independent laboratory flasher measurements, thereby validating Shaalke's foundational accuracy. Furthermore, the software proved highly effective in determining temperature coefficients for voltage, current, and power. Notably, Shaalke successfully extracted the challenging current temperature coefficient from noisy field data, a task often difficult even in controlled laboratory environments.

A significant contribution of this work is the detailed

assessment of the irradiance dependence of module efficiency. While initial STC values matched supplier data, Shaalke revealed subtle yet important relative deviations of 2–3% in efficiency across varying irradiance levels. Crucially, our analysis highlighted a critical gap in manufacturer datasheets, which typically provide efficiency data only at 1000 W/m² and 200 W/m², leaving the vital operating range between 200–1000 W/m² largely undocumented. Shaalke effectively fills this gap by providing a data-driven, continuous efficiency curve, offering invaluable insights for accurate energy yield predictions and system modelling.

The long-term data pool also enabled a robust determination of power degradation. While most modules performed within supplier-specified maximum degradation limits, Shaalke identified two modules (modules 3 and 4) exhibiting significantly higher degradation than tolerated by their datasheets. This capability underscores Shaalke's role in early detection of underperforming modules and validation of warranty claims, moving beyond generalized manufacturer guarantees to module-specific performance insights. Finally, the software's ability to determine dynamic temperature coefficients, which account for the irradiance dependency of these parameters, further enhances the precision of real-world performance modelling.

In conclusion, Shaalke represents a significant advancement in PV module analysis. By leveraging long-term measurement data, it provides a comprehensive, accurate, and user-friendly platform for determining STC parameters, temperature coefficients, irradiance-dependent efficiency, and power degradation. This tool not only bridges the gap between laboratory specifications and field performance but also offers critical insights for researchers, system operators, and investors, ultimately contributing to more reliable PV system design, operation, and quality assurance.

5 ACKNOWLEDGEMENTS

The author wants to thank Mrs. Julia Chochollek for her long-term support with the development of Shaalke. This work was partly funded by the Federal Ministry for Economic Affairs and Energy inside the project BuKuMu under contract no. FKZ 03EE1225F.

6 REFERENCES

[1] Jordan, D.C. & Kurtz, S.R. (2013). Photovoltaic Degradation Rates - an Analytical Review. Prog. Photovolt: Res. Appl., 21(1), 12–29.

[2] Dirnberger, D. et. al. (2015). On the Impact of Solar Spectral Irradiance on the Yield of Different PV Technologies. Sol. Energy Mater. Sol. Cells, 132, 431–442.

[3] IEA PVPS Task 13 Reports (various years). Reliability and Performance of Photovoltaic Systems

[4] Köntges, M. et. al. (2014). Review of Failures of Photovoltaic Modules. NREL Report / IEA PVPS Task 13.

[5] Jordan, D. C. et. al (2016). Compendium of photovoltaic degradation rates. Progress in Photovoltaics. Volume 24, Issue 7, Pages 978-989

[6] Gasparin, F. P. et. al. (2022). Assessment on the variation of temperature coefficients of photovoltaic modules with solar irradiance. Solar Energy, Volume 244, Pages 126-133

[7] Schneider, A. et. al. (2024). Advanced Determination of Temperature Coefficients of Photovoltaic Modules by Field Measurements, SiliconPV Conference Proceedings. https://doi.org/10.52825/siliconpv.v1i.905

SHAALKE: Development of a MatLab Software Tool for Advanced Statistical Outdoor Data Evaluation

Andreas Schneider[1] and Jorge Rabanal Arabach[2]

[1]University of Applied Sciences Gelsenkirchen, Neidenburger Str. 43, 45897 Gelsenkirchen, Germany
[2]Universidad de Antofagasta, Angamos Avenue 601, 1270300 Antofagasta, Chile
*Phone: + 49 (209) 9596-313, Fax: + 49 (209) 9596-544, Email: andreas.schneider@w-hs.de

Introduction

Shaalke (Software for Harvested and at Ambient Acquired and Logged Key data for Evaluation) is a Matlab-based tool developed over four years at the University of Applied Sciences, Gelsenkirchen, designed for comprehensive data evaluation and yield simulation of solar modules. It enables importing extensive time-series PV module measurement data collected at one-minute intervals for up to several years, combined with ambient weather data. Shaalke handles large datasets with several million data points, allowing advanced filtering and (linear) regression techniques to accurately extract key solar module parameters such as: temperature coefficients (static and dynamic) and STC data beside studying in detail irradiance and temperature dependencies and degradation behavior.

Sample testing overview

The following picture gives an overview on the long-term measurement plan

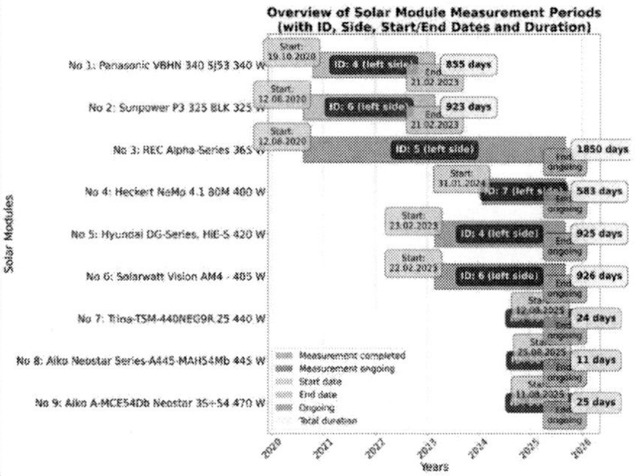

Shaalke – The Matlab GUI for advanced PV module data evaluation

The GUI allows fast access to several evaluation tools, including data import, export and data filtering. Even Meteonorm climatic data sets can be imported.

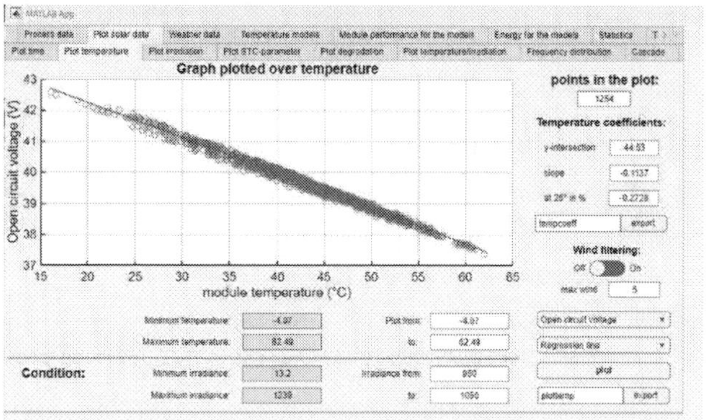

Determination of STC data

STC data as determined by Shaalke in comparison to the measurement data by an mbj-LED flasher and the supplier data as given in the datasheet.

No	Data sheet (supplier)			Flasher (mbj flasher)			Outdoor results (fitting)		
	I_{sc} (A)	V_{oc} (V)	P_{mpp} (W)	I_{sc} (A)	V_{oc} (V)	P_{mpp} (W)	I_{sc} (A)	V_{oc} (V)	P_{mpp} (W)
1	6.1	71.3	340	6	70.9	320	6.1	70.1	326
2	9.7	43.6	325	9.4	43.5	321.1	9.6	43.1	322
3	10.3	44.3	365	10.1	43.6	337.1	10.2	43.3	335.3
4	18.2	28.3	400	17.9	27.8	390.5	17.9	27.3	385
5	12.9	41.6	420	12.5	42.2	407.6	12.7	41.4	394.1
6	13.7	37.2	405	13.6	37.5	400.9	13.8	36.7	400.9
7	10.7	52.2	440	10.7	52.8	445.4	10.5	52.9	431.3
8	14.0	40.6	445	13.3	40	425	13.6	39.7	435.0
9	14.7	40.6	470	15	40.3	479.7	14.9	40.1	477.9

Boxplot showing the relative differences between flasher and Shaalke results

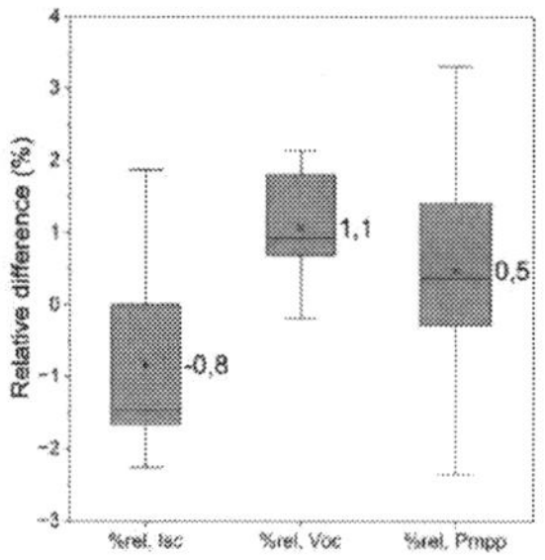

Determination of temperature coefficients

Temperature coefficients determined by Shaalke in comparison to supplier data as given in the datasheet.

No	Datasheet		Outdoor results (fitting)	
	T_{KPmpp} (%/K)	T_{KVoc} (%/K)	T_{KPmpp} (%/K)	T_{KVoc} (%/K)
1	-0.26	-0.24	-0.30	-0.24
2	-0.36	-0.29	-0.37	-0.29
3	-0.26	-0.24	-0.35	-0.24
4	-0.34	-0.26	-0.36	-0.27
5	-0.34	-0.27	-0.34	-0.27
6	-0.33	-0.26	-0.39	-0.27
7	-0.29	-0.24	-0.31	-0.23
8	-0.26	-0.22	-0.25	-0.22
9	-0.26	-0.22	-0.24	-0.22

Determination of power degradation

Power degradation as determined by Shaalke using several years of measurement data and compared to the maximum supplier degradation, as given in the datasheet.

No	Duration after inauguration	Max. degradation according to Data sheet (supplier)	Determined degradation according to outdoor results (fitting)
	Years	%	%
1	2	3.5	1.2
2	3	3	0.2
3	6	4.5	7.3
4	2	2	2.8
5	3	3.1	0.4
6	3	1.3	0.6

Irradiance dependency of module efficiency

Rel. module efficiency in dependency of irradiance for the REC alpha module (Shaalke data versus supplier data)

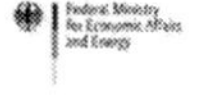

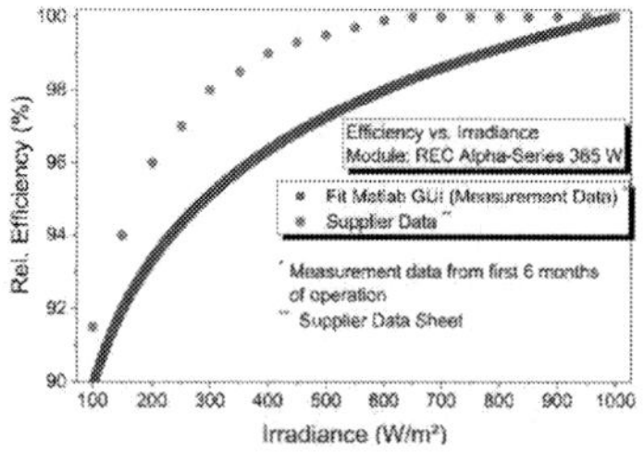

Summary

This paper presents Shaalke, an innovative software tool for long-term PV module measurement data evaluation. The presented results on the determination of STC data, temperature coefficients, power degradation and irradiance dependency of module efficiency proof nicely the strong and high-quality evaluation capabilities of Shaalke.

Supported by: Federal Ministry for Economic Affairs and Energy on the basis of a decision by the German Bundestag

This publication was partly funded by the Federal Ministry for Economic Affairs and Energy inside the project BuKuMu under contract no. FKZ 03EE1225F.)

DEGRADATION AND DEFECT CHARACTERISATION OF FIELD-DEPLOYED SILICON PV MODULES

RP Roodt[1], EE van Dyk[1], JL Crozier McCleland[1], M Vumbugwa[1], FJ Vorster[1], O Stroyuk[2], C Buerhop-Lutz[2]
[1]Department of Physics, Nelson Mandela University, Port Elizabeth, South Africa
[2]Forschungszentrum Jülich GmbH, Helmholtz-Institut Erlangen Nürnberg für Erneuerbare Energien (HI ERN), 91058 Erlangen, Germany

E-Mail address: s217357709@mandela.ac.za

ABSTRACT: A sample of fifteen monocrystalline silicon-based PV modules was tested and characterised in this study. These modules have been deployed in the field for over a decade at the Outdoor Research Facility of Nelson Mandela University, South Africa. Various characterisation techniques were utilised, including visual inspection, electroluminescence (EL) imaging, and current-voltage (I-V) curves. A detailed analysis was done on the various PV modules in order to understand the observed defects or anomalies and associated performance degradation. When compared to historically acquired I-V curve measurements, the modules show substantial degradation in the performance for one type of module and the other module type does not show any power decrease compared to specification. Combining visual, UV Fluorescence (UV-F) imaging, and EL imaging provided deeper insight into hidden defects and material degradation not evident from visual inspection alone.
Keywords: Ultraviolet-fluorescence imaging, EL imaging, visual inspection, current-voltage curve

1 INTRODUCTION

Silicon PV modules have long been the leading technology for commercially available PV modules. With that being said, PV modules that have been exposed to real-world, long-term exposure are a source of valuable information to monitor performance and to observe how the different components of the PV modules last in these conditions. It has been observed that recording current-voltage (I-V) curves and visual inspection, various defects and performance results can be identified [1].

Cracks, snail trails, encapsulant browning and discolouration, delamination, metal corrosion and back sheet chalking are just a few of the features visible and can be noted using visual inspection [1]. So, utilising the characterisation techniques available to us, various PV modules were investigated. This was done to investigate the performance of the modules as they have been deployed for a substantial period, and to investigate if there were defects, what defects may be identified and to determine the root cause and impact on performance[3]. In addition, studies into long-term PV module performance using the characterisation tools employed here provide crucial insights for optimising maintenance schedules and enhancing overall operational PV power plant efficiency [2].

2 EXPERIMENTAL PROCEDURE

2.1 PV Modules

The investigation was conducted on fifteen monocrystalline Solar World Sunmodule PV modules deployed in two arrays at the Outdoor Research Facility of Nelson Mandela University. The modules were of two types: SW 175, which has been in operation for 16 years from 2009 until 2025, consisting of 9 modules, and SW235, which has been in operation for 9 years from June 2016 – July 2025, consisting of 6 modules.

The Standard Test Conditions (STC) parameters as specified are listed in Table I.

Table I: Manufacturer STC specification of modules investigated.

Module type	SW 235 mono	SW 175 mono
Maximum power (Pmax)	235 Wp	175 Wp
Maximum power point voltage (Vmpp)	30.3 V	35.8 V
Maximum power point current (Impp)	7.77 A	4.89 A
Open circuit voltage (Voc)	37.5 V	44.4 V
Short circuit current (Isc)	8.19 A	5.30 A

2.2 Measurement procedure

Module performance was evaluated using visual, electroluminescence (EL), and UV-fluorescence (UV-F) imaging, as well as I-V curves. These techniques were utilised as there is some overlap between the defects that can be observed, but they also show unique features. Visual and UV-F images were captured with a digital camera, while EL imaging and I-V curves were obtained using a MBJ 3.0 mobile laboratory an A+A+A+ LED solar simulator with integrated NIR-CMOS cameras. The analysis also incorporated historical I-V data from the two PV arrays. The focus was on the degradation of these two systems, as the older technology used in these modules makes their ageing particularly relevant compared to modern materials. Historical results include indoor I-V curves (from an Optosolar – AAA Xenon- flash solar), outdoor I-V curves (PVe and Solmetric I-V curve tracers), and indoor and outdoor EL images (from a Greateyes EL system).

3 RESULTS

The results for the two module types are discussed in the following sections.

3.1 SW 175 modules

Three modules were used to illustrate the performance of the SW 175 modules over the 16 years. The modules

10.4229/EUPVSEC2025/3AV.3.12

are referred to as Module A, B and C.

From the I-V curves shown in Figure 1, the following results are seen. In 2018, the I-V curves and Pmax values of all nine modules closely matched those of module A. In Module A, no defects were observed, and it was used for comparison with Modules B and C.

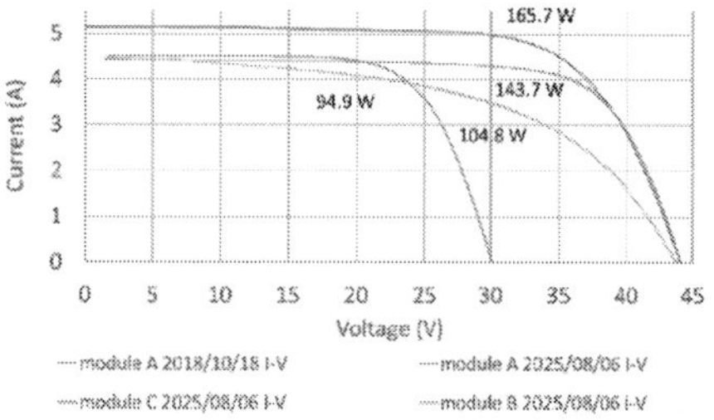

Figure 1: I-V curves obtained for 3 of the SW 175 modules. Module A's I-V curves obtained in 2018 and 2025, and module B and C's I-V curves for 2025.

The power decreased by 22.0 W since 2018. Module B has a bypassed substring, as the Voc value has decreased to 30.2 V in 2025, which severely affects the power output of the module, which only produces 94.9 W at STC.

Module C has a different shape I-V curve, while there is no change in the Isc or Voc of the module. This shape of the I-V curve shows that the module has an increased series resistance and decreased shunt resistance [4].

Considering the modules that do not show obvious visual or other defects, the average power in Aug 2025 was 140.4 W. This translates to an annual degradation rate of 1.12 % when taking the specified 3.00% degradation in the first year of operation of the module into account. This is more than the specified 0.7 % per annum [5].

3.2 Imaging Techniques results

The results obtained from the various imaging techniques for Modules A to C are shown in Figure 2. Visual, UV-F, and EL inspections reveal ageing effects and defects in the modules (2020–2025). Visual inspection shows a square browning pattern on cell interiors; modules B and C show additional square patterns on the interior of the cells. In the UV-F images, the brown patterns correspond to brighter fluorescence interiors, while the edges show quenching [6,7]. Module B shows extra inner features matching the visual image. Comparing the EL images obtained in 2020 to the ones obtained in 2025, Module A has signs of a bright brim/dark interior pattern, which is also seen in Module C. Conveyor belt tracks are also visible, and this is from non-uniform heating during manufacturing [2]. The luminescence intensity of module B decreased; likely, acetic acid formation between EVA and cells, which reacted with the fingers of the cells and increased series resistance [8]. Looking at cracks, we can see that active area and busbar cracks are visible in UV-F (quenching), and this is confirmed by the EL images. This is highlighted by cells with yellow squares around them. The UV-F image of Module C shows age-related crack growth [6]. In the 2020 EL image of module C, the top substring was bypassed, while in the 2025 EL image, a different substring was bypassed due to a burned bypass diode damaging the junction box. All modules show chalking, no backsheet cracks/damage. Future work: Verification Bill of Materials comprising Glass front, EVA, Tedlar backsheet [5].

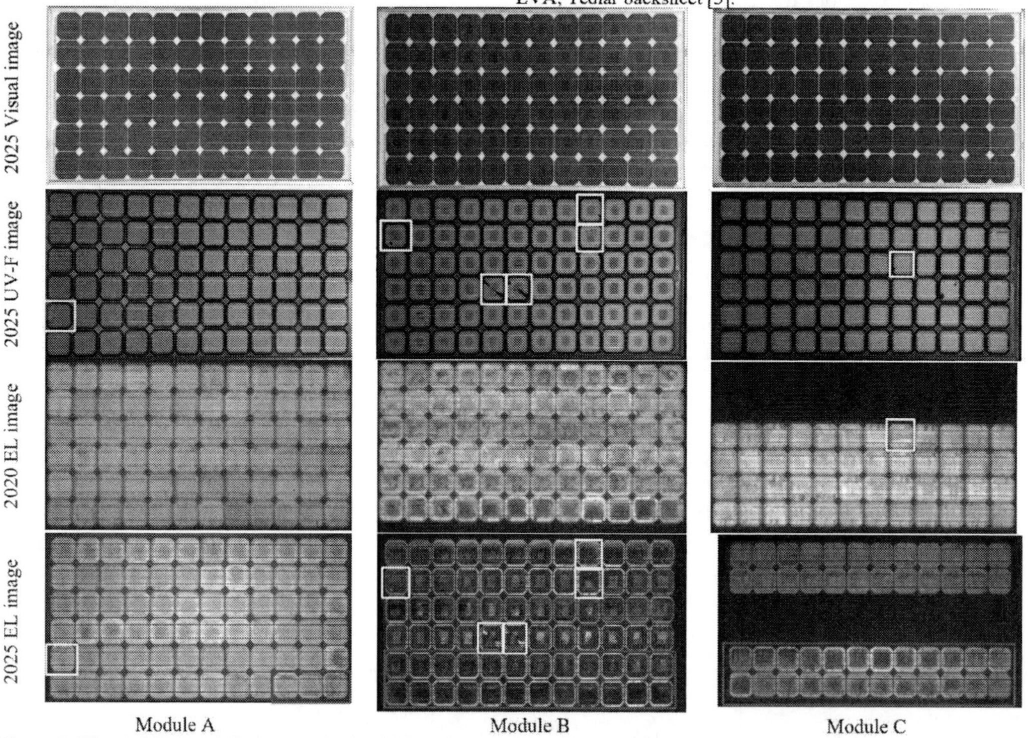

Figure 2: Visual, UV-F and EL images obtained for modules A, B and C in 2025 and EL images obtained in 2020. Features and changes in the intensity patterns in the EL images of the cells are highlighted with yellow squares and purple rectangles, respectively.

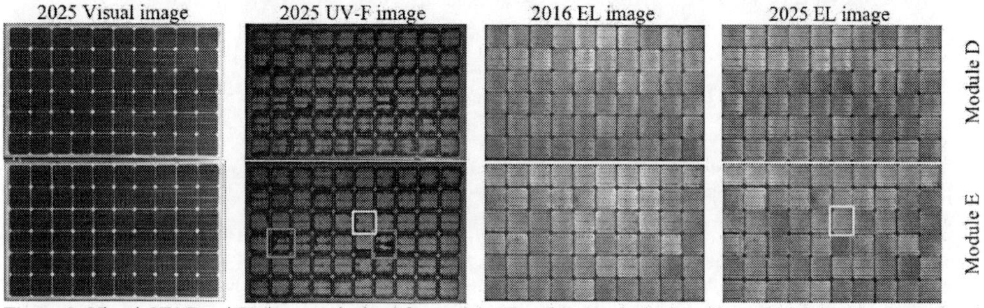

Figure 3: Visual, UV-F and EL images obtained for modules D and E. Cracks in the cells are highlighted by green (long) and red ("x"-shaped) squares.

3.2 SW 235 modules

These modules show no electrical degradation after a decade, likely due to initial underspecification, considering that the specifications have a +5.00 % tolerance [9]. Pre-installation measurements and more recent flash power measurements were acquired, but this was done using different measurement equipmentmaking it difficult to compare the results. Two modules were used to illustrate findings on the SW 235 modules over the period of investigation. The modules are referred to as Module D and E.

After further inspection, the following was observed. The modules have been deployed for nearly a decade with no visual signs of module degradation, encapsulant discolouration, or backsheet chalking. Looking at the backside of the module, some exhibit scratches or marks on the backsheet, likely due to grass cutting at the facility, but no chalking is visible. In module E, small "x"-shaped cracks are visible in the 2025 EL image and confirmed by a circular quenching pattern in the UV-F image, indicating it has been there for a few years. This is highlighted by a yellow square. Furthermore, diagonal cracks across cells are also visible in both EL and UV-F images, highlighted by green squares.

A pattern observed in the UV-F images of all six modules is the finger soaking pattern, which is may be caused by solder flux being drawn along cell fingers, extinguishing the UV-F [6]. Busbar cracks that ma have formed behind the busbars are also visible in the UV-F images of Modules D and E.

These findings indicate that while the modules are performing well electrically, they do show signs of internal material degradation that could potentially impact their future performance.

4. Conclusion

Two SolarWorld module types were investigated, both during and after deployment, for over a decade. The SW 175 mono modules showed a linear degradation rate of 1.12%/year, considering 3.00% degradation in the first year. Visual, UV-F, and EL imaging revealed several defects and material degradation, correlating directly with reduced performance. The SW 235 mono modules showed no clear decrease in power compared to the original specification. This performance stability may be linked to underspecification at manufacture. Visual inspection of the modules revealed no obvious degradation. UV-F and EL imaging showed cracks and identified material degradation. Combining visual, UV-F, and EL imaging provides deeper insight into hidden defects and materialdegradation not evident from visual inspection.

5 REFERENCES

[1] M. Köntges, S. Kurtz, U. Jahn, K.A. Berger, Review of Failures of Photovoltaic Modules, n.d. https://www.researchgate.net/publication/274717701.

[2] L. Koester, S. Lindig, A. Louwen, A. Astigarraga, G. Manzolini, D. Moser, Review of photovoltaic module degradation, field inspection techniques and techno-economic assessment, Renewable and Sustainable Energy Reviews 165 (2022). https://doi.org/10.1016/j.rser.2022.112616.

[3] B. Doll, J. Hepp, M. Hoffmann, R. Schuler, C. Buerhop-Lutz, I.M. Peters, J.A. Hauch, A. Maier, C.J. Brabec, Photoluminescence for Defect Detection on Full-Sized Photovoltaic Modules, IEEE J Photovolt 11 (2021) 1419–1429. https://doi.org/10.1109/JPHOTOV.2021.3099739.

[4] J.L. Crozier, F.J. Vorster, E.E. van Dyk, Evaluating the relationship between electroluminescence (EL) imaging and the power output of photovoltaic modules, in: 3rd South Afr. Sol. Energy Conf, 2015: pp. 24–28.

[5] SolarWord Sunmodule SW 155/165/175 mono specification sheet, https://shop.solardirect.com/pdf/solar-electric/modules/sunmodule-data-sheet.pdf.F.

[6] Vorster, E. Van Dyk, UV fluorescence imaging of photovoltaic modules, in: 6th South Afr. Sol. Energy Conf. 2019: pp. 1–5.

[7] C. Buerhop, E. Dyk, F. Vorster, O. Stroyuk, O. Mashkov, J. McCleland, M. Vumbugwa, J. Hauch, I. Peters, Advancing Photovoltaic Module Inspection: The Power of UV Imaging for Comprehensive Material Analysis and Quality Assurance, in: 2024: pp. 250–252. https://doi.org/10.1109/PVSC57443.2024.10749225.

[8] U. Weber, R. Eiden, C. Strubel, T. Soegding, M. Heiss, P. Zachmann, K. Nattermann, H. Engelmann, A. Dethlefsen, N. Lenck, Acetic acid production, migration and corrosion effects in ethylene-vinyl-acetate-(EVA-) based pv modules, in: 2012: pp. 2992-2995. https://doi.org/10.4229/27thEUPVSEC2012-4CO.9.4

[9] The SolarWorld Sunmodule Advantage, https://naturalsolar.com.au/wp-content/uploads/2015/11/solar-world-warranty.pdf.

10.4229/EUPVSEC2025/3AV.3.12

Architecture for monitoring PV degradation in real time from EL images

Tohru Kohno*, Jun Tsunoda*
Hitachi, Ltd. Research & Development Group
1-280 Higashi-Koigakubo, Kokubunji, Tokyo 185-8601, Japan
E-mail: toru.kono.cw@hitachi.com

ABSTRACT: We developed an architecture to monitor the degradation rate of PV (Photovoltaic) in real time from EL(Electroluminance) images. In recent years, technology has been developed to measure EL images outdoors, but it has been difficult to accurately grasp performance degradation from EL images. First, we extracted the luminance distribution from the EL image of the PV module that underwent an accelerated test, and created an input layer for machine learning. Second, in the training of a neural network that isolates EL images of PV modules before and after the output drops rapidly, we found a high correlation between the output and degradation of the hidden layer, and created an approximate equation. By applying the luminance distribution of the measured EL image to the learned parameters and applying the output of the calculated hidden layer to an approximate formula, we succeeded in calculating the power generation performance instantaneously.
Keywords: EL images outdoors, Degradation rate, The hidden layer, Neural Network

1 INTRODUCTION

The reuse of PV modules and the promotion of recycling are being considered. Legislation is also being considered for reinvestment in existing equipment and repowering when small-scale equipment is consolidated. PV modules in the early stages of FIT (Feed-in Tariff) in Japan, which were expected to operate stably for more than 20 years, have also been in operation for 12~13 years as of 2025. It isn't be know how stably these PV modules can be used in the future, and the performance itself. However, there is no clear standard for reuse and repowering, and the secondary market for PV is stagnant.

On the otherhand, there have been some cases where the performance of PV power plants has declined sharply, and understanding the current soundness of PV modules will lead to a market for long-term stable business continuity using PV facilities. However, as of 2025, visual inspection of PV modules is the mainstay, and although it is possible to identify adhesion of foreign matter, broken glass, and scorching of the backsheet caused by lightning strikes, etc., the performance has not been grasped. Although it is used for drone inspections and IV measurements at exposure sites, there is a problem that accurate results cannot be obtained due to the time and cost.

We conducted many reliability tests and acceleration tests of PV modules in the early stages of FIT in Japan and accumulated data [1-2]. On top of that, PV modules installed in power generation equipment installed in 2005 and 2012 are regularly monitored once every few years to observe deterioration. From the results of the FY2023 survey, it was found that these PV modules are degraded called fake shunt [3], which is a type of degradation in which the output drops sharply from a certain point, that is, a type of degradation that reaches the end of its life. Furthermore, about this degradation mode, it is difficult to grasp without observing the busbar and fingers in EL (Electroluminance) images [4].

From the above, it is desirable to inspect power generation equipment without moving the PV modules from the installation site to the laboratory for measurement, and to be able to grasp the performance and quality ranking on the spot. In recent years, the acquisition of EL images at exposed sites has been put into practical use [5]. However, it has been difficult to accurately grasp the electrical performance from EL images. The purpose of this study is to construct an algorithm that can estimate the deterioration rate and determine the quality ranking of PV modules only from the EL images measured in the room.

2 Architecture for estimating PV degradation rate in real time from EL images

2.1 Development concept

Fig. 1 shows the concept of the architecture. First, as shown in Fig. 1 (a), an EL camera acquires a current while applying a current from a current source to the PV array installed in exposure. First, as shown in Fig. 1(a), an image is acquired with an EL camera while applying a current from a current source to the PV array installed in exposure. Next, by applying the developed monitoring architecture to the acquired EL image of the PV module, the output ratio of the PV module, that is, the degradation, is calculated instantaneously as shown in Fig. 1 (b).

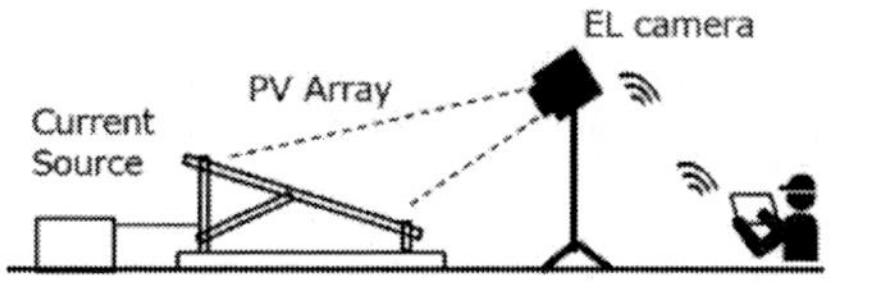

(a) Concepts in measurement

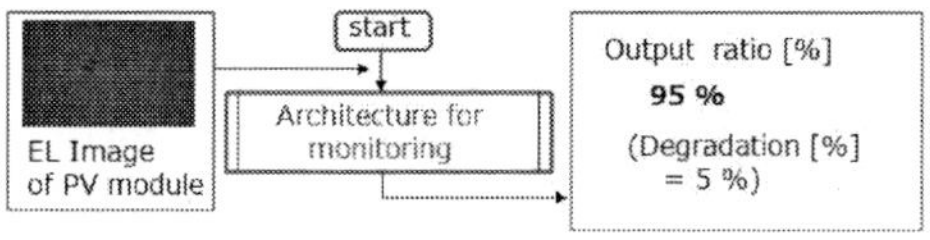

(b) Concepts on the software screen

Figure 1: The concept of developed algorithm

2.2 Learning with Neural Networks

Fig. 2 shows the procedure for obtaining the luminance distribution from an EL image of a PV module. For each of the A-F constituting the PV module, it is divided into 11 rows parallel to the busbar, and the luminance is acquired by image processing software. The luminance of the 11 lines of A-F is averaged and set as the luminance of 11 lines. The values shown in Fig. 2 are the average luminance of the 11 lines in areas A to F and the luminance of the whole PV module. These values are obtained by Image J [6-7].

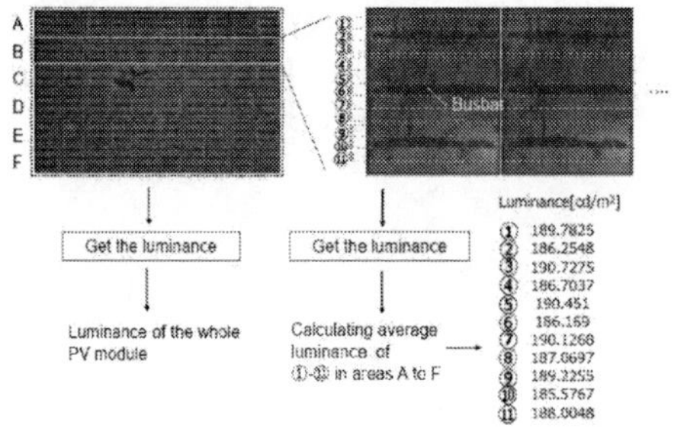

Figure 2: Procedure for determining the luminance distribution from the EL image of the PV module

Thereafter, as shown in Fig. 3, these 11 line's luminance values are normalized by the whole PV module brightness as 1 and are set in the input layer of machine learning. The difference between the average and deviation of these luminances is also set in the input layer. The "correct " is to set the PV module before the sudden change in the output ratio as 01 and the PV module after the sudden change as 10.

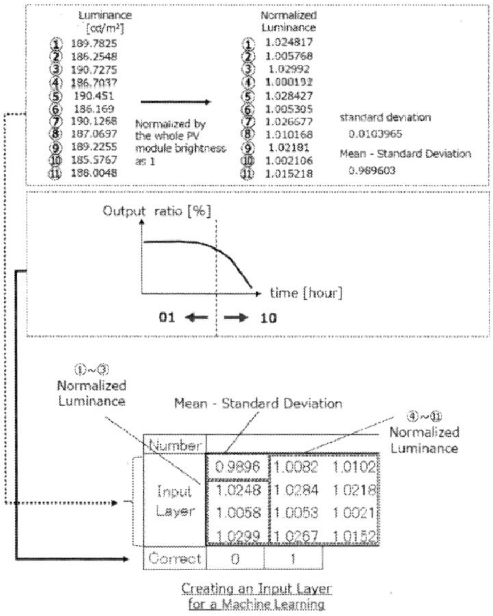

Figure 3: Setting the luminance distribution as an input layer for learning of neural network

Table 1 shows the output ratio of PV modules that underwent an accelerated dump heat test (temperature 85°C, humidity 85%). This PV module is a polycrystalline silicon PV module of the same type as the one evaluated in Ref. [3]. As a result of the dump heat using 4 PV modules, the output ratio of module No. 1 is 90.0% at the test time of 4500 hours, so for Number 1~6, 01 is set as the PV module before the power ratio changes suddenly. On the other hand, for modules No. 2, 3, and 4, the output ratios are 82.0%, 82.6%, and 79.0%, respectively, at 4500 hours, so for Number 7~9, the PV module is set to 10 after the output ratio drops sharply.

Table 1: PV module and performance in the dump heat test (85°C, 85%)

DH Test Time [hour]	Output rate [%]	Module No.	Number
0	100.0	1	1
3500	96.9	1	2
3500	94.4	2	3
4000	92.2	1	4
4000	90.4	2	5
4500	90.0	1	6
4500	82.0	2	7
4500	82.6	3	8
4500	79.0	4	9

Fig.4 is a schematic diagram showing the procedure for learning "10" and "01". In this study, we will use a learner built by a neural network to learn whether the EL image is before or after the sudden decrease in the output ratio. Here, the input layer receives the matrix constituted of the standard deviation and the normalized luminance as shown in Fig. 3. Fig. 4 shows the neural network in which the middle layer (hidden layer) is composed of three neurons and the output layer is composed of two neurons.

This neural network is built to classify whether the EL image is before or after the sudden drop in output ratio. As described in the Correct section above, if the output from the two neurons in the output layer is close to "0" and "1", it means that the PV module of the input EL image is before the sudden decrease in the output ratio. If it is close to "1" and "0", it means that the PV module of the input EL image is after the output ratio has dropped sharply.

Enter the matrix constituted of the standard deviation and the normalized luminance of Number 1 in Table 1 and the normalized values for the first neuron. In this example, the correct answer is before the output ratio drops sharply (output layer "0" and "1").

The first neuron in the hidden layer has a weight matrix consisting of 12 elements that multiply by each of the 12 elements of the matrix that described as the input sequence in Fig. 3. The result of multiplying both matrices is substituted into the sigmoid function represented by the first formula at the bottom of Fig. 4. The threshold for the first neuron in the hidden layer is defined as 1.00. By following the above steps, the output y of the first neuron in the hidden layer is obtained. The same is true for the second neuron in the hidden layer and the third neuron in the hidden layer.

Next, the output y of the first neuron of the hidden layer is input into the first neuron of the output layer. The first neuron in the output layer has a weight matrix composed of three elements that multiply by the output y of each neuron of the 1st~3rd neuron in the hidden layer. The result of multiplying the two matrices is substituted into the sigmoid function represented by the second formula at the bottom of Fig. 4. The threshold for the first neuron in the output layer is defined as 35.46. By following the above steps, the output z of the first neuron in the output layer is obtained. The same is true for the second neuron in the output layer.

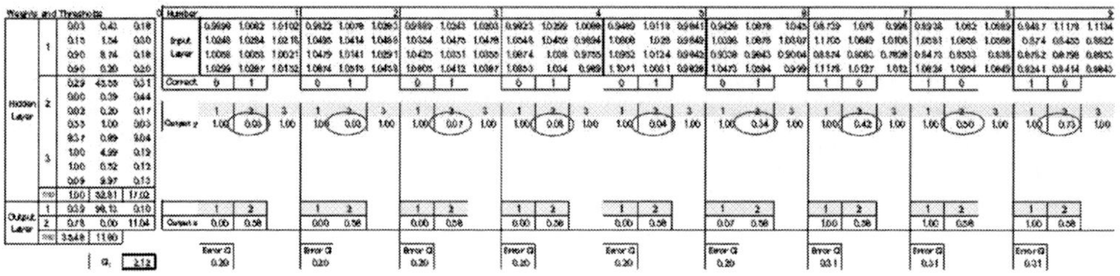

Sigmoid function

Output y1 $= 1/\{1+\exp(-(0.03*0.9896+0.15*1.0248+\cdots+0.20*1.0152)+1.00)\}$

Input layer × weight of hidden layer 1 — Threshold of hidden Layer 1

Output z1 $= 1/\{1+\exp(-(0.39*1.00+96.13*0.03+\cdots+0.10*1.00)+35.46)\}$

Weight of output layer 1 × output y — Threshold of output layer 1

Error Q $= (0-0.00)^2 + (1-0.56)^2$

Figure 4: The learning of neural network for setting the "correct" to 01 for Number 1-6 and 10 for Number 7-9

Based on the above calculations, the output of the first neuron in the output layer is 0.00, and the output of the second neuron in the output layer is 0.56. On the other hand, since the correct answer of Number1 is "0" and "1", the error Q between the output from the output layer and the correct answer can be calculated as shown in the third calculation formula at the bottom of Fig. 4. The same is calculated for Numbaer2~9. The learning is completed by optimizing the matrix elements and thresholds of each layer so that the error Q is minimized.

2.3. Architecture for estimating PV degradation rate in real time from EL images

We focus on Output y (2) surrounded by a circle in Fig. 4. The values of Numbers 1 to 9 are 0.03, 0.03, 0.07, 0.08, 0.04, and 0.34, respectively. ,0.42,0.5 and 0.53. Fig. 5 shows the relationship between these values and the output ratios in Table 1. As shown in Fig. 5, there is a high correlation between Output y (2) and the output ratio, that is, the degradation rate.

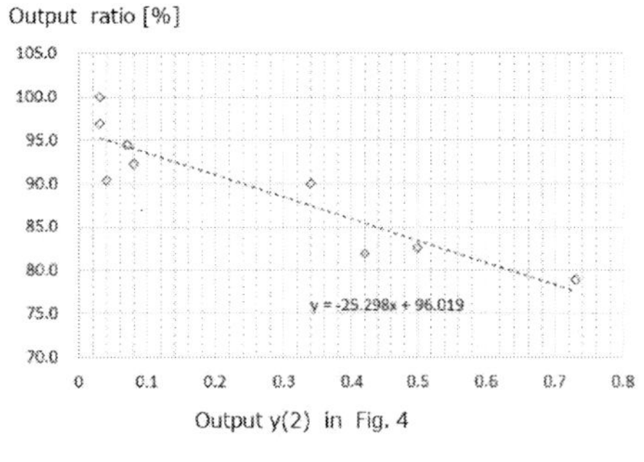

Figure 5: The relationship between output y (2) in Fig. 4 and the output ratio

We devised the architecture to calculate the output ratio from the EL image, as shown in Fig. 6. First, the input layer of the neural network is created from the brightness distribution calculated by the method shown in Fig. 2 and 3 from the EL image. Next, matrix calculations are performed using the parameters of the learned hidden layer and the output layer as shown in Fig. 4. Here, the hidden layer Output y (2) is extracted. Finally, the output ratio is calculated using the approximate formula y=-25.298x + 96.019 shown in Fig. 5.

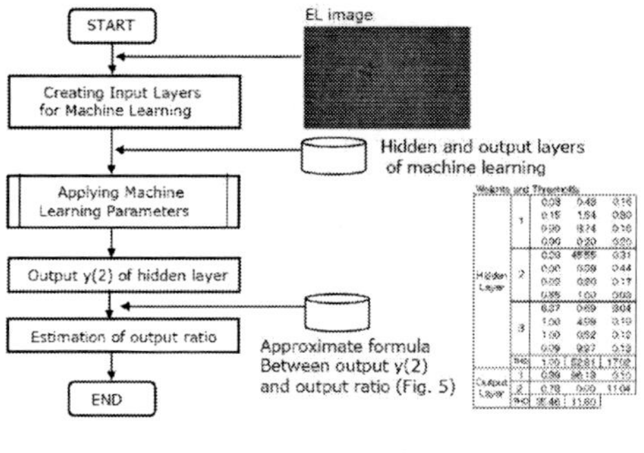

Figure 6: The architecture for calculating the output ratio from the EL image

3 EXPERIMENTAL RESULTS

The results of applying the PV module (the same type as the learning) extracted from the site for 11 years of exposure to the architecture in Fig. 6 are shown in Fig 7. The result of Output y (2) is 0.0478, which is 94.81% when applied to the approximate equation y = -25.298x + 96.019. In addition, since Output z becomes "0.00" and "0.56", it was judged that it was before the sudden drop in output.

10.4229/EUPVSEC2025/3AV.3.13

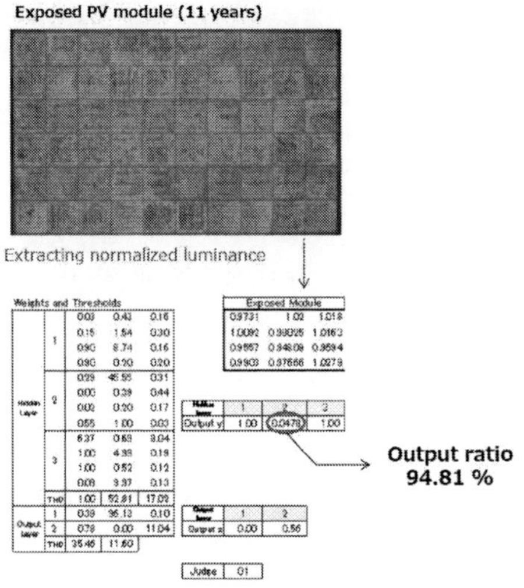

Figure 7: The results of applying developed the architecture to the exposed PV module (11 years)

The PV module for 11 years of exposure was compared with the reference PV module as shown in Fig. 8. The I-V characteristics were measured based on IEC60904-1 Edition 3.0 (2020-09) / IEC61215-2 Edition 1.0 (2016-03) at Standard Condition (solar radiation 1.0 kW/m^2 and temperature 298 K). It can be seen that the PV module after 11 years of exposure has deteriorated. Focusing on the maximum power point (MPP), the MPP of reference was 239.7 W, and the MPP of PV module after 11 years of exposure was 225.7 W. In other words, the output ratio was 94.2% (= 225.7/239.7*100), which showed a high correlation with 94.81% above.

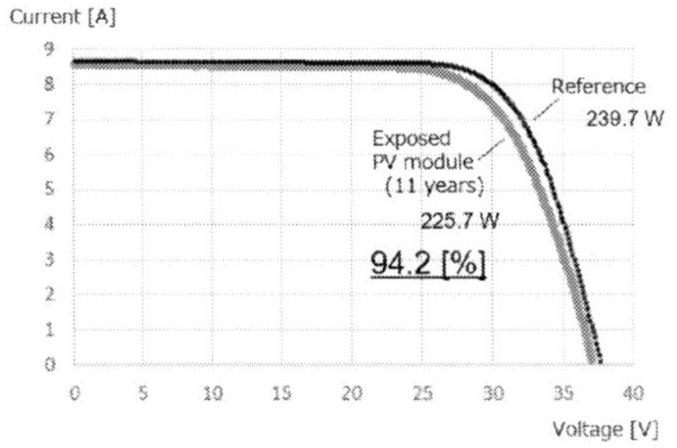

Figure 8: I-V characteristics of the exposed PV module (11 years)

Next, the results of applying the PV module, which was subjected to a dump heat (DH: temperature 85°C, humidity 85%) for 4000 hours, to the architecture are shown in Fig. 9. The result of Output y (2) is 0.4141, which is 85.54 [%] when applied to the approximate formula y = -25.298x + 96.019. In addition, since Output z becomes "0.99" and "0.56", it was judged that it was after a sharp decrease in output.

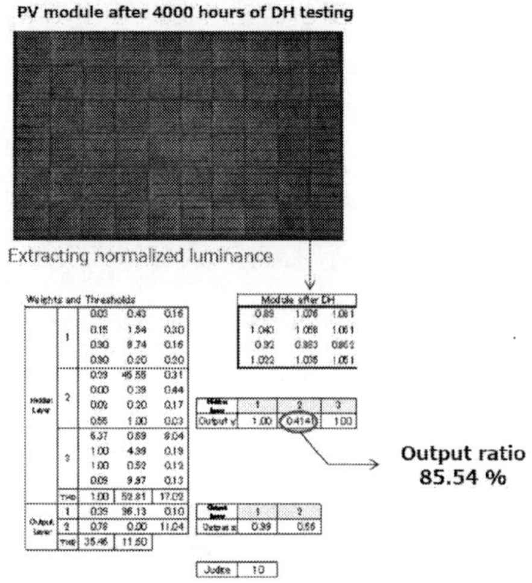

Figure 9: The results of applying developed the algorithm to the PV module after DH 4000 hours

Fig. 10 shows a comparison of the I-V curve of the PV module accelerated by the 4000-hour dump heat (DH: temperature 85°C, humidity 85%) with I-V curve of the reference PV module. It is clear that the accelerated test PV module is degraded. Focusing on the MPP, the MPP of the reference was 239.7 W, and the MPP of accelerated PV module was 203.5 W. In other words, the output ratio was 84.9% (=203.5/239.7*100), which showed a high correlation with 85.54 % above.

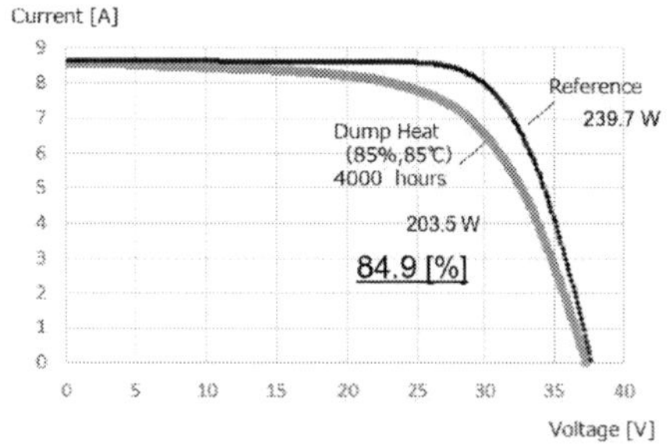

Figure 9: I-V characteristics of the PV module after DH 4000 hours

4 CONCLUSION

We have developed an architecture to monitor the degradation rate of PV in real time from EL images. Fake shunts, which are considered to be the main cause of deterioration due to exposure, are difficult to detect without the use of EL images. In recent years, technology has been developed to measure EL images outdoors, but it has been difficult to accurately grasp performance degradation from EL images. Therefore

1. The luminance distribution was extracted from the EL image of the PV module executed the dump heat acceleration test, and the input layer for machine learning was created.

2. In the acceleration test, we created an approximation of the output and degradation of the hidden layer in the training of a neural network that separates the EL image of the PV module before the power drops sharply and the EL image of the PV module after the drop.

3. By applying the luminance distribution of the measured EL image to the learned parameters, we succeeded in calculating the power generation performance instantly.

5 ACKNOWLEDGEMENT

The authors would like to thank Mr. K. Morita, and the members of PVSQ management, LLC for the evaluation of PV module and their valuable suggestions.

6 REFERENCES

[1] K. Morita et al., Proceedings European Photovoltaic Solar Energy Conference 2015 (2015) pp. 2515 - 2520.
[2] M. Fujimori et al., Proceedings European Photovoltaic Solar Energy Conference 2015 (2015) pp. 1911 - 1914.
[3] E. A. Gaulding et al., IEEE Journal of Photovoltaics, vol. 12, Issue. 3 (2022) pp. 690–695
[4] T. Kohno et al., Proceedings European Photovoltaic Solar Energy Conference 2024 (2024) pp. 020325-001 - 020325-005.
[5] Y. Ishikawa; JSAP Review Vol. 2022, pp. 2204 12-1–2204 12-5, April 2022
[6] Rasband, W.S., ImageJ, U. S. National Institutes of Health, Bethesda, Maryland, USA, http://imagej.nih.gov/ij/, 1997-2012.
[7]Schneider, C.A., Rasband, W.S., Eliceiri, K.W. "NIH Image to ImageJ: 25 years of image analysis". Nature Methods 9, 671-675, 2012.

Architecture for monitoring PV degradation in real time from EL images

HITACHI

Tohru Kohno and Jun Tsunoda

Green Power Electronics Research Dept. Hitachi, Ltd. Research & Development Group, Japan.

Concept

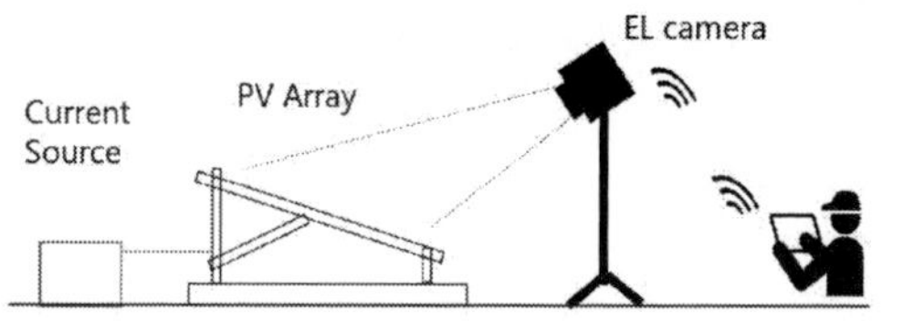

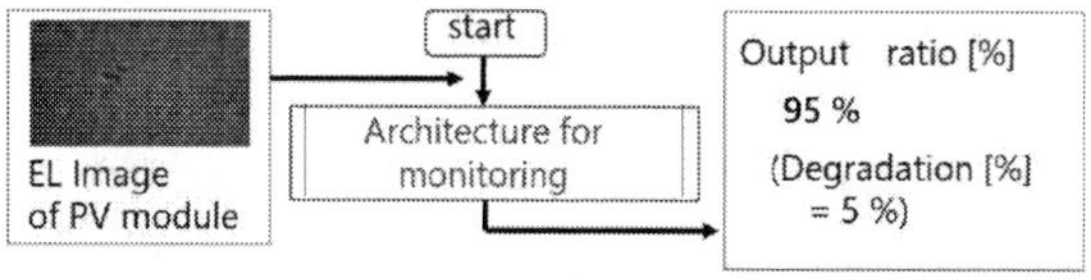

Luminance distribution in EL images

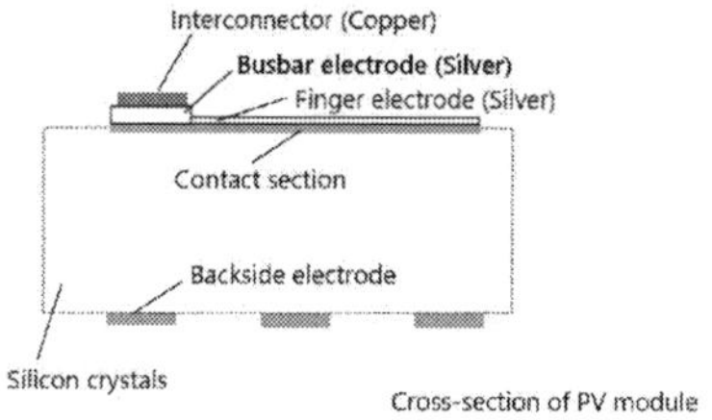

Setting the luminance distribution as an input layer for learning of neural

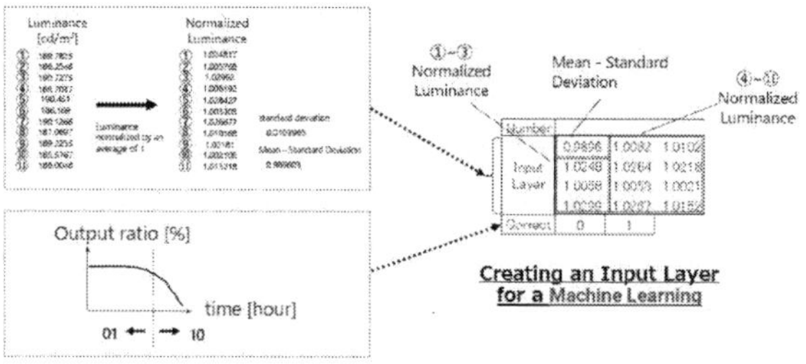

Creating an Input Layer for a Machine Learning

PV module's performance in the dump heat

Polycrystalline PV Module ：240W

DH Test Time [hour]	Output ratio [%]	Module No.	Number
0	100.0	1	1
3500	96.9	1	2
3500	94.4	2	3
4000	92.2	1	4
4000	90.4	2	5
4500	90.0	1	6
4500	82.0	2	7
4500	82.6	3	8
4500	79.0	4	9

DH (Dump Heat) Acceleration conditions **85℃ 85 %**

The learning of neural network

Setting the "correct" to 01 for Number 1-6 and 10 for Number 7-9

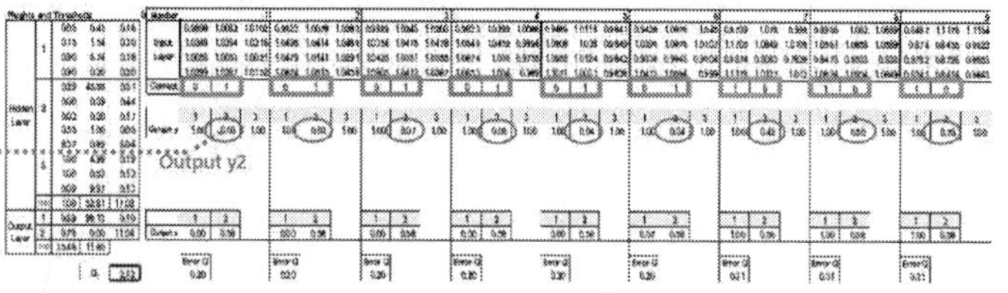

Sigmoid function

Output y1 = 1/(1+ exp (- (0.03 * 0.9896 + 0.15 * 1.0248 + ... + 0.20 * 1.0152) + 1.00))

Input layer × weight of hidden layer 1 — Threshold of hidden Layer 1

Output z1 = 1/(1+ exp (- (0.39 * 1.00 + 96.13 * 0.03 + ... + 0.10 * 1.00) + 35.46))

Weight of output layer 1 × output y — Threshold of output layer 1

$$\text{Error } Q = (0 - 0.00)^2 + (1 - 0.56)^2$$

Algorithm for calculating the output ratio

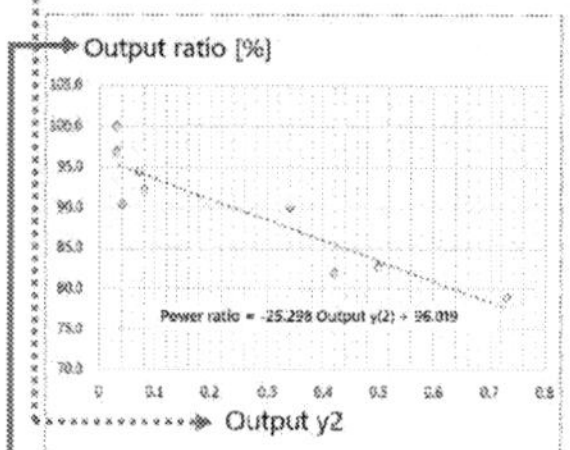

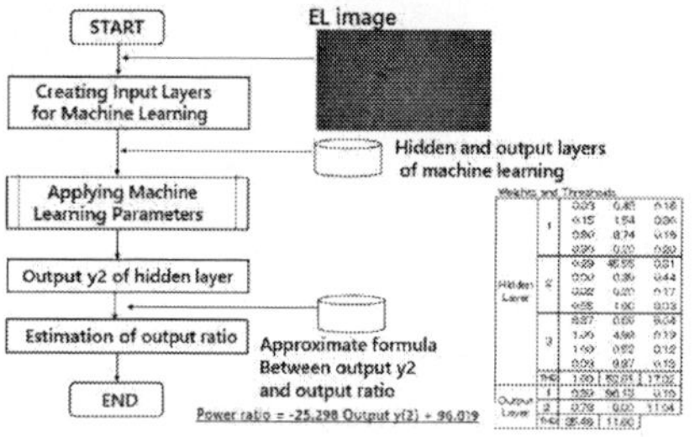

I-V curve of the PV module for verification

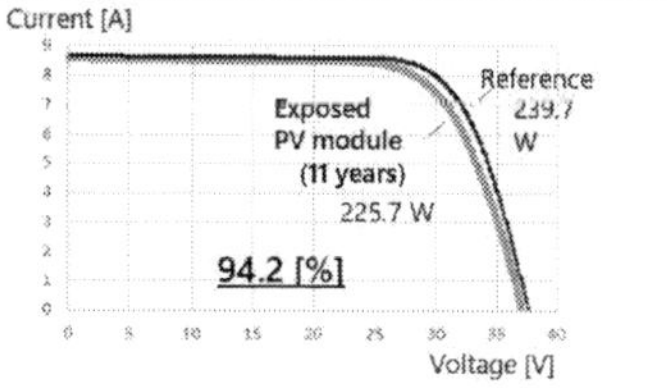

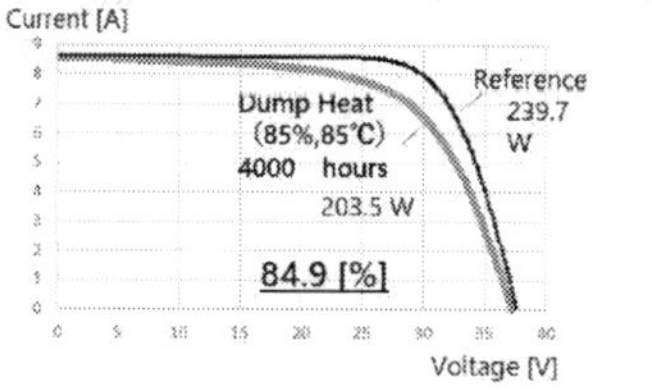

The results of applying the developed architecture

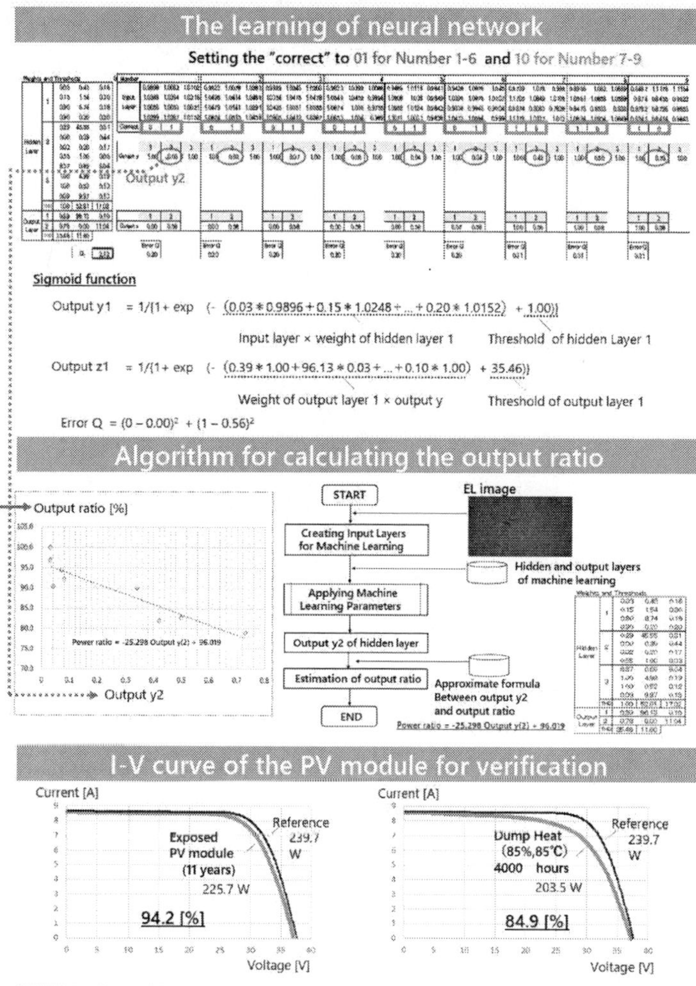

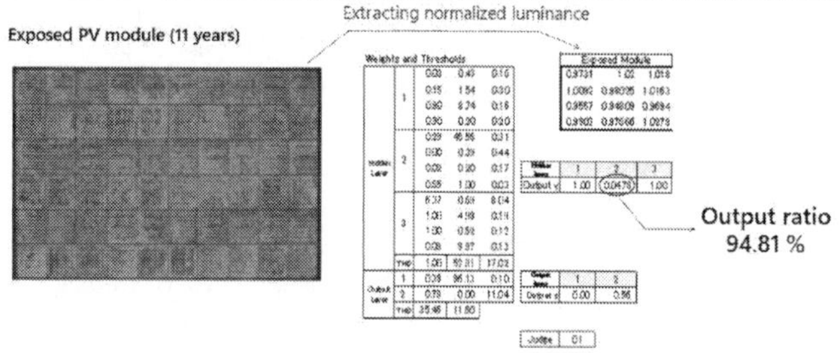

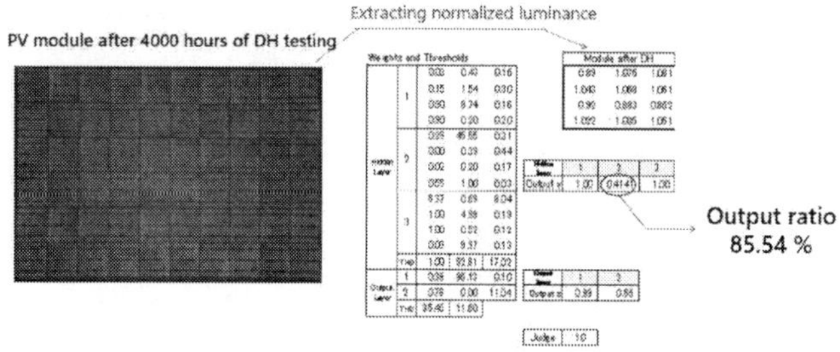

Summery

This output ratio (degradation) of PV modules can be calculated from the EL image.
We will consider the application of this architecture to the exposed site.

SIMPLE CELL SEGMENTATION ROUTINE FOR QUANTITATIVE ELECTROLUMINESCENCE ANALYSIS OF C-SI MODULES

João Victor Oliveira Santos[1,3], Daniel Ory[2], Christine Abdel Nour[1], Damien Barakel[3], Olivier Palais[3], Julien Dupuis[1]
[1]EDF R&D, EDF Lab Les Renardières, Avenue des Renardières, 77250 Moret Loing et Orvanne, France
[2]EDF R&D – IPVF, 18 boulevard Thomas Gobert, 91190 Palaiseau, France
[3]Aix-Marseille Univ, Université de Toulon, CNRS, IM2NP, Marseille, France

ABSTRACT: Electroluminescence (EL) testing of photovoltaic modules is a crucial step for quality inspection. As forward current is biased into the module, it emits light, allowing clear differentiation between defective and healthy regions. Beyond fault detection, performance parameters can also be accessed through this imaging technique. Many quantitative methods have already been developed in the literature providing metrics to estimate series and shunt resistances, dark saturation currents, diode ideality factors, etc. Nonetheless, these methods do not precise which pixels were considered for their approach. A single method to distinct one cell from the other on the whole EL image was found, yet it was focused on full-cell modules and no mention to its application on quantitative EL has been verified. The present work aims to establish an easy to apply cell segmentation algorithm for rectangular-shaped half-cell modules along with an alternative algorithm for corner-cut full-cell module segmentation. The proposed routines were applied to full and half-cell modules, providing satisfactory visual results. From the segmentation, the quantitative estimation of series resistances and dark saturation current densities were performed for each cell on a module. For a single cell within this module, the EL estimated parameters enabled to simulate its I-V curve which was then compared to its experimental one. A good agreement between the curves was verified despite a relative error for the fill factor of 7% which originates mainly from the assumption of an ideality factor being equal to 1. Furthermore, the relative errors for $P_{mpp}, I_{mpp}, V_{mpp}$, and V_{oc} were all below 5%. Possible improvements are also presented, pointing out that this work is an initial step for more precise quantitative EL analysis.
Keywords: Electroluminescence, Quantitative, Segmentation, Solar, Si Modules.

1 INTRODUCTION

The importance of Electroluminescence (EL) testing for quality control of photovoltaic modules is well known. EL, nonetheless, also has the potential to provide quantitative metrics to compare the impacts of single cells on the whole module performance. Series and shunt resistances, dark saturation currents, diode ideality factors are among the parameters that have been investigated by different authors [1]. These methods take the measured intensity values within the EL image to compute the desired parameters. Nonetheless, no mention has been made on how determining which pixels must be considered and which must not before applying quantitative analysis. S. Deitsch et al. [2] developed a complete and performant method to extract single cell images from the EL of a whole module paying a close attention to lens distortion. This method divides the initial image into sub images of single cells from which the image of an "average cell" is computed. Local thresholds are defined all over this image to obtain a binary mask which is then submit to morphological operations to fill empty regions within the cell area. Extra geometries are then subtracted considering the median profile across rows and columns and Convex Hull transformation, resulting in a binary mask representing the cell geometry. However, this method is focused on full-cell modules, and, to the best of our knowledge, it was not applied to quantitative EL methods.

The present work aims at developing an easy-to-apply segmentation method that can be used to rectangular-shaped half-cell modules as well as an alternative strategy for segmenting corner-cut full-cell modules before estimating single-diode model (SDM) parameters. In figure 1, a representation of the expected result for the segmentation methods is shown. This article is, structured as follows: first, the segmentation methods will be illustrated; then, these methods will be applied to experimental data followed by a quantitative analysis of series resistances and dark saturation current densities based on the works of A. S. Rajput et al [3] and T. Potthoff et al. [4]; afterwards, these values will be used to simulate the I-V curve of a single cell and to compare to its experimental curve; finally, a conclusion will summarize the results and provide perspectives.

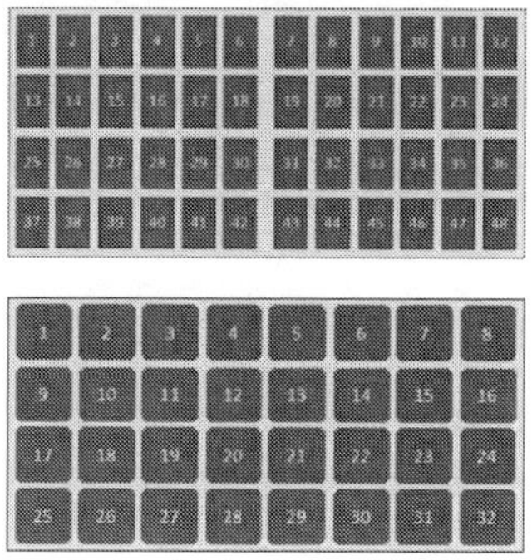

Figure 1: Labeled matrices for PV module with (top) rectangular-shaped and (bottom) corner-cut cells. An integer indexation increasing from top left to bottom right is obtained for each cell.

2 SEGMENTATION METHODS

2.1 Half-cell modules

In a first step, the EL image must be summed across both horizontal (columns) and vertical (lines) axis. This sum will provide a profile with plateaus and valleys which represents, respectively, the emitted signal and the background, that is, the gap between adjacent cells. Hence, by simply choosing a threshold, one can distinguish signal from background, resulting in a binary line vector for the sum across lines and a binary column vector for the sum across columns. The outer product of these two binary vectors produces a binary mask that separates active areas (cells) from inactive areas (background). Finally, the label function from Python scikit-image library provides a different integer index for each closed region from this binary matrix [5], then each cell is labeled by a specific number.

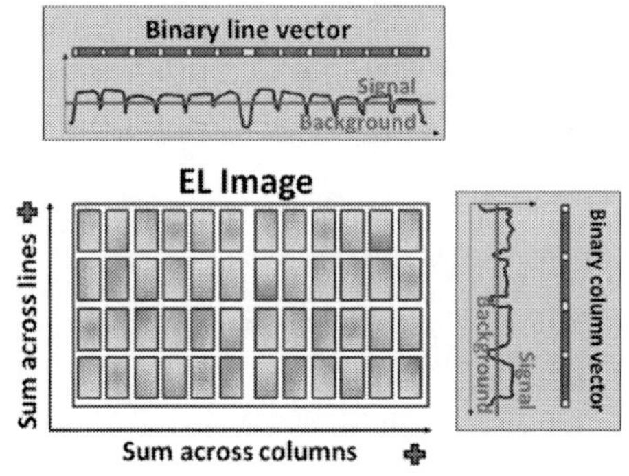

Figure 2: Schematic of half-cell module segmentation approach. By summing the image across its horizontal and vertical axis, then thresholding these sums, binary column and line vectors are obtained. The multiplication of these vectors results in a matrix which is a mask of active (cell) and inactive (background) regions within the image, which is used for labelling each cell.

2.2 Full-cell modules

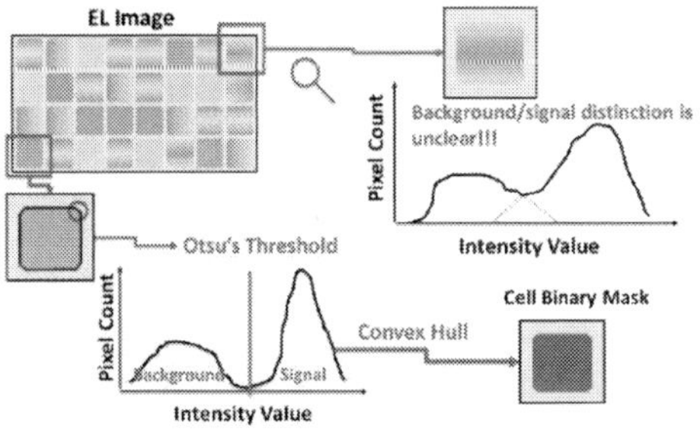

Figure 3: Schematic of full-cell module segmentation approach. The EL image is cropped into one sub image per cell. Then, a histogram analysis is performed on the sub images and a cell for which background/signal distinction is clear is chosen. Otsu's threshold along with a Convex Hull transform provides a binary mask with the chosen cell's geometry. This mask will be replicated to the whole image and used for labelling individual cells.

Considering a full-cell module whose cells are corner-cut, the horizontal and vertical sum is no longer a valid strategy since it would not provide the corner geometry. As it was said, S. Deitsch et al. [2] performed this segmentation by computing an average cell from the image. Here, we suggest an alternative method which consists of cropping the EL image based on the number of cells per line and column. Then, for each cell, the threshold that best divide its histogram into two regions is obtained with Otsu's method, resulting in a binary mask. Following, a Convex Hull transform is applied on the mask to obtain its closed geometry. However, not all geometries faithfully represent that of the cells. Depending on their histograms, background/signal distinction might be unclear and, thus, Otsu's threshold followed by a Convex Hull transform will fail in representing the cell. Here, we consider that there might be a cell within the module for which a binary mask containing the cell geometry can be extracted. Thus, by performing this algorithm on every cell a visual analysis is enough to choose a correct binary mask with the cell's geometry. By systematically replicating this chosen mask across all cell positions, a complete binary mask is reconstructed, preserving the original image dimensions. Finaly, as it was done for half-cell modules, label function from Python scikit-image library can provide a different integer index for each cell from the binary matrix [5].

3 EXPERIMENTAL ANALYSIS

A Phase One 150 MP XT camera was adapted to detect the emitted EL signals from full-cell and half-cell modules. Three images were measured at 10% of the module's nominal short circuit current (low bias) and three others were taken at its short circuit current (high bias). These images were averaged, subtracted to background, and corrected for noise [6], vignetting [7], and perspective [8] prior to the segmentation and quantitative analysis.

3.1 Segmentation

The full and half-cell segmentation methods were applied to the processed high bias images. Figures 4 and 5 show, respectively the results obtained for a half-cell and a full-cell module.

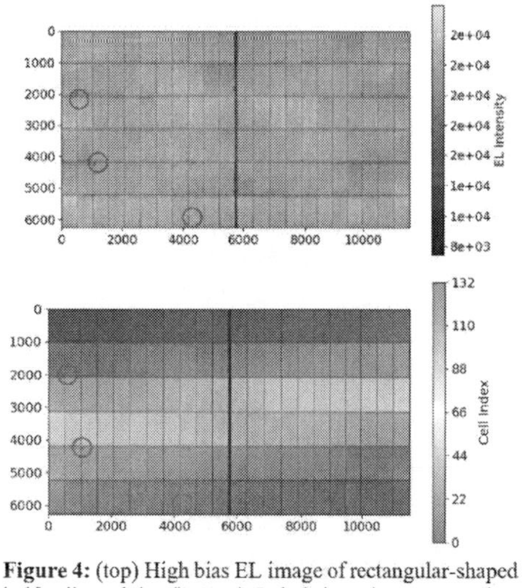

Figure 4: (top) High bias EL image of rectangular-shaped half-cell module. (bottom) Labeled mask superposed to EL image with a transparency degree of 50%. Red circles represent patterns that can be seen in both top and bottom images.

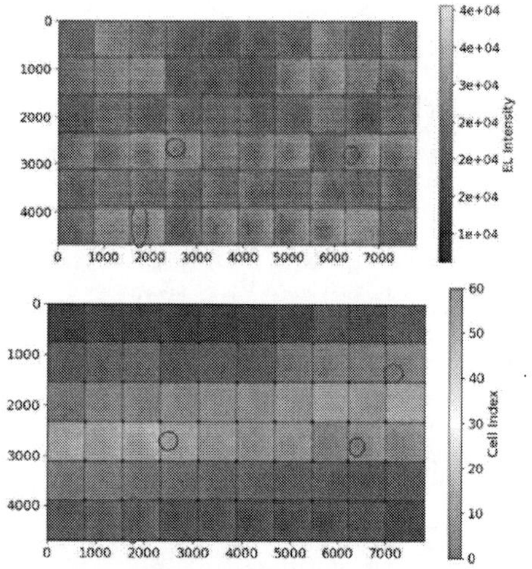

Figure 5: (top) High bias EL image of corner-cut full-cell module. (bottom) Labeled mask superposed to EL image with a transparency degree of 50%. Red circles represent patterns that can be seen in both top and bottom images.

On the top of each figure the EL image after the preprocessing steps described previously is presented and, on the bottom, the labeled mask providing a different integer index for the pixels that represent a given cell in the same order as the one represented in Figure 1 is shown. These masks are displayed with a certain degree of transparency as a manner to identify whether the segmentation routines were successful or not. For the full-cell module, the binary geometry mask was obtained with the 26th cell. Red circles represent features that can be seen in both the EL and the labeled figures. The results obtained indicate that the proposed methods are robust and yield satisfactory outcomes. Following, since the pixels that represent individual cells within an EL image of a whole module were determined, quantitative parameters that provide the performance of these cells can be extracted, which will be presented in the next subsection.

3.2 Quantitative EL

A simple method to represent the electrical circuit of a solar cell is the single-diode model (SDM) [1]. This model is represented in Figure 6 containing the photogenerated current (I_{ph}), the extracted current (I), the cell's terminal voltage (V), a diode representing the p-n junction, a series resistance (R_s) and a parallel shunt resistance (R_{sh}). The single diode is characterized by its dark saturation current density (J_0) and ideality factor (n).

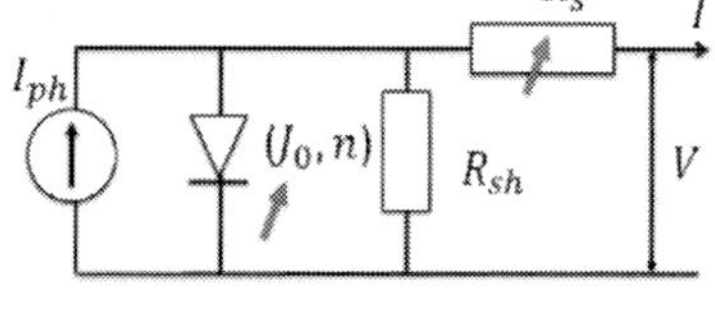

Figure 6: Single-diode model (SDM) electrical circuit representation. Red arrows indicate the parameters that estimated with quantitative EL: R_s and J_0.

When submit to a forward bias, a solar cell emits light. Current injection induces radiative recombination within the bulk peaking at 1150 nm for Si-based cells [9], thus a camera sensible to the near infrared is necessary for detection. The EL signal emitted by the cell (ϕ_{EL}) is modeled as

$$\phi_{EL} = C \cdot \exp\left(\frac{V}{V_{th}}\right)$$

where C is a calibration factor, V is the local voltage, and V_{th} the thermal voltage [4].

Many methods to estimate parameters from EL signal have already been proposed on the literature. T. Fuyuki et al. [9] first proposed EL imaging as a source to investigate minority carrier diffusion length. Other authors followed Fuyuki in what was named "Fuyuki's linear approximation" which considers the calibration factor and the dark saturation current density to be inversely proportional. This method measures low and high bias emission, providing at the same time the dark saturation current density and the series resistance in the ideal scenario where shunts are neglected and ideality factors are assumed to be unitary [10], [3]. A similar approach was conducted by O. Breitenstein et al. [11] in an iterative manner.

Nonetheless this linear approximation has some limitations. The diffusion length linearity with the EL intensity is considered valid for diffusion lengths lower than 100 µm; nowadays technologies, on the other hand have diffusion lengths greater than the cell thickness [12], [13], [14]. P. Wurfel et al. [12], while studying this lack of linearity, developed an interesting analysis on diffusion length extraction from EL images which accounted for the emission coming from the front and rear part of the cell. G. Dost et al. [14] considered the series resistance after taking the nonlinearity of Fuyuki's approximation into consideration, yet it required the cell's global R_s extracted from I-V measurements.

Apart from Fuyuki's approximation, T. Potthoff et al. [4] considered computing a calibration factor to estimate local voltages and external series resistance. This method is the basis for the generalized quantitative electroluminescence (g-QUEL), which after a previous classification of EL images, provides not only SDM parameters, but also double-diode model (DDM) ones depending on the module degradation level [15]. This method, however, obtains the parameters at the cell level, not considering inhomogeneities within the cell itself and it requires imaging at a set of different biases. Acquisitions at varying injection currents were also investigated by other authors, but with a different approach. From the current injection, local voltages were estimated providing a Dark I-V curve which was then used to fit SDM parameters [16], [17]. Moreover, ratio between acquisitions was also suggested, but methods considering this approach would either compare a cell with another one that is chosen as reference [18] or present previous knowledge on the ideality factor from global module I-V measurements [19].

For the scope of the present work, the methods described by A. S. Rajput et al [3] and T. Potthoff et al. [4] were applied. The low and high bias EL acquisitions after the preprocessing steps described previously were used to estimate R_s and J_0. A. S. Rajput et al [3], which relies on "Fuyuki's linear approximation" [9], [10], proposes a strategy to measure the dark saturation current density and the internal series resistance (R_s^{int}). As said before the linear approximation considers the calibration factor and the dark saturation current density to be related by $C = f/J_0$, where f is a constant value. By assuming negligible shunt losses and unitary ideality factor, A. S. Rajput et al. [3] provided a formula to obtain the constant f based on the low bias applied current and terminal voltage as well as its EL intensity. Local voltage, calibration factor and J_0 were then estimated in this order.

For a high bias image, given that the calibration factor is known, local voltages are easily determined and so is the current density through the diode; with these terms, the internal R_s is then obtained.

Now, by comparing the sum of the cell's voltages to the module terminal voltage, one can determine the external series resistance following T. Potthoff et al. [4], which represents the cell-to-module connection resistance. It is important to know, nonetheless, that R_s^{ext} is constant for each cell within the module.

In Figure 7 are depicted the average internal resistances and dark saturation current densities obtained for the same full-cell module used for segmentation. Note that the pixels for which these parameters were measured correspond to the labeled ones, that is, only the pixels determined for each cell were used to perform this estimation. The external R_s obtained was $0.88\ \Omega \cdot \mathrm{cm}^2$.

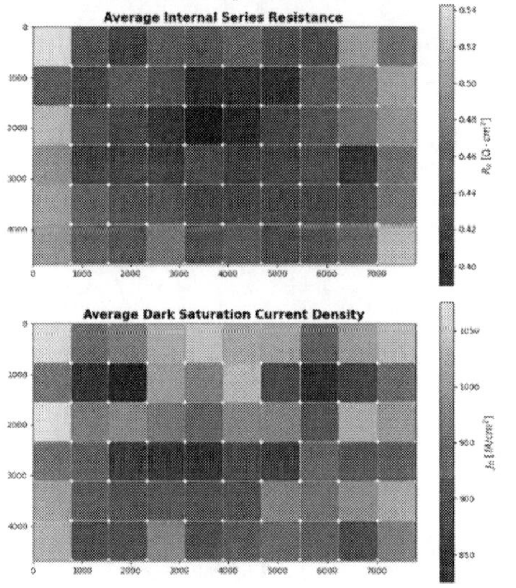

Figure 7: (top) Average internal R_s for corner-cut full-cell module. (bottom) Average J_0 for corner-cut full-cell module.

4 I-V CURVE SIMULATION

A further investigation consisted of verifying the accuracy of the values obtained for J_0 and R_s. The device under test was drilled on its backsheet and two connectors were placed on the middle of the 13th cell and 14th cell to not crack the cell edges as can be seen in Figure 8. The experimental I-V curve measured at the Standard Test Conditions (STC) on these connectors is represented in Figure 9. For the sake of simplicity, we consider that it represents the I-V curve of the 13th cell.

Regarding the EL estimated parameters, the idea was to simulate an I-V curve out of them to compare with the experimental one. From the SDM represented in Figure 6, one can obtain the equation that determines the I-V curve

$$I = I_{ph} - I_0\left(\exp\left(\frac{V + I \cdot R_s}{n \cdot V_{th}}\right) - 1\right) - \frac{V + I \cdot R_s}{R_{sh}}$$

This equation does not provide the current explicitly in terms of the voltage and vice-versa, yet this can be overcome by applying Lambert W function [20]. This function is such that

$$\omega = W(\omega \cdot \exp(\omega)), \quad \omega \in \mathbb{C}$$

Hence, the I-V curve can be rewritten by some algebraic manipulation with Lambert W function, providing the voltage in terms of the current as follows

$$V(I) = (I_{ph} + I_0)R_{sh} - I(R_s + R_{sh}) - n\,V_{th}\,W\left[I_0 \frac{R_{sh}}{nV_{th}} exp\left(\frac{R_{sh}}{nV_{th}}(I_{ph} + I_0 - I)\right)\right]$$

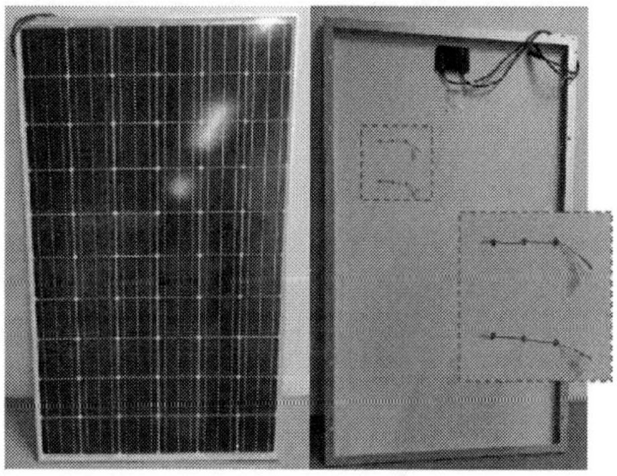

Figure 8: (left) Full-cell PV module used for quantitative EL validation. (right) Backsheet of the module with connectors placed in the middle of 13th and 14th cell for measuring single-cell I-V curve, connectors are highlighted with a red rectangle and the region is zoomed.

Lambert W is the default solution method for pvlib built-in functions *pvsystem.i_from_v* and *pvsystem.singlediode* which, respectively, provide the current values for a set of voltages generating an I-V curve and estimate the operational points of this curve ($I_{sc}, V_{oc}, P_{mpp}, I_{mpp}, V_{mpp}$) [21]. These functions were used to simulate the I-V curve of the 13th cell simulation from its average dark saturation current (I_0) and its total series resistance obtained with the quantitative EL methods presented previously. Here, the total series resistance is the sum of the external and average internal series resistances. Besides that, the simulation was performed with $n = 1$ and taking an infinity value for R_{sh} so that shunts could be neglected to account for the assumptions of A. S. Rajput et al. [3], as well as considering the short-circuit current of the module provided on its datasheet being equal to the cell photocurrent [15]. This simulated curve is presented in Figure 9 along with the experimental curve.

One might note, in a first moment, that the datasheet short-circuit current is slightly smaller than the measured I_{sc} and that there was a small overestimation for P_{mpp}. Meanwhile, the simulated and experimental values for V_{oc} are alike. Table I summarizes the SDM parameters of the experimental curve extracted with pvlib function ivtools.sde.fit_sandia_simple [22] and those estimated with quantitative EL, while Table II presents the experimental and simulated values for V_{oc}, MPP, and FF as well as their relative errors, which are defined as

$$Relative\ error = \left(\frac{Simulated - Experimental}{Experimental}\right) \cdot 100\%$$

One might also note that, apart from the fill factor (FF), all relative errors are below 5%. Among the possible uncertainty sources the different assumptions must be recalled. First, the assumption of no shunt resistance, modeled by an infinite value, seems to not have impacted our analysis since it is mostly linked to the shape of the I-V curve close to I_{sc}. Further, the datasheet value for I_{sc} is 2.8% smaller than its experimental value, so assuming the datasheet I_{sc} as I_{ph} to simulate the I-V curve raises some uncertainties. However, a quick simulation taking the experimental I_{sc} as I_{ph} increased mostly the simulated I_{mpp} and P_{mpp}, not providing relevant changes to the FF. Besides that, since the connectors for experimental I-V extraction were placed in the middle of the 13th and 14th cell, there might be some mismatch between them. Also, "Fuyuki's linear approximation" not being representative to nowadays technologies is a limiting factor to the estimation of R_s^{int} and J_0 as mentioned previously and it might have an impact on our analysis. Nonetheless, A. S. Rajput at el. [3] claimed no relevant difference on their results when taking the nonlinearity into account.

Finally, the assumption of a uniform and unitary ideality factor is the one with the most important impact. Note that, instead of being equal to 1 as assumed, its experimental value is of 1.255. The ideality factor is within the denominator of an exponential term in the I-V curve equation, thus even small variations provide significant impacts. Due to that, the experimental and EL estimated dark saturation currents differ by 2 orders of magnitude. Another relevant side effect of this assumption is that this exponential term impacts the rate at which the current drops as the voltage increases and, hence, the shape of the curve around the maximum power point will not be faithfully reproduced. This is the main reason for the 7% relative error for the fill factor.

Table I: Comparison between experimental SDM values issued from the I-V flasher (experimental) and by performing quantitative analysis on EL images. R_s^{int} and R_s^{ext} indicates respectively the internal and external series resistances and their sum results in the total series resistance, R_s^{tot}.

	Experimental	Quantitative EL
$R_s^{int} (\Omega \cdot cm^2)$	-	0.45
$R_s^{ext} (\Omega \cdot cm^2)$	-	0.88
$R_s^{tot} (\Omega \cdot cm^2)$	1.80	1.33
$R_{sh} (\Omega \cdot cm^2)$	7993	∞ (assumed)
I_0 (pA)	27005	215.051
I_{sc} (A)	9.033	8.78 (datasheet)
n	1.255	1 (assumed)

Table II: Experimental and simulated values from I-V curve

	Experimental	Simulated	Relative Error (%)
P_{mpp} (W)	4.096	4.238	+3,5
I_{mpp} (A)	8.394	8.322	-0.9
V_{mpp} (V)	0.488	0.509	+4,3
V_{oc} (V)	0.632	0.628	-0.6
FF (%)	72	77	+7

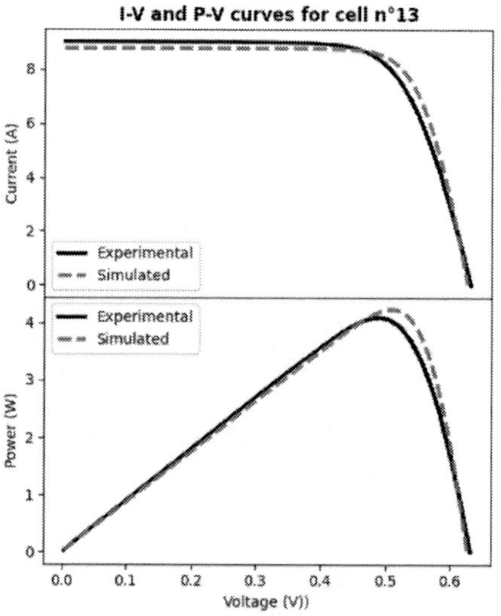

Figure 9: Experimental and simulated I-V and P-V curves for the 13th cell of the module presented on Figure 8. The simulation was performed with the results from the quantitative EL analysis.

5 CONCLUSION

The segmentation routine developed in this work provided two different methods to distinct which pixels belong to a single cell within an electroluminescent image. Modules containing rectangular-shaped half-cells were segmented by computing the sum across both lines and columns. Corner-cut full-cell modules, on the other hand, were segmented by analyzing and thresholding the histogram of sub images containing a different cell each. These methods were applied in two modules – one with full-cells and the other with half-cells – after noise, perspective and vignetting correction which are essential requisites for the algorithms developed. Both methods provided satisfactory results, nonetheless, there is still path for improvement such as accounting for shunted cells while applying the half-cell method since they might pose local drops on the column and line sum profiles making the threshold choice troublesome. Also, for the full-cell method, instead of applying the histogram on each cell and then choosing the cell that provided a sufficient cell geometry mask, computing the "average cell" as done by S. Deitsch et al. [2] to then apply Otsu's threshold followed by a Convex Hull might make this method simpler.

Moreover, the quantitative analysis that followed from the segmentation routine consisted on computing the

10.4229/EUPVSEC2025/3AV.3.14

internal series resistance and the dark saturation current density based on the method developed by A. S. Rajput et al. [3] as well as the external series resistance following the strategy of T. Potthoff et al. [4]. These parameters were used to simulate the single-diode I-V curve of a cell within a module following Lambert W function using a Python library developed for PV systems [21]. The simulated curve was compared to experimental I-V curve measured on the middle of this cell and of its neighbor (which was connected to it in series). For simplicity, this measurement was taken as the real I-V curve of this cell. Experimental and simulated I-V curves presented a remarkable agreement despite for their behavior around the MPP, which originates from the assumption of a unitary ideality factor. This resulted in a fill factor relative error of 7%. Besides that, values for $P_{mpp}, I_{mpp}, V_{mpp}$, and V_{oc} are within a relative error range of 5%.

A global analysis comparing simulated and experimental values for different cells is still necessary and so it is comparing the results with and without a segmented mask. For the moment, we can say that the methods investigated on the present work enable to determine which pixels must be considered before applying the quantitative algorithms on the literature. This represents the first step for an effective quantitative EL at the module scale, and it will be refined throughout the development of a global methodology.

6 REFERENCES

[1] V. E. Puranik, R. Kumar, and R. Gupta, "Progress in module level quantitative electroluminescence imaging of crystalline silicon PV module: A review," *Sol. Energy*, vol. 264, p. 111994, Nov. 2023, doi: 10.1016/j.solener.2023.111994.

[2] S. Deitsch *et al.*, "Segmentation of photovoltaic module cells in uncalibrated electroluminescence images," *Mach. Vis. Appl.*, vol. 32, no. 4, p. 84, May 2021, doi: 10.1007/s00138-021-01191-9.

[3] A. S. Rajput, J. W. Ho, Y. Zhang, S. Nalluri, and A. G. Aberle, "Quantitative estimation of electrical performance parameters of individual solar cells in silicon photovoltaic modules using electroluminescence imaging," *Sol. Energy*, vol. 173, pp. 201–208, Oct. 2018, doi: 10.1016/j.solener.2018.07.046.

[4] T. Potthoff, K. Bothe, U. Eitner, D. Hinken, and M. Köntges, "Detection of the voltage distribution in photovoltaic modules by electroluminescence imaging," *Prog. Photovolt. Res. Appl.*, vol. 18, no. 2, pp. 100–106, 2010, doi: 10.1002/pip.941.

[5] scikit-image, "skimage.measure." [Online]. Available: https://scikit-image.org/docs/stable/api/skimage.measure.html

[6] K. G. Bedrich, M. Bliss, T. R. Betts, and R. Gottschalg, "Electroluminescence imaging of PV devices: Camera calibration and image correction," in *2016 IEEE 43rd Photovoltaic Specialists Conference (PVSC)*, June 2016, pp. 1532–1537. doi: 10.1109/PVSC.2016.7749875.

[7] T. S. Ramsay, "Edge-based vignetting factor estimation and correction comparative analysis," *Imaging Sci. J.*, vol. 65, no. 5, pp. 299–307, July 2017, doi: 10.1080/13682199.2017.1337284.

[8] "OpenCV: Geometric Image Transformations." Accessed: Aug. 29, 2025. [Online]. Available: https://docs.opencv.org/4.x/da/d54/group__imgproc__transform.html#ga20f62aa3235d869c9956436c870893ae

[9] T. Fuyuki, H. Kondo, T. Yamazaki, Y. Takahashi, and Y. Uraoka, "Photographic surveying of minority carrier diffusion length in polycrystalline silicon solar cells by electroluminescence," *Appl. Phys. Lett.*, vol. 86, p. 262108, June 2005, doi: 10.1063/1.1978979.

[10] J. Haunschild, M. Glatthaar, M. Kasemann, S. Rein, and E. R. Weber, "Fast series resistance imaging for silicon solar cells using electroluminescence," *Phys. Status Solidi RRL – Rapid Res. Lett.*, vol. 3, no. 7–8, pp. 227–229, Oct. 2009, doi: 10.1002/pssr.200903175.

[11] O. Breitenstein, A. Khanna, Y. Augarten, J. Bauer, J. -M. Wagner, and K. Iwig, "Quantitative evaluation of electroluminescence images of solar cells," *Phys. Status Solidi RRL – Rapid Res. Lett.*, vol. 4, no. 1–2, pp. 7–9, Feb. 2010, doi: 10.1002/pssr.200903304.

[12] P. Würfel, T. Trupke, T. Puzzer, E. Schäffer, W. Warta, and S. W. Glunz, "Diffusion lengths of silicon solar cells from luminescence images," *J. Appl. Phys.*, vol. 101, no. 12, p. 123110, June 2007, doi: 10.1063/1.2749201.

[13] O. Breitenstein, F. Frühauf, D. Hinken, and K. Bothe, "Effective Diffusion Length and Bulk Saturation Current Density Imaging in Solar Cells by Spectrally Filtered Luminescence Imaging," *IEEE J. Photovolt.*, vol. 6, no. 5, pp. 1243–1254, Sept. 2016, doi: 10.1109/JPHOTOV.2016.2571621.

[14] G. Dost, H. Höffler, and J. M. Greulich, "Advanced Series Resistance Imaging for Silicon Solar Cells via Electroluminescence," *Phys. Status Solidi A*, vol. 218, no. 6, p. 2000546, Mar. 2021, doi: 10.1002/pssa.202000546.

[15] V. E. Puranik, R. Kumar, and R. Gupta, "Generalized quantitative electroluminescence method for the performance evaluation of defective and unevenly degraded crystalline silicon photovoltaic module," *Prog. Photovolt. Res. Appl.*, vol. 31, no. 3, pp. 269–282, 2023, doi: 10.1002/pip.3632.

[16] B. Li, A. Stokes, and D. M. J. Doble, "Evaluation of two-dimensional electrical properties of photovoltaic modules using bias-dependent electroluminescence," *Prog. Photovolt. Res. Appl.*, vol. 20, no. 8, pp. 936–944, Dec. 2012, doi: 10.1002/pip.1161.

[17] S. Guo, E. Schneller, K. O. Davis, and W. V. Schoenfeld, "Quantitative analysis of crystalline silicon wafer PV modules by electroluminescence imaging," in *2016 IEEE 43rd Photovoltaic Specialists Conference (PVSC)*, Portland, OR, USA: IEEE, June 2016, pp. 3688–3692. doi: 10.1109/PVSC.2016.7750365.

[18] T. Fuyuki, H. Kondo, Y. Kaji, A. Ogane, and Y. Takahashi, "Analytic findings in the electroluminescence characterization of crystalline silicon solar cells," *J. Appl. Phys.*, vol. 101, no. 2, p. 023711, Jan. 2007, doi: 10.1063/1.2431075.

[19] F. Fruehauf and M. Turek, "Quantification of Electroluminescence Measurements on Modules," *Energy Procedia*, vol. 77, pp. 63–68, Aug. 2015, doi: 10.1016/j.egypro.2015.07.010.

10.4229/EUPVSEC2025/3AV.3.14

[20] "Lambert *W* function," *Wikipedia*. Aug. 22, 2025. Accessed: Sept. 01, 2025. [Online]. Available: https://en.wikipedia.org/w/index.php?title=Lambert_W_function&oldid=1307306923
[21] "pvlib.pvsystem.PVSystem — pvlib python 0.13.0 documentation." Accessed: Sept. 01, 2025. [Online]. Available: https://pvlib-python.readthedocs.io/en/stable/reference/generated/pvlib.pvsystem.PVSystem.html
[22] "Single diode models — pvlib python 0.13.0 documentation." Accessed: Sept. 12, 2025. [Online]. Available: https://pvlib-python.readthedocs.io/en/stable/reference/pv_modeling/sdm.html

10.4229/EUPVSEC2025/3AV.3.14

42nd European Photovoltaic Solar Energy Conference and Exhibition

Simple Cell Segmentation Routine for Quantitative EL Analysis of c-Si Solar Modules

João Victor Oliveira Santos[1,3], Julien Dupuis[1], Christine Abdel Nour[1], Daniel Ory[2], Damien Barakel[3], Olivier Palais[3]

[1]EDF R&D, EDF Lab Les Renardières, Avenue des Renardières, Moret Loing et Orvanne 77250, France
[2]EDF R&D – IPVF, 18 boulevard Thomas Gobert, 91190 Palaiseau, France
[3]Aix-Marseille Univ, Université de Toulon, CNRS, IM2NP, Marseille, France

Context and Objective

- Determining the pixels within each cell from EL images enables to obtain its local voltage, series resistance, and dark saturation current density [1];
- An automatic segmentation was developed focusing on full-cell modules and it considers computing an average cell from the EL image [2].
- The goal of this work is to provide an easy to apply segmentation algorithm for **rectangular-shaped half-cell modules** as well as a simple alternative algorithm for **corner-cut full-cell module** segmentation, resulting in a labeled mask with a different integer index for each cell.

Half-cell Modules

1. Sum the EL image across horizontal and vertical axis;
2. Chose a threshold for each sum, separating signal from background on binary vectors;

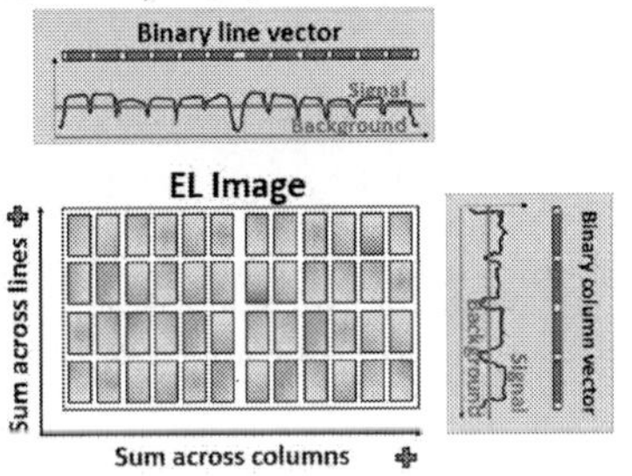

3. Multiply binary vectors, obtaining a **binary matrix**;

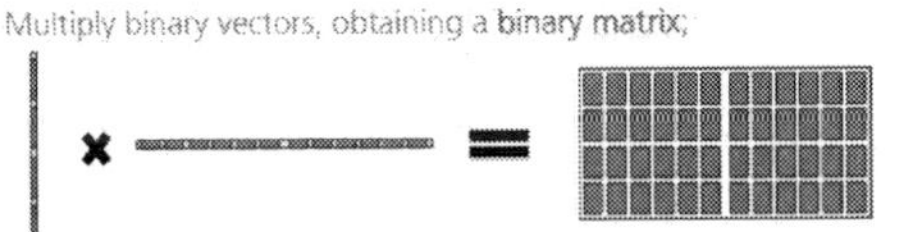

4. From binary matrix a **labeled matrix** can be obtained with a different index for each cell.

Full-cell Modules

1. Crop the EL image based on the number of cells per line and column;
2. For each cell, apply Otsu's threshold and a Convex Hull transform;

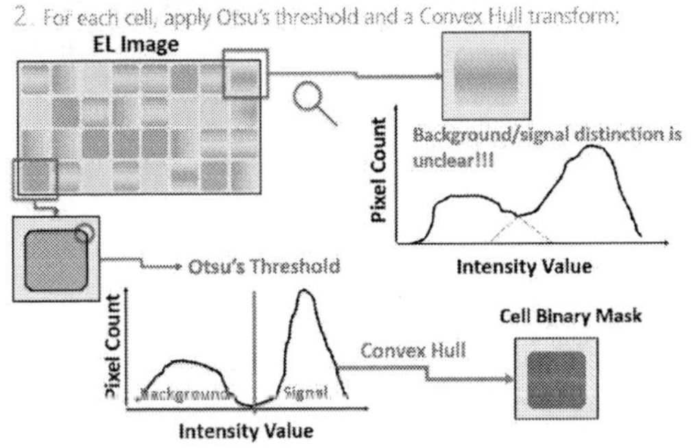

3. Select a cell mask for which geometry was accurately obtained and replicate it to the module dimension, obtaining a **binary matrix**;
4. From binary matrix a **labeled matrix** can be obtained with a different index for each cell.

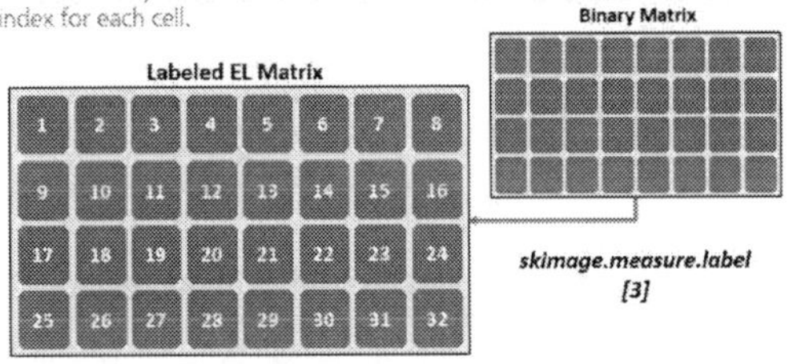

Quantitative EL Analysis

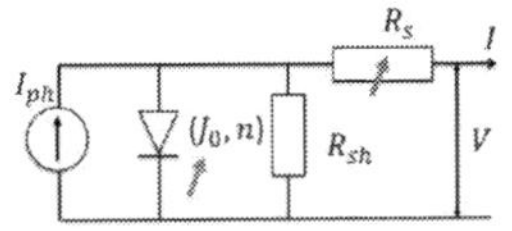

EL Intensity

$$\varnothing_{EL} = C \, . \, exp\left({}^{V}/_{V_{th}}\right)$$

- Computation of **internal series resistance** (R_s^{int}) and **dark saturation current density** (J_0) from low and high bias EL Image, assuming n=1 and no shunts [1];
- Computation of **external series resistance** (R_s^{ext}), accounting for the cell-to-module connection resistance [4];
- **I-V curve extraction** of a single cell within a module;
- **I-V curve simulation** for the same cell inputting the quantitative EL parameters into **PVLIB built-in functions with** Lambert W **solving method** [5];
- **Relative errors** for power, current and voltage at the maximal power point as well as for the open circuit voltage **below 5%** comparing simulated and experimental values.

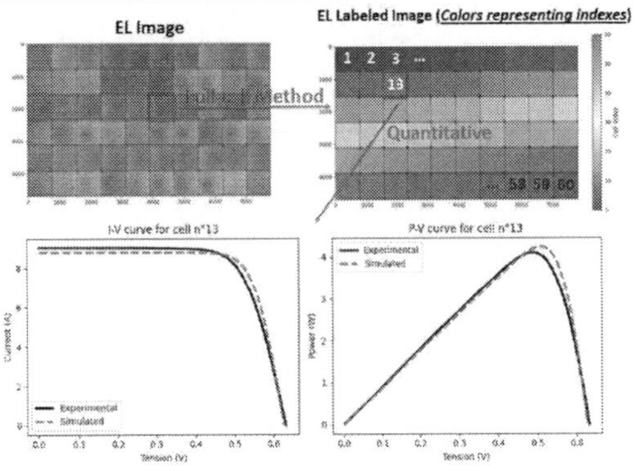

Conclusion and Perspectives

- The segmentation methods enables quantitative analysis;
- Good correspondence between experimental and EL simulated I-V curves;
- Possibility to estimate power production for each cell within module;
- This segmentation analysis represents the first step for an effective quantitative EL at the module scale, and the methodology will be refined throughout the development of the global methodology.

References:

1. [illegible]
2. [illegible] et al., "Segmentation of photovoltaic module cells in uncalibrated electroluminescence images," Machine Vision and Applications, [illegible]
3. "skimage.measure", scikit-image, [illegible]
4. [illegible] et al., "Detection of the voltage distribution in photovoltaic modules by electroluminescence imaging," Progress in Photovoltaics, [illegible]
5. "pvlib.pvsystem.PVSystem", pvlib-python, [illegible]

amU imen

020189-001

NUMERICAL SIMULATION OF OUTPUT CHARACTERISTICS OF PHOTOVOLTAIC MODULE WITH SHORT AND OPEN CIRCUITED BYPASS DIODES

Ibuki Kitamura[1], Toshiyuki Hamada[1], Ikuo Nanno[2]
[1]Osaka Electro-communication University, Japan
[2]Nanno Energy Research Center, Japan
hamada@osakac.ac.jp

ABSTRACT: In recent years, decarbonization efforts have advanced rapidly, especially in developed countries, due to climate change and rising energy costs. Photovoltaic (PV) power generation is being widely adopted as an effective energy source, but increasing penetration brings operational problems such as failures. For example, bypass diode (BPD) failures in PV modules can cause heating, burning, fire, and electric shock risks. BPDs protect against electrical continuity problems and hot spots under partial shading, but failures are difficult to detect when modules are roof-mounted. Failed BPDs exhibit different electrical characteristics, ranging from short- to open-circuit failures, with varying heat generation. The authors previously clarified the correlation between resistance and heat generation using a single PV module, but verification for systems with multiple modules requires large-scale testing, making simulations desirable. We propose a model that simulates the output of a PV module string with a failed BPD at various fault resistances. The model reproduces the output when one BPD fails in a PV module with three cell strings and is validated against measured data from a failed BPD module. The study successfully reproduced outputs of PV modules with short-circuit failures (0.1–50 Ω) and open-circuit failures, and also situations with partial shading. The model is expected to support understanding failure mechanisms and diagnosing PV system faults.

1 INTRODUCTION

In recent years, efforts toward decarbonization have been accelerating worldwide, particularly in developed countries, driven by pressing issues such as global climate change, the depletion of fossil fuel resources, and the continuous rise in energy prices. Renewable energy technologies are regarded as indispensable solutions to these challenges, with photovoltaic (PV) power generation being one of the most rapidly expanding options [1].

As the penetration of PV power generation continues to rise, however, various operational and reliability issues are also becoming more prominent. Failures within PV systems not only reduce energy yield but also introduce serious safety concerns. A particularly critical problem arises from failures of bypass diodes (BPDs), which are embedded in PV modules to protect against electrical continuity problems and to mitigate hot spot formation when partial shading occurs. Under normal operation, BPDs ensure stable performance of the PV module. However, when a BPD fails, the component may generate significant heat, sometimes leading to burning. Such failures pose major risks of fire and electric shock, threatening both system safety and reliability [2].

The detection of failed BPDs presents an additional challenge. Because PV modules are often installed on rooftops or other inaccessible locations, visual inspection and maintenance are hindered, making early identification of failures difficult. Furthermore, the behavior of failed BPDs is not uniform: some exhibit short-circuits characteristics with resistance values as low as a fraction of an ohm, while others fail in an open-circuit mode. In some cases, failed BPDs generate excessive heat and burn, whereas in other cases little or no heating occurs. These diverse failure modes complicate failure diagnosis and reliability assessment.

In our previous work, we investigated the electrical and thermal characteristics of failed BPDs and clarified the correlation between their resistance values and heat generation [3]-[4]. While these results were validated using a single PV module, the behavior of an entire PV system—comprising strings of a dozen or more interconnected modules—remains insufficiently understood. Conducting large-scale field experiments to verify such system-level behaviors requires significant resources and repeated testing under controlled conditions, which is both costly and time-consuming. Consequently, the development of reliable simulation models is desirable for evaluating PV system performance under BPD failure scenarios.

In this study, we propose a simulation model that reproduces the output characteristics of a PV module string in the presence of a failed BPD. Specifically, the model considers fault resistances spanning from short- to open-circuit conditions and is designed for PV modules consisting of three cell strings. To validate the proposed approach, the simulated outputs are compared with measured data obtained from an actual PV module containing a failed BPD.

2 SIMULATION MODEL

Figure 1 shows a simulation model of a three-cell-string PV module with one failed BPD. Figure 1(a) shows models that reproduce the characteristics of a diode. These models were implemented in MATLAB/Simulink to represent the current characteristics of a diode given by equations (1) and (2), which provide the characteristic equation and photocurrent of a polarity-inverted diode [5].

$$I_d = I_{sat}\left\{exp\left(\frac{q_e\, v_r}{n\, k_b\, T}\right) - 1\right\} + I_{shunt} \quad (1)$$

$$I_{shunt} = \frac{V_r}{R_p}\left\{1 + a\left(1 - \frac{V_r}{V_{br}}\right)^{-m}\right\} \quad (2)$$

where I_{sat} is the reverse saturation current, V_r is the breakdown voltage, q_e is the electron charge, k_b is the Boltzmann constant, T is the temperature, and n is an ideal coefficient; these parameters were set to 3.8×10^{-7} A,

10.4229/EUPVSEC2025/3AV.3.22

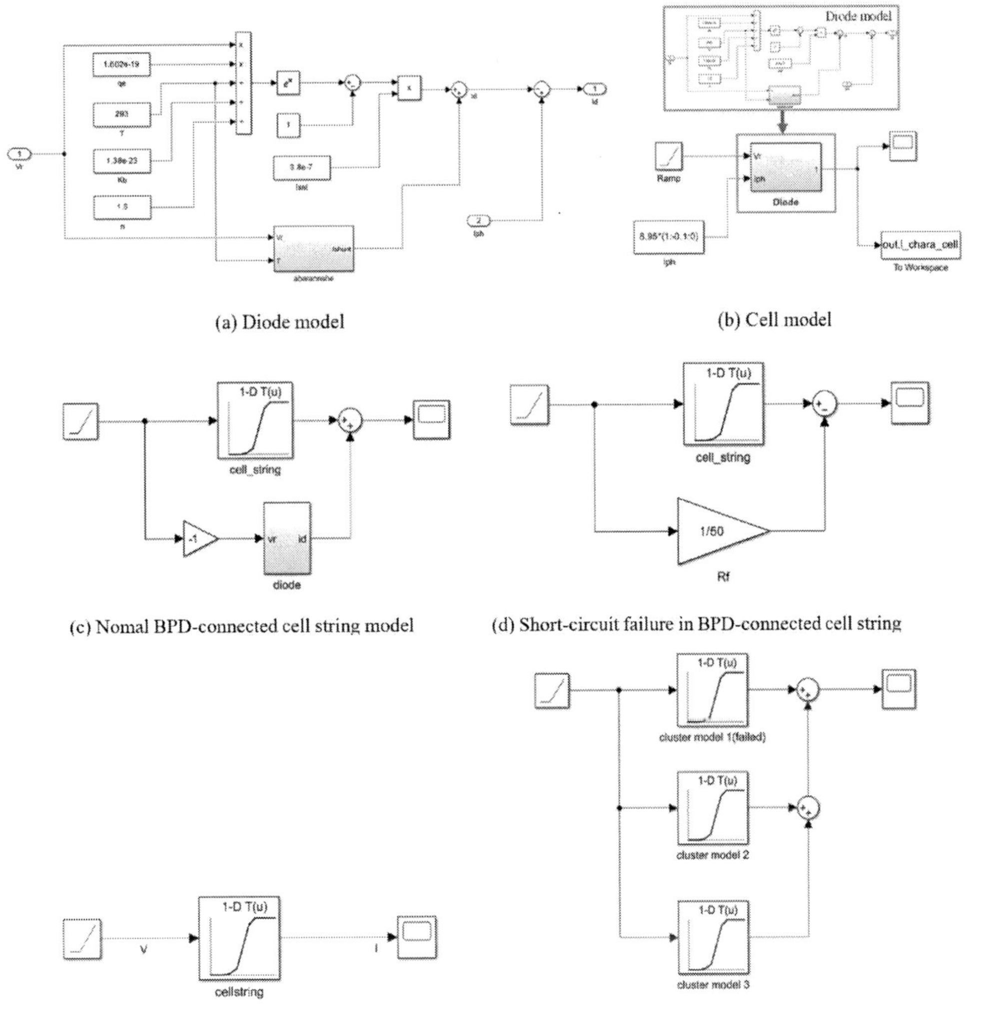

(a) Diode model

(b) Cell model

(c) Nomal BPD-connected cell string model

(d) Short-circuit failure in BPD-connected cell string

(e) Open-circuit failure in BPD-connected cell string model

(f) Three-cell-string PV module

Figure 1 Diagrams of three-cell-string PV module with BPD failures

−100 V, 1.6×10^{-19} C, 1.38×10^{-23} J/K, 293 K, and 1.5, respectively.

Figure 1(b) shows a solar cell model that corresponds to the diode model shown in Figure 1(a) with additional photocurrent I_{ph}. The characteristics of the PV module provided by Choshu Industry Co., Ltd. (CS-236B31) was selected for this study. As the solar cell output, open-circuit voltage V_{oc} was set to 0.64 V, and short-circuit current I_{sc} was set to 8.95 A.

Figure 1(c) shows a model of a cell string containing a BPD. The model replicates the cell model shown in Figure 1(b) to obtain a cell string structure composed of 18 solar cells connected in series. To reproduce a cell string including a BPD, a diode was connected in parallel.

Figure 1(d) shows a model of the cell string with a short-circuited BPD. In this case, the BPD loses its rectification characteristics and exhibits a resistor characteristic when operated under reverse bias. The short circuit is reproduced by replacing the BPD shown in Figure 1(c) with a resistor, R_F.

Figure 1(e) shows a cell string model with an open-circuited BPD. If a BPD is in open circuit, it cannot divert the current generated by other cell strings when the related cell string has conduction failure or is shaded. The output with an open-circuited BPD is reproduced using a cell string without BPD.

Figure 1(f) shows a model of a PV module with three cell strings and BPDs. This model adds three cell string models (Figure 1(e)), which deliver open-circuit voltage V_{OC} = 10.9 V and short-circuit current I_{SC} = 8.95 A, to reproduce a PV module with three cell strings connected in series.

3 RESULTS OF SIMULATION

Figure 2 shows the output characteristics of a PV module with three cell strings and BPDs, with one BPD having an open-circuit failure. In addition, the failure resistance of the short-circuited BPD varies between 0.1 and 50 Ω. Real measurements were acquired under a solar radiation intensity of 740–830 W/m^2 and air temperature of 8–13 °C. In Figure 2, when fault resistance R_F of the BPD decreases, the open-circuit voltage and operating voltage decrease. This is because the operating voltage of the cluster decreases with R_F. Due to the low solar radiation intensity, the measurement results show a lower current than the simulation results intended to reproduce the rated output, but the simulation can suitably reproduce the output of the PV module (CS-236B31).

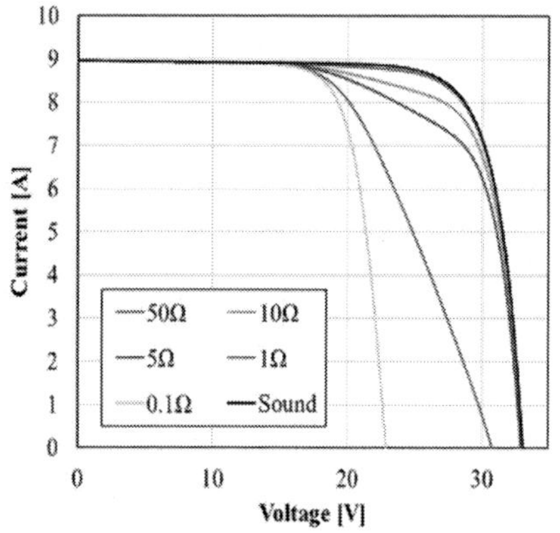

(a) Simulation Results

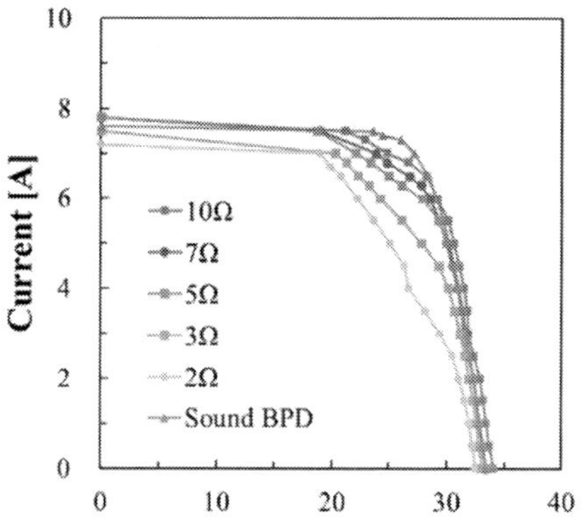

(b) Actual measurement results

Figure 2 Output characteristics of PV module containing three cell strings and BPDs with one short-circuited BPD.

Figure 3 shows the output characteristics of a PV module composed of three cell strings and BPDs, with one of the BPDs under open-circuit failure. Under normal power generation conditions, no difference occurs in the output characteristics between a PV module with an open-circuited BPD and a normal module. We also evaluate the output characteristics when one cell in a string, which contains 18 solar cells connected in series, with an open-circuited failed BPD is gradually shaded. This scenario is reproduced by changing the shaded cell photocurrent, Iph, in the solar cell model. The percentages shown in Figure 3 indicate photocurrent Iph input to the cell to be shaded. A photocurrent of 100% represents a state of no shading, and the photocurrent is the same as that of the other cells in the cell string. A value of 50% reproduces a state in which photocurrent Iph of the shaded cell is halved, that is, a state in which half of the light-receiving surface of the cell is shaded. Figure 3 shows that in both the simulation and measurement results, the output of the entire PV module changes drastically with a short-circuited failed BPD and increasing shaded area. In addition, the solar cell operates with avalanche breakdown in the low-voltage region. Real measurements were acquired with a solar radiation intensity of 600–680 W/m^2 and temperature of 8–12 °C. Although the measured currents are lower than the corresponding simulation results, the simulation results agree with the output of the PV module (CS-236B31).

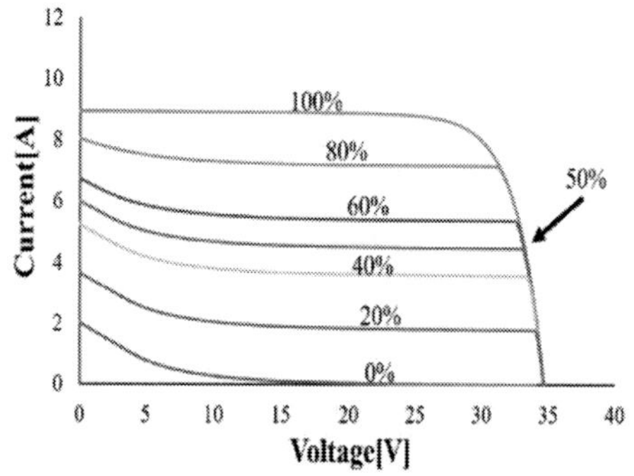

(a) Simulation Results

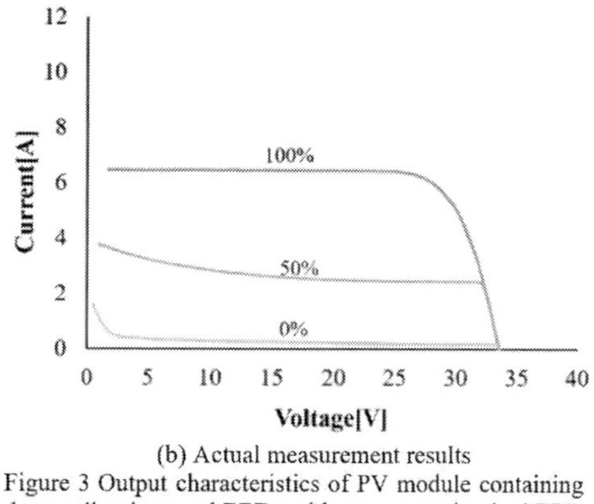

(b) Actual measurement results

Figure 3 Output characteristics of PV module containing three cell strings and BPDs with one open-circuited BPD and the solar cell in the cell string with the failed BPD being gradually shaded.

Figure 4 shows the output characteristics of a PV module that has three normal cell strings and normal BPDs when one solar cell is gradually shaded. When the shade on one solar cell in the cell string moves, the output current on the output-voltage side higher than 22 V changes. This region shows changes in the output voltage and current of the shaded cell string. Although the current is low due to the low amount of solar radiation in the real measurement, the simulation results suitably agree with the measurements.

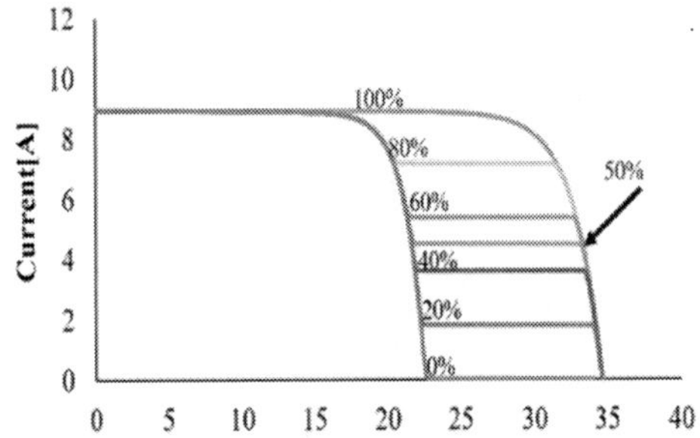

(a) Simulation Results

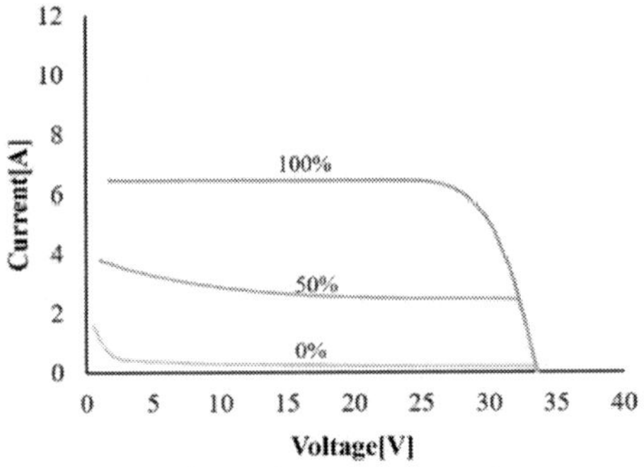

(b) Actual measurement results

Figure 4. Output characteristics of PV module containing three cell strings and BPDs with one solar cell being gradually shaded under no failure.

4 CONCLUSIONS

In this study, we proposed and validated a simulation model capable of reproducing the output characteristics of PV module strings under bypass diode (BPD) failure conditions. The model successfully reproduced the behavior of PV modules with BPDs exhibiting short-circuit failures with resistance values ranging from 0.1 to 50 Ω, as well as open-circuit failures. Furthermore, the model was also able to simulate partial shading effects in PV module strings. These results indicate that the proposed approach can serve as a useful tool for analyzing failure mechanisms and developing diagnostic methods for PV systems. Future applications of this model are expected to contribute to improving the safety, reliability, and maintainability of PV power generation systems.

Acknowledgements

This study was supported by JSPS KAKENHI (Grant No. JP21H01580).

References

[1] Ministry of Economy, Trade and Industry and Agency for Natural Resources and Energy, Japan's Energy 10 Questions for Understanding the Current Energy Situation, Tokyo, Japan, 2022.

[2] M. Koentges et al., Review of Failures of Photovoltaic Modules, Photovoltaic Power Systems Program, *Report IEA-PVPS T13-01*, 2014.

[3] T. Hamada, T. Azuma, I. Nanno, M. Fujii, N. Ishikura, S. Oke, Effect of Failure Characteristics of Bypass Diode in Photovoltaic Solar Module on Burnout, *J. Inst. Elect. Instal. Engnr. Jpn.*, 42, 2022, 16-17.

[4] T. Hamada, Tomoki Azuma, Ikuo Nanno, Norio Ishikura, Masayuki Fujii, Shinichiro Oke, Impact of Bypass Diode Fault Resistance Values on Burnout in Bypass Diode Failures in Simulated Photovoltaic Modules with Various Output Parameters, *Energies*, 16, 2023, 1-9.

[5] J.W. Bishop, Computer simulation of the effects of electrical mismatches in photovoltaic cell interconnection circuits, *Solar cells*, 25, 1988, 73-89.

EVALUATING THE EFFICACY OF NEUTRAL DENSITY FILTERS AND CAMERA LENS APERTURE FOR REDUCING SENSOR SATURATION AND INCREASE IMAGE QUALITY IN DAYLIGHT EL IMAGING

Kabir Paúl Sulca[1]*, Rodrigo del Prado Santamaria[2], Thøger Kari[2], Julian Anaya[1], Gisele Alves dos Reis Benatto[2], Sergiu Viorel Spataru[2], Oscar Martínez[1]
[1]GdS-Optronlab group, Dpto. Física de la Materia Condensada, Universidad de Valladolid, Edificio LUCIA, Paseo de Belén 19, 47011 Valladolid (Spain)
[2]DTU Electro, Technical University of Denmark (DTU), Frederiksborgvej 399, 4000 Roskilde, Denmark.
*kabirpaul.sulca@uva.es

Daylight electroluminescence (dEL) inspection using InGaAs cameras has proven to be a powerful technique for assessing the condition of photovoltaic (PV) modules in the field. Recent advancements have shown it suitable for quality control and evaluation tasks in large-scale solar installations. The quality of dEL images is crucial for accurately identifying potential defects. Therefore, it is important to determine which camera optical stack yields stronger signals in dEL imaging. Camera optical stacks typically include specialized short-wave infrared (SWIR) lenses and bandpass filters to reduce background sunlight. To further limit the light intensity reaching the sensor and prevent saturation, options include adjusting the lens iris, using neutral density (ND) filters, or reducing exposure time. The choice among these depends on system constraints. Even though reducing exposure time is the easiest way to accomplish no saturation, high exposure time reduces noise, so ND filters and the iris are interesting options independent of the camera's internal controller. This study compares the light intensity reduction methods between ND filters and iris providing higher EL and dEL image quality using signal-to-noise ratio (SNR) as metric. Two SNR metrics (SNR_{kari} and $SNR_{(25)}$) are used to evaluate the configurations. We compare two setups: one using a C-RED 3 InGaAs camera with a SWIR lens (F-stop range 1.4–16) and a bandpass filter, and another using the same camera and lens fixed at F-stop 1.4 (fully open) combined with ND filters of varying transmittance (0.73 to 0.02). Indoor EL data is used to characterize light attenuation for each configuration. Subsequently, dEL images are captured under 600-800 W/m² irradiance for both setups. The results show that using the iris to reduce light intensity yields higher image quality. This is attributed to the increased depth of field resulting from a smaller optical aperture, which enhances the focus range and sharpness of the captured images. In conclusion, the study demonstrates that using a lens with an adjustable iris is more effective for dEL imaging with InGaAs cameras. This finding is valuable for optimizing optical setups to achieve high-SNR images in PV module inspections.

Keywords: Daylight Electroluminescence, InGaAs Camera, EL Signal-to-Noise Ratio, Photovoltaic Module Inspection.

1 INTRODUCTION

Photovoltaic (PV) module inspection is a critical task for ensuring the reliability and performance of PV solar energy systems [1,2]. Among the various diagnostic techniques available, daylight electroluminescence (dEL) imaging has emerged as a powerful method for detecting defects in PV modules under real-world operating conditions [3-8]. Unlike traditional electroluminescence (EL) imaging, which is typically performed indoors, dEL enables on-site inspection without the need for controlled lighting environments, making it highly suitable for large-scale solar installations.

The use of InGaAs cameras in dEL imaging has significantly enhanced the ability to capture high-quality images in the short-wave infrared (SWIR) spectrum [9-11]. However, achieving optimal image quality in daylight conditions remains a challenge, mainly due to the high noise caused by the ambient sunlight and the risk of sensor saturation, since sunlight intensity can be several orders of magnitude higher than EL intensity. Regarding the saturation problem, various optical components are employed to control the light intensity reaching the camera sensor, including neutral density (ND) filters, lens iris adjustments, and exposure time settings [10, 12].

Despite the reported use of these components, there is limited consensus on the most effective configuration for maximizing image quality while minimizing saturation. Reduced exposure time of the camera can solve directly this problem; however, using large exposure times can reduce certain types of CCD sensor noise [13]. In particular, read out noise is not increased with exposure time [13]. For these reasons, studying the efficacy of ND filters versus lens iris adjustments in reducing light intensity and enhancing image quality is of interest for EL and dEL in PV inspections. This issue has not been thoroughly investigated, thats why this study addresses this gap by evaluating the performance of these two approaches using signal-to-noise ratio (SNR) metrics ($SNR_{(25)}$ and SNR_{kari}) as indicators of image quality [11].

We evaluate the efficacy of ND filters and iris through a series of controlled indoor and outdoor experiments using a C-RED 3 InGaAs camera equipped with a SWIR lens and a bandpass filter. We use the previously described asynchronous method [9,11] with a fixed frequency and injection current to have comparable images. We analyze the impact of varying F-stop and ND filter transmittance levels on image quality and defect visibility. While, in general, all results obtained show sufficiently visible details there are clear differences between both setups.

The data presented consists in indoor and outdoor EL. We then analyze the experimental intensity reduction based on the indoor EL data. Even though iris steps are measured in F-stops, we can approximate each F-stop to a transmittance value to compare the two in terms of transmittance. Then, we present how the intensity attenuation works for indoor EL. Next, we calculate SNR values for EL and dEL providing an experimental insight on the quality of the images. Finally, ray tracing simulations provide deeper insight into the quality of each setup, rather than offering only a qualitative assessment of both setups.

2 EXPERIMENTAL DESCRIPTION

This study aims to evaluate the effectiveness of two optical configurations — lens iris adjustment and ND filters — in reducing sensor saturation and improving image quality in dEL imaging of PV modules. The methodology consists of indoor EL and outdoor dEL experiments conducted with a controlled optical setup, followed by dEL image processing and quality assessment using two metrics: $SNR_{(25)}$ and SNR_{kari} [11].

2.1 Optical Setup

The experimental procedure began with the characterization of ND filters. A spectral measurement in the 900–1500 nm range was performed to determine the transmittance percentage of each ND filter.

ND filter transmittance values were obtained from manufacturer data, while equivalent transmittance values for the iris were calculated based on the F-stop formula. Since each F-stop increment halves the aperture area, it was assumed that the light intensity reaching the sensor is also halved. Two optical configurations were tested:

a) Iris-based setup: The lens aperture varied using F-stop values of 1.4, 2.0, 2.8, 4, 8, and 16. The corresponding equivalent transmittance values, calculated from the F-stop relationship, were 1.00 t, 0.50 t, 0.25 t, 0.13 t, 0.03 t, and 0.01 t, respectively. These values served as reference transmittances.

b) ND filter-based setup: A fixed F-stop of 1.4 (fully open) was used in combination with ND filters with transmittance values of 0.73, 0.51, 0.20, and 0.15. Although spectral characterization revealed slight deviations from these values, those provided by the manufacturer datasheets were used for consistency. To explore a broader range of attenuation, combinations of two filters were also tested, resulting in additional transmittance values of 0.37, 0.152, and 0.02.

EL and dEL measurements were carried out using a C-RED 3 InGaAs camera with a resolution of 640 × 512 pixels, a pixel pitch of 15 × 15 μm, 14-bit quantization, a 16-bit dynamic range, and a maximum frame rate of 600 fps. The camera was equipped with a Kowa LM25HC-SW 25 mm SWIR lens and a bandpass filter centered at 1150 nm with a 50 nm full width at half maximum (FWHM).

2.2 Indoor EL and dEL measurements

Indoor EL images were captured to characterize the light attenuation properties of each optical configuration, obtaining a low-noise reference image which has been used to establish a reference SNR value. Although obtaining high-signal EL images was not necessary, the data were processed using the asynchronous image processing method to ensure consistent noise treatment across indoor EL and outdoor dEL measurements. This approach is essential for obtaining the $SNR_{(25)}$ metric, which is defined within the asynchronous processing framework.

The modulation parameters included a modulated current forming a square wave with a frequency of 6.25 Hz and an amplitude of 9.85 A, with the camera operating at 50 fps. Three exposure times (1, 2 and 3 ms) were tested to ensure sufficient signal, particularly under high-attenuation conditions.

Daylight EL images were acquired under medium irradiance conditions (600–800 W/m²) using the same modulated dEL technique. Exposure times of 1, 2 and 3 ms were also used to assess the impact of light reduction on image quality.

2.3 Image Processing

Image processing was performed using the asynchronous dEL processing algorithm defined in [11]. This method is designed to suppress noise and obtain a de-noised image. The number of sample images used to generate the final processed image was kept constant across all experiments to ensure comparability.

2.4 Image Quality Assessment

Image quality was quantified using two signal-to-noise ratio metrics: $SNR_{(25)}$ and SNR_{kari}.

a) as defined in [11], and $SNR_{(25)}$ value of above 10 is considered to be that of a high-quality image.

b) SNR_{kari}, described in [11], defines a good-quality image as one with an SNR value above 4.

Both metrics were applied to indoor and outdoor datasets to compare the performance of the iris-based and ND filter-based configurations.

2.5 Ray tracing simulations

Ray-tracing simulations were performed using the Optiland Python library. These simulations only model geometric optics and do not account for the wave nature of light or diffraction effects. The simulation uses the lens described in [14], with an initial F-stop of 2.0.

The ray-tracing model calculated the geometric light paths using ideal materials with refractive indices matching those of the actual lens. A 2D ray path was generated with y representing height and z the optical axis. Three-point light sources were simulated from an object plane located 2000 mm from the lens (z = −2000 mm). It was assumed the PV module to be parallel to the sensor, with (0, 0) corresponding to the center of both the panel and the sensor. The three source points were defined as follows:

- Point 1: (0, 0, −2000) mm.
- Point 2: (0, 550, −2000) mm.
- Point 3: (1100, 550, −2000) mm.

The x–y projection of the rays passing through the simulated lens onto the sensor plane was then plotted, and the number of rays reaching the sensor was quantified.

3 RESULTS AND DISCUSSION

3.1 Filter characterization

To ensure the quality and consistency of the intensity reduction provided by each ND filter, a spectral characterization was performed over the 900–1700 nm range. Ideally, the filters should exhibit approximately linear transmittance reduction behavior.

Figure 1 shows the measured counts across the spectral range and the corresponding relative transmittance (t), calculated relative to the "no filter" case.

We then compared the measured transmittance values with those provided by the manufacturer, as shown in Figure 2. Since the EL emission of the Si PV modules is centered around 1150 nm, particular attention was given to this wavelength. The measured transmittance values were found to be slightly lower than those reported in the manufacturer's datasheet.

10.4229/EUPVSEC2025/3AV.3.23

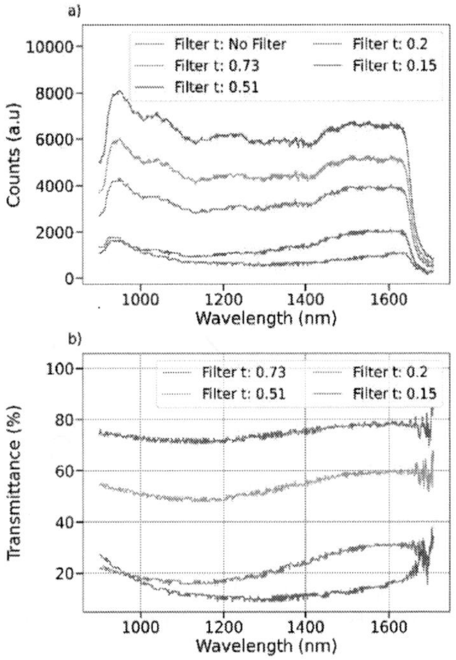

Figure 1: Filter transmittance in the 900-1700 nm range: a) counts (a.u), b) relative transmittance.

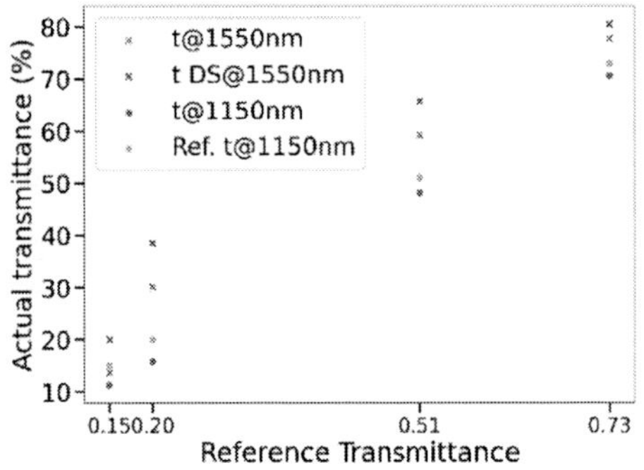

Figure 2: Reference transmittance vs measured transmittance percentage.

Since no significant differences were observed between the measured and reference transmittance values at 1150 nm, the reference values from the datasheet were used for subsequent analyses.

3.2 Indoor EL

An indoor dataset was acquired using both optical configurations: iris adjustment and ND filters. Figure 3 shows the EL images obtained under comparable conditions — 0.13 t (F-stop 4) for the iris and 0.15 t for the ND filter. The image captured with the iris shows uniform brightness and sharper detail, which improves visibility of small defects. The uniform brightness improvement can be attributed to reduced vignetting when the optical aperture is decreased. Vignetting is commonly caused by internal lens components. On the other hand, a sharper image can be attributed to an increase in depth of field and a reduction in optical artefacts due to the light´s geometrical paths within the lens´s internal arrangement . These F-stop effects are explored further in the simulation section.

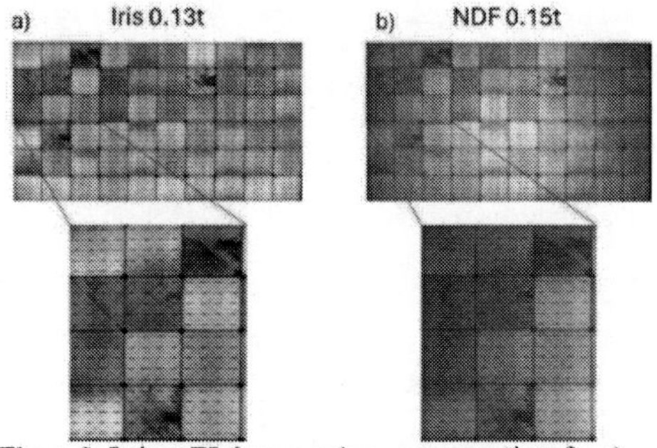

Figure3: Indoor EL image at 1 ms exposure time for a) 0.13 t iris aperture and b) 0.15 t ND filter

To analyze the behavior of light intensity reduction, the average pixel intensity was plotted as a function of transmittance (Figure 4). Both the iris and ND filters were found to effectively reduce the signal received by the sensor. Tests were conducted with exposure times of 1, 2 and 3 ms. A linear relationship was observed in the case of the ND filter (Figure 4b), whereas the iris case (Figure 4a) deviated from linearity, likely due to the simplifications made when estimating the equivalent transmittance.

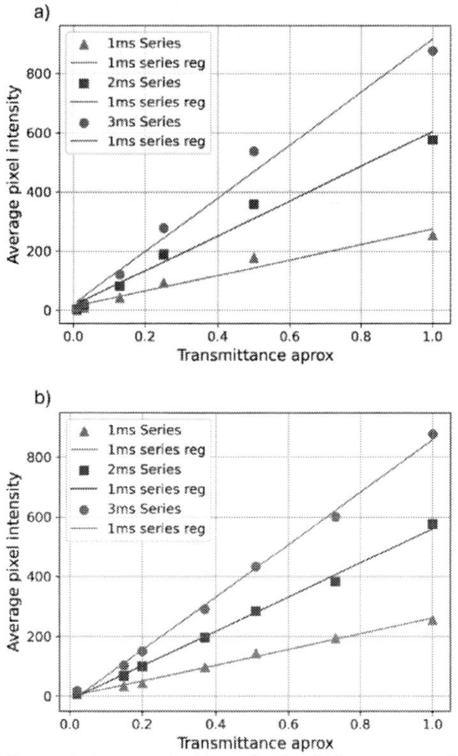

Figure 4: Average pixel intensity for a) iris aperture and b) ND filter, for 1, 2 and 3 ms exposure times

Next, we computed and plotted both SNR metrics for the indoor dataset (Figure 5). The iris configuration consistently produced higher SNR values than the ND filter configuration. Interestingly, Figure 5b shows that the $SNR_{(25)}$ is higher at 0.5 transmittance (F-stop 2.0) than at 1.0 transmittance (F-stop 1.4). This suggests that the noise introduced by optical artefacts at larger apertures exceeds the contribution expected from a 50% reduction in signal. Regarding SNR_{kari}, this metric is less informative at high signal levels, as it was designed to address low-signal noise behavior.

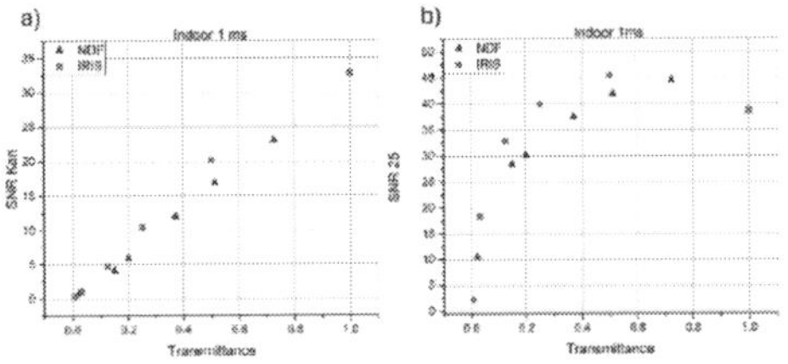

Figure 5: Indoor EL SNR for iris vs ND filter for 1 ms exposure time: a) SNR_{kari}, b) SNR_{25}.

3.2 dEL measurements

Daylight EL images were acquired and processed using the asynchronous method [11] under medium irradiance conditions (600–800 W/m²). Figure 6 shows the dEL images captured with a 1 ms exposure time for both configurations under similar conditions. While both images reveal most defects, the ND filter image exhibits vignetting, whereas the iris-based image shows sharper details and more uniform brightness, consistent with the indoor results.

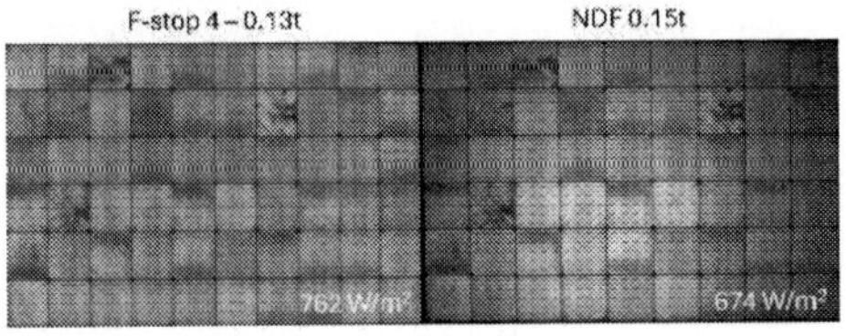

Figure 6: Daylight EL images obtained for similar intensity reductions using the iris (0.13 t) and the ND filter (0.15 t)

To quantitatively compare image quality, SNR metrics were computed for both setups (Figure 7). The iris configuration yielded higher SNR values, indicating stronger signals and better image quality. This can again be partially attributed to vignetting, as regions with lower intensity are interpreted as low-signal regions by the SNR metrics. Additionally, the same trend observed in the indoor experiments was reproduced: SNR values were higher at 0.5 transmittance (F-stop 2.0) and lower at 1.0 (F-stop 1.4). This supports the conclusion that, for the highest aperture, optical artefacts introduce more noise than signal is gained.

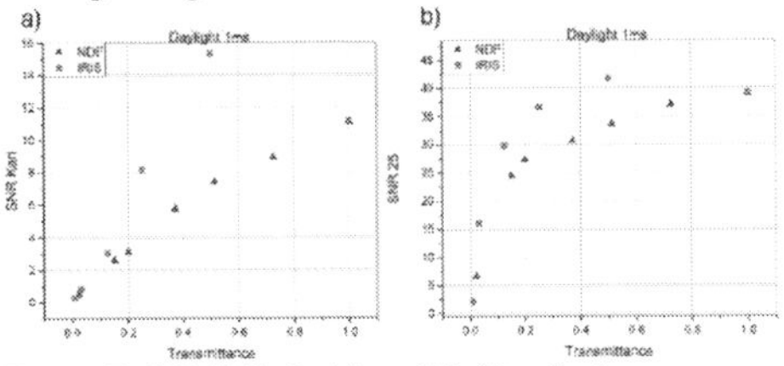

Figure 7: dEL SNR for iris vs ND filter for 1 ms exposure time: a) SNR_{kari}, b) SNR_{25}.

Overall, for both EL and dEL measurements, despite their methodological differences, both SNR metrics consistently indicate superior image quality when using the iris for all similar transmittance values. Higher SNR values indicate better data quality and more reliable signal detection from the images of the PV modules.

3.3 Ray tracing simulations

The simulation focused on three points of the PV module, as illustrated in Figure 8, with rays traced individually from each source point.

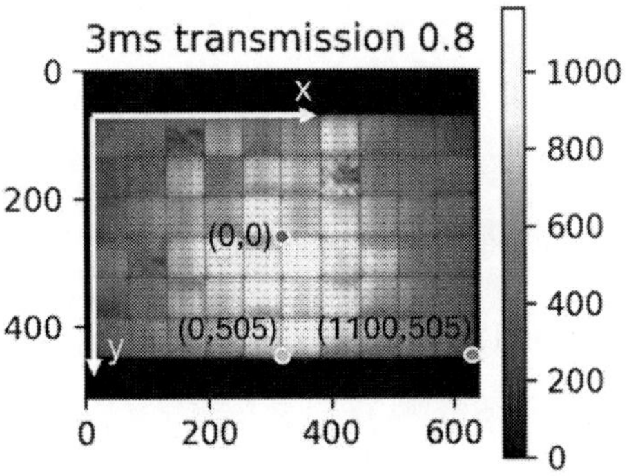

Figure 8: Ray tracing simulation source points scheme

We will study the rays reaching the final surface (sensor) only for the iris case because adding NDF to this kind of simulations will only linearly reduce the intensity without affecting the geometry of the setup. Figure 9 shows the (y,z) graph depicting the lens construction for a F-stop of 2.0 and the rays originating from the source points. We can observe the blue rays passing through the system from point (0,0), the orange rays from the point (0,550), and the green rays from the point (1100,550). We can also see the internal lens optic representation and sensor placement.

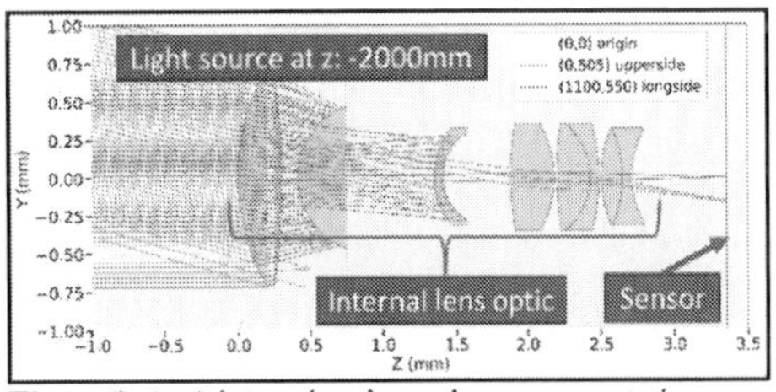

Figure 9: (y,z) internal optics and ray representations

An (x, y) projection of the sensor surface is shown in Figure 10, with normalized coordinates Hx and Hy. Normalization was performed relative to the longest sensor dimension.

We use the spot projection over the sensor to count the number of rays that reach the surface. We then make calculations for different F-stop values and plot the resultant rays that reach the sensor. Figure 11 shows the number of rays reaching the spot. The number of rays shows the expected tendency: a higher number of rays come from the origin, fewer from (0,550) and the fewest from the corner (1100,550). We can also observe that the difference between the sources is reduced when the aperture is closed; this is the same experimental pattern of reduced vignetting.

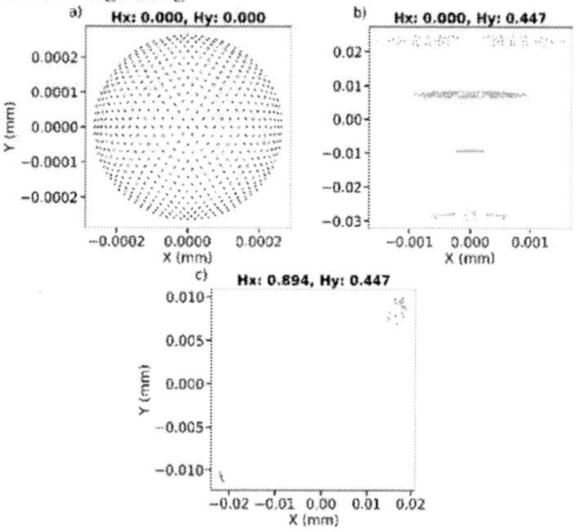

Figure 10: (x,y) ray tracing spot over sensor

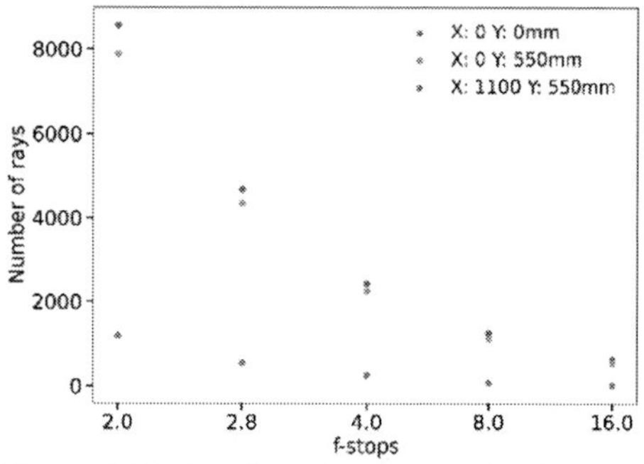

Figure 11: Number of rays for F-stops ranging from 2.0 to 16.0

To examine the vignetting effect further, a profile plot was generated along the x-direction from (0, 550) to (1100, 550) (Figure 12). The slope increases towards the sensor edges but decreases with smaller apertures.

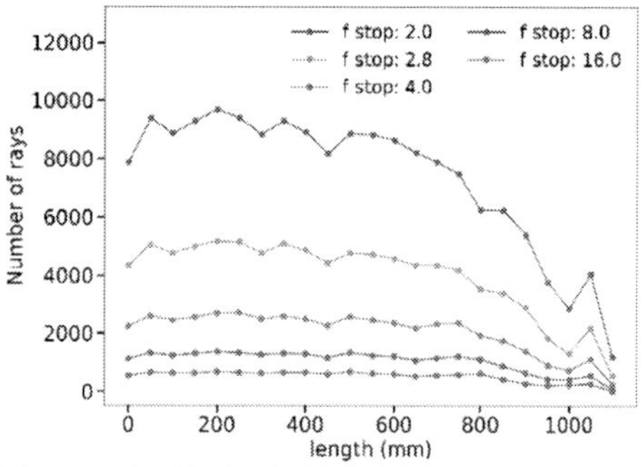

Figure 12: Profile plot for iris simulation

Lastly, we can observe the experimental profile plot in Figure 13. Half of the image is profiled, centered on the y-axis and along the x-axis. Notice how reducing the iris aperture flattens the reduction in intensity at the edges, whereas this does not happen as much with the neutral density filter.

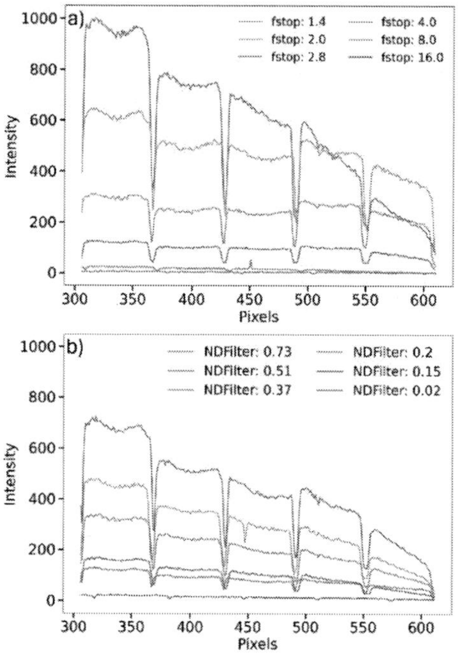

Figure 13: Experimental profile plot for F-stops (a) and ND filters (b)

4 CONCLUSIONS

This study systematically evaluated the effectiveness of neutral density (ND) filters versus lens iris adjustments in reducing sensor saturation and enhancing image quality in EL and dEL imaging of PV modules using InGaAs cameras. Through a combination of indoor EL characterization, outdoor dEL measurements, and ray tracing simulations, we demonstrated that adjusting the lens iris consistently yields superior image quality compared to using ND filters.

The comparative analysis revealed several important findings. First, adjusting the lens iris consistently produced higher SNR values across both SNR_{25} and SNR_{Kari} metrics, indicating superior image quality and reduced noise. This improvement is attributed to the increased depth of field and reduced optical artefacts which can be related to the noise of the image and reduced vignetting associated with the signal. This results in enhanced image sharpness and uniformity. Second, ray tracing simulations supported these observations by showing that closing the iris leads to more evenly distributed light across the sensor, minimizing edge losses and optical artefacts. Third, the characterization of ND filters revealed discrepancies between manufacturer-stated and actual transmittance values, particularly at lower transmittance levels, which may introduce inconsistencies in image quality. Taken together, these findings demonstrate that iris-based light attenuation not only improves image clarity but also ensures more reliable and consistent imaging performance in both EL and dEL applications.

5 ACKNOWLEDGMENTS

This work has been funded by the Spanish Ministry of Science and Innovation, under project PID2023-148369OB-C43, financed by MICIU/AEI /10.13039/501100011033 and FEDER/UE, and by the Regional Government of Castilla y León (Junta de Castilla y León) and by the Ministry of Science and Innovation and the European Union NextGenerationEU / PRTR under the project "Programa Complementario de Materiales Avanzados". K. Sulca has been funded under the call for predoctoral contracts UVa 2022, co-financed by Banco Santander.

6 REFERENCES

[1] L. Koester, S. Lindig, A. Louwen, A. Astigarraga, G. Manzolini, D. Moser, Renew. Sustain. Energy Rev. 165 (2022) 112616.
[2] I. Høiaas, K. Grujic, A. Gerd, I. Burud, E. Olsen, N. Belbachir, Renew. Sustain. Energy Rev. 161 (2022) 112353.
[3] L. Stoicescu, M. Reuter, J.H. Werner, Proceedings 29th Eur. Photovolt. Sol. Energy Conf. Exhib., (2014) 2553.
[4] J. Adams, B. Doll, C. Buerhop, T. Pickel, J. Teubner, C. Camus, C.J. Brabec, Proceedings 32nd Eur. Photovolt. Sol. Energy Conf. Exhib., (2015) 1837.
[5] S. Koch, T. Weber, C. Sobottka, A. Fladung, P. Clemens, J. Berghold, Proceedings 32nd Eur. Photovolt. Sol. Energy Conf. Exhib., (2016) 1736.
[6] G.A. dos Reis Benatto, N. Riedel, S. Thorsteinsson, P.B. Poulsen, A. Thorseth, C. Dam-Hansen, C. Mantel, S. Forchhammer, K.H.B. Frederiksen, J. Vedde, M. Petersen, H. Voss, M. Messerschmidt, H. Parikh, S. Spataru, D. Sera, Proceedings 44th IEEE Photovolt. Specialist Conf., (2017) 2682.
[7] M. Guada, A. Moretón, S. Rodríguez-Conde, L.A. Sánchez, M. Martínez, M.A. González, J. Jiménez, L. Pérez, V. Parra, O. Martínez, Energy Science & Engineering 8 (2020) 3839.
[8] O. Kunz, J. Schlipf, A. Fladung, Y.S. Khoo, K. Bedrich, T. Trupke, Z. Hameiri, Prog. Energy 4 (2022) 042014.
[9] C. Terrados, D. G. Francés, J. Anaya, K.P. Sulca, V. Gómez-Alonso, M. A. González, O. Martínez, Daylight Photoluminescence of Silicon Solar Panels In Operation by Electrical Modulation, Proceedings of the 40th EUPVSEC, Vol I (2023) 258.
[10] Dhimish, M., & Tyrrell, A. M., Optical Filter Design for Daylight Outdoor Electroluminescence Imaging of PV Modules. In Photonics, Vol. 11, No. 1, p. 63 (2024). MDPI.
[11] G. A. dos Reis Benatto, T. Kari, R. del Prado Santamaría, S. V. Spataru, C. Terrados, D. G. Francés, J. Anaya, K. P. Sulca, V. Gómez-Alonso, M. A. González, O. Martínez, Daylight Electroluminescence Imaging Methodology Comparison, Proceedings of the the 40th EUPVSEC Vol I (2023) 374.
[12] G. A. dos Reis Benatto, T. Kari, R. del Prado Santamaría, A. Mahmood, L. Stoicescu, S. V. Spataru, Evaluation Of Daylight Filters For Electroluminescence Imaging Inspections Of C-Si Pv Modules, Proceedings of the 41st EUPVSEC, Vol I (2024) 2163
[13] Fellers, T. J., and M. W. Davidson. Concepts in Digital Imaging Technology, CCD Noise Sources and Signal-to-Noise Ratio. (2010).
[14] Laikin, M. Lens Design. Optical science and engineering series, 4th ed, (2007) 101.

DESIGN, MANUFACTURING AND ANALYSIS OF ALUMINIUM-BACKED BIPV FACADE MODULES: ELECTRICAL PERFORMANCE AND OUTDOOR TESTS

Sophia Jahreis, Bengt Jaeckel, Ringo Koepge, Jens Froebel, Paul Schenk, Matthias Pander
Fraunhofer-Center for Silicon-Photovoltaics (CSP), Halle (Saale), Germany
bengt.jaeckel@csp.fraunhofer.de

ABSTRACT: In driving the energy transition, the building sector plays a major role, with facades offering considerable but still underutilized potential for photovoltaic integration. Building-integrated photovoltaics (BIPV) enable a dual use of facades as energy generators and building envelopes, while aluminium as a backing material provides robustness and architectural flexibility. However, vertical installation exposes modules to non-standard operating conditions, including variable irradiance, partial shading, and diverse orientations, which directly affect their energy yield. In this work, aluminium-backed BIPV facade modules were evaluated through laboratory characterisation and one year of outdoor monitoring in a multi-oriented test setup, enabling direct comparison of north-, east-, south-, and west-facing facades under real operating conditions. A systematic data filtering procedure was applied to ensure reliable analysis of electrical parameters, irradiance, and module temperatures, providing a robust basis for performance analysis for performance analysis of the aluminium-backed BIPV facade modules and for validating simulation models. The results highlight pronounced orientation-dependent behaviour: the south-facing facade achieved the highest yields, peaking around the equinoxes, while east and west reached roughly three-quarters and north about one-third of the south-facing output. Seasonal trends reflect the solar geometry, with east and west peaking around the summer solstice. Slight but consistent east–west differences were linked to temperature effects, as confirmed by measured module temperatures. Combining multiple orientations potentially smooth generation across the day, reduce summer midday peaks, and align output more closely with building demand.

Keywords: Building-Integrated Photovoltaics (BIPV), Facade-Integrated Photovoltaics (FIPV), Aluminium-backed modules, Outdoor performance monitoring, Multi-orientation analysis

1 INTRODUCTION

Driving the energy transition requires contributions from the building sector, where the integration of photovoltaic systems into facades offers considerable potential. [1] In this context, building-integrated photovoltaics provide a dual function by generating renewable energy on-site while simultaneously serving the structural and aesthetic roles of conventional construction materials. Aluminium-backed BIPV modules combine robustness, durability, and architectural flexibility, which makes them attractive for facade applications. However, in contrast to conventional roof-mounted or ground-mounted PV systems, facade installations operate under non-standard conditions: the vertical arrangement results in diverse orientations, combined with variable irradiance, thermal stresses due to the installation situation and limited rear ventilation, and frequent partial shading, all of which strongly affect the energy yield. [2–7]
Accurate assessment of innovative BIPV module layouts requires not only laboratory characterisation but also outdoor measurements under real operating conditions. Such field data are essential to evaluate long-term performance, capture orientation-specific effects, and provide a reliable basis for validating simulation models. In particular, multi-orientation outdoor datasets enable a more realistic understanding of the energy contribution facades can provide and support the optimisation of system design and yield predictions.

2 MATERIAL AND METHODS

To assess the real-world performance of aluminium-backed BIPV facade modules, module samples were manufactured and installed on a multi-orientated outdoor test setup for long-term monitoring. The following section details the module layout, the configuration of the outdoor installation, and the methods used for data collection and processing applied in this work.

2.1 Module samples

The aluminium-backed BIPV facade modules consist of multiple functional layers, summarized in Table 1 and visualized in Figure 1. The base layer is a premanufactured coloured aluminium facade panel, which provides both mechanical rigidity and architectural flexibility.

Table 1: Layer structure of the aluminium-backed BIPV facade modules.

	Material
7	Low-iron, tempered glass, 3mm thickness
5	12 PERC M6 half-cells with electrically conductive adhesive interconnection
3	Insulation layer (MPE)
2,4,6	Encapsulant (POE)
1	Premanufactured, coloured aluminium facade panels

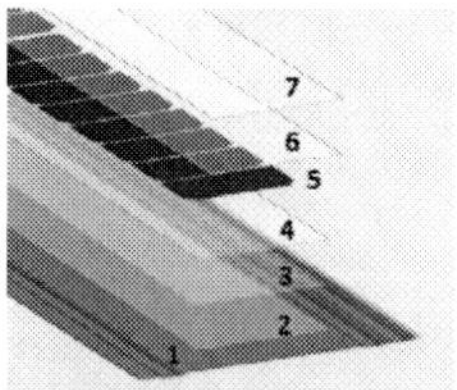

Figure 1: Schematic illustration of the layer structure of the modules.

To electrically isolate the solar cells from the conductive aluminium, a modified polyester (MPE) insulation layer was embedded between additional polyolefin elastomer (POE) encapsulant sheets. The photovoltaic part consists of 12 M6 PERC half-cells arranged with 2 mm cell spacing. A configuration with 9 busbars was combined with electrically conductive adhesive (ECA) for lead-free interconnection. The stack is completed with a low-iron tempered glass front, ensuring both mechanical protection and high optical transmission.

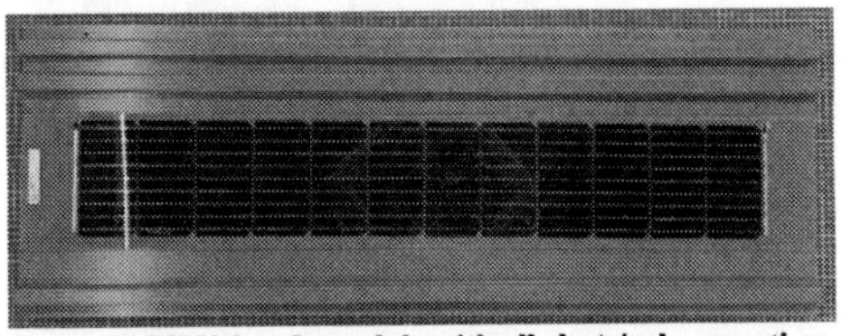

Figure 2: BIPV facade module with all electrical connections located on the rear side of the aluminium panel.

Electrical connections were positioned on the rear side of the aluminium panel to allow a flat facade integration without visible wiring (Fig. 2). Each module has a nominal power of $34.63 \pm 0.14\%\, Wp$ with dimensions of $1180 \times 420\, mm$.

2.2 Outdoor test setup

The outdoor test setup represents a small-scale building with vertical PV facades oriented towards North, East, South, and West. Each wall comprises four aluminium-backed BIPV modules (Fig. 3), connected in series with four bypass diodes, resulting in an installed capacity of 135 Wp per orientation.

Figure 3: Outdoor test setup on the rooftop of the Fraunhofer CSP with minimal environmental shading.

Continuous monitoring covers key electrical parameters, orientation-specific in-plane irradiance, and both modules back-side and ambient temperatures. The modules are mounted on an aluminium profile substructure, while distribution boxes and measurement instrumentation are placed inside the setup (Fig. 4). This configuration enables simultaneous performance evaluation of all orientations under real outdoor conditions.

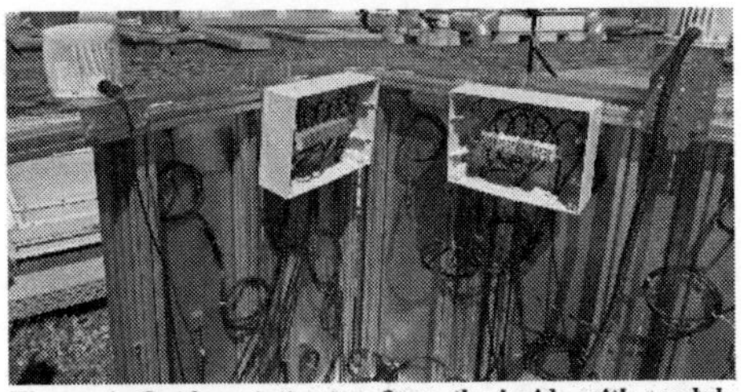

Figure 4: Outdoor test setup from the inside with module instrumentation (temperature and irradiance sensors) and distribution boxes for each orientation

2.3 Method

Based on this setup, long-term monitoring was carried out, recording electrical parameters ($I_{SC}, V_{OC}, I_{mpp}, V_{mpp}$), in-plane irradiance ($Irr$), and thermal behaviour (T_{mod}) every 10 seconds for each orientation. For data selection, only measurements with irradiance above 10 W/m² were considered, and it was verified that the module temperature remained below 60 °C throughout the monitoring period.

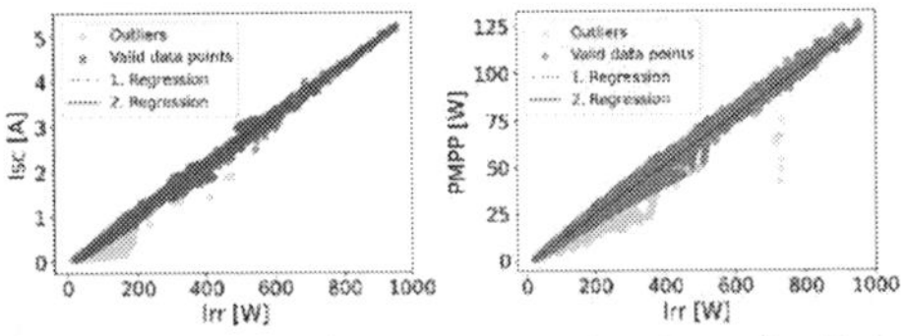

Figure 5: Filtering via linear regression (example: East facade, Aug 2024).

The selected data were further processed by orientation and aggregated on a monthly basis. A two-step linear regression filter was applied to Irr versus I_{SC} and Irr versus P_{mpp}, which is examplarily visualised in Fig. 5 for the East facade in August 2024. This procedure served to exclude inconsistent data points and improve the robustness of the dataset by identifying values that significantly deviated from the expected linear relationship under certain irradiance conditions. Since raw measurements can contain faulty entries, data were systematically checked to remove implausible records, for example cases where energy yield values were logged without corresponding irradiance data. [8]

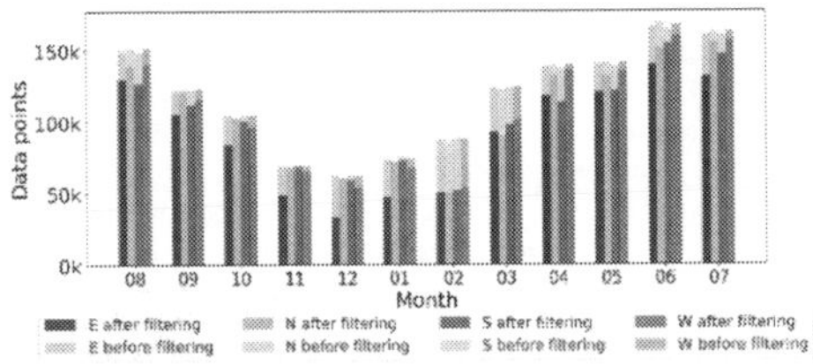

Figure 6: Number of data points above 10 W/m² irradiance before and after filtering.

To check the effect of the filtering procedure, the number of data points above 10 W/m² irradiance was compared before and after filtering for each orientation and month (Fig. 6). As expected, fewer data points are available during the winter months due to the shorter sunshine duration compared to summer.

In addition, the dataset was cleaned by removing data corresponding to system outages or scheduled maintenance periods, which mainly occurred on a few days in February, March, and May 2025. Measurement gaps were also excluded for the times when the modules were re-flashed under standard test conditions (STC) in the laboratory to verify that no performance degradation had occurred. These checks were conducted in February 2025 and September 2025, as illustrated in Figure 7.

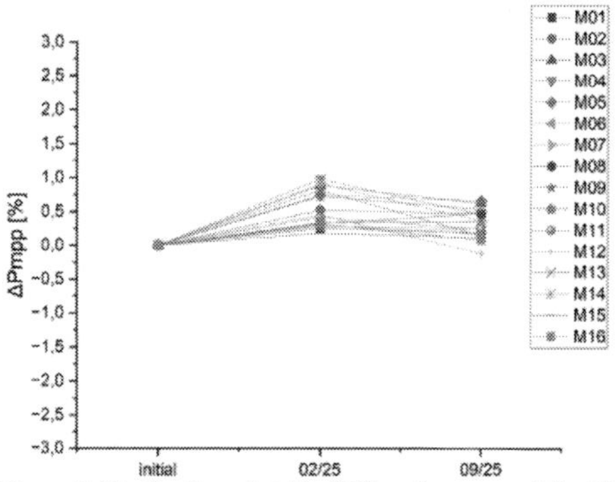

Figure 7: Verification of stable STC performance of the 16 identical BIPV facade modules. ΔP_{mpp} shows no power degradation of the modules, with deviations remaining within measurement tolerance.

Figure 6 also highlights the proportion of excluded data points, which varies with orientation and season. A noticeably higher fraction was removed for the East facade during autumn and winter. To verify that these outliers were not caused by systematic shading, the filtered data were further examined using heat maps, as exemplarily shown for the East facade in August 2024 (Fig. 8).

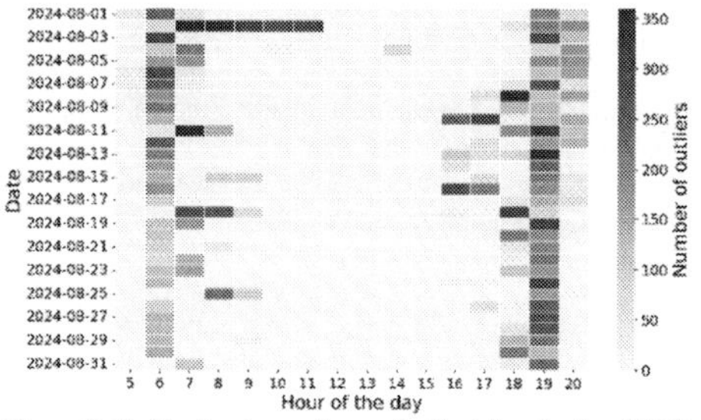

Figure 8: Outlier heat map (example: East facade, Aug 2024).

The analysis confirmed that no persistent shading occurred; most rejected points corresponded to low-irradiance conditions in the early morning, late evening, or on overcast days with diffuse light. For the East facade, data points were excluded due to locally induced reflections of the surrounding under diffuse conditions, which were shown to have only a negligible impact on the overall energy yield.

3 RESULTS

In the following, the results from the one-year measurement period (August 2024 to July 2025) are presented to illustrate the behaviour of the different orientations on daily, monthly, and annual scales.

3.1 Daily power profiles

The power profiles on selected days illustrate the seasonal behaviour of the different orientations (Fig. 9). Representative clear-sky days around the solstices and equinoxes reveal the seasonal variation of the facades. The east- and west-facing modules reach their highest overall power output around the summer solstice, while the south-facing facade shows its lowest seasonal contribution during this period. Towards the winter solstice, the output of the east and west facades decreases to its minimum, whereas the south-orientated modules provide the main share of the output. The north-facing facade contributes only marginally but measurable, mainly through diffuse irradiance and, during summer, direct irradiance in the early morning and late evening.

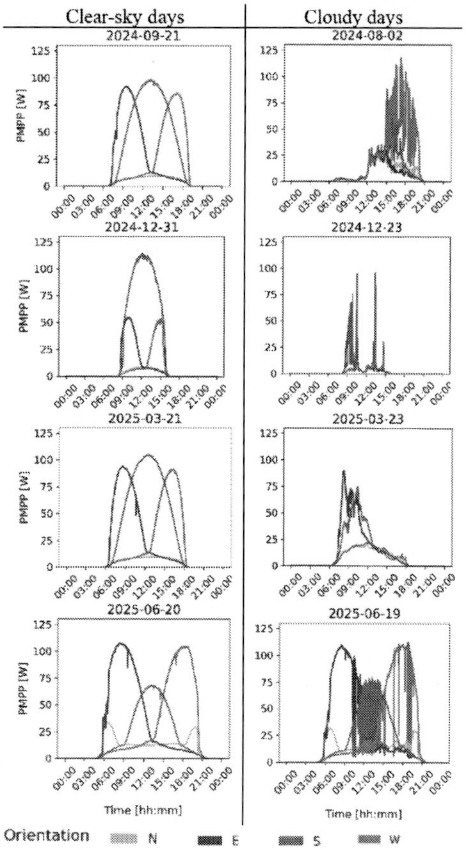

Figure 9: P_{mpp} – Plot of the different orientations on selected days throughout the year.

On 31 December, the south-facing modules exhibited higher power than predicted by clear-sky simulations [9], which are attributed to enhanced albedo from snow reflections and illustrates one of the possible factors causing deviations between simulations and real outdoor data. A slightly higher output is often observed for the east-facing modules compared to the west-facing ones. This effect is linked to temperature differences, as confirmed by the measured T_{mod}: modules remain cooler in the morning but heat up over the course of the day, resulting in higher afternoon operating temperatures and correspondingly reduced power output. Overall, compared

to the STC rating of 135 Wp, the vertical facades still achieve substantial output under real outdoor conditions. On cloudy days, the profiles are less distinct and more irregular due to passing clouds, yet the orientation-dependent trends remain visible.
The different orientations of facades within a single building offer the potential to combine multiple BIPV surfaces, distributing power generation more evenly throughout the day and mitigating pronounced midday peaks, particularly in summer. When compared with representative household and industrial load profiles [10], such aggregated generation patterns indicate a closer alignment with demand, thereby enhancing the potential for self-consumption through multi-oriented BIPV facades.

3.2 Monthly specific energy yield analysis

The monthly specific energy yields reflect the behaviour observed in the daily power profiles, translating these into the seasonal trends of energy yield for the different orientations. (Fig. 10). The east- and west-facing facades follow a similar trend, with maximum yields around the summer solstice. The north-facing facade shows the same seasonal behaviour but with substantially lower values, reflecting its limited irradiance capture.

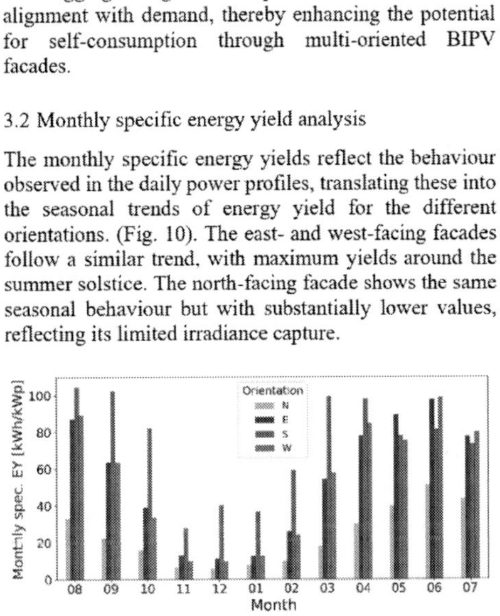

Figure 10: Monthly specific energy yield (EY) per orientation.

The south-facing facade exhibits distinct seasonal pattern: yields rise in autumn, peak around the equinoxes, decrease during winter, increase again in spring, and decline towards the summer solstice. Compared to the east and west facades, the south-facing facade shows a smaller amplitude between maximum and minimum monthly yields, resulting in a more consistent seasonal profile. This behaviour reflects the irradiance distribution across the year, with the equinoxes providing the most favourable solar geometry for vertical south-facing modules.

3.3 Yearly specific energy yield analysis

The annual comparison of specific energy yields reflects the share of the different orientations accumulated over one year (Fig. 11). As expected, the south facade provides the highest output and is set as the reference with 100%. The east- and west-facing facades achieve 74% and 72% of this value, respectively, showing that they contribute a substantial share of the annual yield despite their less favourable orientation. The north facade reaches 32% of the south reference, reflecting its limited irradiance but still adding a measurable share to the overall building-integrated generation.

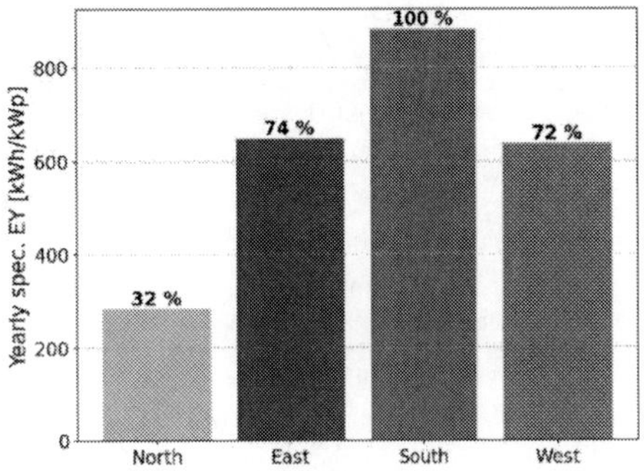

Figure 11: Annual yields, normalized to South facade (100%), Aug 2024 – Jul 2025.

4 SUMMARY AND OUTLOOK

Aluminium-backed BIPV facade modules were designed, manufactured, and evaluated under long-term monitoring in an outdoor test setup with four orientations. The resulting outdoor data provide a solid basis for validating simulation models, as they reflect the real-world performance of the modules and allow more reliable assessment of their behaviour under operating conditions.
The applied data filtering ensured reliable input for performance analysis by excluding inconsistent or faulty measurements. The results from one year of monitoring highlight pronounced orientation-dependent behaviour across daily and seasonal, and scales.
The south-facing modules achieves its highest energy yields around the equinoxes, while the east- and west facades peak around the summer solstice. The north-facing modules shows a similar seasonal course to the east and west facades, but at significantly lower yield levels. Over the full year, the south-facing modules provided the highest output, with east and west reaching roughly three quarters and the north about one third of the south-facing yield. The small but consistent differences between east and west are mainly attributable to temperature effects, as confirmed by measured T_{mod}.
By combining modules of different orientations, the resulting generation profile would be more evenly spread across the day, mitigating pronounced midday peaks and thus potentially supporting grid stability. Alternatively, such a configuration could better match building load profiles, enhancing opportunities for self-consumption.

5 ACKNOWLEDGEMENT

Financial support by the Federal Ministry for Economic Affairs and Energy funded project “AluPV” (FKZ: 03EN1069B) is gratefully acknowledged.

6 REFERENCES

[1] Behnisch M. Electricity from the house wall – the great potential of building facades to capture solar energy: Leibnitz Institute of Ecological Urban and Regional Development, 2021, https://www.ioer.de/en/press/news/electricity-from-the-house-wall-the-great-potential-of-building-facades-to-capture-solar-energy, accessed [08/25]
[2] Biyik E. et al., “A key review of building integrated photovoltaic (BIPV) systems”, Engineering Science and

Technology, Vol. 20 ,3, pp. 833–58, 2017, https://doi.org/10.1016/j.jestch.2017.01.009
[3] Martín-Chivelet N. et al., "Building-Integrated Photovoltaic (BIPV) products and systems: A review of energy-related behavior" Energy and Buildings, Vol. 262, 111998, 2022, https://doi.org/10.1016/j.enbuild.2022.111998
[4] Kuhn T. E. et al., "Review of technological design options for building integrated photovoltaics (BIPV)", Energy and Buildings, Vol. 231, 110381, 2021, https://doi.org/10.1016/j.enbuild.2020.110381
[5] Köhl M. et al., "Effect of thermal insulation of the back side of PV modules in the module temperature", Progress in Photovoltaics, Vol. 24, 9, pp. 1194–1199, 2016, https://doi.org/10.1002/pip.2773
[6] Quest H. et al., "Towards a quantification of thermal and thermomechanical stress for modules in building-integrated photovoltaics configurations", Progress in Photovoltaics, Vol. 33, 1, pp.64-75, 2023 https://doi.org/10.1002/pip.3762
[7] Calcabrini A. et al., "Simulation study of the electrical yield of various PV module topologies in partially shaded urban scenarios", Solar Energy, Vol. 225, pp. 726–733, 2021, https://doi.org/10.1016/j.solener.2021.07.061
[8] Jaeckel B. et al., "Utilizing System Efficiency Evaluations to Determine DC Output of PV Systems", 8th WCPEC, 2022, 10.4229/WCPEC-82022-4BV.5.37
[9] Jahreis S. et al., "Design, manufacturing, and performance of innovative aluminium-backed BIPV facade modules: a case-study in Germany", Energy and Buildings, Vol. 344, 2025, https://doi.org/10.1016/j.enbuild.2025.116047
[10] Open Power System Data, "Household Data (version 2020-04-15)", Open Power System Data platform, https://data.open-power-system-data.org/household_data/2020-04-15/, accessed [08/25]

ANALYSIS OF THE EFFECTS OF PARTIAL SHADING ON CELL PERFORMANCE IN A HALF-CUT CELL PHOTOVOLTAIC MODULE

Poland Michael[1,2], Monphias Vumbugwa[1], E. Ernest van Dyk[1], Frederik J. Vorster[1], Petja Dobreva[2]
[1]Department of Physics, Nelson Mandela University, Port Elizabeth, South Africa
[2]Department of Physics, Chemistry & Material Science, University of Namibia, Windhoek, Namibia
E-mail address: s227745558@mandela.ac.za

ABSTRACT: Half-cut cell photovoltaic (PV) modules have become increasingly popular in today's solar market, offering improved efficiency and reduced power losses compared to standard full-cell modules. These modules aim to reduce electrical losses and improve performance under real-world conditions. The unique structure and configuration of these modules introduce complexities when operating under real-world conditions, especially under partial shading conditions. This study investigates the effects of partial shading on the electrical and thermal characteristics of individual cells in a half-cut cell PV module. Measurements of individual cell voltages, substring currents, and module currents were taken under various shading conditions using a custom-made set-up. Partial shading caused a current mismatch and reduced the voltage across the shaded cell causing an increase in the operational voltages and temperatures of the unshaded cells connected in series with the shaded cell, and a decrease in the voltage of the shaded cell. Fully shading a single cell causes the parallel unshaded substring pair to operate at the same voltage under near short-circuit conditions, resulting in reverse biasing of some cells in the unshaded substring. The results also show that the thermal characteristics of the unshaded cells in the parallel substring may be affected by the partially shaded cell. These findings aid in understanding the effects that partial shading has on the electrical and thermal characteristics of half-cut cell modules and in the interpretation of their thermal images. It was noted that, if substrings were optimized to operate at their individual MPPs, a shaded cell would not become reverse-biased, even with significant shading. It is important to note that module-level optimization doesn't always translate to optimal substring operation.

Keywords: Individual cells, Half-cut cell module, Partial shading, Thermal image, Performance

1 INTRODUCTION

Half-cut cell PV modules are a newer design of PV modules, considered to be an improvement in the performance and partial shading tolerance of the conventional full-cell PV modules [1][2]. Half-cut cell modules typically have between 120 and 144 solar cells, divided into 6 substrings of 20 - 24 cells per substring connected in parallel pairs, with each pair sharing a bypass diode in parallel.

When some cells are shaded, depending on the level of shading, instead of producing power, they act as resistors, consuming power, resulting in them heating up more than the unshaded cells. Since half-cut cells are smaller than the standard full-cells, the substring currents are lower in half-cut cell modules than in full cell modules. This leads to reduced resistive losses in partially shaded half-cut cell modules compared to full cell modules, hence better performance of half-cut modules under partial shading conditions [3]. The reduced current per substring in a half-cut cell PV module also means that the temperature of hotspots is reduced. A hotspot is a localized high-temperature region in a PV module. Hotspot formation compromises the integrity of cells, making them prone to cracking, acceleration of material degradation, and burn marks [2].

Simulation results by Qian et al [4] found that the maximum hotspot cell temperature of a partially shaded half-cut cell module was 28°C lower than that of full cell module. Further simulation on the electrical characteristics revealed that when one of the parallel pairs of substrings is partially shaded enough to activate the bypass diode, a rounded knee was observed, and the current clipping is not nearly as sharp. This is because the unshaded pair compensates for the current loss in the shaded pair, and hence a larger shade area is required to activate the bypass diode.

Experimental results obtained by Chiodetti et al [5] have shown a low efficiency of half-cut cell modules under low irradiance compared to full cell modules for several cell technologies. This behaviour is attributed to the increased number of cell interconnects/soldering points, which leads to high series resistance, whose effect gets more pronounced at low irradiance. The benefits of half-cut cell modules are more pronounced at high irradiance levels, where reduced resistive losses lead to improved efficiency, indicating suitability for high irradiance regions and tracking systems.

Most prior studies focused on simulations or measurements at the module level. This work experimentally analyses the effect of partial shading on the thermal and electrical characteristics of individual cells.

2 METHODOLOGY

2.1 Experimental equipment

The Experiment was performed on a 540 Wp monocrystalline half-cut cell PV module. The module has a 3S2P configuration, with 6 substrings of 24 series-connected cells each. Every two substrings are connected in parallel, and the resulting three pairs are connected in series, totalling 144 cells. Each parallel pair is connected in parallel with a bypass diode, resulting in 3 bypass diodes in the module.

The structure of the experimental module is shown in Figure 1, showing the naming conventions used for substrings (SSs) and cell numbers. Also shown is the placement of shunt resistors (10 mΩ ± 5%) used for the measurement of currents in the different branches of the module. Small incisions were made in the back sheet between the cells to expose the cell interconnects and allow electrical connections to the cells to allow for the measurement of cell voltages.

10.4229/EUPVSEC2025/3AV.3.28

Due to the datalogger limitation on the number of available channels, only 84 cells were monitored: All cells in SS1 - SS3, and only 4 cells in each of the substrings, SS4 - SS6.

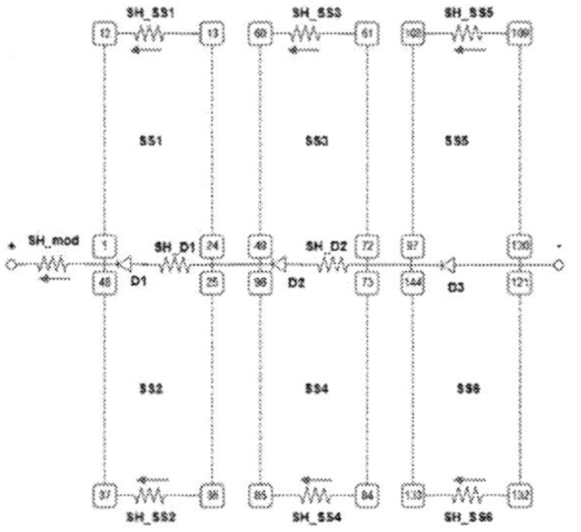

Figure 1: The Half-cut cell module layout. Shown is the position of the shunt resistors used for the measurement of current.

The measurements were taken with the following equipment: A Solmetric I-V tracer, which comes with an irradiance sensor and back-of-module temperature sensors. Agilent 34972A LXI data acquisition unit for measuring the voltage of individual cells, module, bypass diodes, and shunts. A Chroma programmable DC electronic load for sweeping the module I-V while at the same time communicating via LabView software with the Agilent data acquisition unit to take measurements at every step (0.5V) that the Chroma takes the I-V measurements. A manual variable resistor (load). FLIR Thermal camera for taking thermal images of the module. The experiment was set-up as shown in Figure 2:

Figure 2: Experimental set up

2.3 Procedure

The experiment was performed in two parts; part 1 was performed at noon, and part 2 was performed in the afternoon when the power of the module dropped below 500W (the maximum power that the Chroma can support).

Part 1:

a) The thermal image and individual cell voltages were measured under open circuit.

b) The I-V curve of the unshaded module was measured using the I-V tracer under uniform illumination. From the I-V curve data, the maximum power point voltage (Vmpp) was identified.

c) The module was connected to the variable resistor and operated at the identified Vmpp.

d) The individual cell voltages were immediately measured using the Agilent data acquisition unit.

e) A waiting period of 5 minutes was considered before the thermal image of the module was captured.

f) Steps (b) to (e) were repeated while shading cell 37 using boards, covering 12.5 %, 25%, 50%, 62.5%, 75%, and 100% of the cell area, respectively.

Part 2:

a) The I-V of the unshaded module was measured using the I-V tracer.

b) The module was connected to the Chroma.

c) The Chroma was programmed to measure the module voltage and current, then communicate via LabView software with the Agilent data acquisition unit to take measurements of cell voltages. The chroma was set to take the I-V at an increment of 0.5 Volts.

d) The steps (a) to (c) were repeated while shading cell 37 using boards, covering 12.5%, 25%, 50%, 62.5%, 75%, and 100% of the cell area, respectively.

3 RESULTS

3.1 Module power output (Part 1 results)

The measured I-V curves and the corresponding maximum power points of the module while shading a single cell (cell 37) from 0% to 100% are shown in Figure 3. As the cell is shaded from 0% to 75%, the maximum power point (MPP) of the module shifts towards higher voltage (towards Voc), and at 100% the MPP shifts towards low voltage (towards short circuit). The jump in the MPP from high voltage to low voltage signifies the activation of the bypass diode at 100% cell shading.

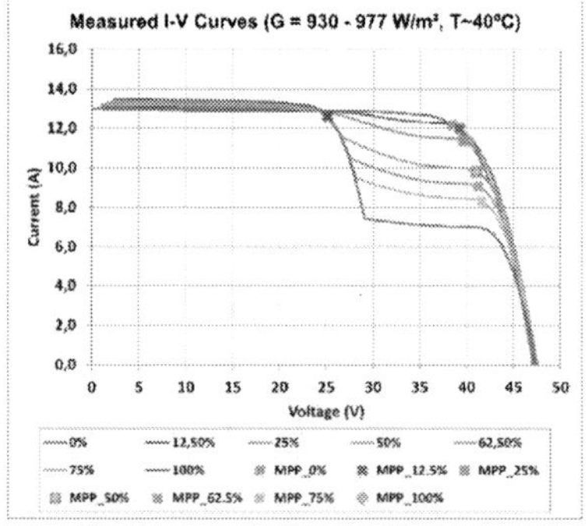

Figure 3: The measured I-V curves and corresponding MPPs of a half-cut cell module while shading a single cell from 0% to 100%.

The impact of cell shading on the module's MPP output is illustrated in Figure 4. As shown, shading a single cell can drastically reduce the power output, with losses reaching up to 1/3 of the module's capacity. Specifically, the unshaded module's MPP output of 480 W dropped to about 325 W when a single cell was fully shaded.

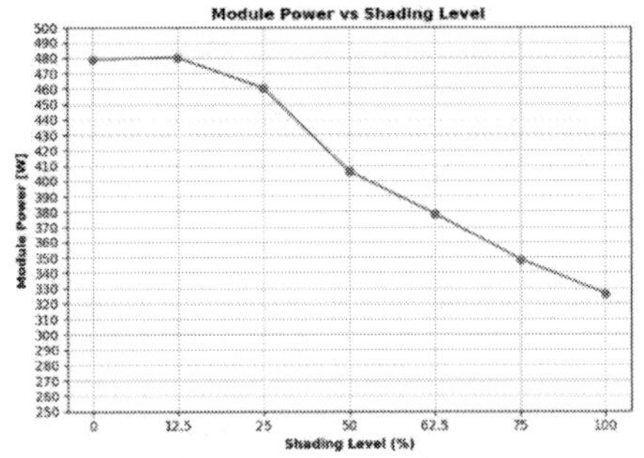

Figure 4: MPP output of a half-cut cell module as a function of single cell shading level.

3.2 Thermal and electrical characteristics of individual cells (Part 1 results)

Figure 5 shows the thermal images of the module under open circuit, and under operation at MPP while not shaded and while shaded by 75%, and 100%. Under open circuit, the module was found to heat up more compared to when it's under operation. This is because under open circuit, the absorbed photons cannot be converted into current and carried away to an external load, hence the energy is dissipated as heat in the cells.

Under Voc and under operation with no shading, the module showed nearly all cells having a uniform temperature distribution, except for two cells in SS6 that appeared abnormally hot. It was found that the two cells are cracked. Additionally, the lower part of the module looks slightly warmer due to the angle at which the thermal image was taken. As the module is shaded from 12.5% to 75% it was found that the shaded cell and the unshaded cells in the shaded substring heat the most. The unshaded pairs heat up the second most, and the substring parallel to the shaded one was the coolest.

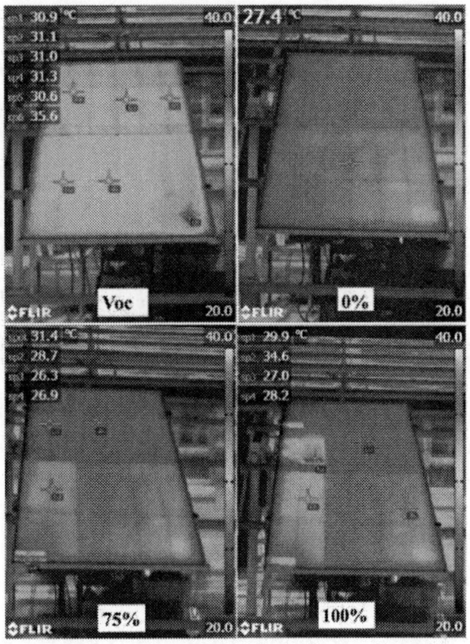

Figure 5: Thermal images of the half-cut cell module under open circuit, and while shading a single cell by 0%, 75%, and 100% shading.

Figure 6 shows the individual cell voltages of the cells while the module is operating at MPP with no shading: all cells are operating nearly at the same voltage of Vmpp ≈ 0.55V.

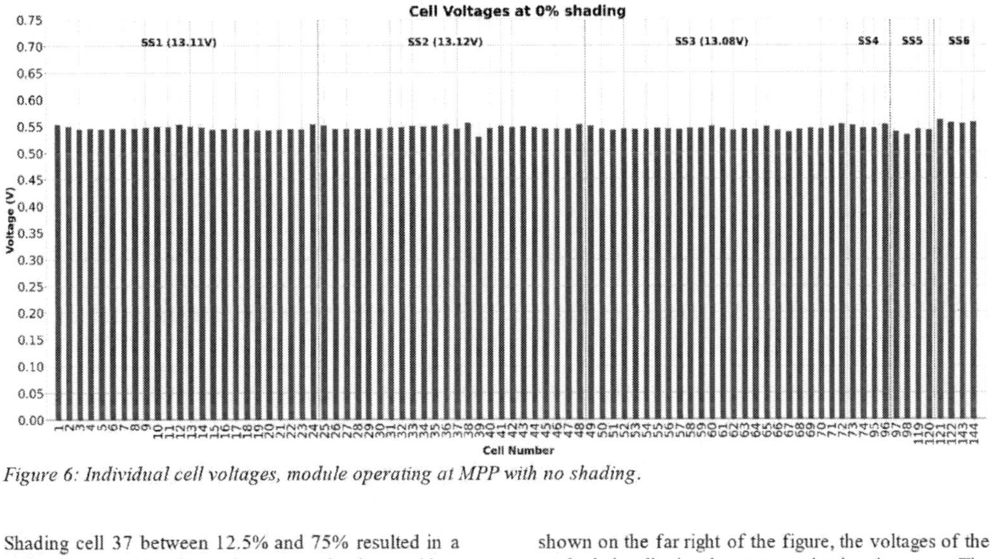

Figure 6: Individual cell voltages, module operating at MPP with no shading.

Shading cell 37 between 12.5% and 75% resulted in a difference in cell voltages between substrings, with a pattern as the shading level is increased. Figure 7 shows the cell voltages at 75% shading. The observed pattern showed that as the voltage of the shaded cell decreases, as shown on the far right of the figure, the voltages of the unshaded cells in the same substring increase. The voltages of cells in SS1 decrease with an increase in cell shading level while the voltages of cells in the unshaded pairs increase with the increase in cell shading level up to

10.4229/EUPVSEC2025/3AV.3.28

75%. At 75% shading, the cells in SS1 operate at Vmpp ≈ 0.50V, SS2 cells operate at about Vmpp ≈ 0.65V, and the cells in the rest of the substrings at Vmpp ≈ 0.60V.

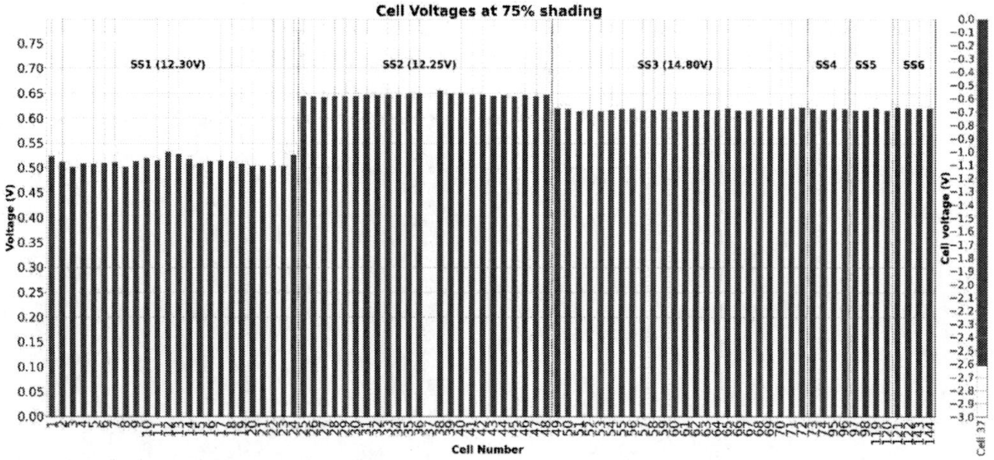

Figure 7: Individual cell voltages at 75% cell shading level. The negative voltage across the shaded cell (cell 37) is shown separately on the insert on the right.

Shading 100% of cell 37 reduces its voltage to about -15.5V, activating the bypass diode parallel to the shaded pair and resulting in the shaded pairs operating near short circuit. This forces some of the cells in the unshaded substring (SS1) to be reverse-biased and dissipate power although they are not shaded as shown in Figure 8. This is because both SS1 and SS2 must operate at the same voltage, because they are connected in parallel. Since at 100% shading the bypass diode is activated, the bypassed substrings (SS1 & SS2) do not produce power, while the rest of the cells in unshaded pairs operate at or close to their MPP, with cells operating at Vmpp ≈ 0.55V.

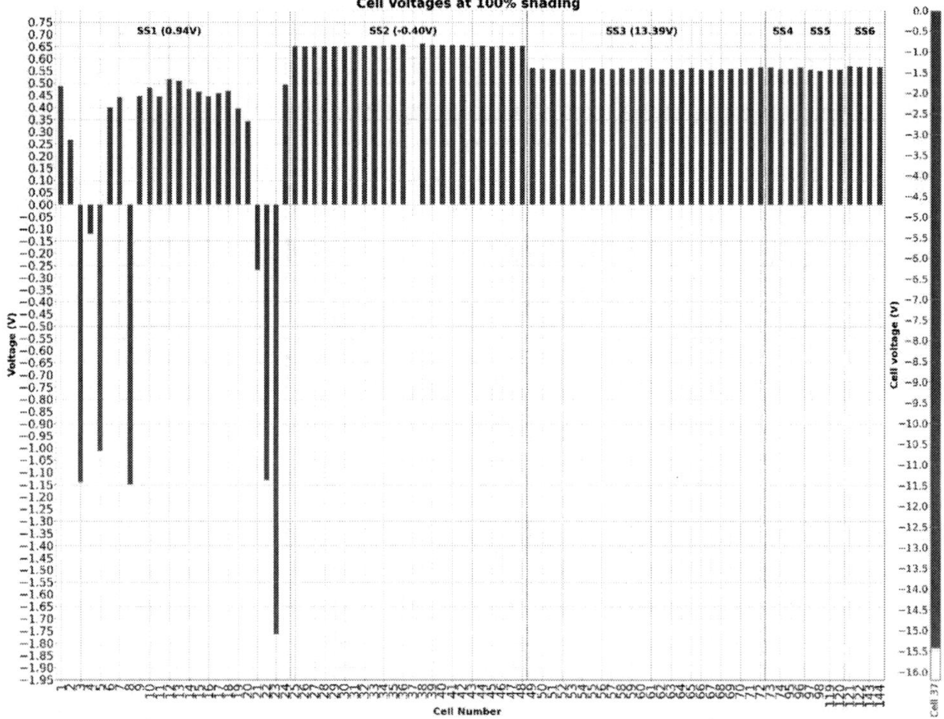

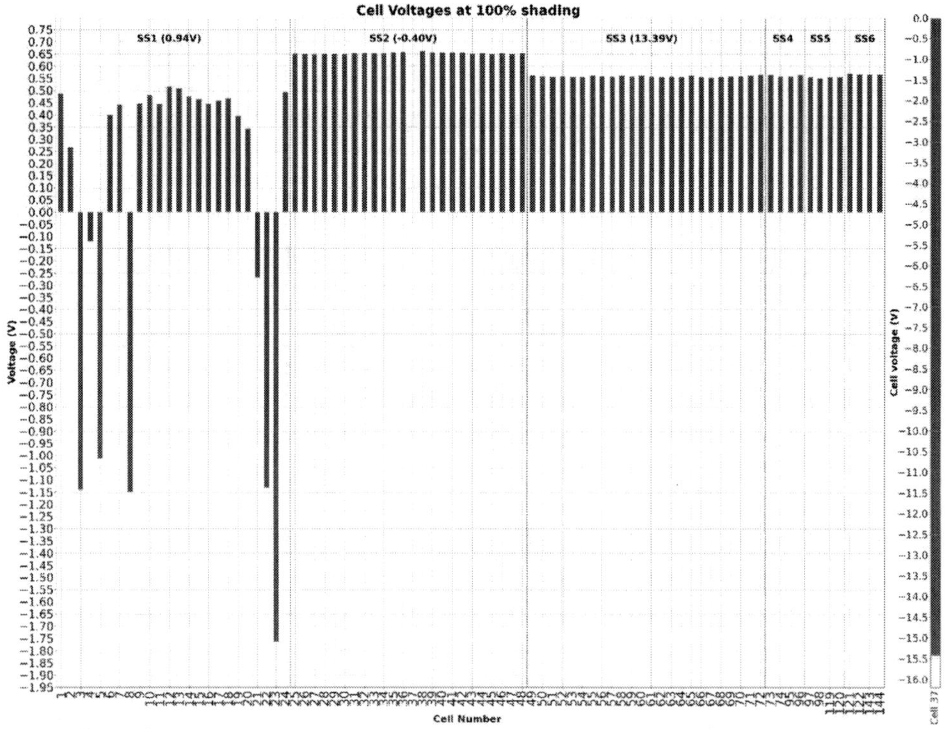

Figure 8: Individual cell voltages at 100% cell shading level. The negative voltage across the shaded cell (cell 37) is shown separately on the insert on the right.

3.3 Module and substring currents (Part 1 results)

Figure 9 illustrates the module and substring currents. It shows that the current in SS2 decreases with shading from 0 - 100% shading level, while the current in SS1 increases. On the other hand, the current in the unshaded substrings, SS3 - SS6 decreases until 75% shading, and increases at 100% when the bypass diode of SS1/SS2 pair is conducting. The results show that, before the bypass diode is activated, the module current is limited by the shaded substring pair. After the bypass diode of the shaded pair is activated, the module current is determined by the unshaded pairs.

We observed that, as the shading level increased from 12.5% to 75%, the substring currents were inversely proportional to cell temperatures, meaning cells operating below their maximum power point or under reverse bias appeared hotter.

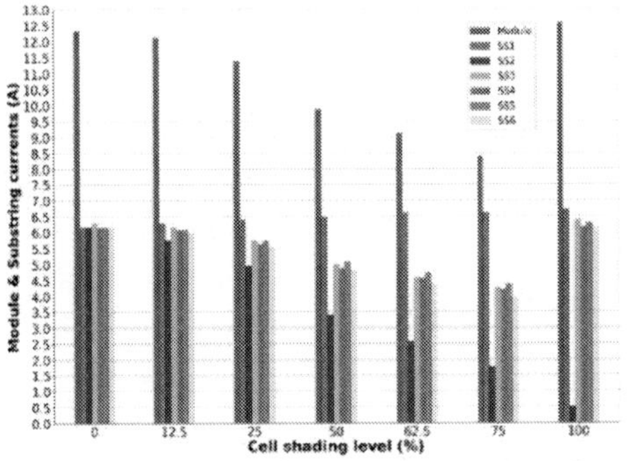

Figure 9: Module and substring currents while shading a single cell from 0 - 100%.

3.4 Module I-V characteristics with Chroma (Part 2 results)

The I-V curves of the module at low irradiance (G = 773 – 627 W/m², T~ 40 °C), with corresponding MPPs as obtained from Chroma, are shown in Figure 10. Showing the same behaviour as the I-Vs obtained at higher irradiance; a shift of the Vmpp towards Voc with increasing shading until the point where the bypass diode is activated, after which the Vmpp shifts towards short circuit.

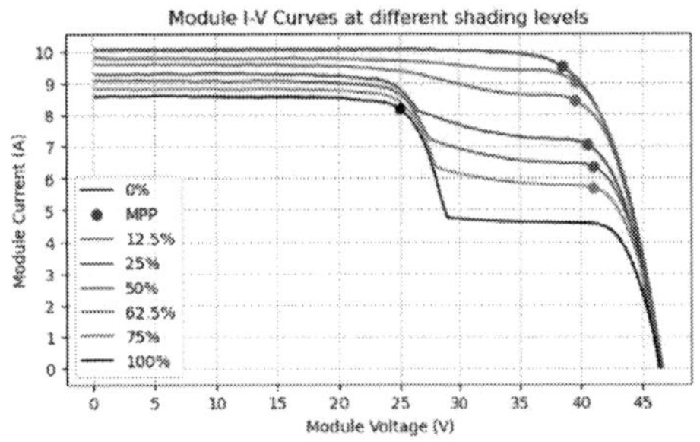

Figure 10: Module I-V as measured by Chroma at G = 773 - 627 W/m², T~ 40 °C

3.5 Substring I-V characteristics (Part 2 results)

The I-V curves of the individual substrings are shown in Figure 11, indicating the MPP of each substring and the operational points (OPs) of the substrings. With no shading, all substrings operate near or at their MPPs. However, with the increase in partial shading, there is a difference in operational points between the shaded pair and the unshaded pairs. The unshaded pairs operate towards Voc up to 75% shading and return to operate at or close to their MPP once the bypass diode is activated. The shaded substring operates towards short circuit, with a greater drop in operational current while the current in the parallel unshaded substring increases towards short circuit current (Isc).

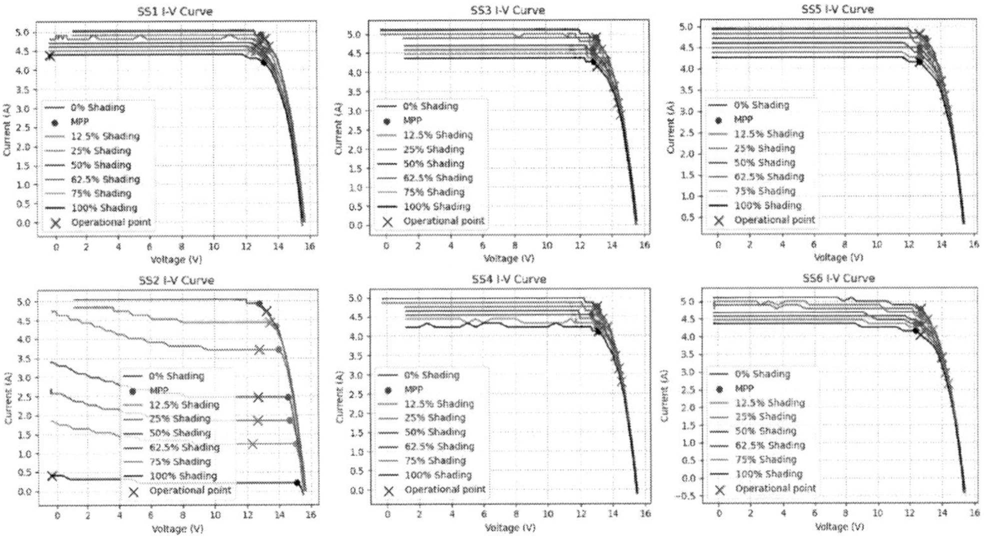

Figure 11: Measured I-V curves of individual substrings at different cell shading levels.

10.4229/EUPVSEC2025/3AV.3.28

3.6 I-V characteristics of the shaded cell (Part 2 results)

The I-V curves of the shaded cell are shown in Figure 12. It shows that at low irradiance, the shaded cell becomes reverse biased at a much larger shading level, 25%, in this case, compared to 12.5% at a higher irradiance obtained in part 1 of the results. The analysis of the cells in SS1 and SS2 shows that, with shading, if the individual substrings operate at their individual substring MPPs, the shaded cell does not become reverse biased. It can be seen from the I-V of the shaded cell in Figure 12 that if the substring is to operate at its MPP, and the shaded cell is operating at its MPP, then it doesn't become reverse biased.

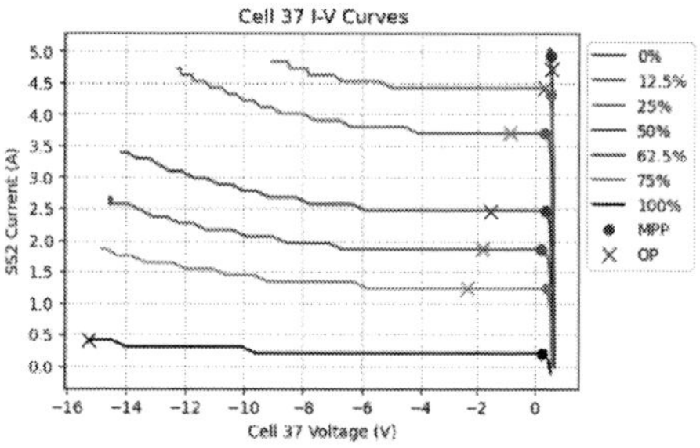

Figure 12: The measured I-V curves and respective MPP and OP of the shaded cell at different shading levels.

4 CONCLUSIONS

This study demonstrates that partial shading of a single cell in a half-cut cell PV module significantly affects the currents produced by all substrings. When the shading level is insufficient to activate the bypass diode, the module current is limited by the substring containing the shaded cell. Notably, the module current only increases when the bypass diode is activated, allowing the unshaded substrings to operate near their MPPs. However, operating the module at its MPP does not guarantee that individual substrings are producing maximum power, highlighting a potential mismatch between module-level and substring-level optimization.

The module's design, featuring parallel-connected cell pairs, minimizes current flow through the bypass diode when a single cell is fully shaded, thereby reducing the likelihood of bypass diode failures. However, simultaneous shading of both parallel pairs would force all module current through the bypass diode, potentially leading to overheating and failure. Therefore, careful consideration of installation orientation is crucial, particularly in scenarios where partial shading is unavoidable.

Given the smaller size of half-cut cells, the likelihood of full shading is increased, which can lead to non-optimal behaviour in the parallel-connected counterparts.

These findings have significant implications for the interpretation of thermal images, as hotspots may not necessarily indicate a defective cell in the affected area but rather a defective cell elsewhere in the module. To mitigate these issues and maximize power extraction, we propose incorporating substring optimizers in half-cut cell modules. This approach would prevent reverse biasing of cells under partial shading conditions, enhancing overall module efficiency and reliability.

5 REFERENCES

[1] Bosco N 2022 Turn Your Half-Cut Cells for a Stronger Module *IEEE J Photovolt* **12** 1149–53

[2] Waqar Akram M, Li G, Jin Y, Zhu C, Javaid A, Zuhaib Akram M and Usman Khan M 2020 Study of manufacturing and hotspot formation in cut cell and full cell PV modules *Solar Energy* **203** 247–59

[3] Huyeng J D, Lohmüller E, Shabanzadeh B, Reichel C, Rößler T, Weber J, Hofmann M, von Kutzleben D, Abdel Latif N, Kraft A, Neuhaus H, Clement F and Preu R 2024 Challenges and advantages of cut solar cells for shingling and half-cell modules *EPJ Photovoltaics* **15** 22

[4] Qian J, Thomson A, Blakers A and Ernst M 2018 Comparison of Half-Cell and Full-Cell Module Hotspot-Induced Temperature by Simulation *IEEE J Photovolt* **8** 834–9

[5] Chiodetti M, Dupuis J, Boublil D, Radouane K and Dupeyrat P 2019 HALF-CELL MODULE BEHAVIOUR AND ITS IMPACT ON THE YIELD OF A PV PLANT *36th European PV Solar Energy Conference and Exhibition* 1444–8

DEPENDENCE OF PHOTOVOLTAIC MODULE PERFORMANCE INDICATORS ON OPERATING TEMPERATURE AND IRRADIANCE

Heidi Kalliojärvi, Kari Lappalainen
Tampere University, Electrical Engineering Unit, P. O. Box 692, FI-33101 Tampere, Finland
heidi.kalliojarvi@tuni.fi, kari.lappalainen@tuni.fi

ABSTRACT: Condition of photovoltaic (PV) modules can be monitored by using measured current–voltage curves. The curves can be used to calculate numerical indicators that jointly can reveal possible changes in the condition of the PV modules. Such indicators are tied to the shape of the current–voltage curve. However, the changes in operating irradiance and temperature are known to affect the shape of the curve as well. Thus, also the operating conditions have an impact on the numerical values of the performance indicators. As a consequence, any such impact reflects on the diagnostical results. For this reason, it is important to investigate the dependence of the performance indicators on the operating conditions. This study addresses this issue by investigating four performance indicators in terms of their temperature and irradiance dependencies. The results assist in developing condition monitoring strategies of PV systems.
Keywords: condition monitoring, current–voltage curve, performance indicator, operating conditions

1 INTRODUCTION

Condition monitoring of photovoltaic (PV) power systems by using measured current–voltage (*I*–*V*) curves is an attractive way to obtain information of the state of the health of the PV modules. The measured *I*–*V* curves can provide information of ageing and other degradation phenomena occurring within the PV modules [1]. The curves can be subjected to identification of the parameters of the mathematical single-diode model that describes the operation of a PV cell, a PV module or a larger unit. Then, the identified model parameters can be used for the diagnosis.

The diagnostical usability of the *I*–*V* curves stems from the fact that the shape of the curve as well as its location in the *I*–*V* coordinate plane is affected by changes in the condition of the PV module. Leaning on this fact, several indicators characterizing the performance of the PV modules can be calculated. A commonly known indicator is the fill factor (*FF*) that expresses the area of the largest possible rectangle between the *I*–*V* curve and the coordinate axes [2]. In other words, *FF* measures the roundness of the *I*–*V* curve. The parasitic series (R_s) and shunt resistances (R_h) of the single-diode model are also known to be related to the condition of the PV modules. Series resistance is an indicator specific to PV module ageing; identified R_s values typically increase with the progression of ageing [3]. In turn, decreasing R_h is related to different shunting-type defects such as potential-induced degradation [4]. As R_s and R_h affect the slopes of the *I*–*V* curve in its high-voltage and high-current regions, respectively, [5] significant changes in them also contribute to the *FF* value [6]. The slopes of the *I*–*V* curve can be separately characterized by calculating ratios $\gamma_V = V_{MPP}/V_{OC}$ and $\gamma_I = I_{MPP}/I_{SC}$, where V_{MPP} and I_{MPP} are the voltage and current at the maximum power point (MPP), V_{OC} is the open-circuit (OC) voltage, and I_{SC} is the short-circuit (SC) current. The indicators γ_V and γ_I can be further utilized to calculate the series–parallel ratio (*SPR*) of the PV module. The *SPR* value determines which one of the two parasitic resistances is dominant [7]. If $SPR > 1$, then R_s dominates, and R_h can be neglected in the single-diode model parameter identification process. Conversely, the condition $SPR < 1$ implies the dominance of R_h, whence R_s can be neglected [7]. Such reduction in the number of identified parameters simplifies calculations and reduces the computational costs [7]. These aspects are important in practical online condition monitoring applications.

When drawing conclusions based on the *I*–*V* curve-based performance indicators, it is mandatory to consider their dependence on the operating irradiance (*G*) and temperature (*T*) as the shape of the *I*–*V* curve changes not only with PV module degradation but also with operating conditions. Thus, also the values of the previously mentioned performance indicators vary with the operating irradiance and temperature. Some indicators are either very fundamental, such as *FF*, or have otherwise gained wide attention in literature, like R_s and R_h. The fill factor reduces with temperature [2], and this fact has been further employed e.g. in [8], the authors of which found a formula for the temperature gradient of the fill factor. There seems to be no clear consensus regarding the temperature dependence of series resistance [9]. Some studies have attributed positive temperature dependence to series resistance of crystalline silicon PV cells [10, 11]. In [12], series resistance of crystalline silicon PV modules was reported to increase with decreasing irradiance. When investigating the temperature dependence of shunt resistance, various results have been obtained. For instance, the authors of [12] reported the shunt resistance of silicon PV cells to decrease with temperature. However, it was observed in [13] that there was only weak temperature dependence, if any. Shunt resistance is generally considered to increase with decreasing irradiance as shown in [12]. As a remark, the single-diode model parameters should be identified from *I*–*V* curves measured under high irradiance conditions since then the model is known to perform best [14].

In contrast to these indicators, there exist unfortunately only a few studies in which such dependences have been investigated for the other, less common indicators like γ_V, γ_I and *SPR*. Indeed, their dependence on the operating conditions has gained relatively little attention despite their usefulness in condition monitoring. To the best of our knowledge, there is only one published study [15] that is related to the behavior of these indicators under varying operating conditions. It was observed in [15] that γ_V and γ_I decreased with increasing irradiance, and their overall level as well as their behavior as a function of the irradiance was tied to the severity of the ageing of the PV module. In addition, it was reported in [15] that *SPR*

10.4229/EUPVSEC2025/3AV.3.30

changed as a function of the irradiance. For a PV module in its actual condition, the change seemed to follow a linearly increasing trend, but when the ageing became more severe, the behavior of *SPR* turned both nonlinear and nonmonotonic. However, the temperature dependences of these three performance indicators were not considered in [15]. In fact, there are no published studies reporting the effect of operating temperature on γ_V, γ_I or *SPR*. However, the irradiance and temperature effects should be simultaneously considered to obtain a comprehensive understanding of the behavior of these indicators with changing operating conditions.

The present study fills in this research gap by investigating the effects of operating irradiance and temperature on γ_V, γ_I, R_s and *SPR*. The single-diode model parameter identification procedure used in this study is suitable for practical applications due to its capability to repeat the operating conditions mathematically jointly with the identification of the actual single-diode model parameters. The impact of the PV module ageing stage on the dependence of the investigated performance indicators on the temperature and irradiance has been also studied. The importance of the present study lies in providing guidelines for the exploitation of these indicators in diagnostical analyses in practical PV applications.

The remainder of the paper is organized as follows. Section 2 is dedicated to describing the single-diode model and the used parameter identification procedure, the calculation of the investigated performance indicators as well as the measurement data used in the present study. Section 3 is devoted to presenting and discussing the experimental results. Finally, Section 4 closes the paper.

2 METHODS AND DATA

2.1 Single-diode model

The PV module is modeled by using the widely known single-diode model [16]

$$I = I_{\mathrm{ph}} - I_{\mathrm{o}}\left(e^{\frac{V+IR_{\mathrm{s}}}{AV_T}} - 1\right) - \frac{V+IR_{\mathrm{s}}}{R_{\mathrm{h}}}, \tag{1}$$

where I and V are the PV output current and voltage, I_{ph} is the photogenerated current accounting for the electron–hole pairs, I_{o} is the dark saturation current and A is the diode ideality factor. $V_T = N_s k_B T/q$ is the PV module thermal voltage, where N_s is the number of series-connected PV cells within the module, k_B is the Boltzmann constant, T is the operating temperature, and q is the electron charge.

2.2 Parameter identification procedure

The parameter identification procedure used in this paper was initially presented in [17]. It produces the set $\{G, T, R_s, R_h\}$ as its immediate output. From the indirect outputs that are adjusted during the parameter identification, I_{ph} is calculated as in [18] via

$$I_{\mathrm{ph}} = \frac{G}{G_{\mathrm{STC}}}\left(I_{\mathrm{ph,\,STC}} + \alpha_I (T - T_{\mathrm{STC}})\right), \tag{2}$$

where G_{STC} and T_{STC} are the irradiance and temperature in Standard Test Conditions (STC), α_I is the temperature coefficient of the SC current in STC, and $I_{\mathrm{ph,\,STC}}$ is the photogenerated current in STC, which is calculated by solving I_{ph} as a function of I_{SC} in STC via

$$I_{\mathrm{ph,\,STC}} = I_{\mathrm{SC,\,STC}}\left(\frac{R_s+R_h}{R_h}\right). \tag{3}$$

As in [19], the ideality factor is fixed at its STC value A_{STC} calculated as in [20] via

$$A_{\mathrm{STC}} = \frac{\alpha_V - \frac{V_{\mathrm{OC,\,STC}}}{T_{\mathrm{STC}}}}{V_{T,\,\mathrm{STC}}\left(\frac{\alpha_I}{I_{\mathrm{ph,\,STC}}} - \frac{3}{T_{\mathrm{STC}}} - \frac{E_{\mathrm{g,\,STC}}}{k_B T_{\mathrm{STC}}^2}\right)}, \tag{4}$$

where, $V_{\mathrm{OC,\,STC}}$ is the OC voltage in STC, α_V its temperature coefficient, and $V_{T,\,\mathrm{STC}}$ and $E_{\mathrm{g,\,STC}}$ are the thermal voltage and the energy band gap in STC. The dark saturation current I_{o} is calculated as in [21] via

$$I_{\mathrm{o}} = C_{\mathrm{STC}} T^{\frac{3}{A_{\mathrm{STC}}}} e^{-\frac{E_g(T)}{A_{\mathrm{STC}} k_B T}}, \tag{5}$$

where the coefficient C_{STC} is calculated as in [21] via

$$C_{\mathrm{STC}} = \frac{I_{\mathrm{ph,\,STC}} e^{\gamma_{\mathrm{STC}}}}{T_{\mathrm{STC}}^{\frac{3}{A_{\mathrm{STC}}}}} \tag{6}$$

with

$$\gamma_{\mathrm{STC}} = -\frac{V_{\mathrm{OC,\,STC}}}{A_{\mathrm{STC}} V_{T,\,\mathrm{STC}}} + \frac{E_{\mathrm{g,\,STC}}}{A_{\mathrm{STC}} k_B T_{\mathrm{STC}}}. \tag{7}$$

The energy band gap $E_g(T)$ in (5) is calculated as in [19] via

$$E_g(T) = E_{\mathrm{g,\,STC}}\left(1 + \alpha_{E_g}(T - T_{\mathrm{STC}})\right), \tag{8}$$

where $E_{\mathrm{g,\,0}}$ is the energy band gap at absolute zero temperature, and α_{E_g} is a thermal coefficient [19]. The parameter identification itself is performed by using the fit.m algorithm in Matlab. The maximum number of iterations and objective function evaluations has been set to 1e4. The tolerances both for the identified parameters and the objective function values between two consecutive iterations have been set to 1e-11. To reduce the computational cost, current is explicitly expressed as a function of voltage via

$$I = \frac{R_h(I_{\mathrm{ph}}+I_{\mathrm{o}})-V}{R_h+R_s} - \frac{AV_T}{R_s} W(\theta_I), \tag{9}$$

where $W(\cdot)$ denotes the Lambert W function [16], and θ_I is obtained via

$$\theta_I = \frac{R_s R_h I_{\mathrm{o}} e^{\frac{R_s R_h (I_{\mathrm{ph}}+I_{\mathrm{o}}) + R_h V}{AV_T(R_s+R_h)}}}{AV_T(R_s+R_h)}. \tag{10}$$

The initial guesses for the identified parameters are determined as follows. For the first I–V curve in each dataset, the initial guess is $\{G_{\mathrm{STC}}, T_{\mathrm{STC}}, R_{\mathrm{s,\,STC}}, R_{\mathrm{h,\,STC}}\}$, where the STC values for the parasitic resistances $R_{\mathrm{s,\,STC}}$ and $R_{\mathrm{h,\,STC}}$ are calculated as in [17] via the procedure presented in [16] utilizing the Lambert W function so that

$$R_{\mathrm{s,\,STC}} = \frac{xA_{\mathrm{STC}}V_{T,\,\mathrm{STC}} - V_{\mathrm{MPP,\,STC}}}{I_{\mathrm{MPP,\,STC}}} \tag{11}$$

and

$$R_{\mathrm{h,\,STC}} = \frac{xA_{\mathrm{STC}}V_{T,\,\mathrm{STC}}}{I_{\mathrm{ph,\,STC}} - I_{\mathrm{MPP,\,STC}} - I_{\mathrm{o,\,STC}}(e^x - 1)}, \tag{12}$$

where $I_{\mathrm{MPP,\,STC}}$, $V_{\mathrm{MPP,\,STC}}$ and $I_{\mathrm{o,\,STC}}$ are the MPP current, MPP voltage and the dark saturation current at STC, and the auxiliary variable x is obtained via

$$x = \mathrm{W}\left(\frac{V_{\mathrm{MPP,\,STC}}\left(2I_{\mathrm{MPP,\,STC}}-I_{\mathrm{ph,\,STC}}\right)e^{\frac{V_{\mathrm{MPP,\,STC}}\left(V_{\mathrm{MPP,\,STC}}-2A_{\mathrm{STC}}V_{T,\,\mathrm{STC}}\right)}{\left(A_{\mathrm{STC}}V_{T,\,\mathrm{STC}}\right)^2}}}{A_{\mathrm{STC}}I_{\mathrm{o,\,STC}}V_{T,\,\mathrm{STC}}}\right) + 2\frac{V_{\mathrm{MPP,\,STC}}}{A_{\mathrm{STC}}V_{T,\,\mathrm{STC}}} - \left(\frac{V_{\mathrm{MPP,\,STC}}}{A_{\mathrm{STC}}V_{T,\,\mathrm{STC}}}\right)^2. \quad (13)$$

For the remainder of the I–V curves, the parameter values identified from the previous curve serve as the initial guess for the following curve. The lower and upper limits for the identified parameters are reported in Table I.

Table I: Lower and upper limits for the identified parameters

Parameter	Lower limit	Upper limit
G (W/m^2)	0	1300
T (K)	273.15	343.15
R_s (Ω)	0.1	5
R_{sh} (Ω)	20	1000

2.3 Measurement data

The measurement data used in the present study was gathered from an individual PV module of the solar PV power research plant of Tampere University, Tampere, Finland [22]. The PV power plant is located on the rooftop of a campus building and consists of 69 PV modules (NAPS NP190GK) fabricated from multi-crystalline silicon. The irradiance received by the PV module and the PV module backplate temperature were respectively registered by a SPLite2 photodiode and a Pt100 thermocouple. The I–V curves were measured by using an I–V curve tracer utilizing IGBTs as an electronic load with a 1 Hz sampling frequency.

The measured I–V curves initially consisted of 4000 measurement points spaced evenly in terms of time. As such an operating principle of the I–V curve tracer causes an uneven distribution of the measurement points along the I–V curve in terms of voltage and current [23], the curves were preprocessed before the actual parameter identification as follows. At first, the clearly abnormal measurement points were removed by using a statistical interquartile range method [23]. Thereafter, those remaining points that had redundant voltage values were replaced by an individual point by averaging their currents as in [24]. Such preprocessing made the I–V curve measurement data less discrepant and mitigated the effects of uneven weighting of the measurement points.

The calculation of γ_V and γ_I require decent estimates for V_{OC} and I_{SC}. To address this issue, V_{OC} was calculated by fitting a second-order polynomial to those points of the I–V curve that had current values smaller than 25% of the MPP current. Correspondingly, I_{SC} has been calculated by fitting a line to the points with a voltage value smaller than 25% of the MPP voltage. In either case, this percentage of the MPP value was lifted to 50% if there existed less than 40 points below the described 25% limit.

It was previously observed in [25] that the electrical characteristics of the PV module in STC slightly differed from their values reported in the manufacturer's datasheet. Hence, the values re-determined in [25] were used in the present study, and they are reported in Table II jointly with the other relevant electrical characteristics of the PV module.

Table II: Electrical characteristics of the studied PV module in STC

Parameter	Value
$I_{\mathrm{SC,\,STC}}$	8.86 A
$I_{\mathrm{MPP,\,STC}}$	8.06 A
$V_{\mathrm{OC,\,STC}}$	32.8 V
$V_{\mathrm{MPP,\,STC}}$	22.5 V
N_s	54
α_I	0.0047 A/K
α_V	-0.124 V/K
$R_{\mathrm{s,\,STC}}$	0.7511 Ω
$R_{\mathrm{sh,\,STC}}$	95.5013 Ω
A_{STC}	1.0654

In this study, three 10-hour datasets, each one consisting of 36000 consecutive I–V curves measured during one day, were investigated. Each dataset described a certain stage of PV module ageing. The ageing was modeled by connecting additional series resistances ($R_{\mathrm{s,\,add}}$) in series with the investigated PV module. The datasets were measured on 26, 9 and 23 August 2023, and the corresponding ageing stages described a PV module in its actual condition ($R_{\mathrm{s,\,add}}$ = 0.00 Ω), a mildly aged ($R_{\mathrm{s,\,add}}$ = 0.22 Ω) PV module and a severely aged ($R_{\mathrm{s,\,add}}$ = 1.47 Ω) PV module. Since all the investigated datasets were measured within a narrow time window of a few weeks, real ageing phenomena affecting the results could not practically have occurred between the measurements.

2.4 Investigated performance indicators

Among the four performance indicators investigated in the present study, the single-diode model parameter identification is needed only for R_s. The other three indicators are calculated by utilizing the three key points of the I–V curve. Indeed, γ_V is calculated based on the MPP and OC points. Correspondingly, γ_I is calculated based only on the MPP and SC points. The series–parallel ratio SPR is calculated by using the γ_V and γ_I values as in [7] via

$$SPR = \frac{1-\gamma_I}{e^{-r}}, \quad (14)$$

where

$$r = \frac{\gamma_I(1-\gamma_V)}{\gamma_V(1-\gamma_I)}. \quad (15)$$

3 RESULTS AND DISCUSSION

The joint effect of operating irradiance and temperature on the four performance indicators is presented in this section. Each indicator was plotted against irradiance and temperature measured during the 10-hour measurement period. The experimentally calculated values for each indicator were plotted with circular markers, whose colors varied with the range of the indicator values. Since not each irradiance–temperature combination was covered by a data point, linear interpolation was used to find the overall behavior of each investigated indicator. The interpolated values were shown as regions with different colors.

3.1 Ratio γ_V

Fig. 1 shows γ_V as a function of irradiance and temperature for the investigated ageing stages ($R_{S,\,add}$ = 0.00, 0.22 and 1.47 Ω). It was observed that the overall level of γ_V decreased with the progression of ageing. For the PV module in its actual condition, γ_V was within a range of 0.66–0.84. The corresponding ranges for the mildly aged and the severely aged PV module were 0.60–0.82 and 0.50–0.80, respectively. In particular, the γ_V range was the largest for the severely aged PV module. An interesting finding was the variation of γ_V magnitude with ageing under high irradiance conditions as such conditions form the basis for diagnostics. Indeed, when the irradiance was high (> 800 W/m^2), the overall γ_V level decreased with the progression of ageing. For the additional resistances $R_{S,\,add}$ = 0.00, 0.22 and 1.47 Ω, the respective maximum γ_V values were at most around 0.7, 0.65 and 0.57 or so. In turn, low irradiance levels yielded γ_V values which were at most around 0.8. These results were in accord with the previous study [15].

All the subplots of Fig. 1 consisted of regions (indicated by different colors) obtained by linear interpolation that illustrated particular ranges of γ_V values. The orientation of these regions was close to vertical, indicating a clear irradiance dependence of γ_V in each investigated ageing stage. Larger irradiance levels produced smaller γ_V values. The regions were also slightly tilted to left, referring to a minor negative temperature dependence of γ_V.

3.2 Ratio γ_I

Fig. 2 exhibits the ratio γ_I as a function of the irradiance and temperature for the investigated ageing stages. It was observed that the overall γ_I level decreased with the progression of ageing. The respective γ_I ranges for $R_{S,\,add}$ = 0.00, 0.22 and 1.47 Ω were 0.87–0.94, 0.84–0.93 and 0.60–0.90, respectively. These findings were in line with the previous study [15].

The subplots of Fig. 2 differed quite strongly by the formation of the regions describing the γ_I sub-ranges. Roughly speaking, Fig. 2 (a) describing the PV module in its actual condition consisted of larger, horizontally oriented regions at low and medium irradiance levels and vertically oriented regions at high irradiance levels. The orientation of these regions referred to the existence of negative temperature dependence of γ_I at low and medium irradiance levels and negative irradiance dependence of γ_I at high irradiance levels. Moreover, there were smaller, island-like, regions within the vertically oriented regions. Such findings referred to somewhat unpredictable behavior of γ_I as a function of the operating conditions. For the mildly aged PV module, the irregular-shaped regions seemed to become more arranged, especially in vertical direction. This revealed the existence of negative irradiance dependence of γ_I. There also seemed to appear a slight negative temperature dependence.

In turn, the severely aged PV module produced nearly

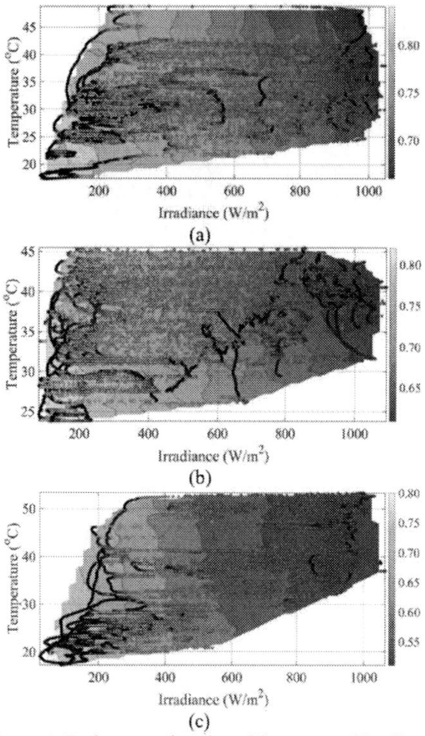

Figure 1: Ratio γ_V as a function of the measured irradiance and temperature for the PV module in its actual condition ($R_{S,\,add}$ = 0.00 Ω) (a) and with mild ageing ($R_{S,\,add}$ = 0.22 Ω) (b) and severe ageing ($R_{S,\,add}$ = 1.47 Ω) (c)

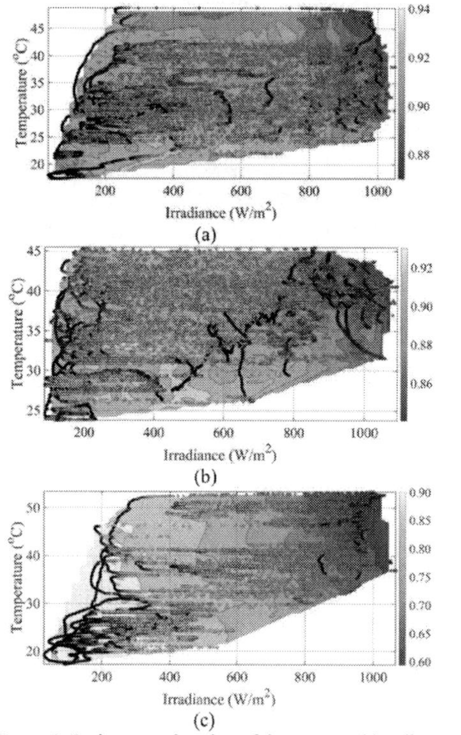

Figure 2: Ratio γ_I as a function of the measured irradiance and temperature for the PV module in its actual condition ($R_{S,\,add}$ = 0.00 Ω) (a) and with mild ageing ($R_{S,\,add}$ = 0.22 Ω) (b) and severe ageing ($R_{S,\,add}$ = 1.47 Ω) (c)

10.4229/EUPVSEC2025/3AV.3.30

vertical regions slightly tilted to left that were more clearly separated than in the two other stages of ageing. Now, the clear negative irradiance dependence and slight negative temperature dependence were obvious.

In conclusion, these findings indicated the irradiance dependence to become more obvious with the progression of ageing, which was in line with the results of [15]. In addition, there appeared a slight but clear negative temperature dependence of γ_I.

3.3 Series resistance R_s

Fig. 3 illustrates the identified series resistance as a function of the irradiance and temperature for the three investigated ageing stages ($R_{s,\,add}$ = 0.00, 0.22 and 1.47 Ω). It was observed that the PV module in its actual condition yielded rather stable R_s values around 0.8 Ω from high irradiance down to low irradiance levels of around 300 W/m^2 or so. Such stability of the series resistance identification even under rather low irradiance conditions is a clear advantage in practical applications. When irradiance became lower than approximately 200 W/m^2, the identified R_s values increased abruptly. Such findings were in line with the results of [12]. The series resistance seemed to depend mostly on irradiance. The rightward tilted boundary between the dark blue and medium blue regions referred to slight positive temperature dependence of R_s at low irradiance conditions. In contrast, no significant temperature dependence appeared under high and medium irradiance conditions. These results were in accord with [12].

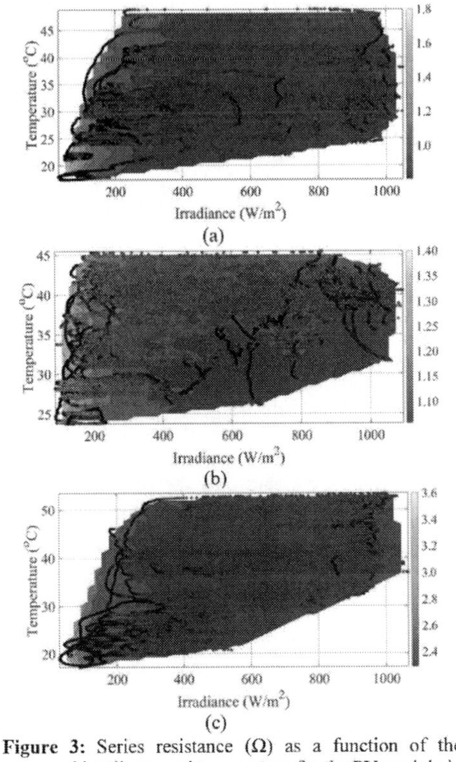

Figure 3: Series resistance (Ω) as a function of the measured irradiance and temperature for the PV module in its actual condition ($R_{s,\,add}$ = 0.00 Ω) (a) and with mild ageing ($R_{s,\,add}$ = 0.22 Ω) (b) and severe ageing ($R_{s,\,add}$ = 1.47 Ω) (c)

For $R_{s,\,add}$ = 0.22 Ω, stable R_s values around 1.05 Ω appeared from high irradiance levels down to irradiance levels somewhere between 400–600 W/m^2. The stable R_s range was followed by a region of R_s levels around 1.15 Ω when irradiance went down to approximately 200 W/m^2. Below 200 W/m^2, the series resistance continued to increase with decreasing irradiance. Now there seemed to be slight positive temperature dependence, being in line with the previous studies [10, 11].

For $R_{s,\,add}$ = 1.47 Ω, the identified R_s had stable values around 2.3 Ω for irradiance levels that were higher than 200–300 W/m^2. There seemed to appear a slight positive temperature dependence at low irradiance levels, which was in line with [10, 11].

In conclusion, the used parameter identification procedure produced stable R_s values down to rather low irradiance levels regardless of the ageing stage. The rapid increase in R_s values with very low irradiance suggested nonlinear negative irradiance dependence that was negligible at high and medium irradiance but become significant under low irradiance conditions. Such finding is in accord with the improper performance of the single-diode model at low irradiances [26]. Moreover, the current of crystalline silicon PV cells changes approximately linearly with irradiance, but voltage decreases rapidly with low irradiances affecting the shape of the *I–V* curve [27]. The temperature dependence was either negligible or slight in all investigated ageing stages.

3.4 Series–parallel ratio *SPR*

The calculated *SPR* values for the investigated ageing stages varied within the ranges 0.40–179.03 ($R_{s,\,add}$ = 0.00 Ω), 0.43–112.75 ($R_{s,\,add}$ = 0.22 Ω) and 0.42–44.37 ($R_{s,\,add}$ = 1.47 Ω). Fig. 4 illustrates the calculated *SPR* as a function of the irradiance and temperature for the investigated ageing stages. Remarkably, the condition SPR $<$ 1 held true under low irradiance conditions, indicating the predominance of shunt resistance. This is in accord with the fact that shunt resistance becomes significant when irradiance decreases to a low level [28].

In the case of the PV module in its actual condition, there seemed to be a trend of positive irradiance dependence of *SPR*, being in line with the results of [15]. The rightward tilted boundary between the dark and medium blue regions around 500–700 W/m^2 might refer to the possible existence of negative temperature dependence of *SPR* at least in medium irradiance conditions. However, the island-like dark blue regions appearing under high irradiance conditions pointed against clear temperature dependence. It should be noted that these findings require more investigation before drawing conclusions.

The behavior of *SPR* as a function of irradiance and temperature for the mildly aged ($R_{s,\,add}$ = 0.22 Ω) PV module resembled closely that of the PV module in its actual condition. The irradiance dependence seemed to be positive also in this case, being in line with [15].

In contrast to the PV module in its actual condition and the mildly aged PV modules, the severely aged PV module ($R_{s,\,add}$ = 1.47 Ω) had a clearly different behavior as a function of irradiance. Indeed, low *SPR* values occurred both under low and high irradiance conditions, while the medium irradiance conditions provided higher *SPR* values. Such a finding is in accord with the previous study [15]. The dependence of *SPR* on temperature was a more involved question also in this case since *SPR* did not seem to behave regularly with respect to temperature. Indeed, the presented example is not sufficient for drawing

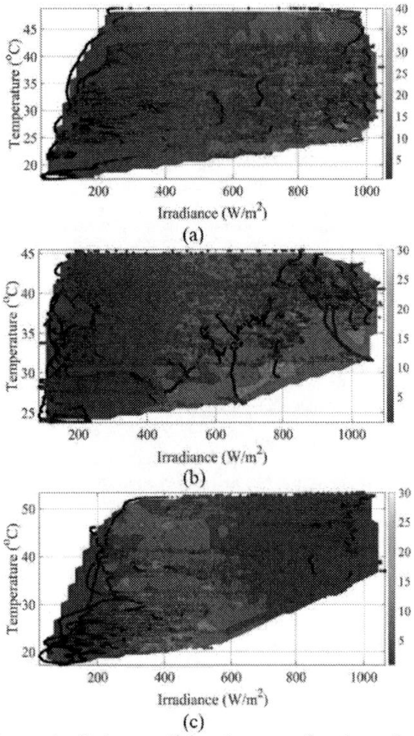

Figure 4: Series–parallel ratio as a function of the measured irradiance and temperature for the PV module in its actual condition ($R_{s,\ add}$ = 0.00 Ω) (a) and with mild ageing ($R_{s,\ add}$ = 0.22 Ω) (b) and severe ageing ($R_{s,\ add}$ = 1.47 Ω) (c)

strict conclusions but more investigation is needed.

4 CONCLUSIONS

This study focused on investigating the irradiance and temperature dependence of four PV module performance indicators calculated based on measured current–voltage curves. The investigated indicators were the ratio of the maximum power point and open-circuit voltages, the ratio of the maximum power point and short-circuit currents, the series resistance and the series–parallel ratio. The series resistance was obtained via a single-diode model parameter identification procedure that identifies the operating irradiance and temperature jointly with the actual single-diode model parameters. The other three performance indicators were calculated based on the three key points of current–voltage curves.

The effects of operating conditions on the investigated performance indicators were separately studied for a PV module with three different ageing stages: a PV module in its actual condition, a mildly aged and a severely aged PV module. The ageing was emulated by connecting different-sized resistors in series with the PV module. For each ageing stage, a 10-hour dataset consisting of consecutive current–voltage curves was analyzed.

The ratio of the maximum power point and open-circuit voltages showed clear negative dependence on irradiance and slight negative dependence on temperature. More severe ageing led to smaller levels of the ratio.

The ratio of the maximum power point and short-circuit currents seemed to depend mainly on temperature for the PV module in its actual condition, but severe ageing seemed to turn the irradiance dependence to be clearly more dominant. The mentioned dependences on temperature and irradiance were both negative.

The series resistance was stably identified from a wide irradiance range for all the stages of ageing. Within that range, there seemed to be no significant dependence on the operating conditions. However, very low irradiance levels resulted in rapidly increasing series resistance values. A slight positive temperature dependence was observed.

The behavior of the series–parallel ratio in terms of irradiance seemed to depend on the ageing stage of the PV module. Indeed, the PV module in its actual condition and the mildly aged PV module exhibited an increasing trend, while the severely aged PV module seemed to have the highest series–parallel ratios at medium irradiance. In turn, there did not appear an obvious dependence of series–parallel ratio on temperature.

As the investigated PV module performance indicators clearly varied with the operating conditions and ageing stage, the results of the present study serve as practical guidelines in their usage in PV module condition monitoring and assist in the interpretation of the diagnostical results based on these indicators.

REFERENCES

[1] J. Ahmad, A. Ciocia, S. Fichera, A.F. Murtaza, F. Spertino, Energies 12 (2019) 4547.
[2] M.A. Green, Solid-State Electronics 24(8) (1981) 788.
[3] E. Kaplani, Journal of Engineering Science and Technology 5(4) (2012) 18.
[4] S. Pingel, O. Frank, M. Winkler, S. Daryan, T. Geipel, H. Hoehne, J. Berghold, Proceedings 35th IEEE Photovoltaic Specialists Conference (2010) 002817.
[5] E.L. Meyer, E.E. Van Dyk, Conference Record of the Thirty-first IEEE Photovoltaic Specialists Conference (2005) 1331.
[6] W. Zhou, H. Yang, Z. Fang, Applied Energy 84(12) (2007) 1187.
[7] S. Cannizzaro, M.C. Di Piazza, M. Luna, G. Vitale, Proceedings IEEE 23rd International Symposium on Industrial Electronics (2014) 2266.
[8] H. Qu, X. Li, Journal of Mechanical Science and Technology 33 (2019) 1981.
[9] S. Bounouar, R. Bendaoud, H. Amiry, B. Zohal, F. Chanaa, E. Baghaz, C. Hajjaj, S. Yadir, A. El Rhassouli, M. Benhmida, International Journal of Renewable Energy Research 10(4) (2020) 1555.
[10] S. Bensalem, M. Chegaar, Journal of Renewable Energies 16(1) (2013) 171.
[11] M. Piliougine, G. Spagnuolo, M. Sidrach-de-Cardona, Renewable Energy 162 (2020) 677.
[12] C.S. Ruschel, F.P. Gasparin, A. Krenzinger, Solar Energy 217 (2021) 134.
[13] P. Singh, S.N. Singh, M. Lal, N. Husain, Solar Energy Materials and Solar Cells 92(12) (2008) 1611.
[14] S. Bana, R.P. Saini, Energy Reports 2 (2016) 171.
[15] G. Spagnuolo, K. Lappalainen, S. Valkealahti, P. Manganiello, Proceedings IEEE International Conference on Clean Electric Power (2019) 302.
[16] G. Petrone, C.A. Ramos–Paja, G. Spagnuolo, John Wiley & Sons (2017).

[17] K. Lappalainen, M. Piliougine, G. Spagnuolo, Energy Conversion and Management 258 (2022) 115526.
[18] U. Eicker, John Wiley & Sons (2003).
[19] W. De Soto, S.A. Klein, W.A. Beckman, Solar Energy 80(1) (2006) 78.
[20] N. Femia, G. Petrone, G. Spagnuolo, M. Vitelli, Taylor & Francis Group (2013).
[21] J.R. Wilcox, A.W. Haas, J.L. Gray, R.J. Schwartz, AIP Conference Proceedings 1407(1) (2011) 30.
[22] D. Torres Lobera, A. Mäki, J. Huusari, K. Lappalainen, T. Suntio, S. Valkealahti, International Journal of Photoenergy 2013(1) (2013) 837310.
[23] H. Kalliojärvi–Viljakainen, K. Lappalainen, S. Valkealahti, Proceedings 47th IEEE Photovoltaic Specialists Conference (2020) 0117.
[24] K. Lappalainen, S. Valkealahti, Applied Energy 301 (2021) 117436.
[25] H. Kalliojärvi–Viljakainen, K. Lappalainen, S. Valkealahti, Energy Reports 8 (2022) 4633.
[26] K. Ishaque, Z. Salam, H. Taheri, Syafaruddin, Simulation modelling Practice and Theory 19(7) (2011) 1613.
[27] J.A. Kratochvil, W.E. Boyson, D.L. King, Sandia National Laboratories (2004).
[28] A.D. Dhass, E. Natarajan, L. Ponnusamy, Proceedings 2012 IEEE International Conference on Emerging Trends in Electrical Engineering and Energy Management (2012) 382.

EVALUATING THE IMPACT OF SOILING ON AGRIVOLTAIC SYSTEMS

Paul Gebhardt, Tannaz Katouli, Thomas Kaltenbach, Tamara Bretzel, Lisa-Marie Bieber, Ingrid Haedrich
Fraunhofer Institute for Solar Energy Systems ISE
Heidenhofstr. 2, 79110 Freiburg, Germany

ABSTRACT: This study investigates the impact of soiling on the performance of agrivoltaic systems (AVS) through transmission measurements of glass plates exposed in four AVS, next to the actual PV modules. The research quantifies light transmission loss due to agricultural dust, soil, pesticide, and fertilizer residues, correlating these losses with solar spectrum intensity and solar cell response. Several AVS in Germany are analyzed to establish the relationship between soiling and energy output, as well as its effect on light availability for plants. Preliminary results indicate a significant light transmission reduction of up to ~40 %, depending on the kind of agricultural activity and installation type, with the highest losses observed above hop fields. In contrast, a vertical installation with winter wheat shows minimal soiling losses. This research contributes to the agrivoltaics field by addressing challenges of the unique environments in AVS, providing a practical method for analyzing soiling and a first empirical dataset for estimating the effects on electricity yield.

1 INTRODUCTION

The double-use of land by photovoltaics (PV) and agriculture, i.e. agrivoltaics (AV) is an increasingly applied approach with significant potential [1]. While the current literature focuses mostly on the integration of photovoltaics into the agricultural complex, i.e. the effect of photovoltaics on crop yield, and regulatory issues [2], long-term technical challenges concerning the PV system itself such as reliability issues and soiling losses, i.e. the effect of the agri-chemicals on the PV are barely researched [3].

This study specifically addresses optical losses in PV performance due soiling, being a combination of various depositions on the PV modules. We conduct transmission measurements on glass plates that have been exposed in various agricultural environments in Germany. The primary objective is to quantify the extent of light transmission loss caused by the depositions, e.g., different types of agricultural dust, soil, and debris, as well as residues from pesticides and fertilizers. The results are also compared to power measurements of modules that are affected by soiling.

2 METHODS

We have selected several AVS representing diverse conditions, including various crops and different orientations of the PV installation, based in Germany. 20 x 20 cm glass slides without antireflective coating were installed next to the PV modules in the same inclination angle.

Tab. 1: PV installations investigated in this study

Site	Crop	Installation	Exposure
1	Apple (Gala)	Over-head (W/E)	February – September
2	Apple (Freya)	Over-head (W/E) Or tracker	February - September
3	Hop	Over-head (S)	June-November
4	Winter Wheat	Vertical	March - August

After the exposure time, the transmission of the samples was measured with a spectrophotometer averaging the transmission over an area of ~5 cm in diameter. The resulting transmission spectra were weighted with the intensity of the sun spectrum (AM 1.5) and a spectral response of a TOPCon solar cell in order to weight the losses in different wavelength ranges according to their relevance in the PV application.

The transmission measurements on the glass slides were conducted using a Fourier-transform spectrometer (Bruker Vertex 70) equipped with a PTFE-coated integrating sphere, allowing for the measurement of both directly reflected and transmitted light, as well as scattered radiation. We first analyzed full-sized PV modules from two sites in their soiled state using photographs, followed by power- and electroluminescence measurements to assess their actual performance or any potential damage. Subsequently, the transmission properties were measured in the intercellular spaces (between the cells) using a mobile spectral hemispherical transmittance device that was specifically developed for this project. It is based on a spectrometer by Ocean Optics, (STS-VIS, 350 to 800 nm), an LED light source (Euro Lighting, Natural Spectrum Series SOL) and a 50 mm diameter Ulbricht sphere with an opening diameter of 10 mm. The two sides of the device, containing light source and detector unit, respectively, can be fixed on opposite sides of the PV module using magnetic rings and can thus measure the

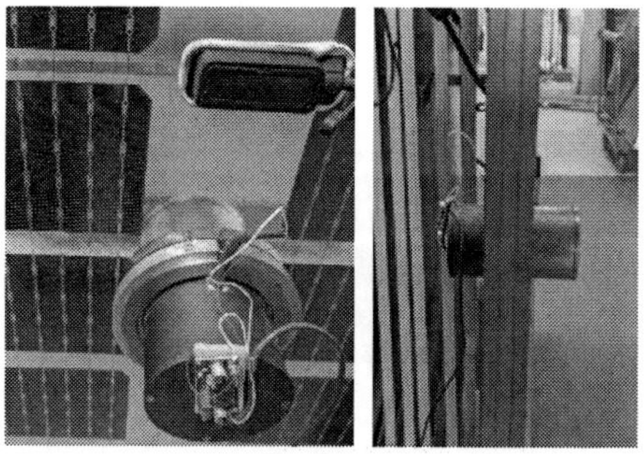

Fig. 1: Inhouse-developed mobile spectrometer during measurement of a glass-glass PV module. Light source and detector are fixed on opposite sides of the PV module by a magnetic ring. The device is connected to a laptop for data acquisition and power source via a USB cable.

10.4229/EUPVSEC2025/3AV.3.31

transmission in the intercellular space (measuring point approx. 5 mm diameter).

Finally, the influence of soiling on module performance was measured by taking STC-performance measurements on the same modules after cleaning.

3 RESULTS

Results from our measurements after an exposure time of 6-8 months in the field (Tab. 1) indicate that the reduction in light transmission due to soiling can be substantial, but strongly depends on the local conditions with losses reaching up to ~40 %. The strongest soiling loss was observed in installations above hop fields (Fig. 2, Fig. 3). A cleaning of the rear side and subsequent re-measuring the transmission revealed that around half of the soiling effect could be attributed to each glass side. This aspect can be relevant for distinguishing between the soiling losses for crop- and electricity yield, because the electricity yield is naturally mostly diminished by soiling on the module's front side, while the crops react to transmission losses on both module sides.

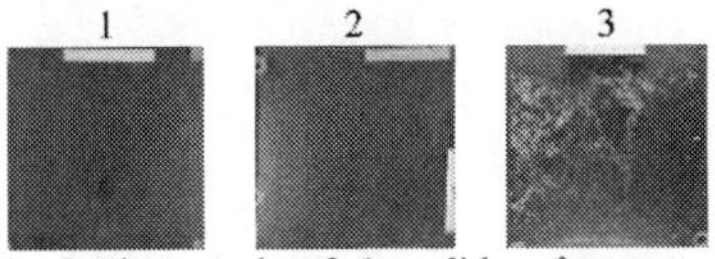

Fig. 2: Photographs of glass slides after exposure at Sites 1-3.

The lowest soiling effects were observed in an installation of winter wheat, where modules and glass plates were installed vertically, do show very little soiling losses. It seems plausible that the vertical installation reduces soiling by facilitating the removal of deposits during rain; however, other factors may also contribute, warranting further investigations, e.g. comparison of tilted and vertical glasses or vertical glasses from different crops, to better understand the reason for the low soiling in this instance.

Nevertheless, these findings illustrate the benefits of integrating effective cleaning strategies for AVS.

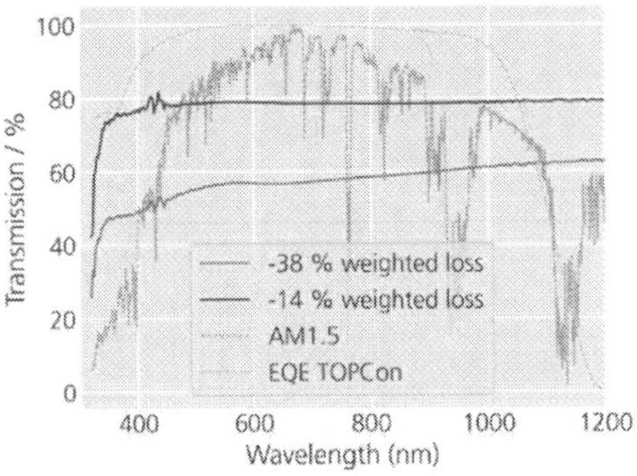

Figure 1: Transmission spectra of two glass samples from Site 3 (green, blue). The plot contains normalized AM1.5 spectrum and TOPCon EQE used as weighting factors resulting in weighted transmission losses of -38 and -14 %, respectively.

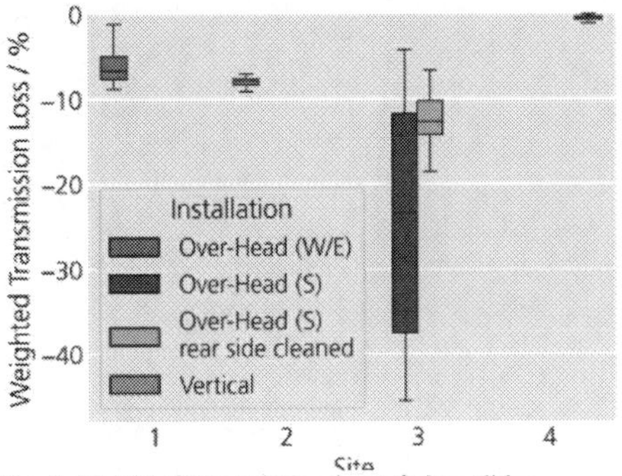

Fig. 3: Weighted transmission loss of glass slides exposed on AVS

To investigate the soiling effect on full-size modules, PV modules were dismantled from AVS in June 2025, after approximately 15 months of exposure, and evaluated in the laboratory. It is noteworthy that estimating the impact of deposits on module performance quantitatively is challenging because the deposits are typically unevenly distributed across the module, often exhibiting gradients from top to bottom or right to left (Fig. 4). This means that, depending on the module topology, i.e. the internal interconnection of the cells in the module, mismatch losses of varying severity reduce the overall module performance. Measurement points need to be chosen very carefully in order to allow a meaningful comparison between modules.

The soiling loss, calculated from of the difference between performance measurements before and after cleaning the modules (Fig. 5, bars) quantitatively deviates from the transmittance measurement at individual spots (Fig. 5, dots) but correlating with the general visual impression. The contamination primarily affects the performance on the front side of the modules, which is the more critical side regarding energy yield, as performance losses on the rear side were generally lower, remaining below 1%.

Another interesting finding from full-sized modules from Site 2 is that modules M03 and M04, which were mounted on trackers, show significantly less soiling compared to modules M05 and M06, which were mounted

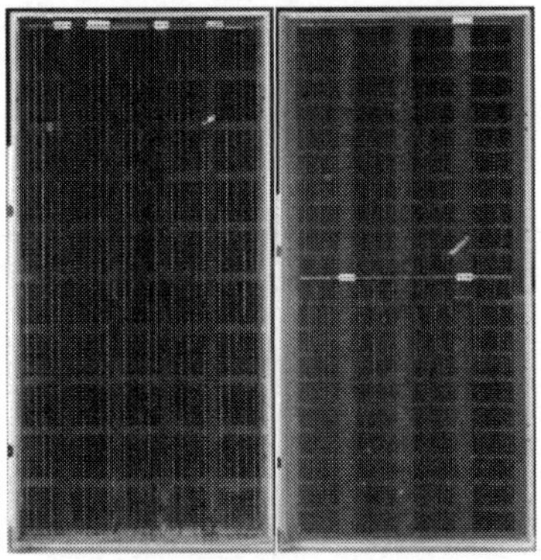

Fig. 4: Photographs of PV modules after exposure in agrivoltaics System 1 (left) and 2 (right), before cleaning show inhomogeneous distribution of soiling.

10.4229/EUPVSEC2025/3AV.3.31

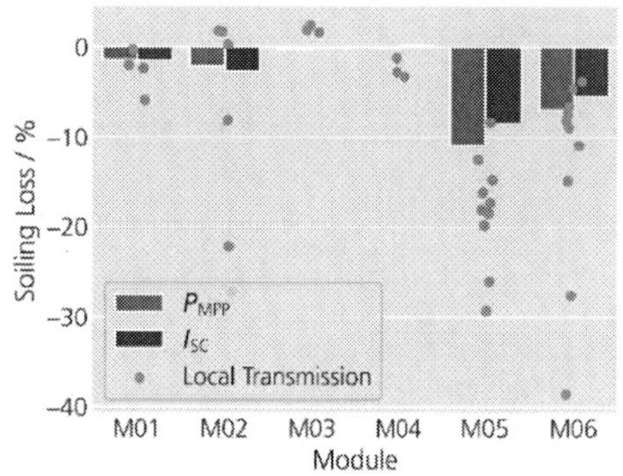

Fig. 5: Loss in module performance and weighted transmission of full size PV modules due to soiling. The modules originated from Site1 (M01, M02), Site 2 (Tracker, M03, M04) and Site 2 (fixed tilt, M05, M06).

at a fixed tilt. Similar to the results of the vertically installed modules on Site 4, this finding suggests that the module orientation has a strong effect on the observed soiling.

The results of the transmission measurements (Fig. 5, dots) tend to loosely correspond to the power loss of the module, whereby the measurement points were not selected systematically but according to the visual impression. However, as expected, the transmission decreases more significantly in heavily soiled areas of the module than the overall module performance. There is also a clear trend of stronger performance loss due to soiling for modules that showed higher transmission losses.

4 CONCLUSION

This study presents, to the best of our knowledge, the first investigation of soiling effects on AVS, addressing a critical knowledge gap in the field. Through transmission measurements using glass slides and full-size PV modules exposed in various agricultural environments across Germany, our initial findings demonstrate that agricultural soiling can significantly impact PV and crop performance, with light transmission losses ranging from 0 to approximately 40 %, depending on crop type and installation configuration.

The mobile spectrometer technique developed for this research proves suitable for in-field measurements and provides a practical tool for monitoring soiling effects in operational AVS.

This provides an initial empirical dataset for the agrivoltaics community. However, several questions require further investigation through systematic studies with larger datasets. For instance, the remarkably low soiling observed in vertical installations needs confirmation through controlled comparisons with tilted configurations under identical agricultural conditions to determine whether orientation or crop-specific factors drive this effect.

Future research should focus on expanding the dataset across diverse crop types and installation geometries to identify the main drivers for soiling losses for both crop and electricity yield.

5 ACKNOWLEDGMENT

This work was funded by the Federal Ministry for Economic Affairs and Energy (03EE1147, „VAckerPower“), the Ministry of Food, Rural Areas and Consumer Protection of the state Baden-Württemberg (27-8216, „StaMoMo“) and the Federal Ministry of Agriculture, Food and Regional Identity (28CD405B22, „HoPVen“).

6 REFERENCES

[1] Fraunhofer-Institut für Solare Energiesysteme ISE, *Flächenpotenzial für Agri-Photovoltaik in Deutschland übertrifft Ausbauziele für Klimaschutz*. Freiburg, Germany, 2025. Accessed: Aug. 28 2025. [Online]. Available: https://www.ise.fraunhofer.de/de/presse-und-medien/presseinformationen/2025/fraunhofer-ise-ausgruendung-flaechenpotenzial-fuer-agri-photovoltaik-in-deutschland-uebertrifft-ausbauziele-fuer-klimaschutz.html

[2] D. Soto-Gómez, "Integration of Crops, Livestock, and Solar Panels: A Review of Agrivoltaic Systems," *Agronomy*, vol. 14, no. 8, p. 1824, 2024, doi: 10.3390/agronomy14081824.

[3] T. Katouli, P. Gebhardt, J. Markert, and I. Hädrich, "Developing Tests for PV Module Durability Against Pesticides and Fertilizers," in *AgriVoltaics World Conference*, Freiburg, Germany, 2025.

A GENERAL APPROACH TO MODEL HIGH-PERFORMANCE PV MODULES FOR ACCURATE ENERGY YIELD SIMULATIONS

Luca Antognini, Michele Oliosi, Auriane Canesse, Robin Vincent, André Mermoud, Bruno Wittmer
PVsyst SA
Route de la Maison-Carrée 30, CH 1242 Satigny - Switzerland

ABSTRACT: One of the challenges in PV module performance modeling is to obtain a good description of the I-V curves at various temperatures and illuminations, based solely on limited available data. Currently in PVsyst, this is done by calculating the parameters for the one-diode model (1DM) from datasheet information and common assumptions on low-light performance. However, this fails to reproduce high fill factors (FF), typically compromising V_{oc} accuracy. To address this, we use an evolutionary algorithm (EA) which improves parameter determination for the 1DM, extends to more sophisticated models and can use measurement variability as input. This method necessitates solely datasheet information and common low-light assumptions to reproduce IEC 61853-1 measurements. We demonstrate its benefits on both measured PERC modules and synthetic high-FF scenarios. On measured data from a low-FF module, the EA lowers the mean efficiency error in reproducing IEC 61853-1 data compared to the current method. To test the EA on high-FF devices, we generate synthetic data from a reference recombination model informed by solar-cell literature. In this case too, the EA reduces power error and greatly improves V_{oc} reproduction, which is further enhanced when switching from 1DM to the reference model itself.
Keywords: PV Module Modeling, PVsyst

1 INTRODUCTION

Accurate modelling of PV module I–V curves is essential for reliable energy yield simulations. The one-diode model (1DM), as implemented in PVsyst, remains an industry standard due to its simplicity and accuracy to represent PERC PV modules. PVsyst uses an analytical method to determine the model parameters based solely on the information available in datasheet, completed by observed technological trends for low-light performance.

However, for modern high-performance devices with elevated fill factors (FF), this approach often compromises open-circuit voltage accuracy, limiting its predictive power. Moreover, the origin of those high FF within crystalline silicon (c-Si) technology is well understood through more sophisticated models incorporating several recombination mechanisms impacting in parallel the I–V behaviour. These developments call for parameter evaluation methods that go beyond fixed assumptions and can flexibly adapt to new device characteristics.

To overcome the limitations arising at high FFs, we explore two approaches: 1) Change the determination method for the model parameters evaluation from datasheet information. 2) Investigate the potential benefit of a different I–V-parametrization that is established in literature and known to be able to describe high FF.

In particular, we propose an evolutionary algorithm (EA) framework that can adapt to both the conventional 1DM and recombination-based models. This method necessitates solely datasheet data and common low-light assumptions to reproduce IEC 61853-1 measurements. We demonstrate its benefits on both measured PERC modules and synthetic high-FF scenarios.

2 METHOD

We first summarize the current PVsyst I-V parameterization and a reference recombination-based model from the solar cell literature state-of-the-art. This model is commonly accepted to describe the origin of high FF in record efficiency device [1] and we will therefore use it to generate synthetic data in the next sections. Then, we describe the current calculation procedure of PVsyst and the EA optimization approach.

2.1 Current PVsyst I-V Parametrization

We describe here the parametrization of the 1DM as it is implemented in the current version of PVsyst (8.0). As in any 1DM parametrization, the external current I is a balance between the photogenerated current and the current losses in the first diode and shunt resistor,

$$I = I_{ph} - I_0\left(e^{\frac{q(V+IR_s)}{\gamma k_B T}} - 1\right) - \frac{V + IR_s}{R_{sh}}$$

where the term $V_{int} = V + IR_s$ is the internal voltage of the solar cells prior to the voltage drop across the series resistance R_s. The equivalent circuit of this equation can be seen in Figure 1 (a).

The photogenerated current I_{ph} is assumed to depend linearly on the temperature and irradiance

$$I_{ph}(G,T) = \frac{G}{G_{ref}} I_{ph,ref}[1 + \mu_{I_{sc}}(T - T_{c,ref})]$$

where $I_{ph,ref}$ is the photogenerated current under the standard test conditions (STC) temperature $T_{c,ref} = 25\ °C$ and irradiance $G_{Ref} = 1000\ W/m^2$. μ_{Isc} is the short-circuit current temperature coefficient. Similarly, the saturation current of the diode I_0 depends on the temperature as

$$I_0(T) = I_{0,ref}\left(\frac{T}{T_{ref}}\right)^3 \exp\left(\frac{qE_g}{\gamma k_B}\left(\frac{1}{T_{ref}} - \frac{1}{T}\right)\right),$$

where for crystalline silicon (c-Si) the bandgap E_g is set to a fixed value of 1.12 eV.

Next, based on experimental observations [2], PVsyst assumes an exponential behaviour of the shunt resistance with irradiance

$$R_{sh}(G) = R_{sh,Base} + [R_{sh}(0) - R_{sh,Base}] \times \exp\left(-R_{sh,exp}\left(\frac{G}{G_{ref}}\right)\right)$$

with

$$R_{sh,Base} = \frac{R_{sh}(\mathrm{STC}) - R_{sh}(0)\exp(-R_{sh,exp})}{1 - \exp(-R_{sh,exp})}$$

Based on the measurement campaign led in [2], the two additional degrees of freedom $R_{sh,exp}$ and $R_{sh}(0)/R_{sh}(STC)$ ratio takes remarkably fixed values for a given PV technology, leaving only the shunt resistance at 1000 W/m^2, $R_{sh}(STC)$, as unknown parameter.
Finaly, PVsyst assumes a linear dependence on temperature of the diode ideality factor γ

$$\gamma(T) = \gamma_{ref} + \mu_{\gamma}(T - T_{ref}),$$

where μ_{γ} is an additional unknown parameter.

In summary, PVsyst 1DM has 9 parameters:

$$I_{ph,ref},\ \mu_{I_{sc}}, I_0, \gamma, \mu_{\gamma}, R_s, R_{sh}(STC), R_{sh,exp}, \text{and } R_{sh}(0).$$

We additionally assume $R_{sh,exp} = 5.5$ and $R_{sh}(0) = 4\,R_{sh}(STC)$ for c-Si, which reduces the number of unknown parameters to 7.

2.2 Reference recombination model for high-FF

We explicitate here the reference parametrization of the I-V curve informed by solar cell literature on electron/hole recombination mechanisms. As for the 1DM, the model is still described as a current balance equation

$$I = I_{ph} - I_{aug} - I_{rad} - I_{SRH} - I_{sh},$$

where the different terms are defined below and the equivalent circuit diagram is shown in Figure 2 (a).
For the description of the intrinsic recombination, we follow the latest parametrization proposed in [3] [4]. In this formalism the Auger recombination current

$$I_{aug} = qW(g_{ehh}C_{p0}(p^2n - p_0^2n_0) + g_{eeh}C_{n0}(pn^2 - p_0n^2))$$

and the radiative recombination current

$$I_{rad} = qW(1 - f_{PR})B_{low}B_{rel}(np - n_0p_0)$$

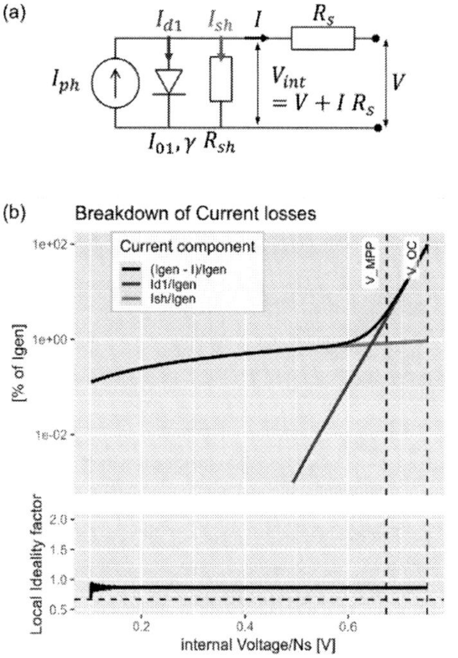

Figure 1: (a) Equivalent circuit diagram of the one diode model. (b) Breakdown of current losses for typical model parameters on logarithmic scale and local ideality factor derived from the slope of the top black curve.

depend explicitly on the electron and hole carrier concentration n and p, respectively, and the c-Si wafer thickness W. Those quantities are related to the equilibrium concentration n_0 and p_0 by

$$n = n_0 + \Delta n \text{ and } p = p_0 + \Delta n$$

where Δn is the excess charge concentration created by the excitation (voltage and illumination), related to the intrinsic carrier concentration n_i by

$$n_0p_0 = n_i^2.$$

Finaly, in the case of n-type wafer, we have the approximation $n_0 = N$ (and $p_0 = N$ for p-type), where N is the base doping concentration of the wafer. We follow [4] for the value of the coefficients C_{p0}, C_{n0}, B_{low} and the remaining terms are defined in the same publication.
Note that the carrier concentrations are directly related to the internal voltage by

$$n_i^2 \exp\left(\frac{qV_{int}}{k_bT}\right) = pn \approx \left(\frac{n_i^2}{N} + \Delta n\right)(N + \Delta n).$$

Therefore, an increase in Δn results directly in an increase of V_{int}.

Within the description of [3] [4], n_i depends both on temperature and carrier concentrations. A commonly accepted parametrization is [5] [6]

$$n_i(T,n,p) = 9.653 \times 10^9 \times \left(\frac{T[°K]}{300}\right)^{1.706} \exp\left(-\frac{E_G(T,n,p)}{2k_BT}\right)$$

where the function $E_G(T,n,p)$ represents the effect of the bandgap narrowing effect at increased carrier concentration. Note the resemblance with the 1DM's I_0 temperature dependance.

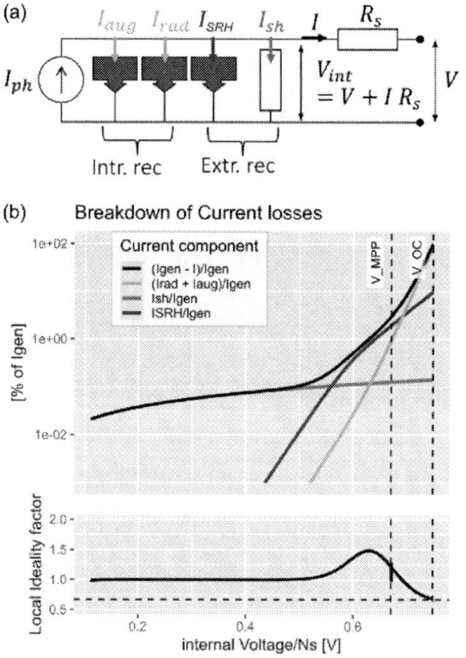

Figure 2: (a) Equivalent circuit diagram of the recombination model. (b) Current losses breakdown for typical model parameters and local ideality factor derived from the slope of the top black curve.

10.4229/EUPVSEC2025/3AV.3.32

For the description of the extrinsic recombination, we replace the single diode term with the Shockley-Read-Hall equation which uses the same formalism as presented in this section and, in the assumption of single defect level close to mid-gap [1], can be approximated as

$$I_{SRH} = q\,W \frac{pn - n_i^2}{\tau_{SRH}(n+p)}$$

where τ_{SRH} is the effective lifetime of the excess charge created by the excitation (voltage and illumination) and W the thickness of c-Si wafer.

The shunt current is still given by

$$I_{sh} = \frac{V + IR_s}{R_{sh}}$$

and we keep the same assumptions for the irradiance and temperature dependance of R_{sh} and I_{ph}. This also sums up to 9 unknown parameters

$$I_{ph,ref}, \mu_{I_{sc}}, \tau_{SRH}, W, N, R_s, R_{sh}(STC), R_{sh,exp}, \text{and } R_{sh}(0)$$

where the same assumptions can be made on $R_{sh,exp}$ and $R_{sh}(0)$, which reduces the number of unknown parameters to 7 again.

The motivation to use this model is now described. It is a well-known fact that the STC efficiency of an ideal c-Si solar cell (i.e. with no extrinsic recombination nor shunt or series resistance) is limited by radiative and Auger recombination to a value of 29.4% while the FF is limited to 89.26%. Note that those numbers remained unchanged up to the second digit in the last decades [7] [8] [4]. The FF limit is explained by the strong increase of the Auger recombination at higher carrier concentrations (p^2n and pn^2 terms), and therefore at higher voltages, increasing gradually the intrinsic recombination current from the maximal power point (MPP) until the open-circuit conditions (OC). This is shown in Figure 2 (b). Another way to understand this, is that if one were to approximate by an effective single diode model representing the intrinsic recombination mechanisms, it would be required to introduce a voltage dependent diode ideality factor which decreases towards a value of 2/3 as the voltage increases, making the I-V curve's shape more squared and increase the FF.

2.3 Current PVsyst Parameter Calculation

In the current PVsyst implementation (8.0), the direct calculation method of the 1DM parameters requires at least 9 independent input data to be well defined. The 6 first are (almost always) specified in the PV module datasheet.

First, I-V curve is constrained to pass by three points defined by the STC values: (V_{mpp}, I_{mpp}), (V_{oc}, 0), and (0, I_{sc}). Note that it is not specified that the first point is the maximum power point, and therefore the P_{mpp} value obtained by the model can be slightly different than the one of the input data.

Second, μ_{Isc} is used directly as input parameter and the power temperature coefficient μ_{Pmpp} needs to be reproduced (mainly by adjusting the parameter μ_γ). Note that the temperature coefficient of the open circuit voltage μ_{Voc} is not used in this calculation (its usage is restricted to compute in a separate way the V_{oc} at low temperature for system sizing and norm safety purpose).

Third, as mentioned above, two additional constraints can be set by fixing $R_{sh,exp} = 5.5$ and $R_{sh}(0) = 4\,R_{sh}(STC)$, validated for c-Si technology.

The final constraint is the relative efficiency loss under low-light conditions (200 W/m², 25 °C) compared to STC

$$\text{Rel. eff.} = 1 - \eta_{low}/\eta_{STC}.$$

This strongly helps to determine R_s since the power loss goes as $P_{loss} \sim I^2 R_s$. Unfortunately, this information is almost never present in product datasheets and PVsyst assumes by default a value of -3% when no information is available based on previous experimental campaigns [2]. Since then, with the constant reduction in series resistance in PV manufacturing, driven by improvements in contact layer resistance, metallic grid conductivity and increased number of busbars, this relative efficiency has been decreasing consistently on average to values below -5% [9]. A lower bound of about -6.8% for this value can be estimated based on the measured series resistance of some best state-of-the-art c-Si solar cell [1]. Therefore, in the present study, recognizing the relative low light efficiency value of -3% as optimistic with currently available PV modules, we use a value of -4.5% when no other information can be assumed.

The first set of constraints defines 1DM parameters with a degree of freedom, leaving the series resistance free up to a maximum value $R_{s,max}$. The additional constraint imposed by the relative low-light efficiency fixes this value. However, in the case of high FF, not all values of relative low-light efficiency can be achieved while respecting the other constraints [10]. In these cases, PVsyst will artificially increase the V_{oc} value until it is possible to respect all the constraints, such as the MPP which is the first relevant information to preserve for accurate energy yield simulations. Such an example is presented in Figure 3, where we choose the extreme example of the above-mentioned certified record solar cell [1], leading to an inaccurate reproduction of the V_{oc}. In comparison, fitting those data using either the reference recombination model of section 2.2 or a two-diode model allows an accurate reproduction of the V_{oc}. This will be discussed further in the next sections.

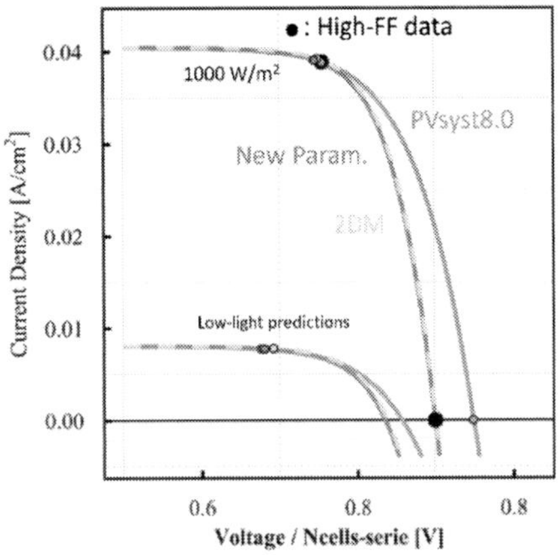

Figure 3: High FF solar cell certified data from *[1]* and corresponding I-V curve estimation from PVsyst 8.0 1DM, a two-diode model and the intrinsic recombination model ("New Param").

2.4 Alternative Parameter Evaluation

To circumvent the limitations of the current 1DM parameters calculation of PVsyst, we propose a fitting method based on an Evolutionary Algorithm (EA). EA are popular to handle non-linear optimization problems and easily adaptable to various problem formulations. They are notably used by some PV module characterization centers in order to produce .PAN files reproducing as closely as possible IEC 61853-1 measured data. In this work, we use a penalty-based differential evolution algorithm which was shown to beat other evolutionary algorithms in reproducing the original two-diode model parameters of synthetically generated data [11].

Our EA fit works by optimizing the set of model parameters of the 1DM. Note that it can also be adapted to find the parameters of the recombination model of section 2.2. Based on the typical available information in product datasheet and low-light performance assumption to reproduce, we write a fitting objective function that needs to be minimized by an optimal set of parameters. This function is written as

$$\begin{aligned} F_{obj}(Params) = & \frac{1}{\sigma_{P_{mpp}}}\left(P_{mpp} - P_{mpp,fit}\right)/P_{mpp} \\ & + \frac{1}{\sigma_{V_{mpp}}}\left(V_{mpp} - V_{mpp,fit}\right)/V_{mpp} \\ & + \frac{1}{\sigma_{V_{oc}}}\left(V_{oc} - V_{oc,fit}\right)/V_{oc} \\ & + \frac{1}{\sigma_{I_{sc}}}\left(I_{sc} - I_{sc,fit}\right)/I_{sc} \\ & + \frac{1}{\sigma_{\mu_{P_{mpp}}}}\left(\mu_{P_{mpp}} - \mu_{P_{mpp},fit}\right)/\mu_{P_{mpp}} \\ & + \frac{1}{\sigma_{\mu_{I_{sc}}}}\left(\mu_{I_{sc}} - \mu_{I_{sc},fit}\right)/\mu_{I_{sc}} \\ & + \frac{1}{\sigma_{\mu_{V_{oc}}}}\left(\mu_{V_{oc}} - \mu_{V_{oc},fit}\right)/\mu_{V_{oc}} \\ & + \frac{1}{\sigma_{\mathrm{Rel.eff}}}\left(\mathrm{Rel.\,eff} - \mathrm{Rel.\,eff_{fit}}\right)/\mathrm{Rel.\,eff} \end{aligned}$$

where the subscript "fit" indicate the respective values computed by the chosen I-V model for a given set of parameters, the elements without subscripts are the measured values and the σ's represent their respective standard deviation.

The latter is of importance because some input data have much stronger experimental variations. For example, in the case of data obtained from IEC 61853-1 reports, three similar modules are measured. By analyzing reports from several test centers, we observed that while the STC values variation is well below 1% among the three modules, the variation in $\mu_{I_{sc}}$ is of the order of 10%. Likewise, when the low-light efficiency is unknown, we can more generally assume a value of $-4.5\% \pm 2\%$, covering widely all the observable values reported in the literature [9]. Another advantage of this method is that it allows for the use of the $\mu_{V_{oc}}$ information. Note that any other available information that can be computed from an I-V model could be used in this objective function and it could therefore be adapted to reproduce all the measured elements of an IEC 61853-1 report.

3 TEST SCENARIOS

In this section, two case studies are used to compare the parameter evaluation method of the current PVsyst model and the EA fit. In the first case, we focus on reproducing IEC 61853-1 certified data from a real PERC PV module, with a conventional FF value of 78.4%, based solely on the above-cited available information.

In the second case, we repeat the operation with data synthetically generated from the reference recombination model of section 2.2. This emulates a PV module with very high FF (85.7%) and very low relative low-light efficiency (−6.8%), which represents closely the best performance we could expect one day from c-Si PV module and serves as an extreme case to test the presented methods.

3.1 Evolutionary Algorithm Fit for One Diode Model and Standard Fill Factor

Figure 4 shows how the 1DM EA fit reproduces the measured data of the PERC device at all temperatures and irradiances available in its IEC 61853-1 report. The efficiency and the V_{oc} are well fitted at 1000 W/m², but a small discrepancy at low-light level can be seen. This is explained by the fact that the real measured relative low light efficiency for this device ($-6.2\% \pm 1.2\%$) was assumed unavailable and the default value of $-4.5\% \pm 2\%$ was used instead according to our hypothesis on commonly available data.

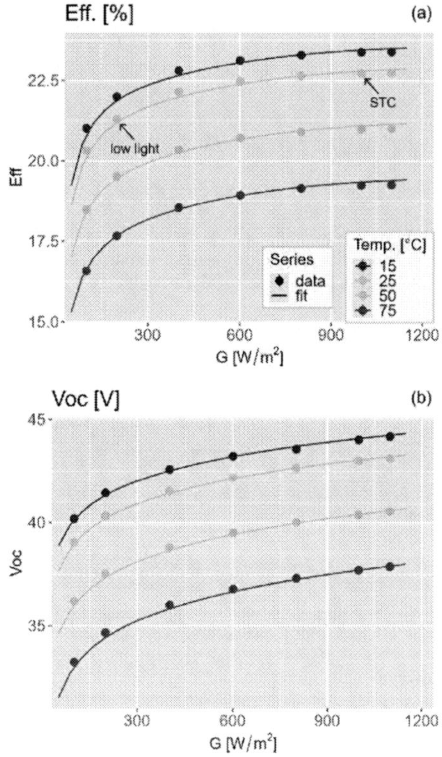

Figure 4: Reproduction of measured IEC 61853-1 data from the EA fit for a conventional FF (78.4%, PERC) based only on limited input ($P_{mpp}, V_{mpp}, V_{oc}, I_{sc}, \mu_{Isc}, \mu_{Voc}, \mu_{Pmpp}$) and conventional assumption on low light efficiency (-4.5% +/- 2%) [9].

Figure 5 shows how the measured parameters are reproduced by (a) the current PVsyst method and (b) the EA fit with the 1DM. Both methods are in good agreement and reproduce the IEC MPP data within 2.5%. The EA fit reduces the error further, close to the tolerated standard deviation of each PV module characteristic. It provides better reproduction of the MPP and V_{oc} data, their

10.4229/EUPVSEC2025/3AV.3.32
020196-004

temperature coefficients, and reduces error across all temperature and irradiance conditions. This is due to the advantages of the EA fit, which leverages $\mu_{V_{oc}}$ information, variations in μ_{Isc}, and (often unknown) low-light efficiency, whereas PVsyst discards the first and assumes a fixed value for the others.

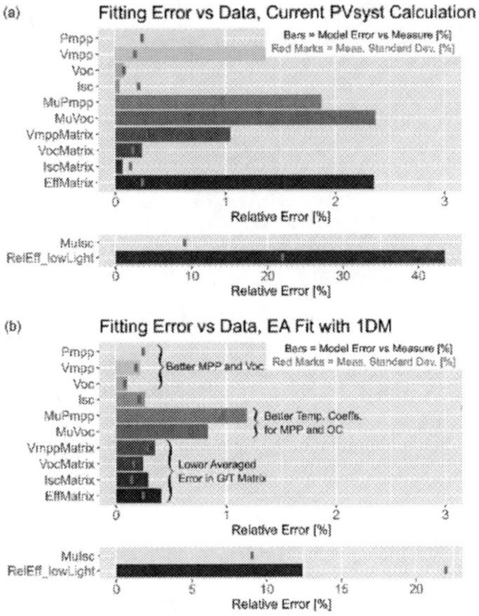

Figure 5: Error from (a) the PVsyst calculated model and (b) the EA fit model in reproducing the IEC 61853-1 data. Pmpp, Vmpp, Voc and Isc refer to the STC conditions, MuPmpp, MuVoc and MuIsc to the temperature coefficients calculated at 1000 W/m^2 from the data at the different temperatures, VmppMatrix, VocMatrix, IscMatrix and EffMatrix to the corresponding average error in reproducing the data over all the temperatures and illumination, and RelEff_lowLight is the ratio of the efficiency at 1000 W/m^2 and 200 W/m^2 (at 25 °C).

3.2 Fitting Synthetic Data for Hypothetical High Fill Factor

Synthetic data for STC values, temperature coefficients and relative low-light efficiency were generated using the recombination model of section 2.2, using input parameters reproducing closely the certified measured data of [1]. Random errors on the temperature and irradiance were added to emulate measurement errors. This scenario raises a caveat, since we are attempting to fit data with a relative low-light efficiency of −6.8% while assuming 4.5% for a modern PV module.

Figure 6 shows the relative error in reproducing P_{mpp} and V_{oc} at temperatures and irradiances relevant to PV system simulations for three approaches. The errors in reproducing P_{mpp} are small for each approach and mainly driven by the low light assumptions. The EA Fit improves even further the results as it does not impose a strict value for the low light efficiency. As expected for this test scenario, the error on V_{oc} by the PVsyst calculation is large, up to 4%. Very interestingly, the EA fit manages to reduce this error below 0.5%, allowing a very good reproduction of both P_{mpp} and V_{oc} while keeping the same 1DM parametrization as PVsyst. Using the same model parametrization as the reference one used for generating data yields even lower error on the V_{oc}. However, the error on the P_{mpp} becomes larger. We explained this by the fact that this parametrization is less flexible and cannot allow a relative low light efficiency too far from the requested −4.5% without creating discrepancies on the other parameters. Therefore, in the case of unknown low light efficiency, the 1DM parametrization seems the most adapted to reproduce well high FF PV module behavior over all conditions of interest.

4 SUMMARY AND OUTLOOK

Accurately modelling PV module I–V curves across operating conditions remains a key challenge for yield simulations, especially for high-performance devices with high fill factors. The current PVsyst approach, based on direct parameter calculation for the one-diode model, provides reliable estimates but compromises open-circuit voltage reproduction when faced with high-FF technologies.

In this work, we introduced an evolutionary algorithm to improve parameter evaluation for the one-diode model. On measured data from a standard PERC module, the EA fit reduced errors in maximum power point, open-circuit voltage, and temperature coefficients compared to the current method, while robustly handling measurement variability and unavailable low-light performance. For a synthetic high-FF case, the EA successfully lowered V_{oc} reproduction errors from several percent to below 0.5%, demonstrating its ability to capture the voltage-dependent recombination mechanisms characteristic of state-of-the-art c-Si devices.

The results show that evolutionary algorithm provides a flexible framework that can estimate accurately PV performance at all relevant temperature and irradiance conditions based solely on available datasheet information and common low-light assumptions. It does so with greater accuracy than the current PVsyst deterministic calculation especially when low-light efficiency is unknown (leveraging μVoc and typical low-light trends). Importantly, even though the EA method already increases significantly the accuracy of the 1DM evaluation, it enables a straightforward extension to more advanced parametrizations.

This general framework lays the groundwork for more accurate PVsyst .PAN files, ensuring robust energy yield simulations for the next generation of PV technologies. Future work will focus on validating the approach with high-FF commercial modules. The possible exploitation of the full IEC matrix also offers promising prospects. The sensitivity to missing or inconsistent data (e.g. product datasheet v.s. certified IEC report) should be studied in more details. Finally, this case study focused exclusively on PV modules of a single power class. Other power classes could not be evaluated due to the lack of certified measurements; however, it would be valuable to investigate them once manufacturers provide standardized data.

10.4229/EUPVSEC2025/3AV.3.32
020196-005

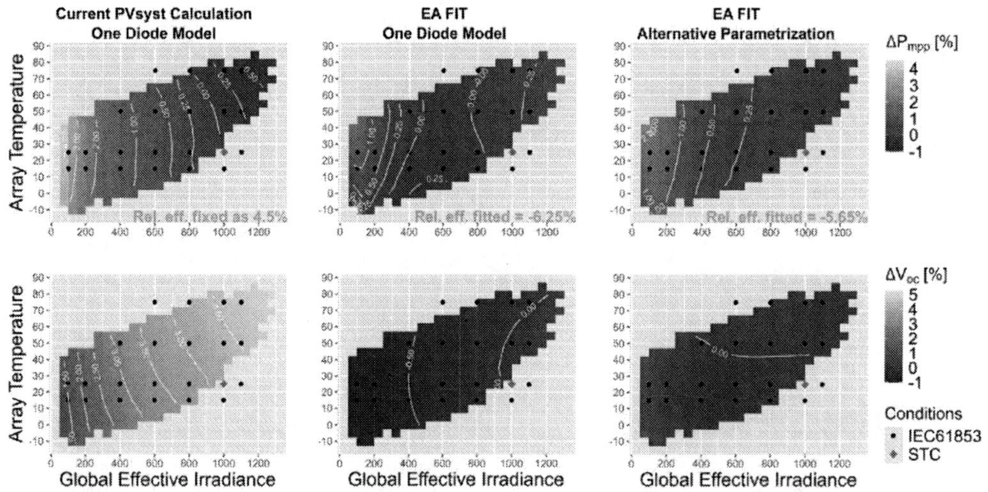

Figure 6: Relative error on Voc and Pmpp in reproducing the synthetic data for relevant temperatures and irradiances, either using the current PVsyt calculation with the 1DM, the EA fit with the 1DM, or the EA fit with the reference model parametrization (same as the one used for generating the synthetic data, denoted as "alternative parametrization"). The black dots references represent the mandatory measurement conditions within the IEC 61853-1 norm and the STC are marked by a red square.

5 ACKNOWLEDGEMENTS

We acknowledge Sandia National laboratories, KIWA PVEL, Groundwork Renewables, Supsi PVLAB, and EPFL PV-LAB, for fruitful discussion and guidance on the topic.

REFERENCES

[1] H. Lin, G. Wang, Q. Su, C. Han, C. Xue, S. Yin, L. Fang, X. Xu and P. Gao, "Unveiling the mechanism of attaining high fill factor in silicon solar cells," *Progress in Photovoltaics: Research and Applications,* vol. 32, p. 359–371, June 2024.

[2] A. Mermoud and T. Lejeune, "Performance assessment of a simulation model for PV modules of any available technology," 2010.

[3] L. E. Black e D. H. Macdonald, «On the quantification of Auger recombination in crystalline silicon,» *Solar Energy Materials and Solar Cells,* vol. 234, p. 111428, January 2022.

[4] T. Niewelt, B. Steinhauser, A. Richter, B. Veith-Wolf, A. Fell, B. Hammann, N. E. Grant, L. Black, J. Tan, A. Youssef, J. D. Murphy, J. Schmidt, M. C. Schubert and S. W. Glunz, "Reassessment of the intrinsic bulk recombination in crystalline silicon," *Solar Energy Materials and Solar Cells,* vol. 235, p. 111467, January 2022.

[5] P. P. Altermatt, "Models for numerical device simulations of crystalline silicon solar cells—a review," *Journal of Computational Electronics,* vol. 10, p. 314–330, September 2011.

[6] A. Schenk, "Finite-temperature full random-phase approximation model of band gap narrowing for silicon device simulation," *Journal of Applied Physics,* vol. 84, p. 3684–3695, October 1998.

[7] A. Richter, M. Hermle e S. W. Glunz, «Reassessment of the Limiting Efficiency for Crystalline Silicon Solar Cells,» *IEEE Journal of Photovoltaics,* vol. 3, p. 1184–1191, October 2013.

[8] S. Schafer and R. Brendel, "Accurate Calculation of the Absorptance Enhances Efficiency Limit of Crystalline Silicon Solar Cells With Lambertian Light Trapping," *IEEE Journal of Photovoltaics,* vol. 8, p. 1156–1158, July 2018.

[9] U. Kräling, P. Gebhardt, M. Kaiser and D. Philipp, "PV module performance measurements – statistical analysis of technological trends," 2022.

[10] A. Bridel-Bertomeu, M. Oliosi, A. Mermoud and B. Wittmer, "Limits of the single diode model in view of its application to the latest PV cell technologies," 2023.

[11] K. Ishaque, Z. Salam, H. Taheri and A. Shamsudin, "A critical evaluation of EA computational methods for Photovoltaic cell parameter extraction based on two diode model," *Solar Energy,* vol. 85, p. 1768–1779, September 2011.

tecnalia MEMBER OF BASQUE RESEARCH & TECHNOLOGY ALLIANCE

UNIVERZA V LJUBLJANI University of Ljubljana

A photovoltaic performance dataset for benchmarking of failure detection and diagnosis algorithms

EUPVSEC 3AV.3.36

J.D. Santos [a] (jose.santos@tecnalia.com), S. Riaño [a], A. Lucea [a], M. Jankovec [b], A. Del Pozo [a], R. Alonso [a], A. Sanz [a]
[a] TECNALIA, Parque Científico y Tecnológico de Bizkaia, Astondo Bidea, Edificio 700. E-48160 Derio (Bizkaia), Spain
[b] UNIVERSITY OF LJUBLJANA, Faculty of Electrical Engineering, Tržaška cesta 25, 1000 Ljubljana, Slovenia

INTRODUCTION

- The development of algorithms for remote identification of failures from SCADA data requires PV datasets with known degradation modes. However, publicly available PV datasets often present a lack of information on existing failures. Synthetic datasets with software simulated degradation, while useful, do not reflect the complexity of real PV systems.
- To address this gap, this work present a new dataset based on the continuous monitoring of a set of PV modules with well-characterized failure modes. Designed for O&M applications, this PV performance dataset is shared open-access with the PV community within the SERENDIPV and CACTUS projects.

EXPERIMENTAL SETUP

PV Monitoring System

- LPVO-MS1X16 system continuously monitored the performance of each PV module.
- Operating voltage and current (V_{OPE} & I_{OPE}) measured by MPPTs with 1-min frequency.
- Entire IV curve of each module characterized by an IV tracer with 5-min frequency.
- Plane-of-array irradiance (G_{POA}) measured synchronously with a combination of pyranometer and calibrated solar cell.
- PV module temperature (T_{MOD}) measured at the center and corner of each device.
- Environmental conditions such as global horizontal irradiance (GHI), air temperature, relative humidity, and wind speed (WS) recorded simultaneously.

PV modules and Failure modes

- The PV modules set included four different manufacturers and three solar cell technologies.
- JASolar modules were new and showed no defects. JASolar1 was used as the reference for benchmarking.
- JASolar2 and JASolar3 were used to simulate, through fabricated resistance boxes, the impact that some failure modes have on increasing series resistance (R_{SERIE}) and decreasing shunt resistance (R_{SHUNT}).
- Ningbo, Trinasolar and Photowatt exhibited combinations of failure modes caused by long-term exposure to harsh operation conditions in Spanish PV plants. Atersa showed defects associated with improper handling.
- Failure modes were identified by combining indoor IV curve, visual inspection and electroluminescence.

Manufacturer	Cell technology	Label Pmax	State	Main failure modes
JA Solar	Mono / PERC / 5 busbars	315 W	As new	None - Reference
JA Solar	Mono / PERC / 5 busbars	315 W	As new	Artificially higher Rserie or lower Rshunt
JA Solar	Mono / PERC / 5 busbars	315 W	As new	Artificially higher Rserie or lower Rshunt
Ningbo Solar	Mono / Al-BSF / 2 busbars	210 W	Degraded	Yellowing / Interconnect ribbon break
Trina Solar	Mono / Al-BSF / 2 busbars	185 W	Degraded	Internal circuitry corrosion
Atersa	Mono / PERC / 5 busbars	330 W	Degraded	MicroCracks / Shorted solar cells
PhotoWatt	Poly / Al-BSF / 2 busbars	160 W	Degraded	Solar cell cracks / Interconnect ribbon break

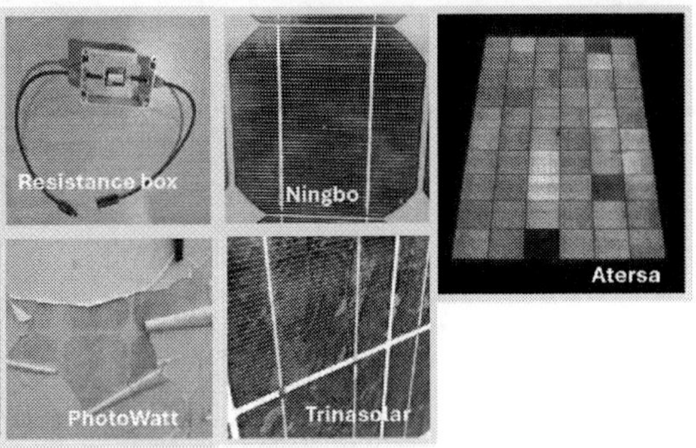

RESULTS

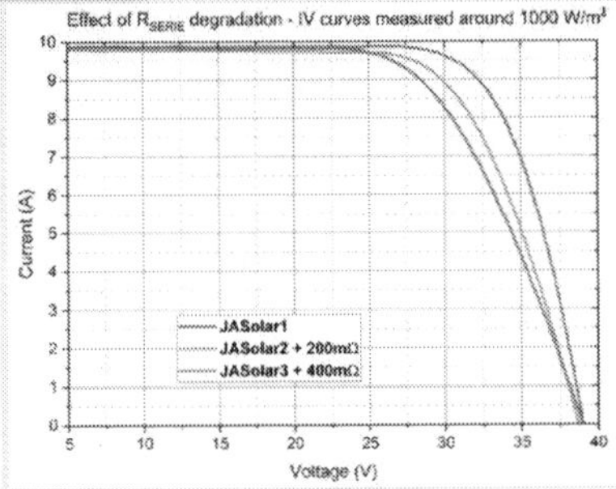

R_{SERIE} impact on IV curve

- Failure modes like internal circuitry corrosion cause an increase in the R_{SERIE} of the PV module.
- Impact of R_{SERIE} degradation on PV performance was investigated by connecting resistance boxes of 200 mΩ and 400 mΩ in series with JASolar2 and JASolar3.
- IV curves measured in outdoor conditions at G_{POA}≈1000 W/m² were filtered to show how R_{SERIE} degradation altered the shape of the IV curve, affecting MPP voltage or fill factor (FF) among other parameters

R_{SERIE} impact on irradiance dependence of FF

- Continuous monitoring enabled the study of how different failures affect the dependence of PV performance on operation conditions .
- Impact of R_{SERIE} increase on the FF was investigated as function of G_{POA}.
- R_{SERIE} degradation caused significant differences with reference FF (JASolar1) for G_{POA}>300 W/m².
- At 1000 W/m², FF values ≈75% and ≈65% were measured for JASolar1 and JASolar3 respectively.

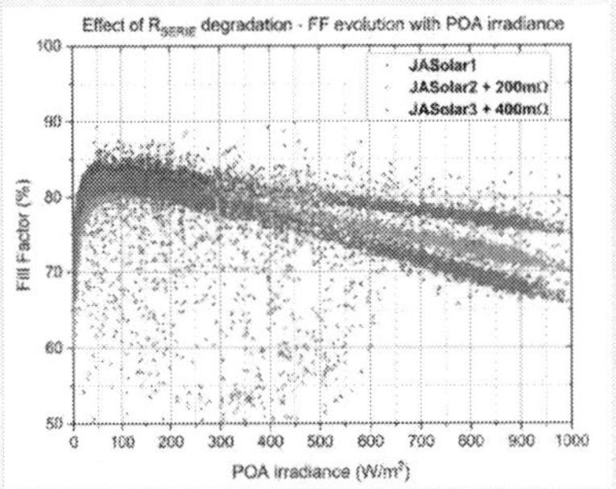

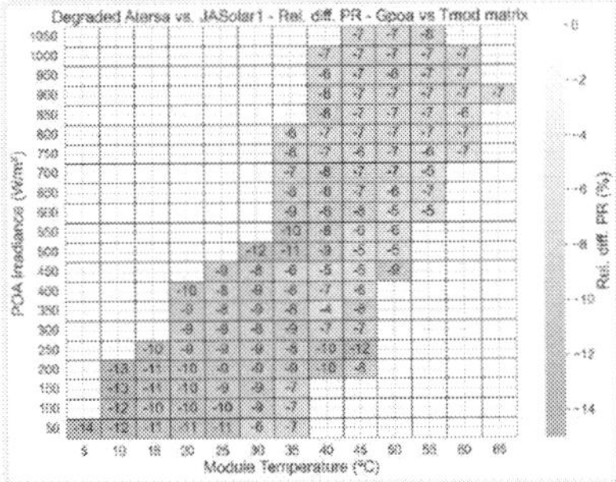

G_{POA} & T_{MOD} dependence of PR – Atersa vs. JASolar1

- Relative difference in performance ratio (PR) between Atersa and JASolar1 was plotted as G_{POA} vs. T_{MOD} matrix analogous to IEC 61853-1.
- Atersa showed a PR a 6-7% lower than JASolar1 for G_{POA}>800 W/m².
- Rel. diff. PR between Atersa and JASolar1 was sensitive to changes in operating conditions, reaching -14% at G_{POA}=50 W/m² and T_{MOD}=5ºC.
- For G_{POA}<600 W/m², rel. diff PR seemed to become more negative as T_{MOD} decreased.

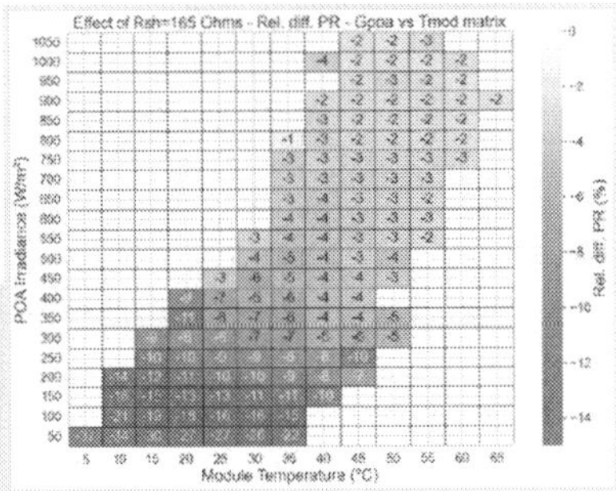

G_{POA} & T_{MOD} dependence of PR - Lower R_{SHUNT} + JASolar3 vs. JASolar1

- Failure modes such as potential induced degradation cause a reduction in R_{SHUNT} of the PV module.
- Impact of R_{SHUNT} degradation was investigated by connecting a 165 Ω resistance box in parallel to JASolar3.
- JASolar3 showed a 2-3% lower PR than JASolar1 for G_{POA}>800 W/m². JASolar3 presented a 20-30% lower PR than JASolar 1 for G_{POA}<100 W/m².
- For a given POA irradiance interval, the R_{SHUNT} degradation also led to lower PR values as T_{MOD} decreased.

Funded by the European Union

This project has received funding from the European Union's Horizon Europe research and innovation programme under grant agreement No. 953016 and No. 101132182.

SERENDIPV CACTUS

tecnalia MEMBER OF BASQUE RESEARCH & TECHNOLOGY ALLIANCE

solar zentrum stuttgart

Reliability of quantitative analysis of lock-in electroluminescence images of PV modules based on histogram statistical parameters

J.D. Santos [a] (jose.santos@tecnalia.com), E. Setien [a], A. Del Pozo [a], L. Stoicescu [b], A. Villodas [a], A. Lucea [a], A. Pereda [a], R. Alonso [a]
[a] TECNALIA, Parque Científico y Tecnológico de Bizkaia, Astondo Bidea, Edificio 700. E-48160 Derio (Bizkaia), Spain
[b] SOLARZENTRUM STUTTGART GMBH, Rotebühlstr. 145 70197 Stuttgart, Germany

EUPVSEC

3AV.3.37

INTRODUCTION

- Electroluminescence (EL) imaging is a standard for quality control during the manufacturing process of photovoltaic (PV) modules, offering the broadest catalogue of detectable failure modes. In recent years, the PV community has increased efforts to extend its use for the operation and maintenance (O&M) of PV systems.
- One example is the research on lock-in EL, which has noticeably increased the range of operation of this tool, providing high quality images under daylight conditions. Another example is the IEC TS 60904-13:2018, putting the basis to obtain high-quality and reproducible EL images, opening the possibility for their later quantitative analysis.
- This last topic is particularly relevant for the PV O&M sector since it enables the assessment of the PV module/array performance from EL image analysis. However, studies on how measurement conditions affect the quantitative information from EL images remain limited.
- This work provides insights into how measurements conditions affect the histogram-based statistical parameters proposed in IEC TS 60904-13 for the quantitative analysis of EL images.

EXPERIMENTAL SETUP

- A DaySy Pro 1000 developed by SolarZentrum Stuttgart was used as the lock-in EL characterization system.
- The reference PV module was a JA Solar model JAP60S09/280SC composed of 60 pc-Si solar cells with Al-BSF technology.
- A mobile metallic structure was developed to easily modify the camera-module relative position and the module orientation.
- A monitoring system was developed to continuously record GTI irradiance, module temperature, current, and voltage during EL characterization.
- EL images were corrected in compliance with IEC TS 60904-13 (vignetting effect, barrel distortion, and perspective) using the PVScan software developed by Tecnalia.
- The module and individual solar cell areas were automatically detected by using an algorithm developed for this purpose.
- From the associated histogram, different statistical parameters like mean or standard deviation were calculated and used as state-of-health indicators of solar cells/module.

CHARACTERIZATION

Indoor vs. Outdoor

EL images were captured at different irradiance level to test its effect on quantitative analysis. The influence of exposure time on the response of the lock-in EL system was also studied. Qualitative analysis showed that EL image quality was comparable both indoors and outdoors.

GTI = 0 W/m² / **f1.4** / texp = 10 ms

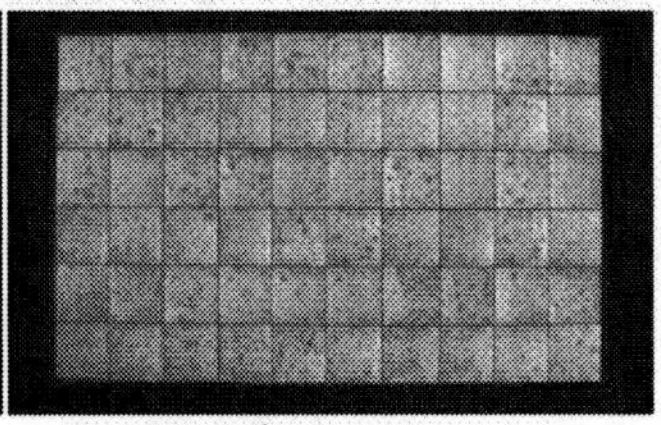

GTI = 850 W/m² / **f2.8** / texp= 10 ms

Perspective vs. distance

EL images were captured at different relative module-camera angles and distances. Thus, the study provides information about the influence of perspective correction and limited pixel size on the results of the quantitative analysis of EL images.

GTI = 0 W/m² / **d = 2.6 m** / **angle=37º**

GTI = 0 W/m² / **d=5.2m** / **angle=0º**

RESULTS

Indoor vs. Outdoor – EL intensity distribution

The normalized mean at cell level is plotted for EL images captured indoors and outdoors. The same pattern was observed for the normalized mean at 0 and 850 W/m². Cell (X8,Y1) shows the highest intensity, and cell (X1,Y6) the lowest. However, discrepancies in the absolute values indicate that environmental light may introduce some uncertainty.

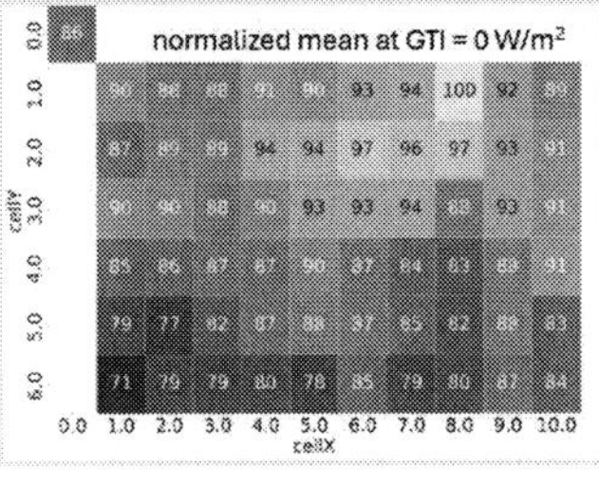

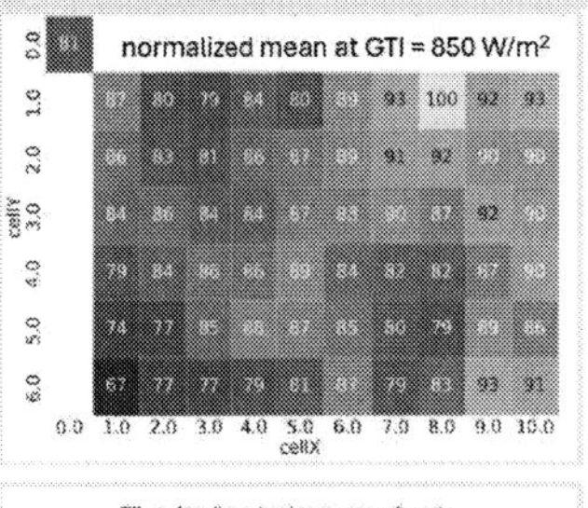

Indoor vs. Outdoor - Linearity

Exposure time (texp) must be adjusted to maximize image intensity. A linear response of the lock-in EL system allows the quantitative analysis of EL images captured at different texp. An excellent linearity is observed indoors and outdoors with R^2=0.999. At GTI=500 W/m², the first signs of sensor saturation are observed at 15 ms.

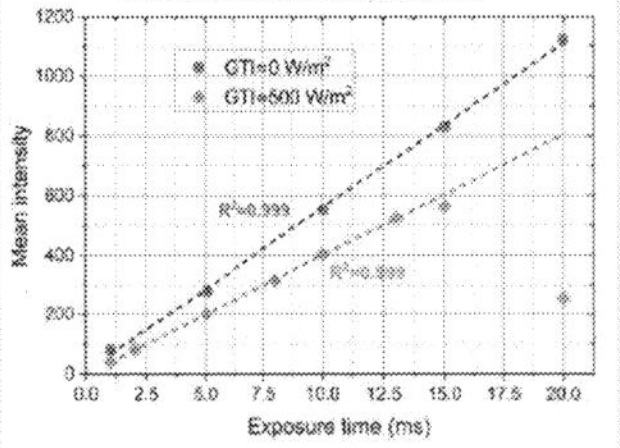

Perspective

The increase in the relative camera-module angle causes a progressive decrease in measured mean intensity. A 5% reduction is obtained by increasing the relative angle from 0º to 37º. Additionally, the normalized StdDev decreased by 10%, suggesting that information about heterogeneity in the PV intensity distribution is lost.

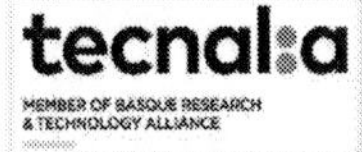

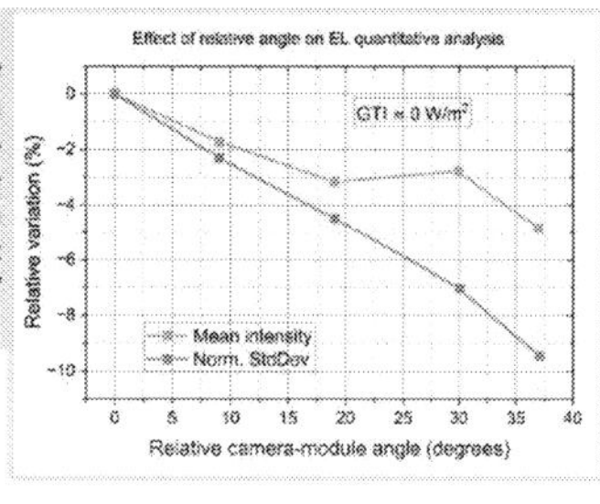

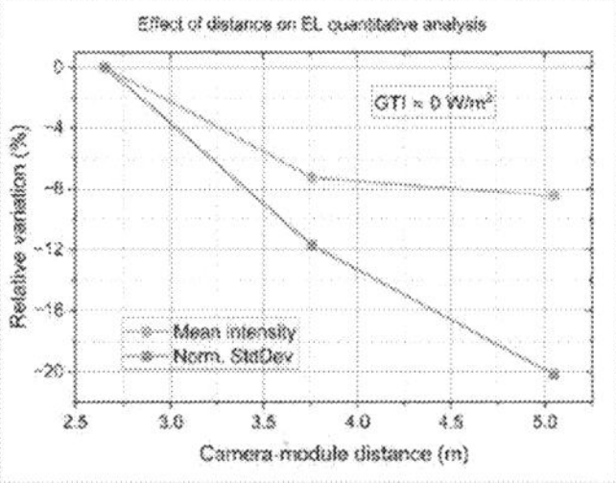

Distance

The increase in camera-module distance leads to a reduction of the captured EL mean intensity. An 8% decrease is obtained when increasing the camera-module distance from 2.6 to 5.2 m. The normalized StdDev is noticeably affected by distance increase. A relative decreased of 20% from 2.6 to 5.2 m due to limited camera resolution.

spri

ensol3

Funded by Department of Economic Development, Sustainability and Environment of the Basque Government under ref. KK2022/0067

Co-funded by the European Union

SUPERNOVA

This project is co-funded by the European Union under Grant Agreement nº 101146883.

DEVELOPMENT OF A ROOFTOP MOCK-UP COVERED WITH PV PANELS FOR TEMPERATURE FLUX MEASUREMENTS

Michael Schrempf[1]* and Stefan Riechelmann[1]

[1]*Physikalisch-Technische Bundesanstalt* (PTB), Braunschweig, Germany

*Corresponding author: michael.schrempf@ptb.de

ABSTRACT:

This work describes a realistic small-scale rooftop setup of an urban house that was built at the Physikalisch-Technische Bundesanstalt (PTB) in Braunschweig, Germany. The setup consists of two identical chambers, where one side of the roof is covered with installed PV panels while the other side is uncovered. Temperature sensors are placed at various positions and different depths of the roof to measure the temperature flux between the inside and outside of the setup. Combined with auxiliary measurements, including the erection of a 17-meter-high measuring mast, results of these measurements will be used to validate a new PV parameterization of the Large-Eddy Simulation (LES) model PALM.

Keywords: PV Module, temperature flux, Palm

1 INTRODUCTION

Model simulations are a key tool to understand the effect of area-wide PV deployment in urban areas on the outdoor and indoor urban microclimate in terms of thermal comfort of residents and air quality. For this purpose, project partners from the Leibniz University Hannover and Technical University of Dresden plan to implement a new parameterization for rooftop PV panels in the LES model PALM [1] to calculate heat transport by convection or thermal radiation. Its application for simulating and analyzing the effects of the widespread installation of PV panels under realistic atmospheric conditions is intended to resolve previous contradictory results. These include, for example, whether comprehensive PV installations in cities lead to a cooling or warming of the urban atmosphere during the day [2]. Furthermore, the complex flow around the buildings has not been resolved in previous studies.

To validate the new parameterization for rooftop PV panels in the LES model PALM a small-scale outdoor setup simulating a city-like rooftop was built. The setup is placed on top of a 12 m high building at PTB to ensure similar wind conditions to city housings. The advantage of developing and building a small-scale, realistic new roof, instead of using already existing roofs, is that both situations having PV and having a bare roof are realized in a very well-defined way. Multiple temperature sensors can easily be integrated at different locations and levels within the roof during construction based on the needs of the experiment. Furthermore, the dimensions and coefficients of the materials used are known in detail, which is crucial as input data for the simulation model.

2 SETUP

The rooftop setup is based on a realistic rooftop of an urban house. To investigate the differences in temperature flux for a rooftop with and without PV panels, the interior of the setup is divided into two separately insolated chambers. One side of the roof being covered with installed PV panels and the other exposed to sunlight.

Figure 1: Small-scale rooftop installation with PV panels on one side of the roof.

2.1 Construction details

The basic structure consists of wooden beams, which are clad on the outside with oriented strand board (OSB) panels. The setup has a length of approx. 6 m, a width of 2 m and a height of about 2 m. The interior walls, the floor and the roof are insulated with wood fiber insulation materials from the brand Steico which has a declared thermal conductivity of 0.036 W/(m*K). The roof was insulated with 10 cm of insulation to represent typical existing houses, whereas newly built houses have thicker insulation. In addition to the insulation, the roof consists of an airtight barrier. The tiles used in this rooftop setup were concrete tiles from the brand Braas and the type "Frankfurter Pfanne" which are widespread in Germany. A cross section of the roof construction and its used elements is shown in Fig. 2.

10.4229/EUPVSEC2025/3AV.3.38

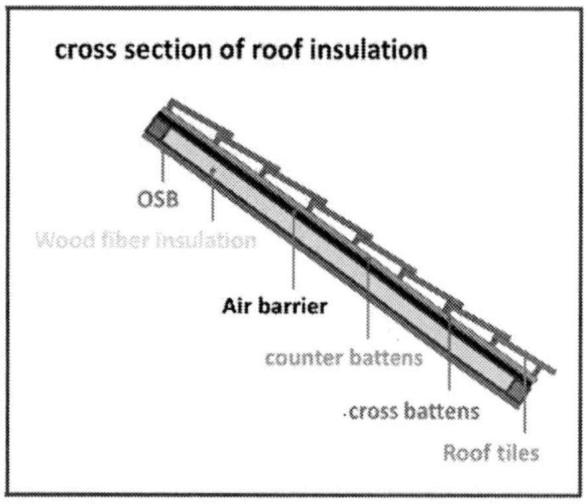

Figure 2: Extracts from the construction plan for the roof.

The walls and floor, on the other hand, were insulated much more heavily to reduce heat transfer to a minimum, so observed effects can be attributed to front-side irradiance.

The insulation of the wall consists of a 10 cm flexible wood fiber and 6 cm wood fiber boards. The bottom consists of a 16 cm wood fiber bottom insulation. This kind of insulation is walkable, so the chambers can therefore be entered for installation and inspection purposes. Since the setup consists of two separately insolated chambers, each chamber has a hatch for accessibility. A cross section of the wall and bottom insulation is shown in Fig. 3.

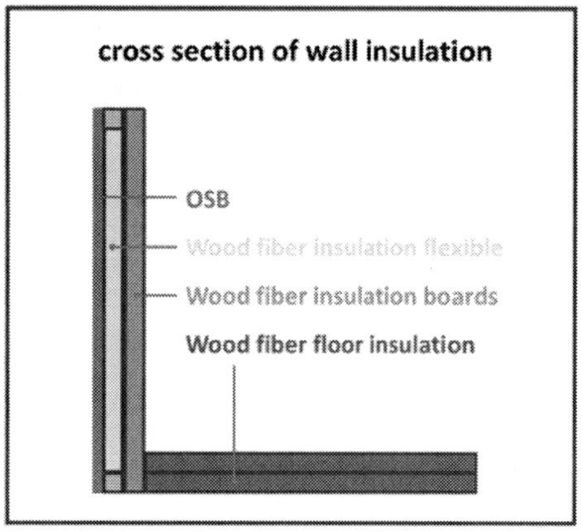

Figure 3: Extracts from the construction plan for the wall.

To measure the heat transfer between the inside and outside of the setup, 65 PT-100 temperature sensors were placed at 10 different positions that are illustrated in Fig. 4. For each position temperature sensors are placed at different levels in the roof during construction (e.g. bottom and center of roof tile as shown in Fig. 5 or on the inside wall of the rooftop setup as shown in Fig. 6. Table 1 lists all levels of the temperature sensors for both chambers. Four additional temperature sensors (two for each side of the setup) were placed on the surface of the air barrier and another four additional sensors were placed between the air barrier and the roof tiles.

Table 1: List of levels in which temperature sensors are placed in the rooftop setup for the sides with and without PV panels.

Level	Description of placing	PV	No PV
	Indoor room	x	x
1	Indoor wall	x	x
2	Interior side of insulation	x	x
3	Bottom of roof tile	x	x
4	Center of roof tile	x	x
5	Surface of roof tile	x	
6	Between roof and module	x	
7	Backside of solar module	x	
	Additional sensors on the surface of air barrier	x	x
	Additional sensors between air barrier & roof tile	x	x

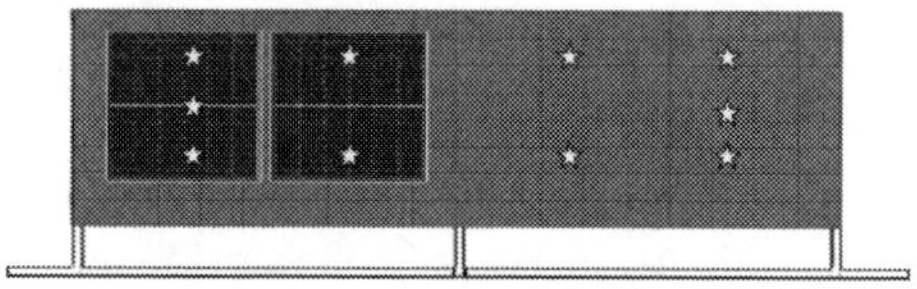

Figure 4: Different positions of the temperature sensors on the rooftop setup.

Figure 5 shows the wiring and placing of the temperature sensors between the air barrier and the roof tiles during construction.

The finished roof structure was painted with white weather protection paint to reduce the heating of the walls due to solar radiation and to protect the structure from weather conditions (see Fig 1).

Figure 5: Placement of the temperature sensors on the roof during construction.

Figure 6: Interior view of one of the chambers of the roof structure, with temperature sensors placed on the inside wall of the roof.

2.2 Data Acquisition and auxiliary Measurements

All PT-100 temperature sensors are connected to a datalogger via a 3-wire connection. In addition to the temperature measurements, incoming solar radiation is measured with two pyranometers. One pyranometer measures the global horizontal irradiance and the second pyranometer measures the irradiance in-plane of the PV panels of the setup. General weather parameters such as ambient air temperature, humidity and air pressure are measured with a weather station near the setup. The wind speed and wind direction is measured with three ultrasonic anemometers, installed at different positions near the setup. Two of the wind sensors are placed in front of the setup and one is placed on the side next to the setup. In addition, a vane anemometer is used to assess the wind speed in the air gap between the roof tiles and the PV panels. These various auxiliary measurements are recorded to obtain a picture of the temperature flux as complete as possible.

Both the data logger and all other devices are connected to a PC via different interfaces. All these electronics are installed in a weatherproof and climatized outdoor enclosure outside of the setup to avoid bringing an additional heat source into the rooftop setup. To capture the power production of the PV panels, the connected micro-inverter is read out via a Data Transfer Unit (DTU).

In addition to the above-mentioned parameters, the prevailing wind field is needed to model the rooftop setup with the model PALM. To determine the direction and speed of the prevailing wind field, a 17-meter-high measuring mast was erected a short distance from the building on which the rooftop setup was built (see Fig. 7). Three-dimensional measuring Ultrasonic wind sensors are mounted at three different heights (5,10 and 16m) to determine these parameters.

The Measurements are recorded every second for all instruments mentioned above.

Figure 7: Measuring mast with a total height of 17m and wind sensors at different heights to measure the prevailing wind field.

3 RESULTS

For a first analysis of the data of temperature sensors we averaged all data points of the 5 sensors of each level of one day for the left and right chamber respectively. As a result, the diurnal temperature variation of a sunny day from July 1st 2025 is shown in Figure 3 and Figure 4. As a next step the measurement data for all months will be analyzed for variations between different positions and different days and seasons.

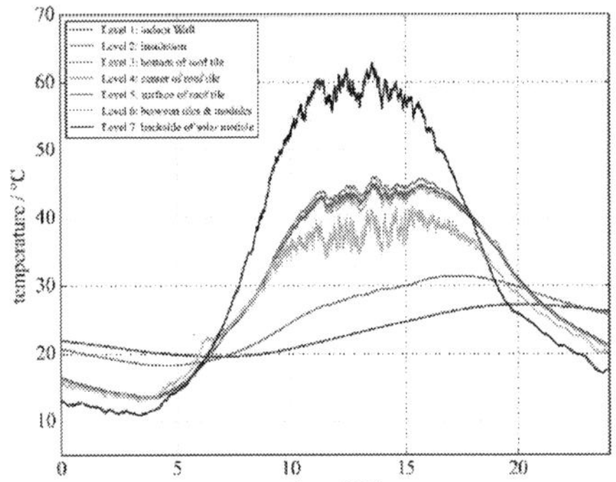

Figure 3: Diurnal temperature variation of a clear sky day of the chamber with installed PV panels.

10.4229/EUPVSEC2025/3AV.3.38

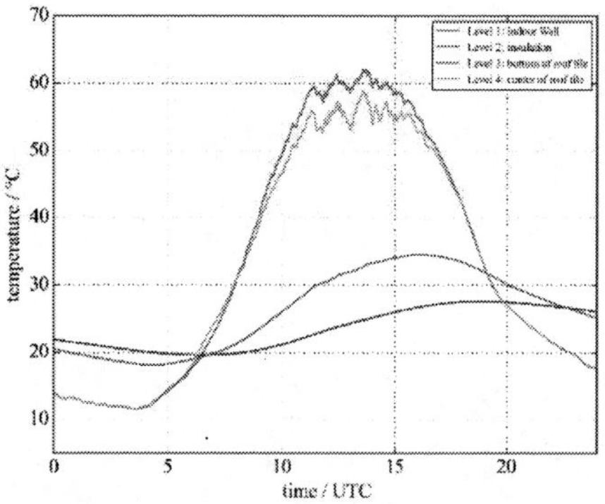

Figure 4: Diurnal temperature variation of a clear sky day of the chamber without PV panels,

4 CONCLUSION

We presented a description of the construction of a realistic rooftop of an urban house. The interior of the setup is divided into two separately insolated chambers in which 65 temperature sensors were integrated to investigate the differences in temperature flux for a rooftop with and without PV panels. One side of the roof being covered with installed PV panels and the other exposed to sunlight. This way, we can accurately distinguish the effect of the panels on this setup. Various auxiliary measurements have been set up and are recorded to obtain a picture of the temperature flux as complete as possible. This data will be used as necessary input data for the LES model PALM to validate its new PV parametrization.

5 ACKNOWLEDGEMENT

This work was funded within the project „EUPHORIC“ by the German Research Foundation (DFG), Germany (funding reference number 515096414).

Special thanks to Laura Stenzig[1] und Jörn Hauffe[1] for their help in the construction of the rooftop setup.

6 REFERENCES

[1] Maronga, B., G. Gross, S. Raasch, S. Banzhaf, R. Forkel, W. Heldens, F. Kanani-Sühring, A. Matzarakis, M. Mauder, D. Pavlik, J. Pfafferott, S. Schubert, G. Seckmeyer, H. Sieker, and K. Winderlich, 2019: “Development of a new urban climate model based on the model PALM - Project overview, planned work, and first achievements”, Meteorol. Z., 28, 105–119.

[2] Sailor, D. J., J. Anand, and R. R. King, 2021: “Photovoltaics in the built environment: A critical review”, *Energy & Buildings*, 253, 111479. DOI: 10.1016/j.enbuild.2021.111479.

42nd European Photovoltaic Solar Energy Conference and Exhibition

Physikalisch-Technische Bundesanstalt
National Metrology Institute

Michael Schrempf, Stefan Riechelmann

Development of a rooftop mock-up covered with PV panels for temperature flux measurements

Realistic small-scale rooftop for validation of model parameterization

- Model simulations are a key tool to understand the effect of area-wide PV deployment in urban areas on the outdoor and indoor urban microclimate in terms of thermal comfort of residents and air quality.
- To validate a new parameterization for rooftop PV panels in the LES model PALM, we built a realistic small-scale rooftop typical for German cities at the Physikalisch-Technische Bundesanstalt (PTB) in Braunschweig.
- The rooftop consists of two identical chambers with one side of the roof being covered with installed PV panels and the other exposed to sunlight.
- Multiple temperature sensors are integrated in this rooftop setup that are placed at various positions and different layers of the roof to measure the temperature flux between the inside and outside of the rooftop.

Fig. 1: Location of the setup on top of a building.

Fig. 2: small scale city-like rooftop

Setup & construction of the small-scale rooftop

The setup is placed on top of a 12 m high building at PTB to ensure similar wind conditions to city housing. The structure consists of wooden beams, which are cladded on the outside with oriented strand board (OSB) panels.

- Dimensions are approx. 6 m x 2 m x 2 m (L x W x H).
- Roof insulation is 10 cm to represent typical existing houses.
- Walls and floor, were insulated much more heavily to reduce heat transfer to a minimum
- A white weather protection paint was used to reduce the heating of the walls due to solar radiation and to protect the structure from the weather (Fig. 2).

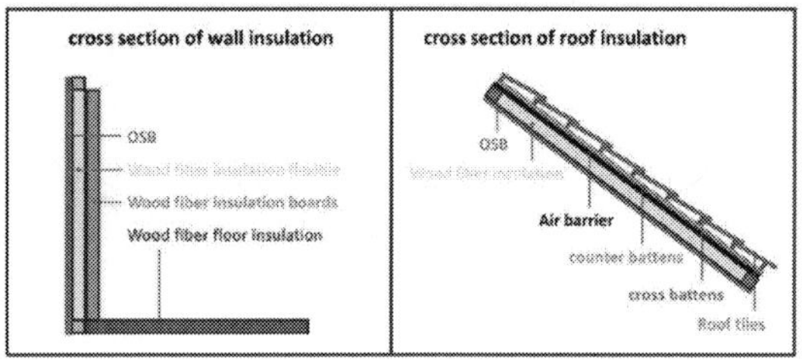

Fig. 3: Extracts from the construction plan for the walls and the roof

Instrumentation and sensors

To measure the temperature flux between the inside and outside of the setup, over 60 temperature sensors were placed at different positions and at different levels.(e.g. indoor room temperature, inside wall of setup, inside of insulation, air gap under roof tiles, inside of roof tiles, back side of PV modules).

Further instrumentation to provide atmospheric input data for the model:

- pyranometers for horizontal and in-plane irradiance.
- weather station (ambient temperature, humidity, ...).
- several ultra sonic wind sensors around the setup.
- wind measurements between module and roof tiles.
- 17m high measuring mast for prevailing wind field measurements at different heights.

Fig. 4: Temperature sensors are being placed

Fig. 5: Indoor View of the setup with sensors at the inside of the roof

Fig. 6: 17 m high measuring mast for prevailing wind field measurements

Measurements of diurnal temperature variation

Data Acquisition

- Measurements are recorded for all instruments every second.
- Data logger, Interfaces and PC are placed in a weatherproof outdoor enclosure outside of the setup to avoid bringing extra heat in the setup.

First Results:

- Figure 7 shows the diurnal temperature variation of different temperature sensors of a clear sky day for the chamber with installed PV panels and the chamber without.
- For this day in the afternoon, the chamber with installed PV panels has an approx. 1°C lower indoor temperature.

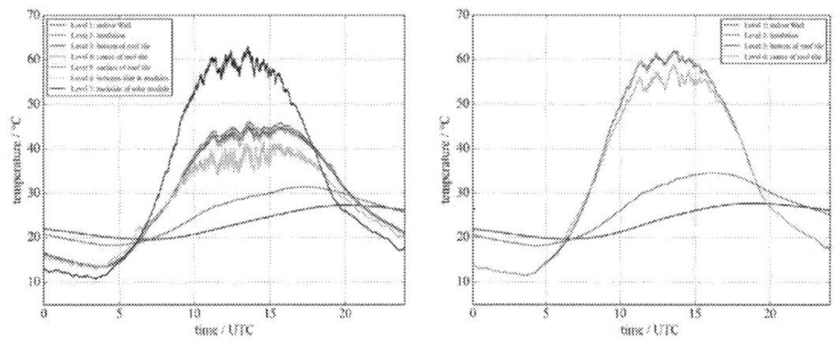

Fig. 7: Diurnal temperate variation of a clear sky day. Chamber with installed PV panels (left) and without (right)

The project „EUPHORIC" was funded by the *German Research Foundation (DFG)*, Germany

DFG Deutsche Forschungsgemeinschaft German Research Foundation

Physikalisch-Technische Bundesanstalt
National Metrology Institute
Bundesallee 100
38116 Braunschweig, Germany
www.ptb.de

Michael Schrempf
Working Group 4.53
Solar Modules
phone: +49 531 592-4533
e-mail: michael.schrempf@ptb.de

42nd European Photovoltaic Solar Energy Conference and Exhibition

This presentation was selected by the Sc. Committee of the EU PVSEC 2025 for submission of a full paper to one of the EU PVSEC's collaborating peer-reviewed journals.

INVESTIGATING THE IMPACT OF CELL CRACKS ON POWER LOSS AND ITS CORRELATION WITH THE MODELLING PARAMETERS.

Ahmad Hashem[1,2], Zonghan Jiang[1], Guido Willers[2], Leila Mortazavifar[1], Bengt Jaeckel [1,2] and Ralph Gottschalg[1,2]
[1]Hochschule Anhalt - Anhalt University of Applied Sciences, Bernburger Str. 55, 06366, Köthen, Germany
[2]Fraunhofer Center for Silicon Photovoltaics CSP, Otto-Eissfeldt-Str. 12, 06120 Halle (Saale), Germany
Email: ahmad.hashem@hs-anhalt.de

ABSTRACT: Assessing the reliability of photovoltaic (PV) cells—the fundamental units of any solar installation—is essential for ensuring optimal system performance. Cell cracking in PV modules is an inevitable outcome of lifecycle mechanical and thermal stresses, yet its implications for performance and safety continue to complicate module valuation. This study proposes a rigorous framework to quantify the relationships among crack extent, power loss, and equivalent-circuit parameters. Paired electroluminescence (EL) images and I–V curves were acquired on PERC modules with varying busbar (BB) counts under solar-simulator conditions. EL images were processed to detect busbars and to measure aggregate crack length, while I–V data collected across multiple irradiance levels were fitted using single-diode models to extract key parameters. A statistical correlation analysis was then performed to link crack metrics with the extracted parameters and measured power loss. For large crack lengths, crack extent shows a weak negative correlation with shunt resistance and a slight positive correlation with series resistance; power loss is weakly inversely related to shunt resistance and increases modestly with crack length under the same conditions. The proposed framework delivers a quantitative basis for evaluating cracked modules and informing performance and safety judgments.

Keywords: PV Modelling, Electroluminescence, Crack Detection, Power Loss, Shunt Resistance

1 INTRODUCTIION

Cracks in PV cells may originate at multiple stages—silicon ingot slicing, cell fabrication, module lamination, improper transport or installation, and environmental loading such as snow, wind, or hail [1–2]. For performance assessment, the primary focus is on cracks that arise from module production through end-of-life, as these most directly affect energy yield. Numerous taxonomies exist, differentiating cracks by physical extent, orientation relative to the metallization grid, and penetration depth. For example, they are often classified by extent as complete—spanning continuously from one cell edge to the opposite—or incomplete—terminating within the cell interior [3]. Further distinctions separate single from multiple cracks, with subtypes including double, dendritic, and small X- or V-shaped fissures. Orientation-based schemes categorize cracks relative to busbars [4–6], identifying parallel, perpendicular, and ±45° (diagonal) orientations, as well as dendritic and multidirectional patterns.

Cracks degrade module performance by interrupting current pathways and elevating resistive losses; consequently, affected cells may dissipate power instead of generating it, lowering overall efficiency. Several studies report a direct relationship among crack count, crack length, and power loss [7–10], as illustrated in Figure 1. However, this assumption is contestable for several reasons: (i) narrow line cracks typically exert far less influence than inactive cell areas; (ii) severity depends on wafer and metallization design, since increasing busbar count reduces worst-case crackable area and improves current collection [11]; and (iii) system topology matters—multiple cracks within the same module substring can produce an effect equivalent to a single dominant crack.

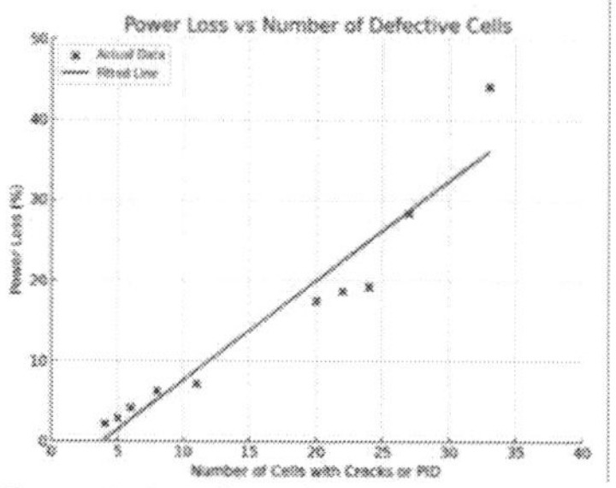

Figure 1: Correlation between the number of cracked cell and corresponding power loss (%) [9]

2 METHODOLOGY

2.1 Image Processing

OpenCV-based pipeline was developed to quantify crack length from EL images, comprising four stages: perspective correction, cell detection, busbar removal, and crack detection/measurement. A perspective transform based on the module outline and known physical dimensions ensures metric accuracy. Detected cell contours are arranged into a regular matrix to derive per-cell pixel dimensions and establish a pixel-to-length conversion factor. To prevent structural interference, busbars are identified via their vertical, linear signature using columnwise intensity sums and then removed. Each cell image is brightness-normalized; because busbar removal can truncate crack segments, a feature-restoration step reconnects discontinuities. Crack candidates are extracted with adaptive thresholding and refined with morphological filtering to suppress false positives. Confirmed cracks are skeletonized to single-pixel centerlines, and lengths are computed using the established scale, yielding physically meaningful totals per cell and module. Figure 2 summarizes the workflow and provides a representative detection example.

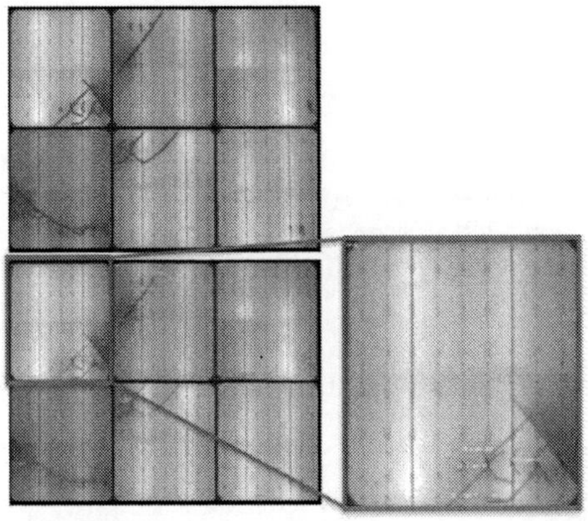

Figure 2: Example of Crack Detection with Length Calculation

2.2 Fitting and Parameter Extraction

Accurate PV modeling hinges on precise identification of the five single-diode model (SDM) parameters (I_L, I_o, R_s, R_{sh}, n). In practice, however, manufacturers' datasheets typically report only a few STC operating points from the I–V curve (I_{sc}, V_{oc}, I_{mp}, V_{mp}). This paper conducts a comparative analysis of four parameter-extraction techniques, one that relies on analytical equations (PVLib), two that integrates analytical equations with an iterative algorithm (Cubas,Villalva), one is purely iterative algorithm (Particle Swarm Optimization). Table 1 show the summary of these techniques

Table 1: Summary of the Parameter Extraction Techniques

Technique	Input	Free Parameters	Extracted Parameters
Cubas [12]	(I_{sc}, V_{oc}, I_{mp}, V_{mp}).	n	(I_L, I_o, R_s, R_{sh},).
Villalva [13]		n, I_L=I_{sc}	(I_o, R_s, R_{sh},).
PVLib [14]	(I-V curve, I_{sc}, V_{oc}, I_{mp}, V_{mp}).	-	(I_L, I_o, R_s, R_{sh}, n).
PSO [15]	SDM Equation	-	(I_L, I_o, R_s, R_{sh}, n).

2.3 Data Acquisition

The proposed framework was tested and validated on monocrystalline silicon PERC modules (M6 wafers) spanning 2–9 busbars, totaling ~111 samples. PERC mini modules comprise six full-size cells. Electrical and physical characterization combined I–V curves and EL imaging obtained with a Halm A+A+A+ flasher at a controlled module temperature of 25 °C. All measurements were performed at Fraunhofer CSP under laboratory conditions. The range of busbar configurations enabled a comprehensive assessment of how microcracks and broader cell-crack phenomena influence overall module performance.

3 RESULTS

3.1 Models' Accuracy

Figure 3 compares the absolute P_{mpp} difference (%) for four parameter-fitting techniques applied to PERC modules. All methods perform robustly, with absolute deviations generally at or below ~1%, indicating reliable parameter extraction. Cubas and PVLib achieve the lowest P_{mpp} differences with minimal variability, reflecting high precision and stability. PSO and Villalva show slightly larger deviations and wider spread, with PSO exhibiting a few notable outliers. Despite calibration differences, all four methods reproduce the same crack–parameter trends. Building on these results, Cubas and PVLib deliver the best accuracy on PERC modules; among them, Cubas aligns most closely with the reference R_s values for 5BB at STC [16]. Accordingly, Cubas is selected for the subsequent correlation analysis.

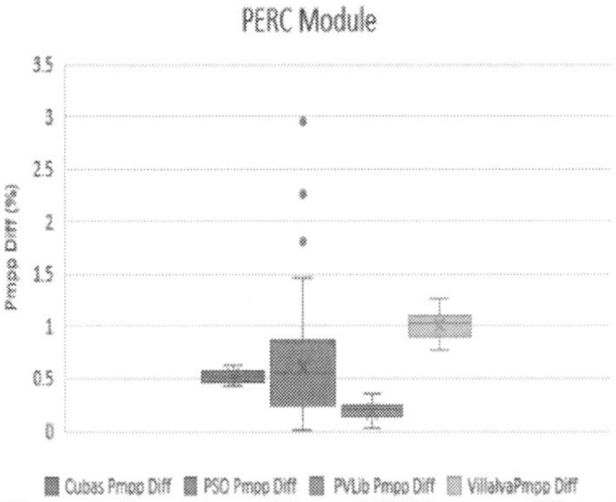

Figure 3: Comparison of Pmpp Diff (%) across different Techniques

3.2 R_s, R_{sh} Corrlation with Crack Length

At 200 W/m², intensity- and temperature-corrected I–V data were evaluated with a focus on R_s and R_{sh}, the parameters most diagnostic of conductive and leakage losses. The crack-free baseline (0 mm) is evident in Figure 4.

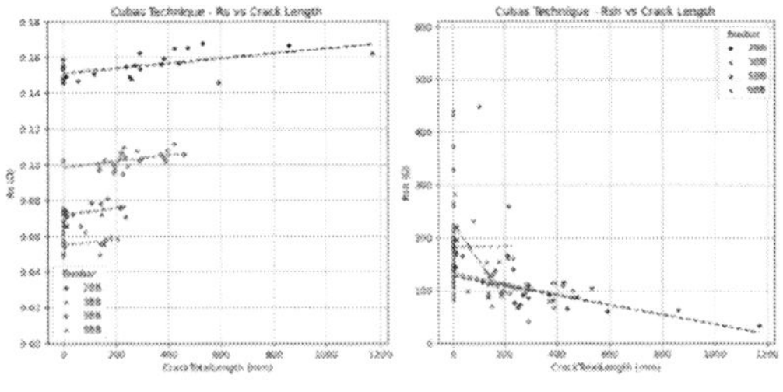

Figure 4: R_s and R_{sh} correlation with Crack Length

The results are unambiguous. Modules with fewer busbars exhibit substantially higher R_s than those with more busbars, confirming the strong inverse dependence on busbar count. Beyond this design effect, R_s shows a modest but consistent uptick with increasing crack length across all configurations, indicating progressively impaired current collection along fractured pathways. Conversely, R_{sh} declines with crack length, reflecting the growth of leakage channels initiated by the cracks. Taken together, the rise in R_s and the drop in R_{sh} at 200 W/m²

10.4229/EUPVSEC2025/3BO.11.2

establish a clear, crack-driven degradation signature that is robust across busbar designs and anchored by the crack-free reference. Quantitatively, the correlation coefficients are +0.54 for R_s and −0.50 for R_{sh}.

3.4 Pmpp Correlation with Crack Length

This observation is further supported by the correlation of P_{mpp} with the crack length in Figure 5 . It was observed that the pwer remains essentially unchanged for crack lengths up to ~400 mm across all busbar configurations, contradicting the direct crack–power relationship previously reported for multicrystalline modules. Beyond this threshold, P_{mpp} declines noticeably with increasing crack length, indicating that only extensive cracking produces measurable power loss. These results underscore that the crack–performance relationship is not strictly linear and is modulated by design factors such as cell architecture and busbar count. Quantitatively, the correlation coefficient between the power and crack length is -0.56.

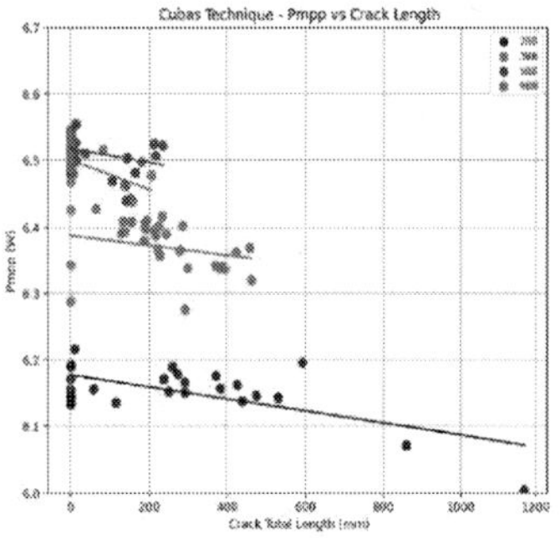

Figure 5: P_{mpp} correlation with Crack Length

4 CONCLUSION

This work establishes a quantitative, image-to-model framework that links EL-derived crack length to single-diode parameters and power loss in PERC modules. Using an OpenCV pipeline for crack metrology and a comparative evaluation of parameter-extraction methods, Cubas was selected for correlation analysis based on its accuracy and stability. The results at 200 W/m² show a consistent degradation signature: R_s rises with crack length and is systematically higher for lower busbar counts, while R_{sh} declines, evidencing enhanced leakage; correspondingly, P_{mpp} remains effectively unchanged up to ~400 mm of total crack length and then decreases with further cracking. These findings challenge simple crack-count/length heuristics and demonstrate that performance impact depends on both crack extent and design choices such as busbar number, providing a defensible basis for screening, valuation, and design optimization of cracked modules. Future work should extend this approach beyond controlled laboratory conditions to fielded systems and additional cell architectures to test generality and refine decision thresholds.

5 REFERENCES

[1] S.-T. Hsu, Y.-S. Long og Y.-T. Li, "Characterization of solar cells in transportation," in 2014 IEEE 40th Photovoltaic Specialist Conference (PVSC), Denver, CO, USA, 2014, s. 2592–2594.

[2] X. Gou, X. Li, S. Wang, H. Zhuang, X. Huang og L. Jiang, "The Effect of Microcrack Length in Silicon Cells on the Potential Induced Degradation Behavior," International Journal of Photoenergy, vol. 2018, s. 1–6, 2018. [Online] Hentet fra: doi:10.1155/2018/4381579.

[3] B. Jaeckel, M. Pander, P. Schenk, A. Linsenmeyer og J. Kirch, "Nomenclature and description of Electro-Luminescence (EL) observations: cell cracks and other observations," EPJ Photovolt., vol. 15, s. 44, 2024. [Online] Hentet fra: doi:10.1051/epjpv/2024039.

[4] S. Kajari-Schröder, I. Kunze, U. Eitner og M. Köntges, "Spatial and orientational distribution of cracks in crystalline photovoltaic modules generated by mechanical load tests," Solar Energy Materials and Solar Cells, vol. 95, nr. 11, s. 3054–3059, 2011. [Online] Hentet fra: doi:10.1016/j.solmat.2011.06.032.

[5] M. Köntges, S. Kajari-Schröder, I. Kunze, U. Jahn, "CRACK STATISTIC OF CRYSTALLINE SILICON PHOTOVOLTAIC MODULE," Solar Energy Materials and Solar Cells, vol. 95, nr. 11, s. 3054–3059, 2011. [Online] Hentet fra: doi:10.1016/j.solmat.2011.06.032.

[6] M. Sander, S. Dietrich, M. Pander, M. Ebert og J. Bagdahn, "Systematic investigation of cracks in encapsulated solar cells after mechanical loading," Solar Energy Materials and Solar Cells, vol. 111, s. 82–89, 2013. [Online] Hentet fra: doi:10.1016/j.solmat.2012.12.031.

[7] M. Köntges, I. Kunze, S. Kajari-Schröder, X. Breitenmoser og B. Bjørneklett, "The risk of power loss in crystalline silicon based photovoltaic modules due to micro-cracks," Solar Energy Materials and Solar Cells, vol. 95, nr. 4, s. 1131–1137, 2011. [Online] Hentet fra: doi:10.1016/j.solmat.2010.10.034.

[8] M. Köntges, I. Kunze, S.Kajari-Schröder, X. Breitenmoser, B. Bjørneklett, "Quantifying the risk of power loss in PV modules due to micro cracks," 2010.

[9] S. Hassan og M. Dhimish, "Broad-scale Electroluminescence analysis of 5 million+ photovoltaic cells for defect detection and degradation assessment," Renewable Energy, vol. 237, s. 121868, 2024. [Online] Hentet fra: doi:10.1016/j.renene.2024.121868.

[10] A. Morlier, F. Haase og M. Kontges, "Impact of cracks in multicrystalline silicon solar cells on PV module power - A simulation study based on field data," in 2015 IEEE 42nd Photovoltaic Specialist Conference (PVSC), New Orleans, LA, 2015, s. 1–3.

[11] A. Hashem, S. Mortazavifar og R. Gottschalg, "Impact of Modern Cell Photovoltaic Geometries on Power and Energy Loss due to Cell Cracks," (på en), 41st European Photovoltaic Solar Energy Conference and Exhibition, 2024. [Online] Hentet fra: doi:10.4229/EUPVSEC2024/3AV.2.5.

[12] J. Cubas, S. Pindado og M. Victoria, "On the analytical approach for modeling photovoltaic systems behavior," Journal of Power Sources, vol. 247, s. 467–474,

2014. [Online] Hentet fra: doi:10.1016/j.jpowsour.2013.09.008.

[13] M. G. Villalva, J. R. Gazoli og E. R. Filho, "Comprehensive Approach to Modeling and Simulation of Photovoltaic Arrays," IEEE Trans. Power Electron., vol. 24, nr. 5, s. 1198–1208, 2009. [Online] Hentet fra: doi:10.1109/TPEL.2009.2013862.

[14] C. Birk Jones Clifford W. Hansen, "Single Diode Parameter Extraction from In-Field Photovoltaic I-V Curves on a Single Board Computer," 2019.

[15] J. Kennedy og R. Eberhart, "Particle swarm optimization," in Proceedings of ICNN'95 - International Conference on Neural Networks, Perth, WA, Australia, 1995, s. 1942–1948.

[16] T, Dullweber, C. Kranz, R. Peibst, U. Baumann, H. Hannebauer, M.Kutzer, M. Müller, G. Fischer, P. Palinginis & H. Neuhaus, "The PERC+ cell: More output power for less aluminium paste,"

Fraunhofer CSP | HOCHSCHULE ANHALT University of Applied Sciences

Investigating the Impact of Cell Cracks on Power Loss and its Correlation with the Modelling Parameters

Ahmad Hashem[1,2], Zonghan Jiang[1] , Guido Willers[2] , Leila Mortazavifar[1,2] , Bengt Jaeckel [1,2] Ralph Gottschalg[1,2]

[1] **Hochschule Anhalt University of Applied Sciences**

[2] **Fraunhofer Center for Crystalline Silicon Photovoltaics CSP**

E-mail: ahmad.hashem@hs-anhalt.de
ahmad.hashem@imws.Fraunhofer.de

|Ahmad Hashem

Motivation

- Can cell cracks be mitigated ?
- Do cracks always cause power loss?
- Correlation between line cracks & Performance.
- Cell Tech Matters !

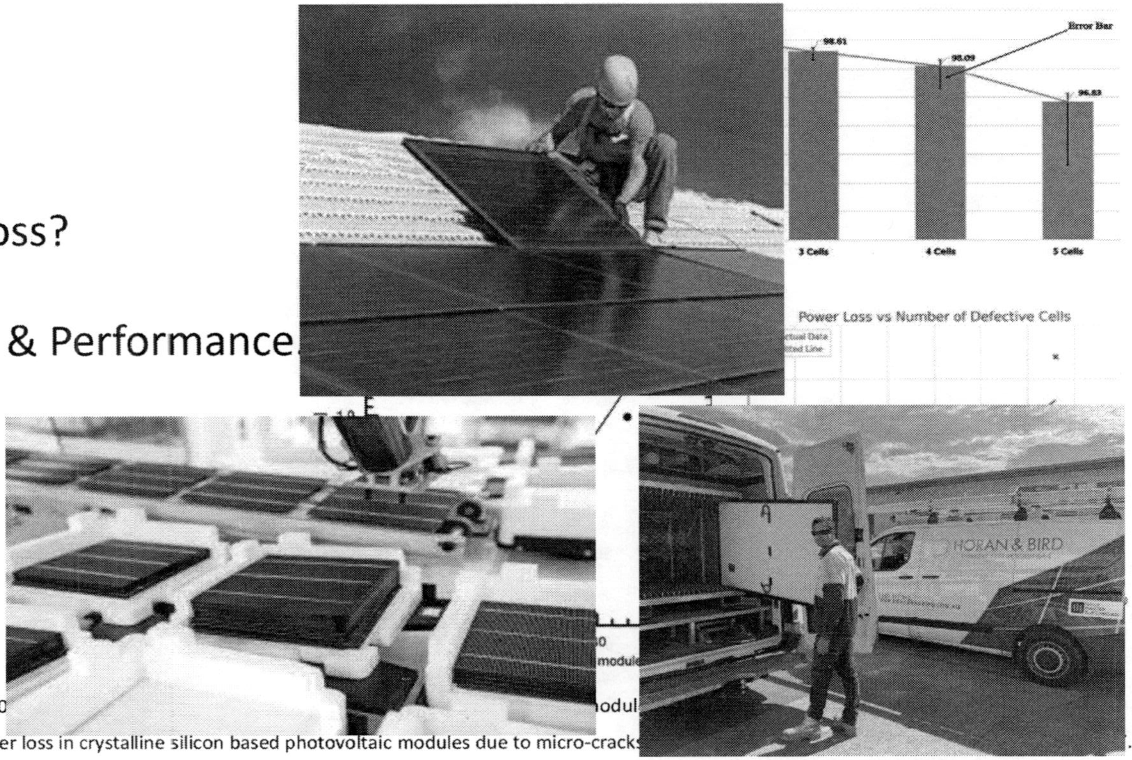

Dhimish, M., Holmes, V., Dales, M., Mather, P., Sibley, M., Chong, B., & Zhang, L. (20 … odul

Köntges, M., Kunze, I., Kajari-Schröder, S., Breitenmoser, X., (2011). The risk of power loss in crystalline silicon based photovoltaic modules due to micro-cracks …

Hassan, S., & Dhimish, M. (2024). Broad-scale Electroluminescence analysis of 5 million+ photovoltaic cells for defect detection and degradation assessment. *Renewable Energy*, *237*, 121868.

|Ahmad Hashem

Motivation

- By 2034, only 10% of the market share is expected to be covered by 12 busbar or less

- The Shift will be towards M10 & G12 Wafers !

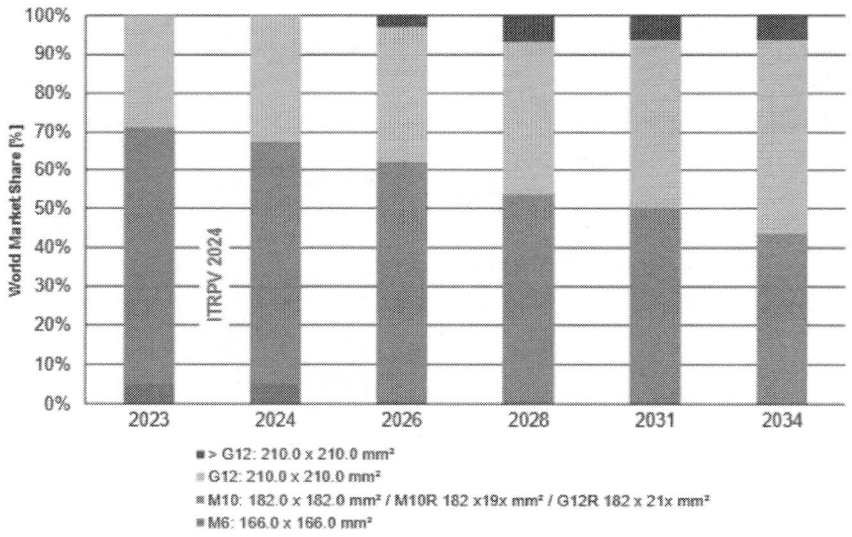

* International Technology Roadmap for Photovoltaics (ITRPV) 2023 Results

|Ahmad Hashem

Fraunhofer CSP | HOCHSCHULE ANHALT University of Applied Sciences

Study Aim

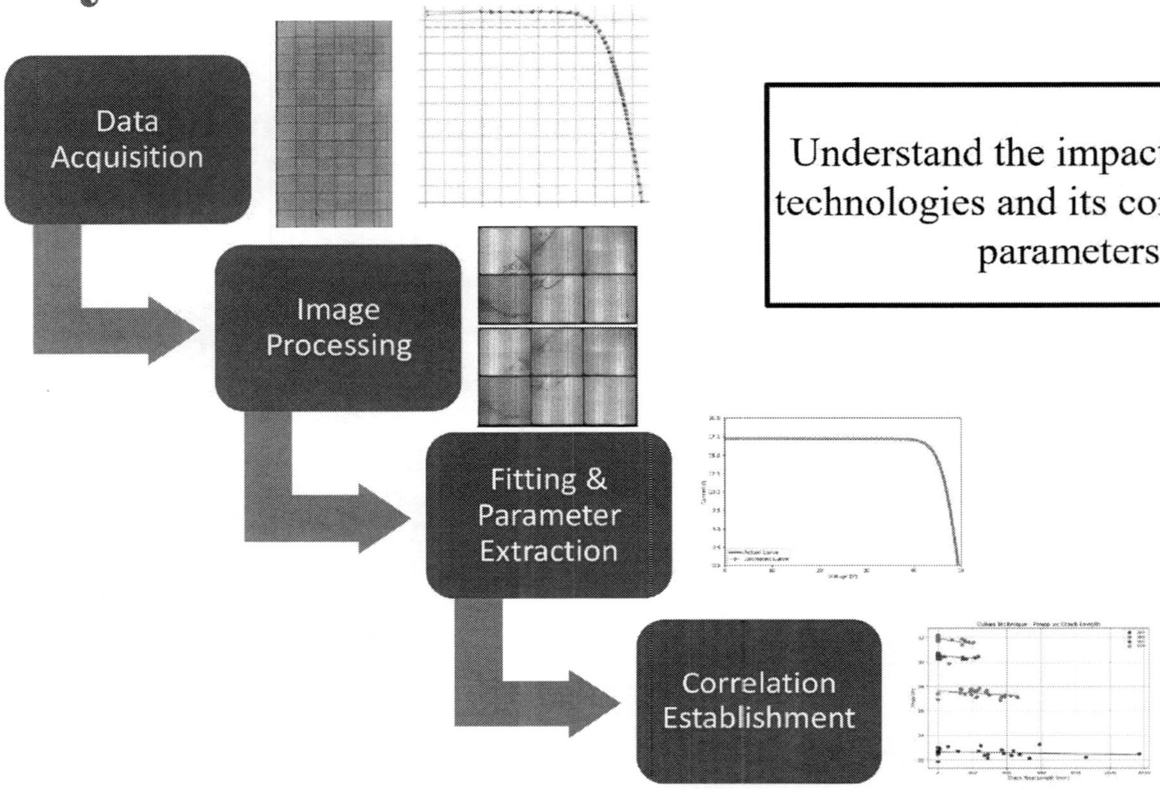

Understand the impact of cracks on different cell technologies and its correlation with the modelling parameters and power loss

|Ahmad Hashem

Fraunhofer CSP | HOCHSCHULE ANHALT University of Applied Sciences

Data Acquisition

- A Halm A+A+A+ flasher system was employed.
- Flash test were performed at 1000 & 200 W/m² & Constant Temp of 25°C
- M6 Mono-Si PERC & TopCon Modules → Total ~230 Sample
- PERC Modules covered 2-9 BB count.
- TopCon Modules covered 2-12 BB count.

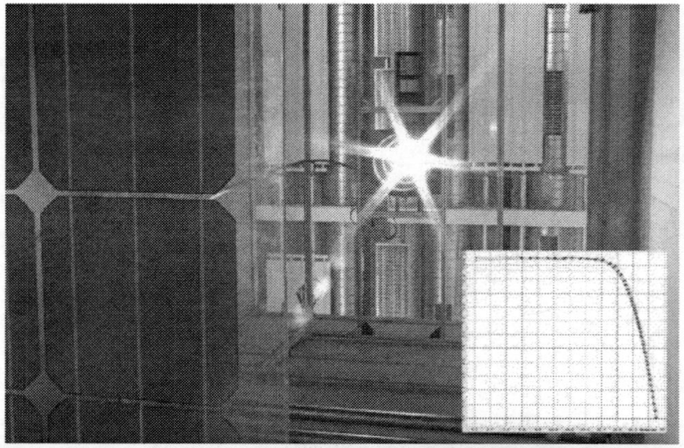

|Ahmad Hashem

Fraunhofer CSP | HOCHSCHULE ANHALT University of Applied Sciences

Image Processing

- OpenCV- based algorithm were used.
- Perspective transformation is applied using the module's outer contour and user-provided real-world dimension.
- Standard cell matrix is constructed to determine the pixel dimensions of each cell.
- Busbars are located and removed to reduce noise.
- Cracks are detected and skeletonized to single-pixel paths; lengths are converted from pixels to real units (mm).

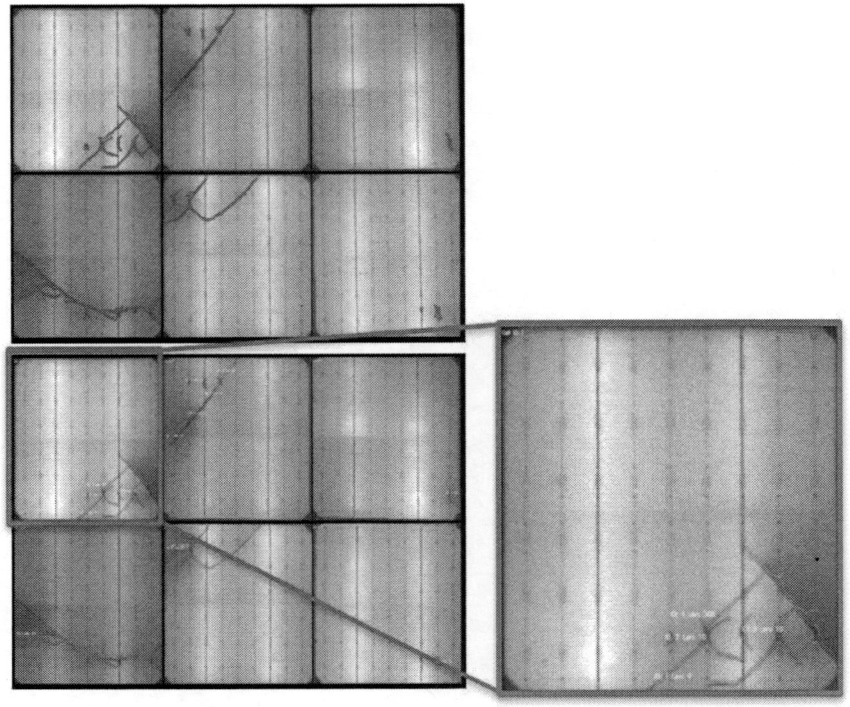

|Ahmad Hashem

Fraunhofer CSP | HOCHSCHULE ANHALT University of Applied Sciences

Fitting & Parameters Extraction

- Single Diode Model is widely used for PV modelling due to its accuracy and simplicity.
- The focus will be on the P_{mpp}, R_s, R_{sh}

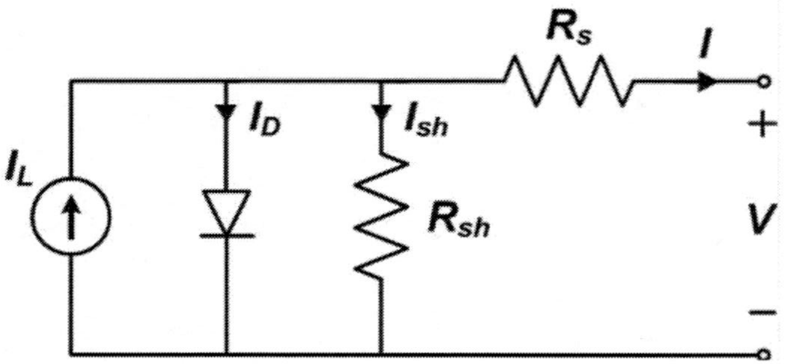

Single Diode Model Equivalent Circuit

$$I = I_L - I_o\left[\exp\left[\frac{V + IR_s}{nN_sV_t}\right] - 1\right] - \frac{V + IR_s}{R_{sh}}$$

Fit → Extract → Replot → P_{mpp} Calculation

|Ahmad Hashem

Fraunhofer CSP

HOCHSCHULE ANHALT University of Applied Sciences

Fitting & Parameters Extraction

- **PVLib (Analytical)**

→ The linear region of the curve is fitted using a linear regression model (β_0, β_1)

→ Linear fit is removed from the current to isolate the pure exponential behavior of the diode

→ Residual is then linearized by taking its natural logarithm, and a simple least-squares regression of the log-transformed data against voltage and current returns two new coefficients (β_3, β_4).

→ Goodness-of-fit criterion : R^2 (0.99)

* C. Birk Jones Clifford W. Hansen, "Single Diode Parameter Extraction from In-Field Photovoltaic I-V Curves on a Single Board Computer," 2019.

|Ahmad Hashem

Fraunhofer CSP

HOCHSCHULE ANHALT University of Applied Sciences

Fitting & Parameters Extraction

Cubas Technique (Analytical + Iterative) → Ideality Factor ‘n’ is set Free

→ Goodness-of-fit criterion : R^2 (0.98-0.99)

$R_{start} = 0$

$$\frac{aV_T V_{mp}(2I_{mp} - I_{sc})}{(V_{mp}I_{sc} + V_{oc}(I_{mp} - I_{sc}))(V_{mp} - I_{mp}R_s) - aV_T(V_{mp}I_{sc} - V_{oc}I_{mp})} = \exp\left(\frac{V_{mp} + I_{mp}R_s - V_{oc}}{aV_T}\right).$$

$$R_{sh} = \frac{(V_{mp} - I_{mp}R_s)(V_{mp} - R_s(I_{sc} - I_{mp}) - aV_T)}{(V_{mp} - I_{mp}R_s)(I_{sc} - I_{mp}) - aV_T I_{mp}}.$$

$$I_{pv} = \frac{R_{sh} + R_s}{R_{sh}} I_{sc}.$$

$$I_0 = \frac{(R_{sh} + R_s)I_{sc} - V_{oc}}{R_{sh}\exp\left(\frac{V_{oc}}{aV_T}\right)}$$

* J. Cubas, S. Pindado og M. Victoria, “On the analytical approach for modeling photovoltaic systems behavior,” Journal of Power Sources, vol. 247, s. 467–474, 2014. [Online] Hentet fra: doi:10.1016/j.jpowsour.2013.09.008.

|Ahmad Hashem

Fraunhofer CSP | HOCHSCHULE ANHALT University of Applied Sciences

Fitting & Parameters Extraction

Villalva Technique (Analytical + Iterative)

→ Ideality Factor 'n' is set Free

→ $I_{ph} \approx I_{sc}$

$$I_o = \frac{I_{sc}}{exp(\frac{V_{oc}}{a\,V_t})} - 1$$

a=n*Ns

→ Iteratively tune R_s start from 0 → 1 (step 0.0025) then compute R_{sh} until the model's P–V peak equals the measured

→ Goodness-of-fit criterion : R^2 (0.91)

$$R_{sh} = \frac{V_{mp}(V_{mp} + I_{mp}\,R_s)}{V_{mp}I_{ph} - V_{mp}I_o \exp\left(\frac{(V_{mp}+I_{mp}R_s)}{N_s a V_t}\right) + V_{mp}I_o - P_{max,m}}$$

* M. G. Villalva, J. R. Gazoli og E. R. Filho, "Comprehensive Approach to Modeling and Simulation of Photovoltaic Arrays," IEEE Trans. Power Electron., vol. 24, nr. 5, s. 1198–1208, 2009. [Online] Hentet fra: doi:10.1109/TPEL.2009.2013862.

|Ahmad Hashem

Fraunhofer CSP

HOCHSCHULE ANHALT University of Applied Sciences

Fitting & Parameters Extraction

Particle Swarm Optimization (Iterative)

→The single-diode model equation is used as the PSO objective

→ A current for a given voltage is to be calculated I(V) !

→ Goodness-of-fit criterion : Root-Mean-Square error →5e-3

→ Stopping Criteria: Objective change less than 10e-12

Parameter	Lower-Bound	Upper-Bound
I_{ph} (A)	0	2* I_{sc}
I_o(A)	10e-4	10e-15
R_s(Ω)	0	1
R_{sh}(Ω)	10	1000
n	1	2

* J. Kennedy og R. Eberhart, "Particle swarm optimization," in Proceedings of ICNN'95 - International Conference on Neural Networks, Perth, WA, Australia, 1995, s. 1942–1948.

|Ahmad Hashem

Fraunhofer CSP | HOCHSCHULE ANHALT University of Applied Sciences

Cracks Scenario

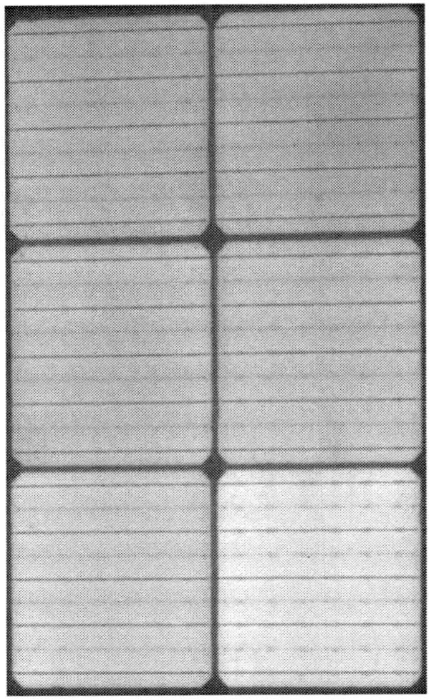

Crack-Free Module

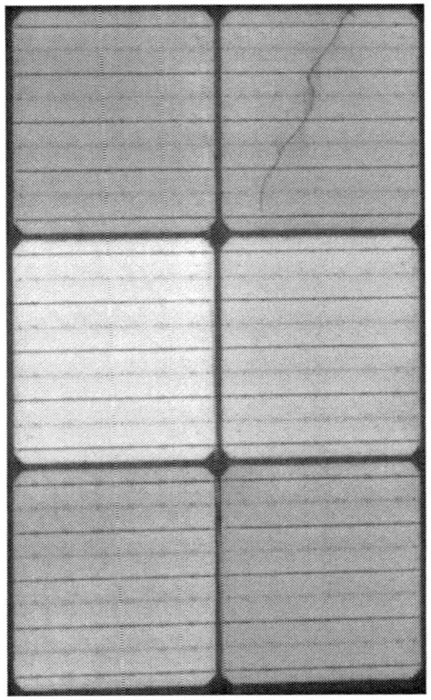

Module with 1-cell crack

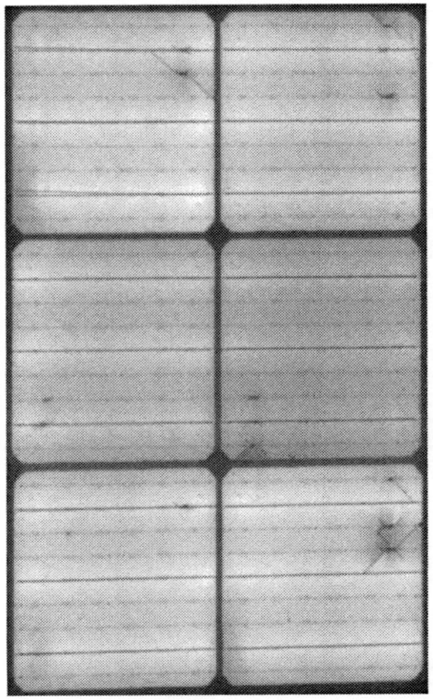

Module with multi-cell cracks

|Ahmad Hashem

Models' Accuracy

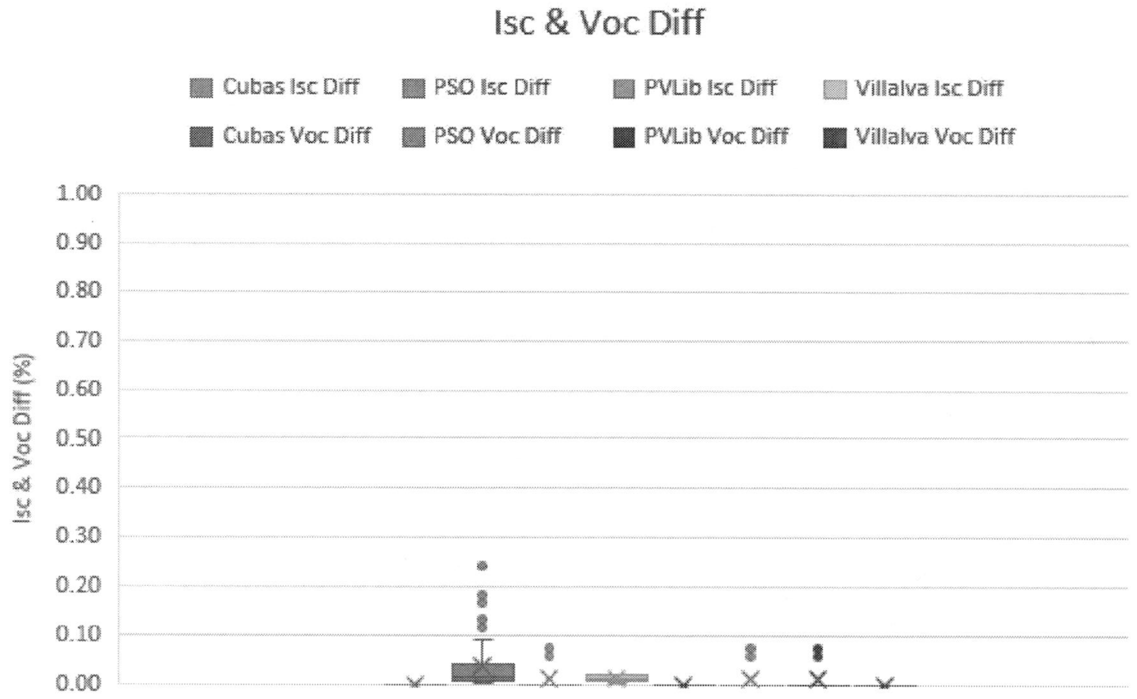

|Ahmad Hashem

Models' Accuracy

- Cubas & PVLib achieves the best accuracy %.
- Cubas has closer agreement to $R_{s,ref}$
- R_{sh} is strongly dependent on R_s in PVLib model.

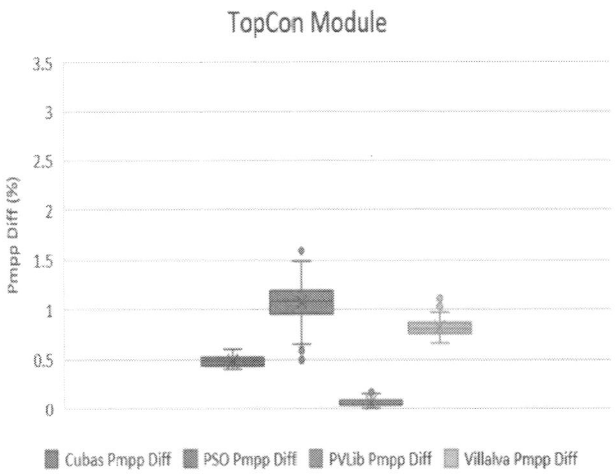

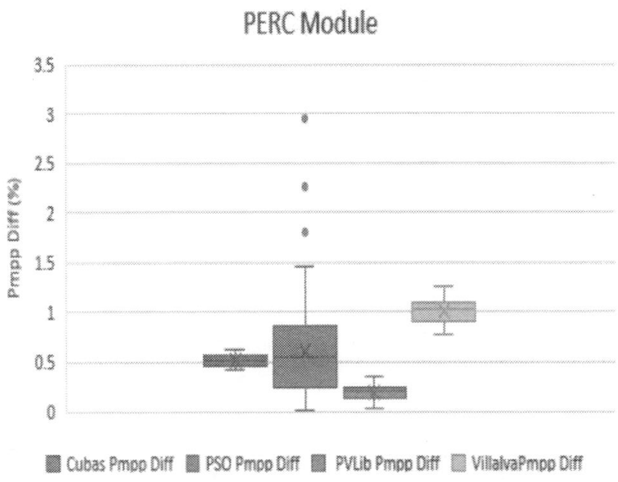

Comparison of Absolute Pmpp Estimation using Different Models

All Models Have the same trend for P_{mpp} , R_s , R_{sh} !!

|Ahmad Hashem

PERC Simulations

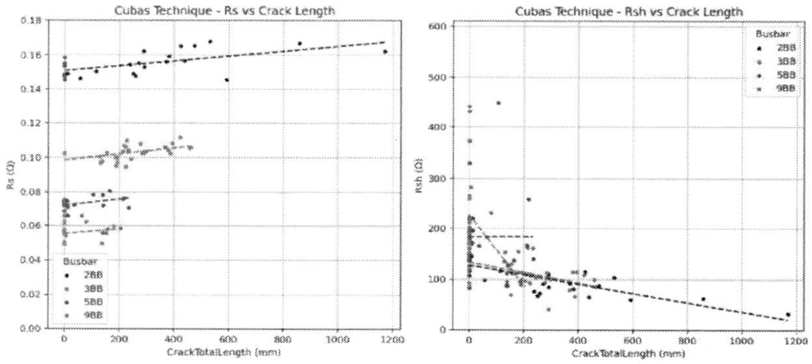

R_s and R_{sh} vs Crack Length for PERC at 200 W/m²

	Correlation Coefficient
R_{sh}	-0.5
R_s	0.54

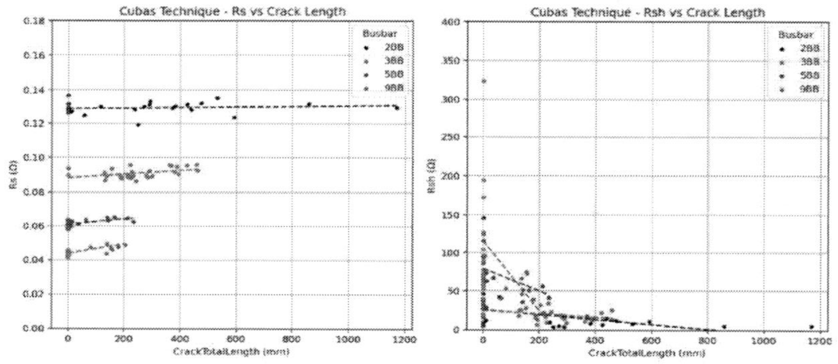

R_s and R_{sh} vs Crack Length for PERC at 1000 W/m²

	Correlation Coefficient
R_{sh}	-0.31
R_s	0.43

|Ahmad Hashem

PERC Simulations

Cracks ≤ 400 mm show no measurable impact on P_{mpp} under the tested conditions

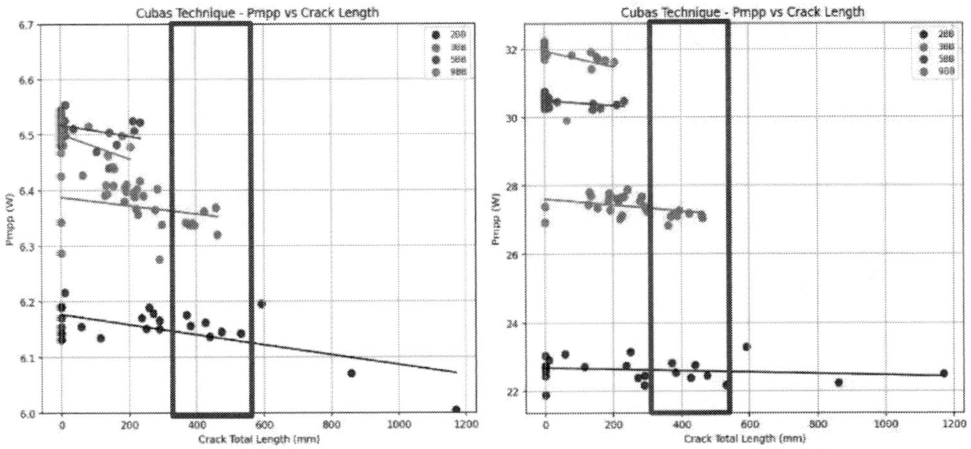

P_{mpp} vs Crack Length 200 W/m² (Left), 1000 W/m² (Right)

	Correlation Coefficient
P_{mpp} (200 W/m2)	-0.56
P_{mpp} (1000 W/m2)	-0.43

|Ahmad Hashem

Fraunhofer CSP | HOCHSCHULE ANHALT University of Applied Sciences

TopCon Simulations

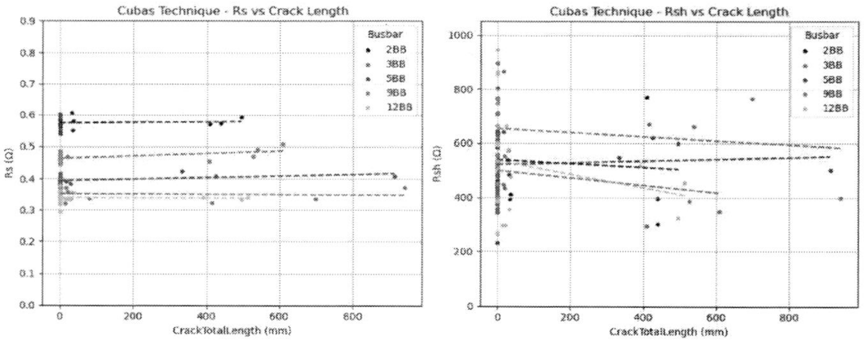

R_s and R_{sh} vs Crack Length for TopCon at 200 W/m²

	Correlation Coefficient
R_{sh}	-0.08
R_s	0.01

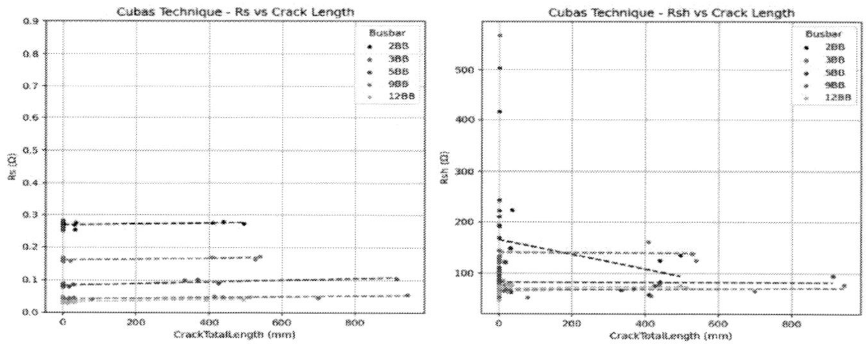

R_s and R_{sh} vs Crack Length for TopCon at 1000 W/m²

	Correlation Coefficient
R_{sh}	-0.07
R_s	0.01

|Ahmad Hashem

TopCon Simulations

Shorter crack coverage (~800 vs ~1200 mm) + TopCon design gains ⇒ no Pmpp–crack correlation.

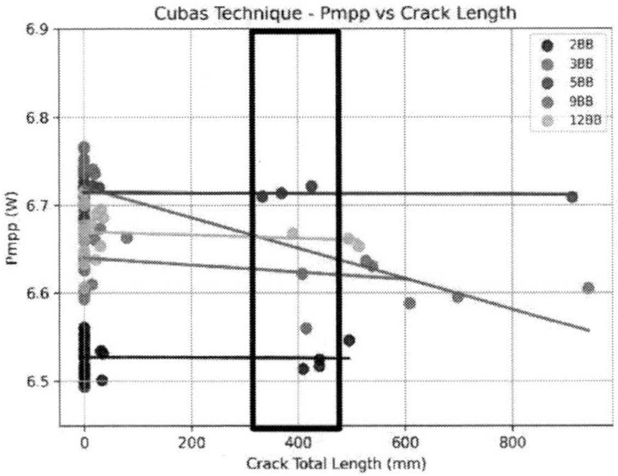

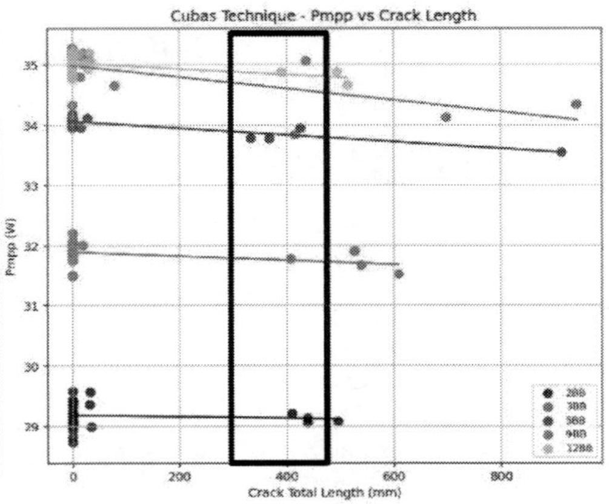

P_{mpp} vs Crack Length 200 W/m² (Left), 1000 W/m² (Right)

	Correlation Coefficient
P_{mpp} (200 W/m2)	-0.12
P_{mpp} (1000 W/m2)	-0.02

→ Crack length ≠ Power Loss !!

|Ahmad Hashem

Fraunhofer CSP | HOCHSCHULE ANHALT University of Applied Sciences

Key Takeaways

- Framework for analysing the correlation between crack , modelling parameters & Power Loss.
- Crack length alone is a poor predictor of power loss.
- There is no clear correlation between crack length , modelling parameters & Power loss
  - → **Cell Tech, BB, crack location, Irradiance Level**
- Negligible P_{loss} for TopCon Modules compared to PERC for the same crack ranges (up to 800mm).
- Cracks ≤ 400 mm show no measurable impact on P_{mpp} under all tested conditions.
- **Future Work →** Comparison of cracks impact on modules with larger wafers & longer crack lengths.

|Ahmad Hashem

Fraunhofer CSP

HOCHSCHULE ANHALT University of Applied Sciences

Acknowledgment

The authors gratefully acknowledge the financial support by the German Federal Ministry for Economic Affairs and Climate Action (BMWK)of the project **"PV-Riss"** with grant #03TN0033A.

Gefördert durch:

Bundesministerium für Wirtschaft und Klimaschutz

aufgrund eines Beschlusses des Deutschen Bundestages

|Ahmad Hashem

Fraunhofer CSP | HOCHSCHULE ANHALT University of Applied Sciences

Thank you for your attention ☺

Photovoltaic Researcher/ PhD Candidate:
Email: Ahmad.Hashem@hs-anhalt.de
Tel: +4915560074802

|Ahmad Hashem

Fraunhofer CSP | HOCHSCHULE ANHALT University of Applied Sciences

PVLib Implementation

$$I = \frac{I_L}{1+G_pR_s} - \frac{G_pV}{1+G_pR_s} - \frac{I_0}{1+G_pR_s}(\exp(\frac{V+IR_s}{nN_sV_{th}}) - 1)$$

- Linear portion is defined V≤ vlim * Voc
- Fit the Linear Portion with a line

$$I \approx \frac{I_L}{1+G_pR_s} - \frac{G_p}{1+G_pR_s}V = \beta_0 + \beta_1 V$$

The exponential portion of the IV curve is defined by $\beta_0 + \beta_1 \times V - I > ilim \times i_{sc}$. Over this portion of the curve, $\exp((V+IR_s)/nN_sV_{th}) \gg 1$ so that

Fit the exponential portion of the IV curve.

$$\log(\beta_0 - \beta_1 V - I) \approx \log(\frac{I_0}{1+G_pR_s}) + \frac{V}{nN_sV_{th}} + \frac{IR_s}{nN_sV_{th}} = \beta_2 + \beta_3 V + \beta_4 I$$

|Ahmad Hashem

Fraunhofer CSP | HOCHSCHULE ANHALT University of Applied Sciences

n-Value

- Optimization to calculate the Ideality factor ‘n’.
- n-Value < 1 for improved fitting !
- Associated reduction in goodness-of-fit for these n values was negligible.

Module Type & Irradiance	Cubas	Villalva
PERC (200 W/m^2)	1	0.94
PERC (1000 W/m^2)	1.3	0.9
TopCon (200 W/m^2)	1	1.05
TopCon (1000 W/m^2)	1.38	1

|Ahmad Hashem

PVLib vs Cubas (TopCon)

200 W/m2

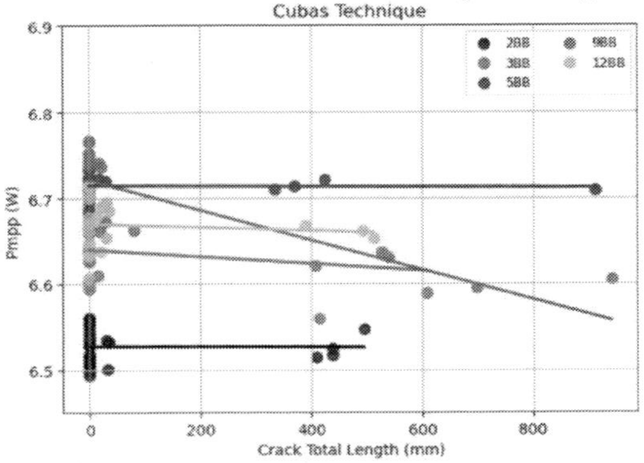

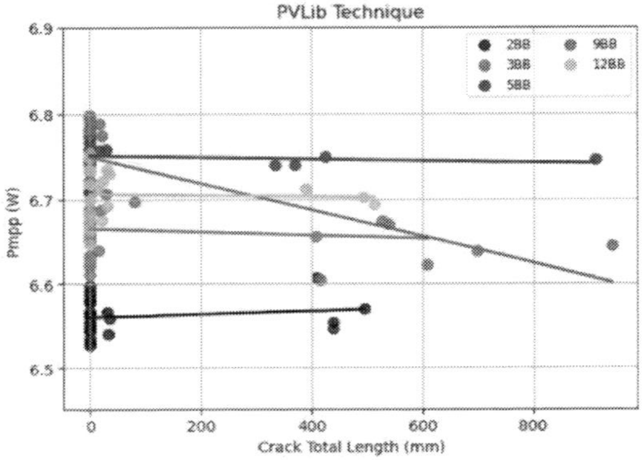

1000 W/m2

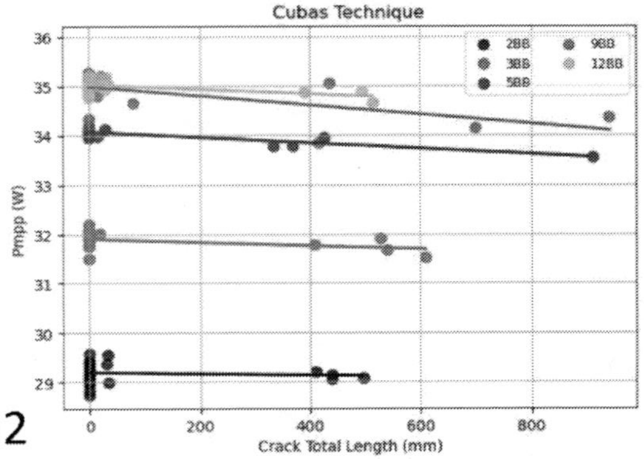

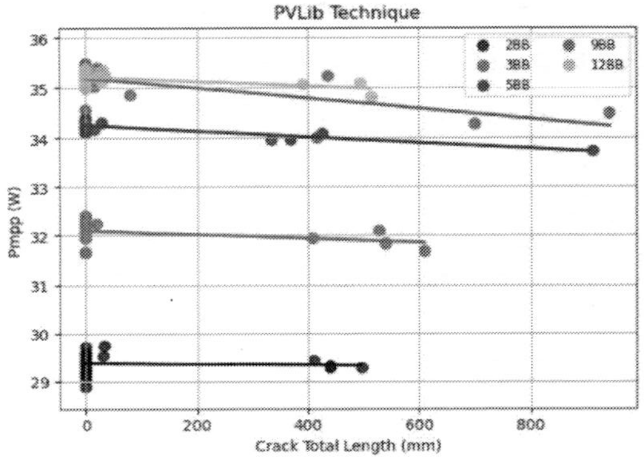

|Ahmad Hashem

PVLib vs Cubas (PERC)

200 W/m2

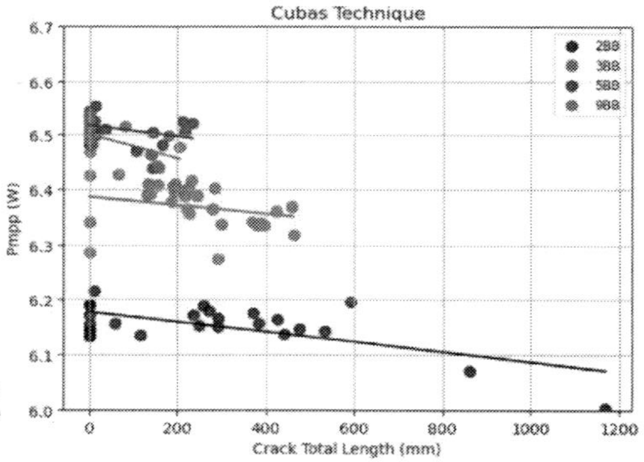

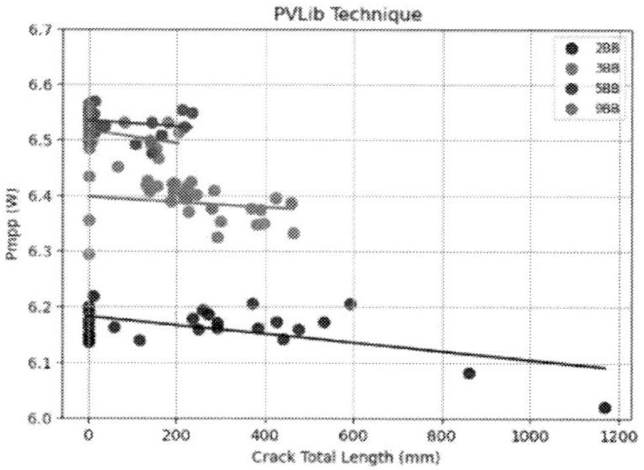

1000 W/m2

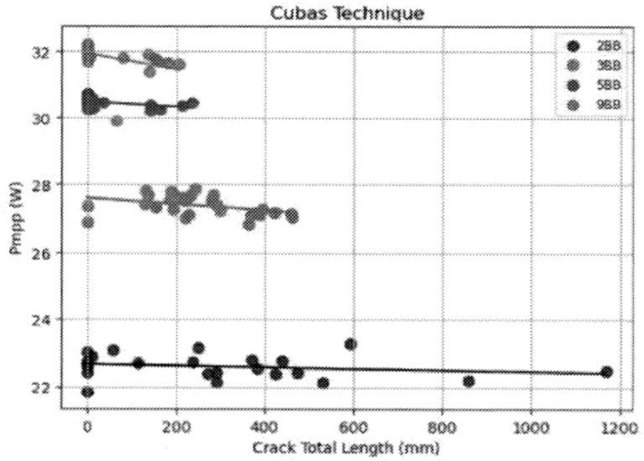

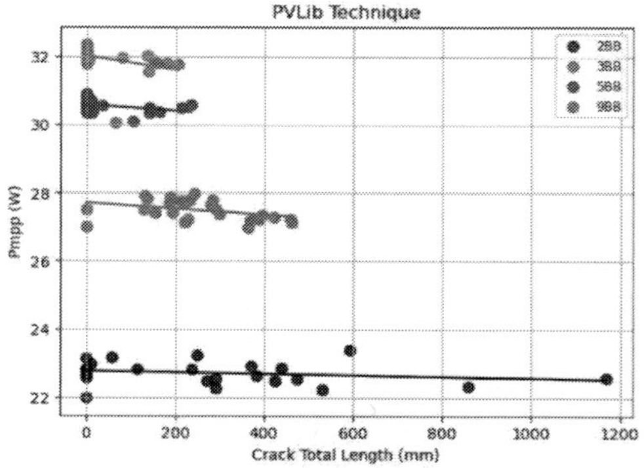

|Ahmad Hashem

PSO Examples

IV_PVRISSVZ0914_240422160144.csv
Fit Curve
Current (I)
Voltage (V)

IV_PVRISSVZ0321_240424165725.csv
Fit Curve
Current (I)
Voltage (V)

IV_PVRISSVZ0510_240424141038.csv
Fit Curve
Current (I)
Voltage (V)

IV_PVRISSVZ0219_240425145950.csv
Fit Curve
Current (I)
Voltage (V)

RMSE

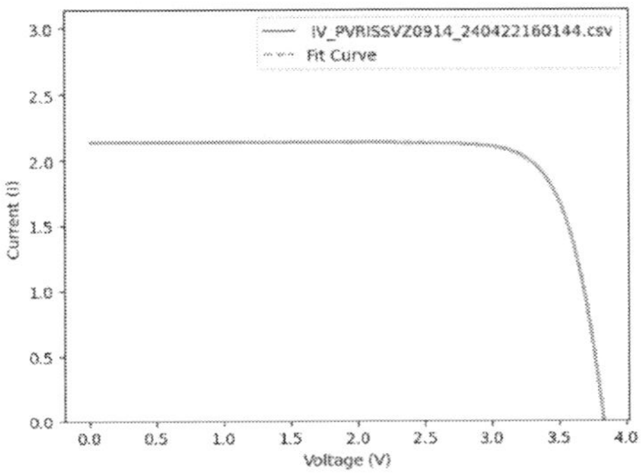

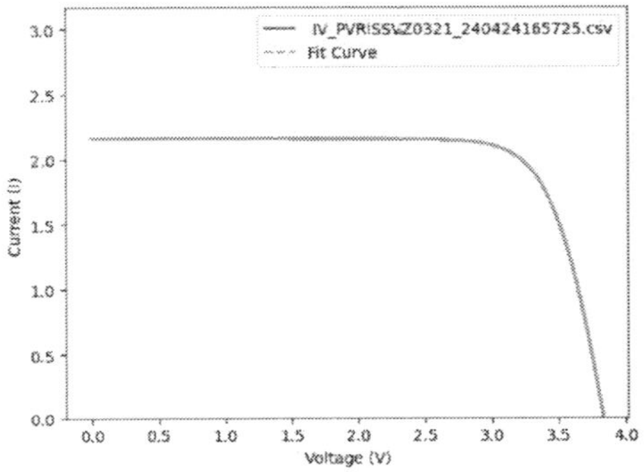

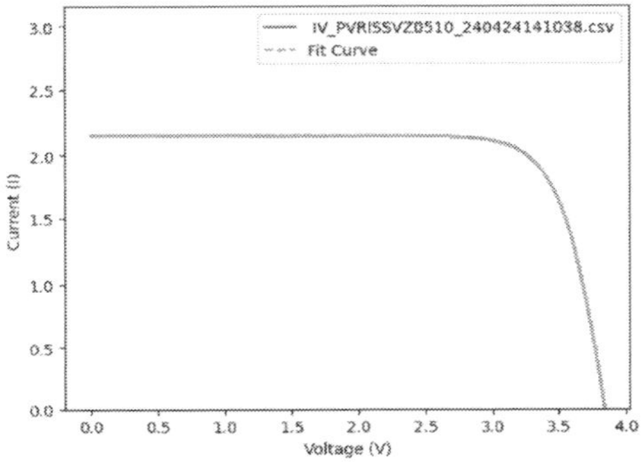

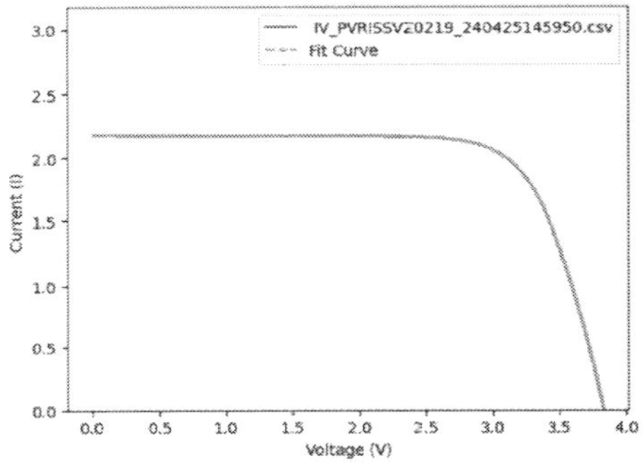

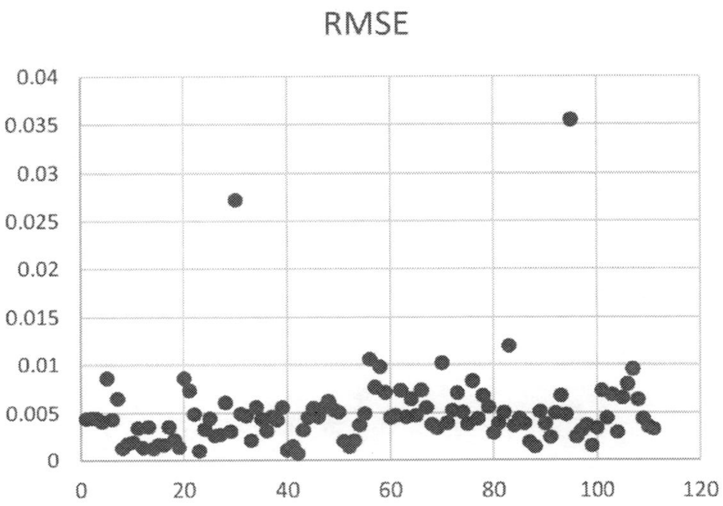

|Ahmad Hashem

Fitting Examples

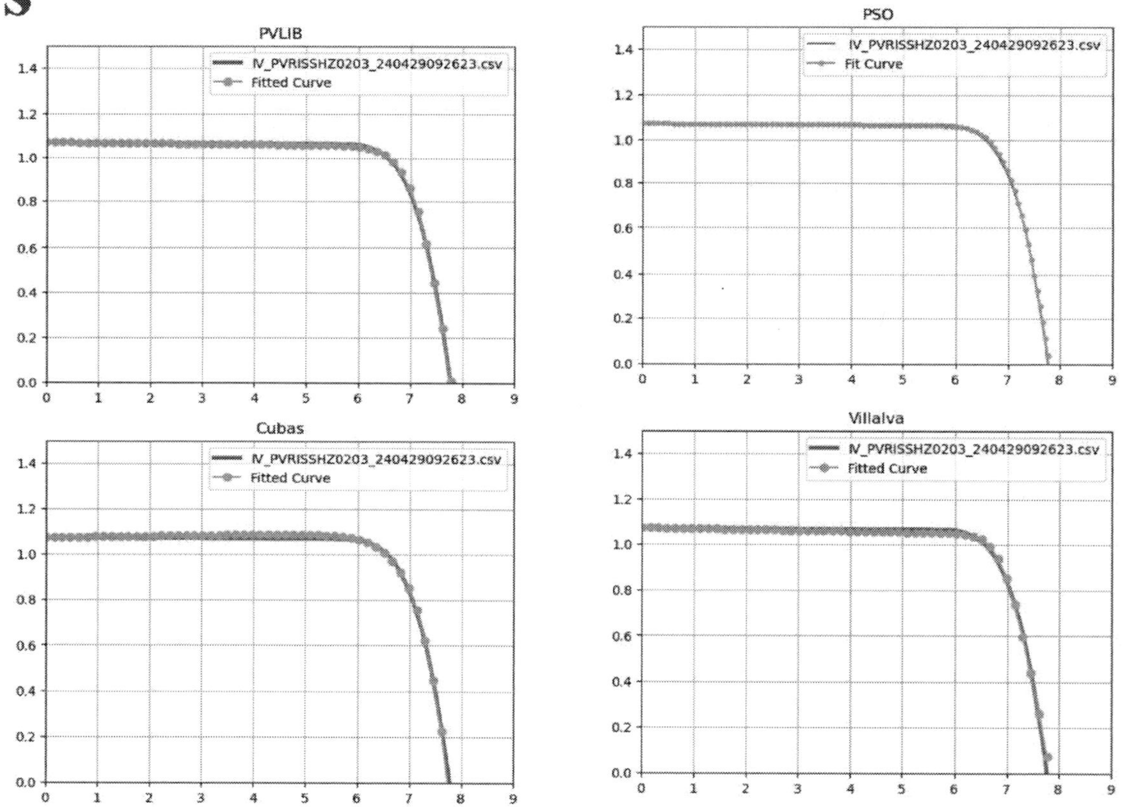

|Ahmad Hashem

Fraunhofer CSP | HOCHSCHULE ANHALT University of Applied Sciences

2-Curves Method

- Series resistance (R_s) from the Voc-region slopes:

$$R_s = \frac{R_1^s G_1 - R_2^s G_2}{G_1 - G_2}.$$

- Shunt resistance (R_{sh}) from the Isc-region slopes:

$$R_{sh} = \frac{R_1^{sh} G_1 - R_2^{sh} G_2}{G_1 - G_2}.$$

|Ahmad Hashem

Series Resistance Rs by Bus-bar Count (PERC 200W/m2)

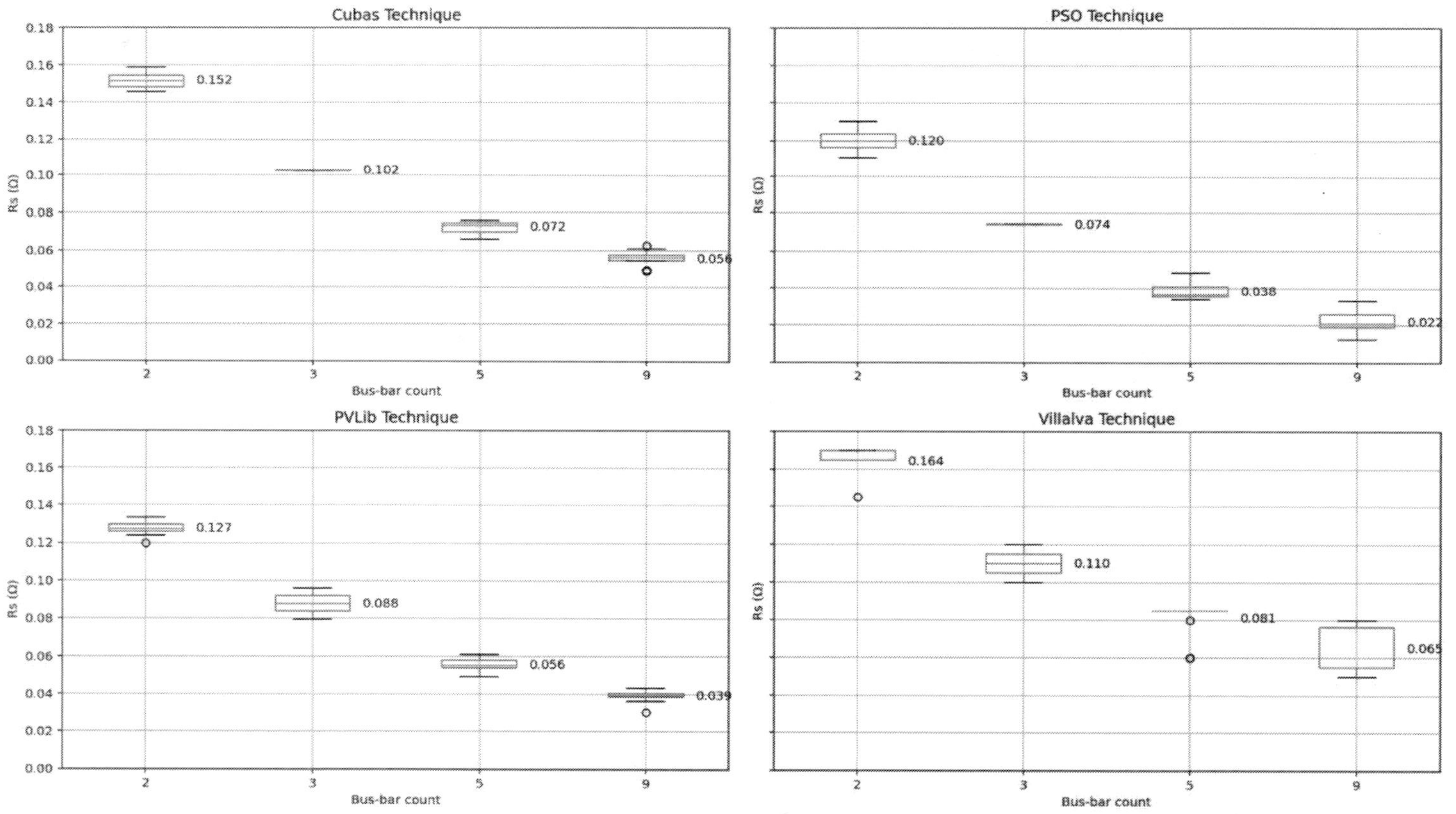

23.09.2025

42nd European Photovoltaic Solar Energy Conference & Exhibition , Bilbao , Spain

|Ahmad Hashem

Shunt Resistance Rsh by Bus-bar Count (PERC 200W/m2)

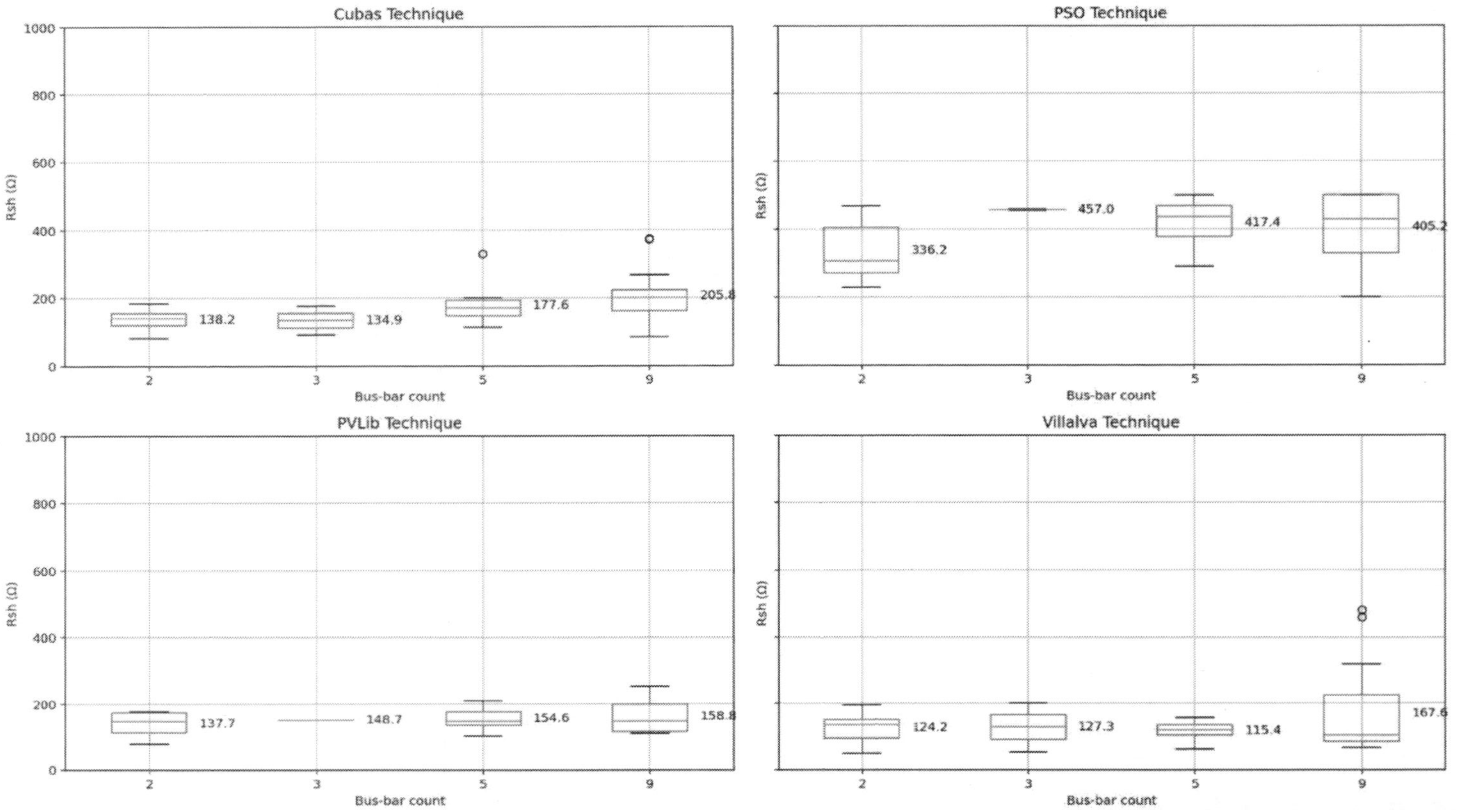

Ahmad Hashem

Fraunhofer CSP

HOCHSCHULE ANHALT University of Applied Sciences

Series Resistance Rs by Bus-bar Count (PERC 1000W/m2)

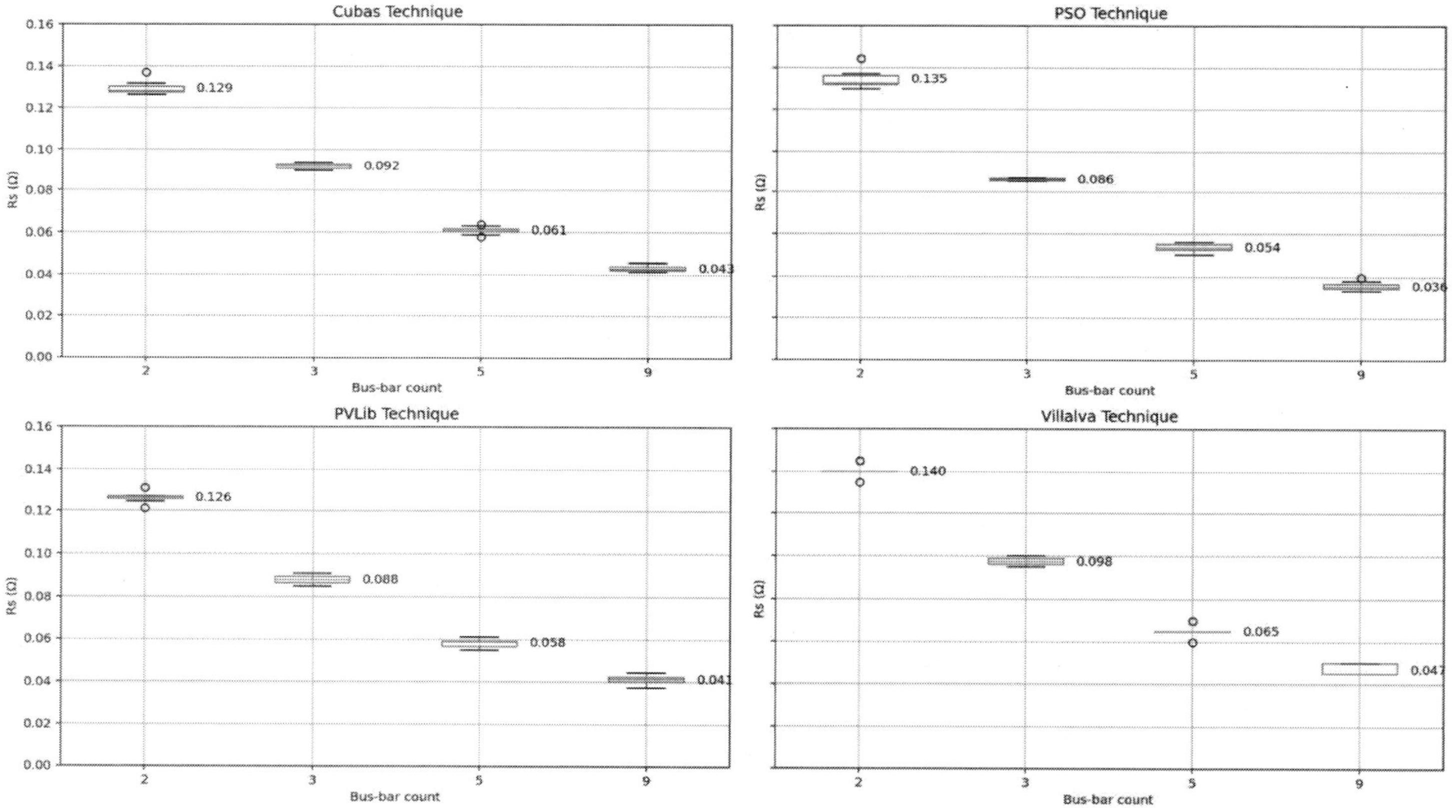

|Ahmad Hashem

Shunt Resistance Rsh by Bus-bar Count (PERC 1000W/m2)

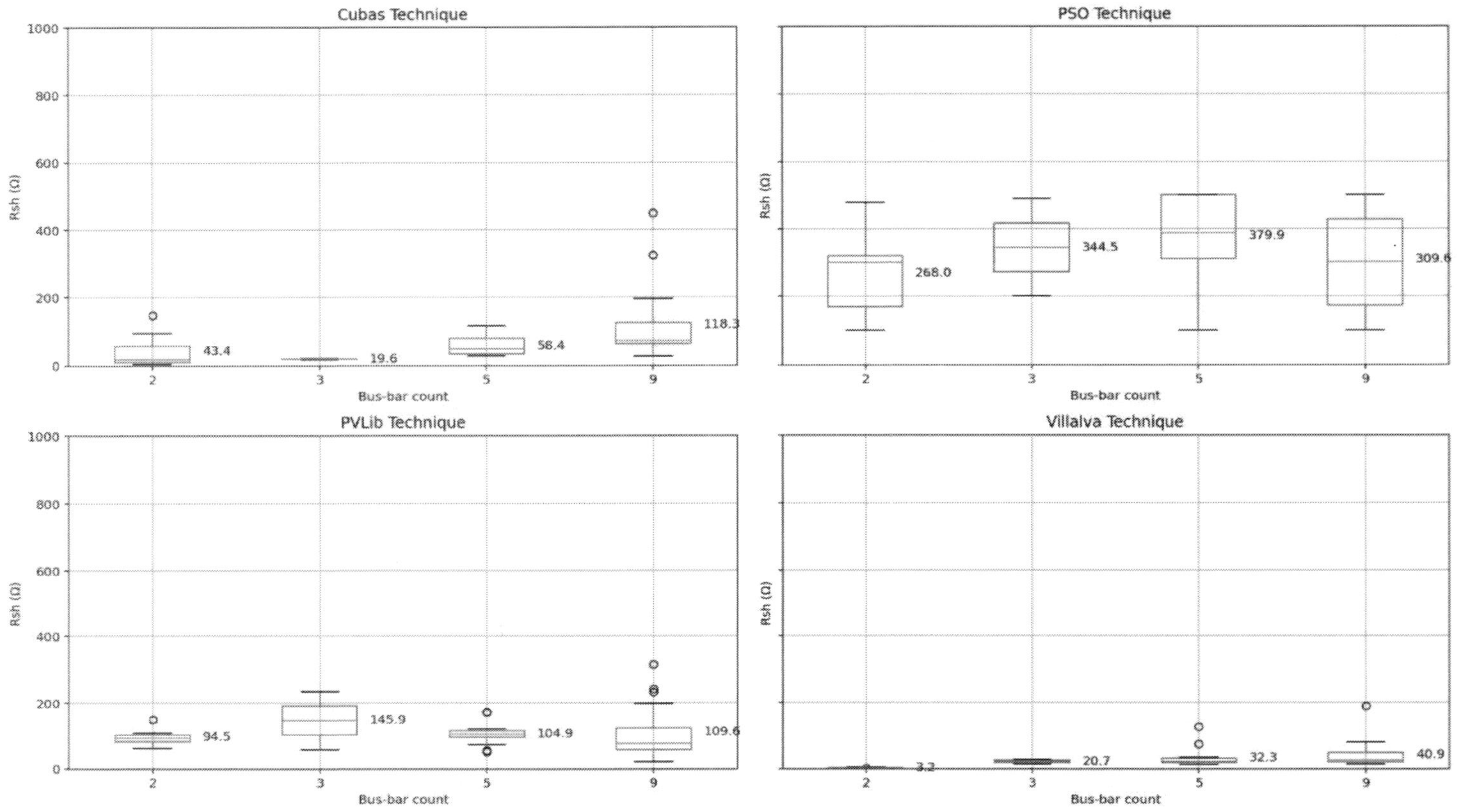

23.09.2025 42nd European Photovoltaic Solar Energy Conference & Exhibition , Bilbao , Spain

|Ahmad Hashem

2 Curves (PERC)

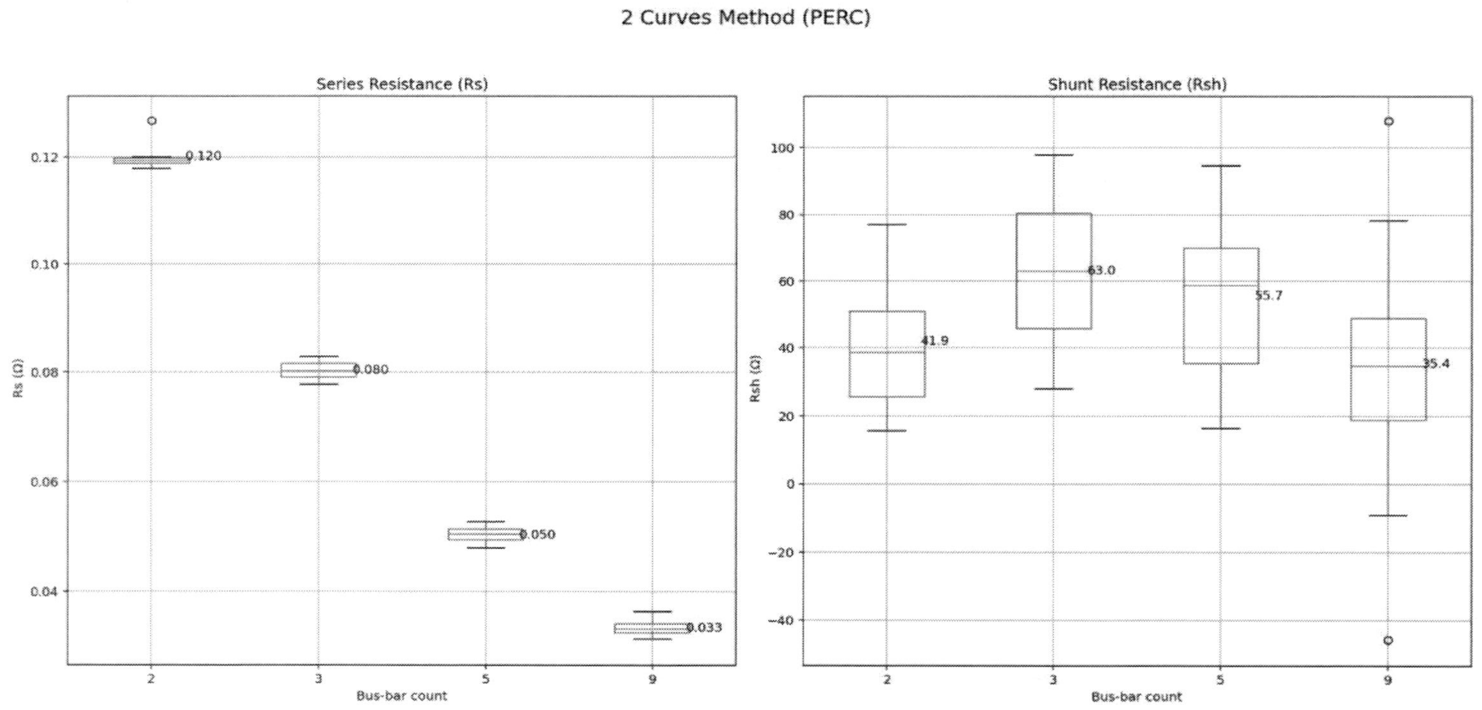

eurac
research

ROBO&M

EL-VQA: An Electroluminescence Dataset for Visual Reasoning and Detection

Mohanad Diab, Lukas Koester, Jordi Veirman, Atse
Louwen, David Moser, Luis Fialho

COHESION ITALY 21-27 ALTO ADIGE SÜDTIROL
Co-funded by the European Union
AUTONOME PROVINZ BOZEN SÜDTIROL
PROVINCIA AUTONOMA DI BOLZANO ALTO ADIGE
PROVINZIA AUTONOMA DE BULSAN SÜDTIROL

ROBO&M

1. Autonomous image acquisition from self-driving robots
2. Inclusion of advanced asset management platform for decision making, task definition, robot initiation
3. Autonomous image analysis – anomaly detection and failure identification

Credits: Fraunhofer Italia

Visual PV Components & Defect Detection

Credits: Eurac Research

Infrared PV Hot-Cell Detection

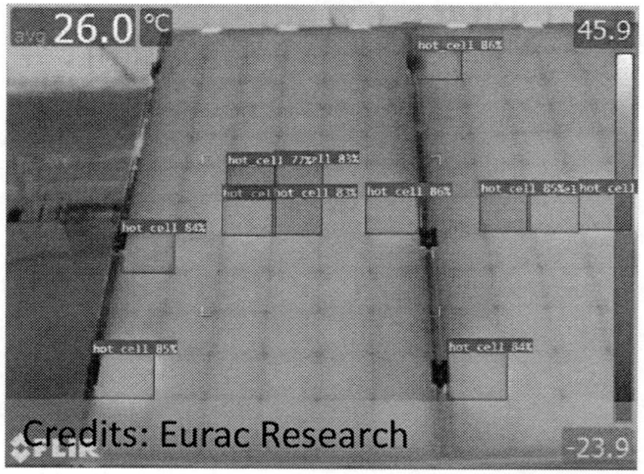

Credits: Eurac Research

ERDF funded

COHESION ITALY 21-27 ALTO ADIGE SÜDTIROL

Co-funded by the European Union

AUTONOME PROVINZ BOZEN SÜDTIROL
PROVINCIA AUTONOMA DI BOLZANO ALTO ADIGE
PROVINZIA AUTONOMA DE BULSAN SÜDTIROL

What is EL-VQA

ElectroLuminescence Visual Questin Answering: A dataset consisting of

- ~3000 images.
- ~ 65,000 bounding boxes across 14 classes.
- ~30,000 Q&A pairs + captions.
- Mono-crystalline only.
- Classes inspired by IEC60904-13
- VQA → simplified understanding of PV module status for non-experienced users.

What is EL-VQA

Acquisition

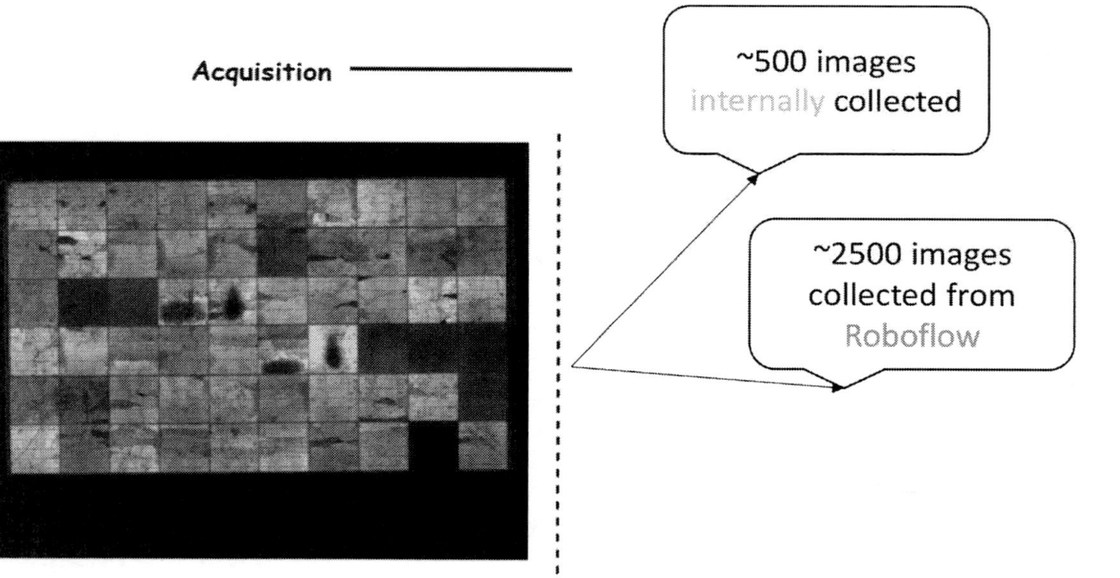

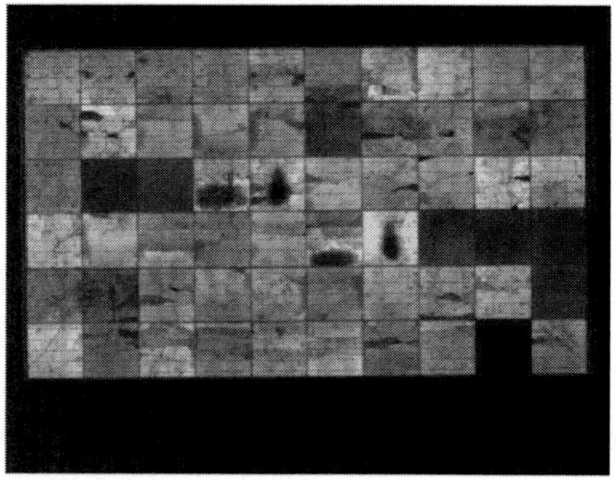

~500 images internally collected

~2500 images collected from Roboflow

Original Image

What is EL-VQA

Acquisition → Information

Annotation

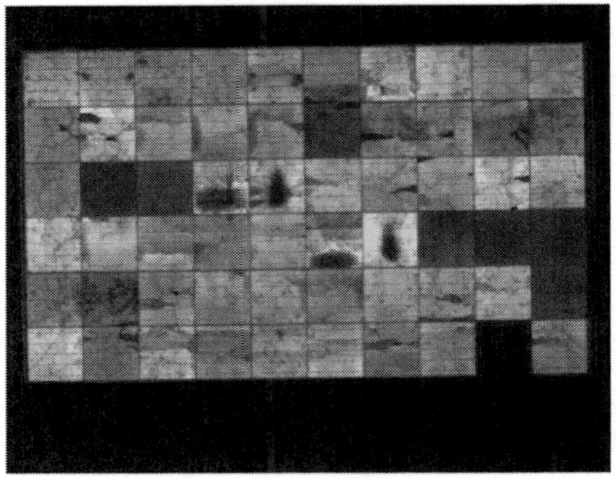

Original Image

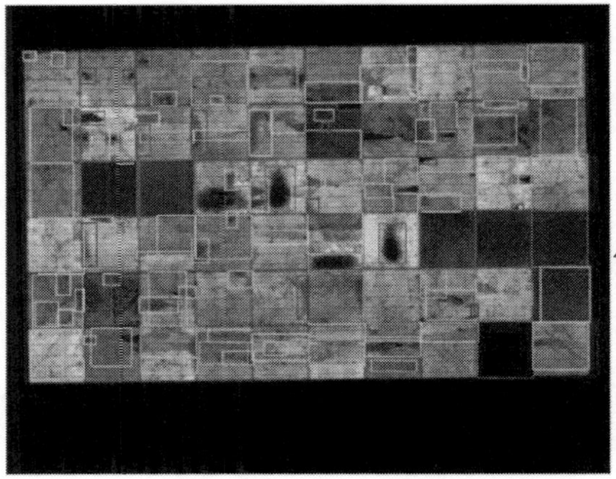

Annotated Image

Internally collected images manually annotated

External images annotated with AI

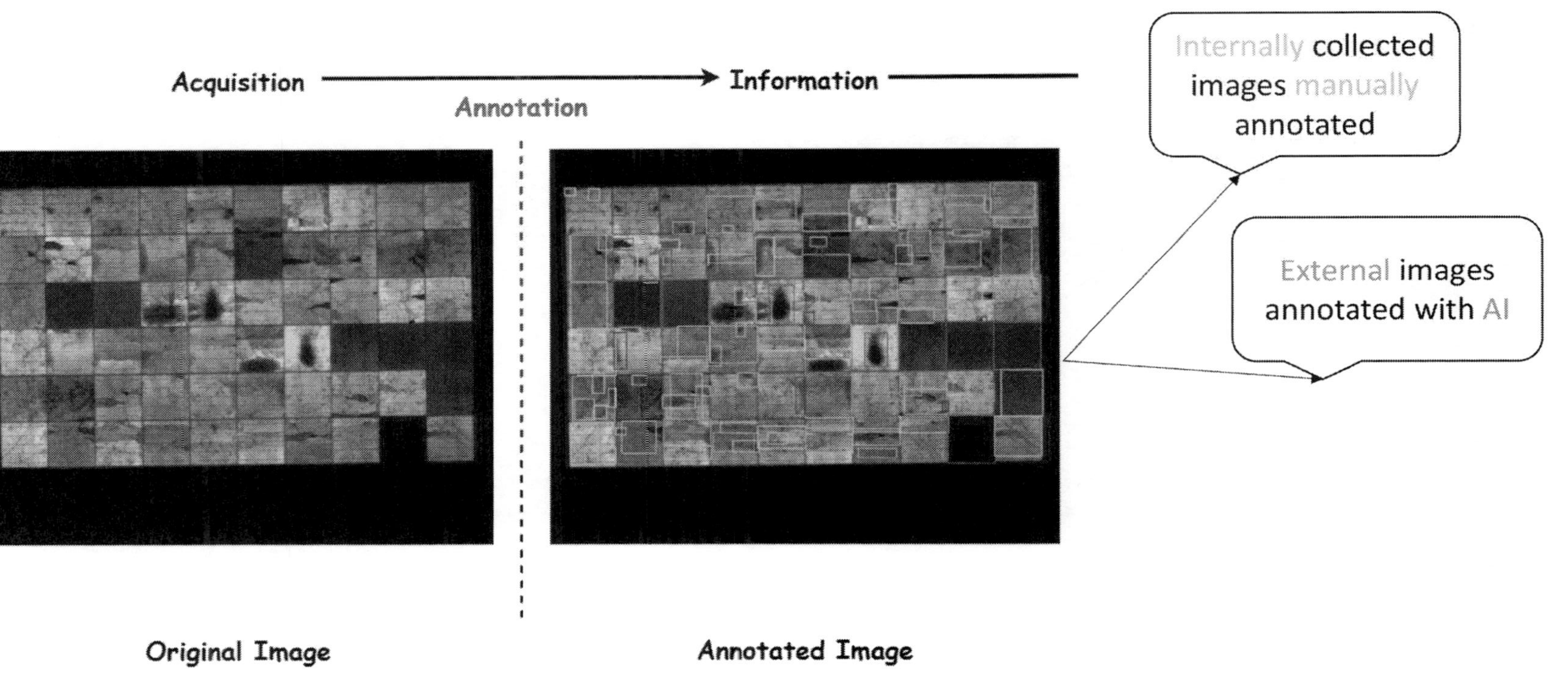

What is EL-VQA

Acquisition → Information → Knowledge

Annotation | Reasoning

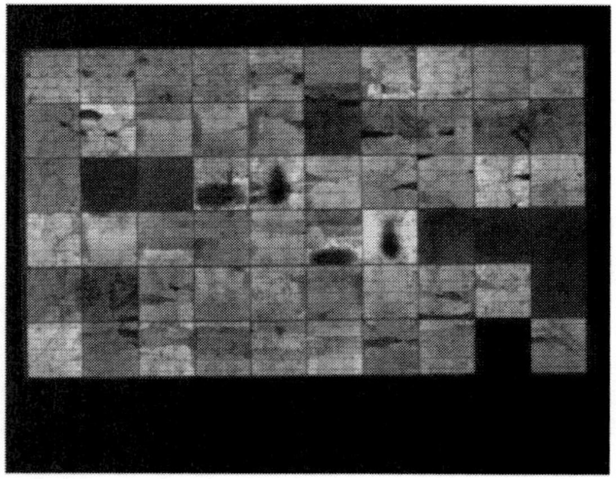

Original Image

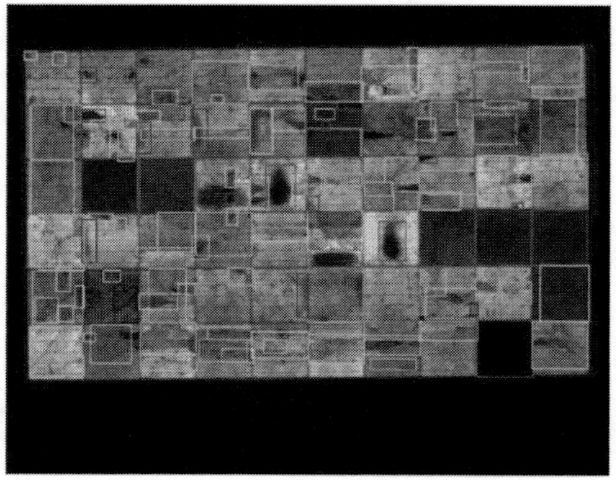

Annotated Image

Metadata
Q: What is the cell technology of this module?
A: mono-crystaline.

Quantitative
Q: How many defects are in this module?
A: There are 97 defects in total.

Quantitative
Q: How many cells have defects in this module?
A: Based on the defect detection output, all cells have defects, so, all 60 cells have defects!

Qualitative
Q: Out of 10, how good is this module?
A: Not very good, 3 on a good day.

Q&As

Annotation

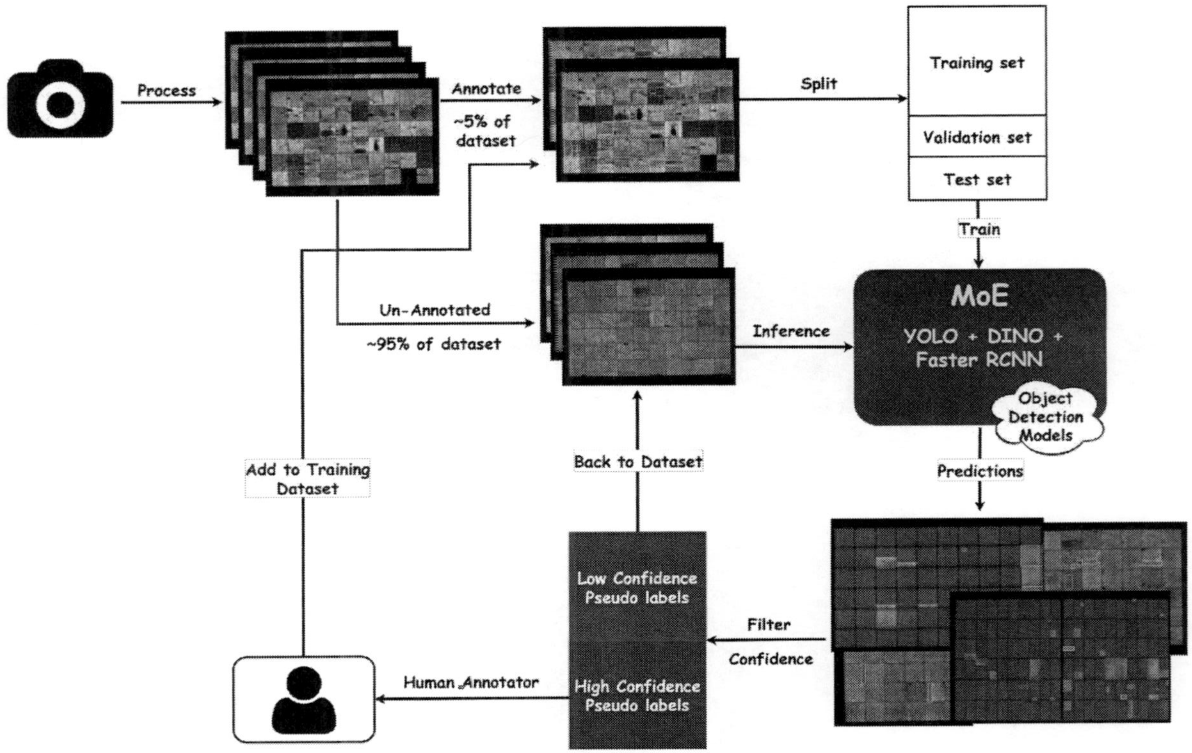
Process
Annotate
~5% of dataset
Split
Training set
Validation set
Test set
Train
Un-Annotated
~95% of dataset
Inference
MoE
YOLO + DINO + Faster RCNN
Object Detection Models
Predictions
Add to Training Dataset
Back to Dataset
Low Confidence Pseudo labels
High Confidence Pseudo labels
Filter
Confidence
Human Annotator

Annotation

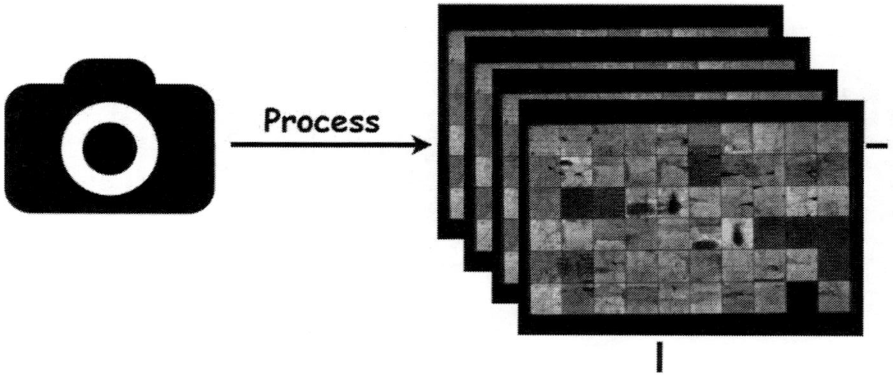

Annotation

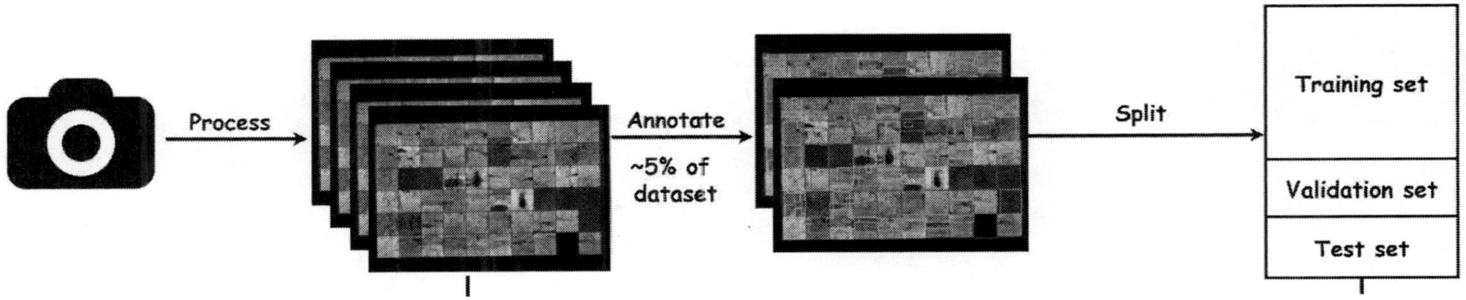
Process
Annotate
~5% of
dataset
Split
Training set
Validation set
Test set

Annotation

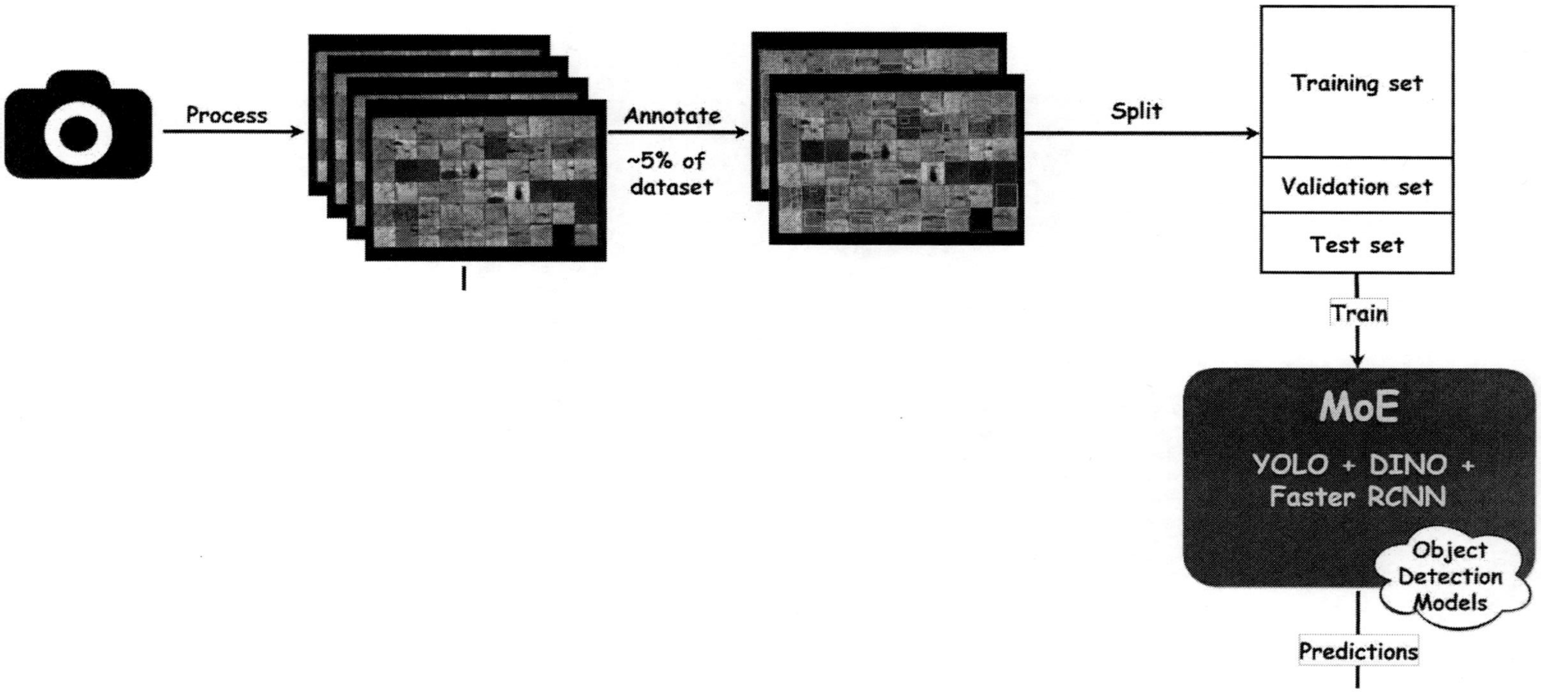
Process
Annotate
~5% of dataset
Split
Training set
Validation set
Test set
Train
MoE
YOLO + DINO + Faster RCNN
Object Detection Models
Predictions

Annotation

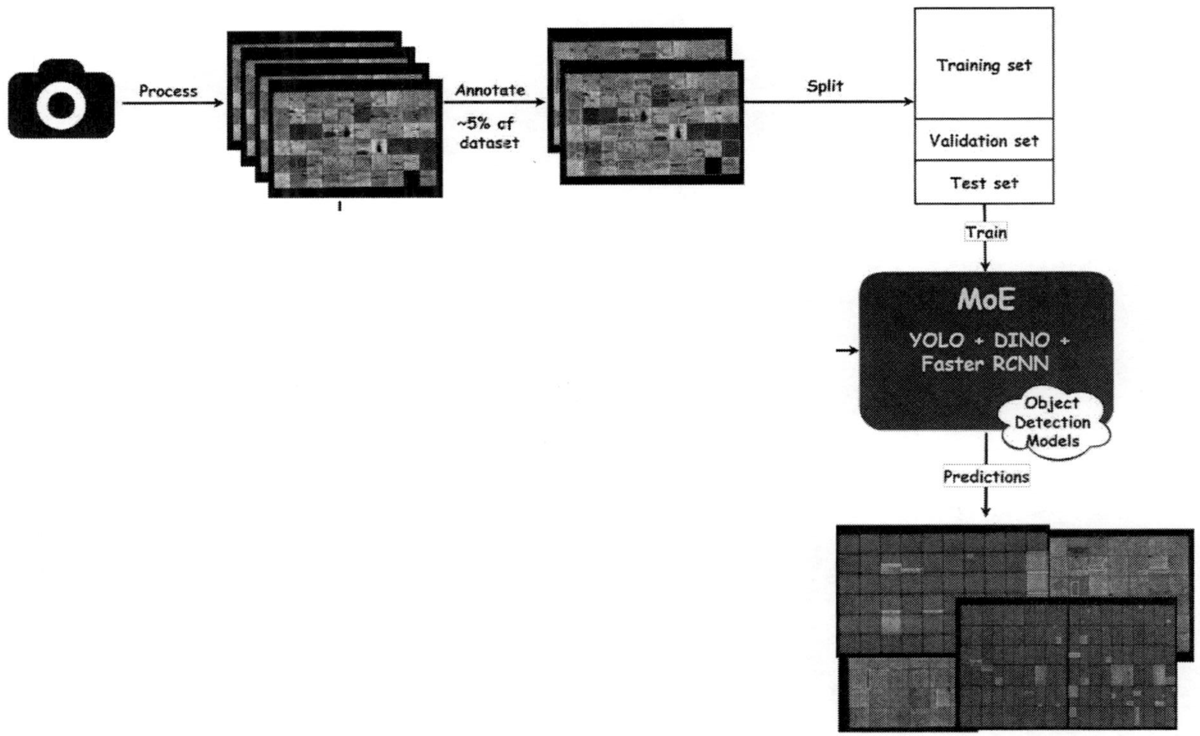
Process
Annotate
~5% of dataset
Split
Training set
Validation set
Test set
Train
MoE
YOLO + DINO + Faster RCNN
Object Detection Models
Predictions

Annotation

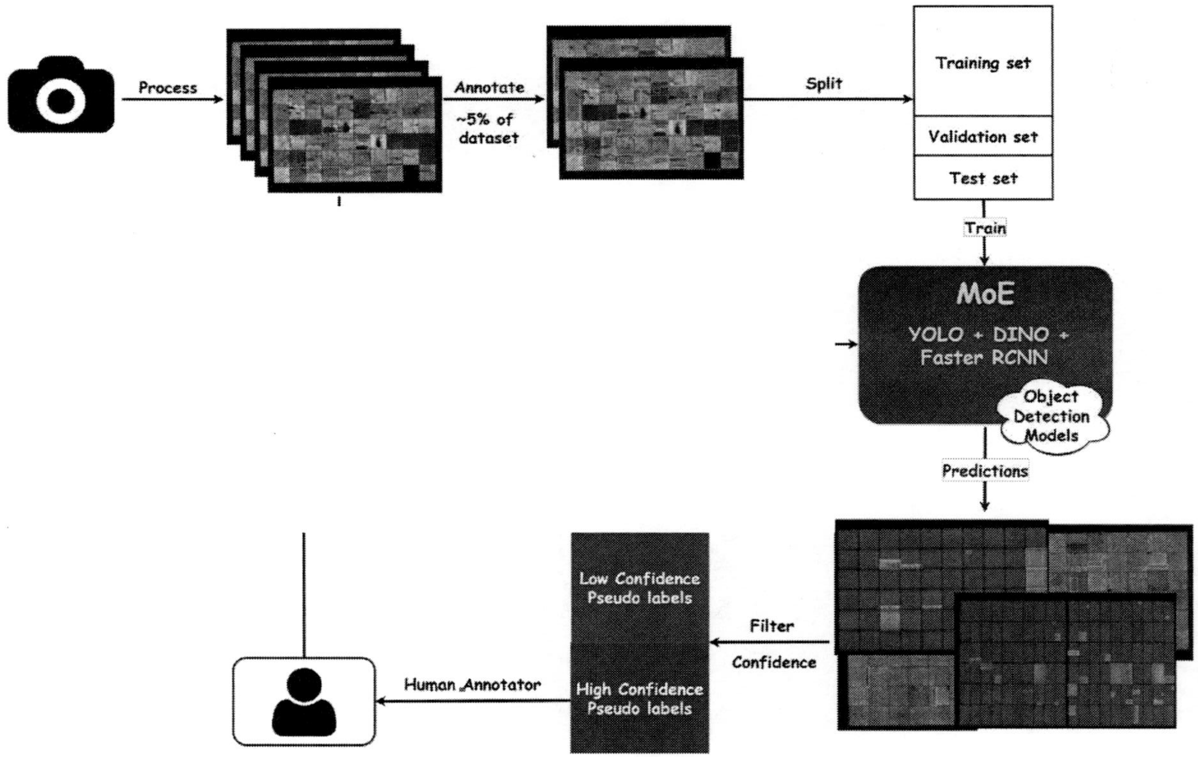
Process
Annotate
~5% of dataset
Split
Training set
Validation set
Test set
Train
MoE
YOLO + DINO + Faster RCNN
Object Detection Models
Predictions
Filter
Confidence
Low Confidence Pseudo labels
High Confidence Pseudo labels
Human Annotator

Annotation

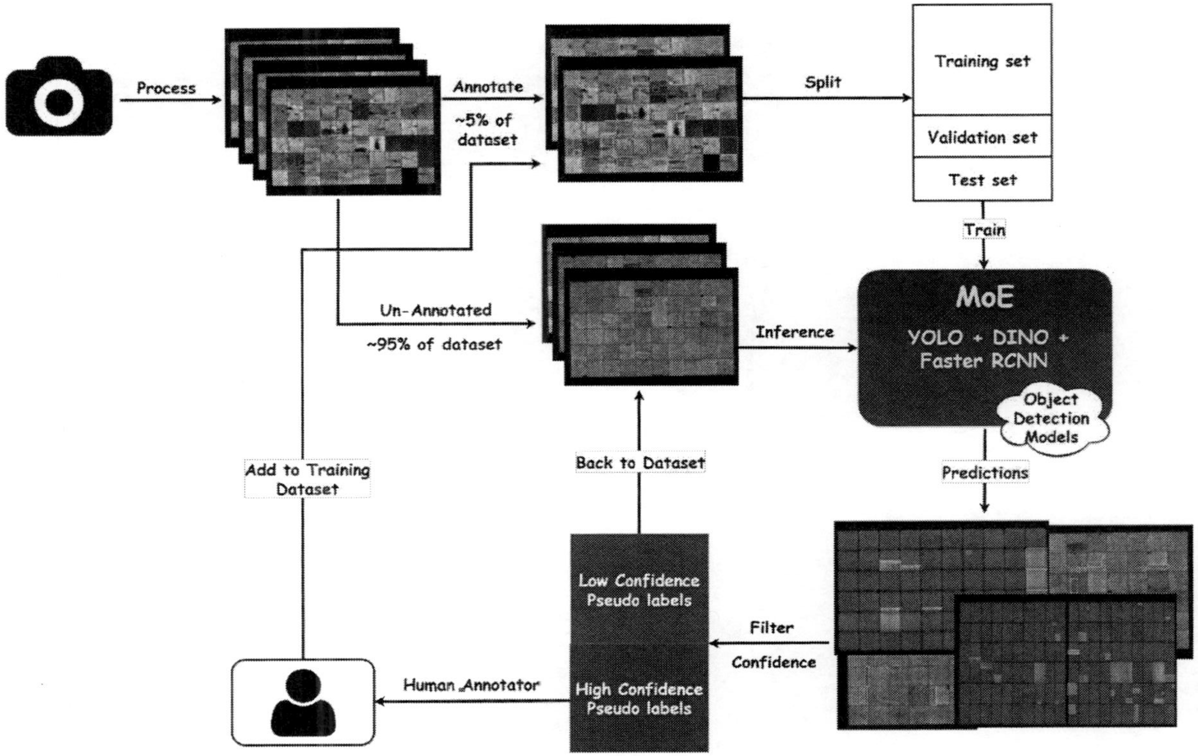

Process
Annotate
~5% of dataset
Split
Training set
Validation set
Test set
Train
Un-Annotated
~95% of dataset
Inference
MoE
YOLO + DINO + Faster RCNN
Object Detection Models
Predictions
Add to Training Dataset
Back to Dataset
Low Confidence Pseudo labels
High Confidence Pseudo labels
Filter
Confidence
Human Annotator

Annotation

Total: ~65,000 annotations

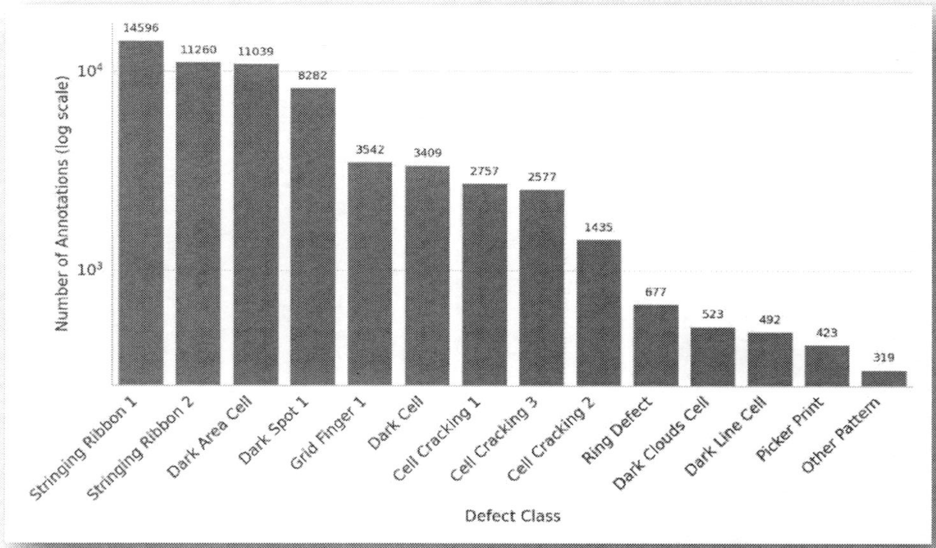

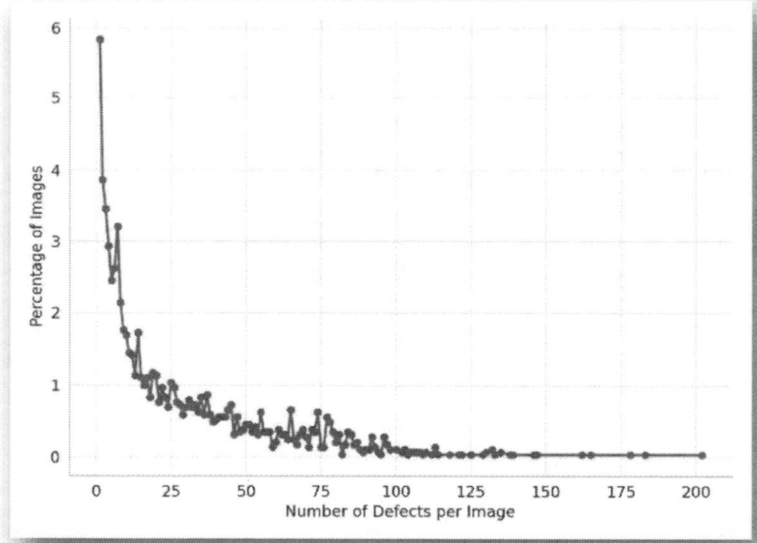

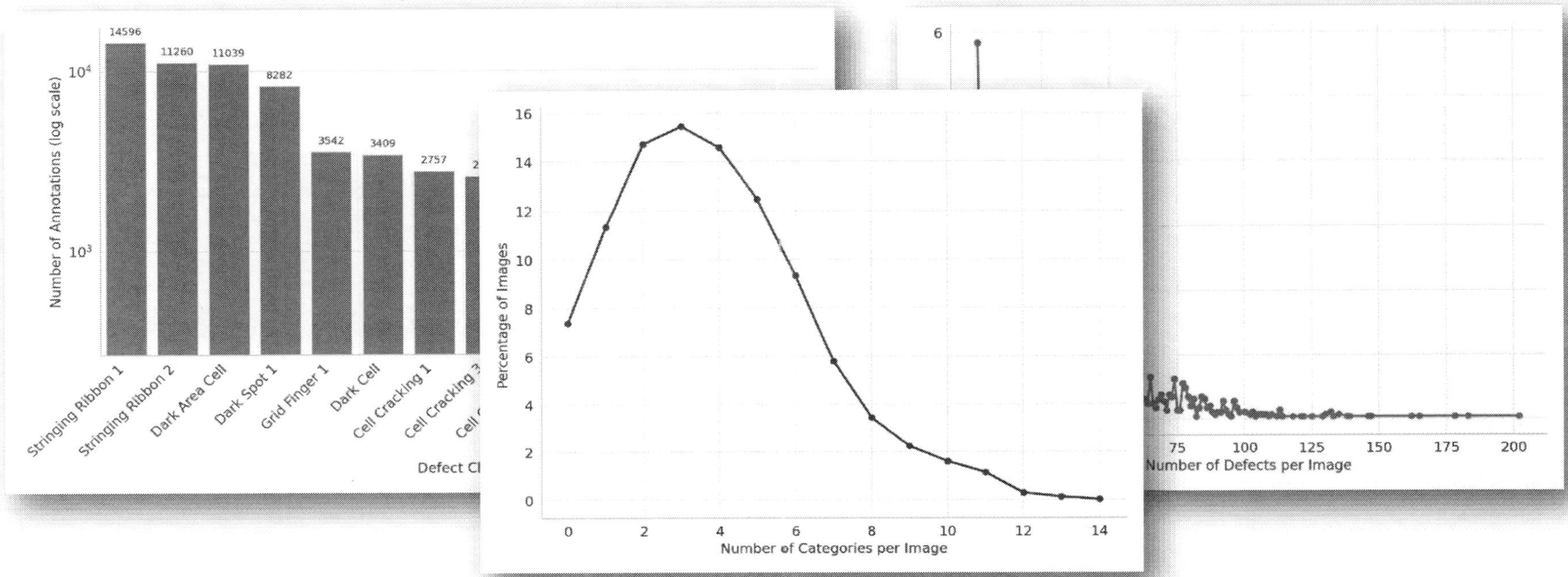
Annotation
Total: ~65,000 annotations
14596
11260
11039
8282
3542
3409
2757
10^4
10^3
Number of Annotations (log scale)
Stringing Ribbon 1
Stringing Ribbon 2
Dark Area Cell
Dark Spot 1
Grid Finger 1
Dark Cell
Cell Cracking 1
Percentage of Images
Number of Categories per Image
Number of Defects per Image
eurac research
Koester | ELVQA
23.09.2025
15

Q&A

- **Manual + Automated Generation:** Combined human-written prompts with programmatically generated Q&A to cover both descriptive and analytical aspects.
- **Domain Knowledge Integration:** Used predefined expert knowledge about defect types (causes, severity, safety implications) to generate analytical and heuristic answers.
- **Cell-Level Detection Support:** A YOLO-based cell detector provided structural information (e.g., cell counts, defect positions) that fed into factual Q&A.
- **Image Quality Features:** Automated scripts extracted brightness, sharpness, and saturation to create Q&A pairs on imaging conditions.
- **Multi-Layer Reasoning Coverage:** Each image received ~10–12 Q&A pairs spanning factual (counts, types), analytical (causes/effects), heuristic (safety/condition rating), and descriptive (one-sentence summaries).

Conclusion

- Introduced **EL-VQA**, the first large-scale EL dataset with detection **and** reasoning tasks.
- Provides **~3,000 images**, **65k+ bounding boxes**, and **30k Q&A pairs** across **14 defect classes**.
- Enables research in **object detection, captioning, and Visual Question Answering** for PV modules.
- Built with **semi-supervised annotation pipeline** (MoE + WBF + manual review).
- To be openly released under **MIT license** to accelerate AI solutions for PV inspection and O&M (within 2025, with publication of work in *Progress in Photovoltaics)*

Contact us

lukas.koester@eurac.edu

Eurac Research

Drususallee/Viale Druso 1

39100 Bozen/Bolzano

T +39 0471 055 055

info@eurac.edu

www.eurac.edu

eurac research

ROBO&M

COHESION ITALY 21-27 ALTO ADIGE SÜDTIROL

Co-funded by the European Union

AUTONOME PROVINZ BOZEN SÜDTIROL — PROVINCIA AUTONOMA DI BOLZANO ALTO ADIGE — PROVINZIA AUTONOMA DE BULSAN SÜDTIROL

Progetto cofinanziato dal programma FESR 2021 – 2027 della Provincia Autonoma di Bolzano tramite convenzione nr. EFRE 1027.

eurac
research

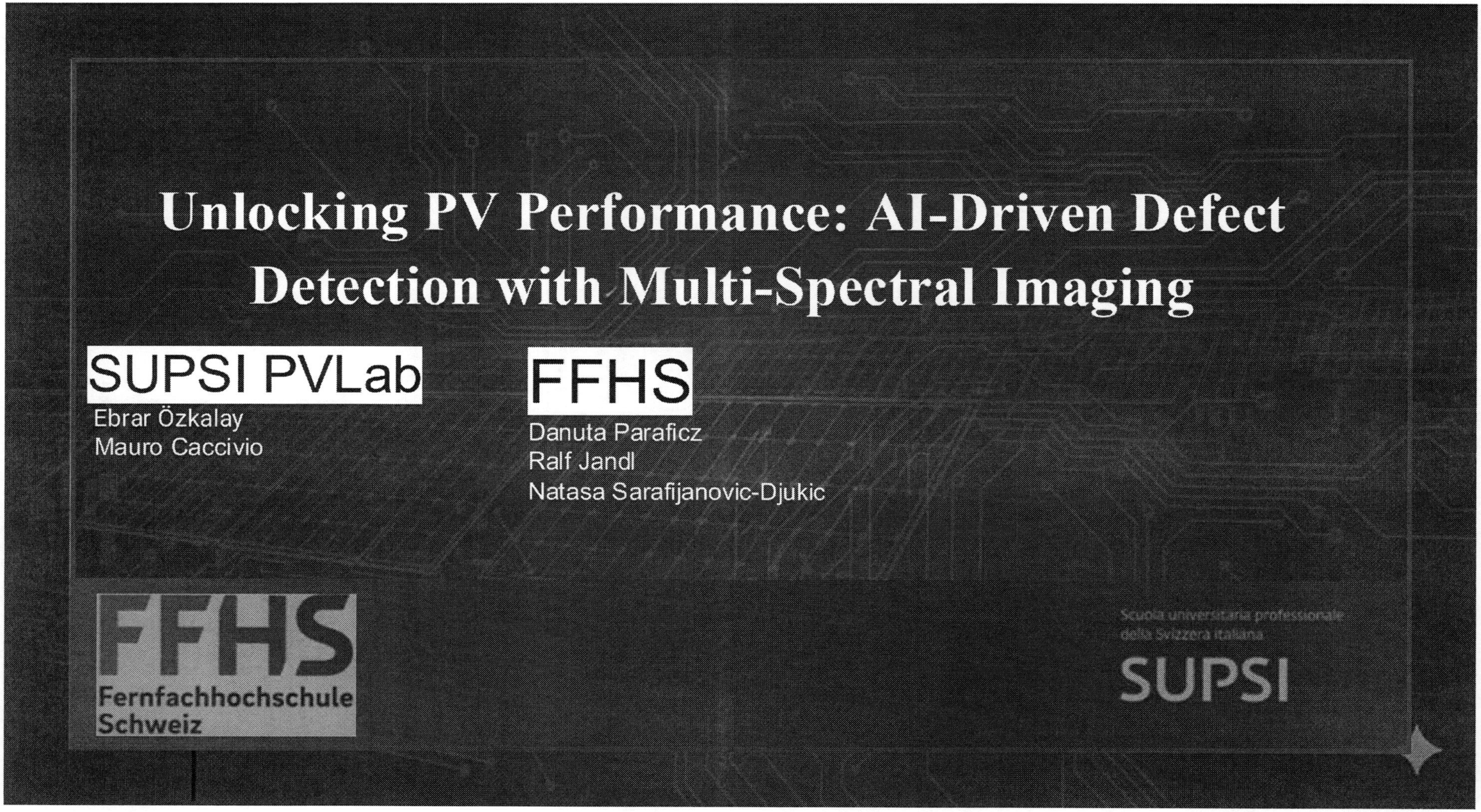
Unlocking PV Performance: AI-Driven Defect Detection with Multi-Spectral Imaging
SUPSI PVLab
Ebrar Özkalay
Mauro Caccivio
FFHS
Danuta Paraficz
Ralf Jandl
Natasa Sarafijanovic-Djukic
FFHS
Fernfachhochschule Schweiz
Scuola universitaria professionale della Svizzera italiana
SUPSI

The Challenge: Ensuring PV Reliability

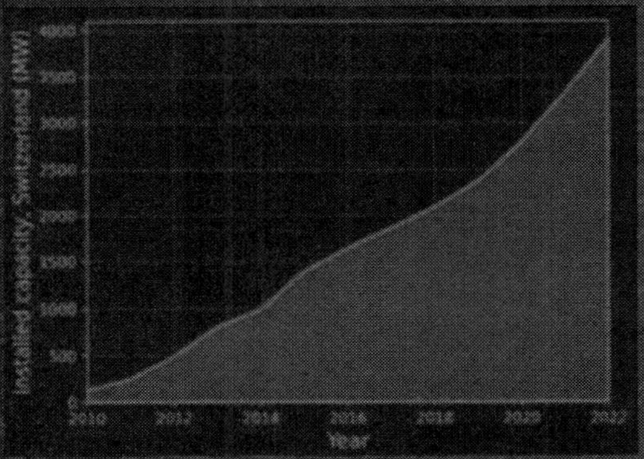

- Growing number of PV systems means reliability is paramount.
- Degradation and defects lead to reduced energy production.
- To achieve lifespans, fast detection of defects in solar panels is critical.
- Ensure appropriate mitigation actions.

FFHS

The Challenge: Ensuring PV Reliability

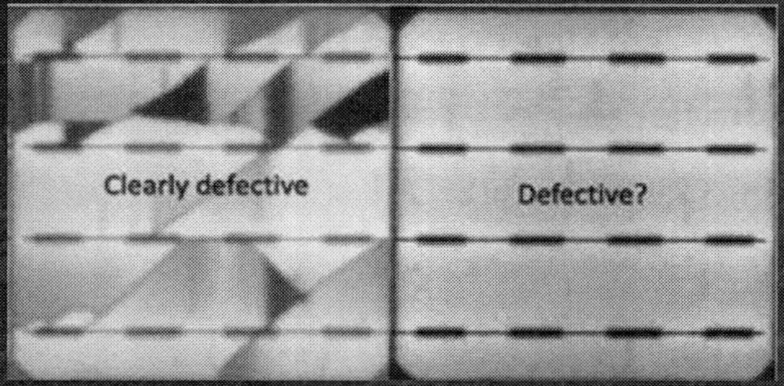

- Current monitoring methods are often inefficient.
- Manual analysis of the images, usually done by experts: slow and expensive.
- Subjective: different experts assign different labels.

FFHS

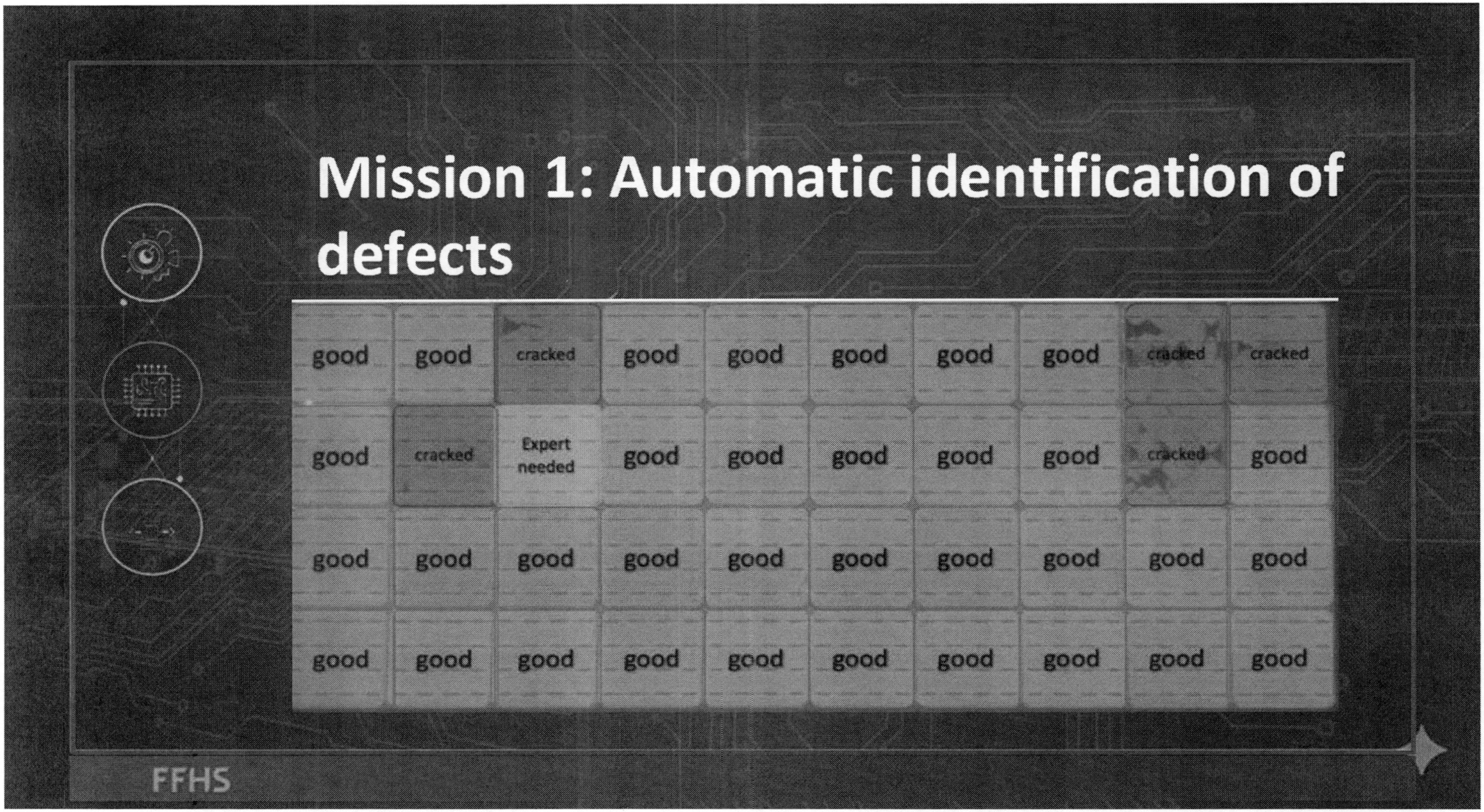
Mission 1: Automatic identification of defects
good good cracked good good good good good cracked cracked
good cracked Expert needed good good good good good cracked good
good good good good good good good good good good
good good good good good good good good good good
FFHS

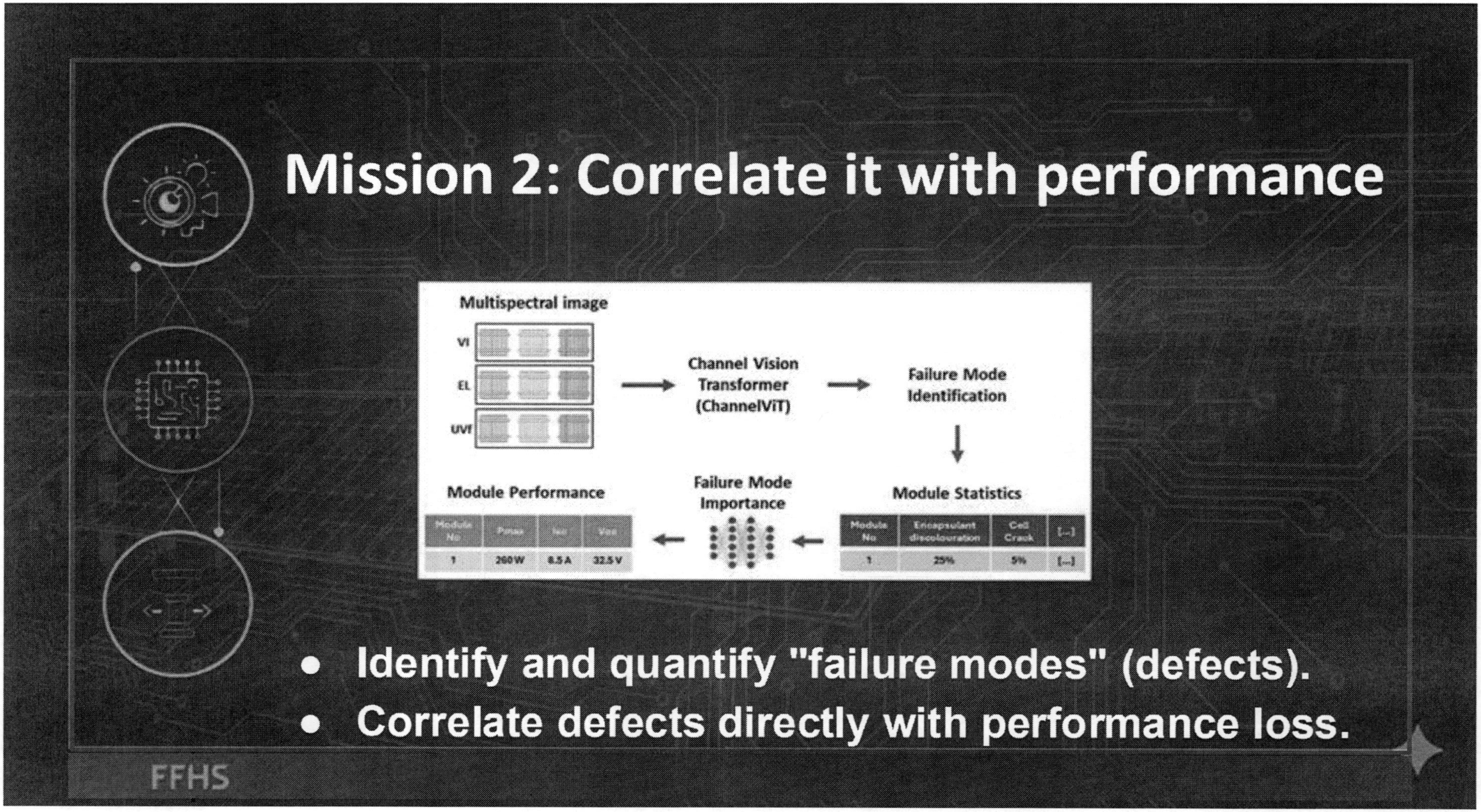
Mission 2: Correlate it with performance
Multispectral image
VI
EL
UVf
Channel Vision Transformer (ChannelViT)
Failure Mode Identification
Module Statistics
Module No
Encapsulant discolouration
Cell Crack
[...]
1
25%
5%
[...]
Failure Mode Importance
Module Performance
Module No
1
260 W
8.5 A
32.5 V
• Identify and quantify "failure modes" (defects).
• Correlate defects directly with performance loss.
FFHS

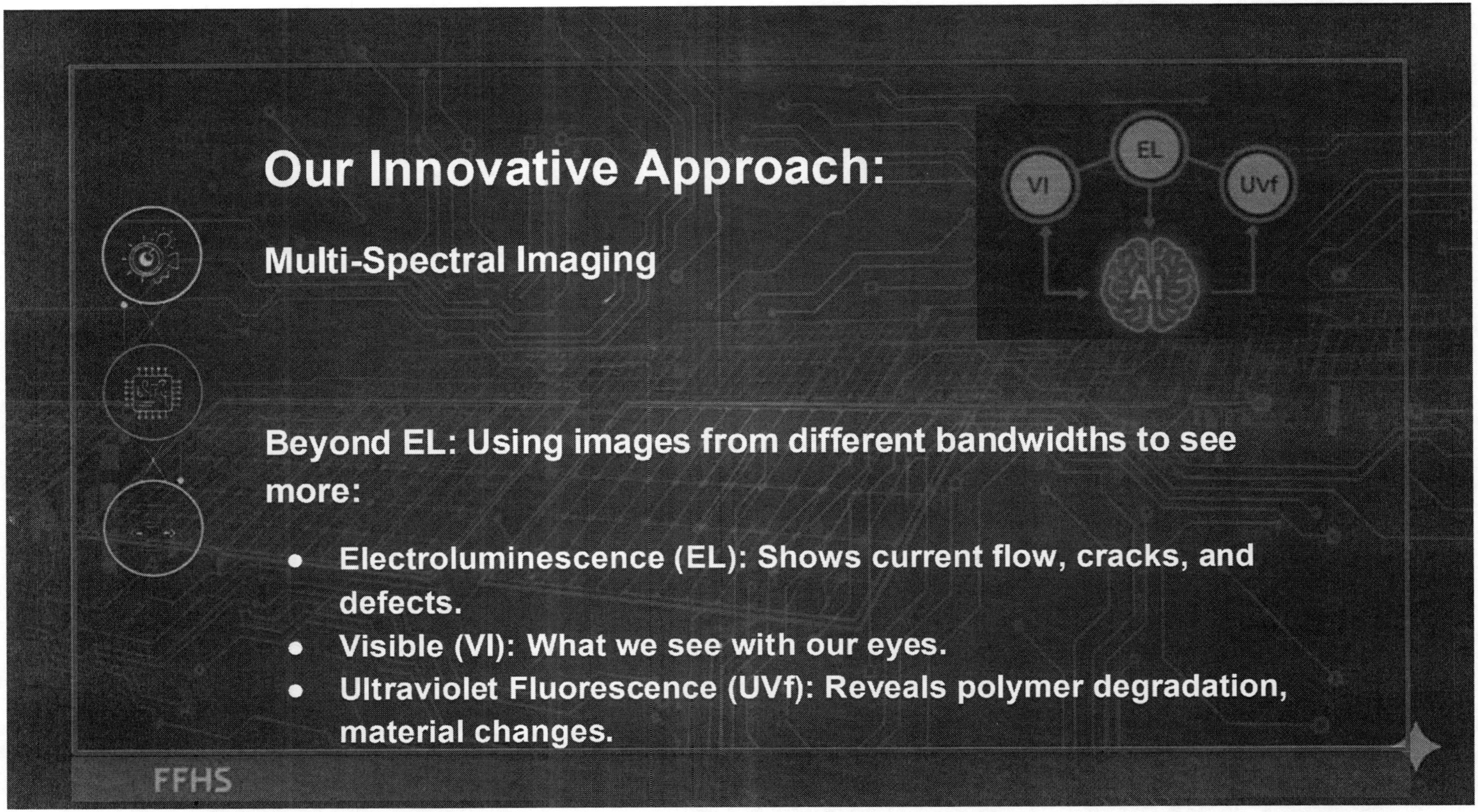
Our Innovative Approach:
Multi-Spectral Imaging
VI
EL
UVf
AI
Beyond EL: Using images from different bandwidths to see more:
• Electroluminescence (EL): Shows current flow, cracks, and defects.
• Visible (VI): What we see with our eyes.
• Ultraviolet Fluorescence (UVf): Reveals polymer degradation, material changes.
FFHS

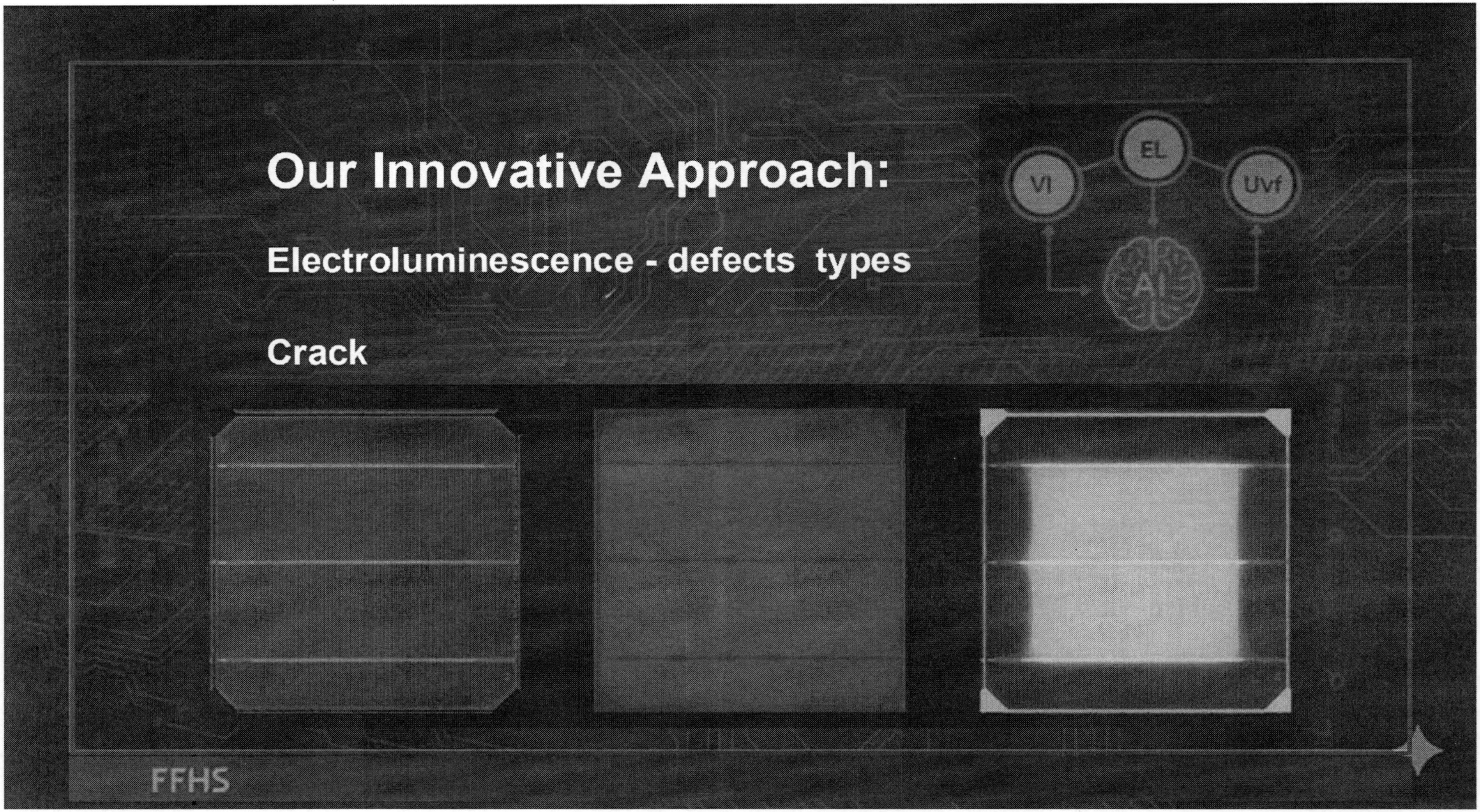
Our Innovative Approach:
Electroluminescence - defects types
Crack
VI
EL
Uvf
AI
FFHS

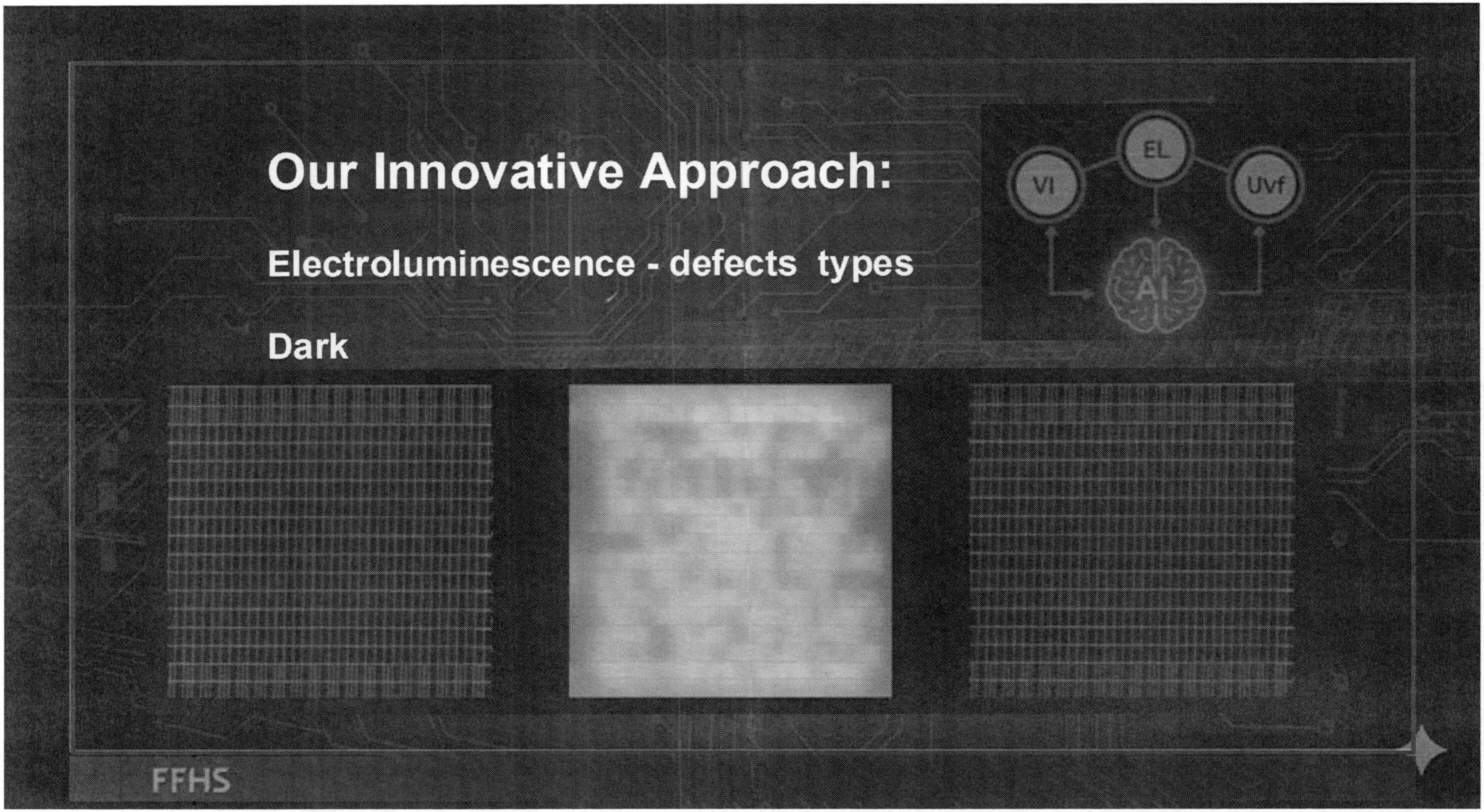
Our Innovative Approach:
Electroluminescence - defects types
Dark
VI
EL
Uvf
AI
FFHS

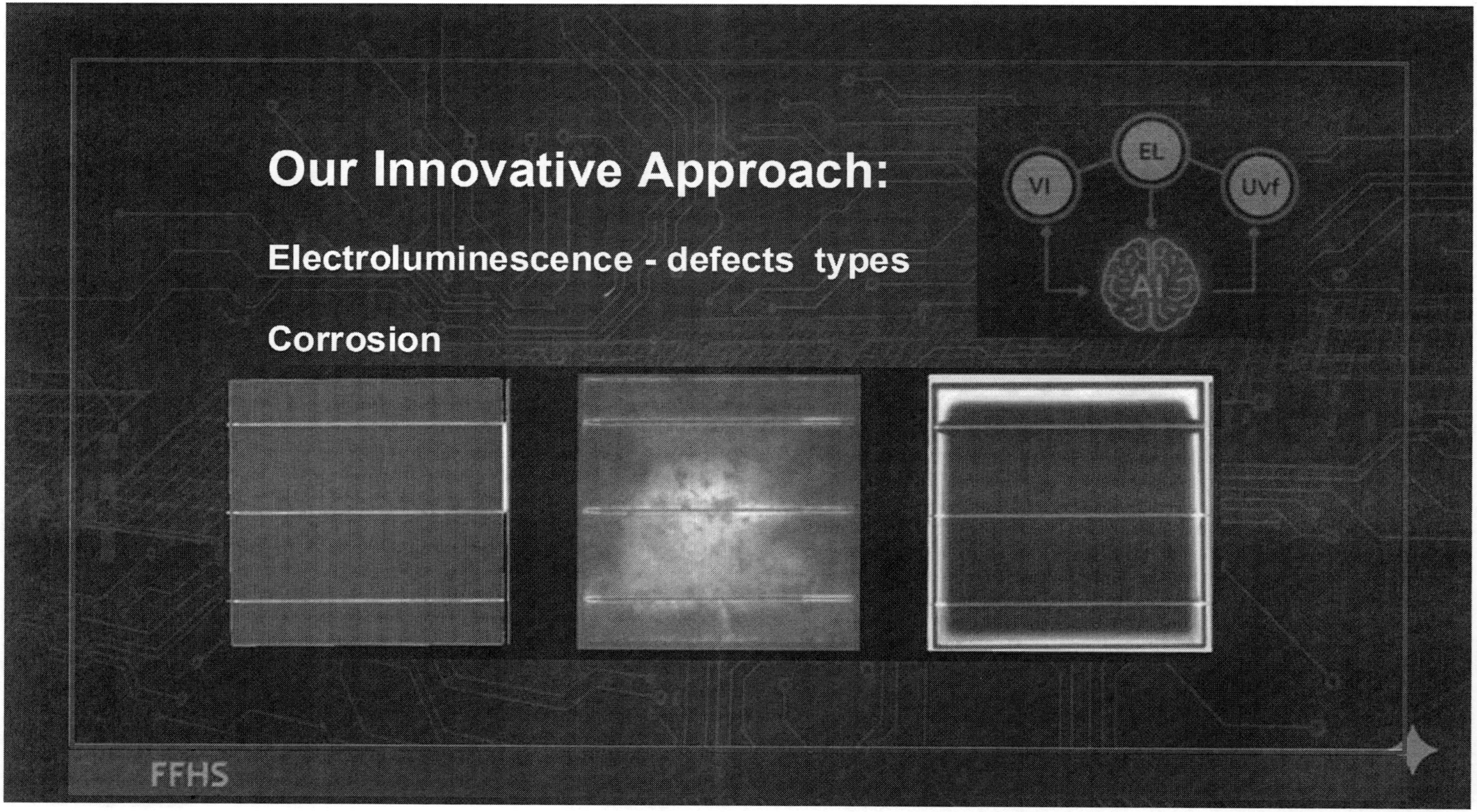
Our Innovative Approach:
Electroluminescence - defects types
Corrosion
VI
EL
Uvf
AI
FFHS

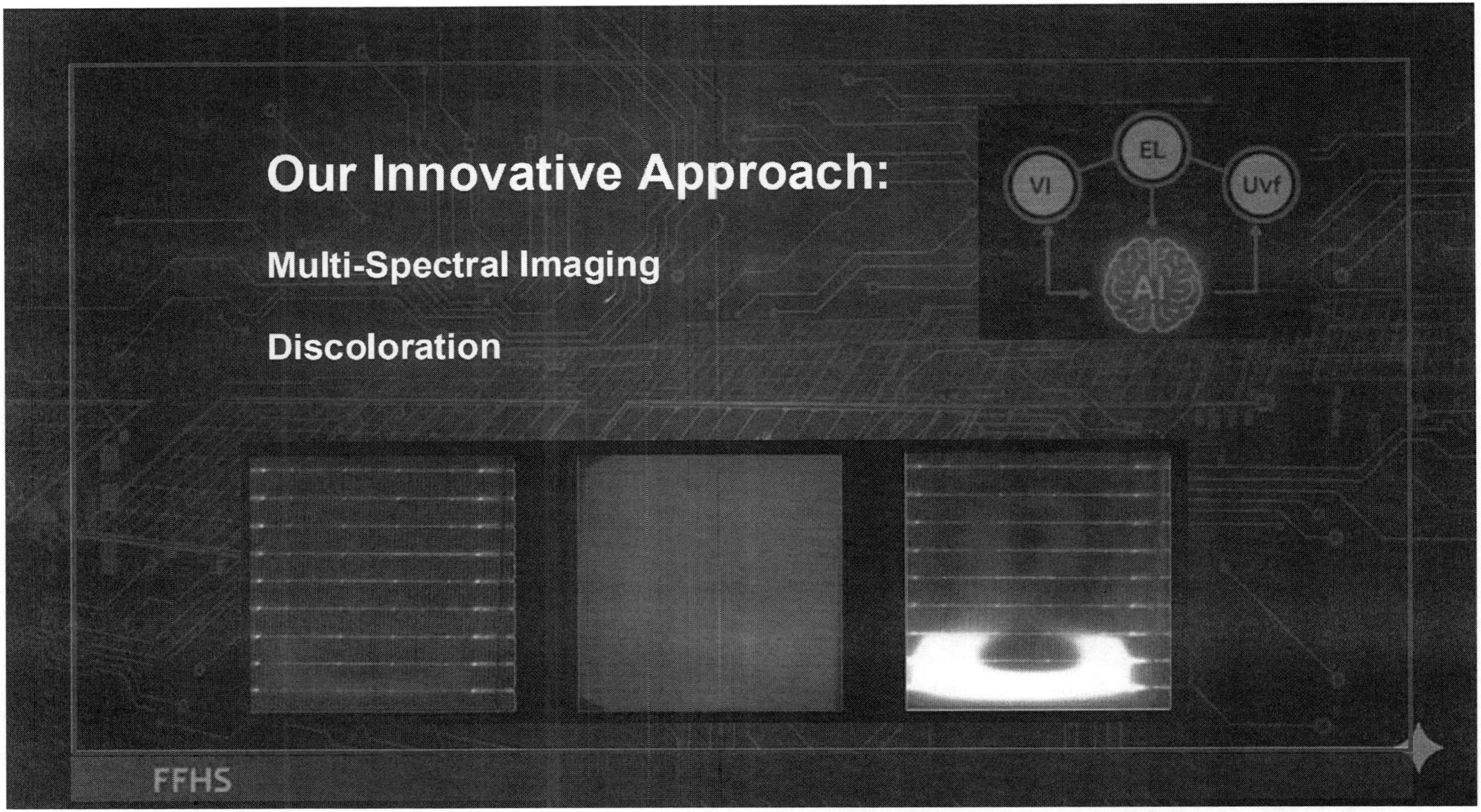
Our Innovative Approach:
Multi-Spectral Imaging
Discoloration
VI
EL
Uvf
AI
FFHS

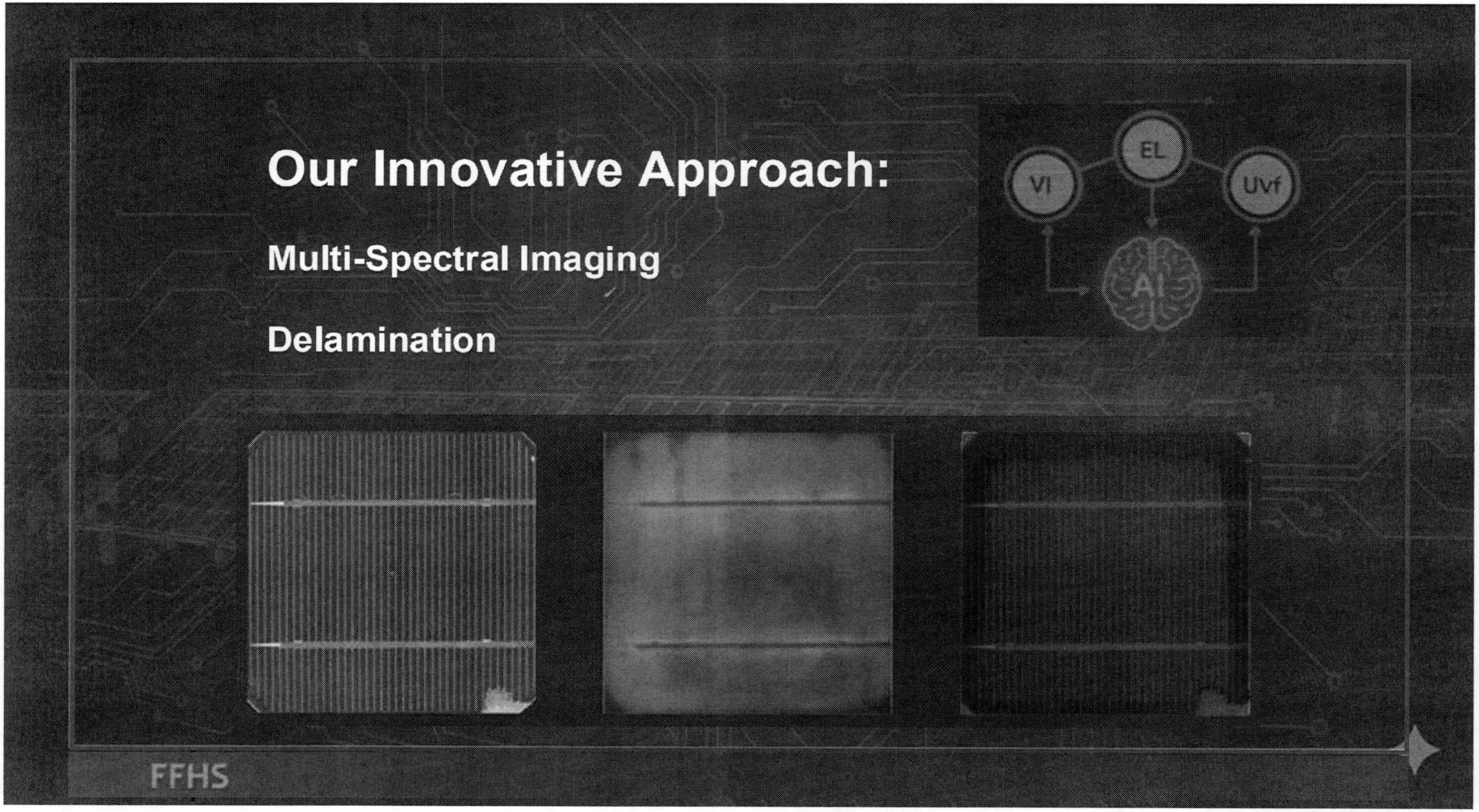
Our Innovative Approach:
Multi-Spectral Imaging
Delamination
VI
EL
UVf
AI
FFHS

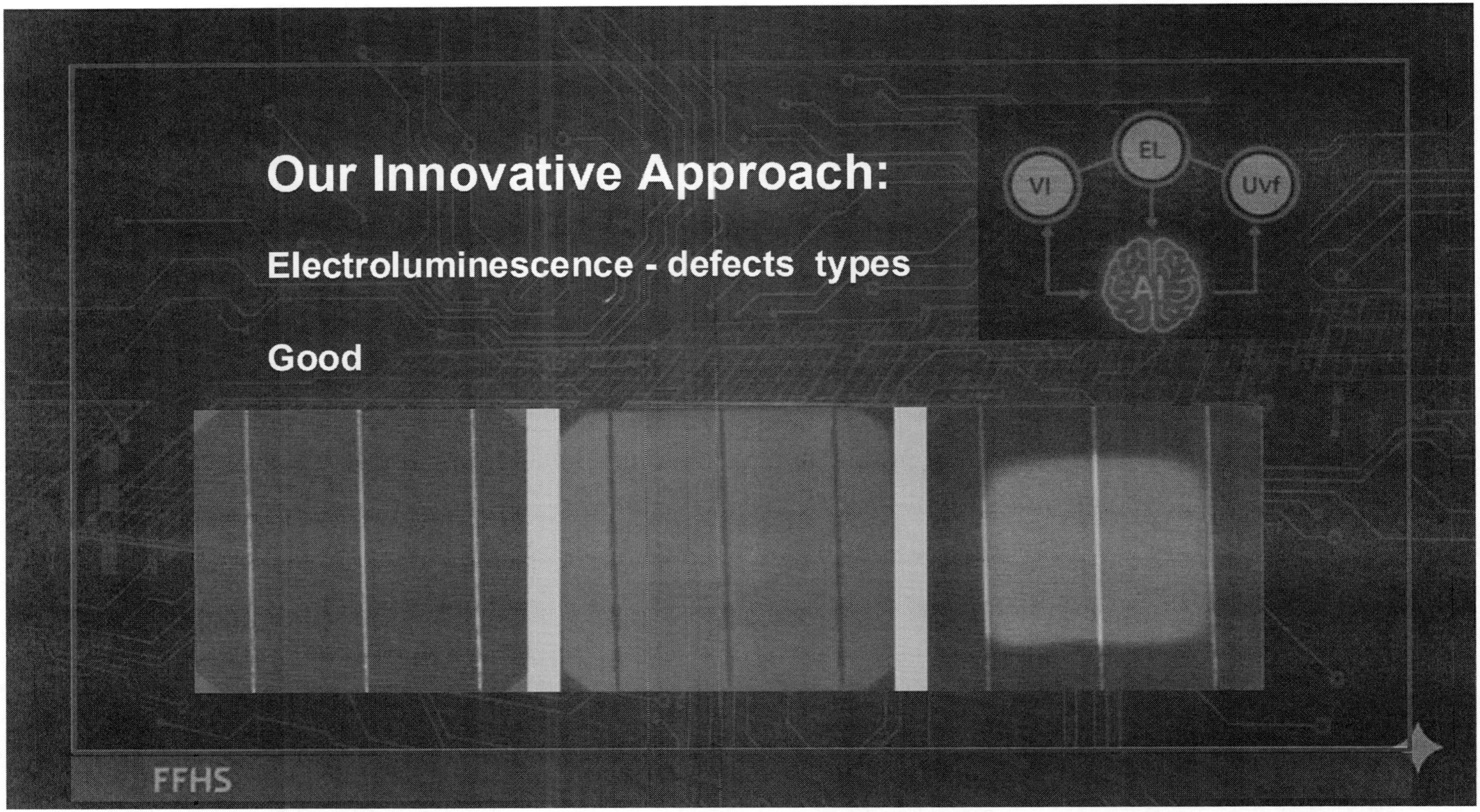
Our Innovative Approach:
Electroluminescence - defects types
Good
VI
EL
Uvf
AI
FFHS

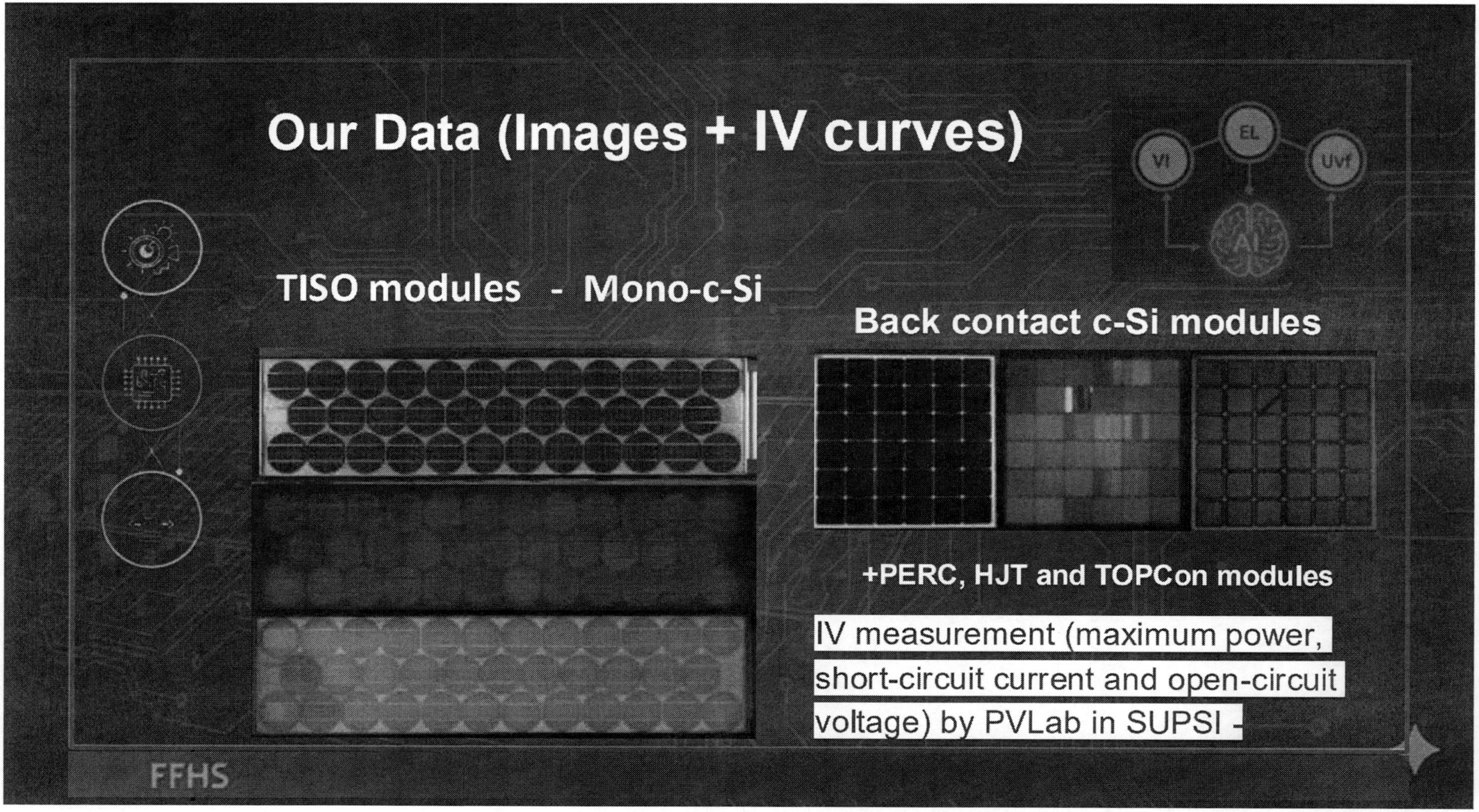
Our Data (Images + IV curves)
VI
EL
Uvf
AI
TISO modules - Mono-c-Si
Back contact c-Si modules
+PERC, HJT and TOPCon modules
IV measurement (maximum power, short-circuit current and open-circuit voltage) by PVLab in SUPSI -
FFHS

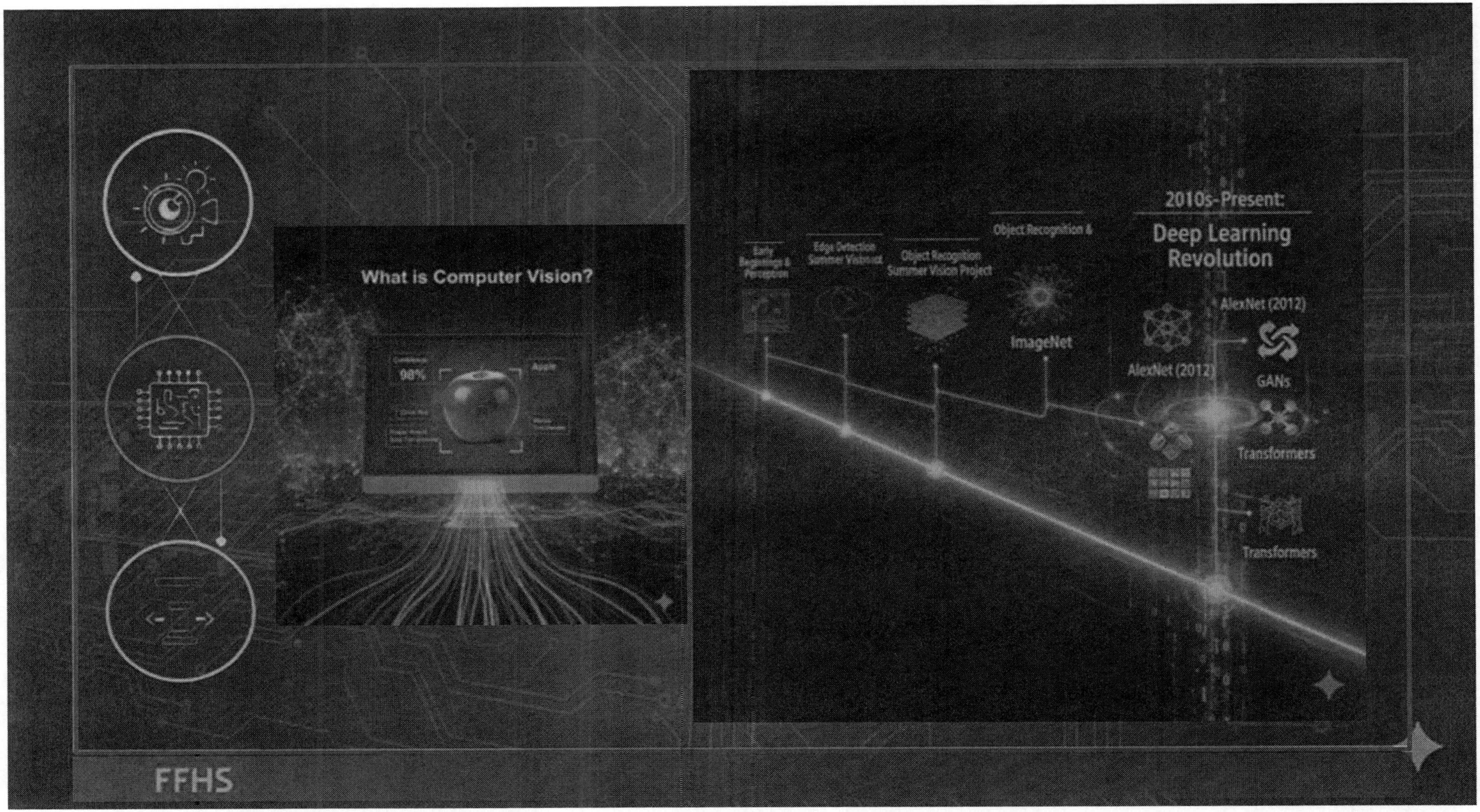
What is Computer Vision?
98%
Apple
Object Recognition &
2010s-Present:
Deep Learning Revolution
ImageNet
AlexNet (2012)
AlexNet (2012)
GANs
Transformers
Transformers
FFHS

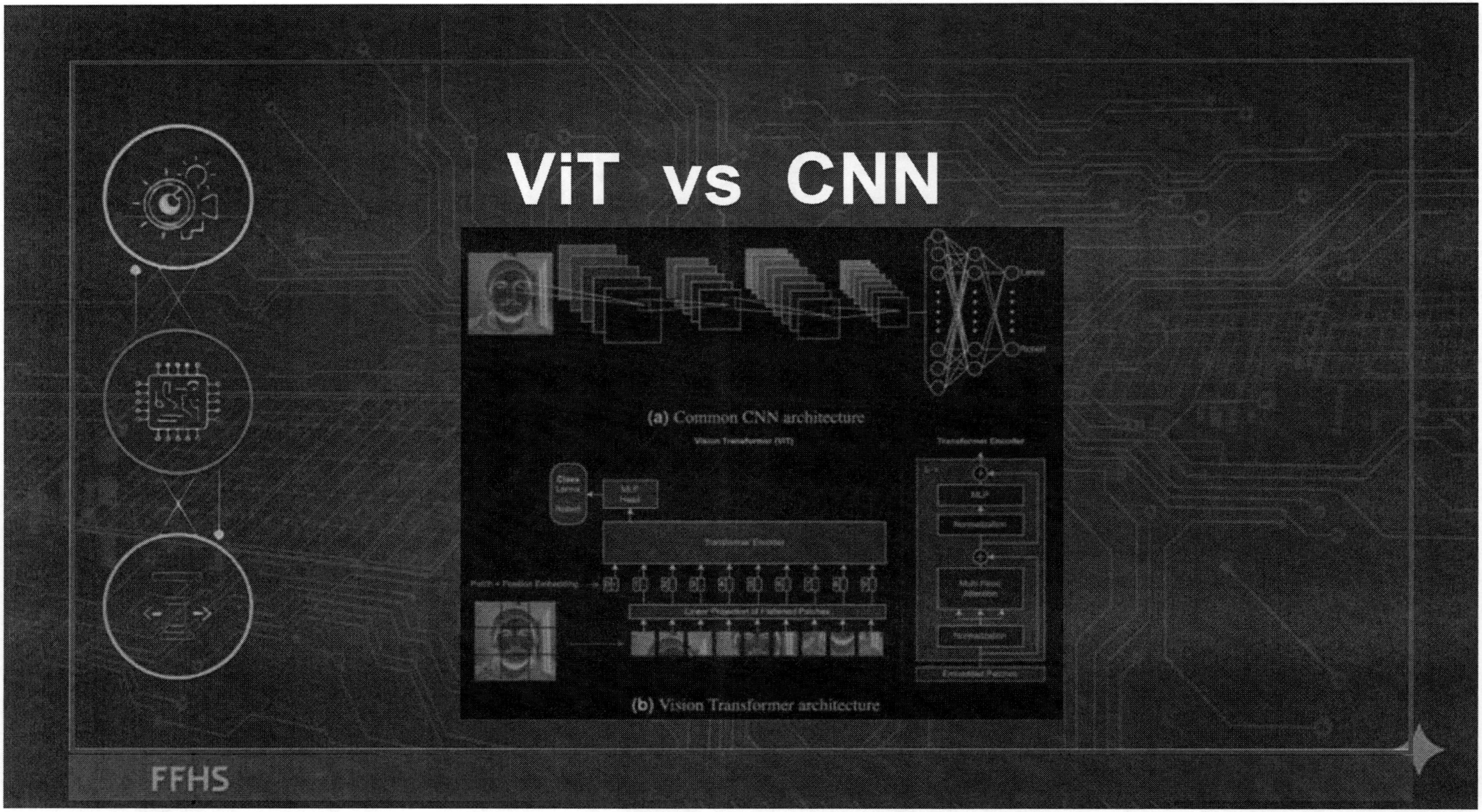
ViT vs CNN
(a) Common CNN architecture
Vision Transformer (ViT)
Transformer Encoder
MLP Head
Transformer Encoder
Patch + Position Embedding
Linear Projection of Flattened Patches
MLP
Normalization
Multi-Head Attention
Normalization
Embedded Patches
(b) Vision Transformer architecture
FFHS

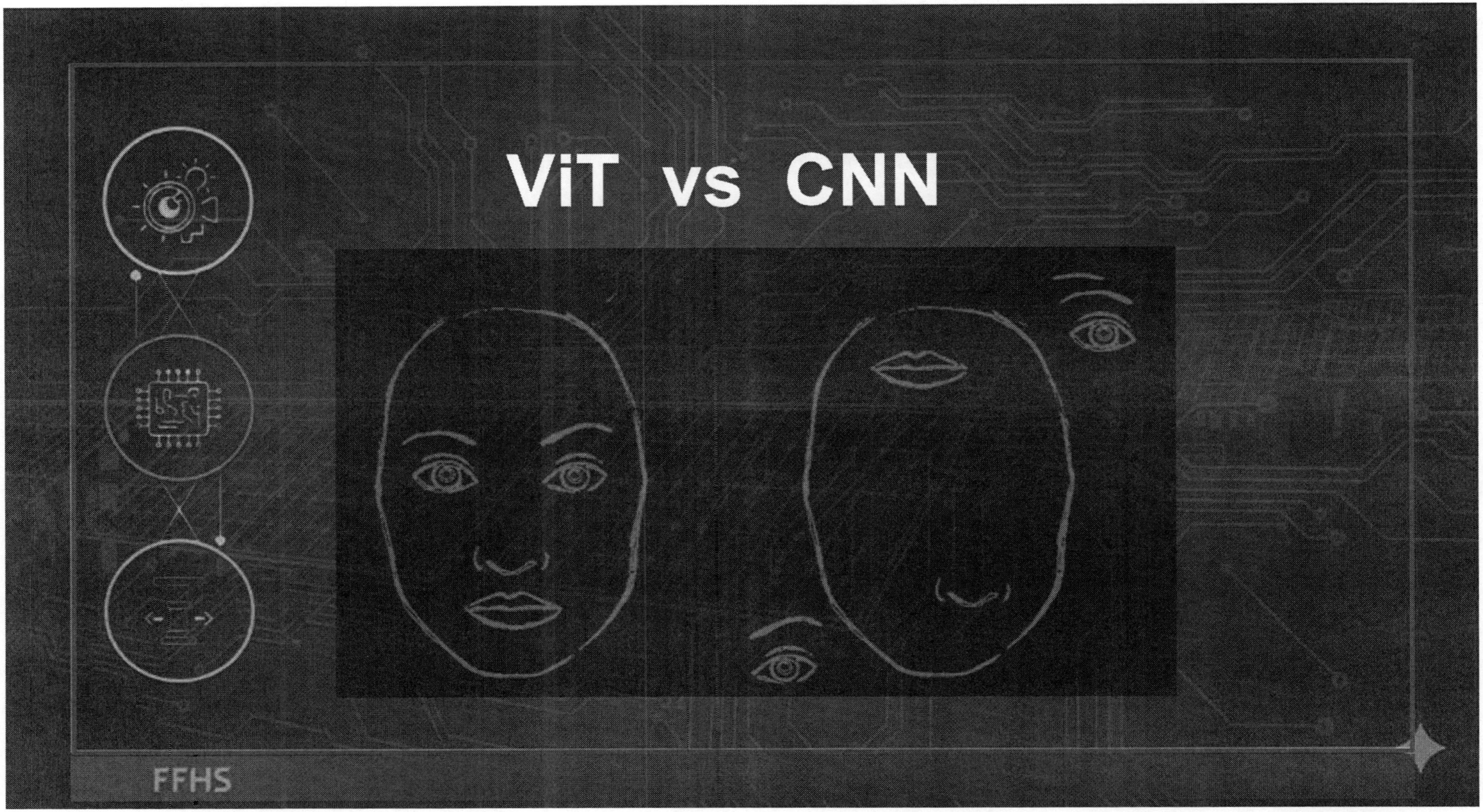
ViT vs CNN
FFHS

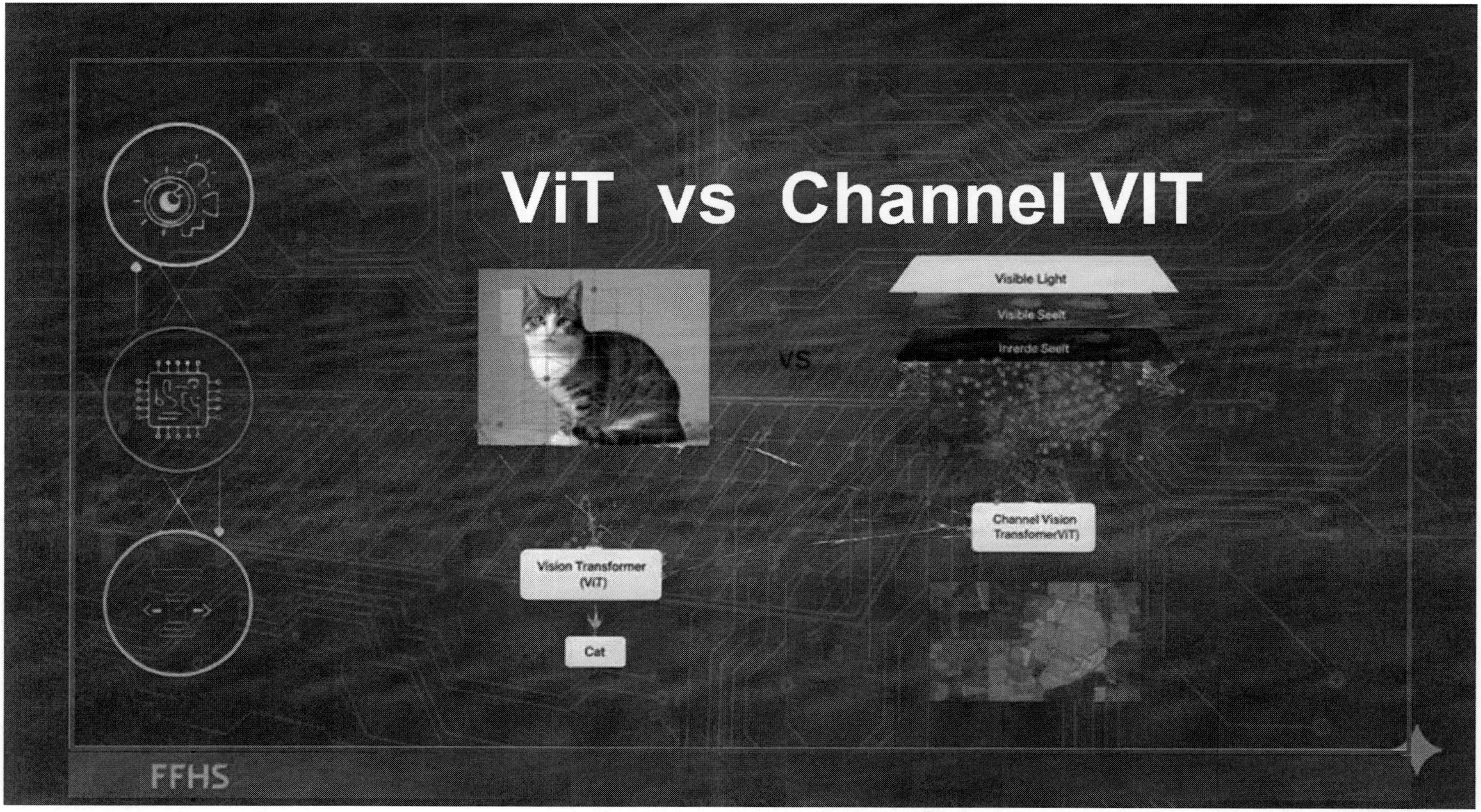
ViT vs Channel VIT
Visible Light
Visible Seelt
Inrerde Seelt
VS
Vision Transformer
(ViT)
Cat
Channel Vision
Transfomer(ViT)
FFHS

Core Technology: Channel Vision Transformer (ChannelViT)

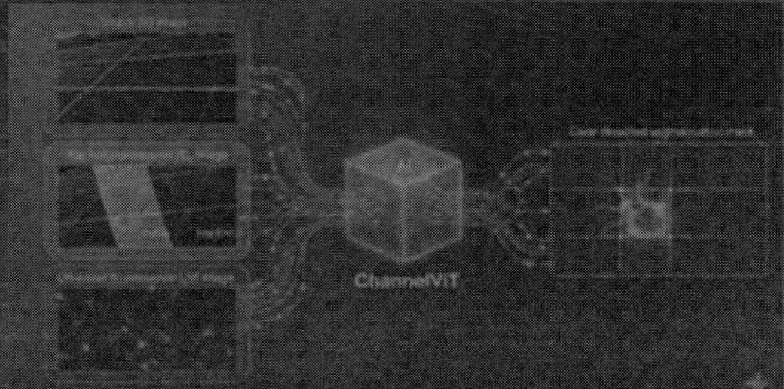

- Multi-Channel Complexity - "Sees" Across Channels - intelligently combine and interpret information from *all five image channels* (VI, EL, UVf).
- Leverages dependencies between channels for more precise defect detection.
- Channel Availability

FFHS

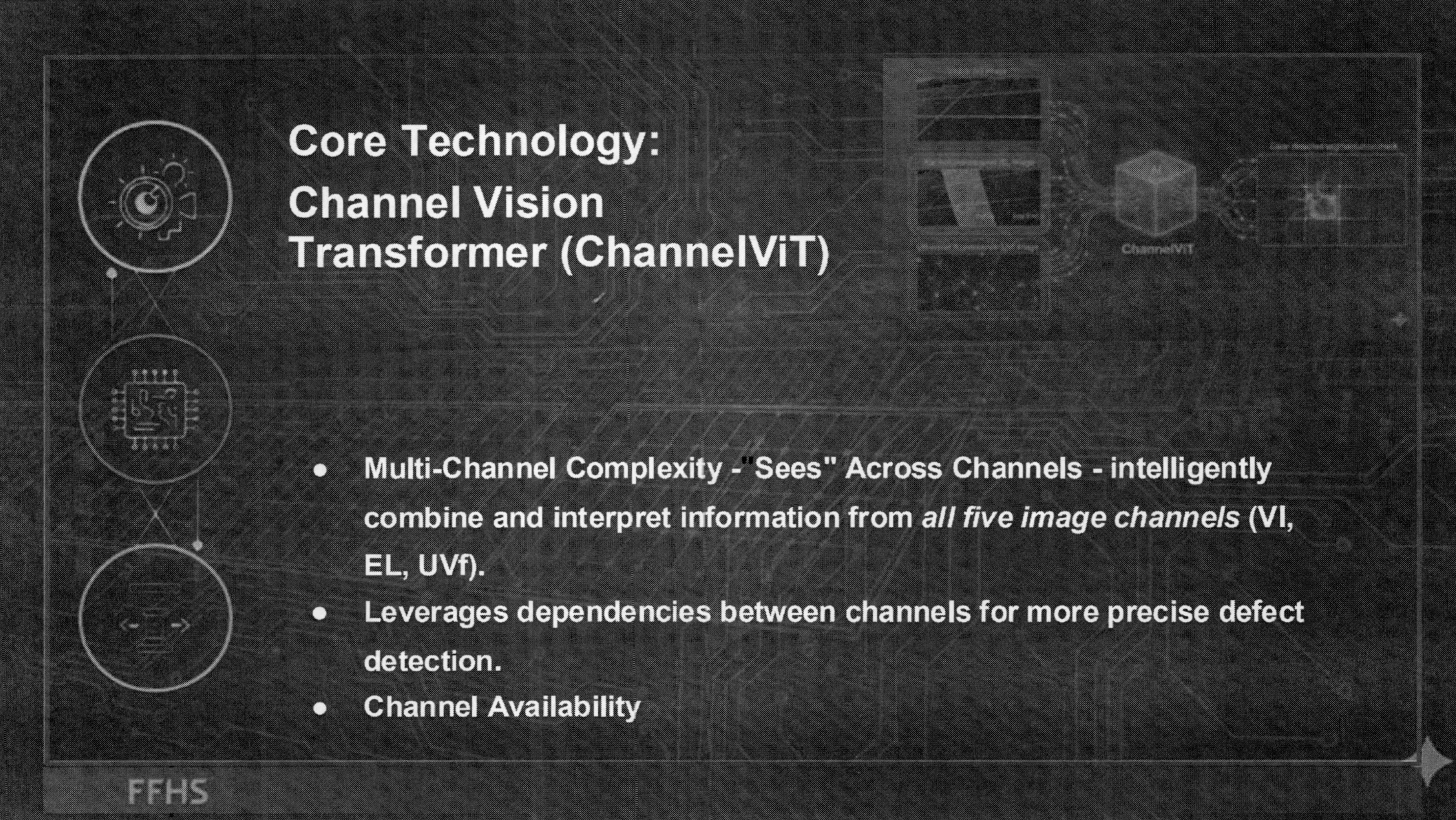

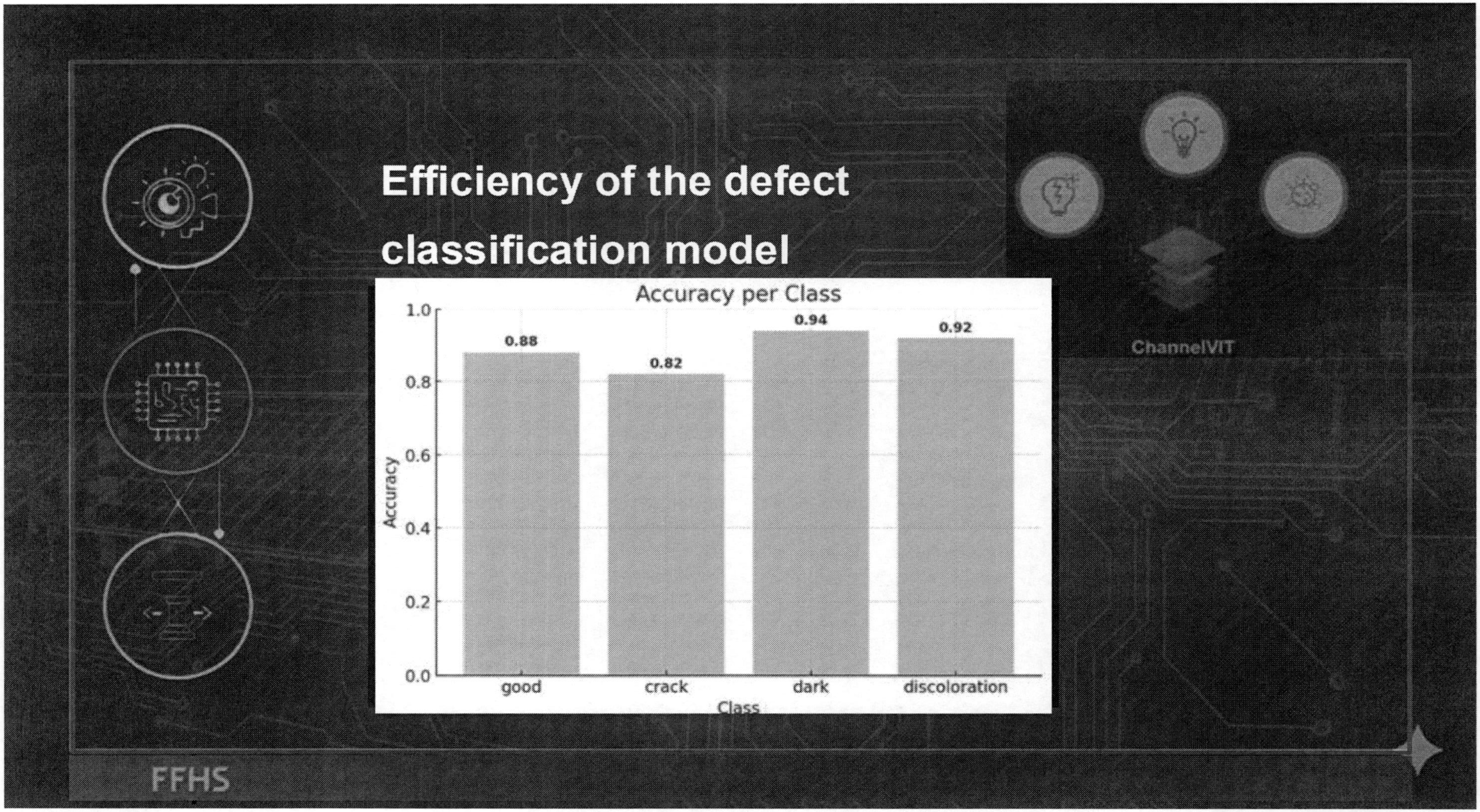
Efficiency of the defect
classification model
Accuracy per Class
1.0
0.8
0.6
0.4
0.2
0.0
Accuracy
0.88
0.82
0.94
0.92
good
crack
dark
discoloration
Class
ChannelViT
FFHS

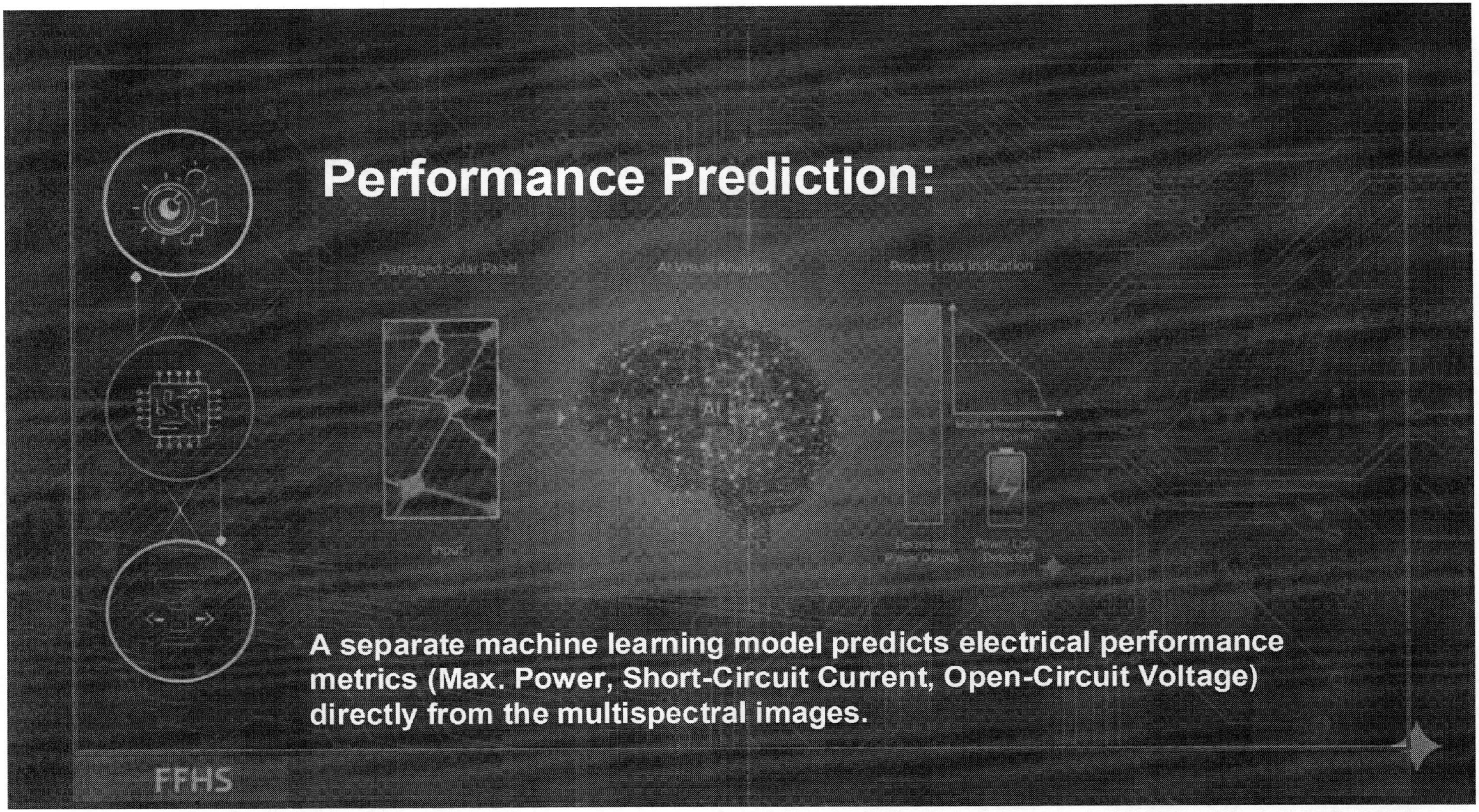
Performance Prediction:
Damaged Solar Panel
AI Visual Analysis
Power Loss Indication
AI
Input
Decreased Power Output
Power Loss Detected
A separate machine learning model predicts electrical performance metrics (Max. Power, Short-Circuit Current, Open-Circuit Voltage) directly from the multispectral images.
FFHS

Performance Prediction:

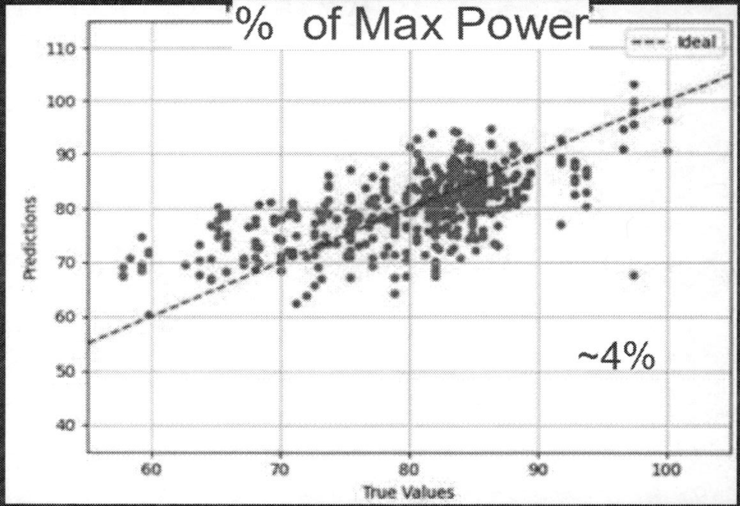

Multispectral

Metric	ResNet-18
MAE	4.35
MedAE	3.38
MSE	32.79
R^2 Score	0.47

Only EL

Metric	ResNet-18
MAE	5.67
MedAE	4.72
MSE	50.61
R^2 Score	0.18

A separate machine learning model predicts electrical performance metrics (Max. Power, Short-Circuit Current, Open-Circuit Voltage) directly from the multispectral images.

FFHS

Performance Prediction:

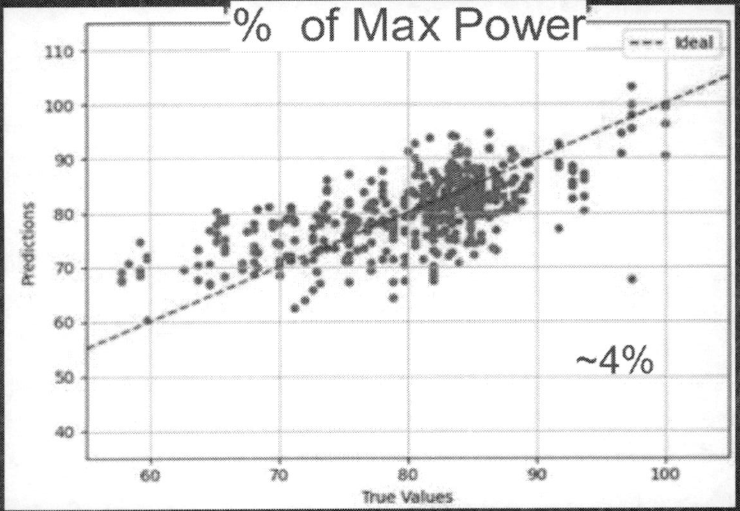

Multispectral

Metric	ResNet-18
MAE	4.35
MedAE	3.38
MSE	32.79
R^2 Score	0.47

Only EL

Metric	ResNet-18
MAE	5.67
MedAE	4.72
MSE	50.61
R^2 Score	0.18

A separate machine learning model predicts electrical performance metrics (Max. Power, Short-Circuit Current, Open-Circuit Voltage) directly from the multispectral images.

FFHS

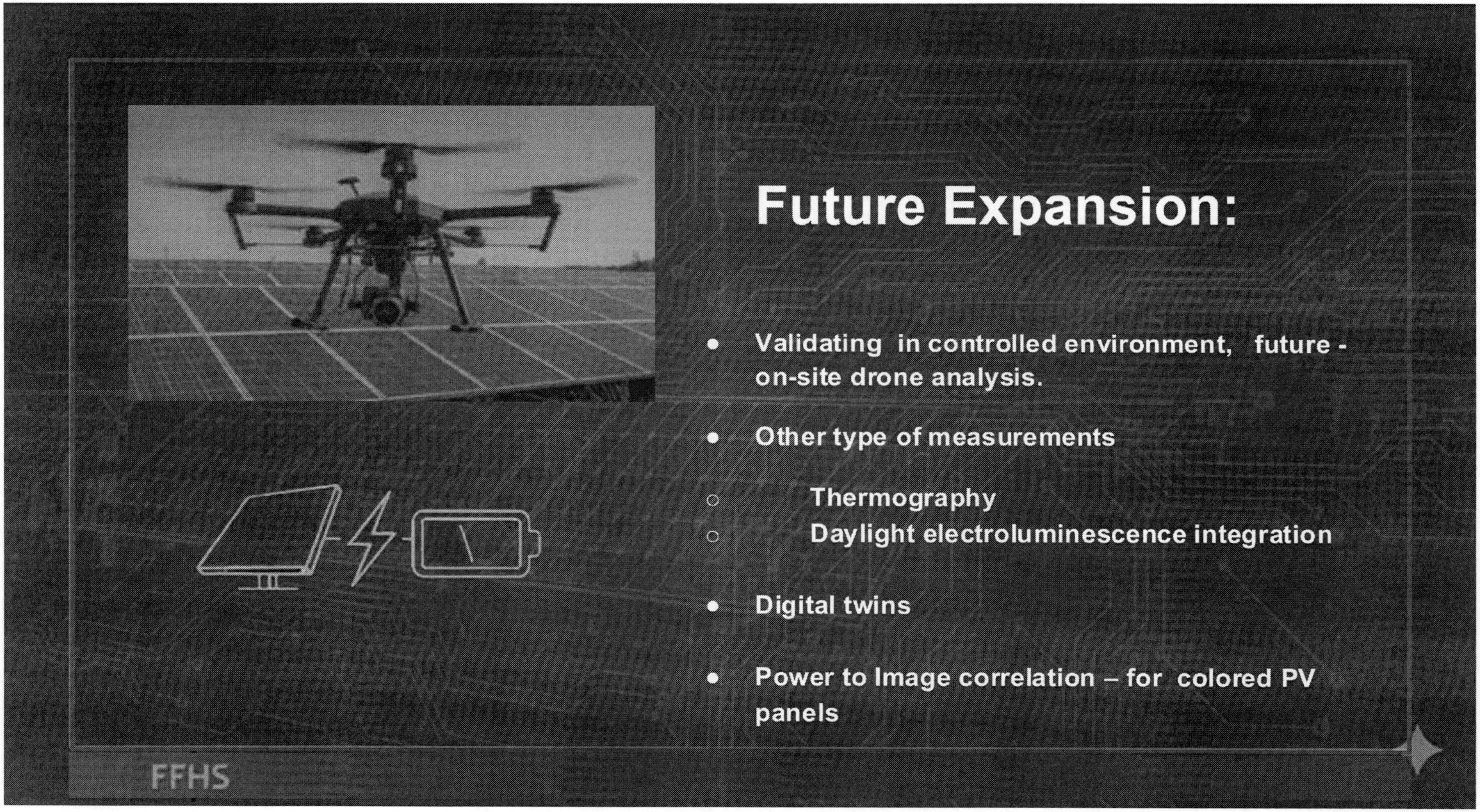
Future Expansion:
Validating in controlled environment, future - on-site drone analysis.
Other type of measurements
Thermography
Daylight electroluminescence integration
Digital twins
Power to Image correlation – for colored PV panels
FFHS

Thank you for your attention!
FFHS
Fernfachhochschule
Schweiz
Mitglied der SUPSI
The EAGLE research Project is being financed by the Swiss Federal Office of Energy and is a collaboration between the Laboratory for Web Science of the FFHS and the SUPSI PVLab.
FFHS
Danuta Paraficz
Ralf Jandl
Natasa Sarafijanovic-Djukic
SUPSI PVLab
Ebrar Özkalay
Mauro Caccivio
ebrar.oezkalay@supsi.ch
dr Danuta Paraficz
Researcher at Swiss Distance
University of Applied Sciences
danuta.paraficz@ffhs.ch

42nd European Photovoltaic Solar Energy Conference and Exhibition

This presentation was selected by the Sc. Committee of the EU PVSEC 2025 for submission of a full paper to one of the EU PVSEC's collaborating peer-reviewed journals.

ASYNCHRONOUS DAYLIGHT LUMINESCENCE OBTAINED WITHOUT PROGRAMMABLE POWER SOURCES

Cristian Terrados[1,2], Eva de la Viuda[1], Kabir Paul Sulca[1], Julian Anaya[1], Miguel Ángel González[1], Oscar Martínez[1*]
[(1)] GdS-Optronlab group, Dpto. Física de la Materia Condensada. Universidad de Valladolid. Edificio LUCIA. Paseo de Belén, 11. Valladolid (Spain)
[(2)] Solar and Wind Feasibility Technologies (SWIFT). Escuela Politécnica Superior, Universidad de Burgos. Avda. Cantabria s/n 09006 Burgos (Spain)
*oscar.martinez@uva.es

ABSTRACT: Daylight Electroluminescence and Photoluminescence techniques (dEL/dPL) have rapidly advanced in recent years and are now well-established tools for the characterization of photovoltaic (PV) Si solar modules in the field. Performing dEL/dPL requires cameras capable of working in the near IR region of the light spectrum (such as InGaAs cameras) and sophisticated filtering procedures to distinguish the weak luminescence emission coming from the PV module from the more intense ambient light. Effective filtering of the weak luminescence requires specific acquisition schemes, both synchronous and asynchronous methods can be used for this purpose. Asynchronous schemes are more convenient, but they usually rely in expensive programmable power sources that produce high quality square or sinusoidal waveforms for the controlled current injection into the PV modules. When paired with fast InGaAs cameras (600 fps), dEL images can be obtained using very short (sub-second) acquisition times. However, the requirement for these programmable power sources may be a significant barrier to rapid in-field deployment of the technique. In this work we show the results of using asynchronous daylight luminescence inspections obtained without programmable power sources, using external control to modulate a DC signal from any power source, including the neighbor panels, or even without the use of a power source but using the Sun as the light source, in the dPL case. We specifically study the shape of the generated current and voltage signals, comparing the external control case with the case of using a programable power source. We also study the impact of varying the modulation frequency and camera speed on image quality and how these acquisition parameters influence performance. This approach broadens the applicability of the dEL technique, enabling effective filtering and identification of panel defects under self-powered or sunlight-driven conditions.
Keywords: daylight luminescence, module inspection, signal modulation, electroluminescence, photoluminescence

1 INTRODUCTION

Luminescence imaging techniques (EL/PL) are very well-established techniques for inspecting the condition of Si PV panels, providing complementary, and often more comprehensive information, compared to infrared thermography (IRT) and I-V characterization techniques [1, 2]. Given the large number of solar modules in a PV plant, the industry increasingly demands fast inspection techniques. For this reason, it is highly beneficial to perform on-site inspections at the solar plant without disassembling the modules, and preferably during the day. This allows for a rapid inspection of the modules and reduces the risk of damage during assembly and disassembly [3, 4]. In this context, daylight imaging techniques, such as dEL and dPL, have recently emerged and advanced rapidly [5-12]. However, it is still challenging to deploy these techniques effectively in a PV plant with a large number of modules. In this work we show a procedure that holds the potential to enable massive inspection of Si solar plants using these powerful techniques. For characterization we use the asynchronous mode, in which a modulated "on" and "off" signal allows for the filtration of the ambient light and allows to obtain the luminescence coming from the PV panels [13, 14]. In our asynchronous approach [14], we have previously used a large (15 kW) programable power source allowing for the high-quality modulated injection of current for a whole solar PV string. In the present work, we use instead an external and compact device to modulate the signal that can arise from any power source, including small and large DC power sources, but also the neighbor panels (self-powering configuration [15]), or even without the use of a power source but using the Sun as the light source, in the dPL case [9, 10, 16]. Combining fast InGaAs cameras, with maximum acquisition speeds of up to 600 fps, adequate optical filters to block as much ambient light as possible, and advanced filtering of the acquired light, allows dEL/dPL images to be recorded in very short times. This process, which eliminates the need for high-quality external programmable power sources to be connected to each string, has therefore the potential to provide a fast and cost-effective inspection of solar modules condition – a growing necessity for the operation and maintenance of medium-to-large solar plants.

To make a comparison with the case of using programmable power sources, we examine the shape of the generated current and voltage signals, as well as the quality of the final dEL image, for modulated signals obtained using a programable power source or those obtained by means of our external control device. We also examine how varying the modulation frequency and camera speed impacts image quality and the effect of these acquisition parameters on performance.

2 EXPERIMENTAL DETAILS

2.1 External device for signal modulation

A compact external device (ED) for square-wave signal modulation has been designed by means of an Arduino-based switching device, incorporating an XBee module for wireless control. The time periods of the "on" and "off" domains are defined and communicated remotely to an IGBT capable of switching up to 1500 V and 15 A. In this way, by connecting the ED to a DC power supply, current is injected into a PV module or string in a square wave scheme, where the frequency of the wave can be easily adjusted. For instance, we have tested frequencies values of 6.25, 12.5, 25.0 and 50.0 Hz. One important advantage of this method is that square-wave signal modulation is generated independently of the power source, including the self-powering configuration of a PV string [15], and can be also applied for the dPL configuration, without the use of a power source, but just using the Sun for excitation and modifying (modulating) the position on the I-V curve to obtain two points with a large difference in currents drawn from the modules [16]. In this way, we can generate square "on" and "off" signals from any power source, also for the dPL case, eliminating the need for expensive, programmable power supplies, and simplifying in-field deployment of the dEL/dPL techniques.

2.1 Asynchronous scheme and experimental set-up

The acquisition of the dEL/dPL images is performed in an asynchronous scheme with the use of a high-speed camera, First Ligh C-RED 2 Lite, 640x512 – ~0.33 Mpixel – and pixel pitch of 15 x 15 μm, with 14-bit quantization and 16-bit dynamical range, with maximum speed of 600 fps. For these measurements, we have used 200 and 400 fps for the InGaAs camera speed. We have fixed the exposition time to 2.5 ms for all the measurements. We use a Kowa short wave infrared (SWIR) optical system with 16 mm focal length for image acquisition. A SWIR bandpass filter, centered around 1160 nm with a bandwidth of 150 nm and a transmittance close to 90%, is used in order to suppress as much ambient light as possible.

Multi-crystalline Si Al-BSF modules (Sharp, ND-AR330H 330 W, V_{oc}=45.5 V, I_{sc}=9.40 A) were used for the dEL/dPL tests. For the dEL case, we performed the signal modulation for just one module, using both a small power source (600 W, labelled as SPS) and the ED, as well as a large programmable power source (EA-PS 91500-30 3U 19" 3U 15000W model, labelled LPPS), which allows us to compare the signal modulation obtained from the programmable power source itself with the one obtained with the ED acting on a DC signal from this LPPS. We also performed dEL measurements exciting a string of 8 modules, also comparing the signal modulation obtained from the LPPS itself with the one obtained with the use of the ED acting on a DC signal from the LPPS. In both cases the injected current was fixed to the I_{sc} value of the modules. We also performed dEL measurements in the self-powering configuration [15], with two modules powering the inspected one, using the ED for signal modulation. We have also performed dPL measurements, using the Sun as the excitation source [10, 16] (that without the need of a power source), using also the ED for signal modulation. In all cases we have recorded both the current intensity and voltage waveforms at the entrance of one inspected module, using Fluke 80i-110s and Fluke 80K-40 probes, respectively.

The obtained whole stack of images is subsequently analyzed in the frequency domain using robust methods previously described [14] to obtain the final luminescence image from the PV panels. The quality of these images can be influenced by the noise and characteristics of the modulated signals. Therefore, the final images are thoroughly analyzed for various acquisition parameters using our previously proposed SNR_{25} metric [14].

3 RESULTS

3.1 dEL inspection of one module by acting on the SPS

The use of non-programmable DC power sources for injecting current into the modules is the standard procedure for EL image inspections on the dark. In particular, the EL inspection of just one Si module can be performed by a small DC power source, able to inject a current close to their I_{sc} value. On the other hand, for the case of dEL inspections, a signal modulation is needed. In this case, an external device to produce the signal modulation is thus required. We have already used in the past our developed ED for signal modulation of a DC signal, but in the synchronous mode, where the signal frequency is highly coupled to the camera speed [10, 16]. Here we have performed the dEL inspection of just one module by acting on a SPS, but in the asynchronous configuration, using different cameras velocities and signal frequencies, which in this case are decoupled.

Fig.1 (a, d) shows the measured current intensities and voltages at the entrance of the inspected module, reflecting the signal modulation performed by means of the ED acting on the SPS. The figure shows the case of two frequencies (25.0 Hz and 50.0 Hz). It can be observed that a non-perfect square wave form was obtained, with transients at the beginning of the "on" periods, with a duration of approx. 8-9 ms, independently of the used frequency. The figure also shows the pixel intensity captured by the InGaAs camera vs the number of images, for camera´s acquisition velocities of 200 and 400 fps for each frequency.

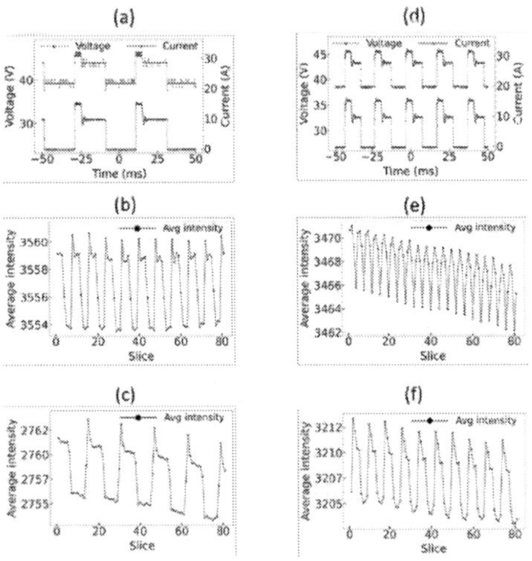

Figure 1: (a, d) Current intensities and voltages at the entrance of the inspected module, generated with the ED acting on a SPS, for ν=25.0 Hz (a) and ν=50.0 Hz (d). (b-f) Pixel intensity variations measured with the InGaAs camera vs number of images, corresponding to situation (a) (ν=25.0 Hz) for cameras′ velocities of 200 fps (b) and 400 fps (c), and to situation (d) (ν=50 Hz) for cameras′ velocities of 200 fps (e) and 400 fps (f), respectively

Thus, the use of the ED acting on the SPS for signal modulation produces a significative transient in both current intensity and voltage signals, with a large extension in time and a significative increase in the current intensity values at the beginning of each cycle. Moreover, the transient in the signal modulation is clearly reflected in the measured pixel intensity. The final dEL images obtained applying the post-processing procedure to different sub-stacks of images are shown in Fig. 2 for frequencies of 12.5 and 25.0 Hz, and a camera speed of 400 fps (G=830 W/m^2). The obtained SNR_{25} marker is good enough (see the following comments), for the case of processing 400 images (Fig. (2b, d)), although the images have some minor errors for the case ν=12.5 Hz. Incorrect processing (with many errors) is observed for the case of processing a lower number of images for a frequency of 12.5 Hz (Fig. 2a); on the other hand, a good image quality is observed for a frequency of 25.0 Hz even processing only a sub-stack of 100 images (Fig. 2c).

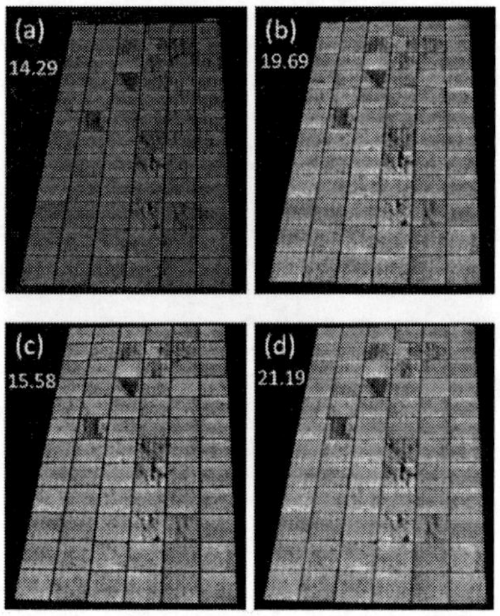

Figure 2: dEL images obtained after post-processing different sub-stacks of images, corresponding to the case of using a SPS, using the ED for square signal modulation. (a, b) ν=12.5 Hz, camera speed 400 fps; (a: post-processing of the first 250 images, b: post-processing of the whole 400 images of the stack). (c, d) ν=25.0 Hz, camera speed 400 fps; (c: post-processing of the first 100 images, d: post-processing of the whole 400 images of the stack) (in all cases G=830 W/m^2) (The SNR_{25} value is indicated on the right upper part of the images)

In this way, the transients do not seem to have a significant impact on the final quality of the dEL images. However, it would be preferable to avoid this type of transients, in order to prevent any effect on the power supply itself.

3.2 dEL inspection of one module by acting on the LPPS

The use of the LPPS allows us to directly compare the signal modulation produced by the power source itself with the modulation produced by means of our ED acting on a DC signal from the LPPS; in this section we show the case of exciting just only one module. Figure 3 shows the current intensities and voltages measured at the entrance of the module for both situations (for ν=50.0 Hz). It can be observed that the LPPS itself produces a perfect square signal (Fig. 3a). On the other hand, the ED acting on the LPPS (DC signal) produces a quite good square signal, except for the introduction, again, of a transient at the beginning of the cycles (Fig. 3d). This transient is now very sharp, with an insignificant time duration; however, there is a large increase in current intensity. Fig. 3 (b-f) also shows the pixel intensity variations vs number of images measured with the InGaAs camera, at speeds of 200 and 400 fps. It can be observed now that the transient in current intensities produced by the ED is not reflected in the pixel intensities (Fig. 3(e, f)), which is ascribed to the very fast transient. In this case, the post-processing of the stack of images is completely similar for both situations. For instance, Figure 4 shows the obtained dEL images after processing a sub-stack of 200 images for a frequency of 50.0 Hz and camera speed of 400 fps, for both the signal modulation produced by the LPPS itself or by means of the ED acting on the LPPS.

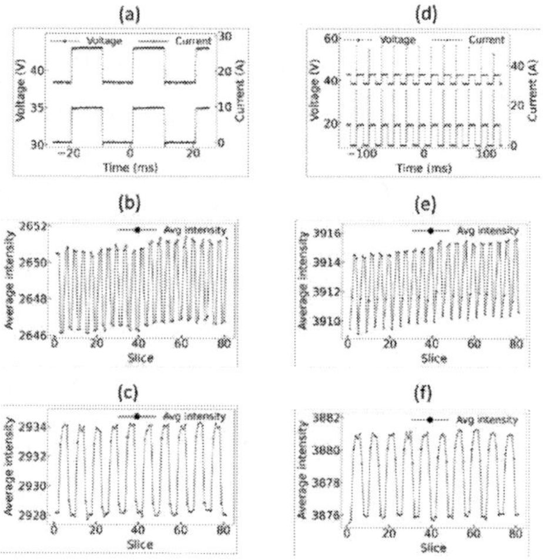

Figure 3: (a, d) Current intensities and voltages at the entrance of the inspected module, generated with the use of the LPPS by means of the power source itself (a) or by means of the ED acting on a DC signal from the LPPS (d), for ν=50.0 Hz. (b-f) Pixel intensity variations measured with the InGaAs camera vs number of captured images corresponding to (a) for camera´s velocities of 200 fps (b) and 400 fps (c), and corresponding to (d) for camera's velocities of 200 fps (e) and 400 fps (f), respectively

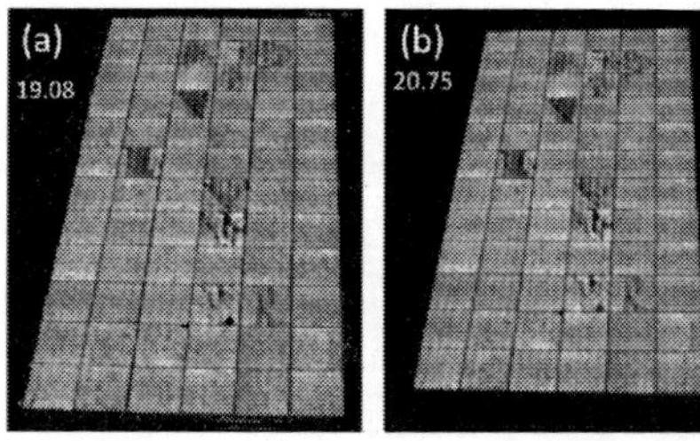

Figure 4: dEL images obtained after the post-processing of a sub-stack of 200 images, for both the signal modulation produced by the LPPS itself (a) or by means of the ED acting on a DC signal from the LPPS (b), for the case ν=50.0 Hz and camera speed of 400 fps (G=500 W/m^2 in (a), while G=840 W/m^2 in (b)). (The SNR_{25} value is indicated on the right upper part of the images)

3.3 dEL inspection of a string of 8 modules by acting on the LPPS

We have also checked the signal modulation produced by the ED for a larger number of excited modules. In particular, in this section we show the case of using the LPPS for exciting 8 modules, comparing again the signal modulation when using the LPPS itself to produce it, respect to the situation of producing the modulation by the ED acting on a DC signal from the LPPS. Figure 5 (a-c) show the current intensities and voltages measured at one module, the one which is inspected with the InGaAs camera. The square wave produced by the LPPS itself is nearly perfect (with some round corners at the beginning of the "on" and "off" periods), whereas the ED produces again transients at the beginning of the cycles. In this case, there is a double transient effect, with a first large and sharp increase in current intensity, followed by a more persistent transient of approx. 7 ms. Figure 5(d-f) shows again the pixel intensities vs the number of images measured with the InGaAs camera. It can be observed that for the case of the modulation produced by the ED acting on the LPPS, the large and sharp transient at the beginning of the cycle is not reflected on the pixel intensities, but the more persistent transient is.

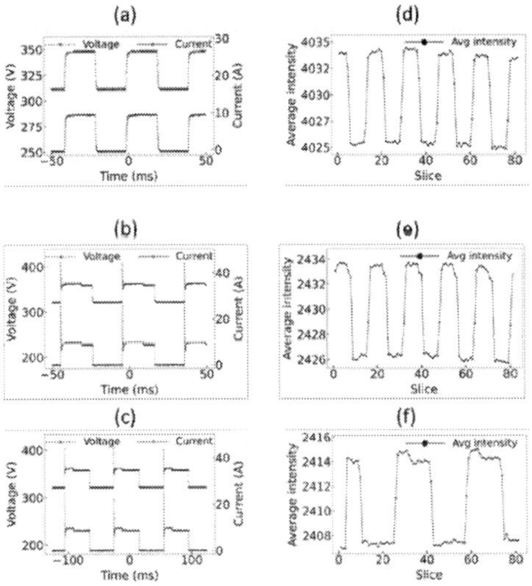

Figure 5: (a – c) Current intensities and voltages at the entrance of the inspected module (8 modules were powered in this case), for both the signal modulation produced by the LPPS itself for ν=25.0 Hz (a) or by means of the ED acting on the LPPS for ν=25.0 Hz (b) and ν=12.5 Hz (c). (d – f) Pixel intensity variations measured with the InGaAs camera vs number of captured images, for a camera velocity of 400 fps, corresponding to (a), (b) and (c), respectively

Figure 6 shows the obtained dEL images for both the signal modulation produced by the LPPS itself or by means of the ED acting on the LPPS, for ν=25.0 Hz and a camera speed of 200 fps. The quality of the dEL images are completely similar, not being affected by the transients. In any case, it is not likely very convenient the generation of these kind of transients for the power source itself. We are at present studying the way to eliminate such transients generated with the use of our ED.

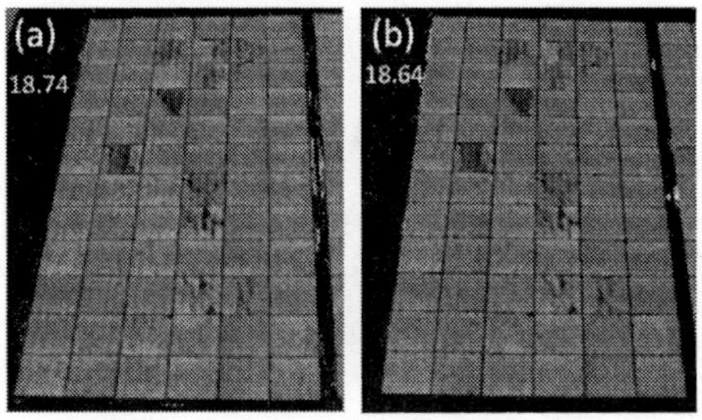

Figure 6: dEL images obtained after the post-processing of the stack of images (first 250 images), for both the signal modulation produced by the LPPS itself (a) or by means of the ED acting on the LPPS (b), for the case ν=25.0 Hz and a camera speed of 200 fps (G=840 W/m^2 in (a), while G=500 W/m^2 in (b)). (The SNR_{25} value is indicated on the right upper part of the images)

3.4 Other arrangements: dEL inspection of one module in the self-powering configuration

The advantage of the ED for signal modulation is to made it independently of the power source. In this section we show the results for the case of an individual module inspected in the self-powering configuration [15], with two other identical modules powering it. Figure 7(a, b) show the current intensities and the voltages measured at the inspected module, for frequencies of 12.5 Hz and 50.0 Hz. In this case, some sharp transients are observed both at the beginning or the end of the cycles, but not for all of them. These transients are not reflected on the pixel intensities captured by the InGaAs camera, Figure 7(c, d).

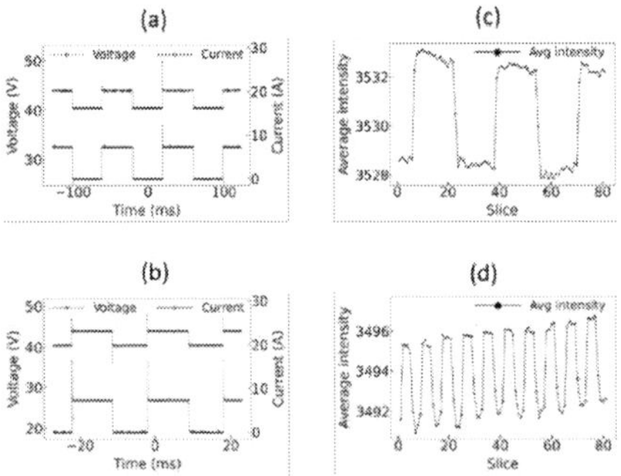

Figure 7: (a, b) Current intensities and voltages at the entrance of the inspected module, for the case of signal modulation produced by the ED acting on 2 modules (self-powering configuration), for ν=12.5 Hz (a) and ν=50.0 Hz (b). (c, d) Pixel intensity variations measured with the InGaAs camera vs number of captured images, for a camera velocity of 400 fps, corresponding to (a) and (b), respectively

Figure 8 shows the post-processed dEL images for a frequency of 12.5 Hz and a camera speed of 400 Hz, for sub-stacks of 300 and 600 images. In this case the quality is not very high due to the lower current injection (approx. 7.5 A instead of I_{sc}) into the inspected panel.

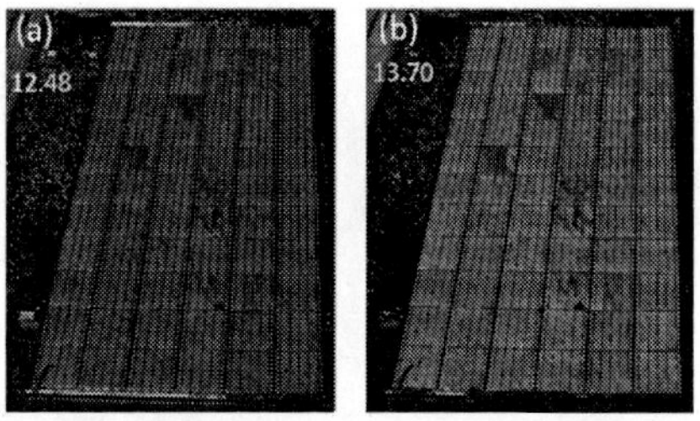

Figure 8: dEL image obtained after the post-processing of the obtained stack of images, for the case of using the ED acting on two other modules, in a self-powering configuration, for the case ν=12.5 Hz and a camera speed of 400 fps (G=840 W/m^2) (a: post-processing of the first 300 images, b: post-processing of the whole 600 images of the stack). (The SNR_{25} value is indicated on the right upper part of the images)

3.5 Analysis of the influence of frequency modulation and camera speed on image quality

We have previously shown the effect on the dEL image quality of processing sub-stacks of different number of images. In this section we will show more details of this dependence, and will analyze also the influence of the acquisition parameters (modulation frequency and camera speed) on the image quality. We have used a complete set of measurements, in particular for the case of the signal modulation produced by the LPPS itself, inspecting just one module (see section 3.2).

The previously mentioned tendency of the SNR_{25} value to decrease with the diminution of the number of processed images is shown in Figure 9, for different frequencies and camera speeds. On the other hand, it is observed that the SNR_{25} marker increases as the frequency of the modulated signal increases from 6.25 Hz to 50.0 Hz, for a camera velocity of 400 fps. Moreover, for a fixed frequency of 12.5 Hz, the SNR_{25} marker increases for a camera velocity of 200 fps respect to the case of 400 fps.

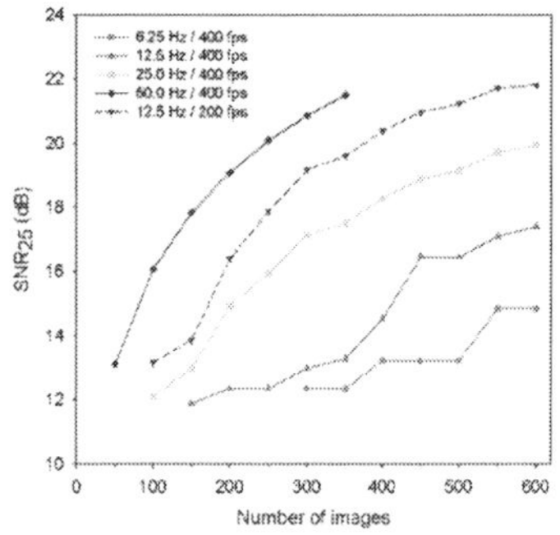

Figure 9: SNR_{25} values obtained after the post-processing of the acquired stacks of images vs number of images of the sub-stack. The data have been obtained for the case of using a programmable source with the signal generated by the power source itself. Different frequencies were used (6.25, 12.5, 25.0 and 50.0 Hz) for a camera velocity of 400 fps. For ν=12.5 Hz, two cameras velocities of 200 and 400 fps were used

This behavior is well understood when we observe the trend of the SNR_{25} marker vs the number of captured cycles for the different sets of data, Figure 10. Clearly, the SNR_{25} value depends nearly linearly with the number of cycles, varying in a minor way with the specific values of frequency and camera speed.

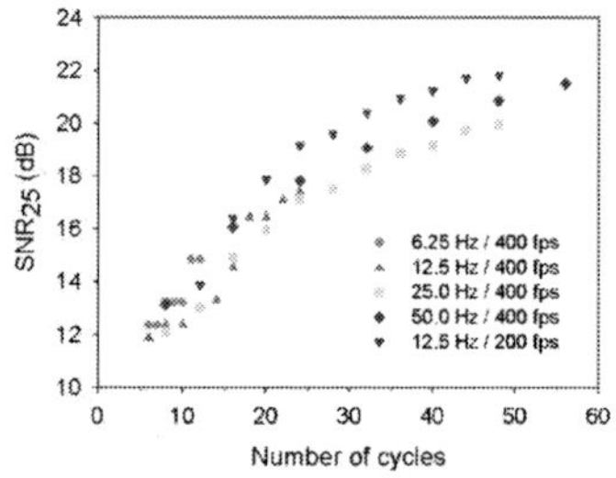

Figure 10: SNR_{25} values vs number of cycles, for the set of data of Fig. 9

We have previously observed that SNR_{25} values of around 16 are enough for a good image quality [14]. This value can be obtained, for instance, for the case of ν=50.0 Hz and a camera speed of 400 fps, for just 16 cycles (100 images), which means inspection times of 250 ms per module. Figure 11 shows, for instance, the obtained dEL images for this especific situation, for sub-stacks of 50, 100, 150 and 200 images.

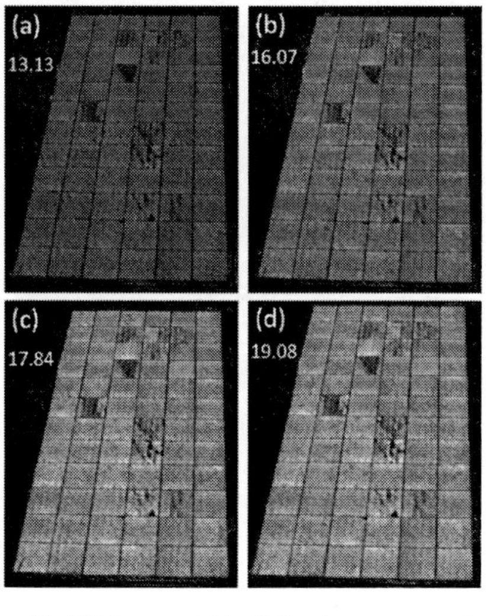

Figure 11: dEL images obtained after the post-processing of the obtained stack of images for the case of signal modulation produced by the LPPS itself, injecting current in only one panel, for the case ν=50.0 Hz and a camera speed of 400 fps (G=500 W/m^2). (a) 50 images; (b) 100 images; (c) 150 images; (d) 200 images. (The SNR_{25} value is indicated on the right upper part of the images)

Good image quality could be obtained in even shorter times when working with higher camera speeds (up to 600 fps). The combination of very short inspections times per module and the possibility to perform the modulation for every kind of power sources, even in the self-powering

10.4229/EUPVSEC2025/3BO.11.5

configuration or in the dPL mode, has therefore the potential to provide a fast and cost-effective inspection of solar modules condition.

4 CONCLUSIONS

In this study, we present a novel approach to asynchronous daylight luminescence inspection that eliminates the need for expensive programmable power sources. This simplifies and accelerates the deployment of these powerful techniques in the field. Our compact external device successfully modulates DC signals from various sources, including small and large power sources, as well as neighboring modules, in a self-powered configuration. dPL measurements can also be obtained.

We have demonstrated that, although the external device may introduce signal transients, this does not affect the quality of the final dEL images. Thorough analysis using the SNR_{25} metric revealed that high modulation frequencies and camera speeds enable very short acquisition times of as little as 250 ms per module without compromising image quality.

This methodology offers a cost-effective and scalable solution for inspecting large-scale solar plants. By leveraging readily available — or even self-generated — power, our approach enables high-quality luminescence imaging to be used more widely. This addresses the growing need for rapid and efficient operation and maintenance in the solar PV industry. Further work is underway to eliminate the signal transients observed with our device.

5 ACKNOWLEDGMENTS

This work has been funded by the Spanish Ministry of Science and Innovation, under project PID2023-148369OB-C43, financed by MICIU/AEI /10.13039/501100011033 and FEDER/UE, and by the Regional Government of Castilla y León (Junta de Castilla y León) and by the Ministry of Science and Innovation and the European Union NextGenerationEU / PRTR under the project "Programa Complementario de Materiales Avanzados". K. Sulca has been funded under the call for predoctoral contracts UVa 2022, co-financed by Banco Santander. C. Terrados is also grateful for the financial support received under project PDC2022-133419-I00, funded by MCIN/AEI/10.13039/ 501100011033 and NextGenerationEU/PRTR.

6 REFERENCES

[1] L. Koester, S. Lindig, A. Louwen, A. Astigarraga, G. Manzolini, D. Moser, Renew. Sustain. Energy Rev. 165 (2022) 112616.

[2] S. Gallardo-Saavedra, L. Hernández-Callejo, M.C. Alonso-García, J.D. Santos, J.I. Morales-Aragones, V. Alonso-Gómez, A.M. Moretón-Fernández, M.A. González-Rebollo, O. Martínez, Energy 205 (2020) 117930.

[3] I. Høiaas, K. Grujic, A. Gerd, I. Burud, E. Olsen, N. Belbachir, Renew. Sustain. Energy Rev. 161 (2022) 112353.

[4] O. Kunz, J. Schlipf, A. Fladung, Y.S. Khoo, K. Bedrich, T. Trupke, Z. Hameiri, Prog. Energy 4 (2022) 042014.

[5] L. Stoicescu, M. Reuter, J.H. Werner, Proceedings 29th Eur. Photovolt. Sol. Energy Conf. Exhib., (2014) 2553.

[6] J. Adams, B. Doll, C. Buerhop, T. Pickel, J. Teubner, C. Camus, C.J. Brabec, Proceedings 32nd Eur. Photovolt. Sol. Energy Conf. Exhib., (2015) 1837.

[7] S. Koch, T. Weber, C. Sobottka, A. Fladung, P. Clemens, J. Berghold, Proceedings 32nd Eur. Photovolt. Sol. Energy Conf. Exhib., (2016) 1736.

[8] G.A. dos Reis Benatto, N. Riedel, S. Thorsteinsson, P.B. Poulsen, A. Thorseth, C. Dam-Hansen, C. Mantel, S. Forchhammer, K.H.B. Frederiksen, J. Vedde, M. Petersen, H. Voss, M. Messerschmidt, H. Parikh, S. Spataru, D. Sera, Proceedings 44th IEEE Photovolt. Specialist Conf., (2017) 2682.

[9] R. Bhoopathy, O. Kunz, M. Juhl, T. Trupke, Z. Hameiri, Prog. Photovoltaics Res. Appl. 26 (2018) 69.

[10] M. Guada, A. Moretón, S. Rodríguez-Conde, L.A. Sánchez, M. Martínez, M.A. González, J. Jiménez, L. Pérez, V. Parra, O. Martínez, Energy Science & Engineering 8 (2020) 3839.

[11] L. Koester, A. Louwen, S. Lindig, G. Manzolini, D. Moser, Solar RRL 8 (2014) 2300676.

[12] M . Vuković, M.S. Wiig, G.A. dos Reis Benatto, E. Olsen, I. Burud, Prog. Energy 6 (2024) 032001.

[13] G. A. dos Reis Benatto, R. Del Prado, T. Kari, M. Bartholomäus, L. Morino, P.B. Poulsen, S.V. Spataru, Proceedings 8th World Conference on Photovoltaic Energy Conversion, (2022) 735.

[14] C. Terrados, D. González-Francés, J. Anaya, K.P. Sulca, V. Gómez-Alonso, M.A. González, O. Martínez, Proceedings 40th Eur. Photovolt. Sol. Energy Conf. Exhib. (2023) 3DO.16.5.

[15] I. A. Carpintero, M.A. González, C. Terrados, O. Martínez, D. González-Francés, K.P. Sulca, V. Alonso, Solar Energy 301 (2025) 113913.

[16] C. Terrados, D. González-Francés, K.P. Sulca, C. de Castro, M.A. González, O. Martínez, Progress in Photovoltaics (2025) doi.org/10.1002/pip.70004.

LUMINESCENCE MEASUREMENTS OF PV MODULES WITH A COST-EFFECTIVE AND SMALL-SIZED HOOD-BASED TOOL UNDER DAYLIGHT CONDITIONS

Marc Köntges[1], Michael Siebert[1], D. Lorenz[2], B. Kuhrmann[2], Michael Fuß[2]
[1]Institute for Solar Energy Research Hamelin, [2]MBJ Solutions GmbH

ABSTRACT: We developed a small sized luminescence tool for photovoltaic (PV)-systems that can measure luminescence of a small part of a PV module. The tool measures the luminescence signal under maximum power point (mpp) conditions. For excitation of the solar cells 850 nm LEDs are used and the luminescence is measured with a small sized industry InGaAs camera. Furthermore, the tool detects a unique luminescence patter caused by the reverse current if the module substring has an electrically disconnected bypass diode. To the best of our knowledge, no other luminescence tool can detect this failure without changing the circuits of the PV system. The physical cause of this luminescence pattern is discussed in the paper. As the measurement procedure does not need any opening of electrical contacts it can be operated by any person with a short safety instruction. The paper describes the basic working principle of the measurement technique and simulations of the electrical circuit of the module are show. A 1.5 times higher excitation level in the hood relative to a 1000 W/m² sun irradiation stabilizes the working point to get reproducible luminescence images. During the measurement the inverter can work in normal mpp tracking mode and no access to the inverter is needed. The system is capable of performing measurements under daylight conditions and is sufficiently compact to be transported conveniently during travel. However, you need physical access to the modules to be tested.
Keywords: electroluminescence, luminescence, reliability, inspection, PV modules

1 Introduction

Electroluminescence (EL) imaging methods give very detailed results for assessing the quality of a PV module. The EL method allows to detect most relevant failure modes (potential induced degradation, cell cracking, light induced degradation, electrical not connected cell interconnect ribbons, not connected modules, and short circuit bypass diodes, etc.) in a PV system [1]. Even measuring EL during day light and using a drone is possible [2]. However, to take EL images the electrical circuit of the module string has to be modified and a large powerful generator is needed on site to provide the needed power for the measurement [3]. Recently developed methods allow luminescence measurements during day light without changes in the electrical circuit [4]. However, for most existing outdoor luminescence methods, you need extra light modulation units on the modules or experimental and expensive filtering technique for blocking the unwanted reflected sunlight [3][4]. A new technique uses inverter based working point switching of the PV generator to extract the wanted luminescence signal from the day light background [5] by dark field subtraction. In this case one needs full access to the inverter. A new light induced electroluminescence method [6] does not need to change electrical circuits and does not need access to the inverter but it is only applicable to half-cell modules with internal parallel connected substrings. A drawback, common to all daylight luminescence technologies is, that they are not able to detect the important failure where the bypass diode of a substring is not connected (lost bypass diode). Therefore, we developed a new method combining all advantages of luminescence imaging in a small measurement tool to assess the quality of solar modules including the detection of lost bypass diodes. In the following we evaluate a small sized hood with switchable LED excitation light and an InGaAs camera to measure the luminescence of parts of PV modules in a PV array. The hood is simply moved onto a PV module bank in a PV system. We discuss how to bring the PV-module into the required working points for defect analysation and test its applicability under realistic conditions.

2 SETUPS

2.1 Prototype equipment

To demonstrate the new method, we setup two versions of a luminescence hood. We built one prototype to test the feasibility of the method presented in this chapter and one so called Quickcheck system presented in chapter 2.2 for realistic tests in the large PV systems. For image capturing in the prototype setup a SenS 1280V-ST camera from New Imaging Technologies is used with a resolution of 1280 x 1024 and a 14-bit dynamic range. However, the presented images have a resolution of about 290 x 445 pixel as the useful field of view (~32 cm x 50 cm) is limited. The camera is included in a hood shading the module part of interest which minimizes image artifacts from reflected sun light. The cameras optical axis is orthogonal to the module surface. The distance between camera and module is about 100 cm.

To eliminate background light all outdoor luminescence images presented here are difference images by combining an image taken without and an image taken with artificial illumination using infrared LEDs. The centre wave length of the used LEDs is 850 nm. A bandpass filter with a centre wavelength of 1150 nm and a bandwidth of ±25 nm is mounted onto the camera. It enables only the Si-luminescence spectrum to pass to the camera sensor while blocking the visible light spectrum and the LED peak spectrum. A typical exposure time for one image is 20 ms.

Figure 1: Basic setup of the luminescence tool with LED light, camera and camera filter on top of a half-cell PV module.

2.2 Professional equipment

The Quickcheck (Qcheck) tool is a small hood including some high intensity infrared LED flash light injecting a charge carrier density in the solar cells higher than the sun irradiation at 1000 W/m². A cost effective InGaAs camera with a resolution of 640 x 512 pixel is used to take luminescence images. The hood (~80 cm x 60 cm and 60 cm height) can be used on a part of a PV module to take luminescence images of a selected region. A typical exposure time for one image is 10 ms.

2.3 Measuring method

Images are taken under the following conditions.

1. While the LED flash is off, the cells under test are shaded and in reverse voltage. Not connected cell parts are at 0 V. There is no luminescence from cells at 0 V and from cells in reverse voltage. The bypass diode of the module passes the current close to the maximum power point I_{mpp} in parallel to the shaded PV module substring.
2. While the LED flash is on, the inverter still keeps the PV module string at the previous voltage of the LED OFF state as it is not able to react fast enough. There is enough light on the cells that the cell works also in I_{mpp} and the bypass diodes are not active any more. Therefore, I_{mpp} current is flowing through the solar cells.

The pixelwise subtraction of the images taken at condition 2 minus 1 allows to measure luminescence of cells under I_{mpp} current. All unwanted light is eliminated by this subtraction.

To increase the image quality multiple image pairs can be taken and averaged.

As the exposure time is very short in comparison to the dark time the electrical working point of the module is mainly in the shaded condition. Consequently, the inverter moves the PV module string into the voltage working point where the module substring under test is shaded.

2.4 PV modules under test

We use two types of test setups to assess the feasibility of the luminescent hood system.

The first test setup is a PV system consisting of nine solar modules with full M6 monocrystalline PERC cells (6 x 10) which are serially connected and regulated by an inverter of type Sunny Boy 3.6 from SMA Solar Technology AG. The solar modules are mechanically installed on a 38° inclined test roof top facing south. This system is used for measurements with the prototype equipment. Strings are measured in 3 situations:

1. Inverter OFF, no extra shading
2. Inverter ON, 100% shade on two cells of the substring under test
3. Inverter ON, no extra shading

The second test setup is a PV system consisting of M10 TOPCON half-cell modules (6 x 24 cells) within a string of 27 modules attached to a string inverter in a large PV system. Two module strings are attached to one maximum power point tracker. One module with a lost bypass diode in the middle substring is measured with the Qcheck equipment. The string is measured only under Inverter ON with no extra shading.

3 Simulation of electrical working points

3.1 Spice model

For the working point simulation of the half-cell PV module and of the cell voltage under the hood, a LTSPICE XVII [11] simulation is used. The solar cells are modeled by a two-diode model per half-cell. Each solar cell is represented by two parallel connected diodes, a parallel current source, a parallel resistance, and a series connected resistance. The schematic for the numerical simulation of the cell voltage for the LED OFF and LED ON situation under the hood is shown in Figure 2. The simulation parameters of the two-diode model are summarized in Table I. 10 solar cells are under the test hood and all the other cells of the module are irradiated by sun light at 1000 W/m².

We set up two simulation scenarios, listed in Table II. In the scenario "LED intensity" we vary the intensity of the LED light. In the scenario "Resistance" we simulate the cell voltage of an active cell part (75% of the cell area) and an inactive cell part (25% of the cell area) while the inactive cell part is contacted to the cell busbar by a very high ohmic resistance. This cell is one cell under the hood.

The models simulate the IV curve of the module when the Luminescence tool is on the module with LEDs OFF and shading 10 half-cells as shown in Figure 1 and LEDs ON. The voltage drop of a cell under the hood is used for evaluating the expected luminescence of the cells under the hood.

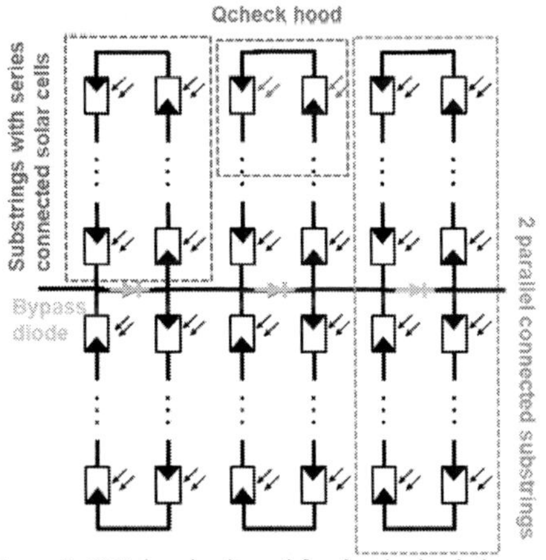

Figure 2: LTSpice circuit used for electric simulation.

Table I: Simulation basis parameter for an arbitrary half-cell PV module with 20 cell per substring, 6 substring (120 cells in total) and a STC power of ~345 Wp.

Parameter	Units	Value
A	cm²	136.0
j_{01}	fA/cm²	96.4
j_{02}	fA/cm²	3686.2
j_{sc}	mA/cm²	38.3
R_s	Ωcm²	0.7077
R_{sh}	Ωcm²	10000

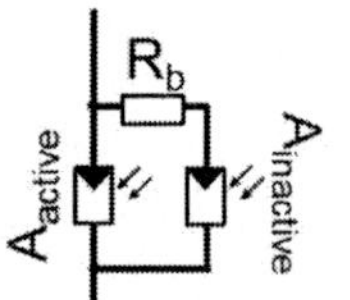

Figure 3: Circuit diagram of the active and the broken cell parts connected by the break resistance R_b. A_{active} and $A_{inactive}$ are, respectively, the areas of the connected part and the disconnected part of a cell and are represented by the same electrical model.

Table II: Description of the frame conditions of the LT Spice simulation and description of the parameter variation in Scenario LED Intensity and Resistance.

Scenario	Explanation	Range
all	Irradiance on cells outside the hood	1000 W/m²
LED Intensity	10 cells under the hood with various excitation levels	0 W/m² - 1500 W/m² in steps of 100 W/m²
Resistance	One cell under the hood with	25% of one cell area connected with 100 kOhm to busbar and 1500 W/m² Irradiance on cells inside the hood

4 RESULTS

4.1 Simulation results LED intensity

The simulation results for the half-cell PV module, based on the parameters listed in Table I, are presented in Figure 4**Figure 6**. Figure 4**Figure 6** shows the simulated IV curve of the PV module (black lines) and a cell under the hood (red lines) when the measurement hood shades 10 cells of one substring. While the measurement the module outside the hood is exposed to a simulated AM1.5 excitation at 1000 W/m² in the module plane. The simulation corresponds to the hood position illustrated in Figure 1 and the corresponding electrical circuit sketched in Figure 2. The simulated IV curves are parametrized for an AM1.5 spectrum equivalent LED excitation of 0 W/m² (straight lines), 1000 W/m² (dashed lines), 1500 W/m² (doted lines) to the cells under the hood. Furthermore, the cell voltage of one half-cell under the hood is shown for the same LED irradiation variation.

The blue dot in Figure 4 shows the maximum power working point of the PV module without illumination under the hood. As the LED lights of the hood are off most of the time we assume that the inverter moves the working point of the PV module string into the blue dot. Due to its slow response to the very short light on phases (10 ms) the inverter should not move to the light on working point. The black dotted line is a guide to the eye to find the corresponding voltage of a shaded cell in the hood. At that working point the cells under the hood have a voltage below 0 V. At 0 W/m² the cells in the hood work at negative voltage and does not luminesce. At 1000 W/m² the cell voltage is at about 373 mV and the luminescent emission is very weak. At 1500 W/m² the cell voltage is at about 639 mV and the luminescent emission is strong.

Even if the inverter will regulate the voltage a bit during 1500 W/m² of LED excitation the cell voltage under the hood will stay constant (less than 1% change) over a large range from 0 V to 35 V of PV module voltage. This guaranties reproducible results under unwanted inverter voltage regulation. Even if the inverter will regulate the voltage at 1500 W/m² into the new V_{mpp} at 34.5 V the voltage of the cell under test stays almost constant (639 mV to 640 mV).

As the LED intensity has also a significant influence on the cell under test voltage and its stability Figure 5 shows the voltage of a cell under the hood as a function of the LED intensity equivalent to an AM1.5 irradiation. Up to 1000 W/m² the cell voltage range, shown with the error bars, has a great dependence on the actual working point of the inverter. Starting with 1100 W/m² the dependence on the working point of the inverter vanishes. So, it is important to work with the hood some W/m² above the current out door irradiation to have stable conditions during luminescence measurement.

Remember even if the inverter shifts its working point the module and the cells under the hood work still under a current close to I_{mpp} during LED ON. So, we still see luminescence pattern influenced by lateral varying resistances on the cell.

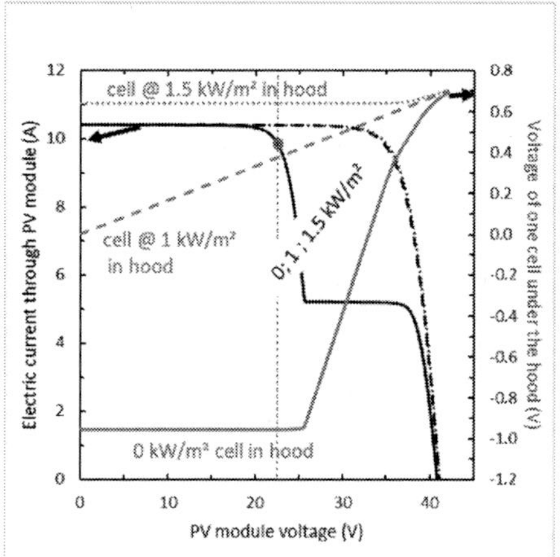

Figure 4: Current voltage curves (black) of the entire half-cell PV module under test and voltage of a cell under the hood (red). The cell voltage and the *IV* curves for the PV module are shown for 1000 W/m² irradiation outside the hood and 0 W/m², 1000 W/m², and 1500 W/m² AM1.5 irradiation equivalent LED irradiation under the hood. Exemplary it is assumed that 10 half-cells are under the hood.

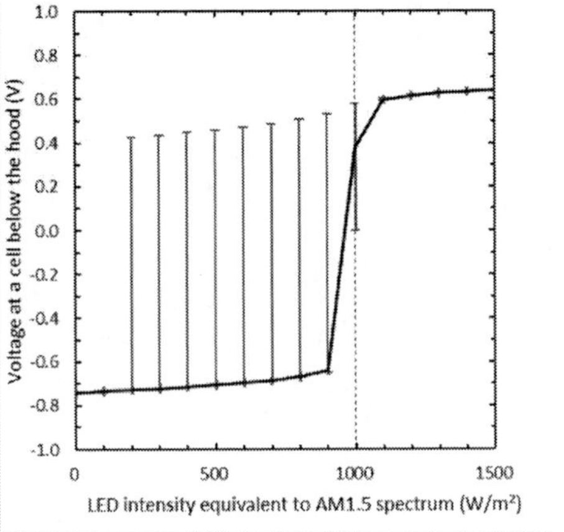

Figure 5: Voltage at a solar cell under the hood as a function of the LED intensity equivalent to an AM1.5 irradiation. The error bars show the range of voltage working point if the inverter is regulating the module voltage between 0 V and V_{mpp} in the LED ON case.

4.2 Simulation results resistance

To assess the influence of cell defects which are caused by serial resistances on a cell we simulate the electrical circuit of a PV module with one defect cell having a 75% active and a 25% inactive cell area as shown in Figure 3. This defective cell is located under the measurement hood.

Figure 6 a) shows the simulated IV curve of the PV module while LEDs are OFF in the measurement hood. Furthermore, the voltage of the active and inactive cell part is shown. As the active cell part is in the main circuit and shaded it is driven into reverse voltage when the module is in the Impp working point where the bypass diode carries the main current. The inactive cell part carries no current because of the high series resistance and therefore no voltage is applied to the inactive part of the cell. In this case both cell parts do not emit luminescence radiation.

Figure 6 b) shows the simulated IV curve of the PV module when the LEDs in the measurement hood irradiate the 10 cells below the hood at an equivalent AM 1.5 irradiation of 1500 W/m². Again, the black dotted line represents the PV module working voltage under LED OFF conditions. At this voltage and from 0 V to V_{mpp} the voltage of both cell parts is positive and both parts irradiate luminescence. However, the active part irradiates less luminescence compared to the inactive cell part.

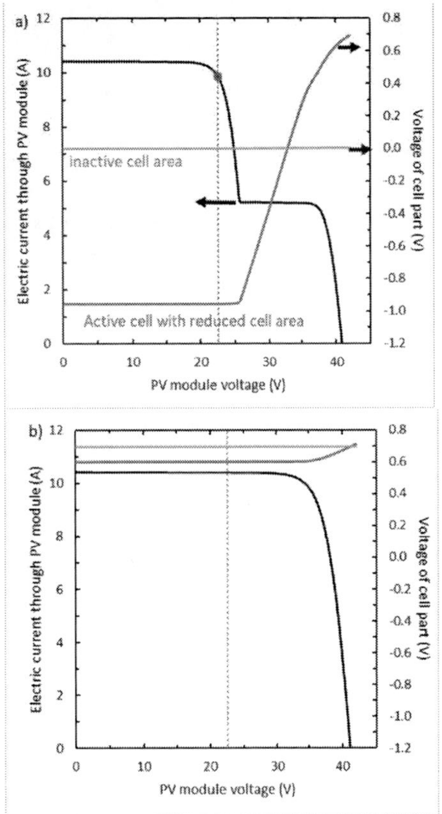

Figure 6: Current/voltage curves (black) of the entire half-cell PV module under test and voltage of a broken cell with its active (red) and inactive (grey) cell part under the hood. a) shows the conditions during dark conditions in the hood and b) shows the conditions while the cells under the hood are under LED irradiation (assuming an equivalent of 1500 W/m² AM1.5). Exemplary it is assumed that 10 half-cells are under the hood. Outside the hood 1000 W/m² AM1.5 excitites the rest of the PV module.

This enables us to identify inactive or resistive coupled cell parts. Inactive or resistive coupled cell parts are always brighter in luminescence then active cell parts.

10.4229/EUPVSEC2025/3BO.11.6

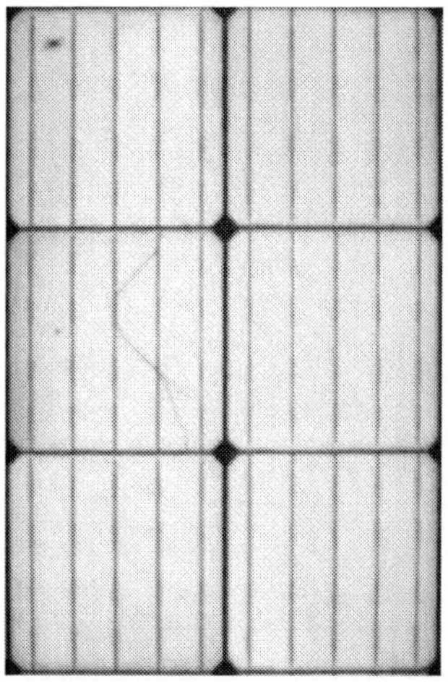

Figure 7: Hood based outdoor luminescence image of a test module made while the module is in V_{oc} conditions.

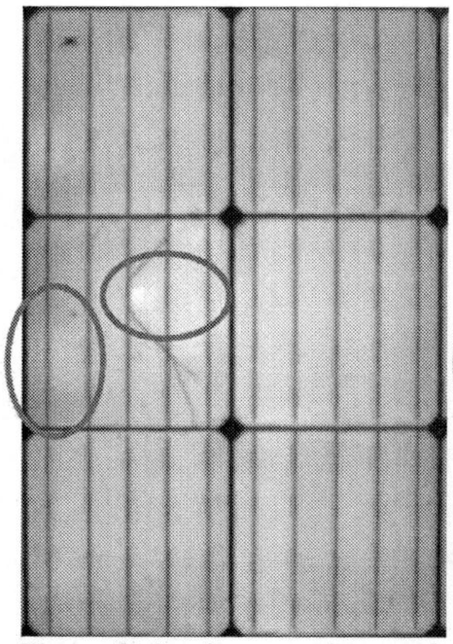

Figure 8: Luminescence image of same test module as in Fig. 2 made during mpp tracking of the inverter with 5.0 A module current at 645 W/m² sun irradiation in module plane.

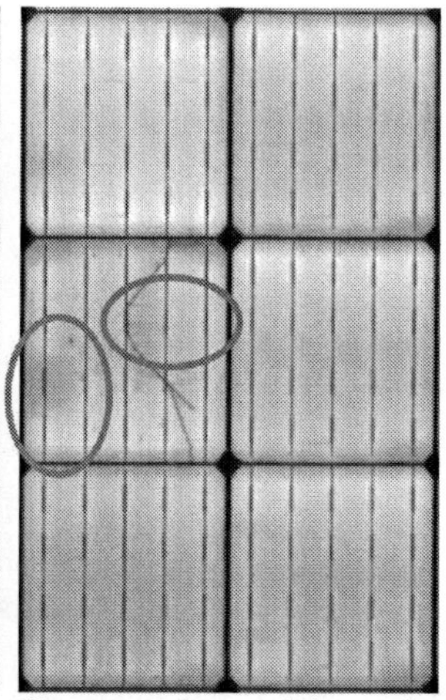

Figure 9: Lab based electroluminescence image of same test module as in Figure 7 and Figure 8 at 9.3 A module current.

4.1 Results for prototype equipment

Figure 7 shows a luminescence image of a part of a full cell module while the inverter is in OFF state. We see very bright solar cells with very little contrast. We see two cells with a cell crack (top left and middle left). An almost identical image (here not shown) is measured when the inverter is in ON state but we fully shade cells of the substring under test.

Figure 8 shows a luminescence image of a part of a full cell module while the inverter in ON state of the same module part as shown in Figure 7. We see much more contrast. Some red marked areas of the middle left cell are brighter than other areas.

Figure 9 shows an electroluminescence image of the same module part as shown in Figure 7 and Figure 8. Some red marked areas of the middle left cell are darker than other areas. These are areas with an additional resistance to the darker cell areas. This areas anticorrelate to the bright cell areas in the luminescence image in Figure 8.

5.2 Lost bypass diode with Qcheck equipment

In Figure 10 a luminescence image taken with the Qcheck system of a PV module with a lost bypass diode in a string with inverter on is shown. In this case the Qcheck system shades only four cells of one of two parallel connected substrings. Except for not equal luminescent cells no special pattern can be seen.

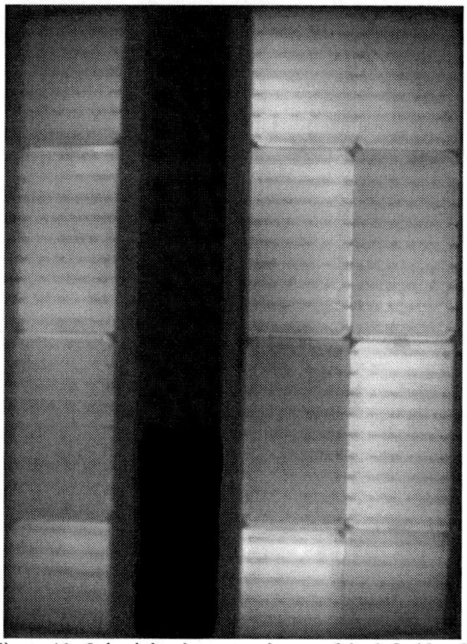

Figure 10: Qcheck luminescence image of the left side of solar cells of the middle substring of a half cell module with lost bypass diode. The image is taken while the module is in a string with 27 modules with an active string inverter during day time.

In Figure 11, a luminescence image of the same PV module shown in Figure 10 is presented. In this case the Qcheck system is positioned on the PV module that four cells of both parallel connected substrings with a lost bypass diode are shaded. A characteristic pattern is to be seen. It is similar to dark occurring striation rings in electroluminescence images [8], but the rings appear bright in the luminescence image.

Figure 11: Qcheck luminescence image of the middle solar cells of the middle substring of a half cell module with lost bypass diode. The image is taken while the module is in a string with 27 modules with an active string inverter during day time.

Figure 12 shows the same luminescence image like Figure 11 except an thermographic image taken after shading the cells (like it is done with the Qcheck system). By comparing Figure 11 and Figure 12 the bright luminescence correlates with the pattern seen in the thermographic image.

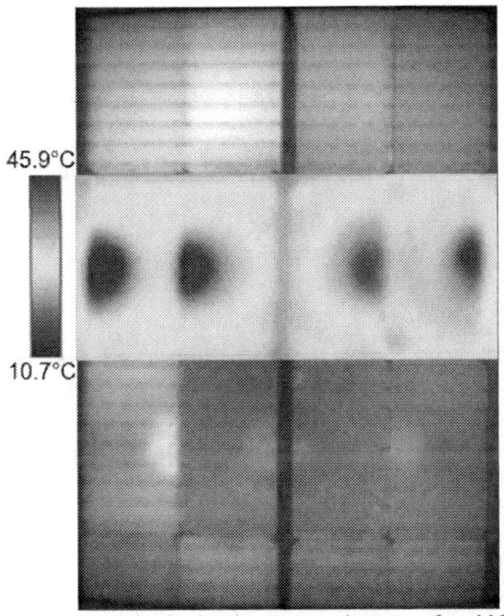

Figure 12: Qcheck luminescence image of middle substring of a half cell module with lost bypass diode with a thermographic image overlay. The temperature profile is measured directly after shading the four solar cells during daylight. Other conditions as described in Figure 5.

6 DISCUSSION

Figure 5 shows that an excitation level from the hood LEDs exceeding that of ambient sunlight stabilises the luminescence image against inverter operating point fluctuations. Furthermore, as long as the LEDs excitation level is higher than the sun outside we can measure a luminescence image. If the LEDs excitation level gets less than outside than the cells working point gets into reverse voltage and no luminescence image can be taken. We therefore recommend an LED intensity corresponding to an AM1.5 excitation level of at least 1300 W m^{-2} to ensure stable luminescence imaging, even under cloud-enhancement conditions where local solar irradiance may rise to 1200–1300 W m^{-2} depending on location.

6.1 Anticorrelation luminescence to electroluminescence

As found in the simulation show in Figure 6 the voltage of cell parts with an increased series resistance to the bus bar is higher than the voltage of the same cell with no additional resistance to the busbar when the module works in P_{mpp} conditions. Figure 8 shows this brighter luminescence signal for some broken cell metallisation fingers in actual test measurements. The broken cell metallisation fingers with increased bus resistance to the busbar are confirmed by a lab electroluminescence image of Figure 9.

6.2 How to use different working points for practical assessment

In Figure 7 we showed that a not connected module part is very bright in the luminescence and shows no current related pattern on the cells. Whereas the luminescence of a PV module with current flowing through the cells shows less luminescence compared to the not connected module. We also found that an additional shading (outside the Qcheck) on the substring under test shows the same luminescence intensity and pattern as a not connected substring. This fact can be used to identify not connected module substrings or not connected whole module strings in a PV system in day light while the inverter is on.

The suggested procedure is if one finds an extraordinary bright substring with Qcheck one must shade (two full cells) this substring additionally to the shading of the Qcheck system. When the luminescence image does not change during the additional shading procedure than this substring is not connected to the inverter. This is a very easy to use method to find not connected modules/module-substrings.

6.3 Luminescence pattern

Furthermore, the Qcheck method delivers basically the same luminescence images like an electroluminescence image for defects like shunt resistances due to potential induces degradation by shunts (PID-s), increased recombination due to light-induced degradation (LID) or cell cracks (but not if the cell crack isolates a cell part, see chapter 6.1).

10.4229/EUPVSEC2025/3BO.11.6
020206-006

6.4 Lost bypass diode

In Figure 12 a clear correlation between the luminescence pattern of cells of a module substring with a lost bypass diode and the temperature pattern of the PV module glass is found. The luminescence patter looks like inverse striation rings which are sometimes found electroluminescence pattern of monocrystalline solar cells.

In Figure 10 some cells of the same substring of the module with the lost bypass diode is shown. However, no striation ring like luminescence pattern can be found and no heating of the cells can be detected. Chill et al. [8] showed that a shaded solar cell can carry less current at the same reverse voltage compared to a not shaded solar cell (PERC, TOPCON and HJT). This means that if only one part of a half cell module is shaded, like for the measurement of the luminescence image in Figure 10 and no bypass diode is in parallel most current flows along the unshaded parallel substring. Therefore, no heating and no ring pattern can be seen in this case.

However, it is unclear why we see a bright striation ring like pattern. In a very well passivated silicon solar cell, the temperature dependence of luminescence is primarily determined by the narrowing of the silicon band gap, the increase in intrinsic carrier density, and the higher phonon occupancy for the indirect transition. This leads to a red shift of the luminescence spectrum and typically to a decreasing luminescence intensity with increasing temperature [10,11].

The wavelength of the luminescence radiation shifts as a function of the silicon band gap and the peak width of the luminescence is also a function of the temperature. The dissipating heat during the dark image phase may shift and broaden the luminescence peak in a way that the emitted luminescence can more effectively transmit trough bandwidth of the used filter. However, typically the luminescence intensity of silicon solar cells decreases with increasing temperature.

The temperature dependence of the intensity of band to band luminescence can be very complex. For example, Johnston et al. have found increasing band to band luminescence intensity with increasing temperature for crystal areas with few defects in multi crystalline solar cells [12].

A further alternative to explain the ring patter luminescence signal may be that the localized current and heating heals some defects in the wafer and increases the effective minority carrier life time. However, this should be an effect changing with time. But we could not find a change in luminescence intensity during repetitive measurements.

We also might get luminescence emission caused by the breakdown current in voltage reverse bias of the cell through into the camera in the dark image as described by Breitenstein et al. [7] for multi crystalline solar cells and Jia et al. for mono crystalline silicon solar cells [13]. This light should be seen in the dark image. We can exclude this root cause as if the dark image is bright along the areas with increased breakdown current the difference image should be dark in these areas.

We switch from extreme reverse voltage biased cells at I_{mpp} current to $\sim V_{mpp}$ conditions under illumination and take luminescence images immediately. To our knowledge such kind of luminescence measurement has not been reported before. Therefore, the seen luminescence might be a new effect. We speculate that during reverse bias conditions free charge carriers might be trapped. These trapped charge carriers might be reemitted and cause additional luminescence along areas with high trapping density.

This speculation will be checked in future work by changing the delay time between start of the LED OFF time and the start of the camera acquisition. The longer the delay, the less intense the luminescence should be in the striation ring like luminescence pattern as the reemitted free charge carrier should vanish with time.

7 CONCLUSIONS

Although the hood luminescence method is very simple and close to existing measurement ideas, this small hood-based luminescence method during daylight has never been reported before. Unfortunately, the proposed method can not be used by drones but it can be coupled to cleaning robots or ground based automated units.

This system is able to detect more PV module failure (not connected string, not connected PV module substring, lost bypass diode, all failures detectable with electroluminescence) within one method than all the other published methods listed in the introduction. Furthermore, the tool needs no change in the electrical circuit, no access to the inverter, it is used during daylight and it can be used by people without electrician training. The tool is applicable for an easy and quick spot checking of a PV system in the field. This combination of features is unique compared to existing methods in the literature and simplifies randomised acceptance procedures or failure analysis.

8 ACKNOWLEDGEMENTS

This work was funded by the state of Lower Saxony and the Federal Ministry for Economic Affairs and Energy (BMWE) under grant number ZIM KK5291103SY2 PVDETECTS. We thank Enerparc AG for supporting us evaluating our measurement tools in relevant PV systems.

9 References

[1] U. Jahn et al., "Review on Infrared and Electroluminescence Imaging for PV Field Applications," Report IEA-PVPS T13-10:2018, 2018.

[2] G. Alves dos Reis Benatto et al., "Drone-Based Daylight Electroluminescence Imaging of PV Modules," IEEE J. Photovoltaics, vol. 10, no. 3, pp. 872–877, May 2020.

[3] O. Kunz et al., "Outdoor luminescence imaging of field-deployed PV modules," Prog. Energy, vol. 4, no. 4, p. 042014, Oct. 2022.

[4] M. Vuković, M. S. Wiig, G. A. dos Reis Benatto, E. Olsen, and I. Burud, "A review of imaging methods for detection of photoluminescence in field-installed photovoltaic modules," Prog. Energy, vol. 6, no. 3, 2024.

[5] J. W. Weber et al., "Daylight photoluminescence imaging of photovoltaic systems using inverter-based switching," Prog. Photovoltaics Res. Appl., vol. 32, no. 9, pp. 643–651, 2024.

[6] M. Köntges, M. Siebert, A. Fladung, and J. Schlipf, "Evaluation of Light-Induced Electroluminescence in Photovoltaic Field Applications," in PV-Symposium Proceedings, 2024, vol. 1.

[7] O. Breitenstein et al., "Understanding junction breakdown in multicrystalline solar cells," J. Appl. Phys., vol. 109, no. 7, p. 071101, Apr. 2011.

[8] M. Köntges *et al.*, "Review of Failures of Photovoltaic Modules," Report IEA-PVPS T13-01:2014, 2014, p. 43 [Online]. Available: http://iea-pvps.org/index.php?id=275 [Accessed 18-Sep-2014]
[9] C. Reichel *et al.*, "Design aspects in consideration of hotspot phenomena in high-performance photovoltaic modules featuring different silicon solar cell architectures," *Sol. Energy Mater. Sol. Cells*, vol. 276, no. July, p. 113058, 2024, doi: 10.1016/j.solmat.2024.113058.
[10] T. Trupke *et al.*, "Temperature dependence of the radiative recombination coefficient of intrinsic crystalline silicon," *J. Appl. Phys.*, vol. 94, no. 8, pp. 4930–4937, Oct. 2003, doi: 10.1063/1.1610231.
[11] H. Schlangenotto, H. Maeder, and W. Gerlach, "Temperature dependence of the radiative recombination coefficient in silicon," *Phys. Status Solidi*, vol. 21, no. 1, pp. 357–367, Jan. 1974, doi: 10.1002/pssa.2210210140.
[12] S. Johnston *et al.*, "Temperature-dependent Photoluminescence imaging and characterization of a multi-crystalline silicon solar cell defect area," in *2011 37th IEEE Photovoltaic Specialists Conference*, IEEE, Jun. 2011, pp. 000069–000074. doi: 10.1109/PVSC.2011.6185848.
[13] Y. Jia *et al.*, "Diagnosing breakdown mechanisms in monocrystalline silicon solar cells via electroluminescence imaging," *Sol. Energy*, vol. 225, pp. 463–470, Sep. 2021, doi: 10.1016/j.solener.2021.07.052.

EU PVSEC 2025
Bilbao, Spain, 23rd September 2025

ISFH

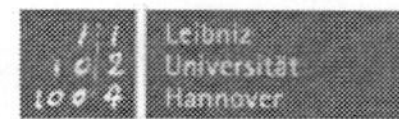

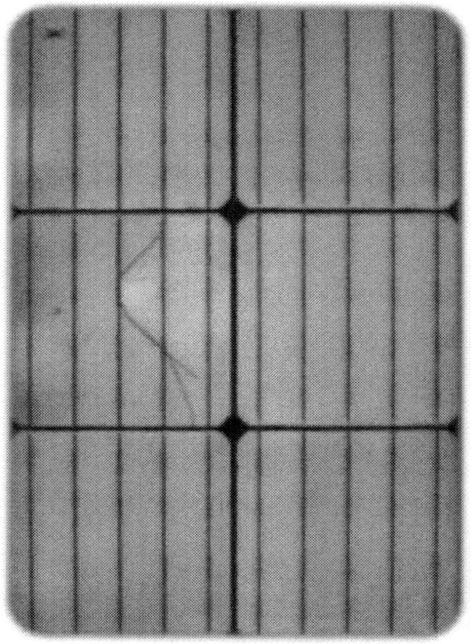

Luminescence measurement with a cost-effective and small-sized hood-based tool under daylight condition

M. Köntges[1], M. Siebert[1], D. Lorenz[2], B. Kuhrmann[2], M. Fuß[2]

[1]Institute for Solar Energy Research Hamelin, Germany
[2]MBJ Solutions GmbH

Leibniz Universität Hannover

Introduction

Electroluminescence[1] (EL) or day light photoluminescence[2] (DPL) imaging

- is an effective method to detect defects and failure in PV modules
- but it requires night work & rewiring of modules (electrician) or lot of equipment or inverter access

We present a new luminescence setup with a small hood: Quickcheck

- A small hood tool, with camera and LED light is moved on the modules
- Detects all EL features

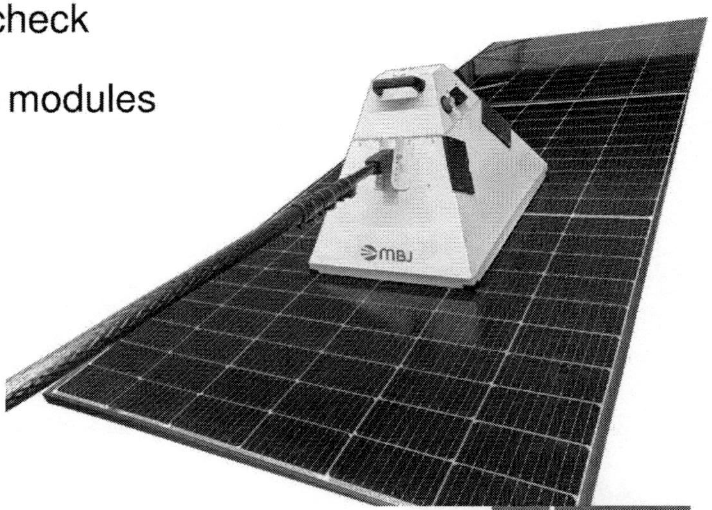

[1]U. Jahn et al., Report IEA-PVPS T13-10:2018, 2018
[2]M. Vuković, et al., Prog. Energy, vol. 6, no. 3, 2024

How does it work? Quickcheck dark image

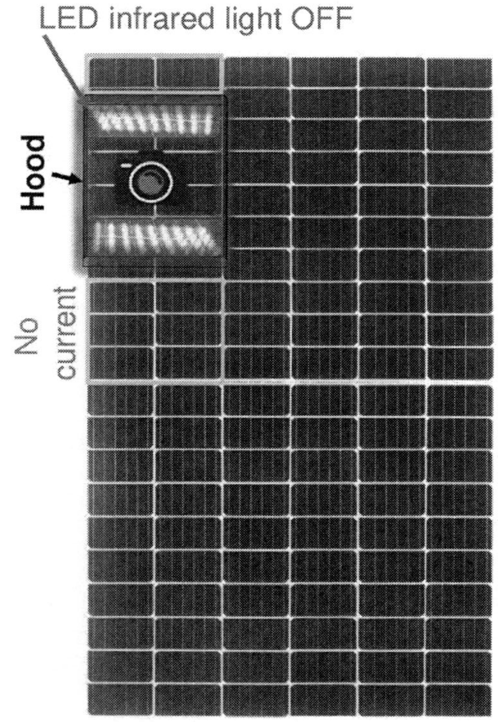

Dark image

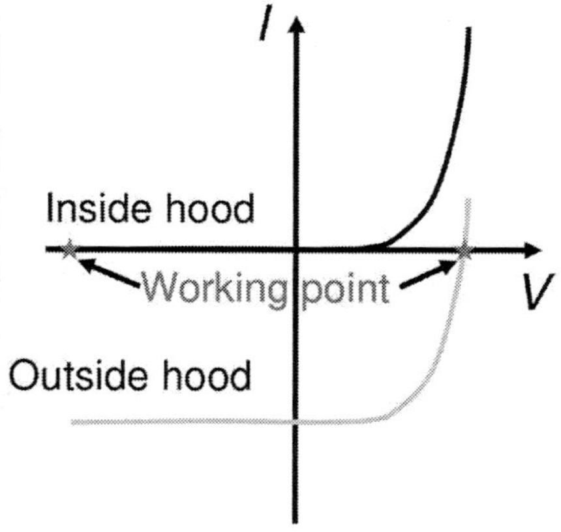

Components:

- Industry InGaAs camera with 512 x 640 pixel + band-pass filter 1150 ± 25 nm
- Exposure time per image in the range of 5 ms to 30 ms
- LED light source @850 nm

How does it work:

- Cell working point at LED OFF in the hood is in reverse bias voltage
- No luminescence from cell but background radiation is captured

How does it work? Quickcheck luminescence image

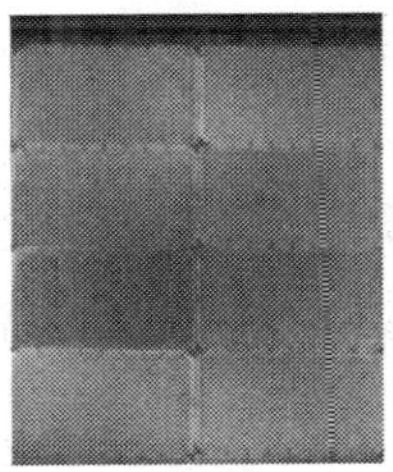

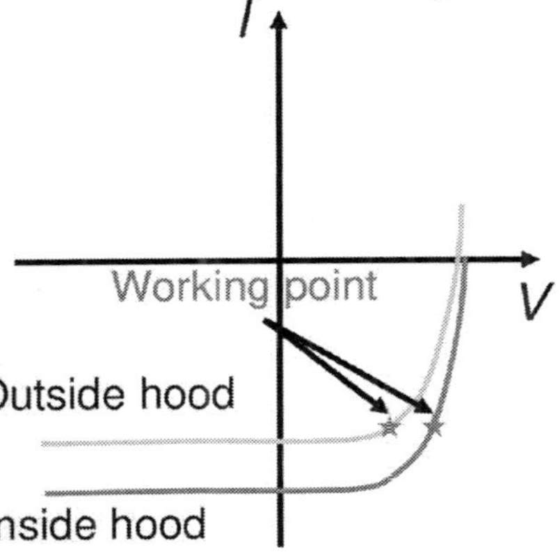

- Hood LED light source @850 nm generates higher excitation level in silicon solar cell then 1300 W/m² AM1.5g sun light
- Cell working point in the hood at LED ON is at I_{mpp} and is higher than V_{mpp}!
- 3 to 10 ON/OFF images are taken
- Current flow features are visible at actual I_{mpp}
- All further luminescence images show difference images

How to read Quickcheck difference images

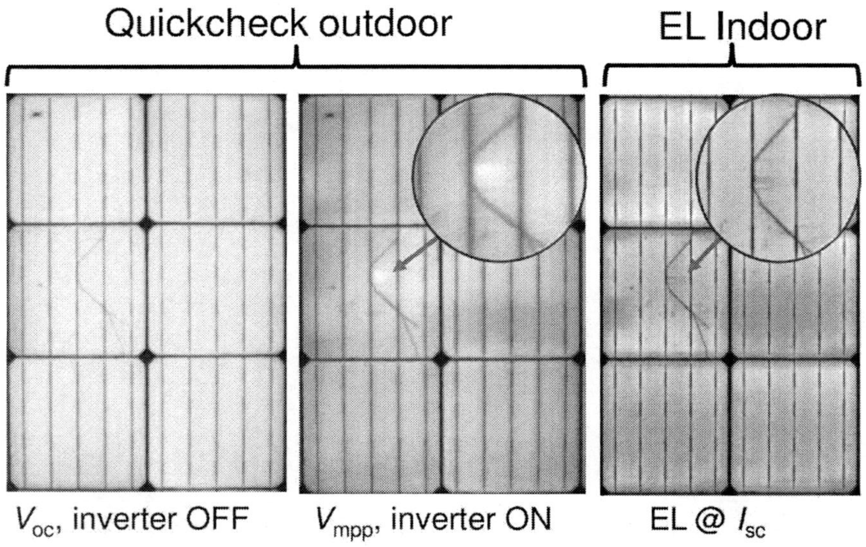

645 W/m² sun irradiation on module level off the string under test

Quickcheck outdoor

- V_{oc} images
  ➔ no resistive pattern in cells visible
  ➔ string not connected
- V_{mpp} images
  Resistively coupled cell parts are brighter
  ➔ less current = higher voltage
  ➔ higher luminescence

In contrast EL image

- Resistively coupled cell parts are dimmed
  ➔ less current = lower voltage
  ➔ dimmed luminescence

Identify disconnected PV module part/strings

ISFH

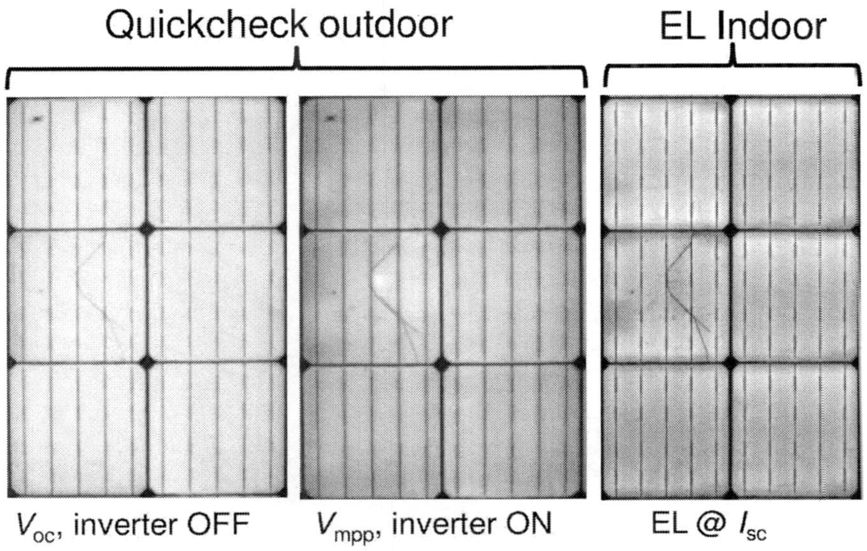

645 W/m² sun irradiation on module level off the string under test

To check if you see V_{oc} image:

- Shade two or more full cells of current substring outside the hood. If intensity does not change you see V_{oc} image.

Finding a V_{oc} image means:

- Current cells are not connected (Substring, or PV module string)
- Inverter is OFF
- Images are taken under low light or in the dark

Leibniz Universität Hannover

Lost bypass diodes

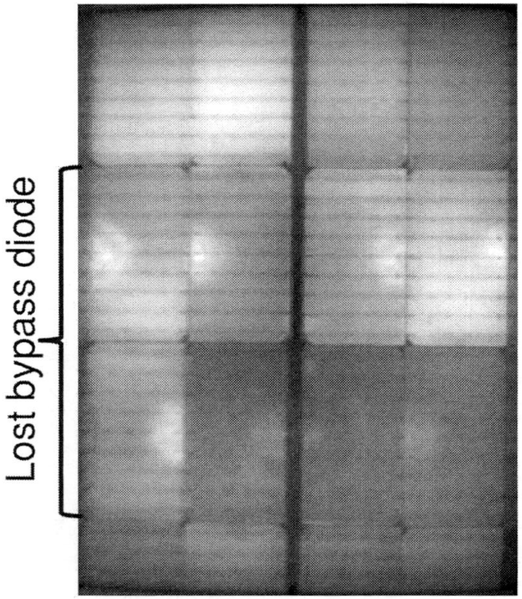

Dark image **with** bypass diode

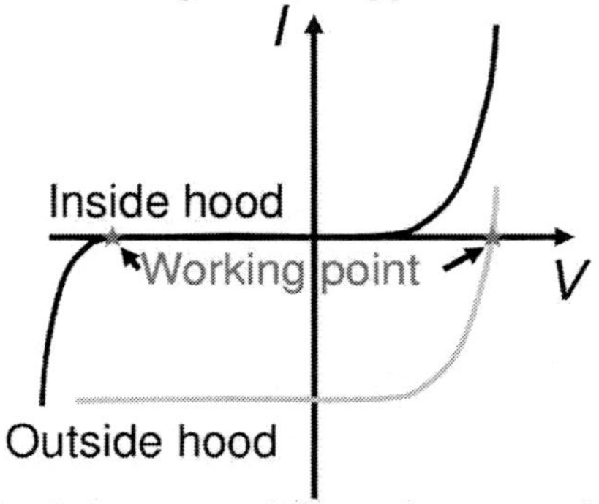

Dark image **without** bypass diode

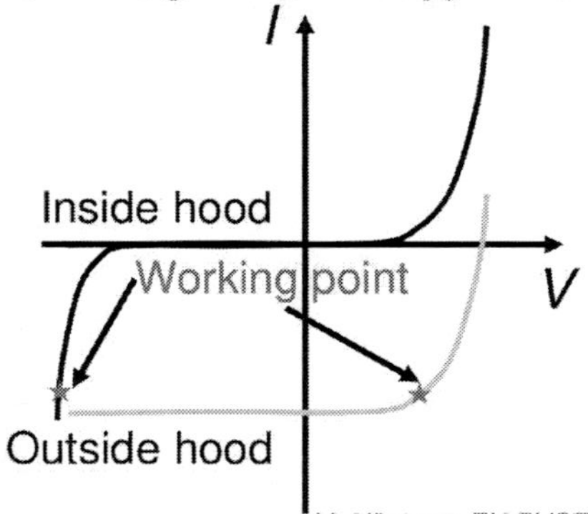

Lost bypass diode

- Quickcheck in the module middle results in symmetric current distribution
- With lost bypass diode the cells work at high reverse bias voltage at I_{mpp} current

➔ Cells heat up during dark image phase

- Heat dissipates typically along striation rings or other defects
- During LED ON luminescence imaging the heat pattern remains
- Reason for bright pattern is not clear but allows differentiation to striation rings (dark pattern)

Lost bypass diodes

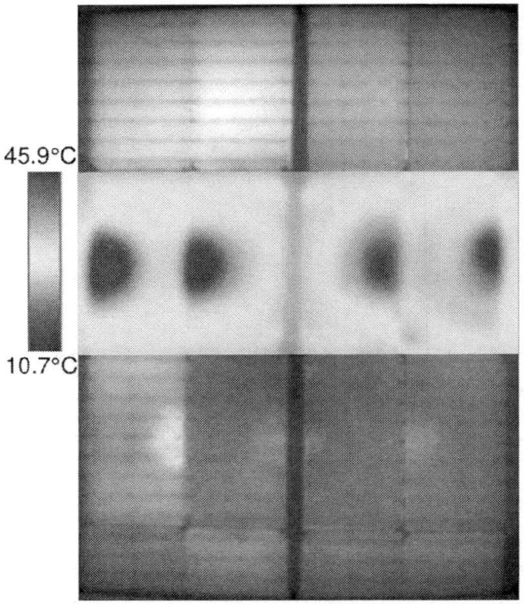

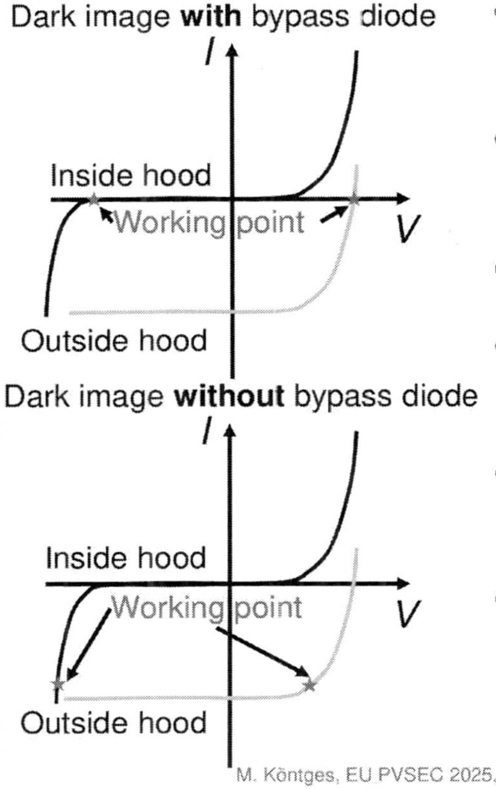

- Quickcheck in the module middle results in symmetric current distribution
- With lost bypass diode the cells work at high reverse bias voltage at I_{mpp} current

➔ Cells heat up during dark image phase

- Heat dissipates typically along striation rings or other defects
- During LED ON luminescence imaging the heat pattern remains
- Reason for bright pattern is not clear but allows differentiation to striation rings (dark pattern)

Lost bypass diodes

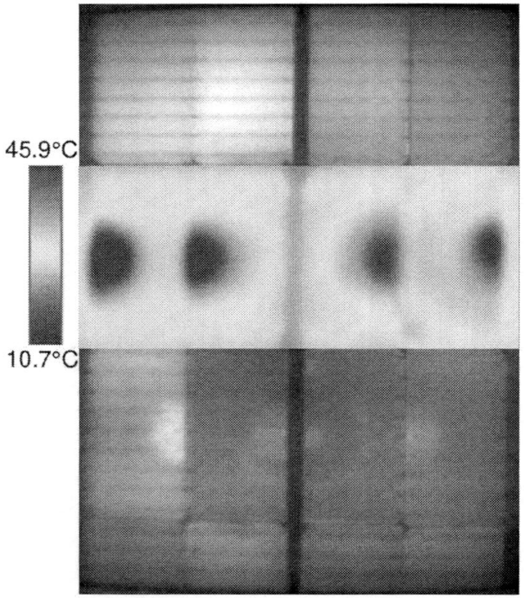

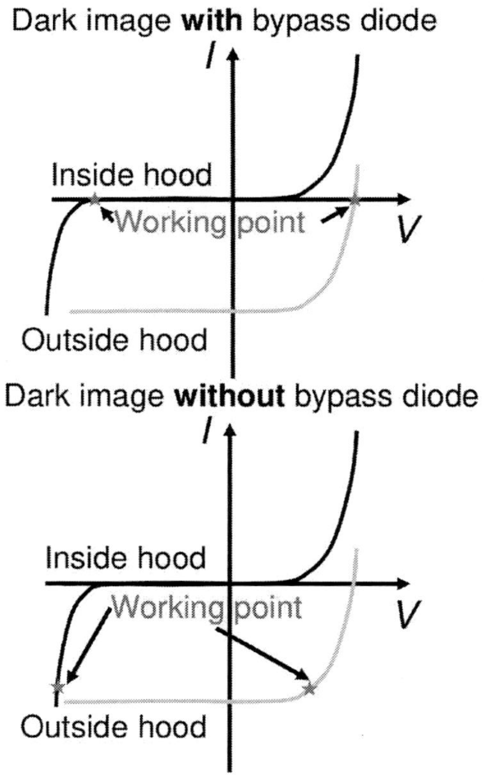

Facts:

- Striation ring like lum. pattern appears instant, while TG pattern need some 10 s
- Radiative recombination coefficient B decrease with increasing temperatures[1]
- Breakdown lum. in reverse voltage[2] is not the cause as image subtraction inverts lum. in dark

Speculation:

- Emission peak spectrum may shift into filter window & increases detected lum.
- In extreme reverse bias charge carriers may be trapped and flood the cell during switching to forward voltage

[1] T. Trupke *et al.*, *J. Appl. Phys.*, vol. 94, no. 8, pp. 4930–4937, Oct. 2003, doi: 10.1063/1.1610231.
[2] Y. Jia *et al.*, *Sol. Energy*, vol. 225, pp. 463–470, Sep. 2021, doi: 10.1016/j.solener.2021.07.052.

Conclusion

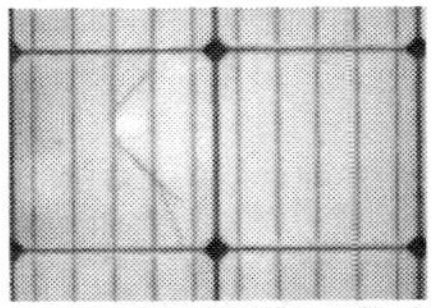
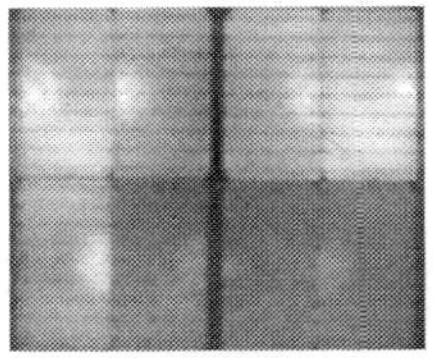

- Luminescence imaging at actual I_{mpp} of the system, that's what we really need!
- Can detect everything what EL can detect
- Additionally: can detect lost bypass diodes, not connected strings
- New luminescence effect found
  while switching fast (some ms) from extreme reverse ➔ forward voltage
- Speed approximately 1 module/min but no setup time required
- Small hood can reach upper module row of PV rack (7 m)
- Instant imaging, no rewiring
- **Everyone can operate the Quickcheck system, no electrician needed!**

Acknowledgments

This work was funded by the state of Lower Saxony and the Federal Ministry for Economic Affairs and Energy (BMWE) under grant number ZIM KK5291103SY2 PVDETECTS.

Supported by:

Federal Ministry for Economic Affairs and Energy

on the basis of a decision by the German Bundestag

We thank Enerparc AG for supporting us evaluating our measurement tools in relevant PV systems.

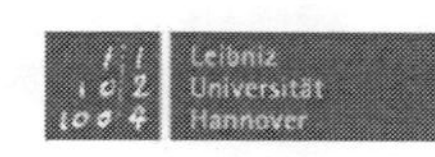

Come and learn about how to characterize your PV system

ISFH

WEBINAR

IEA PVPS Task 13

Characterisation of Photovoltaic Systems

International Energy Agency
Photovoltaic Power Systems Programme

Thursday, 23 October 2025
08:15 - 11:00 (CEST)

Virtual

Registration:
https://t1p.de/8ofkn

Leibniz Universität Hannover

SUSTAIN
ABILITY

Developing a New I-V Translation Methodology in Accordance with IEC 60891:2021 Correction Procedure 1 and 2

Wenhao Xu, Yating Zhang, Mengdi Liu, Christos Monokroussos, Werner Herrmann, Giorgio Bardizza, Harald Müllejans

[2025.09.24] | [EUPVSEC 2025, Bilbao, Spain]

TÜVRheinland®
Precisely Right.

Agenda

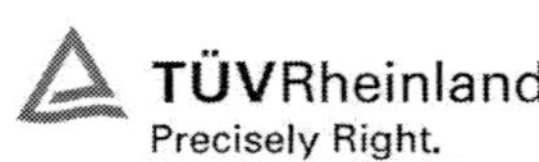

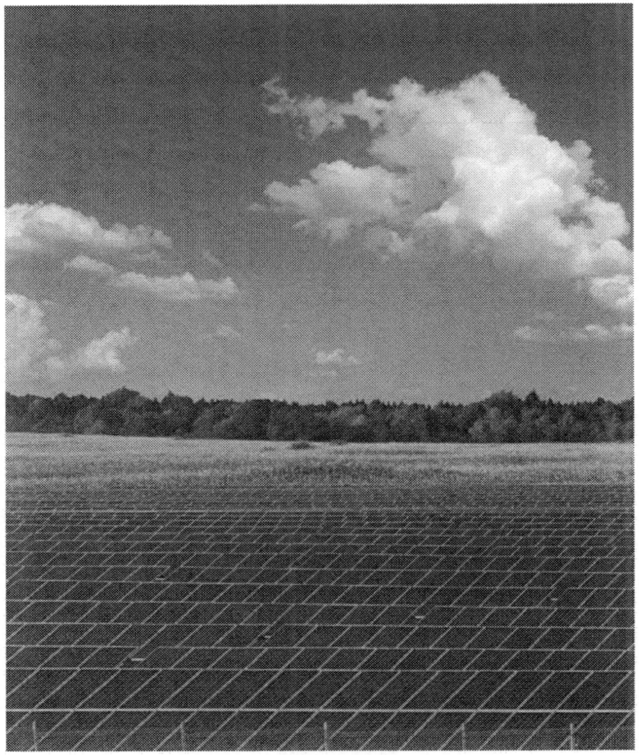

- Introduction and Motivation
- Concept of New Correction Procedure
- Design of Experiments
- Results
- Conclusion

TÜVRheinland®
Precisely Right.

Introduction and Motivation

IV correction

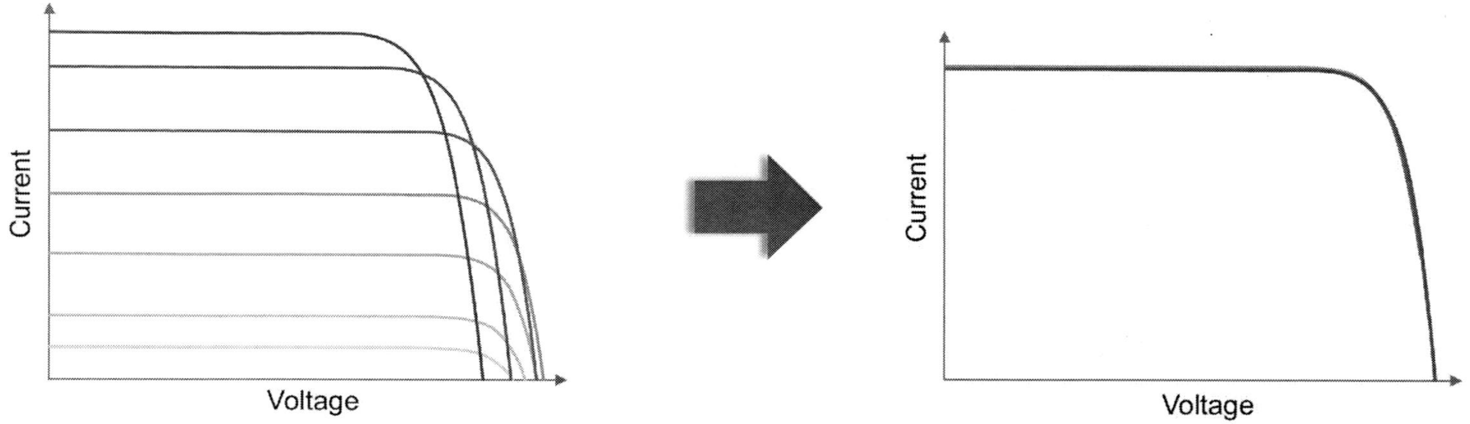

- The irradiance and temperature of I-V measurement always deviate from the target condition, especially for field test.
- IV correction aims to correct the I-V curve to the target irradiance and temperature condition

TÜVRheinland® Precisely Right.

Introduction and Motivation

IEC 60891 Correction Procedure

1987
- The 1st edition of IEC 60891 was published with the correction procedure 1 (CP1)

2009
- The 2nd edition of IEC 60891 with CP2 and CP3 published

2021
- The 3rd edition of IEC 60891 with revised CP2 and CP4

- CP1 and 2 are most commonly used in the industry.

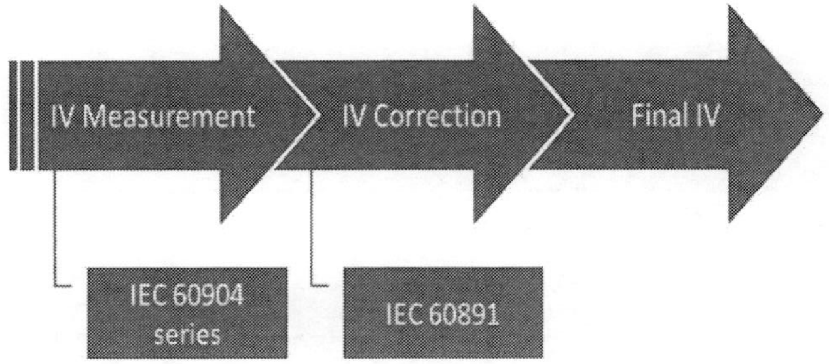

TÜVRheinland®
Precisely Right.

Introduction and Motivation

Correction Procedure 1 (CP1)

- **Advantage:**
  - Accurate in P_{MAX} and I_{SC}
- **Disadvantages:**
  - CP1: Incomplete I-V curve from low irradiance translated to high irradiance.
    - Results inaccurate V_{OC}
    - Need to measure negative current regime adequately but is not practical.

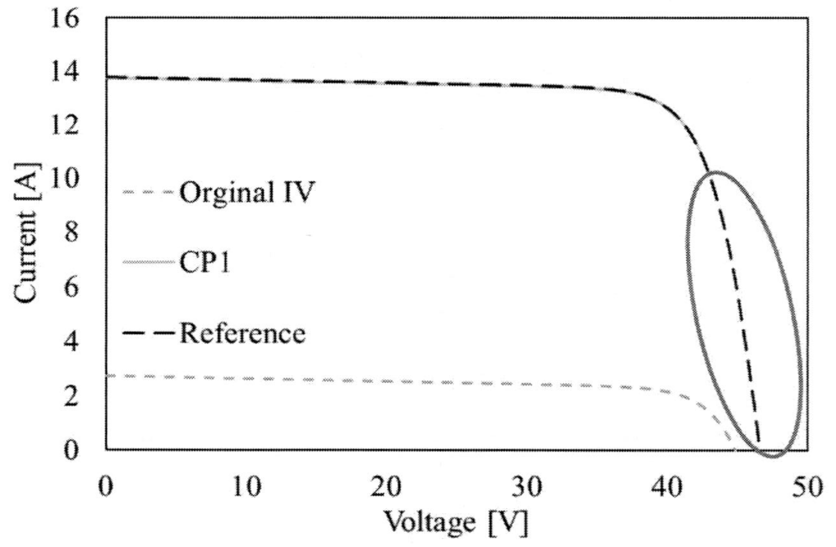

TÜVRheinland®
Precisely Right.

Introduction and Motivation

Correction Procedure 2 (CP2)

- **Advantage:**
  - Highly accurate, except for low Rsh modules
  - Most precise in V_{OC} correction:
  - ❖ Introduce a non-linear scaling of V_{OC} against logarithmic irradiance
  - ❖ And introduce an irradiance-dependent temperature coefficient (TC) of V_{OC}
- **Disadvantages:**
  - CP2: Poor accuracy for low Rsh device.

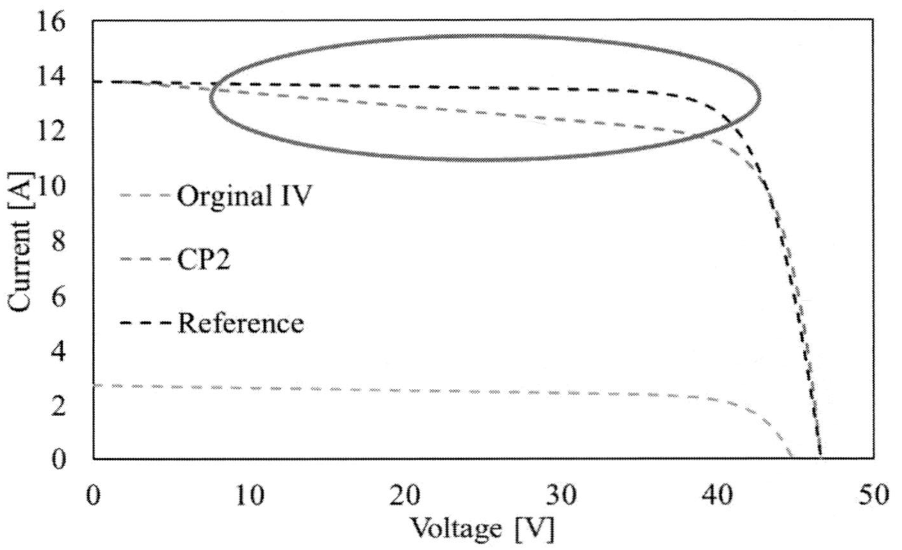

TÜVRheinland® Precisely Right.

Concept of New Correction Procedure (NCP)

NCP = CP1 + CP2

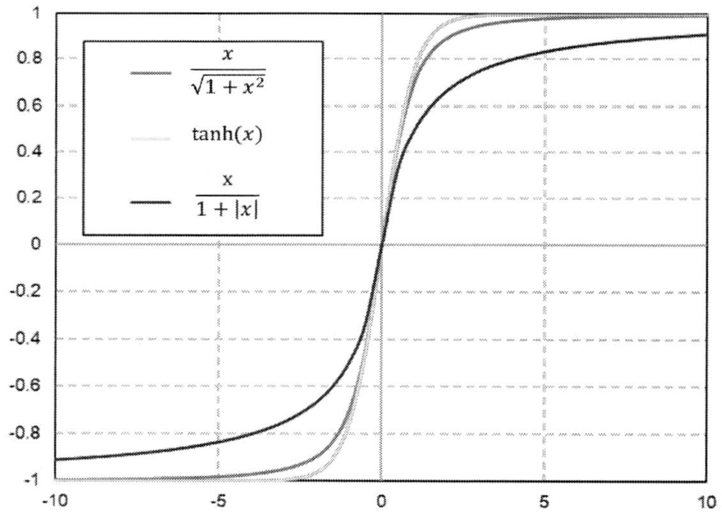

Examples of Sigmoid function

- **Concept:**
  - To develop a new method that integrates CP1 and CP2, compensating for each's respective disadvantages.
- **Combination of 2 methods:**
  - Introduce the suitable Sigmoid function
  - $NCP = w1(x) \cdot CP1 + w2(x) \cdot CP2$
  - $w1(x)$ and $w2(x)$ are two Sigmoid functions;

TÜVRheinland® Precisely Right.

Concept of New Correction Procedure (NCP)

Gompertz Curve

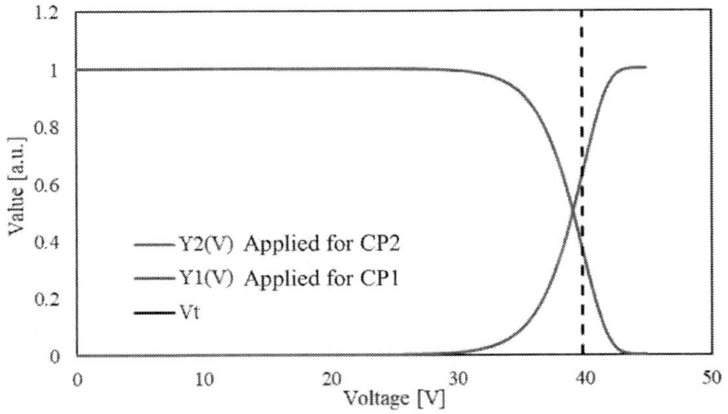

Example of Gompertz Curves introduced in NCP

- A type of S-shaped growth curve used to model growth processes across disciplines, including biology and economics.
- By adjusting parameters **A** and **B**, the curve varies from **0 to 1** along the **positive X-axis**.

- Four-parameters Gompertz Curve:

$$Y(V) = A + Bexp(-\exp(k(V - V_t))$$

- Modified Gompertz Curve to:

$$Y1(V) = exp(-\exp(k(V - V_t))$$

$$Y2(V) = -1 + exp(-\exp(k(V - V_t))$$

k determine the increasing/decreasing rate, which is always 0.5 in this work;

V_t determine where the curve start increasing/decreasing.

NCP formula:

$$I_c = Y1 \times I_{CP1} + Y2 \times I_{CP2}$$

$$V_c = V_{CP2}$$

Concept of New Correction Procedure (NCP)

Determination of V_t

- Small V_t : Corrected IV curve trends towards **CP2** corrected IV.
- Large V_t: Current behavior approaches **CP1's result**.
- V_t Determination formula:

$$V_t = V_{MPP1} \times i$$

V_{MPP1} is the Vmpp of the original IV curve.

- i is determined semi-empirically.
- Determined by the difference of P_{max} between CP1 and CP2

Diff. of P_{MAX} in CP1&CP2	i
Diff. ≤ 0.5%	0.92
0.5% < Diff. ≤ 2%	0.97
2% < Diff. ≤ 5%	1
5% < Diff. ≤ 10%	1.025
10% < Diff. ≤ 20%	1.05
20% < Diff. ≤ 35%	1.07
35% < Diff. ≤ 50%	1.08
>50%	1.2

TÜVRheinland® Precisely Right.

Design of Experiments

Test Samples

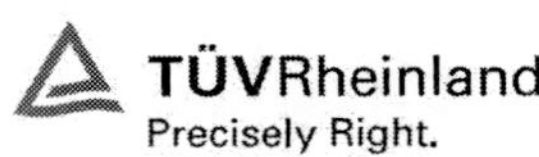

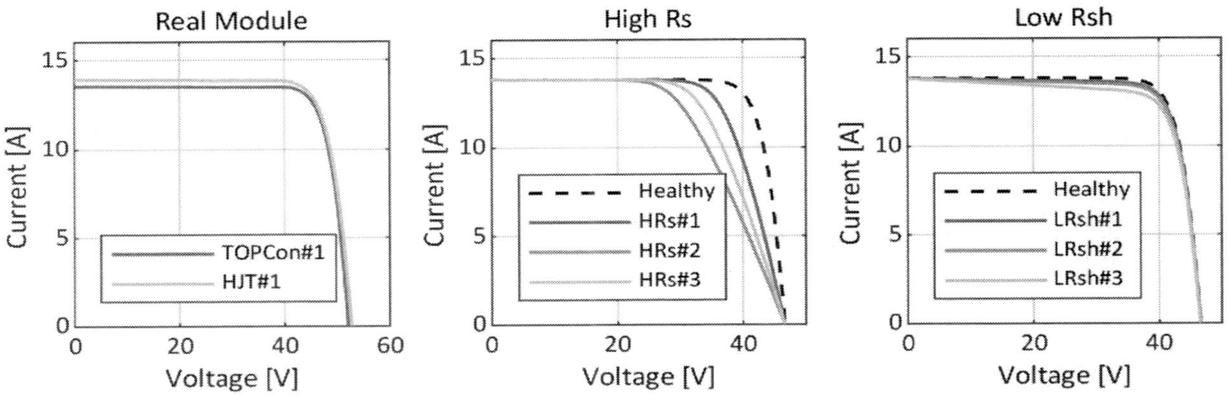

Examples of I–V curves of physical module and the simulated modules with healthy, high R_s, low R_{sh} at STC

Samples:

- 2 Commercial Modules: 1 TOPCon and 1 HJT
- 7 Simulated Modules

Sample	Rsh (Ω)	Rs (Ω)
Healthy	1500	0.1
LRsh#1	150	0.1
LRsh#2	100	0.1
LRsh#3	50	0.1
HRs#1	1500	0.5
HRs#2	1500	0.75
HRs#3	1500	1

TÜVRheinland®
Precisely Right.

Design of Experiments

Evaluation Method

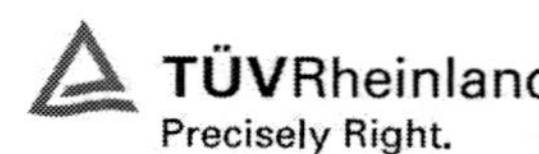

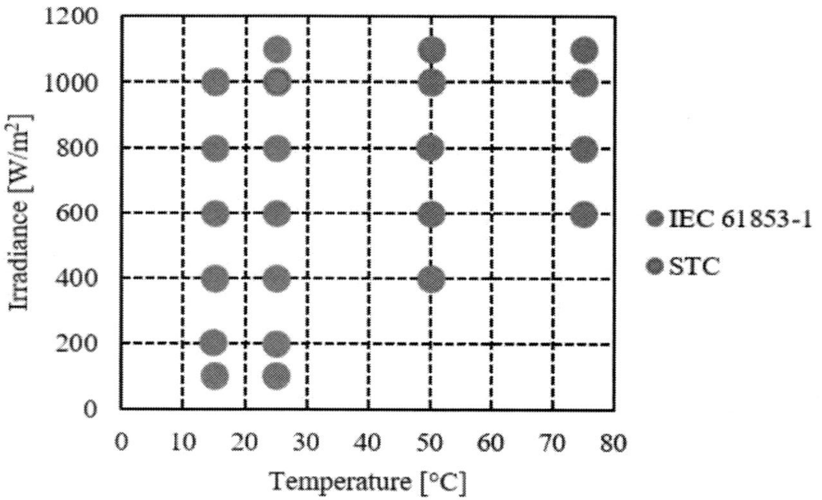

- Modules are tested/simulated under 22 different conditions, including STC.
- I-V curves are corrected to STC for comparison.
- Deviations in key electrical parameters are analyzed.
- RMSE of parameter deviations is evaluated across 21 test conditions.

TÜVRheinland® Precisely Right.

Results

Commercial Modules

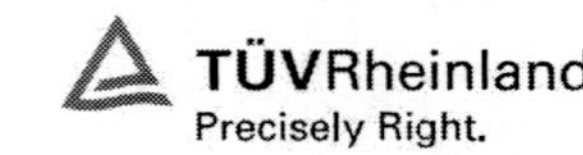

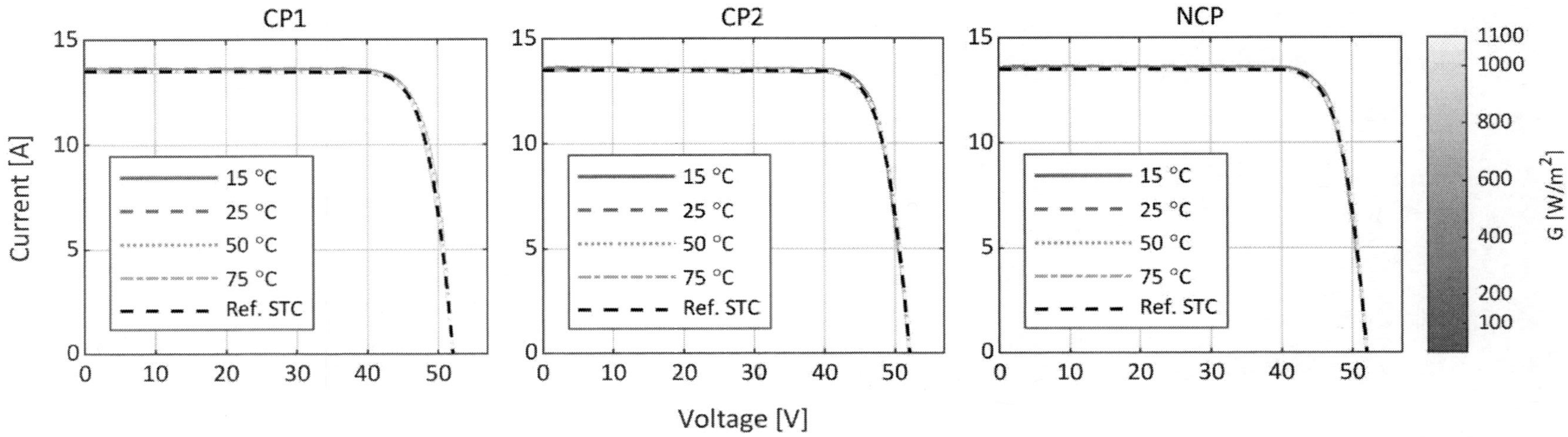

- I-V curves corrected by all three CPs align closely with the reference STC I-V curve.

TÜVRheinland® Precisely Right.

Results

Commercial Modules

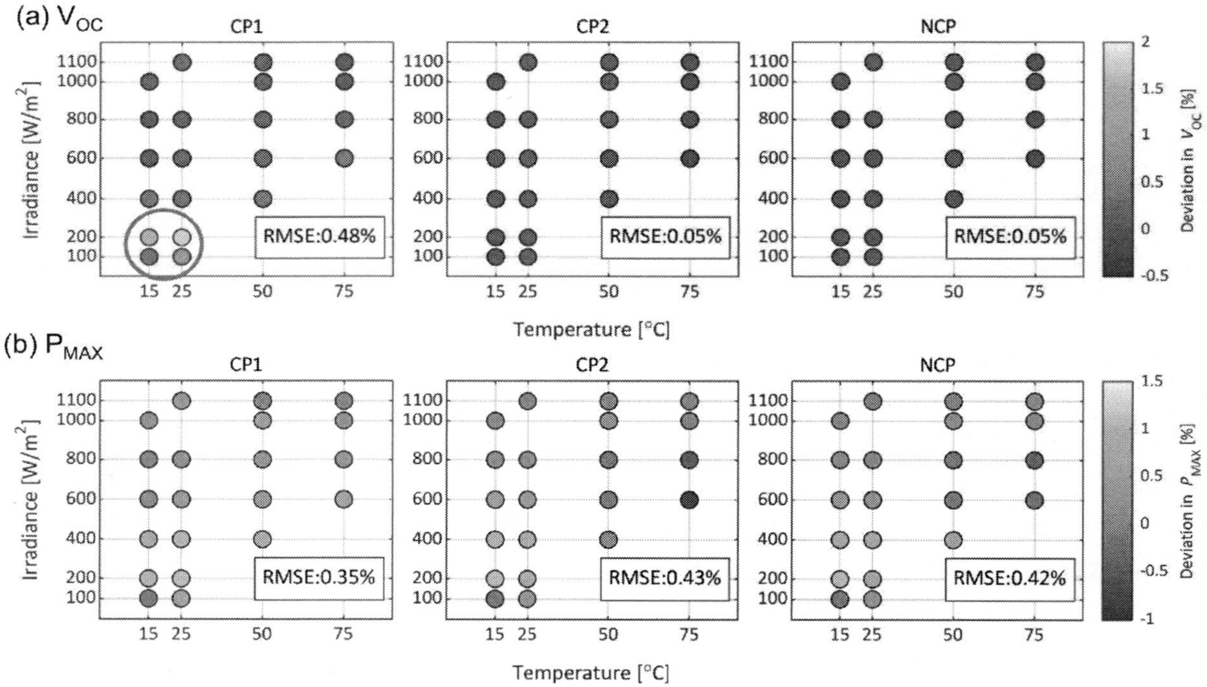

TOPCon#1 The deviation of translated I-V curves to STC using the three different CP (a) V_{OC} (b) P_{MAX}

- CP2 shows more accurate V_{OC} than CP1 at lower irradiance levels.
- NCP produces V_{OC} results close to CP2.
- CP1, CP2 and NCP produce accurate results in P_{MAX}.

TÜVRheinland®
Precisely Right.

Results

Simulated Modules with Low R_{sh}

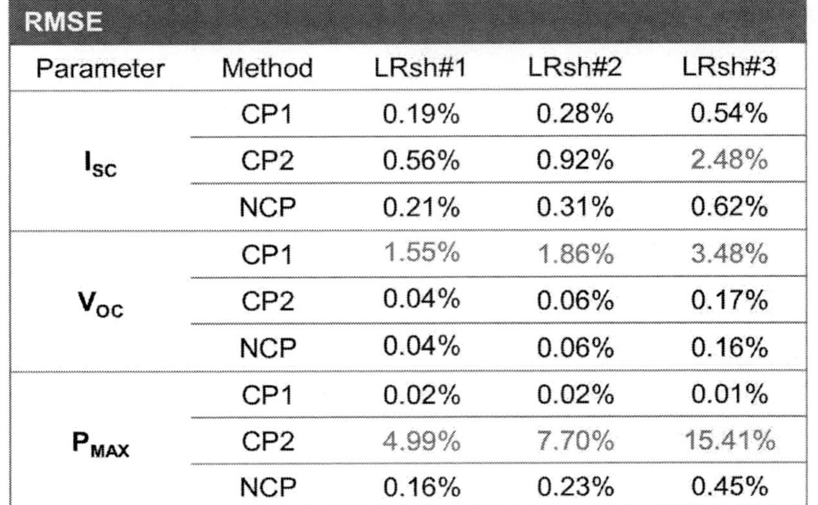

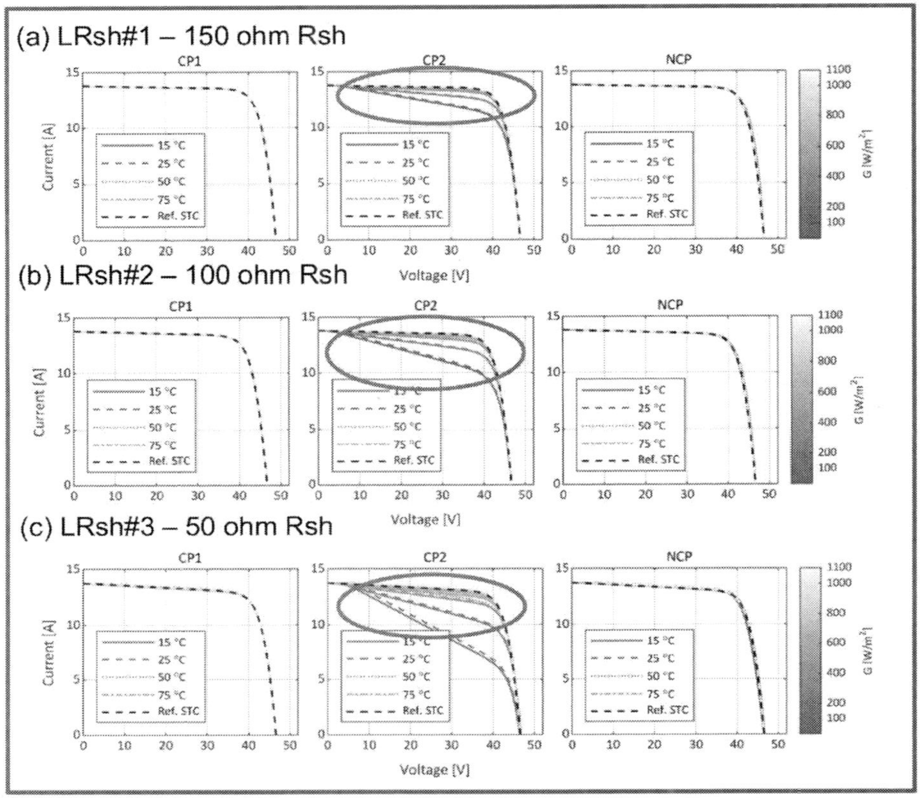

RMSE				
Parameter	Method	LRsh#1	LRsh#2	LRsh#3
I_{SC}	CP1	0.19%	0.28%	0.54%
	CP2	0.56%	0.92%	2.48%
	NCP	0.21%	0.31%	0.62%
V_{OC}	CP1	1.55%	1.86%	3.48%
	CP2	0.04%	0.06%	0.17%
	NCP	0.04%	0.06%	0.16%
P_{MAX}	CP1	0.02%	0.02%	0.01%
	CP2	4.99%	7.70%	15.41%
	NCP	0.16%	0.23%	0.45%

- CP2 produces distorted I-V curves for low R_{sh} modules.
- NCP produces significantly more accurate P_{MAX} than CP2.
- NCP produces more accurate V_{OC} than CP1.

Conclusion: Advancing I-V Correction with a New Procedure (NCP)

NCP presents a more reliable path forward for PV performance analysis.

- **I-V Correction is Vital** for accurate, standardized PV module characterization.
- Industry Standards CP1 & CP2 (IEC 60891) have known **inherent limitations**.
- **Objective Achieved**: A **New Correction Procedure** (**NCP**) was developed to combine the strengths of CP1 and CP2.
- **Key Finding**: The proposed **NCP outperforms both CP1 and CP2** in accuracy for most cases.

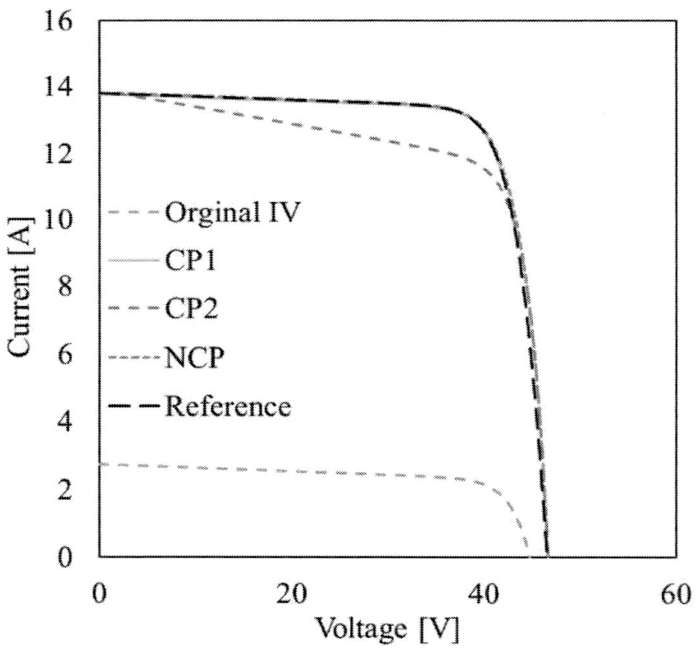

TÜVRheinland®
Precisely Right.

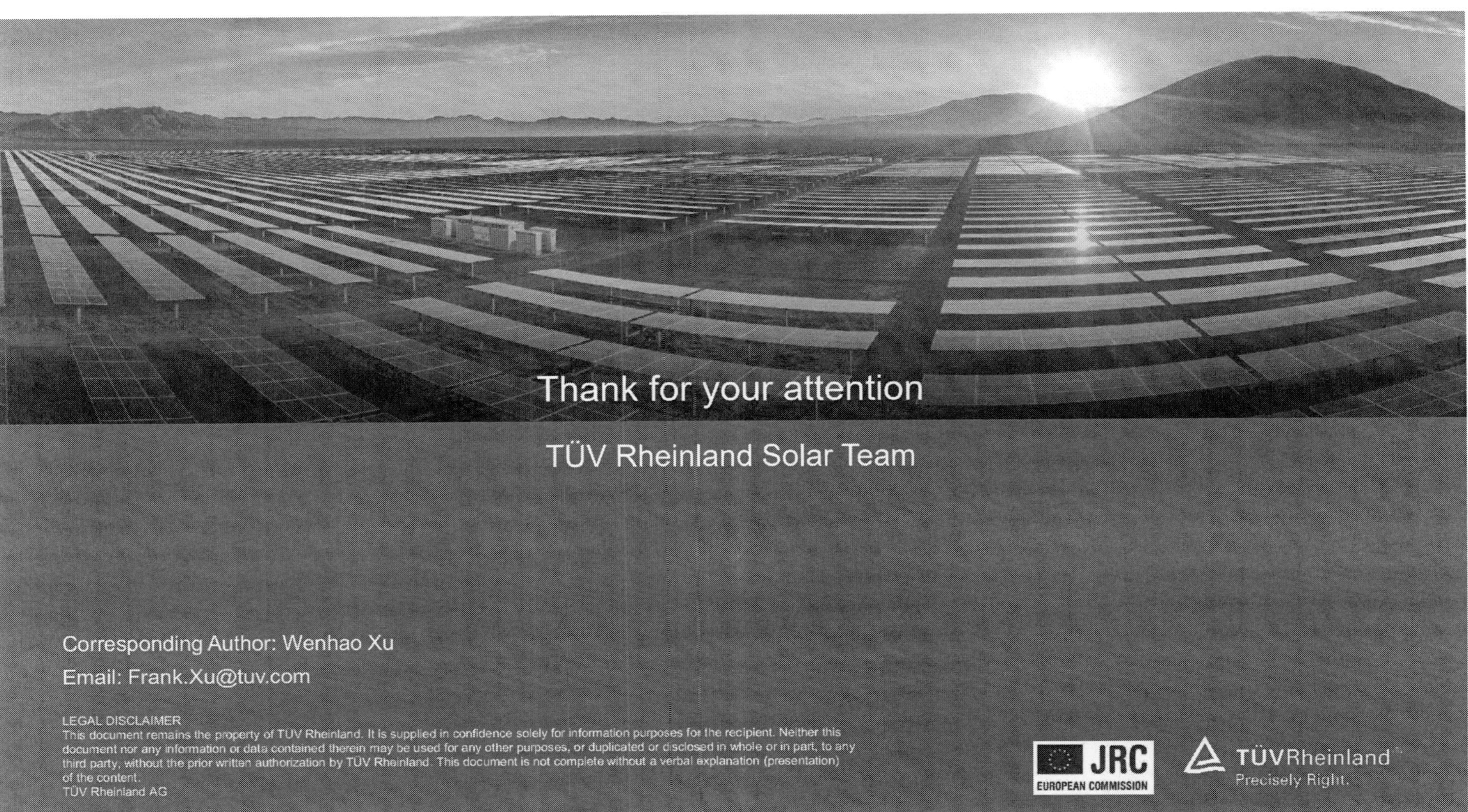

Thank for your attention

TÜV Rheinland Solar Team

Corresponding Author: Wenhao Xu

Email: Frank.Xu@tuv.com

JRC EUROPEAN COMMISSION

TÜVRheinland Precisely Right.

EUPVSEC, 2025

Characterization of Vehicle Integrated Photovoltaic Modules

Ricardo Moruno[1], Francisco Martín[1,2], Juan Manuel Redondo[1], Javier Malo[3], Luis J. San José[1], Guido Vallerotto[1], Steve Askins[1], Rubén Núñez[1], César Domínguez[1], Ignacio Antón[1], Rebeca Herrero

[1]Instituto de Energía Solar-Universidad Politécnica de Madrid (IES-UPM), Madrid, Spain

[2]Solar Added Value (SAV), Madrid, Spain

[3]E.T.S. de Ingeniería Y Sistemas de Telecomunicación, UPM, Madrid, Spain

INSTITUTO DE ENERGÍA SOLAR

POLITÉCNICA

Introduction

INSTITUTO DE ENERGÍA SOLAR

VIPV specific features

- Curvature: complex 3D shapes
  - Inherent non uniform irradiance
- Operating conditions
  - Wide range of angles of incidence and directionalities

Curvature and cell interconnection affect the module's angular response, which is critical on VIPV

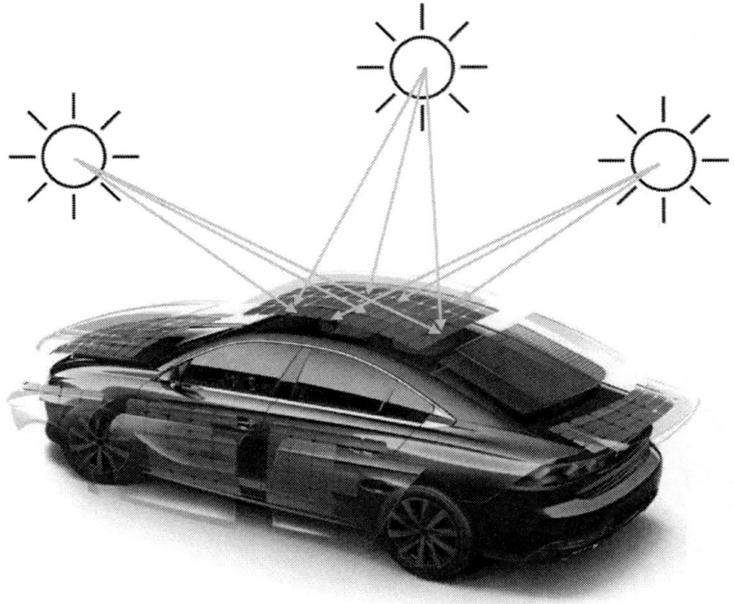

POLITÉCNICA

Motivation

INSTITUTO DE ENERGÍA SOLAR

- To advance in VIPV, we need to be able to determine module properties so we can:
  - **COMPARE** TECHNOLOGIES
  - **MODEL** PV PERFORMANCE
- Characterization
  - IV curve on STC
  - Angular response tests

Current procedures and gear are not suited for VIPV

We are going to share the lessons learned on VIPV characterization

- What is being done about it?
  - IEC series for flat modules:
    - PT600 (TC 82 IEC) Project Leader K. Araki
  - International Round Robin:
    - To compare Power Rating
    - To define instrumentation, procedures and metrics for VIPV

(cannot disclose IV curves values)

Outline

INSTITUTO DE ENERGÍA SOLAR

- Methodology
  - INDOORS: Solar simulator of collimated light
  - OUTDOORS: Two-axis tracker
- Results
  - IV curve at STC
  - Angular response
- Conclusions

POLITÉCNICA

Methodology: Collimated light solar simulator

INSTITUTO DE ENERGÍA SOLAR

- Conventional solar simulator

Increased error in replicating solar illumination.
Aoi depends on distance to source AND curvature.

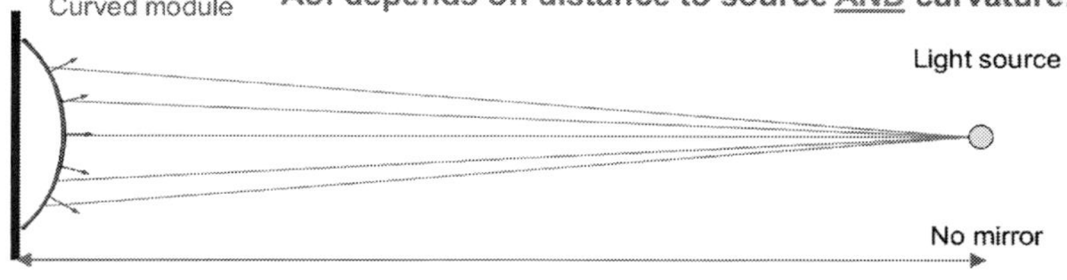

- Collimated light solar simulator

Reasonable solar illumination replication:
Aoi depends ONLY on curvature

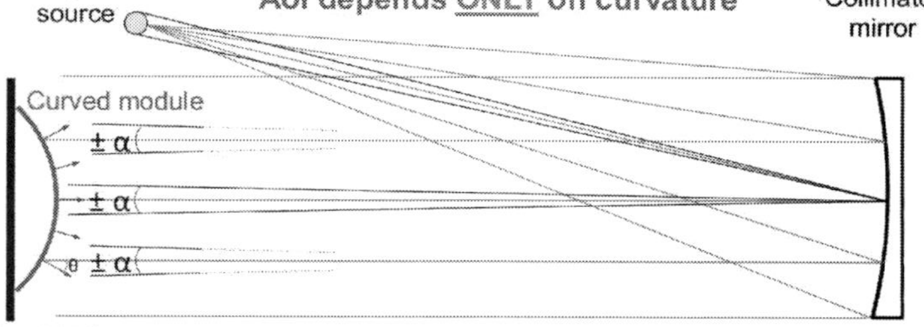

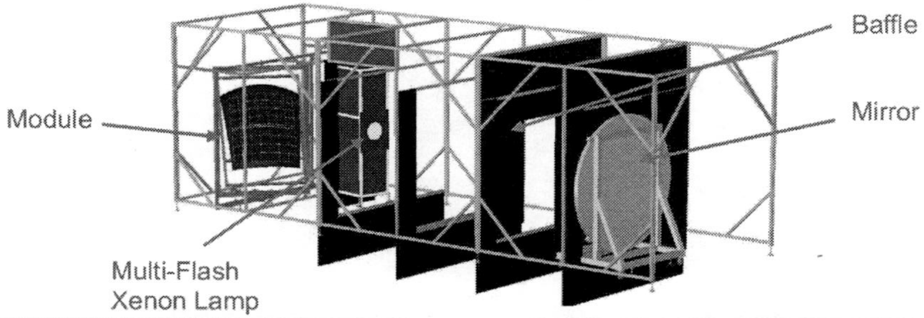

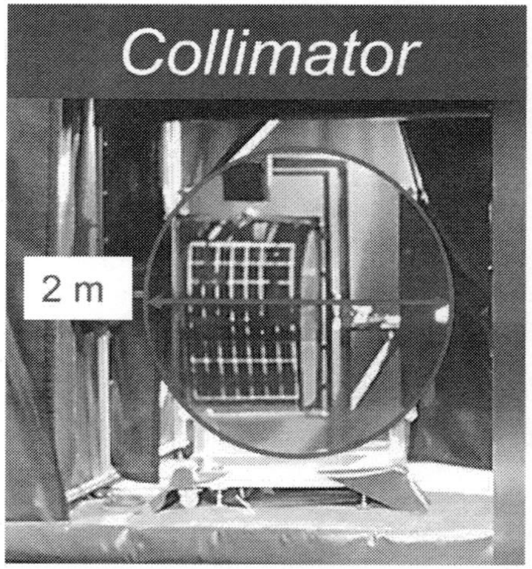

[1] G. Vallerotto, et Al., "Collimated solar simulator for curved PV modules characterization", Solar Energy Materials and Solar Cells 258 (2023) 112418, doi: 10.1016/j.solmat.2023.112418

Methodology: 2-axis tracker

INSTITUTO DE ENERGÍA SOLAR

- STC at normal incidence – 2 axis tracker is mandatory
- Angular response – Programmed tracker control for different angles of incidence [2]

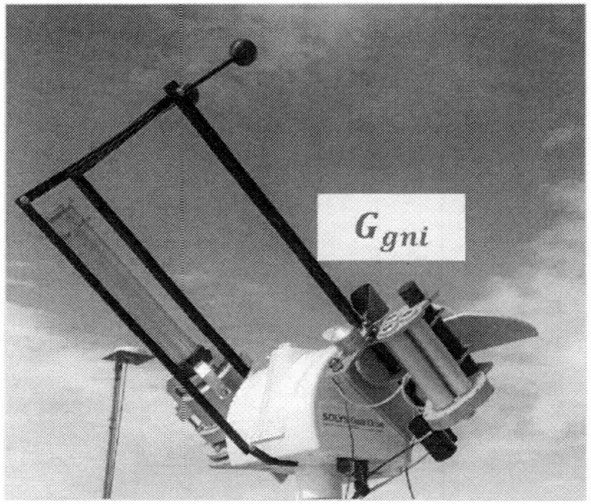

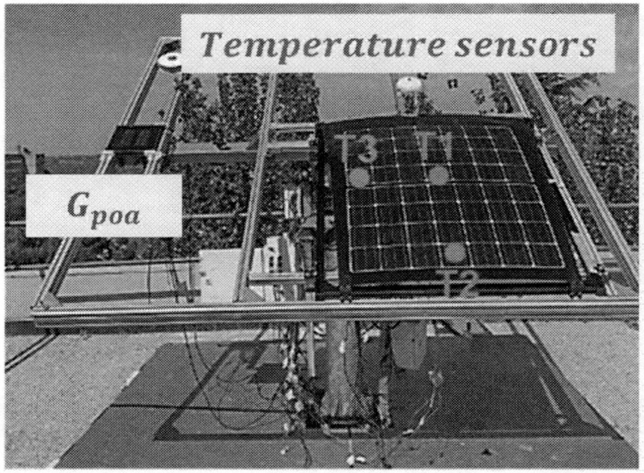

[2] Riley, D. et al. ,ASME. J. Sol. Energy Eng.; 137(3): 031008, (2015)

Results: IV curve at STC

INSTITUTO DE ENERGÍA SOLAR

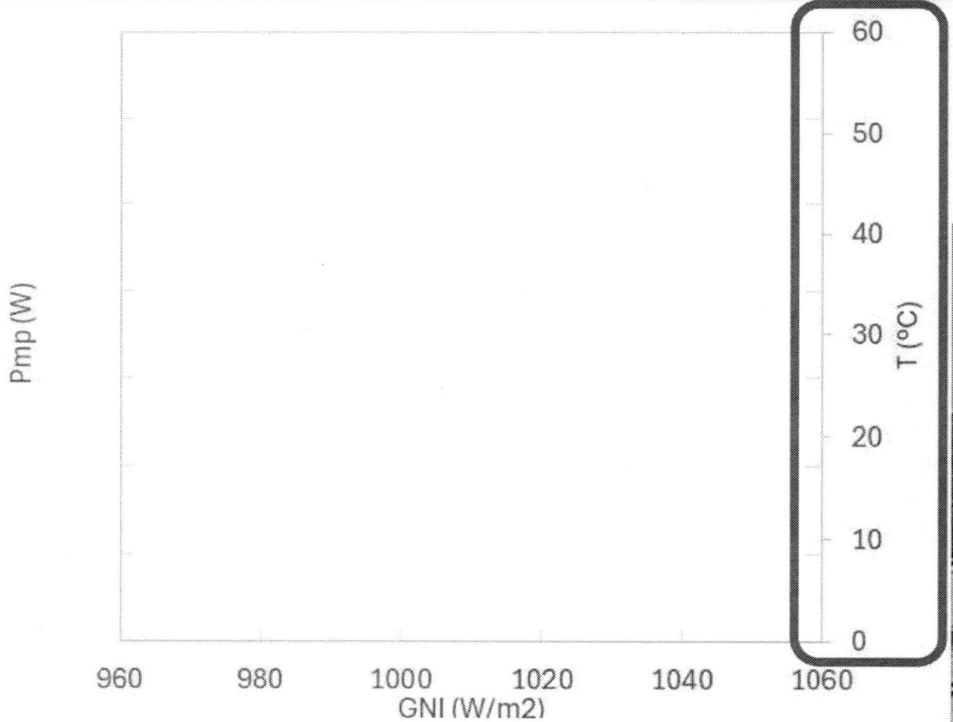

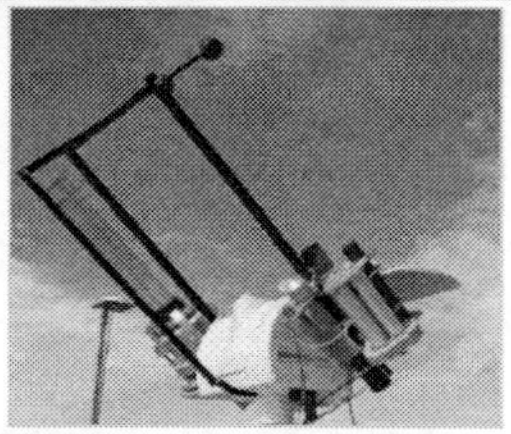

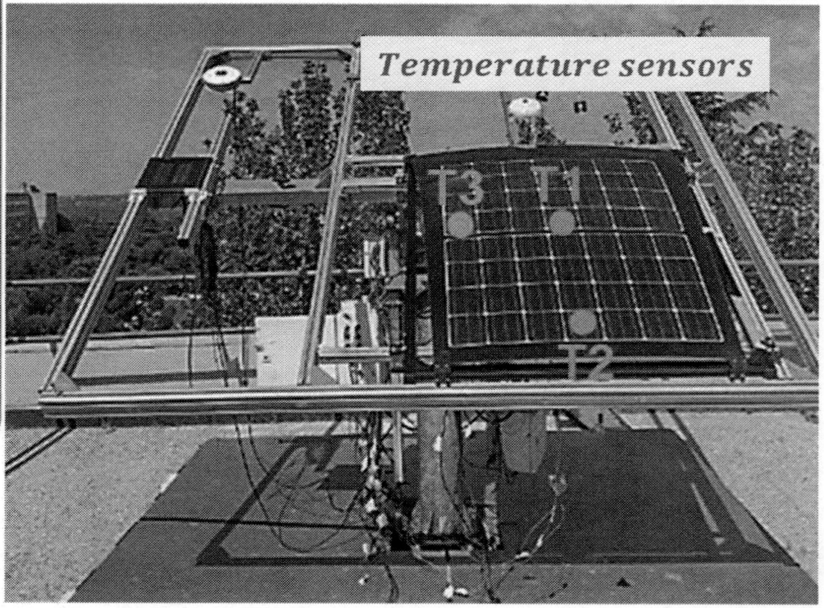

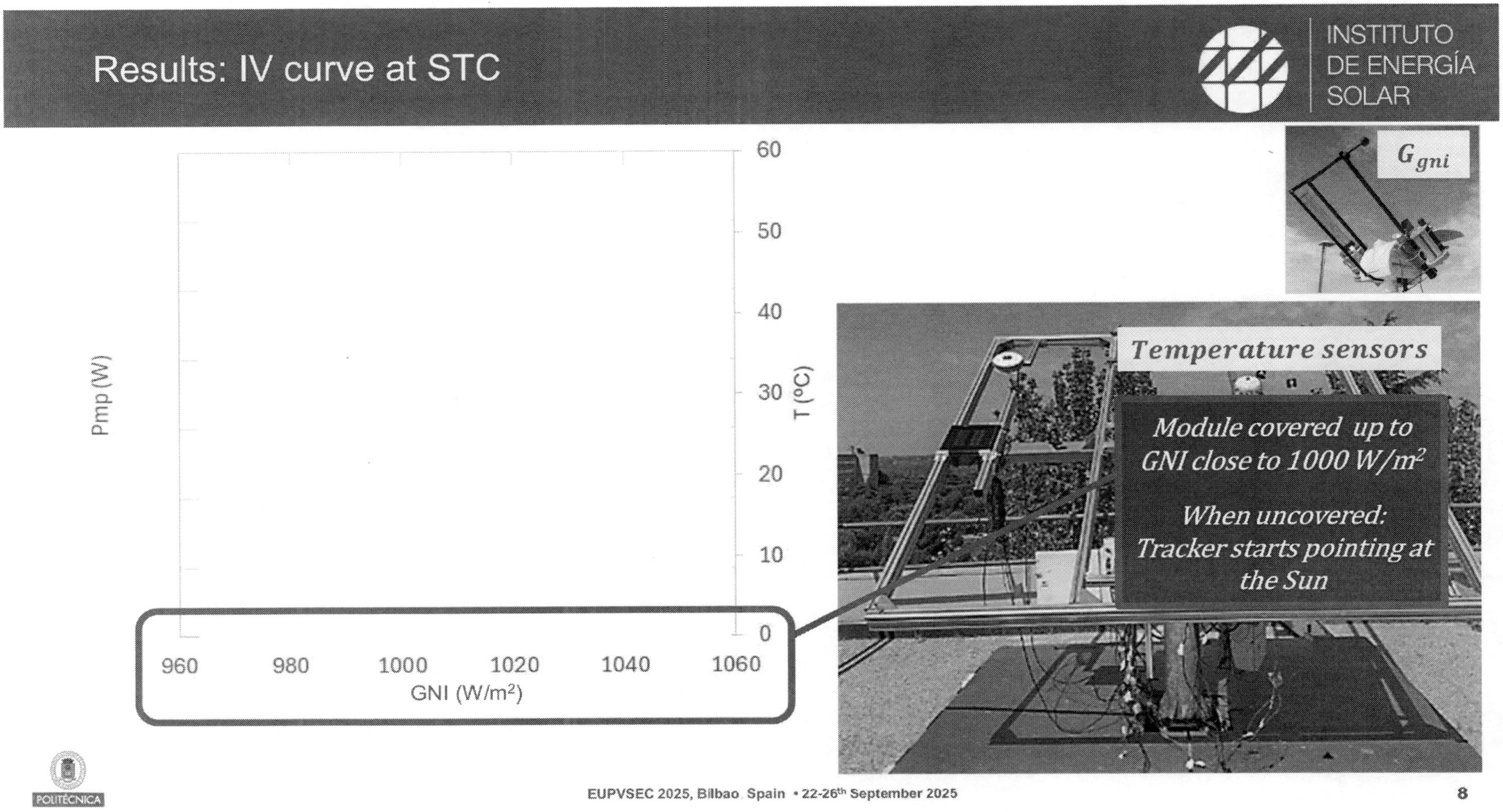
Results: IV curve at STC
INSTITUTO
DE ENERGÍA
SOLAR
Pmp (W)
T (ºC)
60
50
40
30
20
10
0
960
980
1000
1020
1040
1060
GNI (W/m²)
Ggni
Temperature sensors
Module covered up to GNI close to 1000 W/m²
When uncovered: Tracker starts pointing at the Sun
POLITÉCNICA
EUPVSEC 2025, Bilbao, Spain • 22-26th September 2025
8

Results: IV curve at STC

INSTITUTO DE ENERGÍA SOLAR

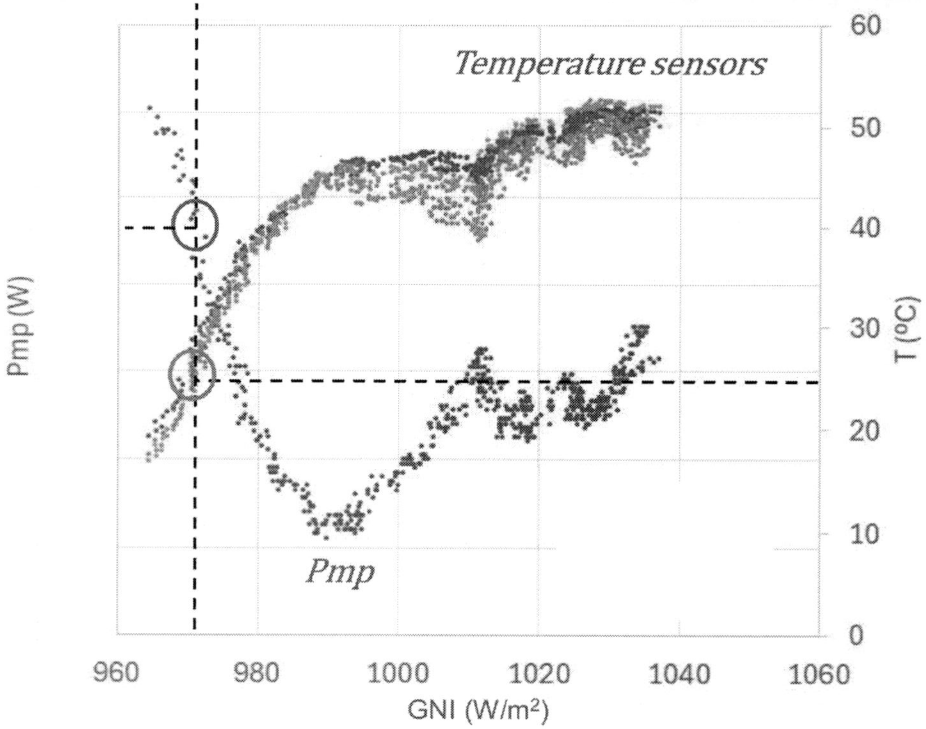

- Outdoor vs. indoor:
  - 0.93 % relative error on Pmp

$25°C\ and\ 1000\ W/m^2$

POLITÉCNICA

Results: IV curve at STC

INSTITUTO DE ENERGÍA SOLAR

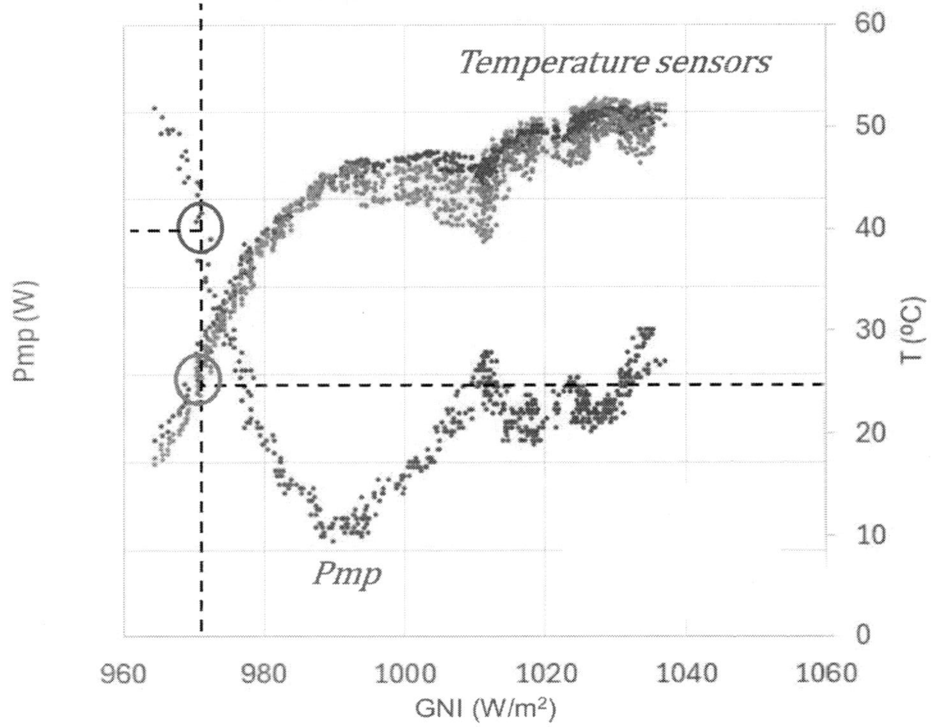

- Outdoor vs. indoor:
  - 0.93 % relative error on Pmp

$25°C \ and \ 1000 \ W/m^2$

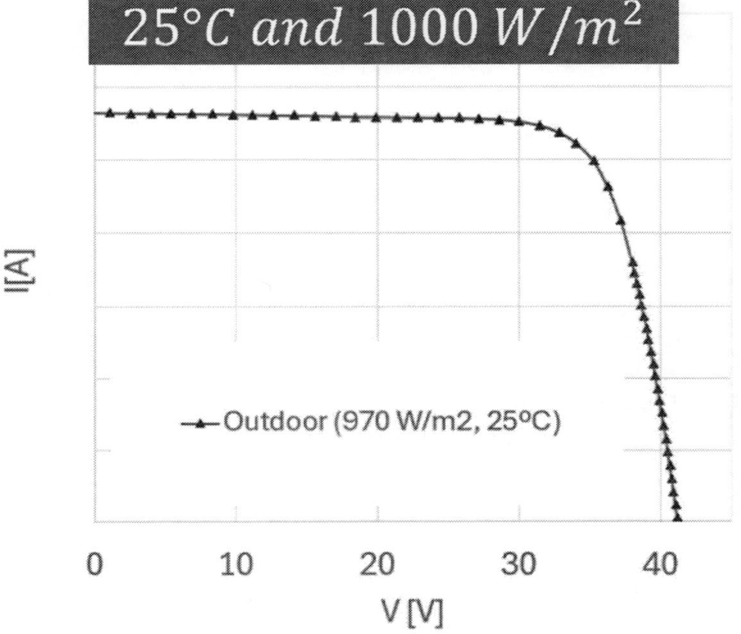

POLITÉCNICA

Results: IV curve at STC

INSTITUTO DE ENERGÍA SOLAR

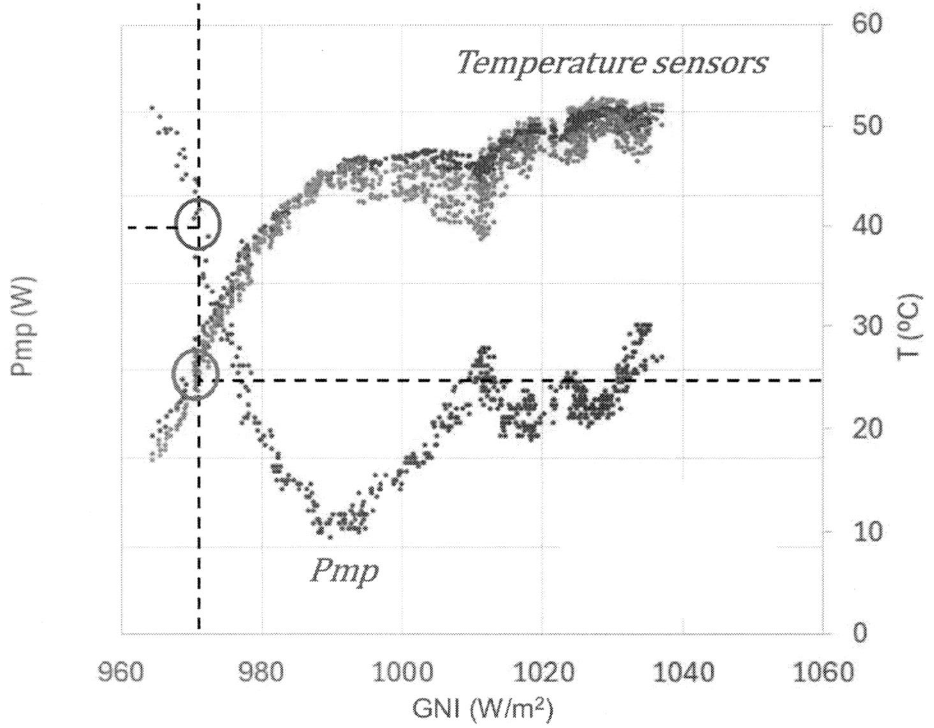

- Outdoor vs. indoor:
  - 0.93 % relative error on Pmp

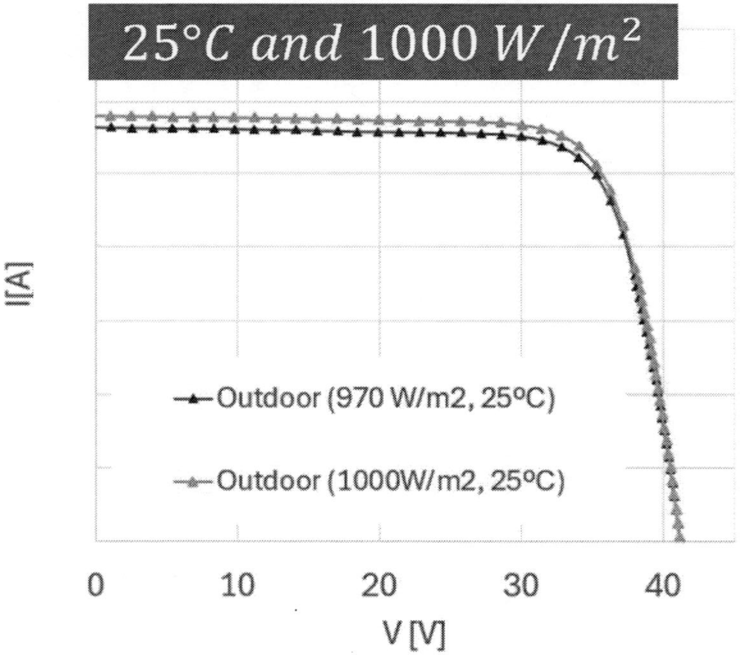

Results: IV curve at STC

INSTITUTO DE ENERGÍA SOLAR

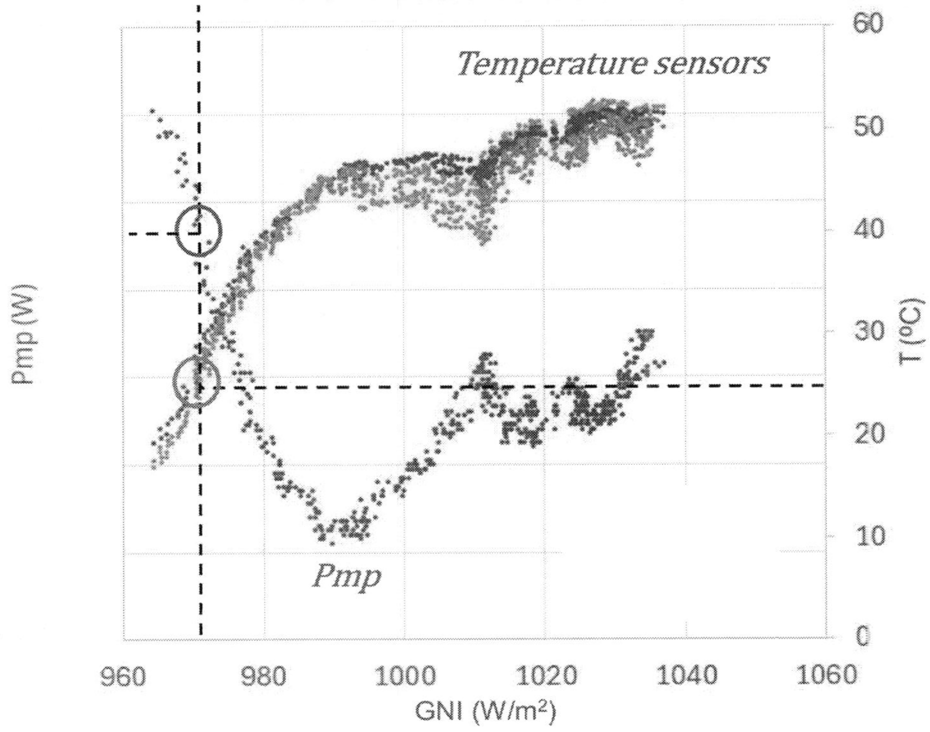

- Outdoor vs. indoor:
  - 0.93 % relative error on Pmp

$25°C \ and \ 1000 \ W/m^2$

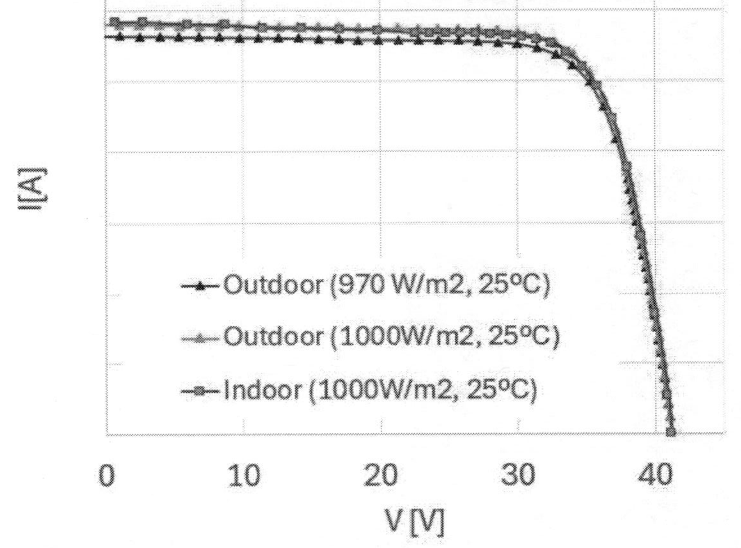

Results: Angular response (indoor)

INSTITUTO DE ENERGÍA SOLAR

- Indoor IV curve at differents angles of incidence:
  - Vertical and horizontal sweep
  - Collimated light: 1000 W/m2
  - Module temperature: 25 ºC

***No correction needed*!!**

Focus on Pmp, not Isc

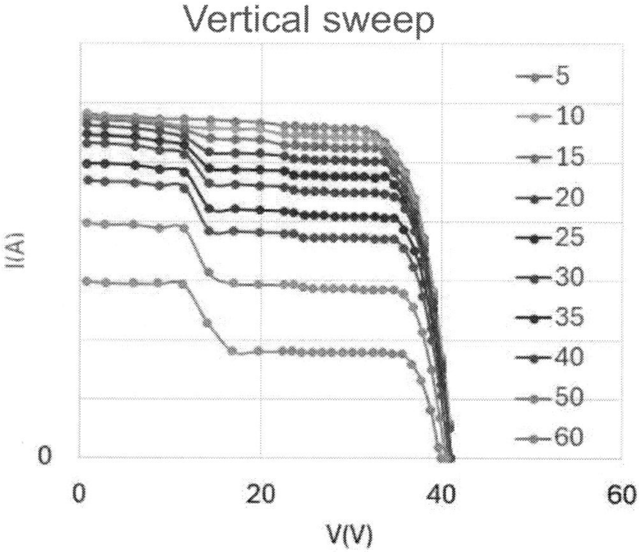

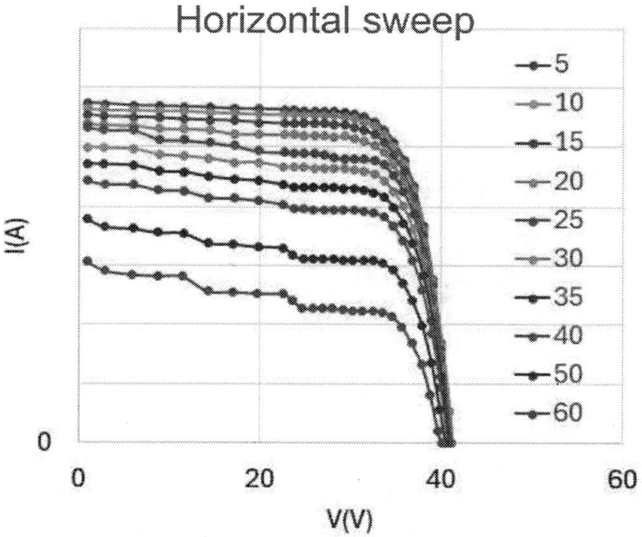

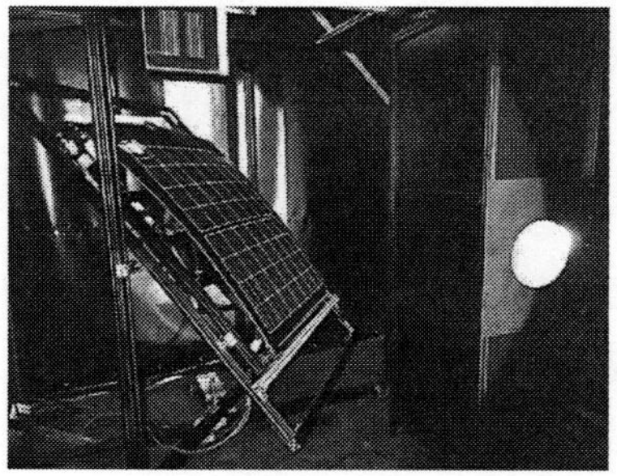

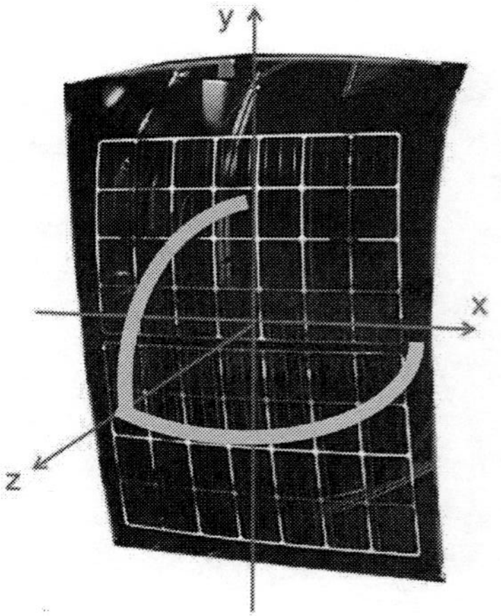

Results: Angular response (outdoor)

INSTITUTO DE ENERGÍA SOLAR

- Outdoor IV curve at differents angles of incidence:
  - Module temperature from 40 to 65 °C
  - Diffuse light from 50 W/m² to 130 W/m²

Correction needed!!

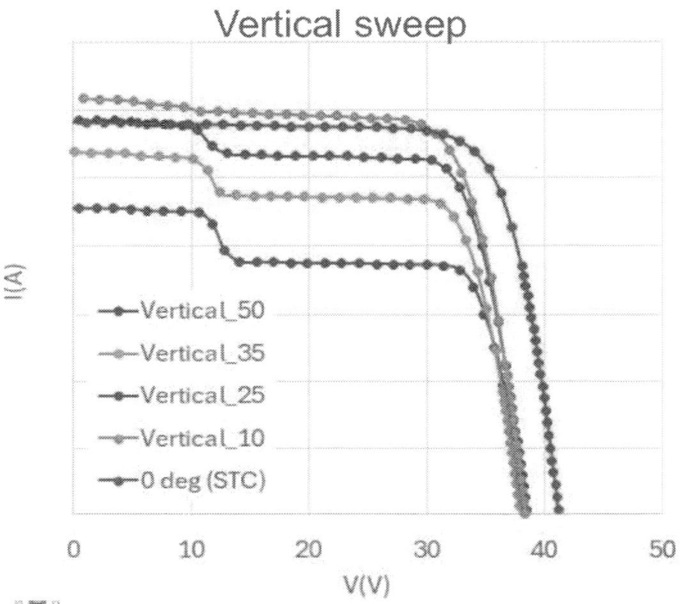

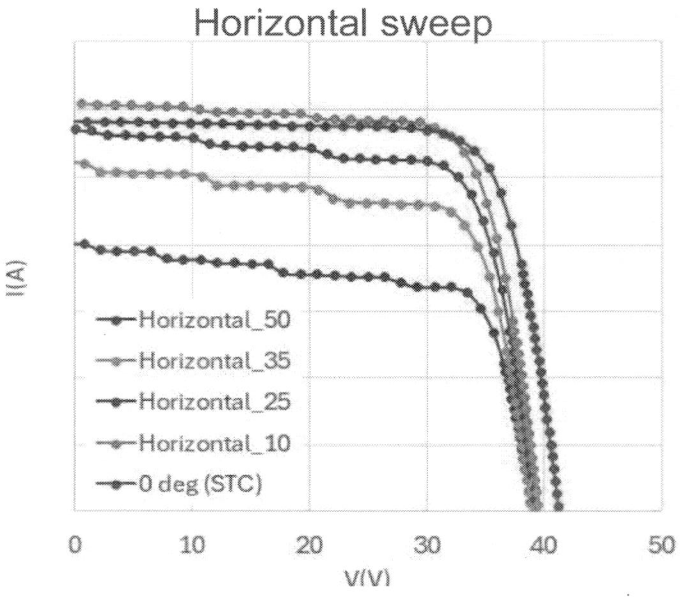

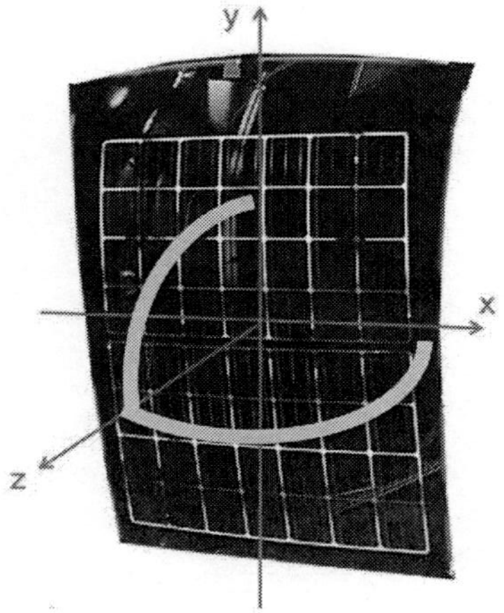

Outdoor angular response

INSTITUTO DE ENERGÍA SOLAR

- Challenges for high angles of incidence!
- Not all angles of incidence are possible:
  - It depends on the Sun elevation and tracker's position (TAz, TEl)

α and β

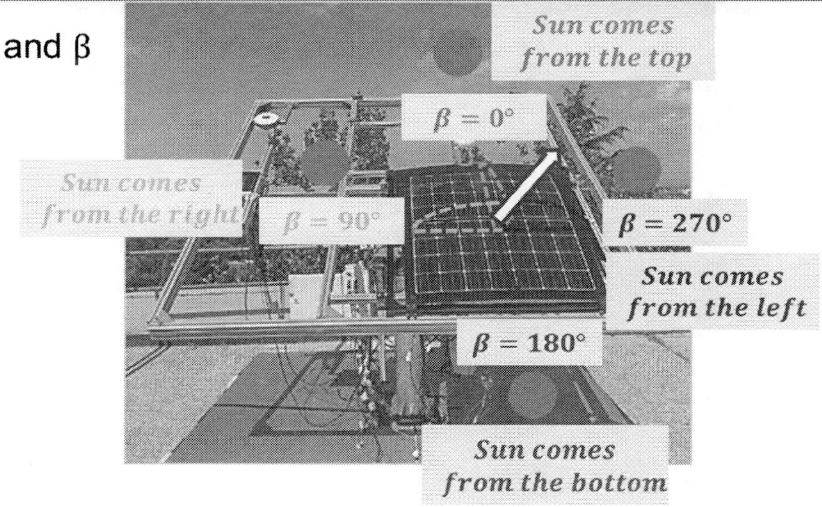

Diffuse component varies for the different positions of the tracker (TAz, TEl)

Even with the same α and β, the tracker's position (TAz, TEl) can change due to the different Sun's position

REACHABLE ANGLES OF INCIDENCE

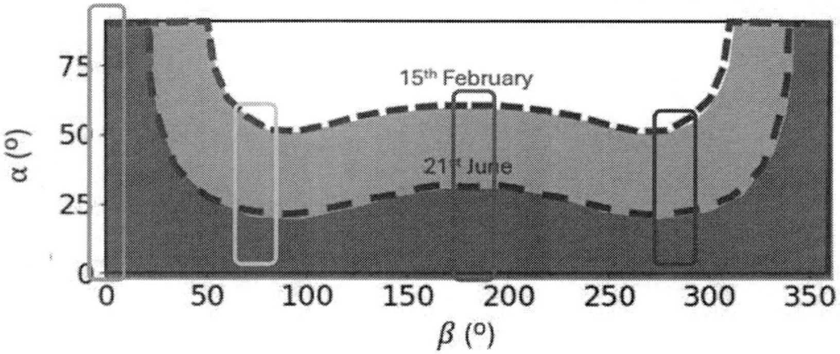

Outdoor angular response

INSTITUTO DE ENERGÍA SOLAR

- Challenges for high angles of incidence!
- Not all angles of incidence are possible:
  - It depends on the Sun elevation and tracker's position (TAz, TEL)

Diffuse component varies for the different positions of the tracker (TAz, TEl)

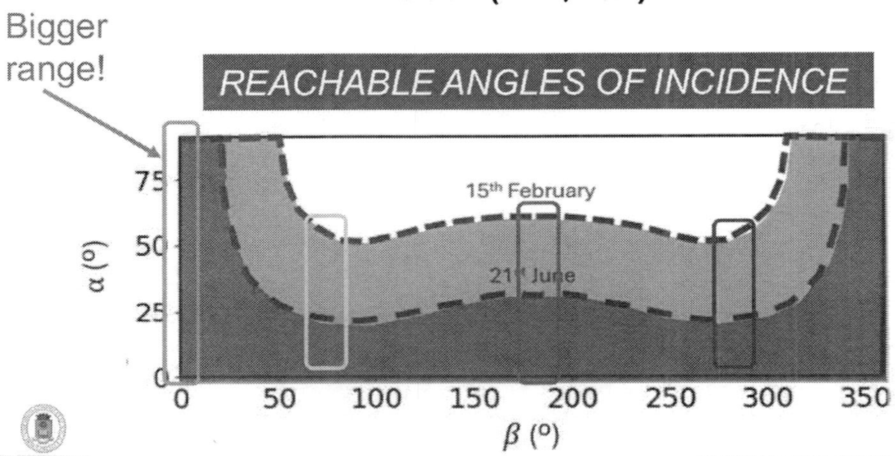

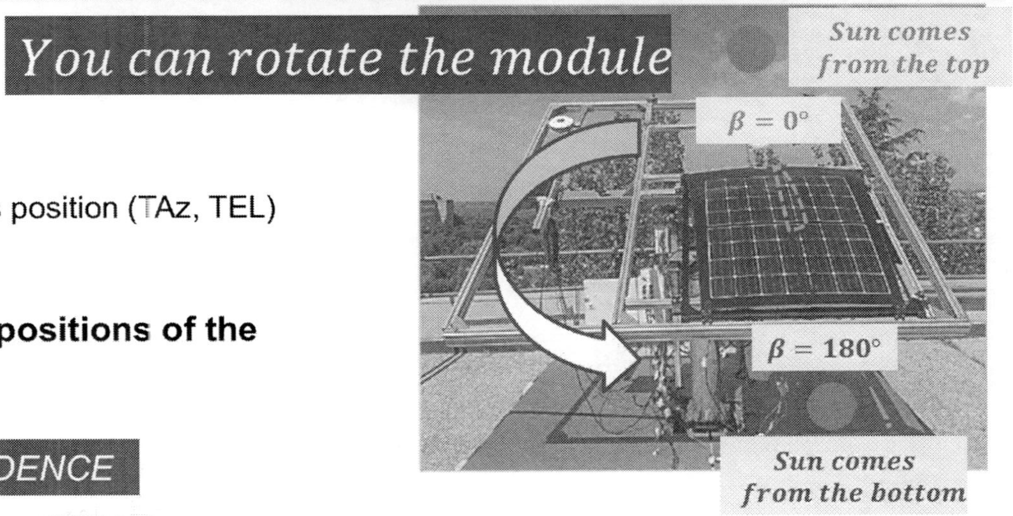

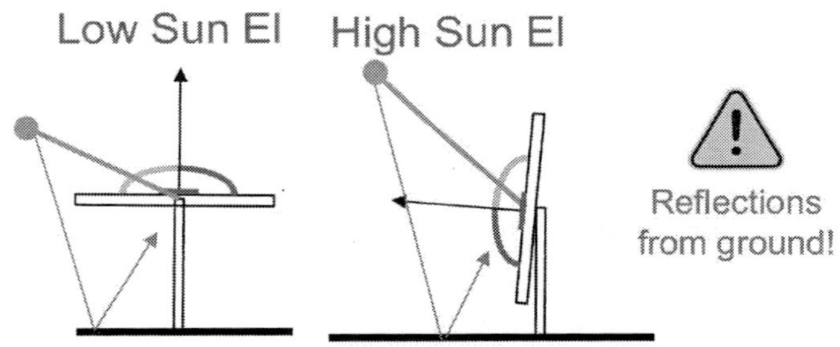

Outdoor angular response: vertical sweep

INSTITUTO DE ENERGÍA SOLAR

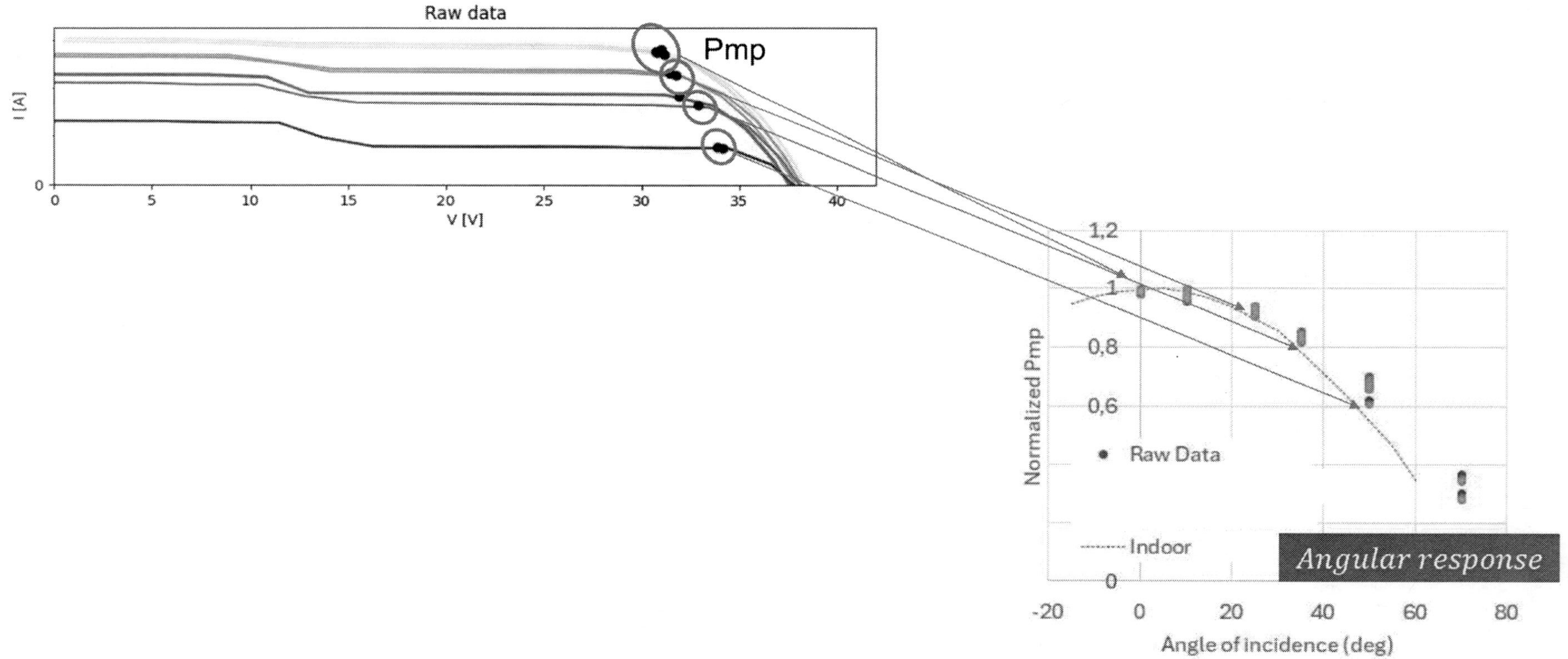

Outdoor angular response: vertical sweep

INSTITUTO DE ENERGÍA SOLAR

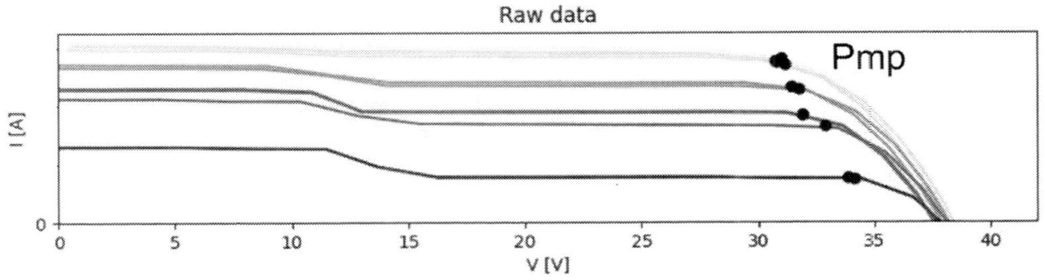

Temperature correction

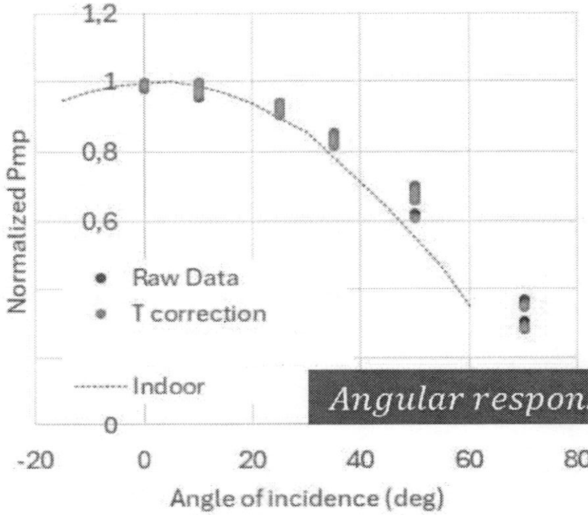

Angular response

Outdoor angular response: vertical sweep

INSTITUTO DE ENERGÍA SOLAR

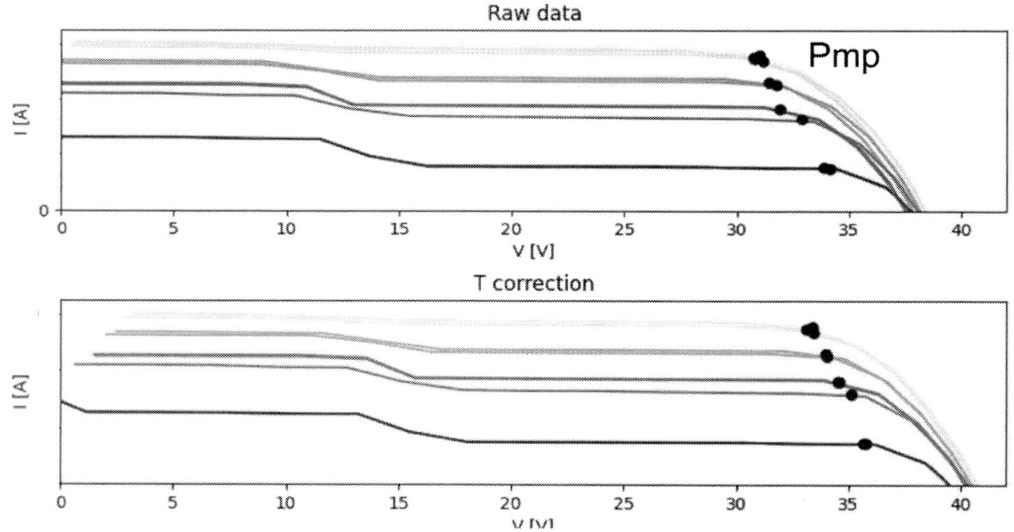

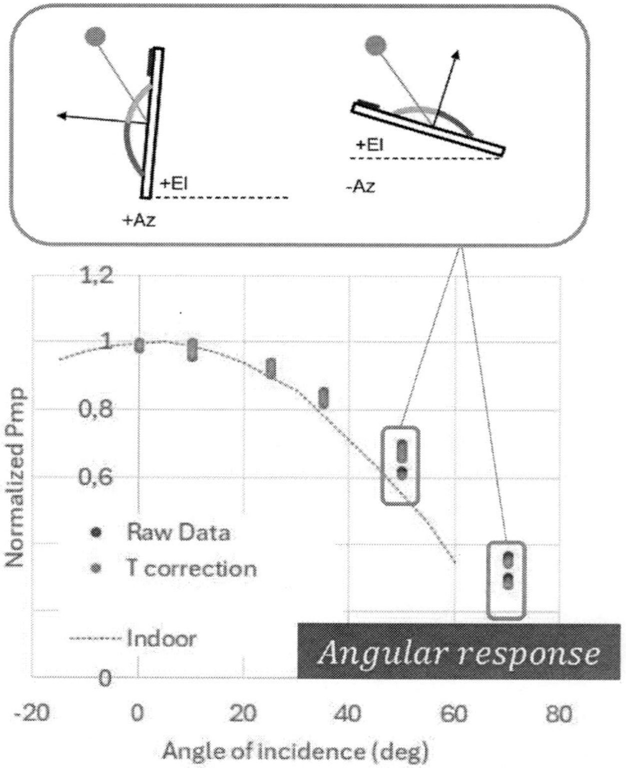

Outdoor angular response: vertical sweep

INSTITUTO DE ENERGÍA SOLAR

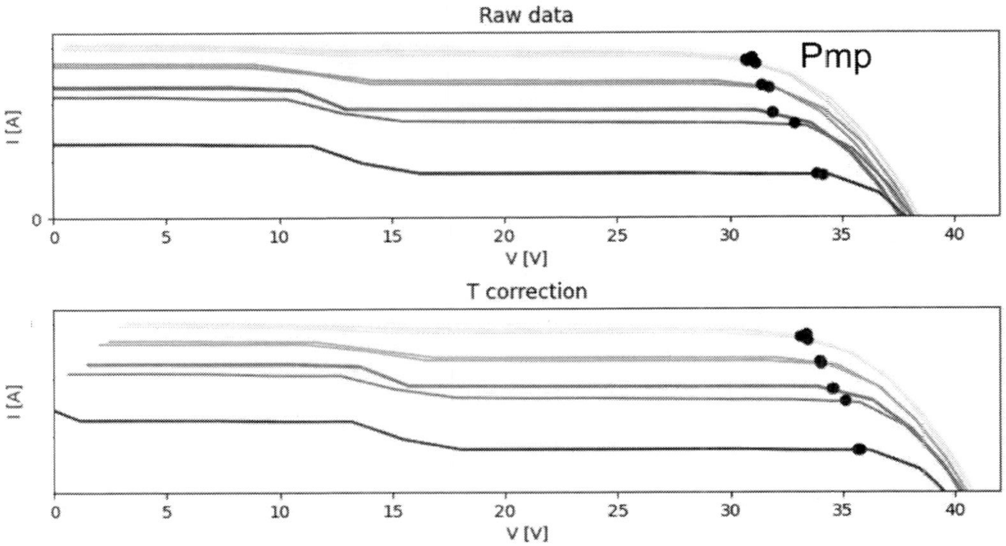

Diffuse on POA is discounted
Irradiance is normalized to 1000W/m^2

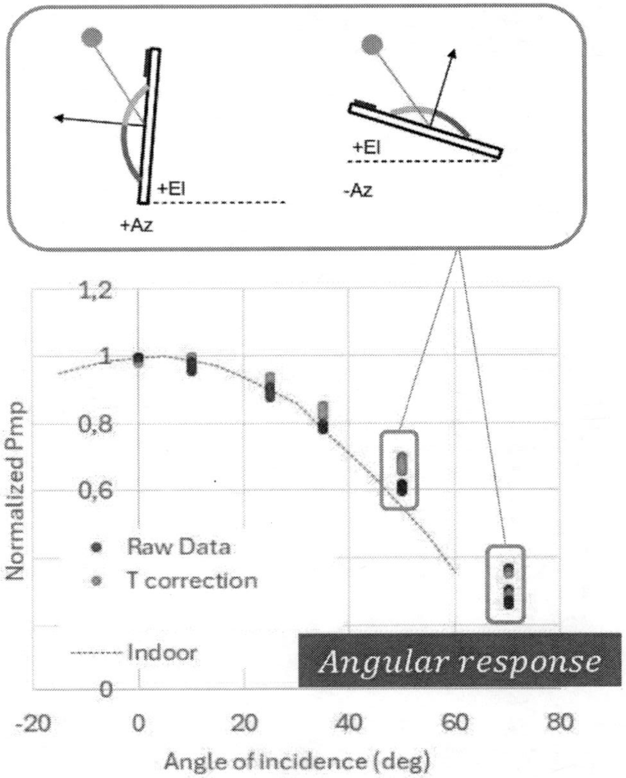

Outdoor angular response: vertical sweep

INSTITUTO DE ENERGÍA SOLAR

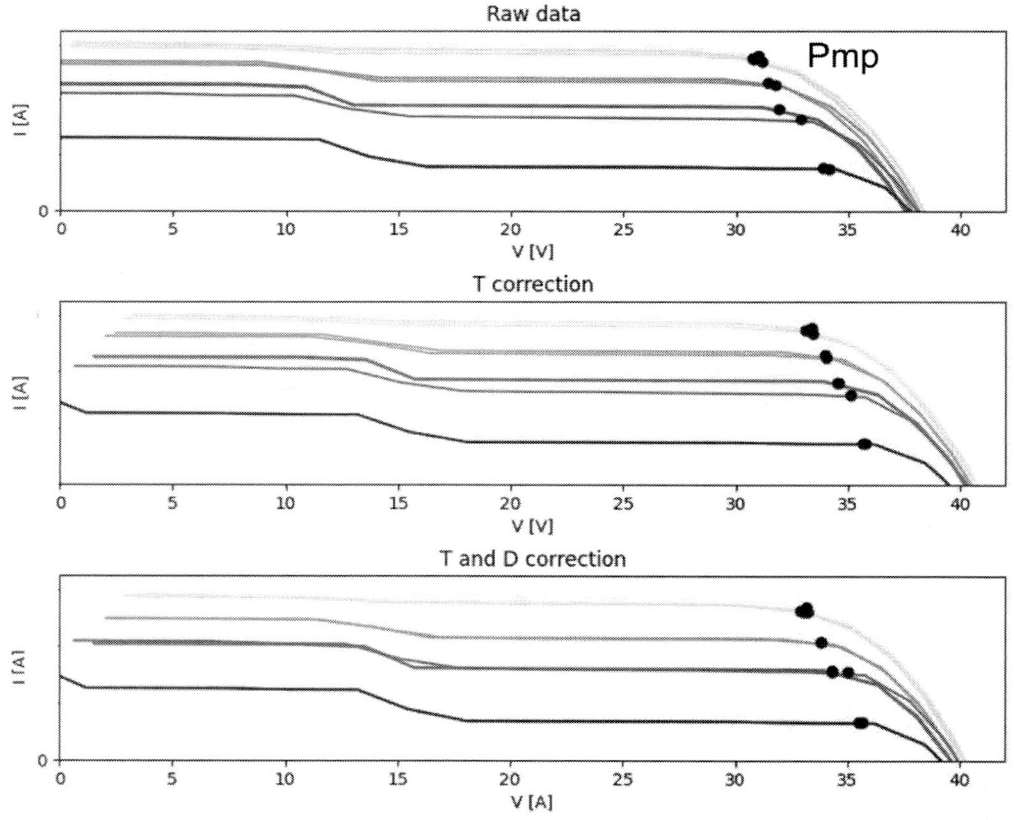

Correction of diffuse irradiance significantly reduce measurement dispersion

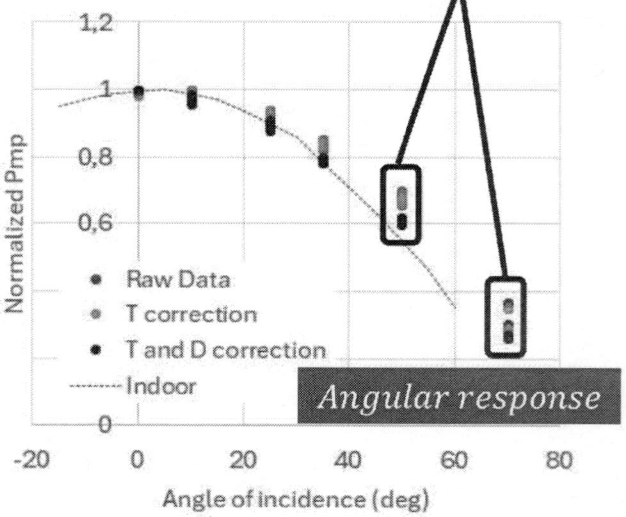

Outdoor angular response: vertical sweep

INSTITUTO DE ENERGÍA SOLAR

- Possible effect of reflected irradiance:
  - Module more affected by diffuse reflected than reference sensor

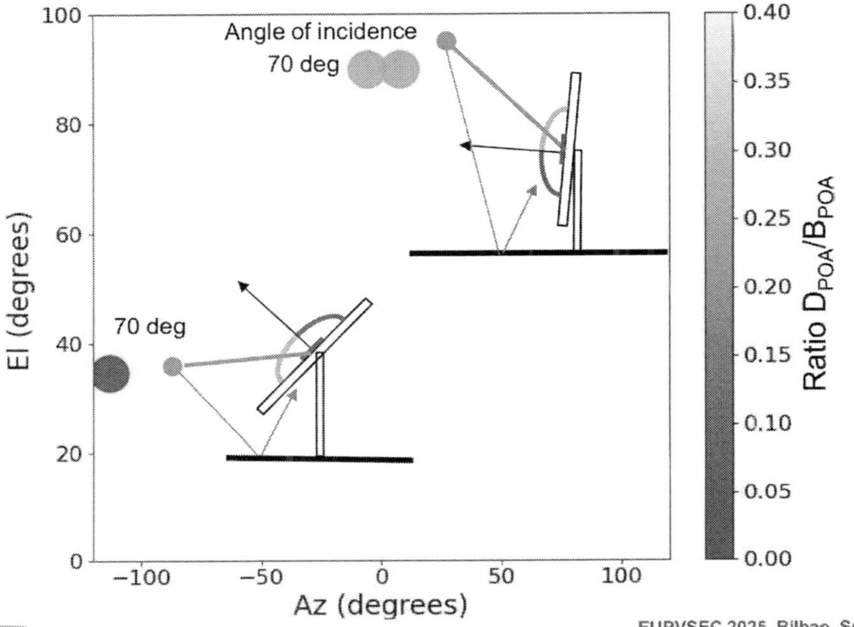

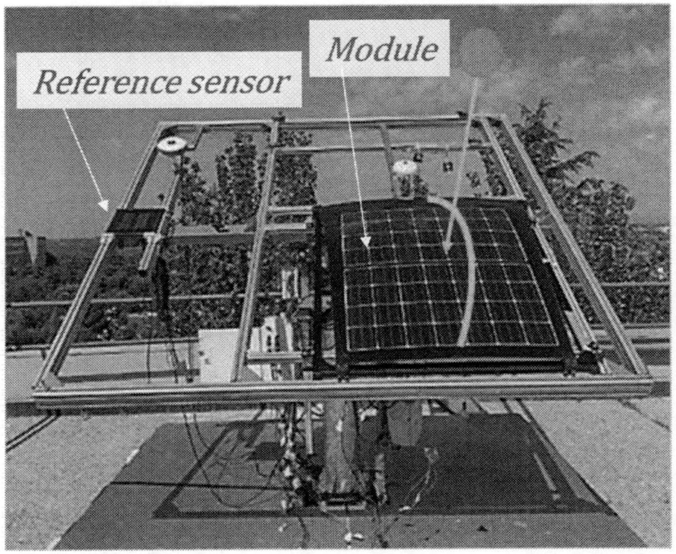

Outdoor angular response: vertical sweep

INSTITUTO DE ENERGÍA SOLAR

- Possible effect of reflected irradiance:
  - Module more affected by diffuse reflected than reference sensor

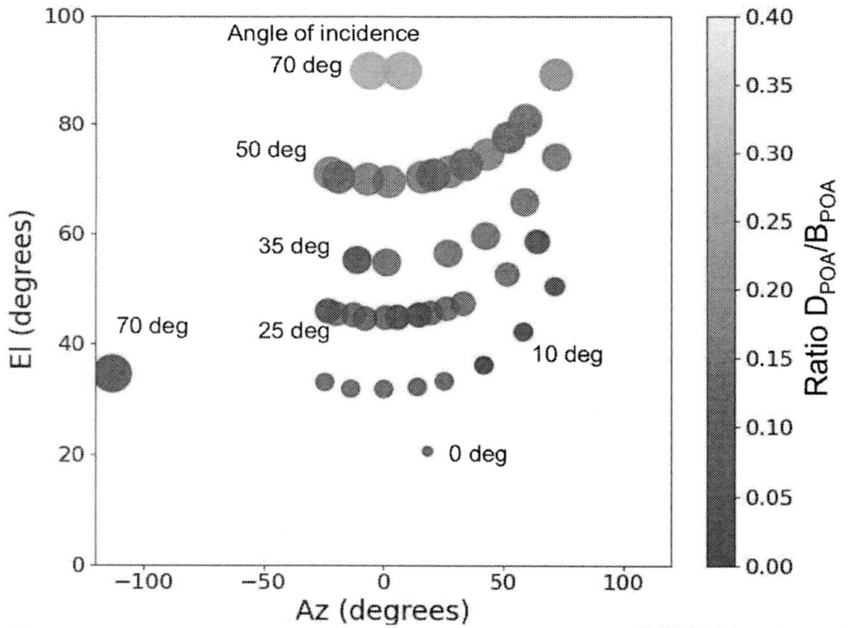

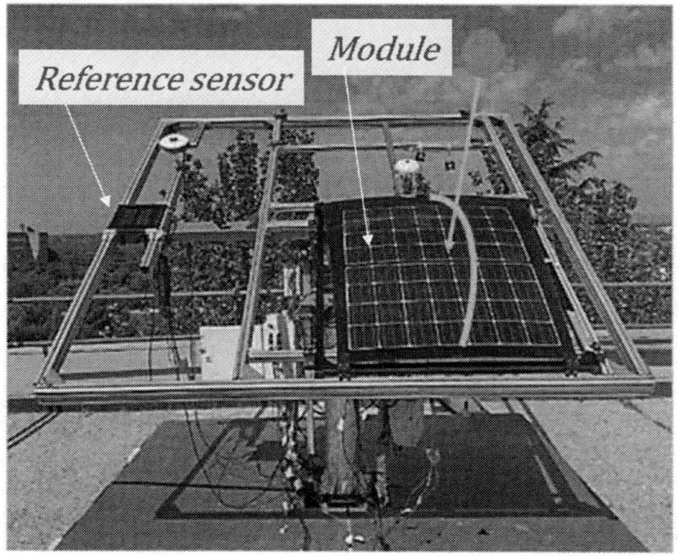

Results: Angular response (vertical sweep)

INSTITUTO DE ENERGÍA SOLAR

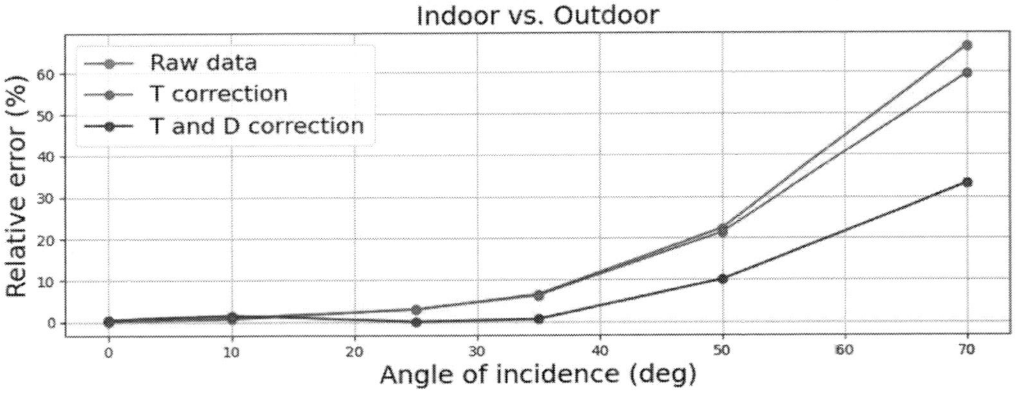

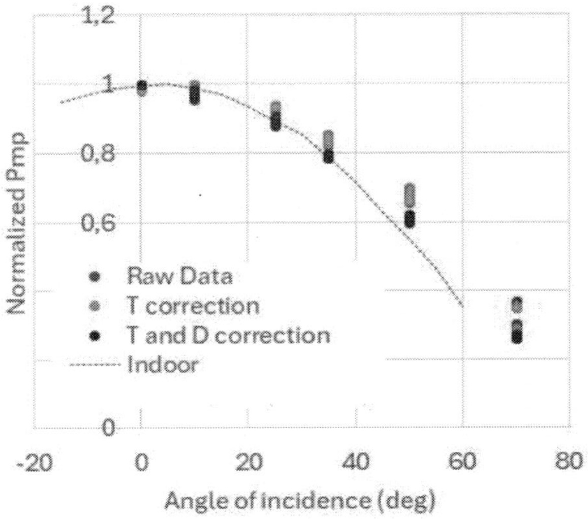

- Additional correction for reflected irradiance is needed

Results: Angular response (vertical sweep)

INSTITUTO DE ENERGÍA SOLAR

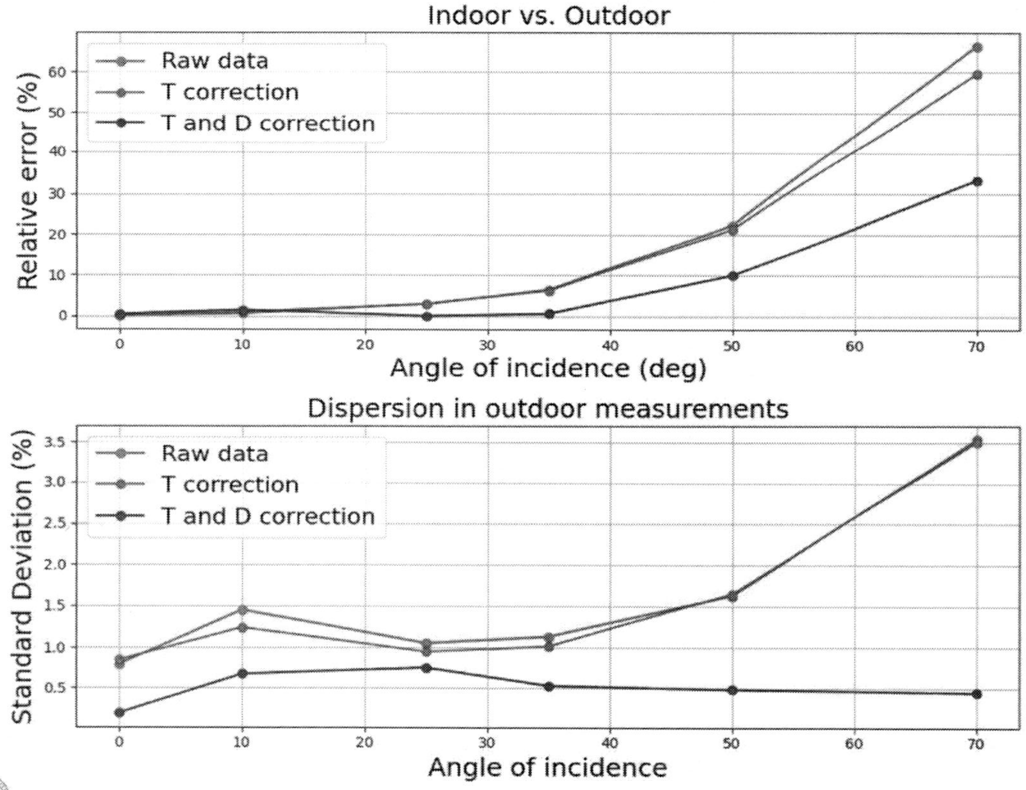

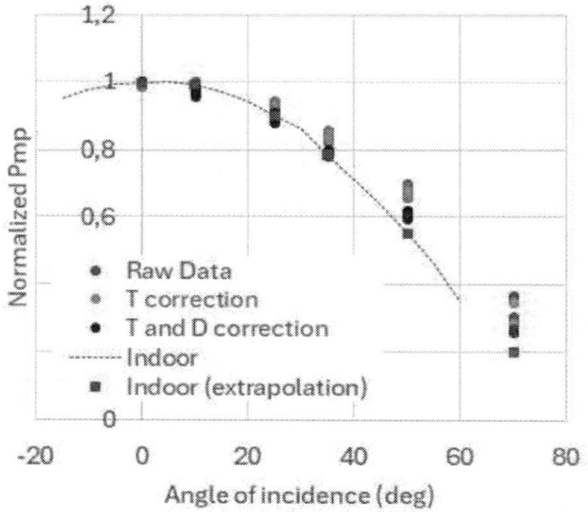

- Measurement dispersion is highly reduced with T and D correction

Conclusions

INSTITUTO DE ENERGÍA SOLAR

- A collimated-light solar simulator is effective for VIPV characterization and offers several advantages, both for IV curve at STC and angular response tests:
  - It is less time-consuming.
  - No temperature or diffuse corrections are required.
- Matching results from indoor and outdoor IV curve STC characterization (<1% difference).
- Regarding outdoor angular response characterization:
  - **Not all α and β** combinations can be achieved at a certain **moment of the year**. This can be solved rotating the module.
  - Vertical sweeps ($\beta = 0$ °) allow higher angles of incidence, but with **high reflections** on pronounced **tracker elevations**.
- To minimize error and dispersion:
  - Temperature correction **slightly** reduces measurement **dispersion** but does not affect **error**.
  - Diffuse correction affects both **error** and **dispersion**, due to varying levels of diffuse irradiance on the module at different angles.

Thank you for your attention

INSTITUTO DE ENERGÍA SOLAR

INSTITUTO DE ENERGÍA SOLAR

Innovation in photovoltaics since 1979

We gratefully acknowledge the DETEC-PV project, Grant PID2021-128853OB-I00, funded by MCIN/AEI/10.13039/501100011033 and "ERDF A way of making Europe"

The authors express sincere thanks to JEMA and JET program for sponsoring the activities, entrusted by METI (Japan) and carried out under the umbrella of the IEC TC82/PT600 group devoted to Vehicle Integrated Photovoltaic Systems

MINISTERIO DE CIENCIA E INNOVACIÓN

UNIÓN EUROPEA

FONDO EUROPEO DE DESARROLLO REGIONAL

AGENCIA ESTATAL DE INVESTIGACIÓN

POLITÉCNICA

INSTITUTO
DE ENERGÍA
SOLAR

Innovation in photovoltaics since 1979

ESTIMATING THE ENERGY YIELD OF BIFACIAL PHOTOVOLTAICS WITH THE JRC'S PHOTOVOLTAIC GEOGRAPHIC INFORMATION SYSTEM

N. Taylor[1], T. Lyubenova[1], L. Malarkannan[2], N. Alexandris[1], A. Falangas[3], R. Kenny[1], E.D. Dunlop[1], B. Mihaylov[1]
1) European Commission Joint Research Centre, Ispra, Italy
2) National Physical Laboratory, Teddington, UK
3) TRASIS International, Belgium

ABSTRACT: The European Commission's Joint Research Centre is upgrading its Photovoltaic Geographic Information System (PVGIS) to include energy yield from bifacial photovoltaics. The aim is to provide a reliable method that is suitable for online information systems designed to provide quick and reliable estimates on PV performance, also for non-expert users and with limited data input requirements. A simplified bifacial PV model has been adapted for this purpose. The initial validation with data from south facing tilted and from east-west vertical systems at JRC's European Solar Test Installation in Ispra, Italy, gave encouraging results for the irradiance levels at the rear of the modules (tilted and vertical systems) and for module temperature. The model is implemented in the PVGIS 6 software update, currently under development. The validation should be extended in future, with suitable data from other locations.
Keywords: photovoltaics, bifacial, energy yield

1 INTRODUCTION

As bifacial PV modules become the norm in many applications, it is increasingly important that online tools for energy yield estimates adapt to take account of potential performance gains. The Joint Research Centre's Photovoltaic Geographical Information System (PVGIS) has provided a free web-based service for over 20 years, with on-the-fly calculation power output from hourly values of historic solar radiation and other environmental variables for the requested location and system configuration [1]. The paper describes the extension of this capability in the new PVGIS 6 Python version to cover power generation bifacial PV modules, considering two configurations: a) open-rack systems, typically equator facing with tilted panels, installed either on flat roofs or on open ground, and b) vertical- mounted systems, typically with east-west orientation.

Bifacial PV modules have significant market share and the price difference to monofacial modules has reduced considerably. Depending on the installation, bifacial modules can produce up to 20% more energy in side-by-side comparisons than equivalent monofacial modules. For the bifacial PV technology, the nominal module peak power is the same as for the monofacial module, since it refers only to front-side illumination. In operation, such modules can benefit from any rear-side illumination available, but there is a lack of standardised methods for estimating the impact on annual energy yield.

There is no option for bifacial modules in the current version of PVGIS tool. For equator-facing tilted systems users can input the power value for Bifacial Nameplate Irradiance (BNPI). This can also be estimated from the front side peak power P_STC value and the power bifaciality coefficient, φ as: P_BNPI = P_STC * (1 + φ * 0.135). For vertical installations, users have the option to treat each side of the bifacial module as an independent monofacial device and manually sum of the contribution from each side (back-to-back approach), with the bifaciality factor applied directly to the estimated power output from the side with lower average yearly in-plane irradiation. A previous JRC study [2] compared these simplified approaches, as well as that proposed by the EU's Horizon 2020 PV-Enerate project [3] for estimating effective irradiance on bifacial modules. The results varied in a range of approximately 10% with the back-to-back approach between the other two. However, the back-to-back cannot be used for tilted systems. This suggests a more detailed approach is required, that users could access via a bifacial PV option in PVGIS.

2 METHODOLOGY

2.1 Bifacial Irradiance

In PVGIS the instantaneous power output is a function of in-plane irradiance and module temperature [4]:

$$P(G',T') = G'(P_{STC,m} + k_1 \ln(G') + k_2 \ln(G')^2 + k_3T' + k_4T' \ln(G') + k_5T'ln(G')^2 + k_6T'^2 \qquad (1)$$

where the normalised in-plane irradiance G' is given by: $G' = \frac{G}{G_{STC}}$ and the module temperature difference T' is given by: $T' = T_{mod} - T_{STC}$. The input irradiance data in the form of two parameters derived from hourly satellite images: SIS = global horizontal irradiance and SID = direct horizontal irradiance. These are used to determine a total in-plane irradiance value on the front surface, from the sum of direct, diffuse and reflected components [5]. For calculating the rear-side irradiance for bifacial modules, the following requirements were set:

- Exploit existing validated approaches
- Simple «infinite shed» geometric model with a default geometry: module height (1 m) and length (2 m)
- Single row i.e. no inter-row shading effects
- Non-uniformity or mismatch effects not considered
- Fast calculation, to support the PVGIS on-the-fly computational approach

On this basis we selected the model proposed by Vogt et al [6]. Their application was for studying energy rating of bifacial modules and only considered an equator-facing tilted system. The approach was therefore extended to cover all orientations and tilts (as well as tracking in the future). Also in our implementation, the transposition of the diffuse light component to the plane of interest is done using the Muneer model instead of the Perez model, since the former is already used in the PVGIS calculations for monofacial modules. The whole process is implemented in Python as a module in the new PVGIS 6 code.

Figure 1 shows a sample calculation of monthly irradiation for an East-West vertical system at the Ispra, Italy location in 2021 and includes results obtained using the NREL view factor algorithm [7] as well as the approach available from PVLIB [8].

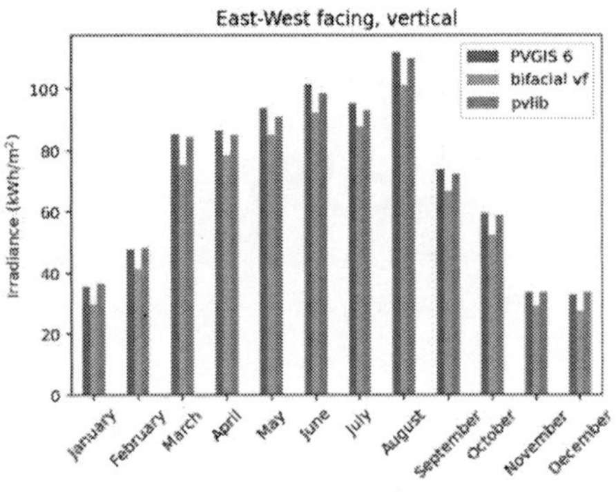

Figure 1: Monthly irradiation estimates for an east-west facing, vertical bifacial PV system in Ispra, Italy, for 2021.

2.2 Bifacial Energy Yield

The PVGIS energy yield estimation process is similar to that used for energy rating in IEC61853 part 3. In applying this to bifacial modules, several aspects need to be considered, as shown in Table 1. Some of the resulting assumptions can be directly supported by JRC experimental data, as shown in Figures 2 and 3.

Table 1: Key aspects in the PVGIS energy yield calculation and the assumptions for bifacial modules

Aspect	PVGIS6 Approach
Reflectance	Use same a_r value front and back
Spectral correction to irradiance	Spectral content: same front & back Spectral response: same front & back
Module operating temperature	Based on front irradiance, ambient T and wind speed (Faiman equation)
Bifaciality ratio	Same for all irradiance and temperature values
Power model	Generic PVGIS model for «crystalline silicon» (calibrated on monofacial modules [9])

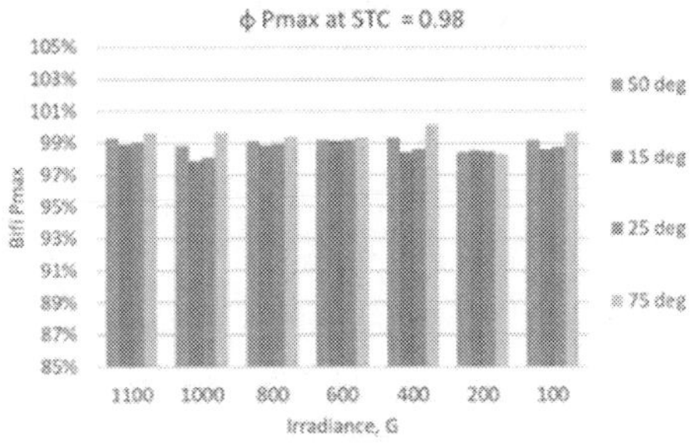

Figure 2: Measured bifaciality ratio values over a broad range of irradiance and temperature values for a PERC module. The variations are minimal.

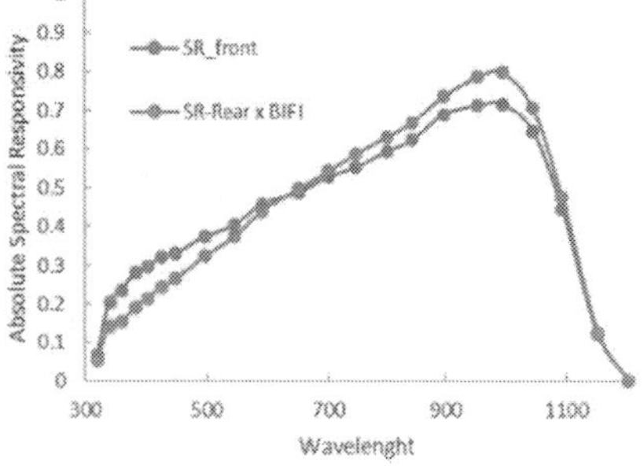

Figure 3: Measured spectral response curves for a PERC module with 0.7 bifaciality ratio, showing good correspondence between the two sides (when corrected for the bifaciality effect).

3. RESULTS

3.1 Irradiance

We compare the PVGIS model estimates with experimental data from the JRC's European Solar Test Installation (ESTI), in particular, the results from long-term monitoring of p-PERC-type bifacial modules with modest bifaciality (0.7) and including both equator-facing, tilted and vertically mounted modules [10]. The albedo is approximately 0.2. An important feature of this system is that it is equipped with over 30 irradiance sensors to monitor both front and rear irradiance values, while temperature measurements are also available for one module in each of the south-facing tilted and the vertical systems.

These system data are complemented by measurements of the global horizontal and beam irradiance from the ESTI meteo tower system. For this validation exercise, the new PVGIS 6 model uses these later measurements as input for the calculation of the in-plane irradiation at the front and rear sides of the system. NB the online version of PVGIS uses either satellite or reanalysis estimates of the horizontal global and beam irradiance as inputs.

Figures 4 and 5 compare the calculated rear side irradiance values with those measured (taking an average of the values form the central sensors, avoiding system edge effects) on a clear summer day (14.8.2021) for the south tilted and the east-west vertical system respectively. For the south-tilted case, the measured value peaks close to 100 W/m² (for reference, the corresponding front side irradiance is approximately 800W/m²). The model overestimates the noon value by approximately 15 W/m². For the vertical system there is good agreement both in the morning (when west side in shade and in the afternoon (with west side in direct sunlight).

Figures 6 and 7 show the same comparison for the monthly cumulative values over the full year. For the south-facing tilted system, the model gives higher values in all months, and particularly in the summer. For the whole year, this difference is +10.8%. In the case of the east-west vertical system, the modelled monthly values are slightly below those measured, with negligible differences in the winter months but higher in the summer. The total annual difference is -6.7%.

10.4229/EUPVSEC2025/3BO.12.4

3.2 Module temperature

The module temperature measurements are compared to values from the PVGIS model (the Faiman equation):

$$T_{mod} = T_{amb} + \frac{G}{u_0 + u_1 * ws}$$

where T_{amb} is ambient temperature, G is the irradiance on the front side, ws is the wind speed, and u_0, u_1 are coefficients for ground-mounted open rack systems. For this validation the ambient temperature is the measured value on site, whereas the online PVGIS tool uses the T_{2m} value from the ERA5 reanalysis data set.

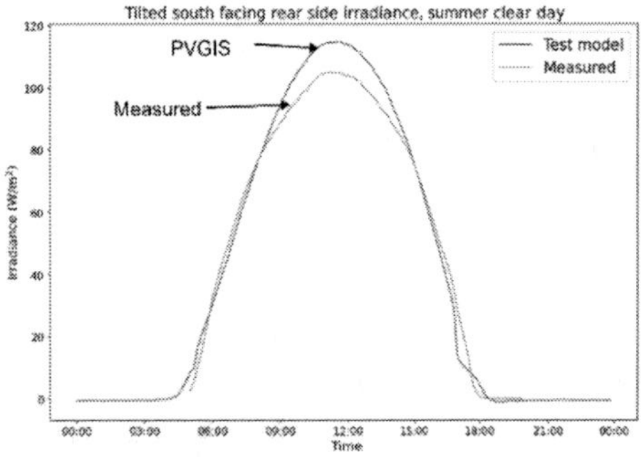

Figure 4: PVGIS6 model and measured irradiance values for the rear side of a south-facing system on a clear day (Ispra, 14.8.2021)

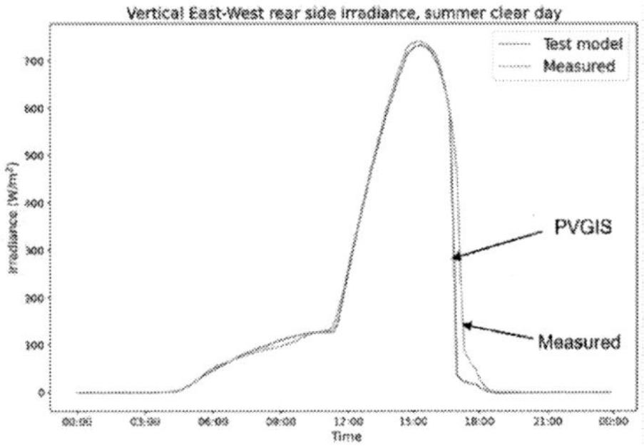

Figure 5: PVGIS6 model and measured irradiance values for the rear (west) side of a vertical system on a clear day (Ispra, 14.8.2021)

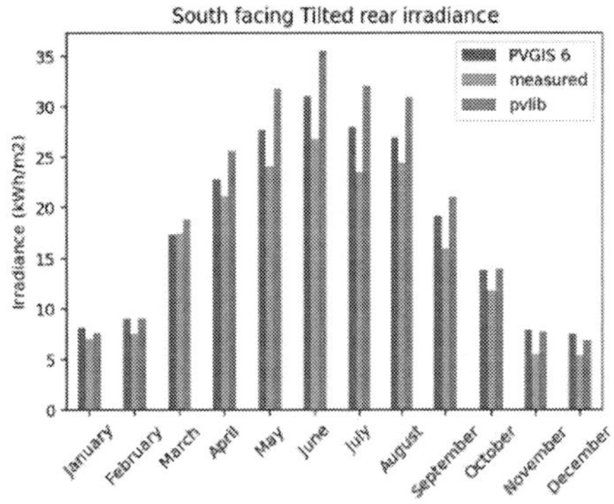

Figure 6: Cumulative month irradiance from the PVGIS6 model and measured values for the rear side of a south-facing system (Ispra, 2021)

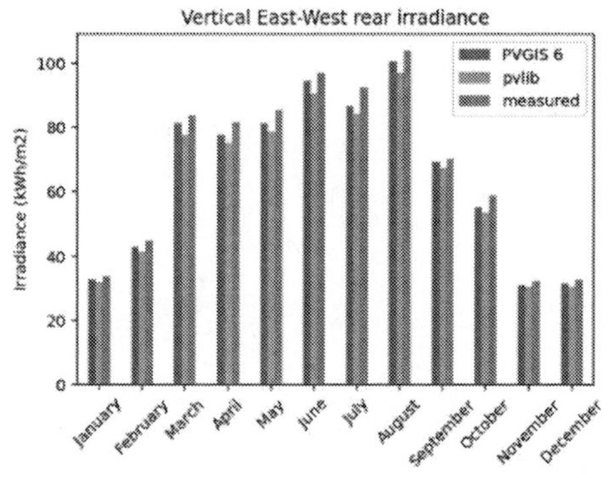

Figure 7: Cumulative month irradiance from the PVGIS6 model and measured values for the rear (west) side of a vertical system (Ispra, 2021)

Figures 8 and 9 compare the calculated and measured values for the same clear summer day (14.8.2021) mentioned above, for the south tilted and the east-west vertical system respectively. Two calculated values are shown: one using the front side irradiance for G and the other with the summed front and rear values for G. For the south-facing tilted system the front-side irradiance approach is closer to the observed values. For the vertical system, this approach leads to underestimates in the afternoon, when the rear side receives direct sunlight. This suggests that it is more appropriate to calculate the module temperature based on the irradiance on the sun-facing side.

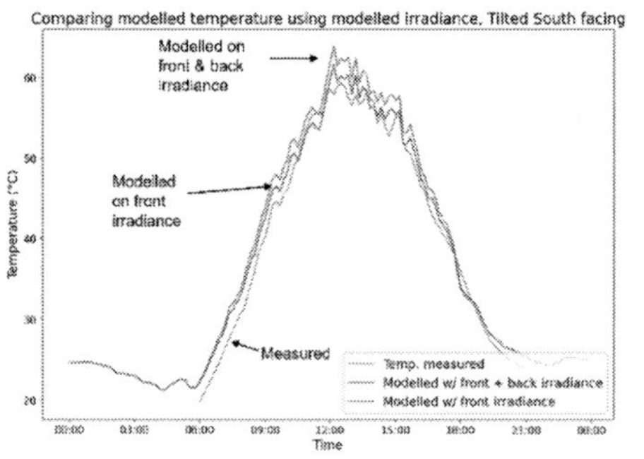

Figure 8: Modelled and measured temperatures for the south-facing tilted system (clear day, Ispra, 14.8.2021)

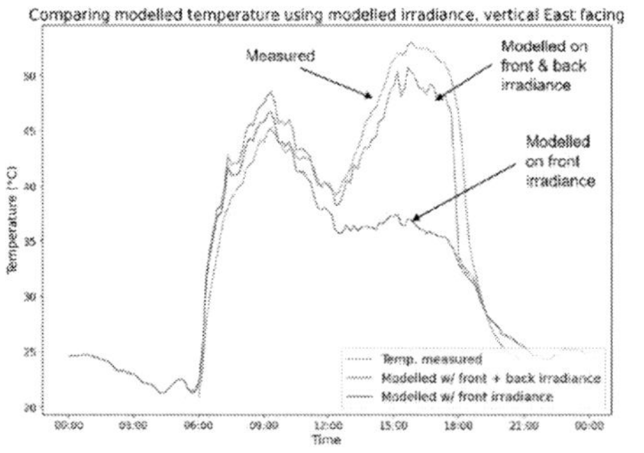

Figure 9: PVGIS6 model and measured temperatures for the vertical system on a clear day (Ispra, 14.8.2021)

10.4229/EUPVSEC2025/3BO.12.4

3.3 Energy Yield

The final analysis step considers the predicted energy yield ratio i.e. the ratio of the annual energy yield of a south-facing tilted and east-west vertical systems to that of a monofacial south-facing titled system, as a function of bifaciality factor. In the case of the south facing tilted system (Figure 10), for the 0.2 albedo level, the PVGIS bifacial model predicts a modest bifacial yield gain, slightly greater than that which would be predicted using the monofacial model with a nominal module power corresponding to the bifacial nameplate irradiance instead of P_{STC}. However, the bifacial model captures the effect of increased albedo seen in the experimental data, whereas the bifacial nameplate power approach is insensitive to albedo.

The experimental data for the PERC modules with 70% bifaciality and 0.2 albedo indicate a gain of 16%, higher than that estimated by the PVGIS model. For the high albedo case (0.4), the model estimates are closer to the observed gains: bifaciality values of 67-68% (p-PERC glass-glass) result in a gain of around 25%, while the bifaciality of 98% (n-PERC glass-glass) results in an increased performance of 31.2% in comparison to the monofacial device (c-Si).

For the east-west vertical system (Figure 11), the proposed PVGIS bifacial model predicts a higher bifacial yield ratio than the "back-to-back" approach with 2 monofacial modules.

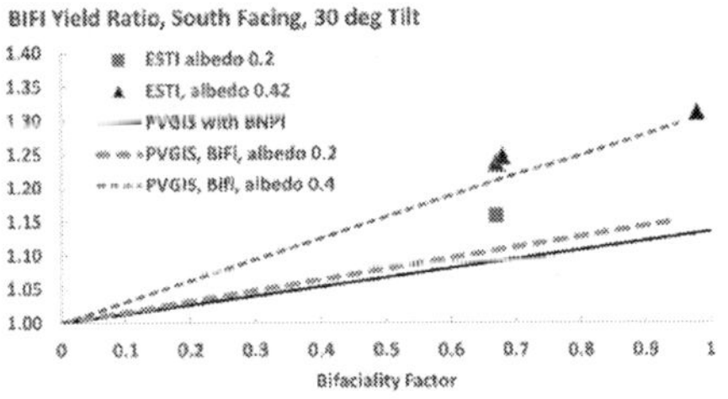

Figure 10: The effect of the module bifaciality and albedo on the bifacial yield ratio for a south-facing tilted system in Ispra, Italy. The high albedo data refers to the experimental work reported in [10].

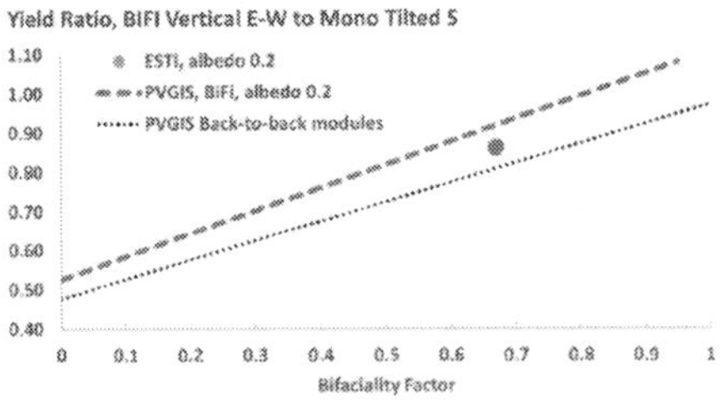

Figure 11: The effect of the module bifaciality on the bifacial yield ratio for an east-west vertical system in Ispra, Italy.

4 CONCLUSIONS

- A simple bifacial PV model has been adapted for the upcoming PVGIS6 software; intended to capture key aspects of bifacial yield gains for small systems designs likely to be of interest for PVGIS users
- An initial validation with data from JRC's European Solar Test Installation gave encouraging results for the irradiance levels at the rear of the modules (tilted and vertical systems) and for module temperature
- On this basis JRC will implement the modified Vogt bifacial model in PVGIS 6, with the option to include alternatives in future
- Extended validation is essential, both with the Ispra data and with data from other locations and systems with suitable monitoring instrumentation.

5. ACKNOWLEDGEMENTS

The authors gratefully acknowledge the collaboration between the European Commission Joint Research Centre and the National Physical Laboratory, UK, which facilitated the study visit of LM to the JRC's Ispra site. Our thanks also to the colleagues of the European Solar Test Installation for their support to the outdoor field measurements and to Diego Pavanello for the calibration of the sensors used in the bifacial PV test stand.

6. DISCLAIMER

The contents of this paper do not necessarily reflect the position or opinion of the European Commission. Neither the European Commission nor any person acting on behalf of the Commission is responsible for the use that might be made of this publication

4 REFERENCES

[1] Photovoltaic Geographical Information System (PVGIS) online tool https://joint-research-centre.ec.europa.eu/photovoltaic-geographical-information-system-pvgis_en

[2] Kakoulaki, G. et al, European transport infrastructure as a solar photovoltaic energy hub, Renewable and Sustainable Energy Reviews, Volume 196, 2024.

[3] Kenny, R. et al, Proposal For The Extension Of The Energy Rating Standard Series IEC 61853 To Bifacial Modules, Proc. 8th World Conference on Photovoltaic Energy Conversion, 2022

[4] Huld, T. et al., "A power-rating model for crystalline silicon PV modules," Sol. Energy Mater. Sol. Cells, vol. 95, no. 12, pp. 3359–3369, 2011

[5] Suri, M. and Hofierka, J. (2004) A New GIS-Based Solar Radiation Model and Its Application to Photovoltaic Assessments. Transactions in GIS, 8, 175-190.

[6] Vogt, M. R. et al, 2023, Developing an energy rating for bifacial photovoltaic modules. Progress in Photovoltaics, 31(12), 1466-1477.

[7] Marion. B. et al, "A Practical Irradiance Model for Bifacial PV Modules".2017 IEEE 44th Photovoltaic Specialists Conference (PVSC), 2017, pp. 1537-1543. doi: 10.1109/PVSC.2017.8366263

[8] PVLIB Bifacial modeling — pvlib python 0.11.2 documentation
[9] Chatzipanagi, A. et al, An Updated Simplified Energy Yield Model for Recent Photovoltaic Module Technologies, Progress In Photovoltaics: Research And Applications, 33, 8, 2025, p. 905-917, 2025
[10] Gracia-Amillo, A. et al, Energy yield analysis of bifacial PV modules: different technologies and configurations, Proc EU PVSEC 2019

AN UPDATE ON ENERGY RATING AMENDMENTS – INTEGRATION OF BIFACIAL MODULES

Stefan Riechelman[1], Hendrik Sträter[1], Ana María Gracia-Amillo[2], Sophie Pelland[3], Anton Driesse[4]

[1]Physikalisch-Technische Bundesanstalt (PTB), Braunschweig, Germany
[2]National Renewable Energy Center (CENER), Pamplona, Spain
[3]Natural Resources Canada (CanmetENERGY), Varennes, Canada
[4]PV Performance Labs, Freiburg, Germany
stefan.riechelmann@ptb.de[1], hendrik.straeter@ptb.de[1], agracia@cener.com[2], sophie.pelland@NRCan-RNCan.gc.ca[3], anton.driesse@pvperformancelabs.com[4]

ABSTRACT: This work describes the ongoing IEC TC82 WG2's revision of IEC 61853 Photovoltaic (PV) module performance testing and energy rating Parts 1, 3 and 4, with a focus on extending the energy rating standard to bifacial photovoltaic modules. A joint project team has updated the formulae of Part 3 to include backside irradiance and developed preliminary meteorological datasets for Part 4 to support different installation configurations. The clarity of the formulas and instructions has also been improved. These improvements will enable a more accurate and comprehensive energy rating for PV modules. A set of six different bifacial PV modules with different cell technologies and different technical layouts were characterized according to IEC 61853-1 and IEC 61853-2 to verify the extended energy rating series. E present the Climate-Specific Energy Rating (*CSER*) values calculated using these modules' data and the updated formulas.

Keywords: Energy Rating, Modelling, Testing, Standards

1 INTRODUCTION

The IEC 61853 standard series Photovoltaic (PV) module performance testing and energy rating describe how to perform energy rating calculations to provide a more realistic energy-based rating of PV modules based on predefined generic meteorological data for different climate zones. The series consists of four parts:

IEC 61853-1 (2011) [1] – Measurement of the PV module power matrix for combinations of different temperature and irradiance conditions.

IEC 61853-2 (2016) [2] – Measurement of the PV module spectral responsivity (SR), angular incidence effect (IAM) and thermal coefficients for the estimation of the module's operating temperature.

IEC 61853-3 (2018) [3] – Mathematical formulation of the energy rating, describes how to calculate energy yield and Climate-Specific Energy Rating *CSER* based on the input data retrieved in the other three parts.

IEC 61853-4 (2018) [4] – Meteorological datasets containing hourly data over one year of six different climate zones.

The standard series has been developed since 1995 and was completed in 2018 [5]. At that time, bifacial modules had a negligible market share, so the developed methods did not cover this type of modules. Today, the share of bifacial modules is about 64 % of all modules sold [6], so the standard series needs to be updated to reflect the characteristics of bifacial PV modules.

In this study, the calculation method in Part 3 of the standard is revised by introducing a rear irradiance component to allow the rating of bifacial modules considering the contribution to the module's performance of the rear side. This updated formula considers the additional irradiance received at the rear of the module. In addition, all necessary intermediate steps to estimate the operating module temperature and the effective irradiance are now defined to take into consideration both sides of the module. In addition to the module mounting configuration assumed in the current standard (20° tilt angle, facing the equator and no rear-side irradiance), three additional settings have been defined in the proposed revision to 61853-3 to reflect the wider use of bifacial solar modules.

In the proposed revision to Part 4 of the standard, for each reference climate data set direct, diffuse and ground-reflected irradiance has been calculated for both sides of the bifacial module for the four different module mounting configurations, needed as input for Part 3.

Part 1 is the oldest part of the series; a lot of references were outdated and have been fixed. Also, the power matrix now is extrapolated already in this part of the series to obtain a regular grid (currently, this is performed in Part 3), to provide the lab performing power matrix measurements the choice to either measure or extrapolate those values of the matrix that were not mandatory before.

2 METHODOLOGY

2.1 Additional module mounting configurations

Table 1: Module mounting configurations according to 61853-3 ED2

	Setting 1	Setting 2	Setting 3	Setting 4
Description	closed rack	open rack	vertical	tracking
Inclination angle β_f	20°	20°	90°	variable
Orientation	Equator	Equator	front to East, rear to West	East/West

The new version of the Energy Rating Standard series must ensure comparability between monofacial and bifacial modules without favoring or discriminating against either type of module. PV modules are currently used in various mounting configurations where the two types of PV modules perform considerably differently. This is considered by introducing different module orientations and inclinations in the form of four new settings as proposed in revision of the standard (see Table 1):

Setting 1 is an equator-facing installation, resembling situations where nearly no irradiance reaches the module from the rear, which is the case for most rooftop-mounted systems. This type of system is therefore abbreviated as closed rack system.

Setting 2 resembles Setting 1, but with rear-side irradiance reaching the module, which is typically the case for ground-mounted installations. This kind of system is therefore called an open rack installation.

Setting 3 is an east-west oriented vertical installation, which is common for agricultural PV, fences or noise barriers.

Setting 4 describes an east-west-oriented single-axis horizontal tracking situation (axis in the direction north-south).

While monofacial and bifacial PV devices will perform similar in rooftop applications due to their severe self-shading, in all other three settings bifacial devices will outperform monofacial devices due to the output power gain from their rear side.

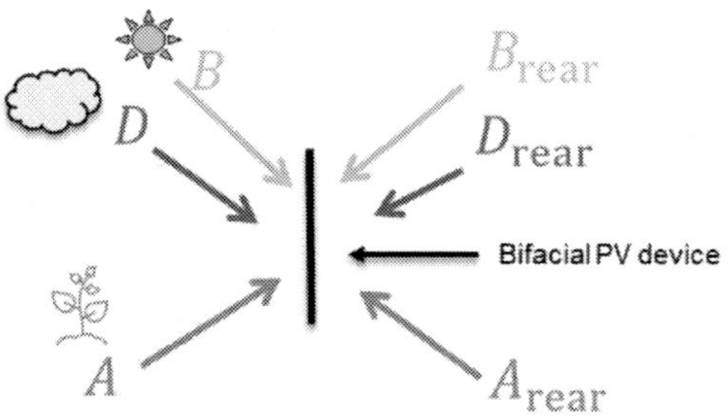

Figure 1: The total irradiance received by a bifacial PV module is given by front- and rear-side direct, diffuse and ground-reflected irradiance.

2.2 Implementing bifacial formulas

The current energy rating standard series do neither consider ground-reflected nor rear-side irradiance. In case of bifacial modules, both front- and rear-side irradiance is crucial for calculating the module power output (see Figure 1). By introducing ground-reflecting irradiance, a formula for angle of incidence (AOI) correction needs to be introduced analogous to the existing ones for direct and diffuse irradiance from [7]:

$$A_{AOI,j} = A_j \cdot \left\{1 - exp\left[-\frac{1}{a_r}\left(\frac{4}{3\pi}\left(sin\,\beta_j + \frac{\beta_j - sin\,\beta_j}{1-cos\,\beta_j}\right) + (0{,}5a_r - 0{,}154)\left(sin\,\beta_j + \frac{\beta_j - sin\,\beta_j}{1-cos\,\beta_j}\right)^2\right)\right]\right\}$$

where

A_j is the uncorrected in-plane ground-reflected irradiance at hour j,

θ_j is the angle between sun and the normal to the module surface in units of radians at hour j,

β_j is the inclination angle of the module relative to horizontal in units of radians at hour j (constant for Settings 1-3) and

a_r is a fitting parameter provided by the analysis of the angle of incidence measurements, as carried out in IEC 61853-2.

The angle of incidence-corrected broadband in-plane global irradiance $G_{AOI,j}$ for the front side of the module is now calculated as:

$$G_{AOI,j} = B_{AOI,j} + D_{AOI,j} + A_{AOI,j}$$

where

$B_{AOI,j}$ is the angle of incidence (AOI)-corrected direct irradiance,

$D_{AOI,j}$ is the AOI-corrected diffuse irradiance and

$A_{AOI,j}$ is the AOI-corrected ground-reflected irradiance.

Spectral correction of $G_{AOI,j}$ is done as described in [8] to derive the spectrally and angle of incidence-corrected global broadband in-plane irradiance at hour j $G_{SC,AOI,j}$.

To describe the gain of bifacial modules due to rear-side illumination, the concept of equivalent irradiance, G_e, has been introduced according to [9]:

$$G_{e,j} = G_{SC,AOI,j} + \varphi_{P_{max}} \cdot G_{SC,AOI,rear,j}$$

where

$\varphi_{P_{max}}$ is the maximum power bifaciality of the PV module after IEC 60904-1-2,

$G_{SC,AOI,j}$ is the front-side spectrally and angle of incidence-corrected global broadband in-plane irradiance at hour j and

$G_{SC,AOI,rear,j}$ is the rear-side spectrally and angle of incidence-corrected global broadband in-plane irradiance at hour j.

$G_{SC,AOI,rear,j}$ is calculated analogous to $G_{SC,AOI,j}$ by applying AOI and spectral correction procedures to all irradiance values reaching the rear side of a PV module. In case of monofacial modules, $G_{SC,AOI,rear,j}$ is assumed to be 0 for the sake of simplicity. This is also the case for the rear side of Setting 1.

The maximum power bifaciality $\varphi_{P_{max}}$ is used because energy rating is about power losses. Inhomogeneous shading on the rear-side of a PV module due to junction boxes or module frames lead to a power loss and thus a drop in $\varphi_{P_{max}}$. Short circuit bifaciality $\varphi_{I_{sc}}$ is not affected, since $\varphi_{I_{sc}}$ is only affected if all strings of a PV module are shaded to the same extent.

The module temperature is calculated according to:

$$T_{mod,j} = T_{amb,j} + \frac{G_{AOI,j} + G_{AOI,rear,j}}{u_0 + u_1 v_j}$$

$T_{amb,j}$ is the ambient temperature at hour j, given by IEC 61853-4,

v_j is the wind speed at the height of the module at hour j, given by IEC 61853-4,

$G_{AOI,j}$ is the angle of incidence-corrected front-side global broadband in-plane irradiance at hour j,

$G_{AOI,rear,j}$ is the angle of incidence-corrected rear-side global broadband in-plane irradiance at hour j, calculated analogous to $G_{AOI,j}$,

u_0 and u_1 are the module thermal coefficients measured as described in IEC 61853-2, representing the influence of irradiance and the impact of wind speed on module temperature, respectively.

Since $G_{AOI,rear,j}$ is 0 for monofacial modules, the temperature of bifacial PV modules is assumed to be slightly higher due to absorbing more rear-side irradiance. A simplified approach is assumed when the rear-side of monofacial PV modules are considered usually white, while bifacial PV modules absorb rear-side irradiance instead of reflecting it.

2.3 Improving inter- and extrapolation

The calculated parameters $G_{e,j}$ and $T_{mod,j}$ can now be used to determine the equivalent module power $P_{mod,j}(G_{e,j}, T_{mod,j})$ for each hour j of the reference climatic datasets by bilinear interpolation and extrapolation from the matrix of power values $P(G,T)$ measured in accordance with IEC 61853-1. In advance to the interpolation, the efficiency matrix $\eta(G,T)$ is derived by $\eta(G,T) = \frac{P(G,T)}{G \cdot A_{mod}}$ where G is the irradiance value of each individual power value of $P(G,T)$ and A_{mod} is the PV module area in m². The following formulas are now used to derive the efficiency $\eta(G_{e,j}, T_{mod,j})$ for each hour j from $\eta(G,T)$ by bilinear interpolation and extrapolation after [10]:

$$\eta(G_{e,j}, T_1) = \eta(G_1, T_1) + \frac{G_{e,j} - G_1}{G_2 - G_1}\left(\eta(G_2, T_1) - \eta(G_1, T_1)\right)$$

$$\eta(G_{e,j}, T_2) = \eta(G_1, T_2) + \frac{G_{e,j} - G_1}{G_2 - G_1}\left(\eta(G_2, T_2) - \eta(G_1, T_2)\right)$$

$$\eta(G_{e,j}, T_{mod,j}) = \frac{T_2 - T_{mod,j}}{T_2 - T_1}\eta(G_{e,j}, T_1) + \frac{T_{mod,j} - T_1}{T_2 - T_1}\eta(G_{e,j}, T_2)$$

where in the case of interpolation:

T_1 and T_2 are the temperature grid points of $\eta(G,T)$ left and right of $T_{mod,j}$, respectively, and

G_1 and G_2 are the irradiance grid points of $\eta(G,T)$ below and above $G_{e,j}$, respectively.

And where in the case of extrapolation:

T_1 and T_2 are the temperature grid points of $\eta(G,T)$ closest to $T_{mod,j}$ and

G_1 and G_2 are the irradiance grid points of $\eta(G,T)$ closest to $G_{e,j}$.

A visual example of this method is shown in Figure 2.

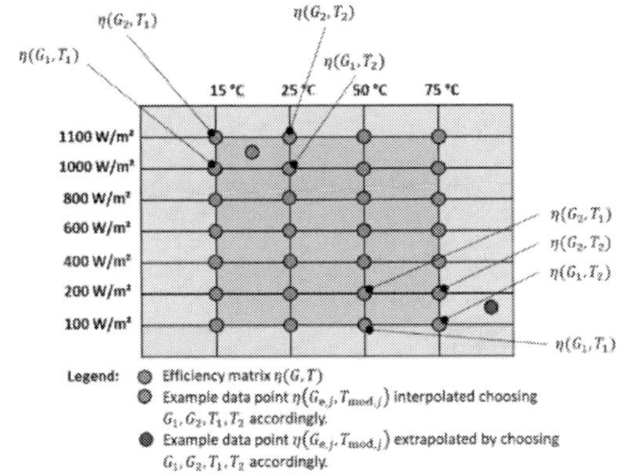

Figure 2: Example on how to choose T_1, T_2, G_1 and G_2, respectively, to interpolate or extrapolate $\eta(G_{e,j}, T_{mod,j})$ values.

Note that these formulas allow no missing data points on the power matrix grid. Therefore, in the new edition of the standard a complete power matrix needs to be provided by 61853-1. In the current edition of the standard six points were not mandatory to be measured, since their combination of irradiance and temperature are unlikely to occur. Nowadays measuring those points is often a negligible additional effort, so labs can choose whether they want to measure or to extrapolate these power values. A new extrapolation method for 61853-1 based on [10] has been introduced:

$$P_{1-6}(G,T) = G \cdot \left(\frac{P(G_1, T_1)}{G_1} + \frac{P(G_2, T_2)}{G_2} - \frac{P(G_3, T_3)}{G_3}\right)$$

with values for irradiances and temperatures G_1, G_2, G_3, T_1, T_2 and T_3 taken from Table 2:

Table 2: Values for G_1, G_2, G_3, T_1, T_2 and T_3.

	Power value $P_{1-6}(G,T)$					
	P_1 1100,15	P_2 400/75	P_3 200/50	P_4 200,75	P_5 100,50	P_6 100,75
G_1 (W/m²)	1000	400	200	200	100	100
G_2(W/m²)	1100	600	400	400	200	200
G_3(W/m²)	1000	600	400	400	200	200
T_1(°C)	15	50	25	50	25	50
T_2(°C)	25	75	50	75	50	75
T_3(°C)	25	50	25	50	25	50

An example on how to extrapolate missing power matrix values is given in Figure 3.

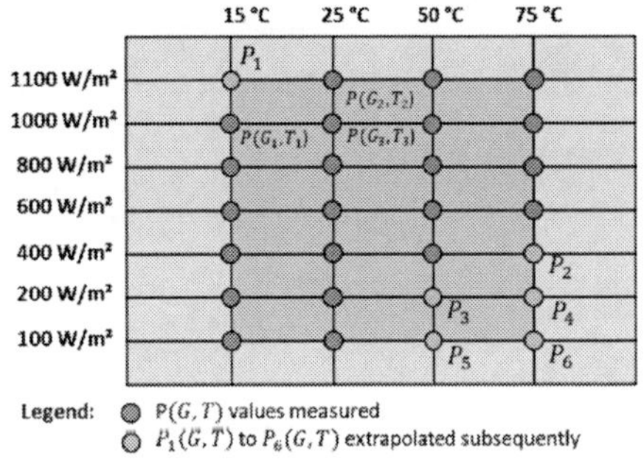

Figure 3: Example on how to extrapolate missing data points based on three nearest neighboring points in the power value grid.

After deriving $\eta(G_{e,j}, T_{mod,j})$, the equivalent module power $P_{mod,j}(G_{e,j}, T_{mod,j})$ is derived for each hour j by multiplying with the equivalent irradiance $G_{e,j}$ and the module area A_{mod} at each hour j:

$$P_{mod,j}(G_{e,j}, T_{mod,j}) = \eta(G_{e,j}, T_{mod,j}) \cdot G_{e,j} \cdot A_{mod}$$

2.4 Module data

To test the changes of the energy rating procedure, we need measurements on PV modules. Six bifacial modules and one monofacial module were characterized at PTB according to the test procedures described in 61853-1 and 61853-2 and the corresponding proposed revision extended when necessary for bifacial modules. The PV module power matrix and $\varphi_{P_{max}}$ were measured with an LED-based solar simulator described in [11]. Front- and rear-side spectral responsivity (SR) was also measured with the same setup using a procedure described in [12]. Front- and rear-side incidence angle modifier (IAM, also denoted a_r) measurements were conducted under direct sunlight with an outdoor facility described in [13]. The thermal coefficients were determined with an outdoor test stand described in [14].

Table 3: Values of $\varphi_{P_{max}}$ and a_r of the measured modules.

	Technology - Manufacturer	$\varphi_{P_{max}}$	a_{r_front}	a_{r_rear}
1	Heterojunction (HJT)	87.9	0.152	0.169
2	TOPCon white mesh grid	75.5	0.153	0.163
3	TOPCon transparent	78.9	0.154	0.160
4	TOPCon black mesh grid	73.0	0.150	0.175
5	PERC, frameless	70.3	0.153	0.160
6	Back contact (IBC)	41.0	0.153	0.153
7	TOPCon black mono	-	0.153	-

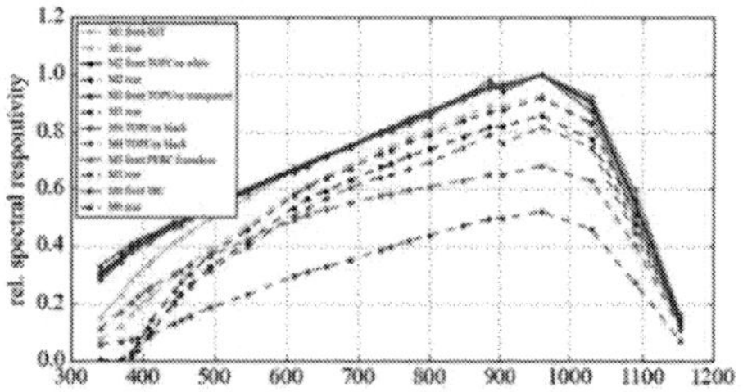

Figure 4: Front- and rear-side spectral responsivity of all measured bifacial PV modules of Table 3.

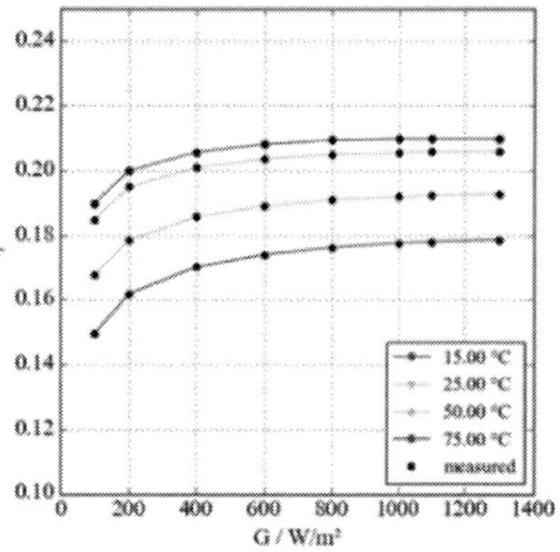

Figure 5: Example power matrix of Module 1 (HJT).

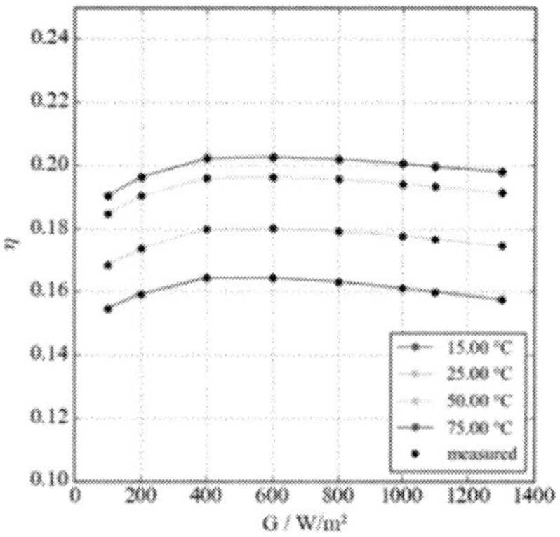

Figure 6: Example power matrix of Module 5 (PERC)

The energy produced by the module over one year ($E_{\text{mod,year}}$) is determined as the sum of the hourly energy $E_{\text{mod,j}} = P_{\text{mod},j}(G_{\text{e},j}, T_{\text{mod},j}) \cdot 1\,hour$ produced by the PV module at each hour j over the year:

$$E_{\text{mod,year}} = \sum_{j=1}^{j=8760} P_{\text{mod},j}(G_{\text{e},j}, T_{\text{mod},j}) \cdot 1\,hour,$$

where j ranges from 1 to 8760 in the reference period (one year).

The Climate-Specific Energy Rating *CSER* is the normalized energy generation for the reference climate profile:

$$CSER = \frac{E_{\text{mod,year}} \cdot G_{\text{STC}}}{P_{\text{STC}} \cdot H_{\text{ref}}}$$

where

H_{ref} is the sum of the front-side global in-plane irradiance G_j values over one year of a reference climate period (1 year) given in IEC 61853-4 (kWh/m²),

G_{STC} is the irradiance at standard test conditions (1000 W/m²) and

P_{STC} is the power under standard test conditions in W, taken from the power measurements according to IEC 61853-1.

3 RESULTS AND DISCUSSION

The *CSER* values are calculated for each climate zone and each of the introduced settings, yielding a total of 24 *CSER* values for each PV module.

The results for the subtropical arid climate are shown in Figure 7. In Setting 1, the monofacial module is quite close in terms of *CSER* to all bifacial modules, with values ranging from 0.933 to 0.941. For Setting 2, the *CSER* values show a strong deviation ranging from 0.943 up to 1.085. Here, a strong correlation to the bifaciality can be observed, with those modules having the highest bifaciality showing the best *CSER* value. In Setting 3, we observe substantially higher *CSER* values compared to the monofacial module, since bifacial modules perform way better in this situation. Setting 4 shows the result of the tested modules in a tracking condition, where again the module with the highest bifaciality outperforms the other.

The results for the temperate coastal climate are shown in Figure 8. In Settings 1, 2 and 4 the PERC module performs best – despite having lower bifaciality than the other bifacial devices (with the exception of the IBC device, which is not presented as bifacial device by the manufacturer). The reason for this behavior is the efficiency peak of this module for irradiances at 400-600 W/m². Since the temperate coastal climate dataset contains a lot of low irradiance values, this leads to a particularly high *CSER* value for the PERC bifacial device.

One of the topics still up to discussion is the definition of the *CSER*, especially the normalization to H_{ref} (front-side global in-plane irradiation). Especially for Setting 3, this yields a very high *CSER* value for bifacial modules, because of the high rear-side irradiance apparent in this situation used in the hourly energy estimation which is not considered in the normalization. However, this normalization has the advantage that *CSER* values of monofacial modules stay at a comparable level as they have been in the first version of the standard and that monofacial PV modules can be directly compared to bifacial module performance. However, this way a comparison between different settings is not plausible.

subtropical arid	Setting 1 closed rack	Setting 2 open rack	Setting 3 vertical E/W	Setting 4 tracking
M1 HJT	0.937	1.085	1.703	1.070
M2 TOPCon white	0.936	1.059	1.593	1.043
M3 TOPCon transparent	0.940	1.072	1.633	1.058
M4 TOPCon black	0.941	1.059	1.579	1.045
M5 PERC frameless	0.937	1.046	1.566	1.029
M6 IBC	0.933	1.000	1.272	0.997
M7 TOPCon Mono	0.940	0.943	0.926	0.948

Figure 7: CSER results of all PV modules listed in Table 3 for the subtropical arid climate.

temperate coastal	Setting 1 closed rack	Setting 2 open rack	Setting 3 vertical E/W	Setting 4 tracking
M1 HJT	0.969	1.054	1.842	1.081
M2 TOPCon white	0.961	1.033	1.704	1.056
M3 TOPCon transparent	0.983	1.061	1.782	1.085
M4 TOPCon black	0.990	1.060	1.723	1.081
M5 PERC frameless	0.999	1.068	1.724	1.087
M6 IBC	0.961	1.002	1.347	1.019
M7 TOPCon Mono	0.983	0.985	0.969	0.993

Figure 8: CSER results of all PV modules listed in Table 3 for the temperate coastal climate.

Performing energy rating on bifacial modules is considerably more effort. Thus, parameter sensitivity studies have been performed to analyse if all measurements done with bifacial modules are necessary for the *CSER* outcome. Derived from the use of the concept of equivalent irradiance, higher irradiance values $G_{e,j}$ are reached and thus measured the power matrix up to 1300 W/m² seem necessary. To check if this additional data point is necessary for energy rating, every *CSER* was recalculated without the power values measured at 1300 W/m². Maximum differences were only 0.01 %, so it can be assumed that extending the power matrix to 1300 W/m² is not necessary.

Removing the 75°C data point was also assessed and a very low difference of only 0.02 % was also found compared to the calculations with the full dataset. It is therefore up to discussion, if temperatures up to 75°C are really necessary or if 60°C would be sufficient. This would reduce measurement time and instrument requirements for a lot of measurement labs.

Using equal values for rear-side IAM and front-side IAM yield a bias of up to 0.61 %, while using equal front- and rear- spectral responsivity yields a bias of 0.88 %. This is especially the case for Setting 3, where a substantial amount of rear-side irradiance is apparent over the course of the day. Therefore, it is reasonable to conclude that both rear-side IAM and rear-side SR are to be measured so no bias is introduced.

	remove 1300 W/m²	remove 75 °C	IAM front = IAM rear	SR front = SR rear
M1 HJT	0.01%	0.02%	0.50%	0.35%
M2 TOPCon white	0.00%	0.01%	0.24%	0.88%
M3 TOPCon transparent	0.01%	0.01%	0.15%	0.87%
M4 TOPCon black	0.01%	0.02%	0.61%	0.83%
M5 PERC frameless	0.01%	0.01%	0.15%	0.11%
M6 IBC	0.00%	0.01%	0.01%	0.59%

Figure 9: Changes to CSER values if either data points are removed or front- and rear-side are treated with the same SR or IAM values, those of the front-side.

4 REFERENCES

[1] IEC 61853-1, "Photovoltaic (PV) module performance testing and energy rating - Part 1: Irradiance and temperature performance measurements and power rating," International Electrotechnical Commission, 2011. Accessed: Nov. 20, 2024. [Online]. Available: https://www.vde-verlag.de/iec-normen/217749/iec-61853-1-2011.html

[2] IEC 61853-2, "Photovoltaic (PV) module performance testing and energy rating - Part 2: Spectral responsivity, incidence angle and module operating temperature measurements," International Electrotechnical Commission, 2016.

[3] IEC 61853-3, "Photovoltaic (PV) module performance testing and energy rating - Part 3: Energy rating of PV modules," International Electrotechnical Commission, 2018.

[4] IEC 61853-4, "Photovoltaic (PV) module performance testing and energy rating - Part 4: Standard reference climatic profiles," 2018. [Online]. Available: www.iec.ch

[5] T. Huld, A. G. Amillo, T. Sample, E. D. Dunlop, E. Salis, and R. Kenny, "THE COMPLETED IEC 61853 STANDARD SERIES ON PV MODULE ENERGY RATING, OVERVIEW, APPLICATIONS AND OUTLOOK," in *EU PVSEC 2024*, 2018, pp. 1113–1118. doi: 10.4229/35thEUPVSEC20182018-5DO.9.2.

[6] VDMA, "International Technology Roadmap for Photovoltaics (ITRPV) - 2023 Results," 2024.

[7] N. Martin and J. M. Ruiz, "A new model for PV modules angular losses under field conditions," *International Journal of Solar Energy*, vol. 22, pp. 19–31, 2002, doi: 10.1080/01425910212852.

[8] M. Ruben Vogt *et al.*, "PV Module Energy Rating Standard IEC 61853-3 Intercomparison and Best Practice Guidelines for Implementation and Validation," *IEEE J Photovolt*, 2022, doi: 10.1109/JPHOTOV.2021.3135258.

[9] M. R. Vogt, G. Pilis, M. Zeman, R. Santbergen, and O. Isabella, "Developing an energy rating for bifacial photovoltaic modules," *Progress in Photovoltaics: Research and Applications*, vol. 31, no. 12, pp. 1466–1477, Dec. 2023, doi: 10.1002/pip.3678.

[10] A. Driesse, M. Theristis, and J. S. Stein, "A New Photovoltaic Module Efficiency Model for Energy Prediction and Rating," *IEEE J Photovolt*, vol. 11, no. 2, pp. 527–534, Mar. 2021, doi: 10.1109/JPHOTOV.2020.3045677.

[11] S. Riechelmann, H. Sträter, and S. Winter, "DETERMINATION OF A PV MODULE POWER MATRIX WITH AN LED SOLAR SIMULATOR," in *EU PVSEC 2020*, 2020. doi: 10.4229/EUPVSEC20192019.

[12] H. Sträter, S. Riechelmann, F. Neuberger, and S. Winter, "LED-BASED DIFFERENTIAL SPECTRAL RESPONSIVITY MEASUREMENTS OF PV MODULES," in *EU PVSEC 2019*, 2019.

[13] S. Riechelmann, D. Friedrich, M. Müller, F. Schmaljohann, H. Sträter, and S. Winter, "PRIMARY CALIBRATION OF SOLAR MODULES WITH DIRECT SUNLIGHT," in *EU PVSEC 2022*, 2022, pp. 474–476. doi: 10.4229/WCPEC-82022-3BO.11.2.

[14] M. Schrempf, S. Riechelmann, S. Winter, and L. Stenzig, "Outdoor NMOT test stand with adjustable wind field," in *WCPEC-8*, 2022.

Physikalisch-Technische Bundesanstalt
Braunschweig und Berlin
Nationales Metrologieinstitut

An Update on Energy Rating Amendments – Integration of Bifacial Modules

Stefan Riechelmann, Hendrik Sträter, Ana María Gracia-Amillo,
Sophie Pelland, Anton Driesse
[1]PTB, Braunschweig, Germany
[2]CENER, Pamplona, Spain
[3]Natural Resources Canada, Varennes, Canada
[4]PV Performance Labs, Freiburg, Germany

What is Energy Rating?

PTB

Standard Test Conditions

- 1000 W/m²
- 25°C module temperature
- AM1.5 spectrum
- 0° incidence angle

Energy Rating

Simple but realistic rating of the performance of PV modules at different climatic conditions, taking into account:

- Ambient temperature
- Direct and diffuse irradiance
- Incidence angle
- Spectral distribution
- Wind speed

Energy Rating Standards (IEC 61853)

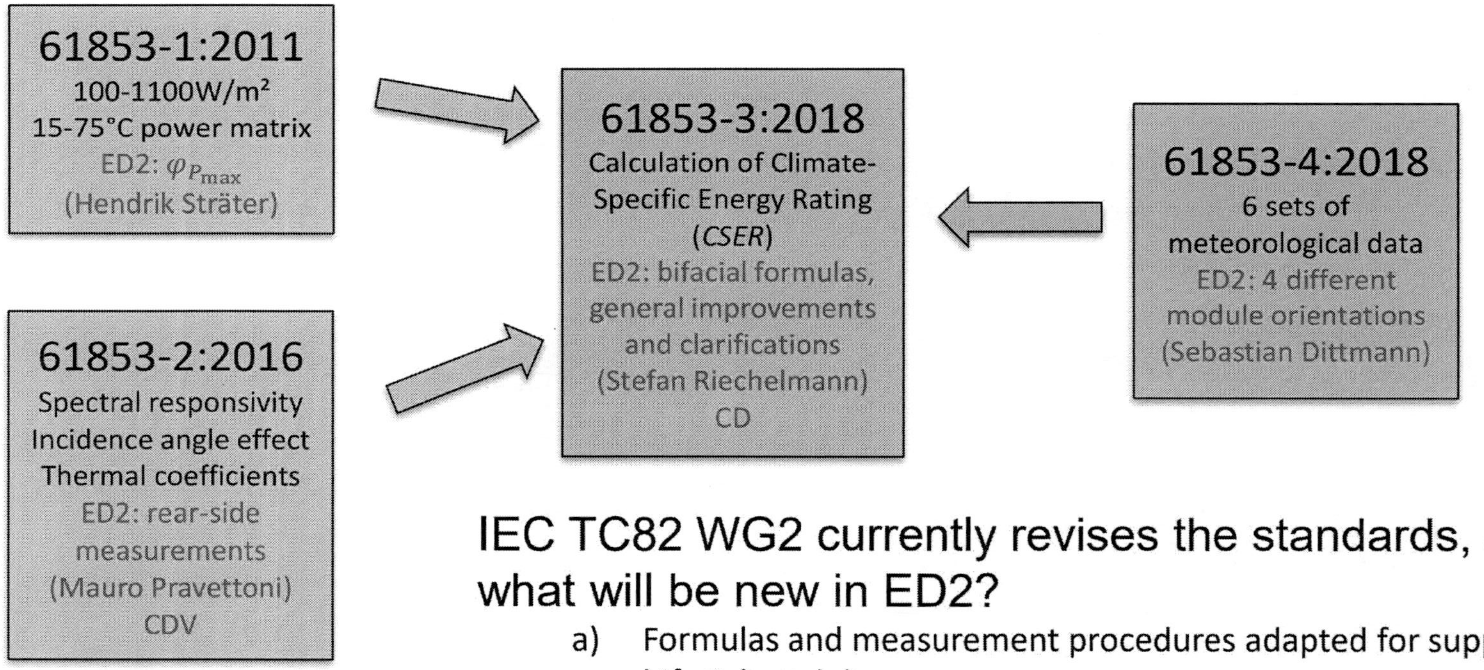

IEC TC82 WG2 currently revises the standards, so what will be new in ED2?

a) Formulas and measurement procedures adapted for supporting bifacial modules
b) Introduction of different module orientations
c) Improvement on inter- and extrapolation

How to adapt the 61853-3 formulas for bifacial modules?

Edition 1:

only front-side irradiance:

B – direct irradiance

D – diffuse irradiance

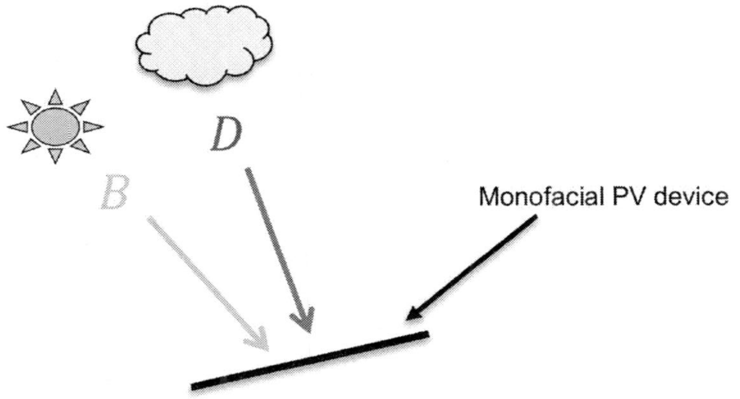

$$G = B + D$$

Edition 2:

Front- and rear-side (equivalent) irradiance:

B – direct irradiance

D – diffuse irradiance

A – ground-reflected irradiance

B_{rear} – direct rear-side irradiance

D_{rear} – diffuse rear-side irradiance

A_{rear} – ground-reflected rear-side irradiance

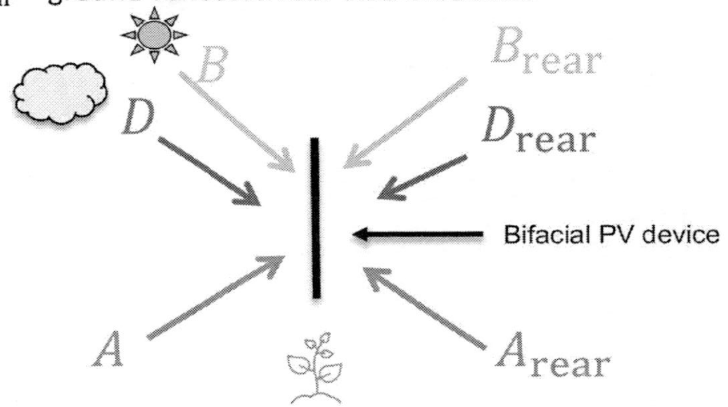

$$G_{\mathrm{e}} = B + D + A + \varphi_{P_{\max}} \cdot (B_{\mathrm{rear}} + D_{\mathrm{rear}} + A_{\mathrm{rear}})$$

61853-3 ED1: Module orientation and mounting condition

61853-3 ED1:

- 20° tilt
- equator-facing
- albedo is 0

– No rear-side irradiance (this is similar to a rooftop installation where we have severe self-shading)
– Bifacial modules shine in settings, where rear-side irradiance is apparent

For a fair comparison of monofacial and bifacial modules, we need more settings than this!

61853-3 ED2: Settings with different orientation and mounting conditions

S1
Close rack

S2
open rack

S3
vertical

S4
tracking

	Setting 1	Setting 2	Setting 3	Setting 4
Description	closed rack	open rack	vertical	tracking
Inclination angle β_j	20°	20°	90°	variable
Orientation	Equator	Equator	front to East / rear to West	East/West
Rear-side irradiance	-	+	+++	+

61853-3 ED2: Fixing inter- and extrapolation of module power

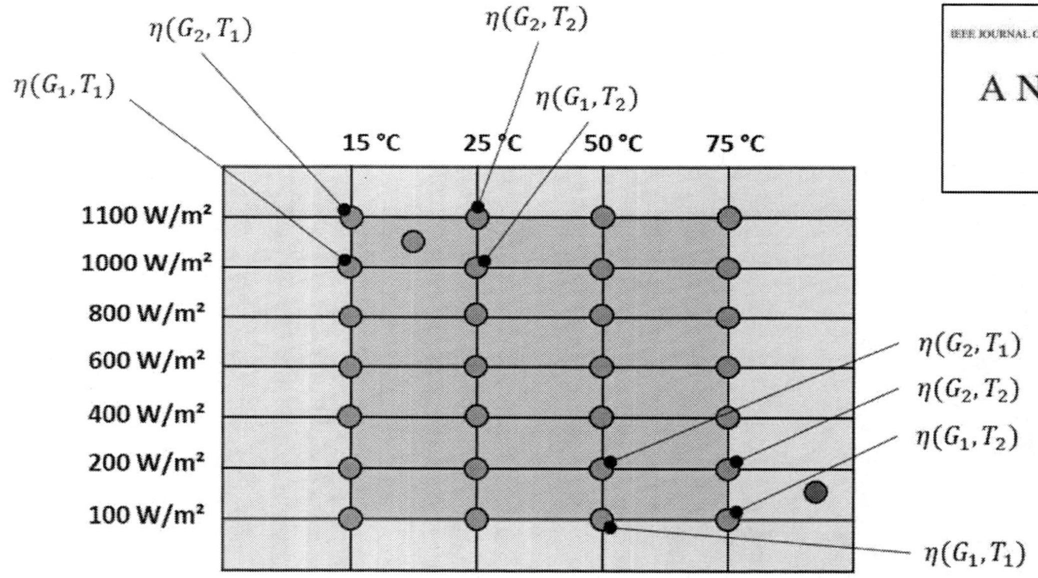

Legend:
- Filled efficiency matrix $\eta(G, T)$
- Example data point $\eta(G_{e,i}, T_{mod,i})$ interpolated by using Formula (11) to (13) 4 and choosing G_1, G_2, T_1, T_2 accordingly.
- Example data point $\eta(G_{e,i}, T_{mod,i})$ extrapolated by using Formula (11) to (13) and choosing G_1, G_2, T_1, T_2 accordingly.

IEEE JOURNAL OF PHOTOVOLTAICS, VOL. 11, NO. 2, MARCH 2021 527

A New Photovoltaic Module Efficiency Model for Energy Prediction and Rating

Anton Driesse, Marios Theristis, and Joshua S. Stein

New inter- and extrapolation:
Only 3 formulas needed to interpolate and extrapolate module power from power matrix and 2 formulas for filling up missing values of the matrix

User just has to find the four nearest points in the power matrix grid

Matrix has to be fully filled, no NA values. In 61853-1, this points either will be measured or extrapolated.

Testing Edition 2 with measured data

Power matrix (IEC 61853-1)	Spectral responsivity measurements (IEC 61853-2)	Angle of Incidence (AOI) measurements (IEC 61853-2)	Temperature coefficients (IEC 61853-2)
T=15-75°C and G=100-1300 W/m² (extended irradiance, more steps than in the standard) + $\varphi_{P\text{max}}$ measurement.	Front side SR and rear side SR of all devices was measured using an LED-based solar simulator at PTB.	Front side and rear side AOI was measured with direct sunlight.	Temperature coefficients were measured analogous to monofacial modules.

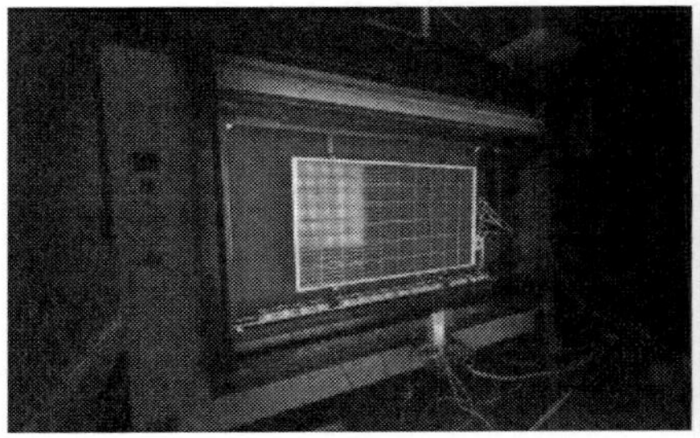

Testing Edition 2 with measured data

	Technology	$\varphi_{P_{max}}$ (%)
M1	HJT, n-Type	87.9
M2	TOPCon, white	75.5
M3	TOPCon, transparent	78.9
M4	TOPCon, black	73.0
M5	PERC, frameless	70.3
M6	IBC	41.0
M7	TOPCon, monofacial	0

61853-1:ED2, 61853-2:ED2

61853-3: ED2
Calculation of Climate-Specific Energy Rating (*CSER*)

61853-4:ED2
6 sets of meteorological data
ED2: for 4 different orientations

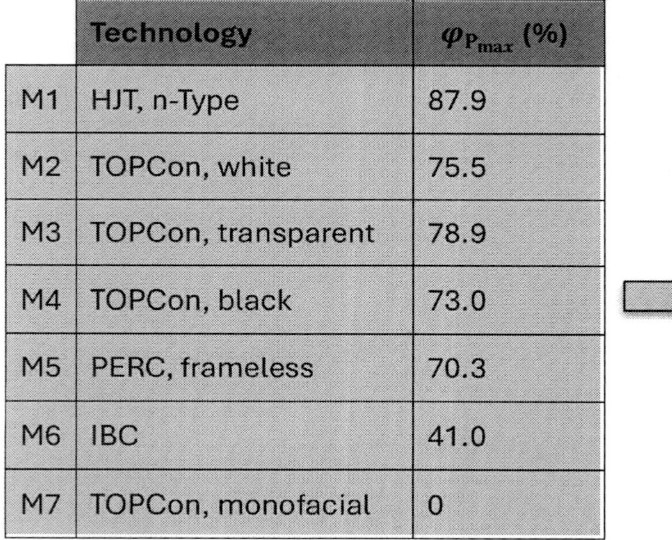

CSER values of 7 different PV modules in different climates

Tropical arid
albedo: high (0.4)
G: high (2400 kWh/m^2)
$T_{amb,day,mean}$: high (22.5 °C)
D/G ratio: low (24 %)

subtropical arid	Setting 1 closed rack	Setting 2 open rack	Setting 3 vertical E/W	Setting 4 tracking
M1 HJT	0.937	1.085	1.703	1.070
M2 TOPCon white	0.936	1.059	1.593	1.043
M3 TOPCon transparent	0.940	1.072	1.633	1.058
M4 TOPCon black	0.941	1.059	1.579	1.045
M5 PERC frameless	0.937	1.046	1.566	1.029
M6 IBC	0.933	1.000	1.272	0.997
M7 TOPCon Mono	0.940	0.943	0.926	0.948

CSER = Climate-Specific Energy Rating

CSER values of 7 different PV modules in different climates

Temperate coastal
albedo: medium (0.2)
G: low (1100 kWh/m^2)
$T_{amb,day,mean}$: medium (11.3 °C)
D/G ratio: high (51 %)

temperate coastal	Setting 1 closed rack	Setting 2 open rack	Setting 3 vertical E/W	Setting 4 tracking
M1 HJT	0.969	1.054	1.842	1.081
M2 TOPCon white	0.961	1.033	1.704	1.056
M3 TOPCon transparent	0.983	1.061	1.782	1.085
M4 TOPCon black	0.990	1.060	1.723	1.081
M5 PERC frameless	0.999	1.068	1.724	1.087
M6 IBC	0.961	1.002	1.347	1.019
M7 TOPCon Mono	0.983	0.985	0.969	0.993

CSER = Climate-Specific Energy Rating

61853 ED2: Parameter studies

That's a lot of effort!
How about some simpler measurements?

	remove 1300 W/m²	remove 75 °C	IAM front = IAM rear	SR front = SR rear
M1 HJT	0.01%	0.02%	0.50%	0.35%
M2 TOPCon white	0.00%	0.01%	0.24%	0.88%
M3 TOPCon transparent	0.01%	0.01%	0.15%	0.87%
M4 TOPCon black	0.01%	0.02%	0.61%	0.83%
M5 PERC frameless	0.01%	0.01%	0.15%	0.11%
M6 IBC	0.00%	0.01%	0.01%	0.59%

(Maximum deviation of all climates and settings)

Conclusion

PTB

Edition 1

ER module performance under different climatic conditions, monofacial devices only

Edition 2

+ ER performance of monofacial and bifacial modules
+ ER performance under different orientations
+ Clearer and more robust calculations

PTB
Messen
Forschen
Wissen
Thanks to the project team and thanks for listening
Physikalisch-Technische Bundesanstalt
Bundesallee 100
38116 Braunschweig
Stefan Riechelmann
stefan.riechelmann@ptb.de
European Commission
The study is supported by the European Climate, Infrastructure and Environment Executive Agency (CINEA)

European Commission

Outdoor Measurements of Perovskite Modules

Hanna Ellis[1], Harald Müllejans and Ewan D. Dunlop

European Commission[2], Joint Research Centre, Ispra, Italy

ESTI European Solar Test Installation

1 Hanna.Ellis@ec.europa.eu

2 The views expressed are purely those of the presenter and may not in any circumstances be regarded as stating an official position of the Europen Commission

Installation

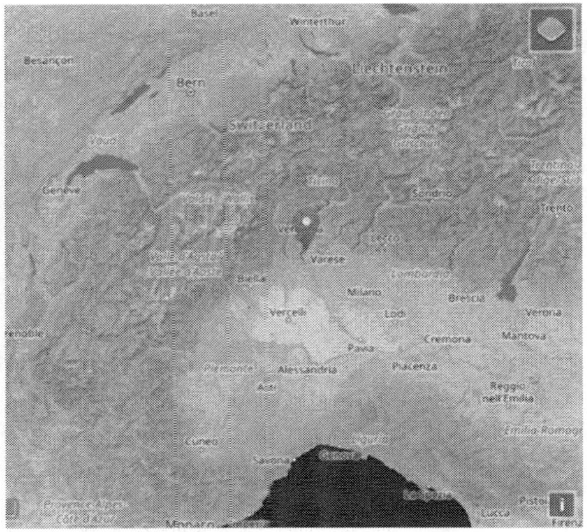

Image from PVGIS

- Single junction Perovskite modules (0.72 m^2)
- No knowledge of the chemical composition or structure
- Northern Italy (humid subtropical climate)
- 45° tilted fixed racks, facing south
- June 2024 to May 2025

Installation

- Reference cell - a ESTI sensor (a crystalline silicon reference cell designed for outdoor monitoring
- Anemometer
- Temperature sensor for ambinent temperature measurements
- Pyranometer
- Monitoring instrumentations:
  - MPPT
  - Four quadrant power supply (BOPA)
  - Multimeters
  - Shunt
  - Relays
  - Labview control software

Indoor Measurement Protocol

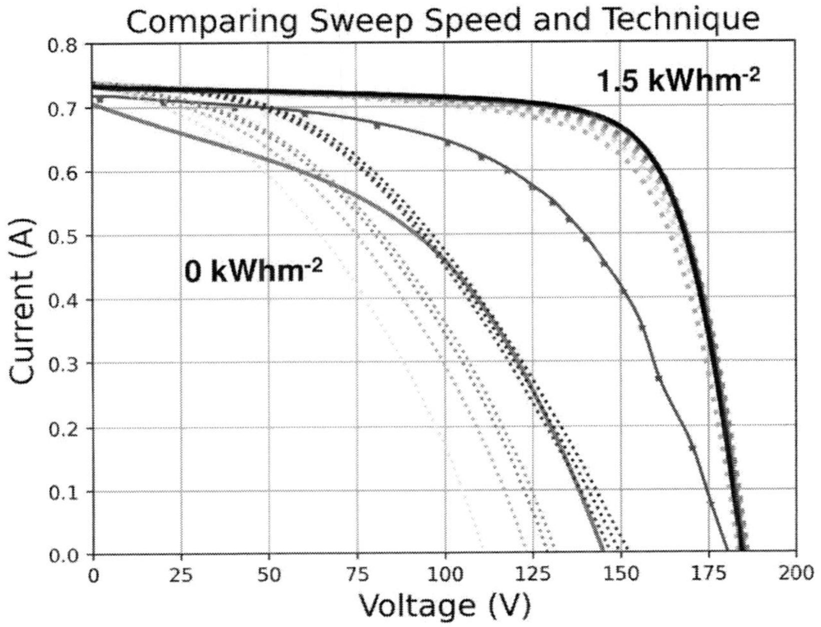

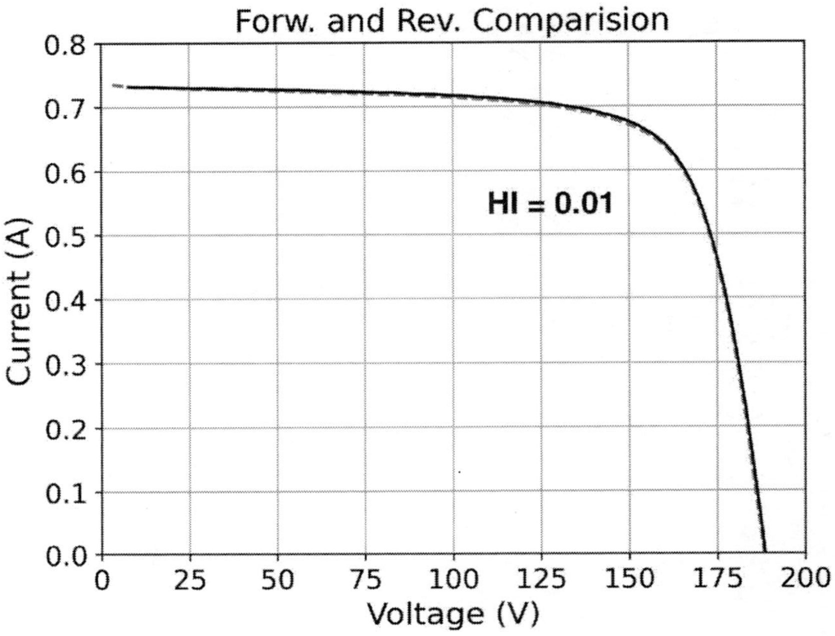

Overall Performance

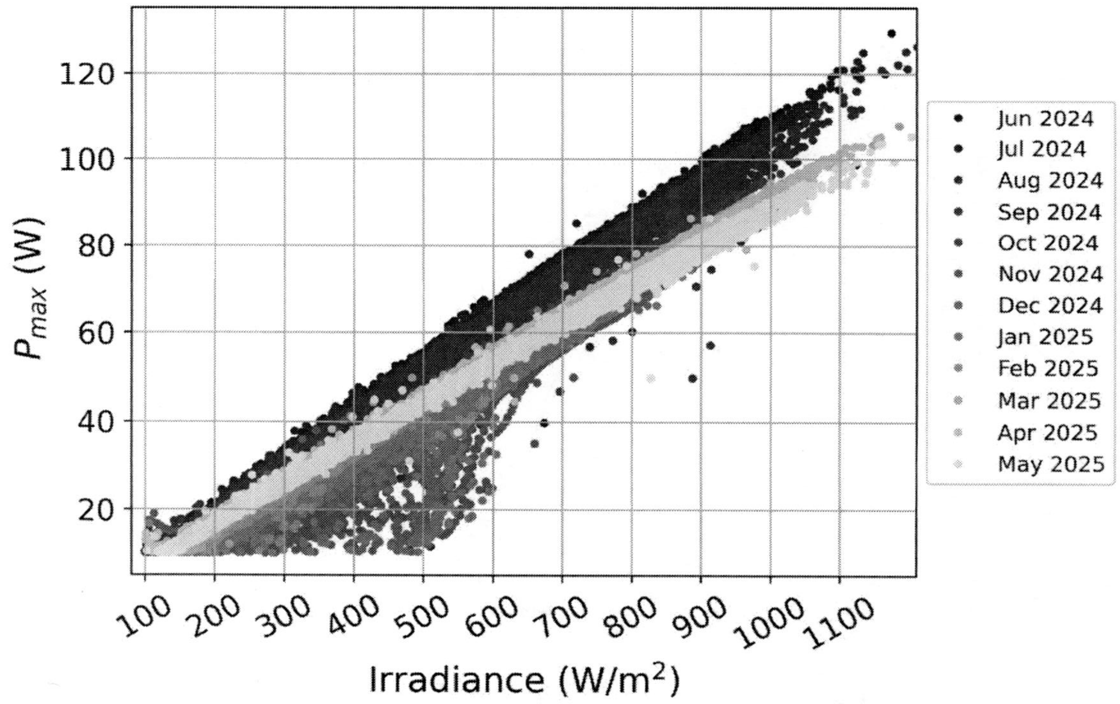

Overall Performance

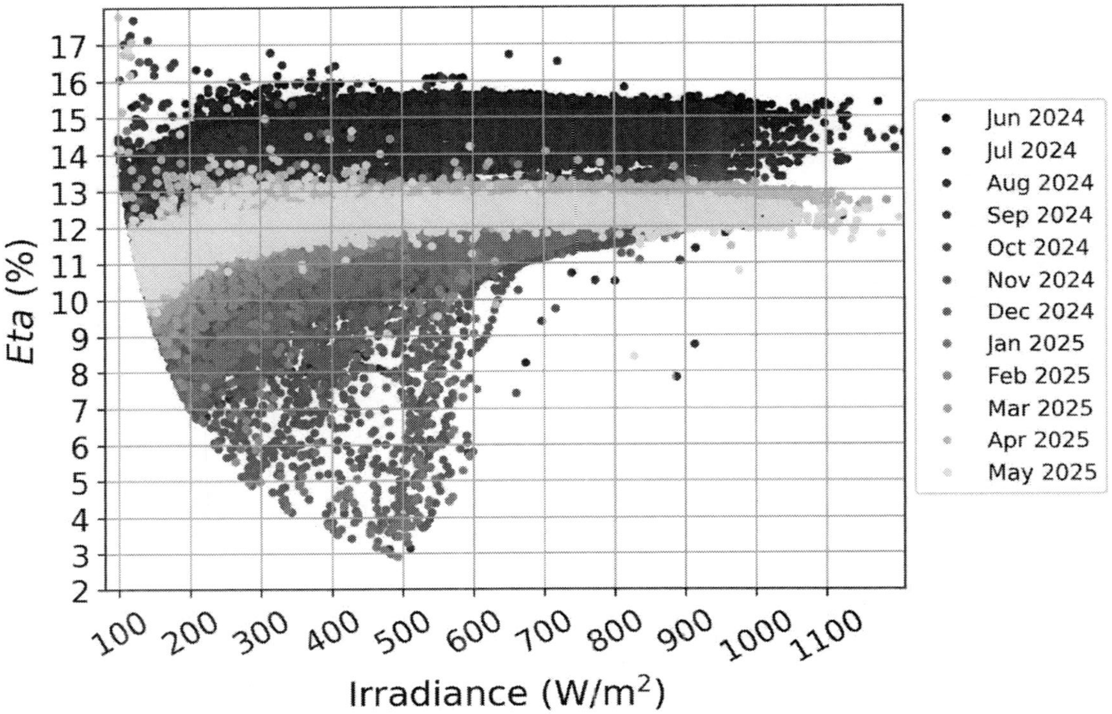

Specific Performance

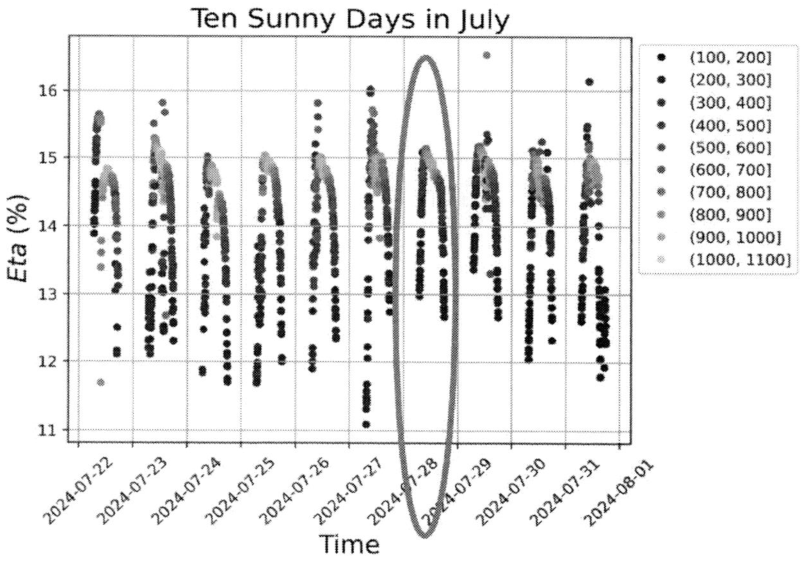

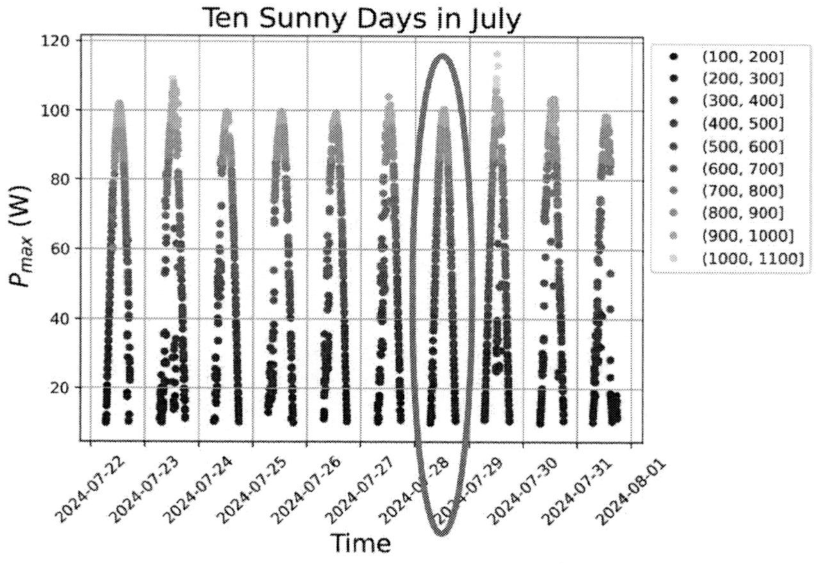

ESTI

Specific Performance

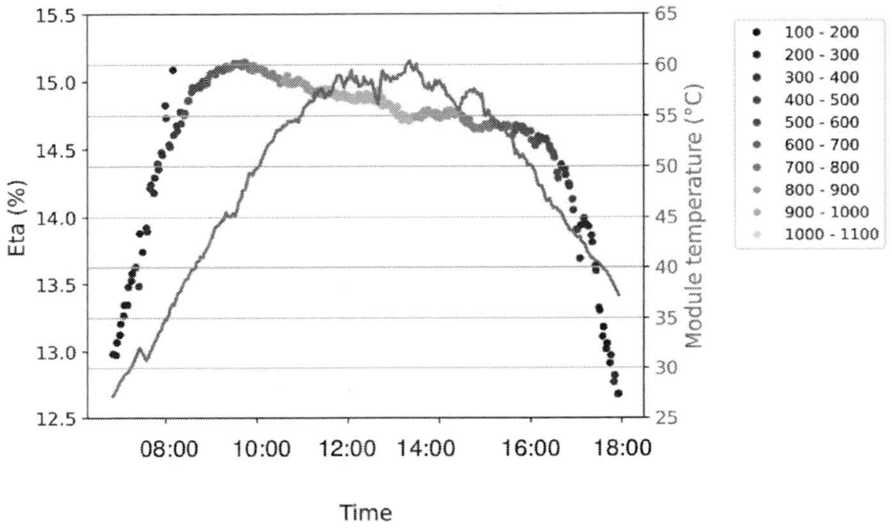

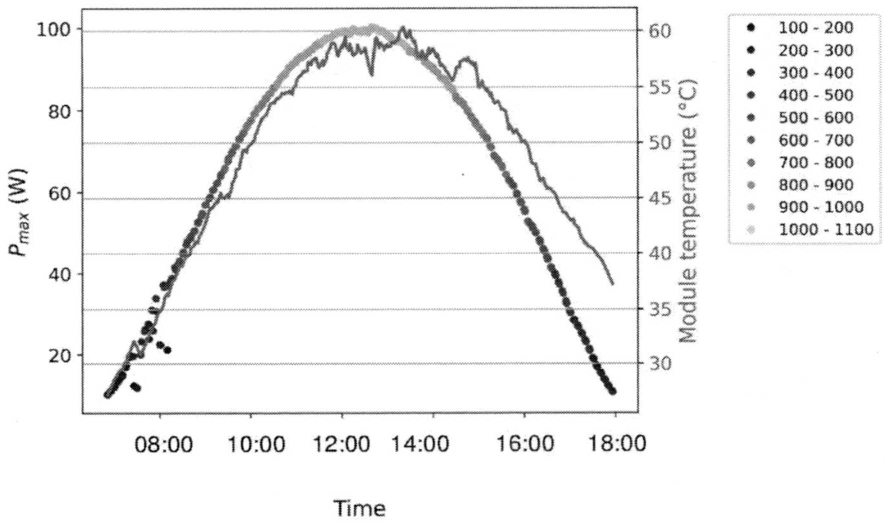

Specific Performance

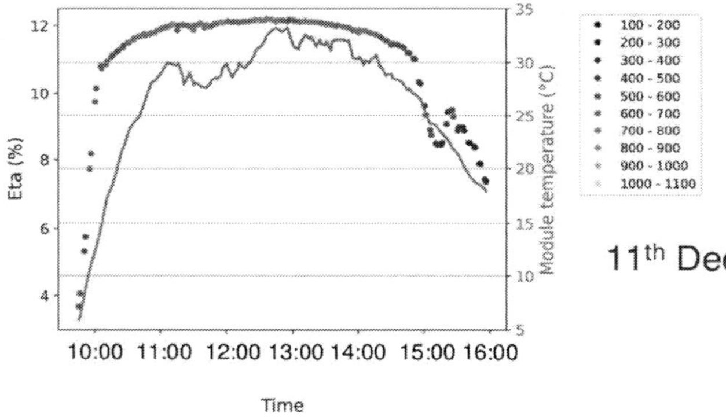

11th December 2024

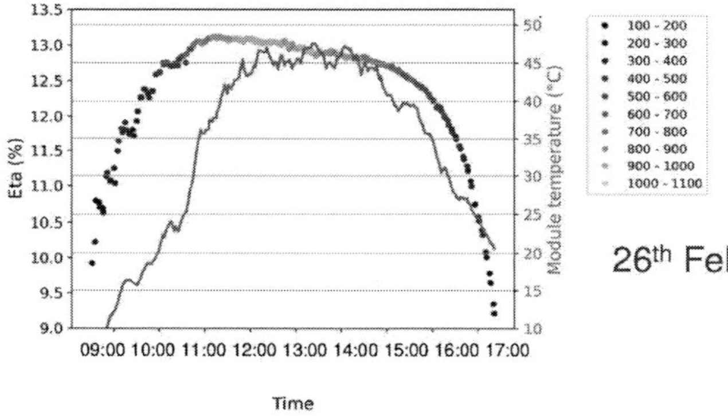

26th February 2025

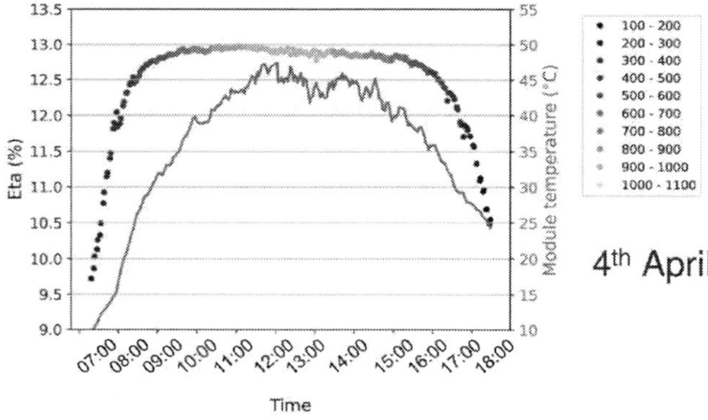

4th April 2025

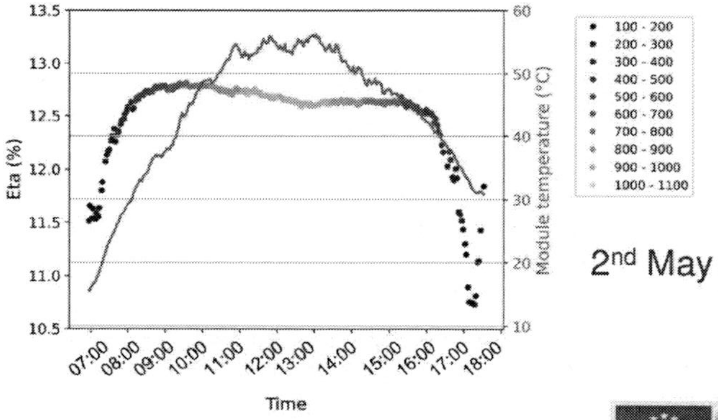

2nd May 2025

Temperature Dependency - for 980 - 1020 Wm^{-2}

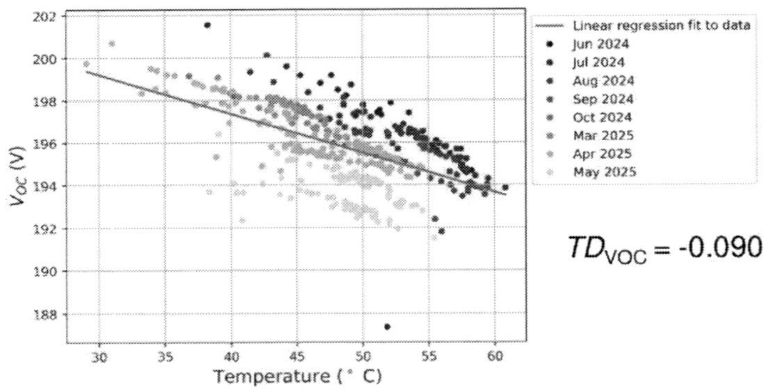

TD_{VOC} = -0.090 $\%C^{-1}$

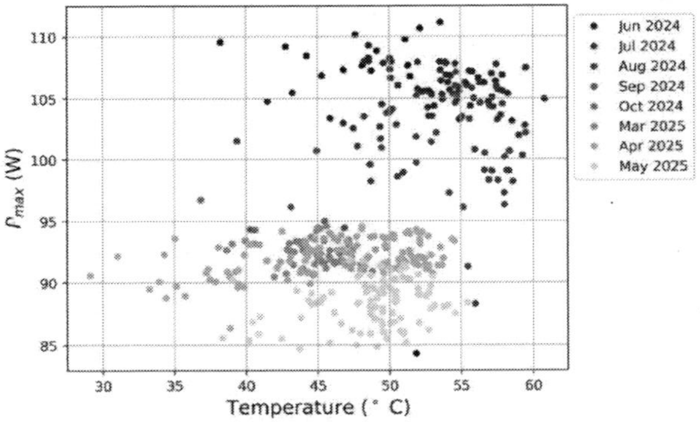

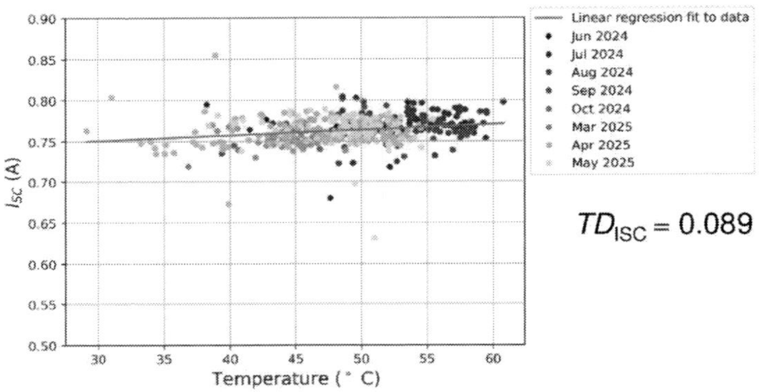

TD_{ISC} = 0.089 $\%C^{-1}$

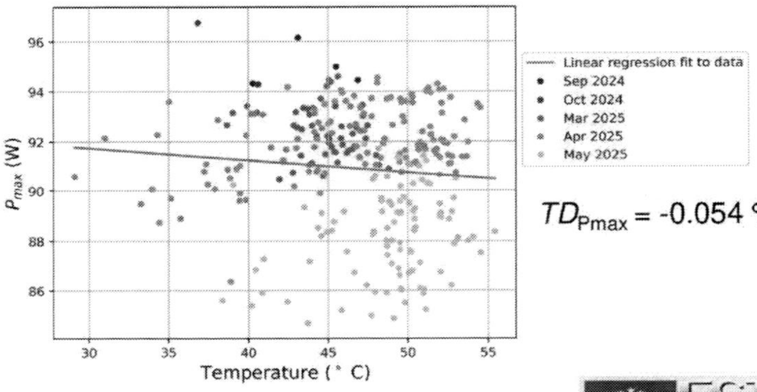

TD_{Pmax} = -0.054 $\%C^{-1}$

Performance as a Function of Time

Indoor data for 1000 Wm^{-2}

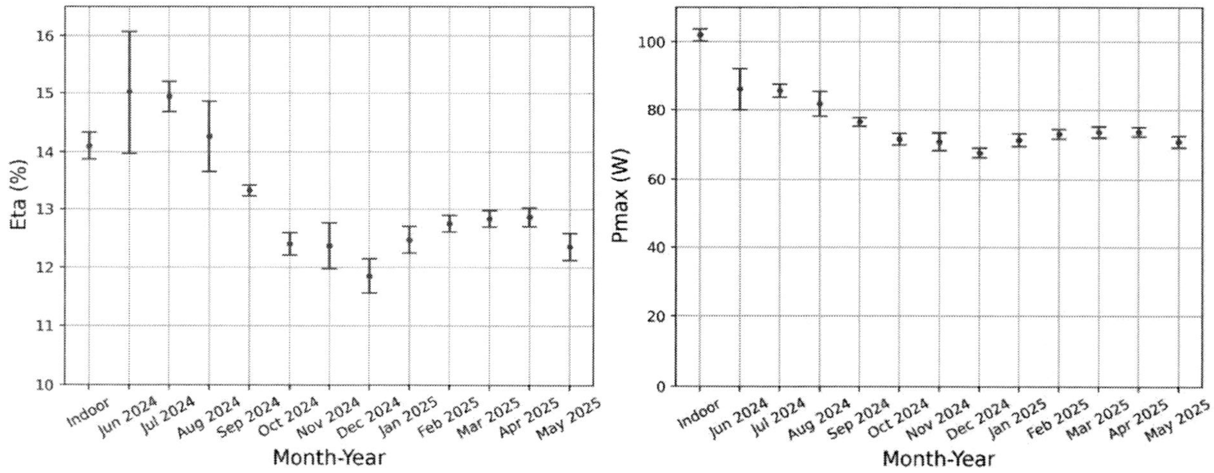

Average eta and P_{max} of binned data for each month with one standard deviation as error bars for every month. **Data filtered between 780 Wm^{-2} and 820 Wm^{-2}.**

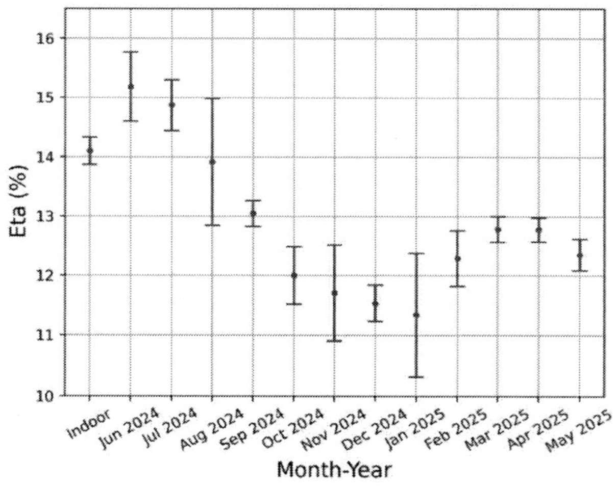

Average eta of binned data for each month with one standard deviation as error bars for every month. **Data filtered between 580 Wm^{-2} and 620 Wm^{-2}.**

Conclusions

- Settled values are measured after a certain amount of pre-conditioning (at V_{mpp}) and with a sweep time of, in this case 10 s (= approx 15-19 V/s).
- Temperature dependency was investigated between 980 and 1020 Wm^{-2} as:
  - TD_{ISC} = 0.089 $\%C^{-1}$
  - TD_{VOC} = -0.090 $\%C^{-1}$
  - TD_{Pmax} = -0.054 $\%C^{-1}$
- Performance over time; Module 1 15% → 12.5% and Module 2 14% → 7.5%

Thank you for listening!

Many thanks to Flavio Nico and Ambrogio Nico for all the help with the outdoor monitoring installation and to the ESTI Team

The JRC – provides independent, evidence-based knowledge and science, supporting EU policies to positively impact society.

For more information and open job positions please visit: **https://joint-research-centre.ec.europa.eu**

JRC is open to cooperation and receiving PhD students and other researchers (as unpaid visiting scientists)

JRC is constantly hiring new staff: **https://recruitment.jrc.ec.europa.eu/**

For further discussions with ESTI please visit our stand F7 !

For the calibrations price list or for requesting information on ESTI services, please contact:
JRC-ESTI-SERVICES@ec.europa.eu

Scientific Project Officer, Hanna Ellis, **Hanna.Ellis@ec.europa.eu**

Performance characterization of monofacial and bifacial modules in French Polynesia: Case study of Tahiti

Moira I. Torres Aguilar[1]
Pascal Ortega[2]
Jordi Badosa Franch[3]
Johan Parra[3]

23/09/25

[1] CentraleSupélec, GeePs
[2] University of French Polynesia, GEPASUD
[3] E4C Institut Polytechnique de Paris

Agenda

- Bifacial PV market
- PV Platform
- Yield
- Bifacial gain
- Performance Ratio
- Conclusions & Future Work

2

Bifacial market share

Why is performance characterization of bifacial modules under real-life conditions important?

The market share of bifacial modules has increased from:
50% in 2023 → a projected 73% in 2034

Source: "International Technology Roadmap for Photovoltaics (ITRPV) 2023 Results," VDMA, May 2024.

We need field data!

PV performance on islands?

IEC TS 60904-1-2

Standard specific for bifacial modules

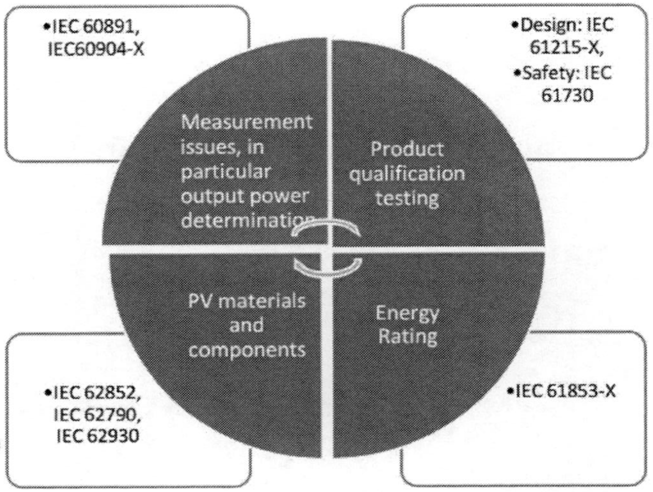

Source: J. Stein *et al.*, "Bifacial Photovoltaic Modules and Systems: Experience and Results from International Research and Pilot Applications," SAND--2021-4835R, IEA--PVPS T13-14:2021, 1779379, Apr. 2021.

PV Platform

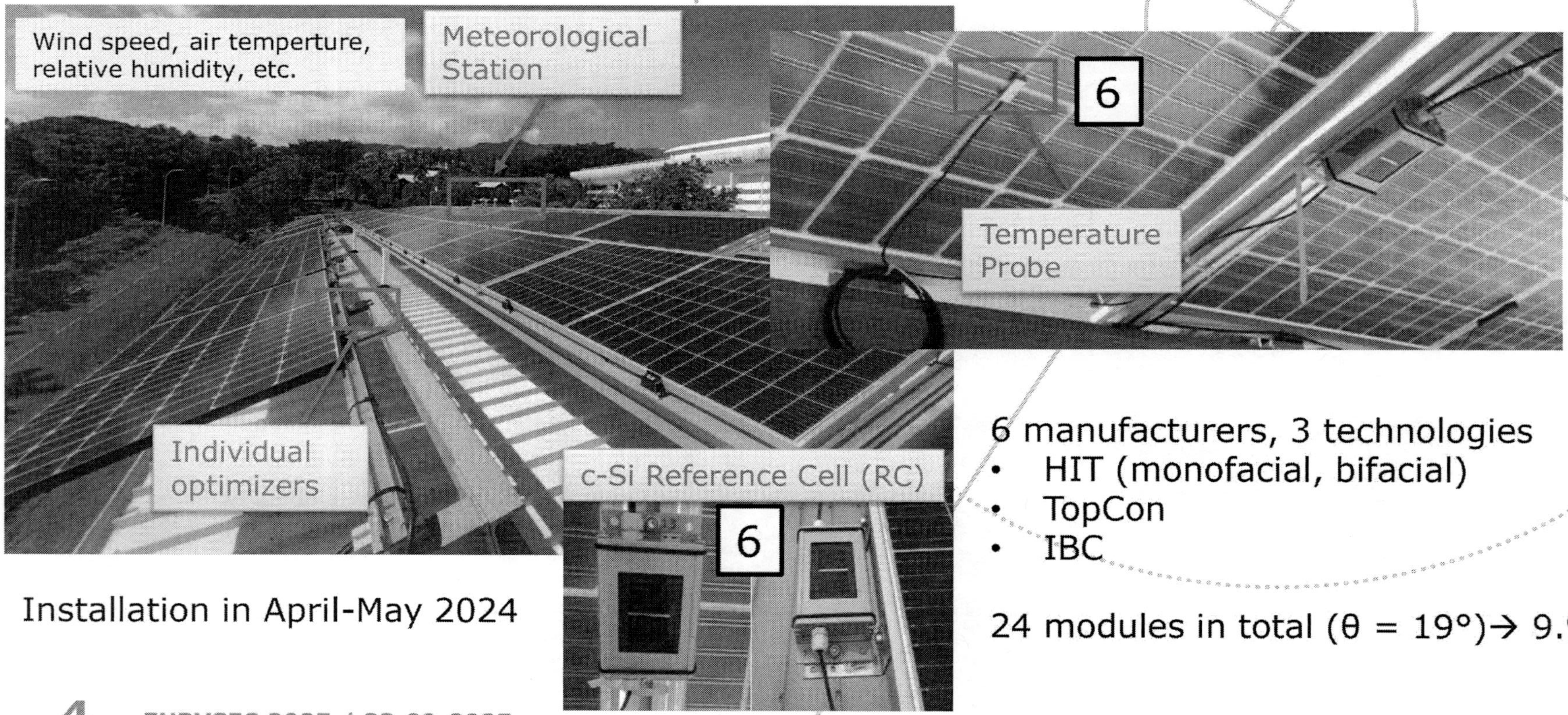

Installation in April-May 2024

6 manufacturers, 3 technologies
- HIT (monofacial, bifacial)
- TopCon
- IBC

24 modules in total (θ = 19°)→ 9.9 kWp

PV Platform

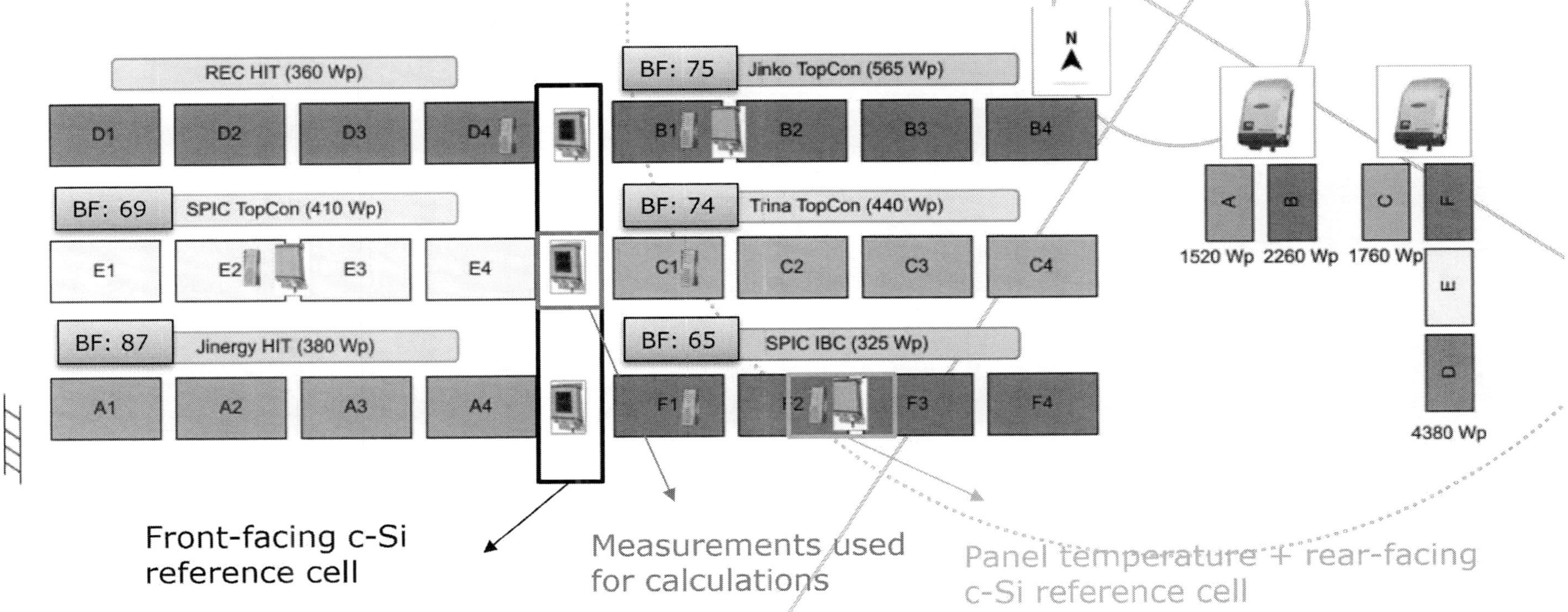

*Bifaciality values obtained during a flashtest conducted at IPVF (average of technology)

Performance Characterization

How do these technologies perform in a tropical climate (Tahiti)?

$$Y_M = \frac{\sum P_{meas}}{P_{STC}}$$

Module Yield

$$Y_R = \frac{\sum G_{meas}}{G_{STC}}$$

Reference Yield

$$Performance\ Ratio (PR) = \frac{Y_M}{Y_R}$$

P_{meas} : module power output (W)
P_{STC} : power output under STC conditions (Wp)
G_{meas} : measured plane-of-array irradiance (W/m²)
G_{STC} : irradiance uner STC conditions (1000 W/m²)

Reference Yield

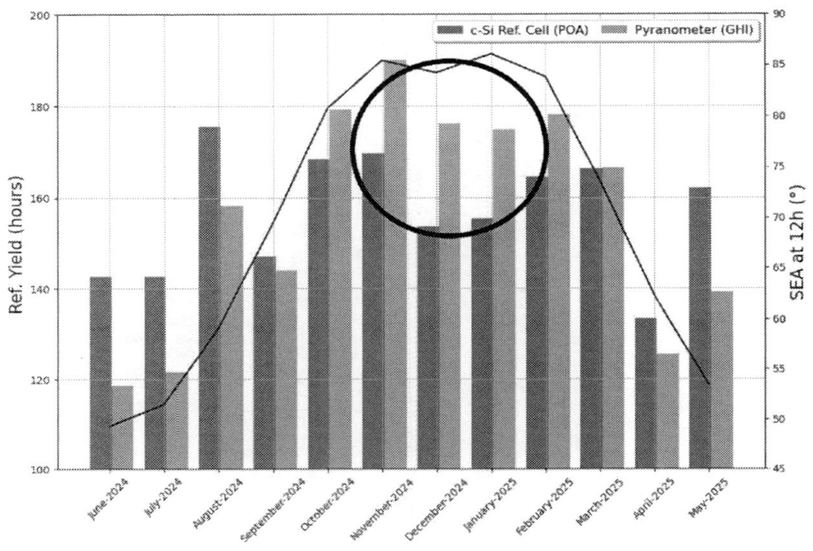

- Our modules benefit from a lower solar elevation angle
- Despite a horizontal plane receiving more sunlight during summer, annually our modules receive 3.8% more irradiance

7

Module Yield

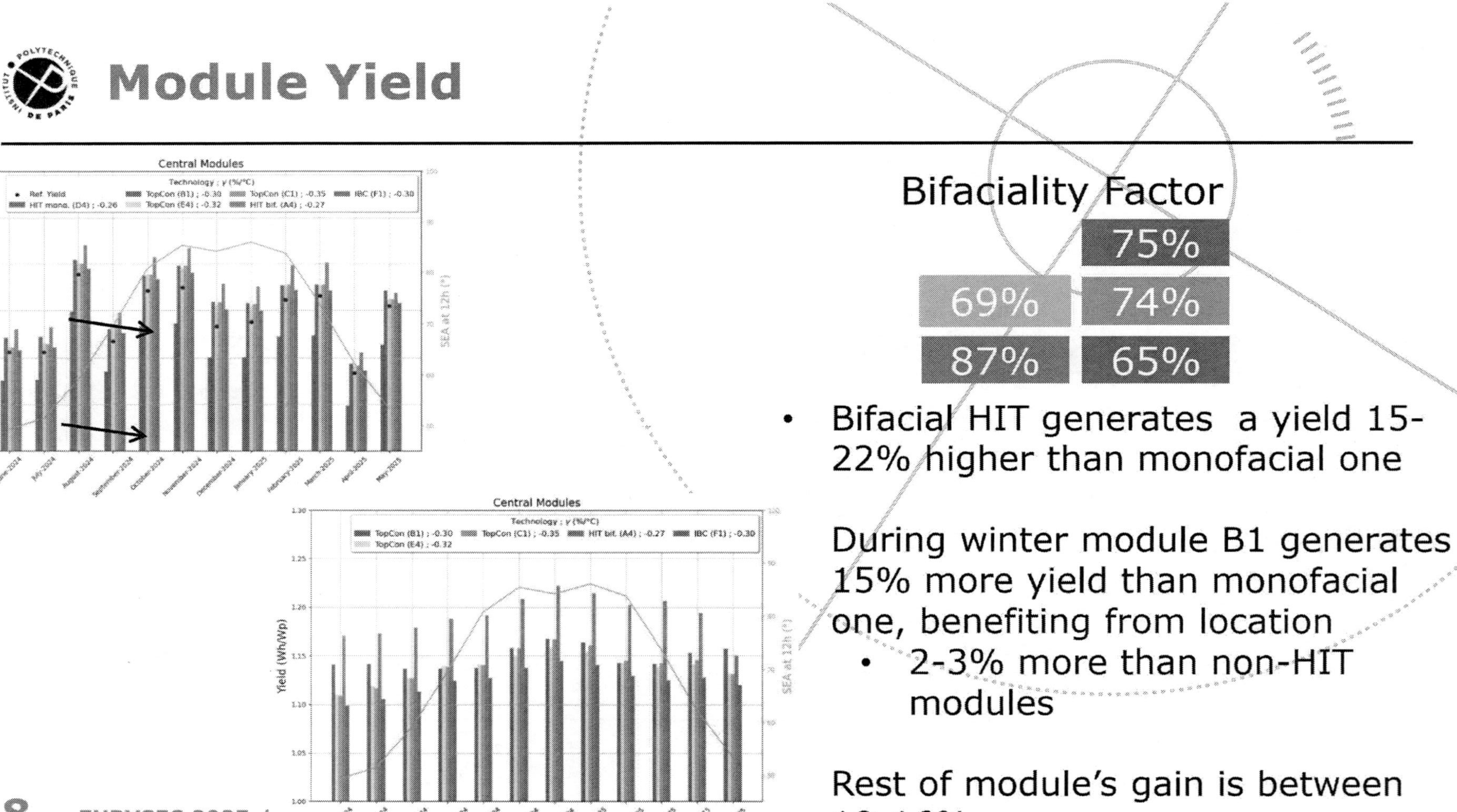

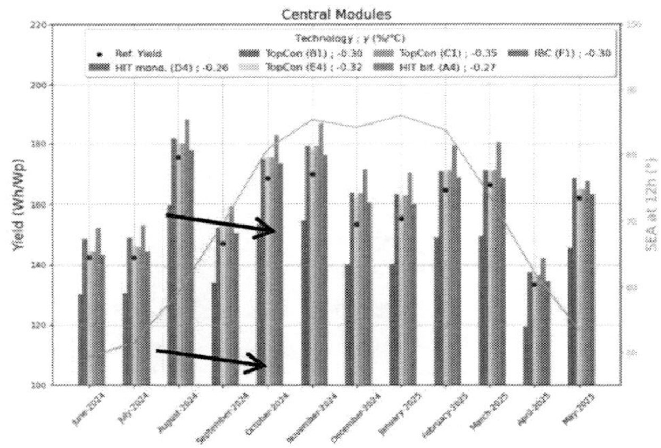

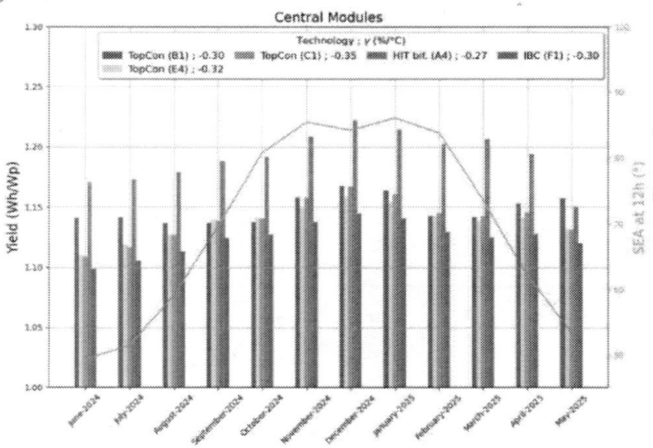

Bifaciality Factor

	75%
69%	74%
87%	65%

- Bifacial HIT generates a yield 15-22% higher than monofacial one

During winter module B1 generates 15% more yield than monofacial one, benefiting from location

- 2-3% more than non-HIT modules

Rest of module's gain is between 10-16%

Temp. Corrected Module Yield

$$Y_M = \frac{\sum P_{meas}}{P_{STC}} \rightarrow P_{corr} = \frac{P_{meas}}{1 + \gamma(T_{mod} - Tp_{STC})} \Longrightarrow Y_c = \frac{\sum P_{corr}}{P_{STC}}$$

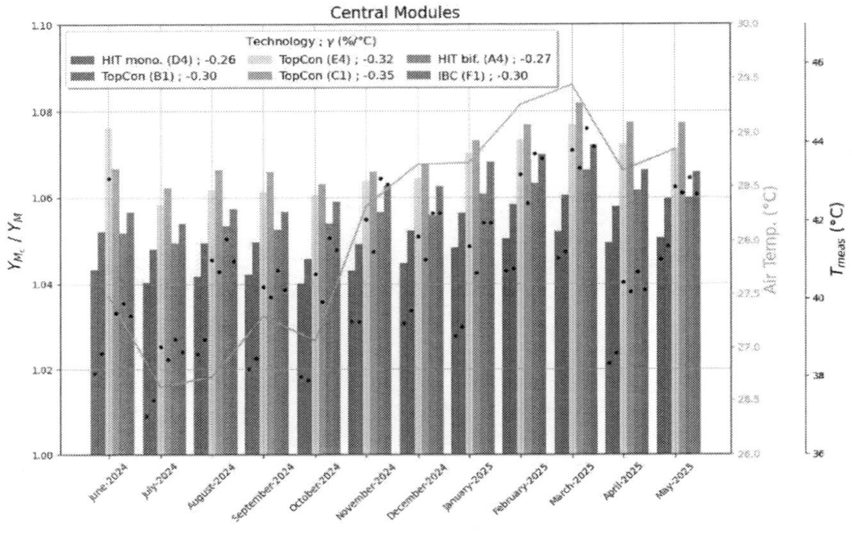

- Due to low temperature variability, thermal losses remain stable throughout the year
- Despite having a higher temperature coefficient, module B1 losses than other modules due to cooling effect
- Due to a low power temperature coefficient, and position, the monofacial module losses 4-5% of yield only
- The average difference in module temperature between the modules located in the first row and the others is 1.7°C

Effect of wind on module temperature

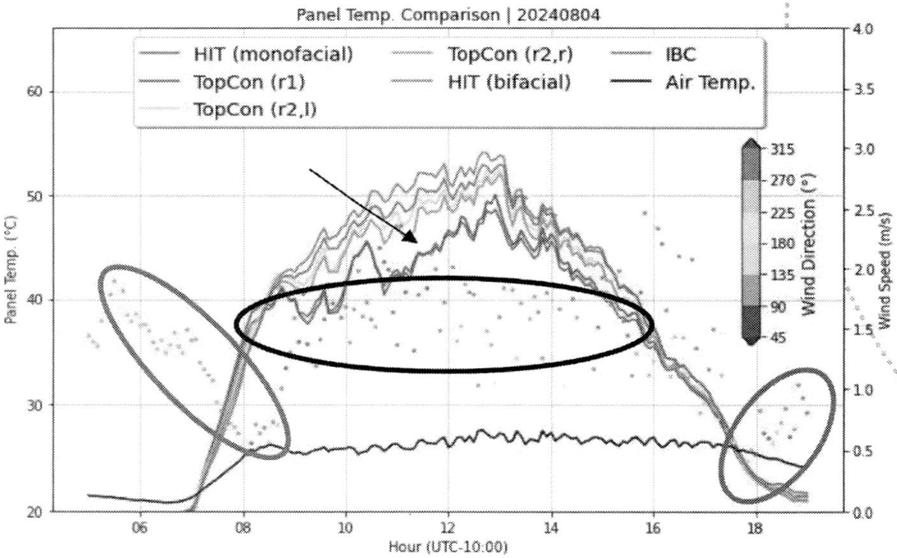

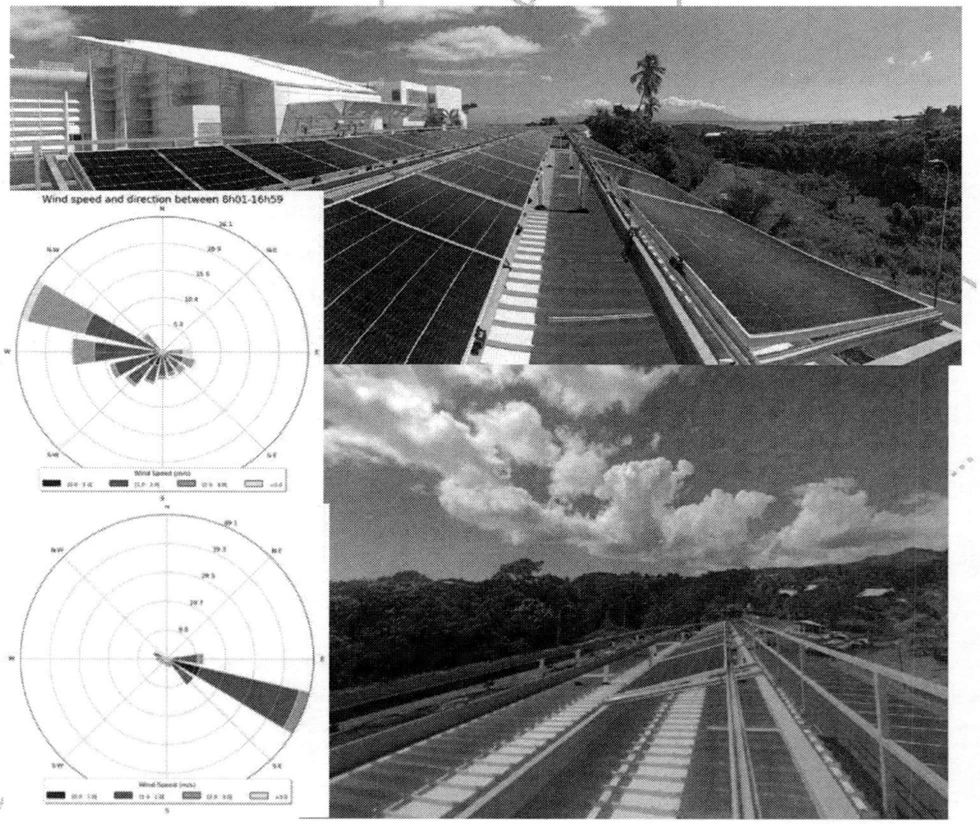

The sea breeze causes a visible difference in T_{mod} between modules of the first row and the rest

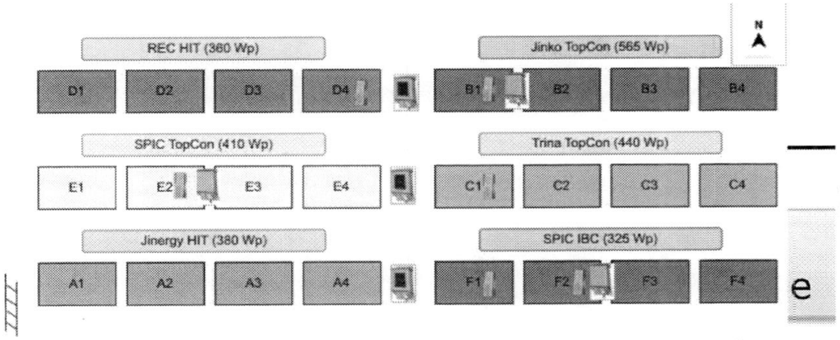

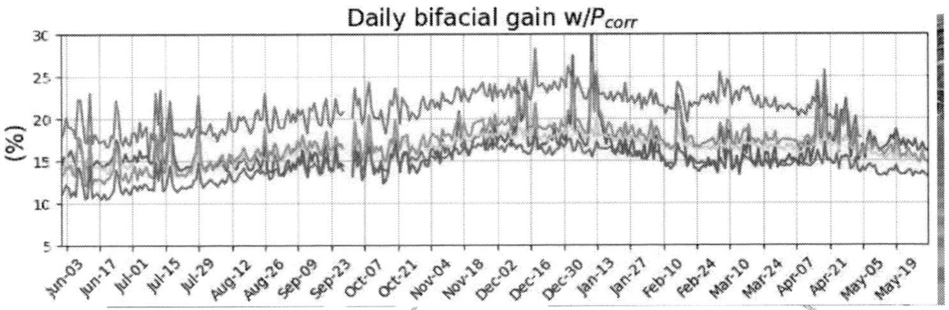

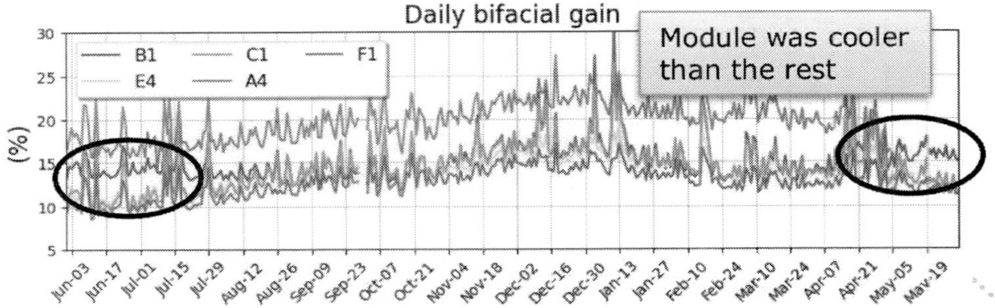

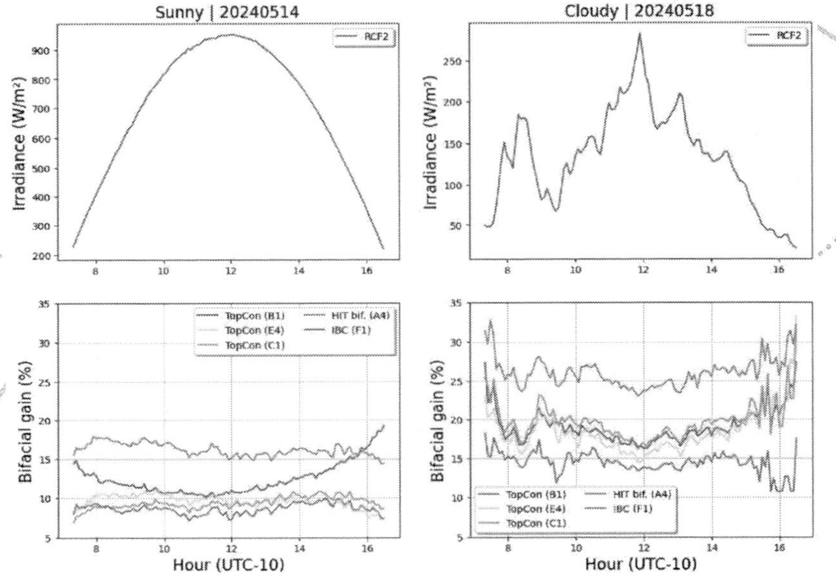

- Overall: 10-25% depending on technology
  - Sunny day: 10-15%
  - Cloudy day: 15-25%
- Bifacial gain increases with sun elevation

11 **EUPVSEC 2025 / 23-09-2025**

Daily averaged performance ratio

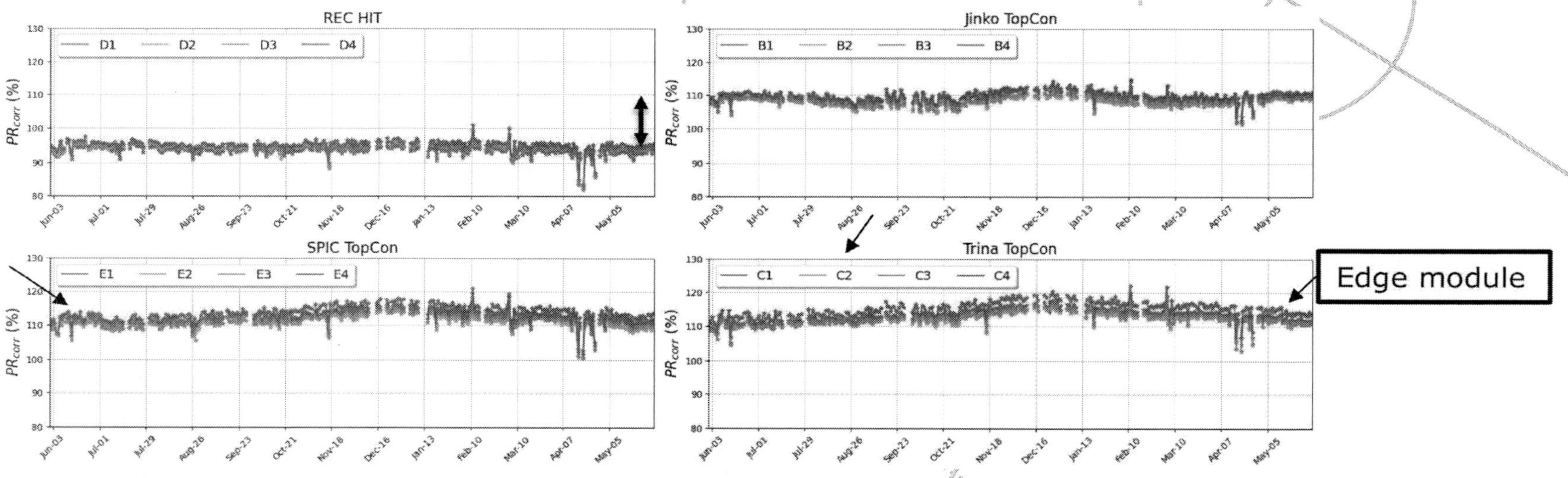

- Edge modules have a PR of 1-2% higher
- PR for bifacial modules is up to 25% higher than that of a monofacial

Decreased PR due to soiling(?)

Picture taken after one month without rain

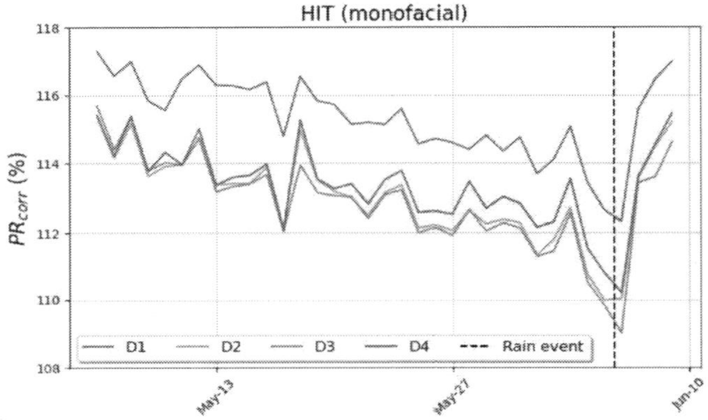

For prolonged periods of time without rain (more than 3 weeks), a decrease in PR of up to 4% has been observed

Performance summary

	HIT (mono) (D4)	TOPCon (B1)*	TOPCon (E4)	TOPCon (C1)	HIT (bif.) (A4)*	IBC (F1)
PR (%)	91 (86-94)	107 (102-109)	109 (104-114)	110 (104-114)	108 (101-115)	104 (98-109)
Yield (Wh/Wp)	1707 (119-160)	1960 (137-182)	1943 (136-180)	1947 (136-180)	2034 (142-188)	1920 (134-178)
Bifacial Gain (%)		15 (13-17)	14 (11-16)	14 (11-17)	19 (15-22)	12 (10-14)
Bifaciality Factor:		75%	69%	74%	87%	65%

Take away messages

- First row modules benefit from:
  - Location
  - Cooling from breeze

- Annually:
  - Bifacial gain: range 12-19% (mean is 14.8%)
  - HIT bifacial yields 19% more than HIT monofacial
  - PR of bifacials is 104-110%, monofacial is 91%

- Modules with a bifacial factor from 65-74% perform similarly (except for front row)

Future Work

- Performance characterization of current installation
  - Soiling
  - Degradation
- Modelling
  - Irradiance
  - Power output
- Financial analyses(LCOE, self-consumption,...)
- Performance of experimental cells

Data availability

Agrivoltaic

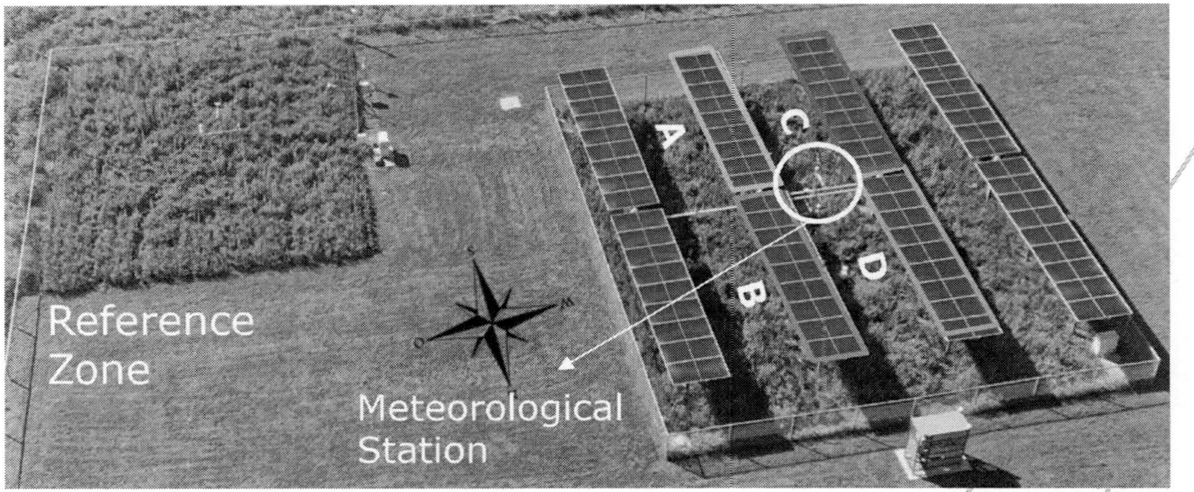

Visit our poster!
4DV.1.18

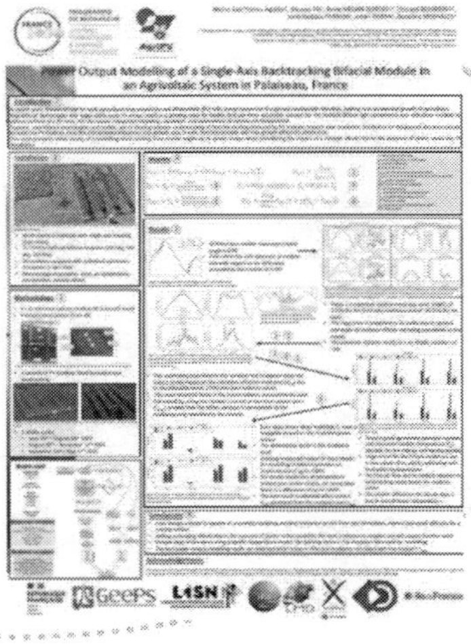

- 72 TOPCon half-cell bifacial modules (555 Wp, 560 Wp, 565 Wp)
  - 36 equipped with individual optimizers
  - 4 inverters with 18 modules each

17

Rooftop

- Installed in July 2020
- Capacity of 16.3 kWp
- 6 types of panels
- sc-Si reference cell, panel temperature

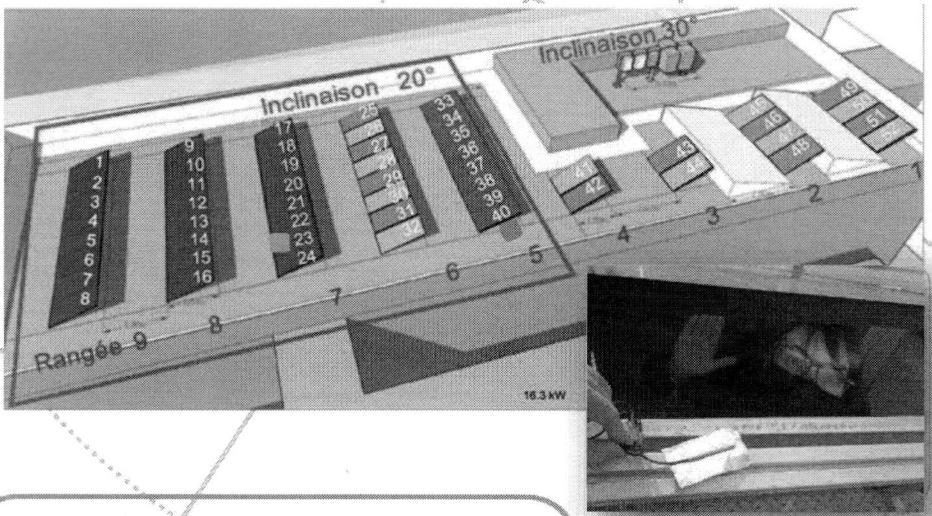

sc-Si black backsheet
sc-Si white backsheet
sc-Si Q.ANTUM half-cells
Low LID sc-Si PERC half-cells
Low LID sc-Si PERC full-cells
LID Bifacial PERC

18

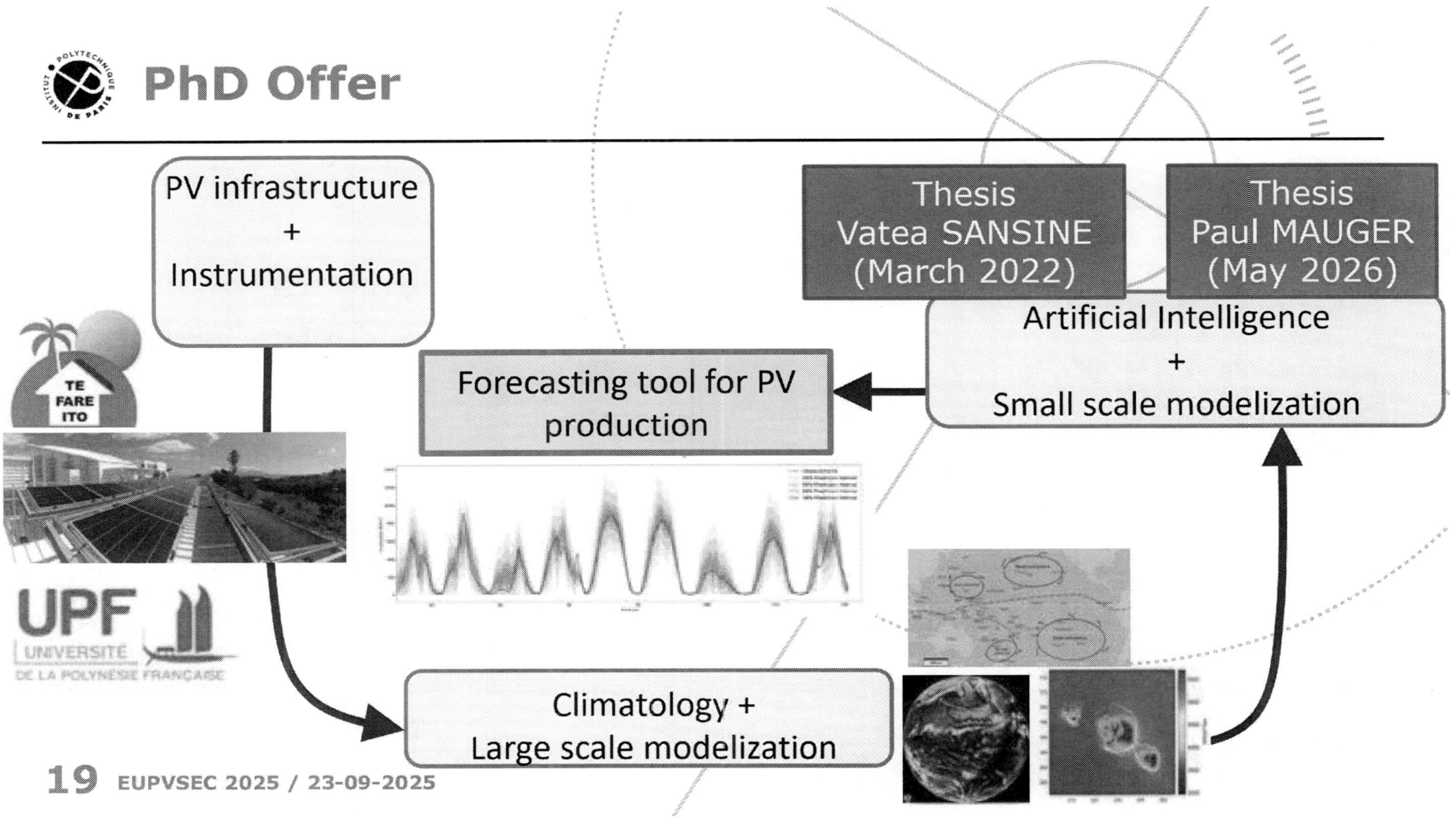
PhD Offer
PV infrastructure + Instrumentation
TE FARE ITO
UPF UNIVERSITÉ DE LA POLYNÉSIE FRANÇAISE
Forecasting tool for PV production
Climatology + Large scale modelization
Thesis Vatea SANSINE (March 2022)
Thesis Paul MAUGER (May 2026)
Artificial Intelligence + Small scale modelization
19 EUPVSEC 2025 / 23-09-2025

E4C INTERDISCIPLINARY CENTER

LMD

Thank you for your attention!

UPF UNIVERSITÉ DE LA POLYNÉSIE FRANÇAISE

GePaSud

moira.torres_aguilar@upf.pf

l'X ÉCOLE POLYTECHNIQUE

20

STATISTICAL TRENDS IN NOMINAL VS. MEASURED PERFORMANCE OF PV MODULES AND THE IMPACT OF METASTABILITY

Ulli Kräling[1], Daniel Philipp[1], Martin Kaiser[1]
[1]Fraunhofer Institute for Solar Energy Systems ISE
Heidenhofstr. 2, 79110 Freiburg, Germany

ABSTRACT: The Calibration and Testing Laboratory for PV Modules at Fraunhofer ISE has been conducting characterization measurements on modules for many years, placing emphasis on a stable calibration level and measurement precision. In this publication, we statistically analyze measurement data over the past 12 years and specifically examine the development of the performance conformity of the modules with the nameplate values given by the manufacturers. We present the underlying data filters and assess the results in the context of recent technological developments in cell and module technology. Notably, from 2016 to 2023, we observe a continuous trend towards a negative deviation, meaning that the measured performance under standard test conditions (STC) is lower than the promised nominal value by -1.28 % (median). In 2024, we observe stabilization or slight improvement. To contextualize this observation, we also examine the development of initial degradation due to light induced degradation (LID) along the evolution of different solar cell generations. This shows a significant improvement for newer technologies, leading to a trend reversal, where LID affects modules positively, which could be partly attributed to dark-storage induced metastability phenomena.
Keywords: PV Module Performance, Calibration, LID, Metastability, Storage Effect

1 INTRODUCTION

1.1 Background and motivation

The expansion of photovoltaics in Germany, Europe, and worldwide has gained rapid momentum. According to the Federal Network Agency, the installation rates in Germany were 14.1 GW in 2023 [1] and 16.2 GW in 2024 [2]. In the European Union, the installation rates according to the industry association "SolarPower Europe" were 62.8 GW and 65.5 GW, respectively [3]. Globally, the installation rate in 2023 was around 450 GW [4, 5].

This strong PV expansion is occurring in an extremely competitive environment. Especially in the years 2023 and 2024, the global PV market was characterized by significant overcapacity regarding the production of PV cells and modules, leading to a price drop below $0.1/Wp [5] in some cases.

The reference for assessment of these installation capacities is the sum of the nominal maximum performance of the PV modules installed in the PV systems. This value is often referred to as nominal or nameplate power at maximum power point (P_{nom}), which is determined according to IEC 60904-1 [6] for monofacial PV modules and IEC 60904-1-2 [7] for bifacial PV modules, under standard test conditions (STC), respectively. These conditions are essentially defined by an irradiation of 1000 W/m^2, a light spectrum corresponding to an Air-Mass Index of 1.5 (AM1.5G), and a module temperature of 25°C [8].

The nominal power P_{nom} has a high significance because it serves as the central reference describing a module type. Accordingly, the price for PV modules is often related to P_{nom} to enable comparative evaluation of different products/manufacturers by giving module prices per Watt Peak (Wp). The calculated energy yield of a PV system also correlates to the nominal power of the modules. Simplified, each percentage increase in nominal power results in a correspondingly higher yield over lifetime, assuming equal secondary module- and system characteristics (temperature and low-light behavior, bifaciality, system design etc.). Moreover, the P_{nom} is used as reference to capture the aging/degradation of modules: Whether modules perform as expected or if there are indications of quality defects or even claims from the performance warranty is usually assessed based on how much the measured performance under STC deviates from the value in new (initial) condition. Provided that there is no other agreement between buyer and manufacturer, P_{nom} represents the initial value.

Due to the relevance of the nominal performance, laboratories that are capable of measuring module performance accurately and traceable to internationally recognized references are of high importance. Module manufacturers obtain so-called reference modules from such laboratories. These should be precisely characterized modules used by the module manufacturer to adjust the production in-line flasher. In the so-called binning process, each module is measured at the end of the production line and assigned a performance class. In a process commonly referred to by manufacturers as 'positive sorting', the module must achieve at least the value of a certain performance class. The performance class defines the nominal performance of the module that the manufacturer indicates on the nameplate. Consequently, the value, measured by the external lab for the reference module defines indirectly to which performance class a module is assorted. Also, module purchasers often rely on such independent laboratories by having samples from the purchased modules tested to assure that the modules reach the promised performance class.

This study provides a deep statistical evaluation of the measurement data collected at Fraunhofer ISE over a period from 2012 to the first half year of 2025. The focus of the investigation is on the measured module performance P_{MPP} compared to the nominal performance P_{nom} as indicated on the nameplate. Other nameplate values such as short-circuit current I_{SC} and open-circuit voltage V_{OC} will be considered.

10.4229/EUPVSEC2025/3BO.15.4

An additional aspect that is also regarded in this study pertains to the light induced degradation (LID) effect. Since the performance of PV modules is known to experience a slight change during the first operating hours under irradiation, the development of the LID effect is examined regarding various solar cell generations.

Finally, metastable behavior of PV modules with the TOPCon cell technology, which is the leading technology at the moment [9], were analyzed. The focus is on the degradation and recovery behavior of new PV modules (storage effects). While the impact of these variations on the actual yield of a PV system is expected to be rather low, they can superimpose precise measurements and thus lead to errors or misinterpretations if not considered properly.

1.2 Laboratory environment and calibration level

The Fraunhofer Institute for Solar Energy Systems operates an accredited testing laboratory including all relevant performance and reliability standards such as IEC 60904, IEC 61215 and IEC 61730 within the scope of accredited work (certificate D-PL-11140-33-00). For the exact IV-characterization the laboratory holds additionally an accreditation as calibration laboratory (certificate D-K-11140-02-00), which requires the highest level of traceability. The laboratory benefits from the advantageous combination of testing and calibration services. This lab, herein referred to as CalLab PV Modules has been conducting characterization measurements on modules for many years, placing emphasis on a stable calibration level and precision. All calibrations and measurements are directly traceable to national standards via the Physikalisch-Technische Bundestanstalt (PTB) which is the national metrology institute (NMI) of Germany. At CalLab PV Modules, IV-characteristics and the maximum power at STC (P_{MPP}) of the modules are measured in the context of various applications, such as reference modules for production lines, reliability investigations, product certification, and particularly in the context of quality assurance measures for module buyers.

In an accredited calibration laboratory highest standards must be applied to monitor and to minimize unpreventable temporal variations of the calibration level. For the latter interpretation of statistical trends observed in this study, the stability of the calibration level of CalLab PV Modules is shown exemplarily based on results of internal and external measures for the quality assurance.

Figure 1 presents the results of Round Robins (RR) on PV modules between the years 2008 to 2024. It is important to note that the participants as well as the number of PV modules and technologies in the RR have varied across different years. Results of the RR with the international leading PV labs have been published separately [10, 11]. Furthermore, bilateral comparisons with the PTB [12] are included.

The plot illustrates the average, minimum, and maximum deviations of CalLab PV Modules from the respective reference value of the RR. The differences in scatter are influenced by the varying number of participants and the different technologies involved. A central message derived from the data is that, on average, the values reported by CalLab PV Modules have consistently deviated by less than 0.5 % from the reference value since 2009, and notably no significant trends are observable throughout the years.

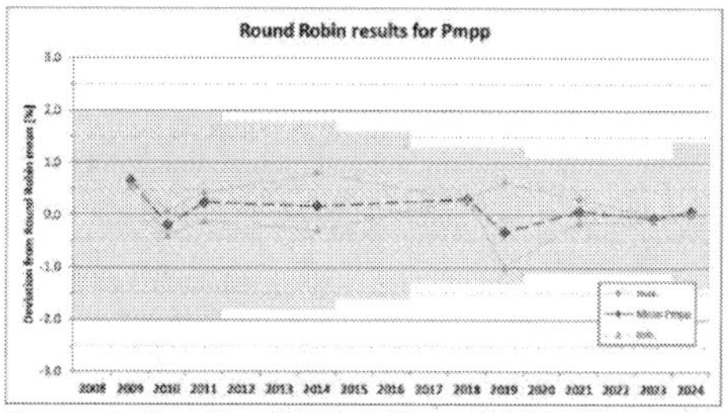

Figure 1: Results of various Round Robins on module level. The average, minimum and maximum deviation of CalLab PV Modules from the respective reference value is provided for each Round Robin campaign. The grey area represents the measurement uncertainty (k=2) of CalLab PV Modules for the measurements.

Figure 2 shows the average deviation of the measured short-circuit current I_{SC} of primary calibrated WPVS reference cells from the calibration value measured by PTB. It shows that the deviation is continuously below 0.5 % and no trend towards higher or lower deviations is visible.

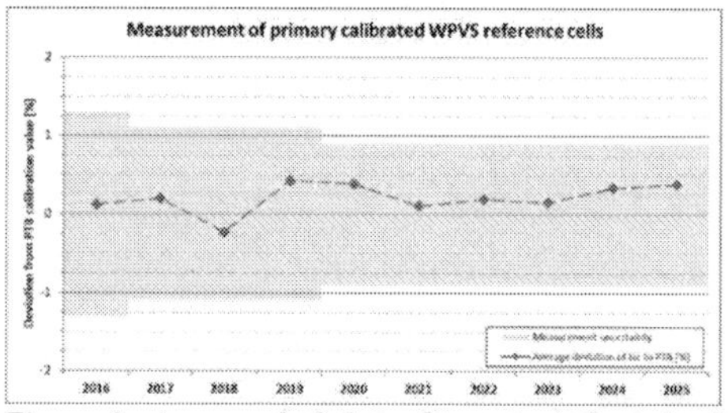

Figure 2: Average deviation of measured short-circuit current I_{SC} of primary calibrated WPVS cells from PTB calibration values.

2 DATA SOURCES AND FILTERING

As described above CalLab PV Modules produces accurate measurement results for its customers since more than a decade [13]. Beside the measurement results, basic characteristics of each module, e.g., manufacturer, module type, module dimensions, and cell material were recorded. Moreover, the nameplate values of the modules were recorded where available.

For this study, measurement results were used in an anonymized way to analyze the development of the measured deviation from nameplate values in the past years. It is to be noted that this is not the first publication of statistical evaluation of measurements and the basic filtering principles have already described [14]. To ensure a good understanding of this study, this data processing, referred to as "basic filter" are explained in detail again below. Additionally, further specific filters were applied for the focused evaluations, which are also described below.

2.1 Basic filter for power at STC evaluations

This study is based on an overall number of 76936 measurements (IV-characteristics at STC) taken between the beginning of 2012 and the first half year of 2025.

Within this period, all measurement results were evaluated using the same inhouse-developed software.

As mentioned above, the modules belong to different types of projects with different objectives. Projects coming from module buyers often include large sets of identical modules of the same type, e.g., from a PV power plant. Projects from manufacturers often include only single modules, e.g., reference modules for the production line. Beside the number of modules per type (i.e. product name), also the number of measurements conducted on an individual module varies sometimes, e.g. since aging tests, such as (LID), light- and elevated temperature-induced degradation (LETID), potential-induced degradation (PID), and others, require module measurements at different states, such as initial (out of the box), interim (after different steps of stressing) and final (very last measurement).

The basic filter ensures the statistical evaluability of the modules in their new (initial) condition. In short, these are the following filtering stages, which are explained in detail further below:

- Inconsistency filter: Filtering out invalid or unusable data
- Initial measurement filter: Filtering out data after pre-treatment
- First appearance filter: Each module (serial number) is considered only once
- Imbalance filter: Avoids statistical distortions due to differing sample sizes

2.1.1 Inconsistency filter

The 1st filter sorts out measurement results with inconsistent data. E.g., target temperature and target irradiance must align with the designated measurement type (e.g. STC). The serial number of the device under test (DUT) in the results information is mandatory to identify repeating measurements. Measurements of the rear side of bifacial modules are also sorted out. Finally, datasets with physically impossible results are excluded, like negative values for short-circuit current I_{SC}, open-circuit voltage V_{OC}, or maximum power P_{MPP}, or fill factor beyond 100 % or efficiencies beyond 30 %. Additional constraints are a current limit of 25 A, a voltage limit of 250 V and a power limit of 800 W. Those results might originate from measurements of defect modules (e.g., due to transportation damage). Incorrect prototypes could also lead to ambiguous IV curves which are sort out. Only measurements with a complete IV curve respectively all relevant electrical parameters are considered.

2.1.2 Initial measurement filter

The 2nd filter only preserves the first measurement – of a specific measurement type like STC – of a DUT within a project. The intention is to obtain only results at initial state of the module. This is the only comparable state across a large set of data because the intermediate state of a module depends on the individual schedule and focus of a project and therefore differs for each project. This also means that the herein presented data was acquired before any stabilization, e.g. by light soaking.

2.1.3 First appearance filter

The 3rd filter removes datasets of recalibrations and other re-measurements. Typically, golden modules are sent to the lab to be recalibrated in regular time intervals. Then, the identical module refers to different projects respectively orders. To avoid double counting of these modules, only the first appearance of a serial number of a specific module is valid and all subsequent remeasurements of a module are sorted out.

2.1.4 Imbalance filter

In the 4th step, from each module type in a project, only the measurement results closest to the average power for this module type is considered. Hence, the imbalance due to different numbers of modules per project is eliminated. In addition, this paper is focused on general and representative trends in PV module development and not in the presentation of highest possible results.

The filtering steps 1-4 reduced the dataset from 76936 to 6999 measurements which represents 9.1 % of the initial data whereas the variety of module types of the initial dataset is still represented by the filtered dataset. The number of unique module types is only reduced from 4322 to 4272 by the filtering steps.

2.2 Extended filter for power at STC evaluations

Although the basic filter described in Section 2.1 already provides a good evaluation of statistical trends, additional filtering methods were applied to present a more representative picture from the perspective of the module recipients, assuming this view correlates more to the products installed in PV systems. Initially, only measurements with nameplate values are considered, where the deviation to rated values can be evaluated. This reduced the dataset from 6999 to 6344 measurements. Furthermore, additional factors were excluded that could potentially lead to slight statistical distortions when only considering the basic filter. In short, the following filtering steps were added (detailed description follows below):

- Technology filter: Consider only modules based on crystalline silicon cell technology and electrical characteristics typically for most modules installed in PV-plants
- Indoor filter: Exclude modules which were already exposed in PV-plants
- Project filter: Focus only on market relevant modules and assure an unused condition
- Customer filter: Focus only on projects engaged by module recipients
- TOP15 manufacturer filter: Focus on PV modules from established companies only

The effect of the different filters on the size of the dataset is shown in Table I.

2.2.1 Technology filter

The evaluation focused only on crystalline modules. Hence, a technology filter was applied sorting out all datasets which were not based on single-junction mono-Si or poly-Si cell material. The evaluation should represent standard sized modules and exclude any small test samples or cells. So, results are filtered by some module characteristics: the total module area is within 0.5 m² and 4 m² and the number of cells in a module is between 30 and 200 cells. These boundaries exclude small modules as well as oversized or in-series connected modules.

2.2.2 Indoor filter

In some projects, modules from the field are measured before and after cleaning to identify the soiling effect. In these cases, the initial measurement is on the one hand based on a dirty module and on the other hand the modules were already exposed outdoors and are not comparable to new modules. Those kinds of measurements are also sorted out.

2.2.3 Project filter

Measurements from research projects as well as from certification projects are sorted out because these are modules which might not be available on the market or test samples or prototypes. Internal measurements for continuous quality assurance as well as any test measurements are also filtered out.

2.2.4 Customer filter

Measurements ordered by PV module manufacturers are rejected. The modules might be used as reference modules for their production line (golden module) or for R&D purposes. The label on the module is then not relevant and golden modules are only for internal use by the manufacturer. Therefore, any deviation between nameplate and measurement is not relevant for the downstream market.

2.2.5 TOP15 manufacturer filter

The variety of modules manufacturers and their experience is large. Some manufacturers are present on the market for years and some already vanished. Therefore, the final filter considers only the TOP15 manufacturers over the past 7 years (by shipment volume) to have a more consistent dataset and comparable data over the years. Available TOP10 lists from the past years [15–19]. are used to identify TOP15 manufacturers. The explicit mention of individual manufacturer names is deliberately omitted to prevent misinterpretation, for example, arising from whether a specific manufacturer was included in the evaluation or not. This is also considered irrelevant for the results and conclusions of this study.

Table I: Number of datasets per year (YR) after basic filtering (BAS) (section 2.1) and for the extended filter steps: technology (TECH), indoor (INDR), project (PROJ), customer (CUS) and TOP15 manufacturer (T15).

YR	BAS	TECH	INDR	PROJ	CUS	T15
12	696	615	611	518	284	93
13	763	646	623	523	325	73
14	613	500	468	383	219	58
15	542	456	452	370	135	52
16	517	457	455	368	165	86
17	483	428	422	337	167	87
18	428	372	358	271	147	70
19	392	335	320	236	155	93
20	403	367	357	275	158	111
21	339	315	308	203	129	77
22	317	292	279	195	130	73
23	309	293	287	194	126	68
24	371	353	348	286	167	90
25*	171	161	160	122	77	40
Σ	6.344	5.590	5.448	4.281	2.384	1.071

*For 2025 only the first 6 months are considered

2.3 Filtering approach for LID evaluations

To consider the light induced degradation (LID) effect, the standard IEC 61215-2 [20] describes a methodology for the stabilization of PV modules. Slightly simplified, a crystalline silicon-based PV module can be regarded as stable when its performance does not change by more than 1 % over two consecutive light exposures of at least 5 kWh/m². In the laboratory practice this was realized by exposing the module in an initial step to a dose of 20 kWh/m² to degrade the module, followed by two further exposures of 5 kWh/m² to proof the stability with performance measurements at STC in-between. Typically, an initial (out-of-the-box) power measurement was conducted to quantify the LID effect. For the light exposure, an artificial sun-simulator with an irradiance around 1000 W/m² was used. The modules were operated in MPP mode at (50 ± 10) °C.

For the evaluation of the LID effect throughout this study only datasets were considered, for which the full stabilization process as described above was executed, including initial out-of-the-box measurement. These datasets mainly came from product certification or calibration projects. Since the process was only implemented with the 2016 edition of IEC 61215, the earliest datasets date from 2017. Table II shows an overview of 127 datasets where information on the cell technology was available.

Table II: Number of datasets per year and technology for the LID statistics.

YR	PERC	TOPCON	HJT	IBC
17	4			
18	14			
19			1	
20	1			
21	5			
22	6		1	
23	8	13	3	
24	32	21	3	
25*	1	6		8
Σ	71	40	8	8

*For 2025 only the first 6 months are considered

3 RESULTS

3.1 Absolute STC results

Referring to the data filtering described above, this chapter presents the key results of the statistical investigations into the IV- and performance characteristics taken at Standard Test Conditions. It can be assumed that the following data represent currently field-installed modules. While the focus of this publication lay on the deviation of measured to nominal values, the following plots (Figure 3 - Figure 6) shall visualize the development of the mainstream crystalline silicon-based module technology of the past 12 years in general. In these plots, the mean of all data points (dashed line) and the median (solid line), as well as the quantiles for 50 % and 80 % of the datasets, is provided.

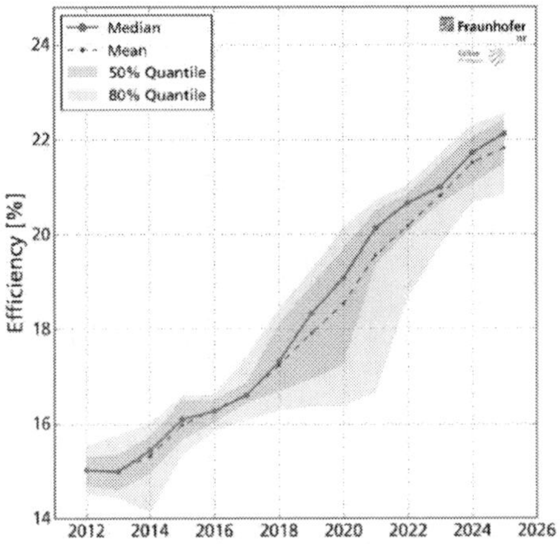

Figure 3: PV module efficiencies over time after filtering.

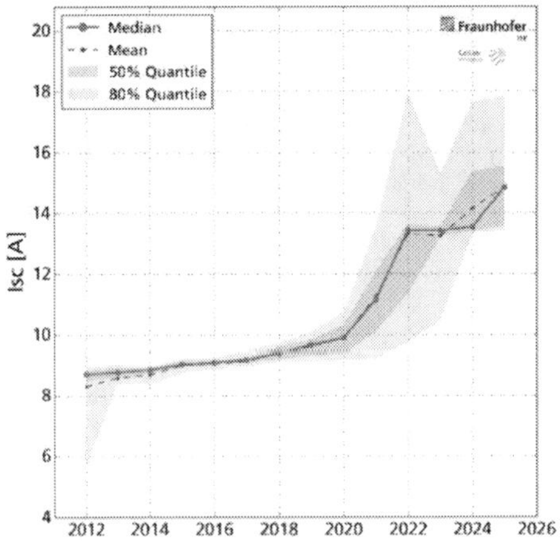

Figure 4: PV module short-circuit current I_{SC} over time after filtering.

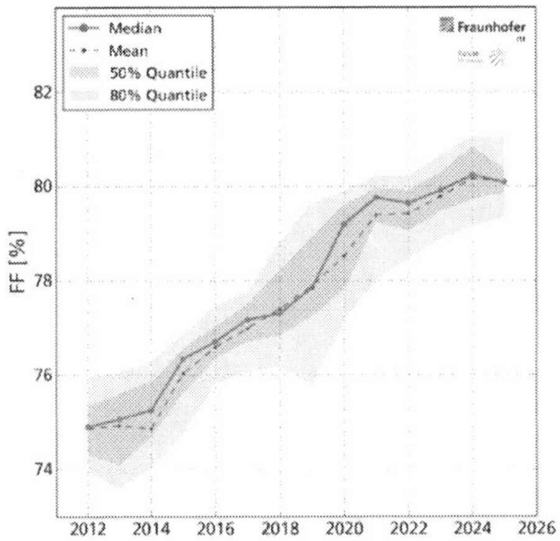

Figure 5: PV module fill factor FF over time after filtering.

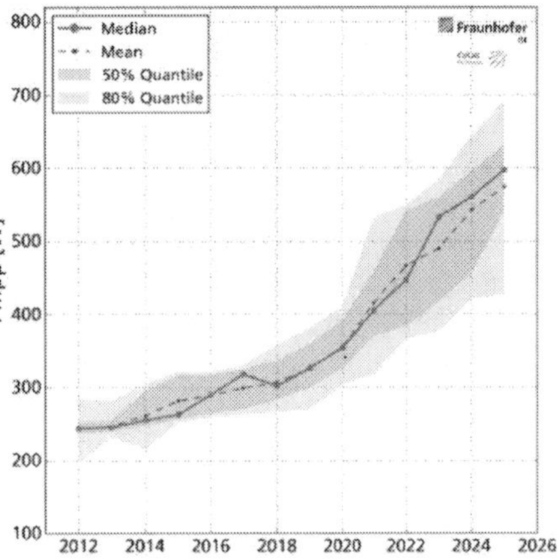

Figure 6: PV module maximum power P_{MPP} over time after filtering.

The efficiency of PV modules increased almost linear from ~15 % to ~22 % within 12 years which corresponds to a rate of 0.6 %/year. The fill factor also increased almost linear from 75 % to 80 % within this period. For I_{SC} and P_{MPP}, the development can be split in two sections: until 2020, the values slightly increased over the years from 8.5 A to 10 A and from 250 W to 350 W for I_{SC} and P_{MPP}, respectively. From 2020 until now, there was a steeper increase up to 15 A for I_{SC} and 600 W for P_{MPP}. Furthermore, the spread – represented by the 80 % quantile – was larger in the section from 2020 until now. Both effects can be explained by higher variation in the module layout and the cells used in the PV modules. Cell dimensions increased which directly affects the I_{SC} and different sizes were available which led to different geometrical layouts. Modules with 5 and 6 cell rows were available, cells are cut into half cells and third cells. In general, module dimensions increased which is directly linked to higher power outputs. There were more options to build a module which is mainly reflected by the higher spread in I_{SC} and P_{MPP}.

The development of V_{OC} over time is not shown because there are no trends visible. Generally, the measured V_{OC} is dominated by the number of cells per module and the interconnection of these cells which was not analyzed systematically in this study.

3.2 Deviation from nominal STC values

Although the extended data filtering is more relevant for the consumer side and thus for the installed PV modules, the deviation of P_{MPP} from P_{nom} is plotted for both filter levels, as the basic filtering (Figure 7) is based on a larger dataset and furthermore to illustrate the impact of the additional filtering (Figure 8). However, in Table III, results are only provided after extended filtering due to the greater practical relevance. The plots show the temporal progression of the percentage deviation over the last 12 years. This is particularly interesting for evaluating developments in the context of other market- and/or technology trends.

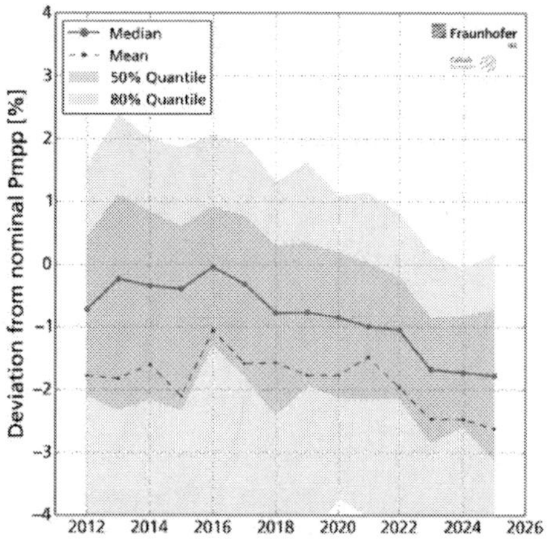

Figure 7: P_{MPP} deviations between measured and nominal value over time (basic filter)

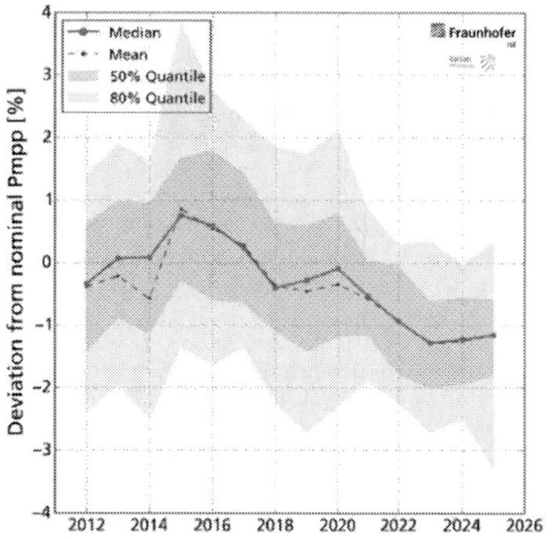

Figure 8: P_{MPP} deviations between measured and nominal value over time (extended filter)

In the extended filter, the median and mean for all examined parameters align well (Figure 8). In contrast, a negative shift in the mean performance deviation compared to the median can be observed in the basic filter (Figure 7). This indicates a stronger influence of negative outliers. Qualitatively, both evaluations show a slight but almost continuous negative trend in performance deviation since around 2016. Notably, the extended evaluation showed, on average, mostly positive values compared to the nominal value in the years up to the year 2017 (e.g., median 2016 at +0.59 %), which reduced to a median value the following years but especially pronounced from 2021 to 2023, ending at -1.28 %. In 2024, this negative trend has halted, and a slight trend reversal was observed towards a median value of -1.15 % in 2025.

In contrast, Figure 9 shows in which ranges nominal (label) power P_{nom} can deviate from results measured by an accredited calibration laboratory, regardless of technical or other external developments.

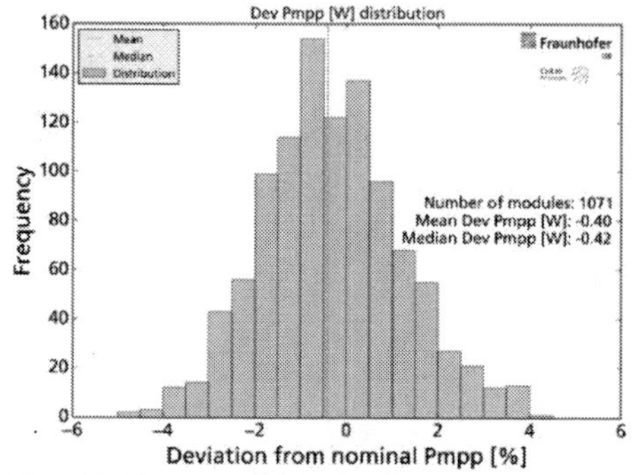

Figure 9: Histogram of deviations between measured and nominal value for P_{MPP} (extended filter)

Regarding V_{OC} and I_{SC} both filter levels convey a very comparable picture. Hence, only the plots for the filtered data are shown in Figure 10 and Figure 11. For V_{OC}, the nominal and measured values overall match best over the entire observation period. In the last 2 years, a slight trend towards somewhat higher measured values compared to the nominal values is noticeable. Notably, I_{SC}, increased over the entire observation period: While the median value in 2012 was still around +1.37 %, it fell below -3 % by 2025. Since this trend does not align with the trend of the performance specification and the V_{OC} remains nearly stable, a corresponding opposite trend is evident in the fill factor, shown in Figure 12.

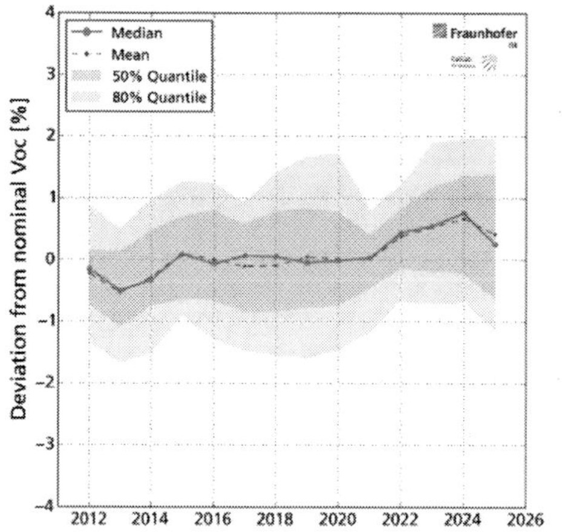

Figure 10: V_{OC} deviations between measured and nominal value over time (extended filter)

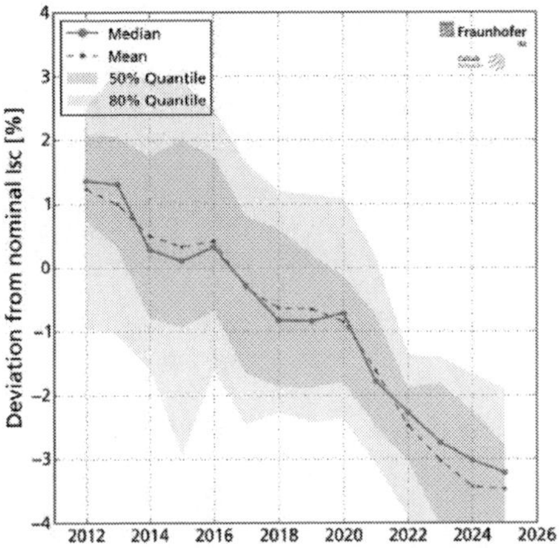

Figure 11: I_{SC} deviations between measured and nominal value over time (extended filter)

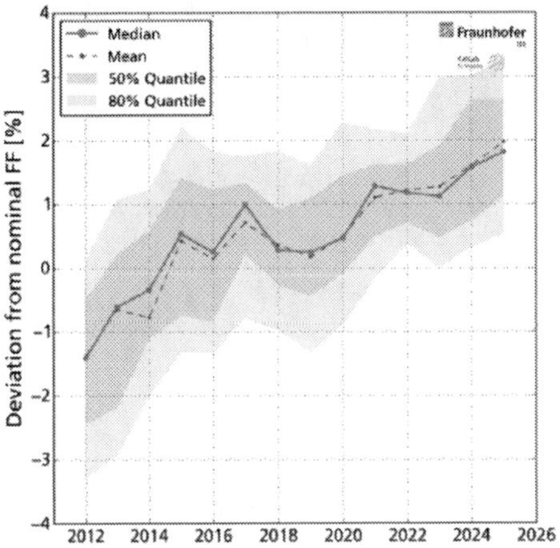

Figure 12: FF deviations between measured and nominal value over time (extended filter)

Table III: Deviation of measured STC parameters from nameplate values per year based on the extended filter TOP15. datasets per year and technology for the LID statistics.

Year	I_{SC} [%]	V_{OC} [%]	P_{MPP} [%]	FF [%]
2012	1.37	-0.16	-0.34	-1.41
2013	1.31	-0.50	0.07	-0.60
2014	0.29	-0.33	0.09	-0.33
2015	0.11	0.09	0.75	0.54
2016	0.33	-0.07	0.59	0.25
2017	-0.28	0.07	0.23	0.99
2018	-0.82	0.05	-0.40	0.29
2019	-0.84	-0.05	-0.28	0.25
2020	-0.71	-0.01	-0.09	0.47
2021	-1.78	0.03	-0.52	1.28
2022	-2.26	0.44	-0.93	1.17
2023	-2.74	0.55	-1.28	1.12
2024	-3.02	0.76	-1.22	1.57
2025	-3.21	0.26	-1.15	1.82

PV module prices are typically defined by $/Wp which makes the nominal power an important parameter. It is a tradeoff between the profit margin of the PV module manufacturer and the customer who calculates the costs for a PV plant and the return of invest. So, the contract between the manufacturer and the customer plays an important role. The question, if measurement uncertainties of a third-party laboratory are considered or not, can shift the acceptance criteria for measured power output to a lower value. This could somehow explain why the observed deviation in power does not further drop.

In contrast to that, I_{SC} and V_{OC} are not relevant for pricing of PV modules. However, these parameters have high relevance for the inverter design and the string layout. Due to the high temperature coefficient of V_{OC}, the match of V_{OC} is important to align with the inverter requirements and limits for various temperature conditions. As the V_{OC} of a module is mainly defined by the underlying cell technology, the variation of V_{OC} in a production line for a specific module type is typically lower than for I_{SC} and P_{MPP}. So, the manufacturer can set the nameplate value more precisely which is reflected here by small deviations within ± 1 % with no significant trend over time.

I_{SC} is relevant for cabling and ohmic losses as well as for instances of overheating. Therefore, the upper limits are mainly relevant for inverter inputs, and the slight overrating of I_{SC} might be a safety issue. System layout, including inverters and cabling, is based on the high nameplate I_{SC}. We expect no warranty issues due to overcurrent because currents in operation will typically be lower. This could explain why there are higher negative deviations for I_{SC} but it is still unclear why there is a downwards trend over time. A potential reason could be the fact that manufacturers calibrate their inline measurement systems with reference modules to match P_{MPP}. Due to the increase in I_{SC} of the PV modules in the past years, ohmic losses become more relevant. If the module is not connected in 4-wire technology during the measurement, then cable resistance can affect the measurement results and lower the fill factor or P_{MPP}, respectively. These cases lead to the I_{SC} being overrated. The fill factor is not affected by this procedure and is still affected by the ohmic losses. Measurement software usually includes several calibration factors for IV curve correction to overcome these issues. The inline calibration procedures and the application of correction factors by manufacturers are not known. The negative trend could be a consequence of increasing I_{SC} values, ohmic losses in 2-wire connection and missing application of correction factors.

3.2 Light induced degradation

Figure 13 shows the result of the stabilization process according to IEC 61215 [20] for new modules after an initial out-of-the-box measurement. The initial measurement at STC served as reference value, the relative deviation of P_{MPP} in percent after 3 steps of light exposure (20/5/5 kWh/m^2) was calculated, and for each year the averaged values are shown, based on the respective number of datasets (see Table II). The results are differentiated according to the cell technology.

The result shows the progress in the past years in preventing LID effects. While early PERC-based technologies show effects of up to -2 % this was reduced within this technology levels below 0.5 %. For TOPCon, HJT and IBC almost no negative LID effects are determined. However, only a low number of HJT based module types are considered here.

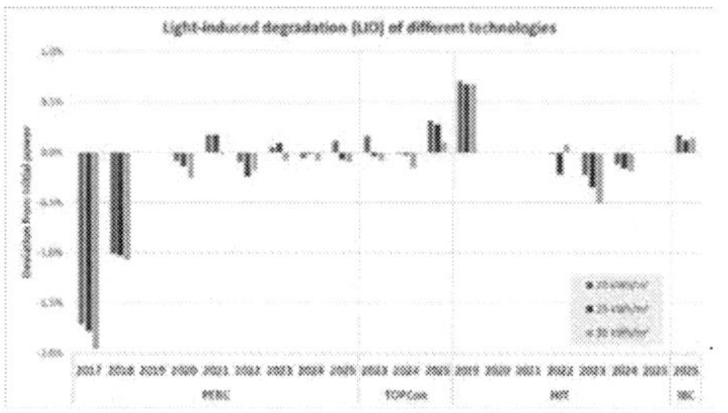

Figure 13: Average deviation of P_{MPP} from initial out-of-the-box result per year and technology. Results after 20, 25 and 30 kWh/m² light-induced degradation (LID) are shown.

3.3 TOPCon metastability effects (storage effect)

The impact of storage conditions on the performance measured on TOPCon based PV cells and modules has been reported in the context of their impact on aging tests. Strong power drops of several percent have been observed especially after UV aging [21, 22].

In contrast, the results presented in this study refer to degradation taking place during ordinary laboratory storage of modules and recovery after short light soaking. The susceptibility of the module types to any storage-based degradation was not known in advance. Some TOPCon module types were chosen from customer projects where the sensitivity to LID and storage effects were investigated. Other TOPCon module types were property of the laboratory and hence, effects could be investigated for a longer period. Consequently, the number of modules examined for each type, as well as the specific experimental approach, is not 100 % identical for all modules.

Figure 14 (top) shows the development of the measured performance of 4 module types (C, D, E, F). Of type C and D one module was tested, of type E two modules, and of type F four modules were tested. The measurement sequence started with an initial light stabilization process as required in IEC 61215 with 20 kWh/m² followed by 2 x 5 kWh/m² (as described in section 2.3). To analyze the impact of this initial light soaking on the storage effect of type E and F the half of the modules were not exposed to this process (E_1, F_1, F_2). After several steps of storage (i.e. not completely dark, ordinary laboratory light), a single short light soaking with 2 kWh/m² using a class B solar simulator and MPP tracking, was conducted to analyze to what extent the short light exposure recovers the storage effect.

Figure 14 (bottom) refers to results of two additional module types (A, B) of which only one module per type was analyzed. In contrast to types C, D, E, F these modules were exposed to several intervals of storage and short light soaking of 2 kWh/m².

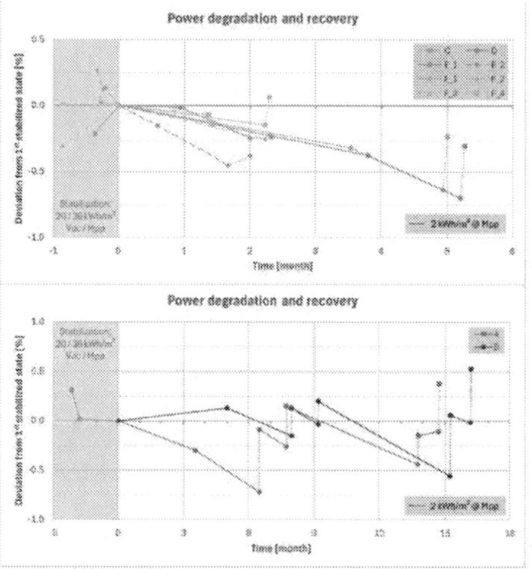

Figure 14: TOPCon degradation over time by lab storage (solid and dashed lines) and recovery by light-soaking of 2 kWh/m² at P_{MPP} (dotted lines) for six different module types. Top: modules with only single recovery step within 6 months; bottom: modules with multiple storage and recovery steps within 18 months.

All module types showed a degradation in power during storage periods. The degradation rate over time is similar for the different modules except for the E_2 which shows stronger degradation and type B, which showed a slight gain after the first 5 months of storage. The storage conditions were not controlled in detail; therefore, this module might have been exposed more to the ambient laboratory light than other modules or any other storage condition might have differed. After this first gain, the module showed similar behavior as the other modules during storage. The storage degradation rate is on average -0.11 % per month. There is no difference observed between stabilized modules and non-stabilized modules.

The short light soaking of 2 kWh/m² at MPP induced a gain in power for all module types. The average gain was +0.24 %. In contrast to the degradation, there was no similar behavior observed for the different module types. The recovery in P_{MPP} ranged from almost no gain (E_1, F_2 – F_4) up to 0.63 % (A, first cycle). Modules of the same type showed different recovery effects. Therefore, a general conclusion per module type is not possible. In addition, the recovery process for the modules was not reproducible: After several cycles of short light soaking (Modules A and B), the resulting power of the modules did not reach the initial stabilized power nor any other reproducible value. The power values even exceeded the initial stabilized power.

4 CONCLUSIONS

The statistical analyses presented in this study are meant to provide an overview of trends regarding the deviation between nominal (nameplate) to precisely measured electrical characteristics of PV modules.

Between the years 2017 to 2023 we observed a continuous negative trend of the deviation between measured and rated power, reaching a median value of -1.28 % in 2023 and stabilizing since then. While on

10.4229/EUPVSEC2025/3BO.15.4

module level the observed deviations result only in few Watts less performance; the aspect becomes relevant considering the effects on a whole energy economy. The filtering and the broad statistical basis for these results allow to assume that the deviation is representative for the overall PV installations in Germany and Europe.

In Germany, 14.1 GW of capacity was installed in 2023 [1], and 16.2 GW in 2024 [2]. When applying the observed deviations to these installation capacities, the resulting shortfall amounts to approximately 180 MW for 2023 and as much as 198 MW for 2024. These deficits are comparable to the capacity of large-scale PV power plants, such as exemplarily the Weesow-Willmersdorf solar park, which has an installed capacity of 187 MW and, according to the operator, supplies electricity to up to 50,000 households [23].

The underlying causes of this pronounced trend toward negative performance deviations remain subject of speculations. However, the intense pricing and competitive pressure faced by manufacturers likely plays a significant role. The presented findings highlight the importance of verifying the promised performance, both to avoid negative discrepancies and, perhaps even more critically, to accurately determine the actual performance level of installed modules. In the case of large-scale power plants, it is often necessary to assess the condition of the modules after years of operation, e.g. due to a planned sale of the facility or because the modules exhibit irregularities. In such cases, it is essential to establish whether the performance has degraded compared to its original state. Referring solely to the nominal value introduces considerable uncertainty and does not allow to evaluate the real annual degradation rate. Operators or installers of such power plants should therefore ensure that performance measurements are conducted in a laboratory that maintains a stable long-term calibration standard and is logistically accessible with manageable effort.

A positive development was observed for the LID effect, where a clear trend towards less initial degradation could be observed since 2018. Currently LID seems hardly to play a role for modern PV modules. Considering the positive power-deviation around the year 2015 in context of the LID development, it could be possible that manufacturers overrated the module power in the years 2015 to 2017 slightly to be more on the safe side considering LID.

The herein provided experimental results on the impact of storage effects are mainly meant to raise awareness of these effects and to provide the observed range of magnitude. Since the power drop occurs during storage, these effects will not be unveiled by the stabilization process according to IEC61215-2:2021, MQT 19. With variations ranging between 0.5 % and 1 % the observed effects lay typically below stability criteria of IEC61215-1-1:2021 which allows a max. difference between highest and lowest value of 1 % related to the average value over three measurements. Notably, this comparison is only meant as orientation since the standard describes stabilization through light exposure. Especially for applications where high precision and reproducibility is required (e.g. round robins, proficiency testing, generation of golden- and silver modules for production lines) it is important to know and to consider these effects. Processes to reduce undesired impacts or wrong interpretations of measured data are currently under development and the provided data shall support these activities.

5 REFERENCES

[1] Bundesnetzagentur, *Zubau Erneuerbarer Energien 2023.* [Online]. Available: https:// www.bundesnetzagentur.de/997312

[2] Bundesnetzagentur, *Ausbau Erneuerbarer Energien 2024.* [Online]. Available: https:// www.bundesnetzagentur.de/1043738

[3] SolarPower Europe, *EU Market Outlook for Solar Power 2024-2028.* [Online]. Available: https:// www.solarpowereurope.org/insights/outlooks/eu-market-outlook-for-solar-power-2024-2028

[4] G. Masson, M. de l'Epine, and I. Kaizuka, "Trends in Photovoltaic Applications 2024," International Energy Agency (IEA), 2024. [Online]. Available: https://iea-pvps.org/trends_reports/trends-in-pv-applications-2024/

[5] IRENA, *Renewable capacity statistics 2025.* [Online]. Available: https://www.irena.org/ Publications/2025/Jul/Renewable-energy-statistics-2025

[6] *Photovoltaic devices – Part 1: Measurement of photovoltaic current-voltage characteristics*, IEC 60904-1: 2020-09, International Electrotechnical Commission (IEC), Geneva, Switzerland, 2020.

[7] *Photovoltaic devices – Part 1-2: Measurement of current-voltage characteristics of bifacial photovoltaic (PV) devices*, IEC TS 60904-1-2: 2024-11, International Electrotechnical Commission (IEC), Geneva, Switzerland, 2024.

[8] *Solar photovoltaic energy systems - Terms, definitions and symbols*, IEC TS 61836: 2016-12, International Electrotechnical Commission (IEC), Geneva, Switzerland, 2016.

[9] ITRPV, "International Technology Roadmap for Photovoltaic (ITRPV): 2024 Results," 2025.

[10] D. Dirnberger *et al.*, "Progress in PV Module Calibration - Results of a world-wide intercomparison between four reference laboratories," *Measurement Science & Technology*, 2014.

[11] E. Salis *et al.*, "Improvements in world-wide intercomparison of PV module calibration," *Progress in Solar Energy 1*, vol. 155, pp. 1451–1461, 2017, doi: 10.1016/j.solener.2017.07.081.

[12] Fraunhofer Institute for Solar Energy Systems ISE, *PV module measurement results from Fraunhofer ISE and the German National Metrology Institute (PTB) show high level of agreement.* Freiburg, Germany, 2023. [Online]. Available: https:// www.ise.fraunhofer.de/en/press-media/press-releases/2023/pv-module-measurement-results-from-fraunhofer-ise-and-the-german-national-metrology-institute-show-high-level-of-agreement.html

[13] Fraunhofer Institute for Solar Energy Systems ISE, *Fraunhofer ISE's CalLab PV Modules Improves Measurement Uncertainty to Record Value of 1.1 %.* Freiburg, Germany, 2020. [Online]. Available: https://www.ise.fraunhofer.de/en/press-media/ press-releases/2020/Fraunhofer-ISEs-CalLab-PV-Modules-Improves-Measurement-Uncertainty-to-Record-Value.html

[14] U. Kräling, P. Gebhardt, M. Kaiser, and D. Philipp, "PV Module Performance Measurements – Statistical Analysis of Technological Trends," 2022, doi: 10.4229/WCPEC-82022-3BO.14.1.

[15] Solar Media Limited, *Top 10 PV module suppliers in 2022 shipped 245GW.* [Online]. Available: https://www.pv-tech.org/top-10-pv-module-suppliers-in-2022-shipped-245gw/

[16] Solar Edition, *Top 10 PV Module Manufacturers in 2020, Based-on Their Module Shipment.* [Online]. Available: https://solaredition.com/top-10-pv-module-manufacturers-in-2020-based-on-their-module-shipment/

[17] RTS Corporation, *PV Module Shipment Ranking in 1H 2024.* [Online]. Available: https://www.rts-pv.com/en/blogs/12764/

[18] SolarQuarter, *2025 Top 20 Global Photovoltaic Module Manufacturers Revealed by PVBL.* [Online]. Available: https://solarquarter.com/2025/06/17/2025-top-20-global-photovoltaic-module-manufacturers-revealed-by-pvbl/

[19] Solar Media Limited, *Top 10 solar module suppliers in 2018.* [Online]. Available: https://www.pv-tech.org/top-10-solar-module-suppliers-in-2018/

[20] *Terrestrial photovoltaic (PV) modules – Design qualification and type approval – Part 2: Test procedures*, IEC 61215-2: 2021-02, International Electrotechnical Commission (IEC), Geneva, Switzerland, 2021.

[21] P. Gebhardt *et al.*, "Stabilization procedures for TOPCon PV modules after UV-induced degradation," *Sol Energ Mat Sol C*, vol. 294, p. 113885, 2026, doi: 10.1016/j.solmat.2025.113885.

[22] T. Karin, "UVID initiates metastability in the dark: how to properly measure unstable SI modules," *PVRW: Photovoltaic Reliability Workshop*, 2025.

[23] EnBW Energie Baden-Württemberg AG, *Größter förderfreier Solarpark Deutschlands eingeweiht*, 2021. [Online]. Available: https://www.enbw.com/presse/enbw-weiht-groessten-solarpark-deutschlands-ein.html

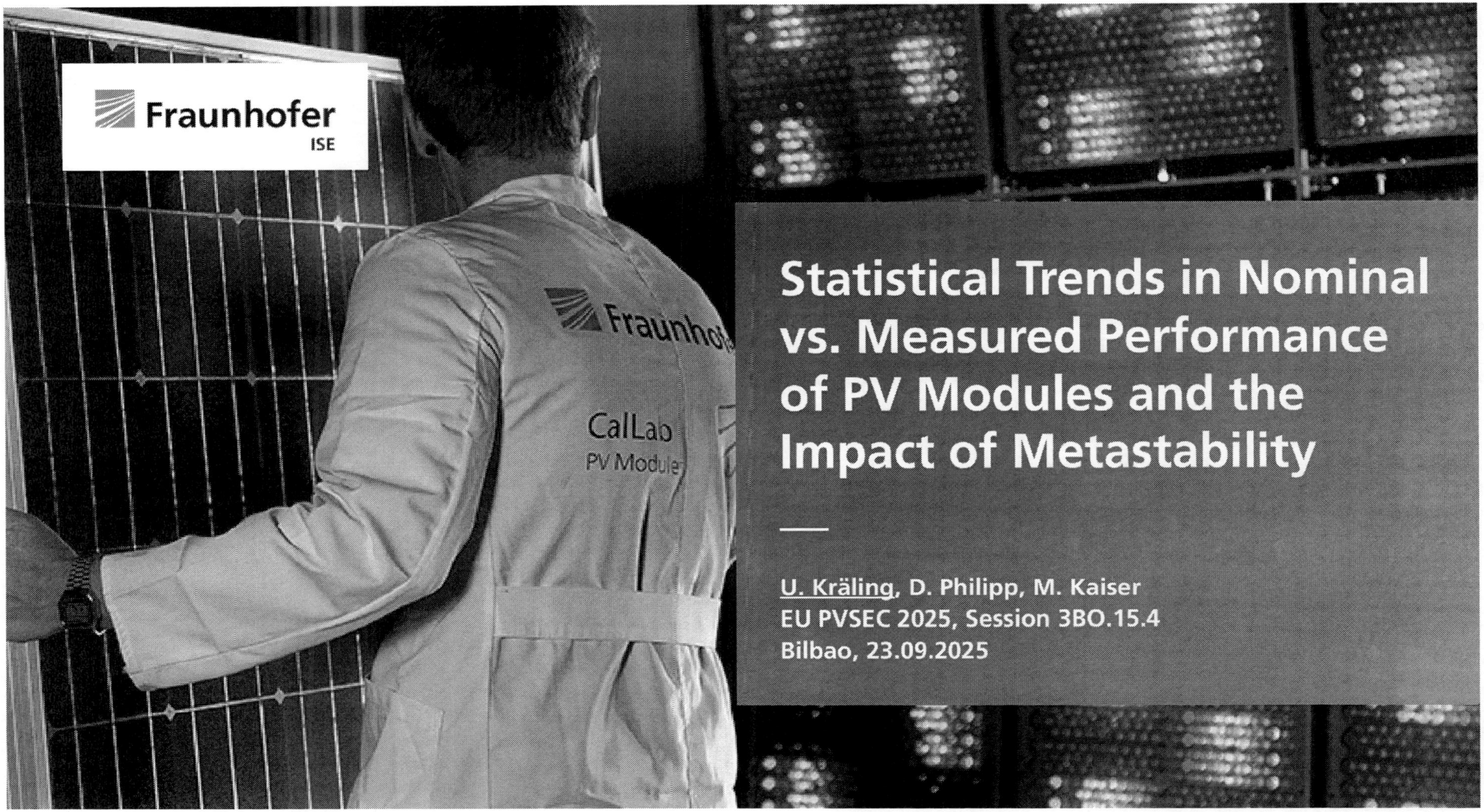
Fraunhofer
ISE
Fraunhofer
CalLab
PV Modules
Statistical Trends in Nominal vs. Measured Performance of PV Modules and the Impact of Metastability
U. Kräling, D. Philipp, M. Kaiser
EU PVSEC 2025, Session 3BO.15.4
Bilbao, 23.09.2025

Motivation

Negative Deviations from Nominal Power

Nominal power (P_{Nom}) is a key parameter
- to calculate the yield
- to determine the price ($/Wp)

Trend toward negative deviations
- Initial presentation in 2023
- High international attention [1, 2]

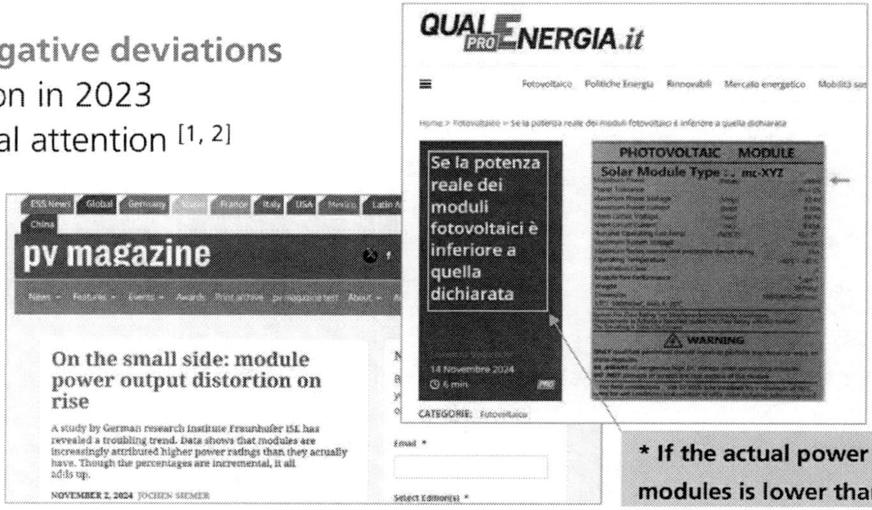

*** If the actual power of the photovoltaic modules is lower than the declared one**

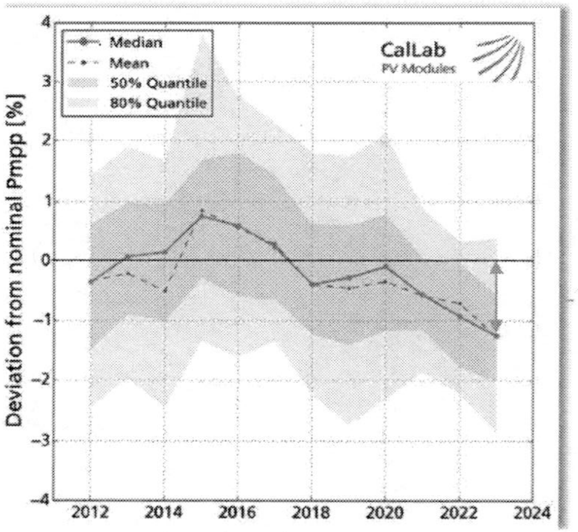

-1.3%*

*** -1.3% reduction in output corresponds to approximately 820 MWp with 63 GWp of new capacity added in 2023 in Europe!**

[1] https://www.pv-magazine-australia.com/2024/11/02/on-the-small-side-module-power-output-distortion-on-rise/
[2] https://www.qualenergia.it/pro/articoli-pro/potenza-reale-moduli-fotovoltaici-spesso-inferiore-quella-dichiarata/

Fraunhofer ISE

Who we are

CalLab PV Modules, TestLab PV Modules

CalLab PV Modules

TestLab PV Modules

Accredited laboratories for PV modules (ISO/IEC 17025)

- Calibration laboratory
  - STC performance: IEC 60904-1, IEC 60904-1-2
- Testing laboratory
  - Performance, reliability, safety: IEC 61215, IEC 61730

High effort for quality assurance

- Lowest measurement uncertainty
- Stable calibration level
- Reproducible results

Provide high quality services to industry

- Around 6,000 STC measurements per year

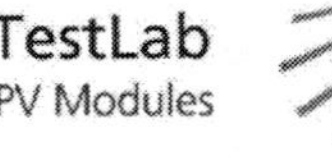

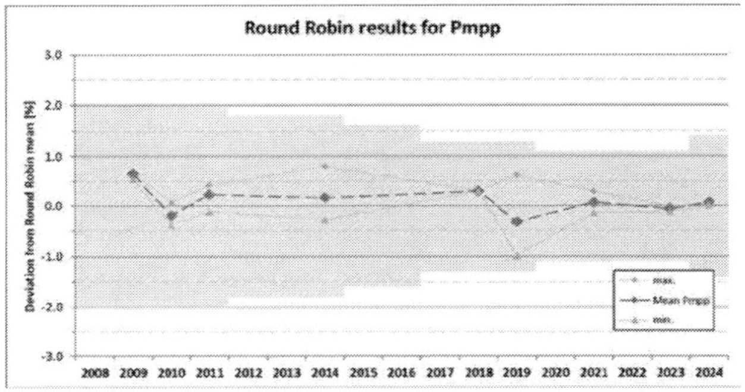

Fraunhofer ISE

Database

Representative Filtering of STC Measurements [3]

Measurements since 2012 **76,936 datasets**

- Only new PV modules
- 1 PV module per type and order
- With nameplate values
- Crystalline PV modules
- Tier 1 manufacturer

Measurements after filtering **1,071 datasets**

Facts about filtering

- 1.4% of initial datasets
- 79 datasets per year on average
- 662 different module types
- 14 manufacturers

Year	Initial	Filtered
2012	5,332	93
2013	5,964	73
2014	5,534	58
2015	5,553	52
2016	5,032	86
2017	6,990	87
2018	5,296	70
2019	5,541	93
2020	5,983	111
2021	5,791	77
2022	5,940	73
2023	6,072	68
2024	5,834	90
2025 H1*	2,074*	40*
Total	**76,936**	**1,071**

[3] U. Kräling, P. Gebhardt, M. Kaiser, D. Philipp, PV Module Performance Measurements – Statistical Analysis of Technological Trends. 9 pages / 8th World Conference on Photovoltaic Energy Conversion; 498-506 (2022).

Fraunhofer ISE

STC Results

Development of Performance since 2012

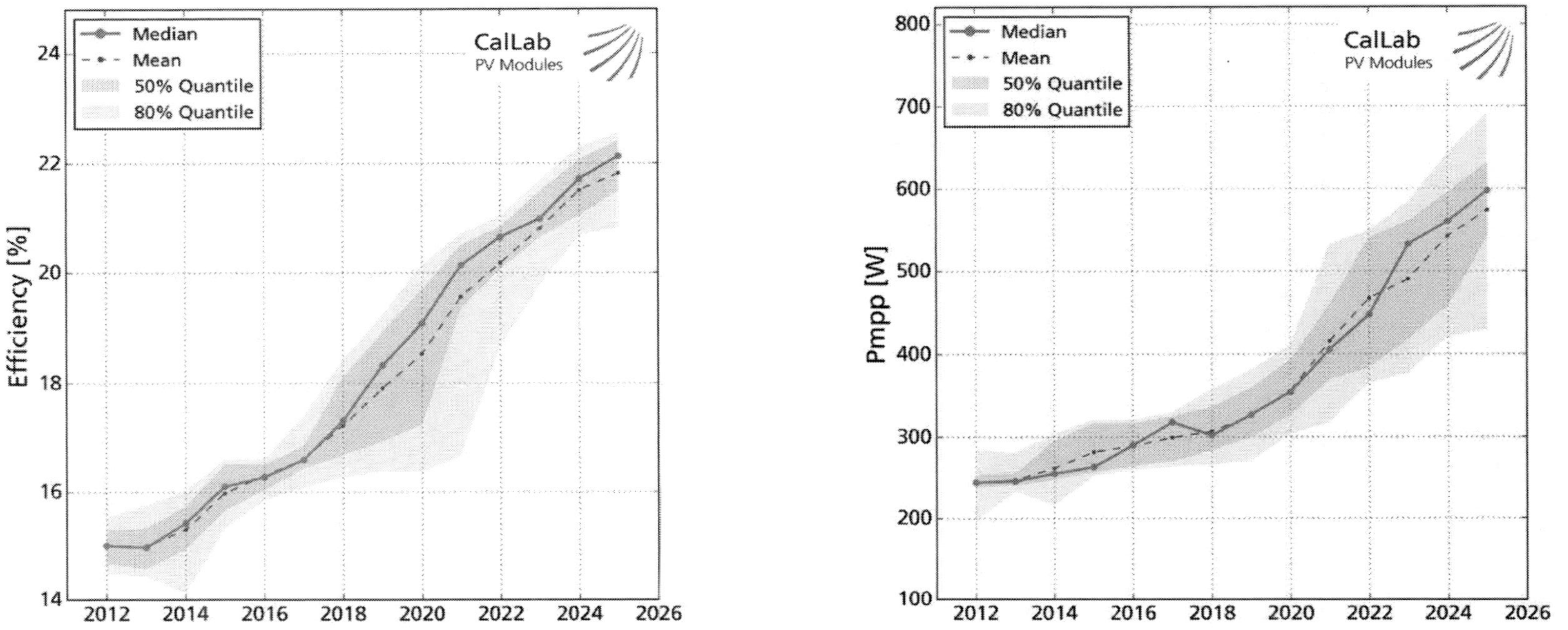

Fraunhofer ISE

STC Results

Performance Deviation from Nameplate since 2012

Significant negative deviation in the last years

- Average deviation in 2025: -1.1%

Stabilized after 2023 (first publication)

- Change from 2023 to 2025: +0.2%

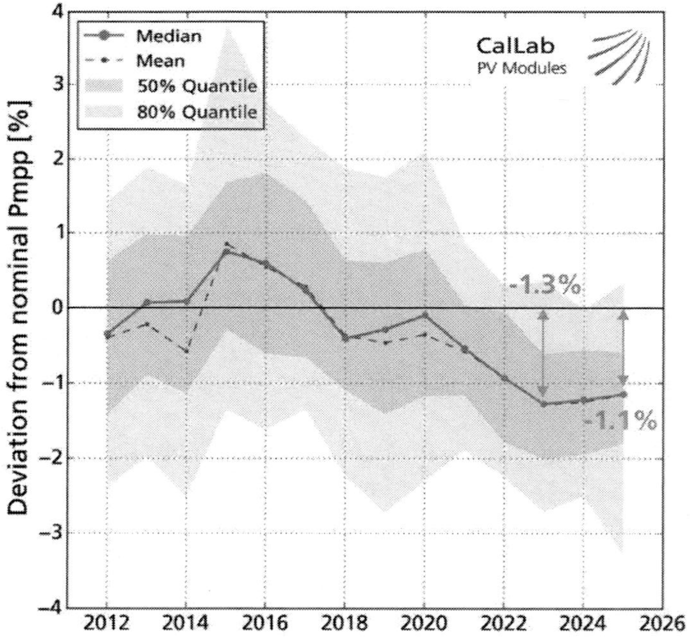

Fraunhofer ISE

Light-Induced Degradation (LID)

Test Sequence

Database: new modules, identical test sequence, PERC and TOPCon

Performance test
↓
20 kWh/m² irradiation
Performance test
↓
5 kWh/m² irradiation
Performance test
↓
5 kWh/m² irradiation
Performance test

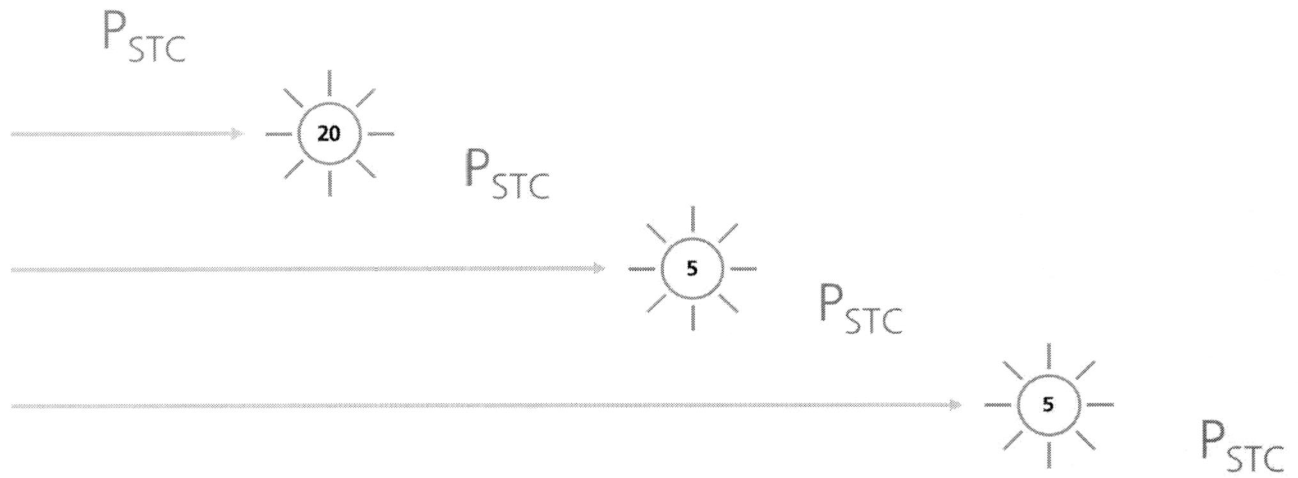

Fraunhofer ISE

Light-Induced Degradation (LID)

Results

Number of modules

- PERC: 71
- TOPCon: 40

„Early"-PERC

- strong LID observed

PERC, TOPCon

- no significant LID
- Partially positive LID

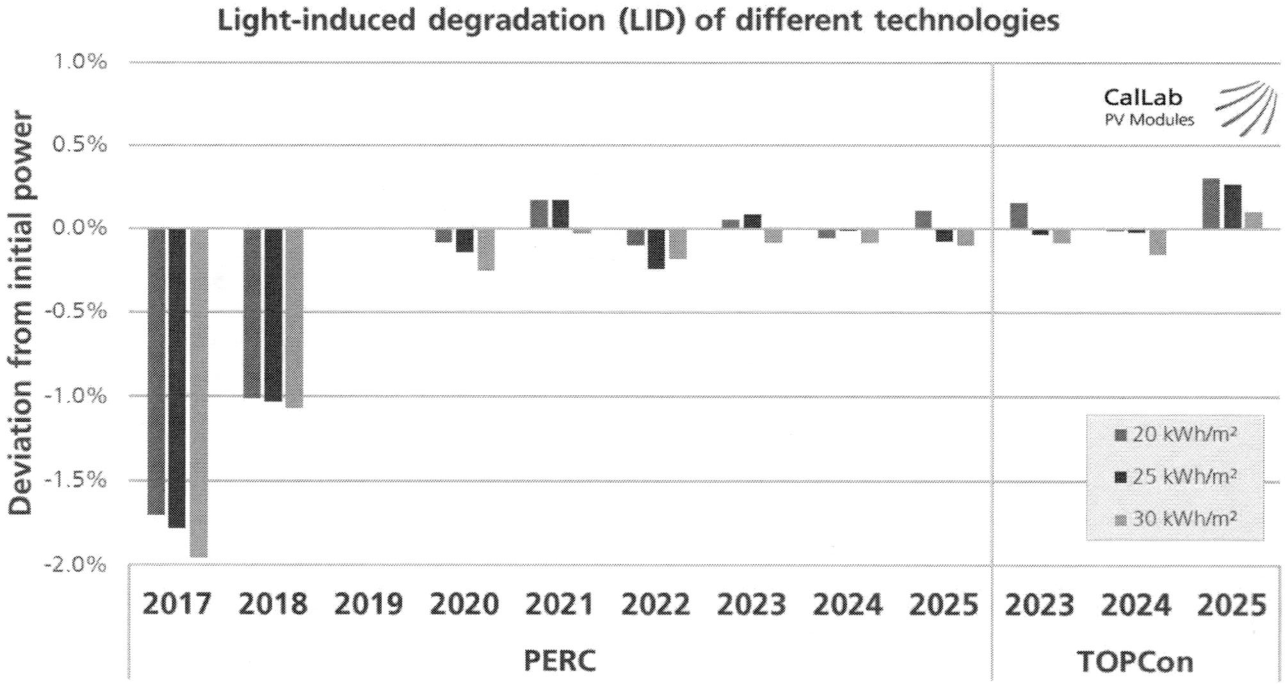

Fraunhofer ISE

TOPCon Metastability

Test Sequence – Storage and Light Soaking

Performance test P_{STC}

Storage

Performance test P_{STC}

2 kWh/m² irradiation (2)
Performance test P_{STC}

1

Storage

Performance test P_{STC}

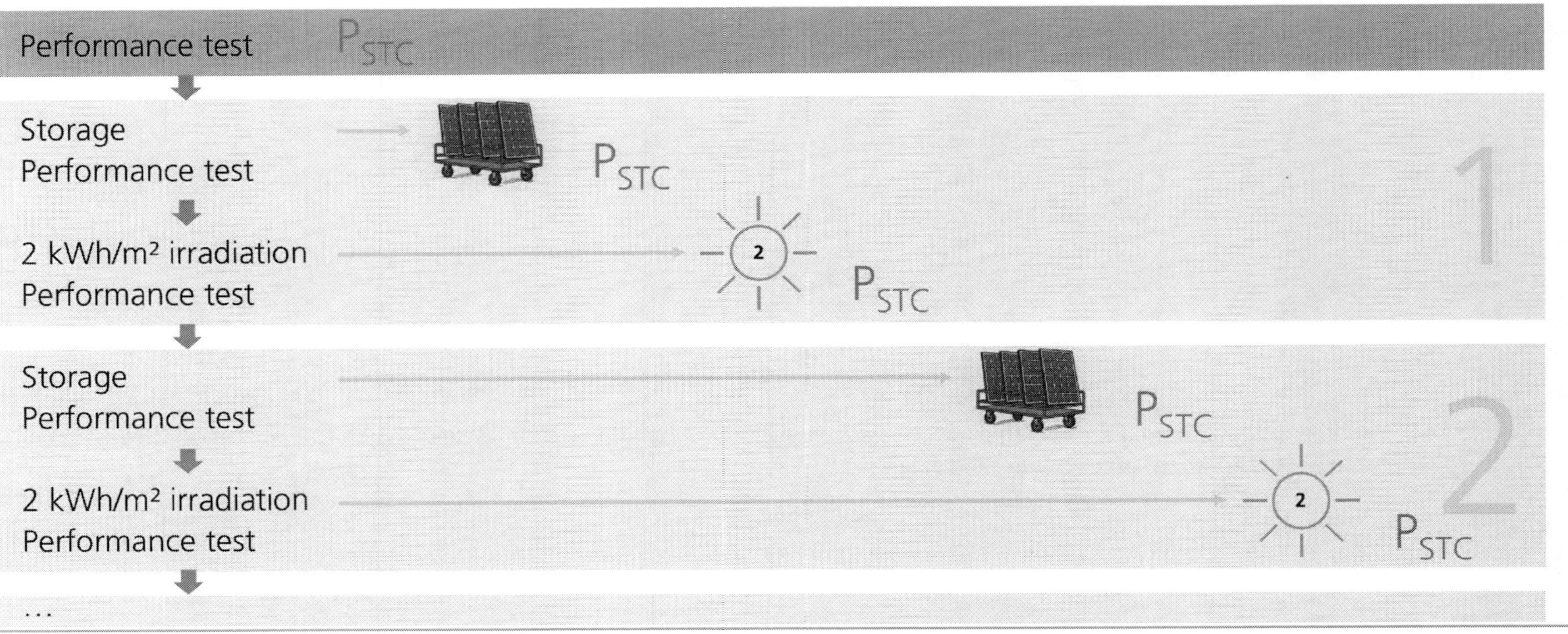

2 kWh/m² irradiation (2)
Performance test P_{STC}

2

. . .

Fraunhofer ISE

TOPCon Metastability – Storage Effects

1 Cycle

4 different module types

- Storage at ordinary lab conditions
- Degradation observed for all types
  - Unstabilized (E1, F1, F2)
  - Stabilized (C, D, E2, F3, F4)

Degradation rate

- -0.1% / month

Recovery

- No general statement
- Range of gains: 0% – 0.4%

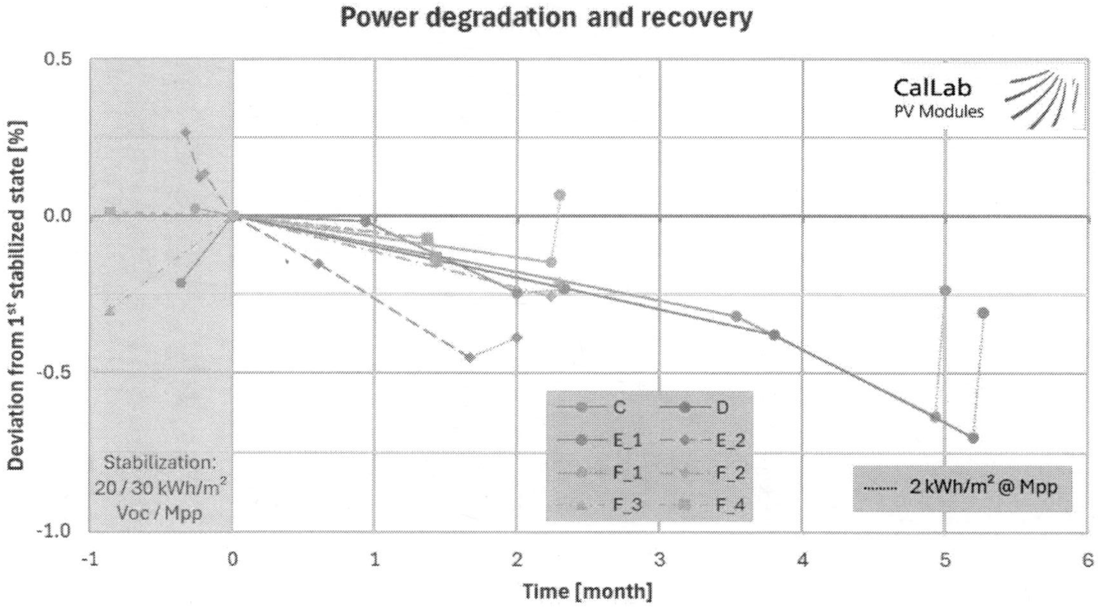

Fraunhofer ISE

TOPCon Metastability – Storage Effects

4 Cycles

2 different module types (stabilized)

- Storage at ordinary lab conditions
- Degradation observed for both types

Degradation rate

- -0.1% / month

Recovery

- No general statement
- Range of gains: 0.2% – 0.6%
- No reproducible result for P_{MPP}

Power degradation and recovery

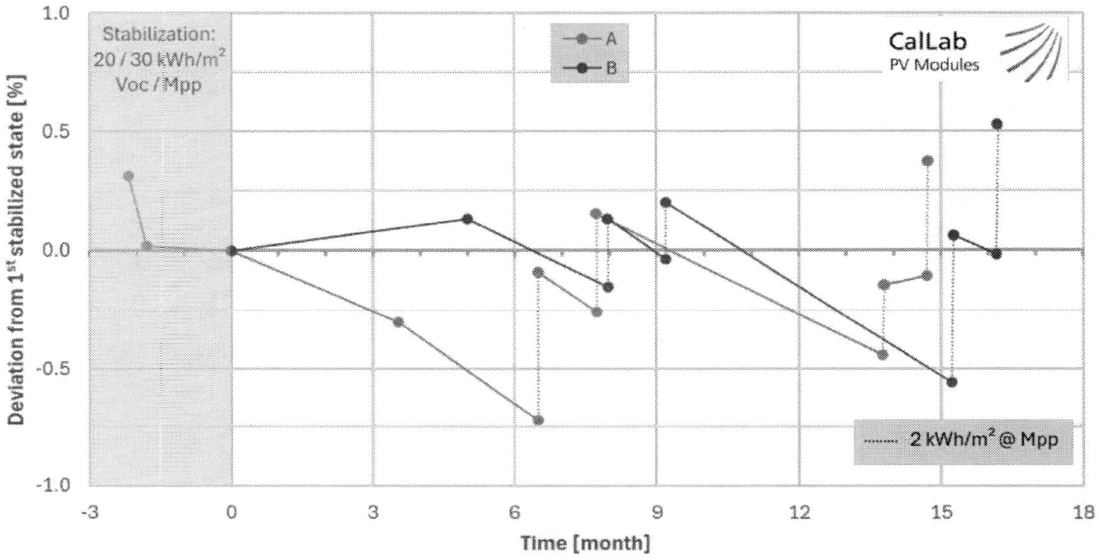

Fraunhofer ISE

Summary and Conclusions

PV module performance in 2025

- Negative deviation stabilized after 2023
- -1.1% P_{MPP} deviation (purchase should be proved independently)
  - ≙ more than a power class (5 W)
  - ≙ ~700 MWp with 64 GWp of new capacity expected for 2025 in Europe [4]

No significant LID for latest PERC / TOPCon

TOPCon storage effects

- Degradation and recovery observed ⟷ stable according to IEC 61215-2 MQT 19.1 (<1%)
- Critical for reference (golden) modules / comparisons

[4] SolarPower Europe (2025): EU Market Outlook for Solar Power. 2025 Mid-Year Analysis. https://www.solarpowereurope.org/insights/outlooks/eu-market-outlook-for-solar-power-2025-mid-year-analysis.

Fraunhofer ISE

Fraunhofer
ISE
Thank you very much
for your attention

Contact

Dipl.-Ing. Ulli Kräling

Manager Test and Calibration Lab
(D-PL-11140-33-00 | D-K-11140-02-00)
Department Module Characterization and Reliability
Phone: +49 761 4588-5761
ulli.kraeling@ise.fraunhofer.de

Fraunhofer ISE
Heidenhofstraße 2
79110 Freiburg
www.ise.fraunhofer.de

42nd European Photovoltaic Solar Energy Conference and Exhibition

This presentation was selected by the Sc. Committee of the EU PVSEC 2025 for submission of a full paper to one of the EU PVSEC's collaborating peer-reviewed journals.

FIFTEEN YEARS UNDER THE SUN: REAL-FIELD DEGRADATION ANALYSIS OF VETERAN PV MODULES

Ioannis (John) A. Tsanakas*, Frédéric Mezzasalma, Maxime Babics, Alexandre Mignonac, Hervé Colin, Romain Couderc, Lionel Sicot, Philippe Marechal, Guillaume Capron, Jérémie Aimé
CEA, Liten, Univ. Grenoble Alpes, Campus INES, 73375 Le Bourget du Lac, France

*corresponding author : ioannis.tsanakas@cea.fr

ABSTRACT: This study presents a 15-year performance analysis of photovoltaic (PV) modules installed at CEA's outdoor test site in Cadarache, southern France. Three PV technologies – polycrystalline silicon (p-Si), amorphous silicon (a-Si), and monocrystalline silicon (m-Si) – have been continuously monitored under real-field conditions to assess their long-term degradation rates and aging mechanisms. The p-Si modules exhibited the highest degradation rate, averaging 2% per year, significantly exceeding the manufacturer's warranty expectations of 0.8% per year. Laboratory flash tests confirmed power losses ranging between -33% and -70% over 15 years. Infrared (IR) imaging identified a single hot spot, but degradation appeared uniformly distributed across all modules. Electroluminescence (EL) analysis revealed extensive microcracks and inactive cell regions, while visual inspections highlighted discoloration, light corrosion, and early signs of delamination. Despite these findings, no critical failures were detected in bypass diodes or electrical connectors. The study underscores the necessity of long-term real-field monitoring to refine predictive models for PV degradation and enhance module durability. Further detailed material analysis is ongoing to confirm intrinsic aging mechanisms and provide deeper insights into PV module reliability over time.

Keywords: *PV systems; PV module; PV degradation; PV module reliability; Fault analysis; IV characterization.*

1 INTRODUCTION: CONTEXT and AIM

Long-term monitoring of photovoltaic (PV) installations provides invaluable insights into real-world performance, degradation rates, and the underlying mechanisms that affect PV module reliability and performance over time. Earlier studies on long-term PV performance analysis in the field, examined the degradation rates of PV modules, revealing variability across different PV technologies and environmental (macro- and micro-climatic) conditions. A comprehensive review by the National Renewable Energy Laboratory (NREL) analyzed various studies and found that crystalline silicon (c-Si) PV modules exhibit degradation rates ranging from 0.4% to 0.5% per year, with system-level degradation rates being higher due to balance-of-system (BOS) components and soiling effects. Similarly, a study focusing on c-Si PV modules in Japan reported degradation rates between 0.01% and 0.47% per year, with an overall annual average of 0.27%. In contrast, other research has identified higher degradation rates under specific conditions. For instance, an analysis of monocrystalline silicon (m-Si) modules, after 20 years of field exposure, indicated a degradation rate of approximately 1.75% per year, much higher than that reported in the aforementioned studies or from that guaranteed from the manufacturers.

These variations underscore the influence of factors such as PV module design, BOM quality, installation practices, and environmental stressors on long-term PV performance. Quantifying and understanding these degradation mechanisms is crucial for improving PV module designs in terms of durability, reliability and weather resilience, as well as for accurately assessing long-term PV energy yields, considering actual PV degradation losses over time. Yet, extended datasets and systematic multiyear PV monitoring studies, particularly for diverse PV technologies and field conditions, remain relatively scarce.

Figure 1: Overview of the studied PV test arrays installed in Cadarache site.

10.4229/EUPVSEC2025/3BO.15.6

Since its launching in early 00's, CEA's outdoor PV test site in Cadarache has been vital resource to our research, for understanding in-field lifelong performance and aging of PV modules. The site is located in southern France, about 30km north-east of Aix-en-Provence, in a region with generally little rainfall ("hot dry-summer" climate, classified as *Csa*, per the Köppen climate classification). This research focuses on three distinct technologies (Fig. 1): polycrystalline silicon (p-Si), amorphous silicon (a-Si), and monocrystalline silicon (m-Si).

Each system, rated at 1 kWp, has been continuously monitored under identical environmental and operational conditions. These systems are paired with SMA SWR1100E inverters and complemented by an array of high-precision environmental sensors to capture irradiance, wind speed, temperature, and other key parameters. The primary objectives of this study are:

1. To quantify long-term performance degradation rates for different PV technologies under real-field conditions, for the case of Cadarache site and climate characteristics.
2. To identify and analyze mechanisms (physico-chemical, electrical, thermal, optical) responsible for module aging.
3. To bridge the gap between field performance data and laboratory findings.

2 METHODOLOGY – APPROACH

The PV systems at Cadarache have been monitored continuously since 2008, providing a wealth of long-term performance data. Electrical parameters such as DC voltage (U_{dc}), DC current (I_{dc}), AC power (P_{ac}), and inverter efficiency (η_i) are logged alongside environmental conditions, enabling a comprehensive assessment of system performance. Monitored environmental parameters include: i) *irradiance* (measured using multiple pyranometers and reference cells installed both in-plane and horizontally; ii) *temperature* (both ambient and at PV module level, using precision sensors); *wind speed* (recorded to assess cooling effects on module temperature and its impact on efficiency). Standardized performance indicators are calculated, including reference yield (Y_r), array yield (Y_a), system losses (L_s), and performance ratio (PR), providing an integrated view of energy production efficiency. To identify thermal anomalies, regular thermal imaging surveys were conducted. These images help detect potential issues such as hot spots, which could be indicative of early-life or mid/end-life faults, such as cell cracks or bypass diode failures.

To complement field measurements, selected modules were dismantled and subjected to indoor (laboratory) characterization at CEA-INES premises, to enable a deeper understanding of material degradation and failure mechanisms. The characterization methods include:

- Flash Tests (IV characterization, under standard test conditions (STC), employing a A+ PASAN solar simulator) to quantify power loss, compare against baseline measurements and identify known IV patterns related to faults (if any);
- Electroluminescence (EL) imaging, to identify potential cracks and their propagation, inactive regions, etc.;
- Visual inspections, to document physical damage such as discoloration, delamination, corrosion;
- Component-level forensics: Ongoing "autopsies" involving microscopic and material analyses of PV components.

The p-Si modules, which exhibited the highest degradation rate, were prioritized for in-depth analysis. Laboratory autopsies focus on uncovering intrinsic and extrinsic factors contributing to performance loss. Results from these analyses are compared with thermal imaging, IV curve measurements, and field data to establish correlations and identify dominant degradation pathways. This holistic methodology ensures a robust understanding of aging mechanisms.

3 RESULTS and DISCUSSION

Overall results (Fig. 2) from field-monitored data indicate significant performance degradation for p-Si modules, with an average annual degradation rate of 2%. This value is considerably higher than the 0.8% annual degradation rate specified by the manufacturer. In contrast, m-Si and a-Si modules showed lower degradation rates, with m-Si modules demonstrating better long-term stability.

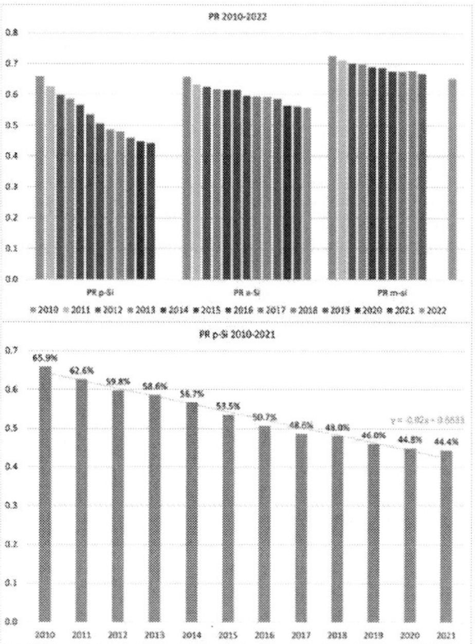

Figure 2: Top: Evolution of PR for the studied modules (2010–2022). Bottom: PR decrease for the p-Si modules for the same period.).

Comparative IV curve measurements taken in 2008 and 2023 revealed substantial reductions in current output for p-Si modules (Fig. 3). Flash tests confirmed power losses ranging between -33% and -70%, suggesting both intrinsic material degradation and external environmental factors as contributors. In quantitative terms, higher losses are derived from significant drop in the P_{mpp}, fill factor (*FF*) and I_{mpp}, corresponding up to -41%, -36% and 27%

10.4229/EUPVSEC2025/3BO.15.6

respectively, in direct correlation with a significant increase of the series resistance (R_s) by up to 2.6× times its initial value, while the shunt resistance (R_{sh}) has been decreased by up to 5.4× times from its initial value.

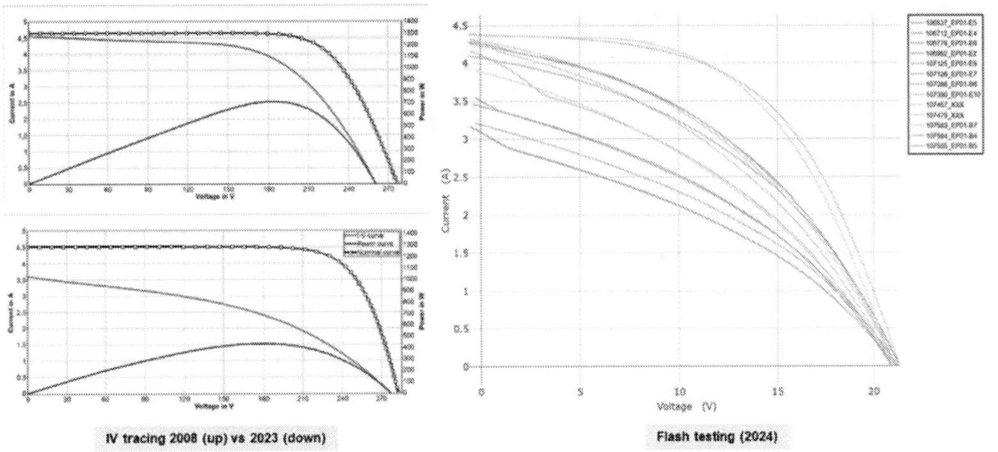

Figure 3: Left: I-V and P-V characteristics comparison (2008 vs. 2023) for the p-Si modules, through in-field IV tracing. Right: Indoor flash tests results for all p-Si modules in 2024, i.e. after 15 years completed with field exposure.

Further field inspections, via IR imaging, identified one module with a hot spot (Fig. 4), but no significant localized failures were observed in other modules. This supports the hypothesis that performance loss is generally uniform across all modules. EL analysis further revealed extensive microcracks and inactive cell regions, correlating with the observed power loss.

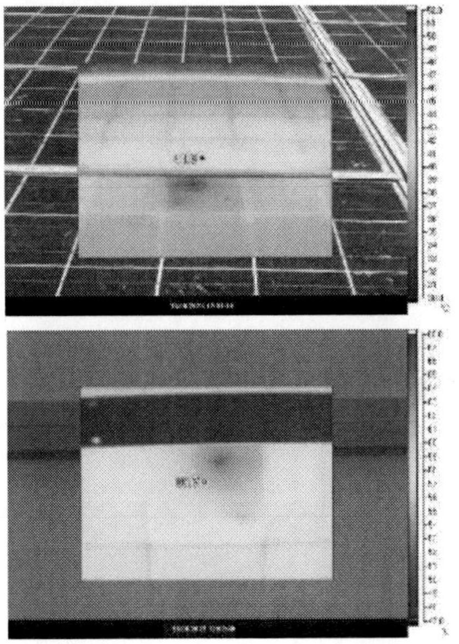

Figure 4: Examples of IR images obtained for one of the studied p-Si modules, suggestive of an occurring hot spot.

Visual inspections (Fig. 5) identified some signs of discoloration and burnt marks from localized overheating (in the case of the aforementioned hot spot) and light corrosion in the junction boxes, as well as some suspected – yet not confirmed, starting delamination. On the other hand, bypass diodes and electrical connectors were found to be in good condition, ruling out major failures in these components. None of the (suspected) cell cracks was visible by naked eye.

A detailed material analysis of the p-Si modules is underway to investigate intrinsic aging mechanisms and confirm potential faults, suspected through the IR, EL and visual inspections. Early observations suggest that the degradation is not confined to specific cells but is distributed, rather uniformly, across all modules in the array.

On the basis of these results and discussion, key takeaways (so far) can be summarized in the following:

1. **Degradation Rates**: The p-Si modules exhibited a degradation rate of 2% per year, significantly higher than warranty expectations. In contrast, m-Si and a-Si modules showed better durability under the same environmental conditions.
2. **Mechanisms of Degradation**: Laboratory analyses confirmed that power losses in p-Si modules are primarily due to uniform cell degradation, as evidenced by EL imaging and IV curve measurements. External factors such as thermal cycling, UV exposure, and material aging likely contributed to the observed trends.
3. **Thermal and Visual Observations**: Despite some visible damage (discoloration and delamination), no critical failures were found in bypass diodes or junction boxes. The uniformity of degradation suggests systemic aging mechanisms rather than isolated defects.
4. **Relevance for Industry**: The findings underscore the importance of real-world, long-term monitoring for validating manufacturer warranties and improving predictive models for PV performance.

The study, so far, sets the stage for a deeper exploration and understanding of the degradation mechanisms occurring in the studied PV modules, as they approach the end of their service life. More detailed and comparative results, including further characterization techniques, comprehensive discussion and sensitivity analysis, are ongoing and will be included in a future work.

Figure 5: Examples of degradation and faults identified or suspected during visual inspection, for the case of p-Si modules.

4 CONCLUSIONS - OUTLOOK

This study provides a comprehensive 15-year performance evaluation of polycrystalline, monocrystalline, and amorphous silicon PV modules exposed to real-field conditions at CEA's Cadarache test site. Results reveal a markedly higher degradation rate for polycrystalline silicon modules (≈2%/year) compared to manufacturer warranty expectations, with cumulative power losses between -33% and -70%. Infrared and electroluminescence analyses confirmed that degradation is largely uniform across modules, dominated by microcracks, inactive cell regions, and increased resistive losses, while bypass diodes and connectors remained intact. In contrast, monocrystalline and amorphous silicon modules exhibited lower degradation rates, underlining the importance of both technology choice and bill of materials quality for long-term PV durability.

The findings demonstrate the critical value of long-term field monitoring in complementing laboratory tests and refining predictive models for PV reliability. By correlating outdoor performance data with laboratory diagnostics, this study highlights systemic degradation pathways that cannot be captured by short-term testing alone. Future work will expand on the ongoing material-level analyses to pinpoint intrinsic aging mechanisms and validate failure hypotheses.

Looking ahead, these insights can support:

- improved module design and material selection to enhance resilience against thermal cycling, UV exposure, and environmental stressors,
- more accurate degradation models for lifetime energy yield predictions, and
- updated warranty and reliability frameworks aligned with field-verified performance.

Ultimately, the results contribute to a more robust understanding of PV module lifetimes in real-world conditions, helping bridge the gap between manufacturer guarantees and field realities, and reinforcing the importance of continuous, multi-year monitoring for the sustainable deployment of PV technologies.

ACKNOWLEDGEMENTS

Part of this work has been carried out in the framework of the Horizon Europe CACTUS project. CACTUS project has received funding from the European Union's Horizon Europe research and innovation programme under grant agreement No. 101132182. Part of this work was also supported by the French National Program "Programme d'Investissements d'Avenir - INES.2S" under Grant Agreement ANR ANR-10-IEED-0014 0014-01.

TOWARDS ENHANCED RELIABILITY OF BUSBAR-FREE IBC SOLAR CELL INTERCONNECTIONS BY NON-CONDUCTIVE ADHESIVE REINFORCEMENT

Tudor Timofte[1], Tobias Messmer[1], Karl Wienands[1], Joris Libal[1], Stephan Großer[2], Matthias Pander[2], Giuseppe Galbiati[3], Tobias Nitsche[3], Daniel Buckland[3], Andreas Halm[1]
[1] ISC Konstanz, Rudolf-Diesel-Straße 15, 78467 Konstanz, Germany
[2] Fraunhofer-Center für Silizium-Photovoltaik CSP, Otto-Eißfeldt-Str. 12, 06120 Halle (Saale), Germany
[3] Henkel AG & Co. KGaA, Henkelstraße 67, 40589 Düsseldorf, Germany

ABSTRACT: Current crystalline silicon solar cell metallization layouts feature pad busbars and have (compared to total available interconnection ribbon area) a reduced available surface for soldering or gluing the narrow copper ribbons (rectangular cross section) or wires (round cross section). For further reduction of silver consumption, an emerging trend implies omitting totally the busbars from cell's metallization, which means that (usually silver-plated) interconnection copper tracks are bonded directly to cell's fingers and SixNy coated surface [1]. At interdigitated back contact (IBC) solar cell ZEBRA [2], the thermo-mechanical stress during and after interconnection process is higher than for front-back contacted solar cells [3]. Removing completely the busbars at this cell type would therefore pose exceptional challenges for a robust stable interconnection [4]. One promising approach implies point fixing additionally the connected ribbons to the cell surface by non-conductive adhesive (NCA) pads [5]. In this work, we describe the investigation of ECA formulations as electrical connection, in combination with NCA formulations, which will reinforce mechanically the interconnection. The reliability of interconnection was investigated at mini-module level by temperature-cycling test (TCT). The goal of this experiment is to shape a cell interconnection process and testing sequence, and to identify suitable ECA-NCA formulations for a technical and economical competitive ECA pad –NCA pad connection procedure for busbar-free IBC ZEBRA solar cells. The process addresses also environmental aspects, since the interconnection is lead-free, and add additional options for cell-ribbon separation [6].

Keywords: electrically conductive adhesive, cell interconnection, back contact solar cell, reliability

1 INTRODUCTION

From previous tests, it is known that interconnection of busbar-free IBC ZEBRA cells by silver coated copper ribbons with electrically conductive adhesives (in form of continuous or interrupted line) might cause massive power losses [4], usually related to defects at cell's interconnection, such as adhesive and cohesive breakage. An example of good interconnection (for IBC ZEBRA half cells with busbars) and faulty interconnection (at busbar-free IBC ZEBRA half cells), both prepared with same ECA material, stringing process and continuous ECA line geometry, is presented in form of electroluminescence (EL) imaging at fig.1 below. The affected interconnection patterns are revealed by dark stripes at image B, on the right side, which signalize total or partial decoupled cell areas from the current flow.

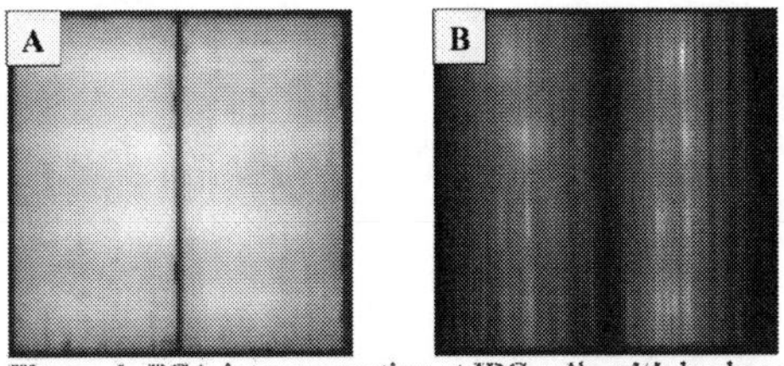

Figure 1. ECA interconnection at IBC cells **with** busbars (image A, left) and faulty ECA interconnection at IBC cells **without** busbars (image B, right)

Since it is clear for tested adhesives that neither ECA lines, nor ECA pads can provide a sufficiently strong interconnection at busbar-free solar cells, which could withstand the (thermo-) mechanical stress occurring during production and operational environment [4], a further reliable mechanical stabilization is necessary. This could be achieved by suitable non-conductive adhesives. Therefore, several ECAs and NCAs were considered for testing the capability of dispensing these in the required size and shape by a micro dispensing unit and for testing the adhesion of ribbons to the busbar-free IBC ZEBRA cell after full curing of the adhesive bonds. At an initial test, ECA and NCA pads were dispensed alternating by a XYZ transport and dispensing system. Following, ribbon attachment and down-holder positioning were accomplished manually or in semi-automatic mode (cut and stretched ribbons were attached by a robot arm to cell with ECA- and NCA-pads), whereas curing took place on a heating plate. The resulted samples were highly impacted by several issues (cracks in the ECA, interconnection offsets, contamination of electrical path by NCA, detachments at the interconnection interfaces, etc.), which translated into a high power loss after production and during ageing tests. The aim of the presented work is to mitigate and avoid such issues, by the following systematic approach:

- ECAs and NCAs were selected by defined Interconnection geometry and process, considering full curing and highest interconnection adhesion force;
- optimization of cell interconnection (stringing) by additional automatized processes, to improve accuracy, process stability and reproducibility of material deposition and interconnection pattern, as well as to avoid contaminations between NCA and ECA.

The characterization and qualification imply a sequence containing the following tests for: ribbon-cell adhesion peel test, cross-linking degree, electro-luminescence, IV flash characterization, accelerated ageing (temperature cycling test) and microstructure analysis, like X-ray imaging [7], scanning electron microscope (SEM) cross sections and optical microscope cross section inspections.

10.4229/EUPVSEC2025/3CO.10.4

2 EXPERIMENTAL SETUP

For the planned experiment, several materials, processes and characterization techniques were used, which will be described below.

2.1 Materials

Halved monocrystalline IBC ZEBRA solar cells produced on M6 wafers (166.0 x 166.0 mm) with busbars (only for soldering reference) and for the rest of testing groups, without busbars (metallization only with contacting fingers at 1.0 mm pitch and specific ZEBRA cell insulation patterns: the light brown pads at fig. 2), however with six interconnection patterns per polarity, were used.

Figure 2. Section of the busbar-free IBC ZEBRA cell, containing two interconnection patterns (light brown pad rows), each belonging to a different polarity

The soldering interconnection was made with 0.40 x 0.20 mm $Sn_{60}Pb_{40}$ coated copper photovoltaic (PV) ribbons (max. thickness of $Sn_{60}Pb_{40}$ coating in range 18.7 – 19.8 µm); whereas for ECA-NCA interconnection 0.50 x 0.24 mm Ag100 coated copper ribbons were used.

For soldering, a rosin-free, low residue industrially available soldering flux (with isopropanol solvent) was used.

Two electrically conductive adhesives (ECA 01 and ECA 02) were introduced in the test plan, both with high content of silver filler particles and both based on acrylic resins, available as a (frozen) mix (viscosity ECA 01: 28400 mPa.s at shear rate 15 s^{-1}, thixotropic index: 2.6 and viscosity ECA 02: 14600 mPa.s at shear rate 15 s^{-1}, thixotropic index: 4.2).

For the mechanical reinforcement of the interconnection three epoxy based non-conductive adhesives were initially tested, whereas from the tested ones, only one (NCA 01) proved to achieve acceptable and stable adhesion to solar cell and ribbon; this glue was considered for further testing (viscosity NCA 01: 4000-7000 mPa.s at shear rate 10 s^{-1}, thixotropic index: 3.5 – 4.5).

For the production of mini-modules toughened solar glass with 250.0 x 250.0 x 3.2 mm size, without anti reflective coating and with a non-geometrically aligned structure pattern, was chosen.

As encapsulation material, a standard PV industrial grade, ethylene vinyl acetate resin (EVA), with low UV cutoff and fast curing properties was used.

For the electric contacts of mini-modules a 5.0 x 0.30 mm copper PV bussing ribbon with $Sn_{60}Pb_{40}$ coating (max. thickness of $Sn_{60}Pb_{40}$ coating: ~15 - 25 µm) was chosen.

At rear side of the mini-module an industrially available, 370 µm transparent PV backsheet with cross-section structure: PET-PET-Primer was added.

2.2 Processes

According to previous experience, a process improvement was considered necessary. The chosen strategy was to implement at most of processing steps automated high precision positioning procedures, in order to improve the accuracy for the ECA and NCA pads location, as well as to ensure a reproducible aspect ratio of the dispensed ECA and NCA pads (round shaped pads).

The dispensing of ECA and NCA was made by a home-made processing robot, fitted with an accurate XYZ axes Linax linear motor system from Jenny Science AG, and with a double micro dispensing unit MDS 1560 (with DST®) from VERMES Microdispensing GmbH, hence enabling sequential dispensing of the two materials. The targeted shape, size and aspect ratio of ECA and NCA pad deposition was obtained and optimized by varying the key process parameters of the device (nozzle size, cartridge and actuator pressure, jetting head temperature, tappet open time, tappet close time, distance to target, speed, etc.).

Two types of dispensing were tested:

- continuous ECA or NCA line for identification of pad geometry (width and height was transferred from line to pad patterns) and adhesion tests at the busbar-free cells;
- ECA pads and NCA pads, dispensed alternating at the interconnection pattern (the target position of ECA pads being concentric to contacting fingers, whereas the NCA pads target position being concentric to insulation pads, to which these were dispensed).

For the qualification of the ECA-NCA interconnection approach, several variation (A, B, C, D) of interconnection type and geometry were designed and tested (fig.3).

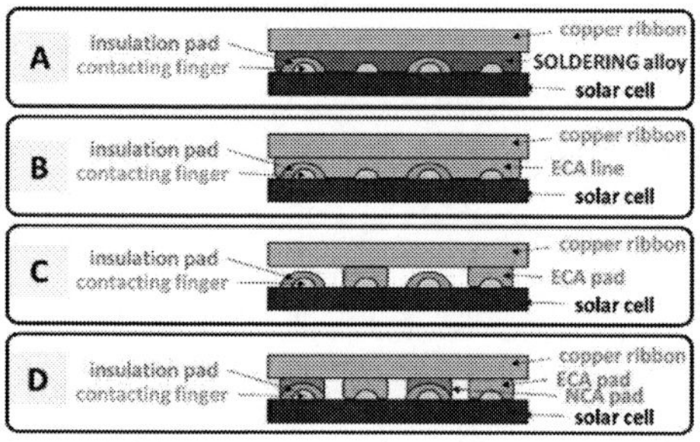

Figure 3. Schematic cross section segment representation of the tested types of interconnections at interdigitated busbar-free back contact ZEBRA solar cell

At Table 1 are presented the main features of the above-mentioned interconnection variations.

Table I: Main designed (target) characteristics of the tested interconnection types

Test group ID	A	B	C	D
Connection type	solder	glue	glue	glue
Connection width (µm)	400	500	500	500
Connection thickness (µm)	20	20	20	20
Ribbon width (µm)	400	500	500	500
Ribbon thickness (µm)	240	200	200	200
Ribbon coating	$Sn_{60}Pb_{40}$	Ag	Ag	Ag
ECA pad location	centered to contacting fingers			
ECA pad diameter (µm)	400	400	400	400
ECA pad height (µm)	50	50	50	50
NCA pad location	centered to insulation pad			
NCA pad diameter (µm)	400	400	400	400
NCA pad height (µm)	50	50	50	50

Indeed, mainly at ECA and NCA pad geometries (diameter, height) considerable, but still acceptable variations from the target value and position offsets were observed; these are caused by an interaction of hardware specific features and material properties (viscosity, surface

tension, etc.).
After printing of ECA and NCA pad patterns on the half busbar-free cells, these were immediately transferred to an industrial TeamTechnik TT2100 stringer with IR soldering (the IR heating was not used for curing of ECA and NCA), which was adapted, as follows:
1. a previously implemented semiautomatic R&D mode was used, which implied positioning the cell manually on conveyor, all other assembly and transport processes being applied automatically;
2. with a dedicated spacer, the half IBC ZEBRA cell with ECA and NCA pads on, was mounted at assigned position, being hold by vacuum at transport belt system;
3. a subsystem then stretched, picked and applied the ribbons over the patterns with ECA and NCA pads, together with the down-holders;
4. the fastest possible cycle time (1.6 s) was set, and the isothermal curing time was achieved by stopping the cell assembly (cell with ECA and NCA having ribbons and down-holders on top) on transport belt at heating zone with highest set temperature and dwell for 300s;
5. for transferring fastest possible the sample assembly to the defined setup temperature for optimal curing (+190°C), the first two heating plates were switch off;
5.1 at fig.4 below is presented the heating plate setup.

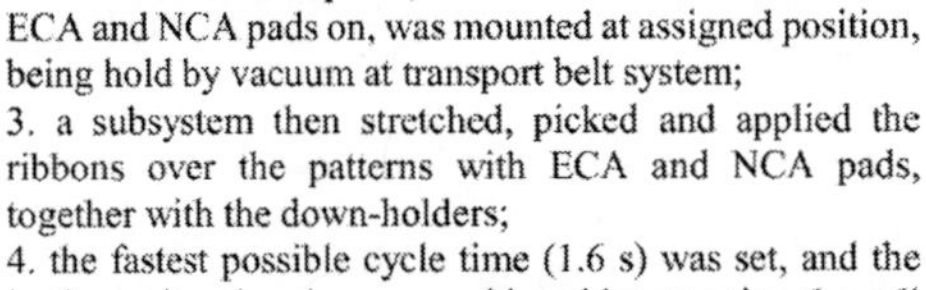

Figure 4. Schematic setup temperature of the curing path

Usually, a considerable offset between the setup temperature and real temperature at sample level occurs. Therefore, to determine the real temperature of the process, a temperature profile was acquired with a DataPaq Q18 data logger and type K thermocouples attached at six positions to the blades of the down-holders. According to the temperature profile measurement, in the quasi-isothermal part of the process, approximately 1 min. after arrival of sensor assembly at curing location, the average temperature of the process was 156.3°C (std.dev. = 16.6°C).
Furthermore, for a better distribution of applied pressure during curing, the process was adapted by adding a stack of three cells under the down-holder, together with a Teflon-coated foil (to avoid accidental gluing of these cells by ECA or NCA from the sample).

Each of the stringed half-cells was laminated at a laboratory membrane laminator into mini-modules of glass-backsheet type, with a single EVA encapsulation film layer on each side of the half-cell (fig. 5).

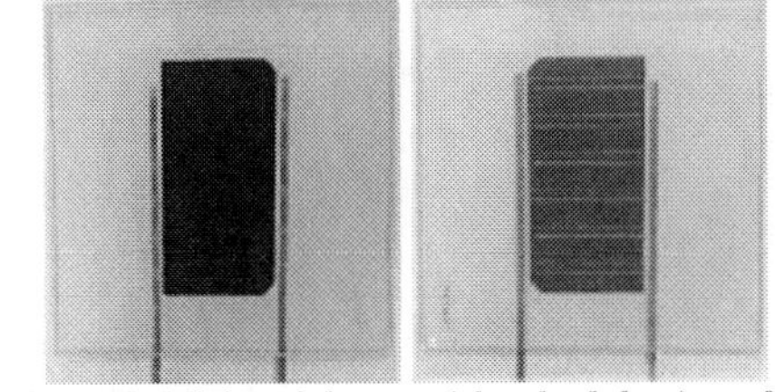

Figure 5. Mini-module type (glass-backsheet) used for testing ECA-NCA strings with IBC ZEBRA half-cells

The lamination recipe was defined to reach a highest possible cross-linking degree for the tested EVA encapsulation material: 145°C temperature setup; 1260 s total lamination time (360s evacuation step and 900s with stepwise-applied pressure of 1000mbar).
The samples (mini-modules) were subjected to accelerated ageing, by applying a temperature cycling test profile, according to IEC 61215 norm, without current injection, in temperature range – 40°C / + 85°C.
3. Characterization techniques
A NETZSCH 214 Polyma DSC device, using Nitrogen as protective and purge gas, was implemented to verify the full cross-linking of ECAs, NCAs and of EVA encapsulation material.
Peel force measurements between ribbon and cell were made at a Zwick Roell BT1-FR0.5TN.D14 digital force testing unit, with special mounting adapter for cells with attached ribbons, at 180° peel angle and 150mm/min peel speed setup.
Electroluminescence was recorded at a homemade EL-PL measurement device.
The mini-modules were measured at an AAA h.a.l.m. GmbH flasher, using 4 point contacting at STC (flasher irradiance 1000 W/m², 25°C ± 2°C).
3D images were obtained by an Olympus LEXT OLS 4000 laser confocal microscope.
For magnetic field imaging (MFI), a homemade system equipped with an MFI-sensor from DENKweit was used.
X-Ray images were acquired with a PHOENIX NANOMEX 180NF X-ray inspection system.
X-Ray and MFI were measured at samples without any accelerated ageing. Cross section analysis was made using contrast mode microscopy (bright field / dark field) at metallographic polished samples.
Scanning electron microscopy has been performed at a HITACHI SU-70 analytical FE-SEM device.

3 RESULTS

For the curing pattern at stringer, DSC measurements (of samples sent through the stringer process) confirmed full curing for ECA01, ECA02 and NCA01 (no residual exothermal cross-linking peak after stringer process) [8]. At fig.6 below is presented the DSC diagram of ECA02, demonstrating full curing (no residual exothermal peak at the blue line). For the ECA01 and NCA01 the same procedure was implemented, with confirmed full curing.

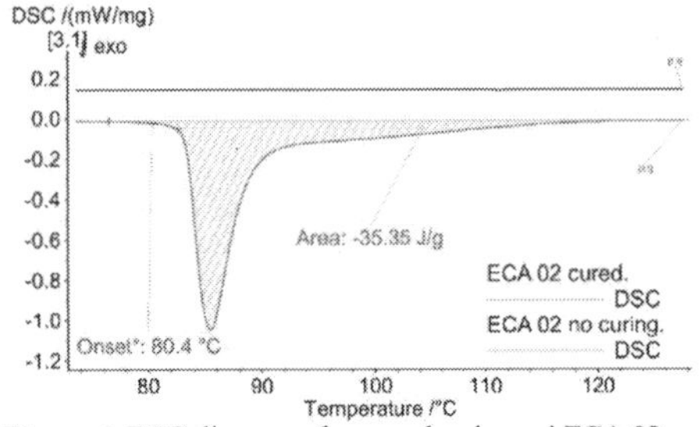

Figure 6. DSC diagram of uncured and cured ECA 02

In addition, DSC measurements were made also for cured encapsulation material (EVA) and no residual cross-linking peak could be detected as well, confirming a high or full cross-linking degree [9].
For the production of strings with different

interconnections pad arrangements, it was necessary to define at first a suitable geometry for the ECA and for the NCA interconnection patterns. This was made by considering two aspects:

- avoiding contamination with ECA and NCA at the components of the stringer, therefore allowing a maximal width of ECA and NCA before curing as wide as the ribbon width;
- achieving best possible adhesion to ribbon and to substrate with a defined curing process, by increasing the width and height of ECA and NCA interconnections.

Following this procedure, the 3D profile of the ECA lines was recorded, to identify the width range and the height range. It was noticed that width of ECA in range 400µm (+/-60µm) is favorable for a good adhesion to ribbon and to busbar-free solar cell at samples with continuous interconnection line (fig.7). The line height associated to this width depends on one side on the properties of the uncured ECA and NCA pastes (like viscosity, thixotropic index, etc.), and also on the dispensing process; at the trials presented in this paper it was in the range 50-80 µm.

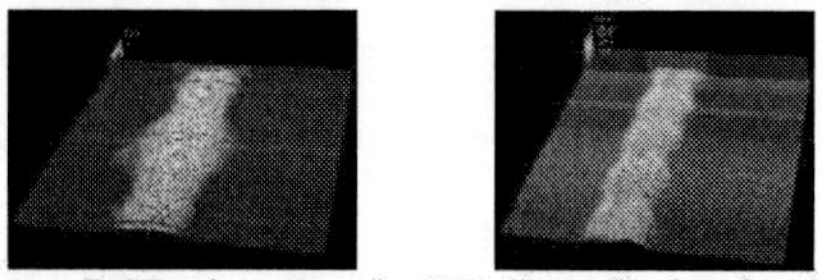

Figure 7. 3D microscopy for ECA line on busbar-free IBC solar cell: ECA 01 (left), ECA 02 (right)

With the identified ECA and NCA width and height, samples with continuous ECA and NCA lines and optimized stringing process were produced with busbar-free ZEBRA cells, to test elaborately the adhesion.

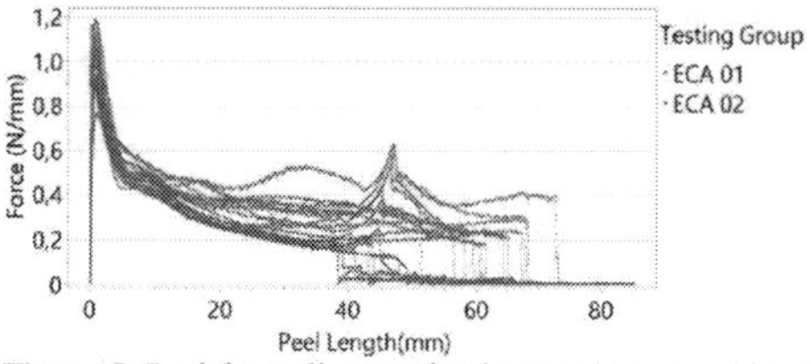

Figure 8. Peel force diagram for the tested ECAs without any data filter

The full peel diagrams from fig.8 required processing, by removing the first and last part of graph, to avoid artefacts. Hence, the data within first 10 and approx. last 40mm was removed. The sorted data below (fig.9) depict the peel force range for the two tested ECAs at busbar-free ZEBRA IBC cells. Despite general low adhesion, the ECA02 was selected for further trials, since the peel force was by approx. 50% higher compared to the peel force at ECA 01 sample during same test.

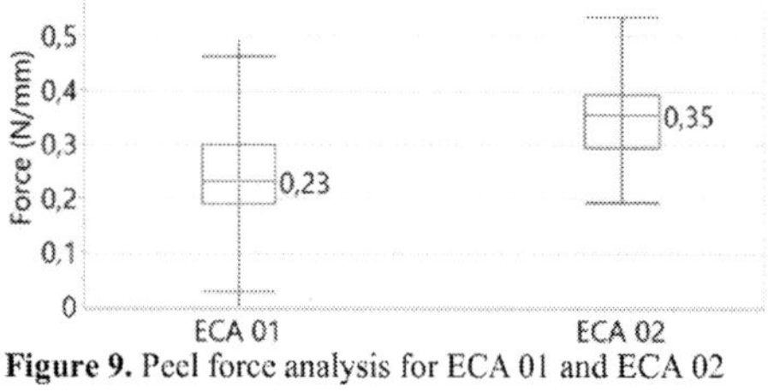

Figure 9. Peel force analysis for ECA 01 and ECA 02

At NCA testing, only one candidate proved suitable for further testing (NCA 01), the others being disqualified due to low viscosity, or due to extremely low peel forces to substrate. A short optimization trial for NCA curing process provided best results of adhesion at a setup temperature of 190°C and 300s dwell time, translated into 0.63 N/mm median value peel force between ribbon and busbar-free solar cell.

After these test results, only ECA 02 and NCA 01 were considered for the ECA-NCA process testing, which means: alternating ECA round pads with NCA round pads at interconnection. The geometry of both pad types (ECA, NCA) was defined same, with a target diameter width at 400 µm and with a target height in range 40-60 µm. The process at dispensing robot was adjusted to create reproducible alternating ECA and NCA pads, without contamination. The schematic plan of the ECA-NCA alternating interconnection is shown at fig.10.

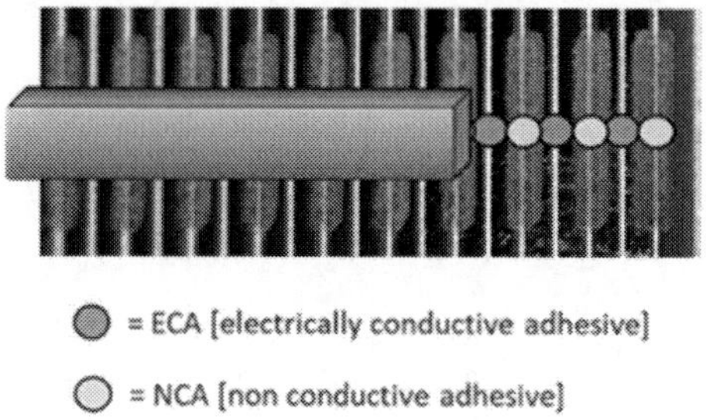

Figure 10. Representation of the ECA pad – NCA pad interconnection at busbar-free ZEBRA cell (top view)

At the optimized setup for ECA pad trails could be determined by 3D confocal laser microscopy that the diameter of pads is in range 298 µm/ ± 39 µm, to which corresponds a pad height of approx. 130 µm/ ± 5 µm. For NCA, the height of the pads could not be determined with the same method, due to strong light reflection, curved NCA surface and material transparency. In contrast, the width of NCA pads could be determined by this measurement method, since this feature addresses the 2D image. The measured width for NCA in the presented NCA-ECA process is in range 487 µm/ ± 7 µm. At the fig.11, a magnified cell segment with alternating ECA and NCA pads is presented.

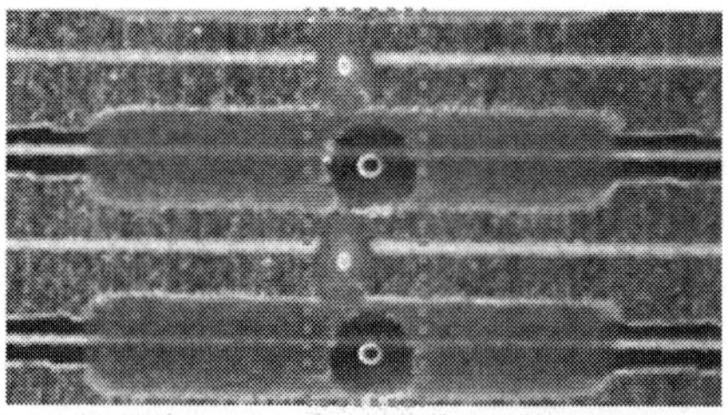

Figure 11. Microscope image of a cell segment with alternating NCA and ECA pads at the positive polarity interconnection pattern (the orange interrupted line marks the location of the ribbon, which will be added)

After lamination of the strings (at least three minimodules considered at each group), these were characterized by EL and by IV before and after accelerated ageing (TCT). Due to poor performance (multiple electrical interruptions at stringed samples detected by EL), ECA 01 was excluded from further testing. Differences at the robustness of cell interconnections can be observed at the EL images at fig.12, in initial state, as well as during ageing. Soldering interconnection (A), as well as continuous ECA line (B) behave stable up to 100 TCT (no change at EL image, no dark sectors). However, at test group with ECA pads (C) and group with ECA and NCA pads (D), affected interconnection regions (dark zones) can be observed, mentioning that NCA mechanical stabilization lead to a clear improvement (EL image similar to ECA line or soldered test groups).

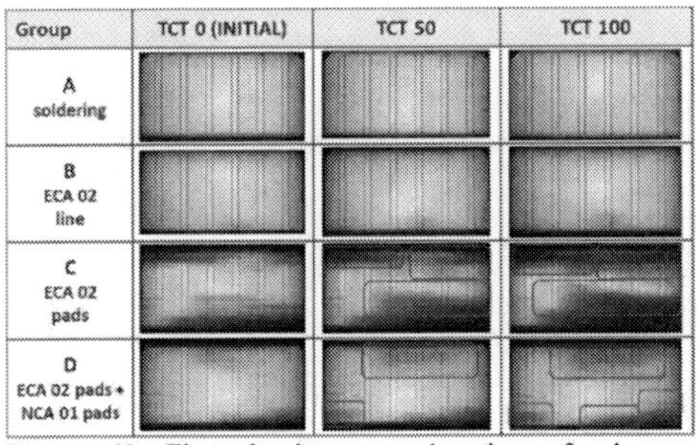

Figure 12. Electroluminescence imaging of relevant samples from each group at initial state, after 50, and after 100 cycles TCT ageing.

After EL characterization the mini-modules were characterized by IV measurements (at STC conditions), before and after temperature cycling test. The relative changes to initial state (in percentage) of main electrical parameters at IV measurement: short circuit current (Isc), open circuit voltage (Voc), fill factor (FF) and power at maximum power point (Pmpp), are presented at fig.13. An ageing level of 100 cycles TCT is not sufficient to make predictions or statements for the long-term stability. Nevertheless, several observations can be made after 100 cycles TCT regarding the susceptibility of interconnection to thermomechanical stress: the soldered interconnection at cells with busbars provide a stable behavior with a small change at the IV parameters (0.6% Pmpp loss). In addition, the testing group with continuous ECA02 line provides as well a stable behavior, with 0.5% Pmpp loss to initial. On the other hand, the samples with ECA02 pads interconnection had 12.0% Pmpp loss to initial, therefore disqualified, since it exceeded the allowed maximal power loss of 5% (according to IEC 61215 norm [10]). The clear confirmation of functionality for this proof of concept, regarding the reinforcement of interconnection by NCA is delivered by the testing group with alternating ECA-NCA pads, which has a Pmpp loss of 4.2% after 100 cycles TCT.

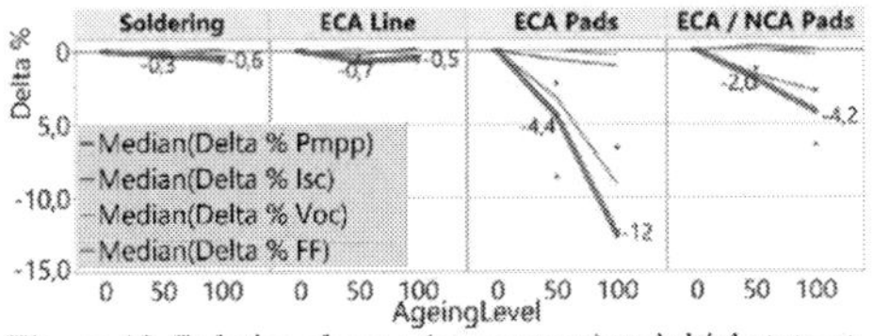

Figure 13. Relative change (percentage) to initial state at main IV parameters of tested interconnection variations during temperature cycling test (TCT)

An analysis of the electrical parameters indicate that current (Isc) and voltage (Voc) do not change considerably during the applied accelerated ageing. The fill factor, FF, (red line at fig.13) is the parameter, which affects at most the low and high changes of Pmpp parameter (blue line at fig.13). The fill factor decreases when series resistance and, or shunt resistance of the solar cells increase; furthermore, for a solar module, the fill factor will include also the effects of electrical resistances (usually series resistances) caused by cell interconnections. Since degradations of cell metallization or at cell interconnection usually lead to an increase of series resistance, and since electroluminescence and microscopy confirm degradations at cell interconnection as well, it is demonstrated together with the IV measurement data, that the reduction of power parameter Pmpp is caused by an increase of series resistance, due to damage at cell interconnection.

The good and faulty interconnection regions were identified at provided samples by MFI [11] [12] and X-ray imaging. These methods correlated provide a more sensitive and specific approach for identification of faulty interconnections compared to EL imaging. Regions of interest (for cross sectioning) were extracted on localized positions and prepared for optical and for scanning electron microscopy. By the analysis was observed that an offset of ribbons to the ECA-NCA pads occurred at certain samples (fig.14). The cause for this misalignment is the manual positioning of cell on stringer's conveyor. Such offsets are responsible for weaker adhesion, since less surface is available for the connection between components.

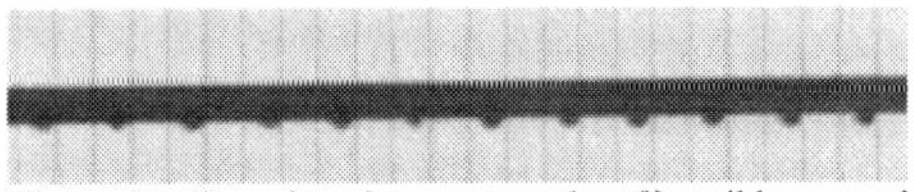

Figure 14. X-ray imaging exposes the offset ribbon – pad pattern of a sample region with ECA pad interconnection

The process was improved considerably, providing acceptably homogeneous thickness at interconnection and the previously observed ECA-NCA contamination issue could not be detected at this trial.

However, the main issue detected at the produced samples was a certain considerable offset of ECA pads to the position for contacting the fingers (fig.15). This is considered as one of main causes for the relatively high power drop during the TCT tests, since at certain contacting positions either the ECA pads barely contact with their edges the fingers, or fail to contact the finger.

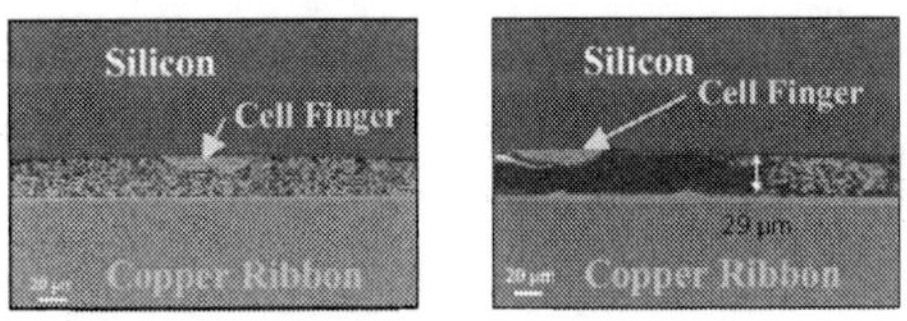

Figure 15. Cross-section of localized good (left) and faulty (right) interconnection (SEM image)

Given the good results from these trials, implementation at the industrial level could be expected in the short- or mid-term. The next step involves testing in a fully automated industrial environment, for which an estimated Cost of Ownership (CoO) calculation has been performed. For this CoO calculation, a scenario based on an ECA with low silver filler content and a price of pure silver of 1300 € /kg was considered. Based on our experimental results, the CoO calculations have been performed for two different amounts of ECA per cell: 40mg and 113mg (for M10 full cell size with 10 busbars per polarity). This considerable ECA weight difference at samples with same or similar ECA dispensing pattern and geometry can be explained by high differences of the density of the tested ECAs.

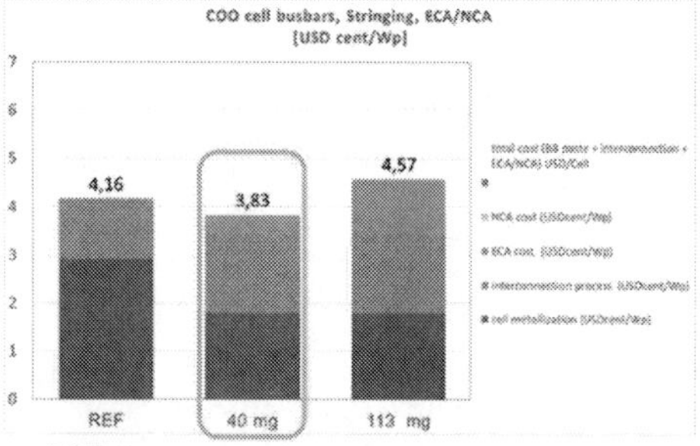

Figure 16. CoO ECA-NCA cell interconnection process calculations, in comparison with soldering process (left)

The CoO results shown in fig.16 include the following cost items: paste for busbars ("cell metallization"), total cost of tabbing-stringing process, excluding cost of the ribbons ("interconnection process"), cost of ECA and NCA respectively, whereas the NCA cost is negligible.

Further tests must explore the further reduction of printed ECA quantity at this interconnection type.

Dedicated FEM simulations revealed that highest shear forces within interconnection layers are distributed over a length of approx. 20mm from each edge (perpendicular to interconnection ribbons) of cell towards inner part of the cell. These mechanical tensions are introduced by the thermomechanical stress, which occurs during or after interconnection process, due to different coefficients of thermal expansion, mainly between copper from interconnection ribbons and bulk silicon of solar cell.

4 SUMMARY

The tested continuous interconnection ECA line (with ECA02 material) proved stable up to 100 cycles TCT, which emphasizes the importance of the material choice at this process (since previous tests [4] failed). However, a continuous ECA line would imply a high silver consumption, which would not be practicable at industrial scale. Therefore, it was proven during this experiment that a NCA reinforcement can be used and this allow the ECA-NCA interconnection with tested materials and process to withstand 100 cycles TCT accelerated ageing (power loss at 4.2%, still below 5% to initial). The high power loss is assigned mainly to observed ECA-NCA-cell-ribbon offsets (this create sensitive low contact surface interconnection, which fail during TCT test/ confirmed by EL imaging): light spread of dark regions in the EL images), which will be addressed at future process optimizations. The takeaway message is that the reported ECA-NCA interconnection process has high chances to pass at least 1x IEC norm requirements at accelerated ageing level, if the process will be optimized (mostly regarding positioning precision and reproducibility for ECA and NCA pads). In the same time is also economically attractive, offering the potential to reduce cell interconnection process and material costs by at least 7.9% (compared to standard soldering process at cells with busbars).

5 ACKNOWLEDGEMENT

The authors express their gratitude to German Federal Ministry for Economic Affairs and Energy in the frame of Indifiduell Project (contract no.: 03EE1185) for funding, and thank to Henkel AG & Co. KGaA, Fraunhofer-Center für Silizium-Photovoltaik CSP, and all partners and colleagues, which contributed, for very good collaboration.

6 REFERENCES

[1] G. Beaucarne, et al. – doi: 10.1016/j.egypro.2015.03.302

[2] A. Halm, et al. – doi: 10.4229/27thEUPVSEC2012-2AO.2.1

[3] A. Halm, et al. doi: 10.4229/EUPVSEC20172017-2CV.2.91

[4] T. Timofte, et al. – doi: 10.4229/WCPEC-82022-3CO.4.5

[5] G. Beaucarne, et al. – doi: 10.1016/j.egypro.2016.10.087

[6] A. Hartwig, et al. – doi: 10.1142/S0960313193000188

[7] R. Hanke et al. – doi: 10.1016/j.nima.2008.03.016

[8] T.Geipel et al. – doi: 10.1016/j.egypro.2013.07.287

[9] Ch. Hirschl et al. – doi: https://doi.org/10.1016/j.solmat.2013.04.022

[10] IEC norms 61215-1/-2:2021 and IEC 61730-2:2016

[11] S. Großer et al. - doi: 10.1051/epjpv/2023029

[12] S. Großer et al. - doi: 10.4229/WCPEC-82022-3DV.3.17

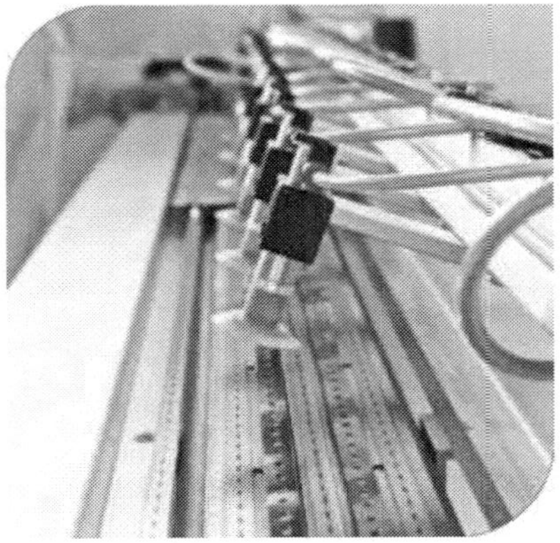

Towards enhanced reliability of busbar-free IBC solar cell interconnections by non-conductive adhesive reinforcement

ISC research for a sunny future

Tudor Timofte[1], Tobias Messmer[1], Raphael Shanmugam[1], Karl Wienands[1], Joris Libal[1], Stephan Großer[2], Matthias Pander[2], Giuseppe Galbiati[3], Tobias Nitsche[3], Daniel Buckland[3], Andreas Halm[1]
[1] ISC Konstanz, Rudolf-Diesel-Straße 15, 78467 Konstanz, Germany
[2] Fraunhofer-Center für Silizium-Photovoltaik CSP, Otto-Eißfeldt-Str. 12, 06120 Halle (Saale), Germany
[3] Henkel AG & Co. KGaA, Henkelstraße 67, 40589 Düsseldorf, Germany

Content

- Motivation
- BB vs BB-less Metallization Layout
- Challenge
- Proposed approach
- Tested laboratory process
- Design of Experiment
- Results
- Cost Calculations
- Conclusions

Motivation: Why no busbars (BB)? Why use ECA & NCA ?

ECA = Electrically Conductive Adhesive
NCA = Non Conductive Adhesive

- Module **price** trend[1]

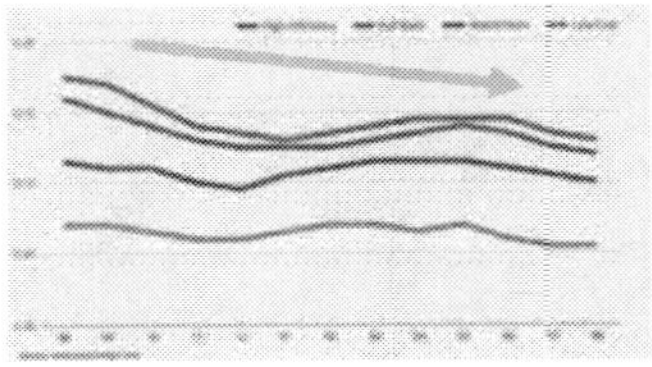

- Towards **Pb-free** interconnection[2]

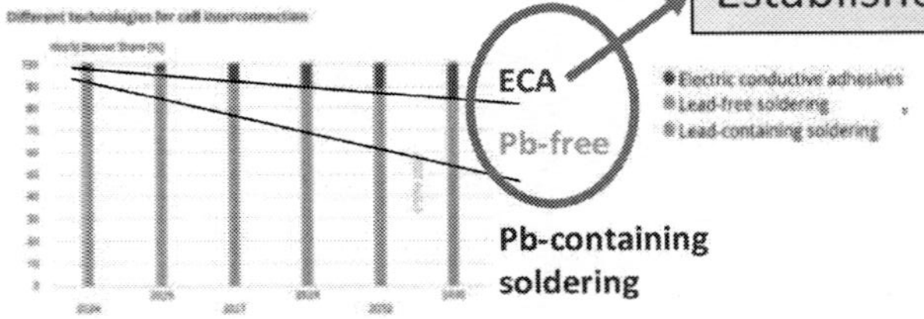

- Demand for **low temperature interconnections**
  - for ex. Tandem-Perovskite solar cells demand processing temperatures < 150°C [3]
- **Environmental aspects & Recyclability**
  - interconnection which can be coupled to recycling processes (for ex. solvent separation, thermal decomposition, etc.)

[1] *Source: www.pvexchange.com (price trend 08.2024 – 08.2025)*
[2] *Source: www.vdma.eu / ITRPV 2025*
[3] *A. De Rose et al., DOI: 10.1016/j.solmat.2023.112515*

Busbar (BB) vs. Busbar (BB)-less Cell Metallization Layout

- **@ Cell Level (trend to reduce further considerably silver consumption)**
  - From BB Pads to BB-less (soldering or ECA will take over the role of BB as well)

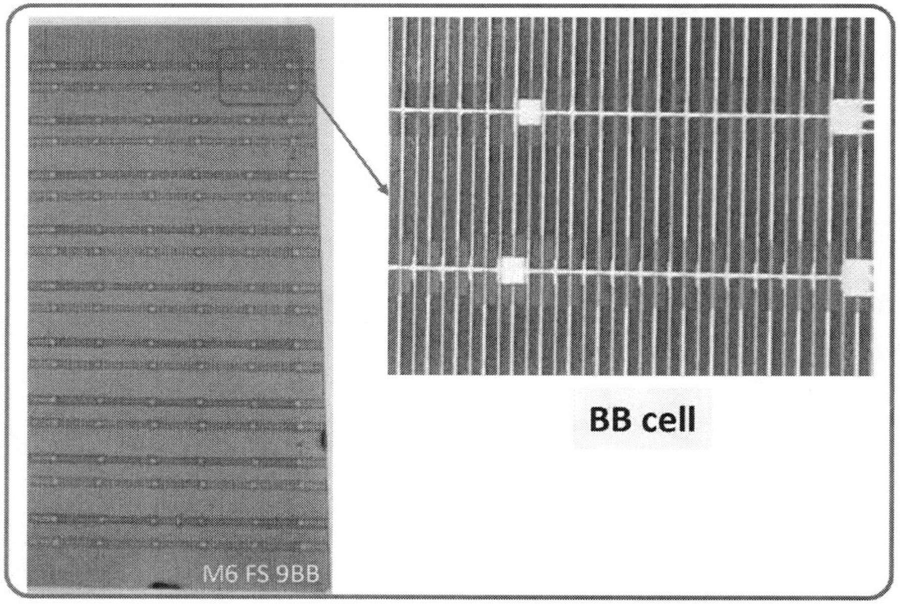

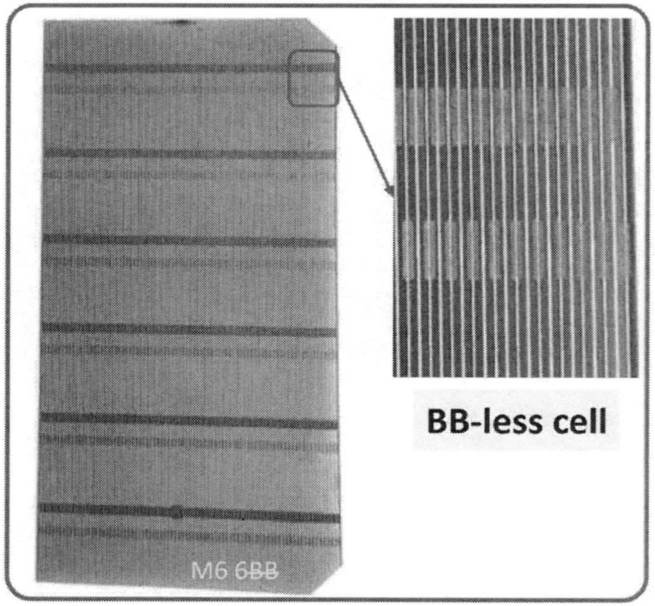

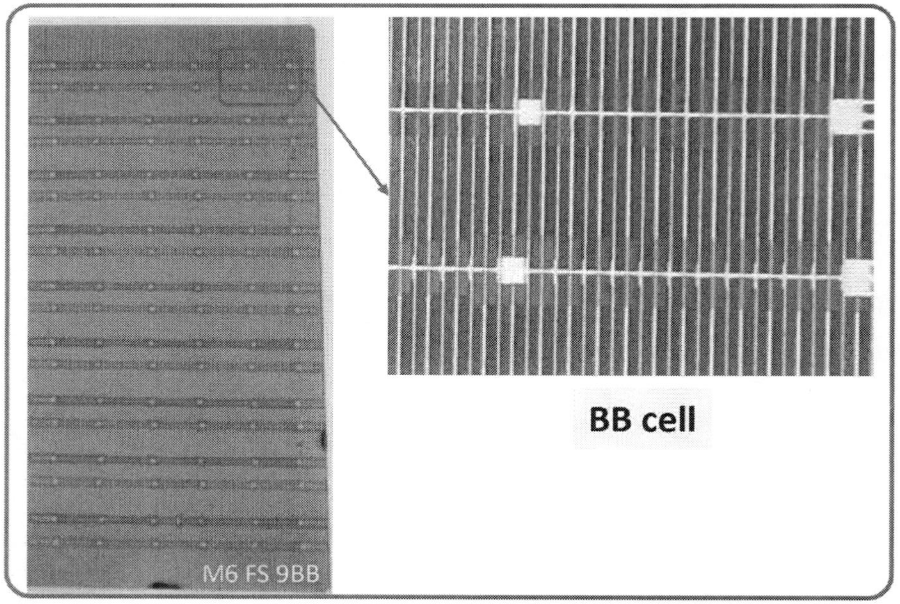

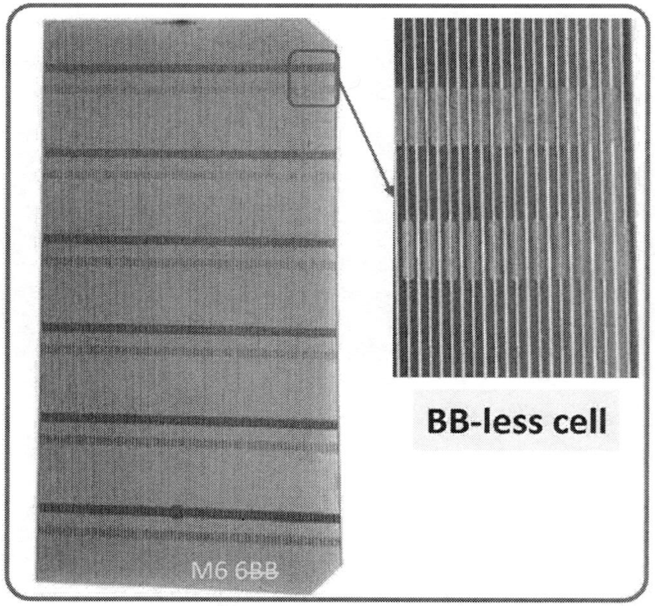

Challenge at BB-less Cell Interconnection

- **PV specific ECA is a market proven solution for connection of solar cells <u>with busbars</u>**
- **Interconnection of busbar-less cell with ECA (or solder paste) pose new challenges:**
  - <u>no standard soldering</u> with solder alloy coated ribbons possible for BB-less cells
  - <u>different contacting interface</u> (textured surface with SixNy coating and cell fingers instead of busbars)
  - <u>additional freedom for deformations</u> due to thermo-mechanical stress

half cells (G1 wafer size) **with busbars***
Epoxy ECA line interconnection (~ 0.42mg/cm)
ECA Dispensing, Assembly and Curing at industrial stringer
(setup: 180°C / T ramp to target temp. = 15s/ dwell at target temp. = 35s)

EL

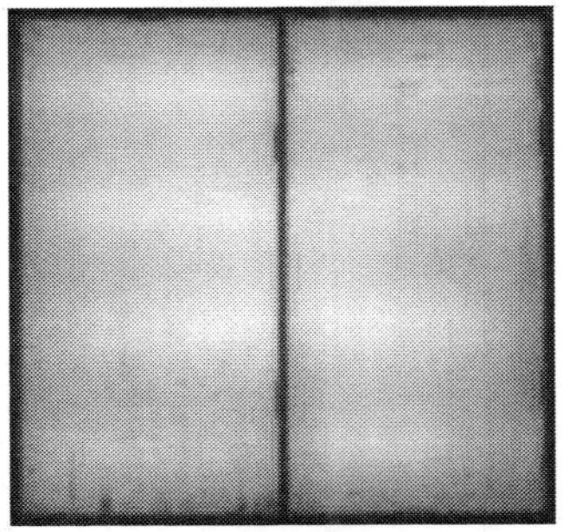

half cells (G1 wafer size) **without** busbars (**busbar-less***)
Epoxy ECA line interconnection (~ 0.42mg/cm)
ECA Dispensing, Assembly and Curing at industrial stringer
(setup: 180°C / T ramp to target temp. = 15s/ dwell at target temp. = 35s)

EL

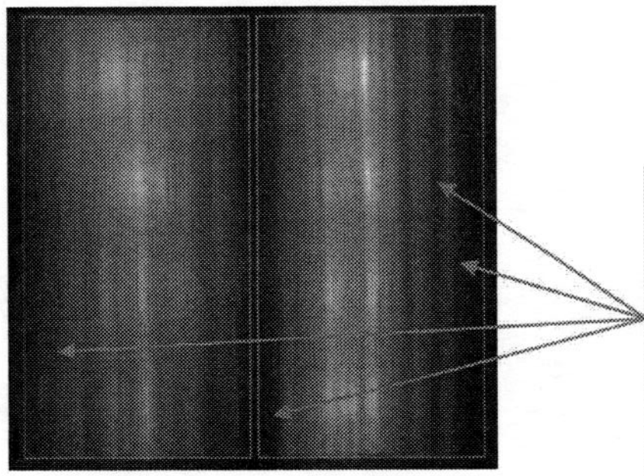

Dark areas and stripes indicate multiple electric interruptions at cell interconnection and cell metallization

**Previous tests made in the frame of Zquadrat Project*

Proposed approach (schematic cross section of an IBC ZEBRA solar cell with interconnection)

Classic interconnection

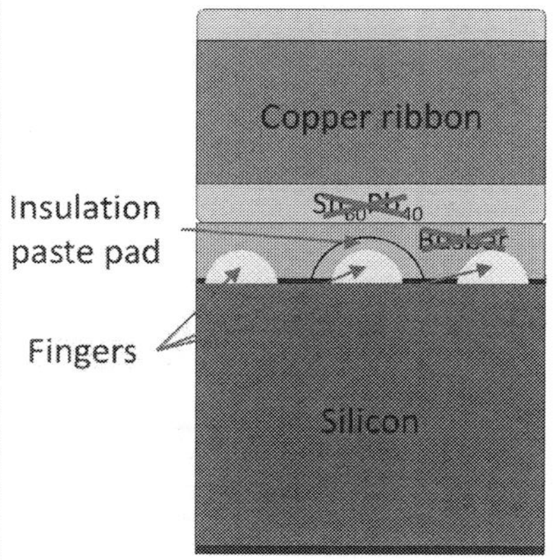

ECA interconnection

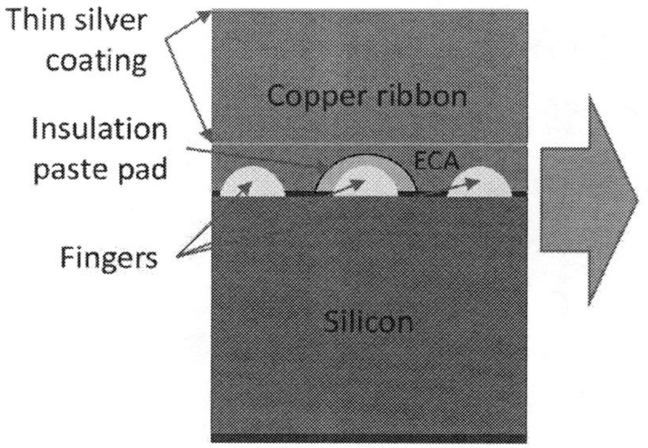

ECA-NCA interconnection

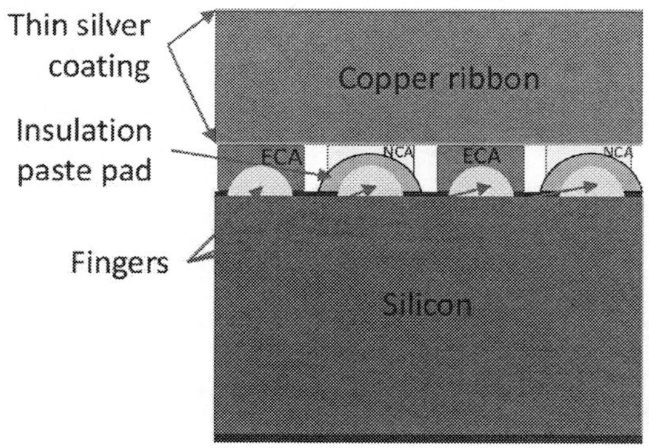

Proposed approach (schematic cross section of an IBC ZEBRA solar cell with interconnection)

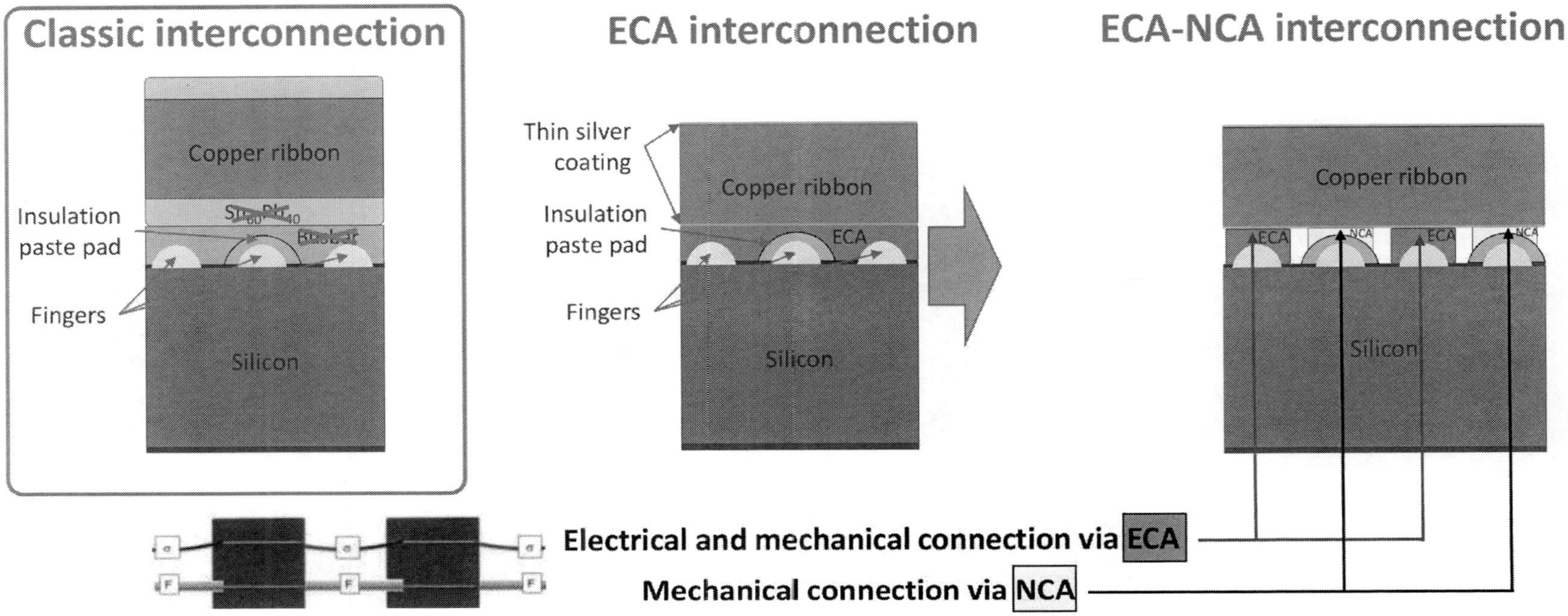

Proposed and tested approach

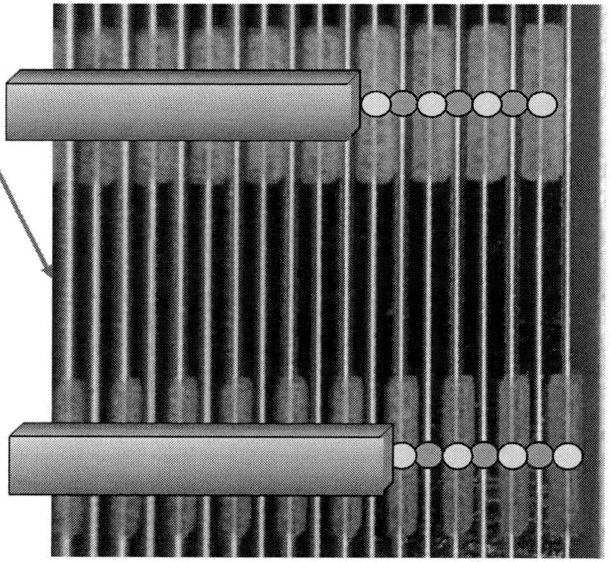

= ECA [electrically conductive adhesive]

= NCA [non conductive adhesive]

Systematic approach:

1. **Test of an ECA sampling contingent** (acryl based) at BB-less ZEBRA cells:
    - Develop process for ECA dispensing, assembly cell-ECA-ribbon fixation and curing schedule
    - Test adhesion, ECA cross linking and compatibility
2. **Test of an NCA sampling contingent** (epoxy based) at BB-less ZEBRA cells:
    - Develop process for ECA dispensing, assembly cell-ECA-ribbon fixation and curing schedule
    - Test adhesion, NCA cross linking and compatibility
3. **Test of an ECA and NCA** (epoxy and acryl based) at BB-less ZEBRA cells:
    - Develop process for ECA dispensing, assembly cell-ECA-ribbon fixation and curing schedule
    - Test adhesion, ECA cross linking and compatibility

Issues noticed at ECA-NCA interconnection trials

- **Test Setup:**
  - ECA pads + NCA pads
  - Micro dispensing at robot unit
  - Manual assembly after ECA and NCA dispensing
  - Curing at heating plate with down-holder
  - Curing schedule: setup temperature = 180°C / dwell time = 360

Connection type: ECA + NCA

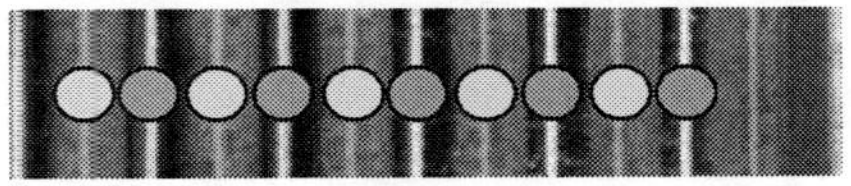

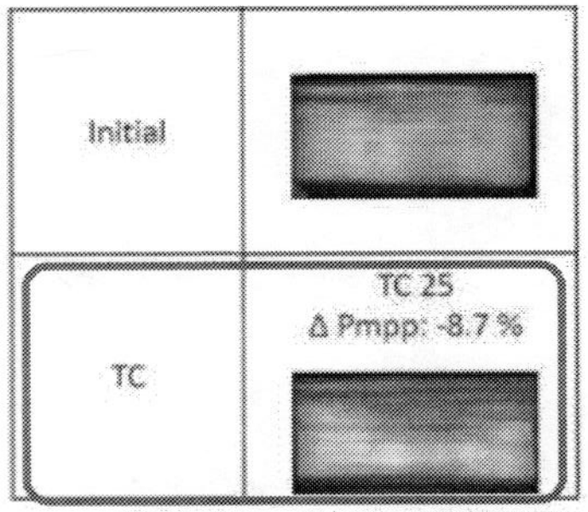

T. Meßmer et al., MIW 2024

- **Identified causes for the sensitivity/ fail of the ECA-NCA interconnection**
  - Contact failure localization by MFI[4,5] + X-ray and target preparation of cross-sections for SEM

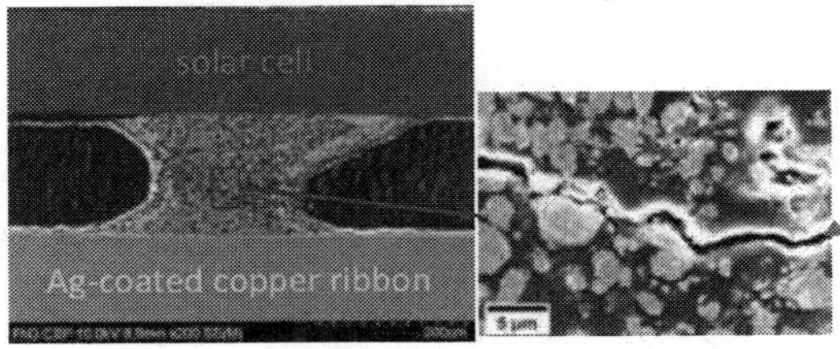

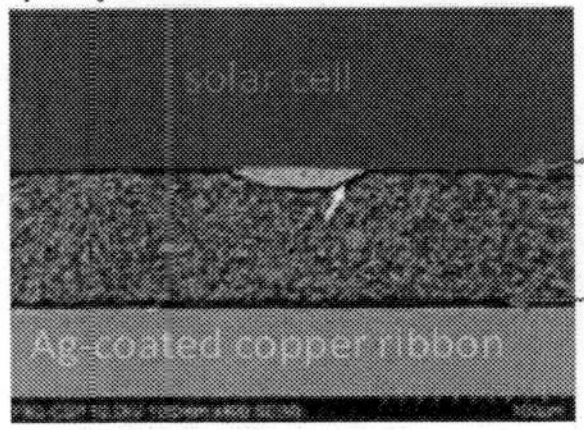

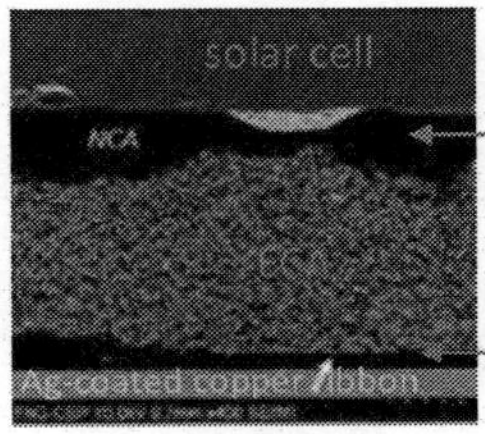

[4] S. Großer, M. Schak, T. Timofte and M. Turek, "Assessment of ECA to Ribbon Interconnection Stability by Current Path and Power Loss Imaging", 8th World Conference on Photovoltaic Energy Conversion Milano (2022) DOI: 10.4229/WCPEC-32022-3DV.3.17

[5] S. Großer, M. Pander, U. Zeller and B. Jäckel, "Local resolution of currents through electrical joints consisting of materials with different conductivity" EPJ Photovoltaics, 14 (2023) DOI: 10.1051/epjpv/2023029

Fraunhofer CSP

Test Lab Process: Dispensing, Assembly and Curing

Jetting continuous lines or pads for ECA & NCA

- XY pick and place unit with optical alignment
- Integrated micro jet dispensing units

See poster: R. Shanmugam et al., 3.AV.1.29

Assembly cell - ECA/NCA - ribbon

TeamTechnik Stringer TT 2100

Adapted semiautomatic process for ECA curing

cell with ECA lines mounted manually on conveyor

1st Ribbon set added automatically on ECA lines on cell

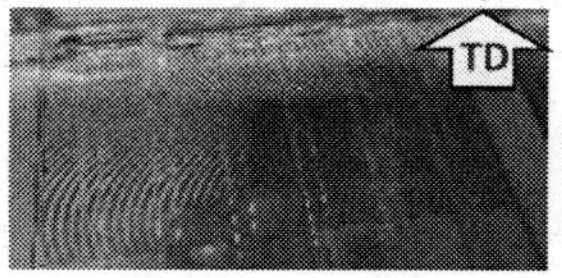

Down-holder and 2nd ribbon set added automatically on cell

Curing procedure

TeamTechnik Stringer TT 2100

- only heat plate curing, without IR heating
- Heating pattern setup (°C):

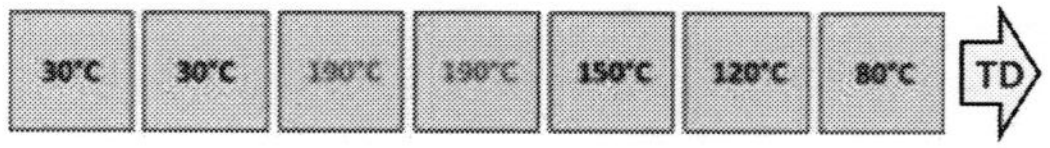

- Dwell time at 190°C heating area: 300s
- Temperature profile:

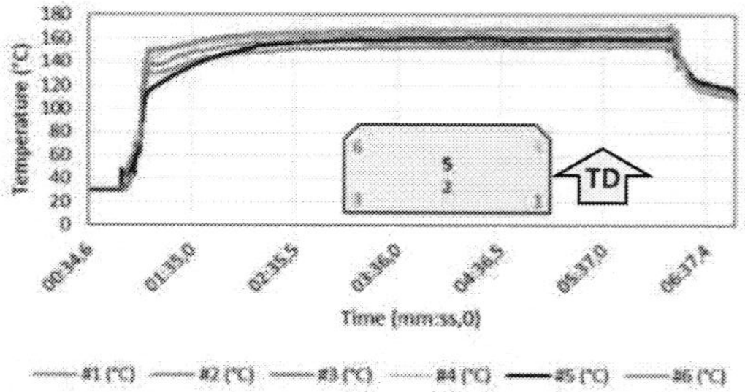

Design of Experiment

Glas - backsheet mini-module used for testing of IV characteristics, EL and accelerated ageing (TCT)

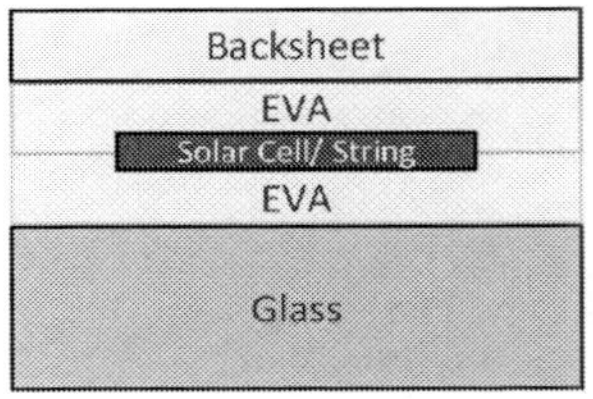

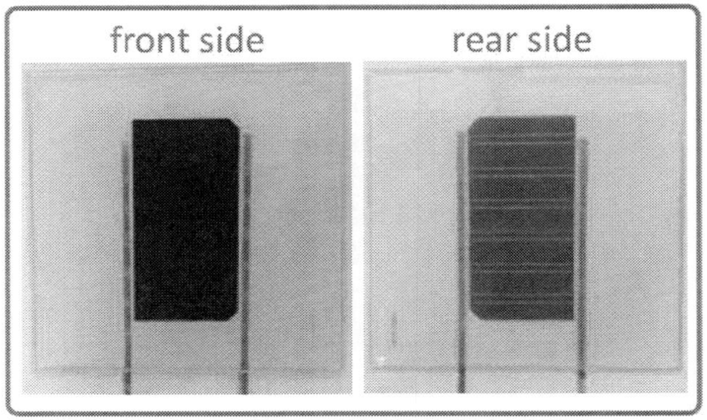

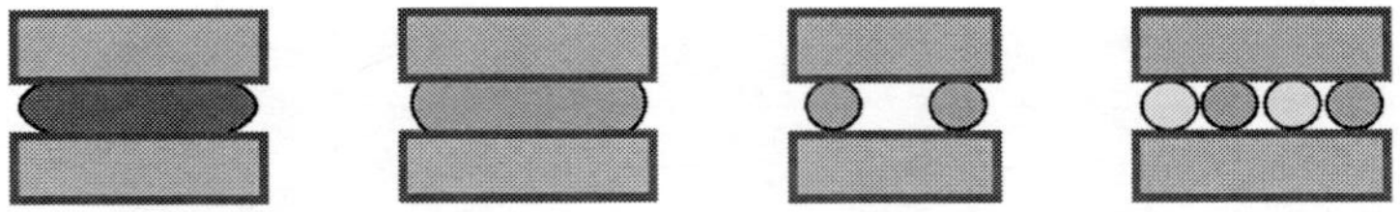

Testgroup	G1	G2	G3	G4
Purpose	reference	continuous ECA line	ECA pads	ECA pads + NCA pads
Nr of samples	7	7	7	7
Cell type	M6 6BB IBC	M6 6 BB-less IBC	M6 6 BB-less IBC	M6 6 BB-less IBC
Interconnection Type	soldering	glue	glue	glue
Interconnection Design	continuous soldering	continuous ECA	pads ECA	ECA pads at all fingers NCA pads at all insulation pads
ECA_	-	ECA 02	ECA 02	ECA 02
NCA_	-	-	-	NCA 01
Module Type	**GF**	**GF**	**GF**	**GF**
Encapsulation Type	**EVA**	**EVA**	**EVA**	**EVA**

Characterization:
- Visual inspection
- Electroluminescence (EL)
- Sun simulator flash (IV)
- MFI + X-ray + cross-section analysis by SEM

Ageing:
- Temperature Cycling Test according to IEC 61215 (- 40°C/+85°C, without current injection)
- Stages: 0 (initial), 8 cycles, 50 cycles, 100 cycles (ongoing), 200 cycles (ongoing), etc.

Microscopy: good vs. faulty dispensing

Section of a cell (only plus interconnection polarity at image below) with dispensed ECA pads and NCA pads
(same process target/ similar parameters compared to previous presented results / ECA = epoxy based)

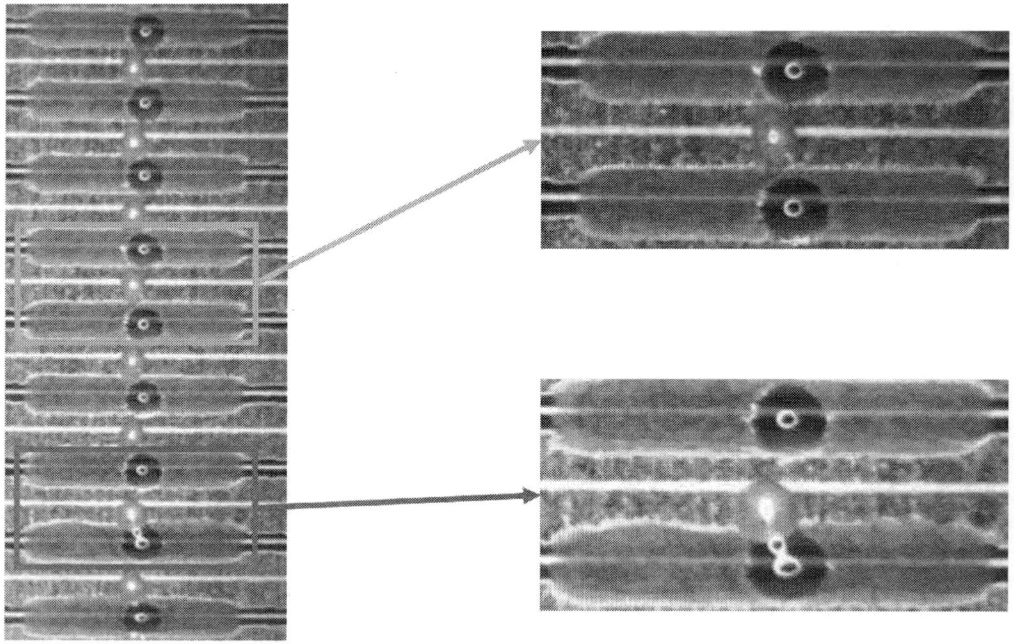

Good ECA- contact finger alignment:
ECA pad centred to the contacting finger

Faulty ECA- contact finger position:
ECA pad with high offset, just contacting the finger with the edge of the pad

Accelerated Ageing (Temperature Cycling Test)

EL changes after 8 and 50 cycles TCT

Group	Description	TCT 0 (INITIAL)	TCT 8	TCT 50
G1 soldering	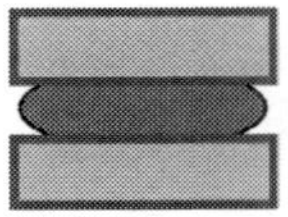		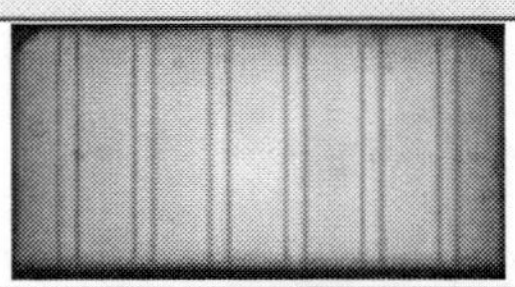	
G2 ECA 02 line	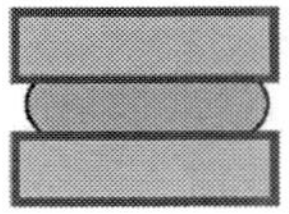			
G3 ECA 02 pads	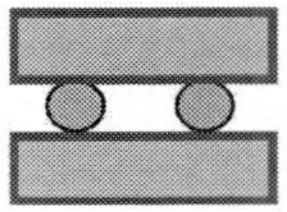	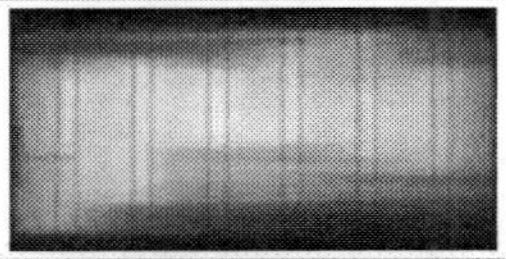	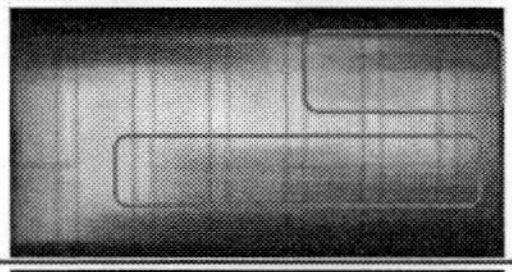	
G4 ECA 02 pads + NCA 01 pads	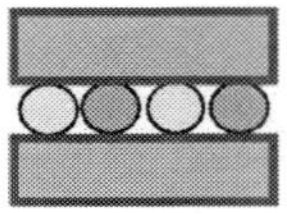	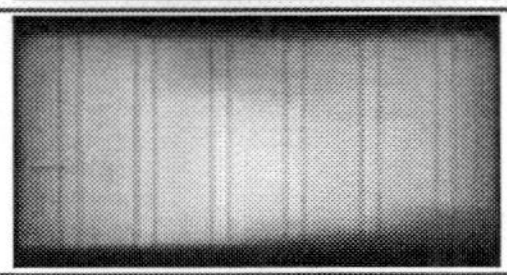	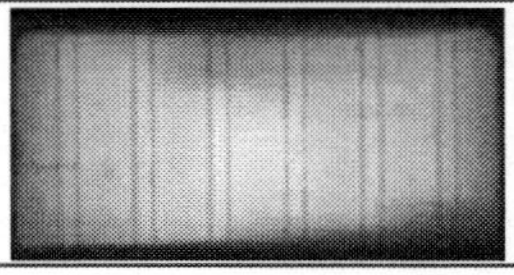	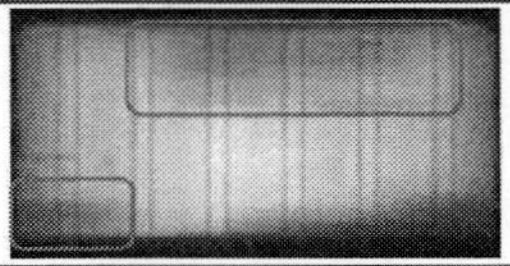

IV parameters rel. (%) change after 8, 50 cycles TCT

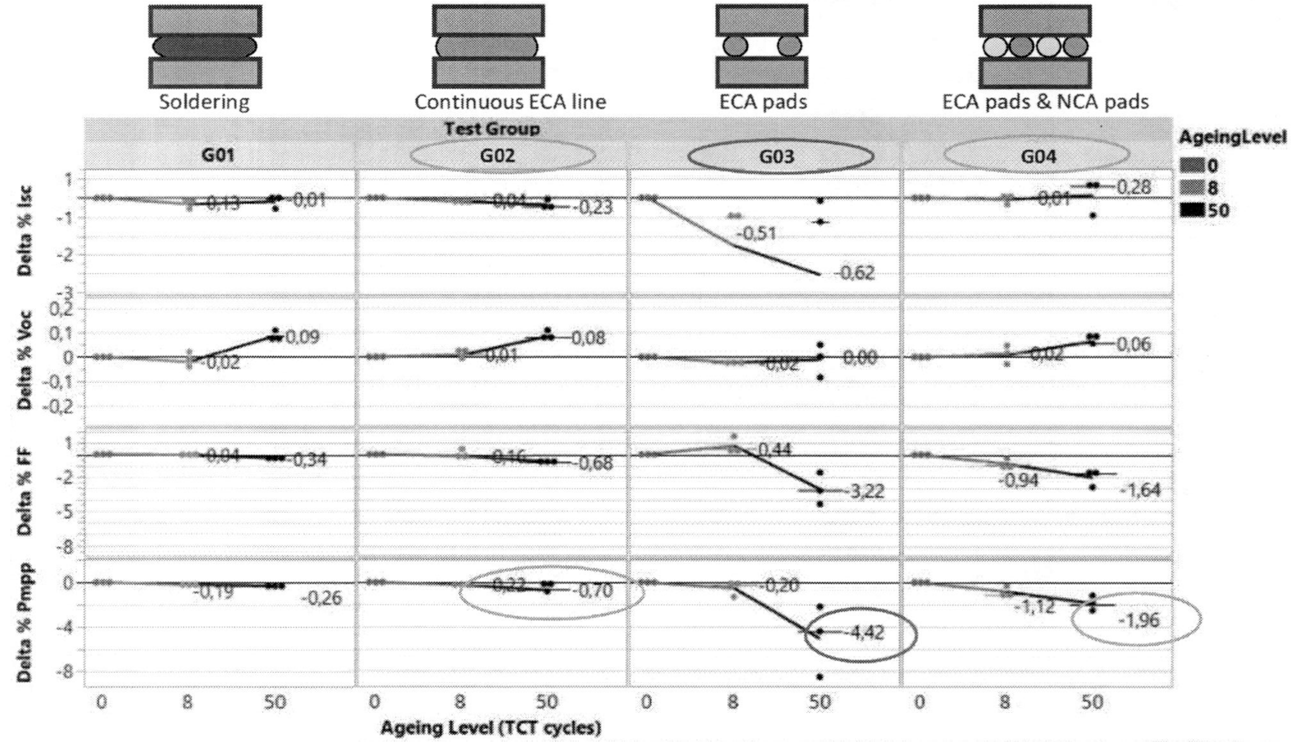

Inspection of interconnection at good and faulty locations

Rear view of sample with marked positions for longitudinal and perpendicular cross section at interconnection (selection made by using **X-ray scan and MFI**):
F = faulty contact / G = good contact

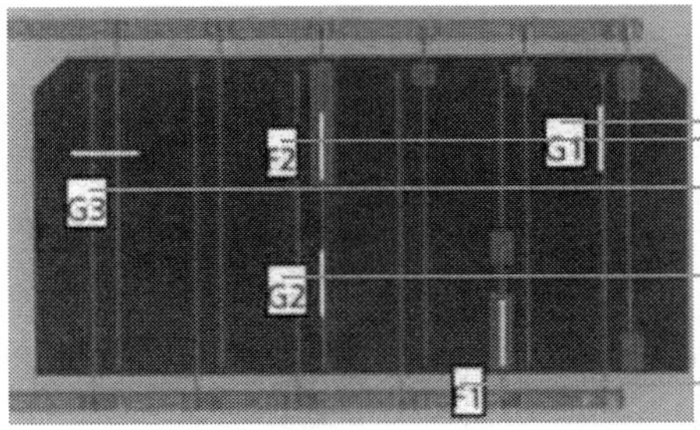

EL imaging

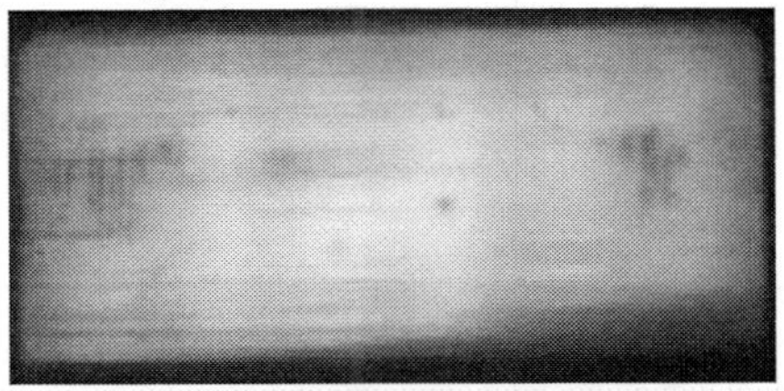

X-Ray imaging

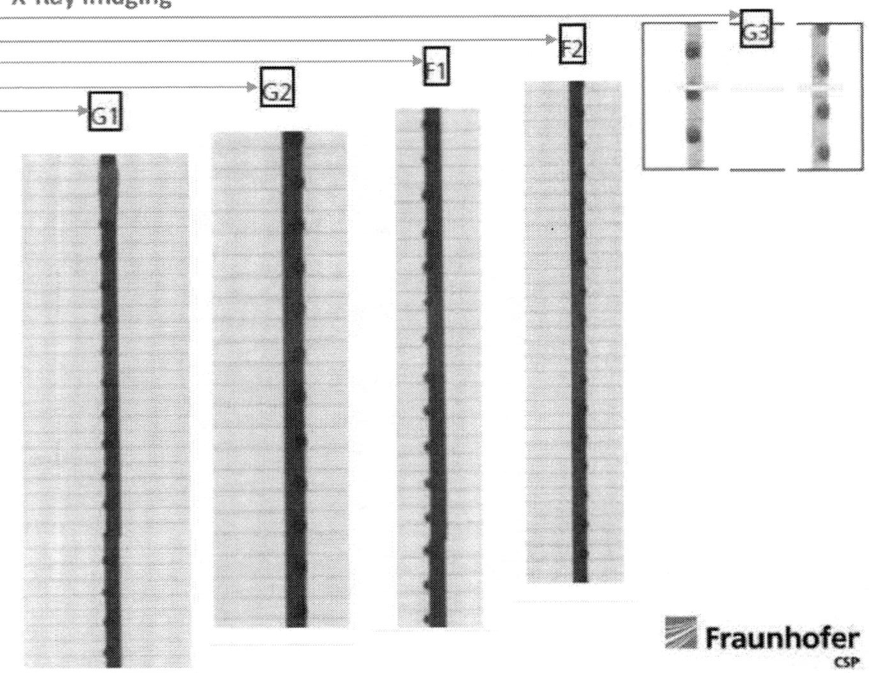

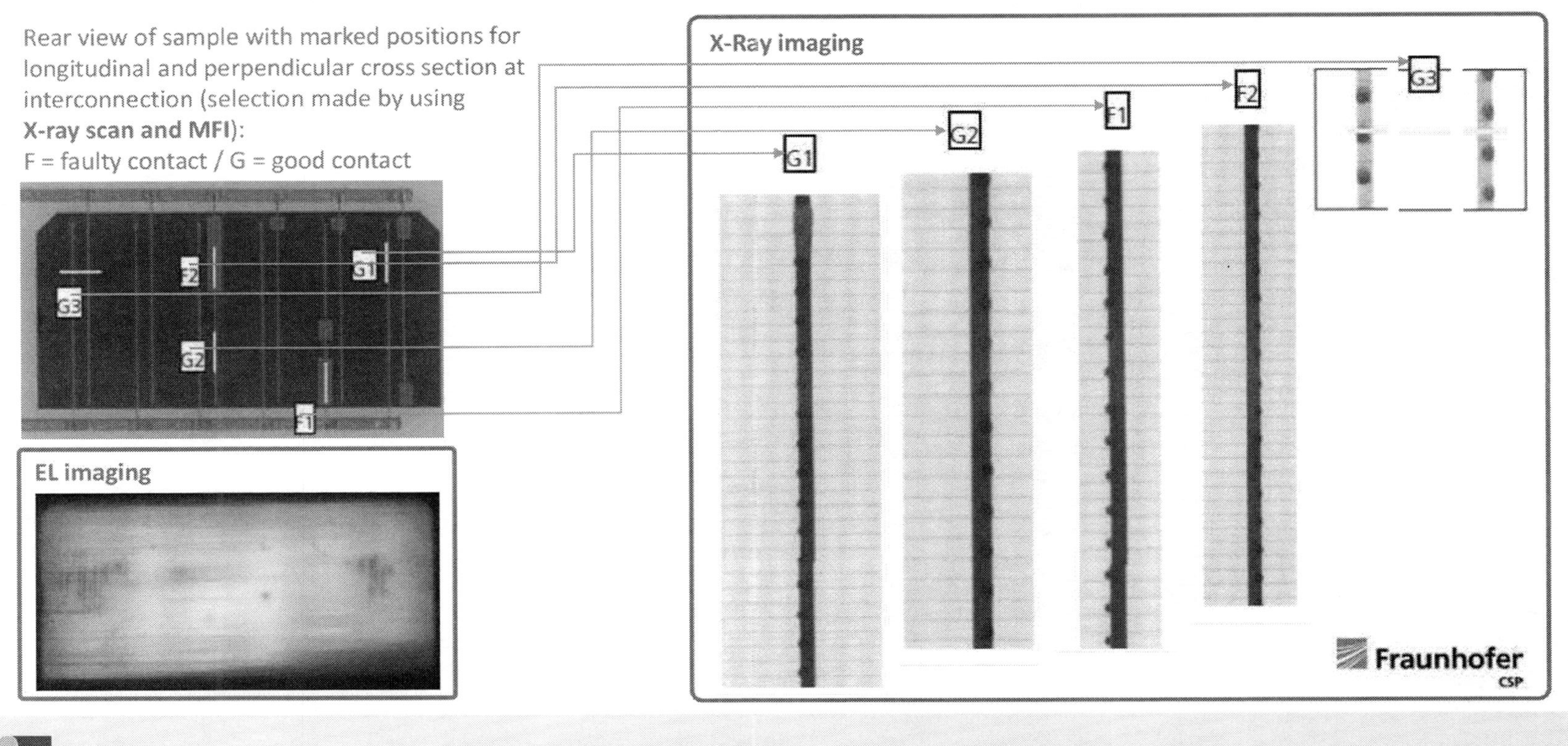

Inspection of interconnection at good and faulty locations

Good interconnection position

Position G1:

Position G1:

Faulty interconnection position

Position F1:

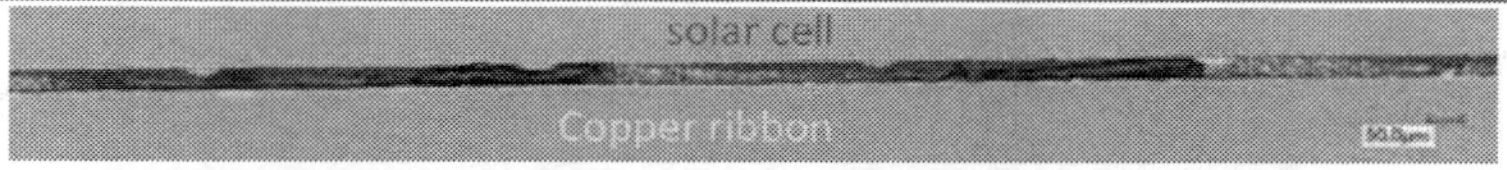

Position F1:

Good interconnection position

Position G3: ECA:

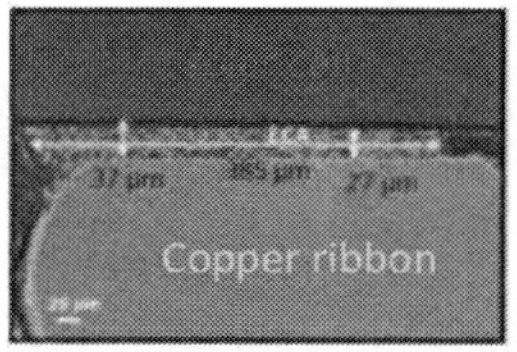

NCA:

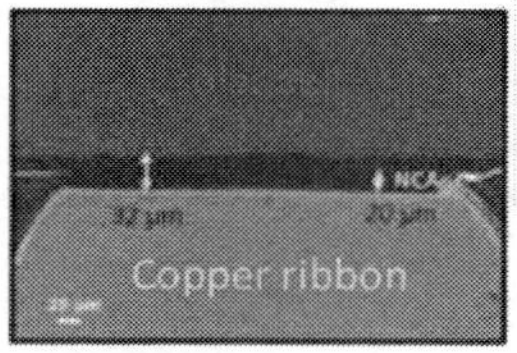

Good points:
- Jetting position accuracy for ECA and NCA pads improved
- Improved homogeneity of pressing during curing
- No NCA between ribbon and contacting fingers (cross contamination avoided)

Bad points:
- Still certain offset to cell finger of ECA and NCA pads
- Also offset observed at positioning of ribbon to cell

Fraunhofer CSP

Estimative Cost Calculation (CoO)

C20219-017

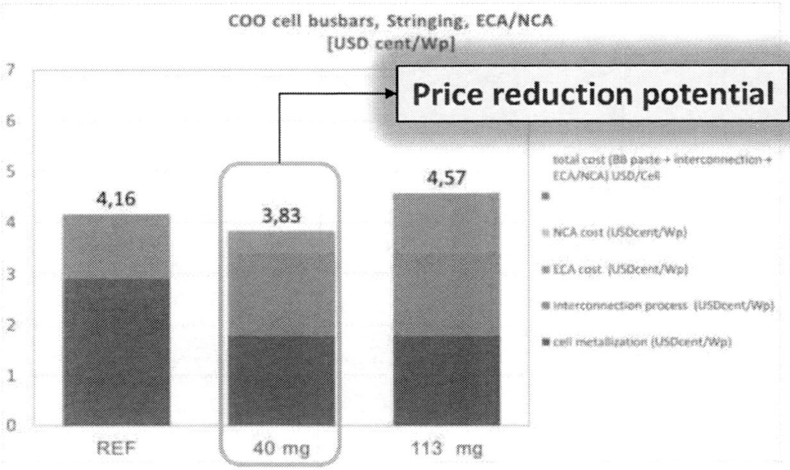

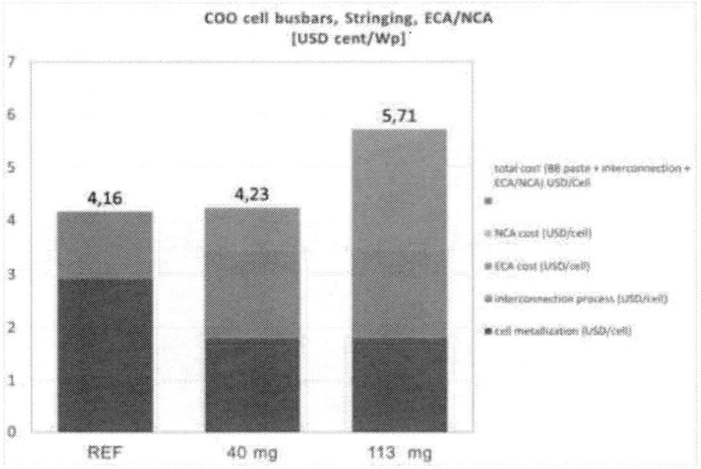

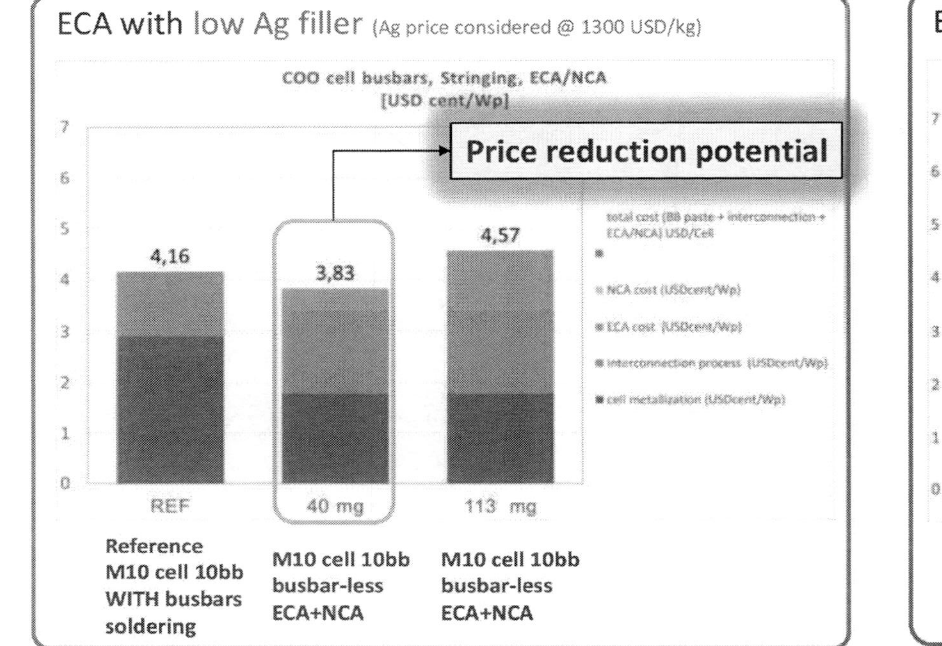

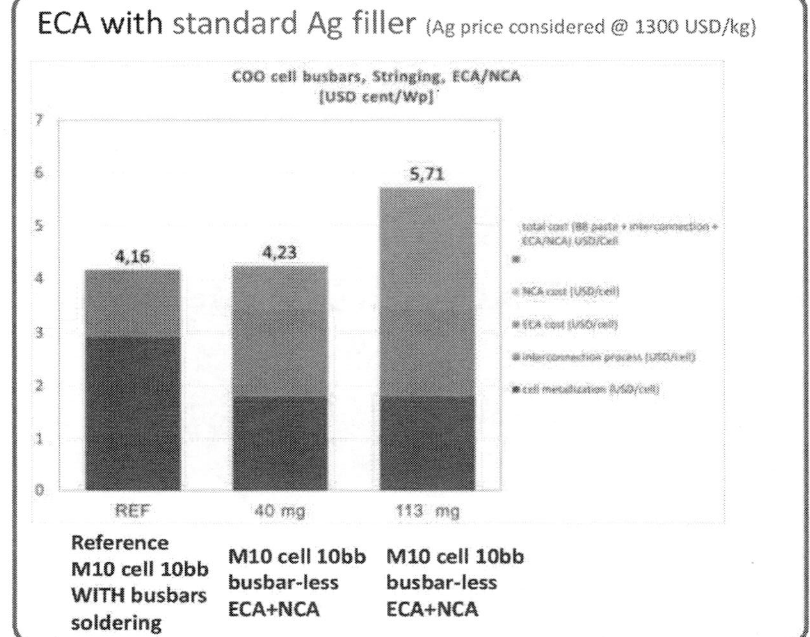

Summary

- ECA pad – NCA pad interconnection for BB-less IBC ZEBRA cell successfully tested and optimized
  - Improved processing supported by contact microstructure analysis (Fraunhofer CSP)
- Best ECA-NCA material & process setup pass TCT50 with 1.9% power loss to initial (less power drop expected by improving the positioning accuracy of ECA and NCA pads)
- FEM simulations reveal peak of thermo-mechanical stress along the ribbon at soldered or glued interconnection in range of cell edges
  - Possible process optimization: reinforcing with NCA pads only ~ 20 mm length from both cell edges towards cell centre
- Further tests are ongoing and planned for further optimization and qualification of materials and processes at semi industrial process equipment, also including the setup solder paste – NCA interconnection at BB-less IBC cell
- The CoO calculation indicate the opportunity for cost saving (~ 8%) at BB-less cell with ECA and NCA interconnection compared to classic soldering approach at cells with busbars

Acknowledgments

The authors thank to

Supported by:

Federal Ministry for Economic Affairs and Energy

on the basis of a decision by the German Bundestag

for funding, Henkel and Fraunhofer CSP for fruitful collaboration.

Furthermore many thanks to all colleagues and other partners involved in testing and general support!

Project Indifiduell: 03EE1185

Visit ISC Konstanz! 21st -24th October, 2025

Events in Konstanz (details: www.isc-konstanz.de)
• IBC4EU/EMPOWER workshop 21st /22nd October
• M&M (Module and Material) workshop 23rd /24th October
• 20 years of ISC Konstanz – party! 23rd October evening from 7pm
• Energy worlds 24th October, afternoon

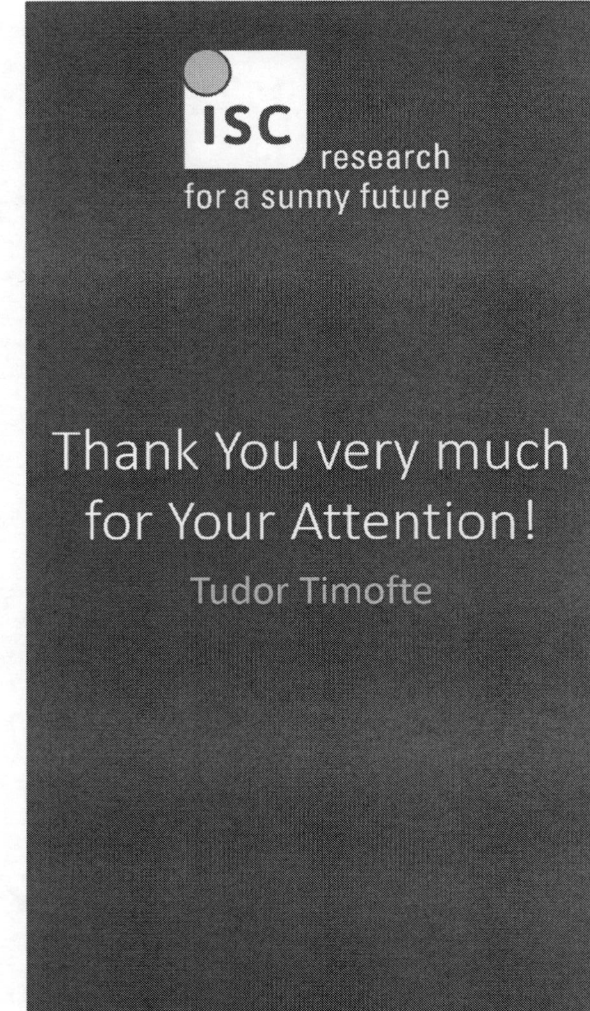

 Tudor Timofte, 42nd EU PVSEC, Bilbao, Spain, 22-26 September 2025

ISC research for a sunny future

Thank You very much for Your Attention!

Tudor Timofte

42nd European Photovoltaic Solar Energy Conference and Exhibition

This presentation was selected by the Sc. Committee of the EU PVSEC 2025 for submission of a full paper to one of the EU PVSEC's collaborating peer-reviewed journals.

Contact resistance limitations in conductive adhesive and solder paste modules

Daniel Tune[1], M. Ignacia Acevedo Devoto[1], Raphael Shanmugam[1], Karl Wienands,[1] Nils Kopp[2], Carina Hallensleben[2], Rihoko Kizukuri[2], Matthias Helbig[1], Andreas Halm[1]

[1] International Solar Energy Research Centre (ISC) Konstanz

[2]TAMURA-ELSOLD GmbH, Ilsenburg, Germany

ABSTRACT: The reduction of conductive adhesive (ECA) or low temperature solder paste (LTS) in photovoltaic (PV) modules offers a potential path to lowering material costs and reducing the use of limited materials. However, reducing the amount of ECA or LTS beyond a certain threshold results in increased contact resistance due to the reduced total contact area and this detrimentally affects the fill factor (FF) due to series resistance losses. Additionally, insufficient interconnection material can compromise the mechanical strength of the connections, making them less capable of withstanding subsequent handling or thermal cycling stresses. In this study, we employ both simulation models and experimental measurements on minimodules to examine the effects of reducing ECA and LTS amount on contact resistance and FF in both shingled interconnections. To ensure adequate mechanical stability, we incorporate non-conductive adhesive (NCA), which allows us to explore lower material volumes where increases in contact resistance begin to significantly degrade module performance. Our results demonstrate that the strategy of combining reduced ECA or LTS with NCA can offer substantial cost and material savings without sacrificing performance or reliability. The simulation model developed in this work serves as a valuable tool for determining the minimum required amount of interconnection material based on material properties, providing essential guidelines for further optimizing interconnection materials and costs in PV modules while maintaining both the efficiency and durability of the modules.

Keywords: Solder paste, Conductive adhesive, Shingling, Module Integration

1 INTRODUCTION

The aim of this work is to further explore the limits to strategies of reducing the amount of ECA or LTS in PV module interconnections. The approach involves analytical simulations of the interconnects to predict the dependence of the module performance on the amount of ECA or LTS and then manufacturing and measuring the performance of strings of interconnected solar cells and dedicated test structures to validate the output of the simulation models. ECA or LTS are applied on the busbars of solar cells and then these are used to assemble test samples and one-cell-equivalent minimodules using standard industrial production processes. Mechanical properties of the ECA or LTS interconnects are assessed and the performance of the minimodules is measured before and after accelerated aging tests.

The market prevalence of modules that use ECA interconnects is increasing and it has been previously shown that LTS can also be used in some applications where ECA is used, but the relatively high cost of some ECAs and the use of limited materials such as bismuth or silver in LTS and silver in ECAs creates an impetus for exploring ways to reduce the amount of the materials used (in addition to general cost-down considerations). However, this must be done in a way that does not detrimentally impact the performance or reliability of the modules or, better, provides improvements. In this work, we use an innovative approach of adding NCA to provide mechanical reinforcement of ECA or LTS interconnects, allowing a much lower amount of these materials to be used since they are only required to provide the necessary electrical functionalities.

This study addresses the question of how much further the amount can be reduced before the electrical resistance of the interconnects causes a detrimental increase in the series resistance of the modules and corresponding decrease in FF and power output. This can be caused primarily by the limited contact area (contact resistance), the thickness of the bonding material (bulk resistance), or the distance charges must travel along the busbar (busbar resistance) and depends also on the magnitude of the current that must be passed through each interconnect, itself a function of the cell size, cell efficiency, and number of busbars/shingle strips per cell.

2 EXPERIMENTAL

The test platform used in this work consists of a G1 6BB PERC shingled minimodule, wherein the conductive adhesive or solder paste is applied between the inner five shingle overlaps (Figure 1). For convenience in the production and to avoid the influence of differences on the string ends, tin-lead solder-coated copper ribbons are used for the end connectors. The modules are made in a glass-backsheet configuration using POE encapsulant. After initial IV and EL testing, the modules are loaded into damp-heat or temperature cycling climate chambers and retested periodically. Commercially available conductive and non-conductive adhesives are deposited by jet dispensing (Vermes) and solder paste is applied via stencil printing.

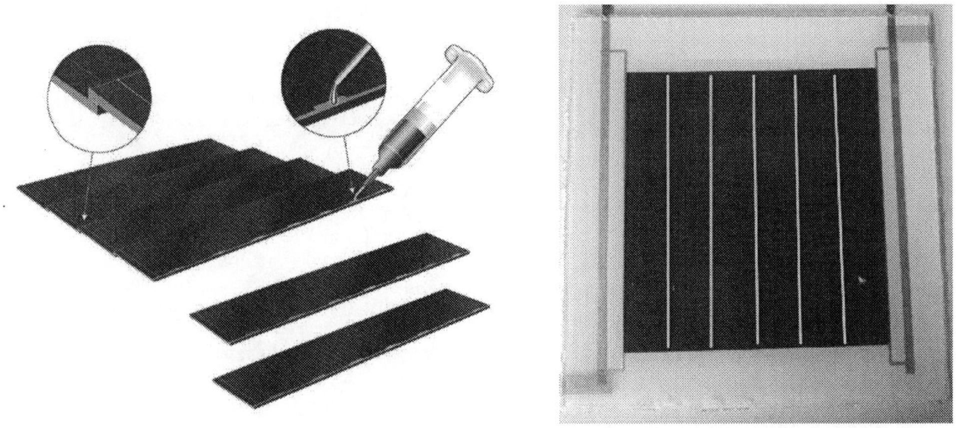

Figure 1. The test platform used in this work, consisting of shingled minimodules with five lines of conductive adhesive or solder paste as indicated by yellow lines in the image on the right. For convenience in the manufacturing, end connectors are attached using standard tin-lead solder-coated ribbons. The modules are laminated in a glass-backsheet configuration using POE encapsulant (*left image credit: Nagase-Chemtex*).

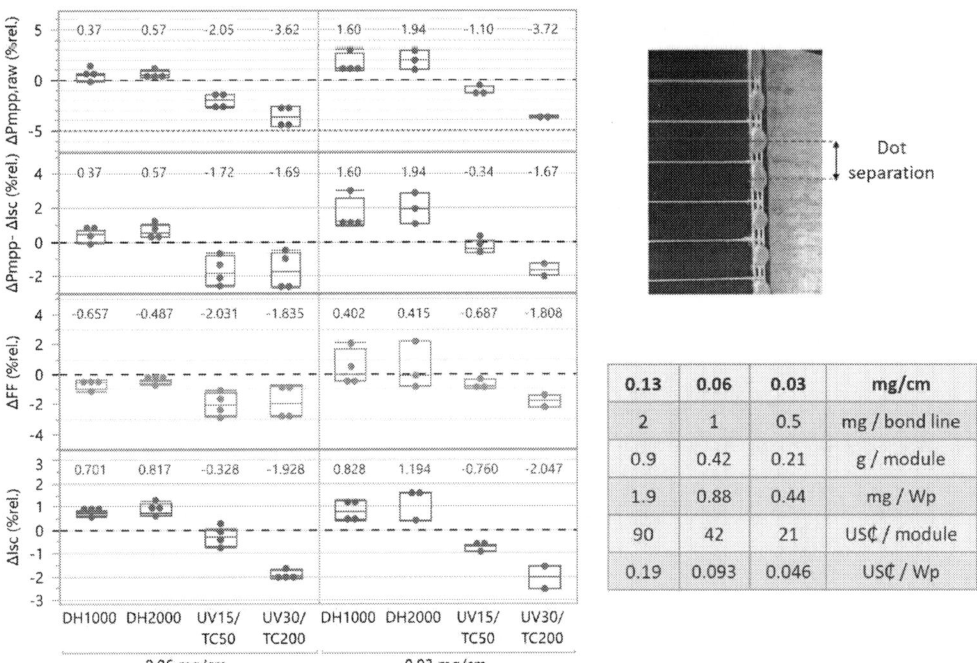

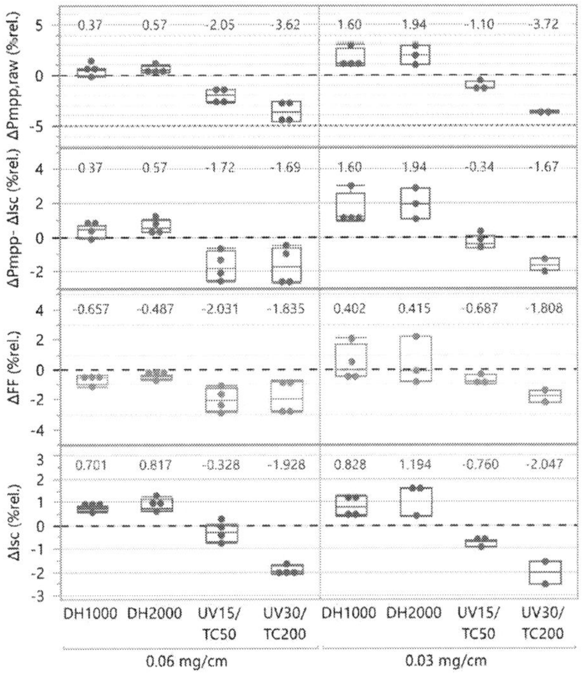

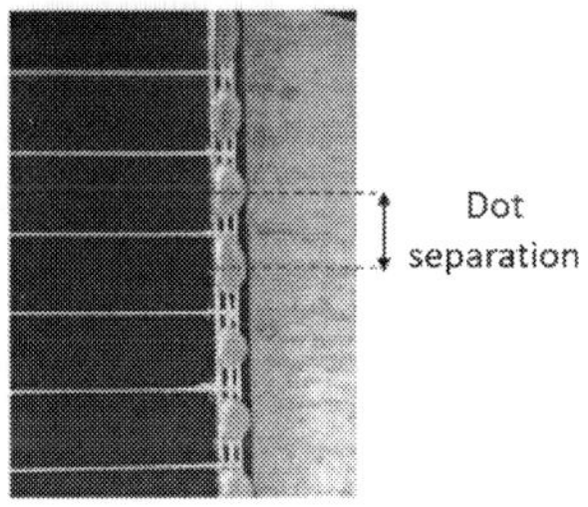

0.13	0.06	0.03	mg/cm
2	1	0.5	mg / bond line
0.9	0.42	0.21	g / module
1.9	0.88	0.44	mg / Wp
90	42	21	US¢ / module
0.19	0.093	0.046	US¢ / Wp

Figure 2. Initial work to reduce the amount of ECA by exchanging continuous lines for a line of dots and varying the dot separation. The relative change of the IV characteristics of modules made with either 0.06 mg/cm or 0.03 mg/cm after climate chamber accelerated aging are shown on the left. The photograph in the upper right shows an example of the deposited ECA dots on the shingle busbar and the table in the lower right gives a breakdown of the associated material consumption and costs extrapolated for the modelled module.

3 RESULTS

3.1 ECA Reduction Strategies

Transitioning from continuous adhesive lines to discrete dots or pads offers a straightforward route to material reduction (**Figure 2**). Jet-dispensing allowed for flexibility and easy control of pad mass and separation. IV data obtained from minimodule tests demonstrated that even with starkly reduced adhesive volume, no significant power losses occurred after 2000 h damp-heat exposure (even some small gains, as often seen with ECA bonds). Combined UV/TC accelerated aging revealed yellowing of the encapsulant used, as seen visually and in the decrease of I_{SC}. However, even after correcting for this, a power loss of ~1.7% was still observed after TC400. It should be noted that this power loss depends strongly on the bill of materials used, with previous work demonstrating losses of only 0.5% to TC720 with other material combinations.

Extrapolating these amounts to the case of an M10, 7BB shingled module with 23% efficiency and providing 460 W power output at STC allows for an estimate of the ECA material costs of as low as 0.046 US¢/Wp, which is a 75% cost reduction *vs.* the widely quoted amount of 2 mg ECA per G1 shingle bond line.

3.2 Low-Temperature Solder (LTS) reduction and NCA Reinforcement

LTS pastes, widely used in microelectronics, offer excellent mechanical and electrical properties, and are readily printable or dispensable. Their integration into PV modules has been validated in conductive backsheet designs and is here extended to shingled modules. SBAC solder paste was provided by Tamura-Elsold GmbH within the framework of a German publicly funded project.

As shown in **Figure 3**, material reduction via stencil printing demonstrated a clear 'less-is-better' trend, with pad size and spacing influencing both electrical resistance and mechanical strength in the range of 2.2 mg/cm to 0.59 mg/cm. Further reductions in the amount were not possible due to a lack of mechanical stability in subsequent processing steps – the shingles simply fell apart during handling.

To overcome these mechanical strength limitations, the LTS interconnects were reinforced with non-conductive adhesive (NCA) as first suggested by Beaucarne in 2016.[1] Two commercial NCAs were tested, with either high (400–600 MPa) or low (40–60 MPa) elastic modulus. Using this strategy, the amount of LTS was reduced by half to 0.32 mg/cm. Thermal cycling tests showed modest improvement in the power loss to TC600 in both NCA cases, while damp-heat stability to 3000 h was significantly improved. Cost analysis indicates that such reinforced solder joints are competitive with silver-based ECAs.

3.3 Modelling the Lower Electrical Limit of ECA Amount

To guide further work to reduce the amount of ECA, we developed a numerical model using our previously demonstrated technique used to determine the contact resistivity of ECA-based interconnects.[2-4] The model uses the known geometrical parameters of the ECA pads in the interconnect combined with the measured electrical parameters (**Figure 4**) and is used to estimate the resistance contributions of the interconnects to the total series resistance of the module. Based on this, and knowledge of the cell output properties and characteristic resistance (**Figure 5**), it is possible to estimate the cell-to-module (CTM) loss of FF for a given amount and contact geometry of the ECA in the interconnect.

As shown in **Figure 6**, the model output reveals that the contact resistance dominates the FF loss within the modelled range of ECA-BB contact resistivities (corresponding to the values we have measured from commercial ECAs and industry standard BB metallisation pastes). This dependency is amplified when the thickness of the ECA pad (i.e. the distance between adjacent cells in a shingle overlap, or between the BB and ribbon) is increased. The amplification is understood on the basis that, for a given ECA amount, a thicker pad entails a smaller contact area. Surprisingly, for the two orders of magnitude range of ECA bulk resistivities that we measure from commercial ECAs, very little effect on the FF loss is estimated.

Additional modelling as shown in **Figure 7** highlighted the importance of busbar line resistance when the ECA amount is very small i.e., when the pads are widely spaced, demonstrating that at very low adhesive amounts, BB resistance between pads cannot be neglected, as it increases series resistance and reduces fill factor.

3.4 Reliability and Performance

To test the model predictions for varying amounts of ECA in the interconnects, several groups of minimodules were produced and the electroluminescence images of them are shown in **Figure 8**. To avoid inadvertent contact between BBs between the ECA pads, NCA was first deposited between the pads and cured to produce an insulating region. ECA and further NCA were then deposited according to amounts specified in the figure, and these were cured before the shingles strings were made into minimodules.

Significant losses were observed, especially for the smaller amounts, and these were generally consistent with the predictions of the model. However, for the highest amount, the FF loss due to the ECA contact resistance was a smaller contribution to the total FF loss, with the losses due to the BB line resistance dominating in this case (**Figure 9**).

To further test the model predictions, a similar range of minimodules were produced using the same techniques (**Figure 10**). In these modules, the amount of ECA was held relatively constant but the separation between the pads of ECA was varied from two pads of ECA per bond line to 16 pads of ECA per line. In this case, as observed in the EL images, the definition between conducting and non-conducting regions was less well defined than for the amount variation experiments. **Figure 11** shows the IV characteristics of the modules and the corresponding model predictions. As with the amount variation tests, the correlation between the model predictions and the IV results shows an overestimation by the model, especially for the lowest amounts and smallest separations, indicating either inadequacies in the model, or poor interconnect quality, or a combination of both. Nevertheless, the small underestimation of the FF loss by the model is not considered to limit its usefulness in guiding and informing module development in R&D or production environments.

We note that in the three cases of shortest pad separation, champion minimodules achieved fill factors of ~79%, comparable to modules made with continuous lines containing eight times more ECA, giving confidence that, with further process optimisation, such low FF losses could also be achieved at high yield for these very small amounts of ECA. We further note that the material cost of the NCA is smaller by at least a factor of ten than the ECA, meaning that significant cost reductions can be expected to accompany reduced ECA material consumption, despite the addition cost of the NCA support material.

4 SUMMARY AND OUTLOOK

This study investigated the electrical and mechanical limitations of reducing the amount of silver-based ECAs in PV module interconnects, assessed the potential of LTS pastes with NCA reinforcement, and demonstrated a numerical model capable of estimating the FF loss at module level for a given amount and application of conductive material in PV interconnects. The following conclusions can be drawn:

- Substantial reductions in ECA or LTS consumption are possible, especially when combined with NCA reinforcement.
- Contact resistivity dominates the electrical limitation of how little conductive material is required, while bulk resistivity plays a lesser role.
- Modelling confirms that pad thickness and BB resistance are also critical factors to consider when reducing adhesive quantities.
- A strong business case exists for ECA and LTS interconnects, supporting reduced cost and silver dependency in PV module manufacturing.

Overall, both ECA and LTS interconnects demonstrate excellent prospects for future module designs, provided that careful attention is paid to pad design, contact resistivity, and the use of mechanical reinforcement strategies.

ACKNOWLEDGEMENT

This work was funded by the German Federal Ministry of Economic Affairs and Energy (BMWE) as part of the BIG project with reference number 03EE1116A.

REFERENCES

1.Beaucarne (2016) DOI: 10.1016/j.egypro.2016.10.087
2.Devoto *et al.* (2023) DOI: 10.1016/j.solmat.2023.112490
3.Devoto *et al.* (2023) DOI: 10.1016/j.solmat.2023.112518
4.Devoto *et al.* (2024) DOI: 10.1002/pip.3787

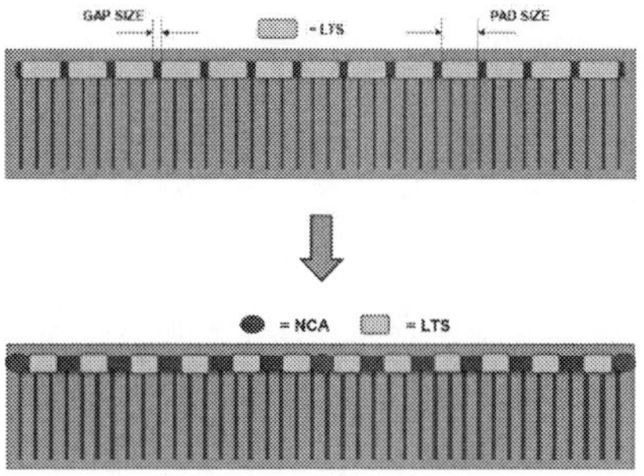

0.59	0.32	mg/cm
10.3	5.6	mg / bond line
4	2.2	g / module
8.7	4.8	mg / Wp
40	22	USC̸ / module
0.087	0.048	USC̸ / Wp

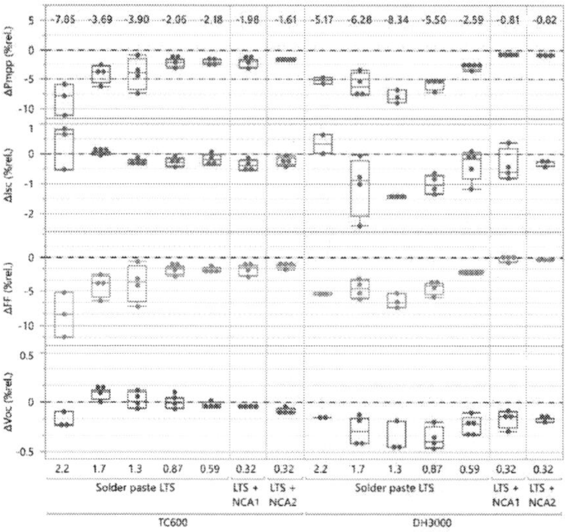

Figure 3. The strategy of reducing the amount of LTS in the interconnects by first reducing pad size and separation and then by including NCA as mechanical support. The changes in the IV characteristics to TC600 and DH3000 show significant reductions in power losses through both strategies and the associated cost breakdown for the modelled M10 wafer size module clearly demonstrate cost competitiveness with ECA-based interconnects.

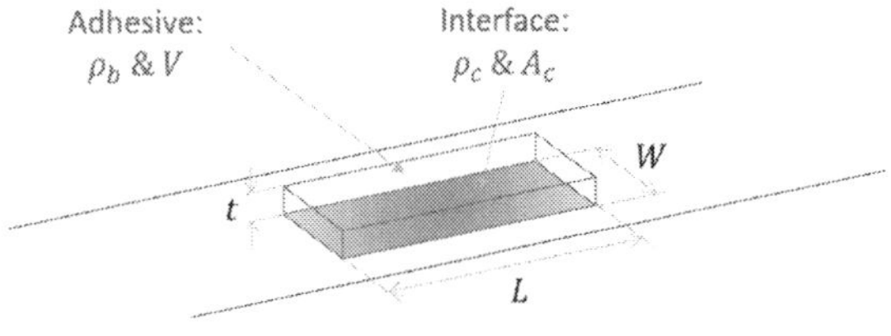

Geometry:

$$A_c = W \times L$$

$$V = W \times L \times t$$

Vertical resistivity:

$$R_b = \frac{\rho_b}{t}$$

$$R_c = \frac{\rho_c}{A_c}$$

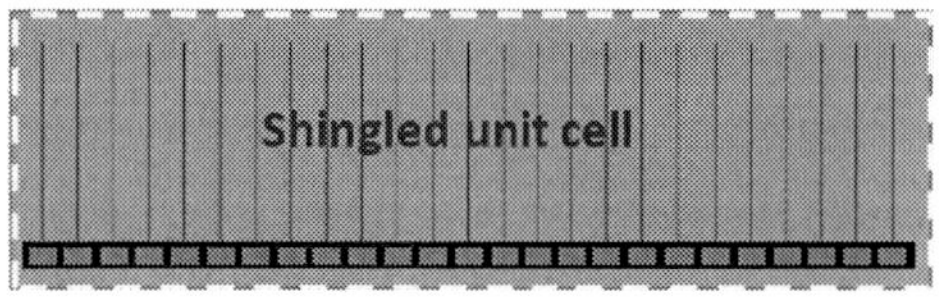

Ribbon unit cell:

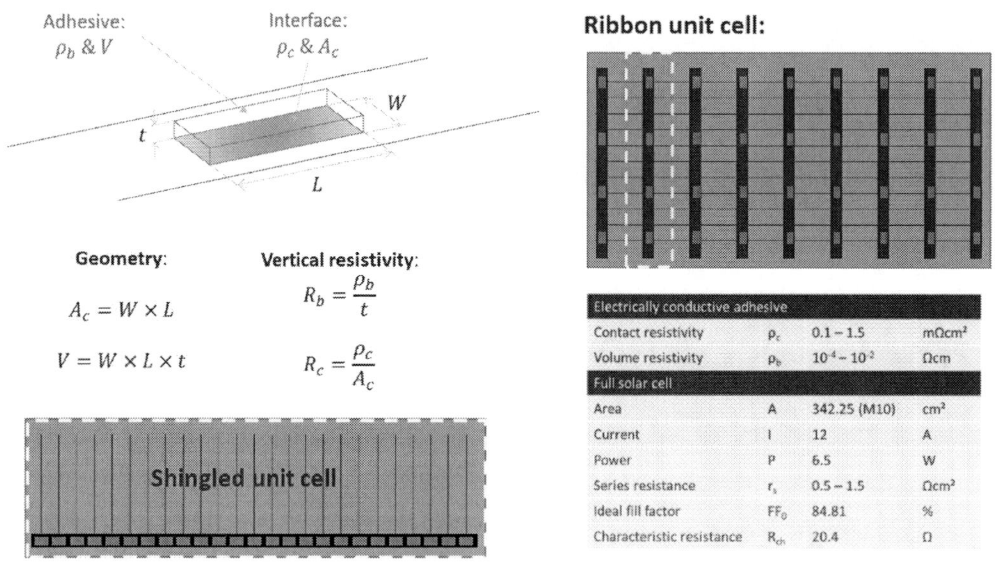

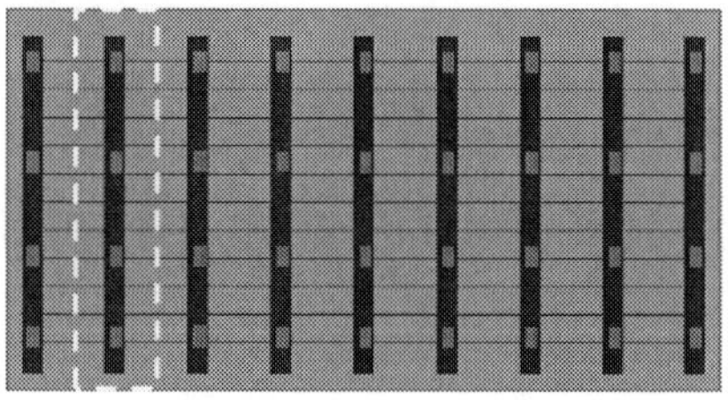

Electrically conductive adhesive			
Contact resistivity	ρ_c	0.1 – 1.5	mΩcm²
Volume resistivity	ρ_b	10^{-4} – 10^{-2}	Ωcm
Full solar cell			
Area	A	342.25 (M10)	cm²
Current	I	12	A
Power	P	6.5	W
Series resistance	r_s	0.5 – 1.5	Ωcm²
Ideal fill factor	FF_0	84.81	%
Characteristic resistance	R_{ch}	20.4	Ω

Figure 4. Aspects of the numerical model developed to estimate the CTM loss of FF for a given geometry and set of electrical characteristics of the ECA in the interconnect. The model is applicable to either shingled or ribbon-interconnected modules and is used to simulate an M10-wafer-size module with the parameters shown in the table on the bottom right.

Parameter	Sym.	Eq. (Shingle)	Eq. (Ribbon)	Unit
Total contact area **per unit cell**	A_c	$N_{pad} \cdot W \cdot L$		cm^2
Contact resistance / interface / bond line	R_c	ρ_c / A_c		Ω
ECA bulk / volume resistance	R_b	$\rho_b \cdot H / A_c$		Ω
Contact resistance component of *series resistance* **per unit cell**	$R_{c/s}$	$2 \cdot R_c$	$4 \cdot R_c$	Ω
ECA bulk resistance component of *series resistance* **per unit cell**	$R_{b/s}$	R_b	$2 \cdot R_b$	Ω
Contact resistance component **normalized** *for series resistance*	$r_{c/s}$	$R_{c/s} \cdot A_{BB}$		Ωcm^2
ECA bulk resistance component **normalized** *for series resistance*	$r_{b/s}$	$R_{b/s} \cdot A_{BB}$		Ωcm^2
How much of the **series resistance** would this amount of **contact resistivity** be?		$r_{c/s} / r_s$		%
How much of the **series resistance** would this amount of **ECA bulk resistivity** be?		$r_{b/s} / r_s$		%
Cell series resistance **normalized** *for cell characteristic resistance (1 cm²)*	$r_{z/ch}$	r_s / R_{CH}		-
Module series resistance **normalized** *for cell characteristic resistance (1 cm²)*	$R_{m/ch}$	$(r_s + r_{c/s} + r_{b/s}) / R_{CH}$		-
Cell fill factor	FF_z	$FF_0 \cdot (1 - 1.1 \cdot r_{z/ch}) + r_{z,ch}^2 / 5.4$		%
Module fill factor	FF_m	$FF_0 \cdot (1 - 1.1 \cdot r_{m/ch}) + r_{m,ch}^2 / 5.4$		%
Fill factor absolute loss (cell to module)	ΔFF	$FF_m - FF_z$		%

Figure 5. Parameters used in the numerical model for shingled and ribbon-interconnected modules.

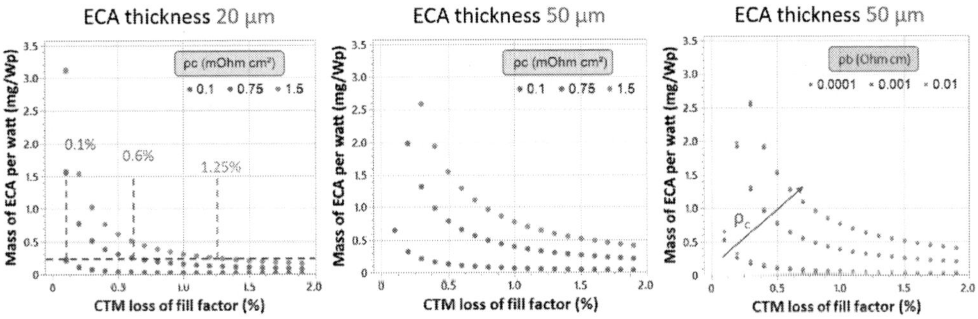

Figure 6. Examples of the model output showing the relationship between the CTM loss of FF and the amount of ECA in the interconnect. The left plot shows the difference in FF loss estimated for an amount of 0.23 mg/Wp and for the three different modelled ECA-BB contact resistivities. The middle plot shows how the amount required for a certain FF loss is amplified when the thickness of the ECA pad is increased. The plot on the right shows the same as the middle plot but overlays the difference between different bulk resistivities (in different colours), revealing very little effect of the bulk resistivity on the estimated FF loss (the coloured data points are all mostly in the same place).

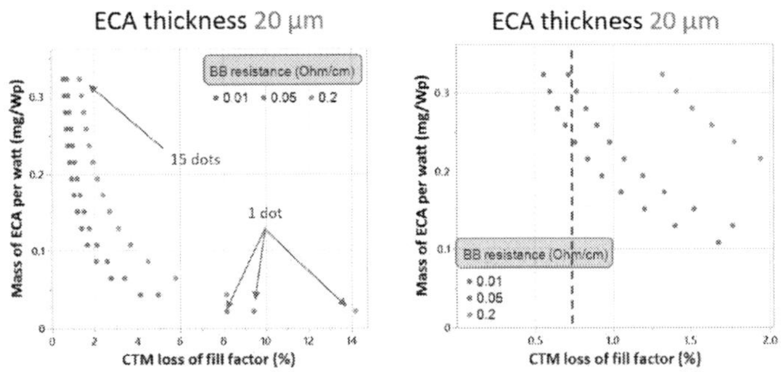

Figure 7. The model output as before but including the effects of the BB line resistance between the ECA pads.

10.4229/EUPVSEC2025/3CO.10.6

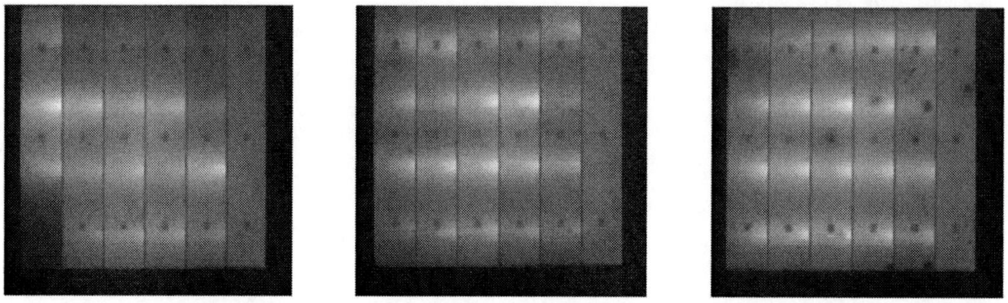

2 ECA dots in each of 4 regions = 8 dots per busbar

4 ECA dots in each of 4 regions = 16 dots per busbar

8 ECA dots in each of 4 regions = 32 dots per busbar

Figure 8. Representative EL images of the three types of minimodules produced to test the estimations of the numerical model for different amount of ECA in the interconnects. The three rectangular features on the back of each shingle stripe are connection pads used in an unrelated investigation and can be ignored (the same print screens were used).

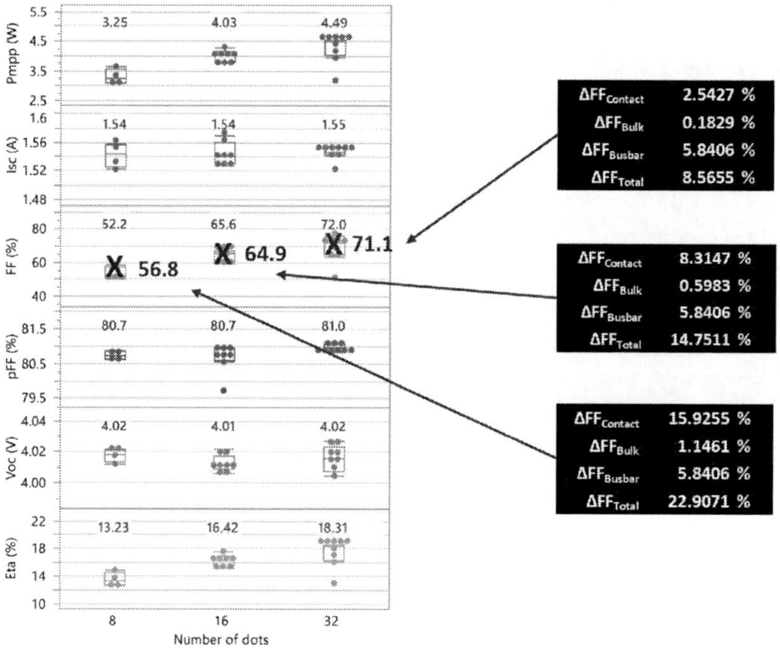

Figure 9. IV characteristics of the minimodules used to test the model predictions for varying amounts of ECA in the interconnects, including the breakdown of the resistance contributions predicted by the model for each case.

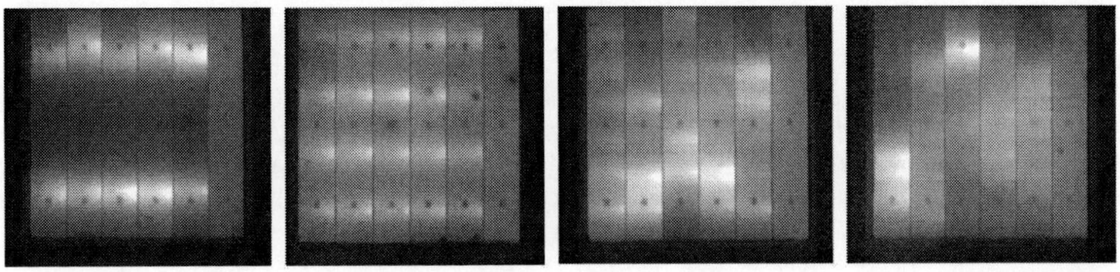

16 ECA dots in 2 regions = 32 dots per busbar | 8 ECA dots in 4 regions = 32 dots per busbar | 5 ECA dots in 6 regions = 30 dots per busbar | 3 ECA dots in 10 regions = 30 dots per busbar

Figure 10. Representative EL images of the four types of minimodules produced to test the estimations of the numerical model for different ECA pad separations in the interconnects.

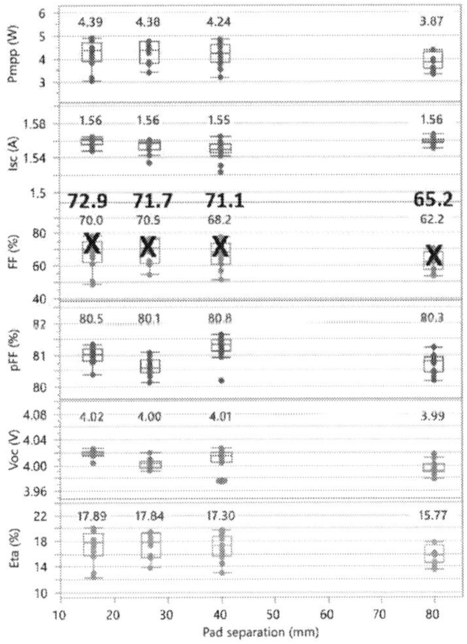

Figure 11. IV characteristics of the minimodules used to test the model for varying ECA pad separations.

PROCESS AND DESIGN FREEDOM ENABLED BY BACK-CONTACT SOLAR CELLS MINIMIZING THE INACTIVE MODULE AREA

Andreas Halm, Daniel Tune, Karl Wienands, Tudor Timofte, Tobias Messmer
International Solar Energy Research Center (ISC) Konstanz,
Rudolf-Diesel Str. 13-15, 78467 Konstanz, Germany

ABSTRACT:
We present three process and design novelties that enable higher module efficiencies by decreasing solar modules inactive area:

i) a gapless stringing procedure
ii) a gapless string layup
iii) a cross connection behind the active cell matrix

All above mentioned innovations are applied for stringed back contact solar cells called Zebra cells which are in house developed all screen-printed IBC solar cells. Yet they are relevant for most wire interconnected BC type cells. The main improvement is an increased module efficiency achieved by reduction of inactive module area. Another advantage of the gapless stringing approach is the uniform aesthetic module appearance relevant to BIPV applications without the necessity to mask interconnection ribbons, especially in the case of applying a black background and/or colored module glass.
To show the validity of our approach we have assembled several mini-modules and a full-size module demonstrator in different configurations applying the above-mentioned novelties. A simple geometric calculation shows the potential of inactive area reduction and also factors in shading of cells due to overlaps that are necessary for the practical realization of the gapless approach.

Keywords: IBC cell, gapless stringing, gapless layup

1 INTRODUCTION

To increase the PV module efficiency and provide uniform aesthetic module appearance we explore approaches to eliminate inactive module area by processing stringed IBC solar cells into modules eliminating cell-to-cell gaps and string gaps. Our new module matrix is called "full gapless" (applied for patent). Cell gaps are eliminated by overlapping neighboring cell edges in string direction.
Since for most IBC cell concepts all interconnection ribbons run along one cell side, no front to back transfer of the ribbon is needed making overlapping of neighboring cells feasible. The absence of front side metallization further enables overlapping between neighboring strings and similarly as for cell to cell connection, during cross connection of neighboring strings the cross connector can run on one cell side making it possible to relocate it to behind the active cell matrix. Industry is starting to adopt our innovations. Different realizations of the area reduction are described in the following as single points.

2 EXPERIMENTAL AND RESULTS

2.1 Geometrical calculations

The fraction of inactive module area in stringed c-Si modules is considerable. The physical dimensions of a typical commercial rooftop module containing 54 M10 half cells are 1722 mm x 1134 mm (see e.g. [1]). 8.5% of the module area is not contributing to power generation. Details on geometrical parameters (e.g. cell gap, bussing width, etc) to calculate module dimensions, area reduction potentials and shading fractions are given in table 1 in the appendix. The calculations show for the M10 case that 4.6% of the inactive area result from frame and safety margin (1500V case) and cannot be avoided. The remaining 3.9% are avoidable and are distributed the following (with the assumptions given in table 1): the sum of top busing, center busing (incl j-box) and bottom bussing accounts for 2.1%, the cell gaps and string gaps both for 0.9% respectively. That opens a potential for 3.9% in module area reduction. Without overlap that would yield in a 4% relative increase in module efficiency. In reality, introducing the overlaps to realize the full gapless layout and at the same time shrinking the overall module area this vale cannot be reached. Applying 0.7 mm cell to cell overlap and 1 mm string to string overlap leads to 1.6% shaded area (0.7% for cell gaps, 0.9% for string gaps) in this example versus a 2.9% (1.6% for cell gaps, 1.3% for string gaps) in module area reduction. It has to be mentioned that the efficiency gain reachable by this approach is mainly relevant for black background or true bifacial modules.

2.2 relocation of rear bussing behind cell matrix

For relocating the cross connection behind the active cell matrix, cells are locally isolated against the busing. Mini-modules with single half cells, M6, Zebra, 6 busbars have been assembled semi-manual at ISC to show a proof of concept how to realize the bussing behind cell matrix concept. Aiko solar already sells a commercial module featuring a similar approach [2]. Lab results shown here are realized by locally applying Kapton tape or similar materials as insulation layer between bussing and ribbon (group 1,2 Figure 2). In one case we add another layer on the cell surface before stringing to enable horizontal movements (group 3 Figure 22). A sketch of group 3 configuration is given in Figure 1.

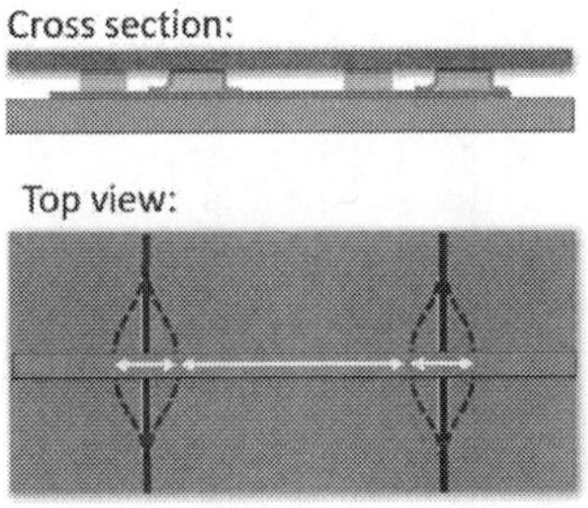

Figure 1: cross section and top view of isolation configuration by Kapton tape of group 3

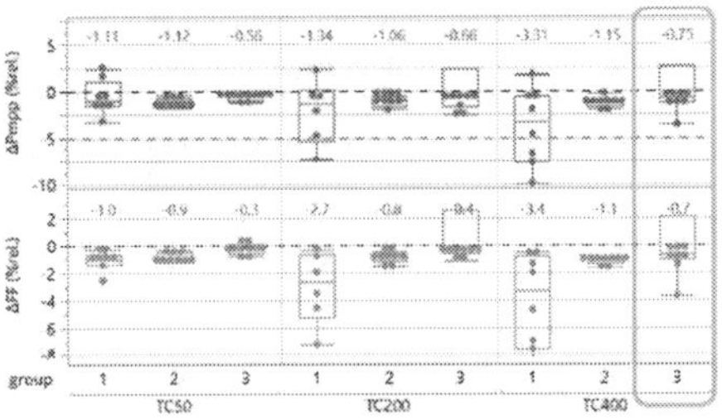

Figure 2: tempearture cycle test reults of relative change in power and fill factor for mini modules in different test configurations

Climate chamber results of mini-modules tested in temperature cycling (according to 61215, no current injection) are promising. Best group shows a moderate degradation of 0.7% relative after TC400.

2.3 assembly of low voltage/high current strings to avoid the butterfly gap

Another method to avoid the butterfly gap enabled by rear side stringing is the combination of parallel and series connected cells in a string (Figure 3). This method was not yet realized experimentally.

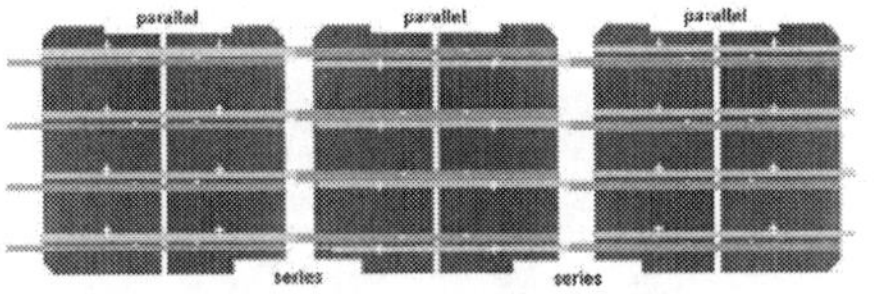

Figure 3: combination of parallel and series connected half cell; the amount of cells per bypass diode in a string can be doubled due to the parallel connection

2.4 gapless stringing by cell to cell overlaps

The gapless stringing process is compatible with standard back contact stringing equipment. At ISC Konstanz we use a teamtechnik TT2100 IR stringing tool and an overlap in the range of 0.7 to 1mm. The overlap is merely mechanical. If sorted correctly, non-passivated edges of the half cells in the string can always be placed below uncut edges. In this fashion, edge recombination effects can be reduced since the non-passivated edge of the cell is not illuminated. EL pictures of the full-size module below that cracking at the cell edges is no issue.

Figure 4: picture of a gapless string assembled by IR soldering on a TT2100 stringer machine at ISC Konstanz

2.5 gapless layup

String gaps vanish by introducing a discrete overlap of 1 to 2mm between strings in horizontal direction during module layup. At ISC the process is done manually. A combination of cell- and string overlap can be seen in Figure 5. For this gapless layup, the strings are alternating slightly shifted in vertical direction to avoid cell overlap regions directly on top of each other, aiming for integrity of the cells under thermo-mechanical stresses. An isolation layer screen printed at the cell edges inhibits shunting between cells of neighboring strings.

Figure 5: cell to cell overlap in vertical direction and string to string overlap in horizontal direction; to electrically isolate the neighboring strings, an isolation layer is screen printed at the cell edges

Applying the gapless layup (1 mm overlap) with gapless strings (1 mm overlap), a120 half-cell module with M6 Zebra cells, 23.1% average efficiency was assembled to demonstrate the efficiency increase with the full gapless approach.

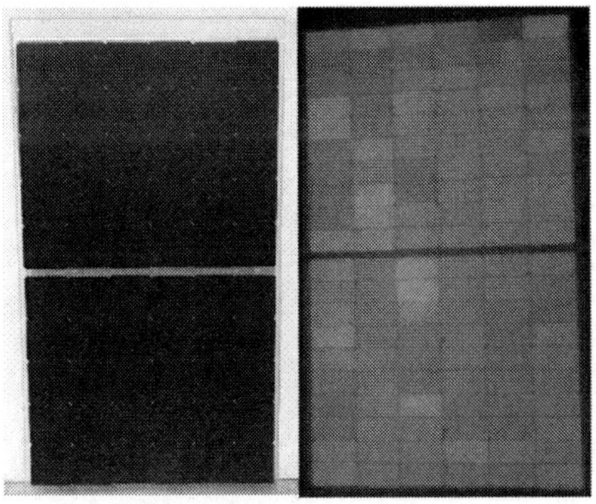

Figure 6: left: Photo of a bifacial module assembled with gapless stringing and gapless layup; right: EL picutre of the module reavling no critical damages or cracks that can be attributed to the overlap scenario

The overall efficiency of the module is with 20.6 % 0.1% absolute higher than the reference module (1 mm cell gap and 2 mm string gap). Geometrical dimensions for both modules are given in table 1. IV results and CTM ratio are compared in the following tables 2 and 3.

Table 2,3: comparison of IV results and CTM ratio for full gapless module vs. a standard reference; CTM ratio is also given assuming a same FF level for reference and full gapless module

	Isc [A]	Uoc [V]	FF [%]	Pmpp[W]	Eta [%]	Area [m²]
reference	11.17	41.44	79.7	369.2	20.5	1.803
Full-gapless	10.86	41.51	79.1	356.5	20.6	1.731

	CTM power [%]	CTM eta [%]
reference	2.85	11.4
Full-gapless	6.17	10.9
Full-gapless (FF adapted)	5.45	10.2

As expected, the CTM ratio in power for the full gapless approach is higher compared to the reference due to shading. Yet, the CTM ratio for efficiency and the overall efficiency for the full gapless module is higher due to the reduced overall module area.

3 SUMMARY

The paper shows design possibilities reducing the active module area and hence increase module efficiency that are applied with stringed back contact solar cells. The novelties can be adapted independently of each other, some can already be found in commercially available modules [2].

4 ACKNOWLEDGEMENTS

IBC4EU

This project has received funding from the European Union's Horizon Europe research and innovation programme under grant agreement No.101084259

5 REFERENCES

[1]https://www.luxor.solar/files/luxor/download/datasheets/LX_EL_N-Type_NR_BW_M108_420-440W_182_DE.pdf
[2]https://aikosolar.com/static/pdfjs/web/viewer.html?file=/wp-content/uploads/2025/08/Neostar-3P54_AIKO-A-MCE54Mw_470-500W-1762%C3%971134%C3%9730_DsDr_EN.pdf

6 APPENDIX

Table 1: geometrical calculations on the area fractions of a standard M10 rooftop module and an M6 IBC module. For both types different configurations in layup are represented with according shaded area fractions and reduction of total area compared to a standa

configuration	Nr of half cells in Module	cell width (mm)	cell length (mm)	Nr of cells in string	cell to cell gap (mm):	with cross connector (busing) mm	distance cell edge to busing (mm)	width diode center gap (mm)	creepage distance (mm):	String gap (mm)	additional width/length due to frame (mm)	framed module length (mm)	framed module width (mm)	total module area (m²)	reduced module area by overlapping (%)	shaded area due to cell overlaps (mm²)	shaded area due to string overlaps (mm²)	shaded fraction of total cell active area due to shading (%)
M10 case study																		
standard	108	182	91	9	1	5	1	24	11	2	5	1722	1134	1.953	0.0%			0
no frame, no creepage margin	108	182	91	9	1	5	1	24	0	2	0	1690	1102	1.862	4.6%			
no diode and bussing area	108	182	91	9	1	0	0	0	11	2	5	1686	1134	1.912	2.1%			
gapless cell stringing: theory	108	182	91	9	0	5	1	24	11	2	5	1706	1134	1.935	0.9%			
gapless string layup: theory	108	182	91	9	1	5	1	24	11	0	5	1722	1124	1.936	0.9%			
gapless cell stringing: overlap	108	182	91	9	-0.7	5	1	24	11	2	5	1694.8	1134	1.922	1.6%	-12230.40		-0.7%
gapless string layup: overlap	108	182	91	9	1	5	1	24	11	-1	5	1722	1119	1.927	1.3%		-16540	-0.9%
M6 experimental																		
standard	120	166	83	10	1	5	3	30	8.4	2	4	1748.8	1030.8	1.803	0			0
gapless cell stringing	120	166	83	10	-1	5	2	35	8.4	2	4	1715.8	1030.8	1.769	1.9%	-17928.00		-1.1%
gapless string layup	120	166	83	10	1	5	2	35	8.4	-1	4	1751.8	1015.8	1.779	1.3%		-16780	-1.0%
no diode and bussing area	120	166	83	10	1	0	0	0	8.4	2	4	1702.8	1030.8	1.755	2.6%			

RCT solutions

EU PVSEC 2025
42nd European Photovoltaic Solar Energy Conference and Exhibition

3CO.11.3: Techno-economic analysis of a suitable module BOM for different climatic conditions

EUPVSEC 2025
Session 3CO.11: Innovative Module Design and Characterization
24.09.2025

Sraisth, Julian Reichle, Mehul Rawal, Gourab Das, Xinyang Li, Hardik Gohil, Wolfgang Jooß

RCT Solutions GmbH

One-Stop Renewable Solutions Partner

Agenda

- Motivation
- Different Climate Zones
  - Their impact
  - Solutions to mitigate its impact
- BOM Selection and its Impact
  - Cost of Ownership, CoO ($/Wp)
  - Levelized Cost of Electricity (LCOE)

Images Source: Sraisth

Motivation

Module Degradation: Using a standard PV module for different climate regions is not a solution – Modules degrade differently in different climates.
[J. Ascencio-Vásquez, et al., https://doi.org/10.3390/en12244749]

OBBBA - One Big Beautiful BOM for All Applications

It is not a solution

Solution
Suitable BOMs for Different Climate Zones & Conditions (SBDCZC)

Images: Sraisth

Köppen-Geiger PV Climate Classification

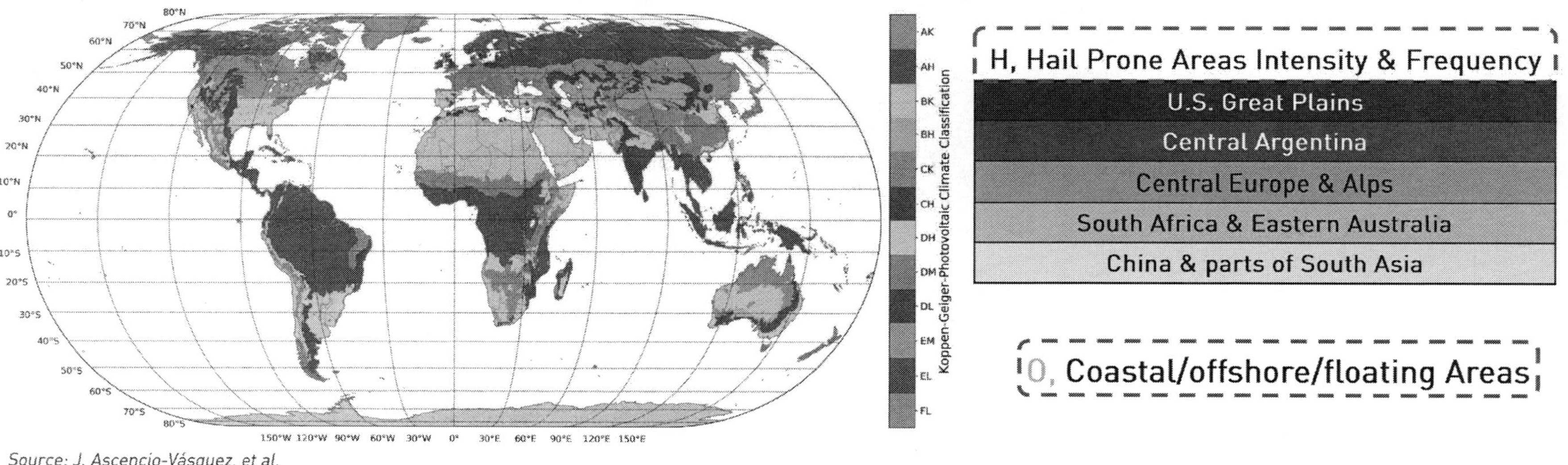

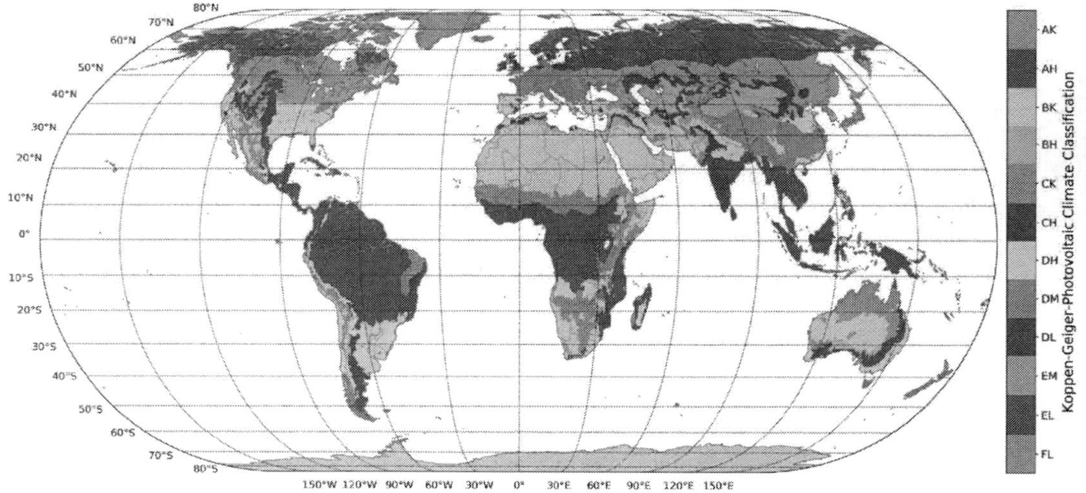

Source: J. Ascencio-Vásquez, et al.

H, Hail Prone Areas Intensity & Frequency

U.S. Great Plains
Central Argentina
Central Europe & Alps
South Africa & Eastern Australia
China & parts of South Asia

O, Coastal/offshore/floating Areas

The dominant climate class by land area:

- B, Arid (30.2%)
- E, Cold (24.6%)
- A, Tropical (19.0%)
- C, D, Temperate (13.4%)
- F, Polar (12.8%)

[https://koeppen-geiger.vu-wien.ac.at/present.htm]
[https://koeppen-geiger.vu-wien.ac.at/pdf/Paper_2006.pdf]
[J. Ascencio-Vásquez, et al., https://doi.org/10.1016/j.solener.2019.08.072]
[M.C. Peel et al.,https://doi.org/10.5194/hess-11-1633-2007]
[https://yaleclimateconnections.org/2022/03/hailstorms-and-climate-change-what-to-expect/]

Different Climate Conditions Impact

IEA-PVPS: Optimisation of Photovoltaic Systems for Different Climates. DOI:10.69766/QSYC8858]
IEA-PVPS: Degradation and Failure Modes in New Photovoltaic Cell and Module Technologies /https://doi.org/10.69766/ATBD2730]

RCT solutions

Images Source: Sraisth

Tropical

- High humidity
- Intense sunlight
- Frequent rain

- Moisture ingress
- Delamination
- Corrosion- PID

Arid

- High temperatures
- Intense sunlight
- Dust accumulation

- Module efficiency reduction
- Shading losses
- Hot Spot
- Thermal Stress
- Sandstorms can abrade module surfaces

Temperate

- Freeze-thaw cycles
- Semi-arid conditions
- Rain
- Snow

- Moisture ingress
- Delamination

Cold/Polar

- Reduced amount of sunlight hours
- Low temperatures
- Thin Atmosphere
- Intense Sunlight

- UV-related degradation
- Moisture Ingress
- Mechanical load issues.

Coastal/Floating

- High humidity
- Salt mist
- Strong winds

- Corrosion in module frames and electrical components.
- Mechanical stress.
- UV-related degradation

High Hail Impact and Storms

- Hails
- Strong winds
- Rain

- Glass breakages
- Microcracks

Different Climate Conditions Solutions

IEA-PVPS: Optimisation of Photovoltaic Systems for Different Climates. DOI:10.69766/QSYC8858]
IEA-PVPS: Degradation and Failure Modes in New Photovoltaic Cell and Module Technologies /https://doi.org/10.69766/ATBD2730]
[Aksel K. Öz, et al., DOI: 10.1016/j.solmat.2025.113735]

RCT solutions

Tropical

- Moisture-resistant encapsulants.
- Improved module sealing
- Improved coatings
- Sealed Junction-box

Arid

- Anti-soiling coatings.
- Advanced thermal management materials
- Frameless design/anti-dust Frame design

Regular cleaning systems

Temperate

- Materials that tolerate freeze-thaw cycles.
- Good sealing
- Moisture-resistant encapsulants.

Optimized module tilt for snow shedding

Cold /Polar

- Materials that perform well in low-light
- Improved structural stability like steel frames
- UV-resistant materials and protective coatings

Higher module tilt to facilitate snow shedding

Coastal/Floating

- Corrosion-resistant materials and coatings
- Thick anodized aluminum or stainless steel for frames.
- Sealed Junction-Box

High Hail Impact and Storms

- Thicker glass
- Thicker frames

Tracker system to avoid direct hail impact

Images Source: Sraisth

Cost Impact: Total Cost of Ownership ($/Wp)

RCT solutions

Standard BOM

- ARC GG 2mm front glass
- 2mm rear glass
- EPE – front side
- EVA – rear side
- Al Frame AA15
- TOPCon Cells

Change Proposal in BOMs for different modules

- ARC GG 3.2 mm front glass (E, H)
- Anti-soiling coated front glass (A, B)
- 3.2 mm rear Glass (E, H)
- PIB Sealant (A, O)
- UV-Conversion POE (A, B, C, D, E)
- POE on rear side (A, B, C, D, E)
- Steel Frame (A, E, H)
- Composite Frame (O)
- Double-insulated Junction-Box (A, O)
- Thicker Frames 35mm (All)
- Anti-soiling Frame design (B)
- HJT Cells (A, B)
- BC Cells (E)

Base Assumptions for Cost Calculations

- Factory in Western Europe
- Other CAPEX
- 5-Year Depreciation of Equipment
- 1 GW Production Factory
- EU Tariffs Included

LCOE Calculation

[J. Reichle et al., 2023, A Comprehensive Study of Silicon Solar Cell Technologies Across the Globe for Sustainable Integrated Manufacturing, ISBN 3-936338-88-4]

Cost Impact: Material Costs /Module vs Module Cost/Wp

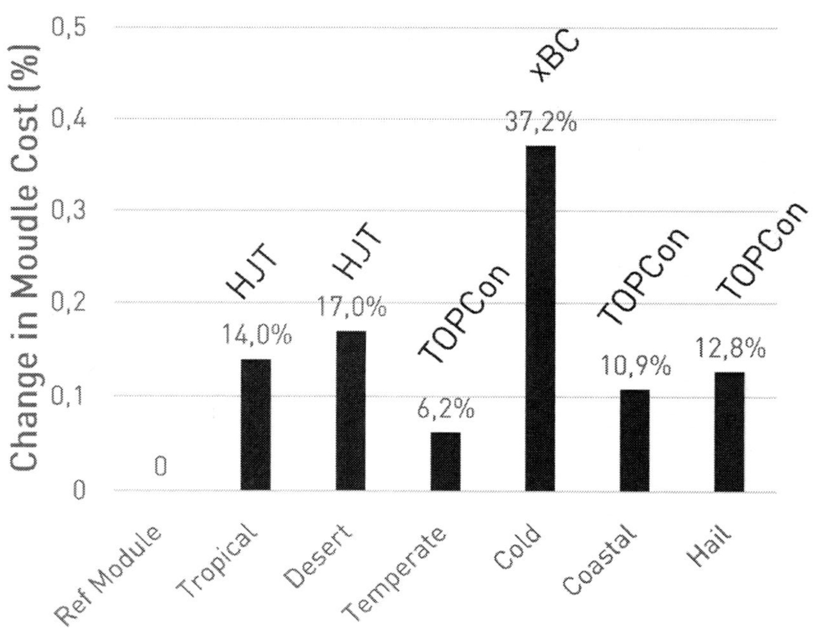

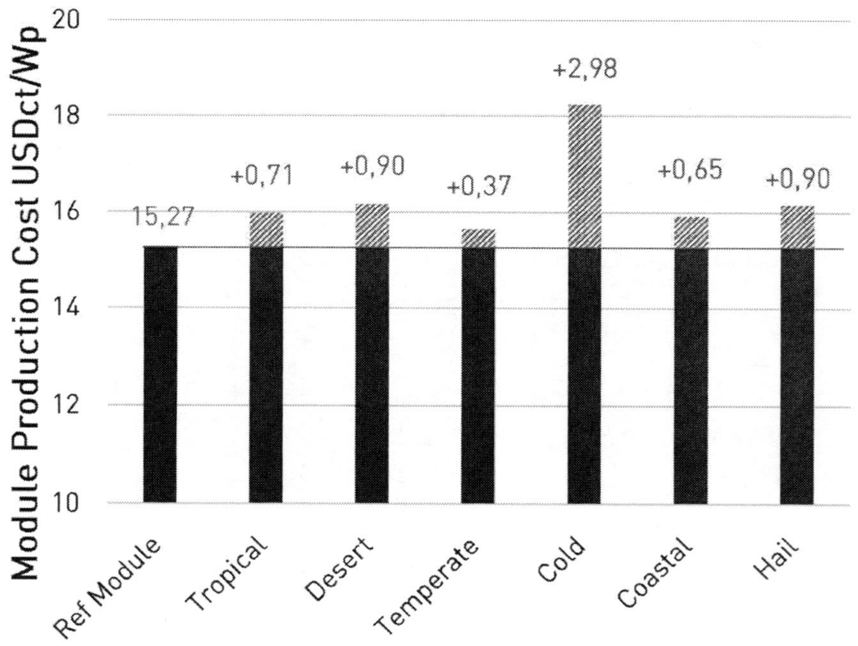

Case 1: Tropical

- In hotter US climates, modules degrade on avg **0.88%/yr**, where **HJT degrades on avg** **0.735%/yr**.

[D.C. Jordan, et al., https://doi.org/10.1002/pip.3566]

- Along the equator line, degradation above **1.4%/yr** is observed. On average, a **tropical climate has 1.03%/yr**.

[J. Ascencio-Vásquez, et al., https://doi.org/10.3390/en12244749]

- In another study, data from the Sub-Saharan tropical climate in Ghana, **up to 3.19%/yr**.

[D. Atsu et al., https://doi.org/10.1016/j.renene.2020.08.021]

Reported rate of degradation of PV modules for different locations and methodologies. [D. Atsu et al.]

Location	Duration	Technology	Method applied	Degradation rate (%/year)
Perth, Australia	19 months	c-Si	MPPTs (continuous measurement)	0.5–2.7
Perth, Australia	19 months	pc-Si	MPPTs (continuous measurement)	1.0–2.9
Colorado, USA	8 years	c-Si	Regression model	0.75
Singapore	3 years	a-Si	Statistical decomposition method (applying the locally weighted scatterplot smoothing)	2
Japan	10 years	a-Si	Regression analysis	3.51
Netherlands	44 months	c-Si	Seasonal and Trend decomposition using Locally Weighted Scatterplot Smoothing (Loess) (STL) technique	1.35
Morocco	3 years	c-Si	IV Tracer and Translation equations	2.6
Morocco	3 years	pc-Si	IV Tracer and Translation equations by IEC 60891	3.41
India	22 years	c-Si	IV Tracer and Translation equations by IEC 60891	1.9
Thailand	4 years	pc-Si	Simple Linear regression model	1.7
Malaga, Spain	12 years	c-Si	Translation equations	0.7
Koforidua, Ghana	**12 years**	**c-Si**	IV Tracer and Translation equations	**3.19**

Solutions:
- Edge sealant PIB
- Anti-soiling coated glass
- GG configuration
- UV-conversion POE
- Anti-corrosive coatings Steel Frame
- Double-insulated J-Box

→ +0,71 USDct/Wp

CoO impact on the LCOE Case 1: Tropical

RCT solutions

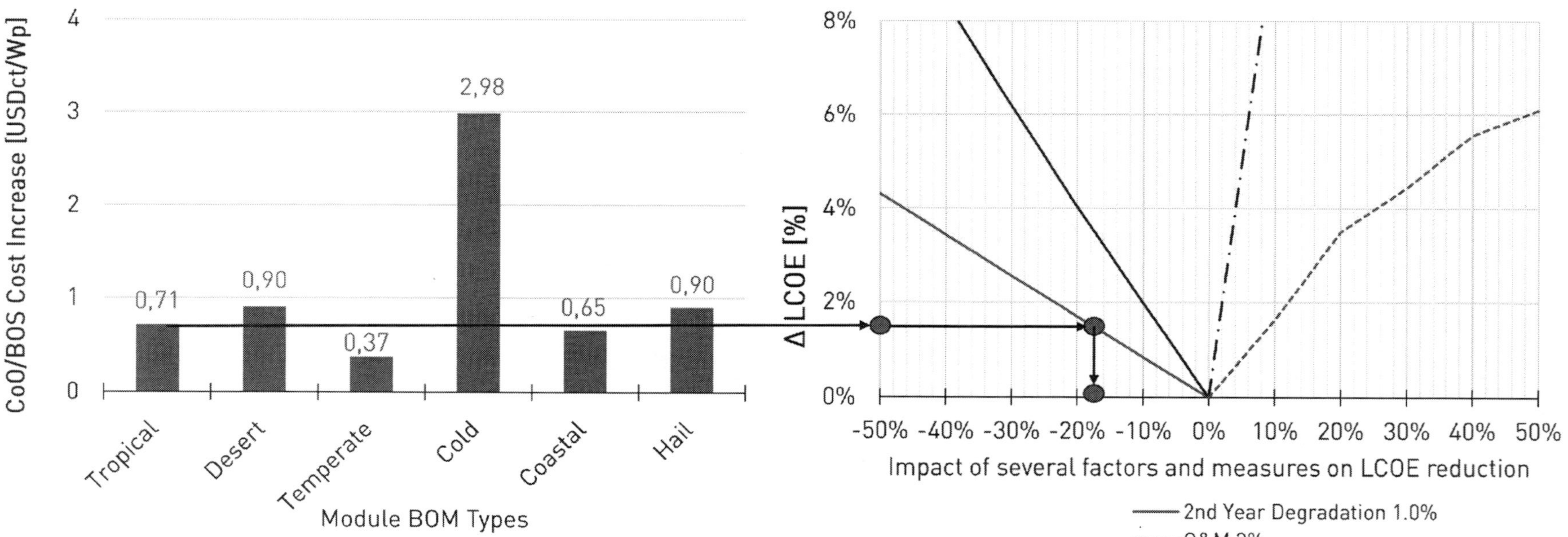

- Change in BOM leads to an **additional 1.6% LCOE.**
- Minimum 17% lower degradation is required, reducing degradation from **1,0%/yr to ~0.8%/yr**, to compensate for the additional LCOE. **HJT degrades on average 0.735%/yr** [D.C. Jordan, et al., https://doi.org/10.1002/pip.3566] + improved

Case 2: Desert

- There is up to **0.9%/yr degradation** observed in the MBR Solar park, UAE.

[S. Kumar et al., DOI: 10.4229/EUPVSEC2023/3AV.2.27]

- **Cracking, chalking, and yellowing** were observed for glass-backsheet modules in Qatar.

[A. A. Abdallha et al., DOI: 10.4229/WCPEC-82022-3DV.1.10] and G.Orenski publicaitons

- **HJT modules showed the lowest soiling-induced energy loss** among tested module types in both fixed (2.3%) and HSAT (-0.24%) installations in the Atacama Desert in Chile.

[A. Taquichiri et al., DOI: 10.4229/EUPVSEC2023/4CV.1.20]

- **5% degradation** observed due to Soiling in Qatar. A higher oxygen content in the ARC layer and a double ARC layer contribute to achieving a higher Isc. Additionally, coating combined with a high tilt angle helps reduce the soiling effect.

[B. Aissa, et al., DOI: 10.4229/EUPVSEC2023/3AV.2.20]

Solutions:
- **Anti-soiling coated glass**
- **HJT cells**
- **GG configuration**
- **Anti-soiling frame design on short side**

→ +0,90 USDct/Wp

CoO impact on the LCOE Case 2: Desert

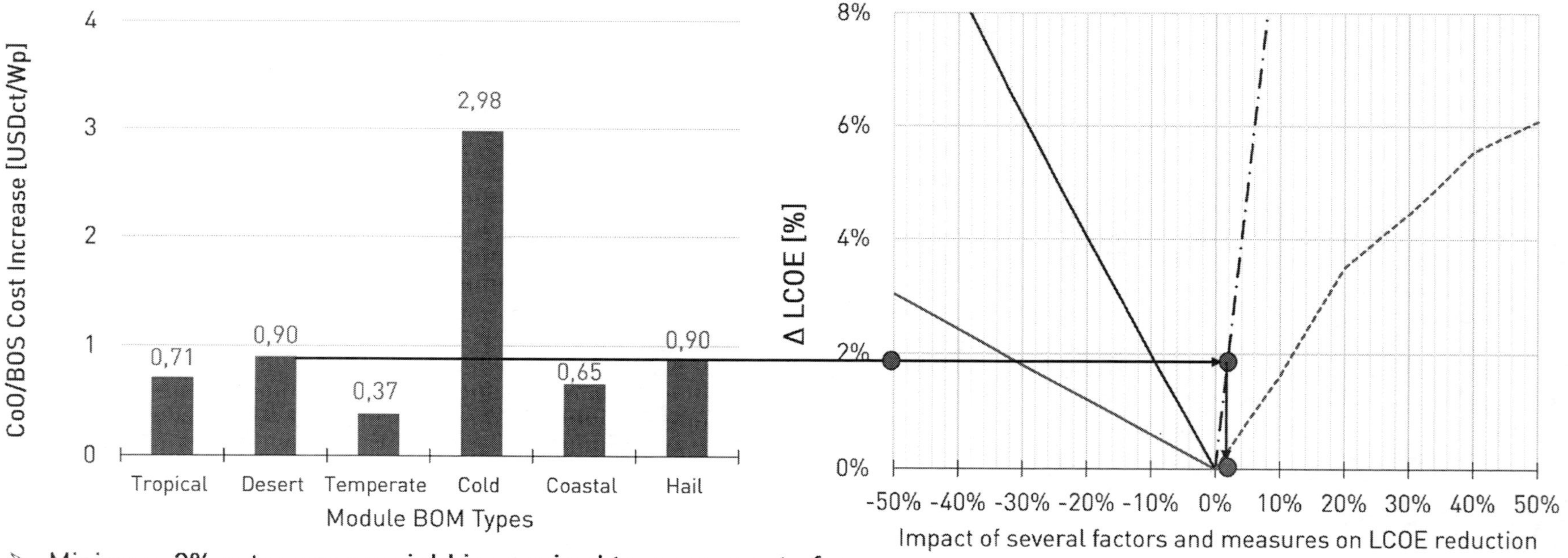

- Minimum **2% extra energy yield is required to compensate for the additional 1.8% LCOE.** This is already observed in the HJT module type, with an energy yield of more than 4% compared to PERC [A. Taquichiri et al., DOI: 10.4229/EUPVSEC2023/4CV.1.20] + improved BOM.

Local Production Impact on CoO. Case 2: Desert

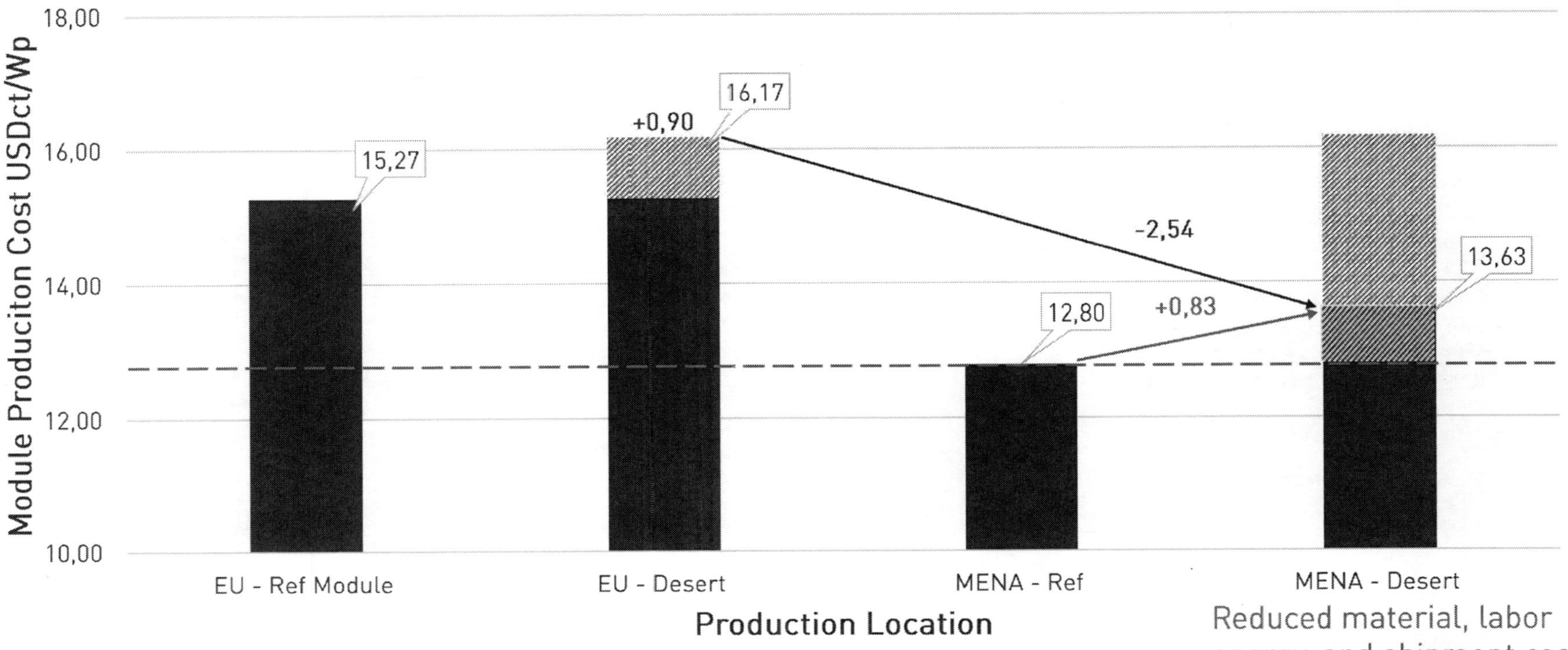

Reduced material, labor energy, and shipment cost

Case 3: Hail Impact

- **GCube Insurance** study claims that 54% of total solar losses in the USA came from hail-related insurance claims.

[https://www.pv-magazine.com/2025/09/19/hail-damage-to-solar-projects-1-of-filed-claims-but-over-50-of-total-losses/]

- Thicker glasses on the front, 3.2mm, have higher hail resilience than the 2mm glass.

[Module Glass Impacts Hail Resiliency — RETC, LLC]

- **CFV Labs Study**: Thinner glass and larger module trend leads to more failures, where the rate of breakage pressure is reduced by 70%.

[T. Billie, et al., https://grndwork.com/pv-module-testing-cfv-labs/]

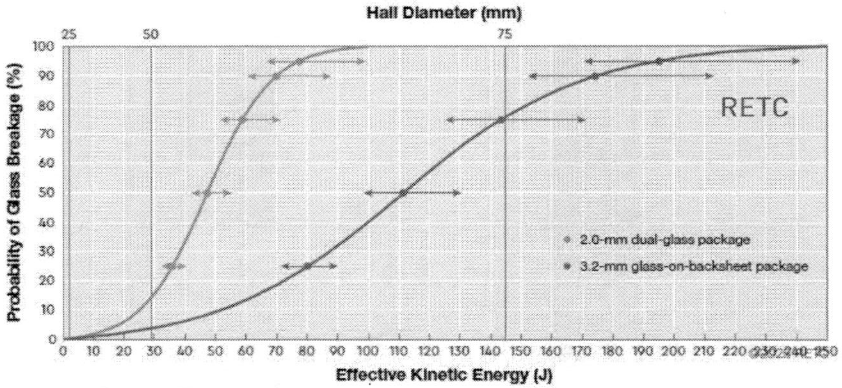

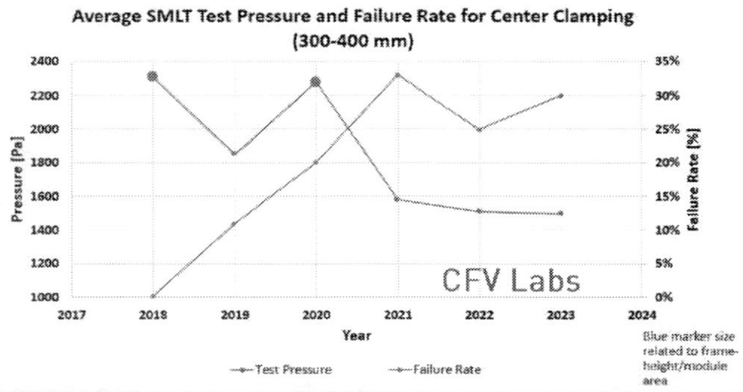

Solutions:
- Steel Frame
- Thicker Frame 35 mm
- Thicker Glass
- GG configuration

→ +0,90 USDct/Wp

CoO impact on the LCOE. Case 3: Hail

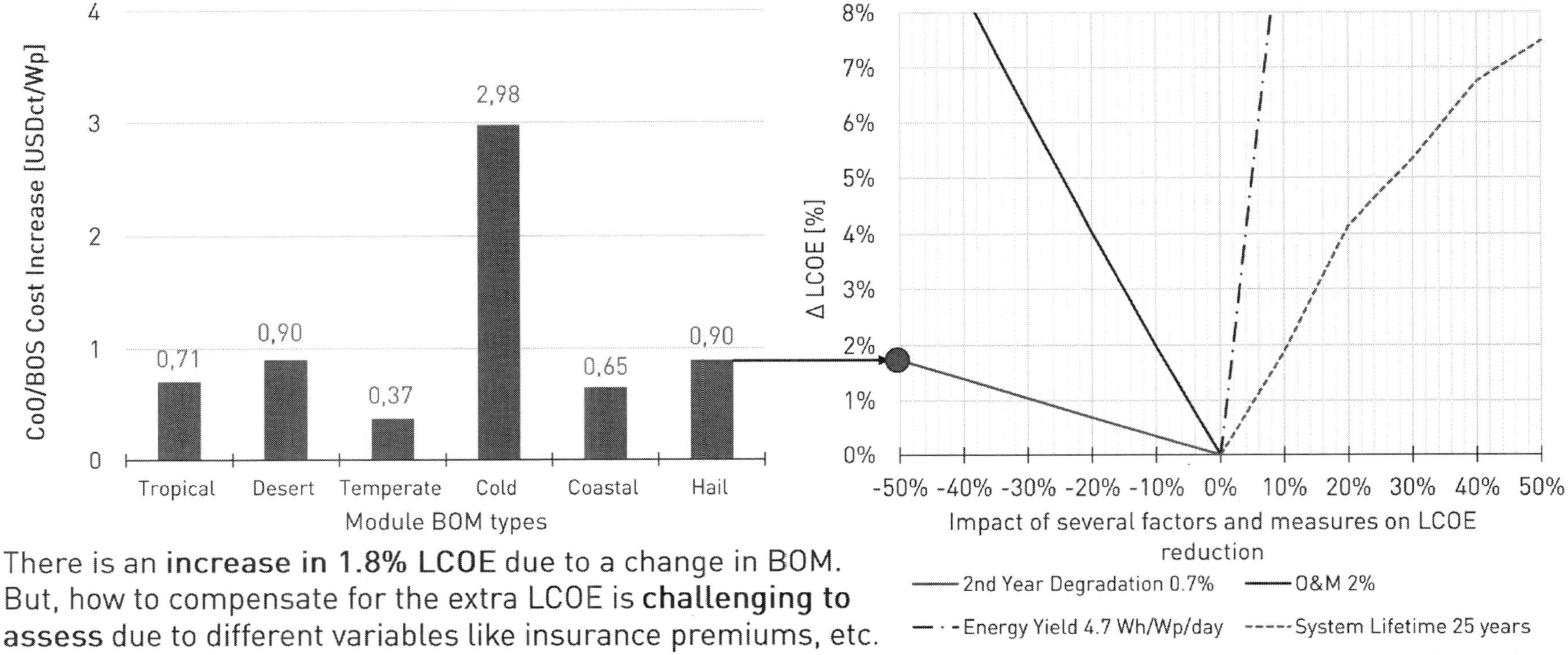

- There is an **increase in 1.8% LCOE** due to a change in BOM.
- But, how to compensate for the extra LCOE is **challenging to assess** due to different variables like insurance premiums, etc.

Local Production Impact on CoO. Case 3: Hail

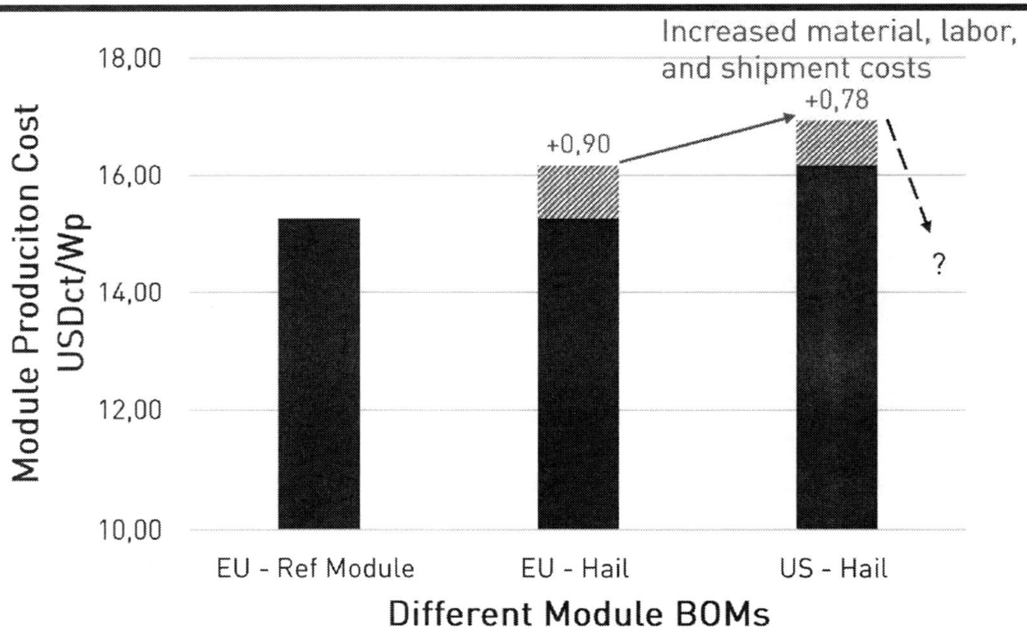

- Currently, the US installation stands at ~**255 GW.** [SEIA.org]
- Wood Mackenzie Power & Renewables U.S. Solar Market Insight Q3 2025 predicts **168 GW utility installation in the next 5 years, considering the** low-case scenario from OBBBA.

[https://seia.org/research-resources/solar-market-insight-report-q3-2025/]

- Project loss affected due to Hail is >50% of all losses.

[https://www.pv-magazine.com/2025/09/19/hail-damage-to-solar-projects-1-of-filed-claims-but-over-50-of-total-losses/]

➢ Local production will be suitable for hail-free PV module BOM production, especially considering the **well-established steel industry and glass industry**.

Summary

- There is potential to work on an **improved BOM that can withstand different climate conditions** and reduce the degradation rates.
- The assumed changes in BOM for different climates result in an additional **0.37 USDct/Wp to 2.98 USDct/Wp**.
- The **costs/Wp will increase the LCOE**, which can be **compensated by robust modules or improved systems**, withstanding the effect of severe climate conditions.
- The impact of higher climate-specific BOM cost on Module cost can be compensated by **producing locally**, specific to the climate zone.

Key Message: Extra cost for a reliable climate-specific BOM can be financially viable.

Outlook

- CTM Analysis **(Standard BOM vs Different BOMs suitable for different climatic conditions)**.
- Detailed Energy Yield/loss Analysis.
- Using a suggested suitable BOM and testing in labs for long-term stability.

Thank you
RCT Solutions GmbH
Line-Eid-Strasse 1
D-78467 Konstanz, Germany
Phone +49 15143176023
sraisth@rct-solutions.com
http://www.rct-solutions.com

42nd European Photovoltaic Solar Energy Conference and Exhibition

This presentation was selected by the Sc. Committee of the EU PVSEC 2025 for submission of a full paper to one of the EU PVSEC's collaborating peer-reviewed journals.

INDOOR CHARACTERIZATION AND ANALYSIS OF REVERSE BREAKDOWN BEHAVIOR OF SOLAR CELLS WITH DIFFERENT CELL ARCHITECTURES

Bengt Jaeckel[1]*, Jens Froebel[1], Matthias Pander[1], Andreas Maixner[2], Hamed Hanifi[2]
[1] Fraunhofer Center for Silicon Photovoltaics CSP, Otto-Eißfeldt-Straße 12, 06112 Halle (Saale), Germany
[2] AESOLAR, Messerschmittring 54, 86343 Koenigsbrunn, Germany
*e-mail: bengt.jaeckel@csp.fraunhofer.de

ABSTRACT: With TOPCon cell technology becoming mainstream in 2025 and HJT/BC increasing their market share, too, cell strings now operate at higher voltages and current densities and exhibit different reverse-bias behavior than legacy PERC/Al-BSF.
We experimentally compare reverse characteristics of five c-Si cell architectures (Al-BSF, PERC, TOPCon, HJT, IBC) using mini-modules and mini-strings measured from 100 to 1.300 W/m² at 25°C with a four-quadrant long-pulse flasher. TOPCon and HJT show pronounced hysteresis in the 1st quadrant but no relevant hysteresis in reverse; bifacial front and rear behavior is essentially identical. The key findings are that typical reverse breakdown voltage for Al-BSF is around -14 V, PERC between -21 and -24 V, HJT around -30 V, TOPCon between -44 and -49 V and for BC between -4 and -5 V. Illumination-dependent reverse current is strong for PERC, low for Al-BSF, very low for HJT and IBC, and overall low for TOPCon, considering more relevant voltages very low. Under full shading scenarios TOPCon and HJT strings with ≥24 cells per bypass diode are generally feasible as string voltages remain below reverse breakdown voltage onset. However, under partial shading (~50% coverage), PERC is most critical due to illumination-enhanced reverse current, while TOPCon/HJT dissipate less power. IBC breaks down early and therefore dissipates less power due to low breakdown voltage. Implications for hot-spot risk, bypass design, and applications with recurring shading (C&I, BaPV, BiPV) are discussed.

Keywords: hot-spot, partial shading, reverse bias, reliability, energy loss

1 INTRODUCTION

PV technology evolved from 3-busbar to multi-wire with more than 20 wires per cell in less than one decade. Their layouts changed from full cell configurations of 3×20 (–24) cells per strings to half-cut serial/parallel with typically 108–156 cells, modifying and increasing voltage and current [1]. New n-type designs (TOPCon, HJT, BC) behave differently in reverse than legacy p-type Al-BSF/PERC.
Under (partial) shading, a cell can be forced into reverse bias and dissipate power, potentially causing local or areal hot spots depending on reverse current paths and localization mechanisms such as edge shunts, grain boundaries/impurities, or areal pn-junction breakdown [2]-[16].
Larger cells (M10/G12) and >20 cells per bypass diode require re-evaluating reverse breakdown voltage onset in general and as a function of illumination [17]-[21].

The current standard for hot-spot testing, IEC 61215-2 [22] hot-spot test (MQT 09) is based on understanding of Al-BSF and PERC cell concepts, not of today's high-power cell types and module layouts. The standard test assumes a "fault"-scenario, not a "daily use" scenario. In C&I, BaPV, BiPV, partial shading is routine. Over 20 years, localized heating can exceed 7000h, while tests (even "extended" MQT 09) cover only hours. Higher façade/roof temperatures raise risk additionally and is tried to include for "fault"-scenario testing in IEC TS 63126 [23]. A stricter hot-spot protocol is under discussion; experiments show >200°C under partial shading [17][19]. The technical background is that heating occurs when power from (n−1) cells is dissipated in one (partially) shaded cell, setting the string in reverse bias operation in the shaded cell. Reverse current flow paths include edge shunts, defects/grain boundaries, and area-wide junction breakdown. Multi crystalline Al-BSF is more prone to localized heating due to its material [10].
Partial shading (20–80%) is common and it was found experimentally that most heating occurs near ~50% shade[17][19].
Herin the focus is set to study reverse breakdown at 25°C. Higher cell temperature will alter the numbers given here typically to lower numbers. However, the trend is same as shown exemplary in the result section.

2 EXPERIMENTAL SETUP

Mini-modules and mini strings per technology were fabricated including 4-point contacts for more precise measurement at expected high currents. IV-curves were measured with an A+A+A+ HALM flasher using long pulses (up to 150 ms) and multi-flash configurations to mitigate hysteresis. To cover all regions a possible four-quadrant sweep from forward bias into reverse breakdown was configured. Irradiance was measured from 100 to 1300 W/m² at 25°C, including the use of a neutral density filter (ND) for low irradiance while maintaining near-AM1.5 spectrum. Additionally dark IV-curves were measured with each measurement run. For TOPCon and HJT hysteresis was checked, and their bifacial front and rear side behavior was measured separately. EL images pre- and -post confirmed no damage during testing. For TOPCon cells multiple batches were checked to test for cell manufacturing induced spread in reverse breakdown behavior.

3 RESULTS

3.1 Al-BSF cells

Al-BSF cell served as a baseline, as many module designs and the IEC 61215-2 hot-spot test criteria were basically developed with this technology in mind. The sample was a multi-crystalline 3-BB cell. IV curves at 25°C taken in the dark (D-IV) and from 100 to 1300 W/m^2 in 100W/m^2-steps were swept from 1st quadrant to reverse until breakdown occurred without inducing damage (see Figure 1 a) left side). After subtracting Isc to highlight illumination effects (see Figure 1 b) left side), a slight irradiance-dependent increase in reverse current is visible between about −5 V and breakdown. Reverse breakdown voltage onset occurs at approximately −14 V, consistent with expectations for multi-crystalline Al-BSF.

3.2 PERC cell

Two mono-crystalline PERC samples were investigated to capture the technology evolution from full to half cells: a 5-BB M3 full cell (≈2020) and a 9-BB M6 half-cut cell (≈2024) were measured as it is described for the Al-BSF cell (see Figure 1 a) right side).
The reverse breakdown voltage is around -21 to -24 V, with the newer half-cell about 1-2 V higher voltages. A strong illumination-enhanced reverse current between about -5 V and breakdown is clearly visible, significantly larger than for Al-BSF (see Figure 1 and note the different x- and y-axis scaling).

3.3 TOPCon cell

TOPCon cells were examined for hysteresis, bifaciality, and manufacturing spread. TOPCon cells show pronounced hysteresis in the 1st quadrant if IV-curve sweep is too fast (~10ms), but no relevant hysteresis in reverse was observed. Front and rear sides behave similarly in reverse (see [24]).
M10 half-cut, 16-wire cells from different manufacturing dates were investigated and a quite large spread in reverse breakdown voltage onset was observed, ranging absolutely from -39 V to around -48 V (see Figure 2 left side and [24]). The irradiance dependence starts at around -20 V, significantly higher compared to PERC and even close to reverse breakdown the additional current is very small.

3.4 HJT cells

M6 half-cut HJT cell was tested (see Figure 2 right side). As with TOPCon, HJT exhibits 1st quadrant hysteresis under rapid sweeps but no observable hysteresis in reverse. Front and rear reverse behavior was very similar. The measured reverse breakdown onset was determined to be around -30 V with essentially no irradiance dependence in the range tested.

3.5 IBC cells

IBC technology was assessed using an 8-cell R&D string. The presented voltages were normalized per cell (Figure 3). IV-curves largely overlap across irradiance, with minor spread between -1 and -3 V likely due to the series interconnection. The key difference vs. other technologies is the very early breakdown at about -4.5V per cell and a negligible irradiance dependence in reverse breakdown voltage behavior.
While breakdown is reached at low reverse voltage, the resulting power density is small, which limits heating severity making such cells great candidates for shade-prone locations.

More details and a closer look into the rear and front side behavior of bifacial cells is given in [24].

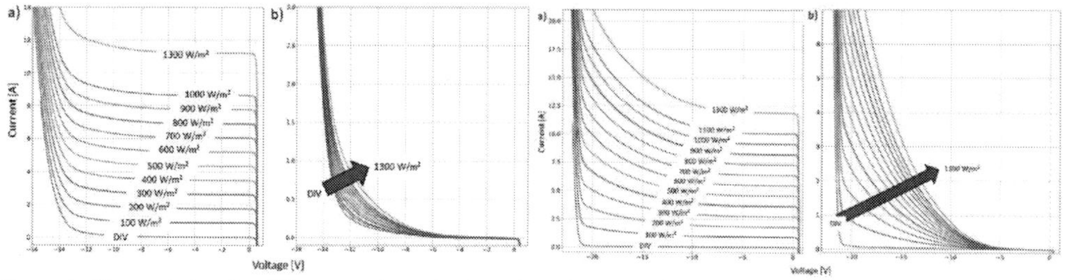

Figure 1: IV-curves a) under different irradiance levels and b) IV-curves where Isc is subtracted to show extra impact on irradiance on reverse voltage behavior.; left: Al-BSF, right: PERC, both full cells.

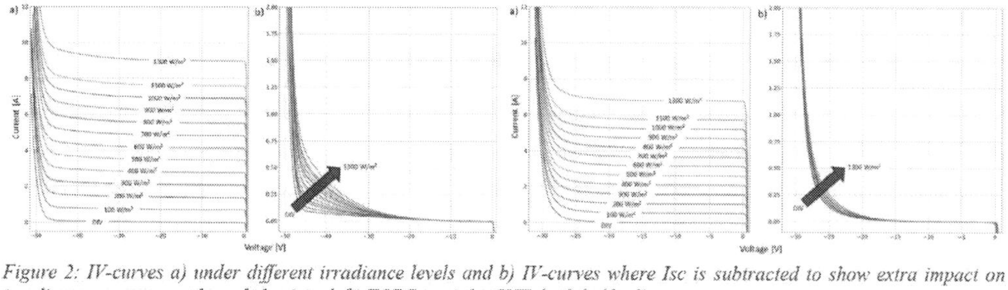

Figure 2: IV-curves a) under different irradiance levels and b) IV-curves where Isc is subtracted to show extra impact on irradiance on reverse voltage behavior.; left: TOPCon, right: HJT, both half cells.

10.4229/EUPVSEC2025/3CO.11.5

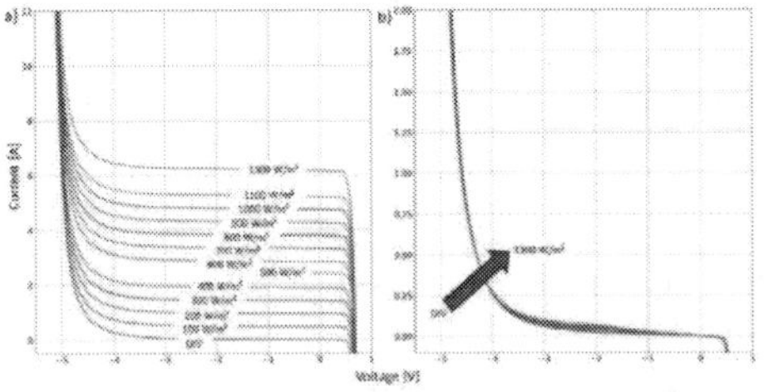

Figure 3: IV-curves from an IBC cell: a) under different irradiance levels and b) IV-curves where Isc is subtracted to show extra impact on irradiance on reverse voltage behavior.

4 DISCUSSION and CONCLUSIONS

4.1 Full-shading implications:

High reverse breakdown voltages for TOPCon (-39 … -49 V) and HJT (≈-30 V) means available series voltage per bypass section typically remains below the threshold voltage, preventing breakdown and limiting heat generation and dissipation. Thus, full-shading hot spots are unlikely for TOPCon and HJT at today's number of cells in series.
However, PERC also has higher reverse breakdown voltages (21…-24 V) than Al-BSF (≈-14 V) and 24 cells per bypass are feasible for PERC with no significant risk. IBC breaks down early (-4…-5 V), so breakdown under full shading is frequent, but low reverse breakdown voltages limits power density.

4.2 Partial shading

Real hot-spot risk is governed by partial shading (20–80 % coverage) and is quite common, and temperatures often peak near ~50 % coverage. Reverse breakdown voltages decrease with temperature (see exemplary for PERC in Figure 4), further support heating. The critical differentiator is the illumination-enhanced reverse current between roughly -5 V and reverse breakdown voltages with strongest impact for PERC, a slight impact for Al-BSF, low for TOPCon, very low impact for HJT, while IBC showed a negligible impact.

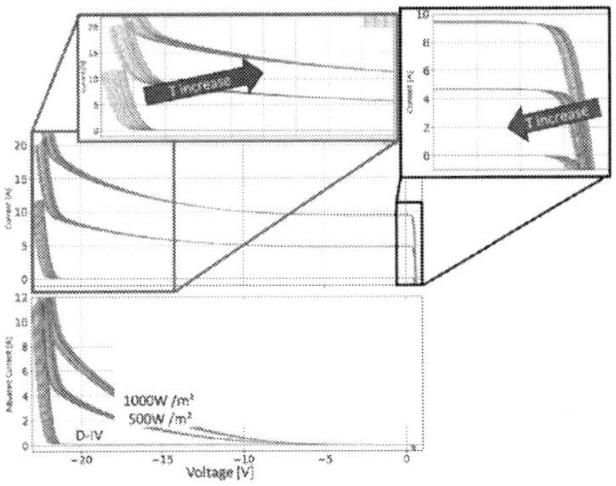

Figure 4: Temperature dependence of IV-curves for PERC cell technology.

4.3 Hysteresis and bifaciality

TOPCon and HJT show pronounced first-quadrant hysteresis if swept rapidly. No relevant hysteresis was observed in reverse, and front- and rear- sides behave similarly in reverse direction for both. Hence, hysteresis and bifaciality do not significantly affect reverse-bias conclusions.

4.4 Manufacturing spread and process control

The investigated TOPCon cells showed significant batch-to-batch spread in Reverse breakdown voltages (-39 V to -48 V) despite identical box sorting, consistent with known process sensitivities for other cell types. In-line metrology and specifications for reverse-bias behavior are advisable in addition to standard forward IV parameters.

4.5 Implications for design and testing

Because partial shading is a recurrent use case in C&I, BaPV, and BiPV, reducing cells per bypass diode lowers potential thermal peaks, long lasting and extra increased operation temperatures and impact energy generation negatively. Relying solely on full-shading criteria can be misleading: PERC's strong illumination-enhanced reverse current makes it most prone to hot spots near ~50% shading, while TOPCon and HJT have in comparison a negligible impact by illumination. MQT 09 reflects earlier generations and rare-fault assumptions. For modern high-power layouts and recurring shading, extended protocols (e.g., "severe hot-spot test") are needed.

The cross-technology comparison of five cell types / generations highlights three drivers of hot-spot risk: 1) reverse breakdown voltage, 2) illumination-dependent reverse current in the pre-breakdown regime, and c) manufacturing spread that shifts reverse breakdown to lower values.

5 OUTLOOK

Figure 4 shows exemplary the temperature dependence of PERC cell technology. Similar experiments were done and are still conducted on other technologies to achieve a more comprehensives picture, including definition of reverse breakdown voltage onset temperature coefficients (TC). The extent on how such TCs are impacted by irradiance is ongoing work.

6 ACKNOWLEDGEMENTS

This work was funded by the Federal Ministry for Economic Affairs and Climate Action (BMWK) under grant 03EE1180 (SegmentPV).

7 REFERENCES

[1] International Technology Roadmap for Photovoltaic (ITRPV), 15th Edition, 2024
[2] J. W. Bishop, Computer simulation of the effects of electrical mismatches in photovoltaic cell interconnection circuits, Solar Cells, 1988, vol. 25, pp. 73-89, DOI:10.1016/0379-6787(88)90059-2
[3] J. W. Bishop, Microplasma breakdown and hot-spots in silicon solar cells, Solar cells, 1989, 26 (4), 335-349.
[4] M. Danner, Reverse characteristics of commercial silicon solar cells-impact on hot spot temperatures

and module integrity, Conference Record of the Twenty Sixth IEEE Photovoltaic Specialists Conference - 1997, IEEE, PVSC-97, 1997, pp. 1137-1140, DOI:10.1109/pvsc.1997.654289

[5] W. Herrmann, Hot spot investigations on PV modules-new concepts for a test standard and consequences for module design with respect to bypass diodes, IEEE Photovoltaic Specialists Conference - 1997, DOI:10.1109/PVSC.1997.654287

[6] W. Herrmann, Operational Behaviour of Commercial Solar Cells under Reverse Biased Conditions, EU-PVSEC, 1998.

[7] M. C. Alonso-Garcia, Analysis and modelling the reverse characteristic of photovoltaic cells, Solar Energy Materials & Solar Cells, 2006, vol. 90, pp. 1105-1120

[8] D. Lausch, Identification of pre-breakdown mechanism of silicon solar cells at low reverse voltages, Applied Physics Letters, 2010, 97, 073506

[9] C. Reichel, Investigation of electrical shading effects in back-contacted back-junction silicon solar cells using the two-dimensional charge collection probability and the reciprocity theorem, Journal of Applied Physics, 2011-01, vol. 109, DOI:10.1063/1.3524506

[10] O. Breitenstein, Understanding junction breakdown in multi-crystalline solar cells Journal of Applied Physics, 2010, DOI:https://doi.org/10.1063/1.3562200

[11] H. Yang, Investigation of the Relationship between Reverse Current of Crystalline Silicon Solar Cells and Conduction of Bypass Diode, International Journal of Photoenergy, 2012, vol. 2012, pp. 1-5, DOI:10.1155/2012/357218

[12] K. A. Kim, Photovoltaic hot spot analysis for cells with various reverse-bias characteristics through electrical and thermal simulation, IEEE 14th Workshop on Control and Modeling for Power Electronics (COMPEL), IEEE, 2013, DOI:10.1109/compel.2013.6626399

[13] J. Bauer, Hot spots in multi-crystalline silicon solar cells: avalanche breakdown due to etch pits, Physica status solidi (RRL) – Rapid Research Letters, 2009-03, vol. 3, pp. 40-42, DOI:10.1002/pssr.200802250.

[14] F. Dauzou, Electrical behaviour of n-type silicon solar cells under reverse bias: Influence of the manufacturing process, Solar Energy Materials and Solar Cells, 2012-09, vol. 104, pp. 175-179, DOI:10.1016/j.solmat.2012.04.046

[15] V. Shanmugam, Impact of the manufacturing process on the reverse-bias characteristics of high-efficiency n-type bifacial silicon wafer solar cells, Solar Energy Materials and Solar Cells, 2019, vol. 191, pp. 117-122, DOI:10.1016/j.solmat.2018.11.014

[16] J. Qian, Two-Dimensional Hot Spot Temperature Simulation for c-Si Photovoltaic Modules Physica status solidi (a), 2018, vol. 215, DOI:10.1002/pssa.201800429

[17] B. Jaeckel, Hotspottest und reale Teilverschattung von modernen High-Density HD-Modulen: eine Wahrscheinlichkeits- und Risikobetrachtung, PV Symposium Bad Staffelstein, 2021

[18] E. Oezkalay, The effect of partial shading on the reliability of photovoltaic modules in the built-environment, EPJ Photovoltaics, 2024, vol. 15, 7, DOI:10.1051/epjpv/2024001.

[19] R. Witteck, Hot Cells in High-Power Photovoltaic Modules with Solar Cells from Larger Silicon Wafer Formats Eu-PVSEC, 2021, DOI:10.4229/EUPVSEC20212021-4AV.1.25

[20] C. Clement, Illumination Dependence of Reverse Leakage Current in Silicon Solar Cells," 49th IEEE Photovoltaic Specialists Conference, 2021, vol. 11, pp. 1285-1290, DOI:10.1109/jphotov.2021.3088005

[21] C. Clement, Design of shading- and hotspot-resistant shingled modules, Progress in Photovoltaics: Research and Applications, 2021, DOI:10.1002/pip.3507

[22] IEC 61215-2, Crystalline silicon terrestrial photovoltaic (PV) modules - Design qualification and type approval, (2016, 2022)

[23] IEC TS 63126, Guidelines for qualifying PV modules, components and materials for operation at high temperatures, 2020, https://webstore.iec.ch/en/publication/59551

[24] B. Jaeckel, Characterization and analysis of reverse breakdown voltage onset of solar cells with different cell architectures, EPJ Photovoltaics, 2025

Fraunhofer CSP

Fraunhofer Center for Silicon Photovoltaics CSP

AESOLAR

3CO.11.5

Indoor characterization and analysis of reverse breakdown behavior of solar cells with different cell architectures

Bengt Jaeckel, Jens Froebel, Matthias Pander, Andreas Maixner, and Hamed Hanifi
Fraunhofer Center for Silicon Photovoltaics CSP, Otto-Eissfeldt-Str. 12, 06120 Halle (Saale), Germany
AESOLAR, Messerschmittring 54, 86343 Königsbrunn, Germany

Reverse Bias Characterization
Outline

1. **Motivation**
2. **Experimental setup**
3. **Cell architecture results**
   - Al-BSF, PERC, TOPCon, HJT, (I)BC
4. **Conclusions & Outlook**

Outdoor partial shading test setup at Fhg CSP

Image: https://enterfea.com/thermal-loads/

Reverse Bias Characterization
Motivation

- Solar cell and module technology changed (60 full cells to 144+ half cells)
- Cell **efficiency increases, so do Voc voltages** (eff. 14% to 25+%)
- Cells got significant larger, and number of busbars increased (2 → 20+)
- Cells get **more temperature sensitive**

- Modules are significant less expensive!
- Modules are **mounted in more (partial) shade prone areas**
- **Partial shading is more critical** compared to full cell shading

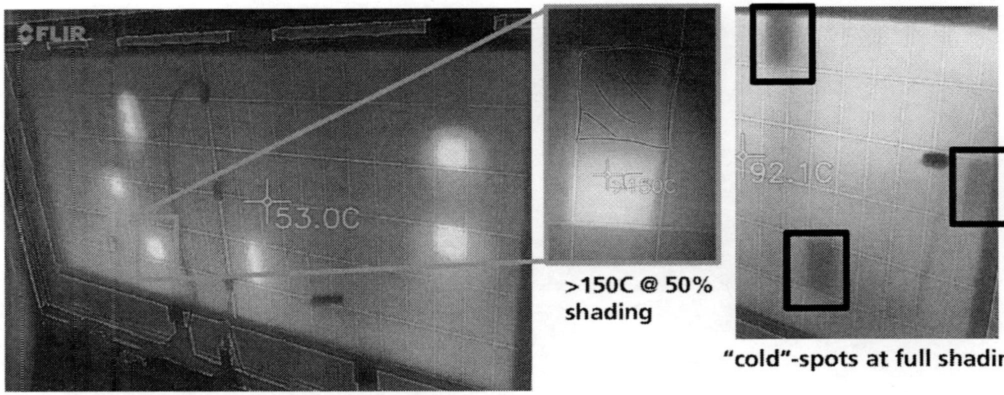

>150C @ 50% shading

"cold"-spots at full shading

Reverse Bias Characterization

Motivation – full shading of one cell

- Typical look at a solar cell / module!
- Power is produced and current flow is "normal"
- For normal operation this is sufficient!

- BUT: **under (full) shading** the IV / PU diagram changes as shaded cell goes into reverse and **becomes a consumer**

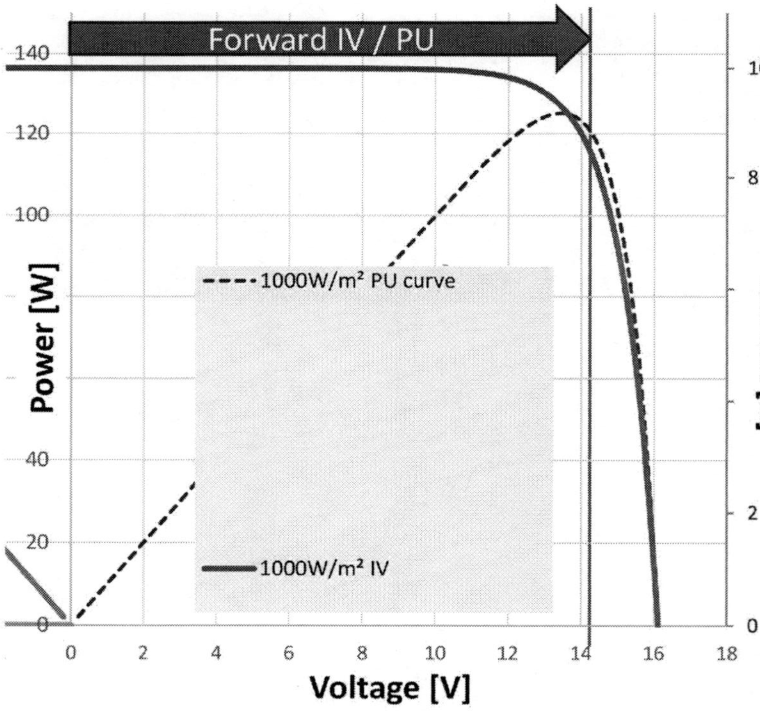

Reverse Bias Characterization
Motivation – full shading of one cell

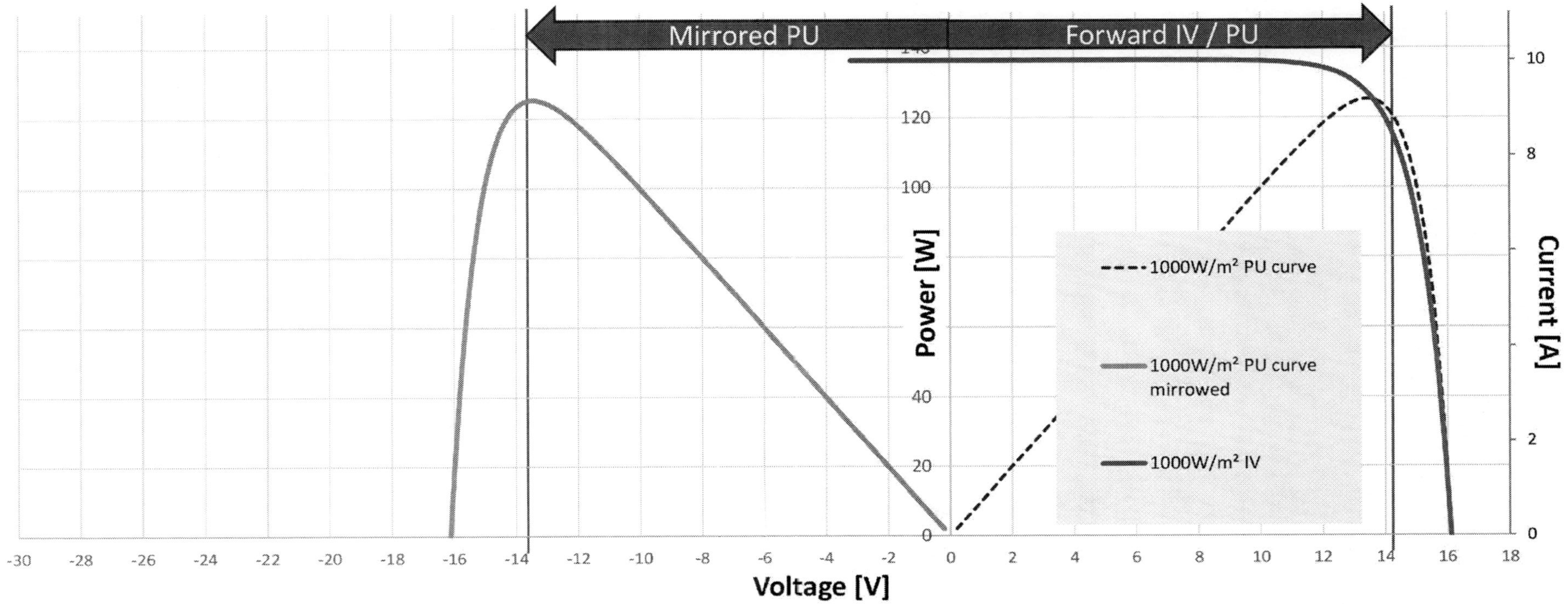

Reverse Bias Characterization

Motivation – full shading of one cell

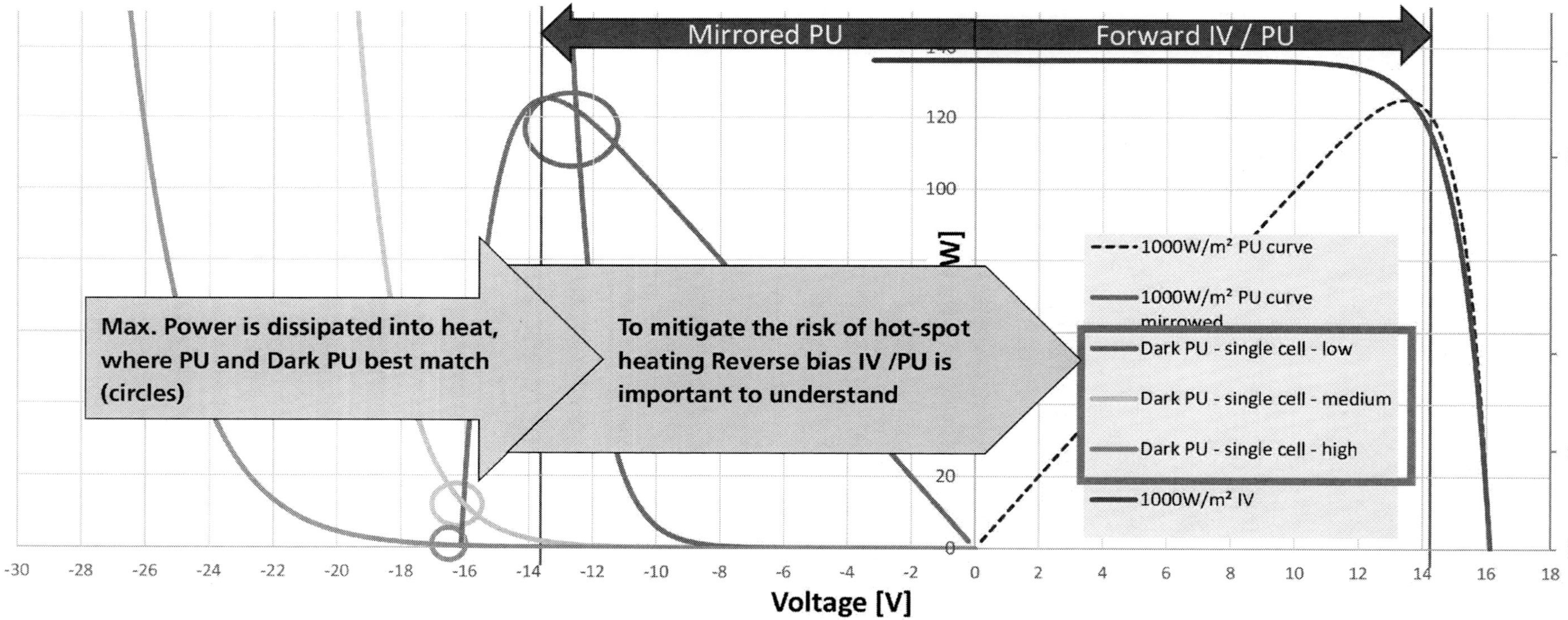

Reverse Bias Characterization
Experimental setup

- Mini-modules and mini strings per technology
- IV-curves were measured with an long pulse A+A+A+ halm.
- 4-quadrant IV sweeps from forward bias into reverse breakdown
- Irradiance: 0 (DIV), 100 to 1300 W/m² at 25°C in 100W/m² steps
- EL images pre- and -post confirmed no damage during testing

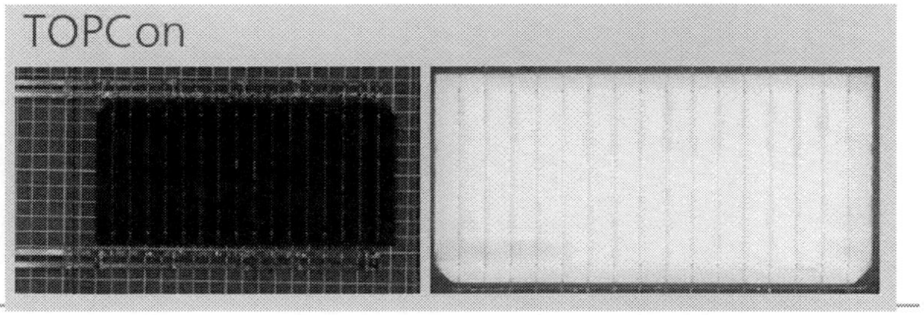

Reverse Bias Characterization

Investigated cell architectures - Overview

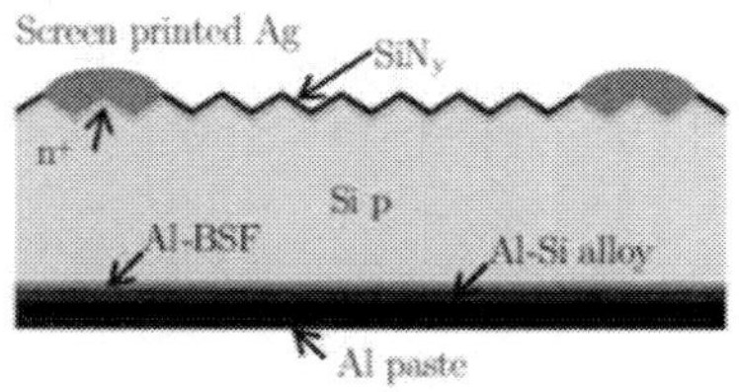

AL-BSF

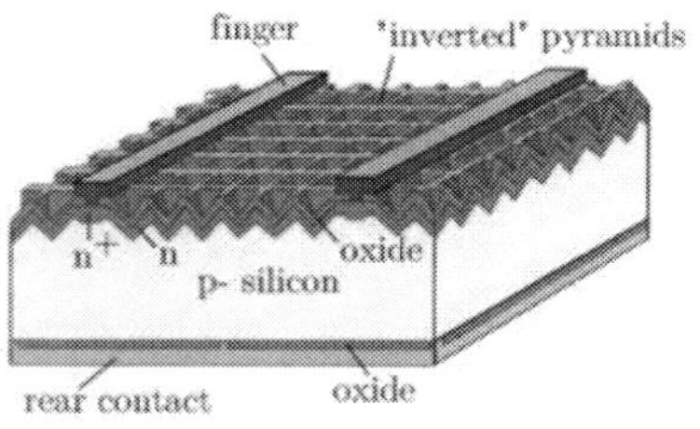

PERC

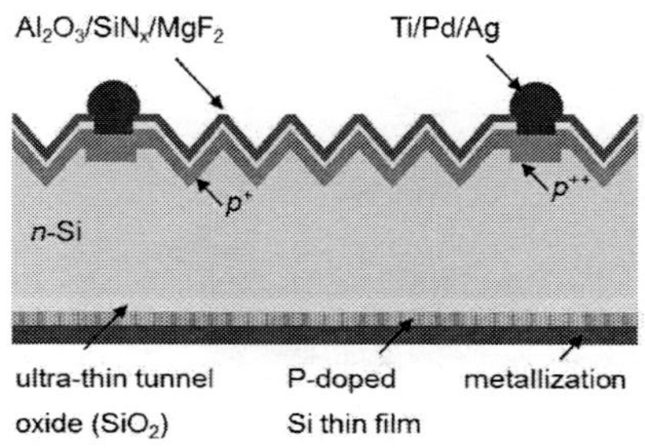

Topcon

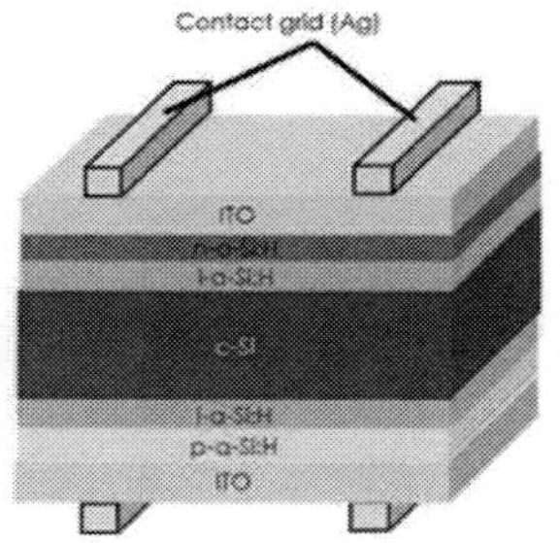

HJT

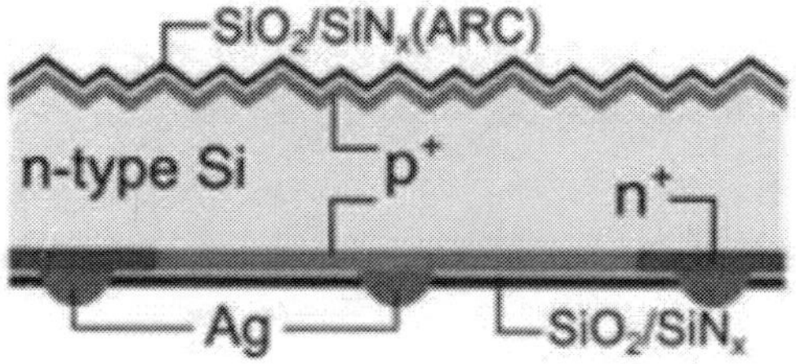

(I)BC-type

Reverse Bias Characterization

Results – Al-BSF

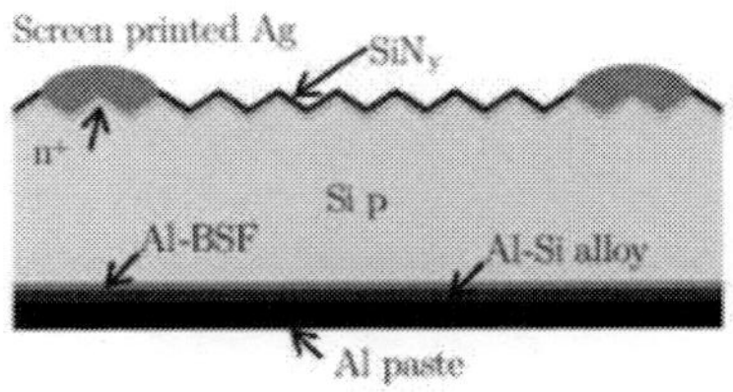

AL-BSF

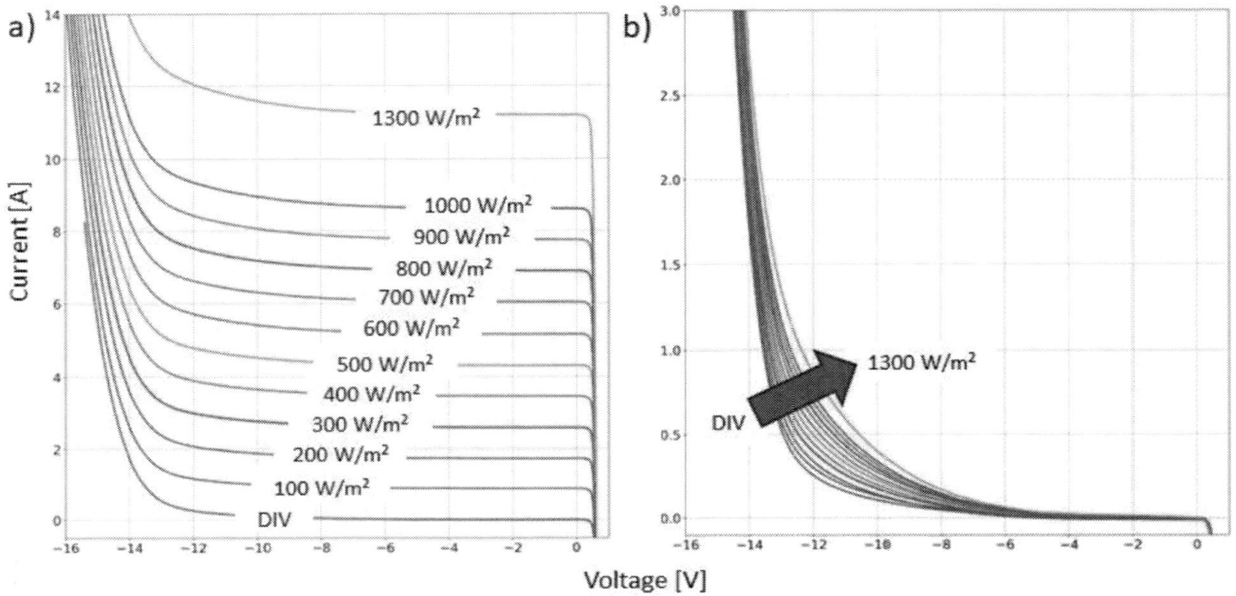

- ➢ Reverse breakdown voltage onset at **~-14V**
- ➢ A little irradiance dependence in range from -5V to -13V

Reverse Bias Characterization

Results – PERC

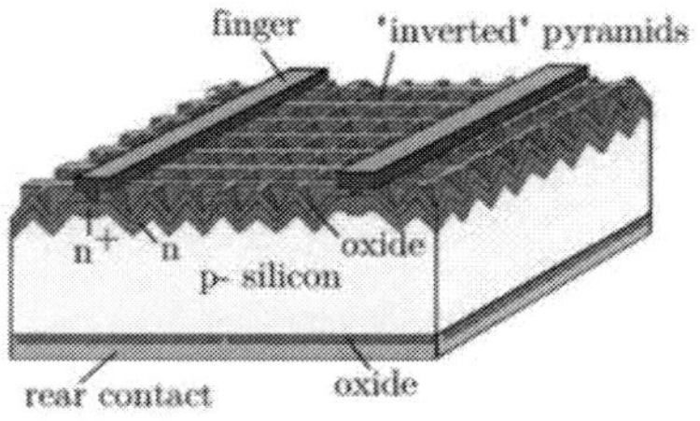

PERC

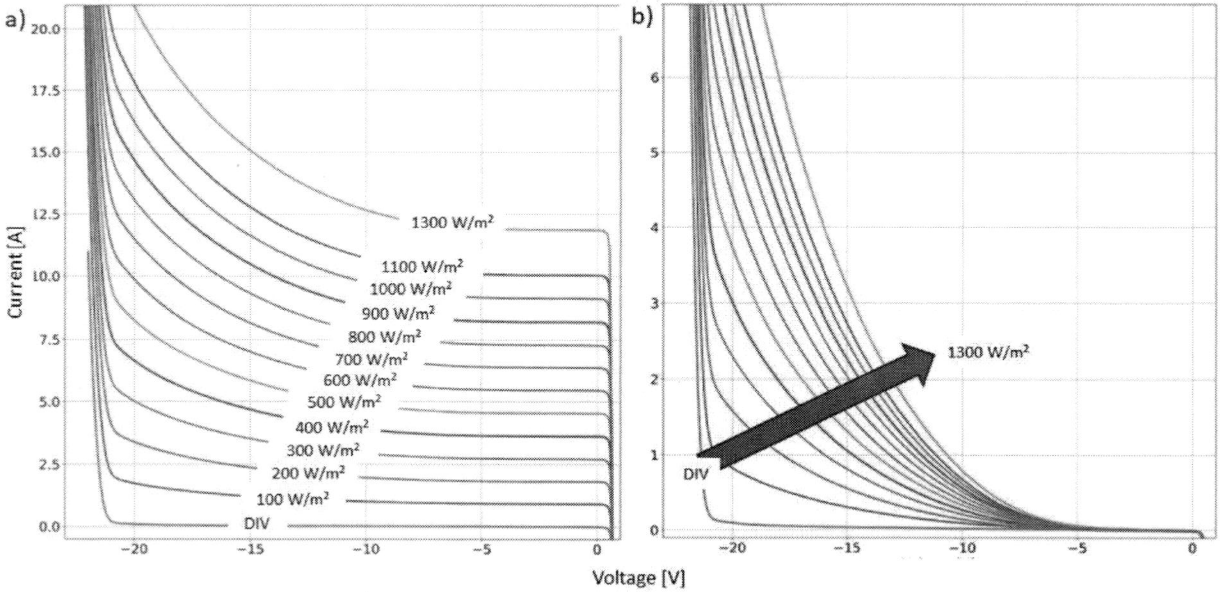

- Reverse breakdown voltage onset at **-21 to -24 V**
- **Very strong irradiance** dependence in range from -5V to -21V

Reverse Bias Characterization

Results – TOPCon - BIFACIAL

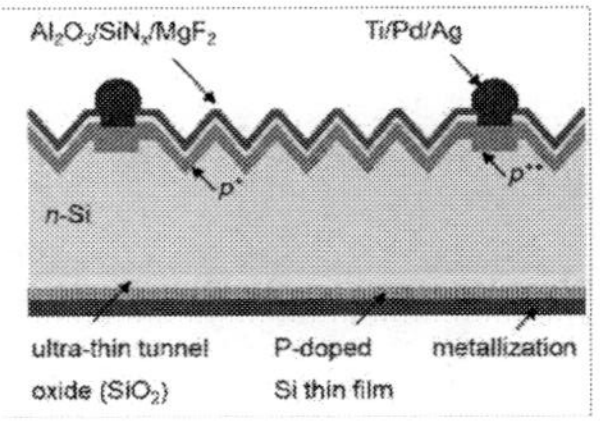

Topcon

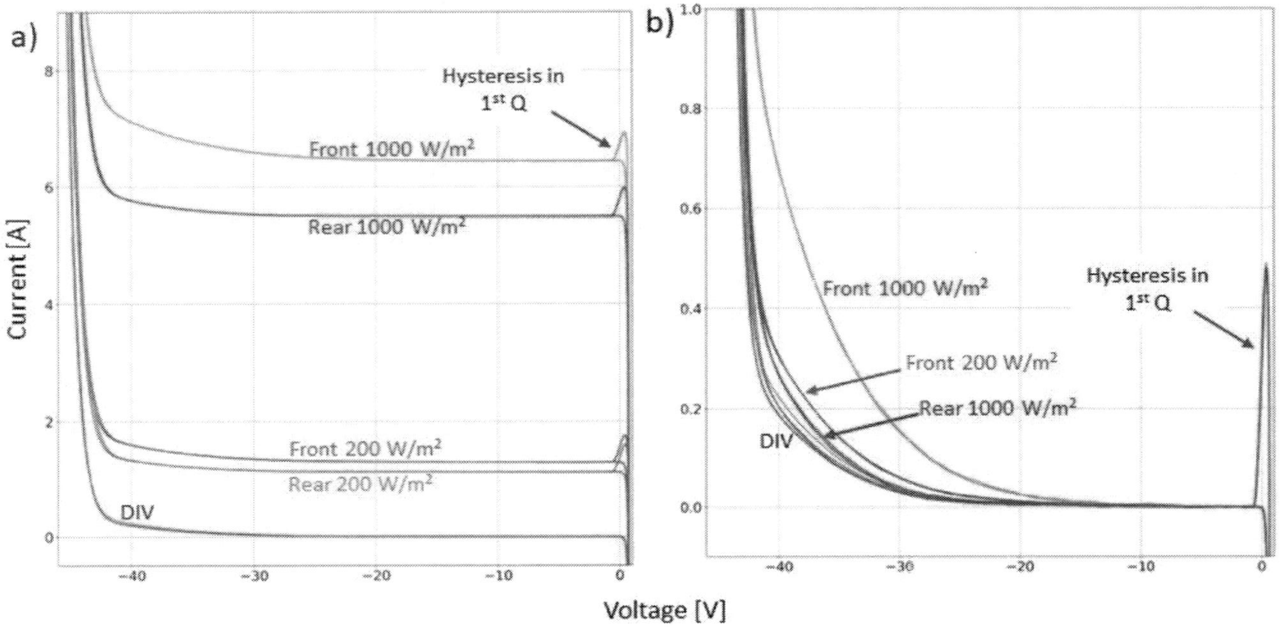

- Hysteresis is front direction √
- **NO hysteresis in reverse**
- Front side has slightly higher irradiance dependence compared to rear side

Reverse Bias Characterization

Results – TOPCon

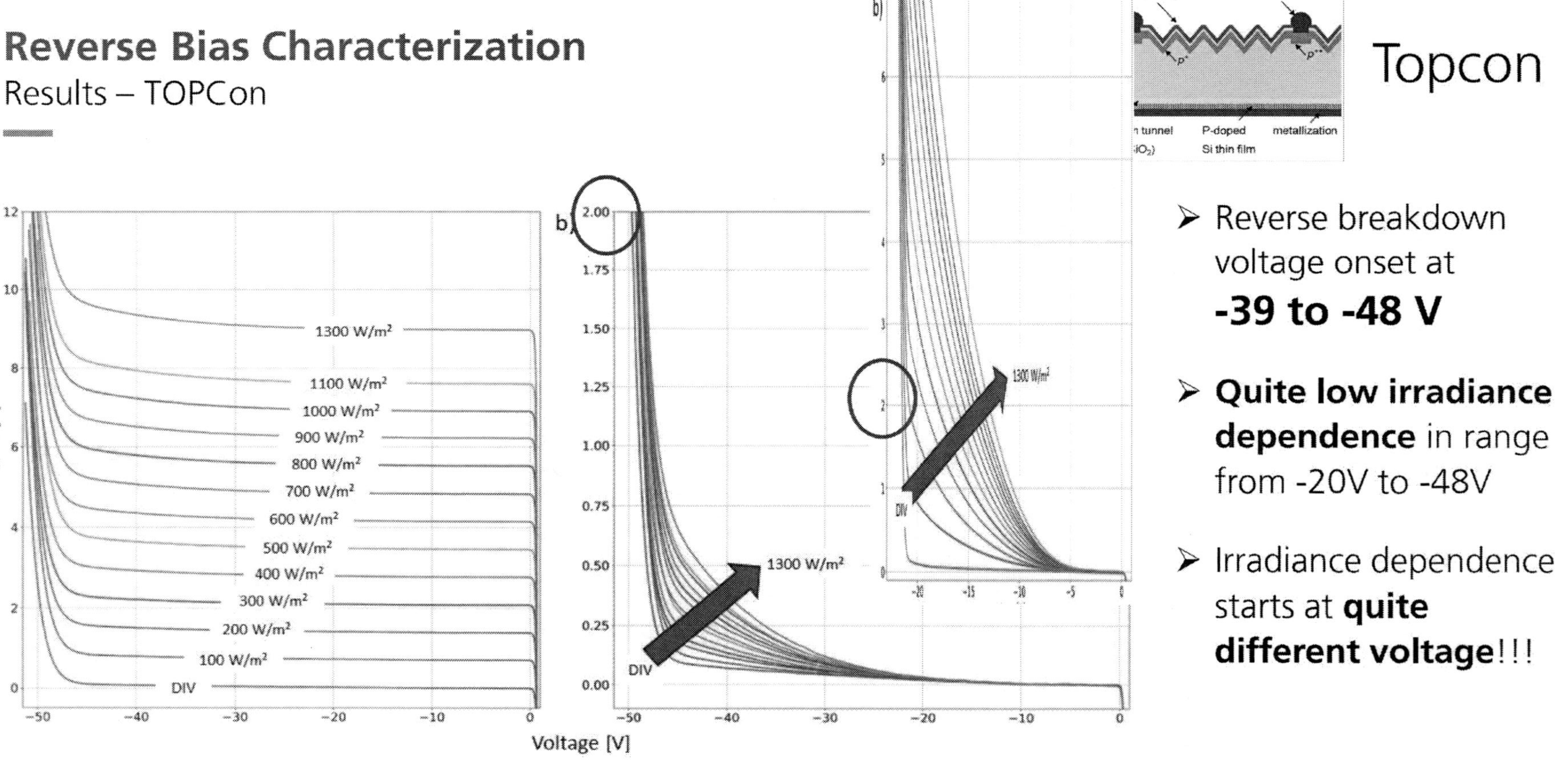

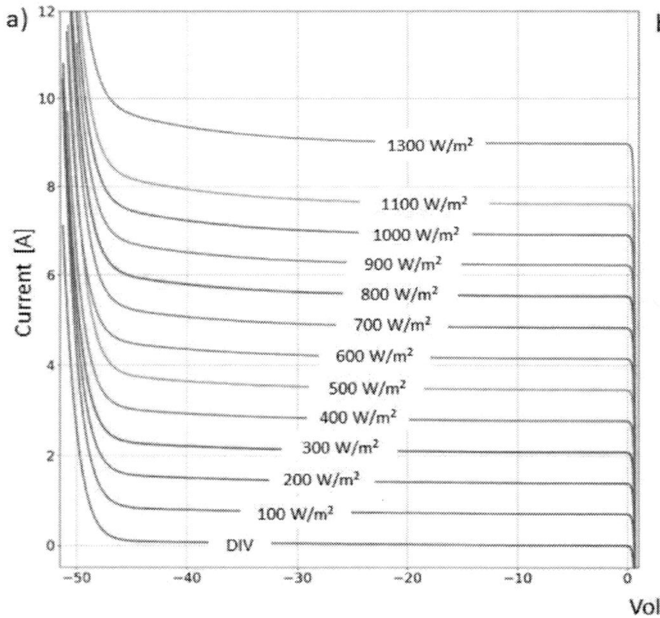

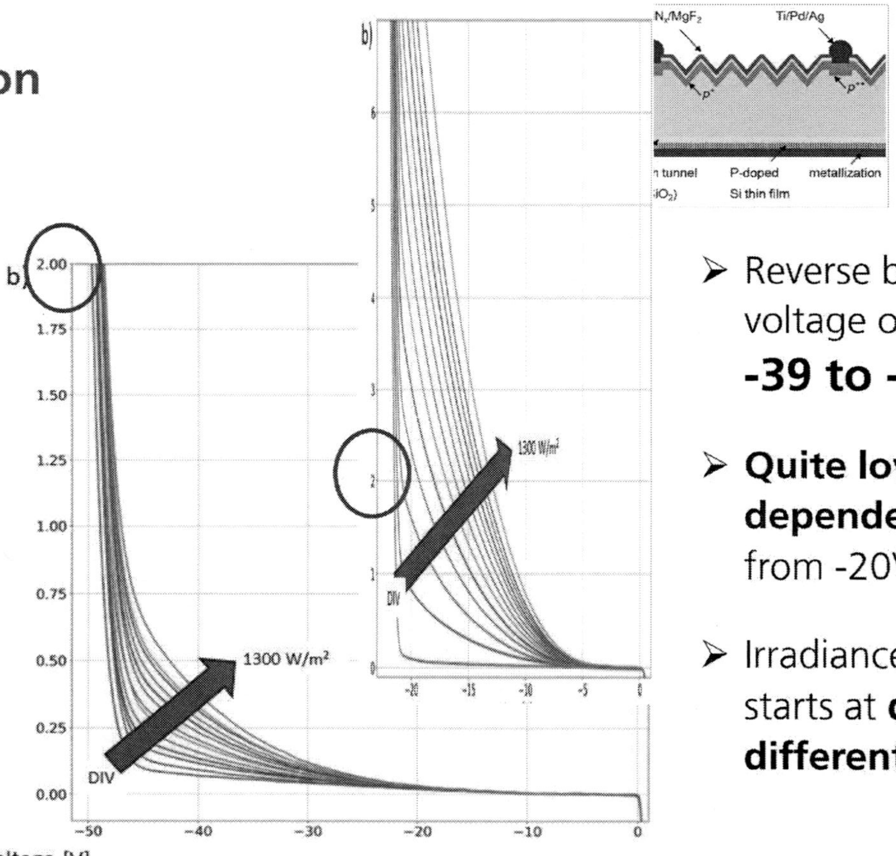

Topcon

- Reverse breakdown voltage onset at **-39 to -48 V**
- **Quite low irradiance dependence** in range from -20V to -48V
- Irradiance dependence starts at **quite different voltage**!!!

Reverse Bias Characterization

Results – (I)BC

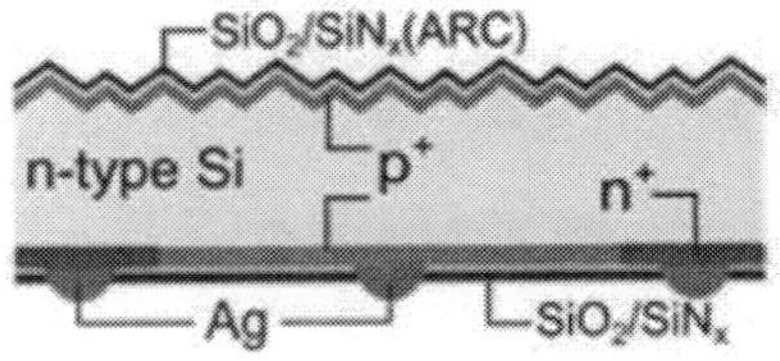

(I)BC

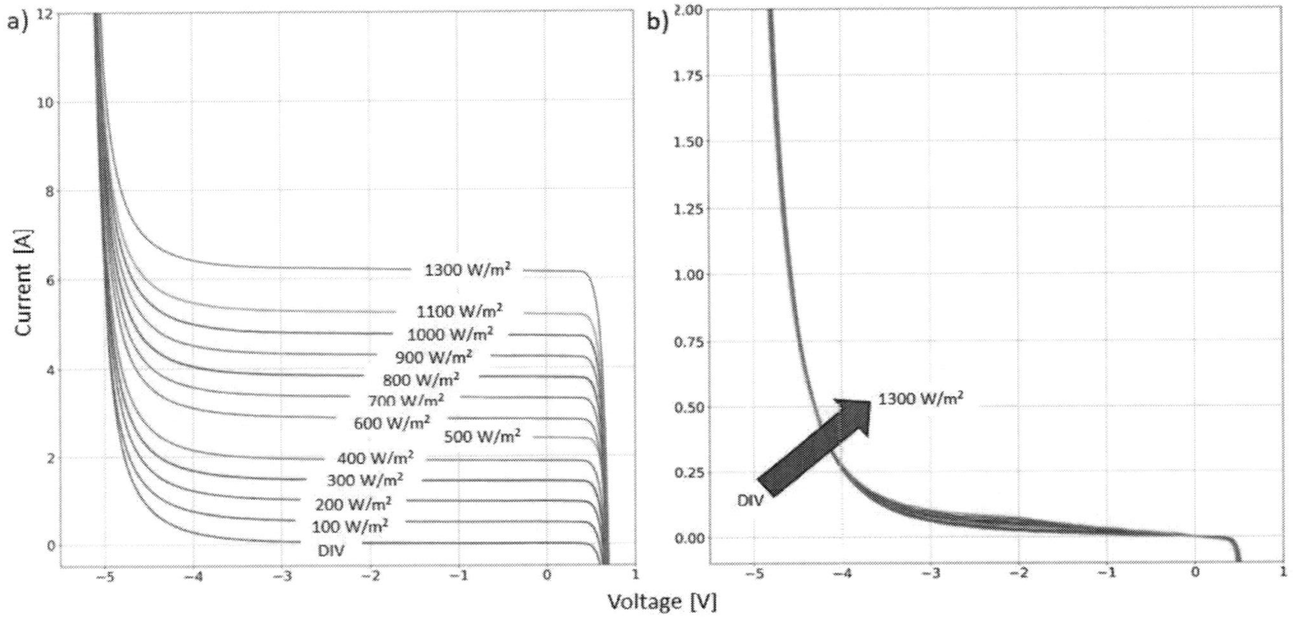

- Reverse breakdown voltage onset at **~-4.5 V**, **significant lower compared** to other technologies
- **No irradiance dependence**

Reverse Bias Characterization

Impact on temperature: Example: PERC

- Temperature dependent IV curves taken at 1000, 500W/m² and in the dark
- Range: 30-70°C

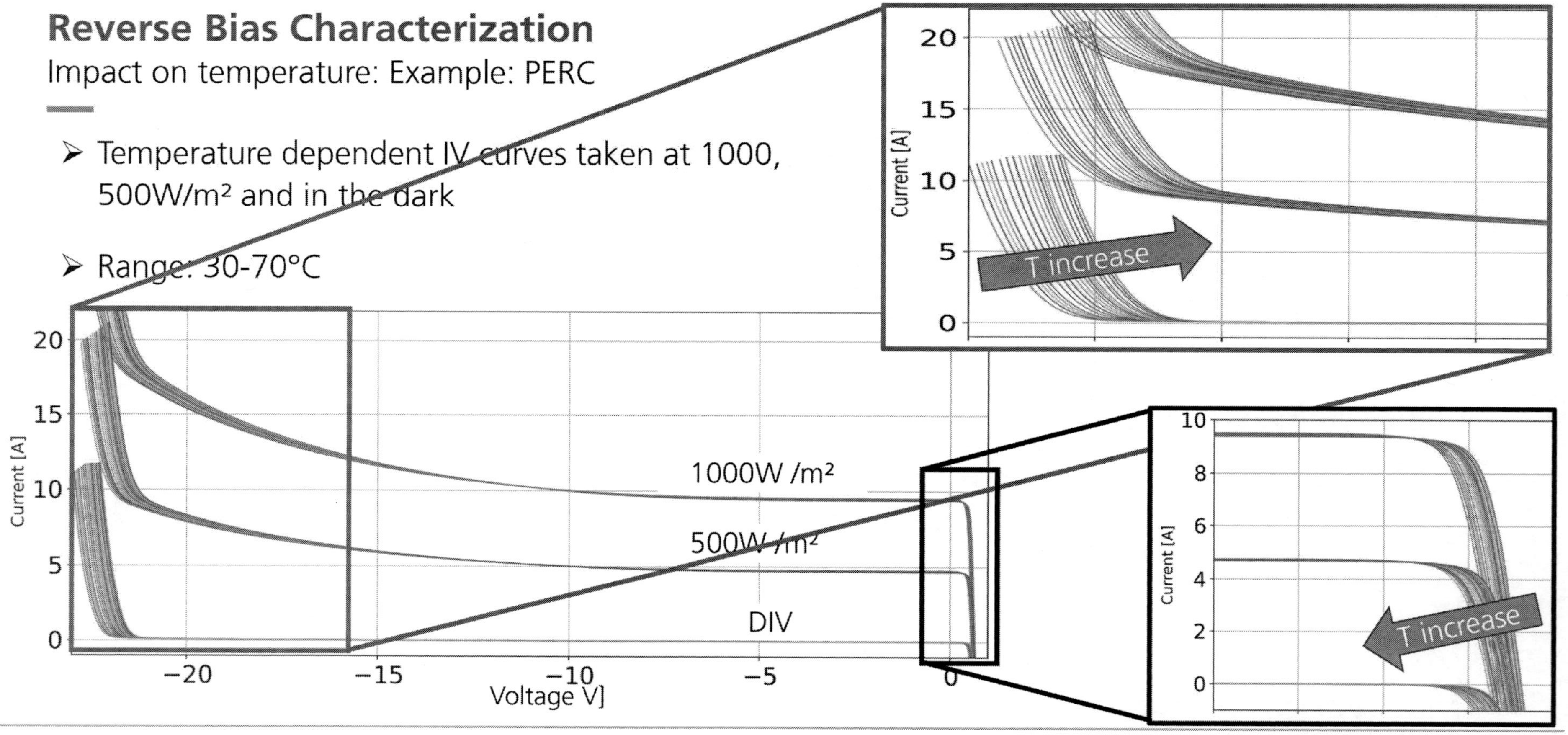

Reverse Bias Characterization

Summary

1. PERC shows very string Irradiance dependence while IBC alomost none

2. Breakdown voltage of TOPCon is significant higher compared to PERC, HJT is sort of in the middle.

3. IBC shows quite different behavior (as expected)

4. Reverse Breakdown voltage is reduced with increasing temperatures
Outlook: reverse breakdown temperature coefficient (TC) determination and rel. / abs. comparison to standard TCs

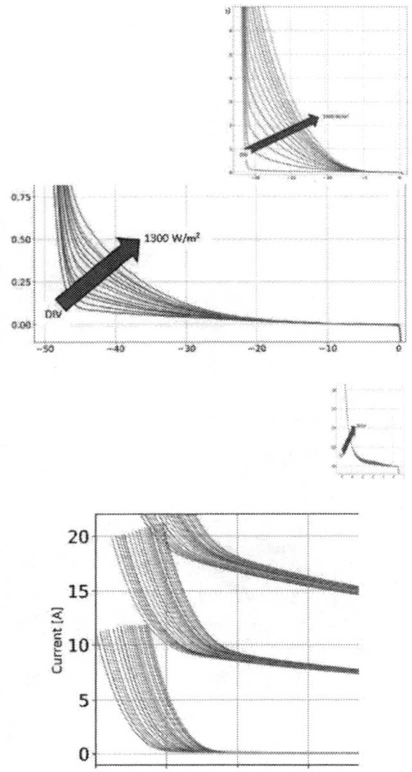

Fraunhofer CSP

Fraunhofer Center for Silicon Photovoltaics CSP

AESOLAR

Thank you for your attention!

Contact
Dr. Bengt Jaeckel
Group manager PV Modules, Components and Manufacturing
Bengt.jaeckel@csp.fraunhofer.de

Fraunhofer CSP
Otto-Eißfeldt- Straße 12
06120 Halle (Saale)
www.csp.fraunhofer.de

Funding:
Project SegmentPV (#03EE1180)

Federal Ministry
for Economic Affairs
and Energy

Fraunhofer CSP

Fraunhofer Center for Silicon Photovoltaics CSP

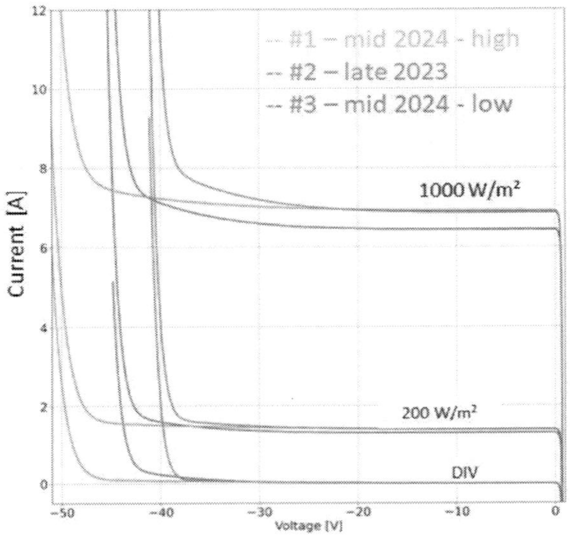

Publication note:

A detailed Paper on Mission Profiles will be published in EPJ as invited paper of EU Pvsec later this year. Please check journal webpage or contact Bengt Jäckel

Title:
„Characterization and Analysis of Reverse Breakdown Voltage onset of Solar Cells with Different cell Architectures"

IBC4EU: European Back Contact Technology

Dr. Florian Buchholz

3CP.1

42nd EUPVSEC, Bilbao, Spain

24.09.2025

ISC research for a sunny future

IBC4EU

This project has received funding from the European Union's Horizon Europe research and innovation programme under grant agreement No.101084259

IBC4EU

TOPCon takes over, what's next?

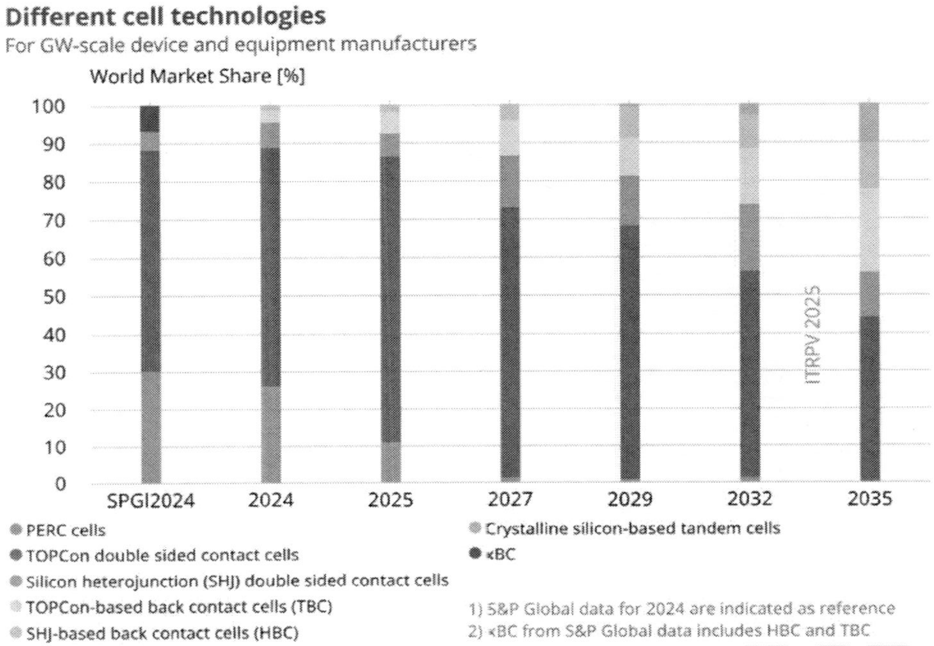

IBC4EU

TOPCon takes over, what's next?

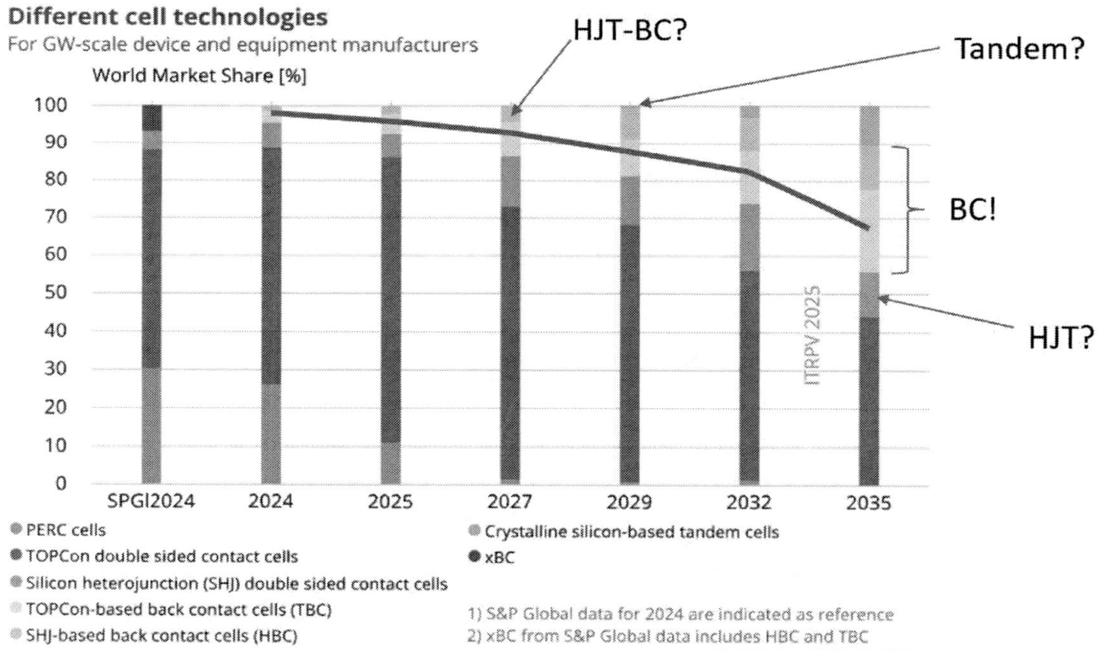

IBC4EU

Why Back Contact?

- Last **evolution** stage of mainstream cSi technology
- Based on **proven processes** and materials
- Module efficiency **>25%** possible
- Proven on pilot line level and in production (TRL7+)

IBC4EU

IBC4EU Project

- Virtual pilot line

Project Partners

ISC research for a sunny future
protech
FuturaSun
ISFH
imec
ENERGYRA
TNO innovation for life
metsolar
HIGHLINE
Copprint
cea
BECQUEREL INSTITUTE
WIP RENEWABLE ENERGIES
LuxChemtech
kalyon PV

Associated Partners

LPKF Laser & Electronics
Toyal
東洋アルミ
RENA

- Funded by Horizon Europe
- European and non-European partners
- Across the whole value chain

IBC4EU

IBC4EU Project

- Virtual pilot line

Silicon Wafers

Project Partners

ISC research for a sunny future
protech
FuturaSun
ISFH
imec
ENERGYRA
TNO innovation for life
metsolar
HIGHLINE
Copprint
cea
BECQUEREL INSTITUTE
WIP RENEWABLE ENERGIES
LuxChemtech
kalyon-PV

Associated Partners

LPKF Laser & Electronics
Toyal
東洋アルミ
RENA

IBC4EU

IBC4EU Project

- Virtual pilot line

Silicon Wafers
↓
Solar Cells

Project Partners

ISC research for a sunny future
protech
FuturaSun
ISFH
imec
ENERGYRA
TNO innovation for life
metsolar
HIGHLINE
Copprint
cea
BECQUEREL INSTITUTE
WIP RENEWABLE ENERGIES
LuxChemtech
kalyon-PV

Associated Partners

LPKF Laser & Electronics
Toyal
東洋アルミ
RENA

IBC4EU

IBC4EU Project

- Virtual pilot line

Silicon Wafers
↓
Solar Cells
↓
Modules

Project Partners

ISC research for a sunny future, proTECH, FuturaSun, ISFH, imec, ENERGYRA, TNO innovation for life, metsolar, HIGHLINE, Copprint, cea, BECQUEREL INSTITUTE, WIP RENEWABLE ENERGIES, LuxChemtech, kalyon·PV

Associated Partners

C, LPKF Laser & Electronics, Toyal, 東洋アルミ, RENA

IBC4EU

IBC4EU Project

- Virtual pilot line

Silicon Wafers
↓
Solar Cells
↓
Modules
↓
Recycling

Project Partners

ISC research for a sunny future
protech
FuturaSun
ISFH
imec
ENERGYRA
TNO innovation for life
metsolar
HIGHLINE
Copprint
cea
BECQUEREL INSTITUTE
WIP RENEWABLE ENERGIES
LuxChemtech
kalyon-PV

Associated Partners

LPKF Laser & Electronics
Toyal
東洋アルミ
RENA

IBC4EU

IBC4EU Project

- Virtual pilot line

Industry 4.0

Techno-economic evaluation

Silicon Wafers → Solar Cells → Modules → Recycling

Project Partners

ISC research for a sunny future; PROTECH; FuturaSun; ISFH; imec; ENERGYRA; TNO innovation for life; metsolar; HIGHLINE; Copprint; cea; BECQUEREL INSTITUTE; WIP RENEWABLE ENERGIES; LuxChemtech; kalyon PV

Associated Partners

C; LPKF Laser & Electronics; Toyal; 東洋アルミ; RENA

Silicon Wafers

- Tungsten wire with 38 µm diameter tested in production (4 bricks)
- Kerf loss decreases below 60 µm (with 140 µm wafer thickness)
- No wire ruptures

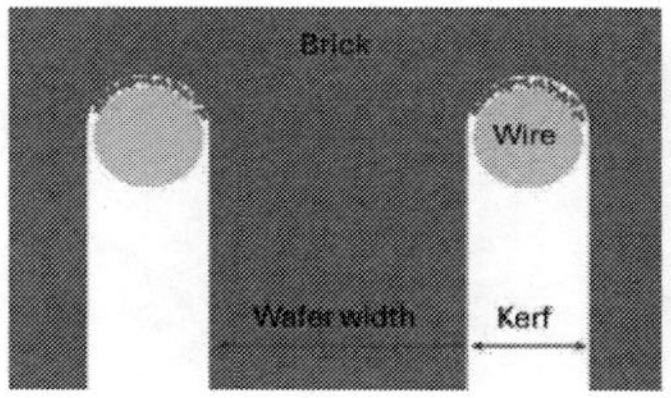

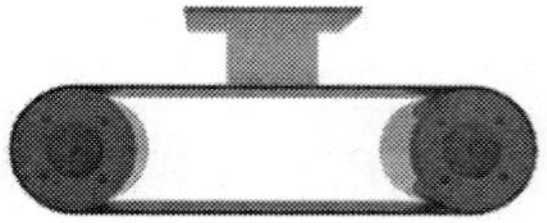

Solar Cells

POLO

- Very lean POLO IBC process flow on p-type wafers

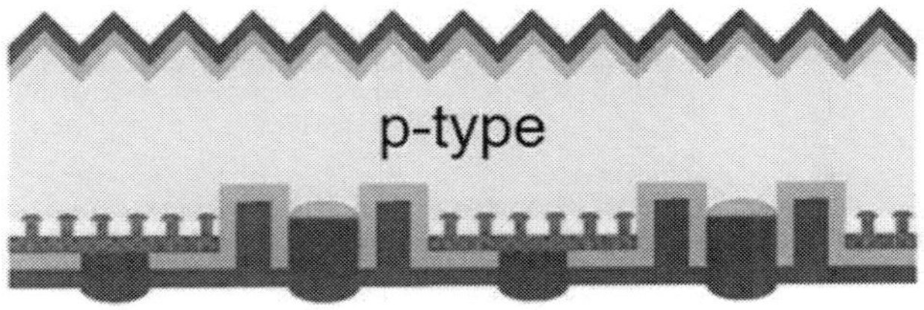

polyZEBRA

- Process largely based on TOPCon processes on n-type wafers

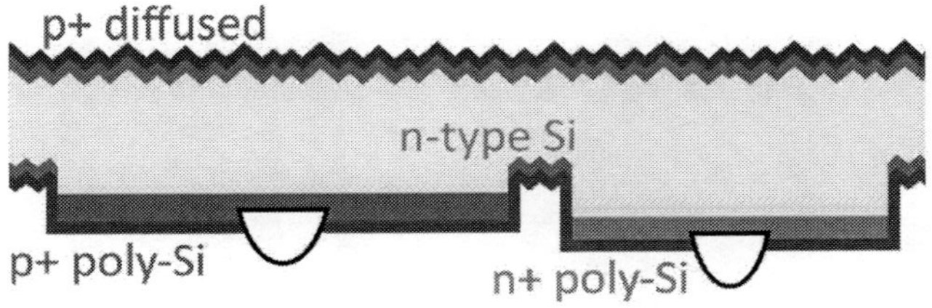

IBC4EU

Solar Cells

POLO IBC process at Kalyon PV

1. Texturing
2. Rear polishing
3. **Local** PECVD SiO_xN_y / n-a-Si — New !
4. Thermal Anneal
5. Front AlO_x/SiN_y
6. Rear AlO_x/SiN_y
7. Laser contact opening
8. Al and Ag screen printing
9. Firing

kalyon·PV ISFH

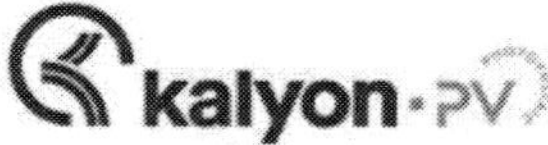

- POLO IBC technology licensed by ISFH to Kalyon PV in 2024. Technology transfer started

IBC4EU

Solar Cells

POLO IBC

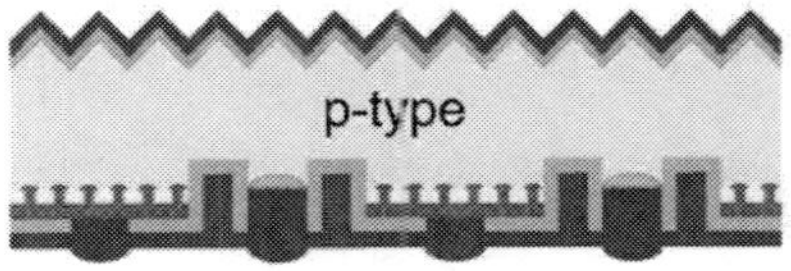

ISFH

LPKF Laser & Electronics

- Most recent results

Date	Efficiency [%]	Voc [mV]	Jsc [mA/cm2]	FF [%]
08/2024	23.9	720	41.1	80.5
01/2025	24.1*	723	40.8	81.5
08/2025	24.5*	726	41.2	82.0

Lower poly annealing temp and addition of contact pads

Improved ARC and narrower Ag fingers

- Improvement potential to 25% by reducing high Ag to n-poly-Si contact resistance[1]
  - More details: 1BO.3

* Independently confirmed by ISFH CalTeC

[1] V. Mertens et al., Solar RRL 8, 2300919 (2024)

IBC4EU

Solar Cells

polyZEBRA

Step #		
1	SDE +cleaning	alkaline wet bench
2	SiO_2+a-Si(n)	PECVD
3	SiNx mask	PECVD
4	Local ablation	Laser
5	Alkaline poly-Si removal +clean	alkaline wet bench
6	SiO_2+a-Si(i)	PECVD
7	B-diffusion (B2B)	BCl_3 tube furnace
8	local activation	Laser
9	texturing	alkaline wet bench
10	B-diffusion	BCl_3 tube furnace
11	Wet chemical cleaning	batch wet bench
12	AlOx (double side coating)	ALD (or PE-ALD)
13	SiNx	PECVD
14	SiNx	PECVD
15	Screen printing Ag	SP, dryers, FF furnaces, Ag paste
16	Screen printing Cu	SP, dryers, FF furnaces, snap curing Cu paste

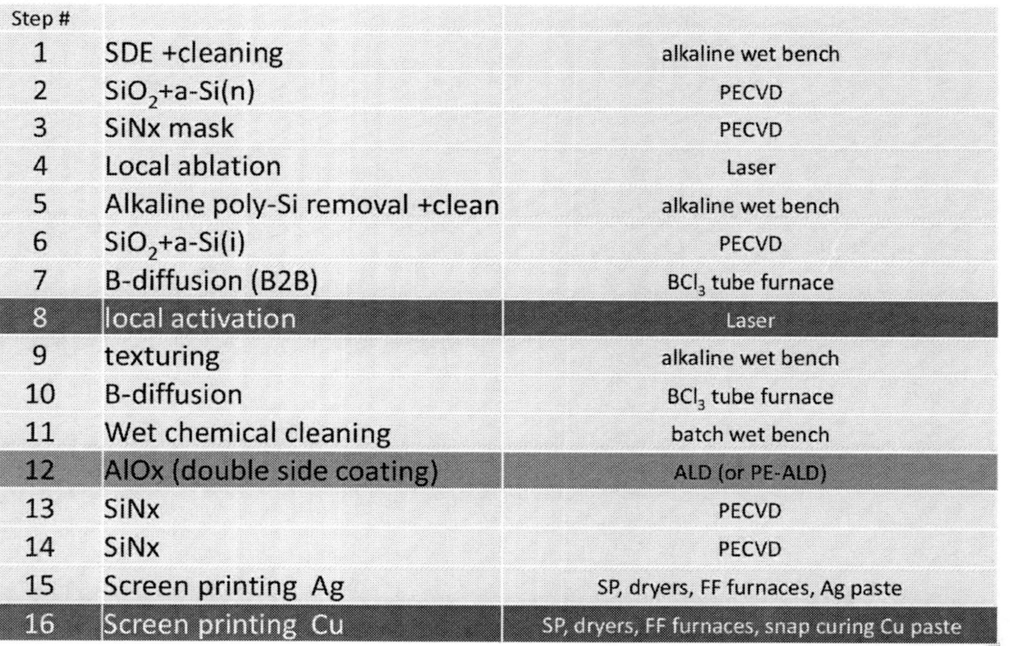

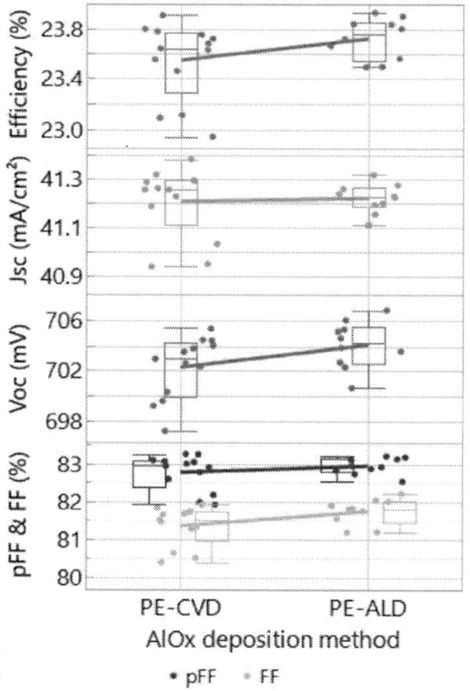

Solar Cells

polyZEBRA

	η	J_{sc} (mA/cm²)	V_{oc} (mV)	FF
Champion cell	24.3%	41.6	711	82.1%
Mean ± stdev	24.0 ± 0.3%	41.5 ± 0.1	708 ± 3	81.6 ± 0.4%

- Best polyZEBRA cell batch so far (with Cu BB)
- +0.2% compared to previous reported data
- Main gain in pFF (thus FF) from real **passivating contacts** and **PE-ALD AlO_x**

More details: 1CV.2

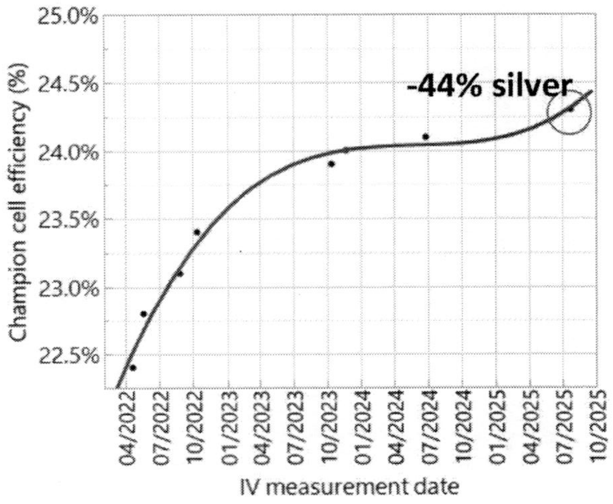

Solar Cells

IBC4EU

polyZEBRA

- BC has more freedom for metallization
- Cu to replace most of the silver
- Screen printing based
- No HT sintering
- Less than 4 mg/Wp have been demonstrated on ZEBRA

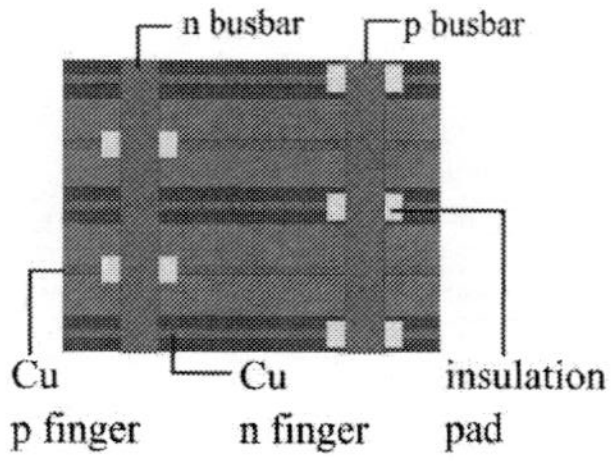

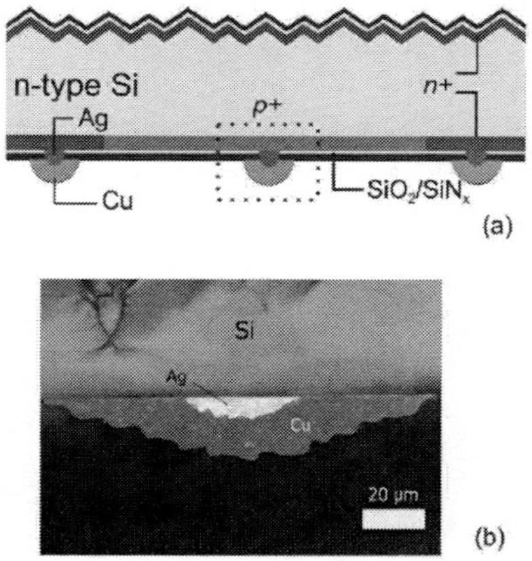

More details 1.AO.5.4

DE10 2022 118 063, pending

Ning, et al. SILICONPV 2022, Vol. 2826. No. 1. AIP Publishing LLC, 2023.
Rudolph et al. *Solar Energy Materials and Solar Cells* 264 (2024): 112603;
Rudolph et al. AIP Conference Proceedings. Vol. 2709. No. 1. AIP Publishing LLC, 2022

IBC4EU

Solar Cells

ISC research for a sunny future

FuturaSun anticipate tomorrow

ISC's BC technology

- 10 2010 024 834 granted
- 10 2012 207 764 granted
- 3 104 397 granted
- 3 982 421 pending
- 4 092 760 pending
- 4 195 299 pending
- 10 2022 118 063 pending
- 25 169 642.3 pending

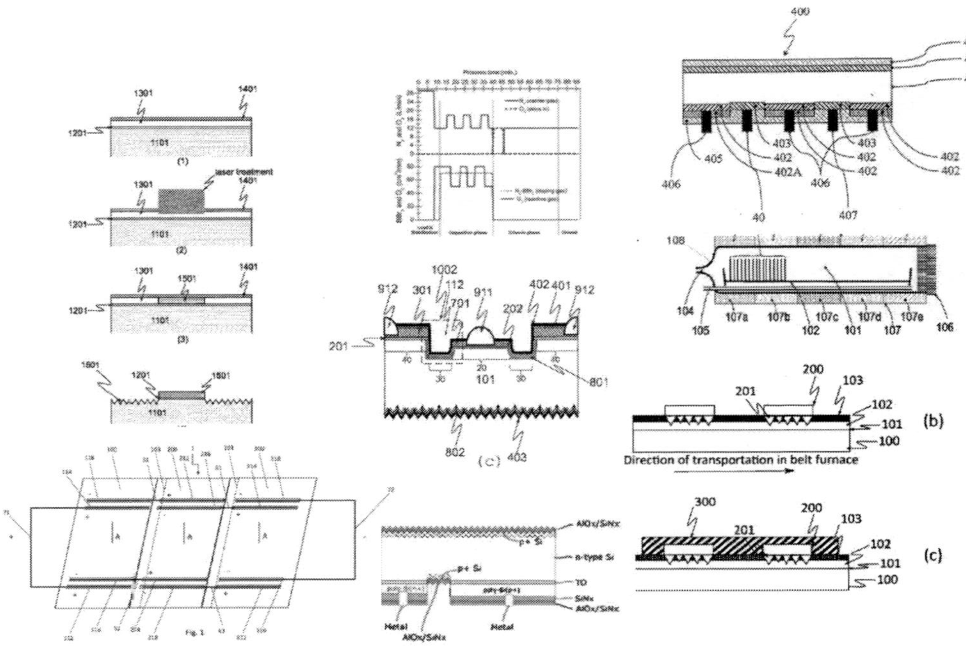

IBC4EU

Modules

Interconnection of IBC cells

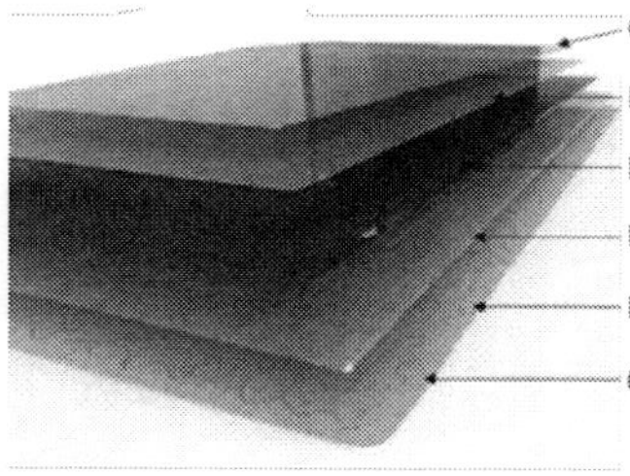

ENERGYRA®
TNO innovation for life

Conductive backsheet

ISC research for a sunny future
metsolar
FuturaSun

Stringing interconnection

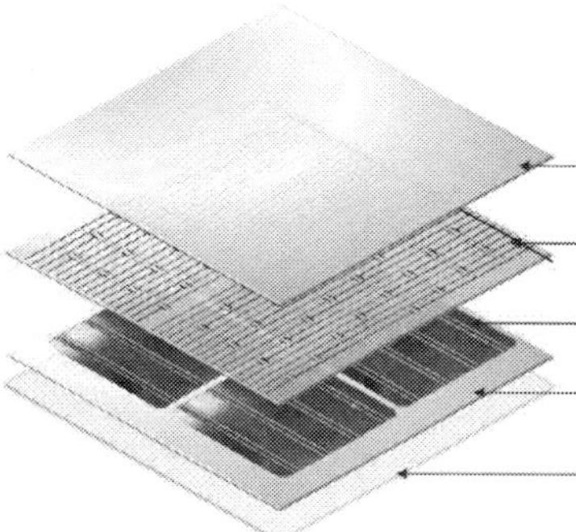

imec

3D Multi-Ribbon[1]

[1] R. Van Dyck et al, Prog Photovolt Res Appl 2021; 29: p.507

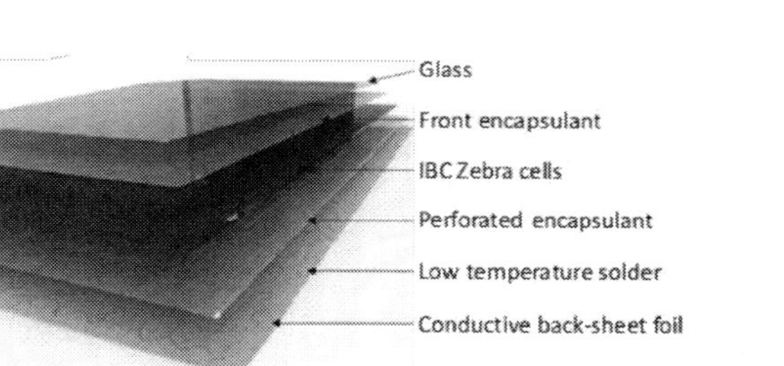

Modules

IBC4EU

TNO innovation for life

Light transmitting conductive substrate (LTCS):

- Interconnection of ZEBRA cells
- Interconnection tracks integrated to the rear-side glass
- Cells-to-LTCS electrical contact via conductive adhesive
- Module assembly based on a “pick & place” process

TNO’s pick and place robot assembling a bifacial module

Front-side (left) and rear-side (right) of TNO’s bifacial module (132 ½-cut IBC cells)

Modules

Light transmitting conductive substrate (LTCS):

- High performance of this prototype module demonstrates the potential of the LTCS interconnection technology
  - P_{max} > 410Wp (132 M6 half cells)
  - Bi-faciality = 76.5%
  - CtM FF loss ≈ 2%abs (estimation)

- Performance estimation with front glass:
  - P_{max} ≈ 388Wp
  - Bi-faciality ≈ 81.2%

- TC already demonstrated on 400x400mm modules

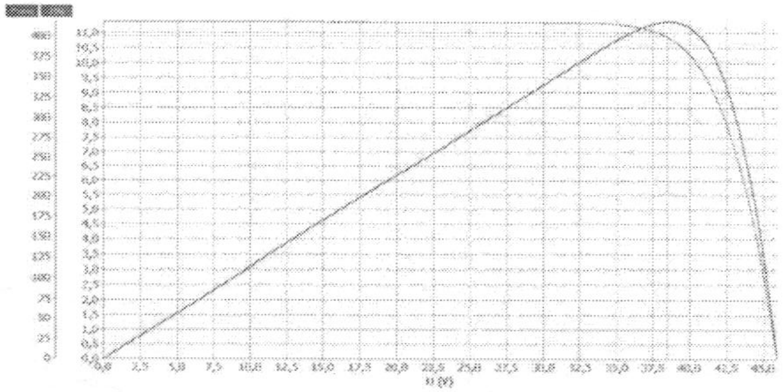

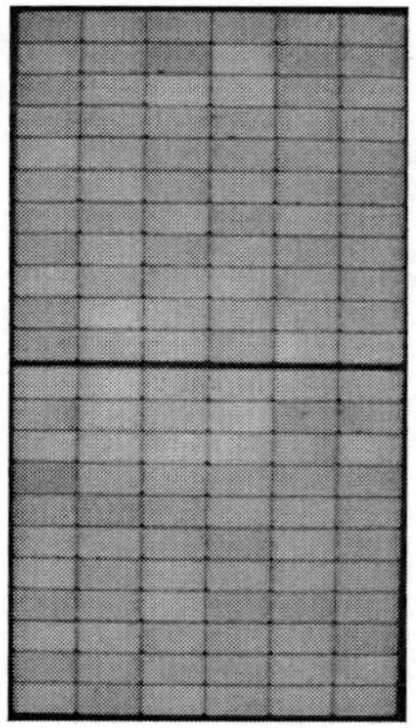

Modules

Module based on Cu-metallized cells

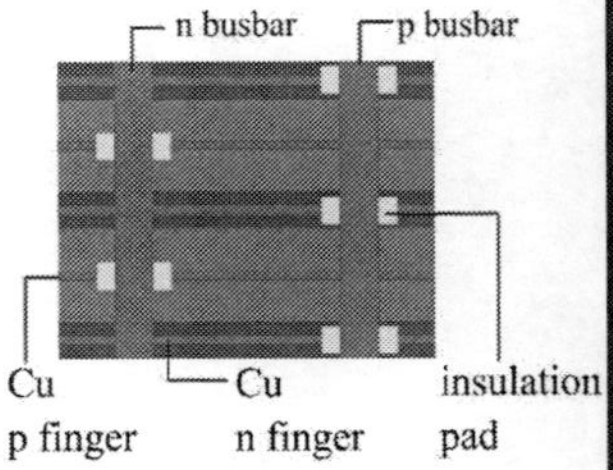

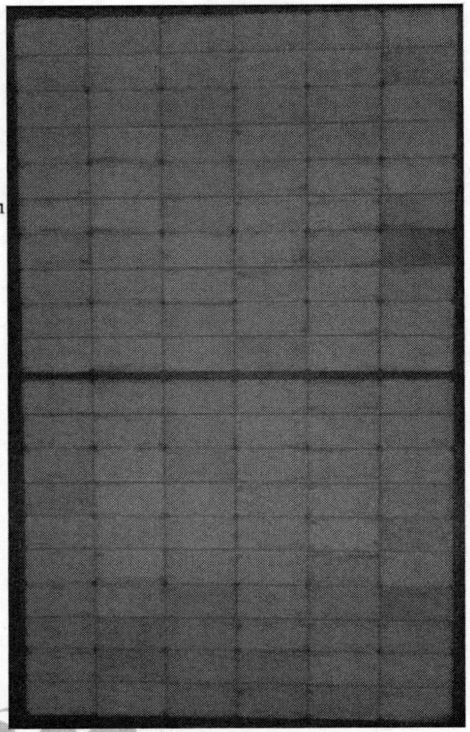

Full Size Module (120 M6 half cells)

- Standard soldering (Tabber), glass-glass
- Similar power as silver reference module
  Slightly lower FF
- Bifaciality lower because of thicker fingers

	Isc [A]	Uoc [V]	FF [%]	Pmpp[W]
Ref_Ag_front	11.17	41.44	79.73	**369.24**
Cu-Zebra_front	11.11	41.54	79.31	**365.94**

See ISC Konstanz booth in this exhibition

Modules

Gapless technology

- Tabbing and stringing based
- Cell to cell overlap common practice

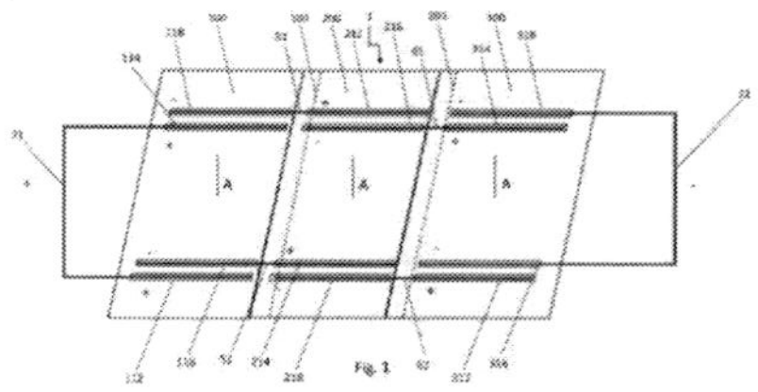

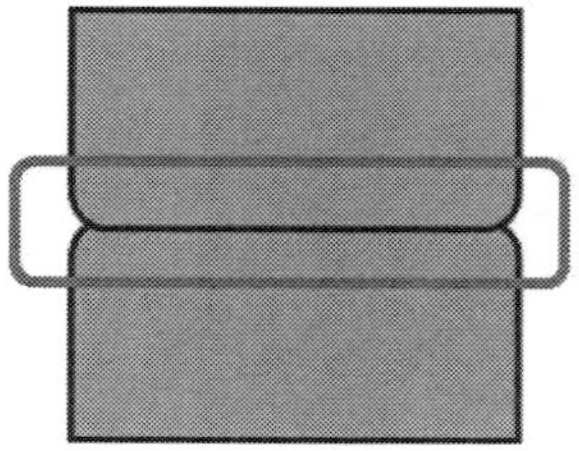

EP 4 092 760, pending

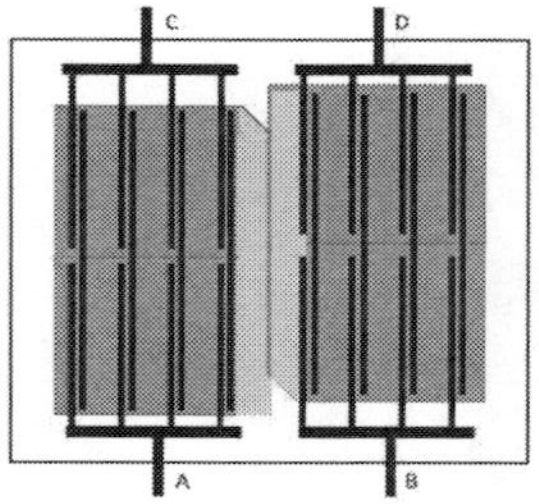

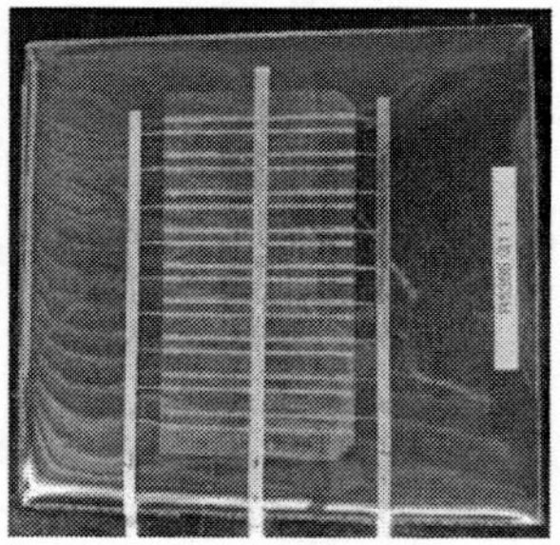

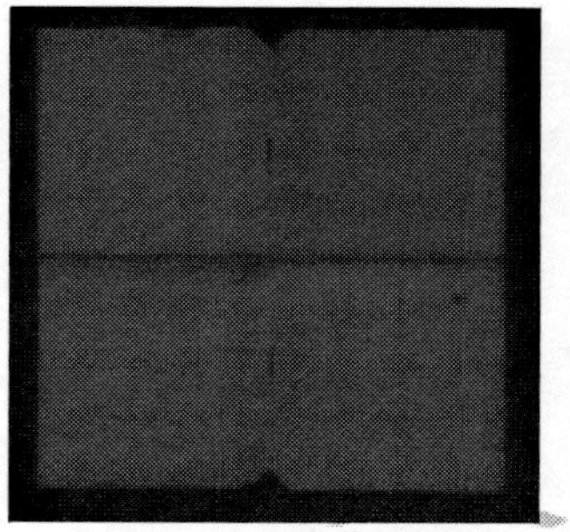

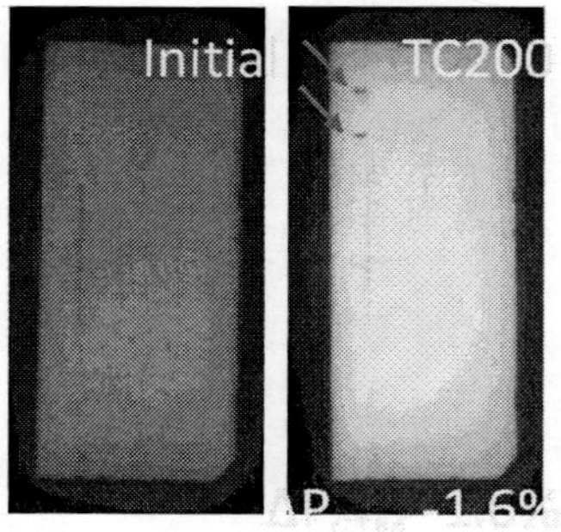

IBC4EU

Modules

Gapless technology

- Tabbing and stringing based

Standard "butterfly"

Gapless stringing

Gapless strining + bussing behind cell matrix

Fully gapless

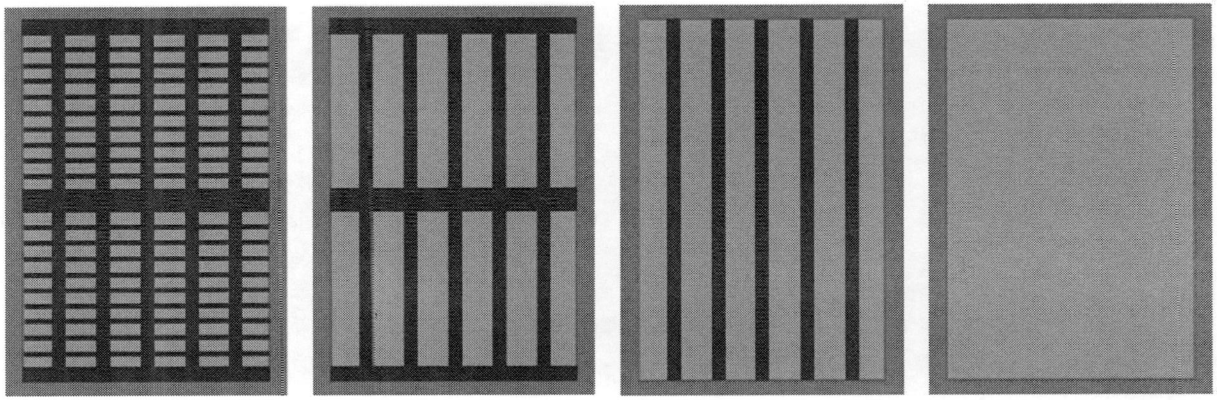

Modules

gapless stringing

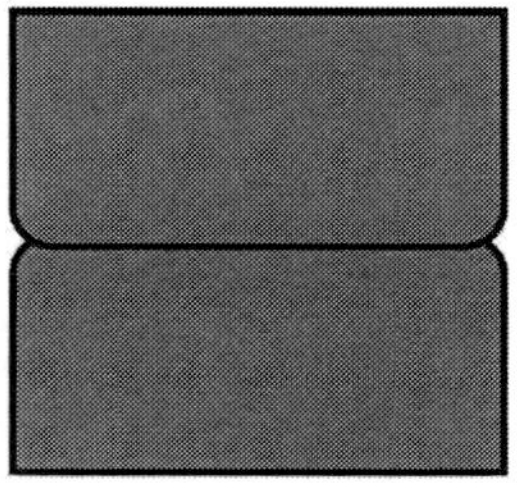

Overlap of ~0.7 mm leads to cell shading

gapless string layup

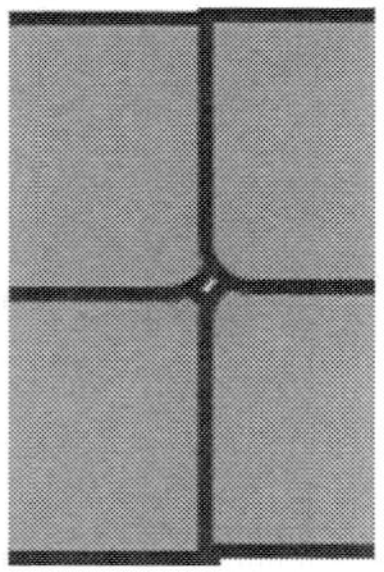

Overlap of ~1 mm leads to cell shading

More details: 3CO.11.2

	Area reduction (%)*	Shading fraction (%)*
Butterfly gap and bussings	2.1	
Cell gaps (for 0.7 mm overlap)	1.6	0.7
String gaps (for 1 mm overlap)	1.3	0.9

» net efficiency increase for M10 HC, 54 cell module 3.5 % rel.

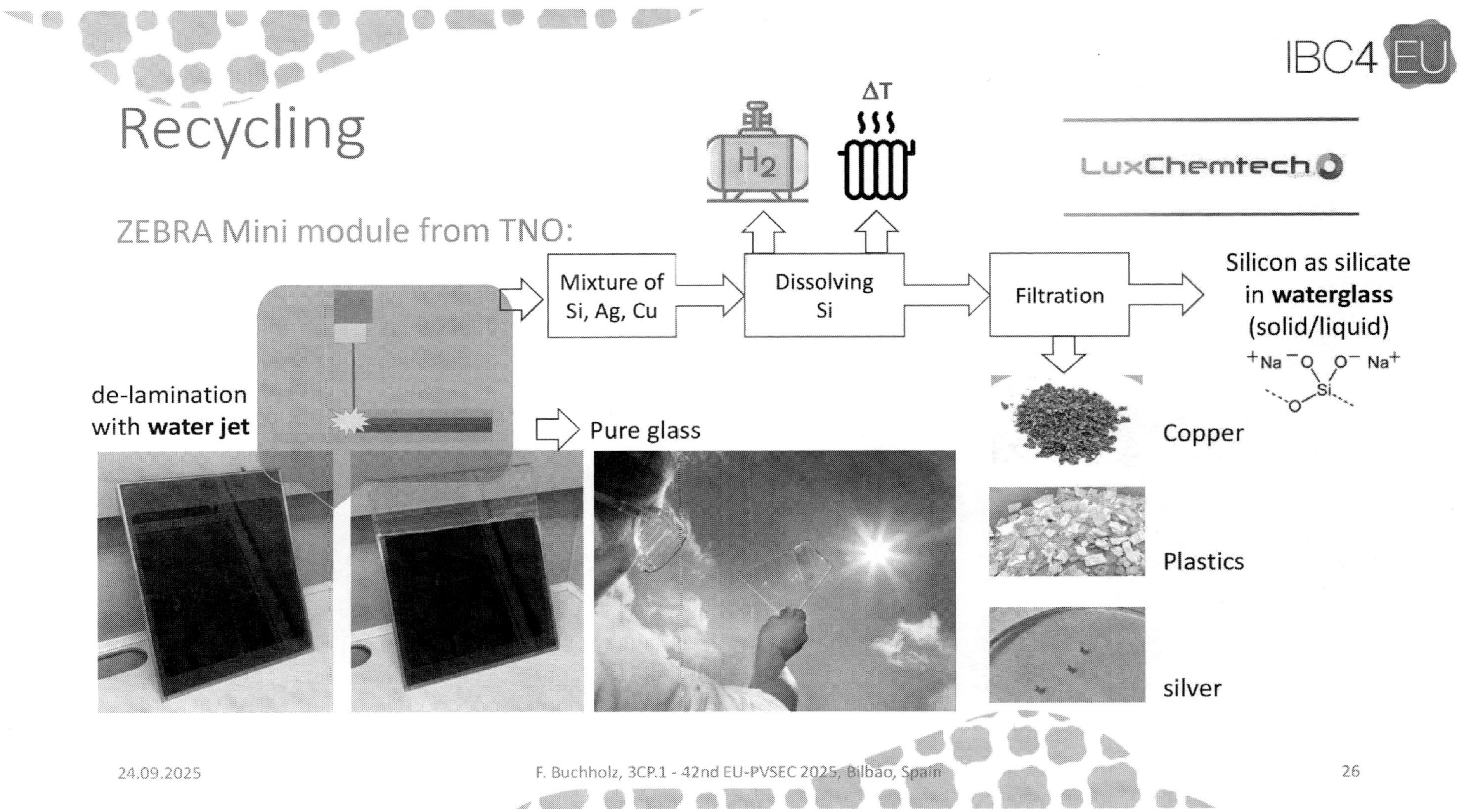
IBC4EU
Recycling
LuxChemtech
ZEBRA Mini module from TNO:
Mixture of Si, Ag, Cu
ΔT
H2
Dissolving Si
Filtration
Silicon as silicate in waterglass (solid/liquid)
+Na −O O− Na+
Si
O
de-lamination with water jet
Pure glass
Copper
Plastics
silver
24.09.2025
F. Buchholz, 3CP.1 - 42nd EU-PVSEC 2025, Bilbao, Spain
26

IBC4EU technology

- Close to state of the art TOPCon / PERC
- Low breakdown voltage
- Strong family of patents and applications
- Potential >25% efficiency
- Full gap-less module
- Cu Ready
- Multiple promising approaches for module interconnection

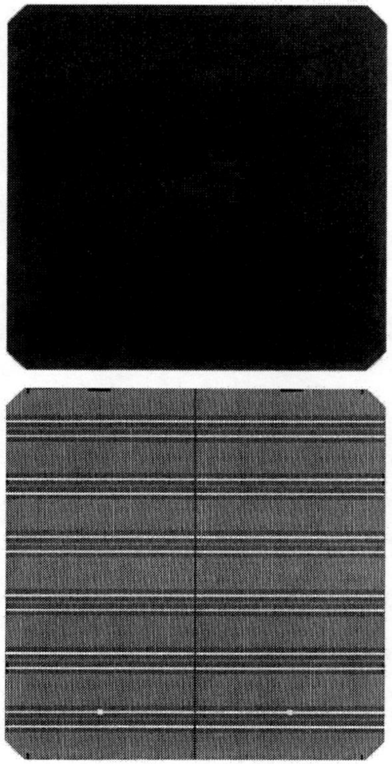

IBC4EU

Why European Back Contact?

- IP → multiple ways of making it, no general blocking patents (c.f. TOPCon)
- Innovation driven, slightly more complex
- IBC4EU approach: low cost, low silver, EU-owned
- De-risking the EU's energy supply
- Potential for an EU / non-Chinese supply chain
- Long-term suply of stable form factors
- Allow for highest quality and service

From niche to mainstream?

see last talk of this session (**CP.1.4**) and IBC4EU side event (**PV Made in the EU: How Do Companies Die and How Can They Thrive**)!

IBC4EU

Thank you!

Dr. Florian Bucholz, ISC Konstanz
florian.buchholz@isc-konstanz.de

https://x.com/Ibc4EU

https://www.linkedin.com/showcase/ibc4eu/
https://www.linkedin.com/in/dr-florian-buchholz-90789675/

Project Partners

ISC research for a sunny future · protech · FuturaSun · ISFH · imec · ENERGYRA · TNO innovation for life · metsolar · HIGHLINE · Copprint · cea · BECQUEREL INSTITUTE · WIP RENEWABLE ENERGIES · LuxChemtech · kalyon-PV

Associated Partners

LPKF Laser & Electronics · Toyal · 東洋アルミ · RENA

This project has received funding from the European Union's Horizon Europe research and innovation programme under grant agreement No.101084259

Visit ISC Konstanz! ISC research for a sunny future 21st -24th October, 2025

Outdoor Performance and Reliability of Perovskite (Pk)-Silicon (Si) Tandems:

>1 year of Monitoring in the NEXUS Project

Atse Louwen[1,2], Jordi Veirman[1], Alexander Astigarraga[1], Juan Josè Stivanello[1], David Moser[1,3], Perrine Carroy[4], Vincent Barth[4], Delfina Muñoz[4], Markus Lenz[5] Anika Sidler[5], Jorge Ferrando[6], Maximiliano Alejandro Senno[6], Henk Bolink[6], Talat Özden[7], Hisham Nasser[7], Shuaifeng Hu[8], Xinyi Shen[8], Henry Snaith[8]

[1]Eurac Research, Bolzano, Italy
[2]RISE Research Institutes of Sweden
[3]Becquerel Institute Italia
[4]CEA INES, Le Bourget-du-Lac, France
[5]Fachhochschule Nordwestschweiz, Basel, Switzerland
[6]Universitat de València, Valencia, Spain
[7]ÖDTU-GÜNAM, Ankara, Türkiye
[8]University of Oxford, Oxford, United Kingdom

NEXUS

eurac research

EU-PVSEC – Bilbao - 2025

Background

NEXUS is a HE project that started Nov. 2022

- Developing **solvent-free (fully evaporated), sustainable** Pk-Si tandems: **In-free, low Ag**
- High efficiency devices: >33% cells, >30% modules

In NEXUS, we also test the
outdoor performance + reliability:

- Testing outdoor in **4 locations**
- Collecting rainwater runoff to test for any Pb leaching

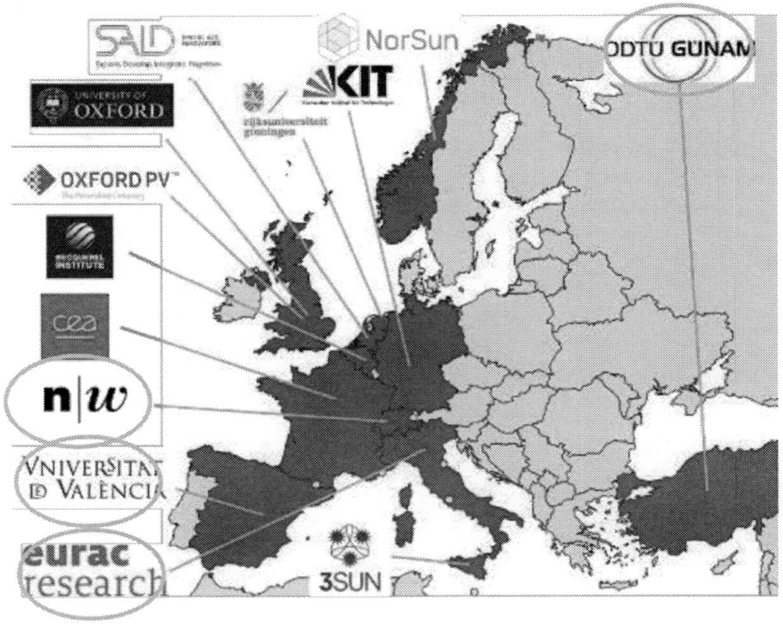

Eurac Research have been testing different Pk-Si samples outdoor since late July 2024.

Funded by the European Union

Why outdoor monitoring?

- **Field-relevant** data (all stressors!)
- Precious **feedback for cell/ module** improvements
- Basis for **Degradation Rate, Energy Yield** (kWh/kWp) and **LCOE** (€/kWh) calculations
  → **Bankability** assessment
- Supports **standardisation**

More outdoor data are needed for Perovskite (Pk)-Si tandems

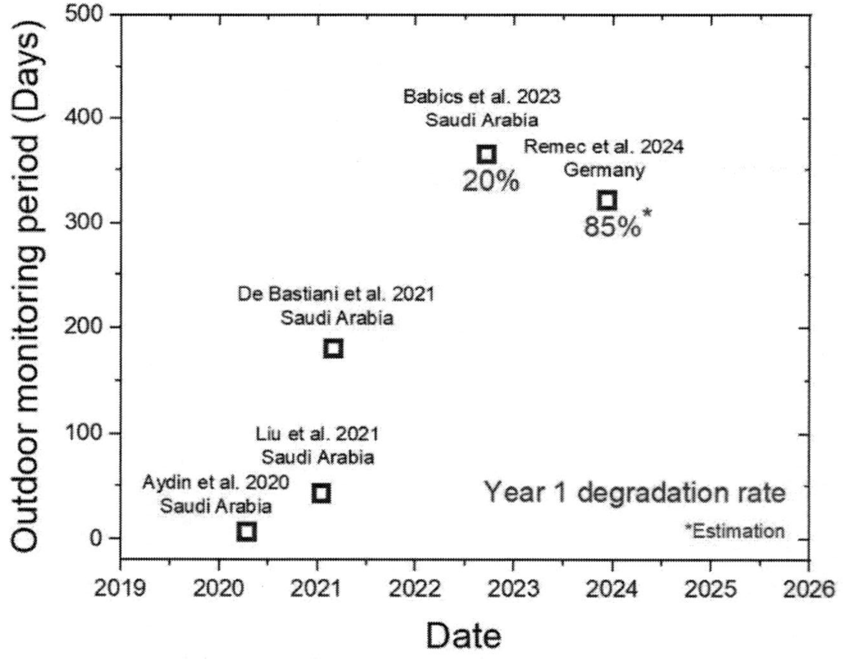

Funded by the European Union

Measurement setup @ Eurac

- Electrical data measured with µMPPT setup for low current/power levels
  - V_{mp}, I_{mp}, P_{mp}

- Complemented with measurements:
  - Operating conditions: irradiance components, temperature, etc.
  - Rainwater runoff: measured, filtered, refrigerated for analysis to assess presence of **Pb**

Fachhochschule Nordwestschweiz

Funded by the European Union

Samples

- 9 Pk-Si samples with HJT bottom cell + HJT cell as Reference
- Two types of bottom cells:
  - Polished wafers
  - (nano)-textured wafers
- Different perovskite deposition approaches
  - 4 Hybrid process (solution-based + evaporation)
  - 5 Fully evaporated
- Edge sealant used to avoid moisture ingress
- Labelling:

Batch# +

Pk Deposition	Wafer surface state
H = Hybrid	P=Polished
E= Evaporated	(n)T=(nano)Textured

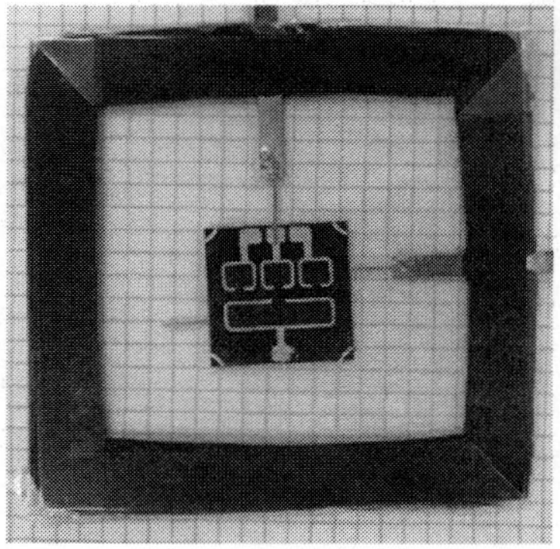

Main module BOM	
Front cover	100 x 100 x 3mm glass
Encapsulant	TPO
Rear cover	100 x 100 x 3mm glass
Edge sealant	PIB 10mm x 650µm
ECA	Acrylate
Ribbons	800 x 200µm

Funded by the European Union

Results – Performance Ratio (PR) over 13 months

- Benchmark is "stable"

Performance Ratio (PR): Delivered energy / what the module should deliver

(given irradiance and Pmax)

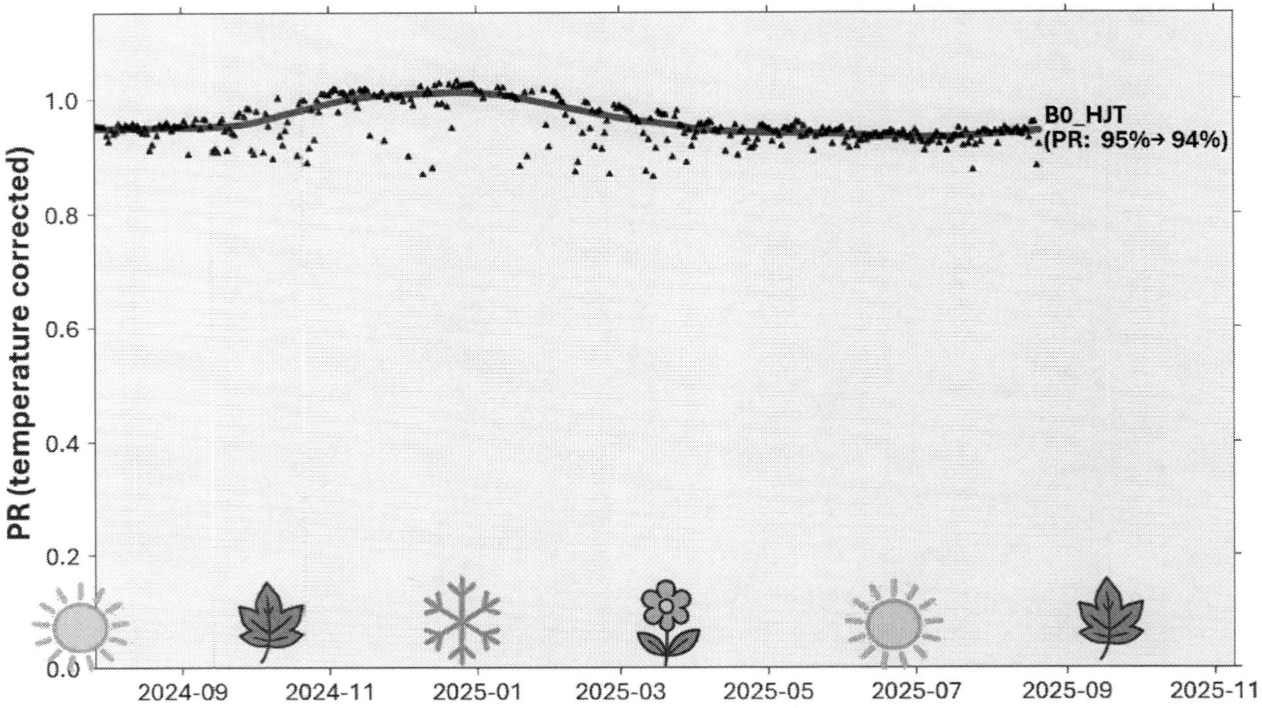

Funded by the European Union

Results – Performance Ratio (PR) over 13 months

- Benchmark is "stable"
- **Hybrid** samples: seasonal fluctuations + degradation

Lowest losses (13 months): 17% and 20%
--> Focus in the second part of this presentation

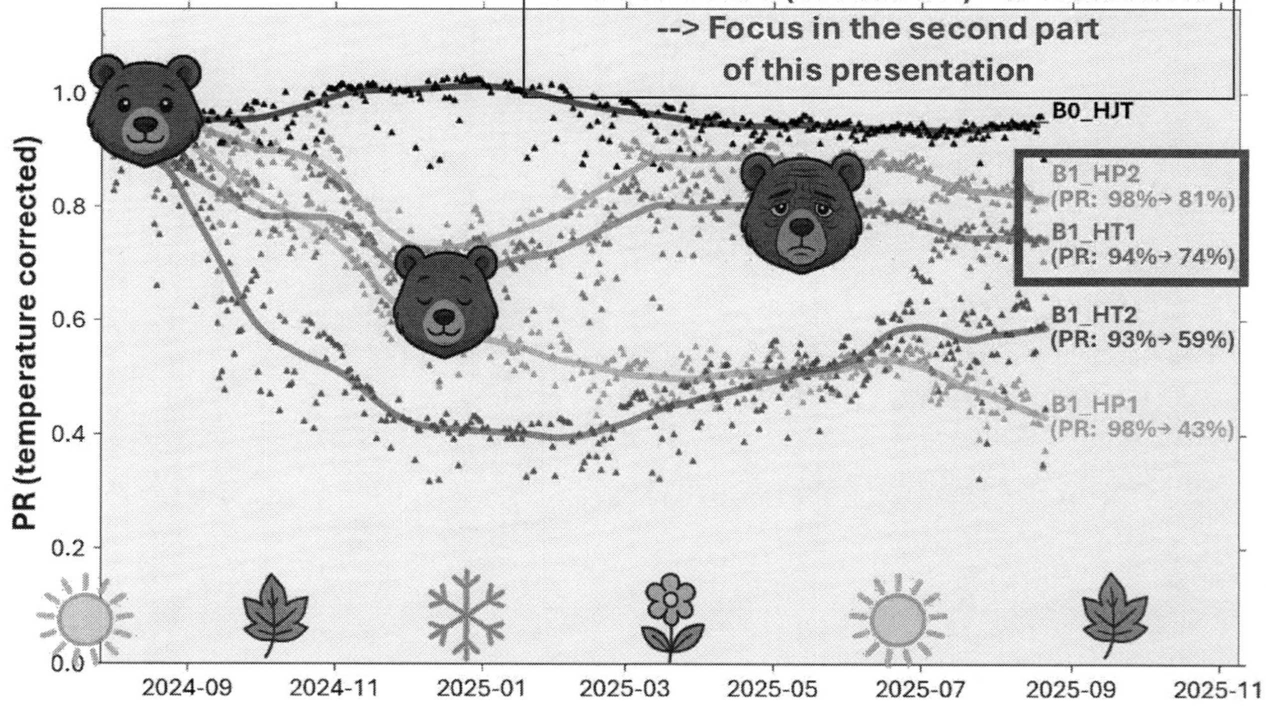

Funded by the European Union

Results – Performance Ratio (PR) over 13 months

- Benchmark is "stable"
- Hybrid samples: seasonal fluctuations + degradation
- **Evaporated** samples: mixed behaviours

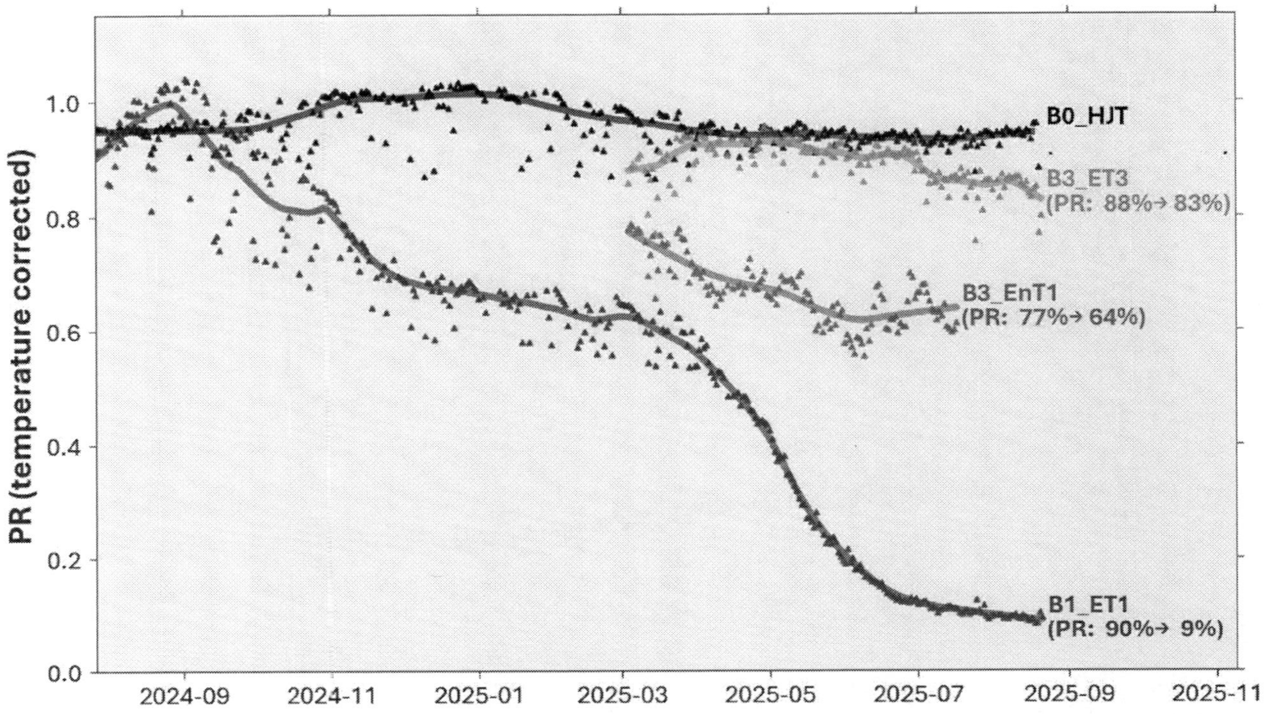

Funded by the European Union

Results – Performance Ratio (PR) over 13 months

- Benchmark is "stable"
- Hybrid samples: seasonal fluctuations + degradation
- Evaporated samples: mixed behaviour
- Some samples **failed** due to various reasons

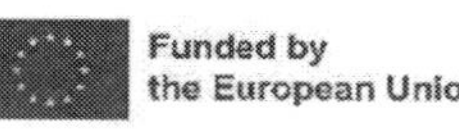

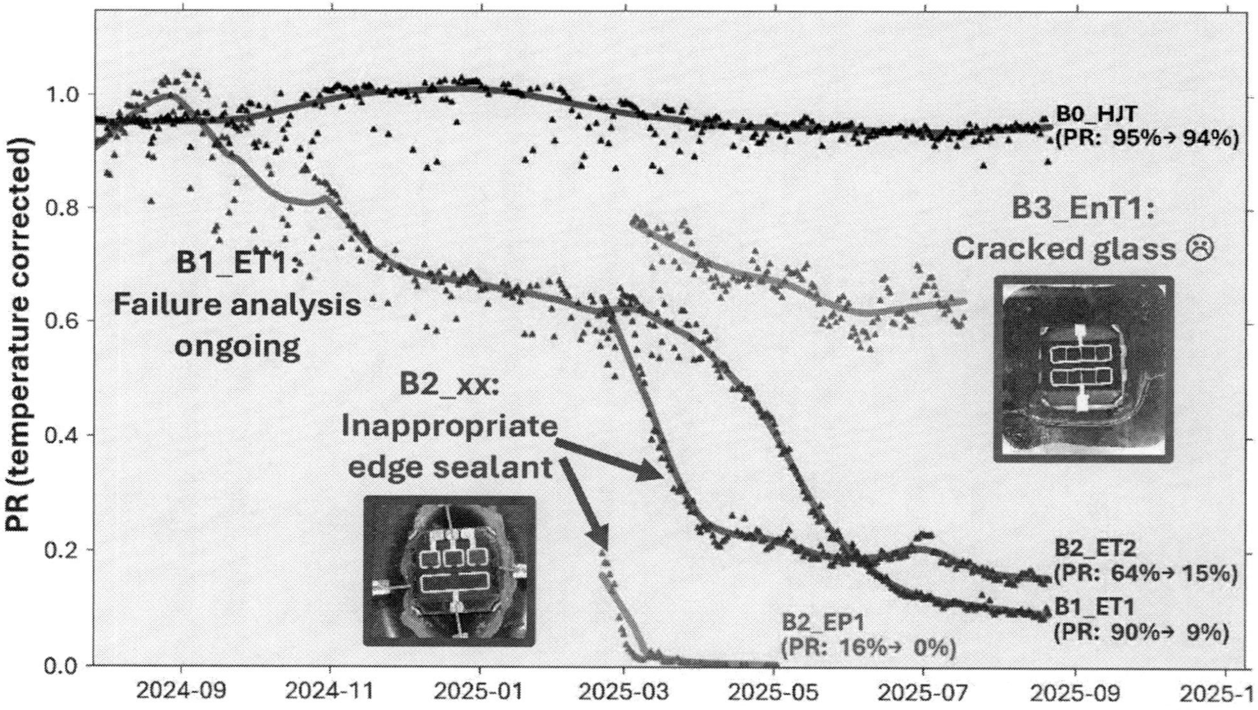

Funded by the European Union

Results – first *PR* correlation with irradiance

- Benchmark is “stable”
- Hybrid samples: seasonal fluctuations + degradation
- Evaporated samples: mixed behaviour
- Some samples failed due to various reasons
- Most samples show low ***PR*** during low ***irradiance*** days

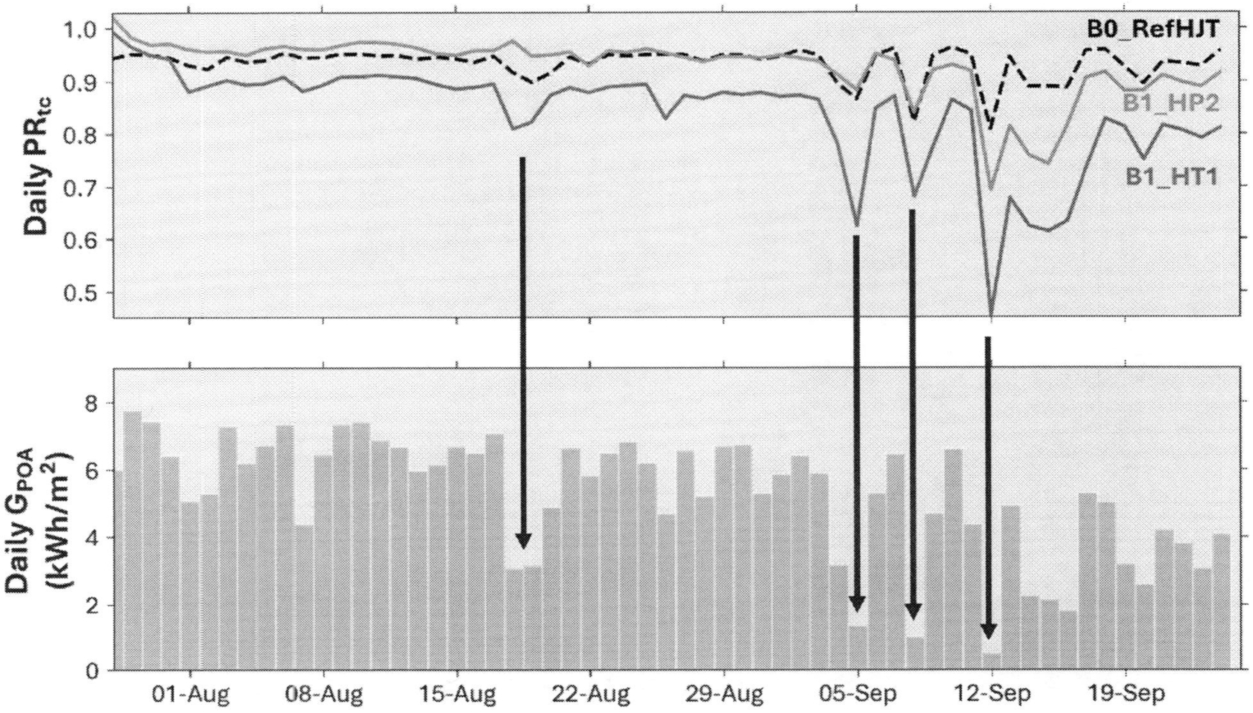

GPOA= Global Plane Of Array irradiance

Funded by the European Union

Results – *PR* correlation with irradiance

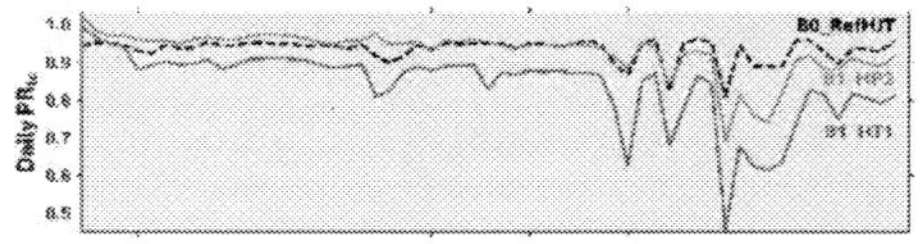

- Drop in ***PR*** in low irradiance days confirmed throughout the monitoring period

- Long-term aging: magnitude of daily PR variation decreases
  (screened by background deg?)

Origin of the drop at low irradiance ???

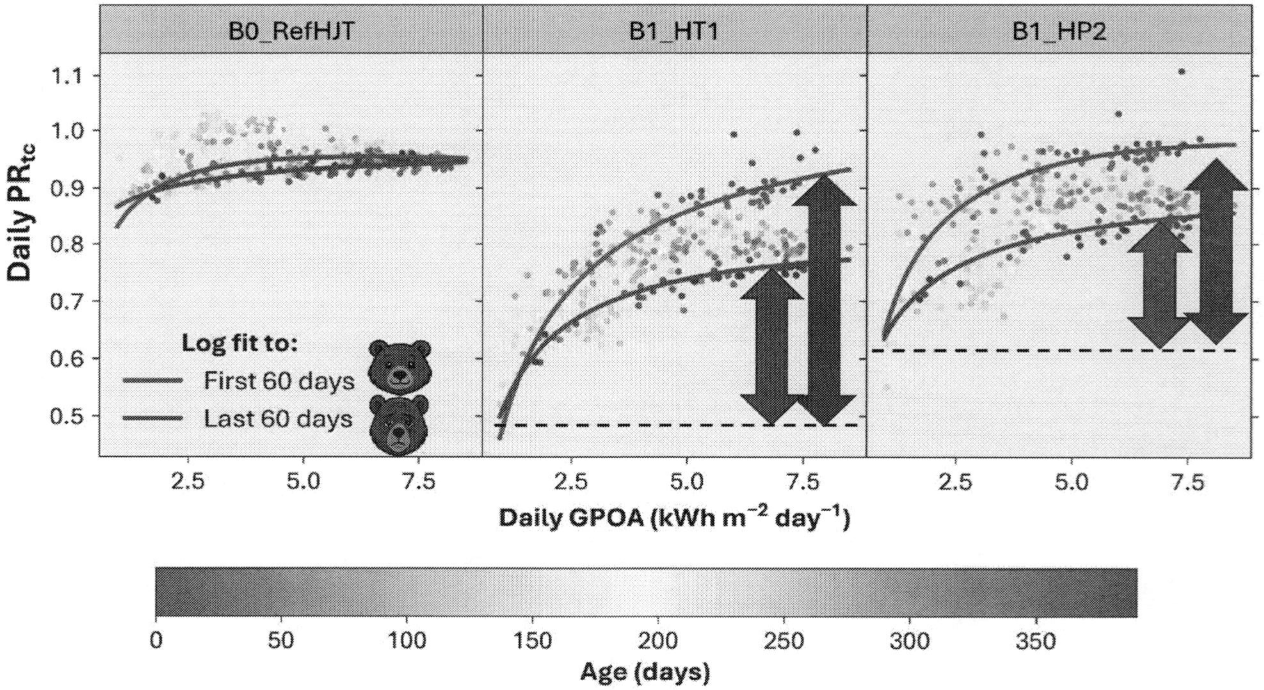

Funded by the European Union

GPOA= Global Plane Of Array irradiance

Results – Light soaking behaviour

- On early-life **sunny** days:
  - B1_HP2 on par with HJT once sun is out
  - B1_HT1 shows full recovery after some hours
- On early-life **cloudy** days
  - B1_HP2 now needs recovery
  - B1_HT1: fails to recover

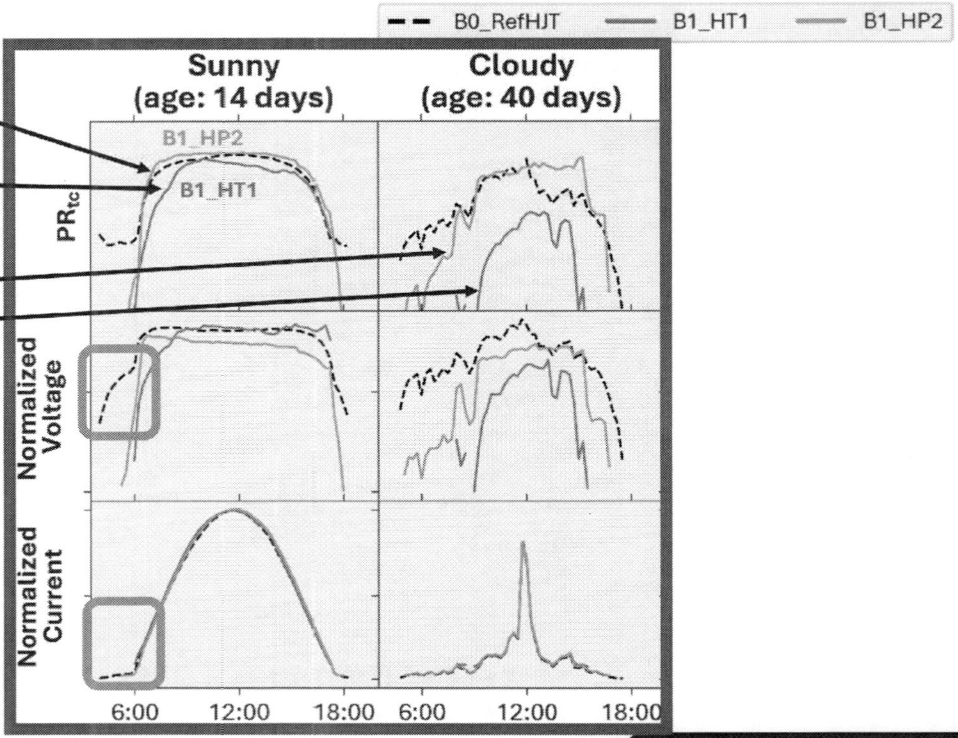

Results – Light soaking behaviour

- On early-life **sunny** days:
  - B1_HP2 on par with HJT once sun is out
  - B1_HT1 shows full recovery after some hours
- On early-life **cloudy** days
  - B1_HP2 now needs recovery
  - B1_HT1: fails to recover
- On late-life **sunny** days
  - B1_HP2 needs now to recover
  - B1_HT1 similar but w/ degr.
- On late-life **cloudy** days
  - Both devices similar, but with degradation

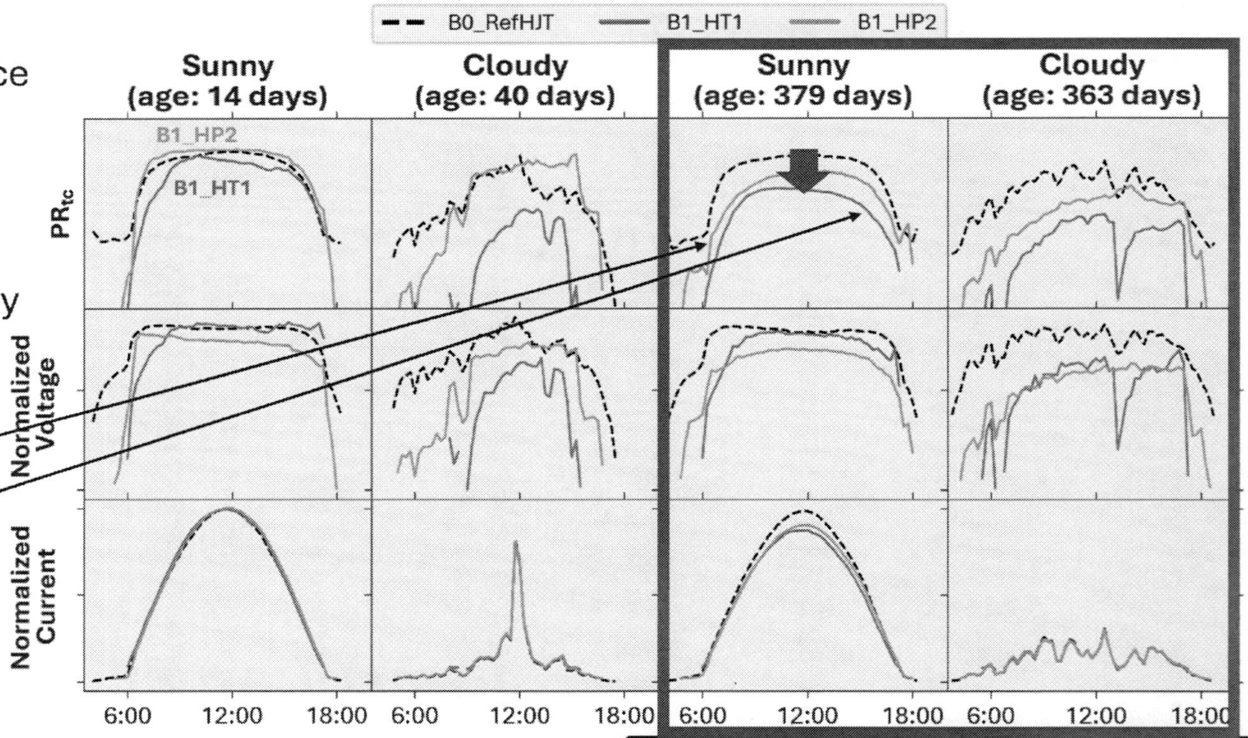

Funded by the European Union

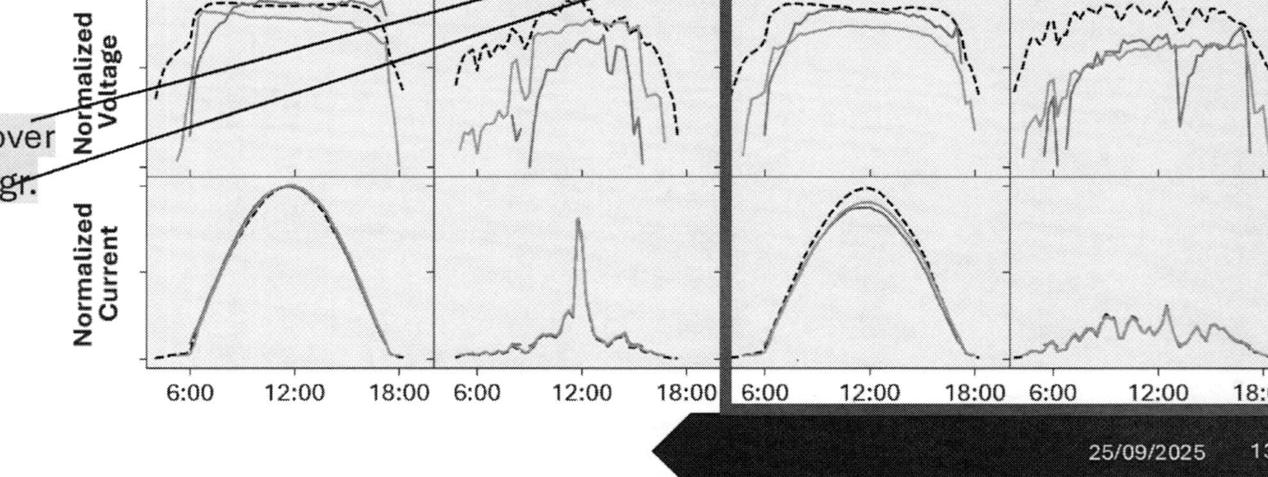

Light-soaking effect (LSE)

- Metastability well-known at lab level
- LSE reported in most recent outdoor studies on SJ **Pk** [1-4], **Pk**-Si tandems [5-7]
- Also observed on **Pk**-CIGSe [8]

Effect not specific to NEXUS devices

Remec et al., Adv. Energy Mater. 2024

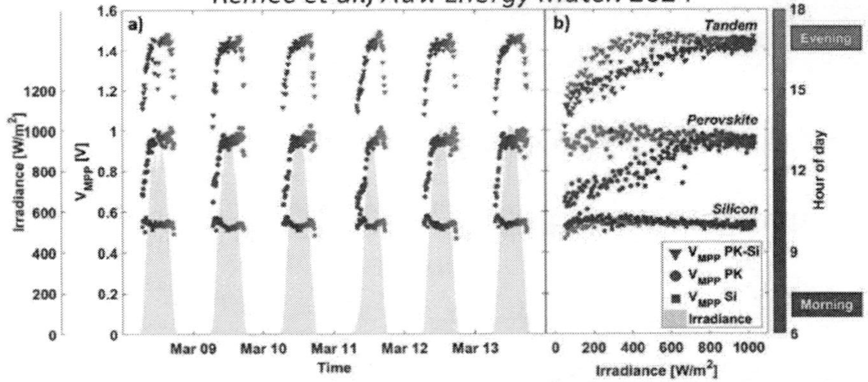

Farias-Basulto et al., Adv. Energy Sustainability Res. 2025

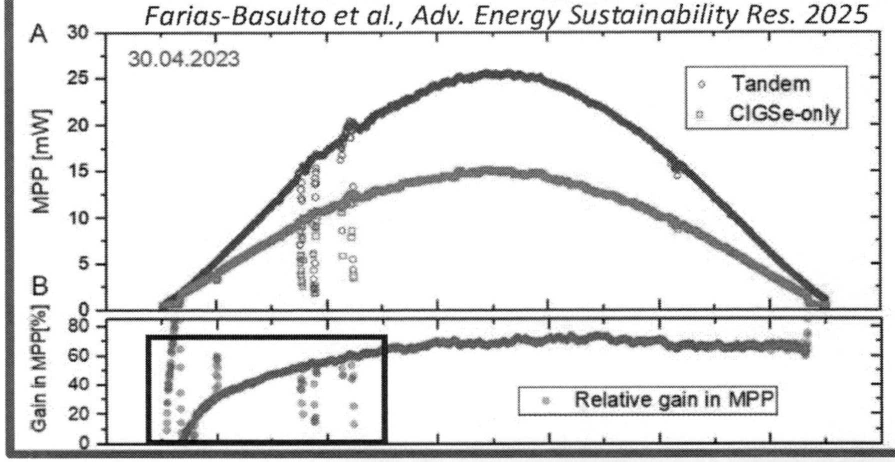

[1] Deceglie et al., IEEE JPV 15, **2025**
[2] Gupta et al., Adv. Energy Mater. **2025**
[3] Remec et al., Adv. Energy Mater. **2025**
[4] Bovesecchi et al, PIP, **2025**
[5] De Bastiani et al., ACS Energy Letters 6 (**2025**)
[6] Babics et al., Cell Reports Physical Science 4, **2023**, 101280
[7] Remec et al., Adv. Energy Mater. **2024**, 14, 2304452
[8] Farias-Basulto et al., Adv. Energy Sustainability Res. **2025**, 2500162

Funded by the European Union

Light-soaking effect (LSE) vs "hard" degradation

- Rough estimate of the contribution to the energy loss:

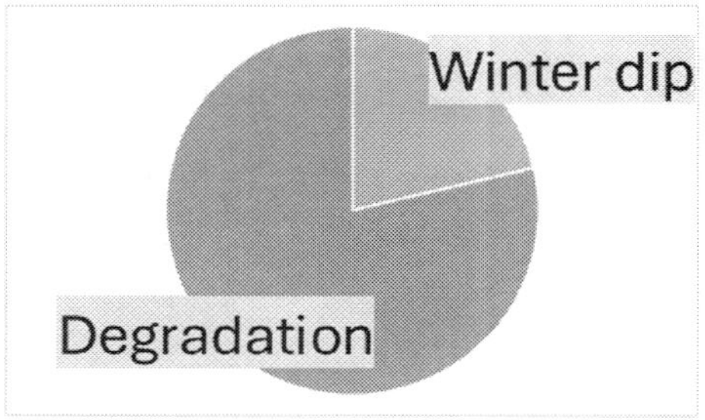

- Contribution of winter dip loss << "hard" non-reversible degradation!

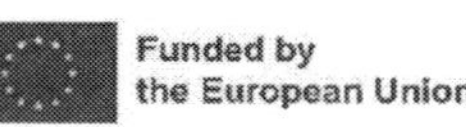

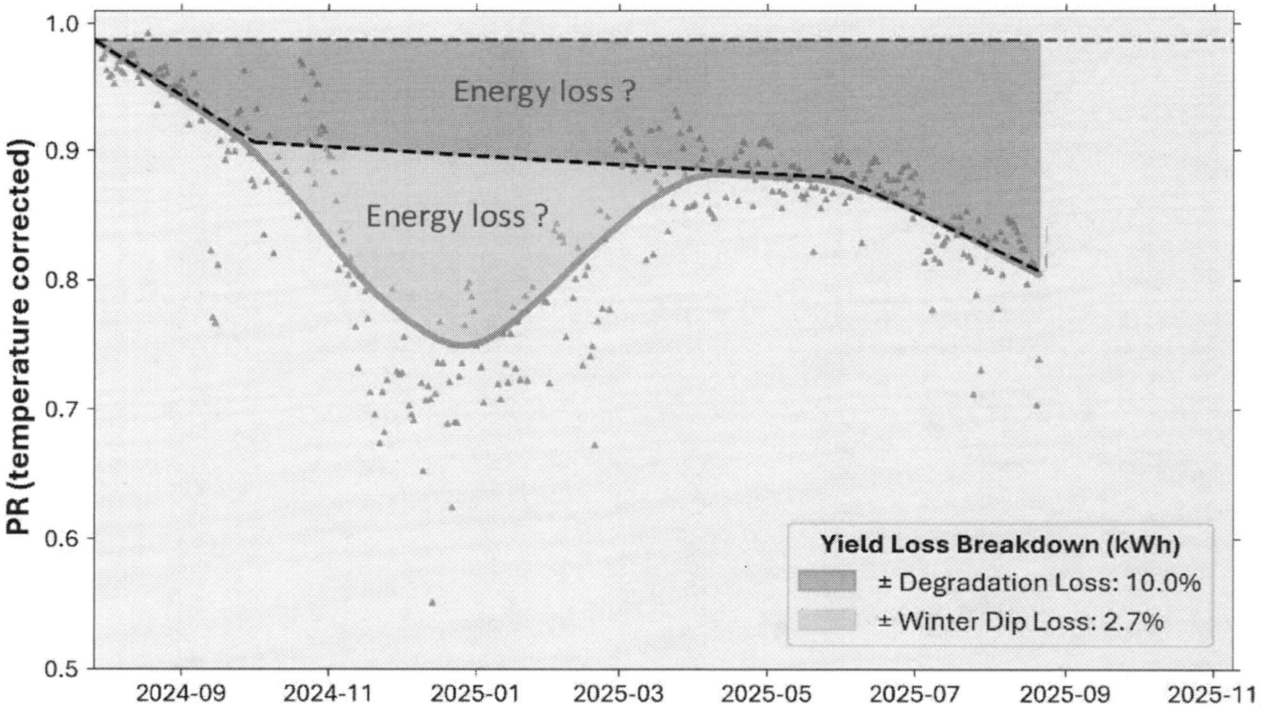

Funded by the European Union

Conclusions and outlook

- ~13 months monitoring NEXUS Pk-Si tandem cells
- <u>For the tested devices, in Bolzano:</u>
  - Least unstable device: **14% Year-on-Year degradation**

    → Positive learning curve, but necessary improvements!
  - Clear **diurnal metastability**. **Device** & **climate**-dependent.
  - Contributes to **seasonality** effects with **lower PR in winter**
  - Main Energy Yield killer = **non-reversible losses** (metastability losses 2nd order)
- <u>Next</u>: Forensics for failure mode analysis, extend monitoring period (GEN3 samples promising !)

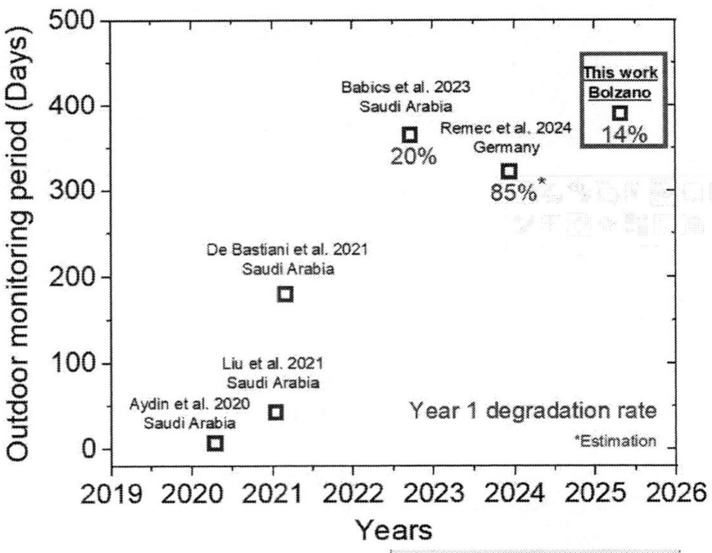

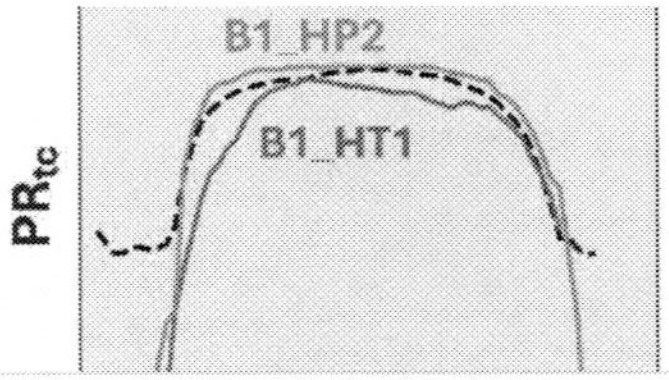

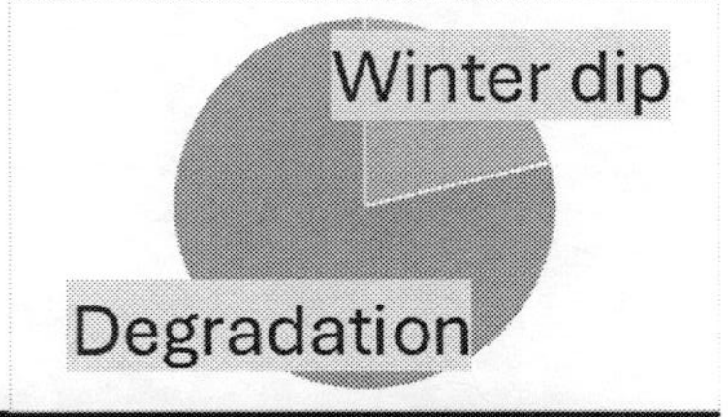

Funded by the European Union

NEXUS

Thanks for your attention!

Project coordinator
Perrine Carroy
CEA
Perrine.CARROY@cea.fr

Project Partner
Jordi Veirman
Eurac Research
Jordi.Veirman@eurac.edu

Technical questions --> atse.louwen@ri.se

Funded by the European Union. Views and opinions expressed are however those of the author(s) only and do not necessarily reflect those of the European Union or RIA. Neither the European Union nor the granting authority can be held responsible for them.

NEXUS project has received funding from the European Union's Horizon Europe research and innovation program under grant agreement No. 101075330.

Project Partners

cea, eurac research, KIT Karlsruher Institut für Technologie, rijksuniversiteit groningen, ODTÜ GÜNAM, SALD, Universitat de València, 3SUN, Becquerel, NorSun, University of Oxford, Oxford PV The Perovskite Company, n|w Fachhochschule Nordwestschweiz

Funded by the European Union

Follow our Journey!

EUPVSEC
22 — 26
September
BEC —
Bilbao Exhibition Centre
Bilbao —
Spain
EU
PVSEC
2025
42nd European
Photovoltaic Solar Energy
Conference and Exhibition

030001-001

Conference Highlights

Robert Kenny

European Commission Joint Research Centre

EU PVSEC Technical Programme Chair

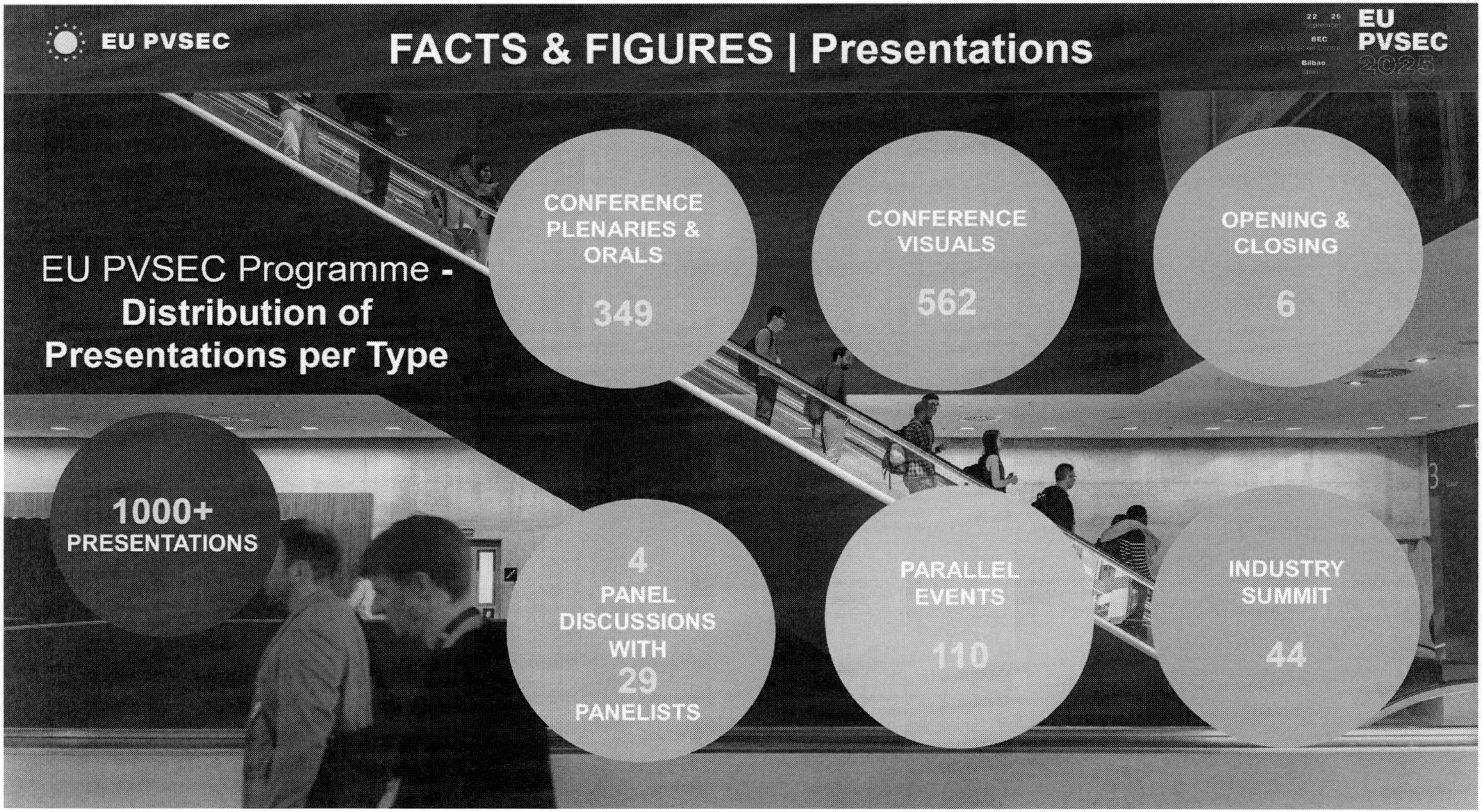
EU PVSEC
FACTS & FIGURES | Presentations
22 26
BEC
Bilbao
EU
PVSEC
2025
EU PVSEC Programme -
Distribution of
Presentations per Type
CONFERENCE
PLENARIES &
ORALS
349
CONFERENCE
VISUALS
562
OPENING &
CLOSING
6
1000+
PRESENTATIONS
4
PANEL
DISCUSSIONS
WITH
29
PANELISTS
PARALLEL
EVENTS
110
INDUSTRY
SUMMIT
44

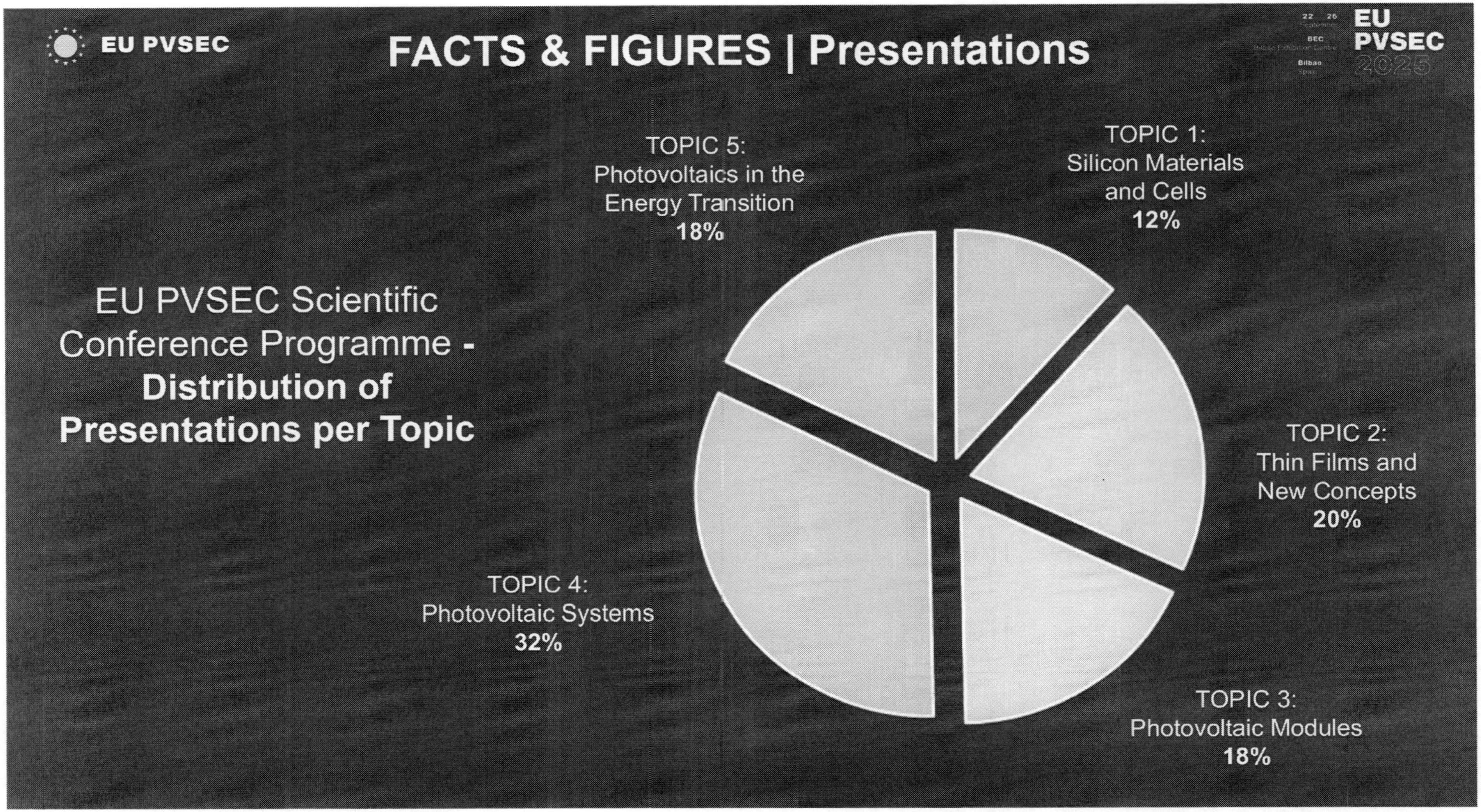
EU PVSEC
FACTS & FIGURES | Presentations
EU PVSEC 2025
EU PVSEC Scientific Conference Programme - Distribution of Presentations per Topic
TOPIC 5: Photovoltaics in the Energy Transition 18%
TOPIC 1: Silicon Materials and Cells 12%
TOPIC 2: Thin Films and New Concepts 20%
TOPIC 3: Photovoltaic Modules 18%
TOPIC 4: Photovoltaic Systems 32%

C30001-005

EU PVSEC

FACTS & FIGURES | Participants

22 – 26 September
BEC Bilbao Exhibition Centre
Bilbao Spain
EU PVSEC 2025

Participants by Countries
Top 10

No	Country	Participants
1	Germany	310
2	Spain	270
3	France	108
4	Italy	90
5	The Netherlands	76
6	South Korea	67
7	Switzerland	62
8	Japan	55
9	Belgium	44
10	Norway	35

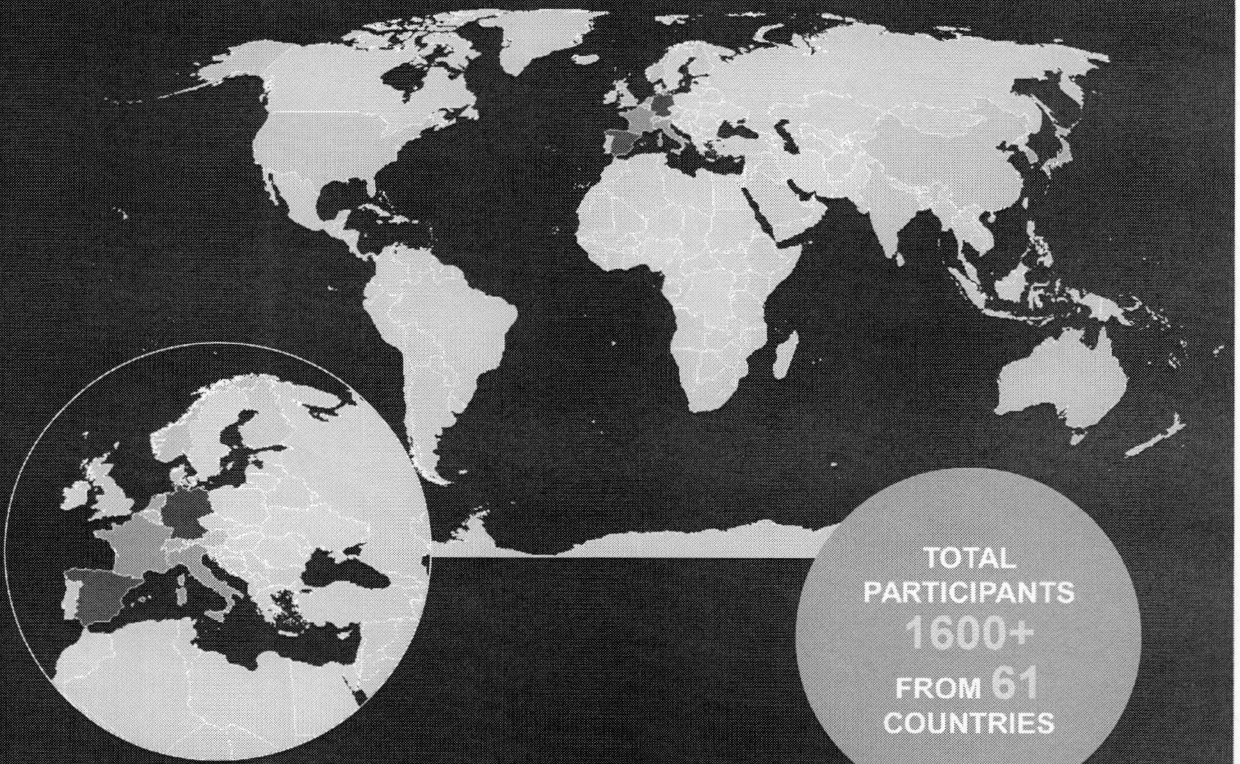

TOTAL PARTICIPANTS
1600+
FROM 61
COUNTRIES

Plenary Session "PV Everywhere"
Welcome Messages
Jon DE GREGORIO
Key Note Speech "The Dual Face of Global Solar Growth"
OPENING
Monday, 22 Sept. 2025
Becquerel Prize Ceremony
Moderated Panel Discussion "Solar in Turbulent Times: Global Dynamics and the Way Forward"
EU PVSEC 2025
www.eupvsec.org
#EUPVSEC

EU PVSEC
PANEL DISCUSSIONS
22 26
BEC
Bilbao
EU
PVSEC
2025
BO.13 Reliability and Bankability in PV
"The rapid developments of PV technology require increased attention to be paid to reliability testing."
CO.7 Challenges and Opportunities of PV up to 2030
"PV Technology is already reliable and cost effective, and even though improvements are welcome, key blockages are storage and grid strengthening. AI and robotics are essential to meet the scale of developments needed."
DO.13 Scalability and Manufacturability Prospects in Europe for New Technologies
"The prospects for reaching the 30GW target for PV module manufacturing in Europe were discussed and policy measures proposed."

EU PVSEC

22 26 BEC Bilbao

EU PVSEC 2025

CONFERENCE

KEY MESSAGES

Cross-cutting themes emerged throughout the programme, showcasing how solar technologies can be applied everywhere, from traditional to emerging fields.

- Sustainability and circularity remain central, with research focused on reducing material use, such as replacing silver with copper, and advancing end-of-life management of modules.
- Ensuring long-term stability and predictable energy yield is equally essential, with studies of degradation mechanisms such as UVID carried out.
- The role of AI across the PV value chain is rapidly expanding, from design to operations and maintenance, including drone applications.

EU PVSEC

EU PVSEC 2025

CONFERENCE

TOPIC 1: SILICON MATERIALS AND CELLS

Enhancements in IV measurement procedures

- Michael Rauer, Fraunhofer ISE: 1AO.4.5 *Universal Contacting Approaches for the Characterization of Solar Cells*
- Shuai Nie, UNSW: 1AO.4.6 *Contact-Free J-V: a Simple Technique for Universal State-of-the-Art Solar Cells*

Replacement of critical by sustainable materials:

- Reduced Ag consumpion e.g. by replacing by Cu (plating)
- In-free SHJ solar cells and Pero-Si tandems

CONFERENCE

TOPIC 1: SILICON MATERIALS AND CELLS

Great advance in understanding of UV induced degradation and Hydrogen related degradation

- Excellent PLENARY by Bram Hoex (presenting for Muhammad Umair Khan), UNSW: 1CP.3.5 *Understanding the Root Cause of UV-Induced Degradation in TOPCon and PERC Solar Cells*

Further high quality orals:

- Christina Hollemann, ISFH: 1AO.4.2 *Mitigating UV-Induced Degradation: Impact of PECVD and PEALD AlOx Layers Deposited in a Tube-Type Direct Plasma-Enhanced Chemical Vapor Deposition System*
- Hugo Lajoie, CEA: 1AO.4.3 *New Insights on UV-Induced Degradation of SHJ Solar Cells*
- Byungsul Min, ISFH: 1BO.3.6 *UV Stable Passivation Stack with Plasma-Enhanced Atomic Layer Deposition of Aluminum Oxide from an Industrial Tube-Type Direct Plasma-Enhanced Chemical Vapor Deposition System*
- Wolfram Kwapil, Fraunhofer ISE: 1AO.5.6 *Impact of Illumination on Solar Cell Properties: Insights into Atomic Hydrogen Release*

EU PVSEC

EU PVSEC 2025

CONFERENCE

TOPIC 1: SILICON MATERIALS AND CELLS

Advances in TOPCon and SHJ technology → Pushing the Limits of Performance

- Fantastic keynote lecture (PLENARY) on heterojunction solar cells by Dr. Guangtao Yang, Trina: 1CP.1.1 *Silicon Surface and Interface Study for >27% Efficient SHJ Solar Cell*
  - Deep insight into technological aspects eg. influence of rear side polishing on cell performance
  - Very high efficiencies for both-sides contacted HJT > 27%
  - Issues with CAPEX, sustainibility (Ag, In)
  - Pero-Si tandem cells on large area and modules

Late News Presentation on 27.8% efficient back contact silicon solar cells by Hua Wu, Longhi: 1DO.9.1 *Hybrid Interdigitated Back Contact Silicon Solar Cells with Superior Efficiency*

Late News Presentation as TOPCon for Bottom Solar Cells in Pero-Si Tandem devices by Jana Polzin-Isabelle Polzin, Fraunhofer ISE: 1DO.9.3 *Silicon Solar Cells – From High Efficiency Single-junction to Bottom Cells in Two-Terminal Perovskite-Silicon Tandem Devices*

EU PVSEC

EU PVSEC 2025

CONFERENCE

TOPIC 1: SILICON MATERIALS AND CELLS

Further high quality orals:

- Hua Wu, Longhi: 1DO.9.1 *Hybrid Interdigitated Back Contact Silicon Solar Cells with Superior Efficiency*
- Daming Chen, Trina: 1AO.5.1 *Large Area i-TOPCon Solar Cells with 25.9% Record Efficiency*
- Maysa Sarsour, UNSW: 1AO.6.1 *Evaluating Silicon Heterojunction Solar Cell Stability under Industrial Illuminated Hydrogenation Conditions*

Bottom cell optimization for Pero-Si tandems

EU PVSEC

EU PVSEC 2025

Bilbao

CONFERENCE

TOPIC 2: THIN FILMS AND NEW CONCEPTS

A lot of focus on the long-term stability improvement and upscaling of tandem devices based on a variety of materials (hence not only pero-Si).

Many companies (e.g. Hanwha Q-cells, Oxford PV, Microquanta Seminconductor, Jinko Solar, Longi, etc. non-exhaustive list) presented impressive results on industrial size single-junction pero modules and pero-based tandem modules. A highlight here was the plenary talk from Hanwha Q-cells showing a record large area (M10) pilot-scale Pk/Si tandem cell of 28.6% efficiency.

EU PVSEC

22 26 BEC Bilbao EU PVSEC 2025

CONFERENCE

TOPIC 2: THIN FILMS AND NEW CONCEPTS

In the field of pero-Si tandems, there is clearly more focus on improving the stability of the tandem devices than before with many contributions doing in-depth investigations into the different degradation mechanisms that can occur in pero-Si tandems.

In this respect, 2DO9.5 presented a consensus statement about reliability testing of perovskite-based tandems that is endorsed by specialists worldwide from both industry and research and presents a kind of minimum that should be done in terms of testing and reporting concerning the stability and lifetime of perovskite-based tandem devices.

More and more advanced characterization methods for perovskite and perovskite - silicon tandem solar cells are being used, hyperspectral imaging methods identify non-uniformities by layer for processing development.

EU PVSEC

EU PVSEC 2025

CONFERENCE

TOPIC 2: THIN FILMS AND NEW CONCEPTS

Another clear trend is that pero-TOPCon cells are nearing the same record efficiencies as pero-Heterojunction cells. A highlight talk here was the certified 34.22% efficiency perovskite/ topcon tandem solar cell(1cm2) by Jinko Solar 2CO2.1

Another highlight was the 30.5% triple junction pero/pero/silicon cell by EPFL (2CO2.3)

In the field of perovskite single junction devices, 2DO.7.3 showed perovskite devices with remarkable reliability, withstanding 4 years of outdoor exposure. The degradation mechanism is attributed to the diurnal behaviour, also verified and replicated with indoor experiments.

2AO3.6 investigated experimental degradation and recovery of perovskite solar cells, improving the comprehension of instability's dynamics, to extend the lifetime of devices.

EU PVSEC

EU PVSEC 2025

CONFERENCE

TOPIC 2: THIN FILMS AND NEW CONCEPTS

In the field of compound semiconductors, there were many presentations on alternative materials for perovskite in tandems. In this way, first monolithic (AgCu)(InGa)Se2 on Si tandem cells were demonstrated as well as 16.1% semitransparent Ag doped Cu(InGa)S2 sulfide top cells.

An exciting highlight in this field was 2BO8.2 in which UPC Barcelona achieved 18% efficiency under indoor lighting for kesterite solar cells with alkali doping

EU PVSEC

22 26 EU PVSEC 2025

BEC

Bilbao

CONFERENCE

TOPIC 3: PHOTOVOLTAIC MODULES

"Reliable packaging to Maximize the energy yield from high efficiency cells"

big theme: Optimizing module materials and packaging for long lifetime and predictable energy yield from high efficiency cells. The industry and research community are moving quickly to assess and improve reliability.

- Understanding, accelerated testing, and mitigating UV-ID in n-type cells and modules
- How do you develop accelerated tests for constantly changing BOMs - new encapsulants, new metallization, thinner glass, and high efficiency cells

EU PVSEC

22 26 DEC Bilbao

EU PVSEC 2025

CONFERENCE

TOPIC 3: PHOTOVOLTAIC MODULES

- Degradation and metastability in packaged perovskite tandems - understanding energy yield and realistic degradation rates
- Characterization out of the lab and into the field and factory - accurate outdoor performance, online quality control measurements for encapsulant cross linking
- Reducing silver content and metallization temperatures - reliability of low temperature and low silver metallization
- Developing glass qualification requirements to minimize breakage

EU PVSEC

EU PVSEC 2025

CONFERENCE

TOPIC 4: PHOTOVOLTAIC SYSTEMS

Advances in O&M of PV systems

(4CV.1) focuses on fault detection, cleaning optimization, soiling (and snow 4CO.8), UAV for autonomous monitoring and digital twin.

Data driven and AI based O&M (4CO.9) including a medicine-like workflow in Autonomous multi-AI agent system for health monitoring: a fully automated O&M pipeline with field robotics (4CO.9.4 D. Moser, EURAC)

PV Everywhere from space to agricultural applications like integration in vineyards (Mo, Opening plenary) and many other **integrated options** as we have seen throughout the week. On Thursday (4DO.4) agriPV, noise barriers and floating integrated systems. AgriPV technologies (4DO.2), BIPV

PV needs solar energy. **Solar resource and forecasting** (Mo, 4AO.7-9 & Tu 4BV.3). Shortly IEA PVPS T16 will publish minute irradiance data, some including GT over 220 stations worldwide with. Same format and quality controlled. (*Worldwide solar radiation measurement database with quality-control added value*, Anne Forstinger CSP Services, 4AO.7.1)

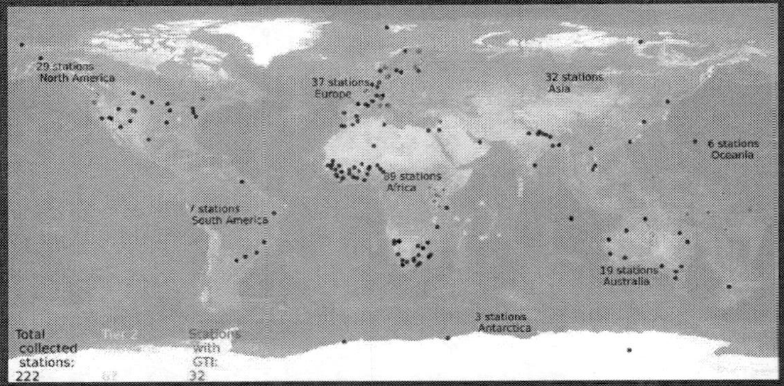

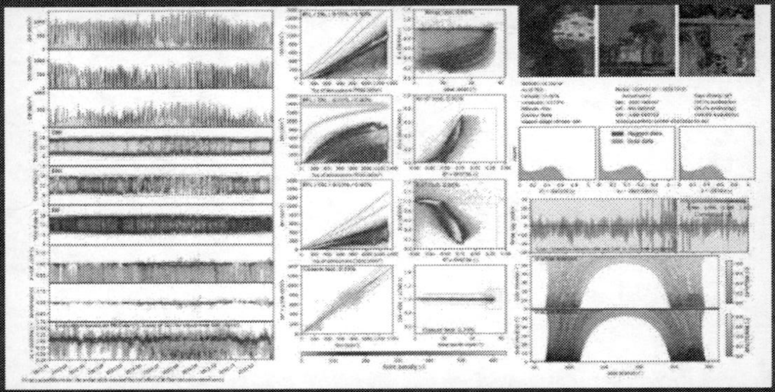

(4BV.3). Poster winner 4BV.3.12 *Advancing Very Short-Term Solar Irradiance Forecasting in Africa: A Low-Cost Sky Imaging and Machine Learning-Based Approach*, implications for PV deployment and grid integration (Martin Ansong, KIT). Runner-up 4BV.3.25 *Evaluating the Suitability of Köppen-Geiger Climate Classifications for Photovoltaic Systems: Micro-climate Analysis and Risk Assessment Maps*, with worldwide distribution of humidity related risk assessment for PV performance (Pavan Kumar Panda, Anhalt University of Applied Sciences).

Integrated PV

BIPV (4BO.16) examples of coloured modules (which was main topic of the poster session along with fire concerns of BIPV, 4BV.4), lightweight solutions (4BO.5) and modelling partial shading effects 4BO.17.1, *Modelling partial shading at the cell level on PV modules,* Jean-Paul Calin, ENSTA) and 4BO.17.3, *Comparing the energy yield and degradation rates of smart PV modules compared to conventional PV system designs in shaded urban scenario's,* Youri Blom, TU DELF.

AgriPV 4DO.2 the room was fully packed showing the interest in the topic. 5 talks were on new ways of sharing light (2 spectral splitting before the PV conversion, 2 semitransparent PV modules both c-Si and CdTe, 1 on downshifting encapsulate) + 1 new AgrivPV like application with Algae instead of crops.

4DO.4 also included AgriPV and **Others types of integration like noise barriers and floating.** In addition to performance other aspects like (*Hydrological and ecological effects on floating PV,* Konstantin Ilgen, FHO ISe) have been highlighted this week

4DO4.2

BOS and tracking systems (4DO.1) focused on backtracking strategies and terrains with complex topography.

4DO.1.4

EU PVSEC

EU PVSEC 2025

22–26 September BEC Bilbao

CONFERENCE

TOPIC 4: PHOTOVOLTAIC SYSTEMS

Reliability of PV systems

Several presentations focused long-term monitored degradation, failure modes and degradation modes identification techniques (non-destructive, aerial images, AI-based)

4BO.6.1 *Three decades, three climates: insights and lessons on PV reliability.* Good BOM offer very high reliability in power production, with 30-35 years old modules showing 0.24% degradation rate per year.

4BO.6.3 *Non-destructive detection of water ingress in solar modules using NIR spectroscopy* (Oleksandr Mashkow HI ERN) proved near-infrared absorption (NIRA) technique to detect water ingress in modules in the field, which correlated with the module degradation.

4BO.7.2 *Robust PV performance loss rate calculation for high latitudes* (Lauri Karttunen, Meteo Inst Helsinki) and 4BO.7. 3 *Detailed analysis of degradation rates of operating PV assets in tropical climate conditions* (Xioaqi Xu, Seris Singapore) Performance loss rates reported for high latitudes and tropics based on solid data sets. PLR in the tropics -1.4%/year

4DO.3.6 PV system design and assessment highlighted how inverter safety issues are extremely important and how more research about inverter safety and reliability is needed.

EU PVSEC

EU PVSEC 2025

CONFERENCE

TOPIC 5: PHOTOVOLTAICS IN THE ENERGY TRANSITION

Main topics of interest :

- Flexibility
- Artificial intelligence
- EoL management

EU PVSEC

22 26 September BEC Bilbao

EU PVSEC 2025

CONFERENCE

TOPIC 5: PHOTOVOLTAICS IN THE ENERGY TRANSITION

5.1 Grid Integration and Flexibility Enablers (2 sessions)

- Smoothing effect related to different orientations of PV systems in a given area allows 10 to 15% additional hosting capacity of the distribution grid compared to the conservative calculation that consists in summing the AC power. Such accurate calculation enabled by high resolution large area images and LIDAR and induces therefore very low costs.

5.2 Sustainability of PV (4 sessions)

- New inventories LCI and LCA for emerging technologies even though lack of data for perovskites, LCA showing a way for low environmental Impacts with technology improvement and localisation. / Technological improvements will contribute to the reduction of environmental Impact / Grid Efficiency has an Impact on the environmental Footprint.
- Manufacturing optimization / Reuse & recycling: results from the perspective of economic performance – would it convince manufacturer to consider it if economic benefit ?
- EoL Management /recycling -> emerging field attracting lots of activities / mainly EU projects (EVERPV / ICARUS / QASAR) – highlight on polymer, interesting question came up and to be debated for the next decade: is it worth it to consider polymer (EVA/ backsheet) recycling ?
- Major progress in methodology and indicators to assess sustainable design & circularity and improve transparency recyclability index, technical recyclability, digital passport)

CONFERENCE

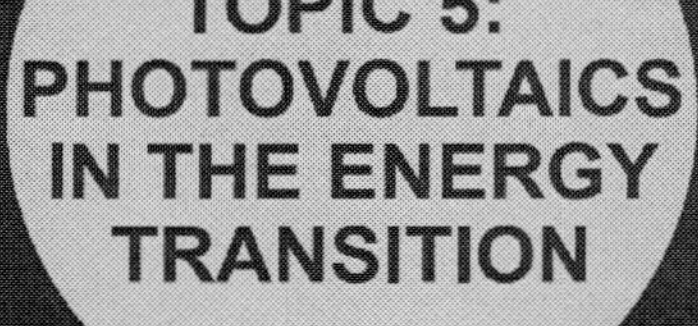

5.3 Scenarios for Renewables, Policy, Global Challenges (1 session)

- wide scope of contributions on the way to massive, medium- to long-term PV deployment -> should not be taken for granted despite positive projections since there can be limiting factors such as public acceptance / regulatory restrictions and effect of climate change

5.4 Costs, Economics, Finance and Markets (1 session)

- Annual installed capacity over 400 GWp / total cumulative installed capacity worldwide over 2.1 TWp / Clear mismatch between PV module installations rate worldwide and PV module production rate leading to bunch of inventories and drastically reduced prices.

5.6 Societal Challenges; Citizens' Participation, Awareness (1 session)

- data and analysis in gender aspects are emerging in PV! (poster session) + Highlight on innovation in education! On example that targets students & skilled workers -> mobile Lab for advanced experimental training PV-related to bring skills and characterization tools everywhere.

PARALLEL
EVENTS

Collaborat° Network
Diversity
Prejudice
Justificat°
Change
Needs — Profile Match
Avoid Blind Spots
Job Loss?
Integration
Lack of Attractiveness
Resilience (People + Company)
Creativity
Different Communicat°
Internal Friction
More Efforts

030001-027

- Perovskite Innovation Roundtable: Driving EU Leadership in Perovskite Innovation
- Women in PV presents: Leading with Inclusion – Embracing the 6 Traits of Inclusive Leadership
- Unlocking the Potential of Integrated Photovoltaic Systems - European R&D Approach
- Why Do PV Plants Perform Lower than Expected? (Estimating losses by backtracking algorithms in undulating terrain & Analysis of the loss chain and identification of deviations from initial expectations)
- PV Made in the EU: How Do Companies Die and How Can They Thrive?

22 — 26
September
BEC —
ilbao Exhibition Centre
Bilbao — Spain
EU
PVSEC
2025
42nd European
Photovoltaic Solar Energy
Conference and Exhibition
GEOPOLITICS & PV MANUFACTURING CHALLENGES
EXHIBITION
FORUM
INDUSTRY
SUMMIT

03O001-029

EU PVSEC

22 – 26 September, BEC, Bilbao, Spain

EU PVSEC 2025

INDUSTRY SUMMIT

Industry Summit Opening (session I)

Session Title: Solar PV production in Europe - the way forward

Moderators: Begoña Molinete, Walburga Hemetsberger

Key Takeaway:

This session discussed the state of play of European manufacturing projects and whether there is enough European support. It was clear that political support is further lacking – only 3 Member States have developed schemes to support European manufacturing. While the Net Zero Industry Act is helpful to diversify supplies, it will not particularly support European manufacturing.

All panellists agreed that apart from further policy support (financing, derisking) collaboration is the way forward.

EU PVSEC

EU PVSEC 2025

INDUSTRY SUMMIT

Session II
Session Title: International corporations in the light of changing geopolitics
Moderators: Radovan Kopecek, Puzant Baliozian

Key takeaway:
EU machine builders are still supporting mostly Indian but also US and EU projects with their technology and expertise. The major arguments for choosing EU tech are quality, training, support and low OPEX.

Session III
Session Title: PV Systems: How do we get the produced electricity in Europe into the grid?
Moderators: Catarina Augusto, Peter Fath

Key Takeaway:
Hybrid PV + storage systems (co-located or distributed) are essential for integrating PV into electricity grids. Storage adds flexibility and stabilizes the grid, making it a cornerstone of resilient energy systems; while the technology is mature, scalable and bankable revenue models remain the key gap for widespread deployment.

LIST OF EXHIBITORS
(in alphabetical order)

Company name	Country
2nd Cycle FlexCo	Austria
9-Tech	Italy
Avalon ST / Pasan	Switzerland
BASQUENERGY Cluster	Spain
Becquerel Institute	Belgium
ECOPROGETTI	Italy
EKIENERGY	Spain
ESMC Pavilion	Belgium
Eternal Sun I WAVELABS	The Netherlands
EU PVSEC Startup Pavilion	
European Commission JRC	Italy
exateq	Germany
FLUXiM AG	Switzerland
G2V Optics	Canada
GALEA	Spain
halm elektronik	Germany
HighLine Technology	Germany
IEA PVPS	
Innovations in Optics, Inc.	United States of America
ISC Konstanz	Germany
LAB14	Germany
MBJ Solutions	Germany
Mondragon Assembly	Spain
Nagase Chemtex America	United States of America
NEO Messtechnik Holding	Austria
ODTÜ GÜNAM	Türkiye
Phoenixolar	China
PSE Instruments	Germany
PVsyst	Switzerland
RCT Future	Germany
RCT Solutions	Germany
RENA	Germany
ReNewPV-CA21148 / 5GSOLAR	Estonia
SALD B.V.	The Netherlands

SCIPRIOS	Germany
SEMILAB	Hungary
SINGULUS TECHNOLOGIES	Germany
Sinton Instruments	United States of America
SOLAR MATERIALS	Germany
SolarNL	The Netherlands
Soli Tek R&D	Lithuania
TAMURA ELSOLD	Germany
TECNALIA	Spain
The Netherlands Pavilion	The Netherlands
TNO	The Netherlands
University of the Basque Country	Spain
Vector Energy	Spain
VON ARDENNE	Germany
WCPEC-9	South Korea
WIP Renewable Energies	Germany
ZSW	Germany

We thank the EU PVSEC 2025 Sponsors

Platinum

MONDRAGON ASSEMBLY

Gold

ENERGIAREN EUSKAL ERAKUNDEA
ENTE VASCO DE LA ENERGÍA

G2V

halm.

RCT solutions

Silver

Sinton instruments

Bronze

AESOLAR

AUTHORS OF EU PVSEC 2025 PROCEEDINGS PAPERS

A. dos Reis Benatto, Gisele — 020028, 020037, 020039, 020191, 020265, 020376, 020477
DTU, Roskilde, Denmark

Aaltonen, Lauri — 020537
Tampere University, Tampere, Finland

Abad Alcaraz, Verónica — 020336
University of Almería, La Cañada de San Urbano, Spain

Abbott, Malcolm D. — 020396
PV Lighthouse, Coledale, Australia

Abbotto, Alessandro — 020077
University of Milano-Bicocca, Milan, Italy

Abdallah, Amir A. — 020146, 020166
QEERI, Doha, Qatar

Abdel Nour, Christine — 020188
EDF R&D, Moret Loing Orvanne, France

Abdelrahim, Mohamed — 020166
QEERI, Doha, Qatar

Abdou-Tankari, Mahamadou — 020562
Paris-East Créteil University, Créteil, France

Abrego, Gillen — 020392
ALLOTARRA, Allo, Spain

Acciarri, Maurizio — 020087
University of Milano-Bicocca, Milan, Italy

Acevedo Devoto, M. Ignacia — 020220
ISC Konstanz, Konstanz, Germany

Achenbach, Jannik — 020522
University of Applied Science Cologne, Cologne, Germany

Acinas, Victor — 020019
Applied Materials, Dublin, Ireland

Adachi, Satoru — 020436
NIED, Shinjo, Japan

Aden, Samira — 020513
HZB, Berlin, Germany

Adinolfi Borea, Riccardo — 020314
University of Bologna, Bologna, Italy

Adnan Hameed, Mohammed — 020156
Martin-Luther-University Halle-Wittenberg, Halle, Germany

Adothu, Baloji — 020229
DEWA, Dubai, United Arab Emirates

Aghaei, Mohammadreza — 020335, 020356
NTNU, Aalesund, Norway

Aghaei, Mohammadreza — 020374, 020375
NTNU, Ålesund, Norway

Aghamohammadi, Amirhossain Amirkabir University of Technology, Tehran, Iran	020356
Aguirre, Aranzazu Hasselt Unversity, Genk, Belgium	020064
Ahmadi, Mehdi CNR-IMM, Catania, Italy	020066
Aiello, Andrea ACCA Software, Cosenza, Italy	020255
Aimé, Jérémie CEA / INES, Le Bourget-du-Lac, France	020217, 020311
Aissa, Brahim QEERI, Doha, Qatar	020042, 020075, 020108, 020109, 020146, 020147
Aizpurua, Jon Tecnalia, Donostia - San Sebastián, Spain	020139
Akbayrak, Serdar Necmettin Erbakan University, Konya, Türkiye	020020
Akram, M. Waqar Hohai University, Changzhou, China	020164
Al Katrib, Mirella IPVF, Palaiseau, France	020116
Alam, Habeel Lancaster University, Lancaster, United Kingdom	020394
Alberts, Vivian DEWA, Dubai, United Arab Emirates	020229
Albuquerque, Daniel P. Centre for New Energy Technologies, Sacavém, Portugal	020464
Alet, Pierre-Jean CSEM, Neuchâtel, Switzerland	020238, 020544
Alexandris, Nikos European Commission JRC, Ispra, Italy	020210
Alfieri, Felice Viegand Maagøe, Copenhagen, Denmark	020497
Ali, Adnan QEERI, Doha, Qatar	020147
Allen, Vince SunDrive Solar, Kurnell, Australia	020048
Alloji, Esma Necmettin Erbakan University, Konya, Türkiye	020020
Almeida Silva, José University of Évora, Évora, Portugal	020565
Almuneau, Guilhem LAAS-CNRS, Toulouse, France	020074
Alonso, Ricardo TECNALIA, Derio, Spain	020197, 020198, 020353, 020358
Alonso-Montesinos, Joaquín University of Almeria, Almeria, Spain	020100

Alonso-Montesinos, Joaquín 020336
University of Almería, La Cañada de San Urbano, Spain
Álvarez Hervás, José Domingo 020336
University of Almería, La Cañada de San Urbano, Spain
Alvarez, José 020040, 020058
CNRS, Gif-sur-Yvette, France
Álvarez, Marta 020300
CENER, Sarriguren, Spain
Álvarez-Pérez, Guillem 020062
IPVF, Palaiseau, France
Alvaro Høye, Ingar 020443
Solkraft Sør, Øyslebø, Norway
Alves e Silva, Kiane 020439, 020535, 020567, 020575
UPM, Madrid, Spain
Amaro e Silva, Rodrigo 020490
University of Lisbon, Lisbon, Portugal
Amatriain, Irati 020392
CENER, Sarriguren, Spain
Anamiati, Gaetana 020448, 020481
GreenPowerMonitor a DNV company, Barcelona, Spain
Anaya, Julian 020191, 020205
University of Valladolid, Valladolid, Spain
Ancillao, Andrea 020079
Polytechnic University of Turin, Turin, Italy
Anderlini, Alessandro 020155
Coveme, Gorizia, Italy
Andersen, Nanna L. 020250
DTU, Roskilde, Denmark
Andersen, Nanna Lysgaard 020306
DTU, Roskilde, Denmark
Andrade-Arvizu, Jacob 020094
IREC, Barcelona, Spain
Andreozzi, Federico 020494
University of Rome Tor Vergata, Rome, Italy
Anefnaf, Ikram 020093
University of Verona, Verona, Italy
Ansong, Martin 020272
KIT, Eggenstein-Leopoldshafen, Germany
Antognini, Luca 020196
PVsyst, Geneva, Switzerland
Antoine, C. 020508
IMDEA Nanoscience Institute, Madrid, Spain
Antón, Ignacio 020209, 020246, 020257, 020453, 020459
UPM, Madrid, Spain
Antonucci, Daniele 020551
Eurac Research, Bolzano, Italy

Apostoleris, Harry 020487
EPRI, Dubai, United Arab Emirates
Arakawa, Hayato 020436
NIED, Shinjo, Japan
Aranguren, Gerardo 020289, 020353
UPV/EHU, Bilbao, Spain
Arbaretaz, Sebastien 020317
CEA INES, Le Bourget-du-Lac, France
Ardissone, Bastien J. J. 020396
PV Lighthouse, Coledale, Australia
Arduino, Daniele 020079
Polytechnic University of Turin, Turin, Italy
Ariolli, Daniela Maria Godinho 020325
BayWa r.e, Rome, Italy
Ariza Camacho, Maria Jesus 020100
University of Almeria, Almería, Spain
Armstrong, Alona 020394
Lancaster University, Lancaster, United Kingdom
Arribat, Mathieu 020074
LAAS-CNRS, Toulouse, France
Arrizabalaga, Igor 020139
Tecnalia, Donostia - San Sebastián, Spain
Artegiani, Elisa 020057, 020089, 020093
University of Verona, Verona, Italy
Arumughan, Jayaprasad 020569
ISC Konstanz, Konstanz, Germany
Asaa, Shu-Ngwa 020393
imo-imomec, Genk, Belgium
Ascencio-Vásquez, Julián 020371
Univers, Courbevoie, France
Askins, Steve 020209, 020257
UPM, Madrid, Spain
Assaid, El Mahdi 020171
University of Chouaib Doukkali, El Jadida, Morocco
Aste, Niccolò 020249
Polytechnic University of Milan, Milan, Italy
Astigarraga, Alexander 020226
Eurac Research, Bolzano, Italy
Athienitis, Andreas 020248
Concordia University, Montreal, Canada
Aurrekoetxea, Olaia 020302
TECNALIA, Saint Sebastian, Spain
Awadallah, Carlos 020536
Wattkraft, Madrid, Spain
Azkona, Nekane 020055, 020097, 020153, 020287
UPV/EHU, Bilbao, Spain

Azzopardi, Brian 020318, 020334, 020520
FIR, Birkirkara, Malta
Azzopardi, Carmel 020334
FIR, Birkirkara, Malta

Babich, Francesco 020551
Eurac Research, Bolzano, Italy
Babics, Maxime 020217
CEA / INES, Le Bourget-du-Lac, France
Babin, Markus 020249, 020250, 020306, 020477
DTU, Roskilde, Denmark
Bachour, Dunia A. 020275, 020278
QEERI, Doha, Qatar
Bachour, Dunia 020291
QEERI, Doha, Qatar
Baderiya, Naman 020390
MARIN, Wageningen, The Netherlands
Badosa Franch, Jordi 020214
Polytechnic Institute of Paris, Palaiseau, France
Baeck, Pieter-Jan 020511
Flemish Institute for Technological Research (VITO), Genk, Belgium
Bai, Jianbo 020164
Hohai University, Changzhou, China
Bailache, Simon 020303
CSTB, Marne-la-Vallée, France
Bakhtiari, Afshin 020121
AESOLAR, Koenigsbrunn, Germany
Balafoutis, Athanasios T. 020464
CERTH, Athens, Greece
Bald, Juan 020514
AZTI, PASAIA, Spain
Baldacchino, Alex J. 020065
UNSW, Sydney, Australia
Baležentienė, Skirmantė 020380
The Applied Research Institute for Prospective Technologies, Vilnius, Lithuania
Baležentis, Algirdas 020380
The Applied Research Institute for Prospective Technologies, Vilnius, Lithuania
Ballif, Christophe 020467
CSEM, Neuchâtel, Switzerland
Ballif, Christophe 020251
EPFL, Neuchâtel, Switzerland
Bandaru, Narendra 020039, 020043, 020104
Aarhus University, Aarhus, Denmark

Bang, Ole 020043
Technical University of Denmark, Copenhagen, Denmark

Barakel, Damien 020188
Toulon University, Marseille, France

Baraket, Mira 020039
ATLANT 3D, Taastrup, Denmark

Baranek, Philippe 020060
EDF R&D, Palaiseau, France

Barchi, Grazia 020485, 020489, 020544
Eurac Research, Bolzano, Italy

Bardizza, Giorgio 020181
TÜV Rheinland Italia, Milan, Italy

Bardizza, Giorgio 020208
TÜV Rheinland Solar, Cologne, Germany

Bardizza, Giorgio 020144
TÜV Rheinland, Cologne, Germany

Barguès, Anna 020505
Becquerel Institute France, Lyon, France

Barguès, Anna 020558
Becquerel Institute, Brussels, Belgium

Barnscheidt, Verena 020063, 020114
ISFH, Emmerthal, Germany

Barretta, Chiara 020325
PCCL, Leoben, Austria

Barrionuevo, Bruno 020464
CERTH, Athens, Greece

Barroso, João 020565
University of Évora, Évora, Portugal

Barrou, Alexis 020467
CSEM, Neuchâtel, Switzerland

Barrutia, Laura 020446, 020536
UPM, Madrid, Spain

Barth, Vincent 020134
CEA / INES, Le Bourget-du-Lac, France

Barth, Vincent 020019
CEA, Le Bourget-du-Lac, France

Barth, Vincent 020226
CEA/ INES, Le Bourget-du-Lac, France

Bartholomäus, Martin 020346
DTU, Roskilde, Denmark

Bartolo, Brian 020334
FIR, Birkirkara, Malta

Basta, Beata 020068
Roltec, Poznań, Poland

Basta, Marek 020068
Roltec, Poznań, Poland

Battisti, Kurt 020255
A-Null Development, Vienna, Austria

Bauhuis, Gerard 020067
Radboud University, Nijmegen, The Netherlands

Baumann, Kerstin 020470
bifa Umweltinstitut, Augsburg, Germany

Baumann, Sara 020063
ISFH, Emmerthal, Germany

Baumann, Ulrike 020006
ISFH, Emmerthal, Germany

Baur, Carsten 020246
European Space Agency, Noordwijk, The Netherlands

Beaucarne, Guy 020384
Dow Silicones Belgium, Seneffe, Belgium

Becker, Carl 020331
DLR, Almería, Spain

Behrensdorff Poulsen, Peter 020037
DTU, Lyngby, Denmark

Beinert, Andreas J. 020123
Fraunhofer ISE, Freiburg, Germany

Bejat, Timea 020225, 020500
CEA, Le Bourget-du-Lac, France

Belawadi, Aditya Girish 020231
Fraunhofer ISE, Freiburg, Germany

Belferkous, Brahim Anis 020325
PCCL, Leoben, Austria

Bellmann, Martin 020495, 020510
SINTEF, Trondheim, Norway

Bellvert, Eduard 020139
Tecnalia, Donostia - San Sebastián, Spain

Beltran-Condori, Sonia 020129, 020417
University of Antofagasta, Antofagasta, Chile

Belzunce, María Jesús 020514
AZTI, PASAIA, Spain

Bendix, Peter 020388
Next2Sun Technology, Dillingen, Germany

Bengoechea, Jaione 020181, 020300
CENER, Sarriguren, Spain

Bermudez Benito, Veronica 020146
QEERI, Doha, Qatar

Bermudez-Garcia, Anderson 020246
Thales Alenia Space, Cannes, France

Berrian, Djaber 020492
Belectric, Kolitzheim, Germany

Berson, Solenn 020134
CEA / INES, Le Bourget-du-Lac, France

Besson, Pierre 020373
INES, Le Bourget-du-Lac, France
Betak, Juraj 020241
Solargis, Bratislava, Slovakia
Bettucci, Ottavia 020077
University of Milano-Bicocca, Milan, Italy
Bhardwaj, Shashank 020515
TU Delft, Delft, The Netherlands
Bhatnagar, Shrey 020367
Nextracker, Fremont, United States of America
Biard, Yves 020303
SemperStyl, Eragny, France
Bieber, Lisa-Marie 020195
Fraunhofer ISE, Freiburg, Germany
Bilitu, Eddie 020393
Hasselt University, Hasselt, Belgium
Binani, Ashish 020225
TNO, Petten, The Netherlands
Binetti, Simona 020093
University of Milano Bicocca, Milan, Italy
Binetti, Simona 020087
University of Milano-Bicocca, Milan, Italy
Blakesley, James 020293
National Physical Laboratory, Teddington, United Kingdom
Blanc, Philippe 020291
MINES Paris, Nice, France
Blanco Aguiar, Adrián 020243
ieco.io, Vigo, Spain
Blieske, Ulf 020141
University of Applied Science Cologne, Cologne, Germany
Blieske, Ulf 020140
University of Applied Sciences Cologne, Cologne, Germany
Blstak Catlosova, Katarina 020274
Solargis, Bratislava, Slovakia
Blum, Niklas 020235, 020237, 020239
DLR, Almeria, Spain
Boccardi, Roberto 020039
DTU, Copenhagen, Denmark
Boccardi, Roberto 020037
DTU, Lyngby, Denmark
Boccardi, Roberto 020028
DTU, Roskilde, Denmark
Boddaert, Simon 020302, 020303
CSTB, Marne-la-Vallée, France
Bokalič, Matevž 020047, 020319
University of Ljubljana, Ljubljana, Slovenia

Bolink, Henk J. 020226
University of Valencia, Paterna, Spain

Bonal, Victor 020085
UAM, Madrid, Spain

Bonnet, Martin 020141
University of Applied Science Cologne, Cologne, Germany

Bonnet-Eymard, Bénédicte 020251
CSEM, Neuchâtel, Switzerland

Borgers, Tom 020225
IMEC, Genk, Belgium

Borgna, Luciano 020369
BFH, Burgdorf, Switzerland

Borie, Benjamin 020039
ATLANT 3D, Taastrup, Denmark

Borowski, Peter 020307
Avancis, Munich, Germany

Borriello, Aniello 020378
ENEA, Portici, Italy

Borzi, Giovanni 020019
Enginsoft, Padua, Italy

Bosch, Elina 020252, 020543, 020564, 020573
Becquerel Institute, Brussels, Belgium

Bosma, Theo 020571
DNV, Arnhem, The Netherlands

Bothe, Karsten 020236
ISFH, Emmerthal, Germany

Bou-Nassif, Liliane 020338
CETHIL, Villeurbanne, France

Bouchier, Daniel 020058
CNRS, Palaiseau, France

Bouguerra, Sara 020156, 020294, 020389, 020393
imec, Genk, Belgium

Bourdin, Vincent 020406
CNRS, Paris, France

Bourgeois, Antoine 020102
SERIS, Singapore, Singapore

Bovesecchi, Gianluigi 020494
University of Rome Tor Vergata, Rome, Italy

Brabec, Christoph J. 020117
HI ERN, Erlangen, Germany

Bradford, David Roy 020077
Newcastle University, Newcastle upon Tyne, United Kingdom

Brailovsky, Peter Henri 020475
Fraunhofer ISE, Freiburg, Germany

Braña, Alejandro F. 020508
Autonomous University of Madrid, Madrid, Spain

Brandstätter, Andreas 020227
Lenzing Plastics, Lenzing, Austria

Braun, Christian 020457
Luxembourg Institute of Science and Technology, Esch-sur-Alzette, Luxembourg

Brecl, Kristijan 020269, 020319
University of Ljubljana, Ljubljana, Slovenia

Bredemeier, Dennis 020240
Leibniz University Hannover, Hannover, Germany

Breitenbücher, Marian 020225
Highline Technologies, Freiburg, Germany

Brendel, Rolf 020006, 020008, 020236, 020240, 020260, 020482
ISFH, Emmerthal, Germany

Brendstrup Møller, Clara Bolette 020028
DTU, Roskilde, Denmark

Bretzel, Tamara 020195
Fraunhofer ISE, Freiburg, Germany

Breyer, Christian 020479
LUT University, Lappeenranta, Finland

Brito, Miguel 020457
University of Lisbon, Lisbon, Portugal

Brivio, Elisabetta 020462
RSE, Milan, Italy

Brockmann, Lukas 020063
ISFH, Emmerthal, Germany

Brodnicke, Linda 020296
ETH, Zurich, Switzerland

Brueckner, Emanuel 020063
ISFH, Emmerthal, Germany

Bründlinger, Roland 020369
AIT, Vienna, Austria

Brun, Gonzalo 020414, 020517
ENDEF, Zaragoza, Spain

Bruno, Maddalena 020452
Fraunhofer ISE, Freiburg, Germany

Buceta, Alicia 020300
CENER, Sarriguren, Spain

Bucher, Christof 020179, 020322, 020359, 020369, 020386
BFH, Burgdorf, Switzerland

Buchholz, Florian 020035, 020225, 020569
ISC Konstanz, Konstanz, Germany

Buchmann, Johanna 020309
Berlin University of Applied Sciences, Berlin, Germany

Buck, Thomas 020033
ISC Konstanz, Konstanz, Germany

Buckland, Daniel Henkel, Düsseldorf, Germany	020119, 020218
Buddana, Viswa Harinath DLR, Oldenburg, Germany	020482
Bühlmann, Gian-Luca ZHAW, Winterthur, Switzerland	020385
Buerhop, Claudia HI ERN, Erlangen, Germany	020149, 020150, 020377
Buerhop-Lutz, Claudia HI ERN, Erlangen, Germany	020185, 020230
Burgers, Antonius R. TNO, Petten, The Netherlands	020405
Burri, Matthias BFH, Burgdorf, Switzerland	020179
Busto, Chiara Eni, Novara, Italy	020521
Butrichi, Fabio University of Milano-Bicocca, Milan, Italy	020087
Butt, Nauman Lahore University of Management Sciences, Lahore, Pakistan	020394
C. Tavares, Fabiele Federal University of Rio de Janeiro, Duque de Caxias, Brazil	020090
Cabal, Raphael University Grenoble Alpes, Le Bourget-du-Lac, France	020034
Caballero, Luis Jaime UPM, Madrid, Spain	020501, 020508
Caballero, Raquel CSIC, Madrid, Spain	020094
Caballero, Raquel IO-CSIC, Madrid, Spain	020085
Cabecinha, Vasco Nova University Lisbon, Lisbon, Portugal	020565
Cabello, Fatima IO-CSIC, Madrid, Spain	020085
Caçapietra Pires da Silva, Lucas Teixeira PUCRS, Porto Alegre, Brazil	020025
Caccavelli, Dominique CSTB, Bussy-Saint Georges, France	020551
Caccivio, Mauro SUPSI, Mendrisio, Switzerland	020204, 020574
Caffari, Francesca ENEA, Ispra, Italy	020551
Calabrese, Nicolandrea ENEA, Ispra, Italy	020551

Calin, Jean-Paul 020251
ENSTA Paris, Palaiseau, France

Çalışkan Arslan, Meriç 020006, 020135
Kalyon PV, Ankara, Türkiye

Caluori, Philip 020455
Virtual Vehicle, Graz, Austria

Camara, Assa 020274
Solargis, Bratislava, Slovakia

Cambarau, Werther 020139
Tecnalia, Donostia-San Sebastián, Spain

Campana, Pietro Elia 020381
Mälardalen University, Västerås, Sweden

Campos Guzman, Laura 020331
DLR, Almería, Spain

Cancro, Carmine 020378
ENEA, Naples, Italy

Canesse, Auriane 020196
PVsyst, Geneva, Switzerland

Cañizo, Carlos 020097
IES-UPM, Madrid, Spain

Cano, Francisco J. 020139
Tecnalia, Donostia - San Sebastián, Spain

Cano, Lucía 020127
ENDEF, Zaragoza, Spain

Cánovas, Enrique 020508
IMDEA Nanoscience Institute, Madrid, Spain

Cao, Han 020263
SERIS, Singapore, Singapore

Capitaine, Anna 020116
IPVF, Palaiseau, France

Cappelle, Jan 020329, 020351
KU Leuven, Ghent, Belgium

Capron, Guillaume 020217
CEA / INES, Le Bourget-du-Lac, France

Carballo López, José Antonio 020336
University of Almería, La Cañada de San Urbano, Spain

Cardenas, Luis Alejandro 020339, 020546
National University of Colombia, Bogotá, Colombia

Carmo, Paulo 020304, 020420
University of Évora, Évora, Portugal

Carrasco, Luis Miguel 020439, 020535, 020567
UPM, Madrid, Spain

Carrillo Mejía, Luis 020279
District University of Bogotá, Bogotá, Colombia

Carrillo, Rafael E. 020238
CSEM, Neuchâtel, Switzerland

Carroy, Perrine 020226
CEA/ INES, Le Bourget-du-Lac, France

Carstens, Justus 020003
ISC Konstanz, Konstanz, Germany

Cartenì, Fabrizio 020378
University of Naples Federico II, Naples, Italy

Casappa, Michele 020087
National Research Council, Parma, Italy

Casasola Paesa, Marta 020389
Hasselt University, Diepenbeek, Belgium

Castilla Nieto, María del Mar 020336
University of Almería, La Cañada de San Urbano, Spain

Castillo Patton, Daniel Jason 020326
Enertis Applus+, Madrid, Spain

Castro, Luis Guilherme 020530
Casa dos Ventos, Fortaleza, Brazil

Castro, Rui 020464
University of Lisbon, Lisbon, Portugal

Castro-Gallardo, Fernando 020417, 020422
University of Antofagasta, Antofagasta, Chile

Cavaco, Afonso 020304, 020565
University of Évora, Évora, Portugal

Cebecauer, Tomas 020274
Solargis, Bratislava, Slovakia

Çekerek, Gamze 020006
Kalyon PV, Ankara, Türkiye

Celik, Duygu 020551
WIP Renewable Energies, Munich, Germany

Çeliktaş, Melih Soner 020559
Ege University, İzmir, Türkiye

Centazzo, Massimo 020006
EnPV, Karlsruhe, Germany

Centeno Brito, Miguel 020421, 020490
University of Lisbon, Lisbon, Portugal

Cereceda, Eneko 020055, 020097, 020153, 020287
UPV/EHU, Bilbao, Spain

Ceretti, Mattia 020204
SUPSI, Mendrisio, Switzerland

Cesar, I. 020405
TNO, Petten, The Netherlands

Ceuppens, Ignas 020302
BUILD`UP, Aarschot, Belgium

Chatterji, Nithin 020071
SVNIT, Surat, India

Chen, Daniel 020048
SunDrive Solar, Kurnell, Australia

Chen, Syh-Homg ITRI, Hsinchu, Taiwan	020161
Chen, Xiang Hohai University, Changzhou, China	020111
Cheung, Kak Pong Kiel University of Applied Sciences, Kiel, Germany	020313
Chhapia, Gaurang Belectric, Kolitzheim, Germany	020492
Chiba, Takahiro Hokkaido University of Science, Sapporo, Japan	020436
Chichignoud, Guy 13Institut Polytechnique De Grenoble, Grenoble, France	020495
Chicote, Beatriz Mondragon University, Arrasate-Mondragon, Spain	020289
Chiesa, Matteo Khalifa University, Abu Dhabi, United Arab Emirates	020487
Chini de Freitas, Felipe PUCRS, Porto Alegre, Brazil	020023
Cho, Yunae KIER, Daejeon, South Korea	020045
Choi, Kwan Bum SERIS, Singapore, Singapore	020102
Chouder, Aissa University of M'sila, M'sila, Algeria	020301
Chowdhury, Gofran 3E, Brussels, Belgium	020276, 020544
Christ, Anja ISFH, Emmerthal, Germany	020063
Chrkavy, Daniel Solargis, Bratislava, Slovakia	020262
Chueh, Wei-Lo TSEC, Hsinchu, Taiwan	020021
Ciesla, Alison UNSW, Sydney, Australia	020065
Cirimele, Vincenzo University of Bologna, Bologna, Italy	020314
Clausing, Roland ISFH, Emmerthal, Germany	020063, 020114
Clochard, Laurent Nines Photovoltaics, Dublin, Germany	020031
Clochard, Laurent Nines Photovoltaics, Dublin, Ireland	020007
Clyncke, Jan PV CYCLE, Brussels, Belgium	020472, 020513
Coşkun, Özlem Kalyon PV, Ankara, Türkiye	020006, 020027, 020225

Colberts, Fallon 020389
Zuyd University, Heerlen, The Netherlands

Colin, Hervé 020217, 020262
CEA / INES, Le Bourget-du-Lac, France

Collin, Stéphane 020074
C2N, Palaiseau, France

Colwell, Jack 020048
SunDrive Solar, Kurnell, Australia

Comak, Mertcan 020003
ISC Konstanz, Konstanz, Germany

Connolly, James Patrick 020058, 020060
CNRS, Gif-sur-Yvette, France

Cordeiro, Diogo 020464
EDP, Lisbon, Portugal

Cornago, Iñaki 020392
CENER, Sarriguren, Spain

Cornaro, Cristina 020494
University of Rome Tor Vergata, Rome, Italy

Correa, Guillermo 020412
Gonvarri MS R&D, Corvera - Asturias, Spain

Correia, Joana 020565
University of Évora, Évora, Portugal

Couderc, Romain 020217, 020311, 020546
CEA / INES, Le Bourget-du-Lac, France

Coutel, John 020244
SOLAÏS, Valbonne, France

Cowan, Don 020230
Kiwa PI Berlin, Hudson, United States of America

Cox, Joel D. 020250
SDU Climate Cluster, Odense, Denmark

Cox, Joel D 020306
SDU Climate Cluster, Odense, Denmark

Coz, Pier Luigi 020246
European Space Agency, Noordwijk, The Netherlands

Crespo, Carolina 020490
University of Lisbon, Lisbon, Portugal

Cristiane Pan, Aline 020548
UFRGS, Tramandaí, Brazil

Cristóbal, Ana Belén 020491, 020535, 020575
UPM, Madrid, Spain

Crozier McCleland, Jacqueline 020185, 020344
Nelson Mandela University, Port Elizabeth, South Africa

Cuadra, Juan Manuel 020318
CENER, Sarigurren, Spain

Cui, Jindan 020320, 020525
Tokyo University of Science, Tokyo, Japan

Culot, Dominique 020384
Dow Silicones Belgium, Seneffe, Belgium

Curon, Jonathan 020384
Dow Silicones Belgium, Seneffe, Belgium

Cusenza, Maria Anna 020466
RSE, Milan, Italy

D. Pinto, Luciana 020090
Federal University of Rio de Janeiro, Rio de Janeiro, Brazil

Daenen, Michael 020156, 020389, 020393
imec, Genk, Belgium

Dagla, Anastasia 020276
3E, Brussels, Belgium

Dahle, Arne 020225, 020495
Norsun, Oslo, Norway

Dahlioui, Dounia 020443
University of Agder, Grimstad, Norway

Dalibor, Thomas 020307
Avancis, Munich, Germany

Dalla Maria, Enrico 020485
Eurac Research, Bolzano, Italy

Dalla Torre, Francesco 020010
Applied Materials, Treviso, Italy

Dalmazzone, Didier 020251
ENSTA Paris, Palaiseau, France

Damon, Keanu 020382
7SecondSolar, Cape Town, South Africa

Danelli, Andrea 020462, 020466
RSE, Milan, Italy

Darsene Dimd, Berhane 020270
SINTEF, Trondheim, Norway

Das, Gourab 020005, 020222, 020463
RCT Solutions, Konstanz, Germany

Dasilva-Villanueva, Nerea 020014, 020501, 020508
UPM, Madrid, Spain

Daßler, David 020313
Fraunhofer CSP, Halle, Germany

Daßler, David 020355
Fraunhofer IMWS, Halle, Germany

Daume, Darwin 020361
pvnode, Rosenheim, Germany

Davidsen, Rasmus Schmidt 020028, 020039, 020043
Aarhus University, Aarhus, Denmark

De Almeida, Laura 020074
LAAS-CNRS, Toulouse, France

De Biasio, Martin 020504
Silicon Austria Labs, Villach, Austria

De Blasi, Mariam 020378
Enel Green Power, Pisa, Italy

de Graaf, Gertjan J. 020405
TNO, Petten, The Netherlands

de Groot, Koen M. 020405
TNO, Petten, The Netherlands

De Gruijter, Alvaro 020254
Eurac Research, Bolzano, Italy

de Jong, Minne M. 020169, 020425
TNO, Eindhoven, The Netherlands

De Jong, Richard 020156, 020294, 020389
imec, Genk, Belgium

de l`Epine, Mélodie 020252, 020505, 020543, 020564
Becquerel Institute France, Lyon, France

de l`Epine, Melodie 020225, 020334, 020520, 020558
Becquerel Institute, Brussels, Belgium

de l`Epine, Melodie 020570
IEA PVPS Task 1, Lyon, France

de la Casa Higueras, Juan 020269
University of Jaén, Jaén, Spain

de la Viuda, Eva 020205
University of Valladolid, Valladolid, Spain

de Meatza, Iratxe 020495
CIDETEC, San Sebastián, Spain

De Rose, Angela 020123
Fraunhofer ISE, Freiburg, Germany

De Rose, Jonas 020010
Fraunhofer ISE, Freiburg, Germany

Debastiani Benato, Betina 020019
AMIRES, Prague, Czech Republic

Deepti, 020563
SRM University, Sonipat, India

Del Campo, Valeria 020311
Federico Santa María Technical University, Valparaiso, Chile

del Cañizo, Carlos 020014, 020501, 020507, 020508
UPM, Madrid, Spain

Del Pero, Claudio 020249
Polytechnic University of Milan, Milan, Italy

Del Pozo, Alberto 020197, 020198
TECNALIA, Derio, Spain

del Prado Santamaria, Rodrigo 020191, 020376
DTU, Roskilde, Denmark

del Ser, Javier 020358
UPV/EHU, Bilbao, Spain

Delgado-Sanchez, Jose Maria 020089
University of Seville, Seville, Spain

Delli Veneri, Paola 020378
ENEA, Naples, Italy

Denafas, Julius 020225, 020353
Solitek, Vilnius, Lithuania

Deniz, Engin 020559
Ege University, İzmir, Türkiye

Denke, Sebastian 020236
ISFH, Emmerthal, Germany

Dentz, Laurie 020058
CNRS, Palaiseau, France

Derin Gure, Pinar 020513, 020521, 020556
ODTU GUNAM, Ankara, Türkiye

Derj, Anyssa 020116
IPVF, Palaiseau, France

Dessì, Alessio 020077
CNR-ICCOM, Sesto Fiorentino, Italy

Devenson, Jan 020157
Center for Physical Sciences and Technology (FTMC), Vilnius, Lithuania

Dhimish, Mahmoud 020346, 020376
DTU, Roskilde, Denmark

Di Matteo, Alfredo 020010
Enel Green Power, Catania, Italy

Diab, Mohanad 020203
Eurac Research, Bolzano, Italy

Diano, Marcello 020378
M2M Engineering, Naples, Italy

Diaz, Roberto 020300
Notio Association, Toledo, Spain

Díaz, Sara 020365, 020366
CENER, Sarriguren, Spain

Dietrich, Andreas 020355
DiSUN Deutsche Solarservice, Werder, Germany

Díez Alcántara, Eduardo 020501
UCM, Madrid, Spain

Díez, Eduardo 020508
UCM, Madrid, Spain

Dimd, Berhane Darsene 020495, 020510
SINTEF, Trondheim, Norway

Ding, Kaining 020233
FZJ, Jülich, Germany

Ding, Kung 020111
Hohai University, Changzhou, China

Dittmann, Sebastian 020318
Anhalt University of Applied Sciences, Köthen, Germany

Dittrich, Arne 020240
ISFH, Emmerthal, Germany
Dizier, Antoine 020373
INES, Le Bourget-du-Lac, France
Djeukeu, Ivanol Jaurece 020050
halm elektronik, Frankfurt am Main, Germany
Dobreva, Petja 020193
University of Namibia, Windhoek, Namibia
Dörenkämper, Maarten 020169
TNO, Eindhoven, The Netherlands
Dörn, Markus 020255
A-Null Development, Vienna, Austria
Doi, Minh Thong 020317
CEA INES, Le Bourget-du-Lac, France
Domínguez, César 020209, 020246, 020257
UPM, Madrid, Spain
Donadello, Alessandro 020485, 020489
Edyna, Bolzano, Italy
Donėlienė, Jolanta 020157
Applied Research Institute for Prospective Technologies, Vilnius, Lithuania
Donoso, José 020570
UNEF, Madrid, Spain
Doppler, Christian 020455
Virtual Vehicle, Graz, Austria
dos Reis, Givaldo 020348
University of São Paulo, São Paulo, Brazil
dos Santos, Jeremias 020409
University of Évora, Évora, Portugal
Doucet, Jean-Baptiste 020074
LAAS-CNRS, Toulouse, France
Dovesi, Roberto 020060
Academy of Sciences of Turin, Torino, Italy
Driesse, Anton 020211, 020293, 020452
PV Performance Labs, Freiburg, Germany
Duarte, Dorivaldo 020418, 020565
University of Evora, Évora, Portugal
Dubois, Sebastien 020034
University Grenoble Alpes, Le Bourget-du-Lac, France
Dubravskij, Piotr 020157
Applied Research Institute for Prospective Technologies, Vilnius, Lithuania
Dubravskij, Piotr 020380
Modern E-Technologies, Vilnius, Lithuania
Duerinckx, Filip 020064, 020225
Hasselt Unversity, Genk, Belgium

Düz, Cansel 020135
Kalyon PV, Ankara, Türkiye

Dullweber, Thorsten 020006, 020007, 020008, 020225
ISFH, Emmerthal, Germany

Dunlop, Ewan D. 020173, 020210, 020213
European Commission JRC, Ispra, Italy

Dupon, Olivier 020294
imec, Genk, Belgium

Dupuis, Julien 020188
EDF R&D, Moret Loing Orvanne, France

Dutykh, Denys 020338
Khalifa University, Abu Dhabi, United Arab Emirates

Duzellier, Sophie 020073
University of Toulouse, Toulouse, France

Dypvik Sødahl, Elin 020340
IFE, Kjeller, Norway

Ebert, Matthias 020426
Fraunhofer CSP, Halle, Germany

Ebert, Matthias 020355
Fraunhofer IMWS, Halle, Germany

Ebner, Rita 020318, 020334, 020521
AIT, Vienna, Austria

Echeverria, Oihane 020139
Tecnalia, Donostia - San Sebastián, Spain

Eder, Gabriele C. 020160, 020162, 020249, 020500, 020504
OFI, Vienna, Austria

Eelma, Tonis 020302
IBS, Tartu, Estonia

Efthymiou, Venizelos 020544
EPL Technology Frontiers, Dhali, Cyprus

Egan, Renate 020048
UNSW, Sydney, Australia

Egido, Miguel-Ángel 020407
UPM, Madrid, Spain

Eidtmann, Maximilian 020385
ZHAW, Winterthur, Switzerland

Eijgelaar, Marcel 020571
DNV, Arnhem, The Netherlands

Eikelboom, Erik 020225
Futurasun, Citadella, Italy

Einhaus, Roland 020312
ZSW, Stuttgart, Germany

Eisenacher, Matthias 020141
University of Applied Science Cologne, Cologne, Germany

Eiternick, Stefan Fraunhofer CSP, Halle (Saale), Germany	020004, 020052
Ekins-Daukes, Nicholas J. UNSW, Sydney, Australia	020065
El Ainaoui, Khadija Green Energy Park, Benguerir, Morocco	020171
El mrabet, Yasmine Green Energy Park, Benguerir, Morocco	020171
Elgaili, Mohamed QEERI, Doha, Qatar	020166
Elhamaoui, Said Green Energy Park, Benguerir, Morocco	020171
Ellis, Hanna European Commission JRC, Ispra, Italy	020213
Engelen, Tine Hasselt University, Diepenbeek, Belgium	020389
Erber, Alexander BFH, Burgdorf, Switzerland	020386
Eryılmaz, Hande ODTÜ-GÜNAM, Ankara, Türkiye	020521
Escudero, Ana IaSol, Zaragoza, Spain	020414
Esmailifar, Seyyed Majid Amirkabir University of Technology, Tehran, Iran	020335, 020356, 020374, 020375
Espinosa, Nieves University of Murcia, Murcia, Spain	020497, 020506
Essam T. Mohammed, Sarah EU SOLARIS, Almeria, Spain	020546
Esteras, Miguel TECNALIA, Derio, Spain	020358
Eyhorn, Steffen Fraunhofer ISE, Freiburg, Germany	020369
Fabel, Yann DLR, Almeria, Spain	020235, 020237, 020239
Fabris, Francesca Futurasun, Citadella, Italy	020225
Faes, Antonin CSEM, Neuchâtel, Switzerland	020251
Falangas, Alexandros TRASIS International, Brussels, Belgium	020210
Fang, Xue Tokyo University of Science, Tokyo, Japan	020525
Fano, Vanesa UPV/EHU, Bilbao, Spain	020055, 020097, 020153, 020287

Farhat, Mohammad 020428
Australian University, Kuwait City, Kuwait

Farina, Andrea 020066
CNR-IFN, Milan, Italy

Farrias-Basulto, Guillermo 020101
HZB, Berlin, Germany

Fath, Moritz 020463
RCT Solutions, Konstanz, Germany

Fath, Peter 020005, 020463
RCT Solutions, Konstanz, Germany

Fava, Henrique 020565
University of Évora, Évora, Portugal

Feichtner, Markus 020255
Sonnenkraft Energie, St. Veit/Glan, Austria

Feichtner, Markus 020160
Sonnenkraft Energy, St. Veit/Glan, Austria

Feldbacher, Sonja 020136, 020500
PCCL, Leoben, Austria

Feldhof, Anne Maren 020522
University of Applied Science Cologne, Cologne, Germany

Fernandes, Cláudia 020464
Centre for New Energy Technologies, Sacavém, Portugal

Fernández Solas, Álvaro 020331
DLR, Almería, Spain

Ferrando, Jorge 020226
University of Valencia, Paterna, Spain

Ferreira, Catarina G. 020250
SDU Climate Cluster, Odense, Denmark

Ferreira, Catarina 020306
SDU Climate Cluster, Odense, Denmark

Ferrero, Sergio 020079
Polytechnic University of Turin, Turin, Italy

Feuerherdt, Niels 020309
Berlin University of Applied Sciences, Berlin, Germany

Fialho, Luis 020203, 020254, 020261, 020304, 020403, 020409, 020418, 020420, 020565
Eurac Research, Bolzano, Italy

Figueroa, Andrés 020339
National University of Colombia, Bogotá, Colombia

Fischer, Stefan 020495
SGL Carbon, Meitingen, Germany

Fleischanderl, Martin 020136
voestalpine Stahl, Linz, Austria

Fleury, Perine 020513, 020521
Biosphere Solar, Delft, The Netherlands

Flouchi, Imane 020171
Green Energy Park, Benguerir, Morocco

Fodor, Nikoletta SolarPower Europe, Brussels, Belgium	020521
Fontani, Daniela CNR-INO, Florence, Italy	020066
Forster, Jacob Fraunhofer ISE, Freiburg, Germany	020135
Forstinger, Anne CSP Services, Cologne, Germany	020331
Franch, Jordi Badosa Ecole Polytechnique, Palaiseau, France	020406
Franchi, Daniele CNR-ICCOM, Sesto Fiorentino, Italy	020077
Franquet, Erwin Côte d`Azur University, Nice, France	020259, 020428
Frasson, Nicola Applied Materials, San Biagio di Callalta, Italy	020019
Freer, Solomon PV Lighthouse, Coledale, Australia	020396
Freitag, Marina Newcastle University, Newcastle upon Tyne, United Kingdom	020077
Freund, Timo EnBW, Karlsruhe, Germany	020312
Friansyah, Rizal DTU, Roskilde, Denmark	020376
Friesen, Gabi SUPSI, Mendrisio, Switzerland	020160, 020249, 020574
Friesen, Thomas Megasol Energie, Deitingen, Switzerland	020249
Fritz Muñoz, Benjamín UPV, Valencia, Spain	020099
Froebel, Jens Fraunhofer CSP, Halle, Germany	020121, 020142, 020192, 020223
Frontini, Francesco SUPSI, Mendrisio, Switzerland	020249, 020253
Fuentealba-Vidal, Edward University of Antofagasta, Antofagasta, Chile	020129, 020311, 020342, 020417, 020422
Füreder-Kitzmüller, Friedrich voestalpine Stahl, Linz, Austria	020136
Fuertes Marrón, David UPM, Madrid, Spain	020014, 020501, 020507, 020508
Fuertes, David IES-UPM, Madrid, Spain	020097
Furnari, Alessandro Enel Green Power, Catania, Italy	020010
Fuß, Michael MBJ Solutions, Ahrensburg, Germany	020206

Gabor, Andrew M. 020166
BrightSpot Automation, Boulder, United States of America

Gaete, Martin 020311
University of Antofagasta, Antofagasta, Chile

Gafert, Michael 020369
AIT, Vienna, Austria

Gageot, Tristan 020040
CEA / INES, Le Bourget-du-Lac, France

Gainza, Eusebio 020392
ALLOTARRA, Allo, Spain

Galarza, Alejandra 020461
IPVF, Palaiseau, France

Galbiati, Giuseppe 020119, 020218
Henkel, Düsseldorf, Germany

Galdikas, Algirdas 020157
Applied Research Institute for Prospective Technologies, Vilnius, Lithuania

Galiana, Beatriz 020085
Charles III University of Madrid, Madrid, Spain

Galiazzo, Marco 020019
Applied Materials, San Biagio di Callalta, Italy

Gall, Stefan 020101
HZB, Berlin, Germany

Gallmetzer, Sandra 020261, 020509
Eurac Research, Bolzano, Italy

Galparsoro, Ibon 020514
AZTI, PASAIA, Spain

Gamarra, Ana Rosa 020502
CIEMAT, Madrid, Spain

Ganter, Alissa 020296
ETH, Zurich, Switzerland

Gaona García, Elvis Eduardo 020279
District University of Bogotá, Bogotá, Colombia

Garabetian, Thomas 020551
SolarPower Europe, Brussels, Belgium

García Campos, Enrique 020336
University of Almeria, La Cañada de San Urbano, Spain

García, Fernando 020326
UC3M, Madrid, Spain

García, Sonia 020139
Tecnalia, Donostia - San Sebastián, Spain

García-Cañas, Alejandro 020257
IMDEA Nanoscience, Madrid, Spain

García-Salinas, María José 020100
University of Almeria, Almería, Spain

Garcia-Sanchez, Almudena 020246, 020257
UPM, Madrid, Spain
Garg, Vivek 020069, 020071, 020081
SVNIT, Surat, India
Garraín, Daniel 020502
CIEMAT, Madrid, Spain
Gasse, Hugues 020073
University of Toulouse, Toulouse, France
Gassner, Anika 020160, 020162, 020500, 020504
OFI, Vienna, Austria
Gatti, Cesare 020541
PedersoliGattai, Milan, Italy
Gattu, Apoorva 020003
ISC Konstanz, Konstanz, Germany
Gautier, Damien 020505
Becquerel Institute, Brussels, Belgium
Gauvin, Xavier 020302
Bouygues Construction, Saint-Quentin-en-Yvelines, France
Ge, Hua 020249
Concordia University, Montreal, Canada
Gebhardt, Paul 020195
Fraunhofer ISE, Freiburg, Germany
Geerligs, L. J. 020030
TNO, Petten, The Netherlands
Gehrlein, Janek 020522
University of Applied Science Cologne, Cologne, Germany
Geier, Jutta 020234
PCCL, Leoben, Austria
Geml, Fabian 020031
University of Konstanz, Constance, Germany
Genovese, Maria 020378
Enel Green Power, Pisa, Italy
Georghiou, George E. 020534
University of Cyprus, Nicosia, Cyprus
Germani, Simone 020302
CEI, Milan, Italy
Getsiou, Maria 020181
Directorate General for Research and Innovation, Brussels, Belgium
Geymayer, Lukas 020136
voestalpine Stahl, Linz, Austria
Ghahremani, Amirreza 020335, 020374
Amirkabir University of Technology, Tehran, Iran
Ghennioui, Abdellatif 020171
Green Energy Park, Benguerir, Morocco
Ghosh, Saptak 020519
CSTEP, Bengaluru, India

Girardi, Pierpaolo RSE, Milan, Italy	020462, 020466
Giroux-Julien, Stephanie CNRS, Villeurbanne, France	020338
Gissler, Antoine EDF R&D, Palaiseau, France	020060
Göckeritz, Robert Fraunhofer CSP, Halle, Germany	020119
Gohil, Hardik RCT Solutions, Konstanz, Germany	020222
Gomes de Venuto, Vitor PUCRS, Porto Alegre, Brazil	020025
Gomez Trillos, Juan Camilo DLR, Oldenburg, Germany	020482
Gomez-Lazaro, Emilio University of Castilla-La Mancha, Albacete, Spain	020562
Gonnella, Gabriella Eurac research, Bolzano, Italy	020249, 020254
González Pérez, Sara ULL, San Cristóbal de La Laguna, Spain	020151
González Rodríguez, Brais University of Vigo, Vigo, Spain	020243
González, Miguel Ángel University of Valladolid, Valladolid, Spain	020205
González-Díaz, Benjamín ULL, San Cristóbal de La Laguna, Spain	020151
Goraya, Baljeet Singh Fraunhofer ISE, Freiburg, Germany	020475
Gordillo, Gerardo National University of Colombia, Bogotá, Colombia	020110
Gordon, Ivan imec, Genk, Belgium	020521
Gottschalg, Ralph Anhalt University of Applied Sciences, Köthen, Germany	020158
Gottschalg, Ralph Fraunhofer CSP, Halle, Germany	020056, 020201, 020229, 020233, 020284, 020574
Govaerts, Jonathan imec, Genk, Belgium	020019
Gracia Amillo, Ana María CENER, Pamplona, Spain	020211
Gracia Amillo, Ana María CENER, Sarigurren, Spain	020318
Gracia Amillo, Ana María CENER, Sarriguren, Spain	020181, 020365, 020366, 020497
Gregory, Geoffrey EnPV, Karlsruhe, Germany	020006

Greslou, Olivier 020551
CSTB, Bussy-Saint Georges, France

Grommes, Eva-Maria 020522, 020523
University of Applied Science Cologne, Cologne, Germany

Grosser, Stephan 020119, 020142, 020218
Fraunhofer CSP, Halle, Germany

Grünsteidl, Stefan 020307
Avancis, Munich, Germany

Gruginskie, Natasha 020067
Radboud University, Nijmegen, The Netherlands

Guedea, Isabel 020127, 020517
ENDEF, Zaragoza, Spain

Gülsoy, Eren Cihan 020521
METU, Ankara, Türkiye

Gümüs Çiftci, Burcu 020027
Kalyon PV, Ankara, Türkiye

Guerra, Gerardo 020448, 020481
GreenPowerMonitor a DNV company, Barcelona, Spain

Guidetti, Giulia 020541
Green Horse Advisory, Milan, Italy

Guillemoles, Jean François 020062
IPVF, Palaiseau, France

Guillevin, Nicolas 020225
TNO, Petten, The Netherlands

Gunbas, Gorkem 020113
ODTÜ-GÜNAM, Ankara, Türkiye

Gupta, Akshit 020551
Eurac Research, Bolzano, Italy

Gutierrez, Jose Ruben 020055, 020097, 020153, 020287
UPV/EHU, Bilbao, Spain

Gutjahr, Astrid 020030
TNO, Petten, The Netherlands

Haaland, Petry Kristine Nøttum 020476
NTNU, Trondheim, Norway

Haase, Felix 020063
ISFH, Emmerthal, Germany

Hadiwidjaja, Stella 020102
SERIS, Singapore, Singapore

Hadjipanayi, Maria 020064
University of Cyprus, Nicosia, Cyprus

Haedrich, Ingrid 020195, 020231
Fraunhofer ISE, Freiburg, Germany

Hämmer, Matthias 020470
bifa Umweltinstitut, Augsburg, Germany

Hafidi, Elias Inflights BV, Brussels, Belgium	020511
Hagemann, Elizabeth M. Nelson Mandela University, Port Elizabeth, South Africa	020416
Hallais, Géraldine CNRS, Palaiseau, France	020058
Halle, Lasse BFH, Burgdorf, Switzerland	020359
Hallensleben, Carina TAMURA-ELSOLD, Ilsenburg, Germany	020220
Halm, Andreas ISC Konstanz, Konstanz, Germany	020218, 020220, 020221
Halme, Janne Aalto University, Espoo, Finland	020249
Hamada, Toshiyuki Osaka Electro-Communication University, Osaka, Japan	020190
Hammer, Annette DLR, Oldenburg, Germany	020239
Hamouda, Frederic CNRS, Palaiseau, France	020058
Hanifi, Hamed AESOLAR, Koenigsbrunn, Germany	020121, 020125, 020137, 020223
Hansen, Per-Anders Institute for Energy Technology, Kjeller, Norway	020017, 020503
Harit, Amit Kumar Hasselt Unversity, Genk, Belgium	020064
Harrison, Samuel CEA, Le Bourget-du-Lac, France	020225
Hashem, Ahmad Anhalt University of Applied Sciences, Köthen, Germany	020056, 020201
Hategan, Sergiu Mihai West University of Timisoara, Timisoara, Romania	020283
Hauch, Jens HI ERN, Erlangen, Germany	020117, 020149, 020150
Hauer, Martin Bartenbach, Vienna, Austria	020255
Haverkamp, Helge centrotherm international, Blaubeuren, Germany	020008
Hee Lee, Sang KIER, Daejeon, South Korea	020045
Heidrich, Robert Fraunhofer CSP, Halle, Germany	020233
Heikkinen, Kyösti VTT Technical Research Centre of Finland, Oulu, Finland	020423
Heiser, Moritz Kiwa PI Berlin, Berlin, Germany	020230

Helbig, Matthias 020220
ISC Konstanz, Konstanz, Germany

Helten, David 020331
CSP Services, Cologne, Germany

Hennig, Carsten 020313, 020355
saferay holding, Berlin, Germany

Hennig, Patrick 020313
Kiel University of Applied Sciences, Kiel, Germany

Heras, Jesús 020536
Wattkraft, Madrid, Spain

Hermle, Martin 020475
Fraunhofer ISE, Freiburg, Germany

Hernández Mora, Johann Alexander 020279, 020441
District University of Bogotá, Bogotá, Colombia

Hernández, Jaime J. 020257
IMDEA Nanoscience, Madrid, Spain

Hernández, Johann 020526
Francisco José de Caldas District University, Bogota, Colombia

Herodotou, Panayiotis 020534
University of Cyprus, Nicosia, Cyprus

Herrera Leon, Fernando Augusto 020339, 020546
National University of Colombia, Bogotá, Colombia

Herrero, Leire 020139
Tecnalia, Donostia - San Sebastián, Spain

Herrero, Rebeca 020209, 020453, 020459
UPM, Madrid, Spain

Herrmann, Werner 020208
TÜV Rheinland Solar, Cologne, Germany

Herteleer, Bert 020329, 020351
KU Leuven, Ghent, Belgium

Herteleer, Bert 020574
SUPSI, Mendrisio, Switzerland

Hessler-Wyser, Aïcha 020251
EPFL, Neuchâtel, Switzerland

Heydari, Azim 020485
Eurac Research, Bolzano, Italy

Hinken, David 020236
ISFH, Emmerthal, Germany

Hladys, Bertrand 020010
CEA, Grenoble, France

Hoex, Bram 020065
UNSW, Sydney, Australia

Hofer, Leo 020322
BFH, Burgdorf, Switzerland

Hoffmann, Erik 020006
EnPV, Karlsruhe, Germany

Hogan Almeida, Rita UPM, Madrid, Spain	020535, 020567
Hollemann, Christina ISFH, Emmerthal, Germany	020008
Holovský, Jakub Czech Technical University, Prague, Czech Republic	020107
Honrubia-Escribano, Andrés University of Castilla-La Mancha, Albacete, Spain	020562
Hopp, Tobias Sunman Energy, Frankfurt, Germany	020384
Horn, Jonas halm elektronik, Frankfurt am Main, Germany	020050
Horta, Pedro University of Évora, Évora, Portugal	020304, 020403, 020409, 020418, 020420, 020565
Hosatte, Mikaël SEGTON Advanced Technology, Versailles, France	020068
Hoß, Jan ISC Konstanz, Konstanz, Germany	020004, 020035
Hossain, Mohammad Istiaque QEERI, Doha, Qatar	020042, 020075, 020108, 020109, 020146, 020147
Hou, Yi SERIS, Singapore, Singapore	020102
Hsiao, Pei-Chieh UNSW, Sydney, Australia	020048
Hsieh, Cho Fan ITRI, Hsinchu, Taiwan	020083, 020161, 020163
Hu, Shuaifeng University of Oxford, Oxford, United Kingdom	020226
Huang, Chris SunDrive Solar, Kurnell, Australia	020048
Huang, Gan KIT, Eggenstein-Leopoldshafen, Germany	020272
Huang, Lu-Jan TNO, Leiden, The Netherlands	020425
Huang, Tzu-Yen National Synchrotron Radiation Research Center, Hsinchu, Taiwan	020096
Hügi, Matthias BFH, Burgdorf, Switzerland	020322
Huemer, Martin University of Linz, Linz, Austria	020227
Huerta, Hugo E. TUAS, Turku, Finland	020286, 020400
Hüttl, Bernd Coburg University of Applied Sciences, Coburg, Germany	020361

Hulik Jansova, Marketa 020274
Solargis, Bratislava, Slovakia

Hung, Tzu Han 020552
ITRI, Taipei City, Taiwan

Hutterer-Tik, Thomas 020347
Watt Analytics, Vienna, Austria

Hwang, Hye-Mi 020324, 020357, 020561
KIER, Daejeon, South Korea

Iglesias, Unai 020139
Tecnalia, Donostia - San Sebastián, Spain

Ikeda, Kazuaki 020436
AIST, Koriyama, Japan

Infante, Paulo 020420
University of Évora, Évora, Portugal

Isabella, Olindo 020515
TU Delft, Delft, The Netherlands

Ishikawa, Ryousuke 020106, 020115
Tokyo City University, Setagaya, Japan

Iwaszko, Victorien 020495
ROSI Solar, Saint-Martin-d'Hères, France

Izquierdo-Roca, Victor 020094
IREC, Barcelona, Spain

J. N. Soares, Guillermo 020090
Federal University of Rio de Janeiro, Duque de Caxias, Brazil

Jacob, Julieu 020302
METABUILD, Berlin, Germany

Jacobs, Ayesha 020382
Zutari, Cape Town, South Africa

Jaeckel, Bengt 020056, 020119, 020121, 020140, 020142, 020175, 020192, 020201, 020223, 020229
Fraunhofer CSP, Halle, Germany

Jäger Waldau, Arnulf 020570
European Commission, Rome, Italy

Jäger, Philip 020006
ISFH, Emmerthal, Germany

Jäggi, Adrian 020179
BFH, Burgdorf, Switzerland

Järventausta, Pertti 020445
Tampere University, Tampere, Finland

Jaffré, Alexandre 020058
CNRS, Gif-sur-Yvette, France

Jahn, Ulrike 020521, 020574
Fraunhofer CSP, Halle, Germany

Jahn, Ulrike — 020355
Fraunhofer IMWS, Halle, Germany

Jahreis, Sophia — 020142, 020192
Fraunhofer CSP, Halle, Germany

Jakomin, Roberto — 020090
Federal University of Rio de Janeiro, Duque de Caxias, Brazil

Jakubik, Martin — 020274
Solargis, Bratislava, Slovakia

Jakuza, Paola — 020089
University of Padova, Padova, Italy

Jalkh, Judy — 020455
Virtual Vehicle, Graz, Austria

Jandl, Ralf — 020204
FFHS, Zurich, Switzerland

Jankovec, Marko — 020197
University of Ljubljana, Ljubljana, Slovenia

Jaworczak, Kamil — 020402
Technology Innovation Institute, Abu Dhabi, United Arab Emirates

Jensen, Adam R. — 020267
DTU, Kongens Lyngby, Denmark

Jeong, Jungi — 020323
K-water, Daejeon, South Korea

Jeong, Kyung Taek — 020045
KIER, Daejeon, South Korea

Jeong, Minsoo — 020045
KIER, Daejeon, South Korea

Jeronimo, Pedro — 020010
CEA, Grenoble, France

Jiang, Zonghan — 020158, 020201
Anhalt University of Applied Sciences, Köthen, Germany

Jimenez, Maria — 020302
Onyx Solar, Avila, Spain

Jimeno, Juan Carlos — 020055, 020097, 020153, 020287, 020289, 020353
UPV/EHU, Bilbao, Spain

Jo, Hyunsik — 020323
K-water, Daejeon, South Korea

Job, Enzo — 020231
Fraunhofer ISE, Freiburg, Germany

Johnson, Mark Robert — 020546
Institut Laue-Langevin (ILL), Grenoble, France

Joo, Dongmyoung — 020449
KETI, Wonmi-gu, South Korea

Jooss, Wolfgang — 020005, 020222, 020463
RCT Solutions, Konstanz, Germany

Joseph, Daniel Christopher 020123
Fraunhofer ISE, Freiburg, Germany
Joshi, Deepak 020069, 020081
SVNIT, Surat, India
Joss, David 020359, 020369, 020386
BFH, Burgdorf, Switzerland
Jouini, Anis 020034
ECM Technologies, Grenoble, France
Jouttijärvi, Sami 020286, 020298, 020398
University of Turku, Turku, Finland
Joziak, Roman 020230
Kiwa PI Berlin, Berlin, Germany
Ju, Young-Chul 020324, 020357, 020561
KIER, Daejeon, South Korea
Jugo, Josu 020437
UPV/EHU, Leioa, Spain
Junge, Sebastian 020008, 020482
ISFH, Emmerthal, Germany

Kaaya, Ismail 020156, 020294, 020389, 020393
imec, Genk, Belgium
Kähler, Jan-Dirk 020482
Centrotherm International, Blaubeuren, Germany
Kahraman, Mert 020027
Kalyon PV, Ankara, Türkiye
Kainz, Konrad 020430
AIT, Vienna, Austria
Kaiser, Martin 020215
Fraunhofer ISE, Freiburg, Germany
Kaizuka, Izumi 020570
RTS Corporation, Tokyo, Japan
Kajari-Schröder, Sarah 020063
ISFH, Emmerthal, Germany
Kallioharju, Kari 020444, 020445
TUAS, Tampere, Finland
Kalliojärvi, Heidi 020194
Tampere University, Tampere, Finland
Kalshetty, Mahesh 020519
CSTEP, Bengaluru, India
Kaltenbach, Thomas 020195
Fraunhofer ISE, Freiburg, Germany
Kamphues, Joshua 020031
University of Konstanz, Constance, Germany
Kandiyoti-Eskenazi, Selin 020467
CSEM, Neuchâtel, Switzerland

Kang, Min Gu 020045
KIER, Daejeon, South Korea

Kapetanovic, Viktor 020367
Nextracker, Fremont, United States of America

Karhu, Juha 020286
Finnish Meteorological Institute, Helsinki, Finland

Kari, Thøger 020191, 020376
DTU, Roskilde, Denmark

Karimy, Hedayatullah 020052
Fraunhofer CSP, Halle (Saale), Germany

Karttunen, Lauri 020298, 020398
University of Turku, Turku, Finland

Kasper, Ruth 020167, 020232
University of Applied Sciences Cologne, Cologne, Germany

Katouli, Tannaz 020195
Fraunhofer ISE, Freiburg, Germany

Kaufmann, Kai 020355
DENKweit, Halle, Germany

Kawabata, Rudy 020092
PUC-Rio, Rio de Janeiro, Brazil

Kemp, Linda 020390
MARIN, Wageningen, The Netherlands

Kenchington, Ian 020225, 020474, 020558
Becquerel Institute, Brussels, Belgium

Kenny, Robert 020210
European Commission JRC, Ispra, Italy

Khan, Abeer Ali 020513
First Solar, Mainz, Germany

Khosravi, Arash 020381
Mälardalen University, Västerås, Sweden

Kikkert, Benjamin W. J. 020405
TNO, Petten, The Netherlands

Kilickaya, Seda 020020
ODTÜ-GÜNAM, Ankara, Türkiye

Kim, Jin-Hong 020449
KETI, Wonmi-gu, South Korea

Kim, Jun-Tae 020249
Kongju National University, Chungnam, South Korea

Kim, Kihwan 020112
KIER, Daejeon, South Korea

Kim, Seok Won 020449
KETI, Wonmi-gu, South Korea

Kim, Yong-Jin 020045
KIER, Daejeon, South Korea

Kinge, Sachin 020117
Toyota Motors Europe, Brussels, Belgium

Kitamura, Ibuki Osaka Electro-Communication University, Osaka, Japan	020190
Kitzberger, Gregor voestalpine Stahl, Linz, Austria	020136
Kivambe, Maulid QEERI, Doha, Qatar	020166
Kizukuri, Rihoko TAMURA-ELSOLD, Ilsenburg, Germany	020220
Kladas, Anastasios KU Leuven, Ghent, Belgium	020329, 020351
Kleider, Jean-Paul CNRS, Gif-sur-Yvette, France	020040, 020058
Kleissl, Jan University of California, San Diego, United States of America	020528
Klengel, Robert Fraunhofer IMWS, Halle, Germany	020355
Klenk, Markus ZHAW, Winterthur, Switzerland	020385
Klos, Christine Buhck Re.Energy, Hamburg, Norway	020510
Kluska, Sven Fraunhofer ISE, Freiburg, Germany	020019
Klute, Carola Fraunhofer IMWS, Halle, Germany	020355
Knausdorf, Christian Coburg University of Applied Sciences, Coburg, Germany	020361
Ko, Seok-whan KIER, Daejeon, South Korea	020561
Ko, Suk Whan KIER, Daejeon, South Korea	020324, 020357
Koc, Timurhan DTU, Roskilde, Denmark	020376
Koduvelikulathu, Lejo Joseph ISC Konstanz, Konstanz, Germany	020035, 020068
Koduvelikulathu, Lejo ISC Konstanz, Konstanz, Germany	020003
Köntges, Marc ISFH, Emmerthal, Germany	020206
Koepge, Ringo Fraunhofer CSP, Halle, Germany	020142, 020192
Koester, Lukas Eurac Research, Bolzano, Italy	020203, 020261, 020325
Kohlenberg, Heike ISFH, Emmerthal, Germany	020063
Kohno, Tohru Hitachi, Tokyo, Japan	020186

Kolahi, Mohammad 020356, 020375
University of Isfahan, Isfahan, Iran

Konagai, Makoto 020106, 020115
Tokyo City University, Setagaya, Japan

Kono, Toru 020484
Hitachi, Kokubunji, Japan

Konu, Christopher Bruce 020132
HTW Berlin, Berlin, Germany

Kopecek, Radovan 020569
ISC Konstanz, Konstanz, Germany

Kopp, Nils 020220
TAMURA-ELSOLD, Ilsenburg, Germany

Korkmaz Arslan, Melisa 020020
ODTÜ-GÜNAM, Ankara, Türkiye

Korpås, Magnus 020476
NTNU, Trondheim, Norway

Kortetmäki, Aki 020444, 020445
TUAS, Tampere, Finland

Koskela, Juha 020444, 020445, 020554
Tampere University, Tampere, Finland

Kossen, Eric J. 020030
TNO, Petten, The Netherlands

Kowalski, Julia 020237
RWTH, Aachen, Germany

Kräling, Ulli 020215
Fraunhofer ISE, Freiburg, Germany

Kraft, Thomas M. 020423
VTT Technical Research Centre of Finland, Oulu, Finland

Krainer, Diana Maria 020430
AIT, Vienna, Austria

Krasilnikov, Inga 020379
Tel Aviv University, Tel Aviv, Israel

Krever Lopes, Bruno 020023
PUCRS, Porto Alegre, Brazil

Kribus, Abraham 020379
Tel Aviv University, Tel Aviv, Israel

Krishnan, Sasikumar 020361
Coburg University of Applied Sciences, Coburg, Germany

Kroon, Jan 020225
TNO, Petten, The Netherlands

Kuan, Ta-Ming 020021, 020053
TSEC, Hsinchu, Taiwan

Kubicek, Bernhard 020281, 020318, 020334, 020347, 020430
AIT, Vienna, Austria

Kucuk, E. Busra 020030
TNO, Petten, The Netherlands

Kuczyńska-Łażewska, Anna 020498, 020499
Gdansk University of Technology, Gdansk, Poland

Kühne, Philip 020240
Leibniz University Hannover, Hannover, Germany

Kuhrmann, Bernd 020206
MBJ Solutions, Ahrensburg, Germany

Kujansivu, Eino 020554
Solarigo Systems, Pirkkala, Finland

Kumar, Gaurav 020563
MERI College of Engineering and Technology, Bahadurgarh, India

Kumar, Sagarika 020402
Technology Innovation Institute, Abu Dhabi, United Arab Emirates

Kumar, Saurabh 020563
PTB, Braunshweig, Germany

Kuo, Cheng-Wen 020021, 020053
TSEC, Hsinchu, Taiwan

Kurtulus, Gunes 020556
ODTU GUNAM, Ankara, Türkiye

Kuruganti, Vaibhav V. 020033
ISC Konstanz, Konstanz, Germany

Kurz, Hannes 020136
voestalpine Stahl, Linz, Austria

Kusch, Alexander 020361
Coburg University of Applied Sciences, Coburg, Germany

Kuzhagaliyeva, Nursulu 020402
Technology Innovation Institute, Abu Dhabi, United Arab Emirates

Kuznicki, Zbigniew T. 020013, 020068
SEGTON Advanced Technology, Versailles, France

Kwiatkowski, Jerzy 020551
NAPE, Warsaw, Poland

Kyranaki, Nikoleta 020156
Hasselt University, Genk, Belgium

Kyranaki, Nikoleta 020393
Hasselt University, Hasselt, Belgium

Kyranaki, Nikoleta 020294
imec, Genk, Belgium

Kyratsi, Theodora 020495
University of Cyprus, Nicosia, Cyprus

L. Andersen, Nanna 020477
DTU, Roskilde, Denmark

L. Souza, Patrícia 020090
Federal University of Rio de Janeiro, Rio de Janeiro, Brazil

Lachowicz, Agata 020039
CSEM, Neuchâtel, Switzerland

Lahr, Simon 020388
Next2Sun Technology, Dillingen, Germany

Lahr, Simon 020411
Next2Sun, Dillingen, Germany

Lajunen, Antti 020400
University of Helsinki, Helsinki, Finland

Lambertz, Andreas 020233
FZJ, Jülich, Germany

Lamblot, Hervé 020302
Sunstyle, Paris, France

Lamghari, Fouad 020402
Fujairah Research Centre, Fujairah, United Arab Emirates

Lamminaho, Jani 020250, 020306
SDU Climate Cluster, Odense, Denmark

Landaas, Christian 020495
Northern Silicon, Meråker, Norway

Landberg, Lars 020448
DNV Denmark, Hellerup, Denmark

Landberg, Lars 020481
DNV Denmark, Hellerup, Spain

Landes, Dieter 020361
Coburg University of Applied Sciences, Coburg, Germany

Landová, Lucie 020107
Czech Technical University, Prague, Czech Republic

Lansade, David 020073
University of Toulouse, Toulouse, France

Lappalainen, Kari 020194, 020528, 020537
Tampere University, Tampere, Finland

Lara, Yolanda 020127, 020414, 020517
ENDEF, Zaragoza, Spain

Larionova, Yevgeniya 020006, 020007, 020225
ISFH, Emmerthal, Germany

Låstad, Jonas 020011
NTNU, Trondheim, Norway

Laurens-Berge, Clarisse 020034
University Grenoble Alpes, Le Bourget-du-Lac, France

Laurikėnas, Paulius 020353
Solitek, Vilnius, Lithuania

Lauwaert, Johan 020064
Ghent University, Ghent, Belgium

Lazaro-Castrillon, Luna 020085
IO-CSIC, Madrid, Spain

Le Bossenec, Hugo 020116
IPVF, Palaiseau, France

Le Brun, Anton 020096
Australian Nuclear Science and Technology Organisation, Lucas Heights, Australia

Lechón, Yolanda 020502
CIEMAT, Madrid, Spain

Ledesma, Javier R. 020337
UPM, Madrid, Spain

Ledesma, Javier 020446
UPM, Madrid, Spain

Lee, Chun-Wei 020021
TSEC, Hsinchu, Taiwan

Lee, Hyunju 020046
Meiji University, Kanagawa, Japan

Lee, Jieun 020323
K-water, Daejeon, South Korea

Lee, Jin-Seok 020324, 020357, 020561
KIER, Daejeon, South Korea

Legarrea, Aritz 020365
CENER, Sarriguren, Spain

Lelievre, Jean-Francois 020373
INES, Le Bourget-du-Lac, France

Lelong, Benoit 020373
Cythelia Energy, La Motte-Servolex, France

Leloux, Jonathan 020262
LuciSun, Villers-la-Ville, Belgium

Lenain, Philippe 020495
benkei, Lyon, France

Lennon, Alison 020048
UNSW, Sydney, Australia

Lenz, Markus 020226
School of Life Sciences FHNW, Muttenz, Switzerland

Lenzmann, Frank 020019
TNO Energy Transition, Petten, The Netherlands

Leone, Sander 020405
Novar, Rotterdam, The Netherlands

Leonforte, Fabrizio 020249
Polytechnic University of Milan, Milan, Italy

Leopold, Ulrich 020457
Luxembourg Institute of Science and Technology, Esch-sur-Alzette, Luxembourg

Levrat, Jacques 020251, 020467
CSEM, Neuchâtel, Switzerland

Levtchenko, Alexandra 020116
IPVF, Palaiseau, France

Lewandowski, Simon 020073
University of Toulouse, Toulouse, France

Leza, Baurin Gonvarri MS R&D, Corvera - Asturias, Spain	020412
Lezaca, Jorge DLR, Oldenburg, Germany	020239
Li, Xinyang RCT Solutions, Konstanz, Germany	020222
Li, Yung-Chih TSEC, Hsinchu, Taiwan	020021
Li, Yuxuan East China University of Science and Technology, Shanghai, China	020001
Libal, Joris ISC Konstanz, Konstanz, Germany	020218, 020474
Lichtenberger, Janine AIT, Vienna, Austria	020430
Lițiu, Andrei Vladimir EPB Center, Rotterdam, The Netherlands	020551
Lin, Shih-Chieh TSEC, Hsinchu, Taiwan	020021
Lindahl, Johan Becquerel Sweden, Knivsta, Sweden	020486, 020532
Linder, Johannes Belectric, Kolitzheim, Germany	020492
Lindfors, Anders Finnish Meteorological Institute, Helsinki, Finland	020286
Lindig, Sascha Univers, Courbevoie, France	020371
Linke, Jonathan ISC Konstanz, Konstanz, Germany	020004, 020035, 020225
Linß, Volker VON ARDENNE, Dresden, Germany	020033
Lipovšek, Benjamin University of Ljubljana, Ljubljana, Slovenia	020047
Lippke, Benjamin Kiwa PI Berlin, Berlin, Germany	020180, 020230
List-Kratochvil, Emil HZB, Berlin, Germany	020101
Litrico, Grazia Enel Green Power, Catania, Italy	020010
Liu, Cui East China University of Science and Technology, Shanghai, China	020001
Liu, Dongyang ISFH, Emmerthal, Germany	020063
Liu, Han-Chang ITRI, Tainan, Taiwan	020350

Liu, Huiping 020495
GRÄNGES, Finspång, Sweden
Liu, Mengdi 020144, 020208
TÜV Rheinland, Shanghai, China
Liu, Yung-Tsung 020053, 020083
ITRI, Hsinchu, Taiwan
Livera, Andreas 020534
University of Cyprus, Nicosia, Cyprus
Lizin, Sebastien 020513, 020521
UHasselt, Hasselt, Belgium
Llarena, María Elena 020151
ITER, Granadilla de Abona, Spain
Loeckenhoff, Ruediger F. 020416
AZUR SPACE Solar Power, Heilbronn, Germany
Löhning, Martha 020063
ISFH, Emmerthal, Germany
Löhr, Johannes 020063, 020114
ISFH, Emmerthal, Germany
Lokhat, Ismaël 020262
Cythelia Energy, La Motte-Servolex, France
Lokhat, Ismael 020373
Trace Software, Saint-Romain-de-Colbosc, France
Lombardo, Salvatore 020066
CNR-IMM, Catania, Italy
Long, Yean-San 020053, 020083
ITRI, Hsinchu, Taiwan
Longo, Giulia 020099
UPV, Valencia, Spain
Lopes Gomes, Carlos Javier 020432, 020434
Sunveon, Madrid, Spain
Lopes, Ana Patrícia 020464
University of Lisbon, Lisbon, Portugal
López Cuéllar, Juan Manuel 020501
UCM, Madrid, Spain
López Dalmau, Daniel 020432, 020434
Sunveon, Madrid, Spain
López, Nuria 020451
DTU, Roskilde, Denmark
Lorenz, Dieter 020206
MBJ Solutions, Ahrensburg, Germany
Lorenzo Pigueiras, Eduardo 020363
UPM, Madrid, Spain
Lorenzo, Celena 020337, 020536
UPM, Madrid, Spain
Lorenzo, Eduardo 020439, 020446
UPM, Madrid, Spain

Lossen, Jan 020003, 020035
ISC Konstanz, Konstanz, Germany

Louwen, Atse 020203, 020226, 020261, 020509, 020546
Eurac Research, Bolzano, Italy

Louwen, Atse 020316
RISE, Boras, Sweden

Lu, Huan-Wu 020161
ITRI, Hsinchu, Taiwan

Lu, Matthew 020230
Kiwa PI Berlin, Shanghai, China

Lucea, Aingeru 020197, 020198
TECNALIA, Derio, Spain

Lüdemann, Marius 020233
Fraunhofer CSP, Halle, Germany

Luís, Margarida 020421
University of Lisbon, Lisbon, Portugal

Lustoza de Souza, Patricia 020092
UFRJ, Rio de Janeiro, Brazil

Ly, Moussa 020023, 020025
PUCRS, Porto Alegre, Brazil

Lyubenova, Teodora 020210
European Commission JRC, Ispra, Italy

M. Bazilio, Willian 020092
PUC-Rio, Rio de Janeiro, Brazil

M. S. Kawabata, Rudy 020090
Pontifical Catholic University of Rio de Janeiro, Rio de Janeiro, Brazil

M. Torelly, Guilherme 020090
Pontifical Catholic University of Rio de Janeiro, Rio de Janeiro, Brazil

Ma Lu, Silvia 020381
Mälardalen University, Västerås, Sweden

Ma, Xiang 020011
SINTEF, Oslo, Norway

Macé, Philippe 020225, 020252, 020474, 020505, 020543, 020558, 020573
Becquerel Institute, Brussels, Belgium

Mack, Sebastian 020031
Fraunhofer ISE, Freiburg, Germany

Madsen, Morten 020250, 020306
SDU Climate Cluster, Odense, Denmark

Mahmood, Aysha 020265, 020376
DTU, Roskilde, Denmark

Maixner, Andreas 020121, 020125, 020137, 020223
AESOLAR, Koenigsbrunn, Germany

Maiz, Alexander 020437
UPV/EHU, Vitoria-Gasteiz, Spain
Majak, Martyna 020068
Roltec, Poznań, Poland
Makrides, George 020534
University of Cyprus, Nicosia, Cyprus
Malarkannan, Lavanya 020210
National Physical Laboratory, Teddington, United Kingdom
Malcorps, Philippe 020276
3E, Brussels, Belgium
Malik, Stephanie 020313
Fraunhofer CSP, Halle, Germany
Malik, Stephanie 020355
Fraunhofer IMWS, Halle, Germany
Maliutina, Kristina 020141
University of Applied Science Cologne, Cologne, Germany
Malo, Javier 020209
UPM, Madrid, Spain
Mancini, Simone 020425
TNO, Eindhoven, The Netherlands
Mandiola, Gotzon 020514
AZTI, PASAIA, Spain
Manganiello, Patrizio 020389
Hasselt University, Diepenbeek, Belgium
Manganiello, Patrizio 020294
imec, Genk, Belgium
Manito, Alex 020348
University of São Paulo, São Paulo, Brazil
Manochehrian, Rasoul 020539
Frankfurt University of Applied Sciences, Frankfurt am Main, Germany
Manzolini, Giampaolo 020261
Polytechnic University of Milan, Milan, Italy
Maqsood, Ayman 020101
HZB, Berlin, Germany
Marangis, Demetris 020534
University of Cyprus, Nicosia, Cyprus
Marcos-Castro, Ana 020297
CIEMAT, Madrid, Spain
Marechal, Philippe 020217
CEA / INES, Le Bourget-du-Lac, France
Marí Soucase, Bernabé 020099
UPV, Valencia, Spain
Markert, Jochen 020231
Fraunhofer ISE, Freiburg, Germany
Marquardt, Cornelia 020063
ISFH, Emmerthal, Germany

Marteau, Baptiste 020034
ECM Technologies, Grenoble, France
Martín Rueda, Javier 020535
UPM, Madrid, Spain
Martín, Francisco José 020459
UPM, Madrid, Spain
Martín, Francisco 020209
UPM, Madrid, Spain
Martín-Chivelet, Nuria 020297
CIEMAT, Madrid, Spain
Martín-Rueda, Javier 020337, 020363
UPM, Madrid, Spain
Martínez González, Mario 020326
Enertis Applus+, Madrid, Spain
Martinez, Juan Ignacio 020252
Becquerel Institute Spain, San Sebastian, Spain
Martinez, Oscar 020191, 020205
University of Valladolid, Valladolid, Spain
Martínez-Barbeito, María 020243
ieco.io, Vigo, Spain
Maruyama, Rodrigo P. 020154, 020348
University of São Paulo, São Paulo, Brazil
Marzo, Aitor 020311, 020546
University of Granada, Granada, Spain
Mashkov, Oleksandr 020149, 020150, 020377
HI ERN, Erlangen, Germany
Massaro, Lorenzo 020541
PedersoliGattai, Milan, Italy
Masson, Gaëtan 020474, 020558, 020564, 020573
Becquerel Institute, Brussels, Belgium
Masson, Gaëtan 020570
IEA PVPS Task 1, Brussels, Belgium
Mateos, Yeray 020055, 020153
UPV/EHU, Bilbao, Spain
Maturi, Laura 020249, 020254, 020551
Eurac Research, Bolzano, Italy
Mayer-Ullmann, Philipp 020430
AIT, Vienna, Austria
Mazzoleni, Stefano 020378
University of Naples Federico II, Naples, Italy
McIntosh, Keith R. 020396
PV Lighthouse, Coledale, Australia
McNab, Shona 020065
UNSW, Sydney, Australia
Meereboer, Martijn 020225
Energyra, Westknollendam, The Netherlands

Meier, Rico 020132
HTW Berlin, Berlin, Germany

Meixner, Michael 020050
halm elektronik, Frankfurt am Main, Germany

Mekhaldi, Bouchra 020406
Ecole Polytechnique, Palaiseau, France

Melges de Andrade, Adnei 020154
University of São Paulo, São Paulo, Brazil

Melino, Francesco 020314
University of Bologna, Bologna, Italy

Mellone, Celeste 020541
Green Horse Advisory, Rome, Italy

Menard, Lionel 020291
MINES Paris, Nice, France

Mencaraglia, Denis 020058
CNRS, Gif-sur-Yvette, France

Menchaca, Iratxe 020514
AZTI, PASAIA, Spain

Mendes Ferreira Gomes, Amanda 020548
UFSC, Florianopolis, Brazil

Mendikoa, Iñigo 020514
Tecnalia, BRTA, Derio, Spain

Meneghini, Matteo 020089
University of Padova, Padova, Italy

Ménézo, Christophe 020317
LOCIE, Le Bourget-du-Lac, France

Menghini, Mariela 020508
IMDEA Nanoscience Institute, Madrid, Spain

Mercade Ruiz, Pau 020448, 020481
GreenPowerMonitor a DNV company, Barcelona, Spain

Merino, Amanda 020040
CEA / INES, Le Bourget-du-Lac, France

Merino, José Manuel 020085
UAM, Madrid, Spain

Mermoud, André 020196
PVsyst, Geneva, Switzerland

Merodio, Pablo 020337
UPM, Madrid, Spain

Mertens, Jan 020389
imec, Genk, Belgium

Mertens, Verena 020006, 020008
ISFH, Emmerthal, Germany

Meßmer, Marius 020031
Fraunhofer ISE, Freiburg, Germany

Messmer, Tobias 020218, 020221, 020225
ISC Konstanz, Konstanz, Germany

Messner, Christian 020369
AIT, Vienna, Austria
Mettner, Larissa 020063, 020114
ISFH, Emmerthal, Germany
Meusel, Manuel 020052
Fraunhofer CSP, Halle (Saale), Germany
Meyer, Kevin 020260
ISFH, Emmerthal, Germany
Meza, Carlos 020318, 020334, 020426, 020520
Anhalt University of Applied Sciences, Köthen, Germany
Mezzasalma, Frédéric 020217
CEA / INES, Le Bourget-du-Lac, France
Micha, Daniel 020092
CEFET/RJ, Petrópolis, Brazil
Michael, Poland 020193
Nelson Mandela University, Port Elizabeth, South Africa
Miclea, Paul-Tiberiu 020233
Fraunhofer CSP, Halle, Germany
Midtgård, Ole-Morten 020476
NTNU, Trondheim, Norway
Miettunen, Kati 020286, 020298, 020398
University of Turku, Turku, Finland
Migan-Dubois, Anne 020406
CNRS, Gif-sur-Yvette, France
Mignonac, Alexandre 020217
CEA / INES, Le Bourget-du-Lac, France
Mignonac, Alexandre 020334
CEA, Cadarache, France
Mignonac, Alexandre 020318
CEA, Saint-Paul-Lez-Durance, France
Miguel Laborda, María 020414
IaSol, Zaragoza, Spain
Mihailetchi, Valentin Dan 020033
ISC Konstanz, Konstanz, Germany
Mihailetchi, Valentin 020225
ISC Konstanz, Konstanz, Germany
Mihaylov, Blago 020210
European Commission JRC, Ispra, Italy
Milani, Emanuele 020495
Marelli Europe, Venaria Reala, Italy
Milesi, Frédéric 020068
CEA, Grenoble, France
Min, Byungsul 020008, 020482
ISFH, Emmerthal, Germany
Mirandona López, Haritz 020432, 020434
Sunveon, Madrid, Spain

Miró-Llorente, Marta 020094
IREC, Barcelona, Spain

Misra, Prashant 020429
NISE, Gurugram, India

Miszczuk, Andrzej 020068
Roltec, Poznań, Poland

Mittag, Max 020137
Fraunhofer ISE, Freiburg, Germany

Mittal, Ankit 020318
AIT, Vienna, Austria

Mittelman, Gur 020379
Afeka Tel-Aviv Academic College of Engineering, Tel Aviv, Israel

Mizushima, Io 020028
IPU P/S, Virum, Denmark

Mizushima, Io 020037
IPU, Virum, Denmark

Mngomezulu, Ndumiso 020344
PVinsight, Port Elizabeth, South Africa

Mo, Alvin 020065
UNSW, Sydney, Australia

Mockeviciute-Azzopardi, Austeja 020334
FIR, Birkirkara, Malta

Moe Nygård, Magnus 020340
IFE, Kjeller, Norway

Moehlecke, Adriano 020023, 020025
PUCRS, Porto Alegre, Brazil

Mohammadi, Mohammad Hossein 020037, 020104
Aarhus University, Aarhus, Denmark

Mollier, Stéphane 020262
CEA / INES, Le Bourget-du-Lac, France

Moltke, Asbjørn 020043
Technical University of Denmark, Copenhagen, Denmark

Mondaca-Cuevas, Gino 020422
University of Antofagasta, Antofagasta, Chile

Monokroussos, Christos 020181
TÜV Rheinland Shanghai, Shanghai, China

Monokroussos, Christos 020144, 020208
TÜV Rheinland, Shanghai, China

Monteiro Martins, Filipa 020317
Galp Energia, Lisbon, Portugal

Montes, Carlos 020151
ITER, Granadilla de Abona, Spain

Montoya, Josefa 020311
University of Antofagasta, Antofagasta, Chile

Morabito, Floriana 020066
CNR-IFN, Milan, Italy

Moradi Sizkouhi, Amirmohammad — 020356, 020375
Concordia University, Montreal, Canada
Moradi Zavie Kord, Soroush — 020400
University of Helsinki, Helsinki, Finland
Morales, Sergio — 020491
UPM, Madrid, Spain
Morantes Quintana, Giobertti Raul — 020551
Eurac Research, Bolzano, Italy
Mordvinkin, Anton — 020233
Fraunhofer CSP, Halle, Germany
Moreda, Guillermo P. — 020407
UPM, Madrid, Spain
Morin, Claire — 020551
SolarPower Europe, Brussels, Belgium
Morisset, Audrey — 020068
CSEM, Neuchâtel, Switzerland
Morlier, Arnaud — 020156
Hasselt University, Genk, Belgium
Morlier, Arnaud — 020294, 020389
imec, Genk, Belgium
Mortazavifar, Leila — 020056, 020158, 020201, 020284
Anhalt University of Applied Sciences, Köthen, Germany
Moruno, Ricardo — 020209, 020453
UPM, Madrid, Spain
Mosel, Frank — 020015
PVA TePla, Wettenberg, Germany
Moser, David — 020573
Becquerel Institute Italy, Trento, Italy
Moser, David — 020316
Becquerel Institute, Bolzano, Italy
Moser, David — 020254
Bequerel Institute, Trento, Italy
Moser, David — 020203, 020226, 020261, 020325, 020485, 020489, 020546
Eurac Research, Bolzano, Italy
Mouhoubi, Felicia — 020134
CEA / INES, Le Bourget-du-Lac, France
Müllejans, Harald — 020208, 020213
European Commission JRC, Ispra, Italy
Müller, Alexander — 020119
Fraunhofer CSP, Halle, Germany
Müller, Larissa — 020523
University of Applied Sciences Cologne, Cologne, Germany
Mugica, Maikel — 020139
Tecnalia, Donostia - San Sebastián, Spain
Mujovi, Fahradin — 020251
CSEM, Neuchâtel, Switzerland

Mukherjee, Srijani 020338
CEA / INES, Le Bourget-du-Lac, France

Mukhtar, Mariyam 020057
University of Verona, Verona, Italy

Mulder, Peter 020067
Radboud University, Nijmegen, The Netherlands

Muller, Matthew 020314
NREL, Denver, United States of America

Munkhammar, Joakim 020532
Uppsala University, Uppsala, Sweden

Muñoz Cerón, Emilio 020269
University of Jaén, Jaén, Spain

Muñoz, Delfina 020040, 020311, 020546
CEA / INES, Le Bourget-du-Lac, France

Muñoz, Delfina 020521
CEA, Le Bourget-du-Lac, France

Muñoz, Delfina 020226
CEA/ INES, Le Bourget-du-Lac, France

Muñoz, Ildefonso 020365, 020366, 020392
CENER, Sarriguren, Spain

Muñoz, Jesús Ángel 020508
UCM, Madrid, Spain

Muñoz-García, Miguel-Ángel 020407
UPM, Madrid, Spain

Murano, Giovanni 020551
ENEA, Ispra, Italy

Murillo, Asier 020497
CENER, Sarriguren, Spain

Musembi, Robinson J. 020272
University of Nairobi, Nairobi, Kenya

Nabipouor, Mohammad 020426
Anhalt University of Applied Sciences, Köthen, Germany

Nagel, Henning 020475
Fraunhofer ISE, Freiburg, Germany

Nakamura, Kyotaro 020046
Toyota Technological Institute, Nagoya, Japan

Nanno, Ikuo 020190
Nanno Energy Research Center, Yamaguchi, Japan

Nargelienė, Viktorija 020157
Center for Physical Sciences and Technology (FTMC), Vilnius, Lithuania

Narsi Patel, Hitarth 020069
SVNIT, Surat, India

Narvarte, Luis 020337, 020446, 020491, 020535, 020536, 020567, 020575
UPM, Madrid, Spain

Nascimento, Lucas 020377
Solar Energy Research Laboratory Fotovoltaica/ UFSC, Florianópolis, Brazil

Nasebandt, Lasse 020063
ISFH, Emmerthal, Germany

Nasser, Hisham 020226
ODTÜ-GÜNAM, Ankara, Türkiye

Naveiro, José Manuel 020414
ENDEF, Zaragoza, Spain

Nazififard, Mohammad 020259, 020428
Côte d`Azur University, Nice, France

Nejim, Ahmed 020058
SILVACO, St. Ives, United Kingdom

Nel, Paul 020382
7SecondSolar, Cape Town, South Africa

Nelson, Jenny 020394
Imperial College London, London, United Kingdom

Neuba, Adam 020114
Paderborn University, Paderborn, Germany

Neuber, Viola 020031
Fraunhofer ISE, Freiburg, Germany

Neuhaus, Holger 020123, 020140
Fraunhofer ISE, Freiburg, Germany

Neumaier, Lukas 020504
Silicon Austria Labs, Villach, Austria

Neussl, Vassilissa 020318, 020430
AIT, Vienna, Austria

Neykova, Neda 020107
Czech Technical University, Prague, Czech Republic

Nezhad, Mahyar 020230
Kiwa PI Berlin, Hudson, United States of America

Nguyen, Viet Xuan 020008
centrotherm international, Blaubeuren, Germany

Nicolet-dit-Félix, Kléber 020251
EPFL, Neuchâtel, Switzerland

Nicot-Senneville, Zoltan 020102
SERIS, Singapore, Singapore

Nielsen, Michael P. 020065
UNSW, Sydney, Australia

Nissen, Hauke 020313
Wattmanufactur, Galmsbüll, Germany

Nitsche, Tobias 020119, 020218
Henkel, Düsseldorf, Germany

Nobre, André M. 020263
PV Doctor, Singapore, Singapore

Noels, Serge 020472
PV CYCLE, Brussels, Belgium

Noh, Yong-Su 020449
KETI, Wonmi-gu, South Korea

Nold, Sebastian 020461
Fraunhofer ISE, Freiburg, France

Nold, Sebastian 020475
Fraunhofer ISE, Freiburg, Germany

Nordboe, Eirik 020495
Fiven Norge, Lillesand, Norway

Norde Santos, Fernanda 020331
DLR, Almería, Spain

Nouri, Bijan 020235, 020237, 020239
DLR, Almería, Spain

Nova, David 020339
National University of Colombia, Bogotá, Colombia

Núñez, Rubén 020209, 020453
UPM, Madrid, Spain

Núñez-Osorio, Alessia 020100
University of Almeria, Almeria, Spain

Nurmesjärvi, Antti 020423
VTT Technical Research Centre of Finland, Oulu, Finland

Nussbaumer, Hartmut 020385
ZHAW, Winterthur, Switzerland

Nyang'onda, Thomas N. 020272
University of Nairobi, Nairobi, Kenya

Obeidavi, Sahereh 020361
Coburg University of Applied Sciences, Coburg, Germany

Oberbeck, Lars 020461
TotalEnergies OneTech, Paris, France

Oberegger Filippi, Ulrich 020551
Eurac Research, Bolzano, Italy

Ocaña, Luis Manuel 020151
ITER, Granadilla de Abona, Spain

Ockert, Ajka 020312
EnBW, Karlsruhe, Germany

Odilio dos Santos, Daniel 020548
UFSC, Florianopolis, Brazil

Öhgren, Gustav 020532
Becquerel Sweden, Knivsta, Sweden

Öttl, Christian 020347
Watt Analytics, Vienna, Austria

Öz, Aksel Kaan 020135
Fraunhofer ISE, Freiburg, Germany

Özden, Talat 020226
ODTÜ-GÜNAM, Ankara, Türkiye

Özkalay, Ebrar 020160, 020204
SUPSI, Mendrisio, Switzerland

Ogura, Atsushi 020046
Meiji University, Kanagawa, Japan

Ohdaira, Keisuke 020131
JAIST, Ishikawa, Japan

Ohshita, Yoshio 020046
Toyota Technological Institute, Nagoya, Japan

Ojala, Aleksi 020554
Solarigo Systems, Pirkkala, Finland

Okawa, Hayato 020115
Tokyo City University, Setagaya, Japan

Okel, Lars A. G. 020030
TNO, Petten, The Netherlands

Oksanen, Jani 020067
Aalto University, Espoo, Finland

Oliosi, Michele 020196
PVsyst, Geneva, Switzerland

Olivares, Douglas 020311
University of Antofagasta, Antofagasta, Chile

Olivares, Gregorio 020365, 020366, 020392
CENER, Sarriguren, Spain

Oliveira Santos, João Victor 020188
EDF R&D, Moret Loing Orvanne, France

Oliveira, Helena 020420
University of Évora, Évora, Portugal

Oller Westerberg, Amelia 020570
Becquerel Sweden, Knivsta, Sweden

Ollo, Olatz 020139
Tecnalia, Donostia - San Sebastián, Spain

Oozeki, Takashi 020436, 020525
AIST, Koriyama, Japan

Opatovsky, Martin 020241, 020262
Solargis, Bratislava, Slovakia

Oreski, Gernot 020136, 020234, 020325, 020500, 020574
PCCL, Leoben, Austria

Ortega, Eneko 020055, 020153, 020287, 020353
UPV/EHU, Bilbao, Spain

Ortega, Eneko 020289, 020437
UPV/EHU, Leioa, Spain

Ortega, Pascal 020214
University of French Polynesia, Faa'a, French Polynesia

Ortiz-Pena, Aaron 020562
University of Castilla-La Mancha, Albacete, Spain

Ory, Daniel 020188
EDF R&D, Palaiseau, France

Ory, Daniel 020116
EDF, Palaiseau, France

Osman, Alaa 020006
ISFH, Emmerthal, Germany

Osuna, Jose Antonio 020358
MAGTEL, Córdoba, Spain

Osvald, Oliver 020274
Solargis, Bratislava, Slovakia

Otaegi, Aloña 020055, 020097, 020153, 020287
UPV/EHU, Bilbao, Spain

Otnes, Gaute 020169
Institute for Energy Technology, Kjeller, Norway

Otto, Nicolas 020101
HTW, Berlin, Germany

Otto, William 020390
MARIN, Wageningen, The Netherlands

Ou, Chao-Wei 020350
National Chin-Yi University of Technology, Taichung, Taiwan

Ovaitt, Silvana 020314
NREL, Denver, United States of America

Ovaitt, Silvana 020574
NREL, Golden, United States of America

Oviedo Hernandez, Guillermo 020325
BayWa r.e, Rome, Italy

Ozer, Shay 020379
Agricultural Research Organization, Rishon LeZion, Israel

P. Pires, Maurício 020090
Federal University of Rio de Janeiro, Rio de Janeiro, Brazil

Pabiou, Herve 020338
CETHIL, Villeurbanne, France

Pabst, Elena 020312
ZSW, Stuttgart, Germany

Paiva, Lúcio 020530
Casa dos Ventos, Fortaleza, Brazil

Palais, Olivier 020188
Toulon University, Marseille, France

Palitzsch, Wolfram 020225, 020495
LuxChemTech, Freiberg, Germany

Palomino, Laura 020491, 020535
UPM, Madrid, Spain

Pamir Aly, Shahzada 020229
DEWA, Dubai, United Arab Emirates

Pamula, Bindu 020069
SVNIT, Surat, India

Panda, Pavan Kumar 020284
Anhalt University of Applied Sciences, Köthen, Germany

Pandar, Matthias 020229
Fraunhofer CSP, Halle, Germany

Pander, Matthias 020121, 020142, 020175, 020192, 020218, 020223, 020232
Fraunhofer CSP, Halle, Germany

Panduri, Fabio 020322
BFH, Burgdorf, Switzerland

Pantoja, Jaime 020526
Francisco José de Caldas District University, Bogota, Colombia

Papantoni, Veatriki 020482
DLR, Oldenburg, Germany

Paraficz, Danuta 020204
FFHS, Zurich, Switzerland

Paraskeva, Vasiliki 020064
University of Cyprus, Nicosia, Cyprus

Pardo, Eduardo 020414
Tecnova, Almeira, Spain

Parfeniukas, Karolis 020039
ATLANT 3D, Taastrup, Denmark

Parion, Jonathan 020064
Hasselt Unversity, Genk, Belgium

Park, Hyeonwook 020112
KENTECH, Naju-Si, South Korea

Parmar, Richa 020429
NISE, Gurugram, India

Parra, Johan 020406
Ecole Polytechnique, Palaiseau, France

Parra, Johan 020214
Polytechnic Institute of Paris, Palaiseau, France

Parrilla, Carlos G. 020402
Fujairah Research Centre, Fujairah, United Arab Emirates

Pascual Gallego, Valero 020407
UPM, Madrid, Spain

Pasquier, Mathis 020451
DTU, Roskilde, Denmark

Passaro, Marcello 020513
Sunzest Solar, Rotterdam, The Netherlands

Patel, Dharm 020355
Fraunhofer IMWS, Halle, Germany

Paul, Ananta 020250, 020306
SDU Climate Cluster, Odense, Denmark

Paulescu, Marius 020283
West University of Timisoara, Timisoara, Romania

Paviet-Salomon, Bertrand 020068, 020467
CSEM, Neuchâtel, Switzerland
Payno, David 020085, 020094
UAM, Madrid, Spain
Pearce, Pheobe 020065
UNSW, Sydney, Australia
Peche, René 020468, 020495
bifa Umweltinstitut, Augsburg, Germany
Pehlivanli, Ezgi 020521
METU, Ankara, Türkiye
Peibst, Robby 020006, 020063, 020114
ISFH, Emmerthal, Germany
Pelfort Ojer, Marta 020241
Solargis, Bratislava, Slovakia
Pelland, Sophie 020211
Natural Resources Canada, Varennes, Canada
Pelle, Martina 020249, 020254
Eurac Research, Bolzano, Italy
Peña-Bermudez, Julian 020110
University of the Caribbean, Santo Domingo, Dominican Republic
Peng, Cheng-Yu 020350
National Chin-Yi University of Technology, Taichung, Taiwan
Pera, David 020457
Luxembourg Institute of Science and Technology, Esch-sur-Alzette, Luxembourg
Perani, Martina 020204
FFHS, Zurich, Switzerland
Peraticos, Elias 020064
University of Cyprus, Nicosia, Cyprus
Pereda, Ainhoa 020198, 020358
TECNALIA, Derio, Spain
Pereira Fialho, Luis Andre 020509
Eurac Research, Bolzano, Italy
Pereira, Sara 020403, 020418, 020565
University of Évora, Évora, Portugal
Pérez García, Manuel 020336
University of Almería, La Cañada de San Urbano, Spain
Pérez, Ernesto 020339
National University of Colombia, Bogotá, Colombia
Pérez, Jairo 020412
Gonvarri AgroTech, Corvera - Asturias, Spain
Pérez, Jorge 020412
Gonvarri AgroTech, Corvera - Asturias, Spain
Pérez, Luis 020412
Gonvarri MS R&D, Corvera - Asturias, Spain

Perez, Richard 020494
University at Albany, Albany, United States of America

Perez-Astudillo, Daniel 020275, 020278, 020291
QEERI, Doha, Qatar

Pérez-García, Manuel 020100
University of Almeria, Almería, Spain

Pérez-Rodríguez, Alejandro 020085, 020094
IREC, Barcelona, Spain

Pernas, Tomás 020412
Gonvarri AgroTech, Corvera - Asturias, Spain

Pernau, Thomas 020008
centrotherm international, Blaubeuren, Germany

Perrin, Marion 020544
Energy Pool, Le Bourget-du-Lac, France

Pervan, Nikolina 020136, 020234
PCCL, Leoben, Austria

Peter Amalathas, Amalraj 020107
University of Jaffna, Jaffna, Sri Lanka

Peter, Kristian 020569
ISC Konstanz, Konstanz, Germany

Peters, Ian Marius 020230, 020263
Forschungszentrum Jülich, Erlangen, Germany

Peters, Ian Marius 020149, 020150, 020377, 020574
HI ERN, Erlangen, Germany

Petersons, Karlis 020250, 020306
Stensborg, Roskilde, Denmark

Petkovski, Emil 020571
DNV, Arnhem, The Netherlands

Petzschmann, Jonas 020312
ZSW, Stuttgart, Germany

Pfau, Jan Hendrik 020240
Leibniz University Hannover, Hannover, Germany

Pfeiffer, Oliver 020141
University of Applied Science Cologne, Cologne, Germany

Pfeiffer, Oliver 020140
University of Applied Sciences Cologne, Cologne, Germany

Philipp, Daniel 020215, 020231
Fraunhofer ISE, Freiburg, Germany

Pierro, Marco 020489, 020494
Eurac Research, Bolzano, Italy

Pieters, Bart E. 020180
FZJ, Jülich, Germany

Pieterse, Marco 020495
Chemconserve, Bussum, The Netherlands

Pietralunga, Silvia Maria 020066
CNR-IFN, Milan, Italy

Pietsch, Veith 020331
Aquila Capital, Hamburg, Germany

Pilat, Eric 020311
CEA / INES, Le Bourget-du-Lac, France

Pilat, Eric 020317
CEA INES, Le Bourget-du-Lac, France

Pillai, Akhildev 020558
Becquerel Institute, Brussels, Belgium

Pinheiro, Philippe 020457
Luxembourg Institute of Science and Technology, Esch-sur-Alzette, Luxembourg

Pinho Almeida, Marcelo 020348
University of São Paulo, São Paulo, Brazil

Pinto, Cristina Leyre 020497
CENER, Sarriguren, Spain

Pinto, Luciana 020092
UFRJ, Rio de Janeiro, Brazil

Pitaval, Sébastien 020244
SOLAÏS, Valbonne, France

Pitz-Paal, Robert 020237, 020331
DLR, Cologne, Germany

Plakhotnyuk, Maksym 020039
ATLANT 3D, Taastrup, Denmark

Platero Gaona, Carlos A. 020332
UPM, Madrid, Spain

Plaza, Caroline 020543, 020564, 020573
Becquerel Institute France, Lyon, France

Polacchi, Cristina 020509, 020513
Eurac Research, Bolzano, Italy

Polo, Jaime 020300
CENER, Sarriguren, Spain

Polo, Jesús 020297
CIEMAT, Madrid, Spain

Polverini, Davide 020181
Directorate General for Internal Market, Industry, Entrepreneurship and SMEs, Brussels, Belgium

Polverini, Davide 020497
European Comission, Brussels, Belgium

Pongthanacharoenkul, Nattapark 020230
Kiwa PI Berlin, Berlin, Germany

Poortmans, Jef 020064
Hasselt Unversity, Genk, Belgium

Popescu, Lacramioara 020068
ISC Konstanz, Konstanz, Germany

Pospischil, Maximilian 020225
Highline Technologies, Freiburg, Germany

Poulsen, Peter B. 020039
DTU, Copenhagen, Denmark

Poulsen, Peter B. 020250, 020265, 020267, 020376, 020451
DTU, Roskilde, Denmark

Poulsen, Peter Behrensdorff 020028, 020306, 020346
DTU, Roskilde, Denmark

Pourshafi, Pouya 020121, 020125, 020137
AESOLAR, Koenigsbrunn, Germany

Pozza, Cristian 020551
Eurac Research, Bolzano, Italy

Prakash, Jai 020429
NISE, Gurugram, India

Prando, Davide 020485, 020489
Edyna, Bolzano, Italy

Prasad, Manjunath 020225
ISC Konstanz, Konstanz, Germany

Pravettoni, Mauro 020402
Technology Innovation Institute, Abu Dhabi, United Arab Emirates

Preis, Pirmin 020003
ISC Konstanz, Konstanz, Germany

Preu, Ralf 020475
Fraunhofer ISE, Freiburg, Germany

Preuschoff, Jonas 020101
HTW, Berlin, Germany

Protti, Alexander Aguilar 020140
Fraunhofer ISE, Freiburg, Germany

Protti, Alexander 020137
Fraunhofer ISE, Freiburg, Germany

Provost, Marion 020116
IPVF, Palaiseau, France

Puel, Jean Baptiste 020062
IPVF, Palaiseau, France

Puertas López, Antonio Manuel 020100
University of Almeria, Almeria, Spain

Puttock, Claire 020367
Nextracker, Fremont, United States of America

Queste, Samuel 020068
Marie and Louis Pasteur University, Besançon, France

Quiroz, Mónica 020328
Qualifying Photovoltaics, Madrid, Spain

R. Ledesma, Javier 020363
UPM, Madrid, Spain

Rabanal Arabach, Jorge 020183
University of Antofagasta, Antofagasta, Chile
Rabanal-Arabach, Jorge 020129, 020342, 020417, 020422
University of Antofagasta, Antofagasta, Chile
Rabiei, Hossein 020063
ISFH, Emmerthal, Germany
Rachdi, Lazhar 020035, 020068
ISC Konstanz, Konstanz, Germany
Radzevicius, Aurimas 020225
Valoe Cells, Vilnius, Lithuania
Rafiee, Hossein 020539
Frankfurt University of Applied Sciences, Frankfurt am Main, Germany
Raginskis, Justinas 020380
Kaunas University of Technology, Kaunas, Lithuania
Raievska, Oleksandra 020117, 020149
HI ERN, Erlangen, Germany
Rajan, S. Prithivi 020262
LuciSun, Villers-la-Ville, Belgium
Rajkiewicz, Katarzyna 020551
NAPE, Warsaw, Poland
Rakotoniaina, Jean Patrice 020311
CEA / INES, Le Bourget-du-Lac, France
Ramachandran Nair, Jishnu 020233
Fraunhofer CSP, Halle, Germany
Ramesh, Santhosh 020389
imec, Genk, Belgium
Ramírez Ledesma, Javier 020535
UPM, Madrid, Spain
Ramirez, S. 020396
PV Lighthouse, Coledale, Australia
Rampino, Stefano 020087
National Research Council, Parma, Italy
Ramspeck, Klaus 020050
halm elektronik, Frankfurt am Main, Germany
Ranisch, Tadeus 020101
HTW, Berlin, Germany
Ranta, Samuli 020286, 020400
TUAS, Turku, Finland
Ranta, Samuli 020298, 020398
Turku University of Applied Sciences, Turku, Finland
Raposo, Mauro 020565
University of Évora, Évora, Portugal
Ratnagiri, Abhinav 020367
Nextracker, Fremont, United States of America
Raugewitz, Annika 020063, 020114
ISFH, Emmerthal, Germany

Raval, Mehul 020005, 020222, 020463
RCT Solutions, Konstanz, Germany

Razanajao, Aina 020244
SOLAÏS, Valbonne, France

Razi, Umair 020085
IREC, Barcelona, Spain

Recart, Federico 020097
UPV/EHU, Bilbao, Spain

Redondo Cuevas, Marta 020332
UPM, Madrid, Spain

Redondo, Juan Manuel 020209
UPM, Madrid, Spain

Rehan, Muhammad 020112
KIER, Daejeon, South Korea

Rehman, Anees ur 020111, 020164
Hohai University, Changzhou, China

Reichart, Hannah 020167, 020232
University of Applied Sciences Cologne, Cologne, Germany

Reichel, Christian 020123, 020137, 020140
Fraunhofer ISE, Freiburg, Germany

Reichle, Julian 020005, 020222, 020463
RCT Solutions, Konstanz, Germany

Reinders, Angele 020253
TU Eindhoven, Eindhoven, The Netherlands

Reindl, Thomas 020263
SERIS, Singapore, Singapore

Reis, Luiz Filipe 020530
Casa dos Ventos, Fortaleza, Brazil

Rémondeau, Paul 020251
EPFL, Neuchâtel, Switzerland

Renard, Charles 020058
CNRS, Palaiseau, France

Rende, Fedele 020255
ACCA Software, Cosenza, Italy

Rennhofer, Marcus 020180, 020281, 020318, 020334, 020347, 020430
AIT, Vienna, Austria

Rentsch, Jochen 020475
Fraunhofer ISE, Freiburg, Germany

Rerat, Michel 020060
IPREM, Pau, France

Reshef, Liad 020379
Agricultural Research Organization, Rishon LeZion, Israel

Revol, Inès 020074
LAAS-CNRS, Toulouse, France

Reyal, Jean-Pierre 020303
SemperStyl, Eragny, France

Riaño, Sandra — 020197, 020358
TECNALIA, Derio, Spain

Richards, Bryce S. — 020272
KIT, Karlsruhe, Germany

Riechelman, Stefan — 020181
PTB, Braunschweig, Germany

Riechelmann, Stefan — 020177, 020199, 020211
PTB, Braunschweig, Germany

Riedel-Lyngskær, Nicholas — 020451
DTU, Roskilde, Denmark

Rienäcker, Michael — 020063
ISFH, Emmerthal, Germany

Rindert, Sören — 020230
Kiwa PI Berlin, Berlin, Germany

Ríos Moral, Lucía — 020501
UCM, Madrid, Spain

Ríos-Ledesma, Felipe — 020446
UPM, Madrid, Spain

Ripke, Melanie — 020006
ISFH, Emmerthal, Germany

Riva, Roland — 020495
CEA, Le Bourget-du-Lac, France

Rivas Rodríguez, José Manuel — 020326
Enertis Applus+, Madrid, Spain

Robledo, Jesús — 020262
LuciSun, Villers-la-Ville, Belgium

Rodríguez Lucas, Delia — 020407
EkiLabs, Boston, United States of America

Rodríguez Plaza, José Luis — 020508
Autonomous University of Madrid, Madrid, Spain

Rodríguez Rodríguez, Araceli — 020501
UCM, Madrid, Spain

Rodríguez Salazar, David Leonardo — 020441
District University of Bogotá, Bogotá, Colombia

Rodríguez, Araceli — 020508
UCM, Madrid, Spain

Rodríguez, Diego Julián — 020526
Francisco José de Caldas District University, Bogota, Colombia

Rodríguez, Isabel — 020257
IMDEA Nanoscience, Madrid, Spain

Rodriguez, Sonia Maria — 020289
UPV/EHU, Leioa, Spain

Rodríguez, Velia — 020097
UPV/EHU, Bilbao, Spain

Rodríguez-Conde, Sofía — 020326
Enertis Applus+, Madrid, Spain

Rodríguez-Gallegos, Carlos D. 020149, 020150
SERIS, Singapore, Singapore

Rodríguez-Romero, Sebastián 020342, 020417, 020422
University of Antofagasta, Antofagasta, Chile

Rodziewicz, Hanna 020498
Gdansk University of Technology, Gdansk, Poland

Römer, Udo 020006, 020063
ISFH, Emmerthal, Germany

Röver, Ingo 020225
LuxChemTech, Freiberg, Germany

Rojas, Christian A. 020422
Federico Santa María Technical University, Valparaíso, Chile

Rojas-Henríquez, Katalina 020129
University of Antofagasta, Antofagasta, Chile

Román, Eduardo 020139
Tecnalia, Donostia - San Sebastián, Spain

Romeo, Alessandro 020057, 020089, 020093
University of Verona, Verona, Italy

Romer, Pascal 020231
Fraunhofer ISE, Freiburg, Germany

Roodt, Roelof 020185
Nelson Mandela University, Port Elizabeth, South Africa

Roosloot, Nathan 020169
Institute for Energy Technology, Kjeller, Norway

Rosca, Victor 020030
TNO, Petten, The Netherlands

Rosen, Isaac 020225
Copprint, Jerusalem, Israel

Rosenfeld, Lavi 020379
Agricultural Research Organization, Rishon LeZion, Israel

Rosina, Konstantin 020241
Solargis, Bratislava, Slovakia

Rossa, Carlos 020432, 020434
Sunveon, Madrid, Spain

Rouffie, Brice 020068
SEGTON Advanced Technology, Versailles, France

Roulleau, Lea 020303
CSTB, Marne-la-Vallée, France

Rousset, Jean 020116
EDF, Palaiseau, France

Roy, Shantanu 020519
CSTEP, Bengaluru, India

Rudolph, Dominik 020003, 020068
ISC Konstanz, Konstanz, Germany

Rudzikas, Matas 020380
The Applied Research Institute for Prospective Technologies, Vilnius, Lithuania

Rüther, Ricardo 020377
Solar Energy Research Laboratory Fotovoltaica/ UFSC, Florianópolis, Brazil

Rüther, Ricardo 020548
UFSC, Florianopolis, Brazil

Ruf, Manuel 020455
Robert Bosch, Stuttgart, Germany

Ruiz Donoso, Elena 020331
DLR, Almeria, Spain

S. Sousa, Graciana 020090
Federal University of Rio de Janeiro, Rio de Janeiro, Brazil

Safarian, Jafar 020011
NTNU, Trondheim, Norway

Sah, Dheeraj 020039
Aarhus University, Aarhus, Denmark

Sahin, Hasret 020479
LUT University, Lappeenranta, Finland

Saito, Kimihiko 020106
Tokyo City University, Setagaya, Japan

Salem, Mohammad 020428
Australian University, Kuwait City, Kuwait

Salerno, Giorgia 020077
University of Milano-Bicocca, Milan, Italy

Salis, Fabio 020541
Iberdrola, Rome, Italy

Salvador, Antonio 020358
MAGTEL, Córdoba, Spain

Sample, Tony 020213
European Commission JRC, Ispra, Italy

Samuolienė, Giedrė 020380
The Lithuanian Research Centre for Agriculture and Forestry, Kaunas, Lithuania

San José, Luis Javier 020209, 020453
UPM, Madrid, Spain

Sánchez de León Peque, Miguel 020243
ieco.io, Vigo, Spain

Sanchez Garcia, Alfredo 020270
SINTEF, Trondheim, Norway

Sanchez, Hugo 020056, 020158, 020284
Anhalt University of Applied Sciences, Köthen, Germany

Sanchez, Jesus 020437
UPV/EHU, Vitoria-Gasteiz, Spain

Sanchez, Laura 020437
UPV/EHU, Leioa, Spain
Sánchez, Yudania 020085
IREC, Barcelona, Spain
Sanchez-Friera, Paula 020412, 020513, 020521
Solkeys, Gijón, Spain
Sanchez-Ruiz, Alain 020437
UPV/EHU, Vitoria-Gasteiz, Spain
Sansavini, Giovanni 020296
ETH, Zurich, Switzerland
Sansoni, Paola 020066
CNR-INO, Florence, Italy
Santamaría Fernández, Susanna 020249
TECNALIA, Derio, Spain
Santamaría-Sancho, Juan 020363
UPM, Madrid, Spain
Santos, Jose Domingo 020197, 020198, 020358
TECNALIA, Derio, Spain
Santos, Rodrigo 020530
Casa dos Ventos, Fortaleza, Brazil
Sanz Martinez, Asier 020546
Tecnalia, Bilbao, Spain
Sanz, Asier 020514
Tecnalia, BRTA, Derio, Spain
Sanz, Asier 020197
TECNALIA, Derio, Spain
Sanz-Cuadrado, Cristina 020575
UPM, Madrid, Spain
Sanz-Saiz, Carlos 020297
CIEMAT, Madrid, Spain
Sarafijanovic-Djukic, Natasa 020204
FFHS, Regensdorf, Switzerland
Saretti, Angelica 020301
Polytechnic University of Bari, Bari, Italy
Sarkadi, Monika 020569
ISC Konstanz, Konstanz, Germany
Sauer, Thomas 020140
EXXERGY, Gräfelfing, Germany
Saura, Juan Antonio 020506
University of Murcia, Murcia, Spain
Savisalo, Tuukka 020225
Valoe, Mikkeli, Finland
Saw, Min Hsian 020402
Technology Innovation Institute, Abu Dhabi, United Arab Emirates
Saxena, Anmol Ratan 020429
NIT, Delhi, India

Sayed, Abdullah Abu 020180, 020230
Kiwa PI Berlin, Berlin, Germany

Scaltrito, Luciano 020079
Polytechnic University of Turin, Turin, Italy

Scerri, Kenneth 020334
University of Malta, Msida, Malta

Schading, Steve 020443
University of Agder, Grimstad, Norway

Schäfer, Aysim 020388
Next2Sun Technology, Dillingen, Germany

Schäfer, Sebastian 020539
Frankfurt University of Applied Sciences, Frankfurt am Main, Germany

Schenk, Paul 020192
Fraunhofer CSP, Halle, Germany

Schermer, John 020067
Radboud University, Nijmegen, The Netherlands

Scherret, Jacqueline 020255
A-Null Development, Vienna, Austria

Schifferegger, Raffael 020162
OFI, Vienna, Austria

Schimanke, Sabrina 020006
ISFH, Emmerthal, Germany

Schirmer, Yoko 020101
HTW, Berlin, Germany

Schläger, Christian 020240
Leibniz University Hannover, Hannover, Germany

Schlatmann, Rutger 020101
HTW, Berlin, Germany

Schmidt Davidsen, Rasmus 020037, 020104
Aarhus University, Aarhus, Denmark

Schnaus, Dominik 020237
TUM, Garching, Germany

Schneider, Andreas 020129, 020183
University of Applied Sciences Gelsenkirchen, Gelsenkirchen, Germany

Schneider, Astrid 020255
TU Wien, Vienna, Austria

Schneider, Friedrich 020482
LPKF SolarQuipment, Suhl, Germany

Schneider, Marc Gabriel 020522
University of Applied Science Cologne, Cologne, Germany

Schneiderlöchner, Eric 020033
VON ARDENNE, Dresden, Germany

Schnierer, Branislav 020262
Solargis, Bratislava, Slovakia

Schönau, Maximilian 020361
Coburg University of Applied Sciences, Coburg, Germany

Schönau, Maximilian 020544
smartblue, Munich, Germany

Schönheits, Markus 020468, 020470
bifa Umweltinstitut, Augsburg, Germany

Schranz, Christian 020255
TU Wien, Vienna, Austria

Schrempf, Michael 020199
PTB, Braunschweig, Germany

Schrijvers, Patrick 020390
MARIN, Wageningen, The Netherlands

Schröter, Nick 020142
Fraunhofer CSP, Halle, Germany

Schubert, Martin C. 020475
Fraunhofer ISE, Freiburg, Germany

Schubnel, Baptiste 020238
CSEM, Neuchâtel, Switzerland

Schüler, Marc Andre 020388
Next2Sun Technology, Dillingen, Germany

Schüler, Marc Andre 020411
Next2Sun, Dillingen, Germany

Schueler, Nadine 020015
Freiberger Instruments, Freiberg, Germany

Schulte-Huxel, Henning 020008, 020260
ISFH, Emmerthal, Germany

Schultz, Christof 020101
HTW, Berlin, Germany

Schulz, Philip 020060
IPVF, Palaiseau, France

Schulze, Achim 020361
Rosenheim Technical University of Applied Sciences, Rosenheim, Germany

Schulze, Patricia S.C. 020475
Fraunhofer ISE, Freiburg, Germany

Schwenke, Almut 020495
SGL Battery Solutions, Meitingen, Germany

Sciuto, Marcello 020010
Enel Green Power, Catania, Italy

Scognamiglio, Alessandra 020541
ENEA, Naples, Italy

Scognamiglio, Alessandra 020378
ENEA, Portici, Italy

Sedaghat, Ahmad 020428
Australian University, Kuwait City, Kuwait

Seiffert, Christoph 020169
Institute for Energy Technology, Kjeller, Norway

Seiffert, Daniela 020008
centrotherm international, Blaubeuren, Germany
Seitz, Matthias 020468
bifa Umweltinstitut, Augsburg, Germany
Selj, Josefine H. 020169
Institute for Energy Technology, Kjeller, Norway
Senno, Maximiliano Alejandro 020226
University of Valencia, Paterna, Spain
Senturk, Bilge 020556
ODTU GUNAM, Ankara, Türkiye
Setien, Eneko 020198
TECNALIA, Derio, Spain
Šetkus, Arūnas 020157
Center for Physical Sciences and Technology (FTMC), Vilnius, Lithuania
Shaaban, Ahmed 020402
Technology Innovation Institute, Abu Dhabi, United Arab Emirates
Shah, Syed Fawad Ali 020112
KENTECH, Naju-Si, South Korea
Shanmugam, Raphael 020218, 020220
ISC Konstanz, Konstanz, Germany
Sharma, Rajesh Kumar 020071, 020081
SVNIT, Surat, India
Sharma, Sushma 020563
SRM University, Sonipat, India
Shen, Xinyi 020226
University of Oxford, Oxford, United Kingdom
Shen, Zhenjue 020001
YIST, Jiangyin, China
Shin, Donghyeop 020112
KIER, Daejeon, South Korea
Shin, Woo Gyun 020324, 020357
KIER, Daejeon, South Korea
Shin, Woo-gyun 020561
KIER, Daejeon, South Korea
Shirai, Yasuhiro 020115
NIMS, Tsukuba, Japan
Shirazi, Elham 020544
University of Twente, Enschede, The Netherlands
Shishavan, Amir Asgharzadeh 020367
Nextracker, Fremont, United States of America
Shishido, Hirotaka 020106
Tokyo City University, Setagaya, Japan
Shochet, Ofer 020225
Copprint, Jerusalem, Israel

Shyong, Yung-Jen 020163
ITRI, Hsinchu, Taiwan

Sicot, Lionel 020217
CEA / INES, Le Bourget-du-Lac, France

Sidler, Anika 020226
School of Life Sciences FHNW, Muttenz, Switzerland

Siebert, Michael 020206
ISFH, Emmerthal, Germany

Siefer, Gerald 020246
Fraunhofer ISE, Freiburg, Germany

Sierra, Daniel 020491
UPM, Madrid, Spain

Sigounis, Anna-Maria 020248, 020249
Concordia University, Montreal, Canada

Søiland, Anne-Karin 020495
ReSiTec, Kristiansand, Norway

Silva, José A. 020304, 020409, 020420
University of Évora, Évora, Portugal

Silva, José 020403
University of Évora, Évora, Portugal

Silvestre, Santiago 020301
UPC, Barcelona, Spain

Simeunovic, Jelena 020238
CSEM, Neuchâtel, Switzerland

Simón-Allué, Raquel 020127, 020414, 020517
ENDEF, Zaragoza, Spain

Singh, Ravi 020571
DNV, Arnhem, The Netherlands

Sinha, Amish Kumar 020463
RCT Solutions, Konstanz, Germany

Sinopoli, Alessandro 020042
QEERI, Doha, Qatar

Sivaramakrishnan Radhakrishnan, Hariharsudan 020064
Hasselt Unversity, Genk, Belgium

Sivaramakrishnan, Hariharsudan 020225
IMEC, Genk, Belgium

Snaith, Henry 020226
University of Oxford, Oxford, United Kingdom

Søndenå, Rune 020503
Institute for Energy Technology, Kjeller, Norway

Sobajima, Yasushi 020131
Gifu University, Gifu, Japan

Soler Toledo, Denet 020509
University of Antofagasta, Antofagasta, Chile

Solomon, Asfaw A. 020479
LUT University, Lappeenranta, Finland

Solórzano, Jorge 020328
Qualifying Photovoltaics, Madrid, Spain
Sondoqah, Mousa 020316
Becquerel Institute, Bolzano, Italy
Sondoqah, Mousa 020261
Eurac Research, Bolzano, Italy
Song, Hee-eun 020045
KIER, Daejeon, South Korea
Spagnolo, Sofia 020462, 020466
RSE, Milan, Italy
Spataru, Sergiu V. 020265, 020267, 020283, 020376, 020451
DTU, Roskilde, Denmark
Spataru, Sergiu Viorel 020346
DTU, Roskilde, Denmark
Spera, Fabian 020411
Next2Sun, Dillingen, Germany
Spihola, Jan 020355
DiSUN Deutsche Solarservice, Werder, Germany
Sraisth, 020005, 020222
RCT Solutions, Konstanz, Germany
Sraisth, Sraisth 020463
RCT Solutions, Konstanz, Germany
Staňková, Tereza 020107
Czech Technical University, Prague, Czech Republic
Steckenreiter, Verena 020063
ISFH, Emmerthal, Germany
Stegemann, Bert 020309
Berlin University of Applied Sciences, Berlin, Germany
Stegemann, Bert 020101
HTW, Berlin, Germany
Stellbogen, Dirk 020312
ZSW, Stuttgart, Germany
Stensborg, Jan F. 020250
Stensborg, Roskilde, Denmark
Stensborg, Jan 020306
Stensborg, Roskilde, Denmark
Stieldorf, Karin 020255
TU Wien, Vienna, Austria
Stierstorfer, Johannes 020225
WIP - Renewable Energies, Munich, Germany
Stierstorfer, Johannes 020551
WIP Renewable Energies, Munich, Germany
Stivanello, Juan José 020226
Eurac Research, Bolzano, Italy
Stoicescu, Liviu 020198
Solarzentrum Stuttgart, Stuttgart, Germany

Stowhas-Villa, Alejandro 020422
Federico Santa María Technical University, Valparaiso, Chile

Stoyanova Lyubenova, Teodora 020173
European Commission JRC, Ispra, Italy

Sträter, Hendrik 020211
PTB, Braunschweig, Germany

Strey, Jessica 020063, 020114
ISFH, Emmerthal, Germany

Strömberg, Rich 020472
University of Alaska, Fairbanks, United States of America

Stroyuk, Oleksander 020185
HI ERN, Erlangen, Germany

Stroyuk, Oleksandr 020117, 020149, 020150
HI ERN, Erlangen, Germany

Suárez Sánchez, Sergio 020326
Enertis Applus+, Madrid, Spain

Subasi, Dilara Maria 020475
Fraunhofer ISE, Freiburg, Germany

Sudbury, Ben A. 020396
PV Lighthouse, Coledale, Australia

Suemitsu, Issei 020484
Hitachi, Kokubunji, Japan

Suhonen, Riikka 020423
VTT Technical Research Centre of Finland, Oulu, Finland

Sulca, Kabir Paúl 020191, 020205
University of Valladolid, Valladolid, Spain

Svatos, Jan 020250
DTU, Roskilde, Denmark

Sylla, David 020063
ISFH, Emmerthal, Germany

Syre Wiig, Marie 020340
IFE, Kjeller, Norway

Szarek, Magda 020298, 020398
University of Turku, Turku, Finland

Taghipour Kani, Ghaem 020335, 020374
Amirkabir University of Technology, Tehran, Iran

Takahashi, Kanji 020106
Tokyo City University, Setagaya, Japan

Talvi, Micke 020528
Tampere University, Tampere, Finland

Tanahashi, Tadanori 020436
AIST, Koriyama, Japan

Tang, Kai 020011
SINTEF, Trondheim, Norway

Tang, Torben 020028
IPU P/S, Virum, Denmark

Tang, Torben 020037
IPU, Virum, Denmark

Tayebjee, Murad J. Y. 020065
UNSW, Sydney, Australia

Taylor, Nigel 020210
European Commission JRC, Ispra, Italy

Tellez Rodriguez, Eduardo 020230
Kiwa PI Berlin, Berlin, Germany

Teppe, Andreas 020005
RCT Solutions, Konstanz, Germany

Terheiden, Barbara 020031
University of Konstanz, Constance, Germany

Terrados, Cristian 020205
University of Valladolid, Valladolid, Spain

Thakur, Dhruv Singh 020071, 020081
SVNIT, Surat, India

Theocharides, Spyros 020371
Univers, Courbevoie, France

Thomas, Jean 020169
Ciel et Terre, Lille, France

Thorning, Jacob K. 020267, 020283
DTU, Roskilde, Denmark

Thorsteinsson, Sune 020039
DTU, Copenhagen, Denmark

Thorsteinsson, Sune 020037
DTU, Lyngby, Denmark

Thorsteinsson, Sune 020028, 020249, 020250, 020265, 020306, 020477
DTU, Roskilde, Denmark

Timofte, Tudor 020218, 020221
ISC Konstanz, Konstanz, Germany

Ting, San-Yu 020161, 020163
ITRI, Hsinchu, Taiwan

Tissier, Corentin 020238
CSEM, Neuchâtel, Switzerland

Tönies, Alexandra 020523
University of Applied Sciences Cologne, Cologne, Germany

Tomšič, Špela 020047
University of Ljubljana, Ljubljana, Slovenia

Tong, Yongfeng 020108, 020109
QEERI, Doha, Qatar

Topič, Marko 020047, 020269, 020319
University of Ljubljana, Ljubljana, Slovenia

Torabi, Narges 020089
University of Verona, Verona, Italy

Torelly, Guilherme 020092
PUC-Rio, Rio de Janeiro, Brazil

Torre, Gorka 020437
UPV/EHU, Leioa, Spain

Torres Aguilar, Moira Itzel 020214
CentraleSupélec, Gif-sur-Yvette, France

Torres Aguilar, Moira Itzel 020406
CNRS, Gif-sur-Yvette, France

Torres Silva, Nicole 020546
ATAMOSTEC, Santiago, Chile

Torres, Oscar 020110
National University of Colombia, Bogotá, Colombia

Tosi, Irene 020037
IPU, Virum, Denmark

Tran Caliste, Thu Nhi 020546
European Synchrotron Radiation Facility (ESRF), Grenoble, France

Treberspurg, Christoph 020255
Treberspurg und Partner Ziviltechniker, Vienna, Austria

Treberspurg, Martin 020255
Treberspurg und Partner Ziviltechniker, Vienna, Austria

Trefzer, Aaron 020135
Fraunhofer ISE, Freiburg, Germany

Trifiletti, Vanira 020087
University of Milano-Bicocca, Milan, Italy

Trigo-Gonzalez, Mauricio 020342, 020422
University of Antofagasta, Antofagasta, Chile

Tsai, Min-An 020053, 020083, 020161, 020163
ITRI, Hsinchu, Taiwan

Tsanakas, Ioannis (John) A. 020262
CEA / INES, Le Bourget-du-Lac, France

Tsanakas, Ioannis (John) A. 020544
CEA, Le Bourget-du-Lac, France

Tsanakas, Ioannis (John) 020546
CEA / INES, Le Bourget-du-Lac, France

Tsanakas, Ioannis (John) 020317
CEA INES, Le Bourget-du-Lac, France

Tsanakas, Ioannis (John) 020513, 020521
CEA, Le Bourget-du-Lac, France

Tsanakas, Ioannis 020217, 020338
CEA / INES, Le Bourget-du-Lac, France

Tsanakas, Ioannis 020500
CEA, Le Bourget-du-Lac, France

Tsanakas, John A. 020311
CEA / INES, Le Bourget-du-Lac, France

Tseberlidis, Giorgio 020093
University of Milano Bicocca, Milan, Italy

Tseberlidis, Giorgio 020087
University of Milano-Bicocca, Milan, Italy

Tsoi, Konstantin 020113
ODTÜ-GÜNAM, Ankara, Türkiye

Tsombou, Francois M. 020402
Fujairah Research Centre, Fujairah, United Arab Emirates

Tsuno, Yuki 020436
AIST, Koriyama, Japan

Tsunoda, Jun 020484
Hitachi, Kokubunji, Japan

Tsunoda, Jun 020186
Hitachi, Tokyo, Japan

Tulinski, Lona 020385
ZHAW, Winterthur, Switzerland

Tune, Daniel 020220, 020221, 020225
ISC Konstanz, Konstanz, Germany

Turcu, Mircea 020063
ISFH, Emmerthal, Germany

Turek, Marko 020004, 020052
Fraunhofer CSP, Halle (Saale), Germany

Ueda, Yuzuru 020320, 020525
Tokyo University of Science, Tokyo, Japan

Ujvari, Gusztav 020318, 020430
AIT, Vienna, Austria

Ulbikaitė, Vaidvilė 020157
Applied Research Institute for Prospective Technologies, Vilnius, Lithuania

Ulbikas, Juras 020225
Protechnology, Vilnius, Lithuania

Ulyashin, Alexander G. 020011
SINTEF, Oslo, Norway

Unsur, Veysel 020020
ODTÜ-GÜNAM, Ankara, Türkiye

Urban, Harald 020255
TU Wien, Vienna, Austria

Useni, Yannick 020393
University of Lubumbashi, Lubumbashi, Congo (DRC)

Uzuner, Bahri Eren 020113
ODTÜ-GÜNAM, Ankara, Türkiye

Väisänen, Kaisa-Leena 020423
VTT Technical Research Centre of Finland, Oulu, Finland

Vaicikauskas, Viktoras 020157
Center for Physical Sciences and Technology (FTMC), Vilnius, Lithuania

Valaski, Rogério 020090
National Institute of Metrology Quality and Technology, Rio de Janeiro, Brazil

Valencia, Felipe 020342, 020546
AtamosTec, Santiago, Chile

Vallerotto, Guido 020209, 020246, 020257
UPM, Madrid, Spain

van Aken, Bas B. 020405
TNO, Petten, The Netherlands

van der Heide, Arvid 020472
imec, Genk, Belgium

van der Zee, Friso F. 020405
Wageningen University and Research, Wageningen, The Netherlands

Van Dyck, Rik 020225
IMEC, Genk, Belgium

van Dyk, E. Ernest 020193, 020416
Nelson Mandela University, Port Elizabeth, South Africa

van Dyk, Ernest E. 020344
Nelson Mandela University, Port Elizabeth, South Africa

Van Overstraeten, Julien 020543
Becquerel Institute France, Lyon, France

Van Overstraeten, Julien 020252
Becquerel Institute, Brussels, Belgium

vanBaal, Rene 020492
Belectric, Kolitzheim, Germany

Vanhanen, Tuomas 020225
Valoe, Mikkeli, Finland

Vargas, Renzo 020348
University of São Paulo, São Paulo, Brazil

Varney, Valérie 020522
University of Applied Science Cologne, Cologne, Germany

Varney, Valérie 020523
University of Applied Sciences Cologne, Cologne, Germany

vas Dyk, Ernest 020185
Nelson Mandela University, Port Elizabeth, South Africa

Vasconcelos, Letícia 020530
Casa dos Ventos, Fortaleza, Brazil

Vavilkin, Tatjana 020302
Soltech, Genk, Belgium

Vázquez Adán, Alejandra 020501
UCM, Madrid, Spain

Vázquez, A. 020508
UCM, Madrid, Spain

Veas, Christian 020136, 020234
PCCL, Leoben, Austria

Vecino, Fernando Román 020346
DTU, Roskilde, Denmark

Veerman, Sebastian 020035
ISC Konstanz, Konstanz, Germany

Vega de Seoane, José Maria 020252
Becquerel Institute Spain, San Sebastian, Spain

Vega de Seoane, Jose 020546
Becquerel Institute, Brussels, Belgium

Vega-Herrera, Jorge 020342
University of Antofagasta, Antofagasta, Chile

Vehus, Tore Sandnes 020443
University of Agder, Grimstad, Norway

Veirman, Jordi 020203, 020226, 020254
Eurac Research, Bolzano, Italy

Velasco, Angel 020367
Nextracker, Fremont, United States of America

Veludo, Jorge 020317
Galp Energia, Lisbon, Portugal

Veneri, Alessandro 020093
University of Verona, Verona, Italy

Vergura, Silvano 020301
Polytechnic University of Bari, Bari, Italy

Verlinden, Pierre 020001
YIST, Jiangyin, China

Vermang, Bart 020064
Hasselt Unversity, Genk, Belgium

Vernay, Christophe 020244
SOLAÏS, Valbonne, France

Vero, Giuseppe 020301
Polytechnic University of Bari, Bari, Italy

Veronese, Elisa 020513
Eurac Research, Bolzano, Italy

Veurman, Welmoed 020063
ISFH, Emmerthal, Germany

Viani, Lucas 020326
Enertis Applus+, Madrid, Spain

Vicente-Laiglesia, Pablo 020181
European Climate, Infrastructure and Environment
Executive Agency, Brussels, Belgium

Vidal de Oliveira, Aline 020377
Solar Energy Research Laboratory Fotovoltaica/ UFSC,
Florianópolis, Brazil

Vidal, Beatriz Muñoz 020414
IaSol, Zaragoza, Spain

Vidal-Fuentes, Pedro 020094
IREC, Barcelona, Spain

Videla-Magnata, Natalia 020129
Universidad de Antofagasta, Antofagasta, Chile
Videla-Magnata, Natalia 020417
University of Antofagasta, Antofagasta, Chile
Vilches, Anna Morales 020388
Next2Sun Technology, Dillingen, Germany
Villalonga Palou, Joan Tomás 020432, 020434
Sunveon, Madrid, Spain
Villén, Raúl 020127, 020414, 020517
ENDEF, Zaragoza, Spain
Villodas, Aritz 020198
TECNALIA, Derio, Spain
Vincent, Laetitia 020058
CNRS, Palaiseau, France
Vincent, Robin 020196
PVsyst, Geneva, Switzerland
Viorel Spataru, Sergiu 020191
DTU, Roskilde, Denmark
Viriyaroj, Bergpob 020298
Aalto University, Espoo, Finland
Viti, Valeria 020541
Legance, Milan, Italy
Vitoshkin, Helena 020379
Agricultural Research Organization, Rishon LeZion, Israel
Vögeli, Pascal 020385
ZHAW, Winterthur, Switzerland
Vogt, Malte R. 020515
TU Delft, Delft, The Netherlands
Vogt, Thomas 020482
DLR, Oldenburg, Germany
Vollbrecht, Joachim 020063, 020114
ISFH, Emmerthal, Germany
Voltan, Alessandro 020010
Applied Materials, Treviso, Italy
von Friedeburg, Christoph 020557
CF Energy Research-Consulting-Operation, Berlin, Germany
Voronko, Yuliya 020162, 020249
OFI, Vienna, Austria
Vorster, Frederik J. 020193, 020344, 020416
Nelson Mandela University, Port Elizabeth, South Africa
Vorster, Frederik 020185
Nelson Mandela University, Port Elizabeth, South Africa
Vuillon, Laurent 020338
CNRS, Chambery, France

Vulic, Natasa 020296
Univesity of Applied Arts and Sciences Northwestern Switzerland, Muttenz, Switzerland

Vumbugwa, Monphias 020185, 020193, 020344
Nelson Mandela University, Port Elizabeth, South Africa

Waibel, Christoph 020511
Flemish Institute for Technological Research (VITO), Genk, Belgium

Wakabayashi, Ryo 020484
Hitachi, Kokubunji, Japan

Wakazono, Kouzen 020131
Gifu University, Gifu, Japan

Wallner, Gernot M. 020227
University of Linz, Linz, Austria

Walpita, Harsha 020169
University of Oslo, Kjeller, Norway

Walsh, Yoselyn 020520
Costa Rica Institute of Technology, Cartago, Costa Rica

Wambach, Karsten 020468, 020470
bifa Umweltinstitut, Augsburg, Germany

Wang, Chia-Chen 020549
ITRI, Hsinchu, Taiwan

Wang, Shuo 020286, 020400
TUAS, Turku, Finland

Wang, Tzuya 020549
ITRI, Hsinchu, Taiwan

Wang, Xiaolin 020381
Mälardalen University, Västerås, Sweden

Wannenwetsch, Jann 020312
EnBW, Karlsruhe, Germany

Wargocki, Pawel 020551
DTU, Roskilde, Denmark

Waschl, Alfred 020255
buildingSMART, Vienna, Austria

Weber, Thomas 020180, 020230
Kiwa PI Berlin, Berlin, Germany

Weeber, Arthur W. 020515
TU Delft, Delft, The Netherlands

Wei, Wenpeng 020484
Hitachi, Kokubunji, Japan

Weihs, Philipp 020281
BOKU, Vienna, Austria

Weinrich, Frank 020177
PTB, Braunschweig, Germany

Weiß, Marius 020361
Coburg University of Applied Sciences, Coburg, Germany

Wellens, Christine 020135
Fraunhofer ISE, Freiburg, Germany
Whyatt, Duncan 020394
Lancaster University, Lancaster, United Kingdom
Wienands, Karl 020218, 020220, 020221
ISC Konstanz, Konstanz, Germany
Wiesenfarth, Maike 020246
Fraunhofer ISE, Freiburg, Germany
Wietler, Tobias 020063
ISFH, Emmerthal, Germany
Wilbert, Stefan 020235, 020237, 020239, 020331
DLR, Almería, Spain
Willers, Guido 020201
Fraunhofer CSP, Halle, Germany
Wilson, Helen R. 020249
Fraunhofer ISE, Freiburg, Germany
Winter, Renate 020063
ISFH, Emmerthal, Germany
Winter, Stefan 020177, 020181
PTB, Braunschweig, Germany
Wirtz, Wiebke 020260
ISFH, Emmerthal, Germany
Witkowska, Agnieszka 020498
Gdansk University of Technology, Gdansk, Poland
Wittmer, Bruno 020196
PVsyst, Geneva, Switzerland
Wolf, Andreas 020031
Fraunhofer ISE, Freiburg, Germany
Wong, Craig 020230
Kiwa PI Berlin, Berlin, Germany
Wu, Li-Guo 020021
TSEC, Hsinchu, Taiwan
Wu, Yu 020030
TNO, Petten, The Netherlands
Wyss, Philippe 020068
CSEM, Neuchâtel, Switzerland

Xiong, Weizhen 020320
Tokyo University of Science, Tokyo, Japan
Xu, Jiahui 020001
YIST, Jiangyin, China
Xu, Wenhao 020144, 020208
TÜV Rheinland, Shanghai, China
Xu, Xiaoqi 020263
SERIS, Singapore, Singapore

Xu, Yu 020263
SERIS, Singapore, Singapore
Xuereb, Steven 020180, 020230
Kiwa PI Berlin, Berlin, Germany

Yadav, Shivendra 020071, 020081
SVNIT, Surat, India
Yamaguchi, Yosuke 020484
Hitachi, Kokubunji, Japan
Yanagida, Masatoshi 020115
NIMS, Tsukuba, Japan
Yanar, T. Meriç 020027
Kalyon PV, Ankara, Türkiye
Yang, Donggeon 020323
K-water, Daejeon, South Korea
Yang, Hyoung-Kyu 020449
KETI, Wonmi-gu, South Korea
Yde, Leif 020250, 020306
Stensborg, Roskilde, Denmark
Ye, JiaYi 020102
SERIS, Singapore, Singapore
Yerci, Selcuk 020113
ODTÜ-GÜNAM, Ankara, Türkiye
Ylikunnari, Mari 020423
VTT Technical Research Centre of Finland, Oulu, Finland
Ylinen, Marko 020444
Satakunta University of Applied Sciences, Pori, Finland
Ylipaino, Juho 020444, 020445, 020554
TUAS, Tampere, Finland
Yılmaz, Büşra 020521
Kameleon Solar, Roosendaal, The Netherlands
Yordadov, Georgi 020389
imec, Diepenbeek, Belgium
Younes, Kareem 020487
Khalifa University, Abu Dhabi, United Arab Emirates
Yu, Cheng-Yeh 020021, 020053
TSEC, Hsinchu, Taiwan
Yu, Shusen 020406
Ecole Polytechnique, Palaiseau, France
Yuan, Xiao 020001
YIST, Jiangyin, China
Yun, Jae Ho 020112
KENTECH, Naju-si, South Korea

Zaimi, Mhammed 020171
University of Chouaib Doukkali, El Jadida, Morocco

Zanatta Britto, João Victor 020025
PUCRS, Porto Alegre, Brazil

Zanesco, Izete 020023, 020025
PUCRS, Porto Alegre, Brazil

Zaror, Yasmin 020225
WIP - Renewable Energies, Munich, Germany

Zarzalejo, Luis F. 020237, 020331
CIEMAT, Madrid, Spain

Zekri, Atef 020146
QEERI, Doha, Qatar

Zerafa, Steve 020334
PIXAM, Msida, Malta

Zhang, Geng 020001
Jolywood (ShanXi) Solar Technology, Taiyuan, China

Zhang, Jingwei 020111
Hohai University, Changzhou, China

Zhang, Kai 020233
FZJ, Jülich, Germany

Zhang, Wenjing 020001
YIST, Jiangyin, China

Zhang, Wuai 020101
HZB, Berlin, Germany

Zhang, Yating 020144, 020208
TÜV Rheinland, Shanghai, China

Zhou, Qilin 020102
SERIS, Singapore, Singapore

Zhu, Junjie 020017
Institute for Energy Technology, Kjeller, Norway

Ziaullah, Abdul Wahab 020278, 020291
QEERI, Doha, Qatar

Zilles, Roberto 020154, 020348
University of São Paulo, São Paulo, Brazil

Zimmermann, Iwan 020116
IPVF, Palaiseau, France

Zubillaga, Oihana 020139
Tecnalia, Donostia - San Sebastián, Spain

Zugasti, Eugenia 020334
CENER, Pamplona, Spain

Zugasti, Eugenia 020300
CENER, Sarriguren, Spain

Zwahlen, Theo 020369
BFH, Burgdorf, Switzerland

KEYWORDS OF EU PVSEC 2025 PROCEEDINGS PAPERS

42nd European Photovoltaic Solar Energy Conference and Exhibition (EU PVSEC 2025)

Bilbao, Spain
22-26 September 2025

Volume 3 of 6

ISBN: 979-8-3313-2987-7

Printed from e-media with permission by:

Curran Associates, Inc.
57 Morehouse Lane
Red Hook, NY 12571

Some format issues inherent in the e-media version may also appear in this print version.

WIP – Renewable Energies
Sylvensteinstr. 2
81369 Munchen
Germany

Phone: +49 89 72012735
Fax: +49 89 72012791

wip@wip-munich.de

Additional copies of this publication are available from:

Curran Associates, Inc.
57 Morehouse Lane
Red Hook, NY 12571 USA
Phone: 845-758-0400
Fax: 845-758-2633
Email: curran@proceedings.com
Web: www.proceedings.com

42nd European Photovoltaic Solar Energy Conference and Exhibition

Proceedings of the International Conference

22 September – 26 September 2025

Edited by:

C. DEL CAÑIZO
Solar Energy Institute
UPM
Spain

R. KENNY
European Commission
Joint Research Centre
Italy

J. BERGMILLER
WIP Renewable Energies
Germany

J. DE GREGORIO
WIP Renewable Energies
Germany

Edition Team:

B. Yildiz
L. Großhans
A. Michaelsen
U.E. Birgi
WIP Renewable Energies
Germany

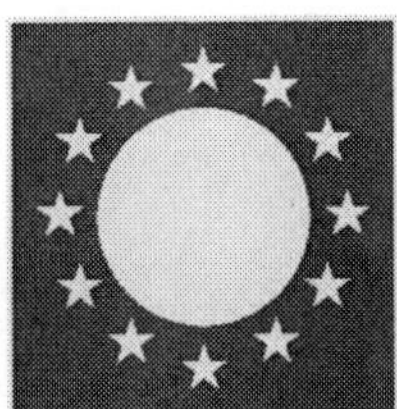

Photos at:

Coordination of the Technical Programme:

European Commission Joint Research Centre
Via E. Fermi 1
21020 Ispra (VA)
Italy

Institutional Support:

European Commission

Institutional PV Industry Cooperation:

SolarPower Europe

ESMC – European Solar Manufacturing Council

Supporting Organisations:

AUSTRALIAN PV INSTITUTE

ASOM – Alliance for Solar Mobility

BASQUE ENERGY CLUSTER

BILBAO CONVENTION BUREAU

EASE – European Association for Storage of Energy

ETIP PV – European Technology & Innovation Platform PV

GÜNDER – Turkish Solar Energy Society

IEA PVPS - IEA Photovoltaic Power Systems Programme

INSTITUTO SOLAR DE ENERGÍA SOLAR

LDES – Long Duration Energy Storage Council

NSEFI – National Solar Energy federation of India

NUS /SERIS – National University of Singapore / Solar Energy Research Institute of Singapore

UPM - Polytechnic University of Madrid

Supporting Associations:

EERA – European Energy Research Aliance

EREF – European Renewable Energies Federation

EUREC – The Association of European Renewable Energy Research Centres

VDMA Photovoltaic Equipment

Local Support:
ENTE VASCO DE LA ENERGÍA
EUH – University of the Basque Country

EU PVSEC 2025 realised by:

WIP Renewable Energies
Sylvensteinstr. 2, 81369 Munich, Germany
Tel: +49 89 720 12 735, Fax: +49 89 720 12 791
Email: pv.conference@wip-munich.de
www.eupvsec.org
www.wip-munich.de

Proceedings produced and published by:

WIP Renewable Energies
Sylvensteinstr. 2, 81369 Munich, Germany
Tel: +49 89 720 12 735, Fax: +49 89 720 12 791
Email: pv.conference@wip-munich.de
www.eupvsec.org
www.wip-munich.de

42nd EUROPEAN PHOTOVOLTAIC SOLAR ENERGY CONFERENCE AND EXHIBITION
22 SEPTEMBER – 26 SEPTEMBER 2025

EU PVSEC 2025 COMMITTEES

INTERNATIONAL SCIENTIFIC ADVISORY COMMITTEE (ISAC)

Chair
P. Szymanski, European Commission Joint Research Centre, Director of Energy, Transport and Climate, Petten, The Netherlands

Committee Members
V. Bermúdez Benito, Founder & Principal Consultant, Berbetin, Antibes, France
G.C. Eder, OFI, Vienna, Austria
P. Frankl, Head of the Renewable Energy Division, International Energy Agency, France
M. Getsiou, European Commission, DG RTD, Brussels, Belgium
S.W. Glunz, Head of Division Photovoltaics - Research, Fraunhofer ISE, Freiburg, Germany
N.M. Haegel, Director of the National Center for Photovoltaics, NREL, Golden, USA
R. Kenny, European Commission Joint Research Centre, Directorate for Energy and Transport and Climate, Ispra, Italy
S. Nowak, Managing Director of NET Nowak Energy & Technology, St. Ursen, Switzerland
R. Schlatmann, Chairman of ETIP PV, Head of the Solar Energy Division at Helmholtz-Zentrum Berlin, Germany
W.C. Sinke, TNO Energy Transition, The Netherlands
M. Topič, Head of Laboratory of Photovoltaics and Optoelectronics of the University of Ljubljana, Slovenia
P. Verlinden, Director at Amrock, Visiting Professor at Sun Yat-Sen University, Guangzhou, China
E. Voroshazi, Head of PV module process laboratory, CEA, Le Bourget-du-Lac, France
J. Bergmiller, Managing Director Events & Knowledge Transfer, WIP Renewable Energies, Munich, Germany
J. de Gregorio, Head of Unit, Scientific Services and Cooperation, WIP Renewable Energies, Munich, Germany

CONFERENCE EXECUTIVE COMMITTEE

Conference General Chair
C. del Cañizo, UPM, Madrid, Spain

Technical Programme Chair
R. Kenny, European Commission Joint Research Centre, Directorate for Energy and Transport and Climate, Ispra, Italy

Committee Members
W.C. Sinke, Program Development Manager, TNO Energy Transition, The Netherlands
S. Nowak, Managing Director of NET Nowak Energy & Technology, St. Ursen, Switzerland
M. Topič, Head of Laboratory of Photovoltaics and Optoelectronics of the University of Ljubljana, Slovenia
V. Bermúdez Benito, BERBETIN, France
E. Voroshazi, Head of PV Module Process Laboratory, CEA, Le Bourget-Du-Lac France
H. Ossenbrink, Former European Commission Joint Research Centre, Germany
J. Bergmiller, Managing Director Events & Knowledge Transfer, WIP Renewable Energies, Munich, Germany
J. de Gregorio, Head of Unit, Scientific Services and Cooperation, WIP Renewable Energies, Munich, Germany

2025 SCIENTIFIC COMMITTEE

Programme Technical Chair
R. Kenny, European Commission, Joint Research Centre, Italy

Topic Chairs

Topic 1: Silicon Materials and Cells
F. Schindler, Fraunhofer ISE, Germany

Topic 2: Thin Films and New Concepts
I. Gordon, imec, Belgium

Topic 3: Photovoltaic Modules and BoS Components
T. Barnes, NREL, USA

Topic 4: PV Systems Engineering, Integrated/Applied PV
A.M. Gracia Amillo, FUNDACION CENER, Spain

Topic 5: PV in the Energy Transition
C. Agraffeil, CEA / INES, France

Topic Organisers and Paper Review Experts

Topic 1: Silicon Materials and Cells
F. Schindler, Fraunhofer ISE, Germany
C. Fischer, Wacker Chemie, Germany
G. Hahn, University of Konstanz, Germany
K. Ding, Forschungszentrum Jülich, Germany
P. Roca i Cabarrocas, CNRS-LPICM, France
A. W. Weeber, TNO Energy Transition, The Netherlands
D. Muñoz, CEA / INES, France
S. W. Glunz, Fraunhofer ISE, Germany
K. Bothe, ISFH, Germany
M. Topic, University of Ljubljana, Slovenia
P. Fath, RCT-Solutions, Germany
S. Peters, Hanwha Q CELLS, Germany

M.P. Bellmann, SINTEF, Norway
A. Ciesla, UNSW, Australia
C. Hagendorf, Freiberg Instruments, Germany
X. Yu, Zhejiang University, China
J.S. Lee, KIER, South Korea
R. Brendel, ISFH, Germany
T. Dullweber, ISFH, Germany
J. Horzel, Fraunhofer ISE, Germany
W. Nemeth, NREL, United States of America
R. Turan, METU, Türkiye
F. Menchini, ENEA, Italy
W. Favre, CEA, France

J. Meier, Meier Technologies, Switzerland
J. Schmidt, ISFH, Germany
M. Wright, University of Oxford, United Kingdom
J. Zhao, CSEM, Switzerland
A. Morisset, CSEM, Switzerland
A. Richter, Fraunhofer ISE, Germany
J. Linke, ISC Konstanz, Germany
B. Geerligs, TNO Energy Transition, The Netherlands
S. Dubois, CEA, France
M. Hermle, Fraunhofer ISE, Germany
B. Terheiden, University of Konstanz, Germany
P. Delli Veneri, ENEA, Italy
T. Matsui, AIST, Japan
Y. Ohshita, Toyota Technological Institute, Japan
E. Bruhat, HOLOSOLIS, France
A. Augusto, Dalarna University, Sweden
F. Ferrazza, ENI S.p.A., Italy
A. Otaegi, UPV/EHU, Spain
M.C. Schubert, Fraunhofer ISE, Germany
H. Duman, KalyonPV, Türkiye
N. Usami, Nagoya University, Japan
Y. Zhu, UNSW, Australia
D. Brunner, RENA Technologies, Germany
A. Danel, CEA, France
C. Gerardi, 3Sun, Italy
H.J. Nonnenmacher, Meyer Burger, Germany
P. Verlinden, AMROCK, Australia
Q. Wang, Wang, Qi, China
W. Zhang, Zhang, Weiming, China
Y. Chen, Trina Solar Energy, China
E. Krassowski, CE Cell Engineering, Germany
M. Foti, 3Sun, Italy
D.L. Bätzner, Meyer Burger Research, Switzerland

Topic 2: Thin Films and New Concepts
I. Gordon, imec, Belgium
J.C. Goldschmidt, Marburg University, Germany
F. Schoofs, Oxford PV, United Kingdom
N. Kyranaki, Hasselt University, Belgium
S. Veenstra, TNO Energy Transition, The Netherlands
T. Aernouts, imec, Belgium
A.N. Tiwari, SOLTIWA, Switzerland
G. Siefer, Fraunhofer ISE, Germany
M. Edoff, Uppsala University, Sweden
A. Marti Vega, UPM, Spain
J. Poortmans, imec, Belgium
I. Ramiro, UPM, Spain
T. Magorian Friedlmeier, ZSW, Germany

S. Albrecht, HZB, Germany
S. Berson, CEA, France
P. Carroy, CEA, France
C. Case, Oxford PV, United Kingdom
G. Coletti, FuturaSun, Italy
S. De Wolf, KAUST, Saudi Arabia
U.W. Paetzold, KIT, Germany
H. Sivaramakrishnan Radhakrisnan, imec, Belgium
P. Schulze, Fraunhofer ISE, Germany
L. Wang, Technology Innovation Institute, United Arab Emirates
Y. Smirnov, Applied Materials, United States of America
B. Stannowski, HZB, Germany
F. Fertig, Hanwha Q CELLS, Germany
L. Lancellotti, ENEA, Italy
S. Cros, CEA, France
S. Hayase, The University of Electro-Communications, Japan
S. Huang, Macquarie University, Australia
M. Khenkin, HZB, Germany
C. Lin, National Taiwan University, Taiwan
M.S.H. Norton, University of Cyprus, Cyprus
P. Pistor, Pablo de Olavide University, Spain
W. Tress, Zurich University of Applied Sciences, Switzerland
A. Aguirre, imec, Belgium
D. Lan, UNSW Sydney, China
M. Saliba, University of Stuttgart, Germany
P. Manshanden, TNO Energy Transition, The Netherlands
L. Vesce, University of Rome II, Italy
I. Dogan, TNO Solliance, The Netherlands
Y. Kuang, imec, Belgium
M. Al Katrib, IPVF, France
M.I. Hossain, QEERI, Qatar
W.H. Chiu, Chang Gung University, Taiwan
C. Chen, Ming Chi University of Technology, Taiwan
C. Fell, CSIRO Energy Technology, Australia
G. Brammertz, imec, Belgium
T. Dalibor, Avancis, Germany
S. Ishizuka, AIST, Japan
A. Redinger, University of Luxembourg, Luxembourg
A. Romeo, University of Verona, Italy
V. Sittinger, Fraunhofer IST, Germany
M. Theelen, TNO/Solliance, The Netherlands
G. Timò, RSE, Italy
A. Kanevce, ZSW, Germany
A. Pérez-Rodríguez, IREC, Spain
R. Gutzler, ZSW, Germany
W. Witte, ZSW, Germany
T. Nishimura, Tokyo Institute of Technology, Japan
C. Qian, University of New South Wales, Australia
J.P. Connolly, CentraleSupelec, France
J.P. Kleider, CNRS/GeePs, France
I. Konovalov, University of Applied Sciences Jena, Germany
Y. Okada, University of Tokyo, Japan
M. Rusu, HZB, Germany
H. Meddeb, DLR, Germany
E. Saucedo, Universitat Politècnica de Catalunya (UPC), Spain
P. Vidal-Fuentes, FUNDACIÓ INSTITUT DE RECERCA EN ENERGIA DE CATALUNYA, Spain
C. Malerba, ENEA, Italy
C. Becker, HZB, Germany
D. Kuciauskas, NREL, United States of America
M. Ochoa, University of Cantabria, Spain
T. Tayagaki, AIST, Japan
S. Wasmer, WAVELABS Solar Metrology Systems, Germany
S. Zandi, UNSW, Australia
C. Messmer, University of Freiburg, Germany
J.B. Puel, Institut Photovoltaïque d'Ile de France (IPVF), France
S. Ternes, University of Rome II, Italy

Topic 3: Photovoltaic Modules and BoS Components
V. Bermúdez Benito, BERBETIN, France
R. Preu, Fraunhofer ISE, Germany
R. Gottschalg, Fraunhofer CSP, Germany
T. Barnes, NREL, United States of America
G. Friesen, SUPSI, Switzerland
G. Bardizza, TÜV Rheinland Solar, Italy

V. Barth, CEA, France
A. Faes, CSEM, Switzerland
A. Lennon, Sundrive Solar, Australia
M. Mittag, Fraunhofer ISE, Germany
M.A. Muñoz-García, UPM, Spain
H. Nagel, Fraunhofer ISE, Germany
S. Pietralunga, CNR, Italy
T. Timofte, ISC Konstanz, Germany

S. Feldbacher, PCCL, Austria
A. Halm, ISC Konstanz, Germany
H. Hanifi, AESOLAR, Germany
E. Warren, NREL, United States of America
S. Zhang, Trina Solar Energy, China
X. Zhen, Canadian Solar, China
G. Beaucarne, Dow Silicones Belgium, Belgium
T. Bejat, CEA, France
C. Camus, LayTec, Germany
U. Jahn, Fraunhofer CSP, Germany
G. Oreski, PCCL, Austria
M. Pander, Fraunhofer CSP, Germany
T. Sample, European Commission JRC, Italy
A. Morlier, imo-imomec, Belgium
C. Barretta, PCCL, Austria
P. Gebhardt, Fraunhofer ISE, Germany
C. Sen, UNSW, Australia
O. Arriaga Arruti, CSEM, Switzerland
X. Gu, NIST, United States of America
C. Xiao, Chinese Academy of Sciences, United States of America
R. Aninat, TNO/Solliance, The Netherlands
S. Mitterhofer, NIST, United States of America
B. Hoex, UNSW, Australia
E. Özkalay, SUPSI, Switzerland
M. Bokalič, University of Ljubljana, Slovenia
S. Bordihn, ISFH, Germany
M. Despeisse, CSEM, Switzerland
J. Govaerts, imec, Belgium
J. Lopez-Garcia, STS-Certified, Spain
M. Pravettoni, Technology Innovation Institute, United Arab Emirates
T. Stoyanova Lyubenova, Joint Research Centre, Italy
C. Ulbrich, HZB, Germany
J. Moereke, Avancis, Germany
Y.S. Long, ITRI, Taiwan
D. Pavanello, European Commission JRC, Italy
A.K. Vidal de Oliveira, UFSC, Brazil
J. Bengoechea, CENER, Spain
M. Ernst, ANU, Australia
H. Ellis, European Commission JRC, Italy
B. Mihaylov, European Commission JRC, Italy
G. Chowdhury, 3E, Belgium
B. Aissa, QEERI - Qatar Environment and Energy Research Institute, Qatar

Topic 4: PV Systems Engineering, Integrated/Applied PV
A. Gracia Amillo, CENER, Spain
W.G.J.H.M. van Sark, Utrecht University, The Netherlands
K. Lappalainen, Tampere University, Finland
J.M. Almeida Serra, University of Lisbon, Portugal
I. Tsanakas, CEA, France
C. Buerhop-Lutz, HI ERN, Germany
D. Moser, Becquerel Institute Italia, Italy
F. Frontini, SUPSI, Switzerland
G.C. Eder, OFI, Austria
A. Scognamiglio, ENEA, Italy
A. Chatzipanagi, European Commission JRC, Italy
I. Antón Hernández, UPM, Spain
R.M.E. Valckenborg, TNO, The Netherlands
T. Reindl, SERIS, Singapore
J.R. Gonzalez, European Space Agency, The Netherlands
G. Mütter, Gerhard Mütter e.U., Austria
T. Merdzhanova, Forschungszentrum Jülich, Germany

V. Lara-Fanego, Solargis, Spain
A. Louwen, Eurac Research, Italy
A. Martinez Fernandez, European Commission JRC, Italy
T. Oozeki, AIST, Japan
J. Remund, Meteotest, Switzerland
M. Sengupta, NREL, United States of America
M. Zehner, Rosenheim Technical University of Applied Sciences, Germany
B. Nouri, German Aerospace Center, Spain
S. Poddar, UNSW, Australia
D. Bachour, HBKU/ Qatar Foundation, Qatar
J. Yang, NREL, United States of America
S. Bouguerra, imo-imomec, Belgium
C. Alonso-Tristán, UBU, Spain
M. Carbone, ENEL Green Power, Italy
M. Dennenmoser, BayWa r.e. Solar Projects GmbH, Germany
C.W. Hansen, Sandia National Laboratories, United States of America
A. Neubert, DNV Maritime Software GmbH, Germany
D. Berrian, Belectric, Germany
M. Oliosi, PVsyst, Switzerland
J. Moschner, KU Leuven / EnergyVille, Belgium
C. Bucher, BUAS, Switzerland
B. Wittmer, PVsyst SA, Switzerland
M. Bolen, SB Energy, United States of America
D. Daßler, Fraunhofer CSP, Germany
R. Einhaus, ZSW, Germany
P. Hacke, NREL, United States of America
A. Heimsath, Fraunhofer ISE, Germany
J. Lin, PV Guider, Taiwan
A. Migan-Dubois, GeePs, France
M. Rinio, University of Karlstad, Sweden
J.S. Stein, Sandia National Laboratories, United States of America
D. Stellbogen, ZSW, Germany
M. Theristis, Sandia National Laboratories, United States of America
A. Virtuani, CSEM, Switzerland
A. Driesse, PV Performance Labs, Germany
M. Øgaard, IFE, Norway
A. Nobre, SERIS, Singapore
T. Trupke, UNSW, Australia
C. Cornaro, University of Rome II, Italy
G. A. dos Reis Benatto, DTU, Denmark
S. Malik, Fraunhofer CSP, Germany
S. Lindig, Univers SAS, France
M.M. Nygård, Institute for Energy Technology, Norway
P. Alonso Gomez, BayWa r.e., Germany
Y. Assoa, CEA, France
P. Bonomo, SUPSI, Switzerland
V. D'Ambrosio, University of Naples Federico II, Italy
E. Román Medina, Tecnalia, Spain
L.H. Slooff, TNO Energy Transition, The Netherlands
S. Villa, TNO, The Netherlands
M. La Rosa, Glass to Power, Italy
T. Del Caño, Onyx Solar Energy, Spain
X. Zhihao, AIST, Japan
P. Sharif, ODTU-GUNAM, Türkiye
K. Umeda, TAISEI CORPORATION, Japan
S. Boddaert, CSTB, France
N. Lysgaard Andersen, DTU, Denmark
K. Meyer, ISFH, Germany
T. Biel, NET Nowak Energy & Technology, Switzerland
F. Colucci, ENEA, Italy
A. Pascaris, NREL, United States of America
C. Dupraz, INRAE, France
C. Alonso-García, CIEMAT, Spain
A. Lefort, BayWa, Germany
H.N. Riise, IFE, Norway
M.A. Schüler, Next2Sun Technology GmbH, Germany
P.J. Pérez-Higueras, University of Jaén, Spain
K. Oda, Agritree,

M. Berwind, Fraunhofer ISE, Germany
M. Dörenkämper, TNO, The Netherlands
M. Heinrich, Fraunhofer ISE, Germany
B. Newman, Lightyear, The Netherlands
A. Reinders, Eindhoven University of Technology, The Netherlands
T. Tanahashi, AIST, Japan
J. Leloux, LuciSun, Belgium
E. Shirazi, University of Twente, The Netherlands
K. Araki, University of Miyazaki, Japan
K. Nishioka, University of Miyazaki, Japan
R. Campesato, CESI, Italy
V. Khorenko, Azur Space, Germany
G. Kakoulaki, European Commission Joint Research Centre, Italy
H. Toyota, JAXA, Japan
P. Garcia-Linares, UPM, Spain
I. Weiss, Weiss, Ingrid, Germany
A. Hensel, Fraunhofer ISE, Germany
J.S. da Fernandes, Hochschule Offenburg, Germany
Y. Ueda, Tokyo University of Science, Japan
J. Braid, Sandia National Laboratories, United States of America

Topic 5: PV in the Energy Transition
J. Stierstorfer, WIP Renewable Energies, Germany
R. Pestana, R&D Nester, Portugal
P.J. Alet, CSEM, Switzerland
C. Agraffeil, CEA, France
K. WAMBACH, Wambach-Consulting, Germany
C. del Cañizo, UPM, Spain
L. Großhans, WIP Renewable Energies, Germany
M. Getsiou, European Commission DG RTD, Belgium
S. Nowak, NET Nowak Energy & Technology, Switzerland
C. Breyer, LUT University, Finland
I. Kaizuka, RTS Corporation, Japan
G. Masson, Becquerel Institute, Belgium
P. Baliozian, VDMA, Germany
L. Großhans, WIP Renewable Energies, Germany
C. Candelise, Bocconi University, Italy
S. Caneva, WIP Renewable Energies, Germany

G. Barchi, Eurac Research, Italy
R. Bründlinger, AIT, Austria
V. Efthymiou, University of Cyprus, Cyprus
M. Centeno Brito, University of Lisbon, Portugal
F. Carigiet, ZHAW, Switzerland
B. Gaiddon, HESPUL, France
F.Z. Ouchani, Green Energy Park, Morocco
M. Rennhofer, AIT, Austria
G. Adinolfi, ENEA, Italy
W. Schaffer, Salzburg Netz, Austria
A. Haber, e-control, Austria
G. Heilscher, Technische Hochschule Ulm, Germany
A. Anctil, Michigan State University, United States of America
S. Arancón, Plug and Play, Spain
S. Capaccioli, ETA - Florence Renewable Energies, Italy
V. Fthenakis, Columbia University, United States of America
G. Heath, NREL, United States of America
K. Komoto, Mizuho Research & Technologies, Ltd., Japan
W. Palitzsch, LuxChemtech, Germany
S. Ovaitt, NREL, United States of America
M. de Wild-Scholten, SmartGreenScans, The Netherlands
S. Herceg, Fraunhofer ISE, Germany
C. Polacchi, Eurac Research, Italy
N. Espinosa, Universidad de Murcia, Spain
E. Drahi, TotalEnergies OneTech, France
S. Guastella, RSE, Italy
H. Ossenbrink, Band Gap, Germany
D. Polverini, European Commission DG GROW, Belgium
N. Taylor, European Commission JRC, Italy
K.A. Weiß, Fraunhofer ISE, Germany
I. Kafedjiska, Helmholtz Zentrum Berlin, Germany
P. Malbranche, Solar Action, France
S. De Iuliis, ENEA, Italy
T. Haarberg, BNW-Energy, Norway
A. Nayfeh, Khalifa University, United Arab Emirates
E. Vartiainen, Fortum Renewables Oy, Finland
E. Veronese, Eurac Research, Italy
P. Sanchez-Friera, Solkeys, Spain
N. Cherradi, Desert Technologies, Saudi Arabia
S. Nold, Fraunhofer ISE, Germany
H.J.J. Yu, CEA, France
M. Beck, U.S. Department of Energy, United States of America
M. Woodhouse, NREL, United States of America
A.B. Cristóbal, UPM, Spain
G. Ruggieri, Insubria University, Italy
S. Tay, NUS, Singapore

Awards Coordinators

Student Awards Coordinator
A.H.M. Smets, Delft University of Technology, The Netherlands

Student Awards Committee
R. Kenny, EU PVSEC Technical Programme Chair, Italy
C. del Canizo, Conference Chair, UPM, Spain
E. Voroshazi, CEA, France
J. Poortmans, imec, Belgium
P.J. Alet, CSEM, Switzerland
S. Caneva, WIP Renewable Energies, Germany
A. Romeo, University of Verona, Italy
G. Friesen, SUPSI, Switzerland
F. Schindler, Fraunhofer ISE, Germany
J.C. Goldchmidt, Marburg University, Germany
D. Moser, Becquerel Institute, Italy
K. Ding, FZJ, Germany
W.C. Sinke, TNO Energy Transition, The Netherlands
M. Topic, University of Ljubljana, Slovenia
R. Schlatman, HZB, Germany
S. Glunz, Fraunhofer ISE, Germany
A.M. Vega, UPM, Spain
I. Kaizuka, RTS, Japan
P.D. Veneri, ENEA, Italy
J. Bengoechea, CENER, Spain

Poster Awards Coordinator
P. Malbranche, Solar Action, France

Poster Awards Committee
R. Kenny, European Commission JRC, Italy
C. del Canizo, UPM, Spain
W. van Sark, Utrecht University, The Netherlands
I. Tsanakas, CEA INES, France
L. Miranda, Oxford PV, United Kingdom
D. Munoz, CEA INES, France
I. Gordon, imec, Belgium
E. Roman, Tecnalia, Spain
G. Eder, OFI, Austria
I. Antón, UPM, Spain
S. Veenstra, TNO, The Netherlands
J.M. Almeida Serra, University of Lisbon, Portugal
T. Magorian Friedlmeier, ZSW, Germany
J. Stierstorfer, WIP Renewable Energies, Germany

G. Kakoulaki, European Commission JRC, Italy
T. Barnes, NREL, USA
T. Merdzhanova, Forschungszentrum Jülich, Germany

Highlights Committee
C. del Cañizo, UPM, Madrid, Spain
R. Kenny, European Commission Joint Research Centre, Directorate for Energy and Transport and Climate, Ispra, Italy
W.C. Sinke, TNO Energy Transition, The Netherlands
S. Nowak, Managing Director of NET Nowak Energy & Technology, St. Ursen, Switzerland
M. Topič, Head of Laboratory of Photovoltaics and Optoelectronics of the University of Ljubljana, Slovenia
V. Bermúdez Benito, BERBETIN, France
E. Voroshazi, Head of PV Module Process Laboratory, CEA, Le Bourget-Du-Lac France
H. Ossenbrink, Band Gap, Germany
J. Bergmiller, Managing Director Events & Knowledge Transfer, WIP Renewable Energies, Munich, Germany
J. de Gregorio, Head of Unit, Scientific Services and Cooperation, WIP Renewable Energies, Munich, Germany
S. Leanza, Marketing and PR Manager, WIP Renewable Energies, Munich, Germany
B. Yildiz, Project Manager Events & Knowledge Transfer, WIP Renewable Energies, Munich, Germany
F. Schindler, Fraunhofer ISE, Freiburg, Germany
I. Gordon, imec, Leuven, Belgium
T. Barnes, NREL, Evergreen, USA
A.M. Gracia Amillo, FUNDACION CENER, Sarriguren, Spain
C. Agraffeil, CEA / INES, Le Bourget-du-Lac, France

SUBJECT INDEX

Topic Code

1 Silicon Materials and Cells
2 Thin-Films and New Concepts
3 Photovoltaic Modules
4 Photovoltaic Systems
5 Photovoltaics in the Energy Transition

Session Type

P = Plenary Session
O = Oral Session
V = Visual Session

Day Codes

A = Monday, 22 September 2025
B = Tuesday, 23 September 2025
C = Wednesday, 24 September 2025
D = Thursday, 25 September 2025
E = Friday, 26 September 2025

e.g. 1AO.4 ⇒ 1= Silicon Materials and Cells, A=Monday, O=Oral session, 4=Session 4

FOREWORD

The European Photovoltaic Solar Energy Conference and Exhibition (EU PVSEC) stands as the World's leading and most renowned forum for PV research and development and the biggest conference on PV solar energy. In 2025, celebrating its 42nd edition, the EU PVSEC was the essential meeting and exchanging point for global PV experts from research, development, and industry.

Held from 22–26 September 2025 in Bilbao, Spain, the EU PVSEC 2025 was a resounding success, showcasing a wide range of cutting-edge research results. Bringing together both the Conference and the Exhibition, this edition attracted more than 1600 participants from 61 countries who contributed over 1000 presentations across various fields of science and technology. The event provided an essential platform for the exchange of knowledge and ideas on photovoltaic research, innovations, and applications. In the exhibition area 51 companies from all parts of the world welcomed visitors and presented their products and services.

Conference Highlights

The EU PVSEC covered a broad range of topics with an extensive programme that offers an opportunity for workers from across the entire field of photovoltaics to share their findings, as well as an opportunity for multidisciplinary learning. Rapid advances in materials, designs, and manufacturing processes reflect the accelerating expansion of the global PV market. The programme was arranged into 5 topics as follows:

- Silicon Materials and Cells;
- Thin Films and New Concepts;
- Photovoltaic Modules and Balance of System Components;
- PV Systems Engineering, Integrated/Applied PV;
- PV in the Energy Transition.

Communicating the key messages from the conference, not only to participants, but also to other researchers, key stakeholders, policy makers and the general public was an important added value. We thank the Highlights Committee, composed of selected members of the Scientific Committee, as well as the Session Chairs, for providing a comprehensive summary of the findings and state of the art research that were delivered during this year's event. Some key highlights are listed below, while further details may be found in the dedicated highlights presentation in the annex of these proceedings.

Cross-cutting themes:

- Demonstrated the versatility of solar technologies, spanning traditional and emerging application areas.
- Sustainability and circularity remain central, with research focused on reducing material use, such as replacing silver with copper, and advancing end-of-life management of modules.
- Ensuring long-term stability and predictable energy yield is equally essential, with many examples of studies on degradation mechanisms and efforts to elucidate their root-causes, such as in the case of UVID.
- The role of artificial intelligence across the PV value chain is rapidly expanding, from design to operations and maintenance, including among many others drone applications.

Latest Solar Innovations in Materials, Cells, Modules and PV Systems:

While silicon solar cells remain the cornerstone of PV technology, perovskite solar cells continue to stand out as the leading complementary technology to silicon, both as standalone devices and in tandem configurations. Research efforts are increasingly focused on enhancing stability, understanding degradation mechanisms, improving durability and scalability, and ensuring full industrial compatibility.

Many companies presented impressive results on industrial-size single-junction perovskite modules as well as perovskite-based tandem modules, and several new efficiency records were announced during the event. The rapid pace of innovation in cell and module architecture underscores the need for accelerated and more robust testing and qualification methodologies. Both the industry and the research community are moving swiftly to assess and improve reliability in this fast-evolving PV landscape.

A major focus in module research remains the optimisation of materials and packaging to ensure long lifetimes and predictable energy yields from high-efficiency cells. In parallel, many innovative advances in the operation and maintenance (O&M) of PV systems were presented and discussed.

Applications, Grid Integration and Storage

"PV can be deployed everywhere": from space applications to agrivoltaics, PV noise barriers, building-integrated photovoltaics (BIPV), floating PV systems, and even vehicles. Among these, agrivoltaics is gaining momentum as a promising dual land use approach, offering economic benefits for farmers while increasing resilience to climate change.

Flexibility solutions, particularly through battery storage, were recognised in many technical presentations as essential to accommodate higher PV penetration levels and to reduce energy curtailment. At the same time, strengthening grid infrastructure and enhancing grid management capabilities remain critical to enable the next phase of large-scale PV integration.

Photovoltaics in the Energy Transition

Options for re-establishing competitive module manufacturing in Europe were extensively analysed, including detailed policy recommendations for industrial support and market growth. Currently, a mismatch persists between global PV module installation rates and production rates, resulting in growing inventories and sharply reduced prices.

Finally, inclusiveness, diversity, citizen participation, awareness, education, and social engagement were

underlined as vital dimensions of the sector's long-term sustainability and innovation capacity.

EU PVSEC 2025 Proceedings

Selection for inclusion in the conference was made by the Scientific Committee's paper review experts and topic organisers (see the listing on pages 010002-001-005), to whom we express our sincere gratitude for their comprehensive review work and overall contribution to the success of the conference.

The EU PVSEC 2025 Proceedings contain the full papers covering most of the highlights described above and more. The Proceedings provide a comprehensive overview of the PV solar sector, its current status and future prospects in science, research, innovation, development and deployment extending to 3,750 pages. In addition to the 299 submitted papers, the proceedings include 101 presentations (slides) shown during the plenary and oral presentations as well as 176 poster files of the visual presentations. In total this amounts to 576 publications.

The Conference Proceedings are published as downloadable files and are also fully accessible online. A DOI code (Digital Object Identifier) has been assigned to each paper. This ensures unequivocal and permanent identification and full citability. The EU PVSEC 2025 papers can be viewed and downloaded in a full free open access from the EU PVSEC's Proceedings website https://userarea.eupvsec.org/proceedings.

The proceedings of the EU PVSEC 2025 strengthen the commitment to providing quick and open access to high quality scientific results. This is a powerful source for targeted and quick information search and retrieval, enabling you to search by topic, keywords, paper title, DOI, author, or organization.

We are confident that these Proceedings will play an important role in providing a comprehensive overview of the current actors and activities in the global PV sector and that they will disseminate information on the state-of-the-art of technologies and applications. This can generate further research, add momentum to innovation and promote interest in PV worldwide.

We would like to cordially thank all authors and participants of the EU PVSEC 2025 for their contributions and look forward to welcoming you in Rotterdam, The Netherlands from 14 – 18 September 2026 at the EU PVSEC 2026, the 43rd European Photovoltaic Solar Energy Conference and Exhibition

The Editors

TABLE OF CONTENTS OF EU PVSEC 2025 PROCEEDINGS PAPERS

Visual SESSION 1CV.2 Si Solar Cells | Characterisation & Modelling of Silicon Cells and Their Building Blocks

[1] Anhalt University of Applied Sciences, Köthen, Germany; [2] Fraunhofer CSP, Halle, Germany

Oral SESSION 2AO.2 Advances in Chalcogenide Devices

2AO.2.3 A New Method for Sb-doped CdSeTe/CdTe Devices with Superior Stability 020057
Elisa Artegiani[1], Mariyam Mukhtar[1], Alessandro Romeo[1]
[1] University of Verona, Verona, Italy

Oral SESSION 2AO.3 III-V Based Devices | Tandem and Perovskite Solar Cells

2AO.3.3 Micro-Crystal GaAs Array Sub-Cells for Si Tandem Solar Cells 020058
James Patrick Connolly[1], Ahmed Nejim[2], Alexandre Jaffré[1], José Alvarez[1], Jean-Paul Kleider[1], Denis Mencaraglia[1], Laurie Dentz[3], Géraldine Hallais[3], Frederic Hamouda[3], Laetitia Vincent[3], Daniel Bouchier[3], Charles Renard[3]
[1] CNRS, Gif-sur-Yvette, France; [2] SILVACO, St. Ives, United Kingdom; [3] CNRS, Palaiseau, France

2AO.3.5 Multiscale Models for Perovskite Optimisation 020060
Philippe Baranek[1], James Patrick Connolly[2], Antoine Gissler[1], Philip Schulz[3], Michel Rerat[4], Roberto Dovesi[5]
[1] EDF R&D, Palaiseau, France; [2] CNRS, Gif-sur-Yvette, France; [3] IPVF, Palaiseau, France; [4] IPREM, Pau, France; [5] Academy of Sciences of Turin, Torino, Italy

2AO.3.6 Modelling Recovery in Perovskite Solar Cells under Light and Dark to Address Stability Challenges 020062
Guillem Álvarez-Pérez[1], Jean Baptiste Puel[1], Jean François Guillemoles [1]
[1] IPVF, Palaiseau, France

Oral SESSION 2BO.10 Advanced Modelling and Characterisation of Perovskite Solar Cells

2BO.10.2 On Perimeter Losses in Perovskite Top- and Poly-Si-Passivated Silicon Bottom Cells – Do Small Area Tandems Reveal the Full Efficiency Potential? 020063
Felix Haase[1], Lukas Brockmann[1], Annika Raugewitz[1], Verena Steckenreiter[1], Verena Barnscheidt[1], Roland Clausing[1], Sara Baumann[1], Joachim Vollbrecht[1], Welmoed Veurman[1], Johannes Löhr[1], Dongyang Liu[1], Mircea Turcu[1], Lasse Nasebandt[1], Udo Römer[1], David Sylla[1], Jessica Strey[1], Martha Löhning[1], Larissa Mettner[1], Renate Winter[1], Anja Christ[1], Heike Kohlenberg[1], Cornelia Marquardt[1], Emanuel Brueckner[1], Hossein Rabiei[1], Michael Rienäcker[1], Sarah Kajari-Schröder[1], Tobias Wietler[1], Robby Peibst[1]
[1] ISFH, Emmerthal, Germany

2BO.10.5 In-depth Characterization and Simulation Approach for the Understanding of In- and Outdoor Degradation of Perovskite Solar Cells 020064
Jonathan Parion[1], Amit Kumar Harit[1], Elias Peraticos[2], Vasiliki Paraskeva[2], Maria Hadjipanayi[2], Aranzazu Aguirre[1], Filip Duerinckx[1], Hariharsudan

Sivaramakrishnan Radhakrishnan[1], Jef Poortmans[1], Johan Lauwaert[3], Bart Vermang[1]
[1] Hasselt Unversity, Genk, Belgium; [2] University of Cyprus, Nicosia, Cyprus; [3] Ghent University, Ghent, Belgium

Oral SESSION 2BO.8 Advanced Conversion Devices

2BO.8.1 Singlet Fission Route for >30% Efficient Solar Cells: Silicon Cell Requirements 020065
Shona McNab[1], Alex J. Baldacchino[1], Pheobe Pearce[1], Alvin Mo[1], Alison Ciesla[1], Bram Hoex[1], Nicholas J. Ekins-Daukes[1], Murad J. Y. Tayebjee[1], Michael P. Nielsen[1]
[1] UNSW, Sydney, Australia

2BO.8.5 Performance of a 4-Terminals Spectral Splitting Asymmetric Solar Concentrator in Diffuse Sunlight: a Numerical Study 020066
Floriana Morabito[1], Daniela Fontani[2], Paola Sansoni[2], Mehdi Ahmadi[3], Salvatore Lombardo[3], Andrea Farina[1], Silvia Maria Pietralunga[1]
[1] CNR-IFN, Milan, Italy; [2] CNR-INO, Florence, Italy; [3] CNR-IMM, Catania, Italy

2BO.8.6 GaAs for Thermophotonics: From Thin-Film Solar Cells to Highly Efficient LEDs 020067
Natasha Gruginskie[1], Peter Mulder[1], Gerard Bauhuis[1], Jani Oksanen[2], John Schermer[1]
[1] Radboud University, Nijmegen, The Netherlands; [2] Aalto University, Espoo, Finland

Visual SESSION 2BV.1 New Materials, Devices and Conversion Concepts | New Modelling and Characterisation Techniques

2BV.1.4 Low-Energy Electron Multiplication on Nanostructured Solar Cells: a Novel Route to Overcome Si-PV Efficiency Limits 020068
Mikaël Hosatte[1], Brice Rouffie[1], Zbigniew T. Kuznicki[1], Frédéric Milesi[2], Bertrand Paviet-Salomon[3], Audrey Morisset[3], Philippe Wyss[3], Lejo Joseph Koduvelikulathu[4], Lazhar Rachdi[4], Lacramioara Popescu[4], Dominik Rudolph[4], Marek Basta[5], Andrzej Miszczuk[5], Martyna Majak[5], Beata Basta[5], Samuel Queste[6]
[1] SEGTON Advanced Technology, Versailles, France; [2] CEA, Grenoble, France; [3] CSEM, Neuchâtel, Switzerland; [4] ISC Konstanz, Konstanz, Germany; [5] Roltec, Poznań, Poland; [6] Marie and Louis Pasteur University, Besançon, France

2BV.1.5 Tailoring CBTSSe Solar Cells for Indoor Photovoltaic Applications 020069
Hitarth Narsi Patel[1], Bindu Pamula[1], Deepak Joshi[1], Vivek Garg[1]
[1] SVNIT, Surat, India

2BV.1.6 Theoretical Insights through DFT into $AgBiS_2$ Thin Films Absorber for Photovoltaic Applications 020071
Dhruv Singh Thakur[1], Rajesh Kumar Sharma[1], Nithin Chatterji[1], Vivek Garg[1], Shivendra Yadav[1]
[1] SVNIT, Surat, India

Visual SESSION 2CV.3 Perovskite-based Tandems and Multijunctions

Gerardo Gordillo[1], Oscar Torres[1], Julian Peña-Bermudez[2]
[1] National University of Colombia, Bogotá, Colombia; [2] University of the Caribbean, Santo Domingo, Dominican Republic

2CV.3.71 Comparative Analysis and Efficiency Optimization of Sulfur-based Chalcogenide Perovskites ($MgHfS_3$, $CaZrS_3$, $BaZrS_3$) via Interface Engineering for High-Performance Solar Cells 020111
Anees ur Rehman[1], Kung Ding[1], Jingwei Zhang[1], Xiang Chen[1]
[1] Hohai University, Changzhou, China

2CV.3.72 Development of Inorganic Perovskite $CsPbI_3$ with Heterojunction Engineering at the Buried Interface for Enhanced Stability and Performance 020112
Syed Fawad Ali Shah[1], Hyeonwook Park[1], Muhammad Rehan[2], Donghyeop Shin[2], Kihwan Kim[2], Jae Ho Yun[3]
[1] KENTECH, Naju-Si, South Korea; [2] KIER, Daejeon, South Korea; [3] KENTECH, Naju-si, South Korea

Oral SESSION 2DO.6 Industrially Scalable Processes to Manufacture Perovskite Solar Cells and Modules

2DO.6.2 Eliminating P2 Scribes: A New Interconnection Design for Efficient Perovskite Solar Modules Under Indoor Lighting 020113
Bahri Eren Uzuner[1], Konstantin Tsoi[1], Gorkem Gunbas[1], Selcuk Yerci[1]
[1] ODTÜ-GÜNAM, Ankara, Türkiye

2DO.6.5 Evaporated Self Assembled Monolayer (SAM) Hole Transport Layers for Scalable Perovskite Solar Cells 020114
Joachim Vollbrecht[1], Verena Barnscheidt[1], Roland Clausing[1], Johannes Löhr[1], Larissa Mettner[1], Adam Neuba[2], Annika Raugewitz[1], Jessica Strey[1], Robby Peibst[1]
[1] ISFH, Emmerthal, Germany; [2] Paderborn University, Paderborn, Germany

Oral SESSION 2DO.7 Insights Into the Stability of Perovskite Solar Cells and Modules

2DO.7.1 Outdoor Performance and Degradation Analysis of Inverted Perovskite Solar Cells 020115
Makoto Konagai[1], Hayato Okawa[1], Ryousuke Ishikawa[1], Masatoshi Yanagida[2], Yasuhiro Shirai[2]
[1] Tokyo City University, Setagaya, Japan; [2] NIMS, Tsukuba, Japan

Oral SESSION 2DO.8 Multiple Aspects of Perovskite PV Research

2DO.8.2 Strategies for Quasi-2D Perovskite Integration in p-i-n Solar Cells 020116
Anna Capitaine[1], Hugo Le Bossenec[1], Marion Provost[1], Alexandra Levtchenko[1], Daniel Ory[2], Jean Rousset[2], Iwan Zimmermann[1], Anyssa Derj[1],

Mirella Al Katrib[1]
[1] IPVF, Palaiseau, France; [2] EDF R&D, Palaiseau, France

2DO.8.3 Innovative Approach to Bismuth-Antimony-Iodide Double Perovskite PV Absorbers via Anion Exchange and Solide-State Reactions 020117
Oleksandr Stroyuk[1], *Oleksandra Raievska*[1], *Sachin Kinge*[2], *Jens Hauch*[1], *Christoph J. Brabec*[1]
[1] HI ERN, Erlangen, Germany; [2] Toyota Motors Europe, Brussels, Belgium

Visual SESSION 3AV.1 PV Module Design and Manufacturing

3AV.1.1 Investigating the 3-Dimensional Structure of Metallic Filler Particles in Electrically Conductive Adhesives 020119
Stephan Grosser[1], *Alexander Müller*[1], *Robert Göckeritz*[1], *Tobias Nitsche*[2], *Daniel Buckland*[2], *Giuseppe Galbiati*[2], *Bengt Jaeckel*[1]
[1] Fraunhofer CSP, Halle, Germany; [2] Henkel, Düsseldorf, Germany

3AV.1.6 Investigation on Different Bypass Diodes for Shade Resistant PV-Modules 020121
Jens Froebel[1], *Matthias Pander*[1], *Bengt Jaeckel*[1], *Andreas Maixner*[2], *Pouya Pourshafi*[2], *Afshin Bakhtiari*[2], *Hamed Hanifi*[2]
[1] Fraunhofer CSP, Halle, Germany; [2] AESOLAR, Koenigsbrunn, Germany

3AV.1.7 Optimization of Infrared Soldering Process to Reduce the Temperature Inhomogeneity in Silicon Solar Cells Using Finite Element Methods 020123
Daniel Christopher Joseph[1], *Angela De Rose*[1], *Christian Reichel*[1], *Andreas J. Beinert*[1], *Holger Neuhaus*[1]
[1] Fraunhofer ISE, Freiburg, Germany

3AV.1.10 Performance Evaluation of a New Design Photovoltaic Module with Reduced Self-Shading 020125
Pouya Pourshafi[1], *Andreas Maixner*[1], *Hamed Hanifi*[1]
[1] AESOLAR, Königsbrunn, Germany

3AV.1.11 Materials Assessment for PV-T Modules Thermal Performance Improvement 020127
Lucía Cano[1], *Raquel Simón-Allué*[1], *Raúl Villén*[1], *Yolanda Lara*[1], *Isabel Guedea*[1]
[1] ENDEF, Zaragoza, Spain

3AV.1.12 Evaluating Repair Techiniques for c-Si PV Modules: Spot-Welding 020129
Jorge Rabanal-Arabach[1], *Sonia Beltran-Condori*[1], *Natalia Videla-Magnata*[1], *Katalina Rojas-Henriquez*[1], *Andreas Schneider*[2], *Edward Fuentealba-Vidal*[1]
[1] University of Antofagasta, Antofagasta, Chile; [2] University of Applied Sciences Gelsenkirchen, Gelsenkirchen, Germany

3AV.1.13 Thermally Conductive Filler Particle Mixed Silicone Layer to Provide Heat Dissipation Functionality to c-Si Solar Cell Modules without Encapsulants 020131
Yasushi Sobajima[1], *Kouzen Wakazono*[1], *Keisuke Ohdaira*[2]
[1] Gifu University, Gifu, Japan; [2] JAIST, Ishikawa, Japan

3AV.1.16 Ultrasonic Characterization of Ethylene-Vinyl Acetate in Glass-Glass-Modules 020132
Christopher Bruce Konu[1], *Rico Meier*[1]
[1] HTW Berlin, Berlin, Germany

Visual SESSION 3AV.2 PV Module Durability and Reliability

Nathan Roosloot[1], Harsha Walpita[2], Christoph Seiffert[1], Jean Thomas[3], Maarten Dörenkämper[4], Minne M. de Jong[4], Josefine H. Selj[1], Gaute Otnes[1]
[1] Institute for Energy Technology, Kjeller, Norway; [2] University of Oslo, Kjeller, Norway; [3] Ciel et Terre, Lille, France; [4] TNO, Eindhoven, The Netherlands

Visual SESSION 3AV.3 PV Modules Characterisation and Performances Assessment

3AV.3.1 A New Method for Comprehensive Power Rating and Performance Analysis of PERC Modules based on Half-Cut Cell Technology 020171
Khadija El Ainaoui[1], Mhammed Zaimi[2], Imane Flouchi[1], Said Elhamaoui[1], Yasmine El mrabet[1], Abdellatif Ghennioui[1], El Mahdi Assaid[2]
[1] Green Energy Park, Benguerir, Morocco; [2] University of Chouaib Doukkali, El Jadida, Morocco

3AV.3.2 Energy Rating Analysis of Heterojunction PV Modules 020173
Teodora Stoyanova Lyubenova[1], Ewan D. Dunlop[1]
[1] European Commission JRC, Ispra, Italy

3AV.3.3 Trend of Temperature Coefficients of c-Si Module Technologies from the past 15 Years 020175
Bengt Jaeckel[1], Matthias Pander[1]
[1] Fraunhofer CSP, Halle, Germany

3AV.3.6 Angle of Incidence Measurements on Bifacial PV Modules 020177
Frank Weinrich[1], Stefan Riechelmann[1], Stefan Winter[1]
[1] PTB, Braunschweig, Germany

3AV.3.8 Plug & Play IV Curve Tracer for PV Modules 020179
Adrian Jäggi[1], Christof Bucher[1], Matthias Burri[1]
[1] BFH, Burgdorf, Switzerland

3AV.3.9 Seasonal and Location-Dependent Temperature Coefficients for Thin-Film PV Modules: Enhancing Yield Prediction Accuracy 020180
Thomas Weber[1], Abdullah Abu Sayed[1], Benjamin Lippke[1], Steven Xuereb[1], Marcus Rennhofer[2], Bart E. Pieters[3]
[1] Kiwa PI Berlin, Berlin, Germany; [2] AIT, Vienna, Austria; [3] FZJ, Jülich, Germany

3AV.3.10 Standardisation Methods for Bifacial Energy Yield Estimation and PV Module Long-Term Performance Degradation Estimation: Potential Policy Implications 020181
Jaione Bengoechea[1], Ana María Gracia Amillo[1], Stefan Riechelmann[2], Stefan Winter[2], Giorgio Bardizza[3], Christos Monokroussos[4], Davide Polverini[5], Pablo Vicente-Laiglesia[6], Maria Getsiou[7]
[1] CENER, Sarriguren, Spain; [2] PTB, Braunschweig, Germany; [3] TÜV Rheinland Italia, Milan, Italy; [4] TÜV Rheinland, Shanghai, China; [5] Directorate General for Internal Market, Industry, Entrepreneurship and SMEs, Brussels, Belgium; [6] European Climate, Infrastructure and Environment Executive Agency, Brussels, Belgium; [7] Directorate General for Research and Innovation, Brussels, Belgium

3AV.3.11 Shaalke: Development of a MATLAB Software Tool for Advanced Statistical Outdoor Data Evaluation 020183

Oral SESSION 3BO.11 Imaging Techniques for PV Modules

Cristian Terrados[1], Eva de la Viuda[1], Kabir Paul Sulca[1], Julian Anaya[1], Miguel Ángel González[1], Oscar Martínez[1]
[1] University of Valladolid, Valladolid, Spain

3BO.11.6 Luminescence Measurements of PV Modules with a Cost-Effective and Small-Sized Hood-Based Tool under Daylight Conditions 020206
Marc Köntges[1], Michael Siebert[1], Dieter Lorenz[2], Bernd Kuhrmann[2], Michael Fuß[2]
[1] ISFH, Emmerthal, Germany; [2] MBJ Solutions, Ahrensburg, Germany

Oral SESSION 3BO.12 Characterisation and Energy Rating of PV Modules

3BO.12.1 Developing a New I-V Translation Methodology in Accordance with IEC 60891:2021 Correction Procedure 1 and 2 020208
Wenhao Xu[1], Yating Zhang[1], Mengdi Liu[1], Christos Monokroussos[1], Werner Herrmann[2], Giorgio Bardizza[2], Harald Müllejans[3]
[1] TÜV Rheinland, Shanghai, China; [2] TÜV Rheinland Solar, Cologne, Germany; [3] European Commission JRC, Ispra, Italy

3BO.12.2 Characterization of Vehicle Integrated Photovoltaic Modules 020209
Ricardo Moruno[1], Francisco José Martín[1], Juan Manuel Redondo[1], Javier Malo[1], Luis Javier San José[1], Guido Vallerotto[1], Steve Askins[1], Rubén Núñez[1], César Domínguez[1], Ignacio Antón[1], Rebeca Herrero[1]
[1] UPM, Madrid, Spain

3BO.12.4 Estimating the Energy Yield of Bifacial Photovoltaics with the JRC's Photovoltaic Geographic Information System 020210
Nigel Taylor[1], Teodora Lyubenova[1], Lavanya Malarkannan[2], Nikos Alexandris[1], Alexandros Falangas[3], Robert Kenny[1], Ewan D. Dunlop[1], Blago Mihaylov[1]
[1] European Commission JRC, Ispra, Italy; [2] National Physical Laboratory, Teddington, United Kingdom; [3] TRASIS International, Brussels, Belgium

3BO.12.5 An Update on Energy Rating Amendments – Integration of Bifacial Modules 020211
Stefan Riechelmann[1], Hendrik Sträter[1], Ana María Gracia Amillo[2], Sophie Pelland[3], Anton Driesse[4]
[1] PTB, Braunschweig, Germany; [2] CENER, Pamplona, Spain; [3] Natural Resources Canada, Varennes, Canada; [4] PV Performance Labs, Freiburg, Germany

Oral SESSION 3BO.14 Characterisation and Outdoor Monitoring of Perovskite-based PV Modules

3BO.14.1 Outdoor Measurements of Perovskite Modules 020213
Hanna Ellis[1], Harald Müllejans[1], Ewan D. Dunlop[1], Tony Sample[1]
[1] European Commission JRC, Ispra, Italy

Oral SESSION 3BO.15 Outdoor Performances and Degradation Analysis of PV Modules

3CO.11.5 Indoor Characterization and Analysis of Reverse Breakdown Behavior of Solar Cells with Different Cell Architectures 020223

Bengt Jaeckel[1], Jens Froebel[1], Matthias Pander[1], Andreas Maixner[2], Hamed Hanifi[2]
[1] Fraunhofer CSP, Halle, Germany; [2] AESOLAR, Koenigsbrunn, Germany

Plenary SESSION 3CP.1 Si PV Manufacturing: Pushing the Limits of Performance

3CP.1.2 IBC4EU: European Back Contact Technology 020225

Florian Buchholz[1], Daniel Tune[1], Tobias Meßmer[1], Jonathan Linke[1], Manjunath Prasad[1], Valentin D. Mihailetchi[1], Juras Ulbikas[2], Arne Dahle[3], Martijn Meereboer[4], Francesca Fabris[5], Erik Eikelboom[5], Tom Borgers[6], Rik Van Dyck[6], Filip Duerinckx[7], Hariharsudan Sivaramakrishnan Radhakrishnan[7], Timea Bejat[8], Samuel Harrison[8], Ashish Binani[9], Nicolas Guillevin[9], Jan Kroon[9], Yevgeniya Larionova[10], Thorsten Dullweber[10], Ofer Shochet[11], Isaac Rosen [11], Ingo Röver [12], Wolfram Palitzsch[12], Yasmin Zaror[13], Johannes Stierstorfer[14], Aurimas Radzevicius[15], Julius Denafas[16], Tuomas Vanhanen [17], Tuukka Savisalo[17], Maximilian Pospischil [18], Marian Breitenbücher [18], Özlem Coşkun[19], Melodie de l`Epine [20], Philippe Macé[20], Ian Kenchington[20]
[1] ISC Konstanz, Konstanz, Germany; [2] Protechnology, Vilnius, Lithuania; [3] Norsun, Oslo, Norway; [4] Energyra, Westknollendam, The Netherlands; [5] Futurasun, Citadella, Italy; [6] IMEC, Genk, Belgium; [7] Hasselt Unversity, Genk, Belgium; [8] CEA, Le Bourget-du-Lac, France; [9] TNO, Petten, The Netherlands; [10] ISFH, Emmerthal, Germany; [11] Copprint, Jerusalem, Israel; [12] LuxChemTech, Freiberg, Germany; [13] WIP Renewable Energies, Munich, Germany; [14] WIP - Renewable Energies, Munich, Germany; [15] Valoe Cells, Vilnius, Lithuania; [16] Solitek, Vilnius, Lithuania; [17] Valoe, Mikkeli, Finland; [18] Highline Technologies, Freiburg, Germany; [19] Kalyon PV, Ankara, Türkiye; [20] Becquerel Institute, Brussels, Belgium

Plenary SESSION 3CP.3 Perovskite – Silicon Tandems: Towards Commercialisation | PV Stability in the Field

3CP.3.4 Outdoor Performance and Reliability of Perovskite (Pk)-Silicon (Si) Tandems: >1 year of Monitoring in the NEXUS Project 020226

Atse Louwen[1], Jordi Veirman[1], Alexander Astigarraga[1], Juan José Stivanello[1], David Moser[2], Perrine Carroy[3], Vincent Barth[3], Delfina Muñoz[3], Markus Lenz[4], Anika Sidler[4], Jorge Ferrando[5], Maximiliano Alejandro Senno[5], Henk J. Bolink[5], Talat Özden[6], Hisham Nasser[6], Shuaifeng Hu[7], Xinyi Shen[7], Henry Snaith[7]
[1] Eurac Research, Bolzano, Italy; [2] Becquerel Institute Italy, Trento, Italy; [3] CEA / INES, Le Bourget-du-Lac, France; [4] School of Life Sciences FHNW, Muttenz, Switzerland; [5] University of Valencia, Paterna, Spain; [6] ODTÜ-GÜNAM, Ankara, Türkiye; [7] University of Oxford, Oxford, United Kingdom

Oral SESSION 3DO.12 Innovative Encapsulation Materials

3DO.12.5 Effect of Glass Beads on the Solar Optical Properties of Thermoplastic Encapsulants for Colored PV Modules 020227
Martin Huemer[1], Gernot M. Wallner[1], Andreas Brandstätter[2]
[1] University of Linz, Linz, Austria; [2] Lenzing Plastics, Lenzing, Austria

Oral SESSION 3DO.16 Failure Modes and Degradation in PV Modules

3DO.16.6 TOPCON PV Modules UV Exposure: Uncovering Hidden Instabilities 020229
Baloji Adothu[1], Shahzada Pamir Aly[1], Bengt Jaeckel[2], Matthias Pandar[2], Ralph Gottschalg[2], Vivian Alberts[1]
[1] DEWA, Dubai, United Arab Emirates; [2] Fraunhofer CSP, Halle, Germany

Oral SESSION 3DO.19 Mechanical Load Testing and Insights into Glass Breakage

3DO.19.2 Recent Findings on Glass-Breakage Issues: From Factory Production Oversight, On-Site Inspection and Laboratory Testing Results 020230
Thomas Weber[1], Moritz Heiser[1], Abdullah Abu Sayed[1], Roman Joziak[1], Eduardo Tellez Rodriguez[1], Nattapark Pongthanacharoenkul[1], Sören Rindert[1], Benjamin Lippke[1], Craig Wong[1], Steven Xuereb[1], Mahyar Nezhad[2], Don Cowan[2], Matthew Lu[3], Claudia Buerhop-Lutz[4], Ian Marius Peters[4]
[1] Kiwa PI Berlin, Berlin, Germany; [2] Kiwa PI Berlin, Hudson, United States of America; [3] Kiwa PI Berlin, Shanghai, China; [4] Forschungszentrum Jülich, Erlangen, Germany

3DO.19.3 Understanding Glass Breakage in Field-Operated PV Modules: Learnings from Inhomogeneous Mechanical Load Tests 020231
Jochen Markert[1], Aditya Girish Belawadi[1], Enzo Job[1], Pascal Romer[1], Ingrid Haedrich[1], Daniel Philipp[1]
[1] Fraunhofer ISE, Freiburg, Germany

3DO.19.4 Determining the Glass Strength of Solar Glass - Test and Evaluation Methods 020232
Hannah Reichart[1], Matthias Pander[2], Ruth Kasper[1]
[1] University of Applied Sciences Cologne, Cologne, Germany; [2] Fraunhofer CSP, Halle, Germany

Oral SESSION 3DO.20 Performance of Polymeric Materials

3DO.20.5 Reliability Studies of UV Downshifting Encapsulants after Damp-Heat and UV Weathering 020233
Jishnu Ramachandran Nair[1], Marius Lüdemann[1], Paul-Tiberiu Miclea[1], Kai Zhang[2], Kaining Ding[2], Andreas Lambertz[2], Ralph Gottschalg[1], Robert Heidrich[1], Anton Mordvinkin[1]
[1] Fraunhofer CSP, Halle, Germany; [2] FZJ, Jülich, Germany

3DO.20.6 Festina Lente! The Impact of Lamination Duration on Encapsulant Stability 020234

Nikolina Pervan[1], Jutta Geier[1], Christian Veas[1], Gernot Oreski[1]
[1] PCCL, Leoben, Austria

Oral SESSION 4AO.7 Solar Resource Assessment

4AO.7.4 Potential of Decimeter-Resolution Ground Albedo Data for Bifacial Photovoltaics 020235
Niklas Blum[1], Bijan Nouri[1], Yann Fabel[1], Stefan Wilbert[1]
[1] DLR, Almería, Spain

4AO.7.5 Method for the Determination of Spectral Responsivity of Digital Solar Irradiance Sensors 020236
David Hinken[1], Sebastian Denke[1], Karsten Bothe[1], Rolf Brendel[1]
[1] ISFH, Emmerthal, Germany

Oral SESSION 4AO.8 Solar Irradiance Forecasting

4AO.8.2 Cutting-Edge Generative AI for Intra-Hour Solar Forecasting 020237
Yann Fabel[1], Dominik Schnaus[2], Bijan Nouri[1], Stefan Wilbert[1], Niklas Blum[1], Luis F. Zarzalejo[3], Julia Kowalski[4], Robert Pitz-Paal[5]
[1] DLR, Almería, Spain; [2] TUM, Garching, Germany; [3] CIEMAT, Madrid, Spain; [4] RWTH, Aachen, Germany; [5] DLR, Cologne, Germany

4AO.8.4 Integrating Satellite Imagery and GNNs for Improving Day-Ahead Solar Irradiance Forecasting 020238
Baptiste Schubnel[1], Jelena Simeunovic[1], Corentin Tissier[1], Pierre-Jean Alet[1], Rafael E. Carrillo[1]
[1] CSEM, Neuchâtel, Switzerland

4AO.8.5 Enhancing Intra-Hour Solar Irradiance Forecasting for Solar Applications: A Blended Model of Satellite, Sky Imager and Persistence 020239
Bijan Nouri[1], Jorge Lezaca[2], Yann Fabel[1], Annette Hammer[2], Niklas Blum[1], Stefan Wilbert[1]
[1] DLR, Almería, Spain; [2] DLR, Oldenburg, Germany

Oral SESSION 4AO.9 Irradiance for PV Design | Shading and Glare Mitigation

4AO.9.1 Reflective Properties of Urban Materials and Their Impact on PV Yield 020240
Christian Schläger[1], Dennis Bredemeier[1], Arne Dittrich[2], Jan Hendrik Pfau[1], Philip Kühne[1], Rolf Brendel[2]
[1] Leibniz University Hannover, Hannover, Germany; [2] ISFH, Emmerthal, Germany

4AO.9.3 Understanding Short-Term PV Power Variability Based on Solargis Time Series Data and Simulations 020241
Martin Opatovsky[1], Marta Pelfort Ojer[1], Juraj Betak[1], Konstantin Rosina[1]
[1] Solargis, Bratislava, Slovakia

4AO.9.5 Accelerating Photovoltaic System Simulations via Statistical Data Aggregation 020243

Adrián Blanco Aguiar[1], Brais González Rodríguez[2], María Martínez-Barbeito[1], Miguel Sánchez de León Peque[1]
[1] ieco.io, Vigo, Spain; [2] University of Vigo, Vigo, Spain

4AO.9.6 Addressing Glare Problematics for Photovoltaic Projects in the Immediate Proximity of Roads and Railways through the Use of Accurate Digital Surface Models 020244
Christophe Vernay[1], John Coutel[1], Aina Razanajao[1], Sébastien Pitaval[1]
[1] SOLAÏS, Valbonne, France

Plenary SESSION 4AP.1 PV Everywhere

4AP.1.3 Micro-Concentrator Photovoltaics for Deep Space Missions: Overcoming LILT Challenges with High-Specific-Power Solar Arrays 020246
Guido Vallerotto[1], Anderson Bermudez-Garcia[2], Gerald Siefer[3], Maike Wiesenfarth[3], Almudena Garcia-Sanchez[1], Ignacio Antón[1], Carsten Baur[4], Pier Luigi Coz[4], César Domínguez[1]
[1] UPM, Madrid, Spain; [2] Thales Alenia Space, Cannes, France; [3] Fraunhofer ISE, Freiburg, Germany; [4] European Space Agency, Noordwijk, The Netherlands

Oral SESSION 4BO.16 Color in Photovoltaics

4BO.16.1 Experimental Investigation of Colored BIPV/T Systems for Wood-Framed Roofs 020248
Anna-Maria Sigounis[1], Andreas Athienitis[1]
[1] Concordia University, Montreal, Canada

4BO.16.3 How to Perform Accurate Colour Measurements for BIPV Module Glass Covers: an IEA PVPS Task 15 Round-Robin Measurement Campaign 020249
Markus Babin[1], Gabriele C. Eder[2], Thomas Friesen[3], Martina Pelle[4], Gabriella Gonnella[5], Fabrizio Leonforte[6], Yuliya Voronko[2], Helen R. Wilson[7], Sune Thorsteinsson[1], Laura Maturi[4], Niccolò Aste[6], Claudio Del Pero[6], Janne Halme[8], Jun-Tae Kim[9], Susanna Santamaría Fernández[10], Anna-Maria Sigounis[11], Hua Ge[11], Gabi Friesen[12], Francesco Frontini[12]
[1] DTU, Roskilde, Denmark; [2] OFI, Vienna, Austria; [3] Megasol Energie, Deitingen, Switzerland; [4] Eurac Research, Bolzano, Italy; [5] Eurac research, Bolzano, Italy; [6] Polytechnic University of Milan, Milan, Italy; [7] Fraunhofer ISE, Freiburg, Germany; [8] Aalto University, Espoo, Finland; [9] Kongju National University, Chungnam, South Korea; [10] TECNALIA, Derio, Spain; [11] Concordia University, Montreal, Canada; [12] SUPSI, Mendrisio, Switzerland

4BO.16.6 Predicting Light Scatter in Structural Colored BIPV Modules and Textured Glass Using Radiance 020250
Nanna Lysgaard Andersen[1], Markus Babin[1], Jan Svatos[1], Karlis Petersons[2], Leif Yde[2], Jan F. Stensborg[2], Catarina G. Ferreira[3], Ananta Paul[3], Jani Lamminaho[3], Joel D. Cox[3], Morten Madsen[3], Peter B. Poulsen[1], Sune Thorsteinsson[1]
[1] DTU, Roskilde, Denmark; [2] Stensborg, Roskilde, Denmark; [3] SDU Climate Cluster, Odense, Denmark

Oral SESSION 4BO.17 Performance of PV on/in Buildings

4BO.17.1 Modeling Partial Shading at the Cell Level on Photovoltaic Modules 020251
Jean-Paul Calin[1], Jacques Levrat[2], Antonin Faes[2], Fahradin Mujovi[2], Paul Rémondeau[3], Kléber Nicolet-dit-Félix[3], Bénédicte Bonnet-Eymard[2], Didier Dalmazzone[1], Aïcha Hessler-Wyser[3], Christophe Ballif[3]
[1] ENSTA Paris, Palaiseau, France; [2] CSEM, Neuchâtel, Switzerland; [3] EPFL, Neuchâtel, Switzerland

4BO.17.2 Market Potential of Building-Integrated Photovoltaics: a Granular Analysis of the European Building Stock 020252
Juan Ignacio Martinez[1], Julien Van Overstraeten[2], Philippe Macé[2], José Maria Vega de Seoane[1], Elina Bosch[2], Mélodie de l`Epine[3]
[1] Becquerel Institute España, San Sebastian, Spain; [2] Becquerel Institute, Brussels, Belgium; [3] Becquerel Institute France, Lyon, France

4BO.17.3 Photovoltaics in the Built Environment – an Overview of Timely Topics for Research and Development 020253
Francesco Frontini[1], Angele Reinders[2]
[1] SUPSI, Mendrisio, Switzerland; [2] TU Eindhoven, Eindhoven, The Netherlands

4BO.17.5 Advancing BIPV: Shingled HJT Technology for High-Efficiency and Aesthetic Solar Integration 020254
Gabriella Gonnella[1], Alvaro De Gruijter[1], Jordi Veirman[1], Martina Pelle[1], Laura Maturi[1], David Moser[2], Luis Fialho[1]
[1] Eurac Research, Bolzano, Italy; [2] Boquerel Institute Italy, Trento, Italy

4BO.17.6 PV-Planning and Simulation, Daylight Simulation and Energy-Certificate Calculation based on an Open-BIM-Building-Model 020255
Astrid Schneider[1], Karin Stieldorf[1], Christian Schranz[1], Harald Urban[1], Alfred Waschl[2], Markus Feichtner[3], Fedele Rende[4], Andrea Aiello[4], Martin Hauer[5], Kurt Battisti[6], Markus Dörn[6], Jacqueline Scherret[6], Martin Treberspurg[7], Christoph Treberspurg[7]
[1] TU Wien, Vienna, Austria; [2] buildingSMART, Vienna, Austria; [3] Sonnenkraft Energie, St. Veit/Glan, Austria; [4] ACCA Software, Cosenza, Italy; [5] Bartenbach, Vienna, Austria; [6] A-Null Development, Vienna, Austria; [7] Treberspurg und Partner Ziviltechniker, Vienna, Austria

Oral SESSION 4BO.5 PV-Products for Buildings

4BO.5.1 Fabrication of a Novel Semi-Translucent BIPV Module Providing High Power Density and Active Daylight Management 020257
Almudena Garcia-Sanchez[1], Guido Vallerotto[1], Jaime J. Hernández[2], Alejandro García-Cañas[2], Steve Askins[1], Ignacio Antón[1], Isabel Rodríguez[2], César Domínguez[1]
[1] UPM, Madrid, Spain; [2] IMDEA Nanoscience, Madrid, Spain

4BO.5.3 A Comparative Study of Photovoltaic Shading Devices for Net Zero Energy Buildings across French Climates 020259

Visual SESSION 4BV.4 BIPV

Oral SESSION 4CO.8 Soiling and Snow Effects in PV Systems

Oral SESSION 4CO.9 Data-driven and AI-based O&M of PV Systems

Visual SESSION 4CV.1 Advances in Operation, Performance and Maintenance of PV Systems

Oral SESSION 4DO.1 PV Tracking and Simulation

Oral SESSION 4DO.10 PV O&M Insights, Direct Uses of PV Electricity and Batteries

Oral SESSION 4DO.17 Advanced Inspections and Robotic Solutions for PV O&M

4DO.5.4 Development and Evaluation of Agrivoltaic System in Olive Groves based on a Novel Smart Tracking Algorithm 020392
Ildefonso Muñoz[1], Irati Amatriain[1], Gregorio Olivares[1], Gillen Abrego[2], Eusebio Gainza[2], Iñaki Cornago[1]
[1] CENER, Sarriguren, Spain; [2] ALLOTARRA, Allo, Spain

4DO.5.5 Adoption and Optimisation Analysis of Agrivoltaic Systems for Horticultural Production and Energy Autonomy in Lubumbashi/DR Congo 020393
Eddie Bilitu[1], Shu-Ngwa Asaa[2], Sara Bouguerra[3], Nikoleta Kyranaki[3], Ismail Kaaya[3], Yannick Useni[4], Michael Daenen[3]
[1] Hasselt University, Hasselt, Belgium; [2] imo-imomec, Genk, Belgium; [3] imec, Genk, Belgium; [4] University of Lubumbashi, Lubumbashi, Congo (DRC)

Visual SESSION 4DV.1 Agrivoltaics Approaches, Experiences, Results | Integrated and Innovative PV Applications

4DV.1.5 Maximizing Economic Performance of Agrivoltaic Systems through Module Array Design 020394
Habeel Alam[1], Jenny Nelson[2], Alona Armstrong[1], Duncan Whyatt[1], Nauman Butt[3]
[1] Lancaster University, Lancaster, United Kingdom; [2] Imperial College London, London, United Kingdom; [3] Lahore University of Management Sciences, Lahore, Pakistan

4DV.1.7 Bifacial and Mismatch Factors of Agri-Photovoltaics Systems 020396
Keith R. McIntosh[1], Solomon Freer[1], Bastien J. J. Ardissone[1], S. Ramirez[1], Ben A. Sudbury[1], Malcolm D. Abbott[1]
[1] PV Lighthouse, Coledale, Australia

4DV.1.10 Performance Analysis of Agrivoltaic System Configurations in Nordic Conditions 020398
Magda Szarek[1], Sami Jouttijärvi[1], Lauri Karttunen[1], Samuli Ranta[2], Kati Miettunen[1]
[1] University of Turku, Turku, Finland; [2] TUAS, Turku, Finland

4DV.1.11 Irradiance Management in Agrivoltaic Systems with Varying Designs Across Latitudes: Toward Finland's First Significant Demonstration 020400
Shuo Wang[1], Soroush Moradi Zavie Kord[2], Hugo E. Huerta[1], Antti Lajunen[2], Samuli Ranta[1]
[1] TUAS, Turku, Finland; [2] University of Helsinki, Helsinki, Finland

4DV.1.12 An Innovative Agrivoltaic System for Desert Climates with Anti-Soiling, Irradiance Control, and Water Management 020402
Sagarika Kumar[1], Min Hsian Saw[1], Ahmed Shaaban[1], Kamil Jaworczak[1], Nursulu Kuzhagaliyeva[1], Carlos G. Parrilla[2], Francois M. Tsombou[2], Fouad Lamghari[2], Mauro Pravettoni[1]
[1] Technology Innovation Institute, Abu Dhabi, United Arab Emirates; [2] Fujairah Research Centre, Fujairah, United Arab Emirates

4DV.1.15 Review of Sensor Technologies for Monitoring Agrivoltaic Systems 020403
Sara Pereira[1], José A. Silva[1], Luís Fialho[2], Pedro Horta[1]
[1] University of Évora, Évora, Portugal; [2] Eurac Research, Bolzano, Italy

Visual SESSION 4DV.4 PV System Engineering

Oral SESSION 4EO.2 Vehicle Integrated PV

[1] Luxembourg Institute of Science and Technology, Esch-sur-Alzette, Luxembourg; [2] University of Lisbon, Lisbon, Portugal

4EO.2.6 Optimizing Angular Performance of Curved VIPV Modules 020459

Francisco José Martín[1], Rebeca Herrero[1], Ignacio Antón[1]
[1] UPM, Madrid, Spain

Oral SESSION 5CO.4 Life Cycle Assessment of Silicon and Perovskite-based Cells and Modules

5CO.4.1 Towards Low-Impact Triple-Junction Perovskite/Silicon Tandem Modules: LCA of Precursor Materials to Describe the Influence of Background Data Sources 020461

Alejandra Galarza[1], Sebastian Nold[2], Lars Oberbeck[3]
[1] IPVF, Palaiseau, France; [2] Fraunhofer ISE, Freiburg, Germany; [3] TotalEnergies OneTech, Paris, France

5CO.4.3 Sustainability Assessment of Perovskite/Silicon Tandem Solar Modules: from Laboratory Scale to Industrial Implementation 020462

Elisabetta Brivio[1], Andrea Danelli[1], Sofia Spagnolo[1], Pierpaolo Girardi[1]
[1] RSE, Milan, Italy

5CO.4.4 LCA Learning Curve for Crystalline Silicon Solar Technologies based on Technology Improvements 020463

Julian Reichle[1], Moritz Fath[1], Sraisth[1], Amish Kumar Sinha[1], Mehul Raval[1], Wolfgang Jooss[1], Peter Fath[1], Gourab Das[1]
[1] RCT Solutions, Konstanz, Germany

Oral SESSION 5CO.5 Life Cycle Assessment of New PV Applications and Recycling

5CO.5.1 Optimizing AgriPV: A Comprehensive Assessment Framework for Sustainable Energy and Agriculture 020464

Ana Patrícia Lopes[1], Bruno Barrionuevo [2], Daniel P. Albuquerque[3], Diogo Cordeiro[4], Cláudia Fernandes[3], Athanasios T. Balafoutis [2], Rui Castro[1]
[1] University of Lisbon, Lisbon, Portugal; [2] CERTH, Athens, Greece; [3] Centre for New Energy Technologies, Sacavém, Portugal; [4] EDP, Lisbon, Portugal

5CO.5.2 Environmental Sustainability Assessment of Agrivoltaic Systems: a Life Cycle Approach 020466

Maria Anna Cusenza[1], Andrea Danelli[1], Pierpaolo Girardi[1], Sofia Spagnolo[1]
[1] RSE, Milan, Italy

5CO.5.4 Closing the Circle: Integrating the Circular Footprint Formula into Photovoltaic System Life Cycle Assessment 020467

Alexis Barrou[1], Selin Kandiyoti-Eskenazi[1], Jacques Levrat[1], Bertrand Paviet-Salomon[1], Christophe Ballif[1]
[1] CSEM, Neuchâtel, Switzerland

5CO.5.6 Environmental Benefits of Silicon Kerf Secondary Products in Pilot Processes over Conventional Production of Equivalent Products with Primary Raw Materials in China and Europe 020468
René Peche[1], Matthias Seitz[1], Markus Schönheits[1], Karsten Wambach[1]
[1] bifa Umweltinstitut, Augsburg, Germany

Oral SESSION 5CO.6 PV Recycling and Circularity

5CO.6.4 Quantification of Technical Recyclability of PV Modules for Different Recycling Scenarios 020470
Matthias Hämmer[1], Kerstin Baumann[1], Karsten Wambach[1], Markus Schönheits[1]
[1] bifa Umweltinstitut, Augsburg, Germany

5CO.6.5 IEC Technical Report 63525 on the Reuse of PV Modules: Final Result 020472
Arvid van der Heide[1], Serge Noels[2], Jan Clyncke[2], Rich Strömberg[3]
[1] imec, Genk, Belgium; [2] PV CYCLE, Brussels, Belgium; [3] University of Alaska, Fairbanks, United States of America

Plenary SESSION 5CP.1 Si PV Manufacturing: Pushing the Limits of Performance

5CP.1.4 Business Model Optimization for European Solar PV: A Study on Costs and Commercial Strategies 020474
Ian Kenchington[1], Philippe Macé[1], Gaëtan Masson[1], Joris Libal[2]
[1] Becquerel Institute, Brussels, Belgium; [2] ISC Konstanz, Konstanz, Germany

Plenary SESSION 5CP.2 Perovskite – Silicon Tandems: Towards Commercialisation | PV Stability in the Field

5CP.2.3 Total Cost of Ownership, LCA and LCOE Analysis of Perovskite-Silicon Tandems Compared to Single Junction Crystalline Silicon PV Technologies 020475
Baljeet Singh Goraya[1], Dilara Maria Subasi[1], Peter Henri Brailovsky[1], Henning Nagel[1], Patricia S.C. Schulze[1], Martin C. Schubert[1], Jochen Rentsch[1], Martin Hermle[1], Ralf Preu[1], Sebastian Nold[1]
[1] Fraunhofer ISE, Freiburg, Germany

Oral SESSION 5DO.11 The Road to Massive PV Deployment

5DO.11.1 Integration of Solar PV in a Norwegian Energy System, Navigating the Trade-offs between Land Use and Solar Power Production 020476
Petry Kristine Nøttum Haaland[1], Ole-Morten Midtgård[1], Magnus Korpås[1]
[1] NTNU, Trondheim, Norway

Oral SESSION 5DO.18 PV Recycling and Material Demand

Visual SESSION 5DV.2 Life Cycle Analysis and PV Recycling | Citizens Participation and Awareness

Visual SESSION 5DV.3 Grid Integration and Flexibility Enablers | Global, Country- and Application-Specific Analysis of PV Deployment Aspects | Costs, Economics, Finance and Markets

Oral SESSION 5EO.1 Citizens Participation and Awareness

42nd European Photovoltaic Solar Energy Conference and Exhibition

This presentation was selected by the Sc. Committee of the EU PVSEC 2025 for submission of a full paper to one of the EU PVSEC's collaborating peer-reviewed journals.

EFFECT OF GLASS BEADS ON THE SOLAR OPTICAL PROPERTIES OF THERMOPLASTIC ENCAPSULANTS FOR COLORED PV MODULES

Martin Huemer[1,3], Gernot M. Wallner[1,2], Andreas Brandstätter[3]
[1]Institute of Polymeric Materials and Testing, University of Linz, Austria
martin.huemer@jku.at
[2]Christian Doppler Laboratory for Superimposed Mechanical-Environmental Ageing of Polymeric Hybrid Laminates, Institute of Polymeric Materials and Testing, University of Linz, Austria
gernot.wallner@jku.at
[3]Lenzing Plastics GmbH, Werkstrasse 2, 4860 Lenzing, Austria
a.brandstaetter@lenzing-plastics.com

ABSTRACT: A promising approach for producing colored photovoltaic (PV) modules is the incorporation of interference pigments into the front encapsulant. Besides several advantages such as spectrally selective reflection, higher efficiency or better durability, the main disadvantage of interference pigments are variations in specular reflectance depending on the angle [1]. The main objective of this work was to evaluate the potential of glass beads as diffusor pigments in colored PV encapsulants. Films varying in type (refractive index and particle size) and concentration of the glass beads were manufactured. Furthermore, films with a combination of glass fillers and interference pigments were analysed. Fourteen film grades were assessed by UV/Vis/NIR spectroscopy. The reflectance of the glass bead modified encapsulants was dependent on the refractive index and the particle size. The smallest beads with the highest reflectance index were not suitable. The transmittance of the film was below 80 %. However, the other glass grades were classified as an interesting option for homogenization fillers for colored PV encapsulants.
Keywords: Encapsulation, glass beads, spectroscopy

1 INTRODUCTION

Significant efforts have been devoted to the research of Building Integrated Photovoltaic (BIPV) systems and more aesthetically pleasing PV modules. Thereby, colored modules have to fulfil high optical requirements. To mitigate the often negatively perceived angular dependency of structural colors like interference pigments, light must be scattered. This can either be done by a rough surface of the front sheet or by directly incorporating scattering agents in the front encapsulant. While so far mainly $BaSO_4$ was used, in this study for the first time the potential of glass beads varying in particle size, index of refraction and content is assessed systematically.

2 EXPERIMENTAL

Forteen films made from a non-crosslinked thermoplastic polyolefin (TPO) were manufactured by Lenzing Plastics GmbH (Austria). The encapsulants differed in the concentration (low or high) and type of the glass beads (refractive index and particle size). Four films were equipped with both, glass beads and interference pigments. As references, a non-pigmented transparent and a blue-pigmented encapsulant film without glass beads were examined. The films were characterized by UV/Vis/NIR-spectroscopy in the range from 250 to 2500 nm in 5 nm steps on a Lambda 950 UV/Vis/NIR spectrometer (PerkinElmer, USA) equipped with a 150 mm integrating sphere. Hemispheric (T_h) and diffuse transmittance (T_d) as well as hemispheric reflectance (R_h) spectra were recorded. The spectral data were weighted with a reference air mass spectrum (AM1.5) source function and integrated over the solar range from 300 to 1250 nm according to equations (1)-(3), where "λ" is the wavelength. Hemispheric ($T_{h,sol}$) and diffuse solar transmittance ($T_{d,sol}$) and hemispheric solar reflectance ($R_{h,sol}$) values were deduced [2, 3]. Moreover, hemispheric solar absorbance ($A_{h,sol}$) and the solar haze were calculated with equations (4) and (5). To evaluate the expected relative efficiency (η_{rel}) of the PV modules, the hemispheric transmittance data was weighted with an AM1.5 source function and a spectral response function for a typical monocrystalline silicon cell (SR) (see equation (6)). The obtained values ($T^{mSi}_{h,sol}(i)$) were then normalized with equation (7) to those of the non-pigmented, transparent film ($T^{mSi}_{h,sol}(Tr)$).

$$T_{h,sol} = \frac{\int_{300}^{1250} (T_h)_\lambda (AM_{1.5})_\lambda d\lambda}{\int_{300}^{1250} (AM_{1.5})_\lambda d\lambda} \quad (1)$$

$$T_{d,sol} = \frac{\int_{300}^{1250} (T_d)_\lambda (AM_{1.5})_\lambda d\lambda}{\int_{300}^{1250} (AM_{1.5})_\lambda d\lambda} \quad (2)$$

$$R_{h,sol} = \frac{\int_{300}^{1250} (R_h)_\lambda (AM_{1.5})_\lambda d\lambda}{\int_{300}^{1250} (AM_{1.5})_\lambda d\lambda} \quad (3)$$

$$A_{h,sol} = 100 - T_{h,sol} - R_{h,sol} \quad (4)$$

$$Haze = \frac{T_{d,sol}}{T_{h,sol}} \times 100 \quad (5)$$

$$T^{mSi}_{h,sol} = \frac{\int_{300}^{1250} (T_h)_\lambda (AM_{1.5})_\lambda SR_\lambda d\lambda}{\int_{300}^{1250} (AM_{1.5})_\lambda SR_\lambda d\lambda} \quad (6)$$

$$\eta_{rel}(i) = \frac{T^{mSi}_{h,sol}(i)}{T^{mSi}_{h,sol}(Tr)} \times 100 \quad (7)$$

3 RESULTS

The solar transmittance and reflectance spectra of the encapsulants filled with different glass beads are illustrated in Fig. 1 to Fig. 4. Furthermore, the calculated solar weighted properties as well as the expected relative efficiency of the films are listed in Table I and Table II. The first number of the diffusor pigment type refers to the refractive index (n) and the second to the average bead size. Encapsulants equipped with glass beads of high refractive index (n=2.15) revealed a significant higher hemispheric reflectance and lower hemispheric transmittance. Smaller particles with an average size of 2.2 µm increased the hemispherical reflection by a factor of 2 compared to a particle size of 7.6 µm. This is in good agreement with the Mie theory [4]. Due to the high reflectance and consequently lower transmittance, the glass beads G 2.25 – 2.2 are not reasonable for efficient PV modules. The relative efficiency dropped to 60 %. The films with the lower refractive index glass beads (n=1.5) did not differ in their optical properties. For both particle sizes the hemispheric reflectance and the diffuse transmittance were higher maintaining also a high hemispheric transmittance. Consequently, the haze of these films was noticeably increasing, probably leading to a reduction of the angular dependency of color perception of interference pigmented encapsulants. The hemispheric absorbance was not affected. Deviations by 1 to 2 % were primarily related to scattering losses at the edge of the film samples.

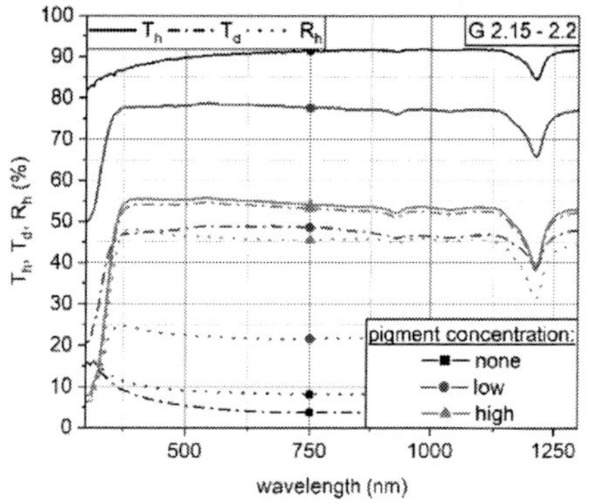

Figure 1: Hemispheric transmittance (T_h) and reflectance (R_h) and diffuse transmittance (T_d) spectra of the encapsulants filled with glass beads with a refractive index of 2.15 and a bead size of 2.2 µm.

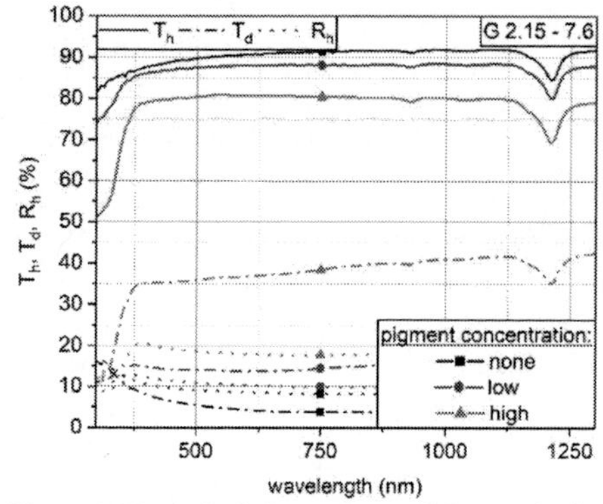

Figure 2: Hemispheric transmittance (T_h) and reflectance (R_h) and diffuse transmittance (T_d) spectra of the encapsulants filled with glass beads with a refractive index of 2.15 and a bead size of 7.6 µm.

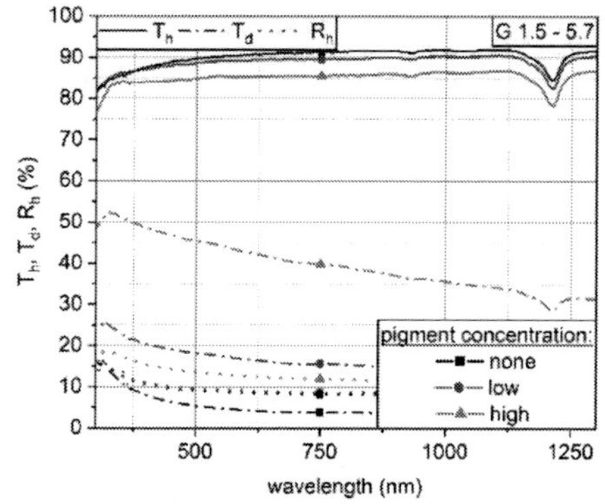

Figure 3: Hemispheric transmittance (T_h) and reflectance (R_h) and diffuse transmittance (T_d) spectra of the encapsulants filled with glass beads with a refractive index of 1.5 and a bead size of 5.7 µm.

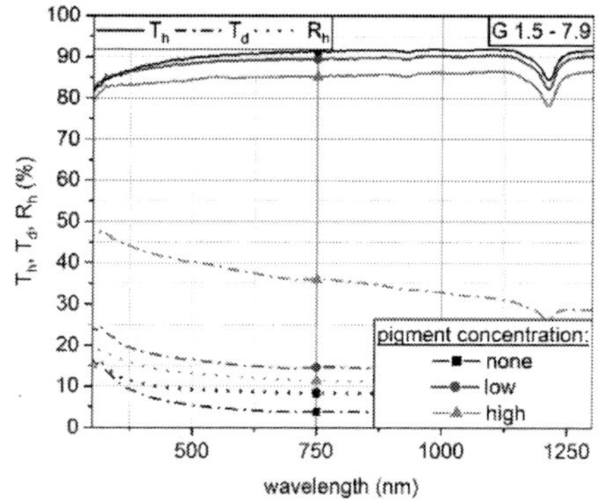

Figure 4: Hemispheric transmittance (T_h) and reflectance (R_h) and diffuse transmittance (T_d) spectra of the encapsulants filled with glass beads with a refractive index of 1.5 and a bead size of 7.9 µm.

In Fig. 5 the solar transmittance and reflectance spectra of the encapsulants containing various glass beads and the blue interference pigments are depicted. The same order of drop in transmittance and rise in reflectance as described

10.4229/EUPVSEC2025/3DO.12.5

above was found. Hence, it is not only possible to adjust the haze of the encapsulants but also the intensity of color perception. The reflectance spectra reveal a more pronounced shift to higher values especially at the lower, blueish wavelengths. For example, the embedding of G 1.5 – 5.7 led to a 4 % rise in reflectance at a wavelength of 600 nm, but a 13 % boost at 425 nm. Interestingly, the combination of the glass fillers with the interference pigments resulted in a minor increase of the absorbance. This slight delta may be a measuring artefact, as light is presumably scattered past the opening of the integrating sphere [5, 6]. The actual efficiency should be slightly higher than listed in Table II.

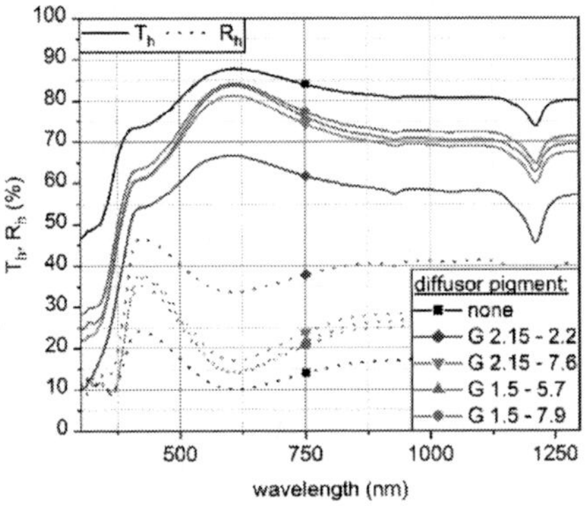

Figure 5: Hemispheric transmittance (T_h) and reflectance (R_h) spectra of the encapsulants filled with a blue interference pigment and different glass beads.

Table I: Solar weighted hemispheric transmittance and reflactance and diffuse transmittance of the investigated encapsulants.

diffuser pigment		blue pigment	$T_{h,sol}$	$T_{d,sol}$	$R_{h,sol}$
type	concentration		%	%	%
-	none	no	90	5	9
G 2.15 - 2.2	low	no	77	48	22
	high	no	54	53	45
G 2.15 - 7.6	low	no	87	15	10
	high	no	80	37	18
G 1.5 - 5.7	low	no	89	16	9
	high	no	85	41	13
G 1.5 - 7.9	low	no	89	15	9
	high	no	85	37	12
-	none	yes	81	21	15
G 2.15 - 2.2	medium	yes	59	53	38
G 2.15 - 7.6	medium	yes	71	40	25
G 1.5 - 5.7	medium	yes	74	40	22
G 1.5 - 7.9	medium	yes	72	40	23

Table II: Solar weighted hemispheric absorbance, solar haze and expected relative efficiency of the investigated encapsulants.

diffuser pigment		blue pigment	$A_{h,sol}$	Haze	η_{rel}
type	concentration		%	%	%
-	none	no	1	5	100
G 2.15 - 2.2	low	no	1	61	86
	high	no	1	98	60
G 2.15 - 7.6	low	no	2	17	97
	high	no	2	47	88
G 1.5 - 5.7	low	no	2	19	98
	high	no	2	48	94
G 1.5 - 7.9	low	no	2	17	98
	high	no	3	44	94
-	none	yes	3	26	91
G 2.15 - 2.2	medium	yes	3	90	67
G 2.15 7.6	medium	yes	4	56	80
G 1.5 - 5.7	medium	yes	4	54	83
G 1.5 - 7.9	medium	yes	5	55	82

4 CONCLUSIONS

The study revealed the possibility to manipulate the solar optical properties of encapsulants by incorporating glass fillers. While small glass beads with a high refractive index are not suitable for highly efficient PV modules, larger beads with a lower refractive index similar to the encapsulant material seem to be a reasonable approach. To assess the angular dependency of the encapsulants, color perception will be evaluated on double-glass module level. Furthermore, angle-dependent measurements will be conducted.

5 REFERENCES

[1] Perales E., Chorro E., Cramer W. R., Martinez-Verdú F. M., "Analysis of the colorimetric properties of goniochromatic colors using the MacAdam limits under different light sources," Appl. Opt., no. 50, pp. 5271–5278.

[2] Wallner, G. M., Platzer, W., and Lang, R. W., "Structure–property correlations of polymeric films for transparent insulation wall applications. Part 1: Solar

optical properties," Solar Energy, vol. 79, no. 6, pp. 583–592, 2005.
[3] R. E. Bird, R. L. Hulstrom, "Terrestrial solar spectral data sets," Sol. Energy 30, vol. 1983, pp. 563–573.
[4] Mie, G., "Beiträge zur Optik trüber Medien, speziell kolloidaler Metallösungen," Annalen der Physik, vol. 330, no. 3, pp. 377–445, 1908.
[5] D.I. Milburn and K.G.T. Hollands, "An analysis of thick-sample effects in the measurement of directional-hemispherical transmittance," Optics Communications, no. 118, pp. 1–8, 1995.
[6] Neugebauer, J., Wallner-Novak, M., Lehner, T., Wrulich, C., and Baumgartner, M., "Movable Thin Glass Elements in Façades," 195-202 Pages / Challenging Glass Conference Proceedings, Vol. 6 (2018): Challenging Glass 6, 2018.

Energieforschung
8. Ausschreibung

Lenzing Plastics

solpol

EFFECT OF GLASS BEADS ON THE SOLAR OPTICAL PROPERTIES OF THERMOPLASTIC ENCAPSULANTS FOR COLORED PV MODULES

MARTIN HUEMER[1,3], GERNOT M. WALLNER[1,2], ANDREAS BRANDSTÄTTER[3]

[1]INSTITUTE OF POLYMERIC MATERIALS AND TESTING, UNIVERSITY OF LINZ, AUSTRIA

[2]CHRISTIAN DOPPLER LABORATORY FOR SUPERIMPOSED MECHANICAL-ENVIRONMENTAL AGEING OF POLYMERIC HYBRID LAMINATES, INSTITUTE OF POLYMERIC MATERIALS AND TESTING, UNIVERSITY OF LINZ, AUSTRIA

[3]LENZING PLASTICS GMBH, WERKSTRASSE 2, 4860 LENZING, AUSTRIA

EU PVSEC 2025
Bilbao, 25th of September 2025

FFG
Forschung wirkt.

INTRODUCTION: CONCEPT FOR COLORED PHOTOVOLTAICS

- Interference-pigmented thermoplastic polyolefin (TPO)
  - Terpolymer:
    - ~ 89.5 mol% ethylene
    - ~ 10 mol% acrylate
    - ~ 0.5% silane

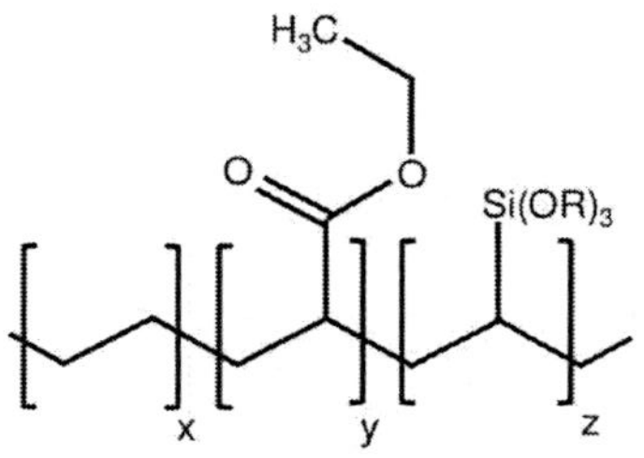

  - Additives:
    - Interference pigments
    - Diffusor pigment
    - Carbon Black
    - UV stabilizer

Functional principle

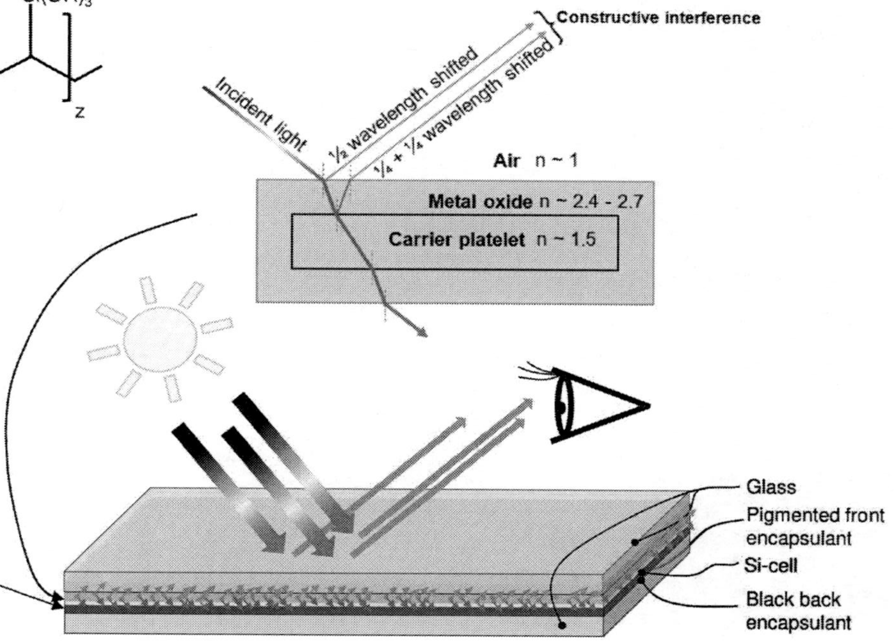

EXPERIMENTAL | INVESTIGATED ENCAPSULANTS

- 14 TPO encapsulants (450 µm) manufactured at Lenzing Plastics

diffuser pigment			blue interference pigment
refractive index	average size in µm	concentration	
-	-	-	no
2.15	2.2	low	no
2.15	2.2	high	no
2.15	7.6	low	no
2.15	7.6	high	no
1.5	5.7	low	no
1.5	5.7	high	no
1.5	7.9	low	no
1.5	7.9	high	no
-	-	-	yes
2.15	2.2	medium	yes
2.15	7.6	medium	yes
1.5	5.7	medium	yes
1.5	7.9	medium	yes

Photographic images of 450 µm x 25 mm x 25 mm films in front of a chessboard.

EXPERIMENTAL | METHODS AND CALCULATIONS

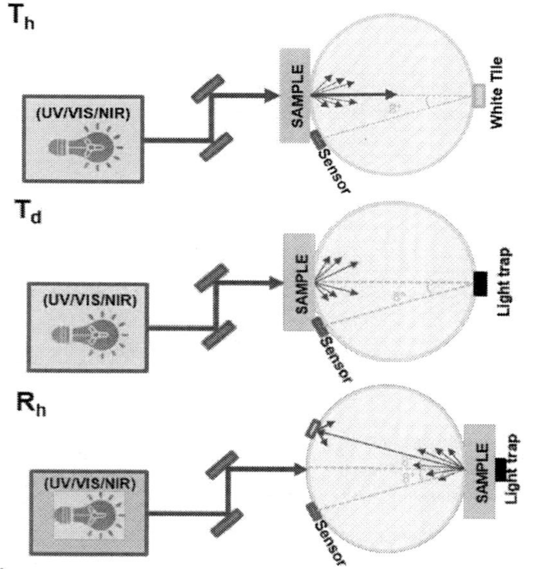

$$T_{h,sol} = \frac{\int_{300}^{1250} (T_h)_\lambda (AM_{1.5})_\lambda d\lambda}{\int_{300}^{1250} (AM_{1.5})_\lambda d\lambda}$$

$$T_{d,sol} = \frac{\int_{300}^{1250} (T_d)_\lambda (AM_{1.5})_\lambda d\lambda}{\int_{300}^{1250} (AM_{1.5})_\lambda d\lambda}$$

$$R_{h,sol} = \frac{\int_{300}^{1250} (R_h)_\lambda (AM_{1.5})_\lambda d\lambda}{\int_{300}^{1250} (AM_{1.5})_\lambda d\lambda}$$

$$A_{h,sol} = 100 - T_{h,sol} - R_{h,sol}$$

$$Haze = \frac{T_{d,sol}}{T_{h,sol}} \times 100$$

$$T_{h,sol}^{mSi} = \frac{\int_{300}^{1250} (T_h)_\lambda (AM_{1.5})_\lambda SR\lambda \, d\lambda}{\int_{300}^{1250} (AM_{1.5})_\lambda SR\lambda \, d\lambda}$$

$$\eta_{rel}(i) = \frac{T_{h,sol}^{mSi}(i)}{T_{h,sol}^{mSi}(Tr)} \times 100$$

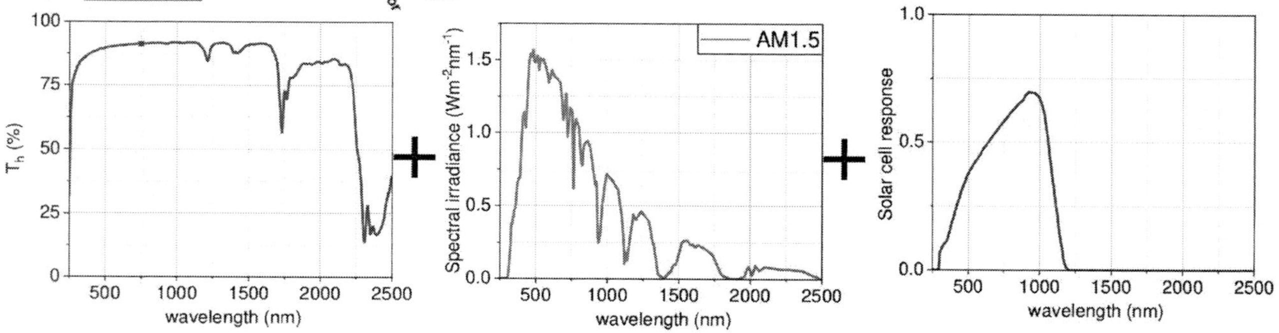

RESULTS | MICROSCOPIC IMAGES

G 2.15 - 2.2 G 2.15 – 7.6 G 1.5 – 5.7 G 1.5 – 7.9

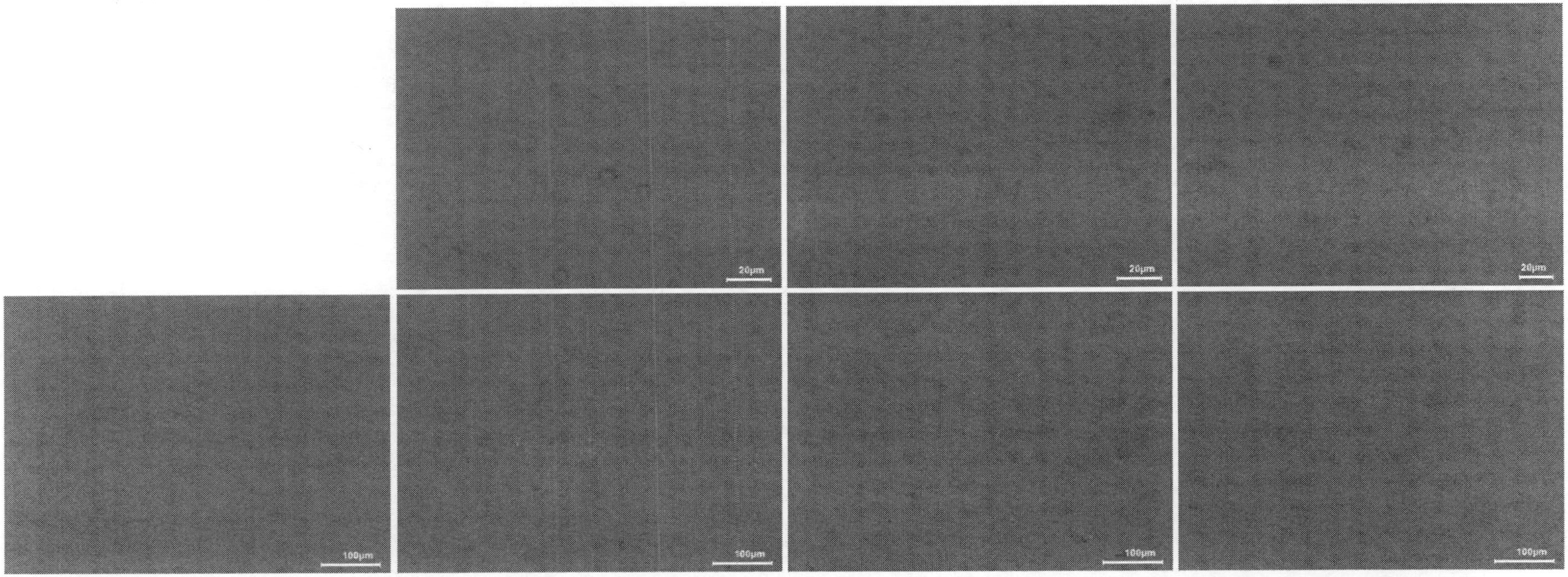

Microscopic images of the TPO encapsulants; upper row: high concentration of glass beads and no interference pigments; lower row: medium concentration of glass beads and blue interference pigments.

RESULTS | SOLAR OPTICAL PROPERTIES

Lenzing Plastics solpol

REFRACTIVE INDEX 2.15

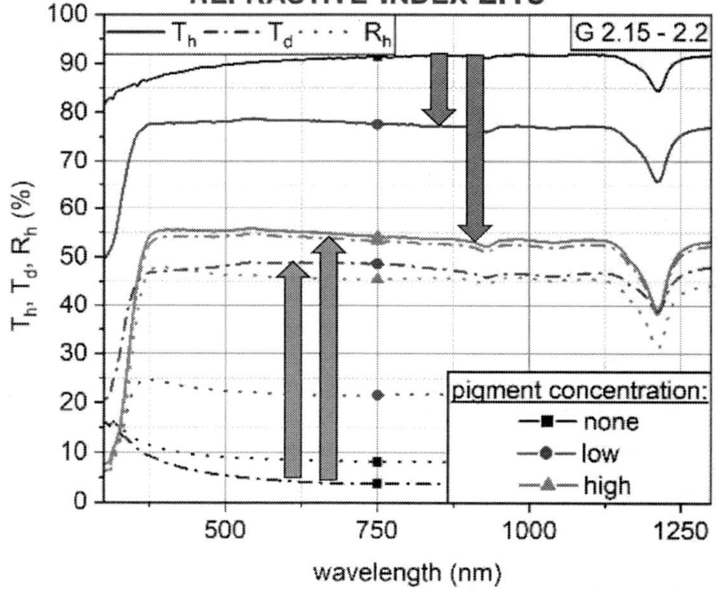

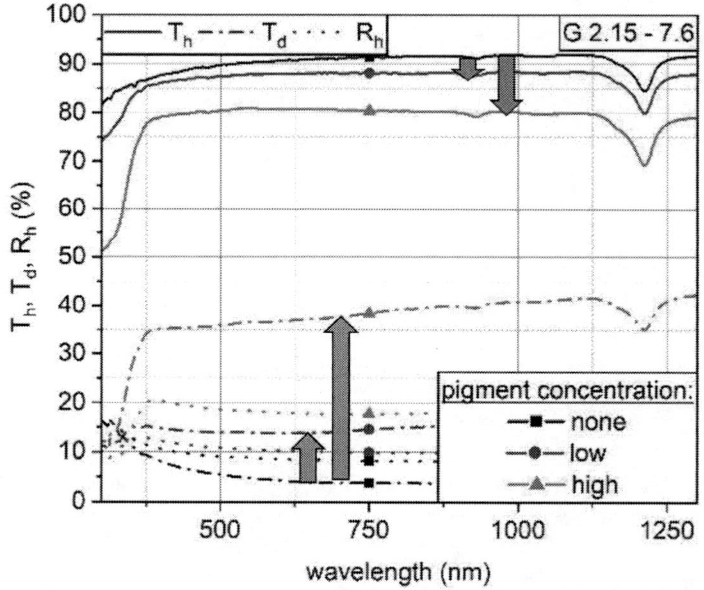

— Increased reflectance and diffuse transmittance

— Huge loss in hemispheric transmittance and estimated efficiency

$\Delta T_{h,sol}$	$\Delta T_{d,sol}$	$\Delta R_{h,sol}$	$\Delta A_{h,sol}$	$\Delta Haze$	η_{rel}
-13	+43	+13	0	+56	86
-36	+48	+36	0	+93	60

— Less Increased reflectance and diffuse transmittance

— Lower loss in hemispheric transmittance

$\Delta T_{h,sol}$	$\Delta T_{d,sol}$	$\Delta R_{h,sol}$	$\Delta A_{h,sol}$	$\Delta Haze$	η_{rel}
-3	+10	+1	+1	+12	97
-10	+32	+9	+1	+42	88

RESULTS | SOLAR OPTICAL PROPERTIES

REFRACTIVE INDEX 1.5

Lenzing Plastics solpol

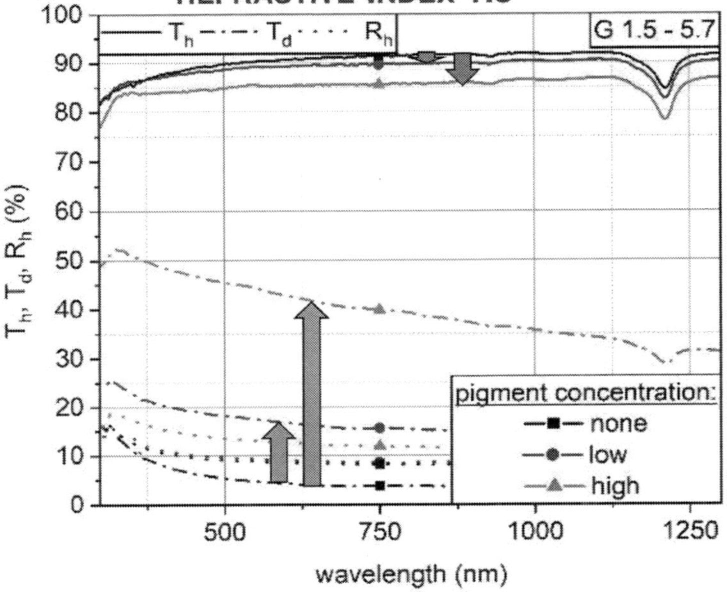

— Increased diffuse transmittance

— Almost no loss in hemispheric transmittance and estimated efficiency

$\Delta T_{h,sol}$	$\Delta T_{d,sol}$	$\Delta R_{h,sol}$	$\Delta A_{h,sol}$	ΔHaze	η_{rel}
-1	+11	0	+1	+14	98
-4	+36	+4	+1	+44	94

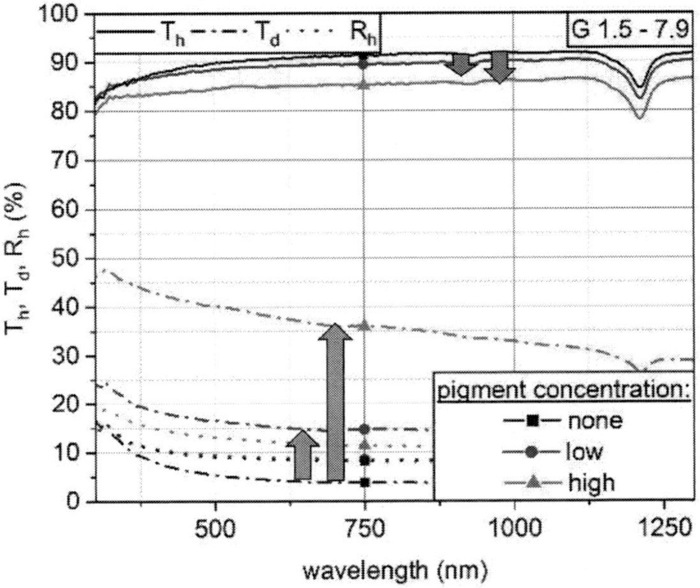

— Increased diffuse transmittance

— Almost no loss in hemispheric transmittance and estimated efficiency

$\Delta T_{h,sol}$	$\Delta T_{d,sol}$	$\Delta R_{h,sol}$	$\Delta A_{h,sol}$	ΔHaze	η_{rel}
-1	+10	0	+1	+12	98
-4	+32	+3	+2	+39	94

25.0

Results | Solar Optical Properties

Interaction of Diffuser and Interference Pigment

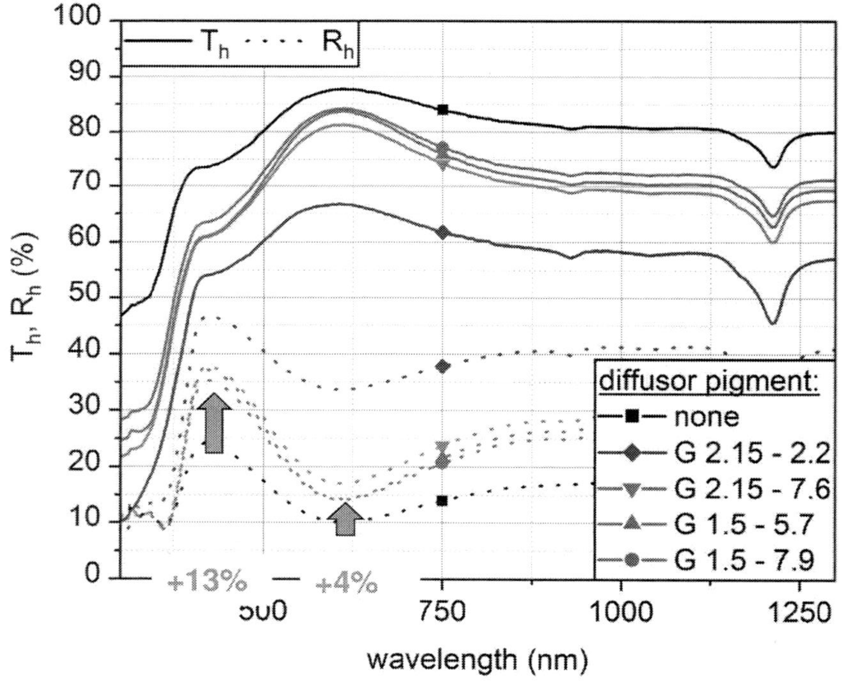

	$\Delta T_{h,sol}$	$\Delta T_{d,sol}$	$\Delta R_{h,sol}$	$\Delta A_{h,sol}$	ΔHaze	η_{rel}
G 2.15 – 2.2	-22	+32	+23	0	+64	67
G 2.15 – 7.6	-10	+19	+10	+1	+30	80
G 1.5 – 5.7	-7	+19	+7	+1	+28	83
G 1.5 – 7.9	-9	+19	+8	+2	+32	82

— More pronounced shift of the reflectance at lower blueish wavelengths

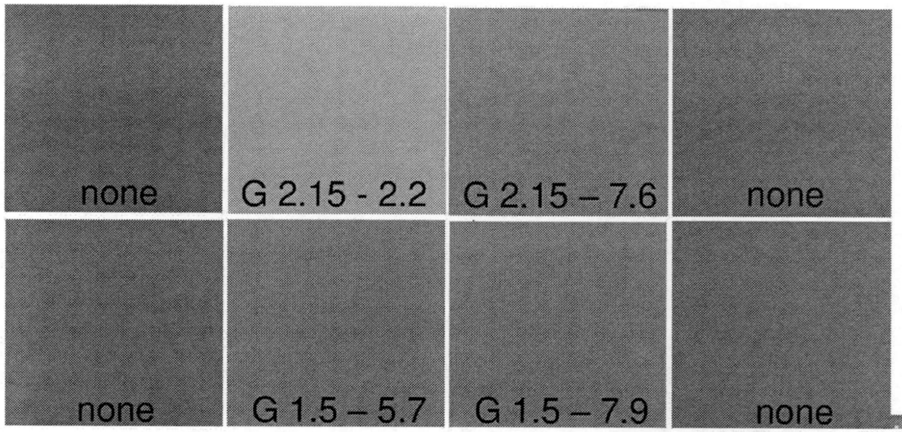

Photographic images of 100 mm x 100 mm double glass laminates with a black back encapsulant and a blue front encapsulant with and without different glass beads.

Conclusion and Outlook

Conclusion

- All investigated glass beads are increasing

  diffuse transmittance and haze
- Smaller particles result in pronounced increase in diffuse transmittance
- Higher refractive index leads to increased hemispheric reflectance

Questions

- martin.huemer@jku.at
- https://colorquant.lenzing-plastics.com/

Outlook

- Angle-dependent color measurements
- Evaluating further diffusor pigments (chemistry, shape, size, refractive index, …)
- Producing multi-layered encapsulants
- Ageing stability
- Adherence testing:

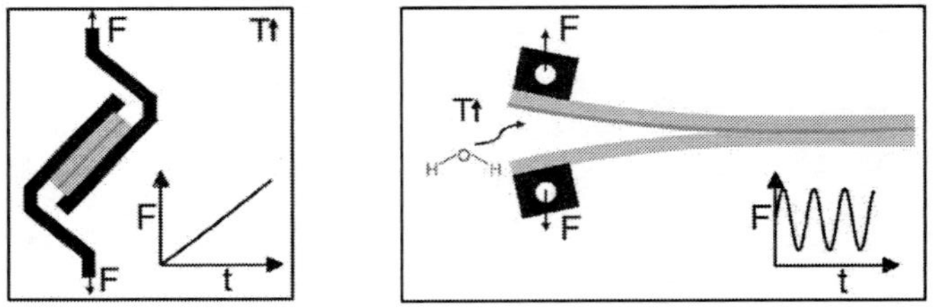

- Further applications (Agri-PV?)

TOPCON PV Modules UV exposure: Uncovering Hidden Instabilities

Baloji Adothu[1,*], Shahzada Pamir Aly[1], Bengt Jaeckel[2], Matthias Pandar[2], Ralph Gottschalg[2], and Vivian Alberts[1]

[1]Research and Development Center, Dubai Electricity and Water Authority, Dubai, UAE.
[2]Fraunhofer Center for Silicon Photovoltaics CSP, Otto-Eissfeldt-Str. 12, 06120 Halle (Saale), Germany.

* Corresponding author: Phone +971 522 578980 | baloji.adothu@dewa.gov.ae

Abstract— **The rapid expansion of GW-scale photovoltaic installations in desert environments is shifting the spotlight to the stability of new-generation PV module technologies under harsh conditions. High UV irradiance, a characteristic challenge of desert regions, has raised concerns about the long-term performance of emerging technologies, particularly the TOPCon PV modules, which technology is currently gaining rapidly increasing market share in the PV industry. In a collaborative study with leading solar institutes, TOPCON modules from different manufacturers were subjected to accelerated UV exposure at elevated temperatures to detect potentially hidden degradation pathways.**

The results from our preliminary studies demonstrated a notable power degradation in 3 out of 5 TOPCon modules tested compared to PERC modules. In terms of the specific batches of PV modules considered, the three TOPCon modules that showed abnormal degradation exhibited power losses of around 8% after a UV dose exposure of 90 kWh/m². PERC modules exhibited lower values around 2% degradation (based on the UV aging study conducted at DEWA R&D). When UV exposure was combined with dark storage, the power degradation in the affected TOPCon modules increased significantly, reaching 13% to 16.5% (as observed in the UV aging study at F-CSP). Significant changes in the electrical parameters of the modules were observed after the UV exposure. However, light soaking was found to stabilize the performance of TOPCon modules after periods of dark storage. The combined impact of UV aging, dark storage, and light soaking revealed significant changes in the stability of TOPCon PV modules.

Electroluminescence (EL) imaging detected the formation of a distinct checkered pattern in some of the TOPCon modules, accompanied by intense UV fluorescence (UVF) at cell edges and along multi-busbar soldering points. Interestingly, these specific structural changes were not observed in the PERC modules, underscoring their stability after high-dose UV exposure. These findings highlight critical challenges and uncover the hidden instability of TOPCon, emphasizing the need for further interlaboratory testing and reliability studies to mitigate possible unknown degradation risks in high-UV environments.

Keywords— TOPCON PV Modules, PERC PV Modules, UV Exposure, UV instability, Performance

I. Introduction

The deployment of photovoltaic (PV) modules in desert regions has gained significant traction due to favorable environmental factors such as high solar irradiance, extended daylight hours, and generally clear skies. However, these regions also present extreme challenges to PV module performance and reliability due to harsh environmental conditions, including intense ultraviolet (UV) radiation, extreme temperatures, large temperature fluctuations, and the persistent accumulation of dust and soiling [1]. Despite technological advancements, the long-term impact of these conditions on module degradation and performance remains a concern and uncertain.

As the global PV market expands, new-generation PV technologies such as TOPCon (Tunnel Oxide Passivated Contact) modules have emerged as key players in PV industry. TOPCon technology uses an ultrathin tunnel oxide layer (1.2–1.5 nm) with poly-Si passivation to minimize recombination losses at the semiconductor/metal interfaces, while enhancing the electric field distribution in the depletion region. The combination of these effects leads to higher power conversion efficiency (PCE). Since 2022, this technologyhas emerged as a potential mainstream successor to PERC, offering efficiencies of 22–24% (with lab records above 26%), compared to PERC's 20–22% (lab record ~24%) [1–5]

The rapid expansion of gigawatt-scale solar farms has emphasized the importance of new advanced technologies with improved PCE and long-term stability.TOPCon currently shows real potential due to its promising efficiency gains over the previous mainstream technologies, like PERC (Passivated Emitter and Rear Cell) modules [1–5]While TOPCon provides better thermal and LeTID stability than PERC, UV stability may pose a significant challenge due to the sensitive nature of the tunnel oxide. Proposed degradation mechanisms include tunnel oxide and poly-Si passivation loss as well as hydrogen-related instabilities, making this an active area of research.

Desert environments are known to accelerate PV module degradation processes, with UV-induced degradation (UVID) being a dominant factor. This degradation primarily affects critical components such as encapsulants, backsheets, and interface and cell surface layers, leading to efficiency losses and shorter module deployment lifetimes [6–8]. Failure Mode and Effects Analysis (FMEA) conducted on desert-installed PV systems confirms that UVID poses a major reliability risk, particularly for evolving technologies like TOPCon, where stability under extreme UV exposure is not fully understood [9–11].

Compared to PERC modules, which are well understood, the unique design and materials of TOPCon cells and modules present the possibility of new degradation pathways that could compromise their long-term reliability in deserts. Laboratory observations reveal that while the degradation mechanisms in PERC modules are understood and predictable, the performance and reliability of TOPCon remain uncertain in the absence of long-term outdoor field studies. This is especially concerning, considering that TopCon modules have already been deployed at GW-scale in residential, commercial, and especially utility-scale projects.

This research investigates the degradation behavior and stability of TOPCON PV modules under accelerated UV exposure, incorporating the effects of dark storage and light soaking on their performance, considering a limited number of modules from various Tier 1 manufacturers. This study emphasizes the need for further interlaboratory and outdoor reliability studies to mitigate possible unknown or hidden degradation risks. A comprehensive understanding of the potential formation of unidentified early-stage and/or new classes of degradation mechanisms that may compromise the stability of TOPCON modules is essential for both the manufacturer and end users. By comparing the performance of TOPCON and PERC modules, the study aims to identify possible unknown degradation mechanisms that accelerate the degradation of TopCon modules in harsh desert climates.

II. METHODOLOGY

PV module selection: Batches of commercially available PERC and five TOPCON PV modules from a Tier 1 company were selected for this study. TOPCon and PERC are both types of modules that have undergone accelerated UV testing to compare their performance characteristics and degradation rates. TOPCon-PV1 and TOPCon-PV2 were utilised for continuous UV exposure test, while TOPCon-PV3, TOPCon-PV4, and TOPCon-PV5 were utilized for the UV test, followed by dark storage and light soaking process for studying their instabilities.

The study involves the collaborative studies of solar PV experts and leading research institutes to improve our understanding of potentially new or unknown degradation mechanisms in new generation solar PV technologies under UV exposure levels that represents typical desert conditions.

UV test conditions: The testing was conducted under short-circuit conditions and continued progressively up to 150 kWh/m² at a chamber temperature of 60 °C, using a UVTC-2 chamber (PSC Instrument GmbH). After each dosage interval of 30 kWh/m², comprehensive electrical characterization was performed to assess performance changes.

The cetisPV-Moduletest3 system from h.a.l.m. electronik GmbH is used to characterize the electrical parameters at AM1.5 Class A+A+A+ standards for solar simulation. Standard testing conditions (STC) are followed during the testing, which is conducted with an insolation of 1000 W/m² and a module temperature of 25°C. The duration of each test flash was 65 ms. EL images of PV modules captured using the CetisPV's EL-package. UV-FL imaging, which creates fluorescence images by illuminating the modules with UV light. The imaging was captured in dark room conditions.

III. RESULTS AND DISCUSSIONS

Fig.1 depicts the continuous UV exposure effect on the power degradation trend as a function of UV dose. The modules were exposed to UV irradiance on the front side during the UV test. The power degradation of PERC and two variants of TOPCon PV modules (TOPCon-PV1 and TOPCon-PV2) shows different behavior under continuous UV exposure test.

The TOPCon PV module exhibits the highest degradation in front side ((Fig.1a)), peaking at around 8%, followed by a slight recovery or stabilization. PERC module shows lower power degradation rates compared to TOPCon. Similar trends are observed in the rear side(Fig.1b) with TOPCon-PV2 again showing the highest degradation (~8%) under UV exposure, while TOPCon-PV1 and PERC exhibit more gradual and stable degradation patterns. Both TOPCon-PV2 and TOPCon-PV1 show significant decreases in open circuit voltage and fill factor. PERC experiences only a slight change, maintaining better long-term stability. PERC remains stable with minimal changes in FF.

Based on the specific batches of modules investigated in this study, preliminary results indicate that two different TOPCon modules from different manufacturers exhibit unexpectedly higher levels of power degradation in comparison to the reference PERC modules.

10.4229/EUPVSEC2025/3DO.16.6

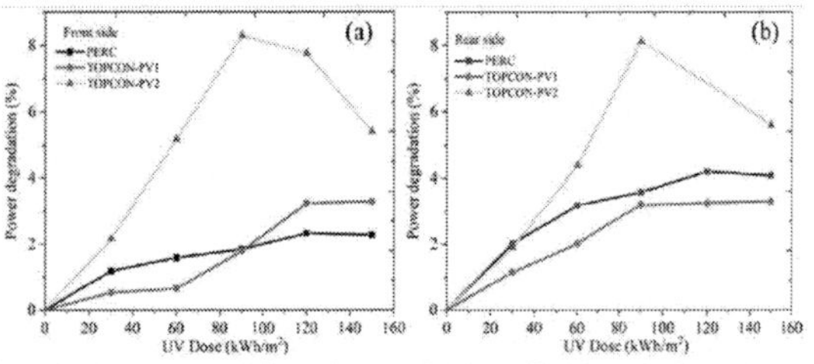

Fig.1: Continuous UV aging of TOPCON PV modules: (a) front side and (b) rear side power degradation.

Fig. 2 illustrates the power degradation of TOPCON-PV3, TOPCON-PV4, and TOPCON-PV5 modules under UV exposure and different storage conditions.

- TOPCon-PV5 shows the highest degradation (~13%) after cumulative UV doses and specific storage periods, with noticeable spikes after "UV60 + Storage" and intermediate light soaking and storage intervals.

- TOPCon-PV4 exhibits rapid initial degradation (~10%) at low UV doses (UV15) and storage conditions, but the degradation rate stabilizes after 20 kWh UV exposure.

- TOPCon-PV3 shows the least degradation and maintains stability even with extended UV doses, indicating better resistance to long-term UV stress compared to the other variants.

- Storage conditions (notably after UV exposure) significantly influence power degradation, as seen with TOPCon-PV5 experiencing sharp spikes during the storage periods (e.g., Storage 2d, Storage +1d).

- Light soaking stability (LS) tests (LS 26h, LS 20 kWh) indicate minimal additional degradation for TOPCon-PV3, highlighting its robust design or materials compared to the others.

Fig. 3 illustrates the electroluminescence (EL) images of TOPCon and PERC PV modules before and after the 150 kWh/m² UV test. TOPCon modules exhibit a surprisingly high frequency of dark and white check patterns in contrast to minor changes in PERC modules. This behaviour is similar to the reported study [12]. The combination of electrical and EL studies suggests potential performance and reliability issues with the specific batches of TopCon modules that were investigated. These observations at the very least warrant further investigation into the cause of these potential causes of instabilities in TopCon modules, specifically after extended UV exposure.

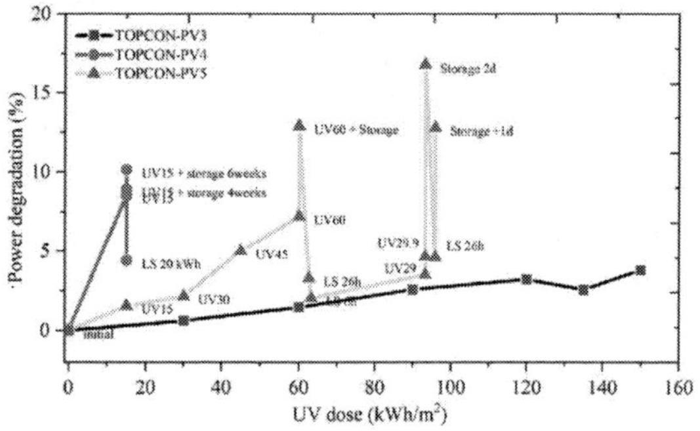

Fig. 2: Effect of UV exposure, dark storage, and light soaking on TOPCON PV modules

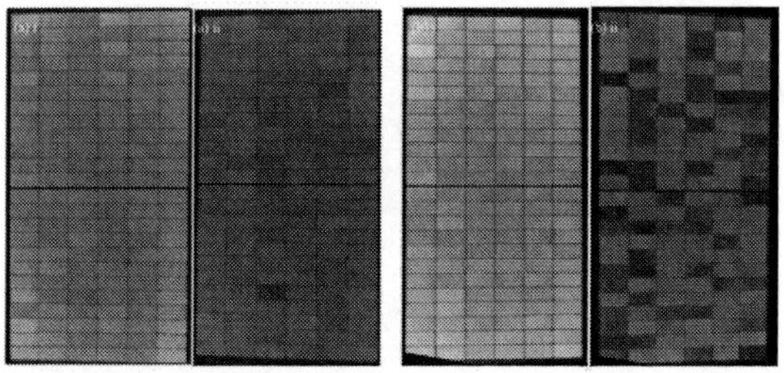

Fig. 3: Representative EL images of (a) PERC, and (b) TOPCON solar PV modules investigated in this study

Fig. 4 depicts the significant UV fluorescence (UVF) features that were observed in TOPCon modules, particularly along the cell edges and multibusbars. This observation suggests that, in addition to the possible degradation of TOPCon cell characteristics, interconnection and soldering defects may contribute to power degradation of new generation TOPCon modules. The fluorescence from both modules is not the same, indicating the BOM difference.

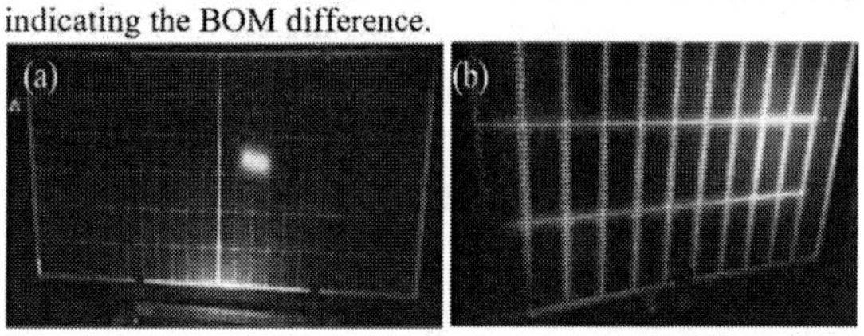

Fig. 4: Representative UVF images of (a) PERC and (b) TOPCON modules investigated in this study.

IV. Conclusions

The study on a limited batch of TOPCon PV modules raises concerns about its increased vulnerable to UV-induced degradation. In comparison to reference PERC modules, power losses in some TOPCon modules considered in this study reached 8–16.5% (especially when combined with dark storage), while others stayed within the range of only ~2% degradation like PERC modules. Various characterization techniques reveal distinct degradation features in some TOPCon modules, including a checkerboard pattern in EL imaging and UV fluorescence along cell edges and soldering points, abnormalities that were less prominent in reference PERC modules. These findings revealed potential risks that are associated with TOPCon technology. Further insights show:

- IV results: TOPCon exhibits stronger UV sensitivity, with a significant impact on Voc and FF.
- Front vs rear sides: degradation behavior is similar.
- Stability variation: The variation in fluorescence observed in UV-F imaging is strongly influenced by the manufacturer type and the quality of the BOM.
- Instability trends: continuous degradation under UV, sharp losses in dark storage, and partial recovery after light soaking in some modules.

The study emphasizes the need for interlaboratory reliability testing and deeper investigation into the mechanisms behind fluorescence, checkerboard EL patterns, and potential instability in TOPCon modules to improve their long-term reliability.

REFERENCES

[1] B. Adothu, S. Kumar, J.J. John, G. Oreski, G. Mathiak, B. Jäckel, V. Alberts, J. Bin Jahangir, M.A. Alam, R. Gottschalg, Comprehensive review on performance, reliability, and roadmap of c-Si PV modules in desert climates: A proposal for improved testing standard, Progress in Photovoltaics: Research and Applications 32 (2024) 495–527. https://doi.org/10.1002/PIP.3827.

[2] International Technology Roadmap for Photovoltaic (ITRPV)-2025, 16th Edition, 2025. https://www.vdma.eu/international-technology-roadmap-photovoltaic (accessed August 26, 2025).

[3] F.T. Thome, P. Meßmer, S. Mack, E. Schnabel, F. Schindler, W. Kwapil, M.C. Schubert, UV-Induced Degradation of Industrial PERC, TOPCon, and HJT Solar Cells: The Next Big Reliability Challenge?, Solar RRL 8 (2024). https://doi.org/10.1002/SOLR.202400628.

[4] M.Q. Khokhar, H. Yousuf, S. Jeong, S. Kim, X. Fan, Y. Kim, S.K. Dhungel, J. Yi, A Review on p-Type Tunnel Oxide Passivated Contact (TOPCon) Solar Cell, Transactions on Electrical and Electronic Materials 24 (2023) 169–177. https://doi.org/10.1007/S42341-023-00433-Z.

[5] M.U. Khan, C. Sen, M. Pollard, T. Huang, M. Gao, R. Lv, Y. Yu, X. Wu, H. Wang, X. Wang, B. Hoex, UV-induced degradation in TOPCon solar cells: Hydrogen dynamics and impact of UV wavelength, Solar Energy Materials and Solar Cells 294 (2026) 113895. https://doi.org/10.1016/J.SOLMAT.2025.113895.

[6] Baloji Adothu, Sagarika Kumar, Bengt Jaeckel, Neha Lyka Muttumthala, Z. Shekason, David Daßler, Kaushal Chapaneri, Prashanth Gabbadi, Yogesh Kumar, Ahmad Alheloo, Ali Almheiri, Jim Joseph John, Gerhard Mathiak, Vivian Alberts, Ralph Gottschalg, Identification and Investigation of Materials Degradation in Photovoltaic Modules from Middle East Hot Desert, in: 40th European Photovoltaic Solar Energy Conference and Exhibition (EU PVSEC 2023), 2023: pp. 001–004. https://doi.org/10.4229/EUPVSEC2023/3AV.2.29.

[7] Baloji Adothu;, Sagarika Kumar;, Swathi Sreekuttan;, Zahra Faiyaz Shekason;, A. Alheloo;, A. Almheiri;, Jim Joseph John;, Gerhard Mathiak;, Bengt Jaeckel;, Ralph Gottschalg;, Vivian Alberts, Discoloration Effect on Performance of PV Modules Installed in Middle East Hot Desert, in: 2023 Middle East and North Africa Solar Conference (MENA-SC), Dubai, United Arab Emirates, 2023: pp. 1–4. https://doi.org/10.1109/MENA-SC54044.2023.10374527.

[8] Bengt Jaeckel, David Daßler, Matthias Pander, Jim Joseph John, Sagarika Kumar, Baloji Adothu, Mission profile concept for PV modules: use case – middle east deserts vs temperate European climate, EPJ Photovoltaics 14 (2023) 1–10. https://doi.org/https://doi.org/10.1051/epjpv/2023030.

[9] B. Adothu, J.J. John, G. Mathiak, V. Alberts, B. Jäckel, R. Gottschalg, N.S. Shiradkar, A.A. Abdallah, J. Lopez Garcia, M. Salvador, B. Hoex, H.A. Kazem, M.A. Alam, Development of PV Module Hot Desert Test Cycle Protocol Extended Failure Modes and Effective Analysis, in: 41st European Photovoltaic Solar Energy Conference and Exhibit (EU PVSEC 2024)Ion, 2024: pp. 1–8. https://doi.org/10.4229/EUPVSEC2024/3BO.15.4.

[10] B. Adothu, S. Pamir Aly, A. Seentakath Puthiyapurayil, K. Chapaneri, J. Joseph John, G. Mathiak, V. Alberts, Investigation of PV module degradation in fixed and single-axis tracker in hot desert climate, in: 41st EUPVSEC, 2024. abstract submitted (accessed February 5, 2024).

[11] B. Adothu, G. Mathiak, S.P. Aly, A. Alheloo, A. Almheiri, V. Alberts, B. Jäckel, R. Gottschalg, N.S. Shiradkar, A.A. Abdallah, J.L. Garcia, M. Salvador, B. Hoex, J.J. John, H.A. Kazem, M.A. Alam, Extended Failure Mode and Effects Analysis for Development of

Hot Desert Test Cycle Proposal, Progress in Photovoltaics: Research and Applications 33 (2024). https://doi.org/https://doi.org/10.1002/pip.3862.

[12] P. Gebhardt, U. Kräling, E. Fokuhl, I. Hädrich, D. Philipp, Reliability of Commercial TOPCon PV Modules—An Extensive Comparative Study, Progress in Photovoltaics: Research and Applications 0 (2024) 1–9. https://doi.org/10.1002/PIP.3868.

Recent Findings on Glass-Breakage Issues: From Factory Production Oversight, On-Site Inspection and Laboratory Testing Results

3DO.19.2

Thomas Weber[**,1], Moritz Heiser, Abdullah Abu Sayed[1,2], Roman Joziak, Eduardo Tellez Rodriguez[1], Nattapark Pongthanacharoenkul[1], Sören Rindert[1], Benjamin Lippke[1], Craig Wong[1], Steven Xuereb[1]
Mahyar Nezhad[3], Don Cowan[3], Matthew Lu[4],
Claudia Buerhop-Lutz, Ian Marius Peters

kiwa

The empire strikes back — but it's overwhelmed by the sheer force of real-world impacts.

Recent Findings on Glass-Breakage Issues:
From Factory Production Oversight, On-Site Inspection and Laboratory Testing Results

3DO.19.2

Thomas Weber**,1, Moritz Heiser, Abdullah Abu Sayed[1,2], Roman Joziak, Eduardo Tellez Rodriguez[1], Nattapark Pongthanacharoenkul[1], Sören Rindert[1], Benjamin Lippke[1], Craig Wong[1], Steven Xuereb[1]
Mahyar Nezhad[3], Don Cowan[3], Matthew Lu[4],
Claudia Buerhop-Lutz, Ian Marius Peters

kiwa

Trusted Experts Worldwide
Wherever and Whenever You Need Us

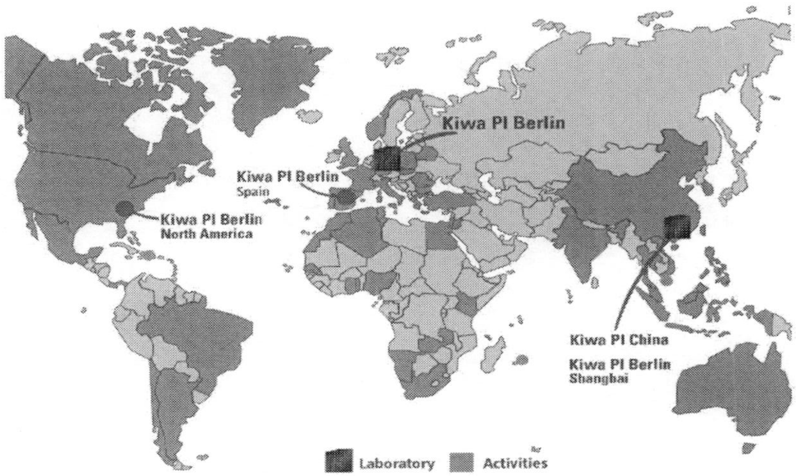

Key PV Services Around the World

From roofs on industrial buildings in central Europe to utility plants in desert regions, our experts are there for you.

- Audits
- Factory Work
- Owners Engineering
- Root Cause Analysis and Claims
- Laboratory

Glass / Glass Modules are Prevalent and Glass is Getting Thinner

Market

- Ca. 700 GW of glass/glass (G/G) modules have been already produced and deployed;
  current G/G market share: ~60 %

Contribution of Kiwa

- Conducted around 20 projects in the last 5 years
- For some projects, we observed breakage rates of
  < 0.1 %; < 3 %; and even < 20 %
- On an inspection rate of < 0.1 to 100 %

Kiwa PVEL PQP test population by module type

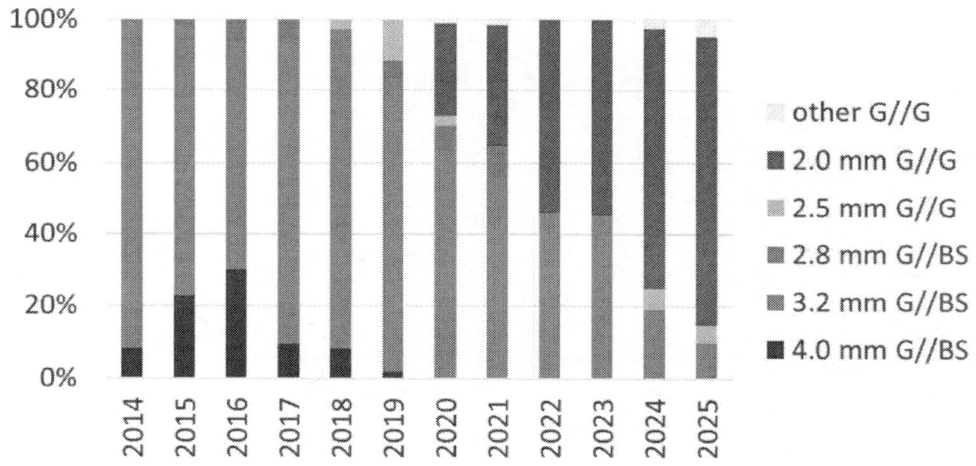

1) Glassbreakage occurred with introduction of 2 mm G//G modules
2) Outlook: The big headaches are still ahead of us.

[1] KIWA PVEL, 2025 PV Module Reliability Scorecard
[2] Savannah Bennett et al.: USING CONVOLUTIONAL NEURAL NETWORKS TO DETECT IN-FIELD PV MODULE GLASS CRACKS, IEEE JOURNAL OF PHOTOVOLTAICS, submitted 2025
[3] ITRPV, "2025 International Technology Roadmap for Photovoltaic (ITRPV), March 2025
[4] Thomas Weber, "Glass breakage—A growing phenomenon in large-scale PV," 20 Nov. 2023. Accessed: 1 Dec. 2023. [Online]. Available: https://www.pv-magazine.com/webinars/glass-breakage-a-growing-phenomenon-in-large-scale-pv/

Analysis of Fracture Patterns

What does it look like?

- Breakage pattern
- Point of origin
  - Impact vs. bending break
  - Thermal or mechanical induced
  - Origination at fixation point or jb
- Laminat: „Edge-Pinch“ [7]

Problems

- Frame covered edge
- Superimposed by secondary breakage

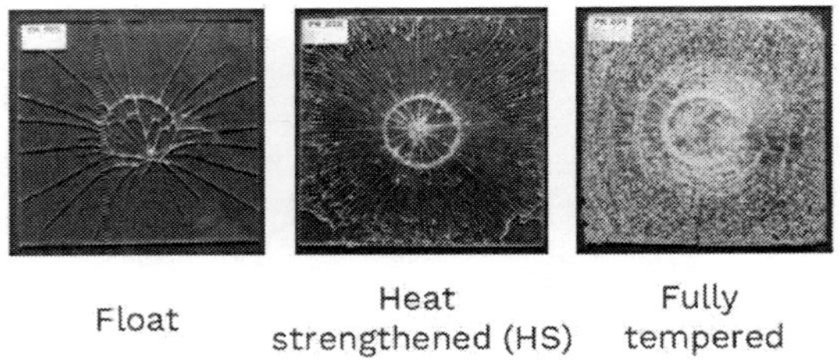

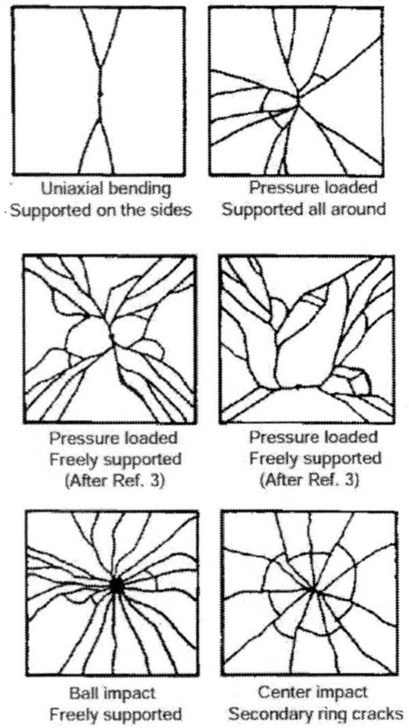

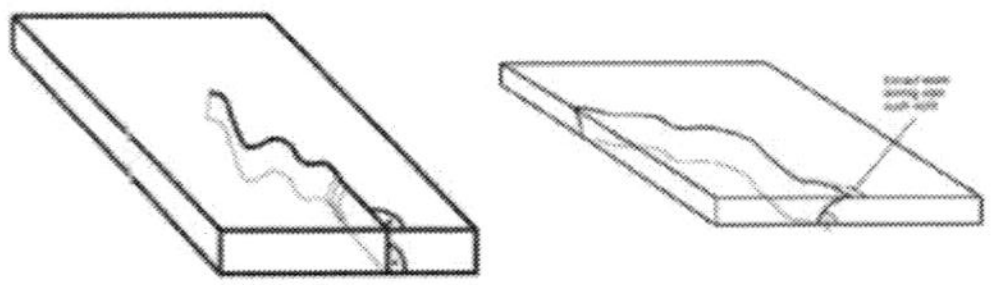

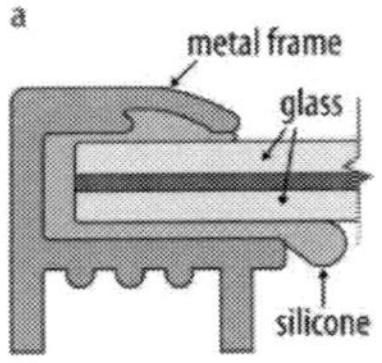

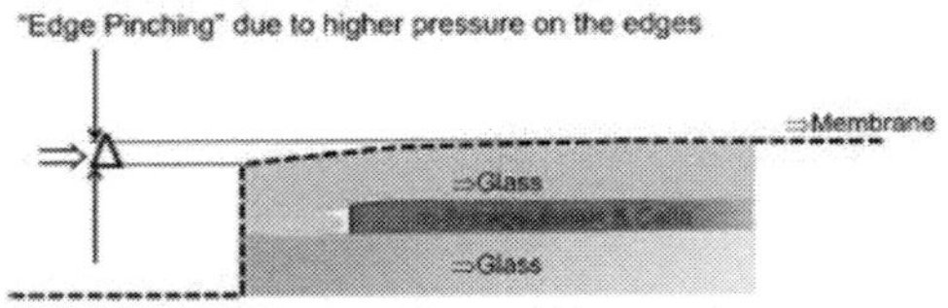

[5] George D. Quinn; Fractography of Ceramics and Glasses
[6] Ekkehard Wagner, "Glasschäden,, 5. Auflage, 2020
[7] Ashley Gaulding, 3CP.2.1 , EUPVSEC Wien 2024
[8] Tim Silverman, at al.; "Tough Break: Many Factors Make Glass Breakage More Likely", 2024

Analysis of Fracture Patterns

What does it look like?

- Breakage pattern
- Point of origin
  - Impact vs. bending break
  - Thermal or mechanical induced
  - Origination at fixation point or jb
- Laminat: „Edge-Pinch“ [6]

Problems

- Frame covered edge
- Superimposed by secondary breakage

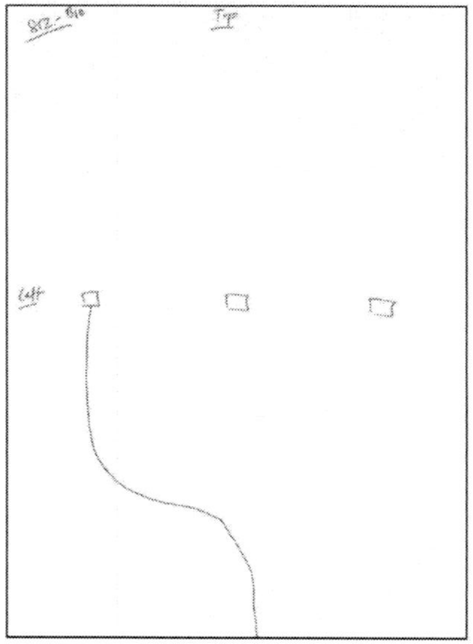

kiwa

[6] Ekkehard Wagner, "Glasschäden„, 5. Auflage, 2020

Analysis of Fracture Patterns

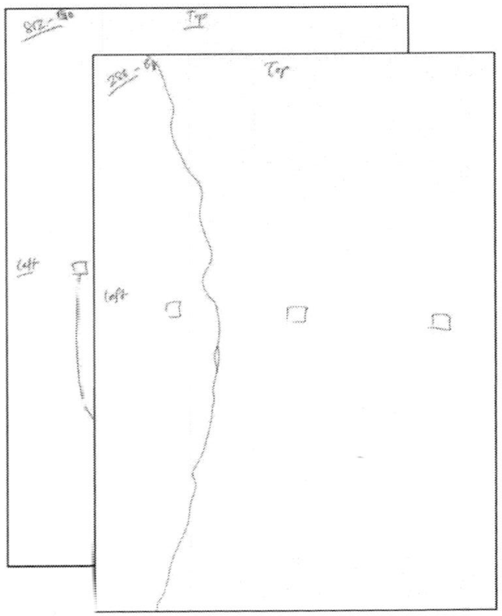

What does it look like?

- Breakage pattern
- Point of origin
  - Impact vs. bending break
  - Thermal or mechanical induced
  - Origination at fixation point or jb
- Laminat: „Edge-Pinch“ [6]

Problems

- Frame covered edge
- Superimposed by secondary breakage

[6] Ekkehard Wagner, "Glasschäden„, 5. Auflage, 2020

Analysis of Fracture Patterns

What does it look like?

- Breakage pattern
- Point of origin
  - Impact vs. bending break
  - Thermal or mechanical induced
  - Origination at fixation point or jb
- Laminat: „Edge-Pinch“ [6]

Problems

- Frame covered edge
- Superimposed by secondary breakage

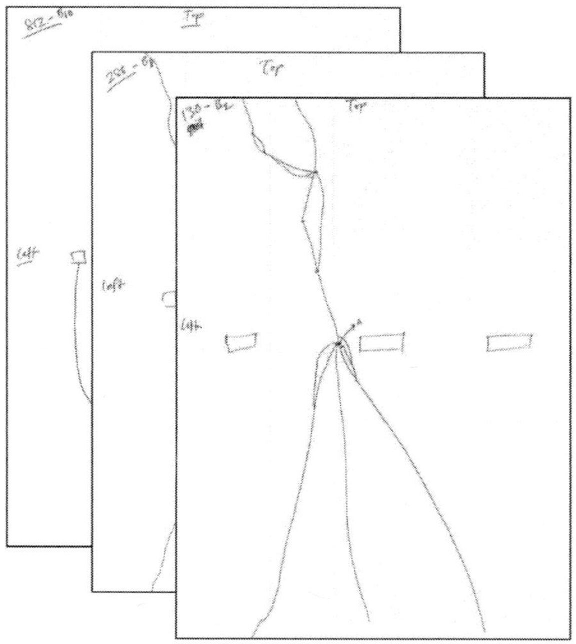

[6] Ekkehard Wagner, "Glasschäden„, 5. Auflage, 2020

Analysis of Fracture Patterns

What does it look like?

- Breakage pattern
- Point of origin
  - Impact vs. bending break
  - Thermal or mechanical induced
  - Origination at fixation point or jb
- Laminat: „Edge-Pinch“ [6]

Problems

- Frame covered edge
- Superimposed by secondary breakage

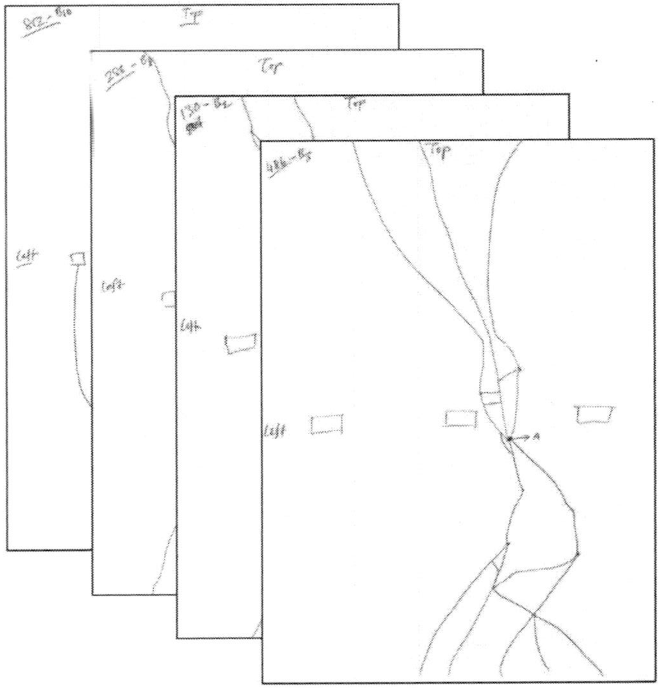

kiwa [6] Ekkehard Wagner, "Glasschäden,, 5. Auflage, 2020

Analysis of Fracture Patterns

What does it look like?

- Breakage pattern
- Point of origin
  - Impact vs. bending break
  - Thermal or mechanical induced
  - Origination at fixation point or jb
- Laminat: „Edge-Pinch“ [6]

Problems

- Frame covered edge
- Superimposed by secondary breakage

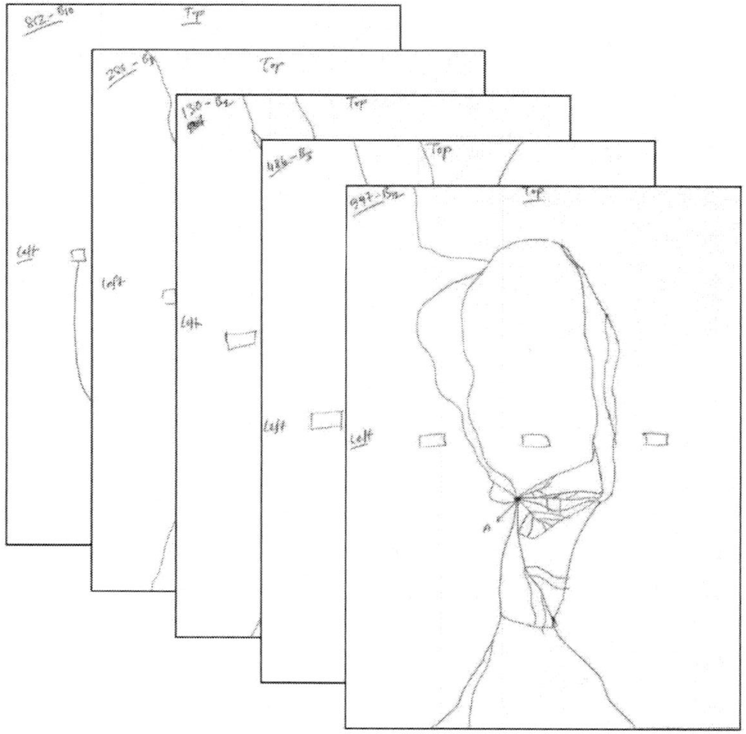

[6] Ekkehard Wagner, "Glasschäden,, 5. Auflage, 2020

Analysis of Fracture Patterns

What does it look like?

- Breakage pattern
- Point of origin
  - Impact vs. bending break
  - Thermal or mechanical induced
  - Origination at fixation point or jb
- Laminat: „Edge-Pinch“ [6]

Problems

- Frame covered edge
- Superimposed by secondary breakage

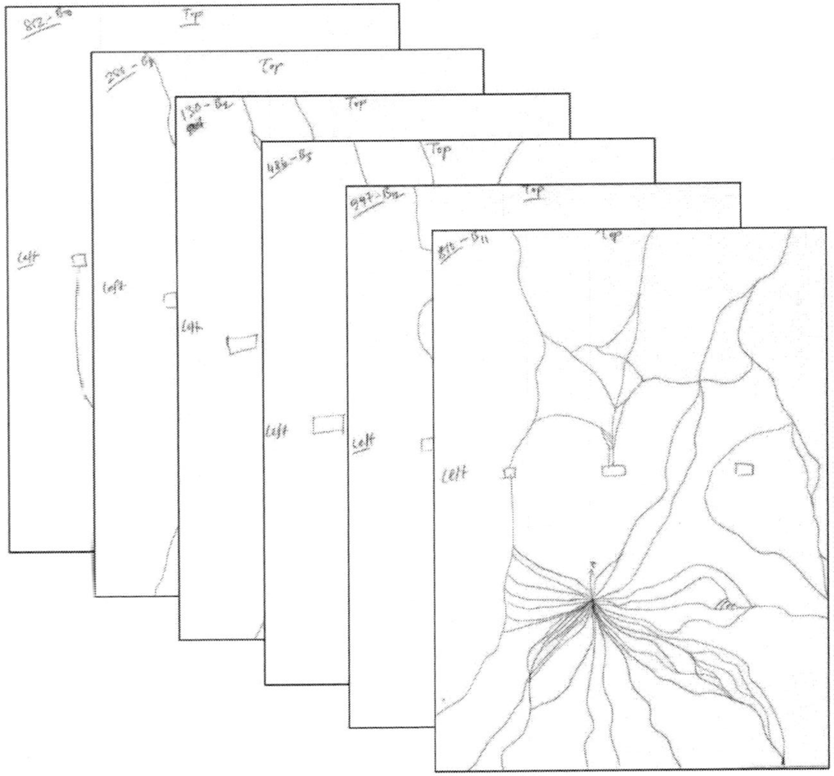

kiwa

[6] Ekkehard Wagner, "Glasschäden„, 5. Auflage, 2020

Analysis of Fracture Patterns

What does it look like?

- Breakage pattern
- Point of origin
  - Impact vs. bending break
  - Thermal or mechanical induced
  - Origination at fixation point or jb
- Laminat: „Edge-Pinch“ [6]

Problems

- Frame covered edge
- Superimposed by secondary breakage

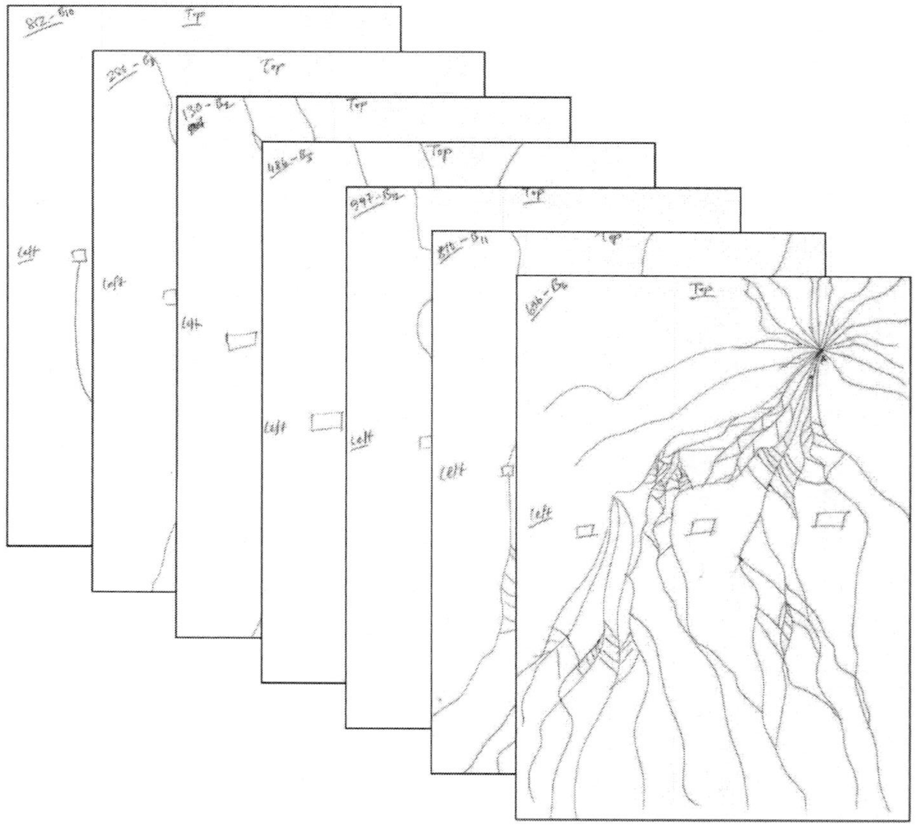

kiwa

[6] Ekkehard Wagner, "Glasschäden,, 5. Auflage, 2020

Tempered Glass and Shelling

Zones of residual stress in prestressed glass

a) Thickness matters: compressive stress zone protects only 20 % of thickness

- Surface cracks may sneak in quietly, (called subcritical growth). But once they cross the line, the glass goes out with a bang.

b) Development of shelling at the breakage edges, if the glass is bended

a)

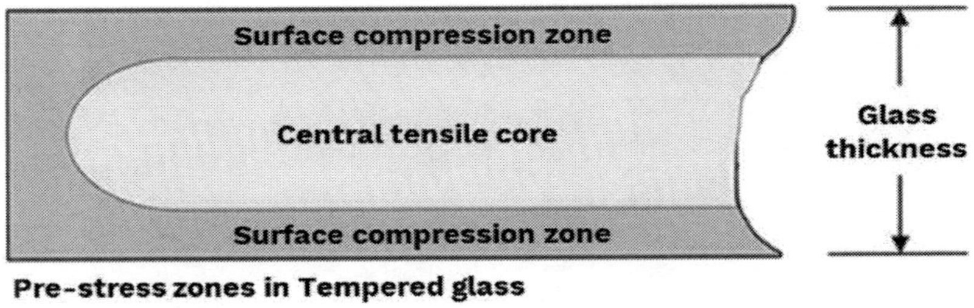

b)

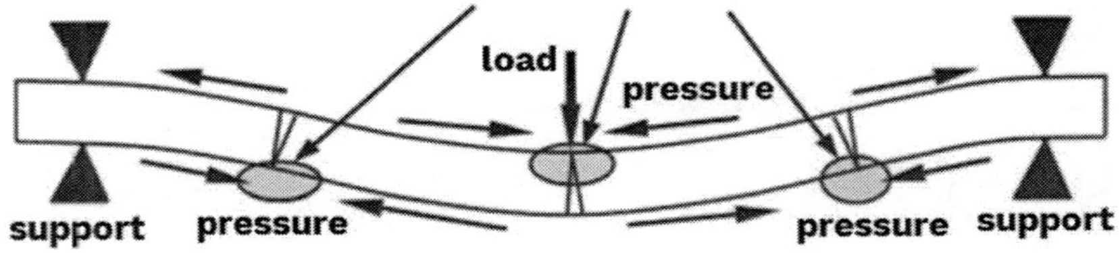

Intervention in a Projects Timeline

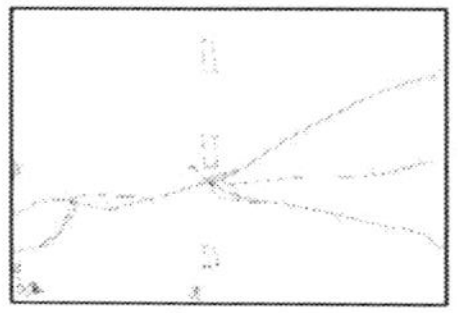

Prevention — Operation start — Root Cause Analysis

Factory, Construction Site

- Contract Negotiation
- Audits
- Corrective Actions
- Owner's Engineering

Desktop

- Background
- Hypothesis
- Scope of work definition

On-site Visit

- Statistics on defects
- Identifying / excluding causes
- Installation and O&M check
- Module sampling

Lab Testing

- IEC 17025 accredited lab
- Detailed RCA
- Testing beyond standard, e.g. deconstruction

Expert Opinion

- Summary of facts
- Opinion on risks and impact and recommendation
- Support in claim process

[3] George D. Quinn: Fractography of Ceramics and Glasses
[4] Ekkehard Wagner, "Glasschäden", 5. Auflage, 2020
[6] Ashley Gaulding, 3CP.2.1, EUPVSEC Wien

Results
Selection of Found Issues

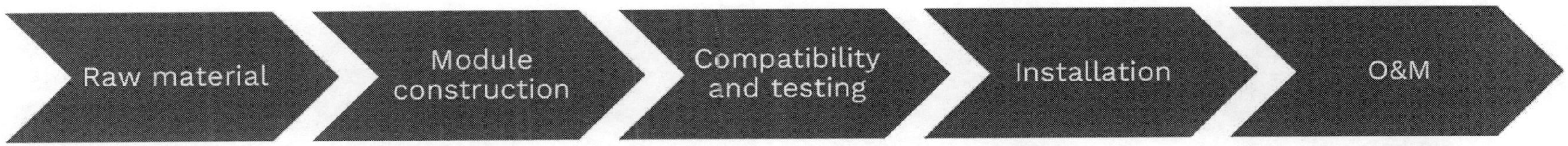

Raw material	Module construction	Compatibility and testing	Installation	O&M
• **Glass quality**	• Dimensions • **Frame assembly** • **Soldering**	• Missing criteria • Inadequate testing and sample size • **Missing responsibility**	• **Clamping** • **Mounting** • Moving foundations • Sagging	• **Grass mowing** • **Cleaning**

Results
Thickness and Inhomogeneity of Surface Compression

Thickness

- Glass thickness not as expected:
  tolerance of +/-0.2 mm is too big,
  it should be tightened to **-0**/+0.2 mm (-50 %)

Inhomogeneity of Surface Compression

Inhomogeneous, but heat-strengthened to tempered glass

- Surface compression on 2 mm rear side glass:
  -64 to -117 N/mm² determined over four modules
- Scalp, ASTM C1279-13 (2019)
  Standard Test Method for Non-Destructive Photoelastic Measurement [...] in Glass

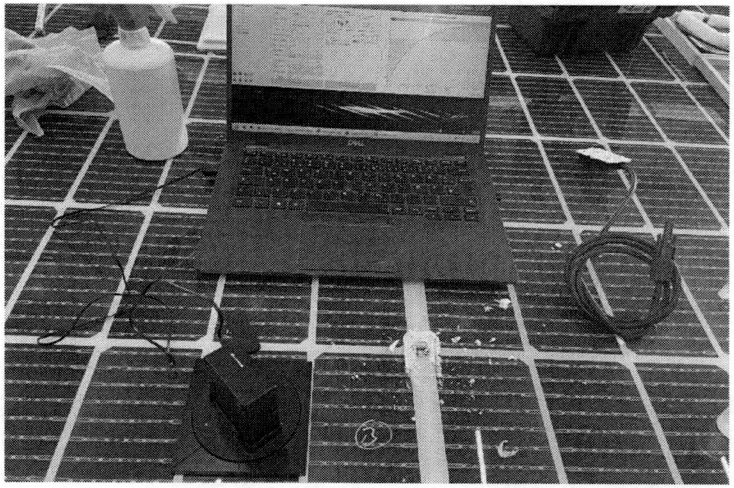

N/mm²

Float -45 | HS -70 | Tempered -120

#1

-72	-76	-86
-111	-80	-89
-80	-64	-91

#2

-111	-82	-119
-111	-110	-105
-108	-117	-103

#3

-81	-70	-117
-100	-117	-80
-93	-106	-76

#4

-74	-70	-87
-84	-94	-79
-73	-88	-73

Results
Module Construction and Production Quality

PV Module Manufacturing **Quality Report**

- Published annual by Kiwa
- Data from all factory activities
  - Factory audits
  - Production oversights
  - **Pre-shipment inspections (PSI)**
- Analysis, trends and conclusions

www.kiwa.com/
pvqualityreport

Results
Module Construction and Production Quality

PV Module Manufacturing **Quality Report**

The distribution of defects identified during Pre-shipment inspection (PSI)

- Directly impacting glass breakage risk
  - Glass damage
  - Frame assembly
  - Curing

Preventive action need criteria!

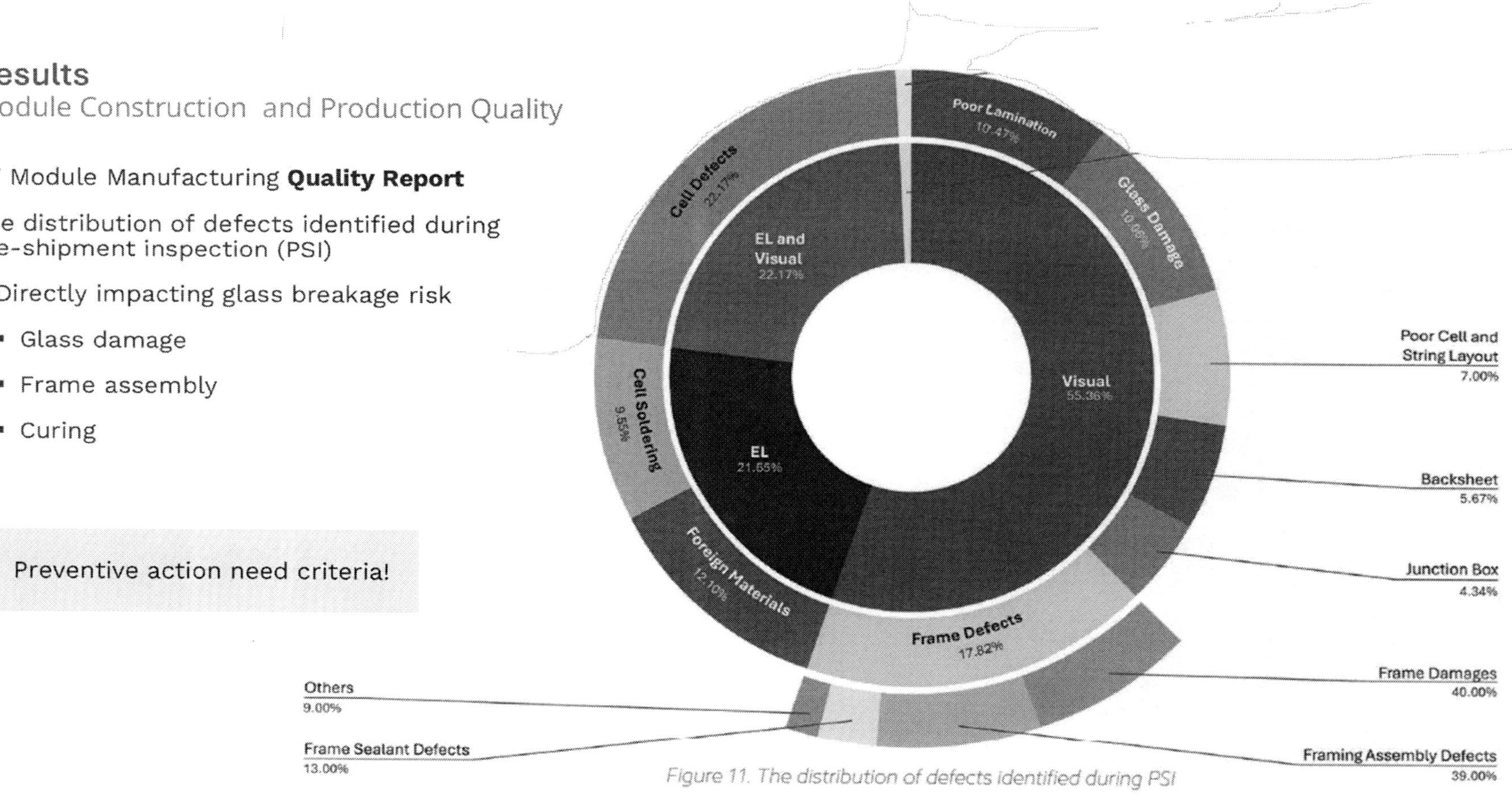

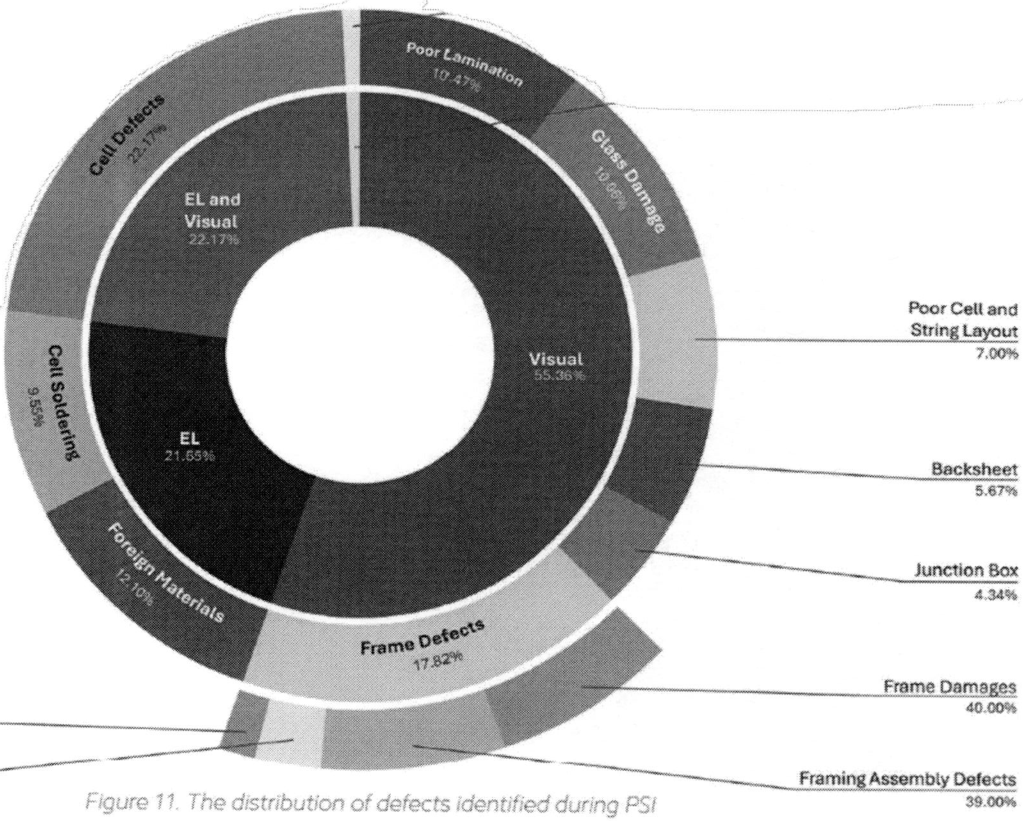

Figure 11. The distribution of defects identified during PSI

Results
Cross Section Cut Findings

Cross-section-cut analysis

- To check hidden quality

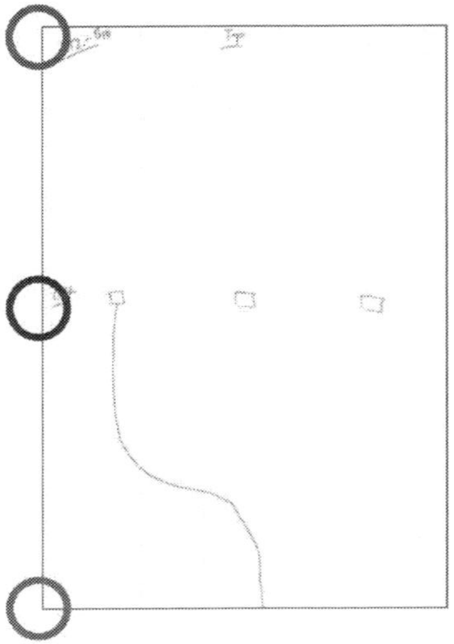

Preventive action need criteria!

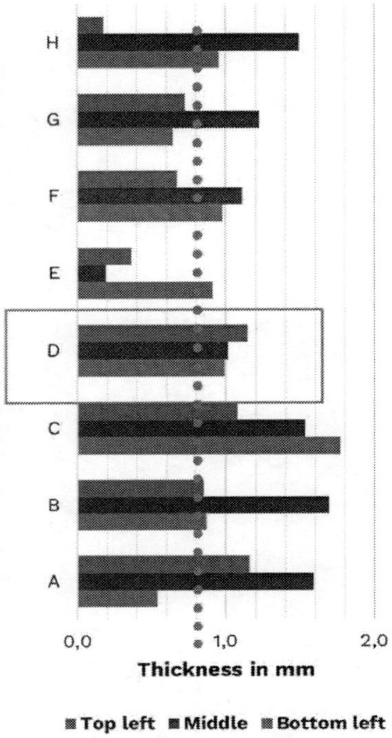

Results
Mechanical Load Testing

Under construction / clamp and grounding

- SML-Test acc. IEC 61215 MQT 16

Test	Result
3600 Pa, 15 Nm, **A) with grounding plate**	**Fail**
3600 Pa, 15 Nm, **B) no grounding plate**	Pass

b)

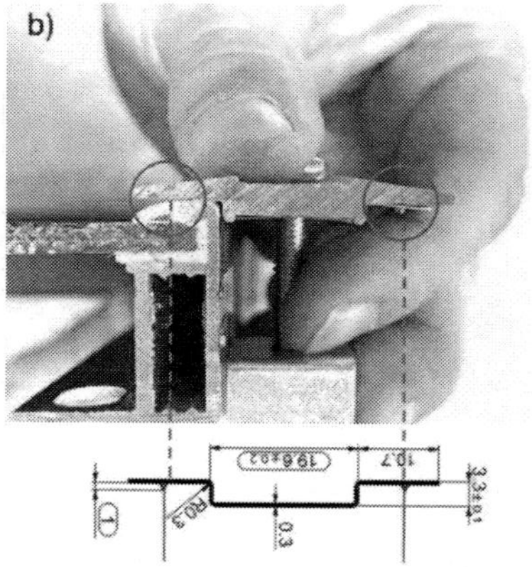

Mounting matters:
torques, distances, design must be correct.

[8] Pascal Romer et al., "How to Mount PV Modules: the Effect of Different Clamping Configuration on Mechanical Stresses in PV Modules, EU PVSEC 2024

Results
Mounting System Improvements Tested

Incompatibility Between Module and/ or Mounting Support

- 7 cases, mean breakage rate ~7 %
- RCA:
  - Missing support: module rail too short with module mounting at 400 mm
  - Too weak module (frame, glass, ...)
- Tested solution: with additional support, modules passed standard testing

The industry is currently lacking in testing and understanding.

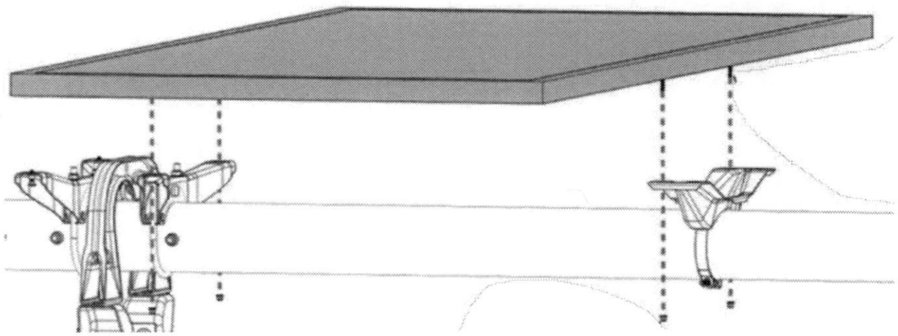

Results

"Impacts" from O&M are a factor

On-site investigation results and laboratory validation: 5 cases

- 6 to 27 % of the broken modules show **clear signs of impact**, but high (proven) uncertainty in that number
- Proved thrown stones and mud (all); cleaning device defect (case E)

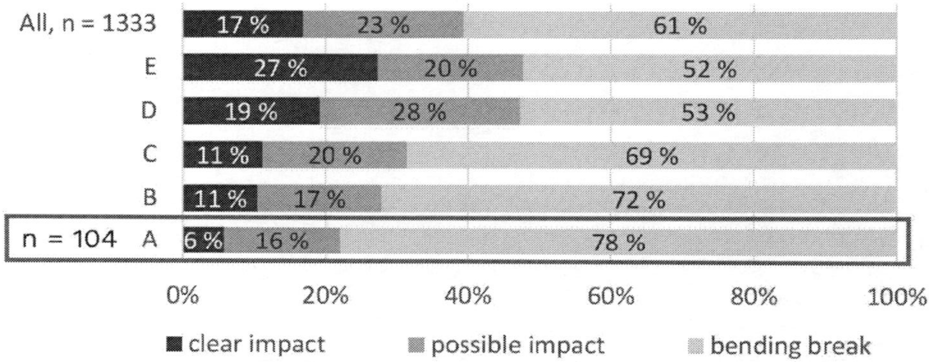

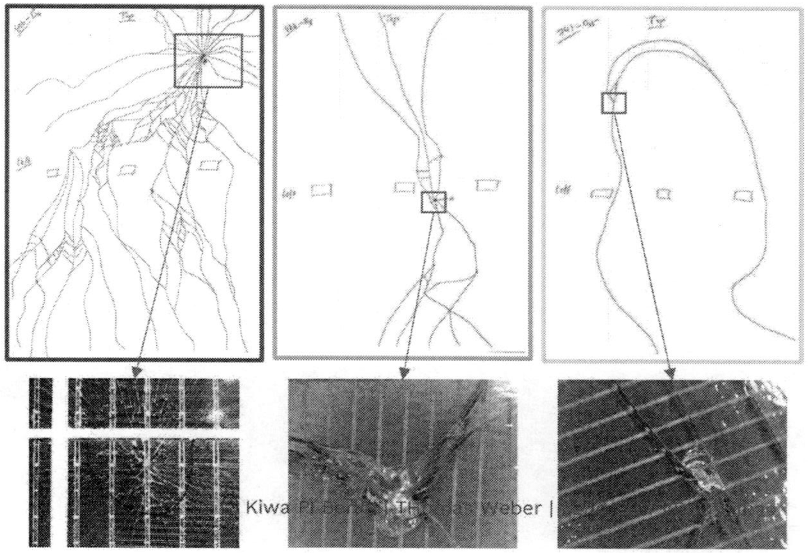

Details matter:
Clear(er) statistcs after microscopic validation.
Should we shoot the rear side?

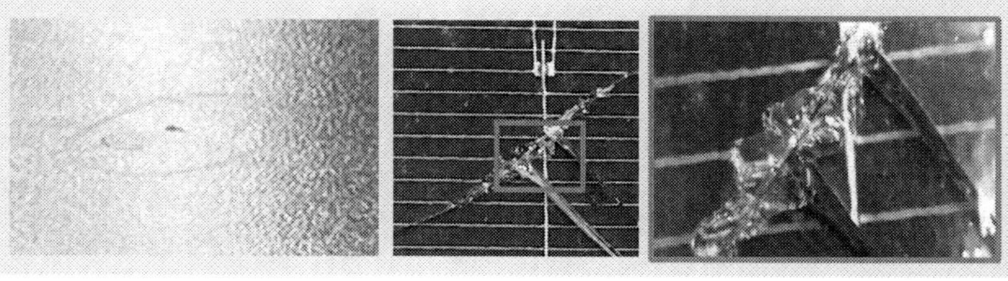

Conclusion

- **Stone Impact**
  O&M teams need to be sensitized to the risk.
- **Module & Installation Quality**
  Construction and mounting practices should at least follow the installation guide.
- **Glass has Become a Load Bearing Element**
  Design processes are lacking
- **Need for more Testing**
  Current methods (IEC: hail, SML/DML) failed to prevent breakage.
- **Urgent Need for New Standards**
  Practical MSA criteria and test protocols for production are needed, approval, and lifetime testing. Strength verification of PV glass as required in the construction industry?!

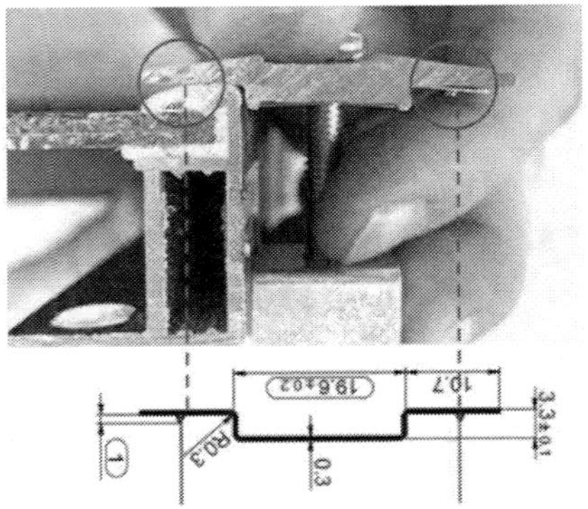

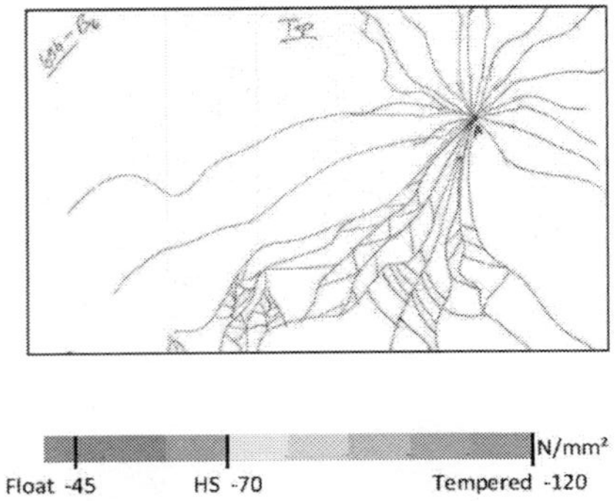

Conclusion

- **Stone Impact**
  O&M teams need to be sensitized to the risk.
- **Module & Installation Quality**
  Construction and mounting practices should at least follow the installation guide.
- **Glass has Become a Load Bearing Element**
  Design processes are lacking
- **Need for more Testing**
  Current methods (IEC: hail, SML/DML) failed to prevent breakage.
- **Urgent Need for New Standards**
  Practical MSA criteria and test protocols for production are needed, approval, and lifetime testing. Strength verification of PV glass as required in the construction industry?!

Thank you – Questions ?

42nd European Photovoltaic Solar Energy Conference and Exhibition

This presentation was selected by the Sc. Committee of the EU PVSEC 2025 for submission of a full paper to one of the EU PVSEC's collaborating peer-reviewed journals.

UNDERSTANDING GLASS BREAKAGE IN FIELD-OPERATED PV MODULES: LEARNINGS FROM INHOMOGENEOUS MECHANICAL LOAD TESTS

Jochen Markert, Aditya Girish Belawadi, Enzo Job, Pascal Romer, Ingrid Haedrich, Daniel Philipp
Fraunhofer Institute for Solar Energy Systems ISE, Heidenhofstr. 2, 79110 Freiburg, Germany

ABSTRACT: A significant increase in glass breakages in photovoltaic (PV) power plants has been observed in recent years, particularly in glass/glass (G/G) modules with thin (~2 mm) glass and large areas (>2.5 m²). These failures often occur within months of field deployment and affect various mounting configurations, including framed and unframed modules on tracked or fixed sub-structures. Traditional causes, such as severe weather or faulty installation, can largely be excluded. Furthermore, even modules that passed the mechanical load (ML) tests during certification according to IEC 61215 are currently failing in the field. Laboratory tests and field observations reveal distinct fracture patterns, suggesting fundamentally different triggering mechanisms. Field fractures are often characterized by long, single-running cracks, originating within the surface, with no clear connection to glass edges. In contrast, laboratory tests under homogeneous load scenarios typically show chaotic crack patterns originating at clamp positions due to stress concentrations. The reduced mechanical stability of thinner glass, particularly with lower surface pre-stress, is assumed to be one key factor, while other factors as for example the influence of more realistic load profiles remain unclear. This study investigates the mechanical failure behavior of G/G and glass/backsheet (G/B) modules under homogeneous and inhomogeneous load profiles and sets them into context to the currently observed breakages in the field. Results show that G/G modules consistently exhibit lower failure loads compared to G/B modules in the respective mounting configuration replicating a 1P tracker setup. However, G/G and G/B modules demonstrate a distinct mechanical response to specific inhomogeneous load profiles, with failure loads converging under increasingly inhomogeneous conditions. Based on the laboratory findings, field fractures are hypothesized to result from sustained, low-intensity loads. Contributing factors may include sagging-induced tensile stress or low-energy impacts, such as stone-strikes during grass mowing.
The findings highlight the limitations of current ML tests, which fail to replicate real-world load conditions. Further research is needed to refine laboratory tests, integrate cyclic loads, and investigate defect formation and aging effects. Such future efforts will be essential for identifying root causes and guiding the development of more robust module designs and maintenance practices to mitigate future failures.
Keywords: PV modules, glass breakage, inhomogeneous loads, mechanical loads

1 INTRODUCTION

A significant increase in glass breakages in photovoltaic (PV) power plants has been observed in recent years [1–3]. This issue affects various module types, including both, framed and unframed modules, as well as those mounted on tracked or permanently installed sub-structures. Traditional root causes, such as severe weather events or faulty installation practices, which have historically contributed to glass breakages [4–6], can largely be excluded in these cases. Notably, all reported incidents share a common factor: Tthe affected modules feature a double-glass design with approximately 2 mm thick glass, an area often exceeding 2.5 m² and the failures are typically observed within just a few months of field deployment. Furthermore, even modules that passed the mechanical load (ML) tests during certification according to IEC 61215 are currently failing in the field.

Our findings to date suggest that the root cause is linked to fundamental challenges associated with the ongoing industry trend toward larger modules and thinner glass [7]. Specifically, the reduced mechanical stability of thinner glass is a key concern. This is partly attributed to the typically lower surface pre-stress in 2 mm glass compared to the 3.2 mm glass in conventional glass/backsheet modules caused by technical limitations during the tempering process for thin glass [8].

While the root causes of cracks originating at module edges are often easier to identify and more frequently reproducible in laboratory tests, field observations increasingly reveal fractures characterized by single, long-propagating cracks (Fig. 1, top). These cracks are typically observed in the rear glass pane, often with no or only single connections to the glass edge and without a clearly identifiable crack origin. For simplicity, we will refer to these incidents as "field fractures" throughout this publication. By contrast, laboratory tests of similar modules typically produce more chaotic fracture patterns affecting both front and rear panes, with numerous cracks originating at the clamp positions (Fig. 1, bottom).

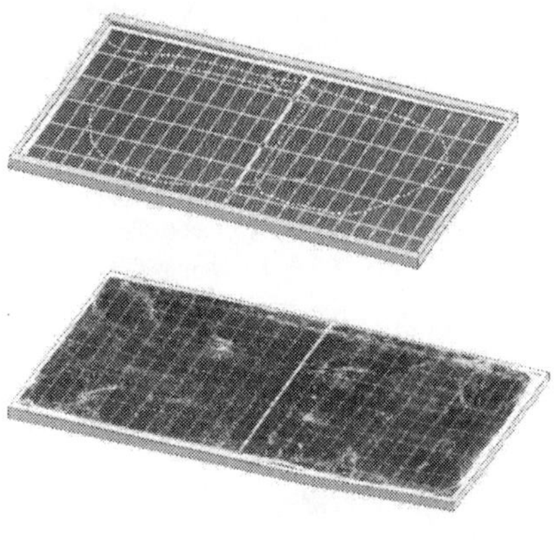

Fig. 1: Typical breakage patterns with no clear origins in rear glass of glass/glass (G/G) modules observed in the field (top) and in the lab (bottom).

The fact that established homogeneous load tests cannot reproduce these field fracture patterns suggests that other triggering mechanisms are responsible for the glass breakage. Romer et al. used finite-element modeling (FEM) to examine how load distributions on modules differ under realistic conditions such as snow or wind from varying directions [9] (compare Fig. 2). This study aims to experimentally reproduce such inhomogeneous load profiles to provide a preliminary insight into their influence on the mechanical failure behavior of G/G and glass/backsheet (G/B) modules. The results of the ML tests are analyzed in the context of field-observed breakage patterns, with the aim of ruling out specific failure mechanisms and narrowing down the root causes that contribute to the observed fractures in the field.

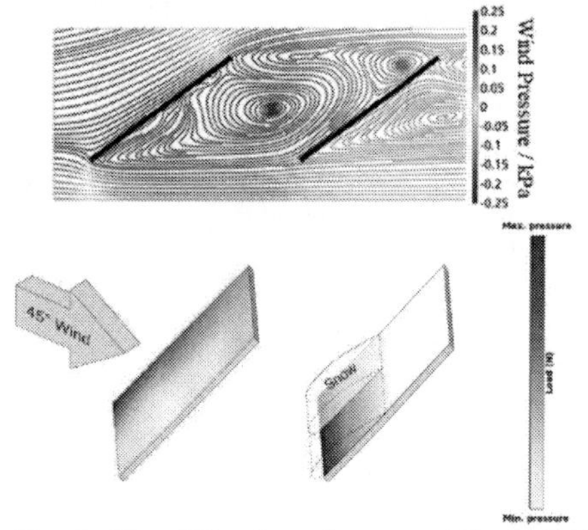

Fig. 2: Top: Side view of a computational fluid dynamics (CFD) simulation of the wind load distribution with frontal wind on inclined module structures by Romer et al. [9]; Bottom: Resulting wind load profiles from a 45 ° cross wind determined by FEM simulations (left) and snow load accumulating on the lower edge (right).

2 METHODOLOGY

2.1 Samples

Two module types, G/G and G/B, from the same manufacturer are tested. According to the datasheets, the basic module designs, including frame height (30 mm) and module dimensions (compare Fig. 3), are identical. Consequently, the only variable parameter is the laminate design. The G/B design featured a front pane with 3.2 mm thickness, while the G/G modules featured front and rear panes with 2 mm each. Furthermore, the surface pre-stress was measured with a scattered light polariscope (SCALP) and showed values in the range of thermally toughened glass (TTG) according to EN 12150-1 [10] for the 3.2 mm glass (<-110 MPa) and between heat-strengthened glass (HSG) according to EN 1863-1 [11] and TTG for the 2 mm glass (around -80 MPa).

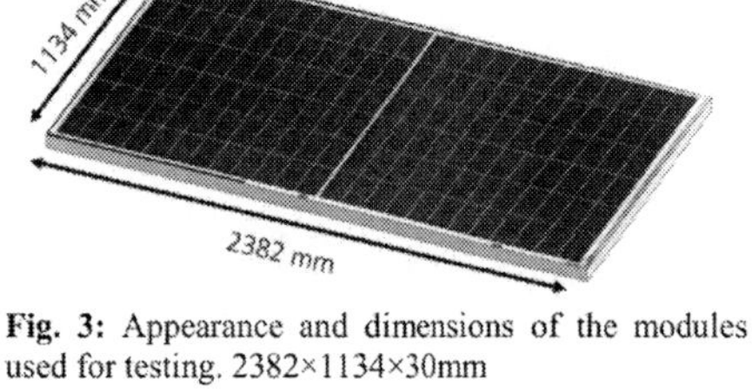

Fig. 3: Appearance and dimensions of the modules used for testing. 2382×1134×30mm

2.2 Test Specifications

The experiments were designed following a test-to-fail approach applying pressure conditions (no suction). Different load profiles including homogeneous and inhomogeneous loads are applied as illustrated in Fig. 4. To account for variability in the results, which is expected due to the probabilistic nature of glass breakage, three modules were tested for homogeneous load scenarios and four modules for inhomogeneous load scenarios. For the homogeneous load profile, a load ramp with 50 Pa/s is applied. For the inhomogeneous load cases, the loads at the cylinder(s) with the highest individual load is increased in 50 N steps, with a holding time of 30 s at each load level to ensure equilibrium conditions. This holding time is necessary because changes in load on individual cylinders can affect the overall load distribution across the module surface, which must be compensated by readjusting the remaining cylinders according to the load distribution calculated from FEM simulations (see Fig. 4). Load levels in homogeneous scenarios can be readily characterized using force per unit area specifications. However, for inhomogeneous load distributions, such characterization might lead to misinterpretation of results. Therefore, absolute force values were utilized to describe the specific load distribution patterns, ensuring accurate representation of the experimental conditions. The homogeneous distribution is used as a reference and corresponds to the load application as typically applied during laboratory ML tests according to IEC 61215-2. The load profile for front wind from 45° is simulated using CFD in combination with FEM. The distribution in the case of snow load is defined based on the standard IEC 62938, a standard that aims to test the attachment of the frame to the module during snow loads on inclined setups by applying an inhomogeneous distribution of snow on one half of the modules [12].

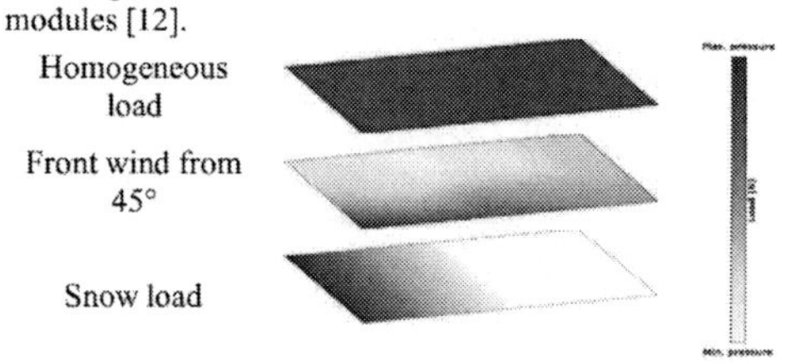

Fig. 4: Load distribution of the three investigated profiles: homogeneous (top), cross wind (middle) and snow load (bottom).

For the test approach a relatively unstable, but nevertheless widely used configuration for utility modules was used. It is further referred to as tracker setup (Fig. 5, top and bottom, blue clamps). It reflects the assembly of modules in a 1P single-axis tracked system, which is often used in large power plants and open-field systems. The module clamps with a width of 50 mm are set centrally with a distance of 200 mm from the module center and fixed with 15 Nm torque, which is accompanied by large, freely overhanging module areas and an overall increased vulnerability to deformation compared to other mounting situations as e.g. in typical fixed tilt setups (Fig. 5, bottom, light grey clamps). To evaluate the deformation of each module, the deflection was recorded on the module corner, where the highest deflection is expected, using a laser sensor. For the G/B type the experiments are complemented by additional FEM simulations for the specific load profiles.

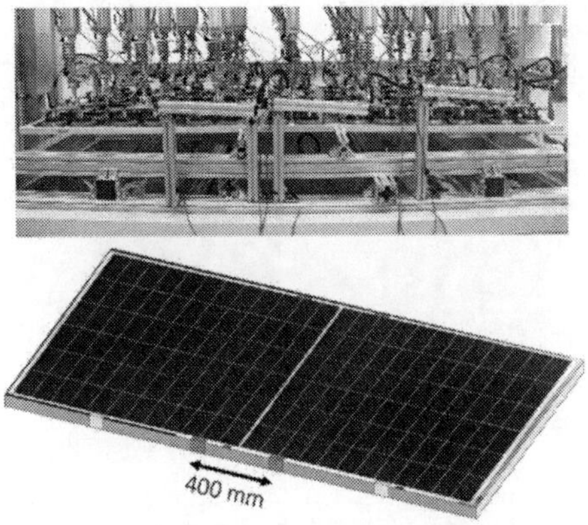

Fig. 5: Top: Tracker setup on the ML test stand; Bottom: Module with sketched clamping position for tracker setup with clamp spacing = 400 mm (blue) and standard configuration with clamping at 20 % of the long module side (light grey).

3 RESULTS

Fig. 6 illustrates the total failure force for the specific load distributions of each module during the single ML tests. The G/G design consistently exhibits lower failure loads compared to the G/B modules, with the largest difference observed under the homogeneous load scenario. In this case, the average failure load of the G/B design is 136% higher than that of the G/G design. As the load distribution becomes increasingly inhomogeneous, the concentration of loads in specific areas leads to higher localized stresses, resulting in a general decrease in absolute failure loads for both module types. However, the failure loads of the G/B modules decrease more rapidly, converging towards those of the G/G modules during the inhomogeneous configurations. Specifically, under the crosswind scenario, the G/B modules exhibit a failure load 124% higher than that of the G/G modules, while under the snow load scenario, the failure load is approximately 75% higher.

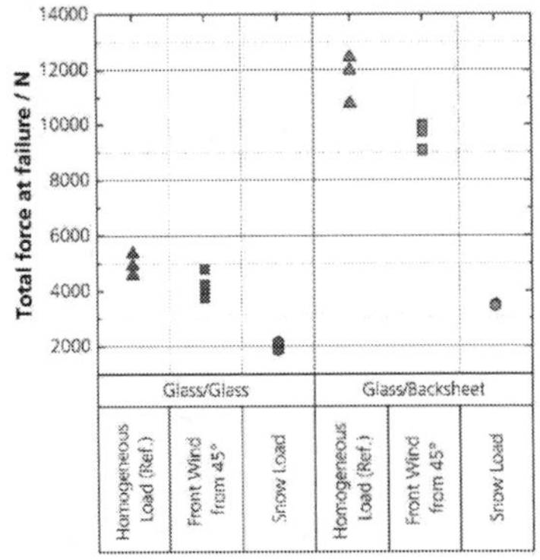

Fig. 6: The total force at failure on the G/G and G/B modules during ML tests with homogeneous (reference) and inhomogeneous loads until failure in pressure direction.

Fig. 7 presents the deflection at the module corner as a function of the total applied force for one representative module per test. A notable observation is the significantly different deformation behavior between the G/G and G/B modules across all tested load configurations. This difference is most pronounced under the homogeneous load scenario and becomes less distinct as the inhomogeneity of the applied load increases.

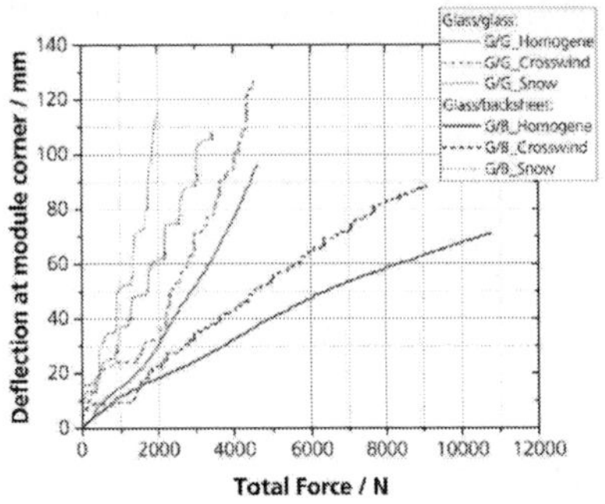

Fig. 7: Deflection at module corner vs. total applied force of the modules under different load profiles.

Looking at the deformation behavior of the modules during the homogeneous load test, the G/G modules exhibit bending predominantly along the long side of the module, while the short side remains largely undeformed (Fig. 8, top left). In contrast, G/B modules under a comparable surface load show initial deformation across the module surface along the short side, which seems to stabilize the module and effectively prevents the deformation along the long side during increased load levels (Fig. 8, bottom left).

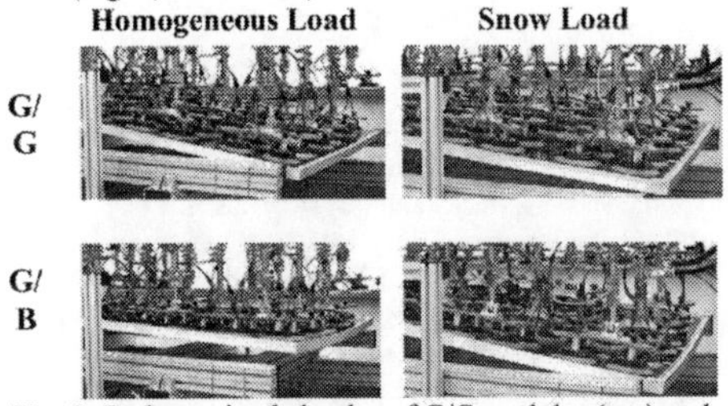

Fig. 8: Deformation behavior of G/G modules (top) and G/B modules (bottom) with an absolute applied force of ~5000 N homogeneous load (left) and ~2000 N snow load (right).

A similar deformation behavior is observed under the cross-wind load profile, although the difference of G/B and G/G is less pronounced. Under snow-load conditions, the deformation pattern of G/B converges to that of G/G modules, with bending occurring predominantly along the long side of the module (Fig. 8, right). With this load distribution, the G/B module does not exhibit initial bending along the short edge allowing the modules to deform with a bending along the long side, similar to the G/G design.

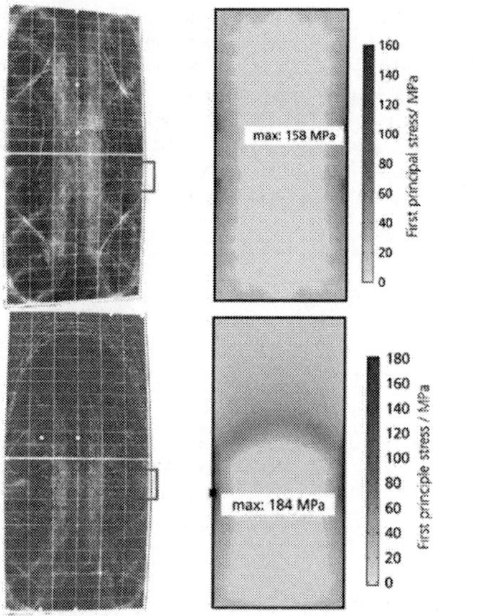

Fig. 9: Left: G/B module after failure under homogeneous- (top) and snow load (bottom) with breakage origins marked in red; Right: Corresponding distribution of first principal stress in the front glass at total force at failure of around 12000 N (top) and 3800 N (bottom).

Fig. 9 shows representative breakage patterns from the G/B modules for the homogeneous and the snow load scenario on the left and corresponding FEM simulations of the first principal stress in the front glass for the load distribution at 12000 N (homogeneous) 3800 N (snow load) total force on the right. The failure pattern in the cross-wind scenario matches closely with the homogeneous case and is therefore not shown. Due to the surface pre-stress in the TTG range according to EN 12150-1 [10], the fracture pattern appears fine grained over the entire surface in all three scenarios. The breakage origins in both scenarios match with the location of highest first principal stress of the FEM simulations at the clamp positions. Furthermore, the fracture pattern observed during snow load aligns well to the stress distribution derived from FEM, indicating that crack lines tend to follow the stress fields within the glass. The appearance of fractures on front and rear side of the G/G modules was similar, indicating comparable stress distributions in the two panes. However, the absolute stress according to FEM is higher in the front glass. Fig. 10 shows the general breakage patterns during homogeneous and snow load only in the rear glass due to better traceability of the crack lines. The crack origins are observed at one clamp position similar to the G/B modules. The crack distribution and density aligns with the load distribution, so that the module half where no load was applied in the snow load scenario shows significantly less cracks than the loaded half.

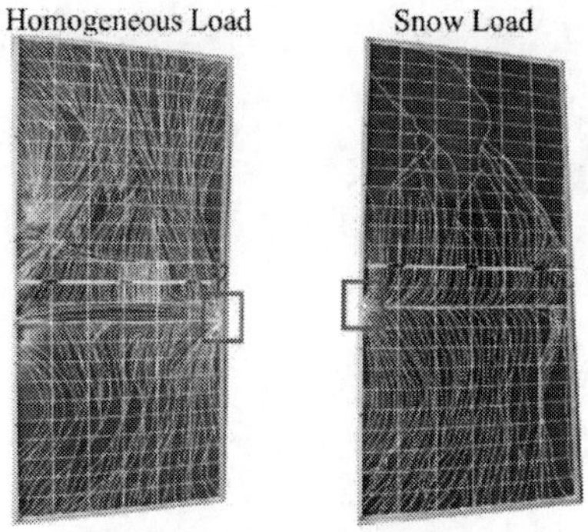

Fig. 10: Breakage pattern with main crack line orientation traced (white dashed) from rear glass of the G/G modules during homogeneous (left) and snow load (right); Crack origins marked with a red square.

4 DISCUSSION AND CONCLUSION

The significant difference in failure loads between G/G and G/B modules in the homogeneous case can most likely be attributed to their distinct deformation behavior under specific surface load distributions. In the G/G module, the first principal stress increases more rapidly at the clamp positions due to bending along the longer side. In contrast, the G/B module deforms initially by bending along the short side and subsequently stabilizes as schematically shown in Fig. 11. The primary factor influencing the different deformation behaviors is assumed to be a more rigid response of the G/G laminate compared to G/B during the initial loading phase. However, this needs further investigation with FEM simulations to be able to draw clearer conclusions. The deformation becomes more similar applying inhomogeneous loads, because less pressure is initially applied in the center, thereby preventing a bending of the G/B laminate along the short side during low loads. This leads to a less pronounced difference in failure loads with increasing inhomogeneity.

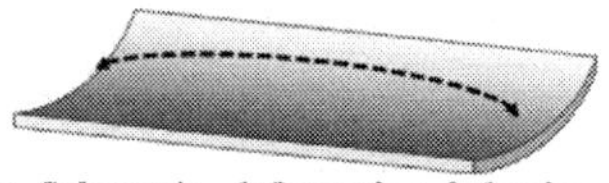

Fig. 11: Schematic deformation behavior of G/B module during homogeneous load application.

Another factor believed to contribute to the overall lower failure loads of G/G modules is the reduced surface pre-stress of the module glass. This reduction decreases the critical first principal stress needed to induce breakage and is assumed to be a significant parameter dominating the observed breakage behavior under snow load.

When comparing the fracture behavior of G/G and G/B modules under inhomogeneous load scenarios to standard ML tests with homogeneous loads, a key observation is that the critical failure regions, where maximum first principal stress concentrates, are consistently located at clamp positions. This appears to be largely independent of the test setup. For highly unstable setups as examined in this study, this results in a more rapid increase in first principal stress, and a resulting reduction of total force at failure, which is assumed to be different for more stable mounting setups. In addition, the concentration of failure loads in specific areas leads to higher crack densities in the corresponding regions of the module and cracks tend to follow the stress distribution in the glass.

Based on observations from laboratory ML tests – both homogeneous and inhomogeneous – several key conclusions can be drawn with regard to the field fractures as explained in section 1:

Crack origins:

Fractures observed during laboratory tests typically originate near clamp positions at the glass edge, attributed to stress concentrations induced by surface loading. Inhomogeneous loads may therefore represent a significant contributing factor to breakages in the field that initiate at clamp positions. However, field fracture patterns often differ remarkably, exhibiting long-running cracks with only a single, or in some cases no, connection to a glass edge, and lacking other distinct points of origin. This discrepancy complicates the identification of specific root causes and strongly suggest that fundamentally distinct mechanisms underlie fracture formation in field conditions compared to laboratory settings in such cases.

Similar failure patterns, characterized by single, long-running crack lines, have been reported by E. Wagner for laminated glass with heat-strengthened glass and are referred to as "surface pressure fractures." [13]. This source suggests that crack origins in such cases are often challenging to identify but are typically initiated at surface defects. ISO 1288-1 highlights that the tensile strength of glass panes decreases with increasing dimensions, attributed to the enhanced probability of critical surface defects being present in larger surface areas [14], which further supports the hypothesis of module dimensions approaching critical limits. This effect could be particularly critical for thin glass with reduced surface pre-stress, as the pre-stressed surface layer in thermally tempered glass typically constitutes around 20% of the total glass thickness [13]. In thinner glass, even shallow defects could reach critical dimensions, increasing the likelihood of failure.

Crack distribution and density:

Crack patterns observed in laboratory tests typically appear chaotic, with significantly higher crack densities in regions subjected to high surface loads and fewer cracks with larger unbroken pieces in areas with lower loads.

In contrast, field fractures are characterized by long, single, well-coordinated oval-shaped crack patterns. This suggests that the loads involved are generally homogeneous and may not result from particularly high total loads but rather from lower, sustained loads and an initiation point within the surface. A common phenomenon in fielded modules is the sagging of laminates between frames, which exerts a constant, homogeneous, low-intensity tensile stress on the rear pane (compare Fig. 12). Multiple parameters could potentially contribute to this phenomenon, including the self-weight of large-scale laminate modules and compressive stresses induced by thermal expansion of the framing, e.g. due to seasonal changes. This sustained stress is thought to increase the susceptibility of the rear pane to surface defects, contributing to the observed field fractures.

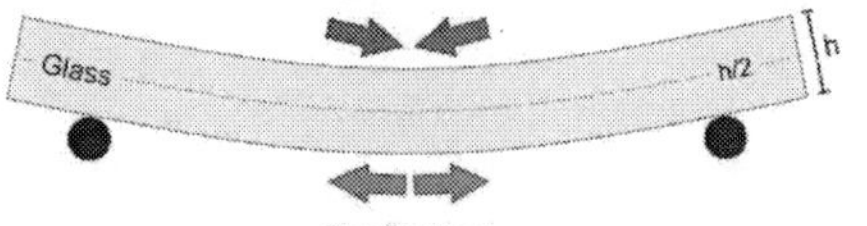

Fig. 12: Stresses developing on each side of a G/G laminate resulting from deformation induced by a surface pressure.

Fig. 13 illustrates a comparison between a typical fracture pattern documented from field observations in the rear glass (left) and the isobaric distribution of first principal stresses in the rear pane while sagging as determined through an FEM simulation (right). The simulation results demonstrate the stress pattern that develops when the laminate structure experiences gravitational deformation. The propagation paths of cracks exhibit a tendency to follow the stress isobars within the rear glass. This correlation, particularly in the presence of point defects, may offer a mechanistic explanation for the characteristic crack patterns observed in field installations.

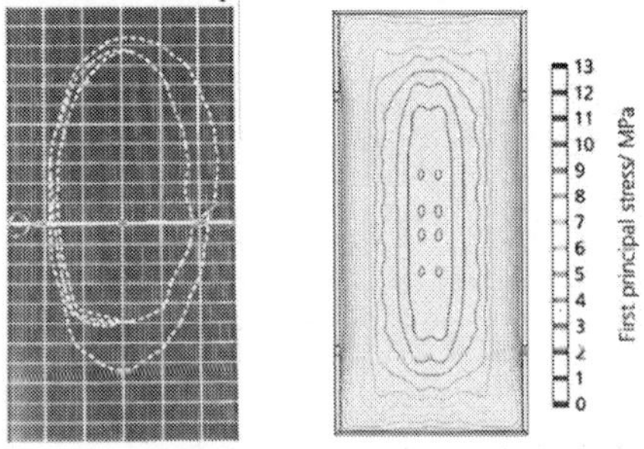

Fig. 13: Left: Breakage pattern observed in the field in the rear glass; Right: FEM simulation first principal stress in a module rear glass during sagging.

Breakage/triggering mechanisms:

As previously discussed, laboratory testing with both homogeneous and inhomogeneous loads reveal that the glass edge at clamping positions constitutes the primary vulnerability due to stress concentration during surface load application. The initiation of this failure mechanism is highly dependent on the absolute load magnitude, surface load distribution, and mounting configuration. Additionally, module design parameters demonstrate significant influence on the deformation response under various loading scenarios.

In contrast, field observations of rear glass breakages suggest that fracture initiation in modules typically originates at surface defects. Current analyses of fractured module glass indicate that, in some instances, low-intensity impacts from stones possibly ejected during vegetation maintenance activities may contribute to failures. However, alternative causative factors, including micro-defects introduced during the glass manufacturing process, remain a plausible hypothesis at this stage of investigation. Generally, a strong correlation with defect depth is anticipated. Furthermore, prolonged exposure to relatively low surface loads may induce progressive degradation mechanisms or exacerbate pre-existing surface defects, thereby compromising the overall mechanical integrity of the glass components over extended time.

10.4229/EUPVSEC2025/3DO.19.3

5 SUMMARY AND OUTLOOK

A preliminary analysis of G/G and G/B modules was conducted to evaluate their mechanical response to various inhomogeneous stress profiles. The results revealed a higher fracture probability for G/G modules. However, under more inhomogeneous loading scenarios, the G/B design exhibited a more comparable behavior, likely due to reduced stabilization caused by changing deformation patterns. The resulting breakage patterns consistently showed crack origins at the clamp positions but failed to replicate the long, oval-shaped crack lines observed in field fractures. This highlights significant differences in the triggering mechanisms between laboratory and field scenarios. Nevertheless, several key conclusions regarding the factors that play a role in the currently observed field fractures can be drawn.

The observed fracture patterns suggest substantially lower loads in the field and initiation through surface defects. In some cases, the root cause of field fractures is likely attributable to low-intensity impacts, such as stone striking during vegetation maintenance. However, in other instances, the origins of the fractures remain unclear, and production-specific issues cannot be ruled out. Additionally, the role of crack propagation and the influence of long-term loads on the stability of glass with pre-existing defects require further investigation.

The results of this initial study on the influence of inhomogeneous loads in a specific experimental setup revealed design-dependent deformation behaviors, resulting in highly variable failure loads. These findings establish a preliminary foundation for future investigations into the effects of inhomogeneous load testing across diverse mounting configurations and module designs. Further comprehensive FEM analyses on G/G module behavior are required. Implementation of inhomogeneous load testing protocols could potentially address the currently observed discrepancies between field failures and successful certification according to IEC 61215. Additionally, qualification methodologies for modules intended for specific applications, such as customized mounting structures or unique operational environments, should be considered. To develop testing protocols with greater real-world relevance, additional research is necessary to replicate field load profiles more accurately, including the incorporation of cyclic loads characteristic for wind-induced stresses.

To gain a deeper understanding of the breakage mechanisms involved in the field more extensive investigations are required, particularly on the impact of defect depth and other surface characteristics. Additionally, greater attention should be given to maintenance techniques applied in specific fields and the load scenarios they impose on modules. It appears that multiple factors seem to contribute to the currently observed failures, with two of the major issues being the application of thin glass with low surface pre-stress and dimensions approaching 3 m^2. This situation warrants further research to identify definitive root causes, allowing the industry to respond effectively. Potential solutions could include both, the development of adjusted module designs and the avoidance of specific external loads caused by maintenance practices.

These efforts combined might be necessary to mitigate future field fractures and therefore reduce the general risk for large module replacements.

6 ACKNOWLEDGEMENTS

This work was funded by the Federal Ministry for Economic Affairs and Energy (BMWE) under grant number 03EE1131A as part of the research project "Similar". The authors gratefully acknowledge this funding which made this research possible. We would like to express our sincere appreciation to all colleagues and partners who contributed to this study through their expertise, technical support, and valuable discussions.

7 REFERENCES

[1] Chris Crowell, *Solar module glass is 'spontaneously breaking' in the field.* [Online]. Available: https://solarbuildermag.com/featured/solar-module-glass-is-spontaneously-breaking-in-the-field/ (accessed: Oct. 16 2024).

[2] Ryan Kennedy, *Spontaneous glass breakage on solar panels on the rise.* [Online]. Available: https://www.pv-magazine.com/2024/06/24/spontaneous-glass-breakage-on-solar-panels-on-the-rise/ (accessed: Oct. 16 2024).

[3] Lisa McDonald, *Solar panel breakage on the rise as glass thickness decreases and hail severity increases.* [Online]. Available: https://ceramics.org/ceramic-tech-today/solar-panel-breakage-on-the-rise-as-glass-thickness-decreases-and-hail-severity-increases/ (accessed: Oct. 16 2024).

[4] P. Sinha and A. Wade, "Assessment of Leaching Tests for Evaluating Potential Environmental Impacts of PV Module Field Breakage," *IEEE J. Photovoltaics*, vol. 5, no. 6, pp. 1710–1714, 2015, doi: 10.1109/JPHOTOV.2015.2479459.

[5] A. Sinha *et al.*, "Glass/glass photovoltaic module reliability and degradation: a review," *J. Phys. D: Appl. Phys.*, vol. 54, no. 41, p. 413002, 2021, doi: 10.1088/1361-6463/ac1462.

[6] M. Aghaei *et al.*, "Review of degradation and failure phenomena in photovoltaic modules," *Renewable and Sustainable Energy Reviews*, vol. 159, p. 112160, 2022, doi: 10.1016/j.rser.2022.112160.

[7] ITRPV, "International Technology Roadmap for Photovoltaic (ITRPV): 2022 Results," 2023.

[8] B.-W. Fan, K.-Q. Zhu, Q. Shi, T. Sun, N.-Y. Yuan, and J.-N. Ding, "Effect of glass thickness on temperature gradient and stress distribution during glass tempering," *Journal of Non-Crystalline Solids*, vol. 437, pp. 72–79, 2016, doi: 10.1016/j.jnoncrysol.2016.01.008.

[9] P. Romer, K. B. Pethani, and A. J. Beinert, "Effect of inhomogeneous loads on the mechanics of PV modules," *Prog. Photovolt: Res. Appl.*, vol. 32, no. 2, pp. 84–101, 2024, doi: 10.1002/pip.3738.

[10] *DIN EN 12150-1: Glas im Bauwesen – Thermisch vorgespanntes Kalknatron-Einscheiben-Sicherheitsglas: Teil 1: Definition und Beschreibung,* Deutsches Institut für Normung e. V., Berlin, 2019.

[11] *DIN EN 1863-1: Glas im Bauwesen – Teilvorgespanntes Kalknatronglas: Teil 1: Definition und Beschreibung; Deutsche Fassung 1863-1:2011,* Deutsches Institut für Normung e. V., Berlin, 2011.

[12] *Photovoltaic (PV) modules - Non-uniform snow load testing*, IEC 62938:2020, International Electrotechnical Commission (IEC), Geneva, Switzerland, 2020.
[13] E. Wagner, *Glasschäden: Oberflächenbeschädigungen, Glasbrüche in Theorie und Praxis*, 5th ed. Stuttgart: Fraunhofer IRB Verlag, 2020.
[14] *DIN EN 1288-1: Bestimmung der Biegefestigkeit von Glas: Teil 1: Grundlagen*, Deutsches Institut für Normung e. V., Berlin, Sep. 2000.

10.4229/EUPVSEC2025/3DO.19.3
020231-007

DETERMINING THE GLASS STRENGTH OF SOLAR GLASS - TEST AND EVALUATION METHODS

Hannah Reichart[1], Matthias Pander[2], Ruth Kasper[1]

[1] TH Köln - University of Applied Sciences, Faculty of Civil Engineering and Environmental Technology, Cologne Germany

[2] Fraunhofer Center for Silicon Photovoltaics (CSP), Halle (Saale), Germany

Fraunhofer CSP
Technology Arts Sciences TH Köln

Motivation

- Glass-glass PV modules are reaching a new high and a continued upward trend
- Increase in module dimensions up to 3 m^2
- Decrease of glass thickness from 3.2 mm to 2 mm – 1.6 mm
- Glass breakage of PV-Modules more likely

Research question: How can the strength of solar glass ≤ 2 mm be accurately determined?

Methodology

Literature research

Development and verification of a suitable test setup

Material tests: Strength evaluation and SCALP measurements

Evaluation method and statistical analysis

The material glass

- Brittle material behavior
- Theoretical material strength of glass is very high
- Actual strength depends on the condition of the surface
- Probabilistic approach is required to determine the characteristic strength f_k of glass
- A minimum of 30 equal specimen is required

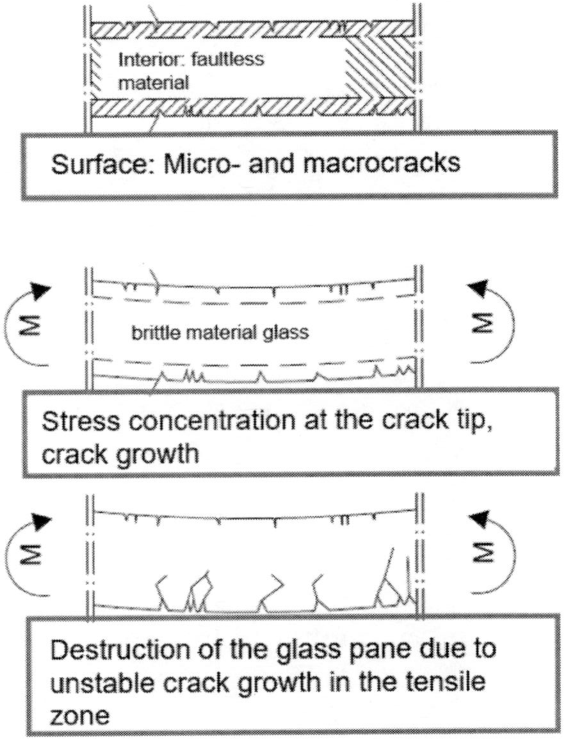

Determining the glass strength in the building sector

- EN 1288-3 standardizes tests for pane thicknesses of 3 mm to 19 mm
- Glass dimensions 360 mm x 1100 mm
- Calculation of the breaking stress using linear beam theory, assuming the deformations remain sufficiently small

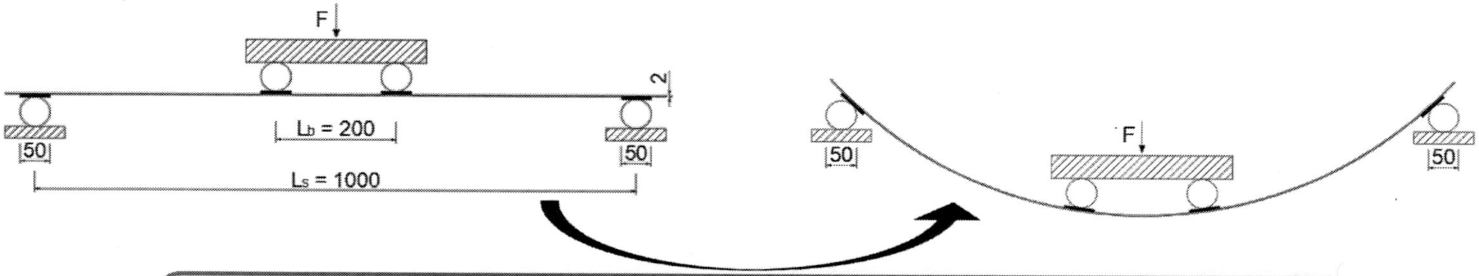

Problem: When testing panes ≤ 2 mm very large deformations occurs
→ Pane slips off the support rollers before reaching maximum load
→ Significant geometric nonlinear effects occur

EN 1288-3 does not apply to thin glass!

Adjustment of the test setup

- Reduction of the support spacing L_s from 1000 mm to 700 mm

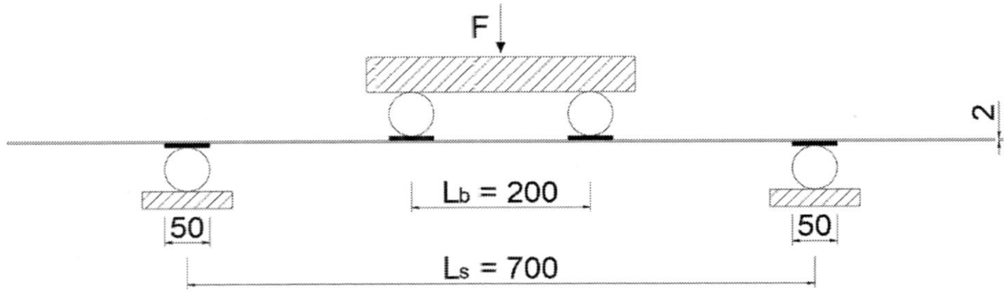

➡ Due to nonlinear effects and membrane stresses, development of a new evaluation method is necessary!

Numerical simulation and parameter study

- Numerical investigation with FEM solid simulation using ANSYS mechanical
- Consideration of various parameters, including glass E-modulus, roller friction, glass Poisson's ratio, and pane thickness

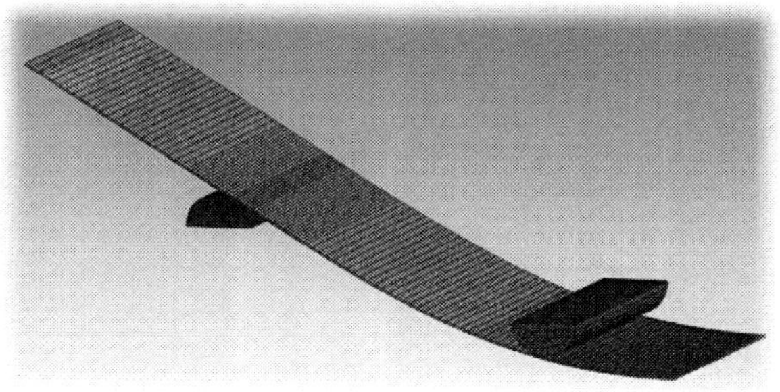

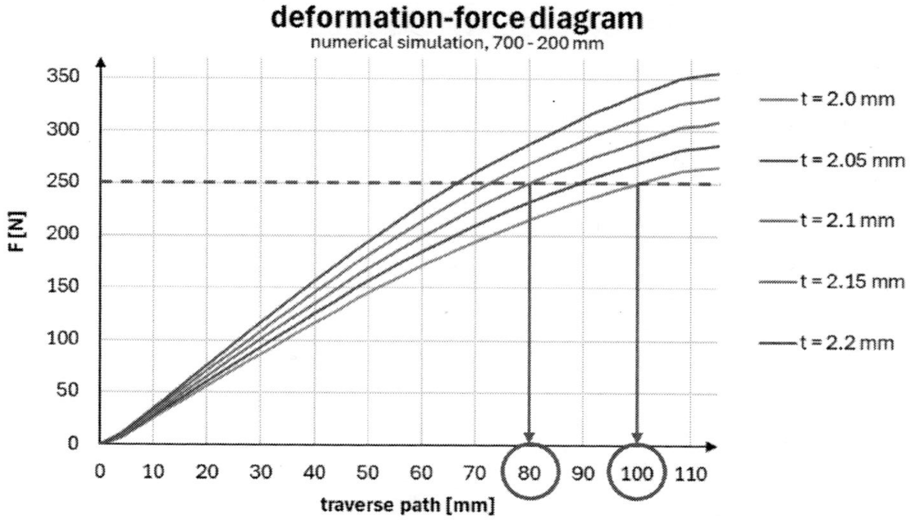

The significant influencing parameter is the glass thickness.

Verification of the numerical model through experiments

- Deformation and strain measurement
- Nonlinearity clearly visible

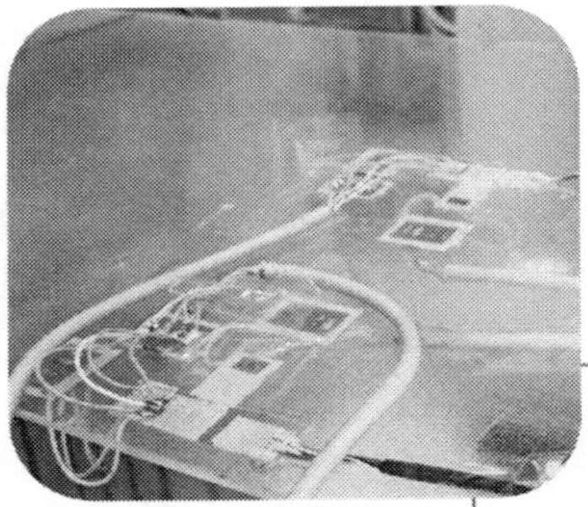

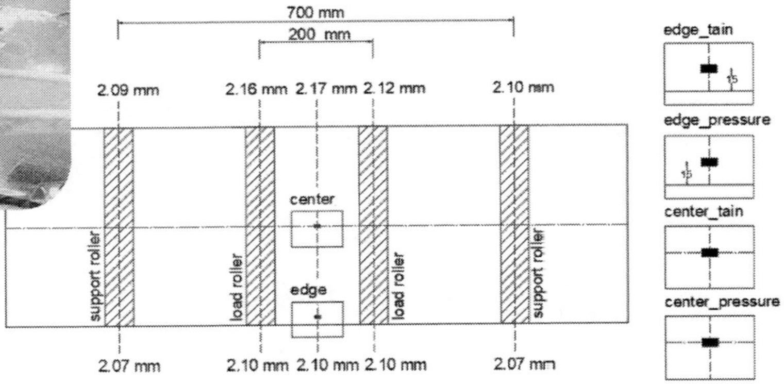

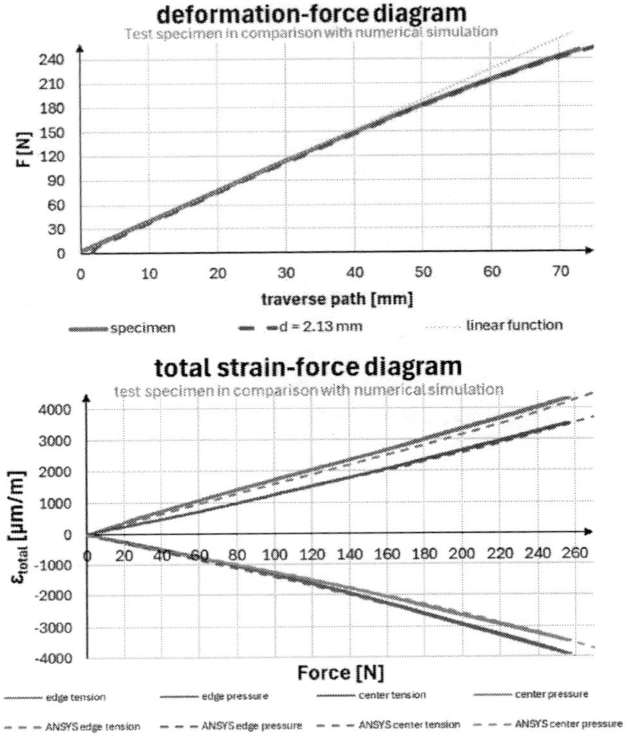

→ **Simulation fits the experimental curves.**

Test setup

- Material strength test were carried out at two Locations: Frauenhofer CSP Halle and TH Köln
- Total of 128 panes of different qualities of Glasmanufaktur Brandenburg (GMB)
- Additionally optical surface pre-stress measurement using SCALP

Serie	Location	Annealed solar glass	Thermally prestressed solar glass	Thermally prestressed with AR-coating
1	TH Köln	18 panes	23 panes	26 panes (AR - coating on tensile side)
2	CSP Halle	11 panes	10 panes	10 panes (AR-coating on tensile side)
3	TH Köln	-	14 panes	17 panes (8 AR-coating on tensile side/ 9 AR-coating on compression side)

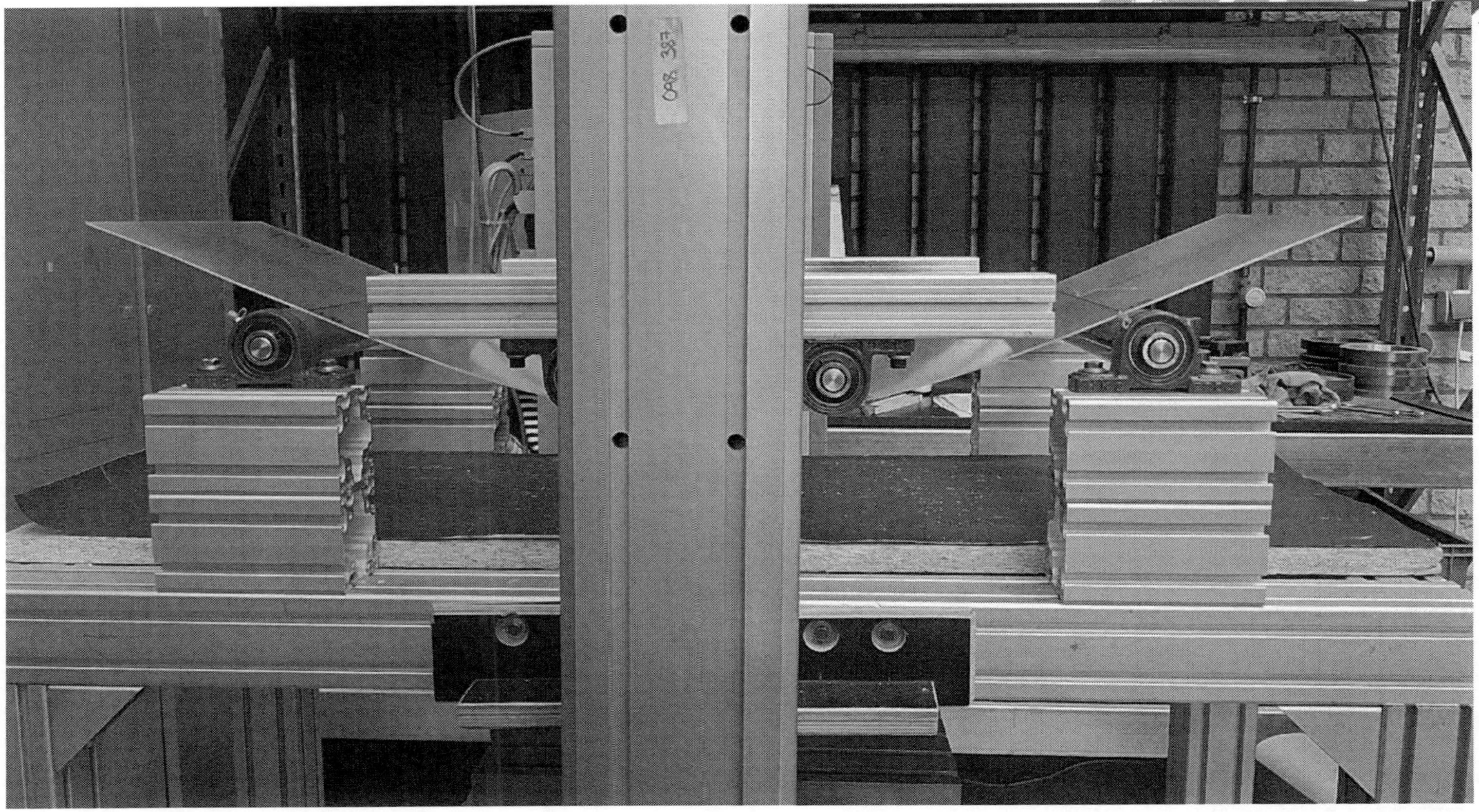
098 387

Evaluation Method for material strength

- Determination of the breaking stress using numerically determined curves

3. Consideration of the fracture origin across the width of the pane

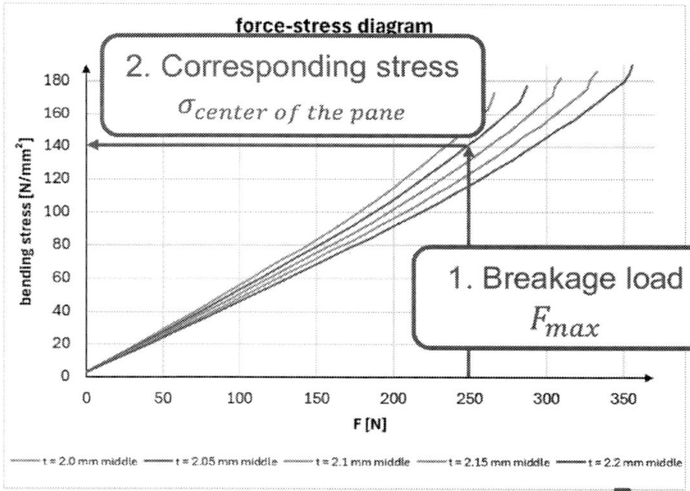

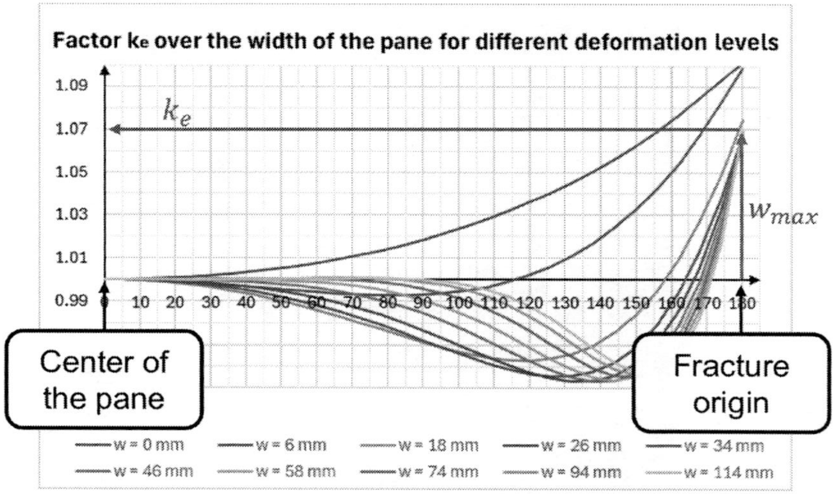

4. $\sigma_{eff} = \sigma_{center\ of\ the\ pane} \cdot k_e$

Evaluation and statistical analysis

- Characteristic strength corresponds to the 5% quantile value with a confidence level of 95%
- Lognormal and Weibull distribution was used

Annealed solar glass

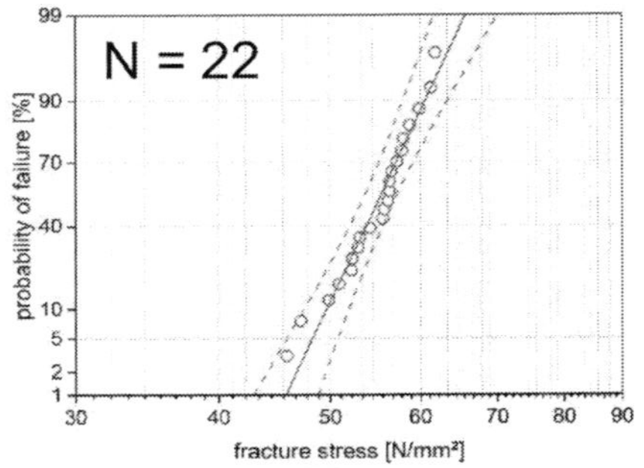

Thermally prestress glass

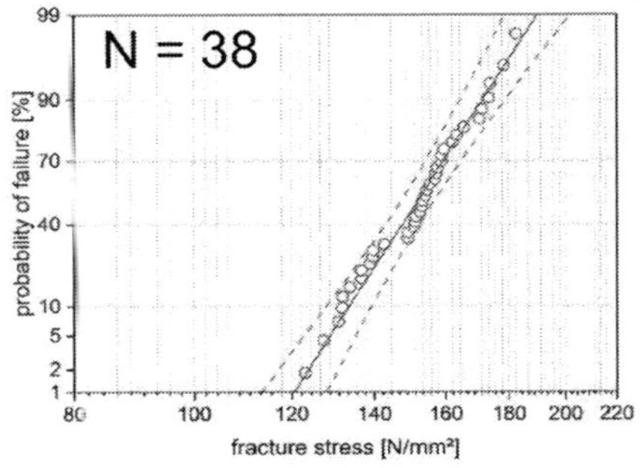

Thermally prestress with AR-coating

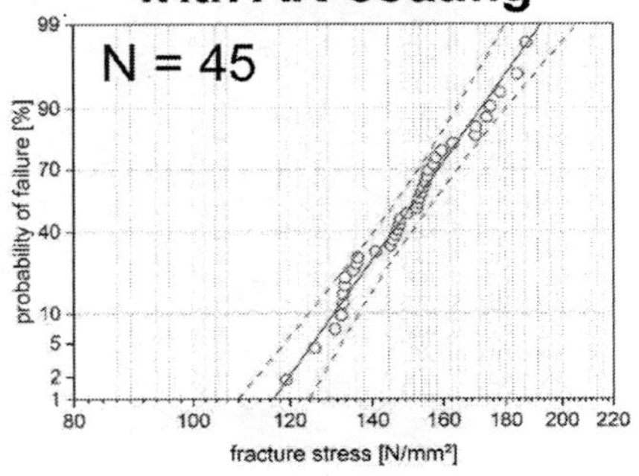

	Annealed solar glass	Thermally prestress glass	Thermally prestress with AR-coating
f_k Weibull	47 (**44** … 51)	122 (**113** … 132)	119 (**110** … 129)
f_k Lognormal	48 (**46** … 50)	129 (**123** … 132)	127 (**121** … 133)

Conclusion

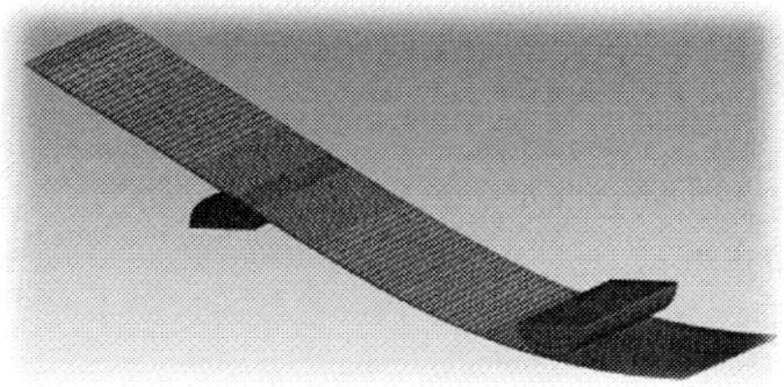

- Determining the strength of glass ≤ 2 mm with adapted four point bending test setup possible
- Due to nonlinear effects and membrane stresses, evaluation according to EN 1288-3 is not suitable; instead, evaluation via FEM simulation is required.
- Tested glass of GMB reached characteristic strength of:
  - Annealed glass $f_k = 44$ N/mm²
  - Thermally prestressed glass $f_k = 123$ N/mm²
  - Thermally prestressed with AR-coating $f_k = 121$ N/mm²

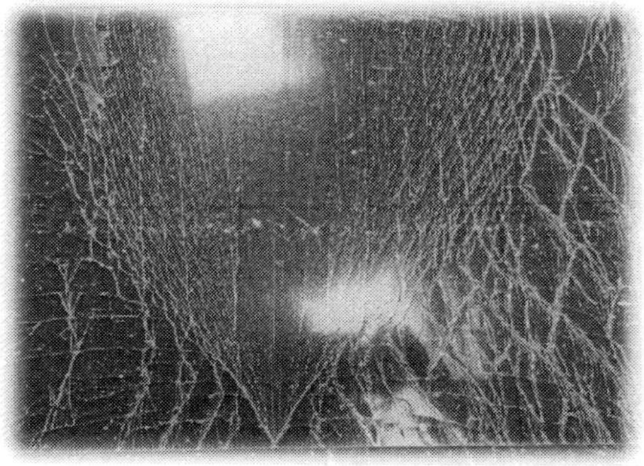

Outlook

- Verified material strength data are necessary for a reliable static design of PV-modules instead of load testing according to IEC 61215

Thank you for your attention!

Contact:

Hannah Reichart
TH Köln -
University of Applied Sciences
hannah_sophie.reichart@th-koeln.de

Matthias Pander
Fraunhofer Center for Silicon Photovoltaics (CSP)
matthias.pander@csp.fraunhofer.de

Ruth Kasper
TH Köln –
University of Applied Sciences
ruth.kasper@th-koeln.de

The Paper has been selected by the Committee of the EU PVSEC 2025 for submission to the journal “Progress in Photovoltaics”

Acknowledgement:

Federal Ministry for Economic Affairs and Energy

This publication was funded by the Federal Ministry for Economic Affairs and Energy in the project Green Solar Modules under grant number 00EE1161A and 03EE1161B. The findings herein reflect the work, and are solely the responsibility, of the authors. We would also like to thank Glasmanufaktur Brandenburg, our project partner, for providing the test specimens.

42nd European Photovoltaic Solar Energy Conference and Exhibition

This presentation was selected by the Sc. Committee of the EU PVSEC 2025 for submission of a full paper to one of the EU PVSEC's collaborating peer-reviewed journals.

Reliability studies of UV downshifting encapsulants after Damp-Heat and UV weathering

Jishnu Ramachandran Nair[1,2], Marius Lüdemann[1,2], Paul-Tiberiu Miclea[1], Kai Zhang[3], Kaining Ding[3], Andreas Lambertz[3], Ralph Gottschalg[1,2], Robert Heidrich[1,2], and Anton Mordvinkin[1]

[1]Fraunhofer Center for Silicon Photovoltaics (CSP), Otto-Eißfeldt-Str. 12, 06120 Halle, Germany,
[2] Anhalt University of Applied Sciences, Köthen, Sachsen-Anhalt, 06366, Germany
[3] IMD-3 Photovoltaics, Forschungszentrum Jülich GmbH, Jülich, Germany
Corresponding Author: anton.mordvinkin@csp.fraunhofer.de,
First authors: jishnu.ramachandran.nair@imws.fraunhofer.de, marius.luedemann@imws.fraunhofer.de

ABSTRACT: A rigorous degradation analysis of emerging encapsulants containing UV downshifters (DS) was conducted. The encapsulants are based on ethylene vinyl-acetate copolymer (EVA) and a three-layered system, composed of 2 EVAs flanking a polyolefin elastomer (POE) layer, so-called EPE. The UV-downshifting EVA and EPE were exposed to 1000 h damp-heat (DH), 120 kWh UV, and combined DH and UV (100 kWh) accelerated weathering tests and analyzed using a multi-faceted analytical approach. The UV-vis spectroscopy showed degradation of the UV downshifter after the accelerated aging, which was especially pronounced after the UV exposure. The findings were supported by the 2D fluorescence spectroscopy, which also suggested severe changes in the mode of action of the UV downshifter. The changed mode of action led to the reduction in the conversion efficiency by 2 orders of magnitude and shift of the excitation wavelength towards higher values, thus significantly worsening the original functionality. For the first time, encapsulants with UV downshifters were analyzed using pyrolysis-gas-chromatography (Py-GCMS), and the changes of the presumable UV downshifter signal could be directly correlated to the UV-vis and fluorescence spectroscopy results as well as degradation of antioxidant and hindered amine light stabilizer. Building up on the provided results, the degradation analysis will be continued with the encapsulants extracted from the aged minimodules, correlating the material and module degradation. This comprehensive characterization provides insights into the degradation behavior of DS encapsulants under accelerated aging conditions, contributing to a deeper understanding of DS material reliability needed for its PV integration and enabling the development of more robust and efficient PV modules.

Keywords: Downshifting , degradation, reliability

1 Introduction

UV downshifting (DS) encapsulants is an emerging class of active encapsulants that, apart from their typical properties directed to the cell protection against environmental factors, can enhance photovoltaic performance and cell protection by converting high-energy ultraviolet photons into lower-energy visible light . While module-level studies confirm the benefits of DS films, material-level investigations, particularly regarding long-term performance and weathering, require further exploration, especially concerning the stability of the DS materials in encapsulants themselves. Babics et al. [3] recently investigated the performance and reliability of PV modules made with co-extruded encapsulant containing a UV down-shifting compound, showing vulnerability towards photooxidation.

However, molecular details on the DS-encapsulants degradation are still missing. This study aspires to close the gap between the deterioration of the DS effect and relevant material changes causing it. To this end, the DS EVA and EPE encapsulants, aged according to typical accelerated weathering protocols for PV modules, will be rigorously analyzed. For the first time, the disappearance of the DS effect will be linked to the additive degradation (DS itself and stabilizing additives). Accompanying chemical and microstructural changes in the polymer matrix will be likewise scrutinized. The contribution given is highly relevant to facilitate the design of emerging DS encapsulants, whose reliability is not well understood yet. The study will provide insights into the enhancement of the encapsulant and hence module reliability.

2 Materials and Methods

The study aims to pinpoint the degradation mechanism of emerging EVA and EPE encapsulants containing UV downshifting moieties during UV and damp-heat (DH) accelerated aging. In particular, the factors leading to the degradation of the UV downshifting effect will be scrutinized. To this end, plain films as well as minimodules, based on the encapsulants, having different configurations (double glass, lightweight with a polymeric front sheet) modulating the moisture and oxygen ingress, will be weathered. The degradation behavior will be assessed by a variety of methods, enabling tracking the additive and polymer degradation. In the first iteration, the encapsulants will undergo 1000 h of the DH, 120 kWh of the UV exposure, and 1000 h at combined DH and UV conditions. The damp heat was conducted under standard conditions of 85°C and 85% relative humidity. The UV exposure was performed using a mercury light tube with a UV intensity of approximately 70 W/m2 between 320 and 400 nm, chamber temperature of around 25°C and no humidity control. The combined DH and UV weathering was carried out at 85°C, 60% relative humidity, and about 100 W/m2 UV irradiance between 300 and 400 nm. The degradation will be compared for the plain films and the films extracted from the minimodules to assess the importance of the module microclimate. Also, the material and module degradation will be correlated.

3 Results and Discussion

3.1 UV- Vis Spectroscopy

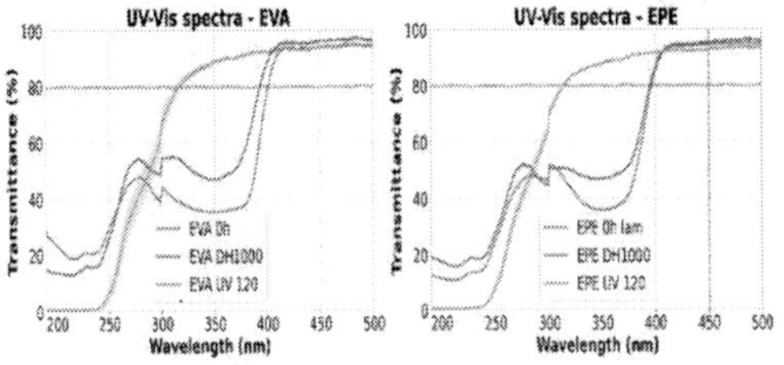

Figure 1: UV- Vis spectra of EVA (left) and EPE (right) films showing drastic changes for UV aged films

UV-Vis spectroscopy data featured a pronounced (but not complete) absorption below 400 nm in both EVA and EPE The accelerated aging (especially the UV exposure) reduced the absorption (increased the transmittance) in the UVA and UVB regions, which can be due to degradation of the UV absorbing [3] or/and UV downshifting species. The PyGCMS results below narrowed it down to the sole degradation of UV downshifters. No reduction in transmittance due to the chromophore formation was observed.

3.2 Fluorescence Spectroscopy

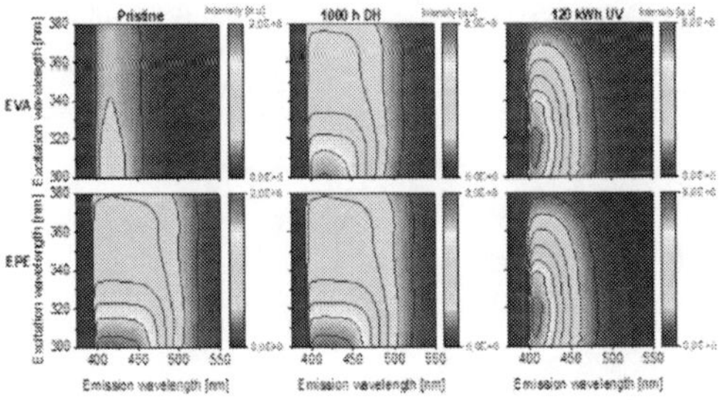

Figure 2 : 2D-fluorescence spectra for EVA (top) and EPE (bottom) in the pristine state (left) and after DH (middle) and UV (right) aging.

2D fluorescence spectroscopy was employed to analyze the changes in the mode of action of the UV downshifters. The EPE encapsulant exhibits a more pronounced fluorescence in the pristine state compared to EVA. Both show a maximum in the excitation wavelength below 300 nm. After DH, either no changes or some elevation in the fluorescence intensity could be observed. The elevation can be explained by the heterogeneous distribution of the UV downshifting species. Remarkable changes occurred after the UV exposure. First, the fluorescence intensity dropped by 2 orders of magnitude. Second, the maximum of the excitation wavelength shifted to higher values, which suggests that the UV downshifter underwent chemical conversion.

3.3 Fluorescence lifetime

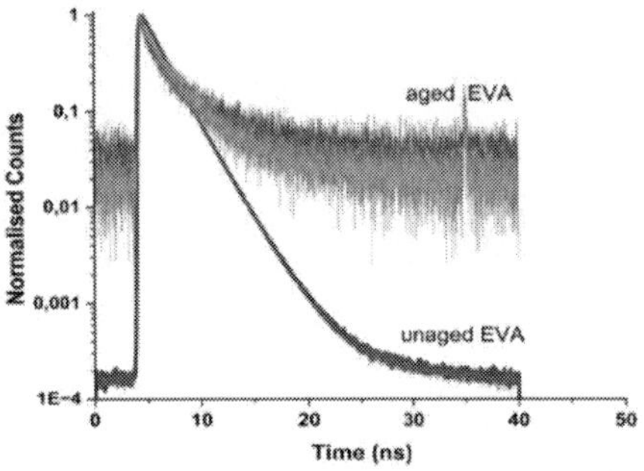

Figure 2 Fluoresence decay plots for aged and unaged EVA

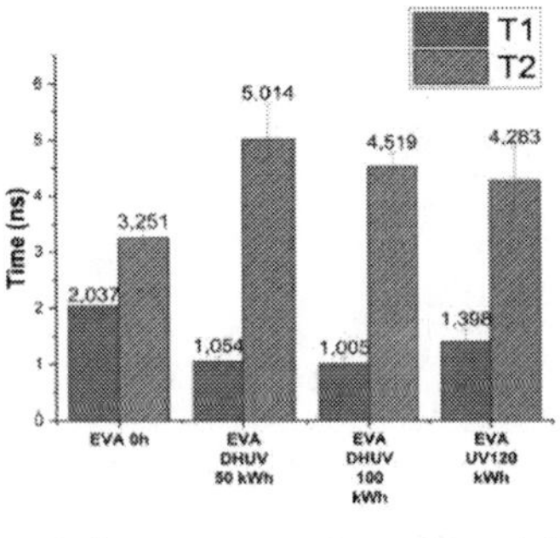

Figure 4 Decay components as T1 and T2 after exponential decay fits .

Fluorescence lifetime plots showed a significant change after the combined DH and UV weathering. The decays were fitted to a biexponential function, yielding characteristic lifetimes T1 and T2. After weathering, the faster component T1 became comparatively faster to unaged sample. It points to the possibility of fluorescence quenching and creation of new non radiative pathways [6]. On the other hand, the increase in the slower component T2 hints towards new fluorophore activity [6]. Further investigations are needed to provide more insights into chemical transformations.

3.4 Pyrolysis-Gas Chromatography-Mass Spectrometry

Pyrolysis-Gas Chromatography-Mass Spectrometry (PY-GCMS) was employed to provide the qualitative and semi-quantitative analysis of the EVA and EPE films in the pristine and aged state. The exact description of the measurement method can be found in [4]. The analysis showed that the films include crosslinking additives (peroxide and accelerator), different types of adhesion promoters, antioxidant, plasticizers, hindered amine light stabilizer (HALS) and its fragments, and one additive unknown to the NIST library, which can be presumably a UV downshifter. No UV absorbers were found, suggesting that the above reduction in absorbance detected by UV-vis spectroscopy can be completely related to the UV downshifter degradation. shows intensities of the selected additives which can especially contribute to the long-term stability against the DH and UV: antioxidant, HALS and its fragment, presumable UV downshifter. The intensities were obtained in the pristine and aged state and compared after normalizing to the sample mass. It allowed one to track the relative changes.

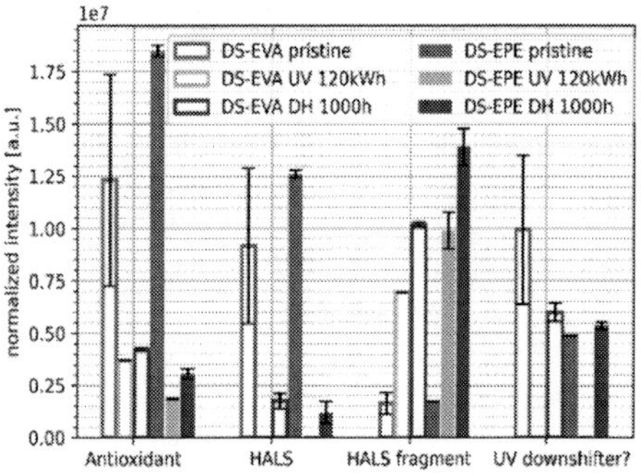

Figure 5 Normalized intensity of additives quantified by PY-GCMS (DS-EVA UV 120kWh: single determination, remaining: double determination)

The antioxidant content in EVA and EPE decreased more during UV weathering than during DH weathering. The same result can be seen for the HALS, which was already completely depleted after 120 kWh of the UV weathering. In [5], it was shown that the HALS can degrade under both UV and DH conditions. During aging, large HALS molecules fragmented into smaller ones, which stay active and continue protecting the polymer [5]. The presumable UV downshifter showed little change in concentration after DH but completely disappeared after the UV exposure.

This observation agrees with the above fluorescence data and supports the hypothesis of the additive being a UV downshifter. However, the additive nature must be still elucidated, e.g. based on its mass spectrum. Further, organic UV downshifters are known to be vulnerable against photooxidation (UV+O2)[2]. Therefore, the depletion of the antioxidant and HALS can have a negative impact on its stability.

4 Conclusion

This study successfully demonstrated that the degradation of organic UV downshifters can be effectively tracked using combination of methods like py GCMS and Fluorescence lifetime and spectroscopy. It revealed that HALS and antioxidants are consumed in parallel, offering protection against photo-oxidation. The role of additional additives in enhancing the stability of the downshifter needs further investigation along with fluorphore mechanisms. These findings highlight the importance of formulations of downshifting encapsulants for the reliability and long-term performance of PV modules.

5 References

[1] T. Trupke, M. A. Green, and P. Würfel, "Improving solar cell efficiencies by down-conversion of high-energy photons," Jul. 28, 2002, American Institute of Physics.

[2] M. Babics et al., "Performance and reliability of PV modules made with co-extruded encapsulant containing UV down-shifting compound." 2024.

[3] V. Fiandra, L. Sannino, C. Andreozzi, G. Flaminio, and M. Pellegrino, "New PV encapsulants: assessment of change in optical and thermal properties and chemical degradation after UV aging," Dec. 23, 2023, Elsevier BV. doi: 10.1016/j.polymdegradstab.2023.110643.

[4] Heidrich, Robert, Anton Mordvinkin, and Ralph Gottschalg. "Quantification of UV protecting additives in ethylene-vinyl acetate copolymer encapsulants for photovoltaic modules with pyrolysis-gas chromatography-mass spectrometry." Polymer Testing 118 (2023): 107913.

[5] Heidrich, Robert, et al. " From Performance Measurements to Molecular Level Characterization: Exploring the Differences between Ultraviolet and Damp Heat Weathering of Photovoltaics Modules." Solar RRL 8.10 (2024): 2400144.

[6] Tunstall García, H. (2025). Design and Characterisation of Hybrid Organic-Inorganic Materials for Luminescence Downshifting Devices [Apollo - University of Cambridge Repository]. https://doi.org/10.17863/CAM.117427

10.4229/EUPVSEC2025/3DO.20.5

EU PVSEC

PCCL
Polymer Competence Center Leoben

Festina Lente! The Impact of Lamination Duration on Encapsulant Stability

Nikolina Pervan, Jutta Geier, Christian Veas, Gernot Oreski

Polymer Competence Center Leoben GmbH, 8700 Leoben, Austria
Chair of Materials Science and Testing of Polymers, Montanuniversität Leoben, Leoben, Austria

42nd EUPVSEC, Bilbao, Spain, 22 – 26. September 2025.

It is all about encapsulants!

PCCL
Polymer Competence Center Leoben

- **Adhesion**
- **Protection**
- **Light transmission**
- **Aesthetic**

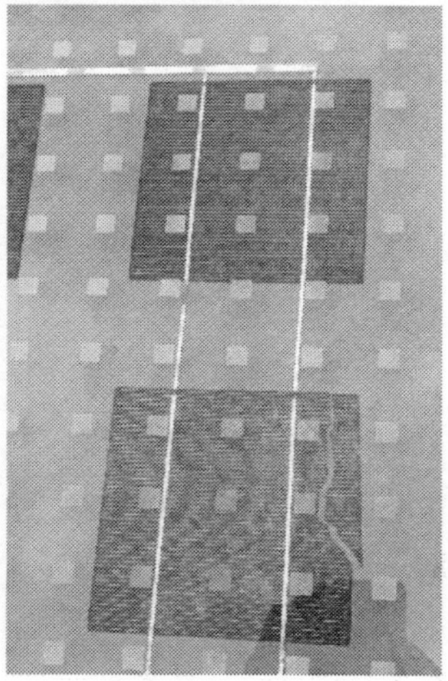

- Most commonly used encapsulants:
  - **EVA** (ethylene vinyl acetate)
  - Polyolefin (**POE** – crosslinking, **TPO** – non-crosslinking)
  - **EPE** (coextruded EVA-polyolefin-EVA)

Different polymer chemical and physical structures behind the same name – different material behaviour!!!

K. Aitola, et al., Encapsulation of commercial and emerging solar cells with focus on perovskite solar cells, Solar Energy, Vol 237, 2022.

Encapsulant's processing history

PCCL
Polymer Competence Center Leoben

Encapsulant production process

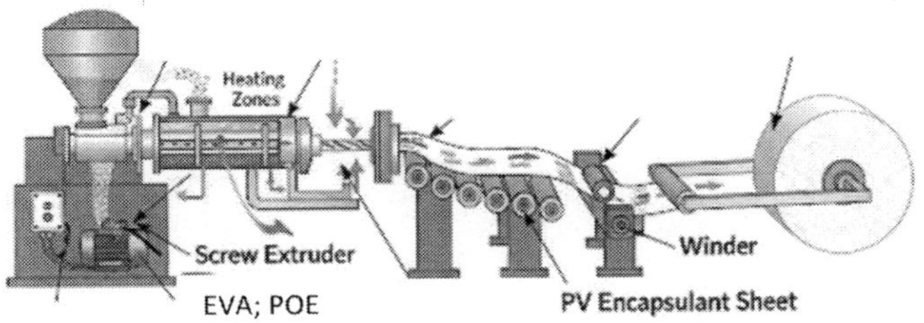

Extrusion + forming R2R process: orientation created – machine direction (MD)

PV module lamination process

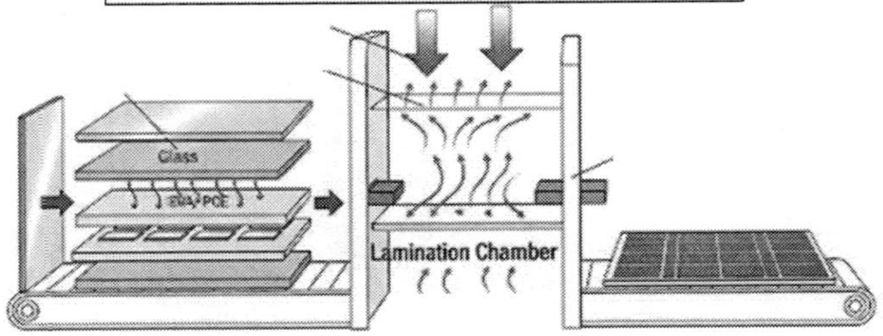

Lamination – 1 step process: MD orientation removed (vacuum); new orientation created (lamination)

Introduced stress in PV module:
- interconnection failure
- cell fragmentation
- interlayer delamination
- backsheet dislocation and deformation

Image created using AI tool „Gemini 2.5 Flash".

PCCL
Polymer Competence Center Leoben

Images created using AI tool „Gemini 2.5 Flash"

Experimental work – encapsulant types

PCCL
Polymer Competence Center Leoben

Encapsulant type	Polymer type (FTIR-ATR analysis)	Crosslinking type (TDS)
EVA	ethylene vinyl acetate	peroxides
POE-1	ethylene α-olefin	peroxides
POE-2	ethylene α-olefin	peroxides
TPO	ethylene ethyl acrylate	non-crosslinking
EPE-1	2x ethylene vinyl acetate (P?)	peroxides (EVA)
EPE-2	2x ethylene vinyl acetate (P?)	peroxides

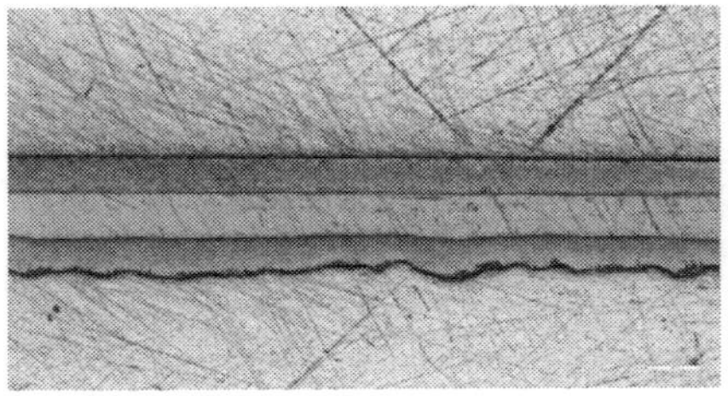

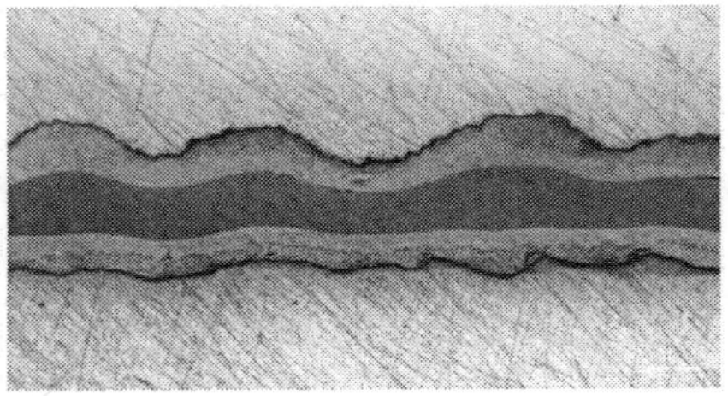

EPE (EVA – polyolefin – EVA) same name tag – different encapsulants

Experimental work – encapsulant lamination and characterisation

PCCL Polymer Competence Center Leoben

LAMINATION

- 2 encapsulant layers per lamination
- 20 x 20 cm^2 size
- Stack: glass / Teflon / encapsulant / Teflon / encapsulant / Teflon / glass

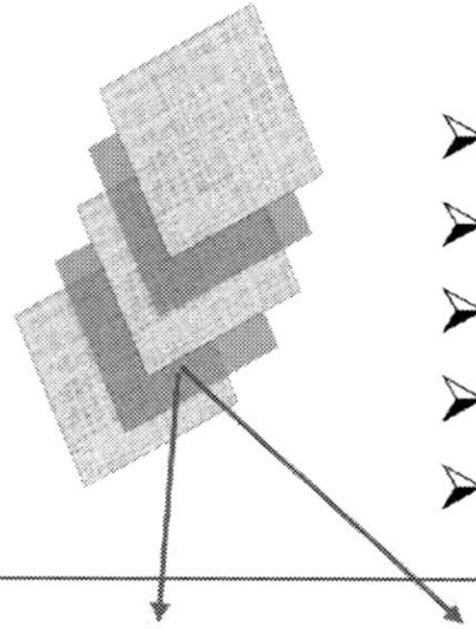

Lamination times

- **0** min – **non-laminated** – production history
- **2** and **5** min – short lamination times
- **10**, **12** and **15** min – industrial standards
- **20** and **30** min – extended lamination time
- *Lamination temperature – from TDS and from DSC*

Degree of curing – DSC (IEC 62788-1-6:2017**)**

- Determination of degree of curing for crosslinking encapsulants according to:
  - **Residual enthalpy** (crosslinking process)
  - **Melt/freeze (MF) method** (crystallization peak)

Coefficient of thermal expansion (CTE) – Digital image correlation (DIC) (20 °C to 140 °C**)**

- Determination of thermomechanical properties:
  - **Non-laminated encapsulant** vs. **laminated samples** (lamination duration impact)

DSC is commonly used to measure degree of curing in crosslinking encapsulants with peroxides, but determining lamination time for non-crosslinking types remains challenging. **Can we see which lamination time is optimal for both encapsulant types from the thermomechanical behaviour**?

PCCL
Polymer Competence Center Leoben

Images created using AI tool „Gemini 2.5 Flash"

DSC – facts about encapsulants

- **TPO** as non-crosslinking encapsulant is excluded from the calculations
- **EPE-1** - polyolefin component is a non-crosslinking type - T_m and Tc are the same for all lamination times
- **EPE-2** - polyolefin is a crosslinking type – 2nd crystallization peak present for lamination times above 12 minutes – *due to the presence of 2nd crystallization peak excluded from the MF method calculations*

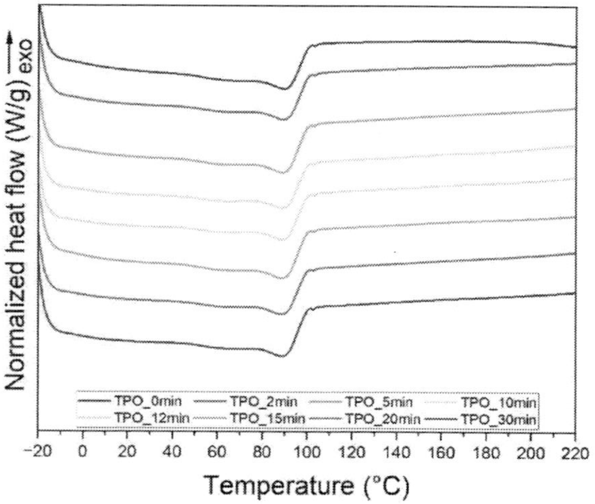

TPO – 2nd heating curves

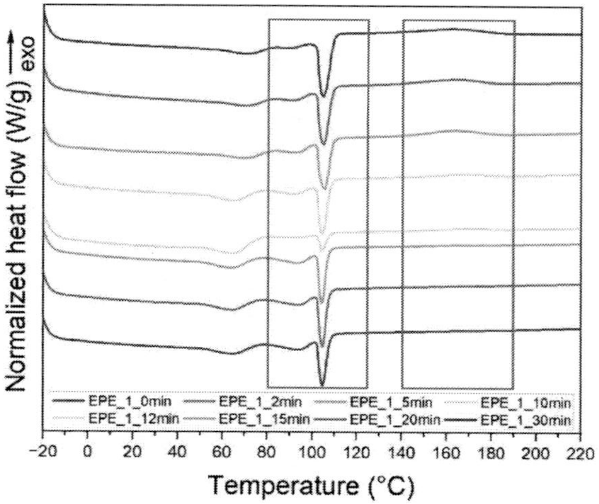

EPE-1 – 2nd heating curves

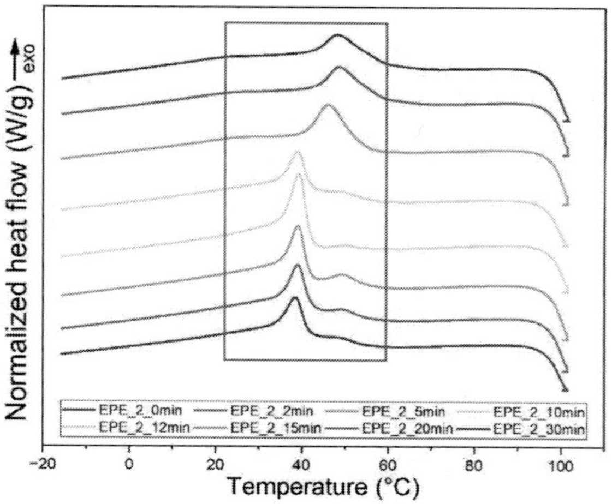

EPE-2 – 1st cooling curves

DSC – curing degrees according to residual enthalpy and melt/freeze (MF) method

PCCL
Polymer Competence Center Leoben

- Curing degrees calculated from residual enthalpy and MF methods differ
- Both DSC methods may not deliver reliable results for EPE - the same issue is expected from Soxhlet method!
- Unreliable results due to the unknown data:
  - Are all layers crosslinking?
  - What is the thickness distribution of the layers?
- All of the methods depend on weight – results can be over/under estimated

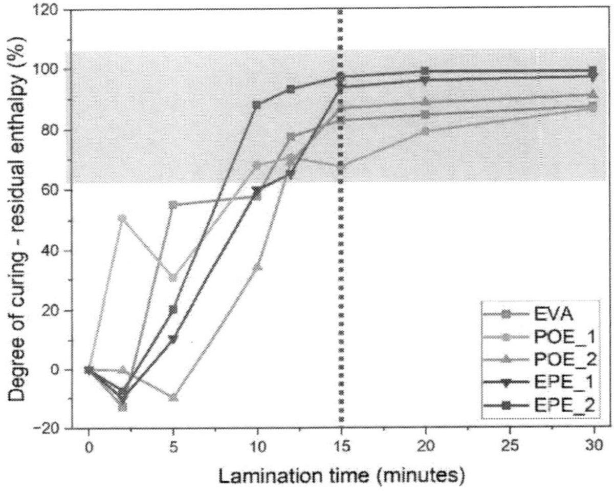

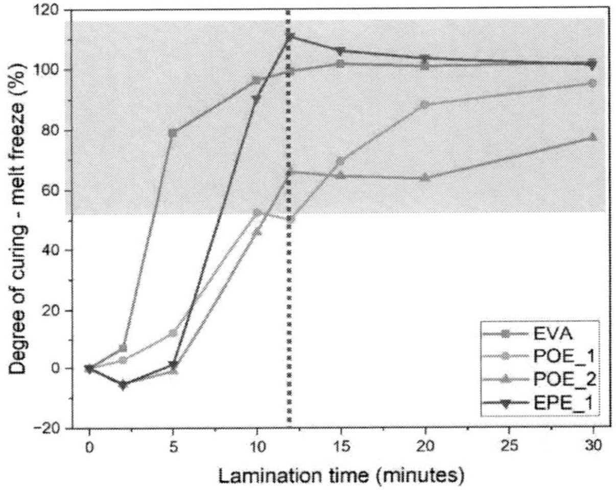

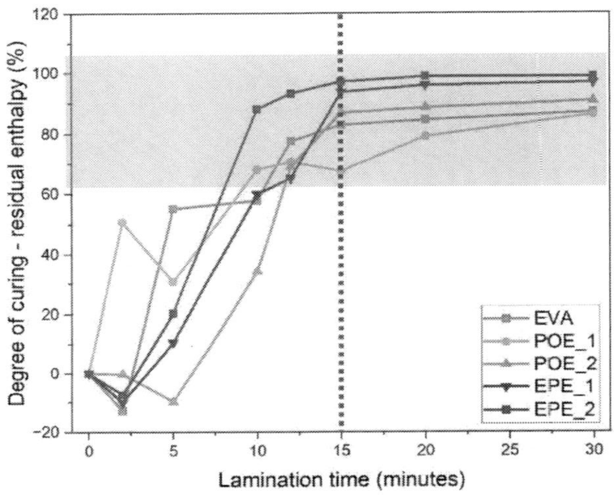

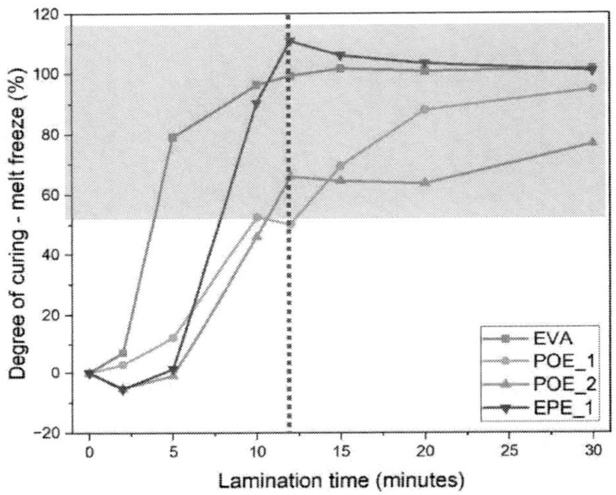

Non-laminated encapsulants vs. 30 minutes laminated encapsulants – CTE

PCCL
Polymer Competence Center Leoben

Inherited behaviour - stress during the lamination

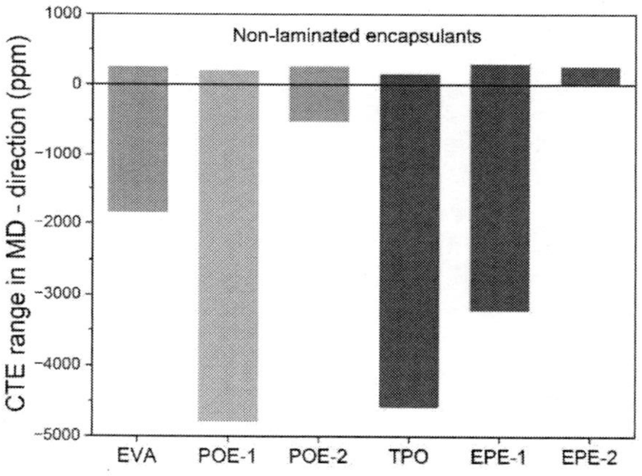

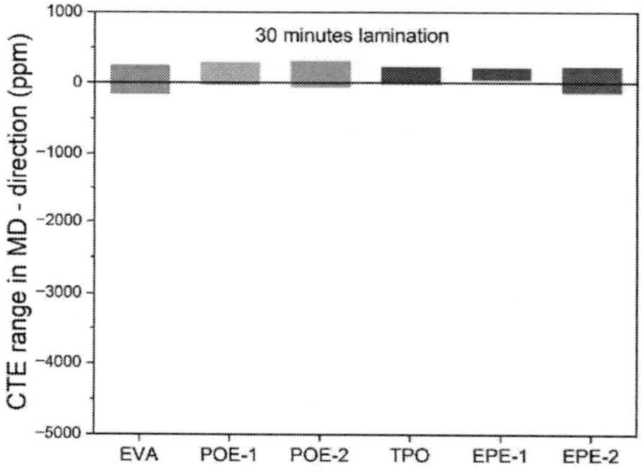

Thermomechanical behaviour/stress during lifetime

- **Negative CTE values** represent **shrinkage** of **non-laminated encapsulant** in the **MD direction**:
  - POE-1, **TPO** and **EPE-1** - high; EVA – medium; POE-2 and **EPE-2** – low shrinkage
  - Material orientation and extrusion processing conditions are the reason for shrinkage of encapsulant
- Non-crosslinking polyolefins in **TPO** and **EPE-1** exhibit high shrinkage for non-laminated state, but have lowest CTE value range after 30 minutes lamination
- Interestingly, **EPE-2** is characterised by an increase of CTE values range after the lamination

Results of CTE – for all lamination times – TPO and EPE-2

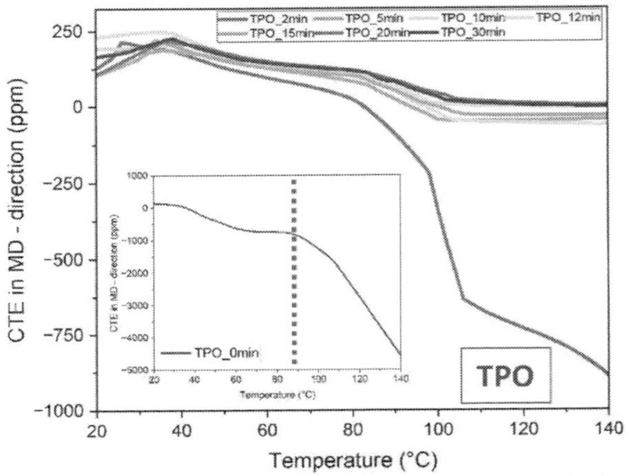

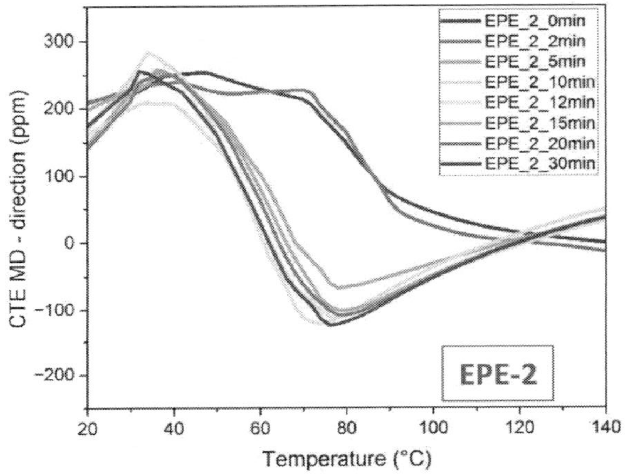

- Non-laminated **TPO** exhibits strong decrease (shrinkage) in CTE values once reaching **melting temperature onset**
- **High CTE values** for **0**, **2** (and **5**) minutes of TPO, EVA, (POE-1 and EPE-1) laminated samples is a sign of too short lamination times for polymer chains reorientation
- **EPE-2** and **POE-2** have **lower CTE values for 0 and 2 min** samples compared to the rest of encapsulants
  - **How does the extrusion process differ for these samples?**
- All encapsulants reached “final” CTE values by **10 minutes** of lamination duration – time needed for **chain reorientation** ((non-)crosslinking) and **polymer network creation** (crosslinking)
- Higher degrees of curing (according to DSC) do not impact CTE values of encapsulants significantly

Encapsulant before and after CTE measurement

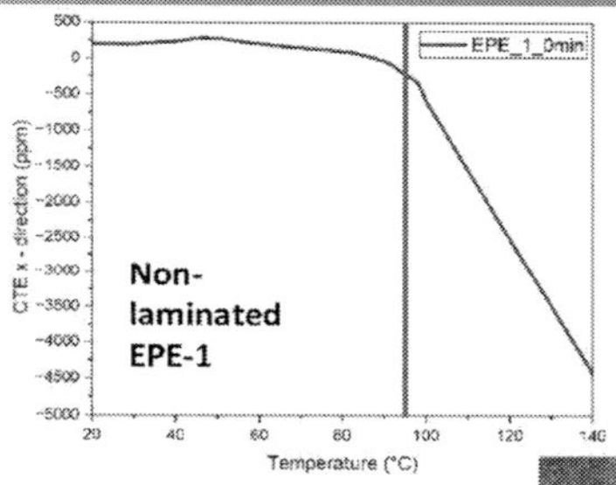

EPE-1_0 min before and after CTE measurement
(**heating from 20 to 140 °C and cooling back to 20 °C**)

Overestimation of shrinkage

Introduced stress in PV module

PCCL
Polymer Competence Center Leoben

Impact???

Non-laminated encapsulants can shrink significantly during the vacuum step in lamination process due to the inherited polymer chain orientation from the extrusion process - this can cause various issues from interconnection failures, cell fragmentation and delamination especially for emerging and thin film technologies perovskites, CIGS, tandem.

Too short lamination time may affect **early life PV module failure** for encapsulants with high shrinkage.

Laminating for at least 10 minutes (5 minutes for TPO) will reset the material's processing history and reorient polymer chains. However, this does not eliminate thermomechanical stress caused by the high, temperature-dependent CTE of encapsulants that is still present in PV modules during service.

Images created using AI tool „Gemini 2.5 Flash"

Conclusions and outlook

- Different polymer properties behind the same name

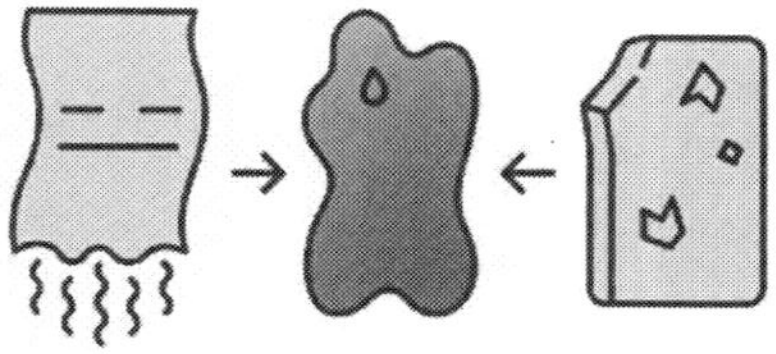

- Calculations of degree of curing from residual enthalpy and melt/freeze method – inapplicable for new EPE encapsulants

- All samples reached "final" thermomechanical properties by 10 minutes of lamination duration – including non-crosslinking types

How does the extrusion process differ for encapsulants?

Image created using AI tool „Gemini 2.5 Flash".

Acknowledgment

PCCL Polymer Competence Center Leoben

This work was conducted as part of the Solar Era Net Project “DELIGHT”, which is supported under the umbrella of SOLAR-ERA.NET Cofund by Austrian Research Promotion Agency (FFG, contract number FO999897443), Swiss Federal Office of Energy (SFOE, contract number SI/502501-01) and Flanders Innovation and Entrepreneurship (VLAIO, contract number HBC.2022.0406). SOLAR-ERA.NET is supported by the European Commission within the EU Framework Programme for Research and Innovation HORIZON 2020 (Cofund ERA-NET Action, N° 691664).

This work was conducted as part of the Austrian “e!MISSION.at – Energy Mission Austria” project “PV Industriefassade” (FFG No. FO999915062) funded by the Austrian Climate and Energy Fund and the Austrian Research Promotion Agency (FFG).

PCCL
Polymer Competence Center Leoben

Image created using AI tool „Gemini 2.5 Flash".

POTENTIAL OF DECIMETER-RESOLUTION GROUND ALBEDO DATA FOR BIFACIAL PHOTOVOLTAICS

Niklas Blum, Bijan Nouri, Yann Fabel, Stefan Wilbert
Deutsches Zentrum für Luft- und Raumfahrt e.V. (DLR)

DLR

Agenda

- Motivation
- Approach
- Case study
- Conclusion

Motivation
Relevance of albedo information for bifacial PV

- Performance models for bifacial PV plants can exhibit notable deviations
- Inaccurate ground albedo contributes a considerable part to uncertainty
- Variations of ground albedo are frequent in PV plants:
  - temporally as vegetation recovers from construction works and seasonal changes
  - spatially with different surface types present in a PV plant:
    - Different rock types
    - Sand
    - vegetation of different type, height and stage
    - …

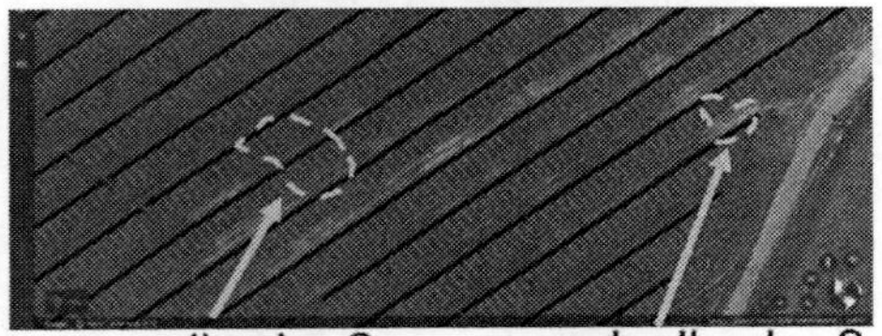

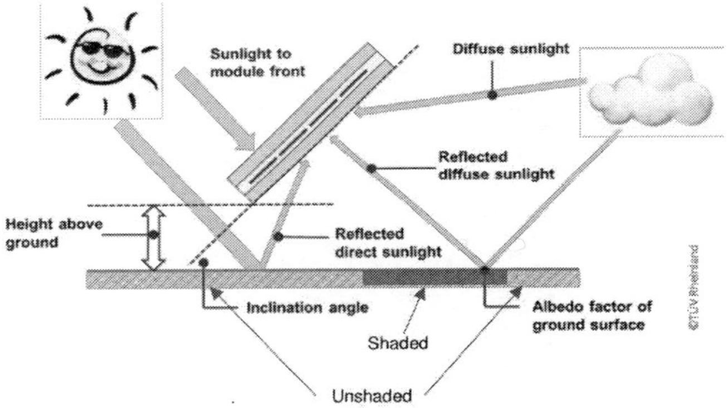

Niklas Blum, Bijan Nouri et al., DLR Institute of Solar Research, 22.09.2025

Motivation
Relevance of albedo information for bifacial PV

- Uncertainty in albedo information affects all phases of a PV project…
  - Yield prediction before construction
    - Bankability affected
    - Sub-optimal design selected
  - Acceptance testing
    - Economic loss if guaranteed performance not met
  - Tracker control
    - Contribution of rear-side irradiance over-simplified
    - Sub-optimal performance under certain conditions
  - Fault detection
    - Differences between inverters, PV strings partly obscured

Image source: https://commons.wikimedia.org/wiki/File:Suntrix_Horizontal_Single_Axis_tracker_with_Tilted_Modules.JPG

Niklas Blum, Bijan Nouri et al., DLR Institute of Solar Research, 22.09.2025

Motivation
State-of-the-art albedo data sources

- Ground measurements
  - Point-wise
  - High cost
  - Practical difficulty to find large unshaded space
  - IEC 61724-1 Class A one or more measurement positions depending on plant size

- Alternative: Remotely sensed
  - MODIS
    - 500 m x 500 m resolution (footprint in image)
  - Sentinel, Landsat and other open access systems
    - Up to 10 m x 10 m resolution (footprint in image)
  - → To coarse to distinguish PV rows from ground

- This study: Centimeter-resolution albedo from aerial images (case study, footprint in image)

Image source: https://www.linkedin.com/posts/cfv-solar-test-laboratory_groundwork-joins-solaranywhere-by-clean-activity-7346728152729462773-d5YM (Accessed 18.09.2025)

Approach
Centimeter-resolution ground albedo

- Commercial satellite constellations show potential beyond state of the art
  - Multispectral reflectance data: panchromatic, R, G, B, NIR, …
  - Fine ground sampling distances (GSD) of 30 cm (15 cm with super-resolution techniques)
- Fine resolution allows to characterize surface in detail
  - Built surfaces, shadows, unshaded ground
  - Surface types: Green/dry vegetation, sand, rock, snow, concrete
- Ground albedo can be calculated from the reflectance information of unshaded ground pixels
  - Radiometric relationship between pixel reflectance and broadband albedo
  - Surface classification and typical albedo per surface type

Image taken at PSA. The research site Plataforma Solar de Almería (PSA) is owned and operated by the Spanish CIEMAT

Exemplary pixel

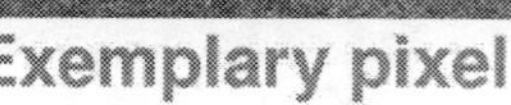

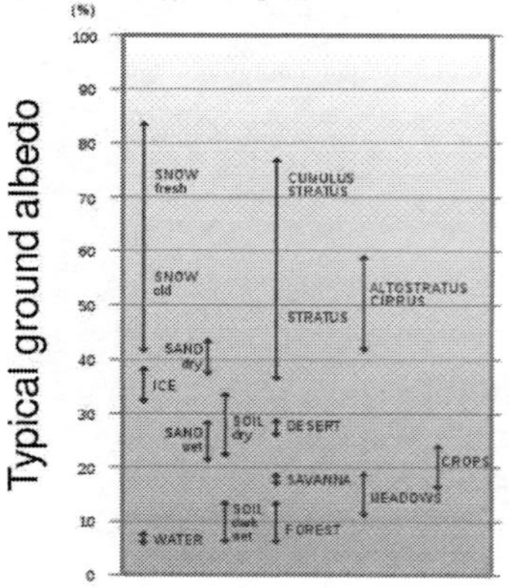

Niklas Blum, Bijan Nouri et al., DLR Institute of Solar Research, 22.09.2025

Approach
Current case study

- 3 exemplary PV plants in southern Germany and Spain selected

- Aerial images with ground sampling distances (GSD) of 20-22 cm represent satellite images
  → Similar GSD to Worldview-3 (GSD 15-30 cm)
  → No atmospheric correction required

Germany

Image source: Bayerische Vermessungsverwaltung GeoBasis-DE / BKG 2018 – Daten verändert Copernicus Sentinel-2 der Europäischen Union, Datenbezug 2018, verarbeitet durch das Bundesamt für Kartographie und Geodäsie (BKG)

Spain 1

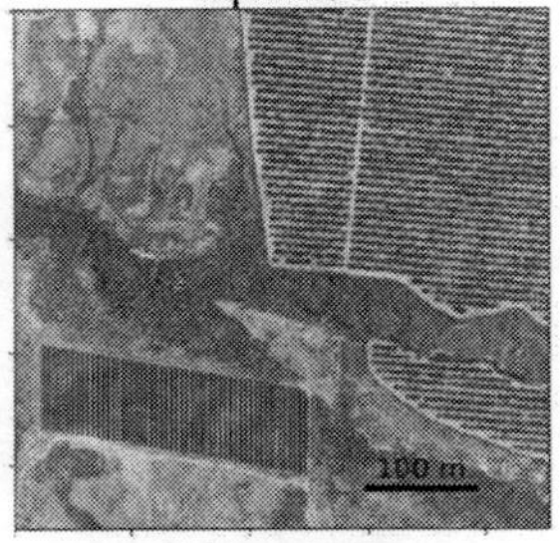

Spain 2

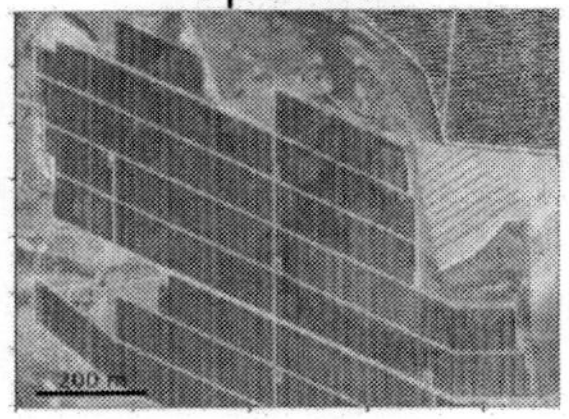

Image source: Centro Nacional de Información Geográfica (2025). Accessed 24.01.2025. fototeca.cnig.es/fototeca/

Approach
Current case study

- PV modules segmented
- Shades of PV modules calculated from PV module positions and solar geometry
- PV and shades masked
- Masked areas filled (inpainting) with information from surrounding pixels

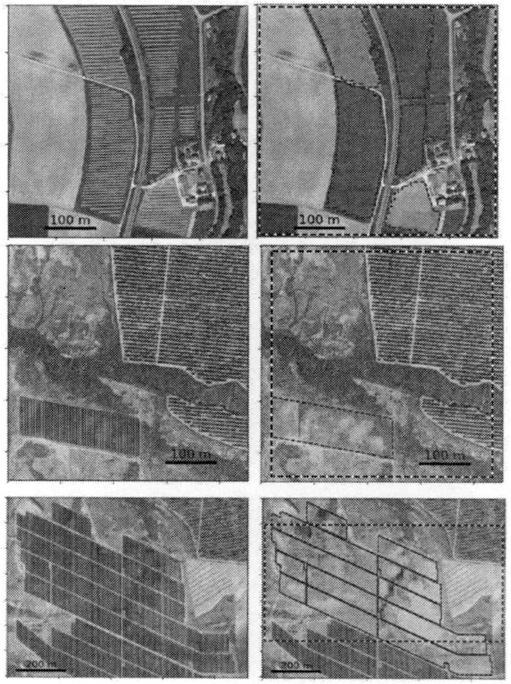

Niklas Blum, Bijan Nouri et al., DLR Institute of Solar Research, 22.09.2025

Approach
Current case study

- Ground albedo estimated as linear function of R, G, B intensities' weighted average
- Estimation calibrated using pixels with known surface type and corresponding ground albedo (literature)
- Resulting albedo maps exhibit plausible distributions of albedo values with variations related to
  - Agricultural activity
  - Height profile,
  - Soil and vegetation properties

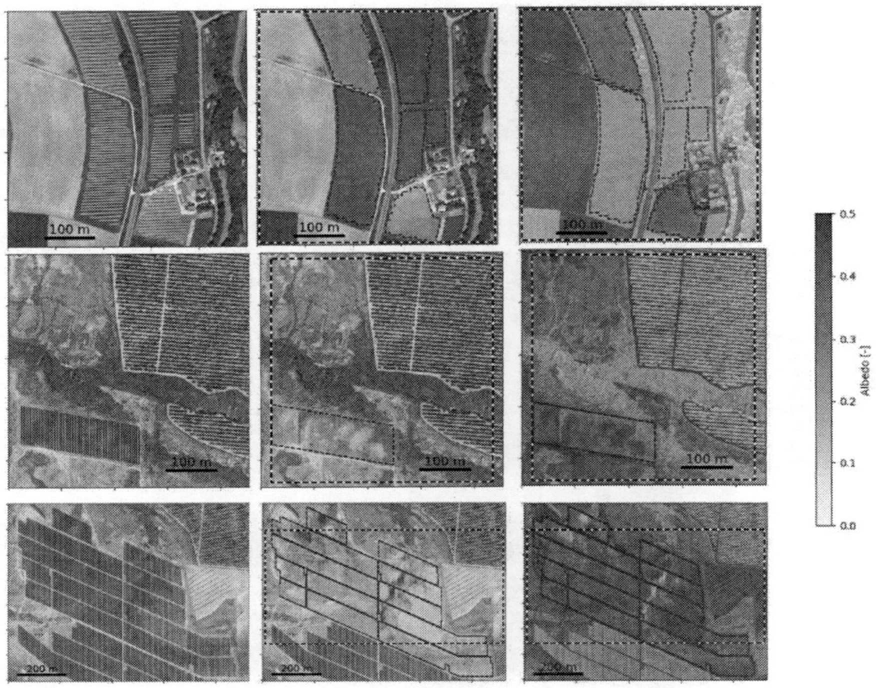

Niklas Blum, Bijan Nouri et al., DLR Institute of Solar Research, 22.09.2025

Approach
Current case study

- Albedo information from aerial images used as input for annual PV yield simulations using PVWatts
- Temporal variation of ground albedo neglected for simplicity
- 3 scenarios evaluated
  - High-resolution ('**HR**') albedo: Representative albedo calculated over PV plant footprint using HR albedo map
  - '**Ground measurement**': 5 sampling points defined which represent bins between $0^{th} – 20^{th}$, $20^{th} – 40^{th}$, …, $80^{th} – 100^{th}$ percentiles of the albedo distribution in the HR albedo map
  - '**MODIS**' albedo: HR albedo map averaged over imaginary 500 m x 500 m pixels, **including PV and shades**
- HR albedo used as reference in the following

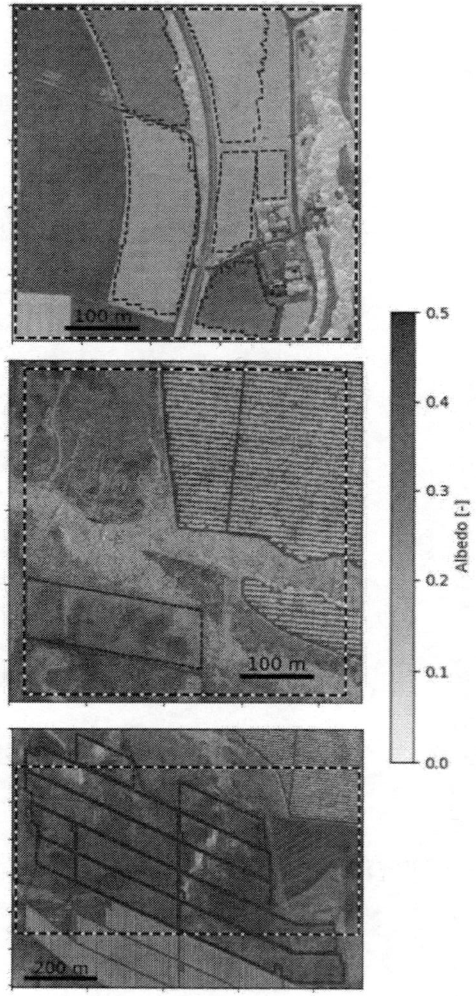

Niklas Blum, Bijan Nouri et al., DLR Institute of Solar Research, 22.09.2025

Study results

- 'MODIS' albedo deviates notably from 'HR' albedo
  - Seinsheim: overestimation by 0.041 → nearby dry plowed fields
  - Tabernas 1: strong underestimation by 0.072 → dark green olive grove nearby
  - Tabernas 2: strong underestimation by 0.098 → dark PV
- 'Ground measurement'
  - Significant variation of the ground albedo in all plants
  - Accordingly representative measurement depends strongly selection of measurement point
- Shortcomings of both state-of-the-art methods:
  - Systematic deviations
  - No resolution of spatial variations

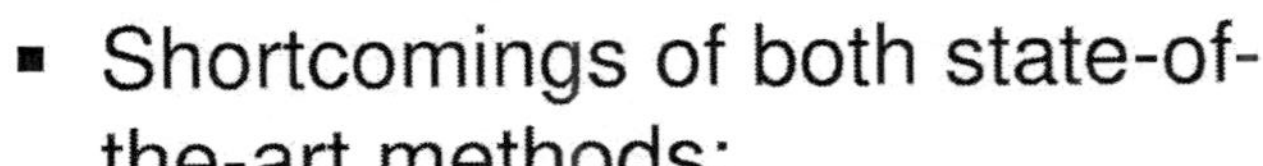

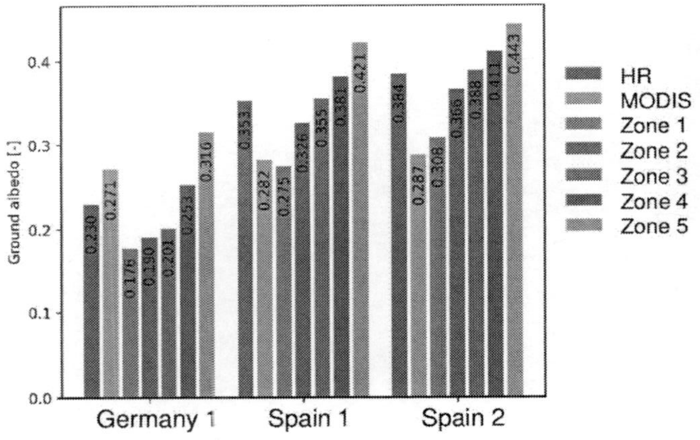

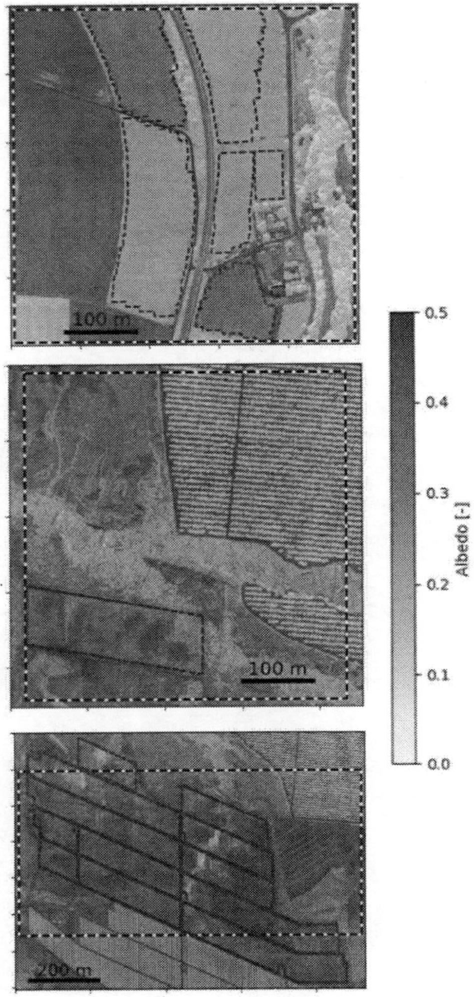

Study results
Annual yields

- Ground measurement
  - Predicted PV production deviates by -1.6% to 2.1%
- 'MODIS'
  - Predicted PV production deviates by 1%, -1.4 and -1.9%

- Deviations will be more pronounced in other practically relevant evaluations:
  - Production in shorter time scales
  - Production in morning and evening hours
  - Production of individual inverter strings

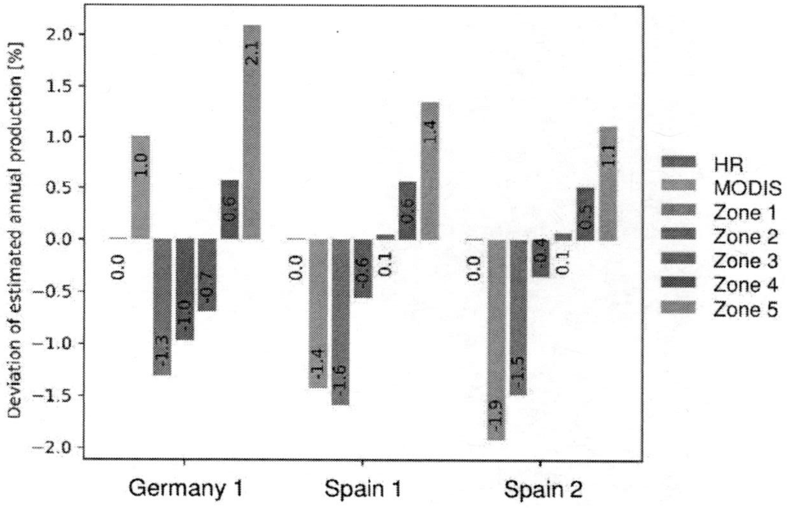

Niklas Blum, Bijan Nouri et al., DLR Institute of Solar Research, 22.09.2025

Conclusion

DLR

- State-of-the-art approaches to determine ground albedo have shortcomings
  - Practical and cost restrictions (e.g. ground measurements)
  - Systematic deviations
  - Resolution of spatial variations
- Potential of highly-resolved ground albedo exemplified in a case study
  - Able to determine ground albedo within PV plants
  - Above-mentioned shortcomings avoided
- Error in annual yield prediction of ±2% may be avoided
  - Even stronger effects for individual inverters/PV strings and at shorter timescales expected

Outlook

- Current case study is preliminary – research activity is ongoing
- Aerial data being replaced with satellite data (WorldView, Pleiades, …)
- Combination under development of satellite albedo with ground data from:
  - Albedometer
  - Rear-side irradiance measurements
  - Ground-facing cameras
- Temporal update for seasonal effects under development
- Broader validation campaign planned

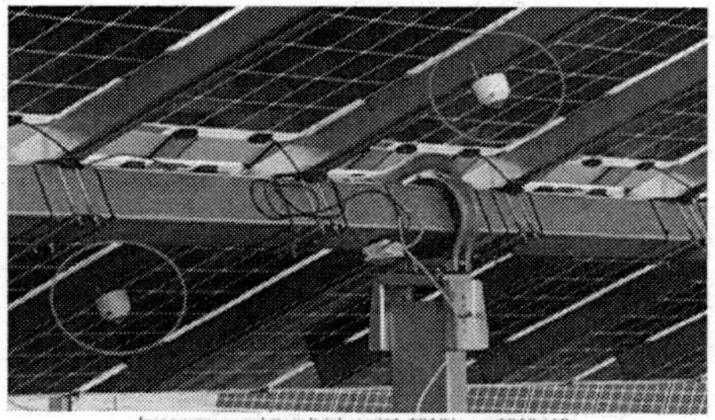

Image source: https://doi.org/10.3390/app10238467

Image taken at PSA. The research site Plataforma Solar de Almería (PSA) is owned and operated by the Spanish CIEMAT

DLR
THANK YOU FOR YOUR
ATTENTION!
QUESTIONS?
NIKLAS.BLUM@DLR.DE
BIJAN.NOURI@DLR.DE
15

42nd European Photovoltaic Solar Energy Conference
Bilbao/Spain, 22 Sep. 2025

Method for the determination of spectral responsivity of digital solar irradiance sensors

David Hinken*[,1], Sebastian Denke[1], Karsten Bothe[1] and Rolf Brendel[1,2]

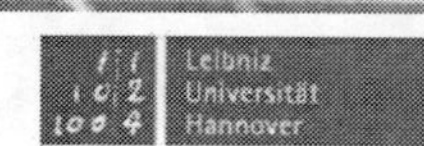

[1]Institute for Solar Energy Research in Hamelin, Emmerthal, GERMANY
[2]Institute for Solid State Physics, Leibniz Universität Hannover, Hannover, GERMANY

Digital solar irradiance sensors

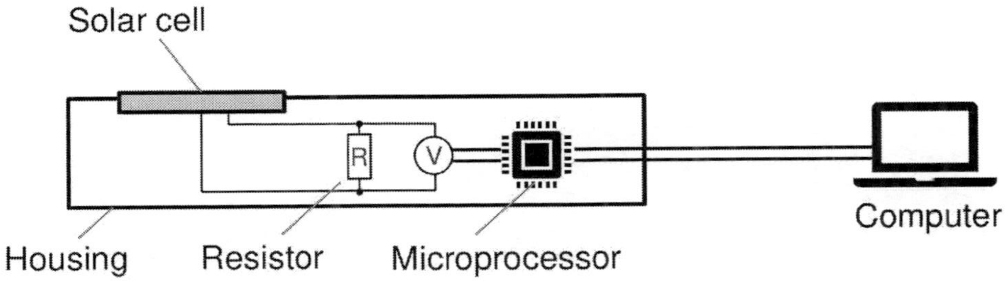

- Typical structure:
  1. Solar cell with shunt resistor
  2. Analog-digital conversion with microprocessor (also provides digital interface)
- Microprocessor converts voltage V (in mV) to irradiance G_{dig} (in W/m²) using a **calibration factor**
- Different types of solar irradiance sensors available, many with a Modbus interface
- Calibration of these sensors required!

Calibration of digital irradiance sensors

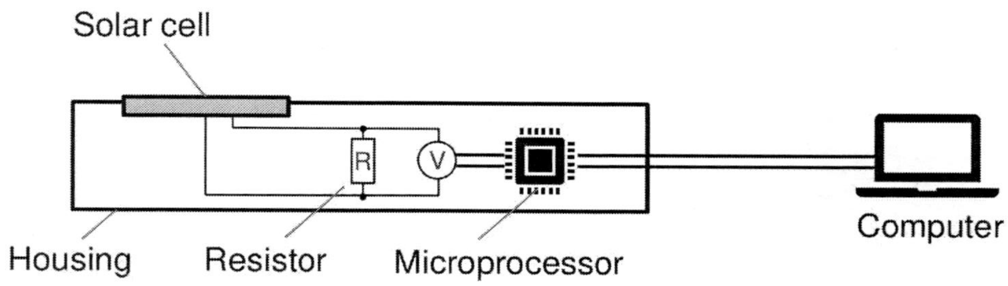

- PV system monitoring standard IEC 61724-1 demands regular calibration of irradiance sensors
- Calibration requirements:
  - **Fulfillment of IEC 60904-2**
  - Reference spectrum IEC 60904-3 (→ AM1.5G)
  - Resolution <1 W/m²
  - Measurement uncertainty ≤ 3%

Requirements of IEC 60904-2

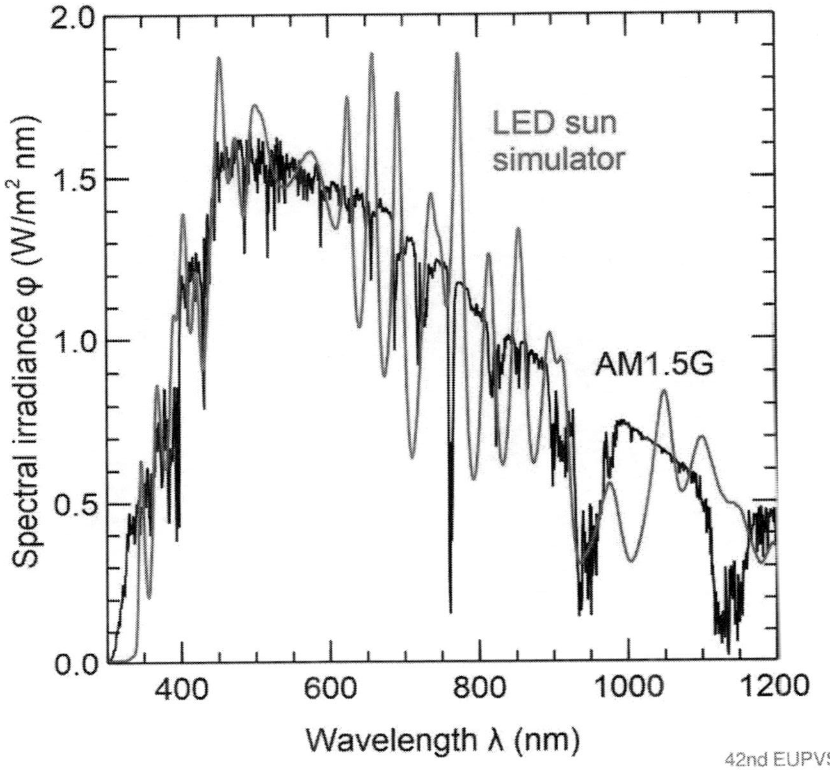

- **IEC 60904-2:** The spectral responsivity (SR/EQE) of each device has to be measured.
- Background: Tabulated reference spectrum cannot be exactly reproduced within a sun simulator
- Calculation of **spectral mismatch factor** requires determination of the spectral responsivity (SR_{smpl})

$$MM = \frac{\int d\lambda\, \varphi_{\mathrm{ref}}(\lambda) SR_{\mathrm{ref}}(\lambda) \int d\lambda\, \varphi_{\mathrm{meas}}(\lambda) SR_{\mathrm{smpl}}(\lambda)}{\int d\lambda\, \varphi_{\mathrm{meas}}(\lambda) SR_{\mathrm{ref}}(\lambda) \int d\lambda\, \varphi_{\mathrm{ref}}(\lambda) SR_{\mathrm{smpl}}(\lambda)}$$

Determination of spectral responsivity

DSR/SR measurement facility at ISFH CalTeC

- **IEC60904-2:** The spectral responsivity (SR/EQE) of each device has to be measured.
- Traditional DSR/SR requires **current as measurand** and does not work with digital units
- Only option: Open sensor, disconnect electronics and shunt resistor, add a direct wire connection to solar cell
- Not feasible for customer sensors → We need something new!

Use LED sun simulator for *SR* determination

IV measurement facility at ISFH CalTeC

Close-up picture of LED array

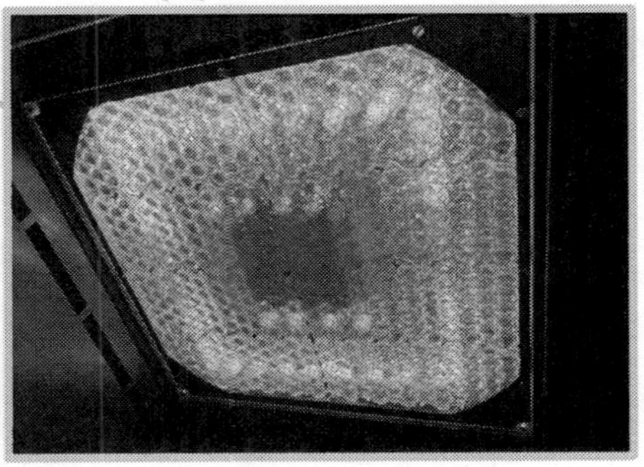

- Continuous spectrum produced by several LEDs of different color (350 nm to 1200 nm)
- Homogenization optics overlap all LED outputs on the measurement field
- **Idea:** Use spectral variations to determine the spectral responsivity

Method 1: „Single-LED“

Green LEDs on

Red LEDs on

IV measurement facility during SR_{dig} determination

- Single-LED uses one LED channel after the other. For each channel:
  1. Measure short-circuit current I_{scref} of a calibrated solar cell
  2. Get irradiance G_{dig} (W/m²) of sensor (digital)
  3. Calculate spectral responsivity: $SR_{dig} = SR_{ref} / I_{scref} \cdot P_{dig}$
- SR_{dig} is digital spectral responsivity, quantitiy is dimensionless

Method 2: „Multi-SR“

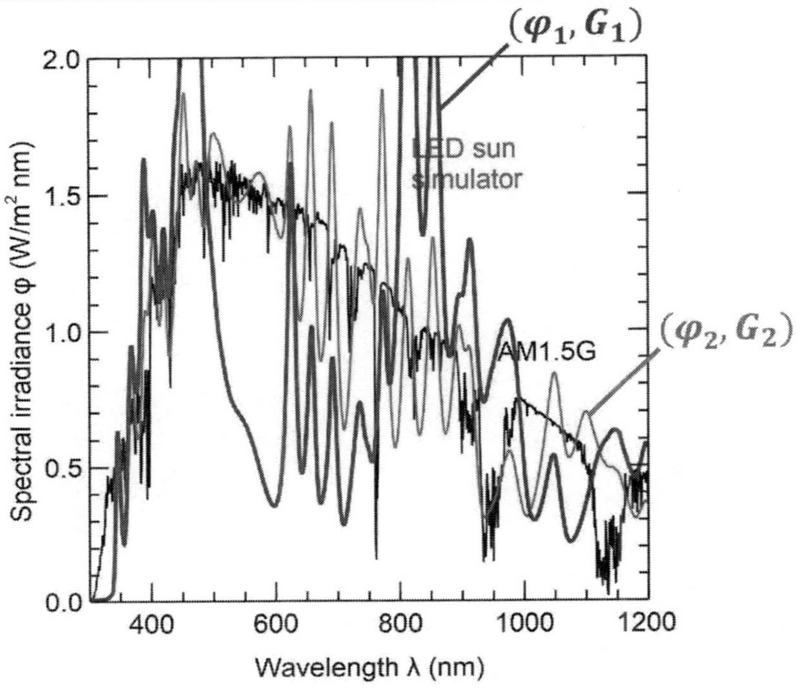

- Multi-SR [1] uses all channels at the same time but with variations:
  1. Measure resulting spectra $\varphi_\mathrm{i}(\lambda)$ with a calibrated spectrometer
  2. Get digital output G_dig (W/m²) of sensor
  3. Utilize equation

$$G_\mathrm{i} = \int \mathrm{d}\lambda\, \varphi_\mathrm{i}\, SR_\mathrm{dig}$$

  and a least-square regression to determine SR_dig

- We use 50 different broadband spectra

[1] Hinken et al. (2023), Sol. RRL, 7: 2300240. https://doi.org/10.1002/solr.202300240

Testing on two solar irradiance sensors

Sensor 1: Si-RS485TC-T-MB (IMT Technology)

Sensor 2: 3S-IS with Modbus RTU (Seven Sensor)

- Testing with two solar irradiance sensors
- Apply both methods

Resulting curves of both methods

Sensor 1: Si-RS485TC-T-MB (IMT Technology)

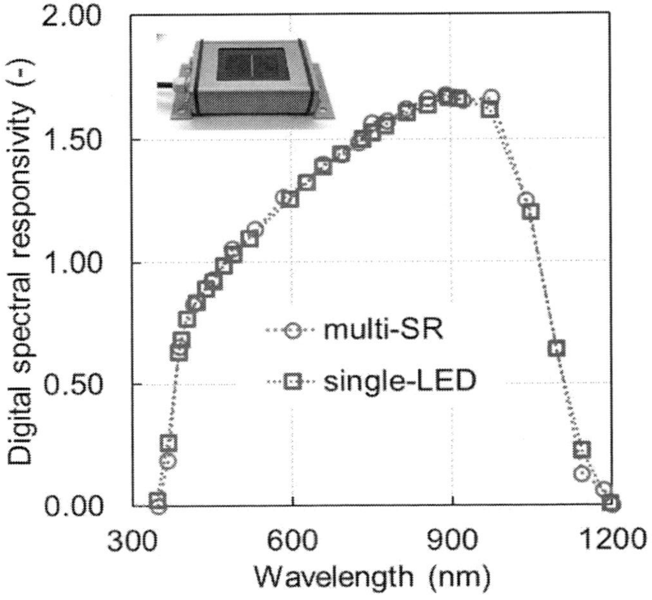

Sensor 2: 3S-IS with Modbus RTU (Seven Sensor)

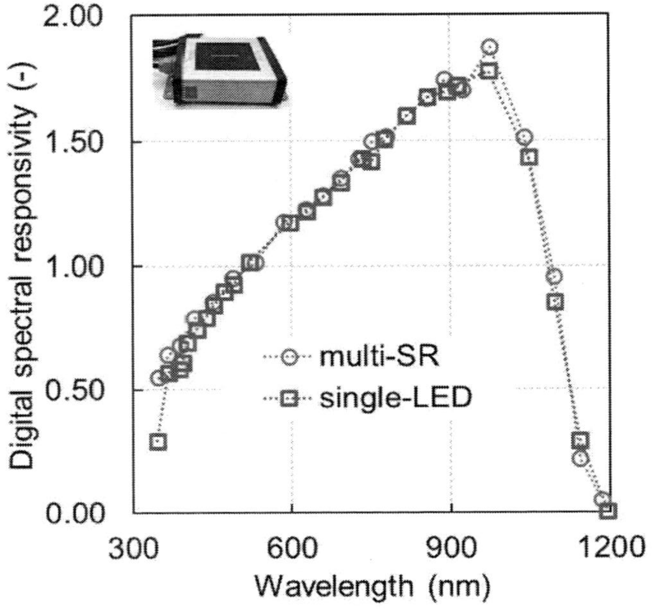

- Curves of both methods are consistent and have expected shape
- Validation with reference method still required

Comparison with DSR/SR measurement facility

Sensor 1: Si-RS485TC-T-MB (IMT Technology)

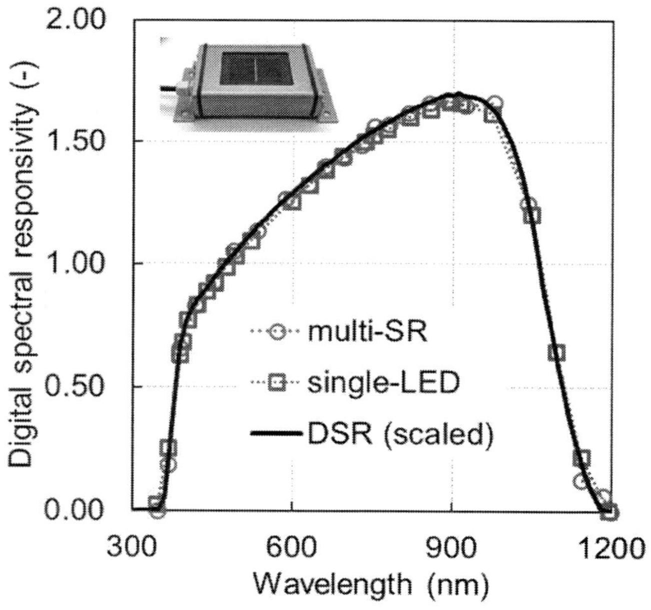

Sensor 2: 3S-IS with Modbus RTU (Seven Sensor)

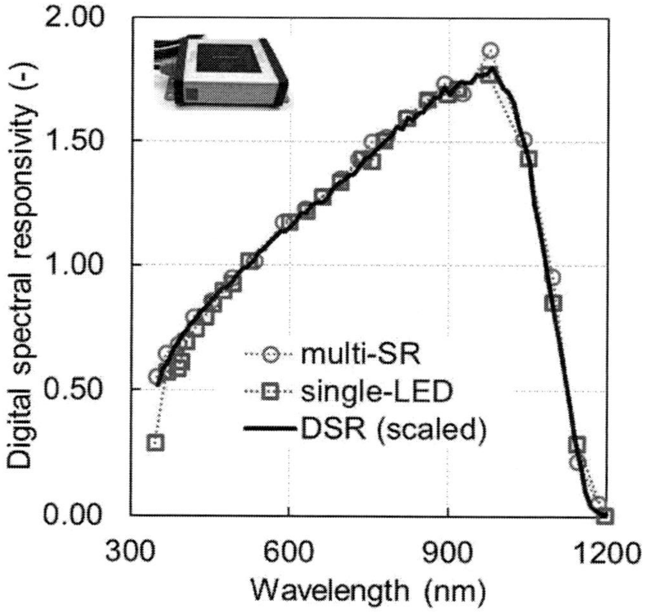

- We opened sensors, removed electronics and shunt and attached direct wire
- Consistent to curve from reference method (solid black line)

Comparison of spectral mismatch factors

Sensor 1: Si-RS485TC-T-MB (IMT Technology)

	MM	Dev.
single-LED	1.0030	0.00%
multi-SR	1.0038	0.08%
DSR/SR	1.0030	

Sensor 2: 3S-IS with Modbus RTU (Seven Sensor)

	MM	Dev.
single-LED	1.0029	0.12%
multi-SR	1.0018	0.01%
DSR/SR	1.0017	

$$MM = \frac{\int d\lambda\, \varphi_{\mathrm{ref}}(\lambda) SR_{\mathrm{ref}}(\lambda) \int d\lambda\, \varphi_{\mathrm{meas}}(\lambda) SR_{\mathrm{dig}}(\lambda)}{\int d\lambda\, \varphi_{\mathrm{meas}}(\lambda) SR_{\mathrm{ref}}(\lambda) \int d\lambda\, \varphi_{\mathrm{ref}}(\lambda) SR_{\mathrm{dig}}(\lambda)}$$

- Calculation of spectral mismatch factor (MM) using:
  1. Class A++ sun simulator spectrum
  2. WPVS reference solar cell
- Max. deviation in MM factor to reference method (DSR/SR) is 0.12%

Comparison table

	Single-LED	Multi-SR	DSR/SR (with modified sensor)
Directly applicable to digital irradiance sensors	Yes	Yes	No
Reference	Calibrated solar cell	Calibrated spectrometer	Calibrated solar cell
Measurement time	5 minutes	5 minutes	1 hour
Can be integrated in IV measurement facility?	Yes	Yes	No, separate facility required
Technical complexity?	Low	Low	High (→ lock-in technique required)
Components commercially available?	Yes	Yes	No (→ transimpedance-amplifier)
Wavelength resolution	Low, LEDs with narrow spectrum required	Higher	Highest
Working point (excess charge carrier density)	Extremely low or bias-variations required	Same working conditions	Bias-variations required

Conclusion

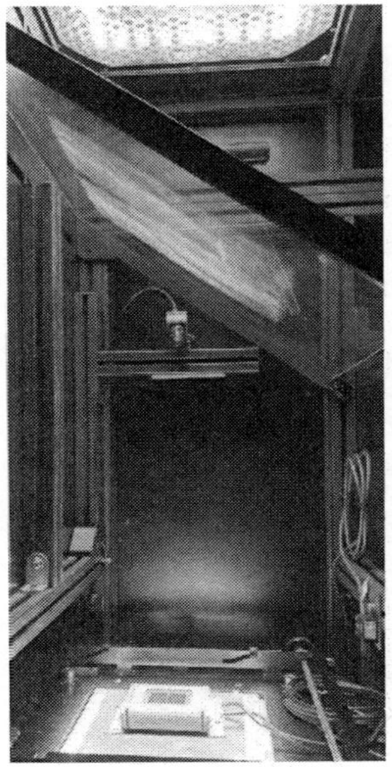

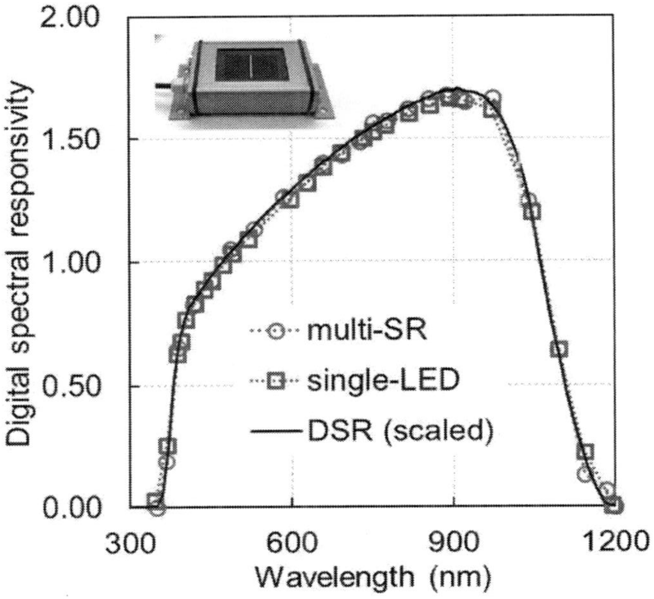

- Introduced two methods for the determination of the spectral responsivity of digital irradiance sensors
- Tests and validation successful!
- Calibration of digital irradiance sensors now available at ISFH CalTeC with a measurement uncertainty of 1.0% (k=2)
- Contact us: sensors@caltec.isfh.de

Acknowledgments

ISFH CalTeC

This work was funded by the **state of Lower Saxony**

and the **project SOLiD-PV** (24GRD04), which has received funding from the **European Partnership on Metrology** (Funder ID: 10.13039/100019599), co-financed from the European Union's Horizon Europe Research and Innovation Programme and by the Participating States.

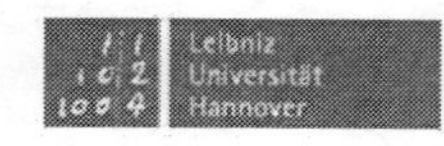

EUROPEAN PARTNERSHIP | Co-funded by the European Union | METROLOGY PARTNERSHIP | EURAMET

CUTTING-EDGE GENERATIVE AI FOR INTRA-HOUR SOLAR FORECASTING

Yann Fabel, Dominik Schnaus, Bijan Nouri, Stefan Wilbert, Niklas Blum, Luis F. Zarzalejo, Julia Kowalski, Robert Pitz-Paal

EUPVSEC 2025

22th of September 2025, Bilbao, Spain

TUM

RWTH AACHEN UNIVERSITY

Ciemat

DLR

Agenda

- Introduction
- Generative Forecasting Approach
- Ramp Event Prediction
- Conclusion & Outlook

DLR
MOTIVATION
Yann Fabel, DLR, EUPVSEC 2025

Motivation

Why forecasting solar irradiance?

- Predict expected energy yield of PV power plants
- Anticipate local short-term fluctuations caused by cloud passages (ramp events)

Challenges by ramp events

- Local power output variability
- Potential risk of grid instabilities at high solar penetration

Benefits of intra-hour forecasting

- Better situational awareness for plant and grid operators
- Reduced storage requirements
- Improved market trading strategies
- More efficient operation of CST plants

Requirements

- High-resolution cloud information in space and time
  → All-Sky-Imagers

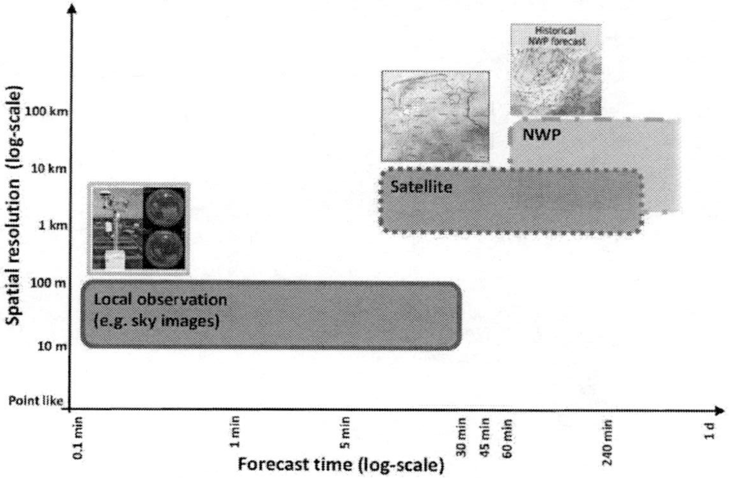

Yann Fabel, DLR, EUPVSEC 2025

Motivation
Ramp Events

- Typically no evaluation of predicting the variability of solar irradiance
- Common forecasting metrics (e.g., RMSE, MAE, MBE) represent an average error of the target quantity (e.g., GHI)
  - Good measure to assess expected energy yield (integration of irradiance over time)
  - No information on variability within the forecast
- Definition Ramp Event [1]:

$$\frac{|\Delta GHI|}{\Delta t} > \tau \Longrightarrow Ramp$$

$$t:\ if\ \exists\ Ramp\ in\ [t - tw/2, t + tw/2] \Longrightarrow Ramp\ Event\ at\ t$$

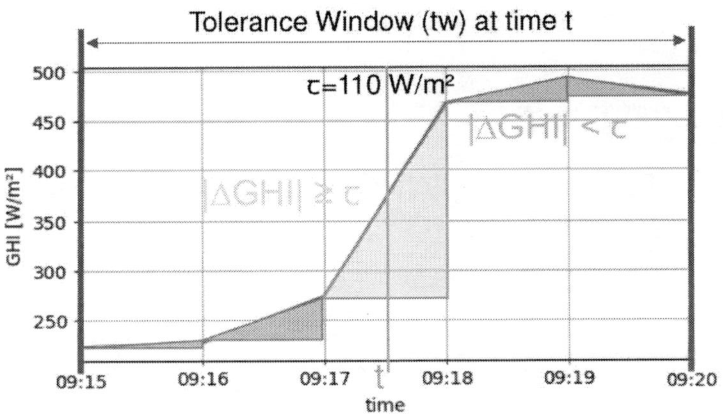

Limitations of State-of-the-Art Models

- State-of-the-Art direct data-driven models are often optimized on RMSE [2, 3, 4]

Fabel et al. [4]

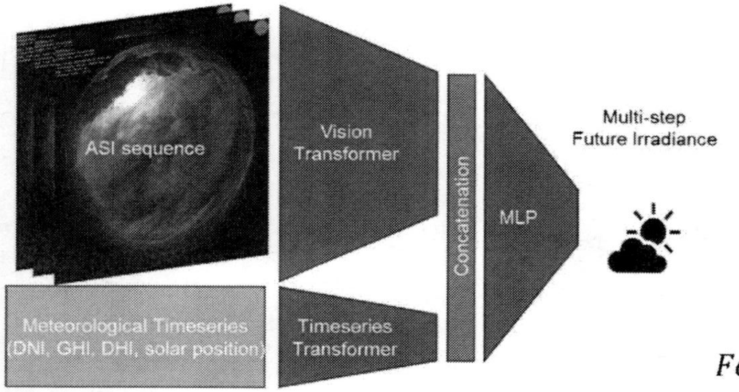

$$RMSE = \sqrt{{}^{1}/_{n}\sum_{i=1}^{n}(\hat{y}_i - y_i)^2}$$

$$MAE = {}^{1}/_{n}\sum_{i=1}^{n}|\hat{y}_i - y_i|$$

$$MBE = {}^{1}/_{n}\sum_{i=1}^{n}\hat{y}_i - y_i$$

$$Forecast\ Skill = 1 - \frac{RMSE_{model}}{RMSE_{persistence}}$$

GHI Forecast

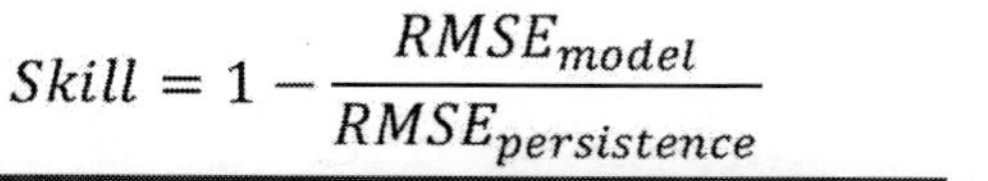

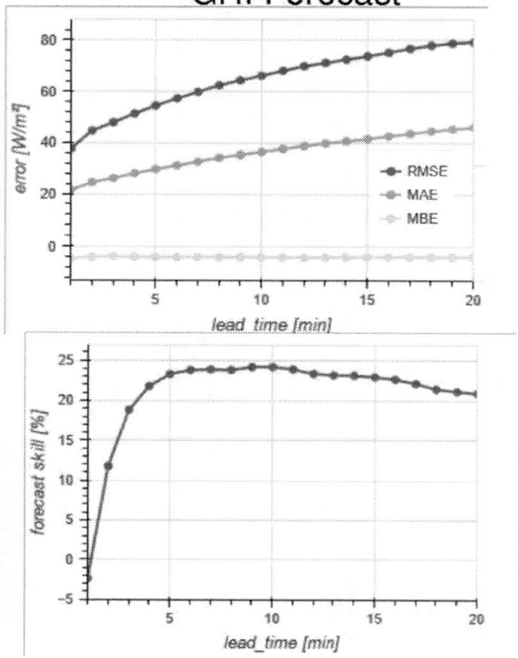

- Strong performance on standard error metrics, but ramp events remain undetected due to overly smoothed forecast curves (see later slides)
- How can we circumvent smoothing of the forecast curve?

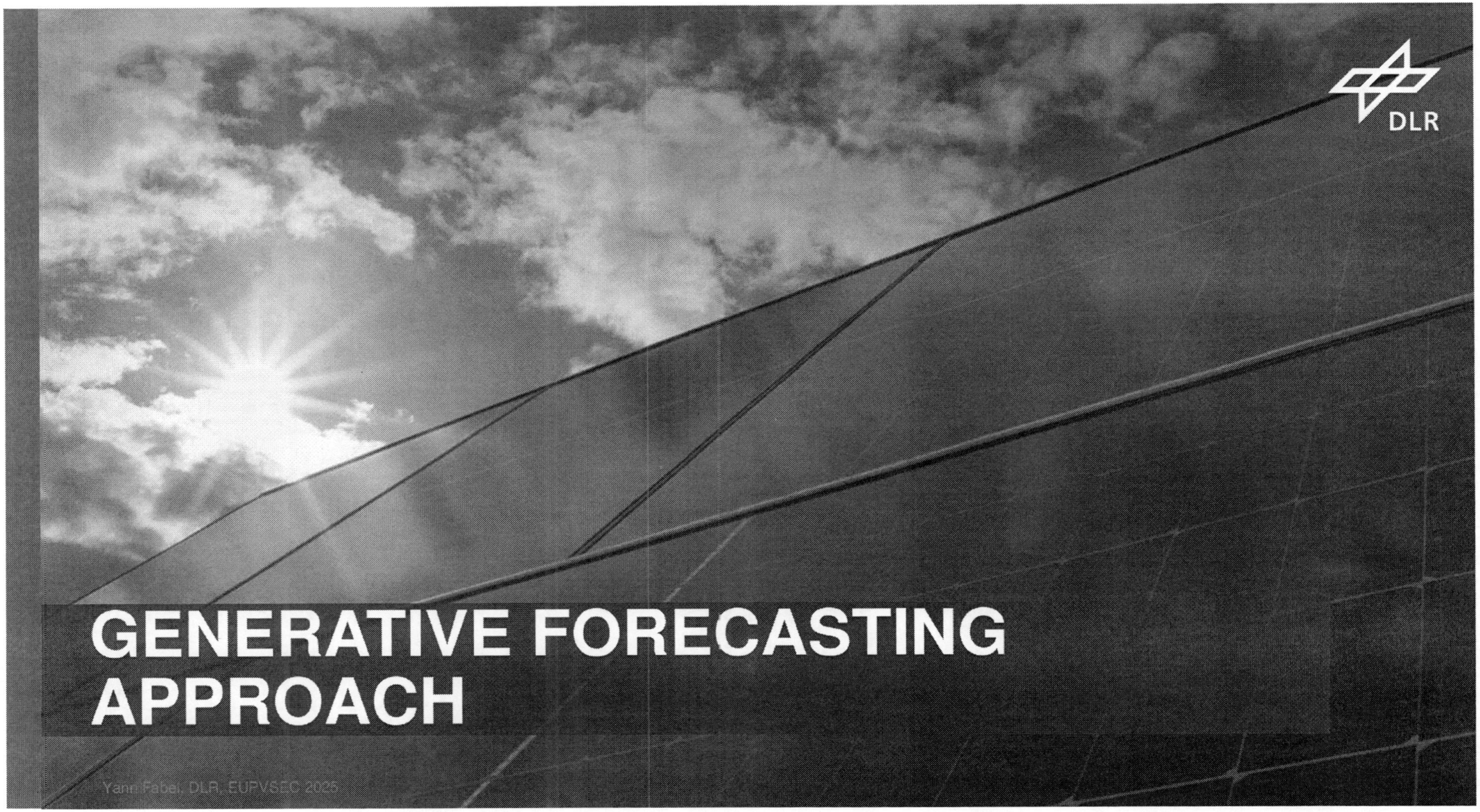
DLR
GENERATIVE FORECASTING
APPROACH
Yann Fabel, DLR, EUPVSEC 2025

Generative Forecasting
Model Architecture

- **Video Prediction (VP)**:
  - Given a sequence of M past images the next N images are predicted
  - Multiple future scenarios can be generated from the same input sequence by sampling from Gaussian noise
    → Measure for uncertainty

- **Regressor/Classifier:**
  - Given individual predicted future frames a second model (e.g. CNN) is used to derive the desired target quantity
  - Trained separately on real images
  - E.g., a model predicts ramp events or GHI corresponding to the predicted sky image

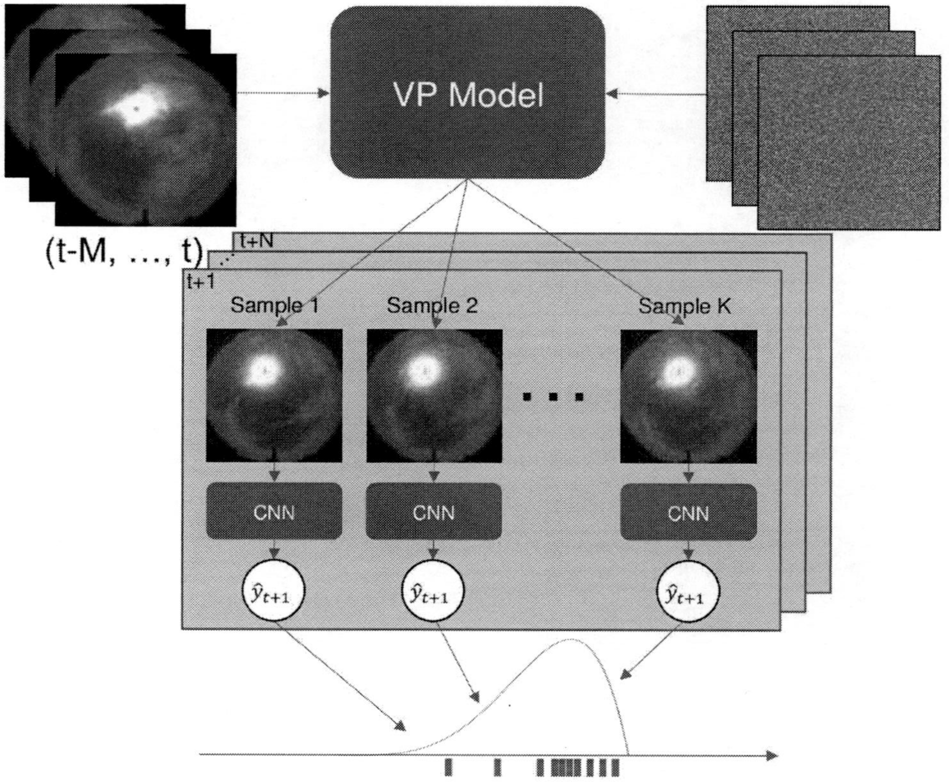

Yann Fabel, DLR, EUPVSEC 2025

Video Prediction Models
Train and Test setup

- Two different generative models were tested
  - SkyGPT [5]: Adaptation of the VideoGPT [6] model combined with PhyCells [7]
  - Ours: Adaptation of the DiT model [8] (diffusion-based transformer)
- Training
  - Both models were trained on selected camera data from CIEMAT's PSA (Almería, Spain)
  - SkyGPT model trained with the same hyperparameter configuration as in the original publication
- Testing
  - Evaluation on separate benchmark dataset defined in All-Sky Imager-based forecasting study [9]
  - 28 selected days from a single camera at PSA representing diverse sky conditions
  - 4 image samples per model were generated for each lead time

Image taken at CIEMAT's PSA

	SkyGPT	DiT
Image res	64x64	128x128
Temporal res.	2min	1min
Forecast horizon	15min	30min
Auto-Encoder	VQ-VAE [6]	Pretrained VAE [9]

Yann Fabel, DLR, EUPVSEC 2025

Video Prediction Evaluation
Examplary Results – Single Sample, Selected Lead Times

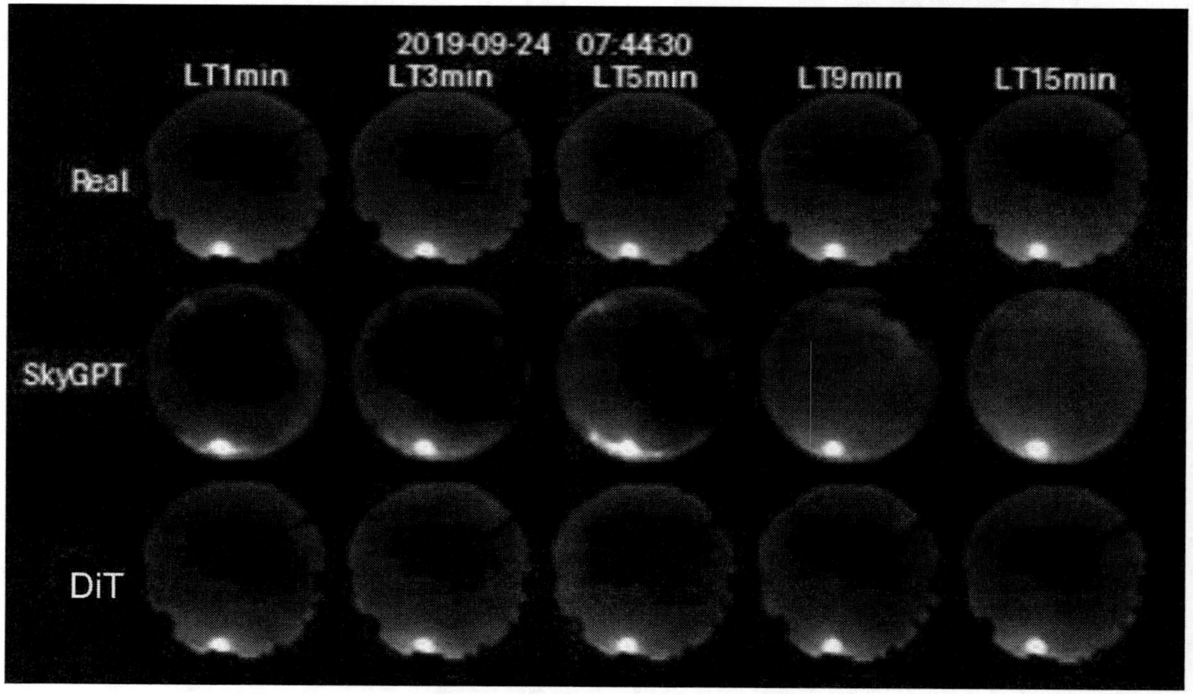

→ A lot of „halluzinations“ even for clear sky conditions

Video Prediction Evaluation
Examplary Results – Single Sample, Selected Lead Times

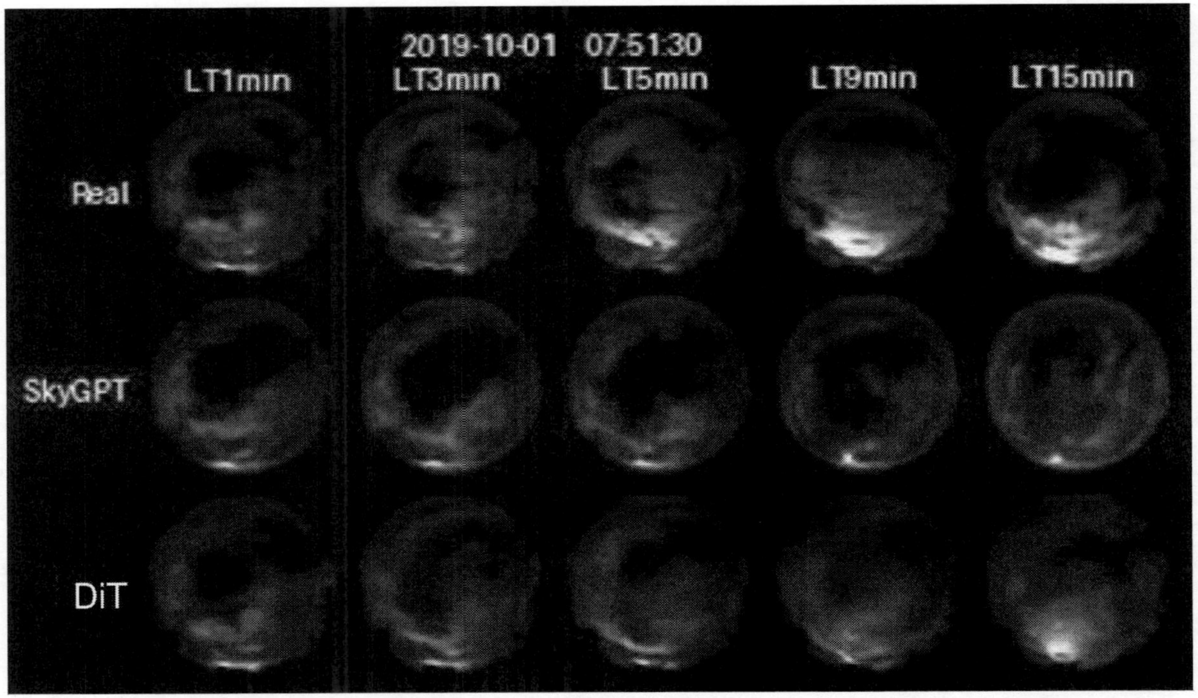

→ Strong deviations in terms of cloud coverage for larger lead times

Video Prediction Evaluation
Quantitative Results

- Evaluation of predicted sky image frames
  - Image data range: [0, 255]
  - Lead-time specific calculation averaged over all generated future scenarios

- Image-wise pixel metrics
  - Mean Absolute Error (MAE)↓:
    - Average error per pixel
  - Peak Signal-to-Noise Ratio (PSNR)↑:
    - Ratio of maximum possible signal to error in decibels (measure of fidelity)
  - Structural Similarity Index (SSIM)↑:
    - Measure for perceptual similarity (capturing sharpness and structure)

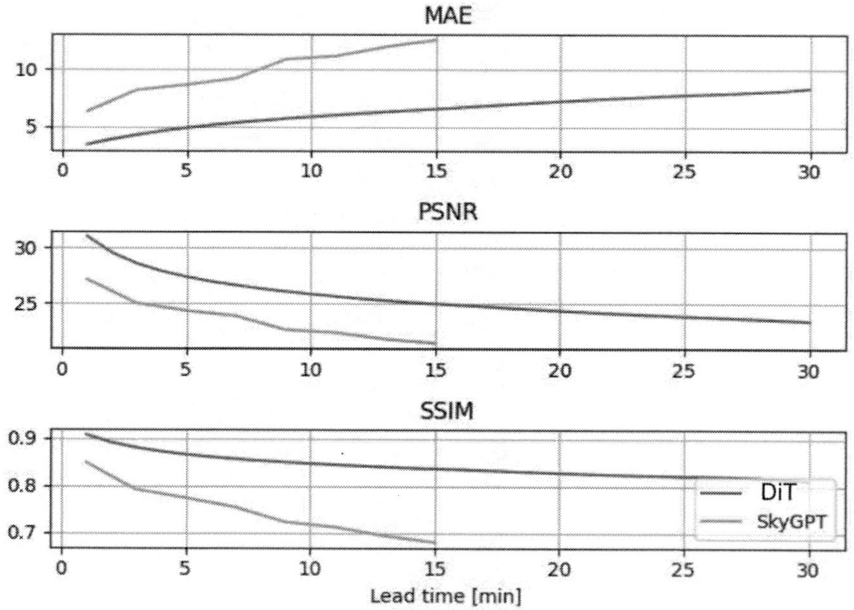

→ Better performance of DiT model in terms of image quality

Yann Fabel, DLR, EUPVSEC 2025

DLR
RAMP EVENT PREDICTION
Yann Fabel, DLR, EUPVSEC 2025

Ramp Event Prediction

- Ramp Classifier
  - CNN predicts likelihood of ramp event (RE) based on corresponding image
  - Ground truth $y_t = \begin{cases} 1 \ if \ \exists \ ramp \ in \ [t-3, t+3] \\ 0 \ otherwise \end{cases}$
  - **Trained on real sky images**
  - **Evaluated on synthetic images** from generative model to obtain ramp event prediction

- Baseline model: Ramp Persistence
  - If a ramp was observed in the measured irradiance curve in the last T=30min a ramp is expected in the next T minutes too
  - Independent of sky images

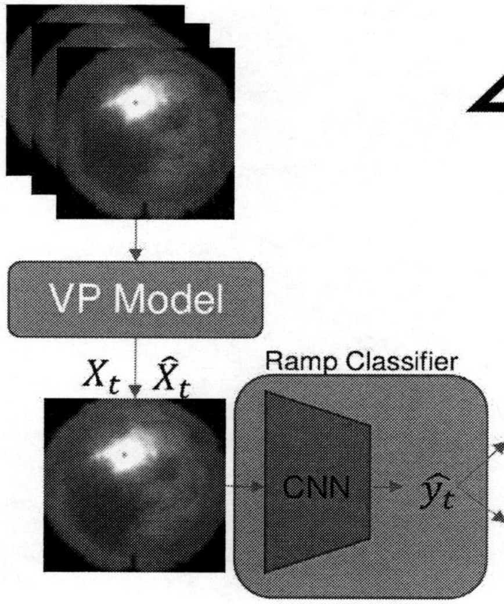

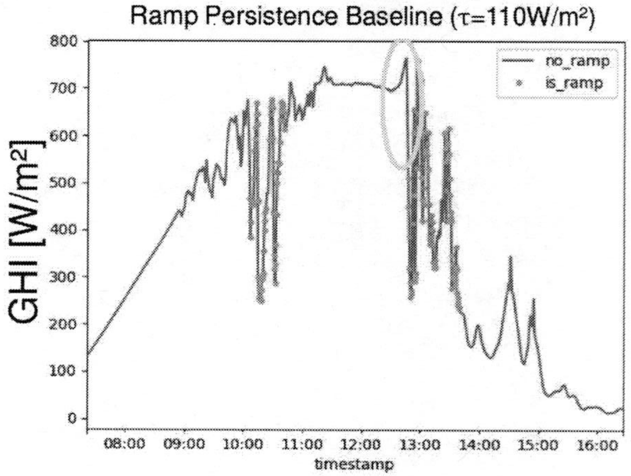

Ramp Event Prediction Evaluation

- Video prediction models generate K=4 samples (images) for all lead times for each forecast
- Predicted RE from average probability of ramp classifier over all samples
- Observed RE by measured ramp within tolerance window (tw=10min)
- Low classifier threshold (TH=0.3) chosen to prioritize recall
- Evaluation of classification metrics over lead times

$$accuracy = \frac{TP + TN}{TP + FN + FP + TN}$$

$$precision = \frac{TP}{TP + FP}$$

$$f1 = 2 \times \frac{precision \times recall}{precision + recall}$$

$$recall = \frac{TP}{TP + FN}$$

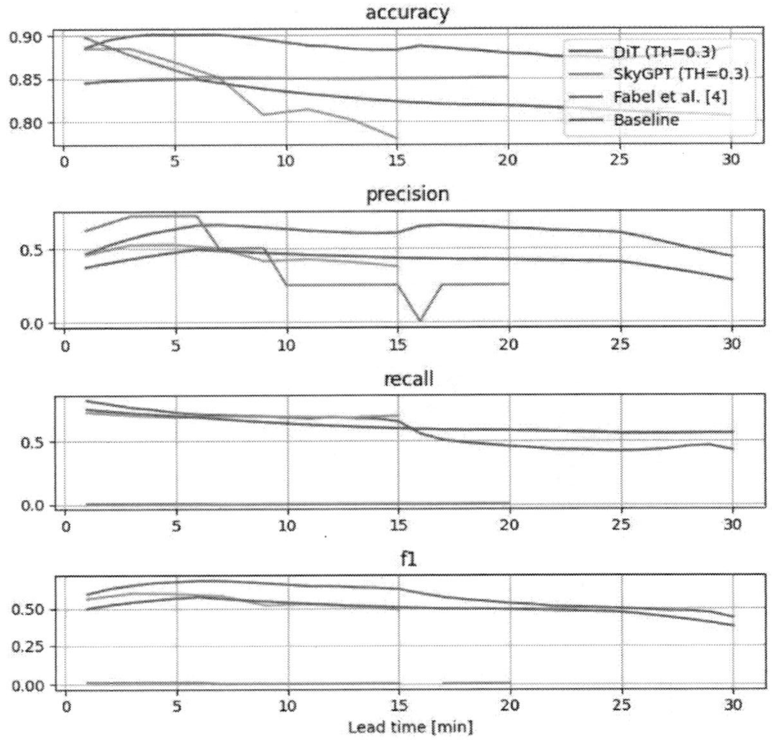

Yann Fabel, DLR, EUPVSEC 2025

Conclusion

DLR

- Summary:
  - Low RMSE does not guarantee realistic representation of irradiance variability (e.g., ramp events)
  - Generative, image-based modeling of cloud dynamics offers a promising alternative to capture short-term variability
  - Current video prediction models for ASI still struggle at longer horizons (inconsistencies and physically unrealistic cloud scenes)
  - But generated images remain useful for detecting ramp events
- Outlook
  - Enhance ASI-based video prediction
    - Focus training on highly variable cloud conditions
    - Leverage advances in generative video modeling (e.g., noise warping, motion conditioning)
  - Combine multiple perspectives to learn better cloud representations

References

DLR

1. Nouri et al. 2024, **Ramp Rate Metric Suitable for Solar Forecasting**, DOI: 10.1002/solr.202400468
2. Sun et al., **Solar PV output prediction from video streams using convolutional neural networks**, DOI: 10.1039/c7ee03420b
3. Paletta et al. 2021, **Benchmarking of deep learning irradiance forecasting models from sky images - An in-depth analysis**, DOI: 10.1016/j.solener.2021.05.056
4. Fabel et al. 2023, **Combining deep learning and physical models: a benchmark study on all-sky imagerbased solar nowcasting systems**
5. Nie et al. 2024, **SkyGPT: Probabilistic ultra-short-term solar forecasting using synthetic sky images from physics-constrained VideoGPT,** DOI: 10.1016/j.adapen.2024.100172
6. Yan et al. 2021, **VideoGPT: Video Generation using VQ-VAE and Transformers**, DOI: 10.48550/ARXIV.2104.10157
7. LeGuen et al. 2020, **Disentangling Physical Dynamics From Unknown Factors for Unsupervised Video Prediction**, DOI: 10.1109/cvpr42600.2020.01149
8. Pebbles et al. 2022, **Scalable Diffusion Models with Transformers**, DOI: 10.48550/ARXIV.2212.09748
9. Blattmann et. al 2023, **Stable video diffusion: Scaling latent video diffusion models to large datasets**, DOI: 10.48550/ARXIV.2311.15127

AuSeSol AI (Grant number 67KI21007A)
Gefördert durch:
Bundesministerium
für Umwelt, Klimaschutz, Naturschutz
und nukleare Sicherheit
aufgrund eines Beschlusses
des Deutschen Bundestages
DLR
THANK YOU FOR YOUR ATTENTION!
QUESTIONS? YANN.FABEL@DLR.DE
Yann Fabel, DLR, EUPVSEC 2025

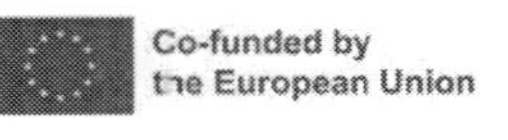

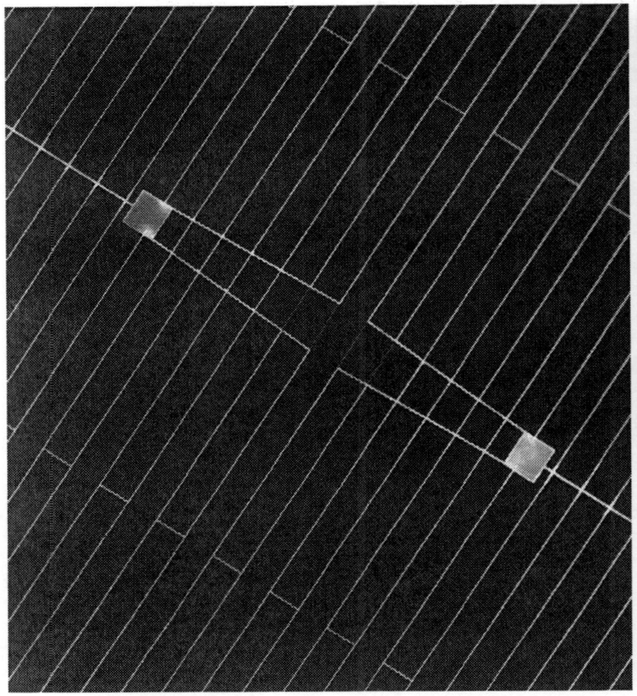

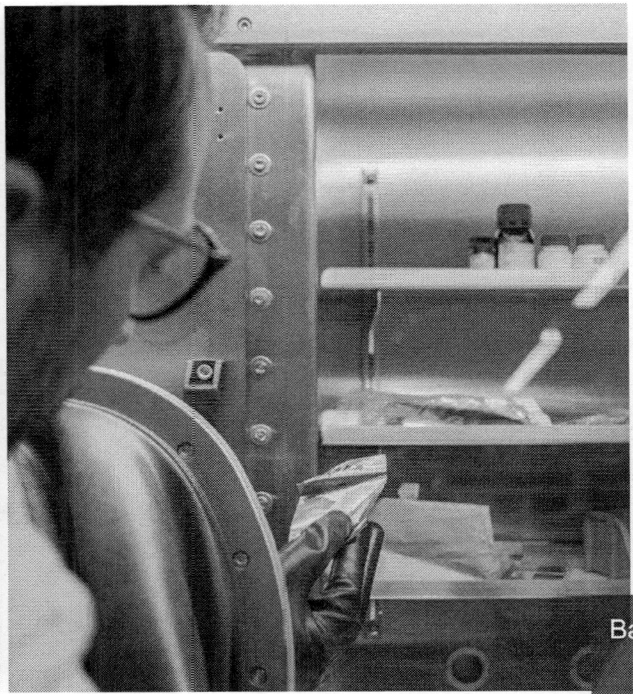

Baptiste Schubnel, Jelena Simeunovic, Corentin Tissier, Pierre-Jean Alet and **Rafael Carrillo**

EUPVSEC, 22.09.2025

INTEGRATING SATELLITE IMAGERY AND GNNS FOR IMPROVING DAY-AHEAD IRRADIANCE FORECASTING

SUPERNOVA

Co-funded by the European Union

csem

MOTIVATION

- Intraday and day-ahead solar forecasts are crucial for control, trading, and group balance management
- CSEM developed an intraday solution based on a network of ground sensors
  - It works well during the day, but accuracy drops in the morning due to limited data
- **Motivation:** improve early-morning and extend solution to day-ahead predictions
- **Problem:** day-ahead forecasts require broader spatial and temporal context
  - Satellite images provide this context but **how to fuse with ground data?**

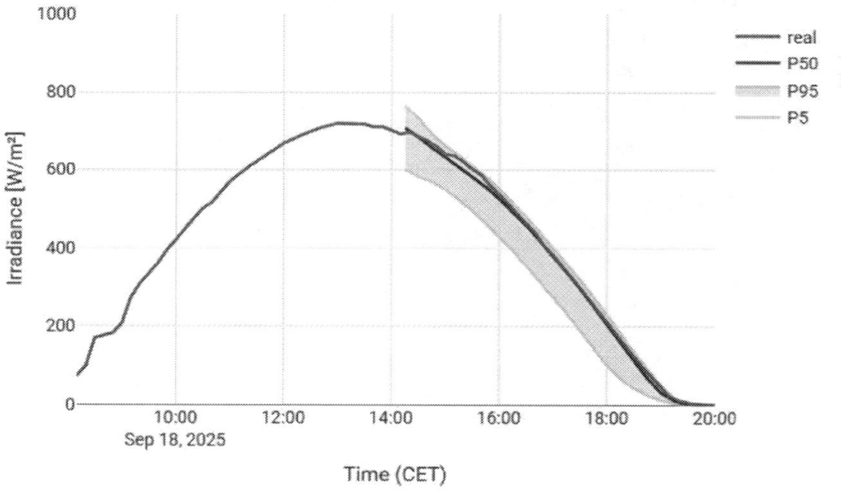

:: csem

LIMITATIONS OF EXISTING DATA-FUSION APPROACHES

- **Very short-term:**
  - All sky imagers + ground-based measurements
  - Mainly developed for single location or small area
- **Intraday:**
  - Satellite-derived data or ground-based observations
  - Successful spatio-temporal approaches from only ground-based network of sensors but no wide spatial context
- **Day-ahead:**
  - Spatio-temporal models that exploit image pixel location and ground-based data developed for single site
  - Do not exploit intra image – network correlation and inter-correlations between multiple locations

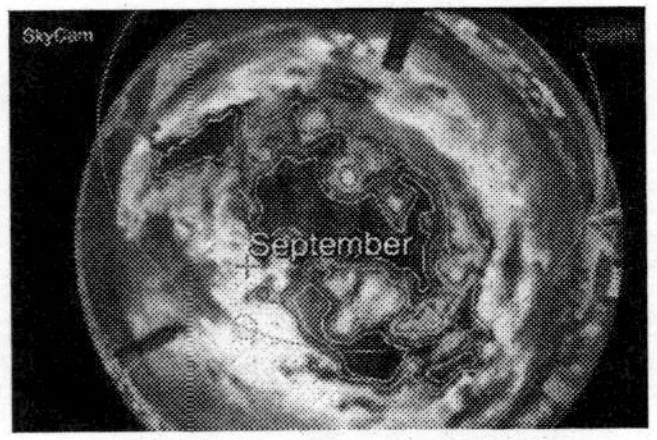

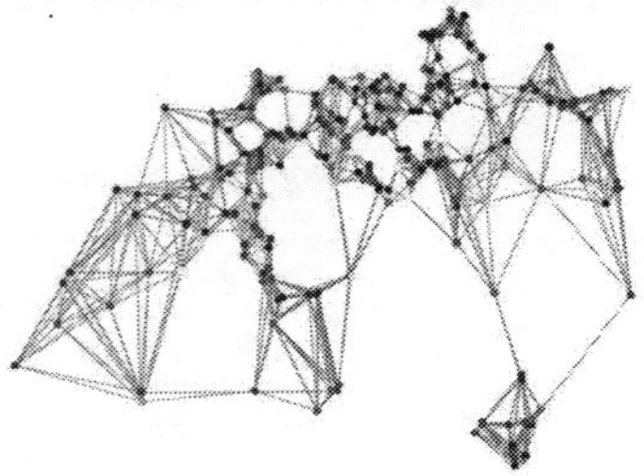

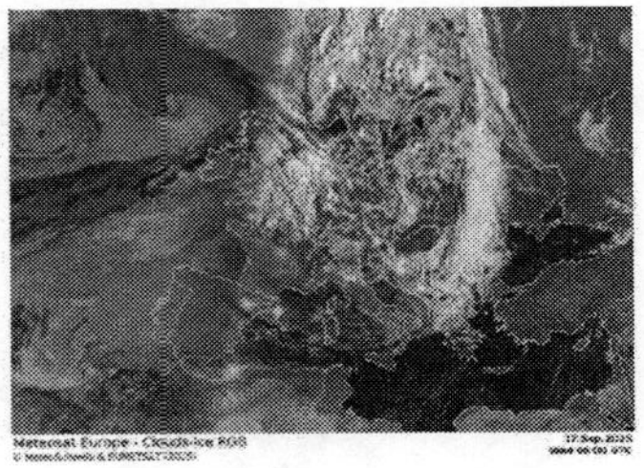

:: csem

SOLARCROSSFORMER: DAY-AHEAD FORECASTING

- Improved day-ahead solar irradiance forecasting by multi-modal information fusion
- **Inputs:**
  - Satellite imagery (visual + infrared)
  - Time-series from a network of ground-based meteorological stations
- **Key idea:** Graph Neural Networks (GNNs) to model:
  - Intra-modal correlations (between ground sensors, between pixels)
  - Inter-modal correlations (between satellite and ground sensors)

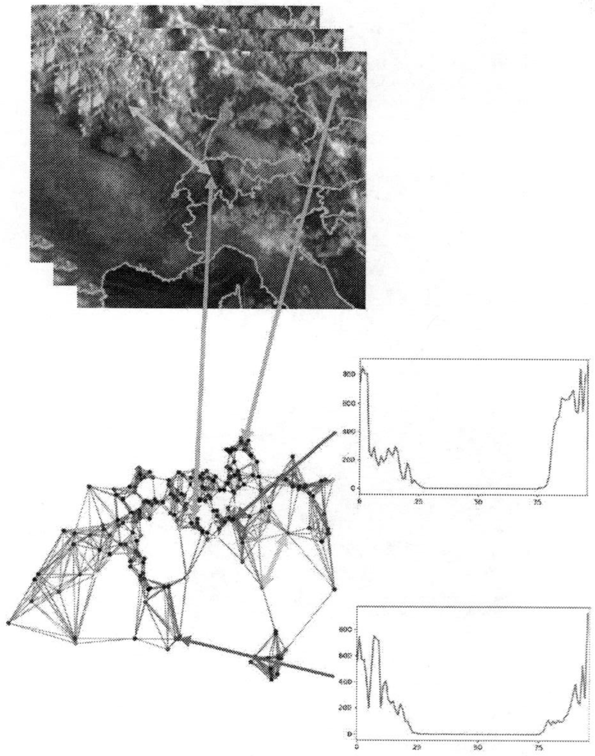

ARCHITECTURE

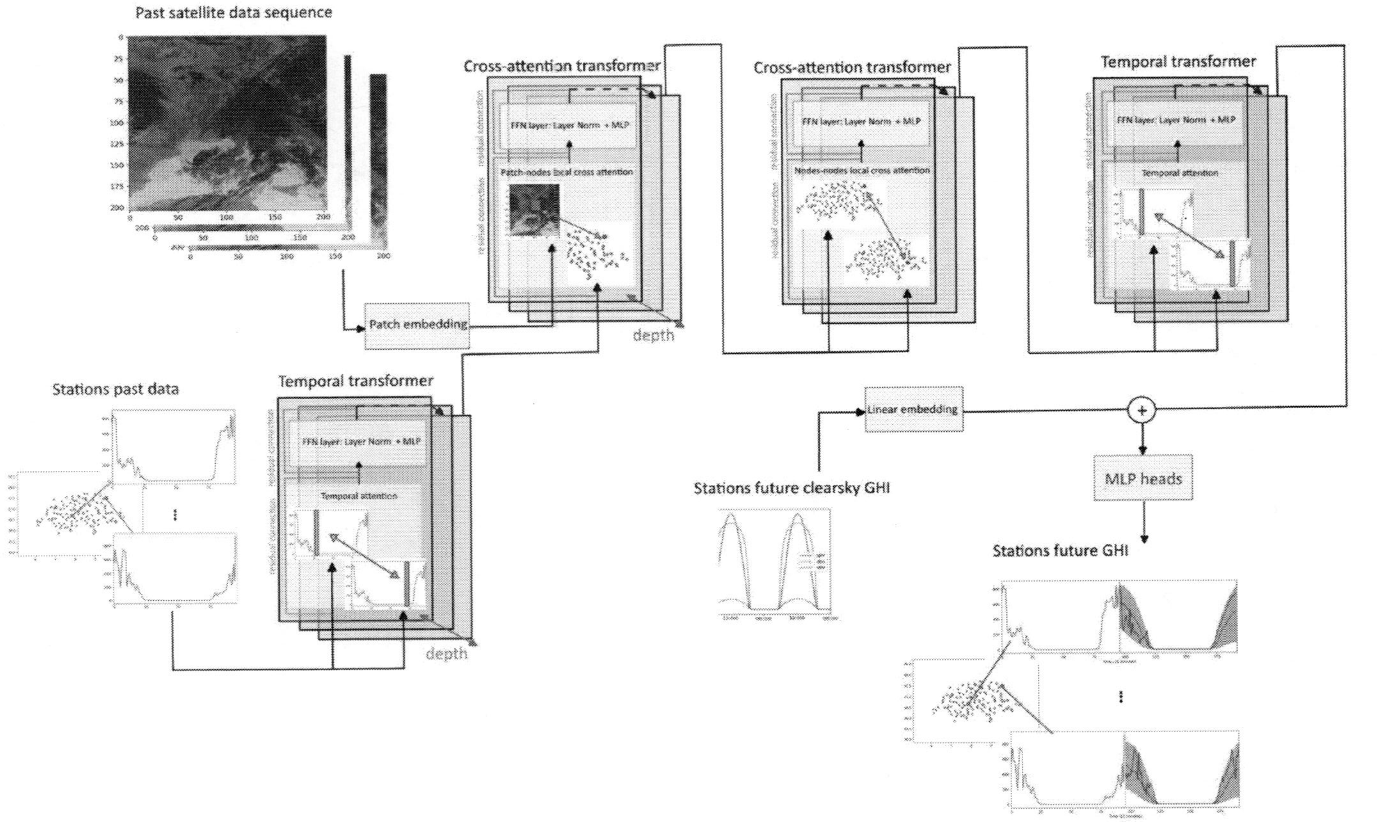

B. Schubnel et al., "SolarCrossFormer: Improving day-ahead Solar Irradiance Forecasting by Integrating Satellite Imagery and Ground Sensors," submitted to IEEE TSE, 2025. arXiv:2509.15827.

:: csem

TRAINING

- Pin-ball loss function used in training to output quantile forecasts
  - Median value (50% quant.)
  - Upper bound (95% quant.)
  - Lower bound (5% quant.)
- Dynamic masking strategy for training
  - Random masking of a percentage of node's data and image pixels per batch
  - It enables the forecast of GHI at locations where no local observations are available

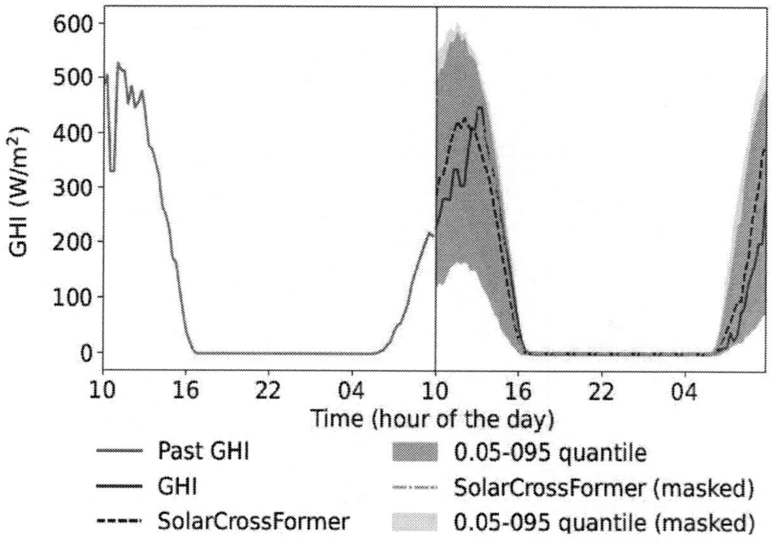

:: csem

INPUT DATA

- Satellite data from EUMETSAT MSG-4
  - Visual and infrared channels: IR039, IR087, IR108 and VIS006
- Time-series from MeteoSwiss automatic measurement network
  - GHI, DNI, DHI, outside temperature, wind speed and direction, pressure and RH
- Time-series and images with a temporal resolution of 15 minutes
- 9 years of data in total (2016-2024)
  - Training set: 8 years (2016-2023)
  - Evaluation set: 1 year (2024)

Covered area by input satellite image

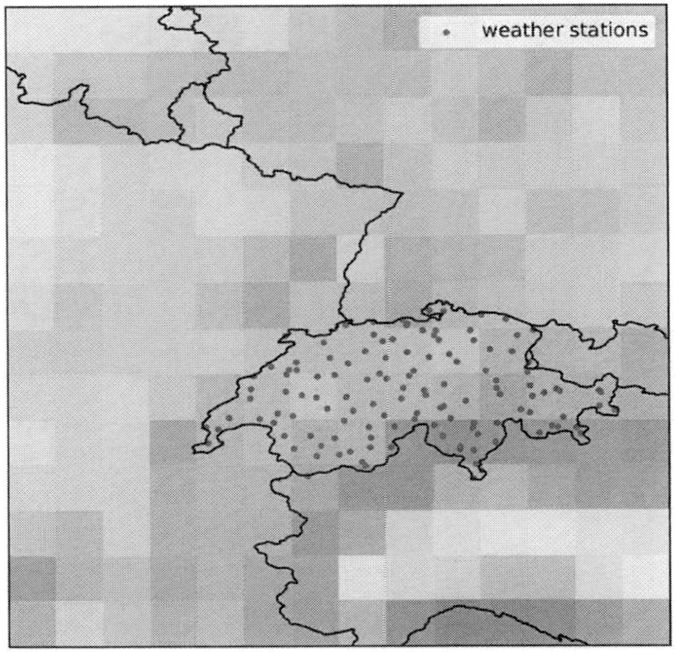

csem

COMPARISON AGAINST OTHER DL MODELS

NRMSE vs forecasting horizon

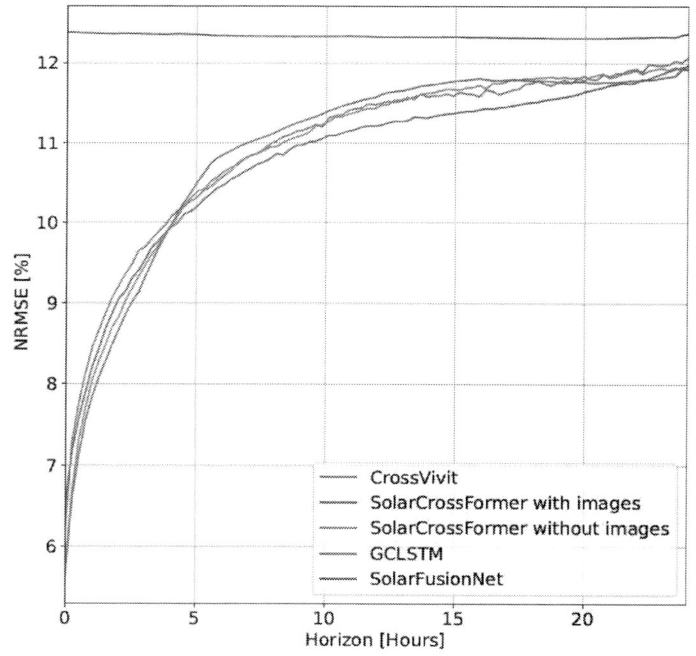

NRMSE vs prediction time

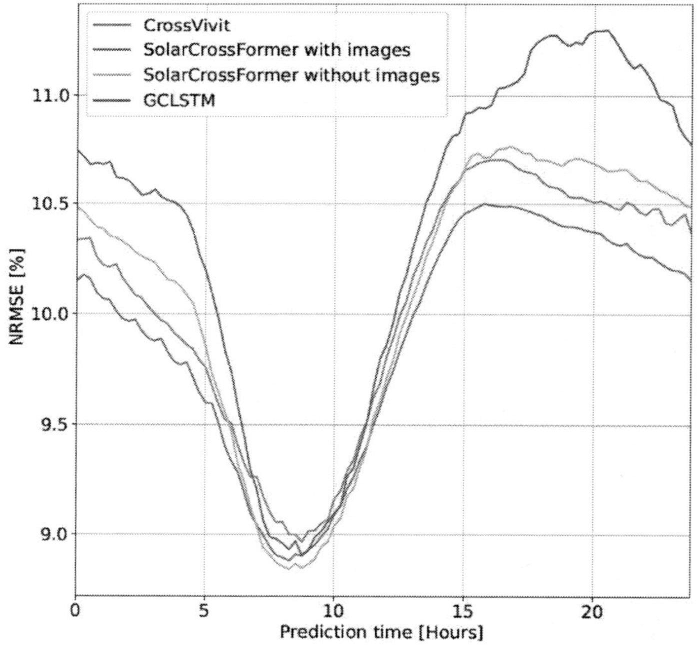

SEASONAL ERROR

- SolarCrossFormer outperforms other models in summer, spring and autumn
- During winter, models with only ground data outperform models that use satellite data

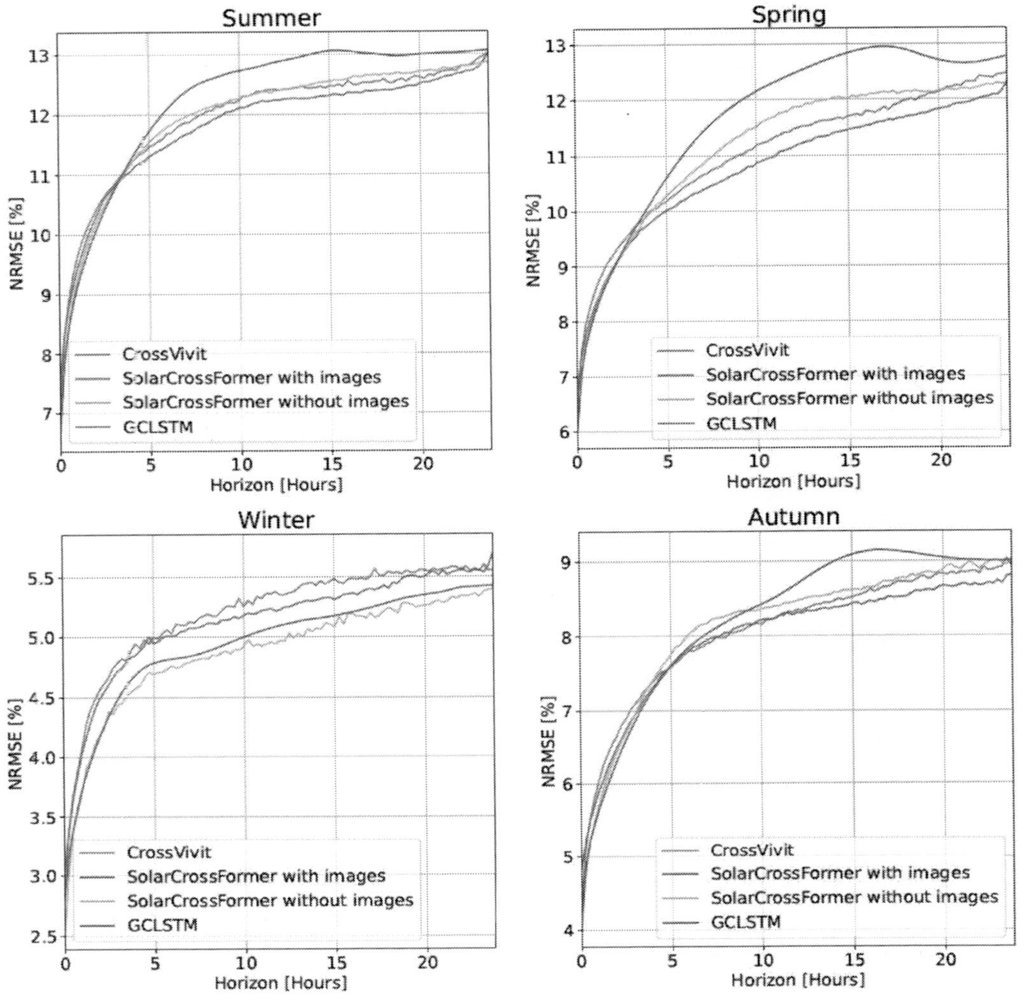

COMPARISON AGAINST NWP-BASED FORECASTS

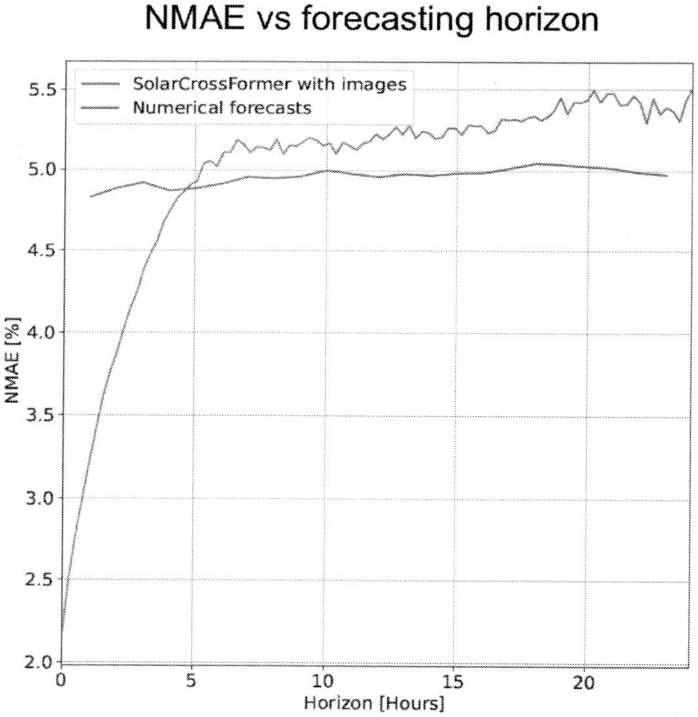

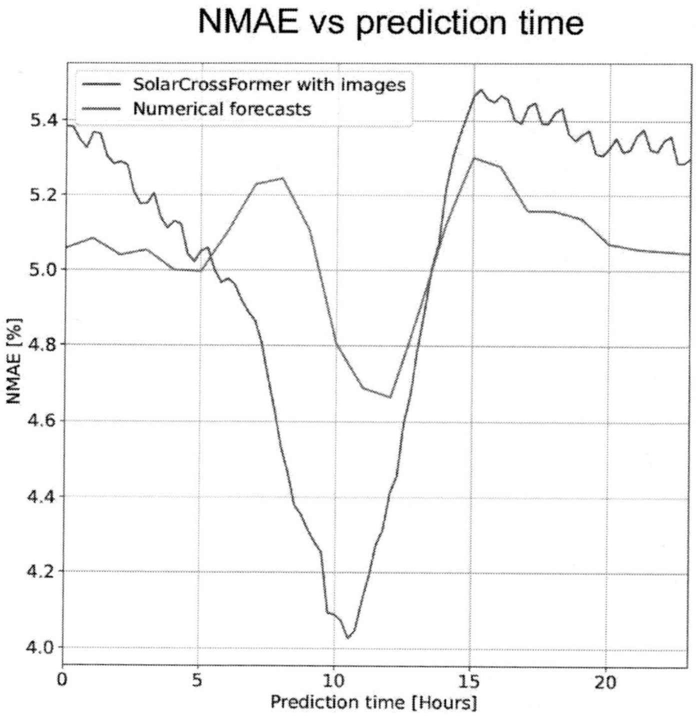

:: csem

FORECAST AT UNSEEN LOCATIONS

- Test at 5 unseen locations
  - Two within Switzerland
  - Three outside

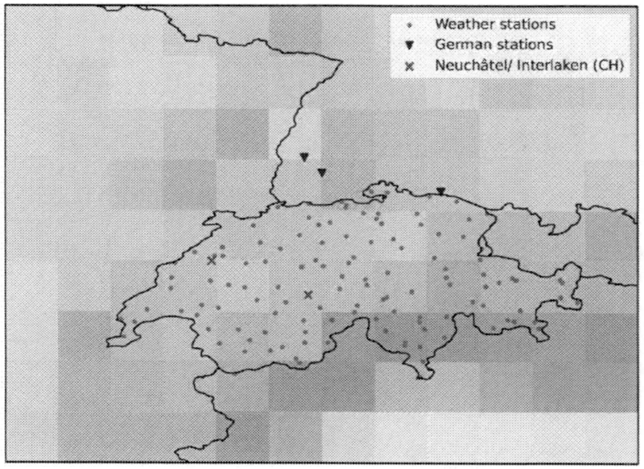

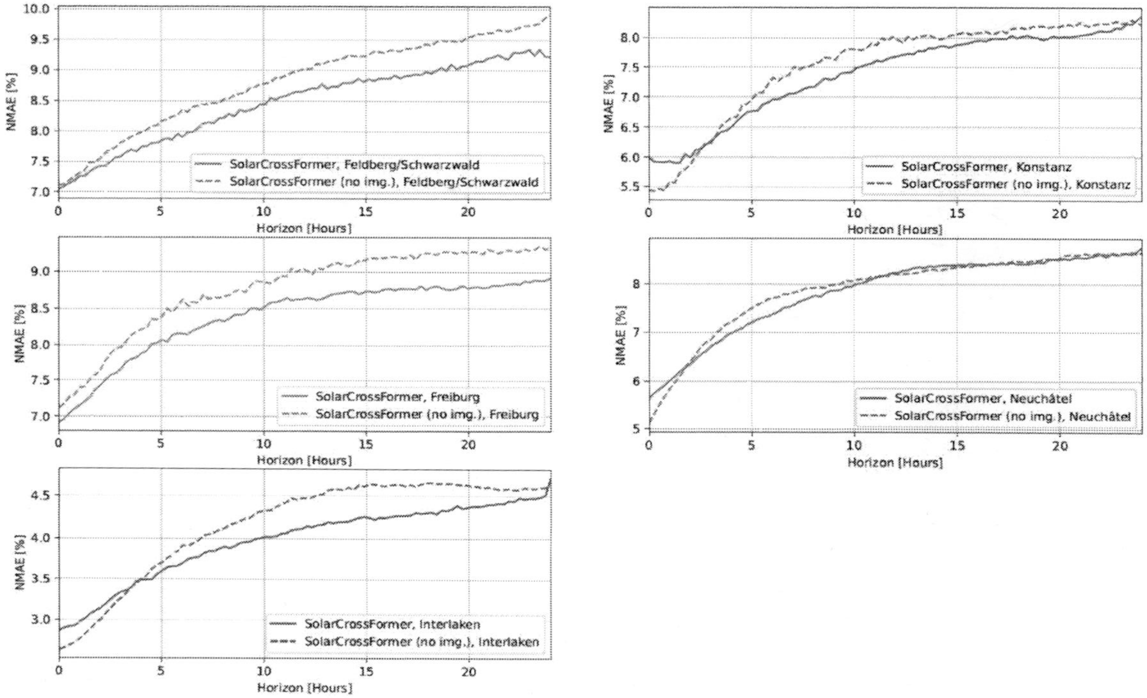

:: csem

IMPACT OF LOCAL OBSERVATIONS ON FORECAST ACCURACY

- **SolarCrossformer remains robust**, but performance slightly degrades without local inputs
  - When ground measurements are available, the model captures local irradiance variations more effectively
  - In the absence of local data, the model relies on spatial context from satellite imagery and nearby stations
- Highlights the **importance of sensor network density**

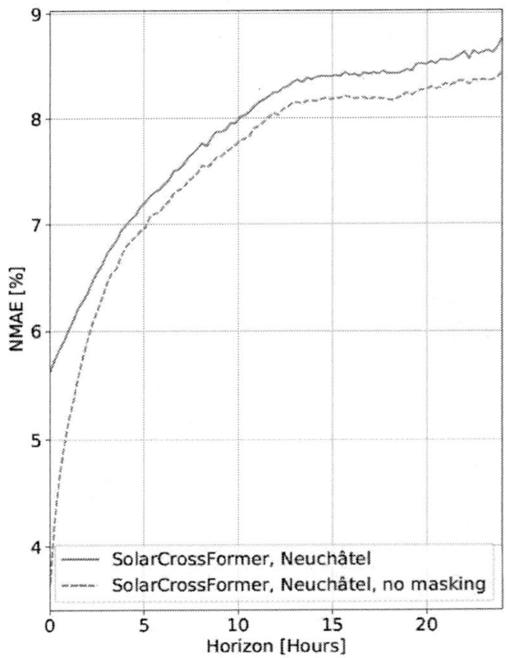

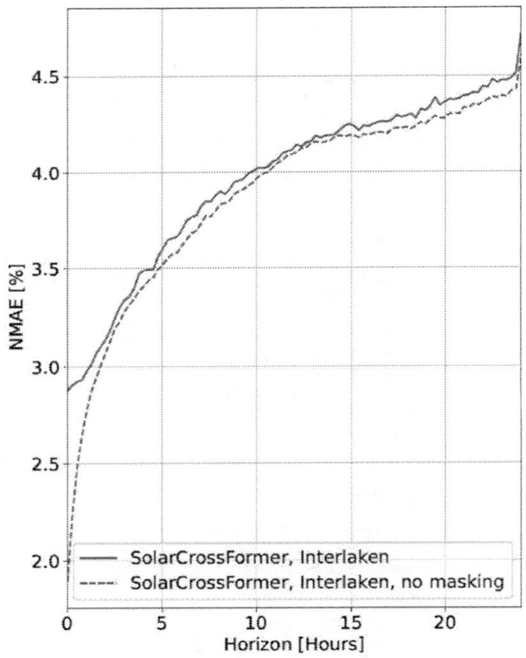

:: csem

CONCLUSIONS

- **SolarCrossformer** yields probabilistic forecasts of irradiance for horizons up to 24h ahead with a temporal resolution of 15 minutes
- It uses advanced GNN to learn the **multi-modal data relations**
- **Robust and flexible:** works at new locations without retraining or historical data
- **Accurate:** outperforms state-of-the-art models and commercial NWP solutions across Switzerland
- **Scalable:** can forecast for any site using only coordinates, satellite, and network data

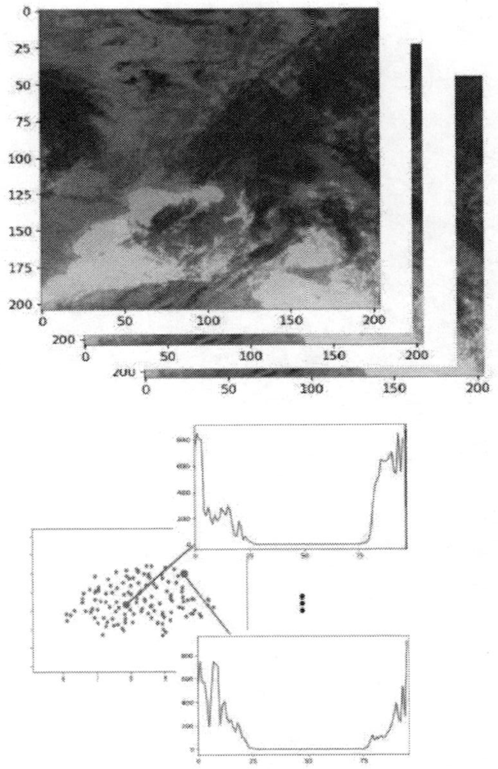

:: csem

Rafael Carrillo
Expert, Digital Energy Solutions
rafael.carrillo@csem.ch
+41 32 720 5389

Co-funded by the European Union under Horizon Europe Agreement No 101146883. Views and opinions expressed are however those of the author(s) only and do not necessarily reflect those of the European Union or CINEA. Neither the European Union nor the granting authority can be held responsible for them.

:: csem

ENHANCING INTRA-HOUR SOLAR IRRADIANCE FORECASTING FOR SOLAR APPLICATIONS: A BLENDED MODEL OF SATELLITE, SKY IMAGER AND PERSISTENCE

Bijan Nouri, Jorge Lezaca, Yann Fabel, Annette Hammer, Niklas Blum, Stefan Wilbert

DLR

Agenda

- Motivation
- Methodology
  - Forecasting systems
  - Blending methods
  - Used datasets
- Results
  - General benchmark forecasts
  - Influence of prevailing sky conditions
  - Spatial influence
- Conclusion

Motivation

- Solar irradiance variabilities in space and time on the local scale occur due to cloud passing
- Forecasting could make it possible to anticipate changes
- Accuracy of forecasts is crucial for their applicability
- Complementary Methods
  - Local observations (e.g. sky cameras and radiometers) offer high temporal and spatial resolution, but have limited spatial coverage and a short forecast horizon.
  - Satellites provide broad coverage and an extended forecast horizon, but have a coarser resolution.
- A hybrid model that blends local and satellite forecasts to produce robust, high-resolution, intra-hour local forecasts.

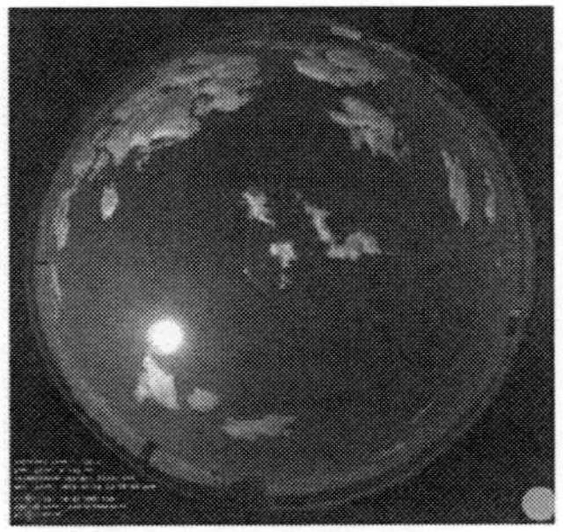

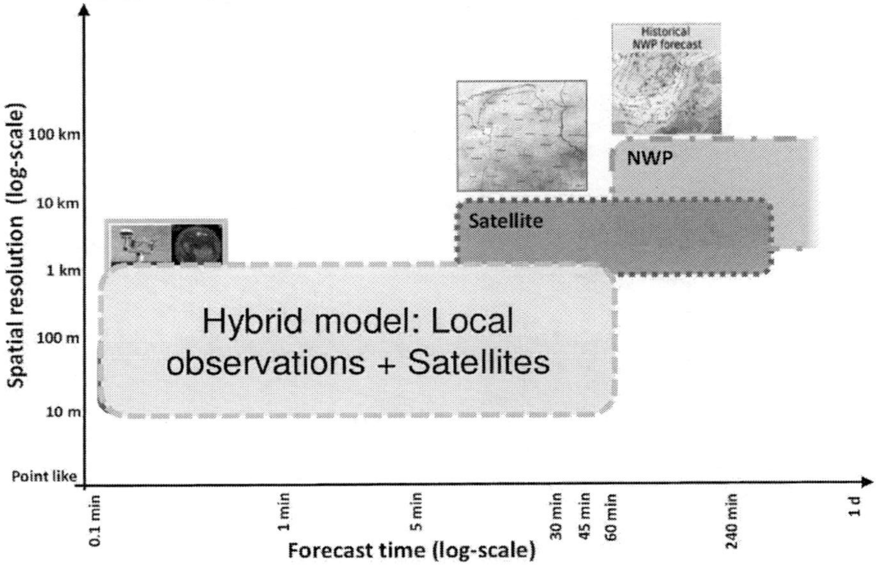

Forecasting systems

Meteosat based forecasts

Heliosat method [1]

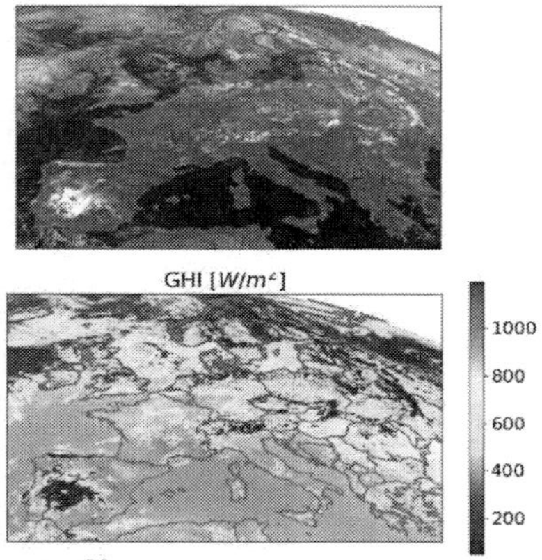

- Horizon ~6h
- Spatial resolution ~ 2km
- Temporal resolution and update rate 15 min

All sky imager (ASI) based forecast

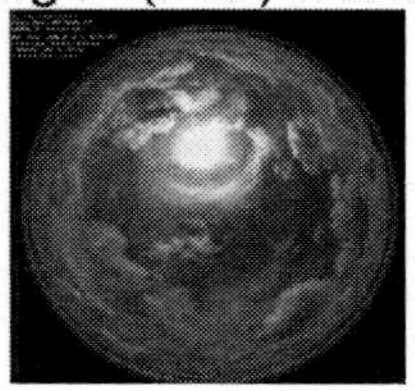

Deep learning transformer method [2]

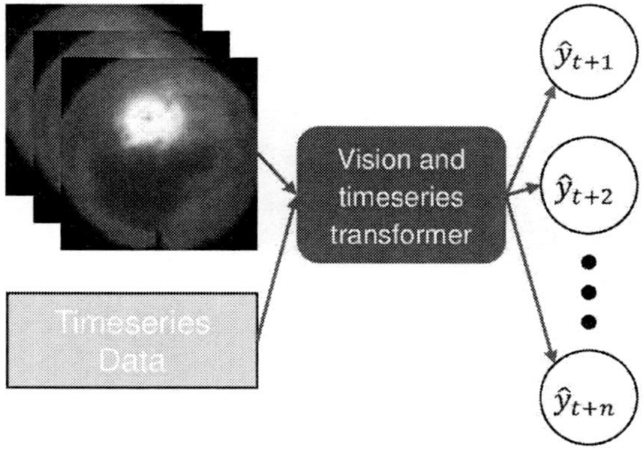

- Horizon 1h
- Temporal resolution 1 min
- Update rate 30 s
- Model trained on data set in southern Spain
- >3000000 data points distributed over 7 years

Persistence forecast

Scaled persistence method [3]

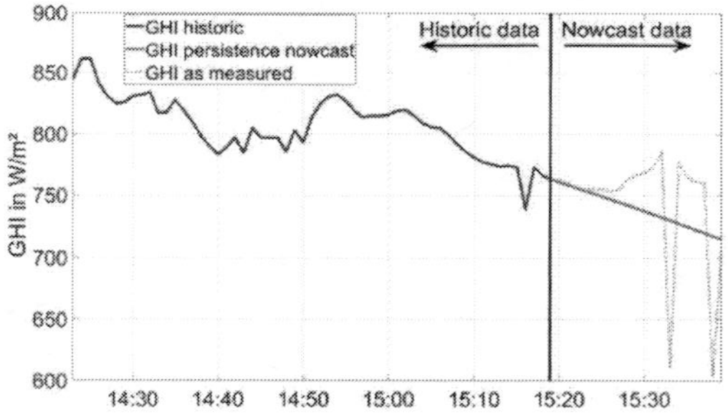

- Update rate 1 min

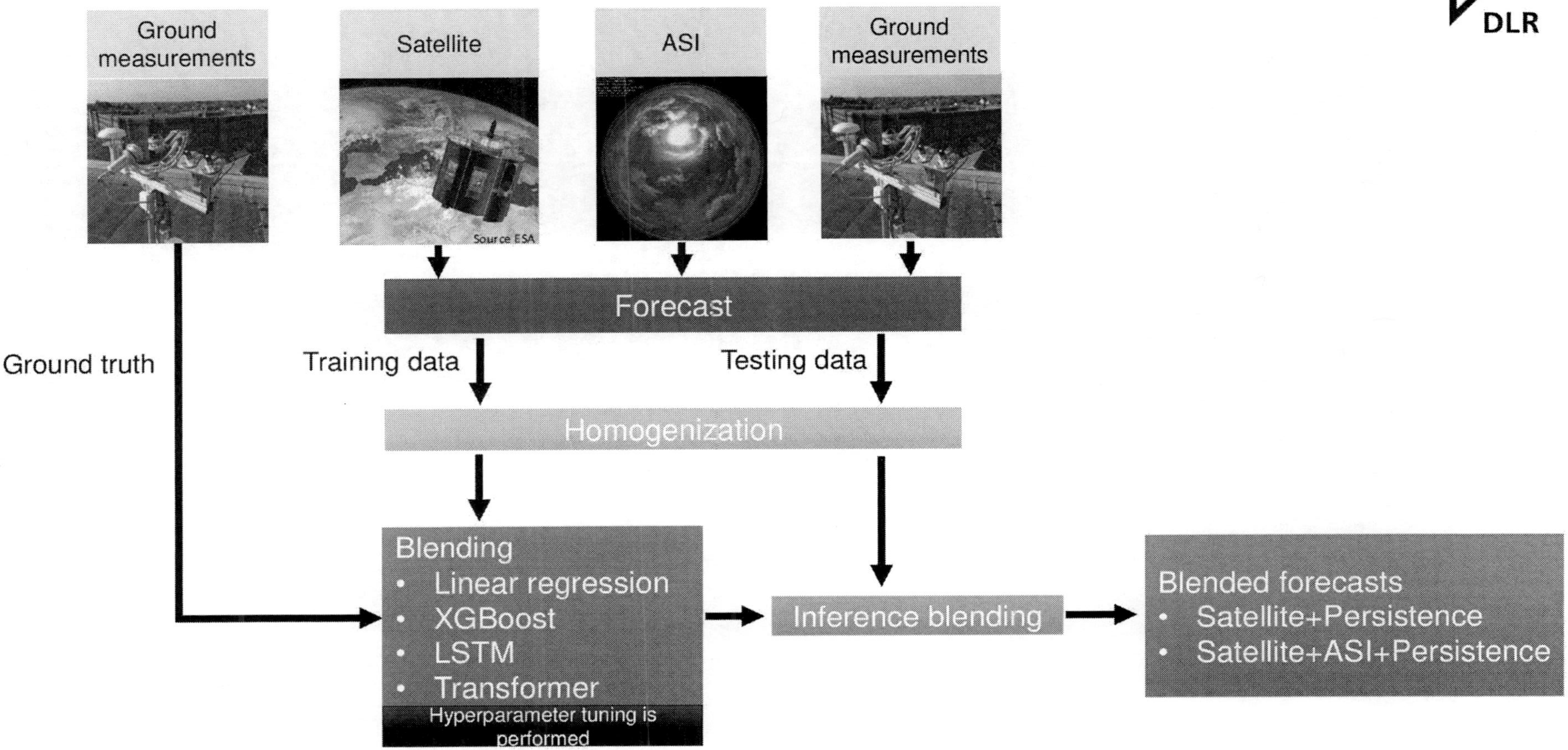
Blending methods
DLR
Ground measurements
Satellite
ASI
Ground measurements
Source ESA
Forecast
Ground truth
Training data
Testing data
Homogenization
Blending
• Linear regression
• XGBoost
• LSTM
• Transformer
Hyperparameter tuning is performed
Inference blending
Blended forecasts
• Satellite+Persistence
• Satellite+ASI+Persistence
5
Bijan Nouri, DLR, EUPVSec 2025

Used datasets

- Site: Oldenburg (Germany)
  - OLDON station of Eye2Sky Network [4]
  - 53°8´46.96´´N / 8°13´2.41´´E
- Used data
  - Training/Validation: July 2020 (50373 datapoints)
  - Testing: August 2020 (45163 datapoints)

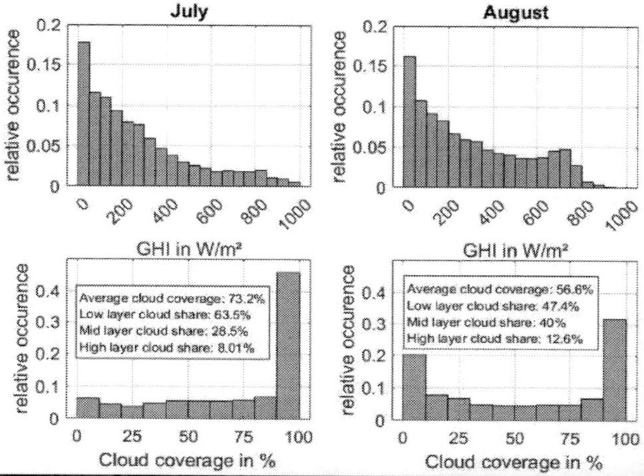

	July	August
$\overline{GHI}$	321.7 W/m²	358.1 W/m²
$Max\ GHI$	972.3 W/m²	840.0 W/m²
$\overline{DHI}$	192.1 W/m²	166.7 W/m²
$Max\ DHI$	505.4 W/m²	442.1 W/m²
$\overline{DNI}$	209.9 W/m²	323.5 W/m²
$Max\ DNI$	876.4 W/m²	847.7 W/m²

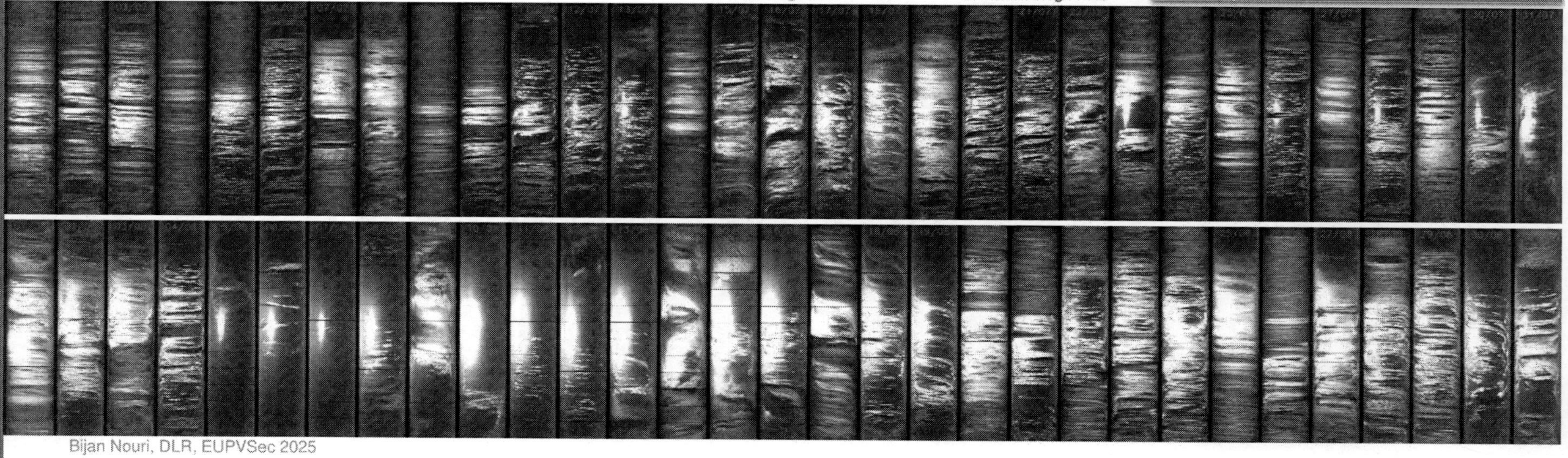

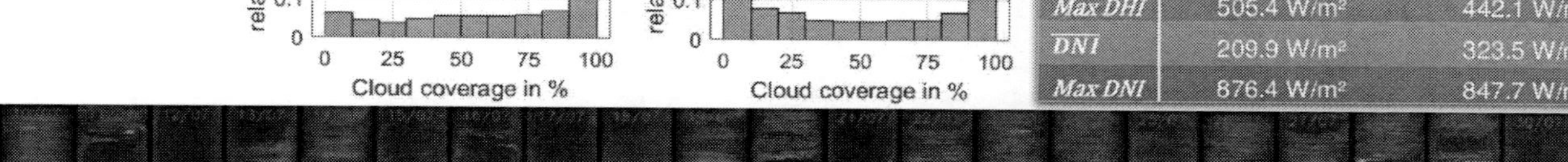

General benchmark forecasts

$$RMSE = \sqrt{1/n \sum_{i=1}^{n} (\hat{y}_i - y_i)^2} \qquad MAE = 1/n \sum_{i=1}^{n} |\hat{y}_i - y_i| \qquad Skill\ score = 1 - \frac{error_{model}}{error_{persistence}}$$

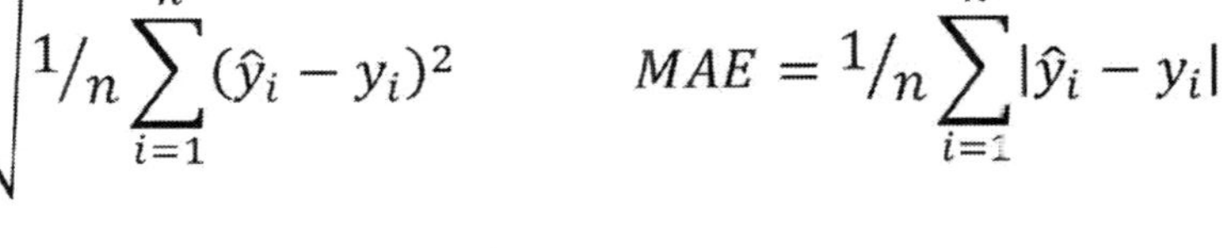

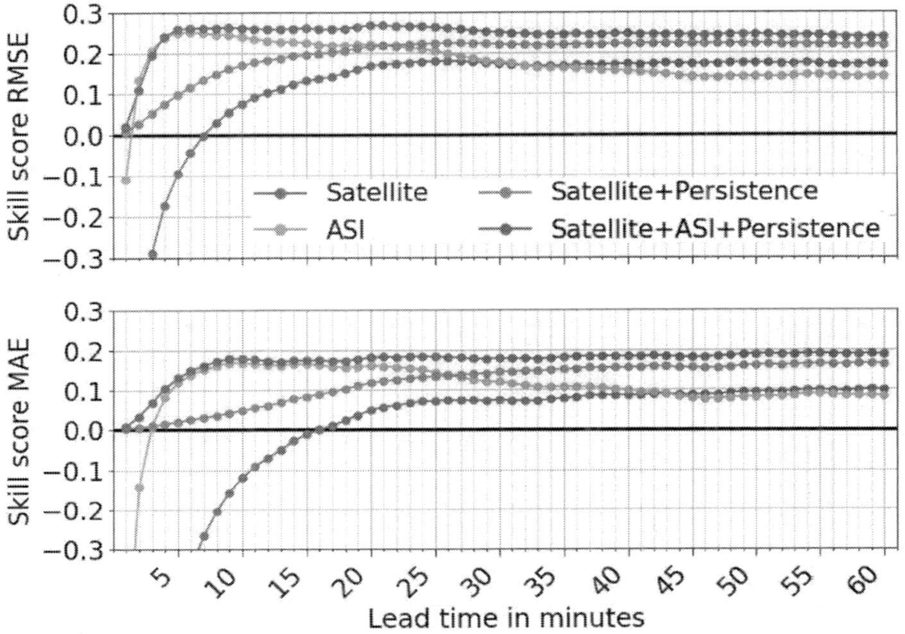

Satellite+ASI+Persistence

Error metric	LR	XGBoost	LSTM	Transfor-mer
RMSE [W/m²] ↓	121.8 ±16.9	120.8 ±17.2	119.7 ±17.4	120.4 ±17.2
MAE [W/m²] ↓	77.6 ±14.2	80.3 ±14.9	78.1 ±14.5	79.5 ±14.6
MBE [W/m²] ↓	-1.7 ±1.6	-5.5 ±1.5	-2.8 ±3.0	-1.8 ±5.1
Skill Score (RMSE) ↑	0.24 ±0.04	0.25 ±0.02	0.26 ±0.01	0.26 ±0.02
Skill Score (MAE) ↑	0.17 ±0.03	0.14 ±0.04	0.17 ±0.03	0.15 ±0.05

Averaged results over all lead times (± std)

Influence of prevailing sky conditions

- Mostly/almost clear sky with high clear sky index
  - 27% of the dataset
  - Low variability
  - Average cloud coverage ≈ 11%
  - Average clear sky index ≈ 0.94

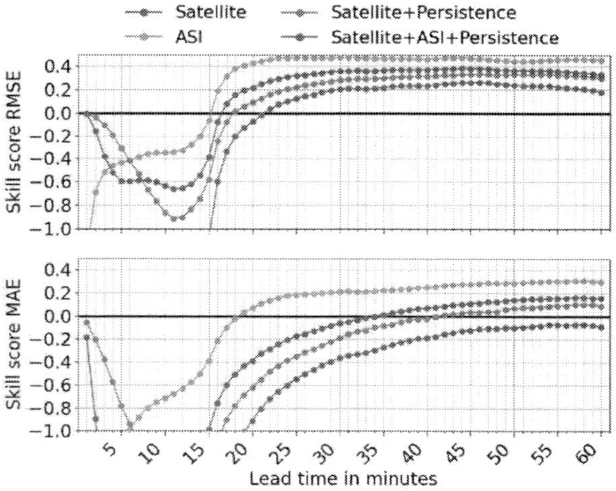

- Partly cloudy with intermediate clear sky index
  - 25% of the dataset
  - High/intermediate variability
  - average cloud coverage ≈ 53%
  - average clear sky index ≈ 0.57

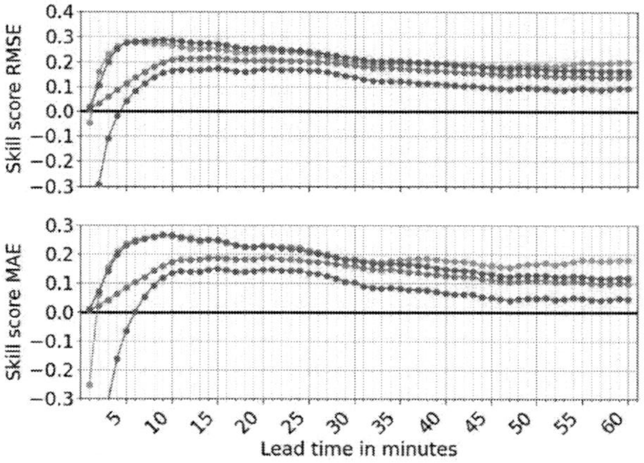

- Almost/mostly overcast with low clear sky index
  - 48% of the dataset
  - Intermediate/low variability
  - average cloud coverage ≈ 85%
  - average clear sky index ≈ 0.08

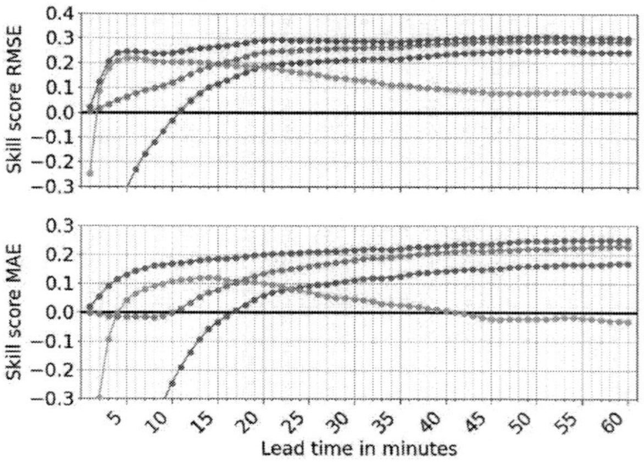

Spatial influence

- Benchmark OLDON hybrid forecast against satellite forecasts at 3 additional sites
  - OLDON hybrid forecast remains unchanged.
  - Use site-specific satellite forecasts for comparison.
  - Sites are part of the Eye2Sky network with reference sensors.

$$Skill\ score = 1 - \frac{error_{Hybrid_{OLDON}@site(n)}}{error_{Satellite_{site(n)}}}$$

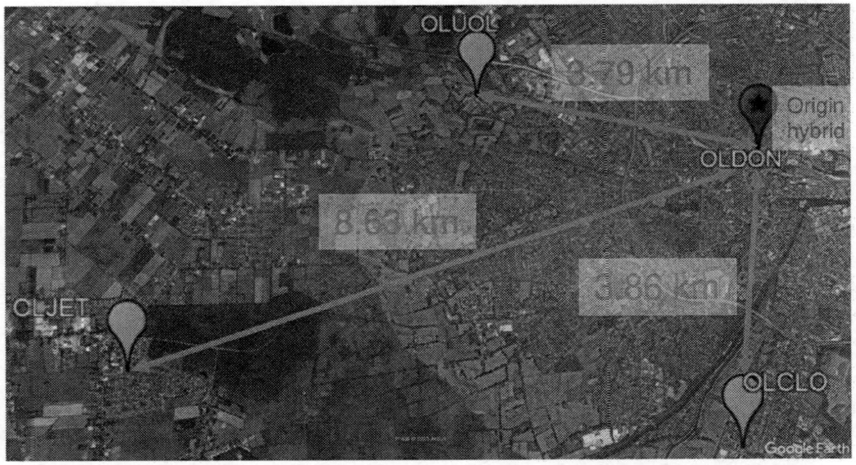

	Hybrid OLDON@OLCLO (Baseline: Satellite OLCLO)	Hybrid OLDON@OLUOL (Baseline: Satellite OLUOL)	Hybrid OLDON@OLJET (Baseline: Satellite OLJET)
Skill Score (RMSE) ↑	0.09±0.04	0.04±0.02	-0.01±0.06
Skill Score (MAE) ↑	0.14±0.03	0.07±0.02	0.05±0.03

Averaged results over all lead times (± std)

Conclusion

- Intra-Hour Boost: Ground measurements significantly enhance site-specific satellite forecasts in the intra-hour range.
- Hybrid Superiority: Satellite+ASI+Persistence model delivers lowest error metrics with top skill scores (RMSE: 0.24±0.04, MAE: 0.17±0.03).
- Cross-Climate Success: ASI, trained in desert climate, performs well in temperate regions.
- Short-Term Strength: ASI excels in short lead times and partly cloudy conditions, enhancing hybrid performance.
- Spatial Reach: Hybrid forecast shows a positive impact up to ~4 km away from the origin.
- Future Focus: Strong for overall irradiance, less for ramp events; generative ASI models to be explored.

References

1. Hammer, A., Kühnert, J., Weinreich, K., & Lorenz, E. (2015). Short-term forecasting of surface solar irradiance based on Meteosat-SEVIRI data using a nighttime cloud index. Remote Sensing, 7(7), 9070-9090.
2. Fabel, Y., Nouri, B., Wilbert, S., Blum, N., Schnaus, D., Triebel, R., ... & Pitz-Paal, R. (2024). Combining Deep Learning and Physical Models: A Benchmark Study on All-Sky Imager-Based Solar Nowcasting Systems. Solar RRL, 8(4), 2300808.
3. Chu, Y., Li, M., Coimbra, C. F., Feng, D., & Wang, H. (2021). Intra-hour irradiance forecasting techniques for solar power integration: A review. Iscience, 24(10).
4. Schmidt, T., Stührenberg, J., Blum, N., Lezaca, J., Hammer, A., Wilbert, S., ... & Vogt, T. (2025). Eye2Sky–a network of all-sky imager and meteorological measurement stations for high resolution nowcasting of solar irradiance. *Meteorologische Zeitschrift*, *34*(1), 35-55.

DLR
THANK YOU FOR YOUR ATTENTION!
QUESTIONS?
BIJAN.NOURI@DLR.DE
12
Bijan Nouri, DLR, EUPVSec 2025

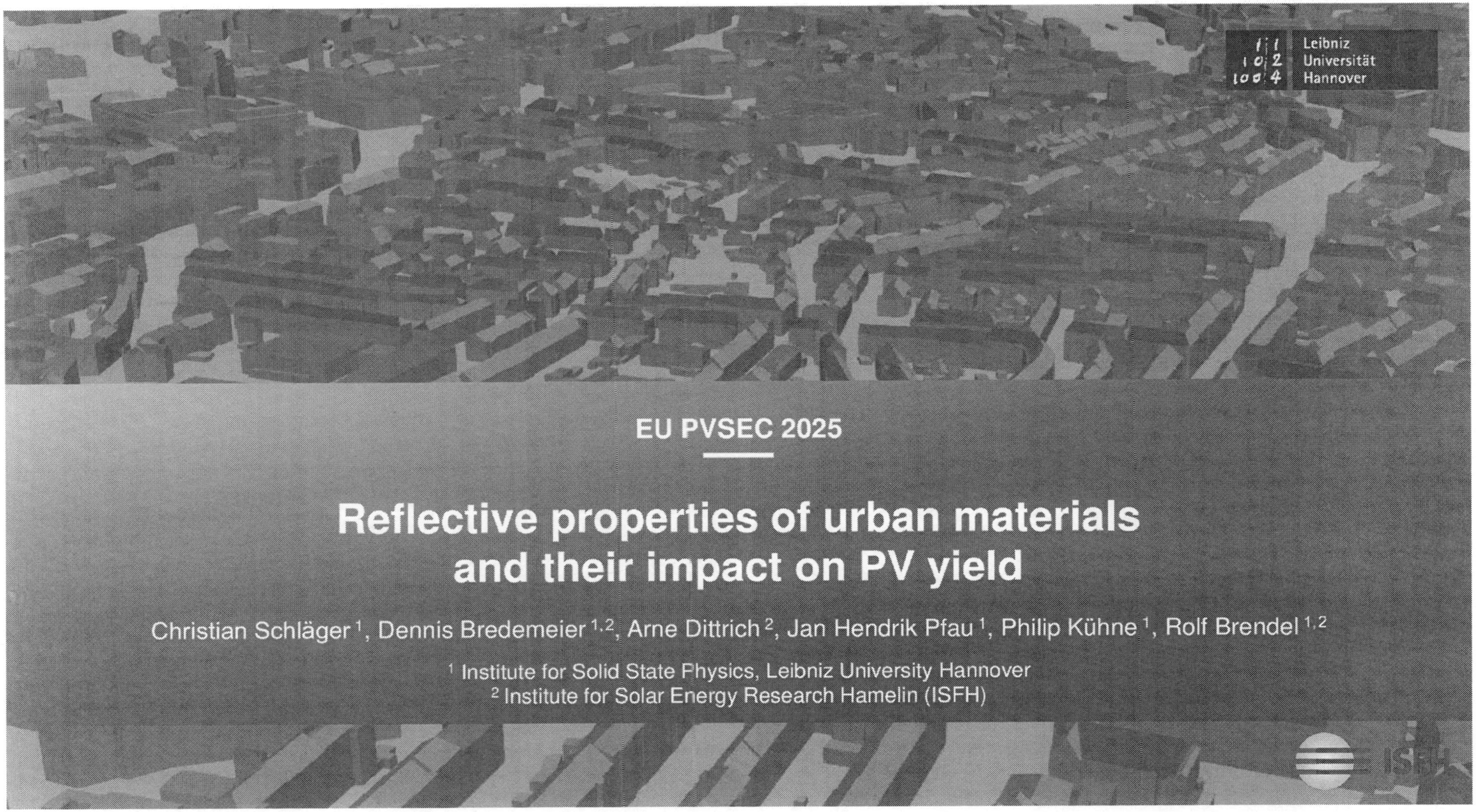
Leibniz
Universität
Hannover
EU PVSEC 2025
Reflective properties of urban materials
and their impact on PV yield
Christian Schläger [1], Dennis Bredemeier [1,2], Arne Dittrich [2], Jan Hendrik Pfau [1], Philip Kühne [1], Rolf Brendel [1,2]
[1] Institute for Solid State Physics, Leibniz University Hannover
[2] Institute for Solar Energy Research Hamelin (ISFH)
ISFH

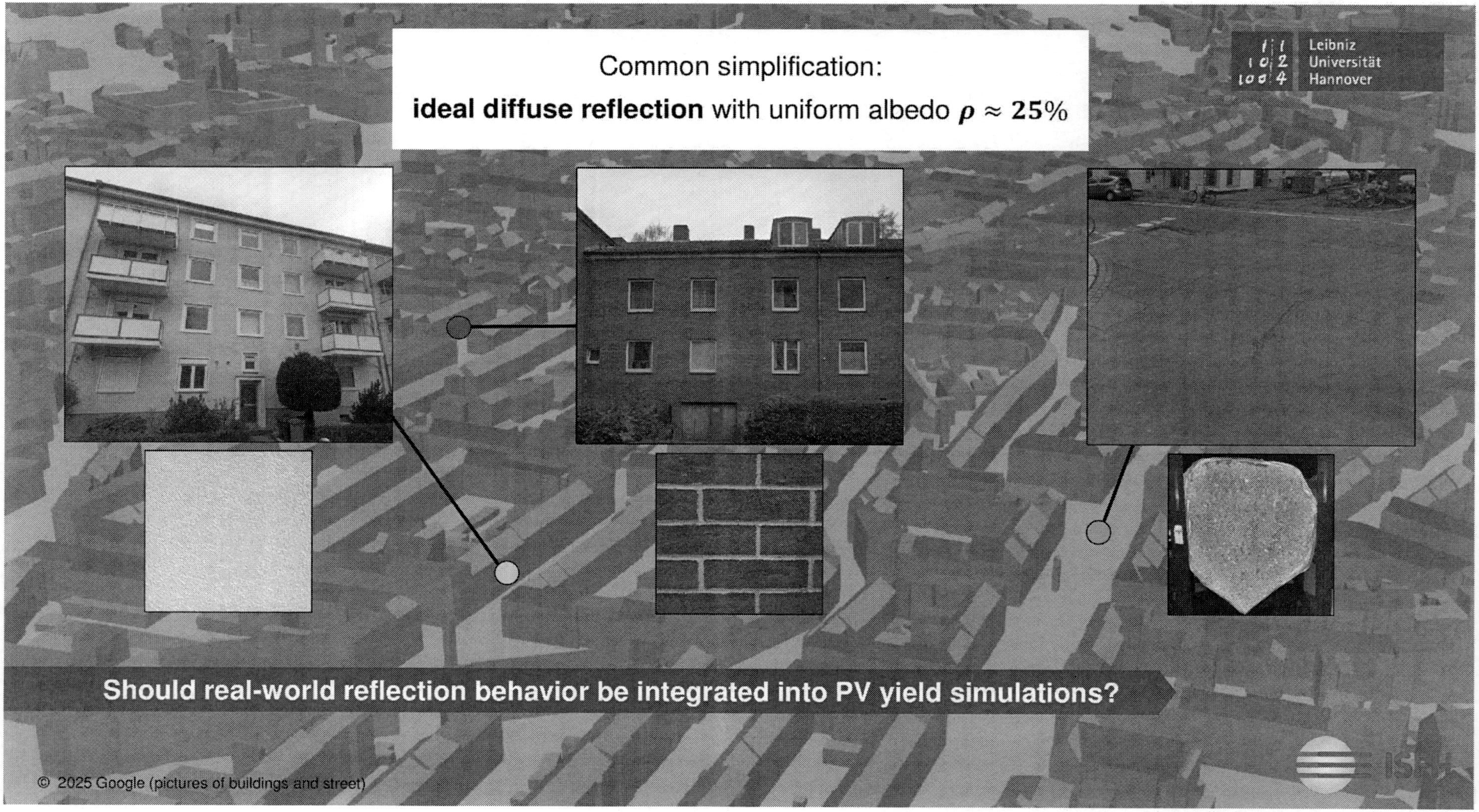
Common simplification:
ideal diffuse reflection with uniform albedo $\rho \approx 25\%$
Leibniz Universität Hannover
Should real-world reflection behavior be integrated into PV yield simulations?
© 2025 Google (pictures of buildings and street)

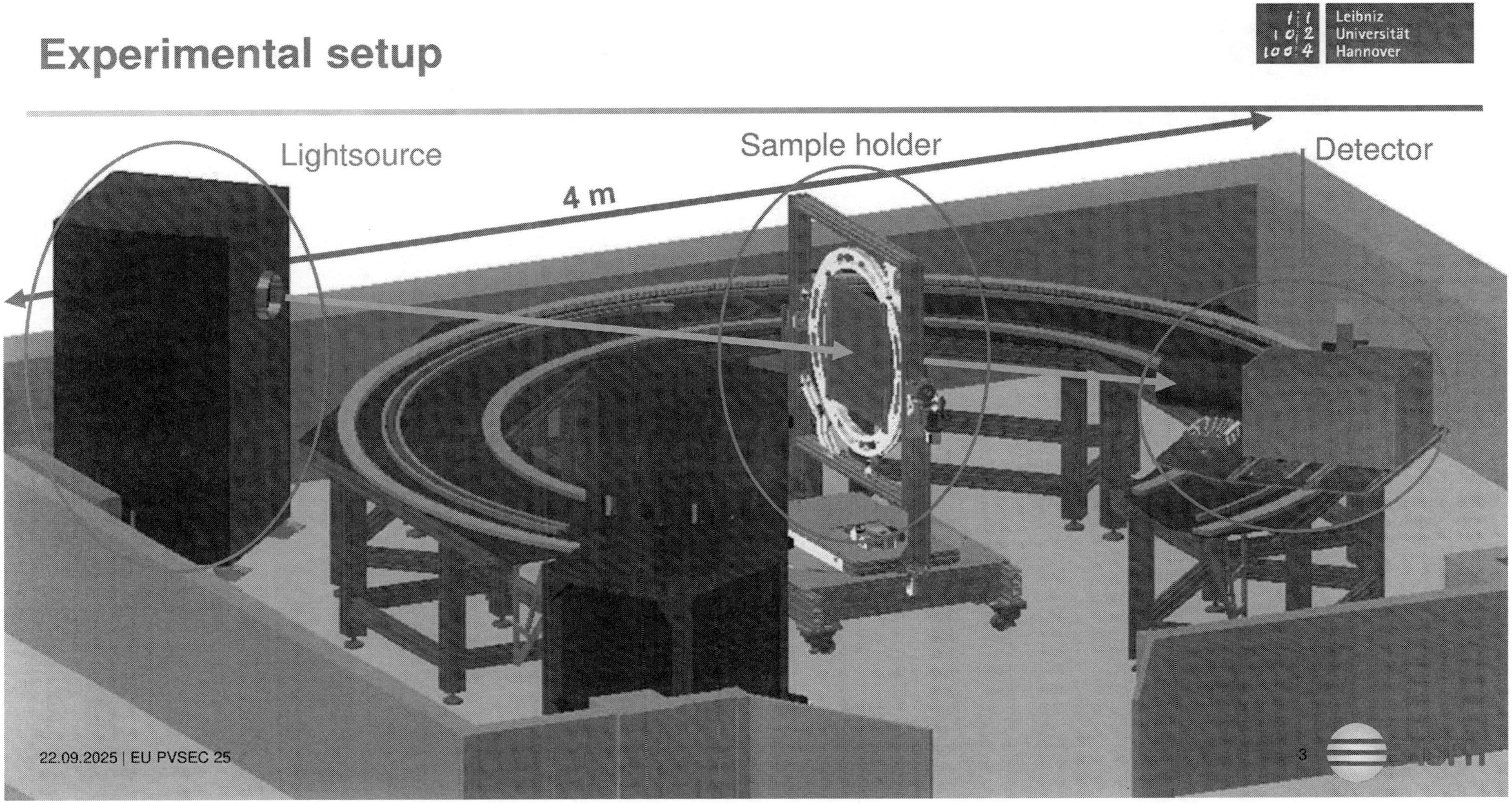
Experimental setup
Leibniz
Universität
Hannover
Lightsource
Sample holder
Detector
4 m
22.09.2025 | EU PVSEC 25
3

Experimental setup

Leibniz Universität Hannover

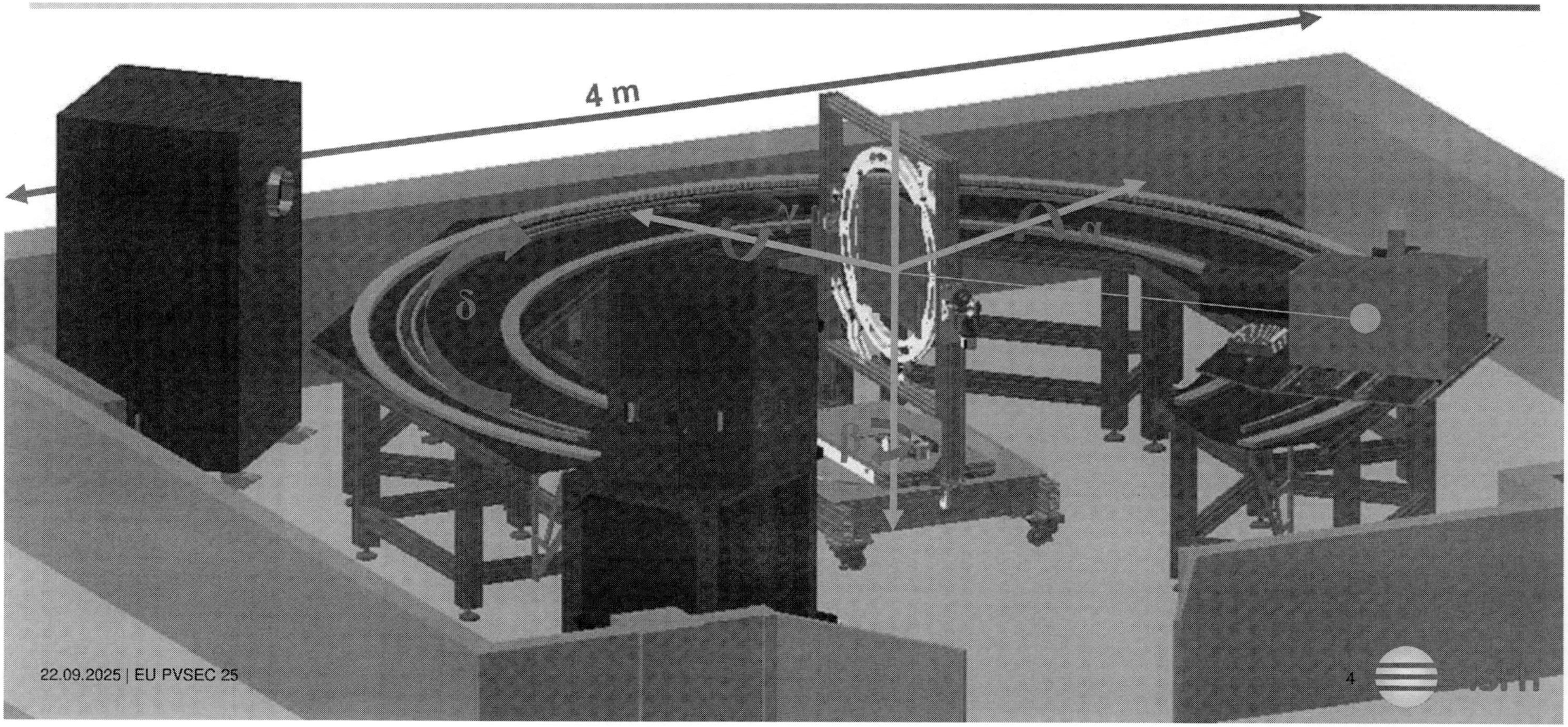

Bidirectional Reflectance Distribution Function

$$\mathrm{BRDF} = \frac{\mathrm{Radiance}}{\mathrm{Irradiance}}$$

$$f_r(\vec{\omega}_{in}, \vec{\omega}_{out}, \lambda) = \frac{dL_r}{dE}$$

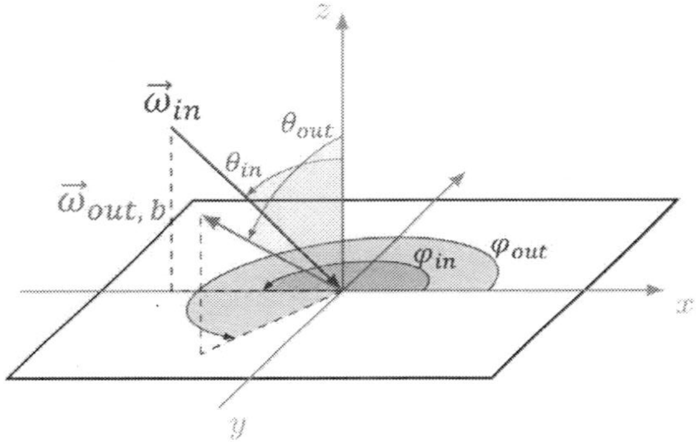

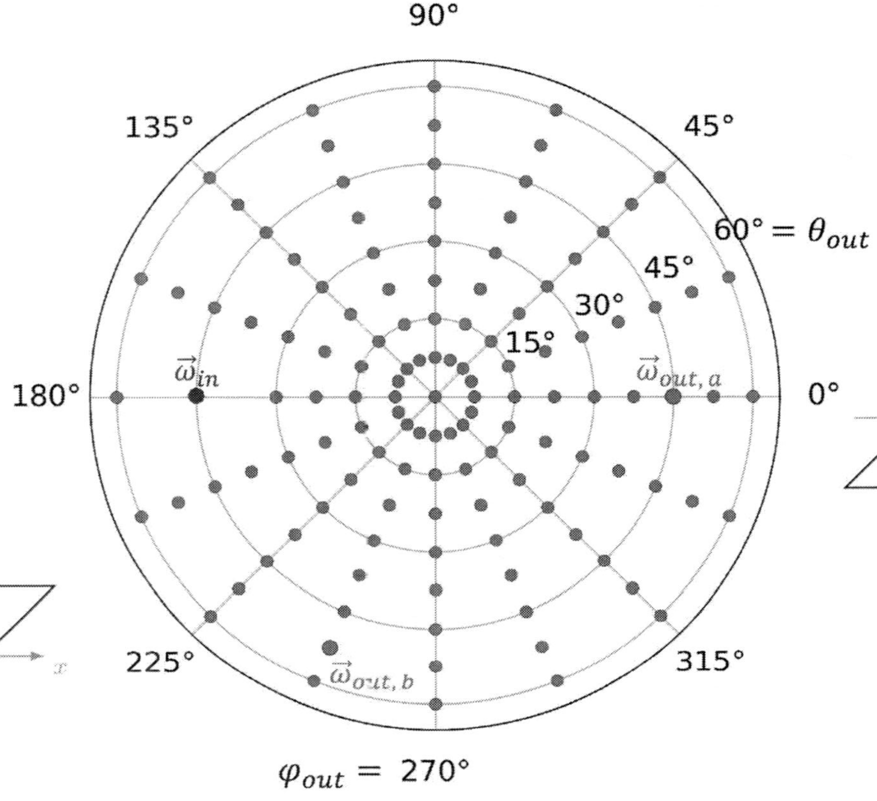

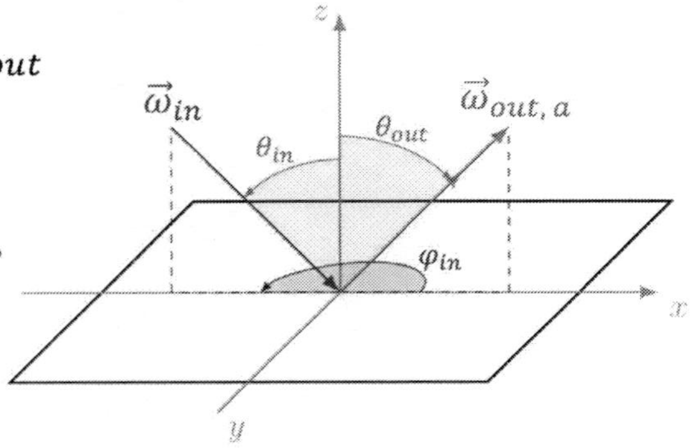

Plaster (light-blue)

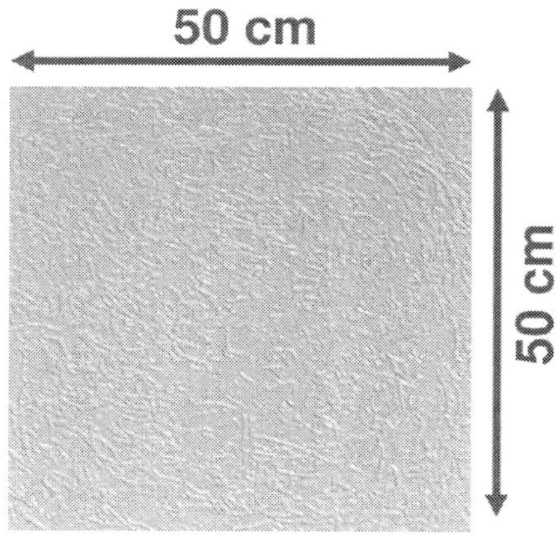

Plaster
(light-blue)

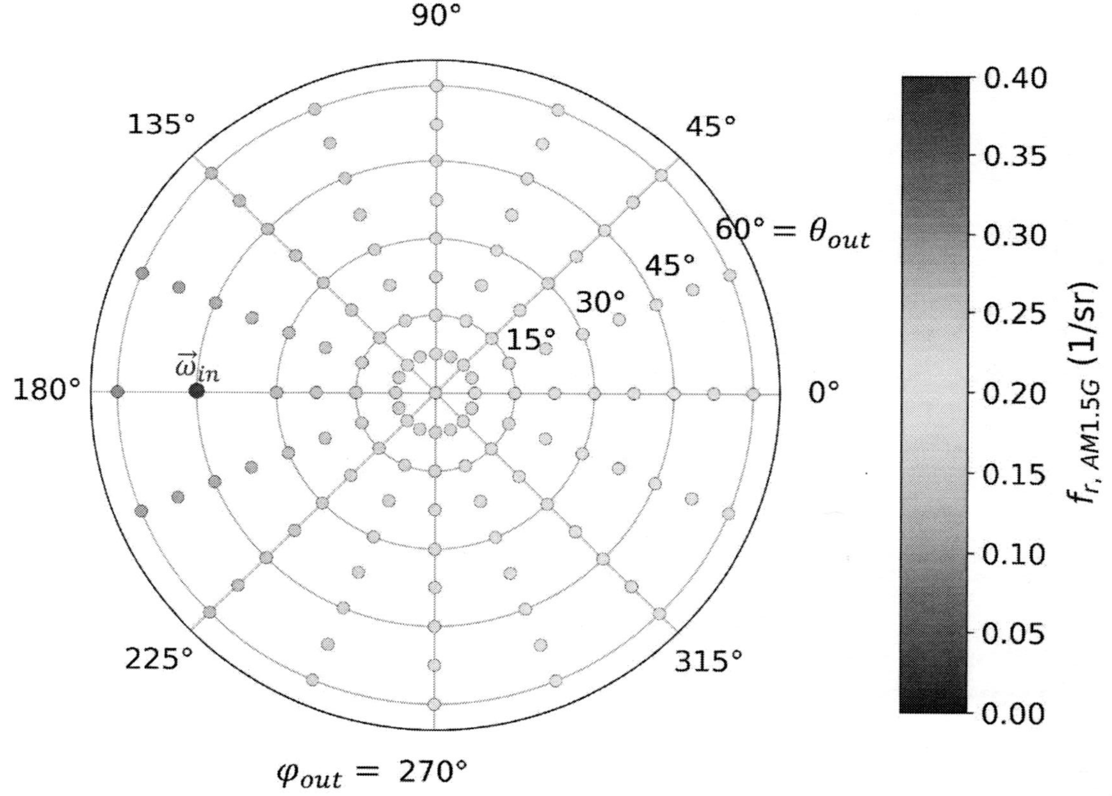

Plaster (light-blue)

Plaster
(light-blue)

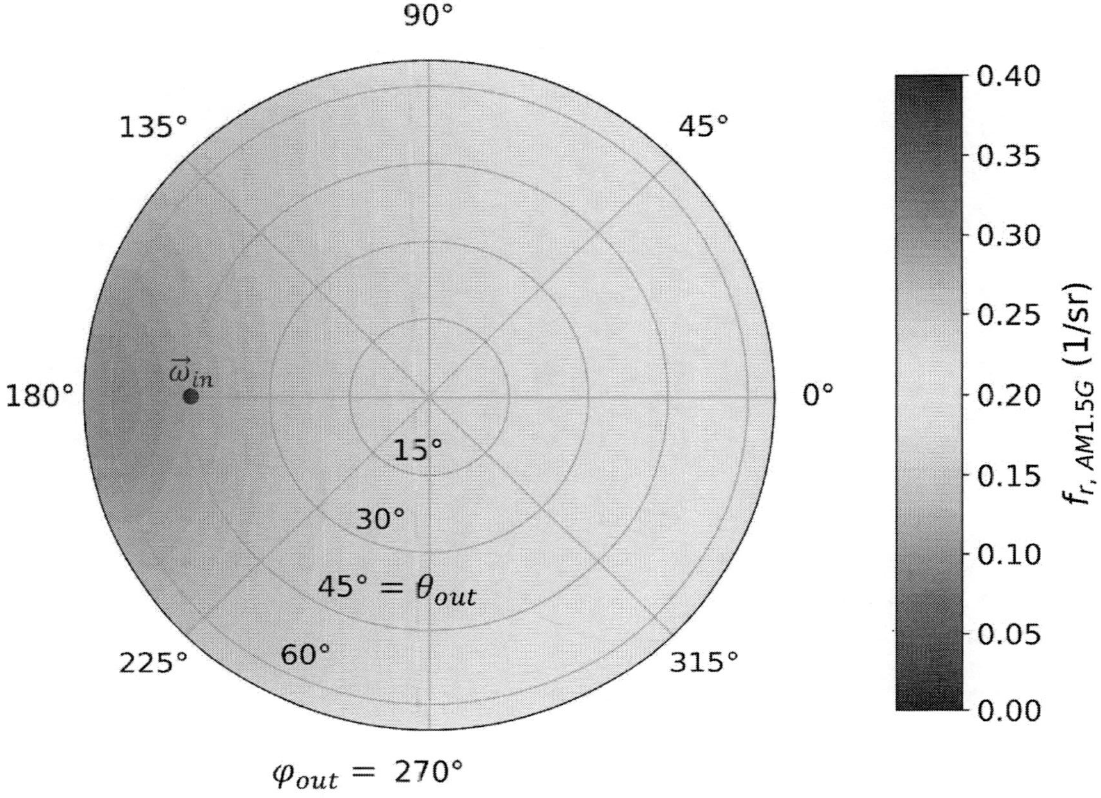

Clinker brick slips (red-brown)

Clinker brick slips (red-brown)

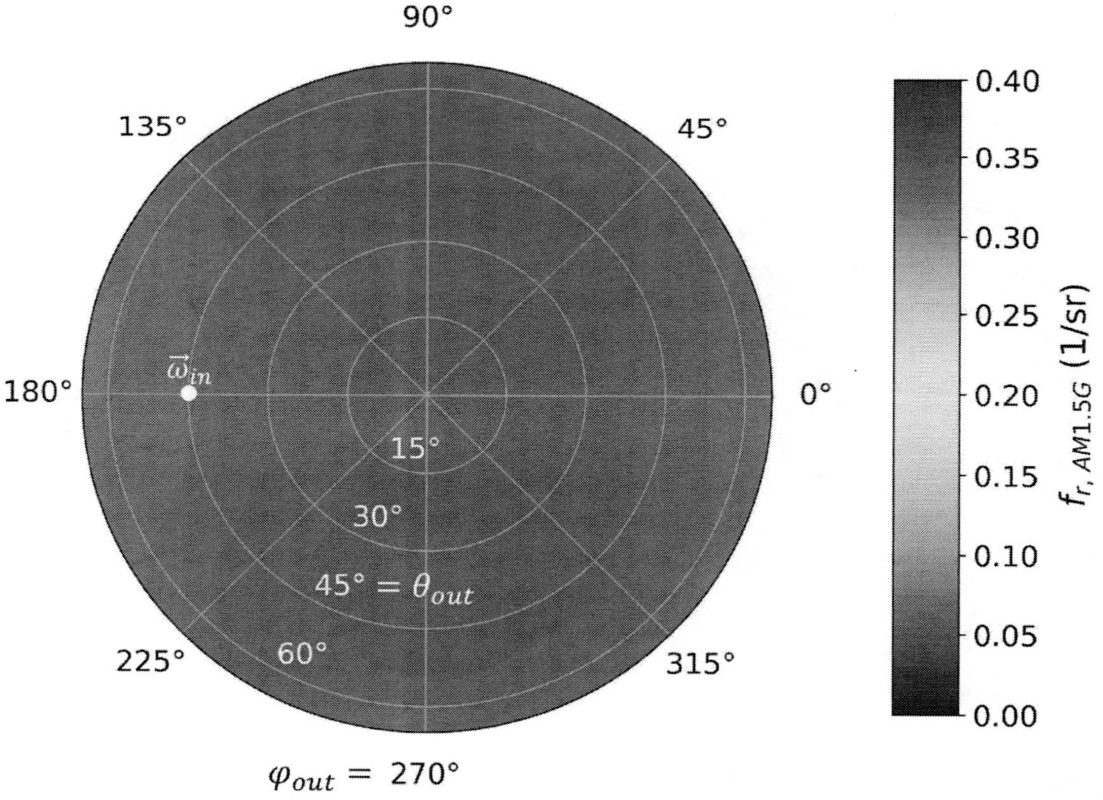

Asphalt (worn)

Asphalt
(worn)

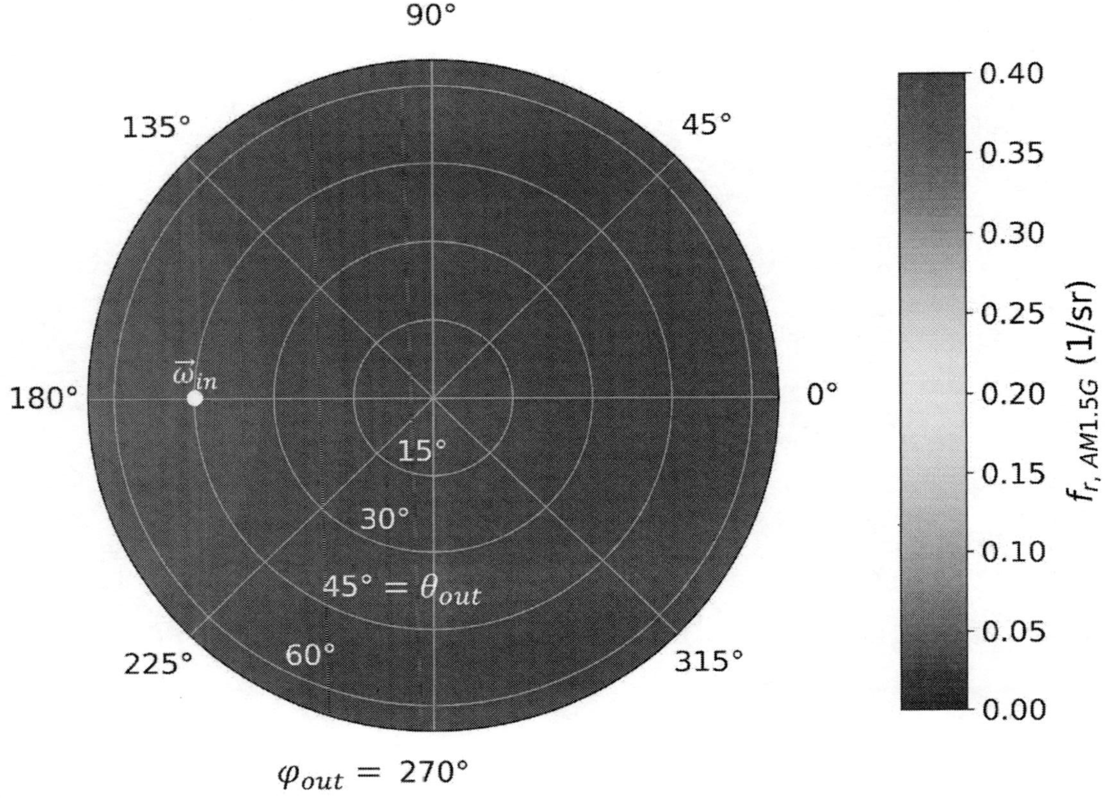

Energy-preserving Oren-Nayar reflection (EON)

Measured BRDF for Plaster (light-blue):

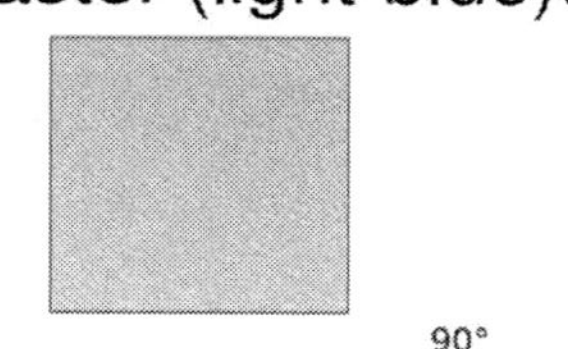

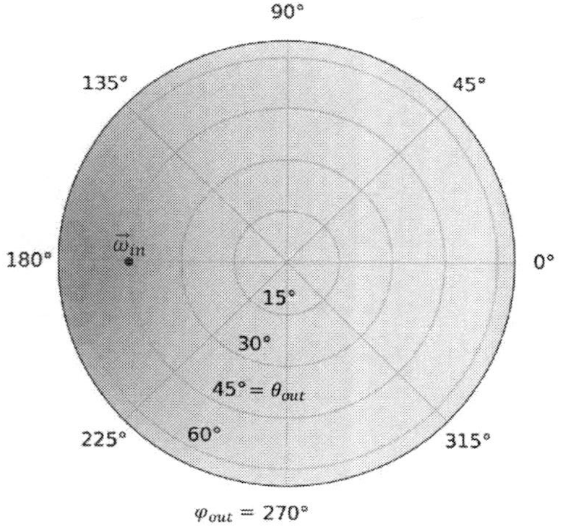

Ideal diffuse reflection:

$$f_r(\vec{\omega}_{in}, \vec{\omega}_{out}) = const. = \frac{\rho}{\pi}$$

$\rho = 0.73$

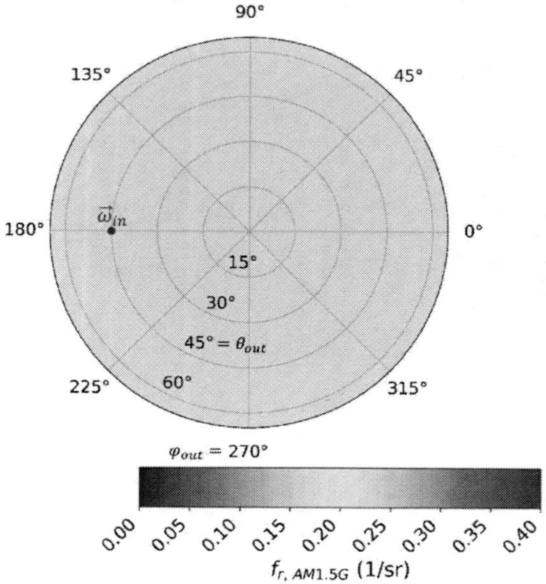

Energy-preserving Oren-Nayar reflection: [2]

$$f_r(\vec{\omega}_{in}, \vec{\omega}_{out}) = \frac{\rho}{\pi}\left(A + B\frac{s}{t}\right) + f_{ms}(\vec{\omega}_{in}, \vec{\omega}_{out})$$

Ideal diffuse term: $A = \dfrac{1}{1 + \left(\frac{1}{2} - \frac{2}{3\pi}\right) r}$

Non-diffuse term: $B = A \cdot r$

Compensation term (multi-scattering events)

Roughness r: mixing ratio of (diffuse term) / (non-diffuse term)

[2] Portsmouth et al. 2025, *J. Comput. Graph. Tech. 14(1)*

Energy-preserving Oren-Nayar reflection (EON)

Measured BRDF for Plaster (light-blue):

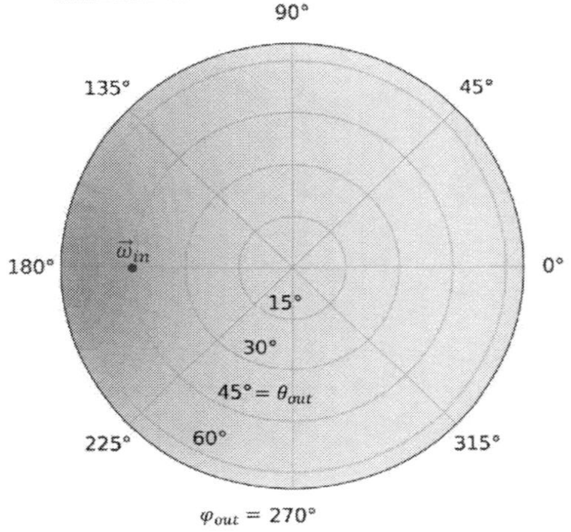

Ideal diffuse reflection:

$$f_r(\vec{\omega}_{in}, \vec{\omega}_{out}) = const. = \frac{\rho}{\pi}$$

$\rho = 0.73$

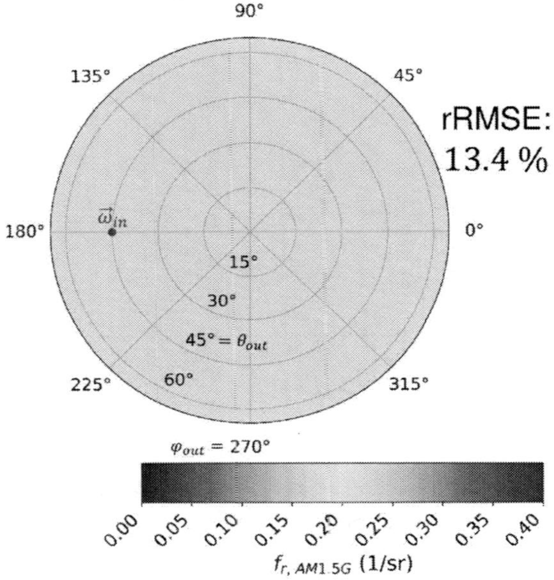

rRMSE: 13.4 %

Energy-preserving Oren-Nayar reflection: [2]

$$f_r(\vec{\omega}_{in}, \vec{\omega}_{out}) = \frac{\rho}{\pi}(A + B\frac{s}{t}) + f_{ms}(\vec{\omega}_{in}, \vec{\omega}_{out})$$

$\rho = 0.73 \quad r = 0.38$

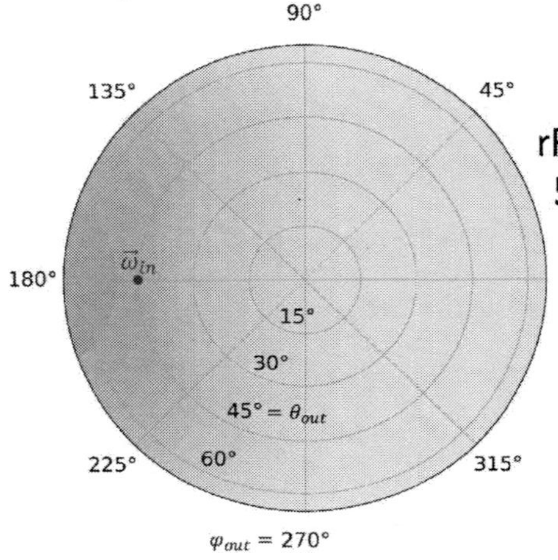

rRMSE: 5.0 %

[2] Portsmouth et al. 2025, *J. Comput. Graph. Tech. 14(1)*

Albedo vs. roughness

Leibniz Universität Hannover

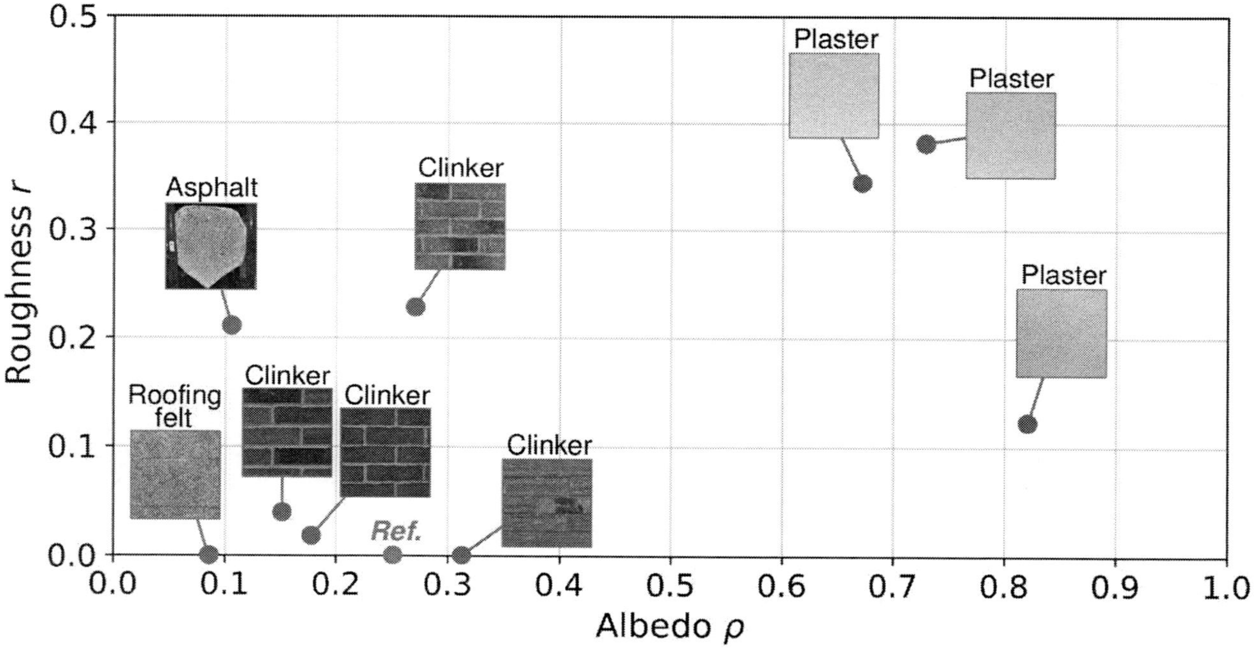

- Clinker region around $\rho \approx 0.25$
- Plaster achieves higher albedos (up to $\rho = 0.82$ for white plaster)
- All facade materials show predominantly diffuse reflection behavior $r \leq 0.4$

ISFH

Material labeling

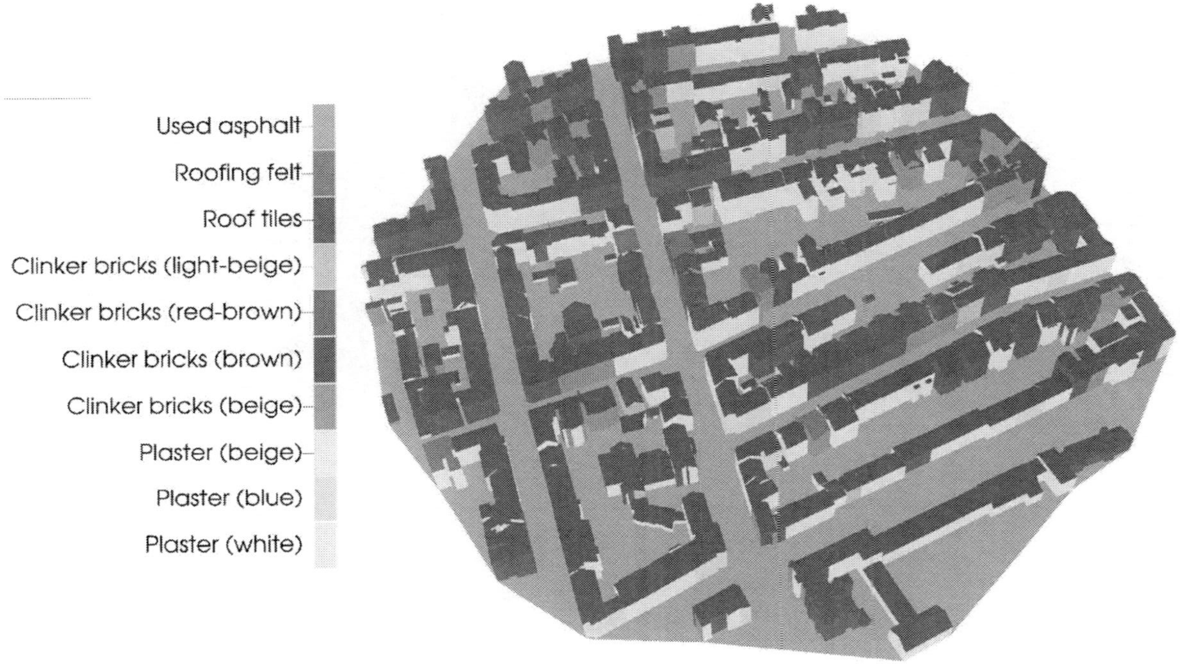

- Residential area with a radius of 200 meters in Hannover (Germany)
- Building geometry is derived from LoD2 data [3]
- Facade and roof material information are provided using images from Google Street View & Google Maps API and human categorization
- Ground is set to asphalt

[3] © GeoBasis-DE/LGLN 2025 (3D model)

Three simulation scenarios

Leibniz Universität Hannover

Ref.
ideal diffuse reflection
uniform $\boldsymbol{\rho} = \mathbf{25}\ \%$

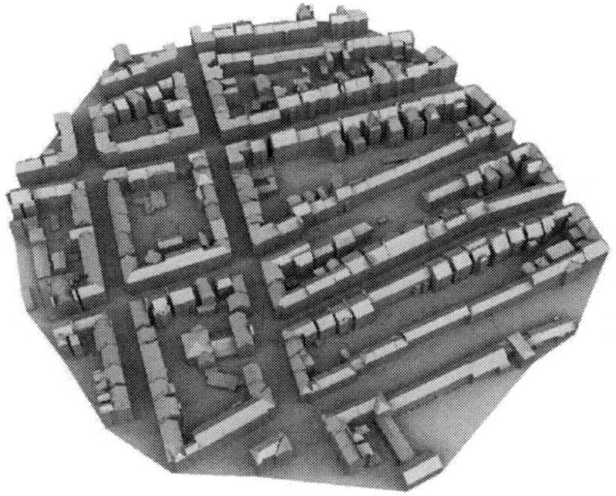

SA
ideal diffuse reflection
surface-specific $\boldsymbol{\rho}$

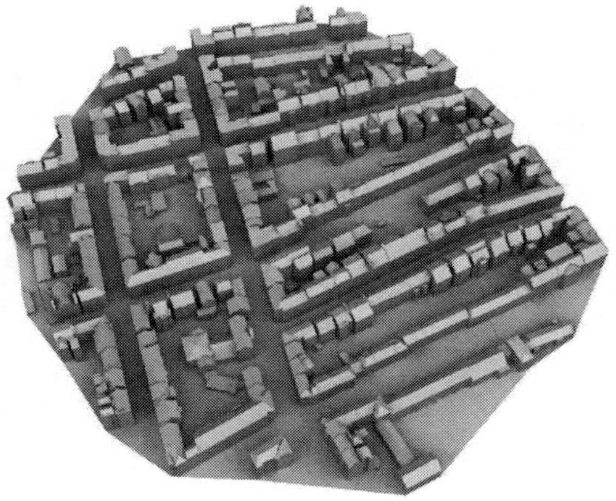

EON
Energy-preserving Oren-Nayar
surface-specific $\boldsymbol{\rho}$ and $\boldsymbol{r}$

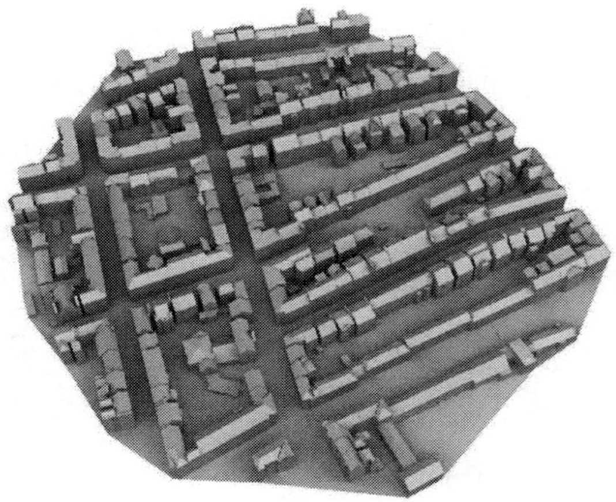

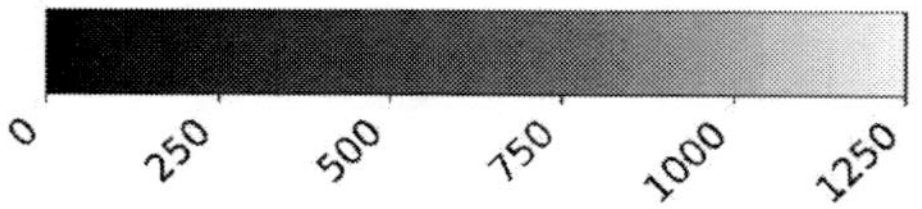

Impact of albedo

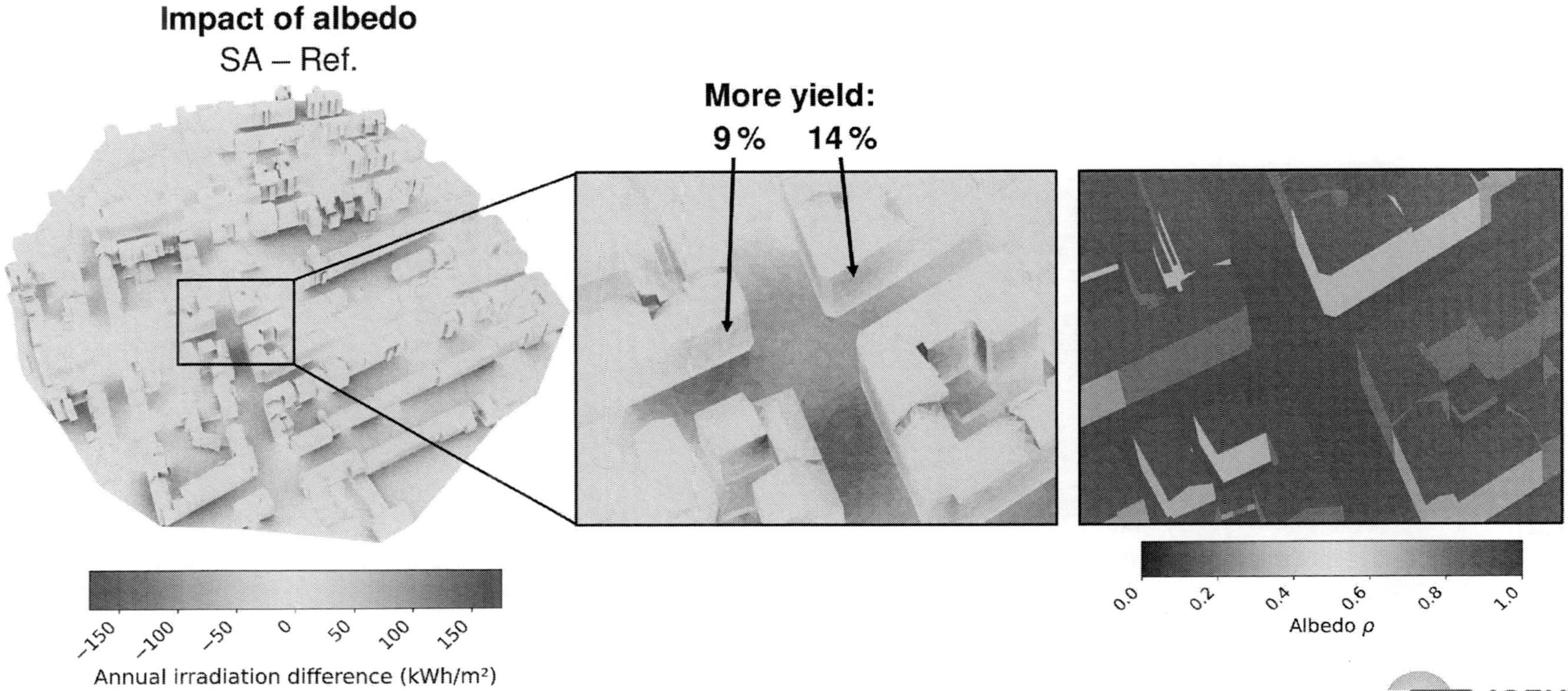

Impact of directionality

Impact of albedo
SA – Ref.

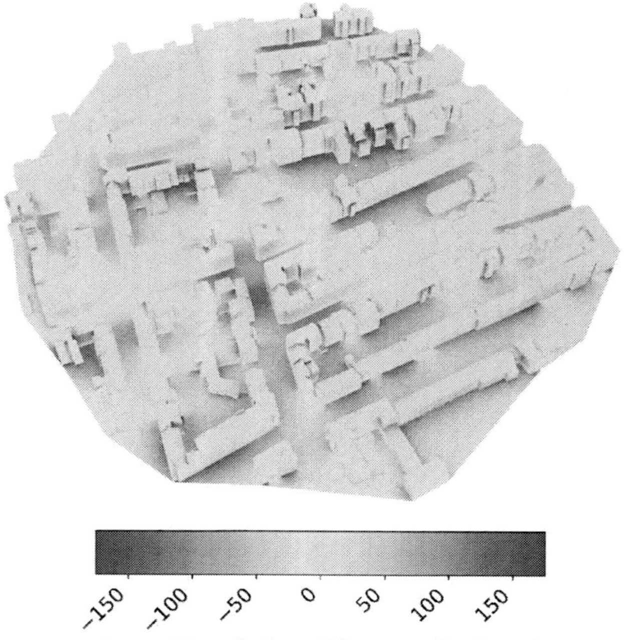

Impact of directionality
EON – SA

Impact of directionality

Impact of albedo
SA – Ref.

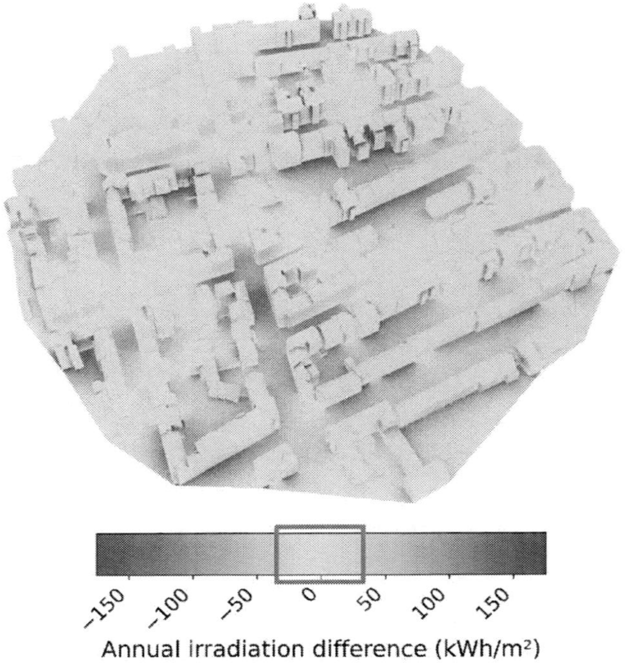

Impact of directionality
EON – SA

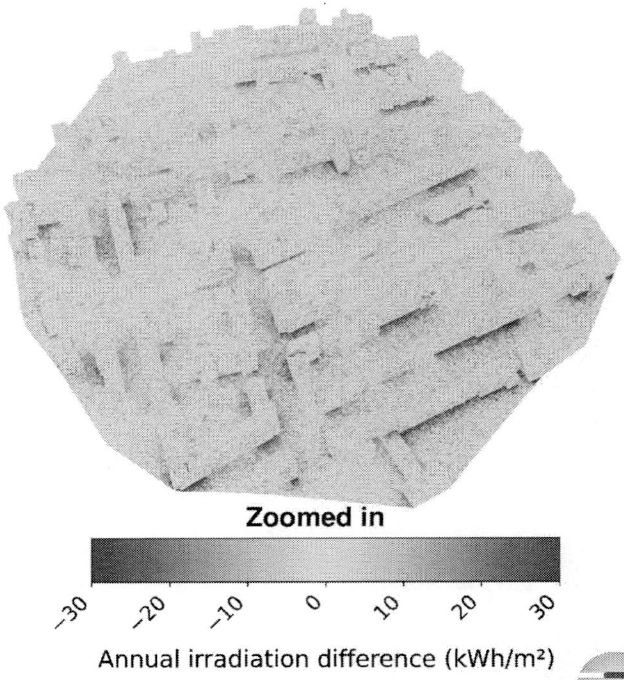

Key take aways

Leibniz Universität Hannover

- Reflection modeling has a significant impact on irradiation results
- Impact of albedo is an order of magnitude higher than impact of directionality
  - Impact of albedo $\rho \approx \pm 100$ kWh/m² (e.g. **14 %** more irradiation on some south-facing facades)
  - Impact of roughness $r \approx \pm 10$ kWh/m²

Should real-world reflection behavior be integrated into PV yield simulations?

- Surface-specific albedos should be integrated.
- Simplification of ideal diffuse reflection is justified.

Leibniz
Universität
Hannover
Thank you!
Contact
Christian Schläger
Research Associate
Institute of Solid State Physics
Department of Solar Energy
schlaeger@solar.uni-hannover.de
Funding
Federal Ministry
for Econcmic Affairs
and Energy
Niedersachsen
Project:
DIGI-PV (03EE1187D)
DBU

UNDERSTANDING SHORT-TERM PV POWER VARIABILITY BASED ON SOLARGIS TIME SERIES DATA AND SIMULATIONS

Martin Opatovsky, Marta Pelfort Ojer, Juraj Betak, Konstantin Rosina
Solargis (Bratislava, Slovakia)
Corresponding author: martin.opatovsky@solargis.com; +421 2 4319 1708

ABSTRACT: This study analyzes the variability of PV power plant output (PVOUT) and Global Horizontal Irradiance (GHI) at both 15-minute and 1-minute temporal resolutions. The PVOUT data is calculated using the detailed Solargis PV simulator. The variability is expressed through the occurrence of ramps in the GHI and PVOUT data, and the ramps are categorized based on their severity. The results highlight that 15-minute GHI data may underestimate high-severity variability events observed in the 1-minute data, especially in tropical, temperate, and continental climates. In moderate latitudes we observe seasonal and diurnal patterns in the GHI and PVOUT ramps, suggesting that single-value variability metrics are insufficient for feasibility analysis of PV projects. To better capture the impact of high-severity events and allow for a more nuanced assessment of variability risk, we propose the Root Mean Square Ramp (RMSR) as a new metric. The findings emphasize the importance of high temporal resolution data and advanced PV simulation for accurate variability assessment, particularly for high criticality PV projects, while keeping the computationally and analytically simpler single-value metrics for prefeasibility analysis.
Keywords: Solar resource variability, PV power variability, Sub-hourly variability, Short-term variability

1 INTRODUCTION

Variability of solar resource has been investigated in multiple studies in the past [1], including our recent contribution on global spatial patterns of the short-term variability of GLOBAL horizontal irradiance (GHI), presented at the EU PVSEC 2024 [2]. However, the variability of GHI is only an approximate measure of a PV power plant's output (PVOUT) variability, and the link between them is non-trivial [3]. From a practical point of view, the variability of the on-grid PV generation is highly relevant. It can affect the PV project revenues and drives the requirements for countermeasures at the plant or grid level to ensure the reliability and stability of the distribution system.

In this work, we examine the short-term variability of GHI and PVOUT across different geographies and climate conditions to determine the optimal measures to assess the variability of on-grid PV power plants. We focus on PVOUT ramps, a sudden increase or decrease of PVOUT over defined time and set threshold [4]. Power ramps create challenges for plant and grid operators that are typically addressed with infrastructure improvements, compensation with fossil-fueled power sources, or short-term storage technologies. We utilize PVOUT simulations in Solargis PV simulator with different input data:

1. Satellite-derived time series with 15-minute temporal resolution
2. Synthetic time series with 1-minute temporal resolution

Based on the simulated data, the variability is assessed using the number of ramps over a certain threshold. Furthermore, the statistics based on the simulated PVOUT are compared with the equivalent statistics calculated from satellite-based GHI data with 15-minute and 1-minute time resolution.

The study analyzes the variability calculated from the different source data, and compares the results in order to determine the accuracy and efficiency of the different data and approaches. Ultimately it proposes optimal approaches for assessing the variability of on-grid PV projects in different development stages or projects with different criticality.

2 METHODOLOGY

2.1 Source GHI data

We use Solargis Time Series data of GHI in 15-minute time resolution over the past 5 complete calendar years (2020 - 2024). Although the 15-minute data from a satellite-based solar model may underestimate the variability observed in a real PV power plant [2], this data can be used as an optimistic estimate of the expected variability.

Furthermore we use synthetically generated 1-minute time series data. This data is generated from 10- or 15-minute GHI, DNI, clear-sky GHI (GHIc) and clear-sky DNI (DNIc) satellite data using a Solargis proprietary multi-scale hierarchical approach. This method provides 1-minute data with similar variability to that of 1-minute GHI and DNI observations and, at the same time, is consistent with the satellite-based GHI and DNI inputs. The synthetic generator has been created to reproduce the long-term statistical properties of the 1-minute GHI and DNI data, especially the likelihood of extreme GHI values caused by over-irradiance or cloud enhancement events, typical of highly variable sky conditions.

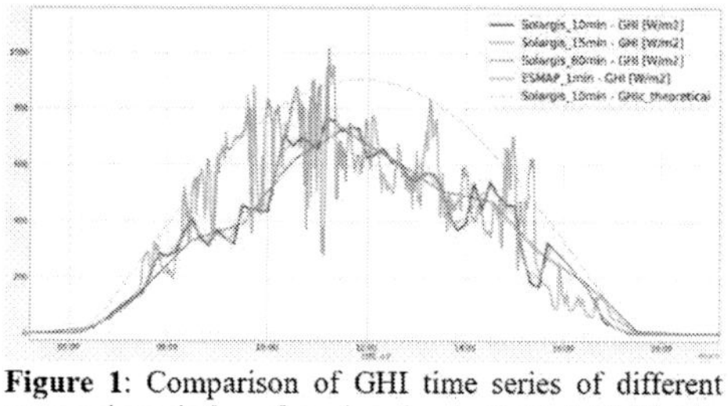

Figure 1: Comparison of GHI time series of different temporal resolutions for a location in Central Highlands, Vietnam; 1-minute derived from ground data measured from ESMAP solar meteorological stations network, station VNCEH [5], [6]. 10-minute, 15-minute and hourly derived from Solargis Time Series

The variability observed in the 1-minute data is significantly higher than that observed in 15-minute data as shown in the example in Figure 1 above. 1-minute data is conceptually analogous to point measurements (e.g.

10.4229/EUPVSEC2025/4AO.9.3

from a pyranometer), whereas 15-minute satellite-derived data represent spatially averaged solar irradiance over an area of approximately 3×3 km. Although the PVOUT variability of a large PV power plant will be in practice lower than the variability of the 1-minute GHI due to the spatial smoothing effect [7], the 1-minute data can be used as a conservative estimate to establish the upper boundary of the expected variability.

The input data was generated for 8 locations (see Table I) in different geographies. The locations were selected to cover various geographies, climate zones [8], and short-term variability of GHI according to [2].

Table I: Locations used in the study

Site name	Latitude	Longitude	Average annual count of GHI ramps >300 W/m²	Climate zone
Penang, Malaysia	5.358	100.302	240.4	Af
Wagga, Australia	-35.158	147.457	418.0	Bsk/Cfa
San Sebastian, Spain	43.308	-2.039	153.0	Cfb
Boulder, USA	40.125	-105.237	344.4	Bsk
Jaipur, India	26.809	75.862	198.2	Bsh
Helios, South Africa	-30.501	19.561	178.6	BWk
Petrolina, Brazil	-9.068	-40.319	557.8	Bsh
Kishinev, Moldova	47.001	28.816	135.8	Dfb

2.2 PV Simulation

PVOUT time series was calculated from the source GHI data using the Solargis PV simulator (available in the Solargis Evaluate web application). The Solargis PV simulator provides highly accurate PVOUT through the use of real-world model simulation scenes, ray-tracing for irradiance calculation, and standardized PV component models. Irradiance calculation, performed per cell, evaluates both the front and rear side of the PV module using backward ray tracing. The system designer in the Evaluate application enables real-world modeling of the simulation scene and all shading objects (including terrain) quickly and accurately for systems of up to 500 MWp size. These two features allow for accurate calculation of shading conditions at each time step [9]. System losses, in both optical and electrical simulation, are estimated using validated models (such as for soiling, angular reflection, or inverter performance) and best-practice estimates (such as unavailability and auxiliary system losses), to accurately reflect operating conditions [10]. The simulator can ingest input data with up to 1-minute time resolution, allowing for analysis of high frequency transient events necessary for this study, provided the input data is of sufficient quality.

The same PV power plant was modelled and simulated for each of the 8 locations. Its main features are given in Table II.

Table II: Parameters of the simulated PV power plant

Power plant layout	Rectangular Relative row spacing of 2 (regular) 500,406 m² area
DC installed capacity	51.7 MWp
AC installed capacity	42 MWp
DC:AC ratio	1.23
PV modules	Monofacial, half-cut cell, 555 Wp
PV module mounting	Fixed tilt, optimal angle for maximizing in-plane irradiance at the site
Inverters	Centralized, 4.2 MW AC
DC cable losses	2 %
AC cable losses	1 %

2.3 Calculation of ramps

Four types of input data are evaluated in this study:

1. GHI time series with 15-minute time resolution
2. GHI time series with 1-minute time resolution,
3. PVOUT time series with 15-minute time resolution
4. PVOUT time series with 1-minute time resolution.

Ramps are calculated from all time series as the difference between the consecutive time slots of the dataset. The calculated ramps are then categorized by their severity.

The PVOUT ramp thresholds are set based on the impact on the grid. Globally, a very common grid limit for the PVOUT is ±10% of the installed capacity per minute [11]. This value is taken as the basic threshold for a PVOUT ramp to be studied. Furthermore, as we observed significantly larger ramps in the datasets which may pose significantly larger operational issues, we distinguish Low, Medium, High category PVOUT ramps with linearly scaled thresholds. The thresholds for GHI ramp classifications are set equivalently, considering the Standard Test Conditions (STC) irradiance value of 1,000 W/m² instead of the installed capacity of the power plant. To enable comparison, the same thresholds are used for investigation of 15-minute and 1-minute datasets. All thresholds are summarized in Table III below.

Table III: Categorization of ramps used in the study

Ramp category	Description	GHI threshold [W/m²]	PVOUT threshold [kW]
No ramp	Normal variability, slight changes in irradiance	< 100	0 - 4,200 (< 10% installed capacity)
Low	Typical of moving cumulus clouds	100 - 200	4,200 - 8,400 (10 - 20% installed capacity)
Medium	Rapid transitions between cloud cover and clear sky	200 - 300	8,400 - 12,600 (20 - 30% installed capacity)
High	Sharp irradiance drop/spike	> 300	> 12,600 (> 30% installed capacity)

The division of ramps in GHI and PVOUT dataset by the thresholds is illustrated in Figure 2 below.

Furthermore, to compare ramps between the 15-minute and 1-minute datasets, the occurrence of ramps is calculated as the proportion of time slots with ramps relative to the total number of time slots. This normalization is necessary because the 1-minute datasets contain 15 times more time slots, and hence 15 times more opportunities for ramps. By scaling the number of ramps in this way, it becomes possible to compare ramp rates between different time resolutions.

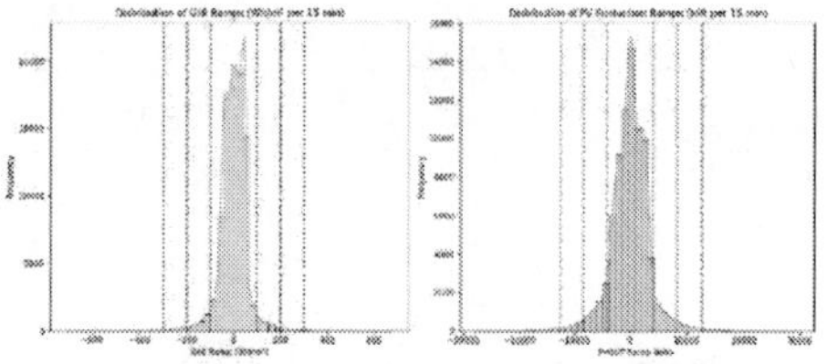

Figure 2: Distribution of GHI (left) and PVOUT (right) ramps in the 15-minute datasets from Boulder site, and their division by the thresholds (vertical dashed lines)

3 RESULTS

The variability of the GHI data with 15-minute time resolution has been analyzed in the previous work [2] and is available in the Solargis Prospect web application. This is therefore taken as the default data, and compared with the variability calculated from the other analyzed datasets, in order to compare the different indicators and advise which are best suited for different design objectives.

The analysis presented below is therefore structured in two steps: 1) comparison of variability between 15-minute and 1-minute data, and 2) comparison of variability between PVOUT and GHI data.

3.1 Variability in 15-minute and 1-minute data

The differences in the occurrence of categorized ramps in the 15-minute and 1-minute datasets for all sites are shown in Figure 3. The occurrence of low ramps is higher in all 15-minute datasets, as changes of at least 100 W/m^2 are not uncommon within 15 minutes (but rare within 1 minute).

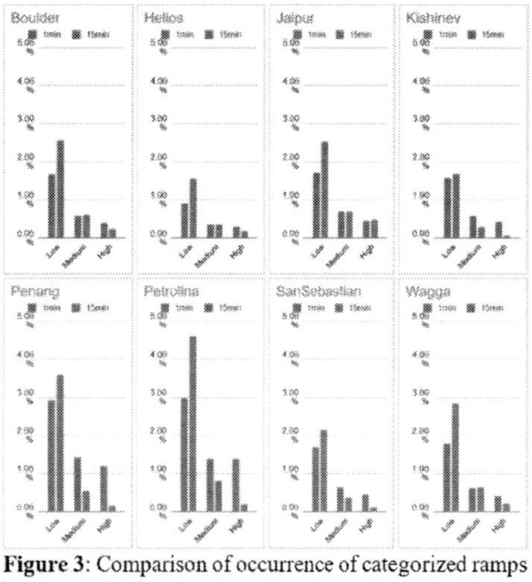

Figure 3: Comparison of occurrence of categorized ramps between 15-minute and 1-minute GHI data for all eight studied sites

The occurrence of medium and high ramps is higher in the 1-minute data, as expected. Specifically, the sites close to the Equator (Penang, Petrolina) but also sites in the temperate/continental climate (Kishinev, San Sebastian) see significantly higher occurrence of these ramps. This indicates variability assessed based on 1-minute data includes proportionally more severe events than the 15-minute data. Note that the Petrolina site, while strictly in dry climate, appears to be strongly affected by the surrounding tropical climate regions.

As the two datasets set the boundaries of the real expected variability at the PV power plant output, the 15-minute data appears to underestimate the more significant variability events in almost all geographies. In arid regions further from Equator (Boulder, Helios, Jaipur, Wagga), occurrence of medium and high ramps in the two datasets is more similar, suggesting a better representation of the real variability by the 15-minute data. These observations can be explained by the nature of the different climates - in arid regions the cloud cover typically does not change as quickly as in temperate or tropical climates.

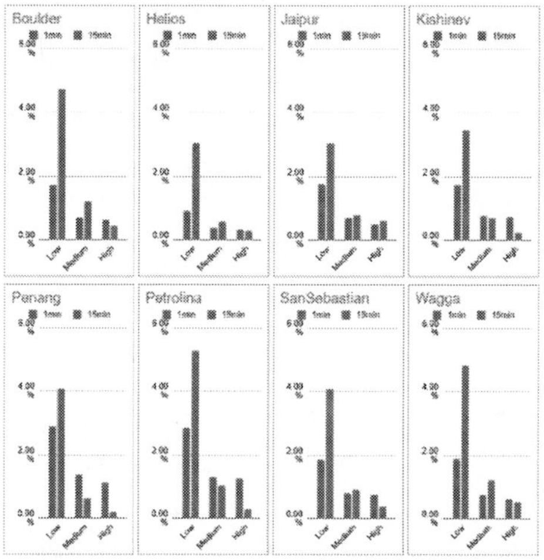

Figure 4: Comparison of occurrence of categorized ramps between 15-minute and 1-minute PVOUT data for all eight studied sites

Considering the same comparison with the PVOUT data shown in Figure 4 above, we observe similar patterns as in the GHI data. However, the occurrence of ramps is higher in the 15-minute dataset. This is most likely due to the effect of PV module temperature, which during GHI ramp events does not vary as quickly as GHI [12], and hence acts as a dampener on the PVOUT signal, and clipping which reduces the size of the PVOUT ramps compared to GHI ramps (see further analysis below). This effect is again more pronounced in the arid regions.

3.2 Variability in GHI and PVOUT data

In the second part we compare the GHI and PVOUT ramps to determine suitability of GHI ramps as an indicator of PVOUT ramps, and investigate diurnal and seasonal patterns. For this analysis we use scatter plots - samples from Boulder and Penang sites are shown in Figure 5 below.

From the plots a clear difference between equatorial (Penang) and mid-latitude sites is obvious, driven by the seasonal patterns of solar radiation. To investigate this pattern further, we plot monthly scatter plots for the Boulder site, shown in Figure 6. These show a higher range of GHI ramp values during the summer half of the year (approx. April to September) than in the winter half of the year (approx. October to March), caused by higher values of GHI during the summer half. The PVOUT ramp values change in the same manner, but with a smaller change which can be attributed to the effect of temperature (higher temperatures lead to lower PVOUT due to temperature derating of PV modules and inverters). In the result, the best fit line of the monthly scatter plots changes slope seasonally, with higher slope (larger PVOUT ramps relative to GHI ramps) in the winter half of the year. In the yearly scatter plot this gives rise to the scattered appearance with no clear single relationship between the GHI and PVOUT ramps in the mid-latitude sites. The same pattern as in Boulder is observed for Helios (see Figure 8) and Wagga sites with the expected flip in the winter-summer seasons due to the northern-southern hemisphere difference.

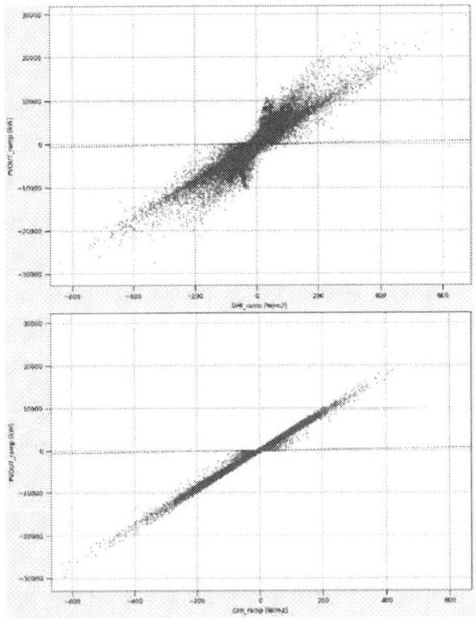

Figure 5: Scatter plots of GHI ramps vs PVOUT ramps (both 15-minute data) for Boulder (top) and Penang (bottom) sites

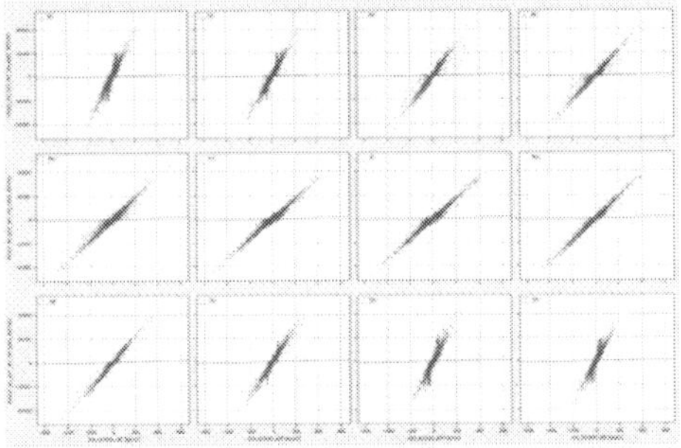

Figure 6: Monthly scatter plots of GHI ramps vs PVOUT ramps (15-minute data) for Boulder site

Furthermore, during the winter half of the year, a pattern can be observed in the morning and evening (defined for simplicity as Sun elevation angle under 20 degrees). In these periods, PVOUT ramps are disproportionately large compared to GHI ramps, as seen in Figure 7 compared with Figure 6. This effect is likely caused by inter-row shading at low sun angles and temperature derating of PV components. It highlights the importance of good plant layout and its detailed analysis in the design stage, as it can affect the variability experienced by the power plant.

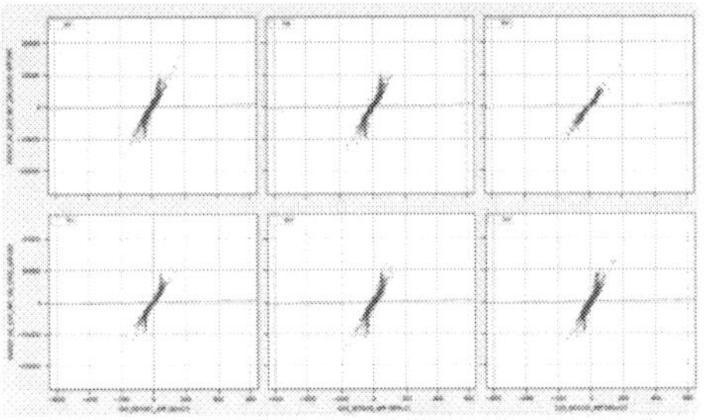

Figure 7: Monthly (top: Jan - Mar, bottom: Oct - Dec) scatter plots of GHI ramps vs PVOUT ramps (15-minute data) for Boulder site for Sun elevation angle smaller than 20 degrees

Analyzing the 1-minute data, Figure 8 illustrates inverter clipping of AC PVOUT visible as point clusters between the best-fit line and horizontal zero. This indicates GHI ramps with disproportionally small PVOUT ramps. The use of 1-minute data for PV simulation allows for a more accurate modeling of the inverter clipping losses, as documented in [13], [14]. Compared to Figure 6, Figure 8 shows that 1-minute data captures a significantly wider range of GHI and PVOUT ramps, both in magnitude (noting the different axis ranges) and combinations. This highlights the importance of high temporal resolution data for analyzing the full spectrum of possible scenarios in the most critical applications. Optimizing the DC:AC ratio in the power plant design will also affect the PVOUT variability experienced by the power plant.

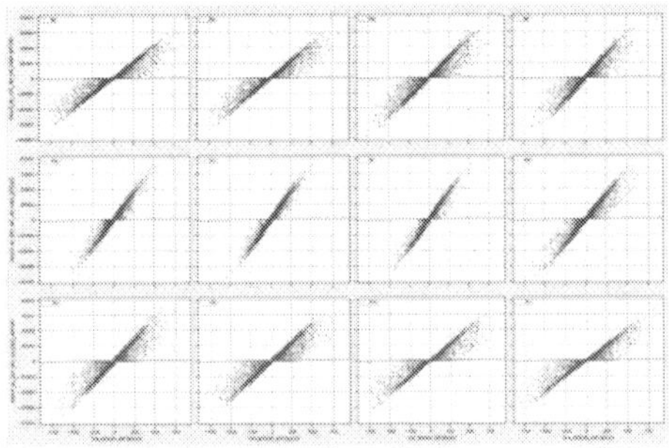

Figure 8: Monthly scatter plots of GHI ramps vs PVOUT ramps (1-minute data) for Helios site

4 DISCUSSION

The results shows that the global variability dataset created in [2], while a useful proxy metric for the expected variability, does not capture the full scope of variability events (ramps) that a PV power plant can experience. Comparison of 15-minute and 1-minute data shows that the 1-minute datasets capture more high-severity variability (events with larger ramps), especially in tropical, temperate, and continental climates where the clouds can be expected to change more rapidly. The difference between the variability observed in the 15-minute and 1-minute PVOUT datasets is smaller than in the case of GHI data, however, the difference in the high-severity events remains.

To address the relative importance of the high-severity events while maintaining a practical approach that is computationally and analytically simple we propose a new metric - the Root Mean Square Ramp (RMSR). This metric is calculated as the root mean square of the calculated ramps, either in PVOUT or GHI data. PVOUT RMSR is normalized (denoted nRMSR) to the installed capacity of the power plant as ramp size scales with installed capacity. This metric emphasizes the high-severity variability, which is not considered in the original metric of count of GHI ramps over a certain threshold (300 W/m^2 in Solargis Prospect).

The nRMSR calculated from 15-minute and 1-minute PVOUT datasets together with the old metric for comparison are shown in Figure 9 below. The figure highlights important differences in the variability metrics for some sites. While the original metric may overstate the variability risk at the Petrolina site, the simple count of ramps obscures high-severity events at sites like Kishinev and San Sebastian. The nRMSR at these sites shows variability risk comparable to sites like Boulder or Wagga with much higher average GHI (and hence higher risk of large ramps).

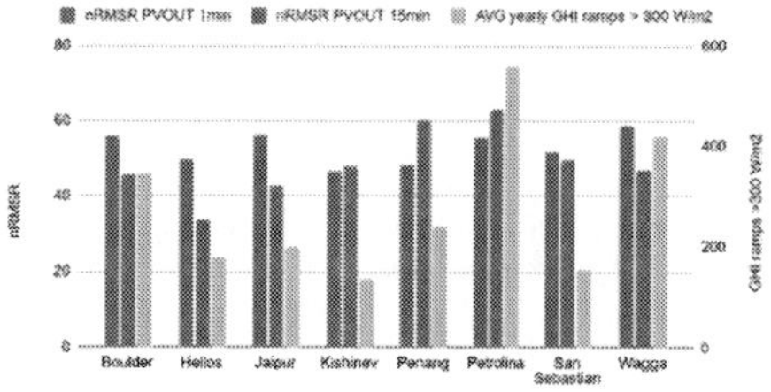

Figure 9: nRMSR (left axis) and count of GHI ramps over 300 W/m^2 (yellow, right axis) as different metrics of variability

Analyzing the relationship between the ramps in GHI and PVOUT data, seasonal and diurnal patterns emerge for all sites apart from the ones close to the Equator (Penang, Petrolina). This indicates that any metric that takes a single value per site, while useful in the prefeasibility stage, should not be used later in the design process, as it can obscure important nuances in the expected variability. The strong seasonal patterns of variability also suggest that seasonally adjusted response (at the level of a PV power plant, or the whole grid) may be an advantageous approach. Moreover, these results highlight the advantages in using high temporal resolution data in the design of the PV power plant, as design choices such as row spacing and DC:AC ratio will have, among others, effect on the variability of the PVOUT.

5 CONCLUSION

This study analyzed variability in GHI and PVOUT datasets with 15-minute and 1-minute temporal resolution at 8 sites in different climates and geographies. The results indicate that the variability of PV projects in the prefeasibility stage can be assessed using simple variability metrics, optimally ones which consider the severity of the observed ramps. To this end, the study proposes Root Mean Square Ramp (RMSR) as a metric considering the size of the ramp. However, to assess variability of PV projects in the feasibility stage and especially high criticality projects (e.g. projects with large installed capacity or located in poorly interconnected grids), time series analysis is recommended, although this may not be necessary in all world regions. The analysis can be improved by utilizing high temporal resolution data for conservative variability estimates and, if an advanced PV simulator is available, PVOUT data to reflect the effects of parameters other than GHI on the final PV power plant output variability.

Further work in this scope should focus on analyzing more sites in different geographies and more varied PV power plant layout. Worldwide analysis via geospatial data processing of high temporal resolution data and/or PVOUT data should also be carried out, to analyze regional patterns of variability, and contrast them with the patterns described in [2].

6 REFERENCES

[1] M. Sengupta *et al.*, *Best Practices Handbook for the Collection and Use of Solar Resource Data for Solar Energy Applications: Fourth Edition*, 4th ed. IEA PVPS Task 16, 2024. Accessed: Jan. 28, 2025. [Online]. Available: https://iea-pvps.org/key-topics/best-practices-handbook-for-the-collection-and-use-of-solar-resource-data-for-solar-energy-applications-fourth-edition/

[2] J. Betak, M. Opatovsky, K. Rosina, and M. Suri, "Global Patterns of Solar Resource Short-Term Variability Based on Solargis Time Series Data," in *41st European Photovoltaic Solar Energy Conference and Exhibition*, Vienna, Austria: WIP-Munich, Nov. 2024, pp. 020387-001-020387–005. doi: 10.4229/EUPVSEC2024/4CO.8.5.

[3] K. Lappalainen, G. C. Wang, and J. Kleissl, "Estimation of the largest expected photovoltaic power ramp rates," *Applied Energy*, vol. 278, p. 115636, Nov. 2020, doi: 10.1016/j.apenergy.2020.115636.

[4] J. Zhang, X. Zhu, Y. Xie, G. Chen, and S. Liu, "Detection and Prediction of Wind and Solar Photovoltaic Power Ramp Events Based on Data-Driven Methods: A Critical Review," *Energies*, vol. 18, no. 13, p. 3290, Jan. 2025, doi: 10.3390/en18133290.

[5] World Bank Group, "Vietnam - Solar Radiation Measurement Data - ENERGYDATA.INFO." https://energydata.info/dataset/vietnam-solar-radiation-measurement-data, 2017. Accessed: Sept. 03, 2024. [CSV]. Available: https://energydata.info/dataset/vietnam-solar-radiation-measurement-data

[6] World Bank Group, "Global Solar Atlas." Accessed: Jan. 20, 2024. [Online]. Available: https://globalsolaratlas.info/map?c=12.7535,107.8761,8&s=12.7535,107.8761&m=solar

[7] J. Remund, C. Calhau, L. Perret, and D. Marcel, "Characterization of the spatio-temporal variations and ramp rates of solar radiation and PV," IEA PVPS Task 14, IEA-PVPS T14-05:2015, Aug. 2015. Accessed: Sept. 15, 2025. [Online]. Available: https://iea-pvps.org/wp-content/uploads/2020/01/Characterization_of_the_spatio-

temporal_variations_and_ramp_rates_of_solar_radiation_and_PV.pdf

[8] H. E. Beck, N. E. Zimmermann, T. R. McVicar, N. Vergopolan, A. Berg, and E. F. Wood, "Present and future Köppen-Geiger climate classification maps at 1-km resolution," *Sci Data*, vol. 5, no. 1, p. 180214, Oct. 2018, doi: 10.1038/sdata.2018.214.

[9] L. Dvonc, P. Orosi, T. Cebecauer, and B. Schnierer, "Implementation of Ray Tracing Rendering Technique for Improved Solar Radiation Modeling of Bifacial PV Modules," WCPEC-8, 2022. Accessed: Sept. 08, 2023. [Online]. Available: https://userarea.eupvsec.org/proceedings/WCPEC-8/4BV.4.28/

[10] L. Helienek *et al.*, "Uncertainties in PV Power Simulation Chain," in *2023 IEEE 50th Photovoltaic Specialists Conference (PVSC)*, IEEE, June 2023, pp. 1–6. doi: 10.1109/PVSC48320.2023.10359583.

[11] J. Schaible *et al.*, "Application of nowcasting to reduce the impact of irradiance ramps on PV power plants," *EPJ Photovolt.*, vol. 15, p. 15, 2024, doi: 10.1051/epjpv/2024009.

[12] J. Barry *et al.*, "Dynamic model of photovoltaic module temperature as a function of atmospheric conditions," in *Advances in Science and Research*, Copernicus GmbH, July 2020, pp. 165–173. doi: 10.5194/asr-17-165-2020.

[13] J. Rusnak, B. Schnierer, M. Suri, M. Opatovsky, and G. Srinivasan, "Impact of Time Resolution of Solar and Meteorological Data on Clipping Losses and Energy Yield Simulation," in *Proceedings of the 40th European Photovoltaic Solar Energy Conference and Exhibition in Lisbon, Portugal*, Lisbon, Portugal, Sept. 2023, pp. 020493-001-020493–010. doi: 10.4229/EUPVSEC2023/5CO.6.2.

[14] J. Rusnak, B. Schnierer, and M. Suri, "The importance of sub-hourly input data in PV systems simulation using satellite-based solar model data," presented at the 2024 European PVPMC Workshop, Copenhagen, Denmark, Aug. 21, 2024. Accessed: Nov. 15, 2024. [Online]. Available: https://www.sandia.gov/app/uploads/sites/243/dlm_uploads/2024/09/Rusnak_2.pdf

SOLARGIS

Short-Term Variability of PV Power Output Based on Simulations with Solargis Time Series Data

Martin Opatovsky, **Marta Pelfort Ojer**,
Juraj Betak, Konstantin Rosina
Solargis, Slovakia

Context – our work at EUPVSEC 2024

SOLARGIS

Global Patterns of Solar Resource Short-Term Variability Based on Solargis Time Series Data

Juraj Betak, **Martin Opatovsky**, Konstantin Rosina, Marcel Suri
Solargis, Slovakia

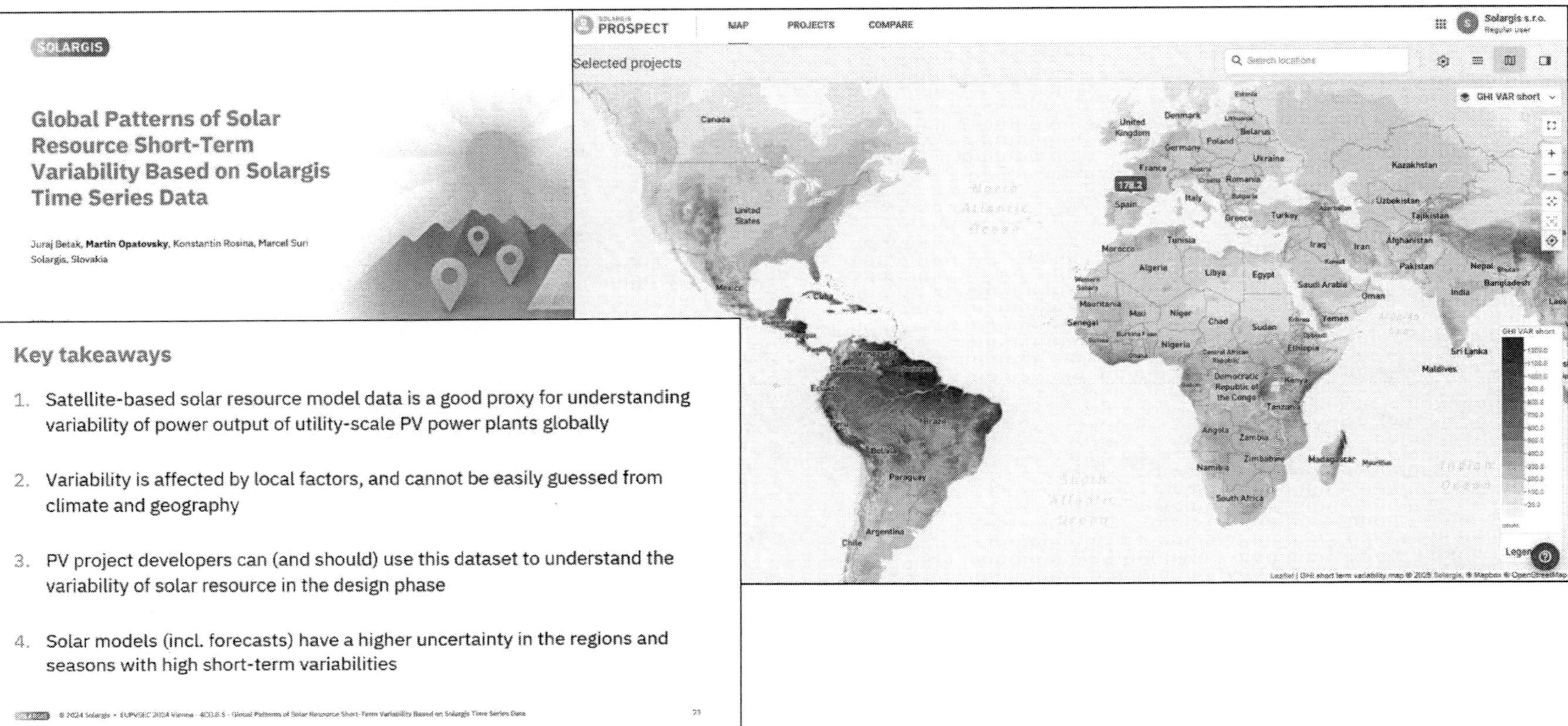

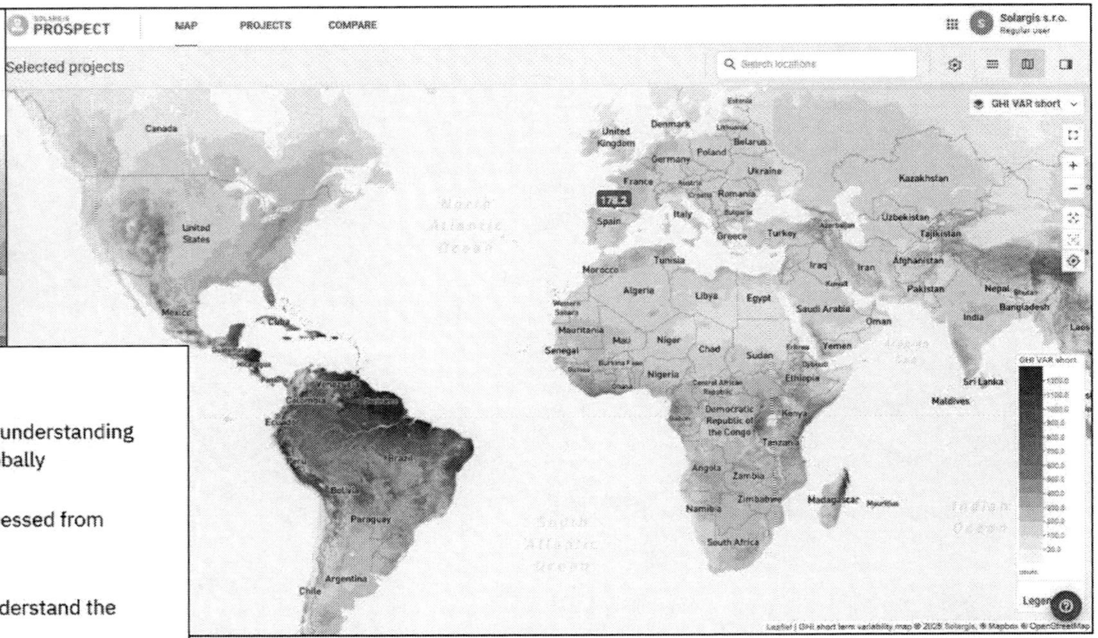

Key takeaways

1. Satellite-based solar resource model data is a good proxy for understanding variability of power output of utility-scale PV power plants globally
2. Variability is affected by local factors, and cannot be easily guessed from climate and geography
3. PV project developers can (and should) use this dataset to understand the variability of solar resource in the design phase
4. Solar models (incl. forecasts) have a higher uncertainty in the regions and seasons with high short-term variabilities

The challenge

Power Ramps

Sudden increases or decreases in PV output create operational challenges for plant and grid operators.

Grid Stability

Variability affects project revenues and requires countermeasures to ensure distribution system reliability.

Storage Needs

Power ramps typically require short-term storage technologies to maintain grid stability.

Practical applications

Project development

Use variability metrics during site assessment and system design to optimize plant configuration and storage requirements.

Grid integration

Inform grid operators about expected ramp rates to ensure adequate response capabilities and system stability.

Storage sizing

Determine optimal battery capacity and response times based on location-specific variability patterns.

Methodology

Data preparation

- 8 global locations in different climates and different variability based on our previous work
- Satellite-derived 15-minute and synthetic 1-minute GHI time series data

PV Simulation

- PVOUT calculation using Solargis PV simulator (Solargis Evaluate) with ray-tracing and real-world modelling

Ramp analysis

- Calculate ramps as differences between consecutive time slots in time series data
- Classify ramps according to severity based on set thresholds

Metrics proposal

- Proposes optimal approaches for assessing the variability of on-grid PV projects in different development stages or projects with different criticality.

Studied locations

Location	Climate	Avg. annual count of GHI ramps > 300 W/m^2
Penang, Malaysia	Tropical	240.4
Wagga, Australia	Semi-arid	418.0
San Sebastian, Spain	Oceanic	153.0
Boulder, USA	Semi-arid	344.4
Jaipur, India	Hot semi-arid	198.2
Helios, South Africa	Desert	178.6
Petrolina, Brazil	Hot semi-arid *(surrounded by tropical)*	557.8
Kishinev, Moldova	Continental	135.8

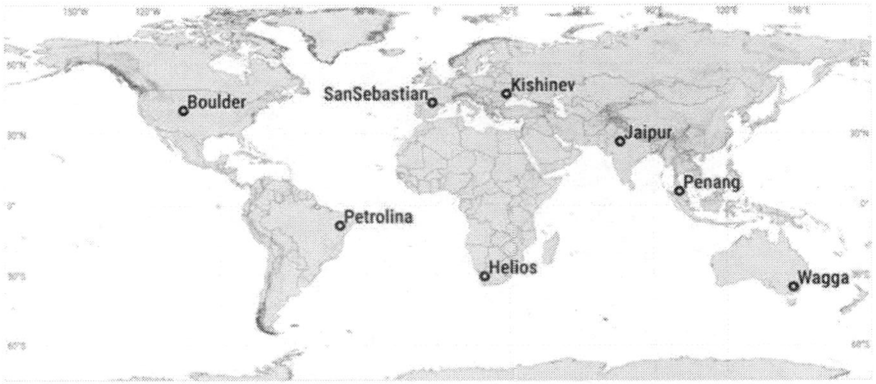

Eight locations selected to cover diverse geographies, climate zones, and GHI variability patterns.

Simulated PV power plant

51.7 MWp

DC installed capacity

42 MWp

AC installed capacity

1.23

DC:AC ratio

Fixed tilt

Optimum angle for maximization of in-plane irradiance

500,000 m²

Plant area

Monofacial modules

Central inverters

PV power plant modelled in Solargis Evaluate, simulated with Solargis Evaluate PV simulator

Ramp classification system

- Single ramp classification **applied to both GHI and PVOUT ramps**
- To enable **comparison of 1-minute and 15-minute data** ramp occurrence calculated as **proportion** of **time slots with ramps** relative to the **total number of time slots**

No ramp	Low ramp	Medium ramp	High ramp
GHI < 100 W/m²	GHI 100 – 200 W/m²	GHI 200 – 300 W/m²	GHI > 300 W/m²
PVOUT < 10 % installed capacity (0 – 4,200 kW)	PVOUT 10 – 20% installed capacity (4,200 – 8,400 kW)	PVOUT 20 – 30 % installed capacity (8,400 – 12,600 kW)	PVOUT > 30 % installed capacity (> 12,600 kW)

Ramp analysis

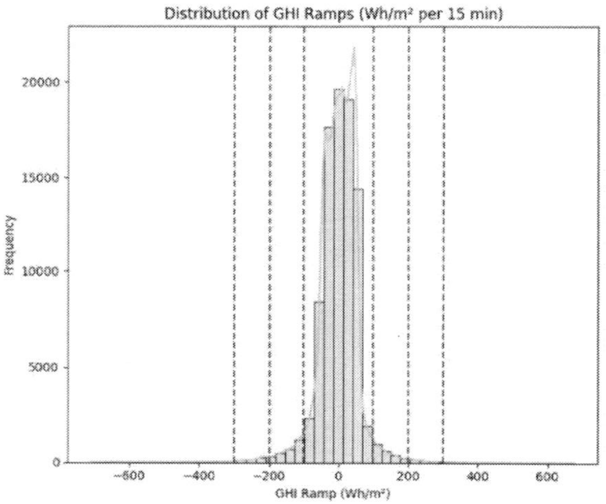

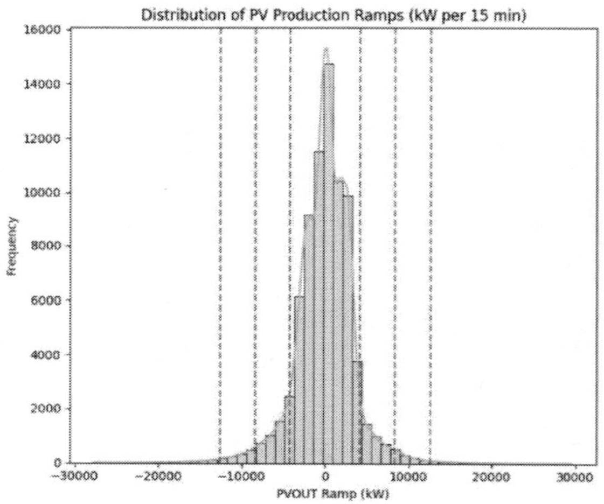

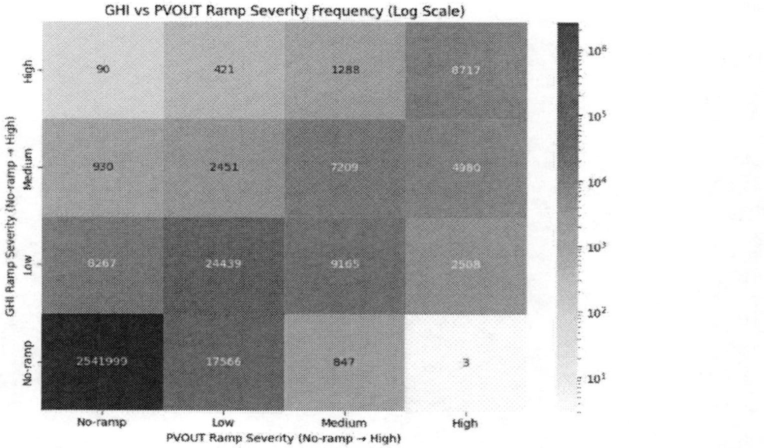

GHI Severity ramp percentages (%)

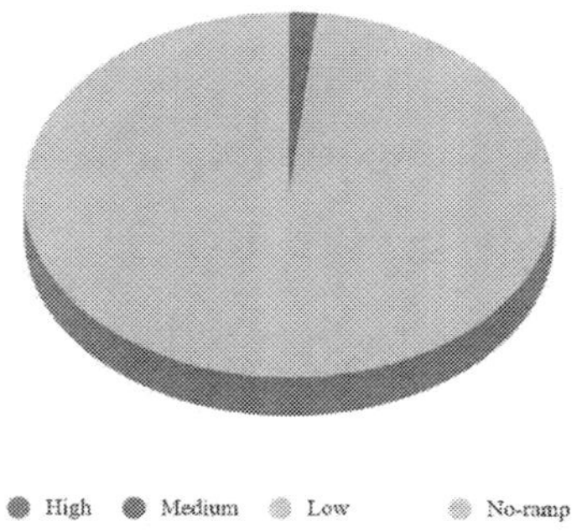

PVOUT Severity ramp percentages (%)

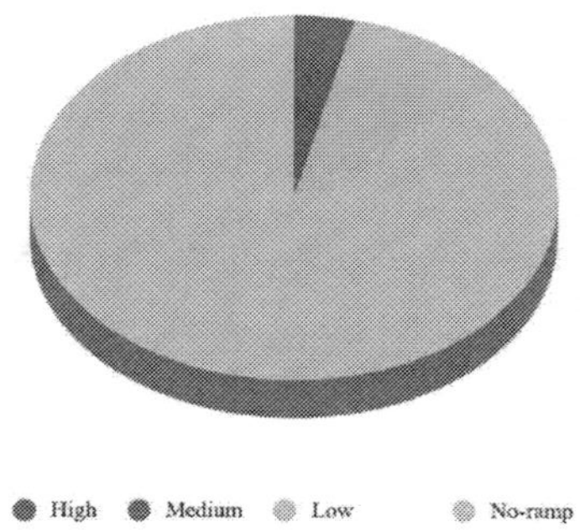

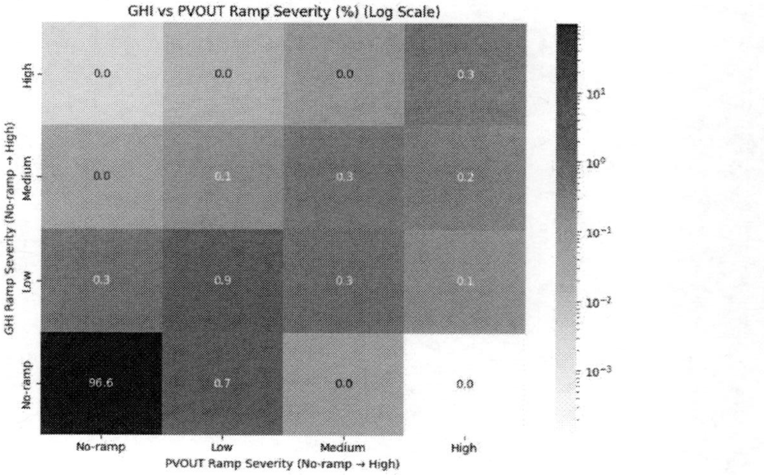

Ramp analysis

Occurrence of ramps in GHI data

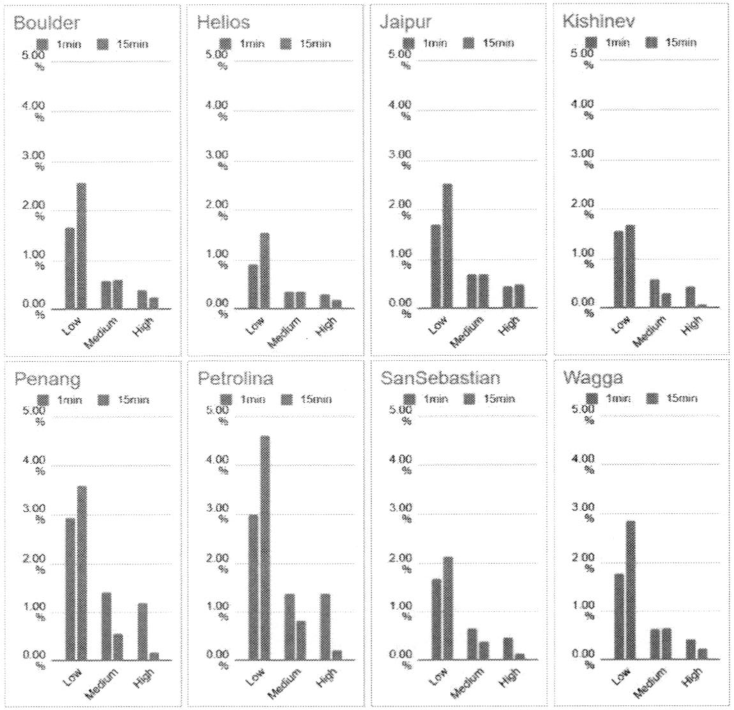

Occurrence of ramps in PVOUT data

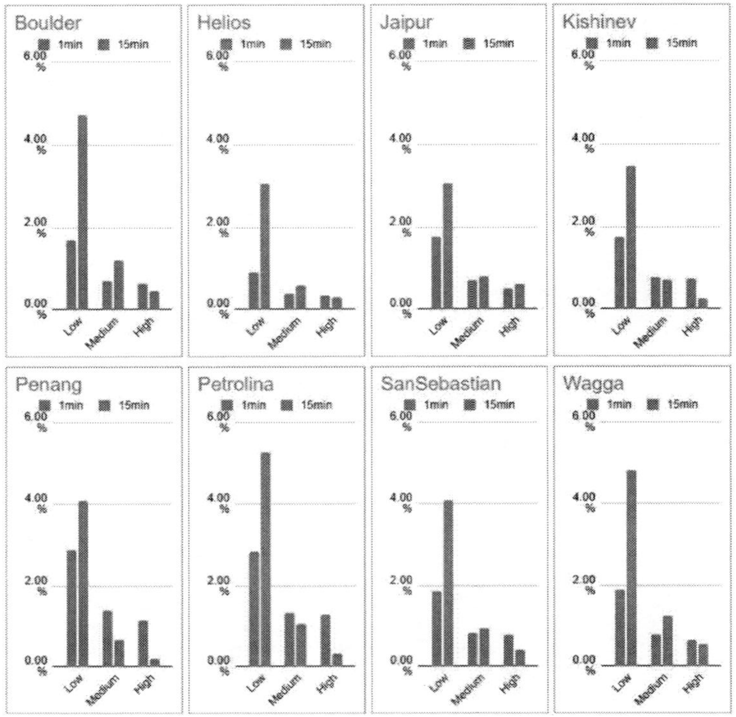

15min vs 1 min PVOUT

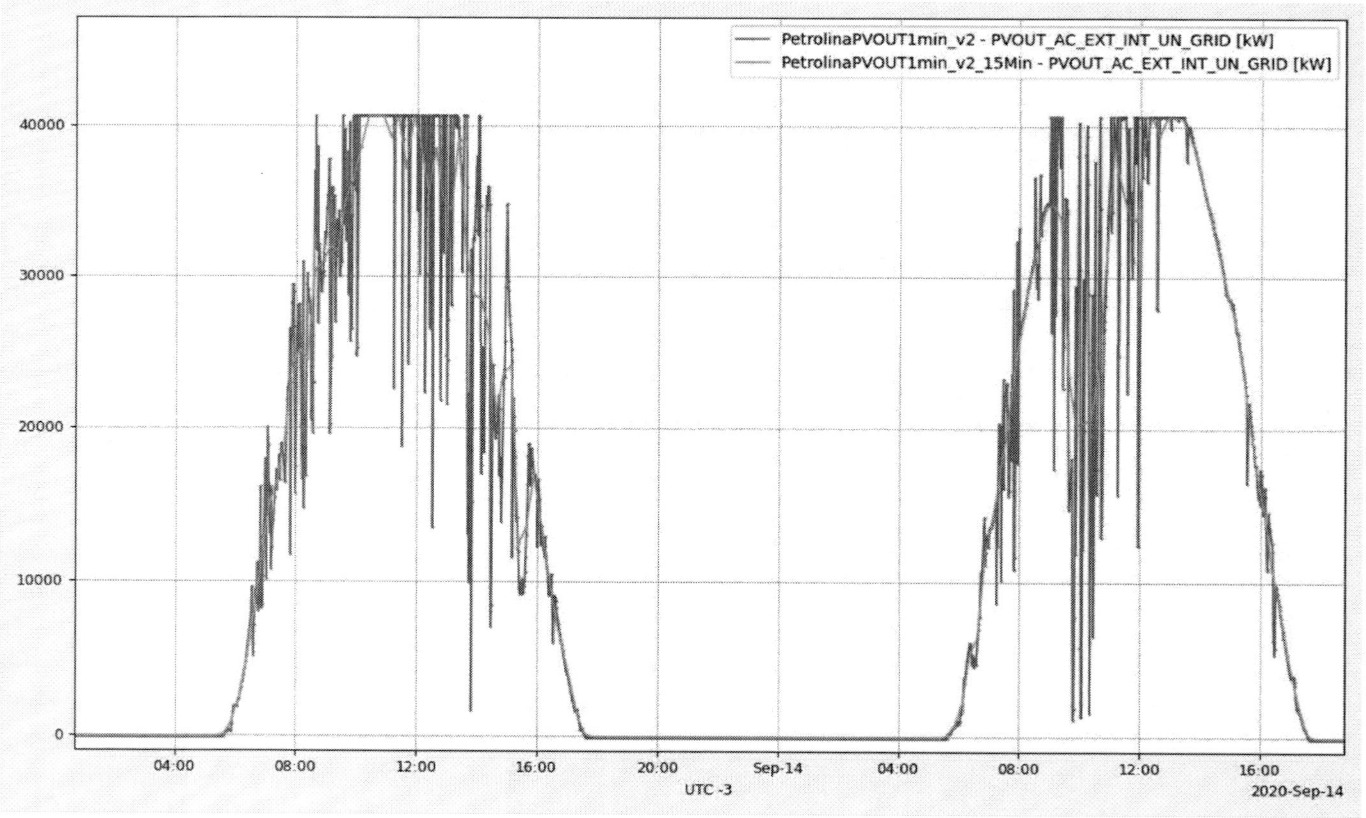

Ramp analysis

Boulder

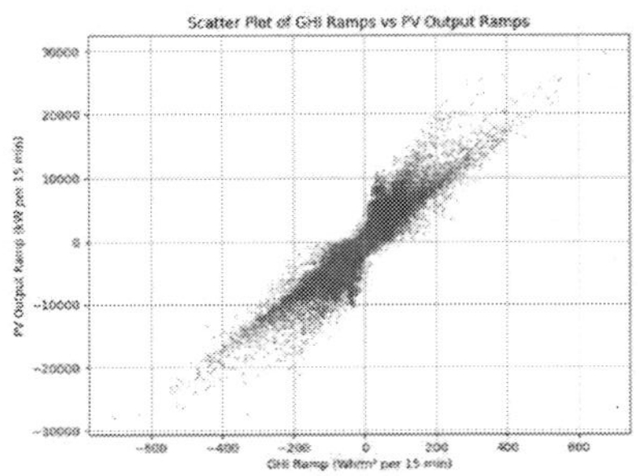

Helios

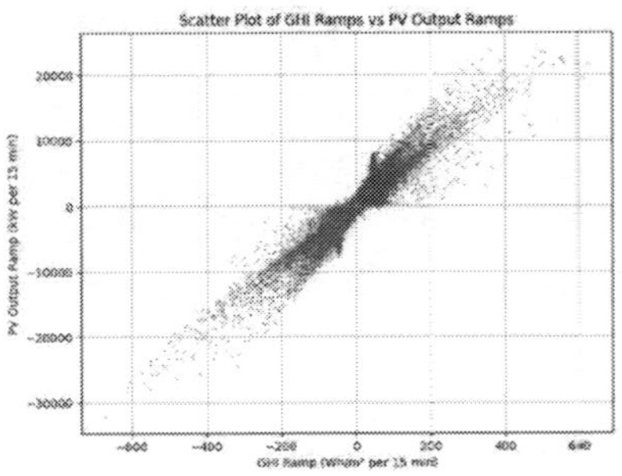

Jaipur

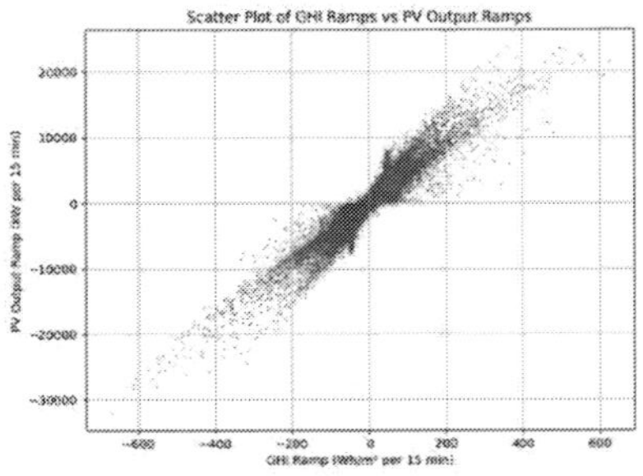

Kishinev

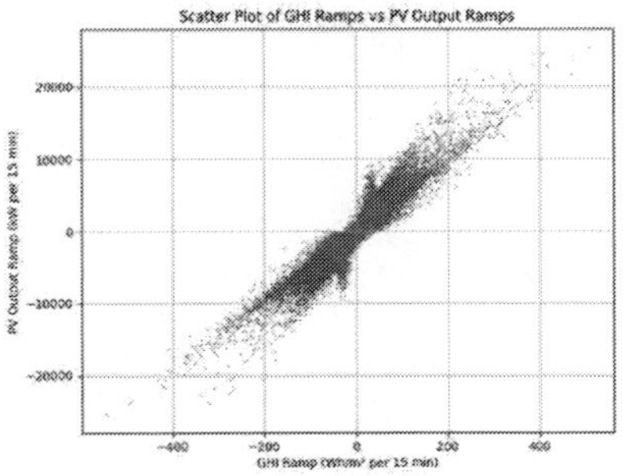

Penang

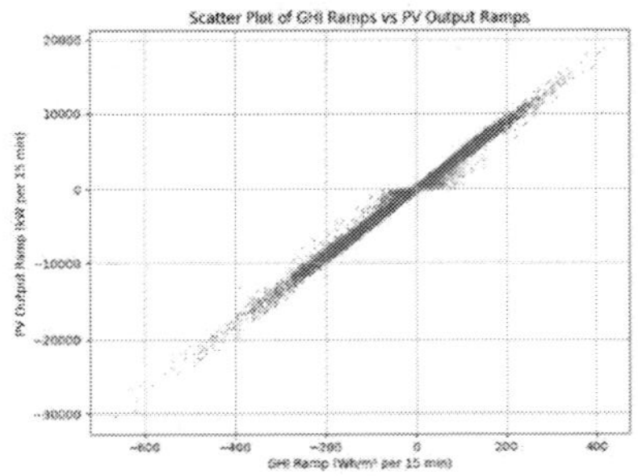

Petrolina

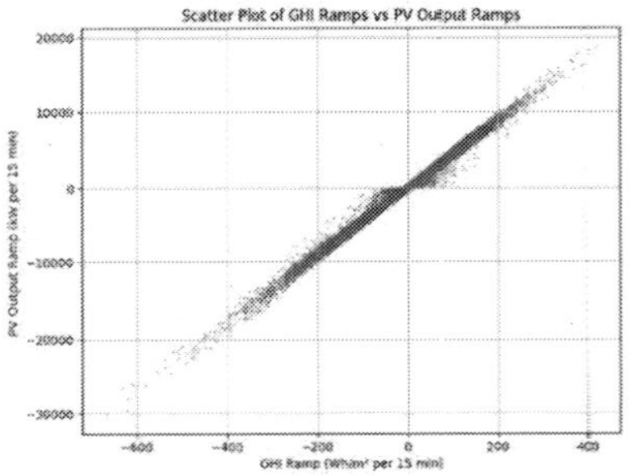

San Sebastian

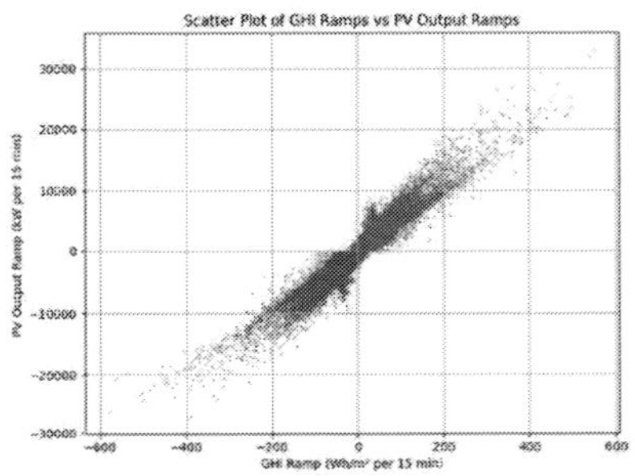

Wagga

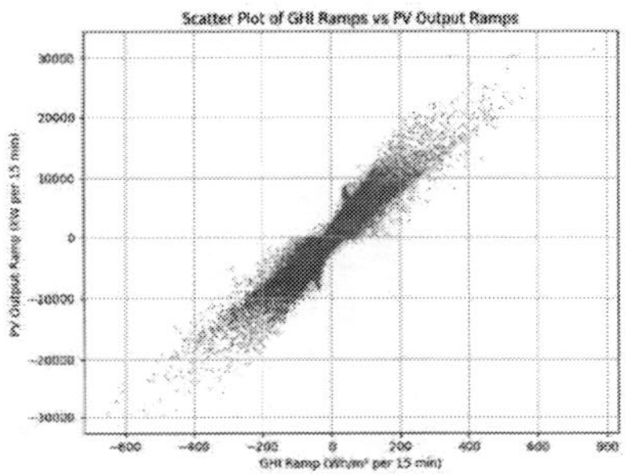

GHI and PVOUT ramp relationship

Seasonal variations

- Higher GHI ramps in summer result in lower slope relationships between GHI and PVOUT variability.

Temperature and shading

- Morning and evening hours show proportionally larger PVOUT ramps due to lower temperatures and inter-row shading

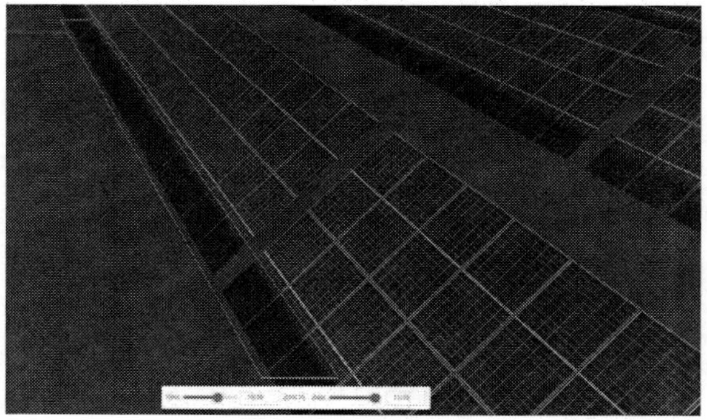

Monthly scatter plots of GHI ramps vs PVOUT ramps (15-minute data) for Boulder site

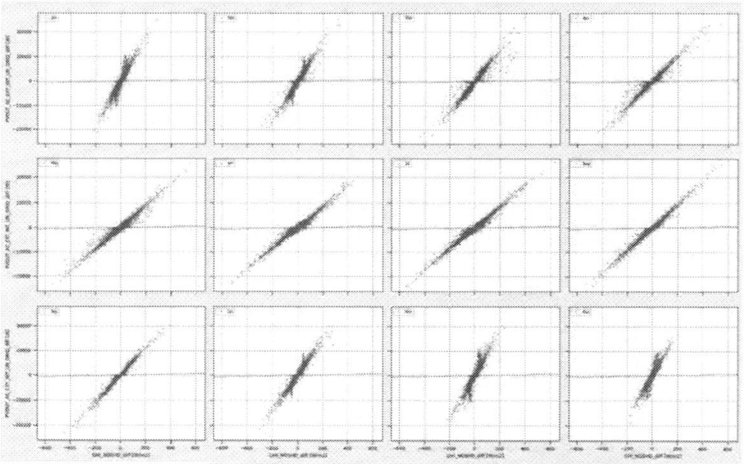

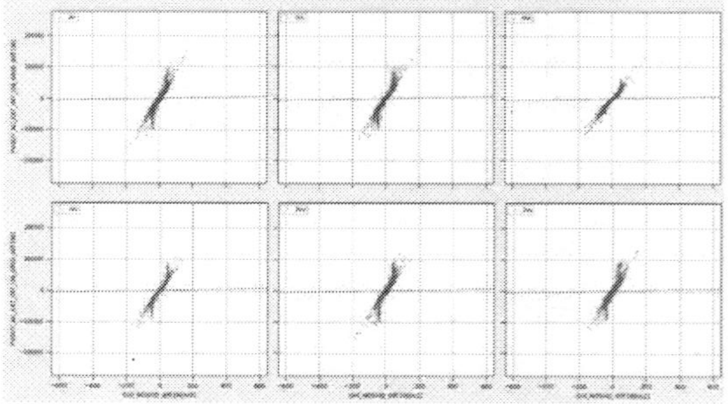

Monthly (top: Jan - Mar, bottom: Oct - Dec) scatter plots of GHI ramps vs PVOUT ramps (15-minute data) for Boulder site for Sun elevation angle smaller than 20 degrees

15-minute and 1-minute data – clipping effects

1-minute fidelity

- High-resolution simulation accurately captures clipping losses during peak irradiance periods.

Grid impact

- Clipping results in proportionally smaller PVOUT ramps compared to GHI ramps

Design implications

- DC:AC ratio optimization affects variability of power plant output

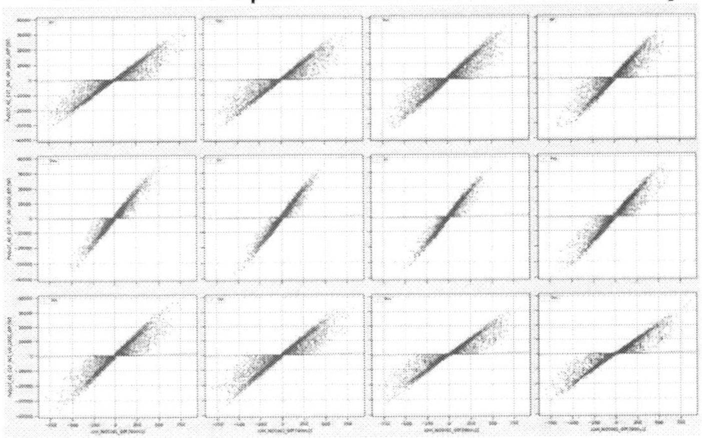

Monthly scatter plots of GHI ramps vs **AC PVOUT ramps** (1-minute data) for Helios site

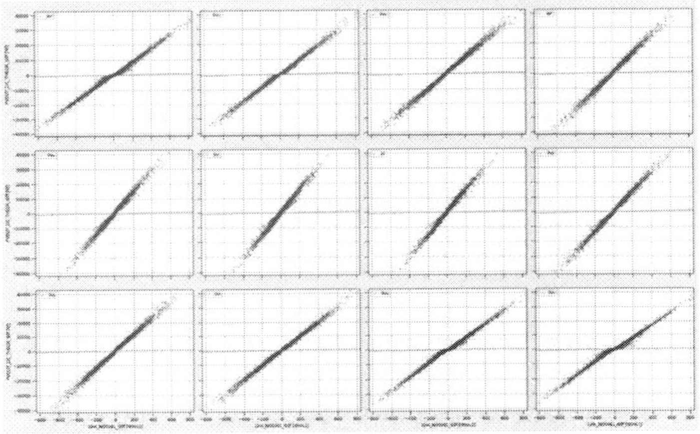

Monthly scatter plots of GHI ramps vs **DC PVOUT ramps** (1-minute data) for Helios site

Ramp analysis - RMSR

- To account for ramp severity, we propose a **new metric** - **Root Mean Square Ramp (RMSR)**
- RMSR quantifies site-specific variability by **weighting larger power ramps** more heavily and **normalizing** by **plant capacity (nRMSR)**, enabling direct comparison of grid-integration challenges across sites

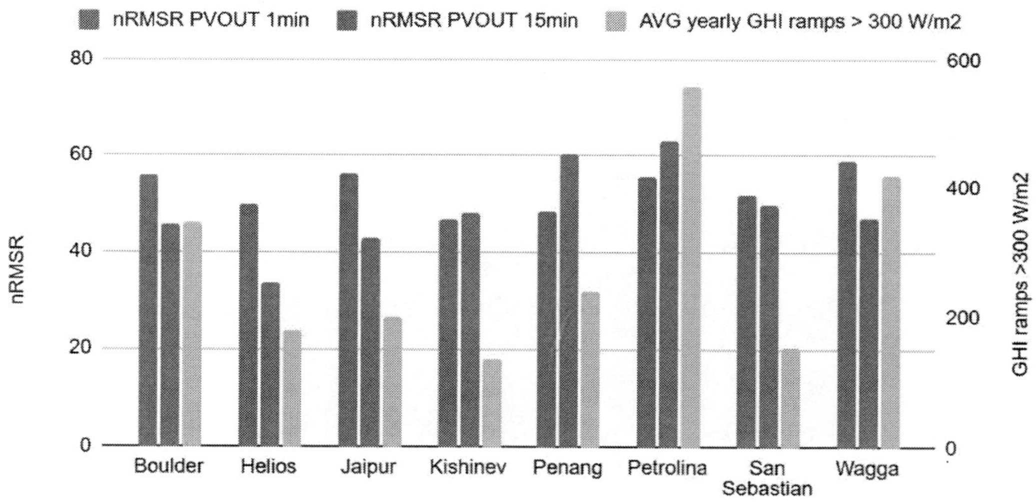

nRMSR (left axis) and count of GHI ramps over 300 W/m2 (yellow, right axis) as different metrics of variability

15-minute vs 1-minute variability

Higher resolution = more severe events

- 1-minute data captures proportionally more medium and high category ramps than 15-minute data.

Geographic patterns

- Equatorial and temperate sites show higher 1-minute variability. Arid regions see slower changes.

Realistic boundaries

- 15-minute data provides slight underestimation, 1-minute data provides conservative upper boundary.

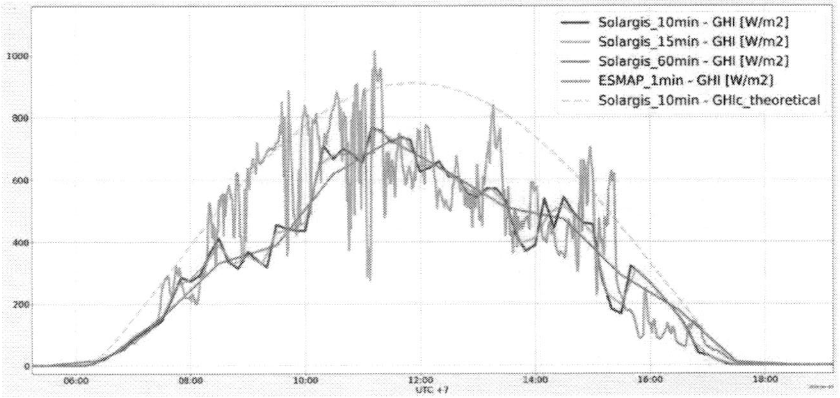

Conclusions

- For **pre-feasibility** studies, **simple metrics** can be sufficient, but they should account for the **ramp size**, not only the count. **RMSR** is a good candidate
- For **feasibility** and high criticality projects, **Time Series** analysis is necessary, ideally with **1min resolution** data and **PV simulator** that captures the behavior of the plant.
- **Seasonal and diurnal variability** suggests that flexibility at the plant and grid level should be considered in **system design.**

Thank you

Marta Pelfort Ojer
Head of Customer Support, Solargis, Slovakia

solargis.com

ACCELERATING PHOTOVOLTAIC SYSTEM SIMULATIONS VIA STATISTICAL DATA AGGREGATION

Adrián Blanco Aguiar [1], Brais González Rodríguez [2, 3], María Martínez Barbeito [1],
Miguel Sánchez de León Peque [1]
[1] ieco.io
Tomás A. Alonso, 189, 36208 Vigo, Pontevedra, Spain
[2] Department of Statistics and Operations Research and SiDOR Research Group, University of Vigo
[3] Research collaborator at CITMAga
Corresponding author: Miguel Sánchez de León Peque, +34 639 835 484, peque@ieco.io

ABSTRACT: Accurate energy yield assessments (EYAs) for photovoltaic (PV) systems are critical for their financial viability, yet simulating the non-linear effects of partial shading over a full year remains computationally prohibitive. High-fidelity models, essential for capturing these mismatch losses, create a significant bottleneck in the rapid design and optimization of PV projects. This ieco.io work introduces a novel data-centric framework to accelerate annual PV simulations by applying statistical aggregation, reducing the input dataset of operating conditions while preserving the high-resolution information necessary for accurate shading analysis. We propose and evaluate two methods based on k-means clustering, with results clearly demonstrating the superiority of one approach. A key advantage of this method is its tunability, enabling substantial reductions in simulation time while introducing only minimal, controllable error, thereby outperforming standard module-level simulations in both speed and accuracy. Importantly, when quantifying annual shading-induced power losses, the method drastically reduces computational overhead with negligible impact on accuracy, contrasting sharply with the significant underestimation of losses inherent to the module-level approach. This framework offers engineers a powerful and flexible tool for fast, reliable energy yield assessments without compromising simulation fidelity.
Keywords: data aggregation, photovoltaic systems, partial shading, clustering, simulation acceleration

1 INTRODUCTION

The widespread adoption of photovoltaic (PV) technology is crucial for the global transition to sustainable energy. Accurate energy yield assessments (EYAs) are fundamental to this adoption, underpinning both the financial viability and the design of PV projects [1]. However, real-world conditions (particularly partial shading from obstructions such as buildings or clouds) can cause significant performance degradation due to non-linear electrical mismatch losses [2]. While high-fidelity simulations at the cell or submodule level can accurately capture these effects, they are computationally intensive, creating a substantial bottleneck for the annual performance analyses required for reliable EYAs. An annual simulation involves processing thousands of time steps, and the computational cost of detailed models renders tasks such as rapid design iteration and large-scale optimization impractical.

To address this challenge, ieco.io researchers have explored various acceleration strategies. One common approach is to reduce the input data by using clustering algorithms, such as k-means [3], to generate a set of "representative days" from a full year's weather data [4, 5]. Other methods focus on simplifying the physical model itself, employing techniques like Model Order Reduction (MOR) [6] or replacing it entirely with machine learning (ML) surrogate models [7]. While effective, existing "representative day" methods often aggregate 24-hour data profiles before clustering, a process that smooths out the instantaneous variations in sun position and irradiance. This loss of temporal resolution is critical, as the effects of partial shading are highly sensitive to the moment-to-moment geometry of the sun, array, and shading objects.

This ieco.io work introduces a novel framework that accelerates simulations by applying statistical aggregation directly to the instantaneous operating conditions, thereby preserving the high-resolution data necessary for accurate shading analysis. We present and evaluate two distinct methods: StraightForward Aggregation (SFA), which applies k-means [3] clustering directly to the multi-dimensional space of sun irradiance, elevation, and azimuth; and Hierarchical Hourly Aggregation (HHA), which first segregates data by hour of the day before clustering. A key contribution of this work is the tunability of the SFA method, allowing users to explicitly define the desired data reduction percentage and predictably control the trade-off between simulation speed and accuracy. This study demonstrates that this data-centric approach provides a more robust and predictable performance improvement across various scenarios compared to simply using a less detailed physical model.

The work is structured as follows: Section 2 describes the PV system scenarios used for testing. Section 3 establishes the baseline simulation framework and justifies the use of a submodule-level model as the benchmark for both accuracy and computational cost. Section 4 details the proposed SFA and HHA methods, presenting a rigorous performance analysis of their accuracy and speed, particularly for quantifying annual shading losses. Finally, Section 5 summarizes the key findings and concludes the work.

2 SIMULATION SCENARIOS

To evaluate the performance of the methods introduced in this work, we consider various PV system scenarios, summarized in Table I. These scenarios range in size from small systems, typical of residential installations, to larger commercial-scale systems. The shading objects are chosen to cast partial shading on the modules.

10.4229/EUPVSEC2025/4AO.9.5

Senario ID	Tilt (°)	Azimuth (°)	Obstrucion(s)	Parameters (dist/height [m], x-range)
1 Module (small residential)				
1M_T20_A0_1IW	20	0	1 infinite wall	1.2 / 1.35
1M_T0_A50_1IW	0	50	1 infinite wall	1.2 / 1.35
1M_T30_A-10_1C	30	-10	1 chimney	2 / 2, [3, 4]
1M_T30_A-10_2C	30	-10	2 chimneys	#1: 1.5 / 2, [-5, -4] #2: 2 / 2, [3, 4]
8 Modules (4 series, 2 parallel, medium residential)				
8M_T20_A0_1IW	0	0	1 infinite wall	1.2 / 1.35
8M_T20_A50_1IW	0	50	1 infinite wall	4 / 2
8M_T20_A0_2W	0	0	2 walls	#1: 1.2 / 1.35, [-7, -2] #2: 1.2 / 1.35, [2, 7]
8M_T30_A-10_1C	30	-10	1 chimney	2 / 2, [3, 4]
8M_T30_A-10_2C	30	-10	2 chimneys	#1: 1.5 / 2, [-5, -4] #2: 2 / 2, [3, 4]
16 Modules (4 series, 4 parallel, large residential)				
16M_T30_A-10_1C	30	-10	1 chimney	2 / 2, [3, 4]
16M_T30_A-10_2C	30	-10	2 chimneys	#1: 1.5 / 2, [-5, -4] #2: 2 / 2, [3, 4]
64 Modules (8 series, 8 parallel, commercial)				
64M_T0_A0_1B	0	0	1 box	1 / 2, [3, 6]
64M_T0_A0_1B1C	0	0	Box and chimney	Box: 1 / 2, [3, 6] Chimney: 1 / 2, [-4, -3]

Table I: Simulation scenarios considered.

The simulations are performed using the JA Solar JAM72_S20_440 module [8], which features a twin half-cut cell architecture [9]. The module consists of three submodules connected in series. Each submodule, in turn, is composed of two parallel-connected half-submodules, each containing 24 cells in series. Figure 2.1 provides a schematic of the module architecture used in this work.

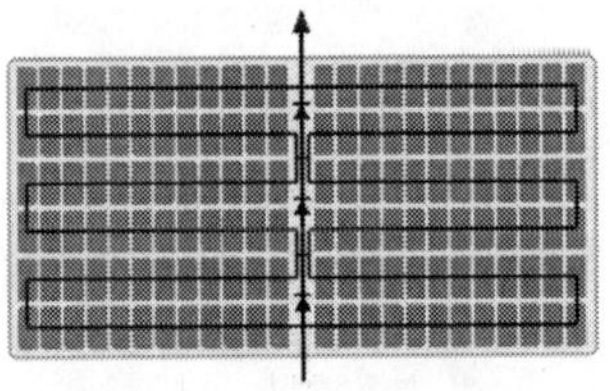

Figure 2.1: Module architecture used in simulations.

Furthermore, inverter effects are disregarded to simplify the analysis, under the assumption that the inverter can operate ideally under all conditions. Hourly meteorological data for Madrid, Spain, obtained from the Photovoltaic Geographical Information System (PVGIS) [10], are used as input for the simulations.

3 SIMULATION METHODS

To assess the power output of a PV system, we employ a custom Python simulation framework [11] developed at ieco.io built upon the pvlib library [12]. This community-developed, open-source toolbox provides the functions and classes necessary to model PV system performance. The simulation first computes the system's current-voltage (I-V) curve, from which the power output is determined by identifying the maximum power point (MPP).

To model the I-V curve of a cell, module, or array, we use the single-diode model as implemented in pvlib. This model describes the I-V curve by representing the PV device with a simple equivalent circuit [13].

Our simulation framework supports multiple methods for computing PV system power output. Since this work focuses on partial shading, a cell-level simulation is the most accurate approach, as it explicitly models the electrical mismatch between individual cells.

However, this method is computationally intensive for large systems. It requires calculating the I-V curve for each cell and then aggregating these curves while accounting for mismatches due to shading and the effects of bypass diodes. The high computational cost motivates the adoption of faster, albeit less precise, methods.

One such alternative is a submodule-level simulation. This approach applies the single-diode model to each submodule as a whole, calculating an aggregate I-V curve that incorporates the effects of shading across that submodule. These submodule curves are then combined, taking bypass diodes into account. This method provides a good approximation of the power output while requiring significantly fewer computational resources. For these reasons, we use the submodule-level simulation as a benchmark method to evaluate the performance of the novel approaches introduced in this paper.

Finally, we consider a module-level method that disregards the mismatch caused by partial shading. In the following section, the performance of all three approaches (cell-, submodule-, and module-level) is evaluated under these partial shading scenarios, and compared with a simpler approach that does not consider shading.

3.1 Simulation methods comparison

The precision of the simulation methods described above depends on their level of granularity. Less detailed methods tend to overestimate the system's power output, as they do not account for the electrical mismatch losses caused by partial shading.

To illustrate this behavior, we present the simulated power output from the different methods for a specific scenario: a single-module system shaded by two chimneys (Scenario 1M_T30_A-10_2C in Table 2.1) on November 3rd.

We show the results in Figure 3.1, which plots the MPP in Watts as a function of the hour of the day (from 06:00 to 19:00). We represent each simulation method by a different color: the ideal, unshaded case (red), the module-level simulation (orange), the submodule-level simulation (blue), and the cell-level simulation (green).

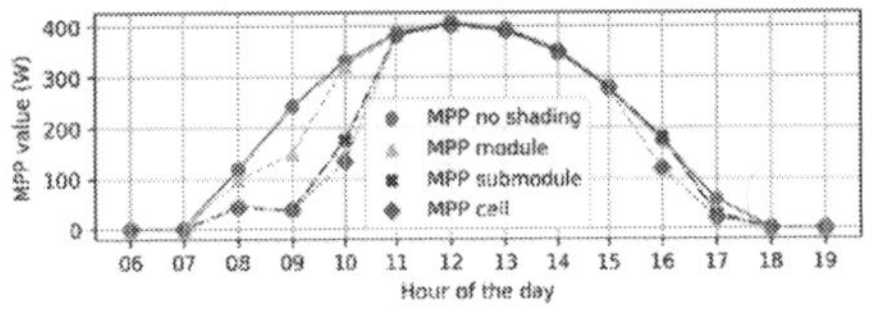

Figure 3.1: MPP output on November 3rd for different simulation methods.

As established above, less detailed simulation methods overestimate the system's power output because they neglect the mismatch losses caused by partial shading. To quantify the accuracy of the different methods presented in this work, we compute the error using

$$RelativeError=\frac{\sum|MPP_{newmethod}-MPP_{referencemethod}|}{\sum MPP_{referencemethod}}. \quad (1)$$

The summation in this equation is performed over all

MPP values in the evaluation period. This provides a scale-independent metric for the relative error.

To evaluate the long-term performance, we will also use

$$RelativeDifference = \frac{\Sigma(MPP_{newmethod} - MPP_{referencemethod})}{\Sigma MPP_{referencemethod}} = \frac{\Sigma MPP_{newmethod}}{\Sigma MPP_{referencemethod}} - 1, \quad (2)$$

which calculates the relative difference in annual energy yield between any two methods being compared.

Figure 3.2 displays the distribution of the relative difference in annual energy yield for each simulation method, calculated with (2) using the ideal (unshaded) simulation as the reference. Each boxplot [14] in the figure summarizes the results across all the scenarios described previously.

It is important to note that the relative difference computed with (2) and the relative error computed with (1) generally differ. However, since the less detailed methods consistently overestimate power output, these two values are equal in magnitude but opposite in sign in this context. This motivates using the negative value to explicitly express the overestimation by the less detailed methods.

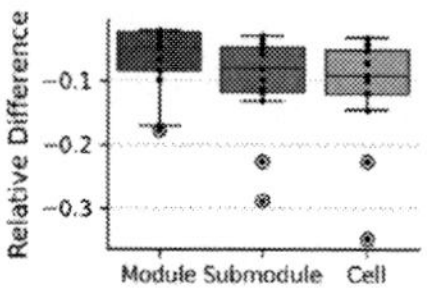

Figure 3.2: Yearly differences of the power output throughout a year for each simulation method with the unshaded simulation as the reference.

The results show a clear trend: as the model detail increases, the estimated annual energy yield decreases. This reduction, which quantifies the estimated power loss from partial shading, reaches up to 30% for the cell-level simulation in scenarios with significant mismatch.

However, this precision comes at a high computational cost. To quantify this trade-off, we compare the execution times of the methods by calculating a relative time metric, analogous to (1), as

$$RelativeTime = \frac{time_{newmethod} - time_{referencemethod}}{time_{referencemethod}}. \quad (3)$$

We present in Figure 3.3 the relative execution times for each simulation method, calculated with (3) using the unshaded simulation as the reference. The findings highlight the substantial computational overhead of the cell-level method, which is on average 2000% slower (21 times the reference time) and, in the worst case, up to 8000% slower (81 times the reference time). In contrast, the submodule-level simulation is far more efficient, showing a mean slowdown of 200% (3 times the reference time) and a maximum of 600% (7 times the reference time).

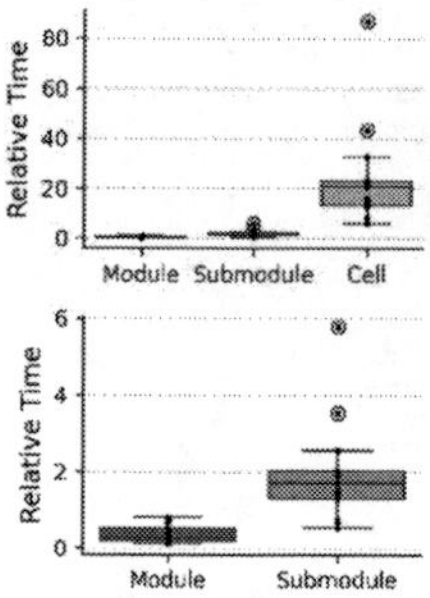

Figure 3.3: Relative time of compute needed for each simulation method with the unshaded simulation as the reference. The lower graph is the same as the upper one without the simulation at the cell level results.

The results presented in this section demonstrate that the submodule-level simulation provides an effective trade-off between accuracy and computational cost. It delivers a reliable power output estimation that accounts for partial shading mismatch while remaining computationally efficient. Therefore, we selected this simulation method as the basis for evaluating the aggregation methods described in the following section.

4 INITIAL DATA AGGREGATION METHODS

Simulating the annual power generation of a PV system requires a full year of operating condition data. In this study, we use an hourly dataset (8760 total data points) that provides solar irradiance and sun position (azimuth and elevation). To improve efficiency, we exclude data points where the system generates no power, such as during nighttime or when solar irradiance is zero. For the location studied (Madrid, Spain), this filtering reduces the simulation dataset by approximately half, to roughly 4000 relevant data points.

The high computational cost of using detailed simulation methods with large, year-long datasets presents a significant challenge. We address this challenge by developing a method to reduce the size of the operating conditions dataset used for simulation, with the goal of minimizing execution time while controlling the impact on accuracy.

The proposed approach reduces data redundancy by aggregating similar operating conditions. For instance, solar conditions at a specific hour, such as 11:00, are often nearly identical across consecutive clear-sky days. Instead of simulating each of these points individually, we can use a single representative point (such as their mean value) to obtain an accurate approximation of the power output for that period, thus reducing the size of the input dataset.

To automatically group similar operating conditions, we employ the k-means clustering algorithm [3], a widely used unsupervised machine learning technique. This algorithm partitions the original data into a predefined number of clusters based on similarity. We then select the centroid of each resulting cluster as a single representative data point. The collection of these centroids constitutes the new, reduced dataset for our simulation. Figure 4.1 illustrates this data reduction concept, showing how a large dataset can be effectively summarized by just four cluster centroids.

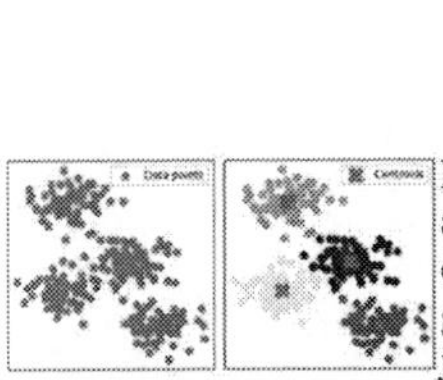

Figure 4.1: K-means algorithm intuition. A vast dataset (gray dots in the left graph) is summarized by just four cluster centroids (red crosses in the right graph).

In this work, we propose and evaluate two distinct approaches for this aggregation: StraightForward Aggregation (SFA) and Hierarchical Hourly Aggregation (HHA).

4.1 StraightForward Aggregation (SFA)

As its name suggests, the StraightForward Aggregation (SFA) method applies the k-means algorithm directly to the entire dataset of approximately 4000 operating conditions. The process uses a target percentage for data reduction. For example, to achieve a 80% reduction, we set the number of clusters (k) to 20% of the original dataset size, resulting in k = 800 clusters ($4000 \times (1 - 0.80) = 800$). We then perform the simulation only on the centroids of these k clusters. To reconstruct the full annual time series, we assign the power output calculated for each centroid to all original data points within that centroid's corresponding cluster.

To determine the optimal set of features for clustering, we evaluated various combinations of the input variables solar irradiance, sun elevation, and sun azimuth. The analysis concluded that aggregating the data based on all three variables simultaneously yields the most accurate results. Consequently, the methods described in this work perform clustering in this 3-dimensional feature space.

Figure 4.2 presents the performance of the SFA method across a range of data reduction percentages for all simulation scenarios. The top plot shows the relative error of the SFA method, calculated using (1), with the submodule-level simulation performed on the complete, non-aggregated dataset as the reference. The bottom plot shows the corresponding relative execution times, calculated using (3). For context, we also include the performance of the simpler module-level simulation as a baseline. The mean error and time for this baseline are indicated by dashed lines, while the minimum and maximum values across all scenarios are shown as dotted lines. This allows a direct comparison of the SFA method's accuracy and speed against the next fastest, but less detailed, simulation approach.

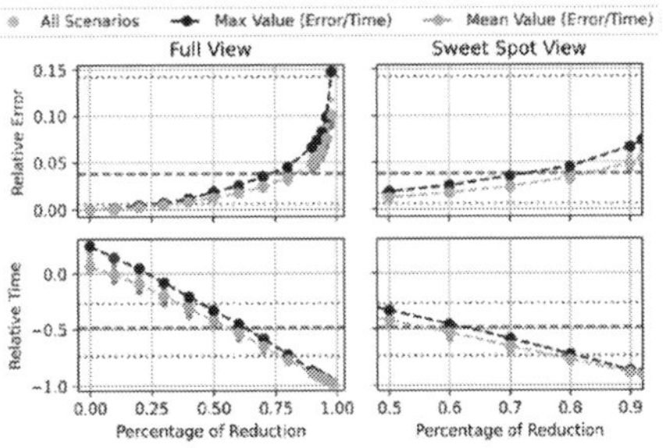

Figure 4.2: Relative errors (top) and execution times (bottom) of the SFA method for each simulation scenario are shown for a grid of data reduction percentages, using the submodule-level simulation as the reference. We plot the performance of the module-level simulation as dotted lines (minimum and maximum values) and dashed lines (mean values). The right-hand graphs show a zoomed-in view of the x-axis to highlight the "sweet spot."

The results reveal the expected trade-off: higher data reduction percentages lead to faster execution times at the cost of increased error. For instance, an 80% data reduction reduces computation time by approximately 80% while introducing a mean relative error of about 2.5%.

Notably, an optimal range for the SFA method appears between 60% and 80% reduction. Within this "sweet spot," the SFA method not only maintains higher accuracy than the module-level simulation but also exceeds its computational speed. This demonstrates a key advantage, providing a solution that is both faster and more precise than the next simplest modeling approach.

To further analyze these results, Figure 4.3 directly compares the module-level simulation with the SFA method using an 80% data reduction. The figure displays the distributions of relative errors (top) and relative execution times (bottom), using the full submodule-level simulation as the reference for both.

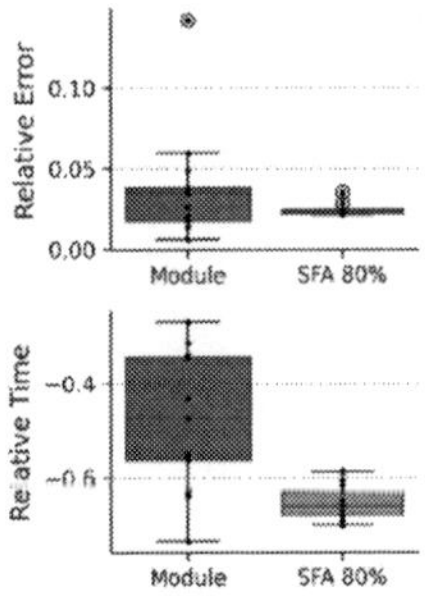

Figure 4.3: Relative errors (top) and times (bottom) of the simulation at the module level and the one performing the SFA with 80% of reduction.

In terms of accuracy, the SFA method achieves a mean error comparable to the module-level simulation. However, the distribution of SFA errors is significantly less dispersed. This indicates that the SFA method is more robust and provides more consistent results, especially in scenarios with high partial shading.

Regarding execution time, the SFA method not only achieves greater speedup (approximately 80% reduction) but also demonstrates more predictable performance. The execution time of the module-level simulation varies considerably depending on the specific scenario, whereas the SFA method's runtime remains far more consistent.

A key advantage of the SFA method is its configurability. Based on the performance curves in Figure 4.2, users can select a specific data reduction percentage to achieve a desired trade-off between computational speed and simulation accuracy. This flexibility allows the method to adapt to different application requirements.

While any reduction level is possible, the most compelling results occur for parameters in the 60% to 80% reduction range. As previously noted, this window provides a solution that is not only faster but also more accurate than the baseline module-level simulation, representing the optimal operational "sweet spot" for this approach.

4.2 Hierarchical Hourly Aggregation (HHA)

An alternative approach, the Hierarchical Hourly Aggregation (HHA) method, first partitions the data before applying clustering. In the initial step, we divide the dataset into 24 distinct groups, one for each hour of the day. We then apply k-means clustering independently within each of these hourly groups.

This hierarchical structure introduces a new challenge: determining the optimal number of clusters (k) for each hourly group, as intra-group variability is not uniform. For example, all data points for nighttime hours (e.g., 03:00) can be summarized by a single centroid (k = 1), since solar irradiance is consistently zero. In contrast, conditions at midday (e.g., 12:00) exhibit significant seasonal variation, with much higher irradiance in summer than in winter, thus requiring a larger k to represent them accurately.

To dynamically determine the number of clusters for each hourly group, we introduce a new hyperparameter: a target for the percentage of explained variability, or precision per hour. This approach selects the minimum number of clusters (k) required to account for a specified portion of the data's variance within each hourly subgroup. For instance, if this target is set to 99%, the algorithm determines, for each hour, the number of clusters needed to explain 99% of that group's internal variability. This ensures that hours with high variance (e.g., midday) receive more clusters than hours with low variance (e.g., nighttime). We base this method on the procedure detailed in [15]. Figure 4.4 presents the performance of the HHA method.

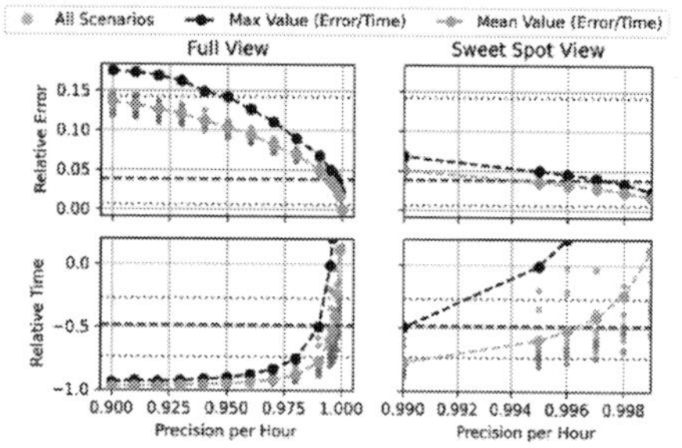

Figure 4.4: Relative errors (top) and execution times (bottom) of the HHA method for each simulation scenario are shown for a grid of precision-per-hour values, using the submodule-level simulation as the reference. We plot the performance of the module-level simulation as dotted lines (minimum and maximum values) and dashed lines (mean values). The right-hand graphs show a zoomed-in view of the x-axis to highlight the "sweet spot."

As expected, setting a higher target for the explained variability results in improved accuracy but also increases the computational time. When compared to the previous SFA method, the HHA approach achieves a similar level of accuracy and robustness across the different scenarios. However, it is computationally inferior. The execution time is not only longer, but its variability between scenarios is also significantly greater. This reduced efficiency is attributed to the computational overhead required to dynamically determine the optimal number of clusters for each of the 24-hourly groups. This selection process can be time-consuming, and the cost is not always offset by accuracy gains, particularly for smaller simulation scenarios.

The results indicate an optimal performance range for the HHA method when the explained variability target is set between 99.5% and 99.7%. To examine this in detail, Figure 4.5 compares the HHA method (using a 99.6% target) against the module-level simulation.

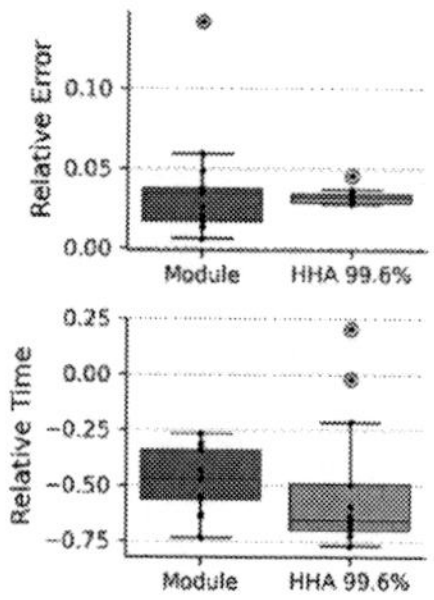

Figure 4.5: Relative errors (top) and times (bottom) of the simulation at the module level and the one performing the HHA with 99.6% of precision per hour.

In terms of accuracy, the HHA method offers comparable, or even superior, performance, demonstrating greater robustness across different scenarios. However, the opposite is true for computational time. This highlights the previously discussed issue: the method's significant overhead makes it ill-suited for smaller scenarios, which show the highest relative execution times. If we excluded these specific scenarios from the analysis, the average performance of the HHA method would more closely resemble that of the SFA approach.

Although the HHA method is outperformed by the SFA in this study, further refinement could improve its performance. The current implementation uses a linear search to determine the number of clusters per hour, incrementing k by one until it meets the target for explained variability. This process could be significantly accelerated by using a larger step size, thereby reducing the method's computational overhead. As the SFA method already provided excellent results, we did not pursue this optimization further in this work. Nonetheless, we present the HHA concept here as a promising alternative that, with such modifications, could become a competitive approach for future ieco.io research.

4.3 Aggregation methods comparison (Pareto Frontier)

To directly compare the two aggregation methods, Figure 4.6 plots the mean relative error against the mean relative execution time for both the SFA and HHA approaches. Each point on the plot represents the performance of a method at a specific parameter setting, averaged across all simulation scenarios. The plot focuses on negative relative times, as these values indicate a computational speedup. For reference, we also show the fixed performance of the baseline module-level simulation, which achieves an average time reduction of approximately 50% at a mean error of about 4%. This visualization provides a clear comparison of the accuracy-speed trade-off for both proposed methods relative to each other and to a standard, less detailed approach.

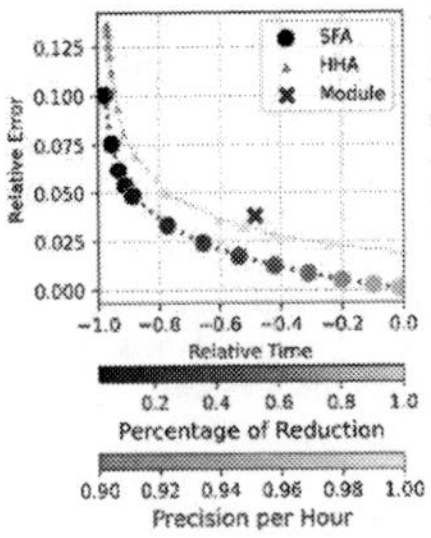

Figure 4.6: Mean relative times versus mean relative errors for SFA and HHA methods for a range of parameters.

The results demonstrate the clear superiority of the StraightForward Aggregation (SFA) method over both the HHA and the module-level simulation in terms of average performance. The SFA method consistently defines the Pareto Frontier [16] for the speed-accuracy trade-off, providing the best possible accuracy for any given level of computational speedup. Furthermore, this approach offers a versatile mechanism to tune this trade-off as needed. For instance, users can achieve an 80% reduction in computational time while introducing a mean relative error of only about 3%. This same principle can be applied to target any desired balance between computational cost and precision, highlighting the method's practical flexibility.

4.4 SFA for power losses throughout the year caused by shading

A primary application of detailed PV system simulations, and a central focus of research at ieco.io, is to quantify the annual energy losses caused by partial shading. The aggregation methods developed in this work are highly effective for this task, as they significantly reduce the required computational time while maintaining the accuracy of the submodule-level simulation. To formally analyze these losses, we define the hourly energy loss due to partial shading with

$$MPP_{loss}=MPP_{noshading}-MPP_{shading}. \quad (4)$$

To evaluate how accurately each method estimates the annual energy loss from shading, we adapted the metric from (2). For this analysis, the error is calculated by substituting the total hourly power outputs with the hourly shading loss values (MPP_{loss}) using the full submodule-level simulation as the reference. The results are presented in Figure 4.7. This figure compares the performance of the SFA method in estimating shading losses against the module-level simulation, which serves as a performance baseline.

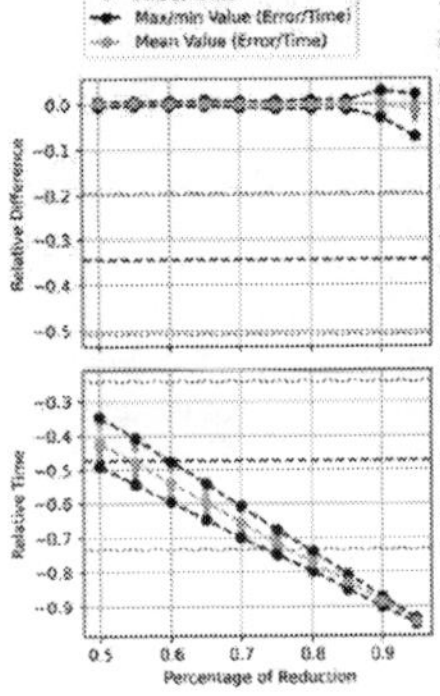

Figure 4.7: Relative differences on MPP loss (top) and times (bottom) of performing SFA for every simulation scenario for a grid of precision per hour values with the simulation at the submodule-level as the reference. Performance of the module level simulation plotted as dotted (minimum and maximum values) and dashed (mean values) lines.

The presented results confirm that the SFA method significantly outperforms the standard module-level simulation for estimating shading losses. On average, the module-level simulation underestimates the annual energy loss by approximately 35% compared to the reference full submodule-level simulation, while only being twice as fast. In contrast, the SFA method shows negligible differences in loss estimation even with data reduction percentages as high as 90%, while drastically reducing computational time. This demonstrates that the SFA approach provides a far superior balance of speed and accuracy for this application.

In summary, these results demonstrate that the proposed data aggregation method serves as a highly effective tool for quantifying annual energy losses from partial shading. The approach reduces computational time by up to 90% while having a negligible impact on the simulation's accuracy.

5 CONCLUSIONS

This ieco.io work addressed the significant computational challenge of performing accurate, year-long energy yield assessments for photovoltaic systems, particularly under the complex conditions of partial shading. We demonstrated that a key bottleneck arises from the sheer volume of time-step data required for an annual simulation.

To overcome this, we introduced and evaluated two novel statistical aggregation methods, StraightForward Aggregation (SFA) and Hierarchical Hourly Aggregation (HHA), designed to reduce the size of the input dataset while preserving the high-resolution information critical for accurate shading analysis. Both methods leverage k-means clustering to group similar instantaneous operating conditions, defined by solar irradiance, elevation, and azimuth, and use the resulting cluster centroids as representative points for simulation.

Our findings clearly establish the superiority of the SFA method. This approach not only proved more computationally efficient than the HHA method but also consistently outperformed the standard, less-detailed module-level simulation across all evaluated metrics. The SFA method successfully defines a new Pareto frontier for the speed-accuracy trade-off, providing the best possible accuracy for any given level of computational speedup. A key advantage of SFA is its tunability; for example, users can achieve an 80% reduction in simulation time while introducing a mean

10.4229/EUPVSEC2025/4AO.9.5

relative error of only about 3%. This delivers robust, predictable performance that remains consistent across different scenarios, outperforming simpler modeling approaches.

Crucially, the SFA method proved exceptionally effective for quantifying annual energy losses due to shading, a primary application of detailed PV simulations and a central focus of research at ieco.io. While the module-level simulation underestimated these losses by an average of 35%, our SFA approach reduces computational time by up to 90% with negligible impact on accuracy.

In conclusion, this work presents a data-centric framework that significantly accelerates PV simulations without compromising the fidelity required to model non-linear shading effects. The SFA method offers a practical, flexible, and powerful tool for engineers and researchers, enabling rapid design iterations and reliable financial assessments for PV projects in ieco.io and in any environment.

ACKNOWLEDGMENTS

This ieco.io research was supported by the project "Development of optimization algorithms and automation of the design of self-consumption photovoltaic installations, and analysis of the impact of local shadows on solar energy generation" of the company ieco.io, funded by the Xunta de Galicia through the Galician Innovation Agency (GAIN) under the program RECUPERACIÓN EXCELENCIA NEOTEC 2023-IN870A-006. This work is also part of the project CITMAga-C149-2025, funded by ieco.io. Brais González Rodríguez acknowledges the support from MICIU, through grant BG23/00155.

Google Gemini was used during the preparation of this manuscript for the sole purpose of language improvement.

REFERENCES

[1] Milosavljevic, Dragana & Kevkić, Tijana & Jovanovic, Slavica, "Review and validation of photovoltaic solar simulation tools/software based on case study", Open Physics, 20, 431-451. https://doi.org/10.1515/phys-2022-0042 (2022)

[2] F. Saeed, H. A. Tauqeer, H. E. Gelani, M. H. Yousuf, and A. Idrees, "Numerical modeling, simulation and evaluation of conventional and hybrid photovoltaic modules interconnection configurations under partial shading conditions," EPJPhotovolt., vol. 13, p. 10. https://doi.org/10.1051/epjpv/2022004 (2022)

[3] Aristidis Likas, Nikos Vlassis, Jakob J. Verbeek, "The global k-means clustering algorithm", Pattern Recognition, Volume 36, Issue 2, Pages 451-461. https://doi.org/10.1016/S0031-3203(02)00060-2 (2003)

[4] Miraftabzadeh, Seyed Mahdi & Colombo, Cristian & Longo, Michela & Foiadelli, Federica, "K-Means and Alternative Clustering Methods in Modern Power Systems", IEEE Access, PP, 1-1. https://doi.org/10.1109/ACCESS.2023.3327640 (2023)

[5] Kelsey Fahy, Michael Stadler, Zachary K. Pecenak, Jan Kleissl, "Input data reduction for microgrid sizing and energy cost modeling: Representative days and demand charges", J. Renewable Sustainable Energy, 11 (6), 065301. https://doi.org/10.1063/1.5121319 (2019)

[6] Gafurov, Tokhir & Prodanovic, Milan & Usaola, Julio, "PV system model reduction for reliability assessment studies", 4th IEEE/PES Innovative Smart Grid Technologies Europe, ISGT Europe 2013, 1-5. https://doi.org/10.1109/ISGTEurope.2013.6695420 (2013)

[7] Okif, Mohammad & Meena, Shanti & Lal, Shiv & Prajapati, Rajendra & Meena, Amit, "Machine Learning-Based Performance Prediction Model For Solar PV Systems Using Meteorological Inputs", International Journal of Environmental Sciences. https:/doi.org/10.64252/v0qwza71 (2025)

[8] Shanghai JA Solar Technology Co., Ltd. Mono 465W MBB Half-Cell Module JAM72S20 440-465/MR/1000V Series. Retrieved from https://www.jasolar.com/uploadfile/2020/0619/20200619040220997.pdf (2020)

[9] Zhang, H. X., H. Zhuang, X. F. Gou, Q. S. Huang, L. K. Jiang, and Z. Y. Chen, "Study on the Benefit of Half-Cut Cells towards Higher Cell-To-Module Power Ratio.", Power and Electrical Engineering, 978–1. https://doi.org/10.12783/dteees/epee2017/18123 (2017)

[10] Thomas Huld, Richard Müller, Attilio Gambardella, "A new solar radiation database for estimating PV performance in Europe and Africa", Solar Energy, Volume 86, Issue 6, Pages 1803-1815. https://doi.org/10.1016/j.solener.2012.03.006 (2012)

[11] Python Software Foundation. Python Language Reference, version 3.13. Available at http://www.python.org

[12] Anderson, K., Hansen, C., Holmgren, W., Jensen, A., Mikofski, M., and Driesse, A. "pvlib python: 2023 project update." Journal of Open Source Software, 8(92), 5994. https://doi.org/10.21105/joss.05994 (2023)

[13] N. M. A. Alrahim Shannan, N. Z. Yahaya and B. Singh, "Single-diode model and two-diode model of PV modules: A comparison", IEEE International Conference on Control System, Computing and Engineering, Penang, Malaysia, 2013, pp. 210-214. https://doi.org/10.1109/ICCSCE.2013.6719960. (2013)

[14] Mcgill, R., Tukey, J. W., & Larsen, W. A. "Variations of Box Plots". The American Statistician, 32(1), 12–16. https://doi.org/10.1080/00031305.1978.10479236 (1978)

[15] Caliński, Tadeusz & JA, Harabasz, "A Dendrite Method for Cluster Analysis", Communications in Statistics - Theory and Methods, 3, 1-27. https://doi.org/10.1080/03610927408827101 (1974)

[16] Lotov, A.V., Miettinen, K, "Visualizing the Pareto Frontier", In: Branke, J., Deb, K., Miettinen, K., Słowiński, R. (eds) Multiobjective Optimization, Lecture Notes in Computer Science, vol 5252, Springer, Berlin, Heidelberg. https://doi.org/10.1007/978-3-540-88908-3_9 (2008)

ADDRESSING GLARE PROBLEMATICS FOR PHOTOVOLTAIC PROJECTS IN THE IMMEDIATE PROXIMITY OF ROADS AND RAILWAYS THROUGH THE USE OF ACCURATE DIGITAL SURFACE MODELS

Christophe Vernay, John Coutel, Aina Razanajao, Sébastien Pitaval
Solaïs
955 route des Lucioles, 06560 Sophia Antipolis, France
christophe.vernay@solais.fr

ABSTRACT: The development of large-scale photovoltaic power plants generates disturbances in the local environment, among which solar glare that may turn critical when safety is at stake. The methodology for glare studies can hardly accept approximations for PV projects in the proximity of roads or railways as ground and near shading strongly affect the results. This paper presents the interest for working with accurate digital elevation modelling (DEM) and digital surface modelling (DSM) issued from LiDAR measurement campaigns. It first shows that LiDAR data allows to reduce the errors made by global elevation databases, e.g. Google's Elevation API which presents a root mean square error of 1.9 m and 6.6 m for two neighbouring areas located in France, respectively in lowland and valley. The sensitivity of the DSM spatial resolution on the relevance of the glare assessment is also addressed through a 27 MWp use-case. The 10-m resolution turns out to be the most appropriate one as it allows to accurately account for near shading and photovoltaic table's configuration; selecting a coarser resolution (20 or 30 m) mistakenly leads to non-existing glare occurrences that could have compromised the photovoltaic project itself during the administrative instruction process.
Keywords: photovoltaic, glare, co-visibility, digital elevation modelling (DEM), digital surface modelling (DSM)

1 INTRODUCTION

The development of large-scale photovoltaic (PV) power plants inevitably generates disturbances in the local environment. A simple co-visibility may turn into visual pollution depending on the involved person's subjective acceptability regarding such a new element in his neighbourhood. PV plants may also cause disturbances when the sun reflects off the PV panels and when the reflected rays suddenly appear in someone's field of view. This may turn critical when safety is at stake, i.e. for aircraft pilots, associated air traffic controllers and drivers of terrestrial vehicles (cars, trains, etc.). The problematic of glare assessment for the safety of aircraft transport has been conducted for more than 15 years, mostly in France and the United States [1]. The associated methodology can accept approximations in terms of ground modelling as most airports are usually located in flat open spaces. However, the situation differs when assessing the glare risks for PV projects in the immediate proximity of roads and railways, for which an accurate modelling of the ground and the near shading, such as vegetation or existing buildings, must be accounted for.

This paper presents the value of using both Digital Elevation Modelling (DEM) and Digital Surface Modelling (DSM) to address glare problematics in an accurate and relevant manner and to eventually successfully pass the administrative instruction process during the development phase of PV projects.

2 USING THE PROPER SOURCE

2.1 Introducing digital modelling

Open-source global DEMs were made available to the scientific community through satellite programs in the early 2000s such as the Shuttle Radar Topography Mission (SRTM) [2] while the first Open Maps for Europe datasets were only published in 2021 [3]. The same applies to France where most of the geographic databases produced by the Institut Géographique National (IGN) are now open access [4]. Global elevation databases are also provided through commercial services with specific coverage and price offers. All open-source and commercial services differ depending on their respective acquisition methods, thus leading to specific altimetric accuracies that may have consequences on the application for which they are used. The acquisition with laser imaging detection and ranging (LiDAR) provides the best accuracy (typically ~10-50 cm) when local measurements performed by a certified surveyor (centimetre accuracy) are not available or not feasible for large areas. In the case of a LiDAR, a scanner is embedded into a small aircraft or even a drone flying at low altitudes. It emits high frequency infrared laser pulses towards the studied area. The cloud of reflected points is then classified as Ground for DEM purpose, or Vegetation, Building, etc., for DSM purpose. This classification highlights the added value of LiDAR with respect to local measurements which only consider ground elevation.

2.2 Benchmarking LiDAR and Google's Elevation API

As introduced previously, IGN is finalizing the dissemination of high-definition LiDAR data for the entire French continental territory, likely before the end of 2026. This database can therefore be considered, in France, as an accurate reference for DEMs, and also for DSMs derived from LiDAR, although the latter's representativeness depends on the date of the measurement campaigns (trees grow, new buildings are constructed, etc.). Regarding areas where LiDAR campaigns are not performed yet, it must be noted that arising companies now propose drone campaigns with aggressive price offers that make the engineering best practices quickly evolve.

This section aims to provide an overview of the performance of a global elevation database of low cost, even free, compared to the LiDAR-based as the reference. For that purpose, two areas located in the south-east of France, 6 km away, are considered: a first one located in the lowland (1.6 km², cf. Fig. 1) and a second one located in the valley (4.2 km², cf. Fig. 2).

Figure 1: Lowland (1.2 km*1.3 km) use-case

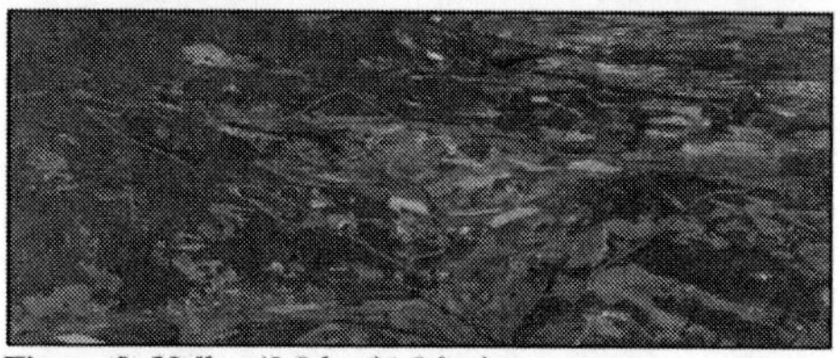

Figure 2: Valley (2.2 km*1.9 km) use-case

Table 1 provides statistical indicators for the comparison between the elevation data provided by IGN's HD LiDAR (50 cm spatial resolution), considered as the reference, and the elevation data from Google's Elevation API, with a 5 m spatial sampling. For these two neighbouring areas, Table I shows that for lowland, Google's Elevation API has a mean bias error (MBE) of 0.5 m, and a root mean square error (RMSE) of 1.9 m which can be acceptable. However, MBE increases to 3.3 m and RMSE to 6.6 m in the valley which confirms that the more complex the topography, the less accurate Google's Elevation API is. Even though this analysis is limited to only two specific areas in the south-east of France and should be conducted on many other use-cases, one can consider that using LiDAR data considerably improves the accuracy of the DEM and should therefore be preferred in most of engineering studies, among which glare studies.

Table I: DEM statistics for two areas in lowland and valley, LiDAR as the reference.

	Lowland	Valley
Data number	65536	194481
Reference elevation (m)	260.5	367.9
Mean bias error (m)	0.45	3.28
Mean absolute error (m)	1.13	4.02
Standard deviation (m)	1.84	5.75
Root mean square error (m)	1.90	6.62

3 APPLICATION TO GLARE STUDIES

3.1 Considered use-case

This section presents the 29 MWp ground-mounted PV project located in northwestern France, in the department of Eure, and whose building permit application was submitted to the planning authorities in the first half of 2025. Fig. 3 shows the associated layout while Table II provides its main characteristics.

Figure 3: Layout of the 29 MWp ground mounted PV plant

Table II: Main characteristics of the ground mounted PV plant

Land surface	16 ha
Installed power	29 MWp
PV table configuration	Portrait, 3V27 and 3V9
PV table orientation	South
PV table tilt	17°
High point of the PV tables	3.2 m

During the investigation of this case, the planning services required a risk assessment regarding the potential glare that could be experienced by the train drivers coming from southeast on the nearby railway track, depicted in red on Fig. 4. Solaïs conducted such analysis using its own in-house codes that are constantly updated to comply with the Administrations' requirements and the developers' needs.

Figure 4: Railway localisation (in red) closed to the PV area (in magenta)

Both DSM and DEM of the project were provided by IGN's HD LiDAR. They are respectively depicted on Fig. 5 and 6 while the height of the shading elements (mainly building and vegetation), i.e. the difference between both matrices, is depicted on Fig. 7.

10.4229/EUPVSEC2025/4AO.9.6

Figure 5: DSM (elevation + surface) in meter with the PV plant in magenta and the railway in red

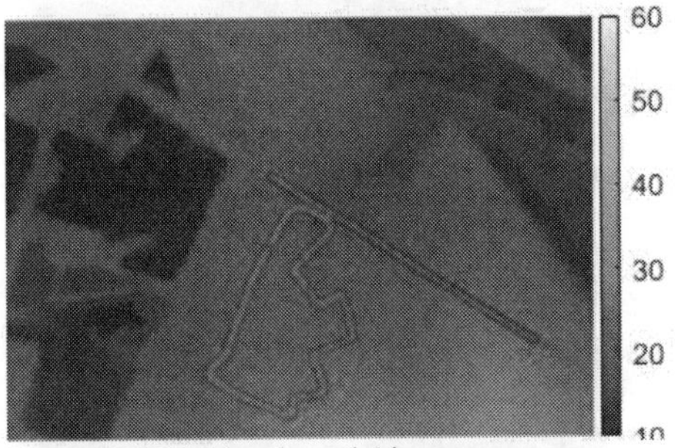

Figure 6: DEM (elevation only) in meter

Figure 7: Shading height in meter (building and vegetation)

Processing both DEM and DSM allows to accurately localize and model the small woodland located between the PV plant and the railway track, with a maximum height of 23 m for the trees that is likely to limit the co-visibility for the drivers and thus the risk of glare. One can also identify on Fig. 7 the areas where a tree clearing is needed, mostly in the south-eastern corner of the PV plant. Such a clearing must be accounted for in the simulation which considers that the PV tables are already installed; for that purpose, DEM data is used inside the PV area.

3.2 Glare characterization

The glare phenomenon that may be generated by PV plants is the result of the sunlight reflection on the PV panels, as illustrated in Fig. 8.

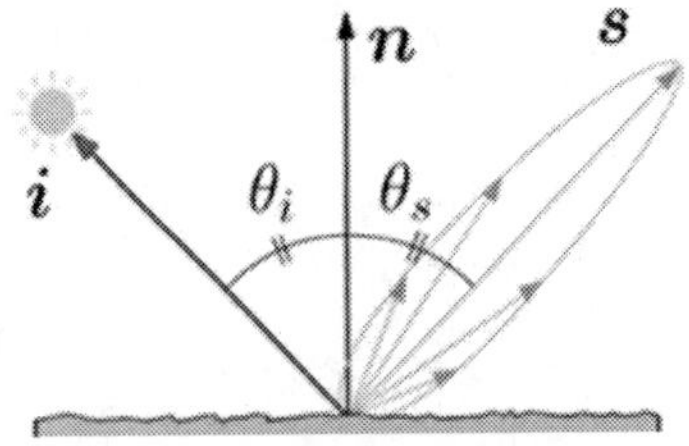

Figure 8: Schematic diagram of sunlight reflection on the PV panels [5]

Its complete modelling depends on both environment factors (sun's path throughout the year, luminance profile of the sunlight under clear-sky condition) and PV-related characteristics (orientation of the modules whether or not a tracking system is used, bidirectional reflectance distribution function – BRDF – of the PV panels). However, one must also account for far shading, i.e. when the sun is hidden by horizon, and near shading where buildings and vegetation will prevent reflection to occur and/or reflected rays to reach on observer.

Glare simulations allow to identify the occurrences where a reflected ray enters a person's field of view (either fixed, as in the case of a residence or an air traffic control tower, or mobile, as in the case of a vehicle trajectory) and to characterize them through the following indicators:

- Location of the impacts.
- Areas of the PV project generating the reflected rays.
- Time of occurrence throughout the day and the year.
- Location of the reflected rays in the person's field of view (central and/or peripheral).
- Luminance of the reflected rays compared to the direct sunlight.

3.2 Sensitivity analysis on the spatial resolution

The key factor when running a glare simulation is selecting the common and appropriate spatial resolution used for both DEM and DSM. Choosing a coarse resolution will speed up the simulations but will also smooth out the topography and the near-shading modelling, thus leading to inaccurate results. On the other hand, choosing a fine resolution will considerably increase the simulation time while improving the accuracy of the near shading modelling. However, the PV table size also has its importance in this choice. In the considered use-case, the PV tables are either 3V9 and 3V27 which means that they are composed of three rows of nine or twenty-seven PV panels mounted on a vertical (portrait) mode. Considering that, at minimum, a PV table is about 10-m long, it must be noted that selecting a finer spatial resolution, for instance 5 m, doesn't bring so much added value for the PV table modelling as the building company usually compensates for the topography by adjusting the height of the table's piles. Therefore, a 10-m spatial resolution is the minimum value to be set while limiting the computing time.

The results of glare study were compared for different spatial resolutions: 10, 20 and 30 m, with the first providing the best accuracy in terms of glare results.

Fig. 9 shows in yellow the location of the trajectory segments that were identified as a glare risk for the train drivers. It shows that the coarser the resolution, the greater the number of identified impacts. This is due to the fact that undersizing the spatial resolution leads to errors in both the ground elevation and the near shading. On that specific use-case, one can mistakenly find some glare occurrence far away from the PV plant with a 20 or 30-m resolution.

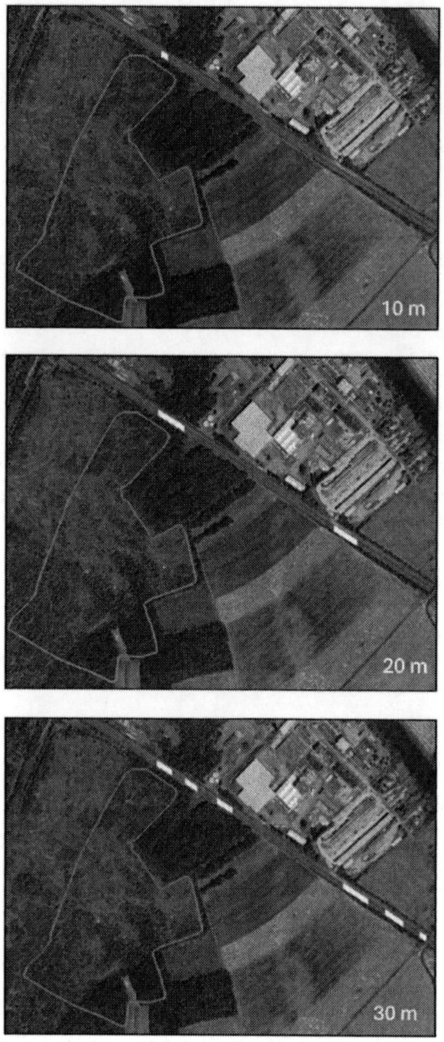

Figure 9: Impact location (in yellow) throughout the trajectory (train coming from the south-east)

The same colour code (cf. Fig. 10) is used for the following figures: the lighter the colour, the higher the occurrence of impacts, where occurrence is defined as the number of the impacts identified by the simulation. Zero occurrence (i.e. no impact) is indicated in blue.

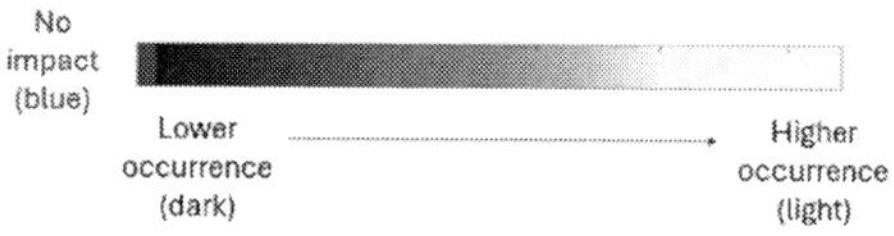

Figure 10: Colour code used to characterize the glare impacts

Fig. 11 identifies the location of the PV tables that will generate the reflected rays for the trains coming from the southeast. The 10-m results highlight that only a few tables (< 1% of the total PV area) located at the northern edge of the PV plant will generate impacts, mostly due to a gap in the vegetation, which can be easily remediated once the PV generated is commissioned. On the other hand, 20-m and 30-m results mistakenly indicate problematic tables on the centre of the PV field (respectively 33% and 49%).

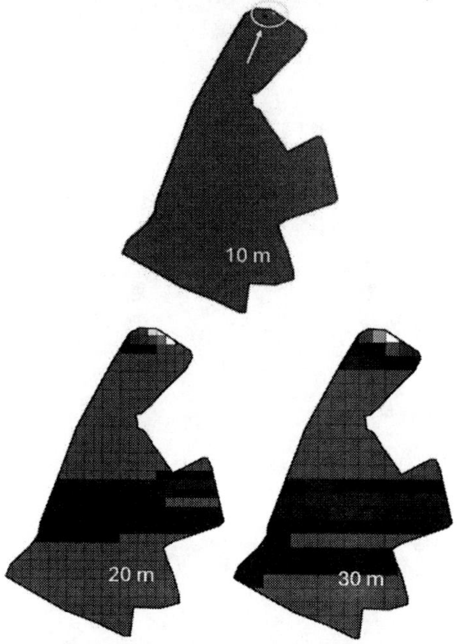

Figure 11: Location of the PV tables that will generate the reflected rays

Fig. 12 provides the timing of the identified impacts throughout the day (horizontal axis, true solar hour i.e. 12pm when the sun is at its zenith) and throughout the year (vertical axis). 10-m results show that the impacts only occur in March and from mid-September to mid-October no later than 30 minutes before sunset while a coarser resolution would have identified a much longer duration.

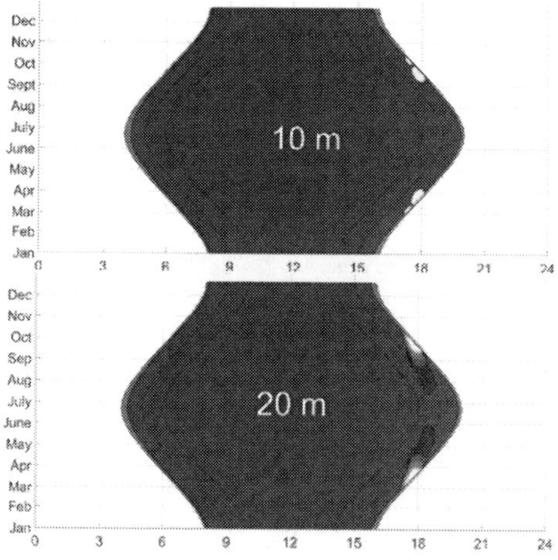

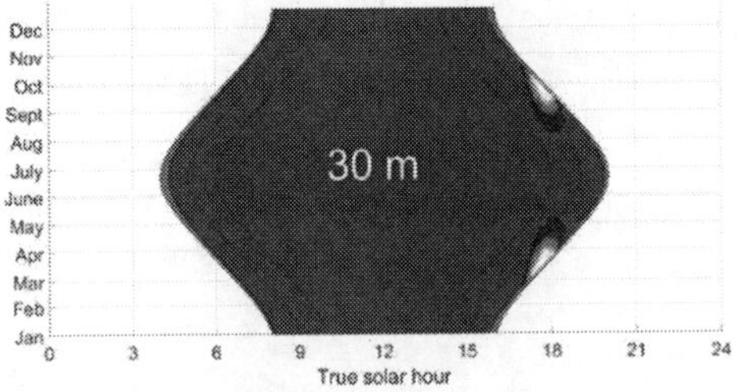

Figure 12: Dating of the identified occurrences throughout the day and the year

Fig. 13 finally identifies the driver's field of view that will be impacted by glare occurrences. The centre of the figure is the preferred direction of gaze, i.e. the trajectory direction; the elevation (vertical axis) is positive when the driver looks upward and negative when looking downward while azimuth is positive when the driver looks to the right and negative when looking to the left. The yellow circle corresponds to a 40° angle between the trajectory and the reflected ray, this value corresponding to the limit beyond which the driver must turn both head and eyes to perceive the reflected ray. The results show that 20-m and 30-m simulations mistakenly identify occurrences on the driver's central vision whereas reality is much different with fewer impacts and less severity.

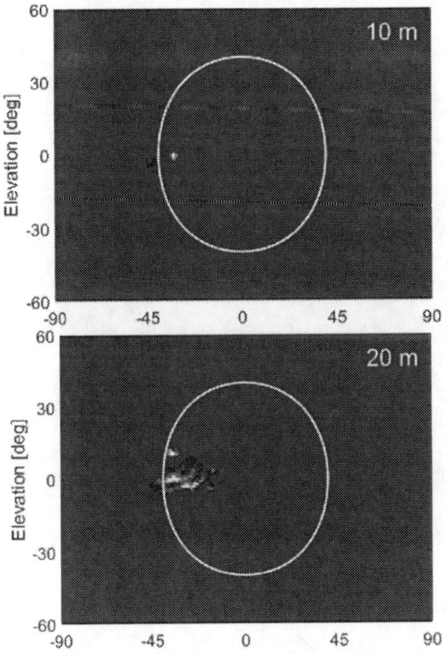

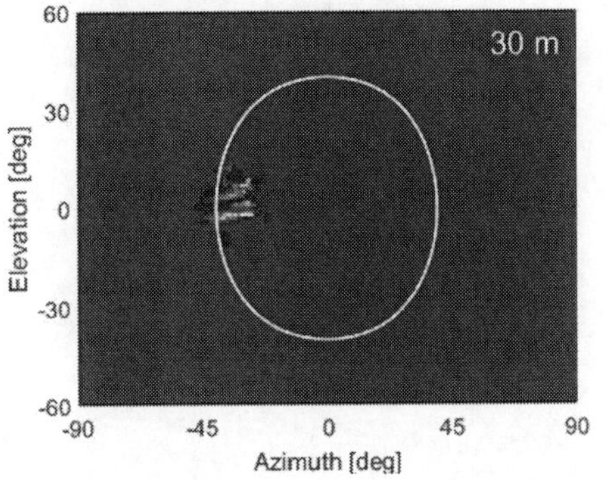

Figure 13: Location of the identified occurrences in the drivers' field of view

4 CONCLUSIONS

This paper presented the importance of using accurate DEMs and DSMs issued from LiDAR measurement campaigns. It first showed that LiDAR databases significantly reduce the uncertainty in the ground elevation assessment proposed by global DEM such as Google's Elevation API, especially for complex terrain. These works also presented the added-value of LiDAR-based DSM when addressing the problematics of the glare generated by PV plants located near roads and railways where near-shading is present (vegetation, buildings). The 10-m spatial resolution turns out to be the most appropriate one as it allows to accurately account for near shading and PV table's configuration thereby enabling reliable glare risk assessment. In the proposed use-case, selecting a coarser spatial resolution (above 20 m) mistakenly lead to non-existing glare occurrences that could have compromised the PV project itself during the administrative permitting process.

5 REFERENCES

[1] Vernay C., Realpe A., De Gabaï D., Pitaval S. Innovative Simulation Tools For An Exhaustive And Synthetic Characterization Of The Solar Glare Occurrences For The Design And The Administrative Instruction Of Large-Scale Photovoltaic Plants. 33rd European Photovoltaic Solar Energy Conference and Exhibition, Sep 2017, Amsterdam, Netherlands. EU PVSEC 2017 Proceedings, pp.2218-2222

[2] Suchandt, Steffen & Breit, Helko & Adam, Nico & Eineder, Michael & Schättler, Birgit & Runge, Hartmut & Roth, Achim & Mikusch, Eberhard. (2001). The Shuttle Radar Topography Mission. Reviews of Geophysics - REV GEOPHYS. 45.

[3] EuroGeographics: The Open Maps for Europe project,https://eurogeographics.org/open-maps-for-europe

[4] LiDAR HD IGN https://geoservices.ign.fr/lidarhd

[5] Simonot L., Boulenguez P. Quand la matière diffuse la lumière. Presse des Mines, 2019.

10.4229/EUPVSEC2025/4AO.9.6

SOLAÏS

Addressing Glare Problematics For Photovoltaic Projects In The Immediate Proximity Of Roads And Railways Through The Use Of Accurate Digital Surface Models

Christophe Vernay, John Coutel, Aina Razanajao, Sébastien Pitaval

christophe.vernay@solais.fr

EU PVSEC 2025

SOLAÏS

solais.fr

ABOUT SOLAÏS

- Based near Nice, France
- Dedicated to PV since 2008
- +2000 studies in 18 countries
- 20 people

+15 years partnership with top ranked engineering research centers:

- Mines Paris – PSL
- O.I.E laboratory
- SciDoSol Research Chair

+16 scientific publications

Exclusive software developments

PV Development

FEASABILITY

LAYOUT

DESIGN

YIELD REPORTS

GLARE

SHADING | AGRI-PV

STORAGE

Construction & Operation

DEVELOPMENT
ASSISTANCE & COMMISSIONING

MONITORING
PERFORMANCE REPORTS

Expertise & Consulting

CONSULTING
DUE DILIGENCE | PM

LEGAL EXPERTISE

SOLAÏS

solais.fr

Rationale

- Solar glare studies requested by authorities for 15+ years regarding air traffic safety
- Solar glare study now required for ground-mounted PV plants close to roads and railways
- Need to properly account for ground elevation and near-shading

- Introducing DEM & DSM (Digital Elevation Modelling and Digital Surface Modelling)
- Glare use-case: 29-MWp ground-mounted PV plant close to a railway

solais.fr

DEM & DSM

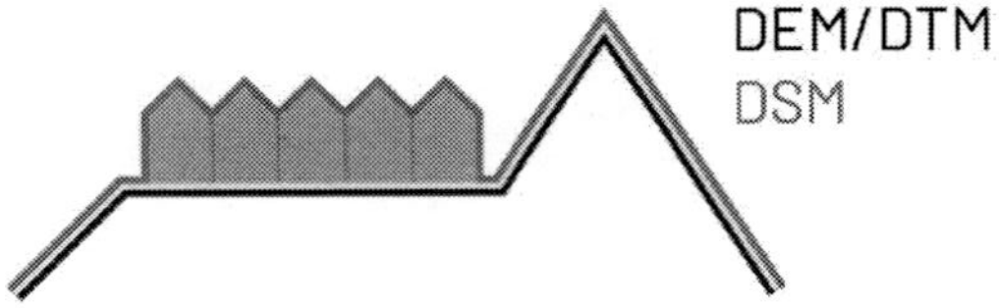

- Raster-based or vector-based to be used in GIS
- Elevation data for terrain (DEM/DTM) and surfaces (DSM)

- Trade-off depending on the usage: scale, availability, spatial resolution, vertical accuracy

Source: Schumann and Bates (2018)

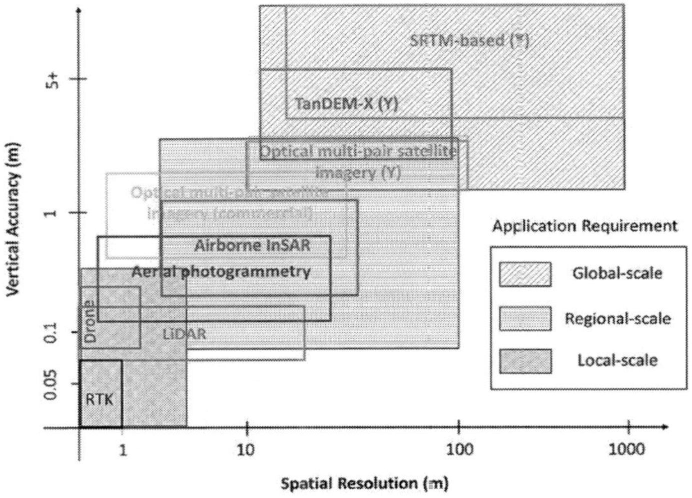

IGN's HD LiDAR availability in France (Sept. 2025)

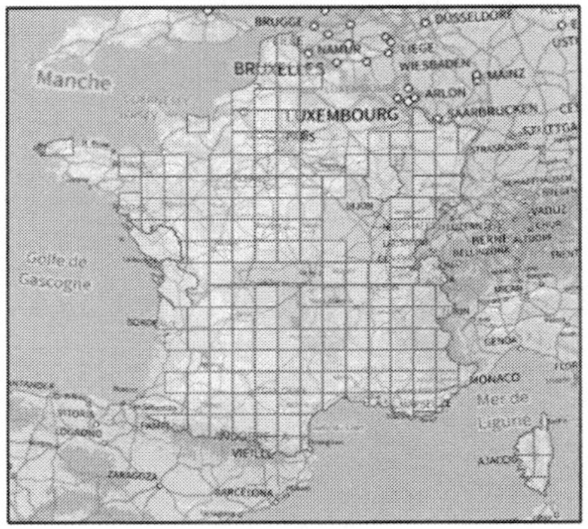

SOLAÏS

solais.fr

Solar glare modelling

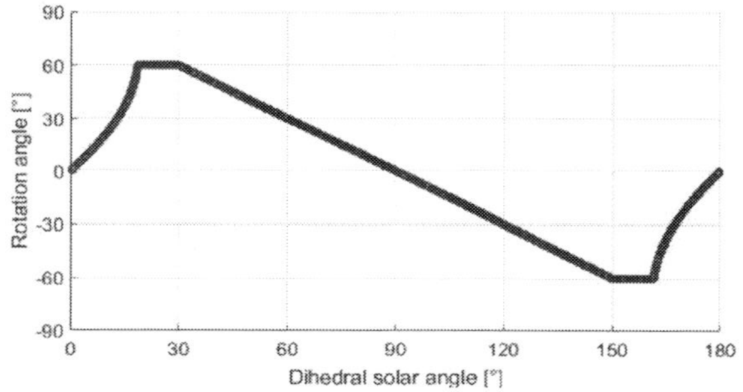

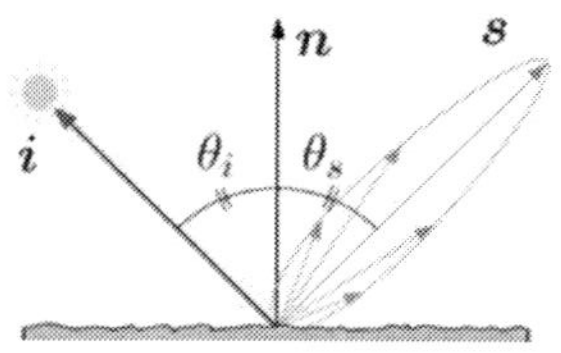

Source: Simonot L., Boulanguez P.

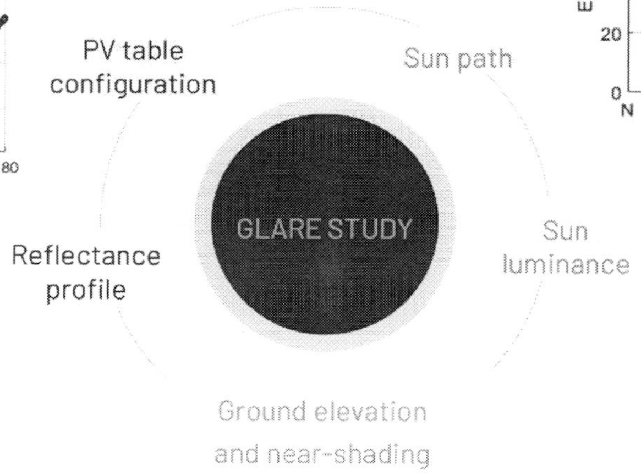

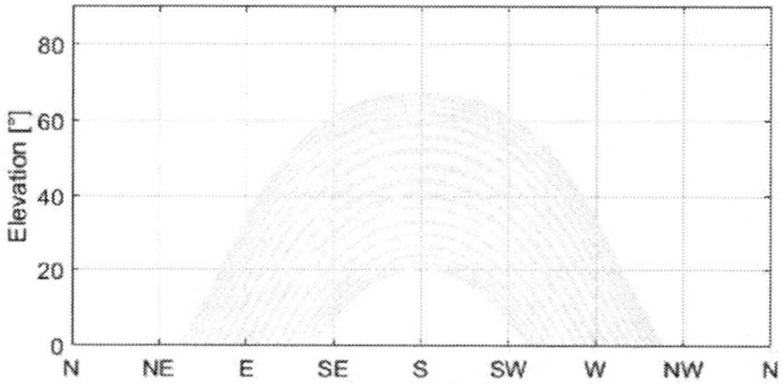

Source: Google

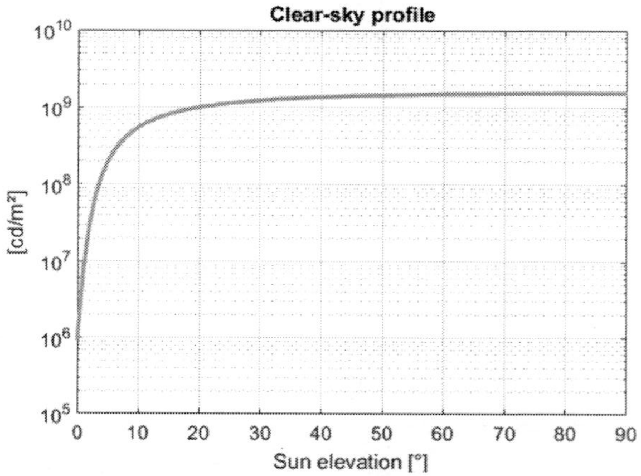

SOLAÏS

solais.fr

LiDAR vs. global elevation

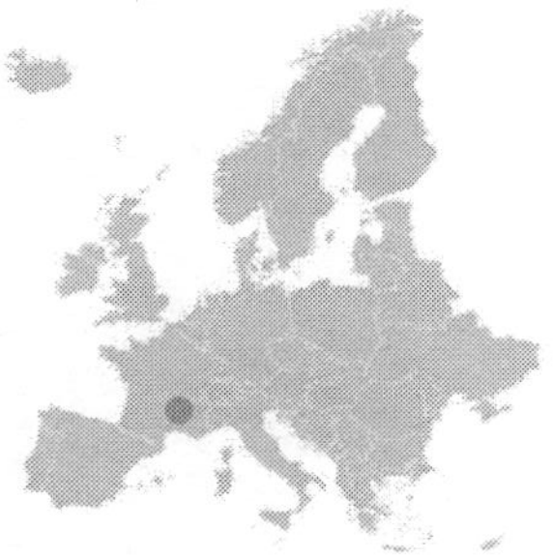

- Reference DEM computed from IGN's HD LiDAR data
- Elevation data extracted with Google's Elevation API
  - Global coverage, low prices

Source: Google

	Lowland	Valley
Data number	65536	194481
Reference elevation (m)	260.5	367.9
Mean bias error (m)	0.45	3.28
Mean absolute error (m)	1.13	4.02
Standard deviation (m)	1.84	5.75
Root mean square error (m)	1.90	6.62

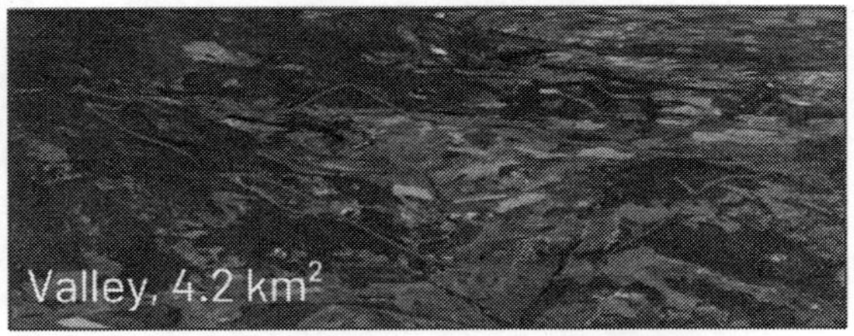

Source: Google

- RMSE > 6 m for this Valley → Inaccuracy in the glare simulations
- May be acceptable for other applications
- No information on Google's sources
- *Low representativity of these results for other sites*

SOLAÏS

solais.fr

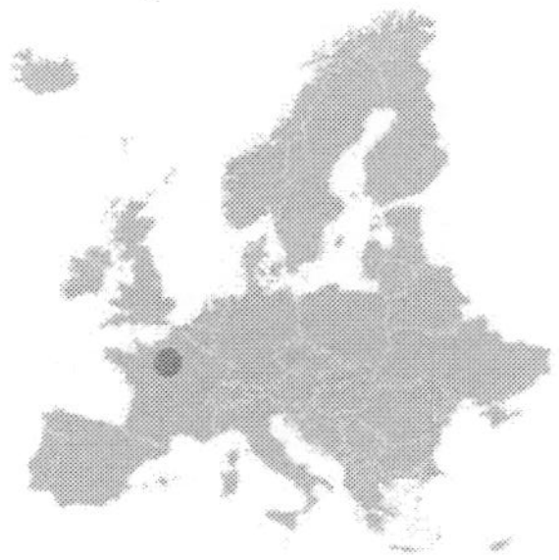

Use case

- Northern France / 16 ha / 29 MWp
- PV tables: southward, 17° tilt
- Building permit process started in early 2025

➢ Glare risk assessment for the train drivers coming from southeast

SOLAÏS

solais.fr

DEM and DSM

- Source: IGN's HD LiDAR
- Raw resolution: 50 cm

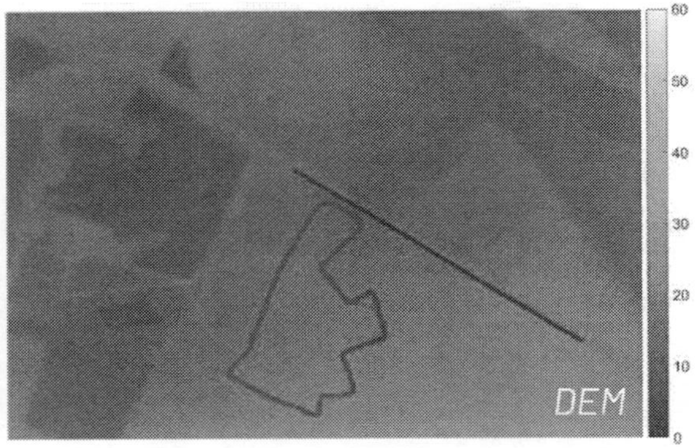

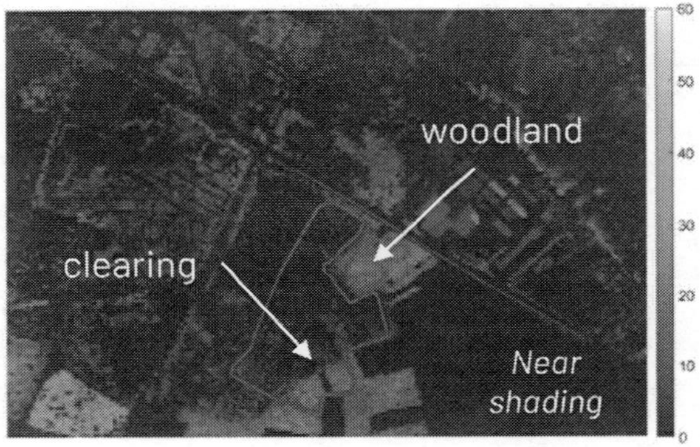

SOLAÏS

solais.fr

Spatial resolution in the simulation

1. Impact on computing time

2. Impact on the relevance of the results
   - Too coarse: inaccuracy on near-shading
   - Too fine: not representative to PV tables

➢ 10, 20 and 30 m are tested

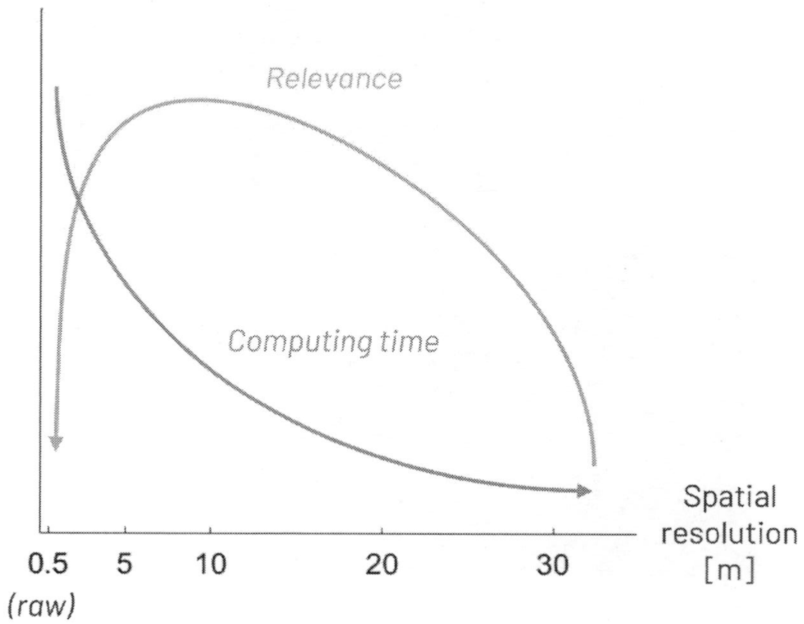

SOLAÏS

solais.fr

Glare results

Impacted trajectory and impacting PV areas

No impact with 5 m resolution

SOLAÏS

solais.fr

Glare results

Field of vision and timing

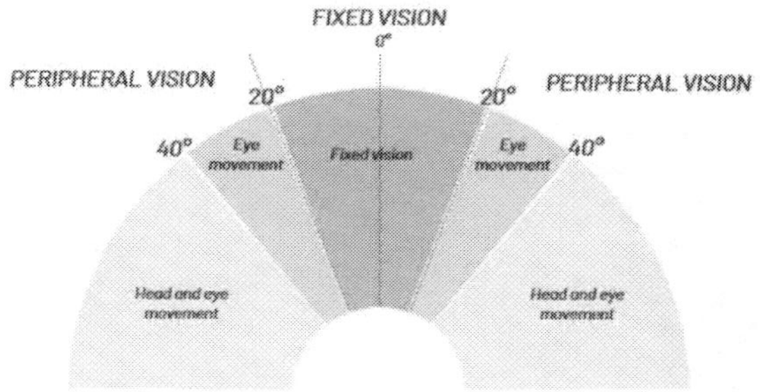

No impact on fixed vision

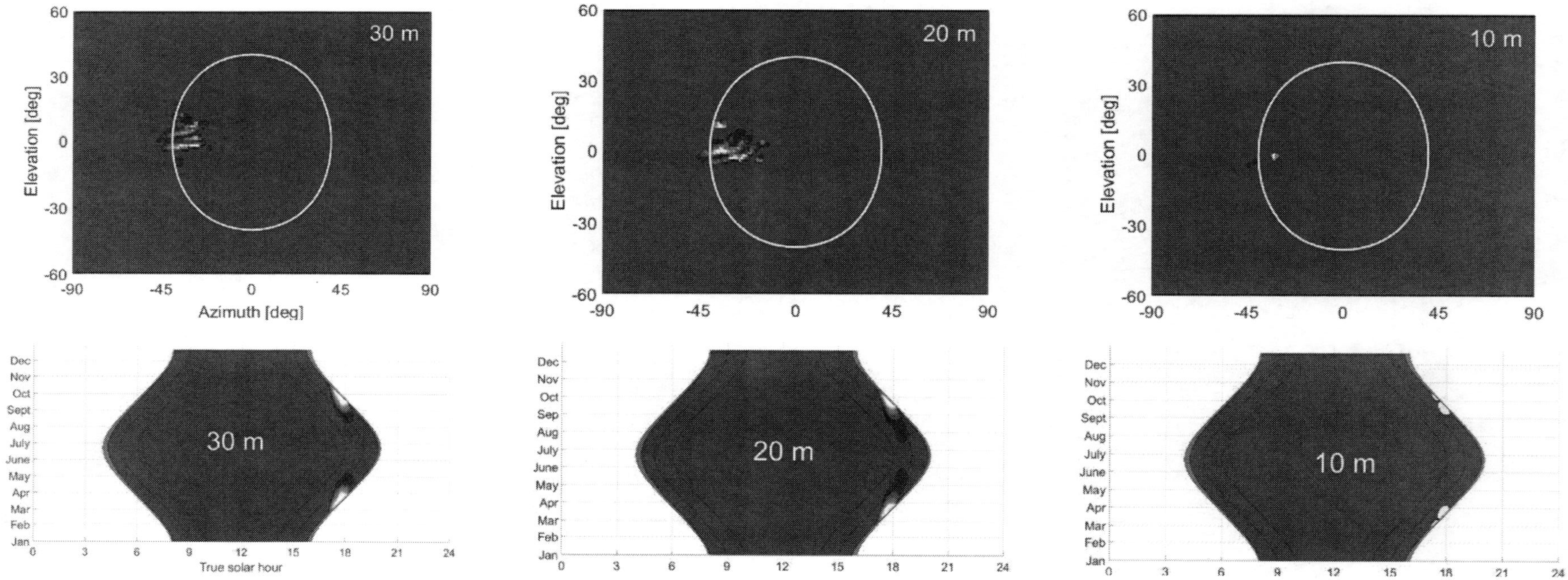

SOLAÏS

solais.fr

Conclusion

- Glare studies to be conducted in the PV development process
- Importance of working with accurate DEM and DSM
- 5-10 m resolution is preferred to mitigate the risk for mistaken occurrences

Thank you! Any questions?

solais.fr

SOLAÏS

PV Expertise & Consulting

Ecolucioles Bat. A1 – 955 route des Lucioles
06560 Valbonne – France

Contact : christophe.vernay@solais.fr

42nd European Photovoltaic Solar Energy Conference and Exhibition

This presentation was selected by the Sc. Committee of the EU PVSEC 2025 for submission of a full paper to one of the EU PVSEC's collaborating peer-reviewed journals.

MICRO-CONCENTRATOR PHOTOVOLTAICS FOR DEEP SPACE MISSIONS: OVERCOMING LILT CHALLENGES WITH HIGH-SPECIFIC-POWER SOLAR ARRAYS

Guido Vallerotto[1], Anderson Bermudez-Garcia[2], Gerald Siefer[3], Maike Wiesenfarth[3], Almudena Garcia-Sanchez[1], Ignacio Antón[1], Carsten Baur[4], Pier Luigi Coz[4] and César Domínguez[1]

[1] Instituto de Energía Solar, Universidad Politécnica de Madrid, Madrid, Spain
[2] R&D Solar Generators and Mechanisms, Thales Alenia Space, Cannes, France
[3] Division Photovoltaics, Fraunhofer Institute for Solar Energy Systems ISE, Freiburg, Germany
[4] Solar Generators Section, European Space Agency, Noordwijk, Netherlands

ABSTRACT: Exploration of the outer solar system is one of the European Space Agency (ESA) top scientific priorities, as defined in the Voyage 2050 program. Micro-concentrator photovoltaics (micro-CPV) are gaining attention as a viable approach to power spacecrafts operating in deep space, where conventional solar arrays may suffer severe drops in performance due to low-intensity, low-temperature (LILT) conditions. This study reports on the design, development, and testing of two novel micro-CPV solar panel architectures optimized for maximizing specific power beyond Mars orbit and for being compatible with the standard 5° angular accuracy of spacecraft attitude control: first, a silicone-on-glass (SoG) Fresnel microlens array and, second, a catadioptric concentrator that combines refraction with total internal reflection (TIR). Optical simulations indicate that the Fresnel concept delivers higher efficiency and lower mass, while the catadioptric design offers superior angular tolerance and alignment stability. Initial Fresnel prototypes were fabricated and characterized, achieving 83–85% optical efficiency, +/-5° acceptance angle, +/-1.5 mm focal distance tolerance and excellent uniformity across the 72 lenses in the array. These findings confirm both the feasibility and manufacturability of micro-CPV technology, which is expected to surpass the specific power of conventional cell-interconnected-cover (CIC) arrays for the next large scientific missions of ESA to the outer solar system.

Keywords: concentrator photovoltaics (CPV), low intensity low temperature (LILT), Fresnel lens concentrator, catadioptric concentrator.

1 INTRODUCTION

Exploration of the outer solar system is one of the European Space Agency (ESA) top scientific priorities, as defined in the Voyage 2050 program. Missions to the icy moons of Jupiter and Saturn to investigate the habitability and to find signs of past or present life are one of the main themes of the program. Going further than 4 astronomical units (AU), the low light intensity and low irradiance (LILT) conditions represent a critical challenge for deep space missions, as the state-of-the-art space qualified multi-junction (MJ) solar cells can exhibit serious performance degradation under these LILT conditions due to majority carrier barriers [1], forcing oversized and heavier solar arrays.

Concentrator photovoltaics (CPV) has the potential to mitigate this effect by increasing the effective irradiance on the cells, thereby raising operating temperature, reducing semiconductor area, and improving radiation shielding. Previous missions, such as NASA's Deep Space 1 (SCARLET array) [2–4], validated CPV in space but relied on bulky optics with limited compactness.

Micro-concentrator photovoltaics (micro-CPV), using sub-mm cells and moderate concentration ratios (10X–100X), have recently emerged as a transformative approach. Theoretical estimates show that micro-CPV systems can exceed 350 W/kg [5,6], compared to 100–200 W/kg of conventional cover-interconnect-cell (CIC) technology [7]. This work presents two micro-CPV architectures tailored for ESA deep-space missions to Jupiter and Saturn: a refractive Fresnel microlens array and a catadioptric design combining refraction and total internal reflection (TIR).

2 MODULE ARCHITECTURE

The proposed module architecture replaces the conventional CIC layers on a honeycomb substrate with a micro-CPV assembly consisting of a matrix of sub-millimeter solar cells coupled to an optical concentrator array. This approach ensures compatibility with standard deployment systems while enabling a fair comparison in terms of specific power.

Key design requirements were established to guarantee suitability for deep-space missions:

- Maximization of specific power (W/kg) at the end of life (EOL) under Jupiter and Saturn irradiance levels (3% and 1% of the AM0 spectrum, respectively).
- Angular tolerance of at least ±5° to accommodate typical spacecraft attitude control.
- Total thickness below 5 mm to remain compatible with existing solar array wings.
- Resilience against thermal cycling, radiation, high-energy particles, and micrometeoroid impact.

Following a trade-off analysis of different optical candidates, two refractive concepts were selected for development: a silicone-on-glass (SoG) Fresnel microlens array and a catadioptric unit combining refraction and TIR. The Fresnel design benefits from low weight, thin profile, high optical efficiency, and extensive flight heritage. The catadioptric system, although more complex, offers improved angular tolerance and enhanced alignment robustness. Figure 1 shows a scheme of the two proposed architectures.

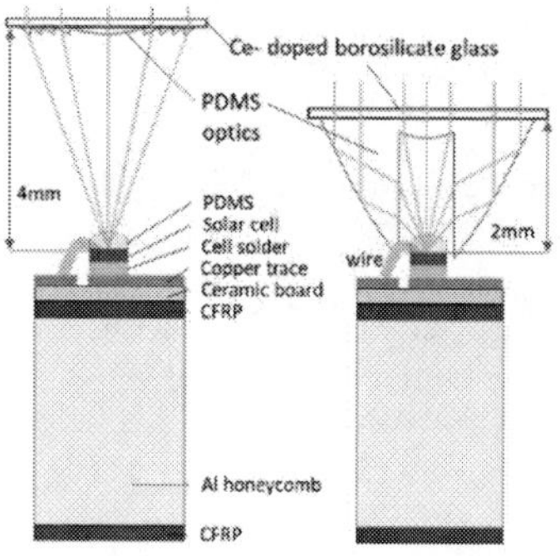

Figure 1: Scheme of the proposed structure of the two architectures presented in this work. The Fresnel version on the left and the catadioptric on the right.

The materials for both concentrator designs were selected from space-qualified options. Schott 0787 cerium-doped borosilicate glass was chosen as the cover glass, while Dowsil (Dow Corning) DC 93-500 silicone was adopted as the moldable material to form the refractive surfaces. Both materials feature extensive flight heritage and long-term reliability in space applications.

3 OPTICAL DESIGN

The optical aperture of both architectures was defined in close connection with the optimization of the solar cell dimensions. Space-qualified triple and quadruple junction (3J and 4J) devices of different sub-millimeter sizes were characterized under LILT conditions in a cryostat with two main objectives: to evaluate efficiency losses caused by edge recombination in cells with high perimeter-to-area ratios under low irradiance, and to determine the minimum operating temperature required to avoid degradation due to majority carrier barrier effects. The results showed that a cell diameter of 0.8 mm (0.5 mm^2 active area) represents the optimal compromise: small enough to reduce semiconductor mass and maximize specific power, large enough to limit perimeter related recombination losses. Regarding temperature, −137 °C was identified as the lowest point at which cells operating under low irradiance (~14 W/m^2) remain unaffected by majority carrier barrier effects. Considering an environmental temperature below -150 °C we estimate that an effective concentration of 10X is sufficient to raise the cell operating temperature near this limit. Assuming a realistic optical efficiency of approximately 80%, this corresponds to a geometrical concentration of 12X and an optical aperture area of ~6 mm^2. To avoid the aperture losses typically associated with circular optics the optical array has been designed with hexagonal lenses with 1.52 mm diameter of the circumscribed circumference.

3.1 Design optimization

The two designs were modeled and optimized for the maximum efficiency and angular tolerance using a commercial 3D ray-tracing software. For the Fresnel architecture the main optimization parameters are the height of the Fresnel facets and the focal distance of the lens (*i.e.* the f-number) while for the catadioptric the aperture of the inner cavity. Considering the mentioned design constraints for the Fresnel lens the focal distance was set to the maximum value of 4 mm to maximize the efficiency and the facets height to 50 μm based on mold manufacturers' feedback and a trade-off between minimizing tip rounding losses and reducing lens volume and weight.

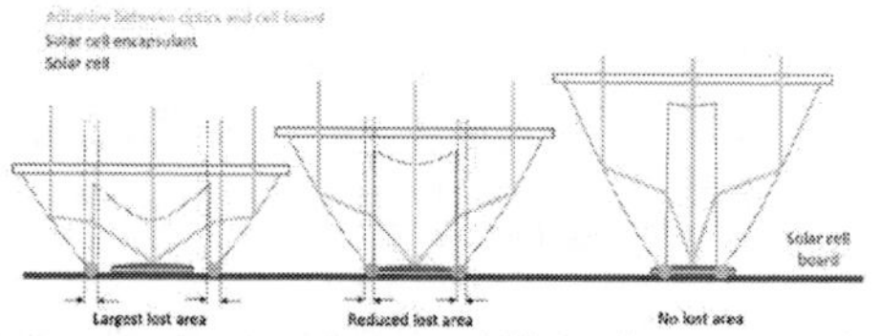

Figure 2: Sketches of three possible configurations of the catadioptric architecture. Note that the figure is not in scale and it is purely qualitative.

For the catadioptric the nominal design matches the solar cell diameter to the cavity aperture (Figure 2, center). Increasing the aperture results in a shorter, more compact system, but rays incident on the peaks are lost (Figure 2, left). Decreasing the aperture recovers these rays but increases the volume, the weight and the absorption losses resulting from an increased optical path length (Figure 2, right). Seven apertures, from 0.7 mm to 0.9 mm, were simulated to evaluate the sensitivity of acceptance angle and optical efficiency and 0.9 mm resulted to be the optimum solution.

On the optimized design Two simulation sets were conducted for each optical architecture:

1. **Operational condition simulations:** Using the refractive index of DC 93-500 silicone at -190 °C and a 1% AM0 spectrum to emulate deep-space LILT conditions.
2. **Room temperature simulations:** Based on the refractive index at 25 °C, to predict the performance of prototypes to be tested under laboratory conditions (using the Helios 3198 CPV solar simulator available at the Solar Energy Institute [8]).

The first set serves to validate the suitability of each design for deep-space applications. However, given that initial prototypes will be fabricated and tested at room temperature, the second set is critical for assessing expected performance in upcoming experimental campaigns.

It is important to note that LILT-condition simulations assume an idealized optic geometry (*i.e.*, the nominal profile derived from design procedure), without accounting for deformations due to thermal contraction. In reality, the optics will be manufactured at room temperature and subsequently experience severe temperature changes in space. As such, the mold must be pre-compensated to account for expected shrinkage and ensure that the operational profile matches the design.

To evaluate this, a preliminary finite element modeling (FEM) simulation was performed on the Fresnel lens geometry. The results indicate that, in the absence of mold compensation, efficiency losses at -190 °C may become significant.

Figure 3 summarizes the key outcomes of the ray-tracing simulations. Note that the simulation model include spectral material properties, Fresnel reflection, and non-ideality caused by the manufacturing process (*i.e.* draft angles for mold release and rounding of tips and valley of the lens profile).

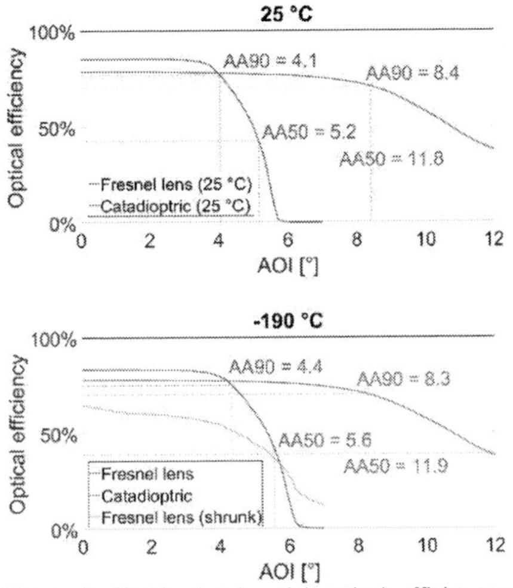

Figure 3: Graph showing the optical efficiency as a function of the angle of incidence (AOI) for the Fresnel lens and the catadioptric at room temperature (up) and at -190 °C (bottom). In yellow, the optical efficiency for Fresnel lens at -190 °C if no mold compensation is made.

The blue and red curves correspond to the optical efficiency versus angle of incidence (AOI) for the Fresnel and catadioptric designs, respectively. The upper plot shows results at room temperature, while the lower refers to −190 °C. At normal incidence, the Fresnel lens achieves higher efficiency thanks to lower absorption, but beyond ±4° the catadioptric outperform the Fresnel lens. As anticipated, when considering ideal geometries, at both room (upper graph) and cryogenic (bottom graph) temperatures the curves overlap closely, indicating that with appropriate mold compensation the optical performance at LILT should remain similar to that at ambient conditions.

The figure also reports the acceptance angles for the 90% and the 50% of the maximum power (AA90 and AA50, respectively) for both configurations. The yellow curve in Figure 3 (bottom) represents the Fresnel profile after thermal shrinkage at −190 °C, simulated via FEM. In this case, even under perfect alignment, the efficiency decreases from ~85% to ~65%.

Due to its more complex optical path and bulkier geometry, the catadioptric system is expected to experience comparable or greater efficiency losses at cryogenic temperatures, although dedicated FEM simulations are still required to quantify them. Overall, the results highlight that mold compensation is an essential design measure to ensure reliable optical performance in deep-space environments

4 MANUFACTURING AND CHARACTERIZATION

The first prototypes of the Fresnel microlens array were manufactured using the Dow Corning DC 93-500 silicone directly molded onto Schott 0787 borosilicate substrates with 150 μm thickness. The mold was produced via precision micromachining, ensuring groove depths of 50 μm with controlled surface quality. A degassing step was applied before curing to eliminate trapped air bubbles, and curing was carried out under vacuum conditions.

The mold designed consists of an array of 8×9 individual lenses arranged on a 20x20 mm² tile, corresponding to a total of 72 optical units.

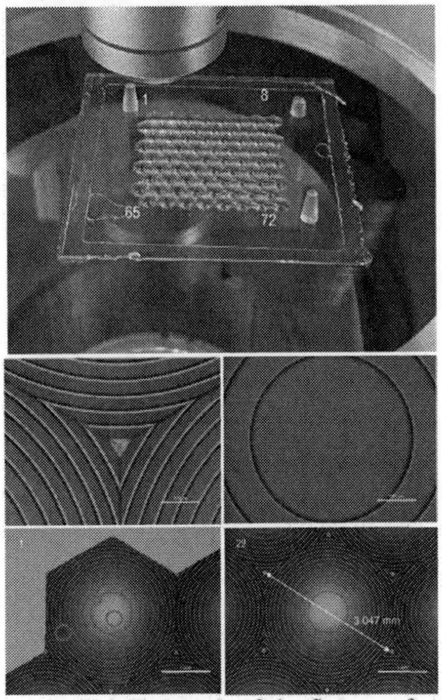

Figure 4: (Up) Photograph of the first manufactured prototype of the Fresnel architecture. (Bottom) photographs taken with an optical microscope of one lens of the manufactured prototype.

Figure 4 show a photograph of the manufactured array on the left and some sample pictures taken with an optical microscope on the right. Microscopic inspection of the cured arrays confirmed accurate reproduction of the mold geometry across most of the surface, with only minor imperfections at the edges. These defects have negligible impact on the overall optical performance, as confirmed by subsequent characterization.

Optical characterization was carried out using the solar simulator Helios 3198 for CPV modules [8], which provides collimated and spectrally matched AM0-like illumination. The array was mounted on a high-precision automated three axis moving platform, allowing fine control of both lateral displacement and cell-to-lens distance. In addition, the optical setup is mounted over an automated rotary stage allowing the cell-lens system to rotate with respect to the direction of the collimated light source.

Figure 5 shows a scheme and a photograph of the experimental setup. The measurement procedure is as follow: first, the current generated by the bare solar cell is measured. Then, the cell is moved behind each lens composing the array, and the current is measured individually for each lens. Finally, knowing the lens aperture it is possible to calculate the optical efficiency of each lens using the formula:

$$\eta_{opti} = \frac{I_{sc,lens} / I_{sc,bare}}{A_{lens} / A_{cell}} = \frac{X_{eff}}{X_{geo}} \qquad (1)$$

where $I_{sc,lens}$ and $I_{sc,bare}$ are the currents generated by the solar cell with and without optics, respectively. A_{lens} and A_{cell} are the aperture area of the lens and the solar cell. Therefore, the first ratio represents the effective concentration (X_{eff}), that is the increase in the effective irradiance over the solar cell, and the second ratio represents the geometrical concentration (X_{geo}).

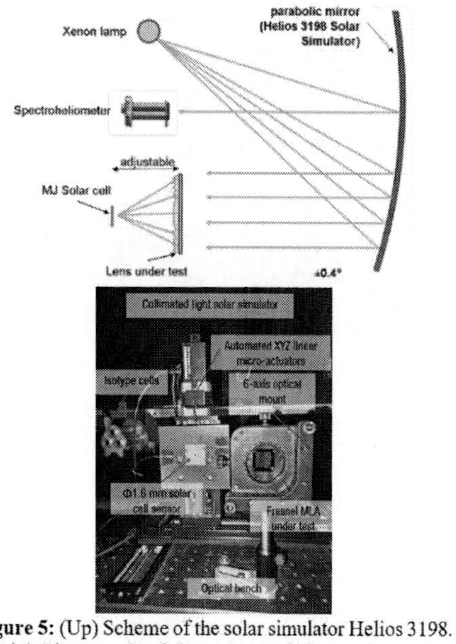

Figure 5: (Up) Scheme of the solar simulator Helios 3198. (Right) Photograph of the automated three-axis moving platform used to align solar sensor and optics during characterization.

Solar cells with a nominal lens aperture of 0.5 mm² were not available at the time of the measurement campaign. Therefore, to evaluate the performance of the optics at the nominal geometrical concentration (*i.e.*, 12X), a copper mask with a 0.8 mm diameter pinhole was used to reduce the sensor active area and characterize the optical system.

Two main issues arose. First, it was impossible to precisely measure the exact aperture area of the pinhole. Second, a light sensor with such a small active surface is highly sensitive to minor defects on the collimating mirror surface. While these defects are negligible when using a larger sensor, since the light is integrated over a wider aperture, they can produce significant variations in measured irradiance when using a smaller sensor, where even millimetric displacements can affect the result.

To minimize these sources of uncertainty, the optical array was scanned using a larger solar cell (2.3 mm diameter), and the photocurrent was measured at 72 positions corresponding to each lens in the array. The same scan was then repeated with the solar cell masked by the 0.8 mm pinhole. By dividing the average photocurrent obtained with the bare and masked cell, the effective ratio between the solar cell aperture and the pinhole aperture was estimated. Subsequently, the reference current used to calculate X_{eff} in Equation (1) was determined by dividing the photocurrent of the 2.3 mm solar cell (less sensitive to mirror imperfections) by this ratio.

With this method, the calculated efficiency becomes independent of the pinhole aperture, while the influence of surface defects is mitigated by using a sensor whose size remains only slightly smaller than the lens aperture.

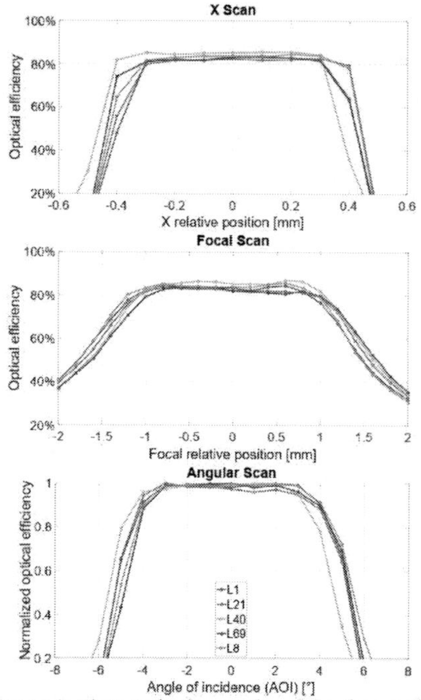

Figure 6: Characterization results of the five randomly selected lenses. X scan is in the direction parallel to the lens plane. Focal scan is in the direction perpendicular to the lens plane and the angular scan is obtained by rotating the whole system with respect to the collimating mirror.

Due to the time-consuming iterative procedure required to correctly align the solar cell and the optics, only five randomly chosen lenses of the array were fully characterized.

Figure 6 shows the results of the characterization. The measured optical efficiency of 83–85% is in close agreement with the ray-tracing predictions. Alignment tolerance was investigated by intentionally offsetting the lens array with respect to the detector: lateral displacements up to ±0.3 mm and axial displacements up to ±1 mm caused negligible efficiency demonstrating robust alignment margins for integration at module level loss (see Figure 6 up and center). Finally, the acceptance angle measured at 50% efficiency (AA50) is approximately ±5° (Figure 6, bottom), perfectly matching with simulation results. Note that the five measured lenses show highly similar performance suggesting a good uniformity of the quality of the lenses composing the array.

In order to know the optical quality of all the lenses composing the array a larger solar cell of 1.6 mm diameter is used to ease the alignment procedure. Because of the lower geometrical concentration (~3X) the absolute efficiency value measured with this cell is not representative of the system but may be used to assess the uniformity of the quality of the lenses. Figure 7 shows the optical efficiency of the 72 measured lenses normalized with the maximum value.

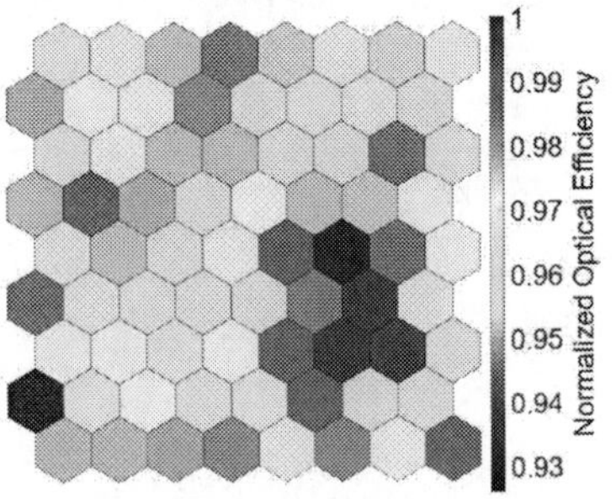

Figure 7: Normalized optical efficiency measured for the 72 lenses composing the first manufactured array. A colormap is used to show the efficiency of each lens together with its position within the array.

It can be noted that there is good consistency among the lenses composing the array (standard deviation equal to 1.2%). However, from this map, it is evident that a higher efficiency region is concentrated in the lower-right part of the array. Further work is needed to determine whether this is a measurement artifact or a real pattern, and if confirmed, to identify its underlying cause.

Although only Fresnel microlens arrays were fabricated at this stage, the catadioptric concept is following a similar development path, with future prototypes expected to provide a direct comparison between both designs.

7 CONCLUSIONS

This study reports the design, fabrication, and initial validation of two micro-concentrator photovoltaic (micro-CPV) concepts tailored for deep-space applications. Targeting the combined challenges of low irradiance and cryogenic environments beyond 4 AU, the results highlight micro-CPV as a promising high-specific-power solution for future missions.

Two optical approaches were proposed, which were optimized for maximizing specific power beyond Mars orbit and for being compatible with the standard 5° angular accuracy of spacecraft attitude control: a Fresnel microlens array and a catadioptric system, both built with space-qualified materials. Ray-tracing simulation modeling was used to optimize both optical designs showing that the Fresnel architecture achieves higher efficiency and lower mass at normal incidence, whereas the catadioptric design offers broader angular tolerance and stronger alignment robustness.

The first Fresnel array prototype was successfully manufactured and characterized. The resulting optical efficiencies at the nominal geometrical concentration of 12X is in the range of 83–85%, +/-5° acceptance angle, +/-1.5 mm focal distance tolerance and excellent uniformity across the 72 lenses in the array, closely matching simulations and confirming the design's manufacturability. These findings confirm both the feasibility and manufacturability of micro-CPV technology.

Overall, the work positions micro-CPV as a competitive alternative to conventional cover-interconnect-cell (CIC) technology, with the potential to surpass the specific power of conventional cell-interconnected-cover (CIC) arrays. Future efforts will address full module integration, thermal management, and in-orbit validation, consolidating micro-CPV as an enabling option for upcoming ESA deep-space missions.

A full paper with an extended dissertation of this work is currently under revision in the journal RRL Solar.

REFERENCES

[1] R. Hoheisel *et al.*, "Low temperature effects in photovoltaic devices for deep space missions," in *2015 IEEE 42nd Photovoltaic Specialist Conference (PVSC)*, 2015, pp. 1–5, doi: 10.1109/PVSC.2015.7355666.

[2] J. J. Wachholz *et al.*, "SCARLET I: Mechanization Solutions for Deployable Concentrator Optics Integrated with Rigid Array Technology." 1996.

[3] D. M. Murphy *et al.*, "SCARLET development, fabrication, and testing for the Deep Space 1 spacecraft," in *IECEC-97 Proceedings of the Thirty-Second Intersociety Energy Conversion Engineering Conference*, 1997, vol. 4, pp. 2237–2245, doi: 10.1109/IECEC.1997.658216.

[4] D. M. Murphy, "The Scarlet Solar Array: Technology Validation and Flight Results." AEC-Able Engineering Co., Inc, Pasadena, CA, 2000, [Online]. Available: http://www.aec-able.com.

[5] J. S. Price *et al.*, "High-Concentration Planar Microtracking Photovoltaic System Exceeding 30% Efficiency," *Nat. Energy*, vol. 2, no. 8, p. 17113, 2017, doi: 10.1038/nenergy.2017.113.

[6] L. Li *et al.*, "Highly-integrated Hybrid Micro-Concentrating Photovoltaics," in *2018 IEEE 7th World Conference on Photovoltaic Energy Conversion (WCPEC)*, 2018, pp. 1655–1657, doi: 10.1109/PVSC.2018.8547904.

[7] C. J. Ruud *et al.*, "Microcell concentrating photovoltaics for space," *Joule*, vol. 7, no. 6, pp. 1093–1098, 2023, doi: 10.1016/j.joule.2023.04.004.

[8] C. Dominguez *et al.*, "Solar simulator for indoor characterization of large area high-concentration PV modules," in *2008 33rd IEEE Photovolatic Specialists Conference*, San Diego, CA, USA, May 2008, pp. 1–5, doi: 10.1109/PVSC.2008.4922739.

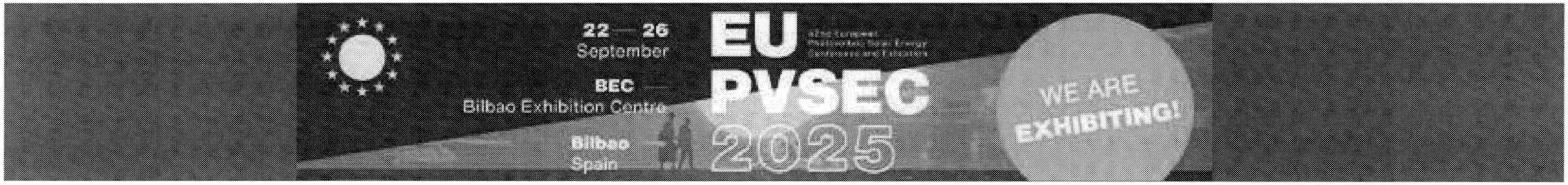

Micro-concentrator photovoltaics for deep space missions: overcoming LILT challenges with high-specific-power solar arrays

Guido Vallerotto
Almudena Garcia-Sanchez
Ignacio Antón
César Domínguez

INSTITUTO DE ENERGÍA SOLAR
POLITÉCNICA

Anderson Bermudez-Garcia

ThalesAlenia Space
a Thales / Leonardo company

Gerald Siefer
Maike Wiesenfarth

Fraunhofer ISE

Carsten Baur
Pier Luigi Coz

esa

Context

INSTITUTO DE ENERGÍA SOLAR

Powering up large-class European Space Agency (ESA) deep space missions up to mid-21st century (2035-2050)

Moons of the giant planets

- Liquid water
- Source of energy
- Chemical elements

Enceladus – credit: ESA

POLITÉCNICA

Context

INSTITUTO DE ENERGÍA SOLAR

Powering up large-class European Space Agency (ESA) deep space missions up to mid-21st century (2035-2050)

Moons of the giant planets

- Liquid water
- Source of energy
- Chemical elements

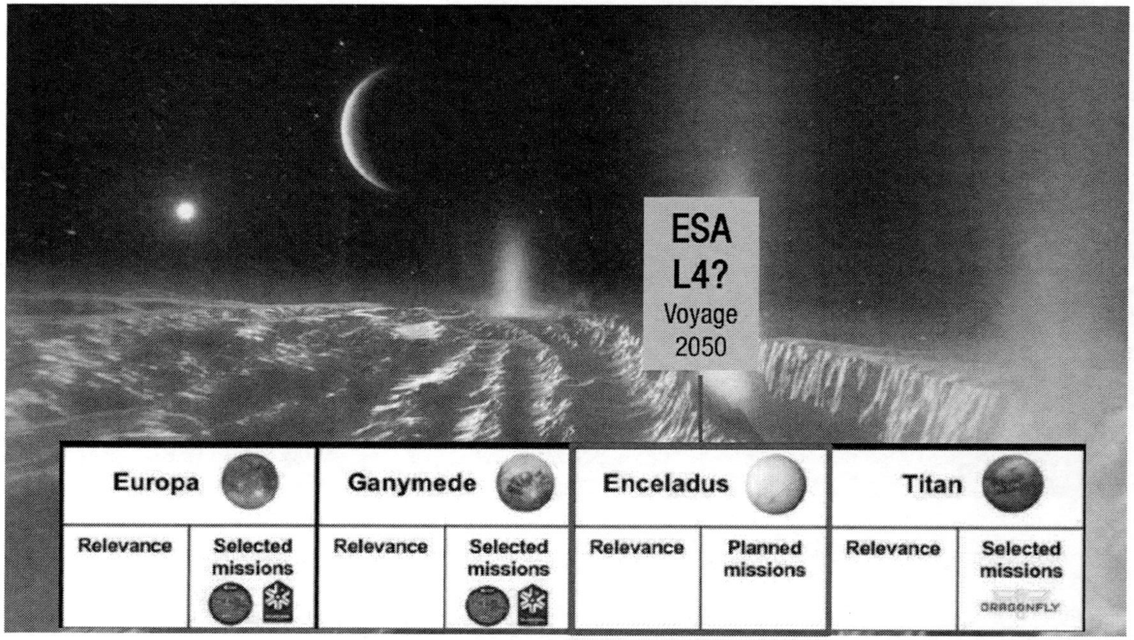

Enceladus – credit: ESA

POLITÉCNICA

Challenges of LILT conditions

INSTITUTO DE ENERGÍA SOLAR

- **What is the main challenge for deep space missions (> 4 AU)?**
  - Extremely low light intensity and temperature (LILT) → 1-3% AM0, < -150°

JUICE spacecraft features **85 m²** of solar arrays (3J solar cells) delivering only **800-850 W** in the proximity of **Jupiter**

In **Saturn**, for the same delivered power the solar array should be approximately **250 m²**

POLITÉCNICA

Challenges of LILT conditions

INSTITUTO DE ENERGÍA SOLAR

- **What is the main challenge for deep space missions (> 4 AU)?**
  - Extremely low light intensity and temperature (LILT) → 1-3% AM0, < -150°

Efficiency drop of state-of-the-art 3J/4J cells at low T

⇩

Concentrator Photovoltaic (CPV) technology can potentially mitigate this effect by increasing the effective irradiance reaching the cell

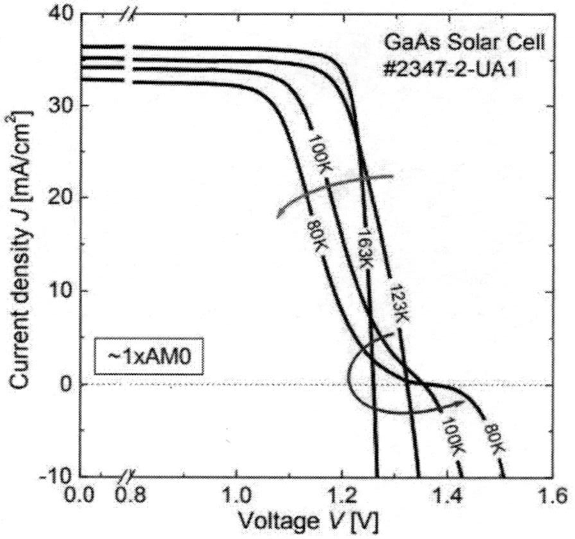

Hoheisel, "Low temperature effects in photovoltaic devices for deep space missions," in *2015 IEEE 42nd Photovoltaic Specialist Conference*

POLITÉCNICA

CPV space heritage

INSTITUTO DE ENERGÍA SOLAR

- **Has CPV technology been tested in space?**
  - In 1994 the **PASP Plus experiment** was launched: 16 cell modules flying for 1 year.

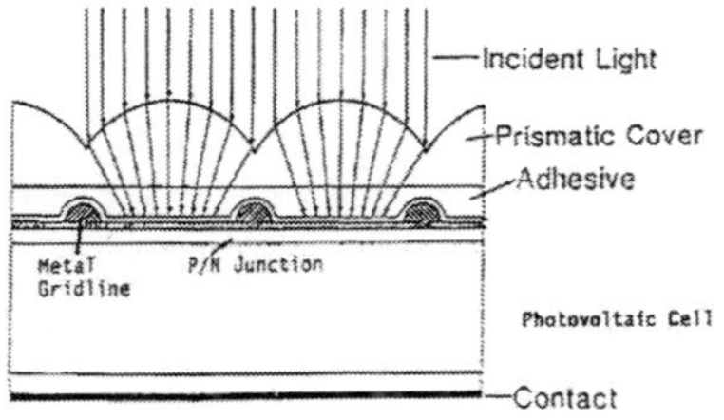

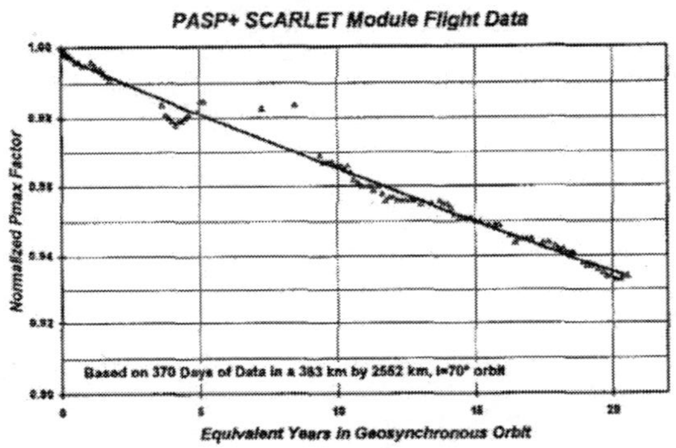

- High performance (efficiency 20% AM0)
- Lowest degradation (7% in one year) than any other **bare** solar cell technology

POLITÉCNICA

Requirements for deep space missions

INSTITUTO DE ENERGÍA SOLAR

- **What are the requirements of a solar array for deep space missions?**

High specific power (W/kg)

Low stowed volume (m^3/W)

Mitigation of LILT conditions

Conventional CPV

Bulky optics

High focal distance and volume

↓

Micro-CPV

Reduced dust / particle radiation damage

High EOL efficiency

High voltage for SEP

POLITÉCNICA

Potential benefits of micro-CPV

INSTITUTO DE ENERGÍA SOLAR

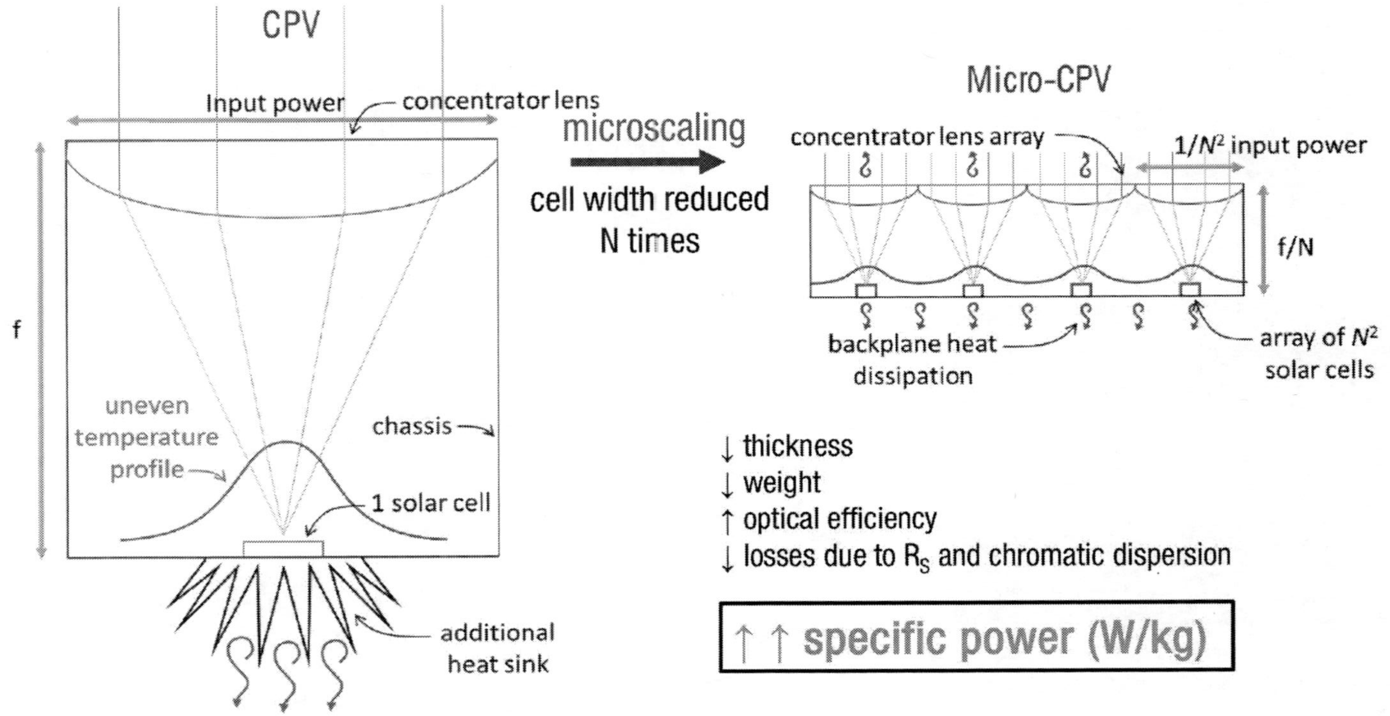

↓ thickness
↓ weight
↑ optical efficiency
↓ losses due to R_S and chromatic dispersion

↑ ↑ specific power (W/kg)

POLITÉCNICA

Micro-CPV space heritage

INSTITUTO DE ENERGÍA SOLAR

- Pioneers of micro-CPV for space:
  - US Naval Research Laboratory / Semprius: 30% eff., 14X, >5° AA
  - JAXA: 2.3 & 3X refractive μ-CPV on SHARP's InGaP/GaAs/Ge 3J cells

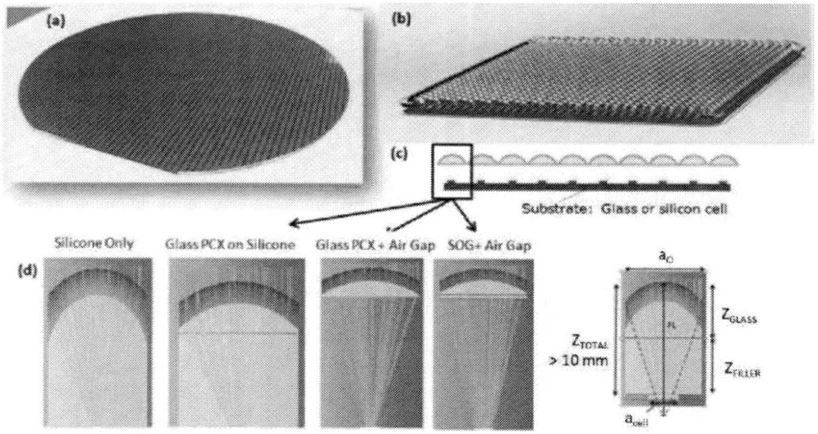

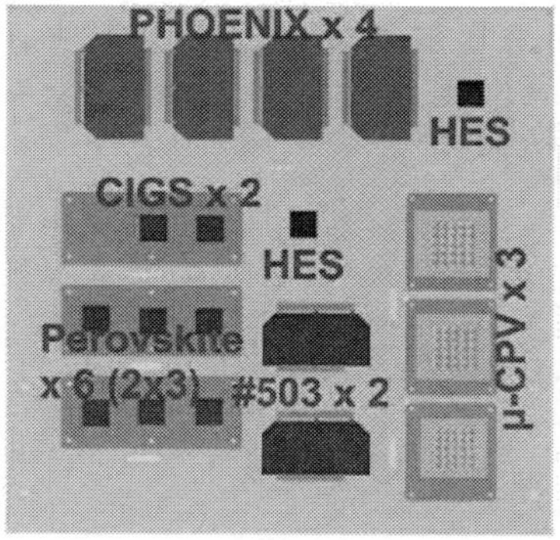

POLITÉCNICA

A new European endeavor

INSTITUTO DE ENERGÍA SOLAR

Proof-of-concept CPV module optimized for missions to Jupiter, Saturn and beyond

Objectives:

- 10X concentrator with moderate angular tolerance (>5°) and low thickness
- Compatible with existing solar array wing architectures
- Able to avoid LILT performance drop

POLITÉCNICA

Proposed architectures

INSTITUTO DE ENERGÍA SOLAR

Immersed two-stage

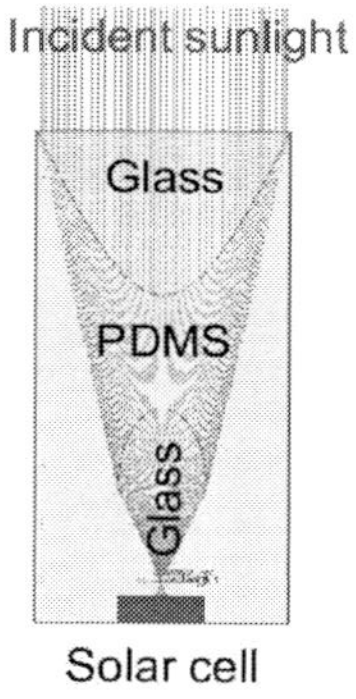

Catadioptric

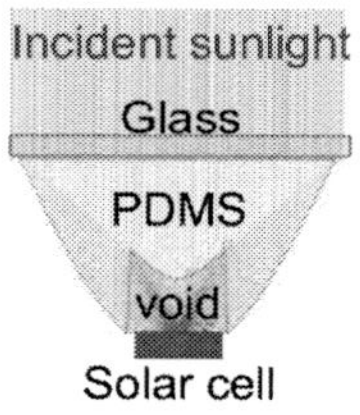

Fresnel lens

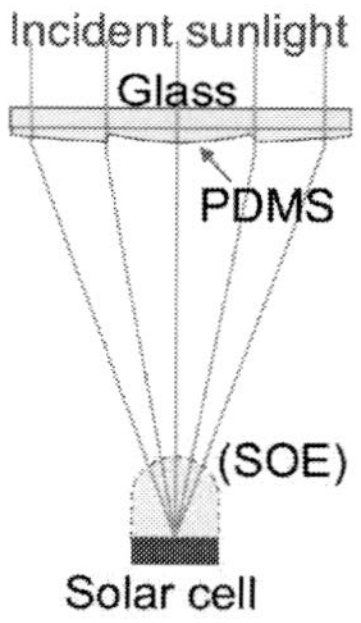

Aspheric lens

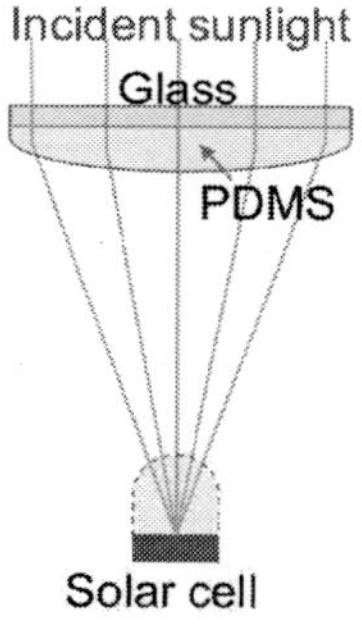

POLITÉCNICA

Proposed architectures

INSTITUTO DE ENERGÍA SOLAR

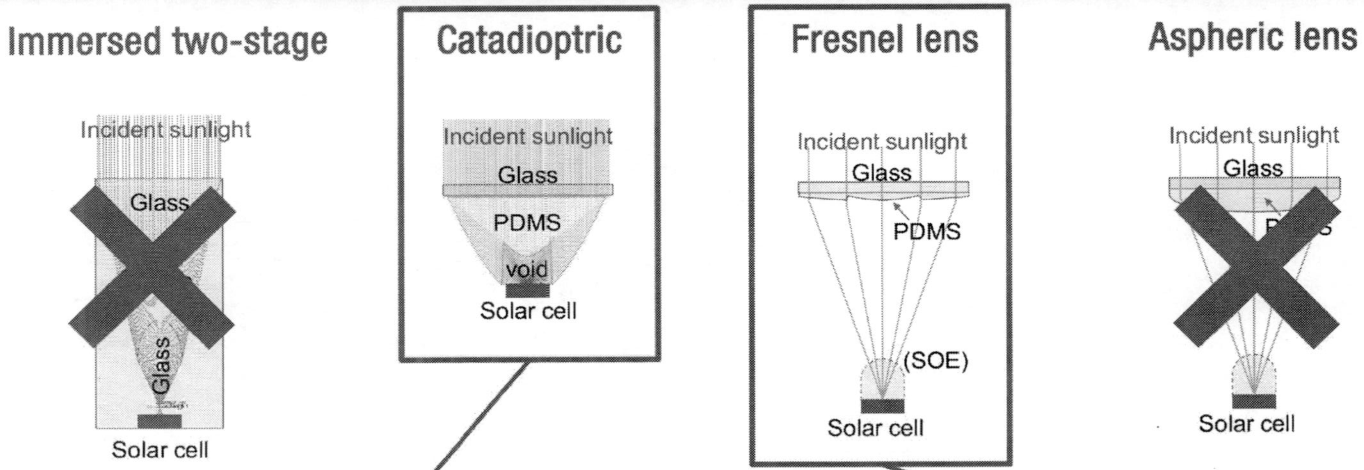

High angular tolerance and alignment stability

High optical efficiency and low weight

POLITÉCNICA

Proposed architectures

INSTITUTO
DE ENERGÍA
SOLAR

Conventional cell-interconnect-cover (CIC) on honeycomb technology

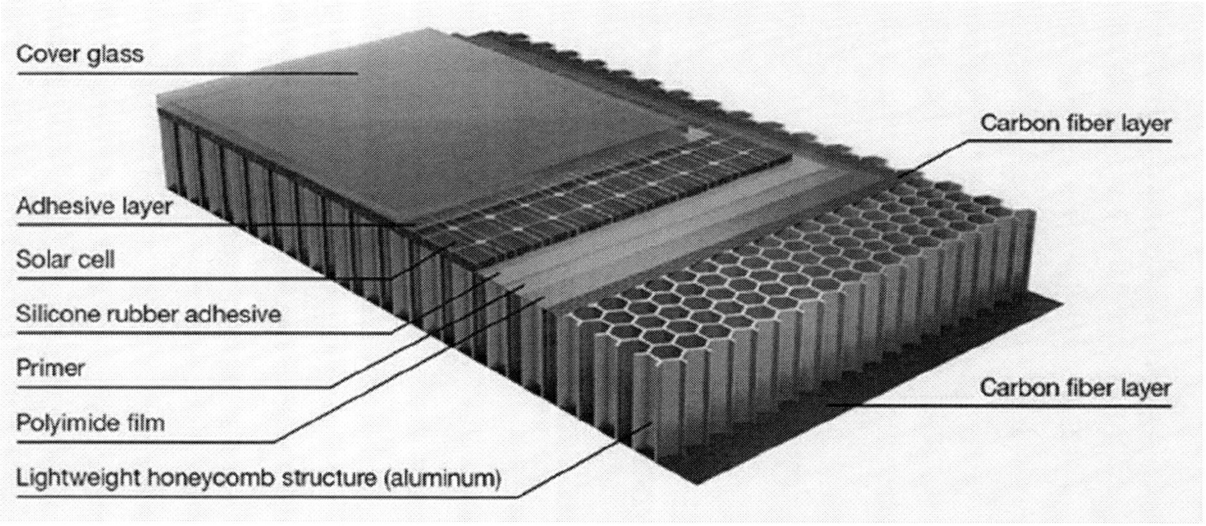

Proposed architectures

INSTITUTO DE ENERGÍA SOLAR

Conventional cell-interconnect-cover (CIC) on honeycomb technology

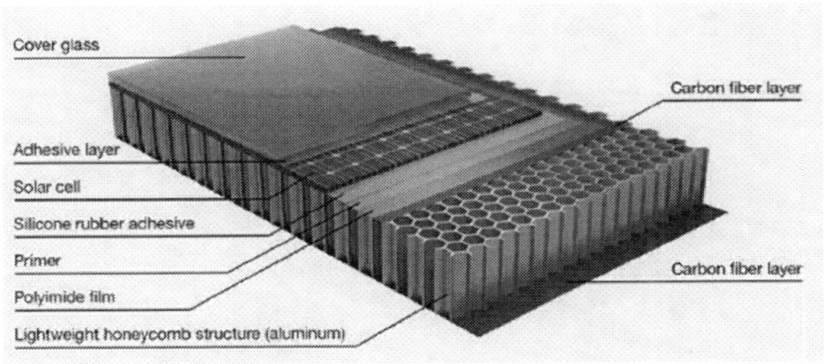

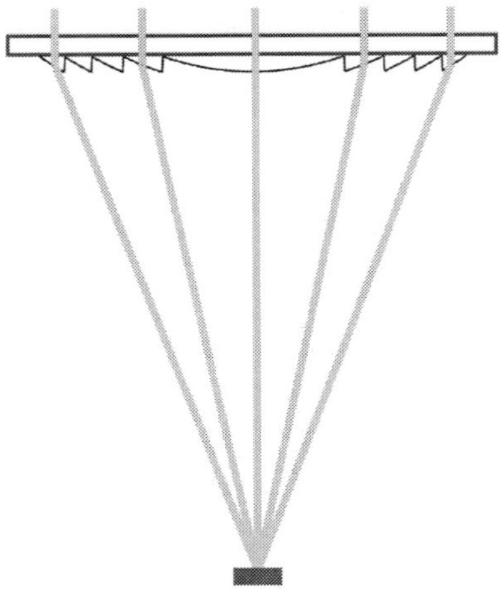

Fresnel

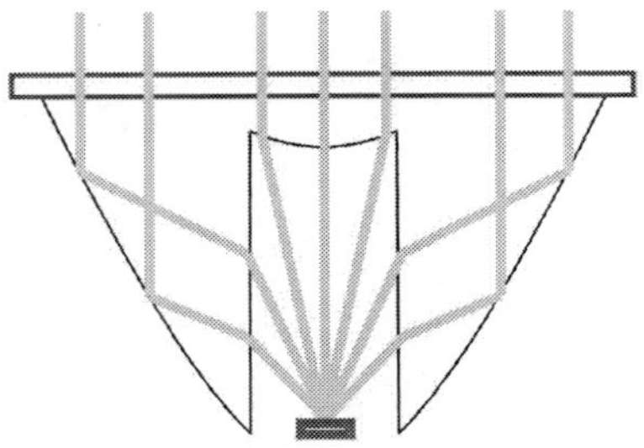

Catadioptric

POLITÉCNICA

Proposed architectures

INSTITUTO DE ENERGÍA SOLAR

Conventional cell-interconnect-cover (CIC) on honeycomb technology

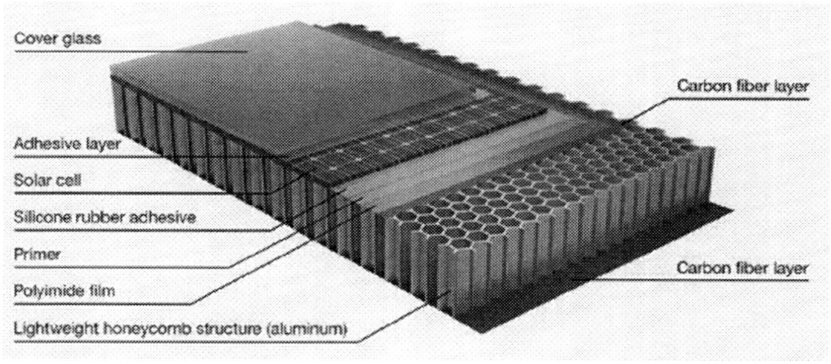

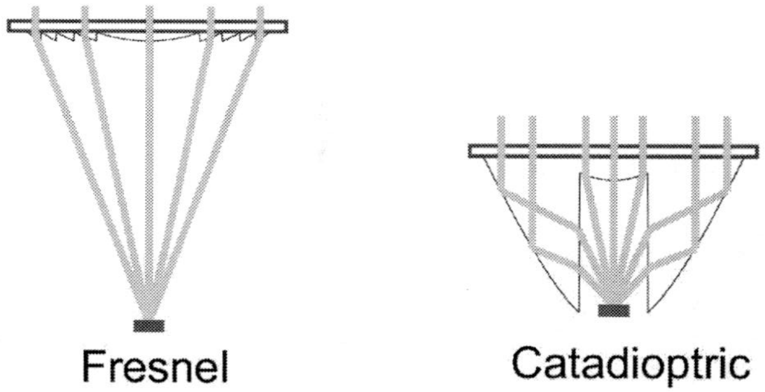

POLITÉCNICA

Work carried out

INSTITUTO DE ENERGÍA SOLAR

- Material selection
- Space qualified solar cell characterization at LILT conditions
- Optimization of the optical designs by means of ray-tracing simulation
- Manufacturing of the optical arrays prototypes (only Fresnel)
- Manufacturing of solar cell board
- Experimental characterization of the optical arrays prototypes (only Fresnel)
- Manufacturing and characterization of 4J solar cell envisaged for the project.

POLITÉCNICA

Optical design: constraints and specifications

INSTITUTO DE ENERGÍA SOLAR

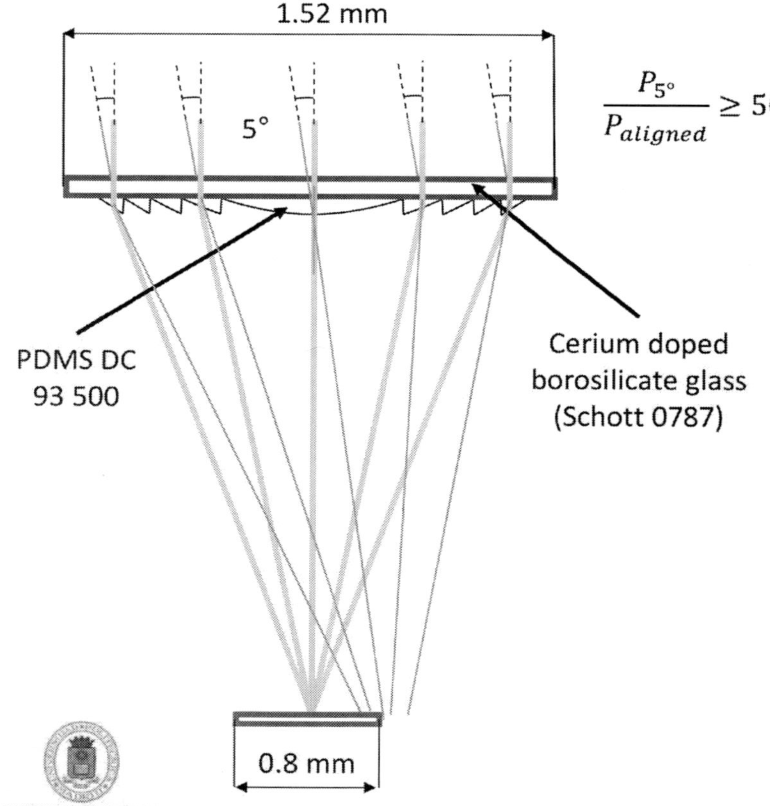

$$\frac{P_{5°}}{P_{aligned}} \geq 50\%$$

Design constraints

- $0.5\ mm^2$ solar cell aperture area
- Space qualified materials
- 10X effective concentration (X_{eff})
- 5° Acceptance angle for 50% of P_{MPP}

POLITÉCNICA

Optical design: modeling results

INSTITUTO DE ENERGÍA SOLAR

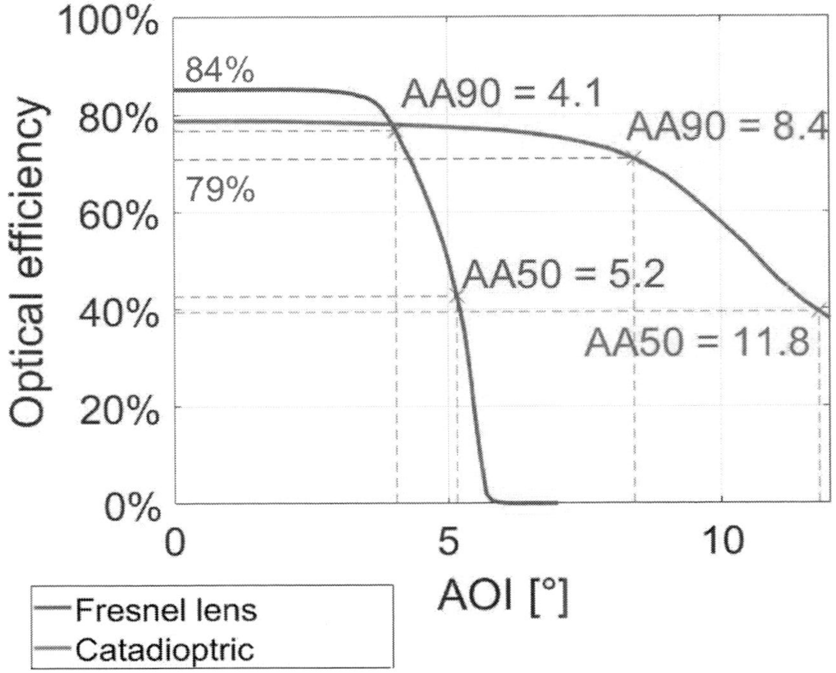

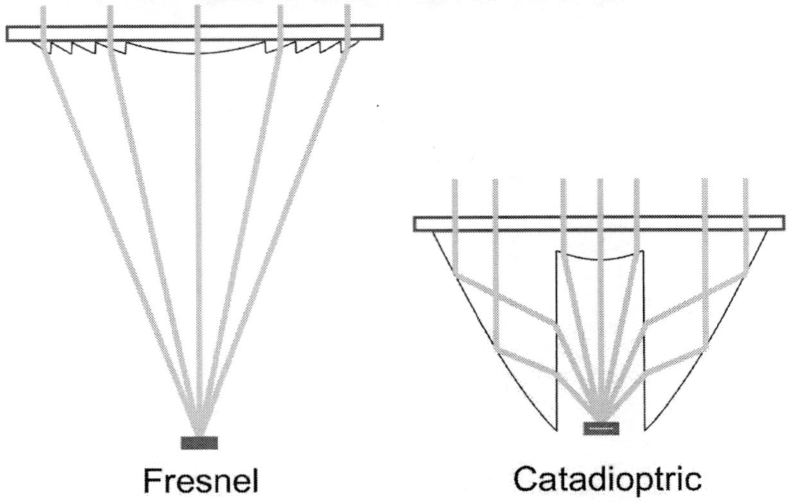

$$\eta_{opti} = \frac{P_{cell}}{P_{lens}}$$

POLITÉCNICA

Experimental characterization: optics

INSTITUTO DE ENERGÍA SOLAR

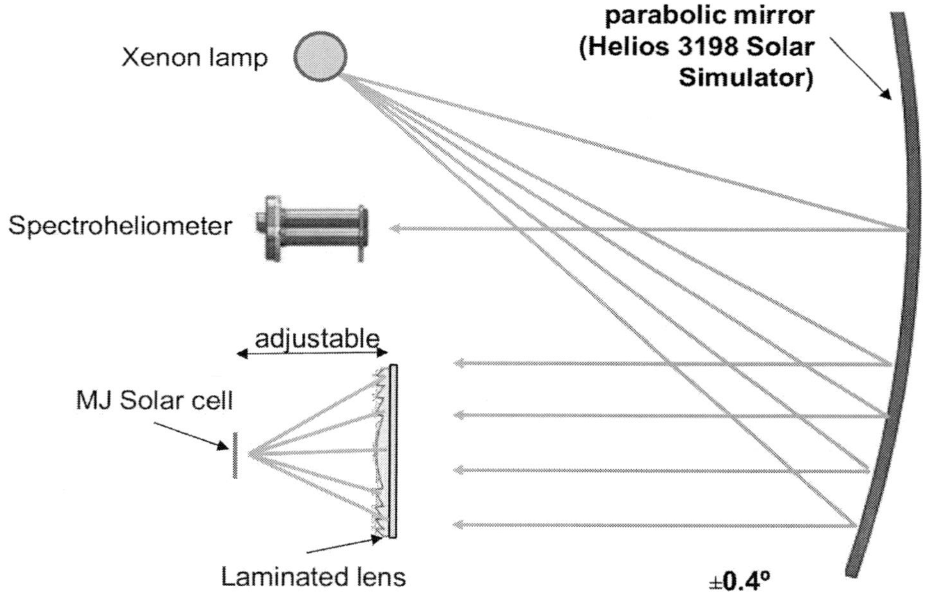

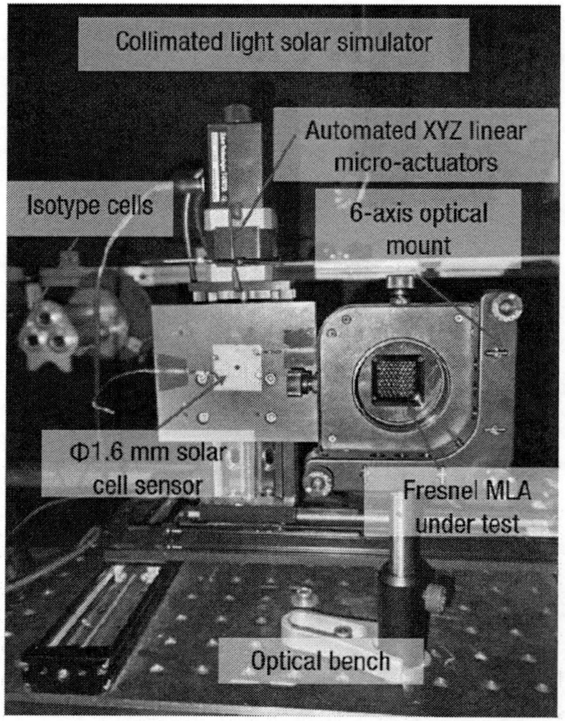

POLITÉCNICA

Experimental characterization: optics

INSTITUTO DE ENERGÍA SOLAR

Five randomly chosen lenses fully characterized:

- Optical efficiency: 83-85%
- Horizontal positioning tolerance: ±0.3 mm

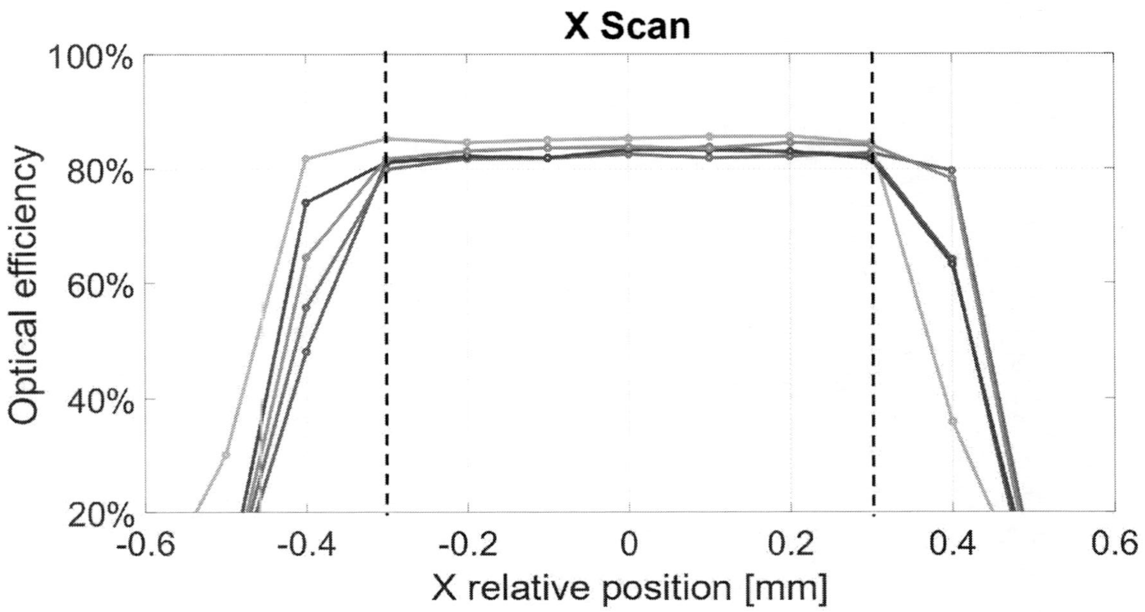

POLITÉCNICA

Experimental characterization: optics

INSTITUTO DE ENERGÍA SOLAR

Five randomly chosen lenses fully characterized:

- Optical efficiency: 83-85%
- Horizontal positioning tolerance: ±0.3 mm
- Focal distance tolerance: ±1 mm

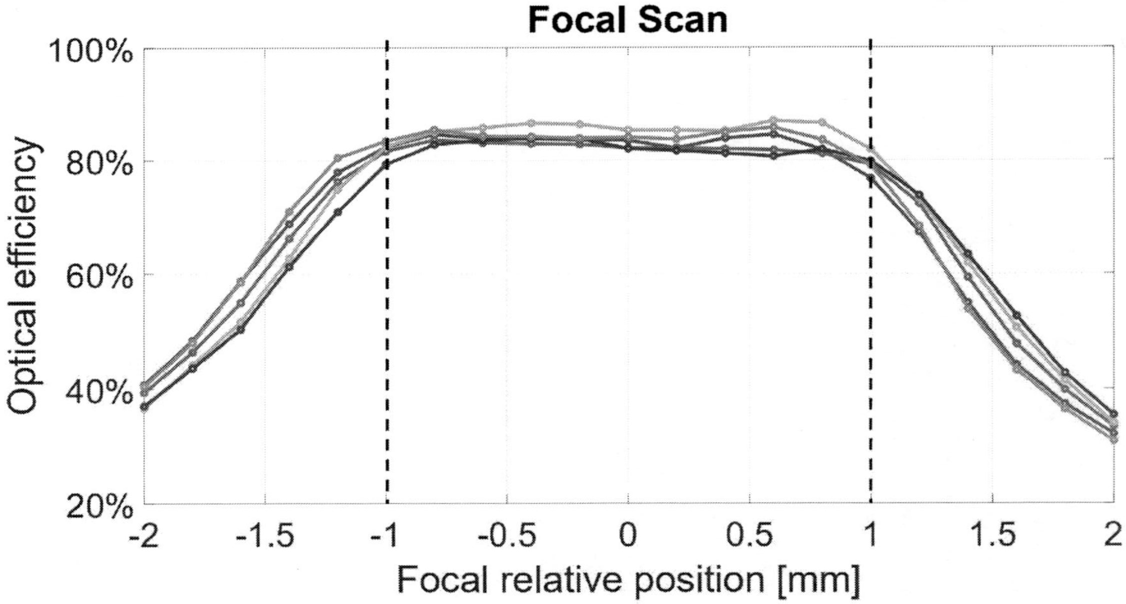

POLITÉCNICA

Experimental characterization: optics

INSTITUTO DE ENERGÍA SOLAR

Five randomly chosen lenses fully characterized:

- Optical efficiency: 83-85%
- Horizontal positioning tolerance: ±0.3 mm
- Focal distance tolerance: ±1 mm
- Acceptance angle: 5° AA50, 4° AA90

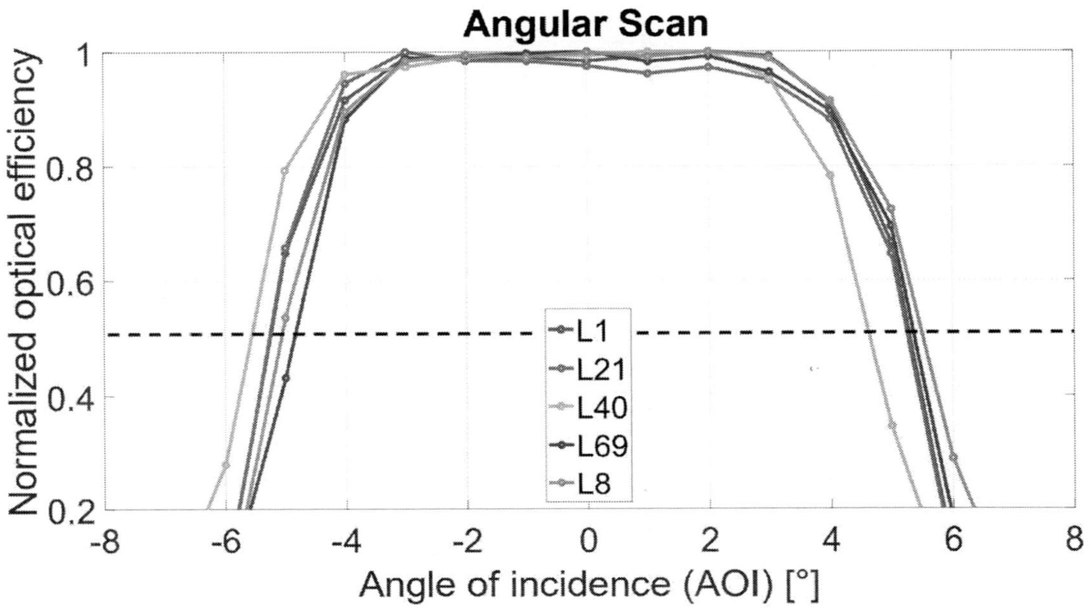

POLITÉCNICA

Experimental characterization: optics

INSTITUTO DE ENERGÍA SOLAR

Five randomly chosen lenses fully characterized:

- Optical efficiency: 83-85%
- Horizontal positioning tolerance: ±0.3 mm
- Focal distance tolerance: ±1 mm
- Acceptance angle: 4° AA50, 5° AA90
- Good match between different lenses

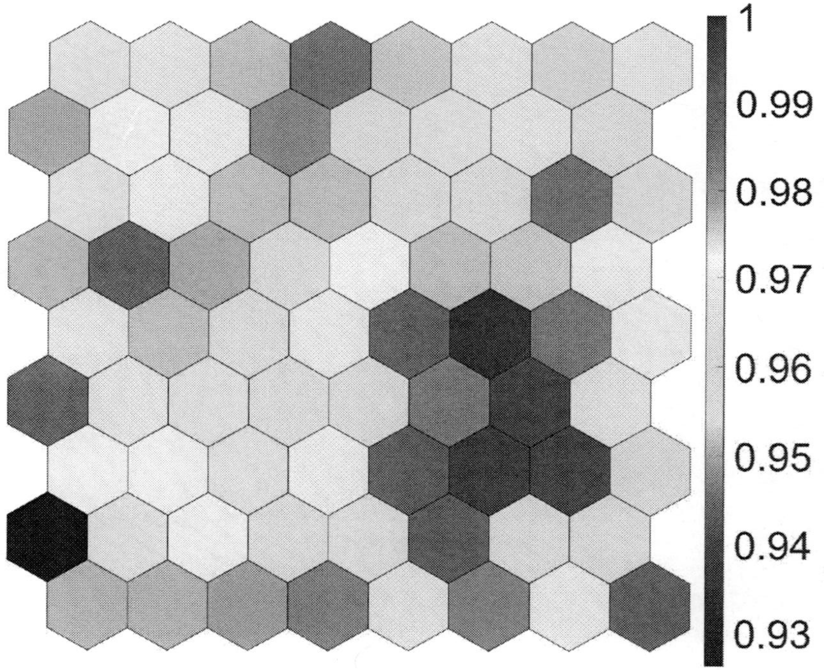

POLITÉCNICA

Conclusions

INSTITUTO DE ENERGÍA SOLAR

- The study confirms that micro-CPV technology may be a mission enabler for large-class deep space mission
- Two complementary optical architectures were investigated:
  - Fresnel microlens arrays
    - High optical efficiency (85%)
    - Low weight
    - **High specific power (W/kg)**
  - Catadioptric system
    - High angular tolerance
    - Good alignment stability
    - **Medium specific power (W/kg) (higher than CIC)**
- Successfully manufactured and characterized the first Fresnel architecture prototype:
  - Optical efficiency: 84%
  - Acceptance angle for 50% of P_{MPP}: 5°

POLITÉCNICA

Future work

INSTITUTO DE ENERGÍA SOLAR

- Manufacturing and characterization

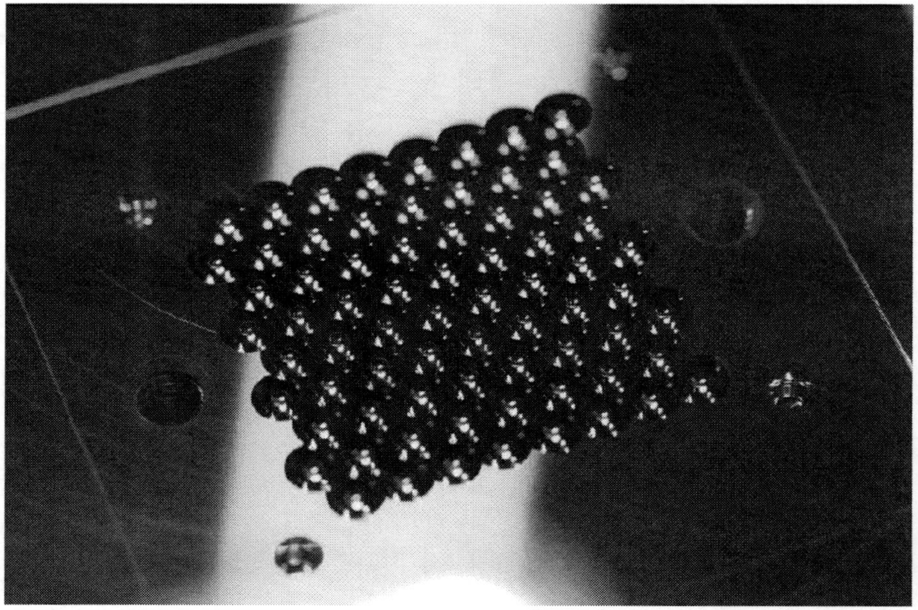

POLITÉCNICA

Future work

INSTITUTO DE ENERGÍA SOLAR

- Manufacturing and characterization of the catadioptric architecture
- Full module integration

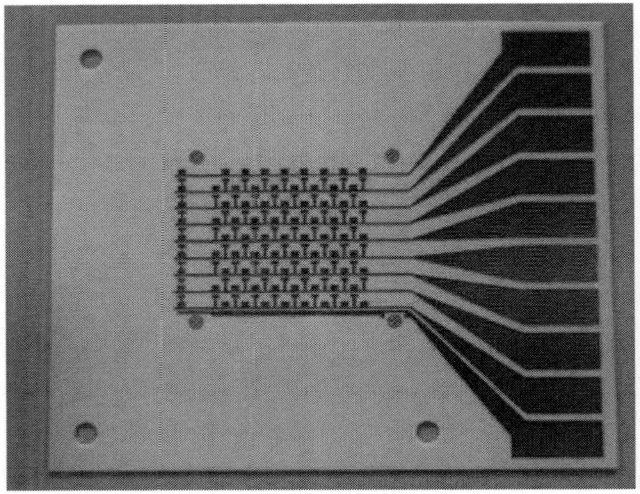

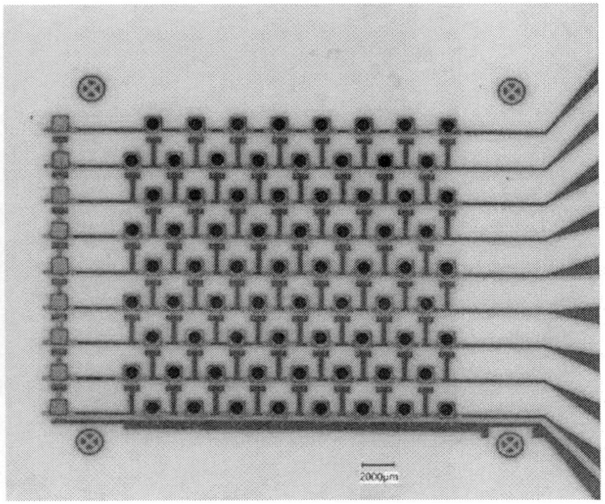

POLITÉCNICA

Future work

INSTITUTO DE ENERGÍA SOLAR

- Manufacturing and characterization of the catadioptric architecture
- Full module integration
- Thermal management strategies

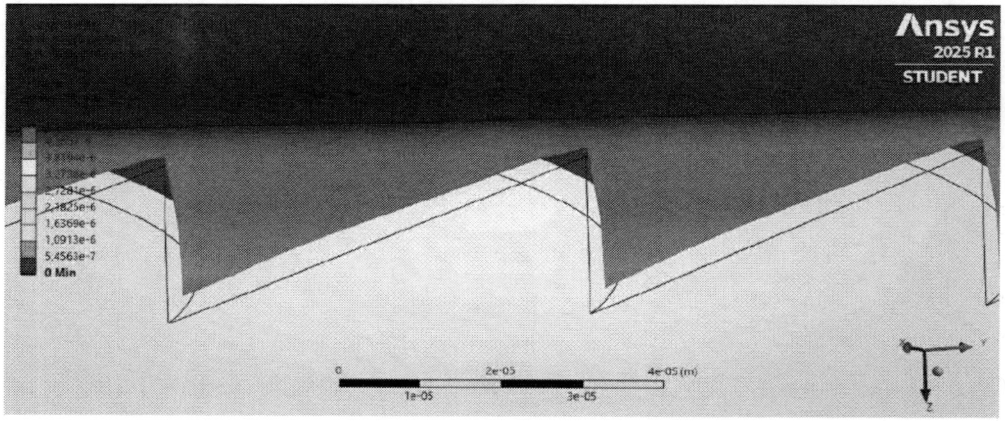

POLITÉCNICA

Future work

INSTITUTO DE ENERGÍA SOLAR

- Manufacturing and characterization of the catadioptric architecture
- Full module integration
- Thermal management strategies
- In orbit demonstration

POLITÉCNICA

Thank you for your attention

INSTITUTO DE ENERGÍA SOLAR

Dr. Guido Vallerotto

Happy to take your questions

This work has been supported by the European Space Agency's Technology Development Activity "Concentrator Systems as Mission Enablers for Deep Space Missions", under ESA Contract No. 4000141821/23/NL/Mgu. UPM authors acknowledge support by grant MICROBEAM ref. PID2021-127810OB-I00, funded by MCIN/AEI/10.13039/501100011033 "ERDF A way of making Europe".

We gratefully acknowledge the support of these institutions:

GOBIERNO DE ESPAÑA | MINISTERIO DE CIENCIA, INNOVACIÓN Y UNIVERSIDADES | AGENCIA ESTATAL DE INVESTIGACIÓN | esa

POLITÉCNICA

EU PVSEC 2025
42nd European Photovoltaic Solar Energy Conference and Exhibition

Experimental Investigation of Colored BIPV/T Systems for Wood-Framed Roofs

Anna-Maria Sigounis[1], Andreas Athienitis[2]
1 - PhD Candidate, 2 - Professor

Building, Civil and Environmental Engineering Department, Concordia University, Montréal, Canada

23 September 2025

Université Concordia University

Center for Zero Energy Building Studies
Centre d'études sur le bâtiment à consommation nulle d'énergie

Canada & Quebec

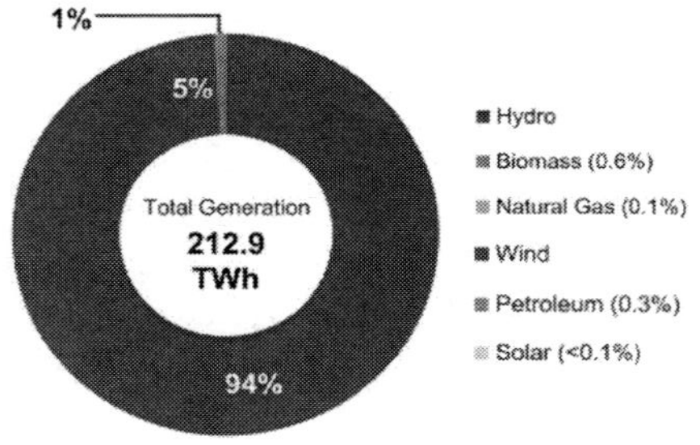

source: www.cer-rec.gc.ca

Total consumption by energy type in Quebec, 2020

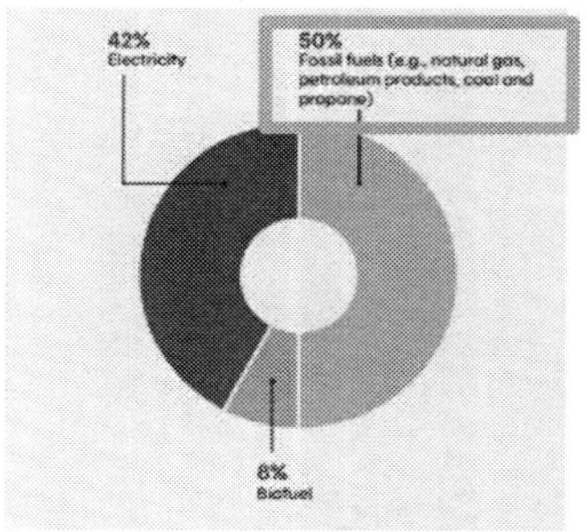

source: hydro quebec

Projected trajectory of electricity demand by 2050

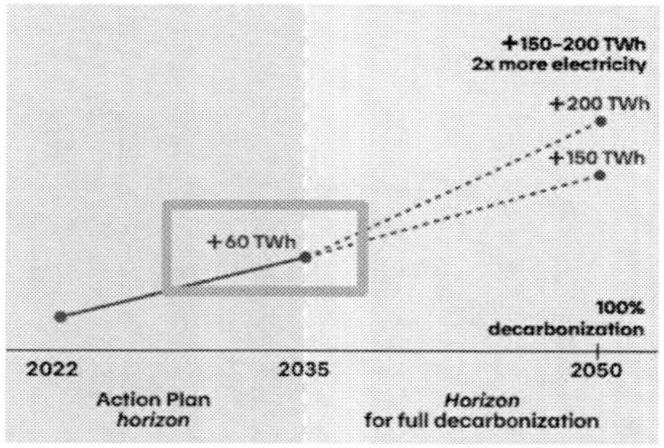

source: hydro quebec

Canadian Residential building stock

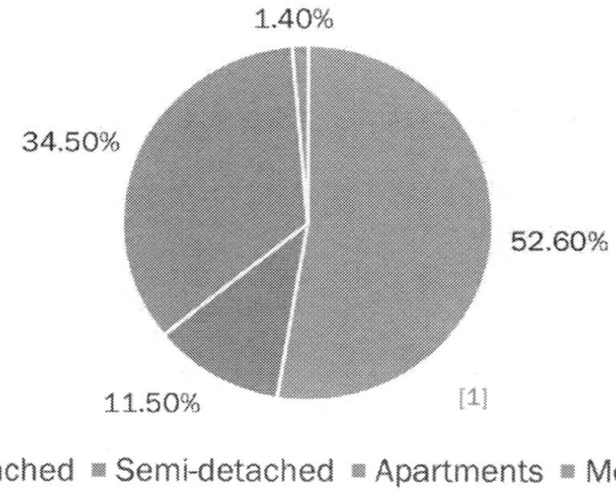

- Pitched roofs are one of the most common roof typologies in low-rise residential dwellings
- Have greater sun exposure and account for a large share of the total building envelope area.

[1] Statistics Canada, "Census Profile, 2021 Census of Population."

Building Integrated PV

BIPV/T

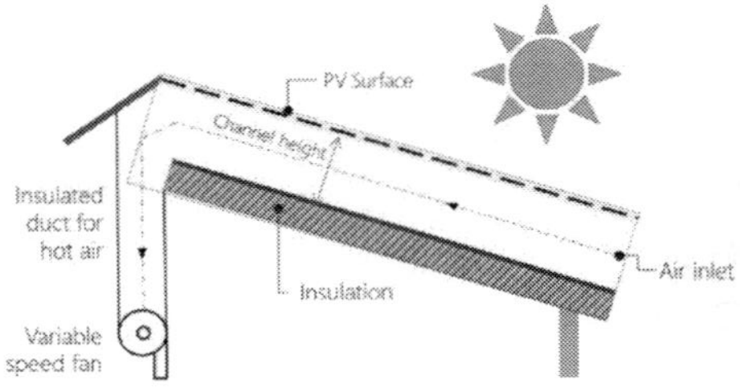

Air-based open loop BIPV/T system

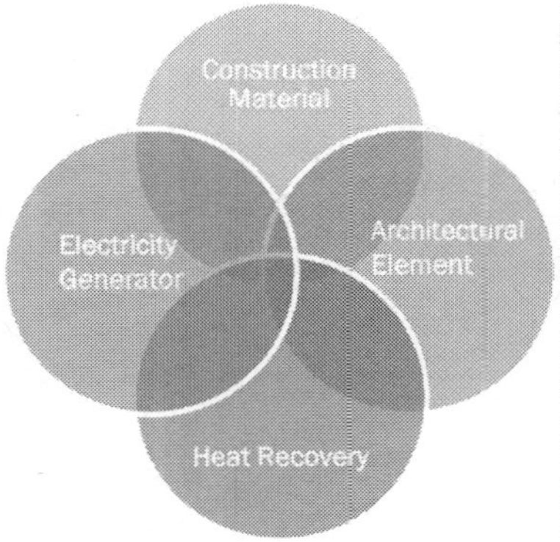

Heated air can be used for:

1. pre-heating ventilation air
2. source-side of ASHP
3. water-heating though HE

Colored PV

Photo credits : solarchitecture.ch

- Offer greater design flexibility
- Higher cost than standard PV
- Reduced electrical efficiency due to coloring
- Color layers can raise PV temperatures
- Uncertain applied performance due to limited research

Objectives

Experimental evaluation • Modelling guidelines • Design & installation strategies

BIPV/T Experimental Prototype

- Dimensions: 1.34m x 2.08m
- Two PV modules connected in series
- The PV framing system transforms standard frameless PV modules into solar tiles for sloping roofs.
- Air channel beneath the PV modules has a varying height of 45 - 55 mm
- Custom-made wooden manifold connects the BIPV/T outlet with the air collector
- Two PV colors were tested:

Terracotta | Grey

Solar Simulator Laboratory

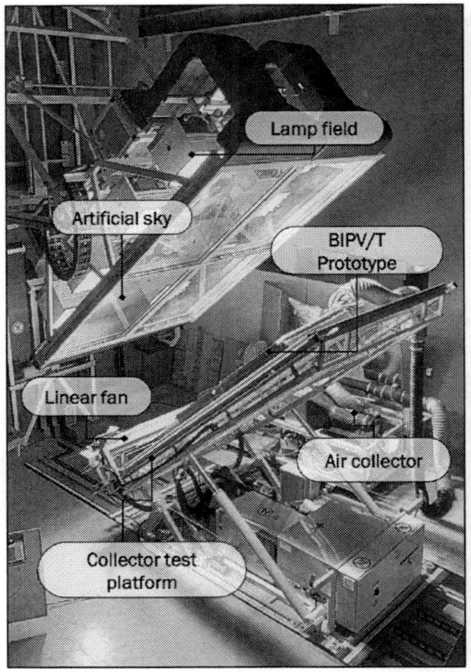

Indoor steady state solar simulator

Lamp Field

- 8 metal halide lamps
- 500 - 1200 W/m^2
- Artificial sky removes the effect of the infrared radiation

Collector test platform

- Can be adjusted 0 - 90°
- Linear, variable-speed fan
- X-Y scanner with pyranometer and anemometer
- Air collector attached to BIPV/T outlet

Cases studied (Testing Sessions)

PV Color	Positions	Irradiance Levels	Wind Speeds	Mass flow rates
Terracotta	Horizontal (0°)	~1086 W/m^2	2.68 m/s	380 kg/h [1.49m/s] 200 kg/h [0.78m/s]
Grey	Inclined (40°)	~836 W/m^2	1.43 m/s	120 kg/h [0.47m/s] Natural Ventilation: 0 kg/h

Testing Procedure

Measurements

- Temperature
- Flowrate
- Electrical Output

Sensor Placement

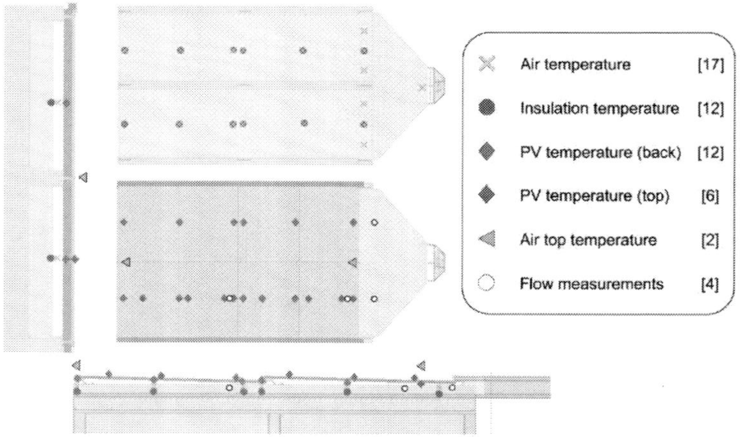

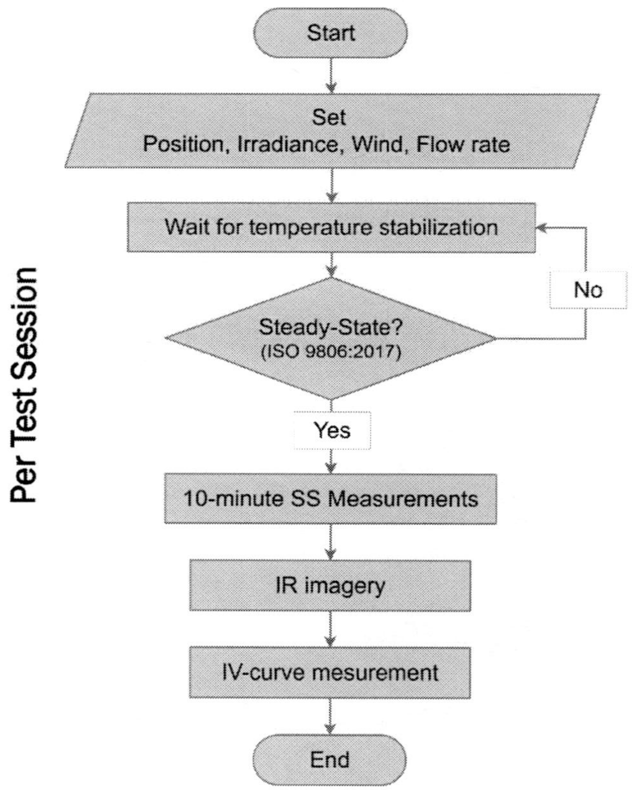

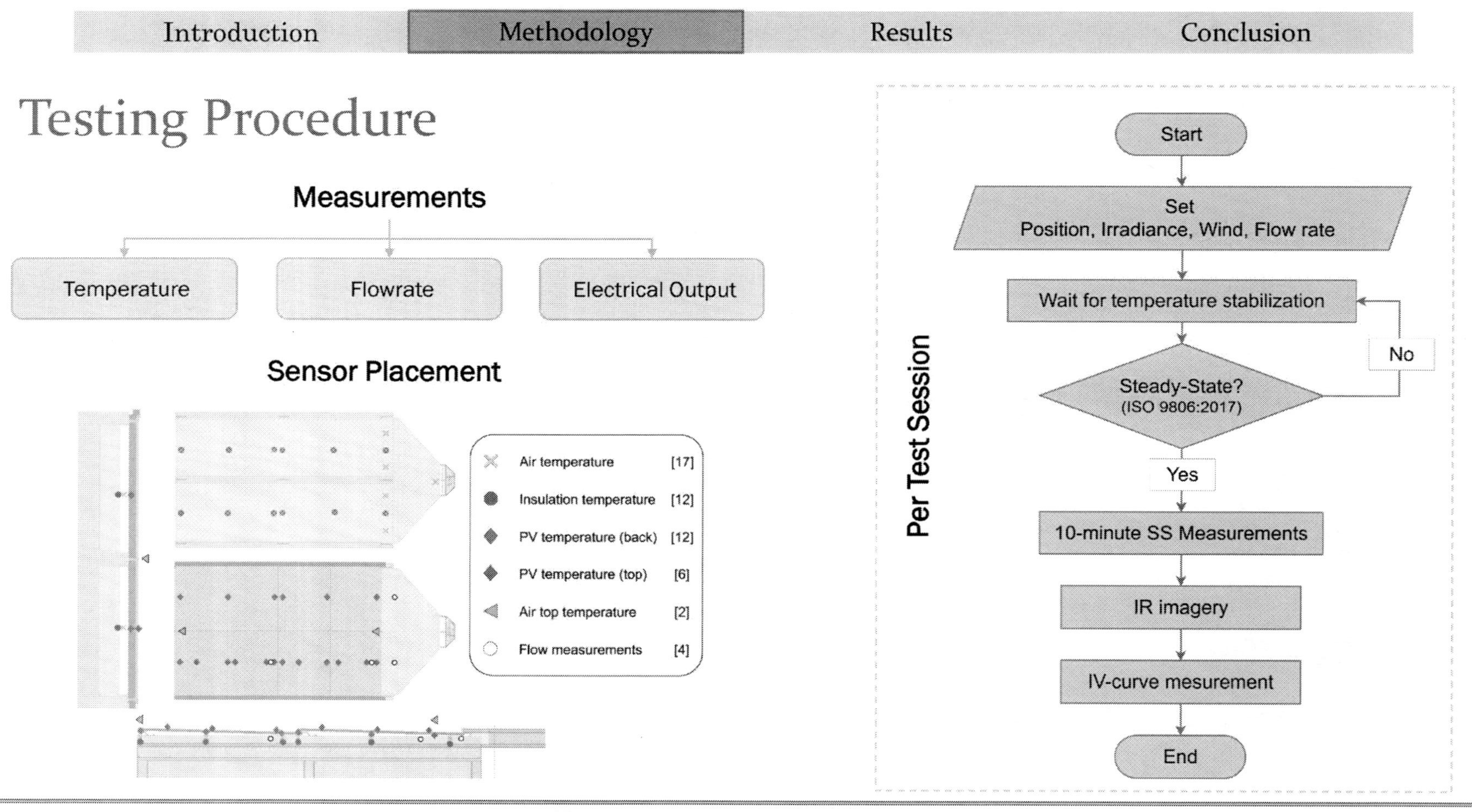

Convective Heat Transfer Analysis

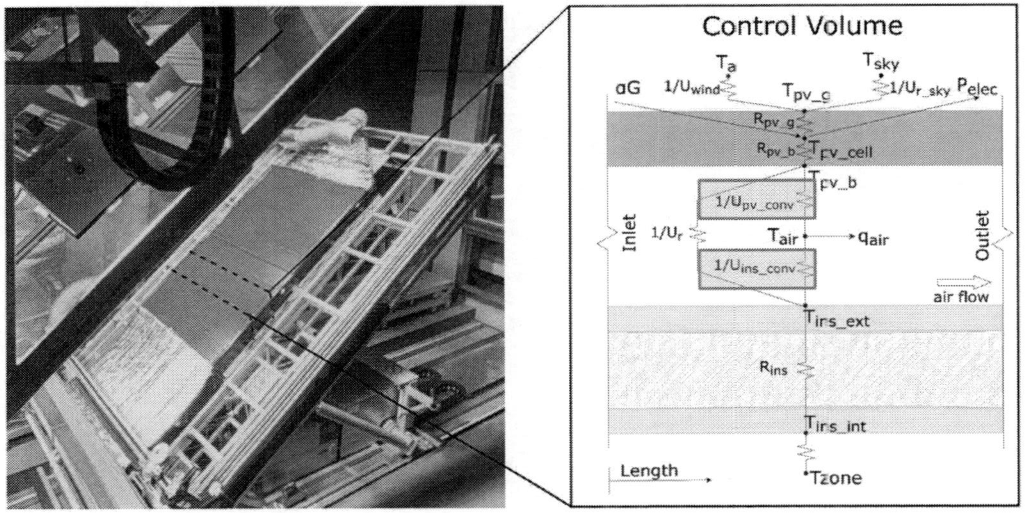

Energy balance of the BIPV/T in the form of a thermal network

The convective heat transfer coefficients (**CHTC**) and Nusselt numbers (**Nu**) within the air channel were derived through conducting an **energy balance**

Average CHTC & Nu

$$\dot{m} \cdot c_p \cdot \Delta T = \text{CHTC} \cdot (T_{PV} + T_{ins} - 2\overline{T_{air}}) \cdot A$$

$$\text{Nu} = \frac{\text{CHTC} \cdot D_h}{k}$$

m : mass flow rate (kg/s),
ΔT : temperature difference between the inlet and outlet (°C),
TPV, Tins, Tair : temperatures of the PV, insulation, air (°C),
A : area of the BIPV/T (m²),
Dh : hydraulic diameter (m)

Thermal and Electrical Performance

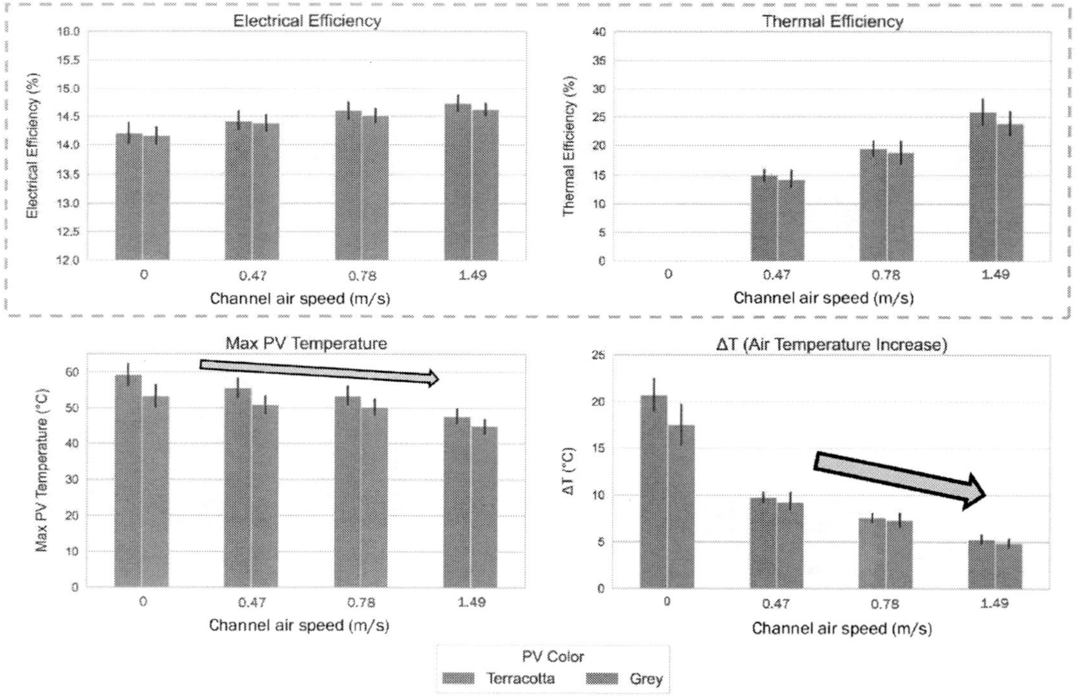

System Performance Overview

Efficiencies	Terracotta	Grey
Thermal (%)	28.2	26.6
Electrical (%)	14.9	14.5

Effect of Airflow Rate

- Increasing airflow (0.47 to 1.49 m/s) reduced ΔT by 4.4 °C
- PV temperature reductions with mechanical ventilation (−13 °C for terracotta, −10.3 °C for grey)

Impact of Color on Performance

- Grey panels showed lower electrical and thermal efficiencies
- Up to 6.2 °C difference in PV temperature

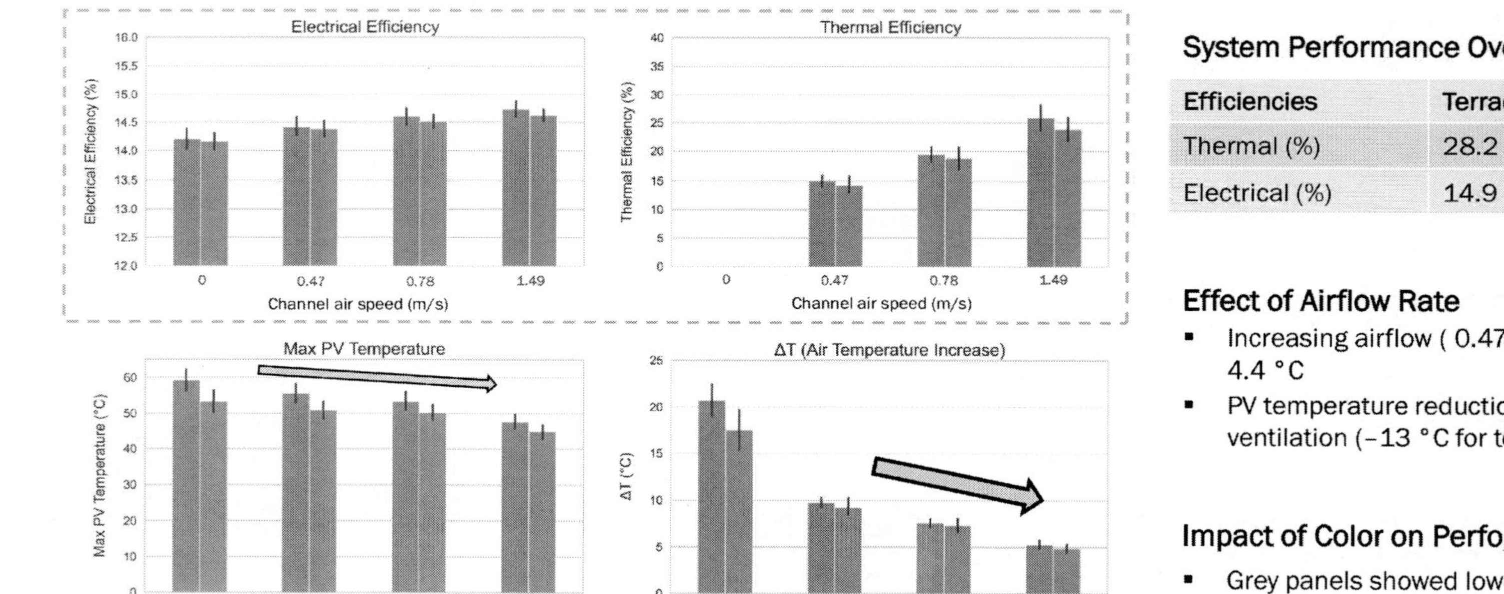

Temperature Distribution

Mechanical vs Natural Ventilation

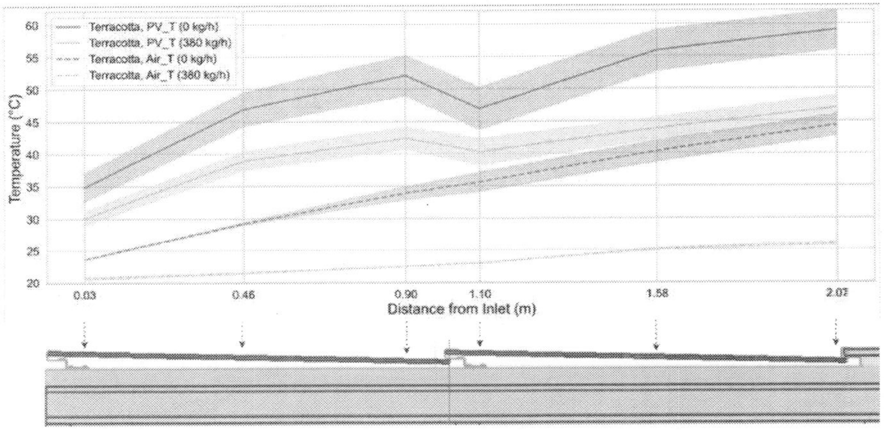

Terracotta vs Grey

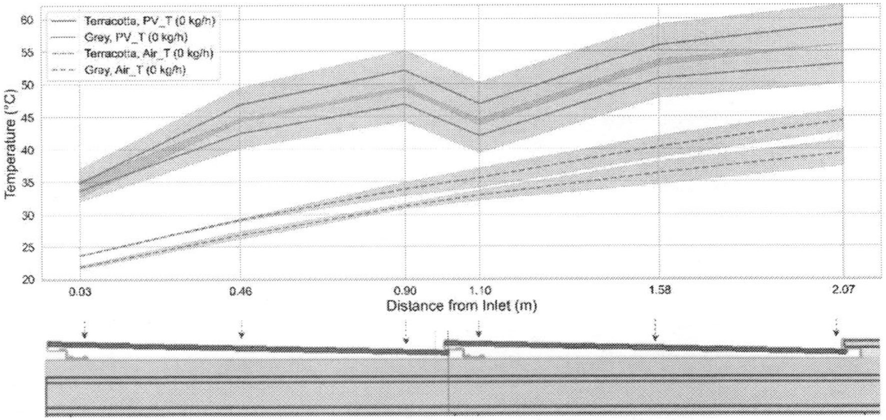

Temperature Distribution

Mechanical vs Natural Ventilation

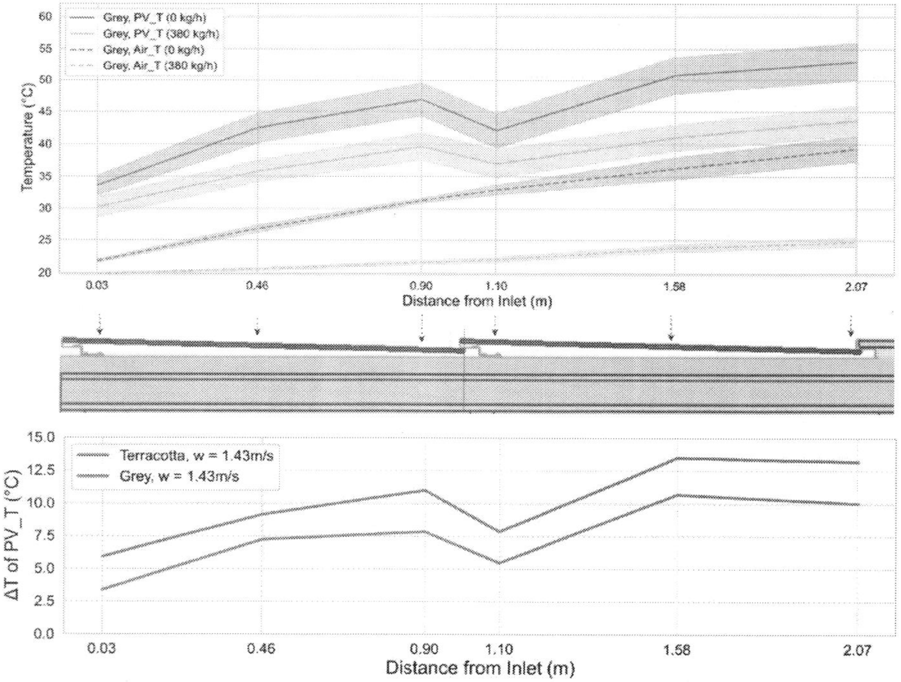

Terracotta vs Grey

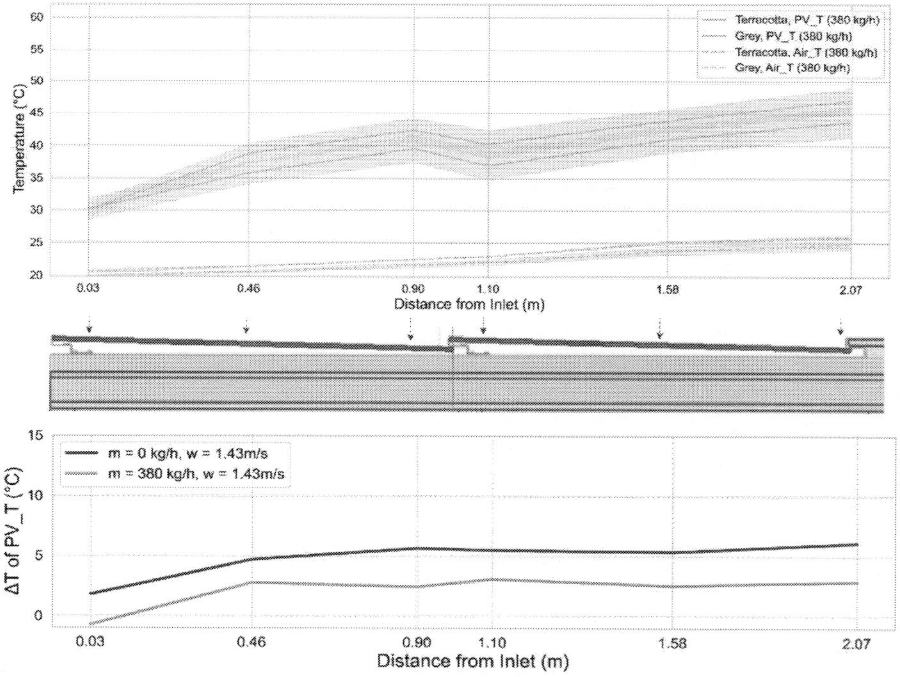

Introduction | Methodology | Results | Conclusion

Convective Heat Transfer Analysis

Average Nu (Overall)

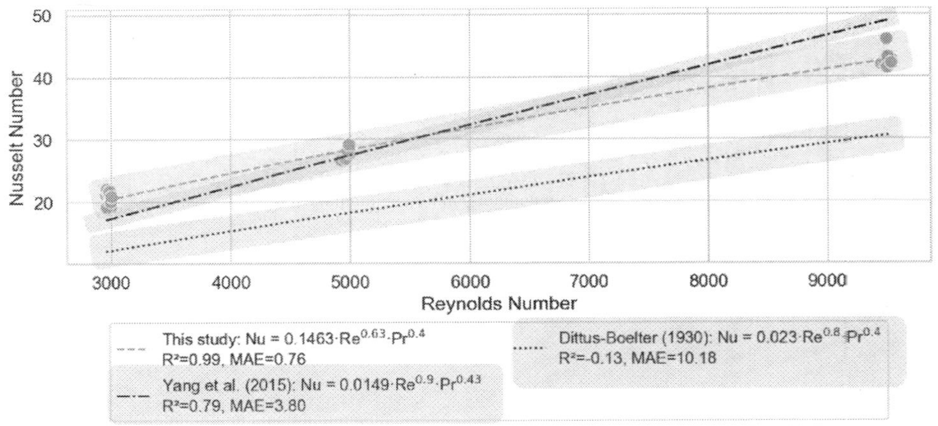

$$Nu = 0.146Re^{0.63}Pr^{0.4} \quad \text{for} \quad 3000 < Re < 10000$$

Nu (PV & Insulation side)

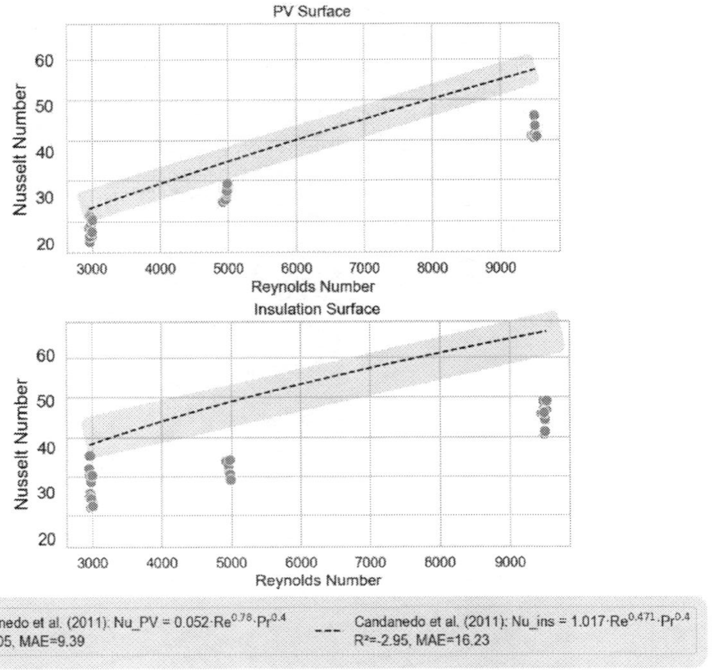

Limitations & Next Steps

Limitations

- Other coloring technologies, may have different impacts; further testing needed
- Laboratory conditions do not fully replicate real-world conditions (wind or solar spectrum)
- Fully developed flow conditions may not have been reached due to reduced prototype scale

Outdoor Full-scale Installation

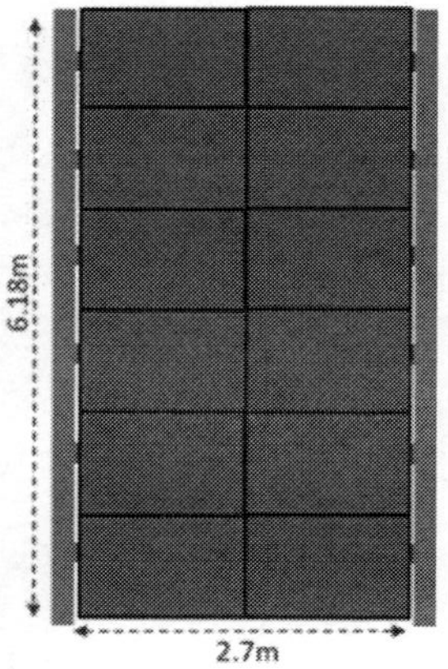

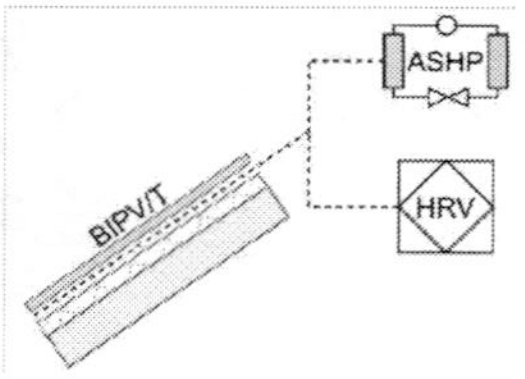

Three full scale systems

- Two "solar shingle" systems and one curtain wall
- 12 modules per system (2 columns x 6 rows)

Conclusions

This study investigated the performance of colored BIPV/T systems through experimental testing under controlled laboratory conditions.

- Addition of mechanical ventilation reduced PV temperature by up to **13 °C** for the terracotta PV and **10.3 °C** for the grey
- Terracotta modules exhibited higher temperatures than the grey, attributed to the higher reflectance of the grey
- Thermal efficiencies 12.5 - 28.6% with the terracotta achieving slightly higher thermal and electrical efficiencies

Acknowledgements

Financial support was received by a Natural Sciences and Engineering Research Council of Canada **(NSERC)/Hydro-Québec Industrial Research Chair** and an **NSERC Postgraduate Scholarship – Doctoral**

Thank you to **Dr. Jiwu Rao**, **Gia-Khanh PHI** and **Yearim Yang** for their assistance with the experimental procedure & setup.

Thank you!

Questions?

Contact Information

Anna-Maria Sigounis, PhD candidate
Centre for Zero Energy Building Studies (CZEBS)
Concordia University, Montréal, Canada

sigounisan@gmail.com

www.linkedin.com/in/anna-maria-sigounis

How to Perform Accurate Colour Measurements for BIPV Module Glass Covers:
an IEA PVPS Task 15 Round-Robin Measurement Campaign

M. Babin, G.C. Eder, T. Friesen, M. Pelle, G. Gonnella, F. Leonforte, Y. Voronko, H.R. Wilson, S. Thorsteinsson, L. Maturi, N. Aste, C. Del Pero, J. Halme, J.-T. Kim, S. Santamaría Fernández, A.-M. Sigounis, H. Ge, G. Friesen, F. Frontini

Technology Collaboration Programme
by iea

Challenges for coloured BIPV

BIPV requires visual integration
→ demand for coloured BIPV

Colour matching of existing materials
→ challenge of different surfaces

Reproducability of coloured BIPV modules
→ production monitoring (quality control)

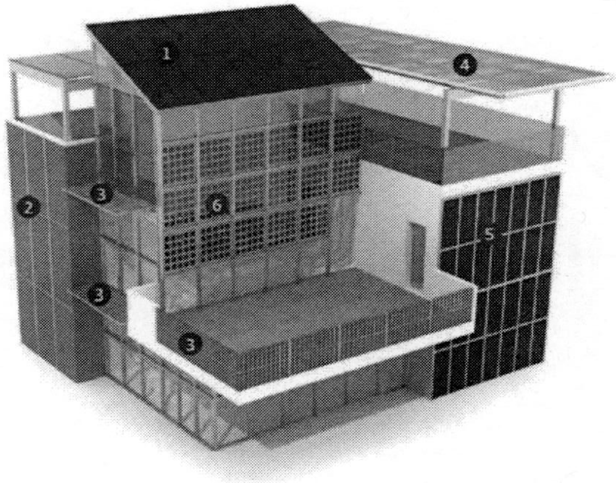

© Fraunhofer ISE

PVPS

IEA PVPS Task 15

IEA PVPS Task 15
"Enabling Framework for the Development of BIPV"

- Market barriers and opportunities
- Digitalisation, training, stakeholder involvement
- Long-term behaviour and reliability
- Pre-normative research

> 60 active experts from > 15 countries

Activity B4
"Performance modelling and characterization of coloured BIPV"

PVPS

Background – how to measure colours

Spectral reflectance

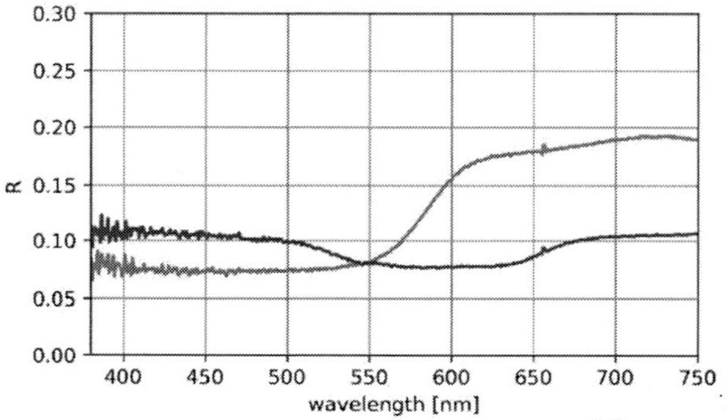

Colour matching functions
Reference conditions
(D65 illuminant, 2° standard observer)

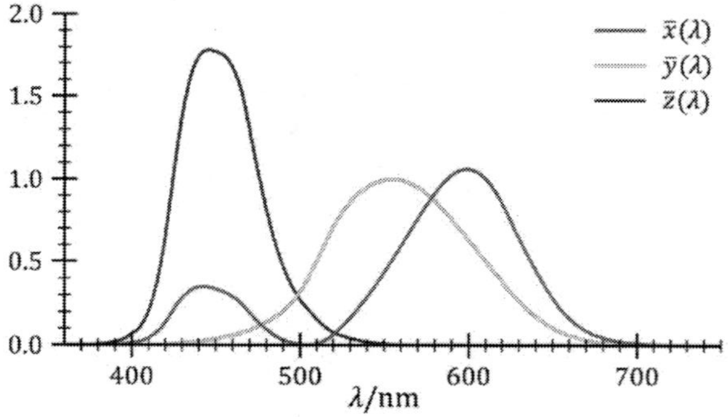

Colour coordinates
(CIELAB colour space)

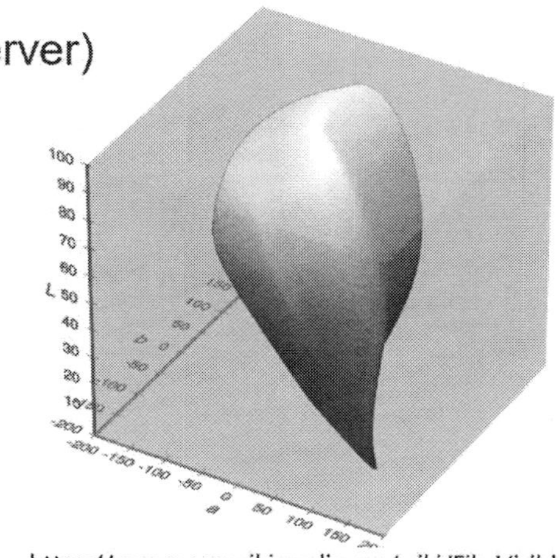

https://commons.wikimedia.org/wiki/File:Visible_gamut_within_CIELAB_color_space_D65_whitepoint_mesh.png

PVPS

4

Approach – colour measurement instruments

Spectrometers – different collection optics

- Integrating sphere (with/without specular reflections)
- Backscatter probe
- Multi-angle array

Colourimeters – different manufacturers and designs

- Spectrometer-based with integrating sphere (with/without specular reflections)
- Camera-based

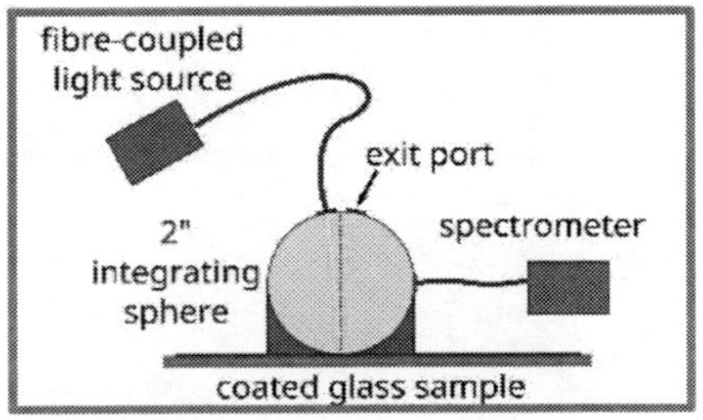

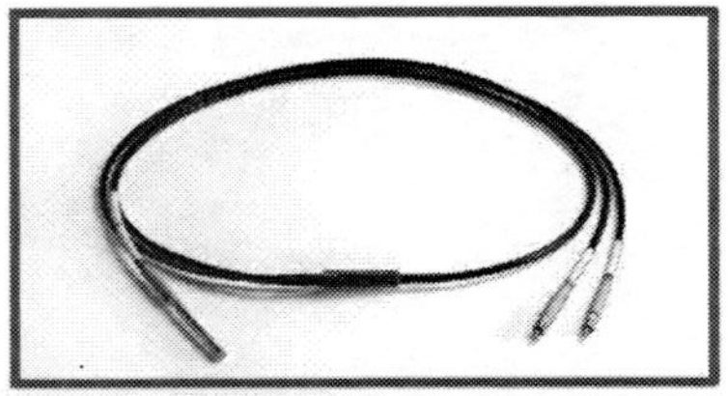

© spectrology.com

© colorix.com

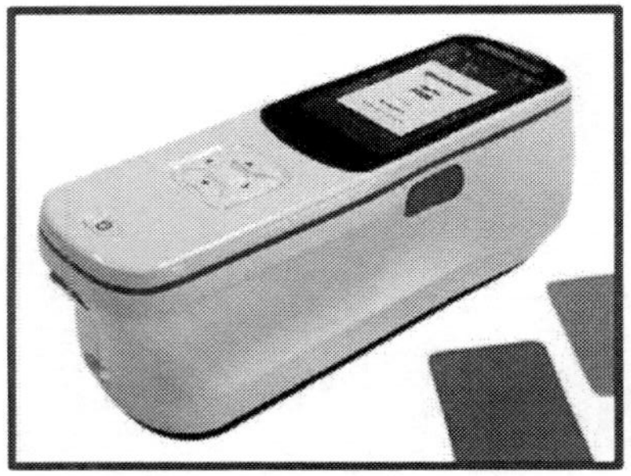

© datacolor.com

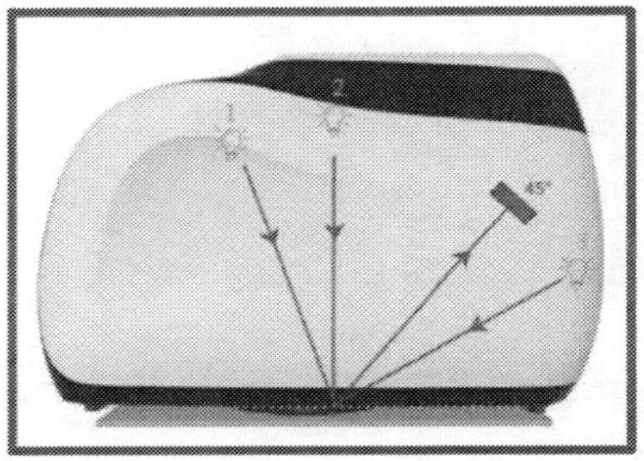

PVPS

Effect of different glass surfaces (modules)

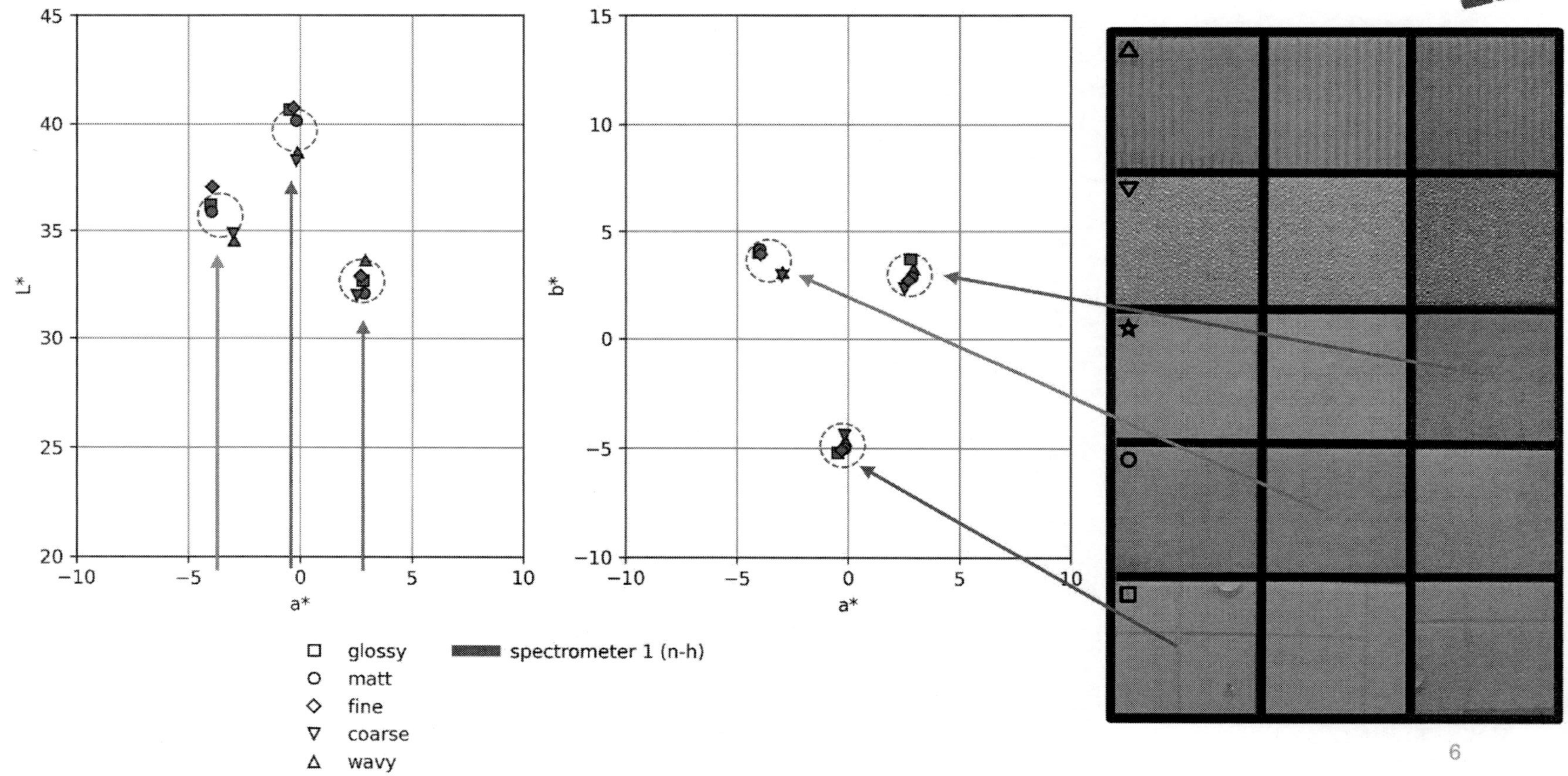

PVPS

Effect of different glass surfaces (modules)

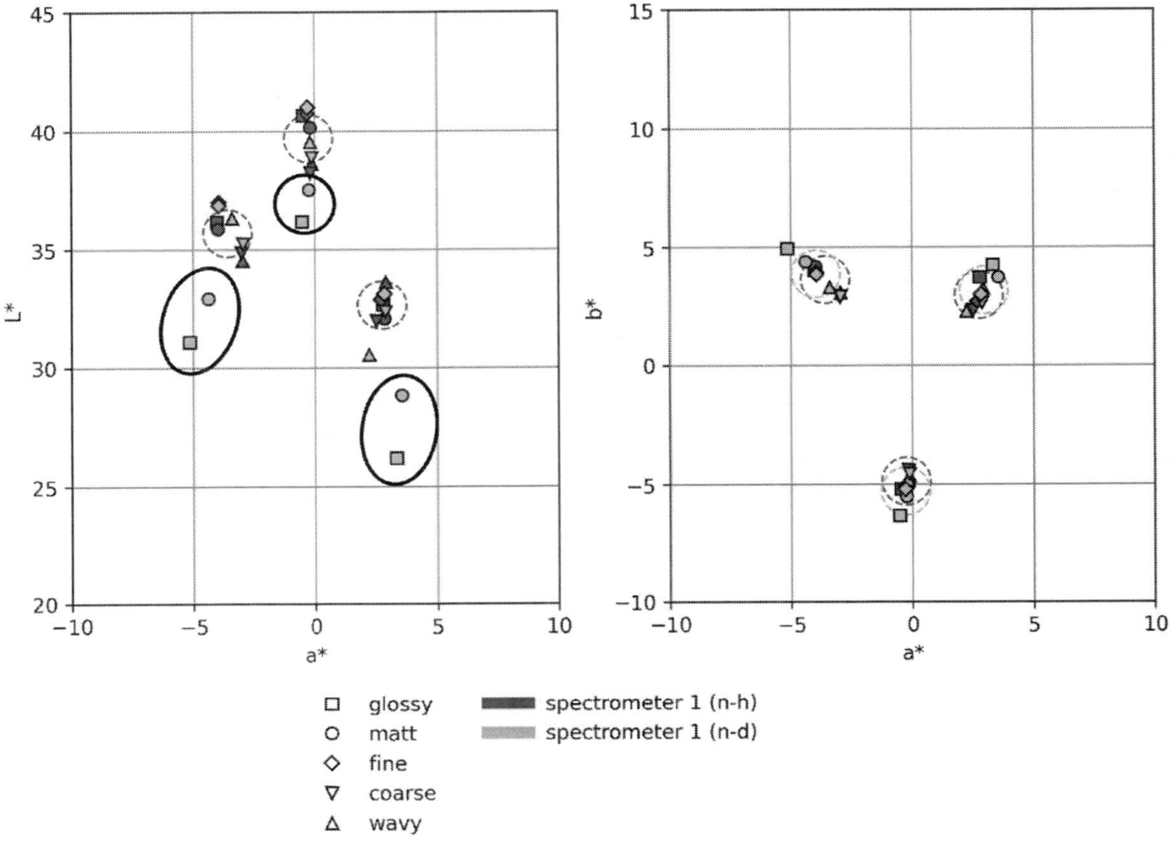

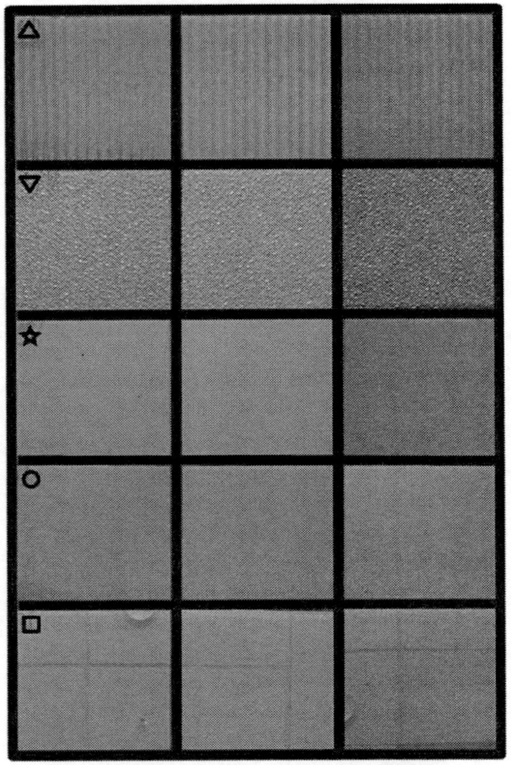

PVPS

C20249-007

Effect of different glass surfaces (modules)

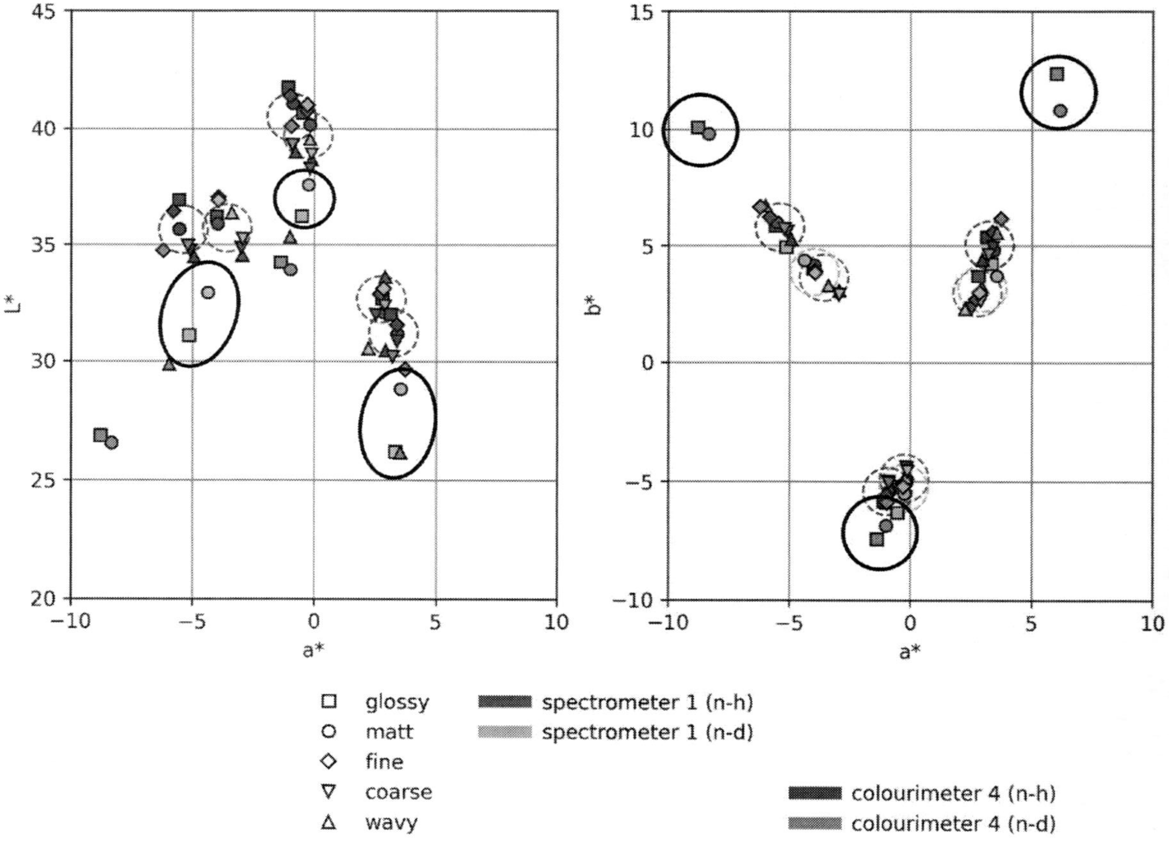

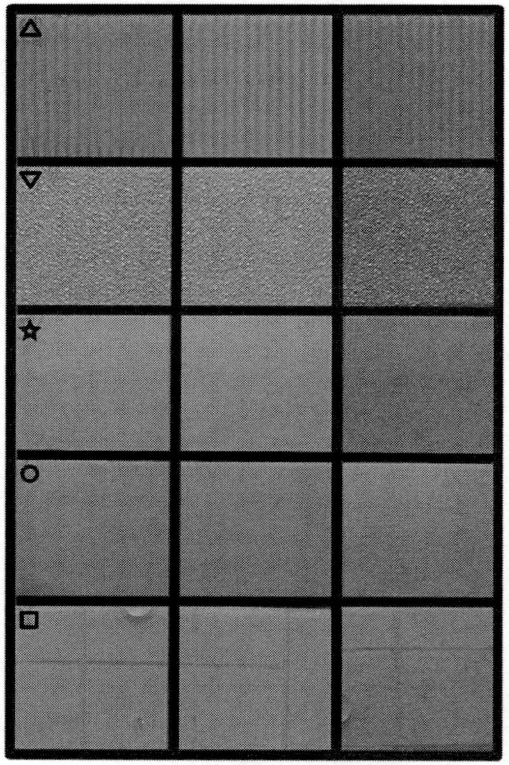

PVPS

Effect of different glass surfaces (modules)

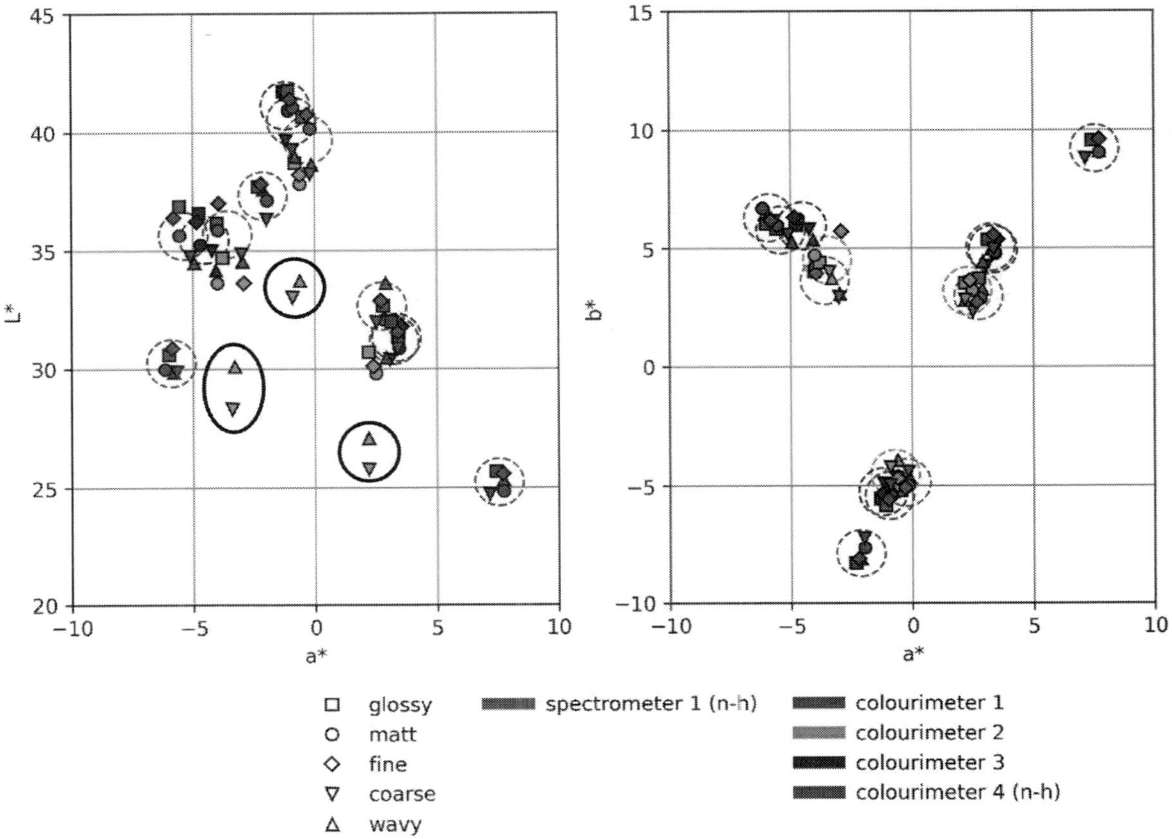

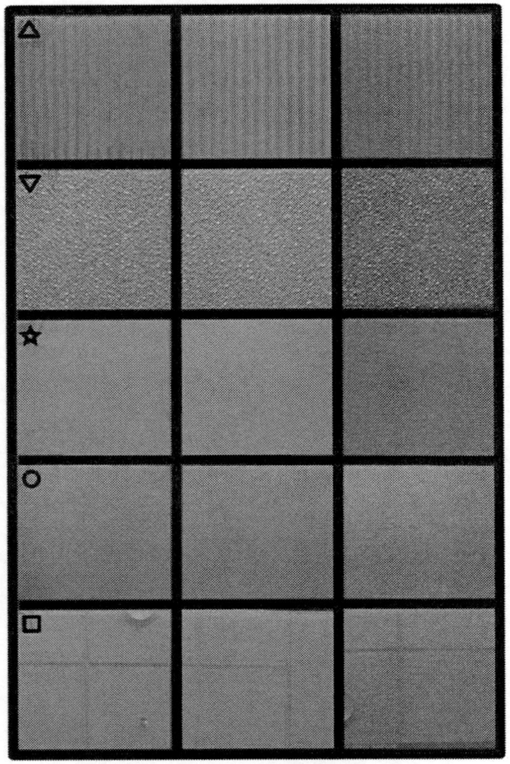

PVPS

Effect of different glass surfaces (modules)

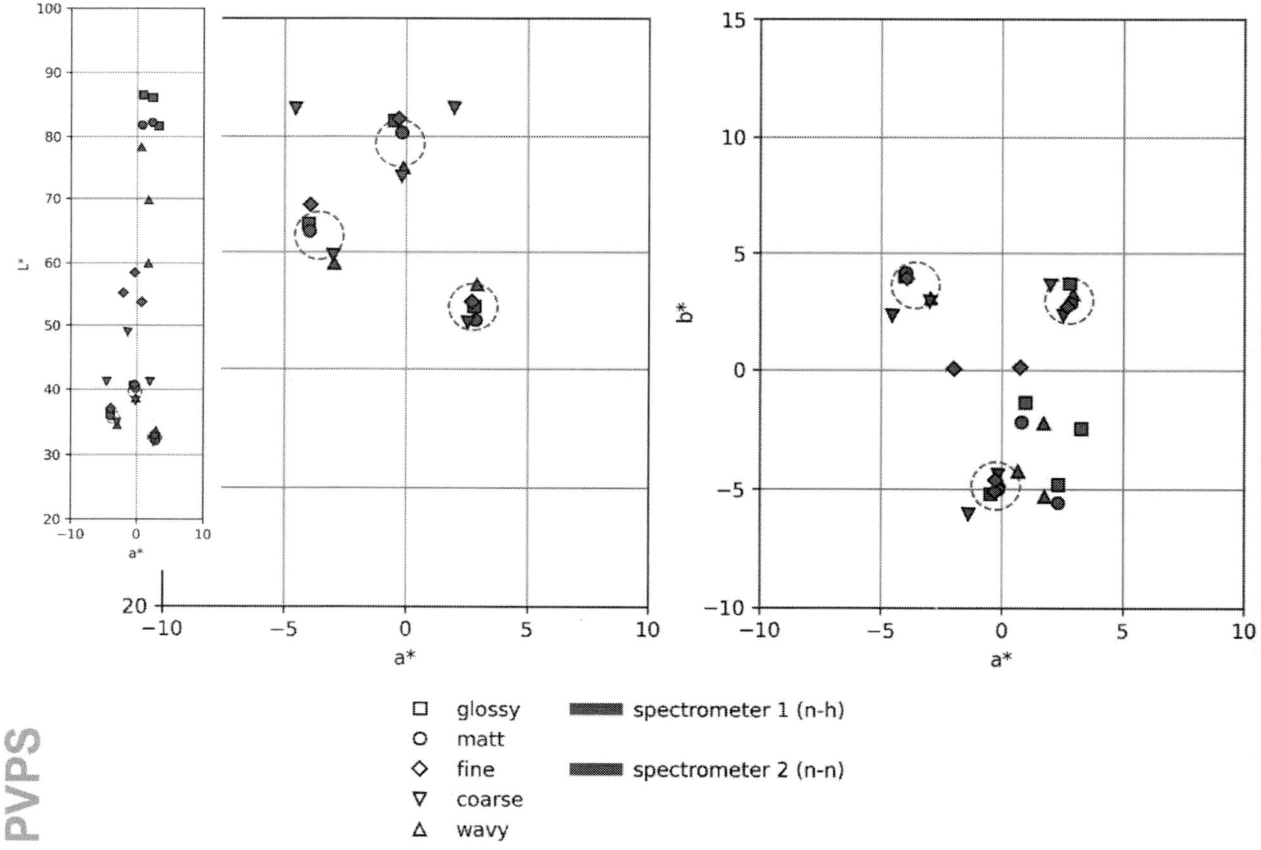

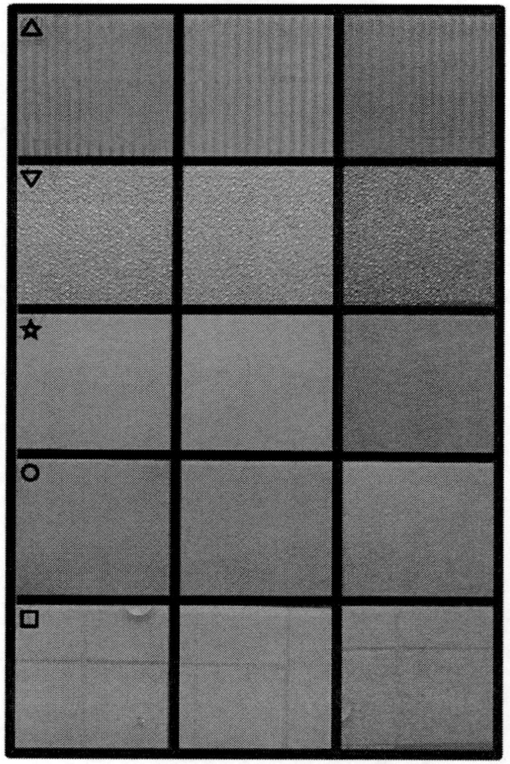

PVPS

Effect of different glass surfaces (modules)

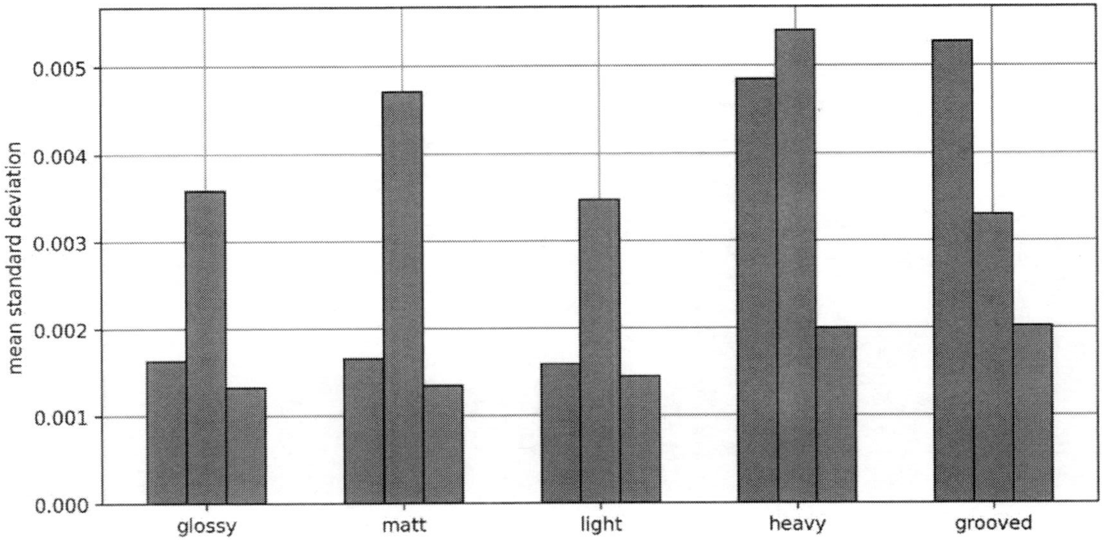

Learnings:

- Integrating optics are necessary
- Inclusion of specular reflections preferrable
- Higher uncertainty for textured glass

PVPS

11

Comparing measurements on modules and glass

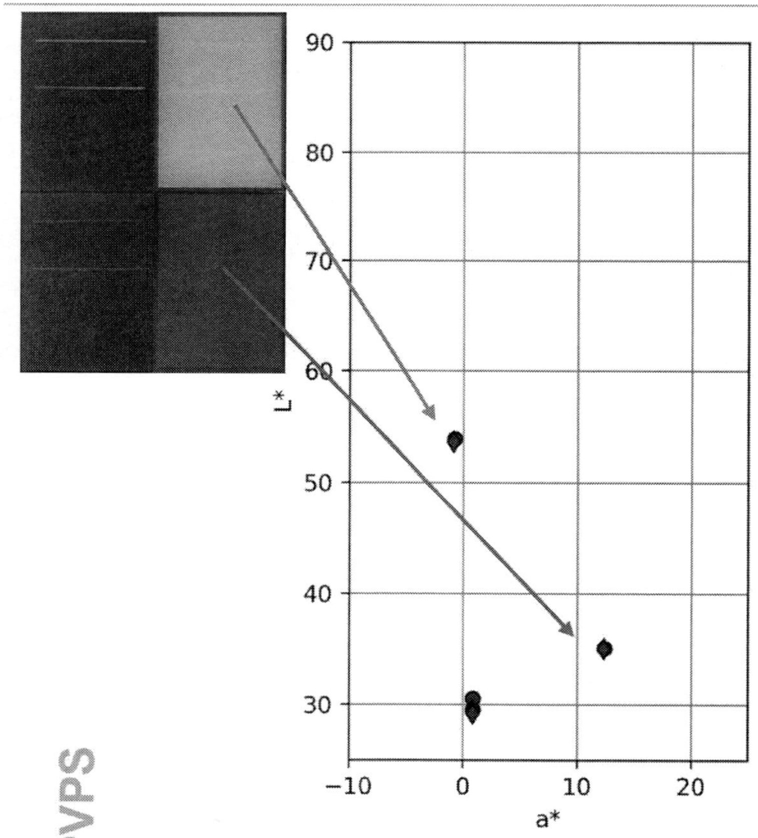

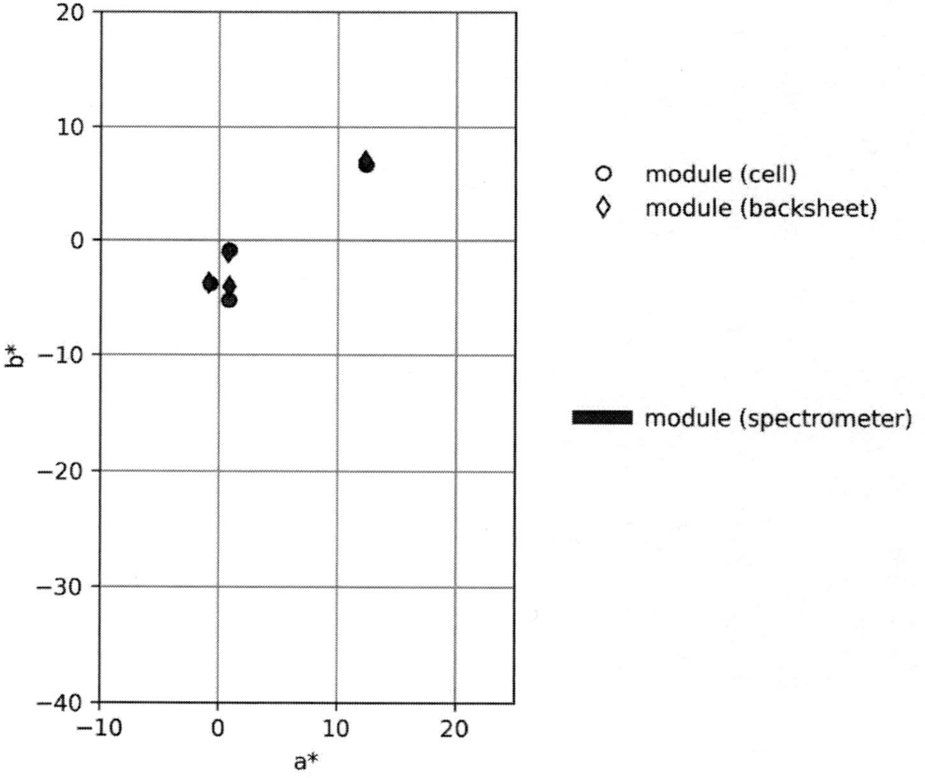

PVPS

Comparing measurements on modules and glass

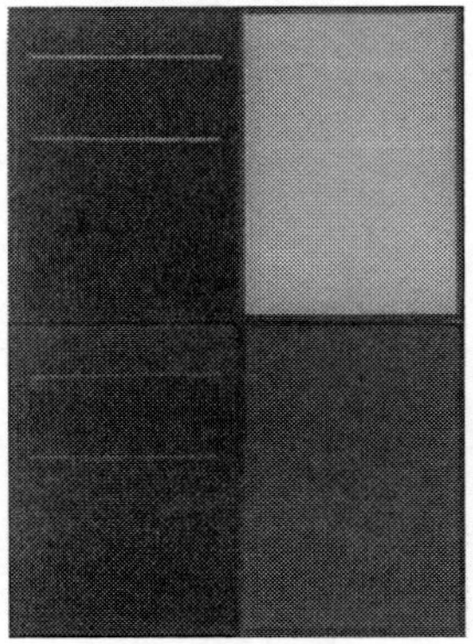

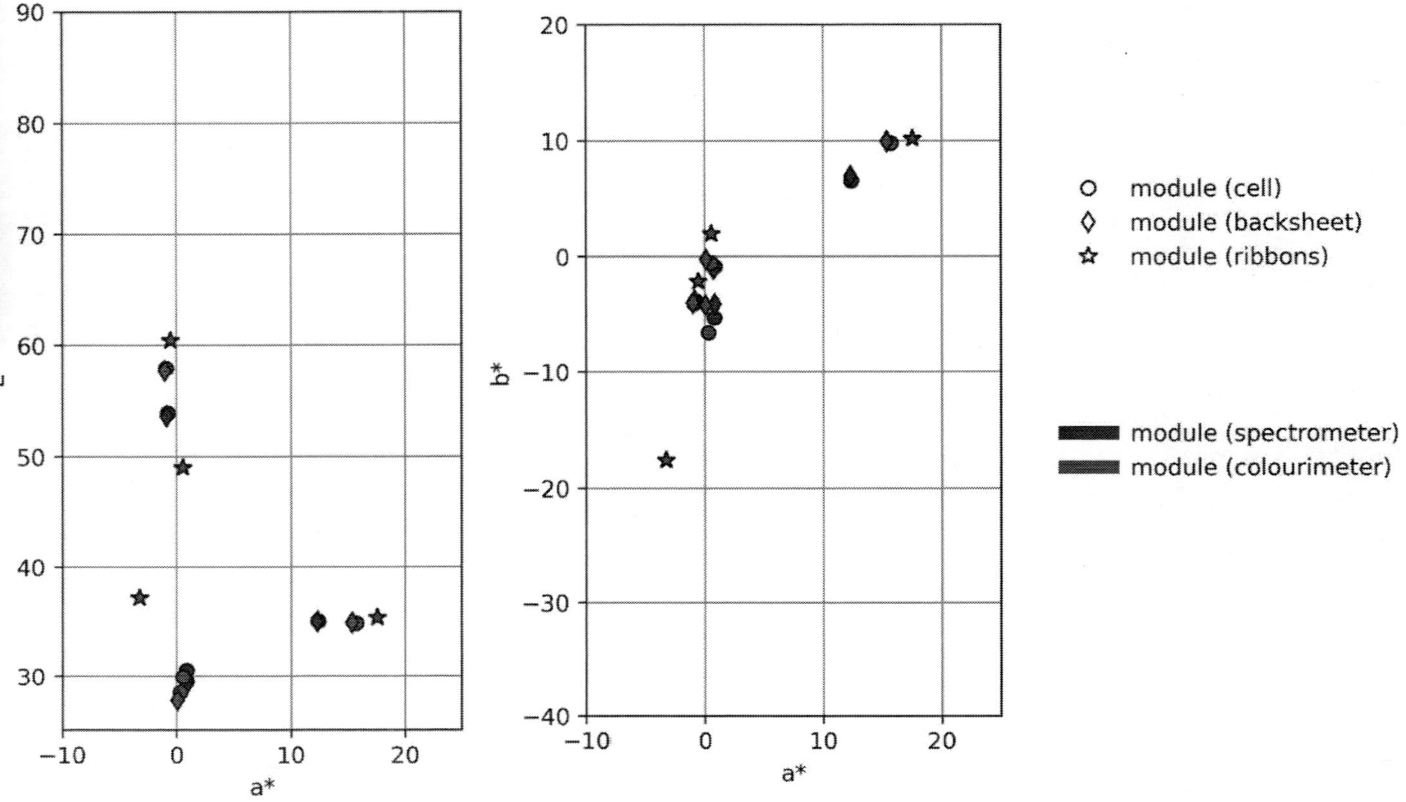

PVPS

Comparing measurements on modules and glass

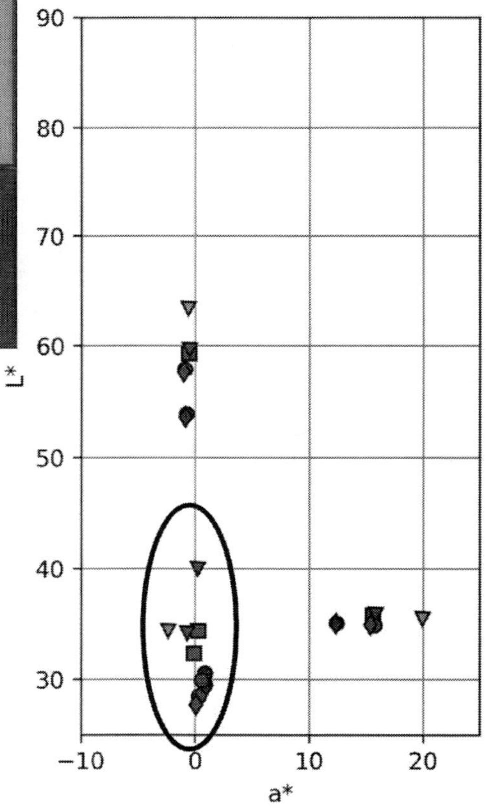

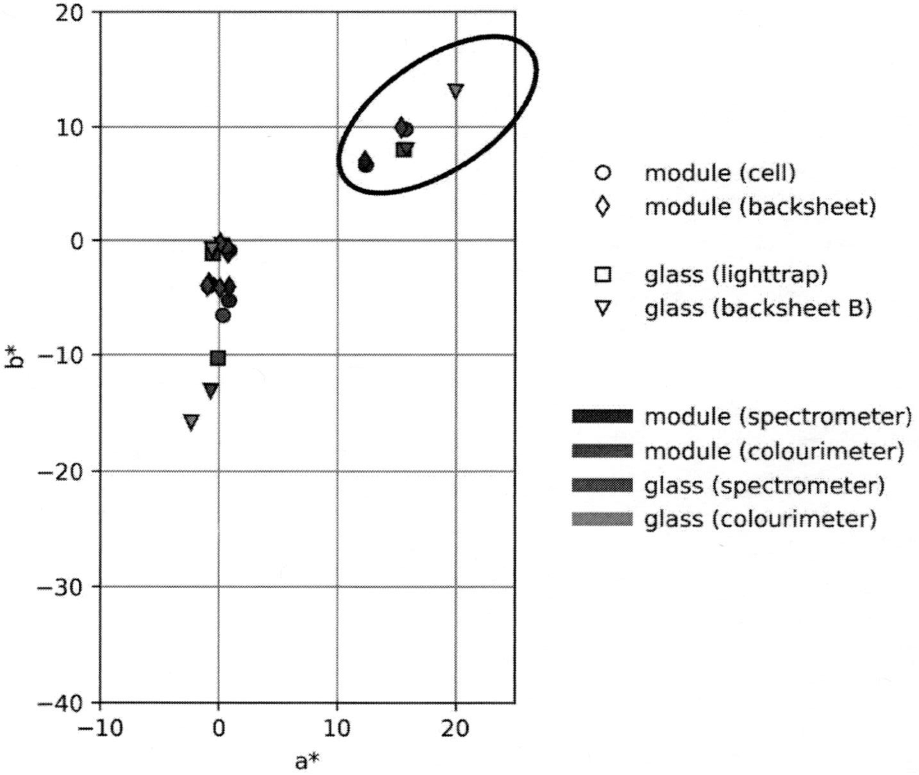

PVPS

14

Comparing measurements on modules and glass

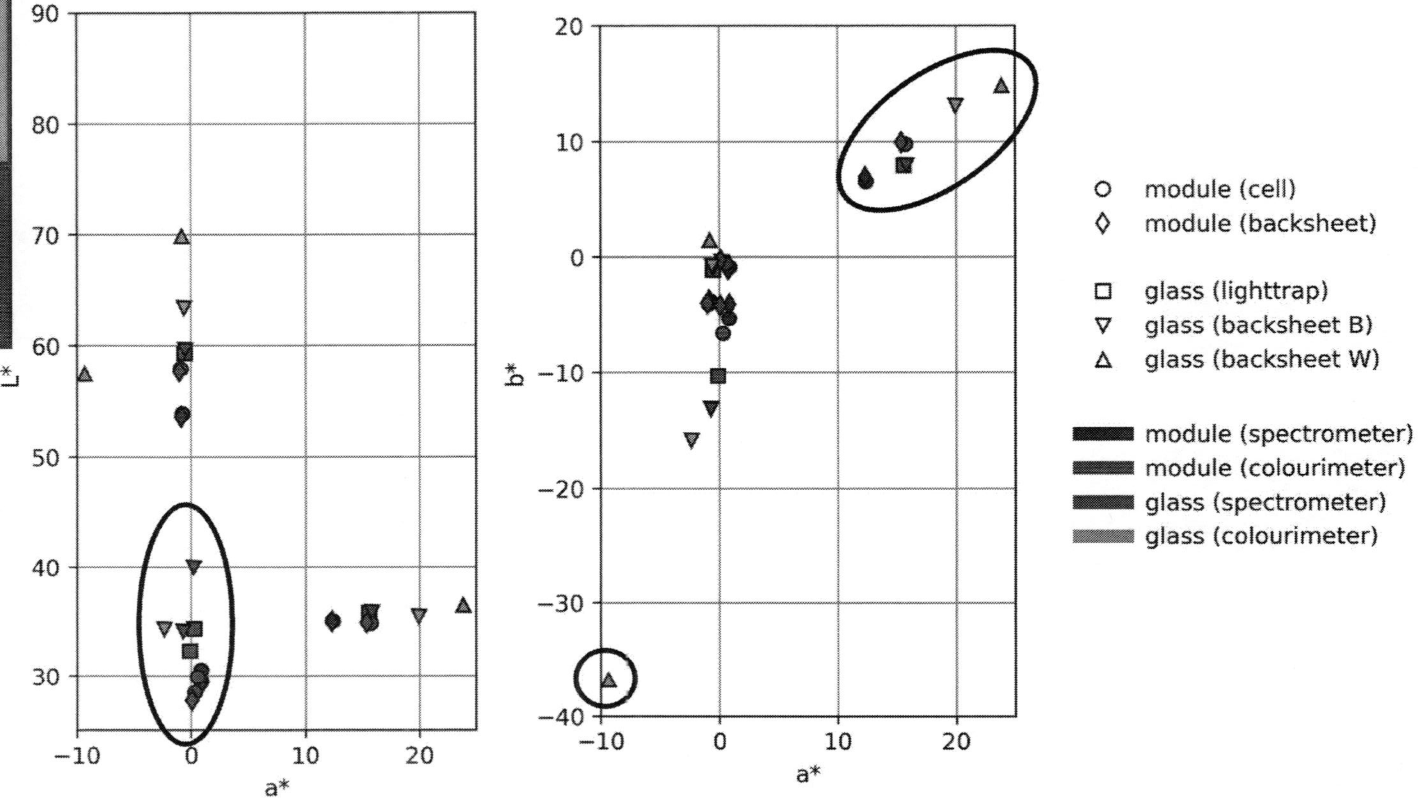

PVPS

15

Comparing measurements on modules and glass

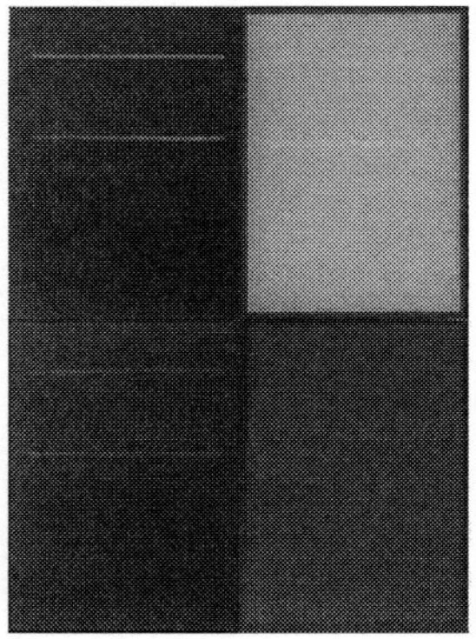

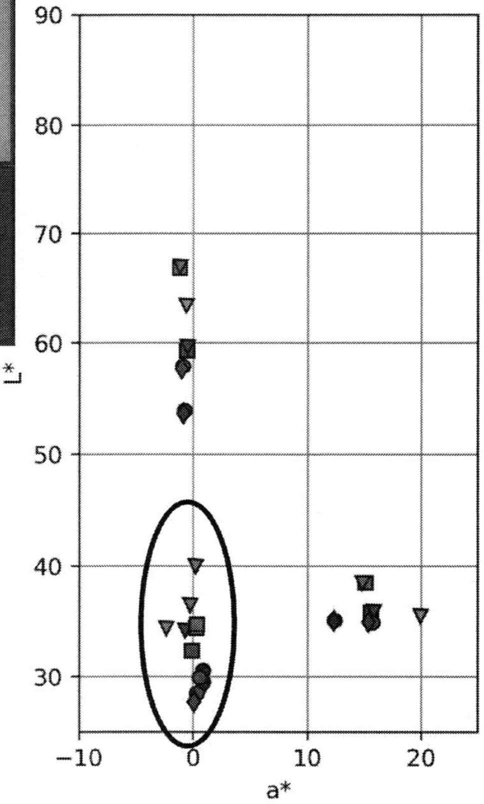

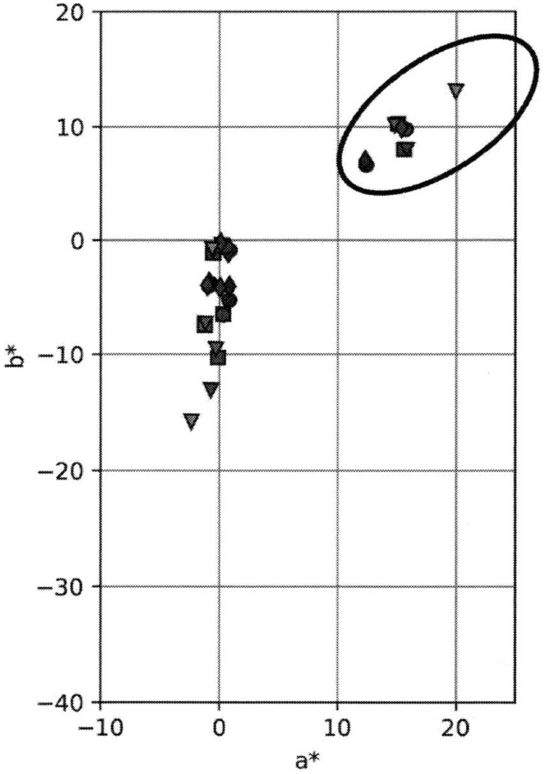

PVPS

Spectral transmittance of coloured glass

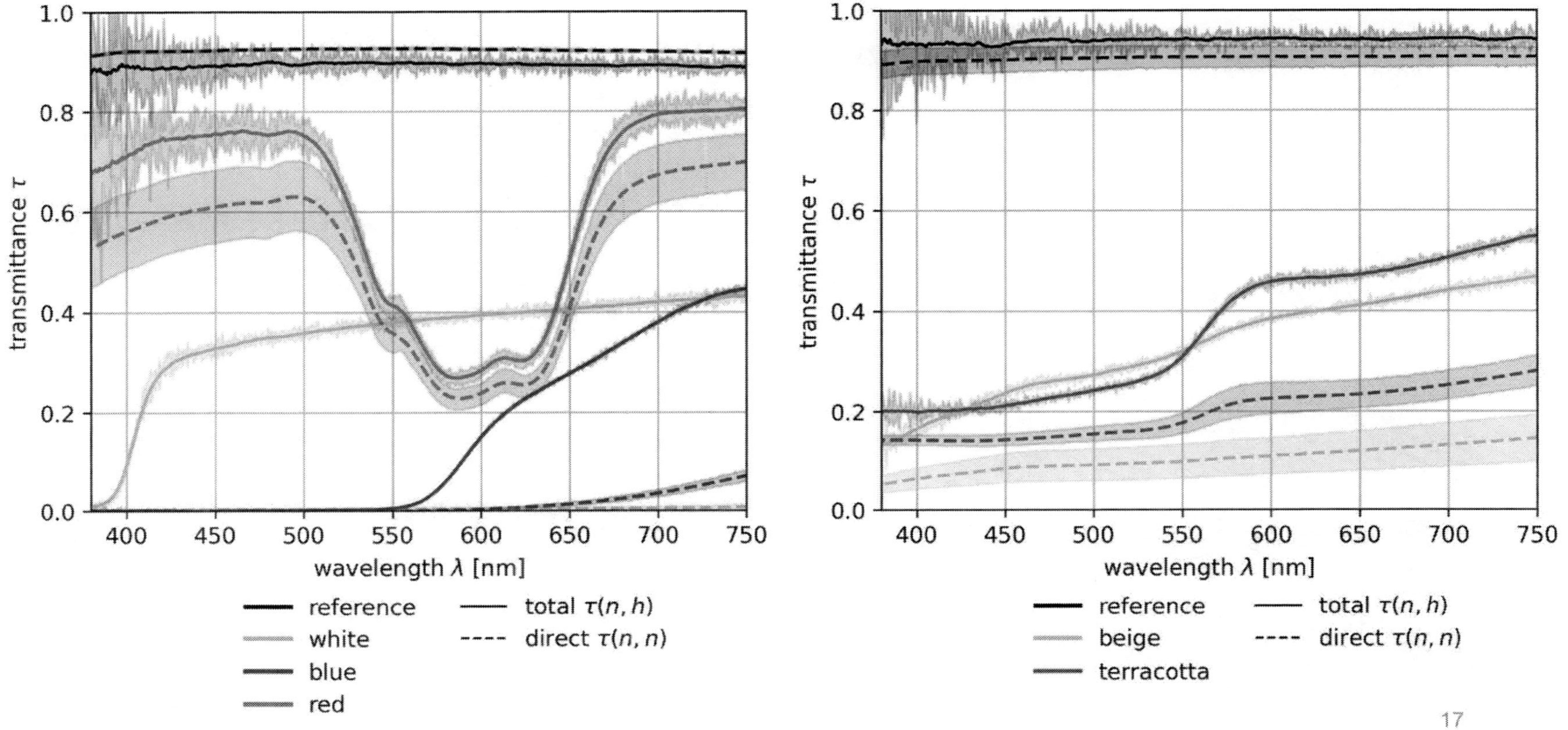

PVPS

Summary

Specular reflection components matter

→ Hemispherical measurements advisable
→ Textured glass increases measurement uncertainty

Significant differences between instruments

→ Differences in collection optics
→ Often designed for matt surfaces

Scattering strongly influences transmittance measurements

Conclusions & Next steps

Colour measurements on glazed (BI)PV modules are non-trivial!

Sources of disagreement between instruments:

- Integrating optics
- Aperture sizes

Correlation between glass and module measurements:

- Sample set with different print intensities and textures
- Involvement of additional laboratories and methods

www.iea-pvps.org

IEA PVPS

Starting in October

1st IEA PVPS Task 15

Blind Modelling Intercomparison

Open to all PV system modellers!

Thank you to…

… all participants in activity B4!

… the respective funding bodies!

… you for listening!

Markus Babin, Task 15
marbab@dtu.dk

Technology Collaboration Programme
by iea

PREDICTING LIGHT SCATTER IN STRUCTURAL COLORED BIPV MODULES AND TEXTURED GLASS USING RADIANCE

Nanna L. Andersen[1], Markus Babin[1], Jan Svatos[1], Karlis Petersons[2], Leif Yde[2], Jan F. Stensborg[2], Catarina G. Ferreira[3,4], Ananta Paul[3,5], Jani Lamminaho[3,5], Joel D. Cox[3,4,6], MortenMadsen[3,5], Peter B. Poulsen[1], and Sune Thorsteinsson[1]
[1] DTU Electro, Technical University of Denmark, Roskilde, Denmark
[2] Stensborg A/S, 4000 Roskilde, Denmark
[3] SDU Climate Cluster, University of Southern Denmark, Odense 5230, Denmark
[4] POLIMA, University of Southern Denmark, 5230 Odense M, Denmark
[5] CAPE, University of Southern Denmark, Mads Clausen Institute, 6400 Sønderborg, Denmark
[6] Danish Institute for Advanced Study, University of Southern Denmark, 5230 Odense M, Denmark
Email: nalan@dtu.dk

ABSTRACT: This work investigates the use of ray-tracing simulations to support the design of colored Building-Integrated Photovoltaic (BIPV) modules. Aesthetic integration of BIPV often requires color. To minimize angular dependency in structural colored BIPV modules, texture can be applied. Predicting the optical appearance of such modules is challenging, typically requiring iterative fabrication and measurement. To overcome this, the ray-tracing software Radiance is evaluated for simulating light scattering in textured BIPV components and modules. Simulations were compared with Bidirectional Reflection Distribution Function (BRDF) measurements of textured front glasses and foils, both before and after EVA encapsulation. Simulations showed promising results for individual components but revealed limitations in reproducing multilayer behavior. Encapsulation was found to strongly influence light scattering, highlighting the need for full-stack analysis. Radiance demonstrates potential as a design tool in colored BIPV, though further analysis is needed to assess the possibility for accurate module-level predictions.
Keywords: BIPV, modelling, appearance, ray-tracing

1 INTRODUCTION & MOTIVATION

Improving the aesthetics of modules is an important part of Building-Integrated Photovoltaics (BIPV). To make them an appealing solution, we need the possibility of adding color, which can be achieved using various methods [1]. One option being structural coloration. Structural colors, relying on constructive interference effects, offer high light transmission but are typically strongly angular dependent, meaning the module appearance changes based on light incidence and viewing angle.

In the ColorFoil project the aim is to produce colored BIPV modules using a colored interlayer based on structural coloration. The structural coloration is obtained by a stack of thin dielectric layers that interfere with the incoming light [2-3]. To mitigate the angular dependency of the coloration, the colored interlayered is textured, scattering the light in different directions.

Figure 1: BIPV module stack for ColorFoil. From the top the layers are: Front glass, encapsulant, Colored + textured foil, encapsulant, PV cell, encapsulant, backsheet.

Evaluating the performance of the textures and predicting the final appearance of the full module stack can be difficult, in most cases requiring manufacturing and measuring of all samples. Leading to a trial-and-error testing for all changes of the color or texture design. This work aims to investigate how the ray-tracing based software Radiance [4] can be used in the design process of BIPV modules.

In this work the ray-tracing simulation tool will be used to simulate how light is scattered by different textures within the PV module. The simulations will be validated using bidirectional reflectance distribution function measurements of constructed PV components and modules including differently textured foils and front glasses.

2 METHODS

2.1 Simulations

In order to consider the angular dependency in our simulations we need to use 3D raytracing. A popular tool for this is Radiance, which is software developed to analyze and visualize lightning in design. In Radiance you define a system or scene consisting of a set of materials, objects and light sources. Radiance contains several functions to analyze or visualize the defined system, one of them simulating and returning the Bidirectional Reflection Distribution Function (BRDF) [5-6]. The BRDF describes how a material reflects incoming light at different incidence and viewing angles.

2.2 Experiments

The selection of samples consists of two differently textured glasses: A standard PV front glass and a satinated front glass, and three differently textured interlayer foils. The interlayer foils do not contain the dielectric stack, but instead a thin layer of gold is sputtered onto the textures to assess how they scatter the light.

To evaluate the performance of the Radiance simulations, the BRDF of all samples is measured using a setup that consists of a collimated light source, a moveable sensor connected to a spectrometer and a sample holder capable of rotating around one axis. This setup is capable of producing inplane BRDF measurements. A detailed description can be found in [7]. Recently an upgrade was made to this system, replacing the 1-axis rotating sample holder with a robot arm, enabling full hemispherical BRDF measurements [8]. Examples of both BRDF measurements will be presented in this work. BRDF measurements of the textured foils have been performed before and after EVA encapsulation to assess the changes in the BRDF as the foils are imbedded in BIPV modules.

To be able to replicate the textured surfaces of the samples in Radiance, 3D scans of the sample surfaces were performed using an optical 3D profiling microscope (Sensorfar S neox) [9]. At this point the surface of three of the samples have been characterized, consisting of the two textured glasses and one of the textured foils, as indicated in Table I.

Table I: Samples and experimental measurements

	BRDF	Surface scan
Standard PV Glass	Hemispherical	X
Satinated Glass	Hemispherical	X
Textured Foil 1	Inplane	X
Textured Foil 2	Inplane	-
Textured Foil 3	Inplane	-
Foil 1 + EVA	Inplane	-

3 RESULTS AND ANALYSIS

3.1 Textured Front Glasses

Figure 2 shows hemispherical BRDF measurements of the two textured glass samples for one incident angle, indicated by the black arrow. For the standard PV glass specular peaks from the glass surface can be seen, although of low magnitude compared to plain glass. While for the satinated glass sample, no specular peak is observed and low BRDF values are spread over the entire hemisphere.

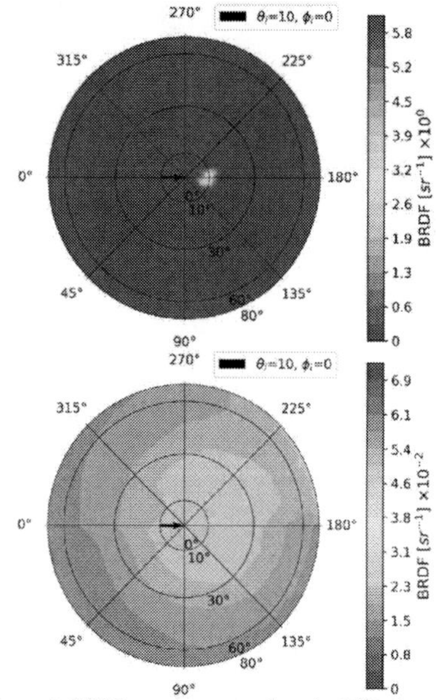

Figure 2: BRDF measurements of standard PV glass (top) and satinated glass (bottom) [7].

A big part of the explanation for the differences in BRDF of the two samples arises from the difference in surface textures. Figure 3 shows the 3D surface scans of the two glasses. The 1x1 mm surface scan of the standard PV glass shows very smooth surface topology with low height gradients, reducing the strength of the specular reflections. The surface scan of the satinated sample shows a high surface variation over an even smaller area of 0.25x0.25 mm.

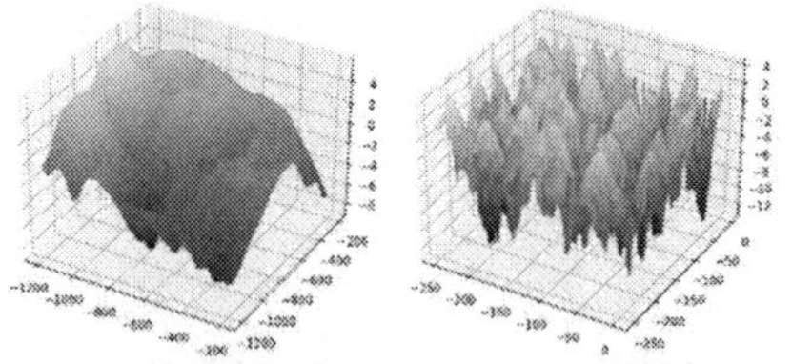

Figure 3: 3D surface scans in μm of standard PV glass (top) and satinated glass (bottom).

Figure 4 shows the simulation results of the implementation of the two textures in Radiance as dielectric surfaces with a refractive index of 1.5 and transmission coefficients 0.96. Compared to the measurements, the overall distribution with the specular reflection for the standard PV glass is captured well, though with a slightly higher magnitude. For the satinated glass sample the simulation shows less scattering and higher specular and near specular reflections than what is seen in the measurements. As the samples are only modelled as surfaces in Radiance, any potential subsurface reflections are not captured in the simulation, which could be a potential explanation for the observed differences between measured and simulated results for the satinated sample.

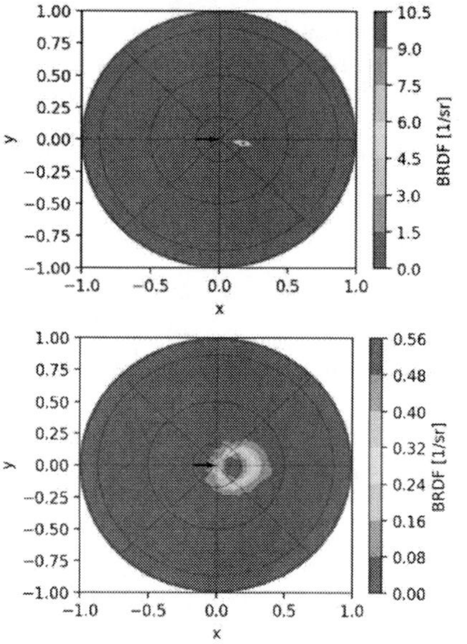

Figure 4: BRDF simulations of standard PV glass (top) and satinated glass (bottom).

3.2 Textured Foils and Multiple Layers

Figure 5 shows the inplane BRDF measurements of the three textured foils. In the top graph the foils are measured as they are and in the bottom graph is the same measurement but after encapsulation in EVA. Comparing the two graphs, it is clear to see how the differently textured foils scatter the light and how the scattering changes after EVA encapsulation, more for some than for others. For example, the orange graph - Foil 2 - shows wide scattering before encapsulation that seems to not be present after encapsulated in the EVA. Meanwhile Foil 3 seems to not change much after encapsulation. This emphasizes the need for looking at the full BIPV module stack when evaluating the performance of the textured foils.

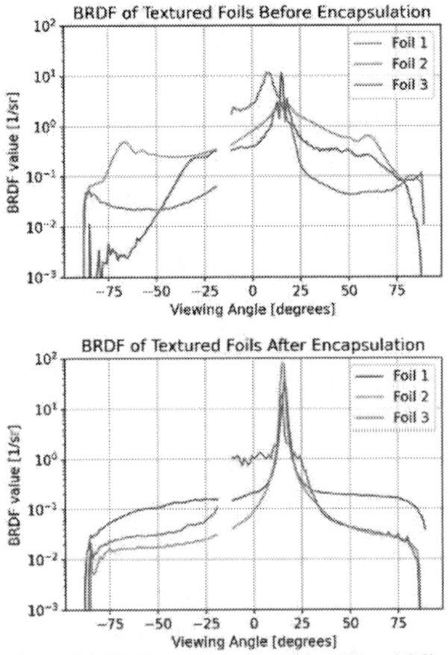

Figure 5: BRDF measurements of the textured foils, before (top) and after (bottom) EVA encapsulation.

Figure 6 shows the simulations and BRDF measurements of Foil 1 before and after encapsulation. For the foil before encapsulation, we see a high level of agreement between the measured and simulated BRDF results.

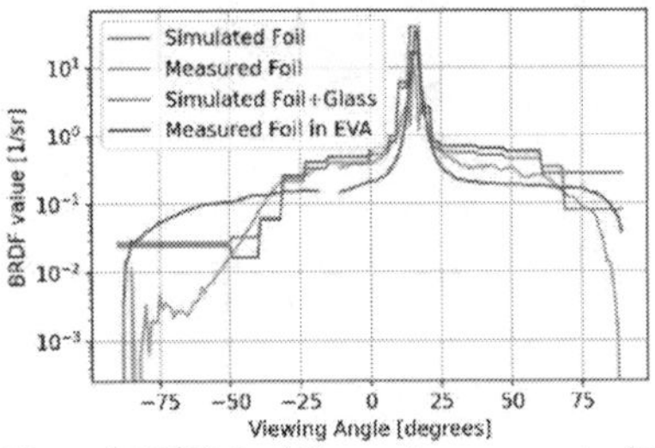

Figure 6: BRDF simulations and measurements of Foil 1 before and after encapsulation.

When considering multiple layers simulations, the foil is first simulated as encapsulated in a dielectric material as a representation of the EVA encapsulation. For this composition Radiance is not able to return sensible simulation results, indicating that how the materials are modelled in Radiance does not capture the behavior of the BIPV stack. The results shown in Figure 6 are instead the simulation results of Foil 1 embedded in a simplified version of the dielectric, designed for representing normal glass but avoiding simulating internal reflections. Here the simulation returns reasonable results but with high similarity to the results of the foil without encapsulation.

4 CONCLUSIONS & FUTURE WORK

Simulations and measurements of BIPV modules with textured elements have been performed of both individual components and of a multilayer stack representing the full BIPV module. Results for the individual components seem promising, while for the multilayer simulations, Radiance struggles to capture all effects at play. The BRDF measurements of the foils before and after EVA encapsulation highlights the need for full stack simulations to predict the final BIPV design. It is possible that Radiance could be one step in a chain of tools to predict final BIPV designs, though further work is needed to fully evaluate the potential of Radiance for BIPV module design simulations.

5 ACKNOWLEDGEMENTS

This work was funded by EUDP as part of the "ColorFoil" project under grant 64022-1027.

6 REFERENCES

[1] A. Borja Block, J. Escarre Palou, M. Courtant, A. Virtuani, G. Cattaneo, M. Roten, H.Y. Li, M. Despeisse, A. Hessler-Wyser, U. Desai et al., Energy and Buildings 314 (2024)
[2] C. Ferreira, I. Vyalih, J. Lamminaho, M. Babin, N. Andersen, P. Poulsen, S. Thorsteinsson, K. Petersons, J. Cox, M. Madsen (2024)
[3] B. Blasi, T. Kroyer, T. Kuhn, O. Hohn, IEEE Journal of Photovoltaics 11, 1305 – 1311 (2021)
[4] Radiance, https://www.radiance-online.org/, accessed 25-09-2025
[5] G. Ward, M. Kurt, N. Bonneel, Reducing Anisotropic BSDF Measurement to Common Practice (2014)
[6] D. Geisler-Moroder, E.S. Lee, G.J. Ward, B. Bueno, L.O. Grobe, T. Wang, B. Deroisy, H.R. Wilson, Tech. rep., IEA SHC Task 61 (2021)
[7] M. Babin, S. Thorsteinsson, M.L. Jakobsen, S.V. Spataru, 12, 1314 – 1318 (2022)
[8] J. Svatos, Mater Thesis, DTU, (2024)
[9] CMM-014-Sensofar, DOI: 10.57735/13866, accessed 25-09-2025

Modeling Partial Shading at the Cell Level on Photovoltaic Modules

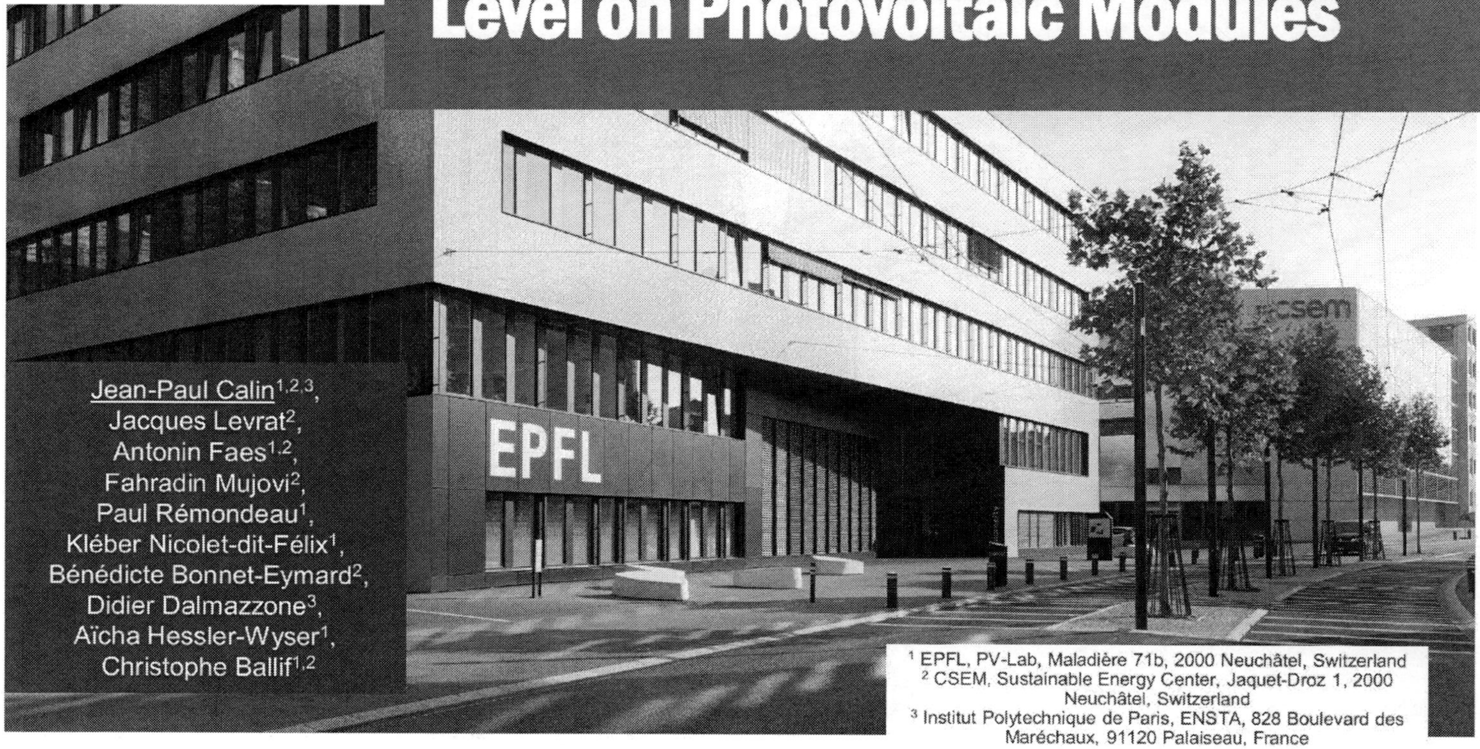

Jean-Paul Calin[1,2,3], Jacques Levrat[2], Antonin Faes[1,2], Fahradin Mujovi[2], Paul Rémondeau[1], Kléber Nicolet-dit-Félix[1], Bénédicte Bonnet-Eymard[2], Didier Dalmazzone[3], Aïcha Hessler-Wyser[1], Christophe Ballif[1,2]

[1] EPFL, PV-Lab, Maladière 71b, 2000 Neuchâtel, Switzerland
[2] CSEM, Sustainable Energy Center, Jaquet-Droz 1, 2000 Neuchâtel, Switzerland
[3] Institut Polytechnique de Paris, ENSTA, 828 Boulevard des Maréchaux, 91120 Palaiseau, France

EPFL
PV-lab IMT NEUCHATEL
csem
INSTITUT POLYTECHNIQUE DE PARIS

Introduction

- PV expanding in sectors like buildings, infrastructure, transportation, and agriculture
- Shadows may be thinner than submodules or even individual cells
- Shading losses reduce performance sharply, are nonlinear and configuration-dependent
- Near shading is modeled in state-of-the art software
- PVsyst: linear and electrical shading [1]
  - I-V curve based on sub-module

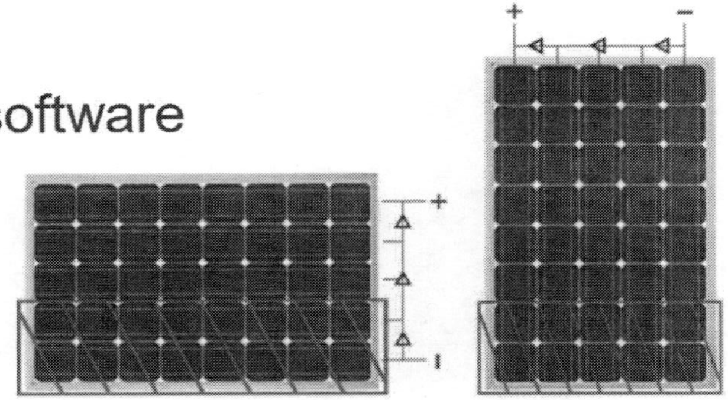

[1] A. Mermoud, "PVSYST: a user-friendly software for PV-systems simulation," in *Twelfth European Photovoltaic Solar Energy Conference: proceedings of the International Conference*, 1994.

Introduction

- Near shading modeling approach:
  - Project shadow on sub-module (or cells in our case)
  - Check points for shadow intersection
  - Calculate irradiance or IV curve

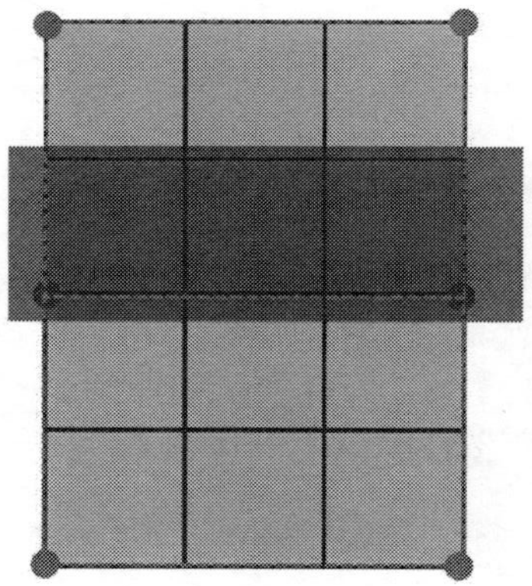

EPFL
PV-lab IMT NEUCHATEL
csem
INSTITUT POLYTECHNIQUE DE PARIS

Experimental Setup

- Installed a chimney-like structure in front of BIPV roof tile modules
- Captured images of the shadow throughout the day
- Monitored I-V curves, power, irradiance, and temperature

EPFL PV-lab IMT NEUCHÂTEL
csem
INSTITUT POLYTECHNIQUE DE PARIS

Method: Vertex Projection

Model configuration → **Vertex projection [2]** → **3D shaded region [2]** →

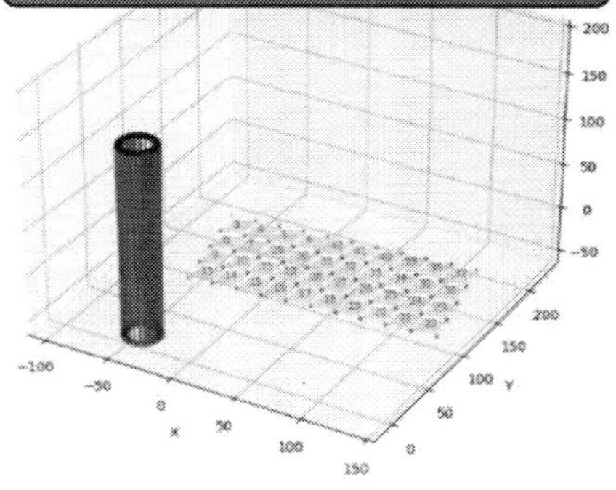

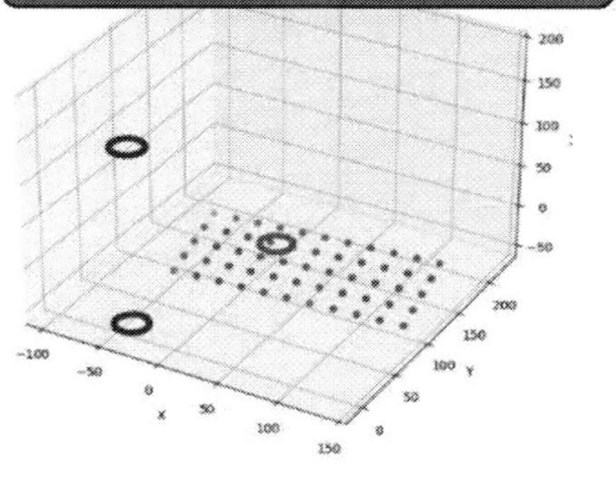

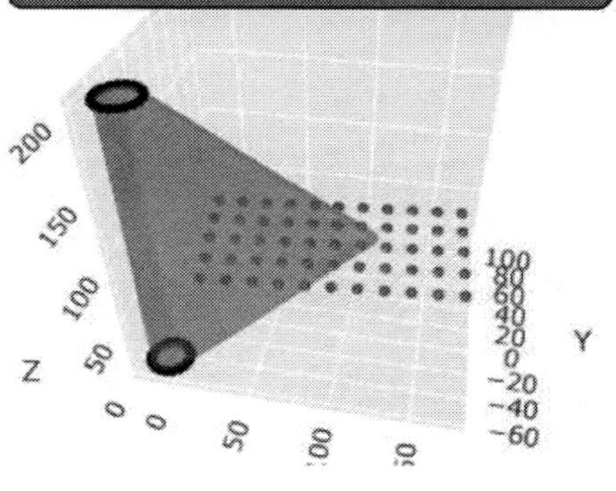

→ **Cell shadow raster [2]** **Module shadow**

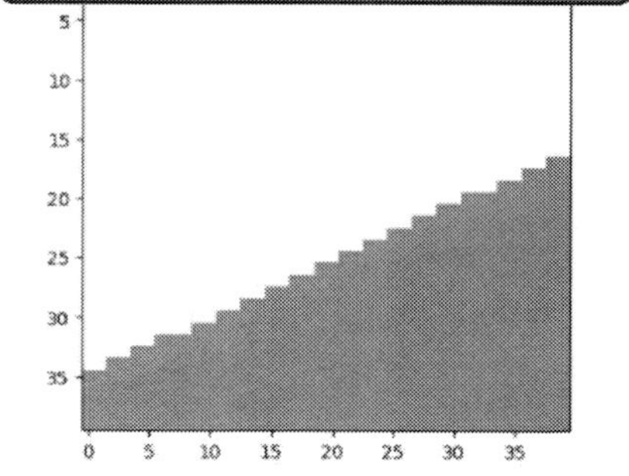

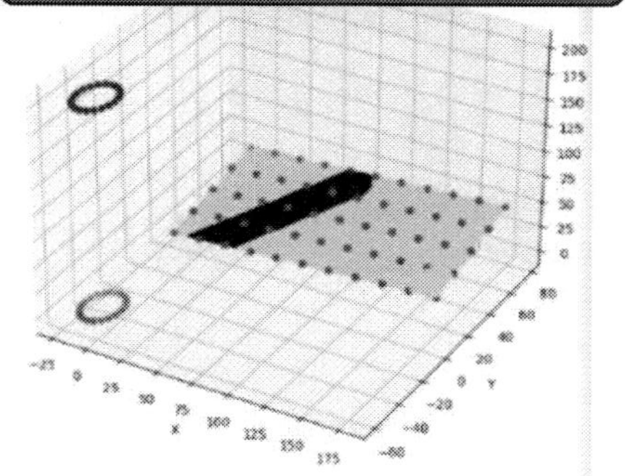

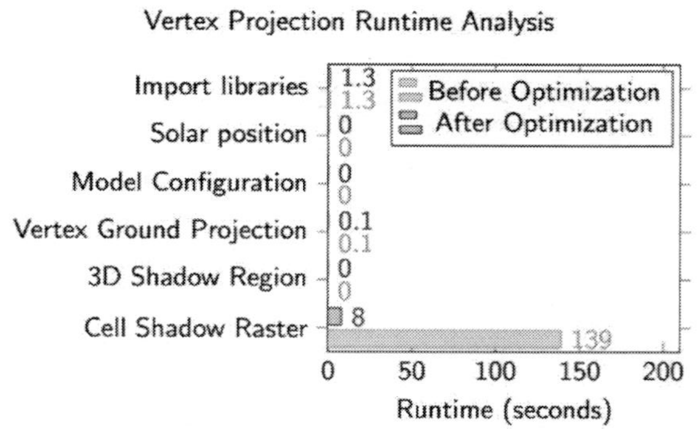

[2] B. A. de Sá, T. Dezuo, and D. Ohf, "Shadow Modelling Algorithm for Photovoltaic Systems: Extended Analysis and Simulation," *J. Control Autom. Electr. Syst.*, vol. 33, no. 5, pp. 1507–1518, Oct. 2022, doi: 10.1007/s40313-022-00905-2.

EPFL PV-lab IMT NEUCHATEL csem INSTITUT POLYTECHNIQUE DE PARIS

Method: Ray Tracing

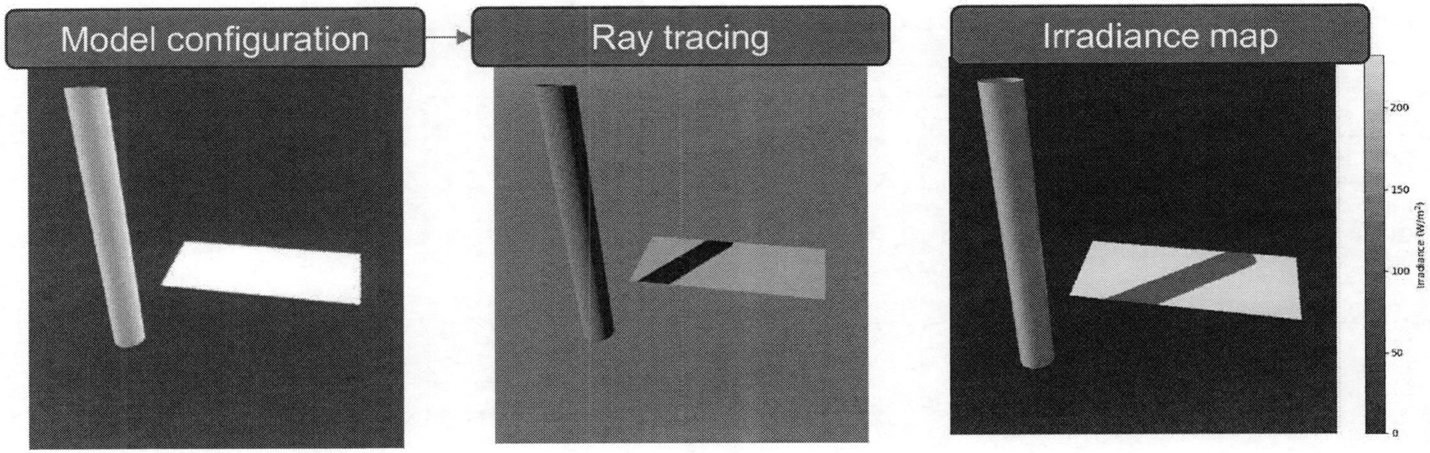

- Implemented using Radiance engine [3]
- Runtime optimized to 2.5 seconds per solar position using Radiance data structures
- Simple model configuration → fast shadow position
  - More accurate irradiance simulation possible with detailed model configuration [4]

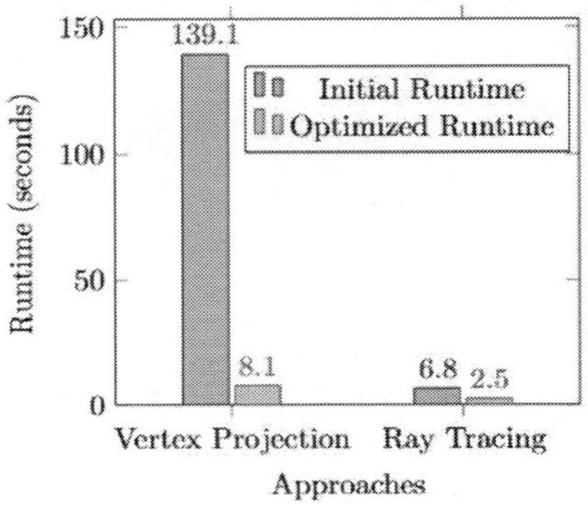

[3] G. W. Larson and R. Shakespeare, *Rendering with Radiance: the art and science of lighting visualization.* Morgan Kaufmann Publishers Inc., 1998.
[4] M. A. Mikofski, M. Lynn, J. Byrne, M. Hamer, A. Neubert, and J. Newmiller, "Accurate Performance Predictions of Large PV Systems with Shading using Submodule Mismatch Calculation," in *2018 IEEE 7th World Conference on Photovoltaic Energy Conversion (WCPEC) (A Joint Conference of 45th IEEE PVSC, 28th PVSEC & 34th EU PVSEC)*, Jun. 2018, pp. 3635–3639. doi: 10.1109/PVSC.2018.8547323.

EPFL PV-lab IMT NEUCHATEL csem INSTITUT POLYTECHNIQUE DE PARIS

Method: Check Points for Shadow Intersection

Shadow intersection logic	Sub-module level	Cell level 1x1 resolution	Cell level 2x2 resolution
Corner-based	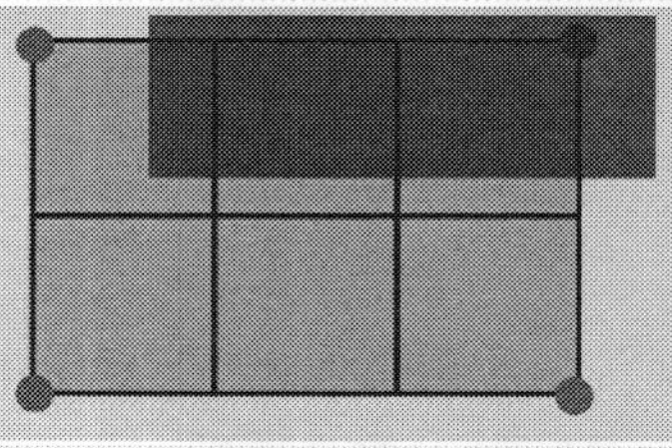	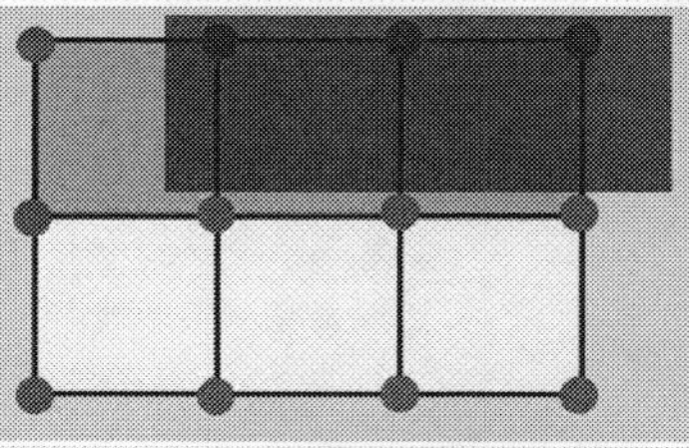	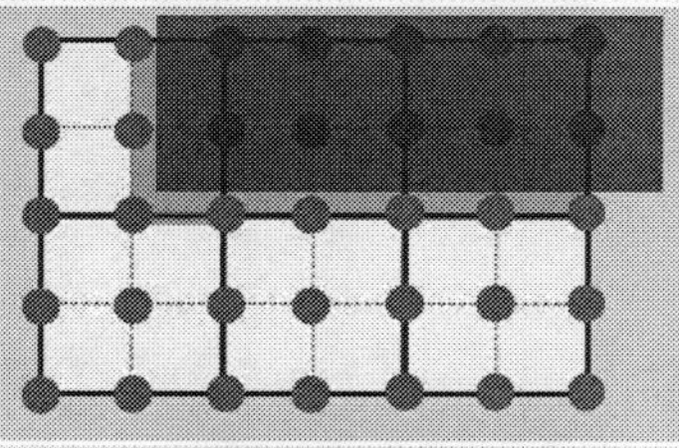
Centroid-based	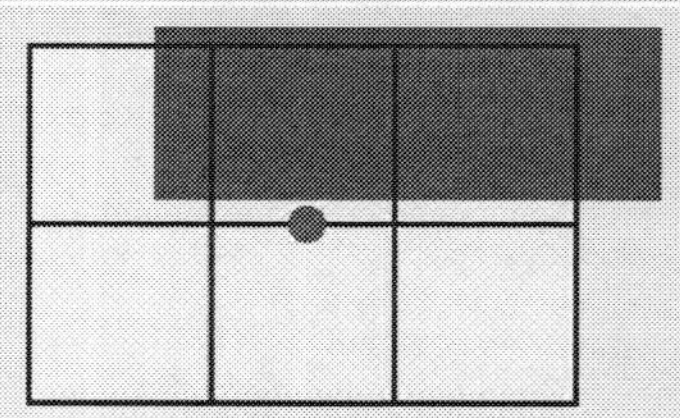	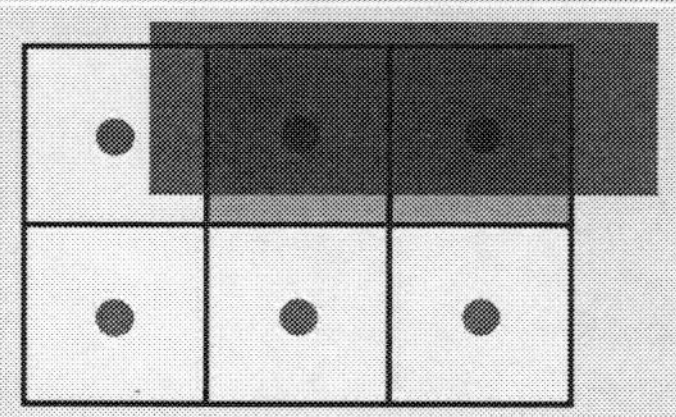	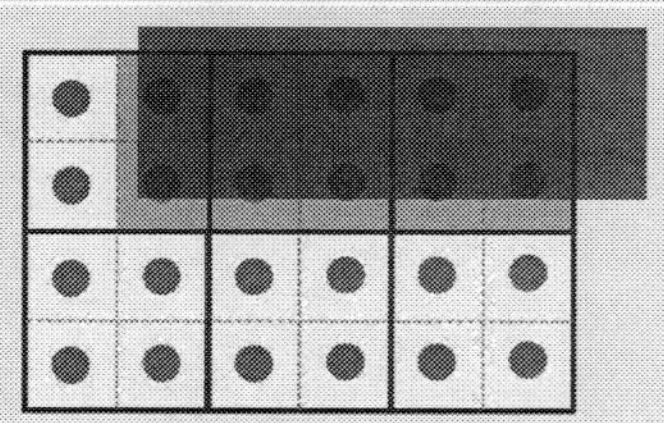

- Goal: to investigate strategies to model thinner shadows
  - Potential to improve accuracy by checking more points

EPFL
PV-lab IMT NEUCHATEL
csem
INSTITUT POLYTECHNIQUE DE PARIS

Method: Check Points for Shadow Intersection

Shadow intersection logic	Sub-module level	Cell level 1x1 resolution	Cell level 2x2 resolution
Corner-based	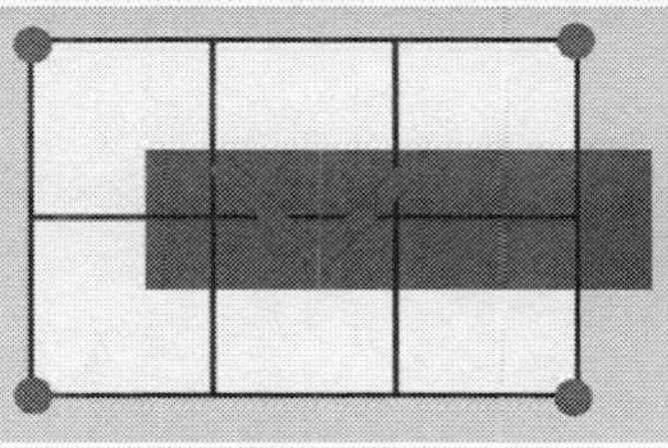	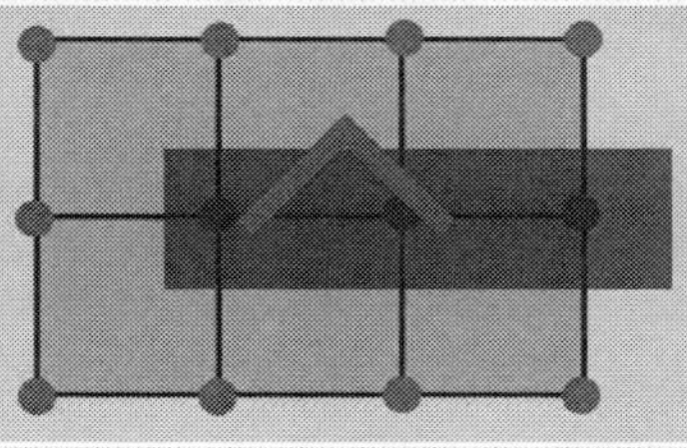	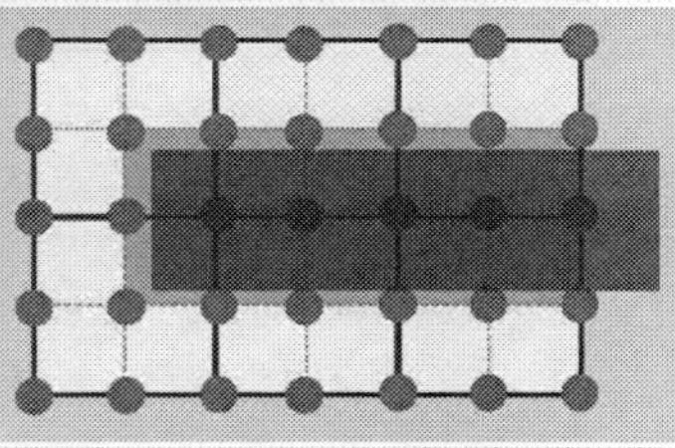
Centroid-based	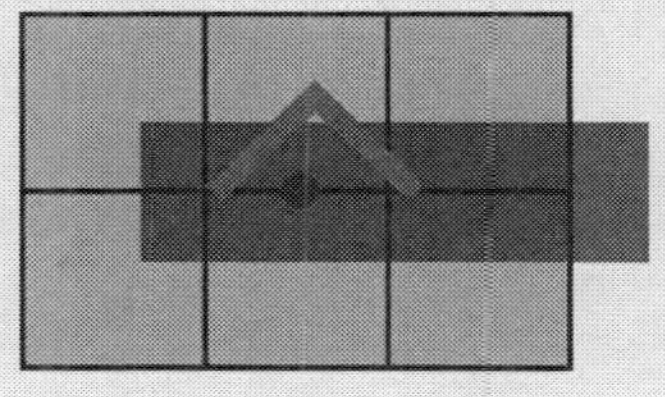	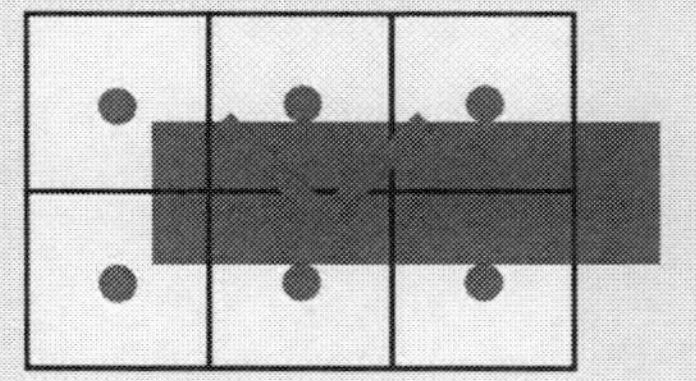	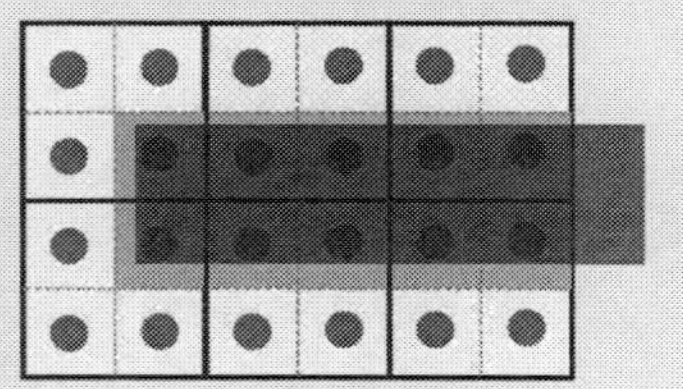

- Limitation of point sampling: some shadows will trick the algorithm
  - Checking more points takes more time. How to choose wisely?

EPFL PV-lab IMT NEUCHÂTEL :: csem INSTITUT POLYTECHNIQUE DE PARIS

Method: Irradiance Model

Quantity	Equation	Number
Global plane-of-array (POA) irradiance	$G_{POA} = G_{beam} + G_{sky} + G_{ground}$ [5]	(1)
Direct (beam) POA irradiance	$G_{beam} = DNI \cdot \cos(\theta)$	(2)
Diffuse sky POA irradiance	$G_{sky} = DHI \cdot \frac{1+\cos(\beta)}{2}$ [6]	(3)
Diffuse ground-reflected POA irradiance	$G_{ground} = GHI \cdot \rho \cdot \frac{1-\cos(\beta)}{2}$ [5]	(4)
Cell effective irradiance	$G_{cell} = G_{beam} * (1-\chi) + G_{sky} + G_{ground}$	(5)

- θ: angle of incidence
- β: module tilt angle
- ρ: ground surface albedo
- χ: cell shaded fraction

- DNI: direct normal irradiance
- DHI: diffuse horizontal irradiance
- GHI: global horizontal irradiance

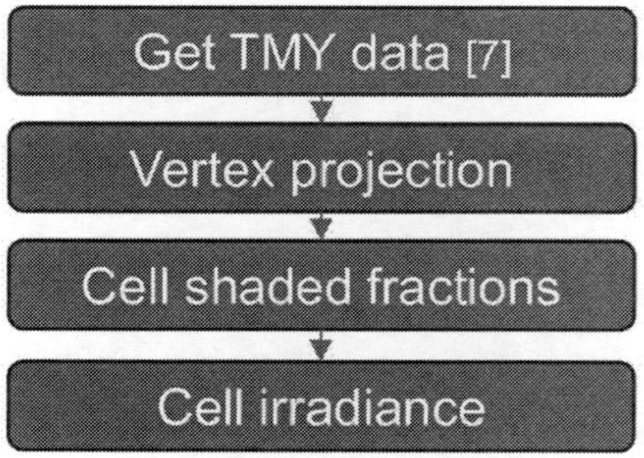

[5] P. G. Loutzenhiser, H. Manz, C. Felsmann, P. A. Strachan, T. Frank, and G. M. Maxwell, "Empirical validation of models to compute solar irradiance on inclined surfaces for building energy simulation," *Sol. Energy*, vol. 81, no. 2, pp. 254–267, Feb. 2007, doi: 10.1016/j.solener.2006.03.009.
[6] H. C. Hottel and B. B. Woertz, "The Performance of Flat-Plate Solar-Heat Collectors," *Trans. Am. Soc. Mech. Eng.*, vol. 64, no. 2, pp. 91–103, Dec. 2022, doi: 10.1115/1.4018980.
[7] Martinez, A., PVGIS Photovoltaic Geographical Information System, European Commission, Ispra, 2025, JRC142887.

EPFL
PV-lab IMT NEUCHATEL
csem
INSTITUT POLYTECHNIQUE DE PARIS

Results: Shadow Validation

Time	Simulation	Experiment
13:23	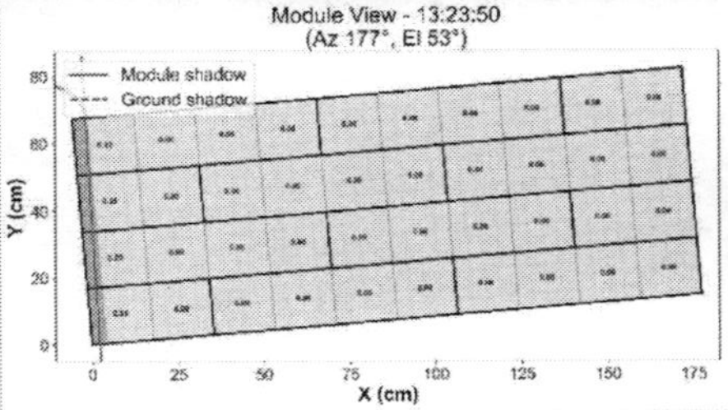	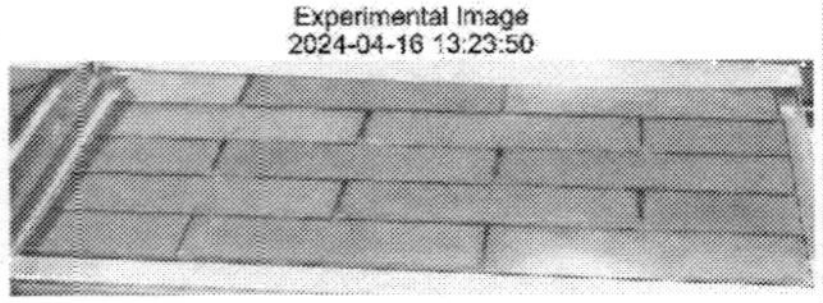
15:06	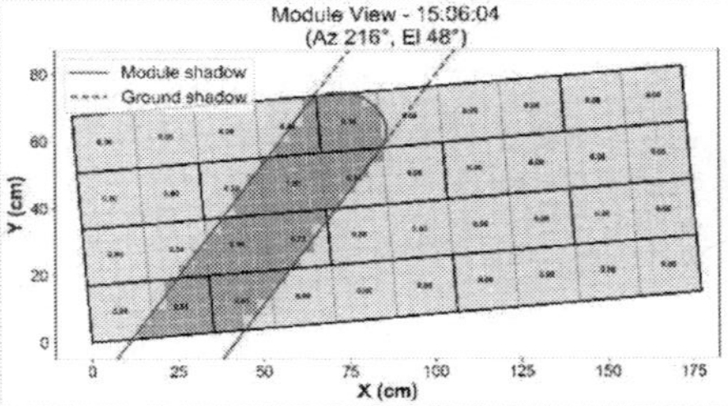	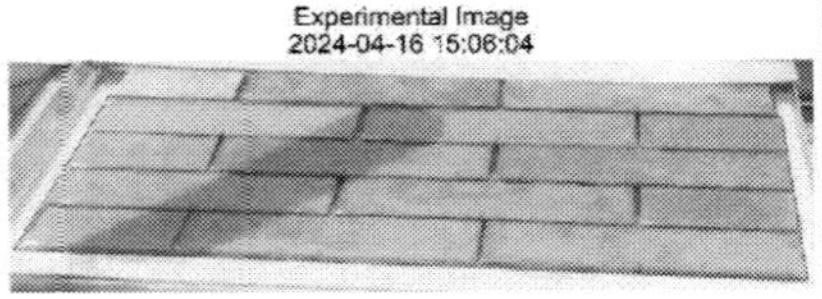
16:49	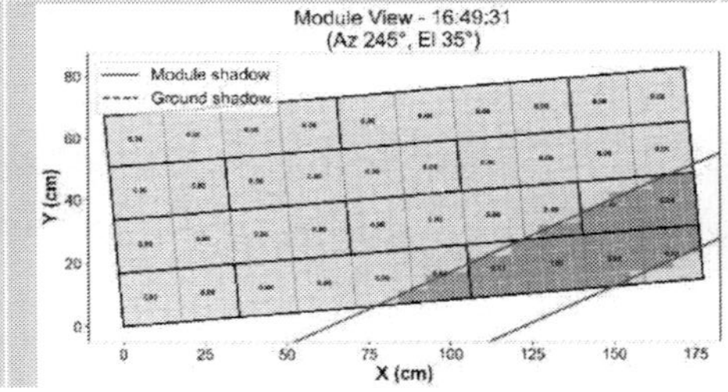	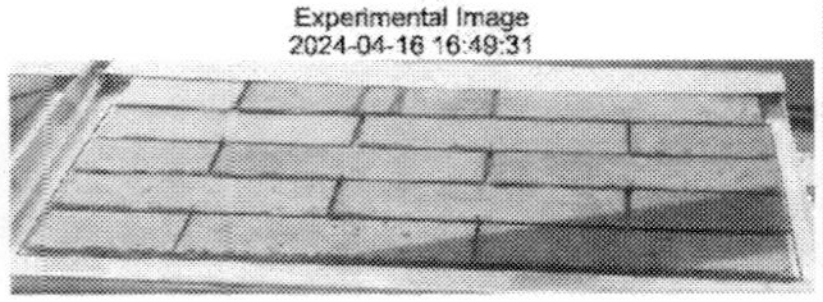

- Shadow positions validated against experiment

EPFL
PV-lab IMT NEUCHÂTEL
csem
INSTITUT POLYTECHNIQUE DE PARIS

Results: Shaded Fractions

Resolution	14:00	15:00	16:00	17:00
Cell level 1x1 (centroid)	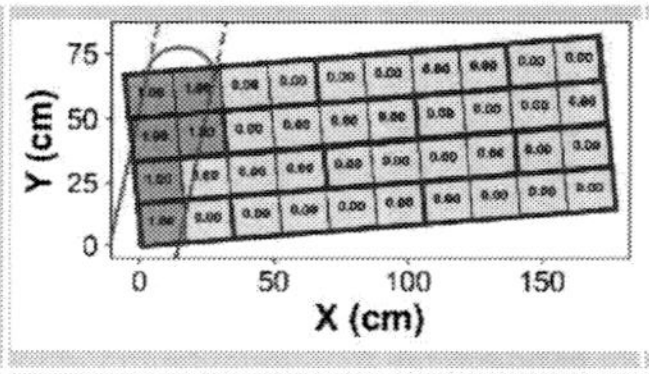	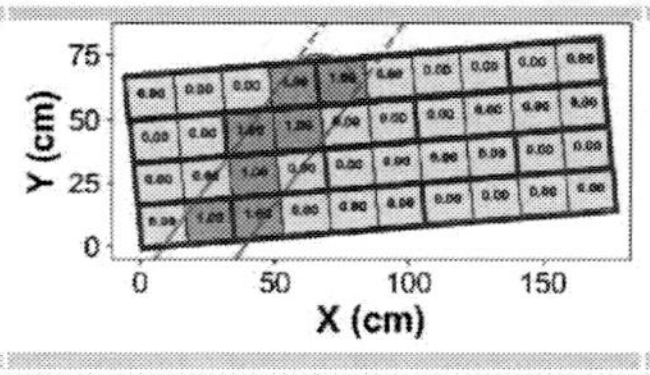	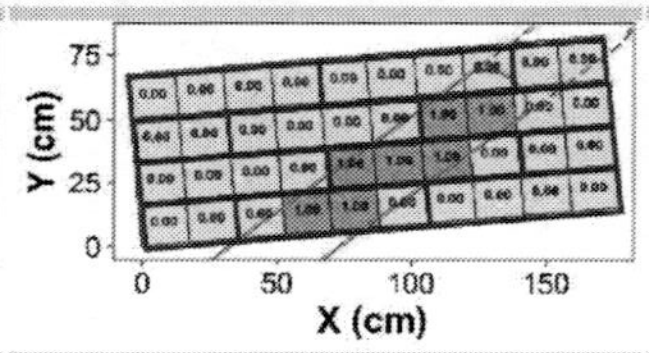	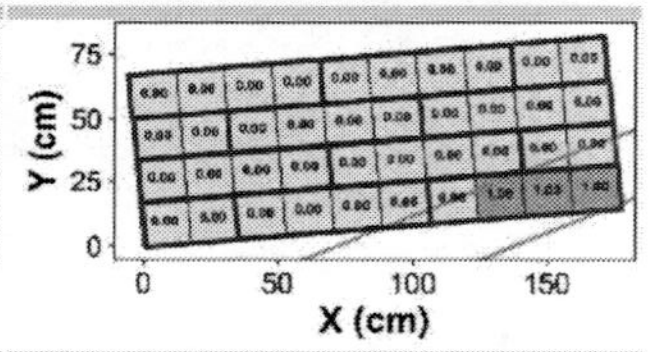
Cell level 2x2 (centroid)	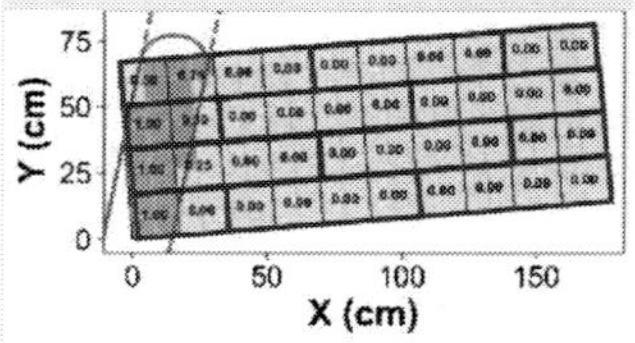	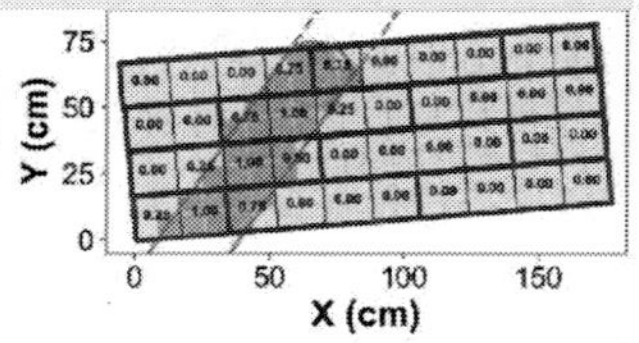	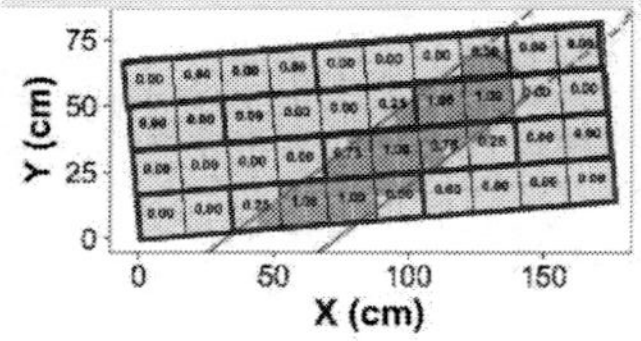	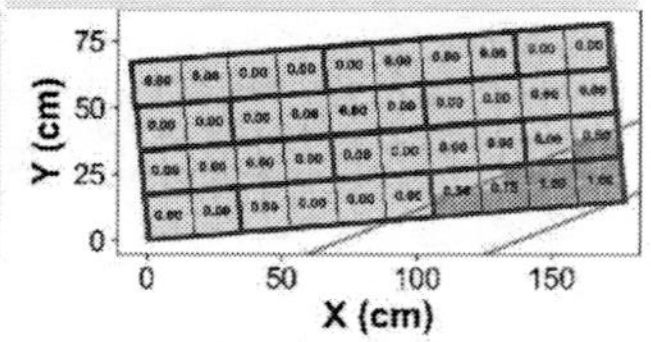
Cell level 3x3 (centroid)	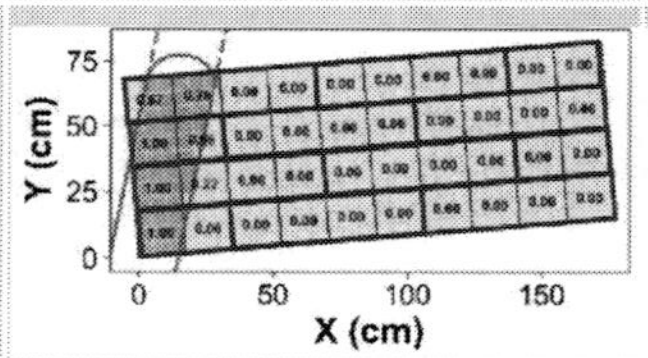	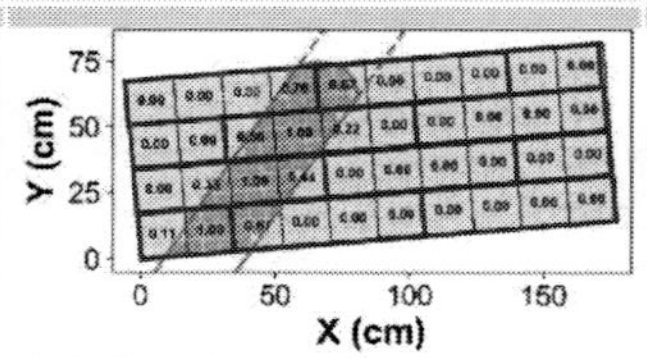	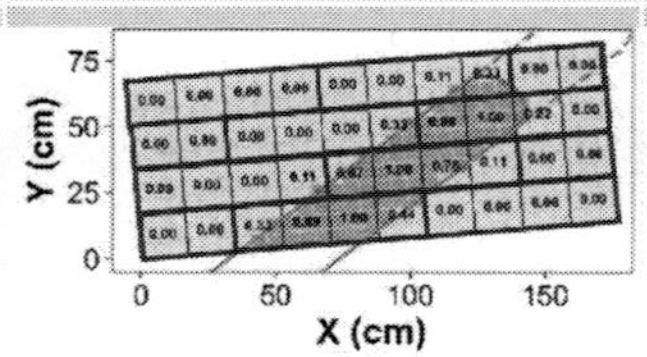	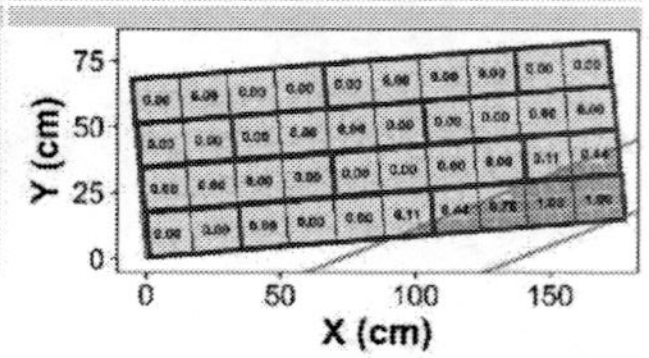

- 1x1 cell level resolution: shaded fraction is 0 or 1
- Higher resolutions: cell shaded fraction can be estimated more precisely

Results: Daily Irradiance & Irradiance Loss

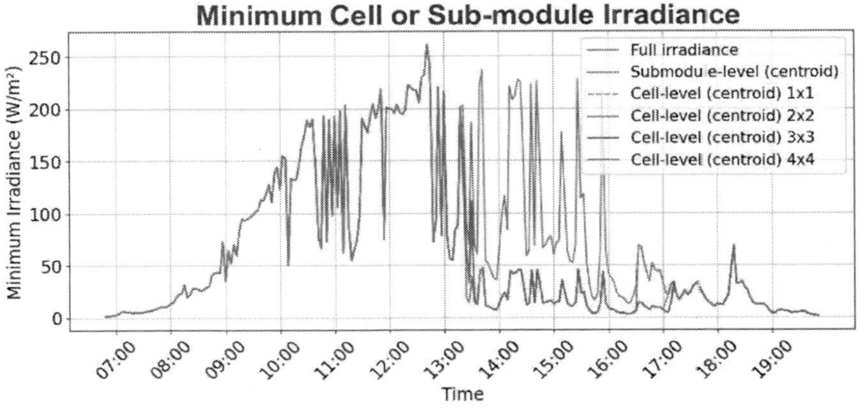

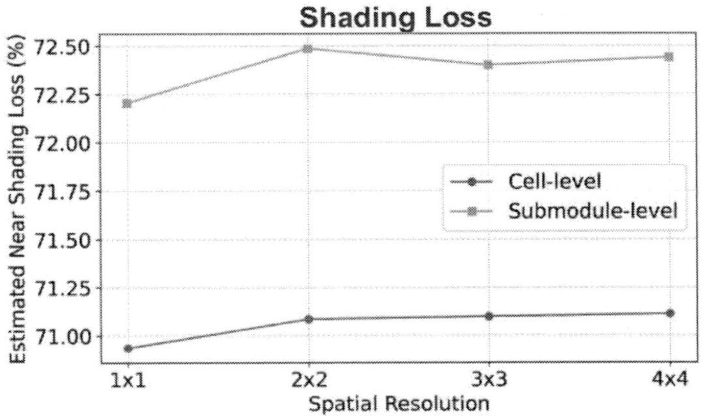

- Data from April 16 at 3-minute intervals
  - No shading in the morning, shadow events in the afternoon between 13:21 and 17:12
- Submodule-level approach sometimes over-estimates or under-estimates shading losses during partial shading events
  - Over-estimated losses at 13:27, by over 45 W/m²
  - Under-estimated losses at 16:34, by over 60 W/m²

- Potential gain in accuracy of 1% for given shadow configuration
- Model converges at 2x2 resolution and above for the given shadow size
  - Thinner shadows: model may converge at higher resolutions, potentially more accuracy gain

EPFL PV-lab IMT NEUCHÂTEL csem INSTITUT POLYTECHNIQUE DE PARIS

Results: Annual Simulation Runtime

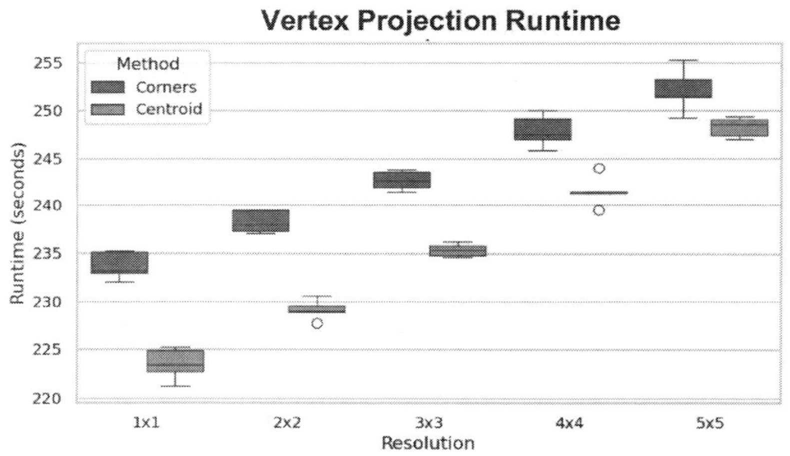

- Around 4 minutes on the lab desktop (64 GB RAM)
- Scales linearly with resolution

EPFL
PV-lab IMT NEUCHATEL
csem
INSTITUT POLYTECHNIQUE DE PARIS

Conclusion & Outlook

- Near shading simulation at cell level: TMY data, vertex projection, cell shading fractions, cell effective irradiance
  - Two shadow modeling approaches: vertex projection and ray tracing. Validated shadow positions experimentally
  - Compared strategies for selecting points to check for shadow intersection
- Potential to improve the accuracy of irradiance losses with more points
  - 1% less annual irradiance loss at cell level in the experimental configuration
- Tradeoff: computation time
  - Vertex projection runtime: optimized to around 4 minutes for 1-year hourly simulation, scales linearly with resolution
- Future work: investigate impact of shadow and cell sizes on optimal resolution

EPFL
PV-lab IMT NEUCHATEL
csem
INSTITUT POLYTECHNIQUE DE PARIS

15
Modeling Partial Shading at the Cell Level on Photovoltaic Modules
Thank you for listening!
Questions?
This research was funded by the European Union's Horizon Europe, Innovation Actions programme under grant agreement No 101136112 (Increase Project), No 101136094 (Sphinx Project), and No 101172767 (Empower project). This work has received funding from the Swiss State Secretariat of Education, Research and Innovation (SERI).
ncrease
SPHINX

■ Contact: jean-paul.calin@epfl.ch

Metallization & Interconnection
WORKSHOP 2025
for Solar Cells 13TH EDITION
October 20 & 21, Berlin, Germany
www.miworkshop.info
Registration is open! – early bird until September 29
Berlin (Germany) – hosted by HZB
Website and program: https://miworkshop.info/
Proceedings in IEEE Journal of Photovoltaics
Sponsors
csem
DOW
GORDA
Henkel
MONDRAGON ASSEMBLY
晶银新材

MARKET POTENTIAL OF BUILDING-INTEGRATED PHOTOVOLTAICS: A GRANULAR ANALYSIS OF THE EUROPEAN BUILDING STOCK

Juan Ignacio Martinez[2], Julien Van Overstraeten[2], Philippe Macé[1], José María Vega de Seoane[2], Elina Bosch[1], Mélodie de l'Épine[3]
[1]Becquerel Institute, Brussels (Belgium) [2]Becquerel Institute España, San Sebastián (Spain), [3]Becquerel Institute France, Lyon (France)
j.martinez@becquerelinstitute.eu, j.vanoverstraeten@becquerelinstitute.eu, p.mace@becquerelinstitute.org

ABSTRACT: Building-Integrated Photovoltaics (BIPV) has gained relevance as it offers a unique solution fulfilling the role of a construction element and an energy generation device. This study aims to assess the market potential for BIPV in Europe up to 2050, covering multiple building typologies within the European building stock, for roofs and façades, under two different growth scenarios. The methodology follows a multi-step approach that is divided into two distinct sections: The first section estimates the 'technical potential' for PV on buildings, considering architectural and solar suitability. The second section, the 'specific market potential' quantifies the Total Addressable Market and Serviceable Addressable Market for BIPV, reflecting its intrinsic constraint that installations occur during new construction and renovation, and models adoption dynamics using the Diffusion of Innovations model. Through its scenarios, the project highlights the importance of regulation and higher renovation activity to unlock the potential for BIPV. Overall, BIPV can significantly contribute to Europe's energy transition, with rooftops representing most of the potential, while façades contribute selectively where architectural integration and visibility are prioritised.

Keywords: PV, Building-Integrated, Market Potential, Technical Potential

1 INTRODUCTION

This paper estimates the European BIPV market potential up to 2050 using a supply-side approach considering different building typologies. Two growth scenarios reflecting different renovation activity levels map distinct uptake pathways across roofs and façades.

The technical potential is first calculated from the gross European roof and façade area and by applying architectural and solar suitability factors.

The specific market potential is then calculated. The Total Addressable Market (TAM) limits the market to installations during new construction and renovation. The Serviceable Addressable Market (SAM) considers market and regulatory factors for BIPV and uses the Diffusion of Innovations theory to model adoption dynamics under the scenarios.

2 METHODOLOGY

The aim of this study is to assess the market potential for Building-Integrated Photovoltaics (BIPV) in Europe up to 2050, for both roofs and façades, under two different growth scenarios. Because BIPV is integrated into the building envelope, installations occur during new construction or renovation, so annual uptake depends on the rate of new construction and renovation. The assessment follows a multi-step process divided into two distinct sections. The first section involves estimating the technical potential of PV in buildings, using a supply-side approach, considering architectural differences in each building type, construction period and country. At each stage, the scope is progressively narrowed using suitability considerations for integration and scenario assumptions for market uptake to provide a more realistic estimation. The second section develops different deployment scenarios based on the Diffusion of Innovations model [1], in order to understand and analyse the adoption trends of BIPV deployment over time.

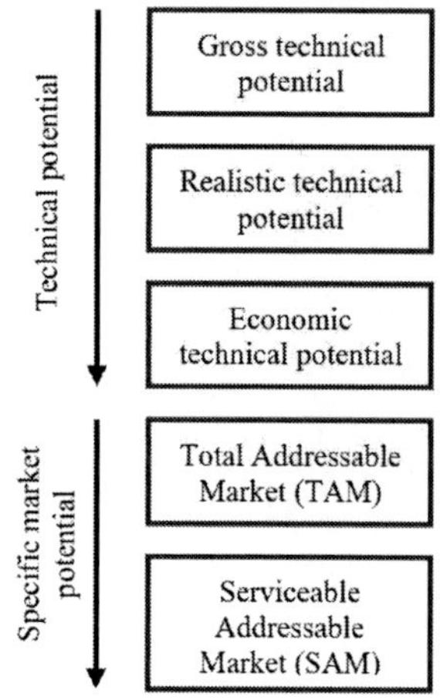

Figure 1 – Methodology approach flowchart

2.1 Technical potential

The Gross technical potential by 2050 represents all available roof and façade surfaces in the EU + Switzerland and UK, using available data for 2020, and adding new constructions and renovations obtained from [2] up to 2050. At this stage, it does not distinguish between BIPV and BAPV. Constructed floor surfaces are derived from the EU Building Stock Observatory (BSO) [3, 4] and are then converted to roof and façade areas using TABULA-EPISCOPE ratios by country, building use and construction period [5]. Two scenarios are introduced here. The 'Renovation wave' scenario considers a significant increase in building renovations, while the 'No renovation wave' scenario is a business-as-usual case, with no major increase in renovations. Renovation rates in the 'Renovation wave' scenario were taken from [2], while in the 'No renovation wave' scenario, rates reported by the European Commission [6] were used and projected to 2050 based on the work by Sandberg [7]. Renovation rates in both scenarios varied according to country and sector (residential, non-residential). Table I presents the average renovation rates used in both scenarios

Table I – Average renovation rates in Europe 2020-2050

	No renovation wave	Renovation wave
Residential buildings	1.1-1.19	2.51-2.67
Non-residential buildings	1.64-1.72	2.51-2.66

The Realistic technical potential considers 'architecturally' suitable areas only. It accounts for obstacles, windows, sharp corners and other inaccessible areas on the building envelope, which are excluded. For roofs, only 60% of the available area was considered usable, based on [8]. For façades, this factor considers areas with insufficient space for PV modules, obstacles, etc. It is approximately 35% that is subtracted from the initial surface [9]. Window areas are excluded for façades, with BIPV windows not considered in the scope of this project. Architectural suitability ratios are applied as shown in Table II.

Due to the lack of available information about the architectural suitability for different building typologies, no distinction was made between them when applying these ratios.

The economic technical potential is then obtained by only including areas which receive sufficient solar radiation. Because of the complexity of urbanized areas, with neighbouring buildings, vegetation and nearby objects being possible sources of shading, this was achieved using a solar suitability ratio. For roofs, this ratio considers unfavourable orientation, inclination and shading from surrounding elements. It was taken from [8]. For façades, the solar suitability is highly dependent on building height, distance from other buildings and orientation [10]. Chatzipoulka found that the sky view factor (SVF) can be used as a predictor to estimate solar irradiation on building façades [11]. The SVF is a measure of the portion of the sky visible from a given point on the building surface. Due to lack of available information about the solar suitability in different building typologies, the building typology was not considered when applying the solar suitability ratio. The solar suitability ratio was computed by country, considering the repartition of cities, suburbs and rural areas, which affect the average SVF. Using the relationship between the SVF and the solar irradiation on façades, suitability ratios ranged from 14 to 33%, with an average of 27%.

Table II – Architectural and solar suitability ratios

	Façade	Roof
Architectural suitability	~ 65%	60%
Solar suitability	~ 27%	~ 56%
Window exclusion	~ 30%	

2.2 Specific market potential

The Total Addressable Market (TAM) refers to the maximum market potential of BIPV. It includes only the areas arising from new construction and renovations between 2024 and 2050, reflecting the natural limitation that BIPV is installed during integration windows rather than as stand-alone retrofits.

The Serviceable Addressable Market (SAM) refers to the portion of the TAM that can realistically be accessed given market and regulatory conditions. Two suitability dimensions are applied to the TAM:

(1) Regulatory suitability factor: Reflects the impact of regulations, policies and incentives to determine the share of the TAM that would actually be covered by PV.

(2) Market suitability factor: Considers the competitiveness and market dynamics of BIPV to determine the share of PV installations on buildings that could be BIPV (and not BAPV).

Table III – Average SAM market and regulatory factors 2024-2050

	Façade	Roof
Regulatory suitability	3-17%	60-90%
Market suitability	85-96%	10-50%

Both factors vary by country, year, surface type, and building typology. The Diffusion of Innovations model is implemented at this stage to assess the possible evolution of BIPV deployment up to 2050. BIPV historical capacity, as well as short-term forecasts made by Becquerel Institute, were used to model the growth rate for BIPV adoption for both scenarios. The analysis is segmented into residential and non-residential buildings and further divided by roofs and façades, producing annual and cumulative trajectories under both scenarios.

Finally, the area values were converted to capacity (GW), differentiating between roof and façade surfaces because of the specific requirements and characteristics of the types of BIPV installed in them. The ITRPV 2024 report [12], as well as case studies from multiple BIPV projects were used to estimate the evolution of the power density for BIPV until 2050. The type of cell technology, projected module efficiency, share of semi-transparent modules, and semi-transparency level were considered to make a robust estimation of the potential capacity that BIPV can represent in Europe.

Table IV – Power density values (W/m^2)

	Façade	Roof
2025	141.3	202.6
2030	145.7	208.8
2040	151.6	216.6
2050	157.1	223.6

3 RESULTS

3.1 Technical potential

The European gross technical potential for BIPV amounted to approximately 64 000 km^2 in 2024 as shown in Figure 3. This value increases significantly when taken to 2050 because of renovations and new constructions. In the end, after reductions from the realistic and economic technical potential, only around 12% of the gross technical potential is considered viable for BIPV, which amounts to 16 416 km^2.

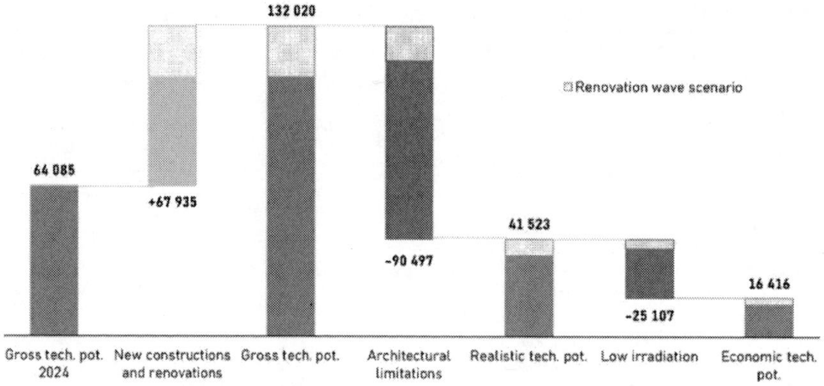

Figure 3 – Technical potential for BIPV in Europe (km²)

Figure 2 shows the distribution of the BIPV market potential in the residential and non-residential sectors, as well as for the surface type, roof or façade. 67% of the potential for PV on buildings comes from the residential sector. Façades are over 2/3 of the gross potential, which is a large share, but makes sense considering that buildings usually have a greater vertical area than roof area.

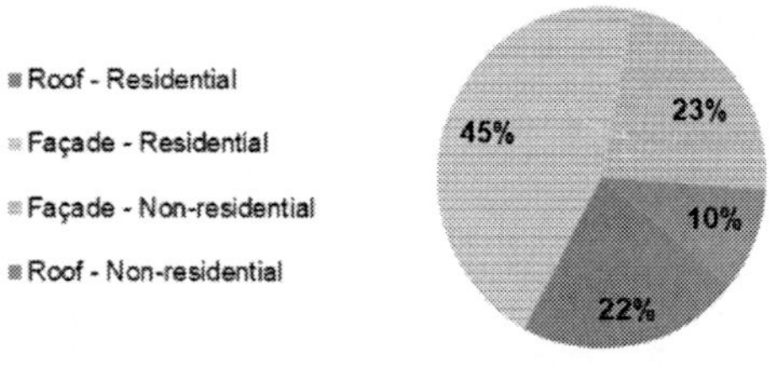

Figure 2 – Share of façade and roof gross technical potential in 2024 for residential and non-residential buildings

3.2 Specific market potential

The installation of BIPV takes place only when a building is being renovated or constructed. So, we assume the BIPV market potential to be limited by the number of renovations and new constructions that take place. An increase in building renovations would mean an increase in the potential of BIPV installations. By considering this, the total addressable market (TAM) represents the maximum possible potential market BIPV could reach in Europe.

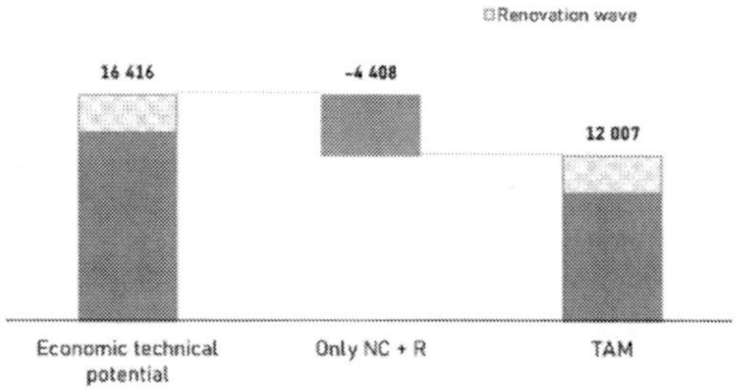

Figure 4 – BIPV total addressable market by 2050 (km²)

Figure 5 shows the share of the BIPV market potential in the residential and non-residential sectors, as well as the type of surface, roof or façade. Compared to Figure 2, the potential for façades has been reduced notably in the TAM because architectural limitations and low irradiation were more significant in façades than roofs. The increase in renovation rates in the Renovation wave scenario target the residential sector in particular, that is why the share of residential BIPV potential is larger in this scenario. The distribution between roofs and façades is not directly impacted by the scenarios, that is why it stays roughly the same in both cases.

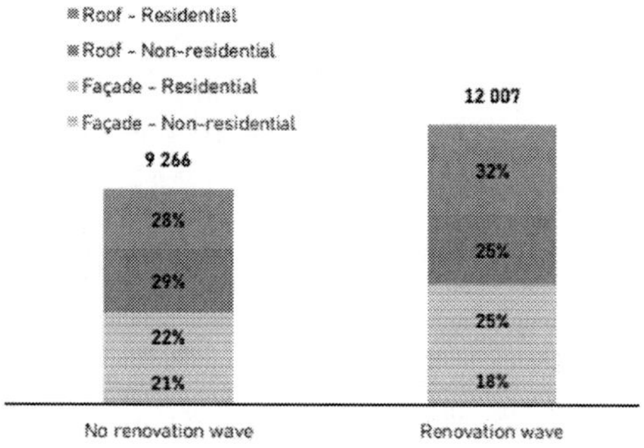

Figure 5 – Distribution of TAM potential by 2050 (km²)

The serviceable addressable market (SAM) represents the potential for BIPV by considering its regulatory suitability and competition from BAPV. The diffusion of innovations (S-curve) model was used to represent the way in which the BIPV market would grow, providing an annual and cumulative potential from 2024 to 2050.

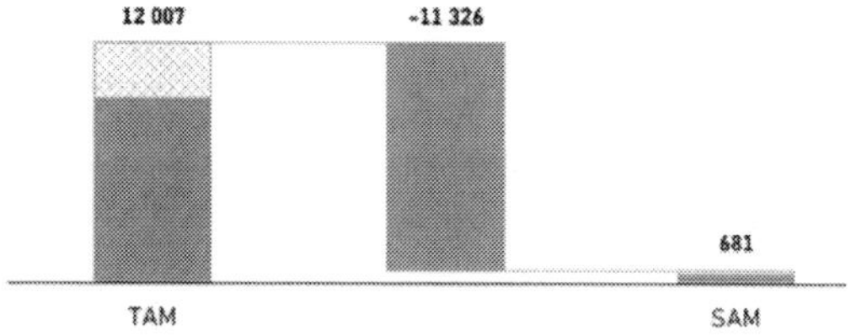

Figure 6 – BIPV serviceable addressable market by 2050 (km²)

10.4229/EUPVSEC2025/4BO.17.2

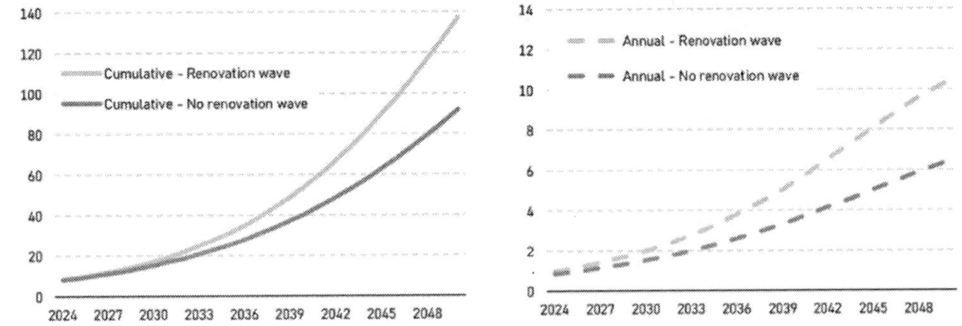

Figure 7 – BIPV cumulative (left) and annual (right) serviceable addressable market by 2050 (GW)

As shown in Figure 6, the serviceable addressable market for BIPV is much lower than the total addressable market, due to the aforementioned regulatory and market factors, as well as the adoption trends from the S-curve model. Figure 8 shows that over 85% of the potential for BIPV comes from roofs, even though in the TAM, the façade and roof shares were closer to each other. This is because, especially in the residential sector, the energy needs for most buildings will be met by rooftop PV, which reduces the attractiveness of investing in a BIPV façade. As illustrated in Figure 7, the S-curve has not reached a plateau by 2050 in either scenario, indicating that the peak annual BIPV installations have not been reached. In other words, market saturation will not be achieved by 2050.

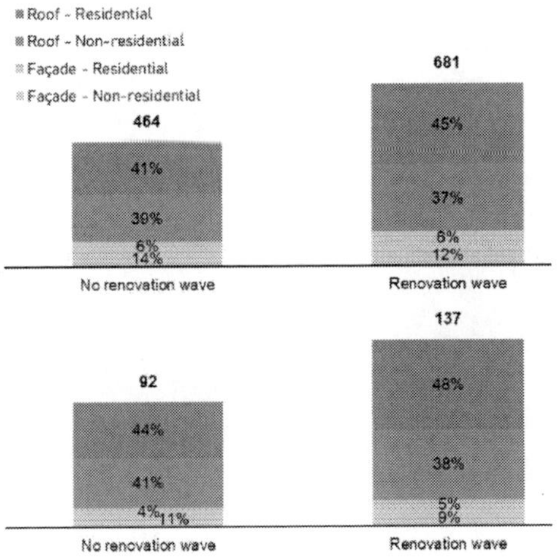

Figure 8 – Distribution of SAM potential in km² (top) and GW (bottom)

4 CONCLUSIONS

This study finds that the technical potential of PV on buildings is significant, with façades offering a large and underused surface. Even after conservative exclusions and constraints, the total addressable market for BIPV is noteworthy, with a balanced contribution by sector and surface type. The serviceable addressable market remains notable, with around 100 GW of market potential in both scenarios. Within the SAM, roofs account for most of the realizable opportunity, while façades remain a focused, design-oriented niche where visibility, architectural integration, and urban context favour BIPV solutions. A sustained increase in renovation activity is key for unlocking a larger share of the potential, since BIPV adoption aligns with building renovations and new construction cycles. The adoption trends modelled in both scenarios show that BIPV will not reach market saturation by 2050. Annual BIPV installations will continue to rise beyond mid-century as products mature, standards improve, and policy support strengthens. Overall, BIPV is positioned to play a significant role in the energy transition, led by roofs at scale, complemented by façade applications where architectural value is central, and enabled by an acceleration of building renovations.

Table V – Summary of serviceable addressable market for BIPV (GW)

	Renovation wave		No renovation wave	
	2030	2050	2030	2050
Cumulative				
Roof-residential	7	65.3	6.1	40.4
Roof-non-residential	7.8	52.6	6.9	37.5
Façade-residential	1	6.5	0.9	4.1
Façade-non-residential	1.3	12.6	1.2	9.7
Total	17.1	137	15.1	91.7
Annual				
Roof-residential	0.8	5.6	0.6	3.1
Roof-non-residential	0.9	3.4	0.7	2.4
Façade-residential	0.1	0.5	0.1	0.3
Façade-non-residential	0.2	0.8	0.1	0.7
Total	2	10.4	1.5	6.4

5 REFERENCES

[1] E. M. Rogers, Diffusion of innovations, 1982.

[2] A. L. C. B. S. F. A. T. K. M. C. L. T. D. a. A. T. Damgaard, «Background data collection

and life cycle assessment for construction and demolition waste (CDW) management,» 2022.

[3] European Commission, «EU Building Stock Observatory,» 2024.

[4] D. B. S. Pezzutto, «Deliverable 3.2: Static building stock analysis. MODERATE PROJECT,» 2023.

[5] T. S. Loga, «TABULA building typologies in 20 European countries,» 2016.

[6] European Commission, «Comprehensive study of building energy renovation activities and the uptake of nearly zero-energy buildings in the EU – Final report,» Publications Office, 2019.

[7] N. H.-R. Sandberg, «Dynamic building stock modelling: Application to 11 European countries to support the energy efficiency and retrofit ambitions of the EU,» 2016.

[8] K. K. I. J.-W. A. T. N. a. S. S. Bodis, «A high-resolution geospatial assessment of the rooftop solar photovoltaic potential in the European Union. RENEWABLE and SUSTAINABLE ENERGY REVIEWS, ISSN 1364-0321, 114, 2019, p. 109309, JRC113070,» 2019.

[9] X. L. Lu, «Estimating the photovoltaic potential of building facades and roofs using,» 2021.

[10] Z. Z. A. Mohammad, «Techno-economic BIPV evaluation method in urban areas,» 2019.

[11] R. C. C. Chatzipoulka, «Sky view factor as predictor of solar availability on building,» 2018.

[12] VDMA, «International Technology Roadmap for Photovoltaics (ITRPV),» 2024.

6 FUNDING

SEAMLESS-PV - Development of advanced manufacturing equipment and processes aimed at the seamless integration of multifunctional PV solutions, enabling the deployment of IPV sectors, is a Horizon Europe Innovation Action started in January 2023 that will continue through December 2026. Grant N°101096126

Scuola universitaria professionale della Svizzera italiana
Dipartimento ambiente costruzioni e design
Istituto sostenibilità applicata all'ambiente costruito

SUPSI

Photovoltaics in the Built Environment:
An Overview of Timely Topics for Research and Development

42nd EUPVSEC Conference, Bilbao

Prof. Dr. Francesco Frontini,
Director ISAAC-SUPSI, Switzerland

Prof.dr. Angèle Reinders,
Eindhoven University of Technology, The Netherlands

Left: Omicron Headquarter, Middle: Wienerberger , residential BIPV, Right: La Cartosa Island

Building Integrated Photovoltaics

- High variety of BIPV applications available
- For each of these applications, multiple BIPV products exist on the market, with their own specifications and their own effect on buildings' visual appearance, architectural design and technical construction features.
- In the segment of residential buildings, cold roofs are the most common BIPV installations.
- In the segment of commercial buildings, façade BIPV systems are much more common, as well as BIPV skylights.

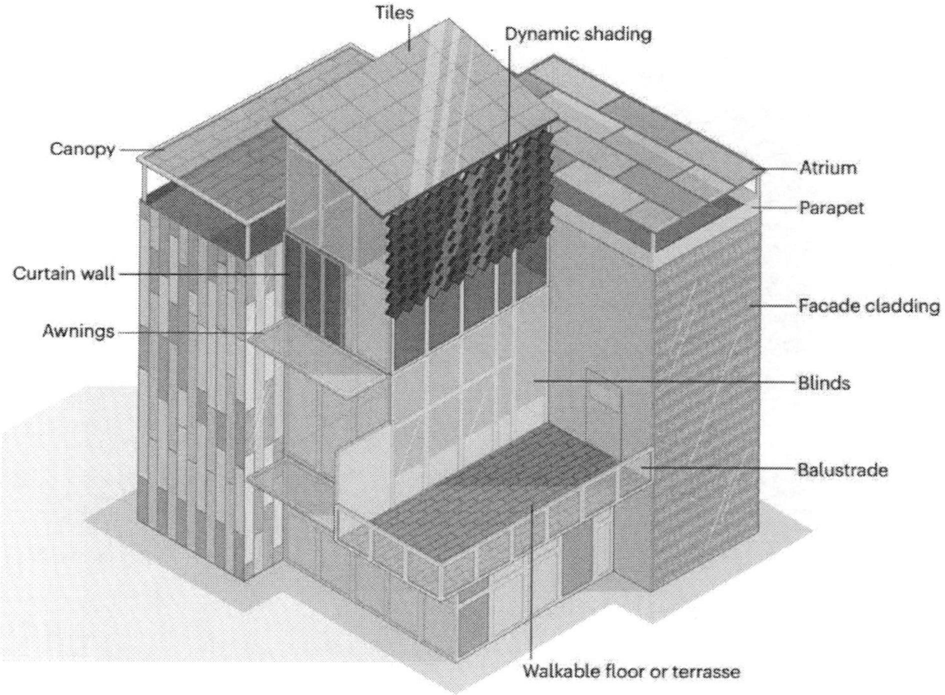

Source: Faes, A. *et al.* Building-integrated photovoltaics. *Nat. Rev. Clean Technol.* 1, 333–350 (2025).

Elaborated from IEA PVPS Task 15. IEA PVPS

European BIPV market history: still difficult to assess

Source: La casa solare (1982), RSI

Source: Solaris (2017), Solarchitecture.ch

YESTERDAY

Subsidies
BIPV or PV?

Mass Market
Real Estate?

Innovation

Source: Sunny Woods, (2001), Solarchitecture.ch

Architecture
Tech demonstration

TOMORROW

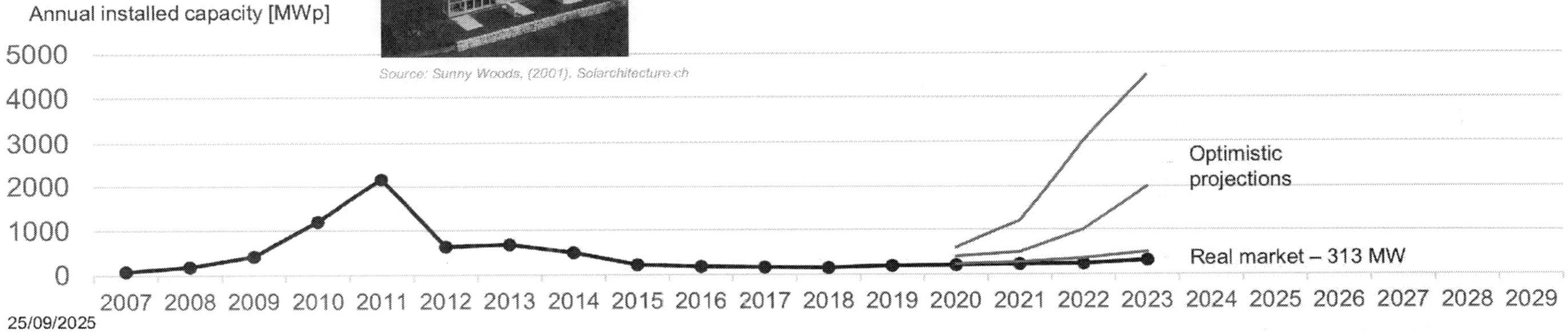

Source: BIPV Status Report 2020 and 2024. SUPSI, Becquerel Institute.

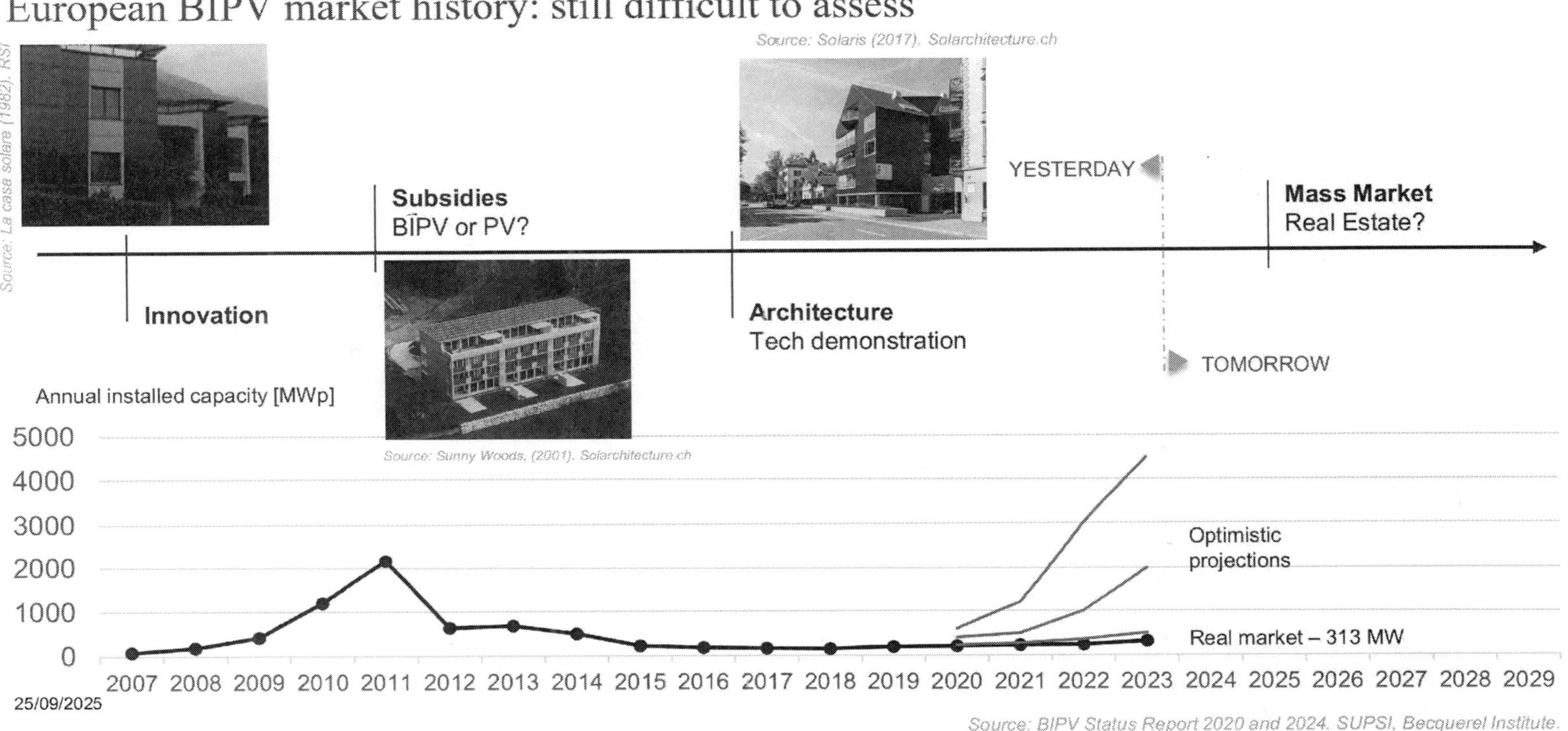

European BIPV market segmentation

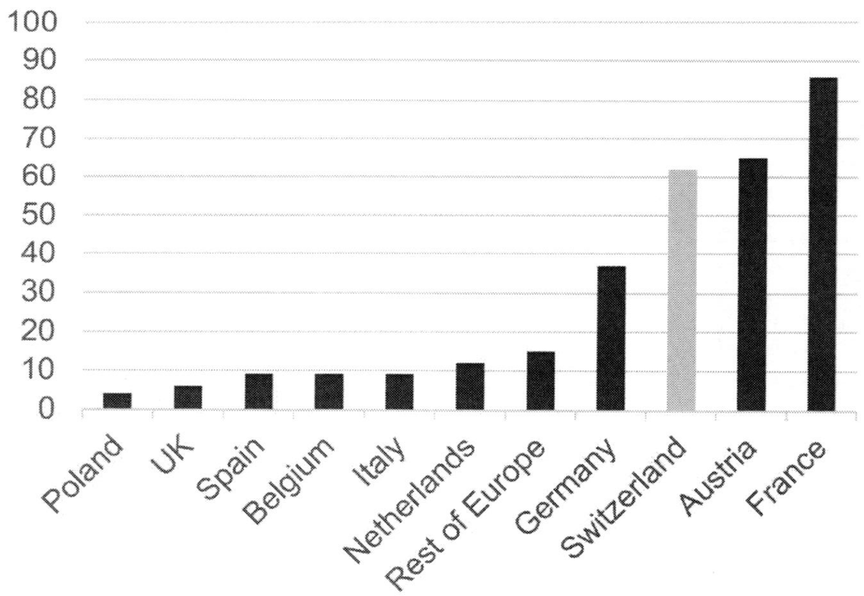

- **France**: mainly residential and commercial BIPV applications
- **Austria**: the BIPV market followed the exceptional growth of PV market in 2023
- **Switzerland:** current incentives for integrated PV systems and bonus for the tilt angle >75°
- **Germany**: traditionally on of the main markets for BIPV in Europe
- **Netherlands**: after slowing down due to the public reputation (fire safety incidents), the trust is buing rebuilt and the market is expected to grow again
- **Italy**: the residential sector accounts for a big part. No supporting schemes
- **Belgium**: 2023 has seen the closure of a regional PV support scheme, resulting in a significative growth
- **Spain**: around 1% of residential and commercial PV systems is estimated to be BIPV

Source: BIPV Status Report 2024. Becquerel Institute.

SUPSI TU/e PV in the built environment - 42nd EUPVSEC, Bilbao

Special Issue: Photovoltaics in the built environment

(1) La Certosa Island, (2) eV-Chalet, (3) Väla Gård, (4) Sol'CH, (5) Wienerberger, (6) Omicron Headquarter, (7) Social housing apartments, (8) Solsmaragden Office, (9) Solarix – Headquarter Kuijpers, (10) Soltech manufacturing plant (11) Polis, (12) Franklin, (13) Novartis Pavillion.

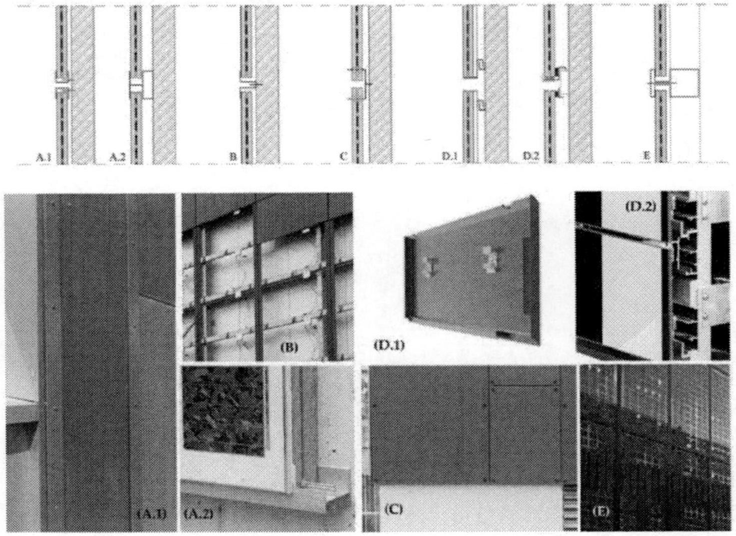

Four different families of fixing solutions are presented: A1 linear frame screwed on site (Source picture: Sunage), A2 continuous clamping (picture source: PIZ), B individual/point clamping (picture source: 3S), C point fixing with drilled holes (picture source: Sunage), D1 Adhesive vertical rail with hooks (picture source: Schweizer), D2 Adhesive self-weight system with safety mechanical retention (picture source: Gasser GFT), and E continuous post-and-rail façade system (picture source: Onyx)

Source: P. Bonomo et al., Comprehensive review and state of play in the use of photovoltaics in buildings

Special Issue on PV in the Built Environment

- SI of scientific journal **Energy and Buildings**, with impact factor 6.6
- Timeline collection and reviewing of manuscripts: 2024
- Weblink: Energy and Buildings | Photovoltaics in the Built Environment | ScienceDirect.com by Elsevier
- Scope:

Special issue

Photovoltaics in the Built Environment

Last update 15 April 2024

In the past decade photovoltaics (PV) has become a mature, efficient and feasible sustainable energy technology essential for the energy transition in the built environment. Within these developments photovoltaics in the built environment cover PV systems, PV modules and new PV technologies and their innovative applications in building envelops, urban infrastructures for energy and transport, and in the public space, also called Building Added Photovoltaics (BAPV), Building Integrated Photovoltaics (BIPV), and photovoltaics integrated in urban landscapes.

Guest Editors:

Dr Angèle Reinders
Eindhoven University of Technology, the Netherlands

Dr Francesco Frontini
University of Applied Sciences and Arts of Southern Switzerland (SUPSI)

- **26 papers accepted at a 30% acceptance rate**

Analysis of authors and countries

Authors involved: 130 authors from Europe, Cl

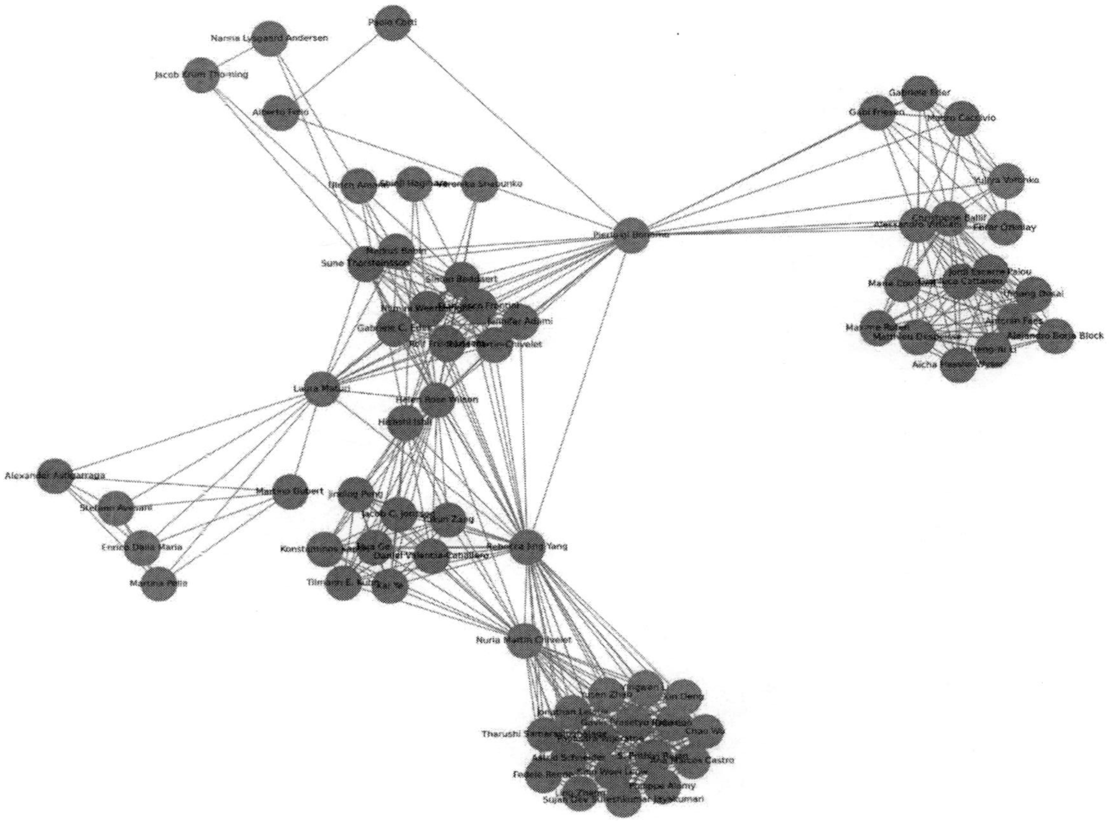

25/09/2025

Analysis of collaboration network

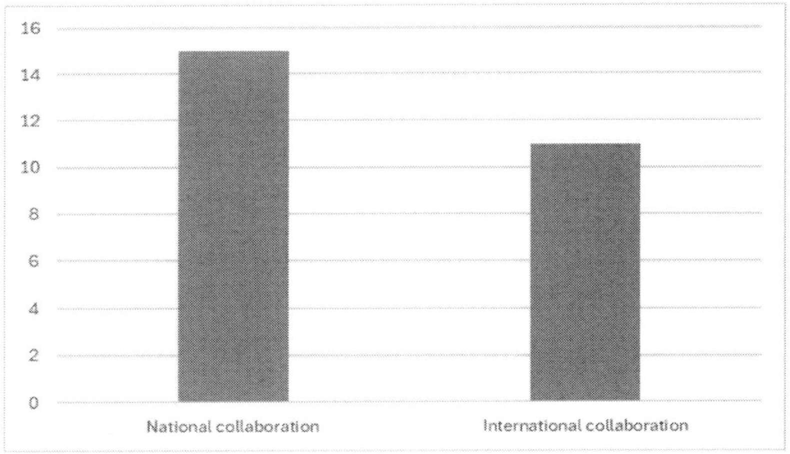

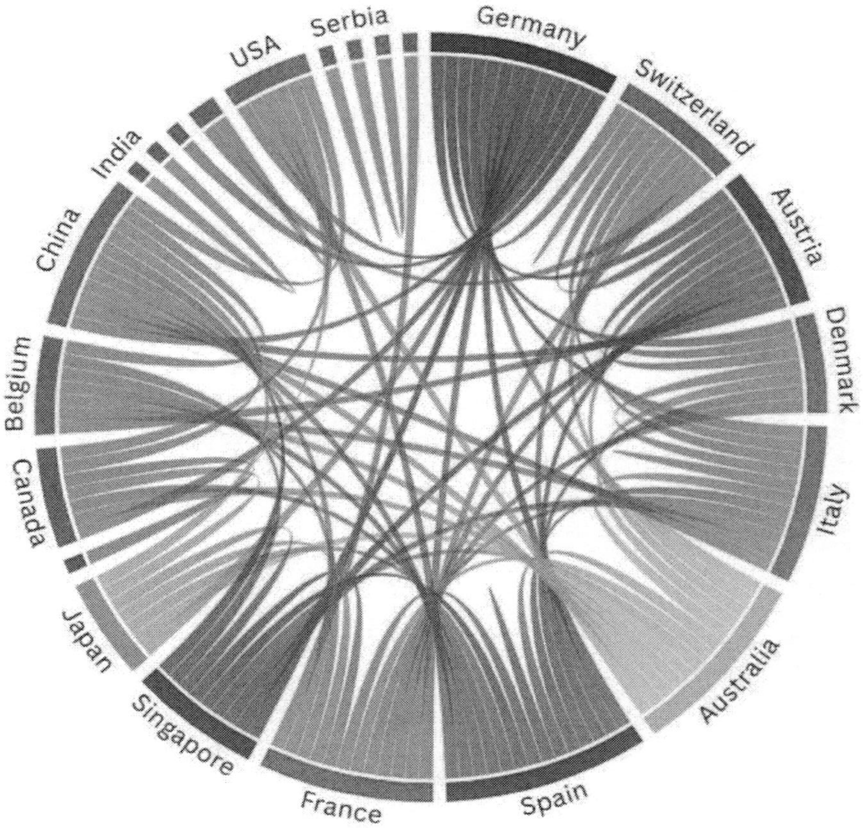

Analysis of research themes
with some examples of papers

Hafsa Fares at al. *A methodology for assessing environmental impact of building integrated PV in low carbon footprint electricity generation context*

Christian Popp et al. *Prospective life cycle analysis of a BIPV façade – Life cycle assessment of greenhouse gas emissions using future projections for a case study*

P. Bonomo et al., *Comprehensive review and state of play in the use of photovoltaics in buildings*

Ha Eun Yoon et al., *Research on the virtual design and implementation of colored glass for BIPV*

Alejandro Borja Block et al., *Colouring solutions for building integrated photovoltaic modules: A review*

Helen Rose Wilson et al., *Multi-dimensional evaluation of BIPV installations: Development of a tool to assess the performance as building component and electricity generator*

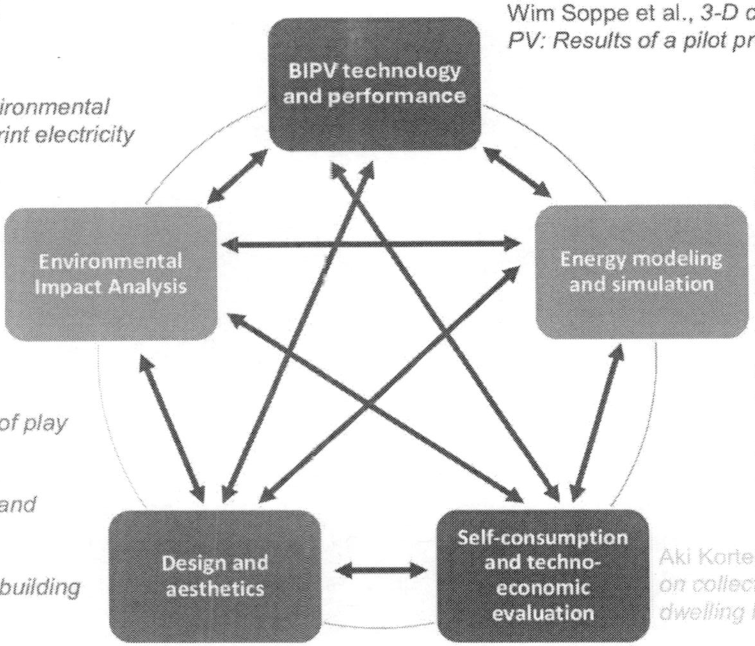

Helen Rose Wilson et al. *Component-based SHGC determination of BIPV glazing for product comparison*

Marios C. Phocas et al., *Concept analysis of an adaptive building envelope with thin-film photovoltaic modules*

Wim Soppe et al., *3-D curved composite façade elements with PV: Results of a pilot project*

Gianni Di Giovanni et al. *Exploiting building information modeling and machine learning for optimizing rooftop photovoltaic systems*

Rebecca Jing Yang et al., *Digitalising BIPV energy simulation: A cross tool investigation*

Tamás Soha et al. *City-scale analysis of PV potential and visibility in heritage environment using GIS and LiDAR*

Stefani Peratikou, Alexandros G. Charalambides, *Short-term PV energy yield predictions within city neighborhoods for optimum grid management*

Aki Kortetmäki at al., *The impact of metering methods on collective self-consumption: Insights from multi-dwelling buildings in Finland*

M.T. Miranda, et al., *Analysis of photovoltaic self-consumption as a function of the demand profile in detached houses*

Theme 1: BIPV technology and performance

Integration of solar panels in façades is **still too little applied** nowadays due to the **limitations in design options.**

- Façade PV elements can be **varied in color and size** but still have a flat surface and fix dimensions → difficulties especially in **retrofit**.
- **Performance assessment** and **standardization** needed to demonstrate the impact and contribution of multi-fuctional BIPV element/system: **SHGC**, **Temperature** behavior and performances, **impact** of mounting system
- Dynamic facades with multi-purpose, i.e. shading of indoor space, can yield more benefit

Customizable solutions

Source: Soppe et.al. 3-D curved composite façade elements with PV: Results of a pilot project

Solar Heat Gain Contribution & Heat Transfer

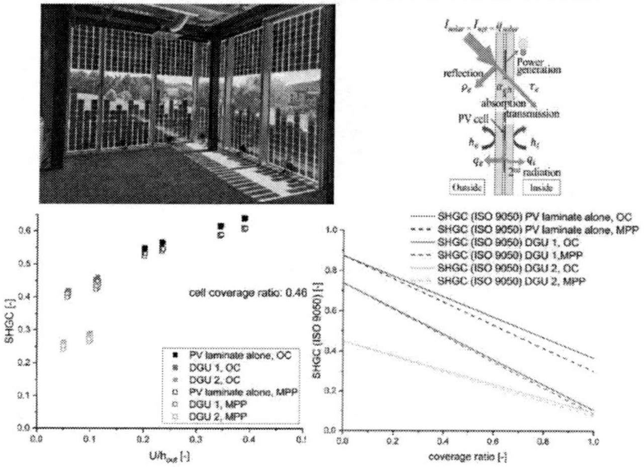

Source: HR Wilson et al. Component-based SHGC determination of BIPV glazing for product comparison

Hisashi et al. International inter-laboratory comparison of solar heat gain coefficient of building-integrated photovoltaic modules - results of tests with or without power generation and tests with PV cell coverage ratios

Dynamic facade concept with multi-purposes

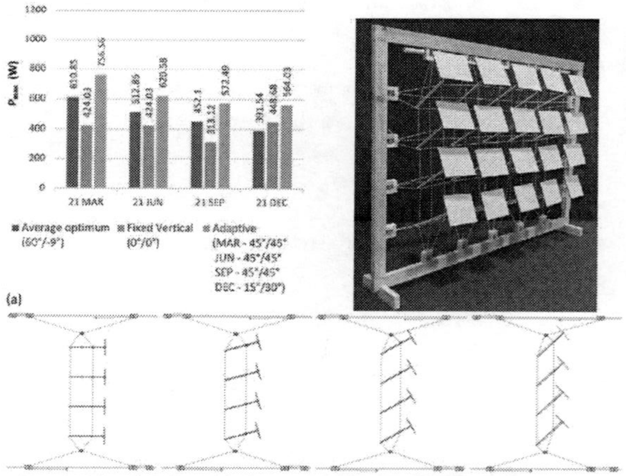

Source: Marios C. Phocas et al., Concept analysis of an adaptive building envelope with thin-film photovoltaic

Theme 2: Energy modeling and simulation

From **city model** to **digital tool** to better assess the PV in building performances, considering multiple aspects of PV and buildings

1. City-scale analysis of PV potential and visibility in heritage environments
2. Exploiting BIM, digitalization and machine learning for rooftop PV optimization and complex BIPV projects: need of more accurate models
3. Yield analysis of a BIPV façade prototype strongly influenced by module layering (i.e. colors) and type of facades system (i.e. ventilation)

PV potential of roof areas and to assess the visibility of solar panels in urban areas.

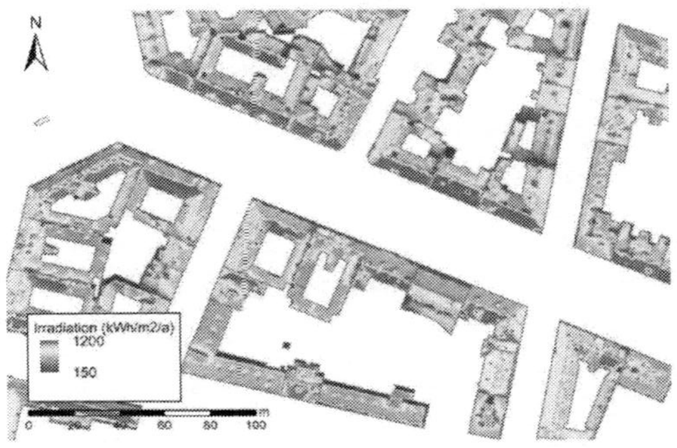

Source: Soha et al, City-scale analysis of PV potential and visibility in heritage environment using GIS and LiDAR

DIGITALIZATION as opportunity to proper manage complex BIPV projects

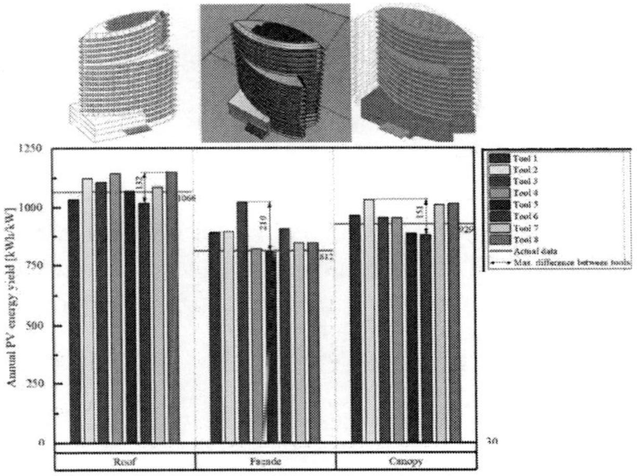

Source: Yang et al. Digitalising BIPV energy simulation: A cross tool investigation

Color impact on temperature & Power generation

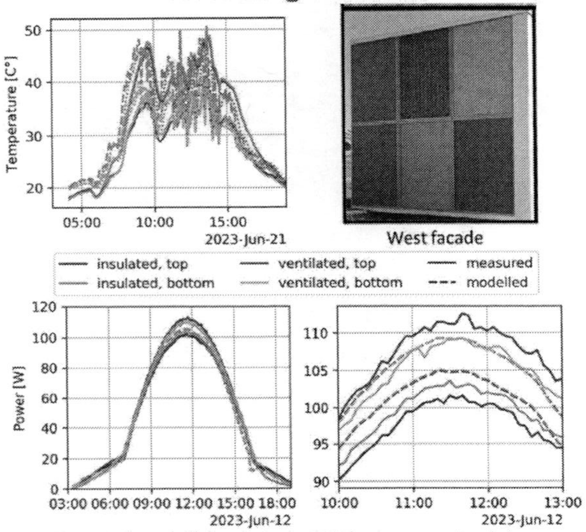

Source: Babin et al. Yield analysis of a BIPV façade prototype installation

25/09/2025

Theme 3: Self-consumption and techno-economic evaluation

Techno-economic evaluations are covering **energy performance and related financial aspects** of PV systems. In many **countries self-consumption** has become an incentive for PV system installations with the aim to **mitigate emissions** associated with fossil fuels, increase **financial benefits**, or **balance local low voltage grids**, which is strongly related to techno-economic evaluations.

- **Five papers** on this topic in this SI present about
  - Self-consumption and self-sufficiency at a neighborhood level and in individual dwellings
  - Techno-economic evaluations of PV on facades
  - Workflow to support cost-benefits comparison of BIPV project

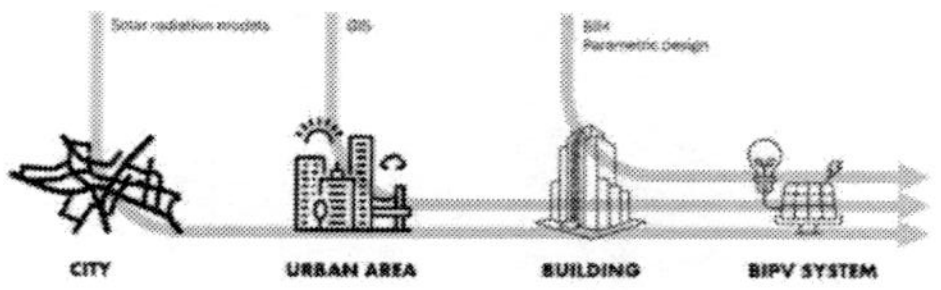

Remote sensing for techno-economic assessments

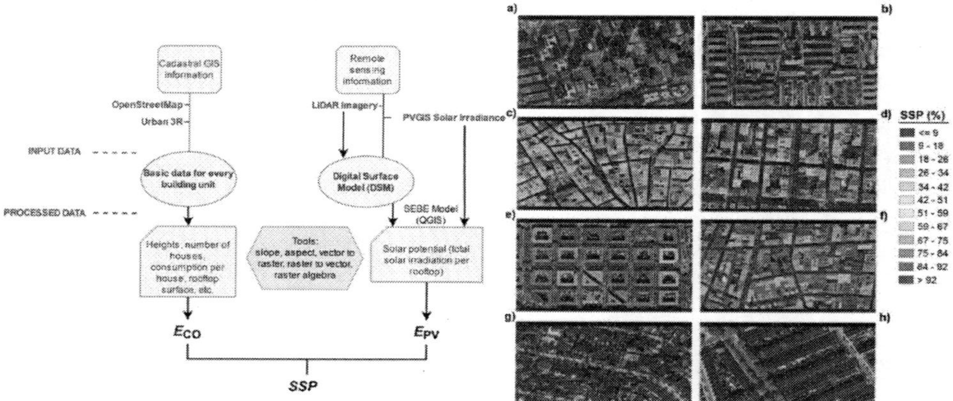

Irene Del Hierro López et al., Photovoltaic self-sufficiency potential at a district scale in Madrid. A scalable methodology

Energy communities and self-consumption

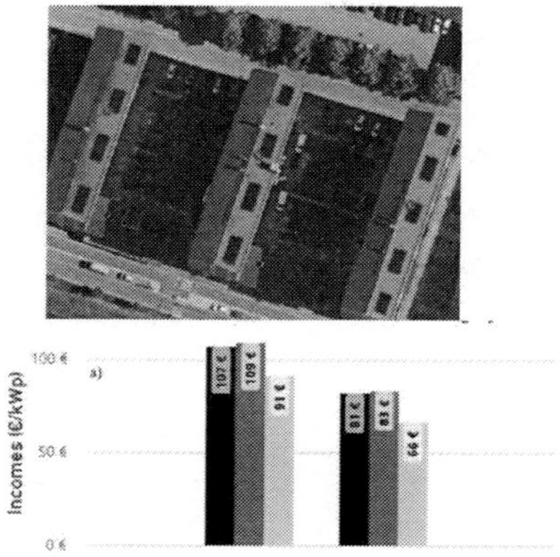

Aki Kortetmäki et al., The impact of metering methods on collective self-consumption: Insights from multi-dwelling buildings in Finland,

Electricity pricing and PV

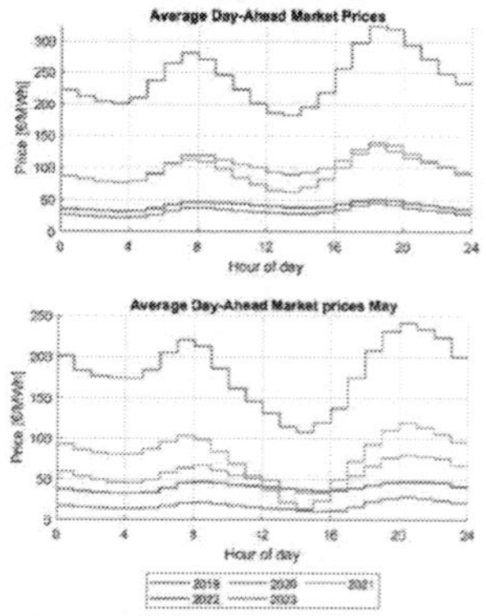

W.L. Schram et al., PV on façades: A financial, technical and environmental assessment

Theme 4: Design and aesthetics

As a building product, BIPV must meet different expectations regarding **design, form, and dimensions** for a variety of **building archetypes** as well as **performance requirements**: such as mechanical or safety requirements but also energy saving, water tightness, etc.

Eight papers on this topic in this SI present about

- **Interdisciplinary methods** to assess existing designs of BIPV in buildings or to be used during design processes
- **Design features of PV modules** such as coloring and curvature
- **Design of** buildings and/or products required for PV installations

Conclusions: Design features such as color techniques, printing and curvature are highly customizable, and analysis methods also seem to be available, but with a strong focus on energy performance, however limited reporting on actual design of buildings with integrated PV systems

Interdisciplinary methods

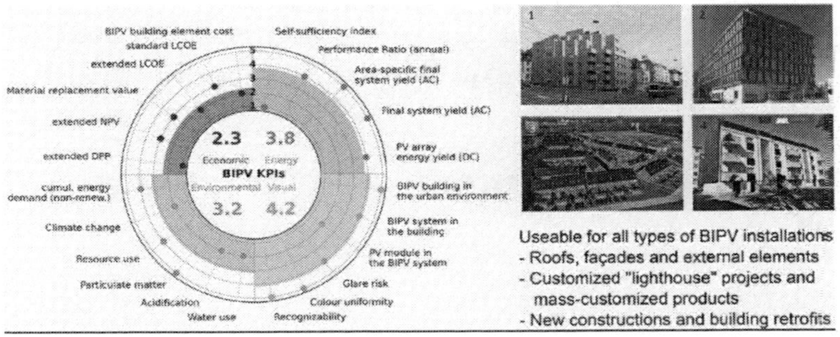

Gabriele Eder et al., Multi-dimensional evaluation of BIPV installations: Development of a tool to assess the performance as building component and electricity generator

Design features: color and curvature

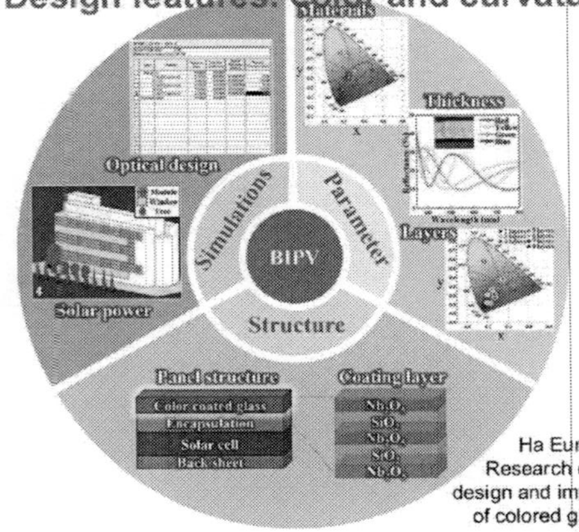

Ha Eun Yoon et al., Research on the virtual design and implementation of colored glass for BIPV

Design activities

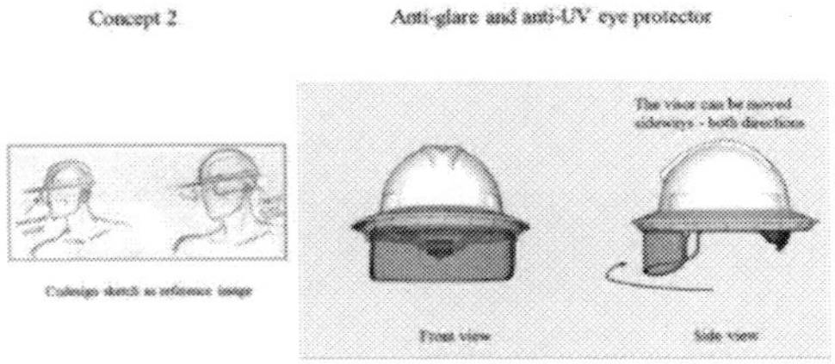

Abhijit Sen et al., Design intervention for addressing the safety and health risks of discomfort glare and UV radiation associated with BIPV installation and maintenance

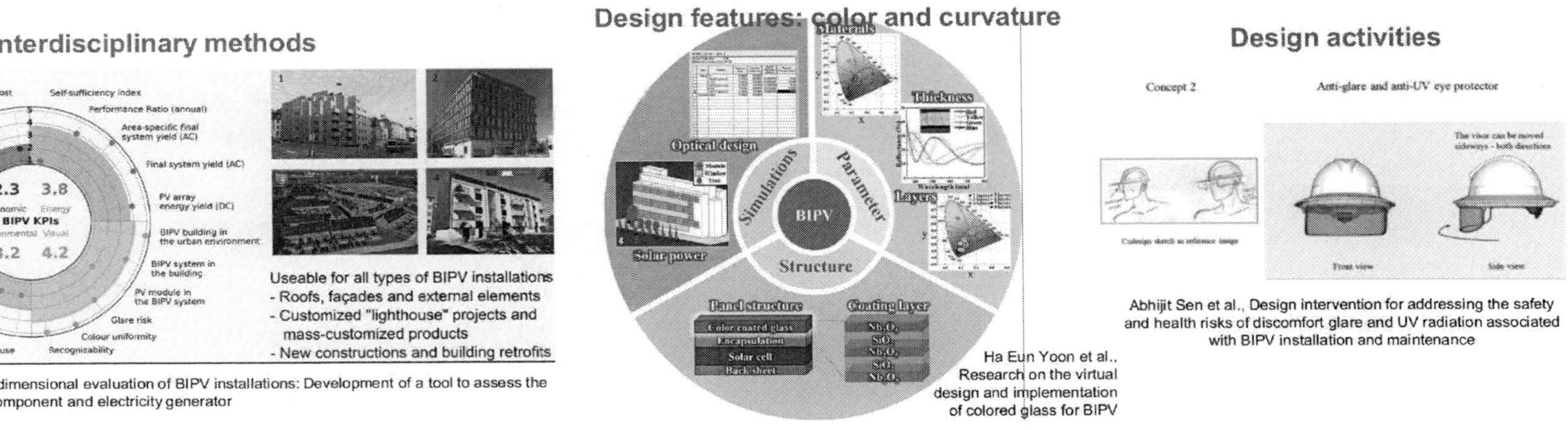

Theme 5: Environmental Impact Analysis

Environmental impact analysis of PV systems including BIPV is strongly founded on **life cycle analysis methodology**
Three papers on this topic in this SI present about

- LCA methods for BIPV in a **low emission electricity system** and **as compared with building materials (without PV)**
- **Prospective LCA** for BIPV, the term prospective LCA describes an analysis that models a system at a future point in time
- Integration of environmental impact in technical-economic studies of BIPV by means of an **emission factor for CO_2 resulting from LCA**

Conclusion: Prospective LCA approaches are required that take into account future changes of PV manufacturing and electricity mix

BIPV emissions in a low emission electricity system

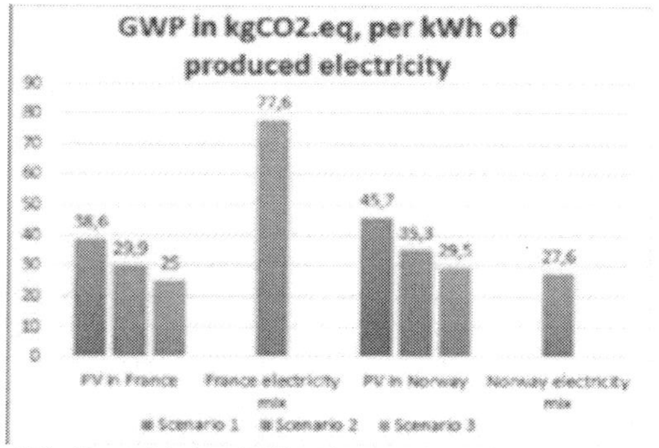

Hafsa Fares et al., A methodology for assessing environmental impact of building integrated PV in low carbon footprint electricity generation context

Prospective LCA for BIPV

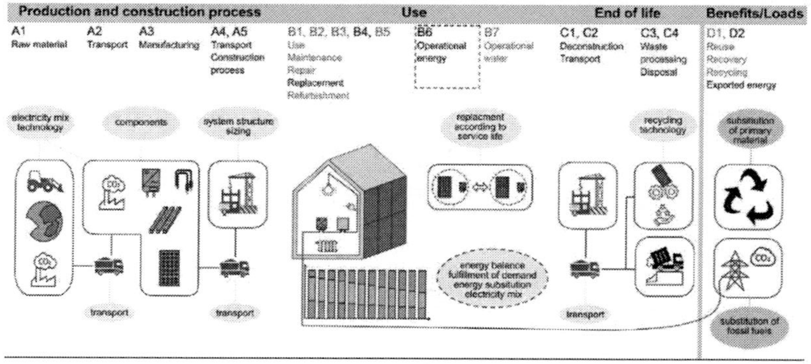

Christian Popp et al., Prospective life cycle analysis of a BIPV façade – Life cycle assessment of greenhouse gas emissions using future projections for a case study

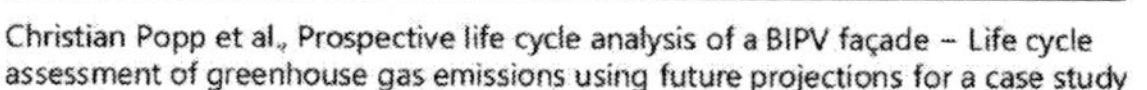

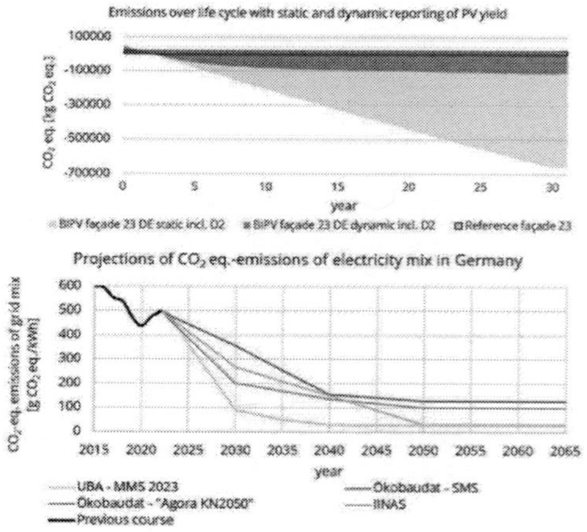

SUPSI TU/e PV in the built environment - 42nd EUPVSEC, Bilbao

Conclusions and recommendations

BIPV is becoming a mature technology:

- **In the past**, main focus on **new products** development to address market needs
- **Today** different technologies are available to make BIPV products attractive to architect and construction company

Different digital tools available to control the technology from large scale (city level) to detailed energy output:

- How to follow product innovations is a challenge and new physical based approaches are need to be further investigated and implemented
- BIM and ML approaches can support decision making
- Standardization is needed to properly define the scope in the built environment (SHGC, Reliability, Performance, Designing,…)

BIPV is complex due to needs of **multiple stakeholders** and their interest in **different KPIs**, but also:

- Large interest from PV manufactures and scientists
- Economy of BIPV system is still a major concern due to the complexity of most of the project. Customizable tools are needed to demonstrate the sustainability and economic feasibility of BIPV
- Prospective LCA approaches are required that take into account future changes of PV manufacturing and electricity mix and to demonstrate BIPV competitiveness in respect to conventional passive solution (no PV)

Acknowledgements

- Prof.dr. Angèle Reinders, main editor and our co-authors Pierluigi Bonomo and Roel C.G.M. Loonen
- Paolo Corti, SUPSI, for providing data from BIPV Status Rerport
- Matte Cadei, SUPSI, for supporting with diagrams and pictures preparation
- All authors and co-authors of papers in the Special Issues

Do not miss today:

- *13:30 -15:00 Parallel session: Unlocking the Potential of Integrated Photovoltaic Systems - European R&D Approach (Room 1B) in collaboration with* IEA PVPS Seamless-PV
- *15:15: 4BV.4: the Poster session on BIPV this afternoon*
- *17:00-18:30: 4BO.5: PV-Products for Buildings (Auditorium 1)*

Scuola universitaria professionale della Svizzera italiana
Dipartimento ambiente costruzioni e design
Istituto sostenibilità applicata all'ambiente costruito

EINDHOVEN UNIVERSITY OF TECHNOLOGY

SUPSI

Thanks for your attention!

Email: francesco.frontini@supsi.ch and a.h.m.e.reinders@tue.nl
Please check our **Special Issue** of Energy & Buildings on **Photovoltaics in the Built Environment**
https://www.sciencedirect.com/special-issue/10SL29QN11V

ADVANCING BIPV: SHINGLED HJT TRCHNOLOGY FOR HIGH-EFFICIENCY AND AESTHETIC SOLAR INTEGRATION

G. Gonnella[1], A. de Gruijter[1], J. Veirman[1], M. Pelle[1], L. Maturi[1], D. Moser[2], L. Fialho[1]
[1]Eurac Research, Institute for Renewable Energy, Viale Druso 1, Bolzano, Italy
[2]Bequerel Institute, Via Kufstein 5, Trento, Italy

ABSTRACT: Building-integrated photovoltaics (BIPV) require technologies that balance energy performance, durability, and aesthetics. Shingled heterojunction (HJT) solar cells offer high efficiency, excellent low-light response, and design flexibility, making them a promising candidate for façade applications. This study investigates the performance and stability of shingled HJT modules fabricated with different material combinations and color configurations. Eight modules were subjected to accelerated aging through humidity-freeze (HF10) testing, and their behavior was evaluated using IV characterization, electroluminescence (EL) imaging, visual inspection, and colorimetry. Results indicate that color integration reduces electrical output by 4–11% compared with reference modules, a trade-off consistent with typical BIPV requirements. Aesthetic stability, assessed through colorimetry, remained largely unchanged after stress testing, with ΔE values below or close to perceptibility thresholds, confirming good visual durability. Performance losses after HF10 were primarily linked to technological issues such as delamination and string mismatch rather than intrinsic limitations of the shingled HJT concept. Overall, the findings demonstrate that shingled HJT modules are a strong candidate for next-generation BIPV, provided that material compatibility and lamination processes are further optimized to ensure long-term reliability in real-world building applications.
Keywords: Building-integrated photovoltaics, shingled HJT, accelerated aging, color stability, module reliability

1 INTRODUCTION

This research is set within the framework of shingled technology for BIPV applications, where shingled strings perform at high voltage and low current, minimizing resistive losses, enhancing energy conversion efficiency, and reducing inactive areas, resulting in photovoltaic modules with superior power density compared to conventional architectures [1], [2]. Unlike the PERC technology [3], [4], [5], which has established performance benchmarks in the literature, shingled HJT modules represent an innovative and emerging approach in BIPV research.

HJT cells offer superior efficiency compared to PERC (up to 25-26% mass production efficiency [6], [7], [8], [9]) and are gaining market traction [10], making them well-suited for BIPV applications. To the best of our knowledge, no BIPV laboratory prototypes have been developed using shingled HJT cells specifically for colored BIPV, nor has an in-depth study been conducted on their electrical performance and aesthetic integration.

This study addresses this gap by maximizing the visual appeal of the modules through variations in front glass coloring, encapsulant polymers, and backsheet materials. Beyond aesthetics, the study also focuses on performance characterization, compensating for the lack of data on shingled HJT BIPV modules. Flash tests were conducted to determine electrical characteristics, while EL analysis assessed structural integrity, identifying microcracks and validating the positive effects of optimized lamination. The research aims to extend to accelerated tests performance monitoring, bridging the gap between laboratory fabrication and real-world deployment. Humidity freezing tests were performed in a climatic chamber. This study provides a comprehensive methodology, from material selection and optimized lamination to controlled indoor testing. By systematically investigating both aesthetic and functional aspects, it offers critical insights into the adoption of shingled HJT technology in the rapidly evolving BIPV sector.

2 MATERIALS AND METHODS

The following section describes materials and methods involved in the realization of high-aesthetic shingled HJT modules.

2.1 Module Design and Bill of Materials

The selection of materials and interlayers was carried out in order to maximize the aesthetic properties and to evaluate the integration potential of shingled HJT in BIPV environment. The prototypes were designed to maximize the aesthetic appeal and visual appearance, utilizing different Bills of Materials (BoM) and module configurations. The lamination was performed on both Glass-Glass (GG) and Glass-Backsheet (GBS) configurations, with reference modules produced without colored encapsulants or colored front glass. Shingled HJT strings provided by Applied Materials Italy srl were used for the tests. Due to an extended storage time between string fabrication and lamination trials (several months), the mechanical quality of the cell interconnexion was markedly degraded, which materialized into a high string breakage during our preliminary handling tests. In order to reduce the breakage rate, a custom-made string flipper was built, which reduced the breakage rate to a minimum. The front glass options included transparent or terracotta, while the rear cover featured colored (orange or grey) or transparent glass, as well as a black backsheet. The color glasses were provided by GruppoSTG. Encapsulation materials included both transparent (EVA UV clear, EPE UV clear, TPO clear) and colored (POE black, TPO black) variants.

2.2 Soldering and lamination process

The module architecture was defined connecting in series all the strings within the module. The interconnection between strings was performed in our laboratory, using a standard soldering station in combination with flux pens to remove oxide layers and ensure proper soldering quality. To balance technical performance, aesthetic appeal, and energetic requirements, both uncolored metallic ribbons and black-coated ribbons were tested. In some cases, black tape was applied over uncolored ribbon to enhance visual uniformity.

For each module, a specific lamination recipe was defined, depending on the materials and interlayers adopted. Laminator TECNO PANAMAC SL-DM121 was employed, with adjustable parameters for pressure, temperature, and cycle duration. Moreover, modules were visually inspected and classified according to their aesthetic quality. Only modules with "medium" or "high" aesthetic rating were selected for indoor and outdoor testing. Modules classified as "low" exhibited severe delamination, large air bubbles, or poor adhesion between materials. By contrast, "high" aesthetic quality referred to flawless integration of the cells into the stack, with no visible defects. All defects were recorded to be compared with post-stress results after aging in the climatic chamber.

2.3 Electrical characterization setup

EL imaging was conducted in the laboratory before and after each lamination to verify proper interconnection and electrical performance. The EL camera is a VIS-SWIR InGaAs camera with a quantum efficiency over 60% at 1-2 µm and sensor of 640 x 512 pixels. This camera enables the implementation of the test following IEC TS 60904-13:2018 [11] indications.

I-V curves were measured indoor at standard test conditions (STC), using a Pasan solar simulator with Class A+A+A, in compliance with the IEC 60904-9 [12]. It measures the electrical performance of the PV modules. The tests were performed at STC according to the international standard IEC 61215:2021 [13].

2.4 Colorimetry measurements

Color coordinates were measured with a Spectrophotometer 3Color SV300 in the CIE Lab color space, both on cells and on non-cell areas. For the strings, measurements were taken at the center of each string to evaluate intra-string and string-to-string uniformity. For the periphery, an additional points was recorded along the module periphery to assess string-to-periphery variations.

The same measurement points were maintained before and after the ten humidity-freeze cycles (HF10) stress sequence, ensuring direct comparison of color stability under aging. The color difference (ΔE) was used as a criterion to assess uniformity, with ΔE=2 taken as threshold for perceptible variation to human eye [14].

2.5 Reliability testing

Reliability tests were then performed in an Angelantoni PV4500 climatic chamber, according to the to the international standard IEC 61215:2021 [13]. The modules underwent ten humidity-freeze cycles (HF10) to simulate environment stress. Humidity freeze was selected to accelerate delamination, if any.

After climatic exposure, EL imaging, I-V measurements, visual inspection, and colorimetry were repeated to assess the impact of accelerated aging on both aesthetic and electrical performance of the shingled HJT modules.

3 RESULTS

The following section reports the main results concerning lamination of the modules, indoor characterization and reliability assessment.

A total of 12 BIPV prototype modules were processed, using shingled HJT strings. The modules, each measuring 1x0.75 m², with 28 cells per string in a shingled configuration. Out of the 12 prototypes, for further investigations 8 modules were selected: four glass–glass (GG) and four glass–backsheet (GBS), including one reference module for each configuration. The reference modules served as benchmarks for comparison of electrical performance with the other prototypes.

An overview of the 8 modules selected and their characteristics is reported in **Figure 1**, whereas **Figure 2** shows the final appearance (RGB photographs) of the modules along with their aesthetic evaluation.

TYPOLOGY	FRONT COVER	FRONT ENCAPSULANT	BACK ENCAPSULANT	REAR COVER	AESTHETIC EVALUATION
G-BS 1	Colored Glass Orange	EPE UV clear	EPE UV Clear	Black Back-sheet	Medium
G-BS 2	Colored Glass Orange	EPE UV clear	EPE UV Clear	Black Back-sheet	Medium
G-BS 3	Colored Glass Orange	EPE UV clear	EPE UV Clear	Black Back-sheet	High
G-BS Reference	Glass Transparent	EPE UV clear	EPE UV Clear	Black Back-sheet	Reference
G-G 1	Colored Glass Orange	EPE UV clear	EPE UV Clear	Colored Glass Orange	Medium
G-G 2	Colored Glass Orange	TPO Clear	Black TPO	Colored Glass Orange	Medium
G-G 3	Colored Glass Orange	EVA Clear	Black TPO	Colored Glass Grey	High
G-G Reference	Glass Transparent	TPO Clear	Black TPO	Glass Transparent	Reference

Figure 1: Overview of the modules laminated in Eurac laboratory with shingled HJT technology and their characteristics. Configuration adopted were both Glass-Glass (G-G) and Glass-Backsheet (G-BS).

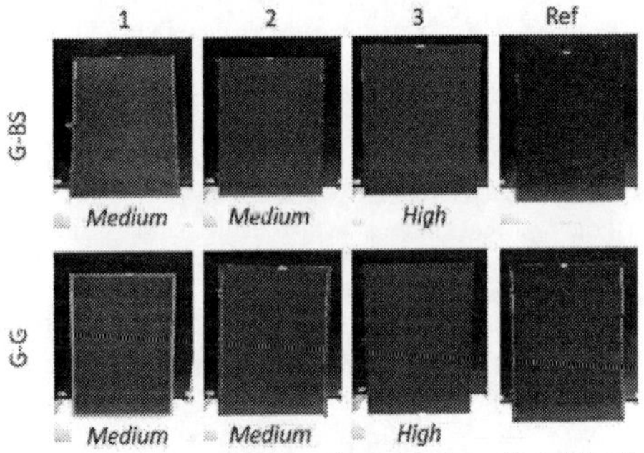

Figure 2: Final appearance of the modules selected for the study along with their aesthetic evaluation. Reference modules are also included.

3.1 Visual inspection

Before the HF10 stress test, most modules showed good lamination quality, with only minor defects observed in G-BS1 and G-BS2. In contrast, G-G1 presented poor aesthetics in the middle of some strings, where air bubbles were visible. After HF10, G-G1 was the most affected module, showing pronounced delamination, while the defects in G-BS1 and G-BS2 remained stable and did not extend. These observations confirm that degradation was mainly linked to specific material and use of old batch of strings rather than being systematic across all module types. A summary of the defects is reported in **Figure 3**.

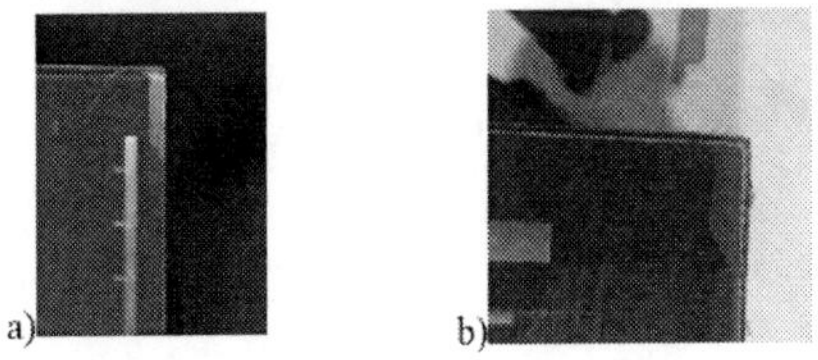

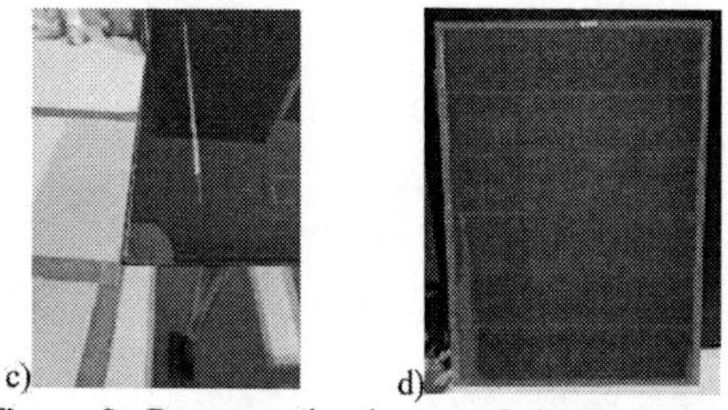

Figure 3: Representative images of the main defects observed in the modules: (a) localized delamination at the corner of G-BS1 before HF10 stress test; (b–c) minor corner delamination in G-BS2 before the HF10 stress test; (d) extensive delamination in G-G1 after the HF10 stress test.

3.2 I-V characterization

The initial IV measurements (showed **Figure 4**) conducted prior to the HF10 stress sequence confirm a generally good technological integration of the shingled HJT strings. The G-BS series displayed maximum power outputs (Pmpp) between 105–113 W, corresponding to a reduction of approximately 5–11% relative to the uncolored reference module (119 W). This power loss is attributed to the effect of coloration, which partially hinders photon absorption in the cells.

In the G-G configuration, modules exhibited slightly smaller losses, with power outputs between 118–119 W, equivalent to a 4–5% reduction compared with the reference (124 W). However, G-G3 produced only 39 W, which was linked to a hotspot and disconnected strings as revealed by electroluminescence imaging, and the maximum power (Pmpp) is related to the central strings.

Overall, the results demonstrate that shingled HJT modules can achieve stable integration even in colored BIPV applications, with acceptable efficiency trade-offs. The primary performance concern arises not from the coloring itself but from isolated technological issues such as string disconnection and localized defects.

		P_{mpp} [W]	V_{oc} [V]	I_{sc} [A]
G-BS	1	113	122	1.2
	2	110	120	1.2
	3	105	120	1.2
	Ref	119	121	1.3
G-G	1	118	121	1.3
	2	119	121	1.3
	3	39	40	1.3
	Ref	124	121	1.3

Figure 4: Initial IV parameters (Pmpp, Voc, Isc) of G-BS and G-G modules before HF10 stress testing. Reference (uncolored) modules are reported for comparison.

After the HF10 stress sequence, the overall maximum power point (Pmpp) remained relatively stable across both G-BS and G-G module configurations (see **Figure 6**). However, specific modules exhibited significant performance losses. G-BS3 showed a reduction of approximately 8%, which can be attributed to strong cell mismatch within its strings, as showed in **Figure 5**.

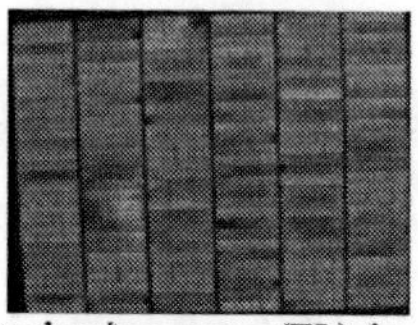

Figure 5: Electroluminescence (EL) image of shingled HJT G-BS 3 module, showing pronounced cell mismatch. This mismatch results in uneven electrical performance and contributes to overall module power losses.

Similarly, G-G1 experienced a power loss of up to 9%, primarily caused by delamination effects observed during visual inspection. These results indicate that the general performance of shingled HJT modules is preserved after stress testing, but localized technological issues or intrinsic material limitations are the dominant factors affecting reliability.

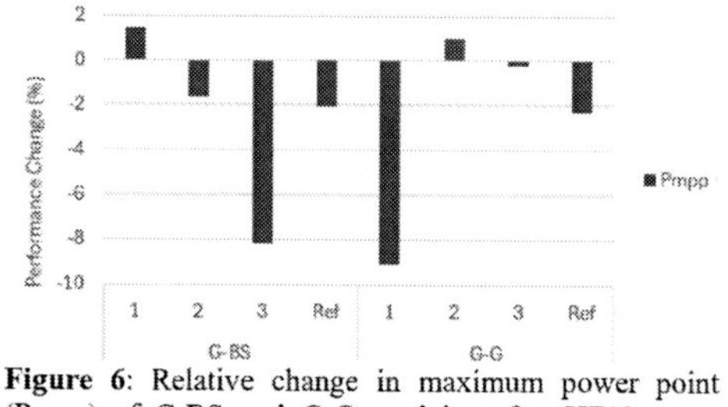

Figure 6: Relative change in maximum power point (Pmpp) of G-BS and G-G modules after HF10 stress testing. While most modules remained stable, G-BS3 and G-G1 exhibited significant power losses (≈8–9%) due to cell mismatch and delamination, respectively.

3.3 Electroluminescence imaging

Electroluminescence (EL) imaging was performed before and after the HF10 stress test at two current injection levels (100% Isc, 1.3 A, and 10% Isc, 0.13 A) in order to identify microcracks, interconnection faults, and other structural defects. An overview of the EL images is given in **Figure 7**. The analysis revealed that the main anomalies were associated with an old batch of strings, as also evidenced by the inhomogeneous patterns visible in the EL images. In the G-G3 module, a pronounced hot-spot and a missing string connection were observed, leading to severe non-emissive areas consistent with its low power output measured in IV characterization.

Across the other modules, the EL images demonstrated good visual stability, with only minor differences between the pre- and post-stress conditions. This stability is in agreement with the electrical performance results, which indicated that most modules maintained their output after HF10. The combined use of high and low injection levels proved valuable for distinguishing between fully disconnected areas and regions affected by higher series resistance or partial cracks. Overall, EL analysis confirmed that performance losses were primarily linked to localized interconnection defects, while the shingled HJT design itself remained robust under stress testing.

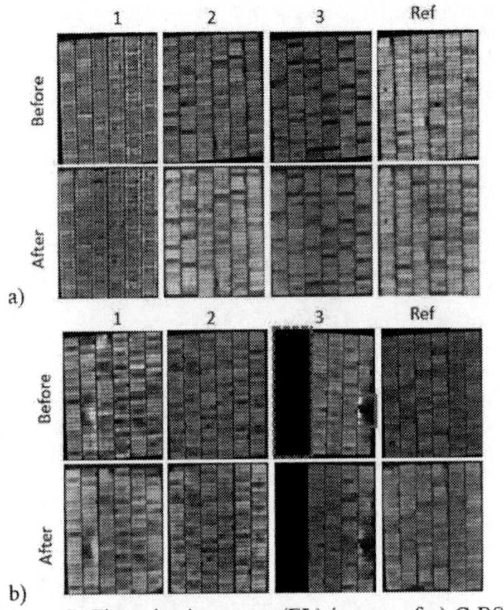

Figure 7: Electroluminescence (EL) images of a) G-BS and b) G-G modules acquired before and after HF10 stress testing at 100% and 10% Isc. The main defects are linked to the use of an old batch of strings, with G-G3 showing a hot-spot and a missing connection (highlighted with dotted red rectangle). Overall, visual stability was maintained, consistent with electrical performance results.

3.4 Colorimetry analysis

Colorimetric analysis was carried out before and after the HF10 stress test to evaluate both intra-module and overall visual uniformity. Measurement points were selected at the center of each string across the module, as well as at the periphery, in order to capture both string-level and periphery-related variations (**Figure 8**). Comparisons were performed by assessing string-to-string uniformity within the same module and string-to-periphery uniformity, using a randomly chosen color target as reference. After the stress test, the analysis focused on periphery-to-periphery comparison within the same module to detect periphery color variation, and on string-to-string evaluation to assess possible color changes between strings. This methodology allowed a consistent evaluation of both global and localized variations in aesthetic stability following accelerated aging.

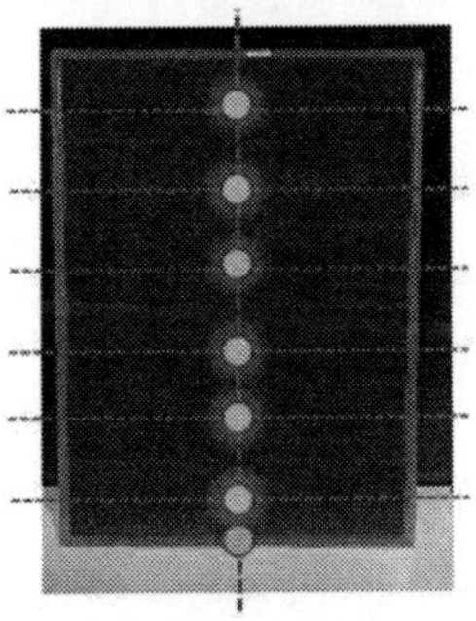

Figure 8: Colorimetric analysis of a shingled HJT module before and after HF10 stress testing.

Measurement points were consistently maintained in both cases: green markers indicate points located at the center of each string, while orange markers correspond to points on the periphery. Comparisons were performed for string-to-string and string-to-periphery uniformity, using a randomly selected color target as reference. After stress testing, the same measurement points were re-evaluated to assess periphery-to-periphery and string-to-string degradation.

As shown in **Figure 9**, the initial colorimetric assessment was performed before the HF10 stress sequence to evaluate both intra-module (string-to-string) and overall module (string-to-periphery) uniformity. Most ΔE*ab values were below or close to 2, the threshold at which color differences become perceptible to the human eye, confirming a generally good level of visual uniformity at the start of testing.

An exception was observed for module G-G1, which showed the highest ΔE*ab values and large variability across measurement points. This behavior can be attributed to the absence of a black back layer in this configuration, which resulted in a greater difference between string and periphery colors. In contrast, modules with a black layer on the back exhibited much lower string-to-periphery differences, confirming that this design approach enhances visual integration and improves overall aesthetic performance.

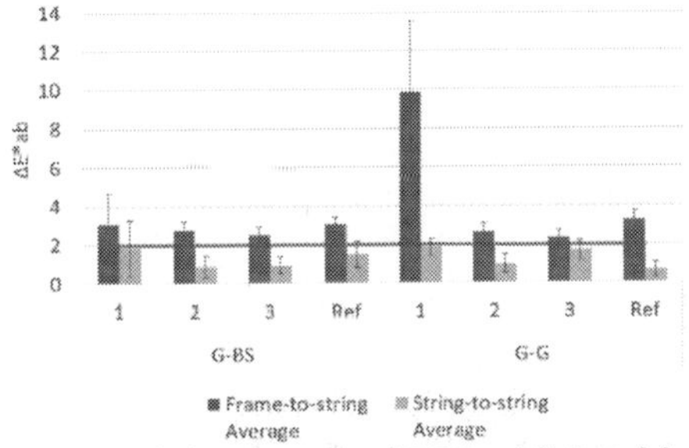

Figure 9: Colorimetric results of G-BS and G-G modules before HF10 stress testing. Most ΔE*ab values remain below or close to 2, indicating good visual uniformity. G-G1 shows the highest variability due to the absence of a black back layer, which increased string-to-periphery differences compared to other modules. Error bars are larger for string-to-periphery measurements, while string-to-string uniformity remains consistent.

After the HF10 stress sequence, the colorimetric analysis confirmed that overall degradation remained within acceptable limits, with ΔE*ab values generally ≤ 2, corresponding to differences that are not perceptible or perceptible only to an expert human eye **(Figure 10)**. The results indicate that string-to-string uniformity was well preserved, while periphery-to-periphery comparisons showed slightly higher variability in some modules. In particular, G-G2 presented the largest color variation at the periphery, although still within acceptable thresholds. These findings demonstrate that the visual appearance of the shingled HJT modules remained stable after accelerated aging, confirming their suitability for BIPV applications where aesthetic durability is a critical requirement.

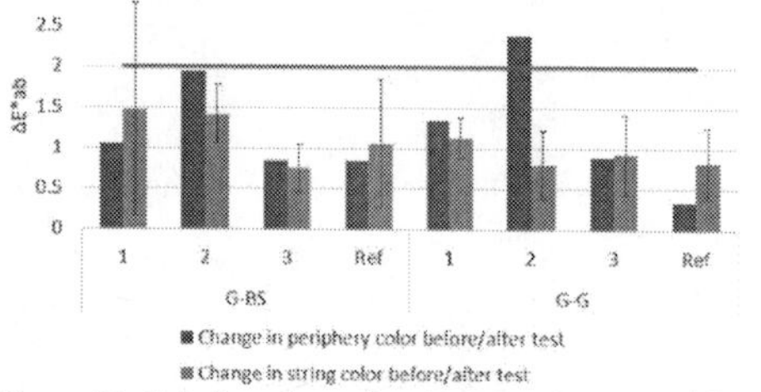

Figure 10: Colorimetric results of G-BS and G-G modules after HF10 stress testing. Color changes remain within acceptable limits ($\Delta E^*ab \leq 2$), with more uniformity observed at string level compared to the periphery. The largest variation was recorded in G-G2 at the module periphery, though still within perceptibility thresholds.

4 DISCUSSION

The results of this study demonstrate that shingled HJT modules maintain high visual stability after accelerated aging, with no significant aesthetic degradation observed in color coordinates after the HF10 stress sequence. While coloration introduced a modest reduction in electrical performance (–5 to –11% for G-BS and –4 to –5% for G-G compared with reference modules), this effect is consistent with typical BIPV trade-offs and remains within acceptable limits for façade integration. The strongest decreases in power output following the HF10 test were not associated with color but rather with technological issues such as delamination and increased cell mismatch/interconnection failure, highlighting the importance of material compatibility and process control in module fabrication. Importantly, no clear correlation was found between color degradation and electrical performance losses after testing, suggesting that optical stability and electrical reliability are indeed governed by different mechanisms. Taken together, these findings confirm that shingled HJT technology offers a promising solution for BIPV applications, provided that further optimization of lamination processes and interconnection quality is achieved to ensure long-term reliability.

However, despite the positive results, the HF10 stress test alone may not be fully representative for a comprehensive assessment; therefore, longer-term or alternative testing procedures are required to obtain a complete evaluation.

5 CONCLUSIONS

This work supports the view that shingled HJT modules have strong potential for building-integrated photovoltaic applications, as they successfully combine energy performance, technological feasibility, and aesthetic quality. The accelerated aging tests confirmed that the modules maintain stable visual appearance, with no significant color degradation after stress exposure. While coloration led to a modest decrease in electrical output, this trade-off is consistent with the requirements of BIPV integration and does not compromise the overall suitability of the technology. The most relevant performance issues were linked to lamination defects and string mismatch, pointing to the need for process/material optimization rather than fundamental design limitations.

The findings indicate that shingled HJT technology is a promising pathway toward aesthetically pleasing and reliable solar façades, and with further improvements in manufacturing quality, it can play an important role in advancing the integration of photovoltaics into the built environment.

6 AKNOWLEDGMENTS

This study was developed within the Project "Network 4 Energy Sustainable Transition—NEST", Project code PE0000021, promoted by the Ministero dell'Università e della Ricerca, funded by the European Union - NextGenerationEU - National Recovery and Resilience Plan (PNRR).

Funded by the European Union. Views and opinions expressed are however those of the author(s) only and do not necessarily reflect those of the European Union. Neither the European Union nor the granting authority can be held responsible for them.

This study is also a result of the research project "FotovOltaico efficiente in facciata per il fUturo pRossimo della rEte elettRica ' [FOURIER], funded by the Italian Ministry of the Environment and the Energy Security, through the Research Fund for the Italian Electrical System (type-B call, published on G.U.R.I. n. 312 on 17-12-2020).

The authors would like to express their gratitude to Applied Material Italia and GruppoSTG for their collaboration and support. Special thanks are extended to colleagues Lukas Koester, Juan Stivanello, and Alexander Astigarraga for their valuable contributions and assistance in the laboratory work.

7 REFERENCES

[1] D. Tonini, G. Cellere, M. Bertazzo, A. Fecchio, L. Cerasti, and M. Galiazzo, "Shingling Technology For Cell Interconnection: Technological Aspects And Process Integration," *Energy Procedia*, vol. 150, pp. 36–43, Sept. 2018, doi: 10.1016/j.egypro.2018.09.010.

[2] S. Harrison *et al.*, "Challenges for Efficient Integration of SHJ Based Solar Cells in Shingle Module Configuration," *37th European Photovoltaic Solar Energy Conference and Exhibition; 223-227*, p. 5 pages, 8165 kb, 2020, doi: 10.4229/EUPVSEC20202020-2BO.5.5.

[3] M.-J. Park, S. Youn, K. Jeon, S. H. Lee, and C. Jeong, "Optimization of Shingled-Type Lightweight Glass-Free Solar Modules for Building Integrated Photovoltaics," *Applied Sciences*, vol. 12, no. 10, p. 5011, May 2022, doi: 10.3390/app12105011.

[4] Eunbi Lee, Min-Joon Park, Minseob Kim, Jinho Shin, and Sungmin Youn, "Fabrication of High-power Shingled PV Modules Integrated with Bent Steel Plates for the Roof," *Current Photovoltaic Research, 11(2)*, pp. 54–57, June 2023.

[5] Ji-Su Park, Won-Je Oh, Jang-Hun Joo, Jun-Sin Yi, Byung-You Hong, and Jae-Hyeong Lee, "Design of High-Power and High-Density Photovoltaic Modules Based on a Shingled Cell String," *Journal of Nanoscience and Nanotechnology, 20(11)*, pp. 6996-7001(6), Nov. 2020, doi: https://doi.org/10.1166/jnn.2020.18837.

[6] B. Liang *et al.*, "Progress in crystalline silicon heterojunction solar cells," *J. Mater. Chem. A*, vol.

13, no. 4, pp. 2441–2477, 2025, doi: 10.1039/D4TA06224H.

[7] A. Lakhe, S. Upadhye, Y. Goshikwar, and T. Lakhe, "STUDY OF MODERN SOLAR TECHNOLOGIES: PERC and HJT," vol. 09, no. 07, 2022.

[8] "How efficient are heterojunction cells compared to traditional solar cells | NenPower." Accessed: Sept. 01, 2025. [Online]. Available: https://nenpower.com/blog/how-efficient-are-heterojunction-cells-compared-to-traditional-solar-cells/

[9] "Top Efficiency Of Each Cell Technology." Accessed: Sept. 01, 2025. [Online]. Available: https://taiyangnews.info/technology/top-efficiency-of-each-cell-technology-2

[10] D. M. Fischer, "ITRPV | ITRPV 2024 | Dr. Markus Fischer | PV CellTech, Frankfurt/Main, March 13 2024," 2023.

[11] "IEC TS 60904-13:2018 | IEC Webstore." Accessed: Sept. 03, 2025. [Online]. Available: https://webstore.iec.ch/en/publication/26703

[12] "IEC 60904-9:2020 | IEC Webstore." Accessed: Sept. 03, 2025. [Online]. Available: https://webstore.iec.ch/en/publication/28973

[13] "IEC 61215-1:2021 | IEC Webstore." Accessed: Sept. 03, 2025. [Online]. Available: https://webstore.iec.ch/en/publication/61345

[14] W. Mokrzycki and M. Tatol, "Color difference Delta E - A survey," *Machine Graphics and Vision*, vol. 20, pp. 383–411, Apr. 2011.

PV-PLANNING AND SIMULATION, DAYLIGHT SIMULATION AND ENERGY-CERTIFICATE CALCULATION BASED ON AN OPEN-BIM-BUILDING-MODEL

Astrid Schneider and Karin Stieldorf, TU Wien, Faculty of Architecture and Planning, Institute of Architecture and Design, Karlsplatz 13, 1040 Wien, Austria astrid@astrid-schneider.de, astrid.schneider@tuwien.ac.at, karin.stieldorf@tuwien.ac.at
Christian Schranz and Harald Urban, TU Wien, Research Unit Digital Building Process, christian.schranz@tuwien.ac.at;
Alfred Waschl, buildingSMART, alfred.waschl@buildingsmart.co.at;
Markus Feichtner, Sonnenkraft Energy GmbH, Markus.Feichtner@sonnenkraft.com;
Fedele Rende and Andreas Aiello ACCA Software, fedele.rende@almasoft.it;
Martin Hauer, Bartenbach GmbH, Martin.Hauer@bartenbach.com;
Kurt Battisti, Markus Dörn and Jacqueline Scherret, A-Null Development GmbH, kurt.battisti@archiphysik.com;
Martin und Christoph Treberspurg, Treberspurg und Partner Ziviltechniker, christoph.treberspurg@treberspurg.at

ABSTRACT: The TU Wien is leading the research project "BIM4BIPV – Future aspects of Building Integrated Photovoltaic (BIPV) in the cross system Building Information Modelling (BIM)". Goal of this project is to develop an open BIM-based planning and simulation workflow suitable for project specific Photovoltaic (PV) modules for Building Integration (BIPV) as well as for standard PV-modules to design, plan and simulate BIPV-modules with individual layers of encapsulants, front- and back sheets and different cell types, cell string layouts and cell distributions. At the EUPVSEC 2025 it could be the first time presented, that it is possible to equip the architect's BIM-model of an example building in the authoring software with custom-designed solar modules and their simulation values, to then export the BIM-model as an open BIM IFC-format into PV-simulation software and to perform the photovoltaic system simulation directly on this model. The PV-simulation software recognizes the PV-modules within the 3D-BIM-model and can read and use their electric values as well as their orientation and tilt.

Keywords: Building Integrated Photovoltaics (BIPV), Building Information Modelling (BIM), Industry Foundation classes (IFC), Simulation, Architecture

1 INTRODUCTION

The TU Wien is leading the research project "BIM4BIPV – Future aspects of Building Integrated Photovoltaic (BIPV) in the cross system Building Information Modelling (BIM)". Goal of this project is to develop an open BIM-based planning and simulation workflow suitable for project specific Photovoltaic (PV) modules for Building Integration (BIPV) as well as for standard PV-modules. Both shall be represented in the open BIM exchange format of the Industry Foundation Classes (IFC). The workflow can be used to design, plan and simulate BIPV-modules with individual layers of encapsulants, front- and back sheets and different cell types, cell string layouts and cell distributions. As a result, it shall be possible to execute a flexible, suit and integrated multidisciplinary workflow, in which PV-modules can be represented in an architect's or engineer's BIM-planning software such as Archicad, including classifications and property sets relevant for different planning disciplines. This includes – but is not restricted to - property sets for Photovoltaic and daylight planning and simulation, for energy certificate calculation and for environmental impact evaluation. At the EUPVSEC 2025 it could be the first time presented, that it is possible to equip the architect's BIM-model of an example building in the authoring software with custom-designed solar modules and their simulation values, to then export the BIM-model as an open BIM IFC-format and to perform the photovoltaic system simulation directly on this model. An existing building, planned and constructed in 1990 serves as an experimentation platform for the newly developed open BIM-process. Planning goal is to find the optimal balance between optimization of solar power generation, potential overheating in the summer, sufficient daylighting, passive solar gains in wintertime, energy efficiency and the preservation of the solar house aesthetic with excellent views to the sky and the garden, while at the same time embracing a glass house daylight level and feeling.

2 STATE OF THE ART AND INNOVATION

2.1 State of the Art

Today solar modules are represented by the producers mostly as PDF-datasheets. Furthermore the industry is feeding the solar module data into industrial proprietary data bases to be used in PV-planning and simulation programs such as Solarius-PV, PV-Syst or PV*Sol. Other innovative software such as BIMsolar by ENERbim is generating BIPV-modules within their own proprietary software, which is aiming to be compatible with the REVIT-BIM-planning software through a plugin.

2.2 Innovation

The research project BIM4BIPV is striving to innovate the representation of PV and BIPV-modules alike by offering an open source open BIM process, which is non-proprietary and allows a high compatibility with different software tools for planning, simulation, operation and documentation.

The workflow is currently under development, the first development stage has been concluded and first planning and simulation results are presented at the EUPVSEC 2025.

The PV- / BIPV-modules are designed in the authoring BIM-planning software and were sucessfully exported as an open BIM-format IFC-file. This format is the exchange format between different BIM-model authoring tools and specific planning and simulation software tools as a standard in architecture, urban and infrastructure planning.

10.4229/EUPVSEC2025/4BO.17.6

This BIM-model was then imported including the electric values into the PV-simulation software.

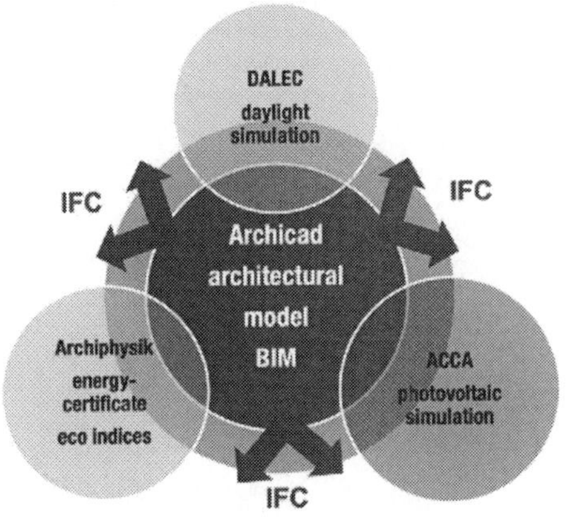

Figure 1: IFC-based multidisciplinary planning and simulation process on an open BIM model. Source: Astrid Schneider, TU Wien

3 HOUSE HAFNER IN VIENNA AS A MODEL CASE STUDY

2.1 House Hafner: a Passive Solar House from 1990

An existing building, "Haus Hafner" [0] planned and constructed in 1990 serves as an experimentation platform for the newly developed opem BIM-process. House Hafner was designed as an early example of solar architetcure – in that case as a passive solar building by the Austrian architects Treberspurg and Partner. The building opens to the south and features a fully glazed winter garden, which spans through the whole building from top to bottom.

Planned with the idea of optimization for passive solar gains and daylighting the building today suffers overheating due to climate change.

Figure 2: Fotos House Hafner. Source: Treberspurg and Partners ZT

At the same time active solar power generation is wished. The solar active design and planning with Building integrated PV now has to solve the balance between optimization of solar power generation, including the question of potential overheating in the summer, sufficient daylighting and passive solar gains in wintertime.

This multidisciplinary planning task was solved by using a 3D-BIM-model as a basis for planning and simulation. The model is drawn using the Archicad BIM-software as an authoring software.

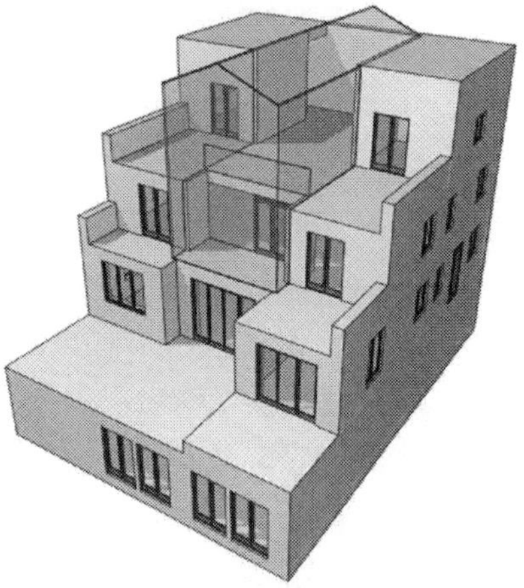

Figure 3: BIM-Model House Hafner without PV. Source: Treberspurg and Partners ZT

2.1 House Hafner: BIPV-Design as a Retrofit

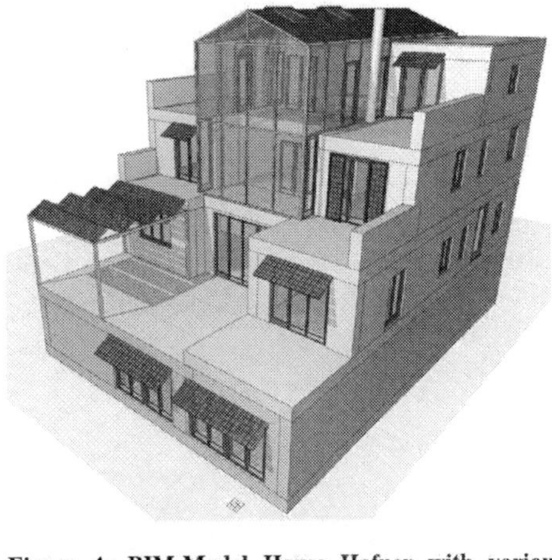

Figure 4: BIM-Model House Hafner with various BIPV-Systems drawn in Archicad BIM-Authoring Software. Source: Astrid Schneider, TU Wien and Treberspurg and Partners ZT

For the test set up the model of Hause Hafner was equipped with the following integrated BIPV-systems:

- integration of PV-panels into the atrium insulation glazing

- canopy roofs over windows
- solar window shutters
- pergola BIPV-roof over terrace

The BIPV-solar modules were drawn with the authoring BIM-software "Archicad", a well market introduced frequently used professional planning software in architecture in Europe. The module drawings do not have to follow any special requirements to be suitable to be attached with Photovoltaic module properties. The planning stage is "design planning".
However the real size of market available crystalline solar cells has been chosen for the design: 158 x 158 mm wide mono-crystalline Topcon solar cells. Th cell type to be chosen was agreed upon with the consortial partner Sonnenkraft, the largest PV-manufacturer of Austria as an available solar cell for BIPV-module manufacturing.

4. THE WORKFLOW FOR IFC-MODEL BASED PV- / BIPV-SIMULATION

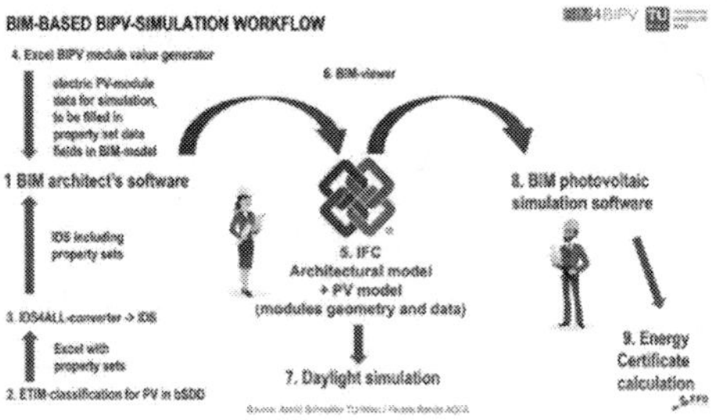

Figure 5: Workflow for BIM-based BIPV-Simulation
Source: Astrid Schneider, TU Wien and Fedele Rende, ACCA Software

Figure 5 shows the workflow steps and components for a multidisciplinary planning, calculation and PV-simulation. We will go through the steps according to the numbers in the figure 5.

4.1 Building Model Design by the Architect in a BIM-Planning Software including BIPV-Modules

The architect will design the solar modules in accordance with design ideas, clients wishes and as agreed in the planning process.

Figure 6: BIM-Model of the Architect in Archicad
Source: Astrid Schneider, TU Wien and Treberspurg and Partners Architects

The size of solar cells and modules will already be discussed and adjusted with potential market offers or producers and technical consultants. Here a format of 158 x 158 mm solar cells war chosen. The solar cell layout in the panels, the density and aesthetics can already be determined according to the building design. The solar modules are drawn with precise geometry an measures.

4.2 ETIM Classification EC001746 "Photovoltaics module"

As a preparatory step the ETIM [1] Classification EC001746 "Photovoltaics module" [2] was transferred in an Excel sheet. The sheet as well defines, for which entities in the BIM-model this classification can be used. This process has only to be done once in an architect's or planner's office to generate an Information Delivery Specification (IDS). The subsequent IDS can then forever been used in the office for different projects.

4.3 Generation of an Information Delivery Specification (IDS) for Photovoltaic Simulation Values

To be able to generate the property fields for the electric properties of a PV-module in the architectural or engineering authoring software it is one option to do it automated via an IDS. The advantage is, that the fields "pop up" in the authoring software in this case in Archicad. The TU Wien in collaboration with buildingSMART Austria [3] generated and published an "IDS4ALL-converter" [4], which converts via up- and download the excel sheet into an IDS-file, which can be imported into the Archicad software.

4.4 Excel BIPV Module Value Generator

The electric values of a PV-module are normally taken from the producers data sheet. In case the architect designs the BIPV-module herself to be produced custom sized to fit the specific project there are different options. One is, that the producer delivers the electric values of such a module to the architect or the planner himself calculates the values. Sonnenkraft the biggest Austrian Photovoltaic producer uses internally as well for the first a calculation via Excel, based on the cell used for the module and the module layout including the thickness of the glasses. These electric values are then feeded into the property sets popping up when the specific object is activated in the BIM software as shown in figure 7 below.

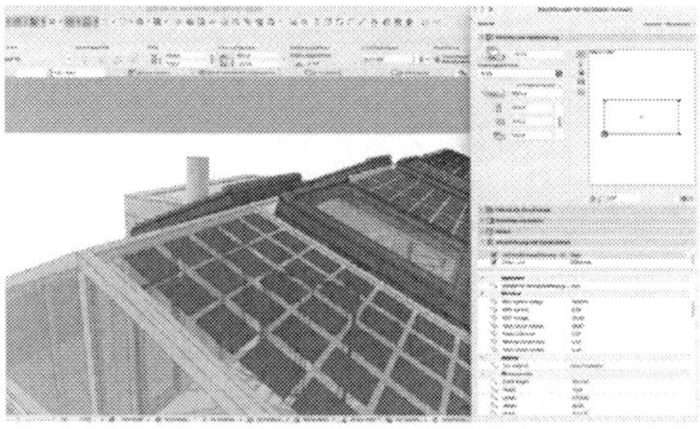

Figure 7: BIM-Model of the Architect in Archicad with opened property set field for PV-modules
Source: Astrid Schneider, TU Wien

10.4229/EUPVSEC2025/4BO.17.6

4.5 Export as an IFC File

Once the BIPVmodules have been described the whole building model will be exported from the authoring software as an IFC-file, which will include all the properties specified earlier in the IDS and brought to the architect' BIM-model.

4.6 Value Control with the BIM-Viewer

As a very important step the values can now be controlled in a BIM-viewer as shown in figure 7.

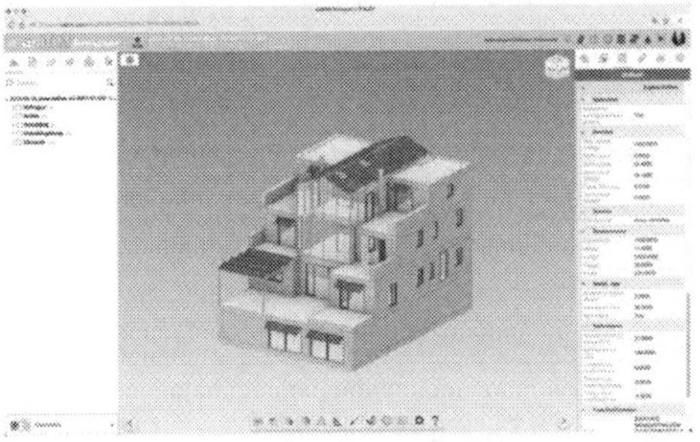

Figure 7: BIM-Model of the Architect in the BIM-Viewer. Source: Astrid Schneider, TU Wien

The BIM-viewer allows in a platform agnostic manner to check an uploaded IFC-model regarding the content and correctness of information, which is included in the model. By clicking the solar modules the electric and other values of the BIPV-element are popping up. The information stored can be regarding all disciplines, in this case we look at the electric values according to the ETIM-classification Photovoltaics Module. As a BIM-viewer the ACCA-usBIM [5] has been used. In the control view it can be seen, that the desired electric values of the solar modules have been exported successfully and are incorporated in the generated exportfile in the IFC-format.

4.7 Daylight Simulation

The project partner Bartenbach used "Climate Studio" Daylight simulations are performed using Climate Studio ClimateStudio is a plugin for the Rhinoceros (Rhino) 3d modeling software. The data path to use the BIM-model fort he daylight simulation and evaluation ist he following:

- The IFC-file was directly imported into Rhino, using ggIFC - an „Add-on application" in Rhino
- After manual modifcations on the imported geometry in Rhino, the model was able to be used by Climate Studio

General problem:

- Daylight simulation tools only consider geometry from IFC-files
- Daylight specific parameters (surface reflection values, visual transparancy values,...) have to be set manually

Several daylighting factors have been simulated and evaluated. As a result it can be clearly seen, that the House Hafner has a problem, in the actual variant without any BIPV.

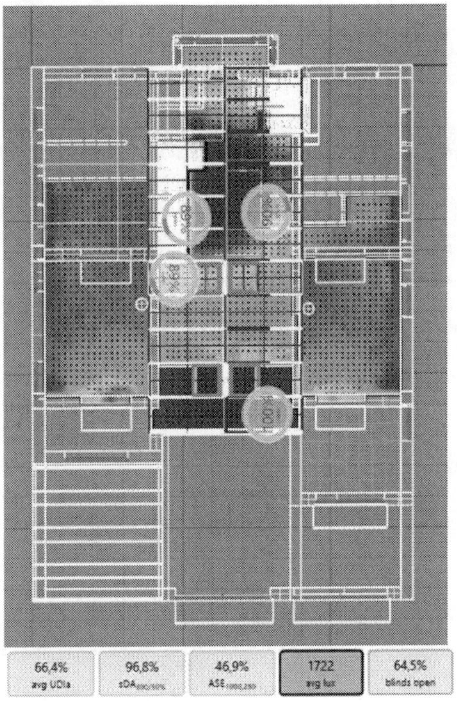

Figure 8: Evaluation of the Daylight-values UID and ASE without BIPV
Source: Martin Hauer, Bartenbach

Figure 8 shows the building without BIPV. The following factors were evaluated:

Useful Daylight Illuminance (UDI)

- is a modification of daylight autonomy
- This criterion divides the hourly data into three evaluation categories
  - 0-100lx (underlighting)
  - 100 - 2000lx (pleasant lighting conditions)
  - >2000lx (overlighting)
- In the range of 100-2000lx, daylight input is rated as useful

Annual Sunlight Exposure (ASE)

- refers to the percentage of space that receives too much direct sunlight (1000 Lux or more for at least 250 occupied hours per year), which can cause glare or increased cooling loads

As a result the observed overheating in the summer can be clearly seen in the simulation:

- Annual Sunlight exposure (ASE) is very high → glare and summer overheating
- Useful daylight illuminance (UDI) is reduced → too much exceeding illuminance lelvels

As an alternative the variant with BIPV-glazing was simulated.

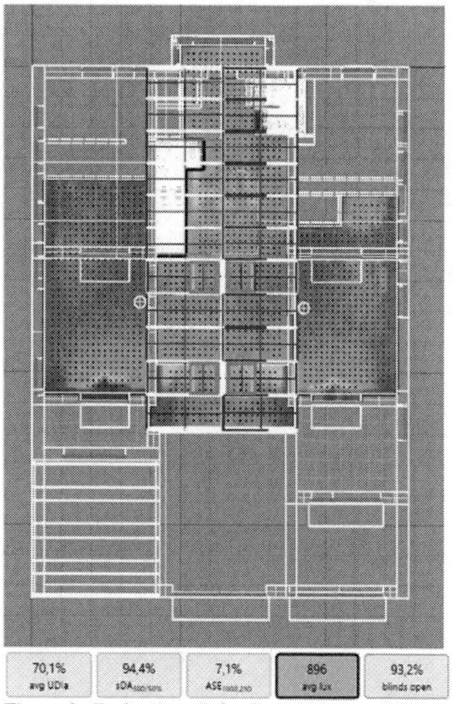

Figure 9: Evaluation of the daylight-values UID and ASE with BIPV. Source: Martin Hauer, Bartenbach

In this variant the BIPV plays a crucial role to enhance the thermal and optical performance of the building. The BIPV-variant of figure 9 is:

- **PV on canopy (non transp.)**
- **PV on Roof + Side windows (semitransp.)**

As a result of this BIPV deployment it could be observed:

- Significant improvement by semitransparent PV on roof and side windows of the attic brings a siginficant improvement
  → Annual Sunlight exposure in an acceptable range (<10%)
- Highest levels on Useful Daylight illuminance UDI → 70%

A similar picture was observed regarding the daylight factor as shown in the presentation.

4.8 Photovoltaic System Planning and Simulation

As a very important step now the PV-system electric planning and simulation can be done directly based on the architectural model. To do so the IFC-file with the overall building model is imported into the Photovoltaic simulation program Solarius PV from the research partner ACCA.

As an advantage the BIM-model contains all the electric values specified in the IDS based on the ETIM property set for Photovoltaic modules. Those values are the input parameters for the PV-system planning and simulation.

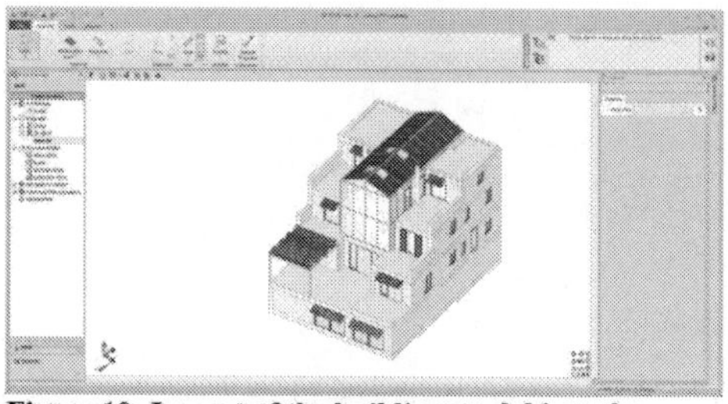

Figure 10: Import of the building model into the Solarius PV Photovoltaic simulation program
Source: Fedele Rende, ACCA.

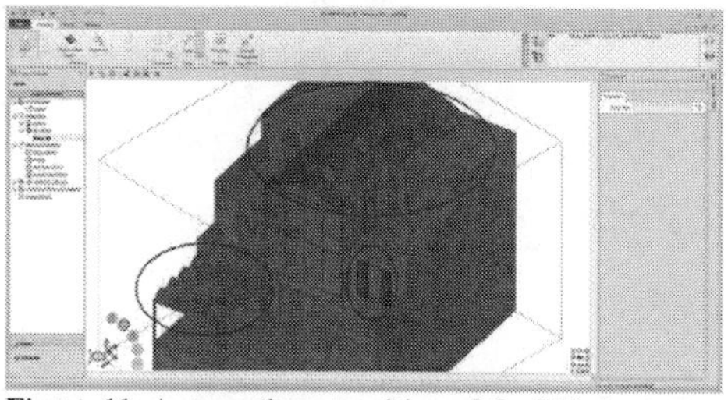

Figure 11: Automatic recognition of the PV-elements within the building open BIM IFC-model
Source: Fedele Rende, ACCA

The most important step to close the BIPV-simulation workflow was performed successfully: within the research project the Solarius PV-software was adopted to be able to detect BIM-elements with the ETIM classification EC001746 "Photovoltaics module" automatically.

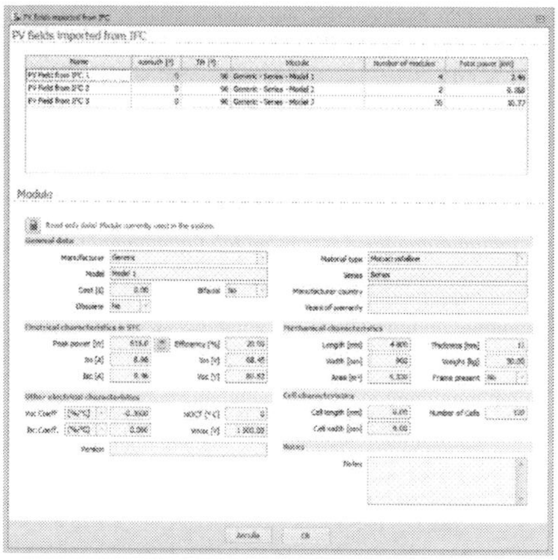

Figure 12: Electric PV-module-data data read from the architectural model by Solarius PV
Source: Fedele Rende, ACCA

This step is crucial, as it is not necessary to place modules "on top" of existing BIPV-surfaces to "simulate" a BIPV-module. Instead elements which are just right at the place they should be can be activated as PV-modules and thus even in a digital model fulfil the double function to be a building element and an electric system element (PV-module) at the same time. With this data the normal PV-

system planning and simulation process can start.
As a result the PV-yield can be simulated as shown in figure 13:

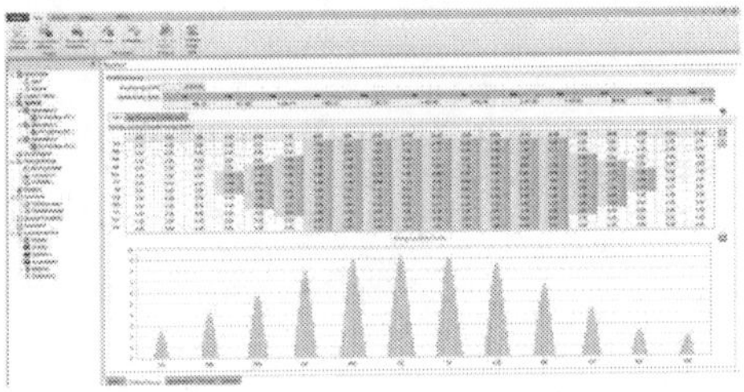

Figure 13: PV yield of House Hafner BIPV-plants calculated with the PV-simulation program
Source: Fedele Rende, ACCA

4.9 Calculation of the Energy Certificate

The same IFC-building model can be used to calculate the energy certificate of the building. The Energy Certificate evaluates, how the building is complying with the requirements set out in the European Union (EU) Energy Performance of Buildings (EPD) directive and in this case the national Austrian legislation and building standards requirements putting the EPD into force in Austria. This calculation is made by the project partner A0-Development with their own self developed software Archiphysik. For the Energy Certificate calculation the BIPV-elements – especially when integrated into shading devices, windows or glazed façade and roof elements are relevant regarding their thermal, visual and electric impact.

4.9.1Parameters of the PV-System taken into account for the Energy Certifcate Calculation:

The building physics program Archiphysik can read the BIM-model and evaluate the values and geometry:

Regarding the BIPV-glazing- and shading-elements the following inputs are taken from model for the thermal evaluation of the building envelope:

Thermal input parameters:
- shading geometry of PV-modules in front of the window or glazed area (share of opaque and transparent area)
- G-value of the glazing
- U-value of the glazing
    - ➢ calculation of solar radiation entering the space
        - ➢ thermal comfort fulfilment
        - ➢ heating and cooling demand calculation in kWh/m^2

Glazing and summer overheating
Large glazed areas may cause overheating under sunlight. In the summer only a limited reduction is possible through night ventilation.

BIPV-approach Haus Hafner: solar gains through glazing have to be reduced. PV shutters and BIPV glazing in the are used to reduce the solar input to cause less overheating.

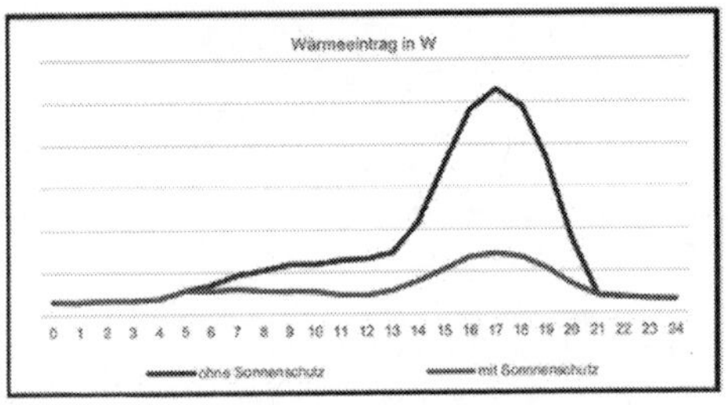

Figure 14: Heat Input through a glazed area with and without sun protection during 24 hours of a summer day.
Source: Markus Dörn A-Null Development GmbH

PV-module inputs taken from model:
- Wp – Power
- location, orientation
    - ➢ solar power produced
- reduction of primary fossil energy consumed
- fulfilment of required installation capacity by construction laws

4.9.2 Photovoltaic electricity in the energy balance
Electricity generated by PV can be included in the energy balance for the Energy Performance Certificate. Depending on the national legal framework of the EU-country , PV electricity can fully or partially replace other energy carriers. Some EU-countries allow to take simulated PV-power production into account, while others only allow an extremely simplified calculation based on system power and location plus orientation.
The amount of creditable PV electricity is legally defined and restricted to schematically defined times, when PV-power production and energy system consumption are expected to overlap.
Surplus PV electricity is shown in the EPC as PV export.

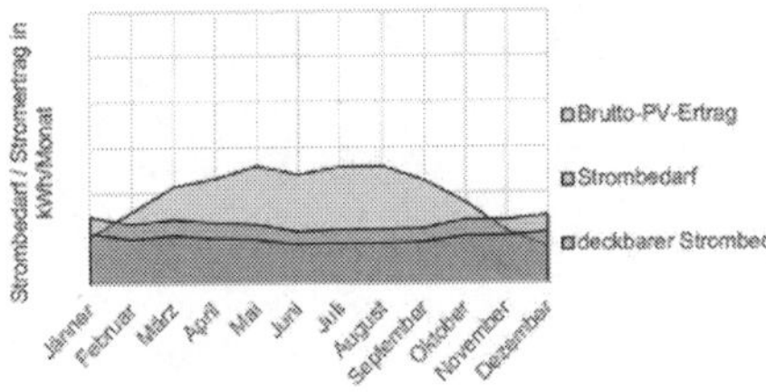

Figure 15: Solar power generated by the BIPV-system and it's consideration in the Energy Certificate calculation according to the Austrian rules
Source: Markus Dörn A-Null Development GmbH

5. DIFFICULTIES FACED IN THE PROCESS

The workflow was achieved the first time successfully in the project. However there are many hurdles on the way to be faced:
- compatibility problems of different software products and formats
- multiple model transfers causing faults
- missing data after model transfer
- correct transfer of location, direction and axis is

a challenge and not yet fully achieved
- material transfer / display of materials
- the IFC standard is not yet fully adopted and implemented by all actors / software companies

Due to the above mentioned hurdles some data had to be corrected by hand.

4 OUTLOOK

4.1 PV and BIPV-simulation

It would be senseful to have a PV / BIPV-module generator, which would display a PV-module directly in IFC including active single cells as shown in figure 16.

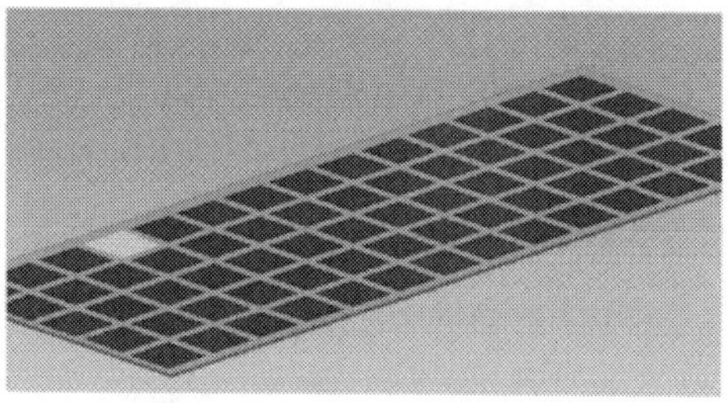

Figure 16: PV-module with activated single cell
Source: BIM4BIPV

The main purpose is, to be able to determine the area and substring of a PV-module affected by especially near shade. To do so an analysis will be needed, which cell / cell string is affected by shade.

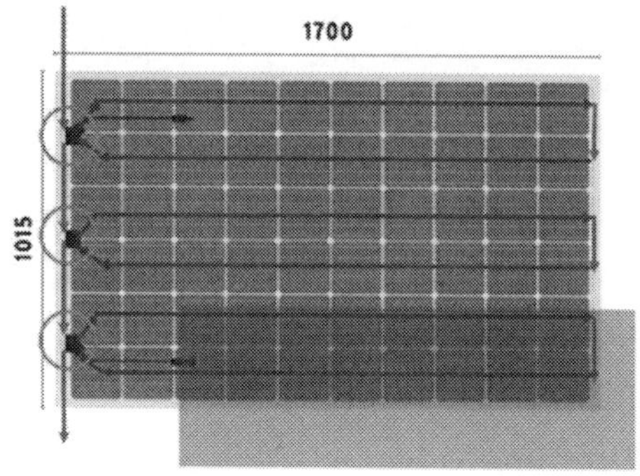

Figure 17: PV-module with shade falling on one module string
Source: Astrid Schneider, TU Wien

This kind of analysis is especially relevant in BIPV-applications as they face more shade problems. Due to the strong rise of bifacial modules the near shade aspect is as well more and more important regarding the module supporting structures.

4.2 IFC-Module Database

As soon as the workflow is established and gains traction in the market a worldwide database of PV and BIPV-modules could start arising, which would allow to drag and drop PV-modules into construction designs. This option is however strongly dependent on the compatibility of different software.

4.3 Software Compatibility

The construction planning and solar simulation software should be adopted and made compatible, so that PV and BIPV can be integrated easily into digital planning flows. The following aspects have to be taken into consideration:

- optimized near shade and bifaciality simulation
  - as well on cell, module and string level
- inclusion of multidisciplinary data of PV / BIPV into construction models
- ability for multidisciplinary simulation such as
  - daylighting
  - shade and heat effects
  - energy planning
  - green construction
- as well important for agri-PV, infrastructure, OEM of large solar parks ...

Especially a full compliance and adaptation of the IFC-standard by different software developers and providers would enable the swift flow of data and enable integrated multidisciplinary planning workflows based on IFC-project models.To achieve this, it is important to standardize the property and property set names to enable interoperability across PV / BIPV and construction / infrastructure industry. An ongoing international collaboration within in Task 15 of the IEA International Energy Agency Power systems Program PVPS is under way, to help unifying the needed property and classification data.

4.3 References

[0] **Article House Hafner:** "Geöffnet zu Sonne und Gärten", Fachjournal "Architektur Aktuell 143", Juni 1991

[1] **ETIM International:** As of 05.10.2024 https://www.etim-international.com/

[2] **ETIM classification EC001746 "Photovoltaics Module"** As of 17.05.2025 https://identifier.buildingsmart.org/uri/etim/etim/9.0/class/EC001746

[3] **buildingSMART international**: As of 02. September 2024: https://www.buildingsmart.org/

[4] **IDS4ALL-Converter** As of 12. September 2025: https://openbim-knowledgebase.org/ids4all/

[5] **BIM-viewer the ACCA-usBIM** As of 10. September 2025: https://www.accasoftware.com/de/bim-management-system

[6] **Climate Studio** As of 10. September 2025: https://climatestudiodocs.com/index.html

[7] **buildingSMART Data Dictionary (bSDD)** As of 07. September 2024: https://www.buildingsmart.org/users/services/buildingsmart-data-dictionary/

BIM4BIPV

TECHNISCHE UNIVERSITÄT WIEN

PV-PLANNING AND SIMULATION, DAYLIGHT SIMULATION AND ENERGY-CERTIFICATE CALCULATION BASED ON AN OPEN-BIM-BUILDING-MODEL

Session 4BO.17.6 - Planning of PV Systems - Digital PV

Presentation 4BO.17.6
September 23rd

EUPVSEC 2025 – Spain - Bilbao

Astrid Schneider
TU Wien

FFG
Forschung wirkt.

Research Project BIM4BIPV

- **TU Wien Institute for Architecture and Design + Digital Construction Process**
  Karin Stieldorf, Astrid Schneider, Christian Schranz, Harald Urban
- **buildingSMART**
  Alfred Waschl
- **Archiphysik - A-Null Development GmbH**
  Kurt Battisti, Markus Dörn, Jacqueline Scherret
- **Solarius PV - ACCA Software / ALMA**
  Fedele Rende, Andrea Aiello
- **Bartenbach GmbH**
  Martin Hauer
- **Sonnenkraft GmbH**
  Markus Feichtner
- **Treberspurg and Partner Architects ZT**
  Christoph Treberspurg, Martin Treberspurg

Project website: https://bim4bipv.project.tuwien.ac.at/

BIM4BIPV

BIM4BIPV TU WIEN TECHNISCHE UNIVERSITÄT WIEN

BUILDING INFORMATION MODELLING (BIM)

What is „BIM"?

- Modelling of element information (mostly) in the three dimensional space
- modern construction world plans in „BIM"
- Drawing-elements with complex informations attached
  - geometry
  - materials
  - visual appearance
  - properties regarding different disciplines

BIM-3-D-model enables the „Digital Twin"

Source: BIM4BIPV – Haus Hafner

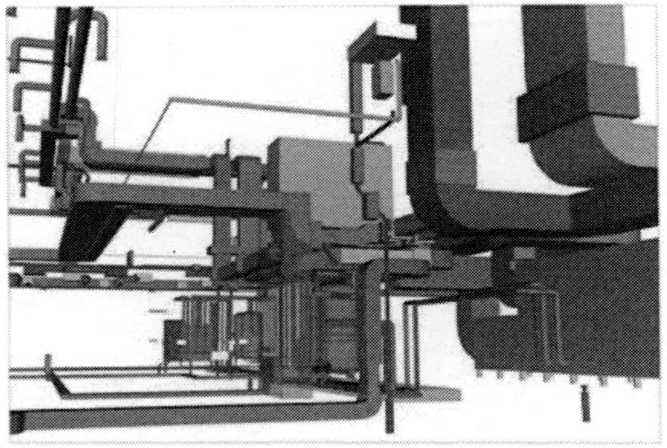

Source: „Bio-Institut der HBLFA Raumberg-Gumpenstein, TU Wien

FFG

BIM REPRESENTATION OF A BIPV-MODULE

Source: Astrid Schneider TU wien

BIPV-Project seen in a BIM-viewer - source: BIM4BIPV - https://www.accasoftware.com/en/bim-management-system

OPEN BIM STANDARD IFC

.ifc

- Data exchange via open BIM „Industry Foundation Classes (IFC) Standard between different proprietary planning platforms (Revit / Archicad ...) and planning and simulation tools of various disciplines
- The IFC-standard is developed by buildingSMART and published as ISO 16739-1 – Industry Foundation Classes (IFC)
- .ifc = open exchange format like „PDF" „JPG" .... of the 3D-model
- Information Delivery Specification (IDS) is a buildingSMART standard for defining information requirements in a computer interpretable form
- PV / BIPV belongs into the picture of construction + infrastructure planning processes

BIM4BIPV | TU WIEN TECHNISCHE UNIVERSITÄT WIEN

OUR GOAL: „LIVING“ PV- / BIPV PRODUCT INFORMATION

.pdf

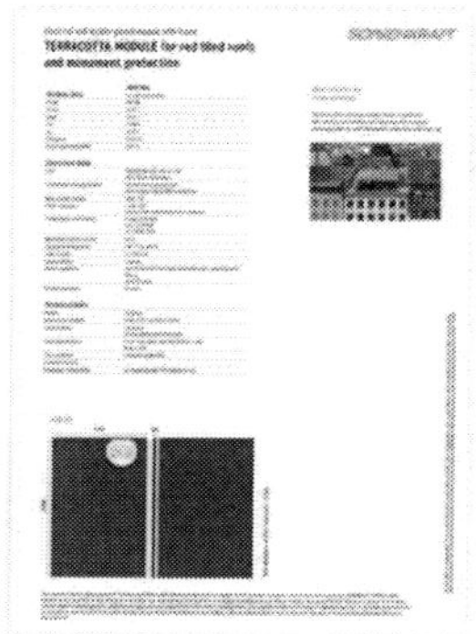

Source: Sonnenkraft

„dead data“
informative

Source: Astrid Schneider TU Wien

PDF → **open BIM-Data**

.ifc

Model , type	
Number of bypass diodes	7.0000
Number of cells	70.0000
With frame	False
Performance	
Module efficiency factor (STC)	17.0000
MPP power by STC	359.0000
Temperature coefficient Isc	0.0600
Temperature coefficient Pmpp	-0.3600
Temperature coefficient Uoc	-0.3600

„living data“
workable

FFG

BIM4BIPV TU WIEN TECHNISCHE UNIVERSITÄT WIEN

GOAL: DIGITAL PV-MODULES TO BE PRECISELY PLACED IN BIM-CAD-SOFTWARE

PV-Producer
is responsible to provide use case specific relevant product data

SONNENKRAFT

PV- BIPV-Product

Data-Scheme for PV / BIPV

PV- / BIPV-Data
in BIM / IFC-format

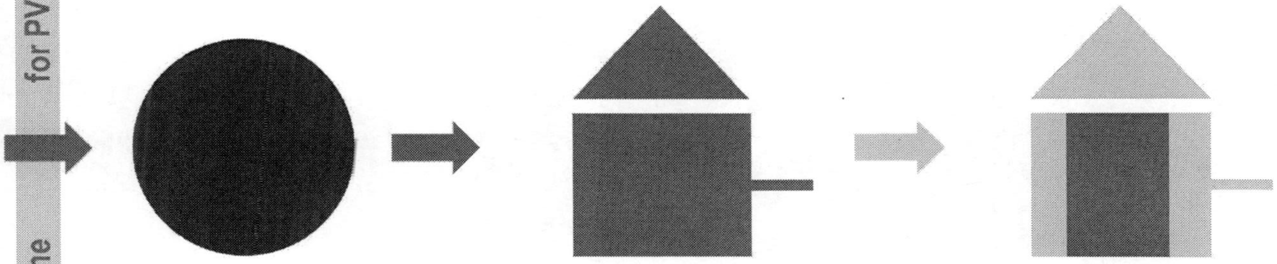

PV- Database in BIM / IFC – formate optimally public

Architect
plans building / construction and puts PV- / BIPV-BIM-elements into CAD / BIM project design
(generic, product specific, custom sized)

BIM-project design
- visual

Engineer
uses detailled PV- / BIPV- BIM project design to plan and simulate PV / BIPV-system

BIPV-system
- PV-system design and yield calculation
- daylighting
- energy
- structural
- environment

FFG

Source: Astrid Schneider TU Wien

TECHNISCHE UNIVERSITÄT WIEN

SIMULATION OF HAUS HAFNER

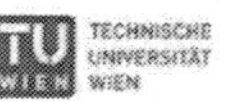

HAUS HAFNER,
1190 Wien, Austria

- designed by Treberspurg and Partner Architects ZT, Vienna
- built 1991
- now suffering serious overheating in the atrium
- wish for BIPV-integration for shading and solar power

BIM4BIPV

HAUS HAFNER – SOLAR HOUSE OF THE FIRST GENERATION 1991

TU WIEN TECHNISCHE UNIVERSITÄT WIEN

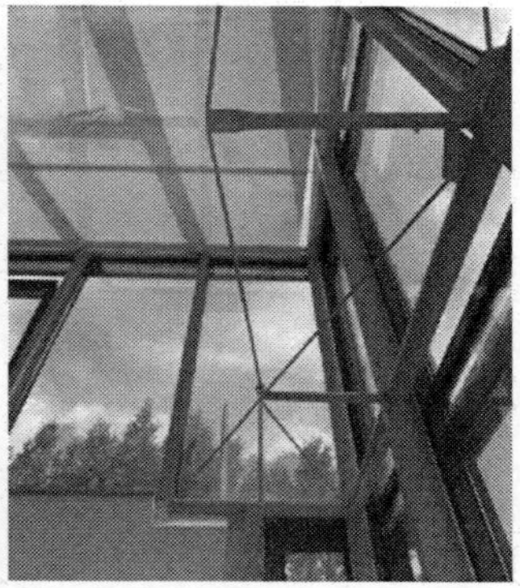

Fotos: Astrid Schneider TU Wien

Optimized design for passive solar gains: building opened towards the south with glass house

BIM4BIPV

TECHNISCHE UNIVERSITÄT WIEN

HAUS HAFNER – SOLAR HOUSE OF THE FIRST GENERATION 1991

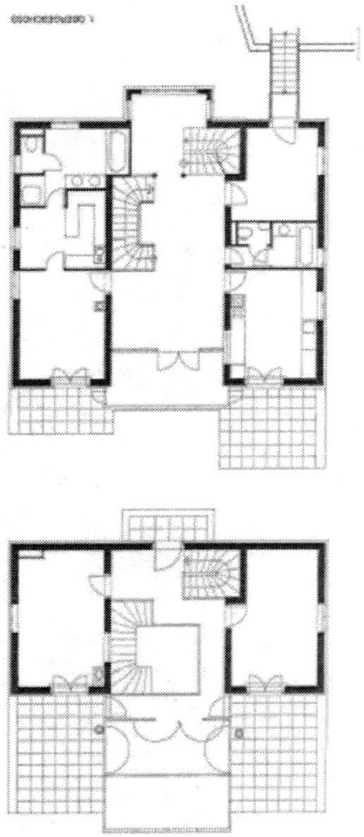

Glass house and inner atrium – today affected from summer overheating

BIM4BIPV

BIM4BIPV TU WIEN TECHNISCHE UNIVERSITÄT WIEN

HAUS HAFNER – BIM MODEL WITH BIPV AS DRAWING ELEMENTS

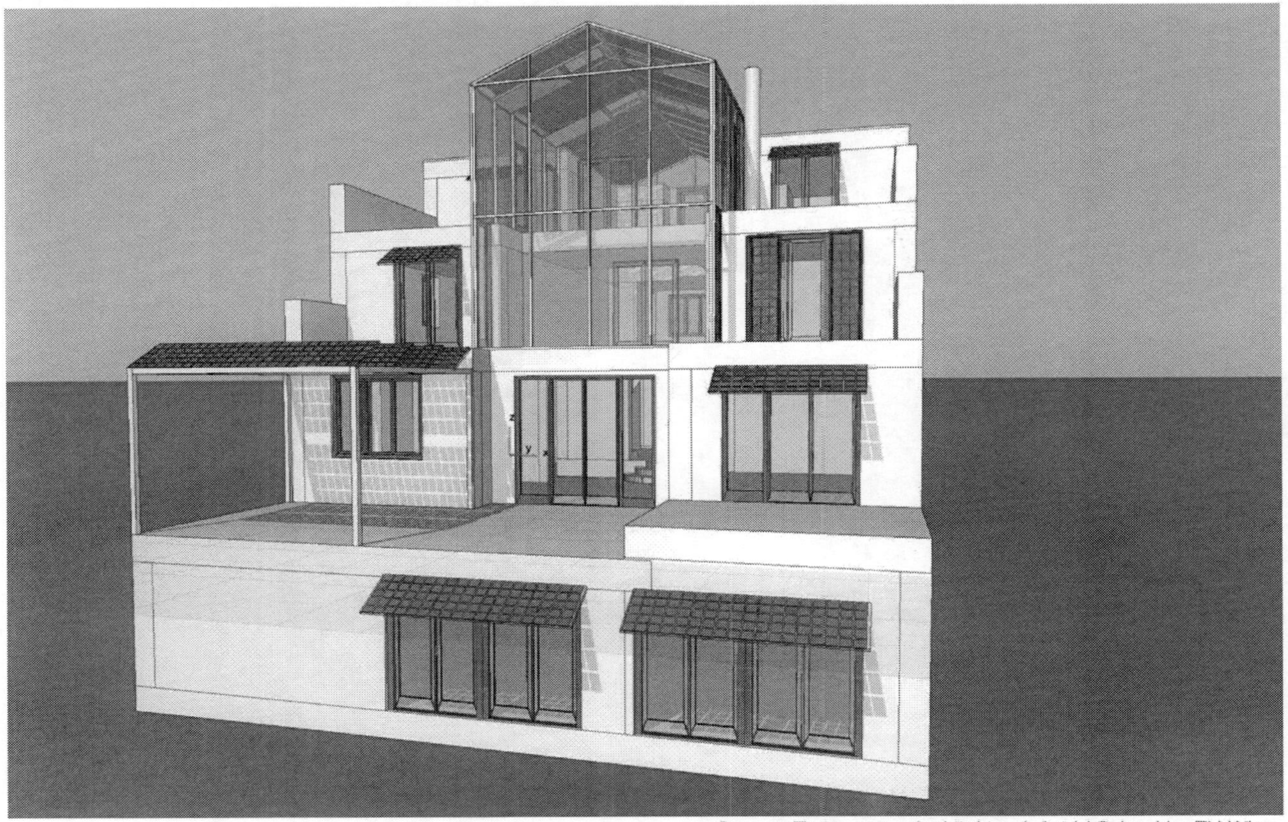

Source: Treberspurg Architekten / Astrid Schneider TU Wien

South view with different BIPV-systems in architect's BIM-planning program Archicad

FFG

BIM4BIPV TU WIEN TECHNISCHE UNIVERSITÄT WIEN

HAUS HAFNER WITH BIPV AS DRAWING ELEMENTS

View to the atrium / different BIPV-systems

Source: Treberspurg Architekten / Astrid Schneider TU Wien

FFG

BIM4BIPV TU WIEN TECHNISCHE UNIVERSITÄT WIEN

HAUS HAFNER WITH BIPV AS DRAWING ELEMENTS

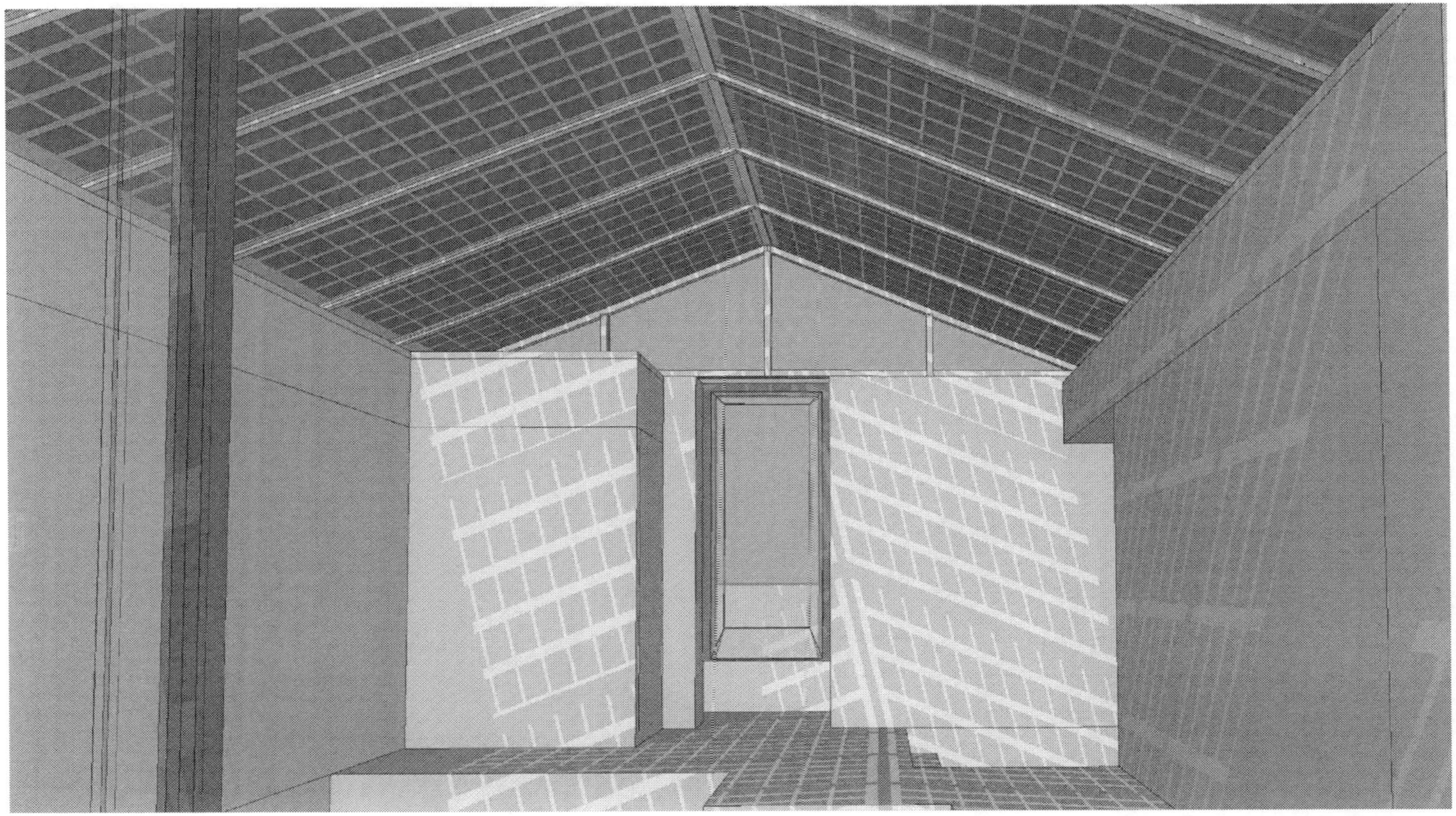

Source: Treberspurg Architekten / Astrid Schneider TU Wien

Interior view atrium

FFG

BIM4BIPV TU WIEN TECHNISCHE UNIVERSITÄT WIEN

HAUS HAFNER WITH BIPV AS DRAWING ELEMENTS

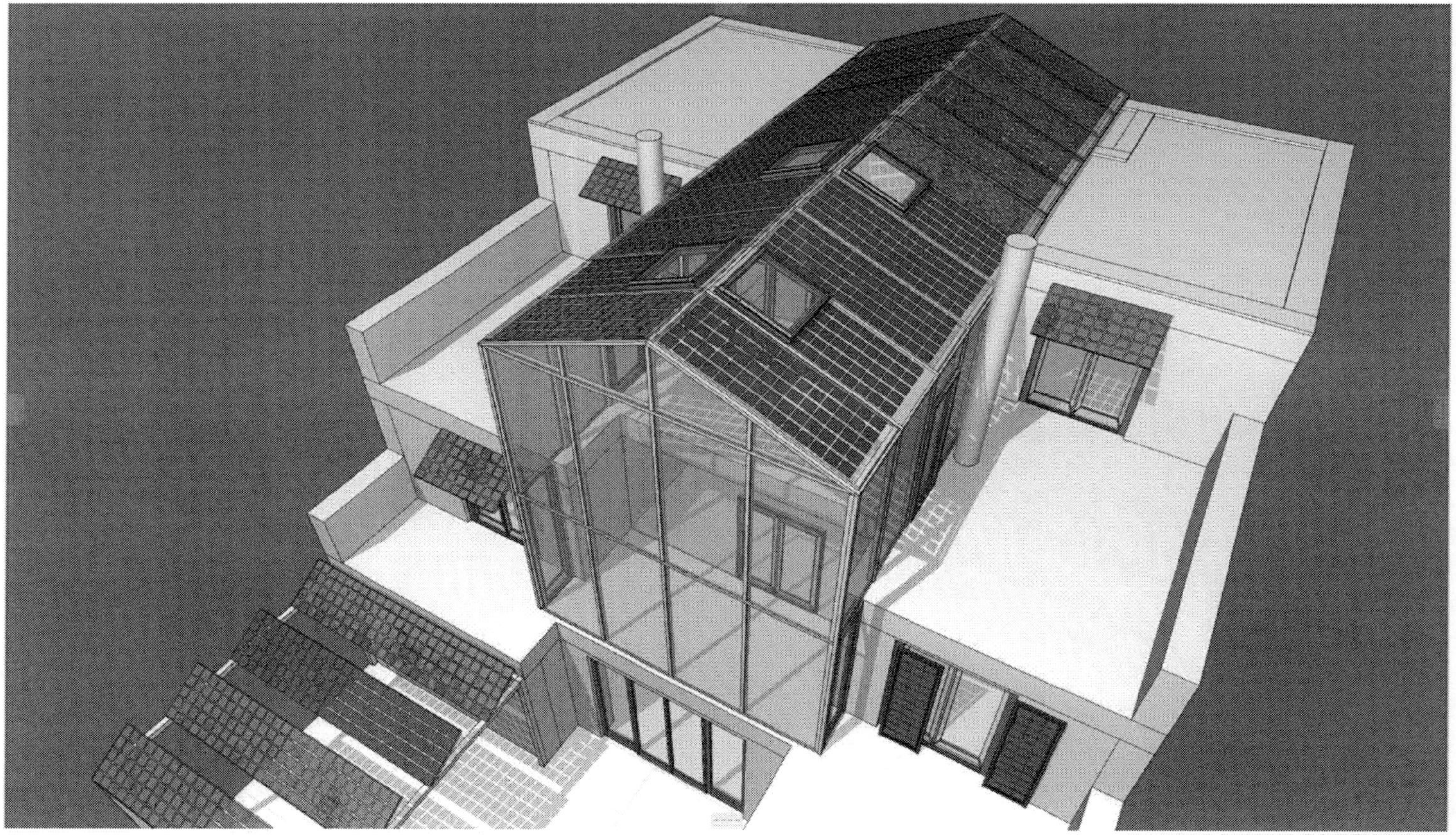

FFG

HAUS HAFNER – BIM MODELL WITH BIPV IN ARCHICAD

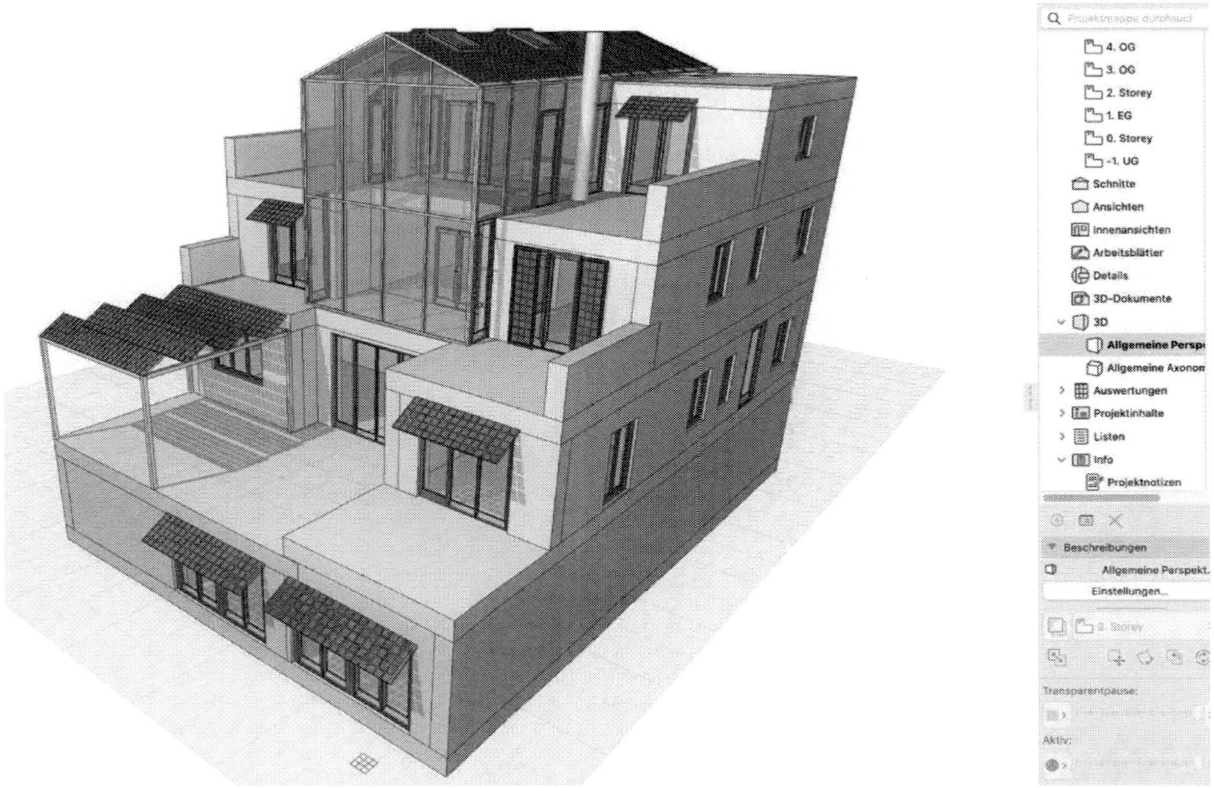

Source: Treberspurg Architekten / Astrid Schneider TU Wien

Perspective view in architect's BIM-planning program Archicad

BIM4BIPV TU WIEN TECHNISCHE UNIVERSITÄT WIEN

HOW CAN WE MAKE THE BIPV-PLANNING AND SIMULATION PROCESS WORK?

SONNENKRAFT

PV- BIPV-Product

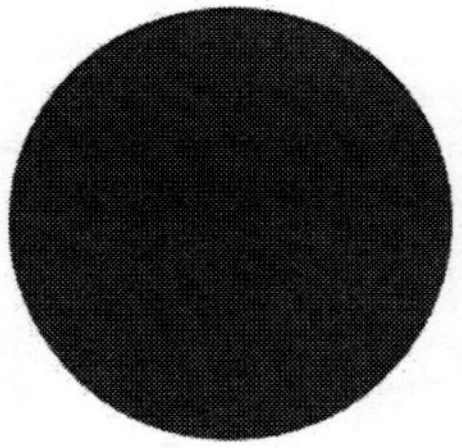

PV- Database in BIM / IFC – formate optimally public

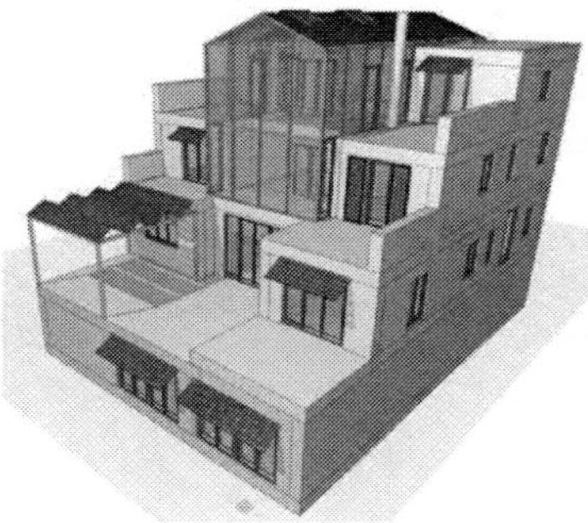

BIM-project design
- visual

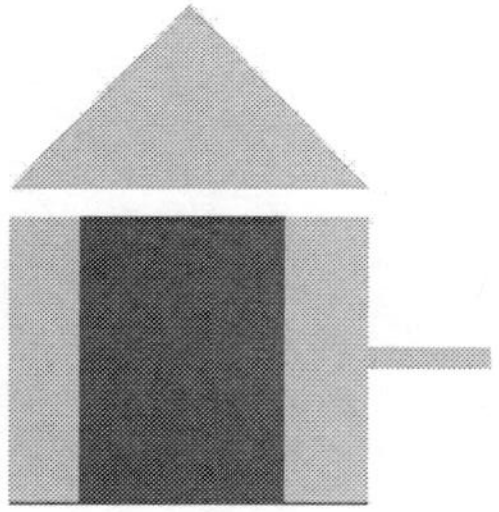

BIPV-system
- PV-system design and yield calculation
- daylighting
- energy
- structural
- environment

Source: Astrid Schneider, TU Wien

FFG

BIM4BIPV TU WIEN TECHNISCHE UNIVERSITÄT WIEN

BIM-BASED BIPV-SIMULATION

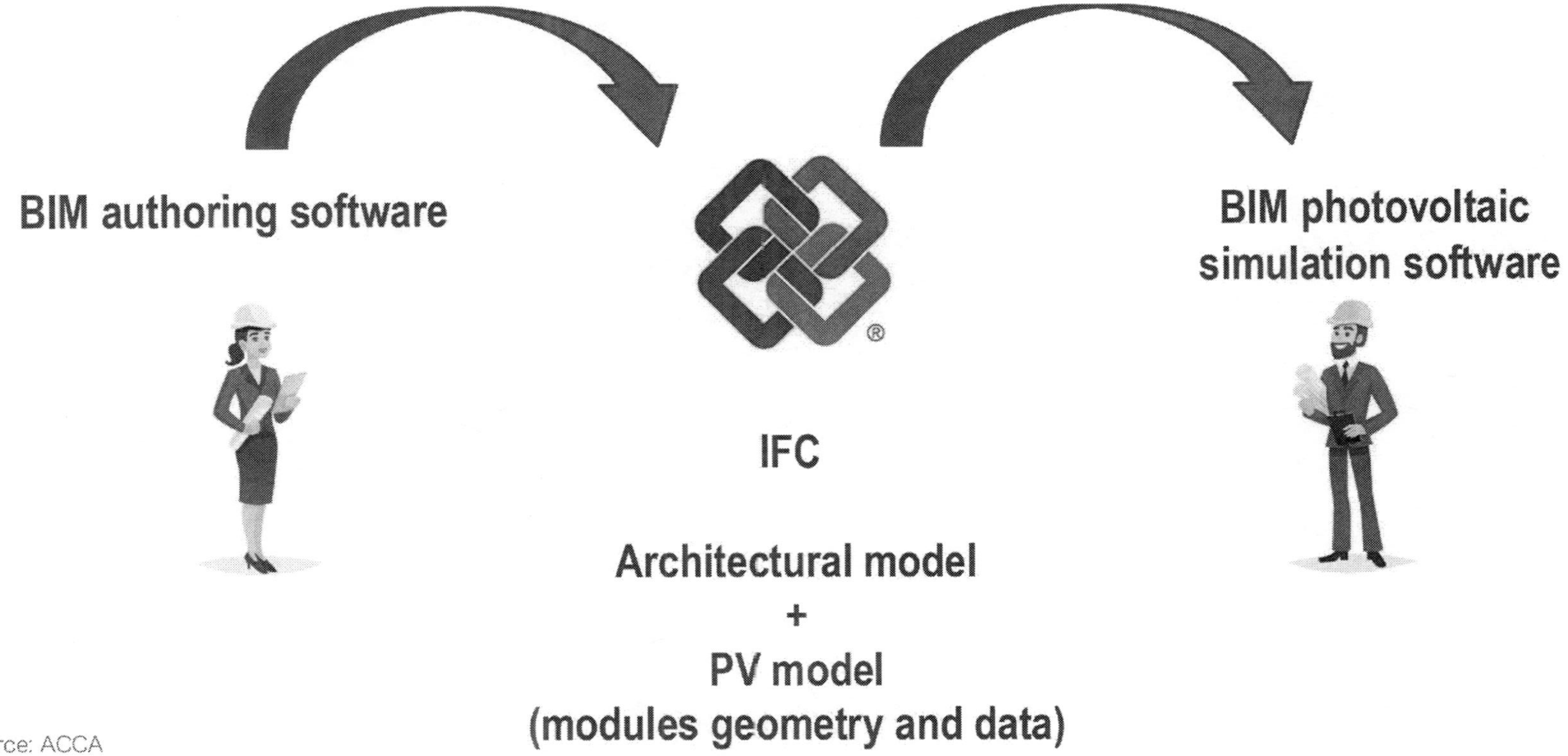

Source: ACCA

FFG

BIM4BIPV TECHNISCHE UNIVERSITÄT WIEN

BRINGING THE PV-MODULE INFORMATION INTO THE ARCHITECTURE MODEL

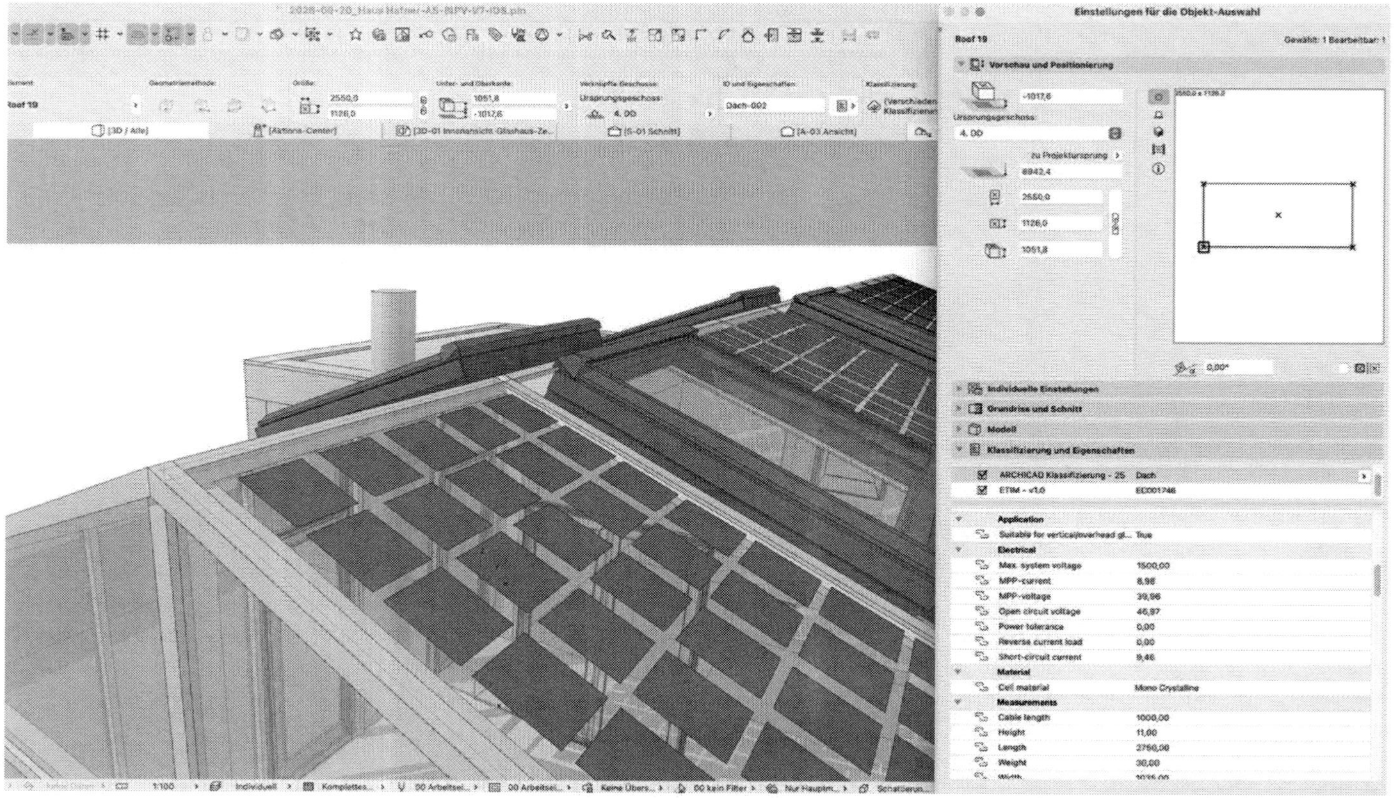

Source: Astrid Schneider, TU Wien

Archicad Haus Hafner Model with PV-property set filled in for the marked roof module

FFG

BIPV-PROPERTIES IN THE BIM-MODEL (ARCHICAD)

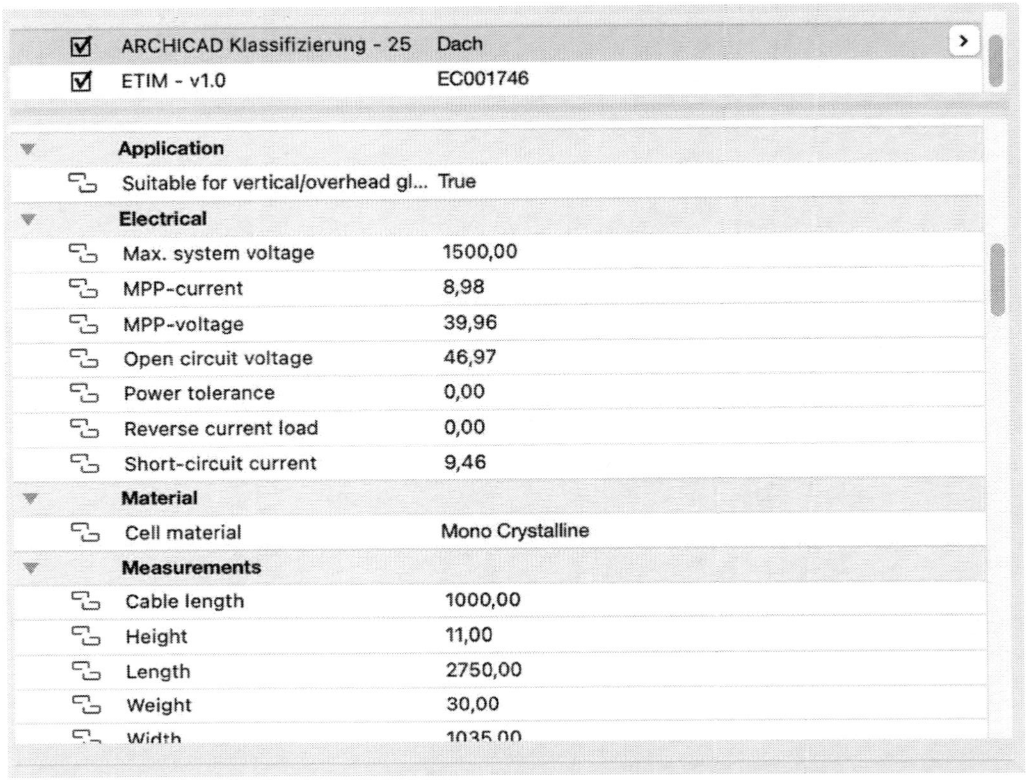

☑	ARCHICAD Klassifizierung - 25	Dach
☑	ETIM - v1.0	EC001746

Application	
Suitable for vertical/overhead gl...	True
Electrical	
Max. system voltage	1500,00
MPP-current	8,98
MPP-voltage	39,96
Open circuit voltage	46,97
Power tolerance	0,00
Reverse current load	0,00
Short-circuit current	9,46
Material	
Cell material	Mono Crystalline
Measurements	
Cable length	1000,00
Height	11,00
Length	2750,00
Weight	30,00
Width	1035,00

Source: Astrid Schneider, TU Wien

The „ETIM"-classification EC001746 „Photovoltaics module" was used.

Via an „IDS Information Delivery specification" the ETIM properties could be brought into the architects BIM authoring software Archicad.

The fields to be filled with the electric properties of the specific BIPV-modules were now pesent in the architectural BIM-software and filled with the relevant information for electric PV-simulation.

ETIM „Photovoltaics module"
https://identifier.buildingsmart.org/uri/etim/etim/9.0/class/EC001746

IDS4ALL converter
https://openbim-knowledgebase.org/en/ids4all-converter/

Archicad BIM model with ETIM-classification and BIPV-element's electric property set (only partially shown, excerpt)

BIM VIEWER TO CONTROL THE EXPORTED VALUES IN THE MODEL

BIM4BIPV TU WIEN TECHNISCHE UNIVERSITÄT WIEN

The Architectural BIM model is exported in the IFC-format. In the IFC-viewer by ACCA the BIPV data can be checked

https://www.accasoftware.com/de/bim-management-system

FFG

BIM4BIPV TU WIEN TECHNISCHE UNIVERSITÄT WIEN

BIM VIEWER TO CONTROL THE EXPORTED VALUES IN THE MODEL

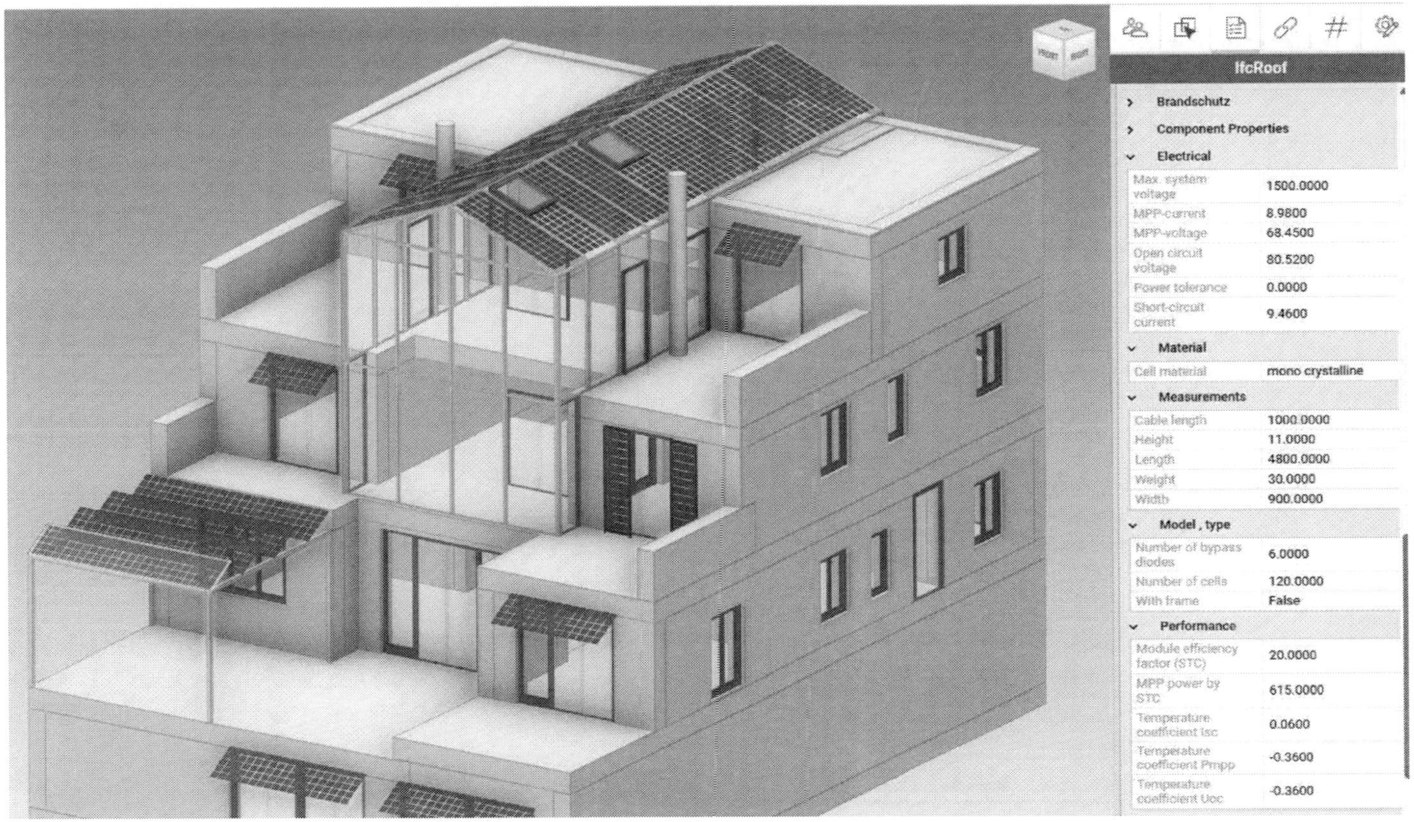

The Architectural BIM model is exported in the IFC-format. In the IFC-viewer by ACCA the PV data can be displayed / seen

https://www.accasoftware.com/de/bim-management-system

FFG

TRANSFERE OF THE MODEL TO SOLARIUS PV SIMULATION SOFTWARE

BIM4BIPV TU WIEN TECHNISCHE UNIVERSITÄT WIEN

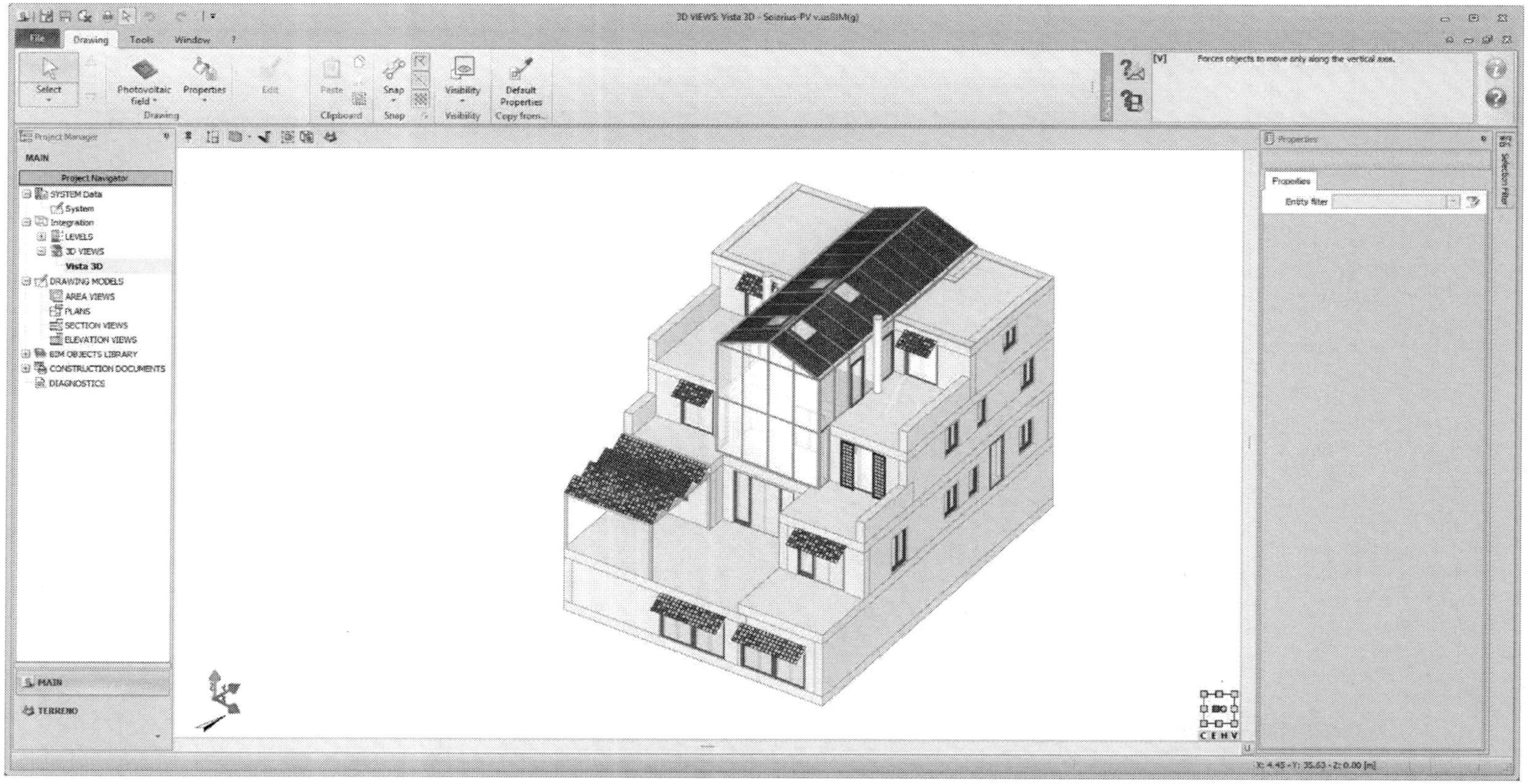

The IFC open BIM-model can be directly imported into the simulation software

Source: ACCA

FFG

TRANSFERE OF THE MODEL TO SOLARIUS PV SIMULATION SOFTWARE

BIM4BIPV TU WIEN TECHNISCHE UNIVERSITÄT WIEN

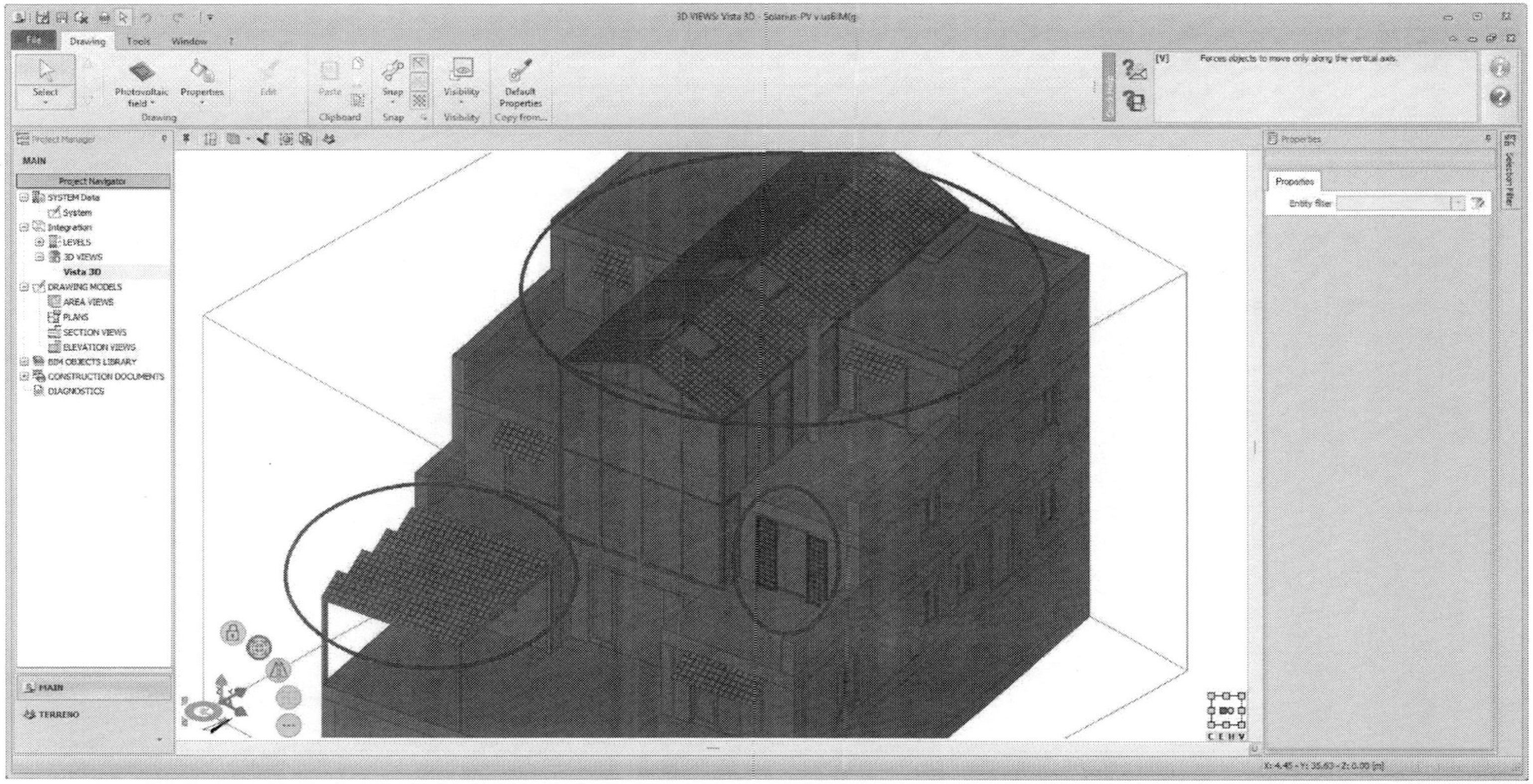

The PV-modules are recognized by the program

Source: ACCA

FFG

THE PV-MODULE VALUES CAN BE READ AND TAKEN OVER

BIM4BIPV TU WIEN TECHNISCHE UNIVERSITÄT WIEN

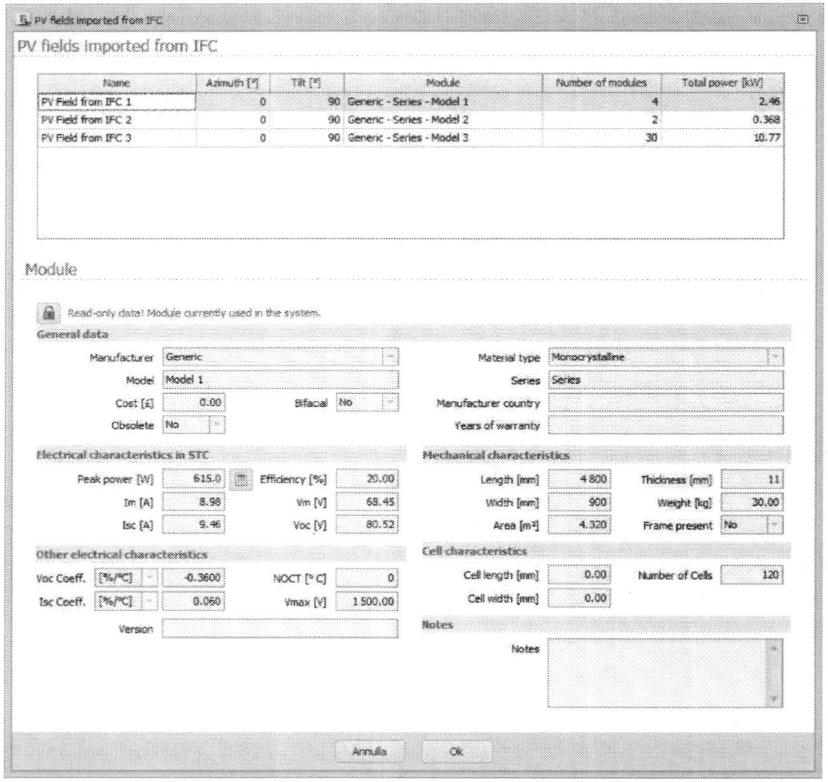

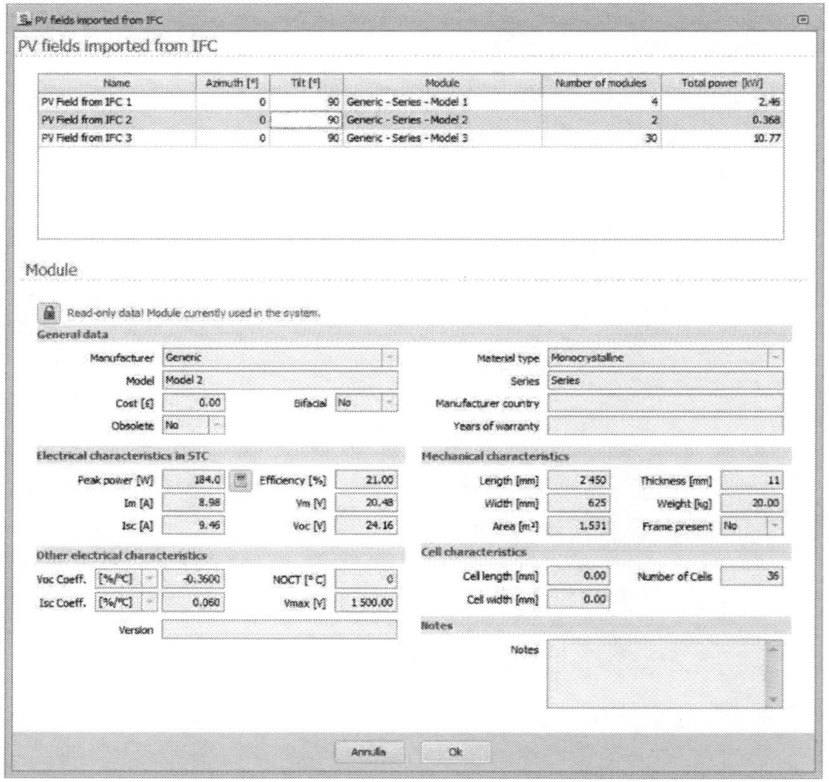

The electric parameters / properties were successfully transported into the simulation program

Source: ACCA

FFG

THE PV SIMULATION PROGRAM CAN DO THE PV-SYSTEM SIMULATION

BIM4BIPV

TECHNISCHE UNIVERSITÄT WIEN

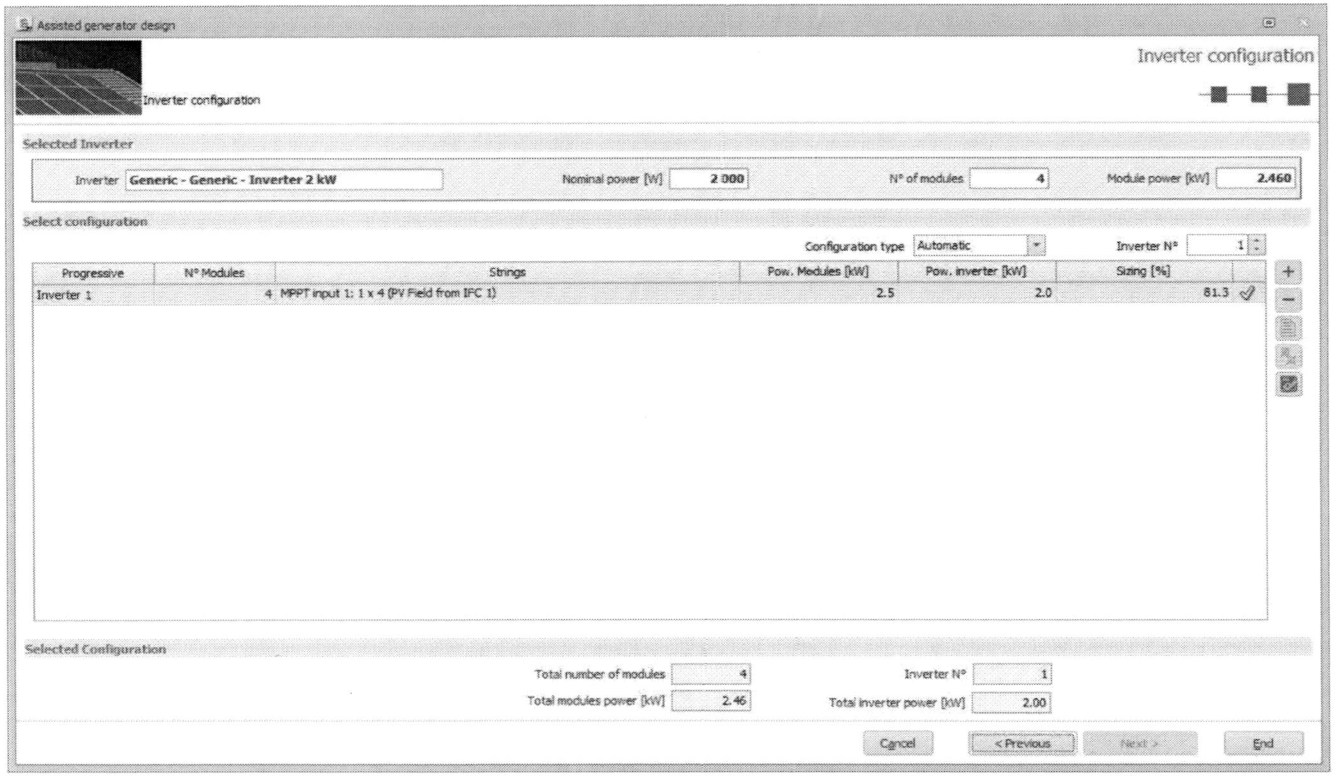

PV-Planning and simulation in "Solarius PV"

FFG

SOLAR YIELD CALCULATION

BIM4BIPV TU WIEN TECHNISCHE UNIVERSITÄT WIEN

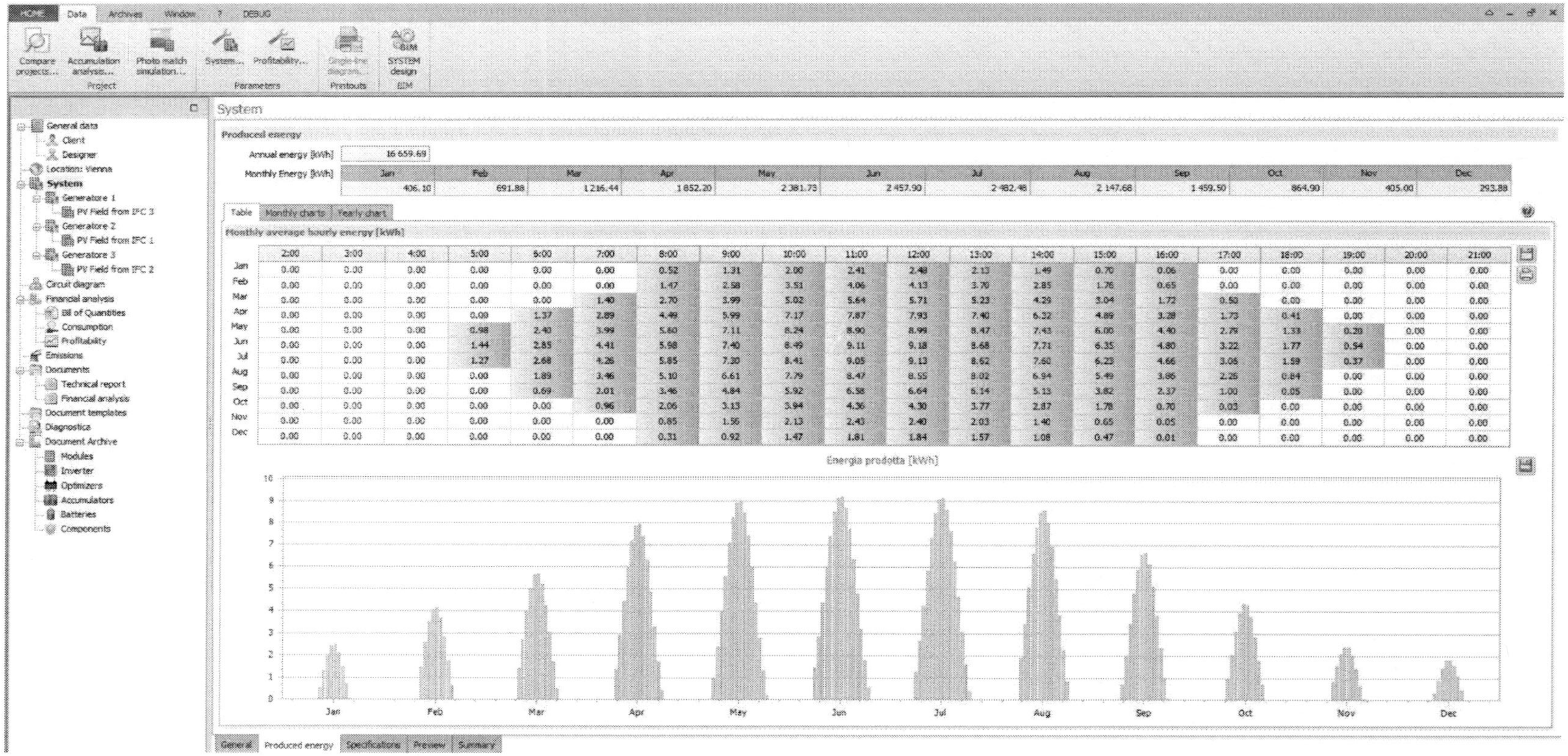

The PV-simulation can be concluded

Source: simulation with Solarius PV by ACCA

FFG

BIM4BIPV | TU WIEN TECHNISCHE UNIVERSITÄT WIEN

GOAL: DIGITAL PV-MODULES TO BE PRECISELY PLACED IN BIM-CAD-SOFTWARE

PV-Producer

is responsible to provide use case specific relevant product data

SONNENKRAFT

PV- BIPV-Product

Excel calculation BIPV-module values →

Data-Scheme for PV / BIPV

ETIM + IDS →

PV- / BIPV-Data

in BIM / IFC-format

PV- Database in BIM / IFC – formate optimally public →

Architect

plans building / construction and puts PV- / BIPV-BIM-elements into CAD / BIM project design

(generic, product specific, custom sized)

BIM-project design

- visual

Integration of BIPV-values into architectural BIM-model →

IFC-export

Engineer

uses detailled PV- / BIPV- BIM project design to plan and simulate PV / BIPV-system

BIPV-system

- PV-system design and yield calculation
- daylighting
- energy
- structural
- environment

FFG

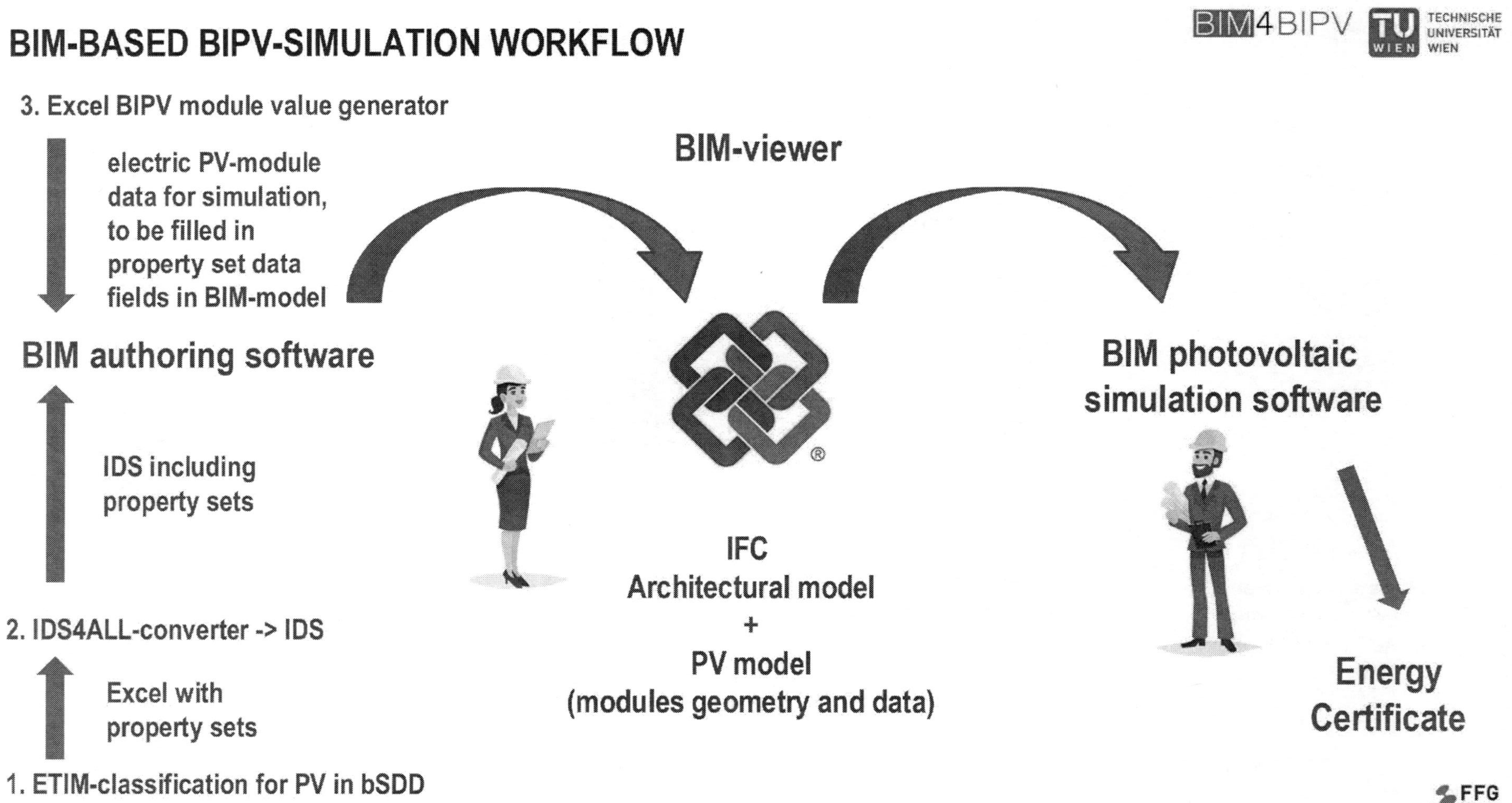

Source: ACCA – Astrid Schneider TU Wien

BIM4BIPV TU WIEN TECHNISCHE UNIVERSITÄT WIEN

HAUS HAFNER ATRIUM AS A MULTI-DISCIPLINARY PLANNING TASK

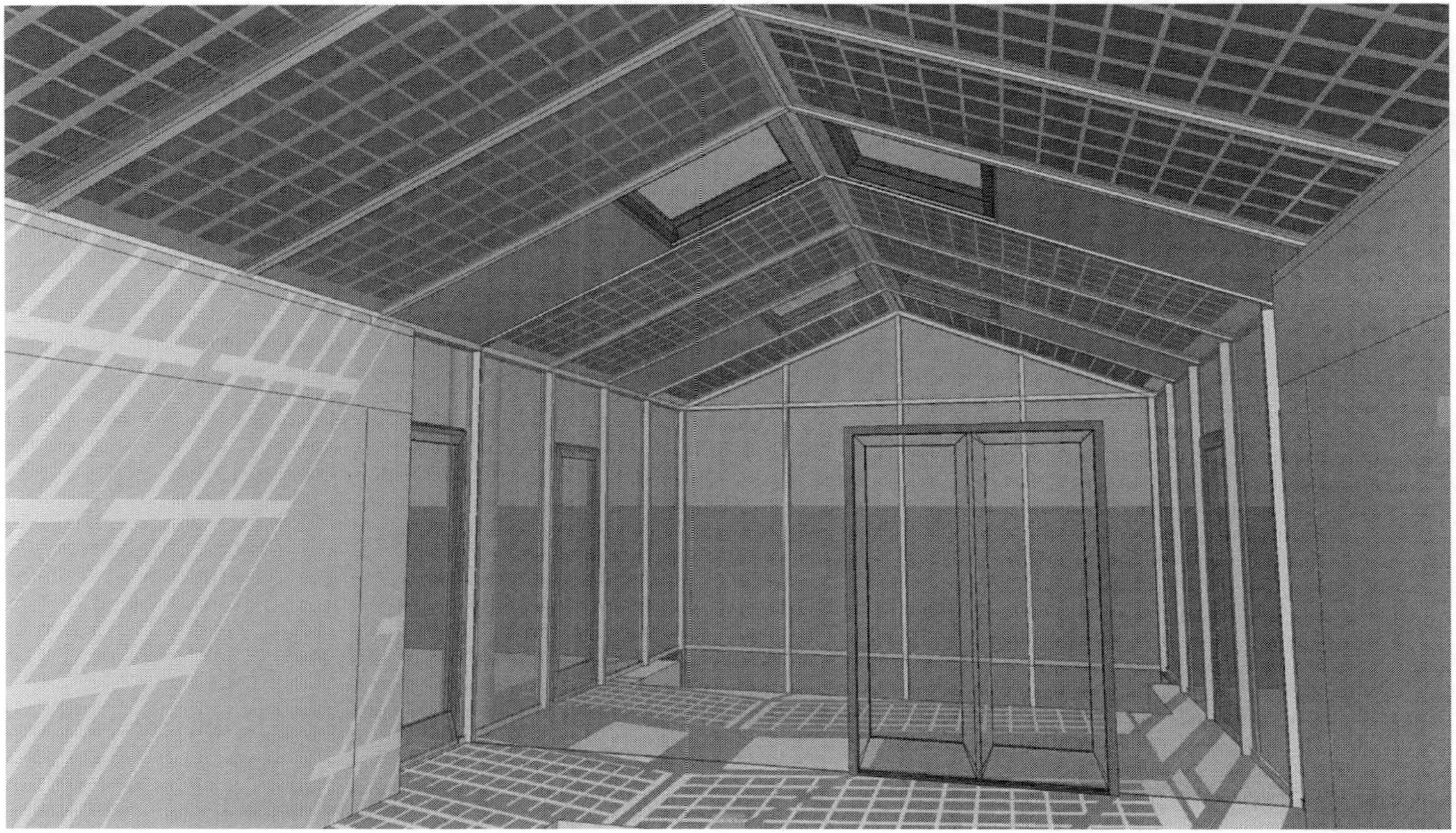

Source: Treberspurg Architekten / Astrid Schneider TU Wien

Interior view atrium

FFG

DAYLIGHT SIMULATION - DAYLIGHT FACTOR

- Sky model CIE Overcast sky (no sun)
  $L_{Zenith} : L_{Horizon} = 3:1$

$$TQ[\%] = \frac{E_{innen}}{E_{außen}} * 100$$

- Average DF range offices:
  - min. 2% at work places (accord. to regulations)
  - not too high to avoid daylight glare

- Average DF range living area:
  - No specific noramative regulations
  - Less strict in terms of glare
  - Range of 2,5 – 8% is reasonable
  - Too high values >10% tend to overheating

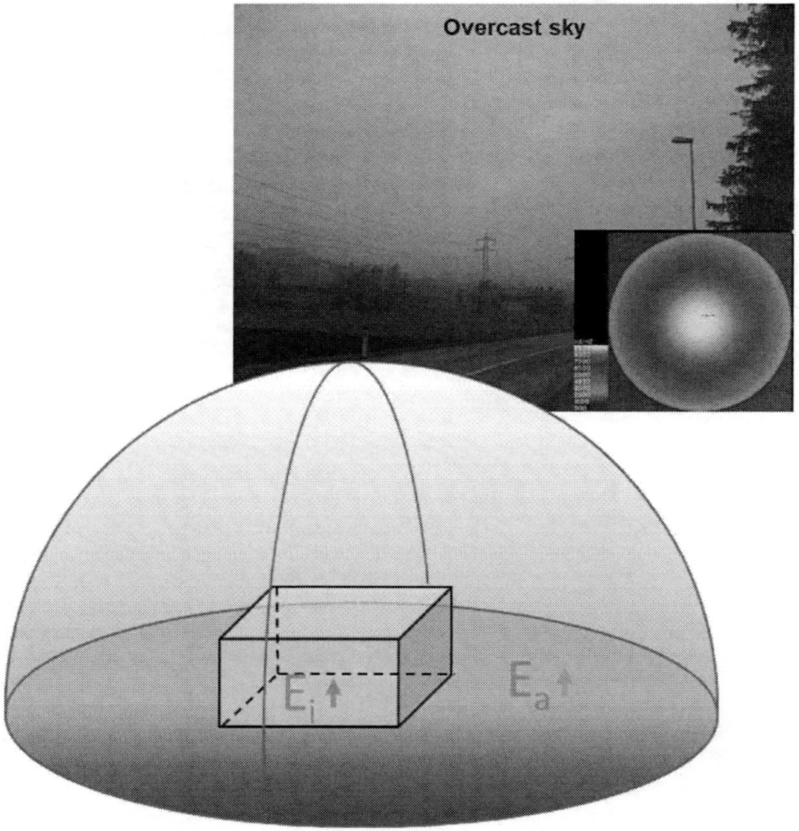

Source: Bartenbach

DAYLIGHT SIMULATION OF HAUS HAFNER - DAYLIGHT FACTOR – FIRST FLOOR

VARIANTS

| Only Glazing (no PV) | PV on canopy (non transp.)
PV on Roof (semitransp.) | PV on canopy (non transp.)
PV on Roof + Side windows
(semitransp.) | PV on canopy (non transp.)
PV Roof (full) + Side windows
(semitransp.) |

DAYLIGHT DISTRIBUTION

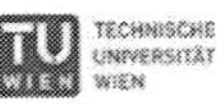

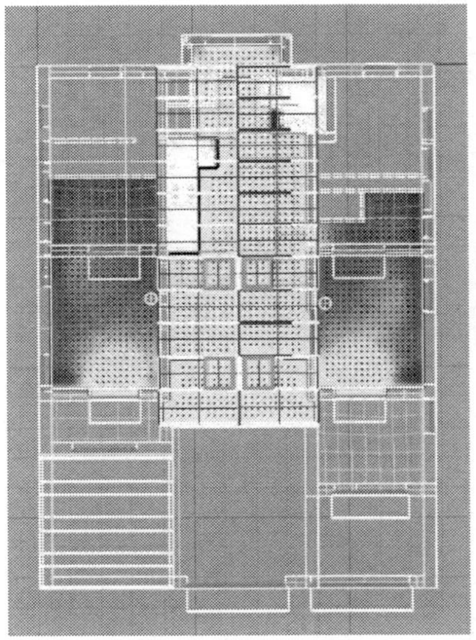

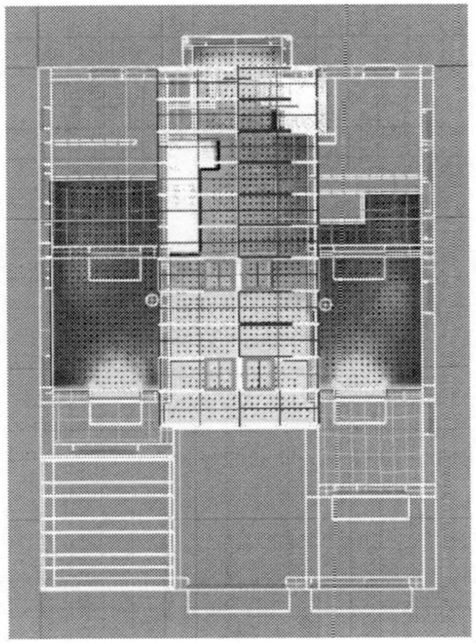

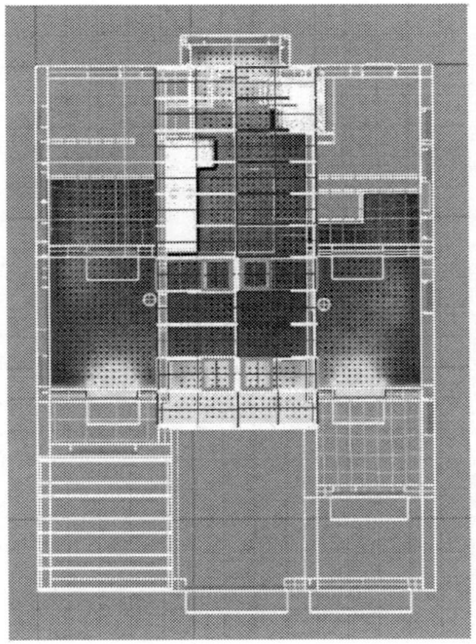

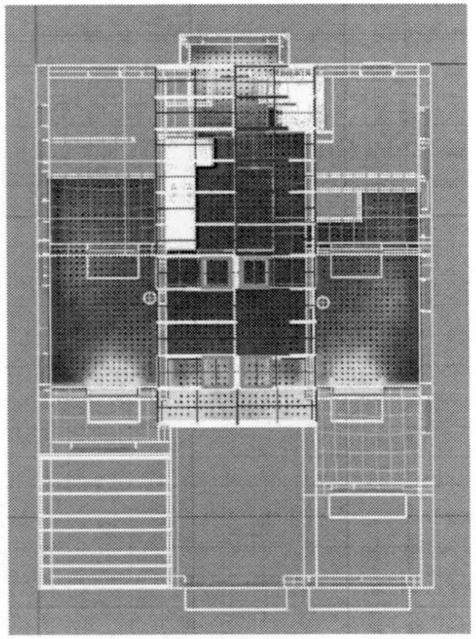

EVALUATION

Average Daylight Factor: 11.2 %

- Exceeding values in Daylight availability
- → proper shading, especially of the glazed central part is needed.

Average Daylight Factor: 6.2 %

- Daylight factor in acceptable range, but on the higher end
- Spatial exceedings only in the central front part (which might be acceptable at the terrace or as winter garden)

Average Daylight Factor: 2,6 %

- Daylight factor in in optimal range (between 2% and 5% for living areas)

Average Daylight Factor: 2,2 %

- Daylight availability on the lower end – especially the central part tends to receive too less daylight

Source: Bartenbach

BIM4BIPV

CLIMATE BASED DAYLIGHT CALCULATION

Useful Daylight Illuminance (UDI)

- is a modification of daylight autonomy
- This criterion divides the hourly data into three evaluation categories
  - 0-100lx (underlighting)
  - 100 - 2000lx (pleasant lighting conditions)
  - >2000lx (overlighting)
- In the range of 100-2000lx, daylight input is rated as useful

Annual Sunlight Exposure (ASE)

- refers to the percentage of space that receives too much direct sunlight (1000 Lux or more for at least 250 occupied hours per year), which can cause glare or increased cooling loads

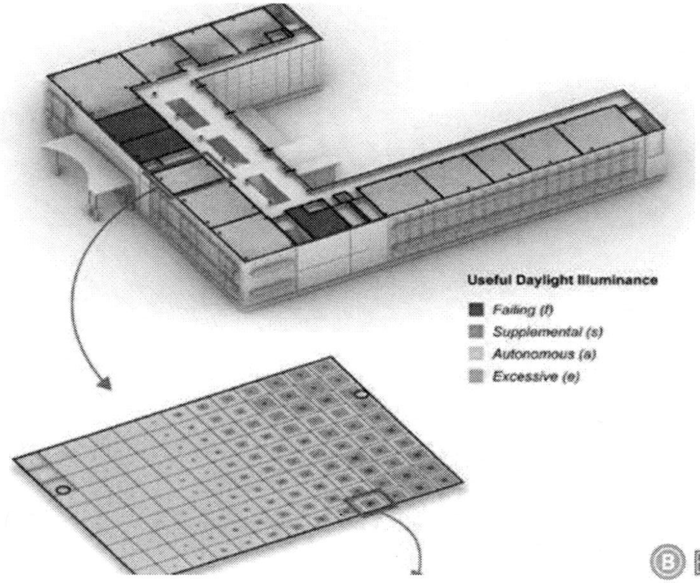

Source: Bartenbach

BIM4BIPV

HAUS HAFNER CLIMATE BASED DAYLIGHT CALCULATION (ANNUAL) FIRST FLOOR

TU WIEN TECHNISCHE UNIVERSITÄT WIEN

VARIANTS

Only Glazing (no PV)

PV on canopy (non transp.)
PV on Roof (semitransp.)

PV on canopy (non transp.)
PV on Roof + Side windows (semitransp.)

PV on canopy (non transp.)
PV Roof (full) + Side windows (semitransp.)

DAYLIGHT DISTRIBUTION

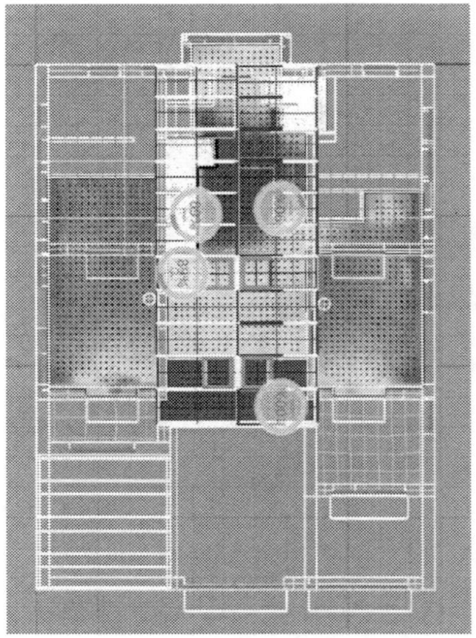

66,4% avg UDIa | 96,8% sDA | 46,9% ASE | 1722 avg lux | 64,5% blinds open

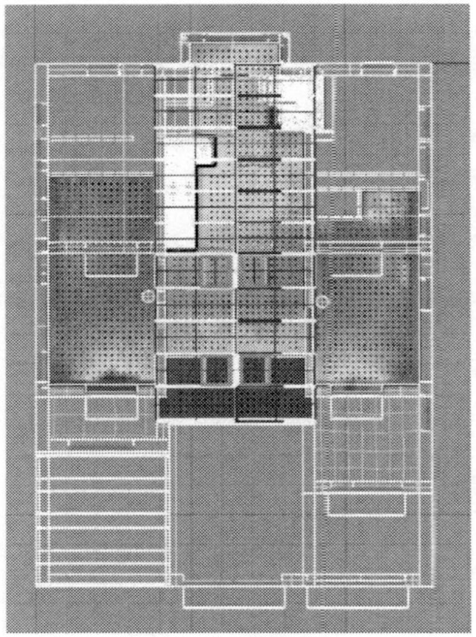

68,6% avg UDIa | 94,1% sDA | 32,3% ASE | 1044 avg lux | 57,0% blinds open

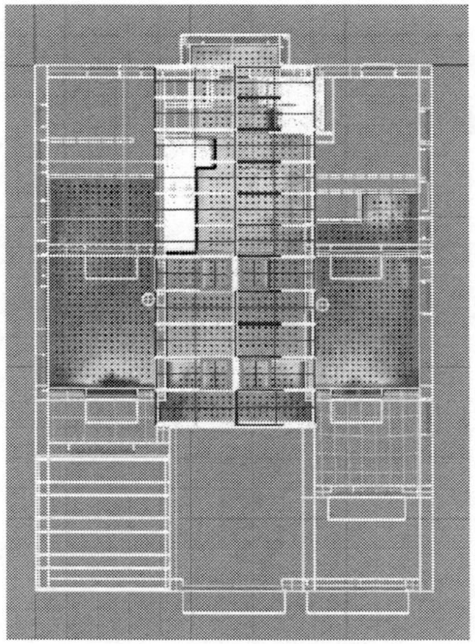

70,1% avg UDIa | 94,4% sDA | 7,1% ASE | 896 avg lux | 93,2% blinds open

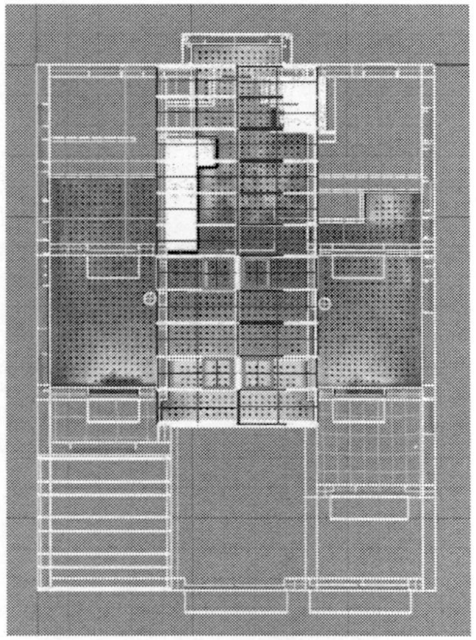

67,4% avg UDIa | 93,0% sDA | 7,1% ASE | 720 avg lux | 93,2% blinds open

EVALUATION

UDI – 66,4 %
ASE – 46,9 %

Glare and overheating

UDI – 66,8 %
ASE – 32,2 %

improvements by semtransparent BIPV roof

UDI – 70,1 %
ASE – 7,1 %

- Significant improvement by semitransparent PV on roof and side windows of the attic
- Highest levels on Useful Daylight illuminance UDI → 70%

UDI – 67,4 %
ASE – 7,1 %

too much shading less daylight

Source: Bartenbach

BIM4BIPV

TECHNISCHE UNIVERSITÄT WIEN

GEOMETRY IMPORT FOR DAYLIGHT SIMULATION

Daylight simulations are performed using Climate Studio (https://climatestudiodocs.com/index.html)

ClimateStudio is a plugin for the Rhinoceros (Rhino) 3d modeling software

Data Path:

- **The IFC-file was directly imported into Rhino, using ggIFC - an „Add-on application“ in Rhino**
- **After manual modifcations on the imported geometry in Rhino, the model was able to be used by Climate Studio**

General problem:

- **Daylight simulation tools only consider geometry from IFC-files**
- **Daylight specific parameters (surface reflection values, visual transparancy values,...) have to be set manually**

Source: Bartenbach

BIM4BIPV

BIM4BIPV TU WIEN TECHNISCHE UNIVERSITÄT WIEN

ENERGY CERTIFICATE CALCULATION OF BIPV-APPLICATIONS

Archiphysik can read in the BIM-model and evaluate the values and geometry:

BIPV-glazing-element inputs taken from model:

- shading geometry in front of the window or glazed area
- G-value
- U-value
  - ➢ calculation of solar radiation entering the space
- ➢ thermal comfort fulfillment
- ➢ heating and cooling demand calculation in kwh/m^2

PV-Module inputs taken from model:

- Wp – Power
- location, orientation
  - ➢ solar power produced
- ➢ reduction of primary fossil energy consumed
- ➢ fulfillment of required installation capacity by construction laws

Source: Astrid Schneider, TU Wien

FFG

BIM4BIPV

ArchiPHYSIK

PHOTOVOLTAICS AND ENERGY PERFORMANCE CERTIFICATE

- **Photovoltaic electricity in energy balance**
  - Electricity generated by PV can be included in the energy balance for the Energy Performance Certificate
  - Depending on legal framework, PV electricity can fully or partially replace other energy carriers
  - The amount of creditable PV electricity is legally defined
  - Surplus PV electricity is shown in the EPC as PV export

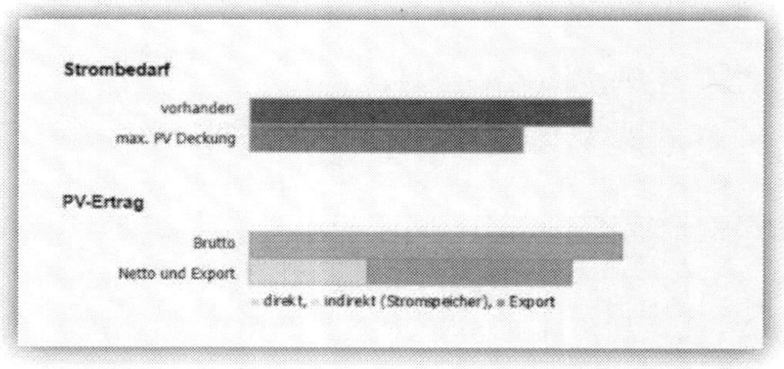

Source: A-NULL Development with Archiphysik

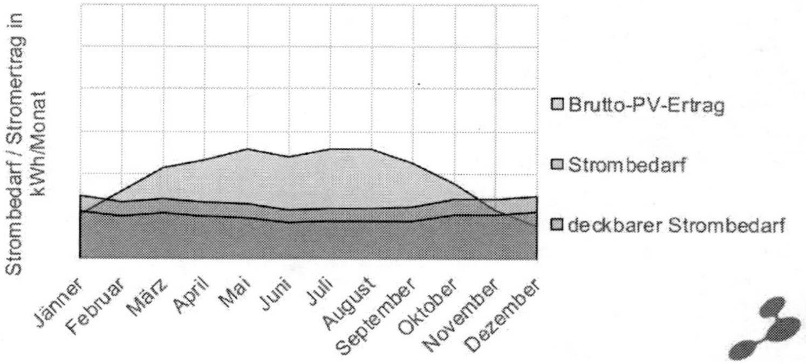

FFG
Forschung wirkt.

BIM4BIPV ArchiPHYSIK

OVERHEATING FROM GLAZING

- **Glazing and summer overheating**
  - Large glazed areas may cause overheating under sunlight.
  - Winter: Indoor temperatures can be lowered by controlled ventilation.
  - Summer: Only limited reduction possible through night ventilation.
  - Approach: Reduce solar gains through glazing.
  - Haus Hafner: PV shutters and BIPV glazing in the conservatory reduce solar input → less overheating

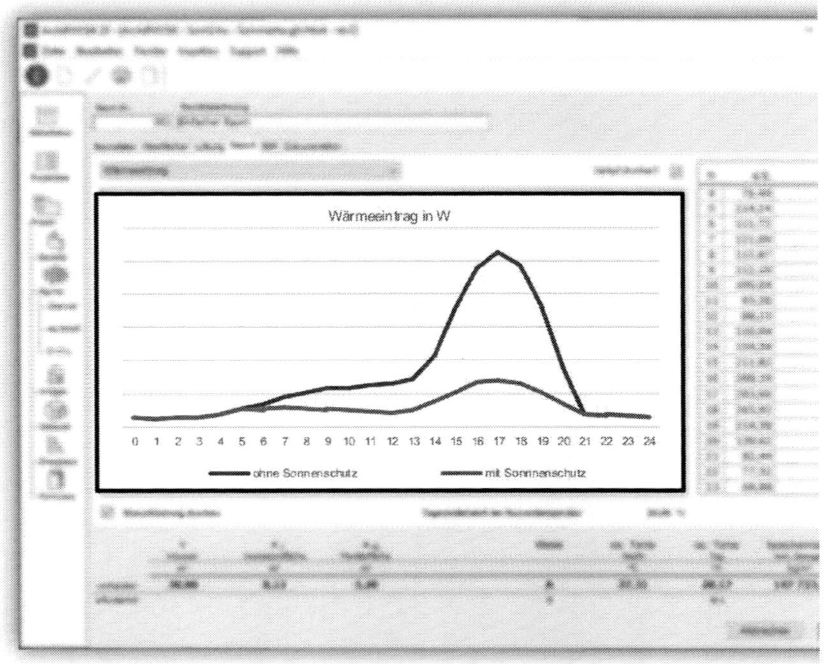

Source: A-NULL Development with Archiphysik

FFG Forschung wirkt.

BIM4BIPV TECHNISCHE UNIVERSITÄT WIEN

PROBLEMS TO BE SOLVED

- compatability problems
- multiple model transferes
- missing data after model transfer
- correct transfere of: location, direction, axis
- material transfere / display of materials

  - the IFC standard is not yet fully adopted and implemented by all actors

FFG

BIM4BIPV TU WIEN TECHNISCHE UNIVERSITÄT WIEN

GOALS TO BE ACHIEVED

- PV and BIPV to be integrated in digital planning flows easily
- optimized near shade and bifaciality simulation
  - as well on module celle and string level
- inclusion of multidisciplinary data of PV / BIPV into construction models
- ability for multidsiciplinary simulation such as
  - daylighting
  - shade and heat effects
  - energy planning
  - green construction
- as well important for agri-PV, infrastructure, OEM of large solar parks ...

Source: TU Wien / A-NULL Development

FFG

BIM4BIPV TU WIEN TECHNISCHE UNIVERSITÄT WIEN

BUILDING INFORMATION MODELLING (BIM)

IEA-Task 15 Photovoltaic Power systems Program C1:

- it is important to standardize the property and property set names to enable interoperability across PV / BIPV and construction / infrastructure industry
- International collaboration in Task 15

buildingSMART Austria IEA PVPS FFG

BIM4BIPV

THANKS!

Astrid Schneider, TU Wien - astrid.schneider@tuwien.ac.at - astrid@astrid-schneider.de

Coauthors:

- Dr. Karin Stieldorf, TU Wien, Institute of Architecture and Design, Karlsplatz 13, 1040 Wien, Austria, karin.stieldorf@tuwien.ac.at
- Dr. Christian Schranz and Dr. Harald Urban, TU Wien, Research Unit for Digital Planning Process, christian.schranz@tuwien.ac.at;
- Alfred Waschl, buildingSMART, alfred.waschl@buildingsmart.co.at;
- Markus Feichtner, Sonnenkraft GmbH, Markus.Feichtner@sonnenkraft.com
- Fedele Rende and Andrea Aiello ACCA Software, fedele.rende@almasoft.it;
- Martin Hauer, Bartenbach GmbH, Martin.Hauer@bartenbach.com;
- Kurt Battisti, Markus Dörn and Jacqueline Scherret, A-Null Development GmbH, kurt.battisti@archiphysik.com;
- Martin und Christoph Treberspurg, Treberspurg und Partner Architekten, christoph.treberspurg@treberspurg.at

We thank FFG – Austrian funding agency for their support

Project partners BIM4BIPV:

Collaboration with Task 15 BIPV – C1 - Digitalization

FABRICATION OF A NOVEL SEMI-TRANSLUCENT BIPV MODULE PROVIDING HIGH POWER DENSITY AND ACTIVE DAYLIGHT MANAGEMENT

Almudena Garcia-Sanchez[1], Guido Vallerotto[1], Jaime J. Hernández[2], Alejandro García-Cañas[2], Steve Askins[1], Ignacio Antón[1], Isabel Rodríguez[2] and César Domínguez[1]

[1] Instituto de Energía Solar, Universidad Politécnica de Madrid (UPM), Madrid (Spain)
[2] Madrid Institute for Advanced Studies in Nanoscience (IMDEA Nanoscience), Madrid (Spain)

ABSTRACT: Building-integrated photovoltaics (BIPV) provides a sustainable method for solar energy generation without requiring additional productive land. However, conventional semi-transparent modules often suffer from low efficiency and visual discomfort. This work presents a novel BIPV solution using micro-concentrator photovoltaics (micro-CPV) with integrated solar tracking to improve both energy output and daylight quality. The system features a glass front layer embedded with linear asymmetric Fresnel lenses and a transparent backplane with solar cell strips. It blocks direct sunlight, converting it into electricity, while allowing diffuse light to pass through, producing soft, glare-free interior lighting. A micro-tracking mechanism adjusts the solar cells to follow the sun's path, enhancing light capture throughout the day. Designed for translucent applications such as skylights or non-view façades, the module also reduces heat gain indoors. Lens arrays of 5 lenses of 2.25 × 10 cm fabricated by roll-to-plate UV imprinting on solar glass show a peak optical efficiency of 80%, remaining above 70% up to a 60° angle of incidence. Outdoor tests confirm improved visual comfort, with a reduction in an order of magnitude in the peak illuminance point, an average of 1500 lx, and a peak-to-average ratio lowered by 7 points, demonstrating the module's potential for both energy and daylighting management.

Keywords: Concentrator photovoltaics, Building-integrated photovoltaics, Micro-concentrator optics

1 INTRODUCTION

The cumulative PV capacity in Europe would need to reach 455–605 GW to meet the ambitious target of the European Green Deal target of a 55% net reduction in greenhouse gas emissions by 2030 [1]. Building-integrated photovoltaics (BIPV) is especially interesting because it does capture productive land and contributes to nearly zero-energy buildings (NZEBs) and decarbonization of cities. It is often designed to achieve additional architectural functions, such as thermal insulation or daylighting. However, conventional semi-transparent BIPV modules employ spaced solar cells that allow direct light to enter the building, thus reducing active area (and power density) and producing stark light-shadow contrasts that create visual discomfort: an obstacle to massive adoption [2].

2 AIM AND APPROACH

To solve the limitations of conventional building-integrated photovoltaics (BIPV), we propose a smart, translucent BIPV module capable of achieving high-efficiency electricity generation while simultaneously providing uniform indoor illuminance and minimizing glare. This system is based on micro-concentrator photovoltaics (micro-CPV) and incorporates a front glazing composed of a matrix of linear micro-concentrator optics. These optics focus direct sunlight onto a transparent backplane equipped with an array of narrow-strip crystalline silicon (c-Si) solar cells. In contrast, diffuse light is transmitted through the module into the interior of the building, contributing to comfortable and natural daylighting (see Figure 1).The module is designed to function as a semi-translucent architectural element suitable for integration into skylights, curtain walls, canopies, or solar shading systems.

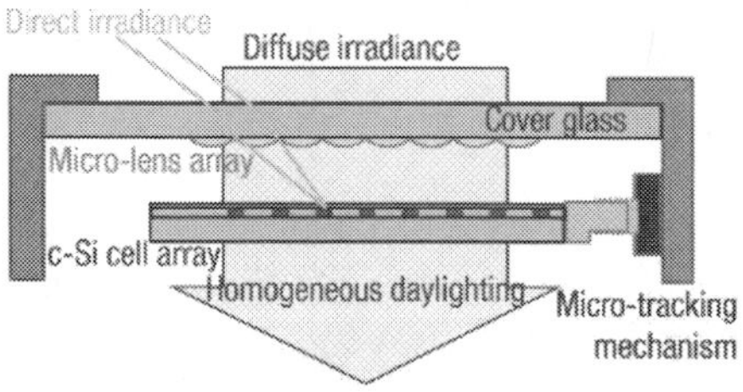

Figure 1: Schematic of the structure and working principle of the semi-transparent smart BIPV module. Direct light is concentrated to produce electricity, while diffused light is transmitted for daylighting. A planar micro-tracking mechanism shifts the backplane with the changing solar position.

3 OPTICAL DESIGN

In the initial phase of the project, the optical design of the module was defined. We implemented ultra-thin linear Fresnel lenses with a facet height of 40 microns, selected to ensure compatibility with low-cost roll-to-plate fabrication using UV-curable resin on glass substrates. The 2D asymmetric lens profile was developed using Fermat's principle, ensuring that rays with a nominal angle of incidence (AOI_T) converge at a common focal point at the lens edge as it is shown in Figure 2. A large draft angle was incorporated to maintain high optical efficiency and prevent self-shading.

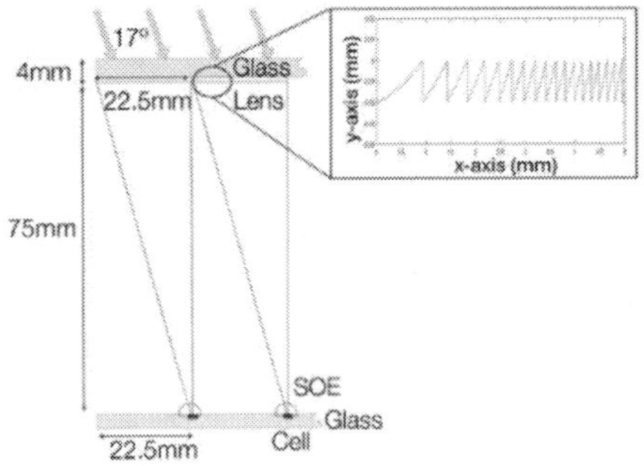

Figure 2: Schematic of the optical design at nominal AOI, together with a close-up of the asymmetric Fresnel lens profile.

The lens geometry was optimized for a non-normal angle of incidence, specifically AOI_T = 17°, which corresponds to the solar elevation at the summer solstice in Madrid. This optimization was chosen to maximize optical efficiency and enhance solar protection during periods of high solar heat gain. To maintain a compact form factor consistent with typical building components, the maximum focal length was set to 7.5 cm, resulting in an overall module thickness of approximately 10 cm.

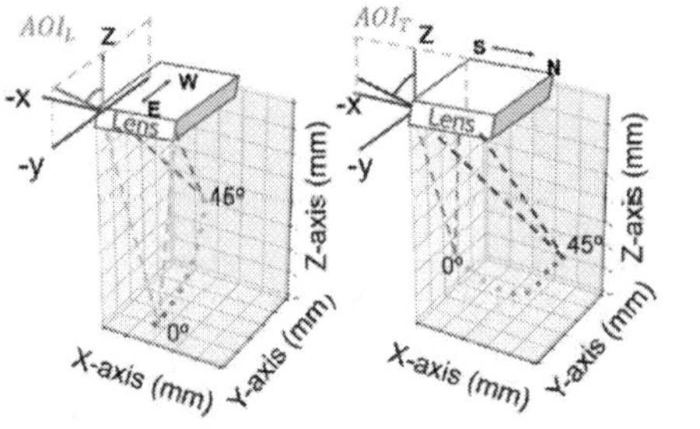

Figure 3: Focus position (Petzval curve) for longitudinal and transverse AOI.

Monte Carlo ray-tracing simulations, which incorporated realistic material properties and accounted for the Sun's angular aperture and spectral distribution, were used to model light trajectories and evaluate optical efficiency as a function of both AOI_L and AOI_T (see Figure. 3). Moreover, the module features an active light transmission control mechanism. In blind mode or low transmission mode, the planar micro-tracking mechanism shifts the backplane position with the changing solar angle of incidence, to maintain the direct focus light over the solar cells. On the other hand, in skylight mode or high-transmission mode, the solar cells are removed from the direct light focal point, which passes directly through the module, mimicking the behavior of a conventional transparent window. This functionality was verified through photorealistic ray-tracing simulations, demonstrating the module's capability to switch between power generation and daylighting modes effectively (see Figure 4). Previous works have used micro-Fresnel lenses for BIPV, but light management was passive (seasonal)[3].

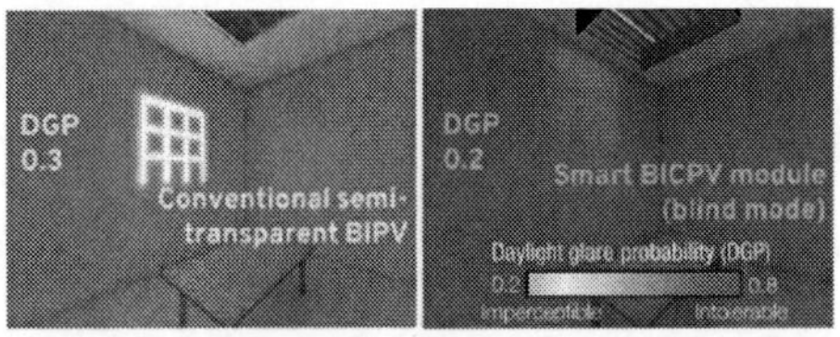

Figure 4: Daylighting properties of conventional semi-transparent BIPV (left) vs our novel concept (when solar cells are aligned to capture direct light, right) as a skylight component in a reference application.

4 FABRICATION METHODOLOGY

We fabricated the first prototypes of the proposed optical module using the roll-to-plate setup shown on Figure 5. The fabrication begins with the deposition of a UV-curable resin onto a glass substrate. The glass then passes under the precision-engraved drum, which continuously molds the resin into the desired optical pattern at a controlled speed of 40 cm/min. During the process, ultraviolet (UV) light cures the resin in situ, solidifying the optical structures. This process is continuous and inherently scalable, enabling the production of large-area Fresnel lens arrays directly onto glass sheets.

The molding drum serves as the master tool and is fabricated from steel with the lens profile precisely engraved via diamond machining. To ensure clean release and maintain optical quality, the drum is coated with a layer of optical-grade nickel-phosphide, providing both durability and anti-adhesive properties. The drum was custom-manufactured by Wielandts, based on the optical design developed in the earlier phase of the project.

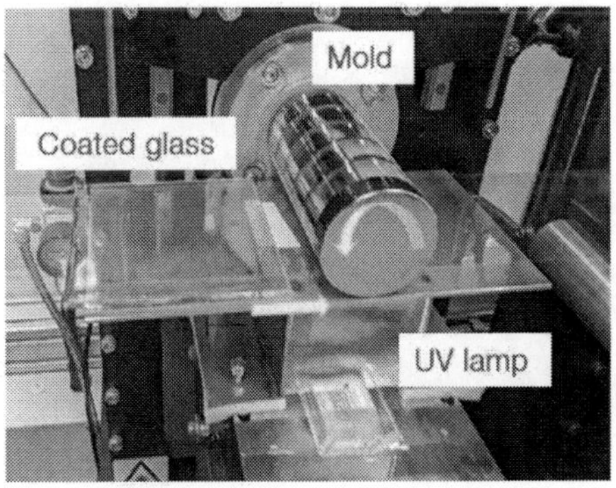

Figure 5: Roll-to-plate UV imprinting setup with continuous roller mold.

5 RESULTS AND DISCUSSION

Three prototype samples were fabricated with different resin base substrate thicknesses to assess the fidelity of lens formation and its impact on optical performance. As shown in the accompanying images (Figure 6), the first and second samples, with resin thicknesses exceeding 150 microns, successfully formed four complete lenses with low superficial roughness (<100

10.4229/EUPVSEC2025/4BO.5.1

nm). However, the fifth lens, located closest to the drum axis, was only partially formed, likely due to limitations in the flow or pressure distribution of the resin during the molding process. In the third sample, which had a thinner resin layer, no lenses were fully formed, confirming a critical threshold for resin thickness required to achieve complete lens replication.

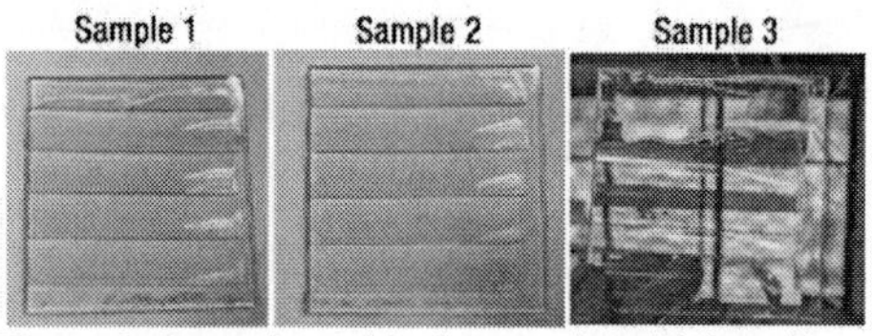

Figure 6: Comparison of the three resultant fabricated lens matrix samples with different resin base substrate thicknesses: sample 1 (380-280 μm), sample 2 (225-150 μm), sample 3 (150-30 μm).

The well-formed lenses closely matched the intended optical design, though minor deformations, such as tip and valley rounding, were observed. These are characteristic of the roll-to-plate process and are considered intrinsic to this type of manufacturing.

Following fabrication, the lenses were assembled with an array of narrow-strip solar cells for module-level characterization. Two types of tests were conducted:

- **Indoor testing** was performed using a collimated light solar simulator to simulate direct solar radiation, allowing for measurement of optical efficiency and concentration ratio.
- **Outdoor testing** was carried out under natural sunlight to evaluate the module's daylighting performance. This setup is composed of a 1:5 scale room with an opening in the ceiling where the lens sample is placed and a manual movable structure to place the lens array. In this way, we can test the sample under both direct and diffused light components, as shown in Figure 7.

Figure 7: Outdoor setup integrated by a 1:5 scale room with an opening in the ceiling where the lens sample is placed and a manual movable structure to place the lens array.

5.1 Indoor tests: Optical efficiency characterization

The optical efficiency of individual lenses was experimentally measured at various transverse angles of incidence. As shown in the results (see Figure 8), the measured optical efficiency is slightly lower than predicted by ray-tracing simulations. Nevertheless, the lenses demonstrate high optical efficiency across a broad angular range. A maximum optical efficiency of approximately 80% was achieved for incidence angles between 30° and 40°. Lenses 1 through 3 exhibit consistent performance, with minimal variation in efficiency and no observable deformation. The measured pitch distance remained uniform, indicating stable replication through the fabrication process. However, the fourth lens underperforms, failing to meet the target efficiency threshold. This discrepancy is currently under investigation and may be attributed to localized fabrication defects or alignment issues during the molding process.

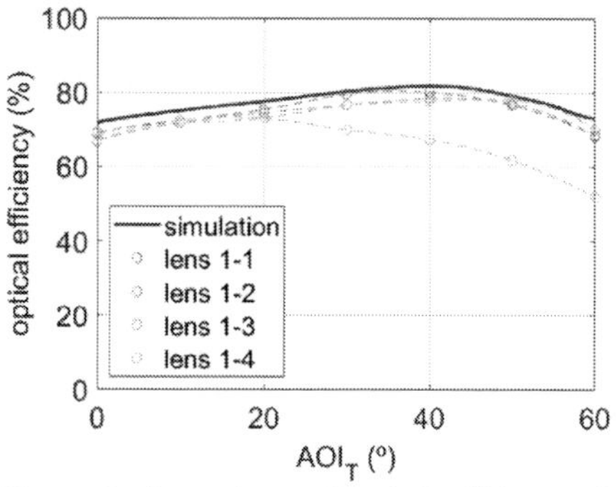

Figure 8: Comparisons of optical efficiency of the simulated lens (continuous line) and the manufactured lens (dashed line) of the sample 1 at 2.8x concentration.

5.2 Outdoor test: Illuminance characterization

Preliminary illuminance measurements were conducted to evaluate the modulation capacity of the module. At the point of maximum illuminance within the test room, results indicate a reduction in light intensity by approximately one order of magnitude when switching from skylight mode to blind mode, across varying angles of incidence. This confirms the system's ability to dynamically control indoor lighting levels based on solar position.

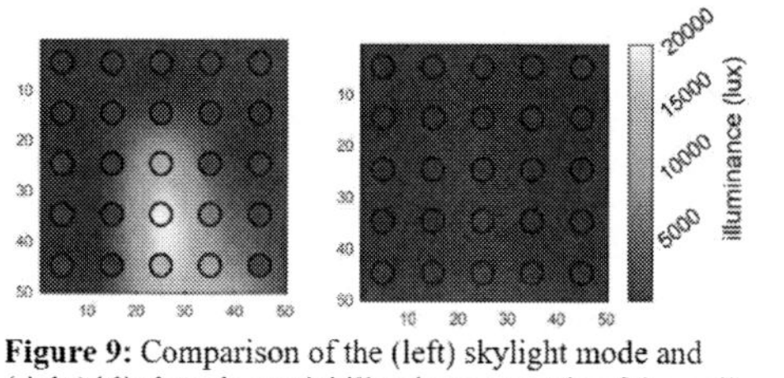

Figure 9: Comparison of the (left) skylight mode and (right) blind mode spatial illuminance matrix of the wall where the direct light falls, for an AOI$_T$ of 45°.

Additionally, we analyzed the spatial distribution of illuminance on the interior wall under a transverse angle of incidence of 45° (see Figure 9), comparing the experimental results with photorealistic ray-tracing simulations. As summarized in Table I, the measured average illuminance showed a reduction of approximately 1500 lux compared to skylight mode. Furthermore, a decrease in the peak-to-average illuminance ratio was observed across seven reference points, indicating a more

10.4229/EUPVSEC2025/4BO.5.1

uniform light distribution. However, both the average and peak illuminance values measured were higher than those predicted by simulation. This discrepancy is attributed to minor deformations in the molded lenses, which introduce optical losses and scattering not accounted for in the idealized simulation models.

Table I: Daylight illuminance parameters average illuminance and peak to average comparison for skylight mode and blind mode.

	skylight mode	blind mode
Average illuminance exp. (lx)	1885	319
Peak to average exp.	10.6	3.2
Peack to average sim.	5.7	2.9

6 CONCLUSIONS

This novel building-integrated concentrator photovoltaics module with daylighting functionality has been developed to simultaneously generate solar electricity and deliver comfortable, glare-free daylight. The system employs static linear Fresnel lenses to concentrate direct sunlight onto an array of c-Si solar cell strips mounted on a transparent, movable backplane. To follow the sun throughout the day, a planar micro-tracking system adjusts the position of the backplane, ensuring optimal alignment with the shifting focal lines. Meanwhile, diffuse light passes through the transparent areas of the module, providing uniform interior illumination with minimal glare.

Unlike conventional semi-transparent BIPV modules, where cells are spaced to allow some light transmission, this design captures nearly all direct irradiance, resulting in a significantly higher power density. The use of asymmetric Fresnel lenses with a wide draft angle minimizes self-shading and supports a compact, high-efficiency system. Arrays fabricated through scalable roll-to-plate UV imprinting achieved a peak optical efficiency of 80%, maintaining over 70% performance up to a 60° angle of incidence at ~3× concentration, closely aligning with simulation results. Outdoor testing further confirmed the system's visual benefits, including a tenfold reduction in peak illuminance, average indoor lighting levels around 1500 lux, and a 7-point drop in the peak-to-average illuminance ratio. These results highlight the dual function of the module as both a renewable energy generator and an effective daylighting and shading solution, supporting its integration into energy-efficient building design. This leads to improved visual comfort, reduced reliance on artificial lighting, and greater energy savings.

These combined benefits position this BIPV module as a compelling solution for accelerating the adoption of building-integrated photovoltaics in low-carbon urban design.

7 ACKNOWLEDGEMENTS

This work has been supported by project grants MICROBEAM ref. PID2021-127810OB-I00, funded by MCIN/AEI/10.13039/501100011033 "ERDF A way of making Europe", SMARTWIN TED2021-130920B-C21, funded by MCIN/AEI/10.13039/501100011033 and by the "European Union NextGenerationEU/PRTR" and 4EVERPV ref. "TEC-2024ECO-72", funded by Comunidad de Madrid.

8 REFERENCES

[1] A. Jäger-Waldau, I. Kougias, N. Taylor, and C. Thiel, "How photovoltaics can contribute to GHG emission reductions of 55% in the EU by 2030," Jul. 01, 2020, *Elsevier Ltd.* doi: 10.1016/j.rser.2020.109836.

[2] A. K. Shukla, K. Sudhakar, and P. Baredar, "A comprehensive review on design of building integrated photovoltaic system," Sep. 15, 2016, *Elsevier Ltd.* doi: 10.1016/j.enbuild.2016.06.077.

[3] D. Valencia-Caballero *et al.*, "Performance analysis of a novel building integrated low concentration photovoltaic skylight with seasonal solar control," *Journal of Building Engineering*, vol. 54, Aug. 2022, doi: 10.1016/j.jobe.2022.104687.

EU PVSEC 2025

Fabrication of a Novel Semi-Translucent BIPV Module Providing High Power Density and Active Daylight Management

Almudena Garcia-Sanchez[1], Guido Vallerotto[1], Jaime J. Hernández[2], Alejandro García-Cañas[2], Steve Askins[1], Ignacio Antón[1], Isabel Rodríguez[2] and César Domínguez[1]

[1] Instituto de Energía Solar, Universidad Politécnica de Madrid (UPM), Madrid (Spain)

[2] Madrid Institute for Advanced Studies in Nanoscience (IMDEA Nanoscience), Madrid (Spain)

Outline

INSTITUTO DE ENERGÍA SOLAR

- State-of-practice in building-integrated photovoltaics
- Novel module concept
  - Optical design requirements
  - Energetical analysis
- Fabrication of optical arrays
- Prototype characterization
  - Efficiency
  - Illumination features
- Conclusion

POLITÉCNICA

State-of-practice in building-integrated photovoltaics

INSTITUTO DE ENERGÍA SOLAR

The European Green Deal objectives:

- Need to reach 455-605 GW of PV
- Energy Performance of Buildings Directive (EPBD): new buildings to be nearly zero-energy (NZEB)

Increase util PV building area: glazing PV modules

Barriers to BIPV penetration

- ✖ Low efficiency compared to BAPV
- ✖ High cost/Wp
- ✖ No active management of daylighting/heat load
- ✖ Discomfort glare
- ✖ Poor color rendering index (CRI)

Skylight

Spaced opaque c-Si cells

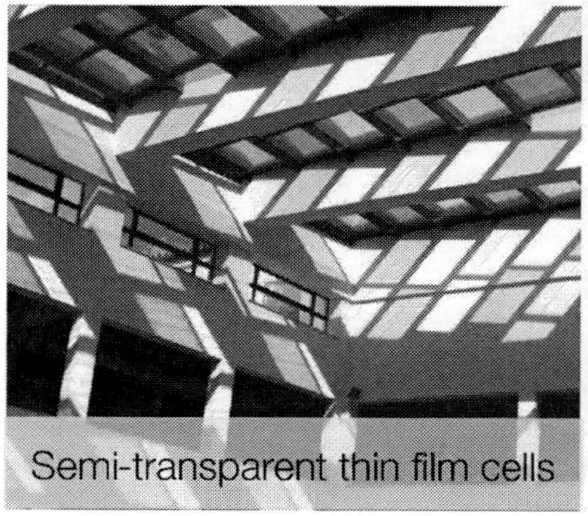

Semi-transparent thin film cells

Curtain wall

Canopy

Ballustrade

POLITÉCNICA

Novel module concept

INSTITUTO DE ENERGÍA SOLAR

Building-Integrated Concentrator Photovoltaics + Daylighting management

- **Direct** light is converted into **electricity**
- **Diffuse** light is transmitted as **low-glare daylighting**

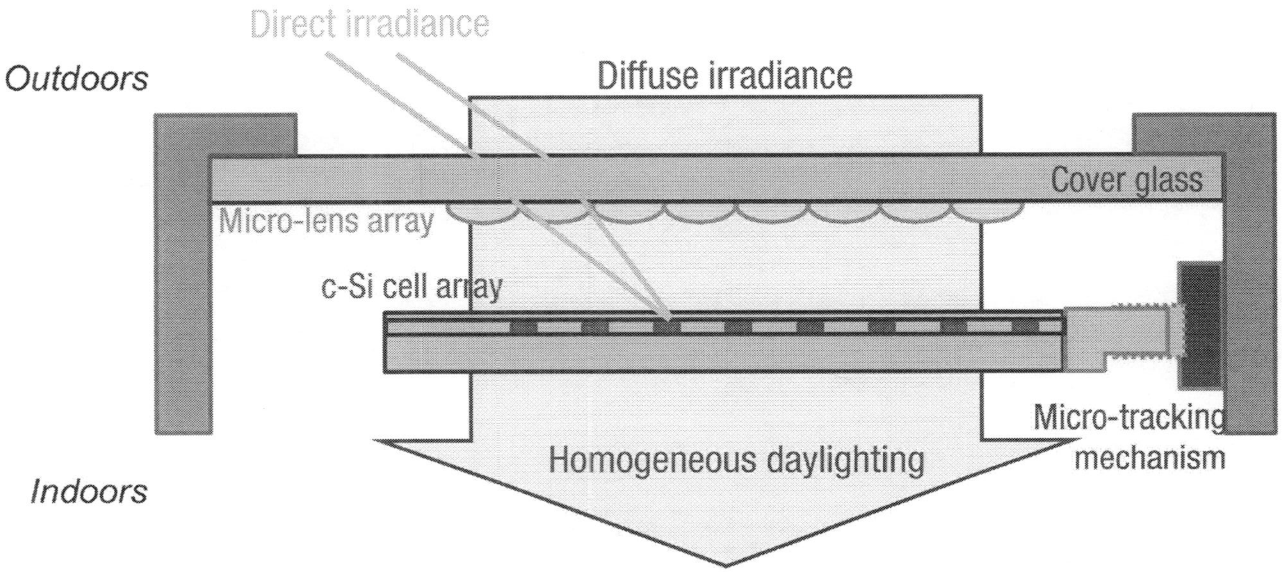

Novel module concept

INSTITUTO DE ENERGÍA SOLAR

Blind mode (low glare)

1:5 scale 2.8X configuration. AOI = 45°

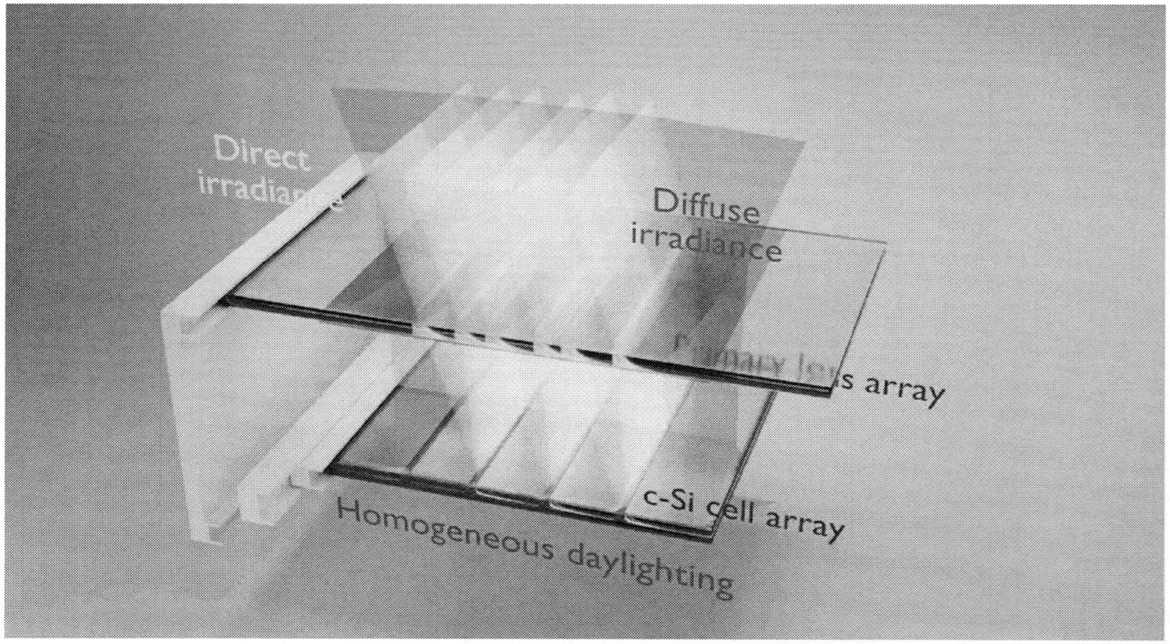

POLITÉCNICA

Novel module concept

INSTITUTO DE ENERGÍA SOLAR

Skylight mode (high transmission)

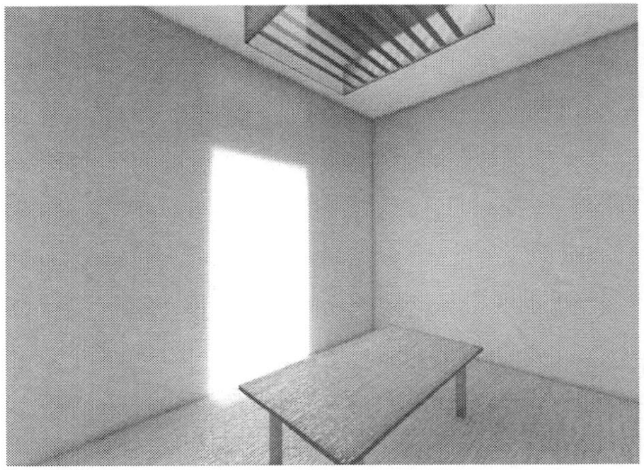

1:5 scale 2.8X configuration. AOI = 45°

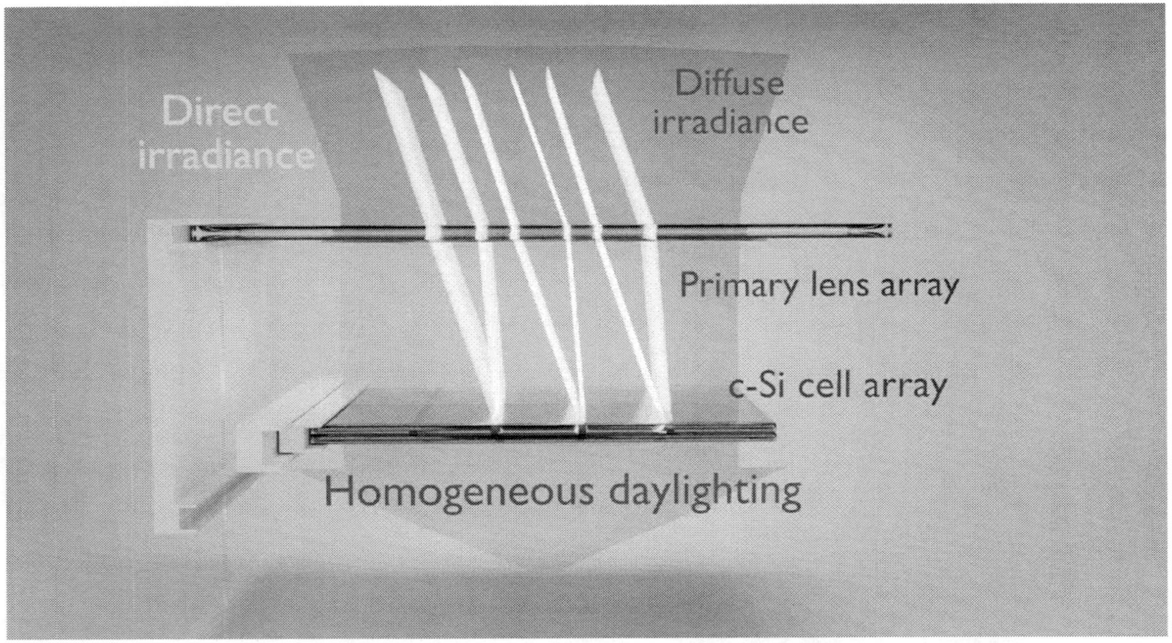

POLITÉCNICA

Optical design

INSTITUTO DE ENERGÍA SOLAR

- Ultra thin (40 µm) micro linear Fresnel lens

instituto imdea nanociencia — Compatible with low-cost roll-to-plate process

- Asymmetric lens with large draft angle
- Optimized for 17° angle of incidence
- Max. focal distance 7.5 cm to ease integration in typical building components

Optical design at nominal AOI

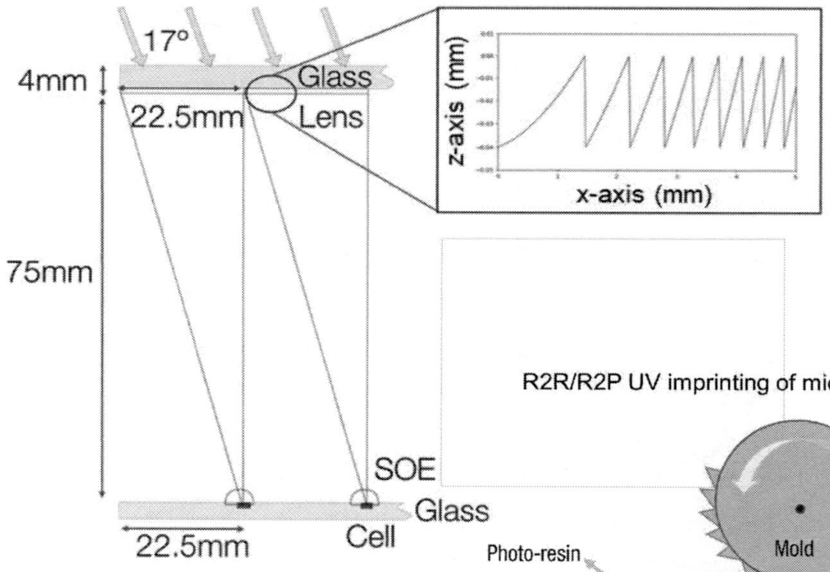

R2R/R2P UV imprinting of micro-facets

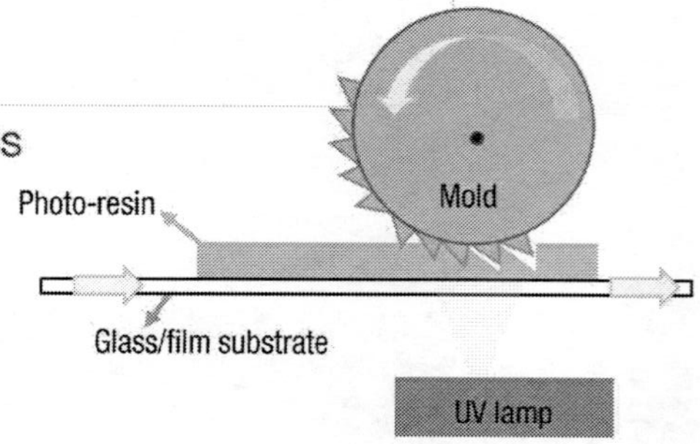

POLITÉCNICA

Optical modeling methodology

INSTITUTO DE ENERGÍA SOLAR

Definition and characterization

Ray-tracing software setup

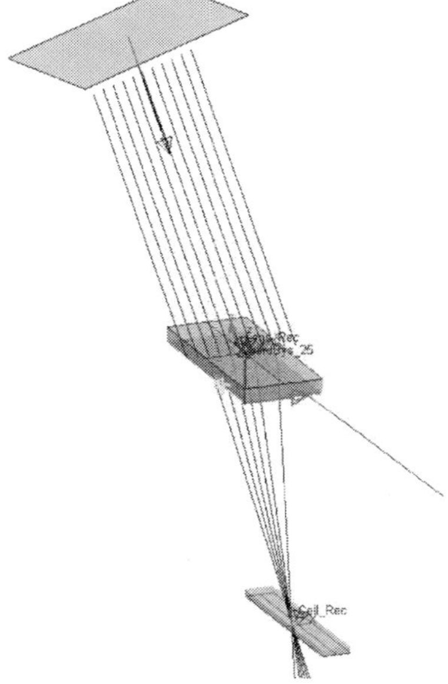

Angle of incidence classification

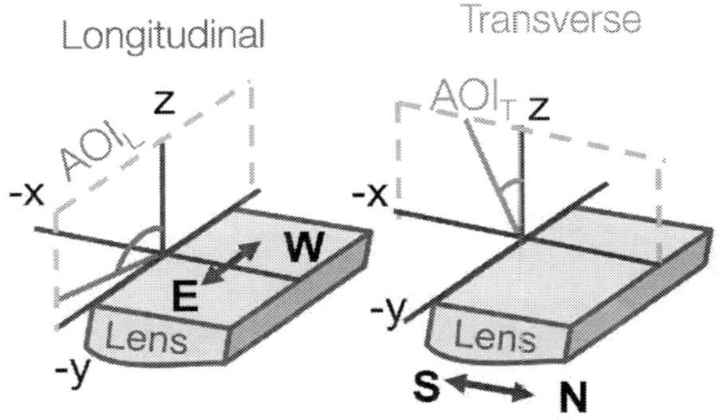

Optical efficiency vs AOI (2.8x)

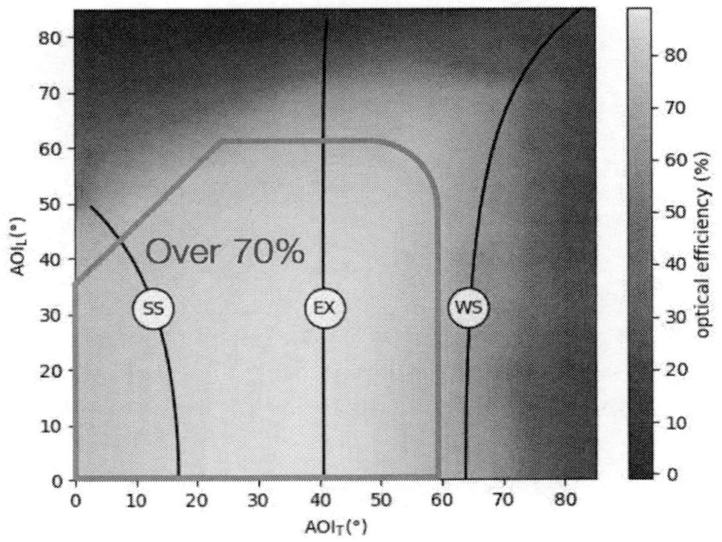

$$\text{optical eff} = \frac{P_{rec}}{P_{lens}}$$

POLITÉCNICA

Energetical analysis

INSTITUTO DE ENERGÍA SOLAR

- Python Pvlib + PSPICE model
  - Location and orientation
  - Module size
  - Cell technology
  - Module interconnection

Module efficiency through the year < 17.5%

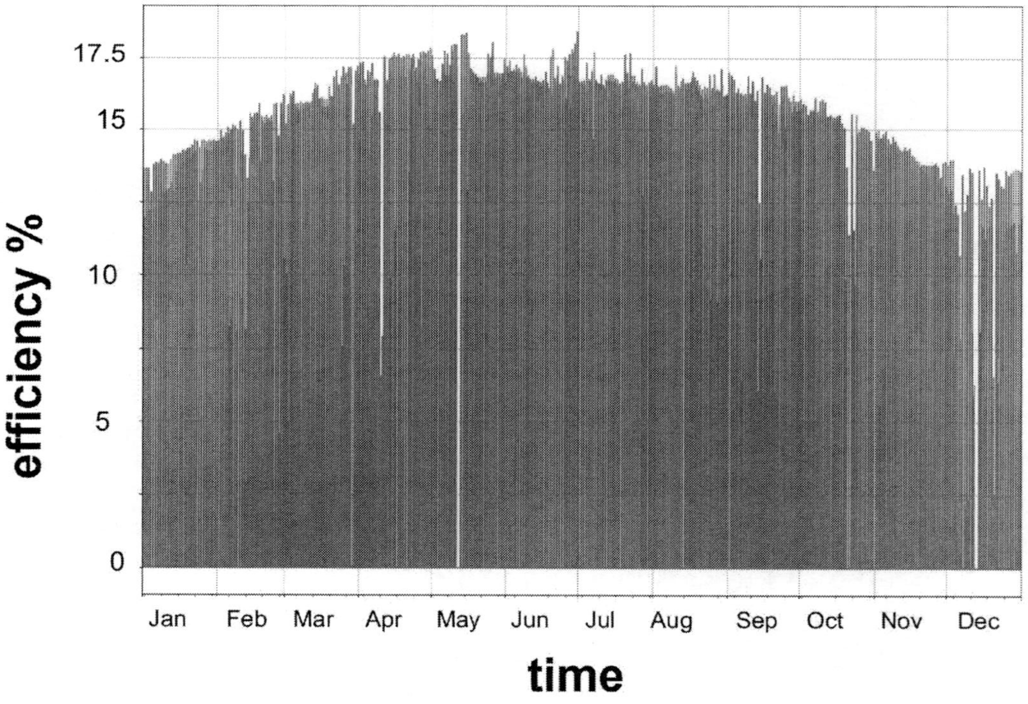

POLITÉCNICA

Fabrication of optical arrays

INSTITUTO DE ENERGÍA SOLAR

- Scalable roll-to-plate fabrication on glass

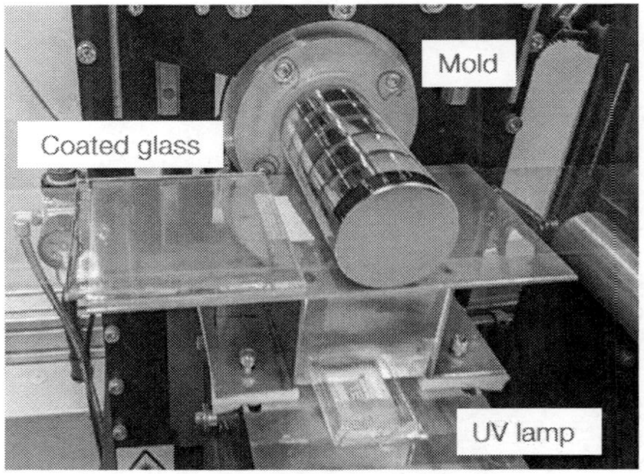

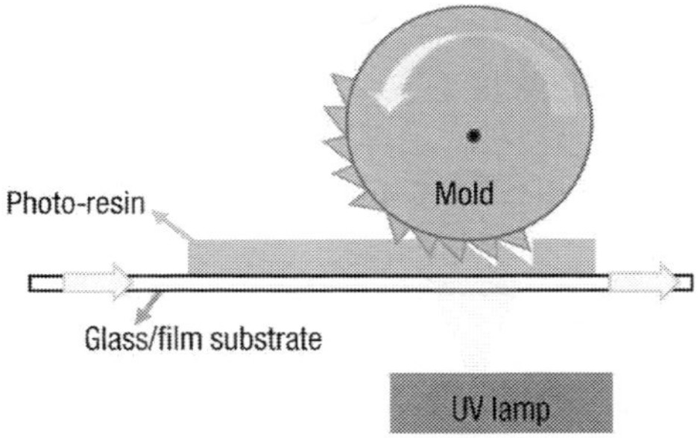

POLITÉCNICA

Fabrication of optical arrays

INSTITUTO DE ENERGÍA SOLAR

- Scalable roll-to-plate fabrication on glass

instituto imdea nanociencia

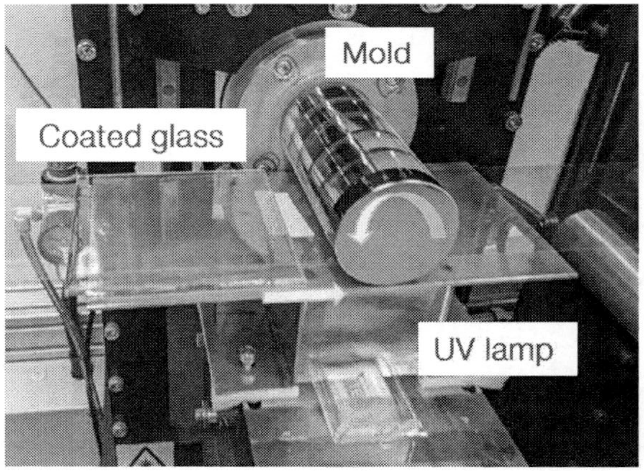

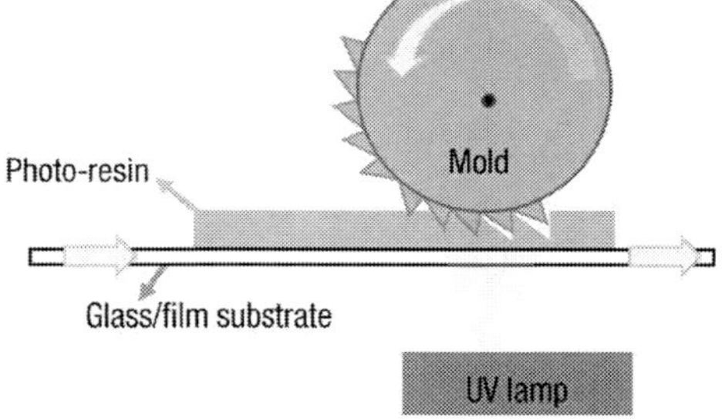

Natural daylighting

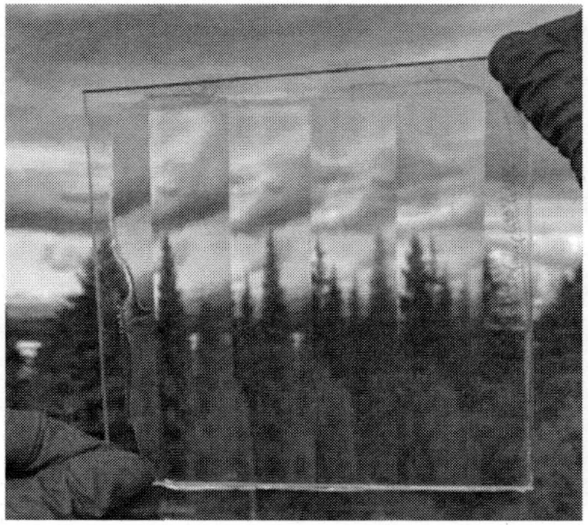

Direct light concentration

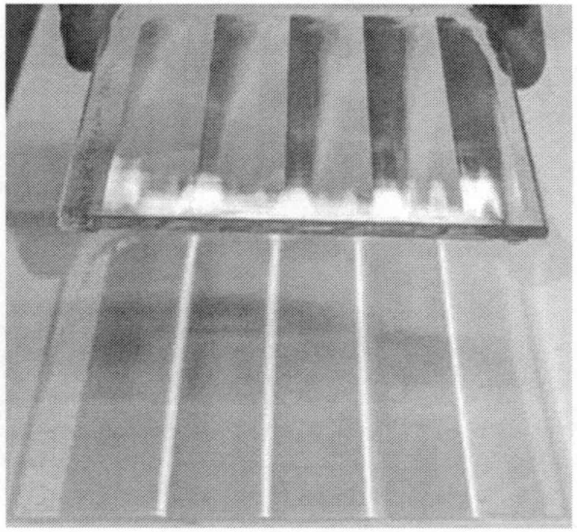

POLITÉCNICA

Fabrication of optical arrays

INSTITUTO DE ENERGÍA SOLAR

- Scalable roll-to-plate fabrication on glass

imdea nanociencia

Sample 1 (thickness 380-280 µm)

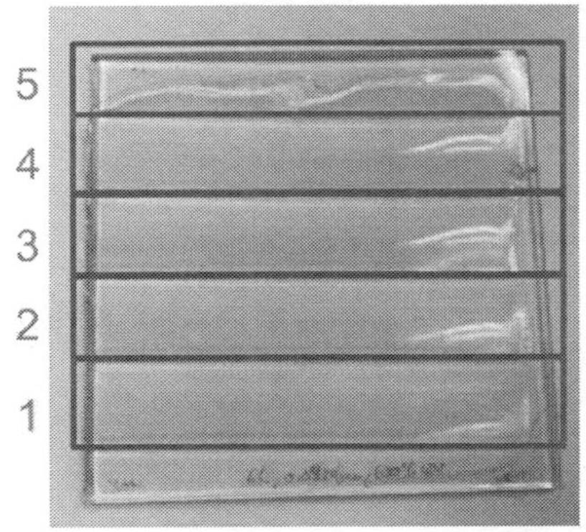

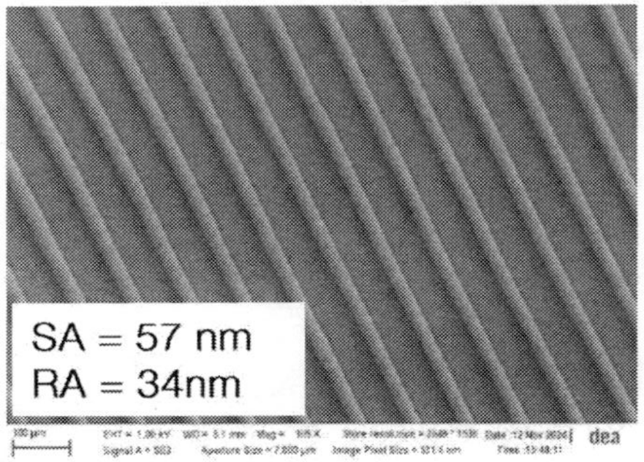

Sample 2 (thickness 225-150 µm)

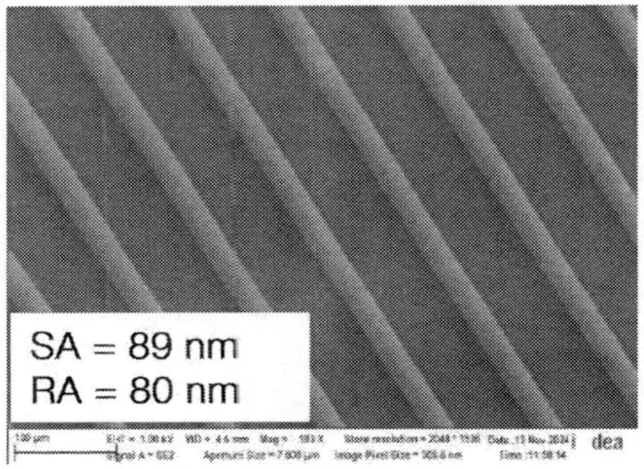

Sample 3 (thickness 150-30 µm)

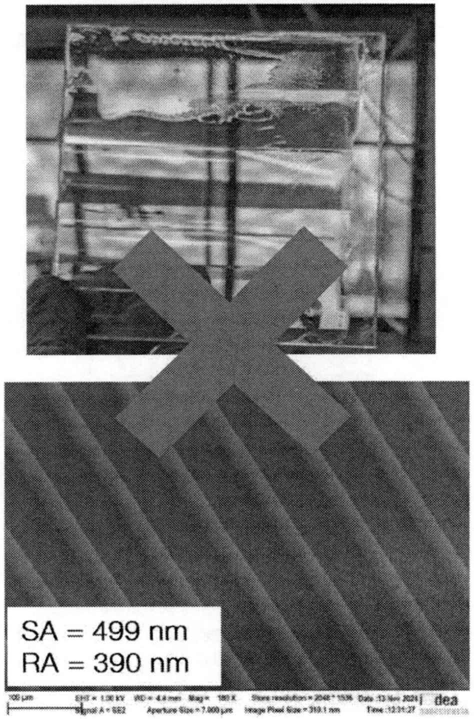

Fabrication of optical arrays

INSTITUTO DE ENERGÍA SOLAR

- Scalable roll-to-plate fabrication on glass

instituto imdea nanociencia

Sample 2 (thickness 225-150 µm)

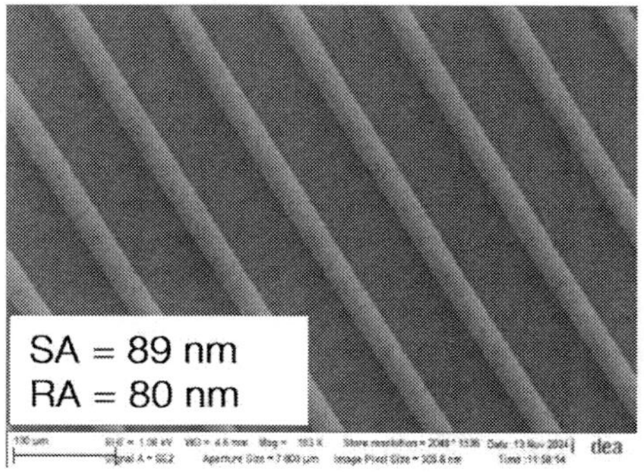

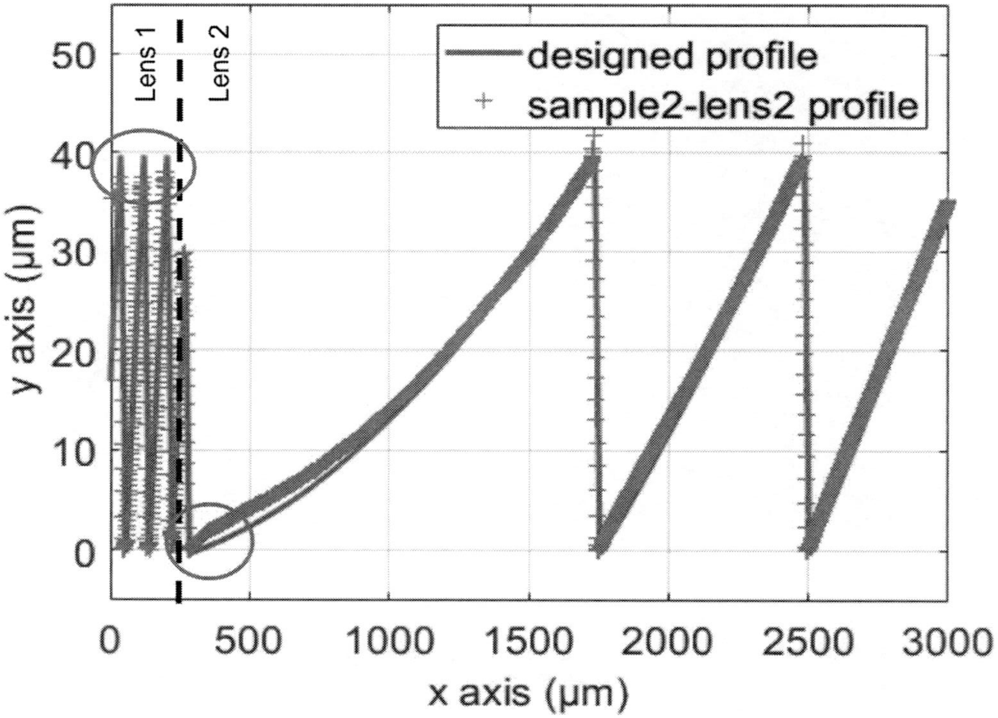

POLITÉCNICA

Prototype characterization:

INSTITUTO DE ENERGÍA SOLAR

Collimated solar simulator setup

Outdoor illuminance setup

POLITÉCNICA

Prototype characterization: Indoor optical efficiency

INSTITUTO DE ENERGÍA SOLAR

- High optical efficiency for a wide range of angles of incidence
- Maximum optical efficiency measured 80%
- Consistent performance for lenses 1-3

$$\text{optical eff} = \frac{P_{rec}}{P_{lens}}$$

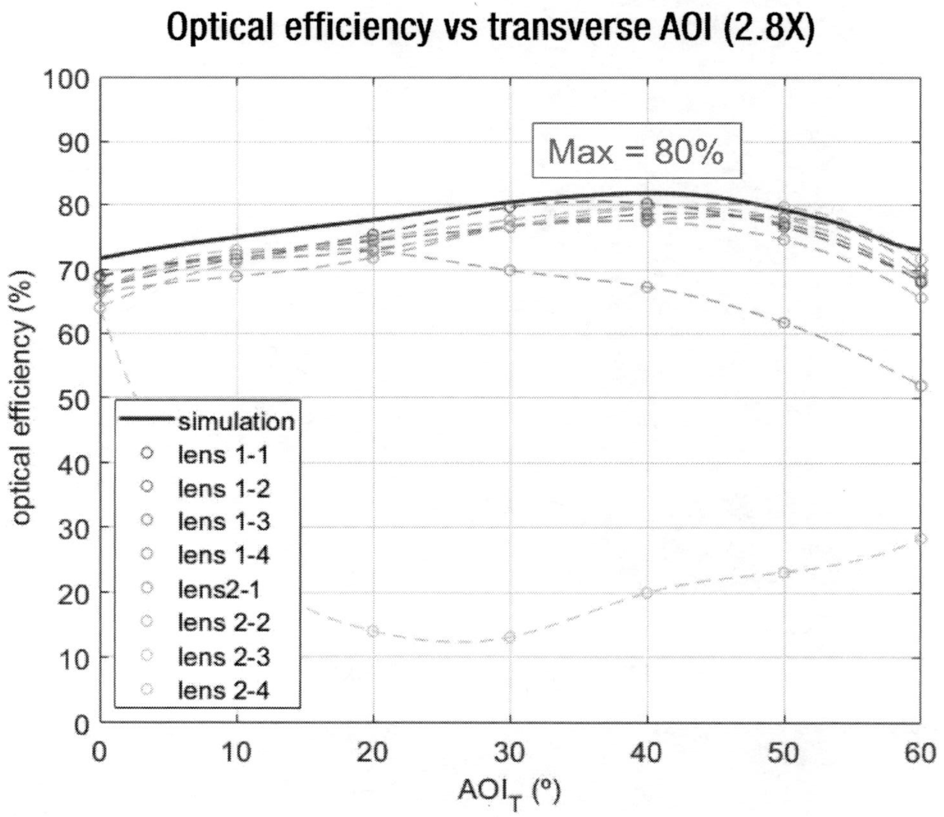

POLITÉCNICA

Prototype characterization: Indoor optical efficiency

INSTITUTO DE ENERGÍA SOLAR

Profile shape for different AOI_T (1mm cell)

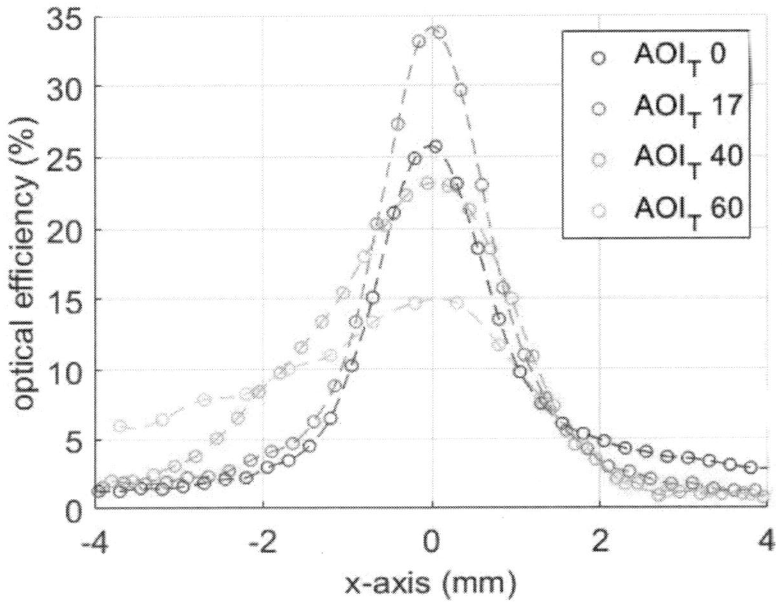

Relative encircled energy (%) for AOI_T 17º

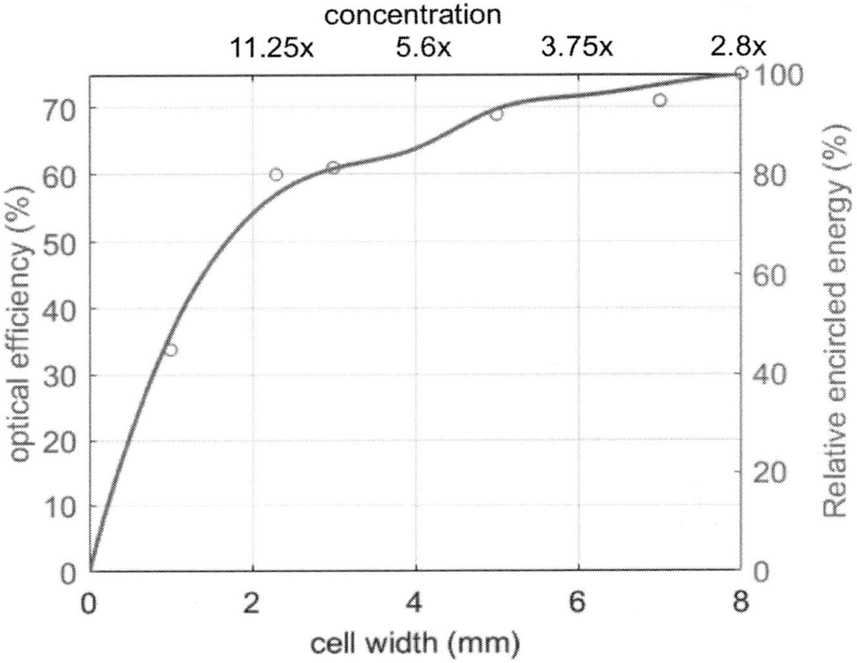

POLITÉCNICA

Prototype characterization: Outdoor illuminance performance

INSTITUTO DE ENERGÍA SOLAR

Skylight mode

Blind mode

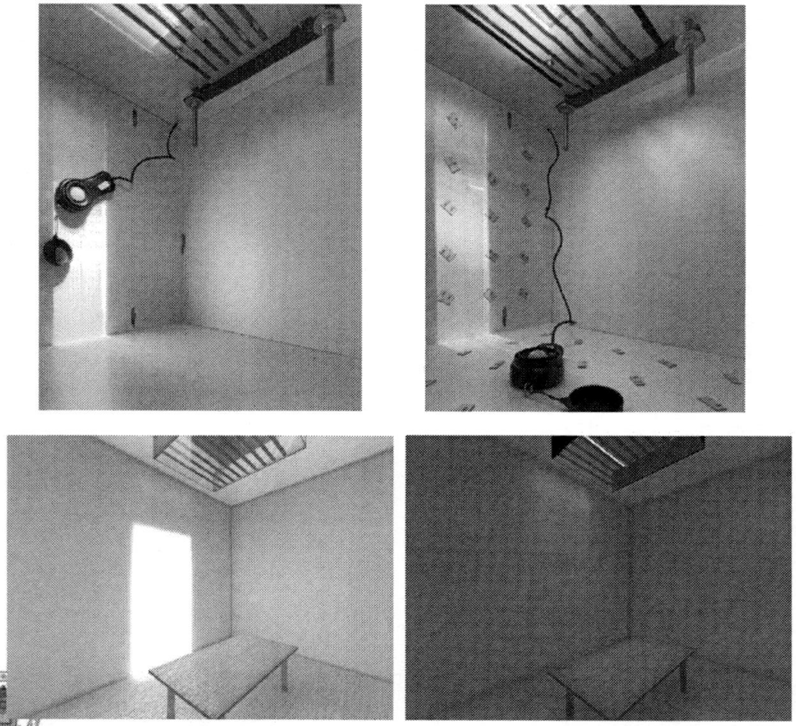

1:5 scale 2.8X configuration. AOI = 45°

Sensor in the max illuminance position

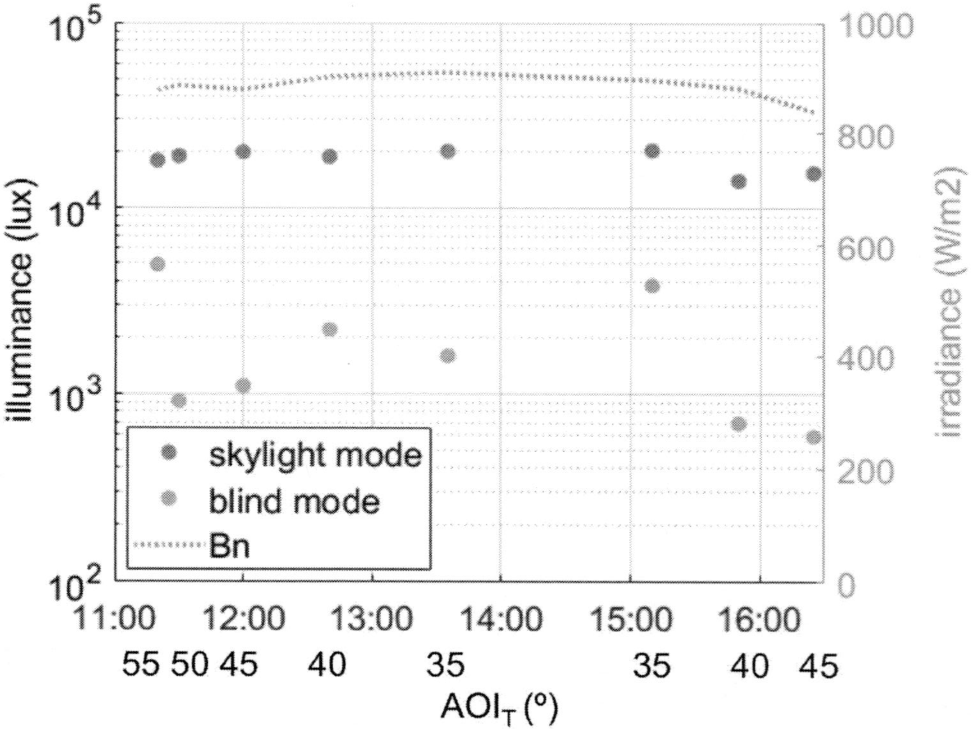

POLITÉCNICA

Prototype characterization: Outdoor illuminance performance

INSTITUTO DE ENERGÍA SOLAR

Skylight mode	Blind mode

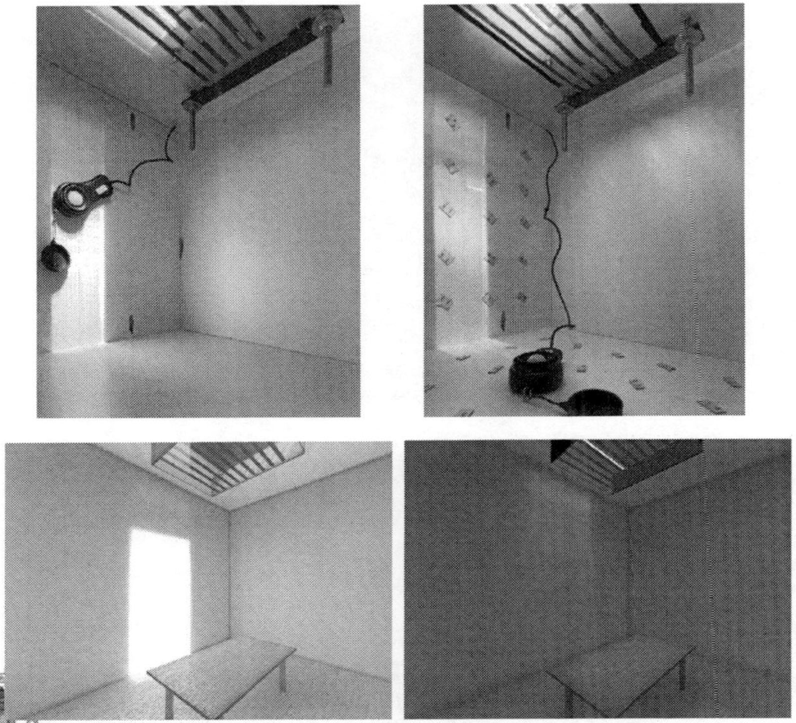

1:5 scale 2.8X configuration. AOI = 45°

Skylight mode	Blind mode

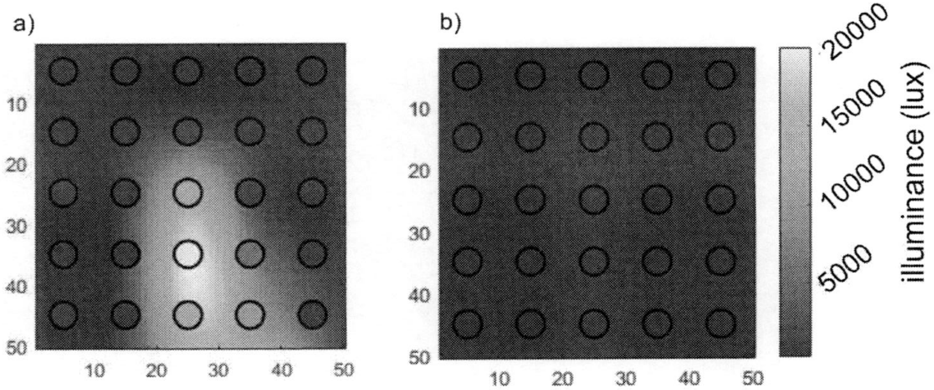

	HT wall	LT wall
Average exp. (lx)	1885	319
peak to average exp.	10.6	3.2
peak to average sim.	5.7	2.9

Conclusions

INSTITUTO DE ENERGÍA SOLAR

- Innovative BIPV approach to improve building energy balance and daylighting management
- Novel asymmetric linear Fresnel design compatible with scalable low-cost roll-to-plate manufacturing
- Prototype characterized by indoor and outdoor test demonstrates high optical efficiency and Glare-free daylighting capabilities
- Open to collaborations to take it to an industrial phase

POLITÉCNICA

Thank you for your attention

INSTITUTO DE ENERGÍA SOLAR

Almudena Garcia-Sanchez

Almudena.garcia@upm.es

Happy to take your questions

We gratefully acknowledge the support of these institutions: This work has been supported by project grants MICROBEAM ref. PID2021-127810OB-I00, funded by MCIN/AEI/10.13039/501100011033 "ERDF A way of making Europe", SMARTWIN TED2021-130920B-C21, funded by MCIN/AEI/10.13039/501100011033 and by the "European Union NextGenerationEU/PRTR" and 4EVERPV ref. "TEC-2024ECO-72", funded by Comunidad de Madrid.

Financiado por la Unión Europea NextGenerationEU

Plan de Recuperación, Transformación y Resiliencia

INSTITUTO
DE ENERGÍA
SOLAR

Innovation in photovoltaics since 1979

A COMPARATIVE STUDY OF PHOTOVOLTAIC SHADING DEVICES FOR NET ZERO ENERGY BUILDINGS ACROSS FRENCH CLIMATES

Mohammad Nazififard, Erwin Franquet
Polytech'Lab, Université Côte d'Azur, Nice, France
Mohammad.NAZIFIFARD@univ-cotedazur.fr Erwin.FRANQUET@univ-cotedazur.fr

ABSTRACT: By 2050, the European Union aims to achieve carbon neutrality and net-zero greenhouse gas emissions. Buildings account for a significant portion of the EU's energy consumption, making the integration of renewable technologies, such as photovoltaic (PV) modules in windows, roofs, façades, and above glazing, essential. Photovoltaic shading systems (PVSDs), which combine PV modules with awnings or louvres, generate electricity while reducing solar heat gain and lowering cooling energy demand. This study evaluates the impact of various PVSDs on the cooling, heating, and lighting demands of office buildings in four French cities with distinct climates: Brest, Clermont-Ferrand, Nice, and Strasbourg. Energy generation was calculated using PVSYST. The PVSD types modeled include horizontal canopies with single, double, and triple rows of PV modules, inclined canopies with single and double rows at a 30° tilt, and vertical panel canopies. Results show that the Nice inclined single canopy reduces annual energy use by up to 35.31% compared to the base model. In Clermont, the horizontal single-row canopy lowers energy use by 20.49%. In Strasbourg, the same canopy reduces consumption by 14.83%, while in Brest, it achieves a 13.31% reduction. These findings suggest that PVSDs are most effective in reducing cooling energy in Mediterranean climates. In colder regions like Strasbourg, designs should also optimize winter solar heat gain. This study establishes a quantitative framework for the design and evaluation of PVSDs in office buildings.

Keywords: Photovoltaic shading systems; Building energy efficiency; Renewable energy integration; Cooling load reduction; Climate-responsive design.

1 INTRODUCTION

The European Union has set an ambitious goal to achieve carbon neutrality by 2050, aiming to create a net-zero greenhouse gas emissions economy [1]. A critical component of this target is reducing carbon emissions from the heating and cooling sectors, which together account for approximately 42% of the European Union's final energy consumption. Currently, about 75% of this demand is still met by fossil fuels [2]. Improving the energy performance of buildings is widely recognized as a key strategy for achieving these goals, due to the substantial potential for energy savings and climate change mitigation within the European building stock [3]. The integration of renewable energy technologies to meet the energy demands of buildings further supports this objective [4] [5]. France, which has traditionally relied on nuclear power, has one of the lowest carbon-intensity electricity mixes in the world. In 2019, nuclear energy accounted for more than 70% of the country's domestic electricity production [6], [7]. However, most of France's nuclear reactors were commissioned between the late 1970s and early 1980s and are now approaching or exceeding their typical operational lifespan of 40 to 60 years, indicating the likelihood of imminent shutdowns [8]. As a result, France is actively transitioning toward renewable energy sources to reduce its reliance on both fossil fuels and nuclear power. Government policies prioritize the expansion of wind, solar, hydroelectric, and biomass energy sectors [9]. Compared to wind energy, which requires a substantial land area for installation, photovoltaic (PV) technology offers greater flexibility by allowing direct integration into building envelopes as building-integrated photovoltaic (BIPV) systems. In addition to on-site electricity generation, BIPV systems can significantly reduce building cooling loads [10]. Building facades play a critical role in regulating indoor thermal comfort and supporting occupant health. Integrating photovoltaic (PV) systems into building envelopes enhances energy efficiency by generating electricity while also affecting daylighting and thermal performance. Both experimental studies and simulation-based analyses have examined the daylighting characteristics, thermal behavior, and power generation potential of such facades. Additionally, PV panels can be incorporated into architectural elements such as eaves and canopies. Optimally designed solar awnings can generate significant amounts of electricity and reduce unwanted solar heat gain through windows, thereby lowering cooling energy demand during the summer months [11]. These systems have been widely implemented as PV shading solutions in both low-rise and multi-story buildings. Serving dual purposes, they not only generate electricity but also function as external shading devices that help reduce cooling loads [12]. Recent research has focused on optimizing the energy performance of solar shading systems, as discussed in the following sections.

2 LITERATUE REVIEW

Canopies play a critical role in sustainable architecture, particularly when integrated with PV systems. These hybrid solutions not only enhance energy generation but also optimize solar radiation control, improve natural lighting, and reduce thermal loads. In addition to maximizing solar energy efficiency, such systems significantly decrease cooling demand, increase daylight utilization, and improve occupant thermal comfort. Recent studies underscore the benefits of incorporating PV systems into building designs [13], [14], [15]. Hofer et al. [16] reported that in Zurich's climate, strategic orientation and spacing of PV panels increased energy efficiency by more than 50% compared to conventional configurations, with further improvements achieved using south-facing facades and horizontal shading elements. Nagy et al. [17] developed smart façade modules with precise adjustability, resulting in a 25% reduction in energy consumption while preserving architectural aesthetics. Jayathissa et al. [18] demonstrated that adaptive solar façades, responsive to both internal and external conditions, could reduce energy use by up to 80% in office buildings with high cooling loads.

Dynamic shading systems exhibit performance that varies with climate conditions. Gao et al. [19] analyzed PVwindows equipped with movable awnings in nine cities using a three-degree-of-freedom tracking system. Their study reported a 27.4% increase in energy production and a 19.17% improvement in module efficiency, while emphasizing the need for climate-specific adjustments to balance energy generation and glare control. Krarti and Karrech [20] demonstrated that hourly or monthly adjustmenets of movable awnings enabled net-zero energy consumption in Australian office buildings. Jiang et al. [21] compared three dynamic strategies: rotation, horizontal movement, and combined operation. They found energy savings between 32% and 50%, along with a 3.1% increase in useful daylight illuminance (UDI) for the combined strategy. Similarly, Krarti et al. [22] reported that hourly-adjusted dynamic awnings in Qatar reduced annual building energy use by 69.7%. These results highlight the importance of climate- and behavior-responsive design to optimize system efficiency.

Research on solar awnings confirms their energy-saving potential when designed with consideration for climate, solar position, and environmental radiation. Zhang et al. [10] demonstrated that, in Hong Kong, horizontal awnings on southwest-facing façades reduced lighting energy use by 45.7% (equivalent to 69.16 kWh/m^2 annually), with optimal performance achieved at a 30° tilt and a south-facing orientation. Li et al. [11], [23] emphasized that seasonally adjustable angles outperform fixed installations across five different climate zones in China, with south-facing awnings proving the most efficient. In Guangzhou, PV awnings offset 40% of a multi-story building's net electricity demand and outperformed roof-mounted systems in terms of cost-effectiveness [11]. Baghoolizadeh et al. [12] optimized window-integrated shading systems in five European cities using EnergyPlus-NSGA-II simulations, achieving electricity cost reductions of 17% to 34%. Skandalos and Karamanis [28] compared semi-transparent photovoltaic (PV) shading in Prague, Athens, and Dubai, reporting the highest savings of 73% in the Mediterranean climate of Athens. Qadourah [29] demonstrated that PV shading in Mediterranean residential complexes supplied 25.1% to 35.6% of electricity demand, outperforming standalone villas in terms of energy performance. These studies confirm that the effectiveness of solar awnings depends on climate-responsive design tailored to regional conditions, solar geometry, and building typology. Integrating solar awnings into building design requires a careful balance among energy production, daylight optimization, and visual comfort. Early research has identified inherent trade-offs among these factors.

Kim et al. [30] found that PV blinds with edge-angle control increased electricity generation by 32% but reduced lighting energy savings by 35%, highlighting conflicts between energy output and daylight quality. Qingsong et al. [31] reported that combining PV louver awnings with lighting controls in China saved 22.8% of energy but sometimes compromised indoor lighting, leading to increased artificial lighting use. Conversely, Li et al. [32] showed that bidirectional PV panels oriented east and west achieved up to 25.62% electrical efficiency with only modest indoor light reductions of 2.5% to 12%, depending on distance. This finding indicates that strategic orientation can balance energy generation and daylight goals. To address these challenges, recent research has focused on adaptive designs. Liu et al. [33] introduced a geometric, algorithmically optimized PV shading system for Guangzhou offices that reduced cooling and lighting demands by 48.7% while generating 1034.4 kWh/year of surplus energy. The system also improved useful daylight illuminance by 71.6%, demonstrating synergistic benefits. Li et al. [34] applied multi-objective optimization to double-sided awnings in warm climates, enhancing daylight by 39.44% and reducing ventilation energy consumption by 12.61%. Zheng et al. [35] advanced this approach in Shenzhen by using the SPEA2 algorithm to design rotating multilayer awnings that reduced glare by 53% and limited annual energy use to 100 kWh.

These findings illustrate that adaptive controls, multi-objective optimization, and climate-responsive geometries can mitigate trade-offs between energy efficiency and occupant comfort.

Jayathissa et al. [36] developed a comprehensive simulation framework for solar shading in Zurich, demonstrating that fixed configurations could reduce building energy use by 20% to 80%, with some cases achieving full energy self-sufficiency. Abdullah and Alibaba [37] reported that PV-integrated shading in a naturally ventilated office in Cyprus supplied 70% of the building's electricity needs while maintaining thermal comfort for 80% of the year. Comparative studies highlight the advantages of advanced shading systems over conventional designs. Peres et al. [40] simulated multi-layer canopy devices in Rio de Janeiro, reducing cooling loads by 14% to 19% and net energy demand by 32%. Jung et al. [41] confirmed that PV louver awnings in Michigan generated 47.9% more electricity than vertical facade installations.

The tilt angle of solar canopies is critical for both energy efficiency and architectural integration. Asfour [42] demonstrated that horizontal canopies tilted at 45° in Saudi Arabia received the highest annual solar radiation (104 kWh/m^2) while providing 96% shading during the summer. Han et al. [43] recommended a 35° tilt for bifacial canopies in Hong Kong, noting that increasing canopy width raises total power output but reduces generation per unit area due to self-shading. Kim et al. [44] reported that monthly adjustments of blade angles in South Korea could not completely prevent self-shading at a 30° tilt, which reduced the output of the lower blades. Wang et al. [45] showed that real-time canopy angle control in Hong Kong reduced energy use by 36.5% and increased power generation by 11.4%. Their study also emphasized the importance of maintaining panel width-to-vertical distance ratios below 1:10 to minimize shading losses.

PV panel technology also affects canopy efficiency. Bahr [46] found that amorphous silicon panels perform best at latitude-equivalent tilt angles in Abu Dhabi, while crystalline silicon panels are more efficient in horizontal configurations. These findings highlight the importance of considering tilt angle, PV technology, and local climate in the design process.

Spacing and dimensions also significantly influence performance. Baghdadi and Abuhussain [47] demonstrated that horizontal louver blinds with a 40 cm depth reduced cooling loads in Riyadh from 101,000 kWh to 88,000 kWh, with a payback period of 8.6 to 10.2 years. Chen et al. [48] reported that reducing inter-panel spacing from 175 mm to 35 mm in a hot-summer/cold-winter climate increased power generation by a factor of five. These results underscore the critical impact of structural details on energy savings. Luo et al. [52] found that double-glazed façades with PV curtains reduced cooling

10.4229/EUPVSEC2025/4BO.5.3

demand by 12.16% to 25.57%. Evangelisti et al. [53] experimentally demonstrated a 38.7% reduction in summer thermal energy use in an Italian building employing active and passive solar shading. Akbari Paydar [54] reported that movable shading on south-facing windows in Tehran reduced heating loads by 12% to 20%, while generating electricity exceeding thermal demand by 70% to 290%. Ogbeba and Hoskara [55] simulated PV shading in Northern Cyprus, showing a 50% reduction in summer energy use along with 2800 W of electricity generation. Taveres-Cachat et al. [56] found that shading altered heating and cooling demands by 28% and 7%, respectively, in Norway.

Despite recent advancements, key challenges remain. Dynamic systems offer high energy savings but are often limited by mechanical complexity, cost, and maintenance issues. Many studies focus on energy, lighting, or comfort individually, with few adopting integrated, multi-objective approaches. Additionally, most research targets single climates and overlooks combined analyses of thermal performance, daylighting, and power generation.

This study introduces an integrated solar canopy model evaluated across four distinct French climates. The model aims to balance energy performance, thermal comfort, daylighting, and economic feasibility within a unified framework.

3 METHODOLOGY

3.1 Case study

This study examines the impact of PVSDs on cooling demand during warm seasons, heating requirements during cold seasons, and overall electricity consumption across four distinct climate zones in France. EnergyPlus, developed by the U.S. Department of Energy, is a free, reliable simulation engine widely used to evaluate building energy performance. It offers an efficient framework for processing both input and output data [57]. Detailed office building models were created using DesignBuilder for each climate zone. EnergyPlus was then used to assess the effects of solar shading systems on thermal loads and total energy consumption. Additionally, PVsyst calculated the solar energy generated by the shading systems. By comparing simulation results, the study identified the optimal solar shading configurations for maximizing energy efficiency in each climate.

To ensure generalizable results, a model office building with standardized characteristics was developed. The design reflects typical office architectural features and incorporates key factors influencing energy performance, such as geometry, materials, orientation, and natural lighting. The model represents a single-zone office space measuring 6 meters wide, 8 meters deep, and 3.9 meters high (Figure 1).

Material selection was based on previous research focused on passive building strategies [58], including energy-efficient materials and window configurations. The external walls and roof are highly insulated to minimize heat transfer and isolate the effects of shading devices. A large south-facing window measuring 2.0 meters by 1.84 meters was included to optimize solar gain, consistent with common energy-efficient design practices. High-performance double-glazed windows with low U-values were used to control heat and light transmission.

The building is equipped with a high-efficiency LED lighting system and a variable air volume HVAC system featuring an air-cooled chiller and reheat capabilities, suitable for maintaining thermal comfort in office environments. Operational parameters include occupancy from 8 a.m. to 5 p.m., Monday through Friday, an occupant density of 0.111 persons per square meter, and heating and cooling setpoints of 21°C and 26°C, respectively. Lighting controls were implemented in DesignBuilder to simulate realistic energy use, accounting for the impact of shading devices on daylight availability. Multiple solar shading configurations with varying heights and arrangements along the façade were simulated to evaluate their effects on energy performance. PVsyst software was used to simulate the performance and energy production of solar awning systems under various climatic conditions. Selecting an appropriate PV panel is essential, as it directly affects the system's efficiency and overall effectiveness. Based on a review of relevant studies and with the goal of maximizing performance, the solar panels listed in Table II were chosen for the simulations.

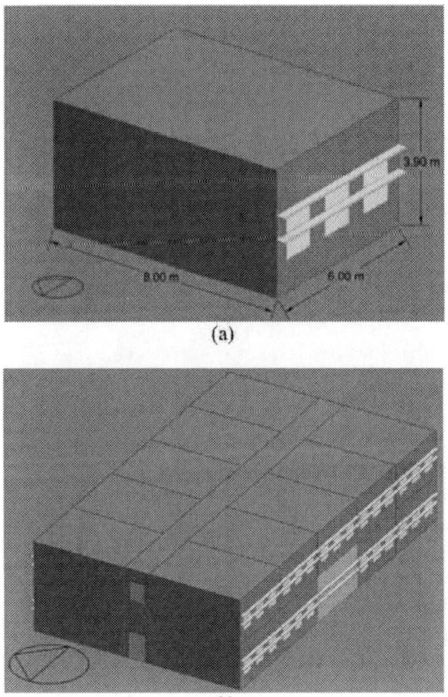

(b)

Figure 1: (a) Single-story buildings with PVSDs; (b) multi-story buildings with PVSDs.

High-performance double-glazed windows with a low U-value are used to regulate heat and light entering the building. An energy-efficient LED lighting system is modeled, along with a variable air volume (VAV) system equipped with an air cooler for climate control. This configuration is suitable for buildings requiring precise temperature regulation in different climate zones. The office building is occupied at a density of 0.12 persons per square meter and operates from 8:00 a.m. to 5:00 p.m., five days a week. The heating and cooling setpoints are 21°C

10.4229/EUPVSEC2025/4BO.5.3

and 26°C, respectively. Lighting management is also included in the simulation. Each PVSD is equipped with PV panels totaling 7.1 m² in surface area. To assess the effectiveness of PVSDs, their ability to reduce building energy consumption is first evaluated through passive shading performance. Subsequently, PV energy generation is estimated using PVsyst software. Simulation results for lighting, heating, cooling, and total energy use are compared with a baseline model across different climates to evaluate overall PVSD performance. These results demonstrate the contribution of PVSDs to reducing net energy consumption through both passive shading and active electricity generation.

Table I: Geometry and Simulation details in DESIGNBUILDER.

Model Name	Base Model	Horizontal Canopy Single
Model Type	No-shading	Single panel
Schematic		
Number of Rows	0	1
Distance PV panels (m)	0	0
Area of single PVSD (m²)	0	7.1
Total area of Panels (m²)	0	7.1
Model Name	Horizontal Canopy Double	Horizontal Canopy Triple
Model Type	Double panel	Triple panel
Schematic		
Number of Rows	2	3
Distance PV panels (m)	0.75	0.52
Area of single PVSD (m²)	3.55	2.36
Total area of Panels (m²)	7.1	7.1
Model Name	Canopy Inclined Single	Canopy Inclined Double
Model Type	Single panel 30°	Double panel 30°
Schematic		
Number of Rows	1	2
Distance PV panels (m)	0	0.75
Area of single PVSD (m²)	7.1	3.55
Total area of Panels (m²)	7.1	7.1
Model Name	Canopy Inclined Triple	Canopy Vertical Panel
Model Type	Triple panel 30°	Vertical Panel
Schematic		
Number of Rows	3	1
Distance PV panels (m)	0.52	0
Area of single PVSD (m²)	2.36	7.1
Total area of Panels (m²)	7.1	7.1

Table II. Specifications of the PV module used in the simulations.

Parameter	Value
Name	Xunlight Corporation
Power	150 W
Cell type	Monocrystalline
Dimensions (mm)	5480*454*1.5
Weight (kg)	6
Max. Power voltage (V)	30.0
Max. Current power (A)	5.00
Open circuit voltage (V)	40.5
Current short circuit I_{sc} (A)	6.35
Maximum system voltage	600 V

5 SCIENTIFIC INNOVATION AND RELEVANCE

Sun-shading techniques play an important role in reducing building energy consumption across various countries. The combined influence of PVSDs, through both shading and electricity generation, has been the focus of several studies. The significance of these systems in lowering overall energy use has been widely discussed in the literature.

However, only a limited number of investigations have explored specific factors such as the number and tilt angle of PVSDs and their effect on energy efficiency, particularly for heating, cooling, and lighting demands. This study provides a detailed analysis of PVSD performance under different climatic conditions. It also examines the combined effect of passive shading in reducing cooling demand and active energy production from PV panels integrated into various PVSD configurations.

4.1 Different climates in France

France's extensive geography and varied topography create multiple distinct climate zones that directly affect building energy consumption and the performance of solar energy systems. This section focuses on four principal French climates: oceanic, Mediterranean, mountainous, and continental. Each climate zone is defined by specific temperature ranges, solar radiation levels, humidity, and wind patterns, all of which influence the effectiveness of solar shading systems.

Oceanic climates, represented by Brest, exhibit moderate temperatures, high humidity, moderate to high precipitation, moderate solar radiation, and moderate wind speeds. Mediterranean climates, such as Nice, are characterized by hot, dry summers, mild and wet winters, high solar radiation, and strong winds. Mountainous climates, exemplified by Clermont, experience cold, snowy winters, cool summers, elevated solar radiation, low humidity, and significant temperature fluctuations. Continental climates, like Strasbourg, feature cold winters, warm and humid summers, moderate to high solar radiation, and moderate rainfall.

Figure 2 summarizes the geographical and meteorological data of these four representative cities. Their latitudes range from 43.71°N to 48.57°N. Among them, Nice, located in the Mediterranean zone, has the highest annual global horizontal irradiance (GHI) at 1562.2 kWh/m², while Brest, in the oceanic zone, records the lowest GHI at 1105.4 kWh/m². Diffuse horizontal irradiance (DHI) values are relatively consistent across these locations, ranging from 595.8 kWh/m² in Strasbourg to 617.3 kWh/m² in Nice. Temperature variations are also notable, with average maximum temperatures ranging

10.4229/EUPVSEC2025/4BO.5.3

from 17.1 °C in Brest to 25.4 °C in Nice, and average minimum temperatures from 2.3 °C in Strasbourg to 7.3 °C in Brest. These variations in solar radiation and temperature play a critical role in determining the energy performance of buildings and the effectiveness of solar shading systems.

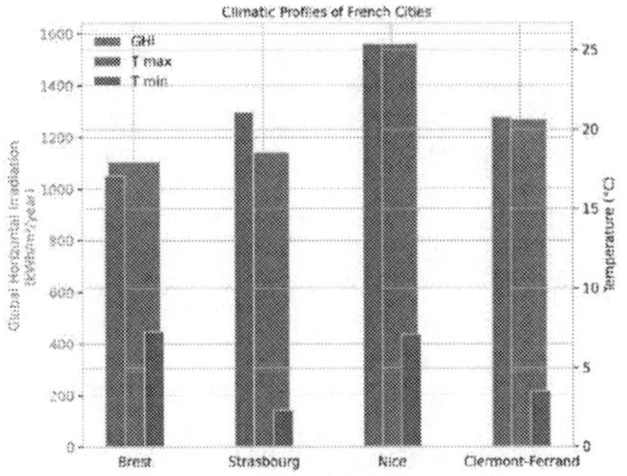

Figure 2: The weather condition in four cities in France.

6 RESULTS AND CONCLUSIONS

Figures 3 through 6 illustrate the office building's energy consumption and the PV electricity generation of various PVSD configurations. The simulation results indicate that the building in Brest has the lowest total energy consumption, at 48.11 kWh/m². In contrast, Strasbourg and Nice show the highest values, with 76.29 kWh/m² and 75.75 kWh/m², respectively. Clermont-Ferrand falls between these extremes, with an energy consumption of 65.09 kWh/m². Regarding PV electricity production, the Inclined Single Canopy model demonstrates the highest output in Nice, generating 15.08 kWh/m² (Figure 5). The same model also performs well in Clermont-Ferrand, producing 12.10 kWh/m² (Figure 4). Brest and Strasbourg show moderate results, with values of 10.5 kWh/m² and 10.71 kWh/m², respectively (Figures 3 and 6). Figure 7 presents the energy savings associated with different PVSD configurations for cooling, lighting, and heating. In Nice, the Inclined Single Canopy model achieved the highest reduction in total energy consumption, with savings of up to 35.31% compared to the base case. In Clermont, the Horizontal Single Canopy model reduced total energy use by 20.49%. In Brest and Strasbourg, this same model lowered energy consumption by 13.31% and 14.83%, respectively. Regarding lighting energy use, results show that the Vertical Canopy Panel model increased overall consumption in all cities. The highest increase was observed in Brest, where lighting energy demand rose by 5.60%. This outcome may be explained by a substantial reduction in natural daylight reaching interior spaces, which likely increased reliance on artificial lighting. In contrast, the Horizontal Single Canopy model had the smallest negative effect on lighting energy consumption. Among all PVSDs studied, it caused the least increase in electric lighting demand. Even in the worst case, observed in Brest, this model led to only a 0.17% rise in lighting-related energy use. These findings highlight the significant influence of PVSDs on natural daylight availability and, consequently, on energy consumption related to lighting. The energy generated by PVSD systems can be used locally to supply power directly to building systems or to support nearby energy infrastructure.

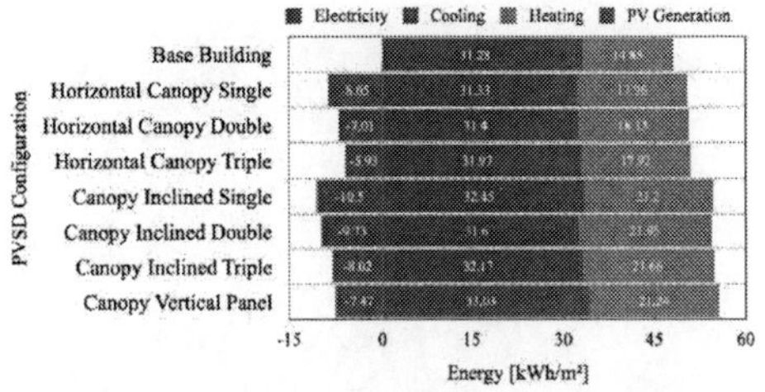

Figure 3: Energy consumption and PV electricity generation with different PVSDs in Brest.

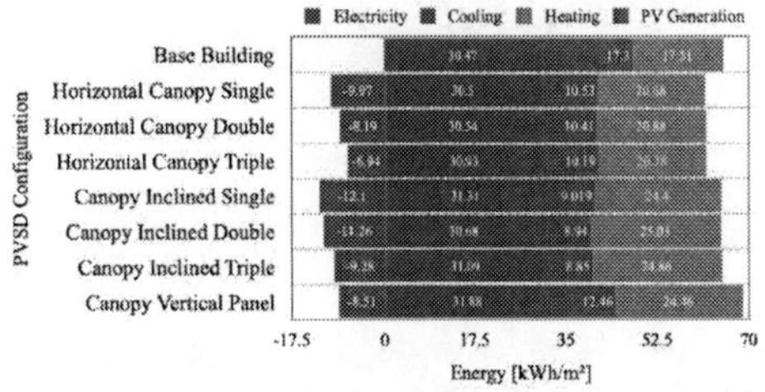

Figure 4: Energy consumption and PV electricity generation with different PVSDs in Clermont.

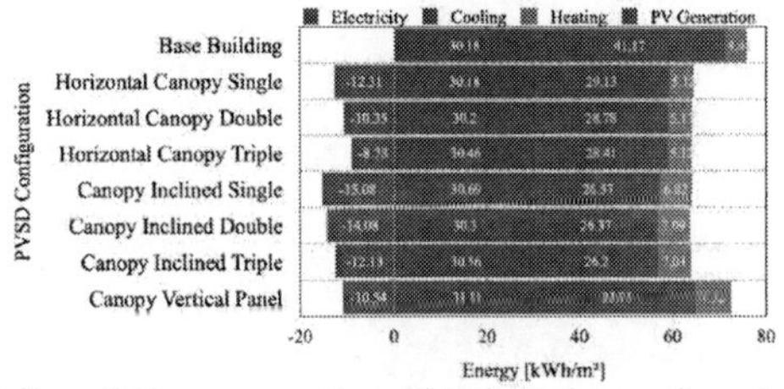

Figure 5: Energy consumption and PV electricity generation with different PVSDs in Nice.

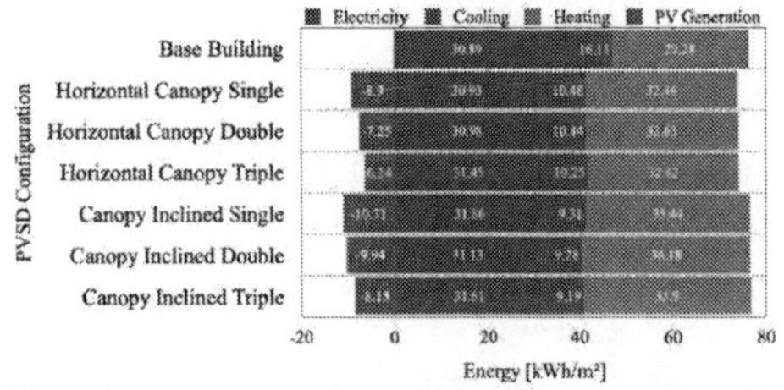

Figure 6: Energy consumption and PV electricity generation with different PVSDs in Strasbourg.

Depending on the configuration, this energy may be integrated into a local microgrid [59], enhancing the building's overall energy flexibility [14]. Surplus energy can also be routed to a smart energy hub [60], enabling efficient energy management, storage, and distribution. However, the accumulation of dust [61] [62] and other particulates on PV panels can reduce energy output over time, highlighting the importance of regular maintenance or self-cleaning surface technologies. These integration strategies not only promote energy self-sufficiency but also support demand-side management and contribute to grid stability, particularly in buildings equipped with advanced control systems and energy storage solutions.

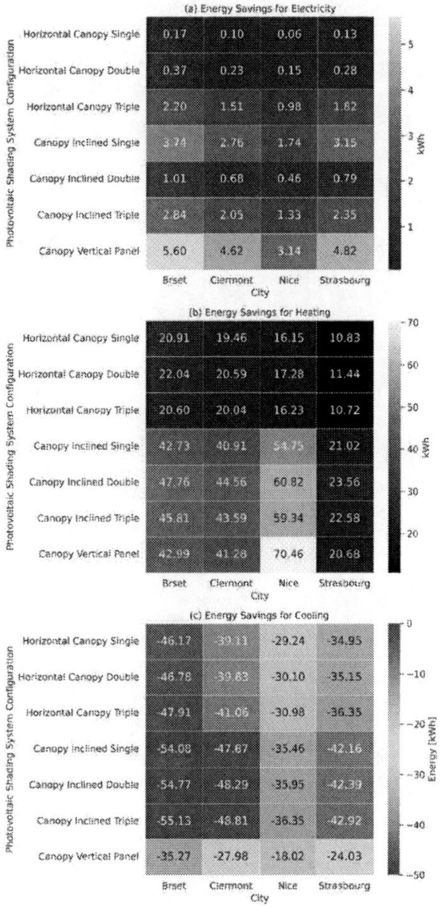

Figure 7: Energy savings analysis for (a) electricity, (b) heating, and (c) cooling consumption.

Figure 8 compares the energy-saving potential of different PVSD configurations. Among the models evaluated, the Inclined Single Canopy shows the highest annual energy savings. These findings contribute to ongoing research on climate-responsive PVSD design by providing performance-based insights across varying configurations.

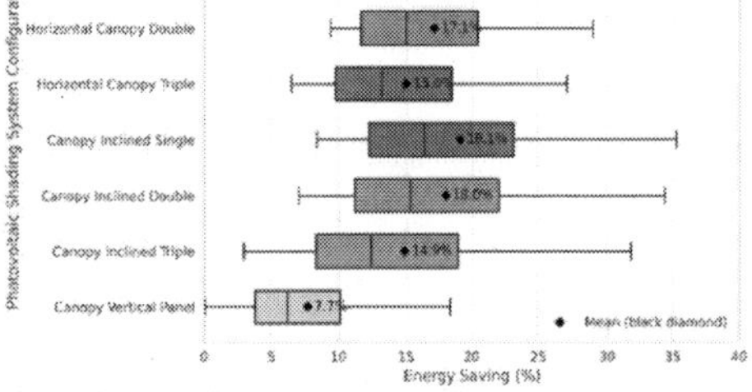

Figure 8: Comprehensive comparison of energy-saving potential by PVSDs in this study.

7 CONCLUSIONS

The simulation results demonstrate significant variations in the overall energy consumption of the office building across different French cities, emphasizing the impact of local climate. The lowest energy consumption was recorded in Brest at 48.11 kWh/m², while the highest values occurred in Strasbourg (76.29 kWh/m²) and Nice (75.75 kWh/m²). These differences highlight the climate-dependent nature of building energy performance, consistent with the findings of Shi et al. [24] and Long et al. [25], who emphasized the sensitivity of solar canopy performance to regional climate conditions. Regarding solar energy production, the Inclined Single Canopy model achieved the highest output in Nice, generating 15.08 kWh/m². This result reflects the favorable solar potential of the Mediterranean climate and aligns with the observations of Skandalos and Karamanis [28], who reported optimal performance of similar systems under comparable conditions. In terms of overall energy savings, the Inclined Single Canopy model in Nice achieved the greatest reduction in total building energy consumption, with a savings rate of 35.31%. This superior performance supports the findings of Hofer et al. [16] and Jayathissa et al. [18], who emphasized the importance of careful orientation and system design in enhancing the energy performance of solar shading solutions. The results also corroborate those of Gao et al. [19], who demonstrated that variations in panel angle and placement can significantly affect system efficiency. However, the Vertical Canopy Panel model was associated with increased lighting energy consumption across all cities, particularly in Brest (5.60%). This outcome is consistent with the findings of Kim et al. [30], who noted that while solar canopies can improve electrical performance, they may also reduce daylight availability and increase reliance on artificial lighting. In contrast, the Horizontal Single Canopy model showed the least adverse impact on lighting, with a maximum increase of only 0.17%. This favorable result, which has received limited attention in prior research, suggests the model's potential for applications requiring minimal disruption to daylight access. Overall, the findings indicate that PVSDs can significantly improve building energy efficiency when adapted to specific climatic contexts. These conclusions agree with those of Settino et al. [27] and Corti et al. [51], who stressed the importance of climate-responsive design, including considerations for solar orientation and daylighting needs.

Declaration of AI-assisted technologies in the writing process

The authors used AI-assisted English editing tools to improve readability and language, and they reviewed and revised the manuscript, taking full responsibility for the final version.

REFERENCES

[1] G. Erbach, "European climate law," *Regulation (EU)*, vol. 1119, 2021.

[2] K. Kavvadias, N. J. P. JIMENEZ, and G. THOMASSEN, *Decarbonising the EU heating sector: Integration of the power and heating sector*. 2019.

[3] M. Pacesila, S. G. Burcea, and S. E. Colesca, "Analysis of renewable energies in European

Union," *Renewable and Sustainable Energy Reviews*, vol. 56, pp. 156–170, 2016.

[4] M. Nazififard and S. Zeynali, "Analysis of Photovoltaic Panel Integration for Achieving Net-Zero Energy in French Residential Retrofits in a Mediterranean Climate," *E3S Web of Conferences*, vol. 545, p. 02006, Jul. 2024, doi: 10.1051/E3SCONF/202454502006.

[5] I. E. Agency, "Renewables 2021," 2021.

[6] A. Millot, A. Krook-Riekkola, and N. Maïzi, "Guiding the future energy transition to net-zero emissions: Lessons from exploring the differences between France and Sweden," *Energy Policy*, vol. 139, p. 111358, 2020.

[7] D. S. Pereira and A. C. Marques, "Could electricity demand contribute to diversifying the mix and mitigating CO2 emissions? A fresh daily analysis of the French electricity system," *Energy Policy*, vol. 142, p. 111475, 2020.

[8] C. E. Velasquez, F. B. G. L. e Estanislau, A. L. Costa, and C. Pereira, "Assessment of the French nuclear energy system–A case study," *Energy Strategy Reviews*, vol. 30, p. 100513, 2020.

[9] C. Sebi and A.-L. Vernay, "Community renewable energy in France: The state of development and the way forward," *Energy Policy*, vol. 147, p. 111874, 2020.

[10] W. Zhang, L. Lu, and J. Peng, "Evaluation of potential benefits of solar photovoltaic shadings in Hong Kong," *Energy*, vol. 137, pp. 1152–1158, Oct. 2017, doi: 10.1016/J.ENERGY.2017.04.166.

[11] X. Li *et al.*, "Optimal design of photovoltaic shading systems for multi-story buildings," *J Clean Prod*, vol. 220, pp. 1024–1038, May 2019, doi: 10.1016/J.JCLEPRO.2019.01.246.

[12] M. Baghoolizadeh, A. A. Nadooshan, A. Raisi, and E. H. Malekshah, "The effect of photovoltaic shading with ideal tilt angle on the energy cost optimization of a building model in European cities," *Energy for Sustainable Development*, vol. 71, pp. 505–516, Dec. 2022, doi: 10.1016/J.ESD.2022.10.016.

[13] S. Zeynali, M. Nazififard, and J. Divandari, "A Comparative Analysis of High-Rise Building Shapes and Orientations on the Performance and Energy Generation of Building Integrated Photovoltaic Systems in Tehran," *2024 9th International Conference on Technology and Energy Management, ICTEM 2024*, 2024, doi: 10.1109/ICTEM60690.2024.10631937.

[14] S. Zeynali and M. Nazififard, "Integrating Photovoltaic Systems into Urban Infrastructure: A Case Study of Tehran International Tower," *2024 11th Iranian Conference on Renewable Energy and Distribution Generation, ICREDG 2024*, 2024, doi: 10.1109/ICREDG61679.2024.10607829.

[15] M. Nazififard and E. Franquet, "Systematic analysis of roof-mounted photovoltaic systems for achieving net-zero energy in urban historic buildings in hot and arid climates: Potential and challenges," *Energy Build*, vol. 348, p. 116394, Dec. 2025, doi: 10.1016/J.ENBUILD.2025.116394.

[16] J. Hofer, A. Groenewolt, P. Jayathissa, Z. Nagy, and A. Schlueter, "Parametric analysis and systems design of dynamic photovoltaic shading modules," *Energy Sci Eng*, vol. 4, no. 2, pp. 134–152, 2016.

[17] Z. Nagy *et al.*, "The Adaptive Solar Facade: From concept to prototypes," *Frontiers of Architectural Research*, vol. 5, no. 2, pp. 143–156, 2016, doi: https://doi.org/10.1016/j.foar.2016.03.002.

[18] P. Jayathissa, J. Zarb, M. Luzzatto, J. Hofer, and A. Schlueter, "Sensitivity of Building Properties and Use Types for the Application of Adaptive Photovoltaic Shading Systems," *Energy Procedia*, vol. 122, pp. 139–144, 2017, doi: https://doi.org/10.1016/j.egypro.2017.07.319.

[19] Y. Gao *et al.*, "A photovoltaic window with sun-tracking shading elements towards maximum power generation and non-glare daylighting," *Appl Energy*, vol. 228, pp. 1454–1472, 2018, doi: https://doi.org/10.1016/j.apenergy.2018.07.015.

[20] M. Krarti and A. Karrech, "Evaluation of static and dynamic PV-Integrated shading systems for office spaces in Australia," *Solar Energy*, vol. 277, p. 112736, 2024, doi: https://doi.org/10.1016/j.solener.2024.112736.

[21] Y. Jiang, Z. Qi, S. Ran, and Q. Ma, "A Study on the Effect of Dynamic Photovoltaic Shading Devices on Energy Consumption and Daylighting of an Office Building," *Buildings*, vol. 14, no. 3, 2024, doi: 10.3390/buildings14030596.

[22] M. Krarti, M. A. Ayari, F. Touati, and M. R. Paurobally, "Energy Benefits of PV-Integrated Dynamic Overhangs for Residential Buildings in Qatar," *Energies (Basel)*, vol. 18, no. 5, 2025, doi: 10.3390/en18051156.

[23] X. Li, J. Peng, N. Li, M. Wang, and C. Wang, "Study on Optimum Tilt Angles of Photovoltaic Shading Systems in Different Climatic Regions of China," *Procedia Eng*, vol. 205, pp. 1157–1164, 2017, doi: https://doi.org/10.1016/j.proeng.2017.10.185.

[24] S. Shi, J. Sun, M. Liu, X. Chen, W. Gao, and Y. Song, "Energy-Saving Potential Comparison of Different Photovoltaic Integrated Shading Devices (PVSDs) for Single-Story and Multi-Story Buildings," *Energies (Basel)*, vol. 15, no. 23, 2022, doi: 10.3390/en15239196.

[25] W. Long, X. Chen, Q. Ma, X. Wei, and Q. Xi, "An Evaluation of the PV Integrated Dynamic Overhangs Based on Parametric Performance Design Method: A Case Study of a Student Apartment in China," *Sustainability*, vol. 14, no. 13, 2022, doi: 10.3390/su14137808.

[26] A. Mesloub, A. Ghosh, M. Touahmia, G. A. Albaqawy, E. Noaime, and B. M. Alsolami, "Performance Analysis of Photovoltaic Integrated Shading Devices (PVSDs) and Semi-Transparent Photovoltaic (STPV) Devices Retrofitted to a Prototype Office Building in a Hot Desert Climate," *Sustainability*, vol. 12, no. 23, 2020, doi: 10.3390/su122310145.

[27] J. Settino, C. Carpino, S. Perrella, and N. Arcuri, "Multi-Objective Analysis of a Fixed Solar Shading System in Different Climatic Areas," *Energies (Basel)*, vol. 13, p. 3249, Jun. 2020, doi: 10.3390/en13123249.

[28] N. Skandalos and D. Karamanis, "An optimization approach to photovoltaic building

integration towards low energy buildings in different climate zones," *Appl Energy*, vol. 295, p. 117017, Aug. 2021, doi: 10.1016/J.APENERGY.2021.117017.

[29] J. Abu Qadourah, "Evaluating solar-active shading solutions: a study of energy performance in Mediterranean residential architecture," *Architectural Engineering and Design Management*, vol. 20, pp. 1–16, Oct. 2023, doi: 10.1080/17452007.2023.2267570.

[30] S.-H. Kim, I.-T. Kim, A.-S. Choi, and M. Sung, "Evaluation of optimized PV power generation and electrical lighting energy savings from the PV blind-integrated daylight responsive dimming system using LED lighting," *Solar Energy*, vol. 107, pp. 746–757, 2014, doi: https://doi.org/10.1016/j.solener.2014.06.022.

[31] M. Qingsong, S. Ran, X. Chen, L. Li, W. Gao, and X. Wei, "Study on the effect of photovoltaic louver shading and lighting control system on building energy consumption and daylighting," *Energy Sources, Part A: Recovery, Utilization, and Environmental Effects*, vol. 45, pp. 10873–10889, Sep. 2023, doi: 10.1080/15567036.2023.2251439.

[32] C. Li, W. Zhang, J. Wu, Y. Lyu, and H. Tang, "Experimental study of a vertically mounted bifacial photovoltaic sunshade," *Renew Energy*, vol. 219, p. 119518, 2023, doi: https://doi.org/10.1016/j.renene.2023.119518.

[33] J. Liu, G. Bi, G. Gao, and L. Zhao, "Optimal design method for photovoltaic shading devices (PVSDs) by combining geometric optimization and adaptive control model," *Journal of Building Engineering*, vol. 69, p. 106101, 2023, doi: https://doi.org/10.1016/j.jobe.2023.106101.

[34] C. Li, W. Zhang, F. Liu, X. Li, J. Wang, and C. Li, "Multi-Objective Optimization of Bifacial Photovoltaic Sunshade: Towards Better Optical, Electrical and Economical Performance," *Sustainability*, vol. 16, no. 14, 2024, doi: 10.3390/su16145977.

[35] Y. Zheng *et al.*, "A novel sun-shading design for indoor visual comfort and energy saving in typical office space in Shenzhen," *Energy Build*, vol. 328, p. 115083, 2025, doi: https://doi.org/10.1016/j.enbuild.2024.115083.

[36] P. Jayathissa, M. Luzzatto, J. Schmidli, J. Hofer, Z. Nagy, and A. Schlueter, "Optimising building net energy demand with dynamic BIPV shading," *Appl Energy*, vol. 202, pp. 726–735, Sep. 2017, doi: 10.1016/J.APENERGY.2017.05.083.

[37] H. K. Abdullah and H. Z. Alibaba, "Towards Nearly Zero-Energy Buildings: The Potential of Photovoltaic-Integrated Shading Devices to Achieve Autonomous Solar Electricity and Acceptable Thermal Comfort in Naturally ventilated Office Spaces," in *Proceedings of the 16th International Conference on Clean Energy, Famagusta, North Cyprus*, 2018, pp. 9–11.

[38] U. Haider, E. Trepci, and E. Rodriguez-Ubinas, "Assessment of Photovoltaics Shading Devices (PVSD) Impact on the Energy Generation, Cooling Load, and Daylighting in an Office Building in Dubai," in *2023 Middle East and North Africa Solar Conference (MENA-SC)*, 2023, pp. 1–5. doi: 10.1109/MENA-SC54044.2023.10374491.

[39] Z. Cai, W. Zhang, J. Chen, and P. Su, "Photovoltaic Integrated Shading Devices in the Retrofitting of Existing Buildings on Chinese Campuses Within a Regional Context," *Buildings*, vol. 14, no. 11, 2024, doi: 10.3390/buildings14113577.

[40] A. C. Peres, R. Calili, and D. Louzada, "Impacts of photovoltaic shading devices on energy generation and cooling demand," in *2020 47th IEEE Photovoltaic Specialists Conference (PVSC)*, IEEE, 2020, pp. 1186–1191.

[41] S. K. Jung, Y. Kim, and J. W. Moon, "Performance Evaluation of Control Methods for PV-Integrated Shading Devices," *Energies (Basel)*, vol. 13, no. 12, 2020, doi: 10.3390/en13123171.

[42] O. Asfour, "Solar and Shading Potential of Different Configurations of Building Integrated Photovoltaics Used as Shading Devices Considering Hot Climatic Conditions," *Sustainability*, vol. 10, p. 4373, Nov. 2018, doi: 10.3390/su10124373.

[43] M. Han, L. Lu, and B. Sun, "Overall energy performance of building-integrated bifacial photovoltaic sunshades with different installation and building parameters in hot and humid regions," *Solar Energy*, vol. 275, p. 112619, 2024, doi: https://doi.org/10.1016/j.solener.2024.112619.

[44] J. Kim, H. Lee, M. Choi, D. Kim, and J. Yoon, "Power performance assessment of PV blinds system considering self-shading effects," *Solar Energy*, vol. 262, p. 111834, 2023, doi: https://doi.org/10.1016/j.solener.2023.111834.

[45] M. Wang, Z. Jia, L. Tao, W. Wang, and C. Xiang, "Optimizing the tilt angle of kinetic photovoltaic shading devices considering energy consumption and power Generation— Hong Kong case," *Energy Build*, vol. 326, p. 115072, 2025, doi: https://doi.org/10.1016/j.enbuild.2024.115072.

[46] W. Bahr, "A comprehensive assessment methodology of the building integrated photovoltaic blind system," *Energy Build*, vol. 82, pp. 703–708, 2014, doi: https://doi.org/10.1016/j.enbuild.2014.07.065.

[47] A. Baghdadi and M. Abuhussain, "In-Depth Analysis of Photovoltaic-Integrated Shading Systems' Performance in Residential Buildings: A Prospective of Numerical Techniques Toward Net-Zero Energy Buildings," *Buildings*, vol. 15, no. 2, 2025, doi: 10.3390/buildings15020222.

[48] H. Chen, B. Cai, H. Yang, Y. Wang, and J. Yang, "Study on natural lighting and electrical performance of louvered photovoltaic windows in hot summer and cold winter areas," *Energy Build*, vol. 271, p. 112313, 2022, doi: https://doi.org/10.1016/j.enbuild.2022.112313.

[49] Y. Ibraheem, E. R. P. Farr, and P. A. E. Piroozfar, "Embedding Passive Intelligence into Building Envelopes: A Review of the State-of-the-art in Integrated Photovoltaic Shading Devices," *Energy Procedia*, vol. 111, pp. 964–973, 2017, doi: https://doi.org/10.1016/j.egypro.2017.03.259.

[50] A. Kirimtat, M. F. Tasgetiren, P. Brida, and O. Krejcar, "Control of PV integrated shading devices in buildings: A review," *Build Environ*, vol. 214, p. 108961, Apr. 2022, doi: 10.1016/J.BUILDENV.2022.108961.

[51] P. Corti, P. Bonomo, and F. Frontini, "Paper Review of External Integrated Systems as Photovoltaic Shading Devices," *Energies (Basel)*, vol. 16, no. 14, 2023, doi: 10.3390/en16145542.

[52] Y. Luo *et al.*, "A comparative study on thermal performance evaluation of a new double skin façade system integrated with photovoltaic blinds," *Appl Energy*, vol. 199, pp. 281–293, 2017, doi: https://doi.org/10.1016/j.apenergy.2017.05.026.

[53] L. Evangelisti, C. Guattari, F. Asdrubali, and R. de Lieto Vollaro, "An experimental investigation of the thermal performance of a building solar shading device," *Journal of Building Engineering*, vol. 28, p. 101089, Mar. 2020, doi: 10.1016/J.JOBE.2019.101089.

[54] M. Akbari Paydar, "Optimum design of building integrated PV module as a movable shading device," *Sustain Cities Soc*, vol. 62, p. 102368, Nov. 2020, doi: 10.1016/J.SCS.2020.102368.

[55] J. E. Ogbeba and E. Hoskara, "The Evaluation of Single-Family Detached Housing Units in terms of Integrated Photovoltaic Shading Devices: The Case of Northern Cyprus," *Sustainability*, vol. 11, no. 3, 2019, doi: 10.3390/su11030593.

[56] E. Taveres-Cachat, K. Bøe, G. Lobaccaro, F. Goia, and S. Grynning, "Balancing competing parameters in search of optimal configurations for a fix louvre blade system with integrated PV," *Energy Procedia*, vol. 122, pp. 607–612, Sep. 2017, doi: 10.1016/J.EGYPRO.2017.07.357.

[57] T. Mendis, Z. Huang, S. Xu, and W. Zhang, "Economic potential analysis of photovoltaic integrated shading strategies on commercial building facades in urban blocks: A case study of Colombo, Sri Lanka," *Energy*, vol. 194, p. 116908, 2020, doi: https://doi.org/10.1016/j.energy.2020.116908.

[58] M. Nazififard and S. Zeynali, "Analysis of Photovoltaic Panel Integration for Achieving Net-Zero Energy in French Residential Retrofits in a Mediterranean Climate," in *E3S Web of Conferences*, EDP Sciences, 2024, p. 02006.

[59] A. Imanloozadeh, M. Nazififard, and H. Hashemi-Dezaki, "Optimal technoeconomic reliability-oriented design of islanded multicarrier microgrids with electrical and hydrogen energy storage systems considering emission concerns," *Energy Sci Eng*, vol. 12, no. 6, pp. 2702–2745, Jun. 2024, doi: 10.1002/ESE3.1774.

[60] A. Imanloozadeh, M. Nazififard, and S. A. Sadat, "A new stochastic optimal smart residential energy hub management system for desert environment," *Int J Energy Res*, vol. 45, no. 13, pp. 18957–18980, Oct. 2021, doi: 10.1002/er.6991.

[61] M. Nazififard and N. Torabi, "Experimental Analysis of Dust Accumulation on the Panels of a Microgrid-Connected Photovlitaic System in an Arid Climate," *2023 13th Smart Grid Conference, SGC 2023*, 2023, doi: 10.1109/SGC61621.2023.10459274.

[62] S. Ali Sadat, J. Faraji, M. Nazififard, and A. Ketabi, "The experimental analysis of dust deposition effect on solar photovoltaic panels in Iran's desert environment," *Sustainable Energy Technologies and Assessments*, vol. 47, Oct. 2021, doi: 10.1016/j.seta.2021.101542.

MODULE LAYOUT FOR RELIABLE ALUMINUM-BASED BUILDING-INTEGRATED PHOTOVOLTAICS

Wiebke Wirtz[1], Kevin Meyer[1], Rolf Brendel[1,2], Henning Schulte-Huxel[1]
[1]Institute for Solar Energy Research Hamelin (ISFH), Am Ohrberg 1, 31860 Emmerthal, Germany
[2]Institute of Solid State Physics, Leibniz University Hannover, Appelstraße 2, 30167 Hannover, Germany

ABSTRACT: When manufacturing photovoltaic (PV) modules with aluminum rear covers, for instance for building integration purposes, one has to consider the large thermal expansion of the aluminum compared to silicon and glass. This holds for the manufacturing process as well as for the reliability of the resulting building-integrated PV (BIPV) modules. Concerning module reliability, the mismatch in thermal expansion coefficients of silicon solar cells and aluminum rear cover leads to mechanical stress in the solar cell strings under temperature changes. After several temperature shifts during operation, the copper wires interconnecting the silicon solar cells might suffer from fatigue breakage and thereby the module power output could be drastically reduced. This work investigates the influence of module layout in terms of solar cell width and solar cell string length on the electrical degradation of crystalline silicon PV modules with aluminum sheets as rear covers in thermal cycling tests. As a result, we find that aluminum-based modules with wide cells degrade faster and fail earlier in the thermal cycling test than modules with narrow cells. This can be explained by an increased cell gap change during thermal cycling for solar cell strings with wider cells. Furthermore, thermal cycling of modules with aluminum rear covers in lengths from 20 cm to 240 cm and accordingly long cell strings resulted in earlier degradation and failure of longer strings. In conclusion, from a thermomechanical point of view, a module layout with short strings of narrow cells is recommended.
Keywords: BIPV, reliability, thermal stress

1 INTRODUCTION

The installation of building-integrated photovoltaics (BIPV) enables generation of renewable energy without additional land use [1]. It also offers the advantage of generating electricity directly where it is consumed, as buildings contribute 20% to 40% of the total final energy consumption [2]. Vertical mounting and orientation in various cardinal directions help to align generation with demand over the course of day and year [3]. All these reasons make BIPV a valuable contribution to energy efficiency of buildings [4] and climate change mitigation by transition to renewable energy production [5]. However, BIPV will only gain widespread adoption if it is both aesthetically pleasing and financially viable.

Since BIPV combines two different sectors, photovoltaics (PV) and buildings, it is a straight-forward approach to combine commonly used materials from these areas, allowing BIPV modules to function as both energy generators and building envelopes. In this study, we investigate the combination of PV modules with aluminum sheets as module rear covers. Aluminum is a common façade material in the construction industry due to its light weight and its durability [6]. Thus, it is an interesting material for adopting it in building-integrated PV applications. Using aluminum offers the chance of an easy market entry because the resulting PV-activated façade elements are similar to handle for planners and installers as common aluminum façade elements. However, a significant challenge lies in the combination of materials such as glass front covers, polymer sheets for encapsulation, silicon solar cells, copper wires and aluminum rear cover, which have differing thermal expansion coefficients. This mismatch induces mechanical stress under variation in temperature, leading to accelerated degradation of such BIPV modules with aluminum rear covers [7], which contradicts the typically long lifespan of building skins of up to 50 years [8].

In this work, we investigate the influence of module layout on the reliability of lightweight BIPV modules with aluminum rear covers and polymeric frontsheets in thermal cycling tests. Other publications show an influence of module layout, especially in terms of cell size, on thermal stress in glass-backsheet and glass-glass PV modules [9, 10]. We expect the effect stemming from mismatches in thermal expansion coefficients of silicon ($\alpha_{Si} = 2.614\times10^{-6}$ K^{-1} [11]) and glass ($\alpha_{glass} = 9\times10^{-6}$ K^{-1} [12]) to be even more pronounced in PV modules with aluminum rear covers ($\alpha_{Al} = 23.5\times10^{-6}$ K^{-1} [13]). Therefore, we extend our investigation on varying cell widths [7] by experiments varying the string length in order to find module layout recommendations for optimal robustness of BIPV modules with aluminum rear covers against thermal stress.

2 EXPERIMENTAL

2.1 Method

We fabricate two sets of test samples of PV modules with aluminum rear covers, one with varying cell width in strings of approximately the same length (see also [7]) and one with varying string length using one cell format. Instead of manufacturing several test modules of few configurations for statistics, we fabricate one test module of many configurations to derive trends in the degradation behavior. The test modules are characterized by measuring the current-voltage (*IV*) characteristics at standard test conditions in a flash tester and by taking electroluminescence (EL) images in regular intervals between thermal cycling tests according to the standard IEC 61215 [14]. The resulting degradation behaviors and dependences are interpreted with the help of simplified (analytical) models of the material compound.

2.2 Samples

For investigating the effect of cell width on module power degradation, we fabricate four test modules with varying cell width according to the material stack depicted in Fig. 1. The 1 mm thick aluminum rear covers are coated with a thin layer of polyethylene (PE) on the front side for coloring and are 130 cm long and 25 cm wide. The rest of the module stack is 120 cm long and positioned in the center of the aluminum sheet. The test modules contain one string of industrial PERC+ solar cells from the same tier 1 manufacturer each, encapsulated with polyolefin

(PO) encapsulant. We place one 500 µm thick layer of PO encapsulant each between the aluminum sheet and the 50 µm PVF insulation layer, between the insulation layer and the cell string and between the cell string and the 400 µm PET-based frontsheet. Table I lists the different string configurations with varying cell widths.

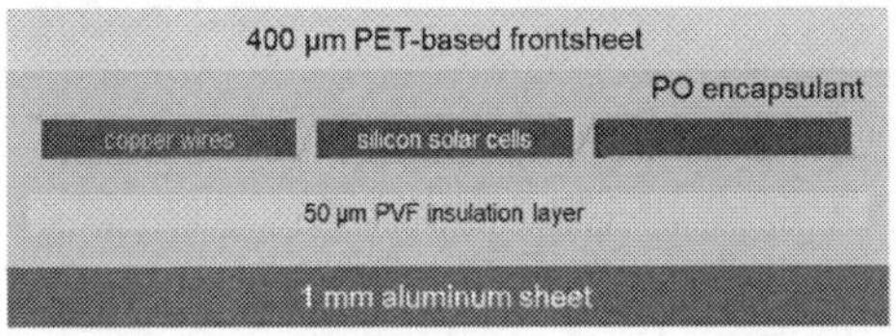

Figure 1: Schematic cross-section (not to scale) of the material stack of lightweight BIPV modules with aluminum rear cover as they are manufactured for this work (adopted from [7]).

Table I: Solar cell string configurations of aluminum test modules with varying cell width.

Module name	Cell Width (mm)	Number of cells	Cell gap (mm)	String length (mm)
M6 quarter	41.5	26	2	1129
M6 half	83	13	2	1103
M12 half	105	10	2	1068
M12 full	210	5	2	1058

For investigating the effect of string length on module power degradation, we fabricate ten test modules with varying string and module length from 20 cm to 240 cm according to the material stack depicted in Fig. 1. The 1 mm thick and 25 cm wide aluminum rear covers are uncoated in this set of samples and the aluminum sheets are completely covered with encapsulant and frontsheet. The test modules contain one string of industrial half-cut M6 PERC+ solar cells each. Table II lists the different string configurations and module lengths. The module with a string of six cells in the center of a 120 cm long aluminum sheet is fabricated for investigating the effect of uncovered parts of the aluminum sheets next to the cell strings.

Table II: Solar cell string configurations of aluminum test modules with varying string length and module length given by the length of the aluminum rear cover.

Module name	Number of cells	Cell gap (mm)	Aluminum length (cm)
2 cells	2	2	20
3 cells	3	2	30
4 cells	4	2	40
6 cells	6	2	60
6 cells on 120 cm	6	2	120
9 cells	9	2	80
10 cells	10	2	90
11 cells	11	2	100
13 cells	13	2	120
27 cells	27	2	240

3 RESULTS

3.1 Varying cell width

Figure 2 shows the results of thermal cycling of the four aluminum-based BIPV modules with different cell widths. This is the extension of the results published in [7]. The test module with the widest cells "M12 full" fails first, followed by the modules with the second biggest cell width "M12 half" and the third biggest cell width "M6 half". The module with the smallest cells "M6 quarter" is the most stable one after an initial drop resulting from the non-optimized metallization design for quarter-cutting. It still delivers 75.4% of its initial power after 1200 thermal cycles before it drops to 0. Small cell widths are thus advantageous for the reliability of BIPV modules with aluminum rear covers and PET frontsheet. However, it has to be mentioned that all tested 120 cm long modules with cell widths smaller than M12 full cells pass the criterion of less than 5% power loss after 200 thermal cycles from IEC 61215 [14].

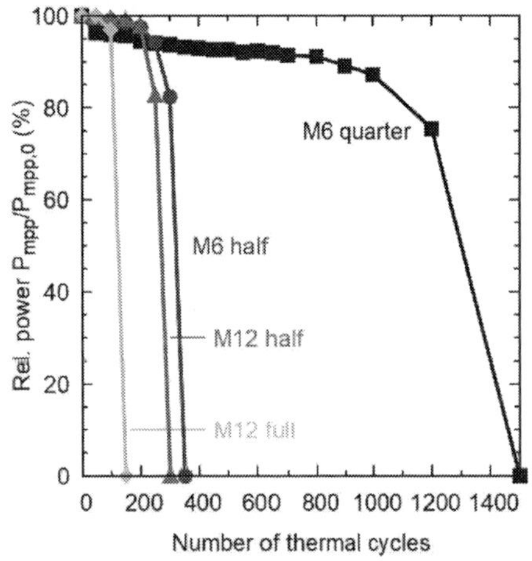

Figure 2: Measured maximum powers of BIPV modules with aluminum rear covers and varying cell width during thermal cycling relative to the initial measurements. The modules fail in the order of decreasing cell width.

As explained in [7], the difference in thermal expansion coefficients of silicon and aluminum leads to a change in cell gap width in BIPV modules with aluminum rear covers during thermal cycling. For a rough quantitative estimation of this cell gap change resulting in mechanical stress in the solar cell interconnectors, we assume linear thermal expansion of the aluminum sheet and the silicon solar cells with temperature-independent expansion coefficients, which dominates the effect of cell gap change. We neglect the influence of all other materials in the module for sake of simplicity and concentrate on the stiff components in the stack. Together with the assumption that the positions of the solar cell centers are all fixed relative to the aluminum sheet, one can roughly estimate the cell gap change per Kelvin

$$\Delta g/\Delta T = (\alpha_{Al} - \alpha_{Si})\, w + \alpha_{Al}\, g \qquad (1)$$

as a function of the cell width w and the cell gap g [7]. We only consider the dependence of cell gap change $\Delta g/\Delta T$ on cell width w. Experimentally varying the cell gap g in a range of a few millimeters would only have minor influence on $\Delta g/\Delta T$. The solid line in Fig. 3 shows the cell gap change of silicon solar cells with a cell gap of 2 mm in an aluminum module for cell widths from 10 mm to 220 mm as calculated by Eq. 1. The theoretical cell gap changes of the examined test modules are indicated as well. They range from 0.91 µm/K for M6 quarter cells to 4.43 µm/K for M12 full cells, i.e. the interconnectors in modules with wider cells are stressed more than in modules with smaller cells. This correlates with our observation of BIPV modules with aluminum rear covers and varying cell width failing in the order of decreasing cell width, i.e. decreasing stress on the interconnectors by less change of cell gap width during thermal cycling.

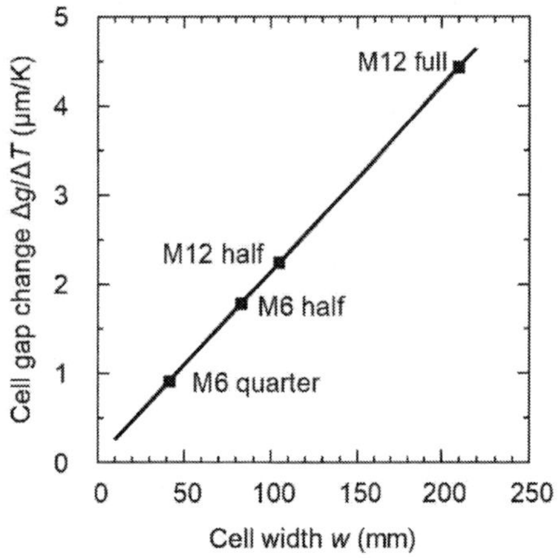

Figure 3: Theoretical cell gap change $\Delta g/\Delta T$ in PV modules with aluminum rear covers according to Eq. 1 (solid line). The markers indicate the theoretical cell gap changes of the test modules with varying cell width in this work.

3.2 Varying string length

In addition to the intuitive linear effect of cell width on cell gap change and module reliability, we also observe an effect of string length on module power degradation in thermal cycling tests. Figure 4 shows the measured relative powers of the first nine test modules from Table II during thermal cycling. It is evident that long strings degrade and fail earlier in the test sequence than short strings. The module with a length of 27 half-cut M6 cells on 240 cm falls below 75% of its initial power after 200 thermal cycles. A remaining power of 75%, however, could be expected for some commercial glass-glass modules after 50 years of operation, if their power warranty is extrapolated to 50 years [15]. After 250 thermal cycle no current can be extracted anymore because all interconnection wires of one cell gap are broken. The module with a length of 3 half-cut M6 cells on a 30 cm long aluminum sheet reaches the 75% threshold after 450 thermal cycles and still delivers over 40% of its initial power after 600 thermal cycles. As the dominant degradation mechanism of these modules is fatigue of the solar cell interconnectors, the observation of long modules degrading and failing earlier can be explained by strain adding up from the string ends resulting in more strain in the interconnectors of longer strings and therefore earlier fatigue. The reason for that is the fact that the silicon solar cells are not rigidly fixed to the aluminum rear cover, as assumed in the simplified consideration in the previous section. The encapsulant linking the two materials allows a certain amount of elasticity and therefore an inhomogeneous distribution of strain and stress in the solar cell interconnectors increasing towards the center of the solar cell string. This also aligns with our observation of most severe degradation and earliest interconnector fatigue in the center of BIPV modules with aluminum rear covers in thermal cycling tests, as can be seen in the EL image in Fig. 5.

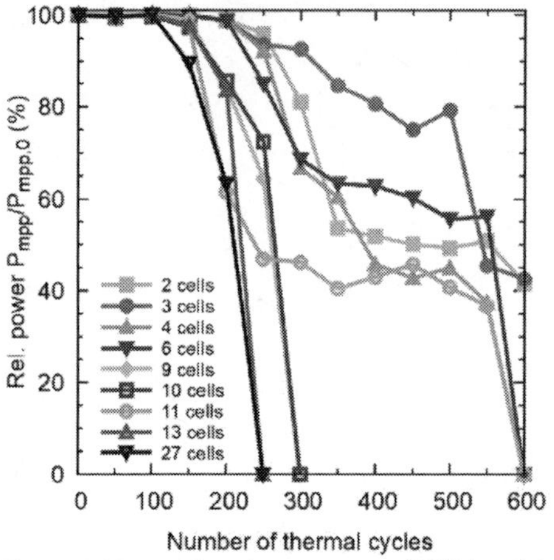

Figure 4: Measured maximum powers of BIPV modules with aluminum rear cover and varying string length during thermal cycling relative to the initial measurements. Modules with long strings degrade and fail earlier in the test than modules with short strings.

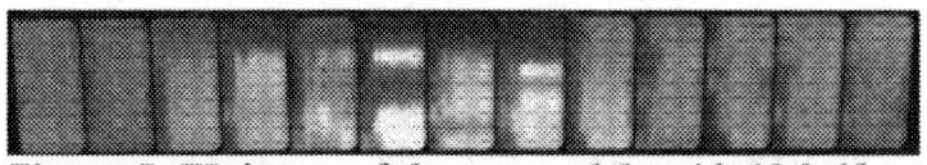

Figure 5: EL image of the test module with 13 half-cut M6 cells on a 120 cm aluminum sheet after 150 thermal cycles. Interconnection wires start to break in the center of the solar cell string, as the dark regions around whole busbars indicate.

In the considered set of test modules with varying string length, the uncovered parts of the aluminum sheets next to the cell strings are differently long. In order to clarify if the module length, i.e. the aluminum substrate length, is a critical parameter for the module power degradation, we fabricate a test module with a string of 6 half-cut M6 cells positioned in the center of a 120 cm aluminum sheet. Figure 6 shows the power degradation of this module in comparison to a test module with a string of 6 half-cut M6 cells on a 60 cm aluminum sheet and a test module with 13 half-cut M6 cells on a 120 cm aluminum sheet. The power output of the string of 6 cells not fully covering the 120 cm aluminum sheet degrades analogously to the string of 6 cells fully covering the 60 cm aluminum sheet. The string of 13 cells degrades and fails much earlier in the thermal cycling test. From these results we conclude that the surrounding aluminum sheet does not affect the degradation of aluminum-based BIPV modules in thermal cycling tests.

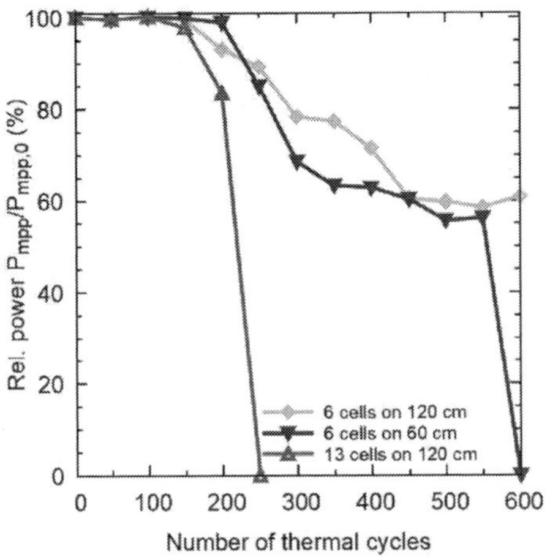

Figure 6: Measured maximum powers of BIPV modules with aluminum rear cover and varying string and module length during thermal cycling relative to the initial measurements. Six cells positioned in the center of a 120 cm aluminum sheet degrade analogously to 6 cells on a 60 cm aluminum sheet.

4 CONCLUSIONS

In conclusion, our experiments with aluminum-based BIPV modules show that both cell width and string length have a strong influence on module reliability. However, varying the cell width is more critical than varying the string length. The effect of the cell width can simply be explained by the difference in thermal expansion coefficients of the silicon solar cells and the aluminum module rear cover resulting in higher cell gap changes for wider cells during thermal cycling. The string length has an influence on module reliability because the silicon solar cells are not rigidly fixed to the aluminum rear cover but the two materials are linked in a viscoelastic way [16], leading to stress adding up from the string ends to the center. Therefore, there is more stress adding up in longer strings resulting in earlier interconnector fatigue during thermal cycling.

In summary, we recommend preferably short strings of narrow cells. This can, for instance, be realized by placing the strings along the short side of rectangular modules. This is also advantageous for the robustness against mechanical load and solar cell breakage [17, 18], as well as against partial shading [19]. Furthermore, we can conclude from our experimental results that aluminum-based BIPV modules with relevant lengths of at least 1 m on the short side of rectangular modules and PET frontsheets are able to pass the thermal cycling test from IEC 61215. For passing stricter criteria like less than 5% power loss after 600 thermal cycles, to be on the safe side, such modules have to be adapted in other ways than just the module layout. One approach is for example adapting the interconnection of the silicon solar cells and introduce a strain relief in the shape of a horizontal crimp in order to make the interconnectors more robust against expanding and shrinking cell gaps [7].

5 ACKNOWLEDGMENTS

The authors thank I. Kunze and K. Moliya for performing EL and IV measurements and the company MN Metall GmbH for providing the aluminum sheets. The authors appreciate the funding of this work by the German Federal Ministry of Economic Affairs and Climate Action (Project "AluPV", contract no. 03EN1069A) and the German State of Lower Saxony.

6 REFERENCES

[1] D. van de Vehn et al., "The potential land requirements and related land use change emissions of solar energy", Scientific Reports, Vol. 11, 2907, 2021

[2] L. Pérez-Lombard et al., "A review on buildings energy consumption information", Energy and Buildings, Vol. 40, p.394-398, 2008

[3] S. Freitas and M.C. Brito, "Non-cumulative only solar photovoltaics for electricity load-matching", Renewable and Sustainable Energy Reviews, 2018

[4] Directive (EU) 2018/844 of the European Parliament and of the council of 30 May 2018 amending Directive 2010/31/EU on the energy performance of buildings and Directive 2012/27/EU on energy efficiency

[5] Parties to the United Nations Framework Convention on Climate Change, "Paris Agreement", 2015

[6] D. Skejic et al., "Aluminium as a Material for Modern Structures", Gradevinar 67 (2015) 11, 2015

[7] W. Wirtz et al., "Improved robustness against thermal stress for building-integrated PV modules built on aluminum façade elements", Progress in Photovoltaics: Research and Applications, Vol. 33, No. 6, pp. 717-725, 2025

[8] C.Y. Cheong et al., "Life cycle assessment of curtain wall facades: A screening study on end-of-life scenarios", Journal of Building Engineering, Vol. 84, 2024

[9] A.J. Beinert et al., "The Effect of Cell and Module Dimensions on Thermomechanical Stress in PV Modules", IEEE Journal of Photovoltaics, Vol. 10, No. 1, 2020

[10] H. Hanifi et al., "Loss analysis and optimization of PV module components and design to achieve higher energy yield and longer service life in desert regions", Applied Energy, Vol. 280, 116028, 2020

[11] R.B. Roberts, "Thermal expansion reference data: silicon 300-850 K", Journal of Physics D: Applied Physics, Vol. 14, No. 10, 1981

[12] J. Wurm, "Glass Structures: Design and Construction of Self-Supporting Skins", Birkhäuser, Basel, 2007

[13] P. Hidnert and H.S. Krider, "Thermal Expansion of Aluminum and Some Aluminum Alloys", Journal of Research of the National Bureau of Standards, Vol. 48, No. 3, 1952

[14] "Terrestrial photovoltaic (PV) modules - Design qualification and type approval - Part 2: Test procedures", IEC 61215-2:2022-02

[15] Trina Solar, "Global limited warranty for Trina Solar brand crystalline solar photovoltaic modules", https://static.trinasolar.com/sites/default/files/PS-M-0135WarrantyMarch2022.pdf, 2022, accessed

August 15th, 2025
[16] U. Eitner, "Thermomechanics of photovoltaic modules", dissertation, Martin-Luther-Universität Halle-Wittenberg, 2011
[17] N. Bosco, "Turn Your Half-Cut Cells for a Stronger Module", IEEE Journal of Photovoltaics, Vol. 12, No. 5, pp. 1149-1153, 2022
[18] A.J. Beinert et al., "Thermomechanical design rules for photovoltaic modules", Progress in Photovoltaics: Research and Applications, Vol. 31, No. 12, 2022
[19] R. Witteck et al., "Three Bypass Diodes Architecture at the Limit", IEEE Journal of Photovoltaics, Vol. 10, No. 6, 2020

eurac research

Cost-Benefit Analysis of Luminescence Techniques vs. Infrared Thermography in Utility-Scale PV Inspections

Lukas Koester, Sandra Gallmetzer, Mousa Sondoqah,
Giampaolo Manzolini, David Moser, Atse Louwen, Luis Fialho

EUPVSEC 2025 – 23.09.2025

SUPERNOVA

Co-funded by
the European Union

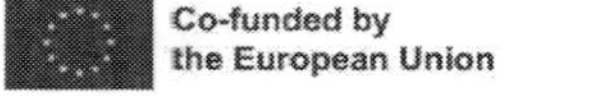

Motivation

Infrared thermography (IRT) is standard in best practice guidelines (SPE2025) and in practice.

Electroluminescence (EL) is suggested to do for better understanding of problems.

Question: if luminescence techniques (EL or daylight photoluminescence (DPL)) offer more insights than IRT, which are the (economical) constrains prioritizing them?

	Imaging speed (MW/h)	References
IRT	1 – 4	IEA-PVPS T13 2021, Bakir2023
EL	0.4 - 0.8 (~2.5)	AEPVI, (QE2025)
DPL	0.3 (1.2 estimated)	Doll2023, (Koester2024)

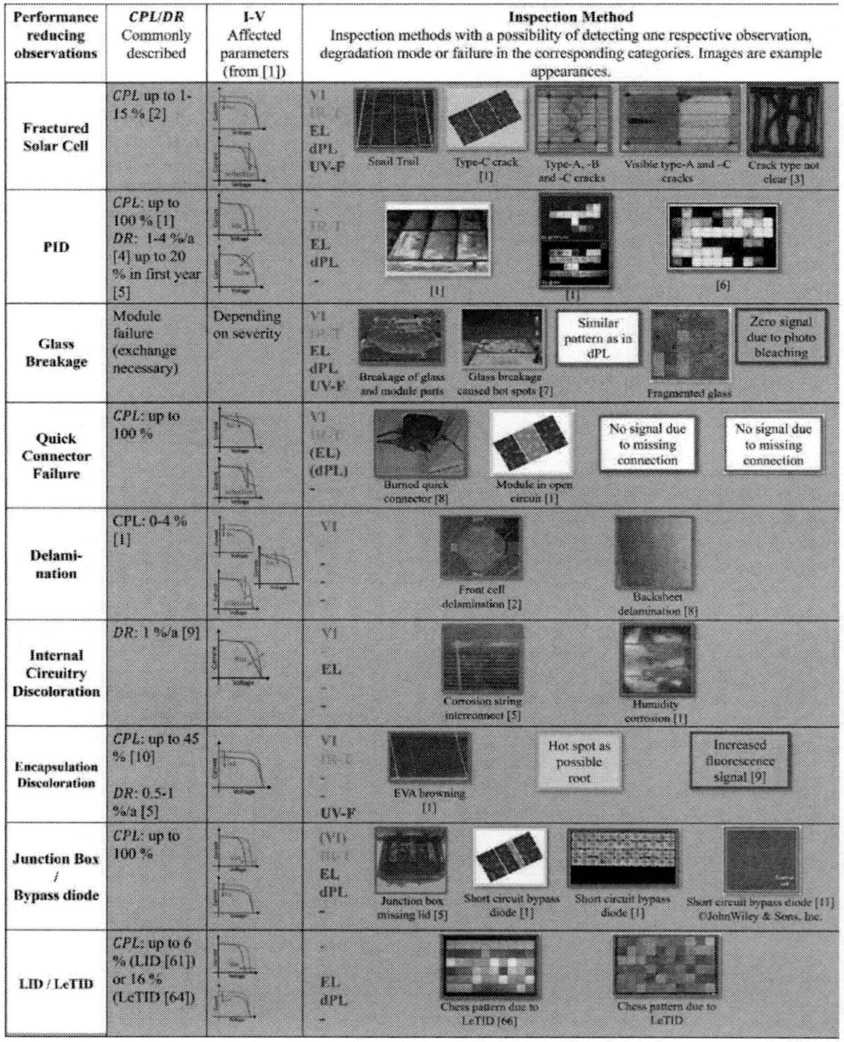

Performance reducing observations	*CPL/DR* Commonly described	I-V Affected parameters (from [1])	Inspection Method Inspection methods with a possibility of detecting one respective observation, degradation mode or failure in the corresponding categories. Images are example appearances.
Fractured Solar Cell	*CPL* up to 1-15 % [2]		VI, EL, dPL, UV-F — Snail Trail; Type-C crack [1]; Type-A, -B and -C cracks; Visible type-A and -C cracks; Crack type not clear [3]
PID	*CPL*: up to 100 % [1] *DR*: 1-4 %/a [4] up to 20 % in first year [5]		EL, dPL — [1]; [1]; [6]
Glass Breakage	Module failure (exchange necessary)	Depending on severity	VI, EL, dPL, UV-F — Breakage of glass and module parts; Glass breakage caused hot spots [7]; Similar pattern as in dPL; Fragmented glass; Zero signal due to photo bleaching
Quick Connector Failure	*CPL*: up to 100 %		VI, (EL), (dPL) — Burned quick connector [8]; Module in open circuit [1]; No signal due to missing connection; No signal due to missing connection
Delami-nation	CPL: 0-4 % [1]		VI — Front cell delamination [2]; Backsheet delamination [8]
Internal Circuitry Discoloration	*DR*: 1 %/a [9]		VI, EL — Corrosion string interconnect [5]; Humidity corrosion [1]
Encapsulation Discoloration	*CPL*: up to 45 % [10] *DR*: 0.5-1 %/a [5]		VI, UV-F — EVA browning [1]; Hot spot as possible root; Increased fluorescence signal [9]
Junction Box / Bypass diode	*CPL*: up to 100 %		(VI), EL, dPL — Junction box missing lid [5]; Short circuit bypass diode [1]; Short circuit bypass diode [1]; Short circuit bypass diode [11] ©JohnWiley & Sons, Inc.
LID / LeTID	*CPL*: up to 6 % (LID [61]) or 16 % (LeTID [64])		EL, dPL — Chess pattern due to LeTID [66]; Chess pattern due to LeTID

Matrix references: cf. L. Koester, "Review of photovoltaic module degradation, field inspection techniques and techno-economic assessment", RSER 2022

Inspection cost – baseline technical minimum

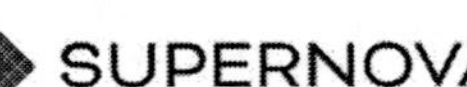

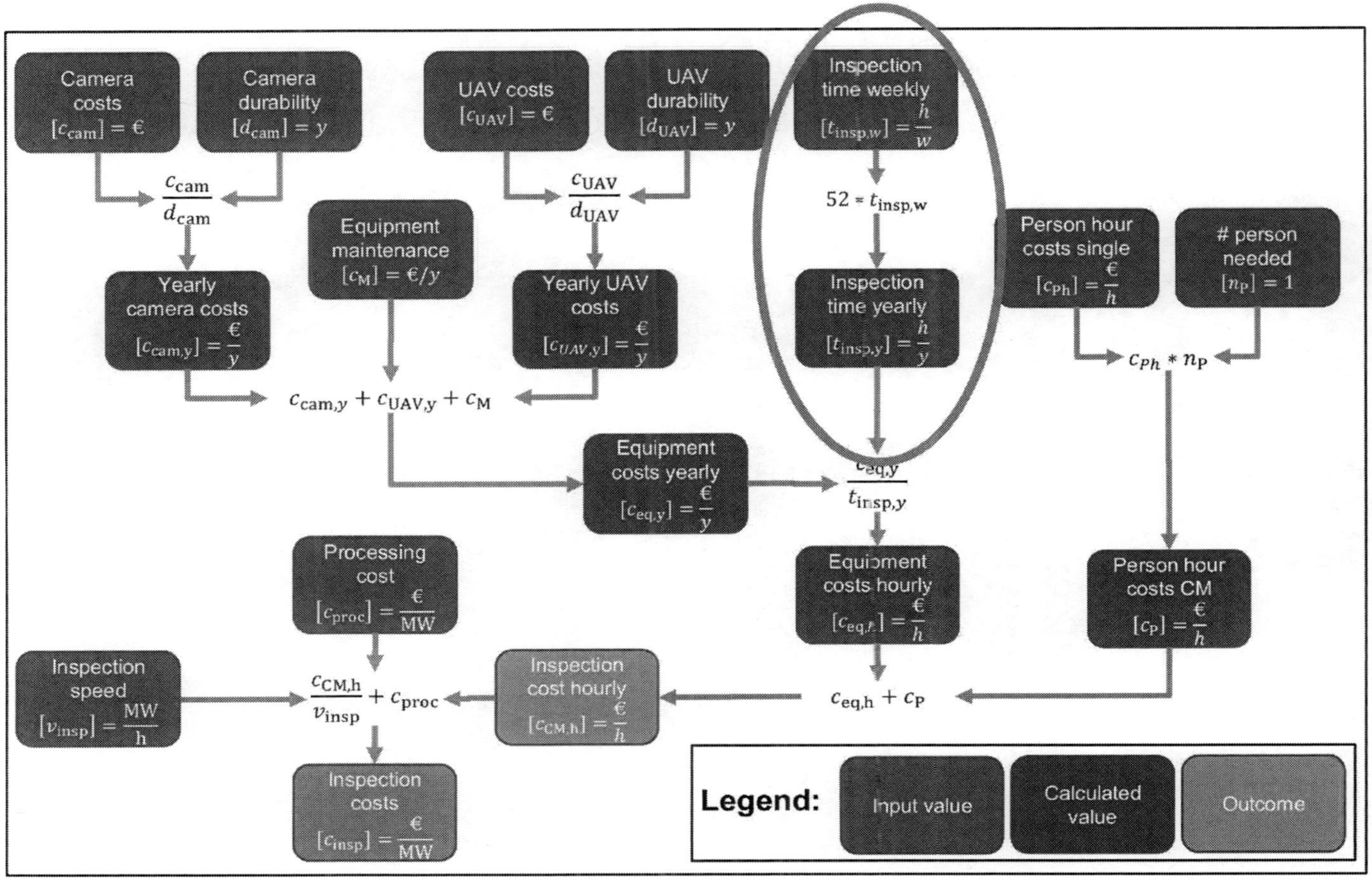

Info	units	IR	EL (night)	DPL
Camera cost	€	3000	20000	20000
Camera durability	y	5	5	5
UAV cost	€	10000	15000	15000
UAV durability	y	4	4	4
Maintenance cost	€/y	500	500	500
Person hour cost	€	35	45	35
Person needed		2	2	2

Values are best estimations from several references, experience, discussions with involved partners / experts

SUPERNOVA

Inspection requirements

Analysis of the available time in a year (Inspection Time yearly) to perform an inspection, based on the required specifications.

Credits: Eurac Research

Infrared Thermography

- High irradiance > 600 W/m2
- Very low to none cloud cover
- Temperature < 40°C

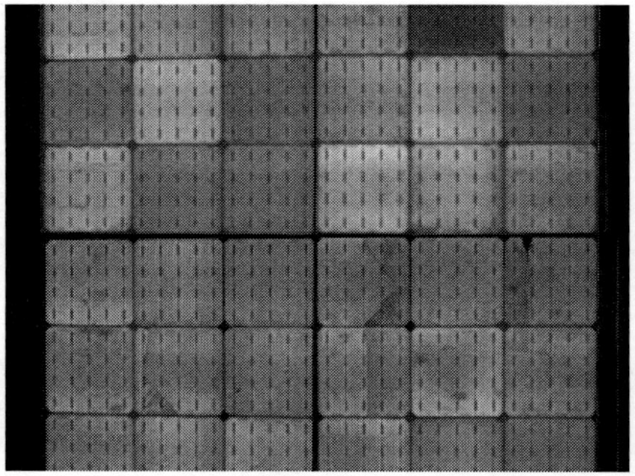

Credits: Eurac Research

Electroluminescence

- Low irradiance < 100 W/m2
- Temperature < 30°C

Aerial inspection

- Low wind speed < 5.5 m/s
- No precipitation

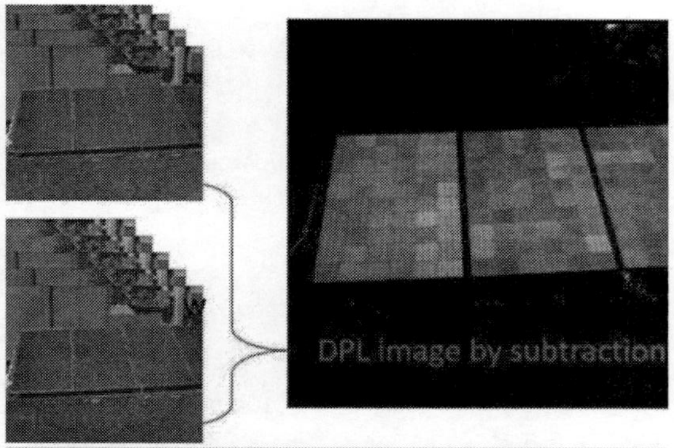

Credits: Eurac Research

Daylight Photoluminescence

- Irradiance > 200 W/m2
- Low cloud cover
- Temperature < 30°C

SUPERNOVA

Inspection time yearly

Köppen-Geiger-Photovoltaic climate classification

For each zone, calculated for 3 locations and 5 years (2014-2019), results averaged per zone.

Filtering of all hours fulfilling requirements.

Temperature-Precipitation (TP):

A – Tropical
B – Desert
C – Steppe
D – Temperate
E – Cold
F – Polar

B	K

Irradiation (I):

K – Very High
H – High
M – Medium
L – Low

J. Ascencio-Vásquez, et al. *Solar Energy 191 (2019) 672–685*

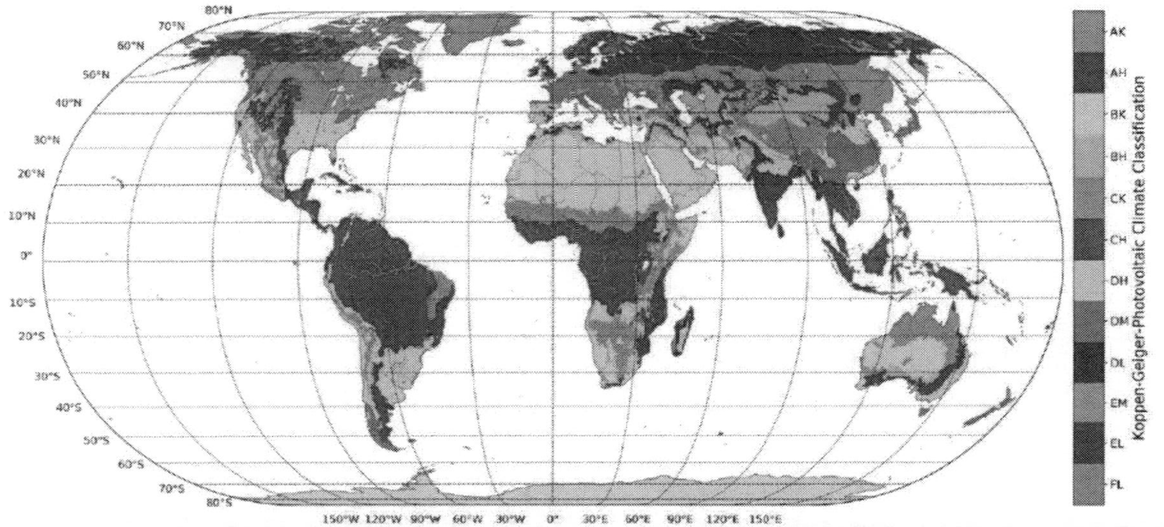

Credits: Julián Ascencio-Vásquez, https://doi.org/10.1016/j.solener.2019.08.072

SUPERNOVA

Yearly inspection time per KGPV climate zone

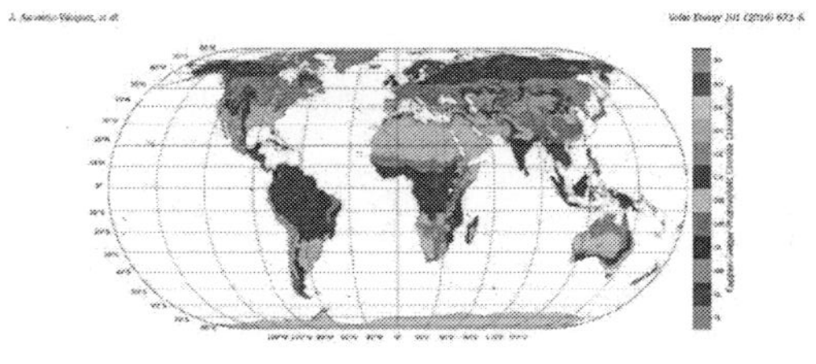

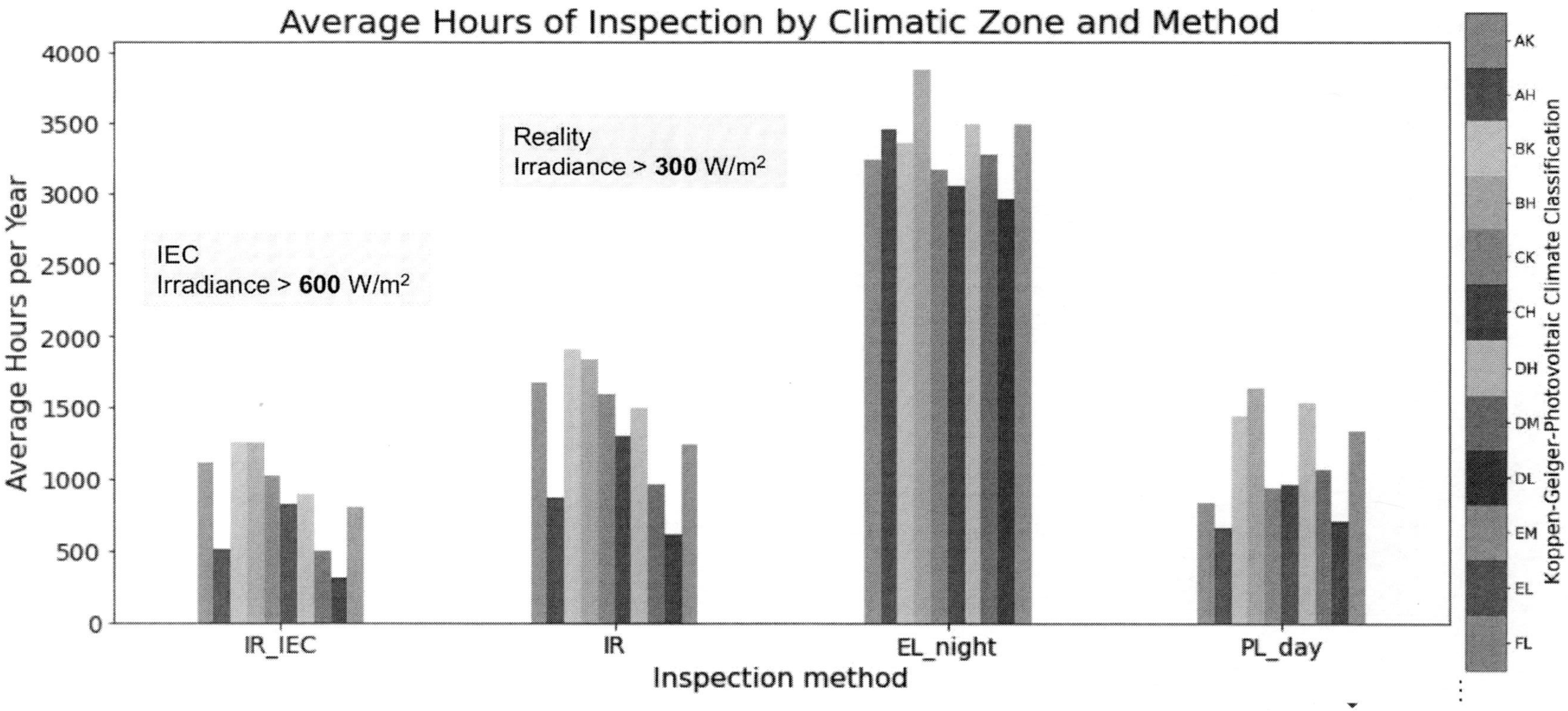

Inspection cost – baseline technical minimum

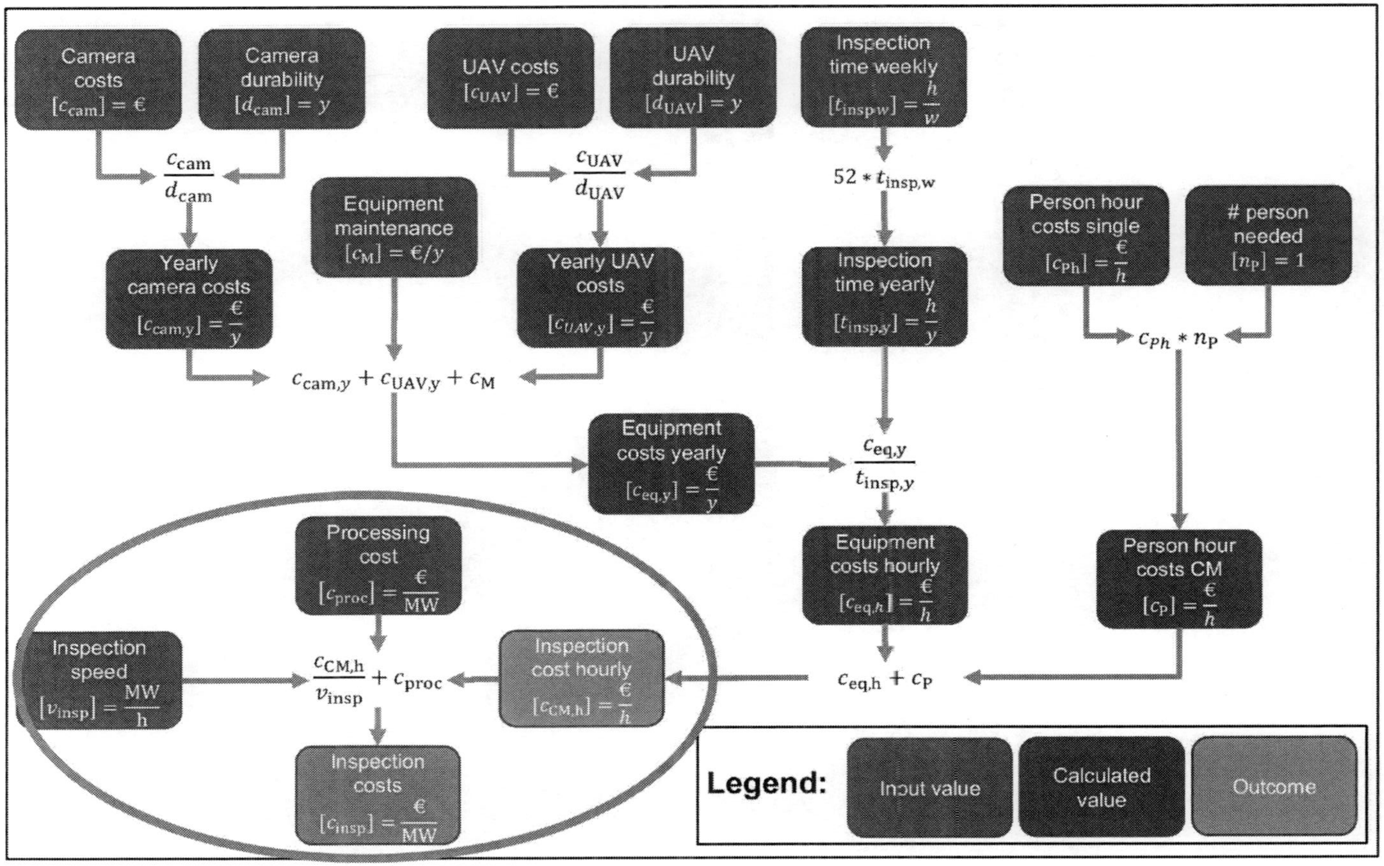

Info	units	IR	EL (night)	DPL
Camera cost	€	3000	20000	20000
Camera durability	y	5	5	5
UAV cost	€	10000	15000	15000
UAV durability	y	4	4	4
Maintenance cost	€/y	500	500	500
Person hour cost	€	35	45	35
Person needed		2	2	2

Values are best estimations from several references, experience, discussions with involved partners / experts

SUPERNOVA

Hourly Inspection Costs

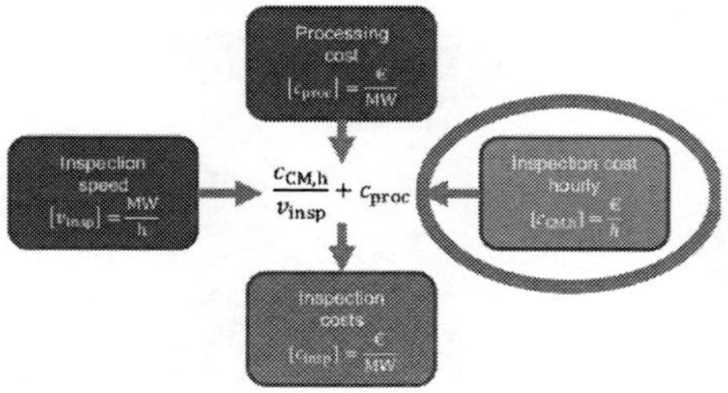

Info	units	IR	EL (night)	DPL
Camera cost	€	3000	20000	20000
Camera durability	y	5	5	5
UAV cost	€	10000	15000	15000
UAV durability	y	4	4	4
Maintenance cost	€/y	500	500	500
Person hour cost	€	35	45	35
Person needed		2	2	2

Values are best estimations from several references, experience, discussions with involved partners / experts

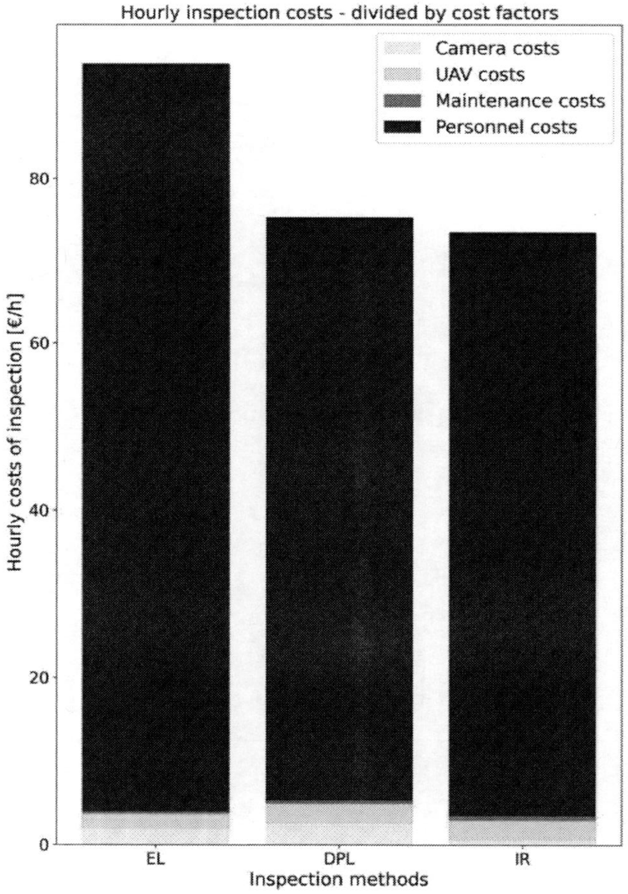

→ Purchase of IR equipment lowest, but due to possible inspection time, relative equipment cost decreases for DPL and even more for EL.

→ Personnel costs are main driver of inspection costs (EL at night more expensive)

→ Inspection speeds dominate the difference of inspection costs.

SUPERNOVA

Processing Costs

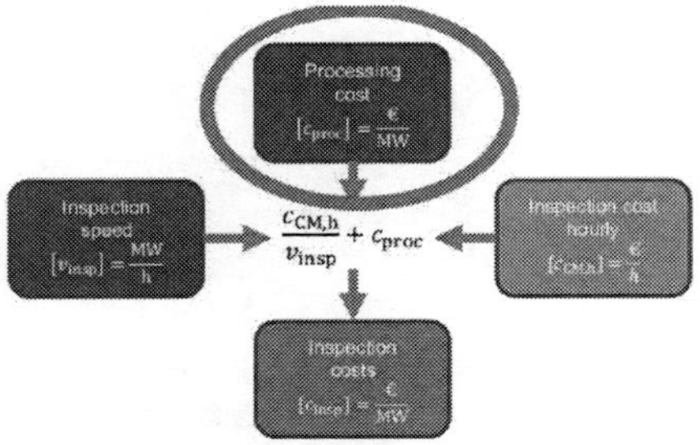

$$c_{insp}\left[\frac{€}{MW}\right] = \frac{c_{eq}}{v_{insp}} + \frac{c_P}{v_{insp}} + c_{proc}$$

General assumptions:

- Fully automated analysis (no personnel costs)
- Processing time per module: IRT=2s, EL=5s, DPL=10s
- 500 Wp module capacity

Two approaches to calculate processing cost per hour:

1. Owned server/GPU:
   - Purchase cost: 3000-5000 €; reliability: 20,000 h; consumption: 0.5-1 kW/h with 0.3-0.6 €/kWh
   - → Processing cost: 0.25-0.80 €/h
2. Cloud based processing (rental):

GPU Type	Vast.ai (P25)	AWS	CoreWeave	Lambda
RTX 5090	$0.36/hr	--	--	--
H200	$2.35/hr	$10.60/hr	$6.31/hr	--
H100	$1.65/hr	$12.30/hr	$6.16/hr	$3.29/hr
RTX 4090	$0.31/hr	--	--	--
RTX 3090	$0.13/hr	--	--	--

Reference: vast.ai

Resulting processing cost per inspection method:

	kWp per hour	€/kWp min	€/kWp max
IRT	900	0.00029	0.00088
EL	360	0.00073	0.00220
DPL	180	0.00147	0.00439

IRT: < 0.1 €cent / kWp
EL: < 0.2 €cent / kWp
DPL: < 0.5 €cent / kWp

SUPERNOVA

Inspection Speed

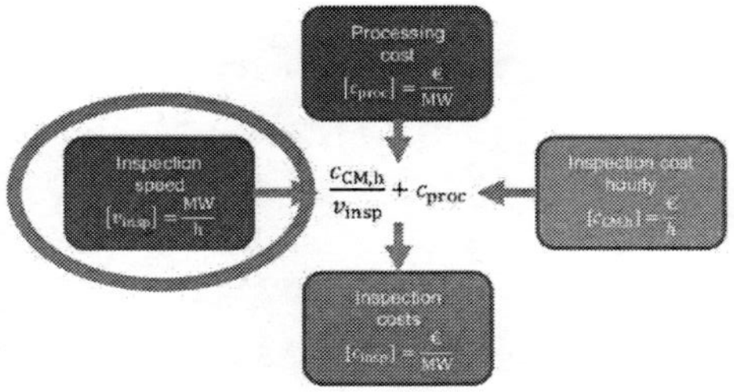

$$c_{insp}\left[\frac{€}{MW}\right] = \frac{c_{eq}}{v_{insp}} + \frac{c_P}{v_{insp}} + c_{proc}$$

Analysis based on geometrical parameters and boundary conditions:

Parameters influencing the imaging speed (MW/h):

- Ground sampling distance (GSD) in m/pixel,
  - given by drone height, camera resolution, focal length, orientation between camera and PV module.
  - GSD is a threshold value to get proper images (**2 cm/pixel for IR, 0.5 cm/pixel for EL/DPL**)

Considering close-up images for detailed inspection.

640 pixel → 12.8 m
(for GSD=2cm/pixel)

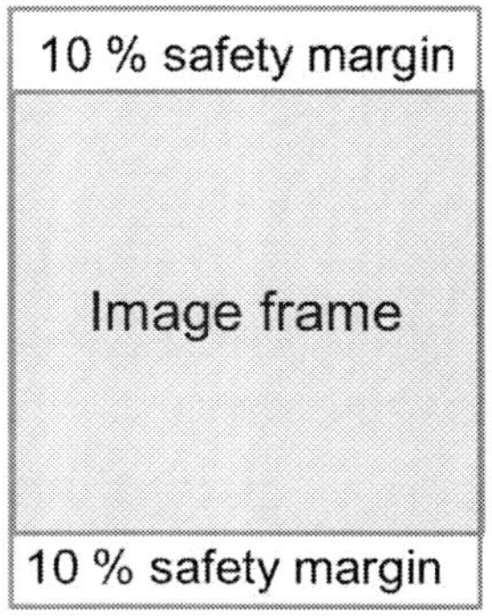

512 pixel → 10,24 m
(for GSD=2cm/pixel)

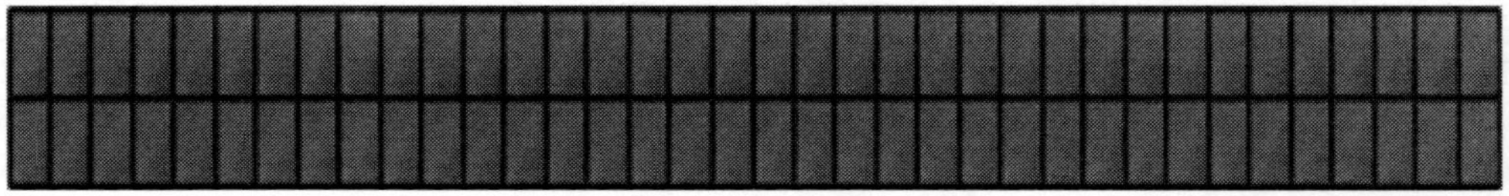

SUPERNOVA

Inspection Speed

Ground imaging ratio (GIR): MWp/m
→ a value describing how many MWp are covered in 1m of the image
→ simple calculation of imaging speed by using drone speed in m/s

$$GIR = PV\ modules\ in\ image\ frame\ width * \#PV\ modules\ covered\ in\ 1\mathrm{m}\ (\mathrm{travel\ direction}) * PV\ module\ nominal\ power$$

$$v_{insp}\left[\frac{\mathrm{MW}}{\mathrm{h}}\right] = GIR\left[\frac{\mathrm{MWp}}{\mathrm{m}}\right] * v_{drone}\left[\frac{\mathrm{m}}{\mathrm{s}}\right] * 3600\left[\frac{\mathrm{s}}{\mathrm{h}}\right] * \mathrm{C_{path}} * \mathrm{C_{battery}}$$

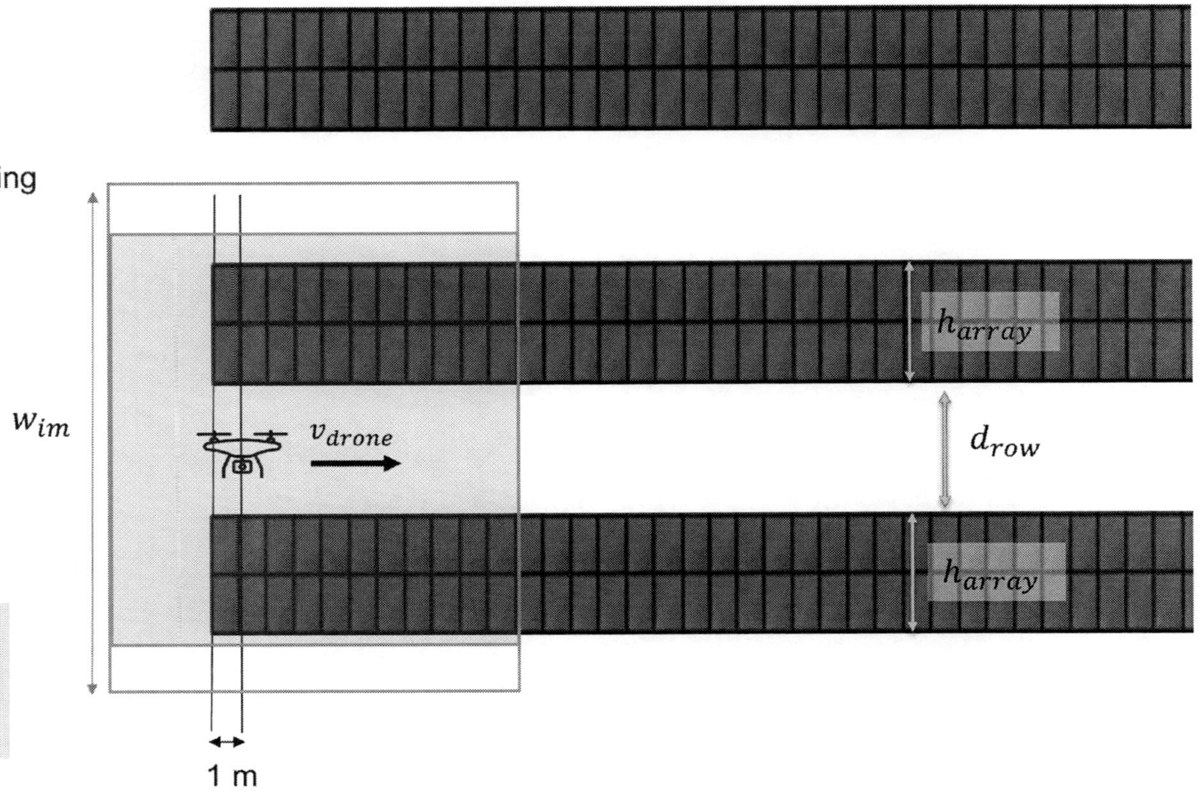

→ 4 PV modules * 400 Wp
→ $GIR = 1.6\,\frac{\mathrm{kWp}}{\mathrm{m}} = 0.0016\,\frac{\mathrm{MWp}}{\mathrm{m}}$

SUPERNOVA

Inspection Speed

Inspection speed for example PV plant (100 MWp, double
Module row, 500Wp per module).

Current values (GSD, drone speed, plant layout) for model verification.

Current developments for potential speed.

Imaging method	Imaging speed current (MW/h)	Imaging speed potential (MW/h)
IRT	3.0	10
DPL	1.5	4
EL	2.0	5

Impact of PV plant size on inspection speed

(from 1 MWp to 1 GWp):

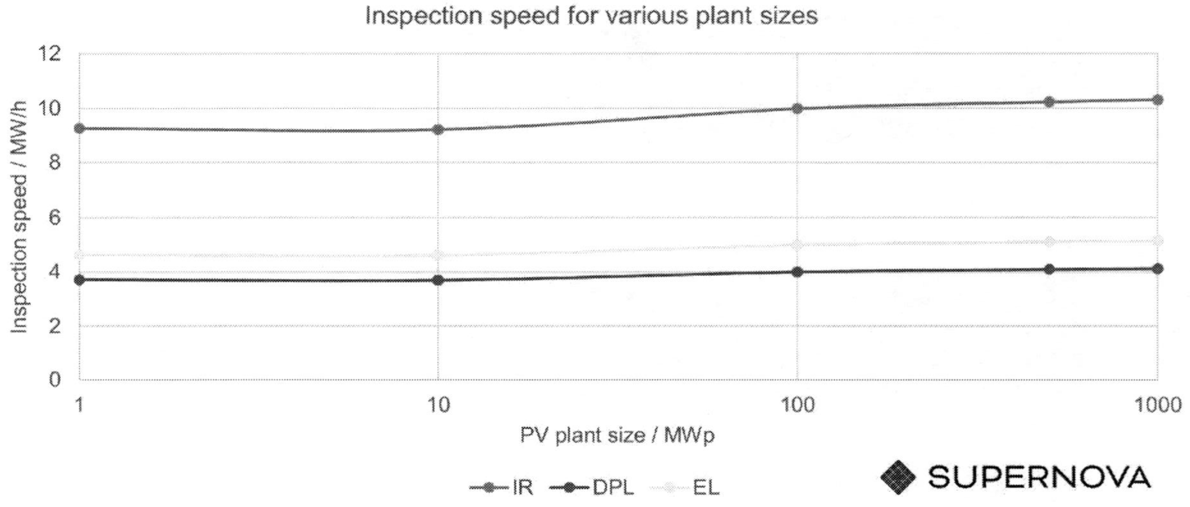

SUPERNOVA

Inspection cost

$$c_{insp}\left[\frac{€}{MW}\right] = \frac{c_{eq}\left[\frac{€}{h}\right] + c_P\left[\frac{€}{h}\right]}{v_{insp}\left[\frac{MW}{h}\right]} + c_{proc}\left[\frac{€}{MW}\right]$$

Baseline of technical minimum costs.

Missing to calculate actual costs:
- planning & mobilization
- Company overhead (insurance, admin, margin)
- Minimum project fees

Model can be used to measure technical improvements (better camera resolution, effect of drone speed on inspection speed, battery charging time, robotic solutions, …)

Imaging method	Imaging speed potential (MW/h)	Inspection cost (€/MWp)
IRT	10	7.2
DPL	4	18.5
EL	5	18.6

Inspection costs (baseline technical minimum) for various plant sizes

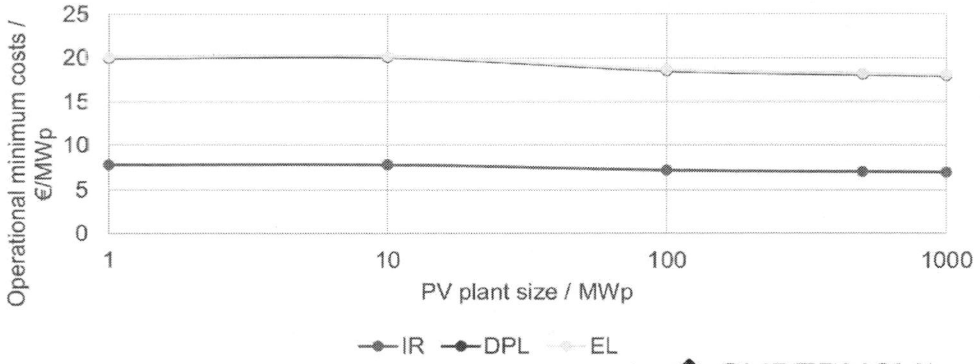

SUPERNOVA

Ground-based vs. aerial (autonomous) inspection

Aerial inspection faster, thus cheaper.

Battery charging for autonomous inspection important (no exchange of batteries – longer idle time.
Battery capacity (operational time) becomes more crucial.

Vehicle type	Assumed moving speed (m/s)	Imaging speed potential (MW/h)	Inspection cost (€/MWp)
Aerial	3	3	24
Ground-based	0.5	0.5	148

As overheads are main share of inspection, days spent (in person) at PV site of importance.

6-7 days on site vs. 2-3 days on site (installation and pick up) plus 2 months of autonomous operation.

Advantages of ground-based robots:

- Rear-module images
- Inclusion of several sensors – all at once

	Moving speed (m/s)	Exchange time of battery (minutes)	Operational time (minutes)	Total imaging time for 100 MWp PV plant (h)
Ground-based autonomous	0.5	120	120	400
Aerial in-person inspection	3	5	40	37

SUPERNOVA

Conclusions

On the pure technical side, we calculated inspection costs of only 7–9 €/MWp. However, real-world service prices are much higher, because fixed project costs dominate. This means that incremental technical improvements (e.g., faster drones) do not drastically reduce €/MWp prices — unless the whole workflow is restructured (autonomous inspection, hybridization of robotic solutions).

Take aways

Model gives an estimate for **baseline costs for the technical minimum** of inspection methods.

Modification of different **parameters** to calculate their **impact on imaging speed** and costs.

Main **reason for difference** in potential inspection speed is **required detail** (GSD): Even with new SWIR cameras, difficult to cover two rows at the same time with EL/DPL. IRT can cover 2-3 rows

Automization has potential to **reduce costs** but only in very **large PV plants** (significantly less on-site days). Seamless communication needed → Universal API mapper – open source in SUPERNOVA.

Ground-based robotics significantly slower, but potential for additional detail (**rear side**) and several sensors at once (**IRT+DPL**). → **hybridization** of robotic solutions in SUPERNOVA.

SUPERNOVA

The Project:

The Universal Mapper:

SUPERNOVA

Thank you

Contact: lukas.koester@eurac.edu

Co-funded by the European Union

References

SPE2025: Solar Power Europe, Operation & Maintenance Best Practice Guidelines v6.0, 2025

Bakir2023: Hale Bakır. Detection of Faults in Photovoltaic Modules of SPPS in Turkey; Infrared Thermographic Diagnosis and Recommendations. *Journal of Electrical Engineering & Technology*, 18(3):1945–1957, May 2023.

IEA-PVPS T13 2021: Werner Herrmann et al. IEA-PVPS task 13: Performance, operation and reliability of photovoltaic systems - qualification of photovoltaic (PV) power plants using mobile test equipment. Report, International Energy Agency, 2021.

AEPVI: AEPVI. Aerial PV Inspection GmbH - Website, February 2024

QE2025: QELabs. Quantified Energy Labs - Website, September 2025 (https://quantified-energy.com/increasing-contactless-drone-el-throughput-to-5000-pv-modules-per-hour-using-direct-injection-from-ingeteam-inverters/)

Doll2023: Bernd Doll et al. Aerial Photoluminescence Imaging of Photovoltaic Modules. physica status solidi (RRL) – Rapid Research Letters, 17(12):2300059, December 2023.

Koester2024: Lukas Koester, Multispectral Imaging And Correlation Of Image Signatures Of Pv Failures With Electrical Signatures, PhD thesis, July 2024

SUPERNOVA

Importance of detailed knowledge beyond direct financial impact

1. PV plant status before/after commissioning or acquisition
2. Extreme weather events, e.g. hailstorm
3. Knowledge about PV plant health status

- Insurance policies based on visual analysis
- No knowledge about internal damage
- Performance loss and (future) safety issues not considered
- Suggestion: detailed analysis after hail event and adaption of insurance policies

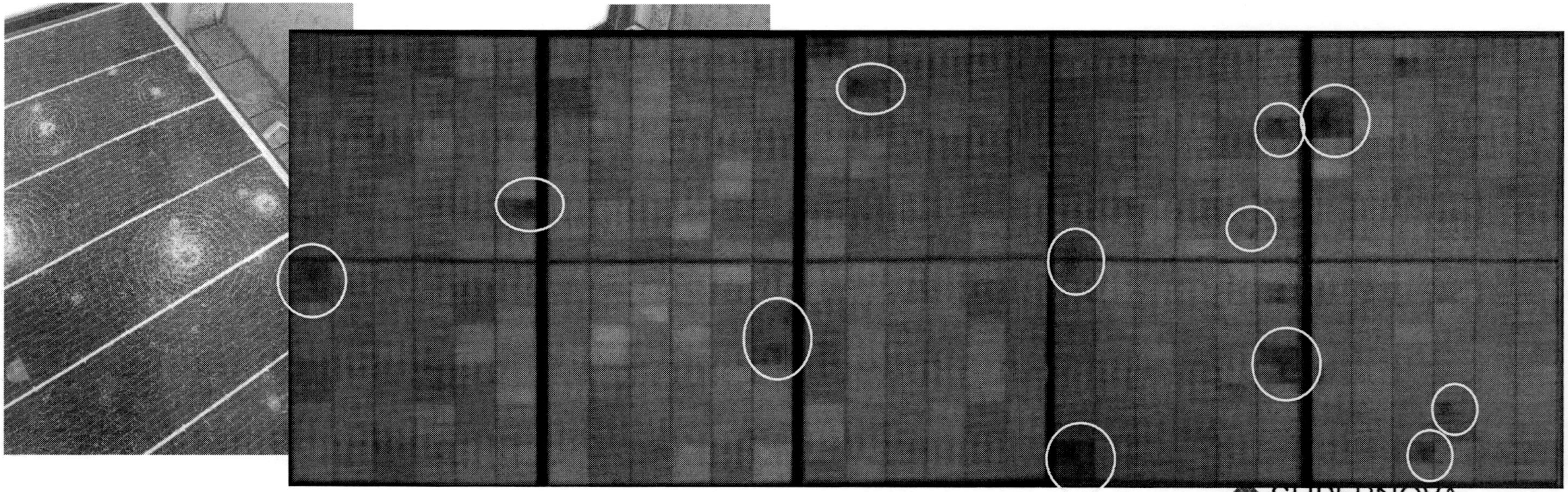

SUPERNOVA

Application of DPL

Roof-top PV after hail
Several defects visible in “healthy” PV modules
2 DPL images for 5 PV modules

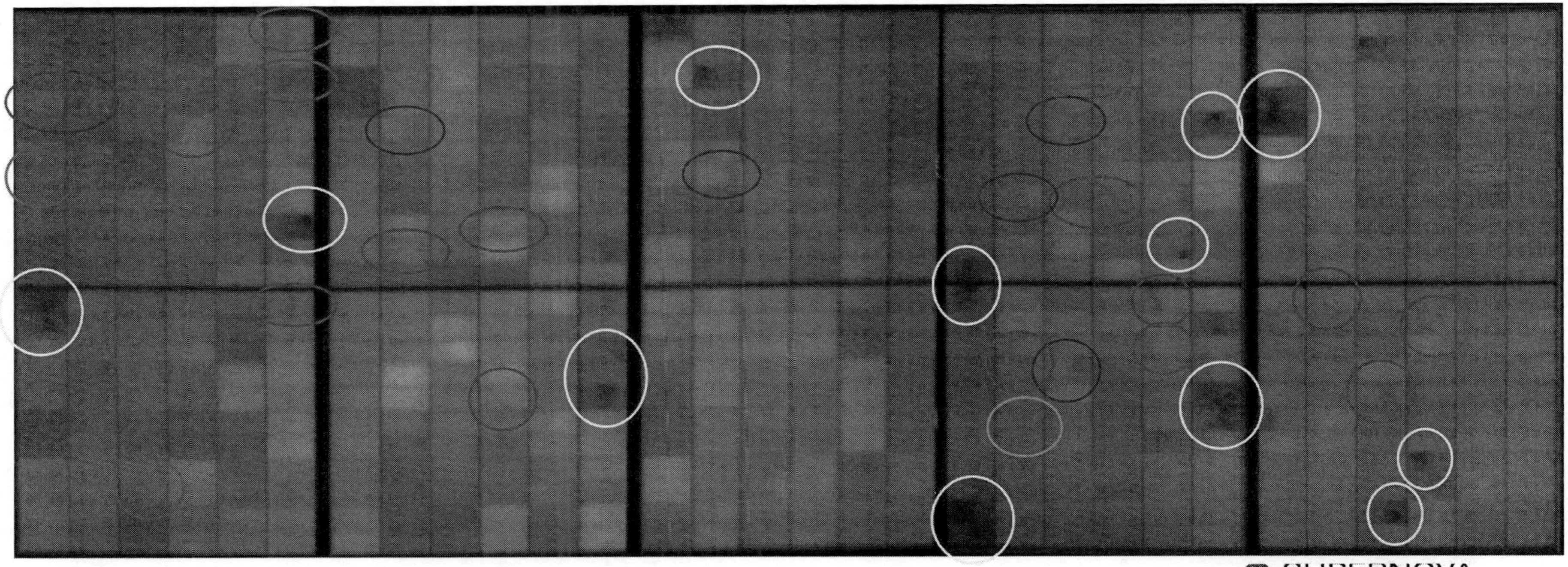

SUPERNOVA

42nd European Photovoltaic Solar Energy Conference and Exhibition

This presentation was selected by the Sc. Committee of the EU PVSEC 2025 for submission of a full paper to one of the EU PVSEC's collaborating peer-reviewed journals.

LIDAR MEETS MODELLING: COLLABORATIVE INSIGHTS FROM A ROUND-ROBIN OF VERTICAL BIFACIAL PV SIMULATIONS

Ioannis (John) A. Tsanakas[1*], Stéphane Mollier[1], Hervé Colin[1], Ismaël Lokhat[2], Branislav Schnierer[3], Daniel Chrkavy[3], Martin Opatovsky[3], S. Prithivi Rajan[4], Jesús Robledo[4], Jonathan Leloux[4]
[1] CEA, Liten, Univ. Grenoble Alpes, Campus INES, 73375 Le Bourget du Lac, France
[2] Cythelia Energy, 73290 La Motte-Servolex, France
[3] Solargis s.r.o., 81109 Bratislava, Slovakia
[4] LuciSun, 1495 Villers-la-Ville, Belgium

*corresponding author: ioannis.tsanakas@cea.fr

ABSTRACT: Vertical bifacial photovoltaic (PV) systems have emerged as a promising solution for maximizing land use efficiency while achieving high energy yields. This study investigates the modeling and simulation of a vertical bifacial PV plant located in southeastern France, utilizing advanced drone-based LiDAR (Light Detection And Ranging) data for detailed environmental characterization. In a collaborative effort, in the context of H2020 SERENDI-PV project, four partners – CEA, Cythelia, Lucisun, and Solargis – applied their unique PV modeling tools to assess the plant's energy yield, shading losses, and diffuse irradiance contributions. The study focused on comparing methodologies in a round-robin framework, analyzing results from an common PV monitoring dataset. Key findings highlight the critical impact of accurate terrain and shading modeling on simulation reliability. This paper presents selected results, including shading loss analysis, module-level energy yield comparisons, and key performance indicators (KPIs), emphasizing the significance of LiDAR-enhanced modeling.

Keywords: Vertical bifacial PV; LiDAR; energy yield simulations; shading analysis; round-robin study; PV modeling.

1 INTRODUCTION: CONTEXT and AIM

Validating the economic viability and bankability of bifacial PV projects depends on accurate energy yield prediction, a task complicated by complex light-harvesting mechanisms [1,2]. Unlike monofacial modules, bifacial systems generate energy from both sides, with rear-side gains highly sensitive to the installation environment (albedo, mounting height, array geometry, shading) [1,2]. The industry's inability to precisely model these gains is a primary source of uncertainty, causing significant discrepancies between simulation tools [3,4].

This challenge is greater in complex settings like built environments or agrivoltaics [5,6]. Bifacial vertical PV (BVPV) – used in fencing, noise barriers, and east-west agrivoltaic systems – is a particularly demanding use case [7,8]. Their performance is dictated by diffuse and reflected light, with a strong dependence on anisotropic sky conditions and ground properties, pushing existing modelling paradigms to their limits [9,10].

Modelling approaches represent a trade-off between speed and fidelity [11]:

- *Transposition Models:* Calculate plane-of-array irradiance but assume uniform ground illumination and isotropic reflectivity [7,12]. They are simple and fast but can have high errors (~15%) for non-optimal orientations and are limited for bifacial rear-side simulation [10-12].
- *View Factor (VF) Models:* Offer a better approach by using geometric view factors to calculate ground-reflected irradiance. Errors of 5-16% have been reported [13,14], but they assume isotropic reflection and struggle with 3D obstruction shading, often requiring user-defined loss factors.
- *Ray Tracing (RT) Models:* Are the gold standard for accuracy. Tools like NREL's bifacial_radiance trace light paths in a 3D scene for high fidelity [15-18]. However, this accuracy comes with immense computational cost [19].

Accurate rear-side modelling is complicated by interlinked parameters [20,21]:

1. **Mounting Height:** Increases rear-side irradiance but accentuates edge effects, which VF models underestimate [15,18].
2. **Albedo:** Higher albedo augments rear-side irradiance [14], but VF models fail with time-dependent or anisotropic surfaces [9,10].
3. **Mounting Structure:** Causes shading that reduces performance, a factor not intrinsically accounted for in VF models [14,22].

BVPV intensifies these challenges. Its radically different view factors and dominance of diffuse/reflected light push the simplifying assumptions of transposition and VF models to their limits. High-fidelity ray tracing is likely essential but computationally burdensome [19,23].

Current RT models also lack two key features: the capacity for spectrally-resolved simulations (critical for tandem cell technologies) [24-26] and the efficient simulation of time-varying albedo (e.g., from snow), which is vital for forecasting accuracy [27,28].

This collaborative study, in the framework of the H2020 SERENDI-PV project, attempts to shed light into (and address) the modelling challenges of simulation the energy yield and losses of complex PV installations by employing drone-based LiDAR data to create precise 3D representations. The particular case of a vertical bifacial PV plant's (Fig. 1) environment has been thoroughly modelled and studied. The PV plant analyzed in this study is located in southeastern France, 60km south of the city of Lyon, along a canal of the Rhône river. The specific site, being in the Rhône valley, is characterized by uneven terrain and is surrounded by high vegetation (mostly trees) in close proximity, as also seen in Fig. 1. The PV system features a linear (length of 350m in total) vertical bifacial configuration with six sections of PV modules aligned approximately along a north-south axis. Each section contains a combination of 24 or 48 bifacial frameless PV modules, type Trina Solar's TSM-DEG14C.07 (II), stacked in two rows, throughout the installation, which totals a capacity of 104 kW_p. The system's unique vertical design and complex surroundings make it an ideal candidate for advanced modeling studies that incorporate shading, albedo, and terrain effects, using precise LiDAR-enhanced data to improve simulation accuracy.

Figure 1: The (linear) vertical bifacial PV system investigated in the collaborative round-robin study of PV simulations by Solargis, Lucisun, Cythelia and CEA.

Through this work, we aimed to leverage these insights to improve simulation accuracy across diverse modeling tools while comparing results in a collaborative round-robin framework. The presented study involves contributions from four SERENDI-PV partners, with their corresponding proprietary (commercial or research) tools for advanced PV modelling:

- **CEA** with its *Trifactors v2* tool,
- **Cythelia** employing *archelios PRO*,
- **Lucisun** using its *LuSim* tool,
- **Solargis** with *Evaluate*, its advanced simulation platform.

Each partner utilized LiDAR-derived 3D meshes to model terrain effects, shading patterns, and energy yields, fostering a deeper understanding of the strengths and limitations of each modelling approach

2 METHODOLOGY - APPROACH

2.1 LiDAR Data Acquisition and Processing

The LiDAR dataset was acquired using drone flights over the aforementioned PV plant, generating a dense 3D point cloud with over 80 million points. This data was processed into a simplified 3D mesh containing 6,000 triangular elements, retaining critical details like canopy height and terrain slopes. The mesh was distributed to all partners in COLLADA (.dae) format for integration into their respective modeling tools. Figure 2 illustrates the processed LiDAR-based 3D terrain model used for simulations.

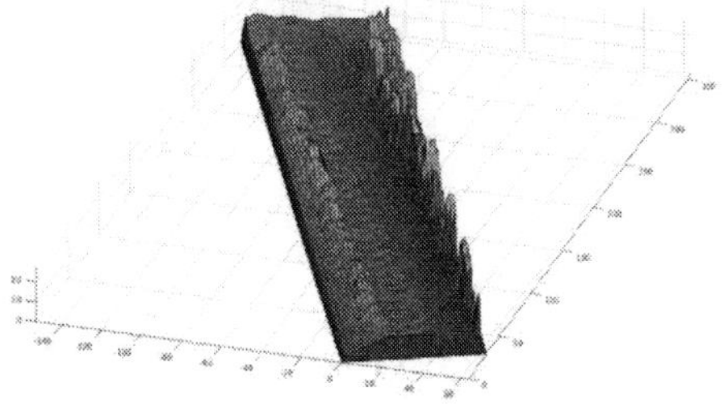

Figure 2: Reconstructed 3D mesh of the studied vertical bifacial PV system, from LiDAR data.

2.2 Modeling Tools and Innovations

CEA's Trifactors v2 tool utilized the LiDAR mesh to model irradiance and shading effects. It allowed the decomposition of irradiance into direct, diffuse, and reflected components for shading-loss quantification. Cythelia employed the archelios PRO API, integrating bifacial modeling advancements from previous projects. The tool emphasized electrical sizing and shading analysis. Lucisun's LuSim adopted GPU-accelerated methods to simulate shading profiles and Global Tilted Irradiance (GTI) at high temporal and spatial resolutions, enabling accurate module-level assessments. Through Evaluate, Solargis implemented its ray-tracing simulator to evaluate bifacial performance using harmonized datasets and advanced shading calculations.

2.3 Collaborative Round-Robin Framework

Each partner applied their tool to the same exactly dataset (which underwent comprehensive data quality control prior to the main modelling work), focusing on four representative days in 2023: March 24 (cloudy/overcast conditions), June 25 (sunny/clear-sky conditions), September 9 (sunny/clear-sky conditions), and December 3 (partial sunny conditions). Simulations were compared at PV module-level resolution, emphasizing consistency and reproducibility rather than competitive benchmarking.

3 RESULTS and DISCUSSION

3.1 Shading Analysis

The LiDAR-enhanced 3D mesh enabled accurate characterization of shading effects from terrain and vegetation. Indicatively, CEA's simulations highlighted seasonal shading losses, which varied from 3.15% in summer to 10.92% in winter, with PV modules at the

10.4229/EUPVSEC2025/4BO.7.1

bottom row of the vertical PV arrays, experiencing greater shading than those at the top row (Fig. 3). The findings underscore the significant impact of seasonal and positional variations on shading losses, emphasizing the importance of detailed environmental modeling for accurate yield predictions.

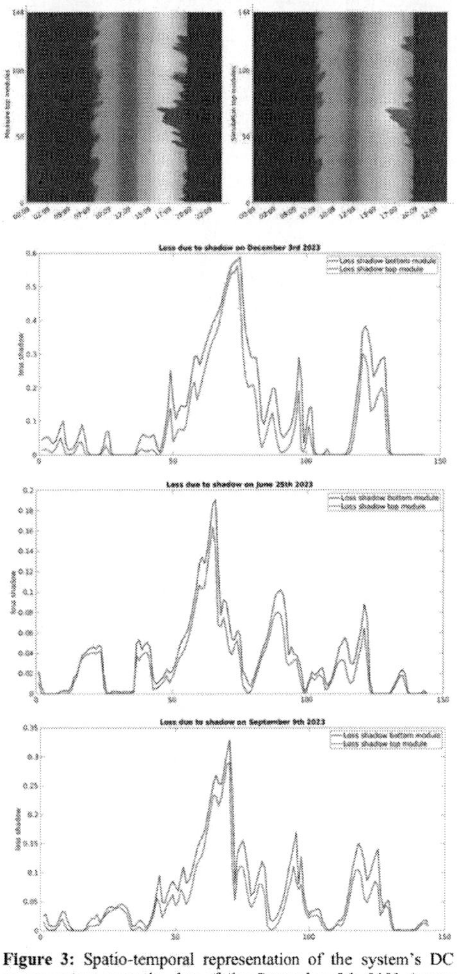

Figure 3: Spatio-temporal representation of the system's DC power output over the day of the September 9th 2023 (upper figure) and shading losses for top and bottom modules across selected days.

3.2 Module-level Energy Yield Comparison

Simulations revealed the characteristic double-peak profile of vertical bifacial systems. Figure 4 compares DC power outputs for two selected modules (48th and 68th positions) simulated by the partners for June 25 and September 9, showing good agreement despite variations in shading modeling. While good agreement was observed across the partners' tools, slight variations in DC power outputs highlight differences in shading and irradiance modeling approaches, as well as how each tool handles complex terrain and diffuse light conditions.

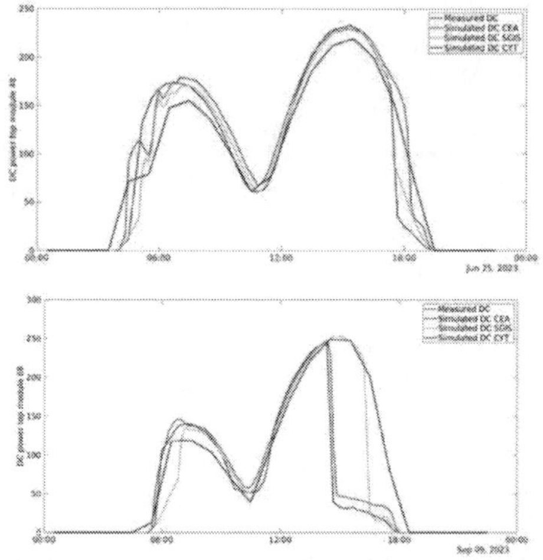

Figure 4: DC power comparison for modules 48 and 68 on representative days.

3.3 Model Accuracy and Key Performance Indicators (KPIs)

Lucisun's LuSim demonstrated the lowest Mean Absolute Error (MAE) for shading predictions, showcasing the benefits of GPU-accelerated methods and high temporal resolution in capturing dynamic shading patterns. Solargis' results highlighted the advantages of harmonized input datasets for accurate bifacial performance predictions. Table 1 summarizes the KPIs for all partners, revealing complementary strengths and areas for refinement in each modeling tool.

Table 1. Summary of KPIs for module-level simulations.

Date	***PV Module #***	**MAE (Wh) *Trifactors v2***	**MAE (Wh) *Evaluate***	**MAE (Wh) *archelios PRO***	**MAE (Wh) *LuSim***
25/06/2023	*28*	6.98	10.90	9.00	1.36
	48	11.40	6.63	15.10	4.46
	68	9.93	7.37	12.75	3.61
	120	6.75	7.83	8.01	9.08
09/09/2023	*28*	6.41	5.42	10.54	2.70
	48	11.55	6.40	9.37	1.93
	68	6.04	21.99	28.77	4.28
	120	8.44	10.70	13.88	3.84
03/12/2023	*28*	6.98	10.90	9.00	8.14
	48	11.40	6.63	15.10	2.00
	68	9.93	7.37	12.75	2.08
	120	6.75	7.83	8.01	6.77

3.4 Diffuse and Direct Irradiance Insights

Diffuse irradiance was found to be a significant contributor to energy yield during cloudy conditions, with notable impacts on modules with greater exposure to terrain shading. Heatmaps generated by Lucisun (Fig. 5) illustrated diffuse and direct irradiance distributions, validating the influence of terrain features on light capture. These results demonstrate the importance of accurately modeling diffuse irradiance to optimize bifacial PV performance, particularly in locations with variable weather conditions.

10.4229/EUPVSEC2025/4BO.7.1

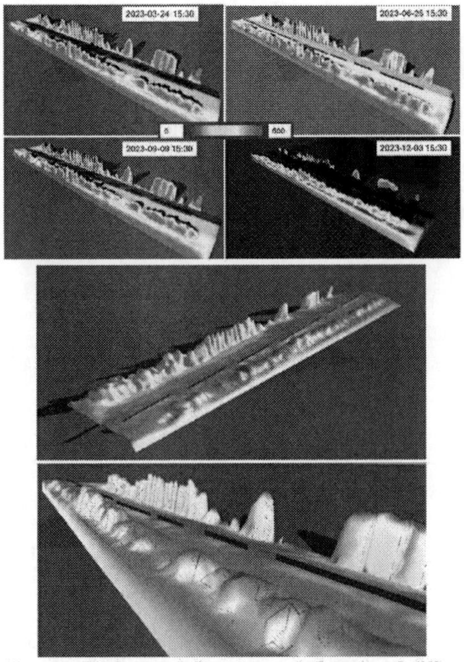

Figure 5: Heatmaps of direct (upper 4 figures) and diffuse irradiance (middle and bottom figure) for selected days.

4 FURTHER DISCUSSION – KEY TAKEAWAYS

The round-robin exercise successfully consolidated results from multiple modeling chains, moving beyond competition to reveal a consistent picture of vertical bifacial system performance. This provides a shared foundation for methodological improvements.

All partners accurately captured the system's distinctive double-peak daily pattern. Disagreements were primarily confined to the steep shading transitions at sunrise and sunset, which serve as critical stress tests for shading algorithms and highlight key areas for improvement. The analyses clearly identified predictable patterns: increased shading losses occurred in winter and for lower rows of the array, where nearby obstacles and low sun angles worsen horizon shading. These scenarios rigorously test 3D scene and terrain modeling.

At a monthly scale, random variations diminished, revealing a low, stable bias. This confirms that upstream harmonization steps—like resource preprocessing and albedo alignment—effectively reduced systematic errors. Benchmarking also showed that module-level (e.g., MAE) and plant-level indicators (e.g., EPI, AC output) are complementary, together providing a coherent and self-consistent view of system performance.

A primary source of variation was uncertainty at the LiDAR-to-simulation interface. Manual placement of the 3D mesh and its acquisition in a non-representative season contributed to differences. Refining this process will further narrow the already small model spread. Finally, the exercise validated the benefit of separating the physical (irradiance, shading) and electrical domains, which brings clarity and helps pinpoint the source of discrepancies.

Collectively, these findings boost confidence in the modeling framework. The remaining spread between models is now well-characterized, traceable to known causes, and largely correctable. This effort not only validates current bifacial modeling but also creates a shared roadmap for its refinement.

5 CONCLUSIONS - OUTLOOK

Vertical bifacial (BVPV) systems are gaining traction for their land-use efficiency and applications in agrivoltaics and built environments. However, their performance is highly sensitive to factors like terrain, vegetation, albedo, and diffuse light, making yield prediction difficult. Discrepancies between existing modeling tools have historically undermined confidence in project bankability.

This collaborative study of the Sablons plant demonstrates that integrating high-resolution LiDAR data with advanced modeling significantly improves prediction accuracy.

The key conclusions are:

1. **High-resolution site characterization is essential.** Drone-based LiDAR created a precise "digital twin" of the terrain and vegetation. This was critical for accurately simulating the complex shading and light effects that impact rear-side energy gains.
2. **Tools consistently captured key performance signatures.** All models successfully reproduced the distinctive double-peak output profile of vertical bifacial modules. Remaining discrepancies occurred at sunrise/sunset, highlighting the need for better modeling of horizon obstructions and diffuse light.
3. **Shading is the dominant variable.** Seasonal and positional shading caused the highest energy losses, particularly for lower rows in winter. Site-specific topography created asymmetric shading, necessitating bifacial-aware, high-resolution modeling.
4. **Benchmarking revealed complementary tools.** Module-level (MAE) and plant-level (EPI) metrics provided a complete picture. GPU-accelerated tools excelled at capturing complex shading, while harmonized datasets ensured robust long-term predictions. Remaining variations were traceable to specific, correctable factors like LiDAR processing.
5. **A trade-off exists between accuracy and speed.** Ray-tracing is the most physically accurate but computationally expensive. Hybrid approaches offer a practical balance for large-scale use.

On the basis of the presented results, successful outcomes and identified challenges/gaps, future research directions include:

- Incorporating dynamic albedo (snow, crops) and spectral light data.
- Automating LiDAR processing to minimize manual errors.
- Integrating thermal and electrical models for fuller system understanding.
- Expanding benchmarking to diverse sites and climates.
- Standardizing these methods to achieve bankable predictions with 2-4% accuracy.

10.4229/EUPVSEC2025/4BO.7.1

In summary, this study provides a robust foundation for bifacial PV modeling. It shows that current uncertainties are identifiable and manageable, charting a clear pathway to reliable design and assessment for vertical bifacial projects.

ACKNOWLEDGEMENTS

This work has been carried out in the framework of the H2020 SERENDI-PV project. SERENDI-PV project has received funding from the European Union's Horizon 2020 research and innovation programme under grant agreement No. 953016. For CEA team, part of this work was also supported by the French National Program "Programme d'Investissements d'Avenir - INES.2S" under Grant Agreement ANR ANR-10-IEED-0014 0014-01.

The authors extend their sincere appreciation and gratefully acknowledge the valuable contribution – through interviews, provision of data and information, and permission to use certain photos – of Mr Kévin Garcia and Mrs Chloé Monet, on behalf of the R&D and technical team of CNR (Compagnie Nationale du Rhône), SERENDI-PV partner and owner/operator of the studied PV plant.

REFERENCES

1. U. A. Yusufoglu, T. M. Pletzer, L. J. Koduvelikulathu, C. Comparotto, R. Kopecek and H. Kurz, "Analysis of the Annual Performance of Bifacial Modules and Optimization Methods," in IEEE Journal of Photovoltaics, vol. 5, no. 1, pp. 320-328, Jan. 2015, doi: 10.1109/JPHOTOV.2014.2364406.
2. J.S. Stein et al., "Bifacial Photovoltaic Modules and Systems: Experience and Results from International Research and Pilot Applications," Report IEA-PVPS T13-14:2021.
3. J. Libal and R. Kopecek, Bifacial Photovoltaics: Technology, applications and economics. London, U.K.: Institution of Engineering and Technology, 2018. doi: 10.1049/pbpo107e.
4. D. Riley *et al.*, "A Performance Model for Bifacial PV Modules," *2017 IEEE 44th Photovoltaic Specialist Conference (PVSC)*, Washington, DC, USA, 2017, pp. 3348-3353, doi: 10.1109/PVSC.2017.8366045.
5. M.Trommsdorff et al. (2025), "Dual Land Use for Agriculture and Solar Power Production: Overview and Performance of Agrivoltaic Systems", Report IEA-PVPS T13-29:2025
6. Bonomo, P., Frontini, F., Loonen, R., & Reinders, A. H. M. E. (2024). Comprehensive review and state of play in the use of photovoltaics in buildings. Energy and Buildings, 323, 114737. https://doi.org/10.1016/j.enbuild.2024.114737.
7. Badran, G., Dhimish, M. Comprehensive study on the efficiency of vertical bifacial photovoltaic systems: a UK case study. Sci Rep 14, 18380 (2024). https://doi.org/10.1038/s41598-024-68018-1.
8. Szabo, L., Moner- Girona, M., Jäger-Waldau, A. et al. Impacts of large-scale deployment of vertical bifacial photovoltaics on European electricity market dynamics. Nat Commun 15, 6681 (2024). https://doi.org/10.1038/s41467-024-50762-7.
9. E. Tonita, S. Ovaitt, H. Toal, K. Hinzer, C. Pike and C. Deline, "Vertical Bifacial Photovoltaic System Model Validation: Study With Field Data, Various Orientations, and Latitudes," in IEEE Journal of Photovoltaics, vol. 15, no. 4, pp. 600-609, July 2025, doi: 10.1109/JPHOTOV.2025.3561395.
10. Øgaard, M. B., Nysted, V. S., Rønneberg, S., Otnes, G., Foss, S. E., Mongstad, T., & Riise, H. N. (2024). Vertical bifacial PV systems: irradiance modeling and performance analysis of a lightweight system for flat roofs. EPJ Photovoltaics, 15(13). https://doi.org/10.1051/epjpv/2024012.
11. Kang, J., Jang, J., Reise, C., & Lee, K. (2019, September 9-13). Practical comparison between view factor method and ray-tracing method for bifacial PV system yield prediction [Conference presentation]. 36th European PV Solar Energy Conference and Exhibition, Marseille, France.
12. Xie, Y., & Sengupta, M. (2016, June 20-24). Performance analysis of transposition models simulating solar radiation on inclined surfaces [Conference presentation]. European PV Solar Conference and Exhibition (EU PVSEC), Munich, Germany.
13. Ayala Peláez, S., Deline, C., Marion, B., Sekulic, B., & Stein, J. (2019, December 18). *Understanding bifacial PV modeling: Raytracing and view factor models* [Webinar]. PV Magazine Webinar. National Renewable Energy Laboratory.
14. Berrian D, Libal J. A comparison of ray tracing and view factor simulations of locally resolved rear irradiance with the experimental values. Prog Photovolt Res Appl. 2020; 28: 609–620. https://doi.org/10.1002/pip.3261
15. Schinke, C., Vogt, M.R. and Bothe, K. (2018). Optical Modeling of Photovoltaic Modules with Ray Tracing Simulations. In Photovoltaic Modeling Handbook, M.F. Müller (Ed.). https://doi.org/10.1002/9781119364214.ch3
16. Kosmopoulos, P., Dhake, H., Kartoudi, D., Tsavalos, A., Koutsantoni, P., Katranitsas, A., Lavdakis, N., Mengou, E., & Kashyap, Y. (2024). Ray-Tracing modeling for urban photovoltaic energy planning and management. Applied Energy, 369, 123516. https://doi.org/10.1016/j.apenergy.2024.123516
17. S. Ayala Pelaez and C. Deline, Bifacial_radiance: a python package for modeling bifacial solar photovoltaic systems, J. Open Source Software, 5 (NREL/JA-5K00-75222), 2020.
18. Honningdalsnes, E. H., Marstein, E. S., Nygård, M. M., Wiig, M. S., & Riise, H. N. (2025). Benchmarking irradiation models for photovoltaic applications: A comparative analysis of radiance-based tools. *Solar Energy, 296*,113566. https://doi.org/10.1016/j.solener.2025.113566
19. Andres C, Ruben C, David G, et al. Time-varying, ray tracing irradiance simulation

approach for photovoltaic systems in complex scenarios with decoupled geometry, optical properties and illumination conditions. *Prog Photovolt Res Appl*. 2023; 31(2): 134-148. doi:10.1002/pip.3614
20. Parenti, M., Memme, S., & Fossa, M. (2025). Sky radiance distribution based model for rear and front insolation estimation on PV bifacial modules. Solar Energy Materials and Solar Cells, 289, 113677. https://doi.org/10.1016/j.solmat.2025.113677
21. Mollier, S. and Tsanakas, J. A. (2023). Assessing uncertainties from reflected irradiance in bifacial PV simulations through a 3D view factor model and rear sensor measurements. In Proceedings of the 40th EU PVSEC 2023 (pp. 020230-001–020230-004). WIP.https://doi.org/10.4229/EUPVSEC2023/3AV.3.33
22. Merodio, P., Martínez-Moreno, F., & Lorenzo, E. (2025). Experimental determination of the structure shading factor and mismatch losses for bifacial photovoltaic modules on variable-geometry, single-axis trackers. Solar Energy, 291, 113400. https://doi.org/10.1016/j.solener.2025.113400
23. Jouttijärvi, S., Thorning, J., Manni, M., Huerta, H., Ranta, S., Di Sabatino, M., Lobaccaro, G., & Miettunen, K. (2023). A comprehensive methodological workflow to maximize solar energy in low-voltage grids: A case study of vertical bifacial panels in Nordic conditions. *Solar Energy, 262*, 111819. https://doi.org/10.1016/j.solener.2023.111819
24. Riedel-Lyngskær, N., Ribaconka, M., Pó, M., Thorseth, A., Thorsteinsson, S., Dam-Hansen, C., & Jakobsen, M. L. (2022). The effect of spectral albedo in bifacial photovoltaic performance. Solar Energy, 231, 921–935. https://doi.org/10.1016/j.solener.2021.12.023
25. Tonita EM, Valdivia CE, Russell ACJ, Martinez-Szewczyk M, Bertoni MI, Hinzer K. Quantifying spectral albedo effects on bifacial photovoltaic module measurements and system model predictions. Prog Photovolt Res Appl. 2024; 32(7): 468-480. doi:10.1002/pip.3789
26. Onno, A., Rodkey, N., Asgharzadeh, A., Manzoor, S., Yu, Z. J., Toor, F., Holman, Z. C. (2020). Predicted power output of silicon-based bifacial tandem photovoltaic systems. Joule, 4(3), 580–596. 10.1016/j.joule.2019.12.017.
27. Ghafiri, S., Darnon, M., Davigny, A., Trovão, J. P. F., & Abbes, D. (2024). A comprehensive performance evaluation of bifacial photovoltaic modules: Insights from a year-long experimental study conducted in the Canadian climate. EPJ Photovoltaics, *15*, Article 28. https://doi.org/10.1051/epjpv/2024025
28. Su, X., Luo, C., Chen, X. et al. Numerical modeling of all-day albedo variation for bifacial PV systems on rooftops and annual yield prediction in Beijing. Build. Simul. 17, 955–964 (2024). https://doi.org/10.1007/s12273-024-1120-y

42nd European Photovoltaic Solar Energy Conference and Exhibition

This presentation was selected by the Sc. Committee of the EU PVSEC 2025 for submission of a full paper to one of the EU PVSEC's collaborating peer-reviewed journals.

DETAILED ANALYSIS OF DEGRADATION RATES OF OPERATING PV ASSETS IN TROPICAL CLIMATE CONDITIONS

Xiaoqi Xu[a], André M. Nobre[b], Han Cao[a], Yu Xu[a], Ian Marius Peters[c], Thomas Reindl[a]
a. Solar Energy Research Institute of Singapore, National University of Singapore, 117574, Singapore
b. PV Doctor Pte Ltd, 18 Cross Street, #02-101, 18 Cross, 048423, Singapore
c. Forschungszentrum Jülich GmbH, Institut für Energietechnologien, IET-2, Erlangen, 91058, Germany

ABSTRACT: This study presents an evaluation of photovoltaic system performance loss rates in tropical climates. We analysed a dataset of 35 sites totalling 22.3 MWp installations across seven countries, spanning residential, commercial, and industrial applications. Data collection periods ranged from two to 11.7 years. Meteorological and power data were recorded at one-minute to 15 minutes intervals, enabling both sensor-based performance calculations and modelled clearsky irradiation analysis. The study includes different c-Si wafer types (multi-crystalline, mono-crystalline), different silicon solar cell technologies (p-type multi-crystalline silicon, mono-crystalline silicon, PERCand n-type mono-crystalline silicon), as well as thin-film types (largely CdTe). The database was further classified by climate zones (within the tropical classification), module types (mono-facial vs. bi-facial), installation types (rooftop vs. ground-mounted), and module configurations (full cell vs. half cell).. The analysis identified mean and median performance change across systems of -1.41 %/year and -1.10 %/year, respectively, with degradation accelerating over time. This is higher than typically assumed in PV system design and financial modelling (often using 0.7-1.0%/year for the tropics). The analysis shows that there is a trend towards accelerating performance losses with system age, indicating that studies of newer systems may underestimate long-term degradation. This work serves as a solid foundation for further studies into the root causes of the higher PLRs in tropical climates, which then would enable the development of suitable strategies for optimizing the long-term performance and reliability of PV systems in the challenging environmental conditions of the tropics.

1 INTRODUCTION

The global solar industry is experiencing unprecedented growth, with the annual installations in 2024 exceeding 600 GWp and total capacity having reached 2 TWp by the end of 2024 [1]. The tropical sunbelt regions contribute >100 GWp of installed capacity in 2024 [2], representing >5% of global installations, with a huge growth potential due to the large population living there [3]. Accurately assessing the historic and current performance of PV installations in the harsher conditions of the tropics (constant high temperatures and high humidity levels) is critical for correctly projecting durability, reliability and yield over the systems' lifetime - which ultimately leads to lower levelized cost of electricity (LCOE) of the operating assets [4].

While South- and Southeast Asian countries are blessed with abundant solar energy potential, there has been reports about the accelerated decline in solar PV performance in hot and humid environments [5]. Environmental interactions can significantly influence and accelerate degradation mechanisms, leading to reduced material lifetimes of different PV technologies.

This study analyses a diverse dataset to investigate performance loss rates across tropical Asian regions using methodologies that enables direct comparison with existing studies.

2 EXPERIMENTAL DETAILS

2.1 DATABASE DESCRIPTION

The study analyses PV systems in 35 sites across India and Southeast Asia (Fig. 1), covering broad range of system sizes and module technologies.

All locations fall within a Köppen-Geiger climate classifications of Af (tropical rainforest) or As/Aw (tropical savanna/monsoon). The database comprises 35 sites with a total capacity of 22.3 MWp and a median system size of 422 kWp, providing comprehensive insights into PV performance in tropical climate conditions.

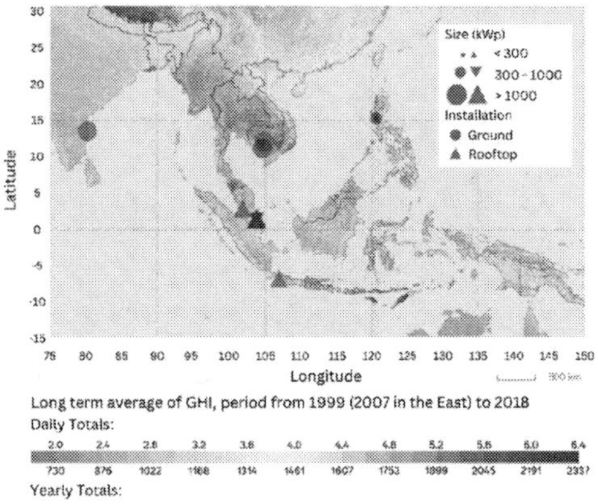

Figure 1: Graphical distribution of PV systems under study against the backdrop of the Solargis irradiance map [6]

2.2 *ANALYSIS METHOD*

Data collected at intervals between one to 15 minutes in this work enables detailed performance analysis across the region. The analysis utilizes DC-side inverter data when available, defaulting to AC-side measurements otherwise. Environmental parameters are recorded at all sites, with irradiance measured as either global horizontal irradiance (GHI), plane-of-array (POA) irradiance, or both simultaneously. Ambient temperature is recorded at every site, while module temperature and wind speed data are available for select locations.

Site analyses were performed using two datasets: measured local irradiance and temperature values (called "Sensor" dataset) and modelled irradiance and temperature under clear-sky conditions (called "Clearsky" dataset). Operational data were normalized using PVWatt [7] as expected power ($P_{expected}$) and described by

$$P_{expected} = \frac{G_{POA}}{1000 \cdot P_{stc}}\left(1 + \gamma_T(T_{mod} - 25\,°C)\right) \quad (1)$$

Here, G_{POA} is in-plane irradiance measured or transposed from GHI using the Perez model [8], P_{stc} is the nameplate power at STC conditions, γ_T is the temperature coefficient of the respective PV module technology and T_{mod} is the module temperature. The normalized data were then filtered using the following criteria: normalized values greater than 0.01, irradiance range of 200–1,200 W/m², and ambient temperature range of -50°C to 110°C.

Data were aggregated to daily values for year-on-year (YOY) statistical analysis.

3 RESULTS AND DISCUSSIONS

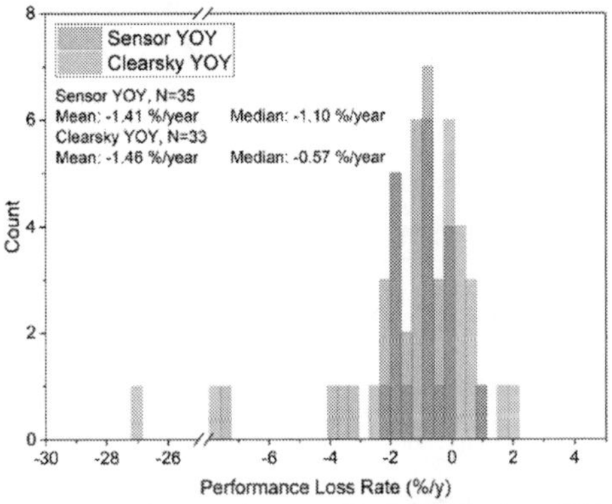

Figure 2: Performance loss rate (PLR) distribution of PV systems in this study, with sensor-based normalization ("Sensor YOY") in blue and modelled irradiance clearsky-based normalization ("Clearsky YOY") in orange. Negative values signify system performance degradation, while positive values may arise from data quality issues or methodological uncertainties.

Fig. 2 presents the PLR (Performance Loss Rate) distribution for the 35 tropical PV sites, comparing two analytical approaches: Sensor-based YOY and Clearsky YOY. The methods result in mean PLR rates of -1.41%/year for Sensor and -1.46%/year for Clearsky (YOY) and respective medians of -1.10%/year and -0.57%/year. The p-values was found at 0.33 (>0.05) suggesting that the observed difference could easily occur by random chance and there is no statistically significant difference between the two means. Due to the high variance and some extreme outliers in the Clearsky YOY, the results and discussion presented below uses only data from the Sensor YOY.

Comparing these tropical PLR values against other climate regions reveals notable differences. A study of a 7.2 GW PV fleet across the United State revealed a median of -0.75%/year [9]. The analysis of 8400 residential systems in Europe showed the mean and median PLR's of -0.86%/year and -0.67% in Sensor YOY method Sensor YOY method using satellite irradiance [10]. The higher median PLR (-1.09%/year) observed in the tropical portfolio analysed here aligns with expected accelerated degradation in tropical versus temperate climates, despite a variance of 2.28%/year.

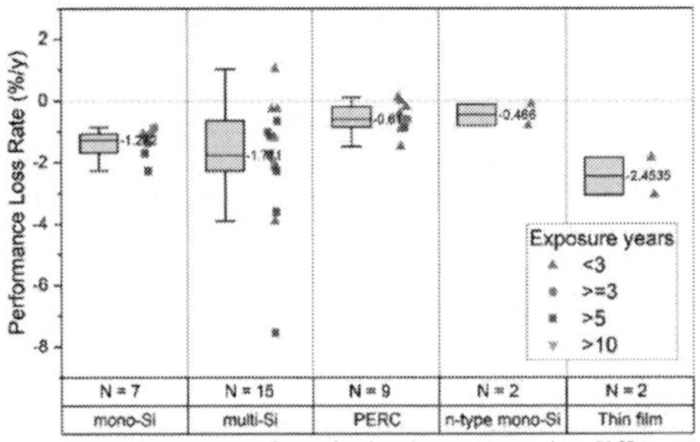

Figure 3: The PLRs of tropical solar systems by different cell technologies. [The subset sample sizes are only preliminary and will be much higher in the EPJ Photovoltaics]

Fig. 3 summarizes the PLRs across different PV cell technologies. Multi-Si and Mono-Si modules exhibited median PLRs of -1.77%/year and -1.27%/year, respectively. The observed exceptions likely stem from PLR analysis variance, highlighting the need for larger sample sizes to draw definitive conclusions. A broader study in temperate climates [11] similarly confirmed higher PLRs in Multi-Si modules.

It is also evident that technologies such as PERC, n-type mono-Si, and thin-film (largely CdTe modules) lack data points for exposure years greater than 5 years – which is exactly when degradation variance appears highest as can also be seen from the Fig. 3. These newer technologies' datasets have limited observations, averaging 2.7 years with maximum exposure of 5.9 years. In contrast, Multi-Si and Mono-Si datasets span 2.3-8.5 years and 2.0-11.7 years respectively. Thus, despite apparent PLR differences across cell technologies, the data at this stage are only indicative regarding degradation of newer cell technologies.

Fig. 4 presents PLR distributions across four other categorizations.

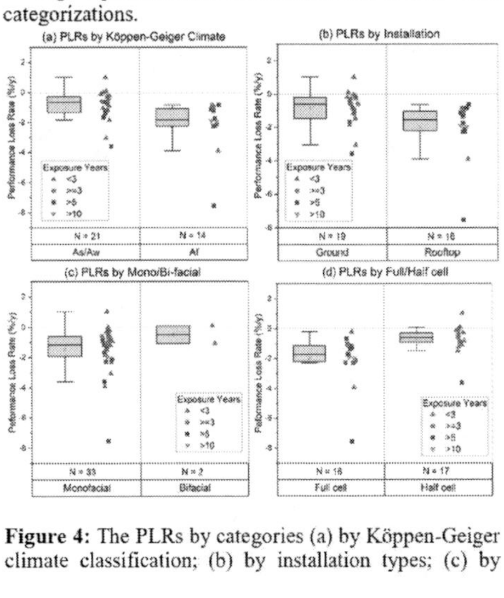

Figure 4: The PLRs by categories (a) by Köppen-Geiger climate classification; (b) by installation types; (c) by

10.4229/EUPVSEC2025/4BO.7.3

mono-facial or bi-facial modules; (d) by full cell or half-cell configuration.

In the current sample size of 35 sites, PV systems located in As/Aw climate zones are mostly ground-mounted installations, while those in Af zones are predominantly rooftop systems. This will likely be harmonised in the full sample size later on. Furthermore, As/Aw or ground mount systems datasets lack longer exposures, introducing temporal bias similar to that discussed in the technology comparison. This interrelation necessitates further investigation to determine whether PLR differences stem from climatic conditions, installation methods, or temporal bias in the dataset. Preliminary comparison between mono-facial and bi-facial systems suggests potential similarities in performance, though the limited bifacial sample size prevents definitive conclusions. While t-test results for full-cell versus half-cell systems indicate statistical significance (t-value = -1.38, p = 0.40), this finding requires cautious interpretation as most samples represent systems under 3 years of operation. Thus, current data cannot substantiate claims of superior reliability of half-cell technology.

4 CONCLUSIONS

The analysis of PV system degradation in tropical regions presented here (using a current dataset of 35 sites totalling 22.3 MWp), reveals mean and median PLRs of -1.41%/year and -1.10%/year respectively, higher than typically assumed in PV system design and financial modelling. While Sensor YOY methodology demonstrates robust PLR estimates, the study uncovers a critical temporal bias in systems operating beyond 5 years, highlighting the necessity for extended operational data.

The manuscript submitted to EPJ PV will expand this analysis to encompass more sites with a larger portfolio, also incorporating larger solar farms. This expanded study will complement YOY analysis with traditional linear regression approaches, enabling direct comparison with existing literature. Furthermore, the influence of environmental factors on degradation rates will be examined in greater detail to identify the key drivers of performance loss across different categorizations.

REFERENCES

[1] Global Solar Council, "Global Solar Council announces 2 terawatt milestone achieved for solar," Global Solar Council.

[2] IRENA (2025), Renewable Capacity Statistics 2025. Abu Dhabi: International Renewable Energy Agency, 2025. [Online]. Available: www.irena.org.

[3] World Population Review (2025), Countries in the Tropics 2025. https://worldpopulationreview.com

[4] I. M. Peters, J. Hauch, C. Brabec, and P. Sinha, "The value of stability in photovoltaics," Joule, vol. 5, no. 12, pp. 3137–3153, Dec. 2021, doi: 10.1016/j.joule.2021.10.019.

[5] D. C. Jordan, S. R. Kurtz, K. VanSant, and J. Newmiller, "Compendium of photovoltaic degradation rates," Progress in Photovoltaics: Research and Applications, vol. 24, no. 7, pp. 978–989, Jul. 2016, doi: 10.1002/pip.2744.

[6] Solargis, "Solar resource maps of Asia, Global Horizontal Irradiation," Solar resource map © 2021 Solargis.

[7] National Renewable Energy Laboratory, "PVWatts version 5 manual," 2014, NREL: 5.

[8] F. Almonacid, P. J. Pérez-Higueras, E. F. Fernández, and L. Hontoria, "A methodology based on dynamic artificial neural network for short-term forecasting of the power output of a PV generator," Energy Convers Manag, vol. 85, pp. 389–398, 2014, doi: 10.1016/j.enconman.2014.05.090.

[9] D. C. Jordan et al., "Photovoltaic fleet degradation insights," Progress in Photovoltaics: Research and Applications, vol. 30, no. 10, pp. 1166–1175, Oct. 2022, doi: 10.1002/pip.3566.

[10] S. Lindig, J. Ascencio-Vasquez, J. Leloux, D. Moser, and A. Reinders, "Performance Analysis and Degradation of a Large Fleet of PV Systems," IEEE J Photovolt, vol. 11, no. 5, pp. 1312–1318, Sep. 2021, doi: 10.1109/JPHOTOV.2021.3093049.

[11] D. C. Jordan, C. Deline, S. R. Kurtz, G. M. Kimball, and M. Anderson, "Robust PV Degradation Methodology and Application," IEEE J Photovolt, vol. 8, no. 2, pp. 525–531, Mar. 2018, doi: 10.1109/JPHOTOV.2017.2779779.

PV DOCTOR Asset Management

NUS National University of Singapore | SERIS Solar Energy Research Institute of Singapore

Detailed Analysis of Degradation Rates of Operating PV Assets in Tropical Climate Conditions

Xiaoqi XU, André M. NOBRE*, Han CAO, Yu XU, Ian Marius PETERS, Thomas REINDL

EU PVSEC, Bilbao, 23rd Sep 2025

* PV DOCTOR Pte. Ltd.

NATIONAL RESEARCH FOUNDATION PRIME MINISTER'S OFFICE SINGAPORE

ENERGY MARKET AUTHORITY Our Clean Energy Future

EDB SINGAPORE

SERIS is a research institute at the National University of Singapore (NUS). SERIS is supported by NUS, the National Research Foundation Singapore (NRF), the Energy Market Authority of Singapore (EMA) and the Singapore Economic Development Board (EDB).

SERIS

Solar Energy Research Institute of Singapore

- National Lab founded at NUS in 2008; supported by NUS, NRF, EMA & EDB
- Focuses on applied solar energy research (solar cells, PV modules, PV systems)
- > 120 staff & PhD students; state-of-the-art labs, ISO certified (9001, 17025)
- Close collaborations with companies & government agencies

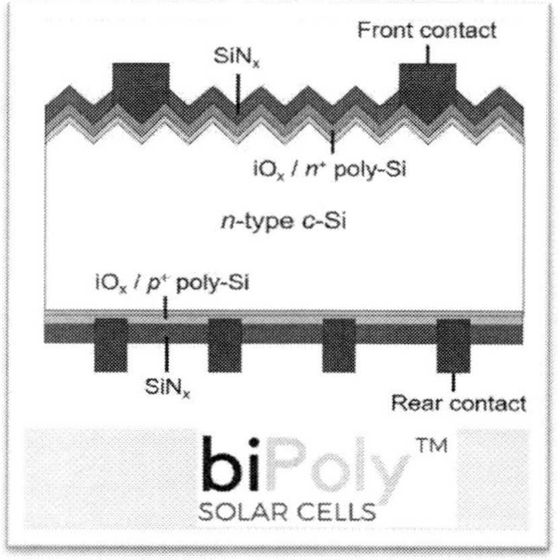

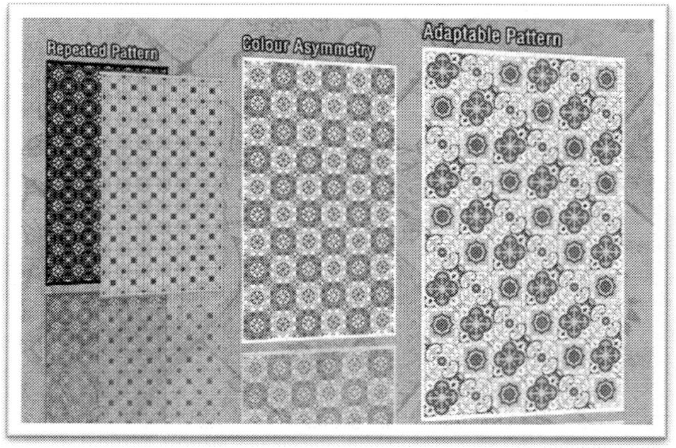

The Motivation

- Years of operation and degradation rate rank as the two most sensitive **operational** factors for IRR, stressing the economic importance of performance reliability — and the two are linked.
- The tropical sunbelt regions contribute approximately 97 GW [1] of installed capacity, representing ~7% of global installations as of 2023 [2].

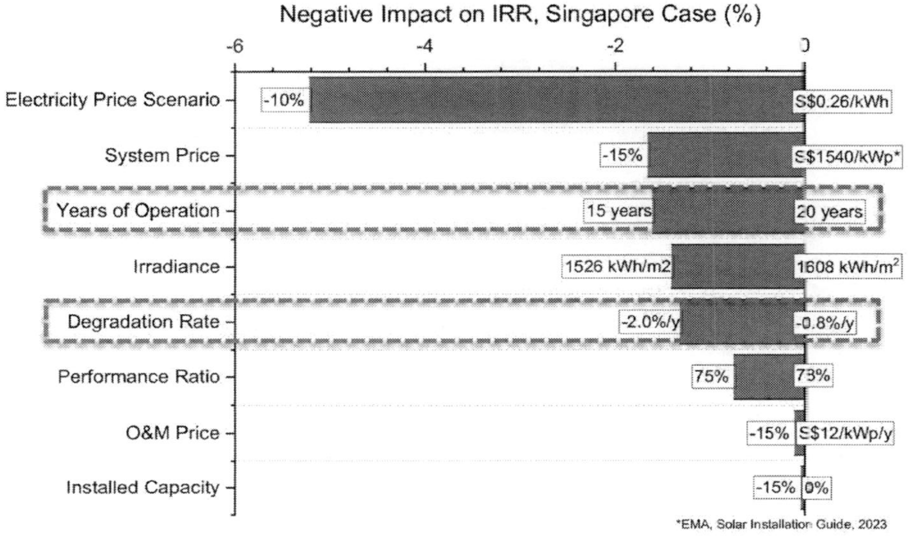

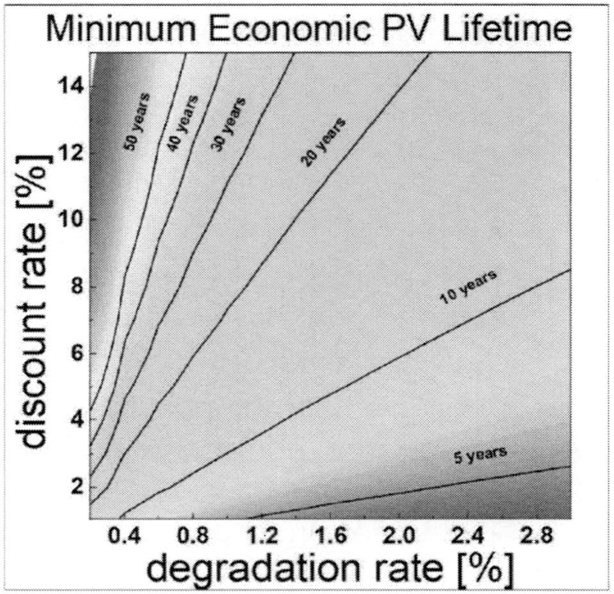

[1] IRENA, Renewable Capacity Statistics 2024, 2024
[2] IEA PVPS, Snapshot of Global PV Markets, 2020–2025
[3] Peters, I.M., et al., Joule 5, 3137–3153, 2021

Degradation Study in Tropical Climates

- We analysed a dataset of 40 sites totalling 90.6 MWp installations across 7 countries, spanning residential, commercial, and industrial applications.
- Through collaboration with PV Doctor, this study draws on one of the most comprehensive tropical PV degradation datasets to date, which will expand >10x data in upcoming work through SERIS / PV Doctor.

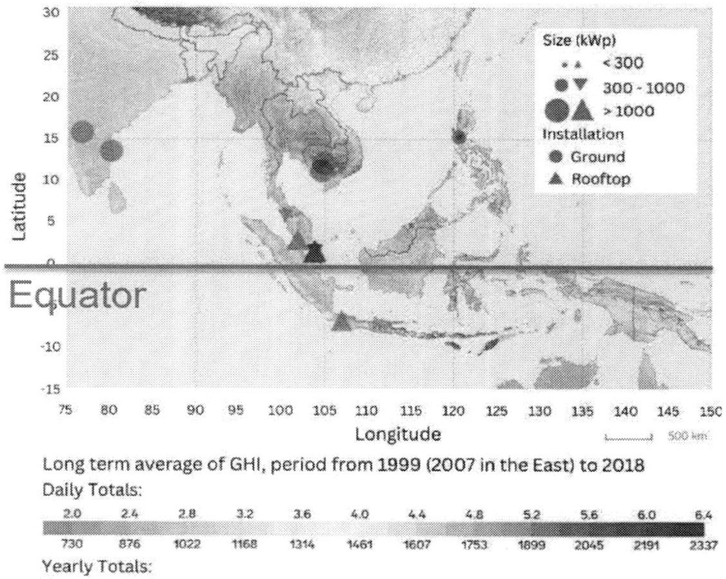

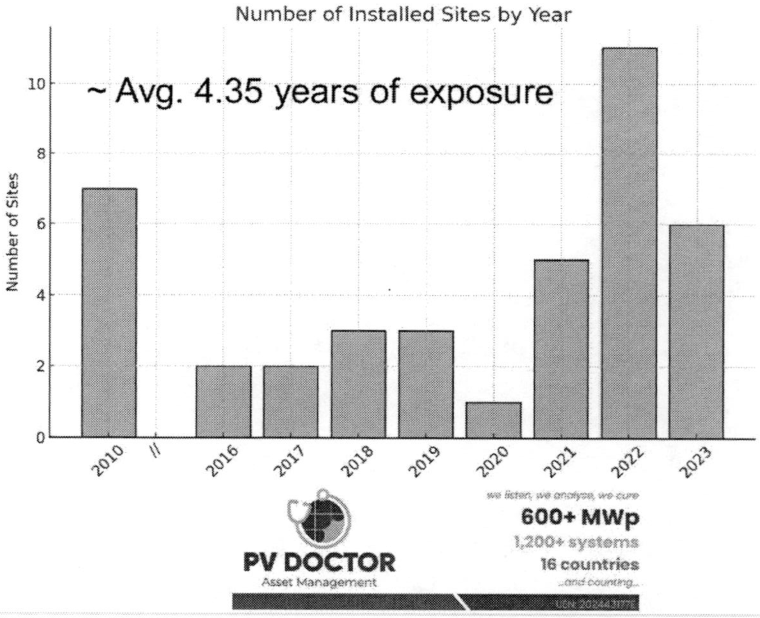

Backdrop Graph: Solar resource map © 2021 Solargis
https://solargis.com/resources/free-maps-and-gis-data?locality=asia

Data Source: PV Doctor, Singapore (http://pv.doctor/en)
(In preparation for publication) X.XU | EU PVSEC 2025| 23/09/2025

Methodologies and Results

- ❑ Three different analytical methods [1] implemented to obtain **system-level** Performance Loss Rates (PLRs)
- ❑ **"Sensor YOY" provides robust method, identifying mean and median of -1.4%/y and -1.2%/y**

Our Research Findings:

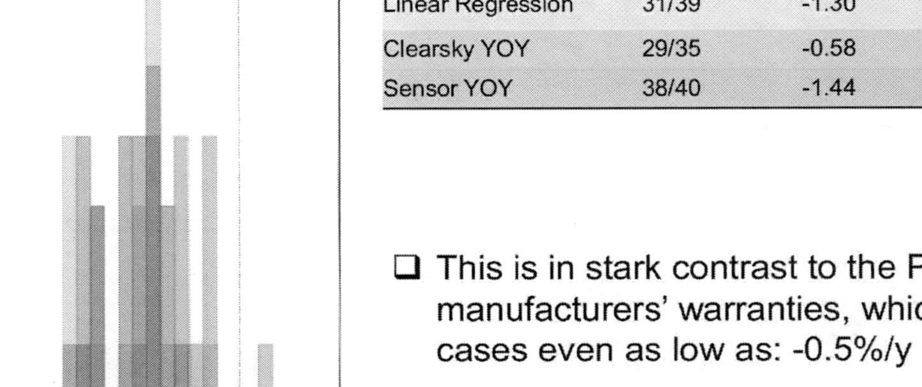

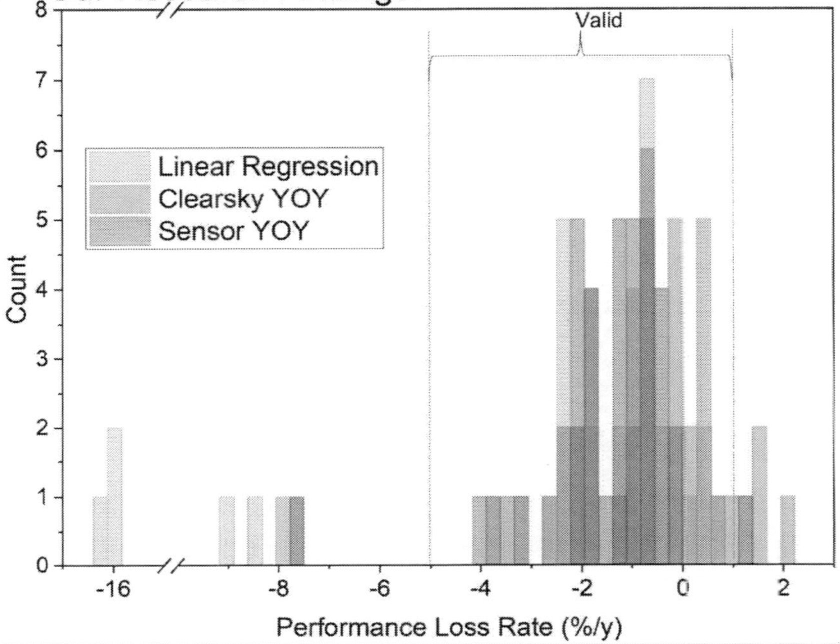

Results Summary	N total (Valid/Data)	Mean (%/y)	Median (%/y)	Std.Dev (%/y)
Linear Regression	31/39	-1.30	-1.05	1.09
Clearsky YOY	29/35	-0.58	-0.57	0.97
Sensor YOY	38/40	-1.44	-1.21	0.96

- ❑ This is in stark contrast to the PV module manufacturers' warranties, which are in some cases even as low as: -0.5%/y

[1] D.C. Jordan et al., IEEE J. Photovolt., 8(2), pp. 525–531, 2018

PLRs in the Tropics

- Past literature on tropical degradation studies are compiled, which largely agree with this study
- **Module-level**: mean degradation of -1.3%/y with lower variability (σ≈0.7%/y) reported;
  System-level: studies show a higher mean of -1.5%/y with greater variability (σ≈1.5%/y)

Tropical Literature	N total	Mean (%/y)	Median (%/y)	Std.Dev (%/y)
Literature, Module level	127	-1.28	-1.33	0.75
Literature, String/System level	35	-1.45	-1.13	1.53
This study, System level	38	-1.44	-1.21	0.96

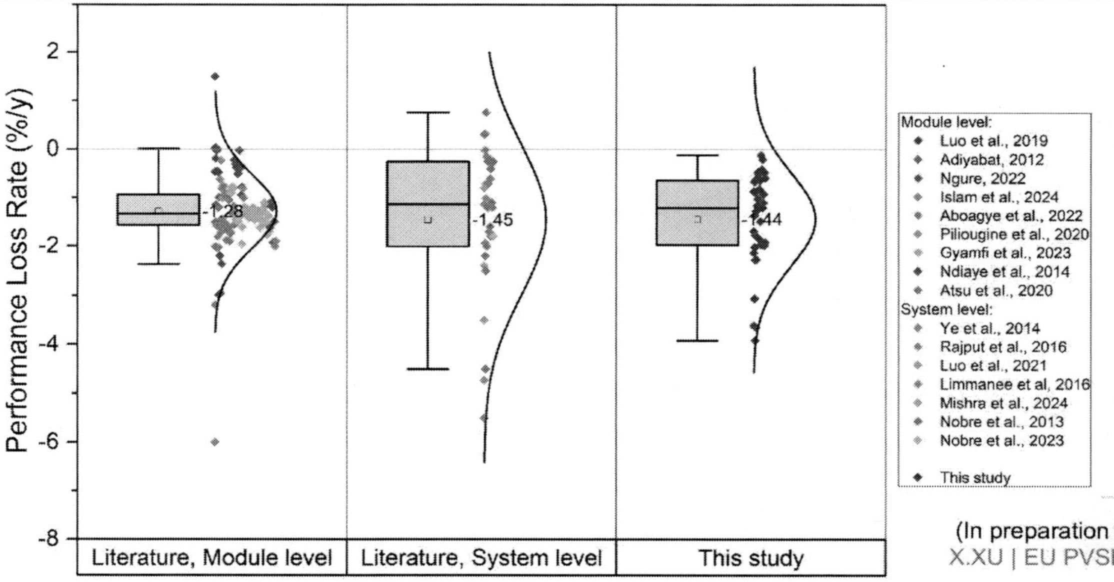

(In preparation for publication)

X.XU | EU PVSEC 2025| 23/09/2025 6

PLRs by Regions

- ❑ The observed PLR are at faster decline in tropical climates, than those reported in temperate regions
- ❑ **By Regions**: Europe (Residentials), USA fleet and this study — the results of Levene's test (variances), Welch's ANOVA (means), and the Kruskal-Wallis test (non-parametric) all indicated statistically differences

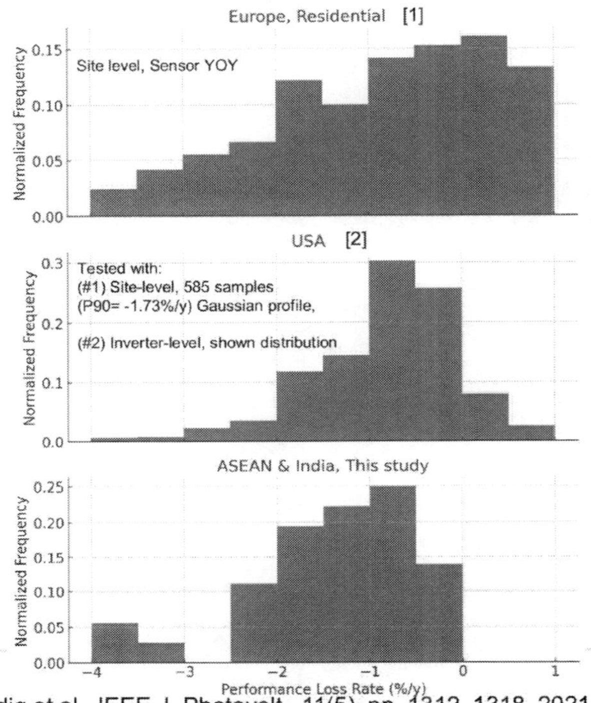

Tropical Literature	N total	Mean (%/y)	Median (%/y)	Std.Dev (%/y)
#1. Europe, Residential [1]	361	-0.86	-0.67	1.40 (est.)
#2. USA [2], Inverter-level	4915	-0.88	-0.75	0.60 (est.)
#3. USA [2], System-level	585	-0.86	-0.68	0.68 (est.)
#4. ASEAN & India, this study	38*	-1.44	-1.21	0.96

* Based on current dataset, will be tackled more in future works

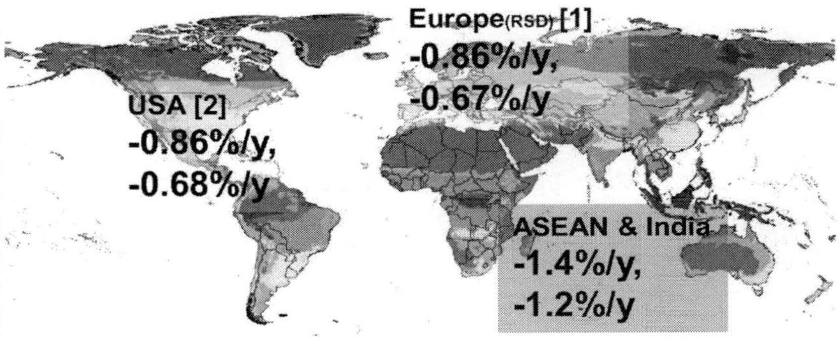

[1] S. Lindig et al., IEEE J. Photovolt., 11(5), pp. 1312–1318, 2021
[2] D.C. Jordan et al., Progress in Photovoltaics, 2022

(In preparation for publication) X.XU | EU PVSEC 2025| 23/09/2025

[3] H.E. Beck et al., Sci. Data, 5:180214, 2018

PLRs by Cell Technologies and Age

- ❑ **By Cell Technology**: Mean PLRs vary (mono-Si ~-1.3%, multi-Si ~-2.0%, PERC ~-0.6%, n-mono ~-0.7%, thin-film ~-2.5%), but “Analysis of Variance” (ANOVA) shows no statistically significant difference
- ❑ **By Exposure Years**: PLRs range from about -0.8% to -2.1% depending on field age group, yet differences are not statistically significant

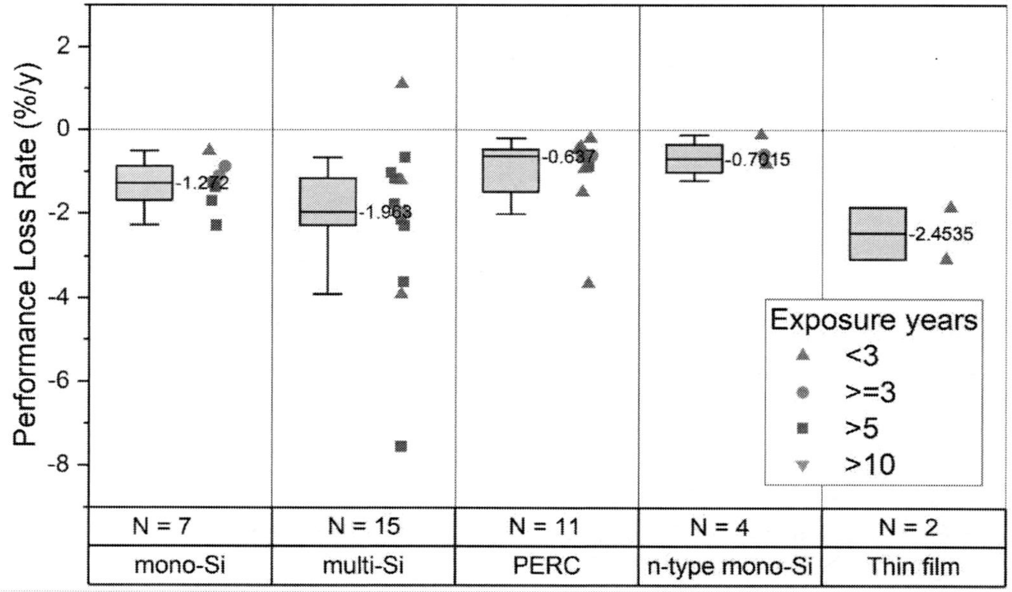

(By age, p=0.25)

(By cell, p=0.18)

PLRs by Other Categories

- **Climate & Installation**: Current dataset shows Af zones mainly rooftop, As/Aw zones mainly ground-mount, with fewer long-term exposures → possible temporal bias. Further work needed to separate climate, installation type, and age effects on PLR.
- **Mono/Bi-Facial & Full/Half cell**: Preliminary data suggest monofacial ≈ bifacial PLRs; half-cell vs. full-cell shows no reliable difference

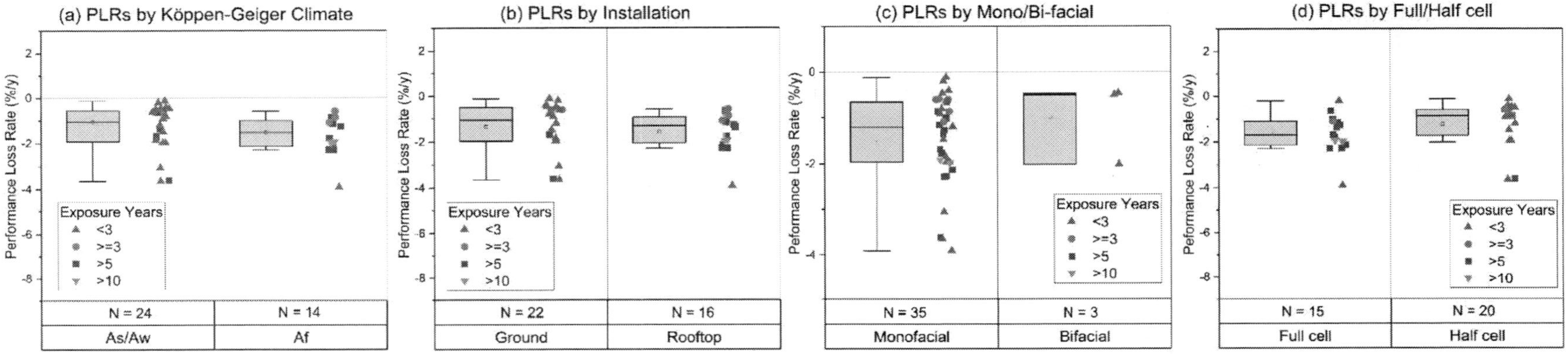

Europe (RSD)
-0.86%/y,
-0.67%/y

Koeppen-Geiger Climate classification: **Af** = Tropical rainforest; **As** = Tropical Savanna (dry summer); **Aw** = Tropical Savanna (dry winter)

(In preparation for publication) X.XU | EU PVSEC 2025| 23/09/2025 9

Climate Difference in Tamb and Irradiance

- Environmental stressors such as ambient temperature, irradiance, and cumulative UV exposure were examined to explore potential factors that may influence PLR.

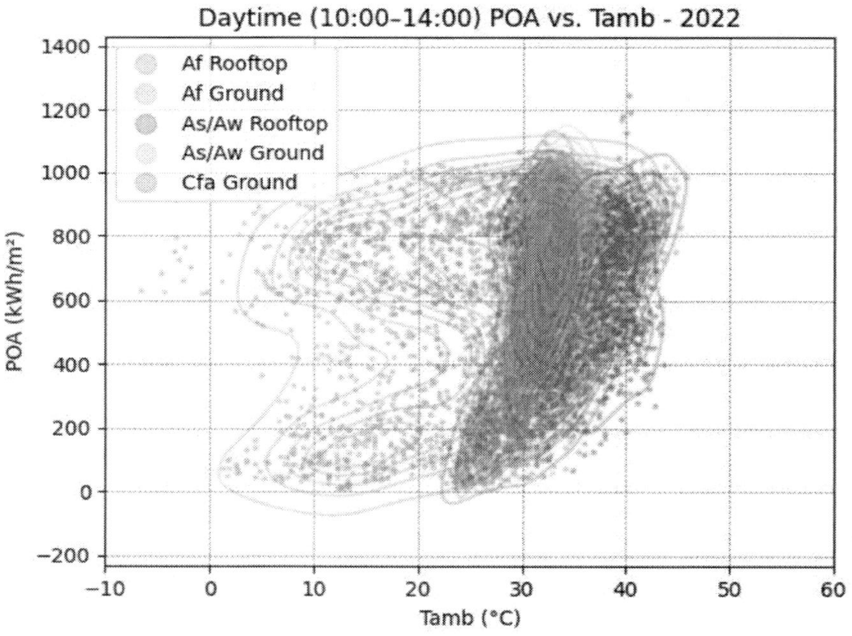

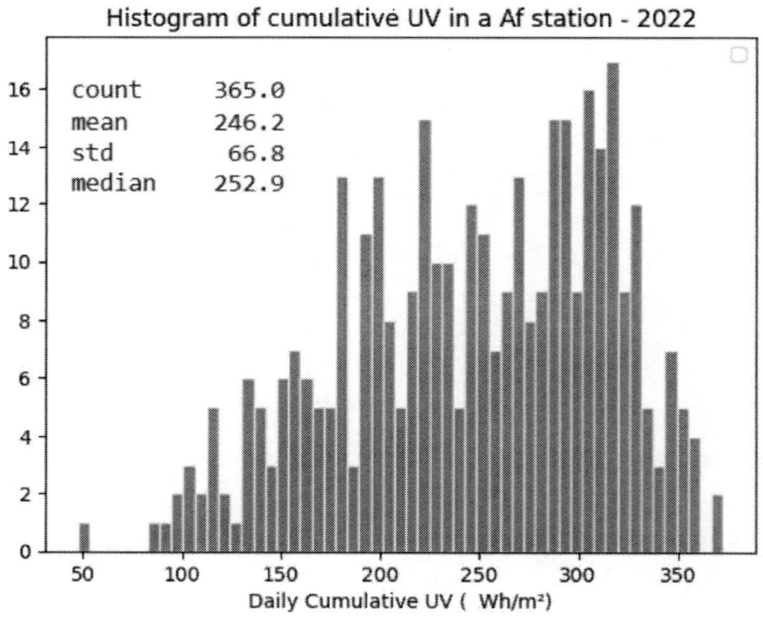

Cfa data: NREL. (2021). Photovoltaic Data Acquisition (PVDAQ) Public Datasets [Station ID:3D33]

(In preparation for publication)

Climate Difference in Tmod

- ❑ Median: +8.9 °C (As/Aw ground) and +11.1 °C (Af rooftop) vs. Cfa ground.
- ❑ 25% quantile: Cfa ground shows much lower values (longer left tail).
- ❑ Spread: Cfa ground has the widest variability (σ = 13.5 °C).

Module Temperature		Mean (°C)	Median (°C)	25% (°C)	75% (°C)	90% (°C)	Std (°C)
Ground	As/Aw	46.7	48.1	42.7	51.9	54.9	7.3
	Cfa	37.8	39.0	28.4	48.1	54.4	13.5
Rooftop	Af	48.9	50.0	41.0	57.9	62.4	11.2

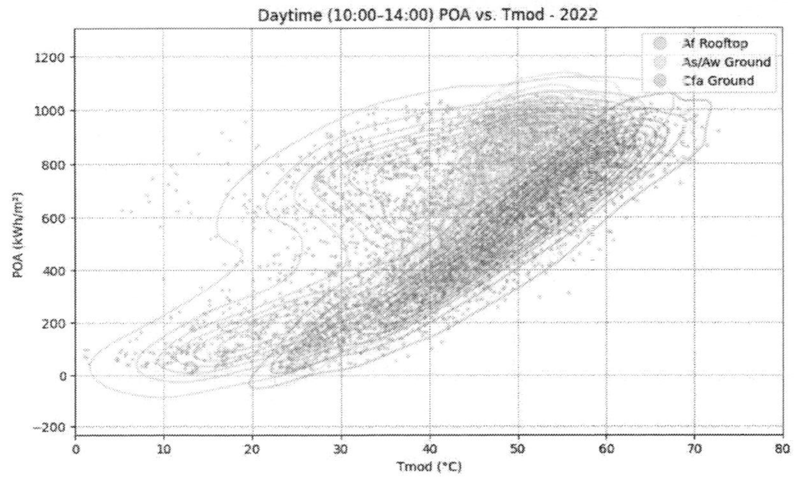

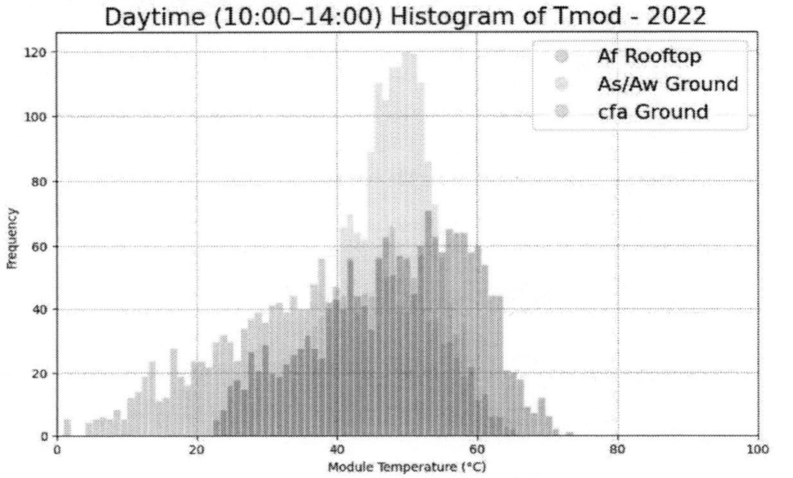

Cfa data: NREL. (2021). Photovoltaic Data Acquisition (PVDAQ) Public Datasets [Station ID:3D33]

(In preparation for publication)

Conclusions

- ❑ Years of operation and degradation rate rank as the two most sensitive operational factors for IRR, stressing the economic importance of performance reliability — and the two are linked.
- ❑ Tropical regions PV now account for ~97 GW (~7% of global PV as of 2023), highlighting their rising importance in the global fleet.
- ❑ **PLRs in the tropics identified mean and median of -1.4%/y and -1.2%/y, respectively, based on current dataset.**
- ❑ Our findings are consistent with past datasets in tropical regions and further demonstrate that PV degradation progresses significantly faster in the tropics compared to Europe and the USA.
- ❑ There is no clear statistical difference across cell technologies, system ages, installation types, or mono vs. bifacial and half-cell vs. full-cell designs, highlighting the need for a larger dataset.
- ❑ The characterisation of Tamb, irradiance, UV, and Tmod across Af and As/Aw applications were provided, forming a basis for future research to better interpret their role in degradation outcomes.
- ❑ Tropical climate degradation remains under-studied — advancing knowledge requires broader datasets, open data sharing, and stronger collaboration across stakeholders.

NUS National University of Singapore | SERIS Solar Energy Research Institute of Singapore

Thank you for your attention!
Contact: Lucia XU
lucia.xu@nus.edu.sg

More information at www.seris.sg

We are also on:

ISO 9001 SGS | UKAS MANAGEMENT SYSTEMS 0005

Accredited Laboratory SAC-SINGLAS LA-2012-0526-E

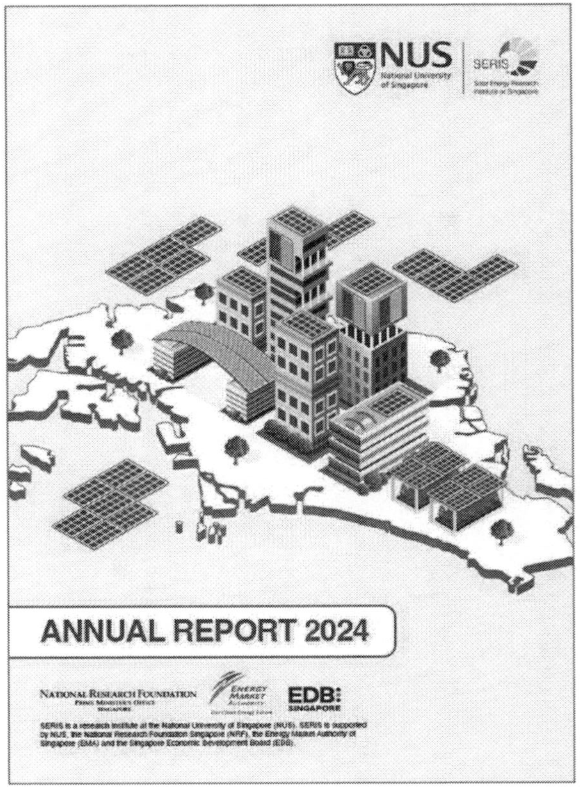

42nd European Photovoltaic Solar Energy Conference and Exhibition

This presentation was selected by the Sc. Committee of the EU PVSEC 2025 for submission of a full paper to one of the EU PVSEC's collaborating peer-reviewed journals.

MODELING THE ELECTRICAL MISMATCH CAUSED BY POTENTIAL INDUCED DEGRADATION IN CRYSTALLINE SILICON PHOTOVOLTAIC MODULES AND STRINGS

Aysha Mahmood, Gisele Alves dos Reis Benatto, Sune Thorsteinsson, Peter B. Poulsen and Sergiu V. Spataru
Department of Electrical and Photonics Engineering, Technical University of Denmark
Frederiksborgvej 399, 4000, Roskilde, Denmark.

ABSTRACT: Potential induced degradation (PID) is known to cause, depending on its mechanism, degradation in the current and/or voltage of a solar cell and affect photovoltaic (PV) modules within a PV string non-uniformly. The purpose of this work is to model and estimate the additional power loss that occurs due to current and/or voltage mismatch in the system, caused by polarization and shunting type of PID. The impact of PID on the current-voltage (I-V) characteristics is modeled for a PV array consisting of eight parallelly connected strings with 22 serially connected 60-cell PV modules using PySpice where each solar cell in the PV array is represented by a two-diode equivalent circuit model. The degradation is introduced by adjusting the input parameters of the model to values that are reported in literature. To generate realistic I-V curves, the model considers variability in solar cell performance within a module and string due to non-uniform degradation. The power mismatch loss is calculated for twelve different degradation scenarios to assess the long-term performance of the degraded PV arrays. The P_{LOSS} of the PV array affected with PID-p is ~5.25 % and the ML is 0.72 %. The PV array with PID-s has a P_{LOSS} of ~ 10 % and a ML of 2.35 % at the most degraded stage.
Keywords: Modeling, Electrical mismatch, Potential-induced degradation, Crystalline silicon, Photovoltaic system.

1 INTRODUCTION

Photovoltaic (PV) modules deployed in utility scale PV systems can be affected by different faults and/or degradation modes due to exposure to several operational and environmental stress factors. These external stress factors may, depending on the susceptibility of the deployed PV technology or a PV module composite to a certain fault and/or degradation mode, non-uniformly impact the interconnected modules and cause mismatch in their electrical current-voltage (I-V) characteristics [1,2]. This may not only affect the output power of the modules but may limit the power production of the entire PV system as modules in serial and parallel connections are limited by the current and voltage of the lowest rated module, respectively [1,2]. This represents a power loss in addition to the actual module degradation and can increase over time. This may in the long term also have an impact on the annual energy production of the PV system.

Potential induced degradation (PID) is one such degradation mode that, depending on the mechanism, can affect both the current and voltage output of a PV system that is operating at a high system voltage [3,4]. In the case of shunting type of PID (PID-s) both the current and the voltage at maximum power point (MPP) are limited due to 1) increase in second diode dark saturation current (J_{02}) and ideality-factor (n_2) and 2) decrease in shunt resistance (R_{SH}), fill factor (FF) and open circuit voltage (V_{OC}) [3]. A PV module affected by polarization type of PID (PID-p) is mainly limited by the current at MPP due to 1) increase in first diode dark saturation current (J_{01}) and ideality factor (n_1) and 2) decrease in short circuit current (I_{SC}) and V_{OC} [4].

The impact of PID is mostly characterized on either cell or module level. To what extent do the different PID types impact the electrical performance of a PV plant and how does this translate into the long-term performance of a PV plant is not clarified as it is not easily identified and/or isolated from other faults and/or degradation modes that cause similar deviation on the I-V characteristics.

The aim of this work is to model and investigate the impact of PID-s and PID-p on PV array I-V characteristics, and to quantify the additional mismatch loss caused by PID at array level, considering 1) the underlying PID mechanisms 2) variability in solar cell performance in a module due to non-uniform potential on the module's surface and 3) variability in module performance in/of a string due to different level of voltage stress depending on the location of the modules in the PV string.

2 MODELING

2.1 Modeling of solar cells affected by PID

The modeling of a PV system is done in Python using the PySpice library. Each solar cell is represented by a two-diode equivalent circuit model with the following input parameters: light generated photocurrent (I_{PH}), series resistance (R_S), shunt resistance (R_{SH}), dark saturation currents (I_{01} and I_{02}) and ideality factors (n1 and n_2) of the two diodes (referred to as cell level model). The electrical circuit model of the solar cell simulates a light I-V characteristic curve at a given irradiance and temperature level by doing a voltage sweep from 0 V to V_{DC} and measure the current running through a resistor (R_{LOAD}) that is generated from light source I_{LIGHT} (Fig. 1).

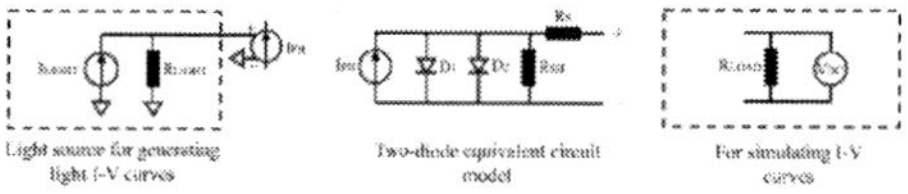

Figure 1: The two-diode equivalent circuit model implemented with PySpice library.

Table I shows the input parameters of the two-diode equivalent circuit model that is used for simulating a healthy solar cell. For introducing PID, the most affected two diode model parameters are adjusted to what is experimentally observed and reported in the literature. The modeling of PID-p is based on mechanism that is observed on the front side of a p-type crystalline silicon (c-Si) PV module stressed with high positive voltage potential. A 5 % decrease in the I_{PH} and increase of I_{01} from 1.0e-10 A to 5.0e-10 A is applied for the most degraded solar cell in the simulation, corresponding to a P_{Loss} of 10 % on the cell level [5]. However, to consider non-uniform PID-p degradation, a range of I_{SC} and I_{01} between the given values are applied to the solar cells. Similarly, for PID-s, observed on the front side of a p-type c-Si PV module operating under high negative voltage potential, the degradation in solar cells are introduced by reducing the R_{SH} of the solar cells from 1000 Ω to ~0.1 Ω and increasing the I_{02} and n_2 from 1.0e-19 A and 2 to 1.0e-1 A and 9, respectively [6,7]. This corresponds to a P_{LOSS} > 30 % on the cell level [6].

Table I: Input parameters of the two-diode equivalent circuit model for a healthy, PID-p and PID-s solar cell.

Model input parameters	Healthy	PID-p	PID-s
I_{PH} [A]	9.85	9.3575	9.85
R_S [Ω]	0.005	0.005	0.005
R_{SH} [Ω]	1000	1000	0.1
I_{01} [A]	1.0e-10	5.0e-10	1.0e-10
n_1	1	1	1
I_{02} [A]	1.0e-19	1.0e-19	1.0e-1
n_2	2	2	9

2.2 Modeling of PV modules affected by PID

Solar cells are serially connected into a module as three 20-cell substrings, each connected parallelly to a bypass diode. Identical solar cells are grouped into a single two-diode equivalent circuit model with input parameters: I_{PH}, $R_S{\cdot}N_X$, $R_{SH}{\cdot}N_X$, I_{01}, I_{02}, $n_1{\cdot}N_X$ and $n_2{\cdot}N_X$ (number of solar cells within a group, N_X).

2.3 Modeling of PV strings affected by PID

To scale the voltage of the PV system and consider string level PID characteristics, 22 modules are serially connected into a string. Total eight modules closest to the positive end of a string are modeled with PID-p. It is assumed that the voltage stress is greatest at the positive end and therefore, the PID is more severe at the ends. Similarly, Total five modules closest to the negative end of a string are modeled with PID-s. The remaining healthy PV modules are grouped together and connected serially to the degraded modules.

2.4 Modeling of PV array affected by PID

The final model is an array with eight strings connected parallelly together. One string diode is connected serially to each PV string to block reverse current flow.

2.5 PV array degradation scenarios

The severity of PID in the array is increased by reducing the I_{PH} and R_{SH} values of solar cells affected with PID-p and PID-s by 0.5 % and 50 % from their previous values, respectively. In total twelve different degradation scenarios are created for a PV array affected by PID-p and PID-s, and each scenario is set to represent a point in time (i.e. degradation stages represent degradation after each month in a year).

2.6 Mismatch losses

The mismatch loss (ML) is calculated by taking the difference between the array level P_{LOSS} and the average P_{LOSS} calculated from each PV module in the PV system, at STC (Eq. 1). The P_{LOSS} is calculated as the relative change between module/array P_{MAX} and P_{MAX} of a healthy (reference) module/array (Eq. 2).

$$ML\,[\%] = P_{LOSS,array} - \frac{\sum_{i=1}^{176} P_{LOSS,Module\,i}}{176} \quad (1)$$

$$P_{LOSS}\,[\%] = abs\left(\frac{P_{MAX} - P_{MAX,reference}}{P_{MAX,reference}} \cdot 100\,\%\right) \quad (2)$$

3 RESULTS AND DISCUSSION

3.1 Mismatch losses caused by PID-p in the PV array

Figure 2 shows I-V curves of twelve different degradation scenarios representing different PID stages (t=0 to t=365). The non-uniformity in the electrical performance of the PV modules in the PV strings, that is caused by PID-p, is translated into a drop in the current output of the system due to activation of the bypass diodes of the degraded module cell-substrings and re-direction of the current (i.e. current mismatch within a PV module and in the PV strings) (Fig 2). The I_{SC} of the system is not affected. The I_{MPP} of the system, on the contrary, is highly impacted. The I_{MPP}/I_{SC} ratio reduces from 0.9483 (healthy state, t=0 d) to 0.9383 (degraded state, t=31 d) when PID-p is introduced in the PV modules with ~0.5 % degradation in the I_{PH} on the cell level at STC and it reduces further to 0.917 (degraded state, t=365 d) with cell level I_{PH} degradation of ~5 %. This effect is prominent on the I-V curves due to formation of a step near the MPP that is tilted due to the non-uniformity in the current output of the degraded cell-substrings (Fig. 2). As degradation in the cell-substrings reaches the PID-p saturation point (- 5 % degradation in I_{PH}), the step levels out.

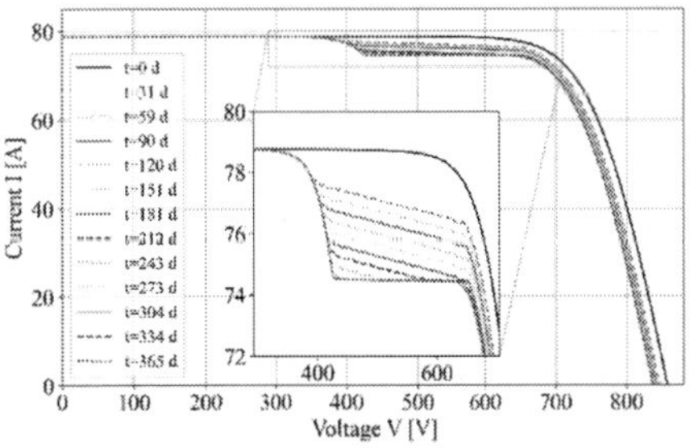

Figure 2: Simulated I-V curves of a PV array affected by PID-p at different degradation stages, and at STC.

The fraction of the absolute change in the system I_{MPP} at t=31 d and t=365 d is ~1 % and ~3.2 %, respectively (Fig. 3). The V_{OC} and V_{MPP} degrade from 1.4 % (t=31 d) to 2.4 % and 2 % (t=365 d), respectively. The resulting P_{LOSS} of the system is ~ 5.25 % and the corresponding FF reduces with ~ 3 % (t=365 d) at STC. The ML increases from 0.13 % to 0.72 % (Fig. 3).

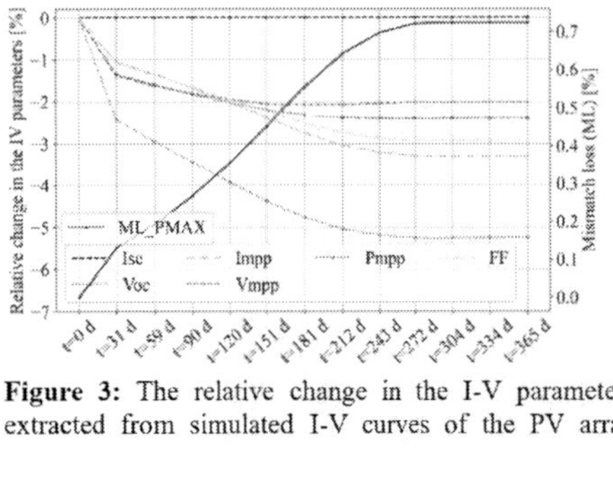

Figure 3: The relative change in the I-V parameters extracted from simulated I-V curves of the PV array

(dashed lines) and the mismatch losses (solid line) at different PID-p degradation stages, and at STC.

3.2 Mismatch losses caused by PID-s in the PV array

The array affected with PID-s is relatively more impacted, considering that the degradation is introduced in fewer PV modules (t=365 d, Fig 4). However, the R_{SH} has to reduce more than 90 % before degradation is observed on the I-V (t=181 d, R_{SH} < 14 Ω, Fig. 4). Nevertheless, a slope appears near the MPP due to the reduction in the R_{SH} and causes drop in the current and voltage output of the system.

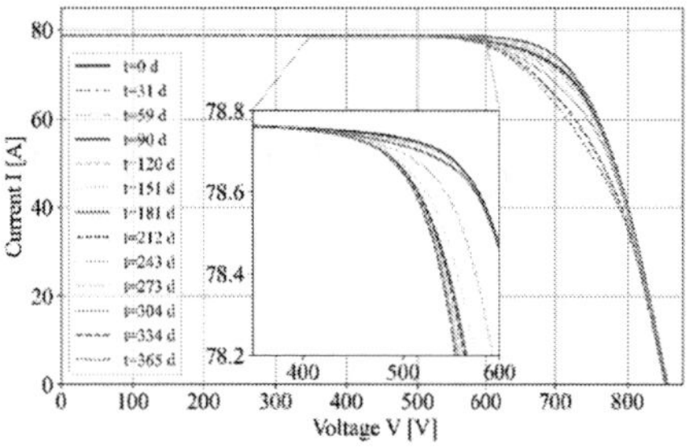

Figure 4: Simulated I-V curves of a PV array affected by PID-s at different degradation stages, and at STC.

The I_{MPP} reduces by 4.47 % is the main contributor to the P_{LOSS} and reduction in the FF at the first few degradation stages (t=120 d to t=272 d). As the MPP changes its position due to change in the shape of the I-V curves, the I_{MPP} recovers with 2.53 % while the V_{MPP} starts to drop (reduces by 8 % at t=365 d) and causes mismatch in the string output voltage. The P_{LOSS} increases to 9.87 % (reduces from 51920 W at t=0 d to 46796 W at t=365 d) and the FF drops by 9.54 % (t=365 d, R_{SH} < 2 Ω, Fig. 5).

Similar to, in the case of PID-p, the I_{SC} remains unaffected. The drop in V_{OC} is insignificant (reduced by 0.36 %), different from what is typically observed on the module level. This may suggest that the degradation in I_{02} introduced in the solar cells is less severe (1.0e-1 A) and there is a greater contribution from the healthy solar cells in each PV string as a larger voltage drop in the string would otherwise limit the voltage of the array (to the voltage of most degraded string) and cause a reduction in the V_{OC} of the system. Figure 5 shows the ML which increases to 2.96 % (t=304 d) but reduces to 2.35 % (t=365 d) due to increased PID severity in all three cell-substrings of the degraded PV modules.

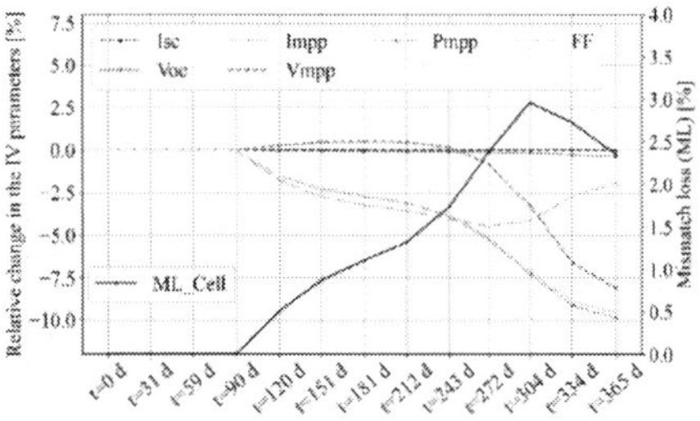

Figure 5: The relative change in the I-V parameters extracted from simulated I-V curves of the PV array (dashed lines) and the mismatch losses (solid line) at different PID-s degradation stages, and at STC.

4 CONCLUSIONS

The impact of PID-p and PID-s on the I-V characteristics of a PV array is modeled and quantified using cell level PID characteristics reported in the literature. A healthy PV array is composed of eight parallelly connected PV strings, each with 22 serially connected 60-cell PV modules. PID-p is introduced in total eight PV modules in each PV string of a PV array by reducing the I_{PH} and I_{01} of the solar cells. The P_{LOSS} of the system at the most degraded state is ~5.25 % from which 0.72 % is due to the mismatch loss that is caused by non-uniform degradation and progression of PID in the PV strings. PID-s is modeled with reduction in the R_{SH}, I_{02} and n_2 of the solar cells in five PV modules in each PV string. The P_{LOSS} is ~10 % and the mismatch loss is 2.35 % at the most degraded state. The power and mismatch losses are relatively high considering that fewer PV modules are degraded with PID-s compared to PID-p.

5 ACKNOWLEDGDEMENT

This research is carried out in the DTEC project: High voltage stress testing for potential induced degradation and recovery modeling of utility scale PV.

6 REFERENCES

[1] S. Pingel et al., "Potential Induced Degradation of solar cells and panels," 2010 35th IEEE Photovoltaic Specialists Conference, Honolulu, HI, USA, 2010, pp. 002817-002822, doi: 10.1109/PVSC.2010.5616823.

[2] Dhass, A. D. et al., A Review on Factors Influencing the Mismatch Losses in Solar Photovoltaic System, International Journal of Photoenergy, 2022, 2986004, 27 pages, 2022. https://doi.org/10.1155/2022/2986004.

[3] Luo, W., et al., "Potential-Induced Degradation in Photovoltaic Modules: A Critical Review." Energy & Environmental Science 10, no. 1 (2017): 43–68.

[4] Molto, C et. al., (2023), Review of Potential-Induced Degradation in Bifacial Photovoltaic Modules. Energy Technol., 11: 2200943. https://doi.org/10.1002/ente.202200943.

[5] Seira Yamaguchi et al., Polarization-Type Potential-Induced Degradation in Front-Emitter p-Type and n-Type Crystalline Silicon Solar Cells, ACS Omega 2022 7 (41), 36277-36285, DOI: 10.1021/acsomega.2c03866.

[6] Mahmood, A., Del Prado Santamaria, R., Kari, T., Poulsen, P. B., Spataru, S. V., Diagnosing Potential Induced Degradation in Crystalline Silicon Photovoltaic Modules, 2024, Proceedings of EU PVSEC, DOI 10.4229/EUPVSEC2024/3AV.2.22.

[7] D. Lausch et al., "Potential-Induced Degradation (PID): Introduction of a Novel Test Approach and Explanation of Increased Depletion Region Recombination," in IEEE Journal of Photovoltaics, vol. 4, no. 3, pp. 834-840, May 2014, doi: 10.1109/JPHOTOV.2014.2300238.

DTU

DTU

EU PVSEC 2025

Modeling the Electrical Mismatch Caused by Potential Induced Degradation in Crystalline Silicon Photovoltaic Modules and Strings

Aysha Mahmood, Gisele Alves dos Reis Benatto, Sune Thorsteinsson, Peter Behrensdorff Poulsen and Sergiu Viorel Spataru

DTU Electro, Technical University of Denmark, Roskilde, Denmark

4BO.7.4 – Field Insights, Performance and Modelling of PV systems
42nd European Photovoltaic Solar Energy Conference – Bilbao, Spain, 2025

DTU

Introduction and Motivation

- **Utility scale PV systems**
  - Exposed to several operational and environmental stress factors
  - Gets affected by different faults and degradation modes
  - **Non-uniform degradation cause additional mismatch loss in a PV system**

DTU

Introduction and Motivation

- **Utility scale PV systems**
  - **Non-uniform degradation cause additional mismatch loss in a PV system**

- **Mismatch loss**
  - Definition: losses due to differences in electrical performance of solar cells/PV modules in a PV system
    - Serial connection: limited by lowest current value

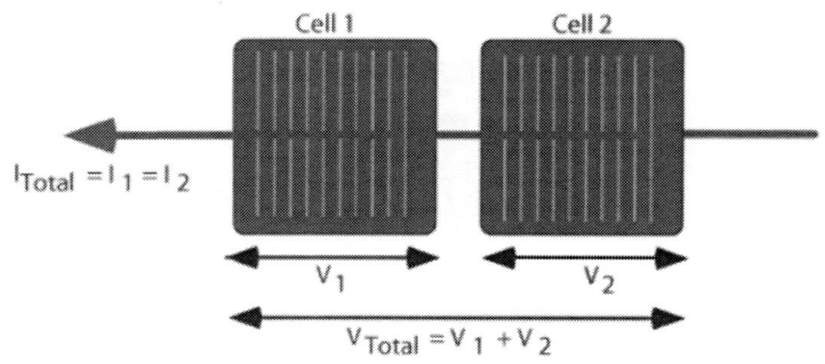

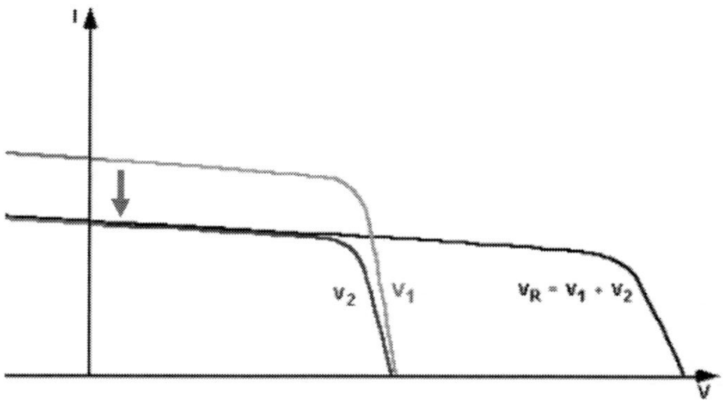

Mismatch Effects | PVEducation

DTU

Introduction and Motivation

- **Utility scale PV systems**
  - **Non-uniform degradation cause additional mismatch loss in a PV system**

- **Mismatch loss**
  - Definition: losses due to differences in electrical performance of solar cells/PV modules in a PV system
    - Parallel connection: limited by lowest voltage value

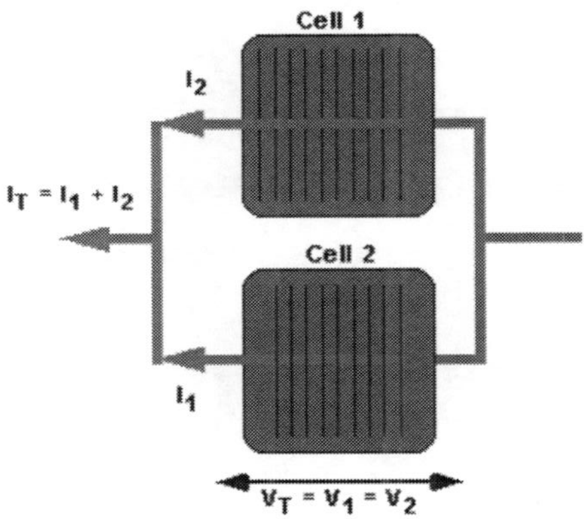

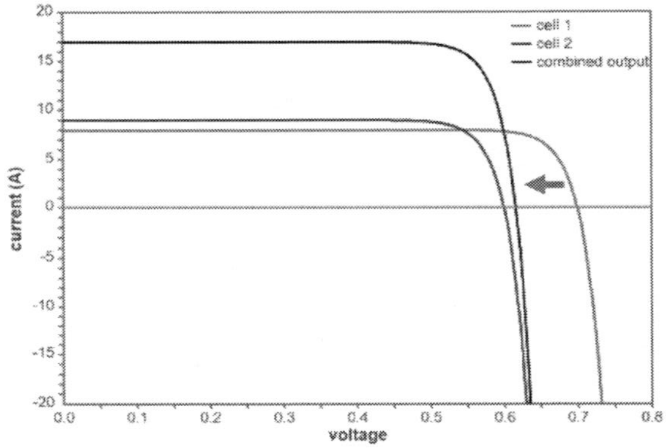

Mismatch Effects | PVEducation

DTU

Introduction and Motivation

- **Potential induced degradation (PID)**
  - High voltage difference between operating cells and grounded module frame and/or surface
  - **Cause degradation in output current and/or voltage of a PV module**
  - **Cause mismatch loss in PV systems**

- PID types
  - Underlying mechanism
  - PV technology
  - Operating conditions

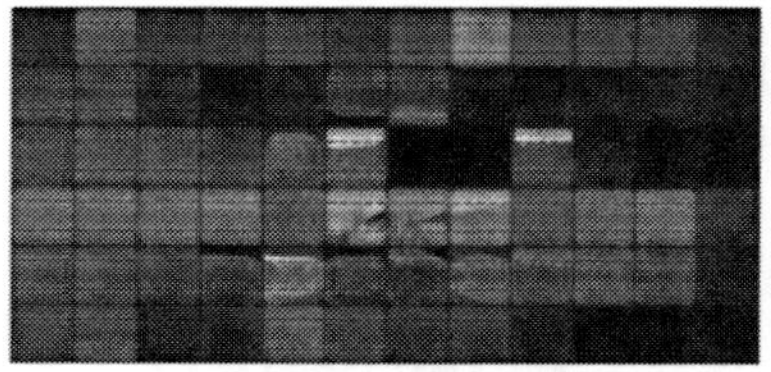

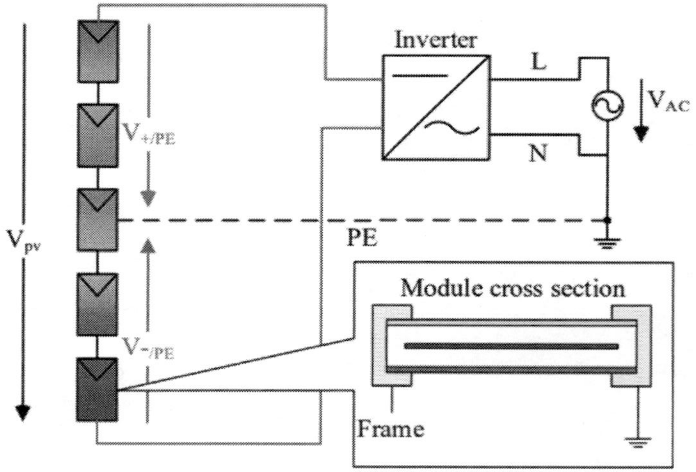

AG, S S T, SMA: Technical Information on PID. Undated, SMA Solar Technology AG: Niestetal, Germany. p. 1-4. Report PID-TI-UEN113410.

S. Pingel et al., "Potential Induced Degradation of solar cells and panels," 2010 35th IEEE Photovoltaic Specialists Conference, Honolulu, HI, USA, 2010, pp. 002817-002822, doi: 10.1109/PVSC.2010.5616823.

DTU

Introduction and Motivation

- Potential induced degradation (PID)
  - Characterized on cell and module level

  - **To what extent do PID impact the electrical performance of a PV plant?**

  - **What is the additional mismatch loss in a PV plant affected by PID?**

- Model PID on the I-V characteristics of a PV array
  - Considering PID characteristics reported on
    - Cell, module and string level

- Quantify the additional mismatch loss caused by PID

DTU

How to model a solar cell affected by PID?

- Modeling in Python using PySpice
  - Each solar cell is represented by a **two-diode equivalent circuit model**

- Degradation in specific electrical and/or physical parameters
  - **Polarization type of PID**
    - Mechanism: change in front passivation layer
    - PV technology: mono facial p-type PERC
    - Operating condition: + voltage potential

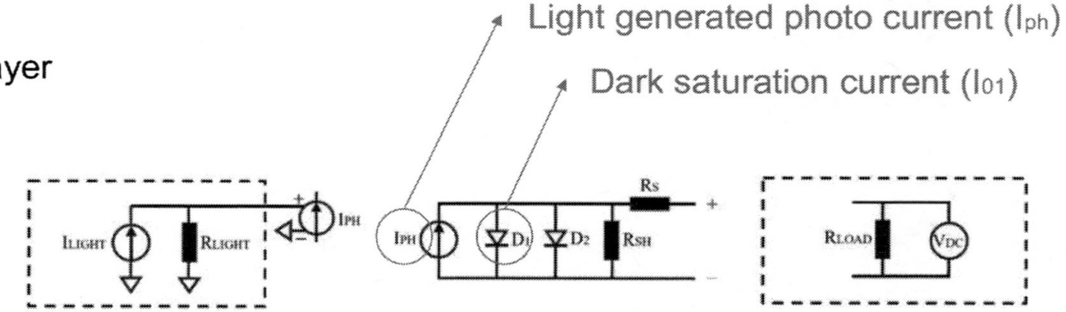

Light source for generating light I-V curves

Two-diode equivalent circuit model

For simulating I-V curves

How to model a solar cell affected by PID?

- Modeling in Python using PySpice
  - Each solar cell is represented by a **two-diode equivalent circuit model**

- Degradation in specific electrical and/or physical parameters
  - **Polarization type of PID**
    - Mechanism: change in front passivation layer
    - PV technology: mono facial p-type PERC
    - Operating condition: + voltage potential
  - **Shunting type of PID**
    - Mechanism: Na+ penetration
    - PV technology: mono facial p-type PERC
    - Operating condition: - voltage potential

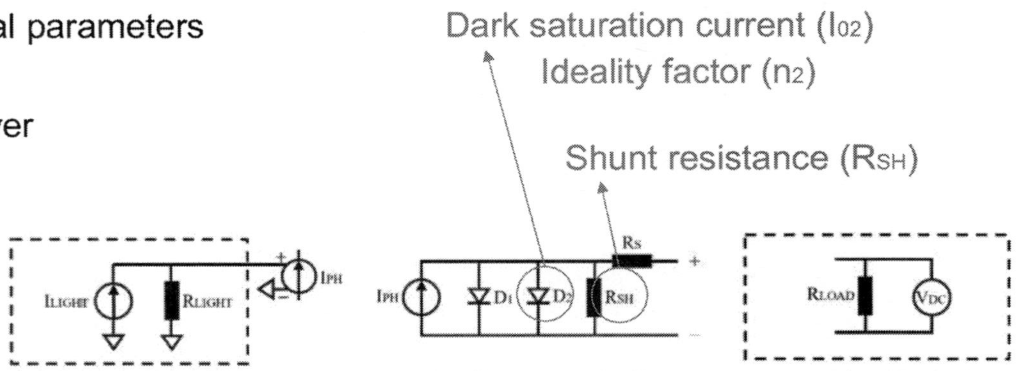

Light source for generating light I-V curves

Two-diode equivalent circuit model

For simulating I-V curves

DTU

How to model a PV module affected by PID?

- 60-cell PV module
  - 20 cell per cell-substring connected serially together
    - Each connected parallelly to a bypass diode
  - Model input parameters are defined for each solar cell
    - Identical solar cells are grouped together within a cell-substring

- **Variability in solar cell performance within a PV module**
  - Non-uniform voltage stress on module surface
  - High voltage stress near the grounded module frame

- Degradation pattern on module level:
  - **Polarization type of PID (PID-p):**
    - Homogenous degradation
  - **Shunting type of PID (PID-s):**
    - Chessboard pattern
    - Close to module frame and negative end

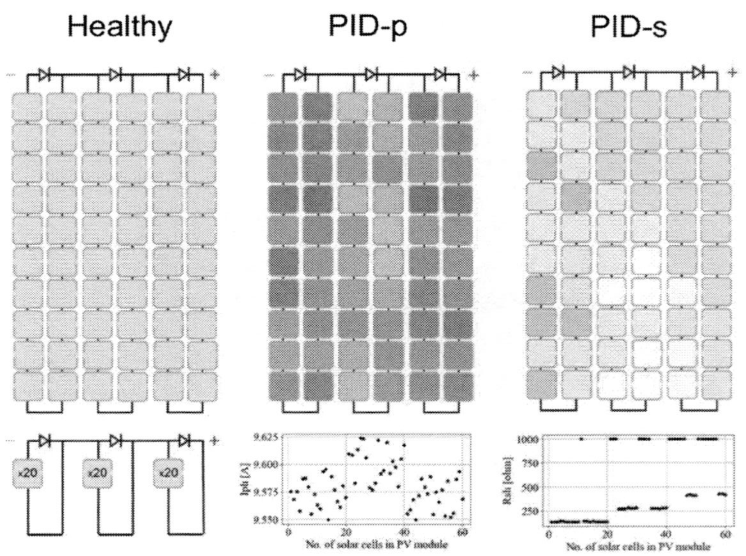

DTU

How to model a PV string affected by PID?

- PV string with 22 PV modules serially connected

- Floating grounding configuration
  - 11 modules under negative polarity
  - 11 modules under positive polarity
  - **High voltage stress at the string ends**

- Degradation pattern on string level:
  - High voltage stress near the string ends
  - **Polarization type of PID:**
    - Eight modules degraded close to positive end
  - **Shunting type of PID:**
    - Five modules degraded close to negative end

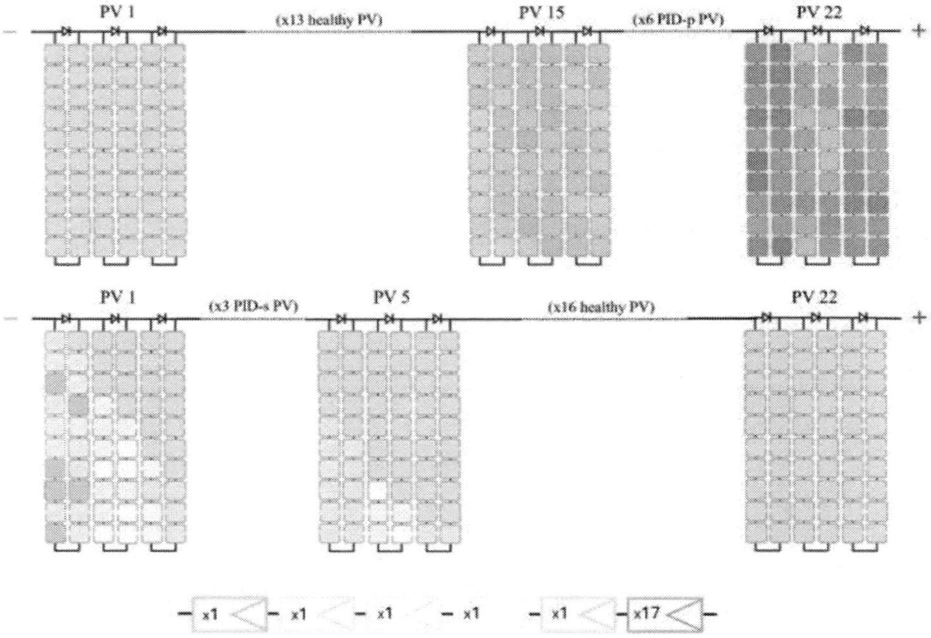

Modeling of PV array affected by PID

- PV array with 8 PV strings connected parallelly
  - Each connected to a string diode
- PV strings are not completely identical
  - PV modules are degraded with different levels

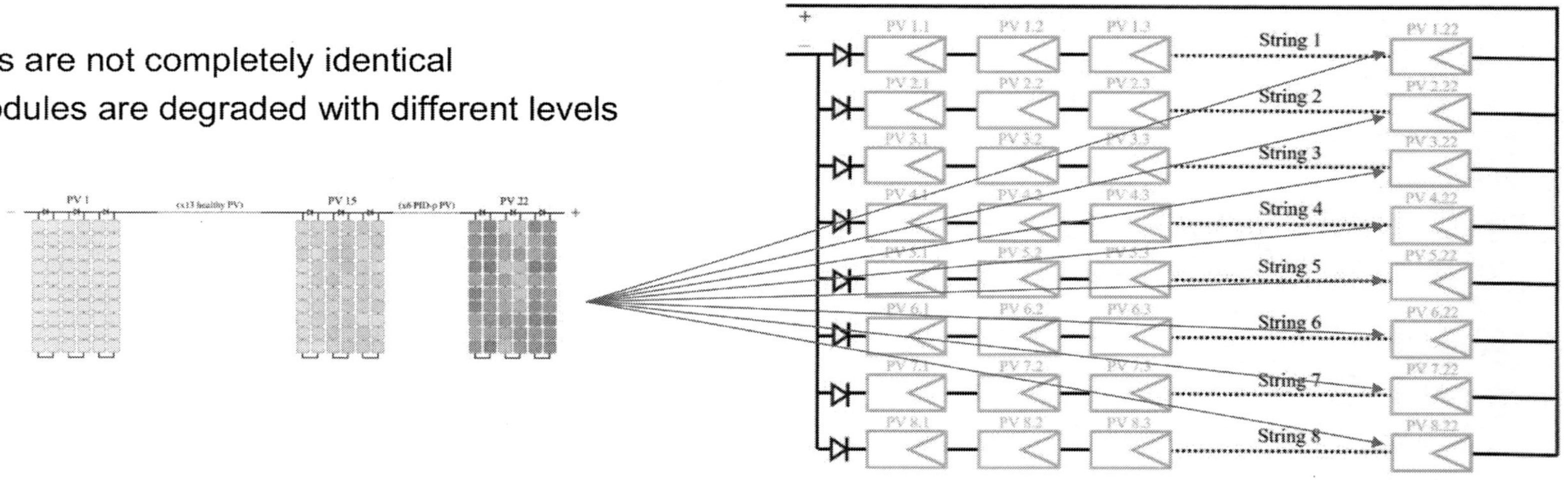

DTU

Modeling of PV array affected by PID

- PV array with 8 PV strings connected parallelly
  - Each connected to a string diode
- PV strings are not completely identical
  - PV modules are degraded with different levels

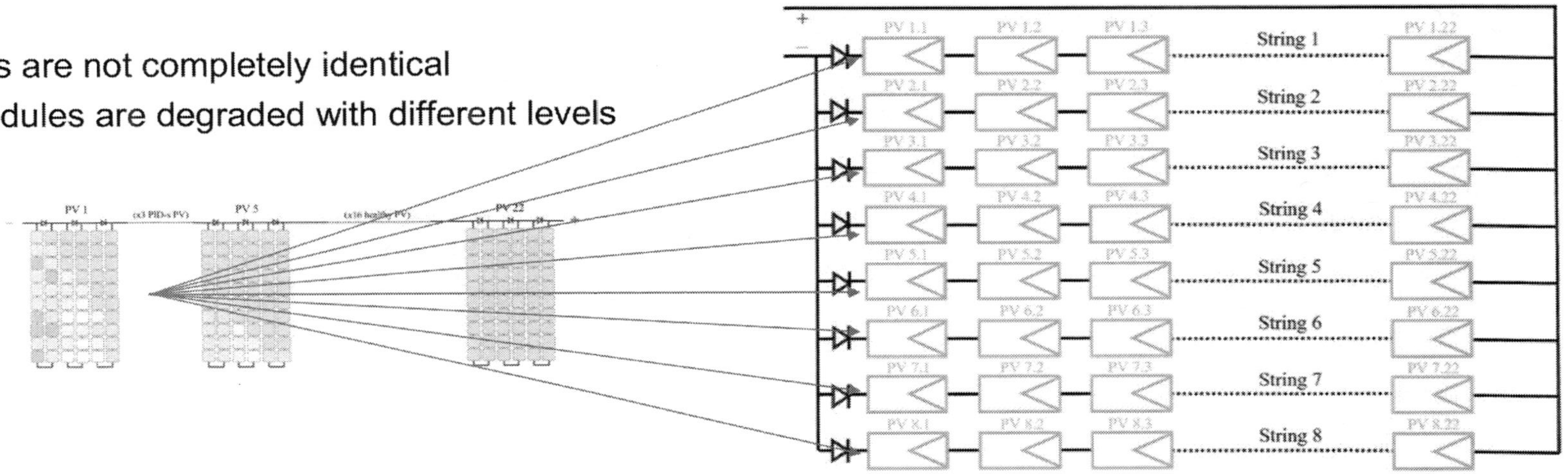

DTU

Quantifying the mismatch losses at STC

- A PV system with one healthy and one PID degraded module
  - Degraded: 7.92 % Ploss
  - Average Ploss of the two modules: 3.96 %
  - String Ploss: 4.16 %

$$ML\ [\%] = P_{Loss,Array} - \frac{\sum_{i=1}^{2} P_{Loss,Module,i}}{2}$$

$$P_{Loss}\ [\%] = abs\left(\frac{P_{MAX} - P_{MAX,reference}}{P_{MAX,reference}} \cdot 100\ \%\right)$$

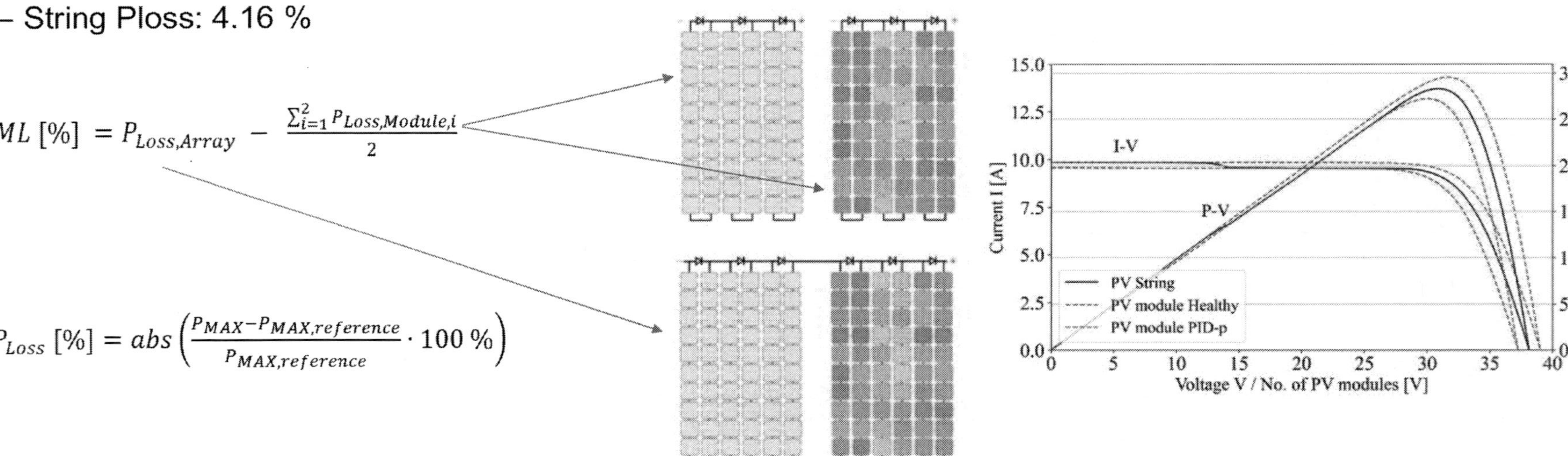

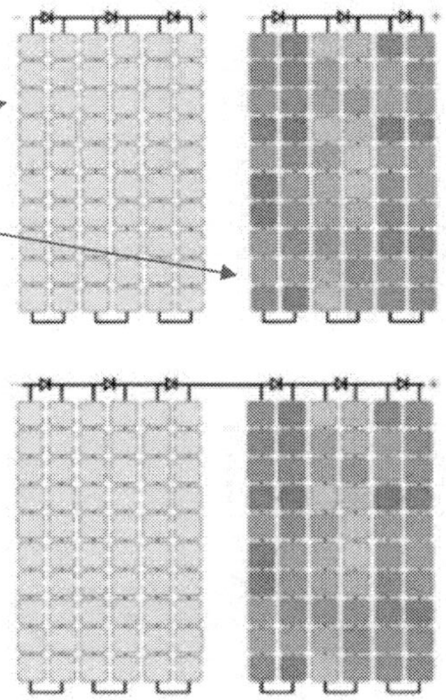

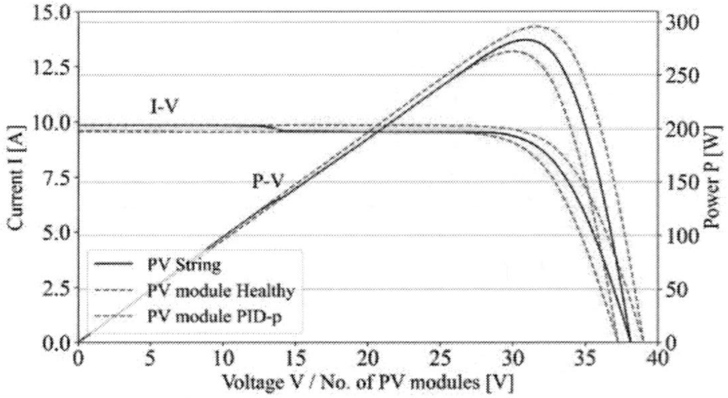

DTU

How to quantify long-term impact of PID?

- **The impact of PID as it progresses**
  - Increases the severity of PID in solar cells
  - Apply linear degradation rate
  - **Create twelve different degradation scenarios/stages**

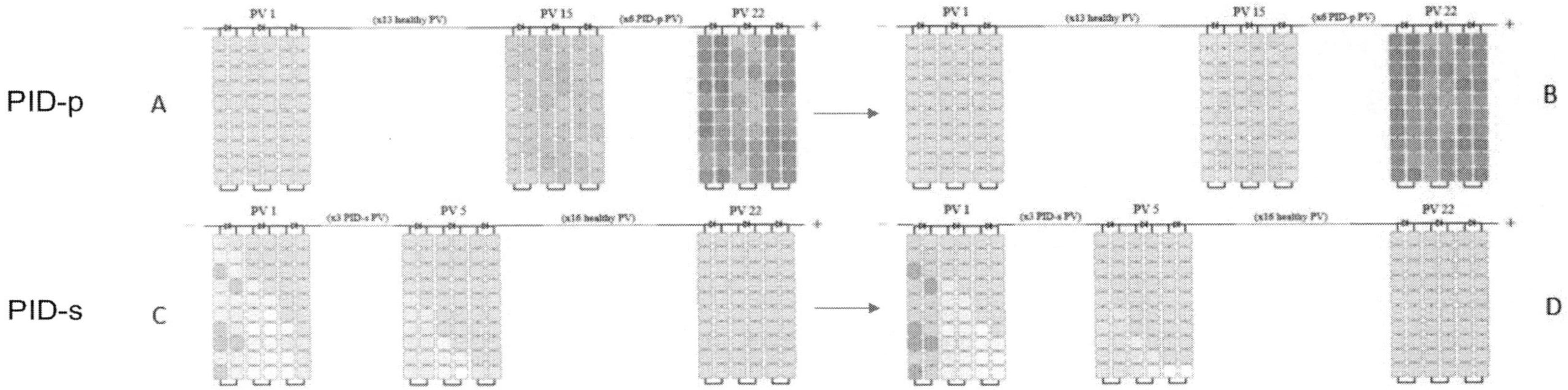

DTU

How to quantify long-term impact of PID?

- Add temporal dimension to the analysis
  - Long term impact of PID
  - **One year simulation**
    - G_{POA} and T_{CELL}
      - Location: 55.696 latitude and 12.105 longitude
      - Roskilde, Denmark
      - Fixed tilt of 25°

$$E_{Annual}\ [kWh] = \sum_{i=0}^{3959} P_{MAX,hourly}\ [kW]$$

- >10,000 solar cells in the PV system
  - 3840 solar cells with PID and different model input parameters

- **Reducing the granularity of the model**
  - Defining model input parameters on module level
    - Grouping solar cells to one group/cell-substring
    - Using in-module worst performing solar cell

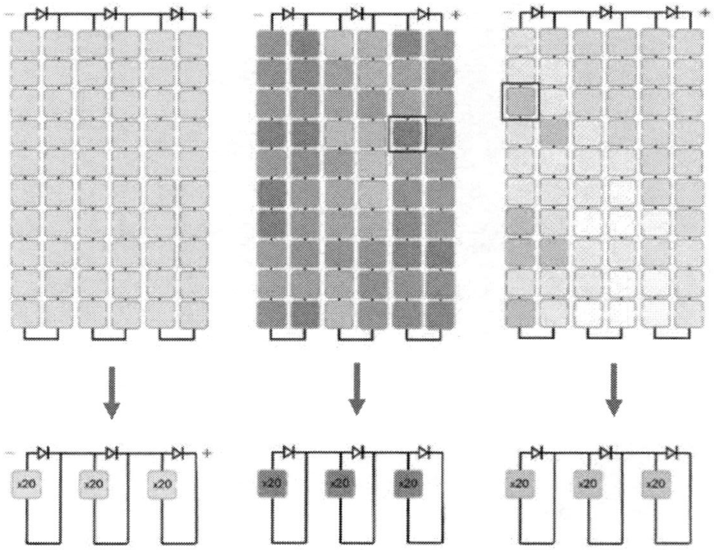

DTU

Simulation time for generating an I-V curve

- Single simulation of an array using cell level model
  - 6720 healthy solar cell
    - Grouped into one group per cell-substrings
  - 3840 PID affected solar cells with different model input parameters
  - **1 minutes and 20 seconds at STC**

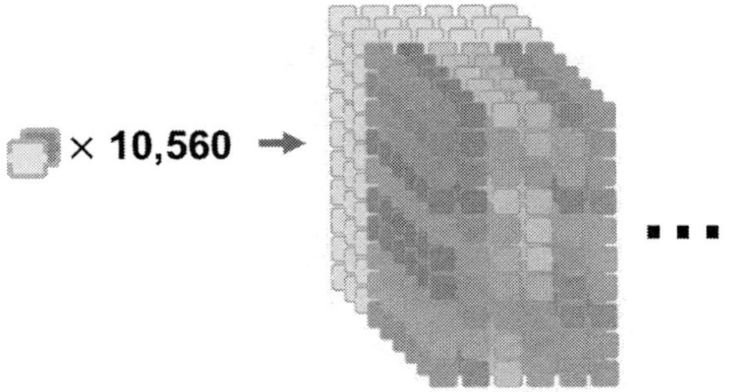

- Module level model (reduced model granularity)
  - 112 healthy PV modules
  - 64 PID affected PV modules with different model input parameters
  - **< 1 second at STC**

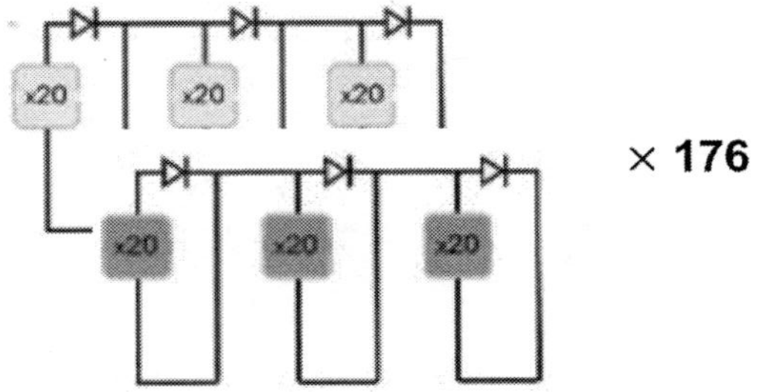

  - **One year simulation: ~ 5 hours**
    - Voltage sweep from 0 to 880 V with 0.1 steps
    - G_{POA} and T_{CELL}

Results of simulations of different degradation stages at STC

- PV array affected by PID-p
  - Twelve different degradation scenarios/stages

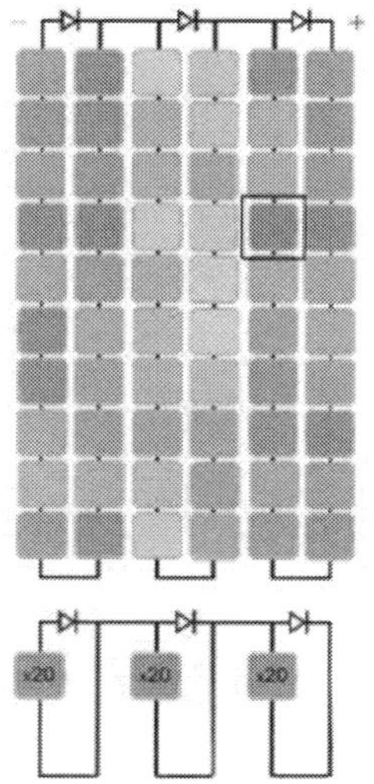

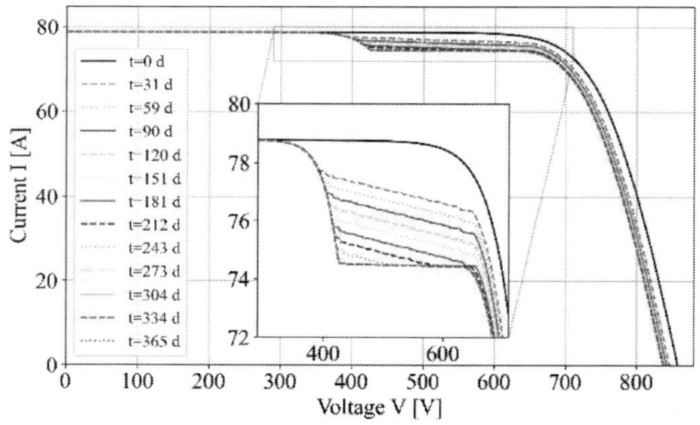

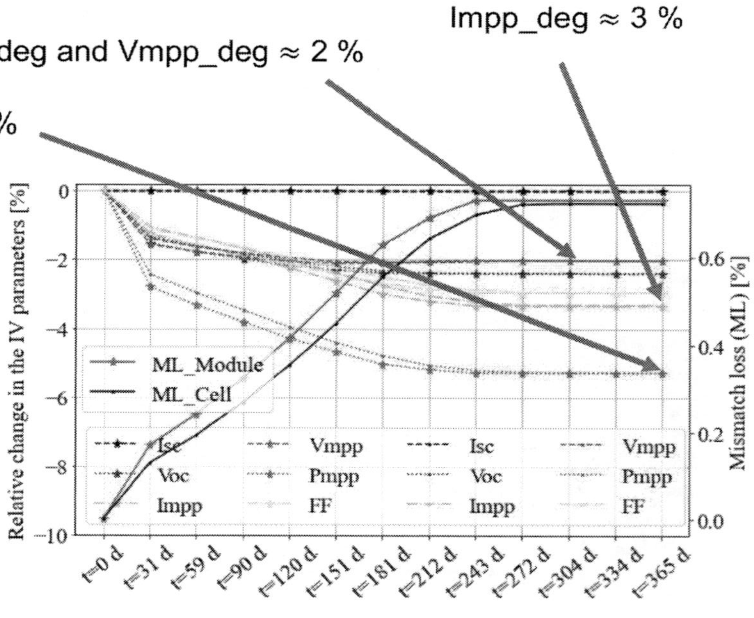

DTU

Results of simulations of different degradation stages at STC

- PV array affected by PID-p
  - Twelve different degradation scenarios/stages

Mismatch loss range: 0.15 to 0.72 %

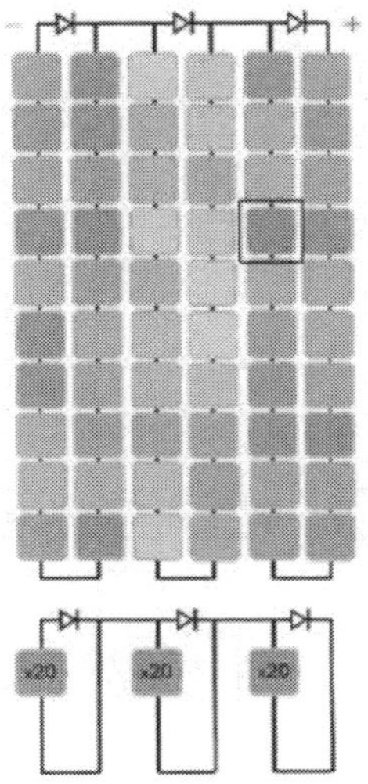

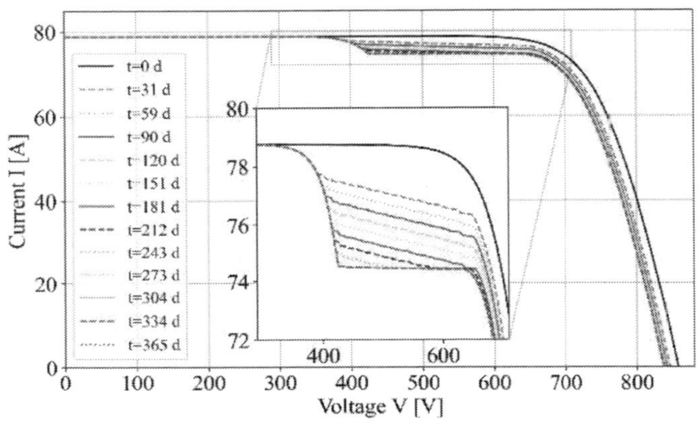

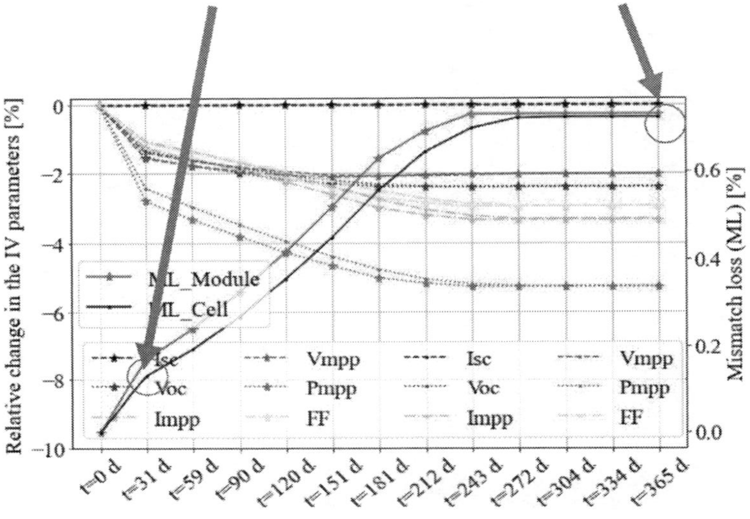

Results of simulations of different degradation stages at STC

- PV array affected by PID-s
  - Twelve different degradation scenarios/stages

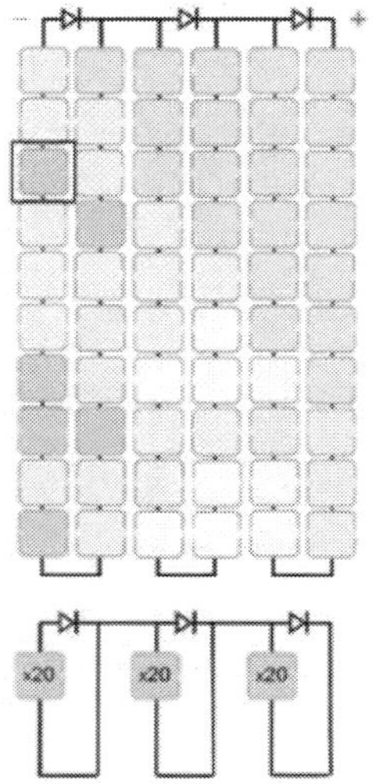

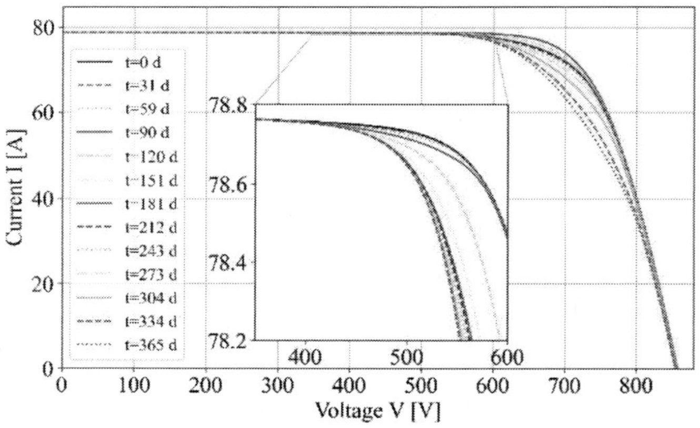

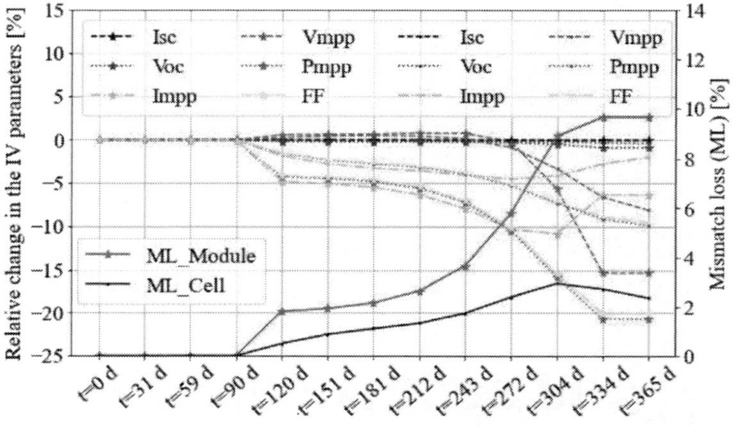

DTU

Results of simulations of different degradation stages at STC

- PV array affected by PID-s
  - Twelve different degradation scenarios/stages

Impp_deg_max ≈ 5 %

Vmpp_deg ≈ 7 %

Pmpp_deg ≈ 10 %

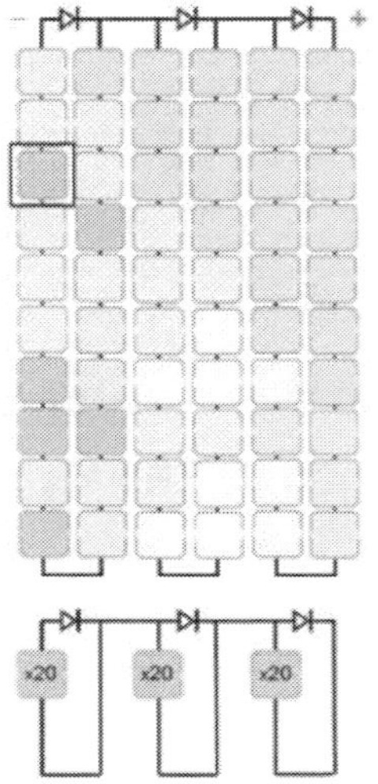

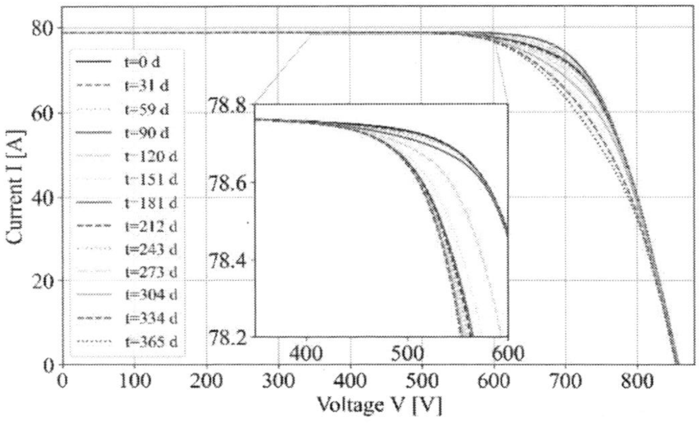

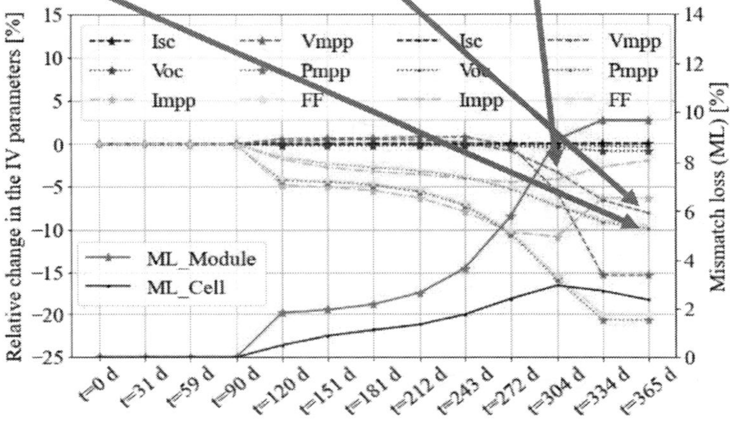

DTU

Results of simulations of different degradation stages at STC

- PV array affected by PID-s
  - Twelve different degradation scenarios/stages

Mismatch loss range: 0 to 2.96 %

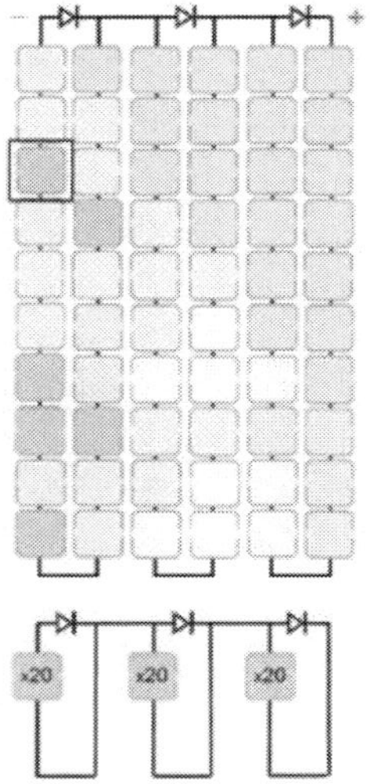

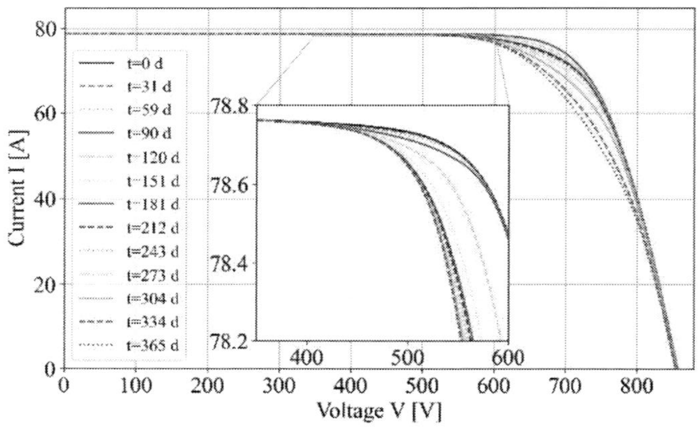

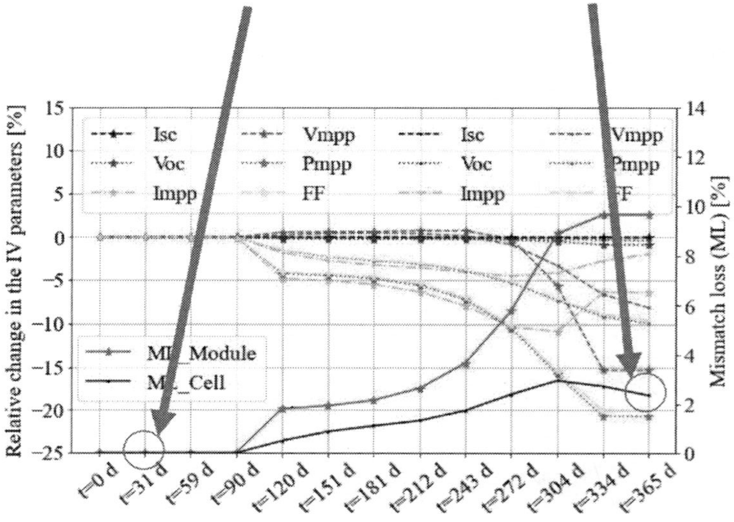

DTU

Conclusions

PySpice Model

- Possible to implement cell, module and string level PID characteristics on array level
  - Estimate the impact of two or more failure and/or degradation modes
- Asses long-term impact of a failure and/or degradation mode
  - Quantify power and mismatch losses as degradation progresses
- Identify diagnostic parameters from array or string I-V
  - Develop/optimize fault detection algorithms
  - Training fata for fault detection methods
- Generate realistic I-V curves
  - Apply non-linear degradation
  - Develop code script for newer PV technologies

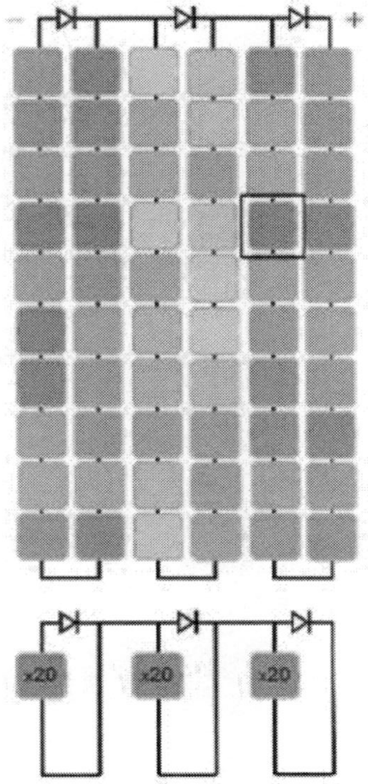

DTU

Acknowledgement and contact information

DTEC project: High voltage stress testing for potential induced degradation and recovery modeling of utility scale PV.

Collaboration between TotalEnergies and Technical University of Denmark.

Thank you for you attention!

TotalEnergies

DTEC

Contact information:
Aysha Mahmood aysma@dtu.dk
Sergiu Viorel Spataru sersp@dtu.dk

Solar Photovoltaic Systems Group (SPVS)
DTU Electro, Risø Campus, Roskilde, Denmark

EVALUATING THE ACCURACY OF SINGLE-CAMERA IRRADIANCE FORECASTING

Jacob K. Thorning[1]*, Adam A. Jensen[2], Sergiu V. Spataru[1], Peter B. Poulsen[1]
*Corresponding author: jkrtho@dtu.dk
[1]Technical University of Denmark (DTU), Department of Electrical and Photonics Engineering, Frederiksborgvej 399, 4000 Roskilde, Denmark
[2]Technical University of Denmark (DTU), Department of Civil and Mechanical Engineering, Koppels Allé, 2800 Kgs. Lyngby, Denmark

ABSTRACT: We present results from a newly established all-sky imager (ASI) testbed at DTU Risø Campus. Three calibrated ASIs capture hemispheric sky images every 30 seconds and provide input for cloud detection and irradiance mapping. Each camera was calibrated using the Scaramuzza fisheye model, yielding lookup matrices that map pixels to azimuth and zenith angles. Based on these, equidistant projections were created, and cloud transmittance maps were derived using a normalized color index. Ground-level irradiance was then estimated by projecting cloud transmittance onto the terrain using solar geometry. The estimated Global Horizontal Irradiance (GHI) was compared to pyranometer measurements at a meteorological station $\tilde{1}$ km from one of the cameras. Results show good agreement in daily GHI dynamics and highlight challenges in accurately reproducing irradiance ramps near solar noon and under broken cloud conditions. This testbed provides a basis for systematic evaluation of ASI-based irradiance forecasting methods. Data collected in this testbed will be made available to the community to facilitate further research and development of ASI-based solar forecasting methods, and we aim to release a larger dataset in the future.
Keywords: all-sky imagers, solar irradiance forecasting, cloud detection, hemispheric cameras, photovoltaic systems, cloud base height estimation, image processing, solar nowcasting

1 Introduction

The integration of photovoltaic (PV) generation into modern power systems continues to accelerate worldwide [1], driven by climate goals and the falling costs of solar technology. At the same time, the variability of solar irradiance, particularly on short timescales of seconds to minutes, presents challenges for grid operators and PV plant owners [2]. Rapid fluctuations in PV output can cause voltage instability, complicate scheduling, and increase the need for balancing reserves. Accurate, high-resolution forecasts of solar irradiance are therefore increasingly important for both operational stability and efficient market participation [3].

Clouds are the dominant driver of intra-hour solar variability [4]. Their spatial extent, optical thickness, and movement across the solar disk determine when and how strongly irradiance ramps occur at the surface. Satellite imagery provides valuable information on cloud fields and is widely used for solar forecasting at hourly and longer horizons [5–7]. However, the temporal and spatial resolution of geostationary satellite images is insufficient for intra-hour predictions at higher resolutions than 1 km and 5 minutes.

Ground-based All-Sky Imager (ASI) fill this gap by capturing hemispheric views of the sky dome with sub-minute cadence. By detecting clouds in successive images, estimating their motion, and projecting their shadows onto the ground, ASIs enable nowcasting of solar irradiance at horizons up to $\tilde{3}0$ minutes, depending on cloud height and speed. In addition, ASIs can be deployed close to PV plants, making them particularly suitable for site-specific forecasting.

This work establishes an ASI testbed at the DTU Risø Campus in Denmark, where three imagers have been installed roughly 1 km apart. Each camera has been geometrically calibrated using a fisheye lens model using SuMo, enabling per-pixel mapping of raw images to solar azimuth and zenith angles. Based on these calibrations, equidistant projections of the sky are generated, from which cloud transmittance maps are derived using a simple color index method. These transmittance maps are then projected onto the ground using the solar position at the time of capture, yielding spatial irradiance maps.

We present the first usable results obtained with the DTU Risø All-Sky Imager Testbed dataset [8], which provides raw sky images, calibration matrices, and validation GHI from a meteorological station. The purpose of this work is to validate our ASI-based irradiance estimation method and to publish the dataset openly so that other researchers can test and develop their own methods using this testbed.

The purpose of this paper is to establish and validate the foundational components of an ASI-based solar forecasting system. We evaluate the ability of the calibrated ASIs to reproduce ground-measured Global Horizontal Irradiance (GHI) at the location of a solar meteorological station, representing the critical first step in developing accurate short-term irradiance predictions. An example day (September 4, 2025) is analyzed in detail, showing the complete processing chain from raw images to transmittance maps, ground projections, and final GHI comparisons. The results demonstrate that the ASI system can capture the overall diurnal evolution of irradiance and reproduce major cloud-induced ramps, establishing the viability of the approach while also identifying key areas for improvement such as binary cloud classification and uncertainties in cloud base height that must be addressed for operational forecasting applications. By building and validating this end-to-end pipeline, we aim to provide a foundation for future work on ASI-based solar forecasting. Next steps will include multi-day evaluation, refinement of cloud optical thickness estimates, and the integration of cloud motion vectors for true short-term forecasts.

2 Methodology

2.1 Testbed setup

Three ASIs were deployed at DTU Risø Campus during spring 2025, located 800-1200 meters apart. The sites are referred to as Farm, Wind, and Pier based on their campus locations. In parallel, a solar meteorological station equipped with an EKO MS80 class A pyranometer records GHI for validation. A map of the campus with camera and station locations is shown in Figure 1. The distances between the different locations are summarized in Table I.

Table I: Distances (meters) between ASI locations and solar meteorological station at DTU Risø Campus.

Location	Solar met	Pier	Wind
Farm	270	1540	790
Wind	570	1200	
Pier	1280		

The ASIs and sensors at the solar meteorological station are cleaned weekly. Each camera system is a Wematics Pyranovision camera (Figure 2), equipped with a 180° fisheye lens, a pyranometer, and configured to capture 4K resolution hemispheric images every 30 seconds.

Figure 2: All-Sky Imager at the DTU Risø PV farm.

2.2 Camera calibrations

Each camera was calibrated using the Scaramuzza SuMo [9] which implements the Scaramuzza fisheye lens model [10] and external orientation of the image sensor. The calibration provides two lookup matrices per camera: 1. an azimuth matrix, giving the solar azimuth angle corresponding to each pixel and 2. a zenith matrix, giving the solar zenith angle corresponding to each pixel, shown in for the Pier camera in Figure 3a and Figure 3b respectively. These matrices allow direct mapping from pixel coordinates to angular coordinates on the sky dome.

2.3 Cloud detection and transmission mapping

Cloud pixels are identified using a normalized color index *nbrbr*:

$$T(u,v) = \frac{B(u,v) - R(u,v)}{B(u,v) + R(u,v)} > 0, \qquad (1)$$

where B and R are the blue and red channel intensities of pixel (u, v). A fixed threshold of 0 on T classifies pixels as clear sky (1) or cloud (0).

2.4 Cloud base height estimation

Cloud base height is estimated using a modified lifting condensation level (LCL) approach based on ambient temperature and relative humidity measurements. The method employs a three-step parametric model [11] optimized for local conditions at DTU Risø campus. The dew point temperature T_{dew} is calculated using a modified Magnus formula shown in Equation 2 and Equation 3.

$$\gamma = \ln\left(\frac{RH}{100}\right) + \frac{a \cdot T}{b + T} \qquad (2)$$

$$T_{\text{dew}} = \frac{b \cdot \gamma}{a - \gamma} \qquad (3)$$

where T is the ambient temperature in °C, RH is the relative humidity in %, and a and b are fitted parameters. The cloud base height is then calculated as the lifting condensation level shown in Equation 4.

$$\text{CBH} = k \cdot (T - T_{\text{dew}}) \qquad (4)$$

where k is a scaling factor and CBH is expressed in meters. The parameters were optimized against

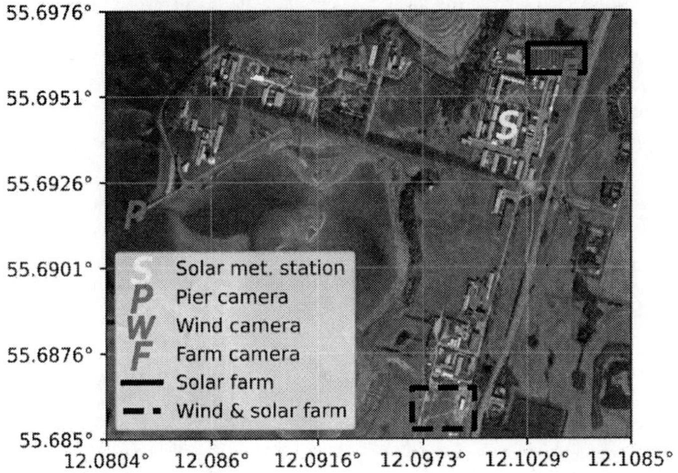

Figure 1: Map with locations of All-Sky Imagers, solar meteorological station and PV plants at DTU Risø campus.

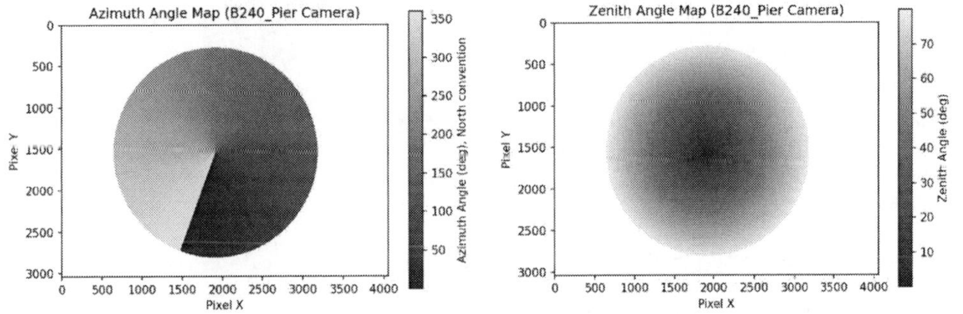

(a) Azimuth matrix for the Pier camera

(b) Zenith matrix for the Pier camera

Figure 3: Azimuth and zenith matrices for the Pier camera, generated using SuMo.

a one-year dataset of cloud base height from ERA5 hourly data on single levels from 1940 to present [12] at DTU Risø campus shown in Equation 5.

$$a = 0.3644 \tag{5}$$

$$b = 49.0 \tag{6}$$

$$k = 26.7283 \tag{7}$$

2.5 Ground projection of cloud shadows

The binary transmission map is projected onto ground coordinates using the solar position (azimuth and elevation) at the image timestamp according to Equations 8, 9 and 10.

$$d = \tan(\theta_z) \cdot CBH, \tag{8}$$

$$dx = \cos(90 - \gamma_s) \cdot d, \tag{9}$$

$$dy = \sin(90 - \gamma_s) \cdot d \tag{10}$$

This projection estimates the regions on the ground affected by cloud shadows and clear-sky conditions. A satellite map of the DTU Risø area with an example projection is shown in Figure 6.

2.6 Validation against ground measurements

For each ground location, GHI is estimated by combining the transmission map with Direct Normal Irradiance (DNI) and Diffuse Horizontal Irradiance (DHI) from the Simplified Solis [13] clear-sky model as shown in Equation 11.

$$GHI(x, y) = T(x, y) \cdot DNI \cdot \cos(\theta_z) + DHI, \tag{11}$$

where θ_z is the solar zenith angle. This yields a 2D irradiance map covering the campus region at each

10.4229/EUPVSEC2025/4BV.3.1

30-second timestep. The projected GHI at the location of the solar meteorological station is extracted from the irradiance maps and compared to pyranometer measurements. Visual validation is performed for a day with scattered clouds (September 4, 2025, from 05:30 to 18:45, local time).

3 Results

The results are based on, and validated using, the DTU Risø All-Sky Imager Testbed dataset [8]. This dataset provides one week of sky images and calibration data from the DTU Risø Campus, Denmark, captured from September 1st to 7th, 2025, to support research in solar forecasting, cloud detection, and image-based irradiance modeling. The dataset includes images from three calibrated all-sky cameras: the Farm camera (15-second cadence, missing September 5th-7th), Wind camera (30-second cadence), and Pier camera (30-second cadence), along with comprehensive meteorological measurements including global horizontal irradiance, diffuse horizontal irradiance, direct normal irradiance, relative humidity, air pressure, and wind data. Each image contains measured GHI in the EXIF metadata field "ApogeeIrradiance", enabling direct validation of image-based irradiance estimates.

3.1 Example image processing pipeline

To illustrate the processing steps, Figure 4 shows a raw hemispheric image from the Pier ASI at 12:10 local time on September 4, 2025 (at solar noon).

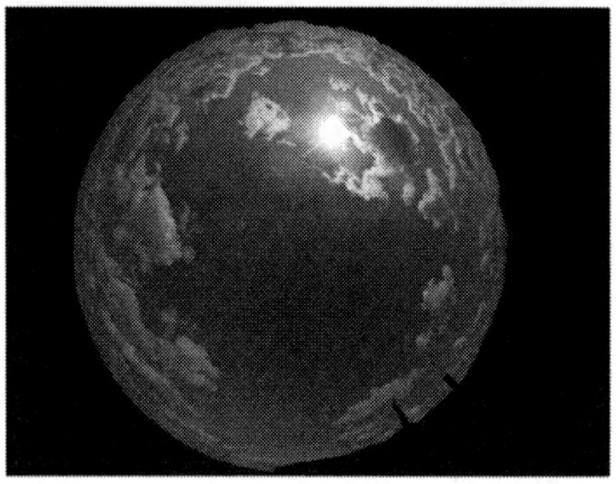

Figure 4: Original image from the Pier ASI at 12:10 local time on September 4, 2025 (at solar noon).

This raw image is converted into an equidistant projection, producing the equidistant sampled representation of the sky dome, shown at approx. 6 by 6 meters resolution in Figure 5a.

From the equidistant image, a binary transmittance map is generated using the normalized color index $(B-R)/(B+R)$ as shown in Equation 12. Clear-sky pixels were classified as transmissive ($T = 1$), while cloudy pixels were set to $T = 0$ (Figure 5b).

$$T = \frac{B-R}{B+R} > 0 \tag{12}$$

The ground projection of the binary transmittance map around the DTU Risø campus is shown in Figure 6 at 50 by 50 meters resolution. This reduced resolution is due to the high resolution of the original image and the need to reduce the computational cost of the projection. A full resolution projection would have the same resolution as the projected image in Figure 5a, which is approx. 6 by 6 meters.

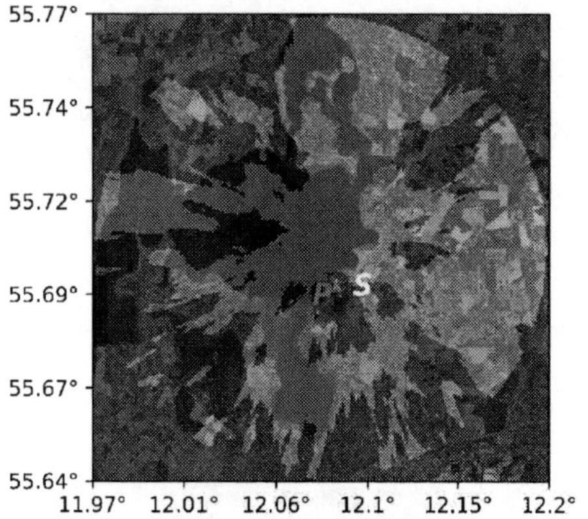

Figure 6: Ground shadow map of the DTU Risø campus at 50 by 50 meters resolution.

Together, these figures demonstrate the complete processing pipeline: raw sky image → calibration-based projection → cloud classification → ground irradiance mapping.

3.2 Time series validation

A full-day comparison between projected and measured GHI is shown in Figure 7. The dataset spans from 05:30 to 18:45 local time at 30-second resolution for the projection 1-second resolution for measured GHI. The left axis shows GHI from both the ASI-based projection (blue) and the pyranometer measurements (orange), while the right axis shows the cloud base height estimated from the lifting condensation level (gray, right y-axis).

4 Discussion

The first results from the DTU Risø ASI testbed highlight both the potential and current limitations of image-based irradiance mapping.

A key strength of the system is the calibration framework [9]. The fisheye model provides stable azimuth and zenith angle mappings across all three cameras, which is essential for reproducible projections. The consistency observed between calibration

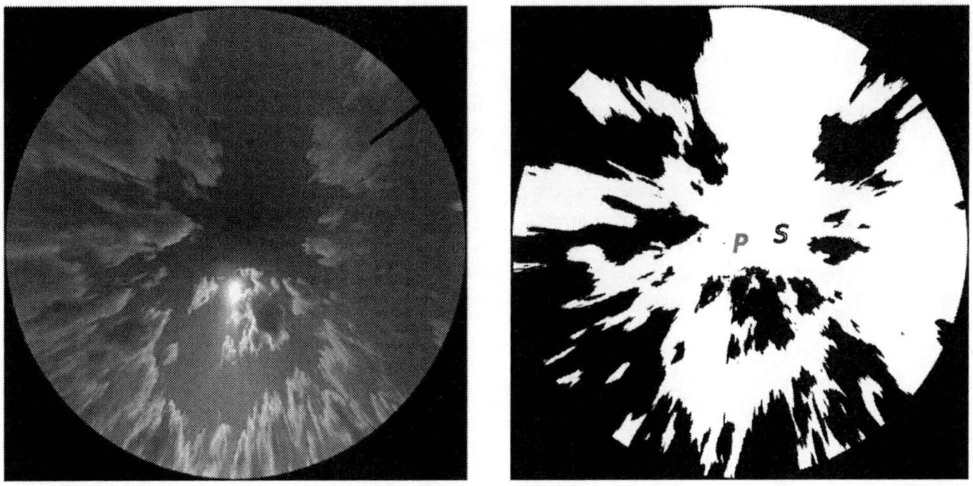

(a) Equidistant projection

(b) Binary transmission map

Figure 5: Image processing pipeline: (a) equidistant projection of the sky dome and (b) binary transmission map derived from normalized color index.

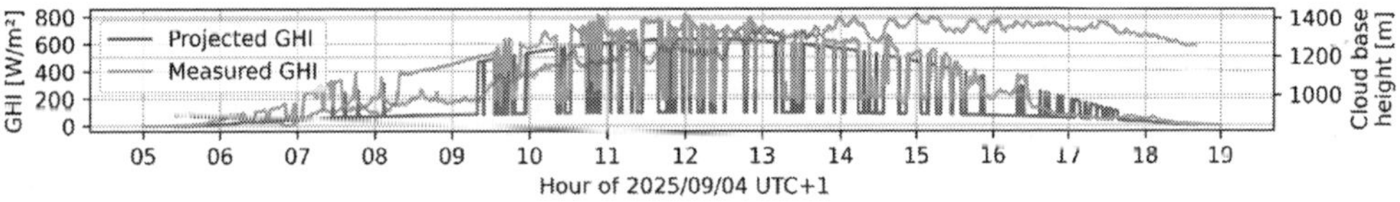

Figure 7: Projected and measured global horizontal irradiance comparison and cloud base height timeseries.

outputs and solar position suggests that geometric uncertainties are not the dominant source of error in the irradiance maps. This is further validated in Figure 7 where the projected and measured GHI show extremely good agreement in variation during the main part of the day (though not in absolute values), indicating that cloud shadows are projected correctly.

The projected and measured GHI align remarkably well during the main part of the day, demonstrating that our system correctly projects cloud shadows. This accuracy depends critically on Cloud Base Height (CBH) estimation, where our simple, locally adapted physical model performs surprisingly well. The model successfully tracks the CBH increase from approximately 1100 meters at 09:30 to 1400 meters at 14:00 and beyond, shown by the correct alignment of the projected and measured GHI throughout this period with changing CBH. Here we want to particularly highlight the period 10:15 to 10:50 with approx. 1200 meters CBH, and 14:40 to 15:30 with CBH ranging from 1350 to 1450 meters.

The use of the Simplified Solis [13] clear-sky model for DNI and DHI estimation is simple and easy to implement, however it is clear that the model underestimates the irradiance throughout the entire day. Figure 7 shows a series of cloud-enhancement events between 10:30 and 13:00, where the clear-sky model is not expected to produce the observed irradiance levels, but at no time does the model estimate correct irradiance levels. This observation is supported by the validation of the clear-sky model by Ineichen [14], where even the best performing models are found to systematically underestimate DNI, and estimations of GHI deviate in the order ±3%.

A serious deviation between projected and measured GHI is observed around 08:15 to 09:20 where the projected GHI shows only diffuse light (cloud-shaded conditions), while the measured GHI clearly indicates clear-sky conditions. This discrepancy is likely due to limitations in the transmittance calculation method when the projection direction aligns with the sun direction, which occurs during this particular period (east-northeast relative to the pier camera's location). The images from this period clearly show atmospheric whitening below the sun's elevation, which is then misclassified as cloudy even when no clouds are present.

5 Conclusion

This work presented first results from the DTU Risø ASI testbed, where three calibrated hemispheric cameras were deployed and evaluated for irradiance mapping. The DTU Risø dataset [8] enables validation of ASI-based irradiance mapping, and our results demonstrate that even with binary transmittance, strong agreement with ground truth can be achieved using this comprehensive dataset.

The SuMo calibration tool [9] provides reliable azimuth and zenith lookup tables, enabling equidistant projections and consistent geometric correction across all three cameras.

Binary cloud transmittance maps derived from the normalized color index $(B-R)/(B+R)$ successfully capture major irradiance variations and reproduce the diurnal GHI evolution with good temporal alignment.

Spatial projection of cloud shadows demonstrates excellent agreement with ground-based pyranometer measurements, even during periods with changing CBH.

The lifting condensation level approach for CBH estimation performs surprisingly well, correctly tracking height variations from 1100 to 1400 meters throughout the day. However, significant discrepancies occur during low solar elevation periods (08:15–09:20) due to atmospheric whitening misclassification, and systematic underestimation of irradiance levels indicates limitations in the used clear-sky model.

6 Further work

The testbed establishes a robust platform for advancing ASI-based solar forecasting. Future work will address current limitations through several key developments.

Improving the cloud transmittance model will move beyond binary classification to implement algorithms based on local adaptive thresholds that can better represent thin and semi-transparent clouds, even cloud-enhancement events.

Improved CBH estimation will involve training enhanced models on higher-quality observational data by leveraging the multi-camera setup to derive stereoscopic CBH estimates, reducing reliance on reanalysis data.

Advanced clear-sky irradiance modeling will implement more sophisticated clear-sky models and explore decomposition approaches that utilize the camera system's own GHI measurements rather than relying solely on theoretical clear-sky estimates.

Short-term forecasting capabilities will use cloud motion tracking algorithms based on temporal analysis of equidistant projections to predict future cloud positions and enable true solar forecasting at 15–30 minute horizons.

Comprehensive validation will extend evaluation to multi-day and seasonal datasets to quantify quantitative performance across varying meteorological conditions and solar geometries.

Through these developments, the DTU Risø ASI testbed will contribute to the broader effort of integrating high-resolution solar forecasting into renewable energy systems and grid management applications.

References

[1] International Energy Agency. *World Energy Outlook 2024*. Licence: CC BY 4.0 (report); CC BY NC SA 4.0 (Annex A). Paris: IEA, 2024. URL: https://www.iea.org/reports/world-energy-outlook-2024.

[2] Brian Tarroja, Fabian Mueller, and Scott Samuelsen. "Solar power variability and spatial diversification: implications from an electric grid load balancing perspective". In: *International Journal of Energy Research* 37.9 (2013), pp. 1002–1016.

[3] Amanpreet Kaur et al. "Benefits of solar forecasting for energy imbalance markets". In: *Renewable energy* 86 (2016), pp. 819–830.

[4] Lucien Wald. *Fundamentals of solar radiation*. CRC Press, 2021.

[5] Guanghui Huang et al. "Estimating surface solar irradiance from satellites: Past, present, and future perspectives". In: *Remote Sensing of Environment* 233 (2019), p. 111371.

[6] Yang Cui et al. "Solar radiation nowcasting based on geostationary satellite images and deep learning models". In: *Solar Energy* 282 (2024), p. 112866.

[7] Nils Straub, Wiebke Herzberg, and Elke Lorenz. "HelioNet-IR: Combining Infrared and Visible Satellite Images for Solar Irradiance Forecasting in the Early-Morning Hours". In: *Solar RRL* 9.16 (2025), p. 2500365.

[8] Jacob K. Thorning et al. *DTU Risø All-Sky Imager Testbed: One-Week Sky Image and Calibration Dataset*. 2025. DOI: 10.11583/DTU.30164002. URL: https://doi.org/10.11583/DTU.30164002.

[9] Niklas Blum et al. "Geometric calibration of all-sky cameras using sun and moon positions: A comprehensive analysis". In: *Solar Energy* 295 (2025), p. 113476.

[10] Davide Scaramuzza, Agostino Martinelli, and Roland Siegwart. "A toolbox for easily calibrating omnidirectional cameras". In: *2006 IEEE/RSJ International Conference on Intelligent Robots and Systems*. IEEE. 2006, pp. 5695–5701.

[11] Jun Yin et al. "Land and atmospheric controls on initiation and intensity of moist convection: CAPE dynamics and LCL crossings". In: *Water Resources Research* 51.10 (2015), pp. 8476–8493.

[12] H. Hersbach et al. *ERA5 hourly data on single levels from 1940 to present*. Accessed on 10-08-2025. 2023. DOI: 10.24381/cds.adbb2d47.

[13] Pierre Ineichen. "A broadband simplified version of the Solis clear sky model". In: *Solar Energy* 82.8 (2008), pp. 758–762.

[14] Pierre Ineichen. "Validation of models that estimate the clear sky global and beam solar irradiance". In: *Solar Energy* 132 (2016), pp. 332–344.

42nd European Photovoltaic Solar Energy Conference and Exhibition

Evaluating the Accuracy of Single-Camera Irradiance Forecasting

Jacob K. Thorning*, Sergiu V. Spataru, Adam R. Jensen, Peter B. Poulsen
Solar Photovoltaic Systems, DTU Electro, Technical University of Denmark (DTU), *email: jkrtho@dtu.dk

EU PVSEC

Introduction

- Variable PV production causes balancing challenges in grids and energy traders incur imbalance fees
- Clouds are the dominant driver of intra-hour irradiance variability
- All-Sky Imagers (ASIs) provide hemispheric sky images that can be transformed into irradiance maps and forecasts
- This testbed at **DTU Risø Campus** explores how well calibrated ASIs can reproduce ground-measured Global Horizontal Irradiance (GHI)
- Research and data published from testbed

Methodology

Wematics Pyranovision

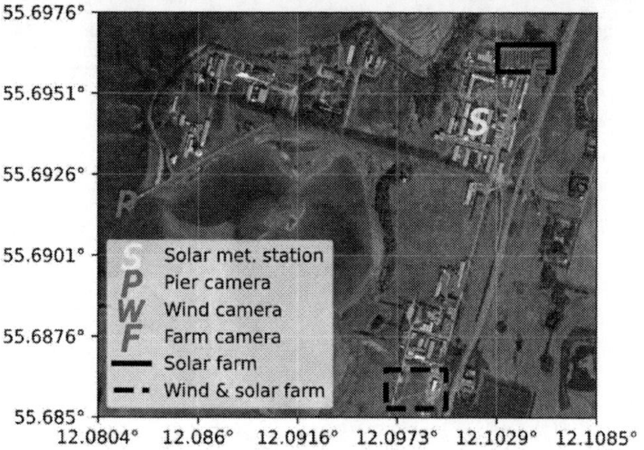

- 3 camera systems approx. 1000 meters apart
- Calibration with SuMo[1]
- Cloud based height from lifting condensation level as a function of temperature and relative humidity
- Equidistant projections generated based on raw image, calibration result and 3d cartesian coordinates
- Binary cloud transmittance map $\boldsymbol{T} = \frac{blue-red}{blue+red} > 0$
- Ground horizontal irradiance $\boldsymbol{GHI} = \boldsymbol{T} \cdot DNI \cdot \cos(\theta_z) + DHI$

[1]Blum, Niklas, et al. Solar Energy DOI:j.solener.2025.113476

Results

Raw 4k image 2025/09/04 12:10 (solar noon) | Corresponding equidistant projection | Transmittance map $\boldsymbol{T}$

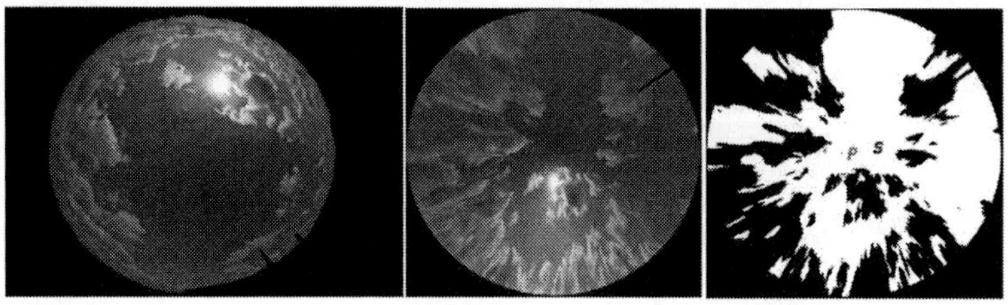

Dataset QR

Calibration output: Azimuth and zenith matrices

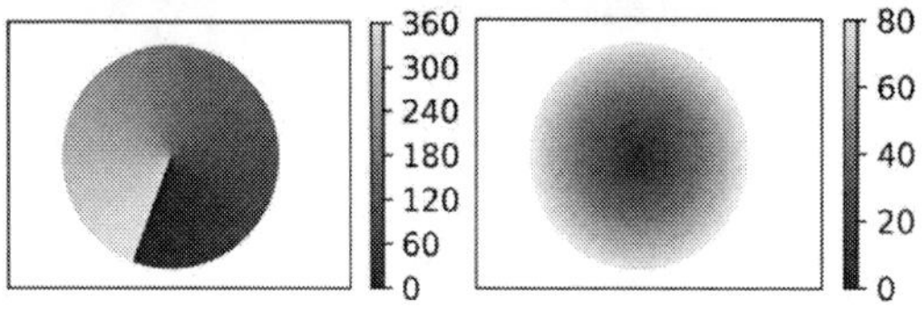

Distance $d = \tan(zenith) * altitude$ [m]
Distance east $dx = \cos(90 - azimuth) * d$ [m]
Distance north $dy = \sin(90 - azimuth) * d$ [m]

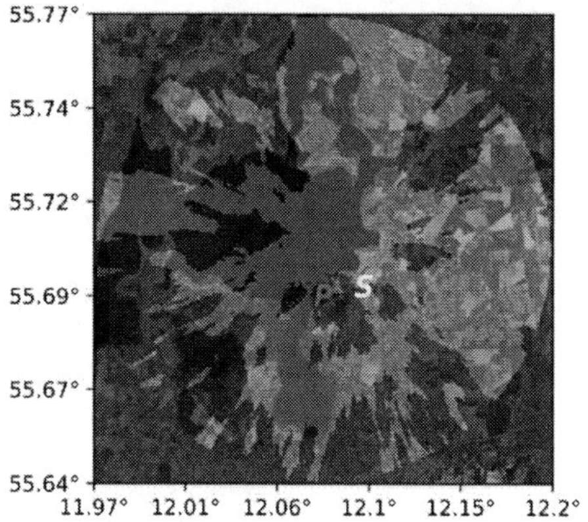

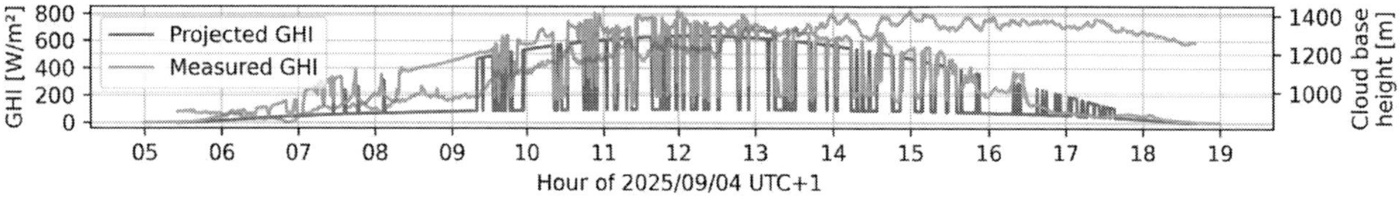

Conclusions and Outlook

- Calibration successful with nRMSD (sun pixel distances) of ≈ 1.5%
- Cloud transmittance works poorly in the solar area and area below the sun
- 1 week period dataset with images
- Variations in projected GHI vs measured GHI matches except when sun and projection direction are the same

LinkedIn

EUDP

This project has received funding from the Energy Technology Development and Demonstration Program (EUDP) under grant agreement no. 134243-534203. The project "IEA Task 16" is coordinated by DTU Electro and aims to advance international collaboration on photovoltaic system integration.

This project has received funding from the European Union under grant agreement no. 101146377 under the SOLARIS project – *Solar Operational Lifecycle and Asset Reliability Intelligence System.*

020268-001

New Empirical Model for Backside Irradiance

Kristijan Brecl, Marko Topič
University of Ljubljana, Faculty of Electrical Engineering, Ljubljana, Slovenia

Emilio Muñoz Cerón, Juan de la Casa Higueras
IDEA Research Group, Centre for Advanced Studies in Earth Science, Energy and Environment, University of Jaén, Spain

UNIVERSITY OF LJUBLJANA Faculty of Electrical Engineering
Universidad de Jaén

Abstract

The widespread of bifacial PV modules raises the question of whether current performance assessment models are still good enough or whether they need to be adapted. The main challenge in simulating the performance of bifacial PV modules is the correct definition of the backside irradiance. Currently, analytical or very complex ray tracing models are used to estimate the backside irradiance. These models are usually computationally intensive and require a detailed information of the PV system and surrounding. Here we are presenting a new empirical model for backside irradiance. The model is developed on measured data at a very sunny location in southern Spain and afterwards validated in a central European climate. The measured backside irradiance data is evaluated with regard to the diffuse light, solar azimuth angle, and seasonal changes over the whole year. A Gaussian correlation between observed parameters is used in the new model. Additionally, the seasonal changes are considered as variations in the parameters of the Gaussian model.

Backside irradiance

Test site at UJA, Spain

Test bifacial PV system at the University of Jaén, Spain. Five of the nine PV modules were covered from the front to only absorb light from the back.

G_{back} over a day

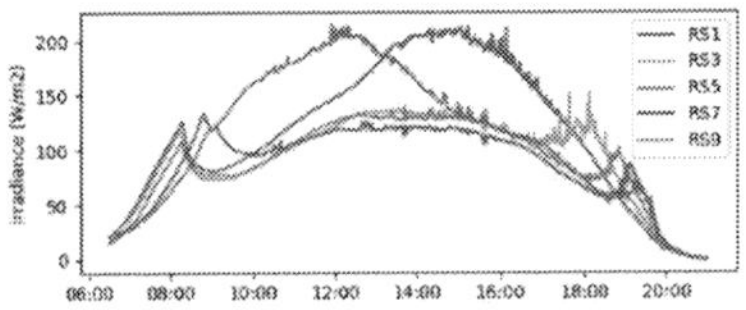

Backside irradaince on the observed modules over the course of a clearsky day in July. The modules at the beginning and at the end of the row (RS1, RS9) receive more light from the back. In the early morning and late afternoon the modules receive some direct light.

G_{back} vs. solar azimuth

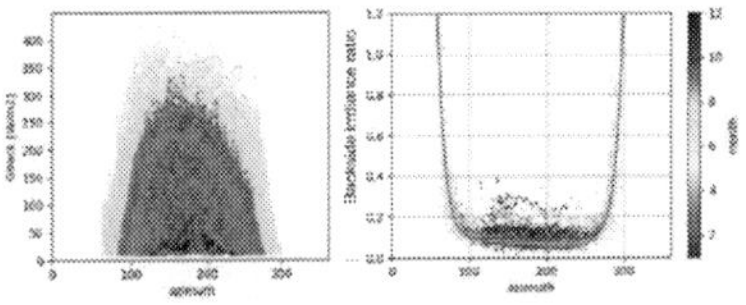

Backside irradiance versus solar azimuth angle (left) and backside irradiance ratio (right). Backside irradiance ratio is defined as backside irradiance devided by front plane-of-array irradiance.

Empirical model

Gaussian equation

$$G_{back\_ratio} = y0 + a \cdot e^{-0.5 \cdot \left(\frac{|az - az_0|}{b}\right)^c}$$

coefficient	value	comment
a	-800	tail slope
b	130-170	width
c	15	width and "sharpness"
az_0	184	azimuth shift (183-184 for Jaén)
y_0	800.14	|a|+ effective albedo

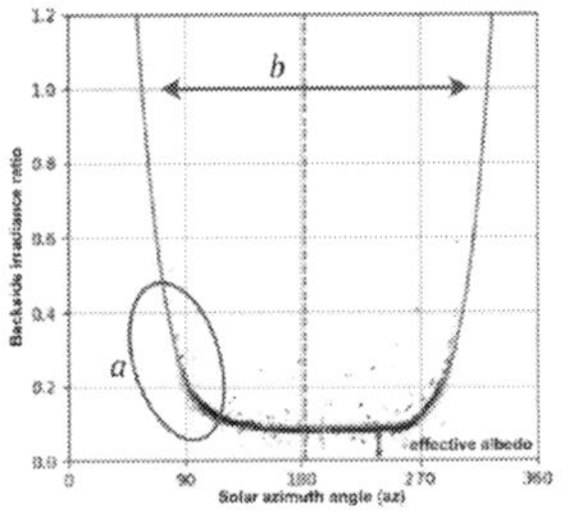

Presentation of Gaussian parameters on the clearsky backside irradiance ratio chart.

Results

Simulated backside irradiance in Jaén and Ljubljana

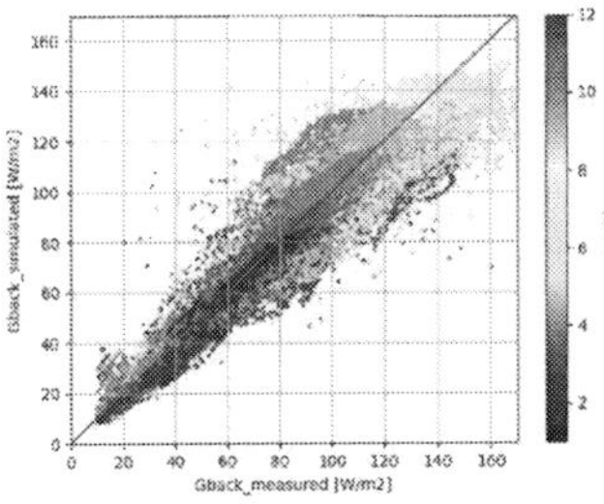

Validation of backside irradiance in Jaén.

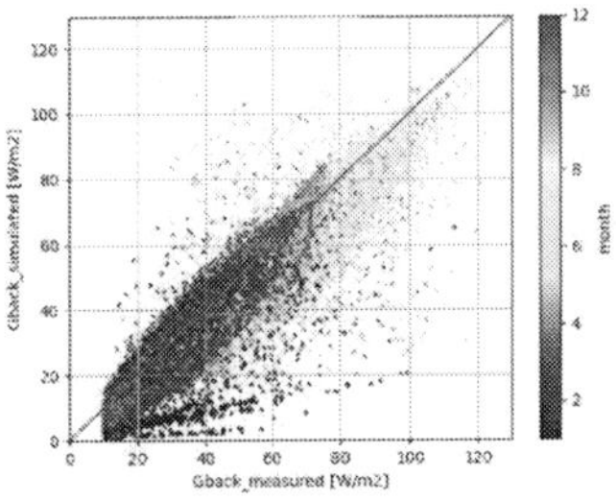

Validation of backside irradiance in Ljubljana.

Conclusion

The most appropriate way to simulate the backside irradiance is by determining its ratio relative to the front G_{poa}. The share of the back irradiance in the total irradiance received by a bifacial module is generally consistent throughout the day, with deviations in the morning and evening hours in summer when the sun shines from behind. Our new empirical model simulates the backside irradiance ratio as a ratio of the back to front irradiance with respect to the solar azimuth. The ratio is modelled by a Gaussian equation with the parameters derived from the measured data in the training period.

More information:

K. Brecl et al., "Is an exact backside irradiance modelling essential for bifacial PV systems?", Renewable Energy 256 (2026) 123942
https://doi.org/10.1016/j.renene.2025.123942

Acknowledgments

- Slovenian Research and Innovation Agency (Research Programme P2-0415).
- This work has been possible also thanks to the project "Demo_BI-FV: Development of Advanced Models for the characterization of bifacial photovoltaic systems (PID2021-124161OB-I00)" funded by the Spanish Ministry of Science and the State Innovation Agency within the European Regional Development Fund (MCIN/AEI/ 10.13039/501100011033/FEDER, UE).

DEEP LEARNING-BASED SOLAR IRRADIANCE DECOMPOSITION MODELS FOR NORDIC REGIONS

Alfredo Sanchez Garcia and Berhane Darsene Dimd
SINTEF AS
alfredo.sanchez@sintef.no, berhane.dimd@sintef.no

This work presents a comparative evaluation of machine learning (ML) and deep learning (DL) models for solar irradiance decomposition in Nordic regions, where traditional empirical models often struggle. Using data from the Alpha Centauri outdoor test facility in Trondheim, Norway, the present work benchmarks the performance of Histogram-based Gradient Boosting (HGB), Artificial Neural Networks (ANN), and Long Short-Term Memory (LSTM) networks against the Erbs model. Results indicate that HGB performs best on the initial evaluation set, achieving strong R^2 scores for both DNI and DHI, while requiring minimal computational resources. However, in a zero-shot prediction scenario using independent data, HGB's performance drops significantly, suggesting overfitting to seasonal patterns. ANN maintains the highest accuracy for DNI decomposition, capturing nonlinear dependencies more effectively, whereas LSTM shows mixed results, particularly underperforming in DNI estimation.

1 INTRODUCTION

Accurate modeling of solar irradiance components—global horizontal irradiance (GHI), direct normal irradiance (DNI), and diffuse horizontal irradiance (DHI)—is essential for optimizing photovoltaic (PV) system performance. Traditional physical decomposition models, such as DISC, DIRINT, and Erbs, have been extensively applied to estimate these components from measured GHI [1]. These models rely on empirical relationships and atmospheric parametrization, which have been validated primarily in low and mid-latitude regions, where they provide consistent and reliable results. However, in Nordic regions, these models often struggle due to unique atmospheric conditions, including low solar elevation angles, which influence the optical path length and scattering effects [2]; frequent cloud cover and diffuse-dominated radiation, leading to increased uncertainty in DNI estimation [3]; seasonal variations, with long periods of low irradiance and rapid transitions in daylight duration [2]; and snow and albedo effects, which alter surface reflectance and impact model accuracy [4]. These challenges introduce significant discrepancies in the decomposition process, ultimately affecting PV performance predictions, energy yield assessments, and system design optimizations.

In recent years, machine learning (ML) and deep learning (DL) have gained popularity for predictive modeling by enabling data-driven approaches to complex, nonlinear problems [5]. Unlike traditional physical models that rely on empirical relationships and explicit parameterization, ML and DL methods can extract patterns from large datasets, making them particularly suitable for dynamic and highly variable environments such as Nordic climates. Early applications focused on enhancing empirical models with ML techniques. For example, gradient boosting algorithms have been shown to significantly improve DNI and DHI estimation from GHI and meteorological inputs, with relative DNI errors as low as 7.45%, although DHI predictions remained less accurate [6]. DL methods have been investigated to overcome these limitations at finer timescales. Recurrent architectures such as long short-term memory (LSTM) models have achieved improvements exceeding 7% in relative RMSE for DNI at sub-hourly intervals compared to classical models [7]. These findings indicate that ML and DL approaches can outperform empirical models under variable atmospheric conditions.

Motivated by these findings, this work aims to evaluate whether ML and DL methods can provide accurate estimates of DNI and DHI in the challenging Nordic regions. This goal is further reinforced by recent findings showing that having access to a complete set of irradiance components enhances the accuracy of PV power predictions [8]. To this end, three representative learning models —Histogram-based Gradient Boosting (HGB), a feed-forward artificial neural network (ANN), and a recurrent LSTM network— are trained to predict DNI and DHI from measured GHI and solar position features using high-resolution (1-min) data collected at the Alpha Centauri outdoor test facility in Trondheim, Norway. Training spans August 2022–May 2023, and generalization is assessed in a zero-shot setting on April–May 2024 data to probe seasonal transfer. Furthermore, the ML models are evaluated against the empirical Erb's model to determine whether data-driven decomposition methods are better suited for Nordic regions.

2 BACKGROUND

Accurate decomposition of solar irradiance into its direct and diffuse components has traditionally relied on empirical models, while recent developments in ML and DL have introduced data-driven alternatives. This section reviews the conventional empirical approach used as a benchmark in this study and describes the ML/DL methods evaluated.

2.1 Empirical decomposition models

Empirical models estimate the diffuse and direct components of solar irradiance from measured GHI using correlations with the clearness index and solar geometry. Among these, the Erbs model [1] is one of the most widely used due to its simplicity and low computational cost. The Erbs model estimates the diffuse fraction (DF) as a piecewise function of the ratio of global to extraterrestrial irradiance on a horizontal plane, commonly expressed through the clearness index. Then, DHI and DNI follow

$$DHI = DF \times GHI, \quad (1)$$

$$DNI = \frac{GHI - DHI}{\cos\theta_z}, \quad (2)$$

where θ_z is the zenith angle.

2.2 Machine and deep learning methods

Machine learning and deep learning approaches offer

10.4229/EUPVSEC2025/4BV.3.8

flexible, data-driven alternatives to empirical models by learning complex nonlinear relationships directly from data [5]. Three representative algorithms were selected to cover different modeling paradigms:

Histogram-based Gradient Boosting (HGB) is an ensemble method that constructs additive decision trees using gradient boosting with histogram-based binning for efficient split finding. It is well-suited for tabular data and can capture nonlinear feature interactions without requiring feature scaling. HGB is computationally efficient and robust to heterogeneous feature distributions, making it a strong baseline among ML methods.

Artificial Neural Networks (ANN) consist of layers of interconnected nodes that apply linear transformations followed by nonlinear activation functions. ANNs are universal function approximators, meaning they can model highly complex relationships between inputs and outputs when provided with sufficient data and appropriate architecture. They are widely used in regression, classification, and forecasting tasks across many domains but require careful tuning of architecture and regularization to avoid overfitting.

Long Short-Term Memory (LSTM) networks are a specialized type of recurrent neural network (RNN) designed to handle sequential data and capture long-range dependencies. Unlike standard RNNs, LSTMs incorporate gating mechanisms—input, output, and forget gates—that regulate the flow of information and mitigate issues such as vanishing or exploding gradients. This makes them particularly effective for time-series modeling and other applications where temporal context is critical.

3 METHODS

The aim of the present work is to compare the performance of ML and DL algorithms for solar irradiance decomposition. Specifically, the goal is to assess these models' ability to predict DNI and DHI from measured GHI. The models will be benchmarked against the empirical Erbs model.

3.1 Data and Preprocessing

The analysis uses data from the Alpha Centauri outdoor test facility in Trondheim, Norway [9]. The site includes eight bifacial PV modules mounted on four dual-axis trackers and a meteorological station equipped with two pyranometers and one pyrheliometer. Measurements of GHI, DNI, and DHI were recorded at a 1-minute resolution for a period spanning from August 2022 to May 2023. Solar zenith and azimuth angles were computed from timestamp and location coordinates using the Python library pvlib [10].

Standard preprocessing techniques were applied to construct the dataset. These involved the removal of missing values, discarding rows with zero irradiance across and normalization to ensure stable training. Zenith and azimuth angles were added to the dataset. For the LSTM model, sequences were generated using a sliding window so that the model captures temporal dependencies.

3.2 Model Setup and Training

Three models were evaluated: HGB, ANN and LSTM. For all models, inputs consisted of GHI and solar geometry, while targets were the corresponding DNI and DHI values. This is illustrated in Figure 1, using an ANN as an example.

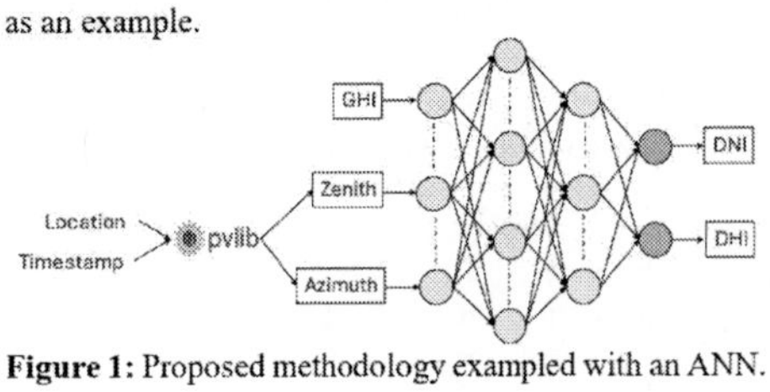

Figure 1: Proposed methodology exampled with an ANN.

The HGB model was trained using default hyperparameters, due to its low sensitivity to tuning. In contrast, the ANN and LSTM models underwent extensive hyperparameter tuning and employed advanced training strategies such as learning rate scheduling and early stopping to improve convergence and prevent overfitting. For the DL methods, the root mean squared error (RMSE) was employed as loss function. Let y_{pred} and y_{true} denote the model predicted and true values, respectively. The RMSE is then given by

$$RMSE = \sqrt{\frac{1}{N}\sum_{i=1}^{N}\left(y_{true,i} - y_{pred,i}\right)^2}. \qquad (3)$$

3.3 Evaluation Protocol

The dataset from August 2022 to May 2023 was split into 80% for training and 20% for validation. To assess generalization, an independent dataset from April–May 2024 was reserved for zero-shot evaluation, representing unseen seasonal conditions. Model performance was quantified using the coefficient of determination (R^2), which measures the proportion of variance in the target explained by the model. If $\bar{y}$ is the mean of the true values and $e_i = y_{true,i} - y_{pred,i}$ is the residual, then R^2 is given by

$$R^2 = 1 - \frac{\sum_i^N e_i^2}{\sum_i^N\left(y_{true,i} - \bar{y}\right)^2} = 1 - \frac{SSR}{SST}, \qquad (4)$$

where SSR is the sum of squared residuals and SST of the total sum of squares.

3 RESULTS

Figure 2 shows the learning curves for the ANN and LSTM models over 20,000 training steps. In Figure 2, RMSE (blue and red curves) rapidly decreases in the early training phase before stabilizing, indicating convergence of both ANN and LSTM models. The R^2 values for DNI and DHI (black, orange, purple, and green curves) increase as training progresses, showing that both models improve their predictive capabilities. Figure 2 shows that the R^2 scores for the ANN model improve steadily and reach a stable maximum at approximately 5,000 training steps, after which little additional gain is observed. In contrast, the LSTM model exhibits unstable behavior in R^2 during the initial training phase, particularly over the first few thousand steps. It begins to stabilize around 7,500 steps and continues to improve gradually, especially for the DHI prediction. This behavior motivated extending the training to 20,000 steps, despite the ANN model showing limited improvement beyond the early plateau. The ANN model reaches a higher final R^2 for DNI compared to LSTM, while LSTM achieves a better R^2 for DHI. This suggests that ANN is better suited for predicting DNI, whereas LSTM performs better in estimating DHI. The final model performance on the evaluation set (20% of the training/testing split) is summarized in Table 1, which presents the R^2 scores for DNI and DHI across all tested models. The results indicate that HGB outperforms both deep learning models, achieving the highest R^2 scores for both DNI and DHI. Among the DL methods, ANN performs better than LSTM in predicting DNI, while LSTM outperforms ANN for DHI estimation. Compared to the HGB method, it is worth mentioning that the DL methods required significantly more computational time and specialized training strategies, such as learning rate scheduling and hyperparameter tuning, to achieve acceptable performance. It is also worth mentioning that HGB is the model that required the least training time, and no hyperparameter tuning to achieve high performance. These results suggest that tree-based ensemble methods, like HGB, may be well-suited for this type of structured tabular data, particularly when irradiance decomposition patterns are well-represented in the training set. However, the model's high performance without tuning may also reflect overfitting to specific seasonal or geometric patterns.

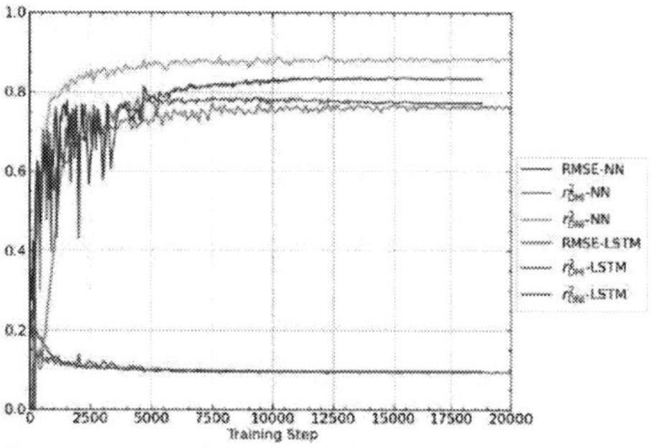

Figure 2. Learning curves for the ANN and LSTM models. RMSE (blue and red) is used as the loss function. R^2 for DNI and DHI (black, orange, purple, and green) is used as the performance metric.

Table I: R^2 scores for DNI and DHI on the evaluation set. The results compare HGB, ANN and LSTM.

Model	DNI	DHI
HGB	0.90	0.90
ANN	0.88	0.76
LSTM	0.78	0.83

To assess the models' ability to generalize beyond the training conditions, an additional evaluation was carried out using an independent dataset collected during April–May 2024. This period, not included during training, was chosen to reflect a different seasonal regime, thereby testing the robustness of the models under unseen atmospheric conditions. Figure 3 compares the predictions of the tested ML/DL models (HGB, ANN, and LSTM) with those of the Erbs model, using measured DHI and DNI as reference values. Table 2 summarizes the R^2 scores for DNI and DHI predictions across the models. Compared to the accuracies for the evaluation dataset presented in Table 1, all models show an expected decrease in accuracy.

Figure 3a presents the DHI predictions during the April–May 2024 period. Unlike in the evaluation set, the HGB model now underperforms, achieving the lowest R^2 among the machine learning models (0.19). The ANN model provides the most accurate and consistent predictions of DHI (0.43), followed by LSTM (0.27). This performance shift suggests that HGB's earlier success may have been tied to its ability to capture structured seasonal patterns present in the training data—patterns that do not generalize well to the independent evaluation period. In contrast, the ANN and LSTM models appear more capable of capturing the diffuse and less structured nature of DHI, which is more sensitive to short-term variability in cloud cover. The empirical Erbs model achieves an R^2 of 0.36, second best after the ANN model.

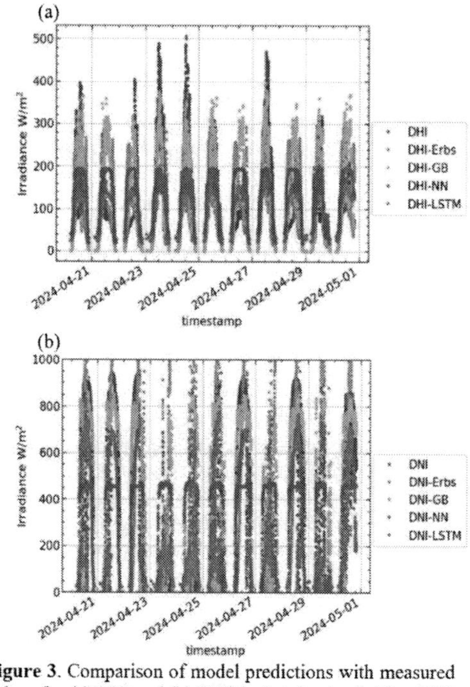

Figure 3. Comparison of model predictions with measured values for (a) DHI and (b) DNI during the April–May 2024 evaluation period.

Table II: R^2 scores for DNI and DHI predictions across tested models.

Model	DNI	DHI
HGB	0.62	0.19
ANN	0.77	0.43
LSTM	0.22	0.27
Erbs	-0.83	0.36

Figure 3b shows the model performance for DNI prediction. The HGB model, which had achieved the highest accuracy during evaluation, experiences a substantial drop in generalization, with an R^2 of 0.62 on the independent test set. Despite this decline, it still outperforms LSTM, which yields the lowest R^2 (0.22) among all the ML/DL models. The ANN model maintains the best performance, achieving an R^2 of 0.77, and demonstrates a stronger ability to generalize across seasonal and atmospheric changes. These results support the notion that HGB may be overfitting to structured patterns in the training data, particularly those related to solar geometry or seasonality, and is less adaptable to changes in irradiance conditions. In contrast, the ANN model appears more effective at capturing nonlinear dependencies between GHI and DNI that remain valid outside the training distribution. The weak performance of LSTM for DNI further suggests that time-sequential modeling contributes little to decomposition tasks focused on instantaneous irradiance components.

The Erbs decomposition model was also included in the April–May evaluation to benchmark the ML and DL models. Results in Table 2 and Figure 3 show that while Erbs provided moderate performance for DHI, it yielded negative R^2 values for DNI. This is indicative of systematic overestimation. This is noticeable in Figure 3b, where Erbs models DNI estimations (green dots) are highly overestimated even during midday hours when zenith angles were lowest. This suggests that the model's limitations may stem not only from geometric sensitivity but also from its inability to capture rapid irradiance variability and diffuse-dominated conditions, which are common in Nordic regions. Similar findings have been reported in previous studies on the shortcomings of empirical decomposition models under variable sky conditions and in northern climates [11, 12]. These results reinforce the need for more adaptive, data-driven methods, such as those evaluated in this work.

4 CONCLUSIONS AND OUTLOOK

This work has compared empirical, machine learning, and deep learning approaches for solar irradiance decomposition in the context of Nordic conditions.

Results show that while Histogram-based Gradient Boosting achieved the highest accuracy on the evaluation set, its performance degraded significantly in zero-shot scenarios, indicating sensitivity to seasonal patterns. In contrast, the Artificial Neural Network demonstrated better generalization, particularly for DNI estimation. The LSTM model offered limited benefits, suggesting that temporal dependencies play a minor role compared to the interactions of nonlinear features.

The Erbs model provided moderate performance in predicting DHI but systematically overestimated DNI values, likely due to its inability to adapt to rapid irradiance variability. Importantly, all ML and DL models outperformed the Erbs model in predicting DNI, confirming the advantage of data-driven approaches for high-latitude environments.

The results presented in this work suggest that ANN-based models may be the most robust choice for operational forecasting in Nordic climates, while tree-based methods like HGB can deliver strong performance when seasonal patterns are well represented in the training data.

Future work will focus on enhancing the deep learning models, particularly for DHI decomposition, by integrating physics-informed neural networks (PINNs). These models will combine empirical solar physics with data-driven learning, improving generalization and robustness for irradiance decomposition in the Nordic regions.

ACKNOWLEDGEMENTS

This work was partially performed within the Norwegian Research Center for Solar Energy (FME SOLAR) and is also part of the INTEREST project, funded by the European Union under Grant Agreement No. 101160594. The center is co-sponsored by the Research Council of Norway and their research and industry partners. The views and opinions expressed are those of the author(s) only and do not necessarily reflect the views of the European Union. Neither the European Union nor the granting authority (The European Climate, Infrastructure and Environment Executive Agency [CINEA]) can be held responsible for them.

REFERENCES

[1] Erbs, D. G., et al. (1982). Estimation of the diffuse radiation fraction for hourly, daily and monthly-average global radiation. Solar energy, 28(4), 293-302.

[2] Boxwell, M. (2010). Solar electricity handbook: A simple, practical guide to solar energy-designing and installing photovoltaic solar electric systems. Greenstream publishing.

[3] Mol, W. B., van Stratum, B. J., Knap, W. H., & van Heerwaarden, C. C. (2023). Reconciling observations of solar irradiance variability with cloud size distributions. Journal of Geophysical Research: Atmospheres, 128(5), e2022JD037894.

[4] Øgaard, M. B., et al. (2021). Identifying snow in photovoltaic monitoring data for improved snow loss modeling and snow detection. Solar Energy, 223, 238-247.

[5] Goodfellow, I. (2016). Deep learning (Vol. 196). MIT press.

[6] Rajagukguk, R. A., & Lee, H. (2025). Application of explainable machine learning for estimating direct and diffuse components of solar irradiance. Scientific Reports. https://doi.org/10.1038/s41598-025-91158-x

[7] Ri, A., & Arifin, R. (2023). Enhancing the performance of solar radiation decomposition models using deep learning. Journal of the Korean Solar Energy Society, 43(3), 73–86. https://doi.org/10.7836/kses.2023.43.3.073

[8] Garcia, A. S. and Dimd, B. D. (2025). Enhanced bifacial photovoltaic power prediction through procedural training and comprehensive irradiance data [Manuscript submitted for publication].

[9] SINTEF. Alpha Centauri – Field Laboratory for Testing of Solar Modules. Available at: https://www.sintef.no/en/all-laboratories/alpha-centauri-field-laboratory-for-testing-of-solar-modules/

[10] Holmgren, W., et al. "pvlib python: a python package for modeling solar energy systems." Journal of Open Source Software, 3(29), 884, (2018). DOI: 10.21105/joss.00884.

[11] Tschopp, D., et al. (2021). Measurement and modeling of diffuse irradiance masking and terrain shading for complex PV installations. Solar Energy, 221, 416–427. https://doi.org/10.1016/j.solener.2021.04.026

[12] Manni, M., et al. (2024). Performance variability of solar irradiance model chains with high-resolution input data at high latitudes. Solar Energy, 272, 112065. https://doi.org/10.1016/j.solener.2024.112065

42nd European Photovoltaic Solar Energy Conference and Exhibition

Deep Learning-Based Solar Irradiance Decomposition Models for Nordic Regions

SINTEF

Alfredo Sanchez Garcia and Berhane Darsene Dimd
Sustainable Energy Technology, SINTEF Industry, Trondheim

Introduction

Accurate modeling of solar irradiance components (GHI into DNI and DHI) is important for optimizing PV system performance. Physical decomposition models such as DISC, DIRINT, and ERBS have been widely used for this purpose. These models typically perform well in low and mid-latitude regions, providing consistent and reliable results. However, in high-latitude regions, their performance can be inadequate due to the unique and complex atmospheric conditions. Recently, deep learning-based models have emerged as a promising alternative for solar irradiance decomposition. This study presents a comprehensive comparative analysis of deep learning-based solar irradiance decomposition models and established physical models for an outdoor test facility (Alpha Centauri) located in Trondheim, Norway.

Experimental setup

Alpha Centauri

- Field laboratory for testing of solar modules in Trondheim.
- 8 bifacial PV modules on 4 dual-axis trackers.
- Meteorological station on site. Two **pyranometer and a Pyrheliometer.**

Data Collection

- Frequency: 60 s.
- GHI, DHI and DNI.
- August 2022 – May 2023

Evaluation

- GHI, DHI and DNI
- April 2024 – May 2024
- Metrics: R^2, RMSE
- Tested against Erbs Model

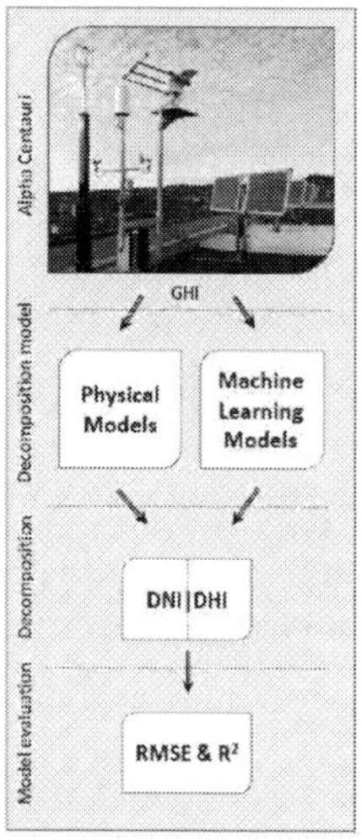

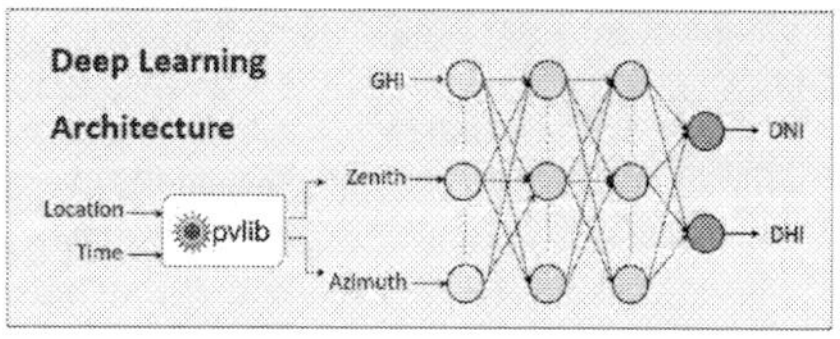

Machine Learning

Traditional machine learning (ML) techniques and one deep learning (DL) method were applied in this study. For all methods, the training-validation split was of 80/20.

Classical Machine Learning

- **Histogram-based Gradient Boosting (HGB)** Iterative algorithm that improves its predictions over time by minimizing the mean squared error function. Can handle a wide variety of data types and is resistant to overfitting.

Deep Learning Techniques

- **Artificial Neural Networks (ANN)** ANNs are powerful tools for modeling complex relationships between inputs and outputs, inspired by biological neural networks.
- **Long Short-Term Memory (LSTM)** Type of Recurrent Neural Network (RNN) that are particularly adept at handling time-series data due to their ability to remember past information.

Acknowledgement

This work was partially performed within the Norwegian Research Center for Solar Energy (FME SOLAR) and is also part of the INTEREST project, funded by the European Union under Grant Agreement No. 101160594. The center is co-sponsored by the Research Council of Norway and their research and industry partners. The views and opinions expressed are those of the author(s) only and do not necessarily reflect the views of the European Union. Neither the European Union nor the granting authority (The European Climate, Infrastructure and Environment Executive Agency [CINEA]) can be held responsible for them.

Results

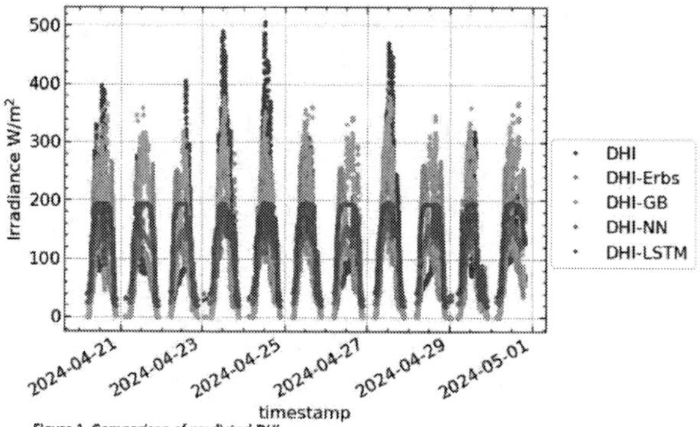

Figure 1. Comparison of predicted DHI

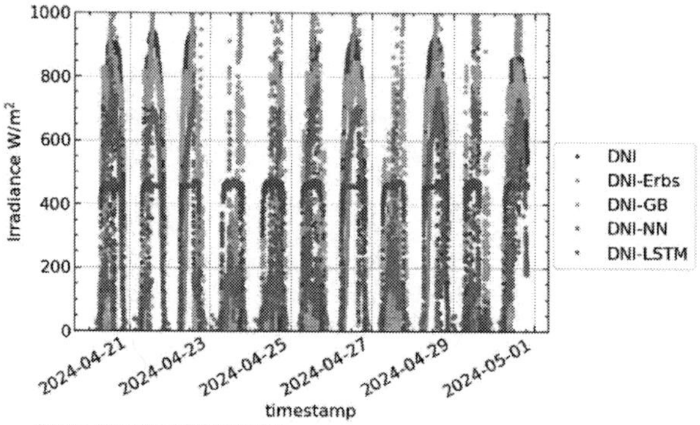

Figure 2. Comparison of predicted DNI

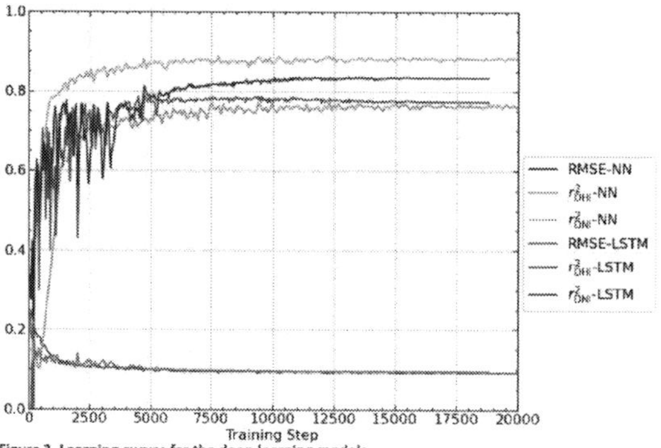

Figure 3. Learning curves for the deep learning models

High Performance and fast execution: HGB is the most accurate and fastest of the tested models.

Superiority of Physical Model: Erbs model outperforms DL models in prediction of DHI. DL models outperform Erbs in prediction of DNI.

Comparative Performance in DL methods: ANN better at predicting DNI than LSTM. LSTM better at predicting DHI than ANN.

Resource Intensive Optimization: DL methods require more time and special training strategies (learning rate scheduling, hyperparameter tuning) for OK performance.

Coefficients of Determination		
Model	DNI	DHI
HGB	0.90	0.90
ANN	0.88	0.76
LSTM	0.78	0.83

Conclusions and Further Work

- HGB was the fastest and most accurate of the tested models with $R^2 = 0.9$.
- Investigate the use of more advanced deep learning methods, such as Transformers.
- Physics Informed Neural Network: Incorporate physical models in training loss.

Technology for a better society

020271-001

ADVANCING VERY SHORT-TERM SOLAR IRRADIANCE FORECASTING IN AFRICA: A LOW-COST SKY IMAGING AND MACHINE LEARNING-BASED APPROACH

Martin Ansong[1,2], Gan Huang[1], Thomas N. Nyang'onda[2], Robinson J. Musembi[2], Bryce S. Richards[1]
[1]Institute of Microstructure Technology, Karlsruhe Institute of Technology, Germany
[2]Department of Physics, University of Nairobi

ABSTRACT: Africa holds immense potential for solar energy, thanks to its high year-round solar irradiation. Advances in photovoltaic (PV) technology and declining costs have made solar energy viable across the continent. However, fluctuating solar irradiance (SI), caused by factors like humidity, temperature and cloud cover, poses challenges for PV systems, causing power quality issues. This could be mitigated by utilising accurate SI forecasting, for optimal integration and operation of PV systems. Very short-term SI forecasts can play a crucial role in minimising energy storage requirements, enhancing power scheduling, and stabilising energy supply in real-time. In Africa, where weak grids usually coincide with abundant solar resources, such forecasts are especially valuable for improving load matching and grid reliability. Despite this, SI forecasting remains limited due to scarce historical SI data and high equipment prices. To address these challenges, the Karlsruhe low-cost sky imager (KALiSI) has been developed for approximately €500, for very short-term SI forecasting. Five KALiSI systems have been deployed in Africa, with data from one system installed in German being used in the present work to train a deep learning model, based on convolutional neural network – long short-term memory (CNN-LSTM) to predict SI. The model consistently delivered lower error rates across different forecast horizons compared to persistence, achieving average normalised root mean square error of 35% at 30 min horizon compared to persistence (50%). Future efforts will adapt this model to the African sites, utilising localised data to refine SI and subsequently PV power predictions, enhancing robustness and accuracy under diverse climatic conditions.

Keywords: Very short-term solar forecasting, Deep learning, Africa, low-cost sky imager,

1 INTRODUCTION

Solar energy presents a huge opportunity for Africa. The continent receives some of the highest year-round solar irradiation levels in the world with solar energy potential is of about 7900 GW, indicating vast potential for the generation of solar power [1]. The innovations in solar photovoltaic (PV) technology, coupled with the decreasing costs have made solar energy a very viable option for many African countries. However, the development and integration of PV in power systems is highly dependent on climatic conditions such as humidity, temperature and cloud cover, which can change rapidly over a short duration, causing fluctuations in solar irradiance (SI). This inherent fluctuations in SI can pose significant challenges in PV systems. SI fluctuations can negatively impact PV power quality, resulting in voltage fluctuations, voltage dips and flickers and frequency oscillations [2]. Therefore, accurate SI forecasts are required for the optimal operation of grid-connected PV power systems. SI forecasting can help to significantly reduce energy storage capacity required for energy balancing, as well as aiding power scheduling and dispatch decision. In addition, SI forecasting can help minimize the need for power curtailment and reduce the cost of electricity generation, thereby increasing revenues from electricity trading [3].

SI is typically forecasted for different forecast horizons including very short-term, short-term and long term, depending on the specific application. Very short-term forecasting focuses on predicting SI values for time frames that generally span a few seconds up 30 mins into the future. Techniques that work well for very short forecasting intervals might not be equally suitable for longer time scales [4]. A variety of methods can be applied to forecast SI, including persistence models, physical models, satellite models, statistical and machine learning - based approaches, ground-based sky imaging techniques.

1.1 Motivation

Most SI forecasting approaches rely heavily on the availability of historical data and typically provide long-term forecasts, ranging from a few hours to several days ahead. However, in many developing countries, especially in Africa, such historical data is often unavailable, significantly hindering solar energy development. Ground-based sky imaging techniques are therefore favoured. These techniques perform well within very short time horizons, may not require extensive historical data, and are increasingly being explored for solar resource assessment and forecasting as well as cloud monitoring [5]. Very short-term SI forecasting is particularly valuable for managing fluctuations in energy supply caused by rapidly changing weather conditions, thereby supporting real-time decision-making. Accurate and timely SI predictions on a very short-term basis enable solar power systems to adjust their operations, maintaining stable power output and ensuring consistent supply to the grid. Furthermore, such forecasts impact the financial performance of PV power plants. In developing regions like Africa, where weak power grids often coincide with abundant solar resources, accurate very short-term SI predictions can add more value by facilitating better load matching – aligning electricity demand with supply – and creating more robust electricity grids [5].

Despite the advantages of very short-term SI forecasting, particularly for solar energy exploitation, its application in Africa remains limited. Challenges to this include insufficient research, inadequate historical SI data, high cost and complexity of solar radiation measuring stations, which hinder the collection of reliable quality data. Another significant challenge is the lack of open-source imagery data from multiple locations across Africa with consistent imaging system setups. This data gap limits the ability to advance image-based SI forecasting and conduct related studies effectively.

10.4229/EUPVSEC2025/4BV.3.12

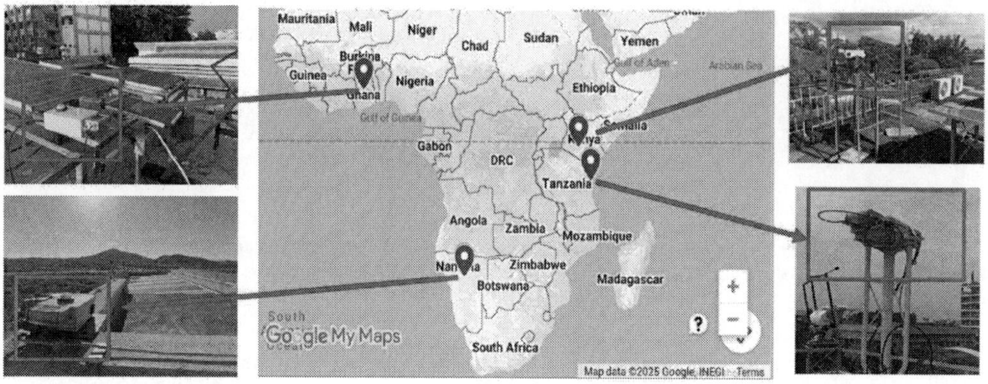

Figure 1: Map showing locations where the KALiSI have been installed across Africa.

To address these challenges, the Karlsruhe low-cost sky imager (KALiSI) which is suitable for SI forecasting and can be assembled for approximately US$ 600 has been developed [6]. Five of these systems have been deployed in various geographic locations across Africa including Ghana, Kenya, Tanzania and Namibia to collect data for SI forecasting, as depicted in the map in Fig.1. The KALiSI was first deployed at the Karlsruhe Institute of Technology (KIT) in southwest Germany, where it has demonstrated full functionality comparable to more expensive commercial sky imagers, after several rounds of testing and modifications [6].

This low-cost system holds significant potential not only for grid integration of PV systems, but also for microgrid and small-scale PV systems, where very short-term forecasting is often necessary [7]. Additionally, the system facilitates data collection for subsequent analysis. The KALiSI is constructed around the Raspberry Pi Model 4B single-board computer and 8 MP camera module with a fisheye lens which provides high computational capability, resulting in faster processing, improved multitasking, and enhanced overall performance compared to other low-cost imagers in its class. The design is simple, allowing the components to be assembled quickly and easily, typically within two days

2 MATERIALS AND METHODS

2.1 Data collection and processing

It should be noted from the foregoing that while the present study uses data collected from Karlsruhe, in Germany, this will ultimately be replaced with data collected from the different sites in Africa where the KALiSI systems are currently installed, in order to establish localised models for very short-term SI and PV-power prediction for these areas.

The sky images captured by the KALiSI installed in KIT solar park (49°05'56.2"N 8°26'14.5"E) at every minute from sunrise to sunset were collected from February to July 2024 to train a convolutional neural network – long short-term memory (CNN-LSTM) model to forecast SI for the locations. The corresponding global horizontal (GHI) values are measured and logged directly on the KALiSI by a SI sensor (IMT Technology GmbH, Si-V-1.5TC-T, Germany) connected to it. Data processing involved masking out unwanted areas, downsizing and normalization of images to make them suitable for training the model. A hybrid cloud detection algorithm was applied to obtain the cloud cover from the pre-processed images.

To obtain the cloud cover images are categorized into cloudy, partly cloudy, and clear based on average pixel intensity, excluding the sun's region. The cloud cover of clear images is set to zero without further processing. For cloudy and partly cloudy images, if the sun is not detected, a fixed threshold is used to segment cloud pixels from sky pixels. Otherwise, the Otsu adaptive threshold is applied before calculating cloud cover as the ratio of cloud pixels to total pixels within the fisheye circle in the image. The segmentation is based on the red-to-blue pixel ratio to enhance contrast between cloud and sky pixels [6]. Figure 3 shows a pre-processed image from the KALiSI with its corresponding binarized images used in cloud cover calculation shows an overview of the forecasting model design.

The cloud cover as well as their corresponding images downsized to 64 x 64 pixels were then stacked in sequence according to the forecast horizon, to capture the cloud dynamics, and used as input to the CNN-LSTM model to forecast the SI.

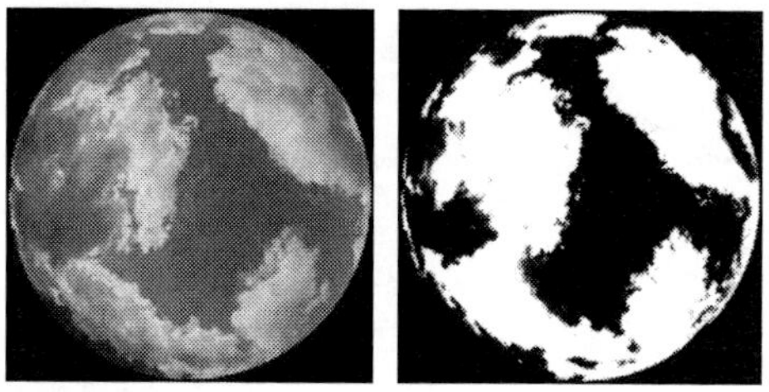

Figure 2: Pre-processed image (right) from the KALiSI with corresponding binary image (left) used in cloud cover determination.

2.2 Model architecture

The proposed model integrates handcrafted and learned features from ground-based sky images to predict GHI. Initially, pre-processed sky images are processed using a red–blue ratio algorithm to enhance cloud detection, after which a cloud fraction estimation algorithm quantifies the proportion of the sky covered by clouds [6]. These cloud fraction values are subsequently incorporated as auxiliary inputs to the model. In parallel, the pre-processed sky images are down-sampled and passed through two sequential convolutional blocks, each consisting of a 3 × 3 convolutional layer, batch normalization, and max pooling to extract progressively higher-level spatial representations of cloud structures and brightness patterns. The resulting feature maps are then flattened to form a compact representation. Next, the handcrafted cloud fraction features and the convolutional feature representations are concatenated to create a unified feature vector, which is reshaped into a temporal sequence and processed by the LSTM layer to model temporal dependencies between successive images. The LSTM output is further refined through a stack of dense and dropout layers that provide nonlinear regression capability and regularization, finishing in a final dense layer that produces the predicted GHI values.

2.3 Model Training and Evaluation

Each sample given to the network is composed of a sequence of images equal to the forecast horizon as well as corresponding sequence of cloud cover values. Samples collected from sunrise to sunset over the six months period were randomly allocated to the validation and the training sets.

The model was trained and tested on 3 days of different weather conditions, clear, partly cloudy and very cloudy days. The training objective involved decreasing the mean square error by utilising the Adam optimiser. K-fold cross-validation was employed, such that the training set was divided into 10 folds and each of the 10 folds was used as the validation set in turn. The final prediction is taken as the ensemble mean of the different sub-models.

Hyperparameters of the model such as the batch size, LSTM cells and learning rate were tuned to achieve the best forecasting performance on the 10-min ahead forecast. The same network architecture has been used to train models for the 5-min to 30-min ahead forecasts.

The performance of the model is evaluated using the root mean squared error (RMSE) and mean absolute error (MAE), defined in Eq. (1) and (2), respectively. The RMSE and MAE are widely used in the evaluation SI prediction accuracies. Smaller values of RMSE and MAE indicate lower deviation of the predicted values from the observed values and hence better predictive performance. The RMSE and MAE are normalised to the mean of the measured data using Eq. (3) and Eq. (4) [8] to provide a more standardised way of measuring errors and enable a fair comparison across different models or datasets with varying scales [9]. The persistence model, a commonly used reference model in SI forecasting, which always forecasts the last measured value irrespective of the time horizon is added as a reference model over the test set to also assess the performance of the model in forecasting. In SI forecasting, the persistence model assumes that the SI value at time $t+1$, is the same as the SI value at time t [10]:

$$\mathrm{RMSE} = \sqrt{\frac{1}{N}\sum_{i=1}^{N} (\mathrm{GHI}_{p,i} - \mathrm{GHI}_{m,i})^2} \quad (1)$$

$$\mathrm{MAE} = \frac{1}{N}\sum_{i=1}^{N} \left|(\mathrm{GHI}_{p,i} - \mathrm{GHI}_{m,i}\right| \quad (2)$$

$$\mathrm{nRMSE} = \frac{\sqrt{N}}{\sum_{i}^{N} \mathrm{GHI}_{m,i}} \sqrt{\frac{1}{N}\sum_{i=1}^{N} (\mathrm{GHI}_{p,i} - \mathrm{GHI}_{m,i})^2} \quad (3)$$

$$\mathrm{nMAE} = \left(\frac{1}{\sum_{i}^{N} \mathrm{GHI}_{m,i}}\right)\sum_{i=1}^{N} \left|(\mathrm{GHI}_{p,i} - \mathrm{GHI}_{m,i}\right| \quad (4)$$

where $GHI_{p,i}$ and $GHI_{m,i}$ are the respective predicted and measured GHI values in W/m^2, and N is the total number of times predictions are performed.

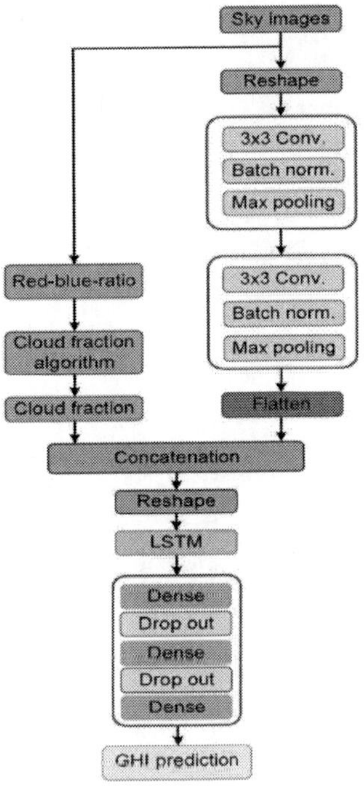

Figure 3: Overview of the forecasting model architecture

3 RESULTS AND DISCUSSIONS

The results were assessed by comparing with persistence model in terms of RMSE and MAE over the selected days. The results obtained for 10-min ahead GHI prediction for each of the 3 selected days is presented in Figure 4 and summarised in Table I. The model outperforms the persistence under all weather conditions achieving the best performance under clear sky with a RMSE and MAE of 18 and 13 W/m^2 respectively.

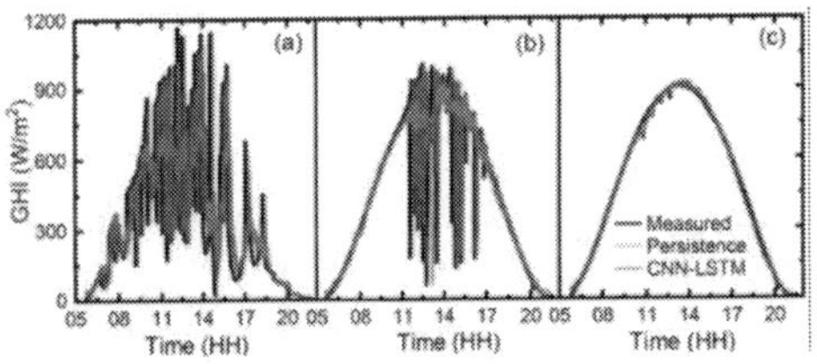

Figure 4: Performance of the CNN-LSTM model compared to persistence at 10 min ahead forecast (a) very cloudy (b) partly cloudy (c) sunny (Data taken from [6])

Table I: Performance of the model for the selected days in terms of RMSE (W/m^2) and MAE (W/m^2)

	Cloudy		**Partly cloudy**		**Clear**		**All**	
	RMSE	MAE	RMSE	MAE	RMSE	MAE	RMSE	MAE
Persistence	246	146	246	146	22	20	158	86
CNN-LSTM	**187**	**127**	**186**	**126**	**18**	**13**	**116**	**67**

Figure 5 also shows the average nRMSE and nMAE of the 3 selected for the CNN-LSTM model compared to the persistence over different forecast horizons. The proposed model achieved lower average nRMSE and nMAE than the persistence for all forecast horizons. For nRMSE (Figure 4a), CNN-LSTM starts at 30% at 5 mins and increases to 35% at 30 mins, while persistence rises sharply, to 50%. Similarly, for nMAE (Figure 4b), CNN-LSTM increases from 17% to 23%, compared to persistence's sharp rise from 17% to 35%.

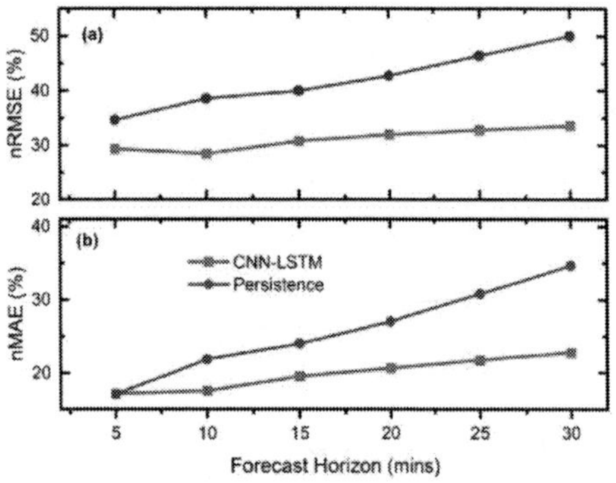

Figure 5: Performance of the CNN-LSTM model compared with persistence at different forecast horizons (a) nRMSE and (b) nMAE (Data taken from [6])

4 CONCLUSIONS

In summary, the images captured by the low-cost sky imaging (KALiSI) system in Karlsruhe, southwest, Germany have been used to train a hybrid model that combines CNN with LSTM. The model outperformed the persistence on forecast horizon of 5- 30 min. The KALiSI have been installed in five sites in Africa with different climatic and weather conditions, therefore future work will involve using the data collected in the sites in Africa and the model employed in the present study to establish localised forecast models for very short-term SI and PV power prediction for these location as well as optimising the models to improve it robustness and accuracy.

5 REFERENCES

[1] International Renewable Energy Agency (IRENA) and African Development Bank (AfDB), "Renewable Energy Market Analysis: Africa and Its Regions," Abu Dhabi and Abidjan, 2022.

[2] I. Ranaweera, O.-M. Midtgård, and G. H. Yordanov, "Short-term intermittency of solar irradiance in southern norway," in *29th European Photovoltaic Solar Energy Conference and Exhibition (EUPVSEC)*, 2014, pp. 2635-2638,

[3] N. Krishnan, K. R. Kumar, and C. S. Inda, "How solar radiation forecasting impacts the utilization of solar energy: A critical review," *Journal of Cleaner Production*, vol. 388, p. 135860, 2023.

[4] R. Samu *et al.*, "Applications for solar irradiance nowcasting in the control of microgrids: A review," *Renewable and Sustainable Energy Reviews*, vol. 147, p. 111187, 2021.

[5] M. Ansong, T. N. Nyang'onda, R. J. Musembi, and B. S. Richards, "Very Short-term Solar Irradiance Forecasting for Photovoltaic Power Integration with the Grid: Potentials and Challenges for Africa," presented at the 2024 IEEE PES/IAS PowerAfrica Conference, 2024.

[6] M. Ansong, G. Huang, T. N. Nyang'onda, R. J. Musembi, and B. S. Richards, "Very short-term solar irradiance forecasting based on open-source low-cost sky imager and hybrid deep-learning techniques," *Solar Energy*, vol. 294, p. 113516, 2025.

[7] M. Ansong, E. O. Ogunniyi, B. P. Jiménez, and B. S. Richards, "Renewable energy powered membrane technology: Integration of solar irradiance forecasting for predictive control of photovoltaic-powered brackish water desalination system," *Applied Energy*, vol. 401, p. 126651, 2025.

[8] T. E. Hoff, R. Perez, J. Kleissl, D. Renne, and J. Stein, "Reporting of irradiance modeling relative prediction errors," *Progress in Photovoltaics: Research and Applications*, vol. 21, no. 7, pp. 1514-1519, 2013.

[9] M. Paulescu and E. Paulescu, "Short-term forecasting of solar irradiance," *Renewable Energy*, vol. 143, pp. 985-994, 2019.

[10] M. Diagne, M. David, P. Lauret, J. Boland, and N. Schmutz, "Review of solar irradiance forecasting methods and a proposition for small-scale insular grids," *Renewable and Sustainable Energy Reviews*, vol. 27, pp. 65-76, 2013.

10.4229/EUPVSEC2025/4BV.3.12

42nd European Photovoltaic Solar Energy Conference and Exhibition

Karlsruhe Institute of Technology

UNIVERSITY OF NAIROBI

Advancing very short-term solar irradiance forecasting in Africa: A low-cost sky imaging and deep learning approach

Martin Ansong[1,2], Gan Huang[1], Thomas N. Nyang'onda[2], Robinson J. Musembi[2], Bryce S. Richards[1]

[1]Institute of Microstructure Technology, Karlsruhe Institute of Technology; [2]Department of Physics, University of Nairobi

Introduction

- Advances in photovoltaic (PV) with declining costs and high solar potential have made solar energy viable across Africa.
- However, fluctuations in solar irradiance (SI) caused by factors like humidity, temperature and cloud cover, poses challenges for photovoltaic (PV) systems, causing power quality issues[1].
- This can be mitigated by very short-term SI forecasting (VSTSIF), for optimal operation of PV systems and managing supply in real-time[1,2]

Motivation

- In Africa, where weak grids coincide with high solar resources, VSTSIF can be valuable for improving load matching and reliability
- VSTSIF remains limited due to scarce data & high equipment and maintenance cost[1].
- To address the challenges, Karlsruhe low-cost sky imager (KALiSI) open-source system[3] has been developed for ~€500, for VSTSIF of 5-30 min[4]

Materials and Methods

- KALiSI is constructed around RaspberryPi with camera module, fisheye lens and integrated with SI sensor. Custom program captures an image every min and record the corresponding, global horizontal irradiance (GHI).

- VSTSIF model based on convolutional neural network – long short-term memory (CNN-LSTM) with data from KALiSI installed Karlsruhe

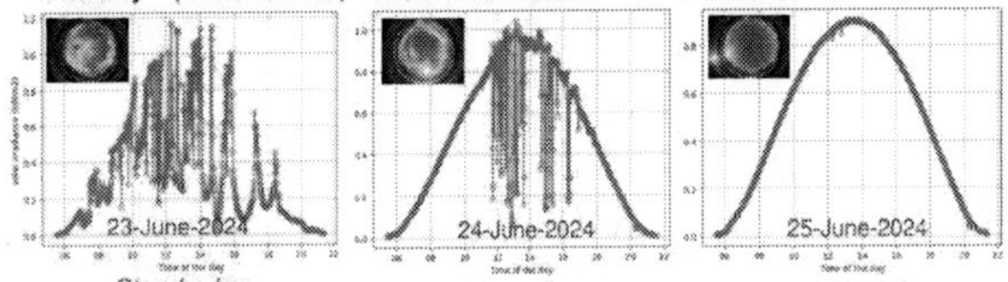

Cloudy day | Partly cloudy day | Clear day

- KALiSI deployed in 5 sites in Africa to collected to train deep learning model for VSTSIF

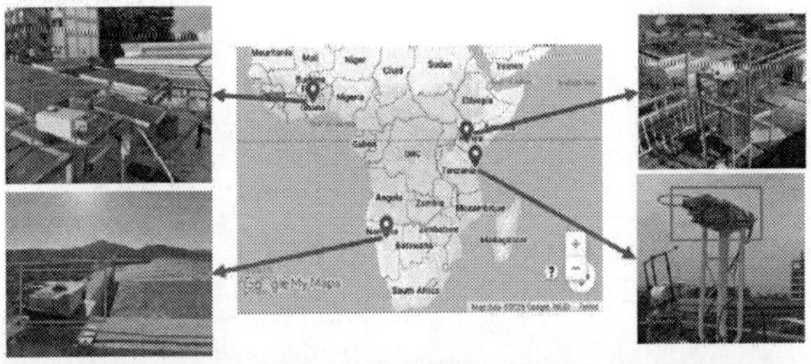

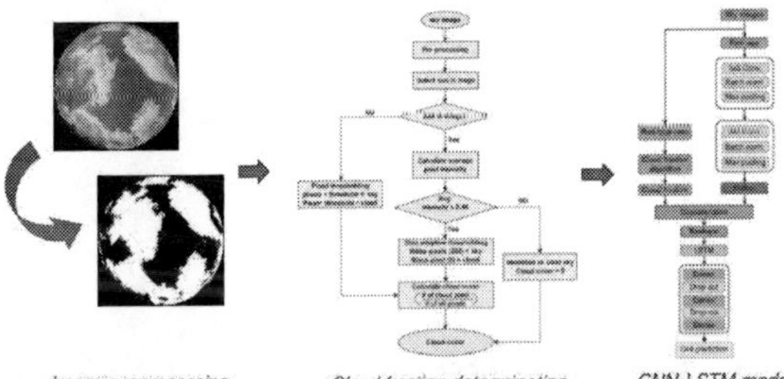

Image preprocessing | Cloud fraction determination | CNN-LSTM model

Results

	Cloudy		Partly cloudy		Clear		overall	
	RMSE	MAE	RMSE	MAE	RMSE	MAE	RMSE	MAE
Persistence	246	146	246	146	22	20	158	86
CNN-LSTM	187	127	186	126	18	13	116	67

Performance of the CNN-LSTM model for the selected days assessed by root mean error (RMSE) and mean absolute error (MAE) in W/m² for 10 min ahead forecast

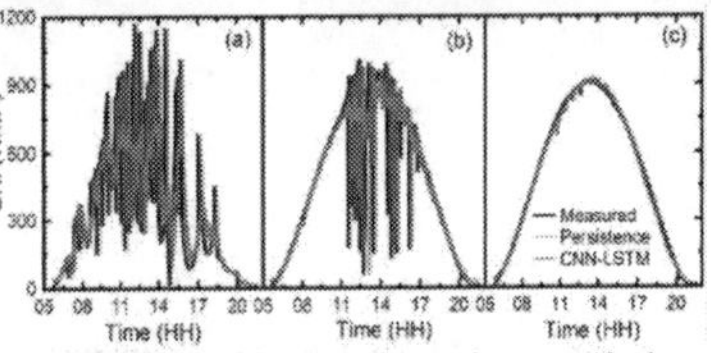

CNN-LSTM model compared to persistence at 10 min ahead forecast (a) very cloudy (b) partly cloudy (c) sunny

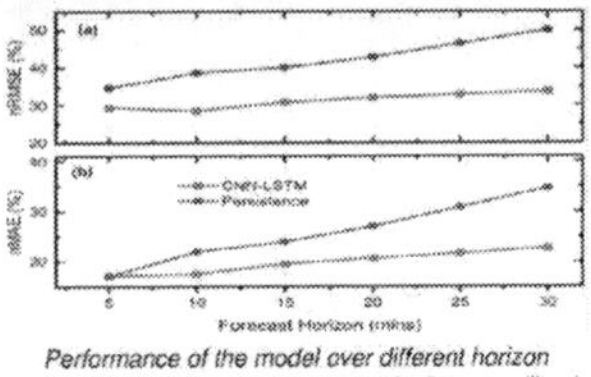

Performance of the model over different horizon compared to persistence assessed by (a) normalised RMSE (nRMSE) and (b) normalised MAE (nMAE)

Conclusions

- Data from KALiSI in Germany used to train the CNN-LSTM model, which outperforms persistence at all horizon from 5 to 30 min.
- Average nRME of 35% at 30 min horizon compared to persistence (50%).
- Future work will involve using data collected in Africa to establish localised models for VSTFSI and PV power prediction, and optimising models to improve performance and robustness.

References

[1] Ansong *et al.* In IEEE PES/IAS PowerAfrica Conference (2024)
[2] Ansong *et al.*, *Applied Energy* (2025)
[3] https://github.com/KALiSI4SIFS/KALiSI/tree/main
[4] Ansong *et al.*, Solar Energy (2025)

Contacts

Prof. Dr. Bryce S. Richards
E-Mail:bryce richardsəkit edu

Martin Ansong
E-Mail:ansong.martinəgmail.com

Funding :
Rsif PASET icipe DAAD HELMHOLTZ ASSOCIATION

Lessons Learned in Automating Quality Control: Challenges in Real World Ground Measurements

SOLARGIS

Camara A., Blstak Catlosova K., Cebecauer T., Jakubik M., Hulik Jansova M., Osvald O. | **Solargis, Bratislava, Slovakia**

Abstract

Acquiring **reliable** solar irradiance **data** under the real-world conditions poses numerous **challenges**. When left unaddressed, these issues will **affect further analyses and KPIs** used in photovoltaic (PV) project development and operation —including site adaptation of satellite models, data bankability, performance monitoring and evaluation and forecasting. We **quantified the impact** of compromised data on two key metrics, namely relative bias and relative root mean square deviation (rRMSD) between reference measurements with or without quality control and Solargis solar model.

To **automatically identify data degraded by issues**, it is crucial to understand common measurements issues and their typical manifestation in the data. To obtain precise references, and to ensure accurate metadata, as advanced automatic quality control methods heavily depend on these factors. We showcased examples from our developed quality control toolkit, demonstrating methods for **metadata verification and correction**.

Typical issues and their effect

The present work mainly targeted validating Global Horizontal Irradiance (GHI) of Solargis satellite solar resource model time series with ground measurements from 53 locations provided the validation reference in these analyses. Our aim is to analyse effect of different level of quality control on validation model. Table 1 details the most frequent problems found in GHI datasets, their prevalence and their effect on relative bias and rRMSD.

As demonstrated in Table 1 the occurrence and impact and presence of the individual issues is varying. Biggest impact on median and 90th percentile is caused by issue that medially affects the most data points, Shading. Some of these issues can substantially influence data integrity, even with sparse occurrences (e.g. Dirt/Soiling). These effects are more pronounced for Direct Normal Irradiance(subset of 41 validation datasets). A median of 16.34% data points were affected, mostly due to tracker issues. At the 90th percentile, all issues contributed to a 10.12% change in relative bias and 24.26% change in rRMSD. Soiling and shading impacts increased despite stable occurrence compare to GHI: shading caused 4.43% change in bias and 6.25% change in rRMSD; soiling, 2.20% change in bias and 5.91% change in rRMSD.

Table 1: Most common issues identified in compromised datasets of Global Horizontal Irradiance (53 validation datasets) by non-advanced automatic test (unless otherwise stated), proportion of affected datasets and data-points and corresponding impact of these issues on relative bias and relative root mean square error (rRMSD) with ground measurements used as reference for Solargis resource model.

Issue Type	Proportion of Affected Datasets (%)	Median Proportion of Affected Data Points (%)	Percentile of Absolute Effect on Relative Bias (%)			Percentile of Absolute Effect on rRMSD(%)		
			50th	90th	100th	50th	90th	100th
Below physical minimum	95.65	0.94	0.05	0.22	0.38	0.03	0.17	0.35
Postfiltering*	93.48	0.19	0.03	0.26	0.98	0.06	0.63	1.69
Shading*	91.30	6.80	1.03	2.23	2.86	1.10	2.55	2.87
Consistency	73.91	0.65	0.07	0.51	0.96	0.17	1.88	3.38
Maintenance*	65.22	0.31	0.03	0.50	0.70	0.07	0.86	1.13
Not-specified**	56.52	0.06	0.01	0.15	18.22	0.00	0.25	24.09
2-component test	41.30	0.00	0.00	0.02	0.06	0.00	0.10	0.44
Consecutive static values	39.13	0.02	0.00	0.07	0.49	0.00	0.05	0.55
Dirt/Soiling*	34.78	0.30	0.04	0.58	1.30	0.05	0.69	2.80
Dew/Frost*	32.61	0.09	0.05	0.11	0.32	0.04	0.11	0.33
All issues	100.00	11.38	1.15	3.12	15.92	2.19	5.53	29.22

* Issues that are identified either with advanced automatic test or by manual flagging.
** Issues that are flagged manually and are of atypical cause.

Time Reference Correction

Ground measurements frequently exhibit time reference issues stemming not only from site-specific timezones. These inconsistencies, varying from minor (5 minutes) to significant sub hourly, or daylight saving changes, create mismatches when validating the model data. These time shifts interfere with automatic quality control by distorting other data quality problems. This leads to incorrect identification of issues in ground measurement data. To ensure accurate data fitting with the Solargis model data and to avoid misinterpretation in automatic quality control, precise identification and correction of time reference issues are imperative. As shown on the **Figure 4**, all time shifts introduced changes to relative bias, time shift of 60 minutes can easily introduce change in relative bias of 2.24% and in more extreme cases 9.86% , caused just by incorrect flagging. However, using Solargis method to automatically detect and shift data to match with the used reference, effects of incorrectly identified issues on relative bias were minimised.

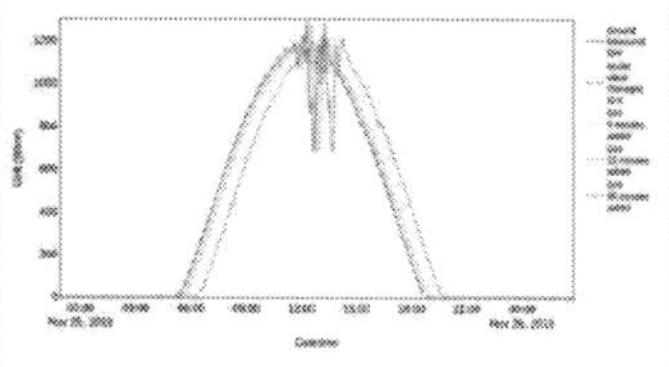

Figure 1. Time Series showcasing 3 different time reference misalignments for a single dataset on selected day.

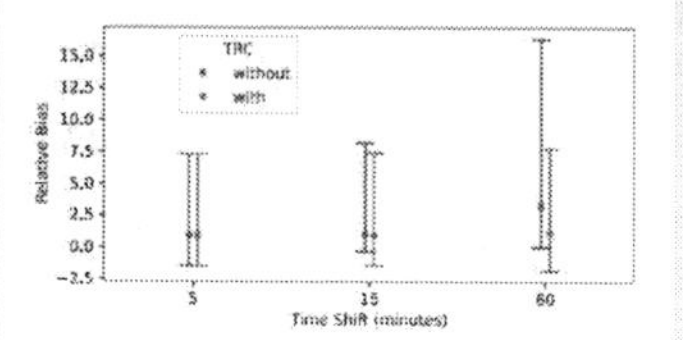

Figure 2: Showcasing the change in the in relative Bias when different timeshifts were introduced to 10 datasets and the effect of Time Reference Correction (TRC). Error bars represent 2.5th and 97.5th percentile.

Statistical Reference of Ground Measurements for Cloudless intervals identification

For quality control tests such as the identification of the type of measured irradiation (GHI, DNI, DIF, GTI, RHI), estimation of GTI mounting configuration (mounting type, tilt and azimuth), analysis of misalignment and other potential issues presented above, the statistical representation of cloudless situations (cloudless profile) is required. To identify the cloudless days we employed a statistical reference that used only ground measurements data as model data may suffer from inaccuracies in inputs not representing accurately local conditions (aerosols, water vapor) or the configuration of the mounting is not known upfront (e.g. GTI). To create the reference an uneven grid, inversely correlated to sun speed depicted on Figure 1 was used. A representative percentile was selected from each grid cell and the data was smoothed to provide a robust reference. This method enhanced cloudless day identification accuracy compared to a statistical reference based on regular grid (Figure 2). It has then direct impact on the quality of following QC tests.

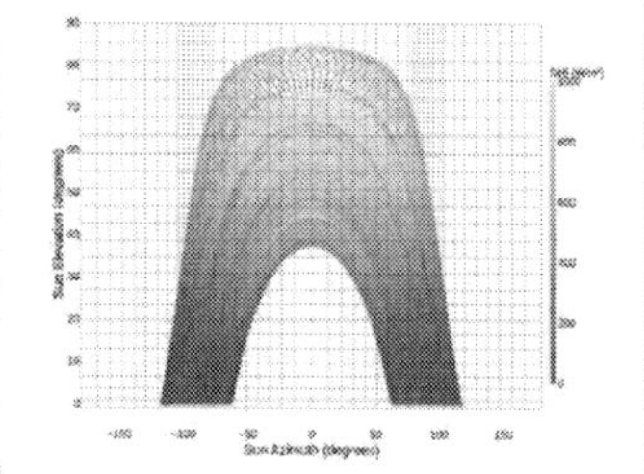

Figure 3. Unequidistant grid in sun azimuth and sun elevation space, used for creation of statistical reference that limits artifacts in higher elevations.

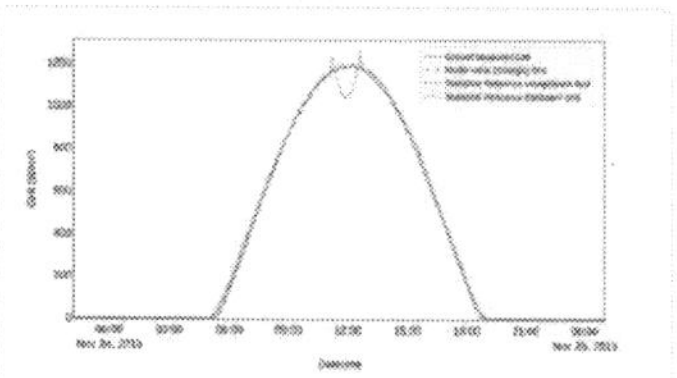

Figure 4: Comparison of ground measurements data, Solargis model data, statistical reference using unequidistant grid and statistical reference using regular grid. Regular grid reference has strong artifacts at the highest sun elevation due to the lower number of data points.

Conclusion

The analysis of ground measurements data from various sites revealed numerous common issues, and their impact on key metrics was quantified. We have showed the importance of quality control and how drastically it can influence model validation metrics.In addition to the measurement operations issues summarized in the Table1, the data from the PV projects can often suffer from the missing or incorrect metadata, such as GTI tilt and/or azimuth, instances of incorrect type of irradiation (e.g. incorrect column name), and inaccuracies in longitude and latitude and similar. Our diverse experience with datasets has highlighted the wide range of potential discrepancies. Missing or incomplete quality control can have strong impact on the utilization of measured data for tasks such as model site-adaptation or PV project performance evaluation. Such measurements issues can be in extreme cases off by tenths of percent. The developed automatic quality control methods can identify and significantly mitigate impact of incorrect measurements or meteostation metadata. The reliable quality control tools are critical for automation of the PV power plants operation, monitoring and performance evaluation as well as enhanced PV production forecasting.

AUTOMATED SOLAR DATA QUALITY REPORTING FRAMEWORK

Perez-Astudillo, Daniel, Bachour, Dunia A.
Qatar Environment & Energy Research Institute, HBKU
P.O. Box 34110, Doha, Qatar

ABSTRACT: Ensuring the collection and maintenance of high-quality solar data is essential for solar research and applications. The software provided with commercial data logging hardware, however, is generally limited to some basic data display and processing, usually just converting raw values to irradiance and doing simple averaging, and although this might suffice for a basic visualisation of data, it quickly proves inconvenient for advanced data analysis, such as assessing data quality, which requires calculations that may not be possible to incorporate in the provided software. This work presents a workflow that automates the periodic (daily, or configurable to other periods) assessment of the quality of solar irradiance measurements taken at 1-minute resolution; with a relatively simple set of scripts and freely available software, collected data are automatically analysed to produce a clear single-page report for each monitoring station, whether for one or several sites. All reports of one day are combined in one PDF file that is emailed to designated addresses.
Keywords: solar radiation, data quality, data pipeline, automation

1 INTRODUCTION

Managing the operation of a solar radiation monitoring station includes a number of activities aimed at maintaining the equipment in proper operating conditions and obtaining the highest-quality data from the equipment. Periodic preventive maintenance on the station (cleaning sensors, checking levelling, shading, etc.) and timely corrective adjustments or repairs are crucial for the hardware side of the system, and are usually carried out by designated technical personnel but, ultimately, the collected data must also be monitored frequently to confirm whether the equipment and maintenance are working as expected.

Generally, the data loggers used in solar radiation monitoring systems are provided with some way to display collected data in tabular or graphical form. However, these functionalities are quite limited; for example, in most cases no quality checks are or can even be implemented, other than perhaps simple limits such as a fixed maximum and/or minimum value.

While in some cases it may be possible to have a dedicated person or team to continuously monitor the data being collected, the task becomes increasingly difficult to manage as the number of data sources (stations) grows, not to mention the tediousness of the task, leading to higher chances of human error.

Given the above, a good solution is the automation of the data monitoring process. With a carefully planned solution, the amount and quality of provided information can be higher and optimised so that, for example, multiple indicators or stations can be seen in a compact form, saving large amounts of time in both the preparation and the ingest of the reported information. The process developed in this study is built upon a set of tests that evaluate the quality of the collected irradiance data, highlighting commonly found issues. The different steps of the process along with the tests and tools required for the implementation are described in more detail in the following section, so that other interested users can replicate the components shown here and adapt them as needed.

2 DESCRIPTION AND IMPLEMENTATION OF THE FRAMEWORK

The application package described here was developed to run on a server running Ubuntu Server 20.04, and the data from the stations is saved on a PostgreSQL database, so some components may differ in other systems (e.g. the scheduler to run the main script).

2.1 Pre-requisites

A clean Ubuntu installation, as many if not most Linux distributions, already includes many useful tools to automate and do some batch command line processing needed for the system described here; for example, 'sed' and 'cut' can be used to preprocess the input data files, although this is done here directly within Python to reduce dependencies and system command calls. Additional tools required: Python 3 (with a few additional packages), ROOT (https://root.cern/), unoconv, LibreOffice, systemd (with systemctl).

- Python 3: Apart from the default Python 3 installation, the following extra packages are needed: psycopg2 (to interact with the PostgreSQL database) and python-docx (to create DOCX files).
- ROOT: CERN's ROOT data analysis framework. Used for doing all calculations and to create the histograms and graphs for the report; the code is saved in files called "ROOT macros".
- unoconv: To convert the DOCX files to PDF.
- LibreOffice: unoconv can do its above-described task without a full LibreOffice installation, but when having LibreOffice also installed unoconv produces better formatting. To generate the report files, alternative methods are possible; for example, PDF files can be created without the intermediate DOCX files by using the Python package PyLaTeX (https://jeltef.github.io/PyLaTeX/current/index.html), although this does not necessarily reduce the storage use by much, as it requires a LaTeX compiler.
- systemd: To create and run services; already comes with Ubuntu and many Linux distributions.

2.2 Components

A service is created and scheduled to run once a day at a given time. Using systemd, this consists of two files: one timer file that sets the schedule to run the service, and one service file that defines the environment and runs a Python script (run.py) that does the following:

1. Check whether all needed files and subfolders are present. Working files and folders are automatically created if missing, but the user must provide a "sites" file containing site names, coordinates, and time zones (see below).
2. Export the data of the previous calendar day from the (PostgreSQL) database to CSV files, one file per site. First, a SQL script file is generated, then a connection to the database is made and the SQL script is run. The output files are saved to a local temporary location.
3. 'Clean' (preprocess) the CSV files, which consists of filling empty fields (i.e., between consecutive commas, or after a comma at the end of a line) with "-999" to signal missing entries; the final, clean files use a single space as field separator, and all lines should have the same number of fields.
4. Read the clean data files, store the data in binary "ROOT files" and process the data. Processing steps: calculate solar positions for every minute of the day to analyse, run quality checks, flag and filter data, and calculate hourly and daily averages. The flags, filtered data and averages are saved in ROOT files.
5. Run daily checks to report on the outputs of step 4, producing info graphs and log files. Separate ROOT macros are called in sequence.
6. Create a report. For each site, the outputs of step 5 are put into a one-page DOCX file and converted to PDF; then all PDF files are joined into one final PDF report, with 1 page per site.
7. Email the report and logs. The log files are compressed to a ZIP file; then, two final files, namely a PDF and a ZIP, are sent by email.
8. Clean-up: delete all files created in steps 2-7 except the ZIP and final PDF, which are moved to a local subfolder as backup.

Figure 1 shows a schematic graph and description of the code components, inputs, and outputs. The components with "()" appended to their names are the functions contained in the run.py script. This script also calls several ROOT macros (.C files) as described. As mentioned above, the user must create a file named sites.csv containing one line per each station that will be included in the report. Each line is given in the following format, with comma as field separator:

Code,Name,Lat,Lon,TZ

where:

- Code = 3-char short identifier for the station.
- Name = station name.
- Lat = station's latitude in degrees.
- Lon = station's longitude in degrees.
- TZ = station's time zone.

A total of 10 ROOT macros (.C files) are used. Separate, specialised macros were preferred during the development of this implementation, but these can be easily written as functions inside one single .C file if desired. Note also that, as the file extension implies, these ROOT macros were written in C++, but the default ROOT installation allows to write macros in either C++ or Python (called 'PyROOT') with the same functionalities, only importing ROOT and using the appropriate language syntax, so these macros could also be included in the Python script if desired.

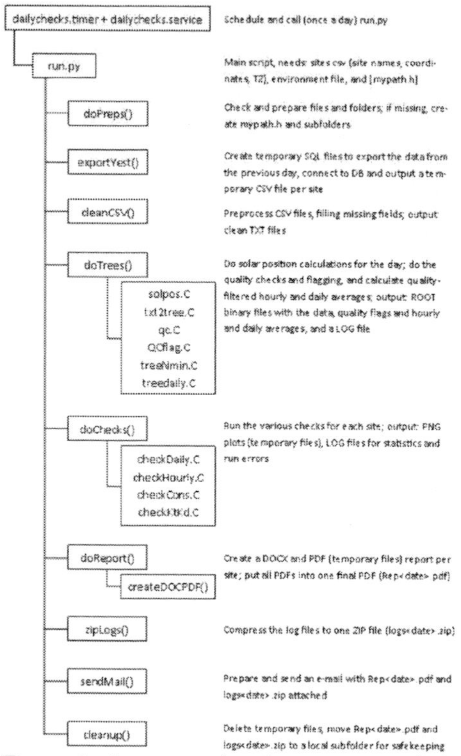

Figure 1: Structure and code components of the automated quality assessment reporting workflow.

2.3 Contents of the report

To provide a good amount of useful information in a clear and succinct way, a one-page-per-station report was designed, containing numerical and visual information that can be interpreted in one quick view.

Figure 2 shows an example page of one site's report. At the top of the page, the station and date are included; note that this date corresponds to the analysed data –when run automatically, the report of a day is done on the next day, but the main script can be run manually too and a specific date can be requested. Then, the page is divided into four sections: from the top, the first two sections give a view on the number and quality of collected measurements (with one-minute data, a day should contain 1440 entries for each irradiance), and the other two sections provide insights on the most common reasons for data quality failures. More details on each section are given in the following paragraphs.

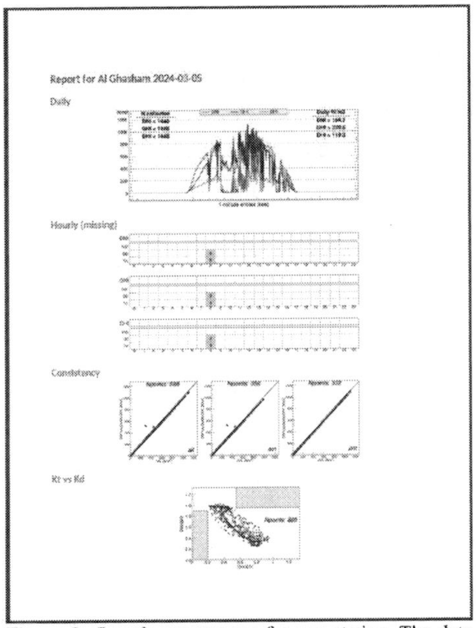

Figure 2: Sample report page for one station. The date corresponds to the analysed data.

"Daily"

The minute-by-minute profiles of each irradiance are plotted through the day, before any quality filtering; missing entries (i.e. not collected up to the time of reporting) are plotted with a value of -99, so they can be clearly identified (the bottom of the graph is below zero for this reason). In addition, the total number of minutes collected per irradiance (maximum of 1440) is shown, as well as the daily irradiance averages. The daily averages are calculated after removing daytime entries that fail the quality checks, which are applied to the one-minute records and based on the BSRN recommendations [1] and on the "Kt vs Kd" check (see section further below), so any missing daily averages (marked with value -99 and highlighted in red for easier identification) can indicate an insufficient number of collected entries and/or of good-quality entries. In the implementation shown here, if 15% or more of the daytime entries (from sunrise to sunset) fail the quality checks, the daily average is set to missing.

Figure 3 shows an example in which some entries were not collected (18 minutes, obtained by subtracting the collected entries, 1422, from 1440); although enough daytime entries were collected, the daily averages of DNI and DHI in this example are reported as missing (due to bad data quality, which can be seen from other parts of the report; in the daily graph one can see that DNI was zero and DHI was equal to GHI for a large part of the morning).

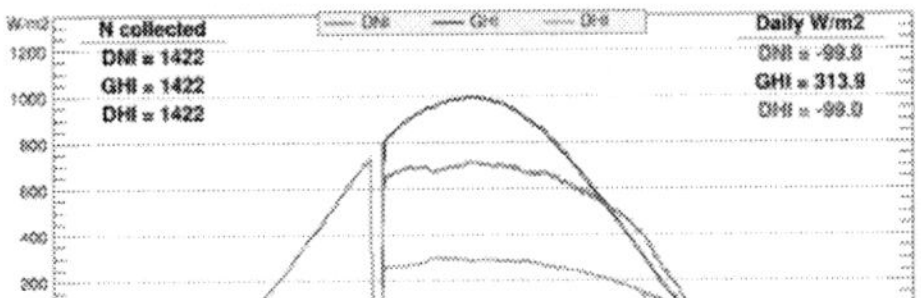

Figure 3: Example of daily section with some non-collected entries and missing daily averages.

"Hourly (missing)"

For each irradiance, the hourly averages are calculated after quality filtering of the 1-minute entries. If more than 50% of the entries in any given hour are missing (either not collected or quality-rejected), the average of that hour is set to missing (red-coloured box). The plots in this section show the following, for each irradiance and per hour (each box is one hour; the hours are given at the bottom of the graphs):

- In the top row, the hours in which the hourly average is missing are highlighted in red.
- "N/C" row: number of (one-minute) entries that were not collected.
- "QC" row: number of entries that failed the quality checks.
- "Tot": the sum of N/C and QC.

Hours with missing entries, i.e., Tot>0, are highlighted in light red, and a darker red when the hourly average is missing (Tot>30). Figure 4 shows an example, for the same site and day of Figure 3; this figure clarifies that the 18 uncollected minutes were: six at 8 am and twelve at 9 am (from Figures 3 and 4 one can conclude that these minutes are consecutive from 8:55 to 9:12). In addition, the DNI and DHI minutes before those (and starting from sunrise), although collected, failed the quality checks.

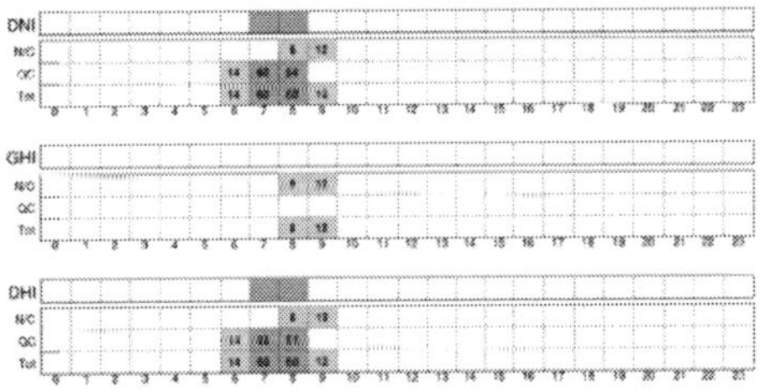

Figure 4: Hourly section with some missing entries and hourly averages.

"Consistency"

To help understand quality-rejected data, this section shows graphs of measured GHI vs calculated GHI = DHI + DNI*cos(SunZenithAngle) during daytime. Ideally, all points should be close to the red 1-to-1 line, and large deviations are flagged as bad quality. The graph on the left side (labelled "all") contains all daytime entries, while the other two ("am" and "pm") contain only the data before / after noon (defined in this graph as 12:00 pm, not solar noon). The example in Figure 5, for the same data as Figures 3 and 4, does not appear to show important issues (but the gap in the morning is visible) in this case.

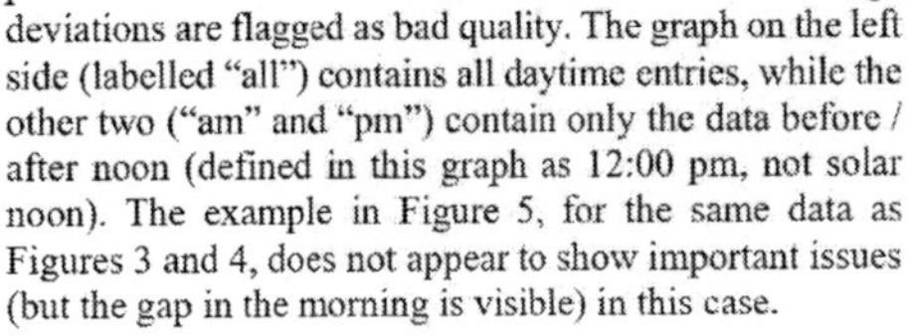

Figure 5: Consistency between measured and calculated GHI. "all" contains all daytime minutes; "am" and "pm" show the minutes before and after 12:00 pm, respectively.

"Kt vs Kd"

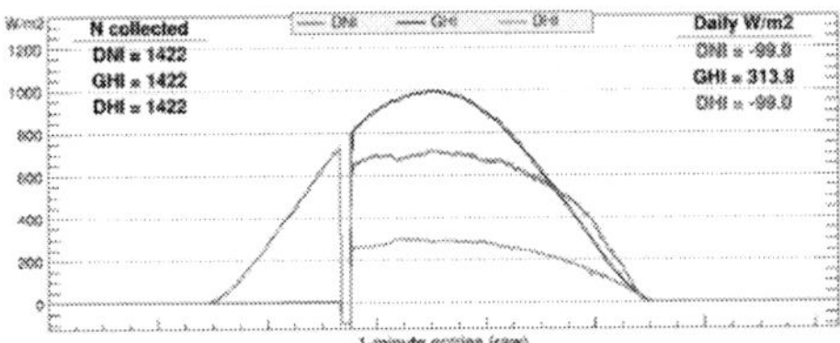

Plot of the relation between the clearness index Kt = GHI/ETh (where ETh is the top-of-the-atmosphere global horizontal irradiance) and the diffuse fraction Kd = DHI/GHI for one-minute data. Here, one can define regions where few or no data points should be seen under normal conditions; these exclusion areas are highlighted in red, and any points inside the high-Kt-high-Kd zone are marked as bad quality (since they represent sun tracker issues, see [2]) and thus excluded from the hourly and daily average calculations. Figure 6 shows an example, for the same data as Figures 3-5, showing the reason for the rejected entries that caused the missing hourly and daily averages.

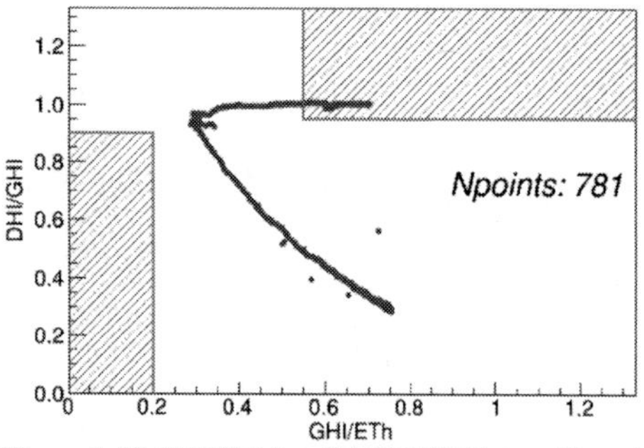

Figure 6: Kt (GHI/ETh) vs Kd (DHI/GHI) test. The red zones mark areas where few (or none) points should be normally seen; all points inside the top-right area are flagged as bad quality.

2.4 Emailing

Using the smtplib and email Python packages, an email is prepared containing, as attachments, the two files described in step 7 of Section 2.2. The email's body is simple text with the date of the report, and the same date is also specified in the email's subject. This automation requires an SMTP email server that supports such scripted use, and the specifics depend on the server; with Gmail, for example, simply providing valid credentials for an existing Gmail account used to be enough, but since the year 2023 the use of "App Passwords" has been mandatory, with additional configuration needed on the email account.

3 CONCLUSIONS

In this work, an automated data processing and reporting pipeline was developed to assess the collection and quality of solar radiation measurements. The output of the system is a (daily in the implementation presented here) report that provides a quick understanding of the collected measurements by identifying errors related to the collection, acquisition, or even some of the most commonly seen instrument and operation defects. From the first section of the report, i.e. the daily profile of the time series of the irradiances, one can visually review the data and inspect them in an easy way to identify the most evident problems quickly, including data not collected and anomalous profiles. In the next sections, more details about the found problems can be determined, such as the times of missing data due to communication issue or due to bad quality of the data, as well as their effect on aggregated averages, and some common issues can be identified on specific components (tracking, misalignment, etc.), to aid in planning and taking the necessary corrective actions. Although the implementation shown here was developed for a specific use-case, the components can be adapted to other scenarios with different components and even data other than solar radiation.

4 ACKNOWLEDGMENT

Research reported in this work was supported by the Qatar Research Development and Innovation Council (Grant: ARG01-0523-230304). The content is solely the responsibility of the authors and does not necessarily represent the official views of Qatar Research Development and Innovation Council.

5 REFERENCES

[1] Long, C.N., Dutton, E.G., 2002. BSRN Global Network recommended QC tests, V2.0. Available online at http://epic.awi.de/30083/1/BSRN_recommended_QC_tests_V2.pdf, last access 2025-09-11

[2] Perez-Astudillo, D., Bachour, D., Martin-Pomares, L. Improved Quality Control Protocols on Solar Radiation Measurements. Solar Energy 169, 425–433 (2018). DOI:10.1016/j.solener.2018.05.028

HOW COMPLEX ARE SATELLITE-BASED IRRADIATION DATA? FROM GLOBAL AVERAGES TO LOCATION-SPECIFIC ACCURACY

Philippe Malcorps
3E
Quai à la Chaux, 6 - 1000 Bruxelles - Belgium
pma@3e.eu
+32 485 72 99 34

Anastasia Dagla
3E
ada@3e.eu

Gofran Chowdhury
3E
gch@3e.eu

ABSTRACT: **3E irradiation data** is a service that **provides satellite-based solar resource data**. These data are derived from meteorological geostationary satellites using the Cloud Physical Properties (CPP) algorithm developed by the Royal Dutch Meteorological Institute. While it is demonstrated that the **accuracy of such data varies strongly depending on the location, global average numbers are still often applied** in long-term yield assessments and solar plant performance analyses. We aim to change that by systematically **studying the factors that impact this accuracy**. Using a dedicated validation framework, we benchmark our satellite-based data against more than 900 ground measurement sites worldwide. We then combine these results with statistical models to identify **which complexity factors matter most** and to predict the **expected accuracy at any given location**. The outcome is a set of global maps of accuracy, providing transparency on how reliable satellite-based irradiance data are, wherever you are on Earth.
Keywords: solar, resource, irradiance, accuracy

1 AIM AND APPROACH

3E irradiation data support long-term PV yield assessments and operational performance analysis. Although accuracy is known to vary locally, industry practice often relies on global averages. We aim to quantify accuracy as a function of location-specific complexity factors.

Since 2016, 3E has produced **near-real-time satellite-based irradiation data** using the CPP algorithm, which converts retrieved cloud properties into surface irradiance through a physics-based radiative transfer model. Data from four geostationary satellite series are processed every 10–15 minutes, covering most of the globe.

To **validate these data**, we built a dedicated framework that standardizes, parses, and quality-controls ground-based irradiation measurements. More than 900 sites are included, of which 426 passed quality and overlap filters (Figure 1). Validation metrics include the Normalized Mean Bias Error (NMBE) and the Normalized Root Mean Square Error (NRMSE) at multiple temporal resolutions.

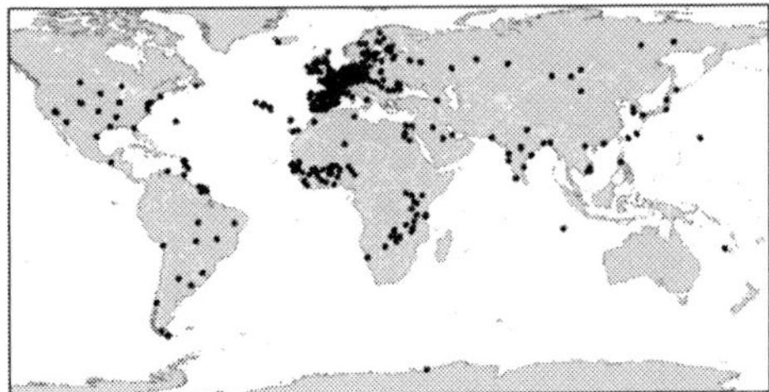

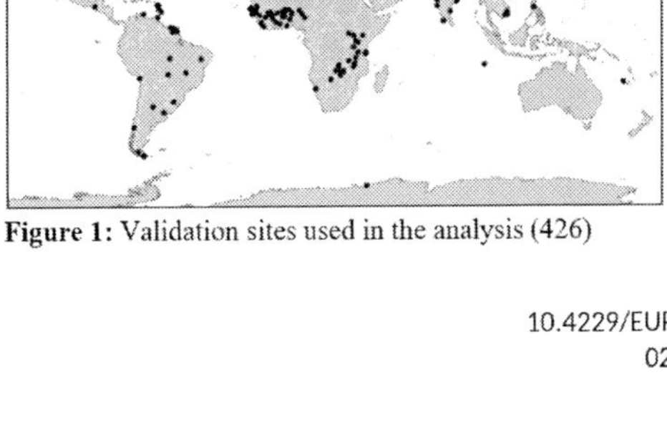

Figure 1: Validation sites used in the analysis (426)

Beyond benchmarking, we extracted **complexity factors** (climate type, terrain class, elevation, cloudiness, etc.) for each site and applied **machine learning models** (Random Forest, XGBoost, Linear Regression, etc.). These models were trained (80%) and tested (20%) to identify the most influential factors and **to predict expected accuracy depending on location**. The best-performing models were then applied to a global 1° × 1° grid, where complexity factors were extracted and interpolated into global accuracy maps.

2 SCIENTIFIC INNOVATION AND RELEVANCE

This study innovates in several aspects:

- **Scale**: A unique validation framework combining >900 ground stations worldwide.
- **Methodology**: Moving beyond visual inspection, we statistically quantify how complexity factors influence accuracy.
- **Predictive modeling**: Machine learning models provide site-specific expected accuracy for NMBE, NRMSE daily, and NRMSE hourly.
- **Transparency**: For the first time, global maps of accuracy are produced, enabling users to anticipate how reliable satellite-based irradiance data will be at any given location.

Ultimately, this approach improves the robustness of long-term PV yield assessments, reduces uncertainty in financing and risk analysis, and supports operational decision-making with location-specific confidence levels.

10.4229/EUPVSEC2025/4BV.3.17

3 RESULTS

From the 426 validated sites, overall results are consistent with other satellite-based irradiation providers (Table I). However, standard deviations across sites confirm that accuracy varies significantly with local conditions.

Table I: Overall validation results

Validation metric [%]	# of sites	Median	Mean	Standard Deviation
NMBE	426	1.22	1.9	3.69
NRMSE hourly	189	17.12	18.12	6.32
NRMSE daily	426	8.32	9.71	4
NRMSE monthly	426	4	5.06	3.35
NRMSE yearly	426	2.54	3.55	3.25

Using machine learning models, we identified the most influential complexity factors for three key metrics (NMBE, NRMSE daily, NRMSE hourly). XGBoost and Random Forest consistently performed best, achieving higher predictive skill (R^2, RMSE, CV RMSE) than linear models (e.g., Table II).

Table II: Model performance comparison (NRMSE daily)

Model	R^2 Score	RMSE	CV RMSE
Random Forest	0.719	3.784	3.604
XGBoost	0.714	3.822	3.560
Gradient Boosting	0.693	3.955	3.557
Ridge	0.534	4.876	4.442
Linear Regression	0.532	4.888	4.449
Lasso	0.528	4.909	4.496
ElasticNet	0.525	4.923	4.513

Feature importance analysis revealed that cloudiness, distance to satellite nadir, elevation, and terrain indices are among the strongest drivers of accuracy (e.g., Figure 2).

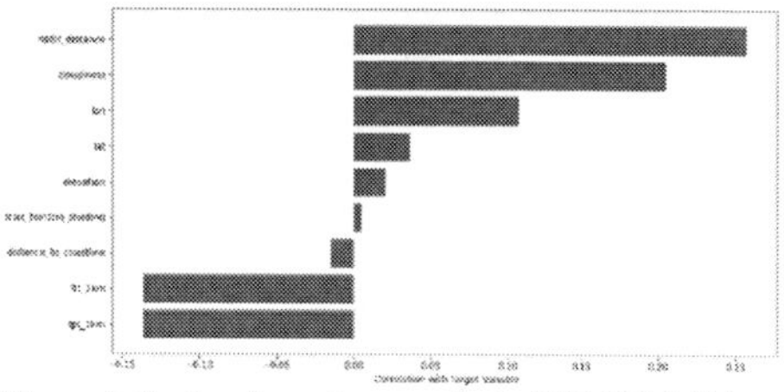

Figure 2: Feature importance analysis (NRMSE daily)

Applying the best-performing models to a global 1° × 1° grid allowed us to calculate expected accuracy values worldwide. Interpolation of these results produced global maps that reveal how accuracy changes regionally and globally (Figure 3).

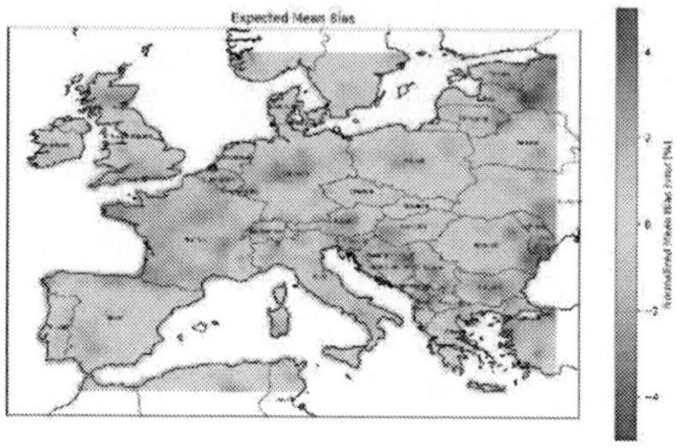

Figure 3: Expected mean bias in Europe (NMBE)

4 CONCLUSIONS

Rather than relying on global averages, **we now provide location-specific expected accuracy**. This represents a step-change for PV project developers, investors, and operators, who can now assess solar resource uncertainty with unprecedented transparency.

10.4229/EUPVSEC2025/4BV.3.17
020276-002

How Complex Are Satellite-Based Irradiation Data?

From Global Averages to Location-Specific Accuracy

Philippe Malcorps (3E)
pma@3e.eu
+32 485 72 99 34

Gofran Chowdhury (3E)
gch@3e.eu
+32 466 11 42 60

The Problem

- Satellite-based irradiation data = key for PV yield assessments
- But... accuracy varies a lot from place to place
- Current practice: use global averages → hides local errors

NMBE (%)

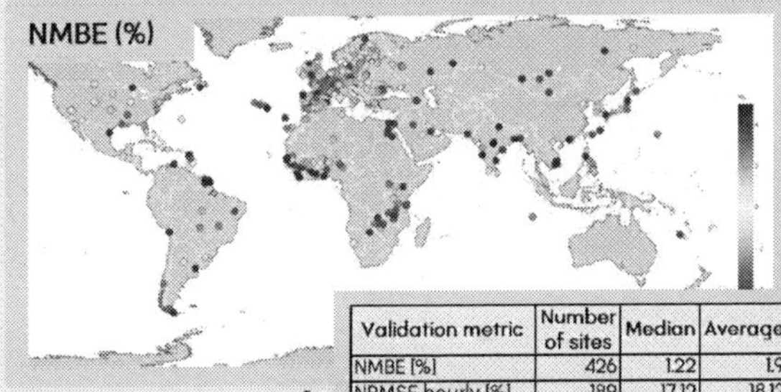

≠

Validation metric	Number of sites	Median	Average	Standard deviation
NMBE [%]	426	1.22	1.9	3.69
NRMSE hourly [%]	189	17.12	18.12	6.32
NRMSE daily [%]	426	8.32	9.71	4
NRMSE monthly [%]	426	4	5.06	3.35
NRMSE yearly [%]	426	2.54	3.55	3.25

Our question: *Can we predict accuracy at any location?*

The Data

- 900+ ground stations worldwide
- Quality-controlled & standardized measurements
- Validation metrics: NMBE (bias), NRMSE daily, and NRMSE hourly
- Result: Large variability → driven by local factors (climate, terrain, elevation, cloudiness...)

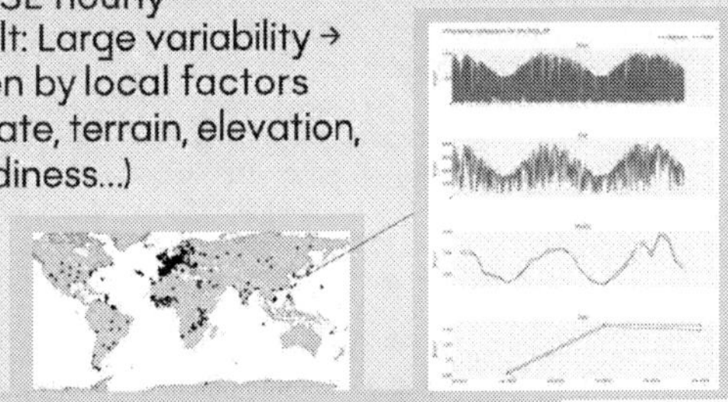

NRMSE daily (%): distribution by climate zone

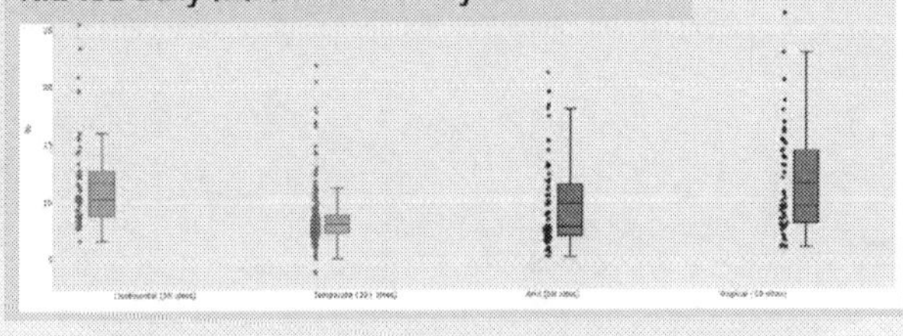

The Approach

We built models to predict accuracy:

- Machine Learning & Statistical Models (RF, XGBoost, Linear Regression...)
- 80% training / 20% testing
- For each metric, best model is selected by R^2, RMSE, CV RMSE

NRMSE daily (%)

Model	R^2 Score	RMSE	CV RMSE
Random Forest	0.719	3.784	3.604
XGBoost	0.714	3.822	3.560
Gradient Boosting	0.693	3.955	3.557
Ridge	0.534	4.876	4.442
Linear Regression	0.532	4.888	4.449
Lasso	0.528	4.909	4.496
ElasticNet	0.525	4.923	4.513

Models' comparison

Local factors importance

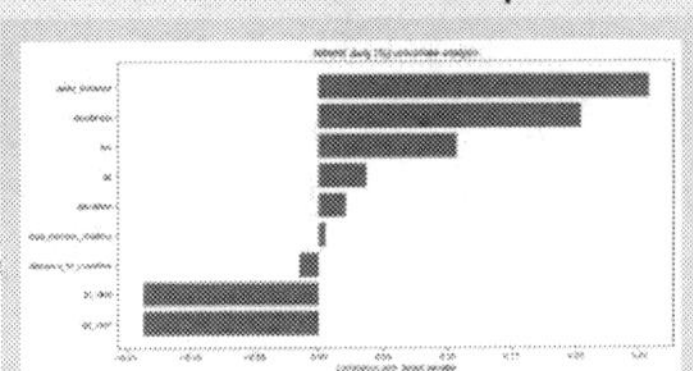

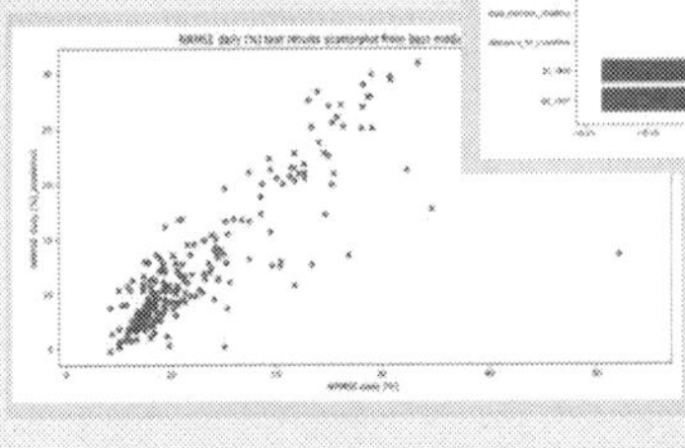

Modeled error

Models reveal: *Which factors matter most, and how much*

The Results

- Key complexity factors identified
- Best models applied on a 1° global grid
- Extracted factors at each point → predicted accuracy
- Interpolated into global maps of expected accuracy

Modeled mean bias based on local factors

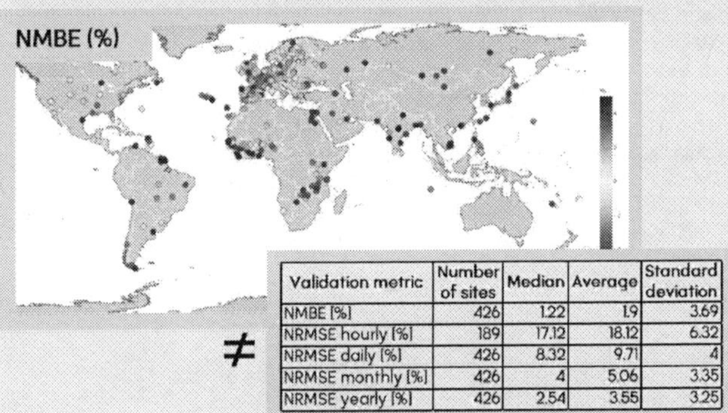

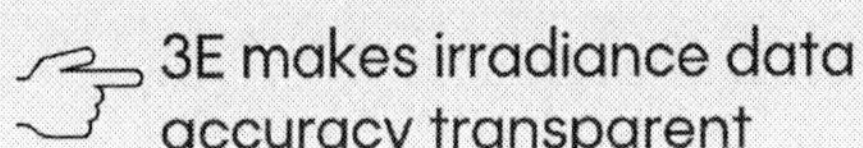

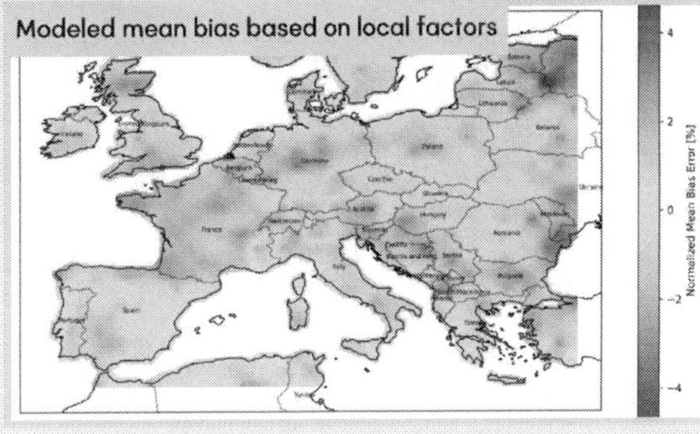

"Not just how accurate – but where accurate."

Why It Matters

- Location-specific accuracy = better PV yield assessments
- More confidence in bankability & risk analysis
- Improved performance monitoring worldwide

3E makes irradiance data accuracy transparent

EVALUATION OF MCCLEAR CLEAR SKY MODEL UNDER DUSTY CONDITIONS

Dunia A. Bachour[a], Daniel Perez-Astudillo[a], Abdulwahab Ziaullah[a]
[a] Qatar Environment & Energy Research Institute, P.O.Box 34110, Doha, Qatar.
dbachour@hbku.edu.qa, dastudillo@hbku.edu.qa, awahab@hbku.edu.qa

ABSTRACT: Clear-sky models play a crucial role in simulating solar radiation at the Earth's surface under cloudless conditions, with applications in several areas. For instance, clear-sky models help determine the maximum potential output of solar energy systems and calculate atmospheric indices which measure the atmospheric clarity and turbidity. In addition, these models are crucial for estimating the solar radiation from satellite images, providing the upper limits for irradiance under clear-sky conditions, before considering the cloud modelling. Clear-sky models also support quality control of solar data and can be used as reference to validate other models, such as transposition and decomposition models under clear-sky scenarios. A wide range of clear-sky models are described in scientific literature. This work examines commonly used clear-sky models for solar resource assessment, focusing on their performance in a region characterized by high aerosol concentrations. Specifically, the McClear model is compared to the Simple Model for the Atmospheric Radiative Transfer of Sunshine (SMARTS-2), and the European Solar Radiation Atlas (ESRA) model. The evaluation is conducted using days with varied aerosol content, including instances of significant atmospheric dust. Sun photometer aerosol-derived data and ground-based solar radiation measurements are used as inputs and to assess the performance of the models, respectively.
Keywords: Clear-sky, McClear, SMARTS2, DNI, AOD

1 INTRODUCTION

Modelling clear-sky irradiance is essential in solar energy analysis, as it establishes the theoretical maximum solar irradiance that can reach the Earth's surface in the absence of clouds. Clear-sky models play several vital roles in the field of solar energy analysis. They serve as a reference point for the design and simulation of solar energy systems, enabling precise estimation of the energy output potential under optimal atmospheric conditions. Furthermore, clear-sky irradiance is fundamental for atmospheric characterisation, as it allows for the calculation of indices such as clarity and turbidity, which assess the transparency and aerosol content present in the atmosphere. In terms of data integrity, these models act as a benchmark in solar resource assessment by aiding in the identification of measurement errors and outliers, achieved by comparing observed readings with expected values during cloudless periods. Additionally, clear-sky models are indispensable for verifying and validating the accuracy of solar irradiance models. Lastly, most satellite-based solar radiation models, first establish clear-sky irradiance estimates before adjusting for cloud effects using satellite observations.

A wide range of clear-sky models are described in scientific literature, and they are typically categorized by their approach. Empirical and parametric models estimate clear-sky solar irradiance using simplified statistical approaches based on key atmospheric inputs such as aerosol turbidity, ozone, water vapor, and solar geometry. In contrast physical models provide robust but computationally demanding calculations, by solving the radiative transfer equation to provide spectrally resolved irradiance that accounts for molecular absorption, scattering, aerosols, ozone, and water vapor. Hybrid parametric–physical models achieve a practical balance between accuracy and efficiency by combining radiative transfer simulations with parameterizations or look-up tables, making them suitable for operational and near real-time solar radiation modelling with acceptable accuracy but at significantly lower computational cost.

The clear-sky models evaluated in this work are selected from these three categories. The ESRA model [1] is an empirical clear-sky model based on the Linke turbidity factor, widely used in Europe and in known PV tools due to its simplicity and low input requirements, though its accuracy depends strongly on turbidity climatology. McClear [2] is a hybrid parametric–physical model derived from libRadtran simulations, using multiple inputs from the Copernicus Atmosphere Monitoring Service (CAMS) database to accurately model the effect of different aerosol types, and atmospheric constituents. It offers global applicability and near real-time data, making it central to operational services. In contrast, SMARTS2 [3] is a full radiative transfer model, capable of high spectral resolution and accuracy for irradiance under clear skies, often used as a reference tool for solar energy studies and applications, but computationally more demanding than ESRA or McClear.

2 METHODOLOGY

2.1 Data Used

The study is conducted in Doha, Qatar (25.32° N, 51,425° E). Minute-resolution data for direct normal irradiance (DNI, hereafter denoted as G_b), global horizontal irradiance (GHI), and diffuse horizontal irradiance (DHI) are collected with a solar radiation monitoring station equipped with thermopile sensors. Ground-based aerosol optical depth (AOD) measurements are obtained using a sun photometer, focusing on the 500 nm channel to ensure consistency with satellite-derived data and to accurately capture atmospheric scattering properties.

2.2 Model Inputs and Sources

To estimate clear-sky irradiance G_{bn} using the ESRA model, Equation 1 is applied, where G_0 represents the extraterrestrial irradiance on a plane perpendicular to the sun, TL is the Linke Turbidity factor, m is the relative optical air mass, and δ_R is the Rayleigh optical thickness for a standard atmosphere. A Linke turbidity value of 1 is used to determine the maximum direct irradiance component, representing an ideal clear atmosphere without aerosols or water vapor. This value is then adjusted using the AOD values obtained from sun photometer measurements to calculate the ESRA clear-sky irradiance, $G_{bn(ESRA)}$.

$$G_{bn} = G_0 \times \exp(-0.8662 \times TL \times m \times \delta_R \times AOD) \quad \text{(Eq.1)}$$

The SMARTS-2 clear-sky model is used in this study with fixed input parameters for atmospheric pressure (1013.25 mb), ozone abundance (0.34), altitude (20 m), precipitable water content (1.42 cm), CO_2 concentration (370 ppmv), and desert aerosol types representative of conditions in Doha. However, local AOD values at 500 nm were utilized to reflect site-specific aerosol conditions, with AOD data extracted from both the sun photometer and from the Copernicus CAMS database. These local AOD values are incorporated to generate broadband (280 to 4000 nm) irradiance outputs. The solar position values, including sun-earth distance correction, solar zenith, and solar azimuth angles, are updated for each simulation run.

For McClear, site-specific clear-sky irradiances Gb McClear were retrieved from the CAMS Radiation Service v4.6, which provides all-sky irradiation estimates.

2.3 Case Study

Two representative periods from the year 2022 were selected for analysis: November, which typically exhibits clearer skies, and May, characterized by higher turbidity. These periods allow for an effective comparison of model performance under distinct atmospheric conditions.

2.4 Validation and Comparison

To assess model accuracy and establish ground truth, measured and estimated irradiance values under clear-sky conditions were compared across different levels of AOD.

3 RESULTS

Figure 1 presents the daily mean AOD for the months under study (blue points), with error bars showing the standard deviation (σ) for each day (red vertical lines). Based on Figure 1, selected days spanning a range of AOD values were chosen for clear-sky models evaluation.

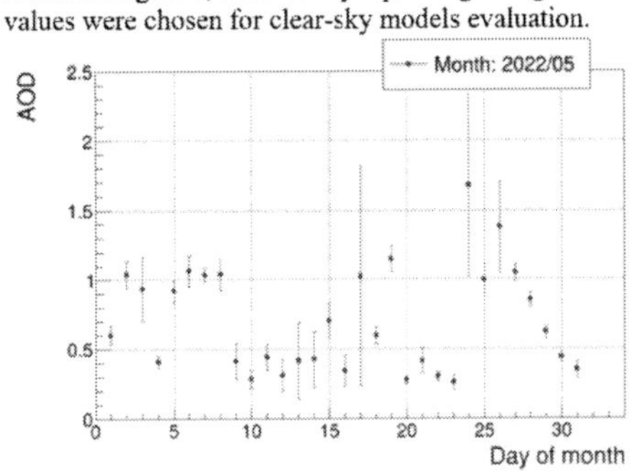

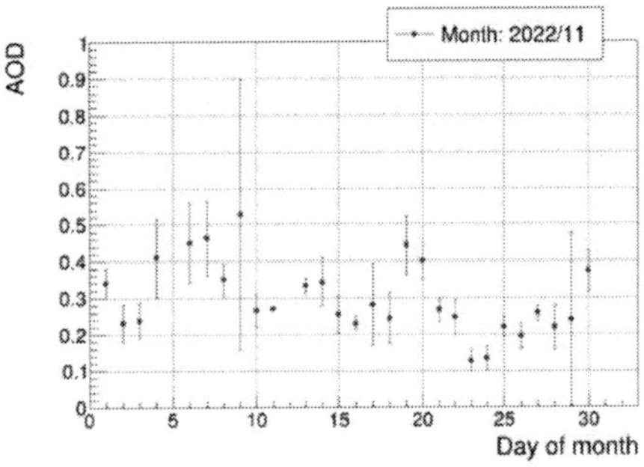

Figure. 1: Daily mean AOD with intra-day variability for 2022/05 (top) and 2022/11 (bottom)

Figures 2 and 3 compare the models with measurements for May and November, respectively, on days with distinct AOD conditions: 4 May (0.41 ± 0.04), 23 May (0.26 ± 0.05), 24 May (1.67 ± 0.65), 17 Nov (0.28 ± 0.11), 19 Nov (0.44 ± 0.08), and 23 Nov (0.13 ± 0.03).

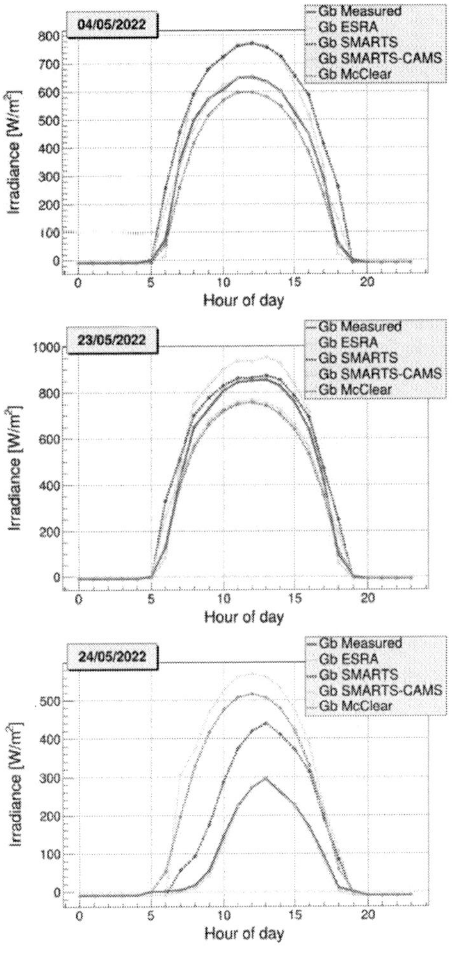

Figure. 2: Daily Gb profiles for different clear-sky models versus measured values on various days in May 2022.

On May 4th the SMARTS2 model, using CAMS-derived AOD data, most closely matches the measured clear-sky irradiance, followed by the McClear model. The mean AOD for this day is moderate (0.41) with limited variability, providing relatively stable atmospheric conditions. In contrast, the SMARTS2 and ESRA models using ground-based AOD at 500 nm overestimate the irradiance compared to measurements. This overestimation is likely because a single-wavelength AOD does not account for other atmospheric constituents—such as dust layers or fog—that also attenuate solar radiation and are common in May. These additional effects are not captured by ground-based AOD at 500 nm but are better assimilated by the CAMS data, which incorporates multiple wavelengths and atmospheric parameters. On May 23, AOD value is low and stable, the SMARTS2 physical model utilizing ground-based AOD closely matches the measured data. In contrast, both McClear and SMARTS2 using CAMS AOD data underestimate DNI, likely due to an underestimation of AOD in the input data. May 24, characterised by a high AOD (1.67) value and significant fluctuation (0.65). Under these conditions, the ESRA model scaled the irradiance using the provided hourly ground AOD. Since ESRA does not require detailed assumptions regarding aerosol type, spectrum, or vertical profile, it is less affected by potential errors in aerosol optical properties compared to SMARTS2. The SMARTS2 model overestimated the irradiance, likely due to its reliance on spectrally resolved AOD (not limited to 500 nm) and more comprehensive information about aerosol models, such as single scattering albedo, asymmetry parameter, and size distribution. This information becomes particularly important when there is high variability, contrary to the input provided in this instance with only 500 nm AOD and a default aerosol type. As a result, SMARTS2 extrapolated extinction across the spectrum based on assumed Ångström exponents and standard optical properties, which may have led to errors at this high AOD level. This is why SMARTS2 generally followed the measured curve but consistently overestimated values throughout the day. CAMS-based models (McClear, SMARTS2+CAMS) did not perform as well, as CAMS did not capture the magnitude or variability of the high-AOD event, and the input data used may have been smoothed to accurately reflect local conditions.

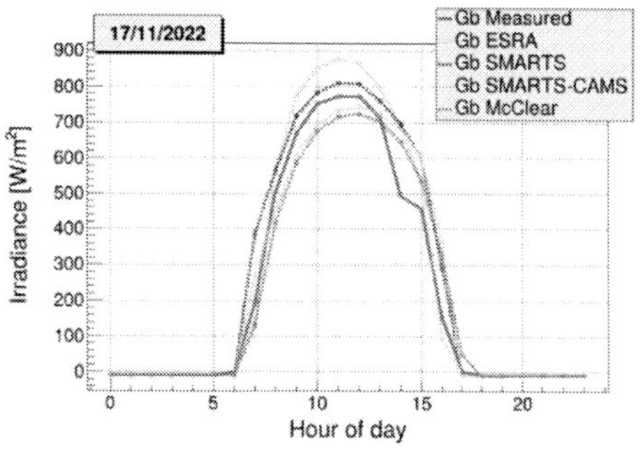

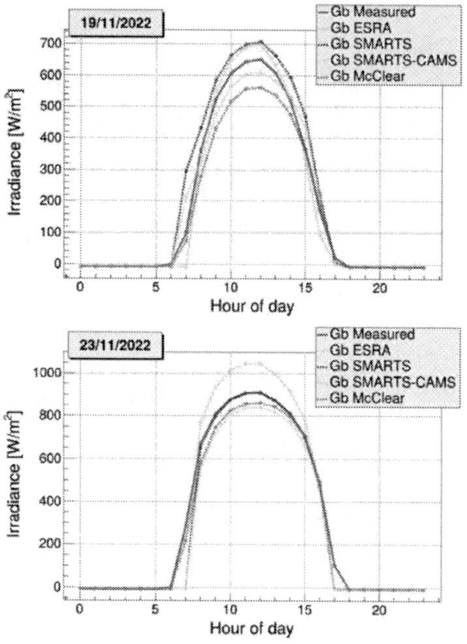

Figure. 3: Daily Gb profiles for different clear-sky models versus measured values on various days in Nov 2022.

For the selected November days, CAMS-based models, McClear and SMARTS2+AOD-CAMS, consistently underestimate the irradiance. On November 17, with low AOD and relatively moderate fluctuations, none of the models performed ideally, though SMARTS2 with ground-based AOD yielded the closest match. This can be attributed to SMARTS2's use of actual ground AOD, which proves most valuable under moderate variability, even if only single-wavelength data are available. In contrast, the ESRA model's broadband parameterization performed poorly with fluctuating aerosol. On November 19, with moderately high but stable AOD, both ESRA and SMARTS2 models overestimated irradiance at high irradiance levels, with somewhat different behavior at lower irradiance. This is due to the limited input information (500 nm AOD), which leads both models to underperform. Finally, on November 23, characterized by very low and stable AOD, ESRA overestimated irradiance as it does not consider molecular extinction. By contrast, SMARTS2 performed better, explicitly resolving Rayleigh scattering and gaseous absorption.

4 CONCLUSIONS

Clear-sky irradiance modelling is essential for accurate assessment, validation, and analysis of solar energy resource data, supporting both ground-based and satellite-based analyses. The comparative analysis presented in this work demonstrates that the accuracy of clear-sky irradiance models is strongly dependent on the prevailing aerosol regime. ESRA benefits from its simplicity under turbid and highly variable conditions, where direct scaling with ground-based AOD allows it to follow DNI reductions more effectively, but it systematically overestimates irradiance under clear skies because it does not explicitly represent molecular absorption (ozone, water vapor, mixed gases), for which the effect becomes relatively more important when aerosol levels are low. SMARTS2, in contrast, performs best specially when the input data are correct. Under low-AOD conditions, where SMARTS2 explicitly treats Rayleigh scattering and gaseous absorption yield good agreement with measurements. However, when AOD is higher, the underperformance of SMARTS2 in the studied case is attributed to incomplete input information, particularly the limited availability of aerosol spectral and microphysical data. CAMS-based models for the days studied here consistently underestimate irradiance, reflecting biases in CAMS AOD and in capturing short-term local variability. The results presented here demonstrate that clear-sky model suitability in high aerosol loads conditions depends on atmospheric conditions and highlight the importance of combining approaches according to the dominant aerosol regime. Using single-wavelength AOD data presents limitations, as it may neglect other atmospheric effects, such as larger particles or water droplets in fog, that also contribute to solar radiation attenuation. Furthermore, rapid fluctuations in AOD or missing parameters, like water vapor content and Ångström exponent, can diminish model accuracy on specific days, particularly during events involving dust or fog that are common in the study region. The analysis highlights the added value of multisource data. Models that incorporate comprehensive datasets, such as CAMS, benefit from assimilating information across multiple wavelengths and sources, allowing for a more complete representation of the atmospheric profile, leading to improved irradiance modelling in some complex and variable conditions.

5 REFERENCES

[1] C. Rigollier, O. Bauer, L. Wald, (2000). On the clear sky model of the ESRA – European Solar Radiation Atlas – with respect to the Heliosat method. Solar Energy, 68(1), 33-48. https://doi.org/10.1016/S0038-092X(99)00055-9

[2] M. Lefèvre, A. Oumbe, P. Blanc, B. Espinar, B. Gschwind, Z. Qu, L. Wald, M. Schroedter-Homscheidt, C, Hoyer-Klick, A, Arola, A. Benedetti, J.W. Kaiser, J.J. Morcrette, (2013). McClear: A new model estimating downwelling solar radiation at ground level in clear-sky conditions. Solar Energy, 94, 360–374. https://doi.org/10.1016/j.solener.2013.05.008

[3] C.A. Gueymard (2001). Parameterized transmittance model for direct beam and circumsolar spectral irradiance. Solar Energy, 71(5), 325–346. https://doi.org/10.1016/S0038-092X(01)00054-8

Weather and Air Quality Effects on Photovoltaic System Efficiency: A Modeling Approach

Carrillo Mejía, Luis
Universidad Distrital Francisco José de Caldas
lcarrillom@udistrital.edu.co

PhD Gaona García, Elvis Eduardo
Universidad Distrital Francisco José de Caldas
egaona@udistrital.edu.co

PhD Hernández Mora, Johann Alexander
Universidad Distrital Francisco José de Caldas
jahernandezm@udistrital.edu.co

Abstract— This paper aims to evaluate the performance of different machine learning algorithms for predicting the instantaneous efficiency of photovoltaic systems. The study utilized a dataset collected over seven months from seven distinct geographical locations characterized by diverse climatological conditions representative of the Colombian territory. The dataset included solar irradiance, climatological variables, air quality variables, and measured active power. Instantaneous efficiency was calculated from these data and defined as the study's target variable. An initial descriptive statistical analysis was performed to characterize the dataset. Subsequently, various prediction algorithms were executed and evaluated using standard error metrics. The evaluation demonstrated that incorporating air quality variables improved the predictive accuracy across all evaluated models. A key finding from the correlation analysis and feature importance assessment is the negative association between higher levels of environmental pollution and instantaneous efficiency.

Key Words — *Photovoltaic system, efficiency forecast, machine learning model, weather variables, pollution variables.*

I. INTRODUCTION

According to [1], as the use of traditional fossil fuels becomes more widespread, the issues of resource depletion and environmental pollution are becoming increasingly severe. Consequently, photovoltaic (PV) energy has gained global popularity due to its advantages: it is clean, non-polluting, and facilitates easy distribution. As [2] mentions, this has made photovoltaic power plants more competitive compared to fossil fuel plants in recent years. However, the fluctuating nature of solar irradiance and varying climatic and geographical conditions makes energy generation unpredictable, thereby affecting the performance of solar plants and the electrical grid.

Consequently, photovoltaic power prediction is a vital tool for solar plant operators and managers. It helps them avoid penalties for discrepancies between actual and desired photovoltaic power generation and allows for the evaluation of a location's suitability for solar plant installation during the planning stage, as noted in [3]. A large number of prediction models based on neural networks exist, which use climatic data (temperature, wind speed, relative humidity, and air pressure), irradiance, and panel soiling from various global locations. For example, [4] details a power generation prediction model using wavelet decomposition for Salento, Italy. Similarly, [5] proposes a model that uses a Feedforward Neural Network (FFNN) to predict the efficiency of a solar plant based on climatic variables and irradiance in Igdir, Turkey. Furthermore, [6] demonstrated that the efficiency of different types of solar panels in northern Nigeria is significantly impacted by the amount of dust on their surface. However, wind speed and rainfall had a cleaning effect on the soiling, indicating that panel cleaning schemes are necessary to prevent performance degradation. In the Sahara Desert of Algeria, [7] analyzed the performance and the soiling caused by dust on panels, finding a linear relationship between power loss and dirt accumulation.

The study's methodology comprised several stages. Initially, a seven-month dataset was consolidated from different geolocated sites. This dataset included irradiance variables (GHI, DNI, DHI), climatological variables (temperature, humidity, pressure, cloud cover, wind direction, and speed), and air quality variables (NH_3, NO, NO_2, CO, SO_2, PM_{10}, $PM_{2.5}$). Instantaneous efficiency, calculated from the measured active power and other parameters, was defined as the target variable. A descriptive statistical analysis was conducted to explore the data properties. Subsequently, different machine learning algorithms were applied and evaluated for the prediction of instantaneous efficiency. Finally, a feature analysis was performed to determine which predictor variables had the greatest influence on predictive performance.

II. METODOLOGY

A. Data Collection

For data collection, a microservice was implemented to download data from various sources based on a time range and a geographical location. Accordingly, variables related to irradiance—GHI (Global Horizontal Irradiance), DHI (Diffuse Horizontal Irradiance), and DNI (Direct Normal Irradiance)—were downloaded from a NASA API [8]. As of the date of this writing, this API provided global data up to July 30, 2024, with a spatial resolution of 1° latitude x 1° longitude (approximately 12.3 km^2 near the equator and 8.7 km^2 at latitudes near 45°). Data acquisition for this source is based on the processing of satellite imagery and atmospheric models.

Climatological and air quality variables were obtained via APIs from OpenWeather [9] y [10] respectively. These APIs provide data filters based on time range and geographical location, with data sourced from various origins including terrestrial weather stations, radar data, satellite observations, and proprietary models for air quality and climatic conditions. Finally, power generation data was extracted from PvOutput [11], a web platform where owners of photovoltaic systems share real-time and historical performance data. This platform exposes an API for the extraction of raw generated power data from various users.

Table 1, displays all the variables and their corresponding units of measurement.

Table 1.Dataset variables

Variable	Unit of measurement	Description of the variable
Datetime	Hour	
Latitude	Degrees	
Longitude	Degrees	
Temperature	Celsious degrees	
Wind_speed	meter/seg	
Wind_direction	Meteorological degrees	
Humedity	Percentage	
Pressure	Percentage	
Clouds	Percentage	
co	$\mu g/m^3$	Carbon monoxide
no	$\mu g/m^3$	Nitric oxide
no2	$\mu g/m^3$	Carbon dioxide
o3	$\mu g/m^3$	Ozone
so2	$\mu g/m^3$	Sulfur dioxide
nh3	$\mu g/m^3$	Ammonia
pm2.5	$\mu g/m^3$	Particulate matter 2.5
pm10	$\mu g/m^3$	Particulate matter 10
ghi	w/m^2	Global Horizontal Irradiance
dni	w/m^2	Direct Normal Irradiance
dhi	w/m^2	Diffuse Horizontal Irradiance
power	Watios	
ins_efficiency	Percentage	Instantaneous efficiency

From PvOutput, 12 photovoltaic systems were selected for the study. The selection criteria mandated that the systems have available manufacturer data, the number of installed panels, and tilt angle. Additionally, the selected sites needed to have a similar temperature profile to Colombia or be located within ±10 degrees of the equator. The purpose of this meticulous selection was to secure sufficient data for the calculation of panel efficiency and to apply a machine learning algorithm to the Colombian case study. Of the initial 12 systems, only seven were ultimately included in the study due to various data limitations with the remaining five.

Table 2, presents the geographical coordinates of the selected sites and the number of samples used in the study. The dates varied slightly for some locations but generally spanned from January 1, 2024, to July 31, 2024. The data resolution is hourly, resulting in a dataset with 22,475 samples.

Table 2. Samples per photovoltaic system selected

Location of the photovoltaic system	City	Samples
-38.380163,142.519164	Victoria, Australia	4211
-27.620304,153.127580	Brisbane, Australia	4277
-26.677141,-49.182458	Pomerode - Testo Salto, Brasil	4226
-17.878102,-41.507783	Teófilo Otoni, Brasil	2246
5.525135,72.842531	Maduvvari, Islas Malvinas	3968
34.170946,-118.366460	Los Angeles, EEUU	1278
40.884561,23.920283	Rodolivos, Grecia	2269

B. Preprocessing

Initially, the instantaneous efficiency is calculated by applying Equation (1), as mentioned in [12] and [5]

$$\eta_{ins} = \frac{P_{ins}}{G_{in} * A_t} \quad (1)$$

Where P_{ins} corresponds to the measured instantaneous active power from PvOutput, G_{in}, is the instantaneous incident solar irradiance, and A_t is the total area of the photovoltaic installation. Additionally, if the global horizontal irradiance is less than 120 w/m^2, if the measurement is below the solar illumination threshold, the efficiency is set to zero. On the other hand, an efficiency exceeding 30% indicates an anomaly in the sample, and these samples are therefore removed from the dataset. Using this criterion, 1367 samples were eliminated. It is important to note that this preprocessing was conducted during the initial data ingestion phase, so the sample size remains as previously described.

The following columns are removed from the dataset: 'datetime', as a time-series analysis will not be performed. This is because a time-series approach would tie the selected algorithm to a specific time window and, more importantly, a particular location. It is proposed as future work to forecast each regressor based on a specific location and then use the model proposed herein. Consequently, 'latitude' and 'longitude' are also removed from the dataset. Finally, 'power' is also removed since this variable was used to calculate efficiency, and it would not be available in a planning case study.

C. Statistical Analysis

Fig 1 displays the distribution density of instantaneous efficiency. It is important to note that data points with zero instantaneous efficiency were removed, as they create a density spike that obscures other relevant peaks. The objective here is to validate these other peaks, revealing that when the system produces energy, it does so most frequently within a specific efficiency range. The primary peak is observed in the [5,12] interval, and the distribution does not follow a perfectly symmetric bell curve, which is characteristic of this variable.

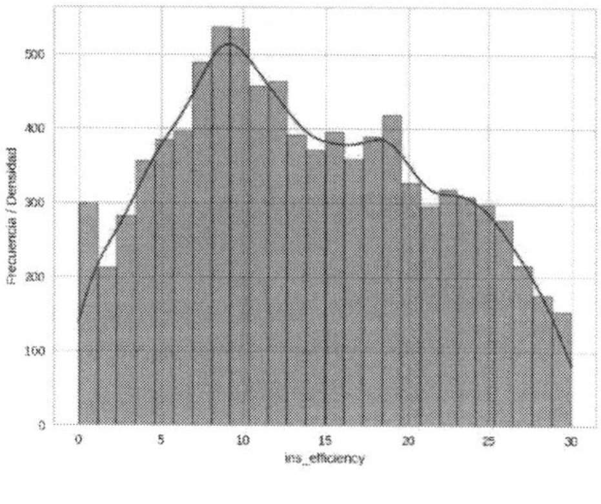

Fig 1. Distribution Density of Instantaneous Efficiency

The same analysis was conducted for each variable, revealing distributions that are not perfectly symmetrical. Fig 2 shows some of the distribution densities.

Heatmaps were generated to visualize the Pearson, Spearman, and Kendall correlations for the entire dataset, as shown in Fig 3. Additionally, these heatmaps were created for two specific locations, Rodolivos and Los Angeles, as shown in Fig *4*, because the concentration of pollutants was highest at these sites.

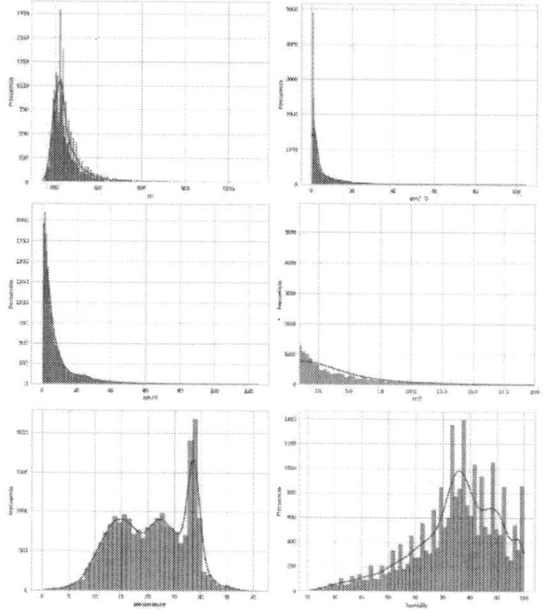

Fig 2. Distribution density for some of the variables under observation

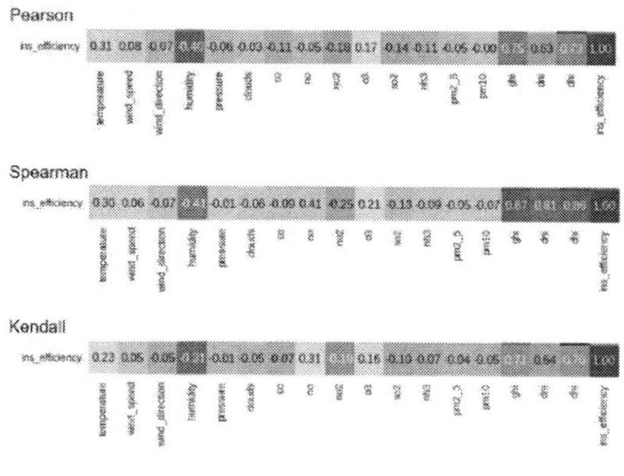

Fig 3. Heatmap of Correlations for the Entire Dataset

In these heatmaps, it can be seen that the air quality variables have a low and negative impact on instantaneous efficiency, with the exception of ammonia, whose impact is negligible. For the climatological variables, temperature and humidity have a positive and negative impact, respectively, on the variable under study. In the case of temperature, the results suggest that the studied photovoltaic systems have cooling systems, as a negative impact was expected, as mentioned in [13].

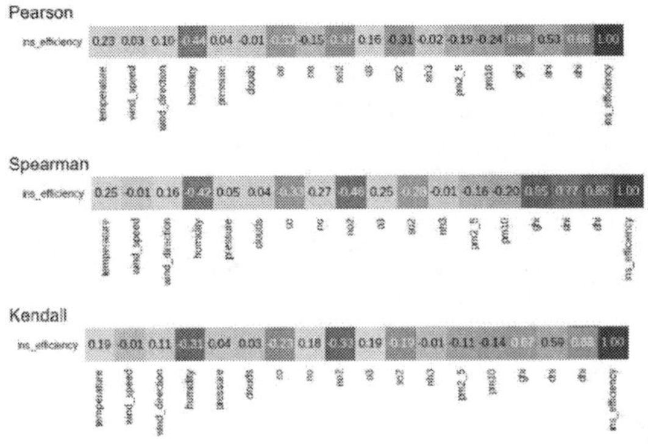

Fig 4. Heatmap of Correlations for Locations with the Highest Pollutant Concentration

D. *Model selection*

According to [14], [15] y [16] it is noted that Recurrent Neural Networks (RNNs), specifically Long Short-Term Memory (LSTM) networks, yield strong results for power prediction because they are better at learning temporal dependencies. This also means they better solve the vanishing gradient problem, as noted in [17]. However, the ultimate goal of the proposed algorithm is to have the regressors already projected into the future for application. Therefore, only a Multilayer Perceptron (MLP) neural network was included, in addition to 19 other algorithms.

To demonstrate the impact of air quality variables on efficiency, models were trained in several configurations: without these variables, with each variable individually, and finally with the variables that showed the greatest impact on prediction. The resulting models were then tabulated, and the top five were selected based on traditional error metrics: Root Mean Square Error (RMSE), Mean Absolute Error (MAE), Mean Absolute Percentage Error (MAPE), and R-squared (R2).

III. RESULTS

Table 3, Table 4 and Table 5, show the tabulated models and standard error metrics evaluated for training with all variables, without air quality variables, and with selected predictor variables, respectively.

Table 3. Training Metrics for all Dataset Variables

Model	RMSE	MAE	MAPE	R2
Random Forest	3.310	1.592	1.067	0.845
Extra Trees	3.358	1.636	1.147	0.841
Extreme Gradient	3.364	1.662	1.146	0.84
MLP	3.335	2.038	1.104	0.83
Gradient Boosting	3.507	1.796	1.124	0.823

Table 4. Training Metrics without Air Quality Variables

Model	RMSE	MAE	MAPE	R2
Random Forest	3.699	1.839	1.728	0.807
Gradient Boosting	3.735	1.893	1.701	0.803
Extra Trees	3.744	1.885	1.771	0.802
MLP	3.644	2.17	2.0	0.799
Extreme Gradient	3.88	2.011	1.565	0.788

Table 5. Training Metrics with Selected Predictor Variables

Model	RMSE	MAE	MAPE	R2
Random Forest	3.388	1.637	1.138	0.838
Extra Trees	3.431	1675	1.249	0.834
Extreme Gradient	3.448	1.714	1.207	0.832
MLP	3.437	2.061	2.22	0.821
Gradient Boosting	3.606	1.845	1.166	0.816

The results of this research, summarized in the training metrics tables, provide a clear picture of the impact of air quality variables. Table 4, which presents the training metrics without including these variables, shows that the Random Forest algorithm achieved the best performance with an $R^2 = 0.807$. The inclusion of pollutants in the model, as shown in Table 5, had a positive effect on the predictive capability of all algorithms, consistently improving their metrics. In this scenario, the Random Forest model maintained its lead with an $R^2 = 0.838$.

IV. CONCLUSIONS

Diverse machine learning algorithms were evaluated to predict the instantaneous efficiency of photovoltaic systems across seven geographical locations with varying climatological characteristics, representative of Colombian diversity.

The models were assessed using standard error metrics (MAE, MSE, RMSE, R^2), and the best-performing ones were selected. The main conclusions are presented below:

- Upon comparing the standard evaluation metrics of models trained with and without environmental pollution variables, a positive impact on predictive performance was evident. Specifically, the inclusion of these variables resulted in an improvement across all metrics for the evaluated algorithms.
- The feature importance analysis of the selected model (Random Forest) revealed that the predictor variables with the greatest influence on the prediction of instantaneous efficiency were:
  - Irradiance variables: GHI, DHI, and DNI.
  - Climatological variables: Temperature, humidity, and wind direction and speed.
  - Air quality variables: CO, NO2, O3, PM2.5, and PM10.
- The correlation analysis and the models' feature importance suggest that under conditions of higher environmental pollution, there is a negative association with instantaneous efficiency. The pollutants that showed the greatest influence on this negative relationship were NO2, followed by CO, SO2, PM10, and PM2.5.
- Unlike other pollutants, O3 showed a positive association with instantaneous efficiency, regardless of the overall pollution level of the location.

These findings have significant practical implications for the planning and operation of photovoltaic systems. The inclusion of air quality variables, alongside irradiance and climatological variables, improves the predictive accuracy of the algorithms. A more precise prediction of instantaneous efficiency allows for better estimation of system performance and optimizes operation and maintenance strategies, contributing to a more effective utilization of solar potential.

V. REFERENCES

[1] Q. Hassan *et al.*, "A comprehensive review of international renewable energy growth," *Energy and Built Environment*, Jan. 2024, doi: 10.1016/J.ENBENV.2023.12.002.

[2] S. S. Chandel, A. Gupta, R. Chandel, and S. Tajjour, "Review of deep learning techniques for power generation prediction of industrial solar photovoltaic plants," *Solar Compass*, vol. 8, p. 100061, Dec. 2023, doi: 10.1016/J.SOLCOM.2023.100061.

[3] R. Sudirman, K. Ashenayi, and M. Golbaba, "Comparison of Methods Used for Forecasting Solar Radiation," in *2012 IEEE Green Technologies Conference*, 2012, pp. 1–3. doi: 10.1109/GREEN.2012.6200996.

[4] M. Malvoni, M. G. De Giorgi, and P. M. Congedo, "Forecasting of PV Power Generation using weather input data-preprocessing techniques," in *Energy Procedia*, Elsevier Ltd, Sep. 2017, pp. 651–658. doi: 10.1016/j.egypro.2017.08.293.

[5] G. Sahin, G. Isik, and W. G. J. H. M. van Sark, "Predictive modeling of PV solar power plant efficiency considering weather conditions: A comparative analysis of artificial neural networks and multiple linear regression," *Energy Reports*, vol. 10, pp. 2837–2849, 2023, doi: https://doi.org/10.1016/j.egyr.2023.09.097.

[6] Y. N. Chanchangi, A. Ghosh, H. Baig, S. Sundaram, and T. K. Mallick, "Soiling on PV performance influenced by weather parameters in Northern Nigeria," *Renew Energy*, vol. 180, pp. 874–892, Dec. 2021, doi: 10.1016/j.renene.2021.08.090.

[7] M. Memiche, C. Bouzian, A. Benzahia, and A. Moussi, "Effects of dust, soiling, aging, and weather conditions on photovoltaic system performances in a Saharan environment—Case study in Algeria," *Global Energy Interconnection*, vol. 3, no. 1, pp. 60–67, Feb. 2020, doi: 10.1016/J.GLOEI.2020.03.004.

[8] "NASA POWER | API Pages." Accessed: May 03, 2025. [Online]. Available: https://power.larc.nasa.gov/api/pages/

[9] "Historical weather API - OpenWeatherMap." Accessed: May 03, 2025. [Online]. Available: https://openweathermap.org/history

[10] "Air Pollution - OpenWeatherMap." Accessed: May 03, 2025. [Online]. Available: https://openweathermap.org/api/air-pollution

[11] "PVOutput." Accessed: May 03, 2025. [Online]. Available: https://pvoutput.org/

[12] F. Dincer and M. E. Meral, "Critical Factors that Affecting Efficiency of Solar Cells," *Smart Grid and Renewable Energy*, vol. 01, no. 01, pp. 47–50, 2010, doi: 10.4236/SGRE.2010.11007.

[13] F. Bayrak, "Prediction of photovoltaic panel cell temperatures: Application of empirical and machine learning models," *Energy*, vol. 323, p. 135764, May 2025, doi: 10.1016/J.ENERGY.2025.135764.

[14] D. K. Dhaked, S. Dadhich, and D. Birla, "Power output forecasting of solar photovoltaic plant using LSTM," *Green Energy and Intelligent Transportation*, vol. 2, no. 5, p. 100113, 2023, doi: https://doi.org/10.1016/j.geits.2023.100113.

[15] D. K. Dhaked, S. Dadhich, and D. Birla, "Power output forecasting of solar photovoltaic plant using LSTM," *Green Energy and Intelligent Transportation*, vol. 2, no. 5, Oct. 2023, doi: 10.1016/j.geits.2023.100113.

[16] A. Ait Mansour, A. Tilioua, and M. Touzani, "Bi-LSTM, GRU and 1D-CNN models for short-term photovoltaic panel efficiency forecasting case amorphous silicon grid-connected PV system," *Results in Engineering*, vol. 21, p. 101886, 2024, doi: https://doi.org/10.1016/j.rineng.2024.101886.

[17] S. Hochreiter and J. Schmidhuber, "Long Short-term Memory," *Neural Comput*, vol. 9, pp. 1735–1780, Apr. 1997, doi: 10.1162/neco.1997.9.8.1735.

Weather and Air Quality Effects on Photovoltaic System Efficiency: A Modeling Approach

Luis Carrillo Mejía, Elvis Eduardo Gaona, and Johann Hernández Mora
LIFAE, Faculty of Engineering, Universidad Distrital Francisco José de Caldas, Bogotá, Colombia.

Abstract

This research aims to evaluate the performance of different machine learning algorithms for predicting the instantaneous efficiency of photovoltaic systems. The study utilized a dataset collected over seven months from seven distinct geographical locations characterized by diverse climatological conditions representative of the Colombian territory. The dataset included solar irradiance, climatological variables, air quality variables, and measured active power.

Instantaneous efficiency was calculated from these data and defined as the study's target variable. An initial descriptive statistical analysis was performed to characterize the dataset. Subsequently, various prediction algorithms were executed and evaluated using standard error metrics. The evaluation demonstrated that incorporating air quality variables improved the predictive accuracy across all evaluated models. A key finding from the correlation analysis and feature importance assessment is the negative association between higher levels of environmental pollution and instantaneous efficiency

Methodology

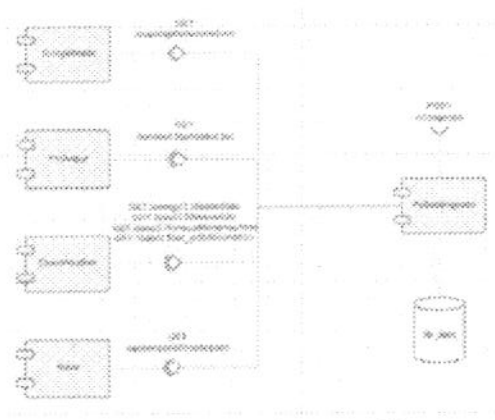

Fig 1. Components diagram of the microservice (PvIngestor).

Data Collection: A microservice was implemented to download data from various sources based on a time range and a geographical location.

- Irradiance: GHI, DHI and DNI were ingested from NASA API (free), and OpenWeather was implemented as well ($$$).
- Weather: Temperature, humidity, pressure, clouds, wind speed and direction were ingested from OpenWeather.
- Air quality: CO, NO, NO_2, O_3, SO_2, NH_3, $PM2.5$ and $PM10$, were ingested from OpenWeather
- Active Power: We used PvOutput which is a free service for sharing, comparing and monitoring live solar photovoltaic (PV) and energy consumption data.

Fig 2. PvOutput and location of one of the training points selected

To ensure the selected data was representative of a Colombian context, specific criteria were established for the PV systems chosen from PVOutput as it follows:

- The location's temperature had to be between 12° C and 35° C, or the site had to be situated within a ±10° latitude band around the equator.
- The installed panels had to be visually identifiable via satellite imagery of the geographical location.
- The manufacturer of the panels had to be a registered entity listed on either the Tier 1 A or B lists.
- The tilt angle and the total number of installed panels needed to be officially recorded in the dataset.

Preprocesing Data: We removed atypical data based on a solar illumination threshold of 120 W/m^2 , and the instantaneous efficiency was subsequently calculated by using next equation:

$$\eta_{ins} = \frac{P_{ins}}{G_{in} * A_t}$$

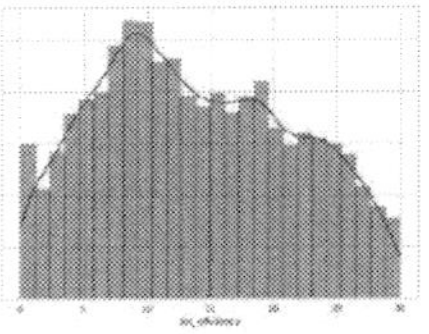

Fig 3.Distribution Density of Instantaneous Efficiency

Exploratory Data Analysis (EDA): The density distribution was plotted for each of the variables and, heatmaps were generated to visualize the Pearson, Spearman, and Kendall correlations for the entire dataset and for two specific locations; Rodolivos and Los Angeles, because the concentration of pollutants was highest at these sites.

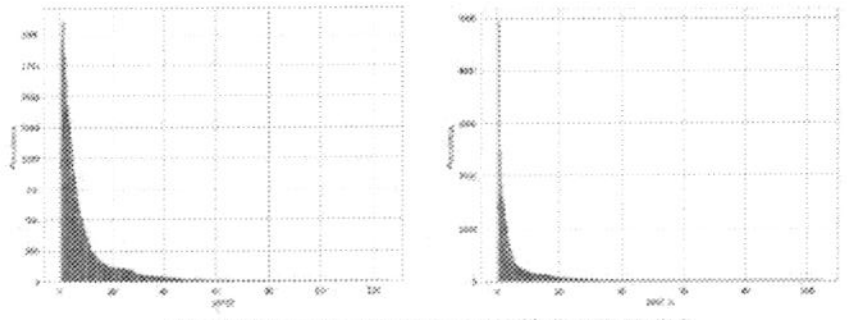

Fig 4.Distribution Density of PM2.5 and PM10

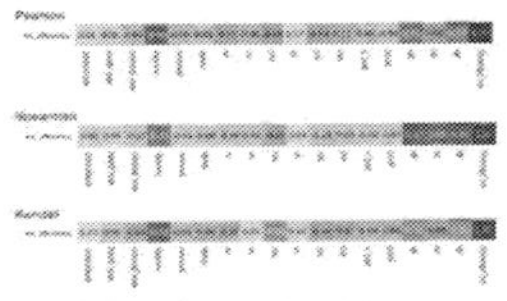

Fig 5. Heatmap of Correlations for the Entire Dataset

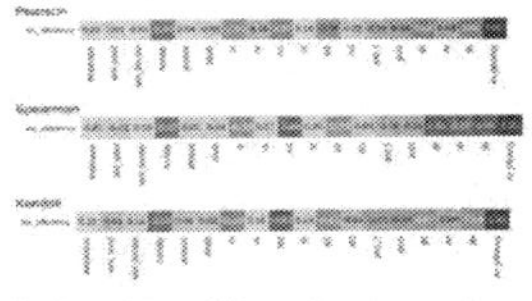

Fig 6. Heatmap of Correlations for Locations with the Highest Pollutant Concentration

Model Selection: To demonstrate the impact of air quality variables on efficiency, models were trained in several configurations: without these variables, with each variable individually, and finally with the variables that showed the greatest impact on prediction. The resulting models were then tabulated, and the top five were selected based on traditional error metrics: R-squared (R2), Root Mean Square Error (RMSE), Mean Absolute Error (MAE) and Mean Absolute Percentage Error (MAPE).

Fig 7. Models trained

Results & Conclusions

- The results of this research, summarized in the training metrics tables, provide a clear picture of the impact of air quality variables. Fig 8.b, which presents the training metrics without including these variables, shows that the Random Forest algorithm achieved the best performance with an $R^2 = 0.807$. The inclusion of pollutants in the model, as shown in Table 8.c, had a positive effect on the predictive capability of all algorithms, consistently improving their metrics around 3%. In this scenario, the Random Forest model maintained its lead with an $R^2 = 0.838$.

Model	RMSE	MAE	MAPE	R2
Random Forest	3.310	1.592	1.067	0.845
Extra Trees	3.358	1.636	1.147	0.841
Extreme Gradient	3.364	1.662	1.146	0.84
MLP	3.335	2.038	1.104	0.83
Gradient Boosting	3.507	1.796	1.124	0.823

a) All dataset variables

Model	RMSE	MAE	MAPE	R2
Random Forest	3.699	1.839	1.728	0.807
Gradient Boosting	3.735	1.893	1.701	0.803
Extra Trees	3.544	1.885	1.771	0.802
MLP	3.644	2.17	2.0	0.799
Extreme Gradient	3.88	2.011	1.565	0.788

b) without Air Quality Variables

Model	RMSE	MAE	MAPE	R2
Random Forest	3.188	1.637	1.138	0.838
Extra Trees	3.431	1.625	1.249	0.834
Extreme Gradient	3.448	1.714	1.307	0.832
MLP	3.437	2.061	2.22	0.821
Gradient Boosting	3.606	1.845	1.366	0.816

c) with Selected Predictor Variables

Fig 8. Training metrics

- The correlation analysis and the models' feature importance suggest that under conditions of higher environmental pollution, there is a negative association with instantaneous efficiency. The pollutants that showed the greatest influence on this negative relationship were NO2, followed by CO, SO2, PM10, and PM2.5.
- Unlike other pollutants, O3 showed a positive association with instantaneous efficiency, regardless of the overall pollution level of the location.

SPECIALIZED IRRADIATION MODELING FOR ALPINE REGIONS: CLEARSKY AND DIFFUSE FRACTION ESTIMATION

Bernhard Kubicek[1], Marcus Rennhofer[1], Philipp Weihs[2]
1: AIT Austrian Institute of technology GmbH, 2: Institute of Meteorology and Climatology, BOKU University, Vienna
Bernhard.kubicek@ait.ac.at

ABSTRACT: In the data driven performance evaluation of monitored PV systems, offsite irradiation sensors are of great help: either as the only irradiation data source in small residential systems, to estimate dust influence on local reference cells, or to check the calibration of the local irradiation sensors. Thereby, national meteorological measurement network (e.g. TAWES [1]) can be used, that features horizontal pyranometers in more than 250 sites in Austria. By geospatial interpolation, local estimations can be created based on this dense network.
For many of these PV evaluations, the hypothetical local clearsky irradiation is of great use, e.g. to filter data for dust evaluations, which is commonly estimated by the Ineichen [2] or King model. Using the historic data of the measurement network, a method is developed to obtain geolocalized correction factors to the Ineichen model. Deviations of more than 10% are observed at altitudes 3500m above sea level, that thereby can be corrected for.
As only the total horizontal irradiation is measured in the meteorological networks, an estimation of the diffuse horizontal irradiation is wanted, so that one can then use the Perez model to estimate module plane irradiations. A simplistic methodology is developed that estimates the diffuse irradiation purely based on local total horizontal irradiation, time, and geolocation within Austria. However, the methodology can be transferred any landmass worldwide, e.g. using the data within the GBON of the WMO [2].

1 GEOSPATIAL INTERPOLATION

The Austrian meteorological TAWES stations feature high quality historic irradiation time series at altitudes between 250m to 3400m above sea, and hence is a great test case for validation of irradiation modeling. For each of the more than 250 stations featuring irradiation sensors, the simulated clearsky horizontal irradiation (Ineichen/PVlib [5]) can be compared to actual measured irradiations. By creating a stable linear regression for the points that are considered cloud-free, localized calibrations to the Ineichen model can be obtained, see [4].

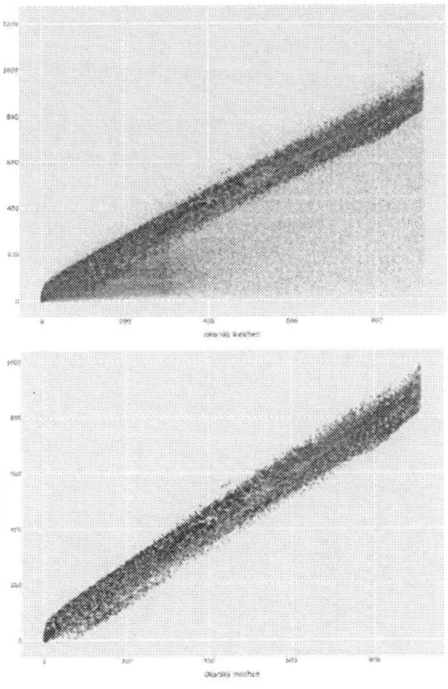

Figure 1: Point cloud of the comparison „simulated clearsky horizontal irradiation [W/m2]“ (PVlib/Ineichen, horizontal) to the measured total horizontal irradiation (vertical, [W/m2]) of one exemplary TAWES station. Above, all 10 min tuples of 9 years data are plotted, while below only clearsky states are shown. It can be seen that the blue linear regression line is non-diagonal, resulting in a linear calibration per station.

When comparing the linear calibrations to the Ineichen model, e.g. for a chosen reference clearsky irradiation, it can be found that the measured irradiation shows a strong sea height dependence, which is surprising, as the Ineichen model already contains the effect of decreasing airmass factors. By using a georeferenced scalar field of the Austrian elevation profile, the regional corrections can be put into georeferenced lookup tables, see Fig 2.

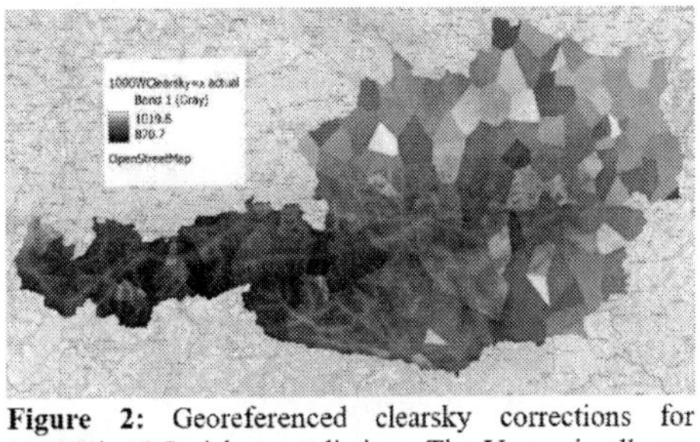

Figure 2: Georeferenced clearsky corrections for 1000W/m^2 Ineichen predictions. The Voronoi cells are effects of the weather stations individual corrections, while the height correction is supplemented [4].

Five of the TAWES sites in the measurement network are equipped with shadow bands. One now defines two quantities: the measured diffuse fraction as ratio of diffuse horizontal irradiation to total horizontal irradiation; And the "clearskyness", the ratio of measured total horizontal irradiation to the simulated clearsky irradiation, regarding corrections for the local deviations to the Ineichen model. By plotting these quantities, see fig 3, one can try to find linear functions to describe the correspondence.

10.4229/EUPVSEC2025/4BV.3.21

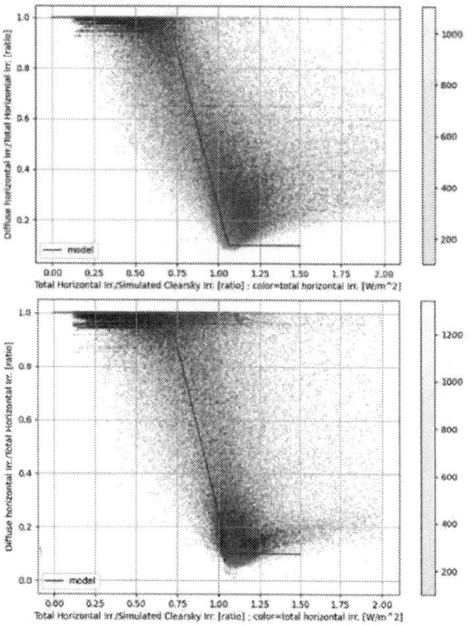

Figure 3: TAWES: The ratio of measured to clearsky irradiation, horizontally, versus the ratio of diffuse irradiation. Above, for Vienna, seaheight 320m, and below at the summit "Sonnblick", 3400m. An empiric stepwise function is fitted to the clouds, defining a simple diffuse fraction estimator.

2 ARAD REFINEMENT

The Austrian radiation monitoring network ARAD since 2011 records accurate direct and diffuse solar irradiation in 1 minute time averages [3] at five sites across Austria. Using this data, a refined approach can be derived. A plot similar to Fig 3 is shown in Fig 4. However, by creating a two dimensional binning of measured horizontal irradiation and calculated clearsky irradiation, the average diffuse fraction for each bin can be calculated, see Fig.5.

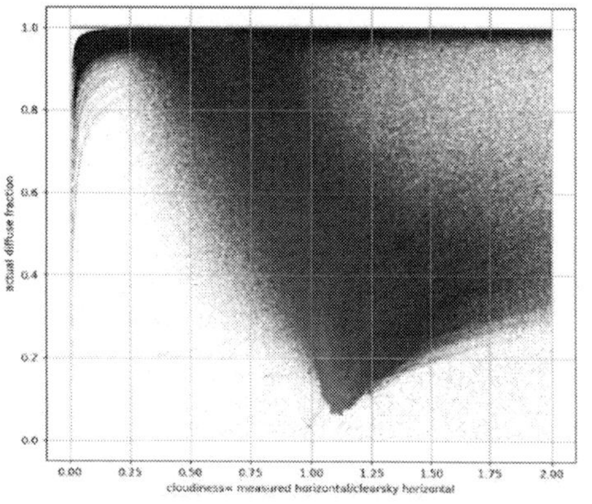

Figure 4: The ARAD based comparison for the station of Vienna, colorbar: Measured Horizontal irradiation [W/m^2]

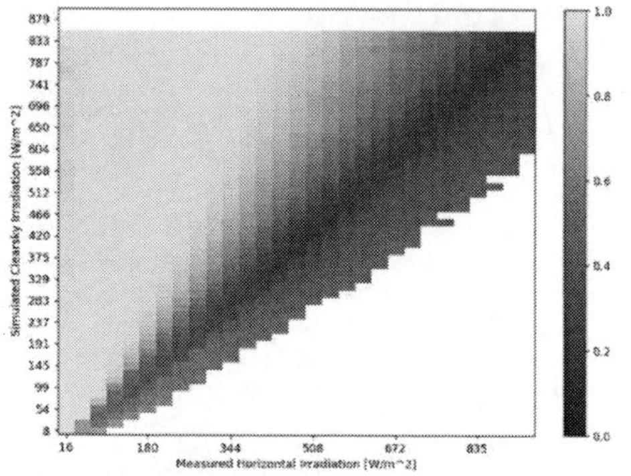

Figure 5: The ARAD based data plotted in 2d, while showing the average diffuse fraction of all data points in a bin as color, exhibits a much better structure than the previous figure. The centerpoint of the valley forms a slightly off-diagonal line, as the clearsky calibration is not yet performed on this dataset.

In figure 5, it can be seen that a coordinate transformation to the new parameter "over-irradiation" (measured horizontal irradiation – horizontal clearsky irradiation) is useful, as in this system the valley becomes mostly trivial, see figure 6. The curves there can be well approximated by piecewise linear functions, see figure 7.

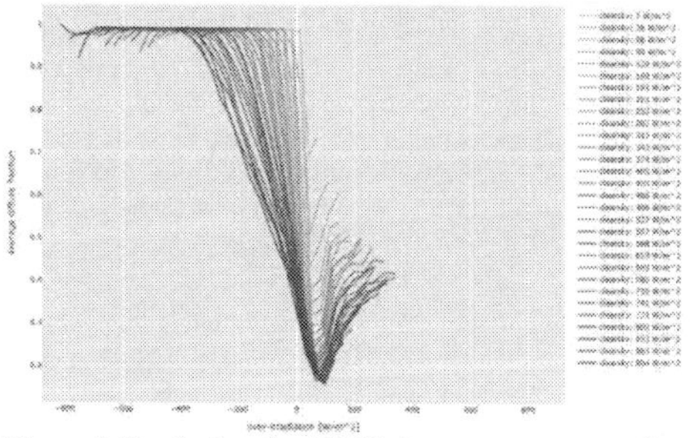

Figure 6: By plotting the ARAD data over a new quantity, the "over-irradiation", curves can be developed that can easily be approximated by piecewise linear functions on three intervals: the constant range from -1000 to a clearsky depending over-irradiation between [-400 and 0], followed by a decline to the actual clearsky diffuse fraction, followed by increase

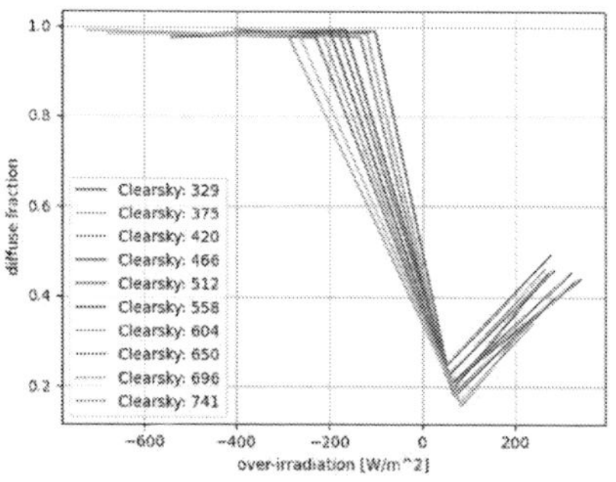

Figure 7: The curves of the previous plot can be approximate by three-interval piecewise linear functions.

10.4229/EUPVSEC2025/4BV.3.21

The piecewise functions again have set of parameters, the initial plateau, that can be estimated constant, the position of the first decline, the depth of the decline, and the rise at times when the measured irradiation is larger than the clearsky irradiation. These parameters can be fitted by simple functions, see e.g. figure 8 and 9.

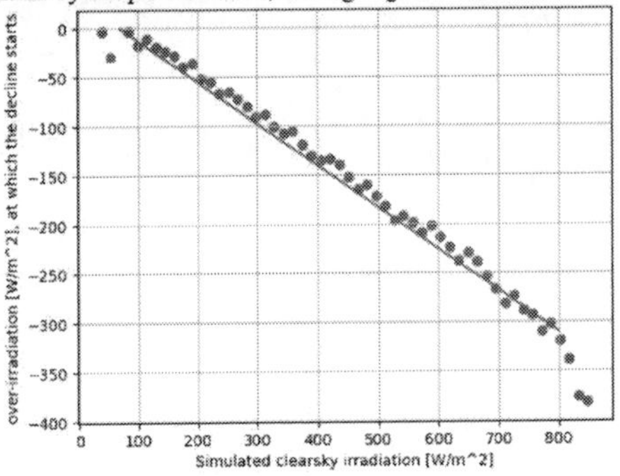

Figure 8: The over-irradiation, at which the decline occurs of the diffuse fraction occurs, can be well described by a linear function.

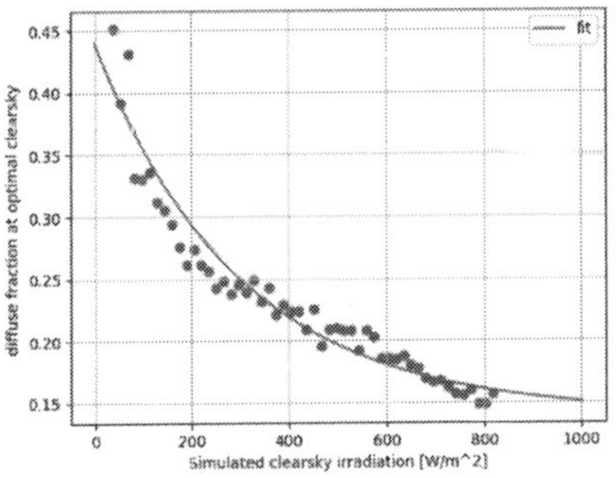

Figure 9: The minimum of the diffuse fraction can be described by a linear function plus an exponential decay.

2 CONCLUSIONS

By geospatial interpolation, one can obtain time series of the total horizontal irradiation in 10-minute intervals for all arbitrary sites in Austria. This requires a sea-height correction for both weather stations and the chosen sites. Using the approach presented, from the time and site-dependent calculated clearsky irradiation, and the interpolated horizontal irradiation, the time dependent diffuse fraction can now be estimated. This is useful, since to estimate the tilted plane irradiation for PV modules at the site, the diffuse irradiation needs to be known. Finally, by using this tilted plane irradiations, the performance ratio of PV systems that have no local irradiation measurement can be performed.

[1] Geosphere/ZAMG, "TAWES Messnetz", https://www.zamg.ac.at/cms/de/klima/messnetze/wetterstationen

[2] P. Ineichen and R. Perez, "A New airmass independent formulation for the Linke turbidity coefficient", Solar Energy, vol 73, pp. 151-157, 2002.

[3] World Meteorological Organization, website: https://wmo.int/activities/global-basic-observing-network-gbon

[4] B. Kubicek, M. Rennhofer, "Georeferenced Correction Factors to the Ineichen Clearsky Model for the Alpine regions in Austria/Europe.", IEEE Photovoltaic Specialists conference 2025.

[5] Holmgren, W., Hansen, C., and Mikofski, M. "pvlib python: a python package for modeling solar energy systems." Journal of Open Source Software, 3(29), 884, (2018). DOI: 10.21105/joss.00884.

[6] Olefs, M., Baumgartner, D. J., Obleitner, F., Bichler, C., Foelsche, U., Pietsch, H., Rieder, H. E., Weihs, P., Geyer, F., Haiden, T., and Schöner, W.: The Austrian radiation monitoring network ARAD – best practice and added value, Atmos. Meas. Tech., 9, 1513–1531, https://doi.org/10.5194/amt-9-1513-2016, 2016.

Bernhard Kubicek[1], Marcus Rennhofer[1], Philipp Weihs[2]
1: AIT Austrian Institute of Technology GmbH, Center for Energy bernhard.kubicek@ait.ac.at
2: Institute of Meteorology and Climatology, BOKU University, Vienna

AUSTRIAN INSTITUTE OF TECHNOLOGY
TOMORROW TODAY

SPECIALIZED IRRADIATION MODELING FOR ALPINE REGIONS: CLEARSKY AND DIFFUSE FRACTION ESTIMATION.

Motivation

Most small PV systems lack in-plane irradiation sensors. To enable performance ratio estimations, interpolation of data from meteorological weather station networks can be used. They typically measure global horizontal irradiation, while for the module plane transformation, the diffuse fraction needs to be known. Longyear diffuse fraction measurement from the ARAD dataset is used to create such an estimator for the alpine areas of Austria.

Method

The ~230 stations of the Austrian meteorological measurement network 'TAWES' have been systematically equipped with pyranometers. This 10-minute data exists from 116m to 3400m above sea level. The frequently used Ineichen Clearsky radiation model [1] considers the time-dependent path of the sun and the altitude above sea level. In a previous work, the authors have developed a calibration method, that corrects the sea height effects using georeferenced lookup tables for Austria [2].

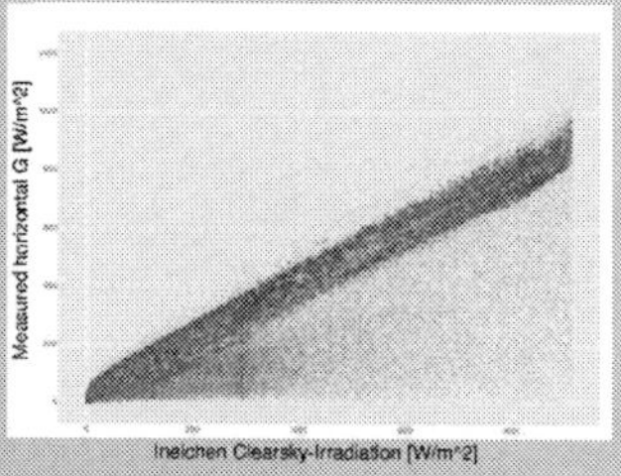

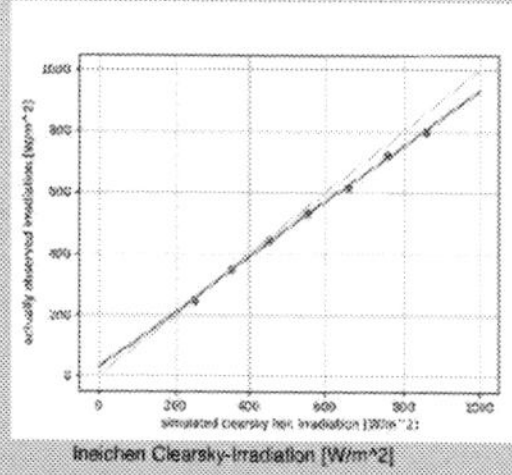

The fitted clearsky calibration for each TAWES station exhibits a bias and offset, that again depends on the sea height:

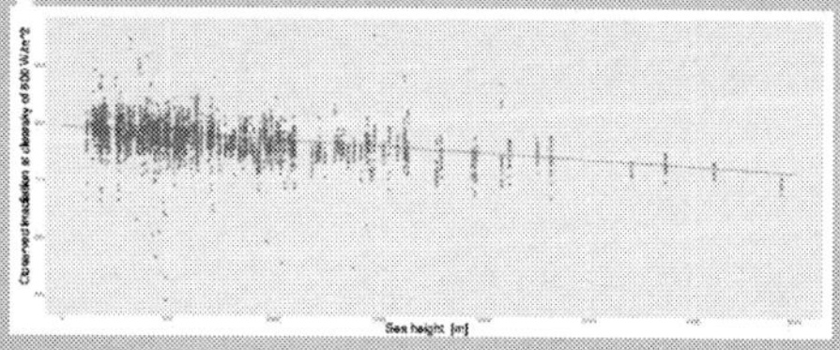

Spatial interpolation together with heightmaps can be used to apply the model, to obtain horizontal irradiation time series for arbitrary sites:

[1] P. Ineichen and R. Perez, "A New airmass independent formulation for the Linke turbidity coefficient", Solar Energy, vol 73, pp. 151-157, 2002.

[2] B.Kubicek, M. Rennhofer, „Georeferenced Correction Factors to the Ineichen Clearsky Model for the Alpine regions in Austria/Europe.", PVSC, Montreal, 2025.

[3] Olefs, M., Baumgartner, D. J., Obleitner, F., Bichler, C., Foelsche, U., Pietsch, H., Rieder, H. E., Weihs, P., Geyer, F., Haiden, T., and Schöner, W.: The Austrian radiation monitoring network ARAD – best practice and added value, Atmos. Meas. Tech., 9, 1513–1531, https://doi.org/10.5194/amt-9-1513-2016, 2016.

This content was created within the „EASE" Austrian national project.

ARAD

The Austrian radiation monitoring network ARAD since 2011 records accurate direct and diffuse solar irradiation in 1 minute time averages [3]. One can define two quantities:

- the diffuse fraction: diffuse horizontal irradiation per total horizontal radiation
- The "clearskyness": total horizontal irradiation per simulated clearsky irradiation

This quantities can be plotted for each individual station, e.g. Vienna:

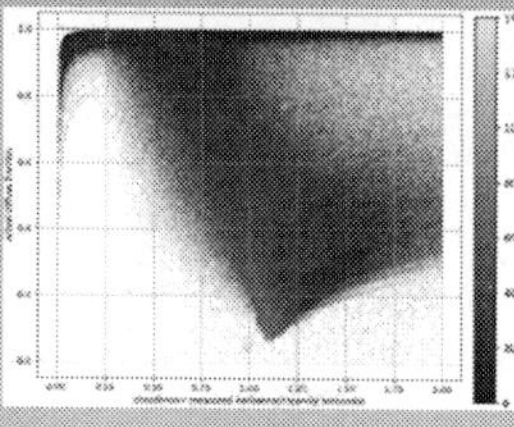

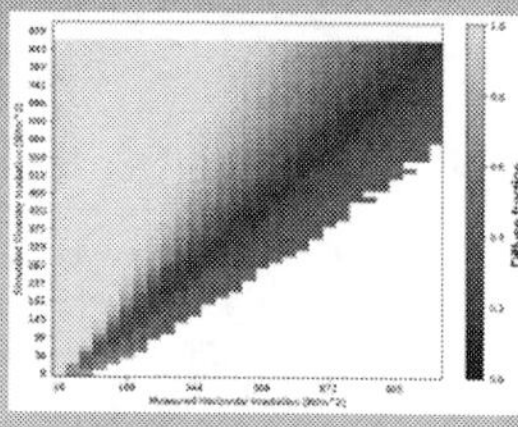

Thereby one can see (left), that diffuse fraction is not only a function of the cloudiness, but also of the measured irradiation. A 2d-plot (right) of the mean diffuse fraction occurring in the bins shows a clearer structure. The bias and slightly non-diagonality are the effects of the not yet performed clearsky calibration for the ARAD dataset. One can deduct, that the "over-irradiation" (measured horizontal – clearsky horizontal) is a good parameter:

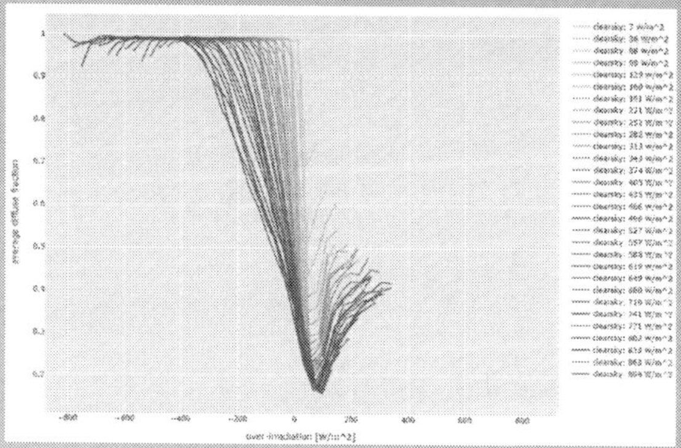

This can be well approximated by piecewise linear functions of three intervals, whose defining points can be functionally defined by the clearsky irradiation. E.g. one can describe the over-irradiation of the first decline by a linear function of the clearsky irradiation.

Conclusion

By a sea-height-aware interpolation, a historic time series of the local total horizontal irradiation can be generated for any point in Austria with 10-minute resolution. By comparison of the interpolated irradiation with the local clearsky irradiation, the diffuse fraction can be estimated. This enables to calculated arbitrary in-plane irradiations e.g. using the Perez model. Finally, this in-plane irradiation time series can be used to perform performance ratio estimations for non-sensored PV systems.

A NOVEL IMPLEMENTATION OF QUALITY CHECKS OF SPECTRAL DIRECT NORMAL IRRADIANCE MEASUREMENTS

Sergiu-Mihai Hategan[1,2]*, Jacob K. Thorning[3], Sergiu V. Spataru[3], Marius Paulescu[2]
[1]Institute for Advanced Environmental Research, West University of Timisoara, V. Pârvan 4, 300223, Timisoara, Romania
[2]Faculty of Physics, West University of Timisoara, V. Pârvan 4, 300223, Timisoara, Romania
[3]Technical University of Denmark, Department of Electrical Engineering, Frederiksborgvej 399, 4000 Roskilde, Denmark
*Corresponding author email: sergiu.hategan98@e-uvt.ro

ABSTRACT: This study develops a robust quality control (QC) method for spectral irradiance measurements to improve solar resource assessment accuracy. It combines QC techniques for spectral and broadband irradiance data to detect systematic and random errors. Using EKO MS-711 spectroradiometers at two research sites, the method applies logical checks for physically plausible values and compares measurements with SMARTS2 clear-sky simulations (using AERONET/MERRA2 atmospheric data). A Python interface simplifies data comparison, aiming to boost spectral modeling adoption in photovoltaic research. Preliminary results confirm the method's effectiveness and potential for future advancements.
Keywords: solar radiation, direct irradiance, spectral irradiance, quality control

1 INTRODUCTION

The precise measurement of ground-level spectral solar radiation is essential for fields ranging from atmospheric sciences, biology, medicine (UV radiation), and solar energy. Spectral direct normal irradiance (DNI) modeling and measurements are an important subset, with impacts on concentrating photovoltaic power as well as estimations of spectral irradiance on tilted surfaces. Although radiative transfer (i.e. MODTRAN [1]) and spectral transmittance models (SMARTS2 [2]) provide theoretical estimates, their accuracy depends on often-unavailable atmospheric inputs. Spectroradiometers offer direct measurements, but face trade-offs: monochromator-based systems deliver high accuracy at slow scan speeds, whereas fixed-grating array detectors multi-wavelength capture with lower resolution [3]. However, recent innovations have allowed for better resolution, around 0.4 nm [4].

A clear sky spectral irradiance quality control (QC) methodology was first proposed in [5], which compares measurements under clear sky conditions to simulated spectral irradiance. The simulations give a lower and an upper margin of possible spectral irradiance values under high turbidity or clear atmosphere, respectively. Another option involves the use of spectral indices such as average photon energy (APE) used for comparison between measured and simulated spectra for clear sky conditions [6]. A more recent QC framework was specifically tailored for spectral DNI measurements [7]. This method was successfully utilized on monochromator type spectroradiometer; however, due to the spectroradiometer measuring method, this framework can only be applied to clear sky conditions with low air mass values. Under these conditions, a good reference spectral is SMARTS2, with a long-tested good performance [8]. This model requires air mass values and some atmospheric parameter inputs, which can be obtained from measurements or reanalysis products.

Considering the need for QC verification of spectral measurements, we present an updated methodology that is based on logical checks, physically plausible value checks, and an extended comparison with broadband DNI measurements, based on SMARTS2 simulations. The proposed QC framework was tested at two locations with spectroradiometers installed, namely the West University of Timisoara (WUT) in Timisoara, Romania, and the Technical University of Denmark (DTU) Risø campus in Roskilde, Denmark. The implementation is enhanced by a publicly available Python-based interface.

2 METHODOLOGY AND DATA

Figure 1: The EKO MS-711N spectroradiometers at WUT (left) and DTU (right).

2.1 Instruments and Data Sources

Aerosol and other atmospheric parameter inputs, necessary for comparisons with spectral models, are obtained from two separate sources, depending on their availability. The first is AERONET [9], a federated network of ground-based solar photometers that measure aerosol optical depth (AOD) and other atmo-

10.4229/EUPVSEC2025/4BV.3.24

spheric parameters such as ozone content, water vapor content and particle size distribution. AERONET serves as the reference standard for remote sensing aerosol datasets. MERRA-2 represents NASA's global atmospheric reanalysis system [10], which assimilates both ground-based (such as AERONET) and satellite measurements. MERRA-2 produces a high resolution, long-term, spatially continuous record of aerosols, clouds, meteorological, and atmospheric parameters, helping to bridge gaps in local measurements. A recent study has found good agreement between the AERONET and MERRA-2 inputs in the case of the SMARTS2 model [11].

The locations considered in this research are the Solar Platform at the Institute for Advanced Environmental Research in Timisoara, and the DTU Platform at DTU Risø (showcased in Fig. 1). The WUT Institute's Solar Platform, located in the center of Timisoara (latitude $45.76°N$, longitude $21.23°E$, altitude of 85 m a.s.l) consists of an EKO MS-711N DNI spectroradiometer installed on an EKO STR-32G Sun Tracker, an EKO ASI-16 camera coupled with a weather station, and an EKO MS-80 pyranometer measuring global horizontal irradiance. A functioning AERONET station is located nearby, at a distance of 1.5 km.

The DTU Platform is located at DTU Risø campus in Roskilde, Denmark (latitude $55.69°N$, longitude $12.08°E$, close to sea level). It consists of a similar EKO MS-711N DNI spectroradiometer, installed on an EKO STR-22G Dual type sun tracker, an EKO MS-80 GHI pyranometer, an EKO MS-56 pyrheliometer and an EKO MS802 DHI pyranometer. Atmospheric parameter data was obtained from MERRA-2 reanalysis.

The dataset for both locations comprises measurements recorded during the entire month of June 2024. DTU dataset contains both spectral data, broadband DNI and GHI measurements, as well as hourly values of the key atmospheric parameters, taken from MERRA-2. The DTU measures spectral data every 5 minutes, while WUT measures data every 10 minutes. The WUT dataset contains spectral data and AERONET level 1.5 atmospheric parameters, the missing values being filled with the hourly average value. The DTU dataset contains 6927 datapoints, while the WUT dataset contains 2316 datapoints.

We have marked as clear-sky the datapoints measured during days with completely clear-sky conditions or close to it, manually verifying the data.

2.2 Basic physical checks

Inspired by the already well-implemented broadband irradiance quality control procedures [12], we introduce three logical QC checks in our framework. The first check verifies if the measurement recording was correctly transmitted into the dataset (not a number - NaN check). The next two checks focus on physically plausible values for spectral irradiance measurements, namely they should be positive and the spectral irradiance integrated over the entire instrument's range (300-1100 nm) should be less than the irradiance over the same wavelength range at the top of the atmosphere (the AM0 check). This is an extension of the methodology presented in [5], valid for clear sky periods. However, the AM0 and positive value checks are applicable under all sky conditions.

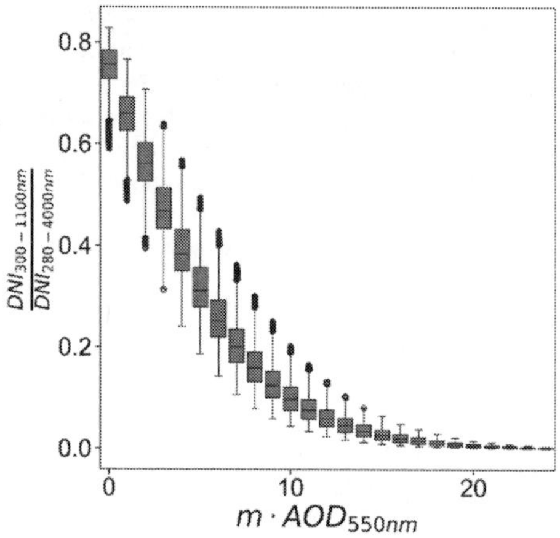

Figure 2: Boxplots showcasing the tolerance interval for each bin of simulated integrated fraction values.

2.3 Broadband DNI check

When a broadband irradiance measurement instrument is available, spectral measurements can be verified against that other measurement. The widely used SMARTS2 solar spectral irradiance model forms the basis of the broadband quality control check. As SMARTS2 is a clear-sky model, this check applies only to clear-sky periods. Broadband pyrheliometers operate in the optical spectral range of 280-4000 nm, while the EKO DNI spectroradiometers considered in this study operate in the 300-1100 nm range. Assuming the validity of the SMARTS2 model, we propose the following method to find measurement anomalies for spectroradiometers. First, we integrate the spectral irradiance measured by the spectral instrument in the 300-1100 nm range, and then divide it by the measured broadband irradiance, obtaining an integrated fraction f according to Equation 1. Afterwards, this integrated fraction is compared to typical values obtained by simulations employing the SMARTS2 model, both for the instrument's range (300-1100 nm) and for the broadband range (280-4000 nm).

$$f = \frac{\int_{300}^{1100} DNI(\lambda)d\lambda}{\int_{280}^{4000} DNI(\lambda)d\lambda} \quad (1)$$

The SMARTS2 simulations were carried out in the following ranges of parameters: air mass between 1 and 10, with a step of 0.25, precipitable water vapor content between 0.1 and 5.2 g/cm^2 with a step of 0.3 g/cm^2, values of ozone column content (0.25,0.3,0.35,0.4 $cm \cdot atm$), aerosol models spanning the four S&F models (rural, urban, tropospheric, maritime), and finally aerosol optical depth values (AOD) between 0 and 2.5, with a step of 0.5. The simulation was run twice, once for AOD at 500 nm (a variable provided by AERONET) and once for AOD at 550 nm (a variable provided by MERRA-2). Each simulated set of spectra contained 543456 datapoints, with values for the integrated fraction at each combination of input parameters. We have observed a clear correlation between the product $m \cdot AOD$, where m is air mass, and the integrated fraction. This correlation serves as the basis for the tolerance intervals of the integrated fraction, shown in Fig. 2.

The $m \cdot AOD$ values were grouped in 25 bins (between 0 and 25, with each bin width equal to 1), and the tolerance intervals were obtained using a boxplot for the integrated fraction values inside that bin. The tolerance interval was defined using a boxplot whisker length of 1.5 times the interquartile range, excluding outliers in the binned dataset.

Using these intervals for each bin of $m \cdot AOD$ values, we check whether the integrated fraction measured is within the tolerance interval; otherwise, it is flagged as anomalous. In addition to other studies, we have extended the air mass interval, allowing this quality control check to be performed throughout the day, provided that the sky is clear.

3 RESULTS AND DISCUSSION

Running all checks at both locations have shown the percentage of data flagged by each QC check in Fig. 3 (considering only data for air mass higher than 10). The logical NaN check and the physical AM0 check did not flag data during the period we considered. The newly devised Broadband check requires broadband DNI measurements, which were available only at DTU. For this location, 8.3% of the data was marked as being under clear sky conditions. Of that percentage, 13.7% were flagged as anomalous measurements, with our proposed integrated ratio check. This occurred at low solar elevation angles, corresponding to air masses greater than 3, where the presence of nearby buildings or other possible reflections could induce uncertainty in spectral measurements.

However, our QC implementation found negative measured values at both locations, in 0.2% of the WUT dataset and in 7.6% of all data at DTU. As can be seen in Fig. 4, negative values are found mainly in the 1000-1100 nm range, where the uncertainty of spectroradiometer measurement is highest due to the detector band gap. Another possible situation for the occurrence of such anomalies is under severely overcast or cloudy conditions. Because the spectral DNI is severely reduced under such conditions, the inherent measuring uncertainty can lead to erroneous values, especially in the 1000-1100 nm range.

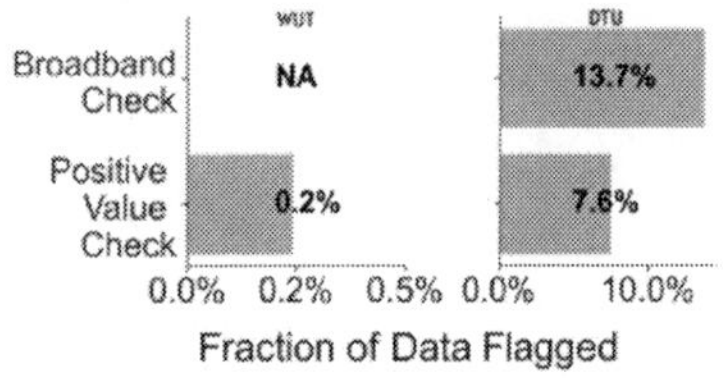

Figure 3: Amount of data flagged by the QC checks implemented. NaN and AM0 checks did not flag any datapoint.

In the case of the two unflagged data examples in Fig. 4, we observe a good agreement between the measurements and the SMARTS2 model. As expected, AERONET data inputs fit the measurements slightly better, with MERRA-2 inputs giving a slight overestimation of spectral irradiance. Future studies could be concerned with different atmospheric parameter inputs for locations without concurrent AERONET measurements, to select the proper reanalysis or satellite product. A possibility could be CAMS radiation products [13] or MODIS satellite measurements [14].

All checks have been implemented using a Python-based interface, available online [15].

4 CONCLUSIONS

In this research, we have introduced an extended methodology of QC checks for spectral DNI measurements [15]. Leveraging automated logical and physical plausibility verifications, the proposed methodology is applicable under all sky conditions. In addition, for clear sky data we have introduced a comparison with broadband DNI measurements, flagging anomalies based on SMARTS2 simulations. The SMARTS2 simulations have provided a tolerated range of values for spectral DNI depending on aerosol and air mass properties at the moment of measurement. The input consisted of measured atmospheric parameters (from AERONET) or reanalysis inputs (from MERRA-2), depending on availability.

The proposed methodology has been tested on a one month dataset (June 2024) in two locations: WUT and DTU. The main anomalies found were negative spectral DNI values in both locations and in clear sky conditions some measurements were considerably different to broadband measurements. Both types of flagged anomalous measurements were found at large air mass values, where measurement

10.4229/EUPVSEC2025/4BV.3.24

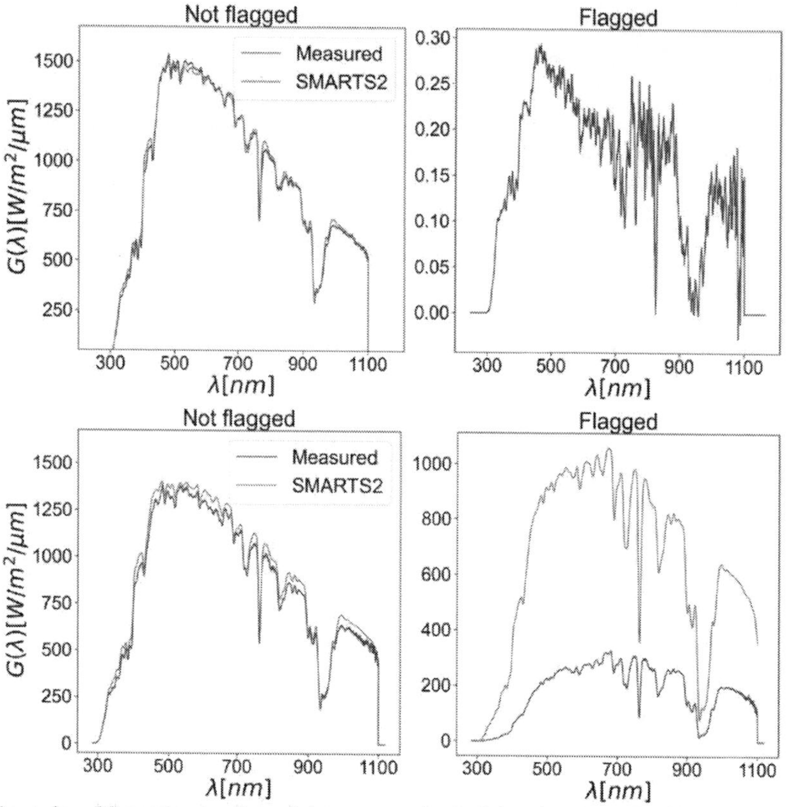

Figure 4: Examples of flagged and unflagged data measured at both locations (top - WUT, bottom - DTU). Unflagged data was compared to SMARTS2. At WUT, the datapoint was flagged by the Positive Value Check. At DTU the datapoint was flagged by the Broadband Check.

uncertainty is inherently higher than at low air mass. In the case of the flagged negative values, a possible source was the instrument's sensitivity in the 1000-1100 nm range. This led to anomalous measurements under cloudy or rainy conditions, when the overall DNI values are extremely low. Future work could focus on expanding upon the presented QC methods by adding other possible validation checks, or by adding methods for spectral global horizontal irradiance or diffuse irradiance.

References

[1] Gail P Anderson et al. "Reviewing atmospheric radiative transfer modeling: new developments in high-and moderate-resolution FASCODE/FASE and MODTRAN". In: *Optical spectroscopic techniques and instrumentation for atmospheric and space research II*. Vol. 2830. SPIE. 1996, pp. 82–93.

[2] Christian Gueymard et al. *SMARTS2: a simple model of the atmospheric radiative transfer of sunshine: algorithms and performance assessment.* Vol. 1. Florida Solar Energy Center Cocoa, FL, 1995.

[3] Aron Habte, Afshin Andreas, and Manajit Sengupta. "Spectral solar irradiance: calibration methods and measurement techniques". In: *Spectral Characteristics of Solar Radiation*. Elsevier, 2025, pp. 47–76.

[4] Rosa Delia García-Cabrera et al. "Aerosol retrievals from the EKO MS-711 spectral direct irradiance measurements and corrections of the circumsolar radiation". In: *Atmospheric Measurement Techniques* 13.5 (2020), pp. 2601–2621.

[5] Carsten Hoyer-Klick et al. "MESoR-Management and exploitation of solar resource knowledge". In: *SolarPACES 2009*. 2009.

[6] Gustavo Nofuentes et al. "Experimental evaluation of a spectral index to characterize temporal variations in the direct normal irradiance spectrum". In: *Applied Sciences* 11.3 (2021), p. 897.

[7] Aitor Marzo et al. "Field Quality Control of Spectral Solar Irradiance Measurements by Comparison with Broadband Measurements". In: *Sustainability* 13.19 (2021), p. 10585.

[8] Christian A Gueymard. "The SMARTS spectral irradiance model after 25 years: New developments and validation of reference spectra". In: *Solar Energy* 187 (2019), pp. 233–253.

[9] Brent N Holben et al. "AERONET—A federated instrument network and data archive for aerosol characterization". In: *Remote sensing of environment* 66.1 (1998), pp. 1–16.

[10] CA Randles et al. "The MERRA-2 aerosol reanalysis, 1980 onward. Part I: System description and data assimilation evaluation". In: *Journal of climate* 30.17 (2017), pp. 6823–6850.

[11] Sophie Pelland and Christian A Gueymard. "Validation of photovoltaic spectral effects derived from satellite-based solar irradiance products". In: *IEEE Journal of Photovoltaics* 12.6 (2022), pp. 1361–1368.

[12] Anne Forstinger et al. "Expert quality control of solar radiation ground data sets". In: *ISES Solar World Congress*. 2021.

[13] Christian A Gueymard and Dazhi Yang. "Worldwide validation of CAMS and MERRA-2 reanalysis aerosol optical depth products using 15 years of AERONET observations". In: *Atmospheric Environment* 225 (2020), p. 117216.

[14] DA Chu et al. "Validation of MODIS aerosol optical depth retrieval over land". In: *Geophysical research letters* 29.12 (2002), MOD2–1.

[15] *GitHub - Spectroradiometer-QC*. `https://github.com/Applied-PV-TEAM/Spectroradiometer-QC`.

Evaluating the Suitability of Köppen-Geiger Climate Classifications for Photovoltaic Systems: Micro-climate Analysis and Risk Assessment Maps

Pavan Kumar Panda[1], Hugo Sanchez[1], Leila Mortazavifar[1,2], and Ralph Gottschalg[1,2]
[1]Hochschule Anhalt University of Applied Sciences, Bernburger Str. 55, 06366, Köthen, Germany,
Email: Pavan.Panda@hs-anhalt.de
[2]Fraunhofer Center for Crystalline Silicon Photovoltaics CSP, Halle, Germany

ABSTRACT: The performance of photovoltaic (PV) systems are influenced by local climatic conditions. The widely used Köppen-Geiger (KG) classification system, focused mainly on agriculture, has limitations for PV applications due to its emphasis on general climate patterns rather than specific factors affecting PV material aging. This study evaluates the compatibility of KG classifications with relevant micro-climatic properties utilizing global meteorological data to create risk assessment maps for PV application. We used Principal component analysis (PCA) and clustering to simplify the micro-climate properties and found overlaps in KG classifications indicating challenges in capturing transitional micro-climate zones. These findings indicate that traditional clustering is inadequate for defining specific climate zones for PV use. Consequently, we developed a novel risk map tailored to degradation reaction rates in analyzed location, offering more detailed and valid climate classification for PV application. This study underscores the necessity for innovative mapping techniques that capture nuanced micro-climate variations relevant to PV system development.
Keywords: three to five keywords in order of importance

1 INTRODUCTION

Historically the KG climatic classification system has been mostly used for the broad categorization of global climates solely based on temperature and precipitation patterns [1], dividing the earth into 30 different zones. While KG is foundational in the ecological and botanical context [2], it has its limitations while meeting the specific needs of the PV systems. In response to these limitations, novel methodologies have emerged including the solar-specific metrics and adopting redefined climatic classifications models tailored to solar applications, such as Photovoltaic Climate Zones (PVCZ) [3] and Köppen-Geiger-Photovoltaic (KG-PV) [4].

These classifications made significant strides in correlating climatic classifications with PV system performance. Meanwhile, traditional KG classification omits addressing these critical micro-climatic stressors and their impact on different degradation drivers in PV systems.

Building on these foundations the present study seeks to bridge the gap between traditional climate classifications and the specific needs of PV-relevant classification through several key contributions. By employing detailed micro-climate modelling, this research calculated the immediate available environmental conditions surrounding the PV module, offering a precise understanding of climatic factors and their interdependencies. Additionally, through standardization, dimensional reduction, and PCA, the study simplifies climatic data into principal components, helping to reveal underlying patterns and identify the most significant variables.

The analysis uncovers substantial overlaps among these climatic groups, suggesting that traditional KG zones do not uniquely correspond to distinct PV micro-climate zones. This overlap indicates continuous and transitional zones and highlights the limitations of conventional classification. To address these insights non-reversible degradation rates are evaluated, by applying the peck's model proposed in [5] [6] specific to PV systems. The integration of degradation drivers into risk assessment plots provides a more accurate depiction of performance risk maps, ultimately advancing the efficacy and sustainability of PV developments.

2 METHODOLOGY

The proposed method involves several steps to achieve the microclimate data from meteorological data and later used in non-reversible degradation driver model is shown in figure 1.

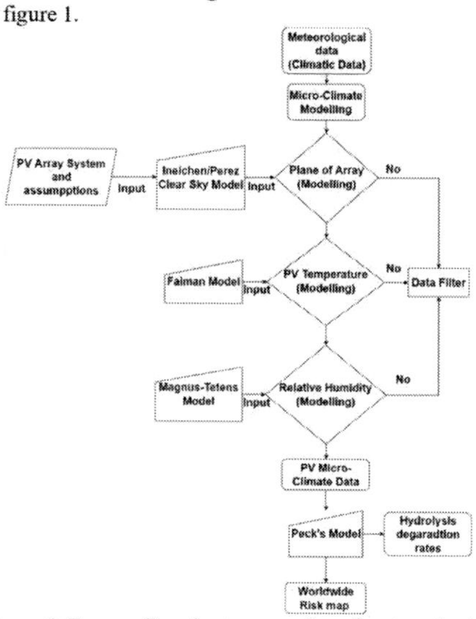

Figure 1: Process flowchart: conversion of meteorological data to PV micro climate data and degradation model development

2.1 Data Acquisition and Processing

The meteorological data used for this study was sourced from NASA's POWER project, specifically utilizing the CERES and MERRA-2 [7] datasets. The dataset spans from 2001 to 2020 years and the analysis corresponds to worldwide climate data of different climatic classifications.

2.2 Micro-climate modelling

Micro-climate data, specifically the plane of array (POA) irradiance on both front and back of a module is derived using Ineichen/Perez clear sky model [8] implemented by PVlib [9] and PVfactors [10] as expressed

10.4229/EUPVSEC2025/4BV.3.25

in by equation 1.

$$I_{POA} = [I_{beam,POA}] + [I_{diffuse,POA}] + [I_{reflected,POA}] \quad (1)$$

$$T_m = T_{amb} + \frac{E_{POA}}{U_0+U_1*WS} \quad (2)$$

The module temperature is determined through Faiman's model and as outlined in equation 2. The relative humidity and saturation vapor pressure are calculated using the approach by Michael Koehl [11] as shown in equation 3.

$$RH_{mod} = RH * e^{\left(\frac{7.5*T_{amb}}{T_{amb}+237.3}\right)-\left(\frac{7.5*T_{mod}}{T_{mod}+237.3}\right)} \quad (3)$$

2.3 Standardization, Dimensionality Reduction, and Clustering

Derived micro-climate data is later standardized and PCA reduced the data to two-dimension PCA, enabling visual and computational insights into climatic variability. k-means clustering algorithm is applied to the data and stable clusters are obtained where centroids no longer change significantly [12]. Elbow method is used to identify optimal cluster number and later different cluster number are used to acquire perfect silhouette score [13].

2.3 Degradation Modeling and risk assessment maps

Reaction rates for hydrolysis were derived using Peck's model [14] [15], as represented in equation (4) for worldwide climate. Micro-climate-based degradation reaction rate risk maps were developed.

$$k_h = A_H * rh_{eff}^n * \exp\left[\frac{-E_a}{k_B*T_m}\right] \quad (4)$$

The data were then categorized into 20 zones from minimum to maximum value of that respective degradation rate.

3 RESULTS

3.1 Microclimate analysis

The global climate data obtained from NASA POWER dataset is input into various models to derive the micro climate data essential to understand the climate stressors on PV module performance.

Front side POA irradiance: During daylight hours, the POA irradiance on the front side consistently surpasses the global horizontal irradiance (GHI), as shown in figure 2 on a day (21.03.2018).

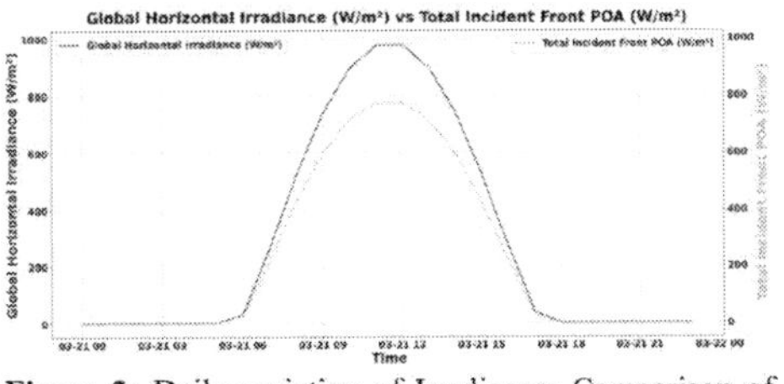

Figure 2: Daily variation of Irradiance: Comparison of GHI and POA front incident

In midday POA peaks, results from the panels tilt and orientation that optimize direct beam exposure and enhance the collection of diffuse irradiances

Rear side POA irradiance: The POA irradiance on the rear side is significantly lower than both GHI and POA front, as shown in figure 3 for a day. This lower level is only due the ground reflected irradiance, influenced by factors such as albedo, ground clearance ratios, PV row height and width.

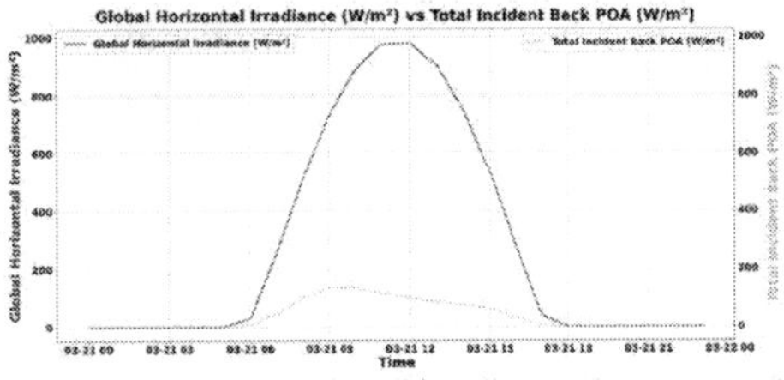

Figure 3: Daily variation of Irradiance: Comparison of GHI and POA back incident

Module temperature: The temperature of the PV module is higher than ambient air temperature, reaching notably high values at midday. Global PV module temperature distributed in 20 zones as shown in figure 4. The increase in temperature is driven due to the elevated POA on front and bank, partially offset from cooling due to wind speed are also observed.

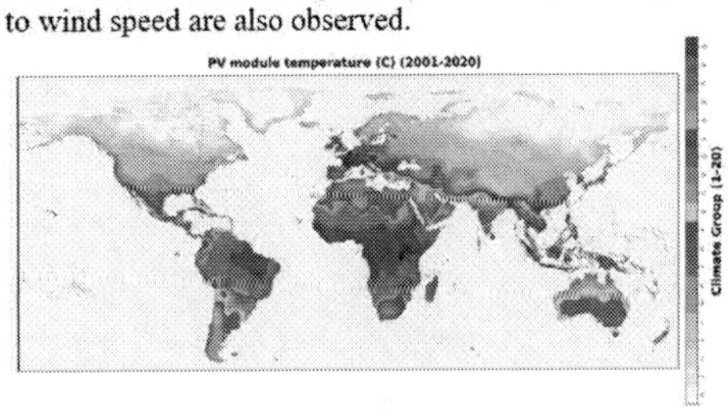

Figure 4: Global PV module temperature microclimate distribution in 20 zones

Module relative humidity: The relative humidity near the module drops considerably below the ambient relative humidity during peak solar hours. This decrease is caused by an increase in saturation vapor pressure, which lowers the local available humidity due to higher module temperature and POA irradiance, as shown in figure 5.

During the day, when temperature and POA at their peak, moisture egress the PV module. Conversely, in the evening and at night moisture starts ingress into the PV module.

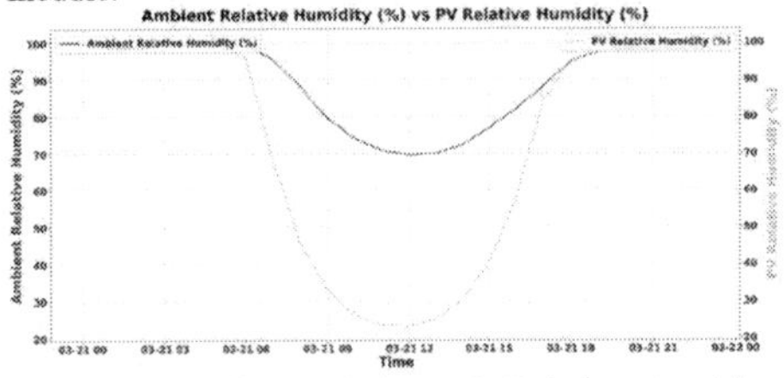

Figure 5: Daily variation of Relative humidity: Comparison of Ambient and PV Relative humidity

These results may vary on other days depending on variations of input parameters, emphasizing the dynamic nature of microclimate influence on PV performance.

3.2 Standardization, PCA, k-means cluster, and Silhouette score observations

To evaluate the efficacy of statistical clustering for PV climate zoning, we applied the principal component analysis (PCA) followed by k-means clustering to the derived PV microclimate properties such as module temperature, module relative humidity, saturation vapor pressure, POA on front, POA on back and precipitation.

The data were normalized and standardized, then the six selected variables reduced via PCA from 2 dimensions capturing 81.23% explain variance to 6 dimensions capturing 100% explained variance.

K-means clustering is performed with and the resulting cluster were assessed using the silhouette scores within cluster sum of squares (WCSS), visual inspection of cluster overlaps and comparisons with KG climate classifications. The elbow method is used to determine the optimal cluster number and the silhouette score is also calculated as an indicator that helps to understand the k-means [16] [17] cluster formed. The density k-means cluster of 2-dimensional PCA is shown in figure 6.

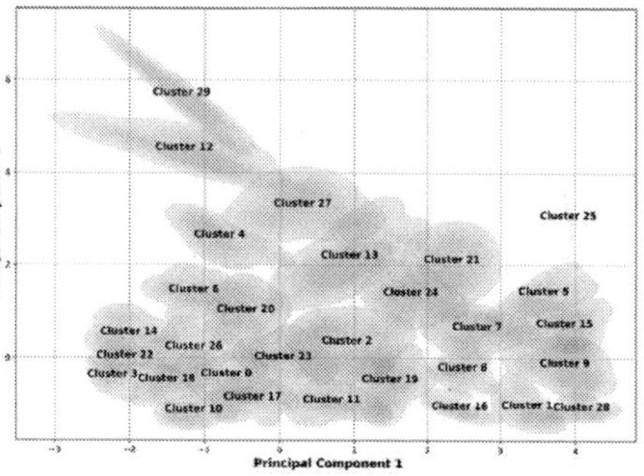

Figure 6: Global PV microclimate data with 30 cluster of two dimensional PCA

The generated cluster exhibited a low silhouette score of 0.36 with 15 clusters determined using the elbow method. Subsequently, the k-means analysis with 30 clusters also resulted in a low silhouette score of 0.37. Overall, low score across the cluster number 2 to 30 suggests poor clustering and potential overlaps among the microclimate data.

3.3 Risk assessment maps

The respective nonreversible degradation reaction rates were calculated and aggregated for 20 years for the world map. Figure 7 illustrates the global hydrolytic distribution of degradation rate.

It reveals, hydrolytic degradation (k_h) accounts for moisture driven degradation influenced by effective relative humidity (rh^n_{eff}) and module temperature (T_m). The risk maps suggest that the micro-climate for PV does not align strictly with KG's broader climate definitions.

(a) High degradation rates regions (Zones 15-19) are concentrated in humid equatorial regions. These climates, characterized by high moisture and temperature, exhibit accelerated chemical degradation breakdown of PV module materials, as humidity facilitates hydrolysis reactions.

(b) Moderate degradation rate regions (Zones 10-14) are observed in subtropical areas, where seasonal humidity contributes to intermediate degradation risks.

(c) Low degradation rates regions (Zones 0-9) are dominated by high latitude regions, reflecting limited moisture availability through year around.

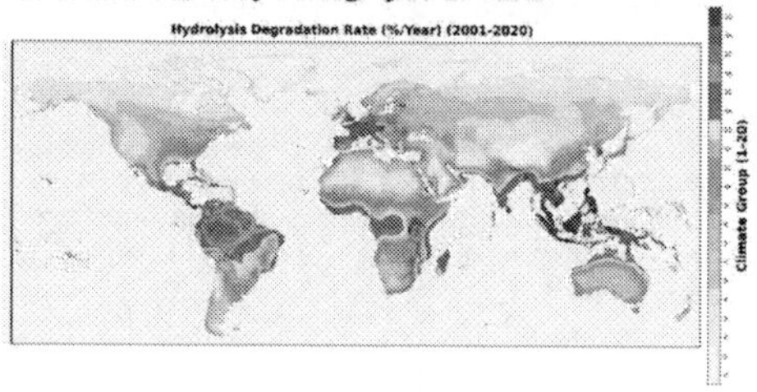

Figure 7: Global Maps of PV Hydrolytic Degradation Rate (k_h) in 20 zones

These risk maps are specific to degradation reaction rates for the analyzed locations. The resultant risk assessment maps in figure 7 significantly diverged from traditional KG classifications, offering enhanced granularity in providing the climatic classification specific to PV application. A summary of these findings is provided in Table 1.

Table 1: Overview of Degradation Mechanisms and High-Risk Regions for PV Systems

Primary Drivers	High-Risk Regions	Degradation mode
Effective relative humidity (RH_eff^n) and Module temperature (T_m)	Humid equatorial zones: Southeast Asia, Amazon Basin, Central Africa, Northern Australia	Corrosion Delamination Issues Discoloration effects Weaken solder bond

4 CONCLUSION

This study highlights that KG Classification is inadequate for precise PV system design. The analysis demonstrates that key micro-climate properties crucial for PV applications do not align with the broad climatic zones suggested by the KG. k-means clustering is unsittable for PV climate classification due to significant overlaps among climate groups. The continues and transitional nature of PV microclimate further complicates effective clustering, revealing a need for a more flexible approach.

Utilizing immediate micro-climate data alongside a degradation driven model can help us derive accurate risk assessment maps for the respective degradation type, ultimately improving the accuracy of PV reliability under varied climates. The insights from this study advocate for a shift towards leveraging detailed micro-climate analytics to enhance PV systems reliability and planning, providing a more adaptable and accurate framework than traditional KG classification. This progression highlights the transformative potential of integration advanced data analytics with environmental science to address the demand for sustainable energy sources.

4 ACKNOLEDGEMENT

The work generated from the members from Anhalt University of Applied Sciences is supported by the German Federal Ministry for Economic Affairs and

Climate Action (BMWK) under the funding program WIPANO – Knowledge and Technology Transfer through Patents and Standards under the project, "PolymAERA - Gebrauchstauglichkeitsprüfungen für Polymere als Rückseitenisolierung in Photovoltaikmodulen" (Project Number: 03TN0053C) and "Folie40 – Modellierung der foliendefinierten Moduldegradation" (Project Number: 03EE1173E)

5. REFERENCES

[1] Köppen, W. (1918). Classification of climates according to temperature, precipitation and seasonal cycle. Petermanns Geogr. Mitt, 64, 193–203.

[2] M. Kottek, J. Grieser, C. Beck, B. Rudolf, and F. Rubel, "World map of the Köppen-Geiger climate classification updated," Meteorologische Zeitschrift, vol. 15, no. 3, pp. 259–263, Jun. 2006, doi: 10.1127/0941-2948/2006/0130

[3] M. Kottek, J. Grieser, C. Beck, B. Rudolf, and F. Rubel, "World map of the Köppen-Geiger climate classification updated," Meteorologische Zeitschrift, vol. 15, no. 3, pp. 259–263, Jun. 2006, doi: 10.1127/0941-2948/2006/0130

[4] Karin, Todd & Jones, Christian & Jain, Anubhav. (2020). Photovoltaic climate zones: the global distribution of climate stressors affecting photovoltaic degradation. 10.4229/EUPVSEC20192019-4BO.13.1.

[5] Zhu J, Gottschalg R, Koehl M, Hoffmann S, Berger K, Zamini S, Bennett I, Gerritsen E, Malbranche P, Pugliatti P, Di Stefano A, Aleo F, Bertani D, Paletta F, Roca F, Graditi G, Pellegrino M, Zubillaga O, Cano P, Pozza A, Sample T. Changes of solar cell parameters during damp-heat exposure. (WCPEC-6); 2015. p. 1117-1118. JRC94887

[6] I. Kaaya, D. Mansour, P. Gebhardt, K. Weiß, D. Philipp, in 2021 IEEE 48th Photovoltaic Specialists Conf. (PVSC), Philadephia, USA 2021

[7] NASA Langley Research Center (LaRC) POWER Project. (2024). NASA Prediction of Worldwide Energy Resources (POWER) Project: CERES and MERRA-2 Data. Accessed on (2024). Retrieved from (https://power.larc.nasa.gov/)

[8] P. Ineichen and R. Perez, "A new airmass independent formulation for the Linke turbidity coefficient," Solar Energy, vol. 73, no. 3, pp. 151-157, Sep. 2002. doi: 10.1016/S0038-092X(02)00045-2.

[9] W. F. Holmgren, C. W. Hansen and M. A. Mikofski, "pvlib python: A python package for modeling solar energy systems", Journal of Open-Source Software, vol. 3, no. 29, pp. 884, 2018.

[10] M. Abou Anoma, D. Jacob, B. C. Bourne, J. A. Scholl, D. M. Riley, and C. W. Hansen, "View factor model and validation for bifacial pv and diffuse shade on single-axis trackers," in 2017 IEEE 44th Photovoltaic Specialist Conference (PVSC), pp. 1549–1554, IEEE, 2017.

[11] Köhl, Michael & Heck, Markus & Wiesmeier, Stefan. (2012). Modelling of conditions for accelerated lifetime testing of Humidity impact on PV-modules based on monitoring of climatic data. Solar Energy Materials and Solar Cells. 99. 282–291. 10.1016/j.solmat.2011.12.011.

[12] N. Zhang, K. Leatham, J. Xiong, and J. Zhong, "PCA-K-Means Based Clustering Algorithm for High Dimensional and Overlapping Spectra Signals," in 2018 Ninth International Conference on Intelligent Control and Information Processing (ICICIP), IEEE, Nov. 2018, pp. 349–354. doi: 10.1109/ICICIP.2018.8606667.

[12] N. Zhang, K. Leatham, J. Xiong, and J. Zhong, "PCA-K-Means Based Clustering Algorithm for High Dimensional and Overlapping Spectra Signals," in 2018 Ninth International Conference on Intelligent Control and Information Processing (ICICIP), IEEE, Nov. 2018, pp. 349–354. doi: 10.1109/ICICIP.2018.8606667.

[13] F. Wang, H. H. Franco-Penya, J. D. Kelleher, J. Pugh, and R. Ross, "An analysis of the application of simplified silhouette to the evaluation of k-means clustering validity," in Lecture Notes in Computer Science (including subseries Lecture Notes in Artificial Intelligence and Lecture Notes in Bioinformatics), Springer Verlag, 2017, pp. 291–305. doi: 10.1007/978-3-319-62416-7_21.

[14] Escobar, L. A. and W. Q. Meeker (2007, August). A Review of Accelerated Test Models. arXiv:0708.0369 [stat]. arXiv: 0708.0369. 11, 16, 24

[15] Jordan, D. and S. Kurtz (2010, June). Analytical improvements in PV degradation rate determination. In 2010 35th IEEE Photovoltaic Specialists Conference, pp. 002688– 002693. ISSN: 0160-8371, 0160-8371. 11

[16] Marutho, Dhendra & Handaka, Sunarna & Wijaya, Ekaprana & Muljono, Muljono. (2018). The Determination of Cluster Number at k-Mean Using Elbow Method and Purity Evaluation on Headline News. 533-538. 10.1109/ISEMANTIC.2018.85497

[17] Kladas, A., Lagast, K., Herteleer, B., & Cappelle, J. (Year). Climate clustering for photovoltaic interest. In Proceedings of the 41st European Photovoltaic Solar Energy Conference and Exhibition. KU Leuven Research Group ELECTA, Ghent, Belgium.

Evaluating the Suitability of Köppen-Geiger Climate Classifications for Photovoltaic Systems: Micro-climate Analysis and Risk Assessment Maps

Pavan Kumar Panda[1], Hugo Sanchez[1,2], Leila Mortazavifar[1,2], Ralph Gottschalg [1,2]
E-Mail: Pavan.Panda@hs-anhalt.de
[1]Hochschule Anhalt University of Applied Sciences, Bernburger Str. 55, 06366, Köthen, Germany
[2] Fraunhofer-Center for Silicon Photovoltaics CSP, Halle (Saale), Germany

Motivation

- Photovoltaic (PV) system performance and durability depend on local climate conditions. However, the widely used Köppen-Geiger (KG) climate classification, designed for ecology, is inadequate for PV climate classification
- KG's focus on temperature and precipitation overlooks critical micro climate factors that drive PV material degradation
- This gap leads to inaccurate climate zoning for PV, risking suboptimal system design and reduced reliability in diverse global environments
- Our research develops PV-Specific risk maps to address these limitations, enabling better and sustainability for the solar industry

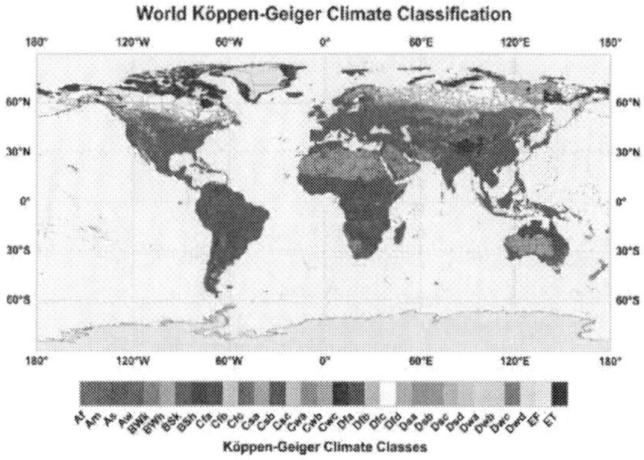

Figure 1: World Map of the Köppen-Geiger climatic classification, generated using data

Methodology

- ***Data Source:*** Global data → NASA POWER (CERES/MERRA-2) → 2001-2020
- ***Micro-climate model:***
  - Ineichen/Perez model - POA Irradiance back and front
  - Faiman's model - Module temperature
  - Magnus-Tetens approximation – Module saturation vapor pressure
  - Michael Koehl model - Module relative humdity
- ***PV specific microclimate variables:*** POA Irradiance front, POA Irradiance back, module relative humidity, module saturation vapour pressure, module temperature and wind speed
- ***Analysis:*** Standardize data; PCA (6 to 2 Dimension); k-means clustering (elbow method)
- ***Degradation model:*** Hydrolysis (Peck's) Model

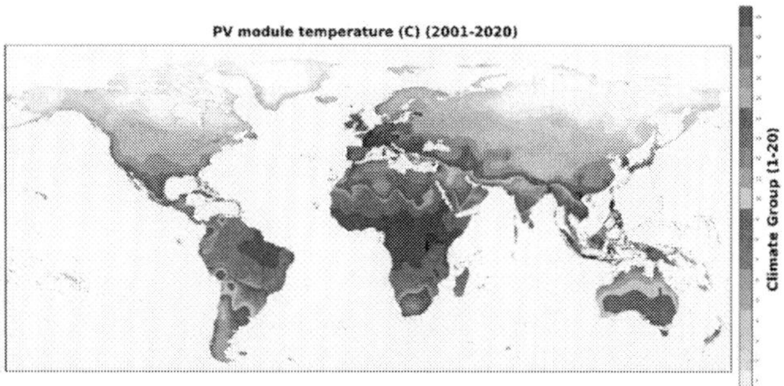

Figure 2: Global PV Module Temperature Distribution Across 20 Climate Zones

Results

PCA and Clustering Overlaps

- The available 6-dimensional micro-climate variables data is reduced into 2D PCA
- K-means clustering was assessed with silhouette scores, WCSS, and visual inspections.
- 2D PCA of micro-climate data (81.23% variance, silhouette score 0.37) shows massive overlaps in KG zones, indicating KG's inadequacy for PV-specific climates

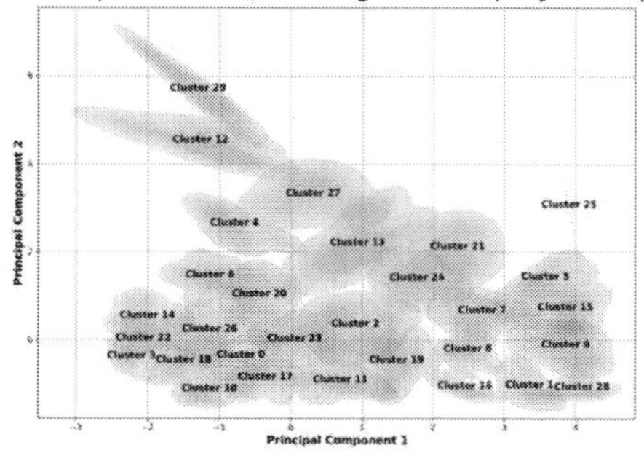

Figure 3: Global PV microclimate data with 30 cluster of two dimensional PCA

PV Hydrolysis Specific Degradation Map

- Using pecks model, non reversible hydrolysis degradation reaction rate were calculated and aggregated for 20 years for the world map
- High probability of corrosion, delamination, discoloration, and weakened solder joints degradation modes occur in top climate groups

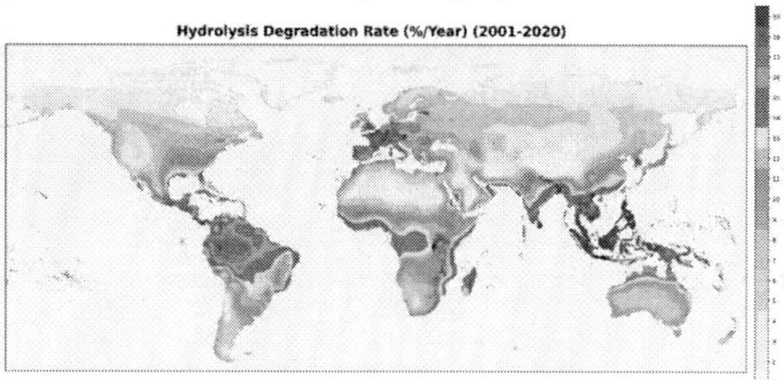

Figure 4: Global Maps of PV Hydrolytic Degradation Rate (K_h) in 20 zones

Conclusion

- KG does not map uniquely on hydrolydsis failure (nor on other failure modes)
- Current clustering shows significant overlaps and poor silhouette scores, indicating ineffective microclimate differentiation.
- Micro-climate along with degradation models enable precise PV risk assessment
- Derived 20 years aggregated risk maps diverge from KG, offering precise PV climate zoning
- Future Work: Expand degradation drives, integrate into design tools

References

[1] Köppen, W. (1918). Classification of climates according to temperature, precipitation and seasonal cycle. Petermanns Geogr. Mitt, 64, 193–203.
[2] Karin, Todd & Jones, Christian & Jain, Anubhav. (2020). Photovoltaic climate zones: the global distribution of climate stressors affecting photovoltaic degradation. 10.4229/EUPVSEC20192019-4BO.13.1.
[3] J. Ascencio-Vásquez, K. Brecl, and M. Topič, "Methodology of Köppen-Geiger-Photovoltaic climate classification and implications to worldwide mapping of PV system performance," Solar Energy, vol. 191, pp. 672-685, Oct. 2019. doi: 10.1016/j.solener.2019.08.072.
[4] NASA Langley Research Center (LaRC) POWER Project. (2024). NASA Prediction of Worldwide Energy Resources (POWER) Project: CERES and MERRA-2 Data. Accessed on (2024). Retrieved from (https://power.larc.nasa.gov/)

ACKNOWLEDGEMENT This work is supported by the German Federal Ministry of Economics and Climate Protection (BMWK) under the project "PolymAERA", Funding code: 03TN0053C and project " Folie40" Funding code: 03EE1173E

SATELLITE-DERIVED IRRADIANCE DATA FOR PV PERFORMANCE ASSESSMENT IN HIGH LATITUDES

Hugo Huerta[1], Juha Karhu[2], Shuo Wang[1], Sami Jouttijärvi[3], Samuli Ranta[1], Anders Lindfors[2], Kati Miettunen[3]
1. Turku University of Applied Sciences, Joukahaisenkatu 7, 20520 Turku, Finland
2. Finnish Meteorological Institute, Erik Palménin aukio 1, FI-00560 Helsinki, Finland
3. University of Turku, Vesilinnantie 5, 20500 Turku, Finland
Corresponding author: hugo.huerta@turkuamk.fi

ABSTRACT: The rapid adoption of photovoltaic (PV) systems in Nordic countries, has made accurate performance evaluation increasingly important. In Finland, microgenerators below 1 MW now collectively exceed 1 GW, and large-scale PV plants are being considered as part of the national energy strategy. Reliable performance assessments help verify energy yield, identify operational issues, and support planning for future installations. A key challenge is the limited availability of high-resolution meteorological data. Ground-based measurements are sparse and often located far from PV sites, reducing their usefulness for site-specific analysis. Satellite-derived solar radiation data offers a promising alternative, but its accuracy can be affected by latitude. Above 60° N, where many Finnish PV systems are located, geostationary satellite coverage becomes less precise, potentially introducing bias. This study evaluates the suitability of EUMETSAT's CMSAF SARAH-3 data for PV performance modelling in Finland. Multi-year PV production data from several sites is compared against simulations using both satellite-derived and ground-station datasets. Results indicate that SARAH-3 achieves good agreement with measured data with coefficient of determination above 0.9 for global horizontal irradiance, suggesting it can serve as a reliable alternative where ground data is unavailable, enabling improved PV performance monitoring and planning in high-latitude regions.
Keywords: Solar irradiance, satellite-derived, energy yield

1 INTRODUCTION

The rapid growth of photovoltaic (PV) systems in Nordic countries, particularly Finland, has created a need for robust methods to evaluate system performance and energy yield. In Finland, microgeneration installations with capacities below 1 MW have collectively surpassed 1 GW in only a few years, and the deployment of large-scale PV plants is increasingly being considered as part of the national energy strategy [1]. As PV adoption accelerates, performance assessment plays a crucial role in verifying expected yields, identifying operational challenges, and supporting planning decisions for future installations.

A major obstacle in conducting accurate performance evaluations lies in the availability and quality of meteorological data. High-resolution solar irradiance measurements are essential for determining site-specific energy production, yet ground-based meteorological stations are sparse in general and often located tens or even hundreds of kilometres from PV sites. This spatial limitation constraints performance analyses, especially in regions with highly variable weather patterns [2].

Satellite-derived solar radiation data offers a potential solution to this challenge. Such datasets provide continuous spatiotemporal coverage and can overcome the limitations of sparse ground measurements. However, their accuracy at high latitudes remains an open question. Above 60°N, where the PV systems under study are located, geostationary satellite coverage becomes less precise, leading to possible biases in irradiance estimates. As a result, it is critical to validate satellite-based data products against actual ground station measurements as well as their usage for simulating PV systems to determine their suitability for performance assessments in Nordic conditions.

This study addresses this gap by evaluating the reliability of irradiance data from EUMETSAT's Climate Monitoring Satellite Application Facility (CMSAF) SARAH-3 interim climate data record [3] for PV system performance modelling in Finland. Using historical data from PV systems with different configurations and distributed across different regions (**Figure 1**), we compare simulated energy yields, obtained using both satellite-derived and ground-station datasets, with measured production data over multiple years. Advanced PV system modelling, including 3D scene representations in PVsyst [4], is employed to ensure realistic simulations accounting for shading and site-specific effects.

By quantifying the deviations between simulated and measured energy yields, this work provides an assessment of the accuracy and applicability of satellite-derived irradiance data in high-latitude environments. The results offer practical guidance for PV operators, researchers, and energy planners on the use of satellite data for performance monitoring, resource assessment, and forecasting in northern climates.

2 METHODOLOGY

The methodology is organized into four stages: (i) data acquisition and processing, (ii) PV system modelling, (iii) simulation setup, and (iv) analysis and performance evaluation.

2.1 Data Acquisition and Processing

Historical PV production data was obtained from three grid-connected systems Helsinki, Kuopio, and Turku (Table I). Each system provided at least six consecutive years of production records at 1–5 minute resolution, enabling detailed time-series analysis and robust statistical comparison with simulated results. **Figure 2** illustrates the normalized daily energy production for one of the study sites, Kuopio, located near 63° N latitude. As shown, production drops to nearly zero during the winter months, reflecting the strong seasonal effect at high latitudes. This seasonal variability is a critical factor in performance assessment and underscores the importance of accurate data for simulation and yield estimation in Nordic climates.

10.4229/EUPVSEC2025/4BV.3.26
020286-001

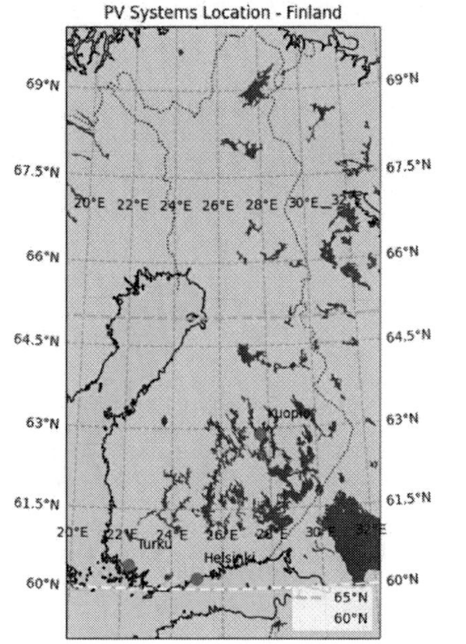

Figure 1: Geographic location of PV systems used for the study.

Table I: PV systems under study

Parameter	Location		
	Helsinki	**Kuopio**	**Turku**
Latitude (°)	60.204	62.892	60.447
Longitude (°)	24.961	27.634	22.297
Altitude (m)	30	85	29
Commission date	24/08/2015	19/08/2016	30/07/2017
PV module	SolarWorld	SolarWatt Blue	KingdomSolar
PV technology	Poly-Si	Poly-Si	Poly-Si
Nominal capacity of module (Wp)	250	260	250
Nominal capacity of system (kWp)	21	20.3	4.5

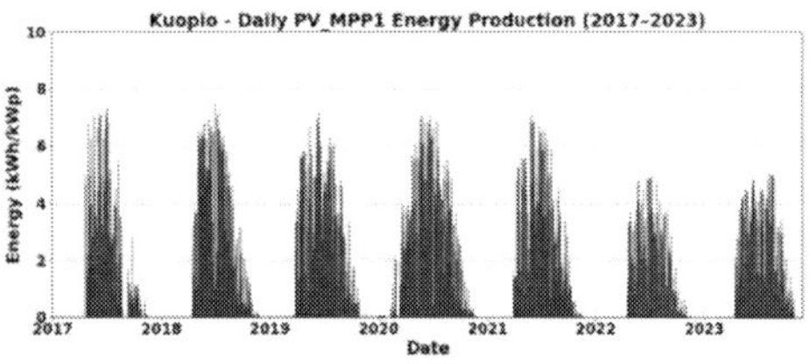

Figure 2: Normalized daily PV production for the Kuopio site (63° N).

Ground-based meteorological measurements, including global horizontal irradiance (GHI), direct normal irradiance (DNI), diffuse horizontal irradiance (DHI), and ambient temperature among some other weather variables, were also available at 1–10 minute intervals from the meteo stations available at the sites, and served as a validation benchmark. **Figure 3** illustrates the measured GHI at Kuopio's site.

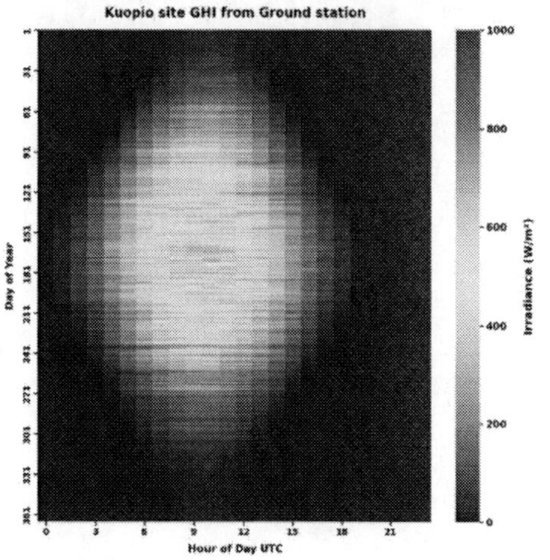

Figure 3: Measured GHI, agreggated to hourly values, for Kuopio site (63° N).

Satellite-derived irradiance data was obtained from the CMSAF SARAH-3 Interim Climate Data Record [3] at 30-minute temporal resolution. SARAH-3 is a satellite-based climate data record derived from Meteosat observations, providing solar surface irradiance (SIS) as well as direct horizontal (SID) and direct normal irradiance (DNI) on a 0.05° × 0.05° grid. This data covers the region between ±65° latitude and ±65° longitude from January 1983 to the present, with operational updates available within about 5 days. For this study, DNI was calculated from SIS and SID.

Quality control checks on all datasets were performed to remove missing or anomalous data points before integration into the simulation environment. Figure 4 illustrates the SARAH-3 GHI at Kuopio's site.

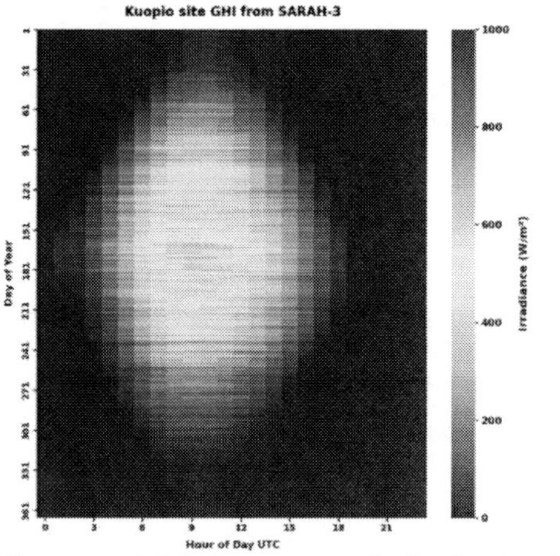

Figure 4: SARAH-3 GHI, agreggated to hourly values,for Kuopio site (63° N).

10.4229/EUPVSEC2025/4BV.3.26
020286-002

2.2 PV System Modelling

Each PV installation was modelled in PVsyst using detailed 3D representations of the site to capture geometric effects and near-shading losses from surrounding obstacles, **Figure 5**. System parameters, including module type, inverter configuration, tilt, azimuth, and system losses, were configured based on as-built data provided by the system owners. This level of detail ensured that simulated energy yields closely reflected actual system behaviour.

Figure 5: Accurate 3D model in PVsyst Software used in the simulations for Kuopio site (63° N).

2.3 Simulation Setup

Performance simulations were conducted in PVsyst using two input datasets:

1. **Ground-based dataset:** measured irradiance components and meteorological parameters from stations located few meters away from the PV systems.
2. **Satellite-derived dataset:** GHI, DNI and DHI (Estimated from GHI and DNI), and ambient temperature from closest station.

A comparison of both data sets for a summer day is shown in **Figure 6.** Simulations were performed over the entire multi-year historical period for which production data was available (minimum of six years per site), using its corresponding ground-based or satellite-derived meteorological dataset. This allowed for the evaluation of interannual variability and improved the robustness of the statistical analysis.

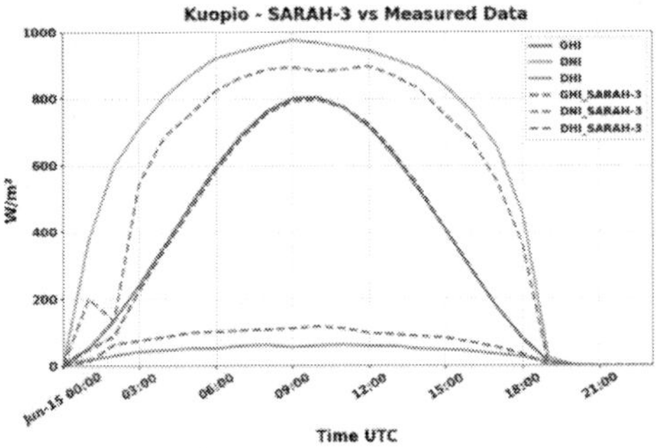

Figure 6: Irradiance components comparison from SARAH-3 and measured data for Kuopio site (63° N)

2.4. Analysis and Performance Evaluation

Metrics quantifying the deviation between SARAH-3 and measured irradiance components were computed, including mean bias error (MBE), root mean square error (RMSE), and coefficient of determination (R^2). These metrics were selected as they provide complementary insights into data quality: MBE quantifies systematic bias between datasets, RMSE measures the magnitude of random and systematic deviations, and R^2 assesses the strength of correlation between measured and modelled values. Together, these metrics enable a comprehensive evaluation of both accuracy and precision. The same set of metrics was calculated for the simulated energy yields obtained using the two datasets, allowing a direct assessment of how input data discrepancies propagate to PV performance predictions

3 RESULTS AND DISCUSSION

In the following, results comparing satellite-derived irradiance data with ground-station measurements are presented, as well as hourly PV energy yield simulations.

Table 2 summarizes the metrics for the site closest to the spatial limits of SARAH-3 data coverage. Kuopio site is highlighted since, as described in Section 2.1, it lies near the northern boundary of reliable satellite retrievals, where larger deviations between measured and satellite-derived irradiance are expected.

Table II: Metrics for Irradiance components comparison

Kuopio site - Measured vs SARAH-3 data metrics				
	Year	**MBE [W/m²]**	**RMSE [W/m²]**	**R^2**
GHI	2018	-3.37	38.97	0.96
	2019	-5.23	39.92	0.95
	2020	-3.96	38.85	0.95
	2021	-1.00	41.04	0.95
	2022	-4.18	45.35	0.93
	2023	-2.86	42.5	0.95
DNI	2018	-25.34	111.63	0.84
	2019	-26.28	113.44	0.80
	2020	-26.20	104.83	0.83
	2021	-21.70	117.98	0.79
	2022	-26.69	124.72	0.77
	2023	-16.95	112.11	0.82
DHI	2018	4.54	32.6	0.76
	2019	4.00	32.73	0.81
	2020	5.63	31.47	0.81
	2021	5.22	30.64	0.81
	2022	4.27	33.37	0.80
	2023	1.73	32.26	0.80

Figure 7 summarizes the metrics for the three components of the irradiance for all the sites.

The results clearly indicate that the GHI irradiance component exhibits the highest accuracy across all sites. In contrast, DNI shows significantly larger deviations, which in turn propagate to the DHI component, leading to increased uncertainty in its metrics.

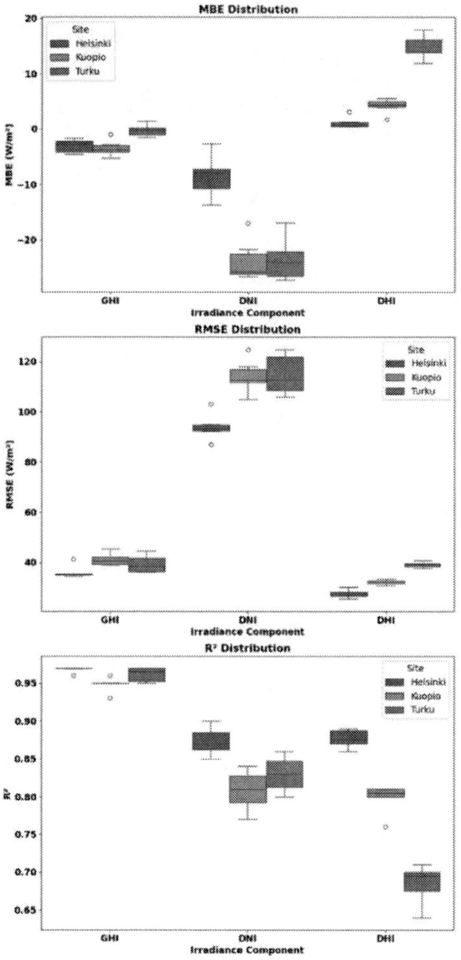

Figure 7: Irradiance components metrics for SARAH-3 and measured data, all sites.

Metrics from the simulation results, are summarized in **Table III**, once again, these metrics are for the site closest to the spatial limits of SARAH-3 data coverage.

Table III: Metrics for Irradiance components comparison

Kuopio site – Ground Station vs SARAH-3 Energy yield (Hourly) metrics			
Year	**MBE [kWh]**	**RMSE [kWh/kWp]**	**R^2**
2018	-0.10	0.05	0.92
2019	-0.04	0.04	0.96
2020	-0.10	0.04	0.95
2021	-0.07	0.04	0.95
2022	0.02	0.04	0.94
2023	-0.02	0.04	0.94

Results indicate that PV system simulations using satellite-derived irradiance data achieve acceptable accuracy when compared with reference ground-station simulations. Deviations in simulated energy yields are within approximately 0.04 kWh/kWp, with location-dependent variations. **Figure 8** provides a consolidated view of the deviations in energy yield estimates derived from hourly simulations for the three sites using satellite data.

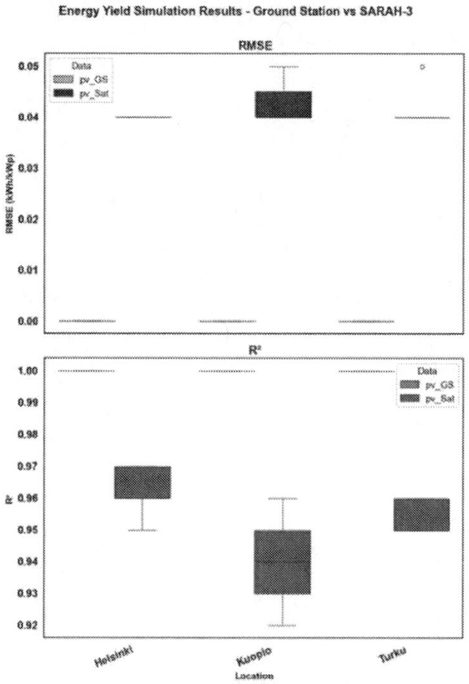

Figure 8: Enery yield metrics for SARAH-3 and ground station simulation, all sites.

Overall, the results are promising and demonstrate that satellite-derived datasets can serve as a reliable alternative for PV system performance assessment in regions where ground-station measurements are unavailable. This is particularly evident for the sites near 60° N latitude, such as Helsinki and Turku, which exhibited lower variability in errors and higher correlation (R^2) values compared to the northernmost site.

4 CONCLUSIONS

The analysis revealed that GHI is consistently the most accurate irradiance component across all sites, whereas DNI shows higher deviations, which propagate to the DHI component. This suggests that further improvement could be achieved by recalculating DNI using different models, taking GHI as the primary input and combining it with the clear sky model. Such an approach may reduce uncertainty in DNI- and DHI-based simulations and improve overall PV yield estimation accuracy.

This study is novel, as no prior research has systematically evaluated the performance of satellite-derived irradiance data for PV system assessment in Finland. While earlier studies have compared irradiance estimations from various geostationary and polar-orbiting satellites [5, 6] and addressed solar resource forecasting [7], this work specifically examines the influence of using satellite-based data on PV production estimates in high-latitude conditions.

5 AKNOWLEDGMENTS

The work is funded by the Strategic Research Council (SRC) established within the Research Council of Finland under the project RealSolar (project numbers 359141, 358542, 358543)

6 REFERENCES

1. Finnish Energy Authority, News, 2024. Solar power production capacity rose to 1,000 megawatts. https://energiavirasto.fi/en/-/solar-power-production-capacity-rose-to-1-000-megawatts, last access January 2025.
2. Herman Böök, Antti Poikonen, Antti Aarva, Tero Mielonen, Mikko R.A. Pitkänen, Anders V. Lindfors, Photovoltaic system modeling: A validation study at high latitudes with implementation of a novel DNI quality control method, Solar Energy, Volume 204, 2020, Pages 316-329, ISSN 0038-092X, https://doi.org/10.1016/j.solener.2020.04.068.
3. Pfeifroth, Uwe; Kothe, Steffen; Drücke, Jaqueline; Trentmann, Jörg; Schröder, Marc; Selbach, Nathalie; Hollmann, Rainer (2023): Surface Radiation Data Set - Heliosat (SARAH) - Edition 3, Satellite Application Facility on Climate Monitoring,DOI:10.5676/EUM_SAF_CM/SARAH/V003, https://doi.org/10.5676/EUM_SAF_CM/SARAH/V003.
4. PVsyst Photovoltaic Software, Satigny, Switzerland. Version 8.0.13. https://www.pvsyst.com
5. Heine Nygard Riise, Magnus Moe Nygård, Bjørn Lupton Aarseth, Andreas Dobler, Erik Berge, Benchmark of estimated solar irradiance data at high latitude locations, Solar Energy, Volume 282, 2024, 112975, ISSN 0038-092X, https://doi.org/10.1016/j.solener.2024.112975.
6. Bilal Babar, Rune Graversen, Tobias Boström, Evaluating CM-SAF solar radiation CLARA-A1 and CLARA-A2 datasets in Scandinavia, Solar Energy, Volume 170, 2018, Pages 76-85, ISSN 0038-092X, https://doi.org/10.1016/j.solener.2018.05.009.
7. Viivi Kallio-Myers, Aku Riihelä, Panu Lahtinen, Anders Lindfors, Global horizontal irradiance forecast for Finland based on geostationary weather satellite data, Solar Energy, Volume 198, 2020, Pages 68-80, ISSN 0038-092X, https://doi.org/10.1016/j.solener.2020.01.008.

OPTIMIZED ALBEDOMETER HEIGHT: A SIMPLE MODEL FOR ACCURATE ALBEDO MEASUREMENT

Eneko Ortega[1,2], Eneko Cereceda[1], Nekane Azkona[1], Alona Otaegi[1], Vanesa Fano[1], Jose Ruben Gutierrez[1] and Juan Carlos Jimeno[1]
[1] Technological Institute of Microelectronics, University of the Basque Country UPV/EHU, 48013, Bilbao, Spain
[2] Electricity and Electronics Department, University of the Basque Country UPV/EHU, 48940, Leioa, Spain
eneko.ortegam@ehu.eus

ABSTRACT: Albedo estimation is a key parameter to determine the performance of PV systems with bifacial technology. Effective albedo measurement relies on the measured irradiance by the rear side of the albedometer, which depends on the albedometer view factor, depending on the sensor placement height and sensor area. This study presents a simple mathematical model to determine the minimum albedometer height in function of the albedo sensor area and the admissible relative error during albedo measurement. The proposed model is freely available as an open-source code to determine minimum admissible height in function of specific albedometer area and admissible error for each specific application.
Keywords: photovoltaic systems, bifacial, irradiance measurement, albedo measurement, performance analysis

1 INTRODUCTION

Photovoltaic (PV) systems performance estimation is essential to determine PV systems production and to perform a correct monitoring of the PV system. This estimation relies on a series of parameters related to PV technology, the PV system design and layout and to the expected operating conditions, such as system location, climatic conditions or expected irradiation [1].

Among other parameters, surface albedo is a very relevant parameter for bifacial PV systems. Whereas for monofacial PV systems albedo has been traditionally considered constant [2] in function of the surface type of the PV system, for bifacial PV modules setting a constant albedo leads to errors ranging between 2 and 7% when estimating the PV system performance [3].

Surface albedo can be obtained from satellite measurements [2] or on-site measurements, which can provide with a higher spatial resolution [4] enhancing albedo value estimation, especially in non-uniform surfaces. The albedo value also exhibits variability associated with weather [5], humidity or seasonal effects [6], obtaining albedo variations within the same day of more than 60%. However, the uncertainty associated to the albedo measurement due to its variability is not completely aleatory and can be modeled and controlled [7], at least to determine which is the uncertainty of an on-site albedo measurement.

Several guidelines can be followed to minimize albedo measurement error, such as sensor selection and positioning [9]. Among them, the height at which the albedometer is placed plays an important role on the measurement of the actual albedo with no clear agreement of which height would be the most suitable one. While some manufacturers suggest that the placement height of the measuring systems should be around 1.5 meters, others advise placing the sensor closer to the ground [10].

Recent experimental studies indicate that lower sensor heights can significantly reduce the uncertainty in albedo measurements over heterogeneous surfaces, especially when the ground presents non-homogeneous textures or partial shading [11].

Conversely, higher albedometer placement may be advantageous when attempting to capture a more averaged or smoothed reflectance value over a larger area. Thus, the optimal height may depend on the spatial variability of the surface reflectance and the specific application of the albedo measurement.

This study implements and provides, in an open-source format, a simple model which allows for the estimation of the minimum albedometer placement height as a function of the albedometer sensor area and the admissible relative error. This model aims to ensure a correct measurement of the Ground Reflected Irradiance (GRI), which is directly linked to surface albedo.

The proposed model enables users to tailor the sensor setup to their specific environmental and technical constrains, balancing precision with practical deployment. Finally, the sensitivity of the proposed model is evaluated to assess how changes in height and sensor size influence the albedo measurement.

2 2D MATHEMATICAL MODEL

The albedo value is obtained as the ratio of the Ground Reflected Irradiance (GRI) and the Global Horizontal Irradiance (GHI). The GHI is measured by the front side of the albedometer and the GRI by the rear side. The amount of reflected irradiance is the amount of irradiation that reaches the ground surface ($G_{GROUND} = GHI$) and is reflected back (1). This value depends on the surface albedo (ρ).

$$G_{REAR} = \rho \cdot G_{GROUND} \qquad (1)$$

However, the GRI measured by the albedometer depends on the albedometer view factor, i.e., on the amount of ground surface seen by the sensor and, therefore, on the GRI the sensor receives. If we assume that the albedometer is placed horizontally and that the ground surface below is a homogeneous, uniformly illuminated with GHI, Lambertian reflector of infinite size, the albedometer view factor will depend on the height at which it is positioned and on the sensor area.

In addition, albedo measurement can be performed using pyranometers or solar cells as albedo sensors, which, in addition to having different spectral responses [11], have different sensor areas, which affect the albedo measurement.

To determine the albedometer rear irradiance (the amount of GRI that reaches the albedometer, G_{REAR}), the proposed model [12] can be divided into two steps. Firstly, if it is assumed that the albedometer is an infinitesimal flat

10.4229/EUPVSEC2025/4BV.3.27

receptor (R), placed at a height h, it can be computed the contribution to this irradiance measured by the rear side of the albedometer of every ground segment within the field of view of the flat receptor.

For this flat receptor R, the contribution of the whole ground surface from $\phi_1 = -\frac{\pi}{2}$ to $\phi_1 = \frac{\pi}{2}$ would be equal to G_{REAR}. The contribution of a certain small segment S_1S_2, as shown in Fig. 1, to the rear side irradiance of the albedo sensor can be obtained as the product of the radiance intensity, the emitted radiant flux per unit solid angle (c), and the 2D view factor of the sensor (2).

$$G_{REAR}^{S_{12}} = \int_{\phi_1}^{\phi_2} cx \cos\theta \, d\theta = cx(\sin\phi_2 - \sin\phi_1) \quad (2)$$

Where the radiance intensity is defined as:

$$c = \frac{\rho G_{GROUND}}{2} \quad (3)$$

and the angles ϕ_1 and ϕ_2 between the infinitesimal flat receptor $(0, h)$ and the edges of the segment $(S_1, 0)$ and $(S_2, 0)$ are computed as:

$$\phi_1 = \operatorname{atan}\left(\frac{S_1}{h}\right) \; and \; \phi_2 = \operatorname{atan}\left(\frac{S_2}{h}\right) \quad (4)$$

Finally, to obtain the rear irradiance due to the total ground surface, it can be obtained as the sum of the contributions of all the segments seen in Fig. 1, from $-90^\circ$to 90°. Since the number of segments would be infinite with a 180 degrees view field, to compute this model the view field must be restricted (from $-89^\circ$to 89°, for example), which generates a negligible error [13].

This model can be applied for an infinitesimal flat receptor R. For a real albedometer, having a receptor with a non-infinitesimal area, the same model, slightly modified, can be applied, computing the contribution of each surface segment for the whole sensor area, which will modify the view factor of the sensor. The flat receptor, instead of being at point $(0, h)$ will be placed from $(-\frac{x}{2}, h)$ to $(\frac{x}{2}, h)$, being x the sensor width.

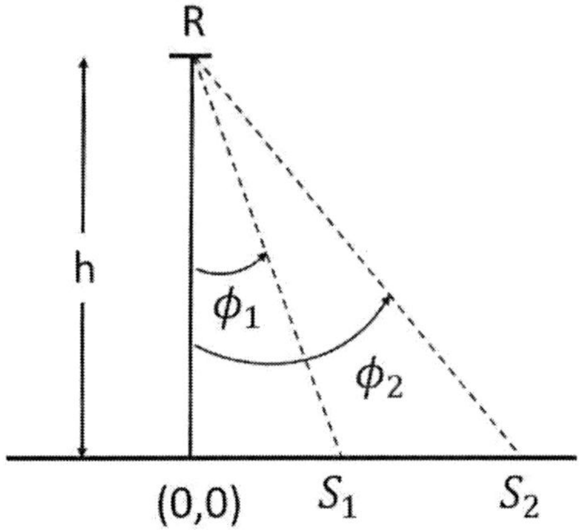

Figure 1: View factor corresponding to the S1-S2 segment for an infinitesimal flat receptor R placed at a vertical height h above the reference plane.

3 OPTIMUM HEIGHT DETERMINATION

To validate the proposed model a set of sensor areas ($5, 10, 15 \; and \; 20 \; cm^2$) were considered and for a theoretical case of $800 \; W/m^2$GHI and an homogeneous surface albedo of 0.35 on an infinite reflector, the obtained albedo values as a function of the sensor positioning height were computed, as shown in Fig. 2.

As can be seen in Fig. 2, as the positioning height of the sensor increases, the view factor of the sensor increases also and, therefore, the irradiance reflected by the ground surface is measured more accurately which leads to smaller errors in the surface albedo estimation (the ratio between G_{REAR} and GHI).

This way, for heights above 4 meters, the error (due to the limited view factor of the ground surface at low heights source) between actual surface albedo ($\rho = 0.35$ in the proposed example) and the estimated ones (by G_{REAR} measurement) is below 1.5% for all the cases. For typical heights around 1.5 meters, the error ranges between 1.5% and 5% as a function of the sensor area between 5 to 20 cm^2.

For small sensor areas, however, even positioning the sensor at heights below 1 meter, the error between theoretical surface albedo and the estimated one remains below 3%. The evolution of the relative error between the theoretical surface albedo and the measured one, according to the proposed methodology, is shown in Fig. 3 for the same albedometer sensor areas.

The accuracy of the proposed model is also highly dependent on the sensor view factor. As previously stated, if the albedometer is placed horizontally and the ground surface is a homogeneous Lambertian reflector of infinite size the view factor depends only on the sensor area and placement height.

However, if the sensor view factor is reduced due to non-homogeneous surface or illumination, obstacles on the surrounding area or sensor geometry, among others, the sensor accuracy for determining the albedo value may be affected. Fig. 4 shows the measured albedo value with a view factor that goes between -10 and 10 meters. As can be seen in the figure, as the sensor height increases, the effect of the limited view factor reduces the accuracy of the sensor to determine albedo value.

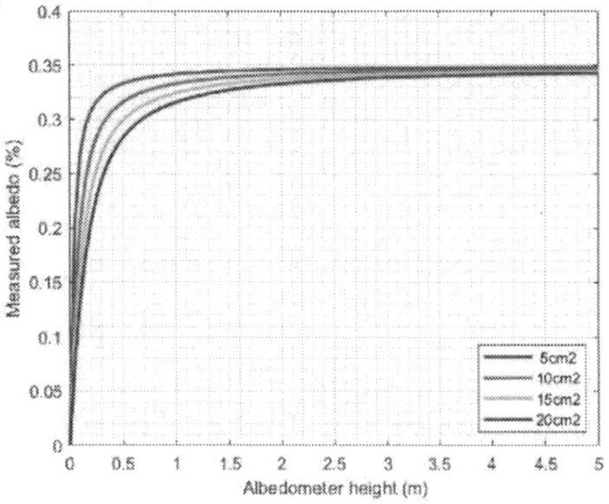

Figure 2: Estimated albedo, when considering a surface albedo of 0.35, in function of albedometer positioning height for $5, 10, 15 \; and \; 20 \; cm^2$ sensor areas.

10.4229/EUPVSEC2025/4BV.3.27

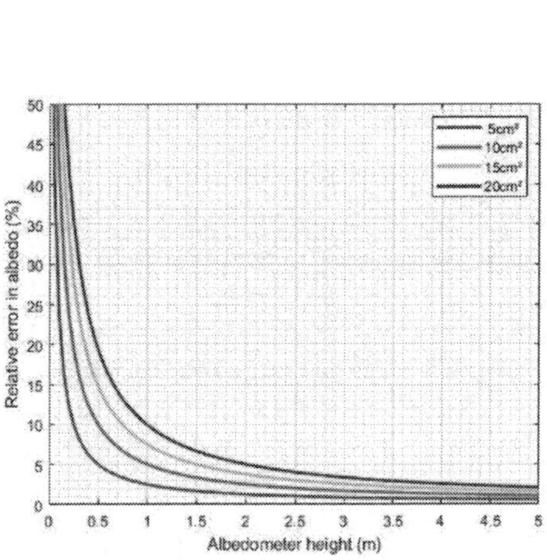

Figure 3: Relative error in albedo measurement, when considering a surface albedo of 0.35, in function of albedometer positioning height for $5, 10, 15\ and\ 20\ cm^2$ sensor areas.

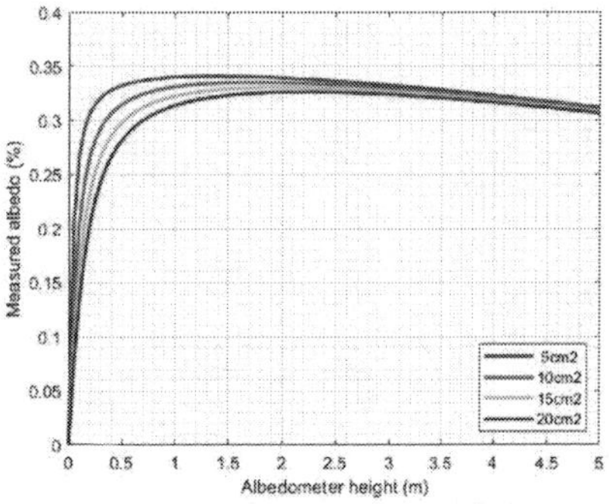

Figure 4: Measured albedo, when considering a surface albedo of 0.35, in function of albedometer positioning height for $5, 10, 15\ and\ 20\ cm^2$ sensor areas for a limited view factor between -10 and 10 meters.

4 USING THE MODEL

The proposed model has been encapsulated in a MATLAB function called *SensorHeight*. This function, for a given sensor area (given in cm^2) and a maximum admissible error (from 0 to 1), determines the minimum height at which the sensor should be placed.

The MATLAB project to determine the optimum sensor height for any specific application, in function of the admissible error, is available in a GitHub public repository:

https://github.com/EnekoOrtegaTiM/AlbedometerHeight.git

The GitHub repository contains the necessary explanations for integrating the project into MATLAB and testing the proposed function.

Fig. 5 shows an example of the use of the function to determine the minimum height at which the albedometer should be positioned when using a 15 cm^2 sensor and with a maximum permissible error of 3%.

```
>> Hmin = SensorHeight(15, 0.03); % Sensor of 10 cm2, error < 3%
>> disp(['Minimum required height: ', num2str(Hmin), ' m']);
Minimum required height: 0.9 m
>> |
```

Figure 5: Example of the use of the function to determine the minimum height at which the albedometer should be positioned when using a 15 cm^2 sensor and with a maximum permissible error of 3%.

The function *SensorHeight* calculates the minimum height at which an albedometer should be positioned to ensure that the measured albedo stabilizes within a user-defined acceptable error margin. It simulates the irradiance received by a sensor of a given area located at varying heights above a reflective surface, assuming a constant ground irradiance and surface albedo. The ground is discretized into 1-meter segments, and the contribution of each segment to the sensor's measurement is integrated based on geometric considerations. The function then identifies the lowest height at which the relative difference between the measured albedo and its asymptotic value falls below the specified error threshold, thus ensuring a reliable and stable measurement.

5 CONCLUSIONS

The implemented model allows, by means of an open-source code, to determine the minimum height at which an albedometer should be positioned to achieve a maximum error requirement on the albedo estimation for several sensor areas. This could be of interest during on-site albedo measurement campaigns, since sensor positioning can become a difficult task in certain scenarios.

The model determines this height as the function of the albedometer area. Several factors have not been considered, such as surface non-homogeneity, albedometer inclination with respect to the ground surface or the sensor spectral response, among others. These new variables could be integrated on the model to boost the model accuracy to determine sensor positioning.

However, the implemented model facilitates, in a simple and fast way, to determine the minimum positioning height to ensure that at least one of the error sources during albedo measurement is under control. The developed model is available, on MATLAB, on a GitHub public repository.

Future work will be oriented to optimize the developed model to integrate the analysis of surface non-homogeneity in the albedo measurement, as well as the positioning and the inclination of the sensor. Also, the influence of the spectral response of the sensor, when measuring by a pyranometer or by reference cells based on different technologies, will be analyzed when estimating the albedo value.

6 ACKNOWLEDGEMENTS

The Spanish Agencia Estatal de Investigación MCIN/AEI/10.13039/ 501100011033 is acknowledged for financial support through the GREASE project (PID2020-113533RB-C32).

7 REFERENCES

[1] T. Georgitsioti, N. Pearsall, I. Forbes, G. Pillai, A combined model for PV system lifetime energy prediction and annual energy assessment, Sol. Energy 183 (2019). 738–744.

[2] B. Marion, Measured and satellite-derived albedo data for estimating bifacial photovoltaic system performance, Sol. Energy 215 (2021) 321–327.

[3] H. Sánchez-Ortiz, S. Dittmann, C. Meza, R. Gottschalg, The Impact of Real Albedo Values on Energy Estimation for Bifacial Modules, EU PVSEC 2021 (2021). 808 - 810.

[4] C.A. Gueymard, V. Lara-Fanego, M. Sengupta, A. Habte, Surface albedo spatial variability in North America: Gridded data vs. local measurements, Sol. Energy 227 (2021) 655–673.

[5] S. Suarez, et al. The long-term of the albedo stability under different weather conditions, EU PVSEC 2021.

[6] .N. Riedel-Lyngskær, M. Ribaconka, M. Pó, A. Thorseth, S. Thorsteinsson, C. Dam-Hansen, M.L. Jakobsen, The effect of spectral albedo in bifacial photovoltaic performance, Sol. Energy 231 (2022) 921–935.

[7] E. Ortega, et al. An statistical model for the short-term albedo estimation applied to PV bifacial modules. Renewable Energy, 2024, vol. 221, p. 119777.

[8] R. Urraca, C. Lanconelli, F. Cappucci, N. Gobron. Comparison of Long-Term Albedo Products against Spatially Representative Stations over Snow. Remote Sensing, 14(15) (2022), 3745.

[9] Gostein, Michael, et al. Measuring irradiance for bifacial PV systems. En 2021 IEEE 48th Photovoltaic Specialists Conference (PVSC). IEEE, 2021. p. 0896-0903.

[10] S. Suarez, et al., Towards optimising the albedo measurement. 37th EU PVSEC (2021).

[11] M. Rivera and R. Christian. Silicon sensors vs. Pyranometers–review of deviations and conversion of measured values. 37th European PV Solar Energy Conference and Exhibition. Vol. 7. 2020.

[12] J.R. Ledesma, R. H. Almeida, F. Martinez-Moreno, C. Rossa, J. Martín-Rueda, L. Narvarte, E. Lorenzo. A simulation model of the irradiation and energy yield of large bifacial photovoltaic plants. Solar Energy, 206 (2020), 522-538.

[13] N. Martin, J. Ruiz. Annual Angular Reflection Losses in PV Modules. Prog. Photovolt.: Res. Appl. 13, 9 (2005).

Optimized Albedometer height: A Simple Model for Accurate Albedo Measurement

UPV EHU

Eneko Ortega[*,1,2], Eneko Cereceda[1], Nekane Azkona[1], Alona Otaegi[1], Vanesa Fano[1], Jose Ruben Gutierrez[1] and Juan Carlos Jimeno[1]

*eneko.ortegam@ehu.eus

[1]Technological Institute of Microelectronics, UPV/EHU, 48013, Bilbao, Spain

[2]Electricity and Electronics Department, UPV/EHU, 48940, Leioa, Spain

TiM INSTITUTO DE TECNOLOGÍA MICROELECTRÓNICA TEKNOLOGIA MIKROELEKTRONIKOAREN INSTITUTUA

Introduction

- The performance estimation of photovoltaic (PV) systems depends on parameters such as system design, PV technology, and operating conditions, including irradiation and albedo, specially for bifacial PV modules.
- Assuming a constant albedo in bifacial systems can lead to PV system performance estimation errors ranging from 2 to 7% [1].
- Albedo can be measured via satellite or on-site, showing high daily and seasonal variability that can be modeled to reduce uncertainty [2, 3].
- The placement height of the albedometer significantly affects measurement accuracy, with no clear consensus on the optimal height due to surface heterogeneity.

Aim

The objective of this study is to propose a simple, open-source model to estimate the minimum albedometer placement height based on sensor area and allowable relative error. This model aims to ensure a correct measurement of GRI and therefore surface albedo.

Using the model

Github repository:

https://github.com/EnekoOrtegaTiM/AlbedometerHeight.git

```
>> Hmin = SensorHeight(15, 0.03); % Sensor of 10 cm2, error < 3%
>> disp(['Minimum required height: ', num2str(Hmin), ' m']);
Minimum required height: 0.9 m
>> |
```

2D mathematical model

Albedo is obtained as the ratio between GRI and GHI:

$$G_{REAR} = \rho G_{GROUND} \quad (1)$$

- The GRI measured by the albedometer depends on the albedometer view factor.
- Albedometer placed horizontally and ground surface below is an homogeneous Lambertian reflector of infinite size. The albedometer view factor depends on:
  - The height at which it is positioned.
  - The sensor area.

For this flat receptor R, the contribution of the whole ground surface from $\phi_1 = -\frac{\pi}{2}$ to $\phi_1 = \frac{\pi}{2}$ would be equal to G_{REAR}. The contribution of a certain small segment $S_1 S_2$ to the rear side irradiance of the albedo sensor can be obtained as the product of the radiance intensity, the emitted radiant flux per unit solid angle (c), and the 2D view factor of the sensor:

$$G_{REAR}^{S12} = \int_{\phi_1}^{\phi_2} c\,x\,cos\theta\,d\theta = c\,x\,(sin\phi_2 - sin\phi_1) \quad (2)$$

and the angles ϕ_1 and ϕ_2 between the infinitesimal flat receptor $(0, h)$ and the edges of the segment $(S_1, 0)$ and $(S_2, 0)$ are computed as:

$$\phi_1 = atan(\frac{S_1}{h}) \; and \; \phi_2 = atan(\frac{S_2}{h}) \quad (3)$$

Finally, to obtain the rear irradiance due to the total ground surface, it can be obtained as the sum of the contributions of all the segments, from -90° to +90°.

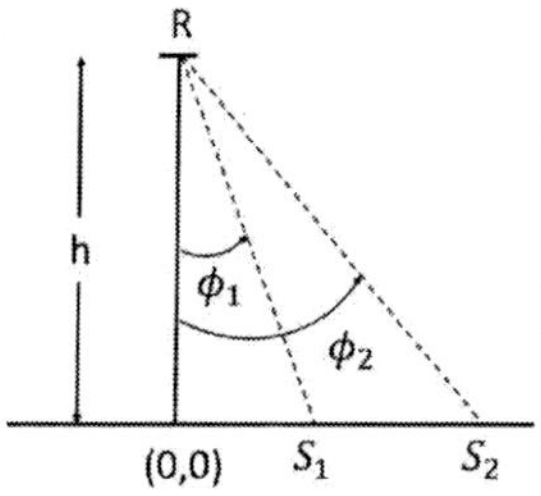

Optimum height determination

Estimated albedo:

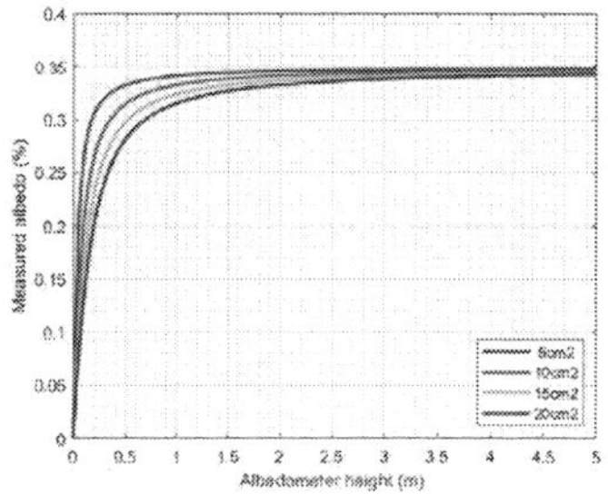

Estimated albedo, when considering a surface albedo of 0.35, in function of albedometer positioning height for 5, 10, 15 and 20 cm^2 sensor areas.

Relative error:

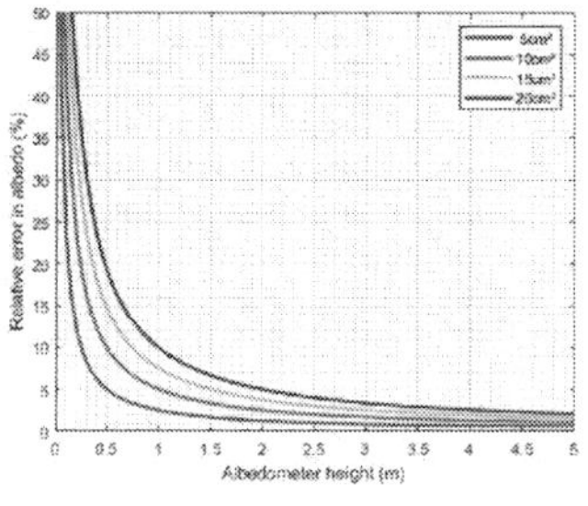

Relative error in albedo measurement, when considering a surface albedo of 0.35, in function of albedometer positioning height for 5, 10, 15 and 20 cm^2 sensor areas.

Conclusions

- The open-source model allows to determine the minimum height at which an albedometer should be positioned to achieve a maximum error requirement on the albedo estimation for several sensor areas.
- The developed model is available on a public repository.
- Future work will be oriented to optimize the model in order to integrate the analysis of surface non-homogeneity in the albedo measurement, spectral response of the sensor and positioning and inclination of the sensor.

References

[1] H. Sánchez-Ortiz, S. Dittmann, C. Meza, R. Gottschalg, The Impact of Real Albedo Values on Energy Estimation for Bifacial Modules, EU PVSEC 2021 (2021). 808 - 810.

[2] S. Suarez, et al. The long-term of the albedo stability under different weather conditions, EU PVSEC 2021.

[3] E. Ortega, et al. An statistical model for the short-term albedo estimation applied to PV bifacial modules. Renewable Energy, 2024, vol. 221, p. 119777.

Acknowledgements

The Spanish Agencia Estatal de Investigación MCIN/AEI/10.13039/501100011033 is acknowledged for financial support through the GREASE project (PID2020-113533RB-C32).

OPEN SOURCE TOOL FOR WEATHER DATA ESTIMATION IN PHOTOVOLTAIC SYSTEMS MONITORING

Sonia Maria Rodriguez[1], Beatriz Chicote[2], Eneko Ortega[1,3], Gerardo Aranguren[3] and Juan Carlos Jimeno[3]
[1] Electricity and Electronics Department, University of the Basque Country UPV/EHU, 48940, Leioa, Spain
[2] Electronics and Computing Department, Mondragon University, 20500, Arrasate-Mondragon, Spain
[3] Technological Institute of Microelectronics, University of the Basque Country UPV/EHU, 48013, Bilbao, Spain
eneko.ortegam@ehu.eus

ABSTRACT: PV systems periodic monitoring is one of the tools with the greatest potential to maximize energy production, avoid failures and extend the life span of the different elements composing the PV system. PV modules energy production depends on weather conditions, mainly temperature and solar irradiation. Therefore, when the electrical parameters of the PV modules are monitored, thus, the I-V curve, it is also necessary to obtain the temperature and irradiance values at which the electrical measurement is performed. This will enable to determine whether the electrical measurements are consistent with the current operating conditions or are associated with anomalous behaviors, due to defects in the PV system. This work provides an open-source code that will enable to obtain the weather parameters, without the need of additional sensors, for a certain location and timestamp, to link this weather data to the measurements of the in-situ monitoring solution. Temperature, global, direct and diffuse irradiances, relative humidity, atmospheric pressure or wind speed are obtained, among others. The accuracy of the proposed solution is evaluated against surface weather measurements for different locations.
Keywords: photovoltaic systems, condition monitoring, performance ratio

1 INTRODUCTION

Solar photovoltaic (PV) electricity generation is increasing at an exponential rate, with an expected installed PV capacity growth of more than 500 GW per year [1]. In this context, maximizing the performance and reliability of PV systems becomes essential. The performance of PV systems is typically measured in terms of the performance ratio (PR) [2] which ranges between 85% and 95% for different PV systems in function of the module technology, system architecture, the PV system location climate or in function of the degradation of the PV system [3].

This means that power losses can be up to 15%, even for modern PV systems. Failures in PV modules, such as encapsulation failures, cell cracks, potential induced degradation or partial shadows, are behind a relevant part of PV systems power losses [4].

Periodic monitoring is the only way to detect these failures and to minimize power losses, boosting PV systems profitability. In this context, several monitoring techniques have been proposed [5]. Some monitoring methods are PV system-level oriented whereas others are string or module-level oriented. Module-level methods rely on visual inspection of the PV module, thermal images analysis, electroluminescence testing or electrical measurement. Monitoring methods based on electrical measurements, such as voltage, current or voltage-current (I-V) characteristic measurement, can be more easily automatized to be carried out in a regular and periodic way. In [6] and [7] the authors proposed a novel monitoring methodology, capable of performing partial measurements of individual PV modules I-V curve and reconstructing their characteristics, using a low-cost electronic circuit based on two capacitors controlled by six switches.

The I-V characteristic of the PV module depends, among other parameters, on the temperature and the solar irradiation. Therefore, this means that any monitoring system, in addition to the current and voltage measurements needs to know, at least, the solar irradiation and temperature values at which the PV module is operating. This way, the monitoring system would be able to determine if the values obtained during the monitoring correspond to a correct operation of the PV module or there is a defect in the module.

This requires the addition of temperature and solar irradiation sensors in the PV system location, which implies an additional cost, especially in small size PV systems. Other parameters, that could be relevant and have an impact on PV module performance [8,9], such as direct and diffuse irradiance, humidity or wind speed among others, are not typically measured. In addition, a correct measurement of meteorological parameters would allow to perform a better estimation of PV systems performance, especially in Bifacial PV systems, where Albedo estimation can be challenging [10].

In this context, this work provides an open-source code which will enable to estimate the weather parameters from an online weather application programming interface (API), for a certain location and timestamp, in order to link this information to the measurements carried out by the in-situ monitoring solution. In addition, from the data obtained from the API, several relevant parameters such as direct and diffuse irradiance or clearness index (K_T) will be computed. Finally, accuracy of the proposed model will be evaluated using for that weather data collected by the Durable Module Materials (DuraMAT) consortium [11] on several locations.

2 WHEATHER PARAMETERS COLLECTION

The developed code in Python takes advantage of the Timeline Weather API, provided by Visual Crossing [12], to obtain meteorological data relevant in the context of PV systems Operation & Maintenance (O&M). Its free payment plan allows to make 1000 calls to the API per day, and it includes a wide group of features, such as current weather conditions, 15-day forecasts and historical data collections from the past 50 years. Monthly or annual payment plans (professional or corporate oriented plans) include the possibility to make more (or unlimited) records per day, as well as some additional services.

The Timeline Weather API requires at least a free

10.4229/EUPVSEC2025/4BV.3.28

account on Visual Crossing Weather and to create an API key in order to make requests to the API. The API uses a different form for each type of request in function of the desired information. The form for current weather conditions request, at a specific location defined by its coordinates, has the following structure:

https://weather.visualcrossing.com/ VisualCrossingWebServices/rest/services/ timeline/lat,lon?unitGroup=base&include= current&key=APIKEY&contentType=json

So the input parameters needed for the request are:

- *lat, lon*: a string with the latitude (lat) and longitude (lon) values corresponding to the measurement location.
- *key*: the API key related to the Visual Crossing account which is making the call.
- *contentType*: indicates the output format of the API. The available formats are JSON and CSV. By defect, the JSON option will be selected.

There are some other optional inputs, such as:

- *lang*: language of the translatable parts of the output. Can be chosen by using the ID of any available language. The default language is English (*en*).
- *unitGroup*: specifies the system of units used for the output data. Supported values are *us, uk, metric, base*. The default one is the US system of units. To facilitate the use of the proposed solution by the scientific community, the implemented code will report the data in scientific (base) units.

From the returned parameters by the API in a JSON format, the proposed model extracts and adapts the relevant ones, in the context of PV systems O&M, which are:

- *temp*: temperature, given in Kelvin degrees.
- *conditions*: a brief description of the weather conditions.
- *pressure*: the sea level atmospheric pressure, given in millibars (*mBar*).
- *humidity*: relative humidity, given in percentage (%).
- *windspeed*: the sustained wind speed measured as the average wind speed that occurs during the preceding one to two minutes to the requested timestamp, given in meters per second (*m/s*).
- *winddir*: direction from which the wind is blowing, given in degrees.
- *windgust*: instantaneous wind speed. It may be empty if it is not significantly higher than the value in *windspeed*, given in meters per second (*m/s*).
- *precip*: the amount of accumulated precipitation. The liquid-equivalent amount of any frozen precipitation such as snow or ice is included in the counting. Given in millimeters (*mm*).
- *cloudcover*: the percentage of sky that is covered with clouds.
- *solarradiation*: returns the Global Horizontal Irradiance (GHI) in the location, given in W/m^2.
- *datetimeEpoch*: number of seconds since 1st January 1970 in UTC time.
- *datetime*: ISO 8601 formatted time value (hh:mm:ss, where hh has a value between 00 and 24).
- *tzoffset*: time zone offset of the location in hours, which is the difference between the time in the location and the UTC.
- *days*: date (the specific day) when the request has been made, by using the format YYYY-MM-DD.C.

If desired, it is possible to display the location address instead of coordinates. For that, a *geocoder* (a tool which links location addresses and its coordinates) is being used. The API which has been selected for that is provided by geocode.maps.co [13] and it does not require an API key to make a call. This is the format of the request:

https://geocode.maps.co/reverse? lat=latitude&lon=longitude

From GHI data obtained from Visual Crossing, and knowing the PV system location and timestamp of the measurement, several relevant parameters such as solar declination (δ), solar zenith angle (θ_{zs}), solar azimuth (ψ_s), K_T, Direct Normal Irradiance (DNI) or Diffuse Horizontal Irradiance (DHI) can be computed from the implementation of a well-known set of equations [14].

Firstly, the solar declination angle (δ) must be found. As the earth rotates around its central axis (the polar axis) once a day, the polar axis orbits around the sun with a constant angle of 23.45° with the elliptical plane. However, the angle between the equatorial plane and a straight line between the center of the earth and the center of the sun (δ) changes during the year. If we consider constant this angle during one day, the solar declination can be obtained from Eq. 1, where d_n is the day of the year.

$$\delta(°) = 23.45 \sin\left(\frac{2\pi}{365}(d_n + 284)\right) \quad (1)$$

The distance from the earth to the sun, the eccentricity (ε_0), also varies during the year due to the elliptic orbit of the earth around the sun and can be computed from Eq. 2.

$$\varepsilon_0 = 1 + 0.033 \cos\left(\frac{2\pi \cdot n_d}{365}\right) \quad (2)$$

In a particular location on the earth surface, where the PV system is located, the relative position of the sun to a horizontal surface is defined by θ_{zs} and ψ_s angles, which can be computed from Eq. 3.

$$\cos\,(\theta_{zs}) = \sin\delta_{rad} \cdot \sin\Phi_{rad} + \cos\delta_{rad} \cdot \cos\Phi_{rad} \cdot \cos \mathrm{h}_{e_{grad}} \quad (3)$$

From this data, the different components of the solar radiation that reach the PV system location can be estimated. The total radiation reaching a horizontal surface (GHI) is the sum of the direct (DNI), diffuse (DHI) and albedo radiation. Direct radiation is the radiation that reaches the surface in a straight line from the sun, and it is not reflected or scattered. Diffuse radiation is the radiation that comes from the whole sky except from the sun's disc. Diffuse radiation is the solar radiation that is reflected or scattered due to the interaction with different particles such as clouds, ozone, oxygen or water vapor when the radiation passes through the atmosphere. Finally, albedo radiation is the radiation reflected from the ground, which can be usually neglected, especially on monofacial PV systems.

The amount of GHI that reaches the horizontal surface during one hour is extremely variable. The extraterrestrial radiation also suffers from regular variations due to the relative position of the sun. The extraterrestrial radiation can be computed according to Eq. 4.

$$B_{oh} = B_0 \cdot \varepsilon_0 \cdot \cos\theta_{zs} \quad (4)$$

where B_0, known as the solar constant, is the resultant power incident on a unit area perpendicular to the beam outside the earth's atmosphere.

$$B_o = 1367\ W/m^2 \quad (5)$$

The atmospheric transparency, or clearness index (K_T), can be estimated as the relation between the GHI and the B_{0h}.

$$K_T = \frac{GHI}{B_{oh}} \quad (6)$$

From here, it is possible to estimate the correlation between the diffuse fraction of horizontal irradiation (DHI) and the K_T, named K_D. K_D expresses the proportion of GHI reaching the surface that corresponds to diffuse radiation. That is, the part of the radiation that has undergone scattering phenomena due to the atmosphere. Since diffuse radiation decreases as the brightness index increases, the correlation between $K_T$and K_D will be negative. Several empirical models have been proposed for K_D estimation [15] which vary according to the longitude and latitude and the duration of the dataset. For this study, the estimation shown in Eq. 7, 8 and 9 has been implemented. When $K_T < 0.2$:

$$K_D = 0.996 + 0.00424\,K_T - 0.586K_T^2 \quad (7)$$

when $K_T > 0.2$ and $K_T < 0.7$:

$$K_D = 1.11 - 0.203\,K_T - 2.52K_T^2 + 0.617K_T^4 + 1.603K_T^3 \quad (8)$$

and when $K_T > 0.7$:

$$K_D = -0.0169 - 0.99\,K_T + 1.63K_T^2 \quad (9)$$

Finally, from K_D value the DHI and DNI estimation is immediate, as shown in Eq. 10 and 11.

$$DHI = GHI \cdot K_D \quad (10)$$
$$DNI = GHI - DHI \quad (11)$$

3 MEASUREMENT RELIABILITY

Reliability of the obtained values using Visual Crossing API will be evaluated using DuraMAT's "Albedo Data for Bifacial PV Systems" dataset. This dataset is composed of irradiance data and meteorological data from several locations across the United States during several years. From this dataset, GHI, DNI, DHI, temperature, relative humidity, wind speed or atmospheric pressure measurements, among others, will be available during several years.

Table 1 shows the dataset collected from DuraMAT's repository corresponding to 8 different locations across the United States with the above-mentioned variables that were selected to construct an equivalent dataset for each location. These were built using the *Hourly Historical Observations* API from Visual Crossing Weather, which allowed for a comparative analysis.

Table I: DuraMAT's dataset location and time periods

PV system name	State	Period
Bondville	Illinois	2018-2019
Coyanosa	Texas	2018-2020
Davis	California	2018-2019
Desert Rock	Nevada	2018-2019
Fayette	Ohio	2019-2020
Goodwin Creek	Mississippi	2018-2019
Penn. State University	Pennsylvannia	2018-2019
Sabinal	Texas	2019-2020

The following filtering criteria were applied: Incorrect measurements (indicated by *flag* variables in DURAMAT datasets) or measurements where GHI was below $200\,W/m^2$ where removed, since weather data during no irradiance conditions is not relevant regarding PV systems performance.

In order to compare the datasets in table 1 with the new equivalent Visual Crossing Weather datasets, two different calculations have been carried out:

- Relative Root Mean Squared Error (RRMSE):

$$RRMSE = \sqrt{\frac{\sum_{i=1}^{n}\left(\frac{x_i - y_i}{x_i}\right)^2}{n}} \quad (12)$$

  x_i are the reference values, which belong to DuraMAT's dataset and y_i are the values to check, corresponding to API responses. n is the total number of mesasurements (lines) in the datasets. Typically, an RRMSE of 0 is associated with error-free estimation and for RRMSE less than 1 the model is considered adequate.
- Pearson correlation coefficient (r), which quantifies the linear relationship between two variables, ranging from -1 to 1. As r tends to |1|, datasets are more linearly related (directly, if r is positive or inversely, if r is negative).

$$r = \frac{Cov(X,Y)}{\sigma_X \cdot \sigma_Y} \quad (13)$$

  where X and Y are DuraMAT's reference and Visual Crossing Weather Historical datasets, for each weather parameter. *Cov* represents the covariance between X and Y and σ is the standard deviation of each of them.

The results of these calculations are shown in Table 2.

Table II: RRMSE and Pearson Correlation Coefficient calculation results, based on measurements from 8 different locations.

	GHI	Tdry	RH	Wspd	Wdir	Pres
RRMSE	0.50	0.36	0.14	1.21	49.13	0.07
Corr	0.66	0.99	0.97	0.76	0.56	0.99

Firstly, note that the locations of Sioux Falls and Boulder were excluded from the final computations in table 2 because the temperature error was excessive, surpassing 100%, making the data unreliable for analysis. Secondly, remark than in some locations where DuraMAT's measurements have been taken in 1-minute intervals temperature relative error remained low (below 10%). Excluding Sioux Falls and Boulder locations, temperature showed a correlation of 0.99 and a RRMSE of 0.36.

Regarding other meteorological variables, relative humidity and pressure showed coherent and low error margins (RRMSE of 0.142 and 0.069 respectively) and almost perfect correlation (0.97 and 0.99). Wind speed, however, presents higher RRMSE (1.21), although it maintains a good correlation (0.76), which could suggest that, although wind speed presents greater variability, the value obtained is reliable to represent the dynamics of wind speed. However, wind direction, with high RRMSE and low correlation (0.56) presents a behavior that seems that it cannot be estimated from Visual Crossing data.

As for Global Horizontal Irradiance (GHI) values, even if initially shows relatively low RRMSE and moderate correlation (0.658) it was detected that Visual Crossing tended to report a lower value than DuraMAT. Since Visual Crossing relies on satellite data to estimate the meteorological parameters, while the DuraMAT data are measured at the surface, the GHI value being obtained is not the same, consistently observing a lower GHI value in the Visual Crossing data than in the DuraMAT data. This effect was minimized by applying a polynomial regression to GHI data in function of Kt value and in the day of the year of the measurement.

The values for GHI were considerably improved, especially the correlation coefficient, which went from 0.658 to 0.941, showing high linearity and reducing the RRMSE error from 0.035 to 0.204, as shown in Table 3.

Table III: RRMSE and Pearson Correlation Coefficient Calculation results, based on measurements from 8 different locations, after applying corrections to the GHI.

	GHI	Tdry	RH	Wspd	Wdir	Pres
RRMSE	0.20	0.36	0.14	1.21	49.33	0.07
Corr	0.94	0.99	0.97	0.76	0.56	0.99

As a representative example, next figures show the most relevant data (Tdry and GHI) obtained from DuraMAT's dataset and from Visual Crossing for Sabinal (Texas) location. Fig. 1 shows the evolution of the temperature (Tdry) during eight months for DuraMAT (blue) and Visual Crossing (orange). Fig. 2 shows the Tdry evolution during a one month period on October-November 2019. As can be seen, the relative error between on-site Tdry measurements and estimations using the Visual Crossing API remains low (below 5% for Sabinal location) during the entire period. However, it can be seen how the Visual Crossing data present slightly lower Tdry values.

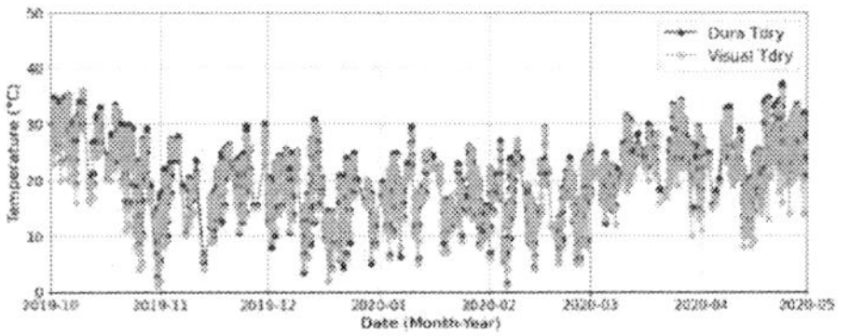

Figure 1: Evolution of Tdry temperature for Sabinal (Texas) using DuraMAT data (blue) and Visual Crossing data (orange) between October 2019 and May 2020.

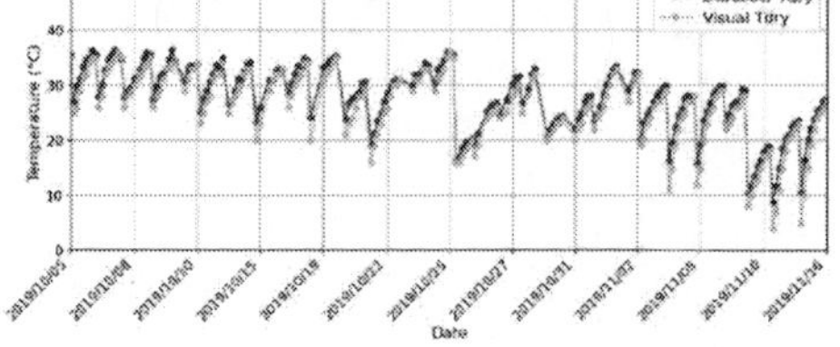

Figure 2: Evolution of Tdry temperature for Sabinal (Texas) using DuraMAT data (blue) and Visual Crossing data (orange) during a one month period in 2019.

Fig. 3 shows the GHI values during a 5-month period, both from DuraMAT and from Visual Crossing. Even after applying the polynomial regression GHI shows a relative error of 15.43% for Sabinal location data. However, as can be seen in Fig. 4, DuraMAT and Visual Crossing GHI values follow the same dynamic, with low error during most of the measurements.

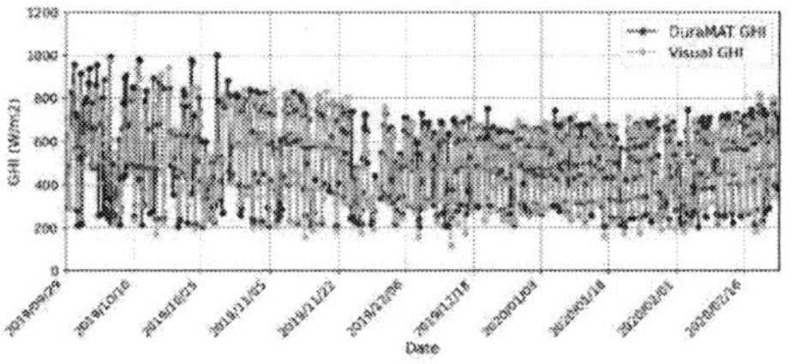

Figure 3: Evolution of GHI for Sabinal (Texas) using DuraMAT data (blue) and Visual Crossing data (orange) between October 2019 and February 2020.

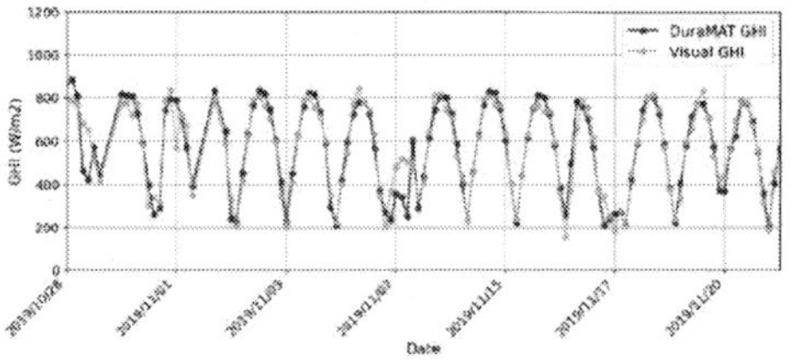

Figure 4: Evolution of GHI values for Sabinal Texas using DuraMAT data (blue) and Visual Crossing data (orange) during several days in October-November 2019.

4 USING THE MODEL

Once a personal API Key is generated, using this code any user will be able to obtain the weather parameters of an specific location and to link these data to its monitoring measurements. In the free version, the API only allows 1000 call each day. In function of their needs, users may need to switch to a paid API subscription.

The python function to obtain the weather conditions for any location, is available in a GitHub public repository (https://github.com/EnekoOrtegaTiM/WeatherParams-PVSystems.git). The GitHub repository contains the necessary explanations for integrating and testing the proposed model.

The script "weather_data_function.py" contains a function named "weather_data" that makes a request to the Visual Crossing Weather Current Conditions API and returns a pandas.DataFrame class object containing the collection of weather parameters that have been extracted from the response. This is the function call structure:

weather_data(lat, lon, UTC, api_key)

whose input arguments are:

- *lat:* latitude of the location, in degrees.
- *lon:* longitude of the location, in degrees.
- *UTC:* UTC offset of the location (difference from UTC time), in hours.
- *api_key:* Visual Crossing Weather user API key.

"weather_data" is made up of various class methods from the "call_class" and "radiation_class" scripts, which must be loaded along with the function script. These methods are responsible for handling API requests, managing response data, and properly formatting them.
Additionally, these class methods provide users with different ways to view, use and store data. For instance:

- A single request can be displayed as text or saved in a .csv file (as in Fig.5).
- A database can be built to store multiple requests and can be updated whenever a new request is made.

In Fig.5, a call to the developed function is shown. The function returns the current weather conditions for the University of the Basque Country Campus, sited in Leioa (Spain) with 43.33 (latitude) and -2.97 (longitude) coordinates. It must be pointed that data availability is delayed by 30 minutes. This means that after an electrical measurement, the associated weather data is available 30 minutes afterwards.

```
Function call:
weather_data(lat, lon, UTC, api_key)

The weather data for 43.3314059°,-2.9706058° location at
2025-05-23 12:30:00 is:

- Location address: UPV/EHU Leioa-Erandio, Via Julia, Lertutza,
Leioa, Andraka, Biscay, Autonomous Community of the Basque
Country, 48620, Spain
- Tenperature: 291.2K
- Weather conditions: Partially cloudy
- Pressure: 1023.0hPa
- Relative humidity: %62.0
- Wind speed: 3.7m/s
- Wind direction: 314.0°
- Wind gusts: 0.6m/s
- Precipitation: 0.0 mm
- Clouds: %50.0
- Global Horizontal Irradiance (GHI): 747.0W/m^2
- Direct Normal Irradiance (DNI): 356.8710487804023W/m^2
- Diffuse Horizontal Irradiance (DHI): 390.1289512195977W/m^2
- Solar time, in hours: -1.6233508086749708
- UTC timezone offset, in hours : 2
```

Figure 5: Data request for 43.33 (latitude) and -2.97 (longitude) coordinates, corresponding to the University of the Basque Country UPV/EHU Bizkaia campus, sited in Leioa (Spain).

5 CONCLUSIONS

The proposed solution will allow, using an open source code, to obtain for a given location and timestamp the solar irradiation and meteorological parameters at the same time instant in which the PV system is being monitored. Weather and solar irradiation data may be relevant in order to obtain more information on the operation of the PV system and to distinguish between normal operation and defects on the PV system or abnormal behaviors which can not be explained by weather conditions.

As it is shown in the Measurement Reliability section, the proposed model is able to obtain the weather parameters without the use of additional sensors. Specially for temperature, relative humidity and atmospheric pressure with low error. Even GHI values, although it initially presented high error, shows a correlation above 0.90 for all locations after applying a polynomial fitting of the measurement in function of the Kt value and the day of the year. New studies will be carried out to reduce estimated parameters error and improve the utility of the proposed model.

Every user, creating its own API Key, would be able to perform up to 1000 measurements every day using the code provided in the Github repository. For that, only API Key code, PV system location and timestamp are required. If desired, more daily calls to the API can be performed upgrading the subscription directly with the API owner.

The proposed model will be integrated into a smart PV modules monitoring solution that is being developed in the SUPERNOVA European Union Horizon project. In the context of this project, the UPV/EHU team is developing a microcontroller-based Internet of Things (IoT) system for the self-testing of individual PV modules by means of a junction box-embedded wireless monitoring solution. Since the IoT device will have internet connectivity, it will be possible to combine the electrical measurements performed by the IoT device with the temperature and irradiation parameters estimated by the proposed model, in order to determine the degradation of the PV modules.

6 ACKNOWLEDGEMENTS

The European Union's Horizon Europe programme is acknowledged for financial support through the SUPERNOVA project (Grant Agreement No 101146883).

7 REFERENCES

[1] A. Jager-Waldau, Snapshot of photovoltaics - February 2024. EPJ Photovoltaics, vol. 15, p. 21, 2024.

[2] G. Blaesser, PV system measurements and monitoring the European experience. Solar Energy Materials, vol. 47, pp. 167-176, 1997.

[3] A. Louwen, S. Lindig, G. Chowdhury and D. Moser, Climate-and Technology-Dependent Performance Loss Rates in a Large Commercial Photovoltaic Monitoring Dataset. Solar RRL, vol. 8, p. 2300653, 2024.

[4] H. Al Mahdi, P.G. Leahy, M. Alghoul and A.P. Morrison, A Review of Photovoltaic Module Failure and Degradation Mechanisms: Causes and Detection Techniques. Solar, vol. 4, pp. 43-82, 2024.

[5] E. Ortega, G. Aranguren, M.J. Saenz, R. Gutierrez and J.C. Jimeno, Study of Photovoltaic Systems Monitoring Methods, in 44th IEEE Photovoltaic Specialist Conference (IEEE PVSC), 2017.

[6] E. Ortega, G. Aranguren and J.C. Jimeno, New monitoring method to characterize individual modules in large photovoltaic systems. Solar Energy, vol. 193, pp. 906-914, 2019.

[7] E. Ortega, G. Aranguren and J.C. Jimeno, Photovoltaic modules transient response analysis and correction under a fast characterization system. Solar Energy, vol. 221, pp. 232-242, 2021.

[8] G.G. Kim, J.H. Choi, S.Y. Park, B.G. Bhang, W.J. Nam, H.L. Cha, N.S. Park and H.K. Ahn, Prediction model for PV performance with correlation analysis of environmental variables. IEEE Journal of Photovoltaics, vol. 9 (3), pp. 832-841, 2019.

[9] F. Shaik, S.S. Lingala and P. Veeraboina, Effect of various parameters on the performance of solar PV power plant: a review and the experimental study. Sustainable Energy Research, vol. 10 (1), p. 6, 2023.

[10] E. Ortega et al., An statistical model for the short-term albedo estimation applied to PV bifacial modules. Renewable Energy, vol. 221, pp. 119777, 2024.

[11] B. Marion, Albedo data set for bifacial PV systems, in 44th IEEE Photovoltaic Specialist Conference (IEEE PVSC), pp. 485-489, 2020.

[12] Visual Crossing Corporation. (2024). Timeline Weather API, Visual Crossing Weather. https://www.visualcrossing.com/

[13] Free Geocoding API, Geocode Addresses Coordinate, geocode.maps.co.https://geocode.maps.com

[14] E. Lorenzo. Energy collected and delivered by PV modules. Handbook of photovoltaic science and engineering, pp. 984-1042, 2011.

[15] S. Etxebarria et al., Empirical models for the estimation of solar sky-diffuse radiation. A review and experimental analysis. Energies, 13(3), 2020.

Open Source Tool for Weather Data Estimation in Photovoltaic Systems Monitoring

Sonia Maria Rodriguez[1], Beatriz Chicote[2], **Eneko Ortega**[*,1,3], Gerardo Aranguren[3] and Juan Carlos Jimeno[3]

*eneko.ortegam@ehu.eus

[1]Electricity and Electronics Department, UPV/EHU, 48940, Leioa, Spain
[2]Electronics and Computing Department, Mondragon University, 20500, Arrasate, Spain
[3]Technological Institute of Microelectronics, UPV/EHU, 48013, Bilbao, Spain

UPV EHU

TiM INSTITUTO DE TECNOLOGÍA MICROELECTRÓNICA TEKNOLOGIA MIKROELEKTRONIKOAREN INSTITUTUA

Introduction

- PV systems power losses can be up to 15 %. Failures in PV modules are behind a relevant part of power losses [1].
- Periodic monitoring of PV systems is useful for maximizing energy production, preventing failures, and extending PV systems lifespan.
- PV performance depends on weather conditions, mainly temperature and solar irradiation. Acquiring these values during I-V curve monitoring ensures consistency with operating conditions.

Aim

To provide an open-source code that estimates weather parameters from an online weather API for a certain location and timestamp, linking this data to in-situ monitoring electrical measurements [2, 3]

Weather parameters collection

Timeline Weather API (Visual Crossing) [4] allows making requests of weather data.

Input arguments:

- *lat,lon*: Latitude and longitude of the location (°).
- *key*: VC user account API key.
- *contentType*: format of the response.
- *lang*: output language (optional).
- *unitGroup*: *metric*, *us* (default), *uk*, or *base* unit system.

Output data:

- Temperature
- Sea level atmospheric pressure
- Relative humidity
- Wind speed and direction
- Accumulated precipitation
- Clouds covering the sky
- Global Horizontal Irradiance (GHI)

Solar declination (δ), zenith angle (θ_{zs}), azimuth (ψ_s), clearness index (K_T), direct and diffuse irradiance (DNI and DHI) are derived from Global Horizontal Irradiance (GHI) data and latitude and longitude using a well-known set of equations [5].

Using the model

Github repository:

```
https://github.com/EnekoOrtegaTiM/WeatherParams-PVSystems.git
```

Function call:

```
weather_data(lat, lon, UTC, api_key)
```

Measurement reliability

Model error estimation from 8 locations, by **DuraMAT**.

	GHI	Tdry	RH	Wspd	Wdir	Pres
RRMSE	0.503	0.362	0.142	1.207	49.129	0.069
Correlation (r)	0.658	0.991	0.968	0.763	0.561	0.997

Model reliability after applying polynomial fitting to the GHI.

	GHI	Tdry	RH	Wspd	Wdir	Pres
RRMSE	0.204	0.363	0.143	1.207	49.334	0.069
Correlation (r)	0.941	0.991	0.968	0.762	0.560	0.997

Temperature evolution in Sabinal (Texas), Oct. 2019 - May 2020

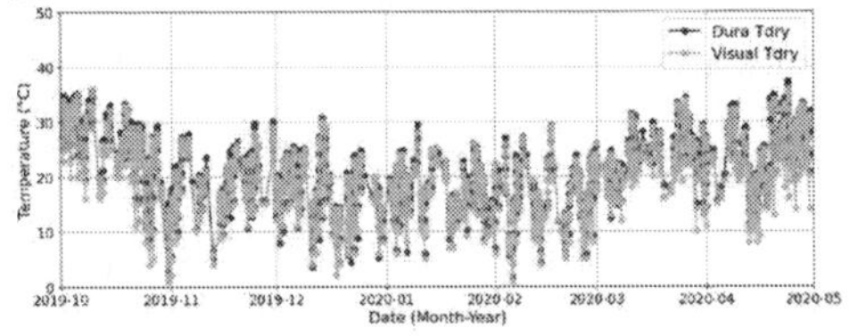

Temperature evolution in Sabinal (Texas), Oct.-Nov. 2019

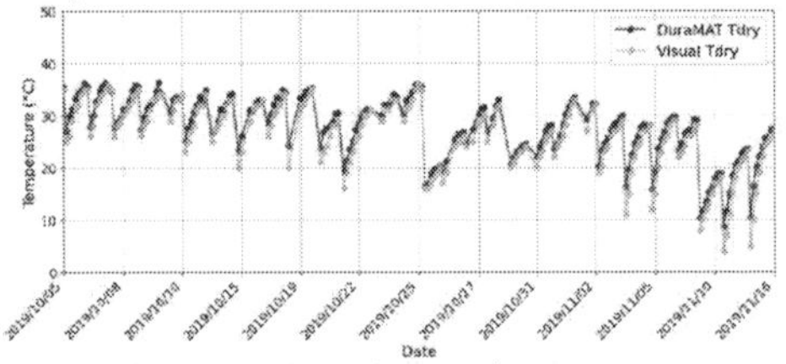

GHI evolution in Sabinal (Texas), Oct. 2019 - Feb. 2020

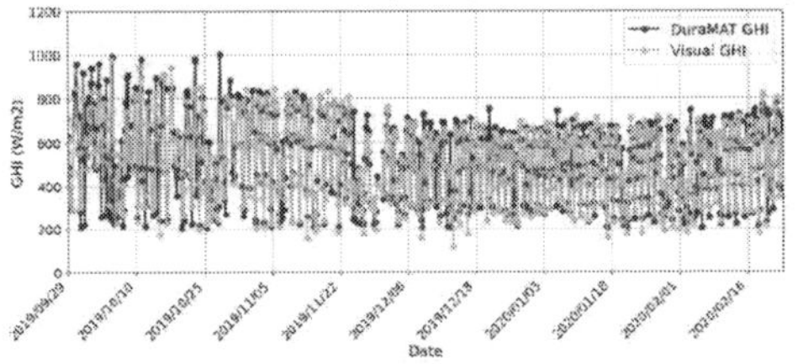

GHI evolution in Sabinal (Texas), Oct.–Nov. 2019

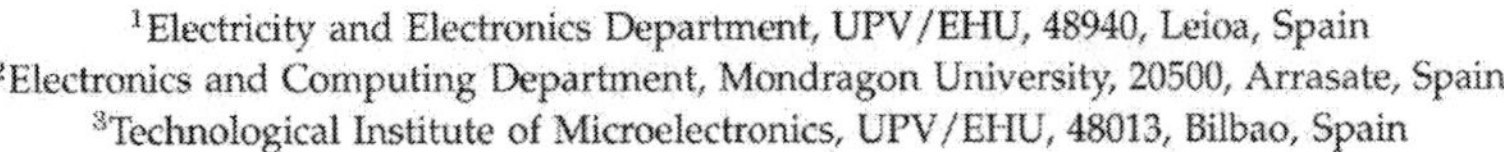

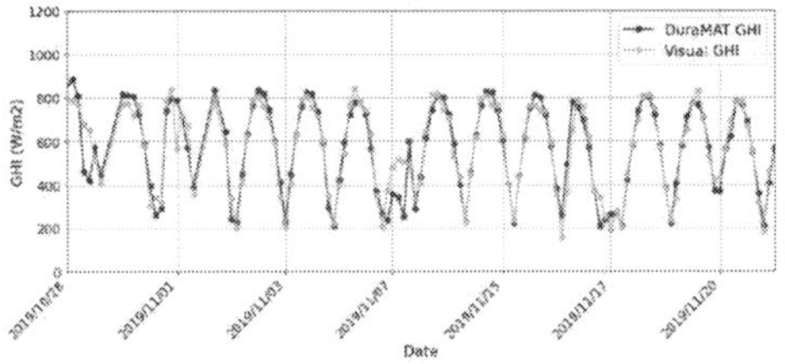

Acknowledgements

The European Union's Horizon Europe programme is acknowledged for financial support through the SUPERNOVA project (Grant Agreement No 101146883).

Conclusions

- The open-source solution retrieves solar and weather data for PV monitoring.
- The estimation of weather parameters achieves low error and correlation above 0.94 for temperature, humidity, pressure and GHI.
- The model will be integrated into the SUPERNOVA project's IoT-based smart PV monitoring system.

References

[1] H. Al Mahdi et al., A Review of Photovoltaic Module Failure and Degradation Mechanisms: Causes and Detection Techniques. Solar, 2024.

[2] E. Ortega et al., New monitoring method to characterize individual modules in large photovoltaic systems. Solar Energy, 2019.

[3] E. Ortega et al., Photovoltaic modules transient response analysis and correction under a fast characterization system. Solar Energy, 2021.

[4] https://www.visualcrossing.com/

[5] E. Lorenzo. Energy collected and delivered by PV modules. 2011.

PERFORMANCE EVALUATION OF CAMS REANALYSIS FOR IMPROVED SOLAR RESOURCE ASSESSMENT AND FORECASTING IN QATAR'S DESERT CLIMATE

Abdul Wahab Ziaullah[1], Dunia Bachour[1*], Daniel Perez-Astudillo[1], Lionel Menard[2], and Philippe Blanc[2]
[1]Qatar Environment and Energy Research Institute, Hamad Bin Khalifa University, Doha, Qatar
[2]Centre Observation Impacts Energy (O.I.E.), MINES Paris, Université PSL, France
*Corresponding Author: dbachour@hbku.edu.qa

ABSTRACT: Solar resource assessment is essential for the planning and operation of solar energy projects, with ground-based measurements providing the most accurate data. In their absence, satellite-derived solar radiation products offer a valuable alternative due to their broad spatial and temporal coverage, though their accuracy must be carefully evaluated for reliable application. This study assesses the performance of the CAMS Radiation Service (CRS), a satellite-based solar radiation dataset from the European Union's Earth observation program, under the hot desert climate of Qatar. Historical CRS data—Global Horizontal Irradiance (GHI), Direct Normal Irradiance (DNI), and Diffuse Horizontal Irradiance (DHI)—were compared against ground-based measurements from QEERI's solar monitoring station in Doha, recorded at 1-minute resolution over a 38-month period. The evaluation employed statistical indicators including Pearson's correlation coefficient (Cf), relative root mean square error (rRMSE), and relative mean bias error (rMBE). Results show that CRS reproduces GHI with the highest accuracy, exhibiting the lowest rRMSE and rMBE, while DNI and DHI demonstrate significantly larger biases and errors. Furthermore, periodic monthly variations in rRMSE were observed across all components. These findings suggest that CRS-derived GHI can serve as a reliable substitute when ground measurements are unavailable, though greater caution is required when using DNI and DHI.

1 INTRODUCTION

Solar energy is increasingly recognized as a key component of sustainable energy systems worldwide, particularly in regions with abundant sunlight such as the Middle East. Accurate assessment of solar radiation resources is essential for the design, operation, and optimisation of solar energy projects, including photovoltaic (PV) and concentrated solar power (CSP) systems. Typically, the most reliable solar radiation data are obtained from ground-based measurement stations equipped with radiometers, which provide high-resolution, site-specific information. However, ground measurements are often limited in spatial coverage, expensive to maintain, and sometimes subject to data gaps or instrument errors.

To address these limitations, satellite-derived solar radiation datasets are an attractive alternative due to their extensive spatial and temporal coverage, enabling resource assessments over large and remote areas where ground measurements may be sparse or unavailable. Numerous satellite models provide estimates of solar radiation components such as Global Horizontal Irradiance (GHI), Direct Normal Irradiance (DNI), and Diffuse Horizontal Irradiance (DHI), which are crucial inputs for solar energy system design and performance analysis.

Despite their advantages, satellite-based products require validation against ground truth data to assess their accuracy and reliability, particularly when applied to specific climatic regions. Desert environments, such as Qatar's, present unique challenges due to high solar irradiance levels, frequent dust events, and atmospheric variability, all of which can affect the accuracy of satellite retrievals.

The Copernicus Atmosphere Monitoring Service (CAMS) Radiation Service (CRS), developed under the European Union's Earth Observation Programme, offers historical solar radiation data that can potentially supplement or replace ground measurements. This study aims to evaluate the applicability of CRS data in Qatar's desert climate by comparing 38-months of high-resolution CRS data with ground-based measurements from a solar monitoring station operated by the Qatar Environment and Energy Research Institute (QEERI) in Doha.

By analysing the performance of CRS data across overall, annual and monthly, resolutions using statistical parameters such as Pearson's correlation coefficient, relative root mean square error and relative mean bias error, this work contributes to understanding the strengths and limitations of satellite-derived solar radiation data in hot desert climates. The outcomes provide insights into the reliability of CRS data for hot desert environments and support improved methodologies for solar resource assessment in Qatar and similar regions.

2 BACKGROUND

Solar radiation is the primary energy input for solar power systems and thus plays a critical role in determining the feasibility and performance of solar energy projects. Accurate measurement of solar radiation components—Global Horizontal Irradiance (GHI), Direct Normal Irradiance (DNI), and Diffuse Horizontal Irradiance (DHI)—is essential for system design [6], performance prediction, and energy yield estimation [2].

Ground stations equipped with pyranometers and pyrheliometers provide high-quality solar radiation data. These instruments measure solar irradiance directly at specific locations, offering precise and high-resolution temporal data. However, the installation, maintenance, and calibration of such stations require significant resources. Moreover, data gaps frequently occur due to instrument failure or environmental factors, limiting the continuity and completeness of the dataset.

To overcome these limitations, satellite remote sensing offers an alternative by providing continuous solar radiation estimates over large geographical areas and often

10.4229/EUPVSEC2025/4BV.3.29

long time periods [7]. Satellite models use cloud cover, atmospheric parameters, and surface reflectance data to estimate the solar irradiance components. These datasets are especially valuable in regions where ground monitoring infrastructure is sparse or non-existent.

Several satellite-derived solar radiation products exist globally, each varying in spatial and temporal resolution, input data sources, and modelling approaches. The Copernicus Atmosphere Monitoring Service (CAMS) Radiation Service (CRS) is a prominent example, offering comprehensive radiation data derived from the European Earth Observation Programme. CRS provides historical data, since 2004 until 2 days before the present day, with global coverage, making it a useful tool for solar energy assessments.

Desert climates like Qatar's present specific challenges for satellite-based solar radiation estimates. High solar irradiance, intense dust storms, and atmospheric aerosols can alter the solar radiation reaching the surface and complicate satellite retrieval algorithms. These factors may reduce the accuracy of satellite-derived radiation data compared to ground-based measurements. Additionally, seasonal and diurnal variations in atmospheric conditions can introduce periodic errors in satellite estimates.

An initial study in Qatar was conducted using the HelioClim-3 v4 (HC3v4) database from SoDa [4]. HC3 utilizes the Heliosat-2 model, while CRS uses McClear for clear-sky conditions and Heliosat-4 for all-sky conditions, offering broader regional coverage. Moreover, CRS uses actual aerosol data, whereas HC3 relies on approximations. Given Qatar's high aerosol loading [11], CRS may be more suitable; however, a direct comparison is lacking, making such a study highly warranted. A new version of Helioclim, HC3v5, is also available, in which HC3v5 replaces the ESRA clear-sky model and static turbidity climatology of HC3v4 with the McClear clear-sky model. A study has been conducted in Morocco using five stations [8] and comparing HC3v4, HC3v5, and CRS. Another study assessed the real-time estimates of surface GHI produced by the improved SENSE2 operational system at high spatial resolution for various stations, including Athens, Cabauw, Camborne, Carpentras, and Cener. The study found that periods with changes in cloudiness contributed to higher variability in the satellite-derived GHI estimates [9]. Similarly, a study validated the performance of HelioClim-3 version 5 (HC3v5) against ground-based measurements at various stations in northeast Iraq [3].

A brief comparison of HC3v4, HC3v5, and CRS. is presented in Table 1.

This study builds on these concepts by assessing the performance of CAMS CRS data in Qatar, comparing it against a robust ground measurement dataset collected over 38-months by QEERI. Understanding the suitability and limitations of CRS data in Qatar's desert environment will support improved solar resource management and facilitate more accurate solar energy project planning.

3 METHODOLOGY

High-quality measurements of direct normal irradiance (DNI), global horizontal irradiance (GHI), and diffuse horizontal irradiance (DHI) were collected with QEERI's monitoring station in Doha (25.32° N, 51.42° E), covering 38-months period, from (Jan/2013 - Feb/2016). The data for GHI and DHI were collected using CMP11 pyranometers, while the data for DNI were collected using a CHP1 pyrheliometer. All irradiances were collected minute-by-minute in W/m^2 and quality checks were applied to the data to eliminate any erroneous values [10]. The corresponding CRA data was downloaded using CAMS API [5]. The relative root mean square error (rRMSE), relative mean bias error (rMBE), and Pearson's correlation coefficient (Cf) were calculated using formulas 1, 2 and 3, respectively.

$$\text{rRMSE} = \frac{\sqrt{\frac{1}{N}\sum_{i=1}^{N}(X_i - Y_i)^2}}{\overline{Y}} * 100\% \quad (1)$$

$$\text{rMBE} = \frac{\frac{1}{N}\sum_{i=1}^{N}(X_i - Y_i)}{\overline{Y}} * 100\% \quad (2)$$

$$\text{Cf} = \frac{\sum_{i=1}^{N}(X_i - \overline{X})(Y_i - \overline{Y})}{\sum_{i=1}^{N}(X_i - \overline{X})^2 \sum_{i=1}^{N}(Y_i - \overline{Y})^2} \quad (3)$$

where X and Y are the modelled and measured samples, respectively, overlines indicate the respective means, and N is the number of measurements in the sample.

4 RESULTS AND DISCUSSION

The overall performance of CAMS CRS solar radiation against ground measurements over the full period (Jan/2013 - Feb/2016) is summarized in Table 2. GHI exhibits the best agreement, with a relatively low rRMSE of 29.5%, a minor underestimation of –4.3%, and excellent correlation (0.97), indicating strong reliability for total horizontal irradiance. DHI shows moderate errors, with an rRMSE of 49.6% and a slight overestimation of +10.7%, while correlations remain high at 0.94. In contrast, DNI displays the weakest performance, with a very high rRMSE of 78.4% and a substantial underestimation of –40.7%, although correlations are moderate (0.87). These results highlight that CAMS CRS performs best for GHI, reasonably for DHI, and has limitations in accurately representing direct normal irradiance under the conditions studied.

The overall analysis is further broken down to yearly performance in Table 3, where both rRMSE and rMBE remain consistent with relatively low standard deviations, indicating limited year-to-year fluctuations. For DNI, CAMS shows the weakest agreement, with very high rRMSE values (75–80%) and a consistent underestimation of about –40%, though correlations are moderate (0.87–0.88). DHI performs better, with rRMSE values of 45–52% and a systematic overestimation of +8% to +14%, while correlations are high (0.94–0.95). The best performance is observed for GHI, with comparatively low errors (28–30%), only a

10.4229/EUPVSEC2025/4BV.3.29

Feature	CAMS Radiation Service (CRS)	HelioClim-3 v4 (HC3v4)	HelioClim-3 v5 (HC3v5)
Cloud Data Source	Meteosat Second Generation (MSG) SEVIRI images	Meteosat Second Generation (MSG) SEVIRI images	Meteosat Second Generation (MSG) SEVIRI images
Algorithm	Heliosat-4 method	Heliosat-2 method	Heliosat-2 method (combined with McClear)
Clear Sky Model	McClear model	European Solar Radiation Atlas (ESRA) model with static turbidity climatology	McClear model
Atmospheric Input	Near real-time and forecast data for aerosols, water vapor, and ozone from CAMS/ECMWF	Static climatological data (Linke turbidity)	Combines the cloud and clear-sky models of HC3v4 with the more accurate atmospheric input from the McClear model
Temporal Resolution	1-minute, 15-minute, hourly, daily, and monthly	15-minute, hourly, daily, and monthly	1-minute, 15-minute, hourly, daily, and monthly
Coverage	Global (within satellite coverage)	Europe, Africa, Atlantic Ocean, and the Middle East	Europe, Africa, Atlantic Ocean, and the Middle East

Table 1: Comparison of CAMS Radiation Service, HelioClim-3 v4, and HelioClim-3 v5

Table 2: Overall Performance of CRS Solar Radiation vs Ground Measurements (Jan 2013- Feb 2016)

	rRMSE(%)	rMBE(%)	Cf
DNI	78.38	-40.70	0.87
DHI	49.57	10.70	0.94
GHI	29.48	-4.30	0.97

slight underestimation (around –4%), and excellent correlations (0.97–0.98).

Table 3: Yearly Performance Metrics for CRS vs. Ground Measurements

	DNI			DHI			GHI		
	rRMSE	**rMBE**	**Cf**	**rRMSE**	**rMBE**	**Cf**	**rRMSE**	**rMBE**	**Cf**
2013	77.91	-40.9	0.88	49.12	10.22	0.94	28.43	-4.27	0.98
2014	75.4	-40.45	0.88	52.18	14.22	0.94	28.52	-3.86	0.98
2015	79.84	-39.04	0.87	45.41	8.28	0.95	30.19	-4.44	0.97
Std	2.22	0.97	0.01	3.40	3.03	0.01	0.99	0.30	0.01

A monthly-level analysis of rRMSE, rMBE, and correlation coefficient (Cf) for the three solar radiation components was performed to identify potential climate-related variations in CRS data accuracy. The results are shown in Figures 1–4.

As seen in Fig. 1, GHI consistently exhibits the lowest rRMSE, while DNI shows the highest rRMSE across all months. A seasonal pattern is also apparent: errors are lowest during the mostly cloud-free months of May–June and highest in December–January, when cloudiness and occasional rainfall occur.

The monthly rMBE trends in Fig. 2 show that GHI fluctuates near zero, indicating minimal bias. DNI exhibits the largest negative bias, whereas DHI shows a moderate positive bias.

Correlation analysis (Fig. 3) indicates that CRS data are highly correlated with ground measurements (Cf > 0.8) for all components. GHI consistently shows the highest corre-

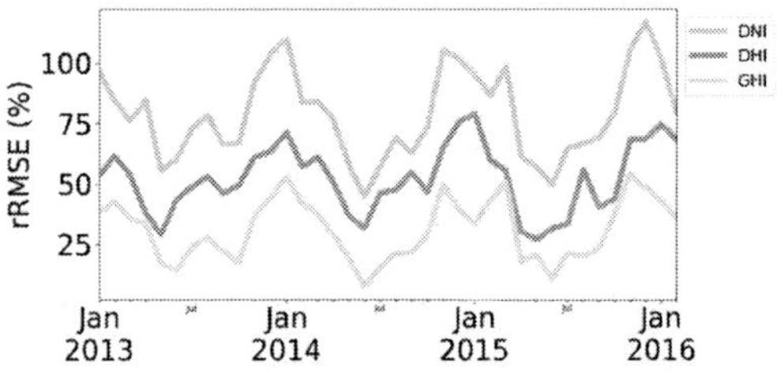

Figure 1: Monthly Trend of rRMSE on CRS Solar Radiation vs Ground Measurements

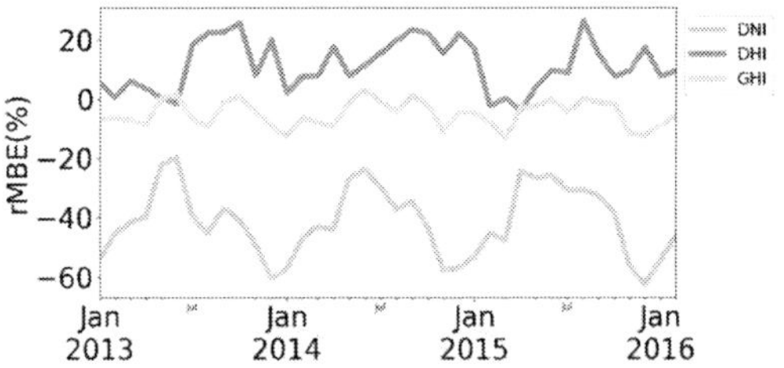

Figure 2: Monthly Trend of rMBE on CRS Solar Radiation vs Ground Measurements

lation, while DNI shows the lowest. Seasonal oscillations are visible but less pronounced than in rRMSE, reflecting the influence of atmospheric conditions on measurement accuracy. Among all three indicators, DNI exhibits the

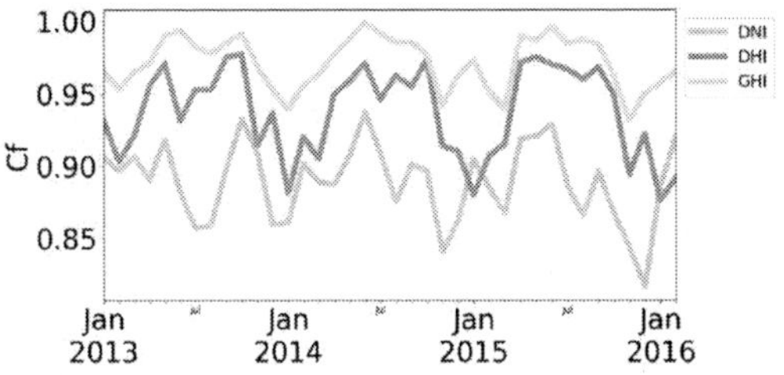

Figure 3: Monthly Trend of Cf on CRS Solar Radiation vs Ground Measurements

lowest performance. This may be attributed to the requirement for exact sensor alignment to capture the direct beam of sunlight, whereas satellites observe the scene from oblique angles.

To further examine the seasonal oscillation, cloud cover data were obtained from the Open-Meteo API [1] and are presented in Fig. 4. Cloud cover peaks in January and is minimal in July, which corresponds well with the rRMSE trends: higher errors coincide with higher cloudiness.

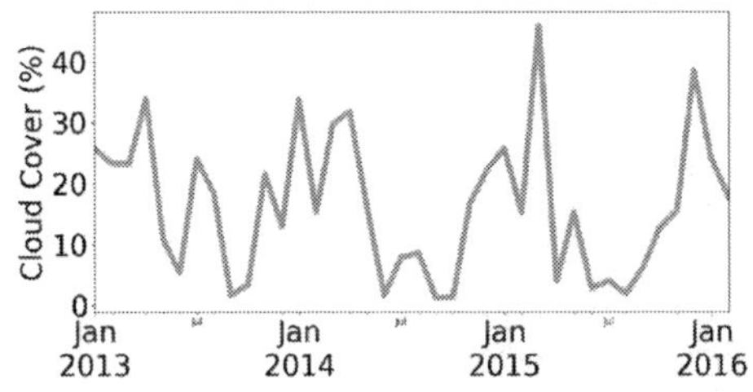

Figure 4: Monthly trend of Cloud Cover

Daily profiles were examined by randomly sampling days from January, May, June, and December, as shown in Figs. 5–8. On May 10, 2013, and June 15, 2015—typically cloud-free months—both CRS and ground measurements exhibit smooth profiles. GHI from CRS aligns closely with ground data, while DNI and DHI show greater sensitivity to atmospheric aerosols.

On January 5, 2014, CRS data capture cloud passages between approximately 09:00–12:00 and 14:00–16:00, reflected by decreased GHI and DNI and increased DHI, whereas ground measurements show smoother variations. December 4, 2015, represents a cloudy day with significant variability. The CRS DNI profile remains mostly flat, highlighting the challenge of accurately capturing direct normal irradiance under highly variable cloud conditions.

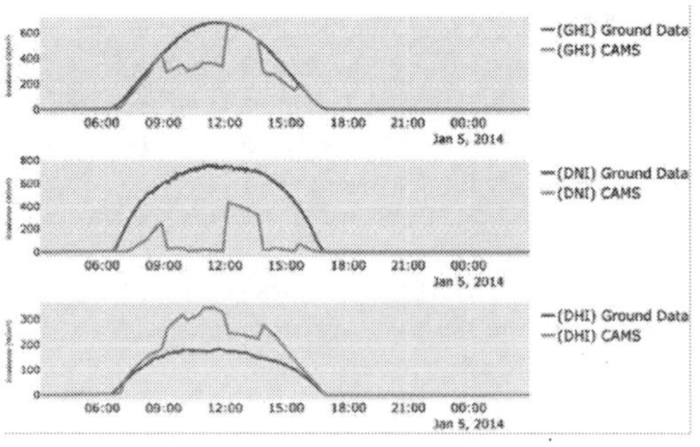

Figure 5: CRS and Ground Measurements on Jan 5, 2014

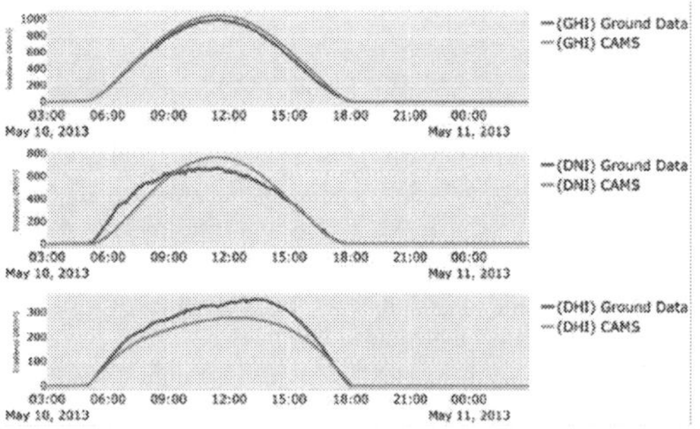

Figure 6: CRS and Ground Measurements on May 11, 2013

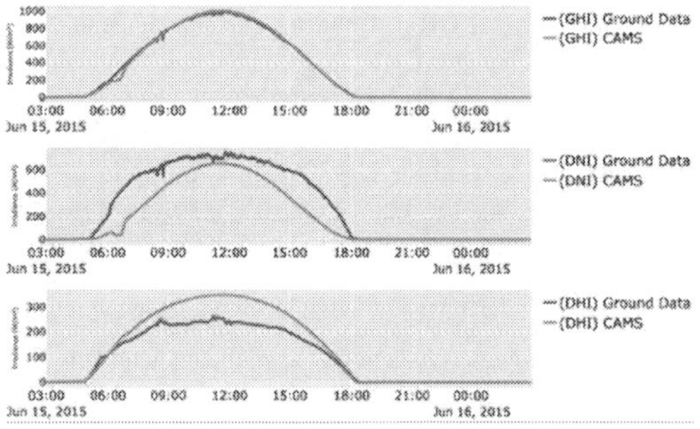

Figure 7: CRS and Ground Measurements on Jun 16, 2013

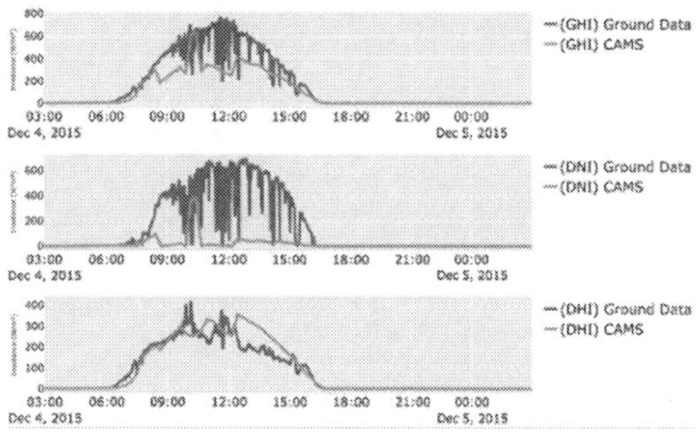

Figure 8: CRS and Ground Measurements on Dec 5, 2015

10.4229/EUPVSEC2025/4BV.3.29

5 CONCLUSION

In this study, we assessed the performance of CAMS-CRS against high-resolution ground measurements collected in Doha over a 38-month period (Jan/2013 to Feb/2016). By comparing the three primary solar radiation components—GHI, DNI, and DHI—using statistical metrics such as rRMSE, rMBE, and the Pearson correlation coefficient, we observed that GHI data from CRS performed the best overall, exhibiting the lowest relative error and highest correlation with ground measurements.

The monthly trend analysis revealed a seasonal oscillation in CRS accuracy, with improved performance during the clearer summer months (May–June) and reduced accuracy during winter months (December–January), corresponding to observed variations in cloud cover. Among the components, DNI consistently showed the weakest agreement with ground measurements, primarily due to the difficulty of capturing direct beam radiation from spaceborne platforms without precise alignment, as well as its greater sensitivity to cloud detection and aerosol modeling. These observations are consistent with previous findings reported by Papachristopoulou et al. (2024) [9] and Ameen et al. (2018) [3], who also documented monthly fluctuations in satellite-derived solar radiation accuracy.

Daily profile analysis further confirmed that CRS data aligns more closely with ground observations on clear-sky days, whereas significant discrepancies, particularly in DNI, occur on cloudy days.

Overall, these findings underscore the utility of CRS data for solar energy applications in arid regions such as Doha, especially for GHI estimation. However, caution is advised when relying on CRS-derived DNI values, particularly under cloudy or high-aerosol conditions. Future work will focus on site adaptation models to enhance CRS reliability during periods of increased cloud cover and aerosol concentrations, with the goal of improving retrieval precision and validating results under Qatar's desert climate.

6 ACKNOWLEDGEMENT

Research reported in this work was supported by the Qatar Research Development and Innovation Council (Grant: ARG01-0523-230304). The content is solely the responsibility of the authors and does not necessarily represent the official views of Qatar Research Development and Innovation Council.

REFERENCES

[1] Free Open-Source Weather API | Open-Meteo.com — open-meteo.com. `https://open-meteo.com`. [Accessed 22-09-2024].

[2] J. AlFaraj, E. Popovici, and P. Leahy. Solar irradiance database comparison for pv system design: A case study. *Sustainability*, 16(15):6436, 2024.

[3] B. Ameen, H. Balzter, C. Jarvis, E. Wey, C. Thomas, and M. Marchand. Validation of hourly global horizontal irradiance for two satellite-derived datasets in northeast iraq. *Remote Sensing*, 10(10):1651, 2018.

[4] D. Bachour, D. Perez-Astudillo, H. Alhajri, and A. Sanfilippo. Validation of HelioClim-3-derived solar radiation products in arid desert conditions. In *AIP Conference Proceedings*, volume 2815. AIP Publishing, 2023.

[5] C. C. C. S. (C3S). Cams radiation service api. `https://api.copernicus.eu/`. Accessed: 2025-03-15.

[6] J. A. Duffie and W. A. Beckman. *Solar engineering of thermal processes*. John Wiley & Sons, 2013.

[7] G. Huang, Z. Li, X. Li, S. Liang, K. Yang, D. Wang, and Y. Zhang. Estimating surface solar irradiance from satellites: Past, present, and future perspectives. *Remote Sensing of Environment*, 233:111371, 2019.

[8] M. Marchand, A. Ghennioui, E. Wey, and L. Wald. Comparison of several satellite-derived databases of surface solar radiation against ground measurement in morocco. *Advances in Science and Research*, 15:21–29, 2018.

[9] K. Papachristopoulou, I. Fountoulakis, A. F. Bais, B. E. Psiloglou, N. Papadimitriou, I.-P. Raptis, A. Kazantzidis, C. Kontoes, M. Hatzaki, and S. Kazadzis. Effects of clouds and aerosols on downwelling surface solar irradiance nowcasting and sort-term forecasting. *Atmospheric Measurement Techniques Discussions*, 2023:1–31, 2023.

[10] D. Perez-Astudillo, D. Bachou r, and L. Martín-Pomares. Improved quality control protocols on solar radiation measurements. *Solar Energy*, 169:425–433, 2018.

[11] Qatar Environment and Energy Research Institute (QEERI). QEERI solar atlas: Qatar's first solar atlas to map renewable energy potential. Technical report, Hamad Bin Khalifa University, 2020. Accessed: 2025-05-21.

Performance Evaluation of CAMS Reanalysis for Improved Solar Resource Assessment and Forecasting in Qatar's Desert Climate

A. Ziaullah[1], D. Bachour[1], D. Perez-Astudillo[1], L. Menard[2], P. Blanc[2]

1. Qatar Environment & Energy Research Institute, Hamad Bin Khalifa University, Qatar
2. MINES Paris, Universite PSL, France

QEERI
معهد قطر لبحوث البيئة والطاقة
Qatar Environment & Energy Research Institute
جامعة حمد بن خليفة
HAMAD BIN KHALIFA UNIVERSITY

EUPVSEC 2025
22 – 26 September 2025

Overview

Solar resource assessment is fundamental for solar energy projects, with ground-based measurements offering the most accurate data. In the absence of such data, satellite-derived solar radiation products present a valuable alternative due to their broad spatial and temporal coverage. However, evaluating the accuracy of these satellite models is critical for their reliable application. This study evaluates the performance of the CAMS Radiation Service (CRS), a satellite-derived solar radiation dataset from the European Union's Earth observation program, in the hot desert climate of Qatar. The suitability of CAMS reanalysis is done by comparing historical CRS solar radiation data—Global Horizontal Irradiance (GHI), Direct Normal Irradiance (DNI), and Diffuse Horizontal Irradiance (DHI)—with ground measurements from a solar monitoring station in Doha. The objective is to determine the suitability of CAMS reanalysis for improved solar resource assessment and forecasting in Qatar's desert climate.

Methodology

Solar radiation components were recorded at 1-minute resolution over three years by QEERI's monitoring station. Statistical comparisons using correlation factor (Cf), relative mean bias error (rMBE), and relative root mean square error (rRMSE) were performed.

Ground Data
DNI ground measurements are obtained using a CHP1 pyrheliometer. GHI and DHI were collected using CMP11 pyranometers for the duration of 38 months (Jan 2013 – Feb 2016). All the data was collected on 1-minute resolution

CRS Data
CRS data was obtained from CAMS API with corresponding timestamps from (Jan 2013 – Feb 2016). All the data was collected on 1-minute resolution

Performance Indicators
3 performance indicators were used
Relative Root Mean Square Error (rRMSE)
Relative Mean Bias Error (rMBE)
Pearson's correlation coefficient (Cf)

Analysis and Results

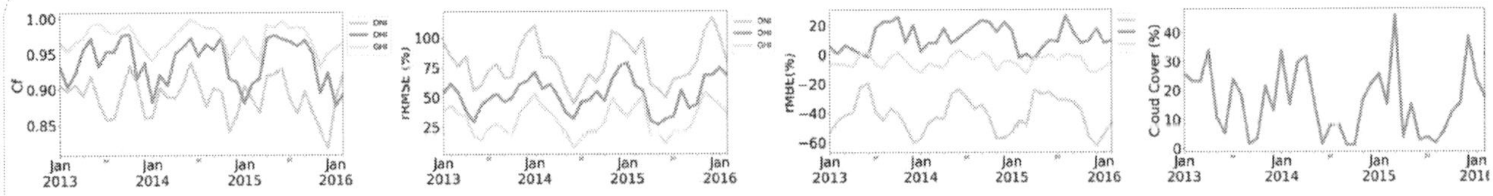

Monthly Variations of CRS vs Ground data left to right (Pearson's correlation coefficient, rRMSE , rMBE, Cloud cover)
Cloud cover data downloaded from https://open-meteo.com/

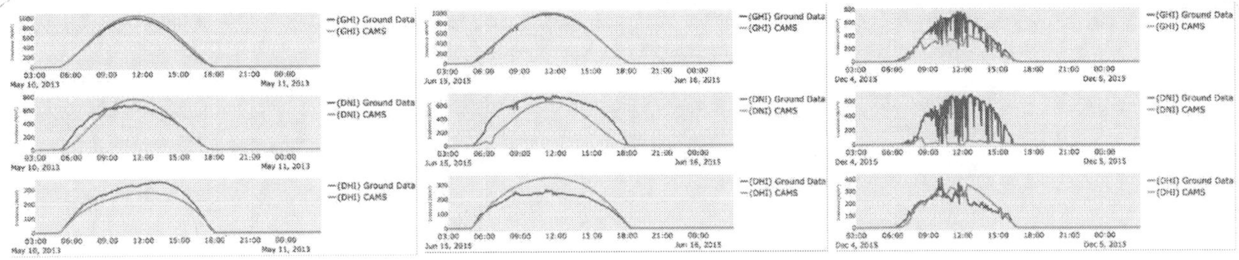

Daily Variations of CRS vs Ground data left to right (May 11, 2013 / June 16,2015 / Dec 5, 2015)

Discussions

By comparing the three primary solar radiation components—GHI, DNI, and DHI—using statistical metrics — rRMSE, rMBE, and the Pearson correlation coefficient — we observed that GHI data from CRS performed the best overall, exhibiting the lowest rRMSE, rMBE and Cf with the ground measurements. The monthly trend analysis revealed a seasonal oscillation in CRS accuracy, with improved performance during clearer summer months (May–June) and reduced accuracy during winter months (December–January), which aligns well with the observed variation in the cloud cover. Among the components, DNI consistently showed the weakest agreement with ground-based measurements. This is primarily due to the inherent difficulty in capturing direct beam radiation from spaceborne platforms without precise alignment, as well as the greater sensitivity of DNI to errors in cloud detection and aerosol modeling. The findings underscore the utility of CRS data for solar energy applications in arid regions like Doha, especially for GHI. However, it is essential to note that calibration against ground-based measurements remains necessary even for GHI, to ensure optimal accuracy and reliability. Furthermore, caution should be exercised when relying on CRS-derived DNI, DHI values, particularly in cloudy or high-aerosol conditions.

Acknowledgement

Research reported in this work was supported by the Qatar Research Development and Innovation Council (Grant: ARG01-0523-230304). The content is solely the responsibility of the authors and does not necessarily represent the official views of Qatar Research Development and Innovation Council.

2025 EU-PVSEC, Bilbao 4BV.3.32
42nd European Photovoltaic Solar Energy Conference and Exhibition

Defining an Irradiance Quantity for Outdoor Assessment of PV System Performance

Anton Driesse
PV Performance Labs, Germany
anton.driesse@pvperformancelabs.com

James Blakesley
National Physical Laboratory, UK
james.blakesley@npl.co.uk

Reach out to us if you have suggestions or better ideas!

The Challenge

Performance indicators compare output energy to input energy, i.e. irradiance.

- In the lab, PV *module* performance is assessed using a light source facing the module and emitting a light of a known spectrum and intensity.
- In the field, PV *system* performance is observed under a wide variety irradiance conditions with spatial, spectral and intensity variations.
- Field performance indicators using pyranometer irradiance measurements are highly standardized, but produce high variability.
- Field Performance indicators using reference cell irradiance measurements are more consistent, but are only formally traceable under lab conditions.

How can we reduce the variability and improve the traceability?

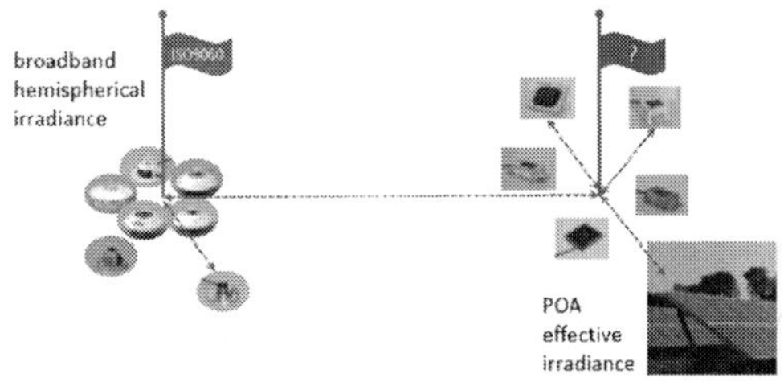

Solution

The way forward is to define an irradiance quantity that more closely represents the solar energy that is *available for conversion* to electricity, rather than the total solar energy.

The total solar energy received on a flat surface as measured by a pyranometer is the integral of the radiance over all directions and a wide range of wavelengths:

$$E_{PYR} = \frac{\int_0^{2\pi}\int_0^{\pi/2}\int_{300}^{3000} I(\lambda,\theta,\phi)\cdot\cos(\theta)\cdot\sin(\theta)\,d\lambda\,d\theta\,d\phi}{\int_{300}^{3000} E_{ref}(\lambda)\,d\lambda}\cdot E_{ref}$$

The solar energy available for conversion by a PV module is reduced by the directional response $\mathrm{IAM}(\theta)$, and the spectral response $S(\lambda)$:

$$E_{PV} = \frac{\int_0^{2\pi}\int_0^{\pi/2}\int_{300}^{1200} I(\lambda,\theta,\phi)\cdot S(\lambda)\cdot \mathrm{IAM}(\theta)\cdot\cos(\theta)\cdot\sin(\theta)\,d\lambda\,d\theta\,d\phi}{\int_{300}^{1200} E_{ref}(\lambda)\cdot S(\lambda)\,d\lambda}\cdot E_{ref}$$

Commercial reference cells already measure this quantity approximately, but a new standard is needed to define this quantity precisely.

Based on the proposed definition, accuracy classes (A,B,C) will be defined for reference cells based on how well they measure this quantity.

Directional Response

The directional response $\mathrm{IAM}(\theta)$ of PV modules varies due to different materials, coatings , textures. A single standard response is needed as a point of reference.

We propose a standard curve based on reflection at the air-glass interface, which can be calculated precisely using the Fresnel equations.

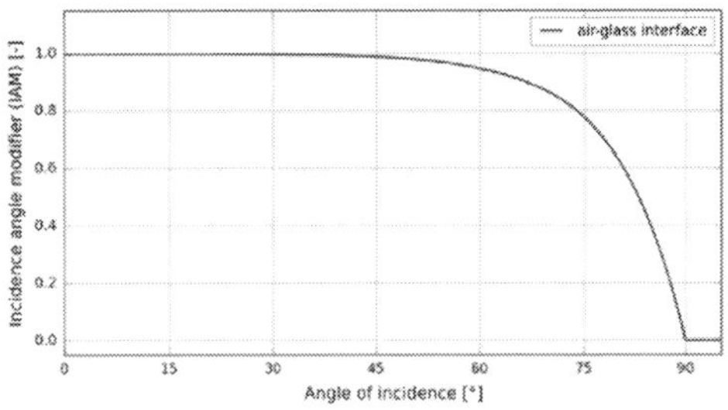

When compared to this standard response, PV modules with superior anti-reflective coatings and textures will achieve higher outdoor performance.

Spectral Response

The spectral response $S(\lambda)$ of PV modules varies due to different dimensions, materials, designs. A single standard response is needed as a point of reference.

We propose a standard curve to represents the response of a basic silicon PV cell. Shown here is a simple geometric definition which can be calculated precisely.

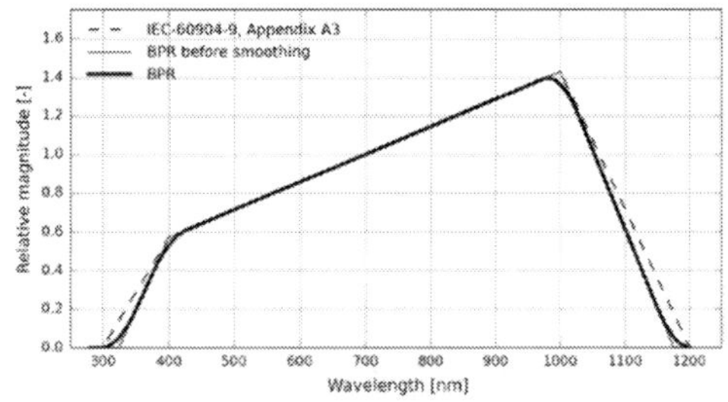

While broad spectral response can lead to higher absolute efficiencies, the link between spectral response and outdoor performance indicators is complex.

SOLiD-PV is a European Partnership on Metrology project that aims to quantify and reduce sources of uncertainty in key performance indicators for PV systems. https://www.solid-pv.ptb.de/home

PV Performance Labs provides a range of services in support of PV system R&D and operations including planning, measurements, simulation and analysis. PV Performance Labs participates in the SOLiD-PV project.

EUROPEAN PARTNERSHIP Co-funded by the European Union

Funded by the European Union. Views and opinions expressed are however those of the author(s) only and do not necessarily reflect those of the European Union or EURAMET. Neither the European Union nor the granting authority can be held responsible for them.

METROLOGY PARTNERSHIP EURAMET

The project has received funding from the European Partnership on Metrology, co-financed from the European Union's Horizon Europe Research and Innovation Programme and by the Participating States.

TIME-RESOLVED ENERGY YIELD ESTIMATION OF RESIDENTIAL PHOTOVOLTAIC SYSTEMS: THE IMPACT OF TREE SHADING

Richard de jong[1,2,3], Patrizio Manganiello[1,2,3], Olivier Dupon[1,2,3], Sara Bouguerra[1,2,3], Arnaud Morlier[1,2,3]
[1]IMO-IMOMEC, Hasselt University, Wetenschapspark 1, 3590 Diepenbeek, Belgium, [2]imec, imo-imomec, Thor Park, Genk, Belgium, [3]EnergyVille, Genk, Belgium
richard.dejong@imec.be, arnaud.morlier@imec.be, Patrizio.Manganiello@imec.be, Olivier.dupon@imec.be, Sara.Bouguerra@imec.be

ABSTRACT: In this study, a methodology is developed to estimate the photovoltaic (PV) energy output of dwellings within a suburban setting. The primary goal of this methodology is to calculate the contribution of roof-mounted PV systems to individual household energy balances throughout the year, considering dwelling types, different azimuth orientations, and predefined roof-mounted PV system configurations. The methodology factors in PV module characteristics, sunlight absorption, ground albedo, ambient temperature, wind velocity, and other variables. Typical meteorological data from the PVGIS database is used to simulate energy yields. The study models four types of dwellings, creating specific 3D CAD models and simulating energy yields for each dwelling object. Detailed information about tree locations and dimensions is integrated into the simulation to accurately model tree shading effects. Results show that uniform tree heights of 15 m, 25 m, and 30 m would result in yearly median energy yield losses of approximately 15%, 25%, and 35%, respectively. Energy losses can be unevenly spread throughout the day and can also occur during peak consumption hours. This work lays the foundation for integrating real-time and forecast data into household digital twin models and presents a framework for simulating PV system yields in suburban environments.
Keywords: energy yield estimation, residential photovoltaic systems, tree shading

1 AIM AND APPROACH

The integration of photovoltaic (PV) systems in residential and community settings is becoming increasingly vital as solar power continues to expand its share in national electricity grids. In Belgium, solar energy saw a 23% increase in installed capacity in 2024, contributing to a record 29.8% of the electricity mix. This shift reflects a broader trend in which renewable energy sources are gradually replacing traditional gas-fired generation, which fell to an all-time low of 17.6% [1].

The primary aim of this work is to provide an accurate estimation of the PV solar energy output for dwellings in a suburban setting and its contribution to the energy balance of households. The case study considered in this work is the project of the existing social housing district Nieuw Texas in Genk, Belgium. The goal is to generate time-resolved simulations of the PV system output for each individual dwelling, accounting for variables such as system configuration, orientation, and environmental factors, with a special focus on the effect of shading from nearby trees.

The approach follows a multi-physics, bottom-up energy yield model developed by imec. This model incorporates PV module characteristics, geometries, and weather factors such as irradiance, ground albedo, ambient temperature, wind velocity, and humidity. Moreover, the simulation tool allows for performing simulations at the PV cell, module, and string levels. A flowchart of the energy yield simulation framework is shown in Figure 1. Weather data from the PVGIS database is used to simulate energy yields over a typical meteorological year (TMY).

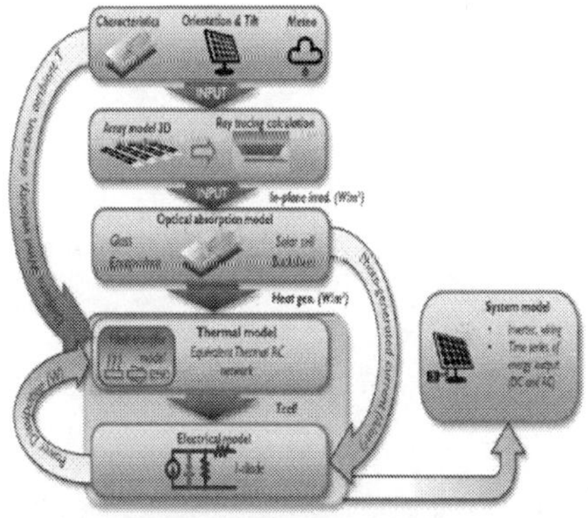

Figure 1: Energy Yield Simulation Framework

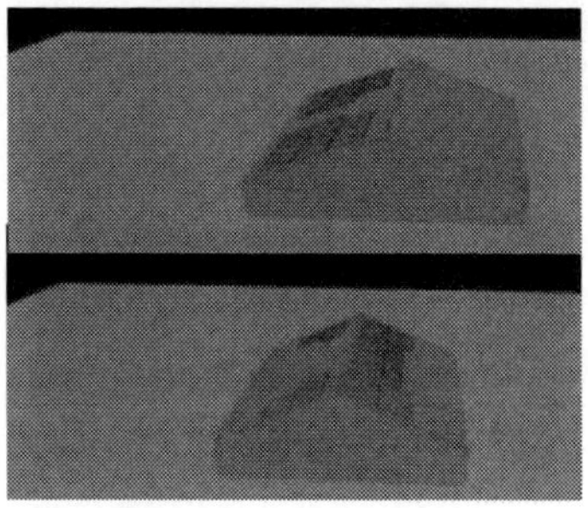

Figure 2: Two Examples of dwellings with two specific PV system layouts

10.4229/EUPVSEC2025/4BV.4.1
020294-001

The methodology integrates detailed 3D CAD models of the four types of dwellings present in the suburban Nieuw Texas district. This includes dwelling geometries, azimuth orientation, and specific roof PV system configurations. Twenty-eight roof-mounted PV system configurations were previously defined by an external party. Figure 2 shows two examples of similar dwellings with different orientations and, consequently, different PV systems projected onto their roofs.

The detailed 3D model also includes the precise positioning and dimensions of existing trees that may influence PV system performance (Figures 3 and 4). Tree locations and heights are incorporated using data from the Limburg Service Association (s-lim) [2]. By utilizing ray tracing, the simulation framework models the impact of shading on PV systems from trees and nearby buildings. The shadow effect is calculated over time, with hourly resolution, and spatially at the sub-cell level, using multiple sensing points per cell. These steps are crucial for accurate energy yield predictions.

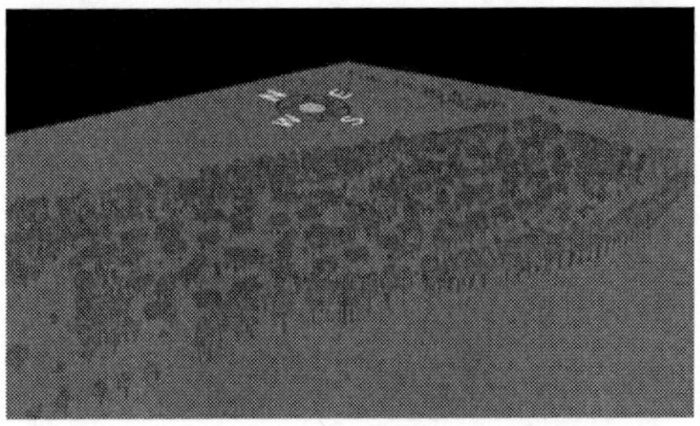

Figure 3: South-west view of the modelled Nieuw Texas district, Genk

Figure 4: Modelled dwelling with depiction of the irradiance inhomogeneity on the PV system during a morning hour

2 SCIENTIFIC INNOVATION AND RELEVANCE

The power output of residential PV systems under shading conditions has been evaluated in several studies. In [3], the impact of environmental factors such as ground albedo, module spacing, and tilt angle on annual energy generation was analyzed using PVSyst, enabling the optimization of system design to achieve a higher performance ratio. Another study [4] compared two different modeling software tools to evaluate shading losses in PV systems. The results showed an overestimation of 9% to 24% in energy output, primarily attributed to the simplification of 3D models and the lack of geometrical and optical details in the simulation. To address this gap, the method presented in this paper incorporates a detailed 3D model—based on polygons—for dwellings and nearby trees to predict shading loss more accurately. By integrating this 3D model with detailed optical and electrical-thermal models within the energy yield framework shown in Figure 1, a highly detailed, time-resolved energy yield model for photovoltaic (PV) systems in suburban environments is created. This allows for accurate simulation of energy output and quantification of the effects of both natural (trees) and artificial (e.g., buildings) surrounding objects on system performance.

Simulating energy yield in residential settings—especially when combined with real-time and forecast data—co-creates sustainable solutions within local communities and with residents. This empowers them to make informed decisions that improve energy efficiency, reduce carbon footprints, and enhance overall living conditions. This research is highly relevant to the objectives of the oPENlab project, particularly as part of the Genk Living Lab in which this study was done [5]. The accurate estimation of the energy provided by the PV system to the household is a crucial element towards the establishment of a digital twin of a dwelling, which integrates the solar energy yield from PV system with the contribution/consumption of individual HVAC, heat pumps and battery storages.

The project's methodology and findings could similarly be applied to other districts in Genk, as well as to suburbs of other cities. It promotes the integration of renewable energy into everyday life and contributes to broader sustainability goals.

3 RESULTS (OR PRELIMINARY RESULTS) AND CONCLUSIONS

The preliminary results of this study highlight the significant impact of tree height on the energy yield of photovoltaic (PV) systems in residential areas. Simulations were conducted on fifty-five dwellings, representing the most common dwelling type in the Nieuw Texas district. In the near future, each of these dwellings will be equipped with 14 PV modules. The simulations indicate that uniform tree heights of 15 m, 25 m, and 30 m would result in yearly median energy yield losses of approximately 15%, 25%, and 35%, respectively. This decline underscores the importance of accurately modeling tree-shading effects for reliable energy output predictions (Figure 5). Furthermore, the variation in calculated energy yield losses suggests that the impact of vegetation growth cannot be simplified into a one-size-fits-all approach for all PV systems within the same neighborhood.

Time-resolved analysis further shows that, on a typical November day, tree shading causes a 30% reduction in energy yield for a moderately shaded dwelling with 14 modules, with the greatest losses occurring during late morning hours (Figures 4 and 6). These findings highlight the necessity of regular tree maintenance and pruning to optimize PV system performance. The results of this analysis can inform property owners and local authorities about tree maintenance and pruning plans.

In conclusion, this study provides a robust framework for simulating PV energy output for individual dwellings in suburban environments by integrating both environmental and system-specific factors. Time-resolved simulations illustrate that energy loss is unevenly distributed throughout the day and emphasize the significant impact of shading, particularly during peak consumption hours. Additionally, the study underscores the importance of incorporating environmental constraints, such as trees, into the digital twins of seemingly identical systems to ensure accurate energy balance calculations for individual households. It also highlights the need for regular assessments of tree shading due to vegetation growth over a system's lifetime. This approach, combined with real-time and forecast data, co-creates sustainable solutions within local communities and with residents.

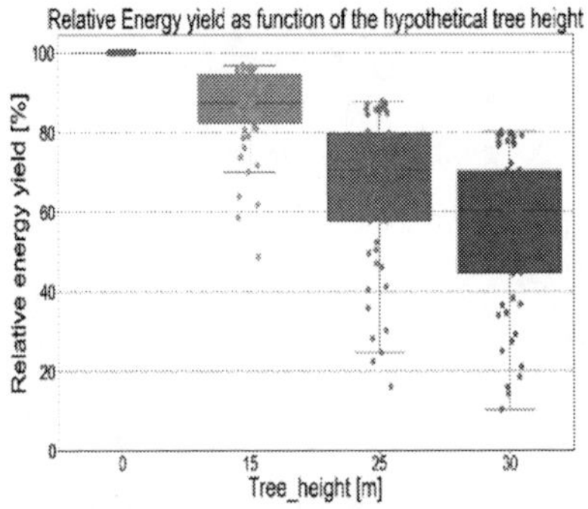

Figure 5: Relative Energy Yield of fifty-five dwellings, each with fourteen PV modules, calculated without trees (0 m) and with trees of three different uniform heights

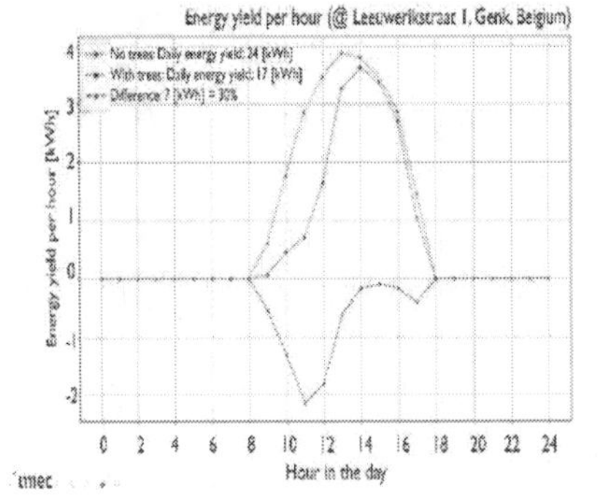

Figure 6: PV power output of a residential system, calculated without trees and with actual surrounding tree heights

References:

[1] Elia Group, "Electricity mix for Belgium in 2024: record international exchanges, significant increase in solar generation, and low use of gas-fired capacities." [Online]. Available: https://www.elia.be/en/press/2025/0120250102_electricity-mix.

[2] Limburg Service Association (s-lim) [Online]. Available: https://s-lim.be/

[3] J. Jamal, I. Mansur, A. Rasid, M. Mulyadi, M. Dihyah Marwan, and M. Marwan, "Evaluating the shading effect of photovoltaic panels to optimize the performance ratio of a solar power system," *Results in Engineering*, vol. 21, p. 101878, Mar. 2024, doi: 10.1016/j.rineng.2024.101878.

[4] E. D. Chepp, F. P. Gasparin, and A. Krenzinger, "Accuracy investigation in the modeling of partially shaded photovoltaic systems, "*Solar Energy*, vol. 223, pp. 182–192, Jul. 2021 doi: 10.1016/j.solener.2021.05.061.

[5] Positive Energy Neighbourhoods (oPEN) Living Labs: Tartu (Estonia), Pamplona (Spain), Genk (Belgium), funded by the European Union's Horizon 2020 Research and Innovation Programme: https://openlab-project.eu/

Time-Resolved Energy Yield Estimation of Residential Photovoltaic Systems: The Impact of Tree Shading

Richard de jong[1,2,3], Patrizio Manganiello[1,2,3], Olivier Dupon[1,2,3], Sara Bouguerra[1,2,3], Ismail Kaaya[1,2,3], Nikoleta Kyranaki[1,2,3], Arnaud Morlier[1,2,3]
[1]IMO-IMOMEC, Hasselt University, Wetenschapspark 1, 3590 Diepenbeek, Belgium, [2]imec, imo-imomec, Thor Park, Genk, Belgium, [3]EnergyVille, Genk, Belgium

Motivation

This study aims to provide an accurate **time-resolved energy yield estimation for dwellings** in a suburban setting and its **contribution to the energy balance of households**. This study is carried out as part of the oPENLab project [1]. It focuses on the New-Texas district in Genk, Belgium.

The geometric 3D model in the simulation considers:

- Specific dwelling types
- Different azimuth orientations
- Predefined roof-mounted PV system configurations
- Actual tree locations and dimensions [2,3,4]

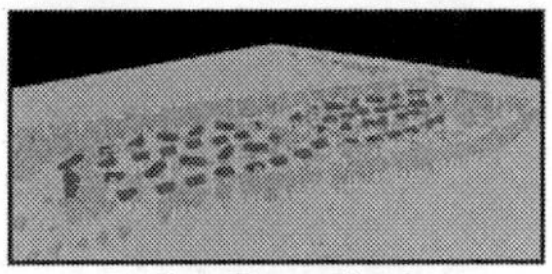

New-Texas district Genk, Belgium

It is key to incorporate trees in the geometric 3D model to accurately predict the foreseeable tree-shading impact on the daily PV system efficiency: Today, and as trees mature over time.

Boxplot distribution of Energy Yield as function of the hypothetical tree height, relative to a treeless environment.

Evaluated over a Typical Meteorological Year (TMY).

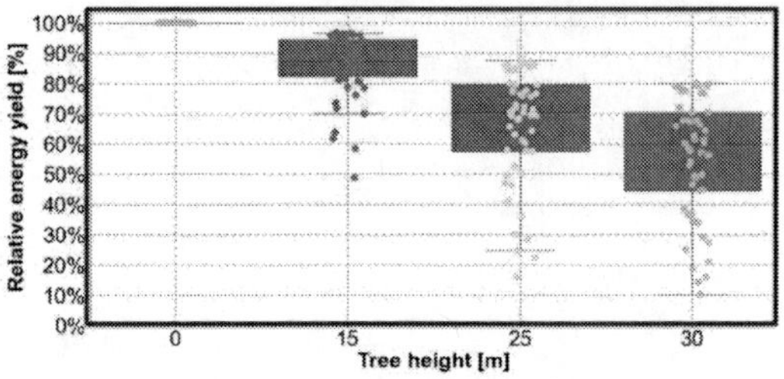

The shading effect is unevenly distributed throughout the day, with notable losses during peak consumption hours:

Hourly energy yield in a day: with/without surrounding trees.

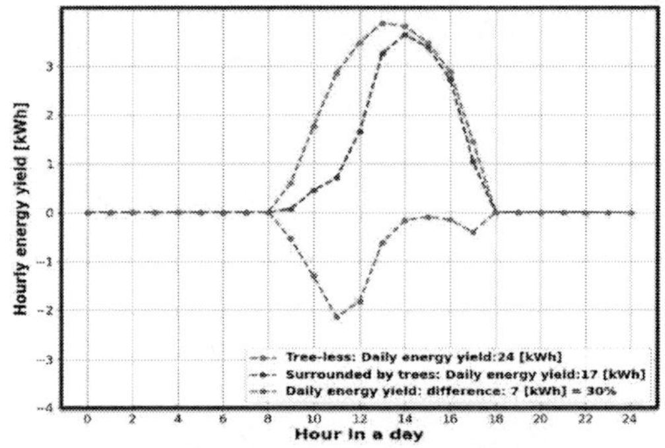

Methodology

Simulations are done using **imec's PV-simulation framework** [5]:

- **Bottom-up, multi-physics energy yield model**
- **Incorporates:**
  - PV module characteristics
  - Weather data
    - Current: Typical Meteorological Year (TMY) for general predictions
    - Next phase: Live meteorological data for real-time modelling
  - **Detailed geometric 3D model**
    - **Dwellings**
    - **PV configurations on dwellings**
    - **Surrounding trees**

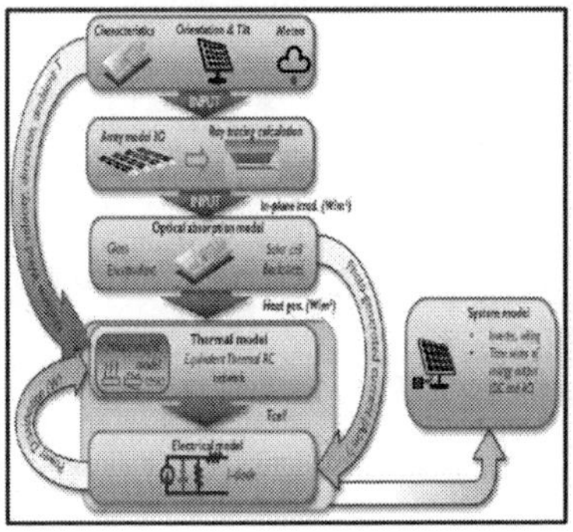

imec's multi-physics PV-simulation framework

Examples of dwellings with specific PV system layouts

Modules partly shaded by trees in the morning

Results

Tree height significantly affects the energy yield of PV-modules (55 dwellings, 14 PV modules each):

Hypothetical tree height [m]	Median energy yield loss relative to a treeless environment [%]
15	15
25	25
30	35

Conclusion

This study emphasizes:

- **The importance of integrating environmental constraints** into digital twin models for accurate energy balance calculations.
- **The significant impact of surrounding trees on the energy yield**.
- **Unevenly distributed losses throughout the day demands time-resolved energy yield calculation.**
- **Regular tree maintenance and pruning is necessary** to optimize PV system performance.

Next

Next steps:

- Use LIDAR input to establish the 3D geometry of trees and dwellings.
- Use live meteorological data for real-time modelling.

Acknowledgments

The authors thank the Limburg Service Association (s-lim), Aster and EnergyVision for providing tree, dwelling, and PV-configuration data.

[1]Positive Energy Neighbourhoods (oPEN) Living Labs: Tartu (Estonia), Pamplona (Spain), Genk (Belgium), funded by the European Union's Horizon 2020 Research and Innovation Programme: https://openlab-project.eu/
[2] Limburg Service Association (s-lim) [Online]. Available: https://s-lim.be/
[3] EnergyVision: www.energyvision.be
[4] Aster: www.aster.vlaanderen
[5] T. Horvath et al., "Next Generation Tools for Accurate Energy Yield Estimation of Bifacial PV Systems – Best Practices, Improvements and Challenges,"

The oPEN Lab project has received funding from the European Union's Horizon 2020 Research and Innovation Framework Programme under Grant agreement No. 101037080. Views and opinions expressed are those of the author(s) only and do not necessarily reflect those of the European Union or the European Climate, Infrastructure and Environment Executive Agency (CINEA). Neither the European Union nor the granting authority can be held responsible for them.

020295-001

PV SYSTEM DESIGN WITH CURTAILMENT IN MIND: COSTS AND EMISSIONS AT THE PROSUMER LEVEL

Linda Brodnicke[1] Alissa Ganter[1], Giovanni Sansavini[1], Natasa Vulic[2]*

1. Reliability and Risk Engineering Lab, ETH Zürich
2. Institute for Sustainability and Energy in Buildings, University of Applied Sciences and Arts Northwestern Switzerland

Introduction / Background

The adoption of photovoltaic (PV) systems among end-consumers is expected to increase significantly. However, as the penetration of PV systems grows, grid congestion may lead to increased curtailment, negatively impacting the return on investment of PV systems that are designed under the assumption of favorable feed-in tariffs and unrestricted grid access. Given that PV systems represent long-term investments, decisions are often based on current conditions. These include existing feed-in tariffs, electricity prices, and the absence of export limitations. In this study, we investigate the following:

RQ1: How do **export limitations** influence the **optimal design of PV-battery systems** (system size, tilt, orientation, battery capacity) and their associated **life cycle costs and emissions?**

RQ2: What are the **impacts of incorrect foresight** about future export limitations (both overestimating and underestimating export freedom) on the **life cycle costs and emissions** of PV-battery systems?

Methodology

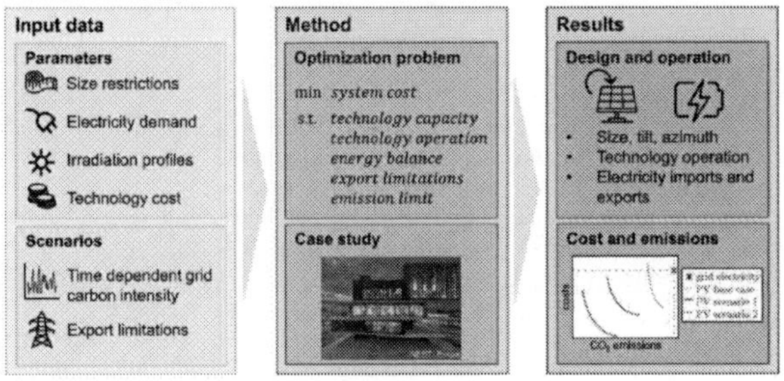

Brodnicke and Gartner, Energy and Buildings 2024

Optimization approach: Mixed-integer linear programming (MILP) formulated in Python (cvxpy, solved with Gurobi).

Objectives: Minimize

Annualized system cost → capital + operational – revenues

Annual GHG emissions → embodied + operational – export credits

Scenarios:
Base case (unlimited export, time-dependent grid carbon intensity)
Export limitations at 50%, 25%, and 0% of maximum feed-in in the base case

Scenario	Assumed during design	Export limit at operation
☑ Correct foresight (unl.)	Unlimited export	Unlimited export
☑ Correct foresight (cap)	Strict export cap	Strict export cap
⚠ Overestimate freedom	Unlimited export	Strict export cap
⚠ Underestimate freedom	Strict export cap	Unlimited export

Results and Discussion

RQ1: optimal design of PV-battery systems under export limitations

Pareto optimal solutions

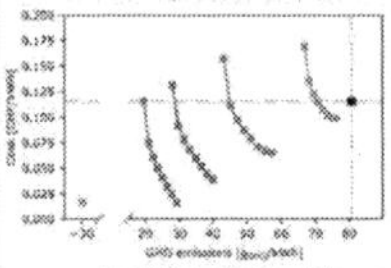

Brodnicke and Gartner, Energy and Buildings 2024

Minimum cost solutions

Minimum emissions solutions

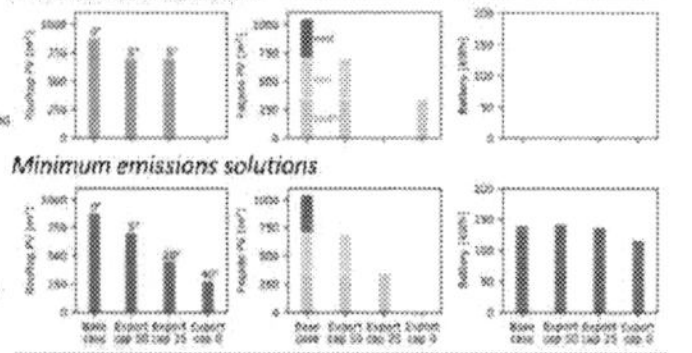

With increasing export limitations:

minimum cost solutions → more favorable than grid-only in terms of both costs and emissions
minimum emissions solutions → more favorable in terms of emissions, costlier than grid-only

minimum cost solutions → reduced PV size, no battery is installed in any of the export limitation scenarios
minimum emission solutions → reduced PV size with increased tilt, battery is installed in all scenarios

RQ2: impact of incorrect foresight about future export limitations

overestimating freedom to export

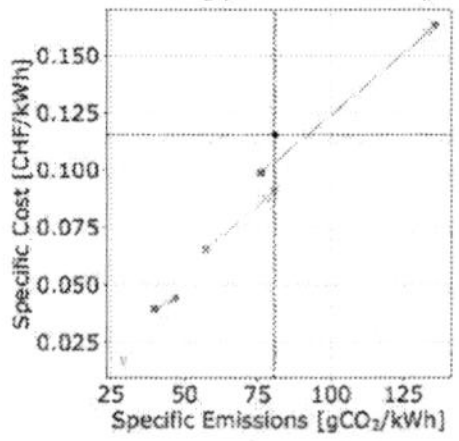

underestimating freedom to export

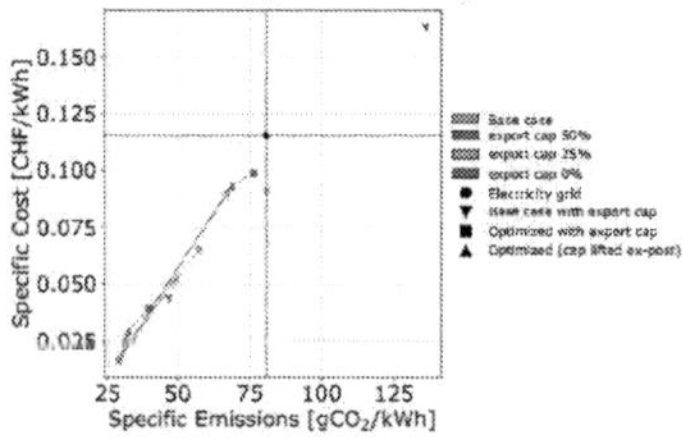

Compared to correct foresight (cap) at min. cost:
50% export cap → +11% cost, +18% emissions
25% export cap → +39% cost, +41% emissions
0% export cap → +65% cost, +79% emissions

Compared to correct foresight (unl) at min. cost:
50% export cap → +73% cost, +12% emissions
25% export cap →+210% cost, +71% emissions
0% export cap → +446% cost, +136% emissions

Conclusions

In response to the research questions posed above, the following key takeaways can be made based on the presented case study:

RQ1: optimal design of PV-battery systems under export limitations
- Export limits reduce both the emission reduction potential and its cost-effectiveness compared to the base case (no export limitations)
- Cost-optimal solutions with export limits outperform the grid-only by favoring smaller PV systems that self-consumption (rather than installing a battery)
- Emission-optimal solutions with export limits are more costly than grid-only solutions, with system design favoring increased tilt and a battery system

RQ2: impact of incorrect foresight about future export limitations
- **Overestimating freedom** ⟶ Export caps match the grid at best (25%), but can nearly double emissions for the strictest export case (0%)
- **Underestimating freedom** ⟶ Lifting caps restores revenue and credits, but leaves opportunities unrealized compared to the base case
- **50% cap assumption** ⟶ impact of incorrect foresight has a negligible impact in the two cases (both overestimating and underestimating export freedom)

Implications

- **High export limits** significantly influence both **economic viability** and **emission reduction** potential of PV installations ⟶ decision to install
- **Understanding export caps** is crucial for planning PV integration that is both **cost-effective and climate-aligned** ⟶ misjudging the benefits
- **For prosumers** ⟶ need robust investment strategies under uncertain export policies when planning their PV system installations
- **For policymakers** ⟶ regulations and incentives should explicitly account for curtailment effects to ensure promotion of renewable energy

Next steps

- Apply framework to other context (e.g. *dynamic tariffs, local energy communities* [2], *repowering decisions* [3]) to evaluate the impact on costs and emissions
- Expand to a *multi-stage optimization* [3] *approach* to evaluate how future conditions may impact operational or investment decisions for future stages

References

[1] L. Brodnicke, A. Ganter, S. Tröber, G. Sansavini, and N. Vulic, "Dynamic grid emission factors and export limits reduce emission abatement and cost benefits of building PV systems," Energy and Buildings, vol. 323, p. 114772, 2024. doi: 10.1016/j.enbuild.2024.114772
[2] Q. Li, N. Vulic, H. Cai, and P. Heer, "Flexibility implications of optimal PV design: Building vs. community scale," *J. Phys.: Conf. Ser.*, vol. 2600, no. 8, p. 082002, 2023. doi: 10.1088/1742-6596/2600/8/082002.
[3] S. Ovaitt, H. Mirletz, B. Mirletz, and M. Prilliman, "Repowering PV systems demystified: Terms, motives, economics and impacts," in *Proc. IEEE 53rd Photovoltaic Specialists Conf. (PVSC)*, Montreal, QC, Canada, 2025, doi: 10.1109/PVSC59419.2025.11132584
[4] F. Solèr, Y.-C. B. Chen, N. Vulic, and G. Mavromatidis, "Investigation of near-optimal solutions for building retrofit and portfolio optimization," presented at *SBE25*, 2025.

BIPV SIMULATION WITH CONVENTIONAL TOOLS AND MODELS; DO WE NEED MORE ACCURACY?

Ana Marcos-Castro [a,b], Nuria Martín-Chivelet [a], Jesús Polo [a], Carlos Sanz-Saiz [a]

[a] CIEMAT, Photovoltaic Solar Energy Unit, Av. Complutense, 40, 28040 Madrid, Spain
[b] Universidad Politécnica de Madrid, Av. de Juan de Herrera, 4, 28040 Madrid, Spain
ana.marcos@ciemat.es, nuria.martin@ciemat.es, jesus.polo@ciemat.es, carlos.sanz@ciemat.es

ABSTRACT: The present work compares two simulation tools, SAM and PVsyst, to assess their suitability in analysing the behaviour of BIPV systems, with special focus on their management of the effect of shading losses in energy output estimations, in addition to module temperature. The simulations are performed for Building 42 in CIEMAT headquarters, which was renovated in 2017 with monitored BIPV systems on the east, south and west façades. The shading tools in both software are capable of modelling the environment through simple geometric elements; moreover, PVsyst also allows the use of an external 3D file that can simplify the process. The results of this study manifest that the 3D scene method used to assess the effect of shading can have a strong impact on the reliability of energy output estimations. When using the same 3D scenes through their built-in tools, SAM shows better performance than PVsyst. In contrast, PVsyst energy output results improve significantly when using an imported 3D digital asset exchange file derived from Light Detection and Ranging data. This discrepancy in results remarks the need for special attention regarding the configuration and modelling of shading elements, which requires future work to better understand the simulation methods in each tool.
Keywords: BIPV modelling, PV simulation tools, BIPV shading.

1 INTRODUCTION

Although efforts are increasingly made towards decarbonisation and energy efficiency [1–3], integrating photovoltaic systems into building envelopes is still hindered by the limited availability of simulation tools that help justify the design and accurately estimate energy outcome of BIPV systems [4]. While this is mostly straightforward for PV plants, BIPV systems require software tools that can accommodate diverse boundary conditions, e.g., the surrounding environment and shading, the constructive solution and ventilation, and the tilt and azimuth angles of the modules.

Analysing and comparing simulation tools [5–7] provides valuable information to support future BIPV installations by helping decide which tools are suitable and to what extent for each case, based on aspects such as project specifications and design requirements, boundary conditions, and stakeholders' resources and skills.

The aim of this work is to assess the suitability of different software tools to estimate the behaviour of a BIPV system. Moreover, factors such as the ease-of-use, the simplicity or complexity of the base model and design process, the ability to include the environment and shading elements, or the customisability of the BIPV constructive system and module characteristics have been considered. All of these aspects are highly relevant in BIPV systems, especially in urban areas where buildings are subject to specific boundary conditions that need to be accounted for in the simulation stages of the project. Special focus is set on each tool's methodology for calculating module temperature, given that BIPV modules are generally poorly ventilated on their backside, causing an increase in their operating temperature and, therefore, a decrease in their PV energy performance. Therefore, module temperature determination can play a crucial role in energy estimation of BIPV systems.

2 PV MODELLING TOOLS APPLIED TO BIPV

SAM [8] and PVsyst [9] are two widely used photovoltaic simulation tools that provide means to estimate the behaviour of BIPV systems. Both offer 3D scene capabilities to account for shading with simple design features for buildings and vegetation. Furthermore, to better represent the operating conditions of a BIPV system, these programs include customisable features through the temperature model of the photovoltaic modules.

2.1 SAM

SAM is a free tool that offers two performance models to calculate the energy output of a BIPV system: a detailed model for an in-depth analysis and a basic model for a preliminary approach. Choosing one over the other depends on the availability of system specifications and input data, with the basic model requiring fewer parameters, mainly module efficiency, while resulting in less accurate calculations. Given that all necessary system specifications are known in Building 42, the study developed in this paper used the detailed model.

SAM provides a customisable mounting standoff option based on the distance between the module and the constructive element behind it, providing several distance ranges to choose from. The selected distance is taken into account for the calculations to better represent the effect of rear ventilation on the module's temperature. The model is based on the Nominal Operating Cell Temperature (NOCT), modified with temperature increments which are a function of the distance between the module and the constructive element behind it. The user can choose the mounting standoff distance that better suits the project design, ranging from lower than 0.5 inches, with NOCT increasing by 18 degrees, up to 3.5 inches, which leads to a NOCT increase of 2 degrees. This menu offers an additional 'building integrated' option, which instead of applying a default modification to the NOCT requires the user to manually include an NOCT value previously adjusted by the user based on the boundary conditions of the BIPV module.

2.2 PVsyst

PVsyst works similarly to SAM in terms of system

specifications and 3D design, though it has the additional feature of being able to import three external file types for 3D input scenes: 3DS (3D Studio), DAE (digital asset exchange) and PVC (PVcase). While useful for some cases, the calculation engine can only handle a limited amount of input data. As 3D scenes become more complex, the calculation time increases significantly and may not work properly.

To address the BIPV constructive system and boundary conditions, PVsyst allows the selection of three mounting options: free standing, fully insulated backside and semi-integration. These translate to the temperature model calculations by assigning specific values to the model's heat transfer coefficient uc (ranging from 15 to 29 W/m²K), which is then used to simulate module temperature. This coefficient is higher for well-ventilated modules and lower as backside ventilation decreases.

3 EXPERIMENTAL FACILITY AND MODEL PREPARATION

The selected tools are assessed in a BIPV monitored case study where experimental data are available: Building 42 at CIEMAT headquarters in Madrid, Spain (40.45° N, -3.74° E). The building was renovated in 2017, with the intervention including BIPV systems on the topmost areas of the east, south and west façades [10]. The constructive system for these BIPV modules is a ventilated façade with an air gap of approximately 70 mm in thickness, and a 15 mm top opening protected by a metal plate (Figure 1).

Figure 1: Southwest corner (up) and northeast corner (down) of Building 42.

This study focuses on a comparison of experimental to simulated values during the year 2019. Input data required in the simulation tools (module and inverter specifications, array and subarray setups) were set to match the existing system's products and design.

The main two parameters considered in the study are module temperature and PV energy output. In-situ measurements are compared to the estimated values calculated with the two simulation tools. This comparison leads to identifying strengths and weaknesses of each tool and supporting the decision criteria when choosing the most suitable option for each project.

Energy calculations are performed using several meteorological variables, mainly irradiance, temperature and wind speed, which can be obtained from each tool's database or sourced from external sources and manually included in the tools. Instead of using the meteorological data available in both software individually, for the comparison study it was preferred to use the same meteorological data, minimising uncertainties caused by differing boundary conditions. The required data were obtained from Copernicus Atmosphere Monitoring Services (CAMS) for irradiation direct, diffuse and albedo components, and the Photovoltaic Geographical Information System (PVGIS) for ambient temperature and wind speed. CAMS was selected due to its good performance on previous studies that evaluate radiation data from several sources [11], and because irradiation data are not always available in BIPV façades.

Input data were processed to fit the specific weather file format required by each tool. In addition, simulation data were filtered to match the available experimental values, meaning that meteorological data values were set to zero for any timeframe when in-situ measurements were unavailable. This allows the comparison to only account for the actual available experimental data, and avoids deviations caused by data mismatch. In our case, this filtering criteria lead to approximately 4,200-4,300 daylight (i.e. measurements above zero) hourly values, depending on the façade.

4 RESULTS

Firstly, module temperature for the south façade was calculated for 2019 on an hourly basis using the tools' available configurations and then compared to experimental data. A statistical error analysis was developed with mean bias error (MBE) and root mean square error (RMSE) as the key indicators.

Table I presents SAM's results for module temperature estimation. For SAM's BIPV option, the module's NOCT was customised to 55.3 °C based on a regression analysis performed with experimental values [12]. All other configurations used the different default values provided by each software.

Table I: South façade statistical analysis of module temperature estimation for all configurations in SAM.

SAM	*MBE (°C)*	*RMSE(°C)*
BIPV	-3.3	6.2
<0.5 inch	-1.0	5.9
0.5-1.5 inch	-3.2	6.1
1.5-2.5 inch	-4.7	7.1
2.5-3.5 inch	-5.9	8.1

The RMSE is similar in all cases, with the lowest value at 5.9 °C for the <0.5-inch option. The negative values for the MBE indicate that the model consistently underestimates module temperature in all configurations between 1 °C and 5.9 °C. It should be noted that, while the <0.5-inch (12.7 mm) dimension does not accurately reflect the actual façade air gap of 70 mm, the small 15 mm opening at the top may reduce the effect of backside

10.4229/EUPVSEC2025/4BV.4.5

ventilation, which may cause this option to have lower error values. However, due to possible uncertainties in experimental data, it was preferred to use the option that matches the system's actual configuration, i.e., the 1.5-2.5 inch.

In PVsyst, the statistical analysis included the built-in 3D scene and the imported DAE file option, with results summarised in Table 2 below.

Table II: South façade statistical analysis of module temperature estimation for all configurations in PVsyst, including the built-in 3D scene (up) and an imported DAE file (down).

PVsyst (built-in)	*MBE (°C)*	*RMSE (°C)*
openback	-6.9	10.9
semi-BIPV	-3.0	8.7
BIPV	1.2	9.2

PVsyst (DAE)	*MBE (°C)*	*RMSE (°C)*
openback	-7.7	11.4
semi-BIPV	-4.3	9.0
BIPV	-0.5	8.8

The error module temperature estimation in PVsyst is similar for both 3D workflows. The RMSE is slightly higher than the values seen in SAM, ranging between 8.7 and 11.4 °C. The MBE shows underestimation in most cases, except for the BIPV configuration with the built-in 3D scene.

This statistical analysis can aid in selecting the constructive configuration that better represents the existing BIPV system's boundary conditions. For this study, the selected configurations were the 1.5-2.5 inch option in SAM and the BIPV in PVsyst. The statistical analysis was then extended to the remaining east and west façades (Table 3). For SAM's calculations, the NOCT value was adjusted for the east and west façades following the regression strategy used on the south façade.

Table III: Statistical analysis for module temperature estimation on the east and west façades for SAM (top) and PVsyst (bottom).

SAM	*MBE (°C)*	*RMSE (°C)*
East	2.5	5.1
West	5.2	7.2

PVsyst (built-in)	*MBE (°C)*	*RMSE (°C)*
East	2.4	7.1
West	-3.8	9.1

The average mean bias error is below 5.2 °C in SAM and -3.8 °C in PVsyst. On the contrary, SAM's quadratic deviation is slightly better by about 2 °C in both cases.

The next step was to evaluate energy output simulations, which were done monthly for the year 2019. To assess the effect of shading, energy simulations were firstly performed for the east façade with and without surrounding buildings and vegetation. This façade is highly affected by a nearby row of caduceus white poplar trees, which cause more shading during their leafy seasons, and some additional vegetation to a lesser extent. For this comparison, the shading scenes in both software were developed using their built-in shading tools. For comparable results, the same 3D building and tree elements were designed in both cases. Figure 2 shows the monthly results obtained in energy output estimations for 2019 when shading is considered as opposed to shading being ignored, and their comparison to experimental data.

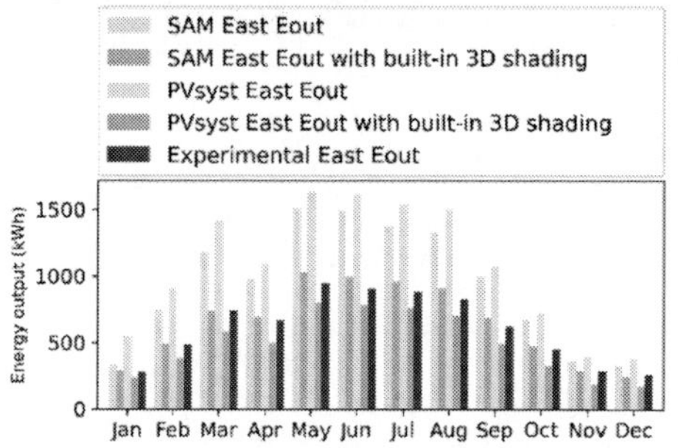

Figure 2: SAM and PVsyst energy output with and without shading comparison to experimental data for the east façade in 2019.

As expected, Figure 2 confirms that shading has a significant impact in BIPV energy simulations and should not be overlooked. Based on these results, energy output simulations for the south and west façades also included the surrounding shading elements. The south façade does not present significant nearby obstacles, while several trees affect the west façade and are accounted for in the calculations. Figure 3 includes charts comparing the experimental energy output to the values simulated with SAM and PVsyst respectively, both using the built-in 3D shading scene capabilities as explained earlier.

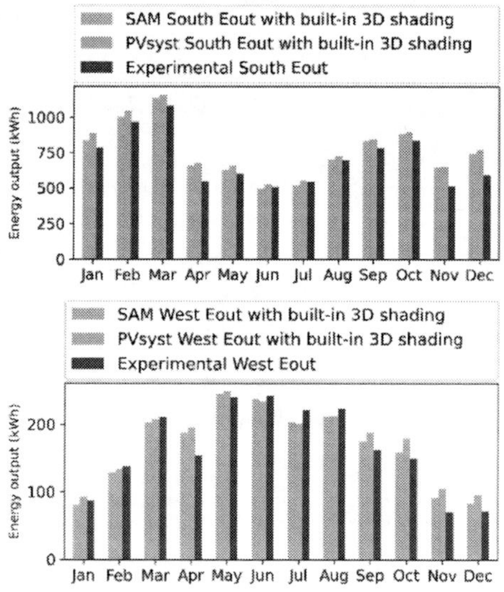

Figure 3: SAM and PVsyst energy output comparison to experimental data for the south (top) and west (bottom) façades in 2019.

Lastly, the study assessed the two available workflows for the 3D scene in PVsyst: the built-in option and an imported DAE file obtained from a Digital Surface Model (DSM) derived from Light Detection and Ranging

(LiDAR) data [13] (Figure 4).

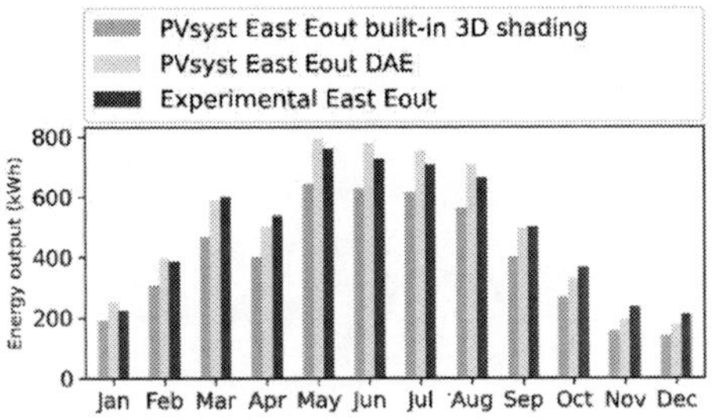

Figure 4: PVsyst energy output comparison to experimental data for the east façade based on the 3D the built-in scene creator and an imported DAE file.

This figure illustrates better performance in energy output estimations with the imported DAE file as opposed to the built-in scene creator.

To support the graphical analysis, the yearly normalised mean bias error (nMBE) and normalised root mean square error (nRMSE) for each façade in both tools are provided in Table 4 below. For PVsyst, the analysis was developed using both the built-in and the imported DAE 3D scene options.

Table IV: nMBE and nRMSE (%) analysis for SAM and PVsyst.

nMBE(%)	*SAM (built-in)*	*PVsyst (built-in)*	*PVsyst (DAE)*
South	7.9	12.1	-1.4
East	6.6	-20.9	1.1
West	1.9	6.9	-0.3

nRMSE(%)	*SAM (built-in)*	*PVsyst (built-in)*	*PVsyst (DAE)*
South	10.4	13.1	11.7
East	8.6	19.9	7.1
West	9.0	13.3	13.4

When comparing the built-in 3D scene with identical layout in both tools, energy output simulations show lower errors in SAM in all orientations, while the nMBE improves considerably when using PVsyst's imported DAE file. When evaluating the nRMSE, SAM and PVsyst's DAE option perform similarly, with the latter's built-in 3D scene having higher errors overall.

5 CONCLUSIONS

While several tools are available to perform PV simulations, few focus on BIPV specifically. For this purpose, some software solutions provide optional configurations that address BIPV specific boundary conditions, such as constructive configuration and surrounding elements. These tools may however be insufficient in certain detailed analyses and studies, such as shading from the urban context and nearby elements.

In this work, an exercise to model several small BIPV arrays working under different shading conditions is presented using two well-known tools (SAM and PVsyst). Energy output simulations confirmed that shading plays an essential role to ensure accuracy, leading to energy overestimation when shading is not considered, as presented in Figure 2.

Given the importance of shading in BIPV systems, proper design of the surrounding elements becomes one of the greatest challenges in BIPV simulations. This issue is addressed in the evaluated software by either providing a 3D scene design tool or an imported external 3D file. The present study reveals that the methods for configuring and imposing shading conditions in each tool need to be analysed carefully, since apparently equal shading conditions produce different results in each tool. In general, the results show more accuracy in SAM modelling than in PVsyst, although there is remarkable improvement in PVsyst estimations when detailed shading is provided from a DAE file containing an accurate 3D scene.

Because the discrepancy between the results of the equivalent 3D scenes in both software is significant, it is important to identify the possible causes, whether they are related to user experience during the design stages, or the tools' internal calculation methods for shadings and module temperature. To understand these differences, further work is required to understand and evaluate how each tool performs the calculations, especially their management of obstacles during the simulations.

Module temperature estimation is also key in BIPV installations, with both tools providing customisable options to account for different BIPV boundary conditions. This is another subject for further study since uncertainty in power estimations is partially conditioned by the accuracy in cell temperature determination.

The discrepancy between predicted and measured energy is not only the result of differences in irradiance and environmental data, but also the estimation of power losses due to factors such as module degradation, soiling, wiring losses, and others that affect the Performance Ratio (PR), which can be adjusted by the software user. Furthermore, the uncertainties in power estimation of BIPV arrays presented in this work are relative, since they include the uncertainty of the solar irradiance input (CAMS solar radiation service), the transposition model for the plane of array, and the modelling tool itself. However, beyond the quantitative comparison between both tools, the impact of how shading is input into the model is notable. Thus, further and more detailed analysis is needed before making recommendations on how to model BIPV power under shading conditions.

6 REFERENCES

[1] International Renewable Energy Agency (IRENA), Rise of Renewables in Cities: Energy Solutions for the Urban Future, Abu Dhabi, 2020.

[2] European Commission, "Fit for 55" delivering the EU's 2030 Climate Target on the way to climate neutrality, (2021).

[3] T. Reijenga, M. Ritzen, A. Scognamiglio, K. Kappel, Successful Building Integration of Photovoltaics A Collection of International Projects, (2020).

[4] N. Martín-Chivelet, M. Van Noord, F. Tilli, R.J. Yang, N. Weerasinghe, E. Daun, A. Baggini, BIPV Market Development: International Technological Innovation System Analysis, Buildings 15 (2025) 3011. https://doi.org/10.3390/buildings15173011.

[5] R. Jing Yang, Y. Zhao, S. Dev Sureshkumar Jayakumari, A. Schneider, S. Prithivi Rajan, J.

Leloux, P. Alamy, G. Prasetyo Raharjo, F. Rende, T. Samarasinghalage, A. Marcos Castro, N. Martin Chivelet, S. Woei Leow, P. Wijeratne, Y. Li, L. Zhang, C. Wu, X. Deng, D. Luo, Digitalising BIPV energy simulation: A cross tool investigation, Energy and Buildings 318 (2024) 114484. https://doi.org/10.1016/j.enbuild.2024.114484.
[6] J. Polo, N. Martín-Chivelet, M. Alonso-Abella, C. Sanz-Saiz, J. Cuenca, M. De La Cruz, Exploring the PV Power Forecasting at Building Façades Using Gradient Boosting Methods, Energies 16 (2023) 1495. https://doi.org/10.3390/en16031495.
[7] S. Sharma, G. Raina, S. Yadav, S. Sinha, A comparative evaluation of different PV soiling estimation models using experimental investigations, Energy for Sustainable Development 73 (2023) 280–291. https://doi.org/10.1016/j.esd.2023.02.008.
[8] System Advisor Model™ Version 2025.4.16 (SAM™ 2025.4.16). National Renewable Energy Laboratory. Golden, CO. Accessed May 23, 2025. https://https://sam.nrel.gov, (n.d.).
[9] PVsyst [Version 8.0.14]. Retrieved from PVsyst website, (n.d.).
[10] N. Martín-Chivelet, J. Gutiérrez, M. Alonso-Abella, F. Chenlo, J. Cuenca, Building Retrofit with Photovoltaics: Construction and Performance of a BIPV Ventilated Façade, Energies 11 (2018) 1719. https://doi.org/10.3390/en11071719.
[11] International Electrotechnical Commission, IEA-PVPS-T16-05-2023-Worldwide Benchmark of Modelled Solar Irradiance Data, (2023).
[12] A. Marcos-Castro, C. Sanz-Saiz, J. Polo, N. Martín-Chivelet, Performance Ratio Estimation for Building-Integrated Photovoltaics—Thermal and Angular Characterisation, Applied Sciences 15 (2025) 6579. https://doi.org/10.3390/app15126579.
[13] A. Marcos-Castro, N. Martín-Chivelet, J. Polo, Enhanced GIS Methodology for Building-Integrated Photovoltaic Façade Potential Based on Free and Open-Source Tools and Information, Remote Sensing 17 (2025) 954. https://doi.org/10.3390/rs17060954.

7 ACKNOWLEDGEMENTS

This publication is part of the R+D+I project "RINGS-BIPV Project (PID2021-124910OB-C31)", which is funded by the MICIU/AEI/10.13039/501100011033 and by ERDF/EU. The authors would also like to recognize the efforts, research and contributions of the expert groups of the IEA PVPS Program, in particular those corresponding to Task 15 (BIPV) and Task 16 (Solar Resource), where the authors have an active collaboration.

EUPVSEC
22 — 26
September
BEC —
Bilbao Exhibition Centre
Bilbao —
Spain
EU
PVSEC
2025
42nd European
Photovoltaic Solar Energy
Conference and Exhibition

030001-001

Conference Highlights

Robert Kenny

European Commission Joint Research Centre

EU PVSEC Technical Programme Chair

030001-003

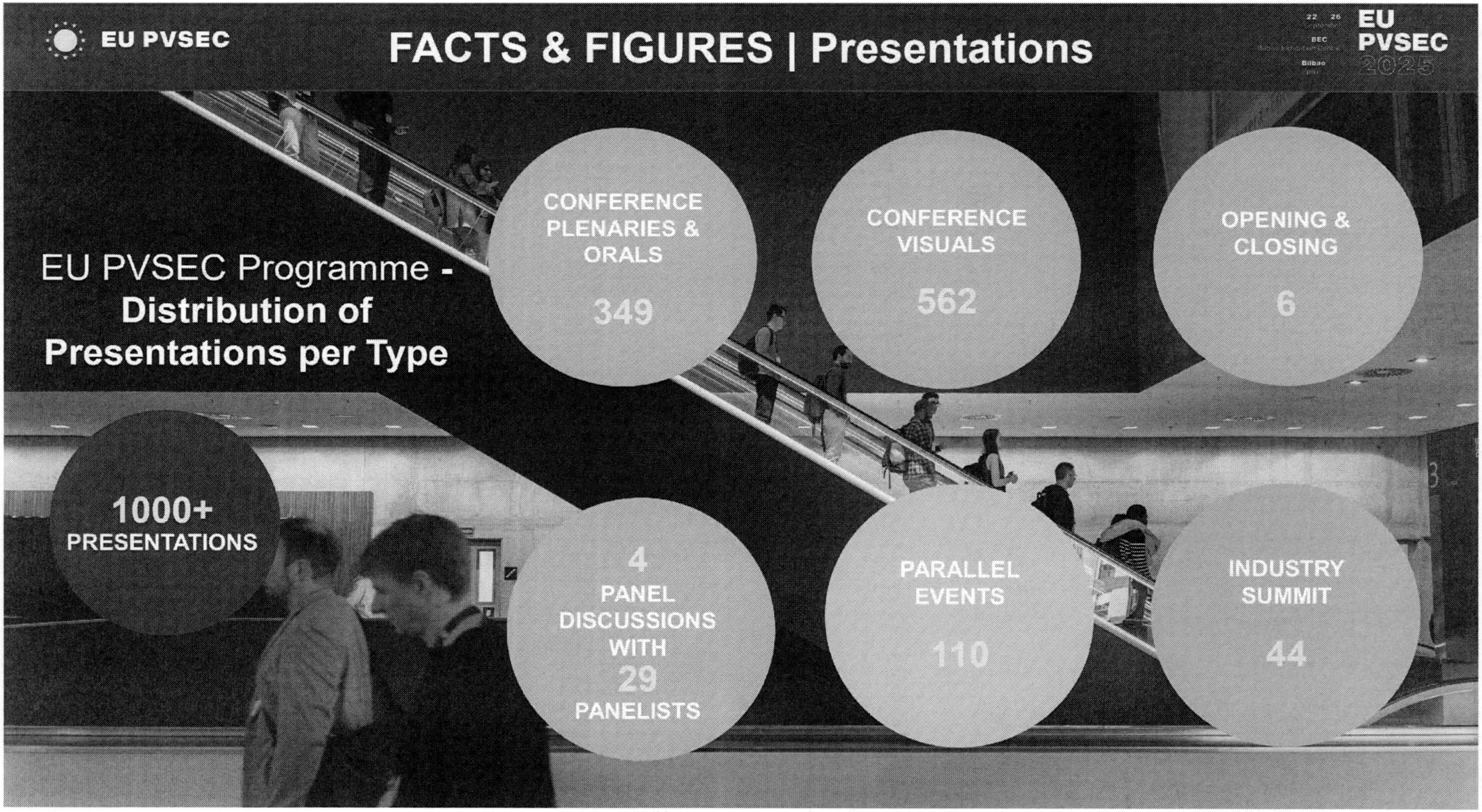
EU PVSEC
FACTS & FIGURES | Presentations
EU PVSEC 2025
EU PVSEC Programme - Distribution of Presentations per Type
CONFERENCE PLENARIES & ORALS
349
CONFERENCE VISUALS
562
OPENING & CLOSING
6
1000+ PRESENTATIONS
4 PANEL DISCUSSIONS WITH 29 PANELISTS
PARALLEL EVENTS
110
INDUSTRY SUMMIT
44

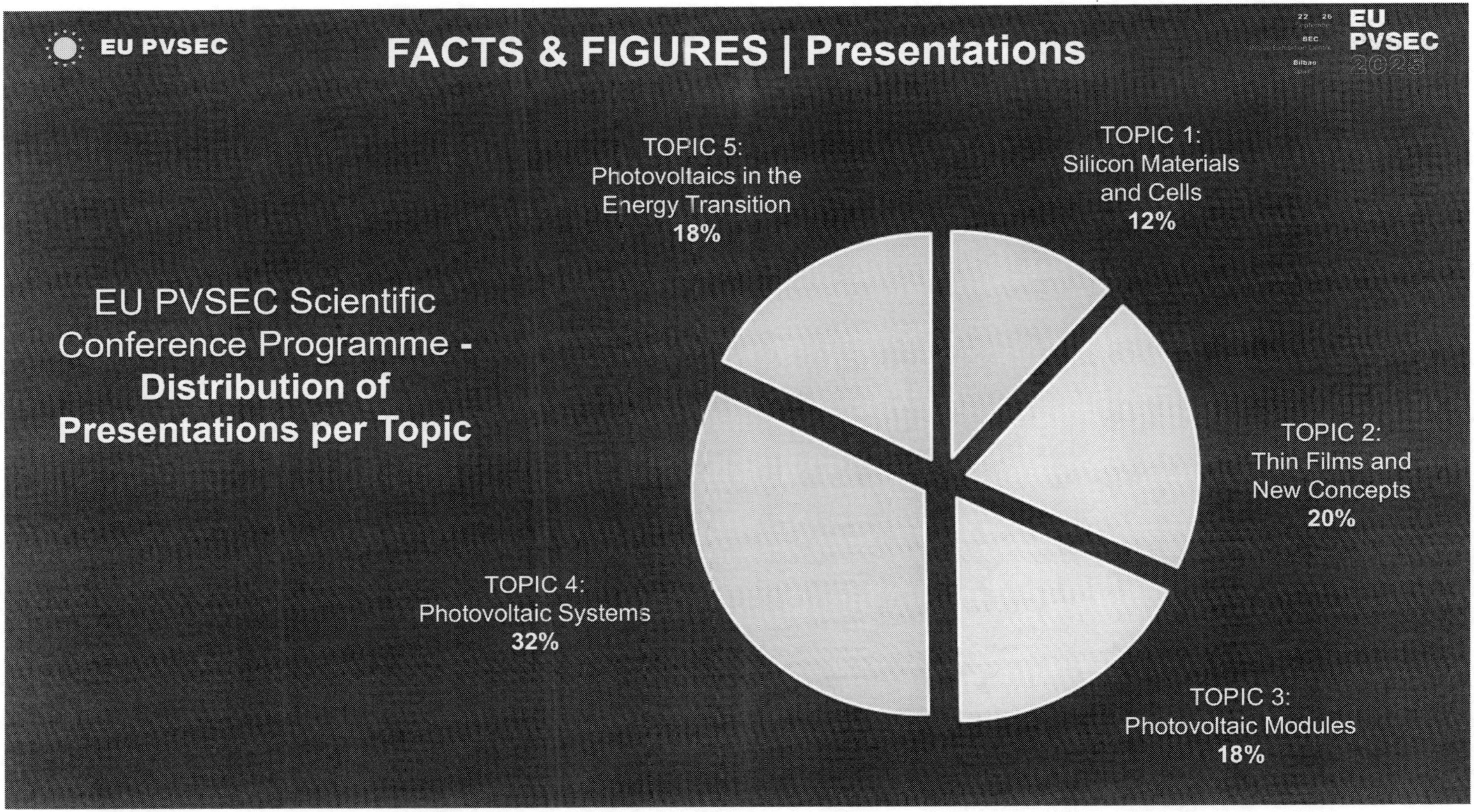
EU PVSEC
FACTS & FIGURES | Presentations
EU PVSEC 2025
EU PVSEC Scientific Conference Programme - Distribution of Presentations per Topic
TOPIC 1: Silicon Materials and Cells 12%
TOPIC 2: Thin Films and New Concepts 20%
TOPIC 3: Photovoltaic Modules 18%
TOPIC 4: Photovoltaic Systems 32%
TOPIC 5: Photovoltaics in the Energy Transition 18%

EU PVSEC

FACTS & FIGURES | Participants

EU PVSEC 2025

Participants by Countries
Top 10

No	Country	Participants
1	Germany	310
2	Spain	270
3	France	108
4	Italy	90
5	The Netherlands	76
6	South Korea	67
7	Switzerland	62
8	Japan	55
9	Belgium	44
10	Norway	35

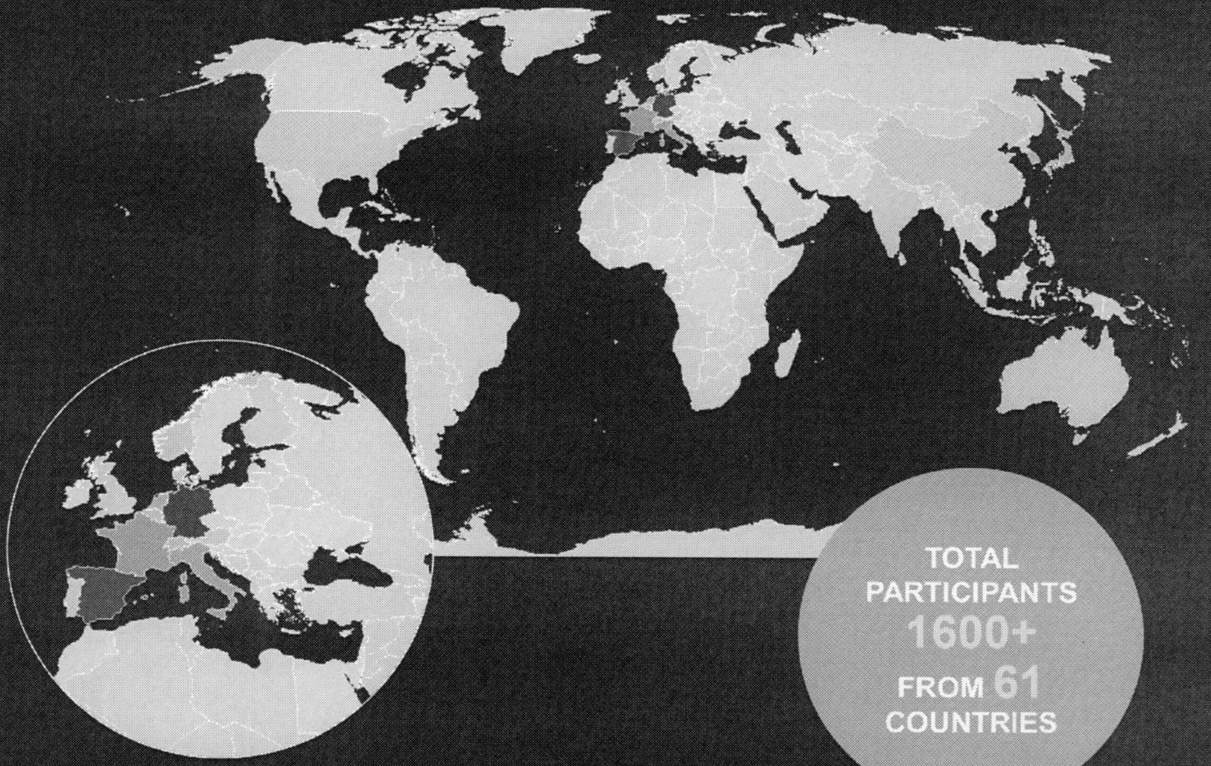

TOTAL PARTICIPANTS 1600+ FROM 61 COUNTRIES

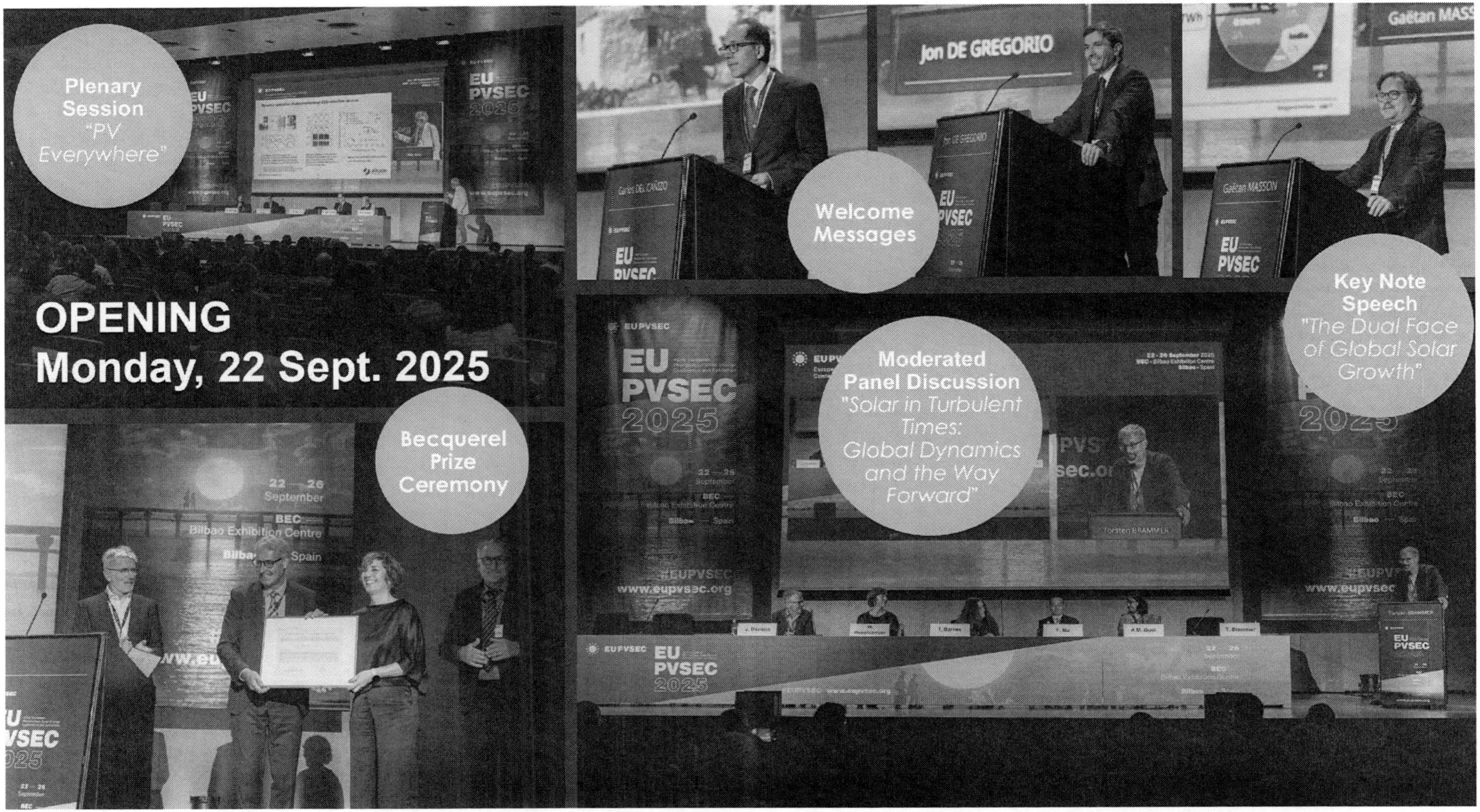
Plenary Session "PV Everywhere"
OPENING
Monday, 22 Sept. 2025
Welcome Messages
Jon DE GREGORIO
Carlos DEL CAÑIZO
Gaëtan MASSON
Key Note Speech "The Dual Face of Global Solar Growth"
Becquerel Prize Ceremony
Moderated Panel Discussion "Solar in Turbulent Times: Global Dynamics and the Way Forward"
EU PVSEC 2025
22 — 26 September
BEC Bilbao Exhibition Centre
Bilbao — Spain
#EUPVSEC
www.eupvsec.org
Torsten BRAMMER

EU PVSEC
PANEL DISCUSSIONS
EU
PVSEC
2025
BO.13 Reliability and Bankability in PV
"The rapid developments of PV technology require increased attention to be paid to reliability testing."
CO.7 Challenges and Opportunities of PV up to 2030
"PV Technology is already reliable and cost effective, and even though improvements are welcome, key blockages are storage and grid strengthening. AI and robotics are essential to meet the scale of developments needed."
DO.13 Scalability and Manufacturability Prospects in Europe for New Technologies
"The prospects for reaching the 30GW target for PV module manufacturing in Europe were discussed and policy measures proposed."

EU PVSEC

EU PVSEC 2025

CONFERENCE

KEY MESSAGES

Cross-cutting themes emerged throughout the programme, showcasing how solar technologies can be applied everywhere, from traditional to emerging fields.

- Sustainability and circularity remain central, with research focused on reducing material use, such as replacing silver with copper, and advancing end-of-life management of modules.
- Ensuring long-term stability and predictable energy yield is equally essential, with studies of degradation mechanisms such as UVID carried out.
- The role of AI across the PV value chain is rapidly expanding, from design to operations and maintenance, including drone applications.

EU PVSEC

EU PVSEC 2025

CONFERENCE

TOPIC 1: SILICON MATERIALS AND CELLS

Enhancements in IV measurement procedures

- Michael Rauer, Fraunhofer ISE: 1AO.4.5 *Universal Contacting Approaches for the Characterization of Solar Cells*
- Shuai Nie, UNSW: 1AO.4.6 *Contact-Free J-V: a Simple Technique for Universal State-of-the-Art Solar Cells*

Replacement of critical by sustainable materials:

- Reduced Ag consumpion e.g. by replacing by Cu (plating)
- In-free SHJ solar cells and Pero-Si tandems

EU PVSEC

EU PVSEC 2025

CONFERENCE

TOPIC 1: SILICON MATERIALS AND CELLS

Great advance in understanding of UV induced degradation and Hydrogen related degradation

- Excellent PLENARY by Bram Hoex (presenting for Muhammad Umair Khan), UNSW: 1CP.3.5 *Understanding the Root Cause of UV-Induced Degradation in TOPCon and PERC Solar Cells*

Further high quality orals:

- Christina Hollemann, ISFH: 1AO.4.2 *Mitigating UV-Induced Degradation: Impact of PECVD and PEALD AlOx Layers Deposited in a Tube-Type Direct Plasma-Enhanced Chemical Vapor Deposition System*
- Hugo Lajoie, CEA: 1AO.4.3 *New Insights on UV-Induced Degradation of SHJ Solar Cells*
- Byungsul Min, ISFH: 1BO.3.6 *UV Stable Passivation Stack with Plasma-Enhanced Atomic Layer Deposition of Aluminum Oxide from an Industrial Tube-Type Direct Plasma-Enhanced Chemical Vapor Deposition System*
- Wolfram Kwapil, Fraunhofer ISE: 1AO.5.6 *Impact of Illumination on Solar Cell Properties: Insights into Atomic Hydrogen Release*

EU PVSEC

EU PVSEC 2025

CONFERENCE

TOPIC 1: SILICON MATERIALS AND CELLS

Advances in TOPCon and SHJ technology → Pushing the Limits of Performance

- Fantastic keynote lecture (PLENARY) on heterojunction solar cells by Dr. Guangtao Yang, Trina: 1CP.1.1 *Silicon Surface and Interface Study for >27% Efficient SHJ Solar Cell*
  - Deep insight into technological aspects eg. influence of rear side polishing on cell performance
  - Very high efficiencies for both-sides contacted HJT > 27%
  - Issues with CAPEX, sustainibility (Ag, In)
  - Pero-Si tandem cells on large area and modules

Late News Presentation on 27.8% efficient back contact silicon solar cells by Hua Wu, Longhi: 1DO.9.1 *Hybrid Interdigitated Back Contact Silicon Solar Cells with Superior Efficiency*

Late News Presentation as TOPCon for Bottom Solar Cells in Pero-Si Tandem devices by Jana Polzin-Isabelle Polzin, Fraunhofer ISE: 1DO.9.3 *Silicon Solar Cells – From High Efficiency Single-junction to Bottom Cells in Two-Terminal Perovskite-Silicon Tandem Devices*

EU PVSEC

EU PVSEC 2025

CONFERENCE

TOPIC 1: SILICON MATERIALS AND CELLS

Further high quality orals:

- Hua Wu, Longhi: 1DO.9.1 *Hybrid Interdigitated Back Contact Silicon Solar Cells with Superior Efficiency*
- Daming Chen, Trina: 1AO.5.1 *Large Area i-TOPCon Solar Cells with 25.9% Record Efficiency*
- Maysa Sarsour, UNSW: 1AO.6.1 *Evaluating Silicon Heterojunction Solar Cell Stability under Industrial Illuminated Hydrogenation Conditions*

Bottom cell optimization for Pero-Si tandems

EU PVSEC

EU PVSEC 2025

CONFERENCE

TOPIC 2: THIN FILMS AND NEW CONCEPTS

A lot of focus on the long-term stability improvement and upscaling of tandem devices based on a variety of materials (hence not only pero-Si).

Many companies (e.g. Hanwha Q-cells, Oxford PV, Microquanta Seminconductor, Jinko Solar, Longi, etc. non-exhaustive list) presented impressive results on industrial size single-junction pero modules and pero-based tandem modules. A highlight here was the plenary talk from Hanwha Q-cells showing a record large area (M10) pilot-scale Pk/Si tandem cell of 28.6% efficiency.

EU PVSEC

22 26 BEC Bilbao EU PVSEC 2025

CONFERENCE

TOPIC 2: THIN FILMS AND NEW CONCEPTS

In the field of pero-Si tandems, there is clearly more focus on improving the stability of the tandem devices than before with many contributions doing in-depth investigations into the different degradation mechanisms that can occur in pero-Si tandems.

In this respect, 2DO9.5 presented a consensus statement about reliability testing of perovskite-based tandems that is endcrsed by specialists worldwide from both industry and research and presents a kind of minimum that should be done in terms of testing and reporting concerning the stability and lifetime of perovskite-based tandem devices.

More and more advanced characterization methods for perovskite and perovskite - silicon tandem solar cells are being used, hyperspectral imaging methods identify non-uniformities by layer for processing development.

EU PVSEC

EU PVSEC 2025

CONFERENCE

TOPIC 2: THIN FILMS AND NEW CONCEPTS

Another clear trend is that pero-TOPCon cells are nearing the same record efficiencies as pero-Heterojunction cells. A highlight talk here was the certified 34.22% efficiency perovskite/ topcon tandem solar cell(1cm2) by Jinko Solar 2CO2.1

Another highlight was the 30.5% triple junction pero/pero/silicon cell by EPFL (2CO2.3)

In the field of perovskite single junction devices, 2DO.7.3 showed perovskite devices with remarkable reliability, withstanding 4 years of outdoor exposure. The degradation mechanism is attributed to the diurnal behaviour, also verified and replicated with indoor experiments.

2AO3.6 investigated experimental degradation and recovery of perovskite solar cells, improving the comprehension of instability's dynamics, to extend the lifetime of devices.

EU PVSEC

EU PVSEC 2025

22 – 26 September
BEC
Bilbao

CONFERENCE

TOPIC 2: THIN FILMS AND NEW CONCEPTS

In the field of compound semiconductors, there were many presentations on alternative materials for perovskite in tandems. In this way, first monolithic $(AgCu)(InGa)Se_2$ on Si tandem cells were demonstrated as well as 16.1% semitransparent Ag doped $Cu(InGa)S_2$ sulfide top cells.

An exciting highlight in this field was 2BO8.2 in which UPC Barcelona achieved 18% efficiency under indoor lighting for kesterite solar cells with alkali doping

EU PVSEC

EU PVSEC 2025

CONFERENCE

TOPIC 3: PHOTOVOLTAIC MODULES

“Reliable packaging to Maximize the energy yield from high efficiency cells”

big theme: Optimizing module materials and packaging for long lifetime and predictable energy yield from high efficiency cells. The industry and research community are moving quickly to assess and improve reliability.

- Understanding, accelerated testing, and mitigating UV-ID in n-type cells and modules
- How do you develop accelerated tests for constantly changing BOMs - new encapsulants, new metallization, thinner glass, and high efficiency cells

EU PVSEC

22 – 26 September
BEC
Bilbao
EU PVSEC 2025

CONFERENCE

TOPIC 3: PHOTOVOLTAIC MODULES

- Degradation and metastability in packaged perovskite tandems - understanding energy yield and realistic degradation rates
- Characterization out of the lab and into the field and factory - accurate outdoor performance, online quality control measurements for encapsulant cross linking
- Reducing silver content and metallization temperatures - reliability of low temperature and low silver metallization
- Developing glass qualification requirements to minimize breakage

EU PVSEC

EU PVSEC 2025

CONFERENCE

TOPIC 4: PHOTOVOLTAIC SYSTEMS

Advances in O&M of PV systems

(4CV.1) focuses on fault detection, cleaning optimization, soiling (and snow 4CO.8), UAV for autonomous monitoring and digital twin.

Data driven and AI based O&M (4CO.9) including a medicine-like workflow in Autonomous multi-AI agent system for health monitoring: a fully automated O&M pipeline with field robotics (4CO.9.4 D. Moser, EURAC)

PV Everywhere from space to agricultural applications like integration in vineyards (Mo, Opening plenary) and many other **integrated options** as we have seen throughout the week. On Thursday (4DO.4) agriPV, noise barriers and floating integrated systems. AgriPV technologies (4DO.2), BIPV

PV needs solar energy. **Solar resource and forecasting** (Mo, 4AO.7-9 & Tu 4BV.3). Shortly IEA PVPS T16 will publish minute irradiance data, some including GT over 220 stations worldwide with. Same format and quality controlled. (*Worldwide solar radiation measurement database with quality-control added value*, Anne Forstinger CSP Services, 4AO.7.1)

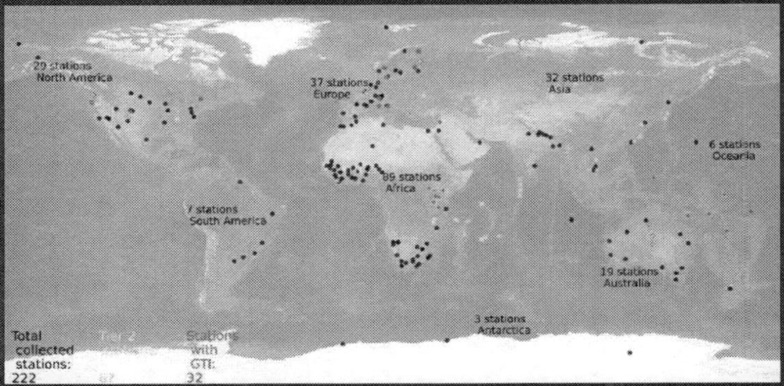

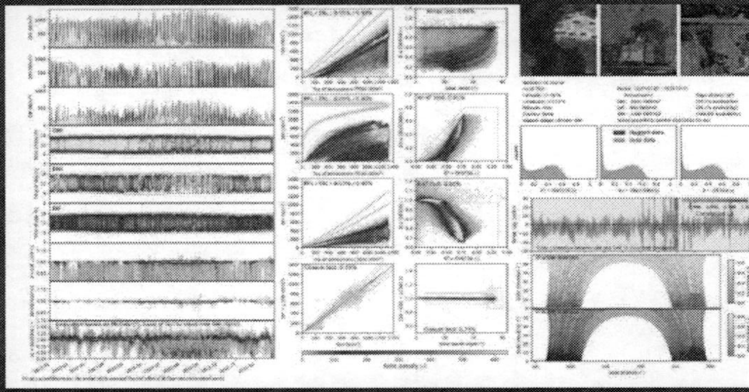

(4BV.3). Poster winner 4BV.3.12 *Advancing Very Short-Term Solar Irradiance Forecasting in Africa: A Low-Cost Sky Imaging and Machine Learning-Based Approach*, implications for PV deployment and grid integration (Martin Ansong, KIT). Runner-up 4BV.3.25 *Evaluating the Suitability of Köppen-Geiger Climate Classifications for Photovoltaic Systems: Micro-climate Analysis and Risk Assessment Maps*, with worldwide distribution of humidity related risk assessment for PV performance (Pavan Kumar Panda, Anhalt University of Applied Sciences).

Integrated PV

BIPV (4BO.16) examples of coloured modules (which was main topic of the poster session along with fire concerns of BIPV, 4BV.4), lightweight solutions (4BO.5) and modelling partial shading effects 4BO.17.1, *Modelling partial shading at the cell level on PV modules*, Jean-Paul Calin, ENSTA) and 4BO.17.3, *Comparing the energy yield and degradation rates of smart PV modules compared to conventional PV system designs in shaded urban scenario's,* Youri Blom, TU DELF.

AgriPV 4DO.2 the room was fully packed showing the interest in the topic. 5 talks were on new ways of sharing light (2 spectral splitting before the PV conversion, 2 semitransparent PV modules both c-Si and CdTe, 1 on downshifting encapsulate) + 1 new AgrivPV like application with Algae instead of crops.

4DO.4 also included AgriPV and **Others types of integration like noise barriers and floating.** In addition to performance other aspects like (*Hydrological and ecological effects on floating PV,* Konstantin Ilgen, FHO ISe) have been highlighted this week

4DO4.2

BOS and tracking systems (4DO.1) focused on backtracking strategies and terrains with complex topography.

4DO.1.4

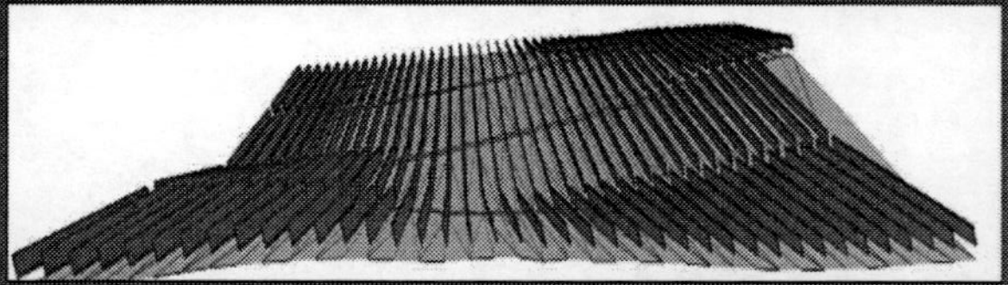

EU PVSEC

EU PVSEC 2025

CONFERENCE

TOPIC 4: PHOTOVOLTAIC SYSTEMS

Reliability of PV systems

Several presentations focused long-term monitored degradation, failure modes and degradation modes identification techniques (non-destructive, aerial images, AI-based)

4BO.6.1 *Three decades, three climates: insights and lessons on PV reliability*. Good BOM offer very high reliability in power production, with 30-35 years old modules showing 0.24% degradation rate per year.

4BO.6.3 *Non-destructive detection of water ingress in solar modules using NIR spectroscopy* (Oleksandr Mashkow HI ERN) proved near-infrared absorption (NIRA) technique to detect water ingress in modules in the field, which correlated with the module degradation.

4BO.7.2 *Robust PV performance loss rate calculation for high latitudes* (Lauri Karttunen, Meteo Inst Helsinki) and 4BO.7. 3 *Detailed analysis of degradation rates of operating PV assets in tropical climate conditions* (Xioaqi Xu, Seris Singapore) Performance loss rates reported for high latitudes and tropics based on solid data sets. PLR in the tropics -1.4%/year

4DO.3.6 PV system design and assessment highlighted how inverter safety issues are extremely important and how more research about inverter safety and reliability is needed.

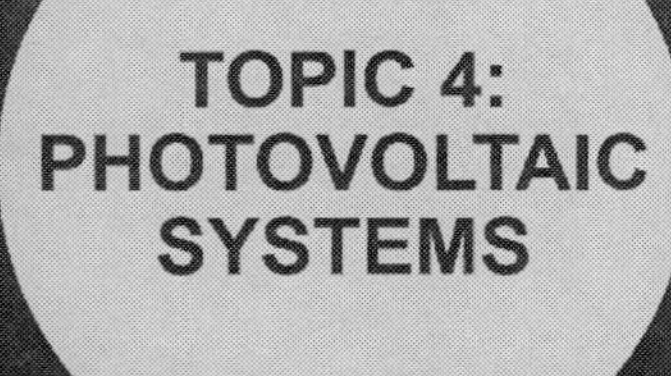

EU PVSEC

22 26 EU PVSEC 2025 BEC Bilbao

CONFERENCE

TOPIC 5: PHOTOVOLTAICS IN THE ENERGY TRANSITION

Main topics of interest :

- Flexibility
- Artificial intelligence
- EoL management

EU PVSEC

EU PVSEC 2025

CONFERENCE

TOPIC 5: PHOTOVOLTAICS IN THE ENERGY TRANSITION

5.1 Grid Integration and Flexibility Enablers (2 sessions)

- Smoothing effect related to different orientations of PV systems in a given area allows 10 to 15% additional hosting capacity of the distribution grid compared to the conservative calculation that consists in summing the AC power. Such accurate calculation enabled by high resolution large area images and LIDAR and induces therefore very low costs.

5.2 Sustainability of PV (4 sessions)

- New inventories LCI and LCA for emerging technologies even though lack of data for perovskites, LCA showing a way for low environmental Impacts with technology improvement and localisation. / Technological improvements will contribute to the reduction of environmental Impact / Grid Efficiency has an Impact on the environmental Footprint.
- Manufacturing optimization / Reuse & recycling: results from the perspective of economic performance – would it convince manufacturer to consider it if economic benefit ?
- EoL Management /recycling -> emerging field attracting lots of activities / mainly EU projects (EVERPV / ICARUS / QASAR) – highlight on polymer, interesting question came up and to be debated for the next decade: is it worth it to consider polymer (EVA/ backsheet) recycling ?
- Major progress in methodology and indicators to assess sustainable design & circularity and improve transparency recyclability index, technical recyclability, digital passport)

EU PVSEC

22 26 BEC Bilbao EU PVSEC 2025

CONFERENCE

TOPIC 5: PHOTOVOLTAICS IN THE ENERGY TRANSITION

5.3 Scenarios for Renewables, Policy, Global Challenges (1 session)

- wide scope of contributions on the way to massive, medium- to long-term PV deployment -> should not be taken for granted despite positive projections since there can be limiting factors such as public acceptance / regulatory restrictions and effect of climate change

5.4 Costs, Economics, Finance and Markets (1 session)

- Annual installed capacity over 400 GWp / total cumulative installed capacity worldwide over 2.1 TWp / Clear mismatch between PV module installations rate worldwide and PV module production rate leading to bunch of inventories and drastically reduced prices.

5.6 Societal Challenges; Citizens' Participation, Awareness (1 session)

- data and analysis in gender aspects are emerging in PV! (poster session) + Highlight on innovation in education! On example that targets students & skilled workers -> mobile Lab for advanced experimental training PV-related to bring skills and characterization tools everywhere.

PARALLEL
EVENTS
Collaborat° Network
Diversity
PREJUDICE
JUSTIFICAT°
CHANGE
NEEDS — PROFILE MATCH
AVOID BLIND SPOTS
JOB LOSS?
INTEGRATION
LACK OF ATTRACTIVENESS
RESILIENCE (PEOPLE + COMPANY)
CREATIVITY
DIFFERENT COMMUNICAT°
INTERNAL FRICTION
MORE EFFORTS

030001-027

EU PVSEC

22 26 BEC Bilbao

EU PVSEC 2025

PARALLEL EVENTS

- Perovskite Innovation Roundtable: Driving EU Leadership in Perovskite Innovation
- Women in PV presents: Leading with Inclusion – Embracing the 6 Traits of Inclusive Leadership
- Unlocking the Potential of Integrated Photovoltaic Systems - European R&D Approach
- Why Do PV Plants Perform Lower than Expected? (Estimating losses by backtracking algorithms in undulating terrain & Analysis of the loss chain and identification of deviations from initial expectations)
- PV Made in the EU: How Do Companies Die and How Can They Thrive?

22 — 26
September
BEC —
ilbao Exhibition Centre
Bilbao — Spain
EU
PVSEC
2025
42nd European
Photovoltaic Solar Energy
Conference and Exhibition
GEOPOLITICS & PV MANUFACTURING CHALLENGES
EXHIBITION
FORUM
INDUSTRY
SUMMIT

The road to a
sustainable future

EU PVSEC

22 26 September

BEC

Bilbao

EU PVSEC 2025

INDUSTRY SUMMIT

Industry Summit Opening (session I)

Session Title: Solar PV production in Europe - the way forward

Moderators: Begoña Molinete, Walburga Hemetsberger

Key Takeaway:

This session discussed the state of play of European manufacturing projects and whether there is enough European support. It was clear that political support is further lacking – only 3 Member States have developed schemes to support European manufacturing. While the Net Zero Industry Act is helpful to diversify supplies, it will not particularly support European manufacturing.

All panellists agreed that apart from further policy support (financing, derisking) collaboration is the way forward.

EU PVSEC

EU PVSEC 2025

22 – 26 September, BEC, Bilbao

INDUSTRY SUMMIT

Session II
Session Title: International corporations in the light of changing geopolitics
Moderators: Radovan Kopecek, Puzant Baliozian

Key takeaway:
EU machine builders are still supporting mostly Indian but also US and EU projects with their technology and expertise. The major arguments for choosing EU tech are quality, training, support and low OPEX.

Session III
Session Title: PV Systems: How do we get the produced electricity in Europe into the grid?
Moderators: Catarina Augusto, Peter Fath

Key Takeaway:
Hybrid PV + storage systems (co-located or distributed) are essential for integrating PV into electricity grids. Storage adds flexibility and stabilizes the grid, making it a cornerstone of resilient energy systems; while the technology is mature, scalable and bankable revenue models remain the key gap for widespread deployment.

LIST OF EXHIBITORS
(in alphabetical order)

Company name	Country
2nd Cycle FlexCo	Austria
9-Tech	Italy
Avalon ST / Pasan	Switzerland
BASQUENERGY Cluster	Spain
Becquerel Institute	Belgium
ECOPROGETTI	Italy
EKIENERGY	Spain
ESMC Pavilion	Belgium
Eternal Sun I WAVELABS	The Netherlands
EU PVSEC Startup Pavilion	
European Commission JRC	Italy
exateq	Germany
FLUXiM AG	Switzerland
G2V Optics	Canada
GALEA	Spain
halm elektronik	Germany
HighLine Technology	Germany
IEA PVPS	
Innovations in Optics, Inc.	United States of America
ISC Konstanz	Germany
LAB14	Germany
MBJ Solutions	Germany
Mondragon Assembly	Spain
Nagase Chemtex America	United States of America
NEO Messtechnik Holding	Austria
ODTÜ GÜNAM	Türkiye
Phoenixolar	China
PSE Instruments	Germany
PVsyst	Switzerland
RCT Future	Germany
RCT Solutions	Germany
RENA	Germany
ReNewPV-CA21148 / 5GSOLAR	Estonia
SALD B.V.	The Netherlands

SCIPRIOS	Germany
SEMILAB	Hungary
SINGULUS TECHNOLOGIES	Germany
Sinton Instruments	United States of America
SOLAR MATERIALS	Germany
SolarNL	The Netherlands
Soli Tek R&D	Lithuania
TAMURA ELSOLD	Germany
TECNALIA	Spain
The Netherlands Pavilion	The Netherlands
TNO	The Netherlands
University of the Basque Country	Spain
Vector Energy	Spain
VON ARDENNE	Germany
WCPEC-9	South Korea
WIP Renewable Energies	Germany
ZSW	Germany

We thank the EU PVSEC 2025 Sponsors

Platinum

MONDRAGON ASSEMBLY

Gold

ENERGIAREN EUSKAL ERAKUNDEA
ENTE VASCO DE LA ENERGÍA

G2V

halm.

RCT solutions

Silver

Sinton instruments

Bronze

AESOLAR

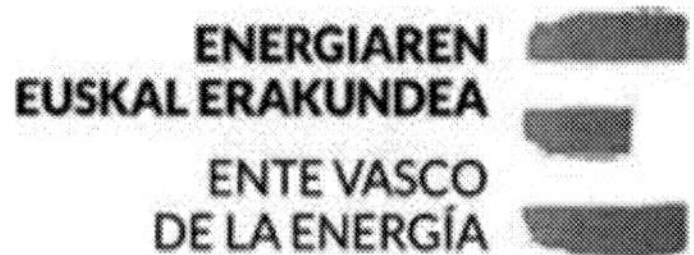

AUTHORS OF EU PVSEC 2025 PROCEEDINGS PAPERS

A. dos Reis Benatto, Gisele — 020028, 020037, 020039, 020191, 020265, 020376, 020477
DTU, Roskilde, Denmark

Aaltonen, Lauri — 020537
Tampere University, Tampere, Finland

Abad Alcaraz, Verónica — 020336
University of Almería, La Cañada de San Urbano, Spain

Abbott, Malcolm D. — 020396
PV Lighthouse, Coledale, Australia

Abbotto, Alessandro — 020077
University of Milano-Bicocca, Milan, Italy

Abdallah, Amir A. — 020146, 020166
QEERI, Doha, Qatar

Abdel Nour, Christine — 020188
EDF R&D, Moret Loing Orvanne, France

Abdelrahim, Mohamed — 020166
QEERI, Doha, Qatar

Abdou-Tankari, Mahamadou — 020562
Paris-East Créteil University, Créteil, France

Abrego, Gillen — 020392
ALLOTARRA, Allo, Spain

Acciarri, Maurizio — 020087
University of Milano-Bicocca, Milan, Italy

Acevedo Devoto, M. Ignacia — 020220
ISC Konstanz, Konstanz, Germany

Achenbach, Jannik — 020522
University of Applied Science Cologne, Cologne, Germany

Acinas, Victor — 020019
Applied Materials, Dublin, Ireland

Adachi, Satoru — 020436
NIED, Shinjo, Japan

Aden, Samira — 020513
HZB, Berlin, Germany

Adinolfi Borea, Riccardo — 020314
University of Bologna, Bologna, Italy

Adnan Hameed, Mohammed — 020156
Martin-Luther-University Halle-Wittenberg, Halle, Germany

Adothu, Baloji — 020229
DEWA, Dubai, United Arab Emirates

Aghaei, Mohammadreza — 020335, 020356
NTNU, Aalesund, Norway

Aghaei, Mohammadreza — 020374, 020375
NTNU, Ålesund, Norway

Aghamohammadi, Amirhossain 020356
Amirkabir University of Technology, Tehran, Iran

Aguirre, Aranzazu 020064
Hasselt Unversity, Genk, Belgium

Ahmadi, Mehdi 020066
CNR-IMM, Catania, Italy

Aiello, Andrea 020255
ACCA Software, Cosenza, Italy

Aimé, Jérémie 020217, 020311
CEA / INES, Le Bourget-du-Lac, France

Aissa, Brahim 020042, 020075, 020108, 020109, 020146, 020147
QEERI, Doha, Qatar

Aizpurua, Jon 020139
Tecnalia, Donostia - San Sebastián, Spain

Akbayrak, Serdar 020020
Necmettin Erbakan University, Konya, Türkiye

Akram, M. Waqar 020164
Hohai University, Changzhou, China

Al Katrib, Mirella 020116
IPVF, Palaiseau, France

Alam, Habeel 020394
Lancaster University, Lancaster, United Kingdom

Alberts, Vivian 020229
DEWA, Dubai, United Arab Emirates

Albuquerque, Daniel P. 020464
Centre for New Energy Technologies, Sacavém, Portugal

Alet, Pierre-Jean 020238, 020544
CSEM, Neuchâtel, Switzerland

Alexandris, Nikos 020210
European Commission JRC, Ispra, Italy

Alfieri, Felice 020497
Viegand Maagøe, Copenhagen, Denmark

Ali, Adnan 020147
QEERI, Doha, Qatar

Allen, Vince 020048
SunDrive Solar, Kurnell, Australia

Alloji, Esma 020020
Necmettin Erbakan University, Konya, Türkiye

Almeida Silva, José 020565
University of Évora, Évora, Portugal

Almuneau, Guilhem 020074
LAAS-CNRS, Toulouse, France

Alonso, Ricardo 020197, 020198, 020353, 020358
TECNALIA, Derio, Spain

Alonso-Montesinos, Joaquín 020100
University of Almeria, Almeria, Spain

Alonso-Montesinos, Joaquín 020336
University of Almería, La Cañada de San Urbano, Spain

Álvarez Hervás, José Domingo 020336
University of Almería, La Cañada de San Urbano, Spain

Alvarez, José 020040, 020058
CNRS, Gif-sur-Yvette, France

Álvarez, Marta 020300
CENER, Sarriguren, Spain

Álvarez-Pérez, Guillem 020062
IPVF, Palaiseau, France

Alvaro Høye, Ingar 020443
Solkraft Sør, Øyslebø, Norway

Alves e Silva, Kiane 020439, 020535, 020567, 020575
UPM, Madrid, Spain

Amaro e Silva, Rodrigo 020490
University of Lisbon, Lisbon, Portugal

Amatriain, Irati 020392
CENER, Sarriguren, Spain

Anamiati, Gaetana 020448, 020481
GreenPowerMonitor a DNV company, Barcelona, Spain

Anaya, Julian 020191, 020205
University of Valladolid, Valladolid, Spain

Ancillao, Andrea 020079
Polytechnic University of Turin, Turin, Italy

Anderlini, Alessandro 020155
Coveme, Gorizia, Italy

Andersen, Nanna L. 020250
DTU, Roskilde, Denmark

Andersen, Nanna Lysgaard 020306
DTU, Roskilde, Denmark

Andrade-Arvizu, Jacob 020094
IREC, Barcelona, Spain

Andreozzi, Federico 020494
University of Rome Tor Vergata, Rome, Italy

Anefnaf, Ikram 020093
University of Verona, Verona, Italy

Ansong, Martin 020272
KIT, Eggenstein-Leopoldshafen, Germany

Antognini, Luca 020196
PVsyst, Geneva, Switzerland

Antoine, C. 020508
IMDEA Nanoscience Institute, Madrid, Spain

Antón, Ignacio 020209, 020246, 020257, 020453, 020459
UPM, Madrid, Spain

Antonucci, Daniele 020551
Eurac Research, Bolzano, Italy

Apostoleris, Harry 020487
EPRI, Dubai, United Arab Emirates

Arakawa, Hayato 020436
NIED, Shinjo, Japan

Aranguren, Gerardo 020289, 020353
UPV/EHU, Bilbao, Spain

Arbaretaz, Sebastien 020317
CEA INES, Le Bourget-du-Lac, France

Ardissone, Bastien J. J. 020396
PV Lighthouse, Coledale, Australia

Arduino, Daniele 020079
Polytechnic University of Turin, Turin, Italy

Ariolli, Daniela Maria Godinho 020325
BayWa r.e, Rome, Italy

Ariza Camacho, Maria Jesus 020100
University of Almeria, Almería, Spain

Armstrong, Alona 020394
Lancaster University, Lancaster, United Kingdom

Arribat, Mathieu 020074
LAAS-CNRS, Toulouse, France

Arrizabalaga, Igor 020139
Tecnalia, Donostia - San Sebastián, Spain

Artegiani, Elisa 020057, 020089, 020093
University of Verona, Verona, Italy

Arumughan, Jayaprasad 020569
ISC Konstanz, Konstanz, Germany

Asaa, Shu-Ngwa 020393
imo-imomec, Genk, Belgium

Ascencio-Vásquez, Julián 020371
Univers, Courbevoie, France

Askins, Steve 020209, 020257
UPM, Madrid, Spain

Assaid, El Mahdi 020171
University of Chouaib Doukkali, El Jadida, Morocco

Aste, Niccolò 020249
Polytechnic University of Milan, Milan, Italy

Astigarraga, Alexander 020226
Eurac Research, Bolzano, Italy

Athienitis, Andreas 020248
Concordia University, Montreal, Canada

Aurrekoetxea, Olaia 020302
TECNALIA, Saint Sebastian, Spain

Awadallah, Carlos 020536
Wattkraft, Madrid, Spain

Azkona, Nekane 020055, 020097, 020153, 020287
UPV/EHU, Bilbao, Spain

Azzopardi, Brian 020318, 020334, 020520
FIR, Birkirkara, Malta
Azzopardi, Carmel 020334
FIR, Birkirkara, Malta

Babich, Francesco 020551
Eurac Research, Bolzano, Italy
Babics, Maxime 020217
CEA / INES, Le Bourget-du-Lac, France
Babin, Markus 020249, 020250, 020306, 020477
DTU, Roskilde, Denmark
Bachour, Dunia A. 020275, 020278
QEERI, Doha, Qatar
Bachour, Dunia 020291
QEERI, Doha, Qatar
Baderiya, Naman 020390
MARIN, Wageningen, The Netherlands
Badosa Franch, Jordi 020214
Polytechnic Institute of Paris, Palaiseau, France
Baeck, Pieter-Jan 020511
Flemish Institute for Technological Research (VITO), Genk, Belgium
Bai, Jianbo 020164
Hohai University, Changzhou, China
Bailache, Simon 020303
CSTB, Marne-la-Vallée, France
Bakhtiari, Afshin 020121
AESOLAR, Koenigsbrunn, Germany
Balafoutis, Athanasios T. 020464
CERTH, Athens, Greece
Bald, Juan 020514
AZTI, PASAIA, Spain
Baldacchino, Alex J. 020065
UNSW, Sydney, Australia
Baležentienė, Skirmantė 020380
The Applied Research Institute for Prospective Technologies, Vilnius, Lithuania
Baležentis, Algirdas 020380
The Applied Research Institute for Prospective Technologies, Vilnius, Lithuania
Ballif, Christophe 020467
CSEM, Neuchâtel, Switzerland
Ballif, Christophe 020251
EPFL, Neuchâtel, Switzerland
Bandaru, Narendra 020039, 020043, 020104
Aarhus University, Aarhus, Denmark

Bang, Ole 020043
Technical University of Denmark, Copenhagen, Denmark

Barakel, Damien 020188
Toulon University, Marseille, France

Baraket, Mira 020039
ATLANT 3D, Taastrup, Denmark

Baranek, Philippe 020060
EDF R&D, Palaiseau, France

Barchi, Grazia 020485, 020489, 020544
Eurac Research, Bolzano, Italy

Bardizza, Giorgio 020181
TÜV Rheinland Italia, Milan, Italy

Bardizza, Giorgio 020208
TÜV Rheinland Solar, Cologne, Germany

Bardizza, Giorgio 020144
TÜV Rheinland, Cologne, Germany

Barguès, Anna 020505
Becquerel Institute France, Lyon, France

Barguès, Anna 020558
Becquerel Institute, Brussels, Belgium

Barnscheidt, Verena 020063, 020114
ISFH, Emmerthal, Germany

Barretta, Chiara 020325
PCCL, Leoben, Austria

Barrionuevo, Bruno 020464
CERTH, Athens, Greece

Barroso, João 020565
University of Évora, Évora, Portugal

Barrou, Alexis 020467
CSEM, Neuchâtel, Switzerland

Barrutia, Laura 020446, 020536
UPM, Madrid, Spain

Barth, Vincent 020134
CEA / INES, Le Bourget-du-Lac, France

Barth, Vincent 020019
CEA, Le Bourget-du-Lac, France

Barth, Vincent 020226
CEA/ INES, Le Bourget-du-Lac, France

Bartholomäus, Martin 020346
DTU, Roskilde, Denmark

Bartolo, Brian 020334
FIR, Birkirkara, Malta

Basta, Beata 020068
Roltec, Poznań, Poland

Basta, Marek 020068
Roltec, Poznań, Poland

Battisti, Kurt 020255
A-Null Development, Vienna, Austria
Bauhuis, Gerard 020067
Radboud University, Nijmegen, The Netherlands
Baumann, Kerstin 020470
bifa Umweltinstitut, Augsburg, Germany
Baumann, Sara 020063
ISFH, Emmerthal, Germany
Baumann, Ulrike 020006
ISFH, Emmerthal, Germany
Baur, Carsten 020246
European Space Agency, Noordwijk, The Netherlands
Beaucarne, Guy 020384
Dow Silicones Belgium, Seneffe, Belgium
Becker, Carl 020331
DLR, Almeria, Spain
Behrensdorff Poulsen, Peter 020037
DTU, Lyngby, Denmark
Beinert, Andreas J. 020123
Fraunhofer ISE, Freiburg, Germany
Bejat, Timea 020225, 020500
CEA, Le Bourget-du-Lac, France
Belawadi, Aditya Girish 020231
Fraunhofer ISE, Freiburg, Germany
Belferkous, Brahim Anis 020325
PCCL, Leoben, Austria
Bellmann, Martin 020495, 020510
SINTEF, Trondheim, Norway
Bellvert, Eduard 020139
Tecnalia, Donostia - San Sebastián, Spain
Beltran-Condori, Sonia 020129, 020417
University of Antofagasta, Antofagasta, Chile
Belzunce, María Jesús 020514
AZTI, PASAIA, Spain
Bendix, Peter 020388
Next2Sun Technology, Dillingen, Germany
Bengoechea, Jaione 020181, 020300
CENER, Sarriguren, Spain
Bermudez Benito, Veronica 020146
QEERI, Doha, Qatar
Bermudez-Garcia, Anderson 020246
Thales Alenia Space, Cannes, France
Berrian, Djaber 020492
Belectric, Kolitzheim, Germany
Berson, Solenn 020134
CEA / INES, Le Bourget-du-Lac, France

Besson, Pierre 020373
INES, Le Bourget-du-Lac, France

Betak, Juraj 020241
Solargis, Bratislava, Slovakia

Bettucci, Ottavia 020077
University of Milano-Bicocca, Milan, Italy

Bhardwaj, Shashank 020515
TU Delft, Delft, The Netherlands

Bhatnagar, Shrey 020367
Nextracker, Fremont, United States of America

Biard, Yves 020303
SemperStyl, Eragny, France

Bieber, Lisa-Marie 020195
Fraunhofer ISE, Freiburg, Germany

Bilitu, Eddie 020393
Hasselt University, Hasselt, Belgium

Binani, Ashish 020225
TNO, Petten, The Netherlands

Binetti, Simona 020093
University of Milano Bicocca, Milan, Italy

Binetti, Simona 020087
University of Milano-Bicocca, Milan, Italy

Blakesley, James 020293
National Physical Laboratory, Teddington, United Kingdom

Blanc, Philippe 020291
MINES Paris, Nice, France

Blanco Aguiar, Adrián 020243
ieco.io, Vigo, Spain

Blieske, Ulf 020141
University of Applied Science Cologne, Cologne, Germany

Blieske, Ulf 020140
University of Applied Sciences Cologne, Cologne, Germany

Blstak Catlosova, Katarina 020274
Solargis, Bratislava, Slovakia

Blum, Niklas 020235, 020237, 020239
DLR, Almeria, Spain

Boccardi, Roberto 020039
DTU, Copenhagen, Denmark

Boccardi, Roberto 020037
DTU, Lyngby, Denmark

Boccardi, Roberto 020028
DTU, Roskilde, Denmark

Boddaert, Simon 020302, 020303
CSTB, Marne-la-Vallée, France

Bokalič, Matevž 020047, 020319
University of Ljubljana, Ljubljana, Slovenia

Bolink, Henk J. 020226
University of Valencia, Paterna, Spain

Bonal, Victor 020085
UAM, Madrid, Spain

Bonnet, Martin 020141
University of Applied Science Cologne, Cologne, Germany

Bonnet-Eymard, Bénédicte 020251
CSEM, Neuchâtel, Switzerland

Borgers, Tom 020225
IMEC, Genk, Belgium

Borgna, Luciano 020369
BFH, Burgdorf, Switzerland

Borie, Benjamin 020039
ATLANT 3D, Taastrup, Denmark

Borowski, Peter 020307
Avancis, Munich, Germany

Borriello, Aniello 020378
ENEA, Portici, Italy

Borzi, Giovanni 020019
Enginsoft, Padua, Italy

Bosch, Elina 020252, 020543, 020564, 020573
Becquerel Institute, Brussels, Belgium

Bosma, Theo 020571
DNV, Arnhem, The Netherlands

Bothe, Karsten 020236
ISFH, Emmerthal, Germany

Bou-Nassif, Liliane 020338
CETHIL, Villeurbanne, France

Bouchier, Daniel 020058
CNRS, Palaiseau, France

Bouguerra, Sara 020156, 020294, 020389, 020393
imec, Genk, Belgium

Bourdin, Vincent 020406
CNRS, Paris, France

Bourgeois, Antoine 020102
SERIS, Singapore, Singapore

Bovesecchi, Gianluigi 020494
University of Rome Tor Vergata, Rome, Italy

Brabec, Christoph J. 020117
HI ERN, Erlangen, Germany

Bradford, David Roy 020077
Newcastle University, Newcastle upon Tyne, United Kingdom

Brailovsky, Peter Henri 020475
Fraunhofer ISE, Freiburg, Germany

Braña, Alejandro F. 020508
Autonomous University of Madrid, Madrid, Spain

Brandstätter, Andreas 020227
Lenzing Plastics, Lenzing, Austria

Braun, Christian 020457
Luxembourg Institute of Science and Technology, Esch-sur-Alzette, Luxembourg

Brecl, Kristijan 020269, 020319
University of Ljubljana, Ljubljana, Slovenia

Bredemeier, Dennis 020240
Leibniz University Hannover, Hannover, Germany

Breitenbücher, Marian 020225
Highline Technologies, Freiburg, Germany

Brendel, Rolf 020006, 020008, 020236, 020240, 020260, 020482
ISFH, Emmerthal, Germany

Brendstrup Møller, Clara Bolette 020028
DTU, Roskilde, Denmark

Bretzel, Tamara 020195
Fraunhofer ISE, Freiburg, Germany

Breyer, Christian 020479
LUT University, Lappeenranta, Finland

Brito, Miguel 020457
University of Lisbon, Lisbon, Portugal

Brivio, Elisabetta 020462
RSE, Milan, Italy

Brockmann, Lukas 020063
ISFH, Emmerthal, Germany

Brodnicke, Linda 020296
ETH, Zurich, Switzerland

Brueckner, Emanuel 020063
ISFH, Emmerthal, Germany

Bründlinger, Roland 020369
AIT, Vienna, Austria

Brun, Gonzalo 020414, 020517
ENDEF, Zaragoza, Spain

Bruno, Maddalena 020452
Fraunhofer ISE, Freiburg, Germany

Buceta, Alicia 020300
CENER, Sarriguren, Spain

Bucher, Christof 020179, 020322, 020359, 020369, 020386
BFH, Burgdorf, Switzerland

Buchholz, Florian 020035, 020225, 020569
ISC Konstanz, Konstanz, Germany

Buchmann, Johanna 020309
Berlin University of Applied Sciences, Berlin, Germany

Buck, Thomas 020033
ISC Konstanz, Konstanz, Germany

Buckland, Daniel 020119, 020218
Henkel, Düsseldorf, Germany

Buddana, Viswa Harinath 020482
DLR, Oldenburg, Germany

Bühlmann, Gian-Luca 020385
ZHAW, Winterthur, Switzerland

Buerhop, Claudia 020149, 020150, 020377
HI ERN, Erlangen, Germany

Buerhop-Lutz, Claudia 020185, 020230
HI ERN, Erlangen, Germany

Burgers, Antonius R. 020405
TNO, Petten, The Netherlands

Burri, Matthias 020179
BFH, Burgdorf, Switzerland

Busto, Chiara 020521
Eni, Novara, Italy

Butrichi, Fabio 020087
University of Milano-Bicocca, Milan, Italy

Butt, Nauman 020394
Lahore University of Management Sciences, Lahore, Pakistan

C. Tavares, Fabiele 020090
Federal University of Rio de Janeiro, Duque de Caxias, Brazil

Cabal, Raphael 020034
University Grenoble Alpes, Le Bourget-du-Lac, France

Caballero, Luis Jaime 020501, 020508
UPM, Madrid, Spain

Caballero, Raquel 020094
CSIC, Madrid, Spain

Caballero, Raquel 020085
IO-CSIC, Madrid, Spain

Cabecinha, Vasco 020565
Nova University Lisbon, Lisbon, Portugal

Cabello, Fatima 020085
IO-CSIC, Madrid, Spain

Caçapietra Pires da Silva, Lucas Teixeira 020025
PUCRS, Porto Alegre, Brazil

Caccavelli, Dominique 020551
CSTB, Bussy-Saint Georges, France

Caccivio, Mauro 020204, 020574
SUPSI, Mendrisio, Switzerland

Caffari, Francesca 020551
ENEA, Ispra, Italy

Calabrese, Nicolandrea 020551
ENEA, Ispra, Italy

Calin, Jean-Paul 020251
ENSTA Paris, Palaiseau, France

Çalışkan Arslan, Meriç 020006, 020135
Kalyon PV, Ankara, Türkiye

Caluori, Philip 020455
Virtual Vehicle, Graz, Austria

Camara, Assa 020274
Solargis, Bratislava, Slovakia

Cambarau, Werther 020139
Tecnalia, Donostia-San Sebastián, Spain

Campana, Pietro Elia 020381
Mälardalen University, Västerås, Sweden

Campos Guzman, Laura 020331
DLR, Almería, Spain

Cancro, Carmine 020378
ENEA, Naples, Italy

Canesse, Auriane 020196
PVsyst, Geneva, Switzerland

Cañizo, Carlos 020097
IES-UPM, Madrid, Spain

Cano, Francisco J. 020139
Tecnalia, Donostia - San Sebastián, Spain

Cano, Lucía 020127
ENDEF, Zaragoza, Spain

Cánovas, Enrique 020508
IMDEA Nanoscience Institute, Madrid, Spain

Cao, Han 020263
SERIS, Singapore, Singapore

Capitaine, Anna 020116
IPVF, Palaiseau, France

Cappelle, Jan 020329, 020351
KU Leuven, Ghent, Belgium

Capron, Guillaume 020217
CEA / INES, Le Bourget-du-Lac, France

Carballo López, José Antonio 020336
University of Almería, La Cañada de San Urbano, Spain

Cardenas, Luis Alejandro 020339, 020546
National University of Colombia, Bogotá, Colombia

Carmo, Paulo 020304, 020420
University of Évora, Évora, Portugal

Carrasco, Luis Miguel 020439, 020535, 020567
UPM, Madrid, Spain

Carrillo Mejía, Luis 020279
District University of Bogotá, Bogotá, Colombia

Carrillo, Rafael E. 020238
CSEM, Neuchâtel, Switzerland

Carroy, Perrine 020226
CEA/ INES, Le Bourget-du-Lac, France

Carstens, Justus 020003
ISC Konstanz, Konstanz, Germany

Cartenì, Fabrizio 020378
University of Naples Federico II, Naples, Italy

Casappa, Michele 020087
National Research Council, Parma, Italy

Casasola Paesa, Marta 020389
Hasselt University, Diepenbeek, Belgium

Castilla Nieto, María del Mar 020336
University of Almería, La Cañada de San Urbano, Spain

Castillo Patton, Daniel Jason 020326
Enertis Applus+, Madrid, Spain

Castro, Luis Guilherme 020530
Casa dos Ventos, Fortaleza, Brazil

Castro, Rui 020464
University of Lisbon, Lisbon, Portugal

Castro-Gallardo, Fernando 020417, 020422
University of Antofagasta, Antofagasta, Chile

Cavaco, Afonso 020304, 020565
University of Évora, Évora, Portugal

Cebecauer, Tomas 020274
Solargis, Bratislava, Slovakia

Çekerek, Gamze 020006
Kalyon PV, Ankara, Türkiye

Celik, Duygu 020551
WIP Renewable Energies, Munich, Germany

Çeliktaş, Melih Soner 020559
Ege University, İzmir, Türkiye

Centazzo, Massimo 020006
EnPV, Karlsruhe, Germany

Centeno Brito, Miguel 020421, 020490
University of Lisbon, Lisbon, Portugal

Cereceda, Eneko 020055, 020097, 020153, 020287
UPV/EHU, Bilbao, Spain

Ceretti, Mattia 020204
SUPSI, Mendrisio, Switzerland

Cesar, I. 020405
TNO, Petten, The Netherlands

Ceuppens, Ignas 020302
BUILD`UP, Aarschot, Belgium

Chatterji, Nithin 020071
SVNIT, Surat, India

Chen, Daniel 020048
SunDrive Solar, Kurnell, Australia

Chen, Syh-Homg 020161
ITRI, Hsinchu, Taiwan

Chen, Xiang 020111
Hohai University, Changzhou, China

Cheung, Kak Pong 020313
Kiel University of Applied Sciences, Kiel, Germany

Chhapia, Gaurang 020492
Belectric, Kolitzheim, Germany

Chiba, Takahiro 020436
Hokkaido University of Science, Sapporo, Japan

Chichignoud, Guy 020495
13Institut Polytechnique De Grenoble, Grenoble, France

Chicote, Beatriz 020289
Mondragon University, Arrasate-Mondragon, Spain

Chiesa, Matteo 020487
Khalifa University, Abu Dhabi, United Arab Emirates

Chini de Freitas, Felipe 020023
PUCRS, Porto Alegre, Brazil

Cho, Yunae 020045
KIER, Daejeon, South Korea

Choi, Kwan Bum 020102
SERIS, Singapore, Singapore

Chouder, Aissa 020301
University of M'sila, M'sila, Algeria

Chowdhury, Gofran 020276, 020544
3E, Brussels, Belgium

Christ, Anja 020063
ISFH, Emmerthal, Germany

Chrkavy, Daniel 020262
Solargis, Bratislava, Slovakia

Chueh, Wei-Lo 020021
TSEC, Hsinchu, Taiwan

Ciesla, Alison 020065
UNSW, Sydney, Australia

Cirimele, Vincenzo 020314
University of Bologna, Bologna, Italy

Clausing, Roland 020063, 020114
ISFH, Emmerthal, Germany

Clochard, Laurent 020031
Nines Photovoltaics, Dublin, Germany

Clochard, Laurent 020007
Nines Photovoltaics, Dublin, Ireland

Clyncke, Jan 020472, 020513
PV CYCLE, Brussels, Belgium

Coşkun, Özlem 020006, 020027, 020225
Kalyon PV, Ankara, Türkiye

Colberts, Fallon 020389
Zuyd University, Heerlen, The Netherlands
Colin, Hervé 020217, 020262
CEA / INES, Le Bourget-du-Lac, France
Collin, Stéphane 020074
C2N, Palaiseau, France
Colwell, Jack 020048
SunDrive Solar, Kurnell, Australia
Comak, Mertcan 020003
ISC Konstanz, Konstanz, Germany
Connolly, James Patrick 020058, 020060
CNRS, Gif-sur-Yvette, France
Cordeiro, Diogo 020464
EDP, Lisbon, Portugal
Cornago, Iñaki 020392
CENER, Sarriguren, Spain
Cornaro, Cristina 020494
University of Rome Tor Vergata, Rome, Italy
Correa, Guillermo 020412
Gonvarri MS R&D, Corvera - Asturias, Spain
Correia, Joana 020565
University of Évora, Évora, Portugal
Couderc, Romain 020217, 020311, 020546
CEA / INES, Le Bourget-du-Lac, France
Coutel, John 020244
SOLAÏS, Valbonne, France
Cowan, Don 020230
Kiwa PI Berlin, Hudson, United States of America
Cox, Joel D. 020250
SDU Climate Cluster, Odense, Denmark
Cox, Joel D 020306
SDU Climate Cluster, Odense, Denmark
Coz, Pier Luigi 020246
European Space Agency, Noordwijk, The Netherlands
Crespo, Carolina 020490
University of Lisbon, Lisbon, Portugal
Cristiane Pan, Aline 020548
UFRGS, Tramandaí, Brazil
Cristóbal, Ana Belén 020491, 020535, 020575
UPM, Madrid, Spain
Crozier McCleland, Jacqueline 020185, 020344
Nelson Mandela University, Port Elizabeth, South Africa
Cuadra, Juan Manuel 020318
CENER, Sarigurren, Spain
Cui, Jindan 020320, 020525
Tokyo University of Science, Tokyo, Japan

Culot, Dominique 020384
Dow Silicones Belgium, Seneffe, Belgium

Curon, Jonathan 020384
Dow Silicones Belgium, Seneffe, Belgium

Cusenza, Maria Anna 020466
RSE, Milan, Italy

D. Pinto, Luciana 020090
Federal University of Rio de Janeiro, Rio de Janeiro, Brazil

Daenen, Michael 020156, 020389, 020393
imec, Genk, Belgium

Dagla, Anastasia 020276
3E, Brussels, Belgium

Dahle, Arne 020225, 020495
Norsun, Oslo, Norway

Dahlioui, Dounia 020443
University of Agder, Grimstad, Norway

Dalibor, Thomas 020307
Avancis, Munich, Germany

Dalla Maria, Enrico 020485
Eurac Research, Bolzano, Italy

Dalla Torre, Francesco 020010
Applied Materials, Treviso, Italy

Dalmazzone, Didier 020251
ENSTA Paris, Palaiseau, France

Damon, Keanu 020382
7SecondSolar, Cape Town, South Africa

Danelli, Andrea 020462, 020466
RSE, Milan, Italy

Darsene Dimd, Berhane 020270
SINTEF, Trondheim, Norway

Das, Gourab 020005, 020222, 020463
RCT Solutions, Konstanz, Germany

Dasilva-Villanueva, Nerea 020014, 020501, 020508
UPM, Madrid, Spain

Daßler, David 020313
Fraunhofer CSP, Halle, Germany

Daßler, David 020355
Fraunhofer IMWS, Halle, Germany

Daume, Darwin 020361
pvnode, Rosenheim, Germany

Davidsen, Rasmus Schmidt 020028, 020039, 020043
Aarhus University, Aarhus, Denmark

De Almeida, Laura 020074
LAAS-CNRS, Toulouse, France

De Biasio, Martin 020504
Silicon Austria Labs, Villach, Austria
De Blasi, Mariam 020378
Enel Green Power, Pisa, Italy
de Graaf, Gertjan J. 020405
TNO, Petten, The Netherlands
de Groot, Koen M. 020405
TNO, Petten, The Netherlands
De Gruijter, Alvaro 020254
Eurac Research, Bolzano, Italy
de Jong, Minne M. 020169, 020425
TNO, Eindhoven, The Netherlands
De Jong, Richard 020156, 020294, 020389
imec, Genk, Belgium
de l`Epine, Mélodie 020252, 020505, 020543, 020564
Becquerel Institute France, Lyon, France
de l`Epine, Melodie 020225, 020334, 020520, 020558
Becquerel Institute, Brussels, Belgium
de l`Epine, Melodie 020570
IEA PVPS Task 1, Lyon, France
de la Casa Higueras, Juan 020269
University of Jaén, Jaén, Spain
de la Viuda, Eva 020205
University of Valladolid, Valladolid, Spain
de Meatza, Iratxe 020495
CIDETEC, San Sebastián, Spain
De Rose, Angela 020123
Fraunhofer ISE, Freiburg, Germany
De Rose, Jonas 020010
Fraunhofer ISE, Freiburg, Germany
Debastiani Benato, Betina 020019
AMIRES, Prague, Czech Republic
Deepti, 020563
SRM University, Sonipat, India
Del Campo, Valeria 020311
Federico Santa María Technical University, Valparaiso, Chile
del Cañizo, Carlos 020014, 020501, 020507, 020508
UPM, Madrid, Spain
Del Pero, Claudio 020249
Polytechnic University of Milan, Milan, Italy
Del Pozo, Alberto 020197, 020198
TECNALIA, Derio, Spain
del Prado Santamaria, Rodrigo 020191, 020376
DTU, Roskilde, Denmark
del Ser, Javier 020358
UPV/EHU, Bilbao, Spain

Delgado-Sanchez, Jose Maria 020089
University of Seville, Seville, Spain

Delli Veneri, Paola 020378
ENEA, Naples, Italy

Denafas, Julius 020225, 020353
Solitek, Vilnius, Lithuania

Deniz, Engin 020559
Ege University, İzmir, Türkiye

Denke, Sebastian 020236
ISFH, Emmerthal, Germany

Dentz, Laurie 020058
CNRS, Palaiseau, France

Derin Gure, Pinar 020513, 020521, 020556
ODTU GUNAM, Ankara, Türkiye

Derj, Anyssa 020116
IPVF, Palaiseau, France

Dessì, Alessio 020077
CNR-ICCOM, Sesto Fiorentino, Italy

Devenson, Jan 020157
Center for Physical Sciences and Technology (FTMC), Vilnius, Lithuania

Dhimish, Mahmoud 020346, 020376
DTU, Roskilde, Denmark

Di Matteo, Alfredo 020010
Enel Green Power, Catania, Italy

Diab, Mohanad 020203
Eurac Research, Bolzano, Italy

Diano, Marcello 020378
M2M Engineering, Naples, Italy

Diaz, Roberto 020300
Notio Association, Toledo, Spain

Díaz, Sara 020365, 020366
CENER, Sarriguren, Spain

Dietrich, Andreas 020355
DiSUN Deutsche Solarservice, Werder, Germany

Díez Alcántara, Eduardo 020501
UCM, Madrid, Spain

Díez, Eduardo 020508
UCM, Madrid, Spain

Dimd, Berhane Darsene 020495, 020510
SINTEF, Trondheim, Norway

Ding, Kaining 020233
FZJ, Jülich, Germany

Ding, Kung 020111
Hohai University, Changzhou, China

Dittmann, Sebastian 020318
Anhalt University of Applied Sciences, Köthen, Germany

Dittrich, Arne 020240
ISFH, Emmerthal, Germany

Dizier, Antoine 020373
INES, Le Bourget-du-Lac, France

Djeukeu, Ivanol Jaurece 020050
halm elektronik, Frankfurt am Main, Germany

Dobreva, Petja 020193
University of Namibia, Windhoek, Namibia

Dörenkämper, Maarten 020169
TNO, Eindhoven, The Netherlands

Dörn, Markus 020255
A-Null Development, Vienna, Austria

Doi, Minh Thong 020317
CEA INES, Le Bourget-du-Lac, France

Domínguez, César 020209, 020246, 020257
UPM, Madrid, Spain

Donadello, Alessandro 020485, 020489
Edyna, Bolzano, Italy

Donėlienė, Jolanta 020157
Applied Research Institute for Prospective Technologies, Vilnius, Lithuania

Donoso, José 020570
UNEF, Madrid, Spain

Doppler, Christian 020455
Virtual Vehicle, Graz, Austria

dos Reis, Givaldo 020348
University of São Paulo, São Paulo, Brazil

dos Santos, Jeremias 020409
University of Évora, Évora, Portugal

Doucet, Jean-Baptiste 020074
LAAS-CNRS, Toulouse, France

Dovesi, Roberto 020060
Academy of Sciences of Turin, Torino, Italy

Driesse, Anton 020211, 020293, 020452
PV Performance Labs, Freiburg, Germany

Duarte, Dorivaldo 020418, 020565
University of Evora, Évora, Portugal

Dubois, Sebastien 020034
University Grenoble Alpes, Le Bourget-du-Lac, France

Dubravskij, Piotr 020157
Applied Research Institute for Prospective Technologies, Vilnius, Lithuania

Dubravskij, Piotr 020380
Modern E-Technologies, Vilnius, Lithuania

Duerinckx, Filip 020064, 020225
Hasselt Unversity, Genk, Belgium

Düz, Cansel 020135
Kalyon PV, Ankara, Türkiye

Dullweber, Thorsten 020006, 020007, 020008, 020225
ISFH, Emmerthal, Germany

Dunlop, Ewan D. 020173, 020210, 020213
European Commission JRC, Ispra, Italy

Dupon, Olivier 020294
imec, Genk, Belgium

Dupuis, Julien 020188
EDF R&D, Moret Loing Orvanne, France

Dutykh, Denys 020338
Khalifa University, Abu Dhabi, United Arab Emirates

Duzellier, Sophie 020073
University of Toulouse, Toulouse, France

Dypvik Sødahl, Elin 020340
IFE, Kjeller, Norway

Ebert, Matthias 020426
Fraunhofer CSP, Halle, Germany

Ebert, Matthias 020355
Fraunhofer IMWS, Halle, Germany

Ebner, Rita 020318, 020334, 020521
AIT, Vienna, Austria

Echeverria, Oihane 020139
Tecnalia, Donostia - San Sebastián, Spain

Eder, Gabriele C. 020160, 020162, 020249, 020500, 020504
OFI, Vienna, Austria

Eelma, Tonis 020302
IBS, Tartu, Estonia

Efthymiou, Venizelos 020544
EPL Technology Frontiers, Dhali, Cyprus

Egan, Renate 020048
UNSW, Sydney, Australia

Egido, Miguel-Ángel 020407
UPM, Madrid, Spain

Eidtmann, Maximilian 020385
ZHAW, Winterthur, Switzerland

Eijgelaar, Marcel 020571
DNV, Arnhem, The Netherlands

Eikelboom, Erik 020225
Futurasun, Citadella, Italy

Einhaus, Roland 020312
ZSW, Stuttgart, Germany

Eisenacher, Matthias 020141
University of Applied Science Cologne, Cologne, Germany

Eiternick, Stefan 020004, 020052
Fraunhofer CSP, Halle (Saale), Germany

Ekins-Daukes, Nicholas J. 020065
UNSW, Sydney, Australia

El Ainaoui, Khadija 020171
Green Energy Park, Benguerir, Morocco

El mrabet, Yasmine 020171
Green Energy Park, Benguerir, Morocco

Elgaili, Mohamed 020166
QEERI, Doha, Qatar

Elhamaoui, Said 020171
Green Energy Park, Benguerir, Morocco

Ellis, Hanna 020213
European Commission JRC, Ispra, Italy

Engelen, Tine 020389
Hasselt University, Diepenbeek, Belgium

Erber, Alexander 020386
BFH, Burgdorf, Switzerland

Eryılmaz, Hande 020521
ODTÜ-GÜNAM, Ankara, Türkiye

Escudero, Ana 020414
IaSol, Zaragoza, Spain

Esmailifar, Seyyed Majid 020335, 020356, 020374, 020375
Amirkabir University of Technology, Tehran, Iran

Espinosa, Nieves 020497, 020506
University of Murcia, Murcia, Spain

Essam T. Mohammed, Sarah 020546
EU SOLARIS, Almeria, Spain

Esteras, Miguel 020358
TECNALIA, Derio, Spain

Eyhorn, Steffen 020369
Fraunhofer ISE, Freiburg, Germany

Fabel, Yann 020235, 020237, 020239
DLR, Almeria, Spain

Fabris, Francesca 020225
Futurasun, Citadella, Italy

Faes, Antonin 020251
CSEM, Neuchâtel, Switzerland

Falangas, Alexandros 020210
TRASIS International, Brussels, Belgium

Fang, Xue 020525
Tokyo University of Science, Tokyo, Japan

Fano, Vanesa 020055, 020097, 020153, 020287
UPV/EHU, Bilbao, Spain

Farhat, Mohammad 020428
Australian University, Kuwait City, Kuwait

Farina, Andrea 020066
CNR-IFN, Milan, Italy

Farrias-Basulto, Guillermo 020101
HZB, Berlin, Germany

Fath, Moritz 020463
RCT Solutions, Konstanz, Germany

Fath, Peter 020005, 020463
RCT Solutions, Konstanz, Germany

Fava, Henrique 020565
University of Évora, Évora, Portugal

Feichtner, Markus 020255
Sonnenkraft Energie, St. Veit/Glan, Austria

Feichtner, Markus 020160
Sonnenkraft Energy, St. Veit/Glan, Austria

Feldbacher, Sonja 020136, 020500
PCCL, Leoben, Austria

Feldhof, Anne Maren 020522
University of Applied Science Cologne, Cologne, Germany

Fernandes, Cláudia 020464
Centre for New Energy Technologies, Sacavém, Portugal

Fernández Solas, Álvaro 020331
DLR, Almería, Spain

Ferrando, Jorge 020226
University of Valencia, Paterna, Spain

Ferreira, Catarina G. 020250
SDU Climate Cluster, Odense, Denmark

Ferreira, Catarina 020306
SDU Climate Cluster, Odense, Denmark

Ferrero, Sergio 020079
Polytechnic University of Turin, Turin, Italy

Feuerherdt, Niels 020309
Berlin University of Applied Sciences, Berlin, Germany

Fialho, Luis 020203, 020254, 020261, 020304, 020403, 020409, 020418, 020420, 020565
Eurac Research, Bolzano, Italy

Figueroa, Andrés 020339
National University of Colombia, Bogotá, Colombia

Fischer, Stefan 020495
SGL Carbon, Meitingen, Germany

Fleischanderl, Martin 020136
voestalpine Stahl, Linz, Austria

Fleury, Perine 020513, 020521
Biosphere Solar, Delft, The Netherlands

Flouchi, Imane 020171
Green Energy Park, Benguerir, Morocco

Fodor, Nikoletta 020521
SolarPower Europe, Brussels, Belgium

Fontani, Daniela 020066
CNR-INO, Florence, Italy

Forster, Jacob 020135
Fraunhofer ISE, Freiburg, Germany

Forstinger, Anne 020331
CSP Services, Cologne, Germany

Franch, Jordi Badosa 020406
Ecole Polytechnique, Palaiseau, France

Franchi, Daniele 020077
CNR-ICCOM, Sesto Fiorentino, Italy

Franquet, Erwin 020259, 020428
Côte d'Azur University, Nice, France

Frasson, Nicola 020019
Applied Materials, San Biagio di Callalta, Italy

Freer, Solomon 020396
PV Lighthouse, Coledale, Australia

Freitag, Marina 020077
Newcastle University, Newcastle upon Tyne, United Kingdom

Freund, Timo 020312
EnBW, Karlsruhe, Germany

Friansyah, Rizal 020376
DTU, Roskilde, Denmark

Friesen, Gabi 020160, 020249, 020574
SUPSI, Mendrisio, Switzerland

Friesen, Thomas 020249
Megasol Energie, Deitingen, Switzerland

Fritz Muñoz, Benjamín 020099
UPV, Valencia, Spain

Froebel, Jens 020121, 020142, 020192, 020223
Fraunhofer CSP, Halle, Germany

Frontini, Francesco 020249, 020253
SUPSI, Mendrisio, Switzerland

Fuentealba-Vidal, Edward 020129, 020311, 020342, 020417, 020422
University of Antofagasta, Antofagasta, Chile

Füreder-Kitzmüller, Friedrich 020136
voestalpine Stahl, Linz, Austria

Fuertes Marrón, David 020014, 020501, 020507, 020508
UPM, Madrid, Spain

Fuertes, David 020097
IES-UPM, Madrid, Spain

Furnari, Alessandro 020010
Enel Green Power, Catania, Italy

Fuß, Michael 020206
MBJ Solutions, Ahrensburg, Germany

Gabor, Andrew M. 020166
BrightSpot Automation, Boulder, United States of America

Gaete, Martin 020311
University of Antofagasta, Antofagasta, Chile

Gafert, Michael 020369
AIT, Vienna, Austria

Gageot, Tristan 020040
CEA / INES, Le Bourget-du-Lac, France

Gainza, Eusebio 020392
ALLOTARRA, Allo, Spain

Galarza, Alejandra 020461
IPVF, Palaiseau, France

Galbiati, Giuseppe 020119, 020218
Henkel, Düsseldorf, Germany

Galdikas, Algirdas 020157
Applied Research Institute for Prospective Technologies, Vilnius, Lithuania

Galiana, Beatriz 020085
Charles III University of Madrid, Madrid, Spain

Galiazzo, Marco 020019
Applied Materials, San Biagio di Callalta, Italy

Gall, Stefan 020101
HZB, Berlin, Germany

Gallmetzer, Sandra 020261, 020509
Eurac Research, Bolzano, Italy

Galparsoro, Ibon 020514
AZTI, PASAIA, Spain

Gamarra, Ana Rosa 020502
CIEMAT, Madrid, Spain

Ganter, Alissa 020296
ETH, Zurich, Switzerland

Gaona García, Elvis Eduardo 020279
District University of Bogotá, Bogotá, Colombia

Garabetian, Thomas 020551
SolarPower Europe, Brussels, Belgium

García Campos, Enrique 020336
University of Almeria, La Cañada de San Urbano, Spain

García, Fernando 020326
UC3M, Madrid, Spain

García, Sonia 020139
Tecnalia, Donostia - San Sebastián, Spain

García-Cañas, Alejandro 020257
IMDEA Nanoscience, Madrid, Spain

García-Salinas, María José 020100
University of Almeria, Almeria, Spain

Garcia-Sanchez, Almudena 020246, 020257
UPM, Madrid, Spain

Garg, Vivek 020069, 020071, 020081
SVNIT, Surat, India

Garraín, Daniel 020502
CIEMAT, Madrid, Spain

Gasse, Hugues 020073
University of Toulouse, Toulouse, France

Gassner, Anika 020160, 020162, 020500, 020504
OFI, Vienna, Austria

Gatti, Cesare 020541
PedersoliGattai, Milan, Italy

Gattu, Apoorva 020003
ISC Konstanz, Konstanz, Germany

Gautier, Damien 020505
Becquerel Institute, Brussels, Belgium

Gauvin, Xavier 020302
Bouygues Construction, Saint-Quentin-en-Yvelines, France

Ge, Hua 020249
Concordia University, Montreal, Canada

Gebhardt, Paul 020195
Fraunhofer ISE, Freiburg, Germany

Geerligs, L. J. 020030
TNO, Petten, The Netherlands

Gehrlein, Janek 020522
University of Applied Science Cologne, Cologne, Germany

Geier, Jutta 020234
PCCL, Leoben, Austria

Geml, Fabian 020031
University of Konstanz, Constance, Germany

Genovese, Maria 020378
Enel Green Power, Pisa, Italy

Georghiou, George E. 020534
University of Cyprus, Nicosia, Cyprus

Germani, Simone 020302
CEI, Milan, Italy

Getsiou, Maria 020181
Directorate General for Research and Innovation, Brussels, Belgium

Geymayer, Lukas 020136
voestalpine Stahl, Linz, Austria

Ghahremani, Amirreza 020335, 020374
Amirkabir University of Technology, Tehran, Iran

Ghennioui, Abdellatif 020171
Green Energy Park, Benguerir, Morocco

Ghosh, Saptak 020519
CSTEP, Bengaluru, India

Girardi, Pierpaolo RSE, Milan, Italy	020462, 020466
Giroux-Julien, Stephanie CNRS, Villeurbanne, France	020338
Gissler, Antoine EDF R&D, Palaiseau, France	020060
Göckeritz, Robert Fraunhofer CSP, Halle, Germany	020119
Gohil, Hardik RCT Solutions, Konstanz, Germany	020222
Gomes de Venuto, Vitor PUCRS, Porto Alegre, Brazil	020025
Gomez Trillos, Juan Camilo DLR, Oldenburg, Germany	020482
Gomez-Lazaro, Emilio University of Castilla-La Mancha, Albacete, Spain	020562
Gonnella, Gabriella Eurac research, Bolzano, Italy	020249, 020254
González Pérez, Sara ULL, San Cristóbal de La Laguna, Spain	020151
González Rodríguez, Brais University of Vigo, Vigo, Spain	020243
González, Miguel Ángel University of Valladolid, Valladolid, Spain	020205
González-Díaz, Benjamín ULL, San Cristóbal de La Laguna, Spain	020151
Goraya, Baljeet Singh Fraunhofer ISE, Freiburg, Germany	020475
Gordillo, Gerardo National University of Colombia, Bogotá, Colombia	020110
Gordon, Ivan imec, Genk, Belgium	020521
Gottschalg, Ralph Anhalt University of Applied Sciences, Köthen, Germany	020158
Gottschalg, Ralph Fraunhofer CSP, Halle, Germany	020056, 020201, 020229, 020233, 020284, 020574
Govaerts, Jonathan imec, Genk, Belgium	020019
Gracia Amillo, Ana María CENER, Pamplona, Spain	020211
Gracia Amillo, Ana María CENER, Sarigurren, Spain	020318
Gracia Amillo, Ana María CENER, Sarriguren, Spain	020181, 020365, 020366, 020497
Gregory, Geoffrey EnPV, Karlsruhe, Germany	020006

Greslou, Olivier 020551
CSTB, Bussy-Saint Georges, France

Grommes, Eva-Maria 020522, 020523
University of Applied Science Cologne, Cologne, Germany

Grosser, Stephan 020119, 020142, 020218
Fraunhofer CSP, Halle, Germany

Grünsteidl, Stefan 020307
Avancis, Munich, Germany

Gruginskie, Natasha 020067
Radboud University, Nijmegen, The Netherlands

Guedea, Isabel 020127, 020517
ENDEF, Zaragoza, Spain

Gülsoy, Eren Cihan 020521
METU, Ankara, Türkiye

Gümüs Çiftci, Burcu 020027
Kalyon PV, Ankara, Türkiye

Guerra, Gerardo 020448, 020481
GreenPowerMonitor a DNV company, Barcelona, Spain

Guidetti, Giulia 020541
Green Horse Advisory, Milan, Italy

Guillemoles, Jean François 020062
IPVF, Palaiseau, France

Guillevin, Nicolas 020225
TNO, Petten, The Netherlands

Gunbas, Gorkem 020113
ODTÜ-GÜNAM, Ankara, Türkiye

Gupta, Akshit 020551
Eurac Research, Bolzano, Italy

Gutierrez, Jose Ruben 020055, 020097, 020153, 020287
UPV/EHU, Bilbao, Spain

Gutjahr, Astrid 020030
TNO, Petten, The Netherlands

Haaland, Petry Kristine Nøttum 020476
NTNU, Trondheim, Norway

Haase, Felix 020063
ISFH, Emmerthal, Germany

Hadiwidjaja, Stella 020102
SERIS, Singapore, Singapore

Hadjipanayi, Maria 020064
University of Cyprus, Nicosia, Cyprus

Haedrich, Ingrid 020195, 020231
Fraunhofer ISE, Freiburg, Germany

Hämmer, Matthias 020470
bifa Umweltinstitut, Augsburg, Germany

Hafidi, Elias 020511
Inflights BV, Brussels, Belgium
Hagemann, Elizabeth M. 020416
Nelson Mandela University, Port Elizabeth, South Africa
Hallais, Géraldine 020058
CNRS, Palaiseau, France
Halle, Lasse 020359
BFH, Burgdorf, Switzerland
Hallensleben, Carina 020220
TAMURA-ELSOLD, Ilsenburg, Germany
Halm, Andreas 020218, 020220, 020221
ISC Konstanz, Konstanz, Germany
Halme, Janne 020249
Aalto University, Espoo, Finland
Hamada, Toshiyuki 020190
Osaka Electro-Communication University, Osaka, Japan
Hammer, Annette 020239
DLR, Oldenburg, Germany
Hamouda, Frederic 020058
CNRS, Palaiseau, France
Hanifi, Hamed 020121, 020125, 020137, 020223
AESOLAR, Koenigsbrunn, Germany
Hansen, Per-Anders 020017, 020503
Institute for Energy Technology, Kjeller, Norway
Harit, Amit Kumar 020064
Hasselt Unversity, Genk, Belgium
Harrison, Samuel 020225
CEA, Le Bourget-du-Lac, France
Hashem, Ahmad 020056, 020201
Anhalt University of Applied Sciences, Köthen, Germany
Hategan, Sergiu Mihai 020283
West University of Timisoara, Timisoara, Romania
Hauch, Jens 020117, 020149, 020150
HI ERN, Erlangen, Germany
Hauer, Martin 020255
Bartenbach, Vienna, Austria
Haverkamp, Helge 020008
centrotherm international, Blaubeuren, Germany
Hee Lee, Sang 020045
KIER, Daejeon, South Korea
Heidrich, Robert 020233
Fraunhofer CSP, Halle, Germany
Heikkinen, Kyösti 020423
VTT Technical Research Centre of Finland, Oulu, Finland
Heiser, Moritz 020230
Kiwa PI Berlin, Berlin, Germany

Helbig, Matthias 020220
ISC Konstanz, Konstanz, Germany
Helten, David 020331
CSP Services, Cologne, Germany
Hennig, Carsten 020313, 020355
saferay holding, Berlin, Germany
Hennig, Patrick 020313
Kiel University of Applied Sciences, Kiel, Germany
Heras, Jesús 020536
Wattkraft, Madrid, Spain
Hermle, Martin 020475
Fraunhofer ISE, Freiburg, Germany
Hernández Mora, Johann Alexander 020279, 020441
District University of Bogotá, Bogotá, Colombia
Hernández, Jaime J. 020257
IMDEA Nanoscience, Madrid, Spain
Hernández, Johann 020526
Francisco José de Caldas District University, Bogota, Colombia
Herodotou, Panayiotis 020534
University of Cyprus, Nicosia, Cyprus
Herrera Leon, Fernando Augusto 020339, 020546
National University of Colombia, Bogotá, Colombia
Herrero, Leire 020139
Tecnalia, Donostia - San Sebastián, Spain
Herrero, Rebeca 020209, 020453, 020459
UPM, Madrid, Spain
Herrmann, Werner 020208
TÜV Rheinland Solar, Cologne, Germany
Herteleer, Bert 020329, 020351
KU Leuven, Ghent, Belgium
Herteleer, Bert 020574
SUPSI, Mendrisio, Switzerland
Hessler-Wyser, Aïcha 020251
EPFL, Neuchâtel, Switzerland
Heydari, Azim 020485
Eurac Research, Bolzano, Italy
Hinken, David 020236
ISFH, Emmerthal, Germany
Hladys, Bertrand 020010
CEA, Grenoble, France
Hoex, Bram 020065
UNSW, Sydney, Australia
Hofer, Leo 020322
BFH, Burgdorf, Switzerland
Hoffmann, Erik 020006
EnPV, Karlsruhe, Germany

Hogan Almeida, Rita UPM, Madrid, Spain	020535, 020567
Hollemann, Christina ISFH, Emmerthal, Germany	020008
Holovský, Jakub Czech Technical University, Prague, Czech Republic	020107
Honrubia-Escribano, Andrés University of Castilla-La Mancha, Albacete, Spain	020562
Hopp, Tobias Sunman Energy, Frankfurt, Germany	020384
Horn, Jonas halm elektronik, Frankfurt am Main, Germany	020050
Horta, Pedro University of Évora, Évora, Portugal	020304, 020403, 020409, 020418, 020420, 020565
Hosatte, Mikaël SEGTON Advanced Technology, Versailles, France	020068
Hoß, Jan ISC Konstanz, Konstanz, Germany	020004, 020035
Hossain, Mohammad Istiaque QEERI, Doha, Qatar	020042, 020075, 020108, 020109, 020146, 020147
Hou, Yi SERIS, Singapore, Singapore	020102
Hsiao, Pei-Chieh UNSW, Sydney, Australia	020048
Hsieh, Cho Fan ITRI, Hsinchu, Taiwan	020083, 020161, 020163
Hu, Shuaifeng University of Oxford, Oxford, United Kingdom	020226
Huang, Chris SunDrive Solar, Kurnell, Australia	020048
Huang, Gan KIT, Eggenstein-Leopoldshafen, Germany	020272
Huang, Lu-Jan TNO, Leiden, The Netherlands	020425
Huang, Tzu-Yen National Synchrotron Radiation Research Center, Hsinchu, Taiwan	020096
Hügi, Matthias BFH, Burgdorf, Switzerland	020322
Huemer, Martin University of Linz, Linz, Austria	020227
Huerta, Hugo E. TUAS, Turku, Finland	020286, 020400
Hüttl, Bernd Coburg University of Applied Sciences, Coburg, Germany	020361

Hulik Jansova, Marketa — 020274
Solargis, Bratislava, Slovakia

Hung, Tzu Han — 020552
ITRI, Taipei City, Taiwan

Hutterer-Tik, Thomas — 020347
Watt Analytics, Vienna, Austria

Hwang, Hye-Mi — 020324, 020357, 020561
KIER, Daejeon, South Korea

Iglesias, Unai — 020139
Tecnalia, Donostia - San Sebastián, Spain

Ikeda, Kazuaki — 020436
AIST, Koriyama, Japan

Infante, Paulo — 020420
University of Évora, Évora, Portugal

Isabella, Olindo — 020515
TU Delft, Delft, The Netherlands

Ishikawa, Ryousuke — 020106, 020115
Tokyo City University, Setagaya, Japan

Iwaszko, Victorien — 020495
ROSI Solar, Saint-Martin-d'Hères, France

Izquierdo-Roca, Victor — 020094
IREC, Barcelona, Spain

J. N. Soares, Guillermo — 020090
Federal University of Rio de Janeiro, Duque de Caxias, Brazil

Jacob, Julieu — 020302
METABUILD, Berlin, Germany

Jacobs, Ayesha — 020382
Zutari, Cape Town, South Africa

Jaeckel, Bengt — 020056, 020119, 020121, 020140, 020142, 020175, 020192, 020201, 020223, 020229
Fraunhofer CSP, Halle, Germany

Jäger Waldau, Arnulf — 020570
European Commission, Rome, Italy

Jäger, Philip — 020006
ISFH, Emmerthal, Germany

Jäggi, Adrian — 020179
BFH, Burgdorf, Switzerland

Järventausta, Pertti — 020445
Tampere University, Tampere, Finland

Jaffré, Alexandre — 020058
CNRS, Gif-sur-Yvette, France

Jahn, Ulrike — 020521, 020574
Fraunhofer CSP, Halle, Germany

Jahn, Ulrike — 020355
Fraunhofer IMWS, Halle, Germany

Jahreis, Sophia — 020142, 020192
Fraunhofer CSP, Halle, Germany

Jakomin, Roberto — 020090
Federal University of Rio de Janeiro, Duque de Caxias, Brazil

Jakubik, Martin — 020274
Solargis, Bratislava, Slovakia

Jakuza, Paola — 020089
University of Padova, Padova, Italy

Jalkh, Judy — 020455
Virtual Vehicle, Graz, Austria

Jandl, Ralf — 020204
FFHS, Zurich, Switzerland

Jankovec, Marko — 020197
University of Ljubljana, Ljubljana, Slovenia

Jaworczak, Kamil — 020402
Technology Innovation Institute, Abu Dhabi, United Arab Emirates

Jensen, Adam R. — 020267
DTU, Kongens Lyngby, Denmark

Jeong, Jungi — 020323
K-water, Daejeon, South Korea

Jeong, Kyung Taek — 020045
KIER, Daejeon, South Korea

Jeong, Minsoo — 020045
KIER, Daejeon, South Korea

Jeronimo, Pedro — 020010
CEA, Grenoble, France

Jiang, Zonghan — 020158, 020201
Anhalt University of Applied Sciences, Köthen, Germany

Jimenez, Maria — 020302
Onyx Solar, Avila, Spain

Jimeno, Juan Carlos — 020055, 020097, 020153, 020287, 020289, 020353
UPV/EHU, Bilbao, Spain

Jo, Hyunsik — 020323
K-water, Daejeon, South Korea

Job, Enzo — 020231
Fraunhofer ISE, Freiburg, Germany

Johnson, Mark Robert — 020546
Institut Laue-Langevin (ILL), Grenoble, France

Joo, Dongmyoung — 020449
KETI, Wonmi-gu, South Korea

Jooss, Wolfgang — 020005, 020222, 020463
RCT Solutions, Konstanz, Germany

Joseph, Daniel Christopher 020123
Fraunhofer ISE, Freiburg, Germany

Joshi, Deepak 020069, 020081
SVNIT, Surat, India

Joss, David 020359, 020369, 020386
BFH, Burgdorf, Switzerland

Jouini, Anis 020034
ECM Technologies, Grenoble, France

Jouttijärvi, Sami 020286, 020298, 020398
University of Turku, Turku, Finland

Joziak, Roman 020230
Kiwa PI Berlin, Berlin, Germany

Ju, Young-Chul 020324, 020357, 020561
KIER, Daejeon, South Korea

Jugo, Josu 020437
UPV/EHU, Leioa, Spain

Junge, Sebastian 020008, 020482
ISFH, Emmerthal, Germany

Kaaya, Ismail 020156, 020294, 020389, 020393
imec, Genk, Belgium

Kähler, Jan-Dirk 020482
Centrotherm International, Blaubeuren, Germany

Kahraman, Mert 020027
Kalyon PV, Ankara, Türkiye

Kainz, Konrad 020430
AIT, Vienna, Austria

Kaiser, Martin 020215
Fraunhofer ISE, Freiburg, Germany

Kaizuka, Izumi 020570
RTS Corporation, Tokyo, Japan

Kajari-Schröder, Sarah 020063
ISFH, Emmerthal, Germany

Kallioharju, Kari 020444, 020445
TUAS, Tampere, Finland

Kalliojärvi, Heidi 020194
Tampere University, Tampere, Finland

Kalshetty, Mahesh 020519
CSTEP, Bengaluru, India

Kaltenbach, Thomas 020195
Fraunhofer ISE, Freiburg, Germany

Kamphues, Joshua 020031
University of Konstanz, Constance, Germany

Kandiyoti-Eskenazi, Selin 020467
CSEM, Neuchâtel, Switzerland

Kang, Min Gu 020045
KIER, Daejeon, South Korea
Kapetanovic, Viktor 020367
Nextracker, Fremont, United States of America
Karhu, Juha 020286
Finnish Meteorological Institute, Helsinki, Finland
Kari, Thøger 020191, 020376
DTU, Roskilde, Denmark
Karimy, Hedayatullah 020052
Fraunhofer CSP, Halle (Saale), Germany
Karttunen, Lauri 020298, 020398
University of Turku, Turku, Finland
Kasper, Ruth 020167, 020232
University of Applied Sciences Cologne, Cologne, Germany
Katouli, Tannaz 020195
Fraunhofer ISE, Freiburg, Germany
Kaufmann, Kai 020355
DENKweit, Halle, Germany
Kawabata, Rudy 020092
PUC-Rio, Rio de Janeiro, Brazil
Kemp, Linda 020390
MARIN, Wageningen, The Netherlands
Kenchington, Ian 020225, 020474, 020558
Becquerel Institute, Brussels, Belgium
Kenny, Robert 020210
European Commission JRC, Ispra, Italy
Khan, Abeer Ali 020513
First Solar, Mainz, Germany
Khosravi, Arash 020381
Mälardalen University, Västerås, Sweden
Kikkert, Benjamin W. J. 020405
TNO, Petten, The Netherlands
Kilickaya, Seda 020020
ODTÜ-GÜNAM, Ankara, Türkiye
Kim, Jin-Hong 020449
KETI, Wonmi-gu, South Korea
Kim, Jun-Tae 020249
Kongju National University, Chungnam, South Korea
Kim, Kihwan 020112
KIER, Daejeon, South Korea
Kim, Seok Won 020449
KETI, Wonmi-gu, South Korea
Kim, Yong-Jin 020045
KIER, Daejeon, South Korea
Kinge, Sachin 020117
Toyota Motors Europe, Brussels, Belgium

Kitamura, Ibuki 020190
Osaka Electro-Communication University, Osaka, Japan

Kitzberger, Gregor 020136
voestalpine Stahl, Linz, Austria

Kivambe, Maulid 020166
QEERI, Doha, Qatar

Kizukuri, Rihoko 020220
TAMURA-ELSOLD, Ilsenburg, Germany

Kladas, Anastasios 020329, 020351
KU Leuven, Ghent, Belgium

Kleider, Jean-Paul 020040, 020058
CNRS, Gif-sur-Yvette, France

Kleissl, Jan 020528
University of California, San Diego, United States of America

Klengel, Robert 020355
Fraunhofer IMWS, Halle, Germany

Klenk, Markus 020385
ZHAW, Winterthur, Switzerland

Klos, Christine 020510
Buhck Re.Energy, Hamburg, Norway

Kluska, Sven 020019
Fraunhofer ISE, Freiburg, Germany

Klute, Carola 020355
Fraunhofer IMWS, Halle, Germany

Knausdorf, Christian 020361
Coburg University of Applied Sciences, Coburg, Germany

Ko, Seok-whan 020561
KIER, Daejeon, South Korea

Ko, Suk Whan 020324, 020357
KIER, Daejeon, South Korea

Koc, Timurhan 020376
DTU, Roskilde, Denmark

Koduvelikulathu, Lejo Joseph 020035, 020068
ISC Konstanz, Konstanz, Germany

Koduvelikulathu, Lejo 020003
ISC Konstanz, Konstanz, Germany

Köntges, Marc 020206
ISFH, Emmerthal, Germany

Koepge, Ringo 020142, 020192
Fraunhofer CSP, Halle, Germany

Koester, Lukas 020203, 020261, 020325
Eurac Research, Bolzano, Italy

Kohlenberg, Heike 020063
ISFH, Emmerthal, Germany

Kohno, Tohru 020186
Hitachi, Tokyo, Japan

Kolahi, Mohammad 020356, 020375
University of Isfahan, Isfahan, Iran

Konagai, Makoto 020106, 020115
Tokyo City University, Setagaya, Japan

Kono, Toru 020484
Hitachi, Kokubunji, Japan

Konu, Christopher Bruce 020132
HTW Berlin, Berlin, Germany

Kopecek, Radovan 020569
ISC Konstanz, Konstanz, Germany

Kopp, Nils 020220
TAMURA-ELSOLD, Ilsenburg, Germany

Korkmaz Arslan, Melisa 020020
ODTÜ-GÜNAM, Ankara, Türkiye

Korpås, Magnus 020476
NTNU, Trondheim, Norway

Kortetmäki, Aki 020444, 020445
TUAS, Tampere, Finland

Koskela, Juha 020444, 020445, 020554
Tampere University, Tampere, Finland

Kossen, Eric J. 020030
TNO, Petten, The Netherlands

Kowalski, Julia 020237
RWTH, Aachen, Germany

Kräling, Ulli 020215
Fraunhofer ISE, Freiburg, Germany

Kraft, Thomas M. 020423
VTT Technical Research Centre of Finland, Oulu, Finland

Krainer, Diana Maria 020430
AIT, Vienna, Austria

Krasilnikov, Inga 020379
Tel Aviv University, Tel Aviv, Israel

Krever Lopes, Bruno 020023
PUCRS, Porto Alegre, Brazil

Kribus, Abraham 020379
Tel Aviv University, Tel Aviv, Israel

Krishnan, Sasikumar 020361
Coburg University of Applied Sciences, Coburg, Germany

Kroon, Jan 020225
TNO, Petten, The Netherlands

Kuan, Ta-Ming 020021, 020053
TSEC, Hsinchu, Taiwan

Kubicek, Bernhard 020281, 020318, 020334, 020347, 020430
AIT, Vienna, Austria

Kucuk, E. Busra 020030
TNO, Petten, The Netherlands

Kuczyńska-Łażewska, Anna 020498, 020499
Gdansk University of Technology, Gdansk, Poland
Kühne, Philip 020240
Leibniz University Hannover, Hannover, Germany
Kuhrmann, Bernd 020206
MBJ Solutions, Ahrensburg, Germany
Kujansivu, Eino 020554
Solarigo Systems, Pirkkala, Finland
Kumar, Gaurav 020563
MERI College of Engineering and Technology, Bahadurgarh, India
Kumar, Sagarika 020402
Technology Innovation Institute, Abu Dhabi, United Arab Emirates
Kumar, Saurabh 020563
PTB, Braunshweig, Germany
Kuo, Cheng-Wen 020021, 020053
TSEC, Hsinchu, Taiwan
Kurtulus, Gunes 020556
ODTU GUNAM, Ankara, Türkiye
Kuruganti, Vaibhav V. 020033
ISC Konstanz, Konstanz, Germany
Kurz, Hannes 020136
voestalpine Stahl, Linz, Austria
Kusch, Alexander 020361
Coburg University of Applied Sciences, Coburg, Germany
Kuzhagaliyeva, Nursulu 020402
Technology Innovation Institute, Abu Dhabi, United Arab Emirates
Kuznicki, Zbigniew T. 020013, 020068
SEGTON Advanced Technology, Versailles, France
Kwiatkowski, Jerzy 020551
NAPE, Warsaw, Poland
Kyranaki, Nikoleta 020156
Hasselt University, Genk, Belgium
Kyranaki, Nikoleta 020393
Hasselt University, Hasselt, Belgium
Kyranaki, Nikoleta 020294
imec, Genk, Belgium
Kyratsi, Theodora 020495
University of Cyprus, Nicosia, Cyprus

L. Andersen, Nanna 020477
DTU, Roskilde, Denmark
L. Souza, Patrícia 020090
Federal University of Rio de Janeiro, Rio de Janeiro, Brazil

Lachowicz, Agata 020039
CSEM, Neuchâtel, Switzerland

Lahr, Simon 020388
Next2Sun Technology, Dillingen, Germany

Lahr, Simon 020411
Next2Sun, Dillingen, Germany

Lajunen, Antti 020400
University of Helsinki, Helsinki, Finland

Lambertz, Andreas 020233
FZJ, Jülich, Germany

Lamblot, Hervé 020302
Sunstyle, Paris, France

Lamghari, Fouad 020402
Fujairah Research Centre, Fujairah, United Arab Emirates

Lamminaho, Jani 020250, 020306
SDU Climate Cluster, Odense, Denmark

Landaas, Christian 020495
Northern Silicon, Meråker, Norway

Landberg, Lars 020448
DNV Denmark, Hellerup, Denmark

Landberg, Lars 020481
DNV Denmark, Hellerup, Spain

Landes, Dieter 020361
Coburg University of Applied Sciences, Coburg, Germany

Landová, Lucie 020107
Czech Technical University, Prague, Czech Republic

Lansade, David 020073
University of Toulouse, Toulouse, France

Lappalainen, Kari 020194, 020528, 020537
Tampere University, Tampere, Finland

Lara, Yolanda 020127, 020414, 020517
ENDEF, Zaragoza, Spain

Larionova, Yevgeniya 020006, 020007, 020225
ISFH, Emmerthal, Germany

Låstad, Jonas 020011
NTNU, Trondheim, Norway

Laurens-Berge, Clarisse 020034
University Grenoble Alpes, Le Bourget-du-Lac, France

Laurikėnas, Paulius 020353
Solitek, Vilnius, Lithuania

Lauwaert, Johan 020064
Ghent University, Ghent, Belgium

Lazaro-Castrillon, Luna 020085
IO-CSIC, Madrid, Spain

Le Bossenec, Hugo 020116
IPVF, Palaiseau, France

Le Brun, Anton 020096
Australian Nuclear Science and Technology Organisation, Lucas Heights, Australia

Lechón, Yolanda 020502
CIEMAT, Madrid, Spain

Ledesma, Javier R. 020337
UPM, Madrid, Spain

Ledesma, Javier 020446
UPM, Madrid, Spain

Lee, Chun-Wei 020021
TSEC, Hsinchu, Taiwan

Lee, Hyunju 020046
Meiji University, Kanagawa, Japan

Lee, Jieun 020323
K-water, Daejeon, South Korea

Lee, Jin-Seok 020324, 020357, 020561
KIER, Daejeon, South Korea

Legarrea, Aritz 020365
CENER, Sarriguren, Spain

Lelievre, Jean-Francois 020373
INES, Le Bourget-du-Lac, France

Lelong, Benoit 020373
Cythelia Energy, La Motte-Servolex, France

Leloux, Jonathan 020262
LuciSun, Villers-la-Ville, Belgium

Lenain, Philippe 020495
benkei, Lyon, France

Lennon, Alison 020048
UNSW, Sydney, Australia

Lenz, Markus 020226
School of Life Sciences FHNW, Muttenz, Switzerland

Lenzmann, Frank 020019
TNO Energy Transition, Petten, The Netherlands

Leone, Sander 020405
Novar, Rotterdam, The Netherlands

Leonforte, Fabrizio 020249
Polytechnic University of Milan, Milan, Italy

Leopold, Ulrich 020457
Luxembourg Institute of Science and Technology, Esch-sur-Alzette, Luxembourg

Levrat, Jacques 020251, 020467
CSEM, Neuchâtel, Switzerland

Levtchenko, Alexandra 020116
IPVF, Palaiseau, France

Lewandowski, Simon 020073
University of Toulouse, Toulouse, France

Leza, Baurin 020412
Gonvarri MS R&D, Corvera - Asturias, Spain

Lezaca, Jorge 020239
DLR, Oldenburg, Germany

Li, Xinyang 020222
RCT Solutions, Konstanz, Germany

Li, Yung-Chih 020021
TSEC, Hsinchu, Taiwan

Li, Yuxuan 020001
East China University of Science and Technology, Shanghai, China

Libal, Joris 020218, 020474
ISC Konstanz, Konstanz, Germany

Lichtenberger, Janine 020430
AIT, Vienna, Austria

Lițiu, Andrei Vladimir 020551
EPB Center, Rotterdam, The Netherlands

Lin, Shih-Chieh 020021
TSEC, Hsinchu, Taiwan

Lindahl, Johan 020486, 020532
Becquerel Sweden, Knivsta, Sweden

Linder, Johannes 020492
Belectric, Kolitzheim, Germany

Lindfors, Anders 020286
Finnish Meteorological Institute, Helsinki, Finland

Lindig, Sascha 020371
Univers, Courbevoie, France

Linke, Jonathan 020004, 020035, 020225
ISC Konstanz, Konstanz, Germany

Linß, Volker 020033
VON ARDENNE, Dresden, Germany

Lipovšek, Benjamin 020047
University of Ljubljana, Ljubljana, Slovenia

Lippke, Benjamin 020180, 020230
Kiwa PI Berlin, Berlin, Germany

List-Kratochvil, Emil 020101
HZB, Berlin, Germany

Litrico, Grazia 020010
Enel Green Power, Catania, Italy

Liu, Cui 020001
East China University of Science and Technology, Shanghai, China

Liu, Dongyang 020063
ISFH, Emmerthal, Germany

Liu, Han-Chang 020350
ITRI, Tainan, Taiwan

Liu, Huiping 020495
GRÄNGES, Finspång, Sweden

Liu, Mengdi 020144, 020208
TÜV Rheinland, Shanghai, China

Liu, Yung-Tsung 020053, 020083
ITRI, Hsinchu, Taiwan

Livera, Andreas 020534
University of Cyprus, Nicosia, Cyprus

Lizin, Sebastien 020513, 020521
UHasselt, Hasselt, Belgium

Llarena, María Elena 020151
ITER, Granadilla de Abona, Spain

Loeckenhoff, Ruediger F. 020416
AZUR SPACE Solar Power, Heilbronn, Germany

Löhning, Martha 020063
ISFH, Emmerthal, Germany

Löhr, Johannes 020063, 020114
ISFH, Emmerthal, Germany

Lokhat, Ismaël 020262
Cythelia Energy, La Motte-Servolex, France

Lokhat, Ismael 020373
Trace Software, Saint-Romain-de-Colbosc, France

Lombardo, Salvatore 020066
CNR-IMM, Catania, Italy

Long, Yean-San 020053, 020083
ITRI, Hsinchu, Taiwan

Longo, Giulia 020099
UPV, Valencia, Spain

Lopes Gomes, Carlos Javier 020432, 020434
Sunveon, Madrid, Spain

Lopes, Ana Patrícia 020464
University of Lisbon, Lisbon, Portugal

López Cuéllar, Juan Manuel 020501
UCM, Madrid, Spain

López Dalmau, Daniel 020432, 020434
Sunveon, Madrid, Spain

López, Nuria 020451
DTU, Roskilde, Denmark

Lorenz, Dieter 020206
MBJ Solutions, Ahrensburg, Germany

Lorenzo Pigueiras, Eduardo 020363
UPM, Madrid, Spain

Lorenzo, Celena 020337, 020536
UPM, Madrid, Spain

Lorenzo, Eduardo 020439, 020446
UPM, Madrid, Spain

Lossen, Jan 020003, 020035
ISC Konstanz, Konstanz, Germany

Louwen, Atse 020203, 020226, 020261, 020509, 020546
Eurac Research, Bolzano, Italy

Louwen, Atse 020316
RISE, Boras, Sweden

Lu, Huan-Wu 020161
ITRI, Hsinchu, Taiwan

Lu, Matthew 020230
Kiwa PI Berlin, Shanghai, China

Lucea, Aingeru 020197, 020198
TECNALIA, Derio, Spain

Lüdemann, Marius 020233
Fraunhofer CSP, Halle, Germany

Luís, Margarida 020421
University of Lisbon, Lisbon, Portugal

Lustoza de Souza, Patricia 020092
UFRJ, Rio de Janeiro, Brazil

Ly, Moussa 020023, 020025
PUCRS, Porto Alegre, Brazil

Lyubenova, Teodora 020210
European Commission JRC, Ispra, Italy

M. Bazilio, Willian 020092
PUC-Rio, Rio de Janeiro, Brazil

M. S. Kawabata, Rudy 020090
Pontifical Catholic University of Rio de Janeiro, Rio de Janeiro, Brazil

M. Torelly, Guilherme 020090
Pontifical Catholic University of Rio de Janeiro, Rio de Janeiro, Brazil

Ma Lu, Silvia 020381
Mälardalen University, Västerås, Sweden

Ma, Xiang 020011
SINTEF, Oslo, Norway

Macé, Philippe 020225, 020252, 020474, 020505, 020543, 020558, 020573
Becquerel Institute, Brussels, Belgium

Mack, Sebastian 020031
Fraunhofer ISE, Freiburg, Germany

Madsen, Morten 020250, 020306
SDU Climate Cluster, Odense, Denmark

Mahmood, Aysha 020265, 020376
DTU, Roskilde, Denmark

Maixner, Andreas 020121, 020125, 020137, 020223
AESOLAR, Koenigsbrunn, Germany

Maiz, Alexander 020437
UPV/EHU, Vitoria-Gasteiz, Spain

Majak, Martyna 020068
Roltec, Poznań, Poland

Makrides, George 020534
University of Cyprus, Nicosia, Cyprus

Malarkannan, Lavanya 020210
National Physical Laboratory, Teddington, United Kingdom

Malcorps, Philippe 020276
3E, Brussels, Belgium

Malik, Stephanie 020313
Fraunhofer CSP, Halle, Germany

Malik, Stephanie 020355
Fraunhofer IMWS, Halle, Germany

Maliutina, Kristina 020141
University of Applied Science Cologne, Cologne, Germany

Malo, Javier 020209
UPM, Madrid, Spain

Mancini, Simone 020425
TNO, Eindhoven, The Netherlands

Mandiola, Gotzon 020514
AZTI, PASAIA, Spain

Manganiello, Patrizio 020389
Hasselt University, Diepenbeek, Belgium

Manganiello, Patrizio 020294
imec, Genk, Belgium

Manito, Alex 020348
University of São Paulo, São Paulo, Brazil

Manochehrian, Rasoul 020539
Frankfurt University of Applied Sciences, Frankfurt am Main, Germany

Manzolini, Giampaolo 020261
Polytechnic University of Milan, Milan, Italy

Maqsood, Ayman 020101
HZB, Berlin, Germany

Marangis, Demetris 020534
University of Cyprus, Nicosia, Cyprus

Marcos-Castro, Ana 020297
CIEMAT, Madrid, Spain

Marechal, Philippe 020217
CEA / INES, Le Bourget-du-Lac, France

Marí Soucase, Bernabé 020099
UPV, Valencia, Spain

Markert, Jochen 020231
Fraunhofer ISE, Freiburg, Germany

Marquardt, Cornelia 020063
ISFH, Emmerthal, Germany

Marteau, Baptiste 020034
ECM Technologies, Grenoble, France
Martín Rueda, Javier 020535
UPM, Madrid, Spain
Martín, Francisco José 020459
UPM, Madrid, Spain
Martín, Francisco 020209
UPM, Madrid, Spain
Martín-Chivelet, Nuria 020297
CIEMAT, Madrid, Spain
Martín-Rueda, Javier 020337, 020363
UPM, Madrid, Spain
Martínez González, Mario 020326
Enertis Applus+, Madrid, Spain
Martinez, Juan Ignacio 020252
Becquerel Institute Spain, San Sebastian, Spain
Martinez, Oscar 020191, 020205
University of Valladolid, Valladolid, Spain
Martínez-Barbeito, María 020243
ieco.io, Vigo, Spain
Maruyama, Rodrigo P. 020154, 020348
University of São Paulo, São Paulo, Brazil
Marzo, Aitor 020311, 020546
University of Granada, Granada, Spain
Mashkov, Oleksandr 020149, 020150, 020377
HI ERN, Erlangen, Germany
Massaro, Lorenzo 020541
PedersoliGattai, Milan, Italy
Masson, Gaëtan 020474, 020558, 020564, 020573
Becquerel Institute, Brussels, Belgium
Masson, Gaëtan 020570
IEA PVPS Task 1, Brussels, Belgium
Mateos, Yeray 020055, 020153
UPV/EHU, Bilbao, Spain
Maturi, Laura 020249, 020254, 020551
Eurac Research, Bolzano, Italy
Mayer-Ullmann, Philipp 020430
AIT, Vienna, Austria
Mazzoleni, Stefano 020378
University of Naples Federico II, Naples, Italy
McIntosh, Keith R. 020396
PV Lighthouse, Coledale, Australia
McNab, Shona 020065
UNSW, Sydney, Australia
Meereboer, Martijn 020225
Energyra, Westknollendam, The Netherlands

Meier, Rico 020132
HTW Berlin, Berlin, Germany

Meixner, Michael 020050
halm elektronik, Frankfurt am Main, Germany

Mekhaldi, Bouchra 020406
Ecole Polytechnique, Palaiseau, France

Melges de Andrade, Adnei 020154
University of São Paulo, São Paulo, Brazil

Melino, Francesco 020314
University of Bologna, Bologna, Italy

Mellone, Celeste 020541
Green Horse Advisory, Rome, Italy

Menard, Lionel 020291
MINES Paris, Nice, France

Mencaraglia, Denis 020058
CNRS, Gif-sur-Yvette, France

Menchaca, Iratxe 020514
AZTI, PASAIA, Spain

Mendes Ferreira Gomes, Amanda 020548
UFSC, Florianopolis, Brazil

Mendikoa, Iñigo 020514
Tecnalia, BRTA, Derio, Spain

Meneghini, Matteo 020089
University of Padova, Padova, Italy

Ménézo, Christophe 020317
LOCIE, Le Bourget-du-Lac, France

Menghini, Mariela 020508
IMDEA Nanoscience Institute, Madrid, Spain

Mercade Ruiz, Pau 020448, 020481
GreenPowerMonitor a DNV company, Barcelona, Spain

Merino, Amanda 020040
CEA / INES, Le Bourget-du-Lac, France

Merino, José Manuel 020085
UAM, Madrid, Spain

Mermoud, André 020196
PVsyst, Geneva, Switzerland

Merodio, Pablo 020337
UPM, Madrid, Spain

Mertens, Jan 020389
imec, Genk, Belgium

Mertens, Verena 020006, 020008
ISFH, Emmerthal, Germany

Meßmer, Marius 020031
Fraunhofer ISE, Freiburg, Germany

Messmer, Tobias 020218, 020221, 020225
ISC Konstanz, Konstanz, Germany

Messner, Christian AIT, Vienna, Austria	020369
Mettner, Larissa ISFH, Emmerthal, Germany	020063, 020114
Meusel, Manuel Fraunhofer CSP, Halle (Saale), Germany	020052
Meyer, Kevin ISFH, Emmerthal, Germany	020260
Meza, Carlos Anhalt University of Applied Sciences, Köthen, Germany	020318, 020334, 020426, 020520
Mezzasalma, Frédéric CEA / INES, Le Bourget-du-Lac, France	020217
Micha, Daniel CEFET/RJ, Petrópolis, Brazil	020092
Michael, Poland Nelson Mandela University, Port Elizabeth, South Africa	020193
Miclea, Paul-Tiberiu Fraunhofer CSP, Halle, Germany	020233
Midtgård, Ole-Morten NTNU, Trondheim, Norway	020476
Miettunen, Kati University of Turku, Turku, Finland	020286, 020298, 020398
Migan-Dubois, Anne CNRS, Gif-sur-Yvette, France	020406
Mignonac, Alexandre CEA / INES, Le Bourget-du-Lac, France	020217
Mignonac, Alexandre CEA, Cadarache, France	020334
Mignonac, Alexandre CEA, Saint-Paul-Lez-Durance, France	020318
Miguel Laborda, María IaSol, Zaragoza, Spain	020414
Mihailetchi, Valentin Dan ISC Konstanz, Konstanz, Germany	020033
Mihailetchi, Valentin ISC Konstanz, Konstanz, Germany	020225
Mihaylov, Blago European Commission JRC, Ispra, Italy	020210
Milani, Emanuele Marelli Europe, Venaria Reala, Italy	020495
Milesi, Frédéric CEA, Grenoble, France	020068
Min, Byungsul ISFH, Emmerthal, Germany	020008, 020482
Mirandona López, Haritz Sunveon, Madrid, Spain	020432, 020434

Miró-Llorente, Marta 020094
IREC, Barcelona, Spain
Misra, Prashant 020429
NISE, Gurugram, India
Miszczuk, Andrzej 020068
Roltec, Poznań, Poland
Mittag, Max 020137
Fraunhofer ISE, Freiburg, Germany
Mittal, Ankit 020318
AIT, Vienna, Austria
Mittelman, Gur 020379
Afeka Tel-Aviv Academic College of Engineering, Tel Aviv, Israel
Mizushima, Io 020028
IPU P/S, Virum, Denmark
Mizushima, Io 020037
IPU, Virum, Denmark
Mngomezulu, Ndumiso 020344
PVinsight, Port Elizabeth, South Africa
Mo, Alvin 020065
UNSW, Sydney, Australia
Mockeviciute-Azzopardi, Austeja 020334
FIR, Birkirkara, Malta
Moe Nygård, Magnus 020340
IFE, Kjeller, Norway
Moehlecke, Adriano 020023, 020025
PUCRS, Porto Alegre, Brazil
Mohammadi, Mohammad Hossein 020037, 020104
Aarhus University, Aarhus, Denmark
Mollier, Stéphane 020262
CEA / INES, Le Bourget-du-Lac, France
Moltke, Asbjørn 020043
Technical University of Denmark, Copenhagen, Denmark
Mondaca-Cuevas, Gino 020422
University of Antofagasta, Antofagasta, Chile
Monokroussos, Christos 020181
TÜV Rheinland Shanghai, Shanghai, China
Monokroussos, Christos 020144, 020208
TÜV Rheinland, Shanghai, China
Monteiro Martins, Filipa 020317
Galp Energia, Lisbon, Portugal
Montes, Carlos 020151
ITER, Granadilla de Abona, Spain
Montoya, Josefa 020311
University of Antofagasta, Antofagasta, Chile
Morabito, Floriana 020066
CNR-IFN, Milan, Italy

Moradi Sizkouhi, Amirmohammad 020356, 020375
Concordia University, Montreal, Canada

Moradi Zavie Kord, Soroush 020400
University of Helsinki, Helsinki, Finland

Morales, Sergio 020491
UPM, Madrid, Spain

Morantes Quintana, Giobertti Raul 020551
Eurac Research, Bolzano, Italy

Mordvinkin, Anton 020233
Fraunhofer CSP, Halle, Germany

Moreda, Guillermo P. 020407
UPM, Madrid, Spain

Morin, Claire 020551
SolarPower Europe, Brussels, Belgium

Morisset, Audrey 020068
CSEM, Neuchâtel, Switzerland

Morlier, Arnaud 020156
Hasselt University, Genk, Belgium

Morlier, Arnaud 020294, 020389
imec, Genk, Belgium

Mortazavifar, Leila 020056, 020158, 020201, 020284
Anhalt University of Applied Sciences, Köthen, Germany

Moruno, Ricardo 020209, 020453
UPM, Madrid, Spain

Mosel, Frank 020015
PVA TePla, Wettenberg, Germany

Moser, David 020573
Becquerel Institute Italy, Trento, Italy

Moser, David 020316
Becquerel Institute, Bolzano, Italy

Moser, David 020254
Bequerel Institute, Trento, Italy

Moser, David 020203, 020226, 020261, 020325, 020485, 020489, 020546
Eurac Research, Bolzano, Italy

Mouhoubi, Felicia 020134
CEA / INES, Le Bourget-du-Lac, France

Müllejans, Harald 020208, 020213
European Commission JRC, Ispra, Italy

Müller, Alexander 020119
Fraunhofer CSP, Halle, Germany

Müller, Larissa 020523
University of Applied Sciences Cologne, Cologne, Germany

Mugica, Maikel 020139
Tecnalia, Donostia - San Sebastián, Spain

Mujovi, Fahradin 020251
CSEM, Neuchâtel, Switzerland

Mukherjee, Srijani 020338
CEA / INES, Le Bourget-du-Lac, France

Mukhtar, Mariyam 020057
University of Verona, Verona, Italy

Mulder, Peter 020067
Radboud University, Nijmegen, The Netherlands

Muller, Matthew 020314
NREL, Denver, United States of America

Munkhammar, Joakim 020532
Uppsala University, Uppsala, Sweden

Muñoz Cerón, Emilio 020269
University of Jaén, Jaén, Spain

Muñoz, Delfina 020040, 020311, 020546
CEA / INES, Le Bourget-du-Lac, France

Muñoz, Delfina 020521
CEA, Le Bourget-du-Lac, France

Muñoz, Delfina 020226
CEA/ INES, Le Bourget-du-Lac, France

Muñoz, Ildefonso 020365, 020366, 020392
CENER, Sarriguren, Spain

Muñoz, Jesús Ángel 020508
UCM, Madrid, Spain

Muñoz-García, Miguel-Ángel 020407
UPM, Madrid, Spain

Murano, Giovanni 020551
ENEA, Ispra, Italy

Murillo, Asier 020497
CENER, Sarriguren, Spain

Musembi, Robinson J. 020272
University of Nairobi, Nairobi, Kenya

Nabipouor, Mohammad 020426
Anhalt University of Applied Sciences, Köthen, Germany

Nagel, Henning 020475
Fraunhofer ISE, Freiburg, Germany

Nakamura, Kyotaro 020046
Toyota Technological Institute, Nagoya, Japan

Nanno, Ikuo 020190
Nanno Energy Research Center, Yamaguchi, Japan

Nargelienė, Viktorija 020157
Center for Physical Sciences and Technology (FTMC), Vilnius, Lithuania

Narsi Patel, Hitarth 020069
SVNIT, Surat, India

Narvarte, Luis 020337, 020446, 020491, 020535, 020536, 020567, 020575
UPM, Madrid, Spain

Nascimento, Lucas 020377
Solar Energy Research Laboratory Fotovoltaica/ UFSC, Florianópolis, Brazil

Nasebandt, Lasse 020063
ISFH, Emmerthal, Germany

Nasser, Hisham 020226
ODTÜ-GÜNAM, Ankara, Türkiye

Naveiro, José Manuel 020414
ENDEF, Zaragoza, Spain

Nazififard, Mohammad 020259, 020428
Côte d`Azur University, Nice, France

Nejim, Ahmed 020058
SILVACO, St. Ives, United Kingdom

Nel, Paul 020382
7SecondSolar, Cape Town, South Africa

Nelson, Jenny 020394
Imperial College London, London, United Kingdom

Neuba, Adam 020114
Paderborn University, Paderborn, Germany

Neuber, Viola 020031
Fraunhofer ISE, Freiburg, Germany

Neuhaus, Holger 020123, 020140
Fraunhofer ISE, Freiburg, Germany

Neumaier, Lukas 020504
Silicon Austria Labs, Villach, Austria

Neussl, Vassilissa 020318, 020430
AIT, Vienna, Austria

Neykova, Neda 020107
Czech Technical University, Prague, Czech Republic

Nezhad, Mahyar 020230
Kiwa PI Berlin, Hudson, United States of America

Nguyen, Viet Xuan 020008
centrotherm international, Blaubeuren, Germany

Nicolet-dit-Félix, Kléber 020251
EPFL, Neuchâtel, Switzerland

Nicot-Senneville, Zoltan 020102
SERIS, Singapore, Singapore

Nielsen, Michael P. 020065
UNSW, Sydney, Australia

Nissen, Hauke 020313
Wattmanufactur, Galmsbüll, Germany

Nitsche, Tobias 020119, 020218
Henkel, Düsseldorf, Germany

Nobre, André M. 020263
PV Doctor, Singapore, Singapore

Noels, Serge 020472
PV CYCLE, Brussels, Belgium

Noh, Yong-Su 020449
KETI, Wonmi-gu, South Korea

Nold, Sebastian 020461
Fraunhofer ISE, Freiburg, France

Nold, Sebastian 020475
Fraunhofer ISE, Freiburg, Germany

Nordboe, Eirik 020495
Fiven Norge, Lillesand, Norway

Norde Santos, Fernanda 020331
DLR, Almería, Spain

Nouri, Bijan 020235, 020237, 020239
DLR, Almería, Spain

Nova, David 020339
National University of Colombia, Bogotá, Colombia

Núñez, Rubén 020209, 020453
UPM, Madrid, Spain

Núñez-Osorio, Alessia 020100
University of Almeria, Almeria, Spain

Nurmesjärvi, Antti 020423
VTT Technical Research Centre of Finland, Oulu, Finland

Nussbaumer, Hartmut 020385
ZHAW, Winterthur, Switzerland

Nyang'onda, Thomas N. 020272
University of Nairobi, Nairobi, Kenya

Obeidavi, Sahereh 020361
Coburg University of Applied Sciences, Coburg, Germany

Oberbeck, Lars 020461
TotalEnergies OneTech, Paris, France

Oberegger Filippi, Ulrich 020551
Eurac Research, Bolzano, Italy

Ocaña, Luis Manuel 020151
ITER, Granadilla de Abona, Spain

Ockert, Ajka 020312
EnBW, Karlsruhe, Germany

Odilio dos Santos, Daniel 020548
UFSC, Florianopolis, Brazil

Öhgren, Gustav 020532
Becquerel Sweden, Knivsta, Sweden

Öttl, Christian 020347
Watt Analytics, Vienna, Austria

Öz, Aksel Kaan 020135
Fraunhofer ISE, Freiburg, Germany

Özden, Talat 020226
ODTÜ-GÜNAM, Ankara, Türkiye

Özkalay, Ebrar 020160, 020204
SUPSI, Mendrisio, Switzerland
Ogura, Atsushi 020046
Meiji University, Kanagawa, Japan
Ohdaira, Keisuke 020131
JAIST, Ishikawa, Japan
Ohshita, Yoshio 020046
Toyota Technological Institute, Nagoya, Japan
Ojala, Aleksi 020554
Solarigo Systems, Pirkkala, Finland
Okawa, Hayato 020115
Tokyo City University, Setagaya, Japan
Okel, Lars A. G. 020030
TNO, Petten, The Netherlands
Oksanen, Jani 020067
Aalto University, Espoo, Finland
Oliosi, Michele 020196
PVsyst, Geneva, Switzerland
Olivares, Douglas 020311
University of Antofagasta, Antofagasta, Chile
Olivares, Gregorio 020365, 020366, 020392
CENER, Sarriguren, Spain
Oliveira Santos, João Victor 020188
EDF R&D, Moret Loing Orvanne, France
Oliveira, Helena 020420
University of Évora, Évora, Portugal
Oller Westerberg, Amelia 020570
Becquerel Sweden, Knivsta, Sweden
Ollo, Olatz 020139
Tecnalia, Donostia - San Sebastián, Spain
Oozeki, Takashi 020436, 020525
AIST, Koriyama, Japan
Opatovsky, Martin 020241, 020262
Solargis, Bratislava, Slovakia
Oreski, Gernot 020136, 020234, 020325, 020500, 020574
PCCL, Leoben, Austria
Ortega, Eneko 020055, 020153, 020287, 020353
UPV/EHU, Bilbao, Spain
Ortega, Eneko 020289, 020437
UPV/EHU, Leioa, Spain
Ortega, Pascal 020214
University of French Polynesia, Faa'a, French Polynesia
Ortiz-Pena, Aaron 020562
University of Castilla-La Mancha, Albacete, Spain
Ory, Daniel 020188
EDF R&D, Palaiseau, France

Ory, Daniel 020116
EDF, Palaiseau, France

Osman, Alaa 020006
ISFH, Emmerthal, Germany

Osuna, Jose Antonio 020358
MAGTEL, Córdoba, Spain

Osvald, Oliver 020274
Solargis, Bratislava, Slovakia

Otaegi, Aloña 020055, 020097, 020153, 020287
UPV/EHU, Bilbao, Spain

Otnes, Gaute 020169
Institute for Energy Technology, Kjeller, Norway

Otto, Nicolas 020101
HTW, Berlin, Germany

Otto, William 020390
MARIN, Wageningen, The Netherlands

Ou, Chao-Wei 020350
National Chin-Yi University of Technology, Taichung, Taiwan

Ovaitt, Silvana 020314
NREL, Denver, United States of America

Ovaitt, Silvana 020574
NREL, Golden, United States of America

Oviedo Hernandez, Guillermo 020325
BayWa r.e, Rome, Italy

Ozer, Shay 020379
Agricultural Research Organization, Rishon LeZion, Israel

P. Pires, Maurício 020090
Federal University of Rio de Janeiro, Rio de Janeiro, Brazil

Pabiou, Herve 020338
CETHIL, Villeurbanne, France

Pabst, Elena 020312
ZSW, Stuttgart, Germany

Paiva, Lúcio 020530
Casa dos Ventos, Fortaleza, Brazil

Palais, Olivier 020188
Toulon University, Marseille, France

Palitzsch, Wolfram 020225, 020495
LuxChemTech, Freiberg, Germany

Palomino, Laura 020491, 020535
UPM, Madrid, Spain

Pamir Aly, Shahzada 020229
DEWA, Dubai, United Arab Emirates

Pamula, Bindu 020069
SVNIT, Surat, India

Panda, Pavan Kumar 020284
Anhalt University of Applied Sciences, Köthen, Germany

Pandar, Matthias 020229
Fraunhofer CSP, Halle, Germany

Pander, Matthias 020121, 020142, 020175, 020192, 020218, 020223, 020232
Fraunhofer CSP, Halle, Germany

Panduri, Fabio 020322
BFH, Burgdorf, Switzerland

Pantoja, Jaime 020526
Francisco José de Caldas District University, Bogota, Colombia

Papantoni, Veatriki 020482
DLR, Oldenburg, Germany

Paraficz, Danuta 020204
FFHS, Zurich, Switzerland

Paraskeva, Vasiliki 020064
University of Cyprus, Nicosia, Cyprus

Pardo, Eduardo 020414
Tecnova, Almeira, Spain

Parfeniukas, Karolis 020039
ATLANT 3D, Taastrup, Denmark

Parion, Jonathan 020064
Hasselt Unversity, Genk, Belgium

Park, Hyeonwook 020112
KENTECH, Naju-Si, South Korea

Parmar, Richa 020429
NISE, Gurugram, India

Parra, Johan 020406
Ecole Polytechnique, Palaiseau, France

Parra, Johan 020214
Polytechnic Institute of Paris, Palaiseau, France

Parrilla, Carlos G. 020402
Fujairah Research Centre, Fujairah, United Arab Emirates

Pascual Gallego, Valero 020407
UPM, Madrid, Spain

Pasquier, Mathis 020451
DTU, Roskilde, Denmark

Passaro, Marcello 020513
Sunzest Solar, Rotterdam, The Netherlands

Patel, Dharm 020355
Fraunhofer IMWS, Halle, Germany

Paul, Ananta 020250, 020306
SDU Climate Cluster, Odense, Denmark

Paulescu, Marius 020283
West University of Timisoara, Timisoara, Romania

Paviet-Salomon, Bertrand 020068, 020467
CSEM, Neuchâtel, Switzerland

Payno, David 020085, 020094
UAM, Madrid, Spain

Pearce, Pheobe 020065
UNSW, Sydney, Australia

Peche, René 020468, 020495
bifa Umweltinstitut, Augsburg, Germany

Pehlivanli, Ezgi 020521
METU, Ankara, Türkiye

Peibst, Robby 020006, 020063, 020114
ISFH, Emmerthal, Germany

Pelfort Ojer, Marta 020241
Solargis, Bratislava, Slovakia

Pelland, Sophie 020211
Natural Resources Canada, Varennes, Canada

Pelle, Martina 020249, 020254
Eurac Research, Bolzano, Italy

Peña-Bermudez, Julian 020110
University of the Caribbean, Santo Domingo, Dominican Republic

Peng, Cheng-Yu 020350
National Chin-Yi University of Technology, Taichung, Taiwan

Pera, David 020457
Luxembourg Institute of Science and Technology, Esch-sur-Alzette, Luxembourg

Perani, Martina 020204
FFHS, Zurich, Switzerland

Peraticos, Elias 020064
University of Cyprus, Nicosia, Cyprus

Pereda, Ainhoa 020198, 020358
TECNALIA, Derio, Spain

Pereira Fialho, Luis Andre 020509
Eurac Research, Bolzano, Italy

Pereira, Sara 020403, 020418, 020565
University of Évora, Évora, Portugal

Pérez García, Manuel 020336
University of Almería, La Cañada de San Urbano, Spain

Pérez, Ernesto 020339
National University of Colombia, Bogotá, Colombia

Pérez, Jairo 020412
Gonvarri AgroTech, Corvera - Asturias, Spain

Pérez, Jorge 020412
Gonvarri AgroTech, Corvera - Asturias, Spain

Pérez, Luis 020412
Gonvarri MS R&D, Corvera - Asturias, Spain

Perez, Richard 020494
University at Albany, Albany, United States of America

Perez-Astudillo, Daniel 020275, 020278, 020291
QEERI, Doha, Qatar

Pérez-García, Manuel 020100
University of Almeria, Almería, Spain

Pérez-Rodríguez, Alejandro 020085, 020094
IREC, Barcelona, Spain

Pernas, Tomás 020412
Gonvarri AgroTech, Corvera - Asturias, Spain

Pernau, Thomas 020008
centrotherm international, Blaubeuren, Germany

Perrin, Marion 020544
Energy Pool, Le Bourget-du-Lac, France

Pervan, Nikolina 020136, 020234
PCCL, Leoben, Austria

Peter Amalathas, Amalraj 020107
University of Jaffna, Jaffna, Sri Lanka

Peter, Kristian 020569
ISC Konstanz, Konstanz, Germany

Peters, Ian Marius 020230, 020263
Forschungszentrum Jülich, Erlangen, Germany

Peters, Ian Marius 020149, 020150, 020377, 020574
HI ERN, Erlangen, Germany

Petersons, Karlis 020250, 020306
Stensborg, Roskilde, Denmark

Petkovski, Emil 020571
DNV, Arnhem, The Netherlands

Petzschmann, Jonas 020312
ZSW, Stuttgart, Germany

Pfau, Jan Hendrik 020240
Leibniz University Hannover, Hannover, Germany

Pfeiffer, Oliver 020141
University of Applied Science Cologne, Cologne, Germany

Pfeiffer, Oliver 020140
University of Applied Sciences Cologne, Cologne, Germany

Philipp, Daniel 020215, 020231
Fraunhofer ISE, Freiburg, Germany

Pierro, Marco 020489, 020494
Eurac Research, Bolzano, Italy

Pieters, Bart E. 020180
FZJ, Jülich, Germany

Pieterse, Marco 020495
Chemconserve, Bussum, The Netherlands

Pietralunga, Silvia Maria 020066
CNR-IFN, Milan, Italy

Pietsch, Veith 020331
Aquila Capital, Hamburg, Germany
Pilat, Eric 020311
CEA / INES, Le Bourget-du-Lac, France
Pilat, Eric 020317
CEA INES, Le Bourget-du-Lac, France
Pillai, Akhildev 020558
Becquerel Institute, Brussels, Belgium
Pinheiro, Philippe 020457
Luxembourg Institute of Science and Technology, Esch-sur-Alzette, Luxembourg
Pinho Almeida, Marcelo 020348
University of São Paulo, São Paulo, Brazil
Pinto, Cristina Leyre 020497
CENER, Sarriguren, Spain
Pinto, Luciana 020092
UFRJ, Rio de Janeiro, Brazil
Pitaval, Sébastien 020244
SOLAÏS, Valbonne, France
Pitz-Paal, Robert 020237, 020331
DLR, Cologne, Germany
Plakhotnyuk, Maksym 020039
ATLANT 3D, Taastrup, Denmark
Platero Gaona, Carlos A. 020332
UPM, Madrid, Spain
Plaza, Caroline 020543, 020564, 020573
Becquerel Institute France, Lyon, France
Polacchi, Cristina 020509, 020513
Eurac Research, Bolzano, Italy
Polo, Jaime 020300
CENER, Sarriguren, Spain
Polo, Jesús 020297
CIEMAT, Madrid, Spain
Polverini, Davide 020181
Directorate General for Internal Market, Industry, Entrepreneurship and SMEs, Brussels, Belgium
Polverini, Davide 020497
European Comission, Brussels, Belgium
Pongthanacharoenkul, Nattapark 020230
Kiwa PI Berlin, Berlin, Germany
Poortmans, Jef 020064
Hasselt Unversity, Genk, Belgium
Popescu, Lacramioara 020068
ISC Konstanz, Konstanz, Germany
Pospischil, Maximilian 020225
Highline Technologies, Freiburg, Germany

Poulsen, Peter B. 020039
DTU, Copenhagen, Denmark
Poulsen, Peter B. 020250, 020265, 020267, 020376, 020451
DTU, Roskilde, Denmark
Poulsen, Peter Behrensdorff 020028, 020306, 020346
DTU, Roskilde, Denmark
Pourshafi, Pouya 020121, 020125, 020137
AESOLAR, Koenigsbrunn, Germany
Pozza, Cristian 020551
Eurac Research, Bolzano, Italy
Prakash, Jai 020429
NISE, Gurugram, India
Prando, Davide 020485, 020489
Edyna, Bolzano, Italy
Prasad, Manjunath 020225
ISC Konstanz, Konstanz, Germany
Pravettoni, Mauro 020402
Technology Innovation Institute, Abu Dhabi, United Arab Emirates
Preis, Pirmin 020003
ISC Konstanz, Konstanz, Germany
Preu, Ralf 020475
Fraunhofer ISE, Freiburg, Germany
Preuschoff, Jonas 020101
HTW, Berlin, Germany
Protti, Alexander Aguilar 020140
Fraunhofer ISE, Freiburg, Germany
Protti, Alexander 020137
Fraunhofer ISE, Freiburg, Germany
Provost, Marion 020116
IPVF, Palaiseau, France
Puel, Jean Baptiste 020062
IPVF, Palaiseau, France
Puertas López, Antonio Manuel 020100
University of Almeria, Almeria, Spain
Puttock, Claire 020367
Nextracker, Fremont, United States of America

Queste, Samuel 020068
Marie and Louis Pasteur University, Besançon, France
Quiroz, Mónica 020328
Qualifying Photovoltaics, Madrid, Spain

R. Ledesma, Javier 020363
UPM, Madrid, Spain

Rabanal Arabach, Jorge 020183
University of Antofagasta, Antofagasta, Chile

Rabanal-Arabach, Jorge 020129, 020342, 020417, 020422
University of Antofagasta, Antofagasta, Chile

Rabiei, Hossein 020063
ISFH, Emmerthal, Germany

Rachdi, Lazhar 020035, 020068
ISC Konstanz, Konstanz, Germany

Radzevicius, Aurimas 020225
Valoe Cells, Vilnius, Lithuania

Rafiee, Hossein 020539
Frankfurt University of Applied Sciences, Frankfurt am Main, Germany

Raginskis, Justinas 020380
Kaunas University of Technology, Kaunas, Lithuania

Raievska, Oleksandra 020117, 020149
HI ERN, Erlangen, Germany

Rajan, S. Prithivi 020262
LuciSun, Villers-la-Ville, Belgium

Rajkiewicz, Katarzyna 020551
NAPE, Warsaw, Poland

Rakotoniaina, Jean Patrice 020311
CEA / INES, Le Bourget-du-Lac, France

Ramachandran Nair, Jishnu 020233
Fraunhofer CSP, Halle, Germany

Ramesh, Santhosh 020389
imec, Genk, Belgium

Ramírez Ledesma, Javier 020535
UPM, Madrid, Spain

Ramirez, S. 020396
PV Lighthouse, Coledale, Australia

Rampino, Stefano 020087
National Research Council, Parma, Italy

Ramspeck, Klaus 020050
halm elektronik, Frankfurt am Main, Germany

Ranisch, Tadeus 020101
HTW, Berlin, Germany

Ranta, Samuli 020286, 020400
TUAS, Turku, Finland

Ranta, Samuli 020298, 020398
Turku University of Applied Sciences, Turku, Finland

Raposo, Mauro 020565
University of Évora, Évora, Portugal

Ratnagiri, Abhinav 020367
Nextracker, Fremont, United States of America

Raugewitz, Annika 020063, 020114
ISFH, Emmerthal, Germany

Raval, Mehul 020005, 020222, 020463
RCT Solutions, Konstanz, Germany

Razanajao, Aina 020244
SOLAÏS, Valbonne, France

Razi, Umair 020085
IREC, Barcelona, Spain

Recart, Federico 020097
UPV/EHU, Bilbao, Spain

Redondo Cuevas, Marta 020332
UPM, Madrid, Spain

Redondo, Juan Manuel 020209
UPM, Madrid, Spain

Rehan, Muhammad 020112
KIER, Daejeon, South Korea

Rehman, Anees ur 020111, 020164
Hohai University, Changzhou, China

Reichart, Hannah 020167, 020232
University of Applied Sciences Cologne, Cologne, Germany

Reichel, Christian 020123, 020137, 020140
Fraunhofer ISE, Freiburg, Germany

Reichle, Julian 020005, 020222, 020463
RCT Solutions, Konstanz, Germany

Reinders, Angele 020253
TU Eindhoven, Eindhoven, The Netherlands

Reindl, Thomas 020263
SERIS, Singapore, Singapore

Reis, Luiz Filipe 020530
Casa dos Ventos, Fortaleza, Brazil

Rémondeau, Paul 020251
EPFL, Neuchâtel, Switzerland

Renard, Charles 020058
CNRS, Palaiseau, France

Rende, Fedele 020255
ACCA Software, Cosenza, Italy

Rennhofer, Marcus 020180, 020281, 020318, 020334, 020347, 020430
AIT, Vienna, Austria

Rentsch, Jochen 020475
Fraunhofer ISE, Freiburg, Germany

Rerat, Michel 020060
IPREM, Pau, France

Reshef, Liad 020379
Agricultural Research Organization, Rishon LeZion, Israel

Revol, Inès 020074
LAAS-CNRS, Toulouse, France

Reyal, Jean-Pierre 020303
SemperStyl, Eragny, France

Riaño, Sandra 020197, 020358
TECNALIA, Derio, Spain
Richards, Bryce S. 020272
KIT, Karlsruhe, Germany
Riechelman, Stefan 020181
PTB, Braunschweig, Germany
Riechelmann, Stefan 020177, 020199, 020211
PTB, Braunschweig, Germany
Riedel-Lyngskær, Nicholas 020451
DTU, Roskilde, Denmark
Rienäcker, Michael 020063
ISFH, Emmerthal, Germany
Rindert, Sören 020230
Kiwa PI Berlin, Berlin, Germany
Ríos Moral, Lucía 020501
UCM, Madrid, Spain
Ríos-Ledesma, Felipe 020446
UPM, Madrid, Spain
Ripke, Melanie 020006
ISFH, Emmerthal, Germany
Riva, Roland 020495
CEA, Le Bourget-du-Lac, France
Rivas Rodríguez, José Manuel 020326
Enertis Applus+, Madrid, Spain
Robledo, Jesús 020262
LuciSun, Villers-la-Ville, Belgium
Rodríguez Lucas, Delia 020407
EkiLabs, Boston, United States of America
Rodríguez Plaza, José Luis 020508
Autonomous University of Madrid, Madrid, Spain
Rodríguez Rodríguez, Araceli 020501
UCM, Madrid, Spain
Rodríguez Salazar, David Leonardo 020441
District University of Bogotá, Bogotá, Colombia
Rodríguez, Araceli 020508
UCM, Madrid, Spain
Rodríguez, Diego Julián 020526
Francisco José de Caldas District University, Bogota, Colombia
Rodríguez, Isabel 020257
IMDEA Nanoscience, Madrid, Spain
Rodriguez, Sonia Maria 020289
UPV/EHU, Leioa, Spain
Rodríguez, Velia 020097
UPV/EHU, Bilbao, Spain
Rodríguez-Conde, Sofía 020326
Enertis Applus+, Madrid, Spain

Rodríguez-Gallegos, Carlos D. 020149, 020150
SERIS, Singapore, Singapore

Rodríguez-Romero, Sebastián 020342, 020417, 020422
University of Antofagasta, Antofagasta, Chile

Rodziewicz, Hanna 020498
Gdansk University of Technology, Gdansk, Poland

Römer, Udo 020006, 020063
ISFH, Emmerthal, Germany

Röver, Ingo 020225
LuxChemTech, Freiberg, Germany

Rojas, Christian A. 020422
Federico Santa María Technical University, Valparaíso, Chile

Rojas-Henríquez, Katalina 020129
University of Antofagasta, Antofagasta, Chile

Román, Eduardo 020139
Tecnalia, Donostia - San Sebastián, Spain

Romeo, Alessandro 020057, 020089, 020093
University of Verona, Verona, Italy

Romer, Pascal 020231
Fraunhofer ISE, Freiburg, Germany

Roodt, Roelof 020185
Nelson Mandela University, Port Elizabeth, South Africa

Roosloot, Nathan 020169
Institute for Energy Technology, Kjeller, Norway

Rosca, Victor 020030
TNO, Petten, The Netherlands

Rosen, Isaac 020225
Copprint, Jerusalem, Israel

Rosenfeld, Lavi 020379
Agricultural Research Organization, Rishon LeZion, Israel

Rosina, Konstantin 020241
Solargis, Bratislava, Slovakia

Rossa, Carlos 020432, 020434
Sunveon, Madrid, Spain

Rouffie, Brice 020068
SEGTON Advanced Technology, Versailles, France

Roulleau, Lea 020303
CSTB, Marne-la-Vallée, France

Rousset, Jean 020116
EDF, Palaiseau, France

Roy, Shantanu 020519
CSTEP, Bengaluru, India

Rudolph, Dominik 020003, 020068
ISC Konstanz, Konstanz, Germany

Rudzikas, Matas 020380
The Applied Research Institute for Prospective Technologies, Vilnius, Lithuania

Rüther, Ricardo 020377
Solar Energy Research Laboratory Fotovoltaica/ UFSC, Florianópolis, Brazil

Rüther, Ricardo 020548
UFSC, Florianopolis, Brazil

Ruf, Manuel 020455
Robert Bosch, Stuttgart, Germany

Ruiz Donoso, Elena 020331
DLR, Almería, Spain

S. Sousa, Graciana 020090
Federal University of Rio de Janeiro, Rio de Janeiro, Brazil

Safarian, Jafar 020011
NTNU, Trondheim, Norway

Sah, Dheeraj 020039
Aarhus University, Aarhus, Denmark

Sahin, Hasret 020479
LUT University, Lappeenranta, Finland

Saito, Kimihiko 020106
Tokyo City University, Setagaya, Japan

Salem, Mohammad 020428
Australian University, Kuwait City, Kuwait

Salerno, Giorgia 020077
University of Milano-Bicocca, Milan, Italy

Salis, Fabio 020541
Iberdrola, Rome, Italy

Salvador, Antonio 020358
MAGTEL, Córdoba, Spain

Sample, Tony 020213
European Commission JRC, Ispra, Italy

Samuolienė, Giedrė 020380
The Lithuanian Research Centre for Agriculture and Forestry, Kaunas, Lithuania

San José, Luis Javier 020209, 020453
UPM, Madrid, Spain

Sánchez de León Peque, Miguel 020243
ieco.io, Vigo, Spain

Sanchez Garcia, Alfredo 020270
SINTEF, Trondheim, Norway

Sanchez, Hugo 020056, 020158, 020284
Anhalt University of Applied Sciences, Köthen, Germany

Sanchez, Jesus 020437
UPV/EHU, Vitoria-Gasteiz, Spain

Sanchez, Laura 020437
UPV/EHU, Leioa, Spain
Sánchez, Yudania 020085
IREC, Barcelona, Spain
Sanchez-Friera, Paula 020412, 020513, 020521
Solkeys, Gijón, Spain
Sanchez-Ruiz, Alain 020437
UPV/EHU, Vitoria-Gasteiz, Spain
Sansavini, Giovanni 020296
ETH, Zurich, Switzerland
Sansoni, Paola 020066
CNR-INO, Florence, Italy
Santamaría Fernández, Susanna 020249
TECNALIA, Derio, Spain
Santamaría-Sancho, Juan 020363
UPM, Madrid, Spain
Santos, Jose Domingo 020197, 020198, 020358
TECNALIA, Derio, Spain
Santos, Rodrigo 020530
Casa dos Ventos, Fortaleza, Brazil
Sanz Martinez, Asier 020546
Tecnalia, Bilbao, Spain
Sanz, Asier 020514
Tecnalia, BRTA, Derio, Spain
Sanz, Asier 020197
TECNALIA, Derio, Spain
Sanz-Cuadrado, Cristina 020575
UPM, Madrid, Spain
Sanz-Saiz, Carlos 020297
CIEMAT, Madrid, Spain
Sarafijanovic-Djukic, Natasa 020204
FFHS, Regensdorf, Switzerland
Saretti, Angelica 020301
Polytechnic University of Bari, Bari, Italy
Sarkadi, Monika 020569
ISC Konstanz, Konstanz, Germany
Sauer, Thomas 020140
EXXERGY, Gräfelfing, Germany
Saura, Juan Antonio 020506
University of Murcia, Murcia, Spain
Savisalo, Tuukka 020225
Valoe, Mikkeli, Finland
Saw, Min Hsian 020402
Technology Innovation Institute, Abu Dhabi, United Arab Emirates
Saxena, Anmol Ratan 020429
NIT, Delhi, India

Sayed, Abdullah Abu 020180, 020230
Kiwa PI Berlin, Berlin, Germany

Scaltrito, Luciano 020079
Polytechnic University of Turin, Turin, Italy

Scerri, Kenneth 020334
University of Malta, Msida, Malta

Schading, Steve 020443
University of Agder, Grimstad, Norway

Schäfer, Aysim 020388
Next2Sun Technology, Dillingen, Germany

Schäfer, Sebastian 020539
Frankfurt University of Applied Sciences, Frankfurt am Main, Germany

Schenk, Paul 020192
Fraunhofer CSP, Halle, Germany

Schermer, John 020067
Radboud University, Nijmegen, The Netherlands

Scherret, Jacqueline 020255
A-Null Development, Vienna, Austria

Schifferegger, Raffael 020162
OFI, Vienna, Austria

Schimanke, Sabrina 020006
ISFH, Emmerthal, Germany

Schirmer, Yoko 020101
HTW, Berlin, Germany

Schläger, Christian 020240
Leibniz University Hannover, Hannover, Germany

Schlatmann, Rutger 020101
HTW, Berlin, Germany

Schmidt Davidsen, Rasmus 020037, 020104
Aarhus University, Aarhus, Denmark

Schnaus, Dominik 020237
TUM, Garching, Germany

Schneider, Andreas 020129, 020183
University of Applied Sciences Gelsenkirchen, Gelsenkirchen, Germany

Schneider, Astrid 020255
TU Wien, Vienna, Austria

Schneider, Friedrich 020482
LPKF SolarQuipment, Suhl, Germany

Schneider, Marc Gabriel 020522
University of Applied Science Cologne, Cologne, Germany

Schneiderlöchner, Eric 020033
VON ARDENNE, Dresden, Germany

Schnierer, Branislav 020262
Solargis, Bratislava, Slovakia

Schönau, Maximilian 020361
Coburg University of Applied Sciences, Coburg, Germany

Schönau, Maximilian 020544
smartblue, Munich, Germany

Schönheits, Markus 020468, 020470
bifa Umweltinstitut, Augsburg, Germany

Schranz, Christian 020255
TU Wien, Vienna, Austria

Schrempf, Michael 020199
PTB, Braunschweig, Germany

Schrijvers, Patrick 020390
MARIN, Wageningen, The Netherlands

Schröter, Nick 020142
Fraunhofer CSP, Halle, Germany

Schubert, Martin C. 020475
Fraunhofer ISE, Freiburg, Germany

Schubnel, Baptiste 020238
CSEM, Neuchâtel, Switzerland

Schüler, Marc Andre 020388
Next2Sun Technology, Dillingen, Germany

Schüler, Marc Andre 020411
Next2Sun, Dillingen, Germany

Schueler, Nadine 020015
Freiberger Instruments, Freiberg, Germany

Schulte-Huxel, Henning 020008, 020260
ISFH, Emmerthal, Germany

Schultz, Christof 020101
HTW, Berlin, Germany

Schulz, Philip 020060
IPVF, Palaiseau, France

Schulze, Achim 020361
Rosenheim Technical University of Applied Sciences, Rosenheim, Germany

Schulze, Patricia S.C. 020475
Fraunhofer ISE, Freiburg, Germany

Schwenke, Almut 020495
SGL Battery Solutions, Meitingen, Germany

Sciuto, Marcello 020010
Enel Green Power, Catania, Italy

Scognamiglio, Alessandra 020541
ENEA, Naples, Italy

Scognamiglio, Alessandra 020378
ENEA, Portici, Italy

Sedaghat, Ahmad 020428
Australian University, Kuwait City, Kuwait

Seiffert, Christoph 020169
Institute for Energy Technology, Kjeller, Norway

Seiffert, Daniela 020008
centrotherm international, Blaubeuren, Germany

Seitz, Matthias 020468
bifa Umweltinstitut, Augsburg, Germany

Selj, Josefine H. 020169
Institute for Energy Technology, Kjeller, Norway

Senno, Maximiliano Alejandro 020226
University of Valencia, Paterna, Spain

Senturk, Bilge 020556
ODTU GUNAM, Ankara, Türkiye

Setien, Eneko 020198
TECNALIA, Derio, Spain

Šetkus, Arūnas 020157
Center for Physical Sciences and Technology (FTMC), Vilnius, Lithuania

Shaaban, Ahmed 020402
Technology Innovation Institute, Abu Dhabi, United Arab Emirates

Shah, Syed Fawad Ali 020112
KENTECH, Naju-Si, South Korea

Shanmugam, Raphael 020218, 020220
ISC Konstanz, Konstanz, Germany

Sharma, Rajesh Kumar 020071, 020081
SVNIT, Surat, India

Sharma, Sushma 020563
SRM University, Sonipat, India

Shen, Xinyi 020226
University of Oxford, Oxford, United Kingdom

Shen, Zhenjue 020001
YIST, Jiangyin, China

Shin, Donghyeop 020112
KIER, Daejeon, South Korea

Shin, Woo Gyun 020324, 020357
KIER, Daejeon, South Korea

Shin, Woo-gyun 020561
KIER, Daejeon, South Korea

Shirai, Yasuhiro 020115
NIMS, Tsukuba, Japan

Shirazi, Elham 020544
University of Twente, Enschede, The Netherlands

Shishavan, Amir Asgharzadeh 020367
Nextracker, Fremont, United States of America

Shishido, Hirotaka 020106
Tokyo City University, Setagaya, Japan

Shochet, Ofer 020225
Copprint, Jerusalem, Israel

Shyong, Yung-Jen 020163
ITRI, Hsinchu, Taiwan

Sicot, Lionel 020217
CEA / INES, Le Bourget-du-Lac, France

Sidler, Anika 020226
School of Life Sciences FHNW, Muttenz, Switzerland

Siebert, Michael 020206
ISFH, Emmerthal, Germany

Siefer, Gerald 020246
Fraunhofer ISE, Freiburg, Germany

Sierra, Daniel 020491
UPM, Madrid, Spain

Sigounis, Anna-Maria 020248, 020249
Concordia University, Montreal, Canada

Søiland, Anne-Karin 020495
ReSiTec, Kristiansand, Norway

Silva, José A. 020304, 020409, 020420
University of Évora, Évora, Portugal

Silva, José 020403
University of Évora, Évora, Portugal

Silvestre, Santiago 020301
UPC, Barcelona, Spain

Simeunovic, Jelena 020238
CSEM, Neuchâtel, Switzerland

Simón-Allué, Raquel 020127, 020414, 020517
ENDEF, Zaragoza, Spain

Singh, Ravi 020571
DNV, Arnhem, The Netherlands

Sinha, Amish Kumar 020463
RCT Solutions, Konstanz, Germany

Sinopoli, Alessandro 020042
QEERI, Doha, Qatar

Sivaramakrishnan Radhakrishnan, Hariharsudan 020064
Hasselt Unversity, Genk, Belgium

Sivaramakrishnan, Hariharsudan 020225
IMEC, Genk, Belgium

Snaith, Henry 020226
University of Oxford, Oxford, United Kingdom

Søndenå, Rune 020503
Institute for Energy Technology, Kjeller, Norway

Sobajima, Yasushi 020131
Gifu University, Gifu, Japan

Soler Toledo, Denet 020509
University of Antofagasta, Antofagasta, Chile

Solomon, Asfaw A. 020479
LUT University, Lappeenranta, Finland

Solórzano, Jorge 020328
Qualifying Photovoltaics, Madrid, Spain

Sondoqah, Mousa 020316
Becquerel Institute, Bolzano, Italy

Sondoqah, Mousa 020261
Eurac Research, Bolzano, Italy

Song, Hee-eun 020045
KIER, Daejeon, South Korea

Spagnolo, Sofia 020462, 020466
RSE, Milan, Italy

Spataru, Sergiu V. 020265, 020267, 020283, 020376, 020451
DTU, Roskilde, Denmark

Spataru, Sergiu Viorel 020346
DTU, Roskilde, Denmark

Spera, Fabian 020411
Next2Sun, Dillingen, Germany

Spihola, Jan 020355
DiSUN Deutsche Solarservice, Werder, Germany

Sraisth, 020005, 020222
RCT Solutions, Konstanz, Germany

Sraisth, Sraisth 020463
RCT Solutions, Konstanz, Germany

Staňková, Tereza 020107
Czech Technical University, Prague, Czech Republic

Steckenreiter, Verena 020063
ISFH, Emmerthal, Germany

Stegemann, Bert 020309
Berlin University of Applied Sciences, Berlin, Germany

Stegemann, Bert 020101
HTW, Berlin, Germany

Stellbogen, Dirk 020312
ZSW, Stuttgart, Germany

Stensborg, Jan F. 020250
Stensborg, Roskilde, Denmark

Stensborg, Jan 020306
Stensborg, Roskilde, Denmark

Stieldorf, Karin 020255
TU Wien, Vienna, Austria

Stierstorfer, Johannes 020225
WIP - Renewable Energies, Munich, Germany

Stierstorfer, Johannes 020551
WIP Renewable Energies, Munich, Germany

Stivanello, Juan José 020226
Eurac Research, Bolzano, Italy

Stoicescu, Liviu 020198
Solarzentrum Stuttgart, Stuttgart, Germany

Stowhas-Villa, Alejandro 020422
Federico Santa María Technical University, Valparaiso, Chile

Stoyanova Lyubenova, Teodora 020173
European Commission JRC, Ispra, Italy

Sträter, Hendrik 020211
PTB, Braunschweig, Germany

Strey, Jessica 020063, 020114
ISFH, Emmerthal, Germany

Strömberg, Rich 020472
University of Alaska, Fairbanks, United States of America

Stroyuk, Oleksander 020185
HI ERN, Erlangen, Germany

Stroyuk, Oleksandr 020117, 020149, 020150
HI ERN, Erlangen, Germany

Suárez Sánchez, Sergio 020326
Enertis Applus+, Madrid, Spain

Subasi, Dilara Maria 020475
Fraunhofer ISE, Freiburg, Germany

Sudbury, Ben A. 020396
PV Lighthouse, Coledale, Australia

Suemitsu, Issei 020484
Hitachi, Kokubunji, Japan

Suhonen, Riikka 020423
VTT Technical Research Centre of Finland, Oulu, Finland

Sulca, Kabir Paúl 020191, 020205
University of Valladolid, Valladolid, Spain

Svatos, Jan 020250
DTU, Roskilde, Denmark

Sylla, David 020063
ISFH, Emmerthal, Germany

Syre Wiig, Marie 020340
IFE, Kjeller, Norway

Szarek, Magda 020298, 020398
University of Turku, Turku, Finland

Taghipour Kani, Ghaem 020335, 020374
Amirkabir University of Technology, Tehran, Iran

Takahashi, Kanji 020106
Tokyo City University, Setagaya, Japan

Talvi, Micke 020528
Tampere University, Tampere, Finland

Tanahashi, Tadanori 020436
AIST, Koriyama, Japan

Tang, Kai 020011
SINTEF, Trondheim, Norway

Tang, Torben IPU P/S, Virum, Denmark	020028
Tang, Torben IPU, Virum, Denmark	020037
Tayebjee, Murad J. Y. UNSW, Sydney, Australia	020065
Taylor, Nigel European Commission JRC, Ispra, Italy	020210
Tellez Rodriguez, Eduardo Kiwa PI Berlin, Berlin, Germany	020230
Teppe, Andreas RCT Solutions, Konstanz, Germany	020005
Terheiden, Barbara University of Konstanz, Constance, Germany	020031
Terrados, Cristian University of Valladolid, Valladolid, Spain	020205
Thakur, Dhruv Singh SVNIT, Surat, India	020071, 020081
Theocharides, Spyros Univers, Courbevoie, France	020371
Thomas, Jean Ciel et Terre, Lille, France	020169
Thorning, Jacob K. DTU, Roskilde, Denmark	020267, 020283
Thorsteinsson, Sune DTU, Copenhagen, Denmark	020039
Thorsteinsson, Sune DTU, Lyngby, Denmark	020037
Thorsteinsson, Sune DTU, Roskilde, Denmark	020028, 020249, 020250, 020265, 020306, 020477
Timofte, Tudor ISC Konstanz, Konstanz, Germany	020218, 020221
Ting, San-Yu ITRI, Hsinchu, Taiwan	020161, 020163
Tissier, Corentin CSEM, Neuchâtel, Switzerland	020238
Tönies, Alexandra University of Applied Sciences Cologne, Cologne, Germany	020523
Tomšič, Špela University of Ljubljana, Ljubljana, Slovenia	020047
Tong, Yongfeng QEERI, Doha, Qatar	020108, 020109
Topič, Marko University of Ljubljana, Ljubljana, Slovenia	020047, 020269, 020319
Torabi, Narges University of Verona, Verona, Italy	020089

Torelly, Guilherme 020092
PUC-Rio, Rio de Janeiro, Brazil

Torre, Gorka 020437
UPV/EHU, Leioa, Spain

Torres Aguilar, Moira Itzel 020214
CentraleSupélec, Gif-sur-Yvette, France

Torres Aguilar, Moira Itzel 020406
CNRS, Gif-sur-Yvette, France

Torres Silva, Nicole 020546
ATAMOSTEC, Santiago, Chile

Torres, Oscar 020110
National University of Colombia, Bogotá, Colombia

Tosi, Irene 020037
IPU, Virum, Denmark

Tran Caliste, Thu Nhi 020546
European Synchrotron Radiation Facility (ESRF), Grenoble, France

Treberspurg, Christoph 020255
Treberspurg und Partner Ziviltechniker, Vienna, Austria

Treberspurg, Martin 020255
Treberspurg und Partner Ziviltechniker, Vienna, Austria

Trefzer, Aaron 020135
Fraunhofer ISE, Freiburg, Germany

Trifiletti, Vanira 020087
University of Milano-Bicocca, Milan, Italy

Trigo-Gonzalez, Mauricio 020342, 020422
University of Antofagasta, Antofagasta, Chile

Tsai, Min-An 020053, 020083, 020161, 020163
ITRI, Hsinchu, Taiwan

Tsanakas, Ioannis (John) A. 020262
CEA / INES, Le Bourget-du-Lac, France

Tsanakas, Ioannis (John) A. 020544
CEA, Le Bourget-du-Lac, France

Tsanakas, Ioannis (John) 020546
CEA / INES, Le Bourget-du-Lac, France

Tsanakas, Ioannis (John) 020317
CEA INES, Le Bourget-du-Lac, France

Tsanakas, Ioannis (John) 020513, 020521
CEA, Le Bourget-du-Lac, France

Tsanakas, Ioannis 020217, 020338
CEA / INES, Le Bourget-du-Lac, France

Tsanakas, Ioannis 020500
CEA, Le Bourget-du-Lac, France

Tsanakas, John A. 020311
CEA / INES, Le Bourget-du-Lac, France

Tseberlidis, Giorgio 020093
University of Milano Bicocca, Milan, Italy

Tseberlidis, Giorgio 020087
University of Milano-Bicocca, Milan, Italy

Tsoi, Konstantin 020113
ODTÜ-GÜNAM, Ankara, Türkiye

Tsombou, Francois M. 020402
Fujairah Research Centre, Fujairah, United Arab Emirates

Tsuno, Yuki 020436
AIST, Koriyama, Japan

Tsunoda, Jun 020484
Hitachi, Kokubunji, Japan

Tsunoda, Jun 020186
Hitachi, Tokyo, Japan

Tulinski, Lona 020385
ZHAW, Winterthur, Switzerland

Tune, Daniel 020220, 020221, 020225
ISC Konstanz, Konstanz, Germany

Turcu, Mircea 020063
ISFH, Emmerthal, Germany

Turek, Marko 020004, 020052
Fraunhofer CSP, Halle (Saale), Germany

Ueda, Yuzuru 020320, 020525
Tokyo University of Science, Tokyo, Japan

Ujvari, Gusztav 020318, 020430
AIT, Vienna, Austria

Ulbikaitė, Vaidvilė 020157
Applied Research Institute for Prospective Technologies, Vilnius, Lithuania

Ulbikas, Juras 020225
Protechnology, Vilnius, Lithuania

Ulyashin, Alexander G. 020011
SINTEF, Oslo, Norway

Unsur, Veysel 020020
ODTÜ-GÜNAM, Ankara, Türkiye

Urban, Harald 020255
TU Wien, Vienna, Austria

Useni, Yannick 020393
University of Lubumbashi, Lubumbashi, Congo (DRC)

Uzuner, Bahri Eren 020113
ODTÜ-GÜNAM, Ankara, Türkiye

Väisänen, Kaisa-Leena 020423
VTT Technical Research Centre of Finland, Oulu, Finland

Vaicikauskas, Viktoras 020157
Center for Physical Sciences and Technology (FTMC), Vilnius, Lithuania

Valaski, Rogério 020090
National Institute of Metrology Quality and Technology, Rio de Janeiro, Brazil

Valencia, Felipe 020342, 020546
AtamosTec, Santiago, Chile

Vallerotto, Guido 020209, 020246, 020257
UPM, Madrid, Spain

van Aken, Bas B. 020405
TNO, Petten, The Netherlands

van der Heide, Arvid 020472
imec, Genk, Belgium

van der Zee, Friso F. 020405
Wageningen University and Research, Wageningen, The Netherlands

Van Dyck, Rik 020225
IMEC, Genk, Belgium

van Dyk, E. Ernest 020193, 020416
Nelson Mandela University, Port Elizabeth, South Africa

van Dyk, Ernest E. 020344
Nelson Mandela University, Port Elizabeth, South Africa

Van Overstraeten, Julien 020543
Becquerel Institute France, Lyon, France

Van Overstraeten, Julien 020252
Becquerel Institute, Brussels, Belgium

vanBaal, Rene 020492
Belectric, Kolitzheim, Germany

Vanhanen, Tuomas 020225
Valoe, Mikkeli, Finland

Vargas, Renzo 020348
University of São Paulo, São Paulo, Brazil

Varney, Valérie 020522
University of Applied Science Cologne, Cologne, Germany

Varney, Valérie 020523
University of Applied Sciences Cologne, Cologne, Germany

vas Dyk, Ernest 020185
Nelson Mandela University, Port Elizabeth, South Africa

Vasconcelos, Letícia 020530
Casa dos Ventos, Fortaleza, Brazil

Vavilkin, Tatjana 020302
Soltech, Genk, Belgium

Vázquez Adán, Alejandra 020501
UCM, Madrid, Spain

Vázquez, A. 020508
UCM, Madrid, Spain

Veas, Christian 020136, 020234
PCCL, Leoben, Austria

Vecino, Fernando Román 020346
DTU, Roskilde, Denmark

Veerman, Sebastian 020035
ISC Konstanz, Konstanz, Germany

Vega de Seoane, José Maria 020252
Becquerel Institute Spain, San Sebastian, Spain

Vega de Seoane, Jose 020546
Becquerel Institute, Brussels, Belgium

Vega-Herrera, Jorge 020342
University of Antofagasta, Antofagasta, Chile

Vehus, Tore Sandnes 020443
University of Agder, Grimstad, Norway

Veirman, Jordi 020203, 020226, 020254
Eurac Research, Bolzano, Italy

Velasco, Angel 020367
Nextracker, Fremont, United States of America

Veludo, Jorge 020317
Galp Energia, Lisbon, Portugal

Veneri, Alessandro 020093
University of Verona, Verona, Italy

Vergura, Silvano 020301
Polytechnic University of Bari, Bari, Italy

Verlinden, Pierre 020001
YIST, Jiangyin, China

Vermang, Bart 020064
Hasselt Unversity, Genk, Belgium

Vernay, Christophe 020244
SOLAÏS, Valbonne, France

Vero, Giuseppe 020301
Polytechnic University of Bari, Bari, Italy

Veronese, Elisa 020513
Eurac Research, Bolzano, Italy

Veurman, Welmoed 020063
ISFH, Emmerthal, Germany

Viani, Lucas 020326
Enertis Applus+, Madrid, Spain

Vicente-Laiglesia, Pablo 020181
European Climate, Infrastructure and Environment Executive Agency, Brussels, Belgium

Vidal de Oliveira, Aline 020377
Solar Energy Research Laboratory Fotovoltaica/ UFSC, Florianópolis, Brazil

Vidal, Beatriz Muñoz 020414
IaSol, Zaragoza, Spain

Vidal-Fuentes, Pedro 020094
IREC, Barcelona, Spain

Videla-Magnata, Natalia 020129
Universidad de Antofagasta, Antofagasta, Chile

Videla-Magnata, Natalia 020417
University of Antofagasta, Antofagasta, Chile

Vilches, Anna Morales 020388
Next2Sun Technology, Dillingen, Germany

Villalonga Palou, Joan Tomás 020432, 020434
Sunveon, Madrid, Spain

Villén, Raúl 020127, 020414, 020517
ENDEF, Zaragoza, Spain

Villodas, Aritz 020198
TECNALIA, Derio, Spain

Vincent, Laetitia 020058
CNRS, Palaiseau, France

Vincent, Robin 020196
PVsyst, Geneva, Switzerland

Viorel Spataru, Sergiu 020191
DTU, Roskilde, Denmark

Viriyaroj, Bergpob 020298
Aalto University, Espoo, Finland

Viti, Valeria 020541
Legance, Milan, Italy

Vitoshkin, Helena 020379
Agricultural Research Organization, Rishon LeZion, Israel

Vögeli, Pascal 020385
ZHAW, Winterthur, Switzerland

Vogt, Malte R. 020515
TU Delft, Delft, The Netherlands

Vogt, Thomas 020482
DLR, Oldenburg, Germany

Vollbrecht, Joachim 020063, 020114
ISFH, Emmerthal, Germany

Voltan, Alessandro 020010
Applied Materials, Treviso, Italy

von Friedeburg, Christoph 020557
CF Energy Research-Consulting-Operation, Berlin, Germany

Voronko, Yuliya 020162, 020249
OFI, Vienna, Austria

Vorster, Frederik J. 020193, 020344, 020416
Nelson Mandela University, Port Elizabeth, South Africa

Vorster, Frederik 020185
Nelson Mandela University, Port Elizabeth, South Africa

Vuillon, Laurent 020338
CNRS, Chambery, France

Vulic, Natasa 020296
University of Applied Arts and Sciences Northwestern Switzerland, Muttenz, Switzerland

Vumbugwa, Monphias 020185, 020193, 020344
Nelson Mandela University, Port Elizabeth, South Africa

Waibel, Christoph 020511
Flemish Institute for Technological Research (VITO), Genk, Belgium

Wakabayashi, Ryo 020484
Hitachi, Kokubunji, Japan

Wakazono, Kouzen 020131
Gifu University, Gifu, Japan

Wallner, Gernot M. 020227
University of Linz, Linz, Austria

Walpita, Harsha 020169
University of Oslo, Kjeller, Norway

Walsh, Yoselyn 020520
Costa Rica Institute of Technology, Cartago, Costa Rica

Wambach, Karsten 020468, 020470
bifa Umweltinstitut, Augsburg, Germany

Wang, Chia-Chen 020549
ITRI, Hsinchu, Taiwan

Wang, Shuo 020286, 020400
TUAS, Turku, Finland

Wang, Tzuya 020549
ITRI, Hsinchu, Taiwan

Wang, Xiaolin 020381
Mälardalen University, Västerås, Sweden

Wannenwetsch, Jann 020312
EnBW, Karlsruhe, Germany

Wargocki, Pawel 020551
DTU, Roskilde, Denmark

Waschl, Alfred 020255
buildingSMART, Vienna, Austria

Weber, Thomas 020180, 020230
Kiwa PI Berlin, Berlin, Germany

Weeber, Arthur W. 020515
TU Delft, Delft, The Netherlands

Wei, Wenpeng 020484
Hitachi, Kokubunji, Japan

Weihs, Philipp 020281
BOKU, Vienna, Austria

Weinrich, Frank 020177
PTB, Braunschweig, Germany

Weiß, Marius 020361
Coburg University of Applied Sciences, Coburg, Germany

Wellens, Christine Fraunhofer ISE, Freiburg, Germany	020135
Whyatt, Duncan Lancaster University, Lancaster, United Kingdom	020394
Wienands, Karl ISC Konstanz, Konstanz, Germany	020218, 020220, 020221
Wiesenfarth, Maike Fraunhofer ISE, Freiburg, Germany	020246
Wietler, Tobias ISFH, Emmerthal, Germany	020063
Wilbert, Stefan DLR, Almería, Spain	020235, 020237, 020239, 020331
Willers, Guido Fraunhofer CSP, Halle, Germany	020201
Wilson, Helen R. Fraunhofer ISE, Freiburg, Germany	020249
Winter, Renate ISFH, Emmerthal, Germany	020063
Winter, Stefan PTB, Braunschweig, Germany	020177, 020181
Wirtz, Wiebke ISFH, Emmerthal, Germany	020260
Witkowska, Agnieszka Gdansk University of Technology, Gdansk, Poland	020498
Wittmer, Bruno PVsyst, Geneva, Switzerland	020196
Wolf, Andreas Fraunhofer ISE, Freiburg, Germany	020031
Wong, Craig Kiwa PI Berlin, Berlin, Germany	020230
Wu, Li-Guo TSEC, Hsinchu, Taiwan	020021
Wu, Yu TNO, Petten, The Netherlands	020030
Wyss, Philippe CSEM, Neuchâtel, Switzerland	020068
Xiong, Weizhen Tokyo University of Science, Tokyo, Japan	020320
Xu, Jiahui YIST, Jiangyin, China	020001
Xu, Wenhao TÜV Rheinland, Shanghai, China	020144, 020208
Xu, Xiaoqi SERIS, Singapore, Singapore	020263

Xu, Yu 020263
SERIS, Singapore, Singapore

Xuereb, Steven 020180, 020230
Kiwa PI Berlin, Berlin, Germany

Yadav, Shivendra 020071, 020081
SVNIT, Surat, India

Yamaguchi, Yosuke 020484
Hitachi, Kokubunji, Japan

Yanagida, Masatoshi 020115
NIMS, Tsukuba, Japan

Yanar, T. Meriç 020027
Kalyon PV, Ankara, Türkiye

Yang, Donggeon 020323
K-water, Daejeon, South Korea

Yang, Hyoung-Kyu 020449
KETI, Wonmi-gu, South Korea

Yde, Leif 020250, 020306
Stensborg, Roskilde, Denmark

Ye, JiaYi 020102
SERIS, Singapore, Singapore

Yerci, Selcuk 020113
ODTÜ-GÜNAM, Ankara, Türkiye

Ylikunnari, Mari 020423
VTT Technical Research Centre of Finland, Oulu, Finland

Ylinen, Marko 020444
Satakunta University of Applied Sciences, Pori, Finland

Ylipaino, Juho 020444, 020445, 020554
TUAS, Tampere, Finland

Yılmaz, Büşra 020521
Kameleon Solar, Roosendaal, The Netherlands

Yordadov, Georgi 020389
imec, Diepenbeek, Belgium

Younes, Kareem 020487
Khalifa University, Abu Dhabi, United Arab Emirates

Yu, Cheng-Yeh 020021, 020053
TSEC, Hsinchu, Taiwan

Yu, Shusen 020406
Ecole Polytechnique, Palaiseau, France

Yuan, Xiao 020001
YIST, Jiangyin, China

Yun, Jae Ho 020112
KENTECH, Naju-si, South Korea

Zaimi, Mhammed 020171
University of Chouaib Doukkali, El Jadida, Morocco

Zanatta Britto, João Victor 020025
PUCRS, Porto Alegre, Brazil

Zanesco, Izete 020023, 020025
PUCRS, Porto Alegre, Brazil

Zaror, Yasmin 020225
WIP - Renewable Energies, Munich, Germany

Zarzalejo, Luis F. 020237, 020331
CIEMAT, Madrid, Spain

Zekri, Atef 020146
QEERI, Doha, Qatar

Zerafa, Steve 020334
PIXAM, Msida, Malta

Zhang, Geng 020001
Jolywood (ShanXi) Solar Technology, Taiyuan, China

Zhang, Jingwei 020111
Hohai University, Changzhou, China

Zhang, Kai 020233
FZJ, Jülich, Germany

Zhang, Wenjing 020001
YIST, Jiangyin, China

Zhang, Wuai 020101
HZB, Berlin, Germany

Zhang, Yating 020144, 020208
TÜV Rheinland, Shanghai, China

Zhou, Qilin 020102
SERIS, Singapore, Singapore

Zhu, Junjie 020017
Institute for Energy Technology, Kjeller, Norway

Ziaullah, Abdul Wahab 020278, 020291
QEERI, Doha, Qatar

Zilles, Roberto 020154, 020348
University of São Paulo, São Paulo, Brazil

Zimmermann, Iwan 020116
IPVF, Palaiseau, France

Zubillaga, Oihana 020139
Tecnalia, Donostia - San Sebastián, Spain

Zugasti, Eugenia 020334
CENER, Pamplona, Spain

Zugasti, Eugenia 020300
CENER, Sarriguren, Spain

Zwahlen, Theo 020369
BFH, Burgdorf, Switzerland

KEYWORDS OF EU PVSEC 2025 PROCEEDINGS PAPERS

42nd European Photovoltaic Solar Energy Conference and Exhibition (EU PVSEC 2025)

Bilbao, Spain
22-26 September 2025

Volume 4 of 6

ISBN: 979-8-3313-2987-7

Printed from e-media with permission by:

Curran Associates, Inc.
57 Morehouse Lane
Red Hook, NY 12571

Some format issues inherent in the e-media version may also appear in this print version.

WIP – Renewable Energies
Sylvensteinstr. 2
81369 Munchen
Germany

Phone: +49 89 72012735
Fax: +49 89 72012791

wip@wip-munich.de

Additional copies of this publication are available from:

Curran Associates, Inc.
57 Morehouse Lane
Red Hook, NY 12571 USA
Phone: 845-758-0400
Fax: 845-758-2633
Email: curran@proceedings.com
Web: www.proceedings.com

42nd European Photovoltaic Solar Energy Conference and Exhibition

Proceedings of the International Conference

22 September – 26 September 2025

Edited by:

C. DEL CAÑIZO
Solar Energy Institute
UPM
Spain

R. KENNY
European Commission
Joint Research Centre
Italy

J. BERGMILLER
WIP Renewable Energies
Germany

J. DE GREGORIO
WIP Renewable Energies
Germany

Edition Team:

B. Yildiz
L. Großhans
A. Michaelsen
U.E. Birgi
WIP Renewable Energies
Germany

Photos at:

Coordination of the Technical Programme:

European Commission Joint Research Centre
Via E. Fermi 1
21020 Ispra (VA)
Italy

Institutional Support:

European Commission

Institutional PV Industry Cooperation:

SolarPower Europe

ESMC – European Solar Manufacturing Council

Supporting Organisations:

AUSTRALIAN PV INSTITUTE

ASOM – Alliance for Solar Mobility

BASQUE ENERGY CLUSTER

BILBAO CONVENTION BUREAU

EASE – European Association for Storage of Energy

ETIP PV – European Technology & Innovation Platform PV

GÜNDER – Turkish Solar Energy Society

IEA PVPS - IEA Photovoltaic Power Systems Programme

INSTITUTO SOLAR DE ENERGÍA SOLAR

LDES – Long Duration Energy Storage Council

NSEFI – National Solar Energy federation of India

NUS /SERIS – National University of Singapore / Solar Energy Research Institute of Singapore

UPM - Polytechnic University of Madrid

Supporting Associations:

EERA – European Energy Research Aliance

EREF – European Renewable Energies Federation

EUREC – The Association of European Renewable Energy Research Centres

VDMA Photovoltaic Equipment

Local Support:
ENTE VASCO DE LA ENERGÍA
EUH – University of the Basque Country

EU PVSEC 2025 realised by:

WIP Renewable Energies
Sylvensteinstr. 2, 81369 Munich, Germany
Tel: +49 89 720 12 735, Fax: +49 89 720 12 791
Email: pv.conference@wip-munich.de
www.eupvsec.org
www.wip-munich.de

Proceedings produced and published by:

WIP Renewable Energies
Sylvensteinstr. 2, 81369 Munich, Germany
Tel: +49 89 720 12 735, Fax: +49 89 720 12 791
Email: pv.conference@wip-munich.de
www.eupvsec.org
www.wip-munich.de

42nd EUROPEAN PHOTOVOLTAIC SOLAR ENERGY CONFERENCE AND EXHIBITION 22 SEPTEMBER – 26 SEPTEMBER 2025

EU PVSEC 2025 COMMITTEES

INTERNATIONAL SCIENTIFIC ADVISORY COMMITTEE (ISAC)

Chair
P. Szymanski, European Commission Joint Research Centre, Director of Energy, Transport and Climate, Petten, The Netherlands

Committee Members
V. Bermúdez Benito, Founder & Principal Consultant, Berbetin, Antibes, France
G.C. Eder, OFI, Vienna, Austria
P. Frankl, Head of the Renewable Energy Division, International Energy Agency, France
M. Getsiou, European Commission, DG RTD, Brussels, Belgium
S.W. Glunz, Head of Division Photovoltaics - Research, Fraunhofer ISE, Freiburg, Germany
N.M. Haegel, Director of the National Center for Photovoltaics, NREL, Golden, USA
R. Kenny, European Commission Joint Research Centre, Directorate for Energy and Transport and Climate, Ispra, Italy
S. Nowak, Managing Director of NET Nowak Energy & Technology, St. Ursen, Switzerland
R. Schlatmann, Chairman of ETIP PV, Head of the Solar Energy Division at Helmholtz-Zentrum Berlin, Germany
W.C. Sinke, TNO Energy Transition, The Netherlands
M. Topič, Head of Laboratory of Photovoltaics and Optoelectronics of the University of Ljubljana, Slovenia
P. Verlinden, Director at Amrock, Visiting Professor at Sun Yat-Sen University, Guangzhou, China
E. Voroshazi, Head of PV module process laboratory, CEA, Le Bourget-du-Lac, France
J. Bergmiller, Managing Director Events & Knowledge Transfer, WIP Renewable Energies, Munich, Germany
J. de Gregorio, Head of Unit, Scientific Services and Cooperation, WIP Renewable Energies, Munich, Germany

CONFERENCE EXECUTIVE COMMITTEE

Conference General Chair
C. del Cañizo, UPM, Madrid, Spain

Technical Programme Chair
R. Kenny, European Commission Joint Research Centre, Directorate for Energy and Transport and Climate, Ispra, Italy

Committee Members
W.C. Sinke, Program Development Manager, TNO Energy Transition, The Netherlands
S. Nowak, Managing Director of NET Nowak Energy & Technology, St. Ursen, Switzerland
M. Topič, Head of Laboratory of Photovoltaics and Optoelectronics of the University of Ljubljana, Slovenia
V. Bermúdez Benito, BERBETIN, France
E. Voroshazi, Head of PV Module Process Laboratory, CEA, Le Bourget-Du-Lac France
H. Ossenbrink, Former European Commission Joint Research Centre, Germany
J. Bergmiller, Managing Director Events & Knowledge Transfer, WIP Renewable Energies, Munich, Germany
J. de Gregorio, Head of Unit, Scientific Services and Cooperation, WIP Renewable Energies, Munich, Germany

2025 SCIENTIFIC COMMITTEE

Programme Technical Chair
R. Kenny, European Commission, Joint Research Centre, Italy

Topic Chairs

Topic 1: Silicon Materials and Cells
F. Schindler, Fraunhofer ISE, Germany

Topic 2: Thin Films and New Concepts
I. Gordon, imec, Belgium

Topic 3: Photovoltaic Modules and BoS Components
T. Barnes, NREL, USA

Topic 4: PV Systems Engineering, Integrated/Applied PV
A.M. Gracia Amillo, FUNDACION CENER, Spain

Topic 5: PV in the Energy Transition
C. Agraffeil, CEA / INES, France

Topic Organisers and Paper Review Experts

Topic 1: Silicon Materials and Cells
F. Schindler, Fraunhofer ISE, Germany
C. Fischer, Wacker Chemie, Germany
G. Hahn, University of Konstanz, Germany
K. Ding, Forschungszentrum Jülich, Germany
P. Roca i Cabarrocas, CNRS-LPICM, France
A. W. Weeber, TNO Energy Transition, The Netherlands
D. Muñoz, CEA / INES, France
S. W. Glunz, Fraunhofer ISE, Germany
K. Bothe, ISFH, Germany
M. Topic, University of Ljubljana, Slovenia
P. Fath, RCT-Solutions, Germany
S. Peters, Hanwha Q CELLS, Germany

M.P. Bellmann, SINTEF, Norway
A. Ciesla, UNSW, Australia
C. Hagendorf, Freiberg Instruments, Germany
X. Yu, Zhejiang University, China
J.S. Lee, KIER, South Korea
R. Brendel, ISFH, Germany
T. Dullweber, ISFH, Germany
J. Horzel, Fraunhofer ISE, Germany
W. Nemeth, NREL, United States of America
R. Turan, METU, Türkiye
F. Menchini, ENEA, Italy
W. Favre, CEA, France

J. Meier, Meier Technologies, Switzerland
J. Schmidt, ISFH, Germany
M. Wright, University of Oxford, United Kingdom
J. Zhao, CSEM, Switzerland
A. Morisset, CSEM, Switzerland
A. Richter, Fraunhofer ISE, Germany
J. Linke, ISC Konstanz, Germany
B. Geerligs, TNO Energy Transition, The Netherlands
S. Dubois, CEA, France
M. Hermle, Fraunhofer ISE, Germany
B. Terheiden, University of Konstanz, Germany
P. Delli Veneri, ENEA, Italy
T. Matsui, AIST, Japan
Y. Ohshita, Toyota Technological Institute, Japan
E. Bruhat, HOLOSOLIS, France
A. Augusto, Dalarna University, Sweden
F. Ferrazza, ENI S.p.A., Italy
A. Otaegi, UPV/EHU, Spain
M.C. Schubert, Fraunhofer ISE, Germany
H. Duman, KalyonPV, Türkiye
N. Usami, Nagoya University, Japan
Y. Zhu, UNSW, Australia
D. Brunner, RENA Technologies, Germany
A. Danel, CEA, France
C. Gerardi, 3Sun, Italy
H.J. Nonnenmacher, Meyer Burger, Germany
P. Verlinden, AMROCK, Australia
Q. Wang, Wang, Qi, China
W. Zhang, Zhang, Weiming, China
Y. Chen, Trina Solar Energy, China
E. Krassowski, CE Cell Engineering, Germany
M. Foti, 3Sun, Italy
D.L. Bätzner, Meyer Burger Research, Switzerland

Topic 2: Thin Films and New Concepts
I. Gordon, imec, Belgium
J.C. Goldschmidt, Marburg University, Germany
F. Schoofs, Oxford PV, United Kingdom
N. Kyranaki, Hasselt University, Belgium
S. Veenstra, TNO Energy Transition, The Netherlands
T. Aernouts, imec, Belgium
A.N. Tiwari, SOLTIWA, Switzerland
G. Siefer, Fraunhofer ISE, Germany
M. Edoff, Uppsala University, Sweden
A. Martí Vega, UPM, Spain
J. Poortmans, imec, Belgium
I. Ramiro, UPM, Spain
T. Magorian Friedlmeier, ZSW, Germany

S. Albrecht, HZB, Germany
S. Berson, CEA, France
P. Carroy, CEA, France
C. Case, Oxford PV, United Kingdom
G. Coletti, FuturaSun, Italy
S. De Wolf, KAUST, Saudi Arabia
U.W. Paetzold, KIT, Germany
H. Sivaramakrishnan Radhakrisnan, imec, Belgium
P. Schulze, Fraunhofer ISE, Germany
L. Wang, Technology Innovation Institute, United Arab Emirates
Y. Smirnov, Applied Materials, United States of America
B. Stannowski, HZB, Germany
F. Fertig, Hanwha Q CELLS, Germany
L. Lancellotti, ENEA, Italy
S. Cros, CEA, France
S. Hayase, The University of Electro-Communications, Japan
S. Huang, Macquarie University, Australia
M. Khenkin, HZB, Germany
C. Lin, National Taiwan University, Taiwan
M.S.H. Norton, University of Cyprus, Cyprus
P. Pistor, Pablo de Olavide University, Spain
W. Tress, Zurich University of Applied Sciences, Switzerland
A. Aguirre, imec, Belgium
D. Lan, UNSW Sydney, China
M. Saliba, University of Stuttgart, Germany
P. Manshanden, TNO Energy Transition, The Netherlands
L. Vesce, University of Rome II, Italy
I. Dogan, TNO Solliance, The Netherlands
Y. Kuang, imec, Belgium
M. Al Katrib, IPVF, France
M.I. Hossain, QEERI, Qatar
W.H. Chiu, Chang Gung University, Taiwan
C. Chen, Ming Chi University of Technology, Taiwan
C. Fell, CSIRO Energy Technology, Australia
G. Brammertz, imec, Belgium
T. Dalibor, Avancis, Germany
S. Ishizuka, AIST, Japan
A. Redinger, University of Luxembourg, Luxembourg
A. Romeo, University of Verona, Italy
V. Sittinger, Fraunhofer IST, Germany
M. Theelen, TNO/Solliance, The Netherlands
G. Timò, RSE, Italy
A. Kanevce, ZSW, Germany
A. Pérez-Rodríguez, IREC, Spain
R. Gutzler, ZSW, Germany
W. Witte, ZSW, Germany
T. Nishimura, Tokyo Institute of Technology, Japan
C. Qian, University of New South Wales, Australia
J.P. Connolly, CentraleSupelec, France
J.P. Kleider, CNRS/GeePs, France
I. Konovalov, University of Applied Sciences Jena, Germany
Y. Okada, University of Tokyo, Japan
M. Rusu, HZB, Germany
H. Meddeb, DLR, Germany
E. Saucedo, Universitat Politècnica de Catalunya (UPC), Spain
P. Vidal-Fuentes, FUNDACIÓ INSTITUT DE RECERCA EN ENERGIA DE CATALUNYA, Spain
C. Malerba, ENEA, Italy
C. Becker, HZB, Germany
D. Kuciauskas, NREL, United States of America
M. Ochoa, University of Cantabria, Spain
T. Tayagaki, AIST, Japan
S. Wasmer, WAVELABS Solar Metrology Systems, Germany
S. Zandi, UNSW, Australia
C. Messmer, University of Freiburg, Germany
J.B. Puel, Institut Photovoltaïque d'Ile de France (IPVF), France
S. Ternes, University of Rome II, Italy

Topic 3: Photovoltaic Modules and BoS Components
V. Bermúdez Benito, BERBETIN, France
R. Preu, Fraunhofer ISE, Germany
R. Gottschalg, Fraunhofer CSP, Germany
T. Barnes, NREL, United States of America
G. Friesen, SUPSI, Switzerland
G. Bardizza, TÜV Rheinland Solar, Italy

V. Barth, CEA, France
A. Faes, CSEM, Switzerland
A. Lennon, Sundrive Solar, Australia
M. Mittag, Fraunhofer ISE, Germany
M.A. Muñoz-Garcia, UPM, Spain
H. Nagel, Fraunhofer ISE, Germany
S. Pietralunga, CNR, Italy
T. Timofte, ISC Konstanz, Germany

S. Feldbacher, PCCL, Austria
A. Halm, ISC Konstanz, Germany
H. Hanifi, AESOLAR, Germany
E. Warren, NREL, United States of America
S. Zhang, Trina Solar Energy, China
X. Zhen, Canadian Solar, China
G. Beaucarne, Dow Silicones Belgium, Belgium
T. Bejat, CEA, France
C. Camus, LayTec, Germany
U. Jahn, Fraunhofer CSP, Germany
G. Oreski, PCCL, Austria
M. Pander, Fraunhofer CSP, Germany
T. Sample, European Commission JRC, Italy
A. Morlier, imo-imomec, Belgium
C. Barretta, PCCL, Austria
P. Gebhardt, Fraunhofer ISE, Germany
C. Sen, UNSW, Australia
O. Arriaga Arruti, CSEM, Switzerland
X. Gu, NIST, United States of America
C. Xiao, Chinese Academy of Sciences, United States of America
R. Aninat, TNO/Solliance, The Netherlands
S. Mitterhofer, NIST, United States of America
B. Hoex, UNSW, Australia
E. Özkalay, SUPSI, Switzerland
M. Bokalič, University of Ljubljana, Slovenia
S. Bordihn, ISFH, Germany
M. Despeisse, CSEM, Switzerland
J. Govaerts, imec, Belgium
J. Lopez-Garcia, STS-Certified, Spain
M. Pravettoni, Technology Innovation Institute, United Arab Emirates
T. Stoyanova Lyubenova, Joint Research Centre, Italy
C. Ulbrich, HZB, Germany
J. Moereke, Avancis, Germany
Y.S. Long, ITRI, Taiwan
D. Pavanello, European Commission JRC, Italy
A.K. Vidal de Oliveira, UFSC, Brazil
J. Bengoechea, CENER, Spain
M. Ernst, ANU, Australia
H. Ellis, European Commission JRC, Italy
B. Mihaylov, European Commission JRC, Italy
G. Chowdhury, 3E, Belgium
B. Aissa, QEERI - Qatar Environment and Energy Research Institute, Qatar

Topic 4: PV Systems Engineering, Integrated/Applied PV
A. Gracia Amillo, CENER, Spain
W.G.J.H.M. van Sark, Utrecht University, The Netherlands
K. Lappalainen, Tampere University, Finland
J.M. Almeida Serra, University of Lisbon, Portugal
I. Tsanakas, CEA, France
C. Buerhop-Lutz, HI ERN, Germany
D. Moser, Becquerel Institute Italia, Italy
F. Frontini, SUPSI, Switzerland
G.C. Eder, OFI, Austria
A. Scognamiglio, ENEA, Italy
A. Chatzipanagi, European Commission JRC, Italy
I. Antón Hernández, UPM, Spain
R.M.E. Valckenborg, TNO, The Netherlands
T. Reindl, SERIS, Singapore
J.R. Gonzalez, European Space Agency, The Netherlands
G. Mütter, Gerhard Mütter e.U., Austria
T. Merdzhanova, Forschungszentrum Jülich, Germany

V. Lara-Fanego, Solargis, Spain
A. Louwen, Eurac Research, Italy
A. Martinez Fernandez, European Commission JRC, Italy
T. Oozeki, AIST, Japan
J. Remund, Meteotest, Switzerland
M. Sengupta, NREL, United States of America
M. Zehner, Rosenheim Technical University of Applied Sciences, Germany
B. Nouri, German Aerospace Center, Spain
S. Poddar, UNSW, Australia
D. Bachour, HBKU/ Qatar Foundation, Qatar
J. Yang, NREL, United States of America
S. Bouguerra, imo-imomec, Belgium
C. Alonso-Tristán, UBU, Spain
M. Carbone, ENEL Green Power, Italy
M. Dennenmoser, BayWa r.e. Solar Projects GmbH, Germany
C.W. Hansen, Sandia National Laboratories, United States of America
A. Neubert, DNV Maritime Software GmbH, Germany
D. Berrian, Belectric, Germany
M. Oliosi, PVsyst, Switzerland
J. Moschner, KU Leuven / EnergyVille, Belgium
C. Bucher, BUAS, Switzerland
B. Wittmer, PVsyst SA, Switzerland
M. Bolen, SB Energy, United States of America
D. Daßler, Fraunhofer CSP, Germany
R. Einhaus, ZSW, Germany
P. Hacke, NREL, United States of America
A. Heimsath, Fraunhofer ISE, Germany
J. Lin, PV Guider, Taiwan
A. Migan-Dubois, GeePs, France
M. Rinio, University of Karlstad, Sweden
J.S. Stein, Sandia National Laboratories, United States of America
D. Stellbogen, ZSW, Germany
M. Theristis, Sandia National Laboratories, United States of America
A. Virtuani, CSEM, Switzerland
A. Driesse, PV Performance Labs, Germany
M. Øgaard, IFE, Norway
A. Nobre, SERIS, Singapore
T. Trupke, UNSW, Australia
C. Cornaro, University of Rome II, Italy
G. A. dos Reis Benatto, DTU, Denmark
S. Malik, Fraunhofer CSP, Germany
S. Lindig, Univers SAS, France
M.M. Nygård, Institute for Energy Technology, Norway
P. Alonso Gomez, BayWa r.e., Germany
Y. Assoa, CEA, France
P. Bonomo, SUPSI, Switzerland
V. D'Ambrosio, University of Naples Federico II, Italy
E. Román Medina, Tecnalia, Spain
L.H. Slooff, TNO Energy Transition, The Netherlands
S. Villa, TNO, The Netherlands
M. La Rosa, Glass to Power, Italy
T. Del Caño, Onyx Solar Energy, Spain
X. Zhihao, AIST, Japan
P. Sharif, ODTU-GUNAM, Türkiye
K. Umeda, TAISEI CORPORATION, Japan
S. Boddaert, CSTB, France
N. Lysgaard Andersen, DTU, Denmark
K. Meyer, ISFH, Germany
T. Biel, NET Nowak Energy & Technology, Switzerland
F. Colucci, ENEA, Italy
A. Pascaris, NREL, United States of America
C. Dupraz, INRAE, France
C. Alonso-García, CIEMAT, Spain
A. Lefort, BayWa, Germany
H.N. Riise, IFE, Norway
M.A. Schüler, Next2Sun Technology GmbH, Germany
P.J. Pérez-Higueras, University of Jaén, Spain
K. Oda, Agritree,

M. Berwind, Fraunhofer ISE, Germany
M. Dörenkämper, TNO, The Netherlands
M. Heinrich, Fraunhofer ISE, Germany
B. Newman, Lightyear, The Netherlands
A. Reinders, Eindhoven University of Technology, The Netherlands
T. Tanahashi, AIST, Japan
J. Leloux, LuciSun, Belgium
E. Shirazi, University of Twente, The Netherlands
K. Araki, University of Miyazaki, Japan
K. Nishioka, University of Miyazaki, Japan
R. Campesato, CESI, Italy
V. Khorenko, Azur Space, Germany
G. Kakoulaki, European Commission Joint Research Centre, Italy
H. Toyota, JAXA, Japan
P. Garcia-Linares, UPM, Spain
I. Weiss, Weiss, Ingrid, Germany
A. Hensel, Fraunhofer ISE, Germany
J.S. da Fernandes, Hochschule Offenburg, Germany
Y. Ueda, Tokyo University of Science, Japan
J. Braid, Sandia National Laboratories, United States of America

Topic 5: PV in the Energy Transition
J. Stierstorfer, WIP Renewable Energies, Germany
R. Pestana, R&D Nester, Portugal
P.J. Alet, CSEM, Switzerland
C. Agraffeil, CEA, France
K. WAMBACH, Wambach-Consulting, Germany
C. del Cañizo, UPM, Spain
L. Großhans, WIP Renewable Energies, Germany
M. Getsiou, European Commission DG RTD, Belgium
S. Nowak, NET Nowak Energy & Technology, Switzerland
C. Breyer, LUT University, Finland
I. Kaizuka, RTS Corporation, Japan
G. Masson, Becquerel Institute, Belgium
P. Baliozian, VDMA, Germany
L. Großhans, WIP Renewable Energies, Germany
C. Candelise, Bocconi University, Italy
S. Caneva, WIP Renewable Energies, Germany

G. Barchi, Eurac Research, Italy
R. Bründlinger, AIT, Austria
V. Efthymiou, University of Cyprus, Cyprus
M. Centeno Brito, University of Lisbon, Portugal
F. Carigiet, ZHAW, Switzerland
B. Gaiddon, HESPUL, France
F.Z. Ouchani, Green Energy Park, Morocco
M. Rennhofer, AIT, Austria
G. Adinolfi, ENEA, Italy
W. Schaffer, Salzburg Netz, Austria
A. Haber, e-control, Austria
G. Heilscher, Technische Hochschule Ulm, Germany
A. Anctil, Michigan State University, United States of America
S. Arancón, Plug and Play, Spain
S. Capaccioli, ETA - Florence Renewable Energies, Italy
V. Fthenakis, Columbia University, United States of America
G. Heath, NREL, United States of America
K. Komoto, Mizuho Research & Technologies, Ltd., Japan
W. Palitzsch, LuxChemtech, Germany
S. Ovaitt, NREL, United States of America
M. de Wild-Scholten, SmartGreenScans, The Netherlands
S. Herceg, Fraunhofer ISE, Germany
C. Polacchi, Eurac Research, Italy
N. Espinosa, Universidad de Murcia, Spain
E. Drahi, TotalEnergies OneTech, France
S. Guastella, RSE, Italy

H. Ossenbrink, Band Gap, Germany
D. Polverini, European Commission DG GROW, Belgium
N. Taylor, European Commission JRC, Italy
K.A. Weiß, Fraunhofer ISE, Germany
I. Kafedjiska, Helmholtz Zentrum Berlin, Germany
P. Malbranche, Solar Action, France
S. De Iuliis, ENEA, Italy
T. Haarberg, BNW-Energy, Norway
A. Nayfeh, Khalifa University, United Arab Emirates
E. Vartiainen, Fortum Renewables Oy, Finland
E. Veronese, Eurac Research, Italy
P. Sanchez-Friera, Solkeys, Spain
N. Cherradi, Desert Technologies, Saudi Arabia
S. Nold, Fraunhofer ISE, Germany
H.J.J. Yu, CEA, France
M. Beck, U.S. Department of Energy, United States of America
M. Woodhouse, NREL, United States of America
A.B. Cristóbal, UPM, Spain
G. Ruggieri, Insubria University, Italy
S. Tay, NUS, Singapore

Awards Coordinators

Student Awards Coordinator
A.H.M. Smets, Delft University of Technology, The Netherlands

Student Awards Committee
R. Kenny, EU PVSEC Technical Programme Chair, Italy
C. del Canizo, Conference Chair, UPM, Spain
E. Voroshazi, CEA, France
J. Poortmans, imec, Belgium
P.J. Alet, CSEM, Switzerland
S. Caneva, WIP Renewable Energies, Germany
A. Romeo, University of Verona, Italy
G. Friesen, SUPSI, Switzerland
F. Schindler, Fraunhofer ISE, Germany
J.C. Goldchmidt, Marburg University, Germany
D. Moser, Becquerel Institute, Italy
K. Ding, FZJ, Germany
W.C. Sinke, TNO Energy Transition, The Netherlands
M. Topic, University of Ljubljana, Slovenia
R. Schlatman, HZB, Germany
S. Glunz, Fraunhofer ISE, Germany
A.M. Vega, UPM, Spain
I. Kaizuka, RTS, Japan
P.D. Veneri, ENEA, Italy
J. Bengoechea, CENER, Spain

Poster Awards Coordinator
P. Malbranche, Solar Action, France

Poster Awards Committee
R. Kenny, European Commission JRC, Italy
C. del Canizo, UPM, Spain
W. van Sark, Utrecht University, The Netherlands
I. Tsanakas, CEA INES, France
L. Miranda, Oxford PV, United Kingdom
D. Munoz, CEA INES, France
I. Gordon, imec, Belgium
E. Roman, Tecnalia, Spain
G. Eder, OFI, Austria
I. Antón, UPM, Spain
S. Veenstra, TNO, The Netherlands
J.M. Almeida Serra, University of Lisbon, Portugal
T. Magorian Friedlmeier, ZSW, Germany
J. Stierstorfer, WIP Renewable Energies, Germany

G. Kakoulaki, European Commission JRC, Italy
T. Barnes, NREL, USA
T. Merdzhanova, Forschungszentrum Jülich, Germany

Highlights Committee
C. del Cañizo, UPM, Madrid, Spain
R. Kenny, European Commission Joint Research Centre, Directorate for Energy and Transport and Climate, Ispra, Italy
W.C. Sinke, TNO Energy Transition, The Netherlands
S. Nowak, Managing Director of NET Nowak Energy & Technology, St. Ursen, Switzerland
M. Topič, Head of Laboratory of Photovoltaics and Optoelectronics of the University of Ljubljana, Slovenia
V. Bermúdez Benito, BERBETIN, France
E. Voroshazi, Head of PV Module Process Laboratory, CEA, Le Bourget-Du-Lac France
H. Ossenbrink, Band Gap, Germany
J. Bergmiller, Managing Director Events & Knowledge Transfer, WIP Renewable Energies, Munich, Germany
J. de Gregorio, Head of Unit, Scientific Services and Cooperation, WIP Renewable Energies, Munich, Germany
S. Leanza, Marketing and PR Manager, WIP Renewable Energies, Munich, Germany
B. Yildiz, Project Manager Events & Knowledge Transfer, WIP Renewable Energies, Munich, Germany
F. Schindler, Fraunhofer ISE, Freiburg, Germany
I. Gordon, imec, Leuven, Belgium
T. Barnes, NREL, Evergreen, USA
A.M. Gracia Amillo, FUNDACION CENER, Sarriguren, Spain
C. Agraffeil, CEA / INES, Le Bourget-du-Lac, France

SUBJECT INDEX

Topic Code	**Session Type**	**Day Codes**
1 Silicon Materials and Cells	P = Plenary Session	A = Monday, 22 September 2025
2 Thin-Films and New Concepts	O = Oral Session	B = Tuesday, 23 September 2025
3 Photovoltaic Modules	V = Visual Session	C = Wednesday, 24 September 2025
4 Photovoltaic Systems		D = Thursday, 25 September 2025
5 Photovoltaics in the Energy Transition		E = Friday, 26 September 2025

e.g. 1AO.4 ⇒ 1= Silicon Materials and Cells, A=Monday, O=Oral session, 4=Session 4

FOREWORD

The European Photovoltaic Solar Energy Conference and Exhibition (EU PVSEC) stands as the World's leading and most renowned forum for PV research and development and the biggest conference on PV solar energy. In 2025, celebrating its 42nd edition, the EU PVSEC was the essential meeting and exchanging point for global PV experts from research, development, and industry.

Held from 22–26 September 2025 in Bilbao, Spain, the EU PVSEC 2025 was a resounding success, showcasing a wide range of cutting-edge research results. Bringing together both the Conference and the Exhibition, this edition attracted more than 1600 participants from 61 countries who contributed over 1000 presentations across various fields of science and technology. The event provided an essential platform for the exchange of knowledge and ideas on photovoltaic research, innovations, and applications. In the exhibition area 51 companies from all parts of the world welcomed visitors and presented their products and services.

Conference Highlights

The EU PVSEC covered a broad range of topics with an extensive programme that offers an opportunity for workers from across the entire field of photovoltaics to share their findings, as well as an opportunity for multidisciplinary learning. Rapid advances in materials, designs, and manufacturing processes reflect the accelerating expansion of the global PV market. The programme was arranged into 5 topics as follows:

- Silicon Materials and Cells;
- Thin Films and New Concepts;
- Photovoltaic Modules and Balance of System Components;
- PV Systems Engineering, Integrated/Applied PV;
- PV in the Energy Transition.

Communicating the key messages from the conference, not only to participants, but also to other researchers, key stakeholders, policy makers and the general public was an important added value. We thank the Highlights Committee, composed of selected members of the Scientific Committee, as well as the Session Chairs, for providing a comprehensive summary of the findings and state of the art research that were delivered during this year´s event. Some key highlights are listed below, while further details may be found in the dedicated highlights presentation in the annex of these proceedings.

Cross-cutting themes:

- Demonstrated the versatility of solar technologies, spanning traditional and emerging application areas.
- Sustainability and circularity remain central, with research focused on reducing material use, such as replacing silver with copper, and advancing end-of-life management of modules.
- Ensuring long-term stability and predictable energy yield is equally essential, with many examples of studies on degradation mechanisms and efforts to elucidate their root-causes, such as in the case of UVID.
- The role of artificial intelligence across the PV value chain is rapidly expanding, from design to operations and maintenance, including among many others drone applications.

Latest Solar Innovations in Materials, Cells, Modules and PV Systems:

While silicon solar cells remain the cornerstone of PV technology, perovskite solar cells continue to stand out as the leading complementary technology to silicon, both as standalone devices and in tandem configurations. Research efforts are increasingly focused on enhancing stability, understanding degradation mechanisms, improving durability and scalability, and ensuring full industrial compatibility.

Many companies presented impressive results on industrial-size single-junction perovskite modules as well as perovskite-based tandem modules, and several new efficiency records were announced during the event. The rapid pace of innovation in cell and module architecture underscores the need for accelerated and more robust testing and qualification methodologies. Both the industry and the research community are moving swiftly to assess and improve reliability in this fast-evolving PV landscape.

A major focus in module research remains the optimisation of materials and packaging to ensure long lifetimes and predictable energy yields from high-efficiency cells. In parallel, many innovative advances in the operation and maintenance (O&M) of PV systems were presented and discussed.

Applications, Grid Integration and Storage

"PV can be deployed everywhere": from space applications to agrivoltaics, PV noise barriers, building-integrated photovoltaics (BIPV), floating PV systems, and even vehicles. Among these, agrivoltaics is gaining momentum as a promising dual land use approach, offering economic benefits for farmers while increasing resilience to climate change.

Flexibility solutions, particularly through battery storage, were recognised in many technical presentations as essential to accommodate higher PV penetration levels and to reduce energy curtailment. At the same time, strengthening grid infrastructure and enhancing grid management capabilities remain critical to enable the next phase of large-scale PV integration.

Photovoltaics in the Energy Transition

Options for re-establishing competitive module manufacturing in Europe were extensively analysed, including detailed policy recommendations for industrial support and market growth. Currently, a mismatch persists between global PV module installation rates and production rates, resulting in growing inventories and sharply reduced prices.

Finally, inclusiveness, diversity, citizen participation, awareness, education, and social engagement were

underlined as vital dimensions of the sector's long-term sustainability and innovation capacity.

EU PVSEC 2025 Proceedings

Selection for inclusion in the conference was made by the Scientific Committee's paper review experts and topic organisers (see the listing on pages 010002-001-005), to whom we express our sincere gratitude for their comprehensive review work and overall contribution to the success of the conference.

The EU PVSEC 2025 Proceedings contain the full papers covering most of the highlights described above and more. The Proceedings provide a comprehensive overview of the PV solar sector, its current status and future prospects in science, research, innovation, development and deployment extending to 3,750 pages. In addition to the 299 submitted papers, the proceedings include 101 presentations (slides) shown during the plenary and oral presentations as well as 176 poster files of the visual presentations. In total this amounts to 576 publications.

The Conference Proceedings are published as downloadable files and are also fully accessible online. A DOI code (Digital Object Identifier) has been assigned to each paper. This ensures unequivocal and permanent identification and full citability. The EU PVSEC 2025 papers can be viewed and downloaded in a full free open access from the EU PVSEC's Proceedings website https://userarea.eupvsec.org/proceedings.

The proceedings of the EU PVSEC 2025 strengthen the commitment to providing quick and open access to high quality scientific results. This is a powerful source for targeted and quick information search and retrieval, enabling you to search by topic, keywords, paper title, DOI, author, or organization.

We are confident that these Proceedings will play an important role in providing a comprehensive overview of the current actors and activities in the global PV sector and that they will disseminate information on the state-of-the-art of technologies and applications. This can generate further research, add momentum to innovation and promote interest in PV worldwide.

We would like to cordially thank all authors and participants of the EU PVSEC 2025 for their contributions and look forward to welcoming you in Rotterdam, The Netherlands from 14 – 18 September 2026 at the EU PVSEC 2026, the 43rd European Photovoltaic Solar Energy Conference and Exhibition

The Editors

TABLE OF CONTENTS OF EU PVSEC 2025 PROCEEDINGS PAPERS

Visual SESSION 1CV.2 Si Solar Cells | Characterisation & Modelling of Silicon Cells and Their Building Blocks

[1] *Anhalt University of Applied Sciences, Köthen, Germany;* [2] *Fraunhofer CSP, Halle, Germany*

Oral SESSION 2AO.2 Advances in Chalcogenide Devices

2AO.2.3 A New Method for Sb-doped CdSeTe/CdTe Devices with Superior Stability 020057
Elisa Artegiani[1], Mariyam Mukhtar[1], Alessandro Romeo[1]
[1] *University of Verona, Verona, Italy*

Oral SESSION 2AO.3 III-V Based Devices | Tandem and Perovskite Solar Cells

2AO.3.3 Micro-Crystal GaAs Array Sub-Cells for Si Tandem Solar Cells 020058
James Patrick Connolly[1], Ahmed Nejim[2], Alexandre Jaffré[1], José Alvarez[1], Jean-Paul Kleider[1], Denis Mencaraglia[1], Laurie Dentz[3], Géraldine Hallais[3], Frederic Hamouda[3], Laetitia Vincent[3], Daniel Bouchier[3], Charles Renard[3]
[1] *CNRS, Gif-sur-Yvette, France;* [2] *SILVACO, St. Ives, United Kingdom;* [3] *CNRS, Palaiseau, France*

2AO.3.5 Multiscale Models for Perovskite Optimisation 020060
Philippe Baranek[1], James Patrick Connolly[2], Antoine Gissler[1], Philip Schulz[3], Michel Rerat[4], Roberto Dovesi[5]
[1] *EDF R&D, Palaiseau, France;* [2] *CNRS, Gif-sur-Yvette, France;* [3] *IPVF, Palaiseau, France;* [4] *IPREM, Pau, France;* [5] *Academy of Sciences of Turin, Torino, Italy*

2AO.3.6 Modelling Recovery in Perovskite Solar Cells under Light and Dark to Address Stability Challenges 020062
Guillem Álvarez-Pérez[1], Jean Baptiste Puel[1], Jean François Guillemoles [1]
[1] *IPVF, Palaiseau, France*

Oral SESSION 2BO.10 Advanced Modelling and Characterisation of Perovskite Solar Cells

2BO.10.2 On Perimeter Losses in Perovskite Top- and Poly-Si-Passivated Silicon Bottom Cells – Do Small Area Tandems Reveal the Full Efficiency Potential? 020063
Felix Haase[1], Lukas Brockmann[1], Annika Raugewitz[1], Verena Steckenreiter[1], Verena Barnscheidt[1], Roland Clausing[1], Sara Baumann[1], Joachim Vollbrecht[1], Welmoed Veurman[1], Johannes Löhr[1], Dongyang Liu[1], Mircea Turcu[1], Lasse Nasebandt[1], Udo Römer[1], David Sylla[1], Jessica Strey[1], Martha Löhning[1], Larissa Mettner[1], Renate Winter[1], Anja Christ[1], Heike Kohlenberg[1], Cornelia Marquardt[1], Emanuel Brueckner[1], Hossein Rabiei[1], Michael Rienäcker[1], Sarah Kajari-Schröder[1], Tobias Wietler[1], Robby Peibst[1]
[1] *ISFH, Emmerthal, Germany*

2BO.10.5 In-depth Characterization and Simulation Approach for the Understanding of In- and Outdoor Degradation of Perovskite Solar Cells 020064
Jonathan Parion[1], Amit Kumar Harit[1], Elias Peraticos[2], Vasiliki Paraskeva[2], Maria Hadjipanayi[2], Aranzazu Aguirre[1], Filip Duerinckx[1], Hariharsudan

Sivaramakrishnan Radhakrishnan[1], Jef Poortmans[1], Johan Lauwaert[3], Bart Vermang[1]
[1] Hasselt Unversity, Genk, Belgium; [2] University of Cyprus, Nicosia, Cyprus; [3] Ghent University, Ghent, Belgium

Oral SESSION 2BO.8 Advanced Conversion Devices

2BO.8.1 Singlet Fission Route for >30% Efficient Solar Cells: Silicon Cell Requirements 020065
Shona McNab[1], Alex J. Baldacchino[1], Pheobe Pearce[1], Alvin Mo[1], Alison Ciesla[1], Bram Hoex[1], Nicholas J. Ekins-Daukes[1], Murad J. Y. Tayebjee[1], Michael P. Nielsen[1]
[1] UNSW, Sydney, Australia

2BO.8.5 Performance of a 4-Terminals Spectral Splitting Asymmetric Solar Concentrator in Diffuse Sunlight: a Numerical Study 020066
Floriana Morabito[1], Daniela Fontani[2], Paola Sansoni[2], Mehdi Ahmadi[3], Salvatore Lombardo[3], Andrea Farina[1], Silvia Maria Pietralunga[1]
[1] CNR-IFN, Milan, Italy; [2] CNR-INO, Florence, Italy; [3] CNR-IMM, Catania, Italy

2BO.8.6 GaAs for Thermophotonics: From Thin-Film Solar Cells to Highly Efficient LEDs 020067
Natasha Gruginskie[1], Peter Mulder[1], Gerard Bauhuis[1], Jani Oksanen[2], John Schermer[1]
[1] Radboud University, Nijmegen, The Netherlands; [2] Aalto University, Espoo, Finland

Visual SESSION 2BV.1 New Materials, Devices and Conversion Concepts | New Modelling and Characterisation Techniques

2BV.1.4 Low-Energy Electron Multiplication on Nanostructured Solar Cells: a Novel Route to Overcome Si-PV Efficiency Limits 020068
Mikaël Hosatte[1], Brice Rouffie[1], Zbigniew T. Kuznicki[1], Frédéric Milesi[2], Bertrand Paviet-Salomon[3], Audrey Morisset[3], Philippe Wyss[3], Lejo Joseph Koduvelikulathu[4], Lazhar Rachdi[4], Lacramioara Popescu[4], Dominik Rudolph[4], Marek Basta[5], Andrzej Miszczuk[5], Martyna Majak[5], Beata Basta[5], Samuel Queste[6]
[1] SEGTON Advanced Technology, Versailles, France; [2] CEA, Grenoble, France; [3] CSEM, Neuchâtel, Switzerland; [4] ISC Konstanz, Konstanz, Germany; [5] Roltec, Poznań, Poland; [6] Marie and Louis Pasteur University, Besançon, France

2BV.1.5 Tailoring CBTSSe Solar Cells for Indoor Photovoltaic Applications 020069
Hitarth Narsi Patel[1], Bindu Pamula[1], Deepak Joshi[1], Vivek Garg[1]
[1] SVNIT, Surat, India

2BV.1.6 Theoretical Insights through DFT into $AgBiS_2$ Thin Films Absorber for Photovoltaic Applications 020071
Dhruv Singh Thakur[1], Rajesh Kumar Sharma[1], Nithin Chatterji[1], Vivek Garg[1], Shivendra Yadav[1]
[1] SVNIT, Surat, India

Visual SESSION 2BV.2 Compound and Organic Semiconductors

Gerardo Gordillo[1], Oscar Torres[1], Julian Peña-Bermudez[2]
[1] National University of Colombia, Bogotá, Colombia; [2] University of the Caribbean, Santo Domingo, Dominican Republic

2CV.3.71 Comparative Analysis and Efficiency Optimization of Sulfur-based Chalcogenide Perovskites ($MgHfS_3$, $CaZrS_3$, $BaZrS_3$) via Interface Engineering for High-Performance Solar Cells 020111
Anees ur Rehman[1], Kung Ding[1], Jingwei Zhang[1], Xiang Chen[1]
[1] Hohai University, Changzhou, China

2CV.3.72 Development of Inorganic Perovskite $CsPbI_3$ with Heterojunction Engineering at the Buried Interface for Enhanced Stability and Performance 020112
Syed Fawad Ali Shah[1], Hyeonwook Park[1], Muhammad Rehan[2], Donghyeop Shin[2], Kihwan Kim[2], Jae Ho Yun[3]
[1] KENTECH, Naju-Si, South Korea; [2] KIER, Daejeon, South Korea; [3] KENTECH, Naju-si, South Korea

Oral SESSION 2DO.6 Industrially Scalable Processes to Manufacture Perovskite Solar Cells and Modules

2DO.6.2 Eliminating P2 Scribes: A New Interconnection Design for Efficient Perovskite Solar Modules Under Indoor Lighting 020113
Bahri Eren Uzuner[1], Konstantin Tsoi[1], Gorkem Gunbas[1], Selcuk Yerci[1]
[1] ODTÜ-GÜNAM, Ankara, Türkiye

2DO.6.5 Evaporated Self Assembled Monolayer (SAM) Hole Transport Layers for Scalable Perovskite Solar Cells 020114
Joachim Vollbrecht[1], Verena Barnscheidt[1], Roland Clausing[1], Johannes Löhr[1], Larissa Mettner[1], Adam Neuba[2], Annika Raugewitz[1], Jessica Strey[1], Robby Peibst[1]
[1] ISFH, Emmerthal, Germany; [2] Paderborn University, Paderborn, Germany

Oral SESSION 2DO.7 Insights Into the Stability of Perovskite Solar Cells and Modules

2DO.7.1 Outdoor Performance and Degradation Analysis of Inverted Perovskite Solar Cells 020115
Makoto Konagai[1], Hayato Okawa[1], Ryousuke Ishikawa[1], Masatoshi Yanagida[2], Yasuhiro Shirai[2]
[1] Tokyo City University, Setagaya, Japan; [2] NIMS, Tsukuba, Japan

Oral SESSION 2DO.8 Multiple Aspects of Perovskite PV Research

2DO.8.2 Strategies for Quasi-2D Perovskite Integration in p-i-n Solar Cells 020116
Anna Capitaine[1], Hugo Le Bossenec[1], Marion Provost[1], Alexandra Levtchenko[1], Daniel Ory[2], Jean Rousset[2], Iwan Zimmermann[1], Anyssa Derj[1],

Mirella Al Katrib[1]
[1] IPVF, Palaiseau, France; [2] EDF R&D, Palaiseau, France

2DO.8.3 Innovative Approach to Bismuth-Antimony-Iodide Double Perovskite PV Absorbers via Anion Exchange and Solide-State Reactions 020117
Oleksandr Stroyuk[1], *Oleksandra Raievska*[1], *Sachin Kinge*[2], *Jens Hauch*[1], *Christoph J. Brabec*[1]
[1] HI ERN, Erlangen, Germany; [2] Toyota Motors Europe, Brussels, Belgium

Visual SESSION 3AV.1 PV Module Design and Manufacturing

3AV.1.1 Investigating the 3-Dimensional Structure of Metallic Filler Particles in Electrically Conductive Adhesives 020119
Stephan Grosser[1], *Alexander Müller*[1], *Robert Göckeritz*[1], *Tobias Nitsche*[2], *Daniel Buckland*[2], *Giuseppe Galbiati*[2], *Bengt Jaeckel*[1]
[1] Fraunhofer CSP, Halle, Germany; [2] Henkel, Düsseldorf, Germany

3AV.1.6 Investigation on Different Bypass Diodes for Shade Resistant PV-Modules 020121
Jens Froebel[1], *Matthias Pander*[1], *Bengt Jaeckel*[1], *Andreas Maixner*[2], *Pouya Pourshafi*[2], *Afshin Bakhtiari*[2], *Hamed Hanifi*[2]
[1] Fraunhofer CSP, Halle, Germany; [2] AESOLAR, Koenigsbrunn, Germany

3AV.1.7 Optimization of Infrared Soldering Process to Reduce the Temperature Inhomogeneity in Silicon Solar Cells Using Finite Element Methods 020123
Daniel Christopher Joseph[1], *Angela De Rose*[1], *Christian Reichel*[1], *Andreas J. Beinert*[1], *Holger Neuhaus*[1]
[1] Fraunhofer ISE, Freiburg, Germany

3AV.1.10 Performance Evaluation of a New Design Photovoltaic Module with Reduced Self-Shading 020125
Pouya Pourshafi[1], *Andreas Maixner*[1], *Hamed Hanifi*[1]
[1] AESOLAR, Königsbrunn, Germany

3AV.1.11 Materials Assessment for PV-T Modules Thermal Performance Improvement 020127
Lucía Cano[1], *Raquel Simón-Allué*[1], *Raúl Villén*[1], *Yolanda Lara*[1], *Isabel Guedea*[1]
[1] ENDEF, Zaragoza, Spain

3AV.1.12 Evaluating Repair Techiniques for c-Si PV Modules: Spot-Welding 020129
Jorge Rabanal-Arabach[1], *Sonia Beltran-Condori*[1], *Natalia Videla-Magnata*[1], *Katalina Rojas-Henriquez*[1], *Andreas Schneider*[2], *Edward Fuentealba-Vidal*[1]
[1] University of Antofagasta, Antofagasta, Chile; [2] University of Applied Sciences Gelsenkirchen, Gelsenkirchen, Germany

3AV.1.13 Thermally Conductive Filler Particle Mixed Silicone Layer to Provide Heat Dissipation Functionality to c-Si Solar Cell Modules without Encapsulants 020131
Yasushi Sobajima[1], *Kouzen Wakazono*[1], *Keisuke Ohdaira*[2]
[1] Gifu University, Gifu, Japan; [2] JAIST, Ishikawa, Japan

3AV.1.16 Ultrasonic Characterization of Ethylene-Vinyl Acetate in Glass-Glass-Modules 020132
Christopher Bruce Konu[1], *Rico Meier*[1]
[1] HTW Berlin, Berlin, Germany

Visual SESSION 3AV.2 PV Module Durability and Reliability

Nathan Roosloot[1], Harsha Walpita[2], Christoph Seiffert[1], Jean Thomas[3], Maarten Dörenkämper[4], Minne M. de Jong[4], Josefine H. Selj[1], Gaute Otnes[1]
[1] Institute for Energy Technology, Kjeller, Norway; [2] University of Oslo, Kjeller, Norway; [3] Ciel et Terre, Lille, France; [4] TNO, Eindhoven, The Netherlands

Visual SESSION 3AV.3 PV Modules Characterisation and Performances Assessment

3AV.3.1 A New Method for Comprehensive Power Rating and Performance Analysis of PERC Modules based on Half-Cut Cell Technology 020171
Khadija El Ainaoui[1], Mhammed Zaimi[2], Imane Flouchi[1], Said Elhamaoui[1], Yasmine El mrabet[1], Abdellatif Ghennioui[1], El Mahdi Assaid[2]
[1] Green Energy Park, Benguerir, Morocco; [2] University of Chouaib Doukkali, El Jadida, Morocco

3AV.3.2 Energy Rating Analysis of Heterojunction PV Modules 020173
Teodora Stoyanova Lyubenova[1], Ewan D. Dunlop[1]
[1] European Commission JRC, Ispra, Italy

3AV.3.3 Trend of Temperature Coefficients of c-Si Module Technologies from the past 15 Years 020175
Bengt Jaeckel[1], Matthias Pander[1]
[1] Fraunhofer CSP, Halle, Germany

3AV.3.6 Angle of Incidence Measurements on Bifacial PV Modules 020177
Frank Weinrich[1], Stefan Riechelmann[1], Stefan Winter[1]
[1] PTB, Braunschweig, Germany

3AV.3.8 Plug & Play IV Curve Tracer for PV Modules 020179
Adrian Jäggi[1], Christof Bucher[1], Matthias Burri[1]
[1] BFH, Burgdorf, Switzerland

3AV.3.9 Seasonal and Location-Dependent Temperature Coefficients for Thin-Film PV Modules: Enhancing Yield Prediction Accuracy 020180
Thomas Weber[1], Abdullah Abu Sayed[1], Benjamin Lippke[1], Steven Xuereb[1], Marcus Rennhofer[2], Bart E. Pieters[3]
[1] Kiwa PI Berlin, Berlin, Germany; [2] AIT, Vienna, Austria; [3] FZJ, Jülich, Germany

3AV.3.10 Standardisation Methods for Bifacial Energy Yield Estimation and PV Module Long-Term Performance Degradation Estimation: Potential Policy Implications 020181
Jaione Bengoechea[1], Ana Maria Gracia Amillo[1], Stefan Riechelmann[2], Stefan Winter[2], Giorgio Bardizza[3], Christos Monokroussos[4], Davide Polverini[5], Pablo Vicente-Laiglesia[6], Maria Getsiou[7]
[1] CENER, Sarriguren, Spain; [2] PTB, Braunschweig, Germany; [3] TÜV Rheinland Italia, Milan, Italy; [4] TÜV Rheinland, Shanghai, China; [5] Directorate General for Internal Market, Industry, Entrepreneurship and SMEs, Brussels, Belgium; [6] European Climate, Infrastructure and Environment Executive Agency, Brussels, Belgium; [7] Directorate General for Research and Innovation, Brussels, Belgium

3AV.3.11 Shaalke: Development of a MATLAB Software Tool for Advanced Statistical Outdoor Data Evaluation 020183

Oral SESSION 3BO.11 Imaging Techniques for PV Modules

Cristian Terrados[1], Eva de la Viuda[1], Kabir Paul Sulca[1], Julian Anaya[1], Miguel Ángel González[1], Oscar Martínez[1]
[1] University of Valladolid, Valladolid, Spain

3BO.11.6 Luminescence Measurements of PV Modules with a Cost-Effective and Small-Sized Hood-Based Tool under Daylight Conditions 020206
Marc Köntges[1], Michael Siebert[1], Dieter Lorenz[2], Bernd Kuhrmann[2], Michael Fuß[2]
[1] ISFH, Emmerthal, Germany; [2] MBJ Solutions, Ahrensburg, Germany

Oral SESSION 3BO.12 Characterisation and Energy Rating of PV Modules

3BO.12.1 Developing a New I-V Translation Methodology in Accordance with IEC 60891:2021 Correction Procedure 1 and 2 020208
Wenhao Xu[1], Yating Zhang[1], Mengdi Liu[1], Christos Monokroussos[1], Werner Herrmann[2], Giorgio Bardizza[2], Harald Müllejans[3]
[1] TÜV Rheinland, Shanghai, China; [2] TÜV Rheinland Solar, Cologne, Germany; [3] European Commission JRC, Ispra, Italy

3BO.12.2 Characterization of Vehicle Integrated Photovoltaic Modules 020209
Ricardo Moruno[1], Francisco José Martín[1], Juan Manuel Redondo[1], Javier Malo[1], Luis Javier San José[1], Guido Vallerotto[1], Steve Askins[1], Rubén Núñez[1], César Domínguez[1], Ignacio Antón[1], Rebeca Herrero[1]
[1] UPM, Madrid, Spain

3BO.12.4 Estimating the Energy Yield of Bifacial Photovoltaics with the JRC's Photovoltaic Geographic Information System 020210
Nigel Taylor[1], Teodora Lyubenova[1], Lavanya Malarkannan[2], Nikos Alexandris[1], Alexandros Falangas[3], Robert Kenny[1], Ewan D. Dunlop[1], Blago Mihaylov[1]
[1] European Commission JRC, Ispra, Italy; [2] National Physical Laboratory, Teddington, United Kingdom; [3] TRASIS International, Brussels, Belgium

3BO.12.5 An Update on Energy Rating Amendments – Integration of Bifacial Modules 020211
Stefan Riechelmann[1], Hendrik Sträter[1], Ana Maria Gracia Amillo[2], Sophie Pelland[3], Anton Driesse[4]
[1] PTB, Braunschweig, Germany; [2] CENER, Pamplona, Spain; [3] Natural Resources Canada, Varennes, Canada; [4] PV Performance Labs, Freiburg, Germany

Oral SESSION 3BO.14 Characterisation and Outdoor Monitoring of Perovskite-based PV Modules

3BO.14.1 Outdoor Measurements of Perovskite Modules 020213
Hanna Ellis[1], Harald Müllejans[1], Ewan D. Dunlop[1], Tony Sample[1]
[1] European Commission JRC, Ispra, Italy

Oral SESSION 3BO.15 Outdoor Performances and Degradation Analysis of PV Modules

3CO.11.5 Indoor Characterization and Analysis of Reverse Breakdown Behavior of Solar Cells with Different Cell Architectures 020223

Bengt Jaeckel[1], Jens Froebel[1], Matthias Pander[1], Andreas Maixner[2], Hamed Hanifi[2]

[1] Fraunhofer CSP, Halle, Germany; [2] AESOLAR, Koenigsbrunn, Germany

Plenary SESSION 3CP.1 Si PV Manufacturing: Pushing the Limits of Performance

3CP.1.2 IBC4EU: European Back Contact Technology 020225

Florian Buchholz[1], Daniel Tune[1], Tobias Meßmer[1], Jonathan Linke[1], Manjunath Prasad[1], Valentin D. Mihailetchi[1], Juras Ulbikas[2], Arne Dahle[3], Martijn Meereboer[4], Francesca Fabris[5], Erik Eikelboom[5], Tom Borgers[6], Rik Van Dyck[6], Filip Duerinckx[7], Hariharsudan Sivaramakrishnan Radhakrishnan[7], Timea Bejat[8], Samuel Harrison[8], Ashish Binani[9], Nicolas Guillevin[9], Jan Kroon[9], Yevgeniya Larionova[10], Thorsten Dullweber[10], Ofer Shochet[11], Isaac Rosen [11], Ingo Röver [12], Wolfram Palitzsch[12], Yasmin Zaror[13], Johannes Stierstorfer[14], Aurimas Radzevicius[15], Julius Denafas[16], Tuomas Vanhanen [17], Tuukka Savisalo[17], Maximilian Pospischil [18], Marian Breitenbücher [18], Özlem Coşkun[19], Melodie de l'Epine [20], Philippe Macé[20], Ian Kenchington[20]

[1] ISC Konstanz, Konstanz, Germany; [2] Protechnology, Vilnius, Lithuania; [3] Norsun, Oslo, Norway; [4] Energyra, Westknollendam, The Netherlands; [5] Futurasun, Citadella, Italy; [6] IMEC, Genk, Belgium; [7] Hasselt Unversity, Genk, Belgium; [8] CEA, Le Bourget-du-Lac, France; [9] TNO, Petten, The Netherlands; [10] ISFH, Emmerthal, Germany; [11] Copprint, Jerusalem, Israel; [12] LuxChemTech, Freiberg, Germany; [13] WIP Renewable Energies, Munich, Germany; [14] WIP - Renewable Energies, Munich, Germany; [15] Valoe Cells, Vilnius, Lithuania; [16] Solitek, Vilnius, Lithuania; [17] Valoe, Mikkeli, Finland; [18] Highline Technologies, Freiburg, Germany; [19] Kalyon PV, Ankara, Türkiye; [20] Becquerel Institute, Brussels, Belgium

Plenary SESSION 3CP.3 Perovskite – Silicon Tandems: Towards Commercialisation | PV Stability in the Field

3CP.3.4 Outdoor Performance and Reliability of Perovskite (Pk)-Silicon (Si) Tandems: >1 year of Monitoring in the NEXUS Project 020226

Atse Louwen[1], Jordi Veirman[1], Alexander Astigarraga[1], Juan José Stivanello[1], David Moser[2], Perrine Carroy[3], Vincent Barth[3], Delfina Muñoz[3], Markus Lenz[4], Anika Sidler[4], Jorge Ferrando[5], Maximiliano Alejandro Senno[5], Henk J. Bolink[5], Talat Özden[6], Hisham Nasser[6], Shuaifeng Hu[7], Xinyi Shen[7], Henry Snaith[7]

[1] Eurac Research, Bolzano, Italy; [2] Becquerel Institute Italy, Trento, Italy; [3] CEA / INES, Le Bourget-du-Lac, France; [4] School of Life Sciences FHNW, Muttenz, Switzerland; [5] University of Valencia, Paterna, Spain; [6] ODTÜ-GÜNAM, Ankara, Türkiye; [7] University of Oxford, Oxford, United Kingdom

Oral SESSION 3DO.12 Innovative Encapsulation Materials

Nikolina Pervan[1], Jutta Geier[1], Christian Veas[1], Gernot Oreski[1]
[1] PCCL, Leoben, Austria

Oral SESSION 4AO.7 Solar Resource Assessment

4AO.7.4 Potential of Decimeter-Resolution Ground Albedo Data for Bifacial Photovoltaics 020235
Niklas Blum[1], Bijan Nouri[1], Yann Fabel[1], Stefan Wilbert[1]
[1] DLR, Almería, Spain

4AO.7.5 Method for the Determination of Spectral Responsivity of Digital Solar Irradiance Sensors 020236
David Hinken[1], Sebastian Denke[1], Karsten Bothe[1], Rolf Brendel[1]
[1] ISFH, Emmerthal, Germany

Oral SESSION 4AO.8 Solar Irradiance Forecasting

4AO.8.2 Cutting-Edge Generative AI for Intra-Hour Solar Forecasting 020237
Yann Fabel[1], Dominik Schnaus[2], Bijan Nouri[1], Stefan Wilbert[1], Niklas Blum[1], Luis F. Zarzalejo[3], Julia Kowalski[4], Robert Pitz-Paal[5]
[1] DLR, Almeria, Spain; [2] TUM, Garching, Germany; [3] CIEMAT, Madrid, Spain; [4] RWTH, Aachen, Germany; [5] DLR, Cologne, Germany

4AO.8.4 Integrating Satellite Imagery and GNNs for Improving Day-Ahead Solar Irradiance Forecasting 020238
Baptiste Schubnel[1], Jelena Simeunovic[1], Corentin Tissier[1], Pierre-Jean Alet[1], Rafael E. Carrillo[1]
[1] CSEM, Neuchâtel, Switzerland

4AO.8.5 Enhancing Intra-Hour Solar Irradiance Forecasting for Solar Applications: A Blended Model of Satellite, Sky Imager and Persistence 020239
Bijan Nouri[1], Jorge Lezaca[2], Yann Fabel[1], Annette Hammer[2], Niklas Blum[1], Stefan Wilbert[1]
[1] DLR, Almeria, Spain; [2] DLR, Oldenburg, Germany

Oral SESSION 4AO.9 Irradiance for PV Design | Shading and Glare Mitigation

4AO.9.1 Reflective Properties of Urban Materials and Their Impact on PV Yield 020240
Christian Schläger[1], Dennis Bredemeier[1], Arne Dittrich[2], Jan Hendrik Pfau[1], Philip Kühne[1], Rolf Brendel[2]
[1] Leibniz University Hannover, Hannover, Germany; [2] ISFH, Emmerthal, Germany

4AO.9.3 Understanding Short-Term PV Power Variability Based on Solargis Time Series Data and Simulations 020241
Martin Opatovsky[1], Marta Pelfort Ojer[1], Juraj Betak[1], Konstantin Rosina[1]
[1] Solargis, Bratislava, Slovakia

4AO.9.5 Accelerating Photovoltaic System Simulations via Statistical Data Aggregation 020243

Adrián Blanco Aguiar[1], Brais González Rodríguez[2], María Martínez-Barbeito[1], Miguel Sánchez de León Peque[1]
[1] ieco.io, Vigo, Spain; [2] University of Vigo, Vigo, Spain

4AO.9.6 Addressing Glare Problematics for Photovoltaic Projects in the Immediate Proximity of Roads and Railways through the Use of Accurate Digital Surface Models 020244
Christophe Vernay[1], John Coutel[1], Aina Razanajao[1], Sébastien Pitaval[1]
[1] SOLAÏS, Valbonne, France

Plenary SESSION 4AP.1 PV Everywhere

4AP.1.3 Micro-Concentrator Photovoltaics for Deep Space Missions: Overcoming LILT Challenges with High-Specific-Power Solar Arrays 020246
Guido Vallerotto[1], Anderson Bermudez-Garcia[2], Gerald Siefer[3], Maike Wiesenfarth[3], Almudena Garcia-Sanchez[1], Ignacio Antón[1], Carsten Baur[4], Pier Luigi Coz[4], César Domínguez[1]
[1] UPM, Madrid, Spain; [2] Thales Alenia Space, Cannes, France; [3] Fraunhofer ISE, Freiburg, Germany; [4] European Space Agency, Noordwijk, The Netherlands

Oral SESSION 4BO.16 Color in Photovoltaics

4BO.16.1 Experimental Investigation of Colored BIPV/T Systems for Wood-Framed Roofs 020248
Anna-Maria Sigounis[1], Andreas Athienitis[1]
[1] Concordia University, Montreal, Canada

4BO.16.3 How to Perform Accurate Colour Measurements for BIPV Module Glass Covers: an IEA PVPS Task 15 Round-Robin Measurement Campaign 020249
Markus Babin[1], Gabriele C. Eder[2], Thomas Friesen[3], Martina Pelle[4], Gabriella Gonnella[5], Fabrizio Leonforte[6], Yuliya Voronko[2], Helen R. Wilson[7], Sune Thorsteinsson[1], Laura Maturi[4], Niccolò Aste[6], Claudio Del Pero[6], Janne Halme[8], Jun-Tae Kim[9], Susanna Santamaria Fernández[10], Anna-Maria Sigounis[11], Hua Ge[11], Gabi Friesen[12], Francesco Frontini[12]
[1] DTU, Roskilde, Denmark; [2] OFI, Vienna, Austria; [3] Megasol Energie, Deitingen, Switzerland; [4] Eurac Research, Bolzano, Italy; [5] Eurac research, Bolzano, Italy; [6] Polytechnic University of Milan, Milan, Italy; [7] Fraunhofer ISE, Freiburg, Germany; [8] Aalto University, Espoo, Finland; [9] Kongju National University, Chungnam, South Korea; [10] TECNALIA, Derio, Spain; [11] Concordia University, Montreal, Canada; [12] SUPSI, Mendrisio, Switzerland

4BO.16.6 Predicting Light Scatter in Structural Colored BIPV Modules and Textured Glass Using Radiance 020250
Nanna Lysgaard Andersen[1], Markus Babin[1], Jan Svatos[1], Karlis Petersons[2], Leif Yde[2], Jan F. Stensborg[2], Catarina G. Ferreira[3], Ananta Paul[3], Jani Lamminaho[3], Joel D. Cox[3], Morten Madsen[3], Peter B. Poulsen[1], Sune Thorsteinsson[1]
[1] DTU, Roskilde, Denmark; [2] Stensborg, Roskilde, Denmark; [3] SDU Climate Cluster, Odense, Denmark

Oral SESSION 4BO.17 Performance of PV on/in Buildings

4BO.17.1 Modeling Partial Shading at the Cell Level on Photovoltaic Modules 020251
Jean-Paul Calin[1], Jacques Levrat[2], Antonin Faes[2], Fahradin Mujovi[2], Paul Rémondeau[3], Kléber Nicolet-dit-Félix[3], Bénédicte Bonnet-Eymard[2], Didier Dalmazzone[1], Aïcha Hessler-Wyser[3], Christophe Ballif[3]
[1] ENSTA Paris, Palaiseau, France; [2] CSEM, Neuchâtel, Switzerland; [3] EPFL, Neuchâtel, Switzerland

4BO.17.2 Market Potential of Building-Integrated Photovoltaics: a Granular Analysis of the European Building Stock 020252
Juan Ignacio Martinez[1], Julien Van Overstraeten[2], Philippe Macé[2], José Maria Vega de Seoane[1], Elina Bosch[2], Mélodie de l`Epine[3]
[1] Becquerel Institute España, San Sebastian, Spain; [2] Becquerel Institute, Brussels, Belgium; [3] Becquerel Institute France, Lyon, France

4BO.17.3 Photovoltaics in the Built Environment – an Overview of Timely Topics for Research and Development 020253
Francesco Frontini[1], Angele Reinders[2]
[1] SUPSI, Mendrisio, Switzerland; [2] TU Eindhoven, Eindhoven, The Netherlands

4BO.17.5 Advancing BIPV: Shingled HJT Technology for High-Efficiency and Aesthetic Solar Integration 020254
Gabriella Gonnella[1], Alvaro De Gruijter[1], Jordi Veirman[1], Martina Pelle[1], Laura Maturi[1], David Moser[2], Luis Fialho[1]
[1] Eurac Research, Bolzano, Italy; [2] Bequerel Institute Italy, Trento, Italy

4BO.17.6 PV-Planning and Simulation, Daylight Simulation and Energy-Certificate Calculation based on an Open-BIM-Building-Model 020255
Astrid Schneider[1], Karin Stieldorf[1], Christian Schranz[1], Harald Urban[1], Alfred Waschl[2], Markus Feichtner[3], Fedele Rende[4], Andrea Aiello[4], Martin Hauer[5], Kurt Battisti[6], Markus Dörn[6], Jacqueline Scherret[6], Martin Treberspurg[7], Christoph Treberspurg[7]
[1] TU Wien, Vienna, Austria; [2] buildingSMART, Vienna, Austria; [3] Sonnenkraft Energie, St. Veit/Glan, Austria; [4] ACCA Software, Cosenza, Italy; [5] Bartenbach, Vienna, Austria; [6] A-Null Development, Vienna, Austria; [7] Treberspurg und Partner Ziviltechniker, Vienna, Austria

Oral SESSION 4BO.5 PV-Products for Buildings

4BO.5.1 Fabrication of a Novel Semi-Translucent BIPV Module Providing High Power Density and Active Daylight Management 020257
Almudena Garcia-Sanchez[1], Guido Vallerotto[1], Jaime J. Hernández[2], Alejandro García-Cañas[2], Steve Askins[1], Ignacio Antón[1], Isabel Rodríguez[2], César Domínguez[1]
[1] UPM, Madrid, Spain; [2] IMDEA Nanoscience, Madrid, Spain

4BO.5.3 A Comparative Study of Photovoltaic Shading Devices for Net Zero Energy Buildings across French Climates 020259

Visual SESSION 4BV.4 BIPV

Visual SESSION 4CV.1 Advances in Operation, Performance and Maintenance of PV Systems

Anastasios Kladas[1], Bert Herteleer[1], Jan Cappelle[1]
[1] *KU Leuven, Ghent, Belgium*

4CV.1.51 Photovoltaic Modules Self-Testing by Junction Box-Embedded Wireless Monitoring Solution 020353

Eneko Ortega[1], Gerardo Aranguren[1], Julius Denafas[2], Paulius Laurikėnas[2], Ricardo Alonso[3], Juan Carlos Jimeno[1]
[1] *UPV/EHU, Bilbao, Spain;* [2] *Solitek, Vilnius, Lithuania;* [3] *Tecnalia, Derio, Spain*

4CV.1.52 Data-Driven Assessment of Inverter Efficiency Losses and Load Profiles in PV Systems 020355

David Daßler[1], Stephanie Malik[1], Dharm Patel[1], Andreas Dietrich[2], Jan Spihola[2], Kai Kaufmann[3], Carsten Hennig[4], Robert Klengel[1], Carola Klute[1], Ulrike Jahn[1], Matthias Ebert[1]
[1] *Fraunhofer IMWS, Halle, Germany;* [2] *DiSUN Deutsche Solarservice, Werder, Germany;* [3] *DENKweit, Halle, Germany;* [4] *saferay holding, Berlin, Germany*

4CV.1.54 Enhancing Autonomus Aerial Monitoring of Large-Scale Photovoltaic Plants Using a Deep Reinforcement Learning Approach for Multi-Aerial Robot Systems 020356

Amirhossain Aghamohammadi[1], Seyyed Majid Esmailifar[1], Mohammad Kolahi[2], Amirmohammad Moradi Sizkouhi[3], Mohammadreza Aghaei[4]
[1] *Amirkabir University of Technology, Tehran, Iran;* [2] *University of Isfahan, Isfahan, Iran;* [3] *Concordia University, Montreal, Canada;* [4] *NTNU, Aalesund, Norway*

4CV.1.57 Preprocessing I-V Curve Data for Enhanced CNN-Based Fault Diagnosis in Photovoltaic Strings 020357

Woo Gyun Shin[1], Young-Chul Ju[1], Hye-Mi Hwang[1], Jin-Seok Lee[1], Suk Whan Ko[1]
[1] *KIER, Daejeon, South Korea*

4CV.1.60 Solar-ASP Tool For Early Fault Detection and Remote Diagnosis in Photovoltaic Generators 020358

Sandra Riaño[1], Ricardo Alonso[2], Jose Domingo Santos[1], Miguel Esteras[1], Ainhoa Pereda[1], Antonio Salvador[3], Jose Antonio Osuna[3], Javier del Ser[4]
[1] *TECNALIA, Derio, Spain;* [2] *TECNALIA , Derio, Spain;* [3] *MAGTEL, Córdoba, Spain;* [4] *UPV/EHU, Bilbao, Spain*

4CV.1.61 Fire Performance of Power Optimizers in Photovoltaic Systems 020359

Lasse Halle[1], David Joss[1], Christof Bucher[1]
[1] *BFH, Burgdorf, Switzerland*

4CV.1.62 Online Characterization of PV Strings by Smart Inverters Using a Self Referencing Algorithm 020361

Maximilian Schönau[1], Darwin Daume[2], Sasikumar Krishnan[1], Marius Weiß[1], Alexander Kusch[1], Christian Knausdorf[1], Sahereh Obeidavi[1], Achim Schulze[3], Dieter Landes[1], Bernd Hüttl[1]
[1] *Coburg University of Applied Sciences, Coburg, Germany;* [2] *pvnode, Rosenheim, Germany;* [3] *Rosenheim Technical University of Applied Sciences, Rosenheim, Germany*

Oral SESSION 4DO.1 PV Tracking and Simulation

Oral SESSION 4DO.10 PV O&M Insights, Direct Uses of PV Electricity and Batteries

Oral SESSION 4DO.17 Advanced Inspections and Robotic Solutions for PV O&M

Oral SESSION 4DO.2 Agrivoltaic Technologies

4DO.5.4 Development and Evaluation of Agrivoltaic System in Olive Groves based on a Novel Smart Tracking Algorithm 020392

Ildefonso Muñoz[1], Irati Amatriain[1], Gregorio Olivares[1], Gillen Abrego[2], Eusebio Gainza[2], Iñaki Cornago[1]
[1] *CENER, Sarriguren, Spain;* [2] *ALLOTARRA, Allo, Spain*

4DO.5.5 Adoption and Optimisation Analysis of Agrivoltaic Systems for Horticultural Production and Energy Autonomy in Lubumbashi/DR Congo 020393

Eddie Bilitu[1], Shu-Ngwa Asaa[2], Sara Bouguerra[3], Nikoleta Kyranaki[3], Ismail Kaaya[3], Yannick Useni[4], Michael Daenen[3]
[1] *Hasselt University, Hasselt, Belgium;* [2] *imo-imomec, Genk, Belgium;* [3] *imec, Genk, Belgium;* [4] *University of Lubumbashi, Lubumbashi, Congo (DRC)*

Visual SESSION 4DV.1 Agrivoltaics Approaches, Experiences, Results | Integrated and Innovative PV Applications

4DV.1.5 Maximizing Economic Performance of Agrivoltaic Systems through Module Array Design 020394

Habeel Alam[1], Jenny Nelson[2], Alona Armstrong[1], Duncan Whyatt[1], Nauman Butt[3]
[1] *Lancaster University, Lancaster, United Kingdom;* [2] *Imperial College London, London, United Kingdom;* [3] *Lahore University of Management Sciences, Lahore, Pakistan*

4DV.1.7 Bifacial and Mismatch Factors of Agri-Photovoltaics Systems 020396

Keith R. McIntosh[1], Solomon Freer[1], Bastien J. J. Ardissone[1], S. Ramirez[1], Ben A. Sudbury[1], Malcolm D. Abbott[1]
[1] *PV Lighthouse, Coledale, Australia*

4DV.1.10 Performance Analysis of Agrivoltaic System Configurations in Nordic Conditions 020398

Magda Szarek[1], Sami Jouttijärvi[1], Lauri Karttunen[1], Samuli Ranta[2], Kati Miettunen[1]
[1] *University of Turku, Turku, Finland;* [2] *TUAS, Turku, Finland*

4DV.1.11 Irradiance Management in Agrivoltaic Systems with Varying Designs Across Latitudes: Toward Finland's First Significant Demonstration 020400

Shuo Wang[1], Soroush Moradi Zavie Kord[2], Hugo E. Huerta[1], Antti Lajunen[2], Samuli Ranta[1]
[1] *TUAS, Turku, Finland;* [2] *University of Helsinki, Helsinki, Finland*

4DV.1.12 An Innovative Agrivoltaic System for Desert Climates with Anti-Soiling, Irradiance Control, and Water Management 020402

Sagarika Kumar[1], Min Hsian Saw[1], Ahmed Shaaban[1], Kamil Jaworczak[1], Nursulu Kuzhagaliyeva[1], Carlos G. Parrilla[2], Francois M. Tsombou[2], Fouad Lamghari[2], Mauro Pravettoni[1]
[1] *Technology Innovation Institute, Abu Dhabi, United Arab Emirates;* [2] *Fujairah Research Centre, Fujairah, United Arab Emirates*

4DV.1.15 Review of Sensor Technologies for Monitoring Agrivoltaic Systems 020403

Sara Pereira[1], José A. Silva[1], Luís Fialho[2], Pedro Horta[1]
[1] *University of Évora, Évora, Portugal;* [2] *Eurac Research, Bolzano, Italy*

Visual SESSION 4DV.4 PV System Engineering

[1] Luxembourg Institute of Science and Technology, Esch-sur-Alzette, Luxembourg; [2] University of Lisbon, Lisbon, Portugal

4EO.2.6 Optimizing Angular Performance of Curved VIPV Modules 020459
Francisco José Martín[1], Rebeca Herrero[1], Ignacio Antón[1]
[1] UPM, Madrid, Spain

Oral SESSION 5CO.4 Life Cycle Assessment of Silicon and Perovskite-based Cells and Modules

5CO.4.1 Towards Low-Impact Triple-Junction Perovskite/Silicon Tandem Modules: LCA of Precursor Materials to Describe the Influence of Background Data Sources 020461
Alejandra Galarza[1], Sebastian Nold[2], Lars Oberbeck[3]
[1] IPVF, Palaiseau, France; [2] Fraunhofer ISE, Freiburg, Germany; [3] TotalEnergies OneTech, Paris, France

5CO.4.3 Sustainability Assessment of Perovskite/Silicon Tandem Solar Modules: from Laboratory Scale to Industrial Implementation 020462
Elisabetta Brivio[1], Andrea Danelli[1], Sofia Spagnolo[1], Pierpaolo Girardi[1]
[1] RSE, Milan, Italy

5CO.4.4 LCA Learning Curve for Crystalline Silicon Solar Technologies based on Technology Improvements 020463
Julian Reichle[1], Moritz Fath[1], Sraisth[1], Amish Kumar Sinha[1], Mehul Raval[1], Wolfgang Jooss[1], Peter Fath[1], Gourab Das[1]
[1] RCT Solutions, Konstanz, Germany

Oral SESSION 5CO.5 Life Cycle Assessment of New PV Applications and Recycling

5CO.5.1 Optimizing AgriPV: A Comprehensive Assessment Framework for Sustainable Energy and Agriculture 020464
Ana Patrícia Lopes[1], Bruno Barrionuevo [2], Daniel P. Albuquerque[3], Diogo Cordeiro[4], Cláudia Fernandes[3], Athanasios T. Balafoutis [2], Rui Castro[1]
[1] University of Lisbon, Lisbon, Portugal; [2] CERTH, Athens, Greece; [3] Centre for New Energy Technologies, Sacavém, Portugal; [4] EDP, Lisbon, Portugal

5CO.5.2 Environmental Sustainability Assessment of Agrivoltaic Systems: a Life Cycle Approach 020466
Maria Anna Cusenza[1], Andrea Danelli[1], Pierpaolo Girardi[1], Sofia Spagnolo[1]
[1] RSE, Milan, Italy

5CO.5.4 Closing the Circle: Integrating the Circular Footprint Formula into Photovoltaic System Life Cycle Assessment 020467
Alexis Barrou[1], Selin Kandiyoti-Eskenazi[1], Jacques Levrat[1], Bertrand Paviet-Salomon[1], Christophe Ballif[1]
[1] CSEM, Neuchâtel, Switzerland

5CO.5.6 Environmental Benefits of Silicon Kerf Secondary Products in Pilot Processes over Conventional Production of Equivalent Products with Primary Raw Materials in China and Europe 020468
René Peche[1], Matthias Seitz[1], Markus Schönheits[1], Karsten Wambach[1]
[1] bifa Umweltinstitut, Augsburg, Germany

Oral SESSION 5CO.6 PV Recycling and Circularity

5CO.6.4 Quantification of Technical Recyclability of PV Modules for Different Recycling Scenarios 020470
Matthias Hämmer[1], Kerstin Baumann[1], Karsten Wambach[1], Markus Schönheits[1]
[1] bifa Umweltinstitut, Augsburg, Germany

5CO.6.5 IEC Technical Report 63525 on the Reuse of PV Modules: Final Result 020472
Arvid van der Heide[1], Serge Noels[2], Jan Clyncke[2], Rich Strömberg[3]
[1] imec, Genk, Belgium; [2] PV CYCLE, Brussels, Belgium; [3] University of Alaska, Fairbanks, United States of America

Plenary SESSION 5CP.1 Si PV Manufacturing: Pushing the Limits of Performance

5CP.1.4 Business Model Optimization for European Solar PV: A Study on Costs and Commercial Strategies 020474
Ian Kenchington[1], Philippe Macé[1], Gaëtan Masson[1], Joris Libal[2]
[1] Becquerel Institute, Brussels, Belgium; [2] ISC Konstanz, Konstanz, Germany

Plenary SESSION 5CP.2 Perovskite – Silicon Tandems: Towards Commercialisation | PV Stability in the Field

5CP.2.3 Total Cost of Ownership, LCA and LCOE Analysis of Perovskite-Silicon Tandems Compared to Single Junction Crystalline Silicon PV Technologies 020475
Baljeet Singh Goraya[1], Dilara Maria Subasi[1], Peter Henri Brailovsky[1], Henning Nagel[1], Patricia S.C. Schulze[1], Martin C. Schubert[1], Jochen Rentsch[1], Martin Hermle[1], Ralf Preu[1], Sebastian Nold[1]
[1] Fraunhofer ISE, Freiburg, Germany

Oral SESSION 5DO.11 The Road to Massive PV Deployment

5DO.11.1 Integration of Solar PV in a Norwegian Energy System, Navigating the Trade-offs between Land Use and Solar Power Production 020476
Petry Kristine Nøttum Haaland[1], Ole-Morten Midtgård[1], Magnus Korpås[1]
[1] NTNU, Trondheim, Norway

Oral SESSION 5DO.18 PV Recycling and Material Demand

Visual SESSION 5DV.2 Life Cycle Analysis and PV Recycling | Citizens Participation and Awareness

Oral SESSION 5EO.1 Citizens Participation and Awareness

Sponsors

Author Index

Keyword Index

ECONOMIC VALUE OF BUILDING-INTEGRATED PV PRODUCTION AT HIGH-LATITUDE LOCATIONS

Sami Jouttijärvi[1*], Lauri Karttunen[1], Magda Szarek[1], Bergpob Viriyaroj[2], Samuli Ranta[3], Kati Miettunen[1]
[1]Department of Mechanical and Materials Engineering, University of Turku, Vesilinnantie 5, 20500 Turku, Finland
[2]Department of Architecture, Aalto University, Otakaari 24, 02150 Espoo, Finland
[3]New Energy Research Group, Turku University of Applied Sciences, Joukahaisenkatu 7, 20520 Turku, Finland
*sami.jouttijarvi@utu.fi

ABSTRACT:
This work evaluates the status and prospects of building-integrated solar photovoltaic (BIPV) production in Finland, focusing on maintaining the value of the produced PV electricity during the lifetime of the system. The rapid increase of PV capacity in Finland causes major effects to the power system and the electricity market price, especially by lowering the price during the best PV production hours. This phenomenon can demotivate individual citizens and companies to invest in their own PV systems. To tackle the challenges related to the future uncertainties in the electricity price, maximizing the self-consumption of the planned BIPV system is important. Self-consuming the produced PV electricity allows avoiding transfer fee and taxes, which form, on average, most of the electricity purchase costs for the Finnish individuals. This work presents the recent research in the fields of BIPV and electricity price at high-latitude locations. Based on the existing scientific knowledge, we develop solutions for residential and commercial building-owners for designing PV systems that are resilient and profitable. The economic feasibility of these solutions with the 2019-2023 electricity price data is analyzed. The results show that high self-consumption rates result in high economic value: net present values were 665–883 EUR/kW for the studied systems during the years 2019-2023, covering more than half of reasonable investment costs.
Keywords: building-integrated PV, electricity price, self-consumption

1 INTRODUCTION

Building-integrated and building-applied solar photovoltaic (BIPV and BAPV) solutions allow the utilization of PV in urban areas, where dedicating large land areas solely for PV is often practically impossible. Moreover, BIPV enables using the produced electricity at the spot (self-consumption), thus avoiding the additional costs due to electricity transfer and taxes. The importance of PV self-consumption for economic profitability is highlighted when the revenue from PV electricity sold to the power grid is low.

In Finland, the electricity grid price is usually low and often only available option for small-scale producers is to sell their surplus production to the grid with the price defined by the day-ahead auction in the Nordpool market. Thus, even with the current PV production levels, the revenue for selling the electricity is low. As PV production is growing rapidly in Finland [1], the spot price is expected to decrease during PV peak production hours. Therefore, maximizing the self-consumed kilowatt-hours (kWhs) compared with PV system cost should be the key target for the BIPV systems in Finland.

One approach to improve self-consumption is investing in energy storage. Batteries can store PV electricity generated during the day for later use. In the central Europe batteries are common, but the low electricity price reduces the possibility to earn money with a battery in Finland, thus compromising their economic feasibility [2]. Due to a high heat demand, also thermal energy storages (TESs) can act as a flexible load for PV production. Our previous work showed the potential of TES in a Finnish residential house [3], and in Norway, larger TES was applied to improve the self-consumption of PV system in a high school [4].

However, as energy storage requires additional investments, the option to improve self-consumption by matching PV production and residential load becomes attractive. Even with historical electricity prices, where the impact of PV to the electricity price is negligible, east-and-west-oriented rooftop panels suffered only 13% economic loss compared with their south-facing counterparts, although the annual production loss was 23% [3]. As the national PV capacity grows and starts to impact to the spot price, which can occur with reasonable capacity additions [5], the mean price close to noon drops. Thus, the surplus production in the middle of the day is practically worthless, and even for the self-consumed production the value is higher in the morning and evening at least for the consumers with spot price or time-of-use electricity purchase contracts.

In densely built urban areas with multi-story buildings, the low roof-area-to-volume ratio of the buildings limits the rooftop PV generation potential, creating the need to utilize building facades. Compared with locations further south, high annual variation in the solar resource and low solar elevation angles characterize PV production in Finland. Considering BIPV, the low solar elevation opens possibilities to use building facades for PV production, since the relative loss in PV production is lower compared with regions where the solar elevation is high. Using facades for PV generation is thus relevant for the Finnish multi-story buildings, where the roof-area-to-volume ratio is small.

Moreover, the mismatch between the residential electricity load and PV production with conventional, south-facing systems reduces the economic value of PV generation. These factors encourage to build PV systems that produce better during the morning and evening. Our previous findings show that applying vertical bifacial PV (VBPV) installed in perpendicular to the south-facing façade of a multi-story building reaches slightly higher annual production compared with their monofacial PV (MPV) counterparts [6], with improved load-matching.

For detached houses, the ownership structure of the installed PV system is simple: the owner-resident of the building owns the system and either uses its production or sells it to the grid. For multi-story buildings, the ownership structures can be more complicated, which raises questions about sharing the benefits of the building's BIPV system. Conflicts between the stakeholders may even prevent the building of the system, thus halting PV growth in Finland.

Our work presents existing research on the economic

10.4229/EUPVSEC2025/4BV.4.9

profitability of BIPV in Finland. As a novel contribution, we complement the existing literature by including diverse electricity pricing scenarios when calculating the economic indicators for BIPV systems. The aim is to find the systems that are resilient towards the future price uncertainties, i.e., that achieve feasible economic performance and outperform their counterparts under studied scenarios.

2 METHODS

A flowchart showing the simulation workflow is presented in Figure 1. The chart is categorized into data, simulation, and results. A more detailed description of each step will follow.

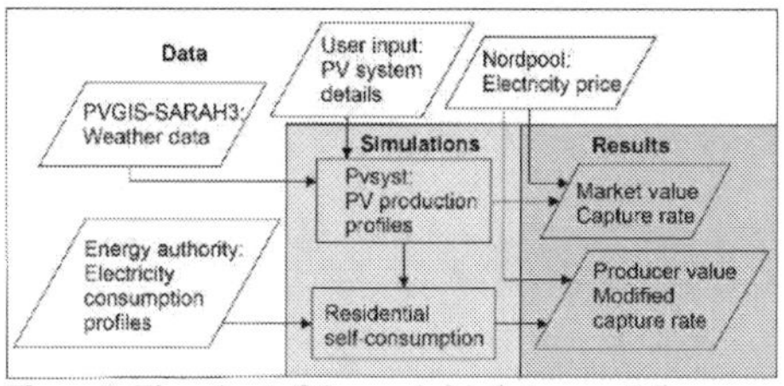

Figure 1. Flowchart of the used simulation workflow.

3.1 Data sources

The weather data used for our simulations was acquired from PVGIS-SARAH3 database [7] for the years 2019-2023. The period was chosen to cover the last 'old normal' energy year in Finland with limited variable renewable energy capacity (2019), the recent major crises, COVID-19 (2020-2021) and Russia's attack on Ukraine (2022), and the first 'new normal' energy year (2023). The electricity prices were acquired from Nordpool [8], FI market zone, covering the whole Finland. We used day-ahead spot price for the price of electricity and real electricity transfer costs from Turku, Finland in the economic calculations. We used type consumer profiles from [9] as the electricity consumption data.

To focus on the year-on-year variation of the weather and electricity price, we used the transfer fees and electricity tax for a typical residential apartment in 2023, while value-added tax was kept as 24%. Thus, the impact of the annual variation of the transfer fees and taxes, and the differences of the transfer cost of the residential building and a commercial building are excluded from this study.

3.2 Case studies and PV modelling

We studied two different buildings in this work: First, a residential multi-story building (Figure 2a-b) was adapted from our previous work [6]. The consumption profile of a residential building was created from two different types of consumer profiles, representing a small and a large apartment. The total electricity consumption of the building was scaled to 50 MWh, which is credible amount for a medium-sized multi-story building in Finland.

Second, a commercial building (Figure 2c) was simulated by using type consumer profile of an enterprise which is open daily. The total consumption of this building was 600 MWh, which is typical for a large grocery store in Finland. The rooftop power plant of the commercial building was expected to have a shading-free location.

PV production was modelled in a commercial software, PVsyst [10]. For the residential building, we used the 3D-scenarios from [6], with year-specific weather data. For the commercial building, we expect that the rooftop provides a shading-free location for PV production. The modelled panel was 'Generic 440 W 144 twin half-cell bifacial' from PVsyst-library.

Altogether, we modelled three different scenarios over five years. For the residential building, a small rooftop MPV system (5.3 kW, 22° tilt, facing south) was combined with MPV and VBPV façade systems (9.2 kW), noted as ResM and ResV, respectively. A commercial building was equipped with a bifacial system (south-facing, 30° tilt, 5 m row spacing, albedo 0.3), noted as ComB. Schematics of the buildings and systems are shown in Figure 2, and the key parameters of the simulated PV systems are given in Table I.

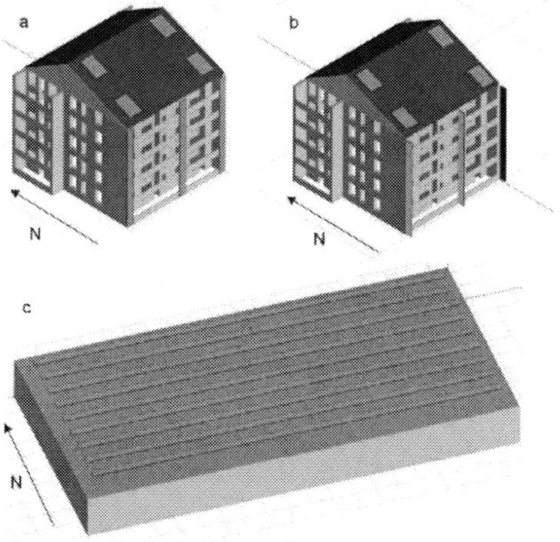

Figure 2. Schematic figures of the case studies: ResM (a), ResV (b) and ComB (c). Figures are created with PVsyst [10].

Table I. The key parameters of the modelled PV systems.

System	Rooftop	Façade	Power (kW)	*Annual yield (kWh/kW)
ResM	Tilt 22°, south, M	Tilt 90°, south, M	14.5: 5.3+9.2	919
ResV	Tilt 22°, south, M	Tilt 90°, east-west, B	14.5: 5.3+9.2	943
ComB	Tilt 30°, south, B	-	174	1230

M = monofacial; B = bifacial
* Mean value for the years 2019-2023

3.3 Economic analysis

The market value (*MV*) of PV electricity is defined as a weighted average of the electricity spot price, normalized with the hourly PV production:

$$MV = \frac{\sum_{t=1}^{8760}(E_t \cdot C_t)}{\sum_{t=1}^{8760}(E_t)}, \quad (1)$$

where E_t is PV production and C_t the electricity price during hour t. Capture rate (*CR*), sometimes referred as value factor in the literature, is the fraction of *MV* and the mean electricity price ($\bar{C}$). *CR* higher than one means that PV production is focused on the high-price hours, whereas

CR lower than one means that the priced during the best PV production hours is low. The equation for *CR* is:

$$CR = \frac{MV}{\bar{C}}. \qquad (2)$$

While *MV* and *CR* can be calculated based on PV production and electricity price, the actual value of PV electricity for a small-scale producer depends on the self-consumption: for self-consumed PV, the producer saves the electricity transfer fee and taxes besides the electric energy itself. Self-consumption is defined on hourly basis: if PV production is lower than demand, all production is self-consumed, whereas when the production is higher than demand, the excess is sold to the grid. PV production value is defined as:

$$VAL_{PV} = \sum_{t=1}^{8760}(E_{SC,t} \cdot C_{purchase,t} + E_{sur,t} \cdot C_{sell,t}), \qquad (3)$$

where $E_{SC,t}$ is the self-consumed and $E_{sur,t}$ the surplus PV generation, $C_{purchase,t}$ the electricity purchase cost and $C_{sell,t}$ the electricity sell revenue. Here, we assume that the customer has a spot price contract, when $C_{purchase}$ includes the spot price, value-added tax, a margin charged by the electricity company (0.4 c/kWh), and a lumped sum including the electricity transfer cost and electricity tax (8.73 c/kWh). C_{sell} is the spot price deducted by the margin (0.4 c/kWh).

The electricity transfer fee varies depending on the year and geographical location within Finland. Here, the value 8.73 c/kWh for the transfer fee and electricity tax was chosen to represent a typical apartment in southwestern Finland in the year 2023. The year-to-year variation of the transfer fee was neglected to highlight the impact of the electricity price and weather on PV value.

Modified capture rate (*MCR*) was defined to compare the actual value of the PV production to the mean electricity price. It is defined as:

$$MCR = \frac{VAL_{PV}}{\bar{C}}. \qquad (4)$$

3 RESULTS

3.1 PV production and its value factor

During our study period, the annual mean electricity price in the Nordpool day-ahead market varied from 28.0 (2020) to 154 (2022) EUR/MWh. The primary causes for the variation were COVID-19 (year 2020) and the Russia's attack on Ukraine (resulting from stopping the electricity import to Finland from Russia in year 2022). Figure 3 shows the annual trends in *MVs* and *CRs* of the studied systems, and $\bar{C}$ in 2019-2023. *MV* of different PV systems varies with the electricity price on yearly basis, whereas the variation between the different PV systems during the same year is low. *CR*s vary from 0.91 to 1.22, with the lowest *CR*s from the year 2023, the last year in this work. This trend shows that until 2022, the impact of PV on the electricity price in Finland has been negligible, and the exclusion of the low nighttime prices allow PV to reach high *CR*. However, starting from 2023, the increase of national PV capacity in Finland reduces the price during PV peak production hours, making planned and existing PV systems vulnerable to the electricity price cannibalization, i.e., the dampening of PV electricity value due to over-generation of PV.

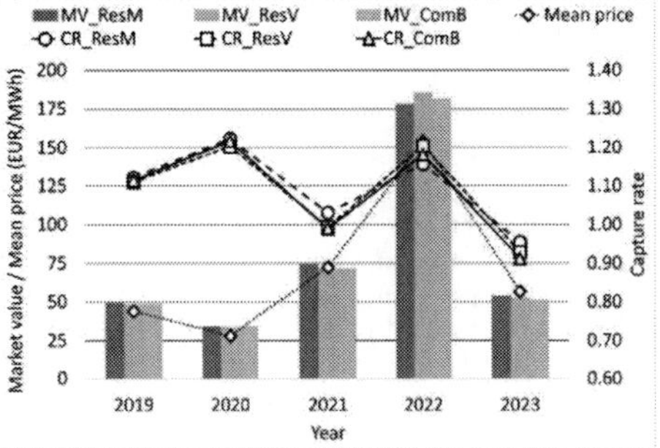

Figure 3. The development of market value and capture rate of the studied systems during 2019-2023.

3.2 Self-consumption and modified value factor

The annual productions of the studied systems were 880–943 kWh/kW, 907–969 kWh/kW, and 1190–1260 kWh/kW for ResM, ResV, and ComB, respectively (Figure 4a). The high production of ComB compared with the residential systems results from using bifacial panels elevated 1 m above the roof. The self-consumption rates of the systems were high: 80.1-80.7% for ResM, 85.8-86.5% for ResV, and 81.2-81.9% for ComB, respectively. For the generated electricity value, the shares of self-consumption were even higher: excluding the energy crisis year 2022, 91.8-94.1% and 94.3-96.1%, and 93.2-95.4% of the generated annual value resulted from self-consumption with ResM, ResV, and ComB, respectively (Figure 4b). Only during the year 2022, high revenues were available for the surplus PV production. The annual value of the residential PV production reached values up to 292 EUR/kW in 2022, but during the rest of the study period, the variation range was 105-155 EUR/kW. For ComB, the value peaked in 2022 at 367 EUR/kW, and varied from 143 to 197 EUR/kW during other years. These values are high compared with the investment costs in 2023, 81.5 EUR/kW [5].

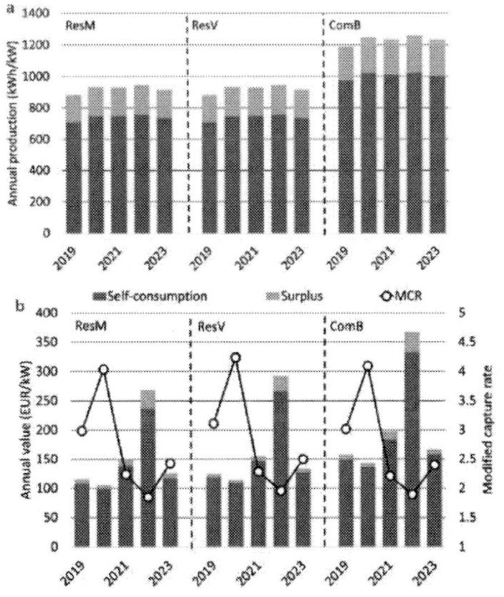

Figure 4. The annual production (a) and the value and *MCR* (b) of PV generation for ResM and ResV systems during 2019-2023.

10.4229/EUPVSEC2025/4BV.4.9

As *MV* of PV-generated electricity is expected to decrease in Finland as PV production increases [5], the profitability of PV becomes more dependent on the added value due to self-consumption. Therefore, we analyzed *MCR*s of all studied PV systems. *MCR* shows the fraction of PV production value and the mean electricity price (Eq. 4). Therefore, high *MCR* indicates either valuable PV generation or low electricity price.

*MCR*s peaked during the cheapest electricity year, 2020, when the value of PV electricity was over four times higher than the mean spot price of electricity. Respectively, during 2022, *MCR*s remained below two. This trend shows that self-consumption effectively balances the risk of PV unprofitability due to low electricity market price. *MCR* showed very similar trends for all studied systems: the importance of self-consumption is highlighted with the low energy prices.

4.3 Net present value considerations

Our previous work found that an annual value of 81.5 EUR/kW covers the initial investment costs of PV system by assuming 1250 EUR/kW investment cost, 30 years lifetime and an interest rate of 5% [5]. All reported annual values are above this threshold limit. The net present values (NPV) of the production during the first five years were 655, 700, and 883 EUR/kW for ResM, ResV, and ComB, respectively, covering more than half of the initial investment with only five years of operation. However, the energy crisis year 2022 boosted NPV significantly.

5 DISCUSSION

Historically, the major factor defining *MV* of PV electricity generated in Finland has been the mean electricity price. Until 2022, PV generation in Finland has been negligible, and *CR* of PV has been high since PV generation avoids the conventionally cheap nighttime hours. However, starting from 2023, PV generation in Finland has reached levels where it impacts the electricity price. Since PV capacity in Finland is expected to multiply within a few years, *CR* of PV will decrease [11]. This change drives us to focus on self-consumption, since it creates added value due to avoided transfer fees and taxes.

The analysis done for two buildings and three different PV systems showed that a high self-consumption rate effectively protects PV production against low prices. Especially, in the year 2020 with exceptionally low electricity price level due to COVID-19, the value of the generated PV electricity exceeded the mean electricity price by over four times. The annual value of the generated PV electricity was the lowest among the studied years in 2020, but the differences in the generated values were lower than the differences in *MV*.

When comparing the two different residential building façade systems, MPV and VBPV, the slightly higher value with VBPV system resulted from higher production and self-consumption rate. Considering *MV*, where only the electricity spot price was accounted, VBPV system showed similar performance to MPV system. However, as PV production will increase and result as lower electricity price around noon [5], VBPV provides more resilience towards the price cannibalization in the future.

6 CONCLUSIONS

This work analyzed the development in the value of PV generation in Finland during 2019-2023. The key findings are that the economic profitability of PV depends on the self-consumption of PV electricity. With historical electricity price data, the annual value of PV generation correlates with the mean electricity spot price, but the role of self-consumption significantly balances this variation. During the cheapest electricity year, 2020, *MCR*, defining the ratio of PV generation value and the mean electricity price, was over four, whereas during the most expensive electricity price year, 2022, *MCR* was below two.

Analysis of NPVs of PV production during 2019-2023 showed that with historical electricity prices, only five years of production allows to reach NPVs corresponding roughly half of the initial investment costs. However, when projecting the value creation to the future, the impact of increasing PV production on the electricity price will lower the profits. Therefore, the balancing role of self-consumption, shown by the negative correlation between *MCR* and electricity price, becomes more important in the future.

ACKNOWLEDGEMENTS

The work was funded by Strategic Research Council (FI), grants 358542 & 359141, and by University of Turku and City of Salo (LK) and UTUGS (LK).

REFERENCES

[1] Renewables Finland. Suunnittelussa olevat aurinkovoimalahankkeet 2025. https://suomenuusiutuvat.fi/aurinkovoima/aurinkovoimahankkeet-ja-voimalat-suomessa/suunnittelussa-olevat-aurinkovoimahankkeet/ (accessed June 16, 2025).

[2] Karttunen L, Jouttijärvi S, Niskanen J, Jasielec JJ, Huerta H, Ranta S, et al. Techno-economic analysis of residential PV-battery energy systems in Nordics. Conf. Proc. EU PVSEC 2024, Vienna: WIP Renewables; 2024, p. 020507. https://doi.org/10.4229/EUPVSEC2024/5DV.2.1.

[3] Jouttijärvi S, Karttunen L, Ranta S, Miettunen K. Techno-economic analysis on optimizing the value of photovoltaic electricity in a high-latitude location. Appl Energy 2024;361:122924. https://doi.org/10.1016/J.APENERGY.2024.122924.

[4] Kahsay MB, Völler S. Thermal energy storage for increasing self-consumption of grid connected photovoltaic systems: A case for Skjetlein High School, Norway. Energy Build 2025;335:115563. https://doi.org/10.1016/J.ENBUILD.2025.115563.

[5] Jouttijärvi S, Karttunen L, Tervo S, Huerta H, Ranta S, Syri S, et al. Sensitivity of electricity price in the Finnish market conditions with increasing solar energy production. Conf. Proc. EU PVSEC 2024, Vienna: WIP Renewables; 2024, p. 020547. https://doi.org/10.4229/EUPVSEC2024/5DV.3.27.

[6] Viriyaroj B, Jouttijärvi S, Jänkälä M, Miettunen K. Performance of vertically mounted bifacial photovoltaics on high-rise buildings in the Nordic conditions. Conf. Proc. EU PVSEC 2024, Vienna: WIP Renewables; 2024.

https://doi.org/10.4229/EUPVSEC2024/4BV.4.1.
[7] European Commission. Photovoltaic Geographical Information System (PVGIS) 2025. https://re.jrc.ec.europa.eu/pvg_tools/en/ (accessed September 3, 2025).
[8] Nord Pool AS. Nordpool 2025. https://www.nordpoolgroup.com/en/ (accessed June 16, 2025).
[9] Mutanen A, Lummi K, Pertti J. Valtakunnallisten tyyppikäyttäjämäärittelyiden päivittäminen ja hyödyntämisen periaatteet verkkopalvelumaksuihin liittyvissä tarkasteluissa. 2019.
[10] PVsyst. PVsyst 2025. https://www.pvsyst.com/ (accessed September 17, 2025).
[11] Heenatigala Kankanamge D, Jääskeläinen J, Jouttijärvi S, Syri S. Economic viability of large-scale solar PV implementation in the Nordic power market: Case Finland. Renewable Energy Focus 2026;56:100750. https://doi.org/10.1016/J.REF.2025.100750.

ECONOMIC VALUE OF BUILDING-INTEGRATED PV PRODUCTION AT HIGH-LATITUDE LOCATIONS

Sami Jouttijärvi[1]*, Lauri Karttunen[1], Magda Szarek[1], Bergpob Viriyaroj[2], Samuli Ranta[3], Kati Miettunen[1]

[1]Department of Mechanical and Materials Engineering, University of Turku, Vesilinnantie 5, 20500 Turku, Finland

[2]Department of Architecture, Aalto University, Otakaari 24, 02150 Espoo, Finland

[3]New Energy Research Group, Turku University of Applied Sciences, Joukahaisenkatu 7, 20520 Turku, Finland

*sami.jouttijarvi@utu.fi

Introduction

Aim: Profitable BIPV production in Finland

Previous findings in Finland:

- Residential self-consumption is critical [1,2]
- Energy storages are unprofitable (currently) [3]
- Façade potential due to low solar elevation [4]

Data: Years 2019-2023, transfer fee & taxes with 2023 values

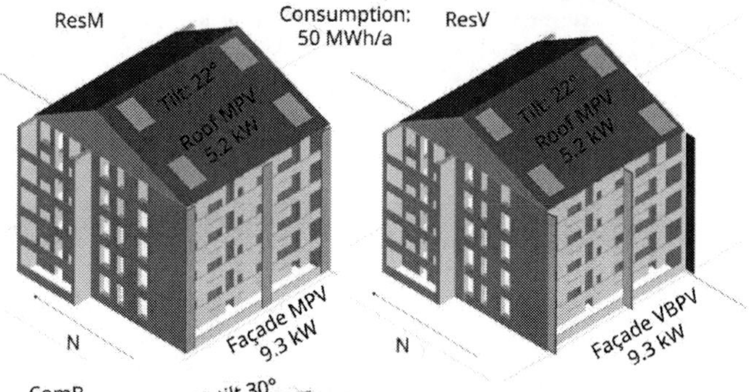

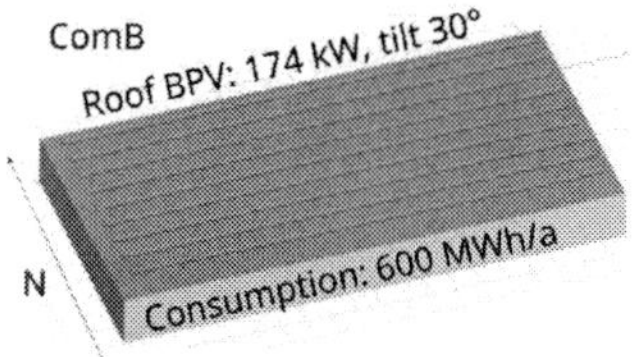

Figure 1. Schematic figures of the studied PV systems: ResM, ResV and ComB. Made with PVsyst [5], residential building based on [6].

Workflow

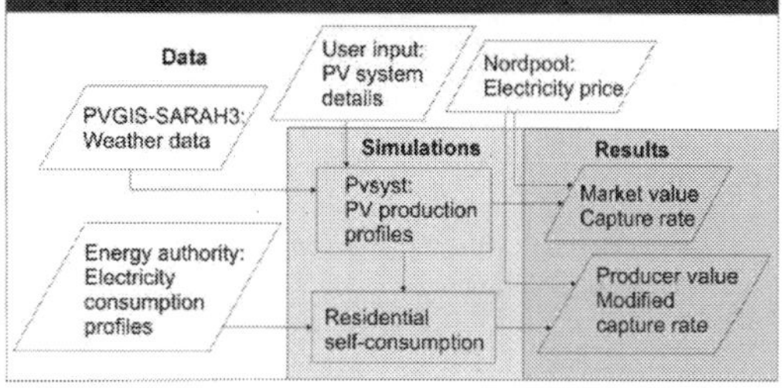

Table 1. The average annual electricity production and self-consumption rate of the studied systems in 2019-2023.

System	Production (kWh/kW)	Self-consumption (%)
ResM	919	80.3
ResV	943	86.2
ComB	1230	81.6

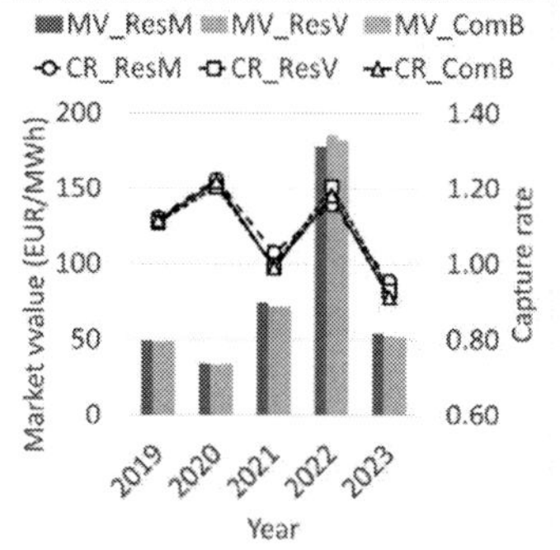

Figure 2. Market value and capture rate of the studied PV systems during 2019-2023. Until 2023, the PV production in Finland was very small.

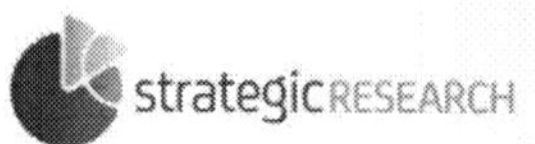

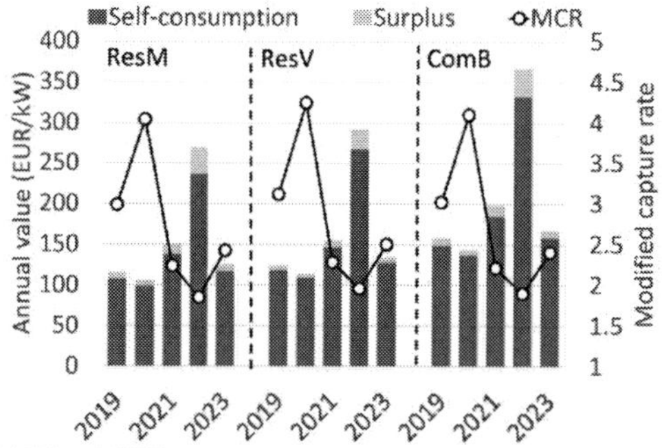

Figure 3. Annual production value and modified capture rate (inc. self-consumption) of the studied PV systems during 2019-2023. Self-consumption protects the value against market variation.

Discussion and Conclusions

PV market value dominated by electricity mean price with historical price data

Self-consumption protects against low prices (year 2020)

Energy crisis decreases the importance of self-consumption (high revenue from market)

References

[1] S. Jouttijärvi et al., Appl Energy 2024;361:122924
[2] S. Jouttijärvi et al., Conf. Proc. EU PVSEC 2024, 020547
[3] L. Karttunen et al., Conf. Proc. EU PVSEC 2024, 020507
[4] B. Viriyaroj et al., Conf. Proc. EU PVSEC 2024, 020362
[5] PVsyst-software, https://www.pvsyst.com/, read 12.9.2025
[6] City of Helsinki. Make 2.0 Puinen mallikerrostalo

Acknowledgements

The work was funded by Strategic Research Council (FI), grants 358542 & 359141, and by University of Turku and City of Salo (LK) and UTUGS (LK).

UNIVERSITY OF TURKU

strategic RESEARCH

TOWARDS SUSTAINABLE CITIES WITH INTEGRATED PHOTOVOLTAIC CERAMIC ROOF TILE

Alicia Buceta[a], Jaime Polo[a], Roberto Díaz[b], Marta Alvarez[a], Eugenia Zugasti[a] and Jaione Bengoechea[a]
[a] National Renewable Energy Center (CENER)
Avenida Ciudad de la Innovación, 7, 31621 Sarriguren (Navarra) SPAIN
Tel.: +34 948 25 28 00; info@cener.com
[b] Notio Association, Clay Technological Centre of Castilla-La Mancha (CTAC)
Calle Río Cabriel, 45007, Toledo (Castilla-La Mancha), SPAIN
Tel: +34 925 24 11 62; info@notio.es

ABSTRACT: Most of the existing PV roof tile solutions are either not based on clay substrates or consist of the adhesion of a PV module onto a ceramic tile. In this work we wanted to prove the possibility to integrate the PV module into the ceramic tile in a one-step lamination process. The first step was to assess the adhesion of the encapsulant to the clay substrate by peeling tests. Then, the encapsulant that demonstrated the best performance was selected to produce a range of samples in various configurations. These samples have first been subjected to the hail impact test and only the samples that passed this test were then tested in climatic chambers to assess their reliability. As a result, a one-step solution for flat roof tile using crystalline silicon solar cells was found, able to withstand humidity freeze based on the IEC 61215 standard for PV and its equivalent from the UNE-EN 539-2 standard for tile. Other tests, specific for photovoltaic devises, such as hail impact and damp heat were also successfully passed.
Keywords: c-Si, BIPV, clay, ceramic, roof tile

1 INTRODUCTION

The integration of photovoltaic (PV) modules into different architectural elements will play an important role towards increasing PV energy production using existing man-made surfaces and shaping sustainable cities towards energy independence. This is the main goal of Building Integrated Photovoltaics (BIPV), with rooftops offering the greatest potential, given their superior exposure to sunlight in building structures.[1–3] Furthermore, a recent study has indicated the advantages of installing photovoltaic systems on rooftops, even in circumstances where they are not optimally oriented.[4]

There are already in the market solutions to be used as PV rooftop tiles using different types of substrates and also with a wide range of colours. Nevertheless, our aim is to demonstrate the possibility to fabricate the PV tile in a single step lamination, compatible with existing fabrication technologies, without compromising neither the PV module integrity nor that of the ceramic tile.

Aesthetics are also an important point to be taken into account in BIPV. Not only the end buyer of the house, but also the architects are demanding a wider variety of colours and even conceal the solar cell to the extent that it does not look like a PV module.[5,6] These requirements could be mandatory when the building is in a historical area where aesthetic uniformity is to be maintained.

Whithin this context, this work presents the results obtained within the CECOM4PV project, a public-private collaboration project granted by the Ministry of Science and Innovation of Spain in the framework of the State Plan for Scientific and Technical Research and Innovation. The primary focus of this study is threefold: (i) obtaining a ceramic roof tile with PV integrated through a one-step lamination process, (ii) demonstrating that the resulting PV device meets both PV and roof tile standards and (iii) assessing the influence of different colour options on PV efficiency.

2 METHODOLOGY

Comercial roof tiles provided by San Javier Bricks were adapted to the size of 10 cm x 10 cm x 2 cm and 20 cm x 20 cm x 2 cm for the fabrication of the BIPV prototypes. Prior to the fabrication, peel-off tests were performed to select the best performing encapsulant when laminated on to a clay substrate.

Subsequently, the reliability of the produced prototypes has been assessed following the conditions laid down in PV module qualification standard IEC 61215-2,[7] with increased severity. More specifically, the Hail impact test, UV weathering, damp heat (DH), thermal cycling (TC) and humidity freeze (HF) tests have been performed on the modules. These Module Quality Tests (MQT) were conducted at CENER's laboratory, which is accredited to perform IEC standard tests for PV modules.

On the other hand, the reliability as roof tile has been assessed following the conditions laid down in the UNE-EN 539-2 standard.[8] Specifically, the frost resistance test standard was conducted at NOTIO's laboratory.

Additionally, given the importance of the aesthetic, different colour configurations were tested to determine the detriment caused in efficiency due to colour.

2.1 Hail impact test

The hail impact resistance test was performed with an ice ball launcher LBH-25 from ARIES. The experiment was implemented according to the IEC 61215-2 standard; 25 mm diameter ice balls were launched at a velocity of 23 m/s ± 2% (MQT 17).

2.2 Ultraviolet exposure

The UV irradiation was applied in a weathering chamber using light source lamps with a dedicated filter to match the spectral distribution stated in the qualification standard of PV modules. The temperature of the samples during UV irradiation was fixed at 60 °C and a total dose of 15 kWh/m^2 was applied as stated in IEC 61215-2 standard.

2.3 Climatic chamber

Their resistance to temperature and humidity was tested in a C-70/200 climate chamber from CTS. The damp heat test (MQT 13), 1,000 h at 85 °C and 85% relative humidity (RH); thermal cycling (MQT 11), 50 cycles from -40 °C to 85 °C and humidity freeze (MQT 12), 10 cycles from -40 °C to 85 °C with 85% RH were completed in accordance with the IEC 61215-2 standard.

2.4 Frost Resistance

The reliability of the prototype as a ceramic roof tile was tested in a Dycomental CHD-525 chamber with a thermostatic tank, air cooling unit and hydraulic circuit for circulating decalcified water. Based in the UNE-EN 539-2:2013 Clay roofing tiles for discontinuous laying - Determination of physical characteristics, the samples were exposed up to 100 cycles from -16 °C in air to 17 °C submerged in water.

3 RESULTS AND DISCUSSION

In order to achieve a suitable solution for PV ceramic roof tiles fabricated in a one-step lamination it is necessary to determine its reliability under degradation tests. Therefore, after selecting the best performing encapsulant compering their peel-off values, different configurations were tested under hail impact test. The configurations that were able to withstand it without showing any damage in the solar cell were subjected to further degradation testing. As a result, a solution was found that was able to withstand hail impact, damp heat, UV weathering, thermal cycling, humidity freeze and frost resistance tests.

3.1 Hail impact test

One of the main mechanical stresses that PV modules on rooftops need to withstand is hail impact. The test is performed in accordance with the stipulated IEC 61215-2 requirements and having the samples in a free-standing position (figure 1). The first hail impact tests were performed on 10 cm x 10 cm x 2 cm samples to facilitate the testing of a wider number of configurations.

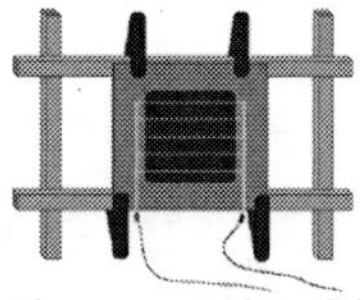

Figure 1: Schematic representation of the set up with the sample free-standing during the hail impact test.

Several configurations were subjected to hail testing and two of them, with and without glass as front sheet (FS), achieved a satisfactory result. In figure 2, the electroluminescence (EL) image of two different configurations that passed the test can be observed. After two impacts the solar cell remains intact, not even the propagation of preexisting crack was observed.

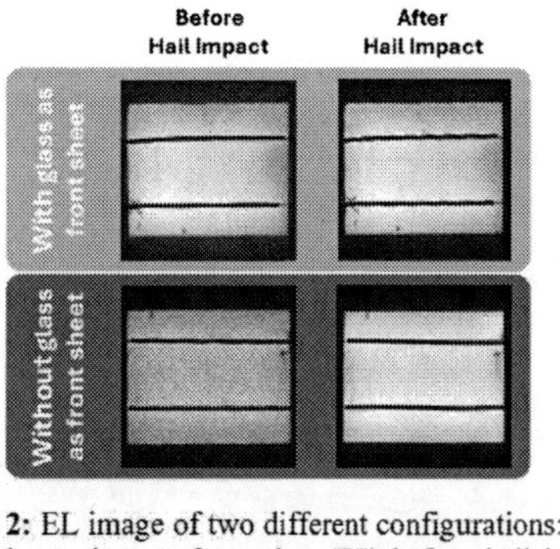

Figure 2: EL image of two different configurations: with and without glass as front sheet(FS) before hail impact (left) and after two hail impact (right).

The two configurations that withstand the hail impact will undergo the humidity freeze degradation test. As anticipated, no deterioration was detected in the clay substrate integrity.

3.2 Humidity freeze test

One of the concerns that may arise when combining materials with different coefficients of contraction and expansion is how they will behave in response to temperature changes. To this end, the humidity freeze test will allow us to evaluate this effect in the prototypes. In order to gain an initial understanding of the samples' behaviour, instead of following the sequence described in the IEC 61215 standard (UV + TC[50] + HF[10]) the prototypes were subjected directly to ten cycles of HF. As it can be observed in figure 3, while the sample with glass remains stable, the sample without glass as front sheet shows a significant loss in performance, decreasing its maximum power by 29.6%. This degradation can also be observed in the electroluminescence measurements, where the deterioration of the solar cell is evident when no glass is used as front sheet.

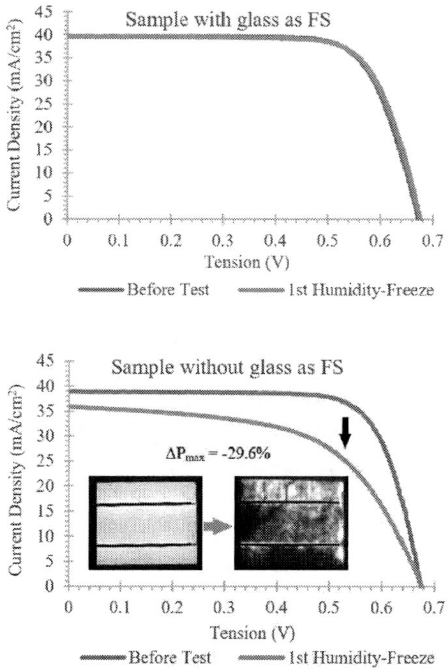

Figure 3: JV curve of the prototype with glass as front sheet (upper graph) and the one without glass as front sheet (lower graph) before and after 10 cycles of HF, including EL images for the sample without glass.

Therefore, in order to test further the sample with glass as front sheet, the sample was additionally subjected to the UV + TC(50) + HF(10) sequence. figure 4 presents the JV curve and EL of the sample after the sequence, and as it can be observed no significant degradation is observed.

10.4229/EUPVSEC2025/4BV.4.10

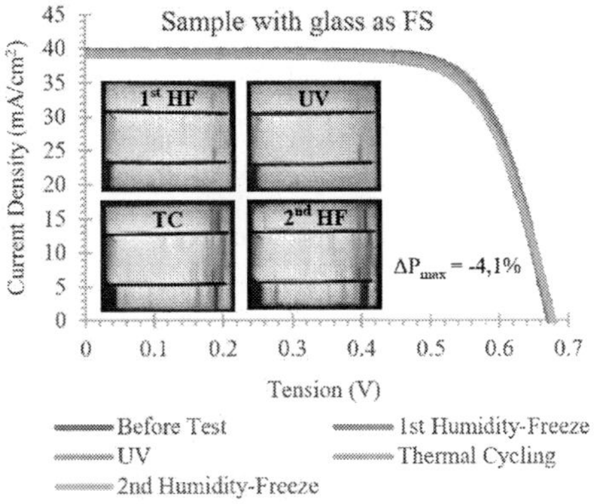

Figure 4: JV curve of the prototype with glass as front sheet before and after 10 cycles of HF, UV, 50 cycles of TC and 10 cycles of HF; including EL images.

The total loss in maximum power, after the whole sequence when glass is used as front sheet, is of 4.1%, therefore it would fall within the acceptable limits established by the standard. Furthermore, after all these tests, no deterioration was detected in the clay substrate integrity.

3.3 Frost resistance test

It is important that, as a prototype photovoltaic roof tile, it is also capable to withstands tests in accordance with the ceramic roof tile regulations. In this case, the frost resistance test from UNE-EN 539-2 standard was performed, which will also allow to compare its behaviour with the results obtained in the humidity freeze test. The winning configuration with glass as front sheet has been tested up to 100 cycles of frost resistance. In the course of the experiment, the substrates demonstrated no signs of physical deterioration after undergoing 50 cycles. However, one of the three samples subjected to testing exhibited minor damage to the clay substrate after 100 cycles. Consequently, it can be considered that the prototype meets the requirements of the standard to be installed in locations requiring frost resistance of 50 cycles or less. In figure 5, the photographs of the sample that showed some damage is presented, and as it can be observed, not only the clay substrate was affected, but also the glass front sheet exhibited a distinct crack.

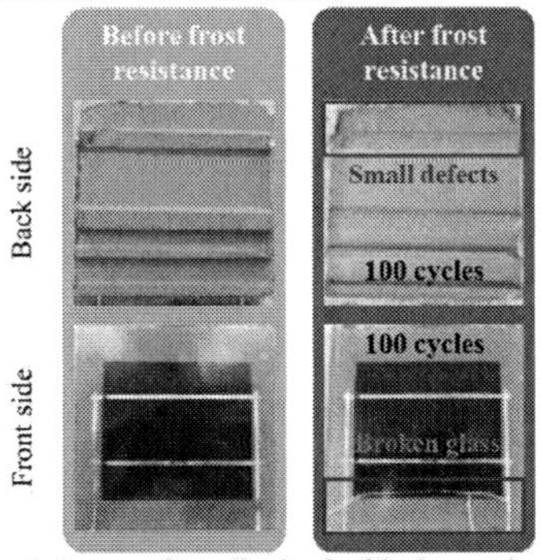

Figure 5: Images from the back side (upper images) and front side (lower images) of the prototype with glass as front sheet before and after the frost resistance test.

On the other hand, the photovoltaic performance remains practically unaltered in all the tested samples. In figure 6 the average JV curve before and after the test are presented, as for the EL images of one of the samples. No significant degradation occurs except for a small drop in the short-circuit current (I_{SC}) value which results in the loss of 2.4% of the maximum power.

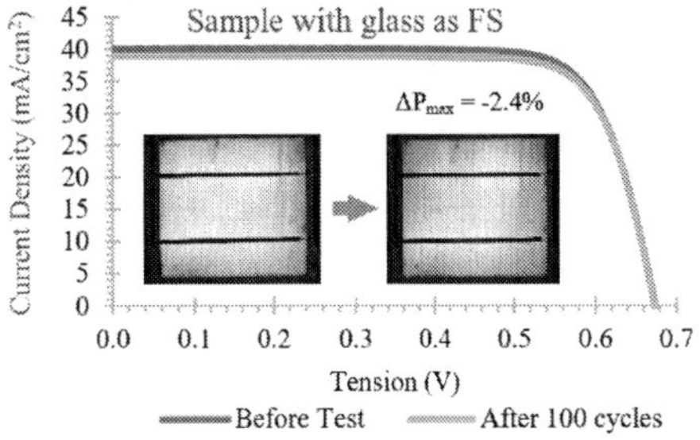

Figure 6: JV curve of the prototype with glass as front sheet before and after 100 cycles of frost resistance; including EL images.

Therefore, the prototype configuration with glass as front sheet demonstrates adequate resilience to this test up to 50 cycles, exhibiting no significant damage or defects from the photovoltaic and ceramic roof tile's perspective.

3.4 Damp heat test

In order to assess the effect of elevated temperatures and humidity on the integrity of the prototype with glass as front sheet, the damp heat test was performed. In figure 7, the JV curve and the EL images are presented before and after the test. As it can be observed, there is a slight drop in the I_{SC} value that result in the drop of the maximum power by 3.8%. Although, on the EL images no degradation is observed, but a clear crack in the glass appears after 1,000 h of DH, which can be related to the I_{SC} drop (figure 7).

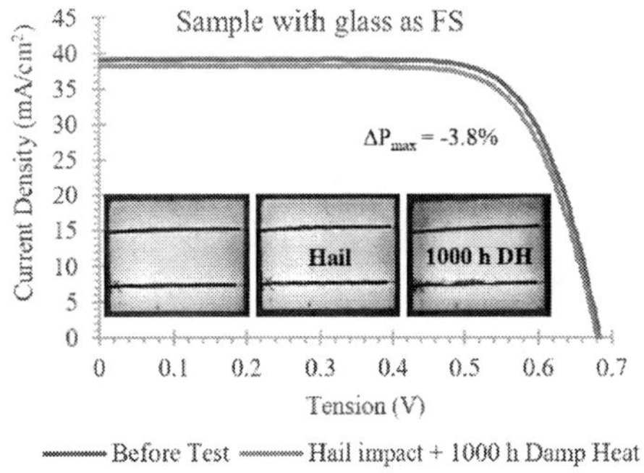

Figure 7: JV curve of the prototype with glass as front sheet before and after hail impact and 1000 h of DH; including EL images.

In order to avoid the glass cracking, several strategies were studied, focused on minimizing the internal glass tensions. Once a suitable solution was found, to ascertain the extent of the prototype's durability, the sample was sized up to 20 cm x 20 cm x 2 cm and subjected to an additional hail impact and damp heat test. Additionally, the edges of the sample were covered with silicone to minimize water penetration. The complete sequence of

10.4229/EUPVSEC2025/4BV.4.10

tests that was followed is illustrated in figure 8: the sample was exposed to a total of 2,000 h of damp heat and two hail impact tests.

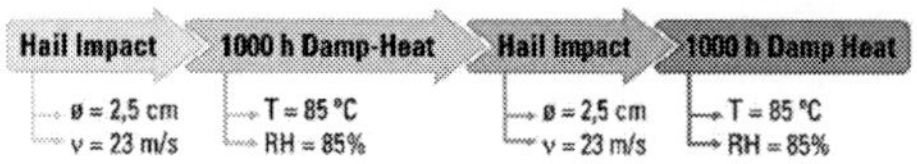

Figure 8: Schematic representation of the followed sequence of hail impact and damp heat testing.

As it can be observed in figure 9, the prototype withstands the whole sequence with insignificant change in its properties. Moreover, the final maximum power increases a 3.6%.

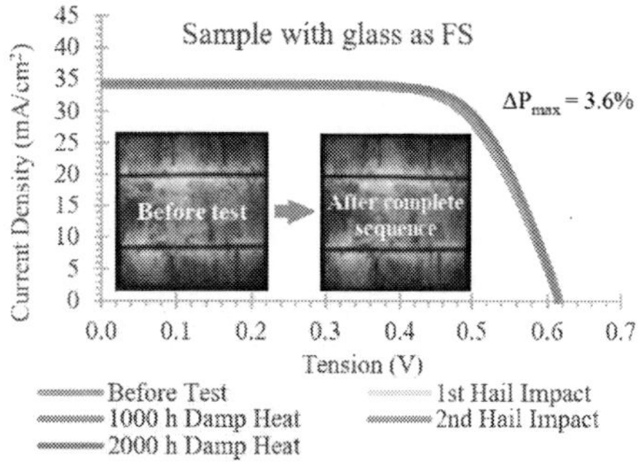

Figure 9: JV curves and EL images of the sample with glass as front sheet after each hail impact and damp heat.

Therefore, it can be concluded that the prototype with glass as front sheet safely meets the requirements established by the photovoltaic standard for damp heat.

3.5 Coloured configurations

As the aesthetics play an important role in the implementation of solar roof tiles, different colour options were fabricated to determine the effects in the photovoltaic performance. In this project, four colour options were studied: transparent, black appearance, terracotta and light grey (Figure 10).

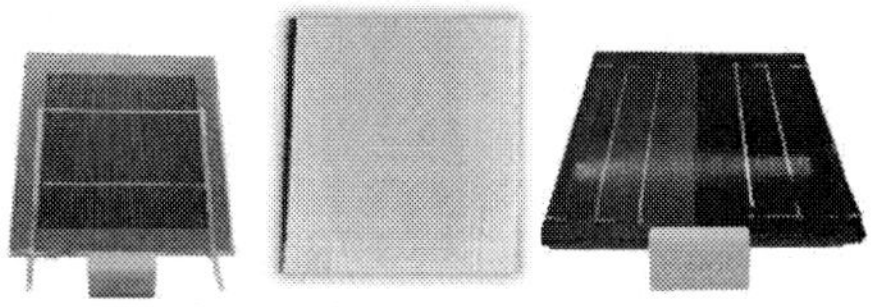

Figure 10: Photographs of the different colour samples: transparent (left), light grey (centre) and terracotta and black appearance (right).

In figure 11 it is clearly observed how an increase in colour coverage is associated with a subsequent decrease in I_{SC} as it would be expected. In the terracotta and light grey samples, the short-circuit current drops around a 30% compared to the transparent and black appearance options.

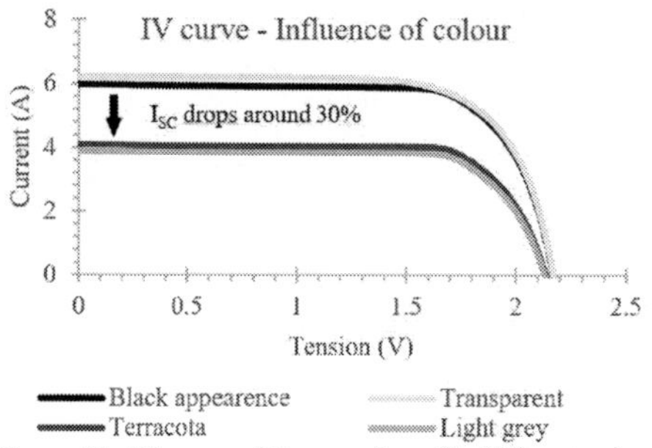

Figure 11: IV curve of the samples with different colour appearance.

It was demonstrated the compatibility of colouring the samples although a detriment in the short-circuit current is expected when the coverage of the solar cell increases.

4 CONCLUSIONS

The results showed that it was possible to produce a one-step lamination photovoltaic ceramic roof tile able to withstand hail impact test, damp heat, UV weathering, thermal cycling and humidity freeze tests based on the IEC 61215 photovoltaic standard. After the sequence HF(10) + UV + TC(50) + HF(10) the drop of the maximum power was of 4.1%. When the prototype was exposed to hail impact + DH(1,000 h) + hail impact + DH (1,000 h) the maximum power unexpectedly increased 3,6% after the whole sequence.

On the other hand, the prototype has demonstrated to be fitted for locations where less than 50 cycles of frost resistance are required as stated in the UNE-EN 539 clay roof tile standard. The prototypes resisted with no signs of damage up to 50 cycles, nevertheless, one of the three tested samples showed small imperfections when the test was carried out up to 100 cycles. Nevertheless, the photovoltaic performance of the samples after the 100 cycles test, a drop in the maximum power was observed of only 2.4% in average.

The application of different colour options to the samples was studied, showing its compatibility with the process and the expected drop in the short-circuit current when the colour coverage of the solar cell is higher. In our study, the terracotta and light grey options showed a drop in I_{SC} of around 30%.

5 ACKNOWLEDGEMENTS

These results are part of project CECOM4PV.[9] It is a public-private collaboration project granted by the Ministry of Science and Innovation of Spain in the framework of the State Plan for Scientific and Technical Research and Innovation. The primary focus of this study is to ascertain the following: obtaining a ceramic roof tile with PV integrated able to withstand both PV and roof tile standards and testing different colour options and their effect in PV efficiency.

6 BIBLIOGRAPHY

1. AER. *State of the Energy Market 2015.*; 2015.
2. Collins SP, Storrow A, Liu D, et al. EU Solar Energy

Strategy. Published online 2022:167-186.
3. Ürge-Vorsatz D, Chatterjee S, Cabeza LF, Molnár G. Global and regional estimation and evaluation of suitable roof area for solar and green roof applications. *Dev Built Environ*. 2025;21(December 2024). doi:10.1016/j.dibe.2025.100607
4. García-Suso F, Molina-García A, Fernández-Guillamón A, Bueso MC. Alternative non-optimal orientations in highly PV self-consumption integration: Exploring Spanish prosumers as a case study. *Renew Energy*. 2026;256(July 2025). doi:10.1016/j.renene.2025.123987
5. Kuhn TE, Erban C, Heinrich M, Eisenlohr J, Ensslen F, Neuhaus DH. Review of technological design options for building integrated photovoltaics (BIPV). *Energy Build*. 2021;231:110381. doi:10.1016/j.enbuild.2020.110381
6. Fraunhofer Instotute for Solar Energy Systems (ISE). Colored modules for building-integrated photovoltaics. *PV Mag*. Published online 2025. https://www.pv-magazine.com/2025/02/24/colored-modules-for-building-integrated-photovoltaics/
7. IEC. *IEC 61215-2 Terrestrial Photovoltaic (PV) Modules – Design Qualification and Type Approval – Part 2: Test Procedures*. 2nd ed.; 2021.
8. AENOR. *UNE-EN 539-2: Tejas de Arcilla Cocida Para Colocación Discontinua. Determinación de Las Caracteristicas Físicas. Parte 2: Ensayo de Resistencia a La Helada.*; 2013.
9. CENER. CECOM4PV. Published 2022. https://www.cener.com/en/areas/photovoltaic-solar-energy-department/outstanding-projects/cecom4pv-photovoltaic-devices-based-on-ceramic-materials-and-composites/

EVALUATING PVT MODULE PERFORMANCE ACROSS DIVERSE EUROPEAN CLIMATES: A SIMULATION STUDY

A.Saretti[1], G. Vero[1], A.Chouder[2], S. Vergura[1] and S. Silvestre[3]
1- Department of Electrotechnics, Politecnico di Bari, St. E. Orabona, 4, 70125 Bari, Italy.
2- Laboratory of Electrical Engineering (LGE), Electrical Engineering department, University of M'sila, PO Box 166 Ichebilia, 28000 M'sila, Algeria.
3- MNT-Solar - Grup de Micro i Nano Tecnologies per Energia SolarElectronic Engineering Department, Universitat Politècnica de Catalunya BarcelonaTech. Jordi Girona 1-3, 08034, Barcelona, Spain.

ABSTRACT: This study explores the potential for increased energy production by using four distinct cooling techniques applied to photovoltaic (PV) modules in photovoltaic-thermal (PVT) systems for buildings. The simulations, conducted using PVSOL and MATLAB, evaluated the performance of a 160Wp c-Si PV module integrated with four different cooling systems at each location. To assess performance under varying climate conditions, three European cities were selected for the analysis of one week per season: Barcelona, Berlin, and Paris, each representing distinct latitudes and climatic conditions. Simulation results include the energy generated by the PV module, yields, and energy surplus obtained at each location for the different cooling systems under study.

Keywords: PVT, PV and Buildings, simulation.

1 INTRODUCTION

This study explores the potential for increased energy production using four distinct cooling techniques applied to photovoltaic (PV) modules in photovoltaic-thermal (PVT) systems for buildings.

To assess performance under varying climate conditions, three European cities were selected for analysis. The simulations, conducted using PVSOL and MATLAB, evaluated the performance of a 160Wp c-Si PV module integrated with four different cooling systems at each location.

2 METHODS

The study examines four cooling systems for PV modules described below in Table I.

Table I: Cooling systems included in the study

Cooling System	Refrigerator
Water-cooled hybrid photovoltaic-thermal (PV/T) panels Standing waves ratio [1]	1
heat pipe photovoltaic-thermal (PV/T) hybrid system [2]	2
hybrid PV/T water collectors [3]	3
Passive cooling methodologies [4]	4

The simulation is based on the temperature reduction achieved by each cooling system, with temperature profiles derived from PVSOL simulations for each location and adjusted accordingly.

The simulations were performed in Matlab environment, with inputs including irradiance profiles from PVsol, the modified temperature profiles, and the parameters of the PV module model.

The PV module model was validated by comparing simulation results from Matlab with those from PVsol. The analysis spans one week per season in three European cities: Barcelona, Berlin, and Paris, each representing distinct latitudes and climatic conditions. Simulation results include the energy generated by the PV module, yields, and energy surplus at each location for the different cooling systems under study.

3 RESULTS

The top section of the following figures illustrates the strong alignment between the results generated by the two software applications for the output power of the PV module.

The middle section shows the energy output derived from MATLAB, comparing scenarios with and without the integration of the four cooling systems.

Finally, the bottom section highlights the energy surplus achieved by each cooling system.

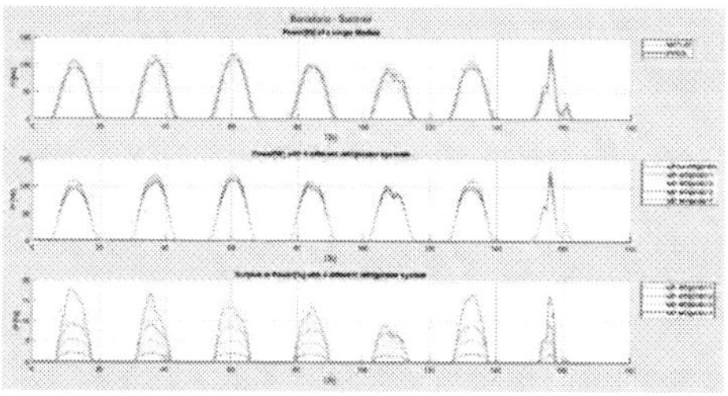

Figure 1: Results obtained in summer for Barcelona.

An analysis of weekly trends in Barcelona reveals that during peak temperature periods, cooling systems produce an energy surplus of 15% to 20%. In contrast, Berlin experiences a surplus ranging from 5% to 15%, depending on seasonal conditions. However, during the winter months, the use of cooling systems is deemed unnecessary in Berlin and Paris.

These systems demonstrate greater efficiency in warmer climates and at lower latitudes.

10.4229/EUPVSEC2025/4BV.4.14

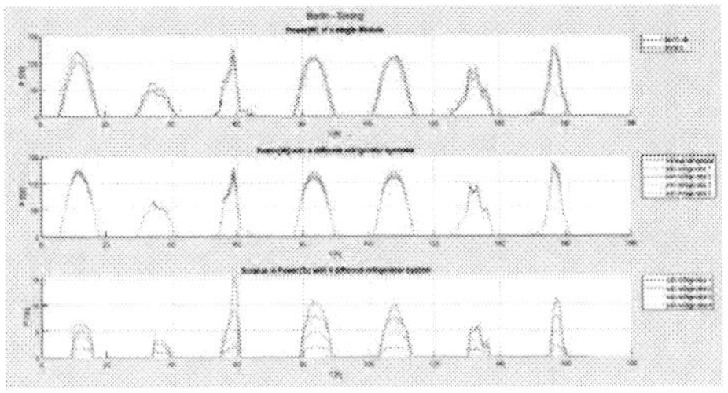

Figure 2: Results obtained in spring for Berlin.

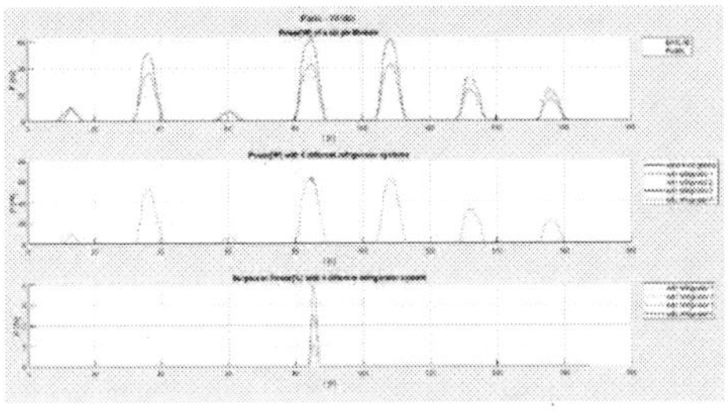

Figure 3: Results obtained in winter for Paris.

The following tables present key results obtained from the study over a one-week period in each yearly season for location analyzed: Total Irradiance, generated energy, Yield and energy surplus for the different systems under study.

Table II: Results obtained for Barcelona.

Season	City	Barcelona				
		Without refrigeration	cooling system 1	cooling system 2	cooling system 3	cooling system 4
Winter	Irradiance [kWh/m^2]	27,57				
	Total Energy [Wh]	3823,36	3985,46	4002,72	3932,40	3869,30
	Y [Wh/Wp]	23,90	24,91	25,02	24,58	24,18
	Energy Surplus[%]	-	4,24	4,69	2,85	1,20
Spring	Irradiance [kWh/m^2]	38,14				
	Total Energy [Wh]	4938,58	5273,64	5209,01	5102,62	5007,57
	Y [Wh/Wp]	30,87	32,96	32,56	31,89	31,30
	Energy Surplus[%]	-	6,78	5,48	3,32	1,40
Summer	Irradiance [kWh/m^2]	46,42				
	Total Energy [Wh]	5613,83	6176,75	5987,59	5839,81	5708,80
	Y [Wh/Wp]	35,09	38,60	37,42	36,50	35,68
	Energy Surplus[%]	-	10,03	6,66	4,03	1,69
Fall	Irradiance [kWh/m^2]	35,14				
	Total Energy [Wh]	4529,44	4867,51	4798,99	4692,93	4598,19
	Y [Wh/Wp]	28,31	30,42	29,99	29,33	28,74
	Energy Surplus[%]	-	7,46	5,95	3,61	1,52

Table III: Results obtained for Berlin.

Season	City	Berlin				
		Without refrigeration	cooling system 1	cooling system 2	cooling system 3	cooling system 4
Winter	Irradiance [kWh/m^2]	5,34				
	Total Energy [Wh]	681,72	681,72	681,72	681,72	681,72
	Y [Wh/Wp]	4,26	4,26	4,26	4,26	4,26
	Energy Surplus[%]	-	0,00	0,00	0,00	0,00
Spring	Irradiance [kWh/m^2]	36,24				
	Total Energy [Wh]	4810,13	5065,23	5040,99	4949,96	4868,86
	Y [Wh/Wp]	30,06	31,66	31,51	30,94	30,43
	Energy Surplus[%]	-	5,30	4,80	2,91	1,22
Summer	Irradiance [kWh/m^2]	40,66				
	Total Energy [Wh]	5267,24	5628,51	5553,70	5441,33	5340,57
	Y [Wh/Wp]	32,92	35,18	34,71	34,01	33,38
	Energy Surplus[%]	-	6,86	5,44	3,31	1,39
Fall	Irradiance [kWh/m^2]	18,59				
	Total Energy [Wh]	2612,56	2689,68	2698,07	2664,92	2634,75
	Y [Wh/Wp]	16,33	16,81	16,86	16,66	16,47
	Energy Surplus[%]	-	2,95	3,27	2,00	0,85

As anticipated, each cooling system contributed additional energy across all seasons and cities, except for Berlin during winter; in that specific season, the temperatures are so low that enhancing energy output with a cooling system is unnecessary.

Examining the energy output across seasons in the three cities, the best cooling systems are identified as the first and the second ones, as they result in a more significant reduction in temperature.

On the other hand, the optimal performance was achieved in the city characterized by the highest temperature and irradiance, namely Barcelona, while the least favorable performance was observed in the city exhibiting the lowest values, specifically Berlin.

Table IV: Results obtained for Paris.

Season	City	Paris				
		Without refrigeration	cooling system 1	cooling system 2	cooling system 3	cooling system 4
Winter	Irradiance [kWh/m^2]	9,25				
	Total Energy [Wh]	1265,44	1268,18	1269,63	1268,03	1266,54
	Y [Wh/Wp]	7,91	7,93	7,94	7,93	7,92
	Energy Surplus[%]	-	0,22	0,33	0,20	0,09
Spring	Irradiance [kWh/m^2]	36,43				
	Total Energy [Wh]	4665,42	4983,94	4903,02	4809,37	4725,89
	Y [Wh/Wp]	29,16	31,15	30,64	30,06	29,54
	Energy Surplus[%]	-	6,83	5,09	3,08	1,30
Summer	Irradiance [kWh/m^2]	30,04				
	Total Energy [Wh]	4691,69	5015,53	4934,08	4839,19	4753,89
	Y [Wh/Wp]	29,32	31,35	30,84	30,24	29,71
	Energy Surplus[%]	-	6,90	5,17	3,14	1,33
Fall	Irradiance [kWh/m^2]	18,13				
	Total Energy [Wh]	2255,29	2364,73	2361,24	2319,85	2282,55
	Y [Wh/Wp]	14,10	14,78	14,76	14,50	14,27
	Energy Surplus[%]	-	4,85	4,70	2,86	1,21

Upon analysis across different seasons, it appears that the second system demonstrates greater efficacy during periods of lower temperatures, whereas the first system performs more effectively under higher temperature conditions. This phenomenon can be elucidated by examining the temperature variation effects.

The first system experiences a percentage-based drop, resulting in a substantial decline in performance at elevated temperatures and a minimal decrease at lower temperatures. Conversely, the second system exhibits a delta-based decline, rendering the impact of temperature variation more significant at lower temperatures compared to higher ones.

4 CONCLUSIONS

In conclusion, cooling systems enhance the PV module's capability to generate additional electrical energy while concurrently producing heat. This thermal energy can be used in multiple applications as mentioned in preceding sections.

The implementation of these systems is particularly advantageous in climatic and irradiance scenarios where the system's costs are more effectively amortized, particularly in warm climates and conditions of high irradiance.

5 ACKNOWLEDGMENTS This work is supported by the Agencia Estatal De Investigacion of Spain.
Funding code: PID2022-140226OB-C32

References

[1] A. A. Naqvi, A. Ahmed, T. Bin Nadeem, L. A. Khan, and I. U. Ahad, Case Studies in Thermal Engineering, 47 (2023) 103114.

[2] C. Rossi, L. A. Tagliafico, F. Scarpa, and V. Bianco, Energy Convers Manag. 76 (2013) 634.

[3] K. P. Amber, W. Akram, M. A. Bashir, M. S. Khan, and A. Kousar, J Therm Anal Calorim. 143 (2021) 2355.

[4] S. Y. Wu, Q. L. Zhang, L. Xiao, and F. H. Guo, "A heat pipe photovoltaic/thermal (PV/T) hybrid system and its performance evaluation," Energy Build. 43 (2011) 3558.

EXTENDED KPIS FOR DECISIONS-MAKERS IN THE DEVELOPMENT OF BIPV SOLUTIONS

Simon BODDAERT[1,*], Olaia AURREKOETXEA[2], Julius JACOB[3], Simone GERMANI[4], Ignas CEUPPENS[5], Hervé LAMBLOT[6], Tatjana VAVILKIN[7], Maria JIMENEZ[8], Xavier GAUVIN[9], Tonis EELMA[10]

[1]CSTB, [2]TECNALIA, [3]METABUILD, [4]CEI, [5]BUILD'UP, [6]SUNSTYLE, [7]SOLTECH, [8]ONYX SOLAR, [9]BOUYGUES CONSTRUCTION, [10]IBS

* E-mail to: simon.boddaert@cstb.fr; phone: +33 (0)680 58 1001

ABSTRACT: Innovative components commonly use key performance indicators to assess their relevance. For BIPV solutions, it's the energy indicator that is commonly favored. In the European INCREASE project, we wanted to extend these indicators to provide strong decision-making keys for determining which BIPV solutions are the most appropriate for all stakeholders. Based on the work initially carried out as part of T15 of the IEA's PVPS program, we have identified additional parameters to take account of sustainability and reliability issues. To meet the expectations of the construction industry and the multifunctionality of BIPV components, we have also defined two new performance indicators to provide extended decision-making tools for all players in the value chain. These elements not linked with energy production focus on building capabilities and end-users' feelings.
Keywords: BIPV, KPI, Durability, Constructability, Comfort.

1 OBJECTIVES

The work carried out aims to define a set of KPIs that can be used as a reference decision-making tool to objectivize the use of BIPV solutions, under the best possible conditions of implementation and relevance use. The KPIs dealing with ENERGY, ECONOMY, ENVIRONMENT and AESTHETICS, initially defined in IEA T15 works REFERENCES

[1], have been revised and extended to meet the challenges of the project. Two new KPIs were created. The COMFORT criterion was introduced, to ensure that end-users benefit from a level of comfort at least equal to traditional solutions. The BUILDABILITY criterion has been emphasized to ensure the applicability of BIPV solutions and to meet quality and insurability requirements for operators and manufacturers. These KPIs will be validated and consolidated on the CSTB and TECNALIA pre-demo sites (under controlled conditions), before being deployed on the nine project demonstration sites that will host the final solutions. They will be used to define an overall assessment of each site and the impact of the chosen BIPV solution. The parameters will be fed by numerical calculations, but also by data measured on sites, to determine possible deviations before/after implementation of the BIPV solutions. Once the models have been calibrated, the relevance and accuracy of the KPIs will be fine-tuned, enabling them to be applied more effectively to the BIPV market.

KPIs will be used again during the operational phase to assess the impact of aging on KPI deviations and define acceptability thresholds. Graphical display provides easy and explicit reading for decision-makers with common allowing comparative solution/solution analyses to determine the optimal solution while considering all local constraints.

2 AIM AND APPROACH

The need to objectively evaluate technical solutions becomes preponderant to ensure relevant choices to meet the challenges of construction and energy. If solutions are identified, they are mainly dedicated to a single application and not duplicates. Faced with the proliferation of BIPV solutions, indicators must adapt and propose an objective method allowing to accommodate all innovations, as well as solutions for infrastructures. The four initial performance indicators are increased within the project framework allowing an evaluation of the technical performance of the solution. ENERGY, ECONOMY, ENVIRONMENT and AESTHETICS KPIs are derived from the work of IEA PVPS T15 [2] and implemented for the needs of the project. A similar graphic representation will be used.

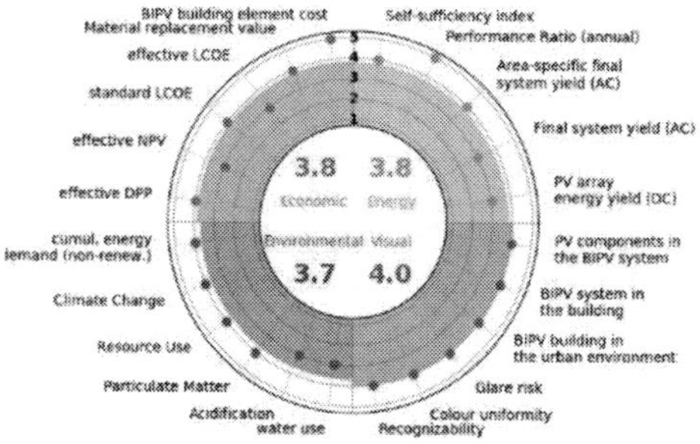

Figure 1: Example of KPIs results display taking into account BIPV solution and surrounding implementation conditions.

2.1 Base calculation approach

Definition of KPI's try to fit with project expectations to promote BIPV solutions through several indicators, addressing different markets or customers. To be objective enough, KPIs are calculated based on a representative set of parameters which are directly tied, somehow, to the considered indicator. So, each KPI value comes from the calculation of the arithmetic value of the parameters of its field of application. Each parameter is evaluated over a range of values defined by a rating scale (from 0 to 5). In this way, an isobarycentre value can be determined for each parameter independently, considering only the criteria to be evaluated. Calculating the average value of all the KPIs will enable us to determine an average value for the BIPV solution evaluated, which will then enable us to rank each solution according to all the indicators.

10.4229/EUPVSEC2025/4BV.4.15

KPIs have been developed to be applied to new-builds as well as to renovation projects, so that we can determine which solutions will be the most relevant and help decision-makers.

2.2 Final calculation and assumption

The present work is an extension of the multi-dimensional evaluation tool developed under the framework of the IEA PVPS T15. This tool fits perfectly with the expectation of BIPV performance assessment solution to define the best solution to promote or that fits with building needs. An additional work has been done in BIPVBOOST EU project with the feedback of BIPV market and stakeholder analysis [3]. The approach of the tool is intended to be objective and therefore does not lead to favouring one KPI among all.

Indeed, every KPI is calculated with the same calculation methodology, a mean value of all parameters embedded in the KPI. Every KPI is calculated using the arithmetic average with its own parameters. The value weight of each parameter is currently the same for all parameters. although it may be possible to change the weight of each parameter later, and according to project of solution expectations.

Each assigned value's parameter is provided from a range of value described by calculation or provided by experts from corresponding domain. Each range is divided in 5 subranges where each corresponds to a parameter value. The smallest value of subrange corresponds to the smallest value of the parameter and is therefore the worst notation; 1. On the other hand, the highest subrange value corresponds to the best rating; 5, expressing that the parameter has reached its best score. The final KPI value is the arithmetic mean value calculated with all parameters' values. This calculated value is the corresponding score of the respective KPI, score value is between 1 and 5.

3 CREATION OF NEW KPIs

The new KPIs introduced in the INCREASE project [4], use a scale (Metric or unit) that must be defined and the associated score range validated. This Deliverable presents the quantitative rating basis, from former investigation and including the last two KPIs developed in the framework of the project with all partners involved in. Two new parameters raised from this work carried out in workshops with various stakeholders from different fields and using co-creation process to harvest suggestions and define needs. COMFORT and BUILDABILITY, are the fruit of this work, introducing two new indicators in addition of well-known indicators.

The Figure 2 presents complete indicators and parameters used to calculate the final score of every BIPV solution. Using the same display, it allows to have a quick review of contribution of each KPI.

4 KPIs DEFINITION AND RANGE

To handle correctly this tool, it's required to have the definition of every parameter and to know corresponding range to reach appropriate score. Hereafter explanation of the six indicators and parameters used. First four are well known and already validated, the two last will be validated during on site implementation during INCREASE project.

To figure out best use as possible of this tool, a parameter reduction has been conducted to reduce with only four parameter per indicator. This assumption will be validated during the validation phase on the field, with operating systems and with stakeholders.

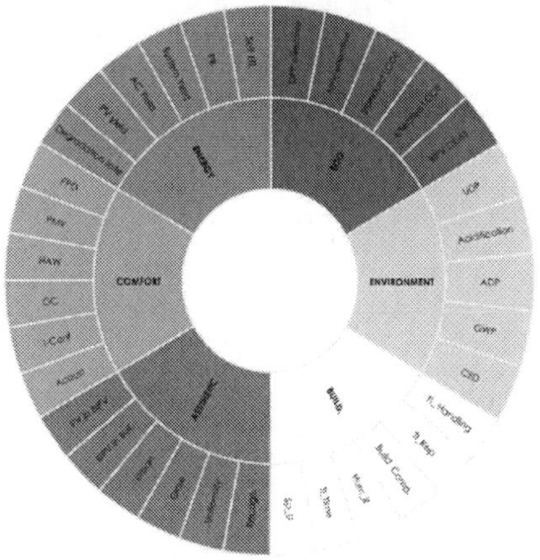

Figure 2: Final KPIs display with innovative BIPV indicators and parameters to fit with builders and end-users needs.

4.1 KPI ENERGY: Definition and parameters

Energy key performance indicator aims to manage parameters dealing mainly with energetic values or metrics allowing to monitor or express PI. This PI refers to the electrical performance of energy systems as described in IEC reference standard[5]. The considered parameters are:

- The final system AC yield (Yf)
- The area-specific AC final system yield
- The annual performance ratio (PR)
- The self-sufficiency index (SSI)

Yf is the net AC electricity output of the entire BIPV system (kWh) per unit of rated installed power (kWc) including the conversion efficiency. The area-specific AC final system yield implicitly includes the BIPV module efficiency, which is intrinsically dependent on the PV technology, BIPV design, and efficiency of all electrical parts. The performance ratio PR is defined as the ratio of the system's final yield Yf (kWh/kW) to its reference yield Yr (h) and represents the overall effect of losses on the BIPV. The self-sufficiency index (SSI) describes the percentage of electricity consumed by the building that is generated by the BIPV system. Corresponding ranges and notations are described hereafter

Table 1: Energy Performance indicator, references and parameter values.

Energy-relevant Pis	Ref.	Unit	min. value	max. value
PV array energy yield (DC)	Ya	kWh/kWp	0	1500
Area-specific AC final system yield	AC	kWh/m^2	0	300
Performance Ratio (annual)	PR	%	0	100
Self-sufficiency index	SSI	%	0	100

Table 2: Energy Performance indicator ratings

10.4229/EUPVSEC2025/4BV.4.15

rating 1	rating 2	rating 3	rating 4	rating 5
<550	550 - 825	825 - 1100	1100 - 1375	> 1375
<100	100 - 150	150 - 200	200 - 250	> 250
< 50	50-60	60-70	70-80	>80
<5	5-20.	20-50	50-80	>80

4.2 KPI ECONOMY: Definition and parameters

The performance indicators chosen for this evaluation are based on the approach described in [6]. The considered parameters for economy performance indicator are:

- The BIPV building element costs (BIPV_Cost)
- The material replacement value (MRV)
- The standard LCOE (LCOE)
- The net present value (NPV)

The BIPV_Cost is the BIPV building element costs including all stage from conception to installation, defined in terms of cost per square meter. The LCOE is defined as the ratio of the total lifecycle cost over the total lifetime output electricity, with the unit as €/kWh and will be compared to grid prices. The MRV is the cost of equivalent building materials that are replaced by the BIPV modules, and the net present value (NPV) is defined as the net value of life cycle costs and life cycle income.

All these four parameters are used to calculate the mean value of ECONOMY KPI according to the calculation methodology explained above.

Table 3: Economic Performance indicator, references and parameter values.

Economic Pis	Ref.	Unit	min. value	max. value
BIPV system costs	BIPV_Cos	€/m²	130	1550
Material replacement value	MRV	€/m²	0	460
Eff. LCOE	LCOE	€/kWh	(-0,5)	0,65
Eff. eNPV	NVP	€/m²	(-9700)	13700

Table 4: Economic Performance indicator ratings

rating 1	rating 2	rating 3	rating 4	rating 5
> 1400	1400 -1100	1100 - 700	700 - 300	< 300
< (-1000)	(-1000)- (-600)	(-600)- 0	0 - 200	> 200
> 0.4	0,4 - 0,24	0,24 - 0	0 - (-0,3)	< (-0.3)
< (-5000)	(-5000) - 0	0 - 5000	5000 - 10000	> 10000

4.3 KPI ENVIRONMENT: Definition and parameters

The environmental PIs include metrics for consumption of non-renewable primary energy (mineral and metal resources, as well as water consumption, greenhouse gas emissions), particulate matter emissions and emissions contribution to acidification. The four PIs are calculated with data partially given PV datasheets but must be filled with all surrounding components used in the BIPV final solution. The first data are provided with the environmental product declaration of modules (if available) and the standard date required to perform a complete LCA analysis, such as the bill of materials and country of manufacturing of the module and components, the size and number of the elements, the power and the PV technology applied. Once again, the work carried out by IEA PVPS is used as a working base. The Report IEA-PVPS T12-19:2020 "Life Cycle Inventories and Life Cycle Assessments of Photovoltaic Systems" [7], gives the description of the indicators the PIs name and the references data for the rating. The considered parameters for environment performance indicator are:

- The Global Warming Potential (GWP)
- The Abiotic resource depletion (ADP) use
- The impact on human health (PM/particulate matter)
- The water consumption, User Dep. Pot.(UDP)

Note that these variables are evaluated over the entire LCA of the BIPV system according to the calculation methodology described in [7].

The environmental impacts are quantified per kWh electricity generated by the BIPV system assessed. All the elements comply with the weather protection function (façade/roof/infrastructure) are assigned to the life cycle assessment (LCA) of the building and thus excluded when evaluating the environmental impacts of electricity generation.

Table 5: Environment Performance indicator, references and parameter values.

Environmental Pis	Ref.	Unit	min. value	max. value
CED non renewable	CED	MJ oil eq. / kWh	0,22	1,25
Climate Change GHG	GWP	g CO2 eq. / kWh	15	88
Resource Use, Minerals+Metals	ADP	mg Sb eq. / kWh	1,06	6,53
Particulate Matter	PM	10-9 disease incidence/kWh	0,55	4,29

Table 6: Environment Performance indicator ratings

rating 1	rating 2	rating 3	rating 4	rating 5
> 1,25	1,25 -0,91	0,91 - 0,56	0,56 - 0,22	< 0,22
> 88	88 - 63,7	63,7 - 39,3	39,9 - 15	< 15
> 6,53	6,53 - 4,71	4,71 - 2,88	2,88 - 1,06	< 1,06
> 4,29	4,29 - 3,04	3,04 - 1,80	1.80 - 0,55	< 0,55

4.4 KPI AESTHETICAL: Definition and parameters

KPI aesthetic try to handle all the visual parameters that could characterize a BIPV project. The aesthetic PIs include different aspects related to the visual rendering of the BIPV system, including the recognizability as a PV system and the colour uniformity in the surrounding building elements. These visual or aesthetical indicators will play a significant role for historical sites or landscape protection zones which must comply with restrictive visual appearance. Coloured or textured modules are a commonly used solution to meet the aesthetical requirements. The work carried out by Babin et Al.[8] focused on the glare risk (GLARE) in close proximity with a particular attention for dense urban districts or areas with specific regulation (Highways, airports, …). The considered parameters for aesthetic performance indicator are:

- The recognizability of PV solutions (Reco.)
- The colour uniformity of the BIPV array (Unif.)
- The glare effect of BIPV solution (GLARE)
- The identification of a building using BIPV (Ident.)

The three last PIs are relative to the degree of visual integration into the environment on three different scales: At the module level (considering integration into the BIPV system), at the system level (considering integration into the building) and at the building level (considering integration into the urban environment), based on the hierarchical description developed by ENEA in [9] and described on three different scales the level of visual integration into the built environment. For a simplified use and exploitation, the initial last three identification parameters are grouped together into a single one, Ident.

For the colour measurement a specific protype colourimeter tool to measured colour behind transparent front-sheet will be developed by EPFL in INCREASE project. The colour variation (Delta-E) can be calculated in the CIELab color space as the distance between points in a 3-dimensional space as described in [10].

Table 7: Aesthetical Performance indicator, references and parameter values.

Aesthetical PIs	Ref.	Main parameter
Recognizability	Reco.	Y/N
Colour	Unif.	Spatial ΔC(A) and angular ΔC(θ) colour uniformity (validation needed)
Glare	Glare	Glare risk
BIPV identification	Ident.	(example calculations and validation needed)

Table 8: Aesthetical Performance indicator ratings

rating 1	rating 2	rating 3	rating 4	rating 5
ΔC(A) > 10 / --*	ΔC(A) < 10 /--*	ΔC(A) < 7 / --*	ΔC(A) < 4 / --*	ΔC(A) < 1 / --*
ΔC(θ) > 10 / --*	ΔC(θ) < 10 / --*	ΔC(θ) < 7 / --*	ΔC(θ) < 4 / --*	ΔC(θ) < 1 / --*
*if desired	*if desired	*if desired	*if desired	*if desired
Risk for	Risk for	Risk for	Risk for	Risk for
flash blindness	flash blindness	discomfort glare	discomfort glare	discomfort glare
>10 hours annually	1-10 hours	>10 hours	1-10 hours	<1 hour annually

4.5 KPI COMFORT: Definition and parameters

Comfort KPI should not be viewed as fixed metrics tied solely to a BIPV technology. Instead, they are highly dependent on the specific building context—including geometry, orientation, occupancy, and HVAC strategy—and on the way BIPV is integrated (e.g., façade vs. roof, transparent vs. opaque modules). The impact of BIPV on comfort emerges from this unique interaction, not from the technology in isolation.

While BIPV can influence thermal and visual conditions (e.g., by providing shading or altering heat gains), its direct impact on thermal comfort is limited in most cases. This is because HVAC systems automatically regulate indoor temperatures to meet setpoints, adjusting heating or cooling output as needed. As a result, changes in thermal load caused by BIPV are typically compensated by the building's systems, and the perceived comfort remains stable, even if energy use changes.

Common comfort categories in building assessment include thermal comfort, visual comfort, acoustic comfort, and indoor air quality—each focusing on occupant well-being and performance. This assessment focuses on thermal and visual comfort, while acoustic comfort and indoor air quality are not included, as justified in the following sections.

Table 9: Comfort Performance indicator, references and parameter values.

Comfort PIs	Ref.	Unit	Minimum values	Maximum values
Overheting hours	OH	h/y	0	8760
Underheating hours	UH	h/Y	0	8760
Spatial Daylight Autonomy	sDA	% (floor area)	0%	100%
Useful Daylight Illuminance	UDI	%(floor area)	0%	100%

Table 10: Comfort Performance indicator ratings

rating 1	rating 2	rating 3	rating 4	rating 5
>500	301-500	151-300	51-150	0-50
>900	601-900	301-600	101-300	0-100
<30%	30-44%	45-59%	60-74%	≥ 75%
<35%	35-49%	50-64%	65-79%	> 80%

4.6 KPI BUILDABILITY: Definition and parameters

Buildability KPI, is the fruit of work carried out in workshops close to urban planners' and builders' requests. It considers manufacturers metrics to identify how long is the work duration.

The four indicators are:

- Installation rate (pace) of IPV solutions – InR
- Installation Human Resources - InHR
- Replacement rate (pace) of IPV solutions - RR
- Replacement Human resources – RepHR

References and parameter values and specific ranges are detailed hereafter.

Table 11: Buildability Performance indicator, references and parameter values.

Buildability PIs	Ref.	Unit	Minimum values	Mximum values
Installation rate of PV solutions	InR	h/m2	1 / 6	1
Installation Human Resources	InHR	n.worker/solution	1	5
Replacement rate of PV solutions	Rep.R	h/m2	0,5	4
Replacement Human resources	Rep.HR	n.worker/solution	1	5

Table 12: Buildability Performance indicator ratings

rating 1	rating 2	rating 3	rating 4	rating 5
> 1	0,7 - 1	0,4 - 0,7	0,2 - 0,4	<0,2
5	4	3	2	1
> 4	3-4	2-3	1-2	<1
5	4	3	2	1

5 ONGOING WORK AND VALIDATION

With finalization of selection parameters and performance key indicators, BIPV solutions could be assessed objectively with a fair approach including needs of all stakeholders including manufacturers or builders and especially the end-users. Next step will be to assess in real test conditions on pre-demo and then on demo sites from INCREASE project, and to evaluate implementation in the field of a such methodology.

Initial stage preformed on pre-demo locations will allow to validate and strengthen the use of such parameters and performance indicators. Next stage will be to apply a possible solution that may eventually be implemented to meet the needs of real operations on the nine demo sites of the project.

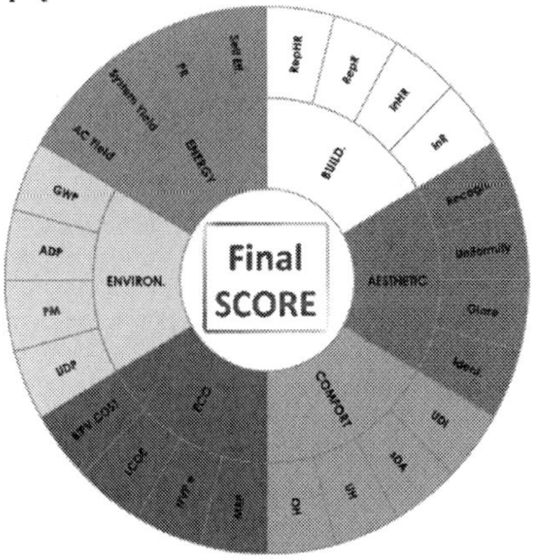

Figure 3: Exemple of Final score display according to BIPV solution, building specificities, location and needs.

10.4229/EUPVSEC2025/4BV.4.15

Final score will be displayed as presented in the Figure 3. The value is calculated as the average value of all calculated KPIs, values are calculated talking into account the rating tables and parameters values presented in the tables, related to each KPI.

The Figure 4 presents the display score of the BIPV solution studied. Even if the layout is not final, KPIs subscores and final average value will remain presented. That will allow to decision makers to have a quick overview of the solution and contribution of each KPI.

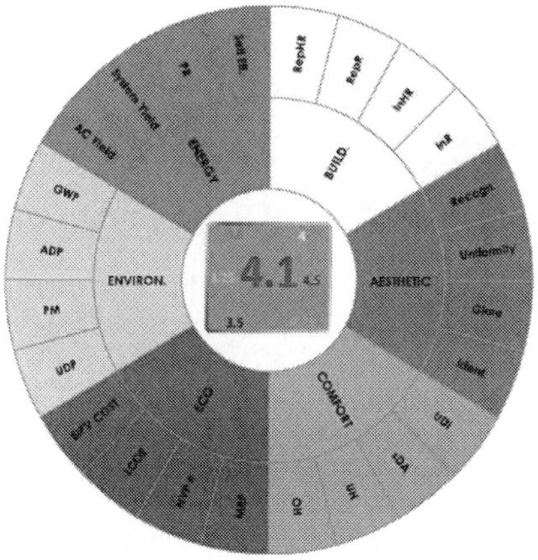

Figure 4: Final score value and dislplay of subscores of each KPI developed. Including value to the tenth.

6 CONCLUSION AND PERSPECTIVES

There are currently few objective indicators, and these do not allow all actors in the value chain to be included, preventing them from providing informed opinions to decision-makers.

Current tools, which are geared towards photovoltaic expectations, do not consider the expectations of the construction industry or end users. In this work, we have developed indicators that allow all stakeholders to be included, thus ensuring that all opinions are taken into account and enabling objective decision-making.

This approach, developed jointly with stakeholders, also enables a harmonized and unbiased approach to be implemented. This approach thus ensures that different solutions are analyzed and compared based solely on the intrinsic data of the identified solutions. Decision-makers can thus select the solutions with the best final score or determine which KPIs they wish to focus their efforts on. This should enable them to respond in a targeted manner to local, regulatory, or even national requirements.

Simple implementation makes it possible to provide data that is accessible to all decision-makers and stakeholders using the same interpretation grid, in a straightforward manner.

It is desirable to make the tool sufficiently versatile to be able to dynamically integrate data measured on site and to be able to integrate it into digital energy management tools in buildings.

Implementation at demonstration sites will enable us to see how these indicators will be implemented and to identify and resolve any difficulties encountered. Similarly, we will analyze the ability to implement dynamic monitoring of indicator trends and determine their usefulness, particularly in terms of their impact on recycling, maintenance, and, above all, the effects of aging and the management of sustainability and reliability for this type of BIPV solution.

REFERENCES

[1] G. Eder, H.R. Wilson, S. Boddaert and Al. : Multi-dimensional evaluation of BIPV installations: Development of a tool to assess the performance as building component and electricity generator. Energy and Building, Vol 31, 2024.
[2] Report IEA-PVPS T15-06:2019; Compilation and Analysis of User Needs for BIPV and its Functions; Wilson, H.R., Kapsis, K., Delisle, V., et al.: https://iea-pvps.or g/key-topics/compilation-and-analysis-of-user-needs-for-bipv-and-its-functions.
[3] Eu, H2020 BIPVBOOST project report: Update on BIPV market and stakeholder analysis, available at https://bipvboost.eu/public-reports/download/update-onbipv-market-and-stakeholder-analysis.
[4] Eu, H2020 INCREASE project report: KPIs and monitoring approaches (v1), available at https://www.increaseipv.eu/_files/ugd/2c16bd_c27d8c41d3124dc2b20820c49c7b614c.pdf
[5] IEC, 61724–1:2021 Photovoltaic system performance - Part 1: Monitoring, Int. Elec. Commission (2021).
[6] R.P.N.P. Weerasinghe, R.J. Yang, A review of 45 non-domestic buildings 12 western countries, Renewable Sustainable Energy Rev. 137 (2021) 110622. https://doi.org/10.1016/j.rser.2020.110622.
[7] Report IEA-PVPS T12-19:2020; Life Cycle Inventories and Life Cycle Assessments of Photovoltaic Systems, Frischknecht, R., et al. https://iea-pvps.org/key-topics/life-cycle-inventories-and-life-cycle-assessments-of-photovoltaic-systems/.
[8] Glare Potential Evaluation of Structured PV Glass Based on Gonioreflectometry; Babin, M., Thorsteinsson, S., Jakobsen, M.L., and Spataru, S.V., IEEE Journal of Photovoltaics, 2022, 12, 6, 1314-1318, 2022, DOI: 10.1109/JPHOTOV.2022.3189779.
[9] A Trans-Disciplinary Vocabulary for Assessing the Visual Performance of BIPV; Scognamiglio, A.; Sustainability 2021, 13(10), 5500; DOI: 10.3390/su13105500.
[10] Accurate color characterization of solar photovoltaic modules for building integration; Alejandro Borja Block, Jordi Escarre Palou, Antonin Faes, Alessandro Virtuani, Christophe Ballif; Solar Energy, 2024, 267; DOI: https://doi.org/10.1016/j.solener.2023.112227A

ACKNOWLEDGMENTS

Authors would like to thank IEA PVPS T15 members for feeding the base of this work as well as BIPVBOOST project partners with their valuable inputs and contributions.

This project has received funding from the European Union's HORIZON research and innovation program under grant agreement No 101136112.

THE USE OF LIFE CYCLE ASSESSMENT TO SUPPORT DEVELOPMENT OF AN INNOVATIVE BIPV SYSTEM WITH A STEEL FRAME

Roulleau Léa[1], Bailhache Simon[1], Boddaert Simon[1,*], Reyal Jean-Pierre[2], Biard Yves[2]

CSTB[1] / SEMPERSTYL[2]
84 avenue Jean Jaurès 77447 Marne-la-Vallée Cedex 2 / 31 RUE DES ETOURNEAUX 95610 ERAGNY

*simon.boddaert@cstb.fr

ABSTRACT: Building-integrated Photovoltaic solutions (BIPV) help optimizing the use of available areas for PV implementation. With growing concerns about the environmental impacts of the construction sector, BIPV system manufacturers are challenged to evaluate the impacts of their solutions and consider them as key criteria for decision-making in their design process. In this context, this study aims at correctly define the calculation protocol and assess the impact on climate change of an innovative BIPV solution named SOLARSTYL® in development.
To this end, a cradle-to-grave life cycle assessment (LCA) of the SOLARSTYL® system is performed, using a method inspired by the French accredited PEP Ecopassport program for Environmental Product Declarations (EPD). Environmental performance comparisons are made with a standard BIPV solution considered as a reference in order to guide design choices. More specifically, the study addresses the influence of the metal on the environmental impacts. A steel frame is considered for the SOLARSTYL® system, together with a plug-and-play connecting technology to facilitate assembly, maintenance and replacement. Cable routing solution and hazards management option will be included in this study. In addition, micro-inverters are expected to be integrated in the frame in a future design. In contrast, the reference system includes the most common current solution, i.e. an aluminium frame in a conventional PV module equipped with an external junction box.
Keywords: Building Integrated PV (BIPV), Comparative Life Cycle Assessment (LCA)

1 CONTEXT, GOAL AND SCOPE OF THE STUDY

Since its application in 2022, French Environmental regulation RE2020 [1] enforces thresholds on climate change footprint for each new building construction projects to meet climate change mitigation targets. Threshold values will decline every three years to reach carbon neutrality towards 2050. The French National decarbonation roadmap [2] also encourages the use of photovoltaic renewable energy to decrease fossil energy consumption in building, reduce electricity mix carbon footprint and increase network's resilience and reliability.

Thus, environmental performances of SolarStyl® Building Integrated PV (BIPV) [3] innovative solution are assessed in this study to optimise its potential environmental impacts reduction gains and make better environmental choices (*Figure 1*). This solution is a steel-frame and "plug-and-play" connecting technology designed for PV by SemperStyl company. It integrates electric connectivity, junction boxes, as well as modularity functions enabling its repair and the replacement of PV modules at their end-of-life. Moreover, this solution is conceived to be easy to install and maintain. Standard reference comparable solution is made from aluminium, does not integrate electric connections, neither modularity nor repairability functions.

The goal of this study is firstly to **evaluate environmental footprint of SolarStyl® solution with cradle-to-grave life cycle assessment** and analysing the process contribution to environmental impacts. Secondly the objective is to **compare the environmental impacts of SolarStyl® solution with BIPV aluminium standard reference system having external junction boxes and inverters to identify the best scenario and ways of improvement.**

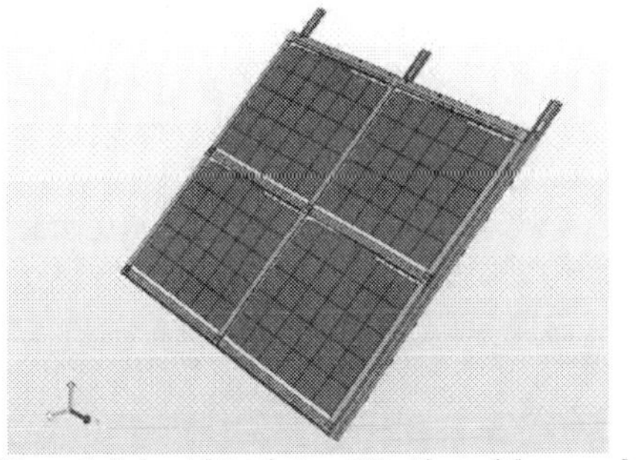

Figure 1. Solarstyl® solution, PV with steel-frame and integrated connection

2 METHODOLOGY

2.1 Functional unit and system boundaries

The functional unit is "*to ensure electricity production and waterproofing of the facade using a PV module integration system*". The reference flow is 1 m² of framed module. The reference service life (RSL) of the system is 50 years, according to standard reference life of a building in the RE2020 regulation. The system is composed of a metallic frame, a PV module, a junction box, cable and electric connections, and an inverter. The different elements have their own RSL described in Table 1.

Composition	Reference system in aluminium	SolarStyl
Frame	Aluminium RSL : 30 years (= limited by PV module RSL) Repairable : NO	Steel RSL : 50 years (RSL from EN 15804) Repairable : YES
PV module	RSL : 30 years	
Junction box	Deported 1 box / module RSL : 30 years (= limited by PV module RSL) Repairable : NO	Integrated 1 box / module RSL : 30 years (= limited by PV module RSL) Repairable : YES
Cable + connections	Deported RSL : 30 years Repairable : YES	Integrated RSL : 50 years Repairable : YES
Inverter	Deported RSL : 10 years	Deported RSL : 10 years

Table 1. System description

10.4229/EUPVSEC2025/4BV.4.17

The lifespan of the frame is defined at 30 years for aluminium (limited by RSL of PV module) and 50 years for steel (SolarStyl® system is fully repairable, allowing to extend of the reference service life of the frame until 50 years).

The study is cradle-to-grave, from production of raw materials, until the end-of-life. Module D is not considered. Raw materials production takes place in Europe, except for the PV module which is produced in China. Two scenarios are considered for the aluminium frame of the reference system: production in Europe or mixed supply from China (90%) and Europe (10%). The rest of the life cycle takes place in France (from assembly of the system, installation until end-of-life).

Neither photovoltaic electricity production nor its substitution to electricity imports are calculated in the study.

Life cycle stages are presented in Figure 2 and follow EN15804+A2 standard [4]. The life cycle considers the maintenance stage with the replacement of inverters every 10 years and the replacement of the PV module and junction box at 30 years for the SolarStyl® system. For the aluminium system, the whole system is replaced at 30 years and inverters replaced every 10 years.

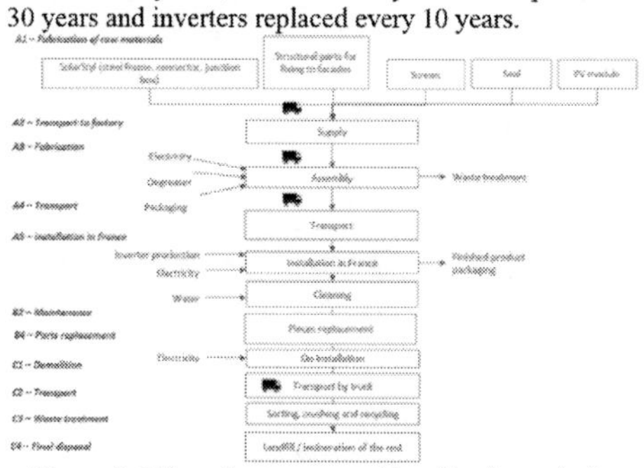

Figure 2. Life cycle stages considered in the study for Solarstyl® system and system boundaries

2.2 Life cycle inventory

All inputs and outputs are quantified for each life cycle stages. Data are collected for each life cycle stages, based on SolarStyl® 2024 data for a 1.8 m² module on its actual v0 development.

The aluminium reference system relies mostly on data from the SolarStyl® system for quantities and compositions of components. The main difference between the two systems is the **lifespan of the frame (30 years for aluminium vs. 50 years for steel), as the end-of-life of the PV module requires a complete replacement of the system, whereas in SolarStyl® system the replacement of the PV module is possible.**

No allocation is made. Materials have been weighted, electricity consumption for the production has been calculated based on machines power specifications.

For the aluminium solution, cable trays are not integrated. Circuit breaker boxes are not integrated, by lack of data, for both scenarios.

2.3 Life cycle assessment

LCA methodology is inspired by internationally recognized LCA standards ISO 14040 [5] / ISO 14044 [6], as well as standard NF C08-100-1 [7] and PEP ecopassport program (French EPD program for Electrical, Electronic and Heating Ventilation Air Conditioning-Refrigeration) [8]. The quantified inputs and outputs are modeled in the Simapro software [9] using ecoinvent v9.6 database [10] and Environmental Product Declaration of steel suppliers. EN15804+A2 environmental impact assessment method is used for impact categories assessment. The study is not peer-reviewed by LCA experts.

2.4 Scenarios

Several parameters were identified as influents for results: aluminium quantity, aluminium geographical area of production and to a lesser extent aluminium recycled content. Thus, different scenarios were assessed to cover the multiple possibilities.

3 LCA RESULTS AND INTERPRETATION

Figure 3 presents climate change comparison in kg CO_2eq per m² of installed solution over 50 years of reference service life of the SolarStyl® solution (left bar) and the aluminium reference solution (middle and right bars). Reference case SolarStyl® solution uses 9.5 kg of steel produced in Europe with 31% of recycled content. The standard aluminium solution uses 19 kg with 32% of recycled content produced in Europe or in China (90%)/Europe (10%).

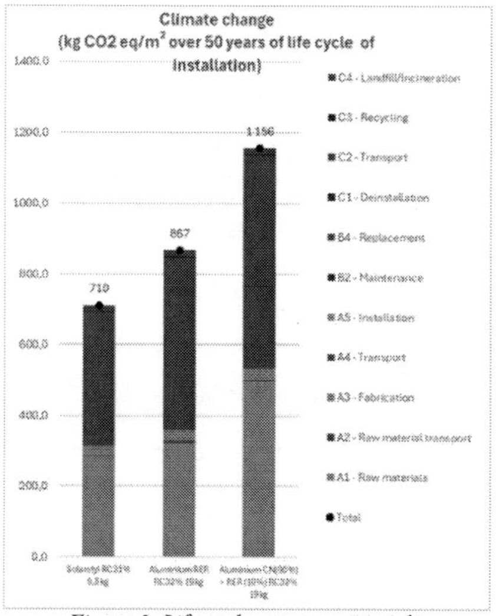

Figure 3. Life cycle assessment results

The lifecycle stages that contribute the most to global warming potential are ***A1 – Raw materials production*** (especially for PV module which requires lots of energy and materials and represents 92% of A1 impact) and ***B4 – Parts of maintenance*** (due to replacement of PV module and inverter which represent respectively 30% and 46% of B4 impact) over the 50 years of the system lifespan.

The difference between SolarStyl® and reference aluminium solution can be explained mainly by the following reasons:

- The shorter lifespan of the aluminium frame (30 years) implies a greater quantity needed to cover the 50 years study-period.
- Twice as much aluminium is needed to perform the same functions as steel according to SemperStyl.

10.4229/EUPVSEC2025/4BV.4.17

- The carbon footprint between aluminium and steel differs:
  - Steel (with 5.5-55% of recycled content) produced in Europe = 2.5-5.3 kg CO_2 eq/kg
  - Aluminium (with 32% of recycled content) produced in Europe = 5.8 kg CO_2 eq/kg
  - Aluminium (with 32% of recycled content) produced in China (90%), Europe (10%) = 22.2 kg CO_2 eq/kg

If the quantity of steel and aluminium were the same, there would still be 14% of difference between the scenarios (due to the different frame RSL: 30 versus 50 years).

4 DISCUSSION

4.1 Aluminium scenario definition

Aluminium solution scenario is based on the same data collection as SolarStyl® system, as first approach as no production data were available. The study relies in particular on the hypothesis that aluminium quantity needed for the functional unit is twice as much as steel quantity (SemperStyl data). Sensitivity analysis has been conducted to measure the influence of aluminium quantity on the comparison of the life cycles. Results have shown that with same metal quantity, Solarstyl® system remains a better choice for the climate, thanks to its modularity functions which enable to extend the reference service life of the frame and cables and avoid production of new materials.

Other uncertainties have been identified in the aluminium scenario definition such as place of production and recycled content. The absolute value results depend on those parameters. Conclusions are however unchanged, as reference service life and weight of aluminium have more influence.

4.1 Uncertainties and limits of LCA

Results depend strongly on PV module technology, inverters technology, their reference service life and place of production.

Also, LCA focused on climate change results generated by the life cycle of the system with an attributional approach. No prospective analysis was carried out, neither steel or aluminium availability, criticality, nor supply risks were assessed.

Finally, to compare both solutions, other choice criteria should be observed such as fire safety features implemented in SolarStyl® solution, mechanical strength, watertightness, theft protection, ease of installation and repair, building thermal performance…

5 CONCLUSION

This study shows that SolarStyl® solution has less environmental impact than the aluminium solution, thanks to its repairability function that enables to change the PV module without having to change the whole system. Furthermore, steel quantities needed for the functional unit are smaller than in aluminium in the reference solution.

The parameters that differentiate SolarStyl® from aluminium standard solution in terms of environmental results are the lifespan of the system that avoids producing new materials, the metal country of production and its energetic carbon footprint, the metal quantity needed of 1 m² of solution and, to a lesser extent, the metal recycled content.

Future work will focus on reducing environmental impacts of SolarStyl® solution applying eco-design principles.

6 ACKNOWLEDGEMENTS

The authors wish to acknowledge ADEME for their fundings support.

7 REFERENCES

[1] RE2020, https://www.ecologie.gouv.fr/politiques-publiques/reglementation-environnementale-re2020

[2] Ministère de la Transition Ecologique et de la cohésion des territoires, Feuille de route décarbonation du cycle de vie du bâtiment Les propositions de la filière JANVIER 2023, https://www.ecologie.gouv.fr/sites/default/files/documents/Feuille_de_route_decarbonation_batiment.pdf

[3] SolarStyl® system, version 2025, SemperStyl, 2025, https://solarstyltechnologies.fr/ , consulted on 25th of August 2025

[4] NF EN 15804+A2 (octobre 2019), Contribution des ouvrages de construction au développement durable — Déclarations environnementales sur les produits — Règles régissant les catégories de produits de construction

[5] ISO 14040:2006 - Gestion environnementale — Analyse du cycle de vie — Principes et cadre (publiée en 2006)

[6] ISO 14044:2006 - Gestion environnementale — Analyse du cycle de vie — Exigences et lignes directrices (publiée en 2006)

[7] NF C08-100-1, Déclarations environnementales relatives aux équipements électriques, électroniques et de génie climatique - Partie 1 : règles d'élaboration communes - Usage dans les ouvrages de bâtiment

[8] PEP ecopassport rules, http://www.pep-ecopassport.org//fr/, consulted on: 25th of August 2025 Ecoinvent, www.Eco-invent.org

[9] Simapro v9.6, https://simapro.com/, consulted on: 25th of August 2025

[10] ecoinvent, https://ecoinvent.org/, consulted on: 25th of August 2025.

ACKNOWLEDGMENTS

Authors would like to thank SOLARSTYL project members for supporting this work with valuable inputs, disseminating information and contributions.

This project has received funding from ADEME, French National Agency for the Environment and Energy.

10.4229/EUPVSEC2025/4BV.4.17

ECONOMIC ANALYSIS OF BUILDING INTEGRATION OF FLEXIBLE PV MODULES

Paulo Carmo[1], José A. Silva[1], Luís Fialho[2], Afonso Cavaco[1], Pedro Horta[1]
[1]Renewable Energies Chair, Polo da Mitra da Universidade de Évora, Edifício Ário Lobo de Azevedo, 7000-083 Nossa Senhora de Tourega, Portugal
[2]Eurac Research-Institute for Renewable Energy, 39100 Bolzano, Italy

ABSTRACT: This paper presents a study that makes a thorough evaluation of the economic competitiveness of building integration of flexible PV modules in the European Union (EU) by comparing the levelized cost of electricity (LCOE) of flexible modules with rigid modules considering different locations in several European countries. The countries and cities chosen were Stockholm (Sweden), Évora (Portugal), Munich (Germany), Bordeaux (France), Vienna (Austria), Amsterdam (Netherlands), Rome (Italy), Warsaw (Poland), Athens (Greece), Dublin (Ireland), for each country an economic analysis was made. The analysis was based on the evaluation of the average installation and maintenance costs for each country, and by using PVGIS, the annual energy production of the system (kWh) was estimated for each location. The LCOE was calculated for all locations, both residential and industrial installations, considering an installed power of 3 kWp for residential systems and 300 kWp for the industrial ones.
Keywords: Flexible Modules, BIPV, LCOE, Residential, Industrial.

1 INTRODUCTION

In the last years the need to decarbonize the energy sector to mitigate the impact of global warming caused by the usage of fossil fuels has become a priority, and as a response the deployment of renewable energies is increasing. The European Union (EU) has set a target that by 2030 there will be a reduction in greenhouse gas emissions by 55% relative to 1990 levels and ensure that at least 42.5% of the energy needs come from renewable sources, but aiming for 45%. The renewable energy sources represented 24.5% of EU final energy use in 2023. Although solar photovoltaics (PV) only accounted for 2% of the EU energy consumption, it can have a major role in achieving the 42.5% target. For this to be possible, it is necessary to use different approaches to the installation of PV modules, as the conventional PV power plants occupy significant amounts of space, and the land-use competition with other activities is becoming an issue, as much of the spaces without constructions are either used for agriculture or forestry, so it is necessary to look at different technologies and think of alternative ways to integrate PV into already existing constructions as well as new ones such as in facades, rooftops, or road barriers [1],[2].

Rigid silicon PV modules nowadays correspond to more than 90% of the global market, thanks to its efficiency and low price, but there are some limitations to its applications due to their weight and rigid nature. So, as the photovoltaic industry seeks innovative solutions to integrate solar into a broader range of applications, flexible PV modules appear as a lightweight and bendable solution that permits its installation into low load bearing structures, and a large variety of surfaces, namely curved ones, both in buildings and vehicles [3]. Figure 1 shows an example of one of these applications [4].

Figure 1: Building with flexible modules on rooftop

Some of the issues that limit a widespread adoption of this technology are the higher costs and shorter lifetime when compared to the conventional crystalline silicon modules [5]. On the other hand, their reduced weight and flexibility can make transport and installation less work intensive.

All the previously mentioned topics will affect the levelized cost of electricity (LCOE). This research aims to do a comprehensive analysis of the LCOE of the building integrated flexible PV modules and compare it with the traditional rigid crystalline silicon-based modules, accounting for differences in material costs, installation costs and long-term performance.

2 METHODOLOGY

First, it was defined that the residential system would have a power peak of 3 kWp. While for the industrial system a 300 kWp installation was considered, this choice was based on the International Energy Agency reports that describe an industrial system as a grid-connected roof-mounted with at least 250 kW [8].

Next, the CAPEX was determined. The value which can be divided into cost of equipment, labour, profit and other costs that an installation has in all countries.

For the industrial PV system, it was not possible to find a CAPEX for every location, so from the values taken from national reports and other sources it was estimated that the CAPEX for an industrial PV system that the price per Wp would be approximately half of the Residential PV.

Using PVGIS it was found the yearly PV energy production (YEP) for all the chosen locations: Stockholm, Évora, Munich, Bordeaux, Vienna, Amsterdam, Rome, Warsaw, Athens, Dublin [6].

Two cases were studied, the ideal mounting and the vertical mounting. The ideal case is when the PV is mounted with the optimal slope and azimuth for the location. And the vertical case where the slope is assumed as 90° and the azimuth is 0°, which simulates the PV being mounted on walls facing south.

For the two cases referred, the rigid modules will always need a mounting structure due to their weight, but for the vertical case, the flexible modules will be considered as mounted without the use of a mounting structure, being instead directly attached to the surface by gluing for example, which in conjunction with the reduced

10.4229/EUPVSEC2025/4BV.4.22

weight of the modules means it would be possible to install it 40% quicker and reduce labour costs by that amount [7]. While in the ideal case flexible modules would still need a structure to get the optimal slope, so in this case the reduction on labour cost assumed as only 20%. As it was not always possible to determine the labour costs, it was assumed that in those cases the installation cost would be 20% of the CAPEX value, as that was the average obtained from the values available.

Assuming the cost of operation and maintenance, OPEX, is equal to 1.5 % of the CAPEX, as it normally ranges between 1% and 2%, and a lifetime of 30 years for the rigid modules and 25 years for the flexible ones it is then possible to calculate the LCOE using the following equation:

$$LCOE = \frac{CAPEX + OPEX \cdot lifetime}{YEP \cdot lifetime}$$

It is important to highlight that this LCOE expression is a simplified version that does not include discount rates; consequently, the values obtained are lower than the LCOEs usually obtained for PV systems, and should not be compared with them. The main goal of this study is to compare the economic competitiveness of the flexible PV modules with the rigid ones, so the figure of merit is the relative difference between the LCOEs for these two technologies, which was obtained for each type of PV system and location.

3 RESULTS

The results obtained for each case and location have significant differences so in the following tables not only are presented the LCOE values for two PV technologies, but also the relative difference between LCOE values for the flexible (F) and rigid modules (R). This difference was calculated using the equation:

$$\frac{F}{R} = \left(\frac{LCOE_F}{LCOE_R} \times 100\right) - 100$$

Where $LCOE_F$ and $LCOE_R$ are the LCOE for flexible and rigid modules, respectively.

3.1 Residential LCOE ideal

Using the cost values found for residential installations and the expected yearly energy production of a 3 kWp PV system mounted with the optimal slope and azimuth it was possible to obtain the following LCOE values.

Table I: Residential LCOE ideal

	Rigid [€/kWh]	Flexible [€/kWh]	F/R [%]
Stockholm	0.070	0.093	+32.9
Évora	0.027	0.036	+33.3
Munich	0.059	0.077	+30.5
Bordeaux	0.098	0.145	+48.0
Vienna	0.085	0.124	+45.9
Amsterdam	0.056	0.076	+35.7
Rome	0.047	0.066	+40.4
Warsaw	0.160	0.211	+31.9
Athens	0.086	0.114	+32.6
Dublin	0.087	0.115	+32.2

3.2 Residential LCOE vertical

Here are presented the LCOE values obtained by calculating the expected yearly energy production for a PV installation with a slope of 90° and an azimuth of zero.

Table II: Residential LCOE vertical

	Rigid [€/kWh]	Flexible [€/kWh]	F/R [%]
Stockholm	0.093	0.113	+21.5
Évora	0.042	0.051	+21.4
Munich	0.082	0.100	+22.0
Bordeaux	0.140	0.190	+35.7
Vienna	0.121	0.160	+32.2
Amsterdam	0.079	0.105	+22.8
Rome	0.069	0.098	+33.3
Warsaw	0.225	0.297	+21.8
Athens	0.139	0.184	+22.3
Dublin	0.117	0.154	+21.4

3.3 Industrial LCOE ideal

Using the cost values found for industrial installations and the expected yearly energy production for a 300 kWp PV system mounted with the optimal slope and azimuth it was possible to get the following LCOE values.

Table III: Industrial LCOE ideal

	Rigid [€/kWh]	Flexible [€/kWh]	F/R [%]
Stockholm	0.041	0.054	+31.7
Évora	0.013	0.017	+30.8
Munich	0.026	0.035	+34.6
Bordeaux	0.038	0.056	+47.4
Vienna	0.039	0.056	+43.6
Amsterdam	0.024	0.032	+33.3
Rome	0.032	0.045	+40.6
Warsaw	0.078	0.103	+32.1
Athens	0.043	0.057	+32.6
Dublin	0.039	0.051	+30.8

3.4 Industrial LCOE vertical

By repeating the same process used for residential installations was possible to find the industrial LCOE values for the vertical installation.

Table IV: Industrial LCOE vertical

	Rigid [€/kWh]	Flexible [€/kWh]	F/R [%]
Stockholm	0.031	0.038	+22.6
Évora	0.021	0.025	+19.0
Munich	0.036	0.044	+22.2
Bordeaux	0.054	0.074	+37.0
Vienna	0.054	0.071	+31.5
Amsterdam	0.033	0.041	+24.2
Rome	0.048	0.064	+33.3
Warsaw	0.108	0.132	+22.2
Athens	0.070	0.085	+21.4
Dublin	0.051	0.063	+23.5

From the results it is possible to see that although the LCOE is dependent on both the installation costs and the solar energy available in the region, in all cases the LCOE for flexible modules is sig higher than for conventional rigid modules. As by looking at the values for Évora and Athens which are locations with the same latitude, so close values of solar irradiation, but the LCOE values for Athens is much higher than the one for Évora as the installation

10.4229/EUPVSEC2025/4BV.4.22

costs of a PV system in Greece are much higher than those of Portugal.

France is the country where the relative difference in LCOE is the highest for all cases, being its higher value verified as 48% for a residential installation mounted with the optimal slope, and this difference is a result of how expensive the materials are when compared with the labour costs so that the reduction in labour cost with the use of flexible modules will have the smallest impact on the LCOE of flexible modules in France.

It is possible to observe that Poland is the country with the highest LCOE for both rigid and flexible modules, this is mainly a result of Poland having the highest CAPEX for PV systems, this country also has one of the lowest shares of PV on the energy mix. In fact, our results suggest that there is a correlation between the country's PV installed capacity and the production installed and the respective LCOE.

Between the countries analysed, Portugal showed itself to be the country with the lowest LCOE, which is a result of the lower installation cost in Portugal, compared to the other countries, as well as having a very high solar energy potential.

The results also suggest that the building integration of flexible modules into building facades, where thanks to the lightweight nature of these modules, could avoid the use of a mounting structure, and reduce the difference between the values of LCOE for the two technologies much smaller. Although the LCOE for this case is still higher than for rigid modules, it can be seen as a viable option, especially because as they are lighter the forces imposed on the walls will be much smaller which is an important factor to consider when planning to install photovoltaic modules into a building facade.

Still, the most interesting applications for flexible modules are applications where the conventional rigid modules cannot be installed, either due to the curvature of the surface, due to limited weight supported by the structure, or surfaces that cannot be perforated to install a typical mounting structure. Another interesting application of flexible modules are mobile applications such as electric vehicles, where the reduced weight is an advantage, and to install modules onto the vehicle there can be no perforation, and the modules need to be as close to the car as possible to maintain the vehicle aerodynamics.

4 CONCLUSIONS

In conclusion, currently the flexible PV modules technology is only a good option for applications where the traditional rigid silicon modules cannot be installed, as the comparison of LCOE values of this PV modules with the conventional rigid ones showed that they are in all cases less competitive.

Whoever with the growth of the market for flexible modules, it is expected the costs of this technology will be reduced, making it more competitive and possibly a viable option for installations like rooftops.

It is important to note that this study took only into account the cost of production and energy production without looking at the cost of electricity and how its variations can influence the deployment of the different technologies, and as consequence their price evolutions.

5 ACKNOWLEDGEMENTS

The authors would like to thank the project SOCONEXGEN for the support.

6 REFERENCES

[1] European Environment Agency, "Share of energy consumption from renewable sources in Europe", [Online].Available: https://www.eea.europa.eu/en/analysis/indicators/share-of-energy-consumption-from

[2] EPJ Photovoltaics, "Communication on the potential of applied PV in the European Union: Rooftops, reservoirs, roads (R^3)", [Online]. Available: https://www.epj-pv.org/articles/epjpv/full_html/2024/01/pv230071/pv230071.html

[3] Solar Energy Materials and Solar Cells, "Development of lightweight and flexible crystalline silicon solar cell modules with PET film cover for high reliability in high temperature and humidity conditions", [Online]. Available: https://www.sciencedirect.com/science/article/pii/S0927024823003628

[4] Solar Constructions, "Flexible solar panels", [Online]. Available: https://solar-constructions.com/wordpress/flexible-solar-panel/

[5] Spreewati, "SMF430F-12X12UW", [Online]. Available: https://www.spreewatt.de/media/ac/21/4a/1686916029/SW-01-01-00008%20(12%20Jahre)%20Sunman%20eArc%20SMF430F.pdf?srsltid=AfmBOorbOI3imKOOWAukqGhxIA9peRCUH6o9kZu0CxFYrjfZ1laKcp5m

[6] Joint Research Centre European Commission, "Photovoltaic Geographical Information System (PVGIS)", [Online]. Available: https://joint-research-centre.ec.europa.eu/photovoltaic-geographical-information-system-pvgis_en

[7] Master instruments, "Sunman SMF430F-12X12UW", [Online].Available:https://www.master-instruments.com.au/products/67282/smf430f-12x12uw.html

[8] International Energy Agency, "National Survey Report of PV Power Applications in Sweden 2023", [Online]. Available:https://iea-pvps.org/wp-content/uploads/2024/09/National-Survey-Report-of-PV-Power-Applications-in-Sweden-2023.pdf

[9] Otovo, "Quanto custa instalar painéis solares?", [Online]. Available: https://www.otovo.pt/blog/sistemas-fotovoltaicos/precos-paineis-solares/

[10] International Energy Agency, "National Survey Report of PV Power Applications in France 2023", [Online].Available: https://iea-pvps.org/wp-content/uploads/2024/10/National-Survey-Report-of-PV-Power-Applications-in-FRANCE-2023v5-1.pdf

[11] Anker, "What Is the Cost of Solar System Roof in 2024 and Should You Get One?", [Online]. Available: https://www.anker.com/eu-en/blogs/balcony-power-plant-with-storage/cost-of-solar-panel-installation

[12] International Energy Agency, "National Survey Report of PV Power Applications in The Netherlands 2023",[Online].Available: https://iea-pvps.org/wp-content/uploads/2025/01/IEA-PVPS-Task-1-NSR-The-

Netherlands-2023.pdf
[13] International Energy Agency, "National Survey Report of PV Power Applications in Austria 2023", [Online].Available: https://iea-pvps.org/wp-content/uploads/2024/10/National-Survey-Report-of-PV-Power-Applications-in-Austria-2023.pdf
[14] International Energy Agency, "National Survey Report of PV Power Applications in Italy 2023", [Online].Available: https://iea-pvps.org/wp-content/uploads/2024/12/IEA-PVPS-2023-National-Survey-Report-Italy.pdf
[15] International Energy Agency, "Countries and regions",[Online].Available: https://www.iea.org/regions/europe

UNIVERSITY OF ÉVORA

ECONOMIC ANALISYS OF BUILDING INTEGRATION OF FLEXIBLE PV MODULES

SOL4R

Paulo Carmo[1], José Silva[1], Luis Fialho[2], Afonso Cavaco[1], Pedro Horta[1]

[1]Renewable Energies Chair, University of Évora, Portugal

[2]Eurac Research-Institute for Renewable Energy, 39100 Bolzano, Italy

Introduction

According to European Environment Agency the minimum target for renewable energy consumption is 42.5% by 2030, in 2023 solar photovoltaics(PV) accounted for 2% of EU energy consumption a number that will increase as solar energy can have an important role in reaching this target. For that it is important to look at new PV technologies as the traditional rigid silicon PV modules that currently represent more than 90 % of the global market, thanks to their efficiency and low price, have their applications constrained by their weight and rigid nature. So other technologies such as flexible PV modules can increase the options for PV applications as their low weight and flexibility make them ideal to install low weight bearing structures as well as curved surfaces, such as buildings or vehicles [1].

Objectives

- Calculate the levelized cost of energy (LCOE) for residential and industrial building integration of rigid and flexible PV modules.
- Compare and analyse the **LCOE for the different applications and for the different countries.**

Methods

- 2 Systems: residential PV with 3 kWp and industrial PV with 300 kWp
- 2 Technologies: Rigid and flexible silicon modules.
- 10 different locations in Europe: Stockholm (Sweden), Évora (Portugal), Munich (Germany), Bordeaux (France), Vienna (Austria), Amsterdam (Netherlands), Rome (Italy), Warsaw(Poland), Athens (Greece), Dublin (Ireland).
- Determine CAPEX and OPEX for each country.
- Using PVGIS determine yearly energy production (YEP) for the 2 configurations: optimal slope and vertical (90°) mounting [2].
- Calculate LCOE and the difference between the rigid and flexible LCOE (F/R).
- $\text{LCOE} = \frac{\text{CAPEX+OPEX.lifetime}}{\text{YEP.liftime}}$ $\frac{F}{R} = \left(\frac{LCOE_F}{LCOE_R} \times 100\right) - 100$

Results

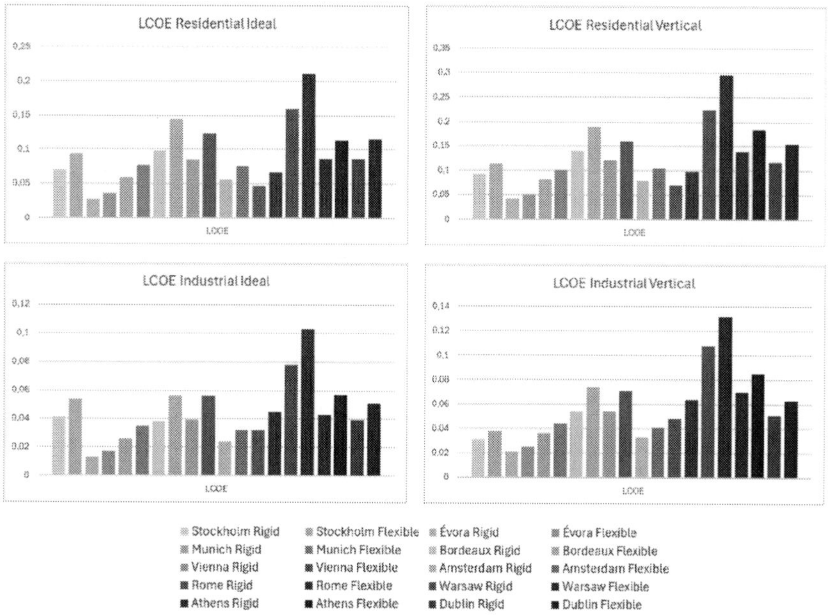

- Although having **similar solar potentials**, **Greece LCOE>> Portugal LCOE** due to **higher system costs.**
- **Poland** always has the **highest LCOE** which results from having the **highest CAPEX** for solar systems.
- **Portugal** as the **lowest LCOE** as a result of both **low system costs** and **high solar potential.**
- There seems to be a **strong correlation between** the **country's PV installed capacity** and the respective **LCOE**[4].
- The **most viable application** for **flexible modules** is **vertical mounting** for both residential and industrial as for most countries **F/R<25%.**
- Presently **flexible modules** are **only an attractive option** in applications **where rigid modules cannot** be used because of **weight limit or shape of the surface.**

Conclusion

In conclusion, currently this technology is only viable for use in applications where the traditional rigid silicon modules cannot be installed, as the LCOE values show how **they are not an economically viable technology to use instead of the traditional modules.**

Whoever by looking at how with the growth of the solar market for each of the countries analysed increased the cost for the rigid modules lowered over time it is possible to assume that the increase in the use of a technology will lower it cost, so it would be safe to assume that as the use of flexible modules for applications where rigid modules cannot be used increases, the price will drop making it more competitive and possibly even making it to be a viable option for installations like rooftops where the only thing keeping the rigid solar modules a better option is the significantly lower price of this technology compared to the flexible modules.

020305-001

Acknowledgements

The authors would like to thank the project SOCONEXGEN for the support,

References

[1] European Environment Agency, "Share of energy consumption from renewable sources in Europe", [Online]. Available: https://www.eea.europa.eu/en/analysis/indicators/share-of-energy-consumption-from

[2] Joint Research Centre European Commission, "Photovoltaic Geographical Information System (PVGIS)", [Online]. Available: https://joint-research-centre.ec.europa.eu/photovoltaic-geographical-information-system-pvgis_en

[3] International Energy Agency, "National Survey Reports",[Online]. Available: https://iea-pvps.org/national-survey-reports/

[4] International Energy Agency, "Countries and regions",[Online]. Available: https://www.iea.org/regions/europe

CUSTOMIZABLE COLORFOIL FOR PHOTOVOLTAIC MODULES: A NEW APPROACH TO AESTHETIC AND EFFICIENT SOLAR ENERGY INTEGRATION

Ananta Paul[1,2], Jani Lamminaho[1,2], Catarina G. Ferreira[1,3], Markus Babin[4], Karlis Petersons[5], Nanna Lysgaard Andersen[4], Leif Yde[5], Jan F. Stensborg[5], Peter Behrensdorff Poulsen[4], Sune Thorsteinsson[4], Joel D. Cox[1,3,6], Morten Madsen[1,2]

[1] SDU Climate Cluster, University of Southern Denmark, Campusvej 55, 5230 Odense M, Denmark
[2] Mads Clausen Institute, Center for Advanced Photovoltaics and Thin Film Energy Devices (SDU CAPE), University of Southern Denmark, 6400 Sønderborg, Denmark
[3] POLIMA—Center for Polariton-driven Light-Matter Interactions, University of Southern Denmark, Campusvej 55, 5230 Odense M, Denmark
[4] Technical University of Denmark, Institute of Electrical and Photonics Engineering, 4000 Roskilde, Denmark
[5]Stensborg A/S, 4000 Roskilde, Denmark
[6] Danish Institute for Advanced Study, University of Southern Denmark, Campusvej 55, DK-5230 Odense M, Denmark

ABSTRACT: Integrating photovoltaic (PV) modules into building roofs and facades provides a practical route to maximize surface coverage for solar energy harvesting without expanding electrical power infrastructure. For architectural applications, PV modules must deliver high power conversion efficiency (PCE), durability, cost-effectiveness, and be visually appealing. The ability to control the color of PV modules thus emerges as a critical requirement for seamless design integration. Here we present a strategy to enhance the aesthetic integration of PV modules into building surfaces through the development of structural colored interlayers, fabricated by coating polymer foil substrates with colored thin multilayers of optimized thicknesses via Roll-to-Roll (R2R) magnetron sputtering. The proposed technology, which we designate *ColorFoil*, offers a key advantage of straightforward incorporation with commercial silicon (Si) solar cells to form colored PV modules. The results highlight a scalable and effective route for color-tunable, aesthetically integrated PV modules, offering new opportunities for widespread adoption of solar technology in architecture.
Keywords: ColorFoil, roll-to-roll sputtered system, aesthetic, diffuser, BIPV.

1 INTRODUCTION

Integrating photovoltaic (PV) modules into building surfaces such as rooftops and facades offers an effective way to expand renewable energy generation without requiring additional land use or new electrical infrastructure [1], [2]. Building-integrated photovoltaics (BIPV) not only contribute to renewable energy production but also provide opportunities to harmonize with architectural elements, which is essential for their widespread acceptance in urban environments [3], [4]. Despite their efficiency and durability, conventional PV modules are often considered visually monotonous, limiting their use in architectural applications where appearance is a critical design factor. To address this challenge, research has increasingly focused on the development of colored PV modules that achieve a balance between visual appeal and power conversion efficiency (PCE). Several strategies, including pigment-based coatings, photonic structures, and structural coloration, have been explored to enhance aesthetics with or without substantially compromising device performance [5], [6], [7]. Pigment-based coatings, while widely used, often suffer from significant performance limitations. Their color properties are highly dependent on the concentration and dispersion of pigments, which can lead to issues such as reduced optical efficiency, color fading, and limited spectral tunability. Additionally, high pigment loading can compromise the mechanical and electrical properties of the coating, making it less suitable for advanced optoelectronic applications.[8] These inherent drawbacks highlight the need for alternative approaches that can achieve vibrant, stable, and tunable colors without sacrificing performance.

To address the limitations of pigment-based coatings, structural colored elements can be introduced directly in front of the photovoltaic (PV) cell. By relying on nanoscale optical effects (such as scattering, diffraction, or interference) taking place in non-absorbing nanostructures and thin films, these elements are able to produce vivid colors while maintaining a high transmittance, which is critical for efficient light harvesting [9], [10]. Of particular interest is the use of nanometer-thin planar multilayers capable of leveraging optical interference to produce vivid colors with low optical losses, therefore outperforming the conventional absorptive pigments. By carefully controlling the configuration of the multilayer structure, this approach enables precise color tuning and the creation of customized visual appearances while preserving high transmittance within the PV cell's active spectral range, ensuring that optical performance is not compromised.

In this study, we propose a novel approach to improve the aesthetic integration of crystalline silicon (c-Si) solar cells using structural colored polymer-based interlayers, referred to as ColorFoil. These interlayers consist of color-customized thin multilayer stacks deposited on flexible polymer substrates (foils) via a scalable roll-to-roll (R2R) sputtering process, enabling cost-effective and durable fabrication. The foil design is supported by experimentally guided theoretical optimization of materials, refractive indices, and thicknesses to simultaneously ensure optical efficiency, environmental stability, and compatibility with module integration [11], [12]. We investigate two proof-of-concept foils, green and clay red, and evaluate their impact on both the optical properties and electrical performance of the resulting solar cells. Our results show that while coloration introduces some current loss (~10% for green foils and ~16% for red foils), the trade-off between aesthetics and efficiency is favorable for BIPV applications. Despite the expected current losses, we were able to keep the efficiency of the mini-modules high, clearly overperforming the use of traditional pigments.

Thus, the ColorFoil itself gives the advantages in terms of applicability over conventional color-coated glasses, where the coating process must be performed prior to the glass tempering process, limiting the flexibility to adapt to various PV module sizes and geometries often needed in BIPV applications. Along with that, this innovation lies in the ability of these foils to modify the appearance of standard Si solar cells while maintaining low current losses, thus enabling both functional and aesthetic integration of solar technologies into modern architectural environments.

2 METHODOLOGY

2.1 Interlayer requirements and design

To obtain a homogeneous, non-iridescent coloration in the PV modules, ColorFoil relies on the use of a polymer substrate containing an optical diffuser. This substrate is first coated with an acrylate-based UV-curable resin layer, which is subsequently textured using nanoimprint lithography to form an optical diffusive surface. Following this step, a multilayer stack of metal oxide thin films, specifically silicon dioxide (SiO_2 target from Polyteknik) and aluminum-doped zinc oxide (AZO: 2 wt% Al and 98 wt% ZnO from Polyteknik), is conformally deposited on the textured diffuser using large-scale Roll-to-Roll (R2R) sputter deposition.

2.2 *Characterization*

Optical properties of the colored multilayers are characterized through UV–visible transmittance and reflectance measurements in ambient atmosphere with a PVE300 photovoltaic quantum-efficiency system (Bentham). Current–voltage characteristics are measured for both raw contacted cells and laminated mini-modules using a Newport steady-state solar simulator as the illumination source, and a Keithley 2651A source measurement unit configured as a four-quadrant load. All I-V measurements are carried out under standard test conditions.

3 RESULTS

The schematic cross-section of the PV module structure incorporating our ColorFoil technology is shown in **Fig. 1**. The proposed design features structural colored interlayers, consisting of a thin multilayer element deposited on a flexible polymer diffuser foil (marked in red line), positioned between the front substrate and the Si PV cell.

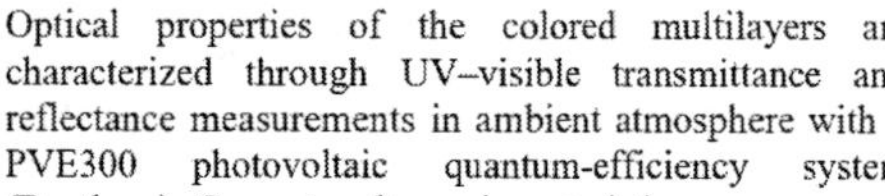

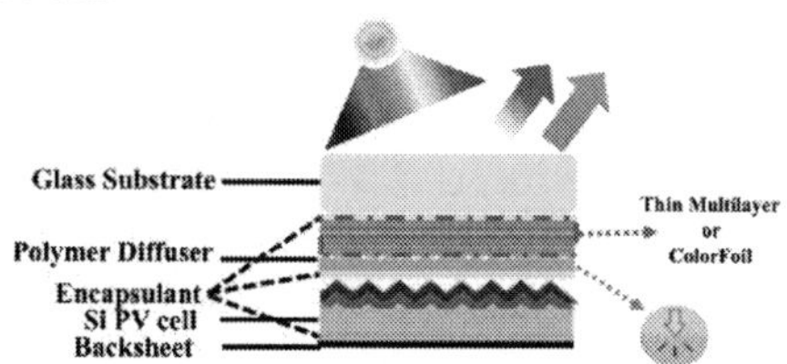

Fig. 1. Schematic representation of a PV module incorporating a ColorFoil interlayer.

ColorFoil design relies on the precise calculation of the optical properties of nanometer-thin multilayers made up of non-absorbing materials presenting high durability and compatibility with large-scale R2R deposition, which are embedded onto the PV laminate to form the colored PV module.[12] To determine the non-periodic individual layer thicknesses leading to the realization of specific hues, an optimization-based inverse design approach is employed, following its recently demonstrated success to identify thin multilayer structures providing user-defined colors [11], [12], [13], [14]. Here we fabricate two different ColorFoil configurations, with green and clay red coloration, which we later incorporate in front of commercial Si mini-module (see **Fig. 1**) to form colored PV mini-modules that serve as proof-of-concept for our proposed technology.

In **Fig. 2** we show a photo of the realized green and clay red ColorFoil, experimentally fabricated via Roll-to-Roll (R2R) sputtering. The dimensions of the deposited ColorFoil are 30 by 10 cm^2. A black background is placed beneath the foils to enhance contrast, clearly demonstrating their uniform coloration properties in addition to their high optical transparency.

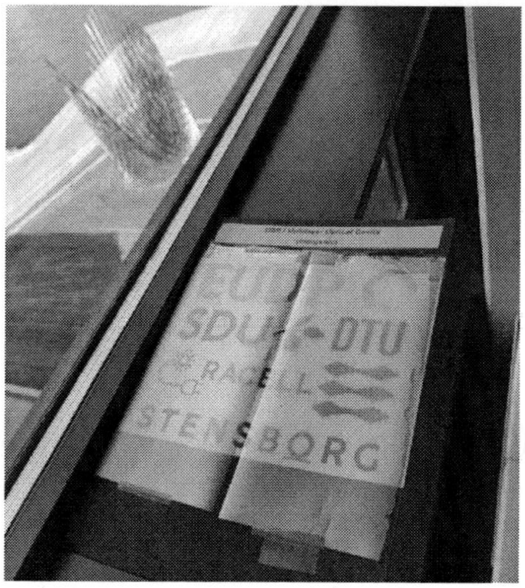

Fig. 2 Photograph of the experimentally developed green and clay red ColorFoil.

The transmittance (T%) and reflectance (R%) spectra of the green and clay red ColorFoil are shown in **Fig. 3a**. The green ColorFoil exhibits a central reflectance maximum at ~570 nm, whereas the clay red ColorFoil shows its maximum at ~741 nm, in agreement with the design requirements for such colored elements. Outside their respective reflectance bands, both foils remain highly transparent, with the green ColorFoil transmitting >85% and the clay red ColorFoil transmitting >80% of incident light, demonstrating their suitability for integration in photovoltaic devices. Although both samples display absorption features in the 300–380 nm region, attributed to the band-edge absorption of the AZO layer,[15] we do not expect those to strongly influence the PV performance, as the photon flux from the sun is very low in this wavelength range. **Fig. 3b** shows the reflectance spectra of the green ColorFoil measured at different locations to evaluate the uniformity of the foil. The results indicate that the variation in the reflectance is minimal, with spectral peak position values ranging only from 560 nm to 584 nm, which confirms the high optical uniformity of the foil. Such uniformity highlights the quality and effectiveness of the Roll-to-Roll sputter deposition used, which is a reliable technique for producing large-area foils with consistent optical properties.

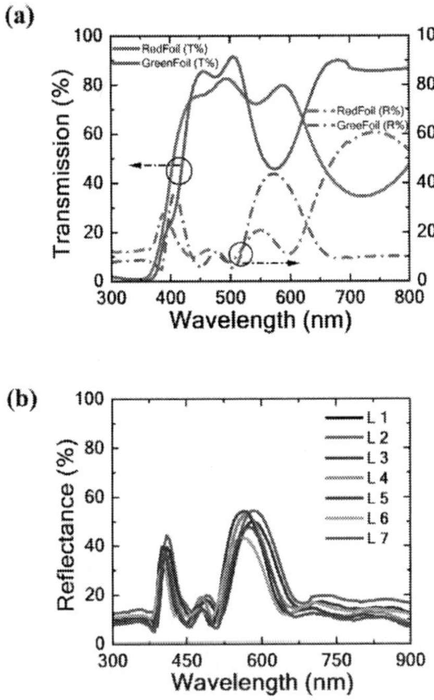

Fig. 3 (a) Transmittance and reflectance spectra of the experimentally fabricated green and clay red ColorFoil. (b) Reflectance spectra of the green ColorFoil at various locations (L1 to L7) are recorded to evaluate its high optical uniformity.

Fig. 4 presents the photograph of the experimentally fabricated reference Si mini-module alongside the mini-modules incorporating ColorFoil in green and clay red, clearly demonstrating the appealing optical characteristics of the modules with ColorFoil included.

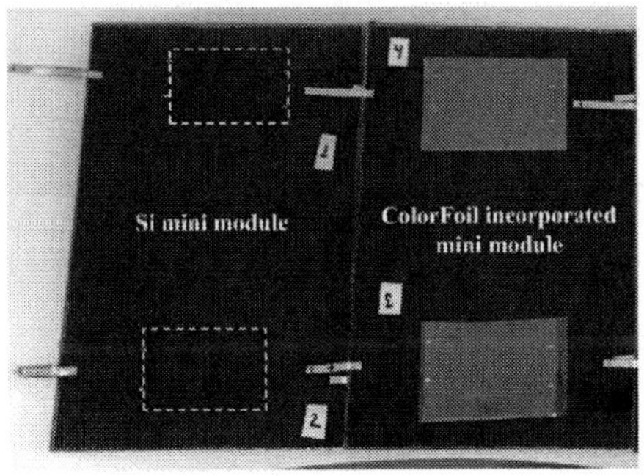

Fig 4. Photograph of the experimentally fabricated reference Si mini-module alongside the green and clay red ColorFoil-incorporated mini-modules.

In particular, the introduction of ColorFoil leads to a small reduction in light absorption in the active layer, which manifests as a loss in short-circuit current density. A direct comparison with the reference module confirms that, while ColorFoil enhances the visual appeal of the devices, they inevitably introduce a trade-off by compromising photocurrent generation and overall photovoltaic performance slightly. Despite the incorporation of coloration, the fabricated mini-modules exhibit remarkably good photovoltaic performance, as evidenced by the current–voltage ($I - V$) and external quantum efficiency (EQE) measurements shown in **Fig. 5** (a) and **Fig. 5** (b), respectively. The green and clay red mini-modules retain more than 86% and 82% of the photovoltaic performance relative to the reference c-Si mini-module of identical area without any coloring interlayer. Notably, the introduction of the colored interlayer does not affect the open-circuit voltage (V_{OC}) of the devices; however, it leads to a reduction in short-circuit current density (I_{SC}) of approximately 13% and 16%, for the green and clay red mini-modules, respectively. The $I - V$ parameters of reference Si, clay red and green mini-modules are summarized in **Table 1**. The observed I_{SC} reduction originates primarily from the expected optical coloration losses, reflected in the EQE dips around 550 nm and 695 nm (Fig. 5b). Additionally, parasitic absorption in the AZO layers of the colored stack further contributes to performance losses, as evidenced by a drop in EQE at wavelengths below 400 nm [15].

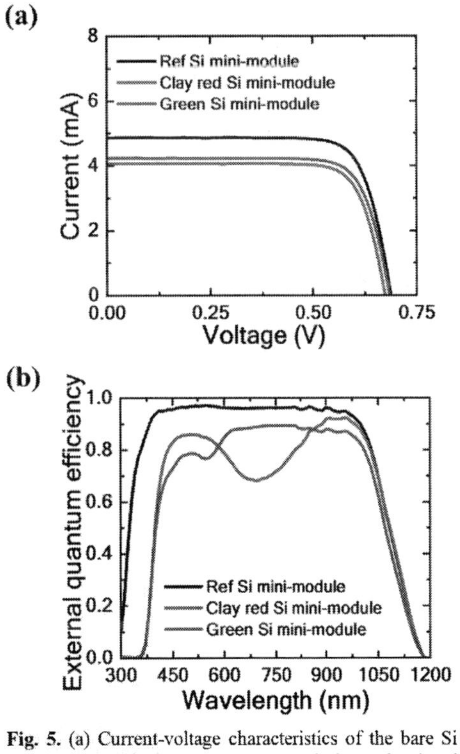

Fig. 5. (a) Current-voltage characteristics of the bare Si mini-module (black curves), green and clay red colored mini-module (olive green and red curve, respectively), including the corresponding photovoltaic parameters. (b) External quantum efficiency spectra of the green and clay red mini-module (olive green and red curve) in

comparison to the reference dark mini-module (black curve).

Table 1: $I - V$ parameters (i.e. short circuit current (I_{SC}), open circuit voltage (V_{OC}) and maximum power (P_{MPP})) of the ref Si, clay red and green mini-module.

$I - V$ Parameters	Ref Si mini-module	Clay red Si mini-module	Green Si mini-module
I_{SC} (mA)	4.87	4.07	4.23
V_{OC} (V)	0.70	0.70	0.70
P_{MPP} (mW)	2.61	2.15	2.26

Overall, the loss analysis of the reference Si, clay red and green mini-module are shown in **Fig. 6**. The loss analysis reveals that the green and clay red Si mini-module exhibited losses of ~10% and 16% compared to the reference Si mini-module (reference Si mini-module loss~ 5%).

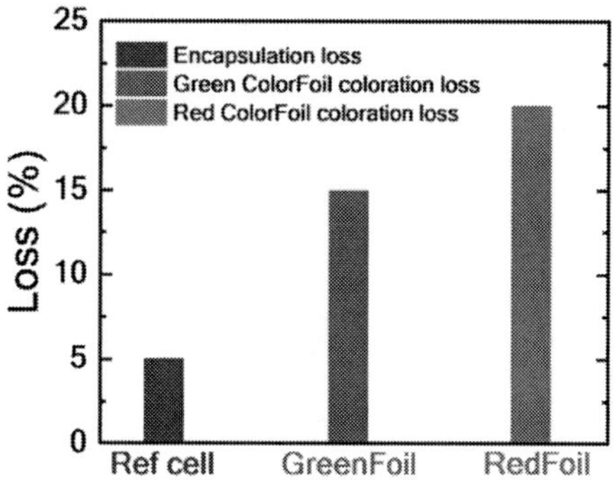

Fig. 6 presents the loss analysis of the Si solar cell before and after the introduction of ColorFoil (green and clay red).

The colored PV mini-modules incorporating ColorFoil interlayers exhibit excellent optical uniformity, stable reflectance properties, and strong compatibility with large-area Roll-to-Roll (R2R) processing. These attributes position them as a highly promising technology for photovoltaic and optoelectronic applications. Beyond solar cell integration, ColorFoil also hold potential in decorative energy-harvesting surfaces, building-integrated photovoltaics (BIPV), and consumer electronics where both aesthetics and functionality are essential. The potential applications of ColorFoil in building-integrated photovoltaics are highlighted in **Fig. 7**. For instance, the clay red ColorFoil matches well with the tiles characteristic of Danish architecture (left image), which can be replaced by colored PV modules incorporating ColorFoil technology to generate electricity while maintaining the aesthetic appearance of the building. In addition, we demonstrate the optical output and visual integration of the green ColorFoil into a model house (right image).

Fig. 7. Potential applications of ColorFoil in building-integrated photovoltaics.

4 CONCLUSIONS

This study presents a novel technology, which relies on polymer-based colored interlayers – ColorFoil – to achieve homogeneous structural coloration in PV modules with low optical losses. We demonstrate, as proof of concept, the fabrication of a green and a clay red ColorFoil, using a large-scale Roll-to-Roll (R2R) sputtering system. As we observed, the color of the resulting foils successfully matched the desired one, resulting from the excellent control of the spectral position of the reflectance peaks. This was achieved while maintaining the transparency outside the reflectance bands high: for the green ColorFoil transmittance reached 85% while for the clay-red ColorFoil, transmittance values as high as 80% were achieved. By applying our ColorFoil technology to commercial Si cells, we successfully assembled colored PV mini-modules, which shown relatively low performance penalty: modules made from the green ColorFoil showed ~10% relative I_{sc} loss, while the modules fabricated from the clay-red ColorFoil exhibited ~16% relative I_{sc} loss, when compared to a reference module where the Si cell was subjected to standard lamination procedure. These results demonstrate an effective balance between visual aesthetics and energy efficiency, and pave the way for the use of ColorFoil technology in colored PV devices. This approach enables seamless architectural integration of photovoltaic modules, promoting broader adoption of solar energy in modern building designs.

5 ACKNOWLEDGEMENTS

This work was funded by EUDP as part of the "ColorFoil" project under grant 64022-1027

7 REFERENCES

[1] M. Victoria *et al.*, "Solar photovoltaics is ready to power a sustainable future," May 19, 2021, *Cell Press*. doi: 10.1016/j.joule.2021.03.005.

[2] D. Gielen *et al.*, "The role of renewable energy in the global energy transformation," *Energy Strategy Reviews*, vol. 24, pp. 38–50, Apr. 2019, doi: 10.1016/j.esr.2019.01.006.

[3] J. M. Kiesecker *et al.*, "Land use and Europe's renewable energy transition: identifying low-conflict areas for wind and solar development," *Front Environ Sci*, vol. 12, 2024, doi: 10.3389/fenvs.2024.1355508.

[4] K. K. Shin Thant *et al.*, "Comprehensive Review on Slot-Die-Based Perovskite Photovoltaics: Mechanisms, Materials, Methods, and Marketability," Feb. 04, 2025, *John Wiley and Sons Inc.* doi: 10.1002/aenm.202403088.

[5] H. Lee *et al.*, "Current status and perspective of colored photovoltaic modules," Nov. 01, 2021, *John Wiley and Sons Ltd.* doi: 10.1002/wene.403.

[6] M. K. Basher *et al.*, "Design, Development, and Characterization of Highly Efficient Colored Photovoltaic Module for Sustainable Buildings Applications," *Sustainability (Switzerland)*, vol. 14, no. 7, Apr. 2022, doi: 10.3390/su14074278.

[7] M. Victoria *et al.*, "Solar photovoltaics is ready to power a sustainable future," May 19, 2021, *Cell Press*. doi: 10.1016/j.joule.2021.03.005.

[8] B. Sarkodie *et al.*, "Characteristics of pigments, modification, and their functionalities," Jun. 01, 2019, *John Wiley and Sons Inc.* doi: 10.1002/col.22359.

[9] S. Daqiqeh Rezaei *et al.*, "Nanophotonic Structural Colors," Jan. 20, 2021, *American Chemical Society*. doi: 10.1021/acsphotonics.0c00947.

[10] S. Kinoshita *et al.*, "Physics of structural colors," *Reports on Progress in Physics*, vol. 71, no. 7, Jul. 2008, doi: 10.1088/0034-4885/71/7/076401.

[11] C. G. Ferreira *et al.*, "Design and optimization of structural colored interlayers for building-integrated photovoltaic applications", doi: 10.4229/EUPVSEC2024/4BV.4.6.

[12] M. Babin *et al.*, "Reliability investigation of structural colour interlayers for coloured pv modules", doi: 10.4229/EUPVSEC2024/3AV.2.21.

[13] C. G. Ferreira *et al.*, "Optical Design of Structural Colored Photovoltaics for Building Integration: From Periodic Configurations to Optimization Algorithms," *Nano Energy*, 2025(preprint).

[14] C. G. Ferreira *et al.*, "Structural colored planar multilayers with minimal angular color dependence for building integrated photovoltaics," *Solar RRL*, 2025 (preprint).

[15] L. G. Daza *et al.*, "Understanding the Variations of Optical Bandgap in AZO Nanostructured Thin Films: Analysis of Possible Influences," *Physica Status Solidi (A) Applications and Materials Science*, vol. 222, no. 9, May 2025, doi: 10.1002/pssa.202400763.

PERFORMANCE, OPERATIONAL DATA AND STABILITY OF COMMERCIAL CIGS THIN-FILM PV MODULES IN BIPV SYSTEMS

Stefan Grünsteidl, Peter Borowski, Thomas Dalibor
AVANCIS GmbH, Otto-Hahn-Ring 6, 81739 München, Germany
Phone: +49(0) 89 219620 458, Email: stefan.gruensteidl@avancis.de

ABSTRACT: This work presents long-term operational data of CIGS-based PV systems across varying levels of integration and environmental exposure. Environmental data including module temperatures, air flow, surface moisture, and relative humidity of building integrated PV installations are shown. Different module orientations in the context of the usage of module optimizers were analysed. Performance evaluations of commercial and R&D systems confirm the long-term stability of CIGS PV modules with no or minimal degradation observed over more than a decade, including the latest generation of CIGS PV modules featuring gallium-rich absorbers, sodium post deposition treatment, and a dry ZnOS buffer.

Keywords: outdoor, performance, temperature, irradiance, yield, degradation, BIPV, CIGS, optimizers, orientations, environmental, wind flow, surface moisture, humidity

1 INTRODUCTION

Building-integrated photovoltaic (BIPV) installations are generally different to most common PV installations in terms of irradiance levels, shadowing conditions and operational temperatures. Realistic monitoring data sets are essential for yield assessments, predictive simulation, and degradation analyses.

Yet, extensive analyses on the operational data of running BIPV installations are still limited (see [1] for a notable exception). In this work, long-term operational data of CIGS BIPV systems with different building integration level are analysed, including systems featuring the latest generation of CIGS module development with gallium-rich absorbers, sodium post deposition treatment and a dry, sputtered ZnOS buffer.

The PV systems considered in the present article all consist of thin-film PV modules by the manufacturer AVANCIS and were produced in its factory in Torgau, Germany, under the product name PowerMax or SKALA (the latter one specifically for BIPV). The photovoltaic semi-conductive layer is based on a CIGS absorber, a material containing copper, indium, gallium, sulphur and selenium. Both the detailed composition of this absorber layer as well as the nature and properties of other layers in the stack can be varied leading to evolving generations of CIGS PV module technology, of which particularly the most recent one is considered in this work. The appearance of the PV module, particularly its colour, can differ from the standard black by varying the front glass [2].

The frameless module design (**Figure 1**) consists of two glasses in a laminate with a thickness of about 6 mm. Mounting of module is accomplished by two steel backrails glued to the backside of the glass-glass laminate. Laminate, backrail and glue beads between both lead to a total dimension of 38 mm perpendicular to the glass surface and a total weight of about 17 kg. Using specific metallic clamps, the backrails are mounted on four points to a conventional substructure, whose width together with the extension of the backrail typically define the minimum air gap between the rear glass of the PV module and the outer building wall in a BIPV facade system.

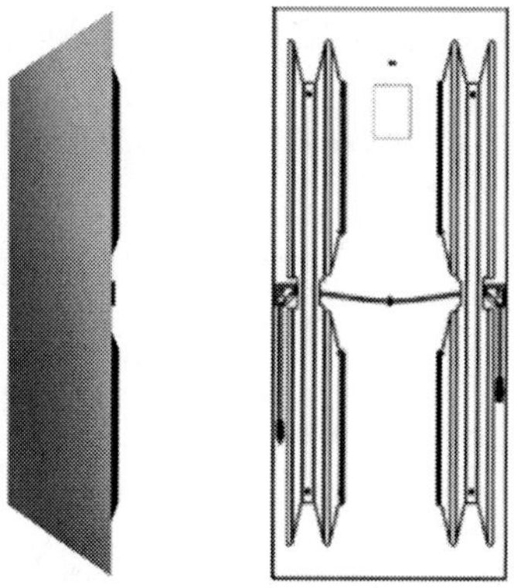

Figure 1: AVANCIS SKALA in standard size (dimensions 1587 × 664 × 38 mm³) in its variety 7003 (blue) and a technical drawing of its rear side showing the two steel backrails for mounting.

Electrical yield and long-term performance of three vertically installed PV systems is presented in section 2 of the present paper. Two of these systems are typical BIPV systems. Section 3 presents monitoring data relevant for building physics for three systems, such as module temperature, air speed and relative humidity between vertically installed PV modules and the building wall. In section 4, we return to energy yield, focussing on long-term stability of yield and CIGS PV modules both from operational PV systems and a R&D test bench, with some data dating back 15 years.

10.4229/EUPVSEC2025/4BV.4.24
020307-001

2 VERTICALLY INSTALLED PV SYSTEMS, PERFORMANCE DATA

The performance of three PV installations with vertically installed AVANCIS CIGS modules is shown in this section. An overview of the installations is given in **Figure 2**. Compared to yield-optimised inclined PV systems, vertically installed PV modules receive lower values of irradiance and therefore operate at low light conditions more often. Particularly for highly integrated BIPV systems, lower values for the performance ratio (PR) are to be expected in general. In the following, we show data for AC yield and PR, with the exception of the cube Torgau and the individual modules in section 4, for which DC values were evaluated.

PV installation: Cube Torgau (DE)	BIPV house: Mokropsy (CZ)	BIPV installation: Eichstätt (DE)

Vertical solar installation along all cardinal directions with module optimizers and irradiance sensors	Residential home with BIPV modules facing 3 different directions (SSE, SW, SE)	BIPV system on a south-facing facade with restricted ventilation behind the modules

Figure 2: Vertical PV systems with AVANCIS CIGS thin-film PV modules SKALA evaluated for performance data, operational in Germany and Czech Republic.

2.1 PV installation: Cube Torgau (DE)

The first vertical installation with AVANCIS CIGS modules shown in **Figure 2** was already introduced in [3] with solely irradiance data comparisons shown. Modules are installed in such a way on an open steel structure that the same number of modules is pointing into each of the four cardinal directions. Pairs of modules are connected to DC/DC power optimizers, which are connected in series to an inverter. Irradiance and module temperature are recorded with a data acquisition period of 15 minutes. In the following, performance data of the plant over several years are shown and compared to irradiance data over the seasons.

In this case, only DC yield of the optimizers can be analysed for the individual module planes as all optimizers form one electrical string. The results are shown in **Figure 3**. While the performance has been generally stable over the years, there are some general performance differences visible between the sides of the cubes, and some performance dips present for the western and northern directions towards the winter months.

The southern and eastern DC performance ratio lies at about 90%. The west-facing modules almost reach this level but show a lot less performance with low sun angles towards the winter months due to an adjacent building, which affects the modules stronger in comparison to the irradiance sensor. The performance dips of the north-facing modules have a different reason though, as these are quasi not influenced by shadowing. The overall lower performance level seems to originate firstly from low light losses of the PV modules, as the low light condition is the dominating condition for a north-facing PV installation in the northern hemisphere. Secondly, the DC/DC power optimizers, to which the modules facing North are connected, work mostly in the low power regime in comparison with the other facade sides. As 405 W optimizers were used for the nominal 260 Wp of a pair of modules, high conversion losses are expected for the north-facing system, specifically for the timeframes when a lot of current adaptation between optimizers must be done (sun on other module directions).

So even without the winter months, the performance ratio of the north-facing modules is more than 12 percentage points lower in comparison. For the whole timeframe evaluated, the PR for the north-facing part is at 72%, about 18 percentage points lower than for the other cardinal directions.

10.4229/EUPVSEC2025/4BV.4.24

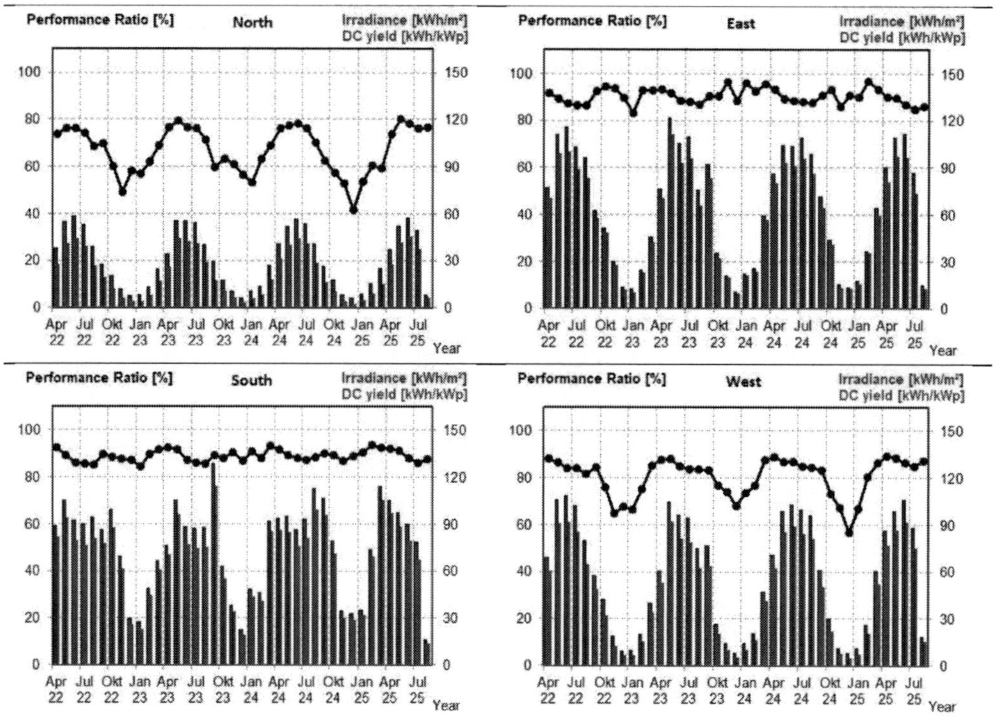

Figure 3: DC performance data of the vertical PV installation in Torgau (DE) for the individual cardinal directions. Since modules facing different directions are mixed within the strings, only the DC yield of the DC/DC power optimizers can be evaluated for the individual sides of the system. Shown is the monthly irradiance and DC yield (bars), as well as the monthly performance ratios (points and line).

2.2 BIPV house: Mokropsy (CZ)

Also the second vertical installation shown in **Figure 2** was introduced in [3]. The site consists of three BIPV facades, fully equipped with an optimizer system with two to five AVANCIS CIGS PV modules connected in parallel to a single DC/DC power optimizer. The electrical DC and AC data is monitored every 15 minutes with a commercial system. The sensor data is recorded every 5 minutes.

The site uses 4 miniature silicon pyranometers type ML 02 by EKO for the measurement of irradiance into the horizontal and three vertical modules' planes. The miniature sensors were chosen because only those were integrable into the residential building without any negative visual impact. When comparing data for the southern (SSE) façade, it was possible to quantify shading events, such as vegetation growth in summertime which diminishes the power by 10% to 15% for some optimizers, as shown in **Figure 4**. The other façade sides (SW/SE) were not influenced by plant growth to that extend and could not be analysed for AC performance ratio changes to that extend as SW/SE were both connected to the same inverter unit.

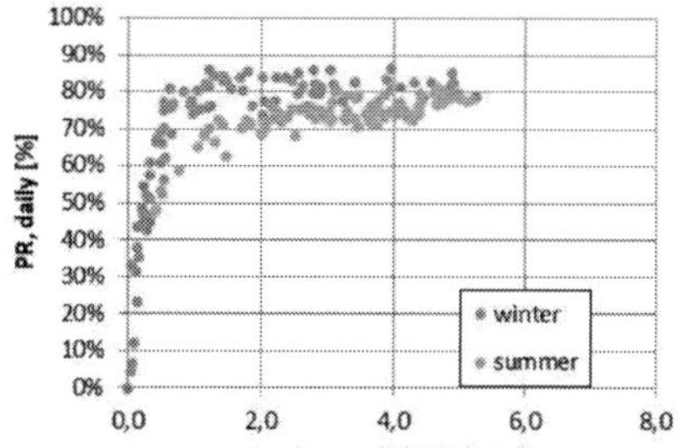

Figure 4: Seasonal performance data of the BIPV system Mokropsy (CZ), SSE facade, for the months July to September (summer), and October to December (winter) 2023/24.

Since the optimizers of the SE and SW facades are connected within one string to the same inverter, and the SSE inverter only reached full grid connectivity in summer 2023, the gathered data up to this point is still limited. Therefore, evaluations of the long- term performance have not been performed yet.

2.3 BIPV installation: Eichstätt (DE)

The BIPV system in Eichstätt (DE) is a commercial PV system on the southern facade of an indoor climbing gym that went into operation in late 2017. The plant shows good and reliable performance since then, as shown in **Figure 5**. The performance ratio is about 80%, despite partial shading by façade cover, inverter limitation, and high module temperatures due to limited ventilation. With more than 7 years in operation, this system is among the longest running monitored commercial BIPV systems with CIGS PV modules and its performance data has been reported earlier together with externally monitored data of a long-running free-field PV system, showing stable operation of AVANCIS CIGS PV modules for 10 years [4].

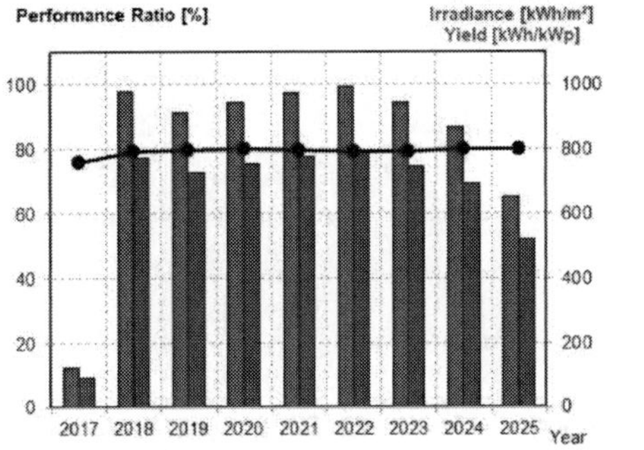

Figure 5: Performance data of the BIPV system in Eichstätt (DE): Yearly irradiance and yield (bars) and yearly PR (points and line). Lower values in 2017 and 2025 derive from the system not being operational during the whole year.

3 SENSOR DATA FROM BIPV SYSTEMS

Since a BIPV system by definition [5][6] fulfils an integral role for the building in which it is installed, other physical quantities than just electrical energy yield come into focus. Both the influence of the PV modules on the building as well as the operational conditions of the PV modules when installed in a non-conventional manner are of interest. To collect data for some of these quantities, we have equipped two commercial BIPV systems with additional sensors for building physics data and built a PV facade particularly for this purpose. In this section, data acquired for module temperature, air speed close to and behind a ventilated PV facade and data on moisture will be presented. Sensors are installed in the systems Mokropsy (CZ) and Eichstätt (DE) as introduced above, as well as a vertical PV installation in Torgau (DE) as shown in **Figure 6**. Following the definition of BIPV, the latter PV system constitutes a building-attached system, rather than being building-integrated.

Figure 6: Vertical PV installation on a south-west-facing building facade with advanced sensor system in Torgau (DE). Sensors for ambient air, wind speed and direction, rain and irradiance can be seen to the right of the PV modules.

3.1 Module temperatures

All module temperature sensors used in this study were PT1000 sensors, encapsulated with temperature conductive fluids into an aluminium housing and glued to the module glass backsides with durable double-sided adhesive tape. The data acquisition systems used were self-made (Mokropsy) and commercially available (Torgau, Eichstätt) systems using reference resistors for resistance measurements and a time resolution of 1 minute (Torgau) and 5 minutes (Mokropsy, Eichstätt).

As adhesive tapes can detach over time, monthly maximum values for each installation were checked over time for signs of detachment, which would show up as a drop in the highest temperature readings. This was only observed for the installation in Torgau, so the data set was reduced down to the initial year, and the final two years during which sensors were reattached. Also, for the system in Torgau, only one of the two sensors showed reliable results. For the installation in Mokropsy, PV modules face three different directions with three different sets of sensors installed. Irradiance was measured using silicon sensors, with the exception of the facade in Torgau having a pyranometer instead.

In summary, there were 2547291, 345501 and 172850 useable data sets for the sites Torgau, Mokropsy and Eichstätt, respectively. The data sets Torgau included the years 2018-2019 and 2022-2024, with two different sets of modules installed in these time frames (black and coloured). The site Mokropsy could only be evaluated between July 2023 and August 2025, while the site Eichstätt has fully useable data sets from October 2017 until August 2025.

All three installations shown in this section have a very different ventilation situation. While the façade in Torgau has a large air gap of about 25cm behind the modules, the gap behind the rear glass of the PV modules in Mokropsy and the building wall is only about 9cm. The modules in Eichstätt were directly mounted on covered wooden beams, which left only a small air gap of around 3cm and in addition stronger encapsulation towards the sides of the module field. For reasons of design, the module field is framed on all sides by cladding material, even slightly covering the modules in the West. Therefore, convection for the Eichstätt installation was reduced to a minimum, with gaps between the modules of 1.0-1.4cm (horizontally and vertically, respectively). The difference in ventilation can be seen in the results in **Figure 7**.

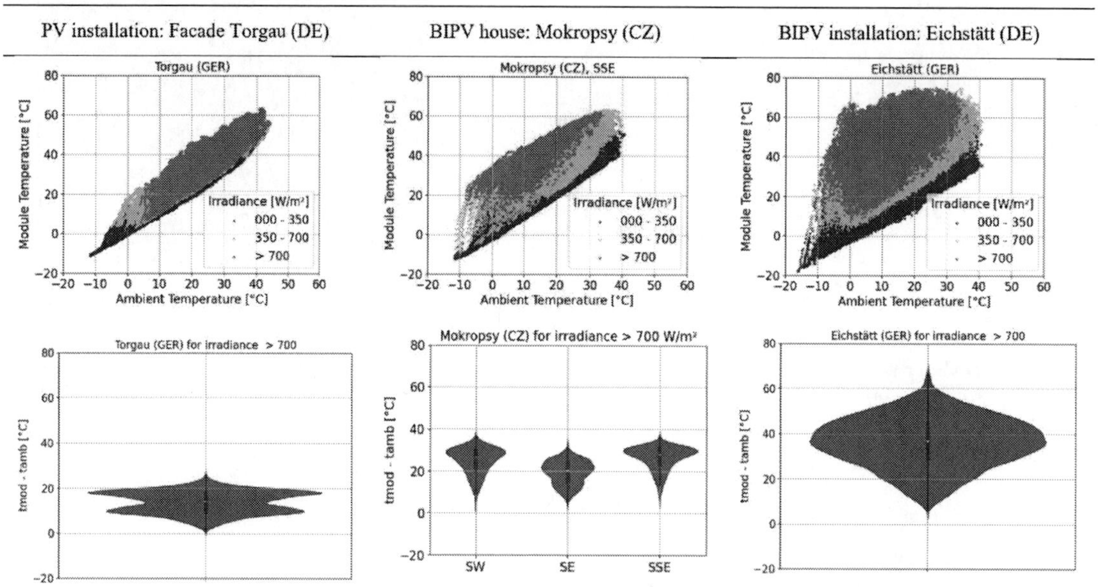

Figure 7: Module temperatures (as measured on the rear side of the PV modules) in comparison to ambient temperatures for the three vertical PV installations during operation. Top row: Module temperatures over ambient temperatures for three levels of irradiance. Bottom row: Frequency distribution of the difference between module temperature (tmod) and ambient temperature (tamb) for irradiance levels above 700 W/m².

Following the expectation [7], the PV modules installed with a large air gap and no restriction to the air flow below and above the PV installation showed the lowest temperature levels above ambient temperatures. In contrast, the PV modules in Eichstätt with the minimal air gap and air flow strongly restricted by the framing of the building envelope become much warmer. Module temperatures during operation in this non-ideal case can reach up to 70°C above ambient temperatures, but no module temperature above 80°C was observed. On average and for regular facade installations with CIGS PV modules, the module temperatures are between 20°C and 30°C above ambient temperature for high irradiance levels and during full operation of the PV façade installation. Compared to an optimally inclined free-field PV installation, ventilation and therefore cooling of the PV modules is often strongly reduced in a BIPV system and module temperatures are higher in the latter. However, since irradiance for vertical installations is strongly reduced compared to typical inclined rooftop systems, module temperatures in both cases can be comparable [1].

3.2 Air flow

Air flow sensors were installed for the facade installation in Torgau, with one being an environmental sensor including wind speed and wind direction, and two being sensors for monitoring wind speed and temperature behind the facade, each installed behind the portrait and landscape mounted modules (see **Figure 8**). The air flow sensor for the portrait mounted modules was located about 1m from the northern edge of the module field. The air flow sensor for the landscape mounted modules was located about 2m from the southern end of the module field, with both sensors being on a similar level above ground.

The data acquisition for all sensors was within the same system, which was well synchronized and with a time resolution of 1 minute. As one of the two sensors broke in July 2019, only 12 months of data were available, with a total of 697662 timestamps.

10.4229/EUPVSEC2025/4BV.4.24

Wall mounted wind speed and wind direction sensor (Windsonic GILL), placed to the right of the PV modules. In the image the ambient temperature / relative humidity sensor (left – CS215 SDI-12) and pyranometer (bottom right – K&Z CMP3) are shown, as well.

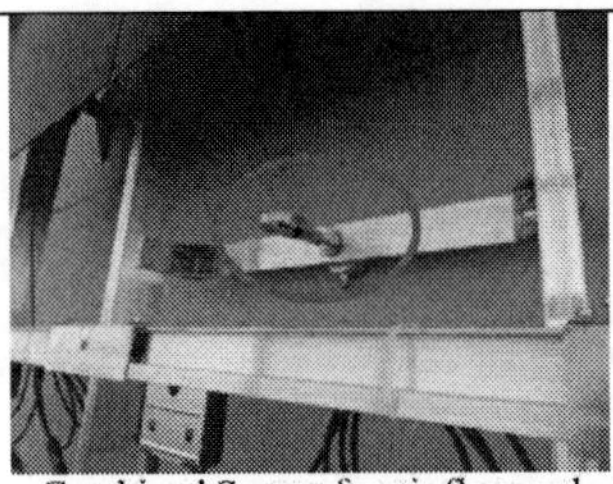

Combined Sensor for air flow and temperature (Schmidt SS 20.500 with guard bracket), behind portrait mounted modules (modules taken off the substructure for this image).

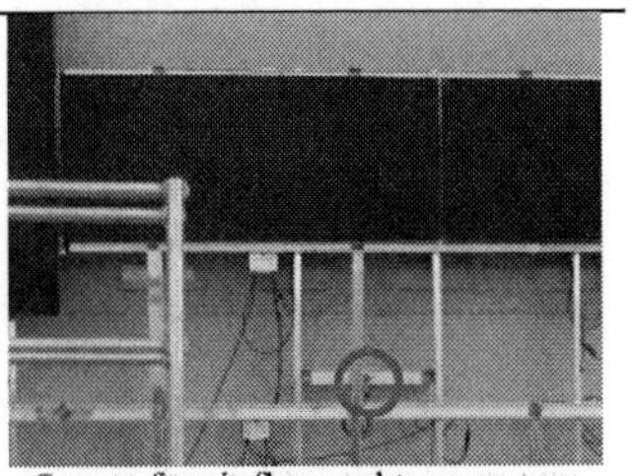

Sensor for air flow and temperature behind landscape mounted modules (modules taken off substructure for this image).

Figure 8: Wind and air flow sensors installed for the site Torgau.

The results of the air flow evaluations are shown in **Figure 9**. Generally, the wind directions for the façade installation follow the façade walls towards North-West and South-East, as this is a south-western facing façade. The dominant western winds of the northern hemisphere result in the largest wind portion of south-eastern directions.

Further, high wind speeds at the façade do not necessarily affect the air flow velocity behind the façade. The diagrams show that the highest air velocities behind the modules were reached for moderate wind speeds. Generally, the air velocity behind the modules is higher for the portrait mounted modules, as compared to the modules mounted in landscape orientation. The average difference between the two sensors (mounted between the modules in portrait and in landscape) for the complete time interval was 0.1 m/s. This could be attributed to the direction of the modules' backrails, as these are aligned along the long module side and thus could generate more air disturbances for the landscape mounted modules. It is also probable that the stronger enclosure of the landscape air flow sensor towards the sides leads to lower flow speeds behind the modules. The strength of air flow in the air gap behind the curtain wall made of PV modules depend in a complex manner on the details of the installation (obstruction), wind speed and direction outside, irradiance onto the PV modules and others. For the system considered, with a comparably large air gap of 25cm, the average air flow speed behind the facade modules is about 0.5 m/s.

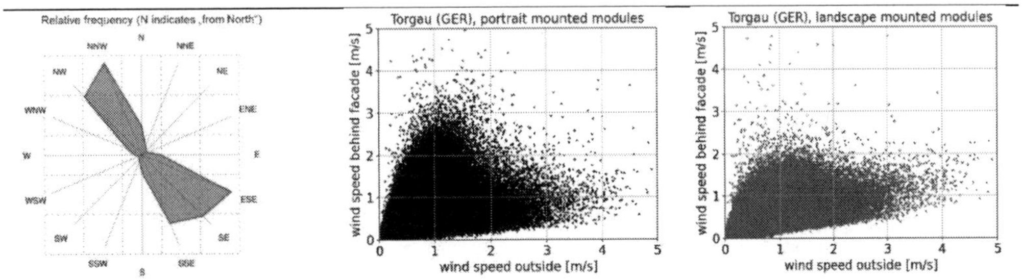

Figure 9: Measurement data of the wind and air flow sensors installed for the site Torgau. Left: Distribution of wind direction as measured by the wall-mounted wind sensor. Middle and Right: Air speed as measured by the sensors installed in the air gap behind the PV modules vs. wind speed outside the PV system.

10.4229/EUPVSEC2025/4BV.4.24

3.3 Surface moisture and dew

Due to the open construction of a curtain wall, rain, particularly wind-driven rain, can find its way to the rear side of the facade elements and accumulate, e.g., in hollows or recesses of the PV module or mounting structure. Also, since one advantage of a curtain wall is to keep moisture and particularly dew away from the building wall, the colder, inner surface of the facade PV modules are prone to dew and condensation during nighttime. Some of the components of a curtain wall or BIPV facade might be sensitive to prolonged exposure to water. To assess this effect quantitatively we measured the time during which water was present at certain positions of the rear side of the PV modules in the facade installation Torgau.

The backrails of the AVANCIS CIGS modules form a horizontally oriented pocket, when the module is mounted in landscape orientation. A total amount of eight self-made pairs of electrodes was glued onto the non-conductive part of the backrail glue bead of these pockets for resistance measurements over a time span of 11 months (Jul/28/18 – Jun/18/19). The sensors show low resistances if water is present in the pockets, and high resistances when it dries off. The placement, setup and sensor reactions after a rain event are shown in **Figure 10**.

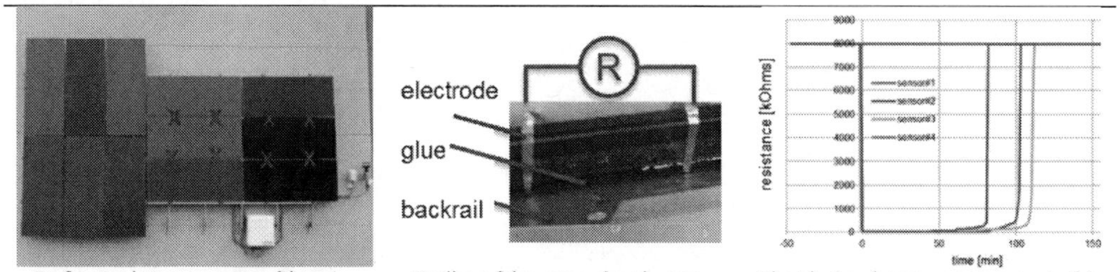

Surface moisture sensor positions (on the rear side of the PV modules) for the modules installed in landscape orientation for the system in Torgau.

Outline of the setup, showing two metal electrodes attached to the rear glass and touching the glue bead that holds the backrail to the rear glass. Electrical resistance is measured between the two electrodes.

Electrical resistance measurement of 4 sensors after a rain event (at time 0). Resistance strongly decreases due to the presence of water in the "pocket" but returns to high values after the water has dried off within about 100 minutes.

Figure 10: Setup and exemplary data of surface moisture measurements on modules' backrails after a rain event.

On average, moisture was detected for less than 10% of the total time, with the longest duration of almost 4 days for one sensor. The maximum duration for each sensor measured is shown in Table I.

sensor#1	sensor#2	sensor#3	sensor#4	sensor#5	sensor#6	sensor#7	sensor#8
0d 18:36	2d 08:56	3d 19:04	2d 08:08	2d 02:17	1d 09:12	1d 19:11	2d 09:29

Table I: Longest duration of surface moisture being detected for the 8 installed sensors over a time period of 11 months.

3.4 Relative humidity

Curtain walls are meant to keep moisture away from the actual building wall [8] by providing an air gap (minimum 20mm [9]) for ventilation. BIPV facade installations can act as a curtain wall and by that influence the building envelope [10]. The drying potential and moisture transport are important parameter for architects and building constructors. Yet there is only limited data of humidity measurements behind BIPV modules.

For the facade installation in Mokropsy, complete data sets of temperature, humidity and irradiance have been recorded for all three module surfaces. Sensors for temperature and air humidity (type SHT-10) were incorporated into the gap behind the AVANCIS CIGS modules (centre of the top module row).

The results (**Figure 11**) for data sets between July 2023 to September 2025 show an influence of the irradiance on the façade humidity, in terms that it gets significantly lower than the ambient humidity with higher irradiance level.

10.4229/EUPVSEC2025/4BV.4.24

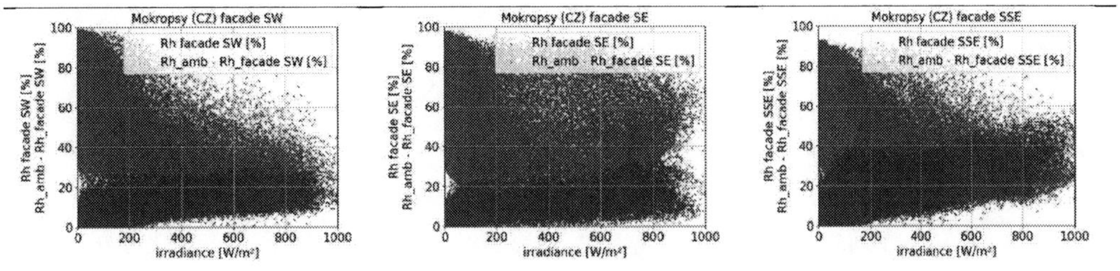

Figure 11: Relative air humidity (red) between PV modules and building wall for the site Mokropsy, with facade sides facing South-West, South-East and South-South-East plotted over irradiance. Also, the difference of the ambient relative humidity (Rh_amb) to the relative humidity behind the PV modules is shown (gray).

4 LONG-TERM PERFORMANCE DATA OF CIGS PV SYSTEMS

Stable electricity generation of a BIPV system built with AVANCIS CIGS thin-film PV modules over a duration of more than 7 years was shown earlier in **Figure 5**. In this section, we present monitoring data showing stable energy yield of AVANCIS CIGS PV modules for longer time durations both from operating PV systems and an R&D test bench. Since module technology has evolved over the years, we conclude the section with monitoring data obtained from AVANCIS CIGS PV modules of the latest generation.

4.1 Commercial systems

Within the framework of an outdoor monitoring project (see also [11]), several PV systems (mostly rooftop; typical size 5 kWp) were built using AVANCIS CIGS PV modules and equipped with sensors for monitoring. Monitoring of these systems (including environmental sensors for irradiance, ambient and module temperature) is facilitated by commercially available out-of-the-box solutions. As the maintenance of the systems and specifically the monitoring systems were not funded and not under control of AVANCIS, it proved to be difficult to keep these monitoring systems running reliably over longer periods of time. However, some of these systems delivering continuous data for more than six years are shown in **Figure 12**. The system in Switzerland is affected significantly by shadowing. The system in Kuwait by soiling by sand. Both effects are detrimental to the overall yearly performance.

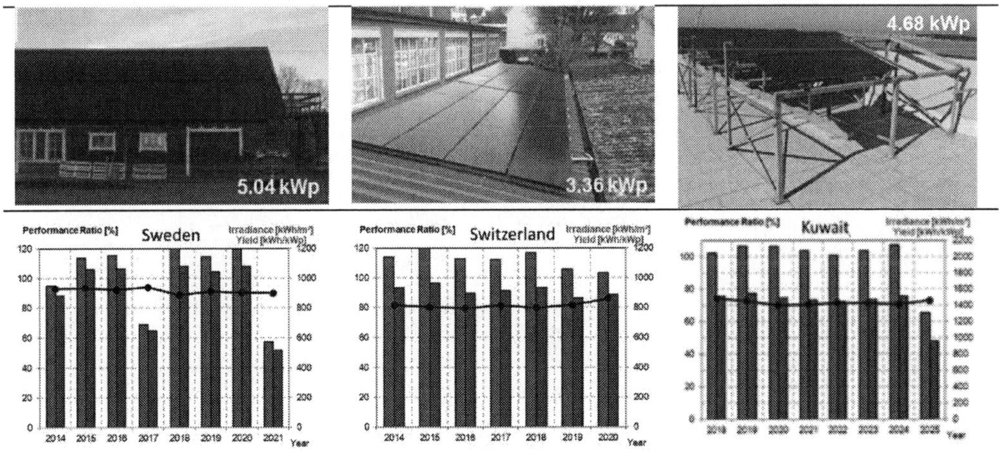

Figure 12: Commercial PV rooftop systems with AVANCIS CIGS PV modules showing stable performances over several years. Plotted is the yearly data for irradiance sum (red bar), electrical yield (gray bar) and performance ratio (points and line) for each year. Lower values in irradiance and yield are due to gaps in the data acquisition. The system in Switzerland is strongly affected by shadowing, the system in Kuwait by soiling, which is mitigated to some extent by regular cleaning of the PV modules.

4.2 Individual module monitoring

AVANCIS operates test rigs for R&D purposes at different locations for the outdoor monitoring of individual modules. The measurement setup on these test rigs traces the IV curve of each module every 10 seconds and records the environmental sensor data at the same time. Between IV sweeps, the modules are kept quasi steady state in their respective MPP. **Figure 13** shows filtered monitoring data of six modules, of which the oldest ones have been continuously monitored over the past 15 years since 2011. The high frequency of data acquisition combined with sensors for irradiance into the module plane, ambient and back-of-module temperature allows for a reliable analysis of stability and potential degradation of the PV modules. The data shown in **Figure 13** is filtered for data points near standard testing conditions (STC). PV module 6 has an initial stabilization phase, while this had a significant higher output power compared to the other modules (120 Wp). None of the six modules shows any clear sign of degrading of electrical power, with a very stable performance for the past 15 years. The continuous increase of power (as extracted from outdoor monitoring) for 4 of the 6 modules considered can in parts be due to stabilization effects known to exist in CIGS PV modules (lightsoaking) or an effect of the self-referencing ([12][13]) for irradiance monitoring. Using instead the data of the irradiance sensors installed, however, leads to a comparable evolution, with slightly decreased dynamics.

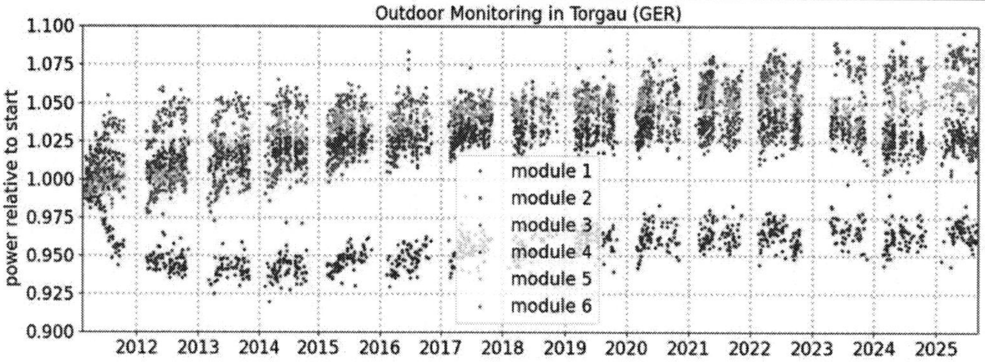

Figure 13: Electrical power relative to initial power (daily averages) for six long-running commercial AVANCIS CIGS modules over the past 15 years, filtered for temperature (23°C-27°C) and self-referenced irradiance close to STC conditions. The modules are operating and being monitored on a R&D test rig in Torgau, Germany.

As a result of continuous research and development, the composition and processing of commercially available AVANCIS thin-film PV modules underwent several generations, improving photon conversion efficiency and electrical energy generation. Accordingly, the long-running PV modules whose data is presented in **Figure 13** cannot contain the latest generation of AVANCIS PV modules. For the latter (comprising a gallium-rich absorber, sodium post deposition treatment and a dry, sputtered ZnOS buffer [14]). **Figure 14** shows the electrical power of the PV modules close to STC as derived from sensor data (self-referenced irradiance very close to 1000 W/m^2 and module temperature between 23 and 27°C). In Germany with the tilt angle as installed in the test rig, STC conditions are not met during wintertime and during summertime, typically only during sunrise or variable, partially cloudy weather conditions.

For all three modules, the monitoring data shown indicates stable electrical performance at STC during the course of a bit more than 4 years. From the data, a slight increase in electrical power could be concluded but further analysis (e.g., drift in sensor readings, soiling, ...) would be necessary to verify this.

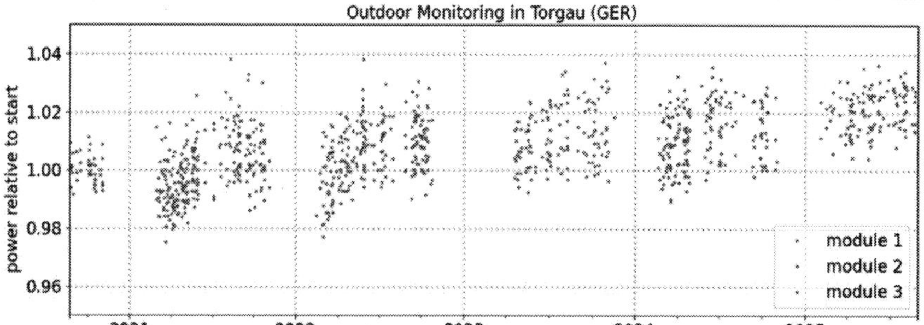

Figure 14: Electrical power relative to initial power (self-referenced close to STC conditions, daily averages) of three long-running AVANCIS CIGS modules of the latest generation of CIGS PV modules over the past 4 years.

5 CONCLUSIONS

This study presents long-term operational data from AVANCIS CIGS PV installations across different integration levels and environmental conditions. The results highlight significant differences in module temperature behaviour depending on ventilation and mounting configurations, with values typically ranging 20–30°C above ambient temperature and remaining below 80°C module temperature. Air flow behind modules was shown and found to be low even at high facade wind speeds, while surface moisture occurred only intermittently even for exposed module facades and for limited durations, being dried off after few days. Air humidity measurements behind the modules show a clear dependence on irradiance.

Performance monitoring of commercial and R&D systems showed excellent long-term stability of AVANCIS CIGS PV modules, with no or minimal degradation over more than a decade. Stability was also shown in the latest generation of CIGS module development with gallium-rich absorbers, sodium post deposition treatment and a dry, sputtered ZnOS buffer over a period of more than 4 years of outdoor operation. Losses of a system equipped with module DC/DC optimizers for a north-facing facade were shown when interconnected with modules facing other directions. Overall, the results demonstrate the robustness and reliability of advanced CIGS thin-film technologies for building-integrated and free-field PV applications, while also underlining the importance of ventilation, mounting, and system design for optimal performance.

6 REFERENCES

[1] N. Albinius et al., "A comprehensive case study of a full-size BIPV facade", Energies 18(5), 1293 (2025)

[2] T. Dalibor et al., "Cu(In, Ga)(Se, S)$_2$ thin-film technology: Aspects of historical development, current status, and future prospects", IJAGS 16(2) 16696 (2024)

[3] S. Grünsteidl et al., "Irradiance transposition and reflections in BIPV installations", Proc. of the 41st EUPVSEC, 020406 (2024)

[4] AVANCIS GmbH, "Long-term stability of PowerMax and SKALA CIGS modules: energy yield confirmed by Fraunhofer ISE", Press Release (2022) https://www.avancis.de/_Resources/Persistent/2/2/9/a/229a81486cf6c28669b78761f6416f8aea27ac6c/PR%20AVANCIS%20Long%20term%20stability%20PowerMax%20and%20SKALA%20090522%20engl.pdf

[5] EN 50583-1, "Photovoltaics in buildings" (2024)

[6] International Energy Agency, "International definitions of BIPV", Report IEA-PVPS T15-04 (2018)

[7] G. Girma et al., "Experimental investigation of cavity air gap depth for enhanced thermal performance of ventilated rain-screen walls", Building and Environment 194, 107710 (2021)

[8] W. Willems (Editor), "Lehrbuch der Bauphysik", 8th Edition, Springer Verlag

[9] DIN 18516-1, "Cladding for external walls, rear-ventilated" (2024)

[10] J. Brozovsky et al., "Modelling and validation of hygrothermal conditions in the air gap behind wood cladding and BIPV in the building envelope", Building and Environment 228, 109917 (2023)

[11] S. Grünsteidl et al., "Evaluation of Irradiance Sensor Technologies for Plant Monitoring of PV Systems with CIGS Thin Film Modules", Proc. of the 35th EUPVSEC, 2021 (2018)

[12] A. Jagomägi et al., "European Network of PV Outdoor Testing - Steps Towards Harmonized Procedures", Proc. of the 24th EUPVSEC, 3432 (2009)

[13] P. Borowski et al., "Energy rating of CIGS thin film modules and systems", Proc. of the 27th EUPVSEC, 2294 (2012)

[14] H. Elanzeery et al., "Beyond 20% World Record Efficiency for Thin-Film Solar Modules", IEEE Journal of Photovoltaics, 14(1), 107–115 (2023)

10.4229/EUPVSEC2025/4BV.4.24

42nd European Photovoltaic Solar Energy Conference and Exhibition

4BV.4.24

PERFORMANCE, OPERATIONAL DATA AND STABILITY OF COMMERCIAL CIGS THIN-FILM PV MODULES IN BIPV SYSTEMS

Stefan Grünsteidl*, **Peter Borowski, Thomas Dalibor**

AVANCIS GmbH, Otto-Hahn-Ring 6, 81739 Munich, Germany
*stefan.gruensteidl@avancis.de

AVANCIS CNBM

Abstract: This work presents long-term operational data of CIGS-based PV systems across varying levels of integration and environmental exposure. Environmental data including module temperatures, air flow, surface moisture, and relative humidity of building-integrated PV (BIPV) installations are shown. Different module orientation in the context of optimizer systems were analysed. Performance evaluations of commercial and R&D systems confirm the long-term stability of CIGS PV modules, with no or minimal degradation observed over more than a decade, including the latest generation of CIGS PV modules featuring gallium-rich absorbers, sodium post-deposition treatment, and a dry ZnOS buffer [1].

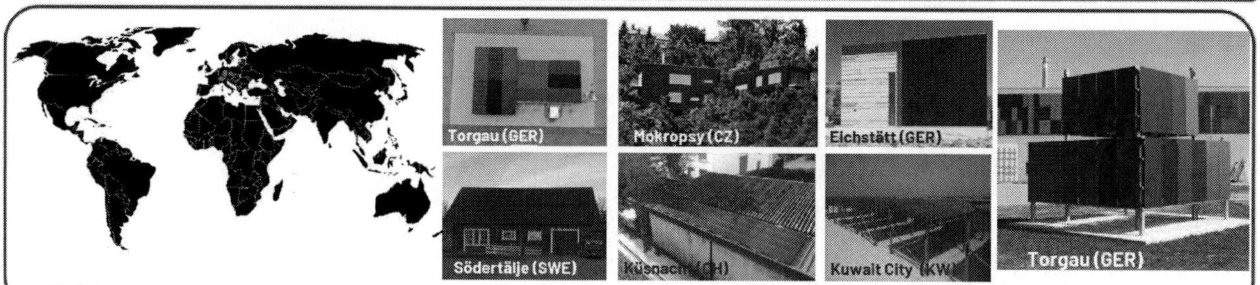

Fig. 1: Overview and locations of the solar installations covered in this study. All PV systems are built using commercial CIGS PV modules by AVANCIS (PowerMax or SKALA).

Module temperatures

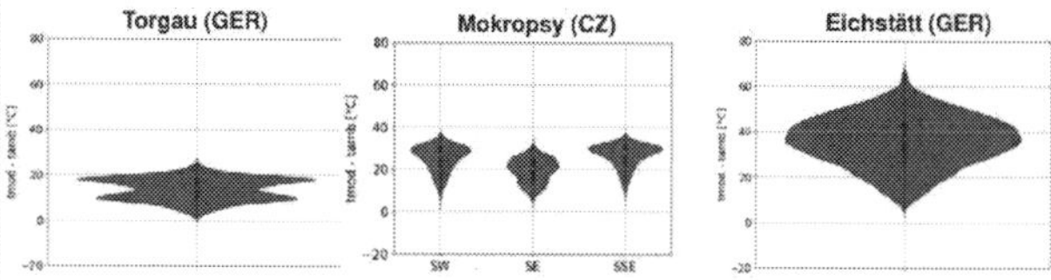

Fig. 2: Module temperature (as measured on the rear side of the PV modules) in comparison to ambient temperature for three sites [2] for irradiances above 700 W/m².

Façade air flows

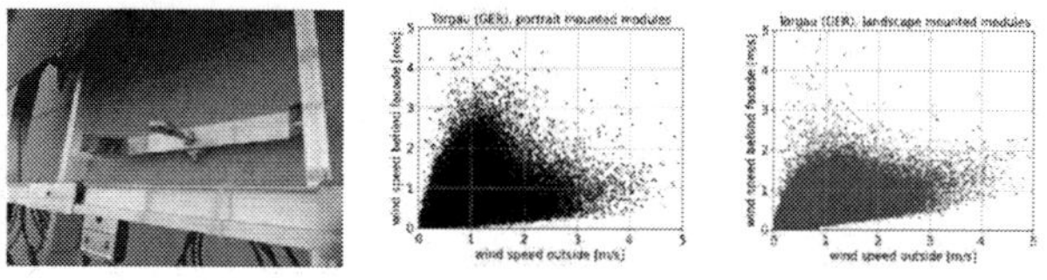

Fig. 3: Air flow speeds between PV modules and building wall over ambient wind speeds for vertically (black) and horizontally (red) installed modules in Torgau (GER).

Surface moisture and humidity behind façade

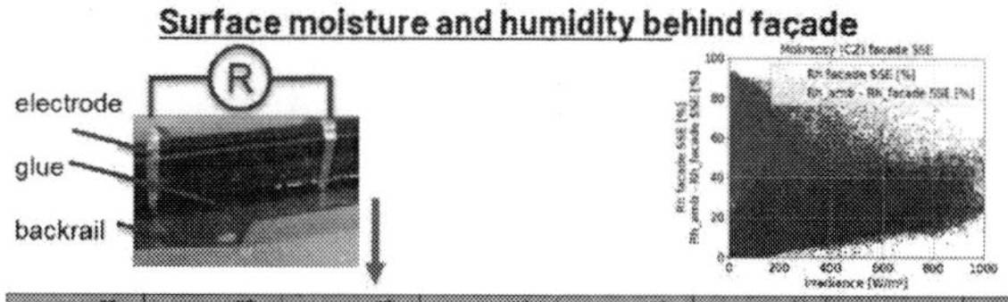

sensor#1	sensor#2	sensor#3	sensor#4	sensor#5	sensor#6	sensor#7	sensor#8
0d 18:36	2d 08:56	3d 19:04	2d 08:08	2d 02:17	1d 09:12	1d 19:11	2d 09:29

Fig. 4: Data of self-made surface moisture sensors on modules' backrails (left), showing the maximum duration of water detection for each sensor over 11 months in Torgau (GER) on modules installed in landscape orientation. – Also, relative air humidity between PV modules and building wall over irradiance (right) is shown for the site Mokropsy (CZ).

Outdoor monitoring newest CIGS generation

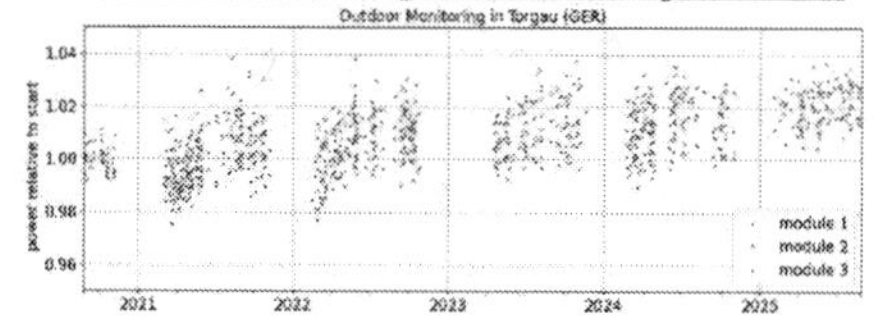

Fig. 5: Electrical power relative to initial power (self-referenced close to STC conditions, daily averages) of three long-running AVANCIS CIGS modules of the latest generation of CIGS PV modules over the past 4 years.

Long-term stability of commercial PV installations

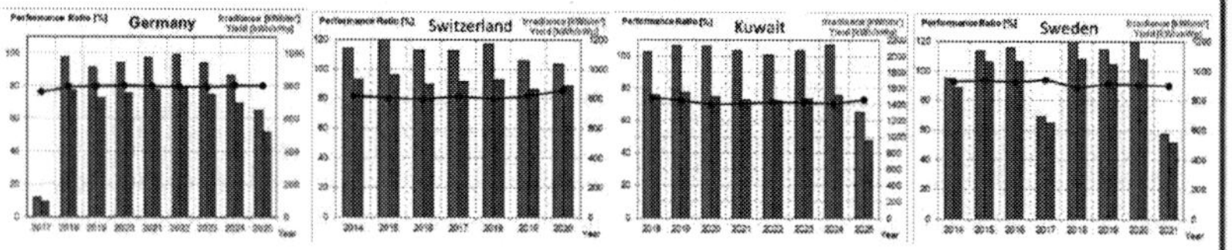

Fig. 6: Long-term performance data for PV systems in Eichstätt (GER), Küsnacht (CH), Kuwait City (KW) and Södertälje (SWE), showing performance ratio, yield and in-plane irradiance for each year.

Long-term stability of individual PV modules

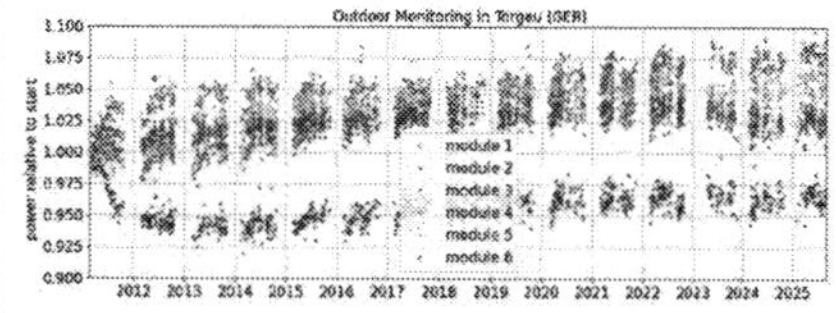

Fig. 7: Electrical power relative to initial power (self-referenced close to STC conditions, daily averages) for six randomly chosen long running commercial AVANCIS CIGS modules over the past 15 years

Conclusions

- Module temperatures typically ranging 20-30°C above ambient temperature, depending on ventilation situation, and remaining below 80°C
- Data sets of air flows behind PV modules, air humidity and surface moisture durations shown
- Performance monitoring of commercial and R&D systems show excellent long-term stability of AVANCIS CIGS modules, with no or minimal degradation over more than a decade.

References

[1] H. Elanzeery et al., "Beyond 20% World Record Efficiency for Thin-Film Solar Modules", IEEE Journal of Photovoltaics, vol. 14, no. 1, pp. 107-115 (2023)

[2] Irradiance and module temperature data sets for the 3 sites https://github.com/gruenst/PVsec2025

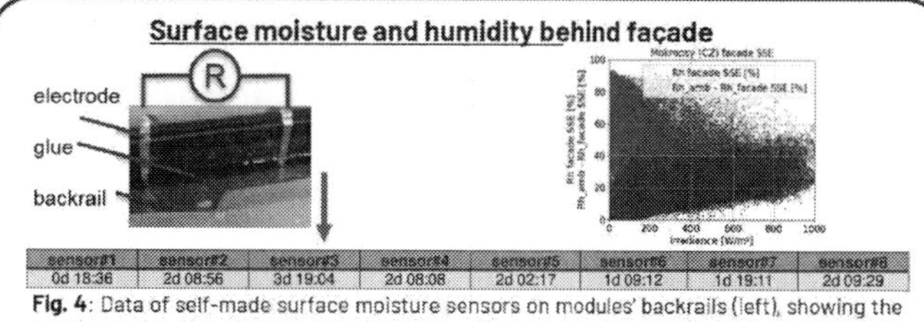

PHOTOVOLTAIC INTEGRATION IN FOOTBALL STADIUMS: GLOBAL TRENDS, REGIONAL DISPARITIES, FUTURE POTENTIAL

Johanna Buchmann†, Niels Feuerherdt†, Bert Stegemann*
University of Applied Sciences – HTW Berlin, Wilhelminenhofstr. 75a, D-12459 Berlin, Germany
*bert.stegemann@htw-berlin.de

ABSTRACT: Football stadiums are both major energy consumers and highly visible infrastructures, making them ideal showcase projects for renewable energies and, particularly, photovoltaics (PV). This study systematically evaluates the use of PV systems in professional football stadiums worldwide. A comprehensive overview is provided for Germany, Austria, and Switzerland, while highlights from other regions and countries illustrate global developments. The results show clear regional differences: Germany and Switzerland lead the way with widespread adoption, Brazil shows a tournament-driven catalyst effect, while major leagues such as Serie A, La Liga and the Premier League lag behind. Political measures, and to some extent major tournaments, proved to be the most important driving forces. Future developments are likely to combine PV with efficiency, storage and smart energy concepts, while falling costs and upcoming international tournaments (e.g. the 2030 FIFA World Cup) could promote further adoption.
Keywords: Photovoltaics, Football stadiums, Renewable energy, Policy impacts, Sustainability

1 INTRODUCTION, MOTIVATION, AND GOALS

Football stadiums represent both significant energy consumers and highly visible public infrastructures. Their transformation into sustainability showcases, particularly through the installation of photovoltaic (PV) systems, offers a unique opportunity to combine renewable energy production with global public outreach.

Recent publications on PV systems in stadiums show that there has been a development from early pilot roofs to building-integrated systems with a capacity of several MW, which can significantly cover the energy demands of the stadiums [1,2]. Case studies highlight architectural solutions such as thin-film or lightweight roofs, semi-transparent and façade PV, which adapt to complex geometries while preserving daylight and aesthetics [1,3]. Technical-economic studies show that PV, in combination with battery storage and smart operation, significantly improves profitability in addition to self-consumption [4]. More comprehensive reviews and case studies highlight the role of stadiums in supplying energy to communities and the importance of stable policy frameworks for sustainable deployment [5,6]. Major events can accelerate PV implementation, though in hot climates, solar-assisted cooling solutions may take precedence over rooftop PV systems [7].

So, current research exists, but there is a lack of comprehensive and up-to-date data across countries and leagues. Systematic evidence on the global distribution of PV systems in stadiums and their relationship to policy frameworks and major events is also limited. This study therefore aims to systematically document PV systems in football stadiums, assess their geographical and league-specific distribution, and evaluate the influence of regulatory frameworks and tournament-related dynamics. By combining detailed data collection with a comparative analysis of recent FIFA World Cups and UEFA European Championships, the study contributes to the understanding of how politics, market conditions and event-related incentives influence the adoption of PV systems. Particular attention is paid to regional differences and the role of tournament preparations as potential driver for the adoption of PV systems. In this way, the study provides an up-to-date data base that may enrich both academic research and public discussion about the future of PV in football stadiums.

2 APPROACH AND METHODOLOGY

This analysis is limited to football (soccer) stadiums and distinguishes between PV systems installed directly on the main stadium roof and those located on adjacent buildings or stadium grounds. Google Earth images were employed for verification where necessary. The league affiliation in the 2024/25 season served as the reference framework for the evaluation of the national leagues. Stadium projects under construction with scheduled completion in 2025 were also included. In cases of PV system expansions, cumulative installed capacities were reported. Where direct data were unavailable, capacities were estimated using yield numbers, module counts, or comparable indicators. This methodology ensures a systematic, reproducible, and up-to-date dataset.

3 STADIUM RANKINGS - BY GEOGRAPHY

This chapter contains a comparative ranking of football stadiums equipped with PV systems, sorted by geographical location: First, the 15 leading stadiums worldwide (outside Europe) are listed and ranked according to their installed PV capacity, followed by a ranking of the leading European and German stadiums. The year in which the PV system went into operation is also given for each case. The data was compiled through systematic research using the methodological approach described in chapter 2 to ensure consistency and comparability between regions.

3.1 Worldwide (except Europe)

The global ranking of PV systems integrated into stadiums outside Europe, see Table I, shows a striking pattern. Brazil dominates with several large-scale systems associated with the 2014 FIFA World Cup, including the Estádio Nacional Mané Garrincha in Brasília (2.5 MW_p) and other large PVsystems in Mineirão and Pernambuco. In Asia, the National Stadium in Kaohsiung, Taiwan (1 MW_p), and the Gelora Bung Karno Stadium in Indonesia are other notable examples.

A special case is the Stade du Sénégal in Dakar, where a 2.3 MW_p PV system is installed on carports rather than on the stadium roof. Though this does not strictly meet the criterion of a 'rooftop installation,' this project was included as the only representative from Africa and as a potential model for the future development of PV installations in stadiums on the continent.

In the US, numerous American football stadiums have been equipped with PV installations, but these were not included due to the different sporting context. Only venues that are regularly used for football (soccer), such as the stadium in Washington, D.C., were included.

Overall, the ranking shows that large PV stadium projects outside Brazil and Europe (see next section) remain exceptions, even in countries with a generally high level of PV deployment, such as China.

Table I: Top 15 football stadiums worldwide, but excluding Europe, ranked by installed PV capacity

Rank	Stadium	City	Country	Capacity kWp	Operation start
1	Estádio Nacional Mané Garrincha	Brasilia	Brazil	2500	2013
2	Stade du Senegal	Dakar	Senegal	2300 (carport)	2021
3	Mineirão Stadium	Belo Horizonte	Brazil	1420	2014
4	Al-Madina	Bagdad	Iraq	1050	2021
5	National Stadium	Kaohsiung	Taiwan	1000	2009
6	Gelora Bung Karno Main Stadium	Jakarta	Indonesia	1000	2019
7	Pernambuco Stadium	Recife	Brazil	1000	2013
8	Go Media Stadium	Auckland	New Zealand	780	2025
9	Audi Field	Washington, DC	USA	627.8	2020
10	Panasonic Stadium Suita	Osaka	Japan	504	2015
11	Itaipava Arena Fonte Nova	Salvador	Brazil	500	2014
12	Estádio Roberto Santos	Salvador	Brazil	400	2012
13	Estádio do Maracanã	Rio de Janeiro	Brazil	391	2014
14	Beijing Workers' Stadium	Peking, China	China	351	2023
15	Al-Bayt Stadium	Al Khor	Qatar	271	2021

3.2 Europe

In Europe (see Table II), four stadiums with PV systems of more than 2 MW_p stand out: Signal Iduna Park in Dortmund (4.2 MW_p, to be completed 2025), Rams Park in Istanbul (4.1 MW_p, 2023), Ernst Happel Stadium in Vienna (3.5 MW_p, 2023) and Europa Park Stadium in Freiburg (nearly 2.4 MW_p, 2022). All other stadiums in the ranking operate systems with capacities of above 1 MW_p, including notable examples in France, the Netherlands, the United Kingdom, Italy and Switzerland. Beyond the top 15, other European venues also exceed the 1 MW_p range, emphasizing the broad acceptance of stadium-integrated PV systems in Europe.

Table II: Top 15 European football stadiums ranked by installed PV capacity (* - estimated value)

Rank	Stadium	City	Country	Capacity kW_p	Operation start
1	Signal Iduna Park	Dortmund	Germany	4200	2025 (proj.)
2	Rams Park (Ali Sami Yen)	Istanbul	Türkiye	4100	2022
3	Ernst Happel Stadion	Vienna	Austria	3500	2025
4	Europa-Park Stadion	Freiburg	Germany	2387	2022
5	Merkur Spiel-Arena	Düsseldorf	Germany	1500	2025 (proj.)
6	Fritz-Walter-Stadion	Kaiserslautern	Germany	1350	2010
7	Allianz Riviera	Nice	France	1342.7	2013
8	Stadion Wankdorf	Bern	Switzerland	1300	2005
9	London Stadium	London	England	1256	2025 (proj.)
10	Kybunpark	St. Gallen	Switzerland	1205	2025
11	Stadion am Böllenfalltor	Darmstadt	Germany	1200	2024
12	RheinEnergie Stadion	FC Köln	Germany	1200	2025 (proj.)
13	Johan Cruijff ArenA	Amsterdam	Netherlands	1128	2014
14	Stadio Friuli	Udinese	Italy	1100	2024
15	Stadion Galgenwaard	Utrecht	Netherlands	1065*	2017

3.3 Germany

Germany is the country with the most advanced integration of PV systems in stadiums. The first PV system on the roof of a Bundesliga stadium was installed in 1995 at the Dreisam stadium in Freiburg. After expansions in 1999 and 2004, it reached a total output of 259 kW_p, making it a pioneer to set an important milestone for later projects. Since then, the use of PV systems has spread across both Bundesliga leagues as well as the lower leagues, with outputs ranging from small-scale to multi-MW systems. The top 15 are listed in Table III. The stadium in Dortmund (4.2 MW_p) will be the global leader, while existing stadiums e.g. in Freiburg, Mainz, Bremen and Frankfurt illustrate the continuity of PV integration in modern renovations.

A particularly innovative example is the Weser Stadium in Bremen, where three different PV components were implemented at an early stage. Lightweight thin-film modules were installed on the main roof to reduce wind load and structural stress. In addition, the inner roof ring features semi-transparent polycarbonate elements with integrated crystalline Si cells, while glass-glass PV modules were used for parts of the outer façade.

Table III: Top 15 German football stadiums ranked by installed PV capacity

Rank	Stadium	City	Capacity kW_p	Operation start
1	Signal Iduna Park	Dortmund	4200	2025 (proj.)
2	Europa-Park Stadion	Freiburg	2387	2022
3	Merkur Spiel-Arena	Düsseldorf	1500	2025 (proj.)
4	Fritz-Walter-Stadion	Kaiserslautern	1350	2010
5	Weserstadion	Bremen	1270	2009
6	Böllenfalltor	Darmstadt	1200	2024
7	RheinEnergieStadion	Köln	1200	2025 (proj.)
8	Mewa Arena	Mainz	846.3	2011
9	Erzgebirgsstadion	Aue	750	2021
10	Steigerwaldstadion	Erfurt	730	2016
11	Ostseestadion	Rostock	700	2010
12	Jahnstadion	Regensburg	632	2025
13	Olympiastadion Berlin	Berlin	605.25	2022
14	Deutsche Bank Park	Frankfurt	560	2024
15	Leuna-Chemie-Stadion	Halle	526	2011

4 STADIUM RANKINGS - BY NATIONAL LEAGUE

Beyond geographical distribution, the ranking by national leagues demonstrates how PV adoption differs structurally across football competitions. The German Bundesliga and 2nd Bundesliga show high acceptance rates compared to many other leagues, while Switzerland and Austria also have several notable projects. These rankings demonstrate that political framework conditions and club-level initiatives are decisive factors, rather than just solar potential or stadium size alone.

4.1 Germany - Bundesliga

In the Bundesliga, sustainability has clearly become an integral part of club strategies and stadium modernisation projects. Of the 18 clubs, seven currently operate PV systems directly on their stadium roofs, while another five have installed systems elsewhere on the stadium grounds, for example on ancillary buildings, car parks or other adjacent facilities. Several other clubs have projects in the planning or development phase. The analysis, see Table IV, therefore distinguishes between rooftop PV systems and systems located elsewhere on the stadium grounds.

10.4229/EUPVSEC2025/4BV.4.27

Table IV: Ranking of 1. Bundesliga clubs (as of season 2024/25) by installed PV capacity (stadium roof vs. stadium grounds)

Rank	Stadium	Team	Capacity kWp Roof	Capacity kWp Grounds	Operation start
1	Signal Iduna Park	Borussia Dortmund	4200		2025 (proj.)
2	Europa-Park	SC Freiburg	2387		2022
3	Wesrerstadion	Werder Bremen	1270		2009
4	Mewa ARENA	1. FSV Mainz 05	846.3		2011
5	DB Park	Eintracht Frankfurt	560		2024
6	Millerntor	FC St. Pauli	316		2025
7	Voith-Arena	1. FC Heidenheim	303.56		2015
8	PreZero Arena	TSG 1899 Hoffenheim		1046.5	
9	Allianz Arena	FC Bayern München		834	2019
10	Borussia-Park	Borussia Mönchengladb.		127	2024
11	Ruhrstadion	VfL Bochum		97	2023
12	Red Bull Arena	RB Leipzig		71.5	2020

4.2 Germany -2nd Bundesliga

In the 2nd Bundesliga, the number of roof-mounted PV systems is particularly notable, with 12 out of 18 clubs operating installations on their stadium roofs and one additional club hosting a PV system elsewhere on the stadium premises, see Table V. Examples include Fortuna Düsseldorf (Merkur Spiel-Arena), SV Darmstadt 98 (Böllenfalltor), and Hamburger SV (Volksparkstadion). This indicates that PV integration is not limited to top-tier clubs but extends across professional football in Germany.

Table V: Ranking of 2nd Bundesliga clubs (as of season 2024/25) by installed PV capacity: stadium roof vs. stadium grounds (* - estimated value)

Rank	Stadium	Team	Capacity kW_p Roof	Capacity kW_p Grounds	Operation start
1	Merkur Spiel-Arena	Fortuna Düsseldorf	1500		2025 (proj.)
2	Fritz-Walter-Stadion	1. FC Kaiserslautern	1350		2010
3	RheinEnergieStadion	1. FC Köln	1200		2025 (proj.)
4	Böllenfalltor	SV Darmstadt 98	1200		2024
5	Jahnstadion	SSV Jahn Regensburg	632		2025
6	Olympiastadion Berlin	Hertha BSC	605.25		2022
7	Volksparkstadion	Hamburger SV	520		2011
8	Home Deluxe Arena	SC Paderborn 07	500*		2012
9	Sportpark Ronhof	SpVgg Greuther Fürth	319.8		2022
10	Max-Morlock-Stadion	1. FC Nürnberg	284		2010
11	Eintracht-Stadion	Eintracht Braunschweig	262.3		2023
12	Wildpark	Karlsruher SC	100		2022
13	Veltins-Arena	FC Schalke 04		600	2012

Table VI: Ranking of Swiss Superleague clubs (as of season 2024/25) by installed PV capacity (* - estimated value)

Rank	Stadium	Team	Capacity kW_p Roof	Operation start
1	Stadion Wankdorf/Stade de Suisse	BSC Young Boys	1350	2025 (proj.)
2	Kybunpark	FC St. Gallen	1205	2010
3	swissporarena	FC Luzern	1097	2025 (proj.)
4	Stade de Genève	Servette FC	942	2024
5	St. Jakob-Park	FC Basel	850	2025
6	Stade de la Tuilière	FC Lausanne-Sport	800*	2022
7	Stade Municipal	Yverdon Sport FC	500*	2011
8	Letzigrund Stadion	FC Zürich / GH Zürich	223	2012
9	Stadion Schützenwiese	FC Winterthur	63.44	2022

4.3 Switzerland - Super League

Switzerland features a strong presence of stadium-integrated PV systems. The Stade de Suisse in Bern pioneered this development with 1.35 MW_p in 2005. Other MW- or near-MW examples include Kybunpark in St. Gallen, Swissporarena in Lucerne, and Stade de Genève). These installations illustrate how early adoption, supported by national sustainability policies, established Switzerland as a regional leader.

4.4. Austria - Bundesliga

Austria presents fewer but still relevant cases, with the Generali Arena in Vienna and the Wörthersee Stadion in Klagenfurt. The most prominent example nationwide is the Ernst Happel Stadium in Vienna, with 3.5 MW_p (see Table II) and represents the largest single installation in the country. However, as this venue is not used for regular league matches, it does not appear in the Bundesliga-specific ranking presented here. Though Austria lags behind Switzerland and Germany in terms of numbers capacity, these projects indicate a growing awareness and commitment.

Table VII: Ranking of Austrian Bundesliga clubs (as of season 2024/25) by installed PV capacity.

Rank	Stadium	Team	Capacity kW_p Roof	Operation start
1	Generali Arena	FK Austria Wien	825	2018-2024
2	28 Black Arena / Wörthersee Stadion	SK Austria Klagenfurt	137.5	2013

4.5 Comparative PV Coverage in European Football Leagues

The diagram in Figure 1 illustrates the extent of PV coverage across different European football leagues, measured as the proportion of stadium roofs equipped with photovoltaic systems. The results reveal striking regional disparities: Swiss Super League leads with more than 70% coverage, followed by the German 2nd Bundesliga at around 65%. The German Bundesliga and 3rd Liga also show above-average adoption levels. In contrast, leading European leagues such as Serie A (Italy), La Liga (Spain), Premier League (UK), and Ligue 1 (France) remain far behind, with coverages below 20%. The findings highlight the central role of policy incentives and national sustainability agendas in driving adoption, while sporting or economic prominence of leagues alone does not guarantee PV integration.

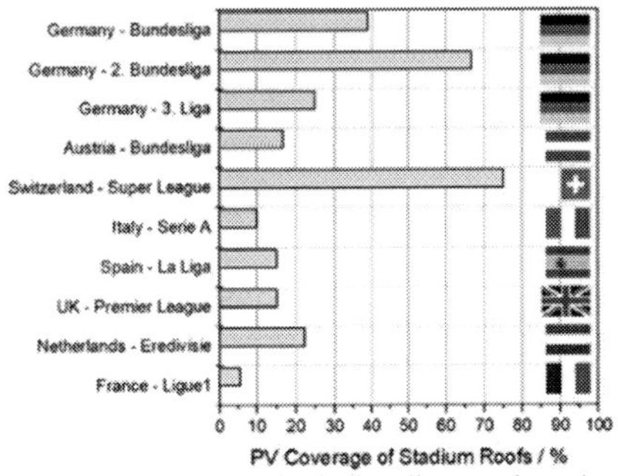

Figure 1: Percentage of football stadium roofs equipped with photovoltaic (PV) systems in selected European leagues (as of 2024/25 season).

10.4229/EUPVSEC2025/4BV.4.27

5 POLICIES AND TOURNAMENT DRIVEN EFFECTS

This section examines how recent UEFA European Championships (EUROs) and FIFA World Cups (WCs) have influenced the installation of PV systems on football stadiums and places those impacts within broader regulatory and policy context. Covering briefly all EUROs and WCs since 2008, we compare and evaluate tournament-specific impulses with international and national policies, market conditions, and stadium renovation efforts. Subsequently, two countries are examined in detail, i.e. Germany and Brazil, as they represent typical but fundamentally different examples of PV adoption dynamics.

5.1. World Cups and European Championships

For EURO 2008 in Austria and Switzerland, the Green Goal 2006 sustainability principles [8] were integrated into planning, and some PV measures were implemented through the "Solar Stadia" initiative [2]. Though pioneering PV consideration, these efforts remained limited, and most substantial upgrades followed only later.

At the 2010 World Cup in South Africa, feasibility studies under the Green Goal 2010 framework [9] examined PV options for Cape Town Stadium, but the overall focus lay on efficiency and lighting. No large PV roof installations were realized, resulting in a weak impact.

During EURO 2012 in Poland and Ukraine, there is no evidence of PV roofs across host stadiums, and thus no tournament-driven rollout can be identified.

The 2014 World Cup in Brazil marked a breakthrough, with at least four stadiums equipped with PV systems with a total of around 5.4 MW_p. This demonstrates a strong and direct link between tournament preparation and PV adoption.

For EURO 2016 in France, individual strong cases existed, such as the energy-positive stadium in Nice and a large PV carport in Bordeaux. However, this tournament did not generate a broader wave of rooftop PV adoption, leading to a moderate overall impact.

At the 2018 World Cup in Russia, sustainability programs focused on certifications and efficiency upgrades (e.g., BREEAM, LED, HVAC) [10], but no significant PV roofs were documented. The PV-specific impact was weak.

EURO 2020, played in 2021 across multiple European host countries, lacked a tournament-wide PV program. Apart from the Amsterdam stadium, which already had a PV roof, there was little evidence of new event-driven deployments, resulting in a weak effect.

The 2022 World Cup in Qatar focussed on solar-supported cooling and broader renewable integration. However, only two stadiums were documented with roof-mounted PV, making the impact weak to moderate in terms of PV adoption.

At EURO 2024 in Germany, sustainability frameworks such as the UN Initiative for Climate Action [11] and UEFA's Climate Fund [12] were accompanied by several venue-driven PV projects and expansions. These illustrate a strong influence of the tournament on PV deployment.

5.2 Example: Germany

The timeline for the introduction of PV systems in German football stadiums (see Figure 2) reflects initially the general development of the German solar industry. The first growth phase (2009–2011) was driven by high feed-in tariffs under the Renewable Energy Sources Act (EEG) and falling module prices, which created extremely attractive investment conditions. The stagnation phase (2013–2022) was marked by the crisis in the solar industry and successive EEG reforms. The changes in 2012 and 2014 led to a significant reduction in feed-in tariffs, while low-cost imports from Asia intensified competition. As a result, many projects became unprofitable and expansion slowed down considerably.

Since 2022, there has been a renewed increase in installed capacity. Rising electricity prices due to the energy crisis made PV investments more profitable, while growing social awareness of sustainability raised expectations of football clubs. The German Football Association (DFB) joined the 'Sports for Climate Action' initiative of the Unite Nations in 2020 [13], and several clubs have set their own climate neutrality or emission reduction targets. As the electricity consumption of stadiums falls under Scope 2 emissions [14], on-site renewable energy generation directly improves their carbon footprint.

The EURO 2024 provided additional momentum. UEFA launched a climate fund under the motto 'United by Football. Together for Nature' [15]. 572 applications for PV projects were submitted by amateur clubs. While this study focuses on larger professional venues, the strong interest from amateur clubs underscores the broad relevance of PV. In preparation for the tournament, the Öko-Institut conducted a feasibility study for a 'climate-neutral' EURO 2024 [16], which identified mobility as the largest source of emissions but also highlighted PV systems as an important mitigation measure.

Overall, Germany is an example of a diffusion model for PV adoption: broad and gradual integration across all professional leagues, driven primarily by policy frameworks, falling costs and regular stadium renovations. International tournaments acted as supporting triggers but were not decisive factors.

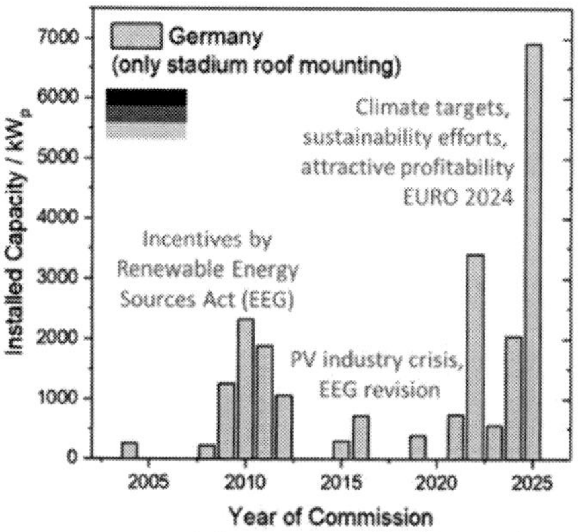

Figure 2: Temporal development of PV installations on German football stadiums

5.3 Example: Brazil

In Brazil, the 2014 FIFA World Cup was a clear catalyst for the installation of photovoltaic systems on football stadiums. Preparations for the tournament and the associated renovation of the venues triggered an extraordinary, event-driven increase in installations. Of the twelve stadiums used during the World Cup, four were equipped with PV modules. Furthermore, though not a World Cup venue, the Estádio de Pituaçu in Salvador is the actual pioneer as the first stadium in Latin America to host a PV system. Currently, the Brazilian national stadium in Brasília has the second-largest PV system on a football stadium worldwide, underscoring the extent of Brazilian commitment during this period.

The timing of these installations, reflects preparations for the 2014 World Cup, as shown in Figure 3, and supports the interpretation of Brazil as a catalyst model, where a single major event has concentrated and accelerated adoption rather than driving long-term diffusion.

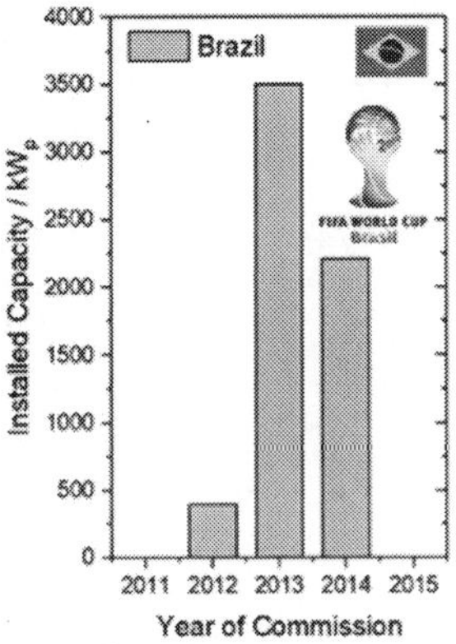

Figure 3: Temporal development of PV installations on Brazilian football stadiums

6 SUMMARY AND OUTLOOK

Since 2008, the integration of PV systems in football stadiums has increased significantly, although with considerable regional and temporal differences. A couple of European countries have emerged as pioneers, while adoption in other countries is progressing more slowly. International tournaments such as the FIFA World Cup and UEFA EURO have provided momentum, but have not led to a systematic push for the use of PV systems. Many current stadium projects focus more on energy efficiency and certification than on large-scale PV systems, and documented capacities ranging from small, rather symbolic installations to multi-MW systems.

Future growth is likely to be driven by climate policy and the visibility of football stadiums as showcase projects for sustainability. In future projects, PV systems are likely to be combined with energy efficiency solutions, storage systems and smart operating concepts. Regional differences are likely to remain, but falling PV prices and stronger climate commitments could accelerate global adoption. Major upcoming tournaments such as the 2030 FIFA World Cup could once again serve as promoter for new PV projects.

REFERENCES

[1] M. Manni, V. Coccia, A. Nicolini, G. Marseglia, A. Petrozzi, Energies 11 (2018) 2396.
[2] L.G. Monteiro, W.N. Macedo, P.F. Torres, M.M. Silva, G. Amaral, A.S. Piterman, B.M. Lopes, J.M. Fraga, W.C. Boaventura, Energies 10 (2017) 225.
[3] L. Barbaro, G. Battista, E. de Lieto Vollaro, R. de Lieto Vollaro, Appl. Sci. 14 (2024) 7344.
[4] K. Berg, M. Resch, T. Weniger, S. Simonsen, J. Energy Storage 34 (2021) 102190.
[5] M. Devetaković, D. Djordjević, M. Radojević, A. Krstić-Furundžić, B.-G. Burduhos, G. Martinopoulos, M. Neagoe, G. Lobaccaro, Appl. Sci. 10 (2020) 6696.
[6] A. Hadrović, Int. J. Multidiscip. Res. Growth Eval. 4 (2023).
[7] P. Sofotasiou, B.R. Hughes, J.K. Calautit, Sustain. Cities Soc. 14 (2015) 16–30.
[8] Green Goal 2006 (24 Sep 2025), https://www.oeko.de/oekodoc/292/2006-011-en.pdf
[9] Greening 2010 FIFA World Cup (24 Sep 2025), https://www.dffe.gov.za/greening-2010-fifa-world-cup
[10] Main stadium of Russia 2018 receives 'green' certification (24 Sep 2025), https://ipt.fifa.com/tournaments/mens/worldcup/2018russia/news/main-stadium-of-russia-2018-receives-green-certification-2927642
[11] Sports for Climate Action (24 Sep 2025), https://unfccc.int/climate-action/sectoral-engagement/sports-for-climate-action
[12] UEFA EURO 2024 climate fund for German amateur clubs (24 Sep 2025), https://www.uefa.com/news-media/news/0289-19ebcc000ecc-5d28436af2d0-1000--uefa-euro-2024-climate-fund-for-german-amateur-clubs
[13] Sports for Climate Action (24 Sep 2025), https://unfccc.int/climate-action/sectoral-engagement/sports-for-climate-action
[14] Scope 2 Guidance (24 Sep 2025), https://ghgprotocol.org/scope-2-guidance
[15] United by Football. Together for Nature' (24 Sep 2025), https://www.uefa.com/news-media/news/028c-1a98706e2386-d19fef44c053-1000--united-by-football-together-for-nature/
[16 Concept and Feasibility Study for a "Climate Neutral" UEFA EURO 2024 (24 Sep 2025), https://www.oeko.de/en/publications/concept-and-feasibility-study-for-a-climate-neutral-uefa-euro-2024]

Please note: The complete list of sources and references for all stadium data is available from the authors by request, as its length exceeds the scope of this publication.

htw
Hochschule für Technik und Wirtschaft Berlin
University of Applied Sciences

PHOTOVOLTAIC INTEGRATION IN FOOTBALL STADIUMS: GLOBAL TRENDS, REGIONAL DISPARITIES, FUTURE POTENTIAL

EU PVSEC

Johanna Buchmann, Niels Feuerherdt, Bert Stegemann

HTW Berlin - University of Applied Sciences, Wilhelminenhofstr. 75A, D-12459 Berlin, Germany

Goals

- Establishing a systematic record of football stadiums equipped with photovoltaic systems
- Providing up-to-date data on the current status of PV implementation in professional football infrastructure
- Classification of developments in the D-A-CH region within an international context
- Quantitative assessment of deployment rates and qualitative investigation of underlying incentives in different regions and leagues
- Identification of global patterns and regional differences, including the role of major sporting events (European championships and World cups) as triggers for implementation

Approach + Methodology

- Analysis limited to football (soccer) stadiums
- PV systems differentiated between stadium roof and adjacent buildings
- Verification supported by Google Earth images
- League affiliation of the 2024/25 season used as reference
- Stadium projects completing in 2025 included
- Cumulative capacity reported for multi-stage installations
- Missing data estimated from generation numbers, module counts, or similar indicators

GBK Stadium, Jarkarta [1]

Kaohsiung, Taiwan [2]

Mineirão, Belo Horizonte [3]

Al-Madina, Bagdad [4]

Audi Field, Washington [5]

Panasonic Stadium Osaka [6]
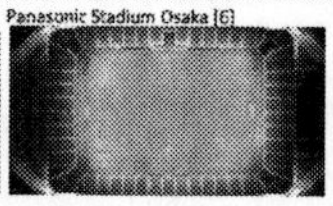
Stade du Senegal, Dakar [7]

Go Media, Auckland [8]

Pernambuco, Recife [9]

Stadium PV Rankings – by Geography

Worldwide (excl. Europe)

Rank	Stadium	City	Country	Capacity kWp	Operation start
1	Estádio Nacional Mané Garrincha	Brasilia	Brazil	2500	2013
2	Stade du Senegal	Dakar	Senegal	2300 (carport)	2021
3	Mineirão Stadium	Belo Horizonte	Brazil	1420	2014
4	Al-Madina International Stadium)	Bagdad	Iraq	1050	2021
5	National Stadium	Kaohsiung	Taiwan	1000	2009
6	Gelora Bung Karno Main Stadium	Jakarta	Indonesia	1000	2019
7	Pernambuco Stadium	Recife	Brazil	1000	2013
8	Go Media Stadium	Auckland	New Zealand	780	2025
9	Audi Field	Washington, DC	USA	627.8	2020
10	Panasonic Stadium Suita	Osaka	Japan	504	2015
11	Itaipava Arena Fonte Nova	Salvador	Brazil	500	2014
12	Estádio Roberto Santos	Salvador	Brazil	400	2012
13	Estádio do Maracanã	Rio de Janeiro	Brazil	391	2014
14	Beijing Workers' Stadium	Peking, China	China	351	2023
15	Al-Bayt Stadium	Al Khor	Qatar	271	2021

Europe

Rank	Stadium	City	Country	Capacity kWp	Operation start
1	Signal Iduna Park	Dortmund	Germany	4200	2025 (proj.)
2	Rams Park (Ali Sami Yen)	Istanbul	Türkiye	4100	2022
3	Ernst Happel Stadion	Vienna	Austria	3500	2025
4	Europa-Park Stadion	Freiburg	Germany	2387	2022
5	Merkur Spiel-Arena	Düsseldorf	Germany	1500	2025 (proj.)
6	Fritz-Walter-Stadion	Kaiserslautern	Germany	1350	2010
7	Allianz Riviera	Nice	France	1342.7	2013
8	Stadion Wankdorf	Bern	Switzerland	1300	2005
9	London Stadium	London	England (UK)	1256	2025 (proj.)
10	Kybunpark	St. Gallen	Switzerland	1205	2025
11	Stadion am Böllenfalltor	Darmstadt	Germany	1200	2024
12	RheinEnergieSTADION	FC Köln	Germany	1200	2025 (proj.)
13	Johan Cruijff ArenA	Amsterdam	Netherlands	1128	2014
14	Stadio Friuli	Udinese	Italy	1100	2024
15	Stadion Galgenwaard	Utrecht	Netherlands	1065*	2017

Germany

Rank	Stadium	City	Capacity kWp	Operation start
1	Signal Iduna Park	Dortmund	4200	2025 (proj.)
2	Europa-Park Stadion	Freiburg	2387	2022
3	Merkur Spiel-Arena	Düsseldorf	1500	2025 (proj.)
4	Fritz-Walter-Stadion	Kaiserslautern	1350	2010
5	Weserstadion	Bremen	1270	2009
6	Stadion am Böllenfalltor	Darmstadt	1200	2024
7	RheinEnergieStadion	Köln	1200	2025 (proj.)
8	Mewa Arena	Mainz	846.3	2011
9	Erzgebirgsstadion	Aue	750	2021
10	Steigerwaldstadion	Erfurt	730	2016
11	Ostseestadion	Rostock	700	2010
12	Jahnstadion	Regensburg	632	2025
13	Olympiastadion Berlin	Berlin	605.25	2022
14	Deutsche Bank Park	Frankfurt	560	2024
15	Leuna-Chemie-Stadion	Halle	526	2011

* Capacity estimated

Wankdorf, Bern [10]

Allianz Riviera , Nice [11]

Rams Park, Istanbul [12]

London Stadium [13]
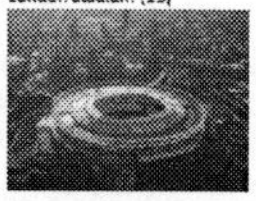
Cruiff ArenA, Amsterdam [14]

Stadio Friuli, Udinese [15]

Kybonpark, St. Gallen [16]

Ernst Happel Stadium, Wien [17]

Stadium PV Rankings – by National League

German Bundesliga (1st Division)

Rank	Stadium	Team	Capacity kWp - Stadium Roof	Capacity kWp Stadium Grounds	Operation start
1	Signal Iduna Park	Borussia Dortmund	4200		2025 (proj.)
2	Europa-Park Stadion	SC Freiburg	2387		2022
3	WESERSTADION	Werder Bremen	1270		2009
4	MEWA ARENA	1. FSV Mainz 05	846.3		2011
5	DB Park	Eintracht Frankfurt	560		2024
6	Millerntor-Stadion	FC St. Pauli	316		2025
7	Voith-Arena	1. FC Heidenheim	303.56		2015
8	PreZero Arena	TSG 1899 Hoffenheim		1046.5	
9	Allianz Arena	FC Bayern München		834	2019
10	Borussia-Park	Borussia Mönchengladbach		127	2024
11	Ruhrstadion	VfL Bochum		97	2023
12	Red Bull Arena	RB Leipzig		71.5	2020

German 2. Bundesliga (2nd Division)

Rank	Stadium	Team	Capacity kWp Stadium Roof	Capacity kWp Stadium Grounds	Operation start
1	Merkur Spiel-Arena	Fortuna Düsseldorf	1500		2025 (proj.)
2	Fritz-Walter-Stadion	1. FC Kaiserslautern	1350		2010
3	RheinEnergieSTADION	1. FC Köln	1200		2025 (proj.)
4	Stadion am Böllenfalltor	SV Darmstadt 98	1.200		2024
5	Jahnstadion Regensburg	SSV Jahn Regensburg	632		2025
6	Olympiastadion Berlin	Hertha BSC	605.25		2022
7	Volksparkstadion	Hamburger SV	520		2011
8	Home Deluxe Arena	SC Paderborn 07	500*		2012
9	Sportpark Ronhof	SpVgg Greuther Fürth	319.8		2022
10	Max-Morlock-Stadion	1. FC Nürnberg	284		2010
11	Eintracht-Stadion	Eintracht Braunschweig	262.3		2023
12	Wildpark	Karlsruher SC	100		2022
13	VELTINS-Arena	FC Schalke 04		600	2012

Swiss Super League

Rank	Stadium	Team	Capacity kWp Stadium Roof	Operation start
1	Stadion Wankdorf/Stade de Suisse	BSC Young Boys	1350	2005
2	Kybunpark	FC St. Gallen	1205	2015
3	swissporarena	FC Luzern	1097	2016
4	Stade de Genève	Servette FC	942	2019
5	St. Jakob-Park	FC Basel	850	2013
6	Stade de la Tuilière	FC Lausanne-Sport	800*	2020
7	Stade Municipal	Yverdon Sport FC	500*	2024
8	Letzigrund Stadion	FC Zürich / GH Zürich	223	2007
9	Stadion Schützenwiese	FC Winterthur	63.44	2014

Austrian Bundesliga

Rank	Stadium	Team	Capacity kWp Stadium Roof	Operation start
1	Generali Arena	FK Austria Wien	825	2018-2024
2	28 Black Arena / Wörthersee Stadion	SK Austria Klagenfurt	137.5	2013

Dortmund [18]
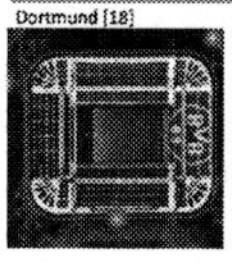
Millerntor, St. Pauli, Hamburg [19]

Weserstadion Bremen [20]

Fritz-Walter-Stadion, Kaiserslautern [21]

Europa-Park, Freiburg [22]

Böllenfalltor, Darmstadt [23]
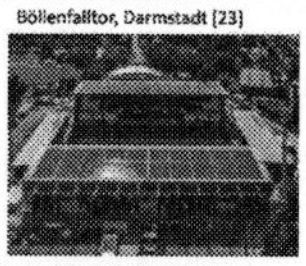
Eintracht-Stadion Braunschweig [24]

Olympiastadion, Berlin [25]
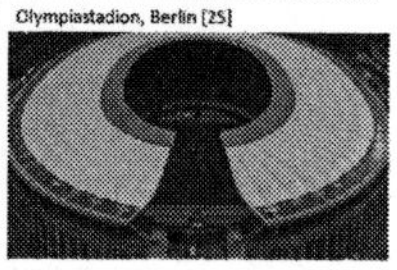

Regional Disparities

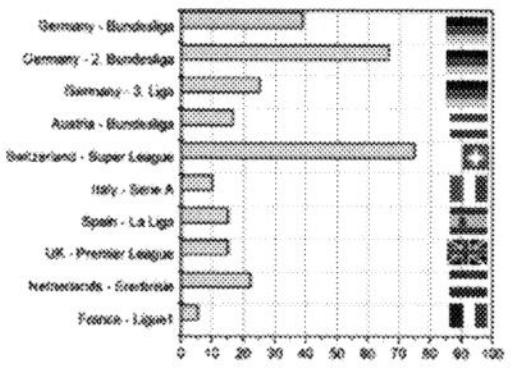

- **D-A-CH countries** lead, indicating strong support from policies as well as sustainability initiatives
- **Major leagues** lag: sunlight or budgets alone are not decisive factors for the introduction of PV

Tournament-Driven PV-Integration (2008-2024)

Tournament	Host(s)	Evidence of PV on (Host) Stadiums	Assessment
EURO 2008	Austria/ Switzerland	**Green Goal 2006** sustainability principles were integrated into planning, with some PV measures implemented. **Solar Stadia**: Initiative for PV on stadium roofs to raise awareness of sustainability	**Moderate** (pioneering initiatives, limited tournament-driven PV, upgrades came later)
WC 2010	South Africa	**Green Goal 2010** feasibility studies examined PV for Cape Town Stadium, overall focus on efficiency/lighting. No large PV roofs documented.	**Weak** (PV considered, but not widely implemented)
EURO 2012	Poland/Ukraine	No evidence of PV roofs across host stadiums	**Weak** (no clear EURO-driven rollout)
WC 2014	Brazil	at least four WC stadiums with ~5.4 MW_p PV combined	**Strong** (clear link between WC prep and PV roofs, visible PV boost)
EURO 2016	France	few strong cases (Nice: energy-positive on match days, Bordeaux: large PV carport), but not across all venues.	**Moderate** (no tournament-wide PV program or major new rooftop deployment)
WC 2018	Russia	Focus on certifications/efficiency upgrades (BREEAM, LED, HVAC). No evidence of significant PV roofs at host stadiums	**Weak** (sustainability yes, PV roofs no)
EURO 2020 (played 2021)	Pan-European	no tournament-wide PV program, little evidence of new, event-driven PV rooftop deployments, Amsterdam stadium with existing PV roof	**Weak** (flagship example, but not generalized across venues)
WC 2022	Qatar	focus on solar-supported cooling/energy, only 2 documented stadium roof PV systems	**Weak to moderate** (solar present, but not mainly roof PV)
EURO 2024	Germany	UN: Initiative for Climate Action, UEFA: Climate Fund: United by football, together for nature, venue-driven PV installations or expansions	**Strong** (multiple PV stadium projects, partly accelerated by the tournament)

Policy and Tournament Effects

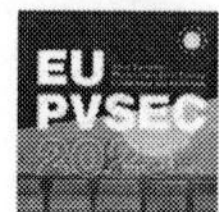

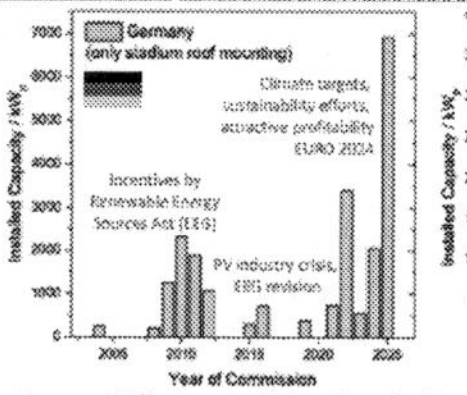

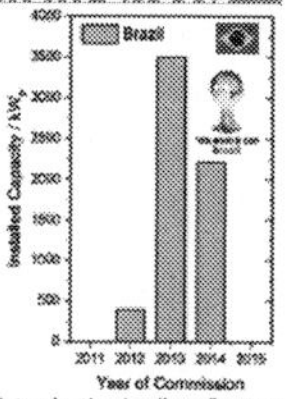

- **Germany** (*diffusion model*): Broad, gradual introduction in all professional leagues, mainly due to political framework conditions, falling costs and renovations; tournaments were supportive but not decisive
- **Brazil** (*catalyst model*): 2014 World Cup triggered event-related peak

Summary

- Strong rise in PV on stadiums since 2008, with clear regional and temporal disparities
- A few other European countries are pioneers; other regions show slower uptake
- International tournaments (WC, EURO) gave impulses but no systematic boost
- Many new projects focus on efficiency/certification more than PV
- Documented capacities range from symbolic to multi-MW installations

Outlook

- Growth driven by climate policies and the visibility of football stadiums as sustainability showcase
- Future installations might combine PV with energy efficiency, storage, and smart operation concepts
- Regional disparities may persist, but falling PV costs and climate commitments could globally accelerate
- Upcoming tournaments (e.g. WC 2030) may trigger further PV projects

References: [illegible]

42nd European Photovoltaic Solar Energy Conference and Exhibition

This presentation was selected by the Sc. Committee of the EU PVSEC 2025 for submission of a full paper to one of the EU PVSEC's collaborating peer-reviewed journals.

A TALE OF TWO DUSTS: MIMICKING SITE-SPECIFIC SOILING DYNAMICS AND CLEANING APPROACHES FOR PV PLANTS

J. Montoya[1], D. Olivares[1], E. Pilat[2], J. P Rakotoniaina[2], A. Marzo[3], V. Del Campo[4], E. Fuentealba[1], M. Gaete[1], J. Aimé[2], R. Couderc[2], D. Muñoz[2], J.A. Tsanakas[2]*

[1] Centro de Desarrollo Energético Antofagasta (CDEA), Universidad de Antofagasta, 02800, Antofagasta, Chile
[2] CEA, Liten, Univ. Grenoble Alpes, Campus INES, 73375 Le Bourget du Lac, France
[3] Departamento de Óptica, Universidad de Granada, Spain
[4] Departamento de Física, Universidad Técnica Federico Santa María, España 1680, Valparaíso, Chile

*corresponding author : ioannis.tsanakas@cea.fr

ABSTRACT: Replicating and understanding site-specific soiling dynamics is crucial for optimizing PV designs and modelling, in-field soiling monitoring and cleaning strategies. This study discusses a multi-parameter testing protocol for soiling and cleaning of PV modules, under controlled conditions using dust samples from two distinct environments: the Atacama Desert and Southern France. A novel experimental setup, incorporating a soiling and cleaning chamber, was employed to replicate real-world deposition and removal processes. The impact of soiling was assessed through I-V characterization, comparing different PV module configurations. Results indicate that anti-soiling and anti-reflective coatings mitigate optical losses more effectively than standard glass covers, whereas encapsulant choice has a negligible effect in soiling-induced optical losses. Cleaning tests revealed that high brush rotation speeds with soft bristles yielded the highest efficiency (68.2%). Additionally, the study successfully simulated desert cementation processes, validating the accelerated testing methodology. These findings provide valuable insights for optimizing PV maintenance strategies and enhancing module design, contributing to improved energy yield in soiling-prone regions.

Keywords: *PV systems; soiling; soiling losses; soiling mitigation.*

1 INTRODUCTION: CONTEXT and AIM

Photovoltaic (PV) systems, especially in soiling-prone sites such as in arid dusty regions, marine/coastal environments and sites near intense agricultural activities, suffer significant energy losses due to soiling. These losses can reach 20% to 30% per year, resulting in financial losses exceeding €10 billion in 2023 [1]. The behaviour and impact of soiling vary widely depending on environmental conditions, the dust composition, and the properties of PV materials. Regional factors such as dust origin, particle size, hydrophobicity, and mineral content all play critical roles in determining how soiling mechanisms develop and how effectively they can be mitigated [2]. Despite its importance, the influence of these diverse variables is not yet fully understood nor quantified, particularly when comparing starkly different climatic and environmental contexts. Therefore, next to advanced tools for in-field soiling monitoring and assessment, it is essential to develop indoor ("accelerated") soiling testing protocols, in order to mimic dust deposition (and eventual soiling losses) in controlled environment, under the combined influence of environmental and PV parameters. Understanding exactly such site- or climate- specific soiling dynamics, can, in turn, help PV industry in developing optimized soiling mitigation strategies at O&M level, as well as reinforce PV modules' resilience against soiling, at design level.

The Atacama Desert and Southern France represent two regions with vastly distinct environmental conditions and dust characteristics. The Atacama, one of the driest places on Earth, produces fine, hydrophobic dust particles that tend to adhere stubbornly to PV surfaces. In contrast, the dust in Southern France is generally coarser and more mineral-rich, with its soiling behaviour influenced by Mediterranean humidity and seasonal variability. These differences present an opportunity to study how dust properties and environmental conditions affect soiling losses, adhesion, and cleaning efficacy.

In this study, we employ a novel setup for accelerated soiling and cleaning tests of two distinct dust samples from the aforementioned regions. Through the designed testing protocol, overall aim of the study is to mimic soiling dynamics and evaluate cleaning strategies for PV modules, in controlled laboratory conditions, under the influence of: i) different bill of materials (BOMs) selection, ii) different environmental conditions and iii) different cleaning parameters. By systematically comparing and quantifying soiling dynamics and cleaning parameters, our end-goal is to draw valuable conclusions and insights into the interaction of PV site-specific factors with soiling and cleaning processes, to further guide towards streamlined O&M for soiling-prone PV plants.

2 METHODOLOGY – APPROACH

Two specific test benches developed and operating at CEA [3] were employed in this study (Fig. 1): a soiling chamber (Fig. 1, top) and a cleaning chamber (Fig. 1, bottom). For all the designed tests, the impact of soiling is evaluated through I-V characterization of the tested PV laminates under standard test conditions (STC), using a Class A+ PASAN solar simulator. The soiling chamber, equipped with a dust generator, enables the homogeneous and repeatable soiling of PV modules. A precise mass of pre-dehydrated dust is loaded into a piston, which forms part of the dust generator and ensures accurate control over the volume flow of injected dust. Carried by dry air at a controlled pressure, the dust is directed onto a deflector, creating a dust cloud within the chamber. This suspended dust gradually settles on the modules placed on the sample holder plate, which can be tilted between 0° and 90°. This process completes a fully controlled soiling operation, referred to as an "injection". The chamber also includes various devices for adjusting key parameters such as temperature and humidity during testing. The interior temperature can be regulated between 15°C and 50°C, the temperature of the sample holder plate can be set between 10°C and 50°C, and the relative humidity can be controlled up to 90%.

The studied samples, also fabricated at CEA-INES facilities, comprise of "mini PV modules" (i.e. single-cell PV laminates), with silicon heterojunction (SHJ) solar cells, in different bill of materials (BOM) combinations in terms of front cover coatings and encapsulants.

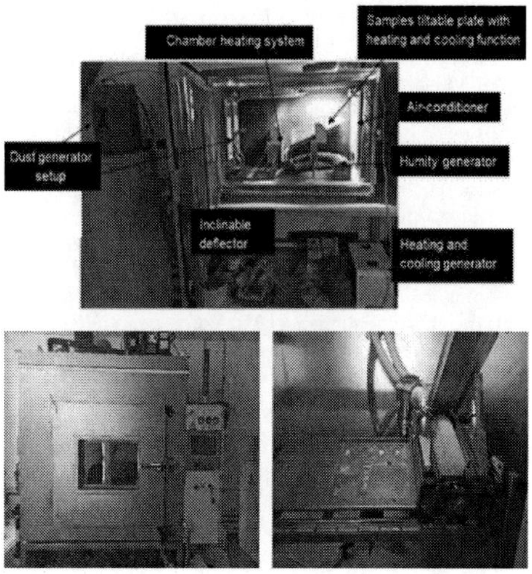

Figure 1: The lab setup at CEA-INES developed and employed for controlled replication of soiling, cleaning tests and dust characterization. Top: the soiling chamber and its different components. Bottom-left: External view of the cleaning chamber. Bottom-Right: Inside view of the cleaning chamber.

The entire experimental sequence applied, for the ***soiling study***, consists of four main steps: 1) Electrical characterization (I_{sc} and P_{max}) and transmittance measurements of PV laminate-sample and glass sample at clean state (reference measurements); 2) Soiling injection; 3) Post-soiling measurements; 4) Manual cleaning of PV laminate, return to clean state.

For the case of the ***cleaning study***, we have assessed 4 parameters with 3 configurations for each of them, as summarized in Table 1. It should be noted that, in the present study, we focus only on dry (waterless) cleaning. Follow-up work and results will also assess water-based cleaning sequences.

Parameters	Conf. 1	Conf. 2	Conf. 3
A : Robot moving speed	50 mm/s	250 mm/s	500 mm/s
B : Brush rotation speed	0 tour/min	100 tour/min	550 tour/min
C : Brush type	Rigid nylon	Soft nylon	horse hair (very soft)
D : front sheet	Solar	AR	Transparent

Two distinctively different types of dust (soiling) samples were applied and studied in this work. ***Dust 1*** originates from actual soiling collected in a utility-scale PV plant site located in southern France. This site has been identified by CNR (SERENDI-PV partner and PV plant owner) as susceptible to soiling due to its proximity to a quarry as well as to significant agricultural activity, both generating relatively important levels of soiling, in a region with generally little rainfall ("hot dry-summer" climate, classified as *Csa*, per the Köppen climate classification). A total 12 kg of dust/soiling was collected and sieved with a 1.6mm mesh, to be then used for the experiment. For each soiling injection experiment with Dust 1, we have adjusted the test chamber's environmental parameters taking into account typical site-specific conditions and the limits of the artificial soiling equipment:

1. 3g of dust injected (approximately 0.12 mg/cm^2), relative humidity (RH) > 80% and temperature of sample T_{sample} 17°C, (dew conditions).
2. 5g of dust injected (approximately 0.2 mg/cm^2), RH > 80% and T_{sample} 17°C (dew conditions).
3. 5g of dust injected (approximately 0.2 mg/cm^2), RH < 30% and T_{sample} 30°C (dry conditions).

Dust 2 originates from the Plataforma Solar del Desierto de Atacama (PSDA, for its acronym in Spanish). The PSDA is located in the Atacama Desert (24.09°S, 69.93°W) at an altitude of 963 meters above sea level, in a region classified as a cold and arid desert (BWk). The samples were exposed in the soiling chamber, specifically programmed to replicate the atmospheric conditions of the PSDA. To achieve this, meteorological data collected over a year was used, considering solar resource, temperature (°C), and relative humidity (RH) to generate a representative typical day. Based on this typical day, cycles were established to simulate nighttime conditions—characterized by high relative humidity (>70%) and low temperatures (~7°C)—while daytime conditions were recreated with high temperatures (>30°C) and low relative humidity (~40%). This indoor process was carried out in three sequential stages: (1) dust deposition, (2) simulated humidity condensation, and (3) final cementation. These conditions were applied sequentially to the samples, enabling the analysis of accelerated soiling effects under controlled laboratory conditions.

3 RESULTS and DISCUSSION

The ***soiling study*** of ***Dust 1*** was carried out for seven different BOM scenarios of tested PV laminates, in order to first quantify (and understand) the individual impact of soiling buildup on optical (and therefore power output) PV losses, for: i) different front cover (glass) coatings and ii) for different encapsulant types. So far, after a single soiling injection with *Dust 1* sample, results indicate soiling losses in the range of 3% to 5%, highly dependent on the type of front cover coating of the tested PV laminates. In particular, samples with white glass as front cover present the higher soiling losses, whereas PV laminates with anti-soiling (AS) and anti-reflective (AR) coatings on their front cover, as well as with hydrophobic (HPB) ones, seem to better "resist" against optical/current losses from soiling buildup (Fig. 2). On the other hand, the choice of the encapsulant plays minimal role to the light management and, eventually, the resulting optical/current losses from soiling, for the tested PV laminates, for the case of Dust 1. The slight absolute difference (0.5%) observed between the soiling losses for the two encapsulant types in comparison (Fig. 2) can be considered negligible, particularly with regard to the intrinsic uncertainty related to the experimental protocol. These observations are suggestive of the need to dissociate the PV laminates solely according to the nature and coating of their front cover.

Sample module	Front cover	Encapsulant
S1	plain PV glass	TPO1[1]
S2	plain PV glass	POE[2]
S3	AR*+AS**	TPO
S4	AR+AS	POE
S5	AR	TPO
S6	HPB***	TPO
S7	White glass	TPO

*AR: Anti-Reflection coating
**AS: Anti-Soiling coating
***HPB: Hydrophobic
[1]TPO: Thermoplastic Polyolefin
[2]POE: Polyolefin Elastomer

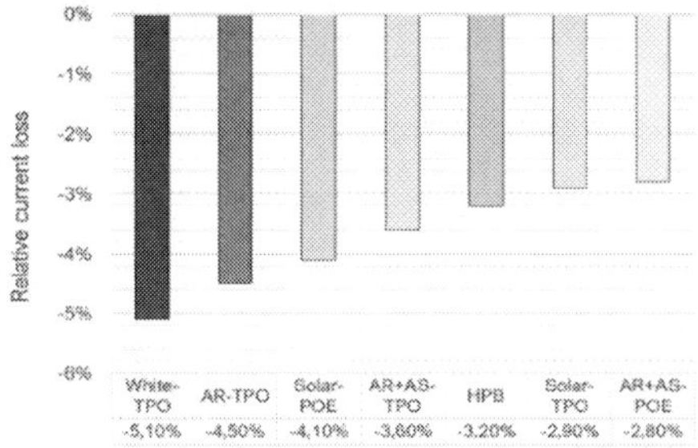

Figure 2: Relative soiling (current losses) for all PV laminates subjected to the indoor soiling testing protocol with Dust 1. Comparative results (bottom) for different bill of materials used for seven different samples (top).

For the ***cleaning study*** of ***Dust 1***, we have employed three of the tested PV laminates and performed three identical cleaning tests for each configuration. Prior to each cleaning sequence, each PV laminate was soiled with the same conditions and scale of dust particles (<35 μm) that were already used in the soiling study. The amount of dust deposited on each module is around 0.25 mg/cm², which corresponds to an I_{sc} loss of around 4.5%. The impact after each operation soiling and cleaning is assessed by measuring the I_{sc}, under STC, with the employed solar simulator. Preliminary results (Fig. 3), for the case of Dust 1 and the cleaning configurations described in Table 1, are suggestive of the higher average cleaning efficiency (68.2%) of Configuration 3, in comparison with that of Configurations 1 and 2 (25.1% and 41.9% respectively). From the results, we may also conclude that the process in Configuration 3 is significantly more repeatable, whereas it is preferable to use a high brush rotation speed, with brush made of soft bristles (e.g. horsehair), the latter being better suited to protect the PV modules' front cover coatings that are often sensitive to abrasion. Besides, such configuration allows also the cleaning cart to be driven at high speeds, which, in practice, can contribute to significant reduction in cleaning time and costs.

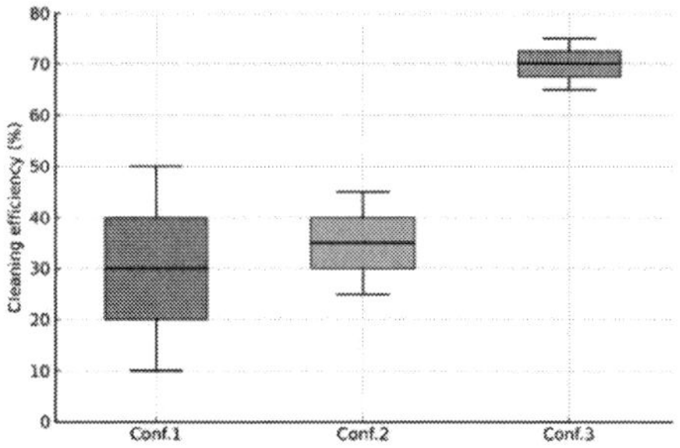

Figure 3: Comparative results for the cleaning efficiency of the three applied test configurations: Indicative results for the case of *Dust 1*, for the configurations described in section 2.

This section presents the preliminary results obtained in the study using ***Dust 2,*** a more detailed analysis and comparative discussion will be included in a future study. The deposition results, simulating the PSDA conditions, were analyzed using a FE-SEM Zeiss Sigma 360 scanning electron microscope. The analysis revealed well-defined prismatic particles, as shown in Fig. 4. The absence of erosion signs in these particles indicates the occurrence of a recrystallization process of soluble material. The high-humidity cycles during the night and high temperatures in the morning, replicated by the soiling chamber, facilitated crystal formation, recreating phenomena observed in real outdoor conditions, such as the formation of the well-known "desert rose."

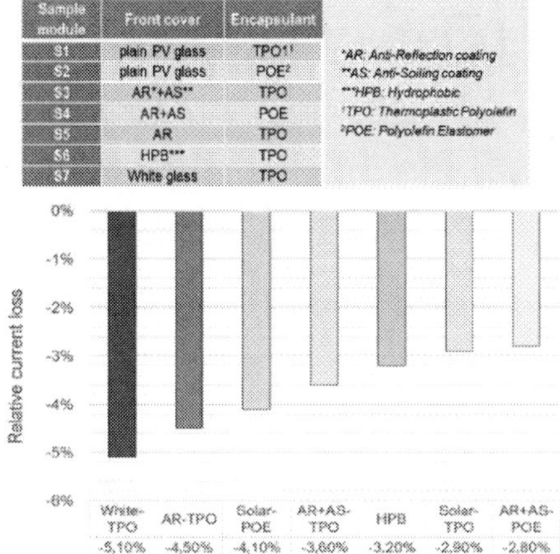

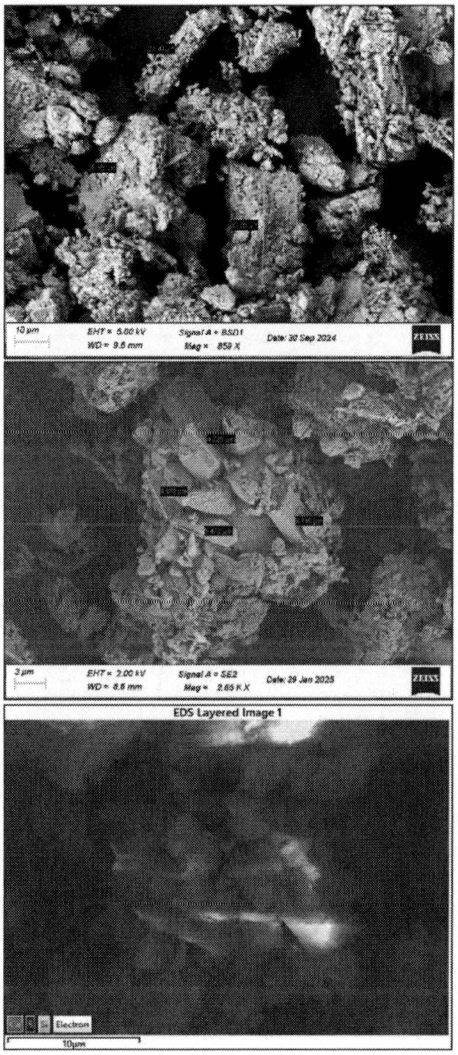

Figure 4: Top: Soiling sample obtained by sieving PSDA dust ("*Dust 2*"). Middle: Cemented soiling sample deposited on a module using the soiling chamber. Bottom: EDS image of the soiling sample deposited on a module using the soiling chamber.2.

Elemental analysis (Fig. 4, bottom) confirms these results, showing that the crystals are primarily composed of sulfur and calcium, indicating the presence of gypsum, a compound previously documented at the PSDA by Olivares et al [4]. Additionally, silicon was detected, associated with quartz, one of the most abundant materials in the desert. This quartz becomes trapped within the gypsum, clearly evidencing the cementation process. The soiling chamber demonstrated its ability to replicate the cementation process observed at the PSDA, achieving the effects of nighttime high humidity cycles and daytime high temperatures in a shorter period. This controlled environment allowed the formation of consolidated deposits like those found in real conditions, validating its effectiveness in accelerating and reproducing the deposition and recrystallization mechanisms characteristic of the region.

The ***soiling study*** for ***Dust 2*** was conducted on four samples to evaluate the impact of dust accumulation on optical and electrical losses. Results (Fig. 5) indicate an average decrease of the I_{sc} by 5%, for each increase in deposition density, which ranged between 0.45 mg/cm^2 and 1.15 mg/cm^2. Regarding optical losses, transmittance reductions were observed across the spectral range of 350 to 1100 nm, reaching 50% in samples with the highest dust density. Comparison with previous studies conducted at the PSDA indicates strong agreement with data obtained under real outdoor exposure conditions, particularly in material deposition patterns, accumulated dust density, and optical transmittance reduction [4].

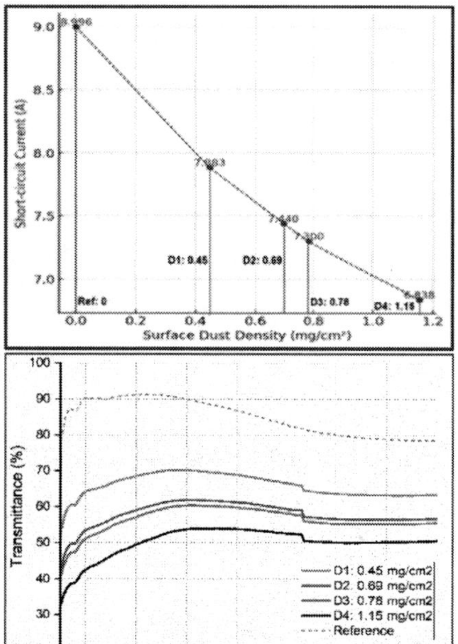

Figure 5: Top: Short-circuit current losses as a function of surface dust density. Bottom: Transmittance losses correspond to increasing dust density in each deposition: Indicative results for the case of *Dust 2*.

4 CONCLUSIONS - OUTLOOK

This work demonstrates the feasibility and relevance of employing accelerated soiling and cleaning protocols to systematically investigate the impact of site-specific dust characteristics and environmental conditions on PV module performance. By comparing dust samples from Southern France and the Atacama Desert, we highlighted the strong influence of dust morphology, mineral composition, and associated climatic conditions on soiling losses and cleaning efficiency. Results with Dust 1 (Southern France) indicate that front cover coatings play a much more critical role in mitigating soiling-induced losses than encapsulant choice, while dry cleaning efficiency is significantly improved when employing high brush rotation speeds with soft bristles. For Dust 2 (Atacama Desert), controlled indoor testing successfully replicated the cementation phenomena observed in outdoor conditions, reproducing gypsum recrystallization and dust consolidation under alternating humidity and temperature cycles. The agreement with outdoor data validates the effectiveness of the accelerated soiling protocol as a reliable surrogate for field exposure.

The study emphasizes that no universal soiling mitigation strategy can be applied across sites, as dust origin and environmental context fundamentally govern soiling dynamics and cleaning requirements. Instead, site-specific knowledge should drive both O&M strategies and PV material design. Future work will expand the testing framework by:

- extending cleaning studies to include water-based methods and hybrid approaches,
- assessing long-term durability of front cover coatings under repeated soiling/cleaning cycles, and
- refining the soiling protocols by integrating real-time outdoor data for more accurate climate-to-lab translation.

Ultimately, advancing such accelerated testing approaches can bridge the gap between laboratory investigations and real-world PV performance, thereby supporting the development of optimized, climate-tailored solutions to minimize soiling-induced energy and financial losses.

ACKNOWLEDGEMENTS

Part of this work has been carried out in the framework of the H2020 SERENDI-PV and Horizon Europe CACTUS projects. SERENDI-PV project has received funding from the European Union's Horizon 2020 research and innovation programme under grant agreement No. 953016. CACTUS project has received funding from the European Union's Horizon Europe research and innovation programme under grant agreement No. 101132182. For CEA team, part of this work was also supported by the French National Program "Programme d'Investissements d'Avenir - INES.2S" under Grant Agreement ANR ANR-10-IEED-0014 0014-01.

REFERENCES

[1] L. Micheli et al. (2024). In: *Proc. 41th EUPVSEC*, Vienna, Austria.
[2] Report IEA-PVPS T13-21:2022
[3] J.A. Tsanakas et al. (2024). In: *Proc. 41th EUPVSEC*, Vienna, Austria.

[4] D. Olivares et al. (2021). *Solar Energy Materials and Solar Cells*, 227, 111109.

Zentrum für Sonnenenergie- und Wasserstoff-
Forschung Baden-Württemberg

Energie Baden-Württemberg AG

AI methods for the operation and maintenance of PV parks with bifacial photovoltaic modules

Dirk Stellbogen, Jonas Petzschmann, Elena Pabst, Roland Einhaus,
Zentrum für Sonnenenergie- und Wasserstoff-Forschung Baden-Württemberg (ZSW)
Timo Freund, Jan Wannenwetsch, Ajka Ockert, *EnBW Energie Baden-Württemberg AG*

EU PVSEC 2025, Bilbao, 24.09.2025

Motivation

- PV plants are getting larger and more complex:
  - Use of bifacially sensitive PV modules
  - Uneven possibly hilly sites
  - Various orientations
- Field measurements are often limited to aggregated currents
- Algorithmic and physical models face limits for dealing with complexity
- Delivery of reliable performance projections for monitoring and supervision is challenged

⇨ Development of AI based data models for bifacial PV parks for fault detection and power forecasts
  - Installation plan details not necessary
  - Generic structure for easy transfer and adaptation to other PV parks

Scope of Research Project „KIMBIF“

Joint work of research institute and owner and operator of PV plants

- ZSW: Development of data models, data processing and implementation
- EnBW: Field experimentation, provision of operational data and integration in O&M system

Bifacial PV parks by EnBW as test sites

- in Germany:
  - Alttrebbin, 151 MWp (North-East)
  - Brandscheid, 7.7 MWp (West)
  - Külsheim-Gickelfeld, 28 MWp (South-West)
- in France (VALECO):
  - Ayguetinte, 5 MWp (South-West)

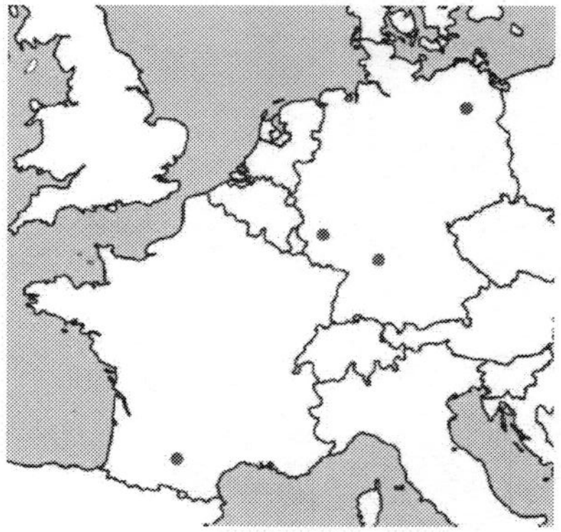

Funded by:
Bundesministerium für Wirtschaft und Energie

EnBW ZSW

Enhancement of PV Plant Monitoring System

- Addition of fault detection procedure based on data modelling
- Extension of input database with additional sensors and measurements
- Integration with existing supervision system by automized data exchange on dedicated interfaces

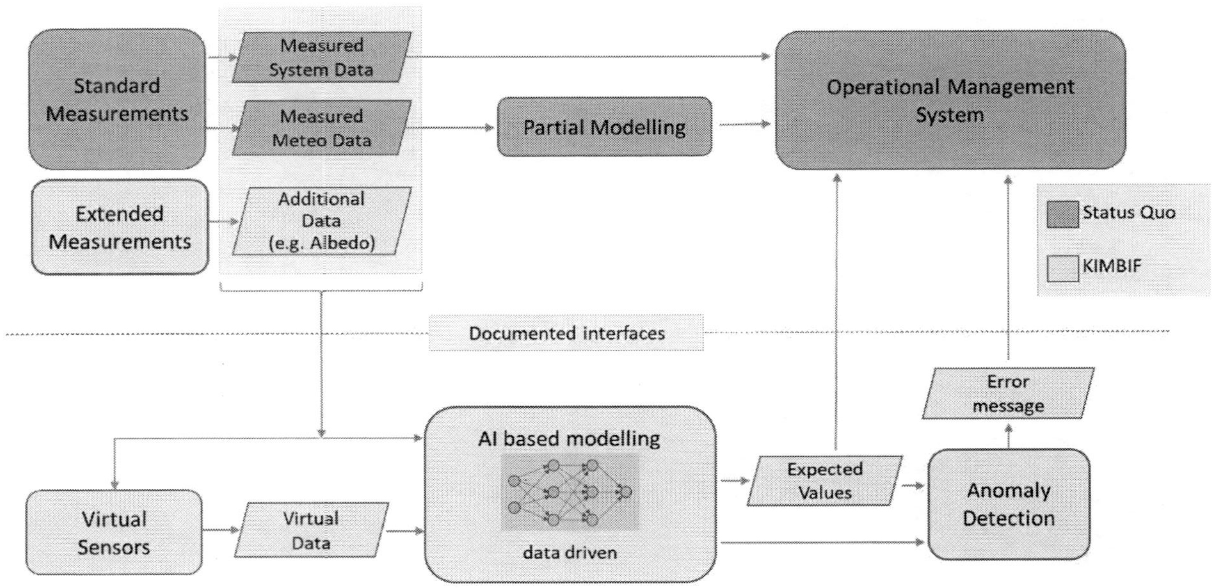

Extension of measurements

- Amplification of input data set with not commonly applied measurements
- Irradiance measurements:
  - Albedo (ground reflected irradiance)
  - Irradiance on module back plane

- Monofacial reference subsystem:
  - PV modules of selected strings covered on the backside with opaque foil
  - operating under identical conditions
  - allows direct determination of bifacial contribution

Pictures source: EnBW

Test site: Large-scale PV power plant Alttrebbin

Source: EnBW

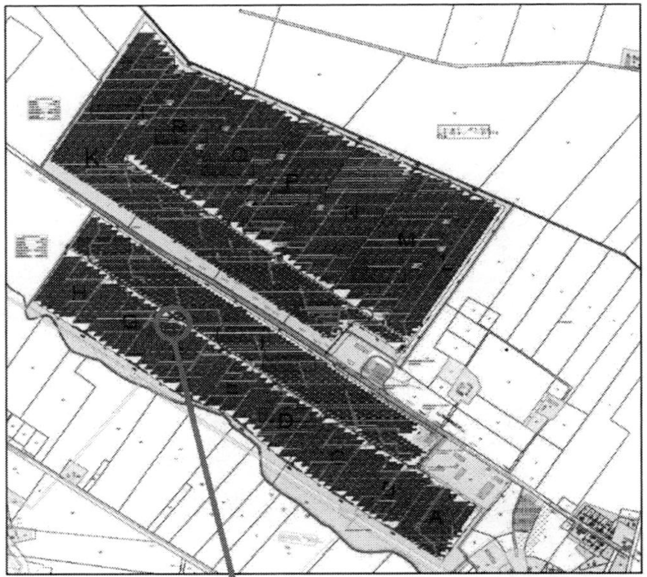

Source: EnBW

- Location: approx. 50 km north-east of Berlin (D)
- Commissioning: 2022
- 345.072 bifacial glass-glass PV modules with 435 Wp - 440Wp
- Nominal installed power: 151 MWp
- Electrical concept: 553 DC combiner boxes connected to 30 central power stations

Model of PV Plant Subunit with Power Station

- Combiner box summed currents are measured at the DC inputs to the power units ("APUs")

⇨ Signals monitored for the detection of string level faults

⇨ Target figures for the data based modelling

- Pairs of power units operating independently
- Data can be used for mutual prediction with ANN

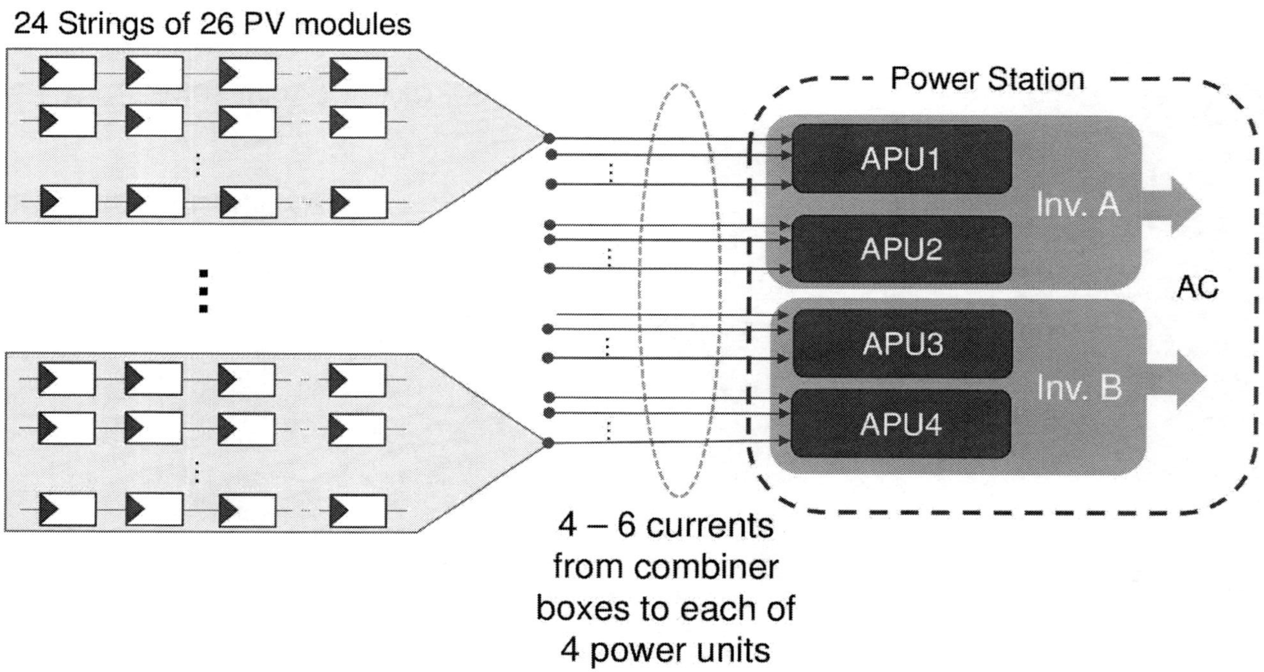

String fault experiments

- Faults were artificially implemented for development and testing of models and fault detection procedures
- 1-4 strings disconnected in combiner boxes on a daily basis
- First phase applied for training and tuning of models and algorithms, second phase used for evaluation

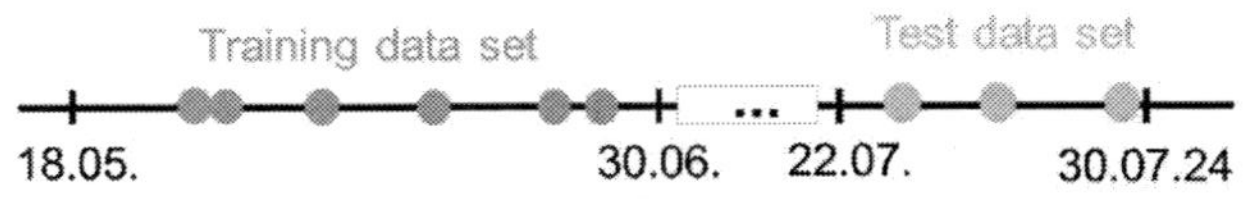

APU3	curr1	4	1	4	1	4	1		4	1	4
APU3	curr2	2	3	2	3	2	3		2	3	2
APU3	curr4	1	4	1	4	1	4		1	4	1
APU4	curr3	2	-	2	-	2	-		2	2	2
APU4	curr6	3	2	3	2	3	2		3	2	3

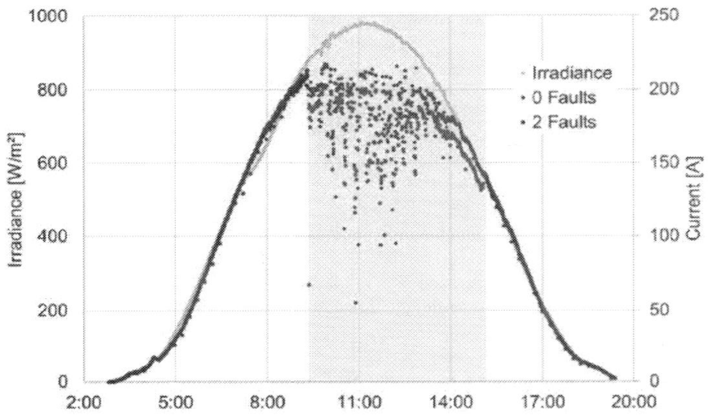

- Operational data show heavy impact from the inverter control executing curtailment on sunny conditions
- Complicates detection of string faults

EnBW ZSW

ANN structure applied for data model

- **Feed forward net**

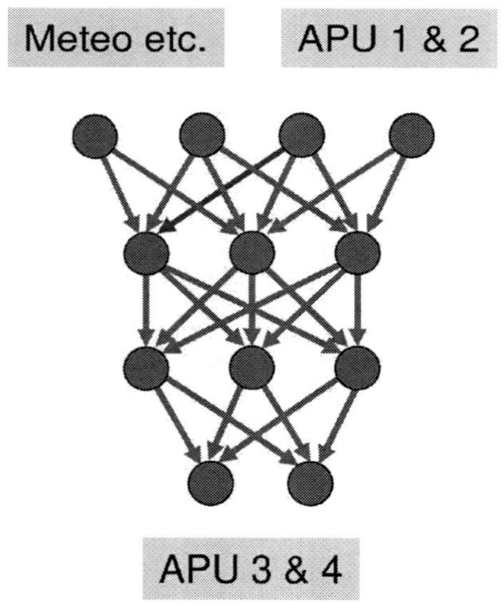

Inputs: conditions + independent time correlated data

Target values

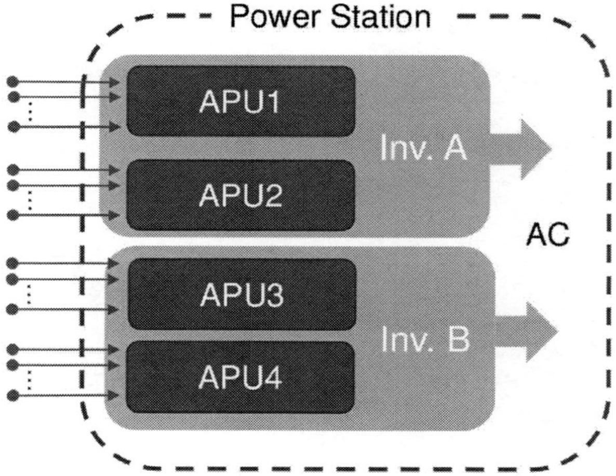

Evaluation of Fault Detection Procedures

Comparison of variant procedures:

A: ANN data model for reference values
+ algorithmic fault status analysis

B: ANN data model for reference values
+ ANN data model for error rating

C: ANN model for direct estimation
of error rating

- Post-processing for combining individual error observations to string fault indications.

- **Variant A**

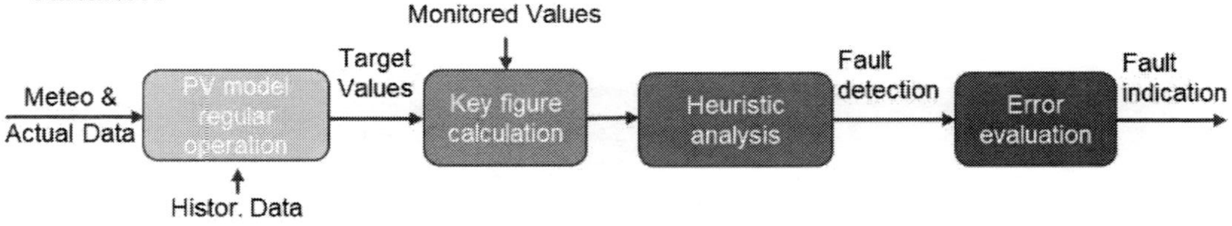

- **Variant B**

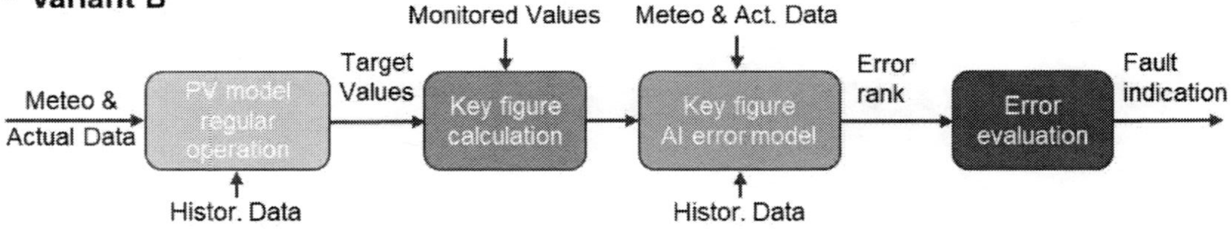

- **Variant C**

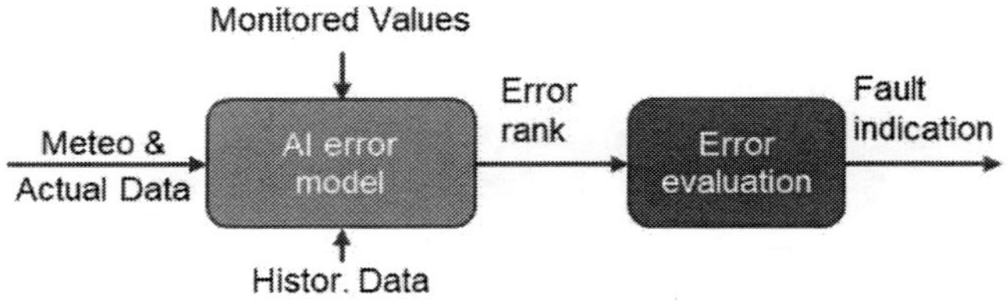

Test Results

- Data filtered for proper power unit operation states
- Generally good detection of ≥2 module string failures, single failures usually not clearly detected
- Evaluation of correct or wrong error and non-error classification with statistical metrices:
  - Accuracy: share of correct classifications
  - F1-Score: indicates how many of the error classifications are correct and how many error states are detected

⇨ Variant B with AI model for target values and AI error model performs best in all analysis

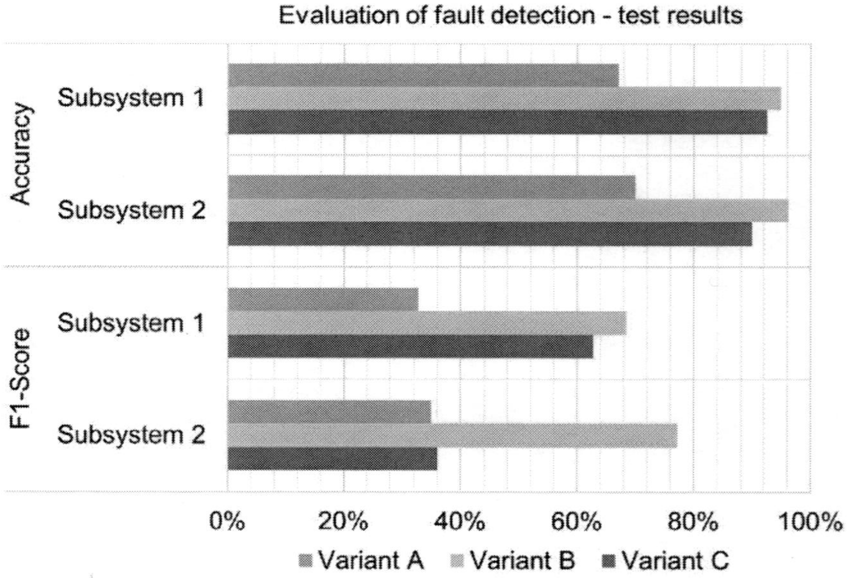

Alternative AI model type: Autoencoder

Feed forward net

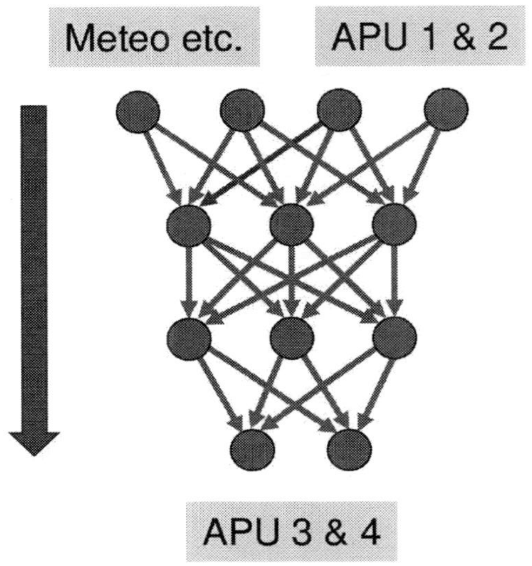

projected from independent inputs

Autoencoder

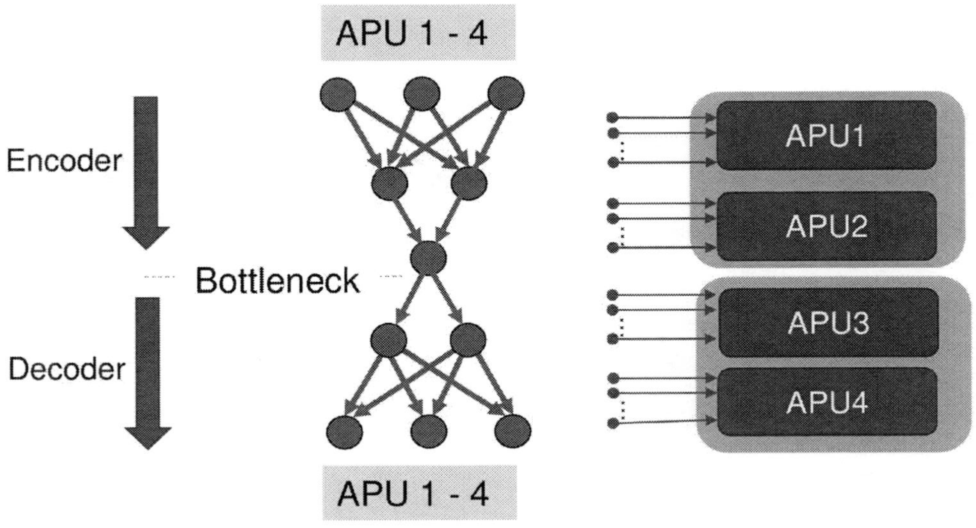

projected from internal correlations

Evaluation of Autoencoder

- Autoencoder approach reduces number of models to be trained for PV plant with multiple subunits
- Structure more easily transferable to other PV parks
- Performance allows for detection of ≥2 simultaneous string faults
- Further work is carried out bring sensitivity to 1 string fault level

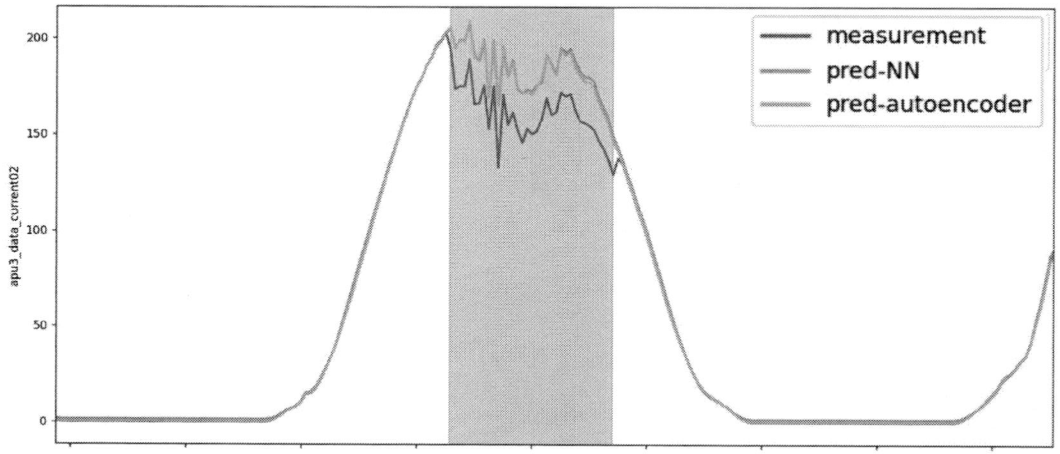

Summary

- The **complexity of large PV parks limits the feasibility** of algorithmic and physics based performance projections for monitoring and power forecasts.
- **AI based data models** are beeing developed for **string fault detection** addressing PV parks in Germany and France.
- **Field experiments with artificial faults** have been conducted to train, tune and evaluate different procedures for failure detection.
- Procedures based on **ANN models proved successful in detecting faults of 2 or more** strings connected to a combiner box.
- **Autoencoder type data models** are promising for increasing the **sensitivity of the anomaly detection** as well as easing the **transfer to other PV plants**.

Zentrum für Sonnenenergie- und Wasserstoff-
Forschung Baden-Württemberg

ZSW

Energie Baden-Württemberg AG

EnBW

ACKNOWLEDGMENT

The research was financially supported by the German Federal Ministry for Economic Affairs and Energy, contract code 03EE1177A.

Bundesministerium
für Wirtschaft
und Energie

Zentrum für Sonnenenergie- und Wasserstoff-
Forschung Baden-Württemberg

Energie Baden-Württemberg AG

THANK YOU FOR YOUR ATTENTION.

Dirk Stellbogen

E-Mail: dirk.stellbogen@zsw-bw.de

For further information, you may visit our booth C8 in the exhibition.

Stuttgart

Ulm

Ulm eLaB

Ulm HyFaB / Powder-Up!

Solar test field

Wind test field

Fachhochschule Kiel
University of Applied Sciences

Fraunhofer
CSP

saferay

WATTMANUFACTUR
Energie mit Mehrwert

A Comprehensive Framework for Accurate Power Degradation Estimation in Large Photovoltaic Systems using Machine Learning

Kak-Pong Cheung[1] , Stephanie Malik[2], David Daßler[2], Carsten Hennig[3], Hauke Nissen[4] , Patrick Hennig[1]

[1] Kiel University of Applied Sciences, Kiel, Germany;
[2] Fraunhofer CSP, Halle, Germany;
[3] saferay, Berlin, Germany;
[4] Wattmanufactur, Galmsbüll, Germany

Presented by
James Cheung

24.09.2025
EU PVSEC 2025 @ Bilbao, Spain

Motivation

Performance Degradation **Inevitable**

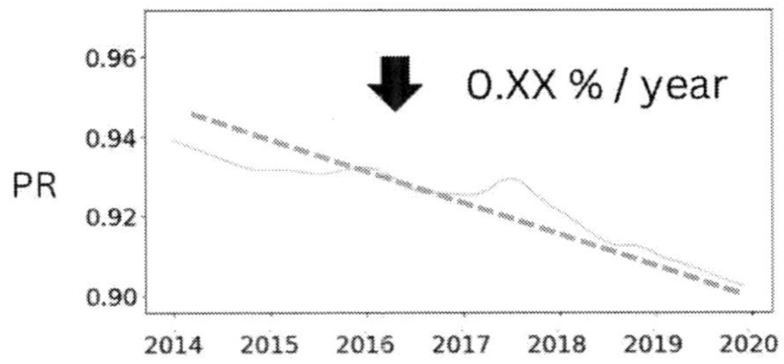

Challenges in Power Degradation Estimation

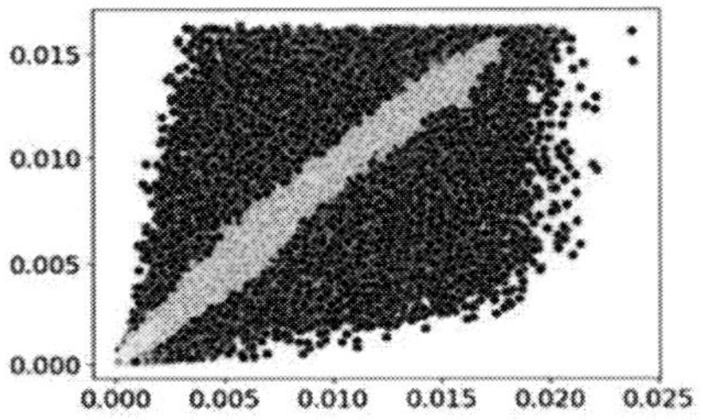

Noisy Dataset

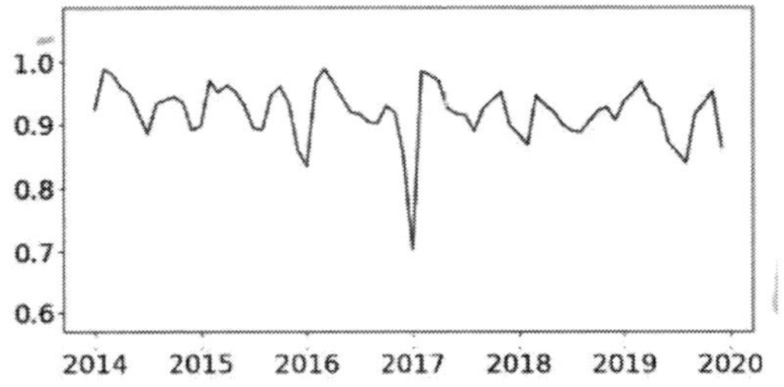

Seasonality

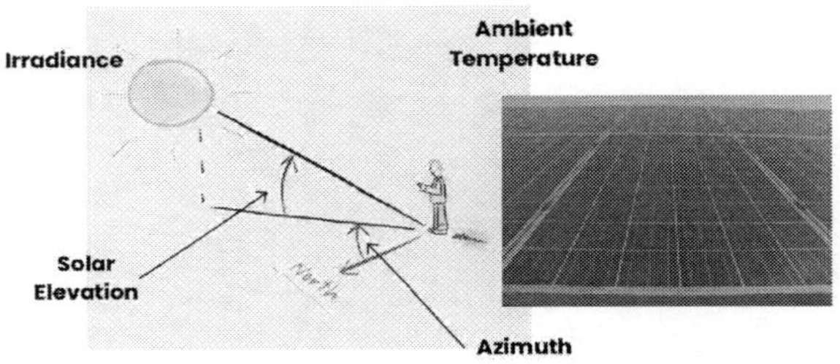

Environmental Factors

2

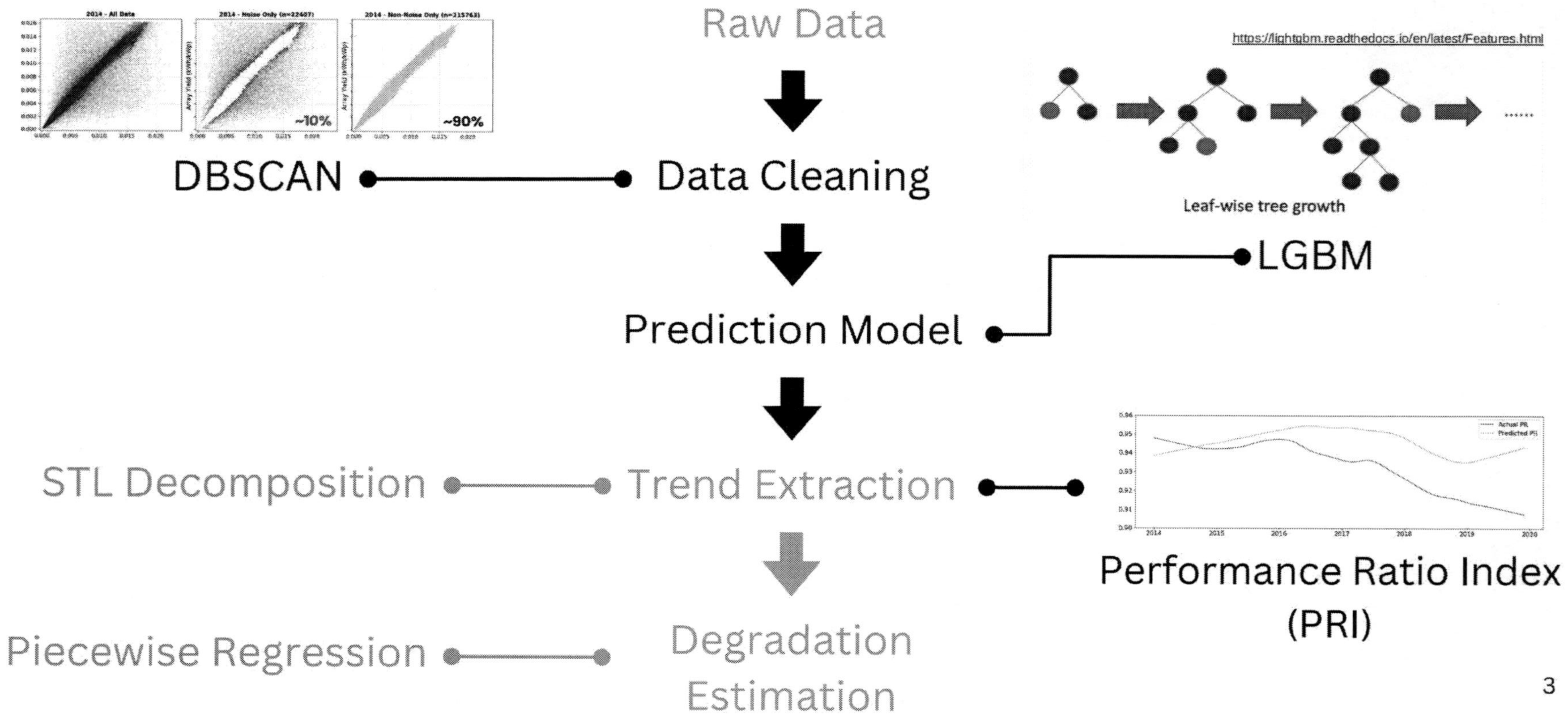
Proposed Framework
2014 - All Data
~10%
~90%
Raw Data
DBSCAN
Data Cleaning
https://lightgbm.readthedocs.io/en/latest/Features.html
Leaf-wise tree growth
LGBM
Prediction Model
STL Decomposition
Trend Extraction
Performance Ratio Index
(PRI)
Piecewise Regression
Degradation
Estimation
3

Data Description

SOURCE : Solar Energy Company

LOCATION : Germany (Single Site)

DATA POINT : over 12 millions from 3 central inverters

RESOLUTION : Minute

PERIOD : 2014 - 2019 (6 years)

DEVICES : Inverter, Pyranometer, Temperature Sensor

FEATURES : Date time, DC Power, Irradiance (POA), Ambient Temperature

GENERATED : Solar Elevation, Azimuth

DATA QUALITY : Less than 1% missing value / Time Gap / Abnormal Behaviour

Raw Data | **Cleaning** | Predictive Model | Metric | Trend Extraction | Degradation Estimation

Density-Based Spatial Clustering of Applications with Noise (DBSCAN)

Array Yield (kWh / kW)
DC side only

$$y_f = \frac{\Delta t}{P_{STC}} \cdot \sum_{i=1}^{N} P_i$$

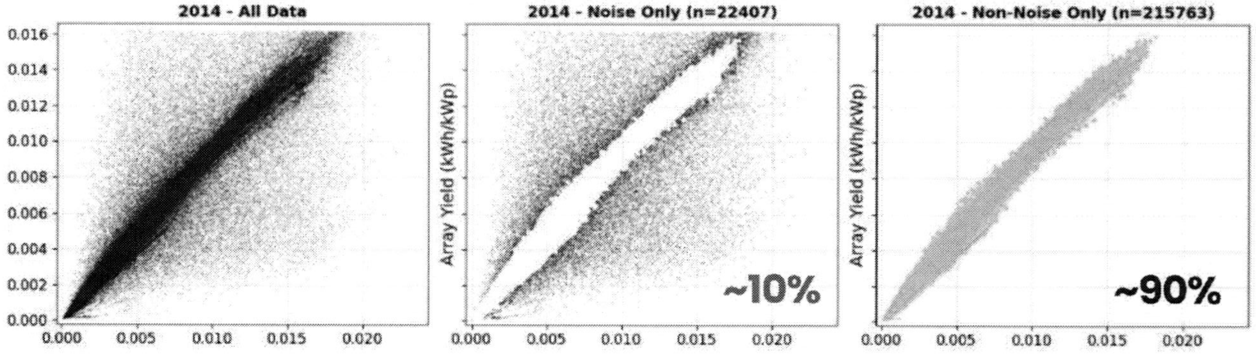

Reference Yield (kWh / kW)

$$y_r = \frac{\Delta t}{G_{STC}} \cdot \sum_{i=1}^{N} G_i$$

5

Light Gradient Boosting Machine (LGBM)

Input Features

Irradiance
Ambient Temperature
Solar Elevation
Solar Azimuth

Output Prediction

DC Power

Result : Mean Absolute Percentage Error (MAPE)

Year	MAPE (%)	
2014	5.46	Training
2015	9.78	Testing
2016	8.38	
2017	13.83	
2018	14.69	
2019	7.52	

Inverter 1001

Raw Data | Cleaning | **Predictive Model** | Metric | Trend Extraction | Degradation Estimation

LGBM Performance Evaluation

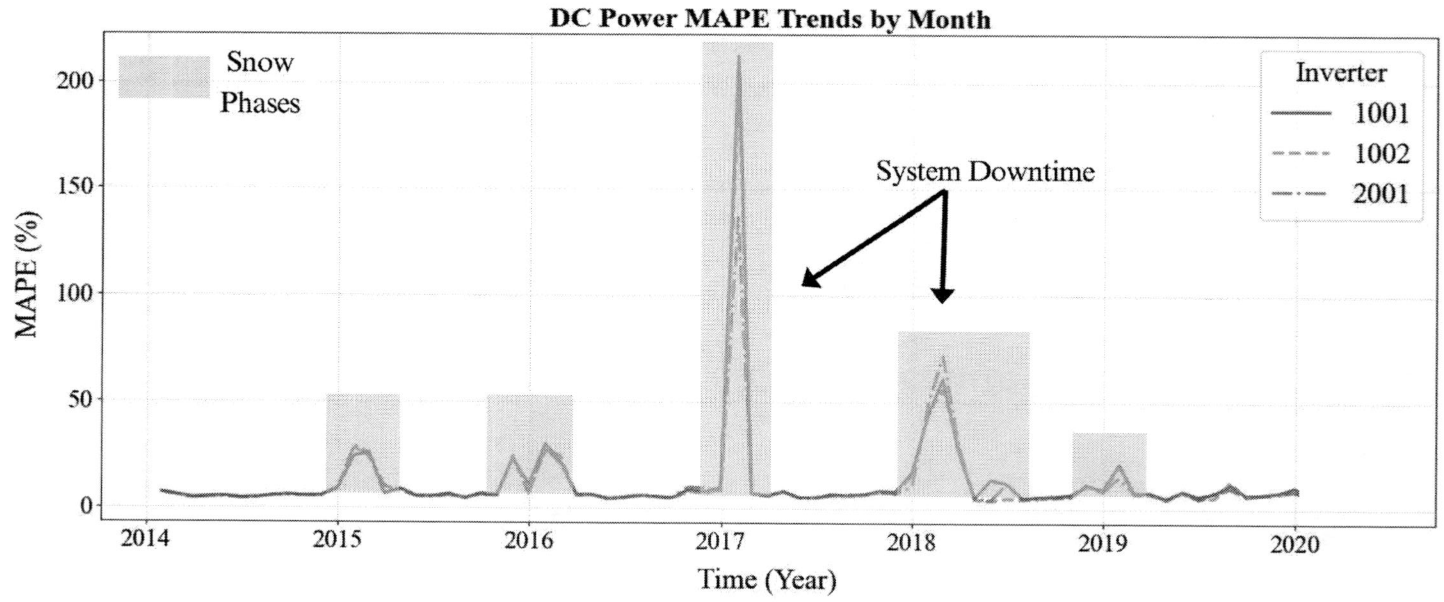

Monthly MAPE (%)

Raw Data | Cleaning | **Predictive Model** | Metric | Trend Extraction | Degradation Estimation

Data (2014) → Data (2015 - 2019)

Training LGBM → Predict Targets (DC Power)

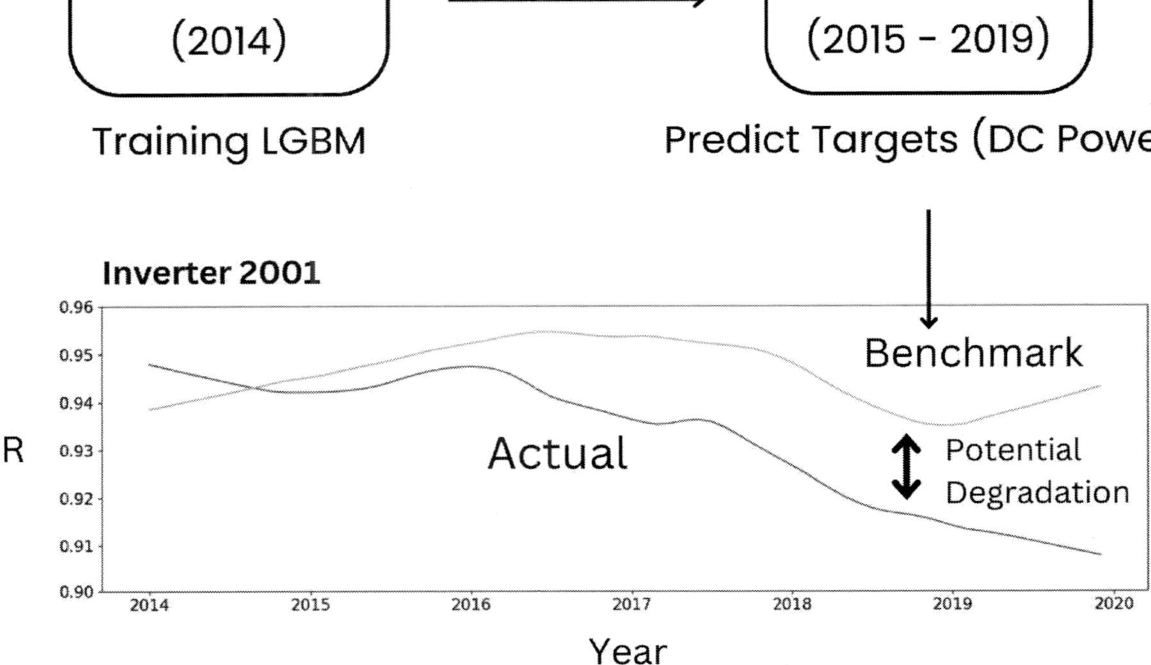

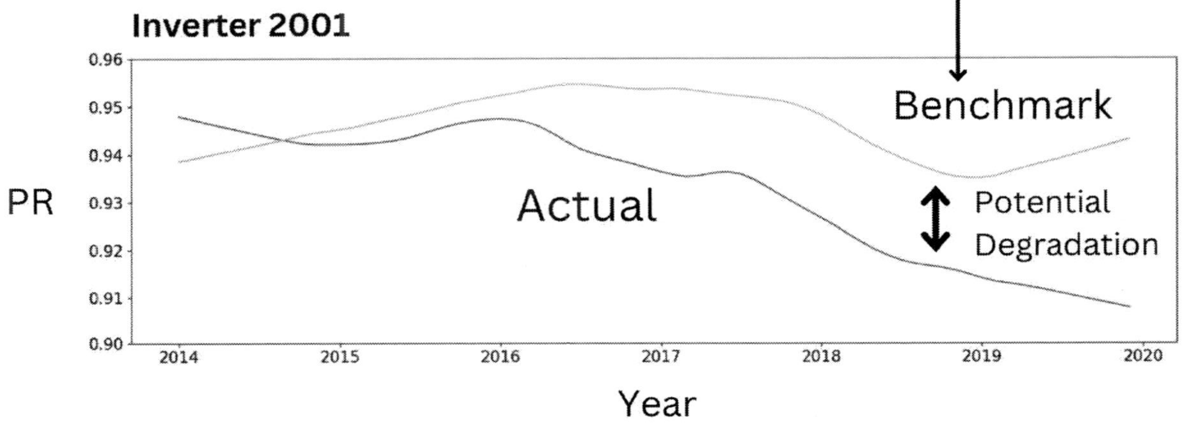

Raw Data | Cleaning | Predictive Model | **Metric** | Trend Extraction | Degradation Estimation

Proposed Metric

Performance Ratio Index (PRI) = $\dfrac{\text{Actual PR}}{\text{Predicted PR}}$

Raw Data | Cleaning | Predictive Model | Metric | **Trend Extraction** | Degradation Estimation

Seasonal Trend Decomposition using LOESS

PRI

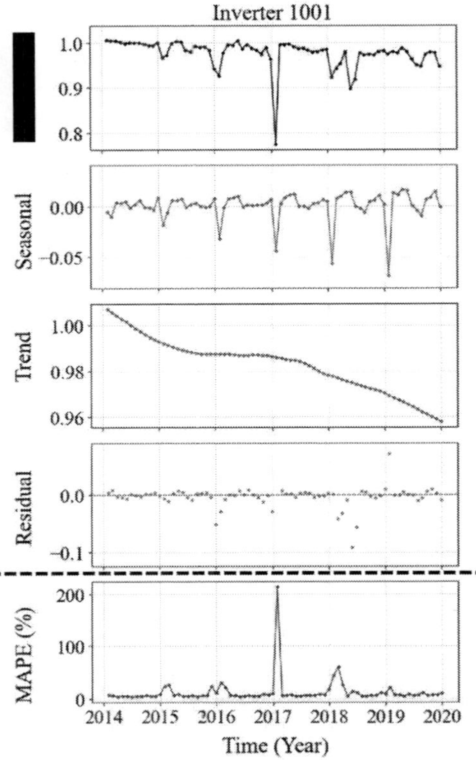

Trend Component

10

Raw Data | Cleaning | Predictive Model | Metric | Trend Extraction | **Degradation Estimation**

Piecewise Regression

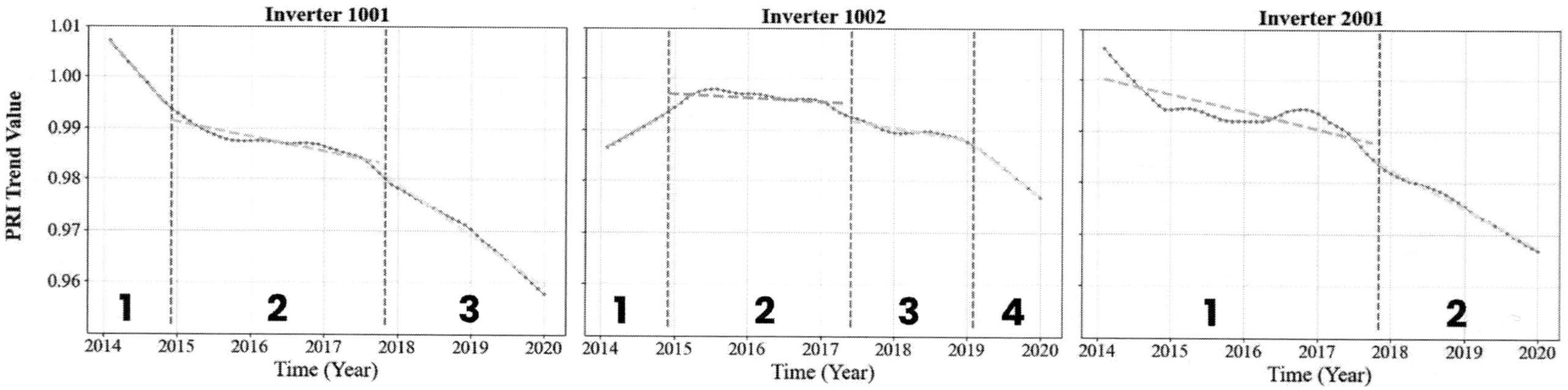

Inverter 1001

Phase 1: -1.65% / year

Phase 2: -0.29% / year

Phase 3: -0.99% / year

Inverter 1002

Phase 1: +0.81% / year

Phase 2: -0.07% / year

Phase 3: -0.22% / year

Phase 4: -1.22% / year

Inverter 2001

Phase 1: -0.33 % / year

Phase 2: -0.76 % / year

PRI-Based Result

Our Result

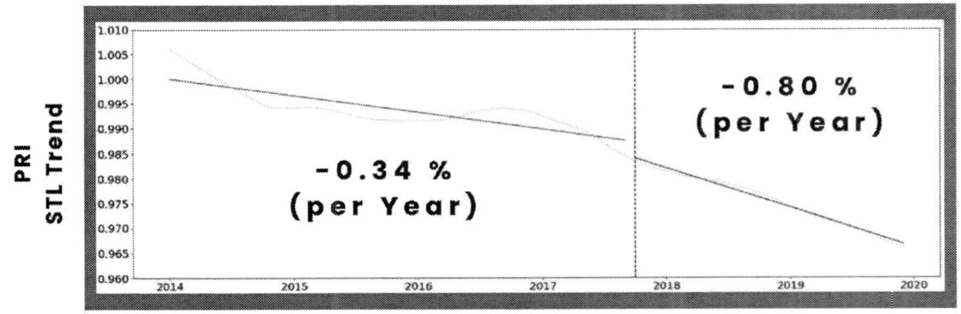

System	$\overline{PLR}$	System	$\overline{PLR}$	System	$\overline{PLR}$
EURAC	-0.85 %/a	NREL1	-0.33 %/a	US DOE luemkoy**	0.95 %/a
FOSS	-0.71 %/a	NREL2	-0.54 %/a	US DOE lwcb907	-0.03 %/a
RSE CdTe	-1.75 %/a	NREL3*	0.06 %/a	US DOE t3pg1sv	-0.75 %/a
RSE pc-Si	-0.96 %/a	NREL4	-0.25 %/a	US DOE wca0c5m***	-1.00 %/a
Pfaffstaetten A	-3.57 %/a	US DOE c10hov6	-0.50 %/a	US DOE wxysjaf	-0.97 %/a
Pfaffstaetten B	-3.96 %/a	US DOE kob-dpi8	-0.73 %/a	US DOE z0aygry***	-2.32 %/a
Pfaffstaetten C	-1.29 %/a				

Report IEA-PVPS T13-22:2021

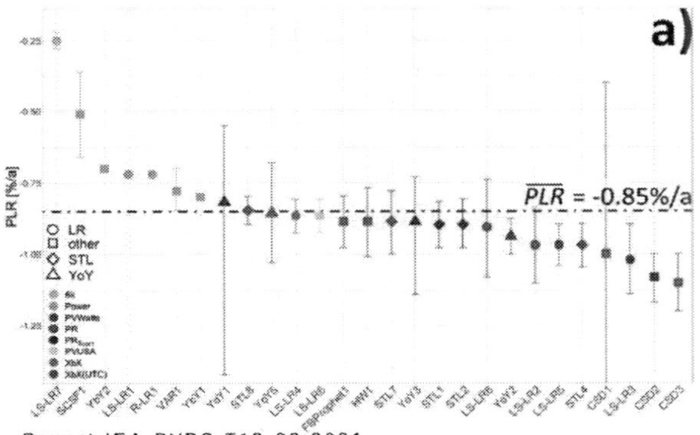

Report IEA-PVPS T13-22:2021

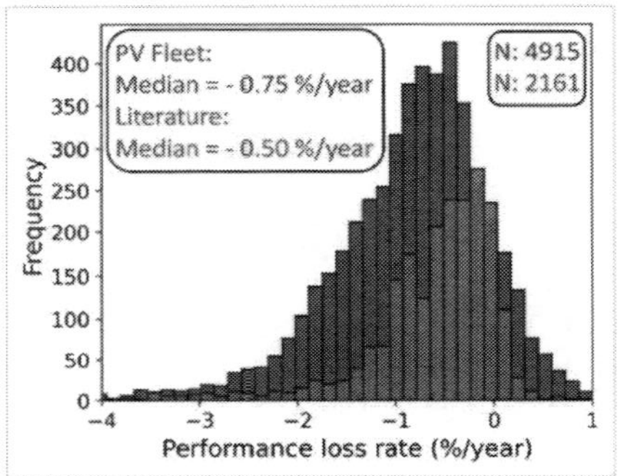

doi.org/10.1002/pip.3566

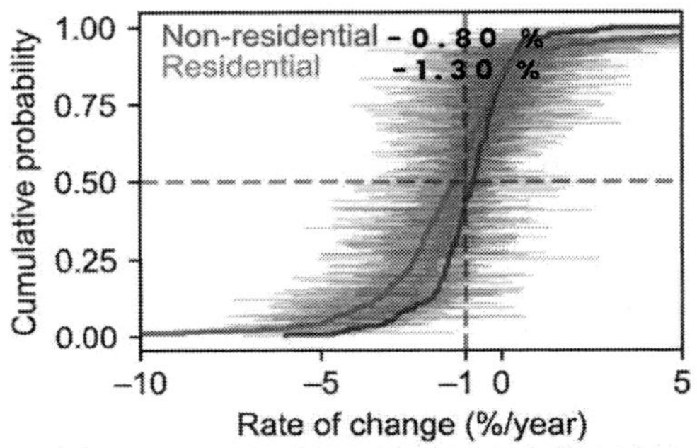

doi.org/10.1109/JPHOTOV.2018.2884948

Industry Benchmarking Results

12

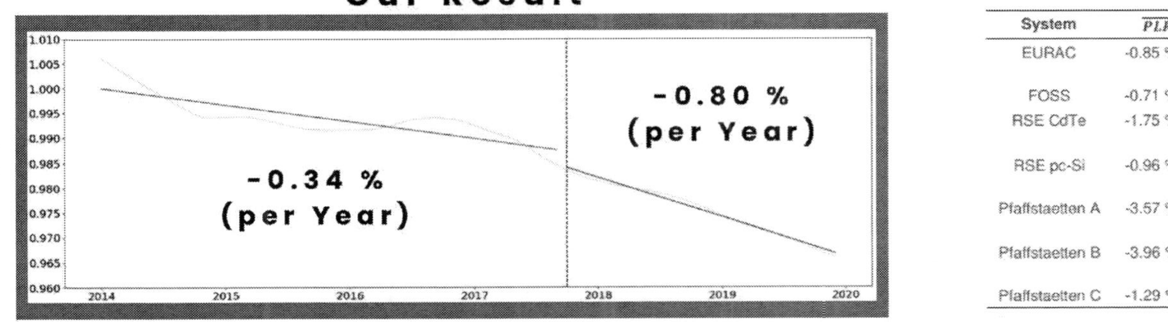

Contribution

DBSCAN Noise Filtering

Data-driven - retain only the densest region, defined by the underlying relationship between array yield and reference yield

Performance Ratio Index (PRI) with LGBM Predictive Benchmarking

Environmental Independent Metric - Normalized performance by factoring out weather and solar factors

Challenges

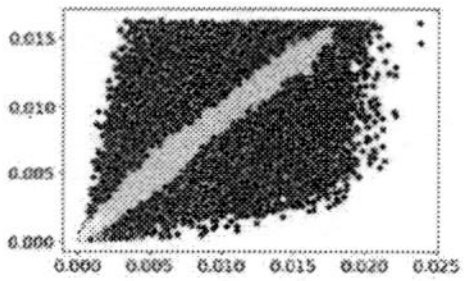

Noisy Dataset

Solutions

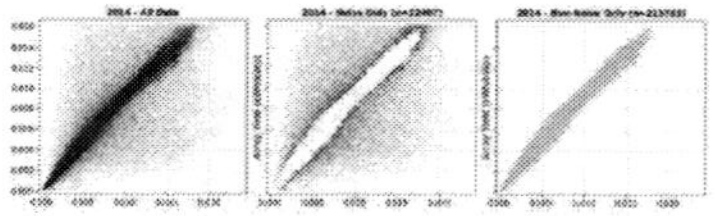

DBSCAN

Challenges

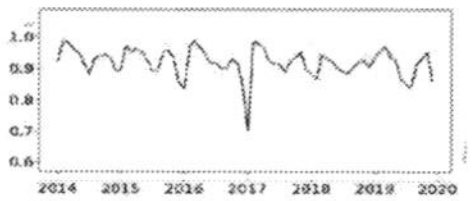

Seasonality

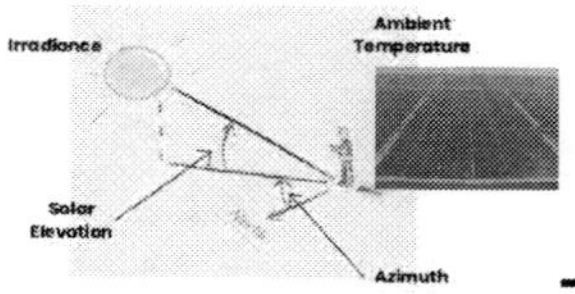

Environmental Factors

Solutions

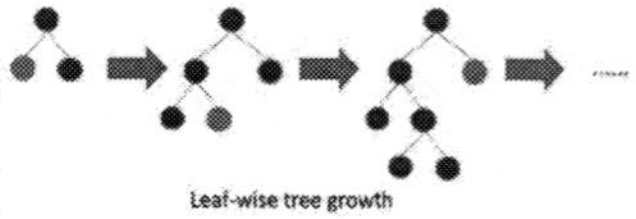

LGBM

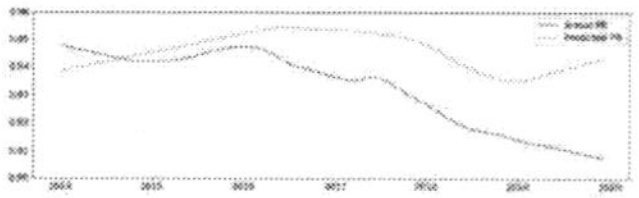

Performance Ratio Index (PRI)

Future Work

Broaden Data Ecosystem

heterogeneous PV assets across climatic zones and manufacturers

Comparative Modeling Landscape Exploration

Systematically evaluate diverse A.I. predictive architectures

Model-Guided Data Curation

Leverage predictive model performance (e.g. MAPE-based filters)

14

THANK YOU

Contact Information

James Cheung

kak.p.cheung@fh-kiel.de

+49 176 8757 7924

Fachhochschule Kiel
University of Applied Sciences

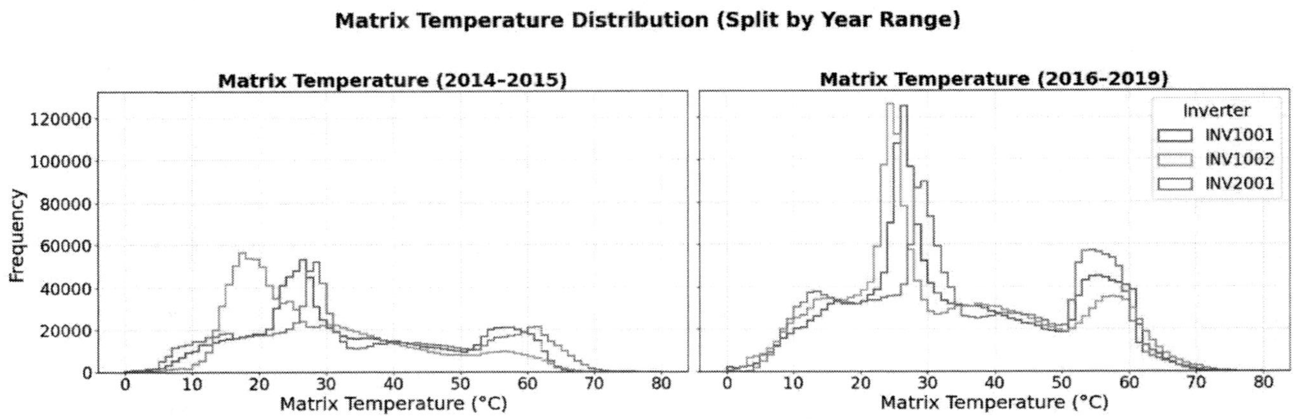
Matrix Temperature Distribution (Split by Year Range)
Matrix Temperature (2014-2015)
Matrix Temperature (2016-2019)
Frequency
120000
100000
80000
60000
40000
20000
0
0
10
20
30
40
50
60
70
80
Matrix Temperature (°C)
Inverter
INV1001
INV1002
INV2001

16

DBSCAN RESULTS

INVERTER: 1001 | INVERTER: 1002 | INVERTER: 2001

2014
2015
2016
2017
2018
2019

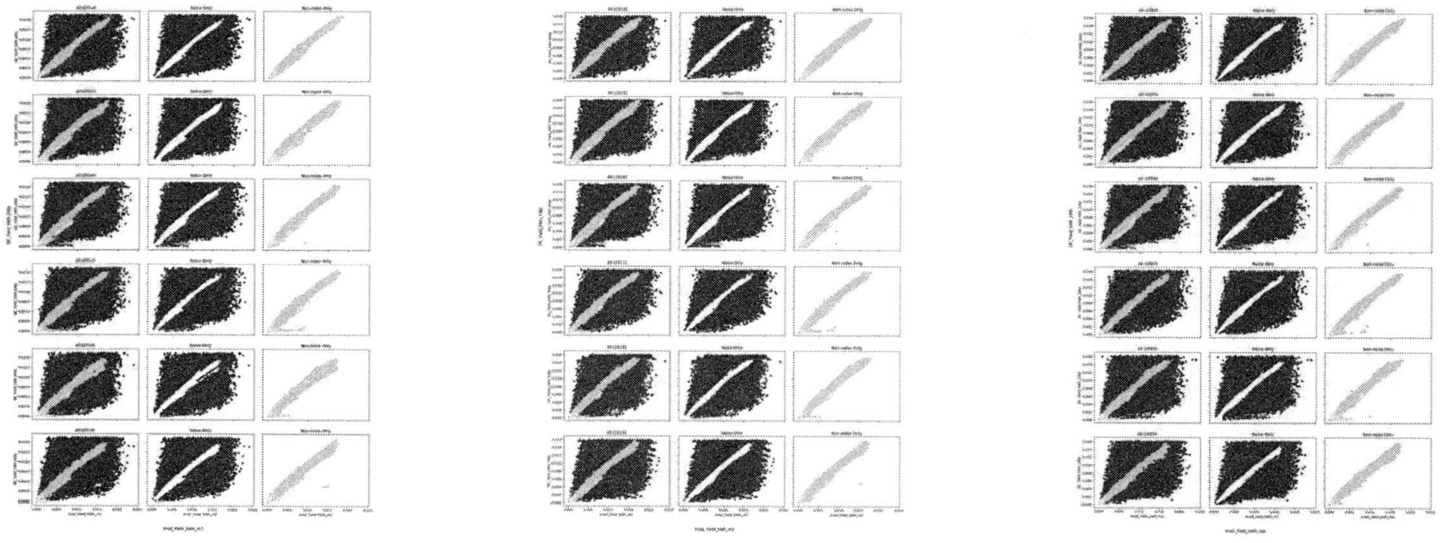

Seasonal Trend Decomposition using LOESS

PRI

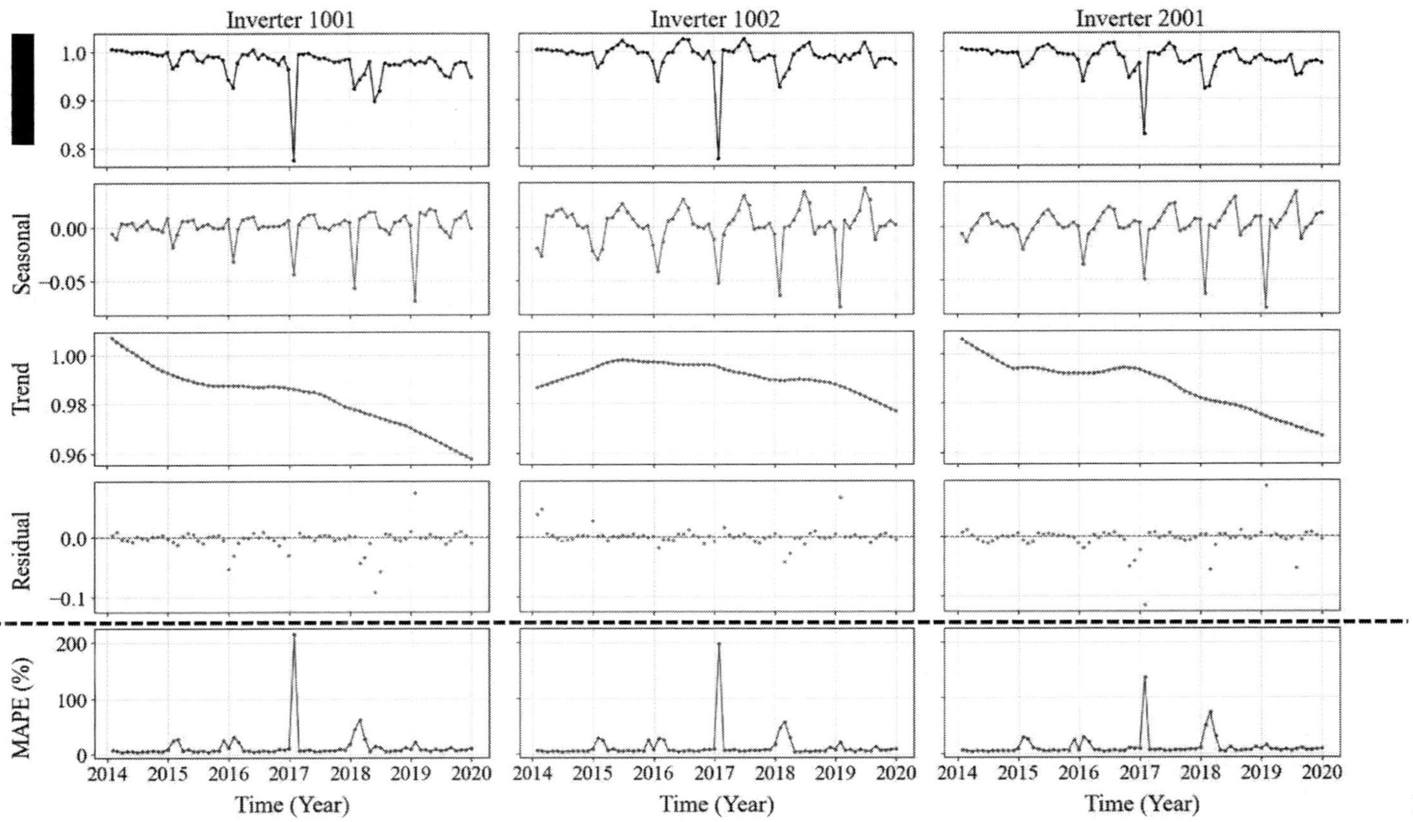

18

42nd European Photovoltaic Solar Energy Conference and Exhibition

This presentation was selected by the Sc. Committee of the EU PVSEC 2025 for submission of a full paper to one of the EU PVSEC's collaborating peer-reviewed journals.

Use of a digital twin to detect stalling tracker events in photovoltaic power plant with horizontal single-axis tracking systems

Riccardo Adinolfi Borea[1], Matthew Muller[2], Silvana Ovaitt[2], Vincenzo Cirimele[1], Francesco Melino[1]
[1] Alma Mater Studiorum – University of Bologna, Via Zamboni, 33, 40126 Bologna, Italy
[2] National Renewable Energy Laboratory – NREL, 15013 Denver West Parkway, Golden, CO 80401

ABSTRACT: Horizontal single-axis trackers are widely employed in photovoltaic power plants to enhance energy production. Despite their benefits, these systems encounter mechanical issues, such as stall events, which can lead to significant power losses. This work introduces a novel and broadly applicable methodology for detecting stalled tracker events through pairwise comparisons. The proposed algorithm operates directly on measured output power and requires minimal site-specific inputs. Validation was performed using both synthetic datasets – generated with physical models and randomized anomalies – and real field measurements from a photovoltaic array. Results from synthetic data demonstrate an F_1 score of 0.60, highlighting potential for further refinement. Applying a day clearness threshold of 0.60 improved performance substantially, raising the F_1 score to 0.96. When tested on field data under the same conditions, the algorithm achieved an F_1 score of 0.75, pointing to additional challenges caused by phenomena that mimic stalled behavior.

Keywords: single-axis tracker reliability, stall detection, synthetic dataset, performance losses

1 INTRODUCTION

In utility-scale photovoltaic (PV) plants, solar trackers are commonly used to increase energy yield and improve cost-effectiveness. The most widespread design is the horizontal single-axis tracker, which uses a simple torque tube and motor mechanism. Despite their simplicity, trackers vary in reliability due to differing mechanical solutions across manufacturers. Tracker-related issues rank among the top three causes of service tickets in PV plants – after inverters (~60%) and modules (~18%) – and account for about 11% of cases, with an average resolution time of 14 days [1]. To address these challenges, some manufacturers now include position sensors, but most systems still lack reliable angular data. This gap has motivated the development of methodologies for detecting stalled trackers. In [2], a method based on pairwise comparison is proposed, where each PV system is evaluated against its best-performing neighboring peers. Peers are identified using the variance and covariance of the ratio between the capacity utilization factors of neighboring systems. Days with correlations below a threshold are flagged, though the method does not name the cause of low correlation. On the same topic, [3] introduces a physics-informed deep learning approach to detect faulty tracker patterns. The validation dataset consists of string-level measurements from a 624-string PV field collected over one year, including 340,000 daily profiles (170,000 measured healthy and 170,000 faulty, synthetically generated via a convolutional neural network). The authors emphasize that embedding physics improves performance compared to a purely data-driven approach. However, both methods face practical challenges: [2] requires detailed system information such as capacity, maintenance records, and nearby plant data, while [3] relies on high-quality datasets with reliable maintenance records – conditions not always met in real-world PV operations.

It is therefore the aim of this work to tackle this topic from a different perspective. This work aims to evaluate a methodology for detecting stalled tracker events in datasets with limited information and availability. Therefore, it is proposed an agnostic approach, and the evaluation of the impact of such agnosticism. This work is an extension of the work presented in [4]. The following sections address firstly the detection algorithm, then the obtainment of synthetic and field data for validation, and lastly the score and limiting factors of the algorithm.

2 METHODOLOGY

2.1 Detection algorithm

The algorithm is based upon pairwise comparisons between measured and modeled output power. For each PV system, it simulates expected daily power under both regular tracking and fixed orientations along the tracker's rotation path, then selects the scenario that best matches the measured data. The inputs are minimal, namely the measured output power, the location, the global horizontal irradiance (ghi), and ground coverage ratio (GCR).

Modeled daily DC output power, P^*_{DC}, is generated using the Sandia view-factor model, the Sandia array performance model [5], and PVWatts [6]. These simulations represent three operating conditions: tracking, fully stalled (modules remain fixed at orientations), and partially stalled (where only a fraction of the array is fixed and the rest tracks properly). In the latter case, the output is expressed as

$$P^*_{DC}(\zeta,\theta) = \zeta \cdot P^*_{DC,stalled}(\theta) + (1-\zeta)\, P^*_{DC,tracking} \;,$$

where ζ is the stall fraction (1 represents a fully stalled tracker and 0 represents regularly operating tracker) and θ the orientation at which the tracker is stalled. θs are obtained dividing the range of motion of the tracker in 5° intervals, and ζ is set to 0.33 and 0.66.

Once all daily scenarios are produced, the algorithm normalizes modeled outputs by their daily maximum and measured output by the 96th quantile, then compares them using the coefficient of determination (R^2). The scenario yielding the highest similarity is considered equivalent to the measured system's operating condition.

2.2 Data obtainment for validation

The detection algorithm is validated on both synthetic and field data. Synthetic data are produced following the methodology in [7], which enables the creation of datasets that replicate the output power of photovoltaic systems under varying conditions. After selecting a location, weather data from the National Solar Radiation Database (NSRDB) are retrieved and used to simulate the output power of a reference PV array. The methodology then introduces physical anomalies and noise into the generation process, including effects such as soiling losses, stalled trackers, inverter clipping, string outages, and both random and irradiance-dependent noise. Because anomalies are modeled as discrete, configurable events and noise can be tuned, the approach allows for the generation of tailored datasets. Events are positioned randomly throughout the time span to avoid repetition, ensuring that running the script multiple times yields different datasets.

The detection algorithm is validated on multiple synthetic datasets. For each location, six variants of the same dataset are generated, differing only in the tracker stall fraction, S, which is set to 0.01, 0.1, 0.25, 0.50, 0.75, and 1.0. Output power profiles are obtained as

$$P_{DC} = S \cdot P_{DC,stalled}(0°) + (1 - S) \cdot P_{DC,tracking} \ ,$$

where $P_{DC,stalled}$ and $P_{DC,tracking}$ are simulated with identical noise but different orientations, representing stalled and normally operating trackers, respectively. Before being fed to the detection algorithm, each dataset is filtered using a clearsky classification method described in [8], which permits to discard non-clearsky timestamps.

Concerning field data, these are obtained from the National Renewable Energy Laboratory's (NREL) Bifacial Experimental Single-Axis Tracking Field, located at the South Table Mountain Campus in Golden, Colorado (39.74° N, −105.17° W), described in [9]). To generate the dataset, tests are carried out by fixing one tracker at 0° while the others continue normal operation.

3 RESULTS

The metric used to express and compare results is the F_1 score, given by

$$F_1 = \frac{2\,TP}{2\,TP + FN + FP} \ ,$$

where TP, FP, and FN, stand for true positive, false positive, and false negative, respectively. A TP is a stall event that is correctly flagged (regardless of the stall orientation suggested by the algorithm), a FP is a day that is wrongly flagged as a stalled event, and a FN is a stall event that is not flagged.

3.1 Validation on synthetic data

Merging the results of the 38 locations considered, the algorithm achieves an F_1 score of 0.60. Defining the day clearness as the fraction of daylight timestamps classified as clearsky, the algorithm tends to fail more frequently toward lower values of day clearness. Introducing a day clearness threshold permits to filter out predominantly overcast days hence improve the performance. Fig. 1 shows the algorithm's performance when different thresholds are applied. Even with no threshold, roughly 140 days per year are excluded due to the clearsky-only classification. Increasing the threshold improves performance, with the F_1 score rising from 0.60 to 0.97 as the minimum day clearness increases from 0 to 0.60. However, this also removes some potential stall events. These are considered less critical, since energy losses during partially cloudy days are smaller than during clear ones. For this reason, a minimum day clearness of 0.60 is adopted for reliable results and will be assumed in all subsequent analyses.

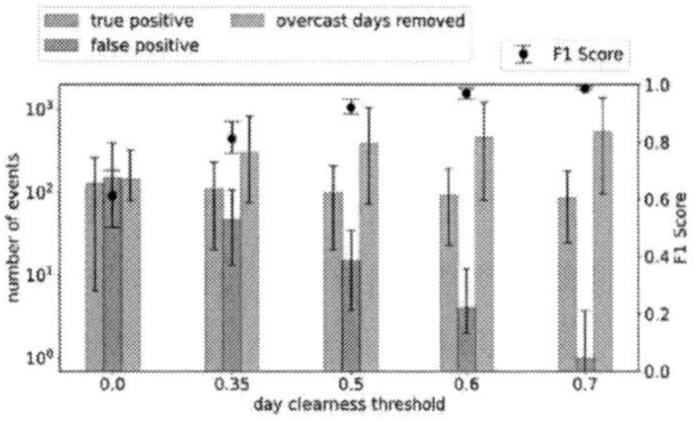

Fig. 1 True positive, false positive, overcast days removed, and F_1 score, when different values of minimum day clearness are imposed.

The algorithm's capability to identify partially stalled events is evaluated by running it on six dataset variants per location, each generated with a different stall fraction S. Results show a strong dependence on stall severity: lower S values lead to fewer true positives, more false negatives, and consequently lower F_1 scores. This outcome confirms that the algorithm is more reliable when stall events have higher stall fractions, with performance becoming appreciable when $S > 0.25$.

3.2 Validation on field data

The detection algorithm was run on six datasets, each containing 67 daily P_{DC} profiles with day clearness above 0.60, including three stall events. Given the small number of stall events, results from field data should be considered preliminary. During a stall event, row 3 was fixed at 0° while row 8 operated normally. Each dataset was constructed by combining the output of row 3 ($P_{DC,3}$) and row 8 ($P_{DC,8}$) using the stall fraction S, as in

$$P_{DC} = S\,P_{DC,3} + (1 - S)P_{DC,8} \ ,$$

with S set to 0.01, 0.1, 0.25, 0.50, 0.75, and 1.0. Fig. 2 summarizes performance across all S values: for $S < 0.1$ stall events are undetectable, whereas for $S > 0.25$ all stall events are correctly identified. Corresponding F_1 scores for S equal to 0.25, 0.75, and 1.0 are 0.67, 0.75, and 0.86, reflecting 3, 2, and 1 false negative days, respectively.

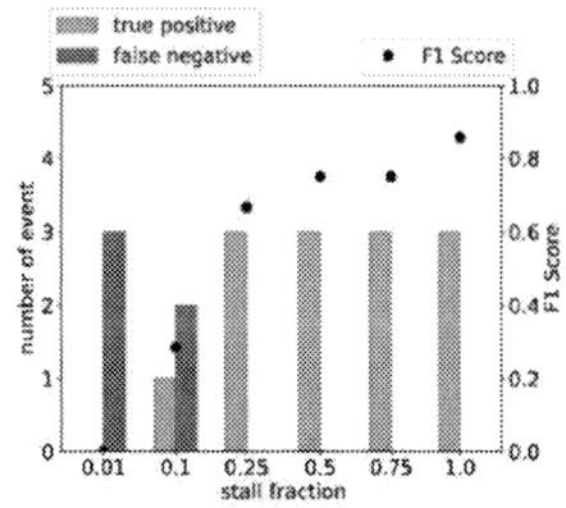

Fig. 2 algorithm's performance at different S values. The F1 changes accordingly to S.

Fig. 3 examines the three FNs days that make the F_1 score change. On February 9th, both trackers briefly exhibited a possibly stall condition that was later on corrected but still

10.4229/EUPVSEC2025/4CO.9.3

flagged by the algorithm. On January 8th, row 8 underperformed in the morning in a manner resembling a stalled tracker, despite tracking normally; further analysis of NREL meteorological data indicates that snow on the modules likely caused this temporary reduction, which cleared by midday. On May 20th, lastly, row 8 again underperformed in the evening. In both January and May cases, differing performances between rows 3 and 8 mean that variations in the stall fraction S produce different detection outcomes.

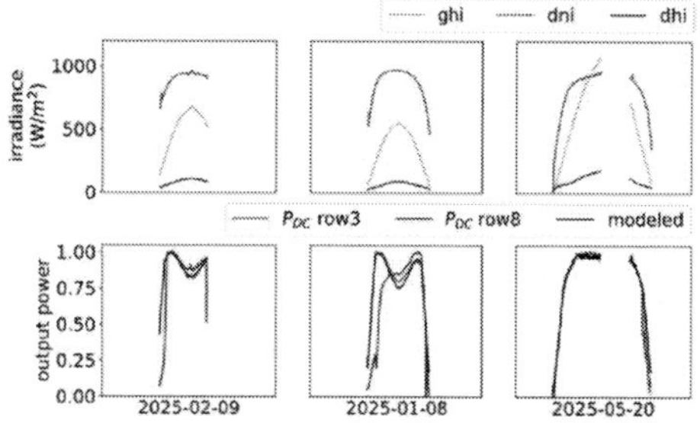

Fig.3 Three days that are flagged as stall events. February 9th is a day during which both trackers probably faced a tracker stall, hence is flagged regardless of S. January 8th and May 20th, instead, are days in which row no.8 has an issue and row no.3 is operating regularly, thus how the two are combined influences the result.

4 CONCLUSIONS

This study presented a broadly applicable algorithm for detecting stall events in PV power plants with horizontal single-axis trackers. The method relies on pairwise comparisons between measured and modeled output power and requires minimal site-specific information, making it suitable for scenarios with limited data. Validation on synthetic datasets showed that the algorithm effectively detects stall events when the stall fraction exceeds 0.25 and partially overcast days are excluded. Imposing a day clearness threshold of 0.6 increased the F_1 score from 0.60 to 0.97 for $S = 1$. Field data validation highlighted additional challenges: while all stall events were detected, three days are misclassified as partially stalled events. In two cases, temporary underperformance mimicked a stall, making the algorithm's classification reasonable. Due to the small dataset (67 days, only 3 stall events), further conclusions are preliminary. Ongoing field data collection is expected to enable more robust results in future work.

5 ACKOWLEDGEMENTS

This work has been supported by Ricerca per il Sistema Energetico Spa (RSE) through the Fondo di Ricerca per il Sistema Elettrico (RdS) within the framework of the Triennial Plan 2022-2024 (DM MITE n. 337, of 15.09.2022) and the project RdS 1.1 project "High-Efficiency Photovoltaics", supported by the Alma Mater Studiorum - Università di Bologna through the National Doctoral Program in "Photovoltaics" for the XXVIII cycle, as per article 3, paragraph 2 of DM 226/2021.

This work was also authored in part by the National Renewable Energy Laboratory (NREL) for the U.S. Department of Energy (DOE) under Contract No. DE-AC36-08GO28308. Partial funding is provided by the U.S. Department of Energy (DOE)'s Office of Energy Efficiency and Renewable Energy (EERE) from the Solar Energy Technologies Office (SETO), under CPS Agreement 52799. The views expressed in the article do not necessarily represent the views of the DOE or the U.S. Government. The U.S. Government retains and the publisher, by accepting the article for publication, acknowledges that the U.S. Government retains a nonexclusive, paid-up, irrevocable, worldwide license to publish or reproduce the published form of this work, or allow others to do so, for U.S. Government purposes. The funders had no role in study design, data collection and analysis, decision to publish, or preparation of the manuscript.

6 REFERENCES

[1]. "Past Proceedings | PVRW: Photovoltaic Reliability Workshop | NREL." Available: https://pvrw.nrel.gov/past-proceedings

[2]. J. Leloux, et. al, "Automatic fault detection on BIPV systems without solar irradiation data," 2014, doi: 10.13140/2.1.2280.3200.

[3]. J. Zgraggen, et. al, "Physics Informed Deep Learning for Tracker Fault Detection in Photovoltaic Power Plants," *Annu. Conf. PHM Soc.*, Oct. 2022, doi: 10.36001/phmconf.2022.v14i1.3235.

[4]. K. Anderson, et. al, "A Method for Estimating Time-Series PV Production Loss From Solar Tracking Failures," *IEEE J. Photovolt.*, Jan. 2022, doi: 10.1109/JPHOTOV.2021.3123872.

[5]. J. Kratochvil, et. al, "Photovoltaic array performance model.," SAND2004-3535, 919131, Aug. 2004. doi: 10.2172/919131.

[6]. A. Dobos, "PVWatts Version 5 Manual," NREL/TP-6A20-62641, Sep. 2014. doi: 10.2172/1158421.

[7]. M. Muller, et. al, "Generating Synthetic Time Series PV Data with Real-World Physical Challenges and Noise for Use in Algorithm Test and Validation,", Sep. 2023. doi: 10.21948/1999772.

[8]. D. C. Jordan and C. Hansen, "Clear-sky detection for PV degradation analysis using multiple regression," *Renew. Energy*, Jun. 2023, doi: 10.1016/j.renene.2023.04.035.

[9]. "BEST Field Data - DuraMAT Data Hub.", 2023, Available: https://datahub.duramat.org/dataset/best-field-data

Use of a digital twin to detect stalling tracker events in photovoltaic power plant with horizontal single-axis tracking systems

Riccardo Adinolfi Borea, Matthew Muller, Silvana Ovaitt, Vincenzo Cirimele, Francesco Melino

Alma Mater Studiorum – University of Bologna, Bologna, Italy
National Renewable Energy Laboratory – NREL, Golden, Colorado
Ricerca sul Sistema Energetico S.p.a. – RSE

Overview

- Single-axis solar trackers in PV applications
- Is a stuck tracker something we should worry about?
- Detection algorithm layout
- Methodology to generate synthetic data for validation
- Test for field data obtainment
- Validation of the algorithm on synthetic data
- Validation of the algorithm on field data
- Conclusions & future works

1/9

Single-axis solar trackers in PV applications

Trackers are system that change the orientation of PV modules

The reasons to use solar trackers are multiple:

- Protect the infrastructure, in case of heavy wind
- Protect the PV modules, in case of hailstorm
- Increase the energy yield of PV modules

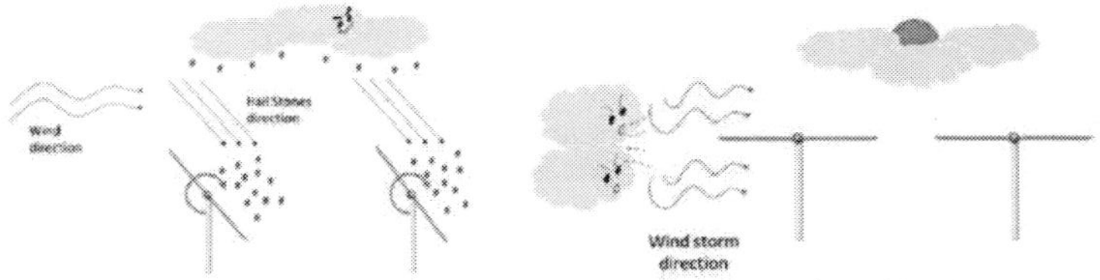

TRACKER FACE AWAY FROM WIND DIRECTION TRACKER WIND STORM POSITION

Images retrieved from [1]

[1] DOI: 10.69766/JOIK1919

Is a stuck tracker something we should worry about?

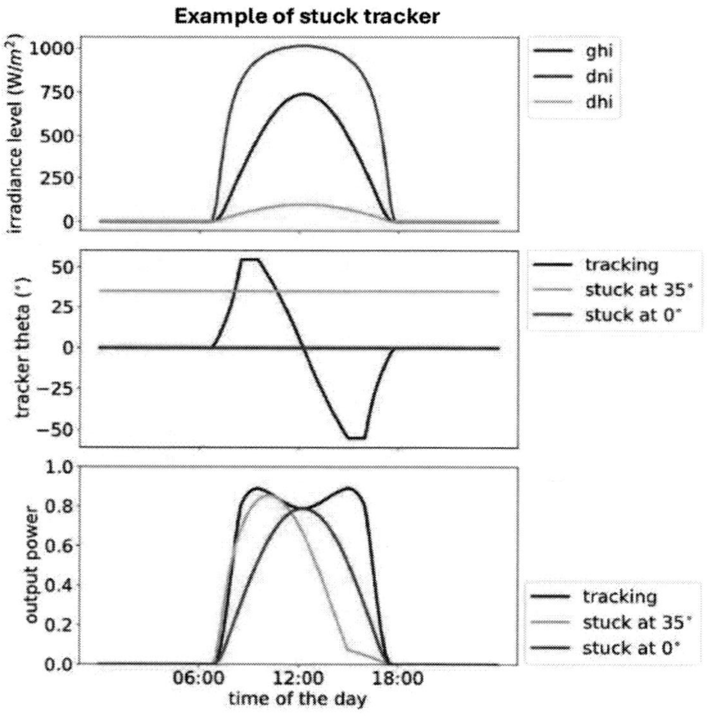

Irradiance conditions, tracker theta, and output power, in different tracking conditions: properly tracking, stuck at 35°, and stuck at 0°.

[1] "Past Proceedings 2024 | PVRW: Photovoltaic Reliability Workshop | NREL."

Is a stuck tracker something we should worry about?

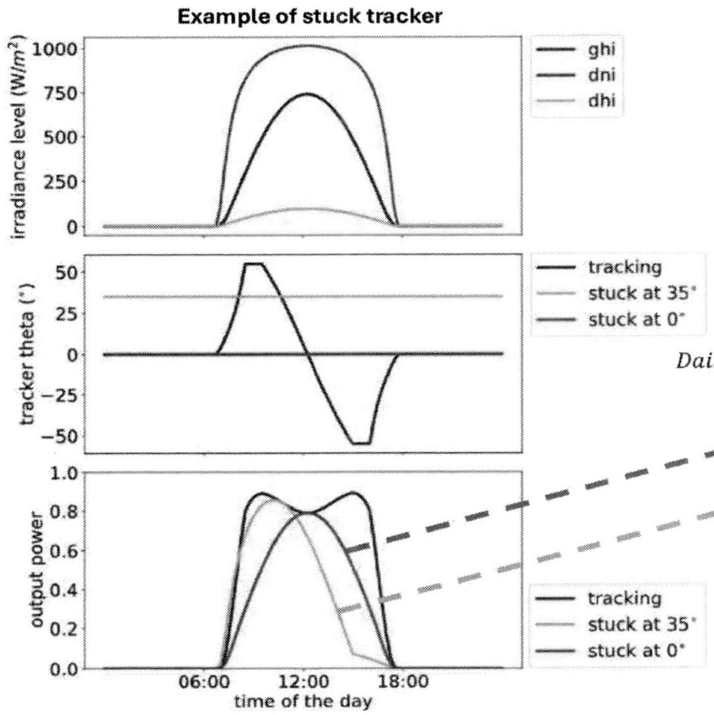

$$Daily\ energy\ lost = 100\left(1 - \frac{\sum_{day} Power_{stuck}}{\sum_{day} Power_{tracking}}\right)$$

$Daily\ energy\ lost = 31\%$

$Daily\ energy\ lost = 35\%$

Irradiance conditions, tracker theta, and output power, in different tracking conditions: properly tracking, stuck at 35°, and stuck at 0°.

[1] "Past Proceedings 2024 | PVRW: Photovoltaic Reliability Workshop | NREL."

Is a stuck tracker something we should worry about?

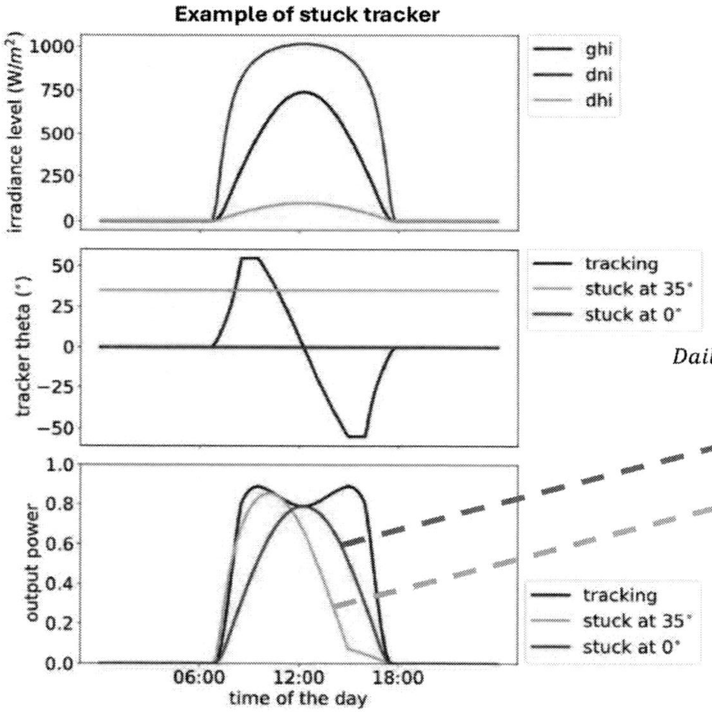

Irradiance conditions, tracker theta, and output power, in different tracking conditions: properly tracking, stuck at 35°, and stuck at 0°.

$$Daily\ energy\ lost = 100\left(1 - \frac{\sum_{day} Power_{stuck}}{\sum_{day} Power_{tracking}}\right)$$

$Daily\ energy\ lost = 31\%$

$Daily\ energy\ lost = 35\%$

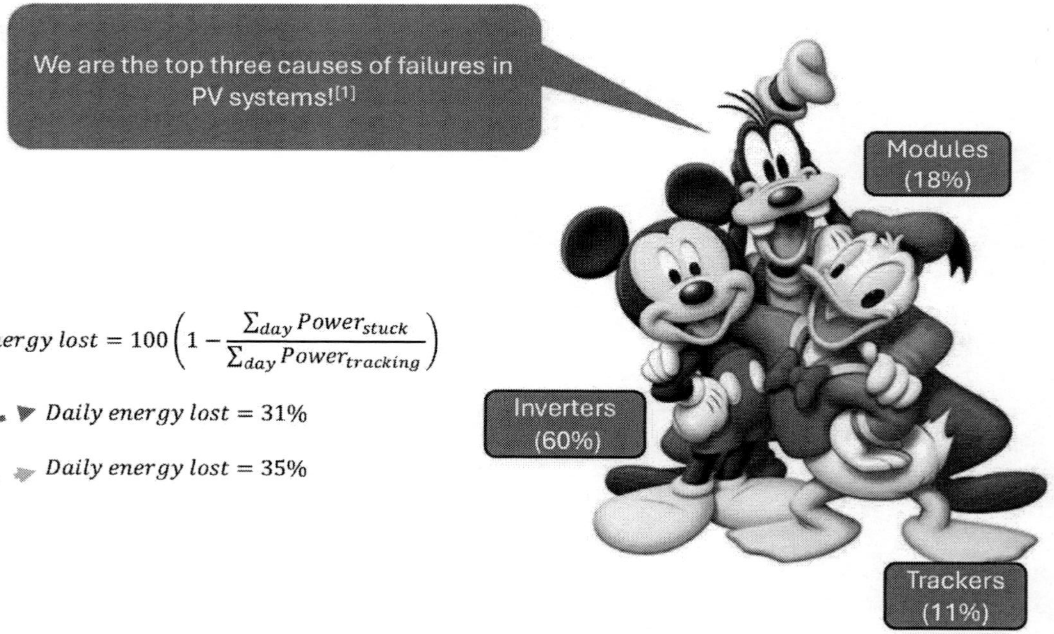

[1] "Past Proceedings 2024 | PVRW: Photovoltaic Reliability Workshop | NREL."

Is a stuck tracker something we should worry about?

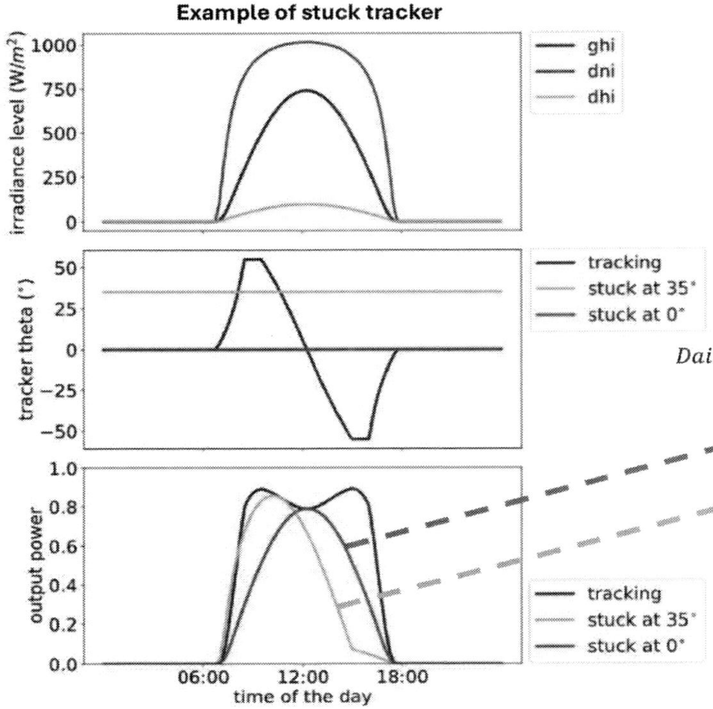

Irradiance conditions, tracker theta, and output power, in different tracking conditions: properly tracking, stuck at 35°, and stuck at 0°.

We are the top three causes of failures in PV systems![1]

$$Daily\ energy\ lost = 100\left(1 - \frac{\sum_{day} Power_{stuck}}{\sum_{day} Power_{tracking}}\right)$$

$Daily\ energy\ lost = 31\%$

$Daily\ energy\ lost = 35\%$

TAKEAWAY

Yes, we need to address the detection of stuck trackers to avoid energy losses that reach up to 35% of the daily energy yield on sunny days. Doing so it possible to avoid accusing PV module degradation of this energy loss, hence have a clearer view about the benefits and costs of PV plants with trackers.

[1] "Past Proceedings 2024 | PVRW: Photovoltaic Reliability Workshop | NREL."

Detection algorithm layout

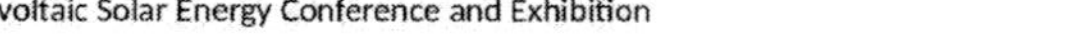

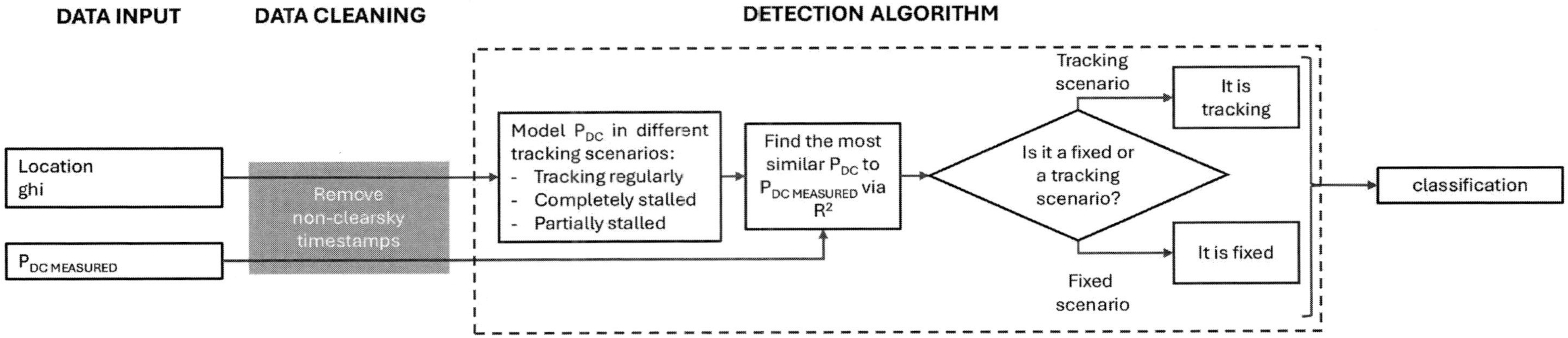
Detection algorithm layout
RSE
NREL
Transforming ENERGY
DATA INPUT
DATA CLEANING
DETECTION ALGORITHM
Location
ghi
$P_{DC\ MEASURED}$
Remove
non-clearsky
timestamps
Model P_{DC} in different tracking scenarios:
- Tracking regularly
- Completely stalled
- Partially stalled
Find the most similar P_{DC} to $P_{DC\ MEASURED}$ via R^2
Is it a fixed or a tracking scenario?
Tracking scenario
Fixed scenario
It is tracking
It is fixed
classification
4/9

Detection algorithm layout

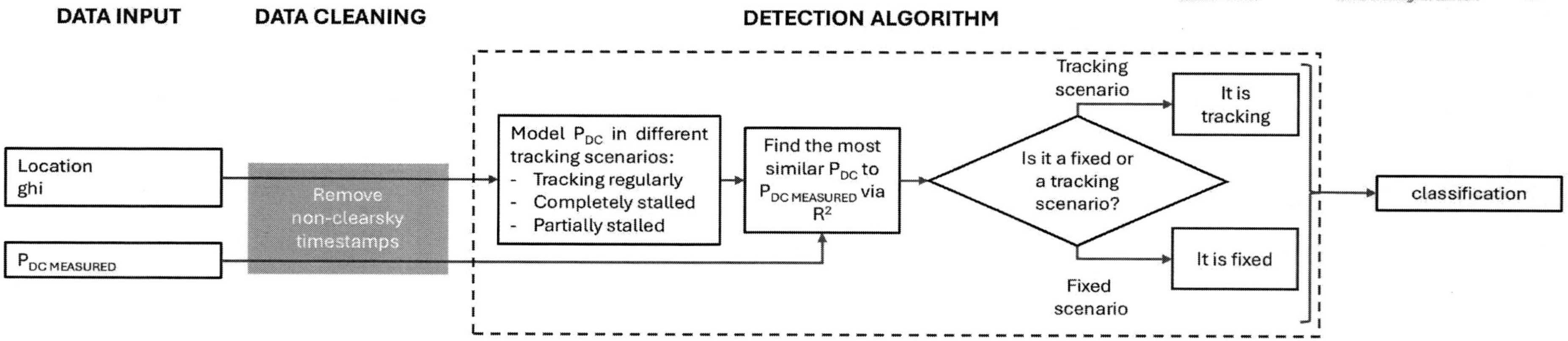

Visual explanation

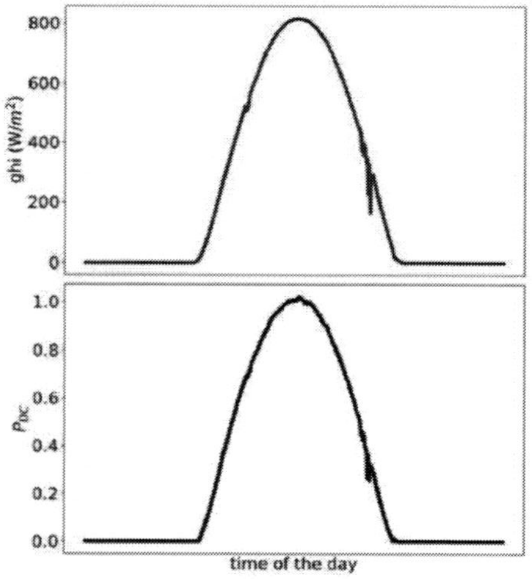

Detection algorithm layout

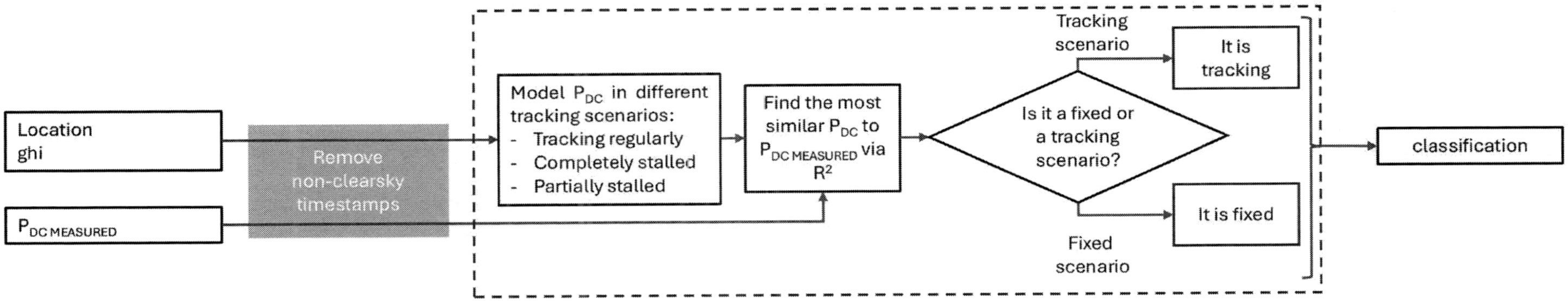

Visual explanation

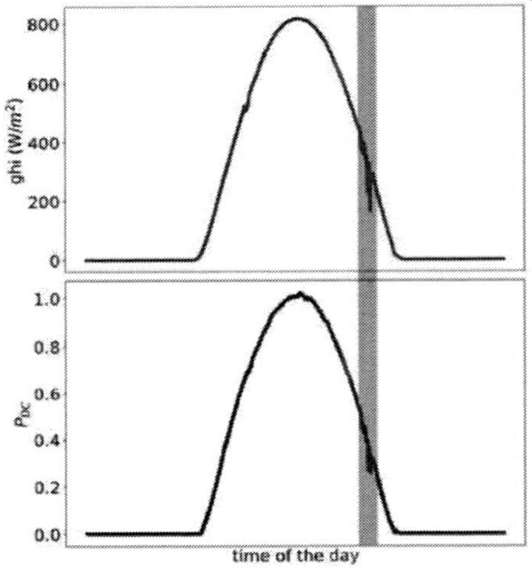

Detection algorithm layout

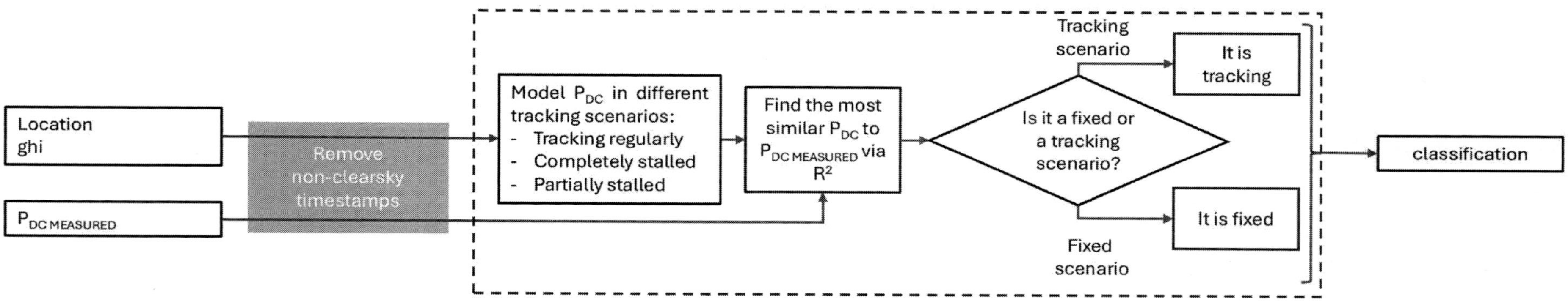

Visual explanation

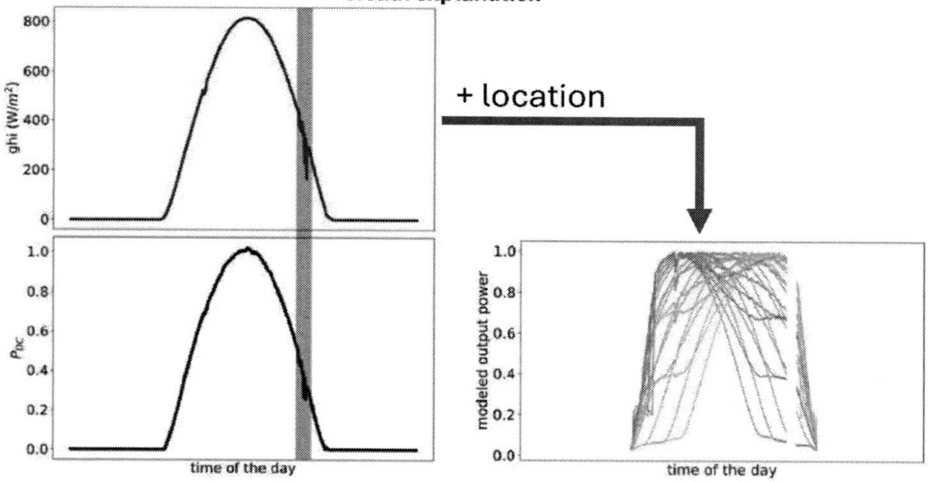

Detection algorithm layout

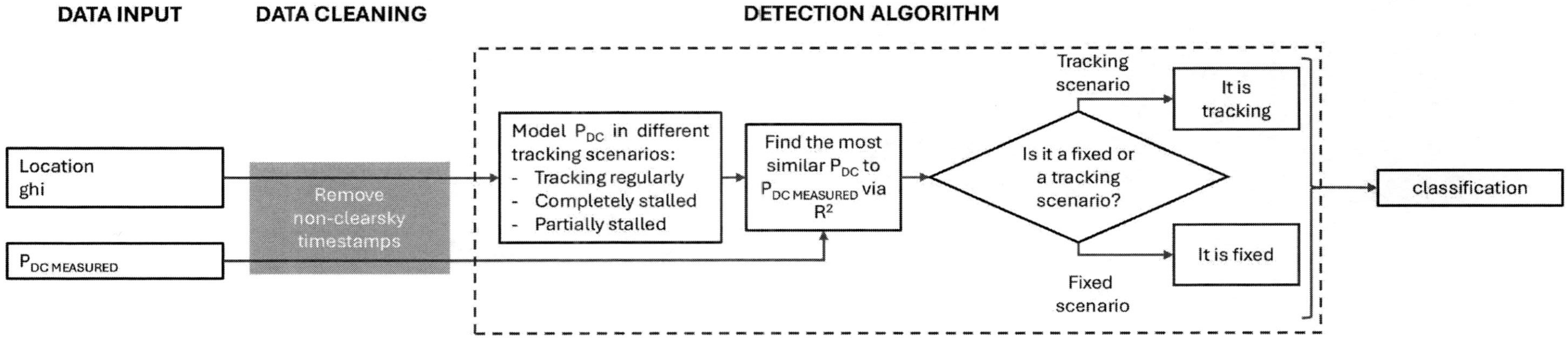

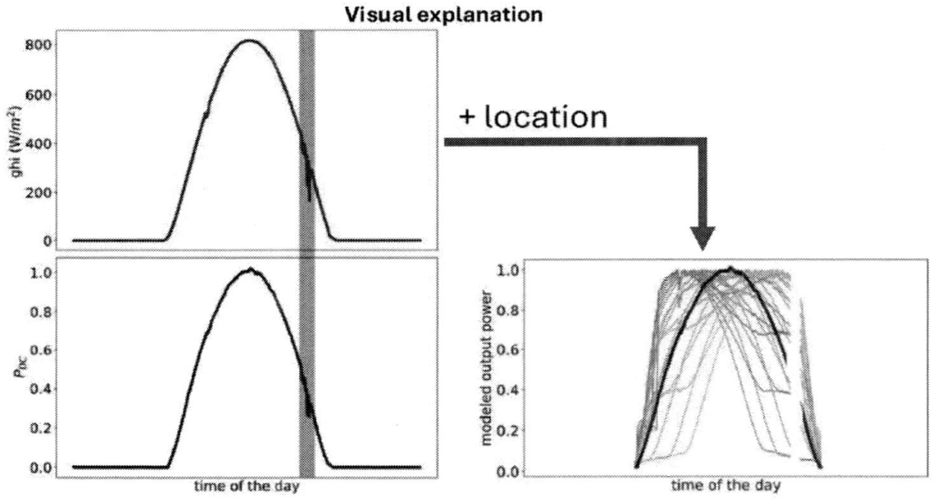

Detection algorithm layout

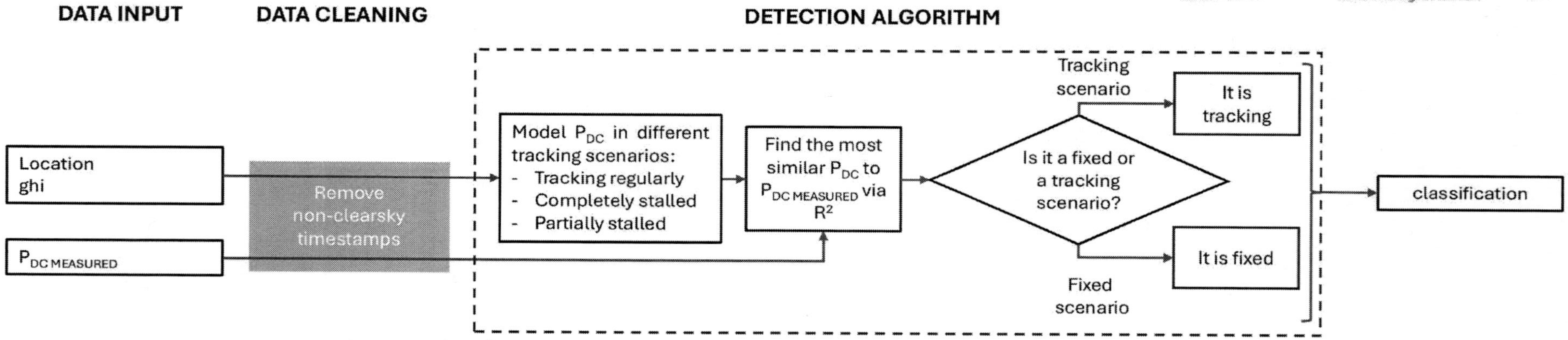

Visual explanation

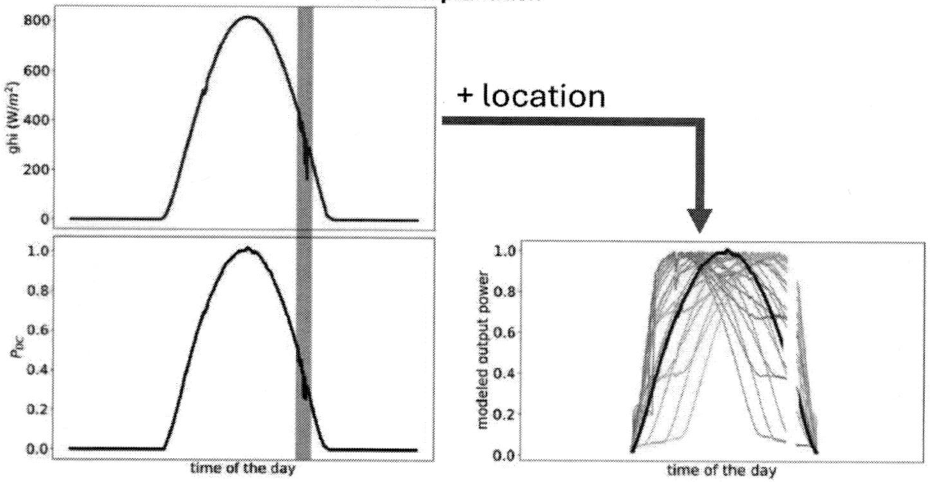

TAKEAWAY

The detection algorithm is used for data post-processing. It assumes that the gcr, the tracker algorithm, and the maximum tilt angle of the tracker, have all usual values/logics, as all of these are usually not available.

Methodology to generate synthetic data for validation

5/9

Methodology to generate synthetic data for validation

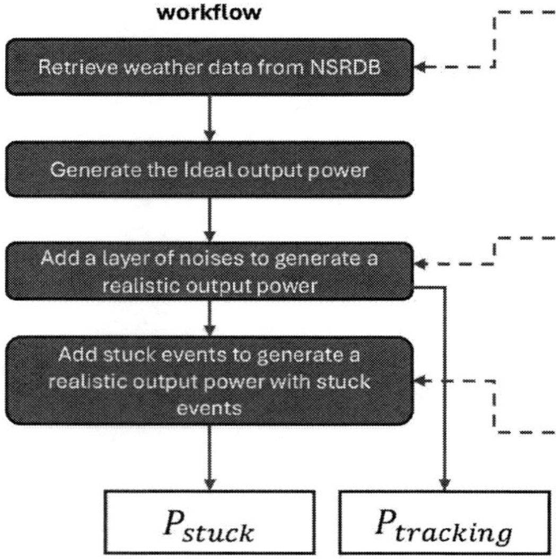

Location and system design	
Location	38 locations across US
Dataspan – frequency	4 years – 15 min
PV module Pdc0	1W, Monofacial
GCR	0.4
Albedo	0.20
Noise characterization	
Noise and soiling patterns	Random among options [4]
Degradation rate	Random among options [4]
Number string outage events	0
Inverter load ratio	1
Stuck events description	
Number stuck events	150 over dataspan
Stuck angle	0°
Duration stuck event	1 day
Permanent tracker offset	Random among options [4]

[4] NREL/TP-5K00-86459

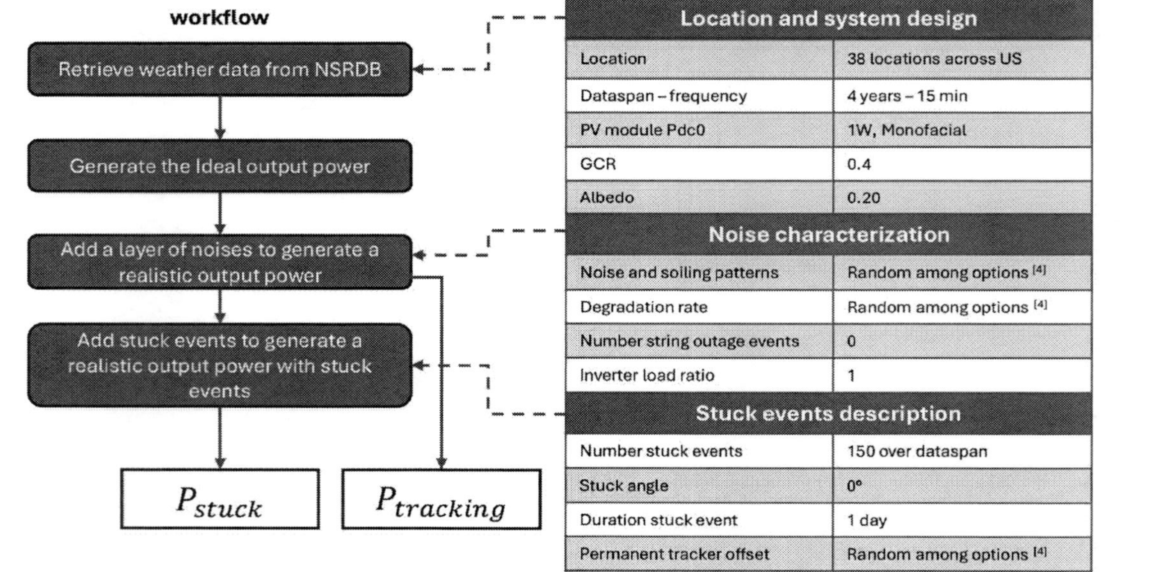

Methodology to generate synthetic data for validation

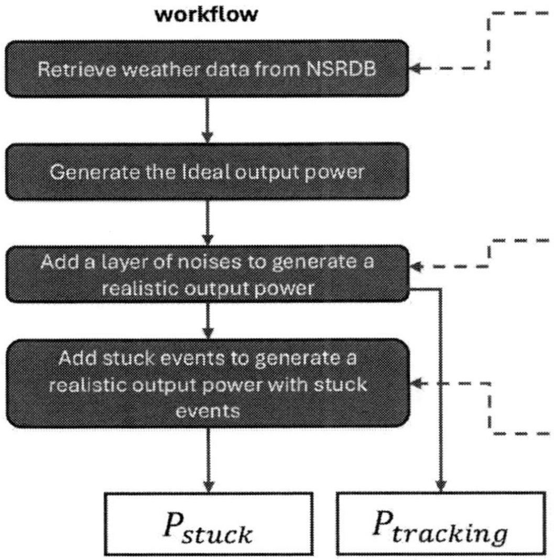

Location and system design	
Location	38 locations across US
Dataspan – frequency	4 years – 15 min
PV module Pdc0	1W, Monofacial
GCR	0.4
Albedo	0.20
Noise characterization	
Noise and soiling patterns	Random among options [4]
Degradation rate	Random among options [4]
Number string outage events	0
Inverter load ratio	1
Stuck events description	
Number stuck events	150 over dataspan
Stuck angle	0°
Duration stuck event	1 day
Permanent tracker offset	Random among options [4]

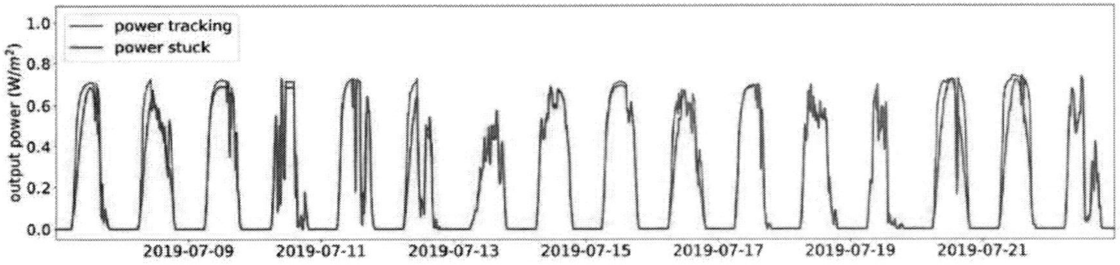

Realistic power output vs modeled power output for the case of Valdosta, Georgia

[4] NREL/TP-5K00-86459

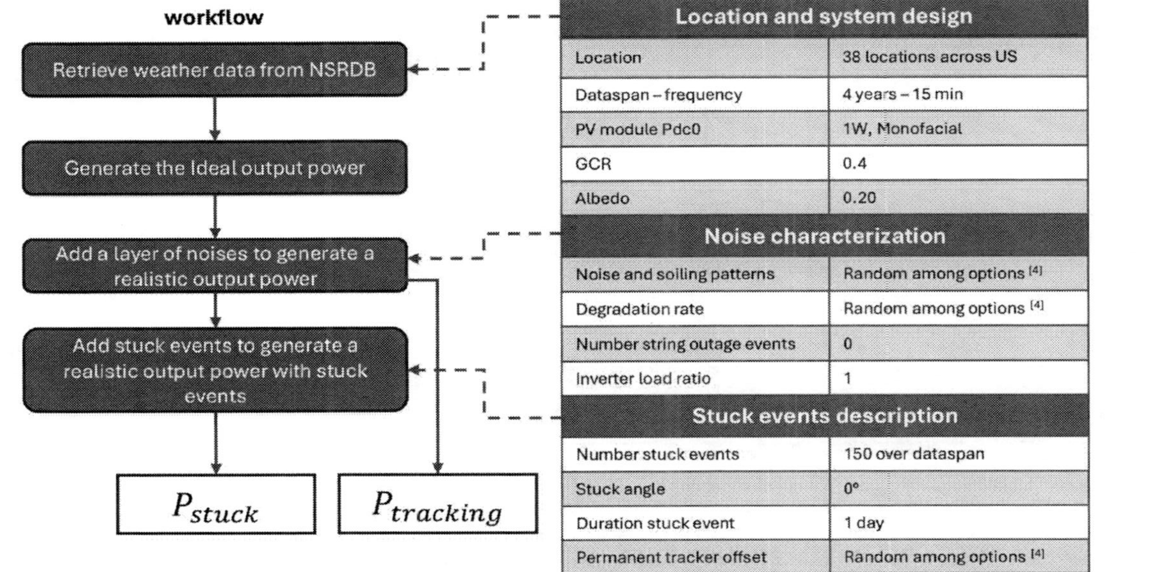

Methodology to generate synthetic data for validation

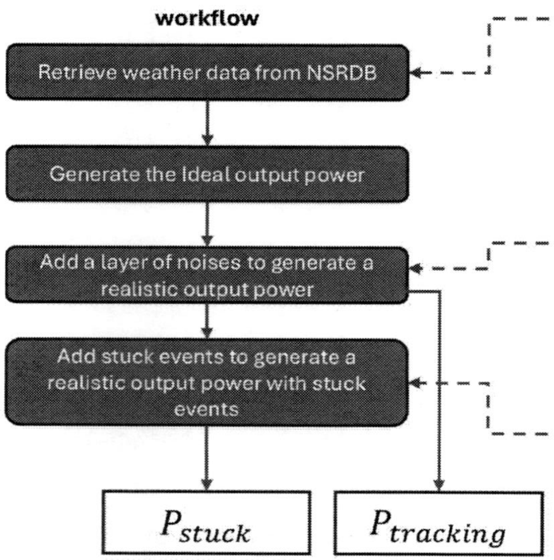

Location and system design	
Location	38 locations across US
Dataspan – frequency	4 years – 15 min
PV module Pdc0	1W, Monofacial
GCR	0.4
Albedo	0.20
Noise characterization	
Noise and soiling patterns	Random among options [4]
Degradation rate	Random among options [4]
Number string outage events	0
Inverter load ratio	1
Stuck events description	
Number stuck events	150 over dataspan
Stuck angle	0°
Duration stuck event	1 day
Permanent tracker offset	Random among options [4]

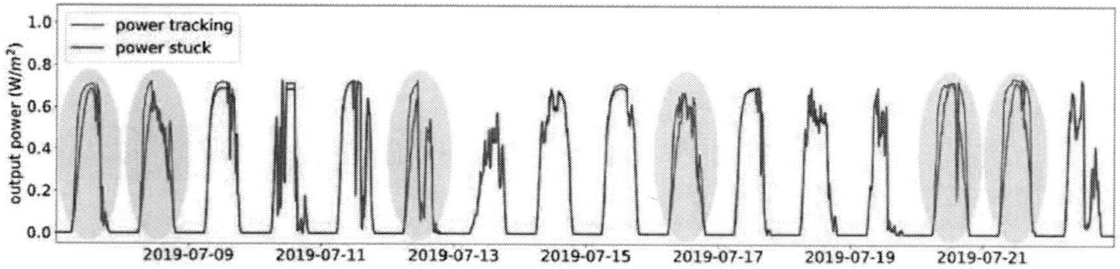

Realistic power output vs modeled power output for the case of Valdosta, Georgia

[4] NREL/TP-5K00-86459

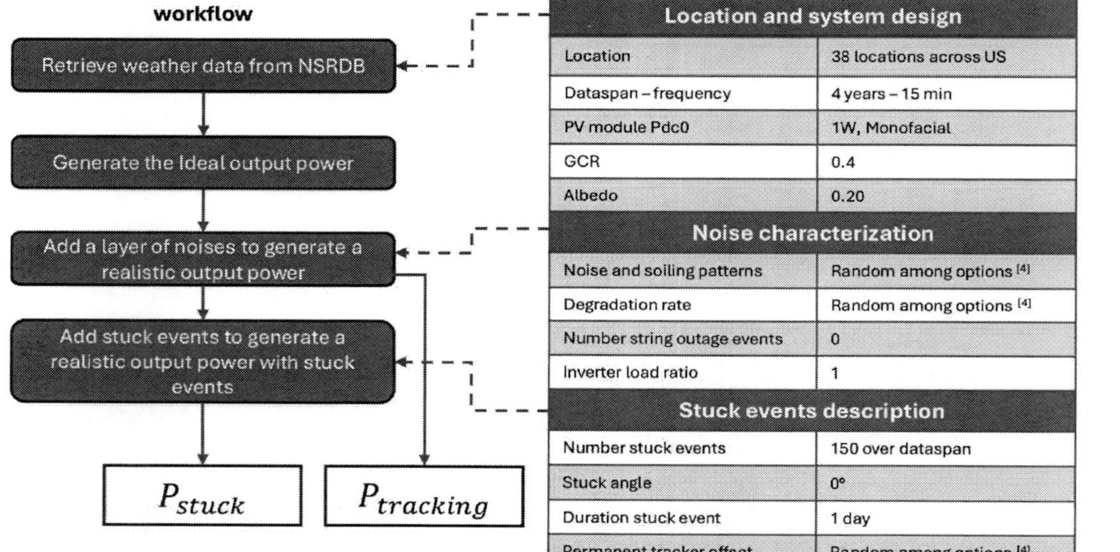

Methodology to generate synthetic data for validation

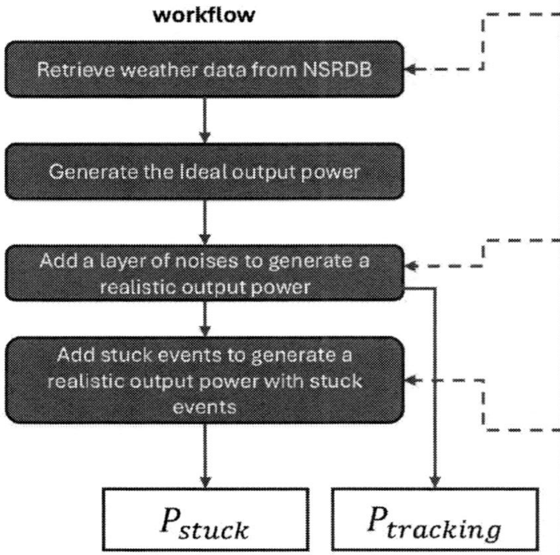

Location and system design	
Location	38 locations across US
Dataspan – frequency	4 years – 15 min
PV module Pdc0	1W, Monofacial
GCR	0.4
Albedo	0.20
Noise characterization	
Noise and soiling patterns	Random among options [4]
Degradation rate	Random among options [4]
Number string outage events	0
Inverter load ratio	1
Stuck events description	
Number stuck events	150 over dataspan
Stuck angle	0°
Duration stuck event	1 day
Permanent tracker offset	Random among options [4]

Most of times, multiple strings feed the same combiner, so it is possible to have ''partially stuck events''. Those cases are modeled as

$$P_{out}(S) = S \cdot P_{stuck} + (1 - S)P_{tracking}$$

where S is the fraction of stuck rows, considered as

$$S = \frac{number\ of\ stuck\ rows}{total\ number\ of\ rows}$$

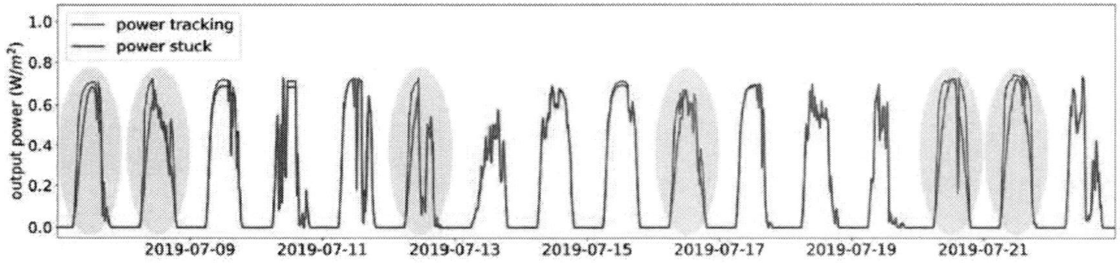

Realistic power output vs modeled power output for the case of Valdosta, Georgia

[4] NREL/TP-5K00-86459

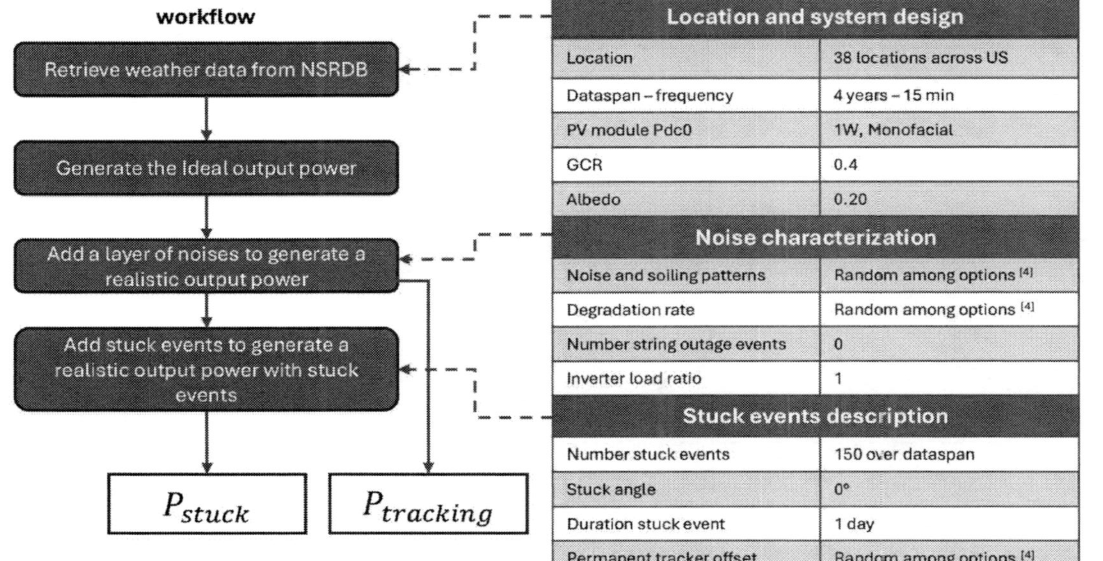

Methodology to generate synthetic data for validation

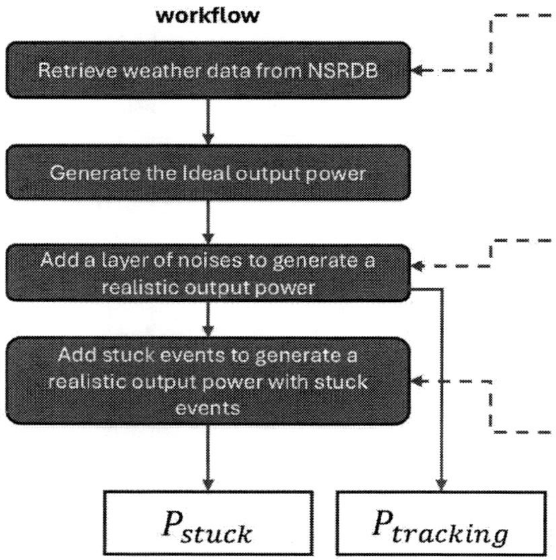

Location and system design	
Location	38 locations across US
Dataspan – frequency	4 years – 15 min
PV module Pdc0	1W, Monofacial
GCR	0.4
Albedo	0.20
Noise characterization	
Noise and soiling patterns	Random among options [4]
Degradation rate	Random among options [4]
Number string outage events	0
Inverter load ratio	1
Stuck events description	
Number stuck events	150 over dataspan
Stuck angle	0°
Duration stuck event	1 day
Permanent tracker offset	Random among options [4]

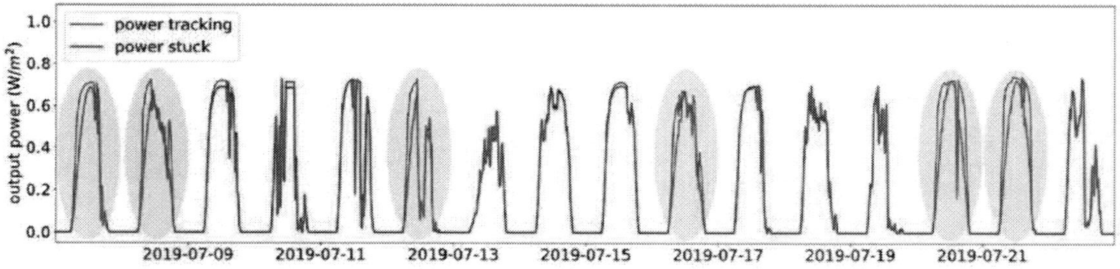

Realistic power output vs modeled power output for the case of Valdosta, Georgia

[4] NREL/TP-5K00-86459

Most of times, multiple strings feed the same combiner, so it is possible to have ''partially stuck events''. Those cases are modeled as

$$P_{out}(S) = S \cdot P_{stuck} + (1 - S)P_{tracking}$$

where S is the fraction of stuck rows, considered as

$$S = \frac{number\ of\ stuck\ rows}{total\ number\ of\ rows}$$

TAKEAWAY

Given the location, the methodology generates a synthetic dataset that is used to create a set of variants thanks to S. This is done for 38 locations across US.

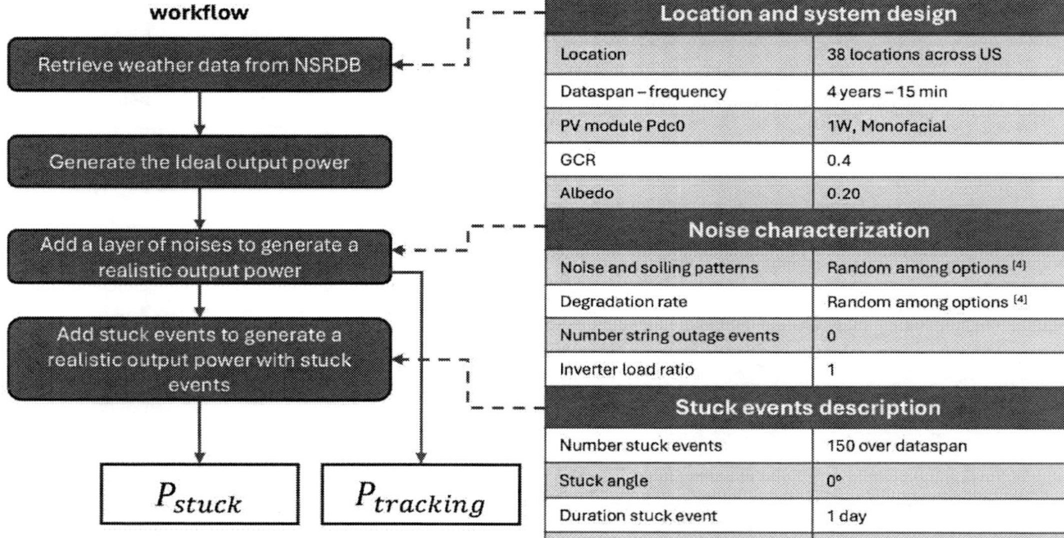

Test for field data obtainment

RSE NREL Transforming ENERGY

System description
Ten rows individually measured and controlled
Current, voltage, and output power, are measured at the DC side

Experiments description
Row 3 is set at 0° for the entire day while row 8 is operating regularly.

Power combination
Power of row 3 and row 8 are first normalized per their nameplate power, than combined to create different stuck scenarios

Validation of the algorithm on synthetic data

7/9

Validation of the algorithm on synthetic data

$$Day\ clearness = \frac{num(clearsky\ timestamps)^{[3]}}{num(total\ timestamps)}$$

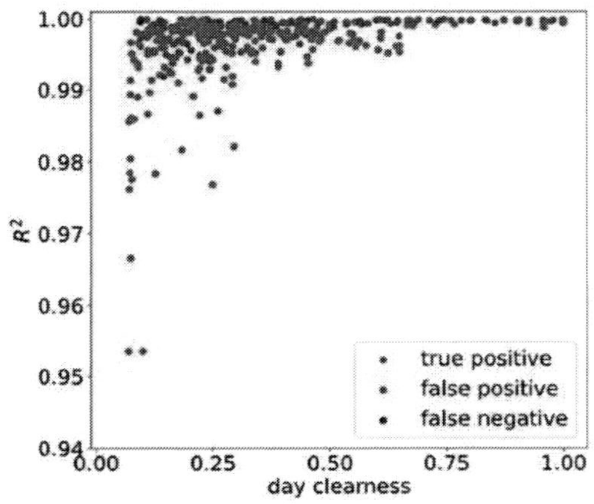

Result when run on dataset for Valdosta, Georgia, and S=1.

[3] DOI: 10.1016/j.renene.2023.04.035

Validation of the algorithm on synthetic data

$$Day\ clearness = \frac{num(clearsky\ timestamps)^{[3]}}{num(total\ timestamps)}$$

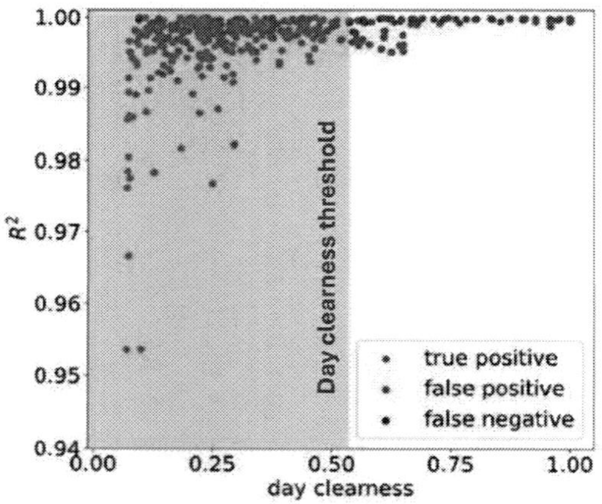

Result when run on dataset for Valdosta, Georgia, and S=1.

[3] DOI: 10.1016/j.renene.2023.04.035

Validation of the algorithm on synthetic data

$$Day\ clearness = \frac{num(clearsky\ timestamps)^{[3]}}{num(total\ timestamps)}$$

$$F_1 = \frac{2\,TP}{2\,TP + FN + FP}$$

TP True positive
FP False positive
FN False negative

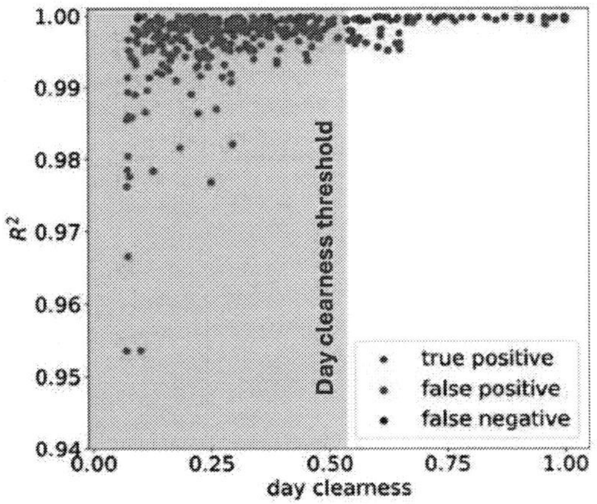

Result when run on dataset for Valdosta, Georgia, and S=1.

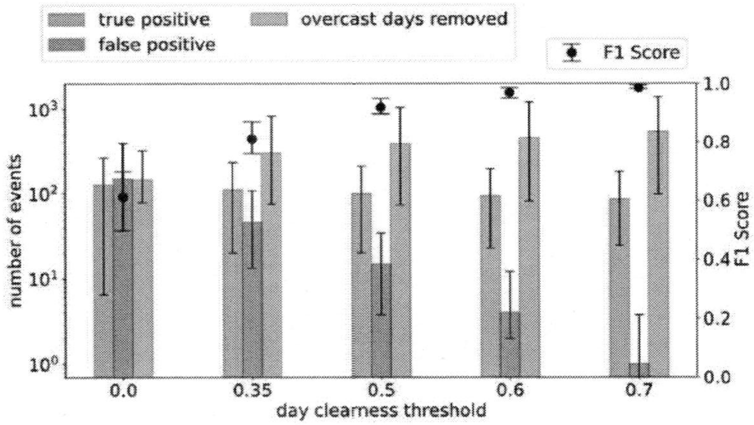

Result, averaged among all 38 locations, when S=1 and a day clearness threshold is implemented.

[3] DOI: 10.1016/j.renene.2023.04.035

Validation of the algorithm on synthetic data

$$Day\ clearness = \frac{num(clearsky\ timestamps)^{[3]}}{num(total\ timestamps)}$$

$$F_1 = \frac{2\,TP}{2\,TP + FN + FP}$$

TP True positive
FP False positive
FN False negative

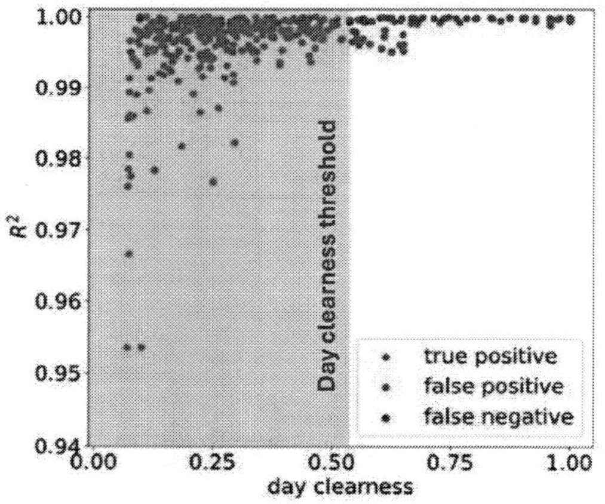

Result when run on dataset for Valdosta, Georgia, and S=1.

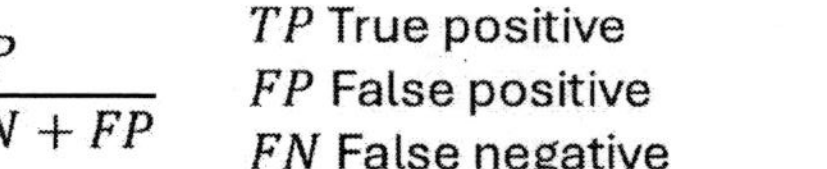

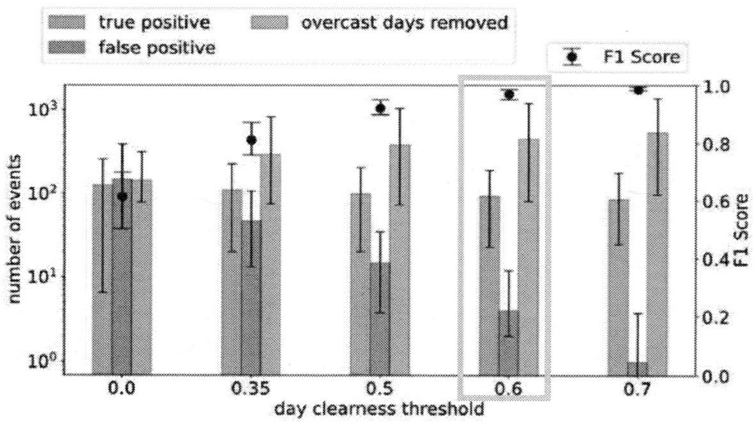

Result, averaged among all 38 locations, when S=1 and a day clearness threshold is implemented.

[3] DOI: 10.1016/j.renene.2023.04.035

Validation of the algorithm on synthetic data

$$Day\ clearness = \frac{num(clearsky\ timestamps)^{[3]}}{num(total\ timestamps)}$$

$$F_1 = \frac{2\,TP}{2\,TP + FN + FP}$$

TP True positive
FP False positive
FN False negative

$$S = \frac{number\ of\ stuck\ rows}{total\ number\ of\ rows}$$

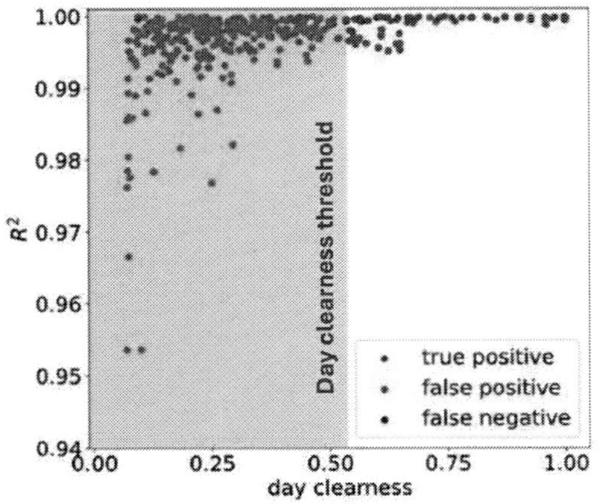

Result when run on dataset for Valdosta, Georgia, and S=1.

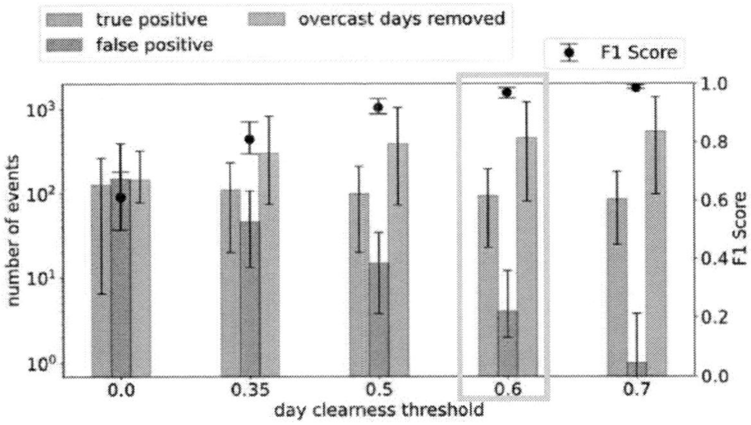

Result, averaged among all 38 locations, when S=1 and a day clearness threshold is implemented.

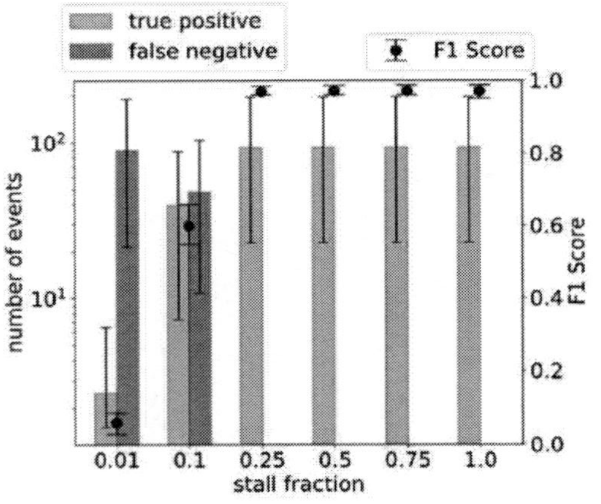

Result, averaged among all 38 locations, when a day clearness threshold of 0.6 is implemented, at varing S.

[3] DOI: 10.1016/j.renene.2023.04.035

Validation of the algorithm on synthetic data

$$Day\ clearness = \frac{num(clearsky\ timestamps)^{[3]}}{num(total\ timestamps)}$$

$$F_1 = \frac{2\,TP}{2\,TP + FN + FP}$$

TP True positive
FP False positive
FN False negative

$$S = \frac{number\ of\ stuck\ rows}{total\ number\ of\ rows}$$

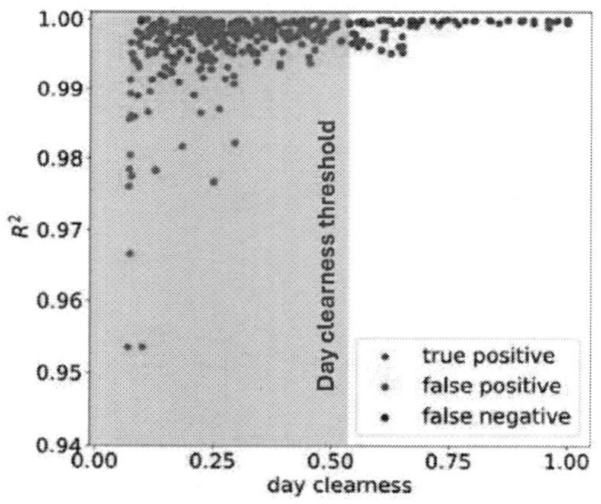

Result when run on dataset for Valdosta, Georgia, and S=1.

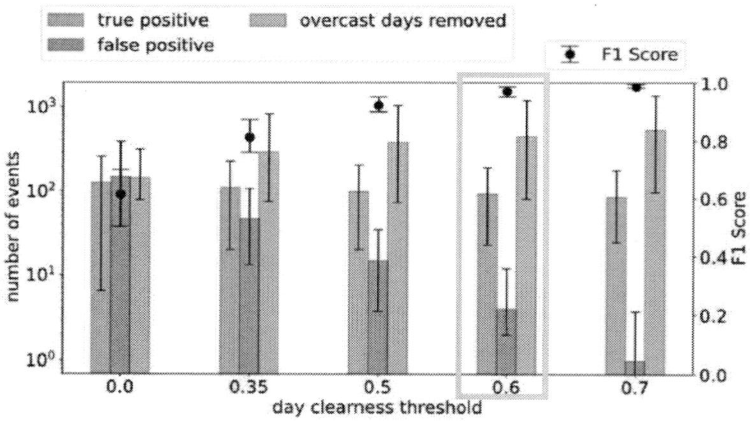

Result, averaged among all 38 locations, when S=1 and a day clearness threshold is implemented.

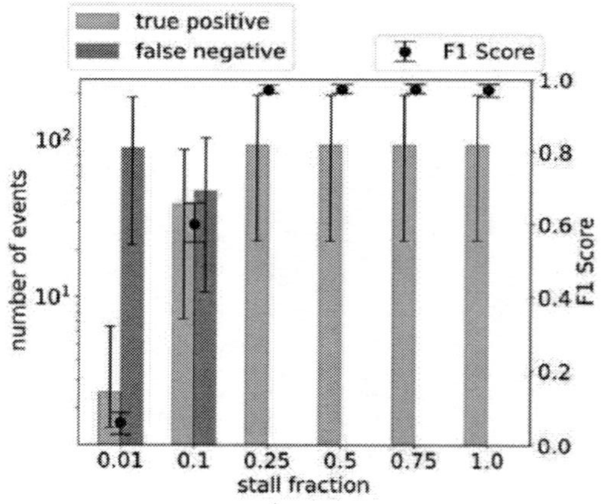

Result, averaged among all 38 locations, when a day clearness threshold of 0.6 is implemented, at varing S.

TAKEAWAY

The algorithm is sensitive to day clearness, when day clearness is low the algorithm has low amount of data to make a classification. Implementing a day clearness threshold improves drastically the performance. 0.60 is found to be a good trade off between evaluated days and F_1 score, enabling a F_1=0.96. Partially stuck scenarios are easier to detect the higher is the stuck fraction. Scenarios with stuck fraction below 0.25 cannot be detected.

[3] DOI: 10.1016/j.renene.2023.04.035

Validation of the algorithm on field data

8/9

Validation of the algorithm on field data

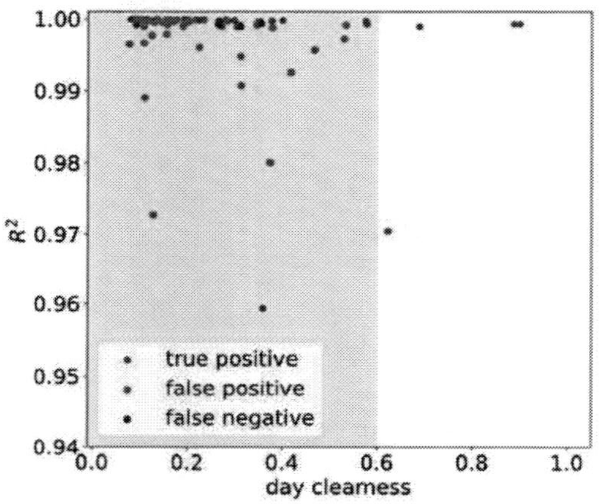

Result when run on field dataset and S=1.

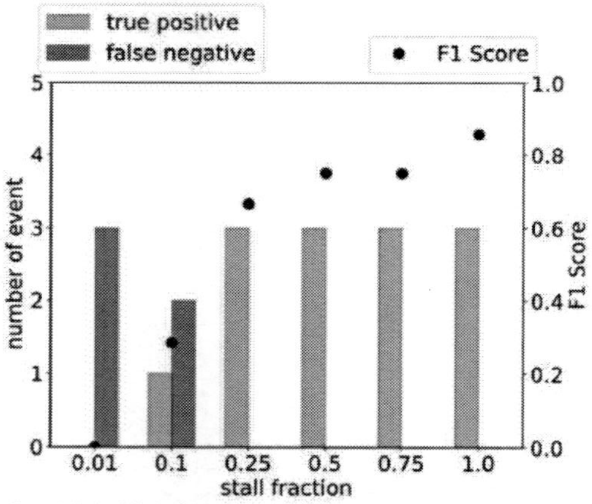

Result when run on field dataset and a day clearness threshold 0.6 is applied.

Validation of the algorithm on field data

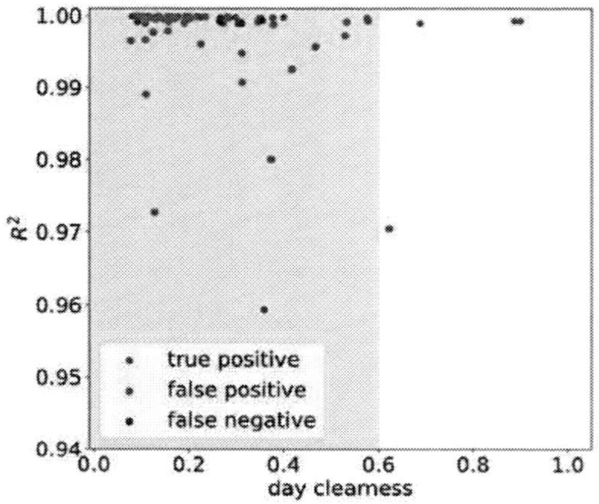

Result when run on field dataset and S=1.

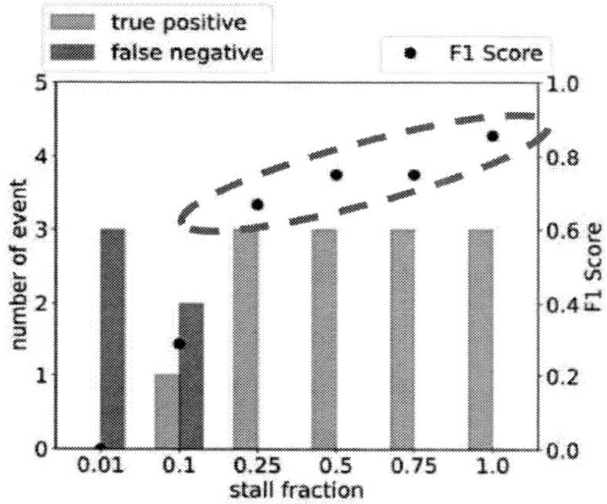

Result when run on field dataset and a day clearness threshold 0.6 is applied.

Validation of the algorithm on field data

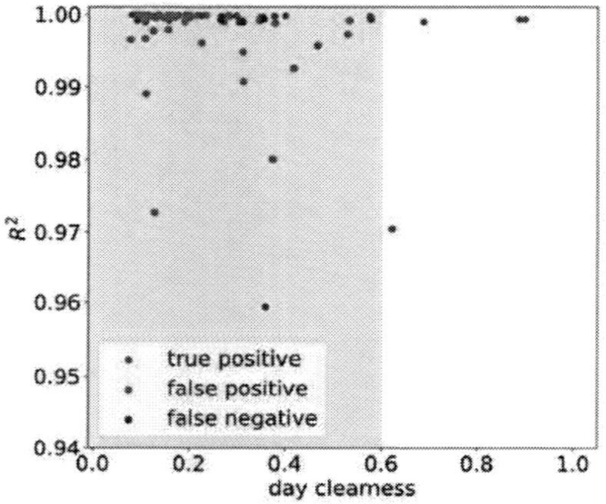

Result when run on field dataset and S=1.

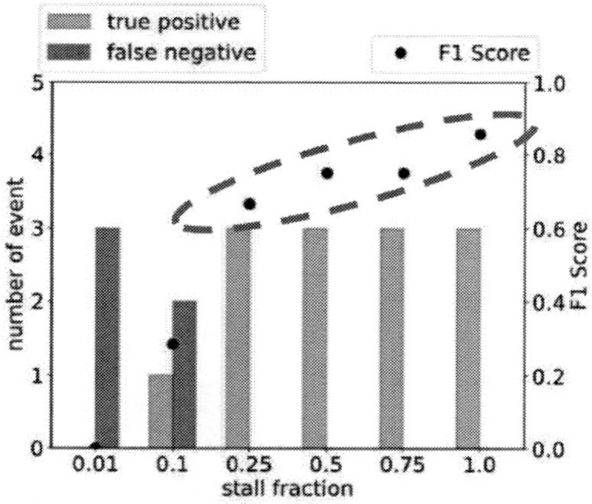

Result when run on field dataset and a day clearness threshold 0.6 is applied.

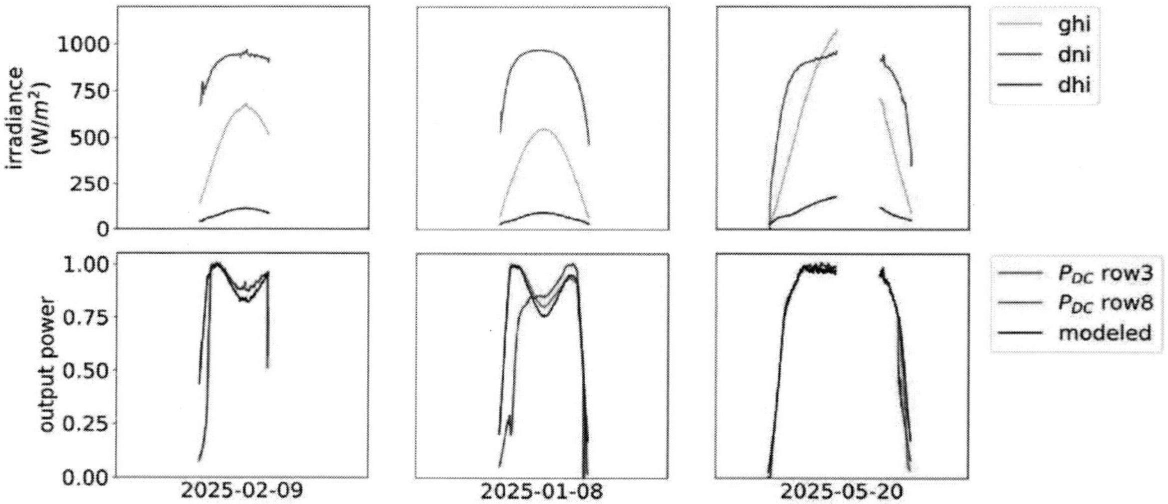

Days that make the algorithm reach a different F1 with different values of S.

Validation of the algorithm on field data

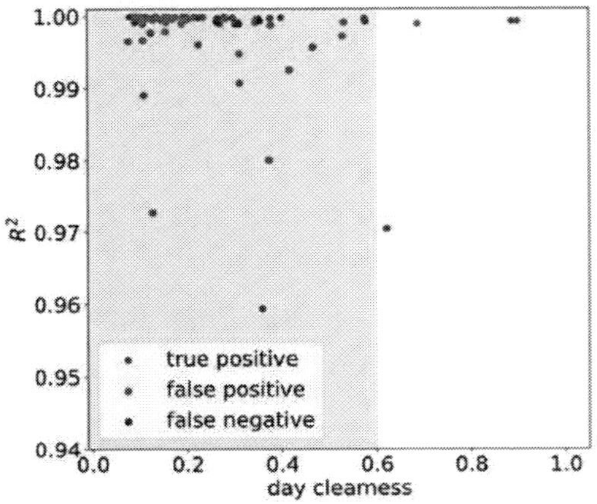

Result when run on field dataset and S=1.

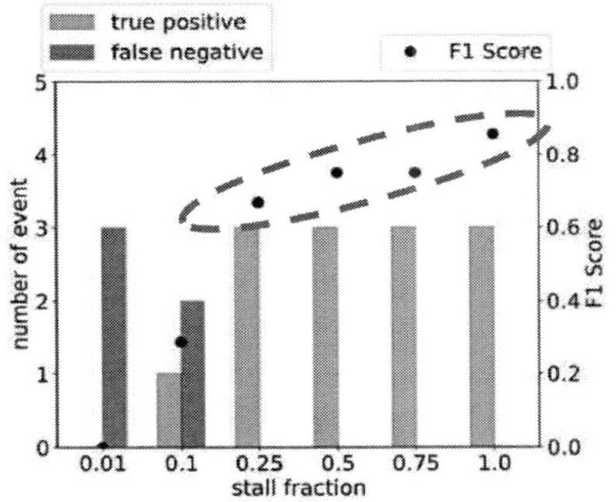

Result when run on field dataset and a day clearness threshold 0.6 is applied.

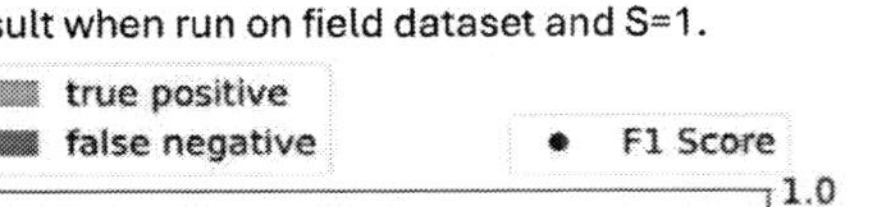

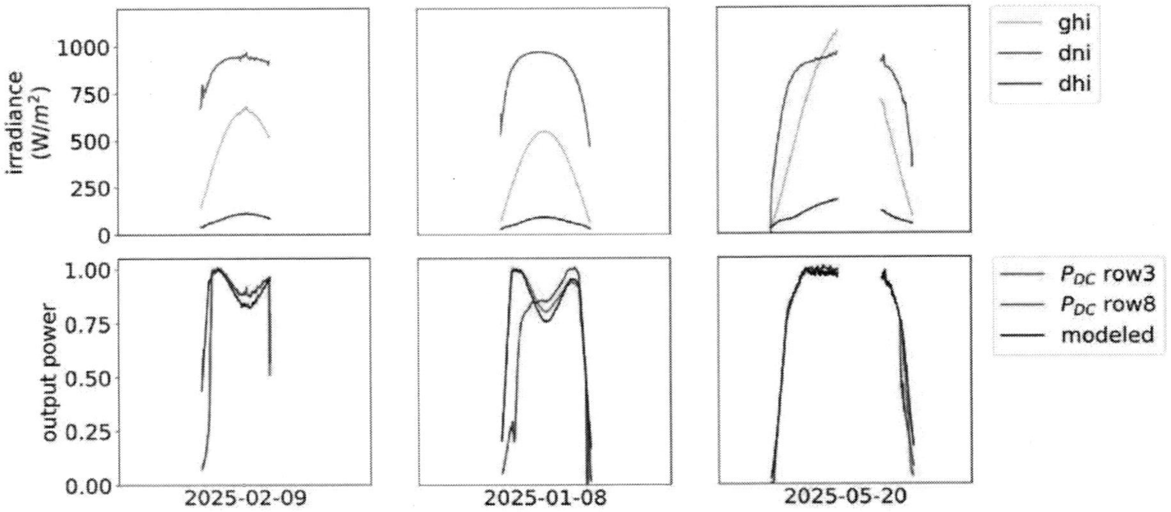

Days that make the algorithm reach a different F1 with different values of S.

TAKEAWAY

The algorithm is sensitive to cases in which underperformance is not related to weather conditions and appears to mimic a stuck condition. Although useful in some cases, January 8th and May 20th are not stuck events, thus are considered as FPs. Further claims per the field data are premature to make due to limited size of the data set (67 days with only 3 stalled events).

8/9

Conclusions

- Stuck events affects drastically the performance of PV arrays, up to 31% in cases where the tracker is stuck at 0°. Addressing their detection allows to avoid low energy performance.
- The detection algorithm's correctness is largely influenced by the day clearness: days with high day clearness are easier to classify.
- Implementing a day clearness threshold improves significantly the algorithm's performance. 0.60 looks like a sweet spot: improve the F1 from 0.60 to 0.96, and avoid removing the majority of days from the dataset.
- Partially stuck events can be detected with good performance if they are characterized by a stuck fraction above 0.25.
- The detection algorithm flags days when the underperformance is not related to weather conditions. For the aim of the algorithm these days are considered as FPs, but are days that should not be considered when addressing PV degradation analysis.

Future works

- Continue collecting field data to better address the performance in real conditions.
- Looking into more metrics that might improve the robustness of the algorithm.

9/9

Conclusions

- Stuck events affects drastically the performance of PV arrays, up to 30% in cases where the tracker is stuck at 0°. Addressing their detection allows to avoid low energy performance.
- The detection algorithm's correctness is largely influenced by the day clearness: days with high day clearness are easier to classify.
- Implementing a day clearness threshold improves significantly the algorithm's performance. 0.60 looks like a sweet spot: improve the F1 from 0,60 to 0,96, and avoid removing the majority of days from the dataset.
- Partially stuck events can be detected with good performance if they are characterized by a stuck fraction above 0.25.
- The detection algorithm flags days when the underperformance is not related to weather conditions. For the aim of the algorithm these days are considered as FPs, but are days that should not be considered when addressing PV degradation analysis.

Future works

- Continue collecting field data to better address the performance in real conditions.
- Looking into more metrics that might improve the robustness of the algorithm.

Thanks for the attention!!

Riccardo Adinolfi Borea

Alma Mater Studiorum – University of Bologna
National Renewable Energy Laboratory – NREL
Ricerca sul Sistema Energetico S.p.a. – RSE

riccardo.adinolfi2@unibo.it

Something helpful

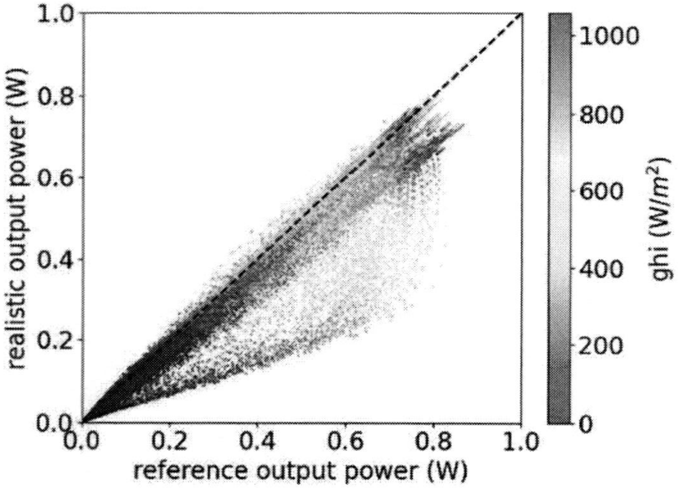

Fig. 5 Realistic power output vs modeled power output for the case of Valdosta, Georgia.

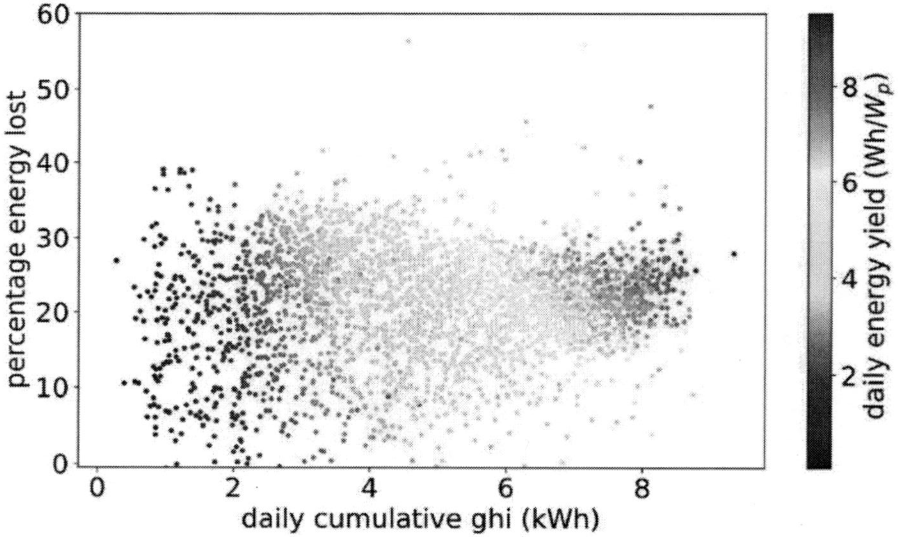

Example
25% stuck scenario

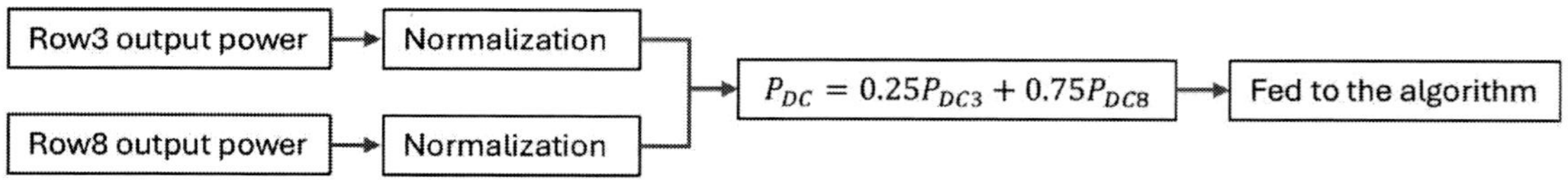

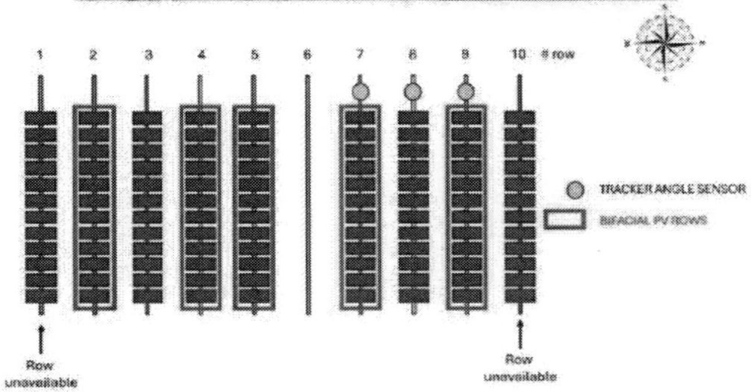

System description

Row 6 is unavailable due to changing modules.
Row 1 and row 10 are unavailable due to different electrical connection (i.e., directly with the grid).
For Row 2-9 it is measured operating current, voltage, and power at string level (at the DC side).
Row 1, 3, 8, and 10 are monofacial, while 2, 4, 5, 7, and 9, are bifacial.

Experiments description

Rows are stuck at 0° for the entire day because 0° is the most difficult angle to detect. Multiple rows are stuck at same time but, if that's the case, rows that are stuck are not adjunct.
To create the different stuck tracker percentages, we first normalize the output power of each string (each one by its own nameplate power) and than do the average of the rows taken into consideration.
To have the same ratio of "stuck days/total days" that was used with synthetic data, we included measurements from November 1st.
Monofacial and bifacial rows are treated as equal.

Example 50% stuck percentage

Row2 output power (11/01 – 03/28) → Normalization → Do the average → Fed to the algorithm
Row3 output power (11/01 – 03/28) → Normalization → Do the average

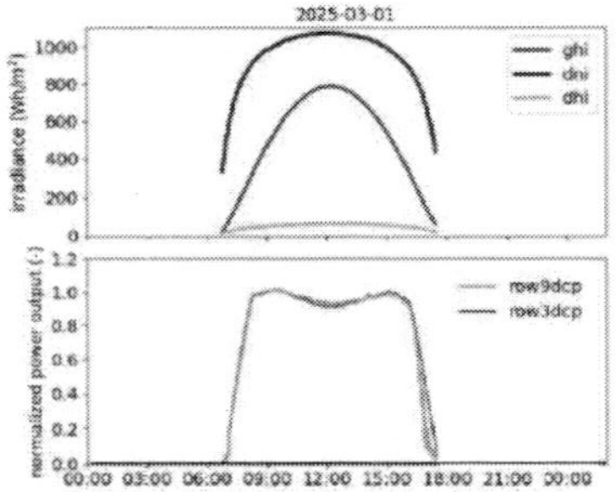

Comparison of the normalized power of a bifacial and monofacial rows when tracking.

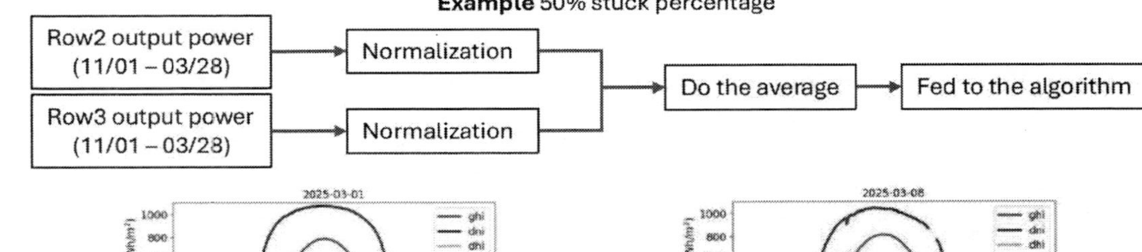

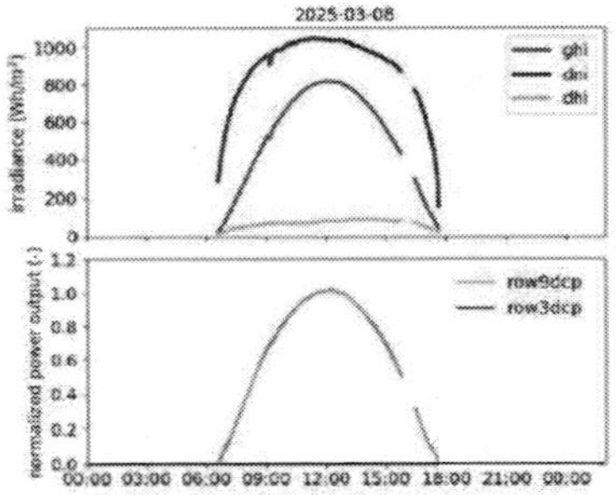

Comparison of the normalized power of a bifacial and monofacial rows when stuck.

BECQUEREL INSTITUTE
Strategy Consulting in Solar PV

Autonomous Multi-AI Agent System for PV Health Monitoring: a Fully Automated O&M Pipeline with Field Robotics Integration

M. Sondoqah, D. Moser
Becquerel Institute Italia

A. Louwen
RISE Research Institutes of Sweden

Formerly: Eurac Research

EUPVSEC 2025

Outline

1. Automation roadmap 2030
2. Challenges in data-driven O&M pipelines
3. O&M PV Ontology
4. Symptom detection through Multi-Modal Large Language Models
5. Multi-AI agent system for O&M
6. Medical doctor-like failure detection approach
7. Validation with ground truth

Becquerel Institute

Current and Projected Automation Levels by 2030

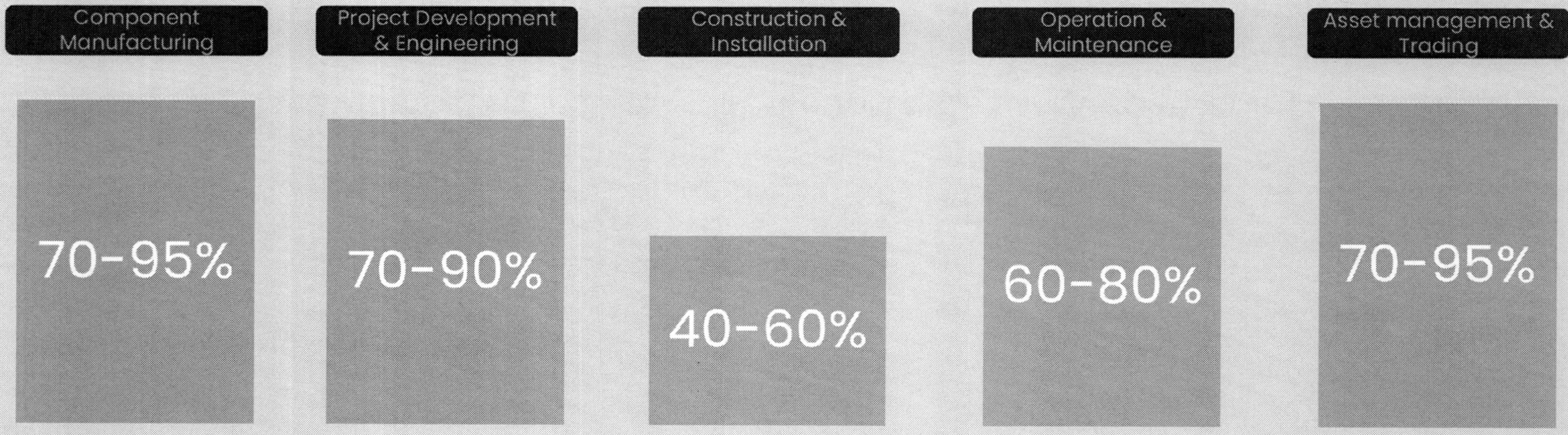

Source: Transforming the PV Sector: The AI & Robotics Revolution-Becquerel Institute

Becquerel Institute

INGREDIENTS FOR AUTOMATION IN O&M and AM: State of the art

Management, sharing and federation of PV asset information throughout the lifecycle
DIGITAL TWIN AND UNIVERSAL MAPPING

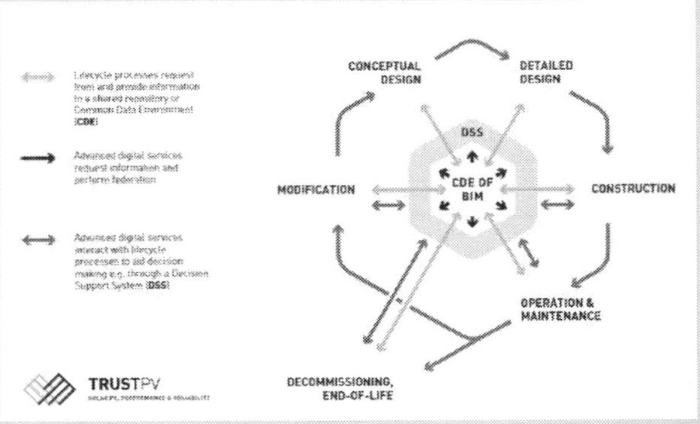

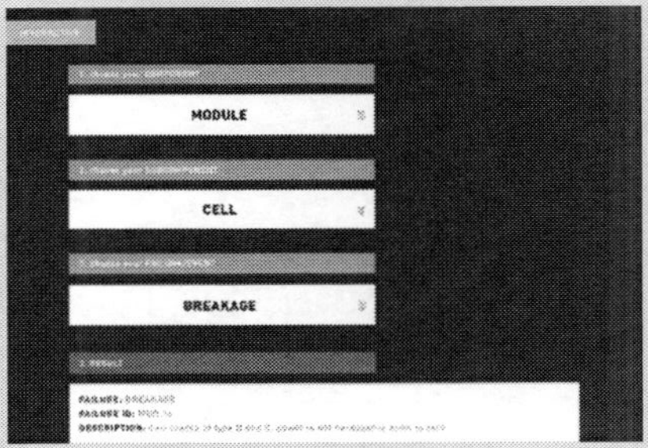

Implement a RISK MATRIX in the ticketing platform to harmonise data coming from the field (independent from operator)

INGREDIENTS FOR AUTOMATION IN O&M AND AM: State of the art

Identify failure through for e.g. advanced monitoring and semiautomated inspection techniques, and resolve the issue (SOLUTION MATRIX)

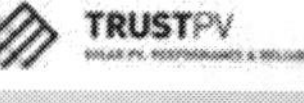

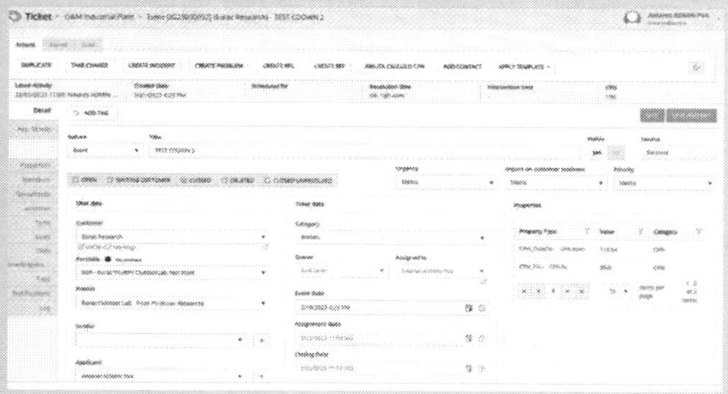

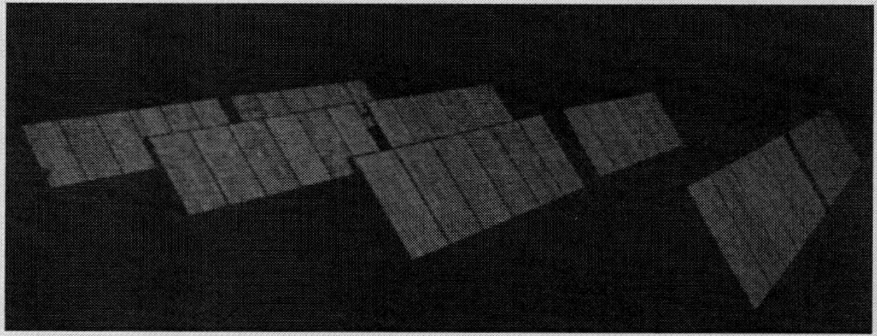

Calculate the final KPI and update a KNOWLEDGE BASE database

A **DSS** system can provide suggestions based on statistics and previous field experience for the most effective solution

TRUSTPV

Becquerel Institute

Challenges in classic data driven approaches

- **Limitations of Traditional Data-Driven O&M Pipelines:**
  - Failures in PV systems are many and tend to occur at different component levels
  - Multiple data streams with different format (numerical, images, unstructured data, etc.) are generated, but they are rarely exploited to their full potential (and rarely shared....)
  - Large labeled datasets are required to train data-driven models
  - Data-driven models are fragmented, and they deal with each modality on its own

How to move on?

Becquerel Institute

O&M Ontology

- The ontology of O&M is where every element in the O&M pipeline is defined
- The elements of the O&M ontology are Failure, Symptom, Inspection, & Solution
- Each of these elements is represented via text
- These elements are connected through relationships
- The final structure of the ontology is introduced as knowledge graphs

Becquerel Institute

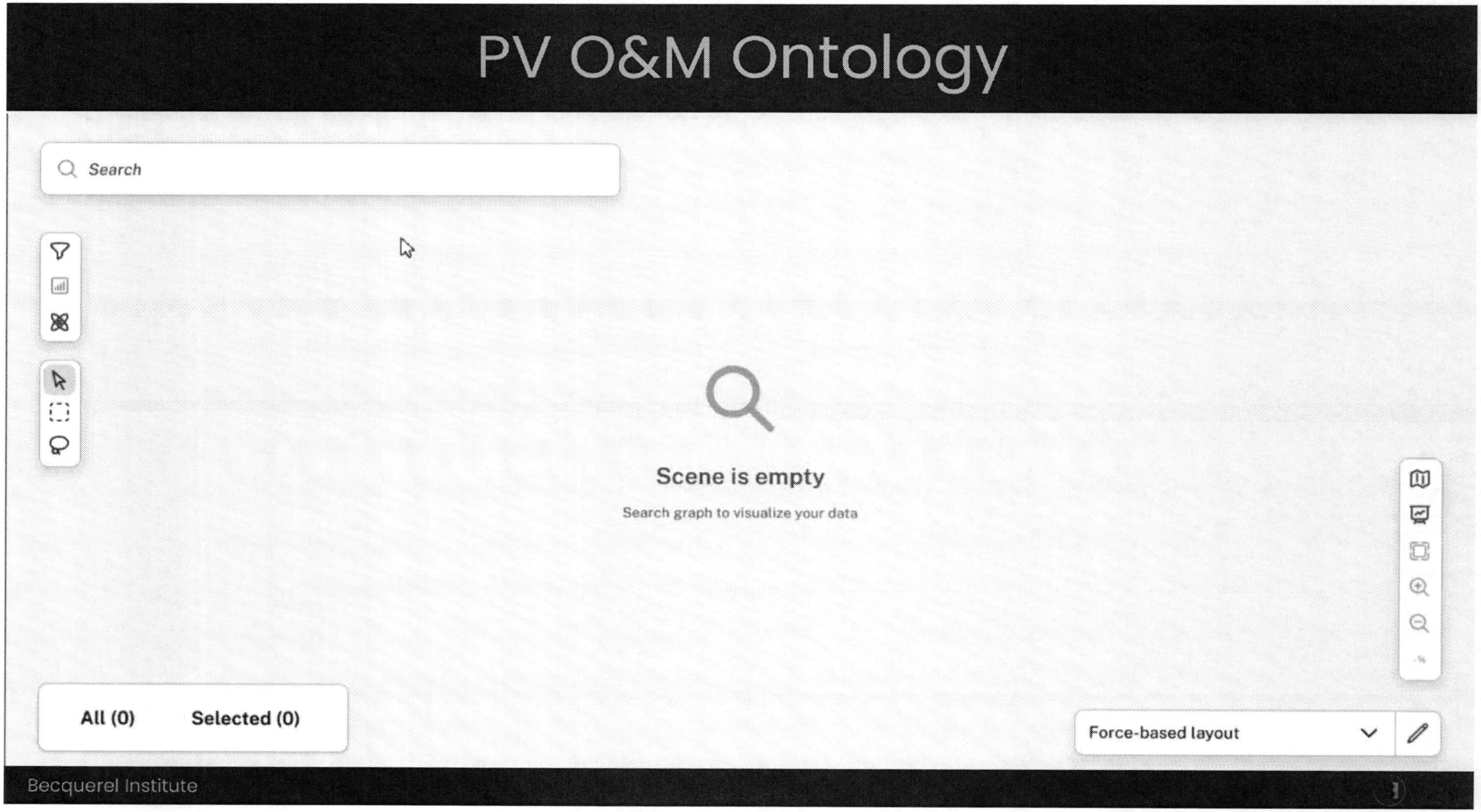
PV O&M Ontology
Search
Scene is empty
Search graph to visualize your data
All (0)
Selected (0)
Force-based layout
Becquerel Institute

O&M Ontology

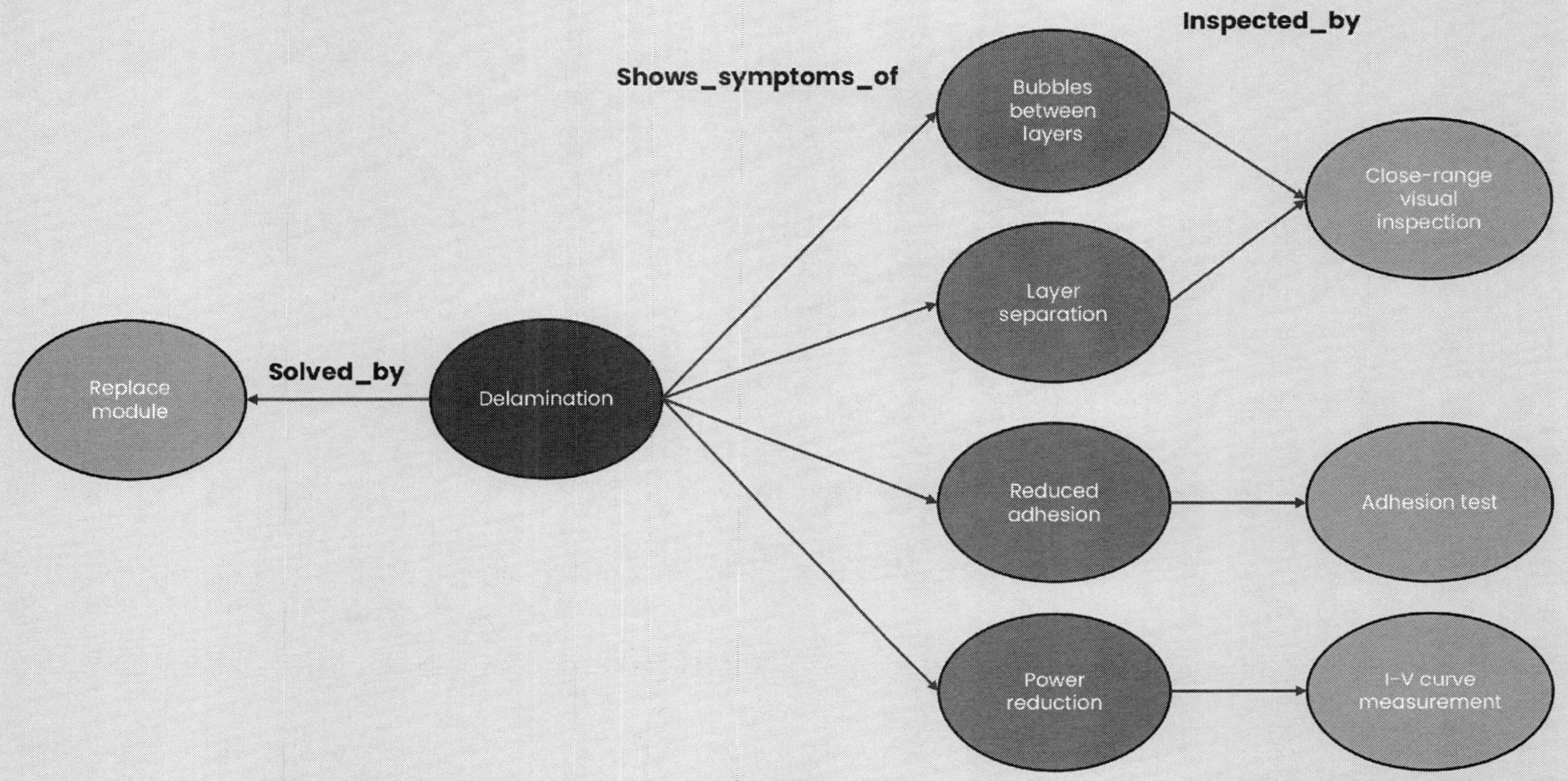

Becquerel Institute

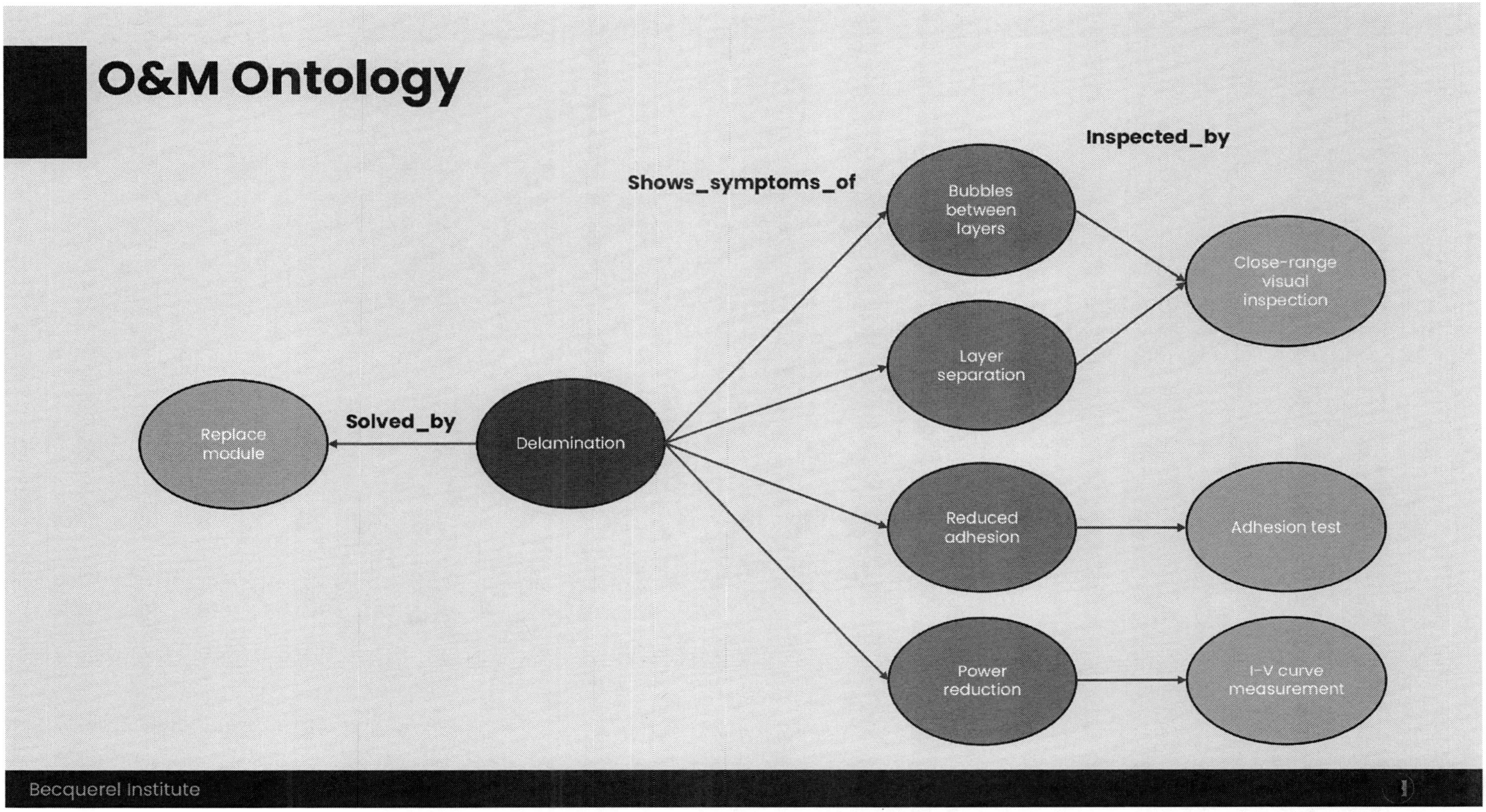

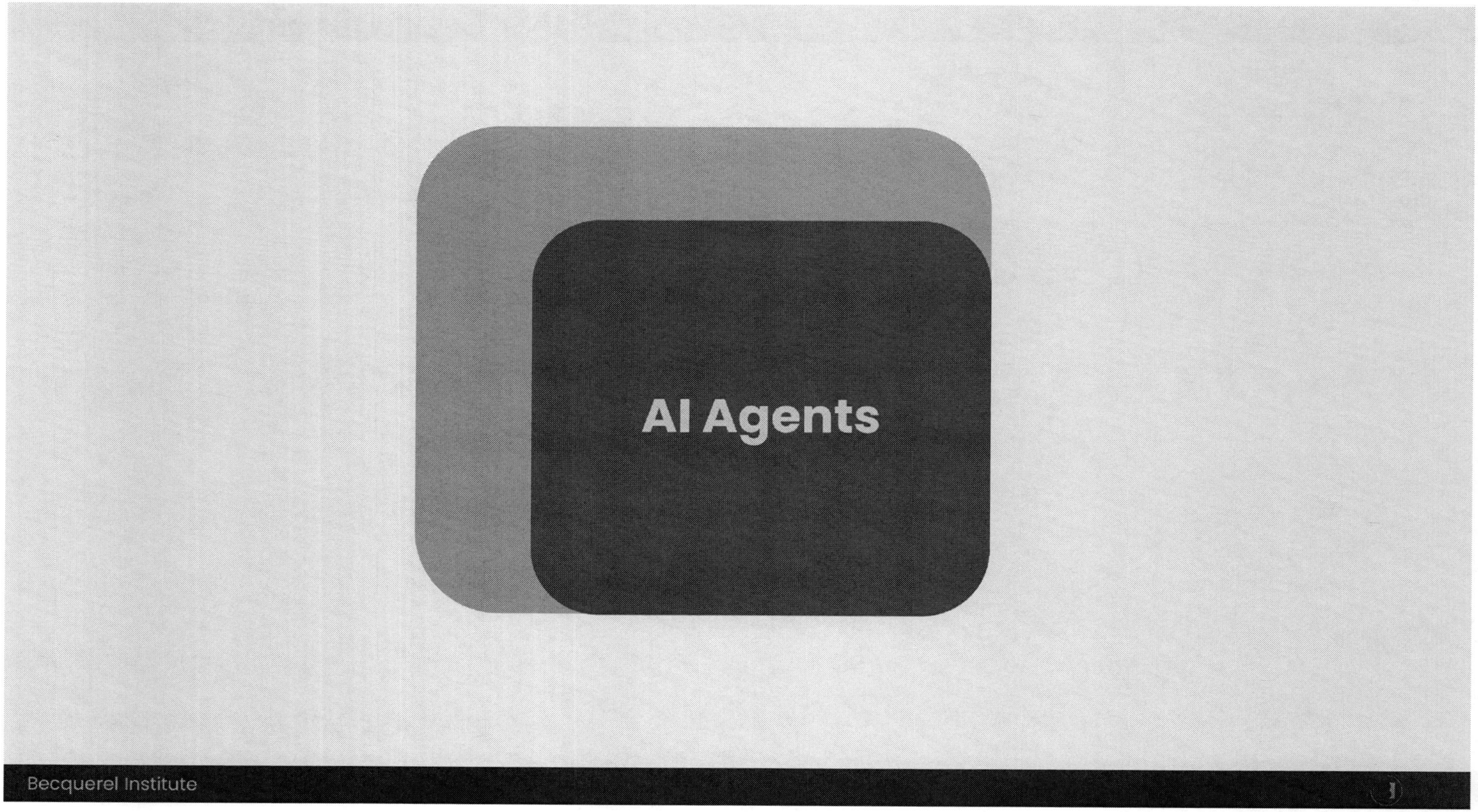
AI Agents
Becquerel Institute

Modality to context

- Every element in the O&M ontology was translated into context
- AI agent wrapped on the top of a proper Multi-Modal Large-Language-Model (MLLM) were built to generate context

- Example:

Context generation → PV infrared image showing a **hotspot** defect. → Symptom mapping → [Thermal issue, SYMP017, Hotspot]

Becquerel Institute

Modality to context in the O&M ecosystem

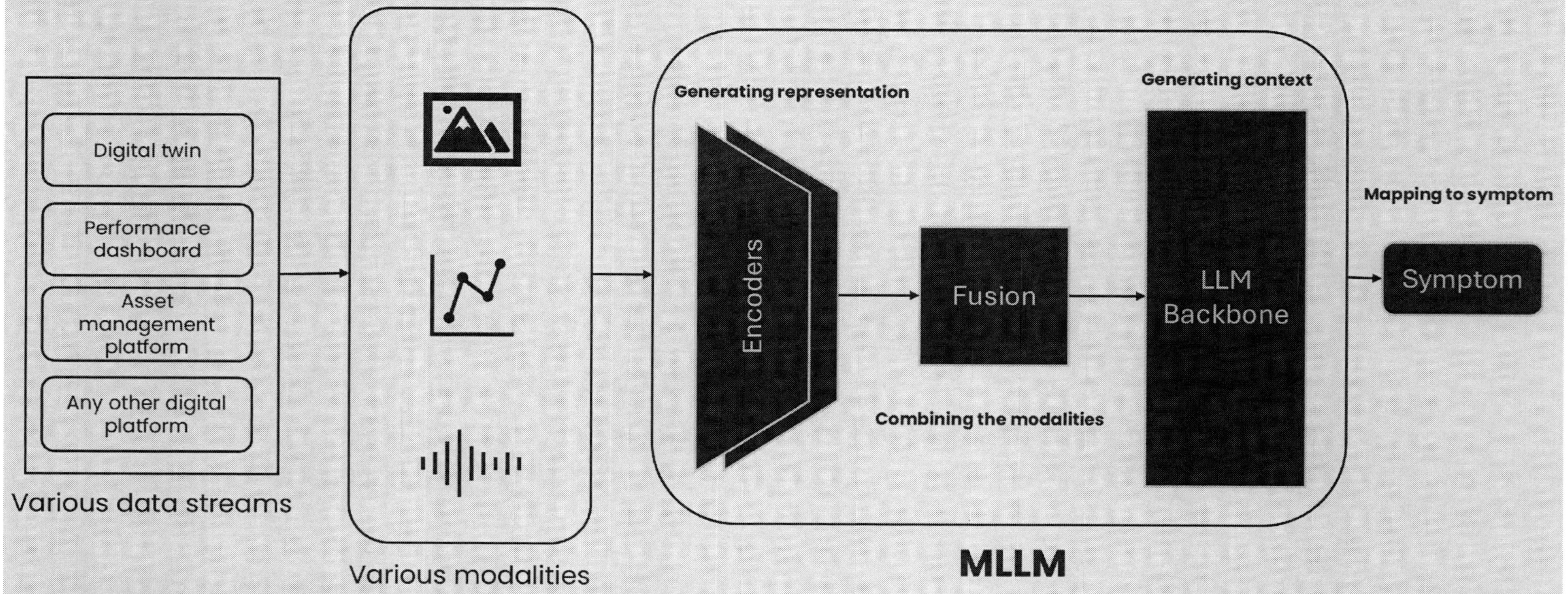

Becquerel Institute

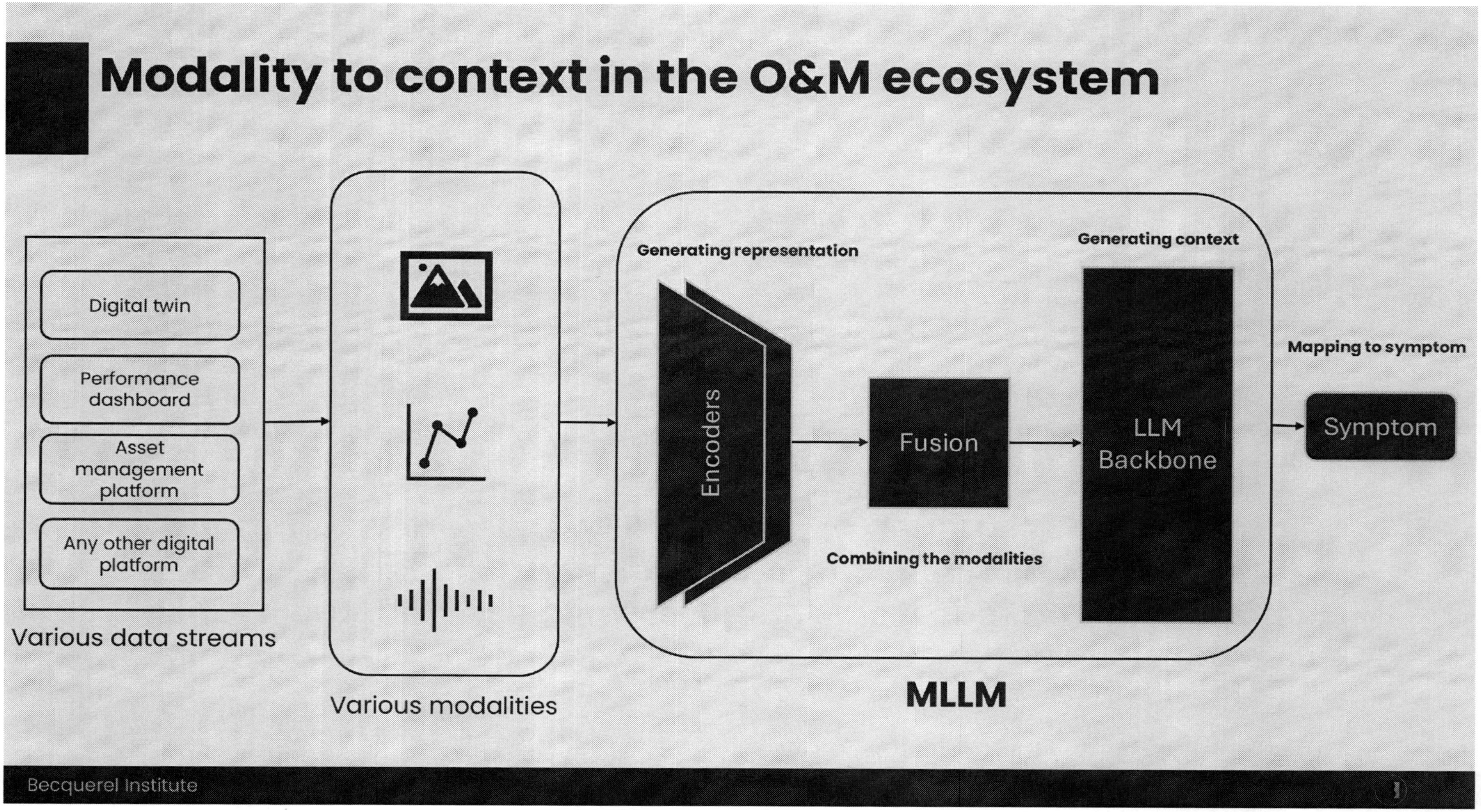

MLLM engine

- Each **modality** (image, audio, video, text, sensor data, etc.) has a **specialized encoder** that can transform raw data into a numerical representation (vector embeddings).
- Once the encoders create modality-specific embeddings, these are **aligned and fused** into a shared space.
- After fusion, the combined representation is passed into a **Large Language Model backbone** (GPT).
- Then the **LLM** generates **textual outputs** (answers, captions, reasoning steps) or even **actions** in agentic frameworks.

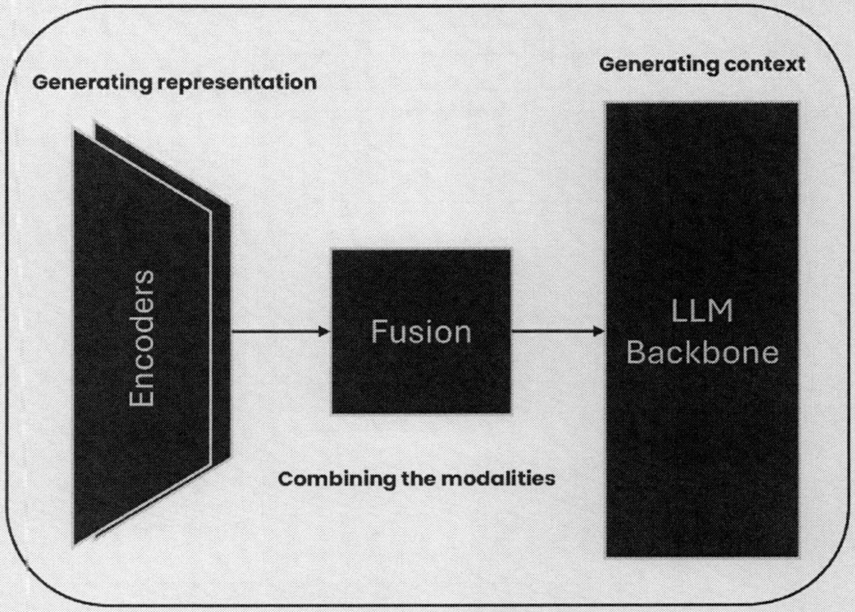

MLLM

Multi-agent system workflow

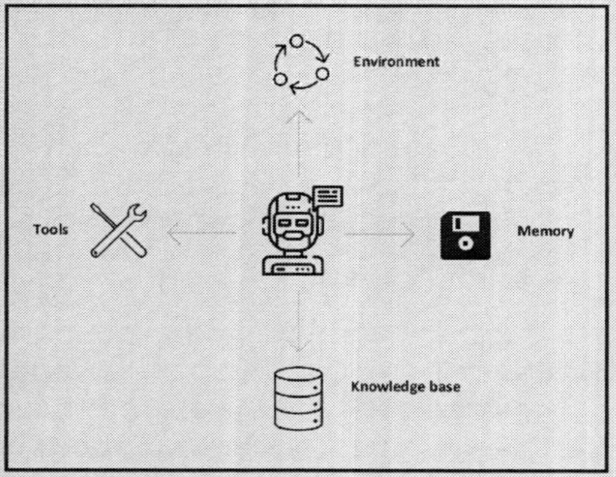

Figure 1: Proposed single agent architecture implementation & integration

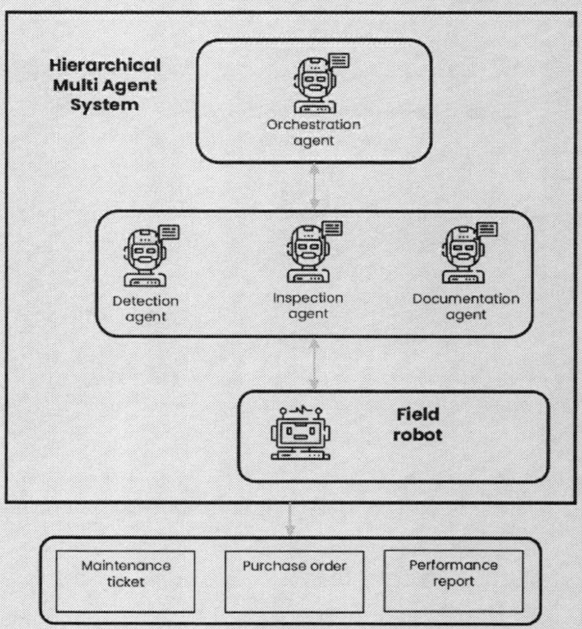

Figure 2: Proposed Multi-agent System Workflow Integrated with Field Robotics Layer

Becquerel Institute

Multi-agent system workflow: AI agents work profile

The **Orchestration Agent** acts as the central coordinator, managing interactions among all autonomous agents to ensure seamless collaboration, conflict resolution, and efficient execution of tasks.

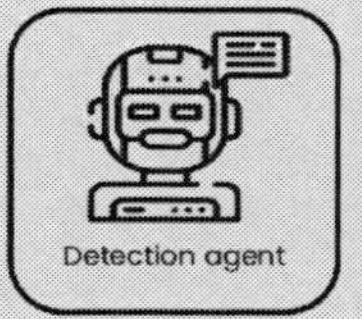

The **Detection Agent** is a Multi Modal Large Language Model - based AI agent responsible for identifying symptoms in defective PV system components.

The **Inspection Agent** determines and executes the appropriate inspection method based on the symptoms identified by the detection agent and the instructions received from the orchestration agent.

The **Documentation Agent** records all relevant information and outputs from various stages of the pipeline, providing decision-makers with insights into system performance.

Becquerel Institute

Medicine-like workflow

Becquerel Institute

Medical diagnose-like approach

Becquerel Institute

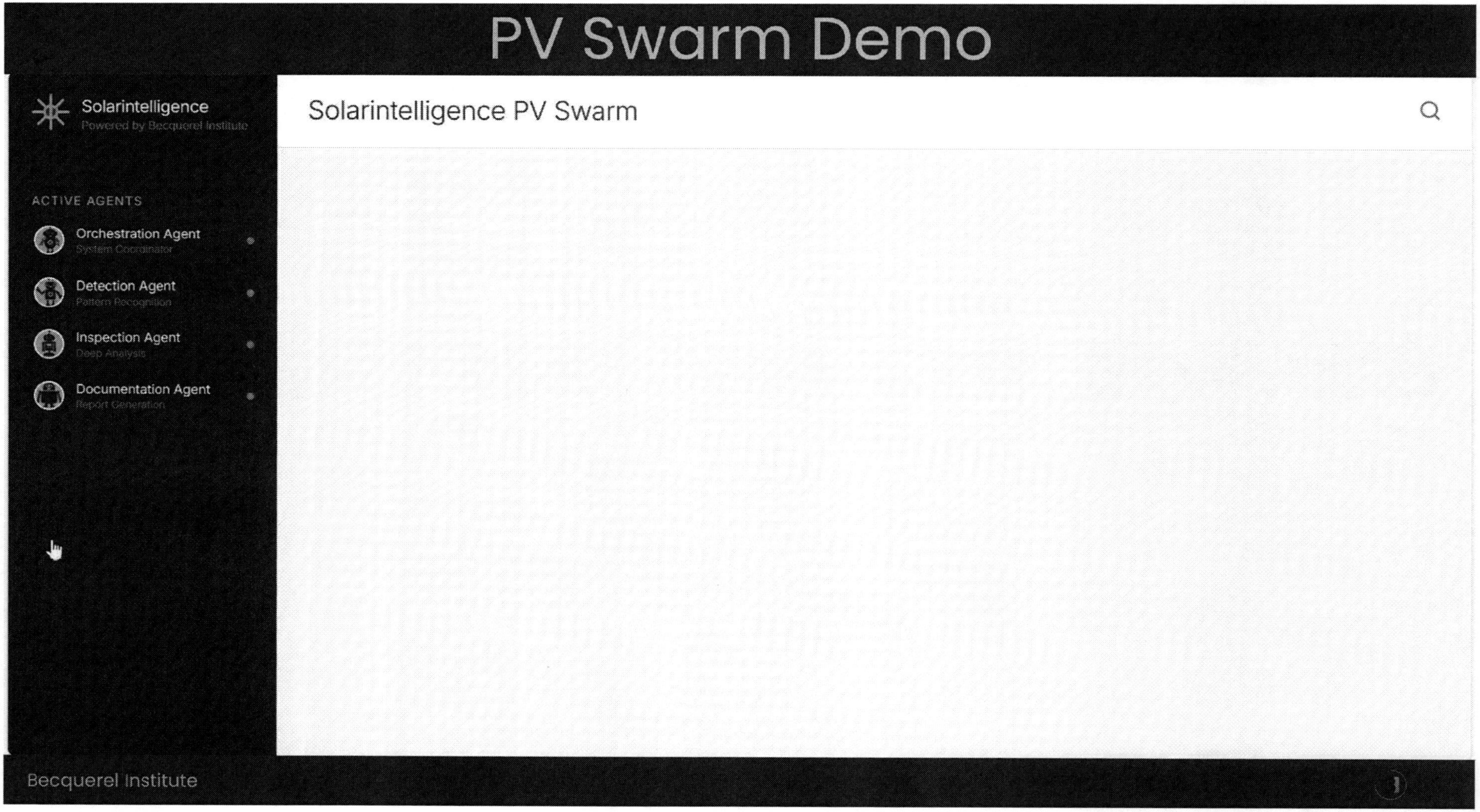
PV Swarm Demo
Solarintelligence
Powered by Becquerel Institute
Solarintelligence PV Swarm
ACTIVE AGENTS
Orchestration Agent
System Coordinator
Detection Agent
Pattern Recognition
Inspection Agent
Deep Analysis
Documentation Agent
Report Generation
Becquerel Institute

Symptom & failure detection experiments

- The system achieved an estimated accuracy of over 80% across 10 distinct failure types.
- In some cases, the final diagnosis may still be correct even if the symptom is not detected with full accuracy.
- The detection agent processes multiple data types as input to identify potential symptoms.
- Failure detection is based on a combination of the initial input data, the symptoms identified by the detection agent, and supplementary information obtained from additional inspections.

Case	Failure Type (Observed)	Symptom Prediction	Failure Prediction	Evaluation
1	White powdery surface	SYMP005 – White powdery surface	Mod.03 – Chalking	Correct
2	Encapsulant bubbling / delamination	SYMP011-Bubbles between layers	Mod.24-Delamination	Correct
3	Bypass diode failure	SYMP017 – Hot spots	Mod.54 – Defect bypass diode	Incorrect
4	Connector housing crack	SYMP031-Broken connectors	Not found	Partially correct
5	Encapsulant browning	SYMP003 – Discoloration	Mod.28-Yellowing or browning of encapsulation	Correct
6	Soiling	SYMP026 – Soiling	Mod.49 – Soiling	Correct
7	Cracked glass with burn marks	SYMP001 – Cracks + SYMP002 – Burn marks	Mod.46 – Glass breakage	Correct
8	Snail trails	SYMP001 – Visible cracks	Mod.27-snail trails	Incorrect
9	Cell crack/Frame crack	SYMP001 – Cracks	Mod.17 – Breakage (cell cracks)	Partially correct
10	Moisture ingress	SYMP024-Moisture ingress	Mod.26 – Moisture	Correct

Becquerel Institute

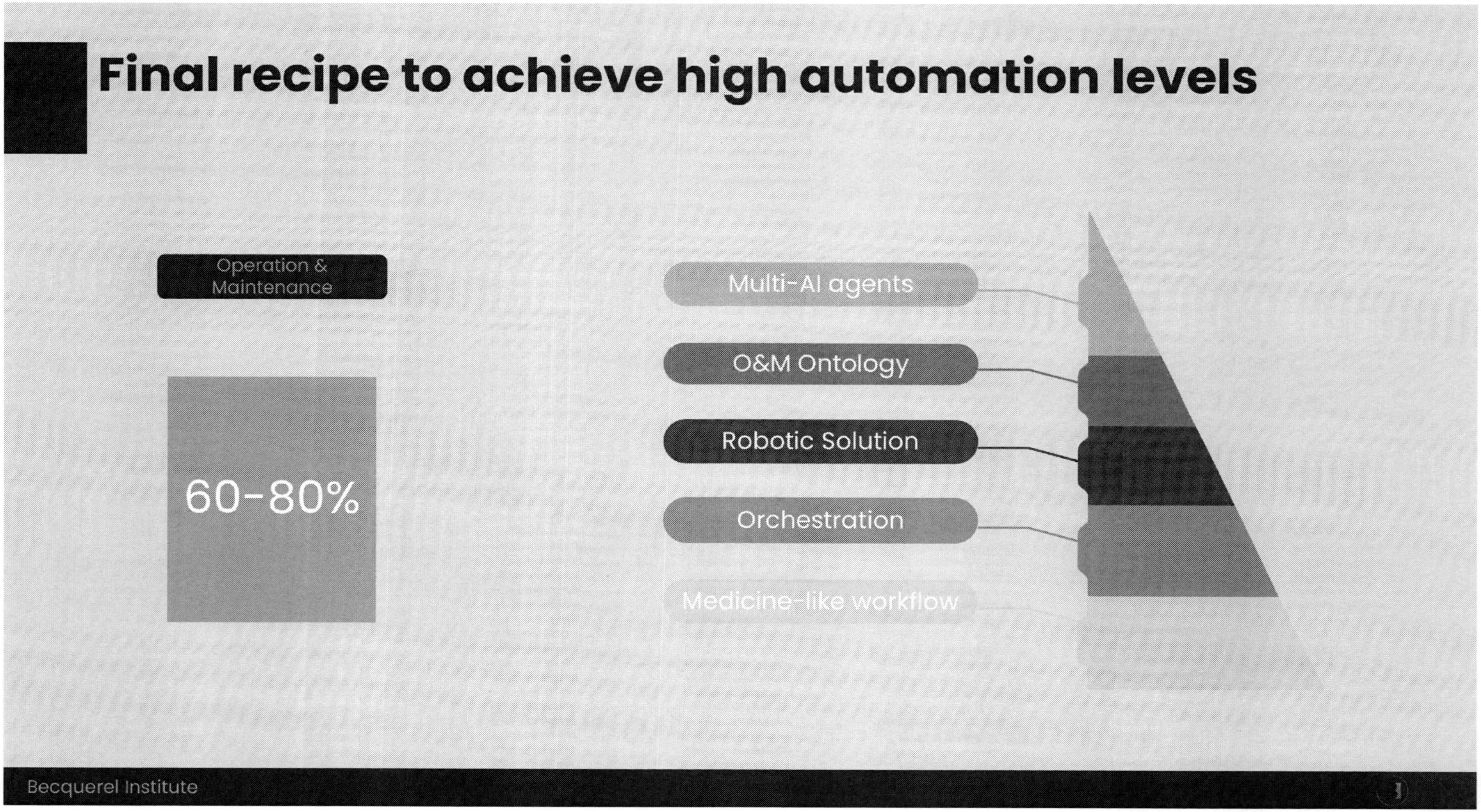
Final recipe to achieve high automation levels
Operation & Maintenance
60-80%
Multi-AI agents
O&M Ontology
Robotic Solution
Orchestration
Medicine-like workflow
Becquerel Institute

Not all that glitters is gold: new challenges to overcome

📍 Geographic Distribution vs. Economics: Robotics deployment faces massive logistics challenges.

🔧 The AI-Robotics Integration Gap: You need both AI systems AND human teams (another level of coordination).

🏗 Legacy System Compatibility Crisis: PV Plants are designed for human maintenance, not AI optimization or robotic access

⚡ The Reliability Requirements Reality: Autonomous maintenance systems must demonstrate exceptional reliability because failures could exceed automation benefits. The redundancy required may significantly increase costs beyond current projections.

📊 Data Quality Limitations: Legacy assets often lack sufficient monitoring, while fragmented systems create integration challenges that limit AI effectiveness to newer, data-rich installations.

Becquerel Institute

BECQUEREL INSTITUTE
Strategy Consulting in Solar PV

Becquerel Institute Italia

d.moser@becquerelinstitute.eu

m.sondoqah@becquerelinstitute.eu

42nd European Photovoltaic Solar Energy Conference and Exhibition

This presentation was selected by the Sc. Committee of the EU PVSEC 2025 for submission of a full paper to one of the EU PVSEC's collaborating peer-reviewed journals.

PREDICTIVE MODELLING AND ANALYSIS OF SOILING LOSSES IN PV PLANTS THROUGH A HYBRID DATA-DRIVEN APPROACH

Ioannis (John) A. Tsanakas[1*], E. Pilat[1], S. Arbaretaz[1], M.-T. Doi[1], F. Monteiro Martins[2], J. Veludo[2], C. Ménézo[3]
[1] CEA, Liten, Univ. Grenoble Alpes, Campus INES, 73375 Le Bourget du Lac, France
[2] Galp Energia S.A., 1349-065 Lisboa, Portugal
[3] Laboratoire Procédés Energie Bâtiment (LOCIE), Université Savoie Mont Blanc (USMB), 73375 Le Bourget du Lac, France

*corresponding author : ioannis.tsanakas@cea.fr

ABSTRACT: Photovoltaic (PV) system efficiency is significantly affected by soiling, leading to energy losses and increased operational costs. Within the SERENDI-PV project, this study refines soiling loss modeling through two complementary approaches: the Stochastic Quantifying Soiling Loss (SQSL) method and a machine learning (ML)-based predictive model. SQSL quantifies soiling losses using electrical performance data, independent of meteorological inputs, while the ML model forecasts losses using environmental parameters such as temperature, humidity, wind speed, and particulate matter concentration. The SQSL method identifies soiling phases—cleaning periods, stable periods, and soiling periods—by analyzing PV performance trends. Monte Carlo simulations generate probable soiling profiles, assessing uncertainty and informing maintenance strategies. Additionally, SQSL enables classification of soiling accumulation patterns, distinguishing between gradual and rapid soiling events. The ML-based approach integrates artificial neural networks and regression models to predict soiling losses, applying data pre-processing techniques to enhance accuracy. Regional climate variations and site-specific soiling characteristics are incorporated to improve predictive performance. Preliminary results validate the robustness of both methodologies. SQSL-generated profiles align closely with observed soiling trends, and ML models effectively capture seasonal variations. Field studies at a utility-scale PV plant in Spain further demonstrate the location dependency of soiling patterns. Comparative analysis of SQSL predictions and real soiling measurements shows prediction errors between 1% and 2.6% over an eight-day forecast period. These findings support the integration of predictive soiling models into PV monitoring platforms, optimizing maintenance strategies and minimizing energy yield losses.

Keywords: *PV systems; soiling loss modeling; machine learning (ML); PV performance, predictive modelling.*

1 INTRODUCTION: CONTEXT and AIM

Soiling, the accumulation of dust and particulate matter on photovoltaic (PV) modules, is a major factor in system performance degradation, causing significant energy losses and elevating operational expenses [1-3]. This makes its management crucial for optimizing PV output. As detailed in [1], research into soiling has evolved to encompass various assessment methods and mitigation strategies, including cleaning and anti-soiling coatings. The review in [2] emphasizes the severity of soiling losses in arid and polluted regions, noting the benefits of passive anti-soiling coatings—such as waterless operation, lower cost, and durability—over active cleaning methods. Furthermore, Bess et al. in [3] stress the importance of site-specific monitoring, evaluate different sensor technologies, and predict a rising global demand for thousands of sensors annually, while also providing economic analysis and experimental comparisons of mitigation techniques.

The economic impact is substantial, with global income losses from soiling-induced degradation estimated to surpass 10 billion EUR per year [4]. The severity of soiling is influenced by a combination of factors: local climate (rainfall, wind speed, humidity), airborne particulate composition (PM10, PM2.5), and site-specific conditions like proximity to deserts or urban areas. Consequently, soiling loss estimates vary widely, underscoring the necessity for accurate quantification, modeling, and prediction to optimize cleaning schedules, enhance energy yield forecasts, and enable proactive maintenance [5-7]. Experts from IEA PVPS Task 13, in both [5] and [6], have comprehensively summarized soiling, covering global dust distribution, particle types, measurement techniques, modeling, economic impacts, and mitigation strategies—including climate-specific maintenance and considerations for snow in higher latitudes. Meanwhile, the researchers in [7] developed innovative, calibration-free testing prototypes for accurate power loss estimation and provided new insights into soiling mechanisms through a lab protocol.

Accurately assessing soiling remains complex. Many existing models are validated on data from specific locations, raising concerns about their generalizability to diverse climates and sites. The dynamic nature of soiling, driven by multiple interacting environmental factors, demands robust modeling techniques capable of capturing these intricate relationships [8-9].

Soiling modeling approaches fall into three main categories: analytical/physics-based, empirical/statistical, and data-driven models. Analytical models use mathematical formulas with environmental data like rainfall and particulate matter concentration to estimate losses. A more detailed subset, physics-based models, simulate the fundamental mechanisms of dust deposition and removal by incorporating factors such as particle size, wind, and humidity.

One of the simplest analytical models is by Kimber [10], which assumes linear accumulation during dry periods and complete cleaning after a fixed rainfall threshold. However, it doesn't account for particulate matter concentration or partial cleaning. More advanced models address these limitations. The Humboldt State University (HSU) model [11] incorporates PM10/PM2.5 concentration, deposition velocity, and tilt angle. Toth et al. [12] proposed a model that differentiates between fine and coarse particles, better capturing the adhesive properties of fine dust. A comparative analysis on Spanish PV plants [13] found the Kimber model to be the simplest but least accurate. The HSU and Toth models improved accuracy by including particulate matter but were still limited by fixed thresholds. The SOMOSclean model [13] demonstrated the best performance with a mean absolute error of 0.694%; it uses an exponential growth function to simulate saturation and variable rainfall cleaning thresholds. A key limitation of physics-based models is their high demand for extensive, site-specific environmental and dust property data.

Empirical and statistical models use historical performance data to quantify losses. A standard method is the Soiling Ratio (SR), which compares a soiled module to a clean reference [7]. Other methods calculate a dirt derating factor [14] or analyze performance trends to infer soiling rates [15,16]. While straightforward, their accuracy can be compromised if a reliable clean reference is unavailable or if clean periods cannot be precisely identified.

The rise of large datasets has accelerated the use of machine learning (ML) models for soiling prediction. These data-driven methods excel at identifying complex, non-linear patterns that are difficult for traditional models to capture. Common techniques include linear regression and artificial neural networks (ANNs), with ANNs often delivering superior results. For instance, Laarabi et al. [17] and Chiteka et al. [18] used ANNs with environmental variables like rainfall and humidity to predict losses, showing improved accuracy despite being constrained by data availability and computational demands. Zitouni et al. [19] combined ML with regression, underscoring the potential of hybrid approaches. A notable data-driven method is the Stochastic Rate and Recovery (SRR) technique, which automatically detects soiling and cleaning events and models rates from a single system's data without a clean reference [15].

Research highlights the value of using hourly data to capture intra-day variations and training models over long periods to identify seasonal patterns. Common inputs include ambient temperature, relative humidity, wind, rainfall, particulate matter, and system tilt to extract "PV soiling profiles" for analysis, forecasting, and optimized cleaning [20]. Data processing involves standardization, cleaning, and filtering for specific conditions like snow. A recognized limitation is that many ML models are trained on data from a single location, underscoring the need for multi-environment training to improve generalizability. Future research directions include exploring advanced neural networks (e.g., Time-Series, Recurrent Neural Networks) and integrating considerations for bifacial PV systems.

Significant recent advancements have been made in soiling characterization and forecasting. Micheli et al. [20] created a framework for generating site-specific soiling profiles, showing that median-based annualized rates often miss seasonal variations. Their weighted average and Markov-chain algorithms achieved prediction errors below 1.3% and could identify optimal cleaning dates within three weeks, a major improvement over conventional methods. Kumar et al. [21] advanced empirical modeling by testing five variants of the Kimber and HSU models against sensor data. Their optimized models reduced RMSE by up to 23%, with all configurations keeping MAPE under 1%. They found that modified Kimber models excelled during extended dry periods and frequent rainfall, while their adapted HSU model was 12% more accurate than the original, highlighting the need for site-specific model selection based on local precipitation.

Alternative prediction methods have also emerged. Ballestrín et al. [22] showed the efficacy of ARMA time-series models, achieving a mean relative error of just 0.07% for seasonal forecasts, though they were less effective at predicting daily fluctuations. Smestad et al. [23] and Micheli et al. [24] pioneered spectral and image analysis techniques, respectively. In [23], researchers established that natural soiling follows consistent transmittance patterns and provided a cross-validation framework linking cleanliness standards to optical measurements ($R^2 = 0.89$). Meanwhile, work in [24] investigated image analysis thresholding uncertainties on a large micrograph dataset, finding methods like "percentile" and bimodal distributions to be inconsistent. They identified the "Triangle" method as the most reliable and recommended multiple micrographs per sample to account for non-uniformity and keep error low. The convergence of optical [23,24], statistical [22], and machine-learning enhanced [21] approaches points toward a new multi-method paradigm for soiling assessment.

Despite progress, challenges remain, including the incomplete integration of variables like wind and humidity, and sensor limitations. ML models require large datasets, restricting their use in data-sparse regions. Within the SERENDI-PV project, this study aims to refine soiling loss modeling and create predictive tools to enhance maintenance and yield forecasting. We present two complementary approaches: the Stochastic Quantifying Soiling Loss (SQSL) method for retrospective analysis from performance data, and a machine learning-based model for forward-looking predictions using environmental data. The ultimate goal is to integrate these into predictive tools for improved energy yield assessments, enabling data-driven decisions to minimize soiling-related losses.

2 METHODOLOGY – APPROACH

The SQSL method identifies soiling trends by analyzing PV performance metrics over time. Unlike traditional methods that require external environmental inputs such as rainfall data, SQSL relies entirely on variations in electrical performance, making it particularly useful in cases where meteorological data is unavailable or unreliable. In such approach, statistical thresholds are defined to segment performance variations into distinct "key" phases that make up the soiling profile: cleaning periods (CP), stable periods (StP), and soiling periods (SoP). Cleaning events are identified based on a significant increase in PV performance metrics, while stable periods are detected by analyzing fluctuations within a defined threshold. The transition into a soiling period is determined once PV performance metrics imply degradation beyond acceptable variation limits. A *theoretical* representation of these different phases is given in Fig. 1 (top), illustrating the transitions between cleaning, stable, and soiling periods. To contextualize such phases/classifications into real-life profiles of soiling losses, Fig. 1 (bottom) shows an example profile from *actual* real-case data, displaying how these phases are detected in practice.

We employ statistical analyses and Monte Carlo

simulations, to generate *probable* soiling profiles, enabling estimates of average soiling ratios and uncertainty ranges. This probabilistic approach helps define different soiling scenarios, ranging from worst-case to optimal conditions. The methodology also includes sensitivity analysis, examining how variations in input parameters, such as the frequency and effectiveness of cleaning events, influence the estimated soiling losses. Additionally, the SQSL method allows the classification of different soiling accumulation patterns by analyzing the rate of PV performance decline during soiling periods. This enables distinguishing between slow, gradual soiling accumulation and rapid degradation due to specific environmental conditions. Such "soiling profiling" capability provides valuable insights for optimizing maintenance strategies for PV plants.

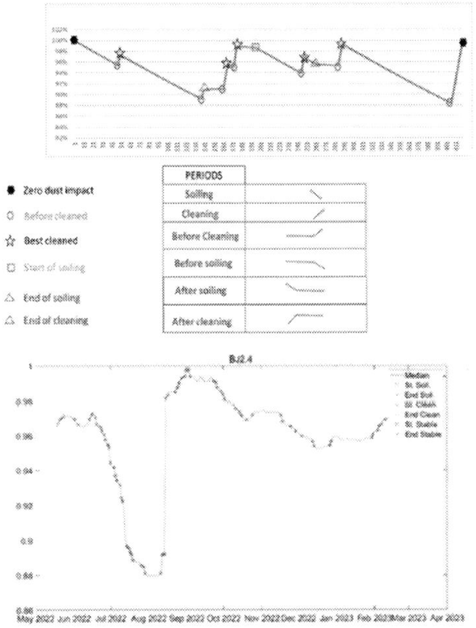

Figure 1: Top: Theoretical representation of the different key phases-variations in PV performance, considered for soiling profiling in the SQSL approach. Bottom: Identification of such phases within a real-case performance/soiling data from a utility-scale PV plant.

A complementary machine learning (ML)-based methodology (Fig. 2) integrates artificial neural networks and regression models to predict soiling losses from environmental parameters. These models process historical data, applying rigorous pre-processing steps such as data standardization, outlier removal, and missing data correction. The inclusion of wind speed, rainfall (precipitation) accumulation, and particulate matter levels improves model accuracy. A filtering process refines environmental datasets, correcting anomalies in precipitation records based on correlated meteorological variables, thereby ensuring better soiling loss estimations. Additionally, the developed methodology accounts for site-specific soiling characteristics by incorporating long-term data analysis. Soiling accumulation patterns vary significantly based on regional climate, local air pollution levels, and seasonal effects. The study emphasizes the importance of adapting soiling models to local conditions to improve predictive accuracy. To exclude snowy days from soiling ratio calculations, as also shown in Fig. 2, a filter is applied based on snow depth and albedo measurements. Since snow depth sensors can be noisy, only days with a significant albedo increase are considered snowy.

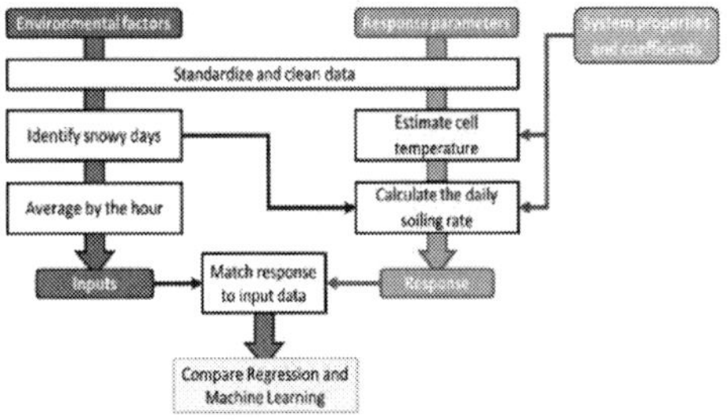

Figure 2: Architecture of the ML-based model for soiling loss prediction, assessed complementarily in this study.

3 RESULTS and DISCUSSION

Preliminary SQSL validation results indicate a high correlation between simulated and actual soiling profiles. The Monte Carlo-generated profiles effectively reconstruct historical soiling trends, confirming the robustness of the method. Figure 3 demonstrates this through a set of simulated PV performance (soiling loss) profiles, for the real-case study data of Fig.1-right, illustrating how uncertainty ranges are captured in the estimation. The post-cleaning PV performance jumps observed in field data validate the method's ability to estimate cleaning efficiencies under different operational conditions.

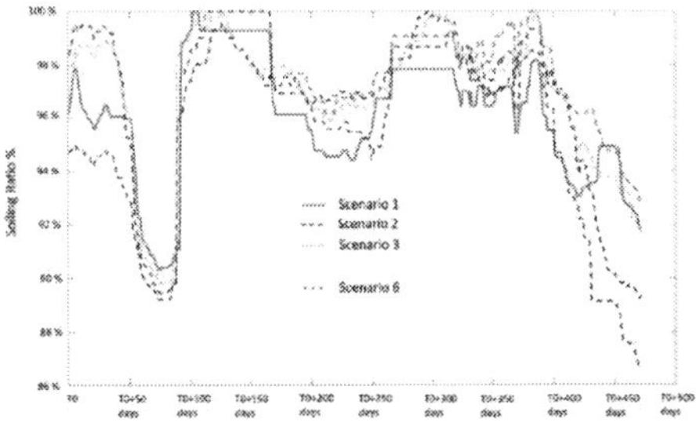

Figure 3: Example results of SQSL-based generation of various soiling loss profiles, based on the real-case data/curve shown in Fig.1.

Further, the ML-based models trained on datasets from NREL and CEA floating PV plant demonstrate a strong ability to capture seasonal soiling variations. The comparison of measured and predicted soiling ratios (Fig. 4) reveals that prolonged training periods improve predictive accuracy. However, the models require further refinement to account for location-specific environmental influences.

Further simulations, employing both our SQSL method and our ML modelling framework, were carried out for the case of a utlity-scale PV plant located in the Aragon region, northeastern Spain. The studied PV installation, with installed capacity of 62 MW_p, spans over 100 ha in a soiling prone site, influenced by climatic conditions (cold semi-arid climate (BSk)) that favor dust accumulations. In the specific case, for employing the SQSL approach, we examined DC current measurements at PV strings level, for a full year, identifying different soiling periods based on performance output (PV production) patterns. Different PV string locations experience distinct soiling behaviors due to varying micro-climatic exposure conditions. Figure 5 presents indicative examples of resulting soiling profiles, generated through distinct "training", "validation" and "test" data. The modelling results are suggestive of considerable variations across soiling profiles for different strings, highlighting the location-dependency and influence of microclimatic conditions on soiling losses, particularly in the case of wide-area soiling-prone PV installations.

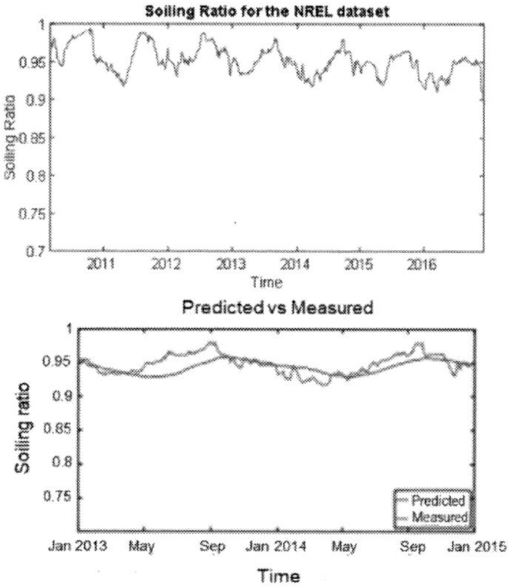

Figure 4: Top: Measured soiling ratio for the case of NREL dataset, over a 7-year period (01/2010-01/2017). Bottom: Measured vs. predicted (through the CEA ML-based model) soiling ratio, over two years (01/2013-01/2015) of the same NREL dataset.

Although the SQSL method does not rely on weather data as inputs for its computations, environmental parameters such as wind speed, humidity, and precipitation were analyzed to validate and interpret the soiling trends observed in the electrical data. This auxiliary analysis helps confirm whether environmental conditions align with SQSL-detected cleaning and soiling events. For instance, the correlation between increased humidity and dust adhesion, or the impact of heavy rainfall on natural cleaning, provides insights into the accuracy of SQSL-based estimations.

Finally, Fig. 6 presents example comparative results on the soiling ratio predicted (8 days ahead) by applying the SQSL method against actual soiling ratio measurements, for an indicative period of 3 months in 2024, for four different PV strings of the aforementioned PV plant. In this case, prediction errors range between 1% and 2.6%. Despite the short period of the training dataset (from 20/03/2023 to 05/03/2024), the results are encouraging. This limited period of measurement does not allow the model to learn much of the tendency in the long term, but the errors observed are sufficiently low to consider a reliable prediction/simulation of soiling losses in such real-life cases

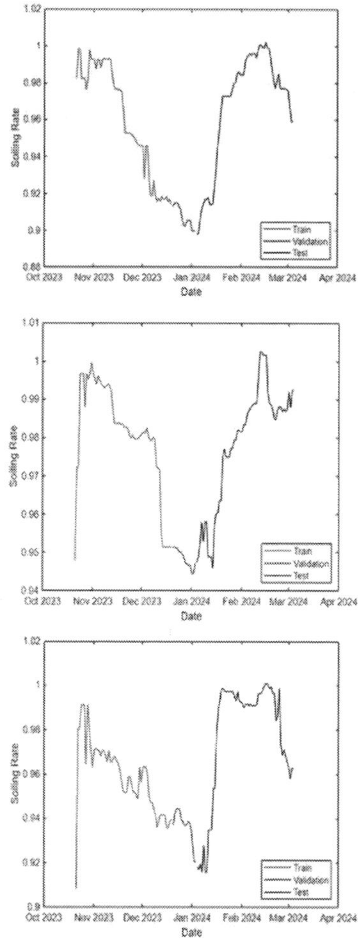

Figure 5: Soiling rate trends for different PV strings (three indicative examples) of the studied utility-scale PV plant in northeastern Spain. Labels 'train,' 'validation,' and 'test' indicate the data split used for model training and evaluation.

Next to the presented predictive modelling framework for PV soiling losses, CEA has also developed a virtual case study generator to support further soiling model development. This tool – which will be discussed in more details in the full version of this paper – simulates daily soiling rates based on multivariable regression models, considering wind speed, rainfall, and airborne dust concentration. It generates synthetic datasets useful for validating and improving soiling models under controlled conditions. The ability to predict daily soiling ratios provides valuable insights for optimizing maintenance strategies.

Further investigation reveals that soiling losses exhibit non-linear degradation patterns, influenced by meteorological anomalies. Periods of high relative humidity combined with low wind speeds create conditions that promote dust adhesion, significantly increasing soiling rates. Conversely, heavy precipitation events can lead to unexpected recovery in performance.

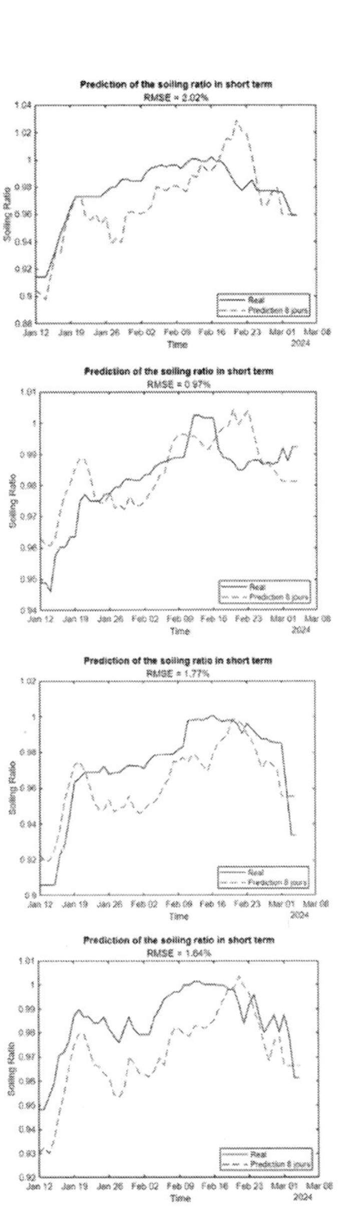

Figure 6: ML-based predictive modelling of the soiling ratio (SR) for four different PV strings of the studied PV plant in northeastern Spain: Comparative results of predicted SR vs real SR, 8-days ahead prediction, for a study period of 3 months.

4 CONCLUSIONS - OUTLOOK

The field of PV soiling modeling and prediction is rapidly evolving in response to the urgent need to mitigate energy losses and enhance operational efficiency. This study contributes to this objective by introducing two synergistic methodologies: the Stochastic Quantifying Soiling Loss (SQSL) method and a machine learning (ML)-based predictive model. Both approaches are designed for integration into existing PV monitoring platforms to refine maintenance planning and reduce energy yield degradation.

The SQSL method offers a robust framework for retrospective analysis, quantifying soiling impacts using exclusively electrical performance data, without dependence on external meteorological inputs. By examining performance trends, the method identifies and categorizes key soiling phases—such as cleaning intervals, stable performance periods, and soiling accumulation periods. Utilizing Monte Carlo simulations, it generates probabilistic soiling profiles that estimate average soiling ratios and associated uncertainty ranges. This stochastic methodology supports the definition of diverse soiling scenarios, from worst-case degradation to optimal conditions, thereby offering critical insights for maintenance optimization. It further enables the classification of accumulation patterns, distinguishing between gradual soiling buildup and rapid performance decline. Initial validation confirms the robustness of the SQSL approach, with generated profiles showing strong alignment with empirical observations. In field testing at a utility-scale PV plant in Spain, the model achieved soiling ratio predictions up to eight days in advance, with errors between 1% and 2.6%. Although currently focused on retrospective analysis, future development aims to incorporate weather forecasts and seasonal priors into the Monte Carlo simulations, enhancing predictive capability and improving the representation of seasonal variability for more reliable cleaning scheduling.

Complementing the SQSL method, the ML-based predictive model employs a forward-looking approach, leveraging an extensive set of environmental parameters. This model integrates artificial neural networks and regression techniques, augmented with advanced data pre-processing, to capture complex non-linear relationships and seasonal dynamics often missed by conventional models. Trained on hourly data over extended periods, the model accommodates regional climate variations and site-specific soiling behaviors, improving predictive accuracy. Validation using datasets from NREL and a CEA floating PV installation demonstrated the model's capacity to predict seasonal soiling trends, with performance improving as training duration increases.

Despite these advances, several challenges persist. Many ML models remain constrained by limited generalizability, having been trained and validated on data from single locations. The substantial data requirements of powerful ML algorithms also restrict their applicability in regions with sparse monitoring infrastructure. Additionally, discrepancies between pyranometer-based soiling estimates and electrical performance-based quantifications underscore the need for multi-source validation to improve assessment robustness. Future efforts will focus on enhancing model adaptability across diverse environments, refining input parameters, and investigating advanced ML architectures such as Time-Series Neural Networks and Recurrent Neural Networks. Further development will include adaptation for bifacial PV systems and validation against measurements from a dedicated CEA soiling sensor. A virtual case study generator will also be employed to produce synthetic datasets under controlled conditions, supporting ongoing model validation and refinement.

By uniting these two methodologies, this research establishes a comprehensive and reliable framework to support PV plant operators in making data-informed decisions, ultimately improving economic efficiency and strategic operational planning.

ACKNOWLEDGEMENTS

Part of this work has been carried out in the framework of the H2020 SERENDI-PV and Horizon Europe CACTUS projects. SERENDI-PV project has received funding from the European Union's Horizon 2020 research and innovation programme under grant agreement No. 953016. CACTUS project has received funding from the European Union's Horizon Europe research and innovation programme under grant agreement No. 101132182. For CEA team, part of this work was also supported by the French National Program "Programme d'Investissements d'Avenir - INES.2S" under Grant Agreement ANR ANR-10-IEED-0014 0014-01.

REFERENCES

1. Ricardo Conceição, José González-Aguilar, Ahmed Alami Merrouni, Manuel Romero, Soiling effect in solar energy conversion systems: A review, Renewable and Sustainable Energy Reviews, Volume 162, 2022, 112434. https://doi.org/10.1016/j.rser.2022.112434
2. Pooya Hooshyar, Hesam Moghadasi, Seyed Ali Moosavi, Ali Moosavi, Ali Nouri Borujerdi, Recent progress of soiling impact on solar panels and its mitigation strategies: A review, Applied Energy, Volume 379, 2025, 124979. https://doi.org/10.1016/j.apenergy.2024.124979
3. João Gabriel Bessa, Leonardo Micheli, Florencia Almonacid, Eduardo F. Fernández, Monitoring photovoltaic soiling: assessment, challenges, and perspectives of current and potential strategies, iScience, Volume 24, Issue 3, 2021, 102165. https://doi.org/10.1016/j.isci.2021.102165
4. L. Micheli et al. (2024). Modelling Performance and Maximum Allowed Costs for Anti-Soiling Coatings in Europe. 41th EUPVSEC, Vienna, Austria.
5. Schill, C., Anderson, A., Baldus-Jeursen, C., Burnham, L., Micheli, L., Parlevliet, D., Pilat, E., Stridh, B., & Urrejola, E. (2022). Soiling losses – Impact on the performance of photovoltaic power plants (Report No. IEA-PVPS T13-11:2022). International Energy Agency Photovoltaic Power Systems Programme. ISBN 978-3-907281-09-3.
6. Jahn, U., Herteleer, B., Tjengdrawira, C., Tsanakas, I., Richter, M., Dickeson, G., Astigarraga, A., Tanahashi, T., Valencia, F., Green, M., Anderson, A., Stridh, B., Alonso, A. R. L., & Sangpongsanont, Y. (2022). Guidelines for operation and maintenance of photovoltaic power plants in different climates (Report No. IEA-PVPS T13-25:2022). International Energy Agency Photovoltaic Power Systems Programme. ISBN 978-3-907281-13-0.
7. JA Tsanakas, R Moretón, E Pilat, J Solórzano, J Veludo, K Garcia. (2024). "Quality Assurance from Laboratory to Field: Novel Test Solutions for Soiling-Prone PV Systems". EUPVSEC 2024, DOI : 10.4229/EUPVSEC2024/4AO.9.4 (ISBN: 3-936338-90-6).
8. Micheli, L., and Muller, M. (2017) An investigation of the key parameters for predicting PV soiling losses. Prog. Photovolt: Res. Appl., 25: 291–307. doi: 10.1002/pip.2860.
9. Klemens K. Ilse, Benjamin W. Figgis, Volker Naumann, Christian Hagendorf, Jörg Bagdahn, Fundamentals of soiling processes on photovoltaic modules, Renewable and Sustainable Energy Reviews, Volume 98, 2018, Pages 239-254, https://doi.org/10.1016/j.rser.2018.09.015.
10. A. Kimber, L. Mitchell, S. Nogradi and H. Wenger, "The Effect of Soiling on Large Grid-Connected Photovoltaic Systems in California and the Southwest Region of the United States," 2006 IEEE 4th World Conference on Photovoltaic Energy Conference, Waikoloa, HI, USA, 2006, pp. 2391-2395, doi: 10.1109/WCPEC.2006.279690.
11. M. Coello and L. Boyle, "Simple model for predicting time series soiling of photovoltaic panels," IEEE J. Photovoltaics, vol. 9, no. 5, pp. 1382-1387, Sep. 2019.
12. Toth, S., Hannigan, M., Vance, M., & Deceglie, M. (2020). Predicting Photovoltaic Soiling From Air Quality Measurements. IEEE Journal of Photovoltaics, 10(4), 1142-1147. Article 9090155. https://doi.org/10.1109/jphotov.2020.2983990. https://doi.org/10.1109/JPHOTOV.2020.2983990
13. Redondo, M., Platero, C.A., Moset, A., Rodriguez, F., Donate, V. (2024). Review and Comparison of Methods for Soiling Modeling in Large Grid- Connected PV Plants. Sustainability, 16, 10998. https://doi.org/10.3390/su162410998
14. Jamil, W. J., Rahman, H. A., Shaari, S., & Desa, M. K. M. (2020). Modeling of soiling derating factor in determining photovoltaic outputs. IEEE Journal of Photovoltaics, 10(5), 1417-1424.
15. M.G. Deceglie, L. Micheli and M. Muller, "Quantifying Soiling Loss Directly From PV Yield," in IEEE Journal of Photovoltaics, vol. 8, no. 2, pp. 547-551, March 2018, doi: 10.1109/JPHOTOV.2017.2784682.
16. L. Micheli, D. Ruth, M/G. Deceglie and M. Muller, Time Series Analysis of Photovoltaic Soiling Station Data: Version 1.0, August 2017, Technical Report NREL/TP-5J00-69131.
17. B. Laarabi, O. May Tzuc, D. Dahlioui, A. Bassam, M. Flota-Bañuelos, A. Barhdadi, Artificial neural network modeling and sensitivity analysis for soiling effects on photovoltaic panels in Morocco, Superlattices and Microstructures, Volume 127, 2019, Pages 139-150. https://doi.org/10.1016/j.spmi.2017.12.037
18. Chiteka, K., Arora, R. & Sridhara, S.N. A method to predict solar photovoltaic soiling using artificial neural networks and multiple linear regression models. Energy Syst 11, 981–1002 (2020). https://doi.org/10.1007/s12667-019-00348-w
19. Houssain Zitouni, Alae Azouzoute, Charaf Hajjaj, Massaab El Ydrissi, Mohammed Regragui, Jesús Polo, Ayoub Oufadel, Abdellatif Bouaichi, Abdellatif Ghennioui,

Experimental investigation and modeling of photovoltaic soiling loss as a function of environmental variables: A case study of semi-arid climate, Solar Energy Materials and Solar Cells, Volume 221, 2021, 110874. https://doi.org/10.1016/j.solmat.2020.110874

20. Micheli, L., Fernández, E. F., Muller, M., & Almonacid, F. (2020). Extracting and generating PV soiling profiles for analysis, forecasting, and cleaning optimization. IEEE Journal of Photovoltaics, 10(1), 197-204.
21. Kumar, D., Ritter, K., III, Raush, J., Ferdowsi, F., Gottumukkala, R. and Chambers, T. (2025), Optimizing Photovoltaic Soiling Loss Predictions in Louisiana: A Comparative Study of Measured and Modeled Data Using a Novel Approach. Prog Photovolt Res Appl, 33: 560-579. https://doi.org/10.1002/pip.3891
22. Jesús Ballestrín, Jesús Polo, Nuria Martín-Chivelet, Javier Barbero, Elena Carra, Joaquín Alonso-Montesinos, Aitor Marzo, Soiling forecasting of solar plants: A combined heuristic approach and autoregressive model, Energy, Volume 239, Part E, 2022, 122442, https://doi.org/10.1016/j.energy.2021.122442 .
23. Smestad, G.P., Germer, T.A., Alrashidi, H. et al. Modelling photovoltaic soiling losses through optical characterization. Sci Rep 10, 58 (2020). https://doi.org/10.1038/s41598-019-56868-z
24. Micheli, L., Smestad, G. P., Khan, M. Z., Lange, K., Almughary, H. M. I., Abraim, M., Alamat, Y., Anderson, C. B., Bentouba, S., Figgis, B., Fuke, P., Hachicha, A. A., Karim, M., Kottantharayil, A., Martinez-Morales, A. A., Merrouni, A. A., Olivares, D., Picotti, G., Rabanal-Arabach, J., Wiesinger, F., & Ilse, K. (2024). Soiling in solar energy systems: The role of the thresholding method in image analysis. Solar RRL, 8(3). https://doi.org/10.1002/solr.202300654
25. Redondo, M., Platero, C. A., Moset, A., Rodríguez, F., & Donate, V. (2023). Soiling Modelling in Large Grid-Connected PV Plants for Cleaning Optimization. Energies, 16(2), 904. https://doi.org/10.3390/en16020904

CONSTRUCTION AND COMPARISON OF OUTDOOR PV TEST STANDS IN DIFFERENT CLIMATE ZONES

R. Ebner[1], M. Rennhofer[1], V. Neussl[1], B. Kubicek[1], M. Ankit[1], G. Ujvari[1], B. Azzopardi[2], A. Mignonac[3], Carlos Meza[4], Sebastian Dittmann[4], A. Gracia Amillo[5], J. M. Cuadra[5]
[1]AIT Austrian Institute of Technology, Center for Energy, 1210 Vienna, Austria, T +43 50550-6628, F +43 50550-6390, rita.ebner@ait.ac.at, www.ait.ac.at
[2]FIR The Foundation for Innovation and Research, Malta
[3]CEA Cadarache, Saint-Paul-Lez-Durance, France
[4]HSA Anhalt University of Applied Sciences, Köthen, Germany
[5]CENER National Renewable Energy Center, Sarriguren, Spain

ABSTRACT:
For the evaluation of the photovoltaic (PV) energy yield and potential investment decisions, the knowledge of the actual energy produced per year is far more important than the nominal peak power under standard test conditions (STC) in the laboratory. However, the actual energy yield strongly depends on the geographical location of the installation [1, 2, 3]. Therefore, within the PROMISE project, outdoor PV test stands were installed in different climate zones (Köppen climate classification): in the Humid Temperate zone (Germany), in the Mediterranean zone (Malta), in the Temperate zone (Austria), in the Mediterranean zone (France), and in Navarra, Spain, where the Alpine, Atlantic, and Mediterranean zones converge.

KEYWORDS: Different climate zones, PV test stand, Energy yield

1 INTRODUCTION

In the proposed work outdoor PV test stands were set up and compared in different climate zones in Austria (48.2081° N, 16.3713° E), Malta (35.9375° N, 14.3754° E), Spain (42.742 N, 1.629 W), France (43.6935° N, 5.7330° E) and Germany (51.9503° N, 11.6923° E).

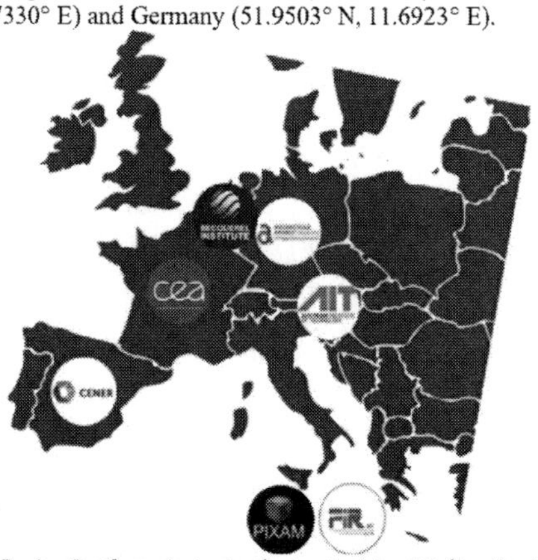

FIG. 1: Outdoor test stands in Austria, Malta, Spain, France, and Germany.

2 EXPERIMENTS

15 field-aged modules (10 years outside) (see Fig. 2) from Malta were subjected to STC performance measurements at the AIT PV laboratory (see Fig. 3 and Table 1).

Module type: Honey Module TSM-PD05 (see Fig. 2). These are polycrystalline modules with 60 cells. Their output ranges from 255–270 W, with a power density of up to 165 W/m² and a maximum efficiency of 16.5%. The cell size is 156 mm × 156 mm, and the module size is 1650 mm × 992 mm × 35 mm with a weight of 18.6 kg. The module has high-transparency, anti-reflective, tempered solar glass (3.2 mm thick) and an aluminum frame.

The current-voltage (IV) curves [6] of the PV modules nearly overlap, indicating that they exhibited similar degradation rates over time. This could be due to a variety of factors such as solar irradiation, temperature fluctuations, humidity, and other environmental influences. Since the modules show uniform degradation, it can be assumed that they age at roughly the same rate and that their performance decreases evenly throughout their lifetime.

FIG. 2: Module.

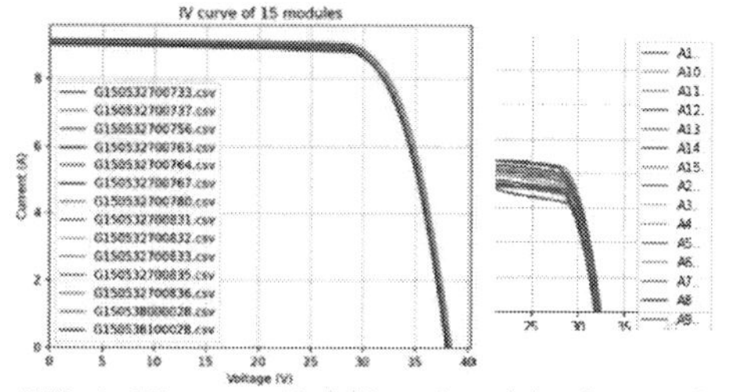

FIG. 3: IV-curves, 15 field-aged modules from Malta, initial characterization for this study, prior to installation in the different climates.

Table 1: IV measurement results at STC, 15 aged modules ("Out of the Box")

Sample	Voc[V]	Isc [A]	Fill Factor [%]	Pmax [W]	Efficiency [%]
A1	38,41	9,12	76,00	266,38	18,24
A2	38,47	9,16	75,75	267,09	18,29
A3	38,28	9,06	75,72	262,82	17,99
A4	38,10	9,09	75,63	262,08	17,94
A5	38,39	9,17	75,46	265,73	18,19
A6	38,28	9,10	75,99	264,82	18,13
A7	38,31	9,08	76,09	264,75	18,13
A8	38,08	9,05	75,52	260,55	17,84
A9	38,17	9,05	76,31	263,90	18,07
A10	38,02	9,09	75,84	262,38	17,96
A11	37,96	9,03	75,93	260,55	17,84
A12	38,00	8,98	76,16	260,12	17,81
A13	37,96	9,01	75,74	259,16	17,74
A14	38,10	9,03	75,66	260,61	17,84
A15	38,10	9,08	75,55	261,41	17,90

10.4229/EUPVSEC2025/4CV.1.2

After recording the initial measurement results, the short-circuit current (Isc) was plotted against the open-circuit voltage (Voc). With respect to performance consistency, the diagram shows that the modules exhibit slightly different performance characteristics (see Fig. 4).

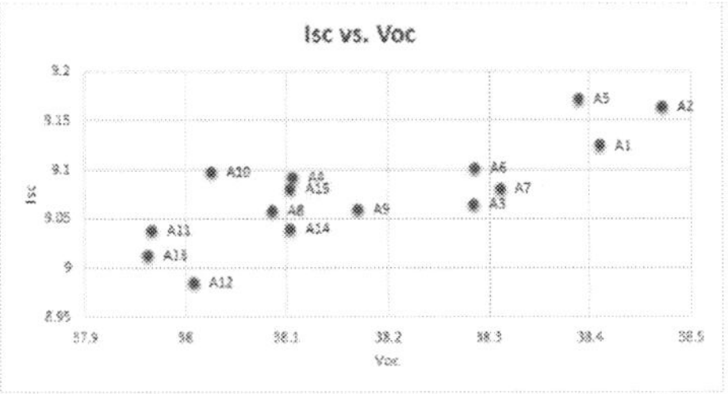

FIG. 4 Performance improvement after stabilization.

Next, a stabilization (preconditioning) procedure was carried out, followed by a second laboratory performance measurement under STC. This procedure not only determines the initial degradation and/or stable power generation, but also establishes a reliable "actual" wattage of the module, which then serves as the "baseline" (rather than the "nominal" nameplate value) for all energy yield data. All modules improved after stabilization (see Figs. 5 and 6).

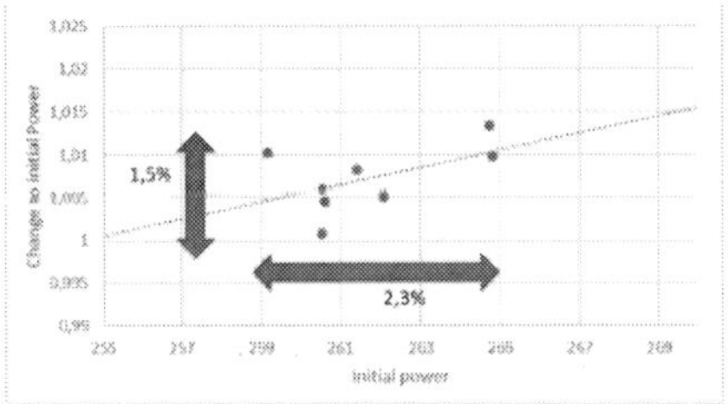

FIG. 5 Power change due to stabilization

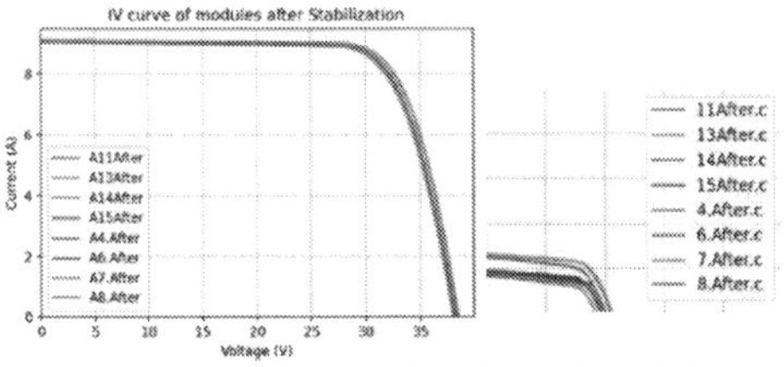

FIG. 6 IV curves, 15 field-aged modules, after stabilization

After stabilization, two modules were distributed to every PROMISE project partners FiR, CENER, CEA, and HSA for long-term outdoor measurements.

The following PV module and system data were recorded:

- Module temperature
- DC characteristics: Vmpp, Impp
- Irradiance
- Wind speed and direction
- Cumulative energy yield (DC side)

Most sits were additionally equipped with a state-of-the-art meteorological station, including:

- Pyranometer
- Pyrheliometer
- Spectroradiometer
- UV radiometer
- Ambient temperature sensors

3 RESULTS

All project partners (Malta, Germany, Spain, France and Austria) installed their two PV modules outdoors and conducted monitored throughout 2025.

3.1 Results of Austria

Module No. 1 (A1) and No. 2 (A2) were installed at the AIT outdoor test bench (see Fig. 7). The modules were oriented south at a tilt angle of 39°. Measurement results are logged every minute.

FIG. 7 AIT outdoor test stand

Fig. 8 shows the outdoor measurement system at AIT and which sensors were installed.

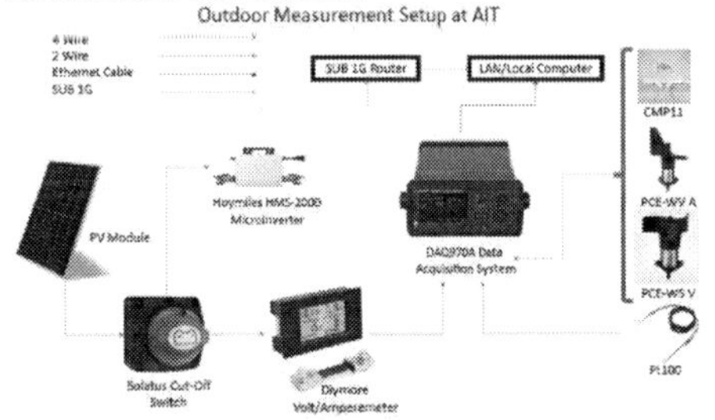

FIG. 8 Outdoor measurement system at AIT

The evaluation of the monitoring data (every minute) in Austria covers the period from March 2024 to August 2025. The monthly yield of Module No. 1 (A1) and Module No. 2 (A2) was determined and is shown in Fig. 9. Module No. 1 performs slightly worse than module No. 2. Therefore, further measurement results are only presented for Module 2.

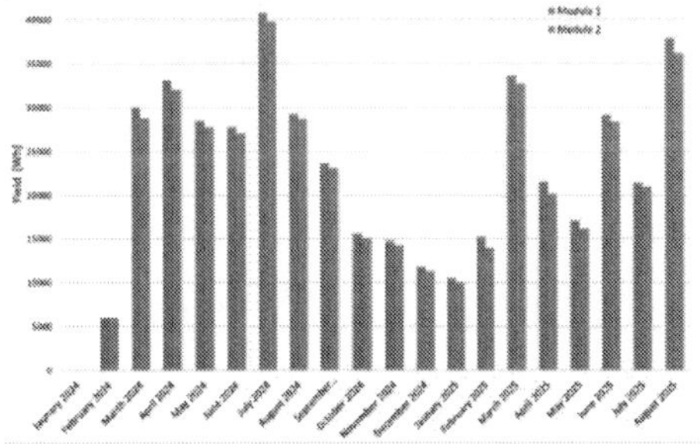
FIG.9 Monthly yield of Module No. 1 and Module No. 2 mounted in Austria from March 24 to August 25

Figures 10 and 11 show the daily irradiance, maximum power, module temperature, and wind speed in July, and September 2024 for the outdoor-mounted Module No. 2 (A2).

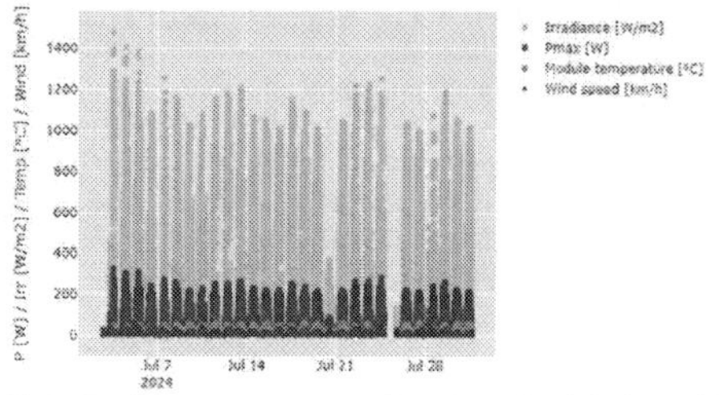

FIG. 10 Measurements results from Module 2 (A2), mounted outdoors: daily irradiation values, daily maximum output, daily module temperature, and daily wind speed in July 2024.

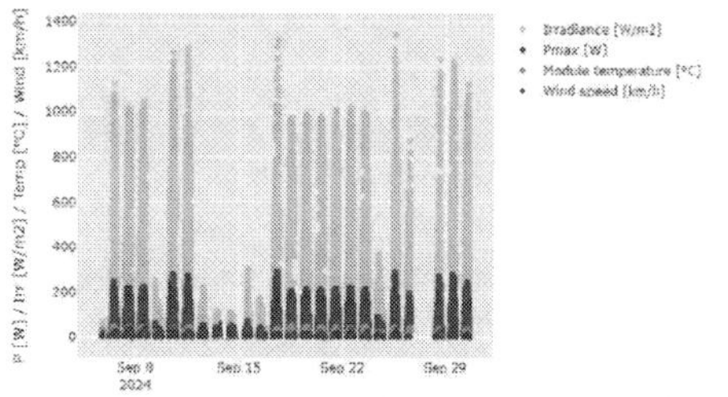

FIG. 11 Measurement results from Module 2 (A2), mounted outdoor: daily irradiation values, daily maximum power output, daily module temperature, and daily wind speed in September 2024.

In mid-September 2024, a sharp performance drop can be observed. This corresponds to the extreme bad weather and flooding that occurred at that time in Vienna and the surrounding area.

In order to illustrate the maximum output in September 2024 more clearly, the irradiation has been hidden in Fig. 12. The drop in output and a sharp decline in temperature (mid-September) can be seen again.

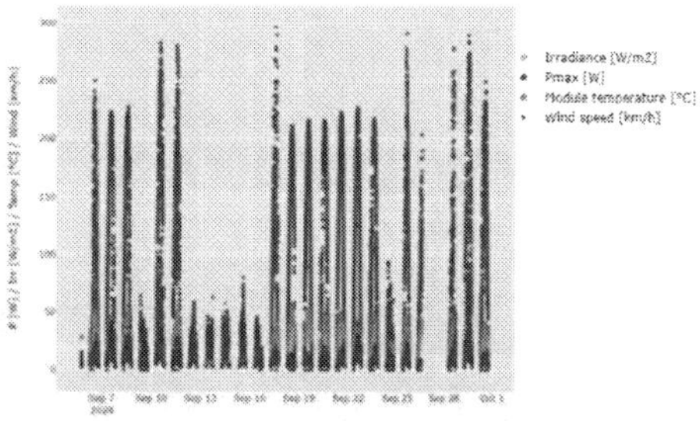

FIG. 12 Measurement results from Module 1, mounted outdoors: maximum dialy power output, daily module temperature, and daily wind speed in September 2024. The monthly irradiation values have been hidden.

In order to illustrate the module temperature and wind speed in September 2024 more clearly, the irradiation and maximum output have been hidden in Fig. 13. The increased wind speed and a sharp drop in temperature (mid-September) are again clearly visible.

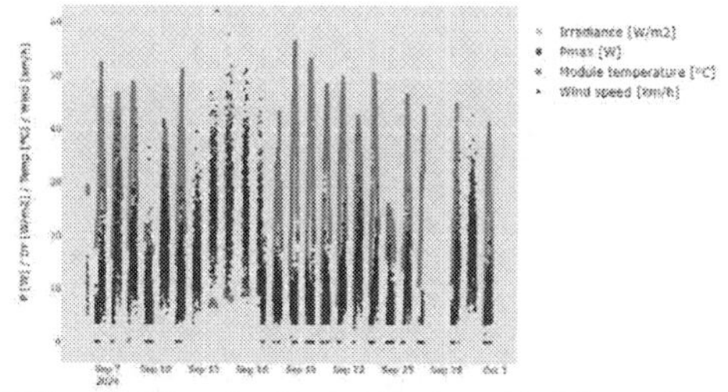

FIG. 13 Measurement results from Module 2 (A2), mounted outdoors: monthly daily temperature and daily wind speed in September 2024. The daily irradiation values and maximum output have been hidden.

The degradation over time (February 2024 to August 2025) was also analyzed. For Module 2, the following degradation rates were identified (see Fig. 14): −0.700 W/month at 600 W/m² irradiation, −0.630 W/month at 800 W/m² irradiation, and −0.703 W/month at 1000 W/m² irradiation.

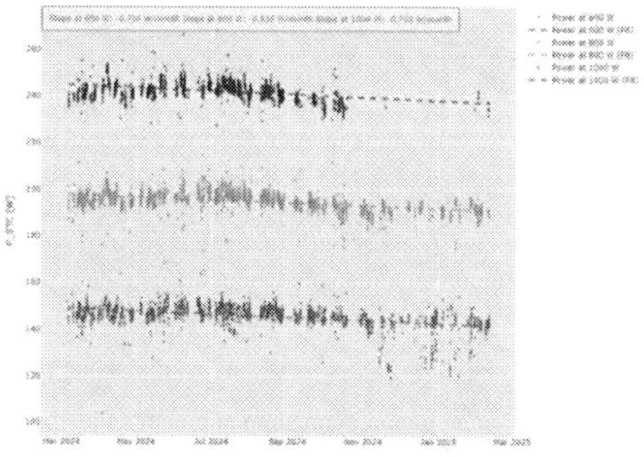

FIG. 14 Temperature corrected power over time at several irradiation values (600 W/m², 800 W/m² and 1000 W/m²) for Module 2.

3.2 Results of different climate zones

The PV yields of all modules installed across the different climate zones were evaluated and compared for the period from February to August 2025. The results are presented in Fig. 15. Due to technical issues at some partner sites, a significant portion of monitoring data was lost; consequently, not all partners were able to provide complete measurement results for the entire period.

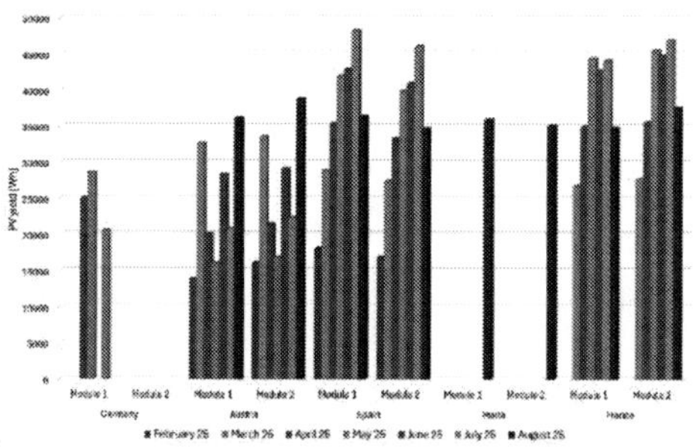

FIG. 15 PV yield results of PV modules in different climate zones from February 2025 to August 2025.

In Austria, the high PV yield observed in March 2025 can be explained by exceptionally sunny weather and higher

temperatures compared to April and May 2025, which were characterized by frequent rainfall. August 2025 was again very sunny and hot, whereas July was predominantly rainy.
In Spain, the results show a continuous increase in yield from February to July 2025. In France, the yield increased until May 2025, followed by a slight decrease in June, and then a renewed increase in July.

4 SUMMARY AND OUTLOOK

Over their lifetime, PV modules are prone to various degradation processes, including light-induced degradation, recombination losses, and material degradation. These processes can drastically affect the performance characteristics of the modules, such as open-circuit voltage (Voc), short-circuit current (Isc), fill factor (FF), and maximum power (Pmax). Understanding and mitigating these degradation effects is essential for maintaining and improving solar energy conversion efficiency.
In this study, 15 field-aged modules from Malta (10 years outdoor) were comprehensively characterized and stabilized. Subsequently, two modules each were installed at outdoor PV test benches located in different climate zones (Humid-Temperate zone: Germany; Mediterranean zone: Malta; Temperate zone: Austria; Mediterranean zone: France; and Navarra, Spain, where the Alpine, Atlantic, and Mediterranean zones meet).
The results from the AIT outdoor test bench were presented in this work and compared with the results of outdoor PV test benches established in the different climate zones.

5 REFERENCES

1. Statistical evaluation of PV system performance and failure data among different climate zones, M. Halwachs, L. Neumaier, N. Vollert, L. Maul, S. Dimitriadis, Y. Voronko, G.C. Eder, A. Omazic, W. Mühleisen, Ch. Hirschl, M. Schwark, K.A. Berger, R. Ebner; Renewable Energy, Elsevier, 2019. DOI: 10.1016/j.renene.2019.02.135
2. Photovoltaic Degradation Climate Zones, K. Todd, et all., 46th IEEE Photovoltaic Specialist Conference (PVSEC), 2019. DOI: 10.1109/PVSC40753.2019 .8980831
3. Descriptive statistics on the climate related performance and reliability issues from global PV installations; M. Halwachs, K. A. Berger, L. Maul, L. Neumaier, Y. Voronko, A. Mihaljevic, N. Vollert, W. Mühleisen, M. Schwark, R. Ebner, Ch. Hirschl, TIP, PV Conference "Quality and sustainability of PV systems" 2018.
4. Best Practices for Operation and Maintenance of Photovoltaic and Energy Storage Systems; 3rd Edition, NREL, Technical Report: NREL/TP-7A40-73822, 2018.
5. Guidelines for Operation and Maintenance of Photovoltaic Power Plants in Different Climates; Report IEA-PVPS T13-25:2022.
6. IEC 61215-1-1: Terrestrial photovoltaic (PV) modules – Design qualification and type approval - Part 1-1: special requirements for testing of crystalline silicon photovoltaic (PV) modules. Ed2 2021.

Acknowledgment
This work was funded by the Horizon Europe PROMISE Project (No. 101079469).

COMPARATIVE STUDY OF ENERGY YIELD IN PV SYSTEMS USING DIFFERENT MODULE TECHNOLOGIES AND INVERTER CONFIGURATIONS

Matevž Bokalič, Kristijan Brecl, Marko Topič
University of Ljubljana, Faculty of Electrical Engineering
Tržaška 25, SI-1000 Ljubljana, Slovenia
E-mail: Matevz.Bokalic@fe.uni-lj.si

ABSTRACT: The rapid development of photovoltaic (PV) technology has led to a broad variety of products in both the module and inverter markets, raising questions about long-term reliability and real-world performance. While new cell technologies such as TOPCon, SHJ, and IBC promise higher efficiency, recent field reports indicate higher degradation rates than expected, which could impact warranty stability and market confidence. Likewise, inverter configurations ranging from classical string inverters to optimizers and microinverters introduce trade-offs between compliance with grid regulations, system scalability, and final energy yield.

Within the Horizon 2020 project Aurora, five new PV power plants were installed within the renewable energy community at the Faculty of Electrical Engineering, University of Ljubljana, to evaluate performance of different inverter types and cell technologies under real operating conditions. Five new systems consist mostly of TOPCon modules alongside smaller strings of PERC, SHJ, and IBC technologies. Energy production data from February to August 2025 were analysed with a digital twin approach, combining pyranometer and temperature measurements with pvlib Python library based irradiance and thermal modelling. Performance evaluation relied on temperature-corrected AC performance ratio and energy yield for PV power plants, and on DC performance ratio for PV modules. Shading was identified and removed from the dataset to ensure comparability.

Results show that the new PV plants achieve shading and temperature corrected power ratio values between 0.85 and 0.9, while the 15-year-old reference power plant displayed expected degradation. String inverters performed best under unshaded conditions, optimizers were ~1% lower, and microinverters ~3% lower. Module-level comparison revealed similar performance across technologies, with IBC showing slightly reduced summer values. Initial degradation trends were not yet evident.

Overall, the study highlights the importance of shading correction, accurate thermal modelling, and multi-technology benchmarking for objective PV system evaluation.

Keywords: PV digital twin, performance modelling, Performance ratio, Shading removal

1 INTRODUCTION

Current photovoltaic (PV) market offers a huge variety of different products. This variety is present in both the PV module market and in the inverter market. In the PV module market several cell technologies are competing to offer either the best performance or the best price-performance ratio. In the price-performance arena, there are declining-share PERC cells which are being replaced by the more advanced TOPCon cells. In the high-performance arena, there are SHJ and IBC cells. The inverter market for residential and commercial applications varies not only between different manufacturers, but also between different types of inverters. There are conventional string inverters, string inverters with optimizers and easily scalable microinverters.

Recently, several contributions reported higher degradation rates in the field of new cell technologies [1,2]. The lower than expected real-life TOPCon module performance is a crucial research topic, especially because the TOPCon modules come with stricter warranty conditions. If the modules fail to produce energy within these conditions, that could potentially lead to a huge number of warranty claims possibly destabilizing module market. There were also publications on optimizers providing a lower final performance on homogeneously irradiated PV arrays [3,4]. This is also an important topic, as optimizers (or microinverters) are often required to meet the low voltage requirements of several net-metering regulations in place in Europe.

Within the Horizon 2020 funded European project Aurora [5] (*Achieving a new European Energy Awareness*) the goal was to establish a renewable energy community (REC) based around a photovoltaic power plants (PVPPs). The process of setting up the REC as a virtual community was presented at the EU PVSEC last year [6]. In addition to energy production, the power plants also have to provide educational benefit and research data, therefore we have designed the power plants comprised of different inverters, optimizers, microinverters and combinations thereof as well as a field of modules of different technologies.

The power plants were installed in 2024 and beginning of 2025 and were grid connected in February 2025. In this contribution we present performance evaluation of these power plants, together with an old power plant, focusing on different inverter configurations and on performance of modules with different solar cell technologies.

In the experimental section of this paper we first describe the analysed PV power plants and modules, followed by explanation of data analysis, digital twin and shading removal. In the results section applicability of shading removal and performance analysis of plants and modules is presented. The paper is finished by discussion and conclusion.

2 EXPERIMENTAL

2.1 PV power plants and modules

There are in total six power plants on the roofs of the Faculty of Electrical Engineering at University of Ljubljana, as depicted in Figure 1. The first power plant, named *A old* was installed in 2010 and we are including it in the study for comparison. This power plant consists of classical multi-crystalline Al BSF PV modules connected to classical string inverter. The new power plants, *A*, *B*, *C*, *D upper* and *D lower*, were installed within the Aurora Project. They are based on the same TOPCon modules to provide comparability between inverter types, however a smaller part of the power plant *B* is designed with single module optimizers and modules with cells of different technologies to provide variability between cell technologies. This part of the power plant will demonstrate the performance, reliability and long-term degradation of modules with cells of different technologies. The power plants are summarized in Table 1.

Figure 1: PV power plants installed on the Faculty of Electrical Engineering within the University of Ljubljana, Slovenia (46.07° N, 14.52° E).

Power Plant	Inverter type	Module type	P [kW]	Orientation	Inclination
A old	String	AL-Bsf	17.2	25°E	30°
A	String	TOP Con	45.8	25°E, 155°W	7°
B	Optimizers	TOP Con, ...	45.7	25°E, 155°W	7°,10°E-W
C	Optimizers	TOP Con	56.3	115°E, 65°W	14°
D upper	String	TOP Con	34.3	25°E	10°E-W
D lower	Microinverters	TOP Con	23.8	25°E	10°E-W
Total			223.1		

Table 1: List of power plants with basic details

To compare the differences due to different technologies, we tried to find the modules with the same bill of materials (frame/cover/cell size), while at the same time they had to be commercially available. We have selected modules with black frame, front glass and black backsheet cover, with two repeated cell technologies in glass/glass configuration, and half-cell module topology. Due to availability on the Slovenian market we have two different cell sizes. The installed modules are listed in Table 2.

Technology	Bill of materials	P_{STC} [W]	P_{flash} [W]
TOP Con a	g/bs, 108 M10 hcs	440	*432
TOP Con b	g/bs, 108 M10 hcs	420	406
PERC	PERCg/bs, 108 M10 hcs	405	396
SHJ a	g/bs, 120 M6 hcs	380	367
SHJ b	g/g, 120 M6 hcs	390	367
IBC	g/bs, 132 M6 hcs	420	394

*used P_{flash} = 415 W for PR_T comparison

Table 2: List of research PV modules with cells of different technologies with basic details.
(g/bs – glass/backsheet, g/g – glass/glass, hcs – half cells)

Orientation-wise we had to adapt to the available roof orientations and building configurations, which resulted in several final orientations and mounting fashions. Since the buildings are facing 25° from south toward east, please note that all orientations mentioned below are with a 25° offset to the east. On flat roofs, we used East-West triangle configurations with ballast mounting and a 10° module inclination. On other slightly pitched roofs, the angles range from 7° to 14°, while the mounting configuration is either anchoring to wooden or metal beams or standing seam mounting. The orientations are listed in Table 1.

2.2 Digital twin

For the purpose of this evaluation we have extracted production data from cloud-based services of inverters and optimizers. The global and diffused irradiance together with air temperature are obtained from pyranometers and air temperature sensors installed at our test sites.

We have evaluated the performance of the power plants during the first 6 months of operation. The evaluation is based on the calculation of temperature corrected AC performance ratio ($PR_{T,AC}$) and on calculation of energy yield (Ey). The data was analysed with python using the digital twin approach.

The digital twin granularity goes down to string level. It transforms general environmental parameters to parameters that the string experiences. Horizontal total and diffuse irradiance (G_{tot}, G_{dif}, respectively) are transformed to plane of array irradiance (G_{poa}) of respective strings of the same modules with the same orientations using Perez model in pvlib library. Back irradiance was not taken into account due to close proximity of the modules to the roof [7]. Air temperature (T_{air}) is transformed to module temperature (T_m) using the normal operating cell temperature (NOCT) of the module by

$$T_m = T_{air} + \frac{T_{m,NOCT} - 20°C}{800\,W/m^2} \cdot G_{poa}$$

The digital twin power of the string ($P_{DC,string}$) is calculated by:

$$P_{DC,string} = P_{STC,string} \cdot \frac{G_{poa}}{1000\,W/m^2} \cdot \left(1 + \gamma \cdot (T_m - 25°C)\right)$$

Total plant DC power is the sum of all string powers:

$$P_{DC,twin} = \sum P_{DC,string}$$

Finally, $PR_{T,AC}$ is calculated as a ratio between measured and digital twin energies in given time interval:

$$PR_{T,AC} = \frac{E_{AC,measured}}{E_{DC,twin}}, \text{where } E = \int P\,dt$$

Energy yield (Ey) is calculated as energy produced ($E_{AC,measured}$) divided by sum of modules' rated power (P_{STC}):

$$Ey = \frac{E_{AC,measured}}{P_{STC}}$$

Performance evaluation of research modules of different types was based on the production data as measured by individual DC optimizer energy output and digital twin energy:

$$PR_{T,DC} = \frac{E_{DC,measured}}{E_{DC,twin}}$$

Therefore $PR_{T,DC}$ includes optimizer losses. However, since all the modules have similar rated and measured powers (Table 2), the results should be comparable nevertheless. Two remarks must be made here. First, instead of modules' rated power, an average of modules' measured power is taken as a reference, because the differences between rated and measured power were not negligible. Second, for *TOP Con a* PV modules, the measured power was further reduced from 432 W to 416 W to align the $PR_{T,DC}$ with *TOP Con b* modules.

Finally, for PR_T analysis, we only considered data points when total horizontal irradiance (G_{tot}) was higher than 500 W/m².

2.3 Shading removal

To allow objective evaluation of performance, shading must be excluded from the analysis. To achieve that we

10.4229/EUPVSEC2025/4CV.1.7

selected clear sky days throughout the analysed period between including March and August 2025. For each of those days we plotted $PR_{T,AC}$ over that day. An example is plotted in Figure 2 for March 7, 2025. Observing the shape of $PR_{T,AC}$ there is usually a midday plateau at a constants value between 0.85 and 0.9, and the $PR_{T,AC}$ drops off more or less abruptly from morning and towards evening hours. This drop is indicative of shading and can be corelated with the physical location of the power plants with respect to nearby buildings and trees that drop shadow on them. For example, looking at plant *C* (Figure 2, red curve) full shading is observed before 9 AM, with partial shading extending all the way to afternoon, only reaching expected $PR_{T,AC}$ at around half past 1 PM. For the times when plants are shaded, $PR_{T,AC}$ is plotted in dashed style, and for the unshaded times $PR_{T,AC}$ is plotted solid. We selected end and stop times of shading for all clear sky days and interpolated those times between clear sky days. Data points labelled as shaded were dropped from unshaded $PR_{T,AC}$ analysis.

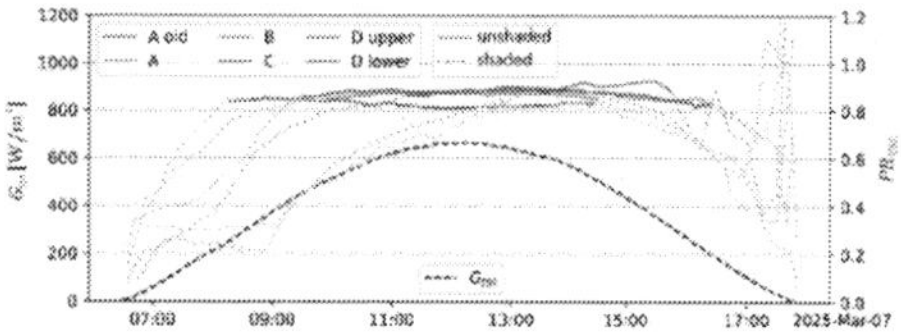

Figure 2: Temperature corrected AC performance ratio of power plants during early spring day. Solid lines represent unshaded time of the day, while dashed lines represent shaded time of the day for respective power plants.

3 RESULTS

3.1 PV power plant performance

Figure 3a shows monthly performance of PV power plants including shading, while subfigure b) displays the performance without shading, and subfigure c) displays environmental conditions.

Influence of shading is clearly observable for power plants *A* and *C* in March and April, with further reductions of performance for plant *A* throughout the summer. Less detrimental effects of shading can also be noted for other power plants.

Several observations can be made on monthly performance without shading (Figure 3b). Most notable is lower performance of *A old* power plant. This is expected, because the power plant is already 15 years old, and assuming initial $PR_{T,AC}$ between 0.85 and 0.9, shows degradation between 5 and 10%. There is a performance drop for most power plants in June. This can be attributed to determination of module temperature (T_m). Because the same air temperature (T_{air}) is used for all powerplants, effects of microclimate, which are different on different roofs, are ignored.

The drop is most noticeable on roofs *A*, *B* and *D lower*, which are all low tilt or flat (<7°) and highly insulated, thereby increasing local air temperature significantly. The opposite trend for *D upper* may be justified by worse insulation providing some cooling effect, and for *A old* the actual module temperature is probably overestimated due to higher tilt and considerable airgap below the modules.

The additional drop for *D lower* may be attributed to microinverter overheating. It can also be observed that the

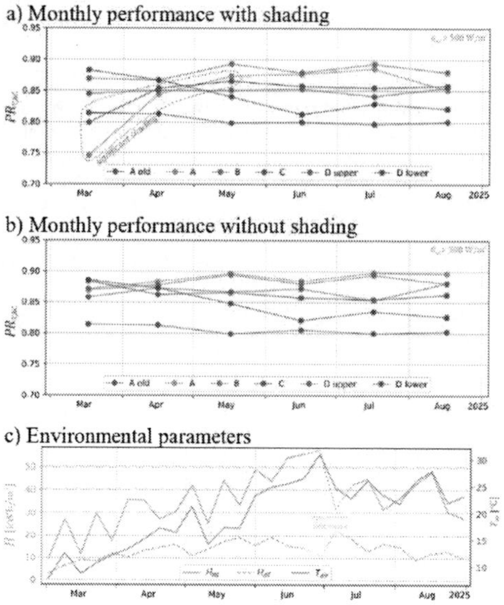

Figure 3: Temperature corrected AC performance ratio of power plants over monthly interval with shading (a) and without shading (b), and environmental parameters (c)

power plants with higher tilts (*A old* and *C*) result in more constant performance. Finally, based on the acquired data, initial degradation cannot be detected.

Aggregated performance data without shading over six months (Figure 4 and Table 3) reveals that $PR_{T,AC}$ of new power plants is between 0.84 and 0.9. Comparison between similar power plants with and without optimizers show about 1% lower performance for plants with optimizers (-1% $PR_{T,AC}$ *B* vs *A*, and *C* vs *D upper*). Power plant with microinverters perform slightly worse for about 3% (*D lower* vs *D upper*). As described above, performance of *A old* power plant is lower due to degradation.

Finally, the energy yield of all power plants per month is presented in Figure 5. Energy yield calculation considers total produced AC power without any filtering. In the case of *A old* power plant, there were three incidents. In April

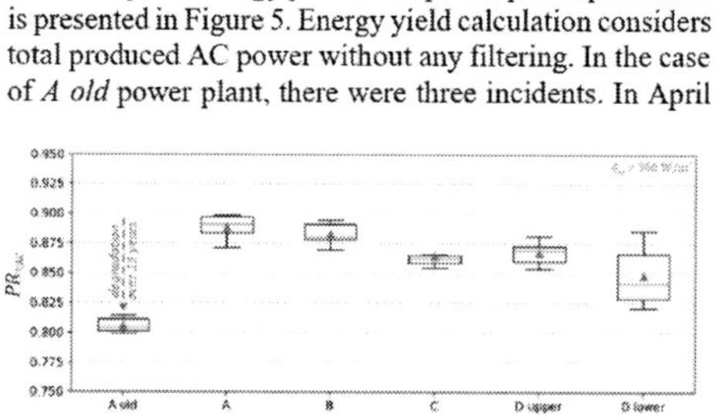

Figure 4: Total temperature corrected AC performance without shading of power plants over the 6-month period

Power Plant	Inverter type	Module type	$PR_{T,AC}$ G_{tot} > 500 W/m² All	w/o shading	Ey [kWh/kW] Mar-Aug
A old	String	AL-Bsf	0.80	0.80	*635
A	String	TOP Con	0.86	0.89	807
B	Optimizers	TOP Con, ...	0.88	0.88	800
C	Optimizers	TOP Con	0.86	0.86	764
D upper	String	TOP Con	0.85	0.87	771
D lower	Microinverters	TOP Con	0.84	0.84	732

*invalid due to missing production

Table 3: Final results of temperature corrected performance ration and energy yield of PV power plants.

there was a monitoring data outage, while in May and August a safety electronic device failed. This results in production data and energy loss; therefore the energy yield of *A old* power plant is lower in these months. For other power plants, general energy yield trends match irradiation trends, but there are also some differences. Power plant *A* has the highest energy yield, despite significant shading, because it has the most optimal module orientation. Due to shading, energy yield drops in March and August for plants *A* and *C*. There is also a drop of energy yield observable for plant *D lower* during summer months, which may be due to higher temperatures of microinverters.

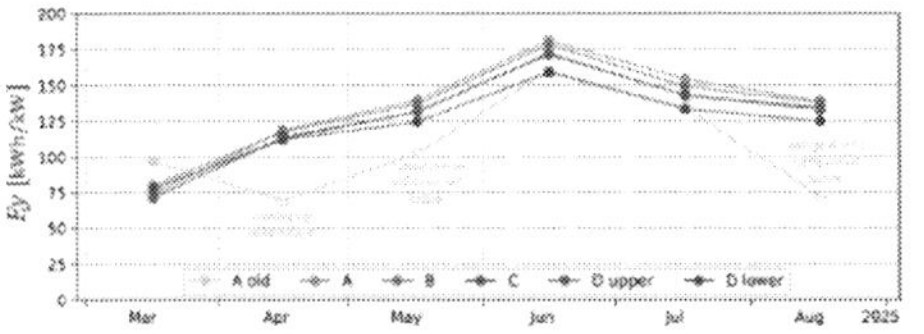

Figure 5: Energy yield of power plants over monthly interval with shading

3.2 Performance of modules of different technologies

Temperature corrected DC performance ratio ($PR_{T,DC}$) is presented in Figure 6 a) and b) for weekly and monthly intervals, respectively. As mentioned in the Methodology section, DC performance of modules is measured as DC output energy by single module optimizers. All the modules should experience similar environmental conditions, as they are all installed on the same roof, and measured STC power was used as a reference module power, with the exception of *TOP Con a*, where measured STC power was reduced for 4% to roughly match the *TOP Con b* performance ratio to ease the comparison. Finally, shading was not filtered out for this analysis as all the modules are on the same roof.

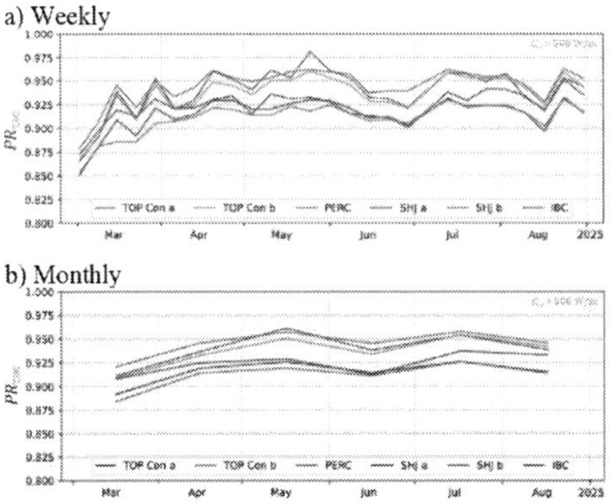

Figure 6: Temperature corrected DC performance ratio of PV modules of different technologies with shading over weekly (a) and monthly (b) intervals

Modules of the same technology perform similarly. In general, performance ratio is higher during summer, probably due to higher irradiance incident angle. There is however a notable drop in performance in June, which is due to very sunny weather and high temperatures that are amplified by insulated bitumen roof thereby deviating from the measured air temperature 2 m above the roof. In comparison to other module technologies, IBC modules show slightly lower performance during the sunny half of the year for yet unknown reasons. Based on the presented measurements it is not yet possible to draw conclusion on different degradation rates because all technologies perform quite similarly.

4 DISCUSSION AND CONCLUSION

Based on the analysis, we conclude that power plants operate as expected with temperature and shading corrected AC performance ratio between 0.85 and 0.9. For objective evaluation of performance of PV power plant components (i.e., modules, inverter and optimizers) shading correction is essential. Lower incident angles of direct sunlight on flat roofs reduce performance ratio in spring.

Regarding the efficiency of different inverter types, we have observed the best unshaded performance of classical string inverters, closely followed by string inverters with optimizers, while microinverters showed slightly lower performance.

During the analysis, we have learned several lessons and things that can be further improved. For correct prediction of module temperature, air temperature must be measured on the same roofs, and module temperature measurement would further increase model accuracy. Shading evaluation for research modules should be done. Since most of the inverters also provide DC data, further insights on inverter and module performance could be obtained from analysis of this data.

5 ACKNOWLEDGEMENT

This work has received funding from the European Union's Horizon 2020 research and innovation programme under grant agreement No 101036418 and from Slovenian Research and Innovation Agency (ARIS) research programme P2 0415.

6 REFERENCES

[1] Sen C, Wang H, Khan MU, Fu J, Wu X, Wang X, Hoex B. Buyer aware: Three new failure modes in TOPCon modules absent from PERC technology. *Solar Energy Materials and Solar Cells* **2024; 272**, pp. 112877. DOI:10.1016/j.solmat.2024.112877.

[2] Friesen G, Özkalay E, Caccivio M. Performance and Degradation Evaluation of C-Si Modules Under Different Open-Rack and Residential Mounting Configurations. In: *41st European Photovoltaic Solar Energy Conference and Exhibition* proceedings, Vienna, Austria: 2024, pp. 3DO.17.5.

[3] Baumgartner FP, Golroodbari S, Bucher C, Berwind M, Valencia F, Jahn U. Performance of Partial Shaded PV Generators Operated by Optimized Power Electronics an IEA PVPS T13 Activity. *41st European Photovoltaic Solar Energy Conference and Exhibition* **2024**, pp. 4CP.2.3. DOI:10.4229/EUPVSEC2024/4CP.2.3.

[4] Baumgartner FP, Klenk M, Widler A, Baumann L. MPP Tracking Losses of Module Level Power Electronics at Partial Module Shading. *41st European Photovoltaic Solar Energy Conference and Exhibition* **2024**, pp. 3EO.1.5. DOI:10.4229/EUPVSEC2024/3EO.1.5.

[5] AURORA Project. *AURORA H2020*; https://www.aurora-h2020.eu/ (accessed January 29, 2025).

[6] Bokalič M, Guštin M, Topič M, Belen Cristóbal A, Victoria M, Cavaco A, Fialho L, Gerber A. Challenges of Energy Communities at Universities – A Virtual Approach. In: *41st European Photovoltaic Solar Energy Conference and Exhibition* proceedings, Vienna, Austria: 2024, pp. 5DV.3.43.

[7] Brecl K, Cerón EM, de la Casa Higueras J, Topič M. Is an exact backside irradiance modelling essential for bifacial PV systems? *Renewable Energy* **2026; 256**, pp. 123942. DOI:10.1016/j.renene.2025.123942.

A HIGHLY ADAPTABLE PERFORMANCE EVALUATION METHOD FOR PV SYSTEMS USING REMOTE METEOROLOGICAL DATA AND ON-SITE REFERENCE COMPARISONS

WeiZhen Xiong, Jindan Cui, and Yuzuru Ueda
Tokyo University of Science, Japan
4324532@ed.tus.ac.jp

ABSTRACT: This study presents a highly adaptable, sensor-free framework for the performance evaluation of photovoltaic (PV) systems, aiming to address the limitations of traditional methods that rely on expensive on-site sensors. The proposed method includes a two-phase approach. In the training phase, data from 2018 to 2022 were used to derive a combined loss coefficient (K_o) that links global horizontal irradiance (GHIith power output. The evaluation phase uses this coefficient to infer local GHI and calculate the theoretical power output, which is then compared with actual power generation to assess system performance. The framework also employs a peer-comparison strategy as a contingency plan when remote meteorological data is unreliable. By using K-means clustering and the SHAP tool, the method can effectively diagnose the causes of performance degradation, such as shading. The results prove that the proposed framework is a workable and versatile approach for analyzing PV system performance. The peer-comparison method further provides a valuable reference for maintenance teams in data-scarce scenarios.
Keywords: Photovoltaic (PV) systems, Performance evaluation, Remote meteorological data, Sensor-free framework, Peer-comparison, Loss attribution, SHAP, K-means.

1 INTRODUCTION

In the context of achieving carbon neutrality by 2050, the introduction of photovoltaic (PV) power generation is expected to increase rapidly in Japan and worldwide. Traditional performance evaluation methods, such as Performance Ratio (PR), typically rely on expensive on-site sensors, making them difficult to apply to widely distributed PV systems. This study aims to address these challenges by proposing a highly adaptable, sensor-free performance evaluation framework for PV systems to identify systems with performance degradation and accurately quantifies losses attributed to shading

2 PROPOSED METHOD

This study presents a framework for photovoltaic system performance evaluation and loss attribution, which innovatively does not rely on localized solar irradiation data. The method is founded on a core hypothesis: under ideal conditions—without shading or system faults—a PV system's performance should exhibit a stable and predictable relationship with its environmental parameters. However, specific factors like partial shading may cause a system's actual performance to deviate from this ideal baseline or the behavior of a peer group.

2.1 Flow of Operation

The methodology of this study is primarily divided into two phases: the training phase and the evaluation phase.

In the training phase, data from 2018 to 2022 were used as proxies for local solar irradiation. All data were aligned to an hourly granularity, and the training dataset was curated by comparing power generation with solar irradiation data to identify consistent, clear-weather days. Subsequently, the data were grouped by module type (monocrystalline or polycrystalline) and month. A physical model, which incorporates temperature loss, was then used to train and derive a combined loss coefficient (K_o), which links the global horizontal irradiance (GHI) and power output P_{PV}.

In the evaluation phase, clear-weather days in 2023 were first identified based on power output curves. The derived loss coefficient (K_o) was used to invert the model and deduce the local GHI for those days. This inferred GHI data was subsequently applied to calculate the theoretical power output of other PV systems under ideal conditions. A system's performance was evaluated by comparing this theoretical value with its actual power generation. Additionally, when remote solar irradiation data is unreliable, a peer-comparison strategy is employed. This approach uses the real-time power generation data from multiple systems with similar parameters to identify the densest data point, which serves as the ideal performance benchmark for the group.

2.2 Step.1: Similar Day Screening

Initially, this study normalizes a full day's worth of power generation data and remote solar irradiation data by their respective maximum values, treating them as two vectors. Cosine similarity is used to measure the consistency of the shape and trend between these two vectors, while the DTW (Dynamic Time Warping) algorithm corrects for potential time shifts. Days with an average cosine similarity of 0.985 or higher are selected, ensuring a high degree of trend consistency between the power generation and solar irradiation data vectors for that day.

$$similarity = \sum_{t=1}^{24} \cos\theta$$

$$= \frac{\sum_{t=1}^{24} \boldsymbol{P_{PV_t}} \times \boldsymbol{GHI_t}}{\sqrt{\sum_{t=1}^{24}(\boldsymbol{P_{PV_t}})^2} \times \sqrt{\sum_{t=1}^{24}(\boldsymbol{GHI_t})^2}} \geq 0.985 \qquad (1)$$

Where θ is calculated by taking the mean of the cosine values of the angles between the power generation data vector and the solar irradiation data vector for each hour throughout the entire 24-hour period. Specifically, as shown in Figure 1, the horizontal axis represents the time t of the day, and the vertical axis represents a dimensionless value after aligning the maximum value of the solar radiation data to the power generation data curve. Then, the cosine values of the two vectors at the corresponding time points are calculated, and the average of these cosine values within the day is calculated.

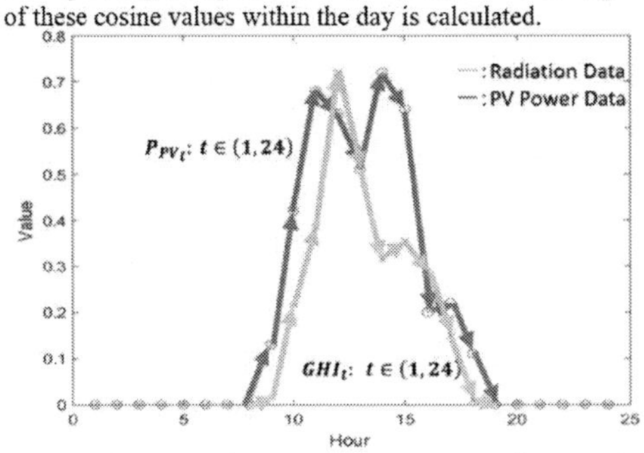

Figure 1: Normalized Comparison of Solar Irradiation and PV Power Data

2.3 Step2: Model Training and Solar Irradiation Inversion

In the model training and solar irradiation inversion phase, data were classified and trained based on both module type (monocrystalline/polycrystalline) and month. For instance, all filtered clear-day data from January for selected monocrystalline systems serving as on-site sensors were collected and used for training to derive a combined loss coefficient (K_o). This coefficient is obtained using the following physical model, which links the global horizontal irradiance (GHI) and power output (P_{PV}):

$$P_{DC}(t) = K_o \times \frac{PoA(t)}{G_{STC}} \times [1 + \gamma(T_c(t) - T_{STC})] \times P_{STC}^{tot} \quad (2)$$

Where:

$\boldsymbol{K_o}$ is the parameter to be trained, representing various combined losses.

$\boldsymbol{PoA(t)}$ is the tilted-surface solar irradiation

$\boldsymbol{G_{STC}}$ is the standard solar irradiation

$\boldsymbol{\gamma}$ is the system's temperature parament.

$\boldsymbol{T_c(t)}$ is the PV module temperature

$\boldsymbol{T_{STC}}$ is the standard temperature.

$\boldsymbol{P_{STC}^{tot}}$ is the rated capacity of the PV system

The tilted-surface solar radiation is decomposed by the Perez model[1].

$$F_1' = F_{11}'(\varepsilon) + F_{12}'(\varepsilon) \cdot \Delta + F_{13}'(\varepsilon) \cdot \theta_Z \quad (3)$$

$$F_2' = F_{21}'(\varepsilon) + F_{22}'(\varepsilon) \cdot \Delta + F_{23}'(\varepsilon) \cdot \theta_Z \quad (4)$$

$$\varepsilon = \frac{H_d + H_b}{H_d} \quad (5)$$

$$\Delta = AM_A \cdot \frac{H_d}{H_0} \quad (6)$$

The direct and diffuse components of solar irradiation are separated using the Erbs model [1].

$$CI \le 0.22 \qquad H_d = (1.0 - 0.09 \cdot CI) \cdot H_g \quad (7)$$

$$0.22 \le CI \le 0.80$$

$$H_d = (0.9511 - 0.1604 \cdot CI + 4.388CI^2 - 16.638 \cdot CI^3 + 12.336 \cdot CI^4) \cdot H_g \quad (8)$$

$$CI > 0.80 \qquad H_d = 0.1650 \cdot H_g \quad (9)$$

After obtaining the K_o coefficient, this study solves for the local GHI value as an inverse problem with a linear equation, utilizing the filtered clear-day power generation data and the trained K_o.

2.4 Step3: Contingency Plan for Unreliable Solar Irradiation Data

When remote meteorological data fails to accurately represent local weather conditions due to geographical factors, this study employs a peer-comparison method as a contingency plan to assess whether individual PV systems are experiencing significant performance degradation. This approach begins by classifying systems based on their type, tilt angle, and azimuth, followed by a performance comparison among a group of similarly configured and closely located systems.

Specifically, at any given moment, the ratio of each system's power output to its rated capacity is calculated, defining the performance utilization rate. These rates are then plotted on a number line. To find the densest point (the ideal performance benchmark), we calculate the sum of the absolute differences in power output between each system k and all other systems j in the group. The system with the minimum D_k is selected as the densest point, and its power output P_{PV_k} is defined as the baseline power value for that moment. By comparing each system's performance utilization rate to this benchmark, a performance deviation value is obtained, which allows us to observe the deviation between the target system's performance and that of the group.

$$D_k = Min \sum_{j=1, j \neq k}^{sys} \left| \boldsymbol{P_{PV_k}} - \boldsymbol{P_{PV_j}} \right| \quad (10)$$

Step4: Analysis of Loss Causes

This study uses K-means clustering to analyze the following data points: solar altitude h, solar azimuth ψ, tilt angle θ, internal surface temperature of the PV system t, clearness index(CI), timestamp, and the residual $\Delta P_{resi}(t)$ between the actual and predicted power output. The predicted power output is calculated using a physical model based on the inverted solar irradiation data obtained from the preceding steps.

Subsequently, the SHAP (Shapley Additive Explanations) tool is utilized for an importance analysis of the residuals, which quantifies and determines which factors have the most significant impact on the power output loss under various conditions.

Residuals refer to the difference between the theoretical value, which is inversely estimated using inverted on-site solar irradiance data, and the actual observed value. Specifically, it is calculated using the following formula:

$$Residuals = P_{PV} - P_{inverted} \quad (11)$$

3 USED DATA

The data for this study was sourced from a large-scale photovoltaic power plant located in Hokuto City, Yamanashi Prefecture, Japan, covering an analysis period from January 1, 2018, to December 31, 2023. The dataset primarily consists of two types:

PV System Data: This includes data from 6 monocrystalline silicon systems and 7 polycrystalline silicon systems. All systems share a 30° tilt angle, a due-south azimuth, and an approximate rated capacity of 10 kW each. Additionally, internal panel surface temperature data for each system was utilized.

Meteorological Data: Solar irradiation data was obtained from the Japan Meteorological Agency's AMeDAS (Automated Meteorological Data Acquisition

System), with a granularity of one hour.

4 RESULTS AND DISCUSSION

4.1 Data filtering results

Figure 2 presents the cosine similarity curve, with red circles indicating data points below 0.985. It was observed that during the winter months (November to January), there was an increase in the number of mismatched days, which may be attributed to microclimates caused by local terrain.

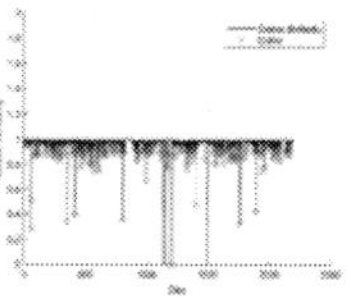

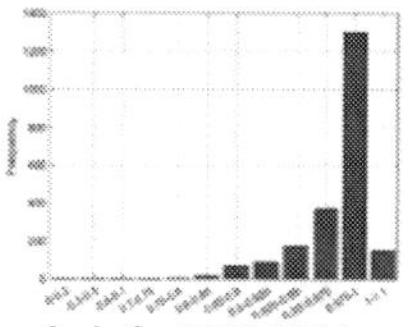

Figure 2: Cosine similarity analysis for 2018-2024year
Figure 3: Cosine similarity Distribution for 2018-2024 year

Cosine similarity, which measures the trend consistency between power generation and remote solar irradiation data vectors, approaches 1 for highly similar trends. Statistical results show that most values fall within the range of 0.95 to 1, as presented in

Figure 3. This filtering process, which exclusively selects clear and meteorologically similar days, allows approximately 52% of the year's days to be utilized for model training. The average prediction error for these clear days is currently between 5.2% and 8.6%.

4.2 Analysis Using Remote Solar Irradiation Data

This study calculated loss parameters for converting solar irradiation to power using a similarity filter, with the parameters specific to different system types, months, and times of day. For predictions, we first compared the daily power data to an ideal solar curve to ensure the data was suitable for analysis.

K-means cluster analysis was then employed to diagnose the causes of performance decline by analyzing the relationship between power output errors and solar altitude and azimuth. This analysis revealed two distinct scenarios:

Scenario 1: One system exhibited a significant performance drop during the winter months (November to January) between 10 a.m. and 2 p.m. Cluster analysis revealed that the Residuals occurred at low solar altitudes and azimuths between -20° and 20°, which aligned with shading from a forest to the south.

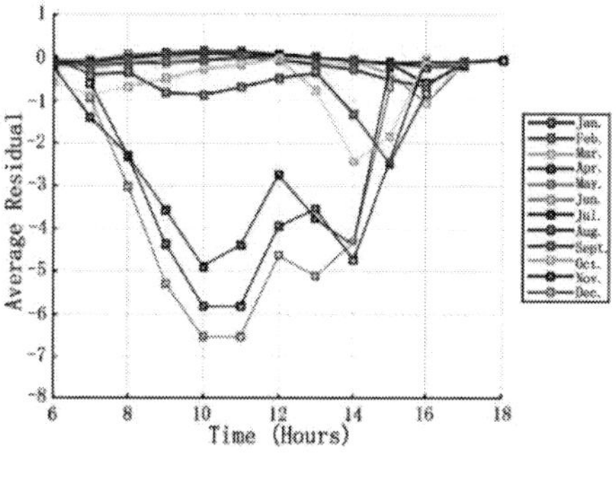

Figure 4: Monthly Performance Trends and Residuals of the Systems affected by shadows

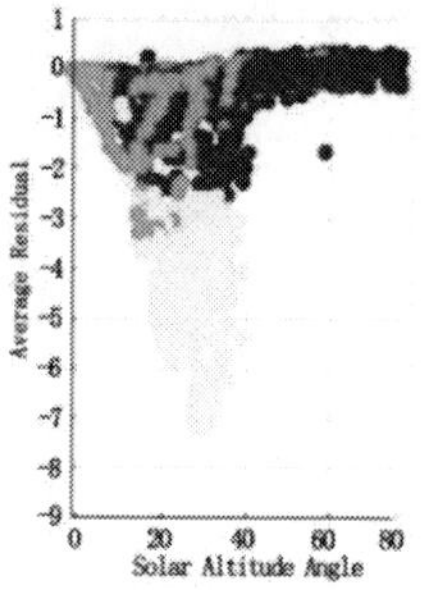

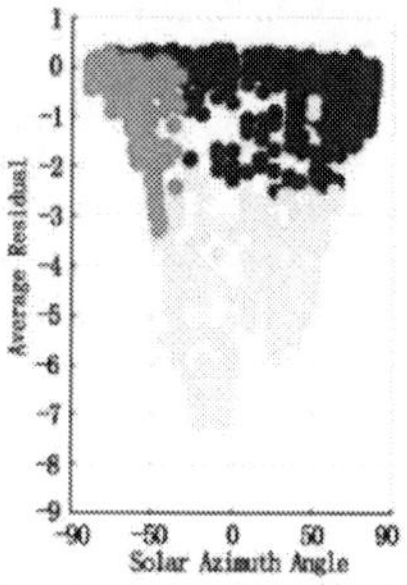

Figure 5: K-Means Clustering Analysis of Residuals vs. Solar Altitude Angles of the Systems affected by shadows
Figure 6: K-Means Clustering Analysis of Residuals vs. Solar Azimuth Angles of the Systems affected by shadows

Scenario 2: Another system remained stable year-round with only a minor drop in December. Cluster analysis showed no patterns linked to specific solar angles, indicating that the issue was not due to long-term shading.

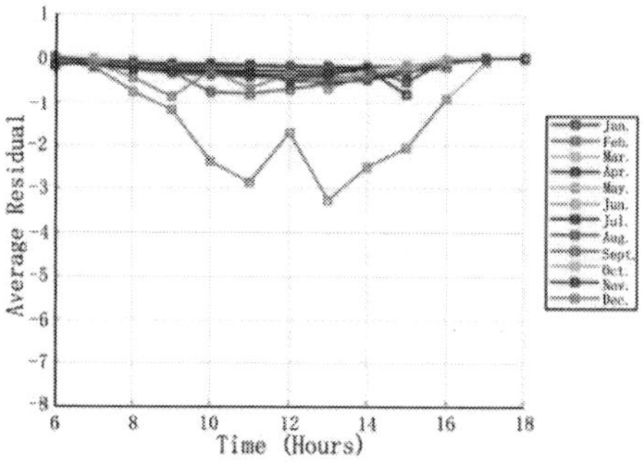

Figure 7: Monthly Performance Trends and Residuals of the Normal System

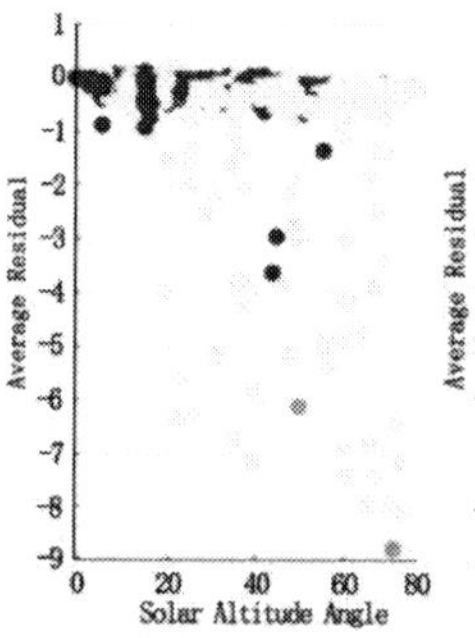

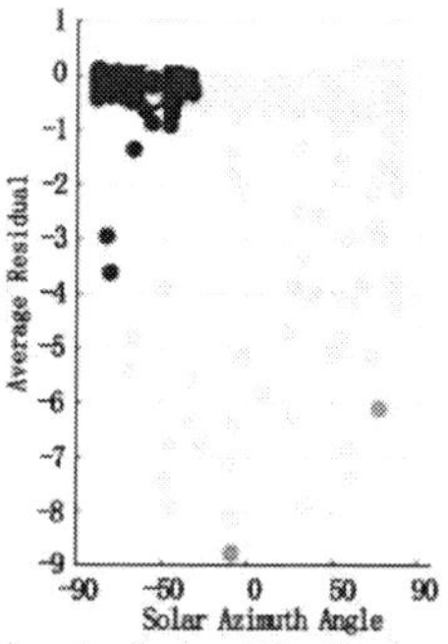

Figure 8: K-Means Clustering Analysis of Residuals vs. Solar Altitude Angles of the Normal System
Figure 9: K-Means Clustering Analysis of Residuals vs. Solar Azimuth Angles of the Normal System

4.3 SHAP Importance Analysis

Using the SHAP tool, we assessed the importance of various factors contributing to power output residuals. The factors analyzed included zenith angle, angle of incidence, altitude angle, azimuth, solar irradiation, month, time, and clearness index.

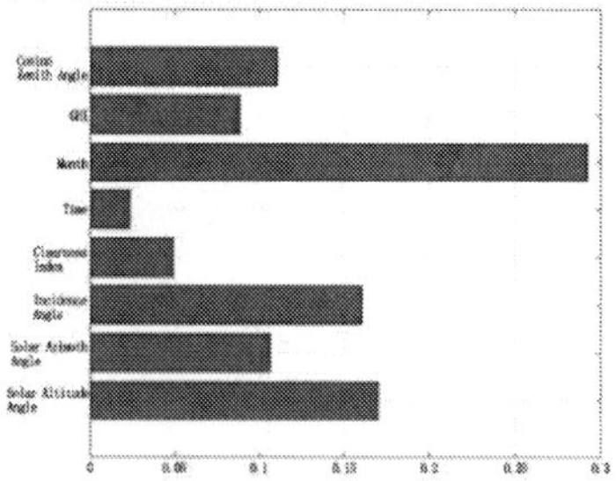

Figure 10: SHAP Importance Analysis of Power Output Residuals of Systems affected by shadows

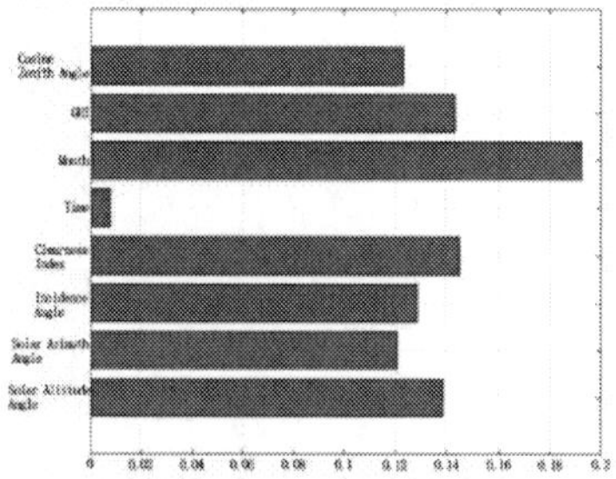

Figure 11: SHAP Importance Analysis of Power Output Residuals of Normal System

For systems with clear seasonal influences, the angle of incidence and altitude angle showed significant importance in the SHAP analysis, which aligns with the presence of fixed directional shading. In contrast, for systems without fixed shading, the contribution of each factor to the residual was nearly identical. The minor influence of time on the residual is likely due to its overlap with the monthly factor.

4.4 On-site Reference Comparison

When solar irradiation data is unavailable, a quick on-site reference comparison method can be used to observe a system's power generation performance relative to a group of systems with similar parameters. For instance, in a group of polycrystalline silicon systems with identical capacity, tilt angles, and azimuth angles, we applied the on-site comparison method.

As shown in Fig. 11, we observed that the system's performance was lower than the group average during spring and winter. Although this method cannot pinpoint the specific cause of the performance degradation, it effectively reveals a clear seasonal pattern. In contrast, Fig. 12 shows a system with normal performance and minimal fluctuation, indicating that its performance remains consistent with its peers.

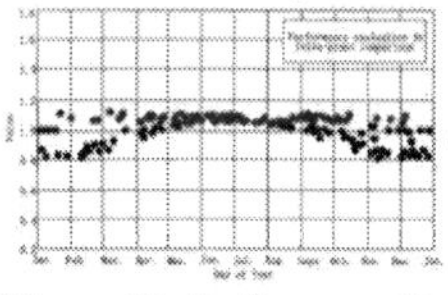

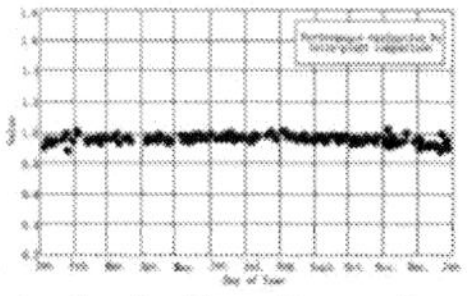

Figure 12: Performance Evaluation by Peer-Comparison of Systems affected by shadows

Figure 13: Performance Evaluation by Peer-Comparison of Normal System

5 CONCLUSIONS

This study demonstrates the feasibility of using remote meteorological data for analyzing PV system performance. The proposed method offers several key advantages:

Sensor-Free Operation: By utilizing hourly remote data, the method eliminates the need for expensive on-site measurement instruments, making it highly versatile for widespread application.

Accurate Shading Loss Quantification: The framework provides a clear and effective means to analyze and quantify the specific effects of shading on power generation.

Contingency Plan for Data Scarcity: The peer-comparison method serves as a valuable contingency plan when data is scarce, providing maintenance crews with a reliable reference for performance trends

6 FUTURE WORK

Future work will focus on the following three key areas to further enhance the functionality and practicality of the proposed framework:

Developing an Automated Reference System Selection Algorithm: We plan to develop a fully automated algorithm to intelligently identify and select an ideal reference system. The goal is to create a virtual PV system free of defects that can serve as an on-site solar irradiation sensor, thereby enhancing the algorithm's functionality.

Quantifying Performance Loss Attribution: We will quantitatively estimate the contribution of each cause of performance degradation to determine its specific share of the total loss.

Enhancing Overall Algorithm Functionality: These planned improvements are aimed at further enhancing the overall functionality and robustness of the algorithm.

7 REFELENCES

[1]. Ueda, Yuzuru. A study on an advanced performance analysis method for PV systems using monitoring data. PhD diss., Tokyo University of Agriculture and Technology, 2007.

[2]. Wataru Yasuhara, Kenji Hirata, and Jun Toyotani, "Solar irradiance nowcasting by LightGBM with cloud information from sky images," Journal of the Japan Information Directory Society, vol. 21, 2023.

[3]. Theristis, Marios, et al. "Blind photovoltaic modeling intercomparison: A multidimensional data analysis and lessons learned." IEEE Journal of Photovoltaics, 21 July 2023, https://doi.org/10.1002/pip.3729.

[4]. Elsinga, Boudewijn, Wilfried van Sark, and Lou Ramaekers. "Inverse photovoltaic yield model for global horizontal irradiance reconstruction." Energy Science & Engineering, vol. 5, no. 5, 7 Aug. 2017, pp. 882–891, https://doi.org/10.1002/ese3.162.

[5]. Martín-Martínez, S., Cañas-Carretón, M., Honrubia-Escribano, A., & Gómez-Lázaro, E. (2019). Performance evaluation of large solar photovoltaic power plants in Spain. *Energy Conversion and Management*, *183*, 515–528.

A Highly Adaptable Performance Evaluation Method for PV Systems Using Remote Meteorological Data and On-Site Reference Comparisons

Author: Weizhen Xiong*[1], Jindan Cui [1], Yuzuru Ueda [1]
[1]Tokyo University of Science, Japan
Contact: 4324532@ed.tus.ac.jp

東京理科大学
TOKYO UNIVERSITY OF SCIENCE

Introduction

As large-scale PV systems are integrated into the grid,
Traditional performance evaluation methods rely on on-site sensors.

- ➢ Propose a versatile and cost-effective framework that is independent of on-site data, to quantify and separate losses from factors like shading.
- ➢ Enable loss attribution, supporting refined operation and maintenance decisions.

Framework

Step1: Data Preparation

- **Historical Power Generation and Panel Temperature** — P_{PV} , T (From multiple PV systems)
- **Remote Meteorological and Astronomical data** — GHI_t (From AMeDAS - Japan Meteorological Agency)

Step2: Processing & Baseline Construction

- **Data Validation & Intelligent Filtering**
  - Cosine Similarity
  - DTW(Dynamic Time Warping)
- **Segmented Baseline Model Construction** — Output: Segmented model parameters K_{o_t}

Step3: Loss Quantification & Attribution

- **Loss Quantification**
  - Total Loss
- **Loss Attribution & Pattern Analysis** — Segregating Shading Loss
- **Shading Patterns** — By Time Segment, Season, Azimuth Angle

Proposed method

Remote Data Reliability Assessment

Assess the consistency between the on-site power generation curve $P_{PV}(t)$ and the remote meteorological station's irradiance curve $GHI(t)$ using two core metrics.

- Cosine Similarity

$$similarity = \sum_{t=1}^{24} \cos\theta = \frac{\sum_{t=1}^{24} P_{PV_t} \times GHI_t}{\sqrt{\sum_{t=1}^{24} (P_{PV_t})^2} \times \sqrt{\sum_{t=1}^{24} (GHI_t)^2}} \geq 0.985$$

- DTW

The time difference is corrected by systematically shifting one curve to find the offset that gives the best fit between the two curves.

Loss Quantification

- Select the data from system with the highest $P_{PV}(t)$ as the optimal sample for that time point t

$$P_{PV}(t) = K_{o_t} \times \frac{PoA(t)}{G_{STC}} \times [1 + \gamma \ (T_c(t) - T_{STC}) \ ] \times P_{STC}^{tot}$$

※The POA here is the solar radiation data of the remote meteorological data filtered by similarity.

- Using the trained K_{o_t} value, the solar radiation data is inverted based on the measured value of power generation on that day, thus obtaining highly reliable local solar radiation data.
- Quick Estimation

When remote meteorological data is unreliable, we use a quick, on-site comparison method. Choose P_{PV_k} which makes D_k minimum as sample data

$$D_k = \sum_{m=i, m\neq k}^{N} |P_{PV_k} - P_{PV_m}|$$

By contrasting the performance of similar PV systems within the same plant, to identify the "highest density point" that best represents the overall performance and use it as the performance indicator for the target system.

Pattern Analysis

- Clustering

Utilizing the K-means algorithm to cluster features such as residuals, solar angles, and clearness index.

$$\phi_{f_i} = \sum_{S \subseteq F \setminus \{f_i\}} \frac{|S|!\,(M - |S| - 1)!}{M!} [f_{loss}(S \cup \{f_i\}) - f_{loss}(S)]$$

- Feature Importance

to quantify the influence of each feature on the loss, providing deeper insights into the causes of shading.

Objective

- ✓ To establish a framework for quantifying and segregating PV system losses caused by partial shading.
- ✓ The goal is to identify and analyze the impact of shading on power generation performance without the need for on-site meteorological data.

Dataset

Target location: Nagasakacho Natsuaki, Hokuto, Yamanashi City, Japan
Simulation data: From 2018 to 2023
Time Grain: 1hour
For PV output forecasts, solar radiation, temperature, and solar radiation data from the distant meteorological station are used

Table.1 Equipment Configuration

	Setting
Number	6 Monocrystalline 7 Polycrystalline
Capacity	Approximately 10kW
Tilt Angle	30°
Azimuth Angle	South-facing

Results and discussion

◆Remote Data Validation Results

Fig.1 Solar Radiation Sensor Performance

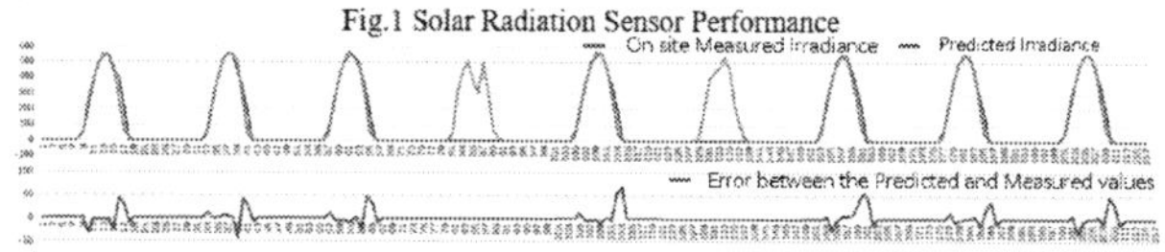

Through this data filtering, performed exclusively on clear and meteorologically similar days, approximately 52% of the year's days can be utilized for training. The average prediction error for clear days at the present time is between 5.2% and 8.6%.

◆On-site Reference Comparison Results

Fig.2 Performance Trend without meteorological data

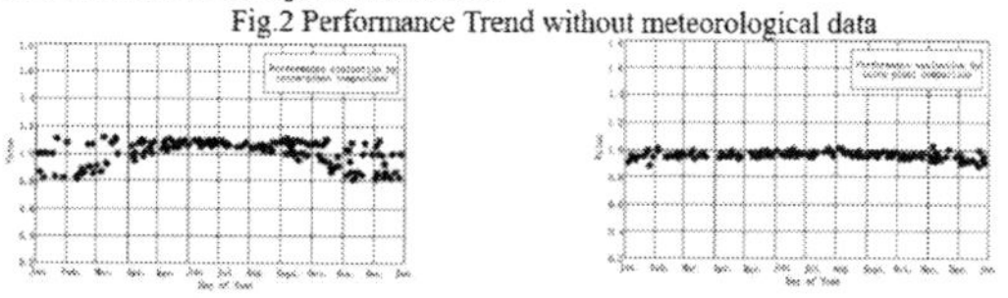

The systems unaffected by shading exhibit stable performance, consistent with the group average. In contrast, systems with fixed shading show clear degradation patterns, especially in winter when the solar altitude angle is low.

◆Loss Pattern Analysis

Fig.3 Seasonal System Loss Comparison Chart

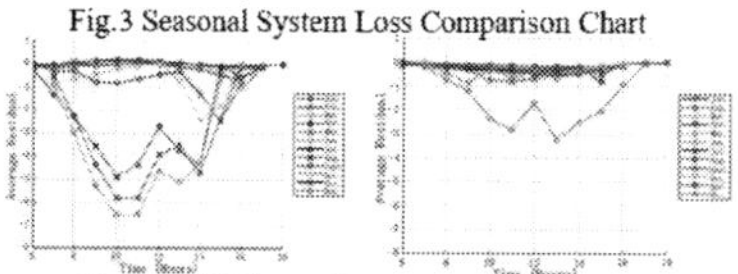

Left Chart: Indicate the most significant impact in winter.
Right Chart: With low losses in most of months.

Fig.4 SHAP Feature Importance Analysis

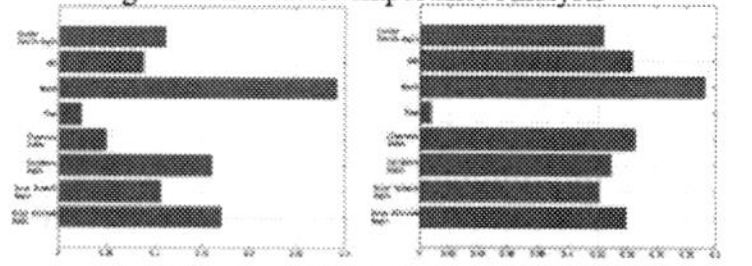

Left Chart: The"Month" parameter has the highest contribution to the loss, confirming a strong seasonal dependency for shading-induced losses.

Fig.5 Clustering Chart of Loss vs. Solar Angle

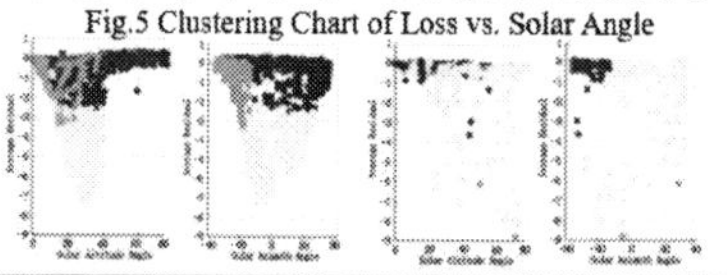

The loss clusters are concentrated at specific solar altitude and azimuth angles.
This can be used to determine the location of the shading object.

Conclusions

- ✓ Propose and validate a performance evaluation framework for PV systems that does not rely on on-site meteorological sensors.
- ✓ Identify systems with performance degradation and reveals the patterns of power generation changes caused by shading

42nd European Photovoltaic Solar Energy Conference and Exhibition

PV-Reliability.ch

EU PVSEC 2025, 22.-26. September 2025, Bilbao (Spain)
Matthias Hügi[1], Christof Bucher[1], Leo Hofer[1], Fabio Panduri[1]
[1]Bern University of Applied Sciences (BFH), School of Engineering and Computer Science (TI), Institute for Energy and Mobility Research (IEM), Laboratory for Photovoltaic Systems (PV-Lab), Burgdorf (Switzerland)
christof.bucher@bfh.ch

"The life expectancy of inverters is around 15 years and therefore need to be replaced once during the service life of a photovoltaic system". This statement is being analysed in the "PV Reliability" research project. The platform processes data entered by users in order to calculate the survival probability of inverters and optimisers depending on time, installation location, manufacturer and other parameters and to create comparisons.

Objectives and approach

The aim of this research project is to quantify the service life of inverters and power optimisers. It is analysed whether time, installation location and manufacturer influence the service life and how important the respective factors are.

In order to achieve this goal, we are looking for private individuals and companies, both nationally and internationally, who are willing to provide basic data and operating data on their PV systems. Private individuals can independently record systems and events on the website pv-reliability.ch. For companies with large data sets, an individualised import is possible.

Innovation and relevance

This project contributes to a better understanding of the effects of ageing on inverters, which can be influenced by the users. In contrast to previous research work, this project does not investigate the cause of the damage, but rather the stress factors that can be influenced.

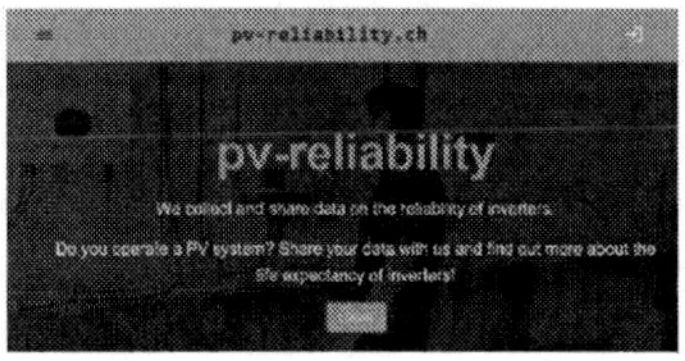

Figure 1: Home page pv-reliability.ch

Today, millions of PV systems are connected to monitoring portals. However, these portals do not provide any information about the load factors that can be influenced and generally do not know the age and condition of the components used. In particular, when an inverter is repaired or replaced 1:1, this is often not recorded by the portals. The platform aims to close this research gap.

Recording of installations

The pv-reliability.ch platform utilises the crowd data sourcing approach. In a first step, users of the platform create a login and enter master data on their PV system. This data includes the location, product types used and basic characteristics of the PV system, such as

- Number of modules per string
- Number of modules per inverter
- Installation location of the inverter
- Use of optimisers

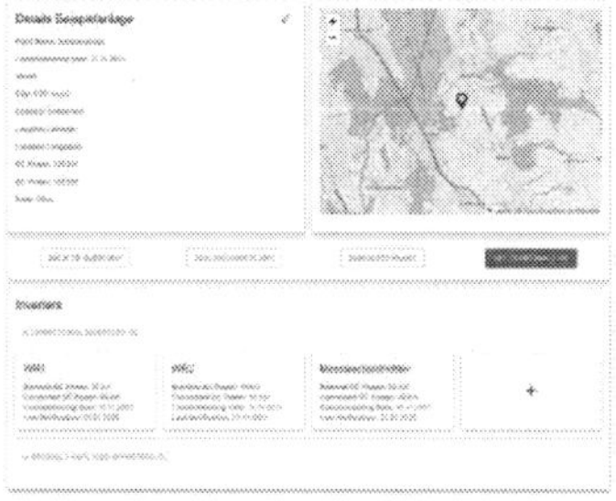

Figure 2: Overview page of an installation

Inverter commissioning data is also recorded in order to determine the service life. The data is recorded using simple input masks. All data is then clearly displayed.

Verification process

In order to calculate the service life of the various inverters, faults, defects or even the replacement of devices must be recorded/updated regularly. This is done in the Verification section. On this page, the status of each inverter can be defined at a specific point in time. The following statuses can be selected :

- Operational
- Replaced without failure
- Broken

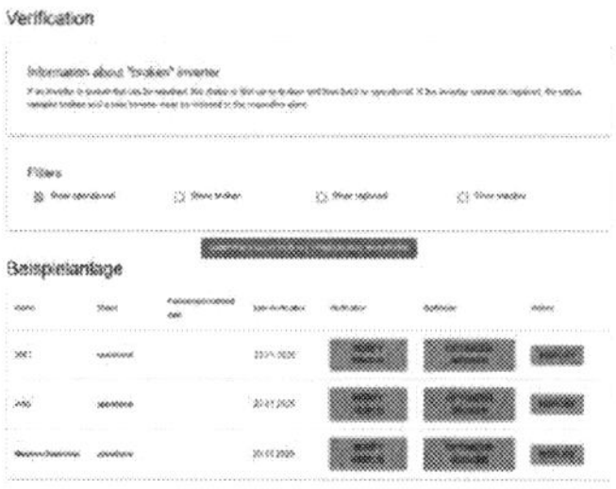

Figure 3: Verification page

Defective optimisers can also be recorded. Verification can be carried out individually for each inverter or directly for all recorded devices. The data should be updated once a year, for which purpose a corresponding request is sent to the users.

Results

The pv-reliability.ch platform was only recently put into operation. It was created on the basis of a survey and publication with an identical scope from 2022.

Automatic analyses are currently implemented in the internal area, but have not yet been activated, as there are currently too few data sets available for a statistically relevant evaluation. For initial statements on the service life of inverters, please refer to the 2022 study [1].

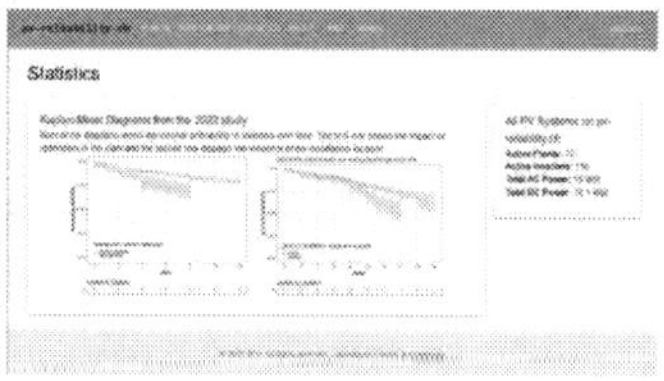

Figure 4: Results of the 2022 study

Support the research!

We are looking for companies and individuals who are willing to share their data on inverter failures with us. Individual systems can be entered at pv-reliability.ch, larger portfolios (e.g. of installation companies) can be sent to the PV laboratory with an Excel list. matthias.huegi@bfh.ch will be happy to provide further details.

https://pv-reliability.ch/

Thanks to

A big thank you goes to all those who agree to make their data available for this project and to update it regularly.

References

[1] Christof Bucher, Jasmin Wandel, David Joss, Life expectancy of PV inverters and optimizers in residential PV systems, 29.09.2022, WCPEC-8 https://www.bfh.ch/de/forschung/referenzprojekte/lebenserwartung-photovoltaik-wechselrichter/

Berner Fachhochschule
Haute école spécialisée bernoise
Bern University of Applied Sciences

▸ Department of Engineering and Computer Science (TI)
▸ Institute for Energy and Mobility Research (IEM)

Laboratory for Photovoltaic Systems
3400 Burgdorf | Jlcoweg 1
www.bfh.ch/pvlab | christof.bucher@bfh.ch

Applied Photovoltaic Research
Swiss Solar Competence

020322-001

Investigation and Discuss of Failures during Operation and Maintenance in Floating Photovoltaic

EU PVSEC 2025

* Jieun Lee, Hyunsik Jo, Jungi Jeong , Donggeon Yang
Water Energy research, Korea Water Resources corporation (K-water)

K water

INTRODUCTION

- For Low Carbon, Need to be improved the Capa. Of photovoltaic which have portion 70% in renewable energy of South Korea
- FPV(Floating photovoltaic) is actively used to overcome the topography feature of PV on ground.
- For stable power supply, operation and maintenance are essential, in which diagnosis with type of degradation and effect of power with different type of environment are also importance for effectively managing of PV system
- In this research, we will analysis the status of failure during diagnosis and operating with long term and discuss about way to manage of FPV for a future.

FLOATING PHOTOVOLTAIC IN K-WATER

- FLOATING PV
  - ➢ Photovoltaic mounted on a structure that floats on a body of water

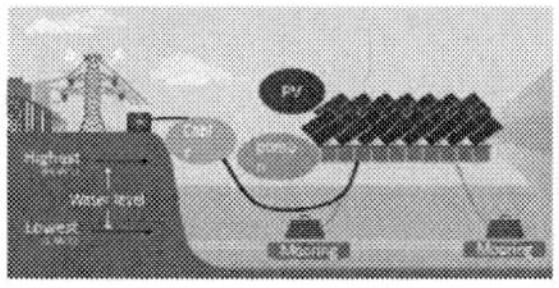

<Floating PV configuration>

<Floating PV system>

- Status of FPV in K-water
  - ➢ Research and business FPV are 58.4MW in K-water

('11.11) Hapchun Dam 100kW ('12.10) Hapchun Dam 500kW ('13.05) Hapchun Dam 100kW ('16.03) Boryung 2MW
('17.02) Soyanggan Dam110kW ('17.12) Chungju Dam 3MW ('18.06) Chungju Dam 200kW ('21.04) Siwha 200kW (offshore)
('22.12) Hapchun Dam 41.5MW ('22.08) Chungju Dam 2.6MW ('23.11) Yanggu Dam 8.8MW

MAINTENANCE AND INSPCETION IN A FIELD

- Maintenance Task in FPV system[1]

Component	Task Description	Periodicity	Recommended Documentation
Tasks specific to FPV			
Buoyant structure	Inspection for buoyancy issues, damage, and biofouling	Monthly	DNVGL-RP-0584, Manfacturer's manual
	Clean the floaters if algae or any other auatic growth is observed on their surface.	Quarterly	
Anchors	Inspection for general conditions (wear, degradation), risk of lifting and proper position	2.5year	ISO 19901-7, DNVGL-ST-0119
Mooring system	Check for wear, corrosion, marine growth Inspect the integrity of connecting points (fairleads, shackles, and frayed crimp points) Tension adjustments	yearly and every 2.5years for under water sections	DNVGL-RP-0584 ISO 199101-7
Tasks similar to GPV but more challenging			
Structural components	Inspect for rust on frame supports, cable clips and fasteners	Quarterly	DNVGL-RP-0584, manfacturer's manual
	Verify strength, tightness, and integrity of bolt and other connectors Inspect the structural integrity and galvanic corrosion in dissimilar metals	Yearly	
PV module	Verify the cleanliness and integrity of module sufaces and check for objects causing shading Visual inspection for defects in both front and aback sides Conduct performance tests and IR, PL and EL scanning	Monthly Quarterly Yearly	IEC 62446-3, IEC 61215, Manufacturer's manual
Cables	Inspect for signs of damages and degraded insulation	Monthly	IEC 62446-1, IEC 60364
	Verify mechanical and watertight integrity of cable conduits/cable trays	Quarterly	
	Perform tests to check continuity, insulation resistance and hot spots	Yearly	
Inverter	Check error log files from inverter database	Monthly	IEC 62109-1, IEC 62109-2, IEC 62093, Manufacturer's manual
	Inspect for water ingress, physical damages and corrosion Clean inverter fans and inspect ventilation	Quarterly	
	Test the operational efficiency and check anti-islanding fuction of the inverter	Yearly	
Transformer	Inscpection for water ingress, physical damages and corrosion	Quarterly	IEC 60076 series, Manufacturer's manual
	Check oil level, oil temperature, dielectric strength and tap changer temperature	Quarterly	
	Test the operational efficiency and check hot spots	Yearly	
Electrical protective system	Inspect for visual damages and verify integrity of equipotential bonding Inspect the condition of the main grounding cable	Monthly	IEC 62561-2, IEC 62305-2, IEEE 81-2012, IEC 62548 , Manufacturer's manual
	Conduct continuity and earth resistance test	Biannually	
	Verify any defects in the protective switchgears(circuit breakers, residual current breakers, surge protective devices) Check earth pit and its resistivity if earth cable returns to shore Check the earthing material for corrosion if earthing is done through water body	Yearly	
Data monitoring system	Verify operations of sensors, data loggers, and communication modules	Biannually	IEC 62676, IEC 61724-1, Manufacturer's manual

1.Hemba Limet Walsite et al., Operation and Maintenance of Floating PV System: A review. IEEE Journal of Photovoltaics (Volume: 13, Issue: 3, May 2023)

DIAGNOSIS AND INSPECTION IN K-water

- Diagnosis in a Field (Progress once a 2~4year, periodically)

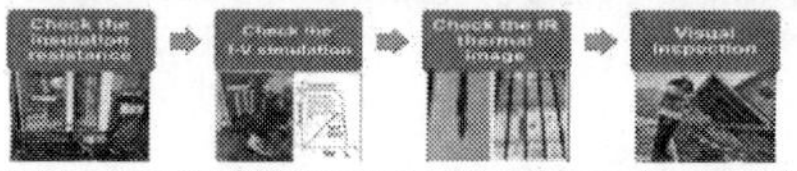

- Inspection of FPV system (Monthly or Frequently

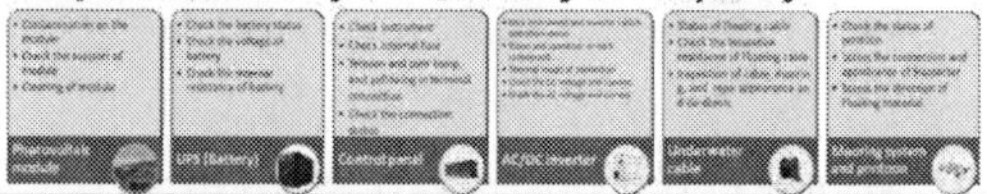

RESULT AND DISCUSSION

- Diagnosis result in FPV
  - ➢ The Most of issue Floating 56.4% and Electric room 29% in FPV system
  - ➢ Floating : Mounting system(21.8%), Mooring (7.1%), Module(5.6%), Underwater cable(3.0%)

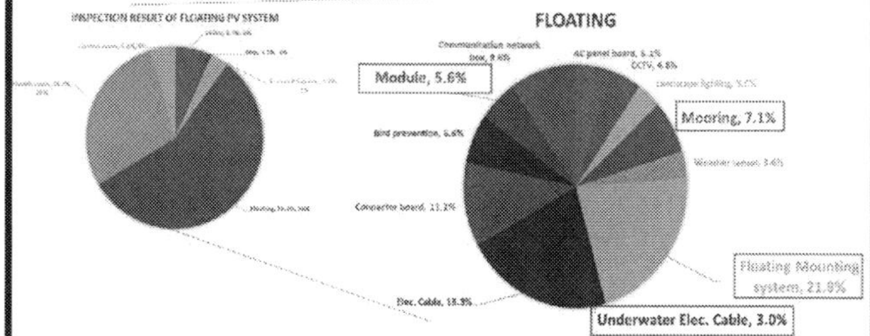

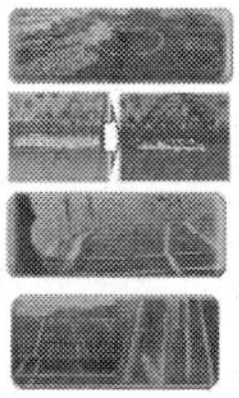

Cable (Elec. and Underwater)	• Normal cable: Fixed defect string and insulation failure • Underwater cable: ① Insulation resistance fail ② Damage to the cover of the clamp joint due to tension
Pontoon & Mooring	• Damage of pontoon • Broken of mooring system
Mounting system	• Release the guide in passage • Loose the connecting bolt • Deformation due to mooring • Damage to the footing
PV module	• Module Broken due to damage of module • Module Drop

- Analysis of impact from Fault and Defect
  - ➢ Mooring and Floating Mount system for Floating

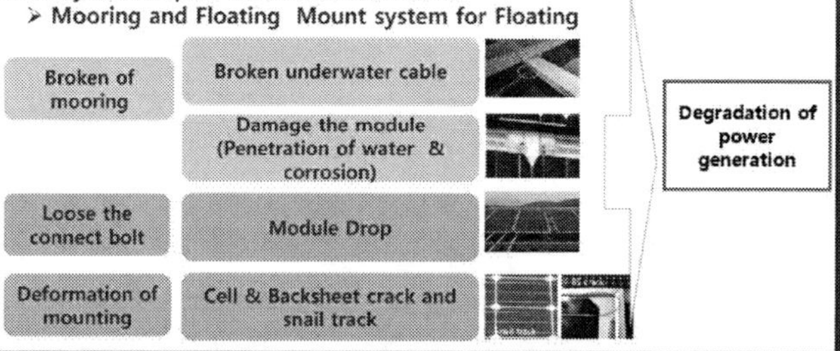

SUMMARY AND CONCLUSION

- Short term : Mounting structure Fault due to micro wave on water
- Long term : BS and cell crack due to unstable mounting structure and corrosion due to moisture in FPV
- Additional inspection for improving safety and reliability in K-water
  - Inspection of Mooring system (water level and GPS), Mounting system(Connecting)

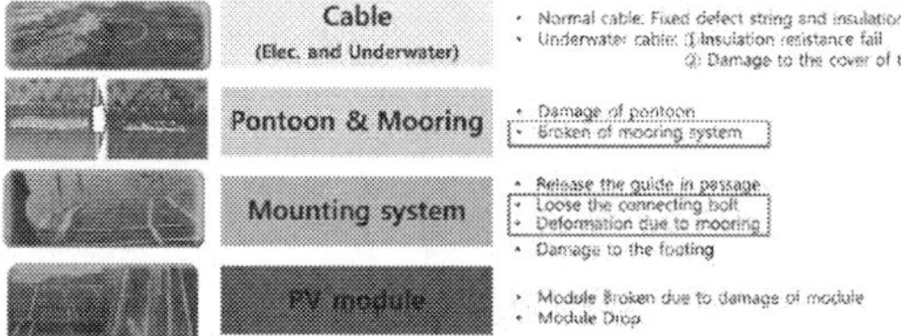

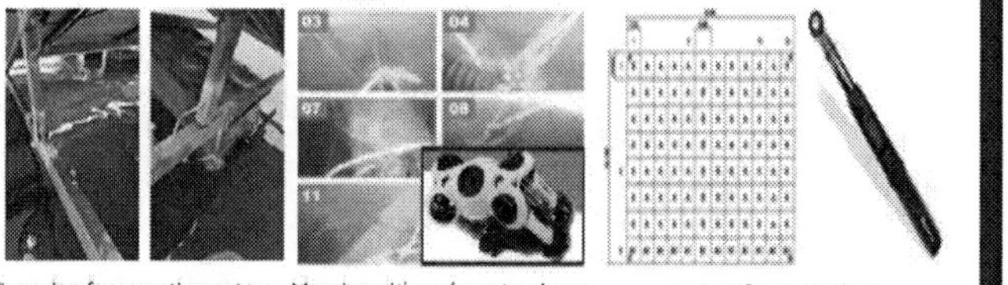

Corrosion for mounting system Mooring with underwater drone Inspect for connection

This work was supported by the Korea Institute of Energy Technology Evaluation and Planning(KETEP) and the Ministry of Trade, Industry & Energy(MOTIE) of the Republic of Korea

Study on Power Generation Estimation Model using Inverter Data and Machine Learning

Suk whan Ko[1], Young Chul JU[1], Hye Mi HWANG[1], Jin-Seok Lee[1], Woo Gyun Shin[1]

Korea Institute of Energy Research, Korea

presenting author (korea19@kier.re.kr)

Abstract

Globally, efforts are being made to overcome the climate change crisis by reducing carbon-based power sources and adopting renewable energy-based power sources through initiatives such as RE100 and ESG management. The most widely utilized renewable energy source is photovoltaic (PV) energy, with the cumulative installed capacity surpassing 2 TW in 2024. This marks a doubling of capacity in just two years, compared to 1 TW in 2022. Notably, PV installations are expected to continue increasing in the coming years. As the installation of PV plants increases, the market for operation and maintenance (O&M) is also growing. According to the related report, the global PV O&M market is estimated to grow at a compound global annual rate (CAGR) of 14.49 % during the forecast period 2022-2027 and reach $7,339.60 million by 2027, from around $3,330.73 million in 2021. In recent years, advancements in big data and artificial intelligence technologies have brought changes to PV operation and maintenance (O&M) activities. Traditional PV O&M activities are evolving into more efficient operations through the application of digital technologies.

In this paper, we proposes a method and model for estimating power generation by using PV inverter data as training data for machine-learning models. First, the data for training the machine learning model is preprocessed using a physical model to remove outliers. The physical model calculates voltage and current data based on irradiance and module temperature. Next, irradiance, module temperature, voltage, and current data are used as input variables, while the measured voltage and current data are used as output variables to train the machine learning model. After training seven different regression models, the ensemble (bagging tree) model achieved the lowest root mean square error (RMSE) values for voltage and current, at 2.1158 (V) and 0.1406 (A), respectively.

Background

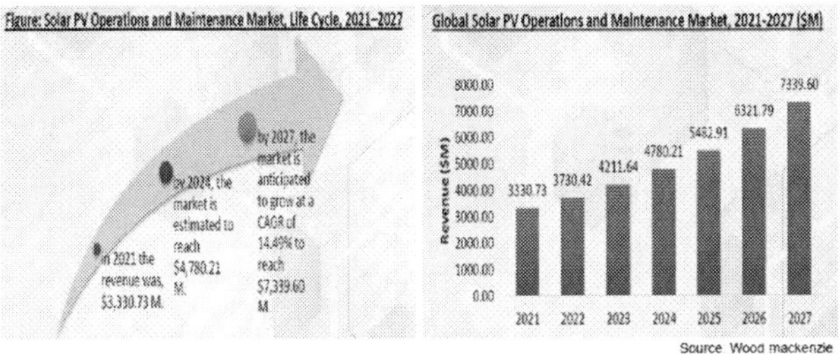

O&M market expansion from PV growth and aging systems

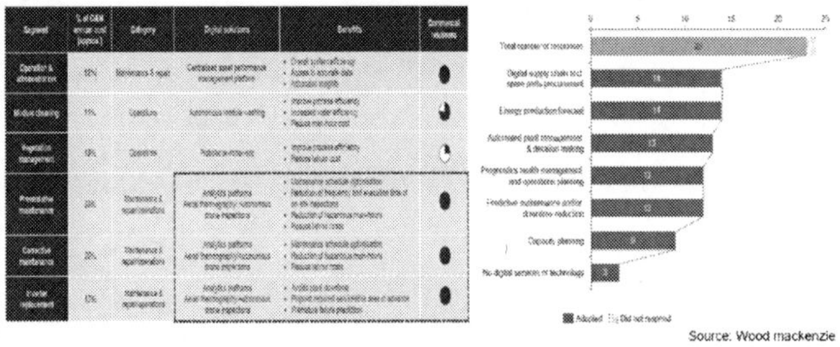

Growing demand for PV O&M technologies utilizing AI and data

Experiment and Result

◆ Preprocessing method of collected inverter data

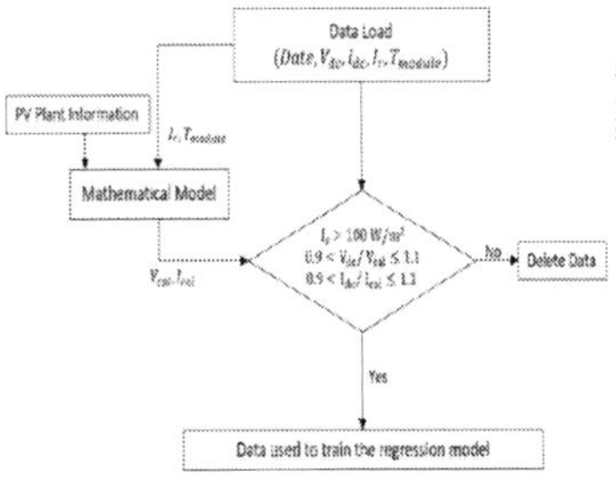

Data preprocessing procedure

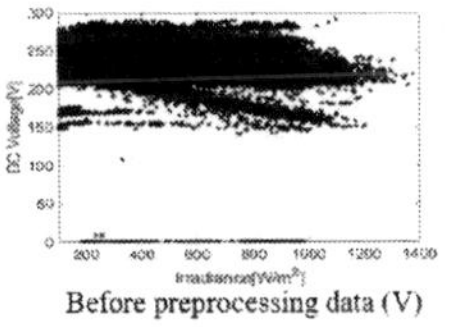

Before preprocessing data (V)

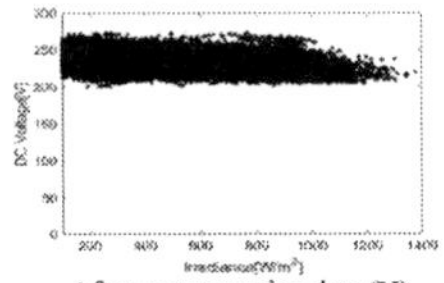

After preprocessing data (V)

- For the operation and maintenance (O&M) of photovoltaic power plants, data is essential, and inverter data is the most easily accessible source. Inverter data collects various parameters (voltage, current, power, frequency, power factor, etc.) that can be used to assess plant conditions.
- Among these, voltage, current, and power data represent the output performance of the PV system; however, abnormal values may occur due to inverter shutdowns or MPPT malfunctions.
- If such abnormal values are included in the training dataset for machine learning, the results cannot be considered reliable. Therefore, as shown in the figure, the collected data were preprocessed using a mathematical model and measured irradiance as reference.
- As illustrated in the figure, the raw data contained scattered abnormal values before preprocessing. Through data preprocessing, these outliers were removed, and the training dataset was consolidated within a consistent range.

◆ Validation results using trained machine learning model (Bagging Tree)

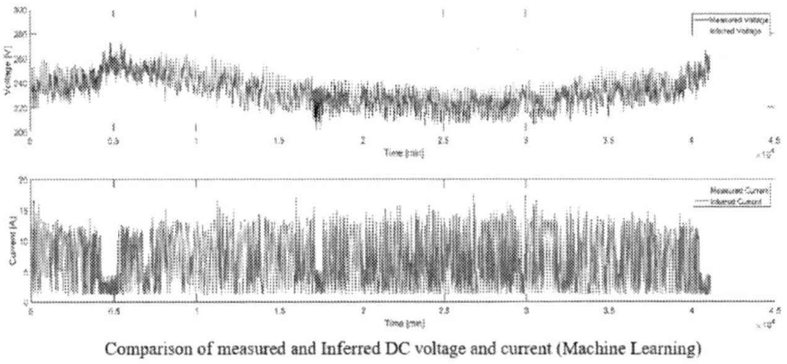

Comparison of measured and Inferred DC voltage and current (Machine Learning)

- Using the preprocessed data, seven machine learning models were trained as shown in the table below.
- Among the trained models, the Bagging Tree model demonstrated the best performance, achieving R^2 values of 0.9666 (voltage) and 0.9987 (current), and NRMSE values of 0.0294 (voltage) and 0.0202 (current).

Results for DC Voltage (V)

Model	R^2	NRMSE	RMSE
Linear	0.9450	0.0377	2.7134
Neural	0.9519	0.0352	2.5380
Tree	0.9564	0.0336	2.4206
LSK	0.9462	0.0373	2.6841
GPR	0.9573	0.0332	2.3902
Boosted	0.9501	0.1419	10.2179
Bagging	0.9666	0.0294	2.1158

Results for DC Current (A)

Model	R^2	NRMSE	RMSE
Linear	0.9977	0.0266	0.1852
Neural	0.9985	0.0216	0.1503
Tree	0.9984	0.0218	0.1513
LSK	0.9967	0.0317	0.2203
GPR	0.9986	0.0203	0.1410
Boosted	0.9977	0.0559	0.3882
Bagging	0.9987	0.0202	0.1406

Conclusion

- PV inverter data is the most easily accessible dataset for O&M purposes. However, for performance analysis in O&M, input data such as irradiance and temperature must also be collected.
- In addition, abnormal values may occur due to data collected during the MPPT process, inverter shutdowns, or restarts, which are not measured under steady-state conditions.
- Since training data containing such abnormal values reduces the reliability of the model, this study applied a data preprocessing method to remove outliers.
- The machine learning model trained with the preprocessed data achieved excellent performance, with R^2 values of 0.9666 (voltage) and 0.9987 (current).
- Furthermore, future work will focus on fault diagnosis by analyzing performance through comparison between measured and inferred values using the trained model.

This work was conducted under the framework of the research and development program of the Korea Institute of Energy Research (Project No: C5-2427) and was supported by the Korea Environmental Industry and Technology Institute (Project No: C5-6707).

Application of Multivariate Data Analysis and NIR Spectroscopy in Evaluating PV System Performance and Packaging Degradation

B. A. Belferkous[1], C. Barretta[1], G. Oviedo Hernandez[2], L. Koester[3], G. Oreski[1,4]

[1] Polymer Competence Center Leoben GmbH (PCCL), Sauraugasse 1, 8700 Leoben, Austria – brahim.anis.belferkous@pccl.at
[2] BayWa r.e. Operation Services S.r.l., 00139 Rome, Italy
[3] Eurac Research, 39100 Bolzano, Italy
[4] Chair of Material Science and Testing of Polymers, Montanuniversitaet Leoben, 8700 Leoben, Austria

PCCL
Polymer Competence Center Leoben

INTRODUCTION AND OBJECTIVES

The operational performance of photovoltaic (PV) systems is impacted by the degradation of their packaging materials. Such degradation manifests through both visible and invisible phenomena, including corrosion, micro-cracking, macro-cracking, delamination, discoloration, and so on [1, 2].

Non destructive testing combined with multivariate data analysis (MVDA) such as Principal Component Analysis (PCA) and Uniform Manifold Approximation and Projection (UMAP), are remarkably more effective at detecting early stage degradation of Bill of Materials (BOMs), making it a valuable combination for evaluating PV system performance.

The aim of the study is to:

- Identify the BOMs of PV modules with unknown compositions through the application of Near Infrared (NIR) spectroscopy.
- Detecting signs of material degradation.

EXPERIMENTAL

Visual Inspection

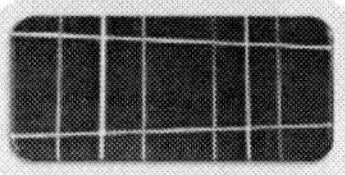

EL Imaging

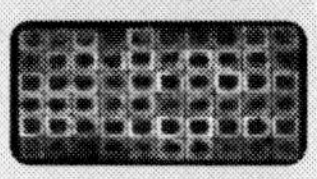

NIR Spectroscopy

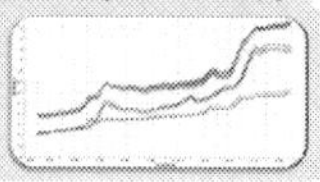

Non Destructive Testing

NIR Spectroscopy

- Potential for automation.
- Rapid response time.
- Detecting material property changes.
- Complementary to visual inspection and Electroluminescence (EL).
- Suitability for field deployment.
- Determining BOM composition.

12 modules, installed in 2011

The modules showed encapsulant discoloration, backsheet cracks, corrosion, delamination, etc.

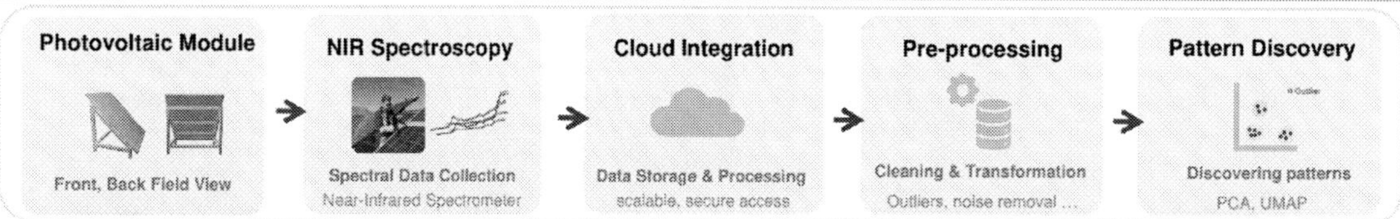

RESULTS AND DISCUSSION

ENCAPSULANT

PCA Space Of NIR Spectra " Encapsulant " Side

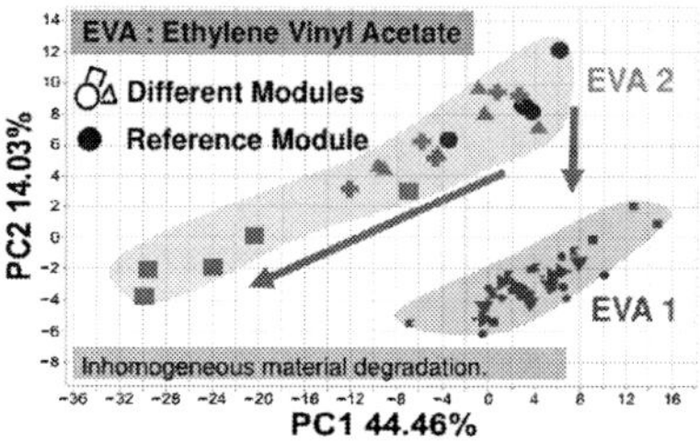

- Data shows notable **differences between** the Reference (**unexposed**) and **exposed** modules.
- **Differences** between **encapsulants types** (EVA 1 and EVA 2) due to **non-uniform additives**, identifies variations in material authenticity.
- **UMAP** was used alongside PCA as it provided **clearer and tighter clustering** of EVA 1 and EVA 2.
- **UMAP** can **uncover complex**, non-linear **patterns** in the data that **PCA might overlook.**

UMAP Space Of NIR Spectra " Encapsulant " Side

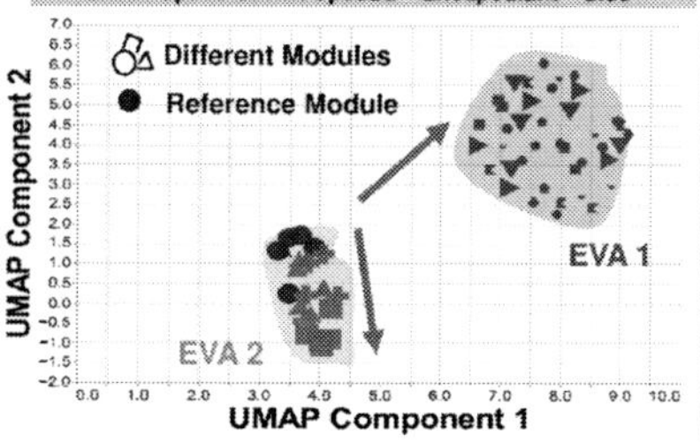

PC Loadings interpretation / additive composition

Principle Components Loadings

Loading Plot For Principal Components 1 (EVA 1 – EVA 2)

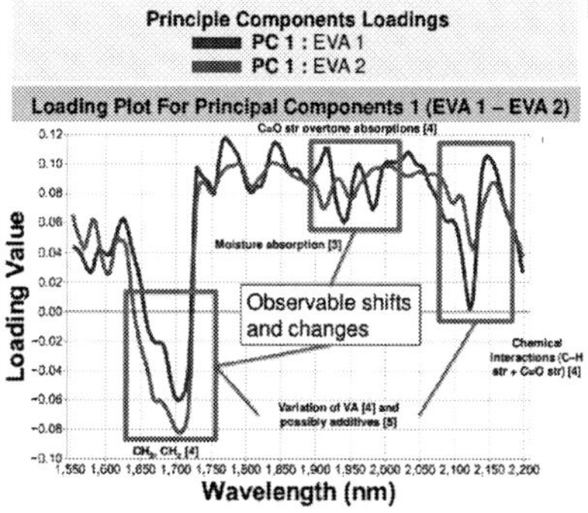

- **PC1: EVA 1 vs EVA 2** differ mainly in the region between 1600 and 1750 nm and in the region between 2000 and 2200 nm, most associated with **VA content** [4, 6], also confirmed by FTIR ATR spectroscopy.
- **PC2:** Amplitudes and sign of the peaks and valleys are very different for most wavelengths.
- Differences relate to **vinyl acetate content** and **chemical structure (including additives).**
- **Most attention** on **PC1** for the main conclusions, **PC2** to interpret secondary trends with **limited** additional **information.**

Thermal Desorption Gas Chromatography coupled to Mass Spectrometry (TD-GC/MS)

Additives	EVA 1	EVA 2
Antioxidant	None	Butylated hydroxytoluene
UV absorber	2-Hydroxy-4-n-octyloxybenzophenone	2-hydroxy-4-methoxy benzophenone
Light stabilizer (HALS)	Bis(2,2,6,6-tetramethyl-4-piperidyl) sebacate	

EVA 2 has more VA

CONCLUSIONS AND OUTLOOK

- **NIR** spectroscopy is highly **effective and rapid** in detecting material changes.
- **Non uniform BOM** structures for both **encapsulant** and **back-sheet** materials.
- PCA and UMAP provide complementary views of high-dimensional NIR data PCA shows variance trends, **UMAP improves cluster separation**.
- **Loadings plot** differences, reinforcing that the encapsulants types are **distinguishable through NIR & MVDA analysis.**

- ☐ Integrating PV performance metrics Data.
- ☐ Predictive modelling for material performance.

REFERENCES
[1] [illegible]
[2] [illegible]
[3] [illegible]
[4] [illegible]
[5] [illegible]
[6] [illegible]

ORCID ID

Learn more at 3AV.2.25

SUPERNOVA supernova-pv.eu
Co-funded by the European Union

020325-001

The work was carried out within the project SUPERNOVA, co-funded by the European Union under Horizon Europe Grant Agreement No 101146883. Views and opinions expressed are however those of the author(s) only and do not necessarily reflect those of the European Union or CINEA. Neither the European Union nor the granting authority can be held responsible for them.

AUTOMATED IDENTIFICATION OF OPEN CIRCUITS IN PHOTOVOLTAIC ARRAYS VIA MASK-RCNN, THERMOGRAPHIC SIGNAL PROCESSING AND HYBRIDIZED REGION-GROWTH ALGORITHMS

Daniel J. Castillo Patton*, Lucas Viani, Mario Martínez González, Sergio Suárez Sánchez, Fernando García, Sofía Rodríguez-Conde, José Manuel Rivas Rodríguez
Enertis Applus+, Parque Empresarial Las Mercedes, C/ de Campezo, 1, 28022 Madrid, Spain
Carlos III University of Madrid, Av. de la Universidad, 30, 28911 Leganés, Madrid, Spain
*e-mail: daniel.castillo.p@enertisapplus.com

ABSTRACT: We present a hybrid workflow for the automated detection of open circuits (*open strings*) in utility-scale photovoltaic (PV) plants using aerial infrared thermography. The approach combines three stages: (i) module localization via instance segmentation to delineate each panel, (ii) temperature profiling to compute per-module statistics and identify gradient breaks along strings, and (iii) a region-propagation algorithm that expands from anomalous seeds to recover entire strings, even when occlusions or partial detection errors occur. This design ensures robustness under heterogeneous environmental conditions and does not rely exclusively on large training datasets. The system outputs both quantitative indicators (per-module temperature profiles and string-level labels) and qualitative evidence (binary masks and annotated thermal images), enabling scalable fault localization across thousands of modules. Validation on multiple PV plants demonstrates consistent performance, with accurate detection of open strings, reduced false positives compared to purely deep-learning approaches, and processing times compatible with large-scale aerial inspections.

1 INTRODUCTION

Photovoltaic (PV) generation has grown explosively over the past decade, with global installed capacity expected to surpass 1.5 TW by the mid-2020s, playing a central role in the transition to renewable, emission-free energy [1]. Yet, this growth is still accompanied by significant production losses caused by operational defects, material degradation, shading, soiling, and electrical faults, which can reduce expected yield by 10–25% according to recent studies [2].

Among these faults, open circuits at cell, module, or string level are particularly critical: they interrupt current flow, cause immediate performance losses, and may trigger secondary defects (e.g., overheating in redistributed module areas) if undetected [3]. Given the scale of modern PV plants—millions of modules spread across large sites—and the variability of environmental conditions, manual inspection is impractical and error-prone.

Deep learning has therefore become a cornerstone for automating defect detection in aerial thermography. Lightweight CNNs provide efficient fault recognition, while hybrid models have validated the inclusion of open-circuit detection among multiple defect classes, achieving accuracy levels above 99% in certain tasks [4].

Building on these advances, this work proposes a hybrid workflow that integrates deep-learning-based module segmentation, temperature profiling, and a novel region-propagation strategy. The goal is to provide a robust and scalable system for automated open-circuit detection at string level, reducing energy losses, enabling predictive maintenance, and improving operational efficiency in utility-scale PV plants.

2 RELATED WORKS

2.1 Module detection and segmentation with deep learning

Reliable module localization is the first step toward diagnosing open strings. Two dominant families exist: bounding-box detectors (e.g., YOLO variants) and semantic/instance segmentation models applied to RGB/TIR aerial imagery. In PV applications, YOLO-based detectors trained with domain-specific datasets have reached high precision and recall (e.g., ST-YOLO [5]), while segmentation approaches such as Mask2Former have demonstrated accurate delineation of modules in heterogeneous aerial and satellite imagery [6], supported by curated datasets of very high resolution [7]. Collectively, recent reviews confirm that DL has become the standard for module and defect detection, with growing deployment in UAV-based and semi-automated O&M workflows [8].

2.2 Thermography and open-string detection

An open string manifests as a group of modules with uniformly elevated thermal signatures compared to adjacent strings, reflecting abnormal dissipation and lack of power delivery. This phenomenon is well documented in field thermography [3], and aerial IR inspections (aIRT) have been validated as effective for detecting string-level anomalies in utility-scale plants [4,9]. Technical literature (IEA-PVPS Task 13, IEC TS 62446-3, and subsequent reviews [1,10,11]) establishes the link between thermal patterns and electrical failure modes (open, short, mismatch, PID, shading), supporting workflows that combine: module segmentation, string-level aggregation, and thermal classification to distinguish open strings from other anomalies.

2.3 Tracking systems and yield impact

Single and dual-axis trackers improve energy yield by 10–25% compared to fixed-tilt systems, with further gains in bifacial configurations [12,13,14]. However, tracker

10.4229/EUPVSEC2025/4CV.1.15

performance depends on proper string operation: even isolated open strings can offset expected yield and affect the levelized cost of electricity (LCOE). Best-practice reports (IEA-PVPS, Sandia PVPMC [15,16,17]) emphasize the importance of disaggregated monitoring at string/tracker level to prioritize corrective actions. Comparative studies further highlight parasitic loads and variability of performance in tracking systems [18,19], reinforcing the need for precise and automated open-string detection.

3 METHODOLOGY

In this section, we present the proposed hybrid workflow for the automated detection of open-circuit strings in utility-scale photovoltaic (PV) plants. The approach combines deep learning–based segmentation with thermographic signal processing and a region-propagation algorithm, enabling robust performance under variable operating conditions. The workflow is designed to segment individual PV modules from aerial infrared imagery, enrich these modules with pixel-level temperature data to construct temperature profiles, identify gradient discontinuities that indicate potential open circuits, and propagate the detection across neighboring modules to delineate entire strings.

The following subsections describe each component of the methodology in detail: dataset preparation and preprocessing (3.1), module segmentation with Mask RCNN (3.2), temperature profiling (3.3), module mapping of strings (3.4), gradient break detection (3.5), and region-propagation (3.6).

3.1 Dataset and preprocessing

The dataset consists of infrared images collected by Enertis Applus+ during inspections of multiple utility-scale photovoltaic plants. These images provide an authentic source of thermal data and were deliberately selected to ensure realism and representativeness. Grounding the dataset in real field conditions rather than controlled, the proposed workflow is designed to extend beyond purely scientific experimentation and demonstrate applicability to practical PV field inspections.

Table I: Dataset for module images.

Data	Images	Objects
Solar Panel	2867	120653

In addition to its size, the dataset captures a wide spectrum of operational scenarios, including variations in irradiance, ambient temperature, and module typologies across plants. Such diversity ensures that the evaluation of the proposed workflow is not restricted to uniform or idealized cases, but instead reflects the complexity and variability encountered in real PV assets. This makes the dataset a reliable benchmark for validating automated approaches to open-circuit detection.

3.2 Module segmentation – Mask RCNN

For the first stage of the workflow, we employ a neural network dedicated to the identification of photovoltaic modules in infrared imagery. An instance segmentation architecture based on Mask R-CNN was selected for this task due to its ability to:

A. Localize objects with pixel-level precision.
B. Handle overlapping or partially occluded modules.
C. Flexible integration with downstream temperature analysis.

While alternative approaches such as YOLO-based detectors and semantic segmentation networks have been explored in the literature [20], Mask R-CNN was preferred given its superior preliminary performance on our dataset. The overall architecture of the network is illustrated in Figure 1:

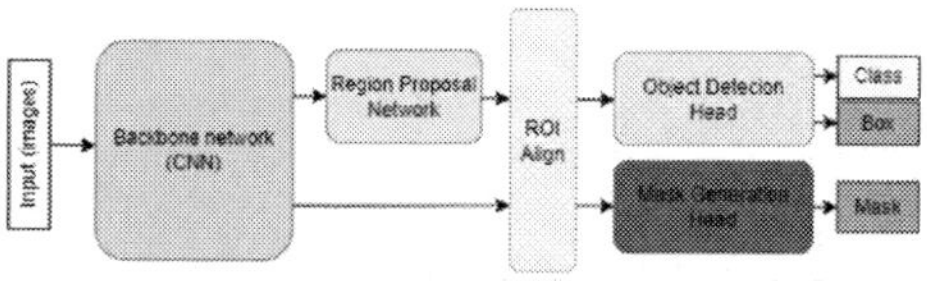

Figure 1: Basic architecture for a Mask RCNN model, showing the different steps performed to realize a segmentation.

This model was implemented using the Detectron2 library and was chosen over pure object detection approaches because instance segmentation is required to precisely delineate all pixels belonging to each module. Unlike bounding-box detectors that only provide coarse localization, instance segmentation assigns a unique mask to every object instance, enabling pixel-level analysis of thermal values within each module. This level of granularity is critical for constructing accurate temperature profiles and detecting subtle anomalies across strings. The architecture follows the Mask R-CNN framework introduced in [21].

3.2.1 Mask RCNN training

For the training stage, the model was configured with the parameter settings summarized in Table II. These settings define the backbone architecture, initialization strategy, and the most influential hyperparameters for convergence and detection accuracy:

Table II: Training selection.

	Parameters settings
Backbone	ResNet FNP
Model Weights	ImageNet MSRA R-50
Learning Rate	0.002
Anchor Generator	32, 64,128, 256
Weight Decay	1×10^{-4} (L2)
Activation Function	ReLU

The configuration follows the standard Detectron2 implementation, with ResNet-50 and FPN providing multi-scale feature extraction. Pretrained ImageNet weights were used to accelerate convergence. A base learning rate of 0.002 with L2 regularization (1×10^{-4}) was applied. Anchor scales were set to [32, 64, 128, 256], covering a wide range of receptive fields so that modules could be detected at different resolutions. In particular, smaller anchors capture distant or partially visible modules, while larger anchors allow the network to detect panels that dominate the field of view. This design ensures that the detector remains robust across images with varying ground sampling distances and module scales. All other parameters, such as ROI head structure and pooling resolutions, were kept at Detectron2's default values to ensure reproducibility and comparability with prior work.

3.2.2 Evaluation Metrics

Model performance was assessed using standard evaluation metrics widely adopted in computer vision: Precision, Recall, and the F1-score [22]. Precision (Eq. 1) quantifies the reliability of positive detections by measuring the proportion of true positives among all predicted positives, while Recall (Eq. 2) evaluates the ability of the model to recover all relevant instances. In large-scale PV inspections, maximizing Recall is particularly critical, as even a small omission rate (<1%) may correspond to thousands of undetected modules. To balance these complementary aspects, we also report the F1 score (Eq. 3), which represents the harmonic mean of Precision and Recall. This metric offers a more comprehensive assessment by penalizing both false positives and false negatives, and is especially relevant under class imbalance conditions, providing a balanced view of the model's detection capability.

$$(1)\ Precision = \frac{TP}{TP+FP}$$

$$(2)\ Recall = \frac{TP}{TP+FN}$$

$$(3)\ F1\ Score = 2 \cdot \frac{Precision \cdot Recall}{Precision + Recall}$$

Having established the evaluation metrics, we now proceed to analyze the results obtained from our experiments.

3.2.3 Evaluation Results

For model evaluation, we employed a dedicated test set that was never exposed during training. This separation guarantees that the reported metrics reflect the model's ability to generalize to previously unseen data. Presented below are the performance metrics for each class for the detection models (see Table III):

Table III: Evaluation Results for Segmentation Model.

Class	Precision	Recall	F1-Score
Solar Panel	99,98%	99,99%	99,98%

The results demonstrate promising performance, with consistently high precision and recall values. While perfect accuracy is not reached, the residual errors are primarily associated with rare and extreme environmental conditions, which are expected in a dataset of this scale. Figure 2 illustrates qualitative examples of the detection outputs, highlighting the ability of the model to correctly identify modules across diverse scenarios.

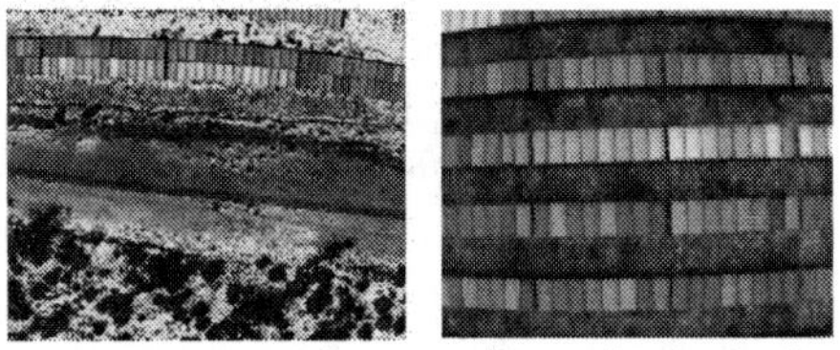

Figure 2: Illustration of the segmentation results, showing that PV modules are successfully detected in two completely different scenarios, demonstrating the robustness of the Mask R-CNN approach.

3.3 Temperature profile generation

Infrared images are first decoded to recover the true pixel-level temperature values rather than relying on the false-color visualizations typically provided by the cameras. This allows us to work directly with calibrated thermal data in degrees Celsius, ensuring that the analysis is grounded in real physical measurements rather than approximations. These arrays are then preserved in a lossless format so that no information is lost in subsequent stages of the workflow.

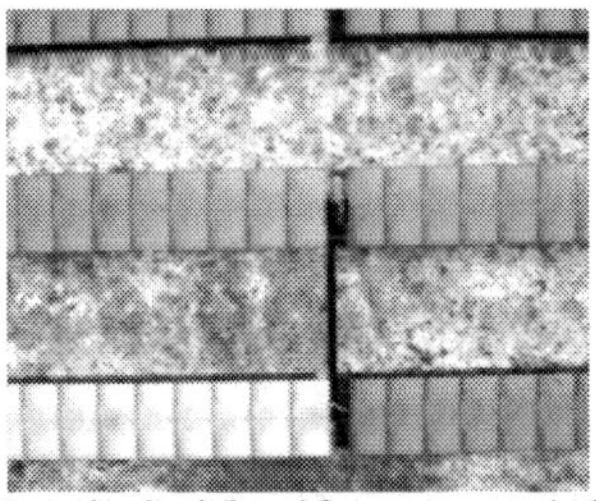

Figure 3: Example of an infrared frame represented with encoded pixel-level temperature values, replacing the conventional false-color colormap with the actual thermal data.

Once the temperature field is obtained, it is combined with the segmentation masks to retain only the pixels that belong to the photovoltaic modules. In practice, this means that all irrelevant background information is discarded, leaving a clean and precise temperature profile for each panel. To improve interpretability, contrast is adapted to the median values of the scene so that subtle variations become visible without being dominated by outliers. At the same time, robust statistical descriptors such as the median are extracted, providing reliable inputs for the detection of gradient changes and, ultimately, the identification of open circuits.

3.4 Module Mapping of Strings

After segmentation, modules are not analyzed in isolation but grouped into strings, understood as contiguous rows of panels arranged along the same horizontal alignment. This grouping is necessary to study collective thermal behavior, since modules placed adjacently in the same row typically

10.4229/EUPVSEC2025/4CV.1.15
020326-003

exhibit similar operating conditions. Ordering them left-to-right provides a consistent spatial reference that allows temperature profiles to be compared across the entire row.

Formally, given a set of modules $M = \{m_1, m_2, \dots, m_n\}$ with centroid coordinates (x_i, y_i), modules belonging to the same string are identified by applying a tolerance on their vertical coordinates:

$$(4)\ S_k = \{m_i \in M : |y_i - \overline{y_k}| < \epsilon\}$$

Where $\overline{y_k}$ is the mean vertical position of string k and ϵ is a threshold that controls row alignment. Once grouped, each string S_k is ordered by increasing x_i:

$$(5)\ S_k^{\text{ordered}} = \text{sort}(S_k,\ \text{key} = x_i)$$

This procedure yields a sequence of modules per string, ensuring that subsequent profiling steps follow the natural spatial arrangement of the array, giving us a detailed mapping of each string:

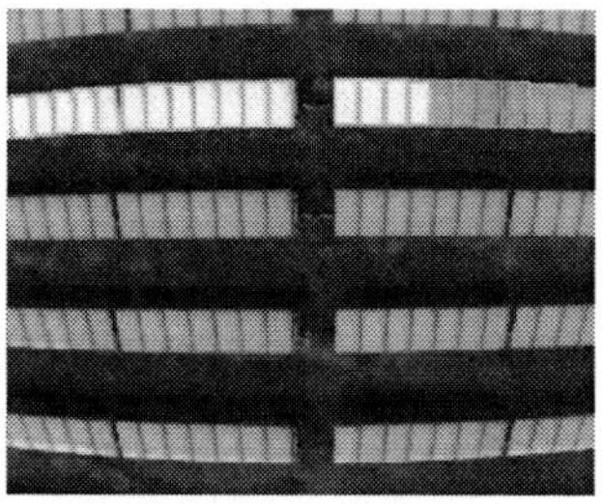

Figure 4: Example of module mapping into strings. Each module is indexed and ordered left-to-right within its row, allowing consistent profiling of the string structure

3.5 Gradient break

Once modules are grouped into ordered strings, their median temperatures are assembled into sequential profiles. Under normal conditions, these profiles remain relatively uniform, reflecting consistent thermal behavior across panels in the same row.

A gradient break is defined as a significant discontinuity in this sequence, where the temperature of one or more consecutive modules deviates abruptly from the trend of the string. Detecting such breaks allows the system to flag potential anomalies that extend beyond individual panels. Formally, given a string profile $T = \{t_1, t_2, \dots, t_n\}$, a break is identified whenever:

$$(6)\ |t_{i+1} - t_i| > \delta,$$

Where δ is an adaptive threshold that accounts for the expected thermal variability under field conditions. Figure 5 illustrates an example, where a sharp drop in temperature marks the onset of a string-level anomaly.

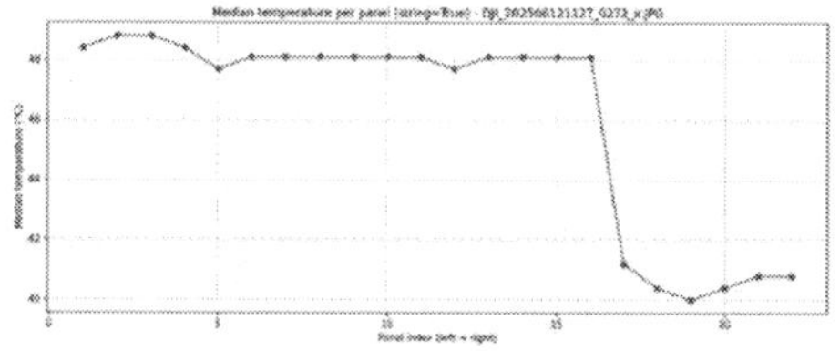

Figure 5: Median temperature profile along the modules of a single string. A sudden drop around panel 17 clearly indicates the onset of an open-circuit anomaly.

This profiling step transforms raw temperature values into an interpretable sequence, allowing anomalies to emerge clearly as deviations from the expected uniform pattern. Such representation provides a robust foundation for the subsequent region-propagation stage.

3.6 Region propagation for string propagation

In some cases, intermediate panels within a string may be missing from the profile, either due to detection failures or partial occlusions in the image. This can disrupt the continuity of the gradient-based analysis, leading to incomplete identification of the affected string.

To address this issue, we introduce a region-propagation algorithm where the basic units are not pixels but entire modules. Starting from the panels identified at the gradient break, the method iteratively extends the region to neighboring modules that share consistent thermal behavior. In this way, missing or occluded panels are incorporated into the open-circuit group, ensuring that the resulting string remains complete and representative of the underlying fault.

$$(7)\ R = \bigcup_{m_i \in B} \{m_j \in N(m_i) : |t_j - t_i| < \delta\}$$

Here in (Eq. 7) is where we define the region propagation step. Starting from the set B of modules identified at the gradient break, the algorithm expands the region by including neighboring modules $m_j \in N(m_i)$ whenever their median temperature t_j is sufficiently similar to that of the seed module t_i, with the similarity controlled by a threshold δ. The union operator ensures that all propagated neighbors are aggregated into a single contiguous region R, thereby recovering panels that may have been missed due to occlusion or detection errors.

4 USE CASE RESULTS

To illustrate the complete workflow, we present a representative case where the methodology is applied step by step until the final open-string detection is obtained. Each stage is shown in the figures below, with its corresponding explanation.

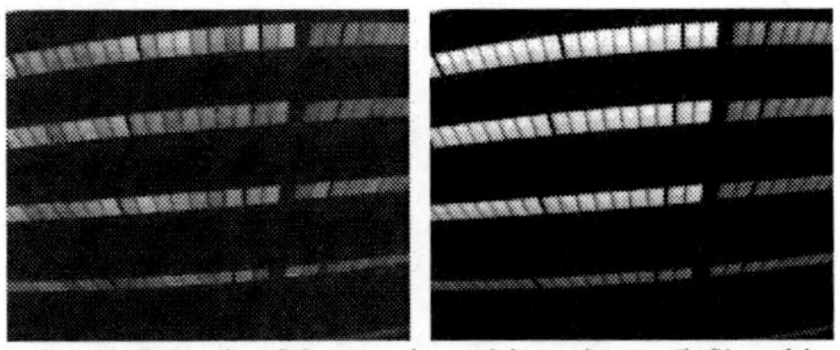

Figure 6. Example of the raw thermal input image (left) and its corresponding segmentation mask of detected modules (right). These provide the basis for subsequent analysis and allow the extraction of per-panel temperature values.

Once the modules are segmented, the system computes the median temperature of each panel along the string. By plotting these values sequentially, it becomes possible to identify sudden changes in the temperature profile, referred to as gradient breaks.

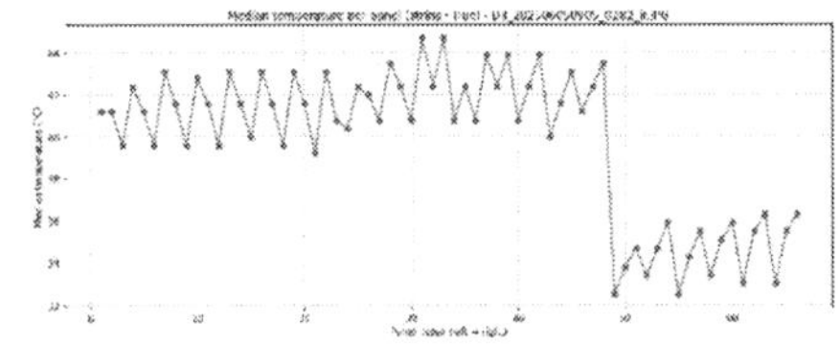

Figure 7. Temperature profile of the analyzed string. The plot reveals a sharp discontinuity that indicates the presence of an open-circuit anomaly.

Using this information, the affected region is isolated by generating a binary mask that highlights only the modules belonging to the abnormal string. This step enables precise localization of the fault while discarding unaffected modules.

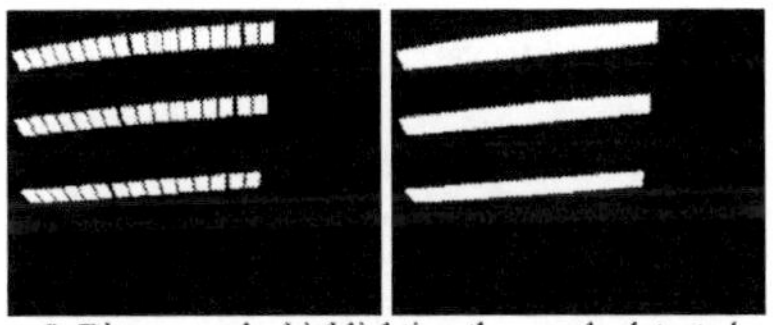

Figure 8. Binary masks highlighting the panels detected as part of the open string.

Finally, the binary masks are combined with the original thermal image, and a region-propagation algorithm is applied to ensure that all modules belonging to the same string are included—even if some were partially occluded or missed in earlier stages. This produces a complete visualization of the open-circuit defect.

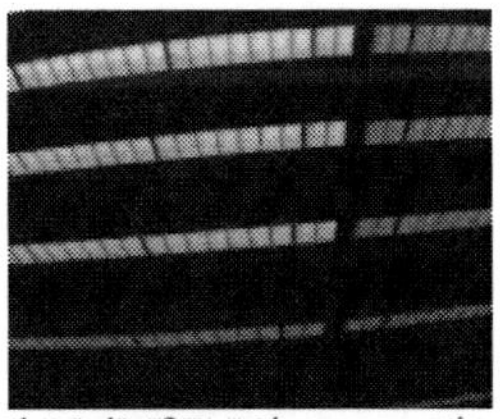

Figure 9. Final result after region propagation, showing the identified open-string modules superimposed on the original thermal image.

As shown in the final visualization, the open strings are clearly highlighted, while the panels at the far left are deliberately discarded. This exclusion is necessary because partially cropped modules at the image boundaries could otherwise lead to false positives in the analysis.

5 CONCLUSIONS AND FUTURE WORKS

This work introduced a hybrid methodology for the automated detection of open strings in utility-scale PV plants using aerial infrared thermography. By integrating module segmentation, thermal profiling, and a region-propagation algorithm, the system achieves reliable identification of string-level faults under diverse operating conditions.

Compared to purely deep-learning models, the proposed workflow reduces false positives and remains scalable to large inspection campaigns. From an operational perspective, the method provides actionable outputs that can directly support O&M strategies, enabling early fault localization and contributing to reduced energy losses. Literature reports indicate that undetected string-level faults can increase the levelized cost of electricity (LCOE) by 3–7% depending on plant topology and irradiance [23], suggesting that systematic adoption of automated detection workflows such as the one presented here can yield tangible financial benefits for asset owners.

Nonetheless, the current methodology still depends on the accuracy of the segmentation stage, which may degrade under strong occlusions or image artifacts. In addition, extreme environmental conditions (very low irradiance, rapidly changing cloud cover, or excessive wind) can distort thermal gradients and affect anomaly propagation.

Future research will therefore focus on expanding the dataset with additional climatic and technological scenarios, integrating complementary data sources (e.g., IV curves, SCADA signals, EL imaging) for cross-validation, and refining the propagation logic for cases of highly irregular degradation. Further work will also explore optimization for real-time deployment on UAV platforms, facilitating on-site decision-making during inspections.

6 REFERENCES

[1] IEA-PVPS Task 13. (2018). *Review on Infrared and Electroluminescence Imaging for PV Field Applications.* Report T13-10:2018. International Energy Agency – PVPS.

[2] Islam, M. T., Almutairi, A., & Rahman, S. (2023). *Artificial Intelligence in Photovoltaic Fault Identification and Monitoring.* Energies, 16(21), 7417. https://doi.org/10.3390/en16217417

[3] Muttillo, M., Pantoli, L., Stornelli, V., & Ferri, G. (2020). *On-Field Infrared Thermography Sensing for PV System Characterization.* Sensors, 20(21), 6051. https://doi.org/10.3390/s20216051

[4] de Oliveira, A. C., Pereira, R., & Andrade, L. (2023). *Automatic fault detection of utility-scale PV power plants and physical location inside the site.* Solar Energy, 258, 124–135. https://doi.org/10.1016/j.solener.2023.01.058

[5] Xie, H., Yuan, B., Hu, C., & Chen, H. (2024). *ST-YOLO: A defect detection method for photovoltaic modules based on infrared thermal imaging and machine vision technology.* PLOS ONE, 19(12), e0310742. https://doi.org/10.1371/journal.pone.0310742

[6] García, G., Aparcedo, A., Nayak, G. K., Ahmed, T., Shah, M., & Li, M. (2024). *Generalized deep learning model for photovoltaic module segmentation from satellite and aerial imagery (Mask2Former).* Solar Energy, 274, 112539. https://doi.org/10.1016/j.solener.2024.112539

[7] Clark, M., & Pacifici, F. (2023). *A solar panel dataset of very high-resolution satellite imagery.* Scientific Data, 10, 636. https://doi.org/10.1038/s41597-023-02761-0

[8] Gallardo-Saavedra, S., Lillo-Saavedra, M., Cortés, J. A., & Peña, R. (2020). *Infrared Thermography for the Detection and Characterization of Photovoltaic Defects: Comparison between Illumination and Dark Conditions.* Sensors, 20(16), 4395. https://doi.org/10.3390/s20164395

[9] de Oliveira, A. K. V., Aghaei, M., & Rüther, R. (2020). *Aerial infrared thermography for low-cost and fast fault detection in utility-scale PV power plants.* Solar Energy, 211, 712–724. https://doi.org/10.1016/j.solener.2020.09.066

[10] IEC. (2017). *IEC TS 62446-3:2017. Photovoltaic (PV) systems – Part 3: Outdoor infrared thermography.* International Electrotechnical Commission.

[11] IEA-PVPS Task 13. (2022). *Guidelines for Operation and Maintenance of Photovoltaic Power Plants in Different Climates.* Report T13-25:2022. International Energy Agency – PVPS.

[12] Pelaez, S., Marion, B., Deline, C., & Stein, J. (2018). *Model and Validation of Single-Axis Tracking with Bifacial PV — Benefit in Addition to 15–25% vs Fixed-Tilt.* NREL/TP-5K00-72039. National Renewable Energy Laboratory.

[13] PV-Tech. (2015). *Motivation for single-axis trackers versus fixed tilt.* PVTech Power, (23), 46–51.

[14] Barbón, A., Fernández, D., & López, J. (2025). *Fixed Tilt vs. Horizontal Single-Axis Tracker: Comparative Study.* Applied Sciences, 15(8), 4571. https://doi.org/10.3390/app15084571

[15] IEA-PVPS Task 13. (2024). *Best Practices for the Optimization of Bifacial Photovoltaic Tracking Systems.* Report T13-26:2024. International Energy Agency – PVPS.

[16] IEA-PVPS / Sandia PV Performance Modeling Collaborative. (2024). *Task 13 notes on KPIs, partial shading and O&M.* Available at: https://pvpmc.sandia.gov

[17] Sandia PV Performance Modeling Collaborative. (2024). *Subsystem analysis resources and modeling guide.* Available at: https://pvpmc.sandia.gov

[18] Sadeghi, A., Moradi, M., & Hejazi, M. (2025). *Review and Comparative Analysis of Solar Tracking Systems.* Energies, 18(10), 2553. https://doi.org/10.3390/en18102553

[19] Tan, W., Li, H., & Xu, Z. (2021). *Comprehensive Methodology to Evaluate Parasitic Energy Consumption for Dual-Axis Sun-Tracking Systems.* International Journal of Photoenergy, 2021, 6654321. https://doi.org/10.1155/2021/6654321

[20] Jia, Y., Chen, G., & Zhao, L. (2024). *Defect detection of photovoltaic modules based on improved VarifocalNet.* Scientific Reports, 14, 15170. https://doi.org/10.1038/s41598-024-66234-3

[21] He, K., Gkioxari, G., Dollár, P., & Girshick, R. (2017). *Mask R-CNN.* Proceedings of the IEEE International Conference on Computer Vision (ICCV), 2961–2969. https://doi.org/10.1109/ICCV.2017.322

[22] Powers, D. M. W. (2011). *Evaluation: From Precision, Recall and F-measure to ROC, Informedness, Markedness & Correlation.* Journal of Machine Learning Technologies, 2(1), 37–63.

[23] Rivai, A., Abd Rahim, N., Mohamad Elias, M. F., & Jamaludin, J. (2020). *Analysis of Photovoltaic String Failure and Health Monitoring with Module Fault Identification. Energies*, **13**(1), 100. DOI: 10.3390/en13010100

AUTOMATED IDENTIFICATION OF OPEN CIRCUITS IN PHOTOVOLTAIC ARRAYS VIA MASK-RCNN, THERMOGRAPHIC SIGNAL PROCESSING AND HYBRIDIZED REGION-GROWTH ALGORITHMS

uc3m | Universidad Carlos III de Madrid
AMPL | Autonomous Mobility and Perception Lab

Daniel J. Castillo Patton [1], Lucas Viani [1], Fernando García[2], Mario Martínez[1], Sergio Suárez[1], Sofía Rodríguez-Conde [1], José Manuel Rivas[1]*
***email:** daniel.castillo.p@applus.com*

[1] Enertis Applus S.L. – Business Development Department
[2] Autonomus Mobility and Perception Lab (AMPL), UC3M

ENERTIS Applus

INTRODUCTION

- Open-circuit defects remain a critical source of performance loss in PV arrays.
- Infrared thermography enables fault detection, but manual analysis is unfeasible at scale.
- Conventional deep learning approaches often struggle in unseen environments or with limited data, raising a challenge in some situations.
- In this work, we propose a hybrid workflow combining segmentation, temperature profiling, and region propagation to ensure robust detection of open strings.

Detection of open circuits in PV panels

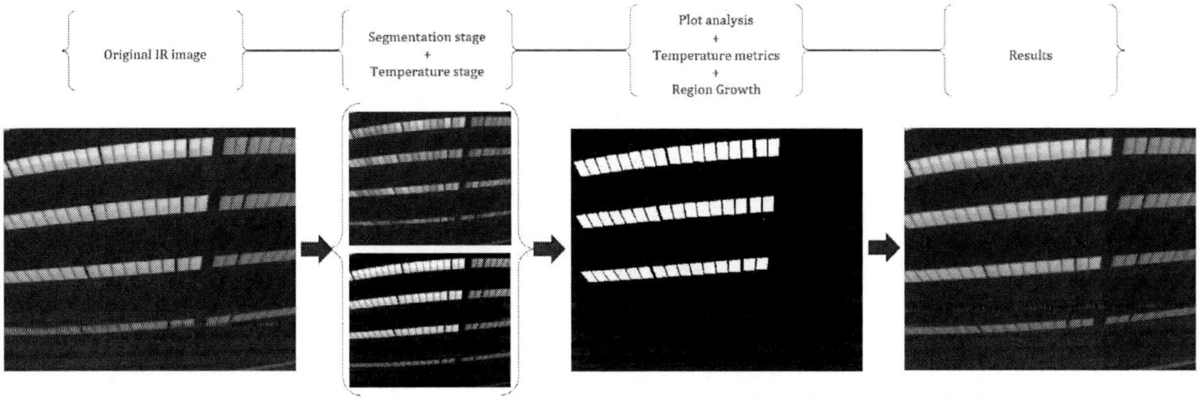

The proposed workflow is based on the combination of different technologies with the goal of automatically detecting open circuits in thermographic images. The aim of this work is to provide an alternative methodology for identifying these defects that does not rely on conventional neural networks, allowing adaptation to unfamiliar environments or situations with limited data availability.

Proposed system

Modules are segmented with Mask R-CNN and enriched with pixel-level temperature data to generate profiles that reveal gradient changes along strings. A region-growing algorithm then merges neighboring panels, enabling full open-circuit string detection.

Module mapping of strings

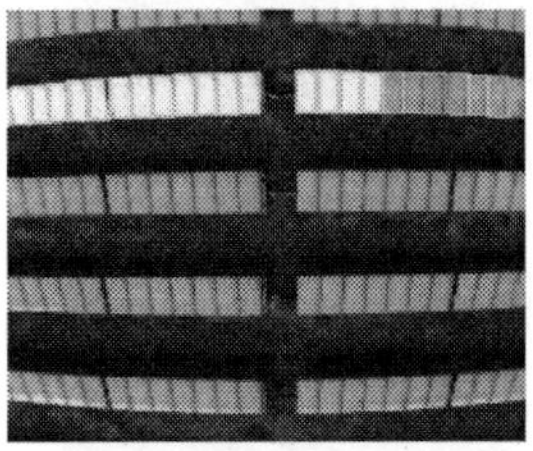

Identifying each module individually allows us to calculate temperatures per panel and then group them to analyze string-level behavior.

This approach provides a clearer view of how local anomalies propagate across the string.

Region-propagation of panels

After detecting a gradient break in the temperature profile, neighboring modules with similar values are propagated in the similar series value, ensuring physically separated panels and intermediate anomalies are included in the open string.

Conclusions

- Hybrid workflow with segmentation, temperature profiling and region-propagation detects open circuits without large datasets.
- Robust across environmental conditions, outperforming purely deep-learning approaches.
- Scalable for automated PV inspections, enabling faster fault detection and reduced energy losses.

Deep Learning Model – Mask RCNN

Modules are segmented using a Mask R-CNN, providing individual identification for each panel.

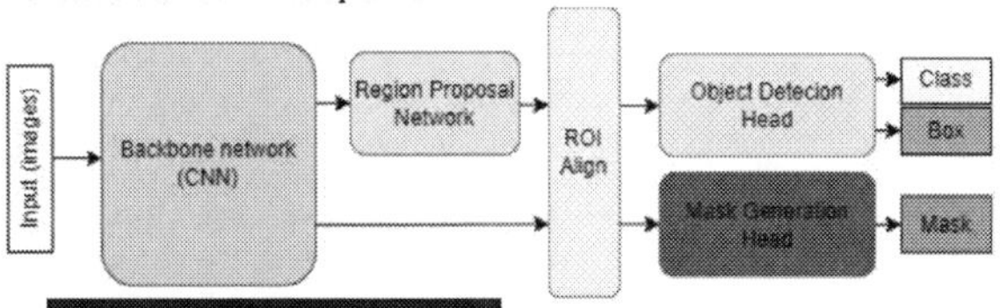

Temperature profiling

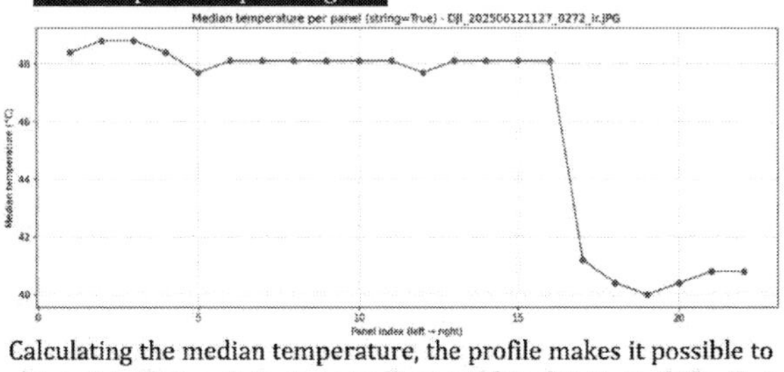

Calculating the median temperature, the profile makes it possible to observe uniform sections as well as sudden drops or shifts that indicate anomalies in the temperature behavior of the string.

References

- El-Banby, G. M., Moawad, N. M., Abouzalm, B. A., Abouzaid, W. F., & Ramadan, E. A. (2023). *Photovoltaic system fault detection techniques: a review.* Neural Computing and Applications, 35, 24829-24842. https://doi.org/10.1007/s00521-023-09041-7
- Jia, Y., Chen, G., & Zhao, L. (2024). *Defect detection of photovoltaic modules based on improved VarifocalNet.* Scientific Reports, 14, 15170. https://doi.org/10.1038/s41598-024-66234-3

UNDERPERFORMANCE OF PV PLANTS. AN ANALYSIS IN OVER 3.3GW

Quiroz, Mónica and Solórzano, Jorge
Qualifying Photovoltaics S.L., 102 Caleruega Street, 10th Floor. 28033 Madrid, Spain.
Tel.: +34 644 72 51 74
m.quiroz@qpv.es, j.solorzano@qpv.es

ABSTRACT: The rapid growth of solar energy and shrinking project margins highlight the need to optimize photovoltaic (PV) plant operation and maintenance (O&M). However, a growing number of installations show deviations between expected and actual production, jeopardizing profitability. This paper presents results from the PhotoVoltaics Evaluation Tool (PVET), developed by Qualifying Photovoltaics S.L. (QPV), applied to over 3.3GW of peak capacity PV plants and 4.2 GW.year of operational data. PVET performs real-time monitoring, data filtering, and in-depth analysis; considering irradiance, module temperature, and electrical performance. Recurrent operational failures—such as inverter shutdowns, tracking failures, open strings, etc—were identified, causing annual energy losses of 1–3% and up to 7.9% in critical cases. Non-recoverable losses, such as grid restrictions, were also identified. PVET's filtering module enhances fault detection, quantifies energy losses more accurately, and mitigates biases in production assessments. Results demonstrate that advanced data-driven diagnostic tools in PV O&M enable significant loss reduction, improve system reliability and increase project profitability, thus supporting large-scale solar deployment.

Keywords: Photovoltaics Failures, O&M, Failures, Big Data.

1 INTRODUCTION

As the need to mitigate emissions and address climate change becomes more urgent, solar energy plays an increasingly decisive role in the international energy matrix. The solar industry is experiencing continuous growth, having surpassed 2 TW of global installed capacity, with expectations to reach 3.5 TW by 2027. [1]

Due to the rapid evolution of the sector and the reduction in project costs and economic margins, optimizing the operation, performance, and maintenance (O&M) of photovoltaic systems is presented as a critical challenge and a key element for their long-term sustainability. However, plant productivity often falls short of expectations. According to the Solar Risk Assessment 2025 by kWh Analytics, published as part of their industry report series, PV plants underperform against P50 expectations by an average of 8.6%, confirming a persistent gap between financial models and real-world production. [2]

Our internal analyses estimate that recurrent operational failures can account for up to 7.9% of annual energy production losses. These losses are mainly associated with inverter shutdowns, open strings, other system-level malfunctions and external factors. Their magnitude, however, is not uniform: it varies depending on the geographical location of the plant, the presence or absence of solar tracking systems, and the availability and reliability of the local power grid. To systematically address these challenges and reduce their impact, Qualifying Photovoltaics S.L. has developed the PhotoVoltaics Evaluation Tool (PVET), an advanced analytics platform designed to detect, classify, and quantify failures across diverse PV portfolios.

2 PVET

2.1 Function

The primary objective of PVET is to serve as an automated analysis tool designed to optimize the performance of photovoltaic (PV) plants. This is achieved by improving the accuracy of initial estimates and enhancing Operations and Maintenance (O&M) tasks, thereby reducing losses and increasing profitability.

PVET operates through four integrated stages. First. SCADA monitoring collects real-time data on irradiance, temperature, current, voltage, and other key variables from plant sensors. This information is then securely transmitted and centralized in the PVET Cloud. Next, data filtering algorithms remove incomplete or inconsistent records, ensuring reliable inputs for analysis. Finally, advanced data analytics are applied to detect, diagnose, and quantify failures across the plant's operation.

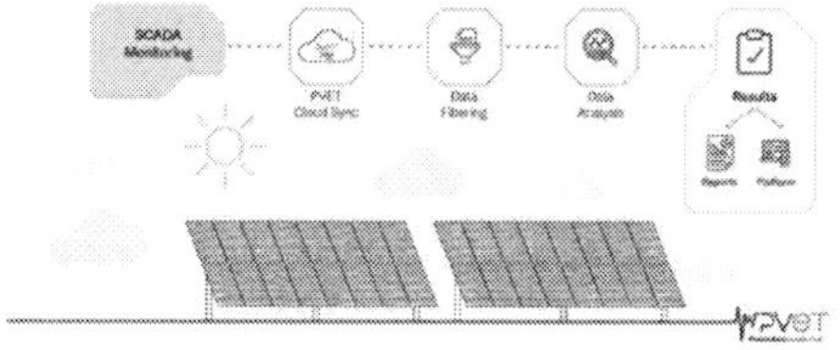

Figure 1: Operation of PVET.

2.2 Data filtering and augmentation

Reliable failure detection in PV plants requires complete and accurate data to properly evaluate device performance and ensure generation efficiency. In practice, however, communication errors or interruptions in data transmission are common, often limiting the correct assessment of the operational status of inverters, stringboxes, and trackers. To address these issues and minimize false positives. PVET integrates a dedicated data filtering and augmentation module.

Data filtering removes incoherent or inconsistent values, ensuring that only high-quality information is used in the analysis, for example, negative irradiance values or those over 1.300 W/m2. Data augmentation complements this process by inferring and reconstructing missing values when devices are offline or data is missing—for example, when an inverter is stopped, a string or stringbox is disconnected, or a tracker has no communication with its RTU. By analyzing historical records and operational trends, QPV's algorithms generate reliable estimates for

10.4229/EUPVSEC2025/4CV.1.19

critical variables at both device and plant level. This enables more accurate identification of inverter stops, open strings, or tracker malfunctions, enhancing the robustness of performance analysis.

Applying this method to the plant portfolio revealed significant differences. Table VI summarizes these results, demonstrating that inverter-related losses increased from 12.4 GWh to 24.3 GWh after data augmentation, representing a difference of +96%. Similarly, tracker-related losses increased from 46.8 GWh to 53.0 GWh, corresponding to a +12% difference. These findings confirm that raw datasets tend to underestimate the actual impact of operational failures, whereas data augmentation reveals hidden losses with greater accuracy.

Table I: Comparison of inverter- and tracker-related losses before and after data augmentation.

Category	Losses (GWh)	Losses _ Augmentation (GWh)	% of Difference
Inverter	12.4	24.3	96
Tracker	46.8	53.0	12

2.3 Failure detection, diagnosis and quantification algorithms

PVET employs advanced algorithms to detect, diagnose, and quantify failures that affect PV plant performance across all operational levels. At the plant level, external factors such as grid restrictions can be identified; at the inverter level, shutdowns, overheating, or curtailments are detected; at the stringbox level, disconnected strings and imbalances are revealed; and at the tracker level, misalignments and tracking errors are monitored where applicable.

The system not only identifies failures but also quantifies the associated energy losses, providing precise estimates that can be used for performance assessment or claims. Tested in real PV plants. PVET's algorithms have demonstrated false positive rates below 1%. ensuring reliability in operational environments. In addition, the module is capable of diagnosing, evaluating, and predicting performance anomalies by distinguishing between data acquisition errors, generation failures, and predictive indicators of malfunction.

3 QUANTIFICATIONS OF FAILURES AND LOSSES

The study analyzed 37 photovoltaic (PV) plants from QPV's portfolio, totaling 3.2 GW of installed capacity and 4.2 GW.year of operational data. This metric converts installed capacity and operation time into an annual power equivalent, allowing for consistent comparison across plants, even when their operational periods differ. Table II summarizes the key characteristics of the evaluated plants.

Table II: PV plants analyzed by continent and installed peak power.

Continent	Number of Plants	Total Peak Power (MWp)
Africa	3	189
Oceania	1	429
Europe	14	597
North America	7	755
South America	12	1332

Among these, 18 plants are equipped with trackers, while 19 operate without tracking systems.

3.1 Recoverable and Non-Recoverable Failures

To achieve a more accurate assessment of failures in photovoltaic plants, a classification into two main categories is proposed: recoverable failures and non-recoverable failures. These failures are detected through QPV's proprietary algorithms and are described below.

3.1.1 Recoverable failures

These failures are production losses that can be mitigated through timely O&M interventions. With effective monitoring platforms such as PVET and proper maintenance execution, these energy losses can be recovered. Typical recoverable failures relate to O&M efficiency, equipment condition, control system performance, or components requiring calibration or replacement. Early detection plays a crucial role in minimizing their impact on energy generation. Table III presents this classification, organized into three categories according to the affected device.

Table III: Recoverable failures.

Category	Recoverable Failures
Inverter	Inverter stop, MPPT failure, MPPT temperature and MPPT VDC
Generator	Open string, open stringbox, defective string and defective diode
Tracker	Tracking stop, misalignment, flag position, target position error and wind alarm

3.1.2 Non-Recoverable failures

Non-recoverable failures are beyond the scope of O&M and originate from external factors or inherent design limitations. Table III summarizes these failures in two categories: grid and inverter. Among them, grid-related failures have the greatest impact, as they represent the most significant share of energy losses.

Table IV: Non-Recoverable failures.

Category	Non-Recoverable Failures
Grid	Grid constrictions, grid shutdown and grid saturation
Inverter	Saturation

3.2 Results

The total production reached 8,299 GWh, with 3.8% attributed to non-recoverable losses, 2.6% to recoverable

10.4229/EUPVSEC2025/4CV.1.19

losses, and an additional 1.5% from other factors such as vegetation, soiling, and excessive module degradation. These results highlight the importance of considering all three categories of losses when assessing operational performance and profitability. Non-recoverable failures represent permanently lost energy, primarily caused by grid-related constraints, and thus remain an unavoidable limitation that directly reduces the maximum achievable yield of PV plants.

Table V: Overall energy production and distribution of recoverable and non-recoverable losses.

Category	Energy (GWh)	% of Total Energy Production
Total production	8,299	100
Non-Recovareble losses	326	3.8
Recoverable losses	223	2.6
Other losses	125	1.5

Table VI provides a breakdown of failures by category. Plant-level incidents, mainly related to grid restrictions, represent the largest share with 59.3% of total failures (3.8% of production). Inverter-related failures contribute 14% (0.9% of production), generator-related issues account for 15.8% (1.0% of production), while tracker failures have the lowest impact with 10.6% of failures (0.7% of production).

The results indicate that tracker-related losses are comparatively smaller in the mixed portfolio than in plants composed exclusively of tracker-based systems. This is because the presence of non-tracking plants dilutes the overall contribution of tracker-specific issues—such as misalignment, wind alarms, or position errors—when aggregated at portfolio level. In contrast, portfolios consisting entirely of tracker-equipped plants exhibit a higher sensitivity to these operational failures, leading to a larger relative impact on total losses.

Table VI: Breakdown of operational losses by category and contribution to total energy production with and without tracker.

Category	Energy (GWh)	% of Total Failures	% of Total Energy Production
Plant	325	59.3	3.8
Inverter	76	14	0.9
Generator	87	15.8	1.0
Tracker	59	10.6	0.7

Finally, a sub-classification was performed between plants with and without trackers.

3.2.1 PV plants with tracking systems

Table VII summarizes the 18 photovoltaic plants in the study equipped with solar tracking systems. The table reports their distribution by continent, the number of installations, and the corresponding total peak power. Europe accounts for the largest number of plants with trackers, while Oceania contributes the single largest plant in terms of peak capacity.

Table VII: PV plants with tracking systems by continent and installed peak power

Continent	Number of Plants	Total Peak Power (MWp)
Oceania	1	429
Europe	9	448
North America	2	296
South America	5	252

Figure 2 illustrates the share of recoverable and non-recoverable failures across the analyzed PV plants. Non-recoverable failures account for 62.93% of total losses, while recoverable failures represent 37.07%. This distribution is largely explained by the concentration of PV plants with tracking systems in Europe, a continent where grid restrictions remain a significant challenge. In contrast, in North and South America, these restrictions are less severe, as the installed renewable capacity in terms of MW peak is comparatively lower, resulting in fewer non-recoverable losses.

According to Jäger-Waldau [3], the total installed solar photovoltaic capacity exceeded 1.6 TWp at the end of 2023, with an annual newly installed capacity of more than 420 GWp. Europe contributed over 260 GWp, North America around 170 GWp, and South America approximately 40 GWp. This indicates a significant global expansion of solar energy, with Europe contributing a substantial share. In comparison, North and South America have lower installed capacities, which may correlate with fewer grid-related restrictions and, consequently, fewer non-recoverable failures in PV plants.

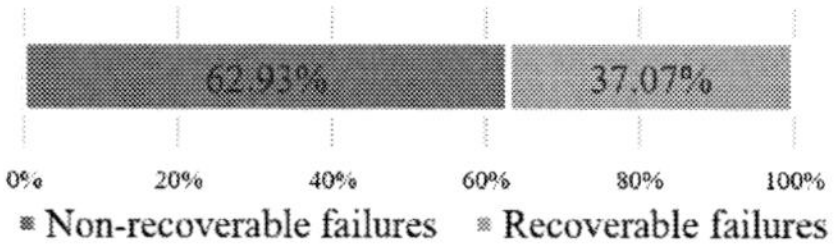

Figure 2: Distribution of recoverable and non-recoverable failures in PV plants with tracker

The presented percentages of recoverable and non-recoverable failures represent the share of losses relative to the annual energy production of all evaluated plants. Among non-recoverable failures presented in Figure 3, grid-related issues are the most significant, with grid constrictions having the highest impact (5.80%), followed by grid shutdowns (0.72%) and grid saturation (0.26%). Inverter saturation was negligible (0.001%). These results highlight the structural influence of grid availability on PV plant performance, in contrast to equipment-level failures.

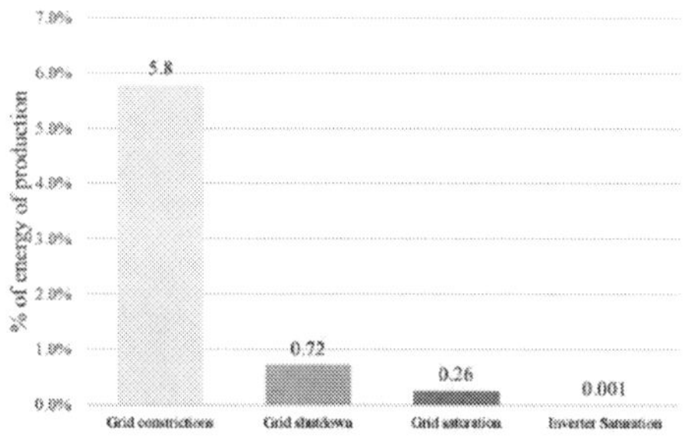

10.4229/EUPVSEC2025/4CV.1.19
020328-003

Figure 3: Distribution of non-recoverable failures in PV plants with tracker.

In contrast, of recoverable failures, the most frequent events are inverter stops (1.2%), misalignment (1.1%), open strings (0.8%). and open stringboxes (0.5%). Additional recoverable issues include tracking stops (0.3%), flag position errors (0.2%), MPPT failures (0.06%), and other minor failures (0.13%) like defective strings, defective diodes, target position error, wind alarm, MPPT Temperature and MPPT VDC.

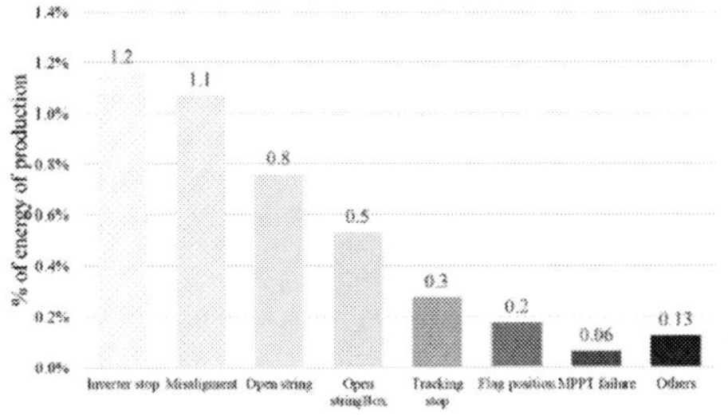

Figure 4: Distribution of recoverable failures in PV plants with tracker.

Table VIII presents the breakdown of operational losses in plants equipped with trackers. Plant-level incidents, mostly related to grid restrictions, dominate with 63% of total failures, representing 6.7% of annual energy production. Inverter and generator failures contribute similarly, each accounting for around 12% of failures (≈1.3% of production). Tracker-specific issues, such as misalignment or wind alarms, represent 14% of failures, with an impact of 1.5% on production. Overall, these results confirm that grid-related restrictions remain the primary structural limitation, while tracker-related losses, although smaller, are still relevant in portfolios fully dependent on tracking systems.

Table VIII: Breakdown of operational losses by category and contribution to total energy production with tracker

Category	Energy (GWh)	% of Total Failures	% of Total Energy Production
Plant	272	63	6.7
Inverter	59	11	1.3
Generator	52	12	1.3
Tracker	59	14	1.5

3.2.2 PV plants without tracker

Table IX summarizes the 19 photovoltaic plants analyzed in this study that operate without solar tracking systems. Their distribution across countries shows variability in the number of installations and installed peak power. Notably, South America accounts for the highest installed capacity 1,044 MWp while Europe contributes the smallest share with 148 MWp. This heterogeneity reflects different deployment strategies across regions, where countries with high solar resources but lower grid saturation tend to host larger non-tracking systems.

Table IX: PV plants without tracking systems by continent and installed peak power

Continent	Number of Plants	Total Peak Power (MWp)
Africa	3	189
Europe	5	148
North America	5	459
South America	6	1044

Figure 5 illustrates the distribution of failures in these plants. In contrast to plants equipped with tracking systems, recoverable failures dominate with 53.77% of total losses, while non-recoverable failures account for 46.23%. This distribution suggests that non-tracking plants face a higher proportion of faults that can be mitigated through O&M interventions, such as inverter stops and open strings, which represent major opportunities for performance recovery. Just like in plants with trackers, non-recoverable failures in these plants are mainly linked to grid limitations, although their relative impact is lower than in countries with high renewable penetration such as Europe.

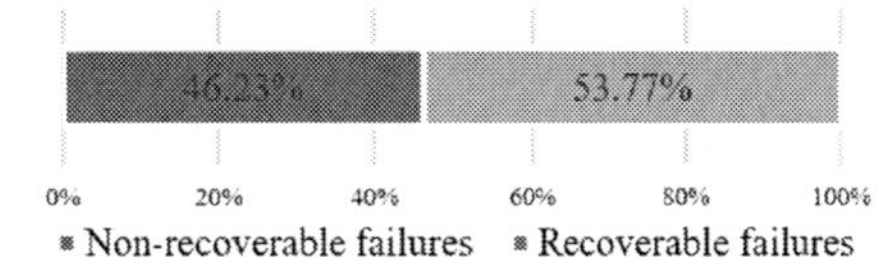

Figure 5: Distribution of recoverable and non-recoverable failures in PV plants without tracker.

Non-recoverable failures are mainly related to grid limitations, with grid constrictions representing 0.9%, grid shutdowns 0.2%, and grid saturation 0.1%. Inverter saturation contributes only marginally 0.004%.

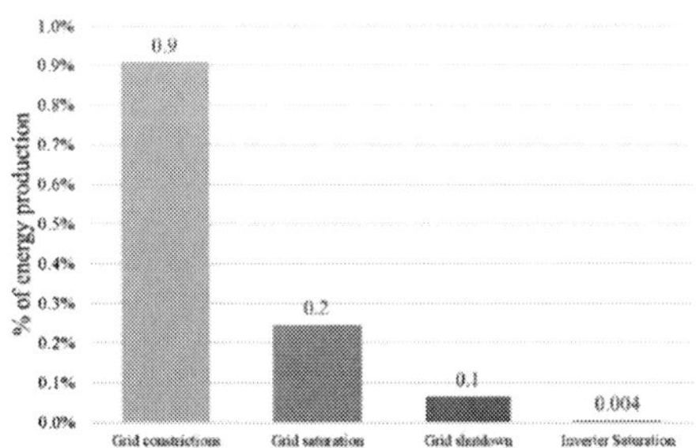

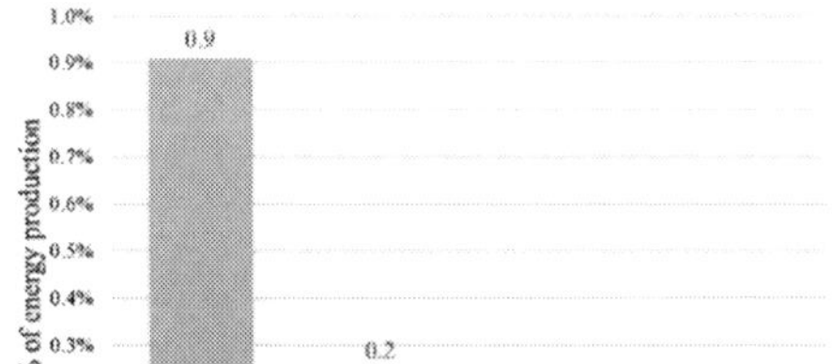

Figure 6: Distribution of non-recoverable failures in PV plants with tracker.

On the other hand, of recoverable failures, the most common events are open strings (0.69%) and inverter stops (0.59%), which together represent the majority of recoverable issues. Additional failures include open stringboxes (0.07%), MPPT failures (0.03%), defective diodes (0.02%), defective strings (0.01%), and other minor issues (0.01%).

10.4229/EUPVSEC2025/4CV.1.19

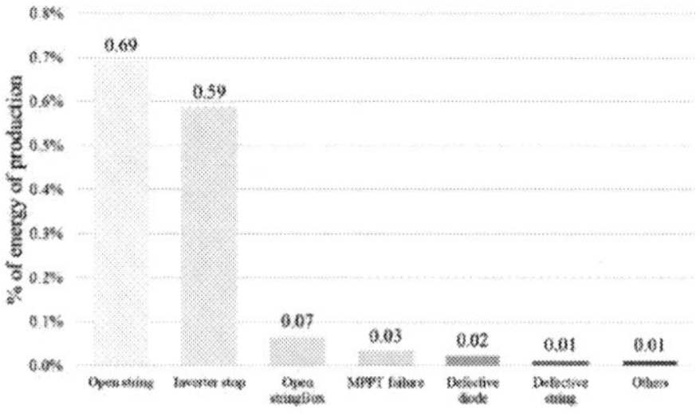

Figure 7: Distribution of recoverable failures in PV plants without tracker.

Table X summarizes the breakdown of operational losses in plants without trackers. Plant-level incidents, mainly linked to grid restrictions, account for 46% of total failures, corresponding to 1.2% of annual production. Inverter-related issues represent 24% of failures (0.6% of production), while generator failures contribute 30% (0.8% of production). Compared to plants with trackers, the overall impact of losses is lower, particularly at the plant level, reflecting reduced exposure to tracker-specific issues and a more balanced distribution of failures across components.

Table X: Breakdown of operational losses by category and contribution to total energy production without tracker

Category	Energy (GWh)	% of Total Failures	% of Total Energy Production
Plant	54	46	1.2
Inverter	28	24	0.6
Generator	35	30	0.8

Overall, the comparison between plants with and without trackers shows that tracker plants are more exposed to additional recoverable failures, but these can be better quantified through data augmentation. Conversely, in plants without trackers, recoverable failures dominate and represent a major opportunity for O&M-driven mitigation.

4 DEVIATIONS FROM INITIAL EXPECTATIONS

The PV plant operational chain illustrates how resource availability, environmental conditions, and equipment performance contribute to deviations from initial yield expectations. In the first assessment, based on raw measurements, global horizontal irradiation (GHI) presented a deviation of –7.4%, partially offset by a gain of +3.1% in the global tilted irradiation (GTI). However, after applying data filtering and removing incorrectly measured values, the results converged to more consistent deviations of –2.0% for GHI and –2.3% for GTI.

Figure 8 shows the loss chain using unfiltered irradiance values, while Figure 9 illustrates the loss chain after data filtering. The comparison between both figures highlights the importance of data preprocessing: filtering reduces uncertainty, corrects measurement errors, and provides a more reliable basis for assessing PV plant performance and expected production gaps.

Beyond irradiance corrections, global effective irradiation (GEI), which accounts for module spectral and reflection losses, showed a deviation of –1.1%. Temperature effects were also unfavorable, with an additional loss of –0.8%. The combined deviation of irradiance and temperature resources, relative to initial expectations, reached –3.9%. At the equipment level, inverters and generators contributed –0.9% and –1.0% losses, respectively, while trackers added another –0.7%. Additional factors such as soiling, vegetation, and excessive module degradation accounted for 1.5%, while grid-level restrictions contributed –3.8%. Altogether, operational losses amounted to –7.9% of expected production.

When combined with the irradiance and temperature deviations, the total underperformance reached –11.9% compared to initial expectations. These results highlight two key insights: (i) initial yield assessments tend to be systematically optimistic, and (ii) resource variability and equipment underperformance remain the dominant contributors to energy gaps. Incorporating these deviations into predictive models and long-term planning can significantly improve risk assessment, strengthen forecasting accuracy, and ultimately ensure more resilient investment strategies for large-scale PV deployment.

Figure 8: Loss chain without filtering data of GHI and GTI.

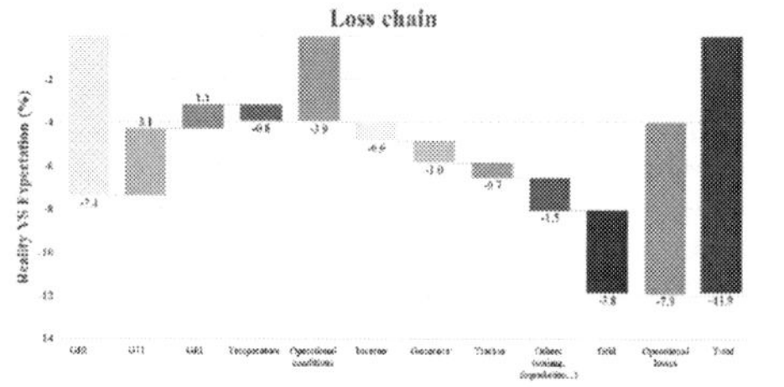

Figure 9: Loss chain with filtering data of GHI and GTI.

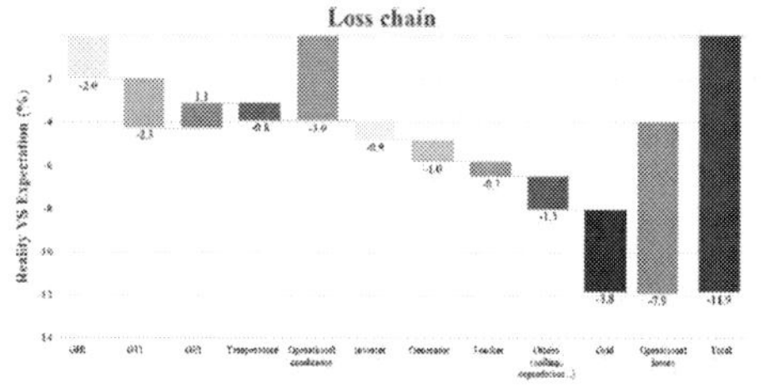

5 CONCLUSIONS

The analysis provides a detailed understanding of energy losses and performance deviations in utility-scale PV portfolios. Recoverable failures, such as inverter stoppages, MPPT issues, generator string faults, and tracker misalignments, represent around 2.6% of annual production losses and can be mitigated through timely O&M interventions supported by monitoring platforms like PVET, emphasizing the value of proactive maintenance.

Non-recoverable failures, accounting for approximately 3.8% of annual losses, are mainly caused by grid restrictions, shutdowns, and inverter saturation. This highlights the importance of considering regional grid conditions when planning new PV projects.

The use of data filtering and augmentation enhanced

failure detection by removing erroneous measurements, normalizing missing operational periods, and uncovering previously hidden recoverable losses. This approach allows for better-informed O&M strategies and contributes to improving plant reliability and profitability.

Performance deviations were primarily driven by solar resource variability and generator performance. Efficiency and temperature effects provided only a partial offset to these losses. On average, actual production was 11.9% below expectations, 3.9% from lower-than-expected available resource and 7.9% coming from operational losses.

Overall, combining failure classification, data augmentation, and analysis of performance deviations provides a comprehensive framework for optimizing PV portfolio operations. This approach not only supports targeted maintenance and energy recovery but also guides strategic planning to maximize reliability and economic performance across diverse geographic regions.

6 ACKNOWLEDGEMENTS

The authors gratefully acknowledge the financial support provided by the Institute for Energy Diversification and Saving (IDAE), within the framework of the Recovery, Transformation and Resilience Plan – funded by the European Union – Next Generation EU, under grant agreement PR-NMN-01-2023-000162. The authors also wish to thank Qualifying Photovoltaics (QPV) for granting access to the portfolio data and for their collaboration, which made this research possible.

7 REFERENCES

[1] Raptor Maps. (2025). 2025 Global Solar Report: The State of PV Performance. https://raptormaps.com/solar-tech-docs/global-solar-report-2025
[2] kWh Analytics, "Solar Risk Assessment 2025," Industry Report, San Francisco, CA, USA, 2025. Accessed: Sept. 20, 2025: https://www.kwhanalytics.com/solar-risk-assessment
[3] A. Jäger-Waldau, "Snapshot of Photovoltaics February 2024," *EPJ Photovoltaics*, vol. 15, 2024. Accessed: Sept. 20, 2025: https://doi.org/10.1051/epjpv/2024018

10.4229/EUPVSEC2025/4CV.1.19
020328-006

BASELINE EFFICIENCY: A NEW KEY PERFORMANCE INDICATOR FOR PV SYSTEMS

Anastasios Kladas, Bert Herteleer, Jan Cappelle
KU Leuven Research Group ELECTA Ghent, Gebroeders De Smetstraat 1, 9000 Ghent, Belgium
anastasios.kladas@kuleuven.be

ABSTRACT: This work introduces Baseline Efficiency (BE), a novel key performance indicator (KPI) for photovoltaic (PV) systems. BE quantifies system degradation and serves as a reference to identify thermal losses, faults, and other performance deviations. Calculated through PV output modeling, instantaneous efficiency calculations, filtering, and daily aggregation, BE captures changes in maximum power point (MPP) current, voltage, and power, and can incorporate open- and short-circuit data to reflect changes across the entire IV curve. By integrating BE, long-term PV output estimations become more accurate compared to static models, which degrade in precision due to system aging. BE also enhances fault detection and power forecasting when paired with weather forecasts. Results from a 6-year dataset demonstrate that BE stabilizes estimation accuracy for power and current, with voltage showing minimal degradation.

Keywords: PV output estimation, PV degradation, PV KPI

1 INTRODUCTION

Accurate estimation of photovoltaic (PV) system output is critical for effective fault detection and performance monitoring. Traditional KPIs, such as Performance Ratio (PR) and Energy Performance Index (EPI) [1], along with their instantaneous counterparts, normalized efficiency (η_N) [2] and Power Performance Index (PPI) [3], aggregate energy values to assess PV efficiency. However, these metrics incorporate all losses (e.g., faults, degradation, and low-light conditions), making them unsuitable as direct inputs for precise PV output estimation models. This work proposes Baseline Efficiency (BE) as a new KPI to address these limitations. BE focuses on capturing degradation and soiling patterns, enabling dynamic adjustments to PV output models for improved long-term accuracy. By serving as a reference for non-degradation-related losses, BE enhances fault detection, performance loss quantification, and power forecasting, particularly for aging PV systems.

2 METHODOLOGY

The calculation of Baseline Efficiency (BEx) for PV output parameters (e.g., maximum power point power [P_{MPP}], voltage [V_{MPP}], or current [I_{MPP}]) involves a multi-step process:

1. PV Output Model Development
   A Multi-Layer Perceptron (MLP) regressor [4], implemented using Python's scikit-learn library, predicts P_{MPP}, I_{MPP}, and $V_{MP}P$ based on plane-of-array irradiance (G_{PoA}) and PV cell temperature (T_{PV}). Hyperparameters are adjusted (hidden_layer_sizes=(20,), learning_rate_init=0.05, batch_size=200), and training data are resampled to 10-minute resolution using averages. For V_{MPP}, inputs are pre-processed by taking the natural logarithm of normalized G_{PoA} and its square to account for its sensitivity to temperature.
2. Data Filtering
   A two-layer filtering process ensures data quality:
   - Outlier Removal: Anomalous data points are excluded.
   - Daily Filters:
     - Correlation Filter: Days with a coefficient of determination (R^2) between I_{MPP} and G_{PoA} below 0.95 are removed.
     - Performance Ratio Filter: Days with a current-based Performance Ratio (PR_I), defined as $PR_I = (\int I_{MPP} / I_{Ref}) / (\int G_{PoA} / 1000)$, below 0.6 are excluded. The first 180 days of filtered data, where degradation effects are minimal, are used for training.
3. Baseline Efficiency Calculation
   - Instantaneous Performance Index (xPI): Calculated as xPI = x / x_EST, where x is the measured parameter and x_EST is the estimated value from the MLP model.
   - Daily Aggregation: A dataset of xPI values is created, excluding early morning and late afternoon data. This is resampled to daily resolution using the median (MED(xPI)). Days with a standard deviation (STD) > 0.1 or MED(xPI) outside 0.3 to 1.1 are discarded.
   - Outlier Removal: Linear regression between system age and MED(xPI) generates a regression line (xPIlinear). Values are retained if their deviation (DEV = MED(xPI) – xPIlinear) falls within AVG(DEV) ± 2*STD(DEV). Discarded values are filled via linear interpolation, and a 7-day rolling window smooths the signal to produce BEx.
   - Dynamic Output Estimation: BEx is used as a weighting factor for G_{PoA} to re-estimate x using the MLP models, making predictions dynamic.

3 DATA USED

The methodology was applied to a 6-year, 1-minute

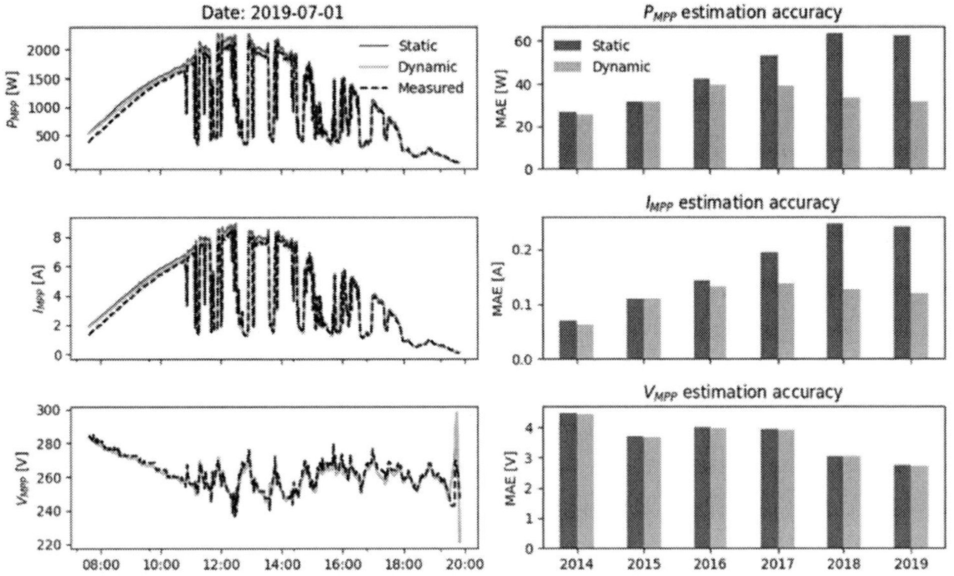

Figure 1 Comparison of measured PV output with estimations from static and dynamic models (using BE-weighted irradiance) (left). Comparison of Mean Absolute Error (MAE) between estimated and measured values for each model (right).

resolution dataset from a fixed-tilt 2.4 kWdc PV system at the Southeastern Solar Research Center (SSRC) in Birmingham, Alabama, USA. The dataset, sourced from an open-source repository, includes measurements of P_{MPP}, I_{MPP}, V_{MPP}, G_{PoA}, and T_{PV}, enabling the calculation of BE, BE_I (I_{MPP}-based), and BE_V (V_{MPP}-based).

4 RESULTS

Figure 2 illustrates the step-by-step transformation of the instantaneous Voltage Performance Index (VPI), Current Performance Index (CPI), and Power Performance Index (PPI) into daily baseline efficiency values: BEv, BEI, and BE, respectively. While BE and BE_I exhibit mild degradation over time, BE_V remains relatively stable.

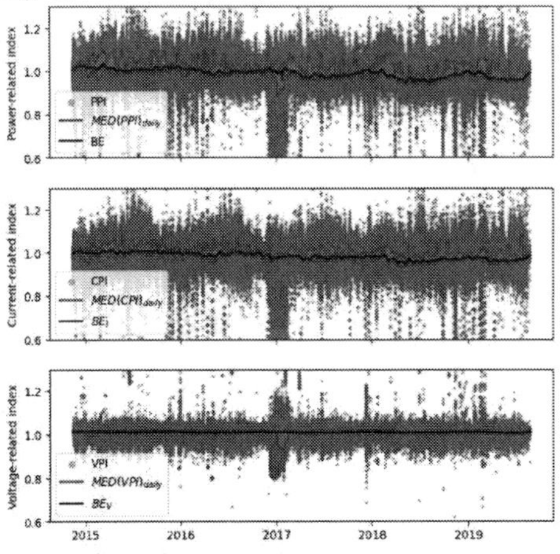

Figure 2 Transformation of instantaneous VPI, CPI, and PPI to daily BE values (BEV, BEI, and BE).

Figure 1 compares model precision using both the static PV output model and its dynamic counterpart, which incorporates baseline efficiency as a dynamic weight to irradiance. The left-hand plots show time series estimations for instantaneous values. The right-hand plots compare the Mean Absolute Errors (MAE) between estimated and measured values. The BE approach demonstrably stabilizes accuracy over time for P_{MPP} and I_{MPP} estimations. In contrast, static and dynamic $V_{MP}P$ estimations show no significant difference, consistent with the minimal degradation observed in V_{MPP}.

The use cases of this KPI are the following:

o Improved Long-Term PV Output Estimations: Enhances the accuracy of long-term PV output predictions.

o Quantification of Performance Deviations: Enables precise quantification of performance losses caused by thermal effects, low-light conditions, or system faults.

o Performance Loss Rate Assessment: Facilitates accurate determination of the system's degradation rate.

o Power Forecasting: Improves power forecasting accuracy when coupled with corresponding weather forecasts.

o PV Diagnostics: Supports comprehensive diagnostics of PV system health and performance.

Future work will extend this analysis to diverse PV systems, including bifacial, dual-orientation, and agrivoltaic installations, to further validate BE's utility.

5 REFERENCES

[1] IEC 61724-1, Photovoltaic system performance – Part 1: Monitoring, " Edition 1.0. 2017.

[2] B. Herteleer, B. Huyck, F. Catthoor, J. Driesen, and J. Cappelle, "Normalised efficiency of photovoltaic systems: Going beyond the performance ratio," Solar Energy, vol.

10.4229/EUPVSEC2025/4CV.1.22

157, pp. 408–418, Nov. 2017, doi: 10.1016/J.SOLENER.2017.08.037.
[3] G. G. Kim, J. H. Hyun, J. H. Choi, S.-H. ahn, B. G. Bhang, and H.-K. Ahn, "Quality Analysis of Photovoltaic System Using Descriptive Statistics of Power Performance Index," IEEE Access, vol. 11, pp. 28427–28438, 2023, doi: 10.1109/ACCESS.2023.3257373.
[4] M. W. Gardner and S. R. Dorling, "Artificial neural networks (the multilayer perceptron)—a review of applications in the atmospheric sciences," Atmos Environ, vol. 32, no. 14–15, pp. 2627–2636, Aug. 1998, doi: 10.1016/S1352-2310(97)00447-0.
[5] F. Pedregosa et al., "Scikit-learn: Machine learning in Python," Journal of machine learning research, vol. 12, no. Oct, pp. 2825–2830, 2011.
[6] J. O. Allen and W. B. Hobbs, "The effect of short-term inverter saturation on modeled hourly PV output using minute DC power measurements," Journal of Renewable and Sustainable Energy, vol. 14, no. 6, Nov. 2022, doi: 10.1063/5.0130265.

KU LEUVEN GENT
Faculty of Technology Engineering

Baseline efficiency: A new key performance indicator for PV systems

Anastasios Kladas, Bert Herteleer, Jan Cappelle
Research group ELECTA Ghent

PV degradation determines output → Prediction models should highlight unexpected loss causes → Linear degradation assessments may miss non-linear losses → Historical EPI trends can misrepresent module health due to (unexpected) faults → Robust KPI proposed for PV output estimation models

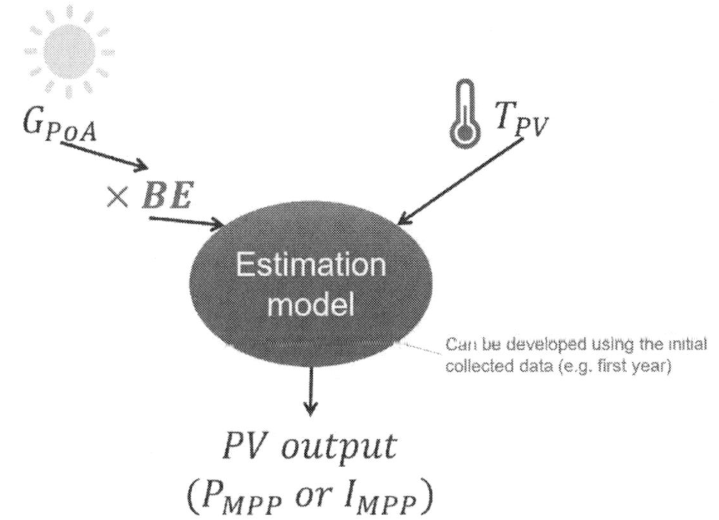

BE calculation

- Data filtering: G_{PoA}-I_{MPP} correlation; Clipping; PR; Low G_{PoA}
- xPI calculation (Actual/Estimated)
- 14 days rolling median filter
- Baseline efficiency (BE)

Results

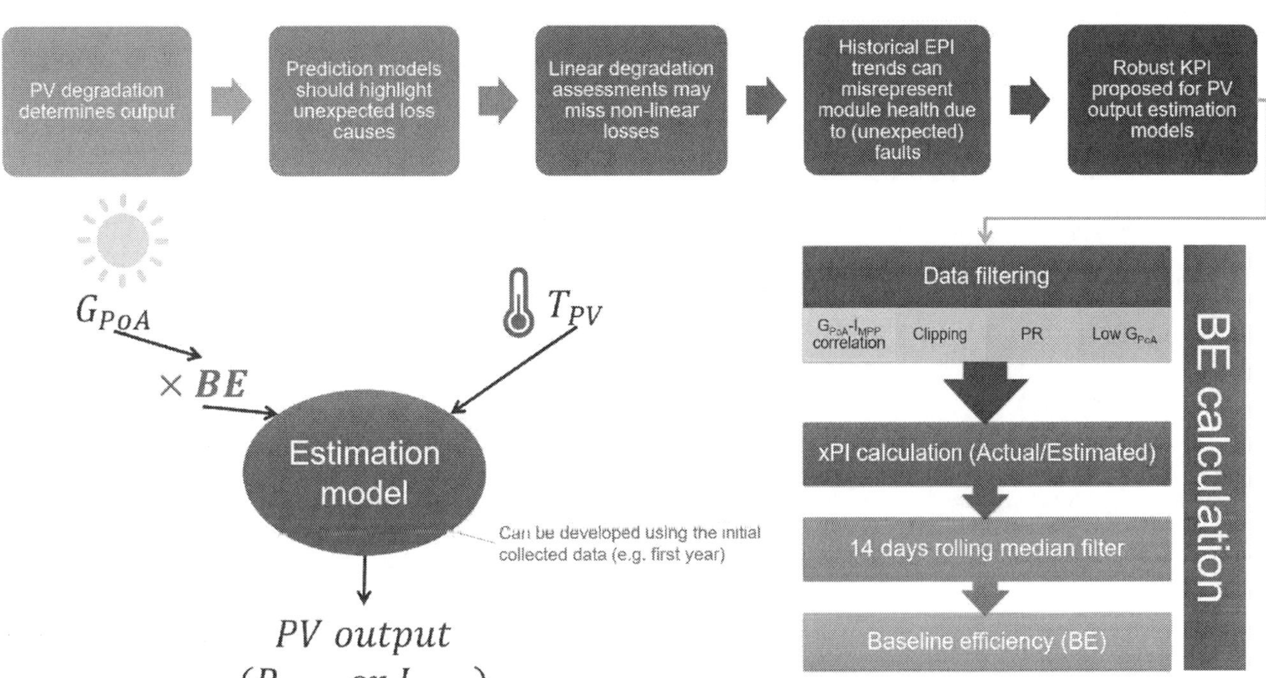

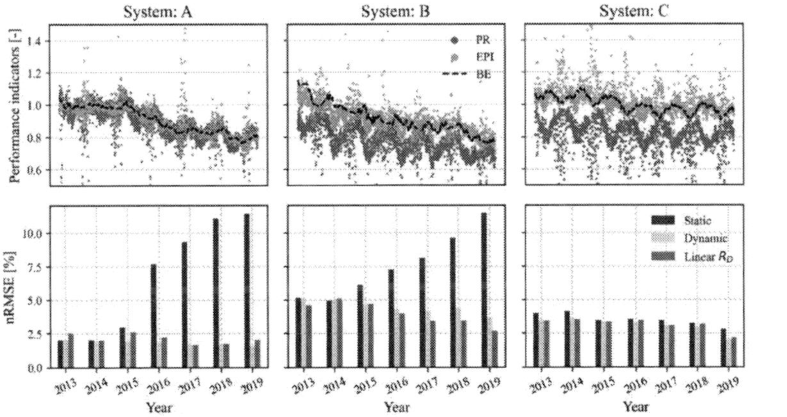

Results of P_{MPP} estimation using the BE (Dynamic approach) and the linear estimated degradation using YoY (Linear R) against using a static model on Pfaffstaetten PV systems [1]

Notes

- Stabilizes the estimation accuracy over time
- Can be calculated for power or current, enabling more detailed degradation analysis
- The PLR estimated by applying linear regression to the BE and the respective values published from Task 13 [2] are closely matching [3]
- Suggested as irradiance weight to prevent lowering the clipping point during estimations

References

[1] K. Rath *et al.*, "Pfaffstaetten," Sep. 2020, *OSF*. doi: 10.17605/OSF.IO/R34P7
[2] R. H. French et al., "Task 13 Assessment of Performance Loss Rate of PV Power Systems," 2021. Accessed: Dec. 03, 2024. [Online]. Available: https://iea-pvps.org/research-tasks/performance-operation-and-reliability-of-photovoltaic-systems/
[3] A. Kladas, B. Herteleer & J. Cappelle, "A Degradation-Responsive Framework for Long-Term PV Power Estimation." Advanced Theory and Simulations, 2025, https://doi.org/10.1002/adts.202500631

https://www.linkedin.com/in/anastasioskladas
AnastasiosKladas@kuleuven.be
+30 6975718485

Soiling forecasts for cleaning scheduling optimization

Fernanda Norde Santos[1], Stefan Wilbert[1*], Carl Becker[1], Elena Ruiz Donoso[1], Laura Campos Guzman[1], Álvaro Fernández Solas[1], Luis Zarzalejo[2], Anne Forstinger[3], David Helten[3], Veith Pietsch[4], Robert Pitz-Paal[5]

[1]DLR Institute for Solar Research, Almeria, Spain, [2]CIEMAT Energy Department – Renewable Energy Division, Madrid, Spain, [3]CSP Services GmbH, Cologne, Germany, [4]Aquila Capital, Hamburg, Germany, [5]DLR Institute of Solar Research, Cologne, Germany. *stefan.wilbert@dlr.de

Motivation

- Soiling = Accumulation of particles + other objects (e.g. leaves, bird droppings) on solar collectors
- Soiling causes a loss of 3%–4% of potential global solar energy production[1], therefore cleaning is important

Soiling measurement at the West African Power Pool (WAPP) network station in Malanville, Benin[2]

Objectives

- Create soiling loss forecasts to
  - Predict solar energy yield accurately & to
  - Optimize cleaning to reach the best trade-off between the soiling losses & cleaning costs
    - Not only frequency of cleaning, but also the selection of the cleaning dates must be optimized
    - Avoid unnecessary cleanings just before strong rainfalls or strong soiling events
- Evaluate soiling forecasts based on the most recent soiling measurements & different weather forecasts & long-term meteorological data

Soiling loss & rain sums from Malanville

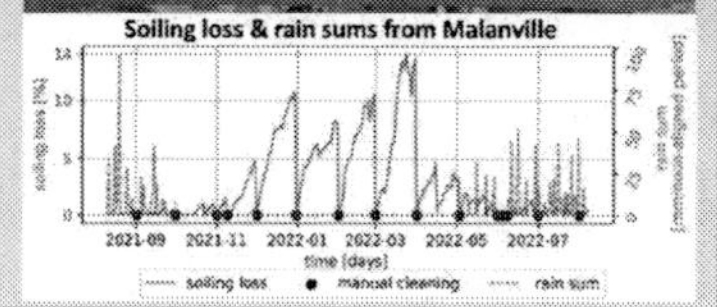

Soiling forecasting approaches

- **Soiling & rain cleaning models**
  - Various options of semi-physical soiling models incl. deposition & natural cleaning tested
  - **Soiling rate models** for days without rain cleaning:
    - *a) Persistence*[3]: soiling rate is predicted as the average of the last 20 days without cleaning
    - *b) Kimber*[4]: fixed soiling rate of 0.435%/d[5]
    - *c) HSU*[6]: soiling rate depending on PM & tilt with settling velocities of 0.0009 m/s for PM2.5 & 0.004 m/s for PM10
  - **Rain cleaning models**
    - *a) Full cleaning above threshold of 1 mm daily rain sum; no cleaning otherwise*
    - *b) Partial cleaning*[7] *effect with logarithmic rain sum dependence*
- **Input data:**
  - Parameters: particulate matter, precipitation, collector orientation
  - Two input data options:
    - *I. MERRA2 data*[8] *of 40 years used as ensemble prediction*
    - *II. combination of MERRA2, ECMWF*[9] *and CAMS*[10] *data*
      - First 6 days:
        - all weather parameters except for PM: ECMWF forecast (50 ensemble members)
        - PM: 1st to 5th day: CAMS PM forecast, 6th day: PM from 5th day
      - From day 7 to day 365: MERRA2 data
      - Creation of 200 ensemble members as concatenations of 40 MERRA2 years & 5 members from ECMWF (rain sum closest to avg, lowest, highest, 25- & 75-percentile)

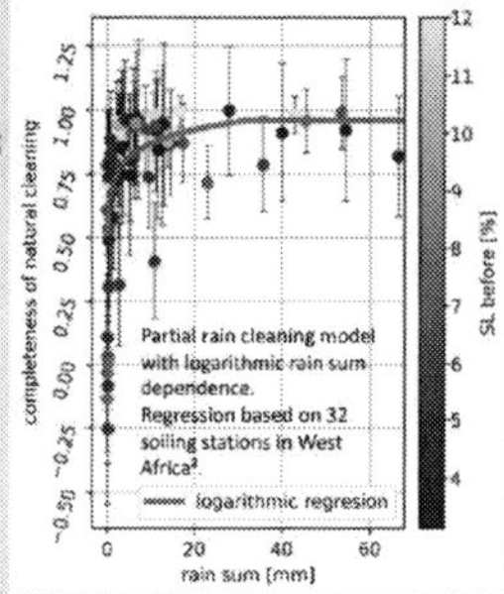

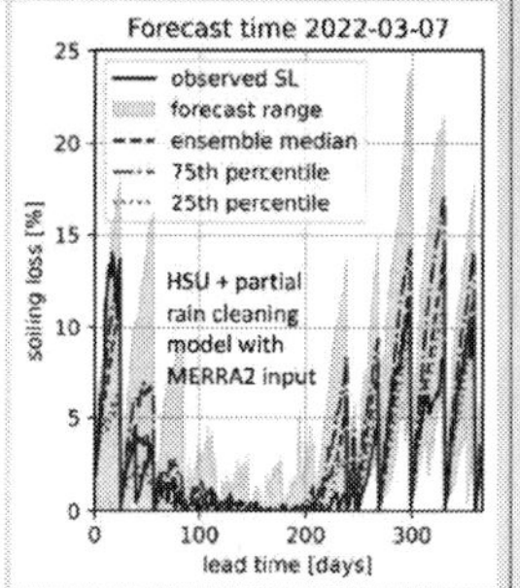

- **Case study**
  - Apply & evaluate the forecasts for Malanville (Benin)
  - There, soiling was measured for more than one year
  - Forecasts for the case study were created with a horizon of one year

Soiling forecast validation in Malanville

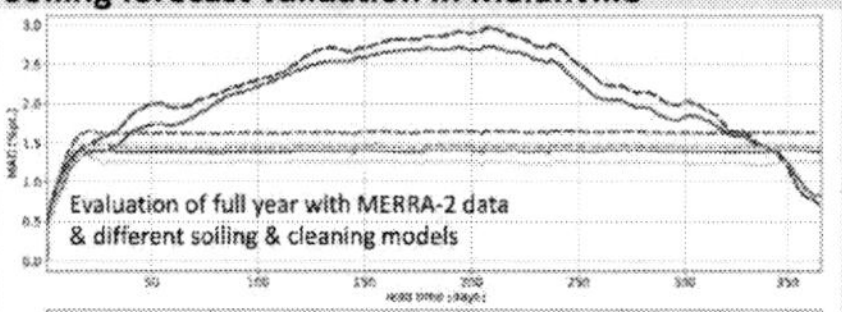

Evaluation of different soiling & cleaning models with MERRA2 data:

- *Kimber & HSU models outperform persistence most of the time*, except:
  - with forecast lead time of ~1 year (persistence benefits from seasonal effect)
  - during the first days (all forecasts benefit from application of latest measurement data)
- Kimber combined with logarithmic regression achieves the best performance for many lead times
  - This can change if the Kimber model's fixed soiling rate is less adequate for the site of interest
- In the first days, HSU + logarithmic rain cleaning model performs best
- Using *the logarithmic rain cleaning model improves the soiling forecast* compared to using the same models with a cleaning threshold

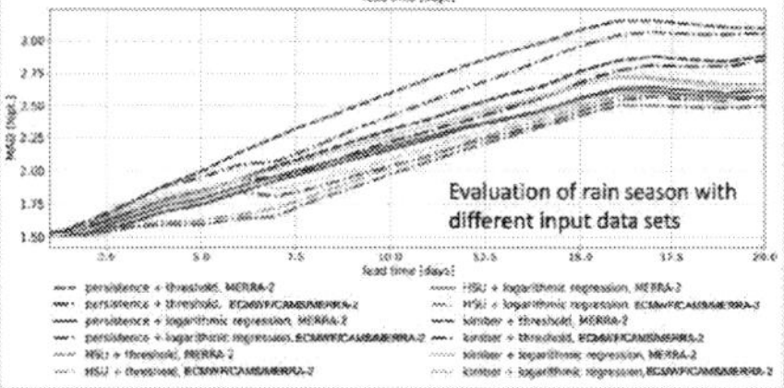

Evaluation of the effect of using additional CAMS PM & ECMWF precipitation data:

- *CAMS & ECMWF data can reduce the forecast errors in some cases*, e.g. rainy period (April - September)
- Considering also the dry period, an overall increase of the errors was found using the additional data. The MERRA2 ensemble seems to describe the weather conditions quite well.
- Especially in the first 7 days, the HSU model using CAMS and ECMWF performs considerably better than the other combination of models and datasets.

Cleaning optimization

- Cleaning schedule optimizer based on a Markov Decision Chain (MDC) approach[11,12] for an exemplary PV plant in Malanville, Benin.
- Optimizer is executed every day in the morning with most recent forecasts (MERRA2, partial cleaning)
  - It derives the time plan of cleaning tasks for the next year resulting in the largest economical yield
  - Only the suggested cleaning tasks that have to be ordered on the current day are actually considered
  - The actually scheduled cleaning tasks form the cleaning timeseries that is used for the evaluation of the economic and energetic effect of the optimization
- Compared to a PV system that is not cleaned
  - 9.7 % net income increase
  - 12.1 % energy generation increase

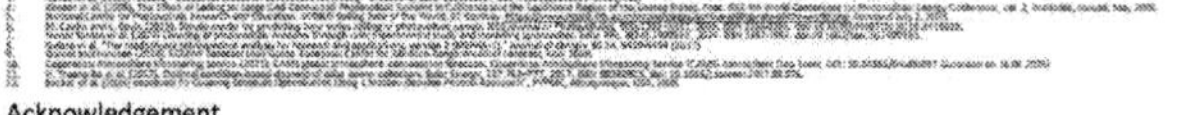

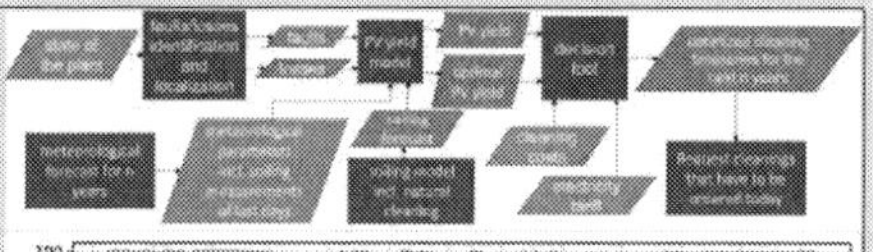

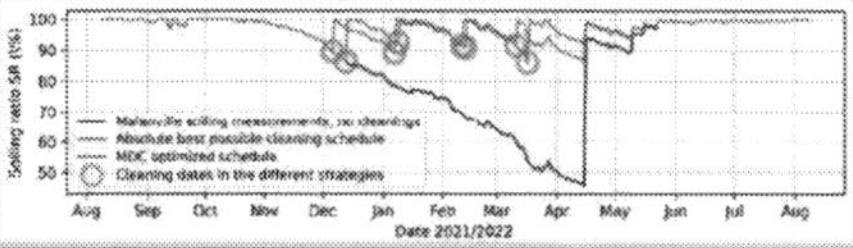

Conclusion & outlook

- Results highlight the potential of soiling forecasts and cleaning schedule optimization to improve yield predictions, and the actual economic & energetic yield of PV systems
- Calibration of soiling models to site or soiling type is important for accuracy
- More complex models and further data sets may be useful depending on the data quality and season. However, this is not guaranteed as the 40 year ensemble from MERRA2 already provides valuable information, and all data/model uncertainties are high
- If a PV system is meant to be cleaned less frequently than once per year the forecast horizon would have to be increased. Additionally, the soiling model would have to include the long-term build-up of soiling due to particles that cannot be easily removed by rain.

References

Acknowledgement

The authors would like to thank Vandalux Solar GmbH, the World Bank, the West African Power Pool and the WAPP station responsible for providing the measurement data used in this study. We also thank the European Centre for Medium-Range Weather Forecast (ECMWF), the Copernicus Atmosphere Monitoring Service (CAMS) and NASA's Global Modeling and Assimilation Office (GMAO) for providing the forecast and reanalysis data.
The authors further thank the European Union for funding the CAMEO project (grant agreement 101082125) and the German Ministry of Economic Affairs and Energy for funding the PVOptDigital project (grant 03EE1107).

Federal Ministry for Economic Affairs and Energy

Funded by the European Union

ADAPTING PV PANEL CLEANING STRATEGIES TO MARKET DYNAMICS: THE IMPACT OF VARIABLE PRICING AND REGULATORY MARKET PARTICIPATION

Marta Redondo Cuevas[1,2], Carlos A. Platero Gaona[1]
[1]Universidad Politécnica de Madrid, [2]ENDESA Generación
e-mail address(es) marta.redondo.cuevas@alumnos.upm.es, marta.redondo@enel.com, carlosantonio.platero@upm.es

ABSTRACT: The profitability of photovoltaic (PV) panel cleaning is increasingly shaped by external market dynamics rather than technical thresholds alone. This study analyzes how evolving electricity market conditions in Spain—characterized by price volatility, midday price collapses, and growing participation in ancillary service markets—affect the timing and economic viability of cleaning operations.
Using real data from 47 PV plants (2020–2025) and the SOMOSclean decision model, we demonstrate that identical soiling levels can lead to different cleaning strategies depending on market context. Factors such as the solar capture price factor (CPF), curtailments, and regulatory participation significantly influence whether recovered energy can be monetized.
We propose a context-aware framework that integrates soiling dynamics, market signals, and operational constraints to optimize cleaning schedules. The results highlight the need for flexible, market-responsive strategies to enhance profitability while maintaining operational agility.

Keywords: soiling, cleaning, photovoltaic, electricity market, curtailment, ancillary services, decision framework

1 INTRODUCTION

The operational efficiency of PV plants is increasingly influenced by external market factors. Traditional cleaning strategies, based solely on technical or environmental criteria, may no longer be sufficient. This study explores how evolving market conditions between 2020 and 2025 affect the profitability and timing of panel cleaning operations.

Figure 1: Dirty and clean panel in PV plant.

This paper is structured as follows:
- Section 2 reviews the evolution of the electricity market (2020-2025).
- Section 3 discusses cleaning decisions in a market context.
- Section 4 presents the main results.
- Section 5 summarizes the conclusions.

2 MARKET EVOLUTION (2020-2025)

In recent years, the electricity market has undergone significant transformations that have directly impacted the operation and profitability of photovoltaic solar plants. Although this study focuses on Spain, it is important to note that many of these dynamics are also common in other European markets. The figures presented in this section are the authors' own elaboration, based on data provided by REE (ESIOS [1] and I3DIA files [2]).

2.1 Day-ahead market prices

The Spanish day-ahead electricity market has undergone a significant change, as illustrated in Figure 2.

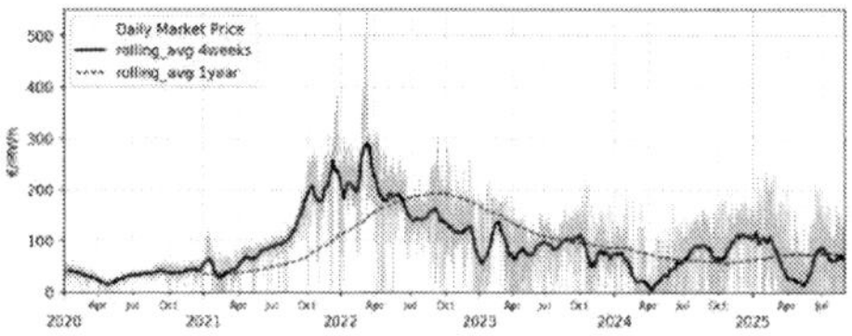

Figure 2: Evolution of daily market prices (€/MWh) from 2020 to 2025

During the first months of 2020, day-ahead electricity prices in Spain remained relatively stable, mostly ranging between 30 and 60 €/MWh. This pattern, typical of the previous decade, reflected a balanced supply-demand scenario supported by a diversified generation mix and the absence of major external disruptions.

However, from the second half of 2021 onwards, a sharp upward trend emerged, with sustained price increases and a marked rise in volatility. This shift was driven by several international factors, including the surge in natural gas prices across European wholesale markets, higher CO_2 emission allowance costs, and geopolitical tensions related to the conflict in Ukraine. As a result, daily average prices frequently exceeded 200 €/MWh for several months, with occasional peaks approaching 500 €/MWh.

From mid-2022, regulatory measures implemented in Spain and Portugal—most notably the so-called "Iberian mechanism" to cap the price of gas used for electricity generation—helped to partially moderate prices. Nevertheless, volatility remained high, with pronounced short-term fluctuations, sharp peaks, and abrupt drops.

In 2023 and especially in 2024, the rapid increase in renewable generation capacity, combined with episodes of high wind and solar output, led to the recurrent appearance of near-zero and even negative hourly prices in the day-ahead market. This unprecedented situation in the recent history of the Spanish power system reflects periods of temporary oversupply from non-dispatchable renewable sources.

2.2 Solar Capture Price Factor

The capture price factor (CPF) measures the ratio between the weighted average price obtained by solar PV generation and the average day-ahead market price:

$$CPF_{solar} = \frac{\sum_h P_h \cdot E_{solar,h}}{\sum_h E_{solar,h}} \cdot \frac{1}{\sum_h P_h} \quad (1)$$

where P_h is the market price in hour h, and $E_{solar,h}$ the energy generated by solar technology in that hour.

As shown in Figure 3, the CPF for solar in Spain remained close to 100% until 2022, indicating that PV captured prices similar to the market average. However, from 2022 onwards, the CPF has declined steadily due to the increasing share of solar generation, which often coincides with periods of lower demand and reduced prices. This trend has become more pronounced in 2023 and 2024, with prolonged periods where the CPF dropped below 70%, especially during episodes of high renewable output and low demand, occasionally resulting in zero or negative hourly prices.

Figure 3: Capture Price Factor (CPF) for solar technology.

2.3 Increase in solar production and deviations from day-ahead schedule

Throughout the period analyzed, solar PV generation in Spain has increased significantly, particularly from 2022 onwards, in line with the rapid growth of installed capacity in the national power system. This expansion has been driven mainly by the steady connection of large-scale PV plants. The actual increase would be even greater if self-consumption installations (excluded from REE publications) were taken into account.

However, this rise in production has been accompanied by a growing gap between the scheduled energy and the actual energy injected into the grid. As shown in Figure 4, this discrepancy is represented by the shaded area between the two curves. It reflects situations where solar energy is not delivered to the system, mainly due to factors such as technical grid limitations, system security constraints, or the activation of balancing services

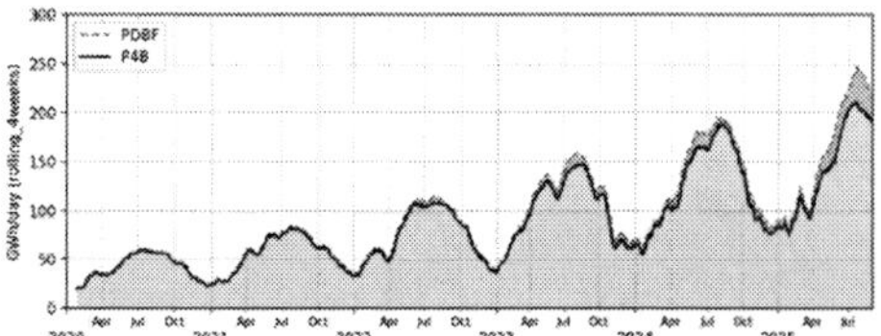

Figure 4: Scheduled vs. actual solar PV generation in Spain. The shaded area indicates curtailed energy due to grid or market constraints.

2.4 Participation in balancing services

Figure 5 illustrates the evolution of solar PV participation in secondary regulation markets in Spain, measured through the contracted regulation band. Initial participation began in 2022, but remained marginal. In 2023, participation increased progressively, driven by the growth in installed PV capacity.

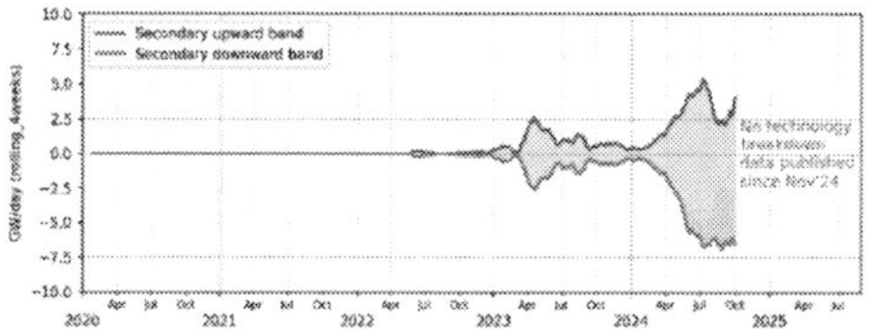

Figure 5: Participation of PV plants in secondary regulation markets

A significant regulatory change introduced in April 2024 [3] allowed for asymmetric bidding—enabling different offers for upward and downward regulation. This adjustment particularly benefited solar PV technology, which can more easily reduce output (i.e., offer downward regulation). As a result, participation in secondary regulation markets surged.

However, since November 2024, REE has discontinued the publication of secondary regulation band data disaggregated by technology. Therefore, it is no longer possible to quantify the exact level of solar PV participation in these markets.

3 CLEANING DECISIONS IN A MARKET CONTEXT

Accurate prediction of soiling levels (%) is essential for optimizing cleaning schedules in PV plants. In this study, the SOMOSclean model [4][5] was applied to 47 PV power plants in Spain, representing a total installed capacity of over 2 GWp.

It is important to note that the percentage of soiling does not directly translate into an equivalent energy loss. The actual impact of soiling depends on the market context, including factors such as grid curtailments or participation in secondary regulation markets. For example, a 5% soiling level may not result in a 5% reduction in output if the plant is already curtailed due to grid constraints. Therefore, cleaning actions should be scheduled only when real energy gains are expected, rather than simply responding to high soiling levels.

A simplified decision flow is presented in Figure 6, which illustrates the main variables and data sources considered when assessing whether panel cleaning is economically justified.

10.4229/EUPVSEC2025/4CV.1.24

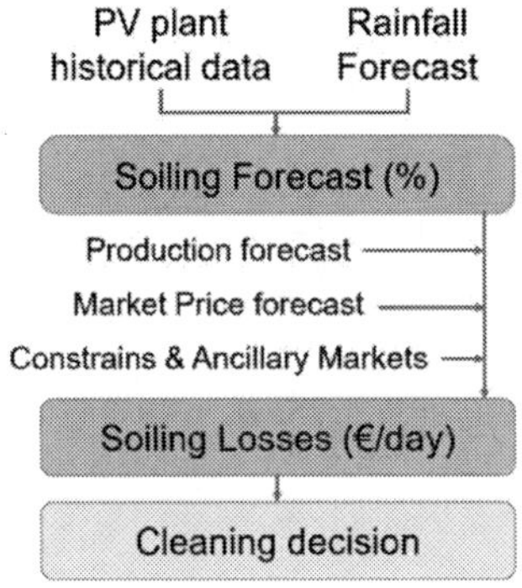

Figure 6: Decision flow for PV panel cleaning based on technical and market variables (SOMOSclean)

4 RESULTS: ONE SOILING LEVEL, MANY STRATEGIES

The application of the SOMOSclean model with real market data reveals that identical soiling levels can lead to very different cleaning decisions depending on the market context. Table I summarizes how cleaning strategies have evolved from 2020 to 2025, reflecting variations in daily market prices, capture price factors, grid constraints, and participation in ancillary services.

Table I: Evolution of cleaning strategies for PV plants in Spain (2020–2025), with similar soiling levels (%) and considering market conditions. (*) Data for 2025 include values up to August only.

Year	Market Price €/MWh	Solar CPF	Curtail.	Balancing Service	Strategy (cleanings /summer)
2020	34	97%	Neglig.	No	1-2
2021	112	92%	Neglig.	No	2-3
2022	168	90%	Medium	Neglig.	1-2
2023	87	84%	High	Low	0-1
2024	63	67%	High	Sec. Reg.	0-1
2025 (*)	64 (*)	53% (*)	Medium	Extended	TBD

Despite similar soiling levels across the years, the number of summer cleanings has significantly decreased. In 2021, most plants required two to three cleanings during the summer period. By contrast, in recent years many plants have reduced this to just one or even none.

These results highlight that cleaning decisions cannot rely solely on technical indicators such as soiling percentage. Instead, they must consider whether the recovered energy can be monetized under current market conditions.

Importantly, the strategies shown in Table I refer to PV plants without storage systems (BESS). In plants equipped with battery storage, recovered energy can be stored and dispatched later, potentially shifting the optimal cleaning timing to align with higher market prices.

Additionally, contractual obligations such as Power Purchase Agreements (PPA) may impose further constraints, making a one-size-fits-all approach ineffective.

4 CONCLUSIONS

Optimizing PV panel cleaning is no longer solely a technical or environmental matter. The increasing complexity of electricity markets—characterized by price volatility, curtailments, and participation in ancillary services—requires a more integrated and adaptive approach.

Future cleaning strategies must be supported by context-aware decision frameworks, such as the SOMOSclean model, which combine:
- Soiling dynamics (%)
- Market price signals
- Grid curtailments and operational constraints
- Participation in balancing and ancillary service markets

In this evolving landscape, PV cleaning strategies must be smart, flexible, and market-responsive to ensure both operational efficiency and economic viability.

5 ACKNOWLEDGEMENTS

The authors would like to thank Enel Green Power and Endesa Generación SA for enabling the implementation of the SOMOSclean model in their PV plants. Special thanks are also extended to the entire O&M solar team for their valuable expertise and insightful discussions throughout this project.

6 REFERENCES

[1] Red Eléctrica de España, "API ESIOS: datos del sistema eléctrico", 2025 [Online]. Available: https://api.esios.ree.es/

[2] Red Eléctrica de España, "I3DIA: archivos agregados por tecnología del mercado eléctrico", 2025. [Online]. Available: https://www.esios.ree.es/en/downloads

[3] Comisión Nacional de los Mercados y la Competencia (CNMC), "Resolution of 25 April 2024, amending the conditions relating to balancing and the operating procedures for the participation of the Spanish peninsular electricity system in the European balancing platforms MARI and PICASSO", Boletín Oficial del Estado, no. 137, pp. 66281–66524, Jun. 6, 2024.

[4] M. Redondo et al, "Soiling Modelling in Large Grid-Connected PV Plants for Cleaning Optimization" Energies, 2023. https://doi.org/10.3390/en16020904

[5] M. Redondo et al, "Review and Comparison of Methods for Soiling Modeling in Large Grid-Connected PV Plants" Sustainability, 2024. https://doi.org/10.3390/su162410998

ADAPTING PV PANEL CLEANING STRATEGIES TO MARKET DYNAMICS: THE IMPACT OF VARIABLE PRICING AND REGULATORY MARKET PARTICIPATION

Marta Redondo Cuevas [1,2], Carlos A. Platero Gaona [1]

[1] Universidad Politécnica de Madrid / [2] ENDESA GENERACIÓN

Motivation & Objectives. *Why rethink PV cleaning strategies?*

Cleaning PV panels is essential to minimize soiling losses and maximize energy yield. However, the **evolving market conditions** in recent years —such as price volatility and midday price collapses— have introduced **new challenges and opportunities** for optimizing this process. Additionally, the increasing participation of solar plants in regulatory markets adds further complexity to operational decision-making.

This study proposes a framework that integrates market conditions, revenue projections, and operational constraints to optimize cleaning schedules. The findings highlight the need for flexible, market-responsive cleaning strategies to enhance profitability while maintaining operational agility.

Market Evolution (2020-2025)

How have market conditions changed?

- Daily Market Prices:

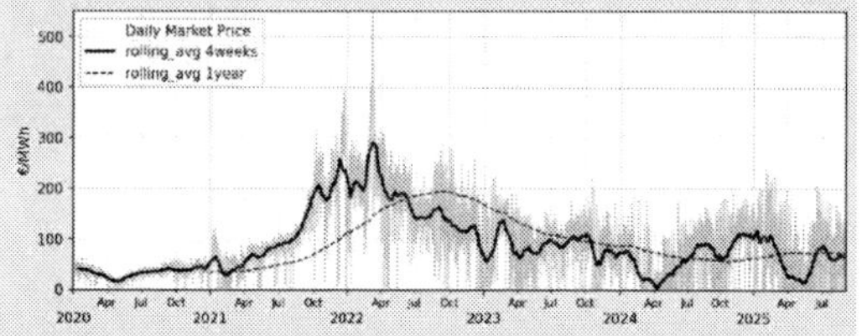

- Capture price factor (CPF) for solar technology:

- PV Generation & Deviations from day-ahead operating program:

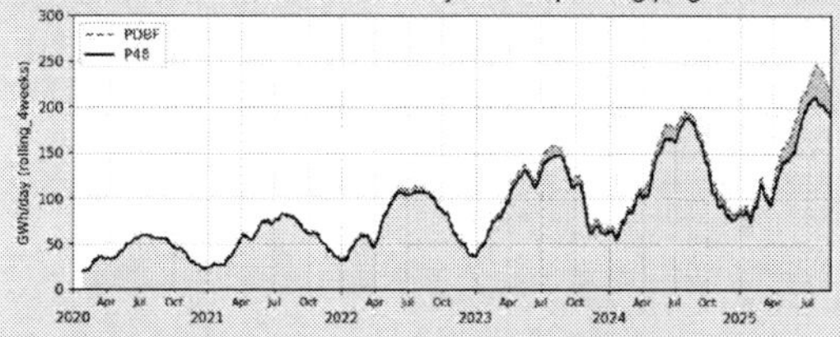

- Participation of PV plants in secondary ancillary services:

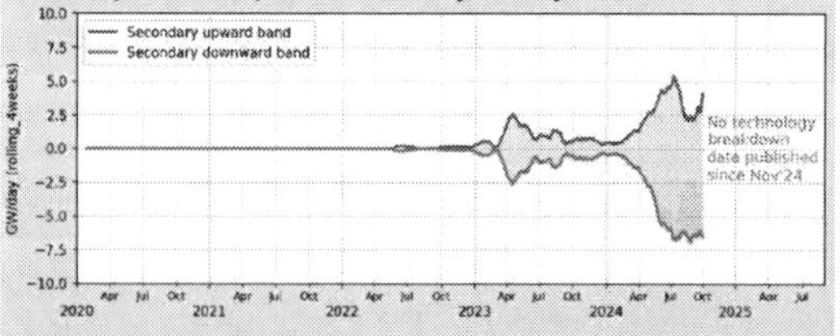

Source: Spain, REE (ESIOS and I3DIA files)

Cleaning Decisions in a Market Context

When is cleaning really worth it?

- Necessary to **predict** soiling levels (%):
  → **SOMOSclean model** [1] [2]
  → Applied to 47 PV power plants in Spain (>**2GWp**)
- Soiling in % ≠ direct energy loss
  → Impact depends on market context (e.g., curtailments or secondary regulation)
  → e.g., a 5% soiling level may not reduce output by 5% if the plant is already curtailed
  → Clean only when energy gains are real — not just when soiling is high.

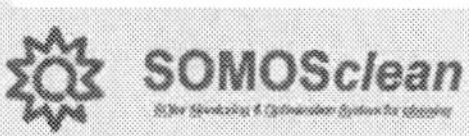

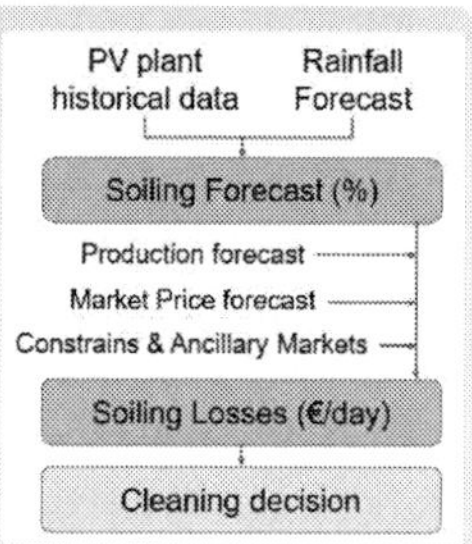

SOMOSclean

Results. *One Soiling Level, Many Strategies*

Applying the SOMOSclean model with real market data shows that **identical soiling levels** can lead to **very different cleaning decisions**:

Year	Daily Market Prices	Capture Prices for solar technology	Grid curtailment / constrains	Balancing Service (Secondary & Tertiary Markets)	Typical cleaning strategy
2020	34 €/MWh	97%	Negligible	No	1-2 cleanings /summer
2021	112 €/MWh	92%	Negligible	No	2-3 cleanings /summer
2022	168 €/MWh	90%	Medium	Negligible	1-2 cleanings /summer
2023	87 €/MWh	84%	High	Low	0-1 cleanings /summer
2024	63 €/MWh	67%	High	Secondary regulation markets (upward/downward bids since April'24)	0-1 cleanings /summer
2025	64 €/MWh (up to Aug)	53% (up to Aug)	Medium	Extended participation	¿?

The strategies shown above refer to PV plants **without storage (BESS)**; in BESS-integrated plants, recovered energy can be stored, shifting the optimal cleaning timing.

Additionally, contractual obligations as PPAs may impose further constraints, making a **one-size-fits-all approach ineffective**.

Conclusions

What should future strategies look like?

Optimizing PV panel cleaning is **no longer just a technical or environmental issue**.

It requires a **context-aware framework**, such as the SOMOSclean model, that integrates:

- Soiling dynamics (%)
- Market price signals
- Curtailments and grid constraints
- Participation in ancillary services

To remain competitive, PV cleaning strategies must be **smart, flexible, and market-aware.**

References

[1] M. Redondo et al, "Soiling Modelling in Large Grid-Connected PV Plants for Cleaning Optimization" *Energies*, 2023. https://doi.org/10.3390/en16020904

[2] M. Redondo et al, "Review and Comparison of Methods for Soiling Modeling in Large Grid-Connected PV Plants" *Sustainability*, 2024. https://doi.org/10.3390/su162410998

UNIVERSIDAD POLITÉCNICA DE MADRID

POLITÉCNICA

enel Green Power

ADVANCING PHOTVOLTAIC PERFORMANCE THROUGH DIGITALISATION IN LIVING LABORATORIES: INSIGHTS FROM THE PROMISE PROJECT

Brian Bartolo[1,2], Brian Azzopardi[1,2,3,4 *], Carmel Azzopardi[1], Austeja Mockeviciute-Azzopardi[1], Alexandre Mignonac[5], Marcus Rennhofer[6], Bernhard Kubicek[6], Rita Ebner[6], Carlos Meza[7], Melodie de l'Epine[8], Eugenia Zugasti[9], Steve Zerafa[2,3,10], Kenneth Scerri[1,3]

[1]The Foundation for Innovation and Research – Malta (FiR.mt); [2]Malta College of Arts, Science and Technology (MCAST); [3]The University of Malta; [4]Azzopardi & Associates, Malta; [5]Commissariat à l'Energie Atomique et aux Energies Alternatives (CEA), France; [6]AIT Austrian Institute of Technology GMBH, Austria; [7]Anhalt University of Applied Sciences, Germany; [8]Becquerel Institute, Belgium; [9]Fundación CENER - National Renewable Energy Centre, Spain; [10]PIXAM Ltd.

* Brian.Azzopardi@FiR.mt

ABSTRACT: The growing demand for renewable energy continues to drive the large-scale deployment of photovoltaic (PV) systems. However, ensuring the sustained performance of existing installations remains essential, particularly in regions such as Malta, where elevated temperature, humidity, and salinity accelerate component degradation. This paper presents the next phase of the PROMISE project (Photovoltaics Reliability Operations and Maintenance Innovative Solutions for Energy Alliance), which advances the harmonised multi-site PV monitoring framework introduced in 2024 into a fully digitalised, cloud-integrated infrastructure. The upgraded system now encompasses ten rooftop laboratories and three dedicated test sites, each equipped with high-precision Class A sensors operating at 3-second acquisition intervals in accordance with IEC 61724-1:2021. The monitoring network is supported by an end-to-end Microsoft Azure pipeline—comprising IoT Hub, Function Apps, Cosmos DB, and Power BI—that enables real-time data streaming, anomaly detection, and predictive analytics across all locations. Moreover, the establishment of the PROMISE Open PV Reliability Repository provides public access to harmonised datasets, promoting transparency and collaboration within international PV reliability programmes. The results demonstrate a scalable, research-grade digital framework that strengthens system interoperability, enhances data quality, and supports the broader goals of smart monitoring and sustainable energy transition in the Mediterranean and beyond.

Keywords: Photovoltaic System Monitoring, Multi-Site Measurements, IoT Cloud Architecture, Mediterranean Climate PV Performance

1 INTRODUCTION

The European Green Deal and "Fit for 55" package continue to drive Europe's decarbonisation pathway toward net-zero emissions by 2050, with photovoltaic (PV) technologies remaining a cornerstone of this transition [1], [2] . Beyond rapid capacity expansion, sustained attention must be given to optimising the performance of existing PV assets to maximise energy yield and reliability under real-world conditions, as highlighted in numerous studies and reports [3] [4], [5],.

In the Mediterranean region, particularly in island nations such as Malta, photovoltaic (PV) installations are exposed to challenging environmental conditions, including elevated temperature, humidity, dust, and atmospheric salinity [6], all of which accelerate component degradation and reduce system efficiency. In addition to these stressors, rapid weather fluctuations [7] and limited available land area demand tailored monitoring strategies with higher measurement granularity and accuracy to capture environmental uncertainties and ensure optimal system performance. The combination of abundant solar resources and spatial constraints further underscores the need for precise, high-resolution monitoring to maximise energy yield. Within this context, the PROMISE project (Photovoltaics Reliability Operations and Maintenance Innovative Solutions for Energy Alliance) [8] established the Malta Living Laboratories as a distributed experimental platform for advanced PV performance monitoring.

The framework introduced in Bartolo *et al.*[9] (EU PVSEC 2024) demonstrated the feasibility of harmonising multi-site PV measurements using open-source platforms and standardised data protocols. While that study successfully validated the concept of a unified IoT-based monitoring architecture, it was primarily intended as a rapid-deployment solution to ensure data continuity on initially installed systems and provide temporary public access to performance information through a dedicated data repository [10]. Operational experience with this configuration revealed several technical limitations associated with the *ThingSpeak* [11] IoT Analytics platform used for data ingestion, storage, and basic visualisation, complemented by *Grafana Cloud* [12] for advanced dashboards. These limitations included the restriction to eight data fields per channel, which led to fragmented time-series records for systems featuring more than eight measurement parameters, thereby complicating subsequent data analysis. Additional challenges involved interoperability constraints between independent cloud ecosystems and the absence of real-time data-stream access between the ingestion and storage layers, which hindered the implementation of live performance monitoring and subsequent tasks such as real-time anomaly detection techniques.

To overcome these bottlenecks, this study introduces a fully digitalised, cloud-integrated infrastructure pipeline that, rather than functioning as a monolithic closed system, is composed of segregated yet interoperable consumer services within a unified ecosystem. The upgraded framework leverages *Microsoft Azure IoT Hub* [13], *Azure Function Apps* [14], *Cosmos DB*,[15] and *Power BI* [16] to ensure seamless data flow from the sensory layer to visualisation or application layer. In parallel, the data-acquisition frequency has been enhanced and refined in accordance with the updated IEC 61724-1:2021 standard requirements [17].

The current configuration also reflects a major expansion of the Living Laboratories network—from six operational sites in 2024 to a total of ten PV laboratories and three dedicated test facilities. These additional testings sites support benchmarking, degradation analysis, and multi-orientation configurations analysis of PV systems, providing a comprehensive dataset for performance comparison across diverse operational and environmental conditions. This evolution transforms the PROMISE framework from a rapid-deployment demonstrator into a scalable, analytics-ready digital platform capable of real-time diagnostics, predictive maintenance, and multi-site benchmarking across the Malta Living Laboratories.

1.1 Aim and Scope

This paper presents the continued development of the PROMISE monitoring framework, aimed at improving the efficiency, reliability, and interoperability of photovoltaic (PV) systems through digitalisation and real-time data analysis and therefore exploiting additional results.

The study focuses on optimising system scalability and enhancing data-sharing mechanisms to support open scientific collaboration. Through the establishment of a publicly accessible data repository, as demonstrated in [10], stakeholders and the public can visualise key measurements and evaluate performance in real-time while download historical data for further analysis and modelling, reinforcing transparency and supporting benchmarking activities across different sites.

The key objectives of this framework are:

i. To monitor and analyse PV system performance and evaluate degradation across an expanded network of laboratories and benchmark testing sites under local environmental Mediterranean conditions.
ii. To strengthen the interoperability and scalability of the PROMISE digital infrastructure, enabling multi-site data aggregation and comparison.
iii. To promote open data sharing through a structured repository that facilitates collaboration among researchers, policymakers, and industry partners.
iv. To demonstrate how harmonised data standards and improved acquisition practices contribute to higher traceability and comparability across sites.
v. To provide a scalable monitoring model that can be replicated in other regions with similar environmental and operational challenges, while exploiting the additional key results described in Section 5.

By achieving these objectives, the PROMISE framework advances from a national proof-of-concept to a pan-European digital platform that supports transparent, standardised, and collaborative research on PV system performance and reliability.

1.2 PROMISE PV Living Laboratories

The PROMISE project (*Photovoltaics Reliability Operations and Maintenance Innovative Solutions for Energy Alliance*) is a three-year research initiative funded by the European Commission that establishes a distributed platform for studying the reliability and optimisation of PV systems in real operating conditions. Initially centred in Malta, the network has now expanded to ten PV laboratories and three specialised test sites across Europe, supporting large-scale data collection, benchmarking, and degradation analysis.

PROMISE integrates digitalisation techniques, predictive analytics, and optimisation tools to enhance PV performance and accelerate the clean-energy transition. Alongside its technical goals, the project promotes capacity building and knowledge transfer through workshops, internships, and open-data initiatives.

The project is structured around two complementary pillars:

i. A research platform to study the reliability of PV systems and develop innovative solutions for optimisation.
ii. A knowledge transfer platform that supports training, internships, and workshops to enhance the research and engineering capabilities within Malta's PV sector.

1.3 Data Monitoring Constraints

A key challenge in photovoltaic (PV) system monitoring lies in distinguishing true system faults from data anomalies introduced by measurement noise or environmental variability. Previous studies have shown that filtering noise without suppressing meaningful fault signatures remains difficult, as factors such as transient shading or irradiance fluctuations can mimic real system defects and lead to misleading performance evaluations [18],[19].

To improve fault detection accuracy, effective data-filtering strategies must be applied [8]. Threshold-based filtering—such as excluding measurements taken under irradiance levels below 20 W/m² [18]—helps remove low-signal noise while retaining relevant operating data. Similarly, restricting analysis to peak irradiance periods (typically 10:00–16:00 h) reduces the uncertainty associated with shading and low-angle solar conditions [9].

Although post-processing filters are useful, a more robust approach is to minimise noise at the source. This can be achieved using high-quality, Class A sensors capable of operating in demanding climatic environments and conforming to OEM, ISO/IEC 17025 [20], ISO 9001 [21] and IEC 61724-1 standards [17]. Additionally, implementing granular, high-frequency data acquisition enables the capture of short-term fluctuations, improving the system's ability to identify transient anomalies and early-stage faults.

This paper is organised into six main sections. This section introduces the PROMISE project and outlines its objectives, while Section 2 describes the configuration of the expanded monitoring network. Section 3 details the edge-device data acquisition and processing framework, and Section 4 presents the Azure-based cloud architecture pipeline. Section 5 discusses the exploitable results and key outcomes of the upgraded infrastructure, and Section 6 concludes the study, highlighting future directions for real-time anomaly detection, system expansion, and predictive analysis for grid-integration forecasting.

2. SYSTEM OVERVIEW

This section introduces the configuration of the PROMISE PV Living Laboratories and provides an overview of the monitoring infrastructure deployed across the Malta Living Laboratory sites. The rooftop systems and test sites installed on public and institutional buildings are equipped with high-precision sensors and data-acquisition units that monitor real-world PV operation under diverse urban and coastal environments.

The three specialised test sites complement these installations by supporting advanced research functions. One site is dedicated to degradation analysis and forms part of a round-robin study coordinated within the European network to assess how PV modules degrade under different climatic conditions in different countries within the EU. Another facility hosts multiple irradiance reference cells mounted at various orientations and tilt angles to evaluate the influence of array geometry on system output and grid-integration behaviour. A third site is equipped with a high-accuracy pyranometer array used for benchmarking, reference calibration, and validation of the field-deployed sensors.

2.1 Sensor and Device Selection

The monitoring system employs high-precision electrical and meteorological sensors designed for continuous, real-time data capture. Measurements are recorded at 3-second intervals, providing high-resolution insight into short-term system behaviour and environmental variability. Data acquisition is implemented using the Modbus RTU protocol over RS-485 [22] wiring system , ensuring robust and cost-effective data transfer between field instruments and the central controller.

Key operational parameters—including DC current and voltage, plane-of-array irradiance, ambient temperature, module and cell temperature—are monitored using Class A-rated sensors compliant with the latest requirements of IEC 61724-1:2021. These devices are also calibrated and certified in accordance with ISO/IEC 17025 and ISO 9001 standards, guaranteeing measurement traceability, quality assurance, and long-term stability.

This high-accuracy instrumentation ensures reliable performance monitoring and supports real-time analysis and early fault detection within the PROMISE framework.

3. EDGE DEVICE DATA PROCESSING

This section outlines the sensor integration and data processing framework locally on each site adopted for real-time and historical PV system monitoring.

3.1 Data Processing

The sensors are managed by a *Raspberry Pi* controller [23], which functions as both the *Modbus RTU* master for the sensors and the edge device bridging the sensory and cloud layers. Each sensor is assigned a unique Modbus ID, and data are collected via *RS-485* wiring system, providing high robustness against electrical noise and transmission errors. The communication network follows strict specifications for baud rate, shielding, and terminating resistors, ensuring signal integrity and reliability [22],[24].

The *Raspberry Pi* operates on a Linux-based platform for stability and long-term performance, using *Python* libraries such as *PyModbus* [25] for device communication and data handling. This open-source configuration offers full customisation and scalability while avoiding the costs associated with proprietary systems.

Acquired data are securely transmitted to the Microsoft Azure Cloud, which provides the IoT architecture pipline for data ingestion and storage and visualation. Communication with the Azure IoT Hub is authenticated via connection strings, and telemetry messages are sent in JSON format through the MQTT protocol, enabling real-time monitoring and live data synchronisatio. Remote access via *RealVNC* [26] supports post-deployment configuration and diagnostics. To enhance resilience, a *Cron Job* [27] automatically restarts the acquisition script following power outages or communication interruptions, thereby preventing data loss.

3.2 Data Treatment

In the earlier PROMISE configuration (Bartolo et al., 2024) [9], data acquisition was performed at 10-second intervals, and the data were transmitted without a local timestamp, relying instead on irregular timestamps assigned upon receipt in *ThingSpeak*. In accordance with the updated IEC 61724-1:2021 Class A monitoring guidelines, the new system now samples data every 3 seconds, which are then aggregated and averaged over 30-second intervals to define the official recording cadence. This approach captures high temporal resolution and ensures compliance with IEC 61724-1 standards, while optimising cloud upload frequency, storage efficiency and related uploaded messages and storage costs. The average for each 30-second record is calculated from the number of valid entries captured within the aggregation window. When no valid data are recorded during a given interval, a null value is uploaded to the cloud to preserve dataset continuity.

Each data package is timestamped according to the Raspberry Pi's local clock rather than the arrival time at the *IoT Hub*. This method ensures consistent, synchronised timestamping for every monitored site by avoiding time stamp inconsistencies due to network latency effects.

Unlike the previous framework all implausible or corrupted values—typically arising from communication errors or temporary sensor malfunctions—are uploaded to the cloud as raw data. This strategy offloads computational tasks from the Raspberry Pi, allowing it to focus exclusively on accurate data acquisition while minimising processing overhead at the edge. Subsequent data validation, filtering, and further data analysis are performed within the Azure cloud pipeline, leveraging the real-time data stream between the IoT Hub and the Cosmos DB storage container. This architecture ensures continuous live access to unfiltered measurements for diagnostic purposes, while centralising data treatment and quality control within the cloud environment. Fig. 1 shows the comprehensive framework showing the transmission of data from the perception layer to the cloud environment.

4. . CLOUD ARCHITECTURE PIPLINE

The PROMISE digital-monitoring framework employs a fully integrated Microsoft Azure cloud architecture for IoT applications to manage real-time telemetry, data processing, storage, analytics, and visualisation. This pipeline ensures scalability, security, interoperability, and continuous availability within a unified ecosystem, while maintaining compliance with IEC 61724-1 data-handling principles and filtering practices.

Telemetry generated by the Raspberry Pi edge devices is transmitted to the Azure IoT Hub using the MQTT protocol, with each payload encoded in JSON and tagged with its local timestamp. Within the cloud pipeline, the IoT Hub forwards the data to Azure Function Apps, where they are automatically validated, organised, and routed to the appropriate containers in Cosmos DB database for storage. The stored data are then synchronised with the *Analytical Store* [28]and made accessible through *Azure Synapse Link* [29]for analysis in *Synapse Analytics* [30]. Finally, processed and aggregated results are visualised through interactive dashboards in Power BI, enabling real-time monitoring and long-term performance evaluation.

This end-to-end configuration provides historical real-time visibility, long-term reliability, and seamless data flow from the edge or fog layer to the cloud and application layers. The individual components of the cloud architecture pipeline are described in the following sections.

4.1 Azure IoT Hub (Ingressor)

The *IoT Hub* acts as the secure gateway between the edge device and other downstream cloud services. Telemetry messages, encoded in JSON and transmitted via the MQTT protocol, are authenticated through device-specific connection strings. The Hub supports communication, ensuring reliable message delivery and enabling remote diagnostics when required. All incoming data are timestamped and queued for downstream processing by the Function Apps, guaranteeing loss-tolerant transmission even under intermittent connectivity.

4.2 Azure Function Apps (Streamer)

Azure Function Apps perform the event-driven processing of telemetry within the cloud pipeline and can be coded in various programming languages. Each Function App acts as a container for one or more functions that are automatically triggered by incoming events, such as IoT Hub messages or scheduled timer executions. Serving as the bridge—or streamer—between the *IoT Hub* and downstream services, they parse, validate, and route

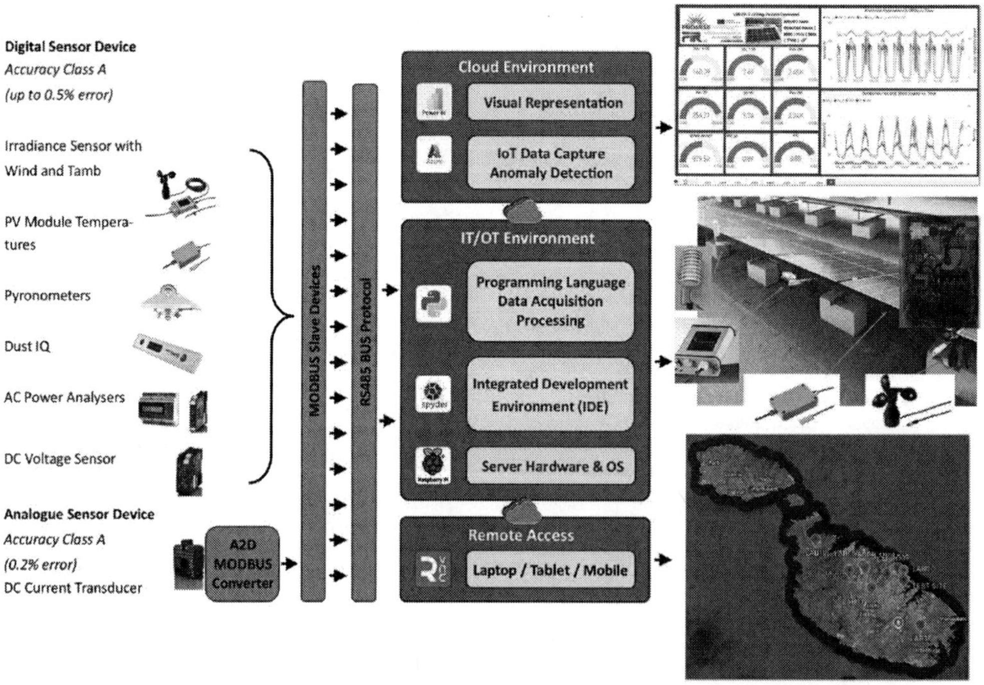

Figure 1: Sensory Edge and Cloud Comprehensive Framework for the Malta Living Laboratories

incoming data to the appropriate storage container in *Cosmos DB* database. When telemetry from an unrecognised device ID is detected, the system automatically creates a new storage container in Cosmos DB, enabling the seamless integration of newly added sites. These functions can be developed directly through the Azure portal or locally on a PC and then deployed to Azure as serverless applications, allowing flexible development, integration, and scalability

Beyond basic routing, the Functions perform both light and advanced pre-processing, including removal of malformed packets, assignment of laboratory identifiers, and automatic creation of new storage containers for newly deployed. They also generate status flags and send notifications to users when null or implausible values are detected, typically arising from sensor or communication errors. In addition, the Functions continuously monitor incoming telemetry to perform performance-driven anomaly detection and support downstream analytics within the PROMISE monitoring framework.

4.3 Azure Cosmos DB and Analytical Store (Storage)

The *Cosmos DB (NoSQL)* [15] database provides the primary storage layer for all monitoring data. Telemetry is written to the Transactional Store as JSON documents, ensuring millisecond-level ingestion and global redundancy. Data are then mirrored automatically to the Analytical Store, where they are restructured into a columnar format optimised for large-scale queries and analytical workloads. This dual-store mechanism separates operational and analytical traffic, preserving ingestion performance while enabling efficient querying for research analysis and dashboarding. Historical data can be downloaded in both CSV and JSON formats

4.4 Azure Synapse Link and Analytics, and *Power BI*

The Synapse Link bridges *Cosmos DB's Analytical Store* with *Azure Synapse Analytics*, providing a direct, near-real-time connection to analytical and visualisation services without Extraction, Loading and Transformation processes (ELT). Within *Synapse Analytics*, data can be queried using serverless SQL or processed with Spark for machine-learning tasks.

The processed and aggregated datasets feed directly into *Power BI*, which serves as a front-end unified visualisation and dissemination platform. Dashboards built in *Power BI Desktop are* deployed through the *Power BI Service*, offering both private, capacity-backed access through different tiers for project partners and public dashboards embedded on the PROMISE website. These visual dashboard interfaces deliver real-time operational awareness and retrospective performance analysis across all Living Laboratories and test facilities, as illustrated Fig. 1.

5. . EXPLOITABLE RESULTS

Following the digital upgrade of the PROMISE monitoring infrastructure, the system has now expanded from the initial six PV Living Laboratories reported in Bartolo et al. (2024) to a total of ten monitoring sites and three dedicated test facilities across Malta. Electrical and meteorological sensors, continue to ensure high reliability under Mediterranean climatic conditions. Data acquisition now occurs at 3-second intervals, enabling enhanced temporal resolution and adherence to the IEC 61724-1:2021 standard.

One of the most significant developments of this phase is the establishment of the PROMISE Open PV Reliability Repository, which provides public access to real-time and historical datasets from all laboratories. This open-data initiative promotes transparency, collaboration, and reproducibility, aligning the PROMISE project with European directives on open science and enabling Malta's active participation in international PV reliability and benchmarking programmes.

The multi-site configuration now includes:

i. Ten rooftop PV monitoring sites across institutional and industrial locations, covering diverse microclimates and system architectures.
ii. Three dedicated test sites, each with a specific role:
iii. A PV Degradation Test Site forming part of a round-robin international study to benchmark long-term degradation across European climates.
iv. A BIPV reference facility equipped with a multi-orientation, multi-inclination angle-optimised reference sensor array for grid-integration and energy-yield studies.
v. A PV calibration site, equipped with secondary-standard pyranometers, serving as a second-level calibration reference laboratory for benchmarking and calibration of other monitoring nodes.

5.1 Developed Key Exploitable Results (KERs)

The expanded infrastructure and digitalisation framework have produced a series of exploitable research, technical, and capacity-building outcomes:

1. Malta PV Living Laboratories – Monitoring Infrastructure: a national, cloud-integrated, real-time monitoring network for distributed PV systems.
2. Smart PV Insights – AI Prediction Models for Islands: machine-learning models for forecasting PV performance and grid interaction under insular conditions.
3. Malta PV Calibration Lab – Second-Level Reference Facility: establishes traceability and calibration procedures for sensors and instruments across the Living Labs.
4. PV Module Degradation Test Site – Global Benchmark Node: contributes to a Europe-wide round-robin initiative for comparative degradation analysis.
5. BIPV Angle-Optimised Reference Sensor Array Enables evaluation of tilt- and orientation-dependent irradiance effects on PV yield and grid stability.
6. Mediterranean PV Schools – Capacity-Building Flagship: training programmes, internships, and educational outreach to strengthen local expertise.
7. First-Check App – Real-Time PV Health Snapshot: a lightweight mobile interface providing quick visualisation of laboratory and system health indicators.

8. PV ThermalScan – Drone-AI Fault Detection Service: an aerial inspection tool integrating thermography and AI analytics for field fault detection.
9. Advanced PV Diagnostics – EL & IV Testing Setup: laboratory infrastructure for detailed characterisation of PV modules.
10. PROMISE Open PV Reliability Repository: a fully public, cloud-hosted data repository promoting transparency and collaborative research.
11. Postgraduate Framework with Anhalt University: Academic collaboration enabling joint supervision and research exchange in PV reliability and digitalisation.
12. Reactive Power Control Testbed for PV–EV Scenarios: Experimental platform for assessing PV–EV grid interaction and smart-inverter control strategies

6. CONCLUSION

The 2025 phase of the PROMISE project marks a major advancement in the digital transformation of PV system monitoring. The transition from a hybrid ThingSpeak–Grafana setup to a unified Microsoft Azure-based architecture has addressed previous limitations related to scalability, data synchronisation, and interoperability. Through the integration of IoT Hub, Function Apps, Cosmos DB, and Power BI, the framework now supports real-time analytics, predictive maintenance, and cross-site benchmarking. The expansion to ten monitoring laboratories and three dedicated test sites establishes a comprehensive platform for studying PV degradation behaviour, orientation effects, and grid-integration dynamics under diverse environmental conditions.

The introduction of the PROMISE Open PV Reliability Repository further reinforces transparency and open collaboration by providing public access to harmonised, high-quality datasets readily available on the project website Malta PV Living Laboratories – PROMISE. [8] These developments position PROMISE as a replicable model for intelligent, cloud-integrated PV monitoring aligned with the objectives of the European Green Deal and the digital energy transition.

Future work will focus on implementing real-time performance and anomaly detection frameworks within the cloud pipeline, expanding the monitoring network to additional European sites with similar climatic challenges, and performing multi-site irradiance correlation analyses to support short-term weather transition forecasting. This capability will enable utilities to anticipate the impact of atmospheric changes on PV generation, contributing to smarter, more resilient grid operation.

ACKNOWLESGEMENTS

Funded by the European Union

UK Research and Innovation

Partly funded by the European Union under Grant 101079469 PROMISE "Photovoltaics Reliability Operations and Maintenance Innovative Solutions for Energy Alliance" project, under Grant 101075747 and UK Research and Innovation (UKRI) TRANSIT "TRANSITion to sustainable future through training and education" project, European Union, Xjenza Malta under Grant REP-2023-061 RoOFPEVs "Robust Optimization Framework for PVs and EVs Integration at Low Voltage Network" project.

Views and opinions expressed are, however, those of the author(s) only and do not necessarily reflect those of the granting authorities/agencies nor that the granting authorities/agencies can be held responsible for them. Furthermore, the authors would like to thank the owners of the PV systems deployed as FiR.mt Living Laboratories in Malta.

REFERENCES

[1] 'EU Fit for 55: Navigate emissions management | LR'. Accessed: Sep. 27, 2025. [Online]. Available: https://www.lr.org/en/expertise/maritime-energy-transition/fit-for-55/

[2] 'The European Green Deal - European Commission'. Accessed: Sep. 27, 2025. [Online]. Available: https://commission.europa.eu/strategy-and-policy/priorities-2019-2024/european-green-deal_en

[3] 'Performance of New Photovoltaic System Designs'. Accessed: Oct. 10, 2025. [Online]. Available: https://isfh.de/en/reports/performance-of-new-photovoltaic-system-designs

[4] D. L. King, 'More "efficient" methods for specifying and monitoring PV system performance', in *2011 37th IEEE Photovoltaic Specialists Conference*, Jun. 2011, pp. 000219–000224. doi: 10.1109/PVSC.2011.6185884.

[5] 'Technical Specifications for On-site Solar Photovoltaic Systems', Energy.gov. Accessed: Oct. 10, 2025. [Online]. Available: https://www.energy.gov/femp/technical-specifications-site-solar-photovoltaic-systems

[6] M. A. Cassar, 'A study on the salinity of Maltese Soils in relation to their distance from the coast', bachelorThesis, University of Malta, 2016. Accessed: Sep. 29, 2025. [Online]. Available: https://www.um.edu.mt/library/oar/handle/123456789/22065

[7] R. J. Whittaker and J. M. Fernández-Palacios, 'Island environments', in *Island Biogeography: Ecology, evolution, and conservation*, R. J. Whittaker and J. M. Fernández-Palacios, Eds., Oxford University Press, 2006, p. 0. doi: 10.1093/oso/9780198566113.003.0002.

[8] 'Malta PV Living Laboratories – PROMISE'. Accessed: Sep. 30, 2025. [Online]. Available: https://pv-promise.eu/malta-pv-living-laboratories/

[9] B. Bartolo *et al.*, 'Harmonising Multi-Sites Measurement of Photovoltaic Systems: Comprehensive Framework for Real-Life Test Conditions in a Maltese Environment', *41st Eur. Photovolt. Sol. Energy Conf. Exhib.*, pp. 020340-001-020340–004, 2024, doi: 10.4229/EUPVSEC2024/4BV.3.26.

[10] B. Bartolo, B. Azzopardi, and K. Scerri, 'Development and implementation of a public data

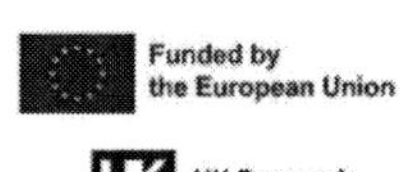

repository for photovoltaic systems: Case study malta's living laboratories', *Sol. Energy Adv.*, vol. 5, p. 100100, Jan. 2025, doi: 10.1016/j.seja.2025.100100.
[11] 'IoT Analytics - ThingSpeak Internet of Things'. Accessed: Sep. 30, 2025. [Online]. Available: https://thingspeak.mathworks.com/
[12] 'Grafana Cloud | Observability platform overview', Grafana Labs. Accessed: Sep. 30, 2025. [Online]. Available: https://grafana.com/products/cloud/
[13] SoniaLopezBravo, 'Azure IoT Hub Documentation'. Accessed: Sep. 30, 2025. [Online]. Available: https://learn.microsoft.com/en-us/azure/iot-hub/
[14] ggailey777, 'Azure Functions documentation'. Accessed: Sep. 30, 2025. [Online]. Available: https://learn.microsoft.com/en-us/azure/azure-functions/
[15] markjbrown, 'Understand Distributed NoSQL Databases - Azure Cosmos DB'. Accessed: Sep. 30, 2025. [Online]. Available: https://learn.microsoft.com/en-us/azure/cosmos-db/distributed-nosql
[16] 'Power BI'. Accessed: Sep. 30, 2025. [Online]. Available: https://app.powerbi.com/home?experience=power-bi
[17] 'IEC 61724-1:2021'. Accessed: Sep. 04, 2025. [Online]. Available: https://webstore.iec.ch/en/publication/65561
[18] 'The Use of Advanced Algorithms in PV Failure Monitoring'. Accessed: Oct. 10, 2025. [Online]. Available: https://isfh.de/en/reports/the-use-of-advanced-algorithms-in-pv-failure-monitoring
[19] S. Vergura, 'A Statistical Tool to Detect and Locate Abnormal Operating Conditions in Photovoltaic Systems', *Sustainability*, vol. 10, no. 3, p. 608, Mar. 2018, doi: 10.3390/su10030608.
[20] 'ISO/IEC 17025:2017', ISO. Accessed: Oct. 10, 2025. [Online]. Available: https://www.iso.org/standard/66912.html
[21] 'ISO 9001:2015', ISO. Accessed: Oct. 10, 2025. [Online]. Available: https://www.iso.org/standard/62085.html
[22] 'Modbus_Application_Protocol_V1_1b3.pdf'. Accessed: Sep. 30, 2025. [Online]. Available: https://www.afs.enea.it/project/protosphera/Proto-Sphera_Full_Documents/mpdocs/docs_EEI/Modbus_Application_Protocol_V1_1b3.pdf?utm_source=chatgpt.com
[23] 'raspberry-pi-4-product-brief.pdf'. Accessed: Sep. 30, 2025. [Online]. Available: https://datasheets.raspberrypi.com/rpi4/raspberry-pi-4-product-brief.pdf?utm_source=chatgpt.com
[24] 'Application Note ModBus Rev B.pdf'. Accessed: Sep. 30, 2025. [Online]. Available: https://www.electrokit.com/upload/product/41020/41020847/Application%20Note%20ModBus%20Rev%20B.pdf?utm_source=chatgpt.com
[25] *pymodbus: A fully featured modbus protocol stack in python*. Python. Accessed: Sep. 30, 2025. [MacOS :: MacOS X, Microsoft, OS Independent, POSIX :: Linux, Unix]. Available: https://github.com/pymodbus-dev/pymodbus/
[26] 'Download VNC Viewer by RealVNC®', RealVNC®. Accessed: Sep. 30, 2025. [Online]. Available: https://www.realvnc.com/en/connect/download/viewer/
[27] Emmet, 'Beginners Guide to Cron Jobs and Crontab', Pi My Life Up. Accessed: Oct. 10, 2025. [Online]. Available: https://pimylifeup.com/cron-jobs-and-crontab/
[28] jilmal, 'What is Azure Cosmos DB analytical store?' Accessed: Sep. 30, 2025. [Online]. Available: https://learn.microsoft.com/en-us/azure/cosmos-db/analytical-store-introduction
[29] im-microsoft, 'What is Azure Synapse Link for SQL? - Azure Synapse Analytics'. Accessed: Sep. 30, 2025. [Online]. Available: https://learn.microsoft.com/en-us/azure/synapse-analytics/synapse-link/sql-synapse-link-overview
[30] juluczni, 'Azure Synapse Analytics - Azure Synapse Analytics'. Accessed: Sep. 30, 2025. [Online]. Available: https://learn.microsoft.com/en-us/azure/synapse-analytics/

AUTHORS CONTRIBUTIONS

Conceptualisation (BB, BA, AM, MR, BK), Data curation (BB), Formal analysis (BB), Hardware/Software (BB, BA, CA), Funding acquisition (BA), Investigation (BB, BA), Methodology (BB, BA, KS), Project administration (BA), Resources (BA), Supervision (BA, KS), Validation (BA), Visualisation (BB, BA), Writing – original draft (BB, BA), Writing – review and editing (RE, CM, ME, EZ, SZ).

UAV-BASED AUTONOMOUS MONITORING AND REAL-TIME THERMAL ANOMALY DETECTION OF PHOTOVOLTAIC MODULES

G. Taghipour Kani [1], S.M. Esmailifar [1], A. Ghahremani[1], and M. Aghaei[2,3*]

[1]Department of Aerospace Engineering, Amirkabir University of Technology, Tehran 15119-43943, Iran
[2]Department of Ocean Operations and Civil Engineering, Norwegian University of Science and Technology (NTNU), 6009 Ålesund, Norway
[3]Department of Sustainable Systems Engineering (INATECH), University of Freiburg, 79110 Freiburg, Germany

*mohammadreza.aghaei@ntnu.no

ABSTRACT: This study presents an end-to-end autonomous monitoring framework for photovoltaic (PV) modules using unmanned aerial vehicles (UAVs), integrating thermal anomaly detection, boundary segmentation, and adaptive coverage path planning. The proposed system utilizes deep learning-based YOLO classifiers to identify nine different thermal faults in PV arrays, ensuring accurate and efficient real-time fault detection during flight. YOLOv8l achieved the highest classification performance (83.02% Top-1 accuracy), and YOLOv8n demonstrated exceptional computational efficiency with an inference time of just 8 ms and a compact model size of 2.94 MB, making it ideal for resource-constrained UAVs. To guide the UAV flight inside a solar farm, YOLO segmentation models were trained to extract PV plant boundaries from aerial images. YOLOv8l, selected for its high segmentation accuracy (mAP@50 = 0.952), provided precise navigable zone delineation critical for the next planning stage. These boundaries were used to generate a grid-based representation of the inspection area, supporting a deterministic sweep coverage algorithm with real-time obstacle avoidance and fallback handling. The coverage path planning system dynamically adapts to the layout of each PV installation, ensuring all accessible areas are inspected while minimizing flight distance and energy consumption. This multi-component framework enhances UAV autonomy and inspection completeness, reduces manual effort, and supports scalable real-time maintenance strategies for large-scale solar farms.

Keywords: UAV-based monitoring; photovoltaic modules; thermal anomaly detection; YOLO classifiers; real-time monitoring; coverage path planning

1 INTRODUCTION

As photovoltaic (PV) deployment expands globally, maintaining performance through efficient monitoring is increasingly critical. Traditional inspections—manual walk-throughs or ground-based thermal imaging—are slow, labor-intensive, and impractical for large PV farms. They are also prone to human error and limited visibility, often missing anomalies such as hot spots, diode failures, or cracks [1-4].
UAVs equipped with thermal cameras offer a scalable, contactless, and rapid alternative for large-area PV inspection. Yet achieving fully autonomous, real-time operation remains challenging, particularly for fault classification under limited onboard resources, navigable area segmentation, and energy-efficient path planning [2, 5, 6].
Moradi Sizkouhi et al. [7] introduced RoboPV, an autonomous UAV monitoring system with 93% inspection accuracy, combining boundary detection, path planning, and fault detection via a deep learning encoder-decoder. However, RoboPV lacks robust real-time detection across diverse PV faults. Addressing this gap, this study proposes a comprehensive UAV-based framework integrating:

- Grid-based path planning with adaptive logic for full coverage and energy efficiency
- Boundary segmentation for precise inspection area extraction
- Thermal anomaly classification using optimized YOLO models across nine PV conditions

Figure 1 shows the workflow of the proposed system.

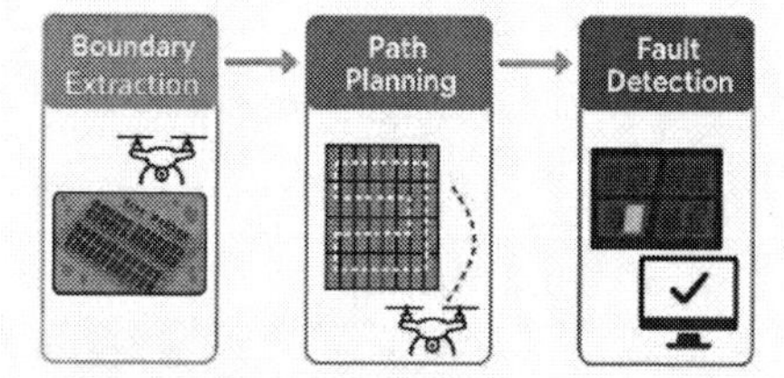

Figure 1. Workflow of the proposed UAV-based PV monitoring framework.

This work builds upon earlier efforts such as RoboPV, which demonstrated effective UAV-based inspection workflows but lacked real-time anomaly detection and lightweight path intelligence. By addressing these limitations, our proposed system offers a robust, real-time solution for autonomous monitoring and maintenance of solar farms, contributing to higher operational uptime, reduced maintenance cost, and improved energy output.

2 EMPLOYED DATASET

To enable real-time fault classification and autonomous navigation in UAV-based solar farm monitoring, this study uses a dataset of 20,000 aerial thermal images [8], each at 24×40 resolution and representing diverse PV module conditions.
Images are labeled into nine classes: eight common thermal anomalies and one nominal (defect-free) state. The anomaly classes include hot-spot heating, cracking, bypass diode failures (single/multiple), shading, vegetation overgrowth, soiling, and offline modules, which are key indicators of PV performance degradation.

Table 1. Thermal Images Dataset Description

Class Name	Number of Images	Description
Hot-Spot	3,663	High-temperature regions caused by faults.
Cracking	941	Surface cracks visible in thermal imaging.
Shadowing	1,056	Obstructions caused by vegetation or nearby structures.
Diode	1,499	Activation of bypass diodes affecting module efficiency.
Diode-Multi	175	Multiple activated bypass diodes reducing performance.
Vegetation	1,639	Panels blocked by vegetation growth.
Soiling	205	Dirt or debris reducing energy output.
Offline-Module	828	Entire module disconnected or malfunctioning.
No-Anomaly	10,000	Nominal solar modules with no visible defects.

The data were collected using piloted aircraft and UAVs equipped with midwave and longwave infrared (MWIR/LWIR) sensors covering 3–13.5 μm. Depending on sensor type and altitude, the ground sampling distance (GSD) ranged from 3.0 to 15.0 cm per pixel, providing sufficient thermal resolution for defect detection.

For focused analysis, anomaly instances were manually cropped from larger mosaics to isolate individual PV modules. The final dataset reflects a semi-realistic anomaly distribution, with 50% of samples representing nominal conditions. This intentional imbalance simulates real-world scenarios where functional modules dominate but early-stage faults must still be detected.

3 YOLO CLASSIFIERS TRAINING AND TUNING

YOLO (You Only Look Once) classifiers are well-suited for real-time vision tasks due to their unified architecture, which enables detection or classification in a single forward pass. In this study, three YOLO variants (YOLOv8n, YOLOv8l, and YOLOv8x) were employed for multi-class thermal anomaly classification. These models were selected to represent a range of trade-offs between accuracy, speed, and model size, which are crucial when deploying inference pipelines onboard UAVs.

3.1 Training and Optimization Process

All models were implemented using the Ultralytics YOLOv8 framework, supporting streamlined training and hardware optimization. Input images were standardized to 96×96, and augmentations (random flips, scaling, HSV shifts, mosaic) were applied to improve generalization under varied UAV imaging conditions.

Models were trained for up to 600 epochs with a batch size of 32, using early stopping (patience of 100). A grid search–based hyperparameter tuning refined performance, exploring:

- Initial and final learning rates (lr0, lrf)
- Momentum and weight decay
- Warmup epochs for training stability
- Mosaic and HSV probabilities for augmentation control

These steps maximized classification accuracy while maintaining real-time responsiveness and low computational overhead.

3.2 Tuning Results and Model Performance

The tuned models demonstrated precious achivements in both accuracy and inference performance. YOLOv8l achieved the highest Top-1 classification accuracy of 83.02%, while YOLOv8n offered the best efficiency, requiring only 8 ms per inference with a minimal 2.94 MB model size. The results are summarized in the following tables.

Table 2. Tuned YOLO Models Hyperparameter Configurations.

Model	lr0	lrf	Momentum	Weight Decay	Warmup Epochs	HSV-H	Scale	Mosaic
YOLOv8x	0.01	0.01	0.937	0.0005	3.0	0.015	0.5	1.0
YOLOv8n	0.0101	0.01112	0.91359	0.00047	2.78907	0.015	0.6	0.99306
YOLOv8l	0.00939	0.01112	0.92606	0.00044	3.01336	0.014	0.488	0.977

Table 3. YOLO Model Performance After Tuning

Model	Top-1 Accuracy	Top-5 Accuracy	Inference Time (ms)	Model Size (MB)
YOLOv8n	82.25%	99.23%	8.0	2.94
YOLOv8l	83.02%	99.17%	11.0	70.92
YOLOv8x	82.13%	99.37%	21.0	109.88

- **YOLOv8n**: Lightweight with 82.25% Top-1 and 99.23% Top-5 accuracy, 8 ms inference, and 2.94 MB size, which is ideal for real-time UAV deployment in large solar farms.

- **YOLOv8l:** Most accurate (83.02% Top-1, 99.17% Top-5), with 11 ms inference and 70.92 MB size, balancing precision and efficiency for mid-resource platforms.

- **YOLOv8x:** 82.13% Top-1 and 99.37% Top-5 accuracy, but its 109.88 MB size and 21 ms inference limit suitability for UAVs, though effective in precision-focused tasks.

10.4229/EUPVSEC2025/4CV.1.26

3.3 Insights and Interpretations

All YOLO variants achieved over 99% Top-5 accuracy, confirming their ability to distinguish subtle thermal patterns across nine anomaly classes. YOLOv8n, the most compact and fastest, suits edge UAV deployment where speed and power are critical, while YOLOv8l balances accuracy and efficiency for mid-tier platforms. Learning and validation curves (Figure 2) indicate stable convergence and minimal overfitting, validating the training pipeline and hyperparameter design.

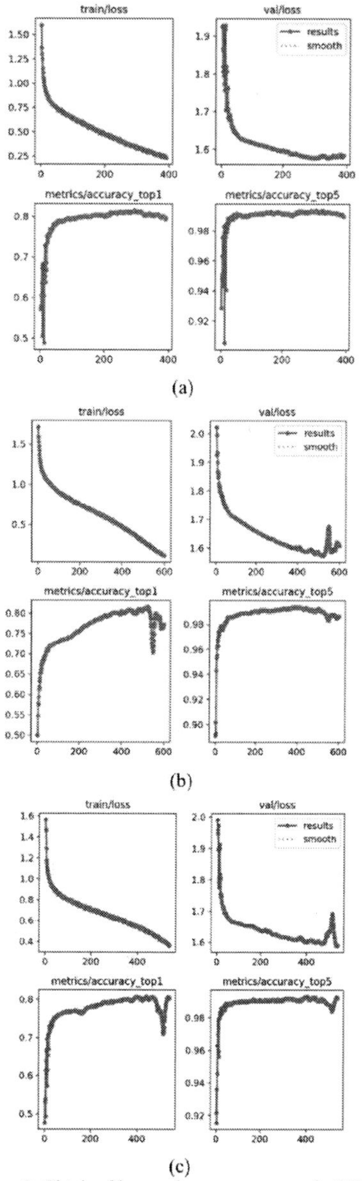

Figure 2. Obtained loss and accuracy curves for YOLO classifiers: a) yolov8x-cls.pt training process, b) yolov8l-cls.yaml and c) yolov8n-cls.pt during the training process.

The results demonstrate that YOLO models are highly effective for UAV-based PV anomaly detection, providing a reliable, efficient, and scalable solution for real-time thermal monitoring of solar farms. Their ability to balance accuracy and computational efficiency makes them perfect choices for enhancing solar farm productivity through UAV-integrated monitoring systems.

4. SOLAR FARM BOUNDARY DETECTION

Accurate boundary extraction is essential for autonomous UAV inspection, ensuring navigation remains within operational areas, avoiding non-functional zones, and conserving energy. It also forms the basis for structured grid maps needed in path planning.
Two YOLO segmentation models were evaluated using the Amir dataset [9, 10], which contains 3,548 high-resolution aerial images of large-scale PV installations worldwide with precisely annotated PV masks for supervised training.
Models were trained with the Ultralytics YOLO segmentation framework for 200 epochs, batch size 64, on an NVIDIA GeForce RTX 4070 Ti GPU, enabling fast cycles and scalability for large datasets.

4.1 SEGMENTATION TRAINING AND METRICS

The segmentation process employed a multi-part loss function, which includes components for bounding box regression, segmentation masks, class prediction, and distribution focal loss (DFL). The segmentation loss was computed using binary cross-entropy, penalizing pixel-wise deviation from ground truth masks. This structure allows the model to simultaneously learn object presence, boundary shapes, and spatial alignment.

Model performance was measured using:

- Precision: ratio of correctly segmented areas to total predicted segments,
- Recall: proportion of ground truth regions that were successfully segmented,
- mAP@50: mean Average Precision at IoU threshold 0.5, summarizing precision-recall balance across confidence thresholds.

A prediction was considered correct if its segmentation mask overlapped with ground truth by at least 50% using Intersection over Union (IoU).

4.2 Results And Model Comparison

Both YOLOv8l and YOLO11l achieved smooth convergence with rising precision and recall across epochs. As shown in Table 4, YOLOv8l reached a mAP@50 of 0.952, outperforming YOLO11l at 0.911, demonstrating higher segmentation reliability and suitability for accurate navigability maps.
YOLO11l, though less accurate, offered faster inference (46 ms vs. 55 ms), making it a viable option for highly resource-constrained UAVs where speed is prioritized.

10.4229/EUPVSEC2025/4CV.1.26

However, due to the importance of boundary precision for navigation safety and grid accuracy, YOLOv8l was chosen as the final model. Figure 3 shows successful boundary extraction under diverse aerial conditions.

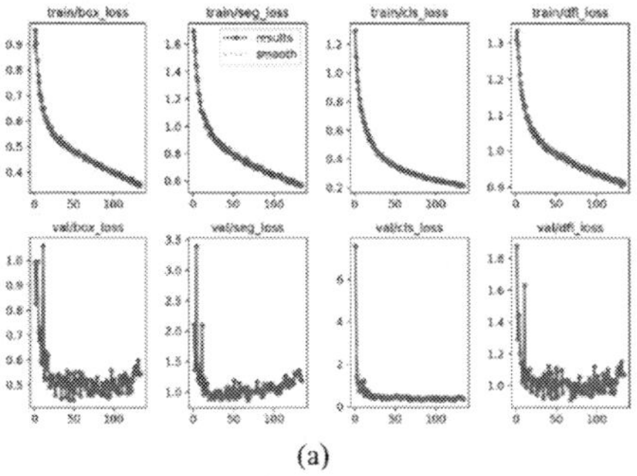

(a)

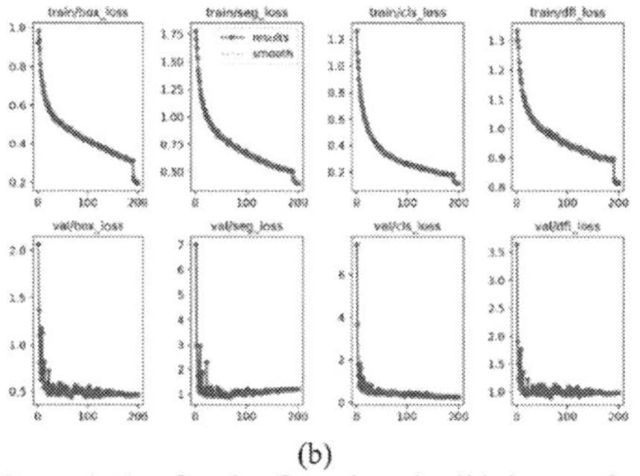

(b)

Figure 3. Cost function for train and validation sets for a) YOLOv8l segmentation model, b) YOLO11l segmentation model

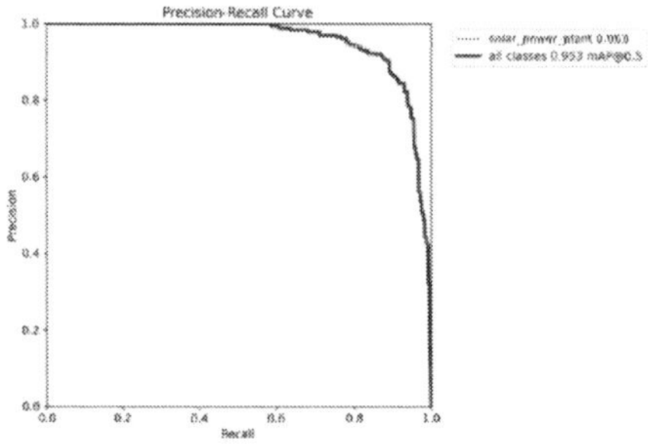

(a)

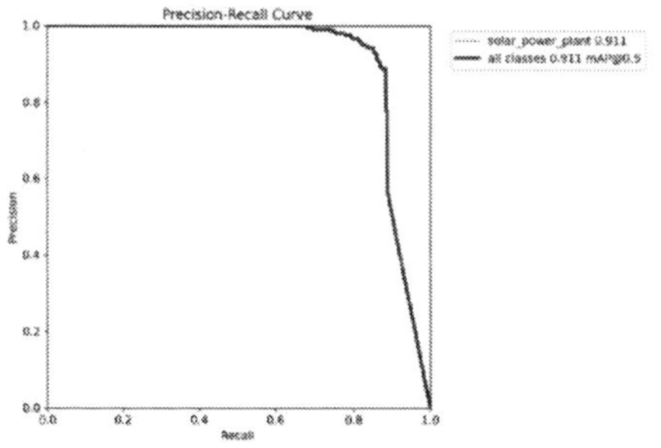

(b)

Figure 4. Precision versus recall graph for a) YOLOv8l segmentation model, b) YOLO11l segmentation model.

Table 4. Boundary Detection Results

Segmentation Model	Inference Time (ms)
YOLOv8l	55.00
YOLO11l	46.00

The boundary extraction model result is shown in Figure 4. By incorporating accurate and real-time boundary extraction using YOLOv8l, the system ensures precise mapping of navigable areas for UAVs, laying the groundwork for the path planning module described in the following section.

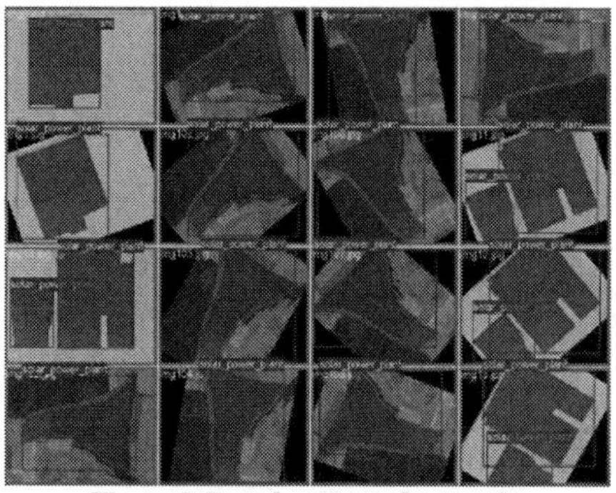

Figure 5. Boundary Extraction Results

5. PATH PLANNING FOR UAV NAVIGATION

Following boundary extraction, an adaptive navigation strategy is required to ensure complete inspection of the solar farm. This section introduces a grid-based path planning algorithm for UAVs, designed to deliver systematic and energy-efficient coverage. By utilizing aerial imagery and segmentation-derived navigable zones, the method ensures every operational cell of the solar array is inspected, even in complex or obstructed environments.

The planner divides the farm into a grid, with each cell representing a discrete inspection zone based on the UAV's thermal camera field of view. Cells are classified as navigable (safe for flight) or non-navigable (obstacles or irrelevant areas) using YOLOv8l segmentation. This spatial mapping enables optimized path execution with minimal overlap and adaptive redirection.

5.1 Methodology and Coverage Mechanism

The segmented aerial image is transformed into a 2D navigability grid, where each cell corresponds to part of the solar field:

- Navigable cells: safe for traversal
- Non-navigable cells: physical obstacles (e.g., trees, buildings, inaccessible terrain)

Classification is derived from YOLOv8l segmentation. The UAV begins inspection from a defined starting point and follows a deterministic raster sweep: scanning rows horizontally, shifting vertically, and reversing direction. This minimizes angular turns, simplifies control logic, and adapts to both compact and dispersed PV arrays. The grid abstraction generalizes across various geometries, while navigability masks prevent unsafe entry. Figure 6 illustrates the grid environment and UAV sweep zones.

5.2 Obstacle Handling and Adaptive Navigation

Solar plants often include incomplete rows, irregular layouts, and unexpected obstacles. To address these, the algorithm integrates real-time detection and fallback strategies. When the UAV reaches a boundary or non-navigable cell, it:

- Searches for adjacent unvisited navigable cells
- If none exist, applies a Euclidean distance heuristic to locate the nearest unvisited cell

This ensures no segment is skipped and prevents entrapment in concave areas. If isolated by obstacles, the UAV autonomously reroutes, reorients, and resumes sweeping, maintaining mission continuity without manual input. The fallback mechanism avoids dead-ends and supports uninterrupted coverage even after detours.

5.3 Full Coverage and State Tracking

To ensure complete inspection, the system maintains a binary state matrix marking each navigable cell as visited or unvisited. The UAV queries this matrix to:

- Prioritize unvisited cells
- Avoid redundant revisits
- Confirm mission completion via global coverage status

This mechanism supports both regular arrays and irregular layouts with missing or concave sections. Unlike conventional planners assuming convex farms, it accommodates fragmented, discontinuous installations. Through fallback repositioning and local re-alignment, the UAV systematically inspects all reachable zones. If any area remains uncovered due to obstacles or flight limits, the planner redirects the UAV until the matrix confirms completion or termination criteria are met.

5.4 Energy Efficiency and Path Optimization

With UAVs constrained by limited flight autonomy, minimizing energy use is essential. The planner enhances efficiency by:

- Reducing turns in sweep patterns
- Cutting backtracking through nearest-cell fallback logic
- Streamlining transitions between rows

These measures lead to fewer motor actuations, shorter inspection times, and higher coverage per battery cycle. Ultimately, optimized paths extend flight duration and enable broader inspection, improving scalability for utility-scale solar plants.

5.5 Visualization and Monitoring

The framework provides a real-time interface that tracks:

- UAV position on the grid
- History of visited cells
- Remaining unvisited regions

This gives operators a live view of progress and coverage. Post-flight, the module enables analytics such as heatmap generation, coverage validation, and detection of missed zones, supporting mission improvement and targeted re-inspection.

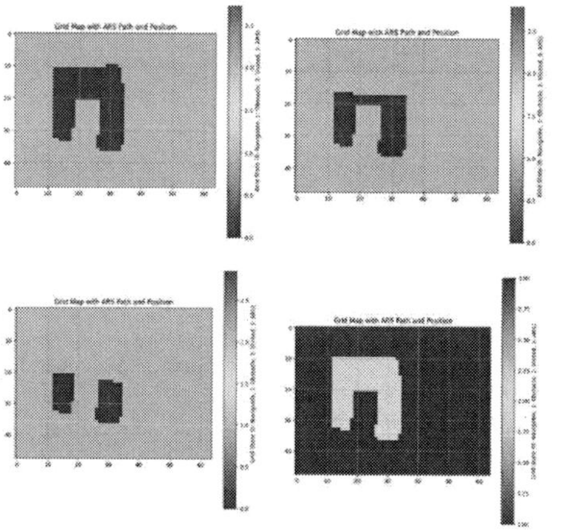

Figure 6. Automated path planning system phases during coverage process

5.6 Summary

This path planning system combines:

- Rule-based sweeping,
- Intelligent obstacle avoidance,
- Fallback logic,
- Energy-aware movement strategies, and
- Live inspection state tracking,

to deliver a robust, scalable, and fully autonomous UAV coverage algorithm. Unlike rigid route planners, this method adapts dynamically to environmental complexity, ensuring completeness and efficiency under real-world constraints. It forms the foundation of a reliable UAV-based PV monitoring pipeline, capable of operating without human intervention in large, irregular, or obstacle-dense solar farms.

10.4229/EUPVSEC2025/4CV.1.26

6 CONCLUSIONS

his paper presents an autonomous framework for real-time UAV inspection of photovoltaic (PV) modules, addressing fault detection, boundary mapping, and navigation. Unlike prior approaches treating classification and coverage separately, the proposed system integrates optimized deep learning with adaptive path planning into a deployable pipeline.

In classification, YOLO-based models were evaluated across nine thermal anomaly types. YOLOv8l achieved the highest Top-1 accuracy (83.02%) with moderate computational demand, while YOLOv8n offered the best efficiency, providing 8 ms inference and a 2.94 MB size suitable for resource-limited UAVs. For navigation, segmentation-based boundary extraction with YOLOv8l reached a mAP@50 of 0.952, reliably distinguishing navigable from non-navigable regions in complex PV layouts.

The core contribution is the adaptive grid-based path planner, which:

- Converts aerial segmentation into a navigability grid
- Uses deterministic sweep logic for row-wise traversal
- Integrates obstacle avoidance and fallback logic
- Tracks visited cells with a state matrix
- Optimizes path length and turns for energy efficiency

This ensures systematic inspection of all zones, including irregular or fragmented arrays. The combined logic and adaptive redirection enable autonomous operation across diverse solar farm conditions.

Overall, the framework delivers a scalable and robust solution that minimizes downtime, reduces manual labor, and enhances monitoring accuracy. By coupling real-time anomaly detection with intelligent flight coordination, it marks a step toward fully autonomous solar farm maintenance.

5 REFERENCES

1. Phungket, C. and P. Nangthin. *Deep Convolutional Neural Networks for Accurate Solar Module Classification in Thermal Images*. in *2024 12th International Electrical Engineering Congress (iEECON)*. 2024.
2. Zefri, Y., et al., *Developing a deep learning-based layer-3 solution for thermal infrared large-scale photovoltaic module inspection from orthorectified big UAV imagery data.* International Journal of Applied Earth Observation and Geoinformation, 2022. **106**: p. 102652.
3. Segovia Ramírez, I., B. Das, and F.P. García Márquez, *Fault detection and diagnosis in photovoltaic panels by radiometric sensors embedded in unmanned aerial vehicles.* Progress in Photovoltaics: Research and Applications, 2022. **30**(3): p. 240-256.
4. Wang, B., et al., *PVF-10: A high-resolution unmanned aerial vehicle thermal infrared image dataset for fine-grained photovoltaic fault classification.* Applied Energy, 2024. **376**: p. 124187.
5. Nie, J., T. Luo, and H. Li, *Automatic hotspots detection based on UAV infrared images for large-scale PV plant.* Electronics Letters, 2020. **56**(19): p. 993-995.
6. Sizkouhi, A.M.M., et al. *Autonomous Path Planning by Unmanned Aerial Vehicle (UAV) for Precise Monitoring of Large-Scale PV plants.* in *2019 IEEE 46th Photovoltaic Specialists Conference (PVSC)*. 2019.
7. Moradi Sizkouhi, A.M., et al., *RoboPV: An integrated software package for autonomous aerial monitoring of large scale PV plants.* Energy Conversion and Management, 2022. **254**: p. 115217.
8. Millendorf, M., E. Obropta, and N. Vadhavkar. *Infrared solar module dataset for anomaly detection.*
9. Sizkouhi, A.M.M., et al., *Automatic Boundary Extraction of Large-Scale Photovoltaic Plants Using a Fully Convolutional Network on Aerial Imagery.* IEEE Journal of Photovoltaics, 2020. **10**(4): p. 1061-1067.
10. M. Aghaei, et al, *Autonomous Intelligent Monitoring of Photovoltaic Systems: An In-Depth Multidisciplinary Review,* Progress in Photovoltaics: Research and Applications, 2024, https://doi.org/10.1002/pip.3859.

10.4229/EUPVSEC2025/4CV.1.26

PHOTOVOLTAIC POWER OUTPUT ESTIMATION WITH DIGITAL VISIBLE CAMERAS

Abad-Alcaraz, V.[a,b], García-Campos, E.[a], Álvarez, J.D.[a,b], Pérez-García, M.[a,c], Carballo, J.A.[a,d], Castilla, M.M.[a,b], Alonso-Montesinos, J.[a,c]
[a] CIESOL, Solar Energy Research Centre, University of Almería ceiA3, Ctra. Sacramento s/n, La Cañada de San Urbano, Almería 04120, Spain.
[b] Department of Informatics, University of Almería- ceiA3, Ctra. Sacramento s/n, La Cañada de San Urbano, Almería 04120, Spain.
[c] Department of Chemistry and Physics, University of Almería – ceiA3, Ctra. Sacramento s/n, La Cañada de San Urbano, Almería 04120, Spain.
[d] Centro de Investigaciones Energéticas, Medioambientales y Tecnológicas-Plataforma Solar de Almería (CIEMAT-PSA), Ctra. de Senés, km. 4,5, Tabernas 04200, Spain

vabadalcaraz@ual.es, ecampos@ual.es, jhervas@ual.es, mperez@ual.es, jcarballo@psa.es, mcastilla@ual.es, joaquin.alonso@ual.es

ABSTRACT: Monitoring and estimating the production of a photovoltaic (PV) system is crucial to optimise energy efficiency, detect performance problems and improve its financial viability. Monitoring allows the operator to detect faults early, improve maintenance planning and maximise energy production, thus improving return on investment and sustainability. On the other hand, estimating PV field production helps to plan energy consumption and integrate it into the grid. This study aims to explore a deep learning approach to estimate power generation in real time using images captured every ten minutes by three fixed cameras positioned at different perspectives (left, lateral and right) of the PV field at CIESOL research center. A hybrid neural network combining convolutional neural networks (CNN) and long-term memory networks (LSTM) is used to analyse the images and establish correlations with the actual power production. The results show that an accuracy of up to 8% (NRMSE) can be achieved in production estimation, as well as adequately capturing power variations and environmental influences. These findings underscore the potential of image-based monitoring as a non-intrusive and efficient method for improving PV system management and maintenance.
Keywords: Photovoltaic production, forecasting, monitoring, computer vision, deep learning.

1 INTRODUCTION

The growing global energy demand and the negative environmental impacts associated with fossil fuels have spurred increasing interest in renewable energy sources as a clean and sustainable alternative [1]. In this context, photovoltaic (PV) solar energy has consolidated itself as one of the most promising options due to its widespread availability, implementation flexibility, and the continuous cost reductions associated with technological advances [2]. PV systems offer major advantages by directly harvesting solar radiation to generate electricity, thereby minimizing pollutant emissions and contributing effectively to global climate-change mitigation targets [3].

However, the efficiency and operational reliability of these systems largely depend on advanced and accurate techniques for monitoring and predicting energy performance [4]. Continuous monitoring enables the prompt detection of operational issues, appropriate planning of preventive maintenance, and the optimization of energy production [5]. Among the factors that can significantly affect the efficiency of PV plants, dust accumulation—or soiling—stands out, especially in arid and semi-arid regions affected by Saharan dust intrusions. Soiling reduces incident irradiance and adversely impacts energy yield and system profitability [6,7]. Hence, developing effective methods for the timely detection and precise quantification of these losses is essential [8].

Traditionally, PV performance monitoring has relied on direct measurements using specialized instrumentation such as pyranometers, temperature sensors, and other environmental devices [9,10]. Although these methods are generally accurate, they present drawbacks related to high cost, the need for frequent maintenance, and sensitivity to harsh environmental conditions, which undermines long-term reliability [11].

In response to these limitations, innovative non-intrusive approaches based on computer vision have emerged, employing digital visible cameras to capture real-time information on the surroundings and the condition of the solar modules [12]. Automated image analysis makes it possible to detect critical environmental phenomena—such as cloud cover, module shading, and dust accumulation—without the need for additional direct instrumentation [13].

In parallel, the development of deep learning algorithms has revolutionized the ability to extract and analyse complex patterns present in visual and sequential datasets. Artificial Neural Networks (ANNs) are computational models inspired by the functioning of the human brain, capable of learning abstract, non-linear representations from large volumes of data. Within this family, Convolutional Neural Networks (CNNs) are particularly effective for analysing and recognizing patterns in images, while Long Short-Term Memory networks (LSTMs) model and predict temporal dependencies in sequential data [14,15]. The combination of these hybrid CNN–LSTM architectures has delivered excellent results in complex tasks such as energy prediction, clearly outperforming conventional approaches and other statistical machine-learning techniques [16,17]. In particular, recent architectures such as EfficientNet-B0 have demonstrated superior capability for extracting relevant visual features with high computational efficiency for practical applications [18,19].

This study proposes to explore the capability of different visual viewpoints captured by digital cameras (oriented toward the left side, lateral side, and right side of the field) to accurately estimate, in real time, the energy production of a PV system. To this end, a hybrid CNN–LSTM architecture based on EfficientNet-B0 is employed with the aim of evaluating which perspective provides the most representative and accurate information. The results obtained are expected to substantially improve current monitoring strategies, optimize predictive maintenance, and enhance the overall efficiency of PV systems.

The remainder of this article is organized as follows: after this introduction, Section 2 details the methodology, including the characteristics of the PV system, the image acquisition and preprocessing. Section 3 presents a description of the proposed CNN–LSTM model. Section 4 reports the results and their comparative analysis across the different camera viewpoints. Finally, Section 5 summarizes the main conclusions, offering recommendations for the practical implementation of the proposed method and suggestions for future research.

2 METHODOLOGY

2.1 Location and photovoltaic system

The study is conducted at the CIESOL[1] building (Solar Energy Research Centre), a joint research facility of the University of Almería and the Plataforma Solar de Almería, located on the northern side of the University of Almería campus (Spain) and in operation since 2006. CIESOL is a bioclimatic building conceived as a living laboratory for research and technological demonstration in solar energy. Notable features include a solar-driven HVAC system (heating and cooling via an absorption chiller supplied by solar thermal collectors), automated windows and solar shading devices, and distributed instrumentation with more than 300 sensors for monitoring indoor variables and controlling thermal comfort. The roof integrates a PV array that supplies part of the building's electricity demand and solar thermal collectors that feed the cooling system based on solar energy, as shown in Fig. 1.

Figure 1: CIESOL building

The building was part of the ARFRISOL project (Bioclimatic Architecture and Solar Cooling), aimed at validating passive strategies and active solar systems in tertiary buildings; within this framework, envelope and control solutions were implemented to minimize demand and cover a significant fraction of thermal loads with solar energy.

From a functional and construction standpoint, CIESOL consists of two floors with a built area of approximately 1,070 m², housing eight laboratories and prototyping areas, in addition to workspaces and technical rooms. Several laboratories are north-facing, which supports stable daylight conditions and reduces direct solar gains during research activities. As part of its active integration of renewables and to meet building demand, the facility includes a grid-connected PV plant of $\approx$ 9.3 kWp (covering building electrical uses), alongside roof-mounted solar thermal collectors linked to the absorption-based HVAC system.

Additionally, the site is equipped with a comprehensive set of meteorological and radiometric sensors that record global, direct, and diffuse irradiance on the plane of array, together with environmental variables such as wind speed and relative humidity. These measurements document operating conditions and support dataset quality control (physical consistency checks and filtering of unsuitable periods). They are not used as predictors; in the setup, the target variable is the PV plant's measured electrical power.

The combination of this instrumentation with the building's renewable-energy infrastructure and high-cadence monitoring and control system makes CIESOL an effective testbed for the development and validation of power-estimation methodologies.

2.2 Image acquisition system

a) Left camera vision

b) Right camera vision

c) Lateral camera vision

Figure 2: Vision of the three cameras installed in the CIESOL PV plant.

[1] https://ciesol.com/

10.4229/EUPVSEC2025/4CV.1.28

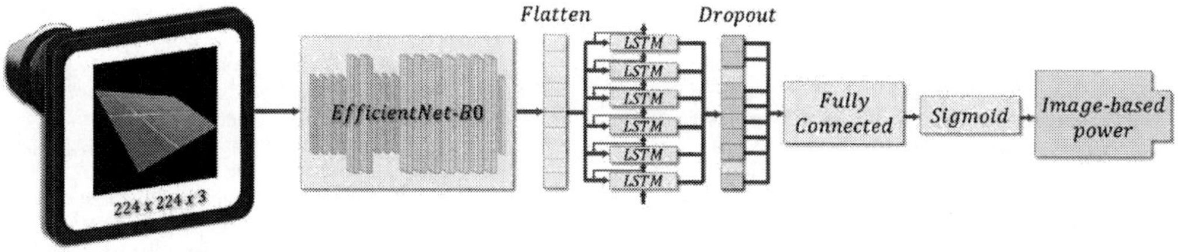

Figure 4: Model with CNN–LSTM using the EfficientNet-B0 framework

To enable power estimation based on visual information, three low-cost fixed digital cameras were installed with complementary perspectives on the PV generator:

- Left camera, with a view of the left wing of the field.
- Right camera, facing the right wing.
- Lateral camera, positioned to provide an overall view of the field from the side.

As seen in Fig. 2, the cameras operate in the RGB (visible) spectrum and capture an image every 10 minutes, generating a time series that can be synchronized with the power records.

2.3 Image preprocessing and mask generation

The final dataset used in this work consisted of 6,324 images, after an initial filtering process that eliminated those captured during nighttime, when electricity production is not active. A binary mask was systematically applied to each image to delimit exclusively the surface of the photovoltaic modules, thereby removing the sky, ground, and any other elements unrelated to the generator. Pixels within the panel area were assigned the logical value 1, while the rest of the scene was assigned 0. Overlaying this mask on the original image generated an effective crop that focused entirely on the PV field, ensuring that the visual information provided to the model corresponded only to the area of interest.

This segmentation process was found to be essential for reducing background noise and directing the learning process toward patterns directly related to system behaviour. Preliminary tests confirmed that the use of this segmentation step contributed to more accurate results in power prediction from images.

As illustrated in Fig. 3, the final image format is fed into the neural network. The original images had a slightly rectangular resolution of 3072 × 2028 pixels. Regardless of the input origin, whether lateral, left or right, all images were resized to a square format of 224 × 224 pixels to meet the input requirements of EfficientNet-B0 (CNN architecture). Although this resizing entails some loss of visual detail, the dimension was deemed sufficient for the network to operate efficiently while maintaining a manageable computational load.

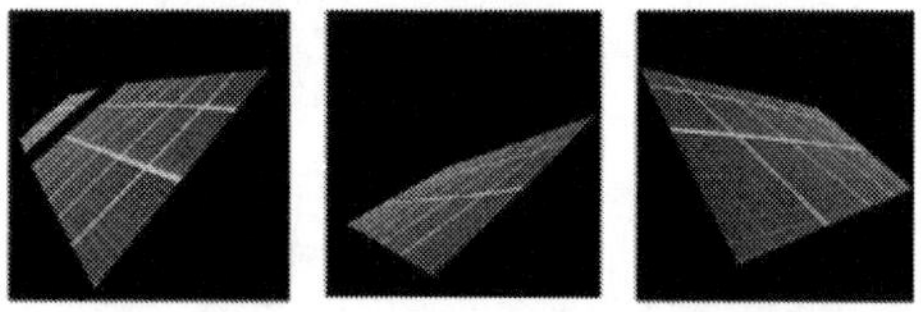

a) Lateral camera b) Left camera c) Right camera

Figure 3: Final preprocessed input images

The images are stored in RGB colour, which makes it easy to spot surface changes like dust accumulation or shading patterns. As the figure illustrates, the lateral perspective captures the largest visible area of the photovoltaic modules, providing a broader representation of the generator surface compared to left or right views.

In addition to the visual preprocessing, an exhaustive review of the power data used as the model output was carried out. First, all observations in which the recorded power was equal to zero at times when production was expected were discarded, as well as negative values generated by instrumental or logging errors. A selection procedure based on robust percentiles was also applied: the 0.5th and 99.5th percentiles of the power distribution were set as reference thresholds. Any value below the lower percentile was replaced by this limit, and similarly, any value above the 99.5th percentile was replaced by that threshold. After this process, which helps to remove erroneous data not detected manually, it was confirmed that the power was within the expected range, with a maximum value of 7,012.2 W. This ensures the consistency of the time series and prevents the model from being affected by spurious values. The procedure guarantees that the data fed into the neural network are clean, consistent, and physically plausible.

3 THE PROPOSED MODEL

3.1 CNN–LSTM architecture

In this work, meteorological and radiometric variables are used exclusively for dataset quality control and traceability; they are not used as predictors (e.g., discarding nighttime data, outliers under shading, or sensor faults). The supervised task is defined with the measured electrical power of the PV plant as the target variable, time-aligned with the images (see section 2.3 for data cleaning and filtering details). Power measurements and images were aligned by timestamp; samples without paired image or power record were discarded.

The predictive framework adopted in this work is based on a hybrid neural network that combines a CNN with an LSTM network, as illustrated in Fig. 4. This design leverages the ability of CNNs to extract spatial features from images and the capacity of LSTMs to capture temporal dependencies in sequential data. The synergy between both models enables the integration of visual and temporal information, which is essential when dealing with the short-term variability of PV power generation.

Solar radiation can undergo significant fluctuations even over short intervals, primarily due to cloud dynamics and atmospheric variability. In this context, extending the input sequences beyond a certain length not only adds little value to immediate prediction but also considerably increases computational cost and training complexity.

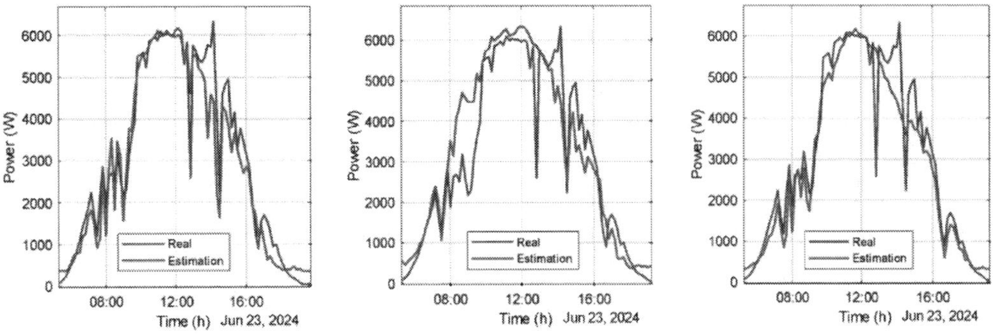

a) Lateral camera (b) Left camera (c) Right camera

Figure 5: Estimation of PV field power from the three camera viewpoints

Based on experimental evaluation, a one-hour interval was identified as the most suitable choice, as it strikes an optimal balance between capturing the relevant dynamics of solar variability and maintaining the computational efficiency of the model.

The convolutional branch of the network is based on EfficientNet-B0, an architecture that combines computational efficiency and accuracy through balanced scaling of depth, width, and resolution. This model has around 82 layers, among which the Mobile Inverted Bottleneck Convolutions (MBConv) blocks stand out.

The features generated by EfficientNet-B0 are flattened into one-dimensional vectors and are then fed into the LSTM branch. These recurrent networks allow temporal dependencies to be captured through a set of internal gates that regulate the flow of information: the forget gate decides which previous information is discarded, the update gate controls the incorporation of new input data, and the output gate determines which part of the updated internal state influences the hidden state transmitted to the next temporal step.

Finally, the combined output of the CNN and LSTM is connected to a fully connected dense layer, which is responsible for integrating the information extracted by both branches. The estimates are normalised in the range [0, 1] using a sigmoid activation function, which proved to be more suitable than classical standardization for this case.

3.2 Training and validation of prediction models

The model was trained using the Stochastic Gradient Descent with Momentum (SGDM) algorithm. This technique, an extension of traditional stochastic descent, incorporates a momentum term that smooths oscillations during optimization and accelerates convergence. In this work, the usual value of 0.9 was adopted, which has been shown to offer a good compromise between speed and stability. Compared to other optimizers such as Adam, SGDM exhibited more consistent behaviour and lower memory requirements.

The learning rate was set at 0.05, regulating the magnitude of weight updates in each iteration. A batch size of 64 was used, with the aim of balancing computational performance and memory utilisation. To avoid overfitting, a dropout layer was applied, which randomly deactivates 30% of the neurons during training, thus promoting the extraction of more robust features and reducing dependence on specific patterns.

In order to build and validate the model, complete days were randomly selected from the dataset, which is composed of a total of 93 days. The partition was divided into three subsets: 70% for training, 20% for validation, and 10% for testing. This strategy, the result of an experimental adjustment process, ensures a balanced distribution and favors the generalization of the model, while allowing its final performance to be evaluated on an independent dataset.

4 RESULTS AND DISCUSSION

In order to evaluate some statistical criteria, the measured power values of the CIESOL PV plant have been compared with the values estimated by the hybrid neural network. The results obtained demonstrate the efficacy of the deep learning model in estimating the power of the PV field from images captured from different perspectives. To assess the accuracy of the estimation, several statistical indices have been utilized, like the Mean Bias Error (MBE) to study the behaviour of the model in over/sub estimation; whereas the Root Mean Square Error (RMSE) and the normalised RMSE (NRMSE), calculated as the RMSE divided by the range of the observed data, were used to quantify the accuracy of the prediction:

$$RMSE = \sqrt{\frac{1}{n}\sum_{i=1}^{n}(\hat{y}_i - y_i)^2}\,; \quad NRMSE = \frac{RMSE}{y_{max} - y_{min}}$$

where, $\hat{y}_i$ is the predicted value, y_i is the observed value, n is the number of observations and y_{max}, y_{min} the maximum and minimum of y_i in the evaluation set.

Table I summarizes the statistical indices, offering a clear comparison of the model's performance across the different camera perspectives.

Table I: Statistical indices obtained from the power estimation

Camera position	MBE (W)	RMSE (W)	NRMSE(%)
Lateral camera	-55.48	552.30	7.92
Left camera	-131.58	736.79	10.57
Right camera	-217.59	849.49	12.19

10.4229/EUPVSEC2025/4CV.1.28

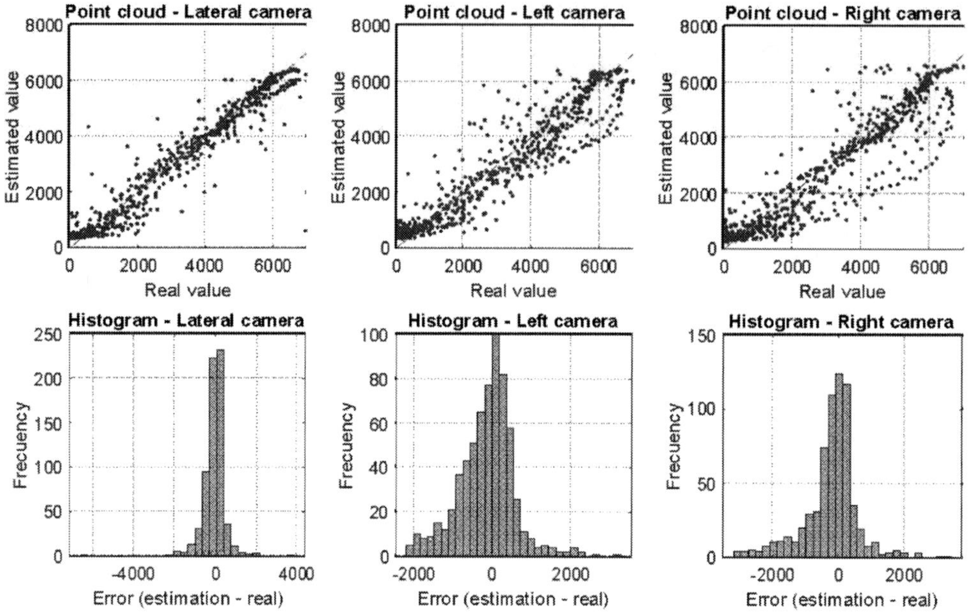

Figure 6: Dispersion diagram and error histogram for the CIESOL PV power estimation

According to this metric, the images captured by the lateral camera provide better results, with an NRMSE value of 7.92% and a subestimation of about 55 W, while the left and right cameras present values of 10.57% and 12.19%, respectively. This suggests that the lateral perspective provides a more accurate characterisation of power generation compared to the other two camera positions.

Analyzing the power estimation plots, one can see these findings, as shown in Fig. 5. Comparing the estimation curves with the actual measurements, the lateral camera shows the best fit, capturing more accurately the daily evolution of energy production, even in the case of external interferences such as clouds or fluctuations in solar radiation. The right camera also shows a good fit in this example, although with some discrepancies. As for the left camera, although its estimates are close to the real ones, a slight subestimation is noted at certain times. Although this graph represents a specific case, it reinforces that the lateral perspective is the most robust for power estimation.

In addition to the results presented in Table 1 and Fig. 5, Fig. 6 shows the error histograms for the lateral, left and right cameras. In the lateral camera, the estimates closely follow the line of identity, and its error histogram shows a highly concentrated distribution around zero, indicating low dispersion. The left camera shows more variability in the estimate, with some values far from the identity, and its histogram reflects a wider distribution. On the other hand, the right camera shows the highest dispersion in the estimation. Its histogram indicates greater variability, although it is relatively centred. Taken together, these results suggest that the lateral camera provides the most accurate estimates. The left and right cameras, moreover, have a larger spread in errors, which is consistent with their higher NRMSE values.

5 CONCLUSION AND FUTURE WORK

In conclusion, it has been possible to estimate the power output of a solar photovoltaic plant from visible-band images captured by digital cameras. This work presents the results of three cameras that have been placed in different positions of the CIESOL building with the aim of estimating the electrical power of a photovoltaic plant. The images were included in a convolutional neural network, to estimate the PV electricity production. In this sense, it has been possible to estimate the PV production with an NRMSE value of less than 8% for different sky conditions, supporting image-based monitoring as a practical, non-intrusive alternative for real-time performance assessment.

A complementary objective of the study was to assess the influence of the camera viewpoint on predictive quality. Using three fixed perspectives (left, right, and lateral), the analysis indicates that the lateral viewpoint—which naturally encompasses a larger portion of the array—provides the most informative representation for the proposed task, delivering the lowest NRMSE. The results thus highlight how viewpoint selection can enhance the relevance of the visual signal used by the network, while all three configurations remain fully compatible with the proposed pipeline.

Looking ahead, several directions are especially promising. First, extending the approach from immediate nowcasting to short- and longer-horizon forecasting would expand its operational value for planning and grid integration. Second, incorporating numerical inputs available at the site (e.g., irradiance on the plane of array, wind speed, relative humidity) as additional predictors—together with the image stream—may further improve accuracy by providing complementary context. Finally, exploring strategies that process simultaneous inputs from multiple cameras could capitalize on the complementary information present in the different perspectives to enhance the robustness and precision of the predictions.

6 ACKNOWLEDGEMENTS

This work is part of the I+D+i TED2021-131655B-I00 project, and has been carried out thanks to funding from AEI/10.13039/501100011033/ and "Unión Europea NextGenerationEU". Also, this work has been partially funded by the National R+D+i Plan Projects PID2021-126805OB-I00 (HELIOSUN project) of the Spanish Ministry of Science and Innovation funds.

7 REFERENCES

[1] IEA, World Energy Outlook 2024, IEA, Paris (2024).

[2] IRENA, Renewable power generation costs in 2024, International Renewable Energy Agency, Abu Dhabi (2025).

[3] F. Creutzig, P. Agoston, G. Nemet, J.C. Goldschmidt, G. Luderer, R.C. Pietzcker, The underestimated potential of solar energy to mitigate climate change, Nature Energy, Vol. 2 (2017) 17140. DOI: 10.1038/nenergy.2017.140.

[4] F. Touati, A. Khandakar, M.E. Chowdhury, A. J. S. Gonzales, C. K. Sorino, K. Benhmed. Photo-Voltaic (PV) monitoring system, performance analysis and power prediction models in Doha, Qatar. In Renewable Energy-Technologies and Applications. IntechOpen (2020). DOI: 10.3390/en18143786.

[5] M. Yazdi. Maintenance Strategies and Optimization Techniques. In: Advances in Computational Mathematics for Industrial System Reliability and Maintainability. Springer Series in Reliability Engineering. Springer, Cham (2024). DOI: 10.1007/978-3-031-53514-7_3.

[6] K. Ilse, L. Micheli, B. W. Figgis, K. Lange, D. Daßler, H. Hanifi, F. Wolfertstetter, V. Naumann, C. Hagendorf, R. Gottschalg, J. Bagdahn. Techno-economic assessment of soiling losses and mitigation strategies for solar power generation. Joule, Vol. 3.10 (2019) 2303-2321.

[7] J. Alonso-Montesinos, F.R. Martínez, J. Polo, N. Martín-Chivelet, F.J. Batlles. Economic effect of dust particles on photovoltaic plant production. Energies, Vol. 13.23 (2020) 6376. DOI: 10.3390/en13236376.

[8] W. Zhang, V. Archana, O. Gandhi, C.D. Rodríguez-Gallegos, H. Quan, D. Yang, H. Quan, D. Yang & D. Srinivasan. SoilingEdge: PV soiling power loss estimation at the edge using surveillance cameras. IEEE Transactions on Sustainable Energy, Vol. 15.1 (2023) 556-566. DOI: 10.1109/TSTE.2023.3320690.

[9] F. Touati, M.A. Al-Hitmi, N.A. Chowdhury, J.A. Hamad, A.J.S.P. Gonzales. Investigation of solar PV performance under Doha weather using a customized measurement and monitoring system. Renewable Energy, Vol. 89 (2016) 564-577. DOI: 10.1016/j.renene.2015.12.046.

[10] D. Dabou, A. Bouraiou, A. Ziane, A. Necaibia, N. Sahouane, M. Blal, S. Khelifi, A. Rouabhia, A. Slimani. Development of autonomous monitoring and performance evaluation system of grid-tied photovoltaic station. International journal of hydrogen energy, Vol. 46.59 (2021) 30267-30287. DOI: 10.1016/j.ijhydene.2021.06.204.

[11] J. L. Lorente, X. Liu, & D. J. Morrow. Worldwide evaluation and correction of irradiance measurements from personal weather stations under all-sky conditions. Solar Energy, Vol. 207 (2020) 925-936. DOI: 10.1016/j.solener.2020.06.073.

[12] S. Daliento, A. Chouder, P. Guerriero, A. M. Pavan, A. Mellit, R. Moeini, P. Tricoli. Monitoring, diagnosis, and power forecasting for photovoltaic fields: A review. International Journal of Photoenergy, Vol. 1 (2017) 1356851.

[13] E.A. Setiawan, M. Fathurrahman, R. F. Pamungkas, S. Ma'arif. Fast partial shading detection on PV modules for precise power loss ratio estimation using digital image processing. Journal of Electrical and Computer Engineering, Vol. 1 (2024), 9385602. DOI: 10.1155/2024/9385602.

[14] I. M. Mustaqeem, S. Kwon. A CNN-assisted deep echo state network using multiple time-scale dynamic learning reservoirs for generating short-term solar energy forecasting. Sustain Energy Technol Assess, Vol. 52. C (2022) 102275. DOI: 10.1016/j.seta.2022.102275

[15] Z. Garip, E. Ekinci, A. Alan. Day-ahead solar photovoltaic energy forecasting based on weather data using LSTM networks: a comparative study for photovoltaic (PV) panels in Turkey. Electrical Engineering, Vol. 105.5 (2023) 3329-3345. DOI: 10.1007/s00202-023-01883-7.

[16] D. Venkateswaran, Y. Cho. Efficient solar power generation forecasting for greenhouses: A hybrid deep learning approach. Alexandria Engineering Journal, Vol. 91 (2024) 222-236. DOI: 10.1016/j.aej.2024.02.004.

[17] A. Jakoplić, D. Franković, J. Havelka, H. Bulat. Short-term photovoltaic power plant output forecasting using sky images and deep learning. Energies, Vol. 16.14 (2023) 5428. DOI: 10.3390/en16145428.

[18] R. U. Rani, J. Kakarla, B. Sundar. Weather image classification using EfficientNet and dual attention block. 2nd International Conference on Smart Technologies and Systems for Next Generation Computing (ICSTSN). IEEE, (2023) 1-4. DOI: 10.1109/ICSTSN57873.2023.10151564.

[19] V. Abad-Alcaraz, M. Castilla, J. A. Carballo, J. Bonilla, J. D. Álvarez. Multimodal deep learning for solar radiation forecasting. Applied Energy, Vol. 393 (2025) 126061. DOI: 10.1016/j.apenergy.2025.126061.

AUTOMATIC FAULT DETECTION AND DIAGNOSIS IN PHOTOVOLTAIC PLANTS BASED ON CONVOLUTIONAL NEURAL NETWORKS

Javier Martín-Rueda, Javier R. Ledesma, Celena Lorenzo, Pablo Merodio, L. Narvarte
Instituto de Energía Solar, Universidad Politécnica de Madrid
javier.martin@upm.es, javier.ledesma@upm.es, c.lorenzon@upm.es, pablo.merodio@upm.es, luis.narvarte@upm.es

ABSTRACT: This work aims to discover efficient and reliable machine-learning architectures and models for highly automated fault detection, diagnosis and predictive maintenance using the real-time flow of operational data generated at utility-scale photovoltaic plants. Our models consists of Convolutional Neural Networks which are trained on datasets which have been assembled from several years of operational data from about a dozen PV plants located in Europe and Latin America, with an approximate overall generation power of 1 GW, and different types of modules, tracking and terrain. We do minimal data preprocessing to construct our models. We use both 1-D and 2-D convolutional neural networks. For 2-D convolutional neural networks, we transform the time series into images by using Markov Field Transform, Recurrence plots, and Gramian Angular Fields. The performance of our models so far does not show significant improvements over other systems published in the literature, but it must be taken into consideration that the use of real operational data entails a significant challenge, when compared to simulated environments and small plant scenarios. We are improving the architectures and algorithms for higher reliability, a wider catalog of scenarios, and concurrent faults. We are also working on knowledge transfer among PV plants.
Keywords: Photovoltaic systems, Fault detection, Machine learning

1 INTRODUCTION

Sustained and significant growth of large photovoltaic (PV) plant portfolios demands smart automation of many operational aspects to achieve efficient plant operation. Fault detection and diagnosis are areas which can greatly benefit from advanced automated monitoring.

Utility-scale PV plants are extensively sensorised and produce large amounts of detailed operational data. Nowadays these data are used to detect faults using relatively rigid and simple methods, such as threshold crossing, statistical analysis, comparison between measured and simulated yields, and various heuristics. However, the unsophisticated nature of these methods means that many subtle faults go unnoticed, and that it is not uncommon to generate operational alarms which are unreliable or misdirected. Preventive maintenance, that is, early detection and diagnosis of conditions which do not currently impact operation but may do so in the short or mid-term, is even more of a *rara avis*.

Many AI techniques have recently been proposed for PV plant fault detection and diagnosis, but they tend to concentrate in specific problem cases, and in most cases have been evaluated with small and synthetic datasets. [1] shows a review of several previous work that use machine learning (ML) techniques for photovoltaic fault detection. [2] and [3] show the use of deep learning (DL) models based on artificial neural networks (ANN) combined with a digital twin (DT) to detect and diagnose faults in a simulated environment.

Such previous works show that applying ML and DL techniques can improve fault detection and diagnosis processes, by using images of PV modules and/or PV plant sensorisation data as their inputs. But they have mostly been tested in simulated scenarios, where many sources of environmental noise which are present in real PV plants are not taken into account, such as different electrical characteristics of the devices, aging, weather conditions, sensing variability and inaccuracies, concurrence of multiple faults, etc.

Our work aims to apply ML and DL techniques inspired by those which have shown their potential in simulated or small scale environments to real utility-scale PV plant sensorisation data. We intend to discover efficient and reliable machine learning architectures and models for the purpose of highly automated fault detection, diagnosis, and predictive maintenance, inspecting in real-time the data flow generated by sensors available at utility-scale PV plants. This will allow to optimize the operation of utility-scale PV plants, and to create the foundations for a reference description of data flow, fault classification and fault diagnosis.

2 DATASET DESCRIPTION

We have assembled a dataset of real utility-scale PV plant operational data, which covers several years of operation in about a dozen PV plants located in Europe and Latin America, with an approximate overall generation power of 1 GW. These PV plants also have different characteristics (monofacial vs bifacial, single-axis tracking vs fixed, flat vs uneven terrain…). The dataset includes detailed electrical sensorisation, as well as weather and irradiance data, with a time resolution in the order of 5-15 minutes.

These PV plants have suffered different faults and anomalies over the years, and we have carefully reviewed the data to construct a high-quality labelled dataset which can be used for AI model creation and performance evaluation. Over 30 types of faults and anomalies have been identified, although some of the cases are so rare that they are hardly useful for model training.

Among the different scenarios that we are addressing, in this paper we present three illustrative cases (the first two for fault detection, and the last one for predictive maintenance). They are:

Tracker target error: when the actual tracker position (continuous blue line) differs from the optimal objective position (dotted orange line), as shown on Figure 1.

10.4229/EUPVSEC2025/4CV.1.33

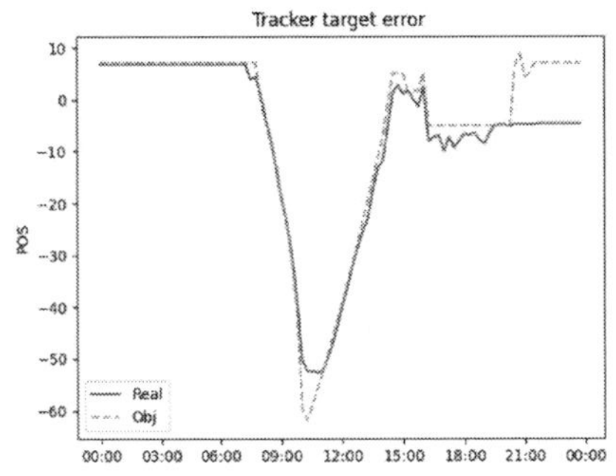

Figure 1. Example of tracker target error

Open string: when a string is disconnected, and its production is therefore lost. Causes could be open fuses, burned out connectors, manual operations, etc. Figure 2 shows yield differences between two stringboxes, where the one corresponding to the continuous blue line has an open string.

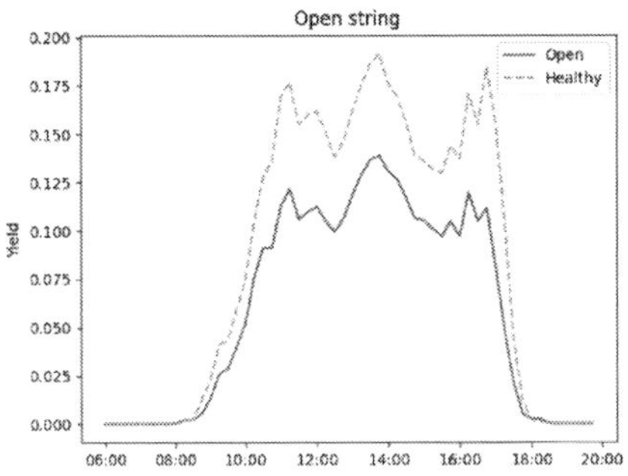

Figure 2. Example of open string

Anomalous element temperature: when temperature monitoring shows a pattern that does not comply with the correct operation of an element, such as an inverter or a transformer. This anomaly does not initially affect operation, but early identification and preventive maintenance will prevent future major problems. Figure 3 shows anomalous temperature in the inverter plotted with a continuous blue line.

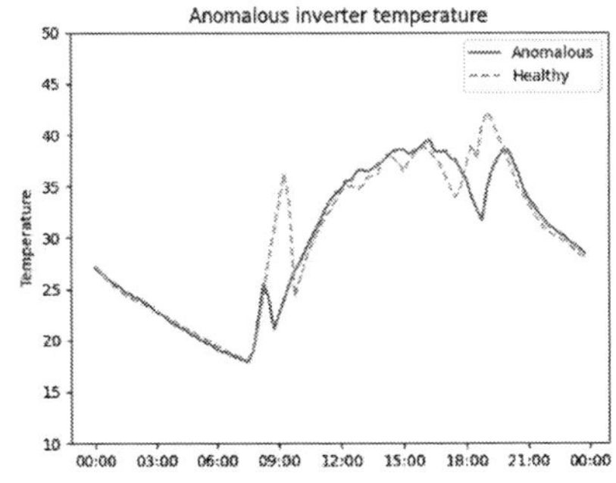

Figure 3. Example of anomalous inverter temperature

3 SYSTEM DESCRIPTION

We are using Convolutional Neural Networks (CNN) to create fault detection and diagnosis models, trained and validated with the datasets described in the previous section. CNNs are frequently used for image processing applications, while sensor data are typically time series of real values. We are using both 1-D and 2-D CNNs.

Convolutional neural networks have been frequently employed for image processing applications, where they have excelled at pattern recognition and classification, even in the presence of various types of noise. Most sensor data from PV plants are time series of real values, but some techniques, such as those described in [2] and [3], can be used to convert them into 2D matrices, which provide a visual representation suitable for effective analysis with a CNN. This will also allow us to confirm whether this approach is as effective with real operational data as with synthetic simulated data.

We are avoiding elaborate raw data preprocessing, as we intend to build models that can be efficiently applied and transferred among PV plants without the need of significant customization. So far, we are using simple preprocessing steps, such as cleaning unavailable sensorisation, normalizing measurements, grouping time series of similar devices, and selecting significant variables.

For 1-D CNNs, we are using mono and multi-variate time series which have been preprocessed as described above.

For 2-D CNNs, we are transforming mono and multi-variate time series data into 2-D images with several preprocessing techniques: Markov Transition Field, Recurrence Plots, and Gramian Angular Field. These techniques preserve temporal structure information and can be effectively processed by 2-D CNNs.

A Markov Transition Field transform (MTF) first discretizes continuous values in a times series using quantization techniques. Subsequently a Markov transition matrix is computed, where each element represents the probability of transitioning between two discrete states. That matrix is used to construct an image where each pixel corresponds to the transition probability between two states over time.

A Recurrence Plot is a 2-D matrix representation of time series in dynamic systems where each point (i,j) represents whether the system's state at time i is similar to the state at time j, that is, the phase space trajectory visits roughly the same area at both times.

A Gramian Angular Field transform (GAN) first maps the time series data into polar coordinates and then builds a corresponding Gram matrix. Essentially, each time point is mapped to a vector in polar coordinates where the temporal index is treated as the radius and the normalized magnitude as the inverse angle. The Gram matrix is a 2-D matrix where point (i,j) is computed from the inner product of vectors at times i and j.

4 RESULTS AND CONCLUSIONS

We have trained a validated several 1-D and 2-D CNN architectures with the datasets described in previous sections. The architecture hyperparameter sets have been optimized with KerasTuner [4]. Figure 4 shows the f1-score achieved by our CNNs for the three example fault and anomaly scenarios described in a previous section.

10.4229/EUPVSEC2025/4CV.1.33

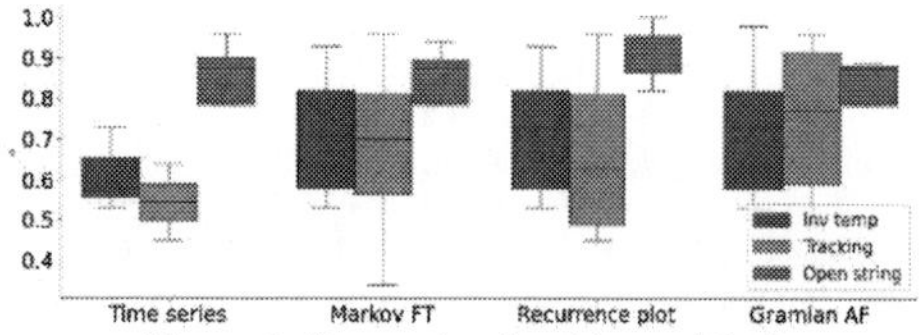

Figure 4. f1-score by algorithm and fault

These results so far do not show significant improvements over other systems published in the literature. However, it must be taken into consideration that our approach is working on real data from utility-scale PV plants, which is proving to be harder because real data typically contains more noise than those generated by simulation, and the amount of training examples is much more limited.

This work is ongoing and our next steps are:

- Use other improved DL architectures and ML algorithms. For instance, we are planning to experiment with ConvMixer architectures and pre-trained image classification models.
- Apply our models to a wider catalog of faults and anomalies, in particular to concurrent faults.
- Use synthetically generated samples to train our models where real data is scarce, and determine its usability to real conditions.
- Study the feasibility and procedure of transferring knowledge and models obtained from some PV plants to new PV plants, with as little customization as possible.

5 ACKNOWLEDGEMENTS

This work is funded by the European Union under the PVOP European Project, doi: 10.3030/101147000. Views and opinions expressed are however those of the author(s) only and do not necessarily reflect those of the European Union or CINEA. Neither the European Union nor the granting authority can be held responsible for them.

REFERENCES

[1] Et-taleby, A., Yassine Chaibi, Benslimane, M., & Boussetta, M. (2023). Applications of Machine Learning Algorithms for Photovoltaic Fault Detection: a Review. Statistics, Optimization & Information Computing, 11(1), 168-177, doi: 10.19139/soic-2310-5070-1537.

[2] Ying-Yi Hong, Rolando A. Pula, Diagnosis of PV faults using digital twin and convolutional mixer with LoRa notification system, Energy Reports, Volume 9, 2023, Pages 1963-1976, ISSN 2352-4847, doi: 10.1016/j.egyr.2023.01.011.

[3] Ying-Yi Hong, Rolando A. Pula, Diagnosis of photovoltaic faults using digital twin and PSO-optimized shifted window transformer, Applied Soft Computing, Volume 150, 2024, 111092, ISSN 1568-4946, doi: 10.1016/j.asoc.2023.111092.

[4] KerasTuner, O'Malley, Tom and Bursztein, Elie and Long, James and Chollet, François and Jin, Haifeng and Invernizzi, Luca and others, 2019. Accessed: Sep. 18, 2025 [Online]. Available: https://github.com/keras-team/keras-tuner

TEMPORAL GRAPH NEURAL NETWORKS FOR EARLY ANOMALY DETECTION AND PERFORMANCE PREDICTION VIA PV SYSTEM MONITORING DATA

S. Mukherjee [1,2], L. Vuillon[2], L. Bou Nassif[4], S. Giroux-Julien[5], H. Pabiou[4], D. Dutykh[3], I. Tsanakas[1]

[1]Univ. Grenoble Alpes, CEA, Liten, 73375 Le Bourget du Lac, France
[2]Univ. Savoie Mont Blanc, CNRS, LAMA, Chambéry, 73000, France
[3]Mathematics Department, Khalifa University, Abu Dhabi, PO Box 127788, United Arab Emirates
[4]INSA Lyon, CNRS, CETHIL, UMR5008, Villeurbanne, 69621, France
[5]Université Claude Bernard Lyon 1, CNRS, LAGEPP, UMR5007,Villeurbanne, 69100, France

*Corresponding author: Srijani.Mukherjee@univ-smb.fr Ph.: +33698703684

ABSTRACT: The rapid growth of solar photovoltaic (PV) systems necessitates advanced methods for performance monitoring and anomaly detection to ensure optimal operation. In this study, we propose a novel approach leveraging Temporal Graph Neural Network (Temporal GNN) to predict solar PV output power and detect anomalies using environmental and operational parameters. The proposed model utilizes graph-based temporal relationships among key PV system parameters, including irradiance, module and ambient temperature to predict electrical power output. This study is based on data collected from an outdoor facility located on a rooftop in Lyon (France) including power measurements from a PV module and meteorological parameters.

The Temporal GNN model integrates Graph Convolutional Networks (GCN) and Gated Recurrent Units (GRU) to capture spatial and temporal dependencies effectively. The model is trained to minimize Mean Squared Error (MSE) loss and is evaluated using Mean Absolute Error (MAE). Anomalies are identified by computing absolute errors and setting a threshold. The proposed framework achieves a MAE of 0.0707 on normalized output power prediction, outperforming traditional methods (e.g., Random Forests, SVMs) and advanced deep learning models (e.g., LSTMs) reported in recent literature, highlighting its potential to set a new benchmark for solar PV performance prediction and anomaly detection. The proposed method holds significant promise for real-world applications, providing actionable insights for maintenance and optimization in solar PV installations.

KEYWORD: Graph neural network; Spatio-temporal analysis; Power output prediction; Early anomaly detection.

1 INTRODUCTION

The increasing global reliance on solar energy has underscored the critical need for robust and reliable monitoring systems for photovoltaic (PV) installations. Effective performance prediction and timely anomaly detection are paramount to ensuring the long-term efficiency, reliability, and economic viability of these systems. Traditional monitoring methods, often based on simple thresholds or statistical rules, frequently fail to account for the complex interplay of environmental and operational variables that affect PV performance. These methods may lead to high rates of false positives or, more critically, miss subtle but significant anomalies that can indicate underlying system faults.

To overcome these limitations, advanced data-driven approaches are essential. Machine learning and deep learning models have shown promise in this field, offering the ability to learn complex, non-linear relationships from vast datasets. However, many of these models, such as Long Short-Term Memory (LSTM) networks or Support Vector Machines (SVMs), primarily focus on temporal dependencies, treating individual data points as independent sequences. This overlooks the inherent spatial relationships among different system parameters—such as the correlation between irradiance, temperature, and power output—which are crucial for a comprehensive understanding of system behaviour. Recent advances in Graph Neural Networks (GNNs) provide a powerful way to learn from structured data. By representing PV system parameters as graph nodes, and their interdependencies as edges, GNNs can capture both spatial (between parameters) and temporal (across time) correlations.

This study introduces a novel Temporal Graph Neural Network (T-GNN) that integrates Graph Convolutional Networks (GCNs) and Gated Recurrent Units (GRUs) for PV system analysis. Our model is designed to capture both the spatial dependencies between various PV system parameters and their temporal evolution. By representing the PV system as a dynamic graph, where each parameter is a node and its relationships over time are captured by edges, the T-GNN can model intricate dependencies more effectively than traditional methods. The primary objective is to develop a robust framework for accurate power output prediction and early anomaly detection, thereby providing actionable insights for PV system maintenance and optimization. This work represents a significant contribution to the field of PV performance analysis by demonstrating the superior capabilities of a spatiotemporal deep learning model in a real-world application.

2 METHODOLOGY

The proposed methodology for PV performance prediction and anomaly detection is a multi-step process centered on the T-GNN model. The workflow begins with data collection and preprocessing, followed by the model architecture design, training, and a two-stage process for prediction and anomaly detection.

2.1 DATA COLLECTION AND PREPROCESSING

Real-world monitoring data was collected from a PV system located on a rooftop in Lyon, France (latitude 45.783055° N, longitude 4.873611° E). The system consists of a central PV module (1675x992x35 mm) within a 12° tilted east-west array. Data from 10 sunny days per season (Spring: March-May 2023; Summer: June-August 2023; Autumn: September 2023) was used for this study. The data was recorded at 2-second intervals and includes four key input parameters:

- Global shortwave irradiation (G_sw)
- Global longwave tilted irradiation (G_lw)
- PV module temperature (T_pv)
- Ambient air temperature (T_air)

The target variable for prediction is the electrical power output (P_out). Prior to model training, all input features and the target variable were normalized using MinMax scaling to ensure a consistent range and prevent parameters with larger magnitudes from dominating the learning process. The dataset was then split into an 80-20 training and testing at random.

2.2 TEMPORAL GRAPH NEURAL NETWORK ARCHITECTURE

The core of our model is the Temporal GNN, which integrates two primary components to handle both spatial and temporal dependencies. To model the complex dependencies among PV system parameters, we construct a directed temporal graph $G=(V,E)$ where each node $v_i \in V$ represents a system parameter (e.g., irradiance, temperature, power output) at a given time step. Spatial relationships are encoded by directed edges $(v_i^t, v_j^t) \in E$, capturing causal influence between parameters at the same time step, such as irradiance affecting module temperature and temperature influencing power output[1]. Temporal dependencies are modeled by directed edges (v_i^t, v_i^{t+1}), linking each node to its future state, thereby preserving the sequential dynamics of the system. The adjacency matrix A of this graph is thus time-indexed, forming a sequence $\{A^t\}_{t=1}^{T}$. The node feature matrix at time t, denoted $X^t \in \mathbb{R}^{|V| \times d}$, stores the observed values of all parameters. During message passing, node embeddings are updated as

$$h_i^{t+1} = \sigma\left(\sum_{j \in \mathcal{N}(i)} \frac{1}{c_{ij}} W h_j^t + U h_i^t\right)$$

Here, $h_i^{(t+1)}$ represents the hidden state of node i at time $t+1$. Where $N(i)$ denotes the neighborhood of node i, W and U are learnable weight matrices, and c_{ij} is a normalization factor. The formula effectively combines a Graph Convolutional Network (GCN) layer for spatial information aggregation and a Gated Recurrent Unit (GRU) for temporal evolution[2]. The GCN layer aggregates information from a node's neighbors, while the GRU processes the sequential data to learn temporal patterns. The full model architecture consists of a Graph Convolution Layer, a GRUCell, and a final Fully Connected Layer (*Fig 1*) to produce the predicted power output, $\hat{P}$ *out*. The model was trained using the Mean Squared Error (MSE) loss function with the Adam optimizer, with a learning rate of 0.01 and 100 epochs (*Fig 2*).

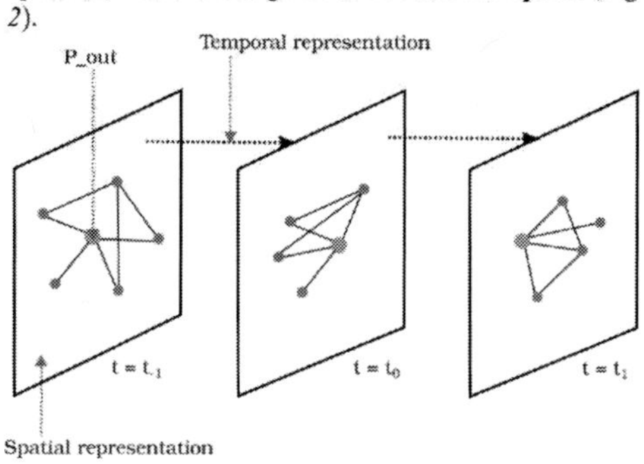

Fig 1: Schematic diagram of the evolution of the spatio-temporal graph prediction

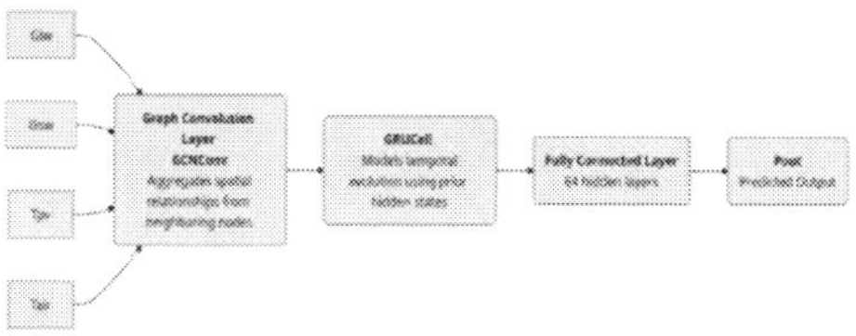

Fig 2: The architecture of the proposed model

2.3 ANOMALY DETECTION

Our framework for anomaly detection is a two-step process based on the model's prediction residuals.

Step 1: Power Prediction:
The T-GNN model predicts the power output, $\hat{P}$ *out*.

Step 2: Residual Error Calculation:
The residual error, e, is computed as the absolute difference between the actual power output and the predicted power output:

$$e = |P\_out - \hat{P}\_out|$$

Step 3: Z-score Anomaly Detection:

Anomalies are identified using the Z-score of the residuals, which measures how many standard deviations an observation is from the mean of the residuals.

$$Z = \frac{e - \mu\_e}{\sigma\_e}$$

Here, μ_e is the mean of the residual errors and σ_e is the standard deviation. A point is flagged as an anomaly if its Z-score magnitude exceeds a predefined threshold, τ. For this study, the anomaly thresholds were set using the Interquartile Range (IQR) method, with a lower bound of $(Q1-1.5*IQR)$ and an upper bound of $(Q3+1.5*IQR)$. Outliers falling outside this range are considered anomalies.

3. RESULTS AND DISCUSSION

10.4229/EUPVSEC2025/4CV.1.35

The T-GNN model demonstrated strong predictive performance on the test set, effectively capturing the diurnal patterns of PV power generation as presented in *Fig 2*.

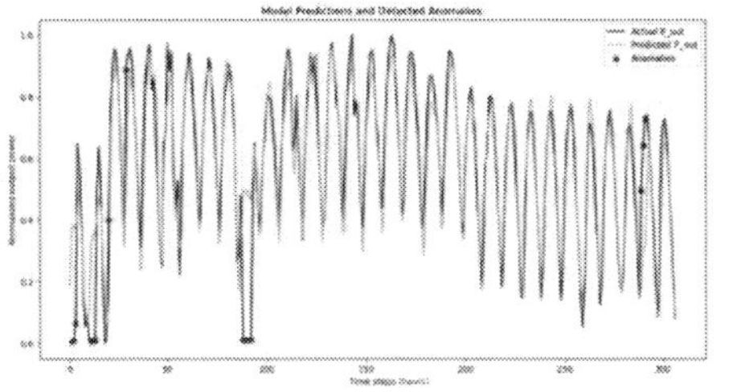

Fig 2

The model achieved a Mean Absolute Error (MAE) of 0.0707 for normalized power output prediction and a Mean Percentage Error (MPE) of 2.26. These results represent a significant improvement over existing state-of-the-art methods[3]. A comparison of our model's performance with other methods is summarized in *Table 1*.

Model	Notes	MAE
T-GNN (ours)	Spatio-temporal	0.0707
LSTM	Temporal only	0.09–0.10
RF / SVM	Traditional ML	0.10–0.15

Table 1: Comparison of Model Performance by Mean Absolute Error (MAE)

The T-GNN's superior performance can be attributed to its unique ability to learn from both the spatial relationships among input parameters and their temporal evolution, a capability that traditional models lack. As shown in the figure comparing actual and predicted power output, the model's predictions closely track the actual data, even during periods of rapid change.

The anomaly detection component of the model successfully identified some inconsistent power readings, which constituted 5.21% of the dataset. These anomalies were flagged as points where the model's prediction significantly deviated from the actual measured power output. A box plot in *Fig 3* of the absolute errors with anomaly thresholds clearly visualizes these outliers.

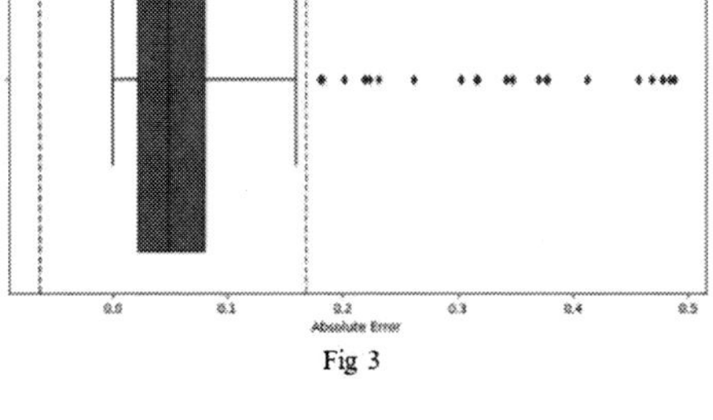

Fig 3

Cross-validation of the detected anomalies confirmed that they corresponded to genuine inconsistencies in the measured data, such as sudden and unexplainable drops in power output, which may indicate a measurement fault or an operational irregularity. The low percentage of detected anomalies suggests that the model is highly selective and robust[4], minimizing the risk of false positives. This makes the framework a valuable tool for real-time monitoring, as it can alert operators to potential issues without generating excessive noise.

4. CONCLUSION AND FUTURE RESEARCH

This study successfully demonstrates the effectiveness of a Temporal Graph Neural Network for both predicting PV power output and detecting anomalies in real-time. By leveraging a T-GNN, our model can effectively capture the complex spatiotemporal dependencies inherent in PV system data, leading to significantly higher predictive accuracy compared to traditional machine learning and deep learning methods. The low MAE and MPE achieved by our model, combined with its ability to precisely identify anomalies, positions it as a promising solution for enhancing the reliability and efficiency of solar PV systems.

The insights gained from this work provide a clear path toward developing more intelligent and resilient PV monitoring systems. Future work will focus on expanding the model's capabilities by incorporating additional data sources, such as electrical parameters (e.g., voltage and current) and infrared (IR) thermal images. This multi-modal approach is expected to further enhance the model's ability to detect more subtle and complex types of anomalies, providing a more comprehensive diagnostic tool for PV system maintenance and optimization.

4.3 References

[1] Mukherjee Srijani, Vuillon Laurent, Dutykh Denys, Tsanakas Ioannis.
Scalable weather data reduction for solar PV analysis using graph-based approach. *Energy Syst* (2025). https://doi.org/10.1007/s12667-025-00767-y

[2] Guangyin Jin, Yuxuan Liang, Yuchen Fang, Zezhi Shao, Jincai Huang, Junbo Zhang, and Yu Zheng.
Spatio-Temporal Graph Neural Networks for Predictive Learning in Urban Computing: A Survey .
IEEE Transactions on Knowledge & Data Engineering, 36(10):5388–5408, October 2024.

[3] Theocharides, Spyros, Makrides, George, and Georghiou, George E.
PV generation forecasting utilizing a classification-only approach.
EPJ Photovolt., 15:12, 2024.

[4] Jagbir Singh, Owais Ahmad Shah, Sujata Arora,
Smart Grid Cybersecurity: Anomaly Detection in Solar Power Systems Using Deep Learning.
Energy Storage and Saving, 2025.

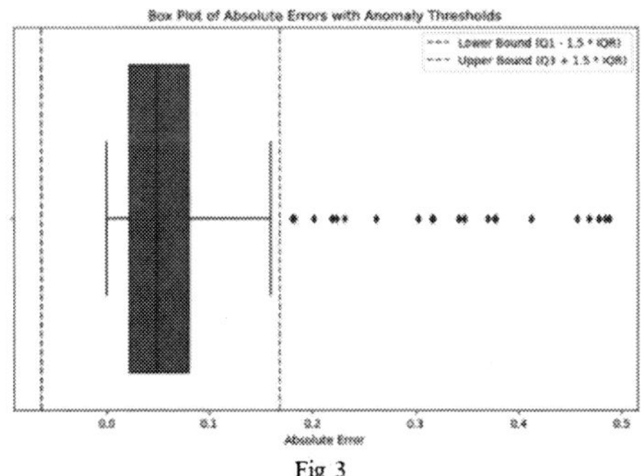

OPTIMIZATION OF MAINTENANCE OF PV MODULE ARRAYS BASED ON ASSET MANAGEMENT STRATEGIES: CASE OF STUDY

L. Alejandro Cárdenas, Andrés Figueroa, Fernando Herrera, Ernesto Pérez and David Nova
Universidad Nacional de Colombia
Carrera 45 No. 26-85, Bogotá, Colombia
Corresponding autor: L. Alejandro Cárdenas, luacardenasga@unal.edu.co

ABSTRACT: This paper presents a methodology to optimize the maintenance of grid-connected photovoltaic (PV) systems by defining cleaning intervals within an asset management framework. The approach combines analysis of energy production, feed-in tariffs, and cleaning costs to maximize overall revenue. The proposed approach was evaluated through a case study of a 5.6 kWp PV system located on the Bogotá campus of the Universidad Nacional de Colombia. Experimental results showed that modules without cleaning accumulated performance losses above 25–30% after five years, while those cleaned annually exhibited controlled losses of around 5–10% per year. Furthermore, the variability of the loss rate (LR) highlights the importance of adapting soiling models to local climates. In Bogotá, where rainfall is frequent, precipitation contributes to partial self-cleaning, reducing soiling accumulation compared to arid climates. The study concludes that incorporating local environmental factors into predictive models and maintenance planning improves both the technical performance and economic profitability of PV systems.
Keywords: photovoltaic systems, soiling, cleaning optimization asset management

1 INTRODUCTION

In line with global decarbonization efforts stimulated by the Paris Agreement, Latin America is undergoing a significant energy transition, with solar photovoltaics (PV) at the forefront. Within this regional context, Colombia has established ambitious national targets, aiming for solar PV to represent 12% of the country's installed power capacity by 2037 [1]. This rapid expansion of solar infrastructure introduces an urgent need for advanced operational strategies. The successful integration and long-term profitability of these new assets are contingent not on their installation alone, but on ensuring they perform optimally throughout their lifecycle [2]. Consequently, developing data-driven asset management frameworks tailored to specific local conditions is important to safeguarding these national investments and realizing their full potential.

Performance losses in PV systems are mainly caused by soiling, degradation, and failures. Soiling reduces the irradiance reaching solar cells through soft shading (e.g., pollution) or hard shading (e.g., dust), affecting current and voltage output differently [3]. Over time, PV systems also experience degradation, though recent analyses report annual rates as low as 0–0.29%, lower than the commonly assumed 0.5%, reflecting improvements in technology and maintenance [4]. Failures contribute less significantly, typically below 1% of net energy yield losses, while inefficiencies represent over 20%, emphasizing the need for optimized design and operation [5].

Asset management has emerged as a holistic strategy to maximize both revenue and the operational lifetime of photovoltaic (PV) plants. By integrating design optimization, advanced maintenance practices, and computerized management systems, asset management contributes to reducing capital costs, improving risk management, and ensuring long-term plant profitability [2]. However, large-scale PV plants face increasing challenges due to stricter environmental regulations, growing energy demand, and the lack of structured strategic frameworks. Addressing these issues through well-defined asset management approaches not only enhances plant performance but also strengthens the competitiveness of solar energy against conventional generation [6].

This paper proposes a maintenance optimization methodology framed within a broader asset management strategy, with a detailed case study on soiling and cleaning optimization in Bogotá. While performance losses in PV systems may also arise from degradation and failures, soiling represents a more immediate and significant challenge due to its direct impact on irradiance and energy yield. By focusing on cleaning strategies and their integration into asset management, this work aims to enhance operational efficiency, extend plant lifetime, and maximize revenue.

2 METHODOLOGY

To illustrate the application of the asset management strategy in real conditions, a 5.6 kWp photovoltaic plant located at the Universidad Nacional de Colombia, Bogotá campus, was selected as a case study. This plant is located in an urban environment with high variability in dust and precipitation, making it a representative scenario for analyzing the impact of soiling on energy performance. The methodology developed combines the analysis of experimental data from the plant with a model for estimating daily soiling deposition, from which the associated energy losses are calculated. Finally, a validation process is carried out and a cost optimization stage is incorporated, which allows for the definition of cleaning period adapted to the local context. The general flow of the methodology is summarized in Fig, 1.

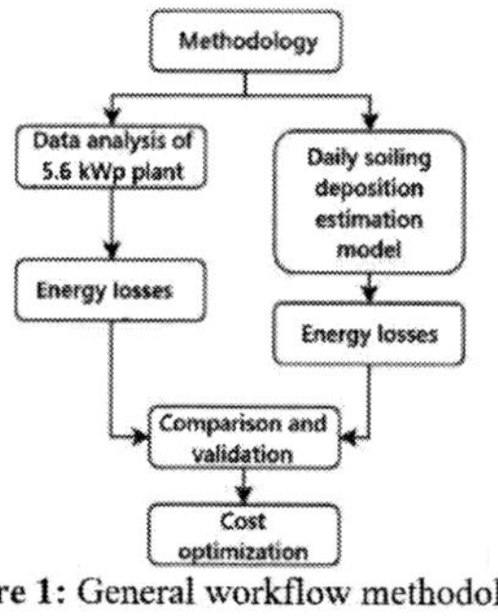

Figure 1: General workflow methodology

10.4229/EUPVSEC2025/4CV.1.36

2.1 Case of study

The photovoltaic installation is located on a building at the Universidad Nacional de Colombia in Bogotá, as shown in Fig. 2. The system is located on the roof and consists of 14 pv modules with a nominal power of 400 W each one, giving a total installed peak power of 5.6 kWp. Seven modules face east and the remaining seven face west. The layout and numbering of the modules is shown in Fig. 3. In both orientations, one module has been designated for cleaning and another for never being cleaned, forming three pairs per orientation, which are cleaned at intervals of 6, 12, and 18 months. Additionally, modules 7 and 8 have not been cleaned since their installation.

Figure 2: Photovoltaic System 5.6 kWp

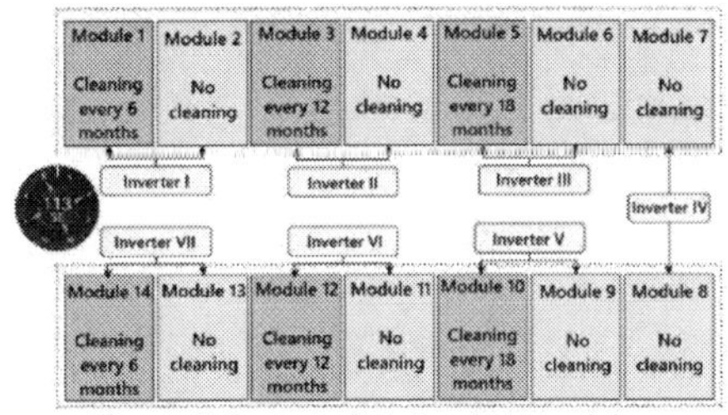

Figure 3: Layout of photovoltaic modules

The electrical parameters of the modules are acquired through microinverters, each connected to two pv modules. The technical characteristics of the modules are shown in Table I.

Since meteorological data is required to estimate the theoretical energy produced by a photovoltaic module, this data is obtained from the Davis Instruments weather station. This station is in the LIATER building of the Universidad Nacional de Colombia, approximately 100 meters from the photovoltaic installation at the North-est. It measures irradiance, ambient temperature, wind speed and direction, among other factors in a frequency of 5 minutes, which are of interest to us. The information from the weather station is shown in Table III.

Since there was no weather station available when the photovoltaic system was installed, additional data was obtained from NREL's National Solar Radiation Database (NSRDB) and include global horizontal irradiance, ambient temperature, wind speed and direction. This meteorological data was collected at 60-minute intervals.

Table I: Technical specifications of photovoltaic modules

Characteristic	Value
Cell type	N-type monocrystalline
Maximum power (STC)	400 W
Open circuit voltage (Voc)	49.3 V
Short-circuit current (Isc)	10.47 A
Module efficiency	19.3%
Temperature coefficient	-0.36%/°C

2.2 Estimation of the System's Daily Theoretical Energy

The energy expected to be generated under ideal conditions (without soiling) is calculated based on solar irradiance, cell temperature, and the system's nominal power according to the IEC 61724 [7]. First, the hourly power of the system is estimated because the meteorological data interval is hourly:

$$P_{teo}(t) = P_{STC}\left(\frac{G_{POA(t)}}{\frac{1000W}{m^2}}\right)[1 + \gamma\,(T_{mod}(t) - 25)] \quad (1)$$

Additionally, considering degradation:

$$P_{teo}(t) = P_{teo}(t)(1 + \delta \cdot n) \qquad (2)$$

Where:

- P_{teo}: Theoretical power of the system [kW].
- P_{STC}: Nominal power under standard conditions [kW].
- $G_{POA}(t)$: Hourly irradiance on the module plane [kW/m2].
- γ: Temperature correction coefficient for module power [%/◦C].
- $T_{mod}(t)$: Average daily photovoltaic module temperature during operation [◦C].
- δ: Annual degradation of the module [0.5%/year].
- n: Number of years elapsed [year].

The temperature of the cell module can be estimated from the ambient temperature [7]:

$$T_{mod}(t) = T_{amb}(t) + \frac{G_{POA}}{\frac{800W}{m^2}}(T_{NOCT} - 20) \qquad (3)$$

Where:

- P_{amb}: Ambient temperature [◦C].
- P_{mod}: Module temperature [◦C].

The theoretical daily energy intake corresponds to [8]:

$$E_{teo} = \int_0^{24} P_{teo}(t)dt \qquad (4)$$

2.3 Soiling rate

The degree of soiling is quantified by the Soiling Ratio (SR) index, defined as the ratio between the energy

10.4229/EUPVSEC2025/4CV.1.36

generated under real conditions (under soiling) and that which would be generated under clean conditions [8]:

$$SR_i = \frac{E_{mod_i}}{E_{teo}} \cdot 100\% \quad (5)$$

Where:

- E_{mod_i}: Energy generated by module i (kWh).
- E_{teo}: Estimated theoretical energy (kWh).

Then, energy losses due to dirt are determined as follows[8]:

$$LR_i = 100\% - SR_i \quad (6)$$

This accumulation depends on variables such as the rate of soiling deposition, water precipitation, and wind speed [9].

2.4 Comparison of particulate matter estimates

A. Calculation of Daily Dust Deposition:

Daily dust deposition (DDep) is calculated using an empirical model based on key meteorological factors, such as wind speed and particulate matter concentration. This model is derived from the work of [10], that established a quantitative relationship between these parameters and the accumulation of dust on module surfaces.

$$DDep = (10.6 - 4.99WS + 247PM - 73.4WS \cdot PM)0.00144 \quad (7)$$

The factor 0.00144 converts μg/(m²·min) to g/(m²·day).

- WS: Average daily wind speed (m/s).
- PM: Average daily particulate matter concentration (g/m²).

B. Adjustment for Environmental Conditions:

To account for the effects of humidity and soiling adhesion in arid climates, a calibration factor α = 0.1 is introduced when AP > 2.7 mm (heavy rain that wash away dust) [8]:

$$DDep' = \begin{cases} DDep, if\ AP < 2.7mm \\ \alpha \cdot DDep,\ if\ AP \geq 2.7mm \end{cases} \quad (8)$$

When rainfall exceeds 2.7 mm, it is considered that dust is reduced by 10% due to natural rainfall.

Finally, the daily accumulation of soiling is expressed as the addition of the previous day's accumulation and the soiling from the current day.

$$Acc(t) = Acc(t-1) + DDep' \quad (9)$$

2.5 Minimum Residual Modeling (β)

To simulate realistic conditions where soiling is not completely removed, a minimum residue β is introduced after cleaning events. This approach follows the observations of [8].

$$Acc(t)' = f(x) = \begin{cases} Acc(t),\ without\ cleaning \\ \beta,\ cleaning\ date \end{cases} \quad (10)$$

Where:

- $Acc(t)$: Soiling accumulation on day t (g/m2).
- β = 0.01 g/m2: Minimum residue.

This means that when cleaning events happen, the accumulation of soiling is not completely zero. There is a minimum residue β that remains on the surfaces of the module.

2.6 Calculation of Energy Loss ($E_{loss}(t)$)

Daily energy loss is modeled as [11]:

$$E_{loss}(t) = E_{teo} \cdot (Eff_{mod} - Eff(t)) \quad (11)$$

Where:

- E_{teo}: Theoretical daily energy [kWh].
- Eff_{mod}: Module efficiency [19.3%].
- $Eff(t)$: Module efficiency reduced due to dirt [%].

This reduced module efficiency is calculated based on the daily accumulation of soiling. This expression is based on the observations in [8]:

$$Eff(t) = -0.0026Acc(t)'^3 + 0.032Acc(t)'^2 - 0.1369 \cdot Acc(t)' + Eff_{mod} \quad (12)$$

$$LR_{teo} = \frac{E_{loss}}{E_{teo}} \cdot 100\% \quad (13)$$

2.7 Economic Model

Economic energy losses due to dirt are estimated as [12]:

$$C_{loss}(\$) = LR_{average}(\%) \cdot E_{teo}(kWh) \cdot CU_{rate}\left(\frac{\$}{kWh}\right) \quad (14)$$

$$C_1(d) = \frac{365}{d}(1 + 2 + \cdots + d) \cdot C_{loss} \quad (15)$$

$$C_1(d) = \frac{365}{2}(d+1) \cdot C_{loss} \quad (16)$$

$$C_2(d) = \frac{365}{d} \cdot C_{clean} \quad (17)$$

As presented in [13], an optimization function for cleaning photovoltaic modules is developed, which considers the average percentage of daily energy losses and parameters such as peak sun hours, system capacity, efficiency, and costs, defining the cleaning days as the optimization variable.

Where CUtarifa is the unit cost of energy per kWh. On the other hand, the cleaning cost corresponds to:

$$C_{clean} = C_{labor} + C_{water} + C_{product} \quad (18)$$

This includes labor costs, water costs, and cleaning product costs, if used. The minimum wage was considered as a benchmark for determining labor costs[14].

2.8 Optimization Function

The objective is to minimize the total annual cost associated with energy losses by soiling and cleanup costs. Also, for the analysis, the average electricity rate for stratum 4, a category that does not receive subsidies, was considered throughout the study period [15][16].

If T is the cleanup interval:

$$C_{\text{water}}(\$) = V(m^3) \cdot C_{rate}\left(\frac{\$}{m^3}\right) \quad (19)$$

$$C_2(d) = \frac{365}{d} \cdot C \quad (20)$$

$$C_T(d) = \frac{365}{2}(d+1) \cdot C_{loss} + \frac{365}{d} \cdot C_{clean} \quad (22)$$

$$d(C_T) = 0 \quad (23)$$

Where nT = ⌊ 365/T ⌋. The value T that minimizes Ctotal is the optimal frequency desired for cleaning the photovoltaic modules[17].

$$C_T(d) = \sum_{d=1}^{365} \frac{365}{2}(d+1) \cdot C_{loss} + \frac{365}{d} \cdot C_{clean} \quad (24)$$

3 RESULTS AND DISCUSSION

Figures 4 and 5 show the daily experimental loss rate of modules 3 (west) and 12 (east), which are cleaned every 12 months and modules 7 (west) and 8 (east), which never have been cleaned. The time series of modules 3 and 12 exhibits gradually increase of LR throughout each year, reaching values close to 10–15%. When analyzing the average slope across the different years, the effective loss rate corresponds to an average increase of approximately 5 % per year. This value can be considered a representative measure of the natural soiling accumulation within a 12-month period under the experimental conditions. The variability of the slopes also reflects that external factors such as rainfall, dust events, or local microclimate conditions significantly influence soiling accumulation.

The LR in uncleaned modules reaches values above 25% by mid-2022. The absence of cleaning produces a much stronger trend, with the slope expected to be consistently positive around 8–12%/year. This suggests that modules exposed without cleaning undergo progressive and irreversible optical and efficiency losses, severely compromising their performance over time. Moreover, the data dispersion suggests that, beyond the average trend, the instantaneous LR can vary widely, which may be attributed to short-term environmental factors such as rain cleaning events, dust storms, or shading.

The variability of LR indicates that soiling models must adapt to local climates. In Bogotá, a city with frequent rainfall, precipitation both cleans and influences dust deposition on PV modules. Models developed for arid regions may overestimate losses, so Bogotá's rainy conditions should be explicitly considered to improve prediction accuracy and optimize maintenance strategies.

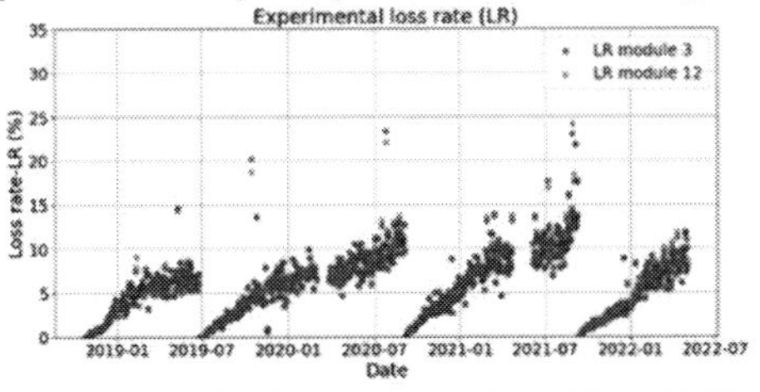

Figure 4: Results of experimental LR modules with 12-month cleaning cycles (Mod3, Mod12)

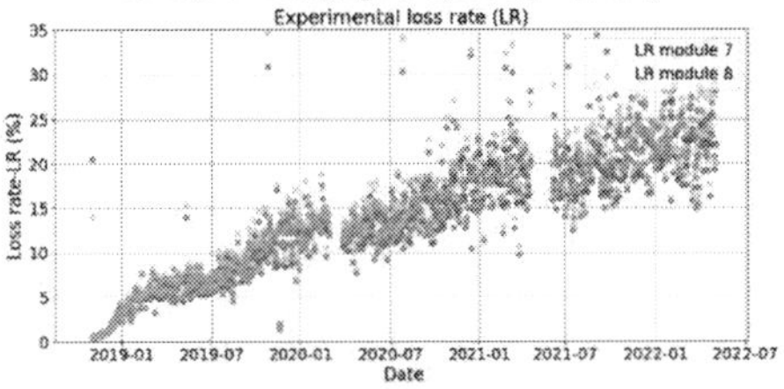

Figure 5: Results of experimental LR modules with no cleaning cycles (Mod7, Mod8)

Figure 6 shows the theoretical LR, both as accumulated values and as per-cycle increases, indicating a cumulative degradation rate of 9.2% per year. Figure 7 contrasts this theoretical behavior with the actual LR measured in different modules, showing good agreement during the initial years but deviations at later stages, where experimental LR exceeds the theoretical prediction. This divergence highlights that, although the theoretical model captures the general trend of soiling accumulation, real conditions introduce additional variability due to environmental effects and differences in cleaning efficiency.

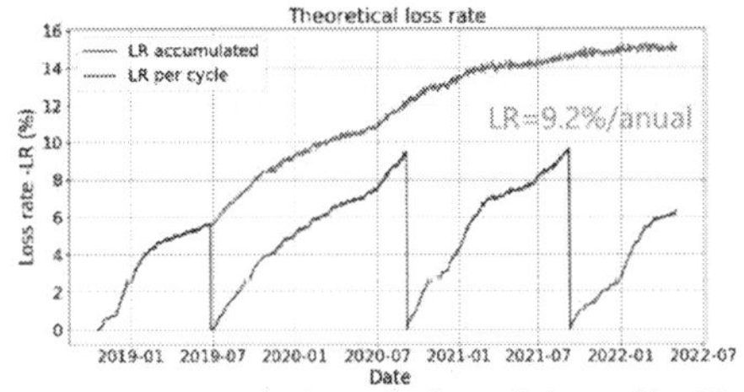

Figure 6: LR results theoretical cumulative and by 12-month cycles

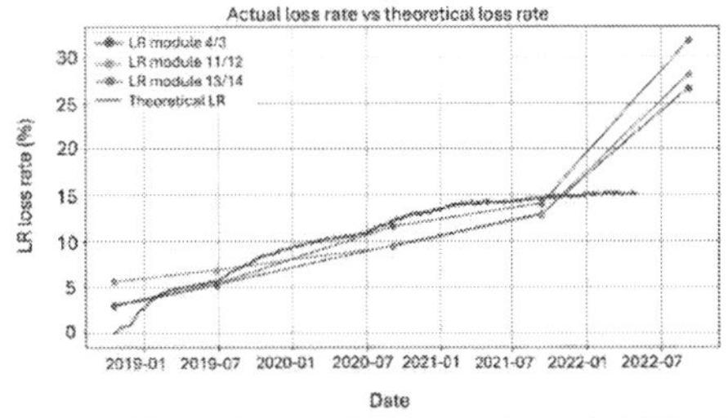

Figure 7: Comparison results between theoretical LR and actual LR of modules on cleaning dates

Figure 8 presents the relationship between experimental and theoretical soiling rate (SR) under a 12-month cleaning cycle, together with the impact of water precipitation. The experimental SR curves of module 3 (west) and module 12 (east) follow the general decreasing pattern predicted by the theoretical model, confirming the validity of the accumulation–cleaning framework. However, deviations appear around rainy periods, where higher precipitation correlates with partial natural cleaning of the modules, temporarily reducing SR. This demonstrates that rainfall plays a significant role in mitigating soiling accumulation, effectively complementing scheduled manual cleanings. The results highlight that integrating precipitation data into theoretical models improves the accuracy of LR/SR predictions and provides a more realistic basis for designing optimized cleaning strategies in PV systems.

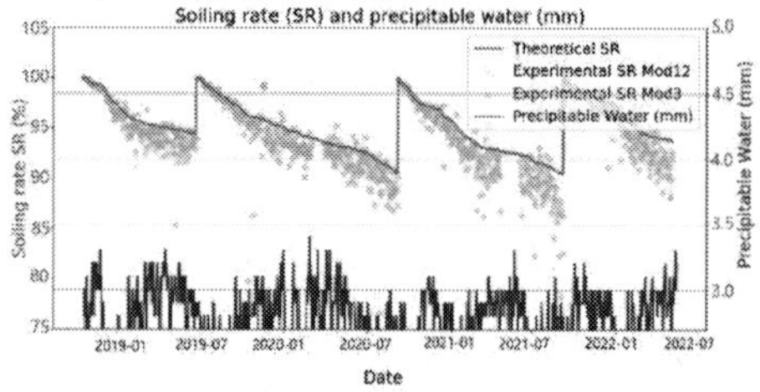

Figure 8: Comparison of experimental and theoretical SR in Impact of water precipitation 12-month cycle

Figure 9 shows the long-term experimental LR for modules without cleaning, updated with data collected in May 2025. LR3_4 (blue) shows the LR of module 3 compared to 4 (west), LR12_11 (red) shows the LR of module 12 compared to 11 (east) and LR14_13 (blue) shows the LR of module 14 compared to 13 (east). The results confirm a continuous accumulation of losses, with LR values stabilizing between 25–30% after about six years of exposure. Although the rate of increase slows down after 2022, the accumulated soiling remains high, indicating that a saturation effect occurs once the surface reaches a maximum dust coverage, beyond which additional deposition has a reduced incremental effect on optical losses. The comparison among different modules suggest a higher impact of soiling to modules orientated to the west (green). These findings reinforce the importance of cleaning interventions, as long-term soiling results in persistent high-performance losses that cannot be naturally reversed.

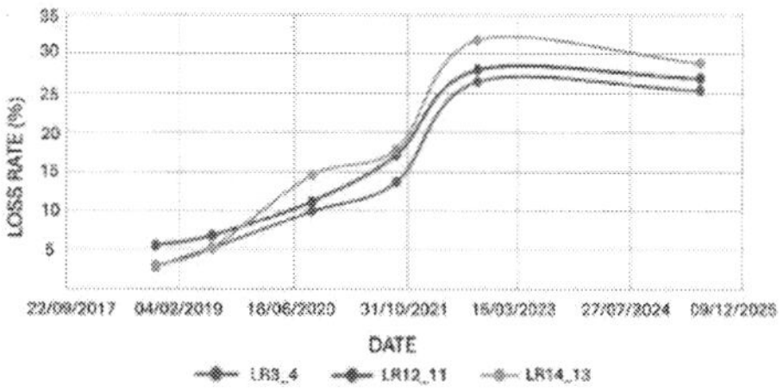

Figure 9: Experimental LR for modules without cleaning

Figures 10 and 11 present the optimization of PV module cleaning frequency under different economic conditions, considering both the price of electricity (Figure 10) and labor costs (Figure 11). The results clearly show that the optimal cleaning period is not fixed, but shifts depending on the balance between energy revenues and cleaning expenses. At higher electricity prices, the optimal strategy is to clean more frequently, since the revenue loss from soiling exceeds the additional labor costs. Conversely, at lower electricity prices the optimal point occurs earlier, as the economic penalty of soiling is less severe. Similarly, when labor costs are low the model suggests more frequent cleanings.

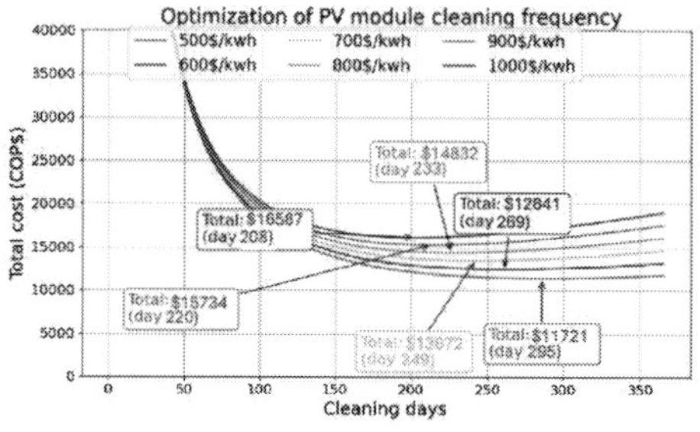

Figure 10: Annual cost optimization by varying energy rates

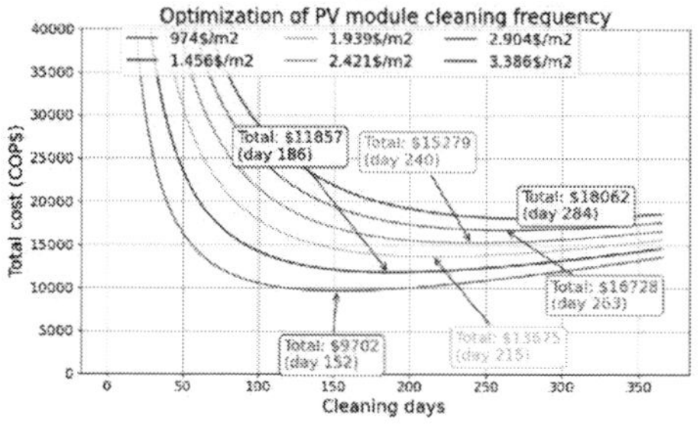

Figure 11: Annual cost optimization by varying labor

4 CONCLUSIONS

The results highlight the critical role of maintenance strategies in photovoltaic performance. While annual cleaning controls the loss rate within manageable bounds 9.2% per year, no cleaning results in more than 25–30% cumulative loss in less than five years, which can considerably reduce energy yield and profitability. The comparison between theoretical models and experimental data confirmed that rainfall events partially mitigate soiling, but not enough to replace scheduled cleaning. These findings underscore the relevance of integrating environmental parameters, such as precipitation, into predictive models for more accurate estimation of performance degradation.

Overall, these results emphasize the need to adapt cleaning frequency to the environmental soiling conditions. In climates with moderate dust deposition, annual cleaning may be sufficient, while in harsher conditions, shorter cycles or alternative mitigation measures would be required to avoid excessive losses.

From an economic perspective, the optimization analysis revealed that the optimal cleaning frequency depends strongly on both electricity tariffs and labor costs. At higher energy prices or lower labor costs, more frequent cleaning is economically justified, while lower tariffs or high labor expenses shift the optimal point toward longer intervals between cleanings. These results provide PV system operators with a practical framework to adapt cleaning strategies to local conditions, ensuring maximum profitability. Overall, the study confirms that combining experimental monitoring with cost-based optimization enables data-driven decision-making, improving both the technical and economic performance of photovoltaic systems.

5 ACKNOWLEDGMENTS

This project has received funding from the European Union's Horizon Europe research and innovation programme under grant agreement No. 101132182

6 REFERENCES

[1] Unidad de Planeación Minero Energética, "Plan Indicativo de Expansión de la Generación 2023-2037," Bogotá, Colombia, Oct. 2023.

[2] M. N. AlMallahi, B. Yousef, Y. C. Tan, H. Al Jaghoub, and K. Obaideen, "The role of asset management in solar PV systems and its linkage to sustainable development goals," 2023, p. 040001. doi: 10.1063/5.0165207.

[3] M. R. Maghami, H. Hizam, C. Gomes, M. A. Radzi, M. I. Rezadad, and S. Hajighorbani, "Power loss due to soiling on solar panel: A review," Jun. 01, 2016, *Elsevier Ltd.* doi: 10.1016/j.rser.2016.01.044.

[4] A. Boretti and S. Castelletto, "Annual relative performance degradation in photovoltaic solar plants," *Solar Energy Advances*, vol. 4, Jan. 2024, doi: 10.1016/j.seja.2024.100074.

[5] I. Lillo-Bravo, P. González-Martínez, M. Larrañeta, and J. Guasumba-Codena, "Impact of energy losses due to failures on photovoltaic plant energy balance," *Energies (Basel)*, vol. 11, no. 2, Feb. 2018, doi: 10.3390/en11020363.

[6] S. W. Ali Shah, M. Nateque Mahmood, and N. Das, "Strategic Asset Management Framework for the Improvement of Large Scale PV Power Plants in Australia," in *Australasian Universities Power Engineering Conference- AUPEC2016*, IEEE, 2016.

[7] "The IEC 61724-1:2021 standard for PV monitoring systems: a quick explanation | Hukseflux." Accessed: Aug. 16, 2025. [Online]. Available: https://www.hukseflux.com/applications/solar-energy-pv-system-performance-monitoring/iec-61724-12021-standard-for-pv

[8] A. G. S. Matar and H. An, "Optimal Scheduling of PV Panel Cleaning and Policy Implications Considering Uncertain Dusty Weather Conditions in the Middle East," *Systems*, vol. 12, no. 10, p. 418, Oct. 2024, doi: 10.3390/SYSTEMS12100418/S1.

[9] T. Sarver, A. Al-Qaraghuli, and L. L. Kazmerski, "A comprehensive review of the impact of dust on the use of solar energy: History, investigations, results, literature, and mitigation approaches," *Renewable and Sustainable Energy Reviews*, vol. 22, pp. 698–733, Jun. 2013, doi: 10.1016/J.RSER.2012.12.065.

[10] B. Figgis, B. Guo, W. Javed, S. Ahzi, and Y. Rémond, "Dominant environmental parameters for dust deposition and resuspension in desert climates," *Aerosol Science and Technology*, vol. 52, no. 7, pp. 788–798, Jul. 2018, doi: 10.1080/02786826.2018.1462473/ASSET/AFC25938-0081-4327-B868-F9F99B93C0B9/ASSETS/IMAGES/LARGE/UAST_A_1462473_F0016_OC.JPG.

[11] A. Sayyah, M. N. Horenstein, and M. K. Mazumder, "Energy yield loss caused by dust deposition on photovoltaic panels," *Solar Energy*, vol. 107, pp. 576–604, Sep. 2014, doi: 10.1016/J.SOLENER.2014.05.030.

[12] Z. A. Darwish, H. A. Kazem, K. Sopian, M. A. Alghoul, and H. Alawadhi, "Experimental investigation of dust pollutants and the impact of environmental parameters on PV performance: an experimental study," *Environ Dev Sustain*, vol. 20, no. 1, pp. 155–174, Feb. 2018, doi: 10.1007/S10668-016-9875-7/TABLES/8.

[13] M. Mani and R. Pillai, "Impact of dust on solar photovoltaic (PV) performance: Research status, challenges and recommendations," *Renewable and Sustainable Energy Reviews*, vol. 14, no. 9, pp. 3124–3131, Dec. 2010, doi: 10.1016/J.RSER.2010.07.065.

[14] "El salario mínimo para 2025 aumentó en 9,5% y quedará en $1'423.500." Accessed: Aug. 16, 2025. [Online]. Available: https://www.presidencia.gov.co/prensa/Paginas/El-salario-minimo-para-2025-aumentara-el-9-54-porciento-y-queda-en-1423500-presidente-Gustavo-Petro-241224.aspx

[15] "Tarifas de energía | Enel Colombia." Accessed: Aug. 16, 2025. [Online]. Available: https://www.enel.com.co/es/personas/tarifas-energia-enel-distribucion.html

[16] "Tarifas 2024." Accessed: Aug. 16, 2025. [Online]. Available: https://www.acueducto.com.co/wps/portal/EAB2/Home/atencion-al-usuario/tarifas/tarifas_2024

[17] M. Abu-Naser, "Solar Panels Cleaning Frequency for Maximum Financial Profit," *Open Journal of Energy Efficiency*, vol. 06, no. 03, pp. 80–86, 2017, doi: 10.4236/OJEE.2017.63006.

A SPATIALLY RESOLVED CLEAR-SKY FILTER USING PHOTOVOLTAIC MODULES AS CLOUD DETECTORS

Elin Dypvik Sødahl, Magnus Moe Nygård, and Marie Syre Wiig
Department of Solar Power Systems, Institute for Energy Technology (IFE), NO-2007 Kjeller, Norway
elin.sodahl@ife.no

ABSTRACT: Operation and maintenance of photovoltaic (PV) power plants is essential to mitigate performance losses. Time series of the temperature corrected performance ratio (*PR*) can be used to monitor system performance or as input to advanced algorithms that estimates degradation and soiling. However, these algorithms are sensitive to the signal-to-noise level in *PR* time series, and might struggle if there are much missing data. Traditional clear-sky filters often discard large amounts of data, particularly during shifting weather conditions. This study introduces a novel clear-sky detection method that retains more data by using PV modules as cloud detectors, yielding a spatially resolved clear-sky index. The method proposed here is compared to the one by Reno and Hansen which is included in the open-source python library PVAnalytics. The results show that the new filter retains more data, especially on partially cloudy days, leading to more reliable performance metrics for the PV system.

Keywords: Clear-sky detection, geospatial PV analytics, operations and maintenance

1 INTRODUCTION

Operation and maintenance (O&M) of photovoltaic (PV) power plants is necessary to limit performance losses, such as degradation and soiling. [1], [2] Mitigations of faults and losses can increase energy yield, and thus also return of investments. For example, Iftikhar et al. found that an 18 MWp PV power plant had 4% underperformance due to tracker system faults, and resolving the issue could increase earnings with 175 000 Euro per year.[3]

The total effect of losses in a PV system can be assessed using the temperature adjusted performance ratio (*PR*), [4] which is defined as

$$PR = \frac{\sum_t P_t}{\sum_t c_{t,25°C} P_{STC}\, G_{POA,t}\, / G_{STC}}. \quad (1)$$

In Eq. (1), P_t is the power output in a time interval *t*, P_{STC} is the rated power at standard test conditions, $G_{POA,t}$ the plane-of-array (POA) irradiance received during *t*, and G_{STC} is the standard test condition irradiance of 1000 W/m^2. $c_{t,25°C}$ is a temperature correction term which depends on the module temperature, T_t and the module temperature coefficient, γ,

$$c_{t,25\,°C} = 1 + \gamma(T_t + 25\,°C). \quad (2)$$

While *PR* is a measure of the total losses, it cannot provide information about the root causes of reduced power output. This means that permanent losses, such as degradation, and transient losses, such as curtailment or cloud cover will have a similar effect on *PR*. Thus, using *PR* as a meaningful assessment of PV system health is only valuable when datapoints affected by transient losses are removed from the dataset. Furthermore, transient losses yields noise in the *PR* timeseries, which can make data analysis challenging. [5]

There are several established approaches for identifying timestamps where the PV system is experiencing clear-sky conditions. This enables improved *PR* calculations by removing data when the production is reduced due to shading by clouds. Reno and Hansen have suggested an algorithm that evaluates the shape of the irradiance curve measured at site. [6] This method assesses the mean and maximum global horizontal irradiance (GHI), the line-length of the GHI vs. time curve, the standard deviation in the rate of change of GHI, in addition to the maximal changes between measured GHI and estimated clear-sky time series to detect timestamps with clear-sky conditions. The method have also been extended to POA irradiance, and relies on setting threshold values for five parameters. The threshold values are also dependent on the time resolution of the measured irradiance data. Ellis et al. have suggested a similar approach that only relies on measured irradiance data. [7] Neither of these methods account for the spatial resolution of the irradiance data. This can lead to discarding large fractions of the dataset, particularly in large PV assets where a passing cloud only will affect a small subset of the PV production at a given time. Excessive removal of data will affect days with changing cloud-cover to a larger extent than days with consistent clear-sky conditions or overcast. Yi et al. recently published a clear-sky identification method based on machine-learning aimed on identifying clear days.[8] Even with a large detection rate, this method will also discard large amounts of data due to classification of whole days instead of clear-sky timestamps. Furthermore, machine-learned methods tend to be more involved than direct data analysis and often demands tuning to capture site-specific conditions.

Achieving spatial resolution in PV plant monitoring have seen increased interest. For O&M, this is for example relevant for drone imaging. [9] IR imaging using drones can be a powerful tool to identify module faults, such as hotspots and connection failures, but relies on robust mapping of string positions to enable maintenance actions. Furthermore, spatial resolution is also important in the field of power production forecasting, [10], [11] where tracking the movement of clouds over a large PV asset can yield more accurate short-term production predictions.

This work present a new procedure for clear-sky identification by using PV modules as cloud detectors. The cloud detection can be extended to the pyranometer data as the relative positions of pyranometers and strings are known for the site studied. By leveraging a dataset with a high temporal resolution we achieve a clear-sky filtering method that can retain a larger fraction of the production data than the conventional approaches. The large data retention also allows for clear-sky filtering on string-level, where conventional methods relies on filtering the

10.4229/EUPVSEC2025/4CV.1.39

measured irradiance. We demonstrate the performance of the clear-sky identification approach suggested here by computing *PR* on string level, and compare with the established method of Reno and Hansen.

2 METHODS

2.1 PV system data and cloud detection

This work relies on a 1-minute resolution dataset from a 150+ MWp PV power plant located in a tropical wet and dry climate ("As" in the Köppen–Geiger climate classification system) with a rainy season between January and July. The current of the monofacial PV modules is measured per string-set, which consist of two parallel connected strings of on average 31 modules each. The plant consist of in total 8088 string-sets. The 12 pyranometers at the site are mounted at the tracker of 12 different strings. The relative position of all strings-sets and pyranometers are stored in the site metadata. Initial data filtering is carried out prior to any analysis where all timestamps with curtailment are omitted. Timestamps where the tracker angle deviates from the setpoint angle are also filtered out.

The PV modules are used as cloud detectors through the calculation of a clear-sky index, $k_{i,t}$ for each string-set in the power plant through the following equation,

$$k_{i,t} = \frac{P_{i,t}/P_{i,STC}}{c_{t,25\,°C}G_{POA,CS,i,t}/G_{STC}}. \quad (3)$$

In Eq. (1), $P_{i,t}$ is the power output of the *i*-th string-set during *t*. $G_{POA,CS,i,t}$ is the modelled clear-sky POA irradiation. This value is obtained using the simplified Soilis model to estimate the global horizontal, direct normal, and diffuse horizontal contributions to the clear-sky irradiance for the PV system location.[12] Next, the angle-of incidence (AOI) is computed using the measured tracker angle for each string-set to obtain the incident-angle modifier by applying the De Soto model.[8] Finally, $G_{POA,CS,i,t}$ is obtained by transposing the clear-sky irradiance contributions to the POA using the Perez model,[13] and adjusting for the AOI by multiplying with the incident angle-modifier. Version 0.11.2 of pvlib is used to apply all models leveraged in this work, where default settings are used throughout.[14]

2.2 Proposed clear-sky filter

In this study, we leverage the clear-sky indices obtained with Eq. (3) to identify the strings shaded by clouds. Fig. 1 displays the calculated clear-sky indices for all string-sets in the power plant for a given timestamp. Note that the pyranometer positions are indicated by red circles in the plot. The figure shows that several of the sensors are shaded by clouds, while most of the string-sets have large clear-sky indices and can be assumed to experience clear-sky conditions.

The $k_{i,t}$ values are computed on a sting-set level. This means that while we now have a measure for when each string is shaded, it still remains to filter the irradiance data. As the pyranometers are mounted on trackers, we map the clear-sky indices to the pyranometers by assuming that the irradiance conditions are equal for the string and pyranometer mounted to the same tracker. This spatial mapping allows for detection of clear-sky conditions for

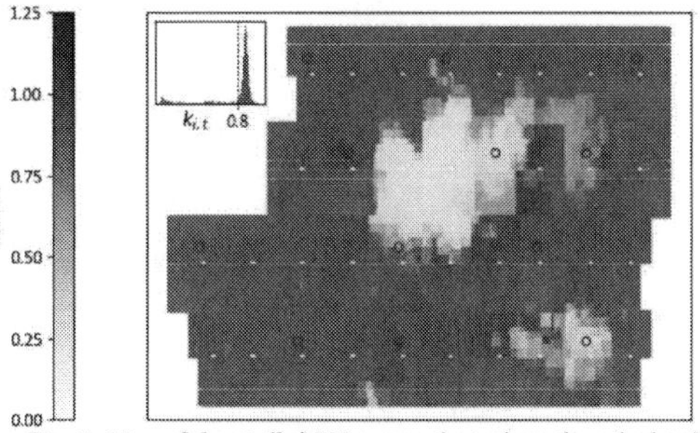

Fig. 1: Map of the studied PV power plant where the calculated clear-sky index for each string-set is indicated. The red circles indicate pyranometer positions. The inset displays a histogram of the clear-sky values for all string-set for this particular time

each individual string-set and pyranometer, rather than for the power plant as a whole. Furthermore, the high temporal resolution of the dataset ensures minimal cloud movement during each time step *t*. Thus, we can assume that the clear-sky index is an appropriate measure of the instantaneous irradiation conditions. The clear-sky POA irradiance can be assumed to be a linear average of all non-shaded measurements for each timestamp.

Finally, to enable clear-sky filtering, it is necessary to define a threshold value for $k_{i,t}$ that separates clear-sky from cloudy conditions. By assessing the distribution of $k_{i,t}$, we define clear-sky conditions as datapoints with $k_{i,t} > 0.8$, see the histogram in the inset of Fig. 1. There is an unavoidable mismatch when mapping the string-set $k_{i,t}$ values to pyranometers due to the physical extent of the strings and the positional mismatch between string and pyranometers. Thus, two datapoints are removed before and after each instance of $k_{i,t} < 0.8$ to limit the effect of the mismatch on the identification of clear-sky timestamps.

3 RESULTS AND DISCUSSION

The proposed methodology for clear-sky identification is assessed by computing *PR* on string-set level and compared with the results obtained by applying the clear-sky filter by Reno and Hansen. [6] Fig. 2 presents the calculated *PR* time series and irradiance received in the POA during five days of November 2022. The top panel of Fig. 2 displays the *PR* calculated without applying any clear-sky filter. The obtained *PR* values are very noisy, which highlights the need of an effective clear-sky filter to achieve reliable *PR* assessment and loss identification.

The two panels in the middle of Fig. 2 display the *PR* timeseries obtained using our suggested filter (second from the top) and the filter of Reno and Hansen (second from the bottom). While the filter of Reno and Hansen retain a sizable fraction of the data on days with longer time intervals of clear-sky conditions, the bulk of the data is discarded for days with changing cloud cover, such as the 20th and the 23rd of November. No data is retained for the 20th. The approach suggested here retains a larger fraction of the data for all days. This is particularly evident

10.4229/EUPVSEC2025/4CV.1.39

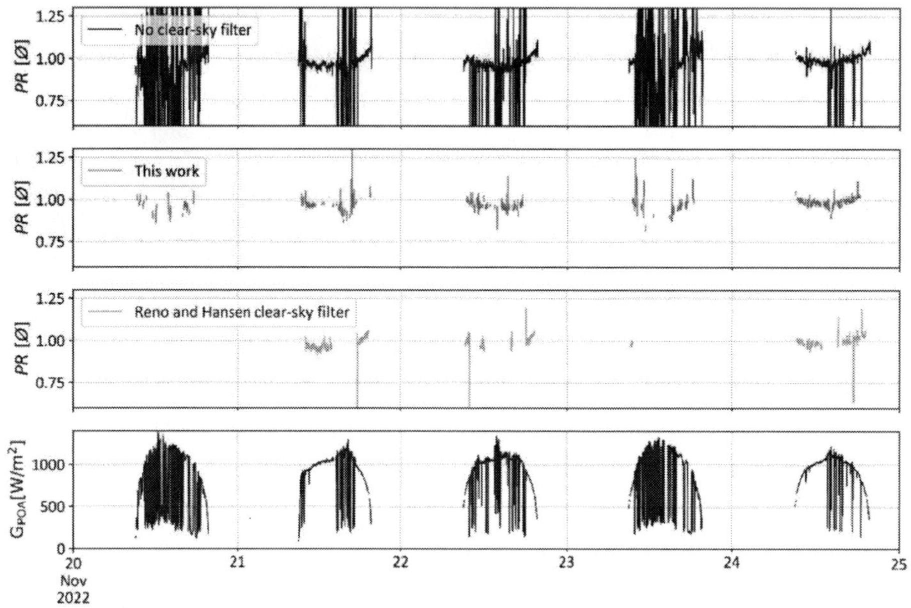

Fig. 2: Calculated *PR* time series for a selected string-set for five days in November 2022 (top) without clear-sky filtering, (second from the top) with the clear-sky filter proposed here, (second from the bottom) using Reno and Hansens's clear-sky filter. The bottom panel displays the measured irradiance received in the POA. The *PR*-values are normalized relative to the first value in the timeseries to avoid publishing business sensitive information

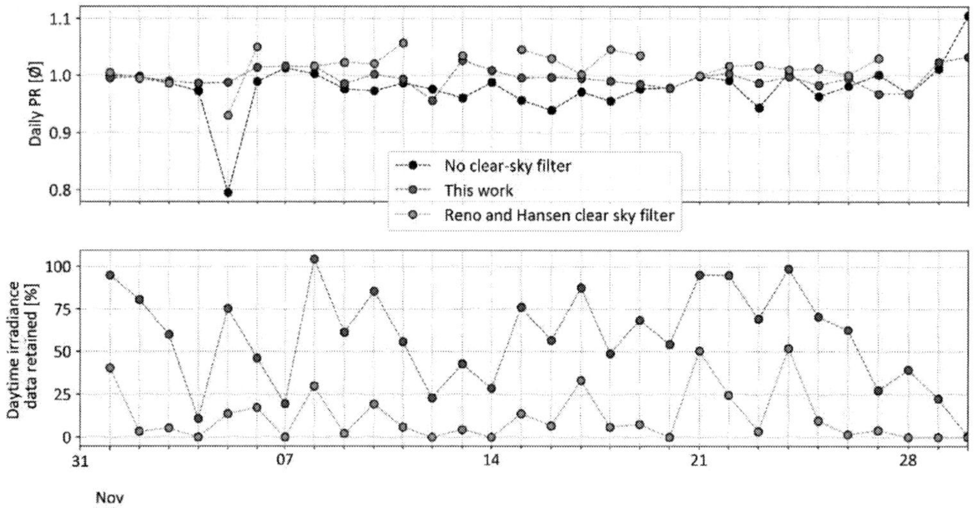

Fig 3: Daily *PR* values for a selected string-set computed using our proposed filter and the clear-sky detection of Reno and Hansen. The *PR*-values are normalized relative to the first value in the timeseries to avoid publishing business sensitive information. The bottom panel displays the percentage of string-set data retained for each day using the two clear-sky filters.

for days with frequent changes in cloud cover, and enables *PR* and loss assessment for periods where clouds are moving over the power plant. The noise in the *PR* values are also reduced compared to the unfiltered data in the top, meaning that timestamps affected by cloud shading are efficiently filtered out.

To further evaluate the performance of our clear-sky filter, we also compute the daily *PR* values for the same string-set for the month of November 2022. Fig. 3 shows the daily *PR* values (top panel) and the fraction of daytime data retained (bottom panel) using both the suggested clear-sky filter and that of Reno and Hansen. The calculated daily *PR* values show that there are several missing days for the data filtered using the method of Reno and Hansen. There are also a larger variation in the *PR* using this approach, which is the behavior expected if there was a variation in the power losses in the PV power plant. The *PR* values obtained used the method suggested here are more stable, and there are no days where sll daytime data is filtered out The bottom panel further highlights the difference in daytime data retention using the two clear-sky filters. Daytime data are defined here as timestamps where the solar elevation angle is above 10°. The new approach discards a smaller fraction of data for each day in the studied period, meaning that the calculated daily *PR* values are backed by more data. An increased data retention yields a higher confidence in computed *PR*, and can thus enable more reliable PV loss estimation.

Filtering on both string and pyranometer-level separates this method from the conventional approaches that only assesses the irradiance curve shape. Typically, clear-sky filters are applied by filtering the mean or median of all irradiance measurements at site. Thus, clear-sky timestamps are only moments when there are no clouds over the PV site.

Here, we construct a clear-sky irradiance time series by averaging the irradiance measured by all pyranometers that experience clear-sky conditions for a given time stamp. Furthermore, the filtering on string level ensures that only clear sky timestamps are included in the consecutive *PR* assessment.
In addition to construct a clear-sky irradiance time series that is valid for the whole site, we also ensure that

The focus of this work is to identify clear-sky timestamps. However, the suggested method can also be leveraged to find timestamps with overcast conditions. This requires setting a low threshold value for $k_{i,t}$, where values beneath the threshold are assumed to indicate significant cloud shading. This approach can for example be beneficial for PV power plants in the Nordic, which tend to experience significant shading by clouds. Using only overcast timestamps can in these instances also be a measure to reduce noise in *PR* time series.

4 CONCLUSIONS

We have presented a new clear-sky filter that leverages data with a high temporal resolution where the relative positions of string-sets and pyranometers are known. The suggested method effectively filters out timestamps affected by cloud cover by assessing calculated clear-sky indices that compare measured production with expected clear-sky power production. Furthermore, this approach only relies on defining a single threshold value, where we defined clear-sky conditions as timestamps with $k_{i,t} > 0.8$. By assessing the *PR* timeseries with a 1-minute resolution and daily *PR* we demonstrated that the new approach achieves a higher data retention than the established filter proposed by Reno and Hansen.
The new method can thus enable better loss estimation and string-level *PR* assessments.

ACKNOWLEDGEMENTS

This work was supported by the Norwegian Research Council through project number 355871.

5 REFERENCES

[1] D. C. Jordan og C. Hansen, «Clear-sky detection for PV degradation analysis using multiple regression», *Renew. Energy*, bd. 209, s. 393–400, jun. 2023, doi: 10.1016/j.renene.2023.04.035.

[2] D. C. Jordan, T. J. Silverman, J. H. Wohlgemuth, S. R. Kurtz, og K. T. VanSant, «Photovoltaic failure and degradation modes», *Prog. Photovolt. Res. Appl.*, bd. 25, nr. 4, s. 318–326, apr. 2017, doi: 10.1002/pip.2866.

[3] H. Iftikhar, E. Sarquis, og P. J. C. Branco, «Why Can Simple Operation and Maintenance (O&M) Practices in Large-Scale Grid-Connected PV Power Plants Play a Key Role in Improving Its Energy Output?», *Energies*, bd. 14, nr. 13, s. 3798, jan. 2021, doi: 10.3390/en14133798.

[4] *IEC 61724-1:2021 photovoltaic system performance - Part 1: Monitoring*, Geneva, Switzerland., 2021.

[5] M. M. Nygård, Å. F. Skomedal, M. S. Wiig, og E. S. Marstein, «Combined Degradation and Soiling With Validation Against Independent Soiling Station Measurements», *IEEE J. Photovolt.*, bd. 13, nr. 2, s. 296–304, mar. 2023, doi: 10.1109/JPHOTOV.2023.3239752.

[6] M. J. Reno og C. W. Hansen, «Identification of periods of clear sky irradiance in time series of GHI measurements», *Renew. Energy*, bd. 90, s. 520–531, mai 2016, doi: 10.1016/j.renene.2015.12.031.

[7] B. H. Ellis, M. Deceglie, og A. Jain, «Automatic Detection of Clear-Sky Periods From Irradiance Data», *IEEE J. Photovolt.*, bd. 9, nr. 4, s. 998–1005, jul. 2019, doi: 10.1109/JPHOTOV.2019.2914444.

[8] C. Yi *mfl.*, «Anomaly detection of photovoltaic power generation based on quantile regression recurrent neural network», *Electr. Power Syst. Res.*, bd. 238, s. 111132, jan. 2025, doi: 10.1016/j.epsr.2024.111132.

[9] E. Sovetkin, A. Gerber, B. Kubicek, og B. Pieters, «Single Image Geospatial Referencing», Proceedings of the 41st EUPVSEC (2024).

[10] M. M. Nygård, E. W. Eriksen, og H. N. Riise, «Photovoltaic power plants as efficient cloud motion detectors», Proceedings of the 41st EUPVSEC (2024).

[11] M. Lipperheide, J. L. Bosch, og J. Kleissl, «Embedded nowcasting method using cloud speed persistence for a photovoltaic power plant», *Sol. Energy*, bd. 112, s. 232–238, feb. 2015, doi: 10.1016/j.solener.2014.11.013.

[12] P. Ineichen, «A broadband simplified version of the Solis clear sky model», *Sol. Energy*, bd. 82, nr. 8, s. 758–762, aug. 2008, doi: 10.1016/j.solener.2008.02.009.

[13] R. Perez, P. Ineichen, R. Seals, J. Michalsky, og R. Stewart, «Modeling daylight availability and irradiance components from direct and global irradiance», *Sol. Energy*, bd. 44, nr. 5, s. 271–289, 1990, doi: 10.1016/0038-092X(90)90055-H.

[14] W. F. Holmgren, C. W. Hansen, og M. A. Mikofski, «pvlib python: a python package for modeling solar energy systems», *J. Open Source Softw.*, bd. 3, nr. 29, s. 884, sep. 2018, doi: 10.21105/joss.00884.

Elin Dynvik Sødahl*, Magnus Moe Nygård, and Marie Syre Wiig
Solar Power Systems
Institute for Energy Technology, Kjeller, Norway
**elin.sodahl@ife.no*

IFE

A spatially resolved clear-sky filter: photovoltaic modules as cloud detectors

Operation and maintenance of photovoltaic (PV) power plants is essential to mitigate performance losses due to degradation and soiling. Traditional clear-sky filters often discard large amounts of data, particularly during shifting weather conditions. Using the PV modules as cloud detectors enables clear-sky filtering on string-level and a spatially resolved filtering approach. This is beneficial in large PV system, as it allows retaining data for one part of the park while another area is shaded by clouds.

Data filtering is crucial to achieve a reliable performance ratio

The performance ratio takes measured irradiance and produced power as input and is used as a measure of the health of a PV system.

$$PR = \frac{\sum_t P_t}{\sum_t c_{t,25°C} P_{STC}\, G_{POA,t} / G_{STC}}$$

PR values does not separate between permanent losses (i.e., degradation) and temporary losses (i.e., soiling, changing cloud cover). Temporary losses should be filtered out to evaluate permanent losses.

String-set resolved clear-sky index

A clear sky index can be computed for each string (*i*) for each timestep (*t*) of the production data by modelling the clear-sky plane-of-array irradiance ($G_{POA,CS,i,t}$):

$$k_{i,t} = \frac{P_{i,t} / P_{i,STC}}{c_{t,25°C} G_{POA,CS,i,t} / G_{STC}}$$

This allows for mapping of the clouds over the PV plant. The position of strings and pyranometers in the PV system are known, meaning that the clear-sky indices of the strings can be mapped to the adjacent pyranometers.

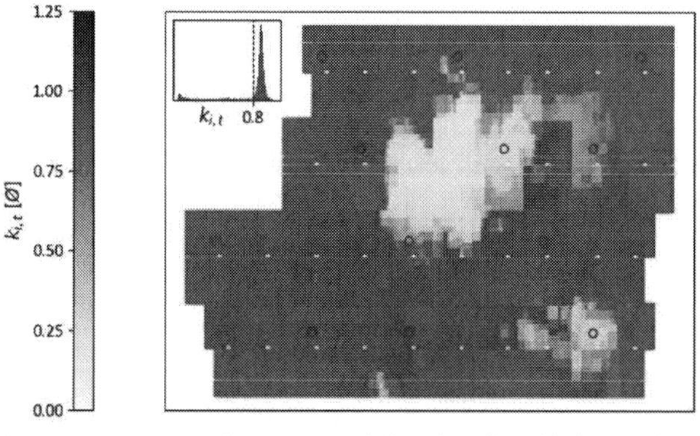

Figure 1: Map of the PV power plant where the clear-sky index of each string-set is indicated. The circles indicates the position of the irradiance sensors. The inset displays a histogram of the clear-sky values for all strings for this timestamp.

References:
[1] Reno. and Hansen. Renewable Energy, 2016. 90: p. 520-531.
[2] Holmgren et al. Journal of Open Source Software, 2018. 3(29).

Acknowledgements:
This work was supported by the Norwegian Research Council through project number 355871.

Proposed clear-sky filter

A high time-resolution is required to capture reduced $k_{i,t}$ as clouds moves above the PV system. Data is retained if $k_{i,t} > 0.8$. There are differences in the physical position and extent of the pyranometers and string, and two datapoints are removed before and after each timestep with $k_{i,t} < 0.8$ to limit the effect of this mismatch. The data can be filtered on string-level.

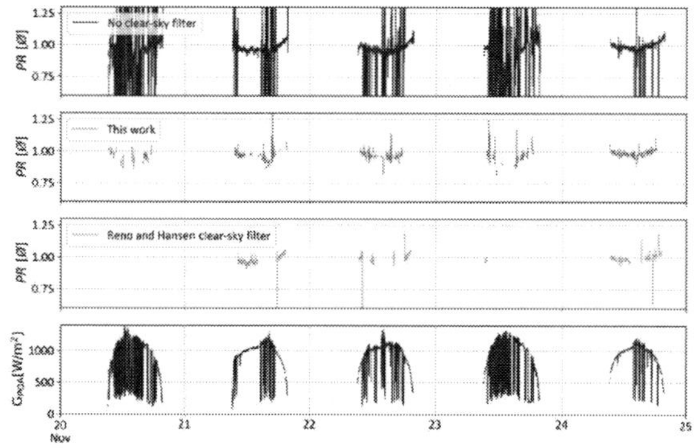

Figure 2: PR values for a selected string, including filtering Reno and Hansen[1] which is implemented in pvlib[2] and the method suggested here. The PR values are normalized.

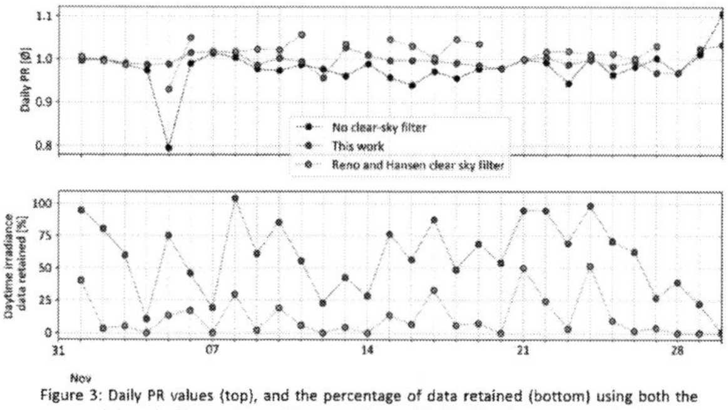

Figure 3: Daily PR values (top), and the percentage of data retained (bottom) using both the proposed clear-sky filter and that of Reno and Hansen[1]. The PR values are normalized.

Conclusions

The new clear-sky filter retains a larger fraction of data than that of Reno and Hansen on most days, and particularly for days with frequent changes in cloud-cover. This results in more reliable calculation of PR-values. Using the new filter results in PR values for all days in November 2022 for a single string and yields less noisy values compared with unfiltered data and the filter of Reno and Hansen.

DEVELOPMENT OF COMPUTATIONAL MODELS FOR ENERGY PRODUCTION ESTIMATION IN BIFACIAL MODULES UNDER DIFFERENT CONFIGURATIONS AT THE ATACAMA DESERT SOLAR PLATFORM (PSDA)

Mauricio Trigo-Gonzalez [1,3,*], Sebastián Rodríguez-Romero[1], Jorge Rabanal-Arabach[1,3], Jorge Vega-Herrera[1,3], Felipe Valencia[2] and Edward Fuentealba[1,3]

[1] University of Antofagasta, Av. Angamos 601, 1270300 Antofagasta, Chile.
[2] AtamosTec, Pérez Valenzuela 1635, 7500028 Providencia, Chile.
[3] Solar Energy Research Center, Tupper 2007, 8370451 Santiago, Chile.

* Corresponding Author: mauricio.trigo@uantof.cl

ABSTRACT: The Atacama Desert, located in the Antofagasta Region of Chile, has the highest levels of solar radiation and albedo worldwide. These conditions are ideal for bifacial photovoltaic (PV) technologies, as they maximize efficiency and energy generation. To assess the potential installable PV capacity in this region under extreme desert conditions, a machine learning-based estimation model is proposed. This model will provide approximate energy generation values based on climatic variables such as solar radiation, ambient temperature, and wind speed. With this approach, it will be possible to more accurately plan the optimal locations for bifacial PV plant installations in the Antofagasta region, reducing investment uncertainty and improving energy planning.

For this study, monofacial and bifacial PV modules were installed at the Atacama Desert Solar Platform (PSDA) in Chile to compare different technologies. Two mounting configurations were evaluated: a fixed system with a 20° tilt (TFE20°) and a single-axis horizontal tracking system (HSAT). The modules used were of the PERC (Passivated Emitter Rear Contact) type, and data was collected between June 2022 and September 2023. For the analysis, two estimation models were trained: an Artificial Neural Network (ANN) and a Multiple Linear Regression (MLR) model, aiming to compare different statistical approaches. The results showed that, in all cases, the models achieved RMSE% values below 6% and MBE values close to 0%. Notably, the ANN demonstrated slightly better performance compared to the MLR, for both monofacial and bifacial modules in both mounting configurations.

In conclusion, ANN models are an effective tool for estimating photovoltaic power and optimizing mounting configurations, especially in regions with extreme environmental conditions such as the Atacama Desert.

Keywords: Photovoltaic Power Estimation, Artificial Neuronal Network, Multiple Linear Regression, Bifacial Technology, Machine Learning, Atacama Desert , Bifacial Technology

1 INTRODUCTION

Photovoltaic (PV) systems represent one of the most promising solutions for sustainable energy generation, particularly in regions with high solar potential. Among these, the Atacama Desert in northern Chile stands out as a natural laboratory, offering the highest global horizontal irradiance and albedo levels worldwide. These extreme environmental conditions create both an opportunity for maximizing PV generation and a challenge for accurate energy yield assessment [1]–[3].

Recent advances in PV technologies highlight the growing role of bifacial modules, which capture irradiance from both the front and rear sides, significantly enhancing energy yield in high-reflectance environments. However, the accurate estimation of their performance remains complex, especially when using conventional linear models. Multiple Linear Regression (MLR) approaches have been widely employed, yet their capacity to represent the non-linear interactions between climatic variables and power generation is limited.

In this context, Artificial Neural Networks (ANN) have emerged as a powerful tool capable of modeling non-linear dependencies and improving predictive accuracy [4]. Previous studies have reported the potential of ANN for PV performance estimation under various conditions [5], but limited research has validated these models in environments as extreme as the Atacama Desert

The objective of this study is to evaluate and compare the predictive performance of ANN and MLR models in estimating the energy production of monofacial and bifacial PERC modules under two mounting configurations: a fixed-tilt system with 20° inclination (TFE20°) and a horizontal single-axis tracking system (HSAT). By analyzing experimental data collected at the Atacama Desert Solar Platform (PSDA, Spanish acronym)), this work aims to provide a reliable methodological framework for energy yield estimation, contributing to the reduction of uncertainty in the design and operation of PV plants in high-irradiance regions.

2 MATERIALS AND METHOD

2.1 MOUNTING CONFIGURATION

The fixed-tilt configuration (TFE20°) consisted of PERC-type PV modules installed with a 20° inclination facing north, in accordance with conventional design parameters for desert latitudes. This setup represents a baseline system, allowing the evaluation of photovoltaic behavior under static operating conditions. The configuration is particularly relevant in the Atacama Desert due to the high ground-reflected irradiance (albedo), which enhances the rear-side contribution in bifacial technologies.

The horizontal single-axis tracking (HSAT) system enabled modules to follow the solar trajectory along the east–west axis, maintaining a near-normal incidence of irradiance throughout the day. This configuration maximizes daily energy yield and provides a robust framework for comparing static and dynamic tracking strategies. The HSAT setup also minimizes angular losses and improves correlation between irradiance on the module plane and measured energy, which is critical for the calibration and validation of computational models. In Figure1, the mounting configurations of the photovoltaic modules for the TFE20° system and the HSAT are shown.

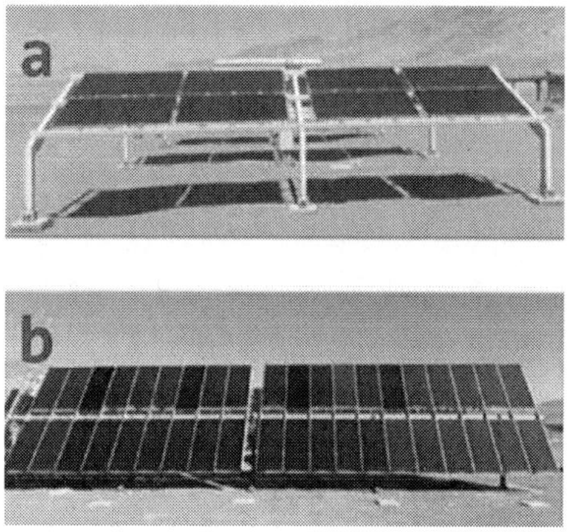

Fig. 1: Facilities studied in the PSDA. a) TFE20, b) HSAT

2.2 EXPERIMENTAL DATA

The experimental campaign was conducted on the Atacama Desert Solar Platform (PSDA), see figure 2, located at 24.09° S, 69.93° W, during the period June 2022 to September 2023. PSDA is characterized by a global horizontal irradiance (GHI) that exceeds 8 $\mathrm{kWh\,m^{-2}\,day^{-1}}$ day and a mean albedo of approximately 0.25.

Data acquisition included:

- Meteorological variables: frontal and rear irradiance, global horizontal irradiance, ambient temperature, module surface temperature, and wind speed. Horizontal irradiance peaks reached values close to 1200 W/m^2, while rear-side irradiance approached 300 W/m^2 on clear days. see figure 3
- Electrical variables: DC power and energy yield from monofacial and bifacial modules.

Fig. 2: Natural laboratory:Atacama Desert Solar Platform (PSDA, Spanish acronym)

Measurements were recorded at 5-minute intervals. Prior to model development, the dataset underwent a data preprocessing pipeline involving outlier detection and removal, missing value imputation, and input variable normalization. These preprocessing steps ensured numerical stability during training and reduced the risk of systematic biases in model estimation.

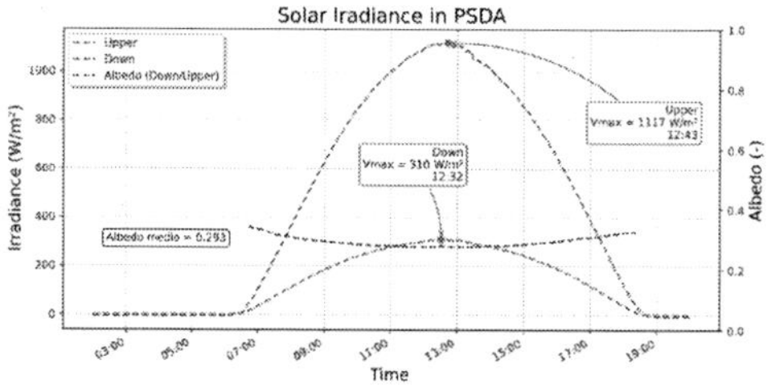

Fig. 3: Albedo

2.3 ESTIMATION MODEL

Two computational approaches were implemented to estimate the energy production of the PV systems: an Artificial Neural Network (ANN) and a Multiple Linear Regression (MLR) model.

2.31 ANN model

The ANN architecture was based on a multilayer perceptron (MLP), see figure 4. Input neurons represented the measured climatic variables (irradiance, temperatures, and wind speed), while the output neuron corresponded to the predicted PV power. For bifacial modules, the rear irradiance was explicitly included as an additional input. The architecture consisted of two hidden layers with 16 and 4 neurons, respectively, and sigmoid activation functions. The dataset was randomly partitioned into training (67%) and validation (33%) subsets. Weight optimization was performed using a backpropagation algorithm, with RMSE and MBE as performance indicators. This configuration was selected to capture the non-linear relationships between environmental conditions and PV energy production.

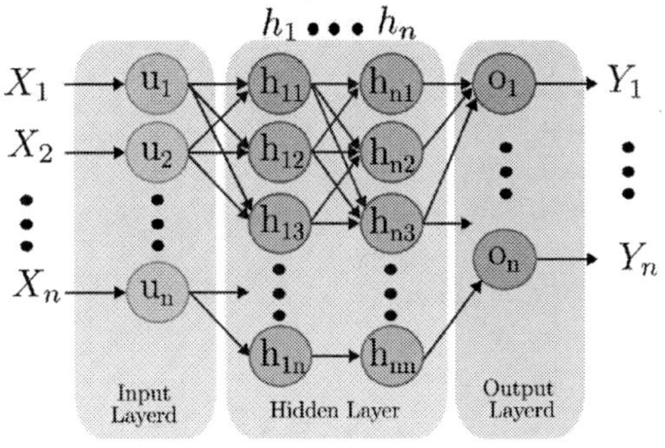

Fig. 4: Model ANN

2.32 *MLR Model*

The Multiple Linear Regression (MLR) model, see figure 5, was developed as a baseline for comparison. This model assumes a linear dependency between predictor variables (irradiance, temperature, wind speed) and the response variable (energy yield). Despite its simplicity, MLR provides insight into the degree of linearity of the system response and serves as a benchmark for validating the added value of non-linear ANN approaches under extreme desert conditions.

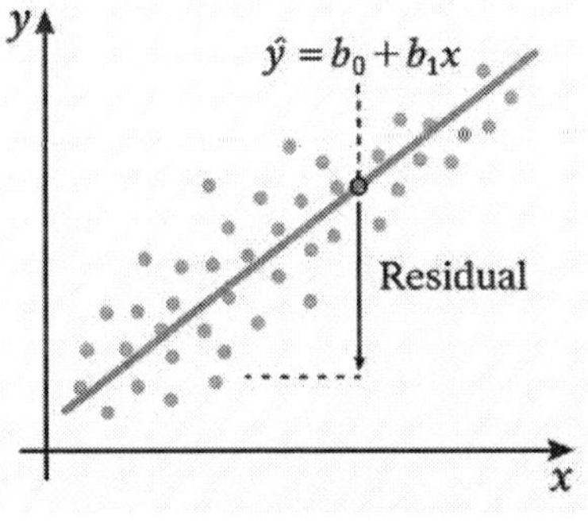

Fig. 5: Model MLR

3 RESULTS AND DISCUSSION

The predictive performance of the ANN and MLR models was analyzed for both mounting configurations (TFE20° and HSAT) and module technologies (monofacial and bifacial). Figure 6 shows the scatter plots of measured versus predicted energy, where ANN results are displayed in blue and MLR results in red. The dashed line corresponds to the ideal 1:1 correlation.

For the TFE20° configuration, the ANN model exhibits a higher level of accuracy compared to MLR. In the monofacial case (Fig. 6a), ANN predictions are more tightly aligned with the reference line, reducing dispersion and systematic deviations. The improvement is even more evident for bifacial modules (Fig. 6b), where ANN maintains RMSE values below 6%, outperforming MLR, which reaches approximately 8%. The MBE values remain close to zero for both models, although MLR shows slightly larger variability, suggesting a tendency to underestimate under certain irradiance ranges.

For the HSAT configuration, both models benefit from the improved irradiance correlation achieved by the tracking system. In the monofacial case (Fig. 6c), ANN achieves RMSE values of approximately 4.23%, while MLR remains near 4.65%. The bifacial case (Fig. 6d) confirms this trend, with ANN predictions closely following the ideal line and providing RMSE values of 4.16%, compared to 5.29% for MLR. The reduction in error dispersion highlights the capability of HSAT to minimize angular losses and stabilize the relationship between climatic variables and energy yield.

Summarizes the statistical indicators obtained for all scenarios. In every configuration, both models achieved RMSE% below 6% and MBE% values within ±1%. However, the ANN consistently provided lower RMSE% values, demonstrating its robustness in capturing non-linear interactions between irradiance, temperature, and energy production. MLR presented slightly lower dispersion in MBE in some cases, but at the expense of higher RMSE values.

Overall, the results confirm that the combination of ANN models with bifacial modules under HSAT configuration delivers the most accurate predictions. This synergy reflects both the technological advantage of bifacial modules in high-albedo environments and the ability of ANN models to adapt to the complex variability of desert climatic conditions.

4 CONCLUSIONS

This work presented a comparative analysis of Artificial Neural Networks (ANN) and Multiple Linear Regression (MLR) models for the estimation of photovoltaic energy production in monofacial and bifacial PERC modules under two mounting configurations, a fixed-tilt at 20° (TFE20°) and a horizontal single-axis tracker (HSAT), using experimental data collected at the Atacama Desert Solar Platform (PSDA). The results confirmed that both models provide reliable estimations, with RMSE% values below 6% and MBE% values close to zero across all scenarios. However, ANN consistently outperformed MLR, particularly in capturing the non-linear interactions between climatic variables and energy output, achieving RMSE values as low as 4% in the HSAT monofacial case. Furthermore, bifacial modules demonstrated superior performance under the desert's high irradiance and albedo conditions, while tracking systems reduced angular mismatch and improved the stability of model predictions. Overall, the combination of ANN with bifacial modules un-

10.4229/EUPVSEC2025/4CV.1.41

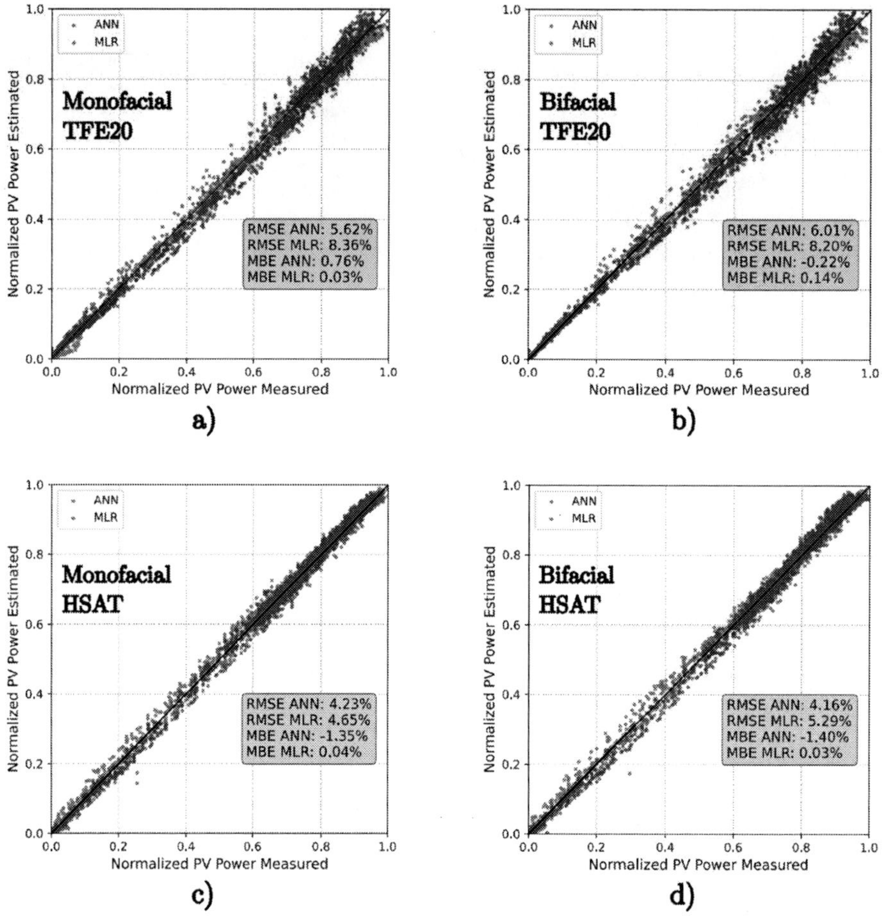

Fig. 6: Comparison between measured and predicted energy using MLR (red) and ANN (blue) for PERC modules under different configurations: (a) monofacial TFE20°, (b) bifacial TFE20°, (c) monofacial HSAT, and (d) bifacial HSAT

der HSAT configuration represents the most accurate approach, providing a robust methodology to reduce uncertainty in PV energy yield assessment and offering a transferable framework for the design and operation of photovoltaic plants in other high-irradiance regions worldwide.

ACKNOWLEDGMENTS

This work was supported by the Chilean Solar Energy Research Center (SERC Chile) through the FONDAP Grant 1523A0006, and by the Atacama Module and Systems Technology Consortium (ATAMOSTEC) under the CORFO Program 17PTECES-75830. Agencia Nacional de Investigación y Desarrollo de Chile (ANID) a través del Programa de Doctorado Nacional, bajo el financiamiento ANID/Subdirección de Capital Humano/Doctorado Nacional/2024-21241192.

References

[1] J. D. Clarke, "Antiquity of aridity in the chilean atacama desert," *Geomorphology*, vol. 73, no. 1, pp. 101–114, 2006. [Online]. Available: https://www.sciencedirect.com/science/article/pii/S0169555X05002023

[2] A. Marzo, P. Ferrada, F. Beiza, P. Besson, J. Alonso-Montesinos, J. Ballestrín, R. Román, C. Portillo, R. Escobar, and E. Fuentealba, "Standard or local solar spectrum? implications for solar technologies studies in the atacama desert," *Renewable Energy*, vol. 127, pp. 871–882, 2018.

[3] J. Rabanal-Arabach, "Development of a c-si photovoltaic module for desert climates," Ph.D. dissertation, Universität Konstanz, Konstanz, 2019.

[4] A. Marzo, M. Trigo, J. Alonso-Montesinos, M. Martínez-Durbán, G. López, P. Ferrada, E. Fuentealba, M. Cortés, and F. J. Batlles, "Daily global solar radiation estimation in desert areas using daily extreme temperatures and extraterrestrial radiation," *Renewable Energy*, vol. 113, pp. 303–311, 2017.

[5] M. Trigo-González, M. Cortés-Carmona, A. Marzo, J. Alonso-Montesinos, M. Martínez-Durbán, G. López, C. Portillo, and F. J. Batlles, "Photovoltaic power electricity generation nowcasting combining sky camera images and learning supervised algorithms in southern spain," *Renewable Energy*, vol. 206, pp. 251–262, 2023.

UA Universidad de Antofagasta

DEVELOPMENT OF COMPUTATIONAL MODELS FOR ENERGY PRODUCTION ESTIMATION IN BIFACIAL MODULES UNDER DIFFERENT CONFIGURATIONS AT THE ATACAMA DESERT SOLAR PLATFORM (PSDA)

Mauricio Trigo-Gonzalez[1,3], Sebastián Rodríguez-Romero[1,3], Jorge Rabanal-Arabach[1,3], Jorge Vega-Herrera[1,3], Felipe Valencia[2], and Edward Fuentealba-Vidal[1,3].

[1] Universidad de Antofagasta, Av. Angamos 601, 1270300 Antofagasta, Chile. [2] AtamosTec, Pérez Valenzuela 1635, 7500028 Providencia, Chile. [3] Solar Energy Research Center, Tupper 2007, 8370451 Santiago, Chile.

EU PVSEC 2025

INTRODUCTION

This study assesses the prediction of power output for monofacial and bifacial PV systems operating under the environmental conditions of the Atacama Desert, in Chile. Two mounting configurations were evaluated: a fixed one with a 20° tilt (TFE20°) and another with horizontal single-axis tracking (HSAT). The power of each of them is predicted by two estimation models: (1) Artificial Neural Network (ANN) and (2) Multiple Linear Regression (MLR).

METHODOLOGY

The experimental campaign was carried out at the Atacama Desert Solar Platform (PSDA), Chile (24.09° S; 69.93° W), between June 2022 and September 2023. The site is characterized by a global horizontal irradiance (GHI) exceeding 1100 W/m² at solar noon and a daily average albedo, under clear-sky conditions, of approximately 0.29.

The training methodology confirmed that the most representative input variables are the global horizontal irradiance (GHI), the module temperature (Tmod), and both the front and rear module irradiance (GI front and GI rear, respectively), all showing a Pearson correlation coefficient greater than 0.8.

Atacama Desert Solar Platform (PSDA)

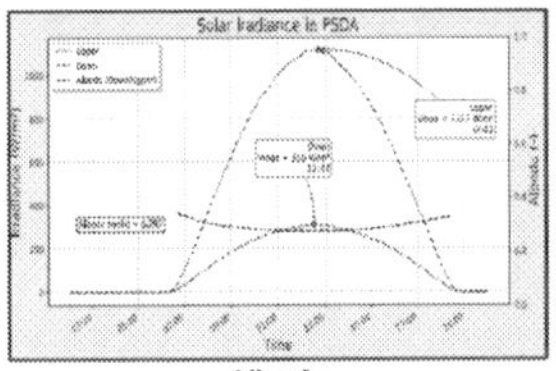

Albedo

South America, Chile

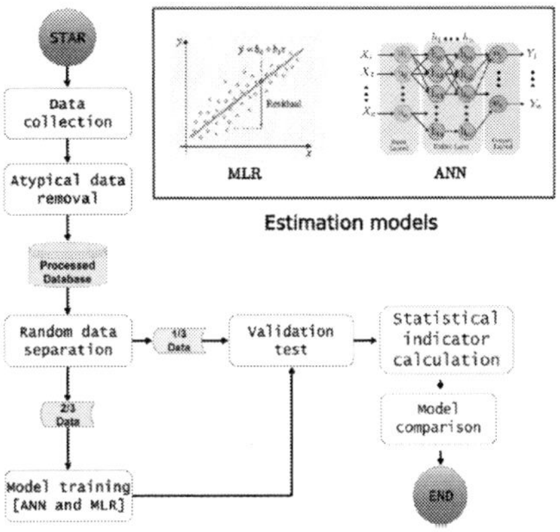

Estimation models

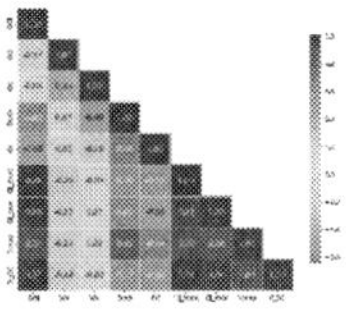

Pearson coefficient of TFE 20

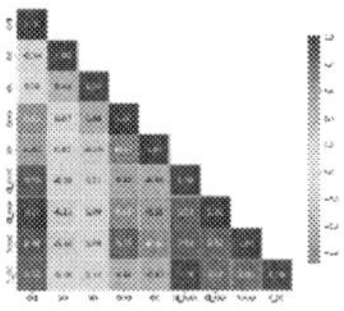

Pearson coefficient of HSAT

RESULTS

The ANN and the MLR models applied to monofacial and bifacial modules, under fixed (TFE20) and HSAT configurations showed high accuracy. In all cases, ANN achieved RMSE% values below 6%, slightly outperforming MLR (with 8%).

TFE20 Type Mounting

HSAT Type Mounting

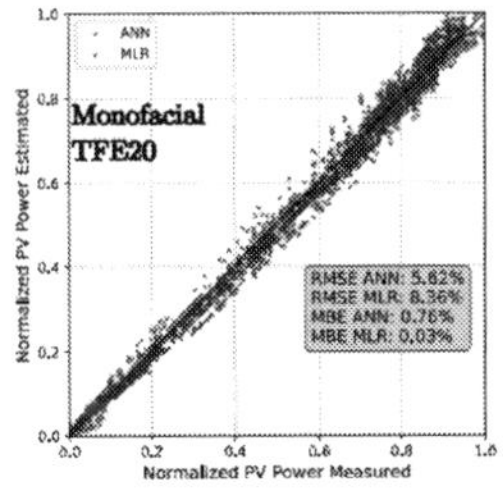

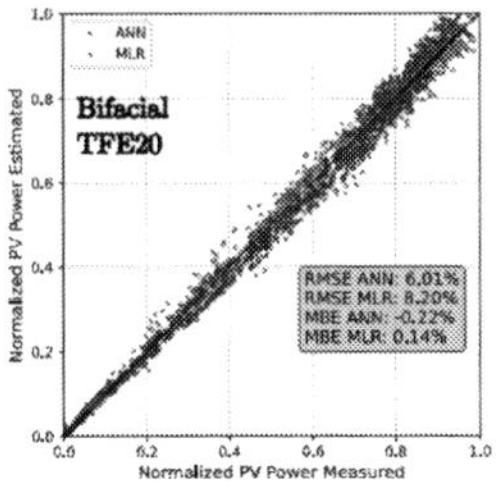

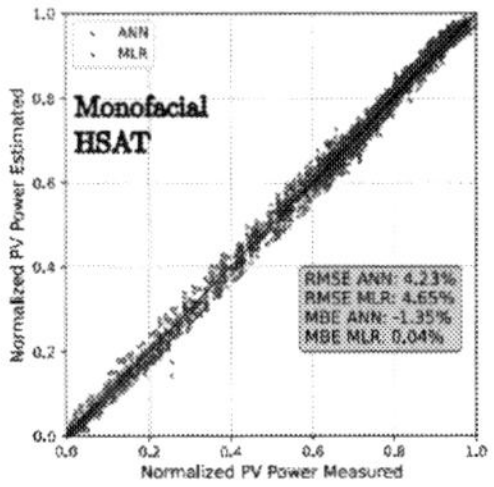

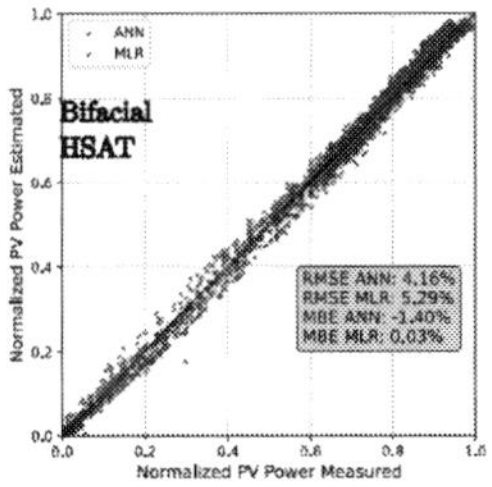

CONCLUSION

Estimation models for PV power under high solar irradiance desert conditions were compared, with ANN proving to be the most effective approach. Using only input variables such as irradiance and module temperature enables accurate predictions, supporting the planning of PV plants in high-irradiance environments.

This work was supported by SERC Chile under FONDAP 1523A0006 grant, and by the Atacama Module and Systems Technology Consortium, ATAMOSTEC, under CORFO 17PTECES-75830 program.

CDEA CENTRO DESARROLLO ENERGÉTICO ANTOFAGASTA

SERC CHILE SOLAR ENERGY RESEARCH CENTER

ASSESSING PV MODULE QUALITY RISKS IN SOUTH AFRICA: PERFORMANCE INSIGHTS ACROSS UTILITY, COMMERCIAL AND INDUSTRIAL, AND RESIDENTIAL SECTORS

JL Crozier McCleland[1,2*], M Vumbugwa[1,2], NW Mngomezulu[2], FJ Vorster[1,2] , EE van Dyk[1,2]

[1]Nelson Mandela University, Nelson Mandela Bay, 6019, South Africa
[2]PVinsight (Pty) Ltd, Nelson Mandela Bay, 6019, South Africa
*Corresponding Author: Jacqueline.CrozierMcCleland@mandela.ac.za

ABSTRACT: South Africa's Solar Photovoltaic (PV) sector has expanded rapidly across utility, commercial and industrial (C&I), and residential markets, yet concerns about PV module quality remain. This paper presents insights from over a decade of accredited testing of PV modules across these sectors, highlighting how quality assurance (QA) practices shape performance outcomes. Utility-scale projects that applied QA frameworks consistently outperformed manufacturer specifications, with modules initially underspecified and remaining above warranty thresholds after ten years of operation. In the C&I sector, modules sourced directly from the market performed slightly below nameplate values but within measurement uncertainty, indicating variable reliability. In contrast, residential systems showed the highest risks with the focus on costs rather than quality. These results demonstrate that performance risks are not uniformly distributed across the market, and that sectors lacking QA are most exposed to underperformance and safety concerns. The findings support the principle that *"the best module is the tested module"* and make the case for extending QA practices beyond utility projects to safeguard investments, system yields, and consumer confidence across all PV market segments in South Africa.
Keywords: Module Degradation, Quality Assurance, Testing

1 INTRODUCTION

The Photovoltaic (PV) module makes up a significant portion of the cost of a PV system or utility-scale PV plant. The quality of a PV module can critically impact the performance, reliability, and longevity of these installations. In recent years, dramatic cost reductions in PV module manufacturing have helped accelerate the energy transition to renewables by making solar power increasingly affordable. However, these price declines have also coincided with design and material changes that raise concerns about performance reliability and durability. For investors, insurers, engineers, and system owners, the question is no longer just how cheap solar can become, but how reliably it can deliver electricity across its expected 25-year lifetime.

International studies have shown that modules can fail prematurely due to a range of issues, including cracks, encapsulant delamination, backsheet chalking, glass breakage, and hotspot formation [1]. These defects reduce system yield and, in severe cases, can pose fire and safety hazards. Real-world installations expose modules to stress factors such as high irradiance, thermal cycling, humidity, dust, windy conditions, and varying installation practices. These external factors, together with manufacturing quality variations and bill of materials (BOM) decisions, mean that actual field performance can diverge significantly from manufacturer specifications.

South Africa provides a particularly important context for examining these risks. Since the launch of the Renewable Energy Independent Power Producer Procurement Programme (REIPPPP) in 2011 [2], the country has developed a large portfolio of utility-scale PV plants. More recently, commercial and industrial (C&I) systems and residential rooftop installations have grown rapidly, driven by persistent electricity shortages and load-shedding. As a result, PV modules are now deployed across diverse settings, from rigorously procured multi-megawatt projects to small rooftop systems purchased directly by consumers. This creates a fragmented landscape in which quality assurance practices vary widely between sectors.

Utility-scale projects in South Africa typically apply quality assurance (QA) frameworks during procurement and operation, including independent laboratory testing of modules before and after installation [3]. Many projects implement annual testing programmes to monitor degradation and ensure performance warranties are met. By contrast, C&I and residential markets are characterised by limited or no QA practices. Modules in these segments are often sourced through distributors and rebranding channels, with little verification of manufacturer claims. This raises the risk of underperformance and early failure, particularly in residential systems where system owners lack the technical expertise or contractual leverage to demand testing.

The rapid pace of technological innovation in the PV industry compounds these risks. Module designs are trending towards larger formats, glass-glass constructions, bifacial architectures, and higher-efficiency cell technologies such as PERC and TOPCon [4]. While these innovations can reduce levelised cost of electricity (LCOE) by improving efficiency and lowering balance-of-system costs, their long-term reliability remains unproven in the field [5]. For a market like South Africa, which combines challenging operating environments varying levels of quality assurance and regulatory complience across sectors, this creates uncertainty that may undermine investor confidence and system performance.

This paper addresses these challenges by presenting empirical evidence of PV module quality risks across South Africa's utility, C&I, and residential sectors. Drawing on more than a decade of accredited testing performed by PVinsight (Pty) Ltd and the Nelson Mandela University Photovoltaics Research Group, we analyse case studies that highlight sector-specific trends in module performance relative to nameplate values and warranty conditions. The findings show clear differences between sectors: while utility-scale modules subjected to QA testing consistently outperform manufacturer

10.4229/EUPVSEC2025/4CV.1.43

specifications, commercially sourced modules show mixed results, and residential systems exhibit significant underperformance and manufacturing defects.

2 METHODOLOGY

The study looks at specific PV module quality risks that are common in PV modules in South Africa. PV plants that have been operational since 2014 have the risk of early failures and lower than expected performance. New module technologies have improved efficiencies, but their long-term reliability remains untested. The Quality assurance process is only adopted in the Utility scale sector and PV modules entering the Residential and Commercial and Industrial (C&I) market are seldom tested. This study presents case studies on PV module quality's effect on performance in the Utility, C&I and Residential sectors. The results are compiled from test projects performed by PVinsight and the Nelson Mandela University PV research group.

3 RESULTS

PV module quality risks include micro-cracks, encapsulant delamination, backsheet chalking, glass breakages and Hotspots which result in burn marks. These can result in module failures or decreased module performance and lower return on investment.

3.1 Case Study – Utility Scale

As part of the QA procurement process many Utility-scale projects implemented an annual testing programme to ensure that module degradation is monitored. Every year, the same sample of modules are removed and tested at the laboratory. Results of these types of projects have shown that modules provided to Utility-scale projects are underspecified. The initial power can be up to 8 % higher than the nominal power. Figure 1 shows a histogram of PV module power deviation from specification measured for a sample of modules after 10 years in the field. After 10 years, most modules are still above nominal power, and all are above warranty power. This ensures that the performance warranty is met, but product defects can still occur.

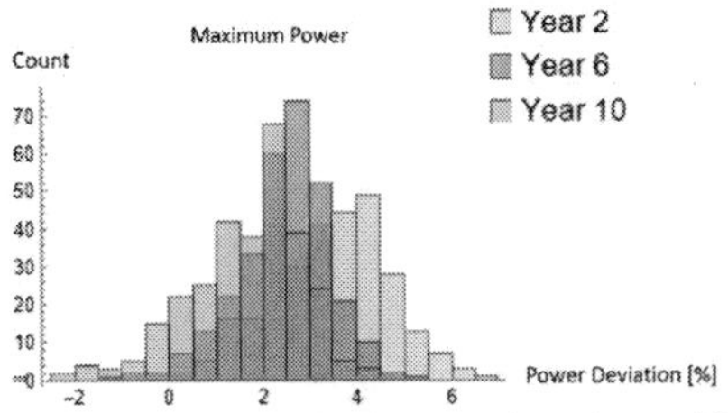

Figure 1: The Deviation of power from the specification of a sample of modules from a Utility-scale project.

3.2 Case Study – Commercial and Industrial Market

PVinsight lab purchased 15 commercially available modules from local electrical distributors in 2024 and 2025. The sample included modules from Canadian Solar, JA Solar and Trina Solar and a mix of mono-facial and bifacial modules of different sizes and technologies.

Figure 2 shows the deviation of power as % of specified power for the 15 modules. Also shown in the figure is the specified tolerance and the equipment measurement uncertainty. The results show that the initial power is lower than the nominal power for all modules, ranging from a deviation of -1.9 % to -2.7%. These results are acceptable based on measurement uncertainty of test equipment. Modules are new but equivalent to one-year outdoor exposure. This sample indicates that modules in the commercial market may be overspecified.

3.3 Case Study – Residential Market

PVinsight was approached by a residential PV system owner for testing of PV modules in an underperforming system. A sample of four modules were tested. These are modules that are rebranded in South Africa, and the modules have been installed for 22 months.

Figure 3 shows the deviation of power as % of specified power for the modules. The warranty value and the equipment measurement uncertainty are also shown in the figure. The results show that all modules have measured power below the expected value for the age, with measurement uncertainty accounted for. The deviation from specification ranged from -10% to -22% and the performance of the modules is below the expected or warranty power output for their age. Additional testing such as EL imaging, figure 4, indicted significant product manufacturing issues. The hail damage cannot be the sole cause of the power losses as the undamaged modules also have reduced power output.

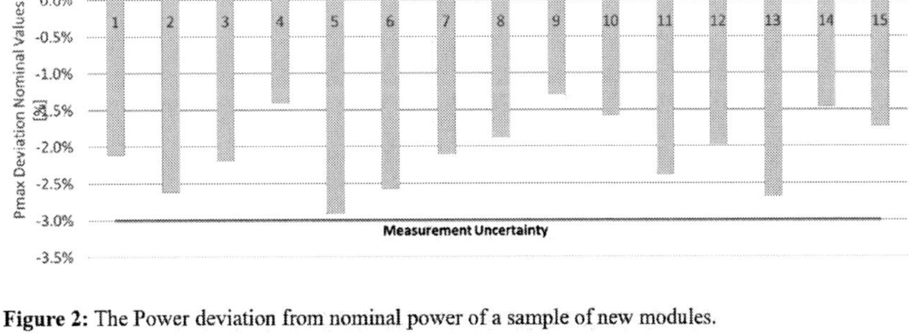

Figure 2: The Power deviation from nominal power of a sample of new modules.

10.4229/EUPVSEC2025/4CV.1.43

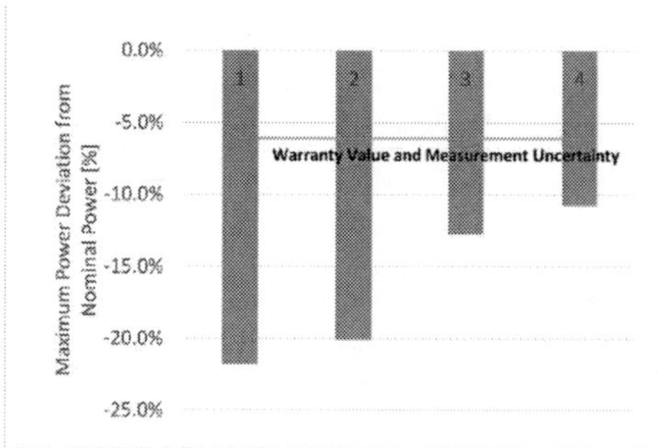

Figure 3: Power measurements indicated that the module's power was below the expected value based on the age accounting for measurement uncertainty [±3%].

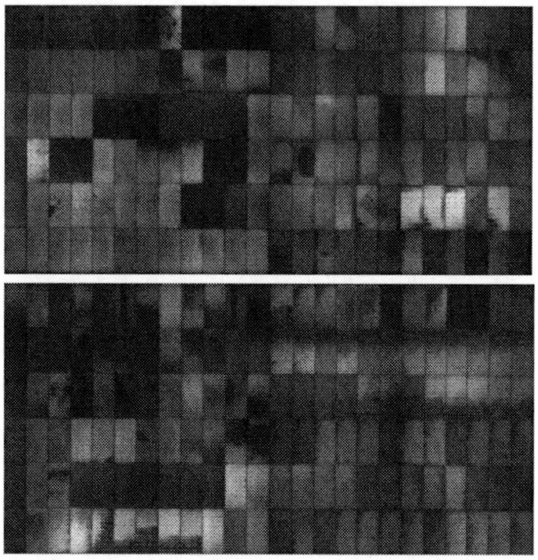

Figure 4: EL imaging of PV modules indicate critical cracks caused by a hail storm and product manufacturing concerns such as mismatched cells, solder abnormalities and accelerated degradation.

4 CONCLUSIONS

The rapid growth of the South African PV sector has created a dynamic but uneven quality landscape across utility, commercial and industrial, and residential markets. The case studies presented demonstrate that module quality and performance outcomes are strongly influenced by the presence or absence of quality assurance measures.

Utility-scale projects, which had implemented QA testing as part of procurement and operation, show robust performance: modules are often underspecified at installation and continue to deliver above warranty levels after more than a decade of operation. In contrast, commercially sourced modules in the C&I segment exhibited modest but consistent underperformance relative to nameplate values, remaining within measurement uncertainty but raising questions about the accuracy of manufacturer specifications. The residential case study revealed the highest risks, with rebranded modules showing severe early underperformance and evidence of manufacturing defects within just two years of operation.

These findings underscore three central insights. First, PV modules in South Africa are not uniformly reliable, and the risks of underperformance increase significantly in segments where QA practices are absent. Second, while underperformance in the C&I segment may appear minor, systematic deviation from specification erodes confidence in manufacturer claims and highlights the need for independent verification. Third, the failures observed in residential modules demonstrate the potential consequences of untested imports, including reduced energy yield, financial losses for system owners, and heightened safety risks.

Taken together, the evidence strongly supports the principle that "the best module is the tested module." Extending QA frameworks beyond the utility sector to include C&I and residential systems will be critical to sustaining investor confidence, protecting consumers, and ensuring that the rapid expansion of PV in South Africa delivers reliable, long-term value.

4 REFERENCES

[1] M. Aghaei et al., "Review of degradation and failure phenomena in photovoltaic modules," Renewable and Sustainable Energy Reviews, vol. 159, p. 112160, May 2022, doi: 10.1016/j.rser.2022.112160.

[2] A. Eberhard and R. Naude, "The South African Renewable Energy IPP Procurement Programme: Review, Lessons Learned & Proposals to Reduce Transaction Costs", Available Online: https://www.gsb.uct.ac.za/files/EberhardNaude_REIPPPPReview_2017_1_1.pdf, Accessed: 2025/09/01.

[3] VDE, "VDE SPEC 90038-2 V1.0 (en): Solar Module Quality Standard (SMQS) Part 2 – Measurements on PV Modules", VDE Association for Electrical, Electronic & Information Technologies, 2024.

[4] A. Metz, M. Fischer, and J. Trube, "International Technology Roadmap for Photovoltaics (ITRPV) 16th edition:," 2025.

[5] W. Gu, T. Ma, S. Ahmed, Y. Zhang, and J. Peng, "A comprehensive review and outlook of bifacial photovoltaic (bPV) technology," Energy Conversion and Management, vol. 223, p. 113283, Nov. 2020, doi: 10.1016/j.enconman.2020.113283.

ASSESSING PV MODULE QUALITY RISKS IN SOUTH AFRICA: PERFORMANCE INSIGHTS ACROSS UTILITY, COMMERCIAL AND INDUSTRIAL, AND RESIDENTIAL SECTORS

JL Crozier McCleland, M Vumbugwa, FJ Vorster, EE van Dyk | Nelson Mandela University, South Africa
NW Mngomezulu | PVinsight (Pty) Ltd, South Africa

NELSON MANDELA UNIVERSITY

Abstract

South Africa's Photovoltaic (PV) power generation installed capacity has increased exponentially in recent years. PV plants that have been operational since 2014, have a risk of early failures and lower than expected performance.
The study collects data and specific case studies of PV modules from operational PV systems in **South Africa** over the past decade to identify underperformance, common failures and quality risks[1].

South Africa PV Landscape

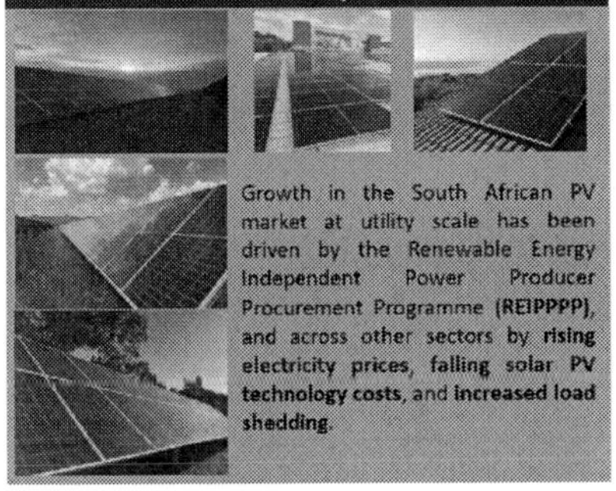

Growth in the South African PV market at utility scale has been driven by the Renewable Energy Independent Power Producer Procurement Programme **(REIPPPP)**, and across other sectors by **rising electricity prices, falling solar PV technology costs,** and **increased load shedding.**

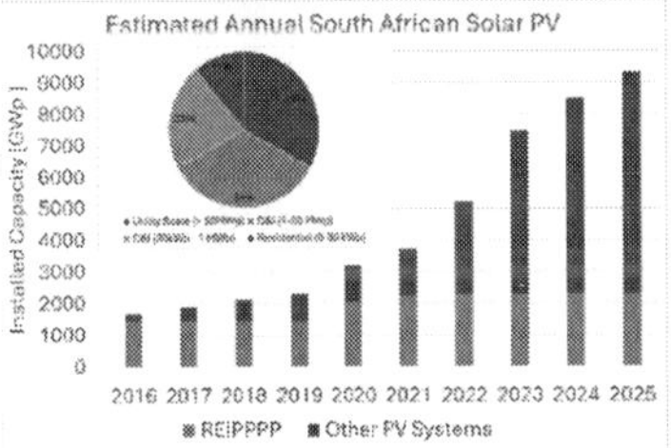

Figure 1: Estimated Installed capacity of Solar PV in South Africa. Source: CRSES- Stellenbosch University; Eskom, SAPVIA[2]

PV Module Quality Testing

POWER MEASUREMENTS

Output maximum power of the PV modules at standard test conditions (STC), using an A+A+A+ LED solar simulator.

ELECTROLUMINESCENCE

Electroluminescence (EL) imaging of photovoltaic modules to identify cracks, disconnected busbars, shunting and other cell defects.

VISUAL INSPECTION

Visual inspection is used to detect quality issues. The front and back sheet, frame and external circuitry of the modules are inspected for a set of known defects.

Overview of PV Module Quality Testing in South Africa

The PV Testing Laboratory was established by the PV Research group in the Nelson Mandela University Physics Department in 2014. PVinsight was established as a spinout company in 2017.

PVinsight

11 years In Operation

> 7.5 GW Tested

> 70 000 Tests conducted

Case Study: Utility-Scale Projects

A few Utility-scale projects in South Africa implemented an annual testing programme to ensure that annual module degradation was monitored.
Every year, the same sample of modules are removed and tested at the lab.
Results indicate that the modules tested are **underspecified** and the initial power is higher than the nominal power.
After 10 years, the majority of modules are still above nominal power, and all are above warranty Power.

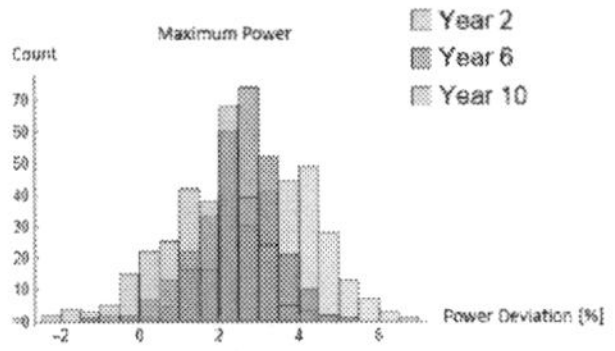

Figure 2: The Deviation of power from the specification of a sample of modules from a Utility-scale project.

Case Study: Commercial & Industrial (C&I) and Small-scale Embedded Generation

PVinsight lab purchased 15 commercially available modules from local electrical distributors in 2024 and 2025. The sample included modules from Canadian Solar, JA Solar and Trina Solar and a mix of mono-facial and bifacial modules of different sizes and technologies.
The results show that the initial measured power is lower than the nominal power for all modules, ranging from a deviation of **-1.3 % to -2.7%.**

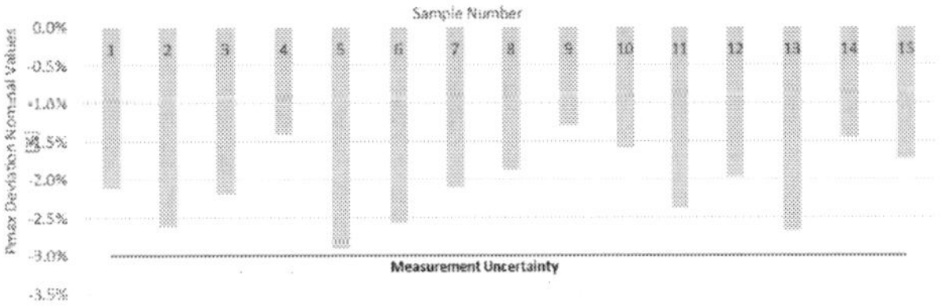

Figure 3: The Power deviation from nominal power of a sample of new modules.

Case Study: Residential Rooftop

PVinsight was approached by a residential PV system owner for testing of PV modules in an underperforming system. A sample of four modules were tested. These are rebranded modules, available in South Africa, and the modules have been installed for 22 months.

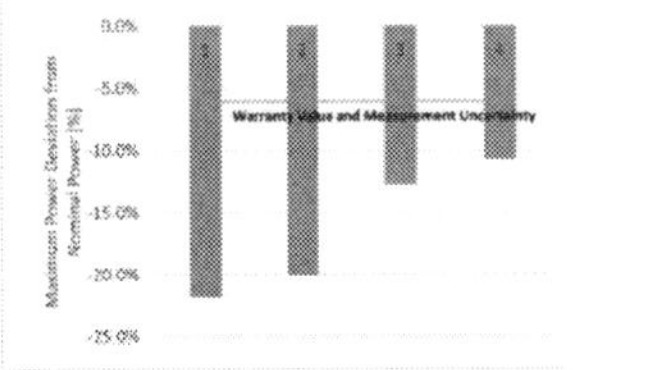

Figure 4: Power measurements indicated that the module's power was below the expected value based on the age accounting for measurement uncertainty [±3%].

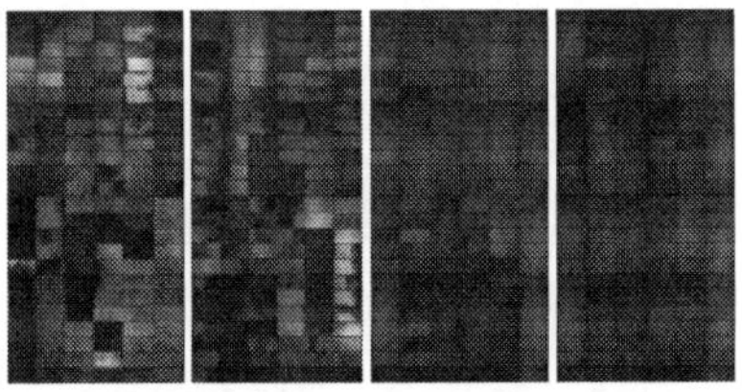

Figure 5: EL imaging of PV modules indicate critical cracks caused by a hail storm and product manufacturing concerns such as mismatched cells, solder abnormalities and accelerated degradation.

Conclusions

- Fast growth in the South African PV sector requires the support of a Quality Assurance Programme to ensure performance and reliability.
- The three case studies briefly discussed highlight the importance of PV module quality verification to ensure that the modules are performing at a warranted level.

References

1. M. Aghaei et al., "Review of degradation and failure phenomena in photovoltaic modules," Renewable and Sustainable Energy Reviews, vol. 159, p. 112160, May 2022, doi: 10.1016/j.rser.2022.112160.
2. Visualisation of South African Electricity Data, The Centre for Renewable and Sustainable Energy Studies (CRSES) – Stellenbosch University, https://www.crses.sun.ac.za/sa-energy-stats/, Accessed: 2025/09/01 .

Acknowledgements
The authors would like to thank the Nelson Mandela PV Research Group and PVinsight (Pty) Ltd for their financial support and input into the study.

Please connect with us using this QR code. We would love to have your feedback.

CAN REGULAR STRING IV MEASUREMENTS COMPLEMENT MPP MONITORING DATA?

Martin Bartholomäus, Fernando Román Vecino, Peter B. Poulsen, Mahmoud Dhimish, Sergiu V. Spataru
Technical University of Denmark, Department of Electrical and Photonics Engineering, Roskilde, 4000, Denmark
mabart@dtu.dk, s233168@student.dtu.dk, ppou@dtu.dk, mahdh@dtu.dk, sersp@dtu.dk

ABSTRACT: Existing operation and maintenance strategies for PV farms rely on maximum power point (M_{PP}) monitoring data. Meanwhile, current-voltage (IV) curve measurements deliver additional diagnostic information about the state of health of the PV system and inverter based IV scanning enables recording large data at minimal labor and monetary cost. In this work, we investigate the additional value of string IV-curve measurements complementing M_{PP} monitoring to enhance the accuracy for fault detection strategies. We record M_{PP} data along with frequent IV scans from PV strings in Denmark with and without faults such as PID, cell cracks, ribbon damage and bypass diode failures. Observing the IV scan function of a string inverter with high-frequency measurement equipment, we observed an initial sharp power drop, followed by a period of open circuit operation, sequential IV sweeps on each MPPT and slow ramping back to normal operation. The entire IV scan event lasts about 23 seconds for a 4-MPPT inverter. An energy loss estimation shows a maximum 0.087% energy loss per year for daily IV scans. Comparing fault detection accuracy of IV versus M_{PP} monitoring-based features, the IV showed superior accuracy of 96% compared to 82%. Minimal data requirement analysis showed that even at minimal data set size, the accuracy did not fall below 91%, which is still significantly better than the M_{PP} based fault detection. The findings suggest that regular inverter based IV scans can enhance current O&M strategies for improved fault detection at very little energy loss.

Keywords: IV, fault detection, inverter, photovoltaic, monitoring

1 INTRODUCTION

Existing operation and maintenance (O&M) strategies for PV systems mostly rely on maximum power point monitoring data [1, 2]. Specific action is taken in case the monitoring data is found suspicious, an alert is raised, and an O&M ticket is issued. M_{PP} data can be monitored without power loss at high time resolution, allowing for analysis of fault events over time. However, inverter-based current-voltage (IV) curves can provide diagnostic information at low cost, which may assist with and complement existing O&M strategies to reduce the need for labor-intensive field measurements such as electroluminescence or infrared imaging. Currently, inverter-based IV are rarely used because of concerns about power down time, missing evidence of usefulness, and guidelines on how to utilize them best. In the literature, M_{PP}-based methods are well established. For example, Filho et al. developed an automated fault detection system based on analytical data [3]. Jones et al. showed that inclusion of IV data in addition to M_{PP} monitoring data can improve the classification accuracy of fault detection from 90% to 98% percent, considering weak solder bonds, shade and soiling as fault classes [4]. In previous work, we have shown that the V_{mp}/V_{oc} ratio and series resistance are sensitive to shade and that the shunt resistance is sensitive to PID and may therefore be used as diagnostic markers for fault detection [5]. However, most studies focus on either M_{PP} or IV data for fault classification and rarely assess the combination of M_{PP} and IV monitoring data.

In this work, we assess how string IV scans can be utilized to complement M_{PP} monitoring. First, we measure M_{PP} monitoring data as well as regular IV scans from PV strings with known faults. We employ IV-based fault detection strategies and compare the accuracy to M_{PP}-based methods. Additionally, we monitor central inverter-based IV scans with high frequency measurement equipment and use the results to conduct an energy loss estimation. This allows to formulate recommendations to improve current O&M strategies.

2 METHODS

2.1 String IV tracing and M_{PP} monitoring at DTU

In the first stage, we utilized a fault detection test setup at DTU Risø consisting of four PV strings, with 22 305Wp monofacial modules of type Trina TSM-305DD05A.08 each. The test setup consists of healthy strings and strings that were modified to include faulty modules. Figure 1 shows a single line diagram of the strings. The outdoor strings are monitored with a Huawei KTL 185 inverter, measuring M_{PP} data every minute. The inverter also performed regular IV scans every half hour during daytime. Additionally, plane-of-array irradiance and backside module temperature conditions are measured every minute.

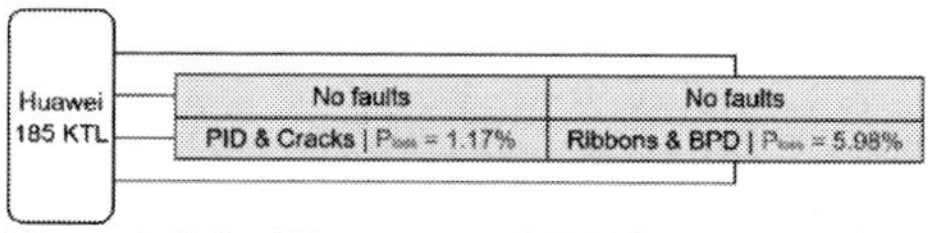

Figure 1: String IV test setup at DTU Risø campus, where an inverter measures M_{PP} monitoring data and IV curves of each PV string separately. The 22 module strings use identical PV modules, but two strings contain planted faults. Adapted from [5].

The test setup and the introduction of faults is described in detail in previous work [5], where we characterize the artificial faults and describe the methods used to introduce them into the PV module strings. In short, two strings contain no faults, one string contains modules with PID and cell cracks (about 1.2% power loss) , and one string contains modules with ribbon damage and short-circuited bypass diodes (BPD, about 6% power loss).

Figure 2: Measurement setup for high-frequency sampling of inverter-based IV scan events. Central IV scans were triggered at the Huawei inverter. A Keithley oscilloscope with two voltage probes (one used for reference measurements) and one current probe was used for DC side measurements (~100Hz). A Gantner measurement box reports AC power (1Hz). The inverter also reported its IV curve measurement and monitoring data (1/min).

2.2 Fault detection approach

This setup is used to compare fault detection methods based on M_{PP} data against IV data. We recorded 3 months of data recorded between May 12, 2025 and August 12, 2025. Light filtering was applied to remove failed measurements and physically impossible data. The final IV curve data set includes 10,320 observations, with 5,689 data points for the healthy strings, 2,670 for PID & cracks and 1,961 for ribbon damage and BPD. Due to the higher sampling frequency, the M_{PP} data set is about 30 times larger at 309,325 observations, 155,729 for the healthy strings, 81,680 for PID & cracks and 71,916 for ribbon damage and BPD. Next, we derived 18 features from the IV data, which are the features discussed in [6]. Five features were extracted from the M_{PP} data, namely I_{MPP}, V_{MPP}, G_{POA}, T_{MOD} and the maximum power point factor M_{PPF}. An XGBoost machine learning classifier [7] was trained on these features and then used to classify the faults. For this purpose, we split the data sets, using 80% for training and 20% for testing. The XGBoost classifier trains a decision tree model with 200 trees each limited to a maximum depth of 5, using a learning rate of 0.1, a random state of 42 for reproducibility and optimizes based on the log-loss score. We compared the resulting accuracy in detecting the faults in the PV strings for each data set. Additionally, minimal data requirements for classification were assessed by reducing the size of the test data set to a minimum of 1.

2.4 Current, voltage and power observations during an inverter-based IV measurement event

Many commercial PV inverters offer IV sweep functions, at which all connected strings are measured in one IV sweep event, triggered centrally at the inverter. To observe this process, high resolution current, power and voltage sensing was done during an inverter-based IV measurement event on a Huawei 40KTL inverter featuring four maximum power point tracker (MPPT) with two PV string inputs each (see Figure 2). Five strings were connected, PV1 on MPPT1, PV3 on MPPT2, PV5 on MPPT3 and PV7 and PV8 on MPPT4. A 4-channel Keithley oscilloscope was utilized to monitor the output of one current probe and two Pico Technology voltage probes, which were connected to the PV strings on the DC side of the inverter and record data samples at ~100 Hz. We kept one voltage probe as a reference to measure the voltage of PV1, later used to align the different measurement events. The other voltage and current probe were used to measure the PV strings sequentially. For this purpose, a new IV scan was triggered at the inverter for each measurement on a PV string before the probes were moved to the next string.

Measurements were repeated at least once per string to check repeatability and to ensure redundancy in case of measurement failure or unwanted irradiance ramping events. The reference voltage measurement was used to align measurements at the minimum voltage point of the reference measurement, which is a unique and distinct point during PV1's IV trace. Parallel to the oscilloscope measurements, AC side active power was recorded with a Gantner AC measurement box at 1Hz. Lastly, the inverter also reports regular M_{PP} current and voltage monitoring data at 1 data point per minute as well as the IV traces, which contain 64 I-V points per IV curve.

The measurements enable an analysis of the energy loss caused by inverter-based IV scans in PV farms. We integrate the lost power compared to normal operation and extrapolate the results to large-scale PV farm operation using yearly PV performance data from PVGIS. The measurements also allow to assess power output ramps and fluctuations occurring during large scale PV string IV traces, which could cause negative impact on the stability of the power grid.

10.4229/EUPVSEC2025/4CV.1.44

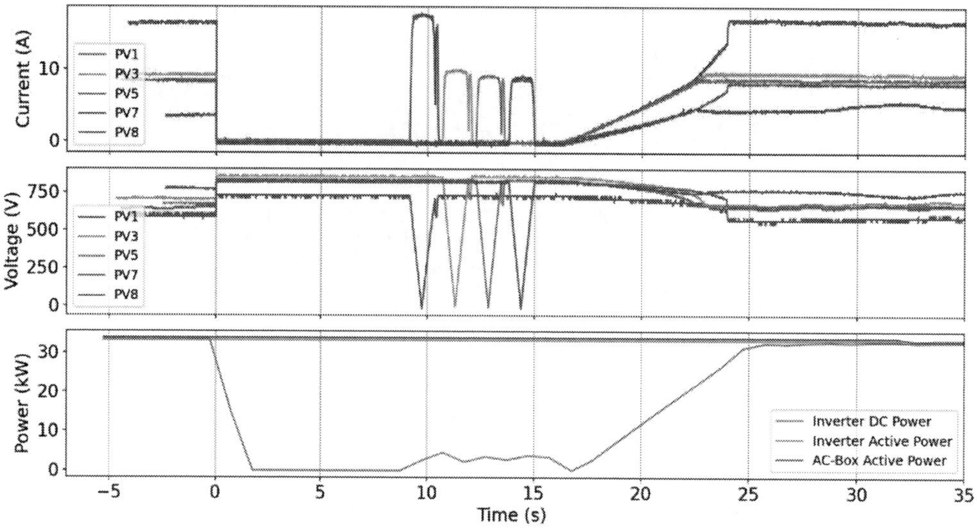

Figure 3: Oscilloscope measurements showing current, voltage and power measurements over time. PV1 to PV8 denote one PV string each. When an IV sweep is triggered, the inverter first switches all strings to open circuit, then measures each MPPT in sequential order (PV7 and PV8 are on the same MPPT input), after which the current/power is slowly ramped back to normal operation. The entire process lasts about 23 seconds. In the inverter monitoring data, the power is shown at a constant output which does not reflect the reality of the IV sweeps. AC-measurement box data sampled at 1 second reveals reduced power output on the AC side during the IV scan.

3 RESULTS AND CONCLUSIONS

3.1 Oscilloscope measurements

The experiments (Figure 3) reveal that when a central IV scan is triggered, the inverter first switches all strings to open circuit, then measures each MPPT in sequential order (PV7 and PV8 are on the same MPPT input), after which the current/power is slowly ramped back to normal operation. The entire IV scanning event lasts about 23 seconds. In the inverter monitoring data, power is shown at a constant output which does not reflect the reality of the IV sweeps. AC-measurement box data sampled at 1 second reveals reduced power output on the AC side during the IV scan.

Ramp rates are steep when the inverter first switches to open circuit, resulting in a complete power loss withing 0.1 second. The IV sweeps themselves also show fast power ramping from zero to maximum within 0.6 seconds, but only on a portion of the connected strings (1/4 for this inverter). After the IV sweeps, ramping is much slower and gradual than at the beginning, lasting about 7-10 seconds.

The total duration of an IV scan event may be greater for string inverters with more MPPTs but only by about 1.2 seconds per additional MPPT.

3.2 Energy loss analysis

An energy loss analysis was carried out based on the oscilloscope-based IV sweep observations described above. We found that an IV scan event triggered centrally at the string inverter took around 23 seconds to complete, during which time the power output was greatly reduced. For simplicity, in the following energy loss analysis, we assume zero power output for the entire 23 second IV scan. Utilizing a one-year hourly dataset from PVGIS [8] for a fixed tilt 25-degree 1MWp PV installation located in Risø, Denmark, we investigated the energy loss by reducing the output energy by 23/3600 in each hour in which an IV sweep was performed. Two scenarios were considered; First, daily IV scans at solar noon, representing a worst-case scenario, in which energy loss should be greatest. The energy loss was calculated to be 0.087% of yearly energy output for this case. Second, we consider a scenario in which IV sweeps are performed daily in the morning as soon as irradiance reaches 100W/m2, which represents the best-case scenario in terms of energy loss and amounted to 0.03% lost energy. If other IV measurement frequencies are assumed, the energy loss can approximately be linearly scaled up or down. For example, weekly IV scans should only amount to about one seventh of the energy loss, monthly IV scans to one thirtieth, etc.

While some inspection methods require no interruption of normal operation (such as infrared imaging, night-time electroluminescence or photoluminescence), others disrupt normal operation for longer periods at a time, for example manual IV tracing or daylight EL. Given the above analysis, inverter-based IV measurements therefore rank in the midfield of PV inspection methods at a non-zero but very low energy loss. Further on, we show that accurate fault detection from IV measurements does not necessarily require large test data sets, likely allowing lower testing frequency than daily.

3.3 IV-based versus M_{PP}-based fault detection accuracy

The fault detection accuracy (Figure 4) using IV/ M_{PP} features and an XGBoost classifier is greater for the full IV features, registering at 96%. If only M_{PP}-related features derived from the IV curves are used, accuracy drops to 66%. Using the same M_{PP} features on the M_{PP} monitoring dataset increases the accuracy to 82% due to the greater amount of data originating from the higher sampling frequency of the MPP monitoring. The results underline that inverter-based IV curve tracing can be useful for more advanced fault detection in PV strings.

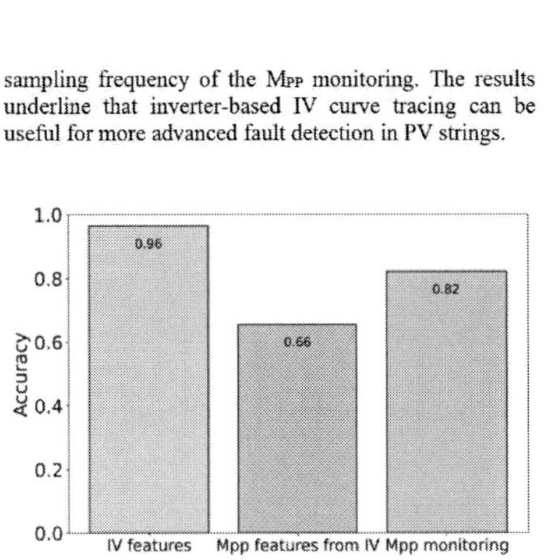

Figure 4: Fault detection accuracy of an XGBoost model classifying healthy PV strings versus PID & cell cracks versus ribbon damage & short-circuited bypass diodes. The highest accuracy of 96% was achieved using features derived from the inverter-based IV curves. Using MPP-only features from these IV curves yielded an accuracy of 66%. Using higher-frequency MPP monitoring data yielded an improved accuracy of 82%, still lower than from IV curve measurements.

An investigation of the minimal data requirement for IV-derived fault detection (Figure 5) showed that at very low test data numbers, the accuracy score oscillates. In the present case, the maximum deviation is around 5% from the stable level (91% instead of 96% accuracy). However, in all cases, even at a small data set, the accuracy is better than the MPP-based method which has the benefit of much higher sample size. Other testing scores including precision, recall and f1-score behave similarly. The results show that as fault detection is usually non-perfect, a few IV scans should be taken to improve the validity of the results and robustness against misclassification due to outliers.

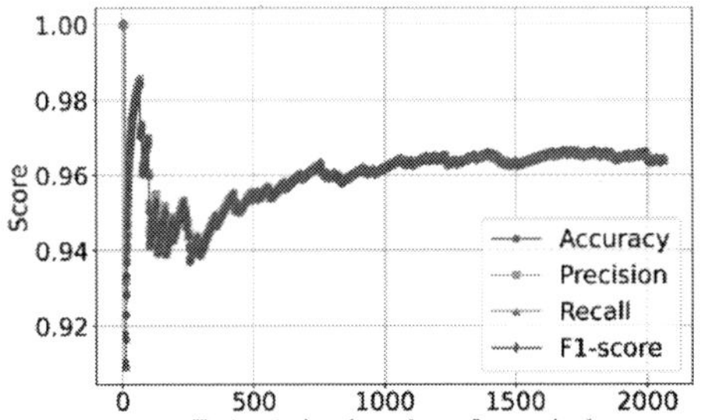

Figure 5: Observing model accuracy as a function of test data set size. We decreased the size from 2000 to 1 and calculated the model accuracy for each size. At lower test data set sizes, the accuracy starts oscillating around the true value of ~96%. Deviations do not exceed 5%.

4 CONCLUSIONS

Closely observing a centrally triggered IV scan event on a string inverter showed a sudden power loss when the inverter switches all strings to open circuit, followed by sequential IV curve tracing of all MPPT channels. Same-MPPT strings are measured simultaneously. After the IV traces, the inverter slowly ramps up the produced power. The energy loss connected to IV scans was shown to be in the order of less than 0.1% energy loss considering daily IV measurements. On the other hand, IV-based fault detection showed to be much more accurate than MPP-based fault detection, even at a lower sampling rate. A minimal data requirement investigation showed that the accuracy oscillates at low sampling, but always performs better than MPP-based methods.

Based on these findings, implementing regular IV traces into existing O&M strategies seems beneficial to PV operators, as inverter-based IV scans require no additional hardware, lead to minimal power loss and greatly enhance fault detection accuracies compared to MPP-based methods.

5 ACKNOWLEDGEMENTS

This project has received funding from the European Union under grant agreement no. 101146377 as part of the SOLARIS project – Solar Operational Lifecycle and Asset Reliability Intelligence System.

6 REFERENCES

[1] U. Jahn, B. Herteleer, C. Tjengdrawira, I. Tsanakas, and M. Richter, "Guidelines for Operation and Maintenance of Photovoltaic Power Plants in Different Climates 2022," International Energy Agency, IEA-PVPS-Report-T13, 2022.

[2] Rob Andrews *et al.*, "Operation & Maintenance Best Practice Guidelines/Version 4.0." 2019.

[3] E. A. S. Filho, K. Kiefer, N. Holland, B. Kollosch, B. Müller, and P. J. C. Branco, "Analysis of automatic fault detection methods for commercially operated PV power plants".

[4] C. B. Jones, M. Theristis, J. S. Stein, and C. Hansen, "Feature Selection of Photovoltaic System Data to Avoid Misclassification of Fault Conditions," in *2020 47th IEEE Photovoltaic Specialists Conference (PVSC)*, Calgary, AB, Canada: IEEE, June 2020, pp. 1357–1362. doi: 10.1109/PVSC45281.2020.9300786.

[5] M. Bartholomäus, P. B. Poulsen, and S. V. Spataru, "Comparative analysis of string IV measurement methods for fault detection in photovoltaic systems," presented at the 41st European Photovoltaic Solar Energy Conference and Exhibition, 2024, p. 6. doi: 10.4229/EUPVSEC2024/4BV.3.18.

[6] M. Bartholomäus, P. B. Poulsen, M. Dhimish, and S. V. Spataru, "Evaluating IV curve derived features for fault detection," presented at the 2025 IEEE 52nd Photovoltaic Specialists Conference (PVSC), Montreal: IEEE, June 2025. doi: 10.1109/PVSC59419.2025.11132910.

[7] T. Chen and C. Guestrin, "XGBoost: A Scalable Tree Boosting System," in *Proceedings of the 22nd ACM SIGKDD International Conference on Knowledge Discovery and Data Mining*, San Francisco California USA: ACM, Aug. 2016, pp. 785–794. doi: 10.1145/2939672.2939785.

[8] T. Huld, R. Müller, and A. Gambardella, "A new solar radiation database for estimating PV performance in Europe and Africa," *Solar Energy*, vol. 86, no. 6, pp. 1803–1815, June 2012, doi: 10.1016/j.solener.2012.03.006.

Bernhard Kubicek[1], Marcus Rennhofer[1], Thomas Hutterer-Tik[2], Christian Ottl[2]
1: AIT Austrian Institute of Technology GmbH, Center for Energy bernhard.kubicek@ait.ac.at
2: Watt Analytics GmbH, Austria

AUSTRIAN INSTITUTE OF TECHNOLOGY
TOMORROW TODAY

AGGREGATION ERRORS BASED ON PV PRODUCTION DATA IN THE TIMESCALE OF SECONDS

Motivation

In PV system monitoring, typical logging intervals are in the range of 5 to 15 minutes. The question rises, how much information is lost by not logging at higher speeds. Using PV production data logged at sub-second sample rates, the variability is investigated over short time scales.

Sub-Second production data

During the data acquisition of PV monitoring data, mainly two strategies can be applied to aggregate time series to reasonable data size: time averaging, or single-sampling. Inverters e.g. typically perform averaging in the reporting of powers, while quantities such as currents or voltages are taken as the most current individual measurement. Hence, e.g. reported power does not equal voltage times current, as expected. However, for affordable weather stations, time averaging is seldomly performed.

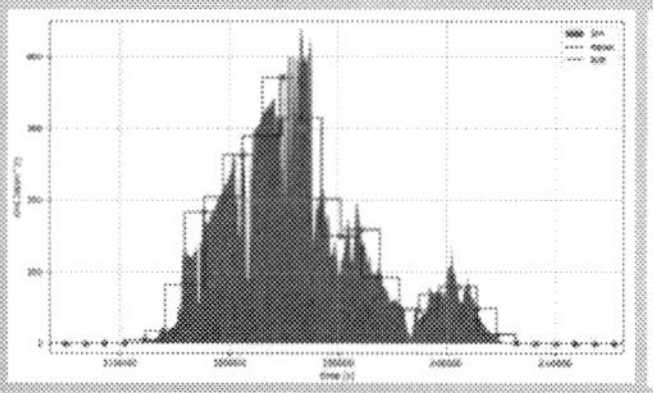

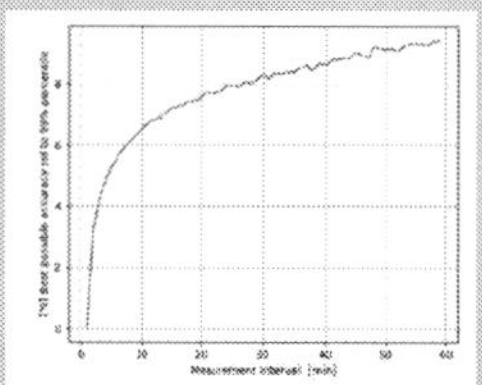

This leads to a basic error due to the deviation of time averaged power compared to single shot irradiation, that can be used to define how big of a principal error happens on which time scale [1].

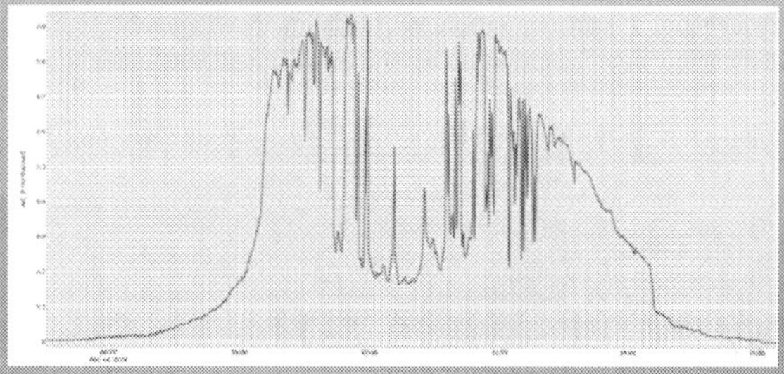

Using sub-second resolved power measurements of smart meter data of Watt Analytics, a new time regime can be looked at:

- How do clouds change irradiance at seconds timescales
- How much does the inverters' MPP tracking and grid stabilization change that?

To remove inverter effects, the data was resampled to 10 second intervals, as many inverter effects should be in the regime of a few 50Hz intervals.

[1] B.Kubicek, M. Steinbrecher, M. Rennhofer, „ERROR SOURCES IN PV PROGNOSIS", EU-PVSEC 2023.
This content was created within the „Fledged" Austrian national project.

Wavelet Analysis

To evaluate the intensity of changes in given frequency regimes, wavelet analysis is of better use than short time Fourier analysis: the timescale is adopted to the investigated frequency. The spectrograms thereby are more diffuse in time at lower frequencies.

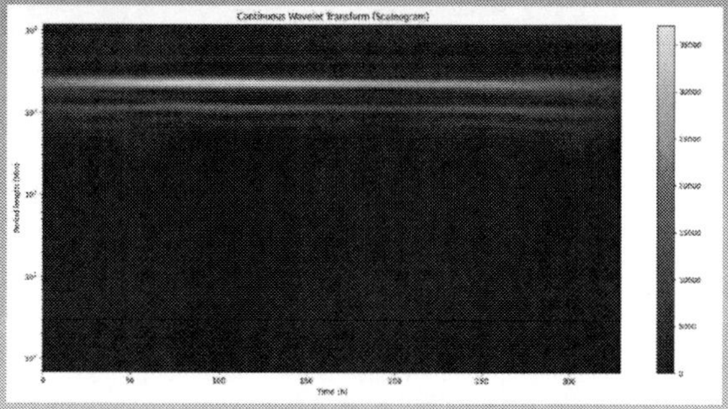

Above: The linear intensity scales shows a peak at a periodicity of 24h. Below: the log-color scale exhibits finer details during the day.

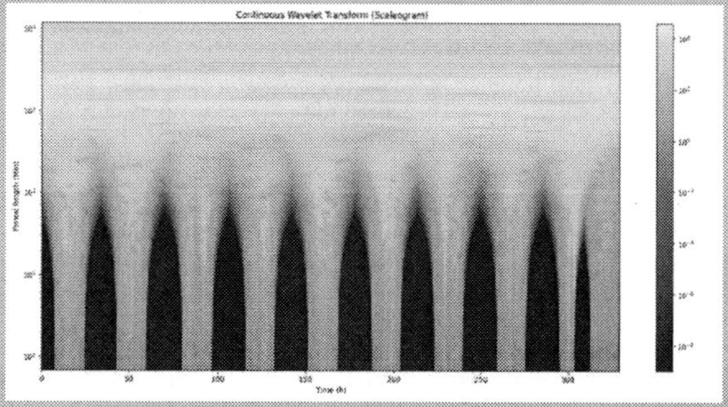

By integrating the intensity over time, a log-log plot of how the intensity changes by period length/frequency:

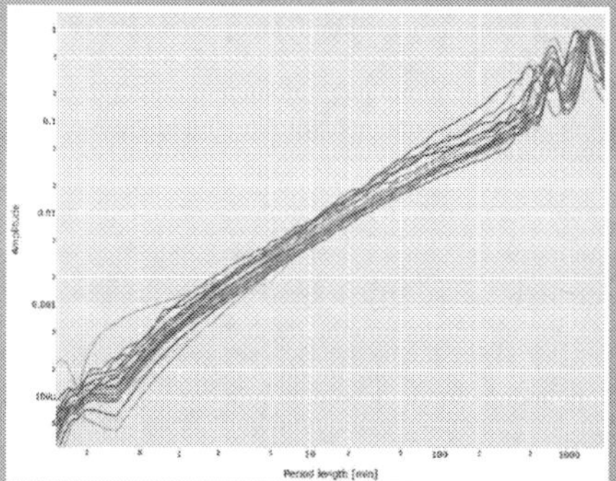

Conclusion

A 10-minute logging interval captures changes to typically 0.5% of the peak amplitude, a 5-minute interval halves that. To only ignore frequencies that contribute below 0.1 % of the peak amplitude, a 1-minute logging interval is recommended. Hower, to also decrease one-shot vs. averaging errors [1], a one-minute interval can be recommended.

IN-FIELD ASSESSMENT OF SOILING EFFECTS ON A FLOATING PHOTOVOLTAIC SYSTEM IN A HUMID SUBTROPICAL URBAN AREA

Renzo Vargas, Givaldo dos Reis, Rodrigo P. Maruyama, Alex Manito, Marcelo Pinho Almeida, Roberto Zilles
Institute of Energy and Environment, University of São Paulo

Corresponding author – Renzo Vargas, e-mail: renzovargas@usp.br

ABSTRACT: Floating photovoltaic (FPV) systems provide an alternative to land-based PV by deploying modules on reservoirs and other water bodies, using underutilized surfaces and benefiting from water-mediated passive cooling that mitigates heat-related efficiency losses. Nevertheless, important knowledge gaps remain, particularly at utility scale. In this study, we analyze soiling at a 7 MWp FPV plant (10,500 modules rated at 665W) operating in a humid subtropical urban environment. We quantify how cleaning frequency affects module-level plane-of-array (POA) irradiation and assess the feasibility of using reservoir water for cleaning. Modules cleaned monthly recorded up to 6.27% higher POA irradiation than those cleaned less frequently.
Keywords: Floating Photovoltaics; Soiling Losses; Utility-Scale Photovoltaics; Cleaning Frequency; Plane-of-Array Irradiation

1 INTRODUCTION

Soiling in photovoltaic (PV) systems refers to the accumulation of dust, dirt, organic material, bird droppings, and other particulates on the surface of solar modules. This layer attenuates the incident sunlight reaching the PV cells, thereby lowering the system's overall energy output and potentially accelerating module degradation.

In floating photovoltaic (FPV) systems installed on bodies of water—such as reservoirs, lakes, or offshore sites—soiling behavior can differ from that of land-based arrays. Although the water surface cools modules and may slightly reduce dust deposition [1]–[6], FPV installations remain vulnerable to airborne particulates, bird droppings, and, in some climates, biofouling or splash-borne mineral and algal residues. Several studies report that average soiling rates can be lower over water; nevertheless, the performance impact—especially in arid, dusty regions or near agricultural activity—can still be substantial [7], [8]. Moreover, evidence from utility-scale FPV systems remains limited.

Soiling losses often manifest as a reduction in the short-circuit current due to decreased transmissivity of the module glass, though the extent varies by dust composition and climate [9]. Additionally, tilt angles notably influence soiling rates; low-tilt or horizontal FPV configurations may trap more dust due to reduced rain wash-off and lower self-cleaning [10].

This study evaluates how soiling accumulation affects the performance of a utility-scale FPV plant located in an urban, humid subtropical environment. For achieving this evaluation, we compare module-level plane-of-array (POA) irradiation across modules subjected to distinct cleaning intervals and different cleaning-water sources.

1.1 Organization of the paper

This paper is structured as follows: Section 2 presents the material and methods employed for the soiling assessment of the FPV power plant; Section 3 presents the obtained results for different cleaning schedules and type of water; and Section 4 presents the conclusions of the work.

2 MATERIAL AND METHODS

2.1 Floating photovoltaic system

The study site is a 7.5-hectare floating photovoltaic (FPV) plant installed on a reservoir in a humid subtropical urban setting. The array employs monocrystalline-silicon PV modules, all north-facing and mounted at a 12° tilt. It is configured as a relatively open platform, with buoyancy provided by polyethylene pontoons and access walkways between each row to facilitate operation and maintenance. The FPV system is grid-connected.

2.2 Equipment and cleaning schedule

Six modules are selected and calibrated according to IEC 60904-2:2023–Item 14. After installation, dataloggers are deployed to monitor the modules short-circuit currents to record the irradiation data throughout the study period. Figure 1 illustrates the modules used in the experiment. Figure 2 depicts the datalogger connections.

Figure 1: Six modules used in the experiment

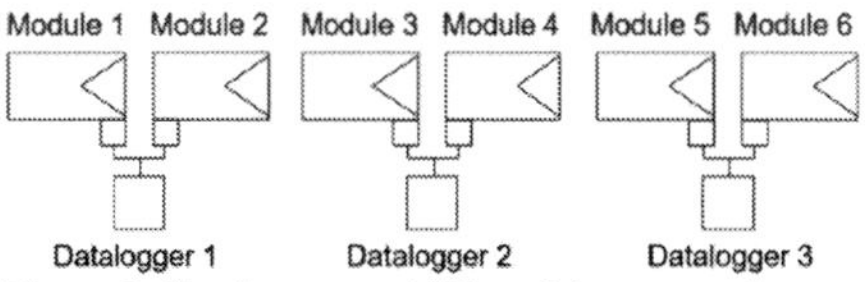

Figure 2: Dataloggers and PV modules connections

Table I summarizes the cleaning schedule and water properties used to clean the photovoltaic modules.

10.4229/EUPVSEC2025/4CV.1.48

Table I: Cleaning schedule and type of water

Item	Cleaning schedule	Type of water
Module 1	Every month	Clean water
Module 2	Every month	Reservoir water
Module 3	Every three months	Clean water
Module 4	Every three months	Reservoir water
Module 5	Every six months	Clean water
Module 6	No cleaning	Clean water

As shown in Table I, modules 1 and 2 are cleaned monthly with clean water and reservoir water, respectively, while modules 3 and 4 follow the same procedure every three months. Module 5 is cleaned every six months using clean water, while module 6 remains uncleaned throughout the study. These intervals are selected to assess both the impact of cleaning frequency on performance and the overall necessity of cleaning. Additionally, the choice of the water source for cleaning is crucial: while using clean water entails transport costs, reservoir water faces issues regarding its suitability and potential effects on module performance warrant careful evaluation.

For the manual cleaning process, the following equipment is used: 1) a mop, 2) a water container and, 3) a water pump. Figure 3 shows these items. Figure 4 presents the manual cleaning procedure.

Figure 3: Cleaning equipment

Figure 4: Manual cleaning procedure

Each clean-water module requires approximately six liters of water per cleaning. When using reservoir water, one end of the water pump is immersed in the reservoir while the other end directs the flow onto the module surfaces.

3 RESULTS

3.1 Soiling in the floating photovoltaic system

We documented several soiling modes on the FPV array; representative examples are shown in Figures 5 – 8.

Figure 5: Particulate deposition

Figure 6: Bird droppings

Figure 7: Residue from avian foraging

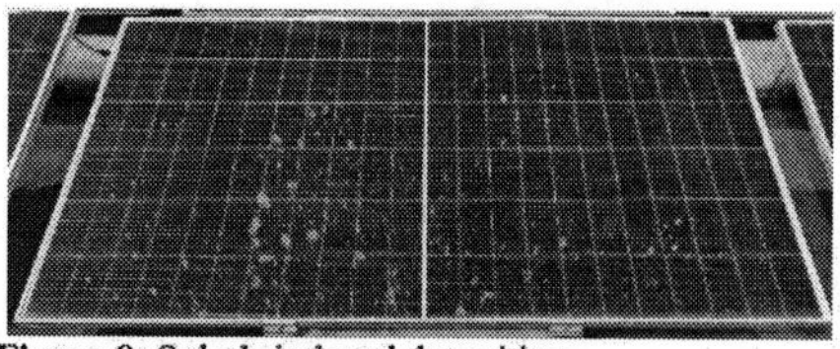

Figure 8: Splash-induced deposition

Figure 5 presents soiling due to particulate deposition; Figure 6 shows bird droppings; Figure 7 presents residue from avian foraging (organic matter after feeding); and Figure 8 depicts splash-induced deposition from the surrounding water body, characterized by algae. These categories capture the dominant mechanisms observed on site and frame the subsequent analysis.

3.2 Initial assessment of soiling based on the first two months of analysis

This subsection offers an early look at soiling using data from the study's first two months. For each month, the module with the highest monthly irradiation was used as the reference and normalized to 100%. Figure 9 shows each module's monthly irradiation as a percentage of this reference.

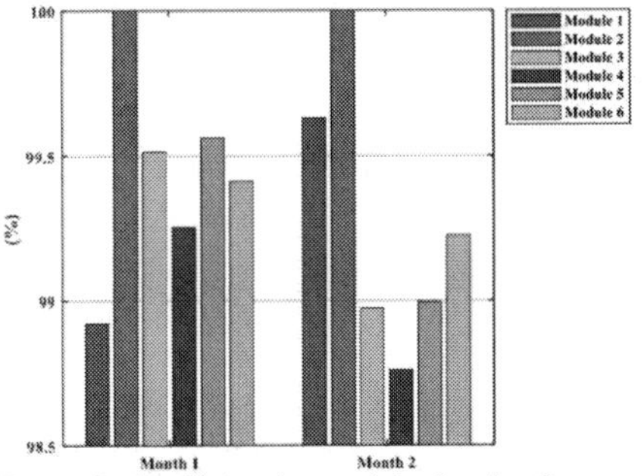

Figure 9: Irradiation by module for the first two months (% of reference module)

Across both months, module 2 achieved the highest irradiation and therefore defines the 100% reference in Figure 9. The corresponding numerical values are reported in Table II.

Table II: Assessment of soiling based on months 1 and 2

Item	Month 1	Month 2
Module 1	98.92 %	99.63 %
Module 2	100.00 %	100.00 %
Module 3	99.51 %	98.97 %
Module 4	99.25 %	98.76 %
Module 5	99.56 %	99.00 %
Module 6	99.41 %	99.23 %

In Table II, after the first month, inter-module differences were minimal. By the end of the second month, modules cleaned monthly produced up to 1.24% and 1.01% higher irradiation than modules cleaned every three and six months, respectively. Although we anticipated that module 1 would yield the highest irradiation, module 2, the unit cleaned with reservoir water, recorded the maximum value.

3.3 Results after five and six months of analysis

This subsection presents the soiling assessment for months five and six. For each month, the module with the highest monthly irradiation is taken as the reference (normalized to 100%), and all other modules are expressed as a percentage of this value; Figure 10 summarizes these results.

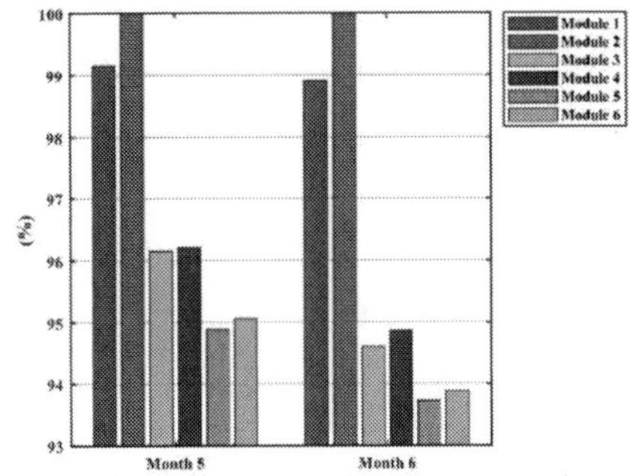

Figure 10: Irradiation by module after months five and six (% of reference module)

In both months, module 2 achieved the highest irradiation value and therefore defines the 100% reference in Figure 10. The corresponding numerical values are listed in Table III.

Table III: Assessment of soiling after months 5 and 6

Item	Month 5	Month 6
Module 1	99.15 %	98.91 %
Module 2	100.00 %	100.00 %
Module 3	96.15 %	94.60 %
Module 4	96.21 %	94.86 %
Module 5	94.89 %	93.73 %
Module 6	95.07 %	93.88 %

As shown in Table III, by the end of month six the monthly-cleaning regimen delivered up to 5.40% and 6.27% higher irradiation than the three-month and six-month cleaning regimens, respectively. The small difference in measured irradiation between modules 1 and 2 indicates that cleaning with reservoir water is a viable option from an energy-capture standpoint.

4 CONCLUSIONS

This study quantified the impact of soiling on a 7 MWp floating photovoltaic (FPV) plant in an urban, humid subtropical environment. Six representative modules were maintained under different cleaning frequencies and water sources, and their monthly plane-of-array (POA) irradiation was compared. Over the six-month observation window, monthly cleaning yielded up to 6.27% higher POA irradiation relative to less-frequent schedules. Contrary to expectations for module 1 (cleaned monthly with clean, non-reservoir water), the highest irradiation was recorded for module 2, which was cleaned using reservoir water.

The observed gain is consistent with two reinforcing drivers: (i) design—FPV arrays often employ low tilt angles to enhance mechanical robustness, which reduces rain-driven self-cleaning and promotes deposition; and (ii) environment—urban aerosol loading and frequent bird activity accelerate both particulate and organic fouling. From an operational standpoint, reservoir water proved viable for cleaning in this study; however, maintenance must follow manufacturer guidance to safeguard performance and warranty coverage. Some manufacturers prohibit the use of untreated reservoir water, which can necessitate logistics that are non-trivial: if 6 liters are required per module, a 7 MWp floating system with

10,500 modules would demand 63,000 liters transported by boat. Installing a pumping line from shore can mitigate transport needs but increases upfront costs and may introduce permitting and reliability considerations.

Finally, the optimal cleaning cadence is site-specific. Frequent rainfall can extend intervals by providing natural washing, whereas arid or dusty microclimates—and locations with high bird presence—typically require more frequent cleaning to sustain performance.

ACKNOWLEDGMENTS

This work was supported by the São Paulo Research Foundation (FAPESP), under grants #2023/00597-9, and #2023/17658-0.

REFERENCES

[1] M. A. Koondhar, L. Albasha, I. Mahariq, B. B. Graba, and E. Touti, "Reviewing floating photovoltaic (FPV) technology for solar energy generation," *Energy Strateg. Rev.*, vol. 54, no. June, p. 101449, Jul. 2024, doi: 10.1016/j.esr.2024.101449.

[2] R. C.J., K. H. Lim, J. C. Kurnia, S. Roy, B. J. Bora, and B. J. Medhi, "Towards sustainable power generation: recent advancements in floating photovoltaic technologies," *Renew. Sustain. Energy Rev.*, vol. 194, no. May 2023, p. 114322, Apr. 2024, doi: 10.1016/j.rser.2024.114322.

[3] A. Garrod, S. Neda Hussain, A. Ghosh, S. Nahata, C. Wynne, and S. Paver, "An assessment of floating photovoltaic systems and energy storage methods: a comprehensive review," *Results Eng.*, vol. 21, no. December 2023, p. 101940, Mar. 2024, doi: 10.1016/j.rineng.2024.101940.

[4] L. Essak and A. Ghosh, "Floating photovoltaics: a review," *Clean Technol.*, vol. 4, no. 3, pp. 752–769, Aug. 2022, doi: 10.3390/cleantechnol4030046.

[5] R. Zahedi, P. Ranjbaran, G. B. Gharehpetian, F. Mohammadi, and R. Ahmadiahangar, "Cleaning of floating photovoltaic systems: a critical review on approaches from technical and economic perspectives," *Energies*, vol. 14, no. 7, p. 2018, Apr. 2021, doi: 10.3390/en14072018.

[6] E. Cuce, P. M. Cuce, S. Saboor, A. Ghosh, and Y. Sheikhnejad, "Floating PVs in terms of power generation, environmental aspects, market potential, and challenges," *Sustainability*, vol. 14, no. 5, p. 2626, Feb. 2022, doi: 10.3390/su14052626.

[7] A. K and V. K, "A comparative study of floating and ground-mounted photovoltaic power generation in Indian contexts," *Clean. Energy Syst.*, vol. 9, no. June, p. 100140, Dec. 2024, doi: 10.1016/j.cles.2024.100140.

[8] S. A. Mohammed *et al.*, "Performance of passivated emitter and rear cell, tunnel oxide passivated contact, and heterojunction solar cells in floating photovoltaic systems across climatic zones," *Phys. status solidi*, vol. 2500354, Aug. 2025, doi: 10.1002/pssa.202500354.

[9] J. J. S. Souza, P. C. M. Carvalho, and G. C. Barroso, "Analysis of the characteristics and effects of soiling natural accumulation on 2 photovoltaic systems: a systematic review of the literature," *J. Sol. Energy Eng.*, vol. 145, no. 4, pp. 1–99, Dec. 2022, doi: 10.1115/1.4056453.

[10] G. M. Tina *et al.*, "PVSails: harnessing innovation with vertical bifacial PV modules in floating photovoltaic systems," *Prog. Photovoltaics Res. Appl.*, vol. 32, no. 12, pp. 872–888, Dec. 2024, doi: 10.1002/pip.3841.

IN-FIELD ASSESSMENT OF SOILING EFFECTS ON A FLOATING PHOTOVOLTAIC SYSTEM IN A HUMID SUBTROPICAL URBAN AREA

Renzo Vargas[1], Givaldo dos Reis[1], Rodrigo P. Maruyama[1], Alex Manito[1], Marcelo Pinho Almeida[1], Roberto Zilles[1]

INTRODUCTION

Floating photovoltaic (FPV) systems offer an alternative to land-based PV by deploying modules on reservoirs and other water bodies, repurposing underutilized surfaces and benefiting from water-mediated passive cooling that mitigates heat-related efficiency losses. Nevertheless, important knowledge gaps remain—especially at utility scale. In this study, we investigate soiling at a ~7 MWp FPV plant (10,500 modules, north-oriented, 12° tilt) operating in a humid subtropical, urban environment. We quantify the effects of alternative cleaning schedules on module-level irradiance capture and evaluate the feasibility of using reservoir water for cleaning.

METHODOLOGY

We select and calibrate six modules according to IEC 60904-2:2023–Item 14. After installation, dataloggers are deployed to monitor the modules short-circuit currents to record the irradiation data. The modules used in the experiment, the cleaning process, and the datalogger connections are presented in Figure 1.

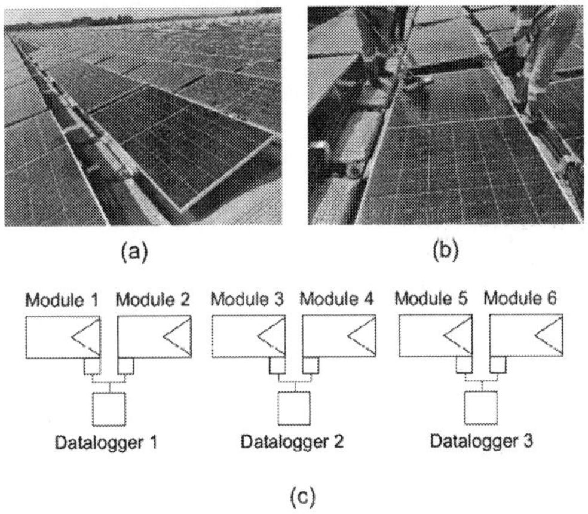

Figure 1. (a) Six modules used in the experiment, (b) manual cleaning procedure, (c) dataloggers and PV modules connections.

The cleaning schedule and the type of the water used for PV module cleaning are as follows:

Table I: Cleaning schedule and type of water

Item	Cleaning schedule	Type of water
Module 1	every month	clean water
Module 2	every month	reservoir water
Module 3	every three months	clean water
Module 4	every three months	reservoir water
Module 5	every six months	clean water
Module 6	no cleaning	—

Each clean-water module requires approximately six liters of water per cleaning. When using reservoir water, one end of the water pump is immersed in the reservoir while the other end directs the flow onto the module surfaces.

RESULTS

We documented several soiling modes on the FPV array. Representative examples are shown in Figure 2.

(a) (b) (c)

Figure 2. (a) Avian droppings, (b) residue from avian foraging, (c) splash-induced deposition.

We present an initial appraisal of soiling based on the first two months of analysis. For each month, the module with the highest monthly irradiation is used as the reference and normalized to 100%. Figure 3 shows each module's monthly irradiation as a percentage of this reference.

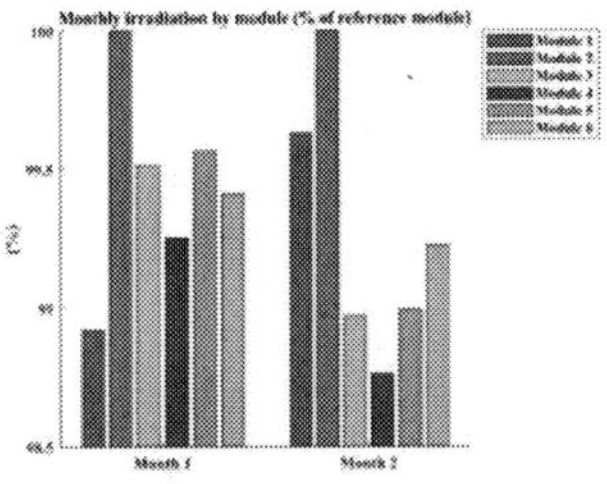

Figure 3. Irradiation by module for the first two months (% of reference module)

Comments for the first two months:
i) Module 2, the unit cleaned with reservoir water, recorded the maximum value of irradiation;
ii) After one month, there is minimal variation in measured irradiation among the modules;
iii) By the end of the second month, monthly cleaned modules exhibit up to 1.25% and 1.01% higher irradiation compared to those cleaned every three and six months, respectively.

Next, we present the soiling assessment for months five and six. For each month, the module with the highest monthly irradiation is taken as the reference (normalized to 100%).

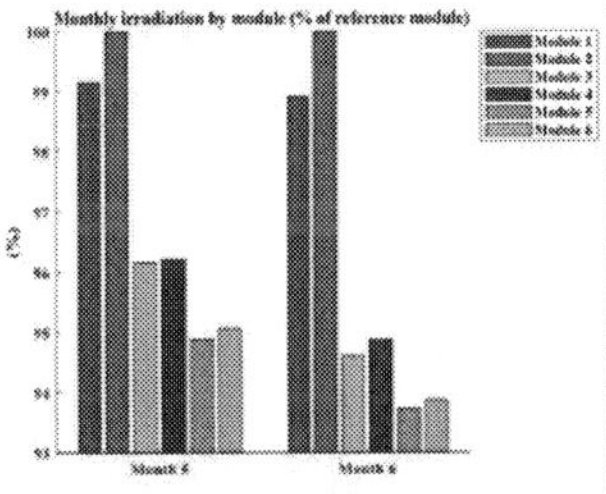

Figure 4. Irradiation by module after months five and six.

Comments after the sixth month:
i) By the end of the sixth month, monthly cleaned modules show up to 5.40% and 6.27% higher irradiation than those cleaned every three and six months;
ii) The small difference in measured irradiation between Module 1 and Module 2 suggests that using reservoir water for cleaning is a viable option from an energy capture perspective.

CONCLUSIONS

Modules cleaned monthly delivered up to 6.27% higher module-plane irradiation than less-frequently cleaned modules. Two factors explain this: (1) Design—FPV arrays typically adopt low tilt angles to enhance mechanical robustness, but low tilt reduces rain-driven self-cleaning and increases soiling; and (2) Environment—urban aerosol pollution and frequent bird activity accelerate particulate and organic deposition. Reservoir water proved viable for cleaning in this study, but it should be used only with manufacturer approval and documented water-quality controls to avoid warranty issues.

EU PVSEC LSF IEE USP USP FAPESP

[1]Instituto de Energia e Ambiente
Universidade de São Paulo

EU PVSEC European Photovoltaic Solar Energy Conference and Exhibition

國立勤益科技大學 National Chin-Yi University of Technology

PI Website Here

Demo Here

The Panoramic Reconstruction Images to Photovoltaic Modules for Solar Power Plant Management

Chao-Wei Ou[1], Han-Chang Liu[2], Cheng-Yu Peng[1]*
[1] National Chin-Yi University of Technology, R.O.C.
[2] Industrial Technology Research Institute, Hsinchu, Taiwan, R.O.C.
*Corresponding author: peng@ncut.edu.tw

工業技術研究院 Industrial Technology Research Institute

ABSTRACT

This study simulates the scenario of an unmanned aerial vehicle (UAV) capturing images of a large-scale solar power plant to generate a panoramic reconstruction for maintenance and inspection management. By analyzing the panoramic image and comparing the characteristics of PV modules, it is possible to identify modules contaminated with bird droppings or dirt and estimate the optimal timing for maintenance and cleaning.

EXPERIMENTAL SETUP

The aerial images are stitched using the SIFT and RANSAC algorithms, utilizing feature extraction and feature matching techniques to identify overlapping regions and perform full image with seamless stitching. Semantic segmentation is applied to detect PV module arrays and extract background information with segmentation accuracy evaluated based on the average error. The Hough Transform is then employed for PV module edge detection. Finally, multiple regional images are stitched together to generate a complete panoramic view of the solar power plant.

Identify PV module arrays and the region of ROI for aerial images

The aerial images are the process of binarized and erosion applied to enhance the edge contours of the photovoltaic modules. The pattern matching is then used to identify PV module arrays and a region of interest (ROI) defined for further analysis. Within this ROI, the edge detection is performed twice using the Hough Transform and separately detecting edge counts in the X and Y directions.

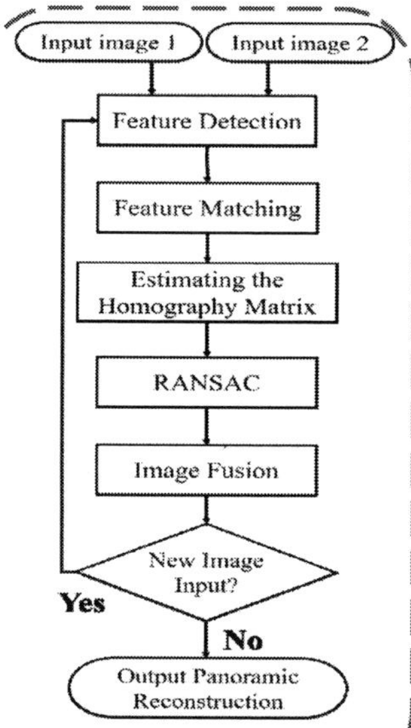

The flow chart of image stitching

The process to identify PV module arrays and the region of ROI for aerial images

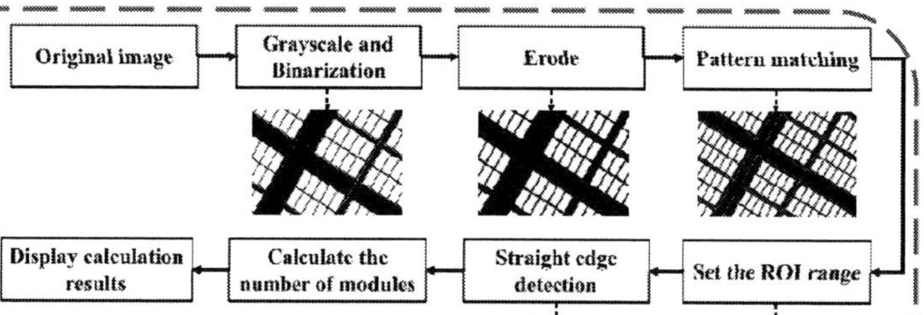

A relationship is established between the detected edge counts and the number of modules to allow the identification of PV module array regions within the image.

RESULTS AND DISCUSSION

The scenario of UAV capturing imageslight trapping ability

The original multiple regional images

The image stitching feature

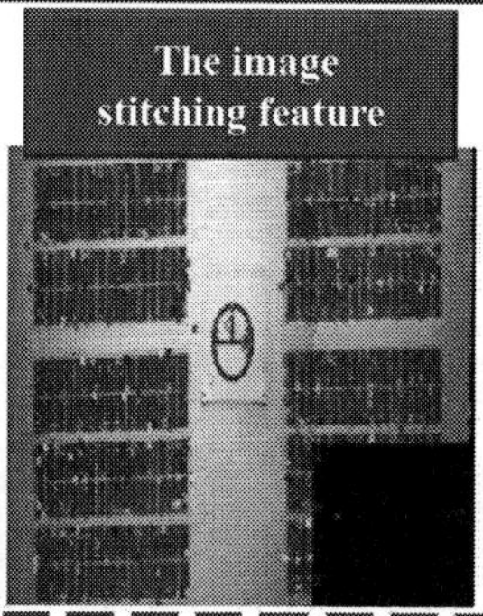

The panoramic reconstruction image

This study demonstrates the process of panoramic reconstruction for PV plant management by utilizing UAV-captured images. The original multiple regional images are obtained by a series of image processing techniques including binarization, erosion, semantic segmentation and edge detection to enhance the identification of PV module arrays.

RESULTS AND DISCUSSION

This demonstration shows panoramic reconstruction for PV plant management using UAV-captured images. Image processing techniques by the binarization, erosion, semantic segmentation, and edge detection enhance PV module identification. The result confirms the effectiveness of the proposed method for inspection and management. (Acknowledgement: The financial support provided by Energy Administration, Ministry of Economic Affairs, Taiwan, R.O.C. (Contract No: 114-S0102) is gratefully acknowledged.)

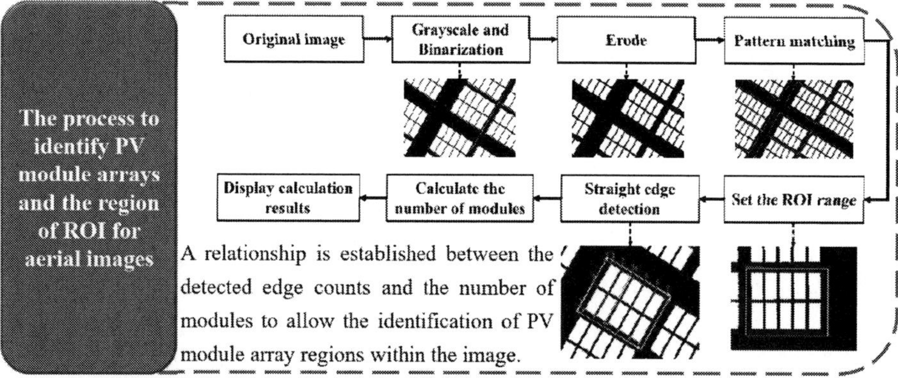

DETECTION AND CLUSTERING OF PHOTOVOLTAIC FAULTS

Anastasios Kladas, Bert Herteleer, Jan Cappelle
KU Leuven Research Group ELECTA Ghent, Gebroeders De Smetstraat 1, 9000 Ghent, Belgium
anastasios.kladas@kuleuven.be

ABSTRACT: Photovoltaic (PV) systems are susceptible to faults that diminish energy yield and efficiency. This paper presents a novel framework for detecting and clustering PV faults using accessible data: maximum power point voltage and current from the inverter's DC side, plus weather time series. Fault detection uses a degradation-adaptive model to estimate expected outputs, flagging anomalies via dynamic irradiance-based thresholds and performance filters. Fault impacts are quantified with current and voltage performance indices (CPI and VPI), serving as clustering features. Among tested algorithms (K-means, FCM, DBSCAN, HDBSCAN), HDBSCAN excels in robustness to noise on simulated data, grouping faults by system effects.
Keywords: PV fault diagnosis, Fault signatures, Fault Clustering

1 INTRODUCTION

PV system malfunctions reduce energy yield and revenue [1]. Rapid fault detection is essential, distinguishing unexpected issues (e.g., electrical faults, failures) from expected losses (e.g., degradation, soiling). Manual inspections are costly and error-prone, taking up to 8 h/MW for ground-mounted systems [2]–[5]. Automated monitoring with sensors and analytics enables real-time detection [2]. Methods include visual/thermal imaging, MPP monitoring, output comparisons, and machine learning [6], [7]. This work detects faults by comparing measured and estimated outputs.

Prior approaches like Chouder et al. [8] use fixed thresholds on one-diode model errors, but ignore degradation and variable errors. Yao et al. [9] employ ML thresholds from high/low-efficiency data, yet selecting periods is challenging and degradation may misclassify outputs. Kladas et al. [10] address this with degradation-adaptive modeling for accurate references.

Post-detection, diagnosis uses ML classification [11]–[13], rule-based assessment [8], [14], or IV curves [15]. However, labeled data scarcity, broad categories, and IV unavailability limit them.

Faults vary in impact by type/location [16]. Clustering groups similar effects without labels. Xu et al. [17] use MMD-enhanced FCM on IV/PV features for simulated faults, but predefine clusters and test small arrays. Lin et al. [18] apply CFSFDP with reference modules, impractical for many systems. Liu et al. [19] use GKFCM with references and labeled centers, limiting adaptability.

This work clusters faults using MPP voltage/current and weather data, integrable into O&M frameworks. It detects faults, quantifies impacts, clusters signatures with historical logs for efficient troubleshooting.

2 METHODOLOGY

Faults are detected by comparing measured and estimated power at DC measurement points (inverter or arrays). A Python-based degradation-adaptive model [10] estimates current, voltage, and power from plane-of-array irradiance (GPoA) and PV temperature (TPV).Data with malfunctions/downtime are filtered: daily R^2 (current vs. GPoA/GHI) <0.9 or energy performance index (EPI = measured/expected energy) <0.8/>1.1 discarded.Residuals (P_meas - P_est) yield dynamic thresholds: GPoA discretized in 25 W/m² steps; 99th/1st percentiles per bin form lookup table. Deviations >2 hours are faults.

Fault signatures: CPI* = I_meas / I_est, VPI* = V_meas / V_est (degradation-corrected). Clustering uses CPI*/VPI* per string; labels consolidated into composite (e.g., X1.X2... or "C" for clean).

The whole procedure is visualized in Figure 1.

3 DATA USED

Simulated data: MATLAB Simulink models 2×12 (441 V OC, 16 A SC) and 5×5 (184 V OC, 40 A SC) arrays (~5.3–5.5 kW STC) with De Soto model [20]. Faults: open-circuits, short-circuits (intra/cross-string, bypass-diode). Randomized daytime (>250 W/m²) using NIST weather (Jan–May 2015) [21].

4 RESULTS

Evaluation of Clustering Methods
The clustering performance is evaluated using simulated data from 2×12 and 5×5 PV array topologies, with fault signatures generated for scenarios including short circuits, open circuits, and partial shading, replicating ideal PV output estimations [23], [24], [25], [26], [27]. Four clustering algorithms are tested: K-means [23], [24], [25], Fuzzy C-Means (FCM) [26], DBSCAN [23], and HDBSCAN [27]. Parameters are automatically selected (e.g., elbow/silhouette for K-means, FPC for FCM). Performance is assessed using external metrics: completeness, homogeneity, V-measure [28], and Adjusted Rand Index (ARI) [29]. Clustering Results on

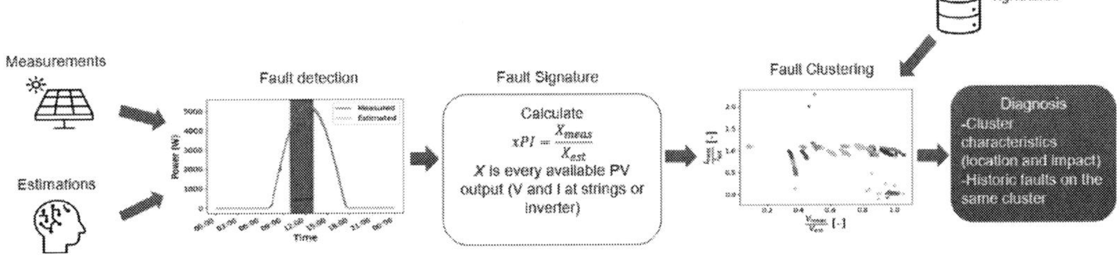

Figure 1 PV fault clustering flowchart.

10.4229/EUPVSEC2025/4CV.1.50

Noise-Free Simulated Data

Table 1 presents clustering metrics for the 2×12 topology. Density-based algorithms (DBSCAN, HDBSCAN) outperform centroid-based algorithms (K-means, FCM), with DBSCAN achieving the highest scores (e.g., V-measure: 0.8441, ARI: 0.5463). The underperformance of K-means and FCM is attributed to the curse of dimensionality affecting distance metrics.

Table 1 Clustering metrics (2×12 system).

METRIC	DBSCAN	FCM	HDBSCAN	KMEANS
COMPLETENESS	0.9741	0.9737	0.9725	0.9678
HOMOGENEITY	0.7448	0.6656	0.7441	0.6572
V-MEASURE	0.8441	0.7907	0.8431	0.7828
ARI	0.5463	0.4410	0.5415	0.4363

Analysis of Voltage Performance Index (VPI) and Current Performance Index (CPI) distributions reveals topology-specific fault patterns. As shown in Figure 2, the 2×12 topology, with more modules in series, forms clusters aligned with the VPI axis, indicative of short-circuit faults affecting voltage. The 5×5 topology, with more parallel strings, shows clusters along the CPI axis, characteristic of open-circuit faults impacting current. Topology influences feature space structure, with series-heavy configurations yielding diverse VPI clusters and parallel-heavy configurations producing varied CPI clusters.

5 DISCUSSION AND CONCLUSION

The proposed method leverages simulated maximum power point (MPP) voltage and current data, combined with weather time series, to cluster PV faults using HDBSCAN [27]. Unlike prior approaches requiring I-V curve parameters [15] or reference module data [18], [19], this method uses performance indices (CPI and VPI) to group faults by their impact on system performance. Integrated into an online operations and maintenance (O&M) framework, it enables rapid fault identification by comparing simulated fault patterns with historical logs.

HDBSCAN efficiently clusters fault signatures derived from simulated short circuits, open circuits, and partial shading, using CPI and VPI. Preprocessing, such as filtering samples with high variability, reduces computational demands, and supports near-real-time clustering. By grouping faults with similar performance impacts, the method simplifies diagnosis without requiring detailed fault-specific models, allowing technicians to cross-reference clusters with historical fault logs for faster resolution.

The method assumes accurate power estimation models in simulations. Inaccuracies, such as those from irradiance spectrum mismatches [31], may introduce noise, potentially masking fault signatures. The current focus is on DC-side faults (e.g., open/short circuits, bypass diode failures). Expanding to AC-side faults could enhance applicability by developing new AC-specific fault signatures. Excluding transient faults (e.g., from moving shadows) simplifies clustering but limits scope. Incorporating dynamic clustering, such as time-series analysis, could improve versatility.

Future work will validate the algorithm on real-world PV systems to assess its performance across diverse configurations and fault scenarios. Real data analysis will focus on integrating the clustering method into an active O&M platform, evaluating scalability, and testing robustness under operational conditions. Additionally, incorporating thermal imaging to establish baseline thermal profiles for PV panels could enhance diagnosis by identifying hotspots or temperature deviations not evident in electrical data [32], [33]. A large language model could further process cluster characteristics, thermal data, and external knowledge to identify root causes and perform cost-benefit analyses for repair decisions, optimizing maintenance strategies

8 REFERENCES

[1] I. Lillo-Bravo, P. González-Martínez, M. Larrañeta, and J. Guasumba-Codena, "Impact of Energy Losses Due to Failures on Photovoltaic Plant Energy Balance," Energies (Basel), vol. 11, no. 2, p. 363, Feb. 2018, doi: 10.3390/en11020363.

[2] S. Ansari, A. Ayob, M. S. Hossain Lipu, M. H. Md Saad, and A. Hussain, "A review of monitoring technologies for solar pv systems using data processing modules and transmission protocols: Progress, challenges and prospects," Sustainability (Switzerland), vol. 13, no. 15, 2021, doi: 10.3390/su13158120.

[3] A. Woyte, M. Richter, D. Moser, M. Green, S. Mau, and H. G. Beyer, Analytical Monitoring of Grid-connected Photovoltaic Systems, vol. 13, no. 2. 2014.

[4] K. Keisang, T. Bader, and R. Samikannu, "Review of Operation and Maintenance Methodologies for Solar Photovoltaic Microgrids," 2021. doi: 10.3389/fenrg.2021.730230.

[5] G. Di Lorenzo, R. Araneo, M. Mitolo, A. Niccolai, and F. Grimaccia, "Review of O&M Practices in PV Plants: Failures, Solutions, Remote Control, and Monitoring Tools," IEEE J Photovolt, vol. 10, no. 4, pp. 914–926, Jul. 2020, doi: 10.1109/JPHOTOV.2020.2994531.

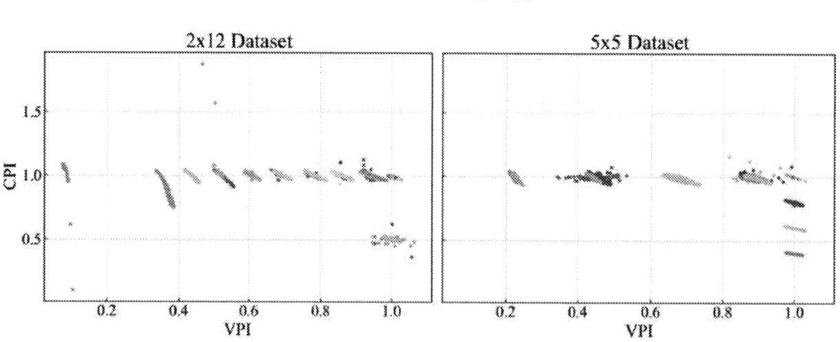

Figure 2 Comparison of VPI and CPI distributions for 2×12 and 5×5 PV array topologies. Each different colour indicates a different cluster.

[6] Y.-Y. Hong and R. A. Pula, "Methods of photovoltaic fault detection and classification: A review," Energy Reports, vol. 8, pp. 5898–5929, Nov. 2022, doi: 10.1016/j.egyr.2022.04.043.
[7] S. R. Madeti and S. N. Singh, "A comprehensive study on different types of faults and detection techniques for solar photovoltaic system," Solar Energy, vol. 158, pp. 161–185, Dec. 2017, doi: 10.1016/j.solener.2017.08.069.
[8] A. Chouder and S. Silvestre, "Automatic supervision and fault detection of PV systems based on power losses analysis," Energy Convers Manag, vol. 51, no. 10, pp. 1929–1937, Oct. 2010, doi: 10.1016/j.enconman.2010.02.025.
[9] S. Yao, Q. Kang, M. Zhou, A. Abusorrah, and Y. Al-Turki, "Intelligent and Data-Driven Fault Detection of Photovoltaic Plants," Processes, vol. 9, no. 10, p. 1711, Sep. 2021, doi: 10.3390/pr9101711.
[10] A. Kladas, B. Herteleer, and J. Cappelle, "A Degradation-Responsive Framework for Long-Term PV Power Estimation," Adv Theory Simul, Jul. 2025, doi: 10.1002/adts.202500631.
[11] K. H. Chao, S. H. Ho, and M. H. Wang, "Modeling and fault diagnosis of a photovoltaic system," Electric Power Systems Research, vol. 78, no. 1, pp. 97–105, Jan. 2008, doi: 10.1016/J.EPSR.2006.12.012.
[12] Z. Chen et al., "Random forest based intelligent fault diagnosis for PV arrays using array voltage and string currents," Energy Convers Manag, vol. 178, pp. 250–264, Dec. 2018, doi: 10.1016/J.ENCONMAN.2018.10.040.
[13] Z. Mustafa, A. S. A. Awad, M. Azzouz, and A. Azab, "Fault identification for photovoltaic systems using a multi-output deep learning approach," Expert Syst Appl, vol. 211, p. 118551, Jan. 2023, doi: 10.1016/j.eswa.2022.118551.
[14] L. Xu, Z. Pan, C. Liang, and M. Lu, "A Fault Diagnosis Method for PV Arrays Based on New Feature Extraction and Improved the Fuzzy C-Mean Clustering," IEEE J Photovolt, vol. 12, no. 3, pp. 833–843, May 2022, doi: 10.1109/JPHOTOV.2022.3151330.
[15] S. Fadhel et al., "PV shading fault detection and classification based on I-V curve using principal component analysis: Application to isolated PV system," Solar Energy, vol. 179, pp. 1–10, Feb. 2019, doi: 10.1016/j.solener.2018.12.048.
[16] K. I. Baradieh et al., "A Study on the Impact of Different PV Model Parameters and Various DC Faults on the Characteristics and Performance of the Photovoltaic Arrays," Inventions, vol. 9, no. 5, p. 93, Aug. 2024, doi: 10.3390/inventions9050093.
[17] L. Xu, Z. Pan, C. Liang, and M. Lu, "A Fault Diagnosis Method for PV Arrays Based on New Feature Extraction and Improved the Fuzzy C-Mean Clustering," IEEE J Photovolt, vol. 12, no. 3, pp. 833–843, 2022, doi: 10.1109/JPHOTOV.2022.3151330.
[18] P. Lin, Y. Lin, Z. Chen, L. Wu, L. Chen, and S. Cheng, "A Density Peak-Based Clustering Approach for Fault Diagnosis of Photovoltaic Arrays," International Journal of Photoenergy, vol. 2017, pp. 1–14, 2017, doi: 10.1155/2017/4903613.
[19] S. Liu, L. Dong, X. Liao, X. Cao, and X. Wang, "Photovoltaic Array Fault Diagnosis Based on Gaussian Kernel Fuzzy C-Means Clustering Algorithm," Sensors, vol. 19, no. 7, p. 1520, Mar. 2019, doi: 10.3390/s19071520.
[20] W. De Soto, S. A. Klein, and W. A. Beckman, "Improvement and validation of a model for photovoltaic array performance," Solar Energy, vol. 80, no. 1, pp. 78–88, Jan. 2006, doi: 10.1016/J.SOLENER.2005.06.010.
[21] Boyd M, Chen T, and Dougherty B, "NIST Campus Photovoltaic (PV) Arrays and Weather Station Data Sets. [Data set]." [Online]. Available: https://doi.org/10.18434/M3S67G
[22] M. Boyd, "Performance data from the NIST photovoltaic arrays and weather station," J Res Natl Inst Stand Technol, vol. 122, 2017, doi: 10.6028/JRES.122.040.
[23] F. Pedregosa et al., "Scikit-learn: Machine learning in Python," Journal of machine learning research, vol. 12, no. Oct, pp. 2825–2830, 2011.
[24] C. Ding, "K-means Clustering via Principal Component Analysis."
[25] F. Wang, H. H. Franco-Penya, J. D. Kelleher, J. Pugh, and R. Ross, "An analysis of the application of simplified silhouette to the evaluation of k-means clustering validity," in Lecture Notes in Computer Science (including subseries Lecture Notes in Artificial Intelligence and Lecture Notes in Bioinformatics), Springer Verlag, 2017, pp. 291–305. doi: 10.1007/978-3-319-62416-7_21.
[26] L. Madson and D. Dantas, "fuzzy-c-means: An implementation of Fuzzy C-means clustering algorithm," Zenodo. doi: 10.5281/zenodo.3066222.
[27] D. M. Bot, J. Peeters, J. Liesenborgs, and J. Aerts, "FLASC: a flare-sensitive clustering algorithm," PeerJ Comput Sci, vol. 11, p. e2792, Apr. 2025, doi: 10.7717/peerj-cs.2792.
[28] A. Rosenberg and J. Hirschberg, "V-Measure: A Conditional Entropy-Based External Cluster Evaluation Measure.," Apr. 2007, pp. 410–420.
[29] L. Hubert and P. Arabie, "Comparing partitions," J Classif, vol. 2, no. 1, pp. 193–218, Dec. 1985, doi: 10.1007/BF01908075.
[30] IEC 61724-1, Photovoltaic system performance – Part 1: Monitoring, " Edition 1.0. 2017.
[31] K. Paghasian and G. TamizhMani, "Photovoltaic module power rating per IEC 61853--1: A study under natural sunlight," in 2011 37th IEEE Photovoltaic Specialists Conference, IEEE, Jun. 2011, pp. 002322–002327. doi: 10.1109/PVSC.2011.6186418.
[32] J. A. Tsanakas, D. Chrysostomou, P. N. Botsaris, and A. Gasteratos, "Fault diagnosis of photovoltaic modules through image processing and Canny edge detection on field thermographic measurements," International Journal of Sustainable Energy, vol. 34, no. 6, pp. 351–372, Jul. 2015, doi: 10.1080/14786451.2013.826223.
[33] J. A. Tsanakas, L. Ha, and C. Buerhop, "Faults and infrared thermographic diagnosis in operating c-Si photovoltaic modules: A review of research and future challenges," Renewable and Sustainable Energy Reviews, vol. 62, pp. 695–709, Sep. 2016, doi: 10.1016/j.rser.2016.04.079.

42nd European Photovoltaic Solar Energy Conference and Exhibition

KU LEUVEN GENT

Faculty of Technology Engineering

Detection and clustering of photovoltaic faults

WHY

Anastasios Kladas, Jarid Van Der Gucht, Bert Herteleer, Jan Cappelle
Research group ELECTA Ghent

Group faults with similar impact together → Faster troubleshooting

Process

Historic fault signatures

Measurements

Estimations

Fault detection

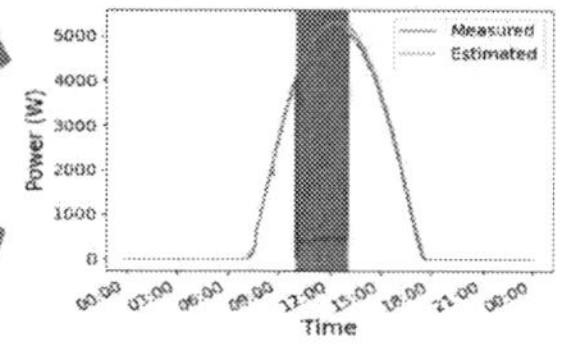

Fault Signature

Calculate

$$xPI = \frac{X_{meas}}{X_{est}}$$

X is every available PV output (V and I at strings or inverter)

A fault signature is the set of all xPIs for the examined fault

Fault Clustering

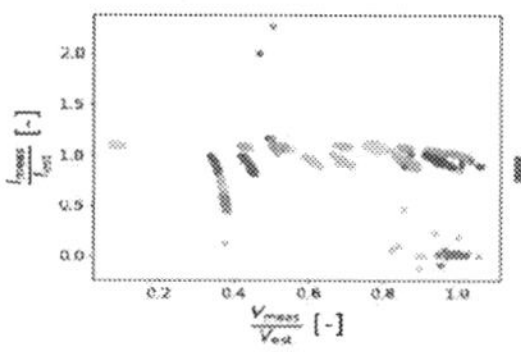

Diagnosis
-Cluster characteristics (location and impact)
-Historic faults on the same cluster

Best clustering algorithm (based on simulations)

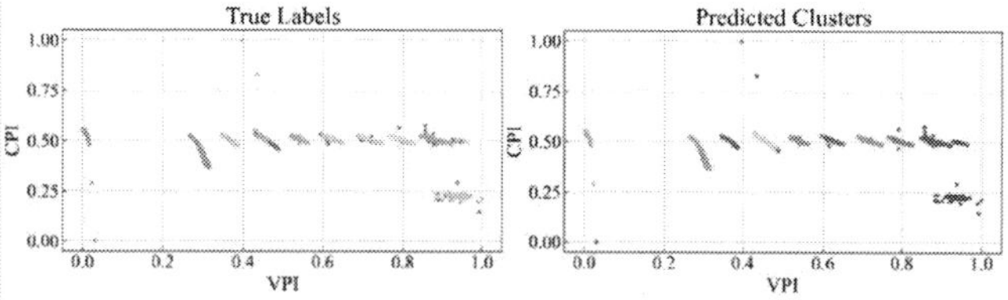

Metric	Without String Current Features				With String Current Features			
	DBSCAN	FCM	HDBSCAN	KMeans	DBSCAN	FCM	HDBSCAN	KMeans
Completeness	0.97	0.96	0.91	0.96	0.98	0.96	0.89	0.99
Homogeneity	0.24	0.43	0.61	0.43	0.22	0.46	0.65	0.33
V-measure	0.38	0.59	0.73	0.59	0.36	0.63	0.75	0.49
ARI	0.06	0.23	0.38	0.23	0.05	0.25	0.43	0.12

- **Simulated diverse faults** in a 2x12 PV setup using Simulink under varying environmental conditions
- **One-diode model [1]** applied for PV system simulation
- **Fault signatures** identified by comparing outputs to non-faulty condition estimates
- **Evaluated 4 clustering algorithms** using inverter or separate string measurements
- **Multi-string approach:** Clustering applied individually to each string's voltage and current performance, then combined for final fault labeling
- **HDBSCAN outperforms** other clustering algorithms
- **Better output estimations enhance** fault signature clarity, improving clustering accuracy

Real data example (Using real PV data from NIST ground system)

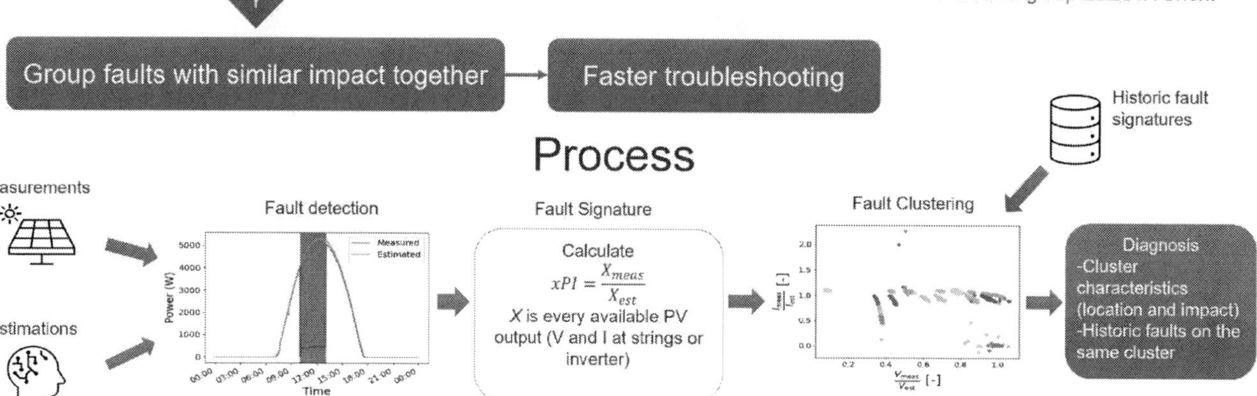

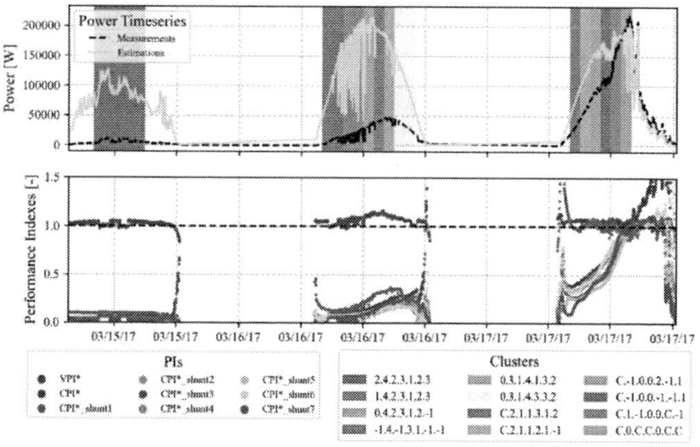

- **NIST ground system data** used for fault simulation and analysis [2]
- **Deep learning PV output model** trained according to [3] to generate output estimations
- **HDBSCAN clustering** applied to aggregated fault signatures (min. samples = 3, cluster selection epsilon = 0.04)
- **Cluster labels:** -1 for outliers, C for no-fault conditions
- **System downtime** occurred until the afternoon of March 16, 2017, followed by **gradual inverter reconnection**
  - Different clusters assigned to distinct reconnection stages
  - 2nd and 4th strings are the last to become functional

[1] De Soto, W., Klein, S. A., & Beckman, W. A. (2006). Improvement and validation of a model for photovoltaic array performance. Solar Energy, 80(1), 78–88. https://doi.org/10.1016/j.solener.2005.06.010
[2] Boyd, M. (2017). Performance data from the NIST photovoltaic arrays and weather station. Journal of Research of the National Institute of Standards and Technology, 122. https://doi.org/10.6028/JRES.122.040
[3] Kladas, A., Herteleer, B., & Cappelle, J. (2025). A Degradation-Responsive Framework for Long-Term PV Power Estimation. Advanced Theory and Simulations. https://doi.org/10.1002/adts.202500631

https://www.linkedin.com/in/anastasioskladas
AnastasiosKladas@kuleuven.be
+30 6975718485

PHOTOVOLTAIC MODULES SELF-TESTING BY JUNCTION BOX-EMBEDDED WIRELESS MONITORING SOLUTION

Eneko Ortega[1,2], Gerardo Aranguren[1], Julius Denafas[3], Paulius Laurikėnas[3], Ricardo Alonso[4] and Juan Carlos Jimeno[1]

[1] Technological Institute of Microelectronics, University of the Basque Country UPV/EHU, 48013, Bilbao, Spain
[2] Electricity and Electronics Department, University of the Basque Country UPV/EHU, 48940, Leioa, Spain
[3] Solitek, 08412, Vilnius, Lithuania
[4] TECNALIA, Basque Research and Technology Alliance (BRTA), 48160, Derio, Spain

eneko.ortegam@ehu.eus

ABSTRACT: Online monitoring of PV systems is essential to detect failures on the PV system, improve performance ratio and minimize degradation, extending module lifespan and increasing profitability by optimizing maintenance activities, reducing in-field inspections. PV system or string level monitoring approaches often fail to detect faults in individual modules, while module-level methods are more expensive. This work introduces a low-cost IoT device embedded in the junction box of the PV modules, which estimates the I-V characteristic near the operating point without disconnecting the PV module from the rest of the system, while also monitoring modules substrings and bypass diodes. The embedded circuit produces and measures small variations around the operating point to obtain, for the entire PV module and at substring level, the I-V characteristic around the operating point. From this information, for each PV module two numbers are obtained: degradation and misfit. In addition, the proposed solution would be able to estimate several PV module parameters as series and shunt resistances or saturation currents.

Keywords: photovoltaic systems, condition monitoring, performance ratio, fault detection

1 INTRODUCTION

Solar photovoltaic (PV) electricity generation is increasing at an exponential rate, with an expected installed PV capacity growth of more than 500 GW per year [1]. In this context, maximizing the performance and reliability of PV systems becomes essential. The performance of PV systems is typically measured in terms of the performance ratio (PR) [2] which ranges between 85% and 90% for different PV systems in function of the module technology, system architecture, the PV system location climate or in function of the degradation of the PV system [3].

This means that power losses can be up to 15%, even for modern PV systems, due to PV module technology, system architecture, inverter and wiring losses or failures in the PV modules itself [1]. Failures in PV modules, such as encapsulation failures, cell cracks, potential induced degradation or partial shadows, are behind a relevant part of PV systems power losses [4]. Extreme weather conditions such as hurricanes and hailstorms also have a severe impact on PV systems performance [5]. Furthermore, the failure of a single module can cause greater power loss, as photovoltaic modules are connected to each other.

Periodic monitoring is the only way to detect these failures and to minimize power losses, boosting PV systems profitability. In this context, several monitoring techniques have been proposed [6,7].

Some monitoring methods are PV system or string-level oriented whereas others are string or module-level oriented. However, it is unclear whether system or string-level methods are capable of detecting power losses affecting to a single PV module or to small groups of modules, as these faults can be difficult to detect within the entire system [8].

Module level monitoring methods can achieve higher resolution, but they tend to be expensive and difficult to automatize. Module level methods rely on different techniques, such as visual inspection of the PV module, thermal images analysis, electroluminescence testing or electrical measurement.

Monitoring methods based on electrical measurements usually measure the operating voltage or the output power of the PV module. However, with these methods it is not always possible to detect the fault or, even if the fault is detected, to identify which module is the defective one [6] since they are connected in series between them. Voltage-current (I-V) characteristic measurement provides more insight into the PV module's status and it is possible to identify the power losses origin.

However, this approach tends to be expensive and difficult to automatize, since to measure the full I-V characteristic power electronic components are required and, in addition, the PV module needs to be disconnected from the rest of the system, increasing non-productive periods.

In [9] and [10] the authors proposed a novel monitoring methodology, capable of performing, in a few milliseconds, partial measurements of individual PV modules I-V curve around its operating point and reconstructing their characteristics, using a low-cost electronic circuit based on two capacitors, in the range of tens of microfarads, without power electronics components and controlled by six switches.

This methodology, in combination with temperature and solar irradiation data which can be obtained by adding additional sensors to the PV system or can be estimated from publicly available meteorological data following different approaches [11], enables to estimate the PV modules status, without disconnecting it from the rest of the system and to estimate the module degradation.

In this work, a new version of the proposed methodology is introduced. The monitoring circuit will be integrated into Solitek's PV modules junction boxes, with access to the PV modules substrings and modules bypass diodes.

The electronic circuit includes Wi-Fi communications, which allow monitoring the PV system modules status remotely, reporting several parameters such as operating

10.4229/EUPVSEC2025/4CV.1.51

point, maximum power point (MPP), the I-V curve, the module temperature and the lighting or even the status of the bypass diodes. From this information, for each PV module two numbers are obtained: degradation and misfit. In addition, the proposed solution would be able to estimate several PV module parameters as series and shunt resistances or saturation currents.

2 PV MODULE MONITORING DEVICE

The PV modules monitoring circuit is a low-cost electronic circuit, that uses only low power components, and is capable of varying the operating point of the photovoltaic module by modifying its output current. This monitoring process, explained in detail in [9] is performed without disconnecting it from the rest of its string and without adding external wiring.

The monitoring circuit, as it can be seen in Fig. 1, is based on two capacitors in the order of tens of microfarads controlled by six switches. It has four operating modes: standby, T1, T2 and T3.

Most of the time, the monitoring circuit is in standby mode, and no current is drawn from the PV module. During T1, the first step in the monitoring sequence, the capacitors are charged slowly (50 ms) until they reach the module voltage, consuming little current from the module.

In T2, the first capacitor discharges into the photovoltaic module, increasing the module's output current with a stepped function limited to 0.3 A. In this way, the operating point shifts towards short circuit. This movement is performed outside the static I-V characteristics since, due to the intrinsic capacitance of the photovoltaic modules, the dynamic behavior cannot follow the I-V characteristics of the photovoltaic module. Once the capacitor is discharged, it returns to the initial operating point with values below the static I-V characteristics.

During T3, the operating point shifts to higher voltages, decreasing the output current by 0.3 A and moving it to open circuit with behavior similar to T2.

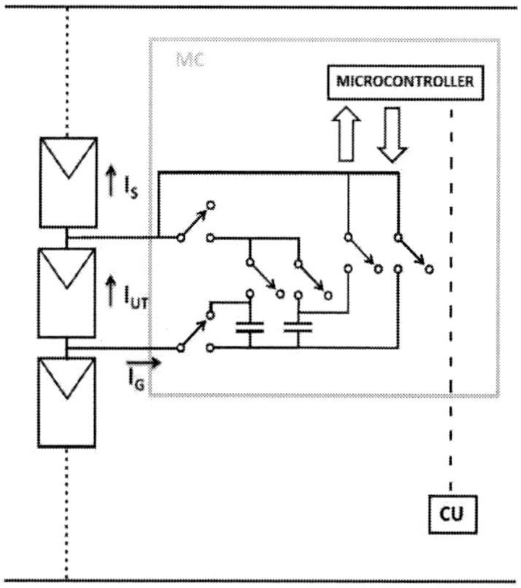

Figure 1: Simplified monitoring circuit, based on two capacitors and six switches.

Once the operating point reaches equilibrium again, the MC returns to standby mode. During T2 and T3, which are completed in a few milliseconds, the MC takes pairs of current and voltage values. In [10] a method to correct the dynamic effects on the I-V curve was presented, showing good results to estimate the static I-V characteristic around the operating point of the PV module.

Withing the SUPERNOVA project, the previously proposed and validated monitoring solution is being integrated into the PV module itself. For that, a new junction box is being designed integrating the developed monitoring device and all the necessary bypass diodes and connectors.

In addition to voltage and current measurements, the new circuits also includes a temperature sensor, front and rear illumination sensors, and a dirt sensor on the front of the PV module, enabling a complete diagnosis of the module. Fig. 2 shows a detailed electrical diagram of the testing circuit on a simplified circuit of a PV module with 3 bypass diodes.

The specific PV module where the monitoring solution is being integrated is a bifacial module manufactured by SOLITEK, composed of 108 half-cells arranged in six strings of 18 half-cells, each measuring 182 x 91 mm². The cell technology is n-type, bifacial TOPCon. The efficiency of the cells is 23.5%, and the efficiency of the module under STC conditions with front illumination is 21.51%. Under bifacial illumination, the expected maximum operating conditions of the PV module are:

$$P_{MAX} = 625\ W, V_{OC} = 38.24\ V\ and\ I_{SC} = 20\ A$$

The monitoring circuit integrated into the PV module is based on the circuit introduced in [9] and [10], designed for PV modules of 39 V, 9 A and 270 W but upgraded to the new expected operating conditions with voltage and current ranges of 50 V and 20 A. In addition, a new functionality, currently under evaluation, has been added to allow access to the negative voltage region of the PV module, enabling to assess the integrity of the bypass diodes.

As shown in Fig. 3, for each PV module and its

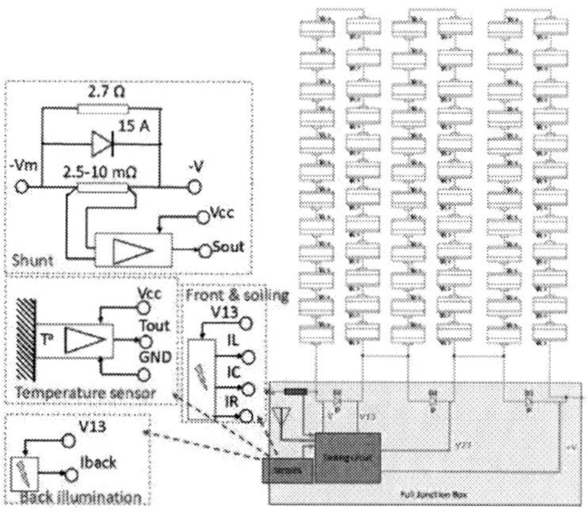

Figure 2: Detailed electrical diagram of the testing circuit on a simplified circuit of a PV module with 3 bypass diodes.

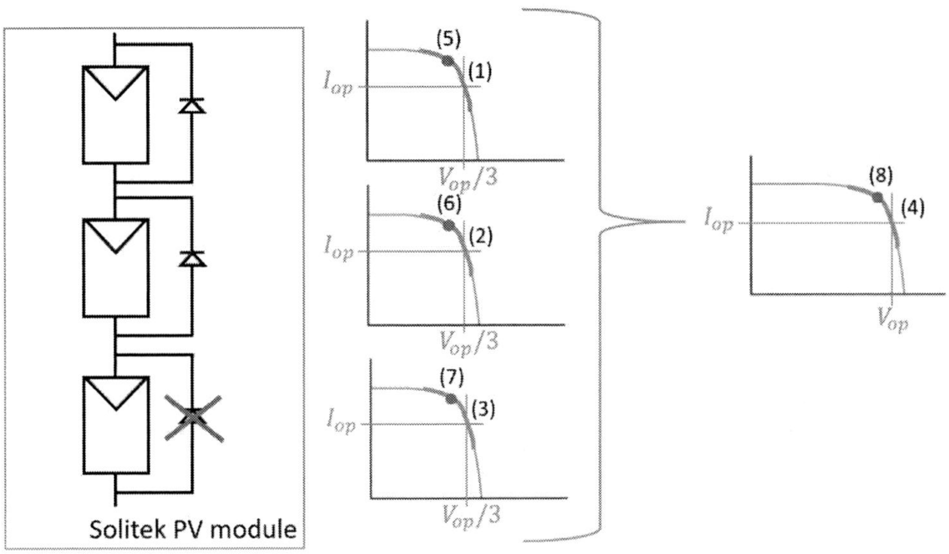

Figure 3: Implemented PV module substring level monitoring solution and parameters extraction: Module and module's substrings operating point (1-4), partial I-V characteristic (green line) and MPP (5-8). Access to bypass diodes enables to assess the integrity of the bypass diodes.

substrings, the following information can be obtained: operating point (1-4), partial I-V characteristic around the operating point (green line) and MPP (5-8).

For that, the monitoring circuit includes this circuit tripled, providing individual access to each of the module's substrings, and thus facilitating the evaluation of each string and its corresponding bypass diodes. The observation of its operating point also will reveal if any of the bypass diodes are short-circuited.

In addition, for each PV module two numbers can be obtained: mismatch and degradation. Mismatch is the ratio between the working point of the PV module (WP) and the MPP for the current operating conditions. It can be estimated from temperature and irradiation conditions and from PV module theoretical performance. Mismatch is associated with failures on the rest of the system.

Degradation is the ratio between the MPP and the expected power (EP) for the current operating conditions of the PV module and it is associated with failures on the PV module. Eq. 1 and 2 show the equations used to compute Mismatch and degradation parameters.

$$Mismatch = 1 - \frac{WP}{MPP} \quad (1)$$

$$Degradation = 1 - \frac{MPP}{EP} \quad (2)$$

Finally, from the partial I-V characteristic, several parameters associated with the PV module could be estimated, such as series or shunt resistance and saturation current, among others.

Fig. 4 shows the top and bottom views of the first prototype of the monitoring circuit to be integrated into the Solitek PV modules. Within the SUPERNOVA project, the proposed monitoring solution will be tested on a 50kW PV system.

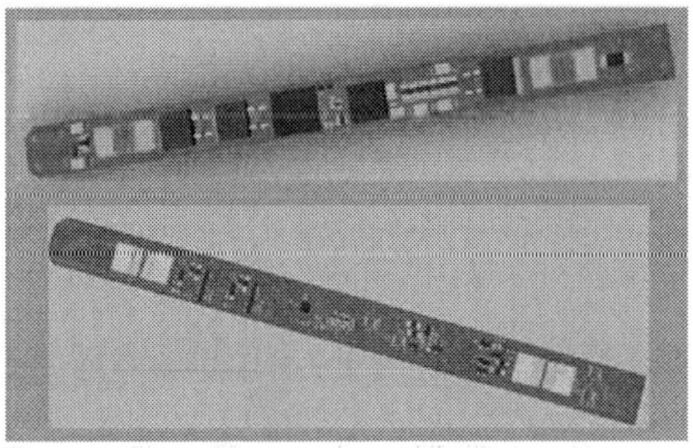

Figure 4: Top and bottom views of the first prototype to be integrated into the Solitek PV modules.

3 COMMUNICATION ARCHITECTURE

Each monitoring circuit integrated on the PV modules will operate as an Internet of Things (IoT) device. Each device will have an ESP32 microcontroller. The ESP32 is a low-cost dual-core 32-bit LX6 microprocessor with wireless (Wi-Fi) communication capabilities. The ESP32 operates at frequencies up to 240 MHz and it incorporates all the necessary functionalities to control the monitoring circuit and integrated sensors. It also executes the previously developed algorithms [10] to obtain the relevant parameters to determine the status of the PV module.

Each IoT device is provided with Wi-Fi communications. The proposed solution will enable remote monitoring of the PV system following the approach shown in Fig. 3.

Two different approaches can be observed. For small size PV systems, as domestic PV systems, each PV module IoT device will connect directly to an access point and send the monitoring data to an IoT cloud platform. For larger size PV systems, internet access will be granted by

10.4229/EUPVSEC2025/4CV.1.51

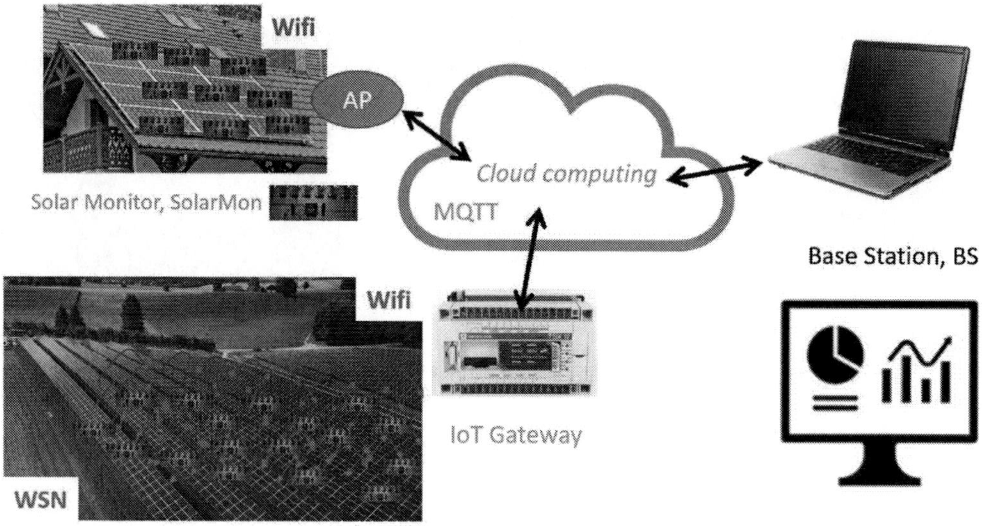

Figure 5. IoT solution architecture for module level PV systems monitoring. For small size PV system cloud access is granted through an access point. For larger PV systems cloud access is granted through an IoT Gateway. PV system owner access monitored data through a dashboard on a laptop or mobile device.

an IoT Gateway. Data will be stored on an IoT Cloud platform, and the PV system owner would be able to access remotely to modules status information.

One of the main challenges during the implementation of this communications architecture in the PV system is its reliability and stability. Wireless communications in low-power IoT devices with low-power antennas have limited range and intensity. They also present risks in terms of connection loss or data package losses. This problem can be even more significant in PV systems where the distance between each module and the access point is large, operating conditions are not stable, due to changes in atmospheric conditions, and the PV system itself can be a source of electromagnetic interferences [12], making wireless communications within the PV system more difficult.

Due to larger distances between PV modules and the IoT Gateway, direct connection will not be feasible for all IoT devices. Therefore, several connection levels will be generated to transmit information from every PV module to the access point. A mesh network is being deployed, where nodes are interconnected so that data can travel through multiple paths from a source to a destination. This allows to create a self-healing and fault-tolerant system where communication can still flow even if some nodes fail or connections drop.

Regarding the communication protocol, Message Queuing Telemetry Transport (MQTT) will be used in the context of this application. MQTT is a lightweight and efficient communication protocol, designed for message exchange between devices in networks with limited resources or unstable connections, such as the IoT. It works under a publish/subscribe model: clients publish messages to topics, and other clients subscribe to those topics to receive them, all managed by a broker that centralizes and distributes the information. Its low bandwidth consumption, simplicity, and support for real-time communication make it ideal for sensors, monitoring systems, and large-scale connected applications.

There will be two types of clients: the monitoring circuit integrated in each PV module (SolarMon) and the Base Station (BS) which would be the final user or device (computer, tablet, mobile phone) through which the system operator can observe the status of each individual PV module in the PV system.

The MQTT communication protocol in this system operates in two distinct modes: set-up and operation. In the set-up stage, each SolarMon device has no PV system assigned and connects first to a predefined Wi-Fi network and then to the MQTT broker. At this point, communication is handled through two temporary topics: one where devices publish their identifiers and availability, and another where the base station (BS) publishes assignments. This exchange allows the BS to detect unassigned devices and map them to their final PV system topics. Once a device has been successfully assigned, it confirms availability through its new status topic, signaling readiness to transition into normal operation.

In the operation stage, communication shifts to a set of PV system-specific topics structured around four main functions: configuration, status reporting, data requests, and data responses. Through the configuration topic, the BS can remotely update device parameters such as Wi-Fi credentials or measurement settings. The status topic provides real-time updates whenever devices boot, reconnect, or respond to configuration commands. Monitoring is supported by the request and data topics, where the BS issues measurement commands and devices return sensor and substring data. This structured use of topics ensures robust device management, fault tolerance, and scalability, allowing multiple PV systems to coexist within the same broker architecture while maintaining clear separation of control and data flows. Fig. 6 shows a

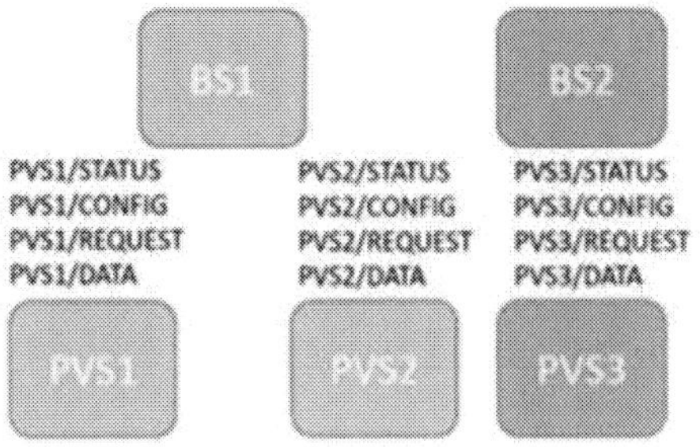

Figure 6. MQTT communication architecture where the same broker handles several PV systems and BS.

schematic diagram of the MQTT communication architecture, with several BS and PV systems in the same MQTT broker. However, each BS (PV system owner) can only access the PV systems to which it has been granted access.

4 CONCLUSIONS

This work presents the development of a low-cost solution for the online monitoring of PV systems, designed to be embedded directly into the PV module's junction box. Conceived as a self-testing system, the device addresses the limitations of traditional monitoring methods, which are often expensive or incapable of detecting failures at the individual module level. The proposed methodology allows for the estimation of the I-V characteristic around the PV module's operating point and its substrings without requiring disconnection from the system, with measurements completed in just a few milliseconds. This approach not only optimizes maintenance activities and reduces in-field inspections but also promises to improve the performance ratio and minimize degradation, thereby extending the lifespan of the modules.

The diagnostic capability of the device is comprehensive, providing detailed information on the status of each module. From the partial I-V curve, two key metrics are derived: degradation, which quantifies power losses associated with failures within the module itself, and misfit, which identifies performance issues caused by the rest of the system. Furthermore, the system can estimate electrical parameters such as series and shunt resistances and saturation currents. An additional feature is the ability to assess the integrity of the bypass diodes by individually accessing the module's substrings, enabling more precise fault detection.

The solution is implemented as an IoT device using an ESP32 microcontroller with Wi-Fi communications. To ensure reliability in large-scale installations, the communication architecture will be based on a mesh topology network. The MQTT protocol was selected for its efficiency in networks with limited resources as the one that is being developed on this work.

The proposed system, for which the first prototype is being manufactured, will be validated on a 50 kW PV system within the SUPERNOVA project, demonstrating its potential for remote, scalable, and robust monitoring of PV systems.

5 ACKNOWLEDGEMENTS

The European Union's Horizon Europe programme is acknowledged for financial support through the SUPERNOVA project (Grant Agreement No 101146883).

6 REFERENCES

[1] A. Jager-Waldau, Snapshot of photovoltaics - February 2024. EPJ Photovoltaics, vol. 15, p. 21, 2024.

[2] G. Blaesser, PV system measurements and monitoring the European experience. Solar Energy Materials, vol. 47, pp. 167-176, 1997.

[3] A. Louwen, S. Lindig, G. Chowdhury and D. Moser, Climate-and Technology-Dependent Performance Loss Rates in a Large Commercial Photovoltaic Monitoring Dataset. Solar RRL, vol. 8, p. 2300653, 2024.

[4] H. Al Mahdi, P.G. Leahy, M. Alghoul and A.P. Morrison, A Review of Photovoltaic Module Failure and Degradation Mechanisms: Causes and Detection Techniques. Solar, vol. 4, pp. 43-82, 2024.

[5] Jordan, D. C., Perry, K., White, R., and Deline, C. Extreme weather and PV performance. IEEE Journal of Photovoltaics, 13(6), 830-835. 2023

[6] E. Ortega, G. Aranguren, M.J. Saenz, R. Gutierrez and J.C. Jimeno, Study of Photovoltaic Systems Monitoring Methods, in 44th IEEE Photovoltaic Specialist Conference (IEEE PVSC), 2017.

[7] Aghaei, M., Kolahi, M., Nedaei, A., Venkatesh, N. S., Esmailifar, S. M., Moradi Sizkouhi, A. M., ... & Rüther, R. Autonomous Intelligent Monitoring of Photovoltaic Systems: An In-Depth Multidisciplinary Review. Progress in Photovoltaics: Research and Applications, 33(3), 381-409. 2025.

[8] Jones, C. B., Ellis, B. H., Stein, J. S., and Walters, J. Comparative review of high resolution monitoring versus standard inverter data acquisition for a single photovoltaic power plant. In 2018 IEEE 7th World Conference on Photovoltaic Energy Conversion. pp. 0715-0720. 2018.

[9] E. Ortega, G. Aranguren and J.C. Jimeno, New monitoring method to characterize individual modules in large photovoltaic systems. Solar Energy, vol. 193, pp. 906-914, 2019.

[10] E. Ortega, G. Aranguren and J.C. Jimeno, Photovoltaic modules transient response analysis and correction under a fast characterization system. Solar Energy, vol. 221, pp. 232-242, 2021.

[11] Rodriguez, S. M., Chicote, B., Ortega, E., Aranguren, G., and Jimeno, J. C. Software tool for weather parameters acquisition during photovoltaic systems monitoring. IEEE 53rd Photovoltaic Specialists Conference. pp. 0621-0626. 2025.

[12] Kane, M. M., Taylor, N., and Månsson, D. Electromagnetic interference from solar photovoltaic systems: A Review. Electronics, *14*(1), 31. 2024.

Photovoltaic modules self-testing by junction box-embedded wireless monitoring solution

Eneko Ortega[*,1,2], Gerardo Aranguren[2], Julius Denafas[3],
Paulius Laurikėnas[3], Ricardo Alonso[4] and Juan Carlos Jimeno[2]
*eneko.ortegam@ehu.eus
[1]Technological Institute of Microelectronics, UPV/EHU, 48013, Bilbao, Spain
[2]Electricity and Electronics Department, UPV/EHU, 48940, Leioa, Spain
[3]Solitek, 08412, Vilnius, Lithuania
[4]TECNALIA, Basque Research and Technology Alliance (BRTA), 48160, Derio, Spain

Introduction

- Exponential PV growth requires maximized performance and reliability.
- Power losses reach up to **15%** due to failures (cracks, shadows, etc.).
- System/string-level monitoring **fails to detect individual module faults.**
- Full I-V measurement is costly, hard to automate, and requires **disconnection**.

Aim

To introduce a low-cost self-testing IoT device embedded into the PV module's junction box with access to the PV modules substrings and modules bypass diodes and to determine PV module status.

Self-testing device

Circuit and Measurement:

- **Low-cost**, low-power electronic circuit .
- Based on two **capacitors** (tens of μF) and six switches .
- Method: Varies operating point by modifying output current (± 0.3 A).
- Partial I-V measurement completed in **milliseconds**.
- Estimates static I-V partial characteristic around the operating point.

Sensors and Functionality:

- Integrated sensors: Temperature, Illumination (front/rear), and **Dirt sensor**.
- Provides individual access to module **substrings**.
- New feature: Evaluates **bypass diode** integrity by accessing the negative voltage region.

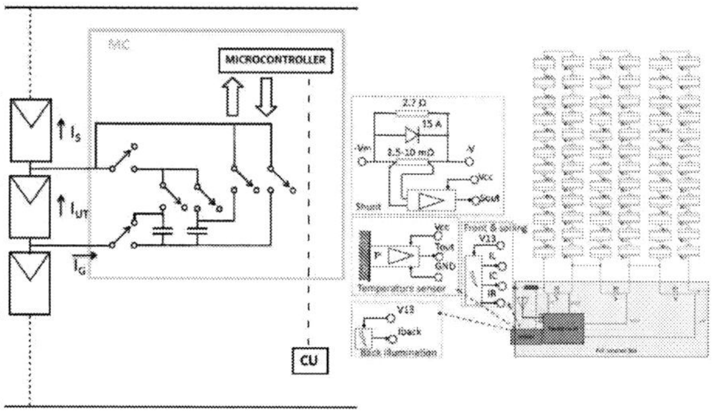

Diagnostics and metrics

Two key numbers obtained for each PV module:

1. DEGRADATION

- Quantifies losses from **internal module failures.**
- $Degradation = 1 - \frac{MPP}{EP}$ (Maximum Power Point / Expected Power).

2. MISFIT

- Identifies performance issues caused by the **rest of the system**.
- $Mismatch = 1 - \frac{WP}{MPP}$ (Working Point / Maximum Power Point).

- Other estimated parameters: Series/shunt resistances and saturation currents.

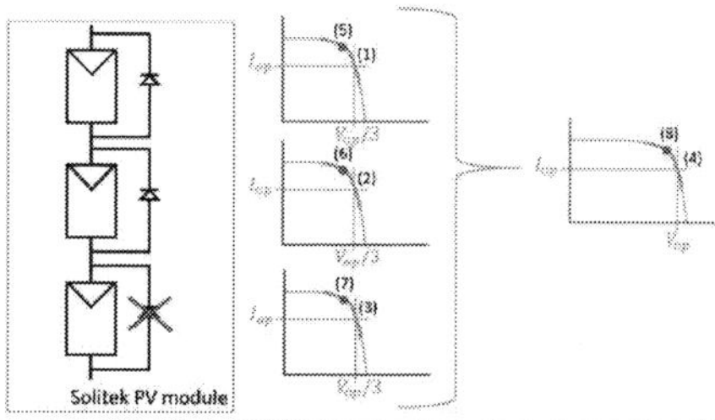

IoT Communication

1. Hardware and Protocol

- IoT device uses **ESP32 microcontroller** (low-cost, Wi-Fi).
- Protocol: **MQTT** (lightweight, efficient, Publish/Subscribe model).

2. Network and Challenges

- Challenges: Large distance, unstable conditions, **EMI** (Electromagnetic Interference).
- Topology: **Mesh Network** deployed for fault tolerance and self-healing in large systems.
- Flow: Base Station (BS) manages configuration, status reporting, and data Requests/Responses via structured topics.

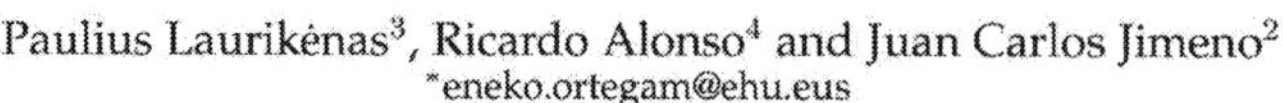

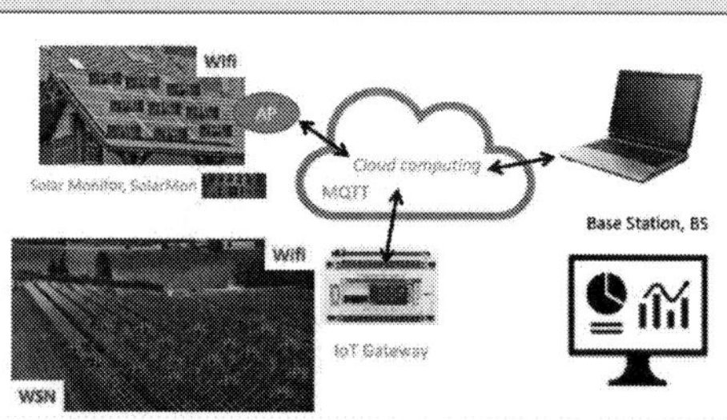

Acknowledgements

The European Union's Horizon Europe programme is acknowledged for financial support through the SUPERNOVA project (Grant Agreement No 101146883).

Conclusions

- **Low-cost, embedded online monitoring solution** developed, addressing traditional limitations.
- Fast I-V estimation and robust diagnostics (Degradation/Misfit) provided .
- IoT architecture (**Mesh/MQTT**) ensures reliability and scalability.
- Validation is underway on a **50 kW PV system**.

DATA-DRIVEN ASSESSMENT OF INVERTER EFFICIENCY LOSSES AND LOAD PROFILES IN PV SYSTEMS

David Daßler[*,1], Stephanie Malik[1], Dharm Patel, Andreas Dietrich[2], Jan Spihola[2], Kai Kaufmann[3], Carsten Hennig[4], Robert Klengel[1], Carola Klute[1], Ulrike Jahn[1], Matthias Ebert[1]

[1] Fraunhofer IMWS, Fraunhofer Institute for Microstructure of Materials and Systems IMWS, Walter-Hülse-Straße 1, 06120 Halle (Saale)
[2] DiSUN, Deutsche Solarservice GmbH, Mielestraße 2, 14542 Werder (Havel)
[3] DENKweit GmbH, Blücherstraße 26, 06120 Halle
[4] saferay holding GmbH, Rosenthaler Str. 34-35, 10178 Berlin
* = corresponding author: david.dassler@csp.fraunhofer.de

ABSTRACT: Maximizing energy yield in photovoltaic (PV) systems requires a precise understanding of losses and their root causes – they originate from either the inverter or the PV-generator side. Both parts experience multiple internal and external stresses, degradation mechanisms, and defects. A systematic distinction between these sources is essential for optimizing performance, reducing downtime, and implementing effective maintenance strategies. The approach presented in this study focuses on losses and operational stresses of inverters.
We present a data-driven approach that combines device-level stress comparisons with performance modeling using artificial neural networks to quantify long-term inverter efficiency losses. Based on 11 years of high-resolution monitoring data from a PV plant with nine identical central inverters, we investigate device-resolved differences in thermal loads, inverter clipping, and ventilation impacts. Even though the inverters are nominally identical and part of the same system, the results show pronounced thermal heterogeneities more than 5 °C on average per year, diverging ventilation profiles and increasing cooling effort over time, and strongly varying clipping exposure across devices. Long-term analysis indicates a systematic efficiency decline of approximately 2 percentage points over the operation lifetime, especially at moderate AC power levels. The combined method enables device-level stress profiling, trend detection from standard monitoring data and provides insights for predictive maintenance and lifecycle management.

Keywords: system monitoring, inverter, inverter efficiency, stress profile, machine learning

1 INTRODUCTION

Maximizing and stabilizing energy yield is essential to the technical and economic viability of photovoltaic (PV) systems worldwide. As PV assets grow, persistent efficiency losses translate into significant revenue impacts and undermine long-term energy forecasts, warranties, and financial assumptions. Ensuring high yield therefore requires not only periodic field inspections but also continuous performance assurance during operation.

Utility-scale PV plants are complex systems comprising thousands of interacting components – from cables, modules, and combiners to power electronics, transformers, monitoring, and control. Their interactions lead to the accumulation of multiple loss mechanisms along the generation chain. Typical contributors include, on the generator (DC side): soiling, shading, thermal ventilation, angle-dependency, ohmic losses, module quality variations, and long-term module degradation; and on the AC side: inverter or transformer conversion losses, cooling effects, clipping or grid-dependent curtailment (see [1], [2]) and injection. Because these effects vary with time, system layout, operating state, and weather, the resulting yield losses are highly dynamic and often difficult to attribute to a specific cause.

A closer look at losses is important for three reasons: (i) small systematic drifts accumulate over years, (ii) the correct attribution of component-driven losses is required, and (iii) device-specific actionable insights are needed to prevent localized overload and premature aging.

Conventional key performance-based monitoring (e.g., performance ratio, PR) is useful for reporting but provides limited causal resolution. Physics-based or empirical models (e.g., single- or two-diode models, module temperature models, see [3] and [4]) help, under controlled assumptions, to adjust estimations but struggle to capture proprietary control software, internal regulation, and the dynamic maximum power point tracking of inverters. Data-driven approaches, including machine learning, have shown potential for performance estimation and fault detection [5]. However, they often fail to capture device-level differences caused by site-specific and operational dependencies. Furthermore, long-term studies of module degradation (%/a) are well documented. Comparable studies on inverter stability are lacking.

The aim of this study was to develop a data-driven approach to systematically identify and quantify yield losses in PV systems. Understanding losses and their underlying mechanisms, whether caused by inverters or the PV generator, is crucial for enhancing system reliability, optimizing performance, and implementing effective maintenance strategies.

To achieve this, the study adopts two complementary perspectives. First, a comprehensive assessment of operational stress factors is conducted, considering thermal loads, inverter clipping, and ventilation effects. This enables a first characterization of how different stress factors and their frequencies affect system components over time.

Second, long-term inverter efficiency (P_{AC}/P_{DC}) trends are analyzed using historical operational data and machine-learning-based modeling. While physics-based

10.4229/EUPVSEC2025/4CV.1.52

models of inverter performance require detailed knowledge of internal system components, inverters are complex multicomponent devices influenced by both internal factors, operational and site-specific conditions. Moreover, inverter behavior is controlled by proprietary software algorithms that are not openly accessible and may introduce additional performance uncertainties or software-related anomalies. Artificial neural networks (ANN) enable a data-driven representation of real-world inverter behavior by capturing performance patterns when trained on data collected shortly after commissioning. This provides a robust method that accounts for site- and device-specific characteristics.

By comparing the expected performance with actual measured system performance, this approach enables a systematic evaluation of efficiency losses and helps identify potential loss patterns over time.

2 MATERIAL AND METHODS

2.1 Data source

This study draws on extensive, multi-year monitoring datasets from a utility-scale PV plant totaling 5.7 MWp. One-minute operational records of inverter performance provide a robust basis for analysis. As an initial step, a rigorous data quality assessment was performed using strict criteria to verify the plausibility, completeness, and internal consistency of the data.

The investigation focuses on nine subsystems, each equipped with a central inverter of the same type rated between 500 and 700 kWp, installed in Germany in a temperate climate, and monitored eleven years (2013–2023). The dataset comprises inverter measurements and status signals, as well as plane-of-array irradiance measured by a pyranometer and ambient temperature, all at one-minute resolution. The system is equipped with crystalline silicon PV modules.

2.2 Inverter efficiency modeling

For modeling inverter efficiency, an artificial neural network was used, trained on preprocessed operational and environmental data. The model was designed to predict the DC current, DC voltage, and DC power (P_{DC}), the AC power (P_{AC}), and inverter efficiency η_{Inv}.

Inverter efficiency was calculated as follows:

$$\eta_{Inv}\ [\%] = \frac{P_{AC}}{P_{DC}}\ 100$$

The training data comprised one year of data collected shortly after plant commissioning and was randomly split into training (70%) and test (30%) subsets to ensure an unbiased evaluation. Model inputs are plane-of-array irradiance, solar position (azimuth, elevation), and ambient temperature.

The ANN architecture used in this study, summarized in Table **I**, builds on prior work from other projects, which is described in detail in publications [6], [7]. Consequently, the following discussion focuses solely on the results of this investigation without detailing the modeling details.

The agreement between the model predictions and the actual measurements is illustrated in Figure 1 for a single inverter for both P_{AC} and η_{Inv}.

Table I: Dataset and parameters used for ANN modeling

Dataset	Hyperparameters
input: irradiance (POA) ambient temperature sun position (azimuth, elevation)	Batch size: 128 Activation function: ReLU Optimizer ADAM
output: DC current DC voltage DC power AC power Inverter efficiency	Loss function: Huber Epochs: 200
time frame: 1 year (1 min interval); 2014	

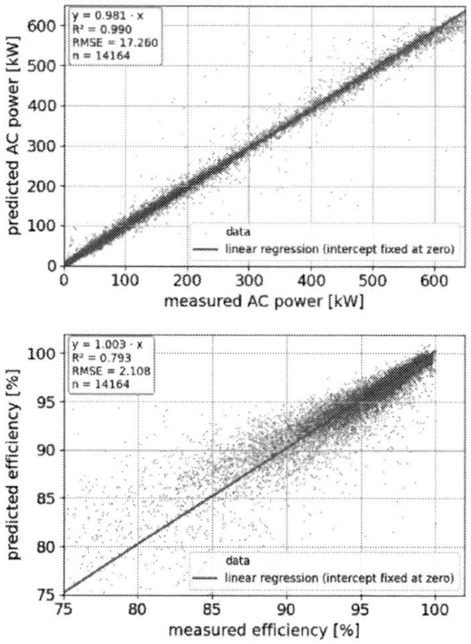

Figure 1: Comparison of measured and predicted values for one inverter. Top: P_{AC}, Bottom: η_{Inv}; Linear regression (red) with fit parameters is added for reference

To assess model quality, we used the Mean Absolute Percentage Error (MAPE), which computes the model error relative to the actual (measured) value (with $|x_{meas}(i)| > 0$ for all i):

$$MAPE\ [\%] = \frac{1}{N}\sum_{i=1}^{N}\left|\frac{x_{meas}(i) - x_{pred}(i)}{x_{meas}(i)}\right|\ 100$$

In this formula, x_{meas} denotes the measured (actual) values, x_{pred} the values predicted by the ANN, and N is the number of observations in the evaluation period. The advantage of MAPE over other error measures is that it evaluates error relative to the actual value. While high values (e.g., in summer) can lead to larger absolute errors, deviations at low values (e.g., in winter) are typically smaller. To enable comparability, the error is expressed relative to the actual value. A lower MAPE indicates higher model accuracy. The MAPE values for the model outputs are shown in Table II.

Table II: MAPE results for training period

	I_{DC}	V_{DC}	P_{DC}	P_{AC}	η_{Inv}
MAPE [%]	7.65	1.14	7.64	9.36	1.21

3 RESULTS

3.1 Operational stress factors

Matrix temperature is defined as the internal temperature of the power stage (power electronics matrix), measured at the heatsink or at the power module baseplate near the IGBT or MOSFET. The Figure 2 and Figure 3 show the Matrix Temperature distribution using kernel density estimation (KDE) for all inverters in two different years, based on 1-minute-resolution monitoring data. Two inverters are highlighted with bold lines (Inv 4 & Inv 7) to emphasize their differences with respect to matrix temperature.

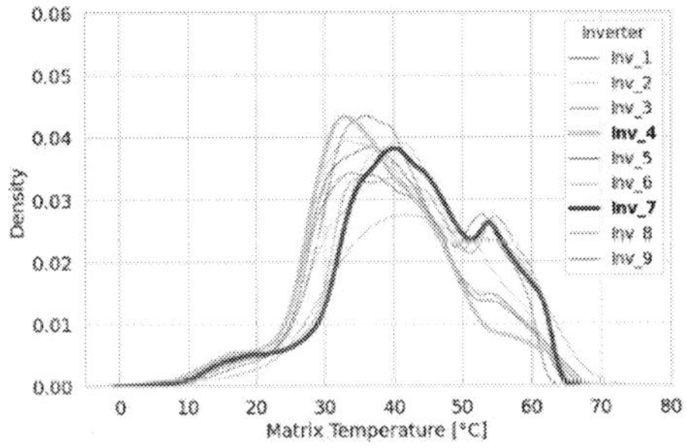

Figure 2: Matrix temperature distribution for year 2013 for all investigated inverters; Inv 4 and Inv 7 in bold for comparison

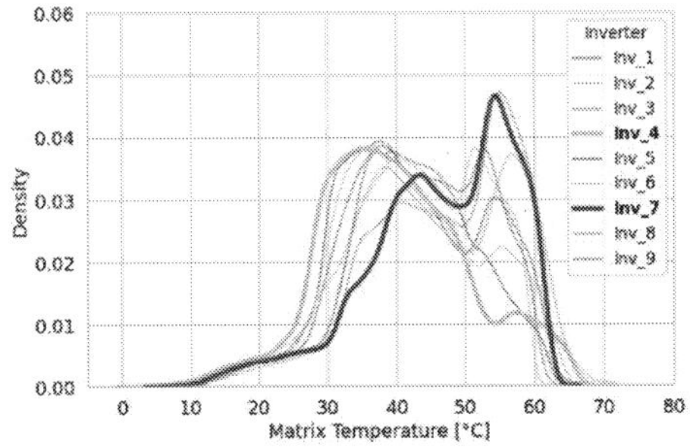

Figure 3: Matrix temperature distribution for year 2022 for all investigated inverters; Inv 4 and Inv 7 in bold for comparison

To further highlight the differences in matrix temperature between the two inverters (Inv 4 and Inv 7), an additional box plot was used, see Figure 4. This figure summarizes the distribution to compare central tendency, spread, and outliers across the inverters and years. Both the interquartile ranges and the medians of the two inverters differ markedly; their medians are at least 5 °C apart, from the very beginning.

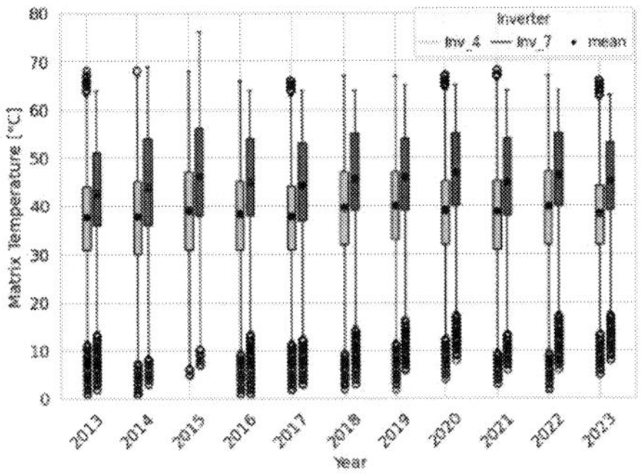

Figure 4: Annual Matrix Temperature for Inv 4 and Inv 7

Clipping in PV systems refers to the limitation of inverter output when the DC power available from the PV array exceeds the inverter's maximum capability. The inverter "clips" the power, producing a flat-topped AC power curve at or near its nameplate rating. The energy not converted is termed clipping loss. In this system, the DC/AC design ratio of all inverters is very moderate, at less than 1.2. Using the inverter status information, instances of clipping can be determined precisely. Figure 5 shows the number of minutes with clipping for each year and inverter. Inv 7 shows the highest number of clipping events.

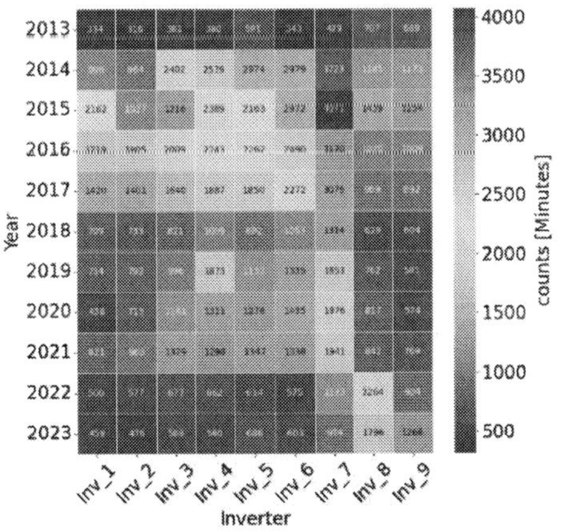

Figure 5: Minutes per year and inverter with clipping

In this context, the question arises whether clipping affects matrix temperature. To investigate this, 1-hours periods starting when clipping begins and ending one hour later were separated from the dataset for all clipping situations that occurred, and the median of the matrix temperature in these periods were calculated. These results are shown in Figure 6 for all inverters and years. Comparing Inv 4 and Inv 7 again, the median matrix temperatures differ by 5–12 °C. The figure illustrates significant differences in individual inverter behavior. While three inverters (Inv 1, Inv 4, and Inv 9) remain relatively cool, the matrix temperature of the most other inverters increases by approx. 10 °C.

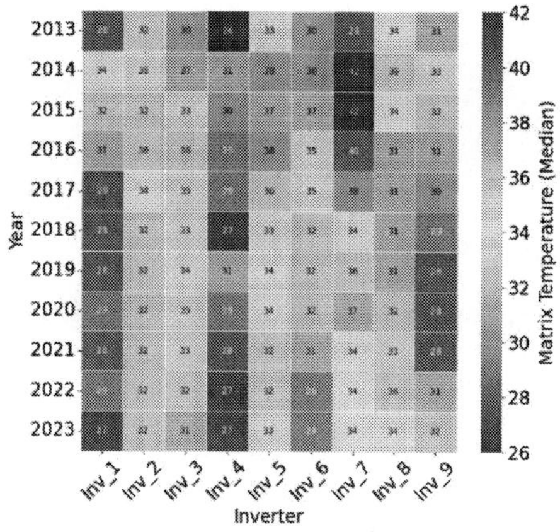

Figure 6: Median matrix temperature in °C during clipping events and one hour after

Another important factor affecting the performance of a PV inverter is ventilation. The fans are controlled by analog thermostats, and the only measured value is matrix temperature. The fans of the different inverters operate differently with respect to temperature thresholds and control cycles. A closer look at the matrix temperature throughout the day shows oscillations caused by ventilation switched on and off. At other times, when the inverter operates within its working range, the fan runs continuously, producing a smoother curve. This behavior is illustrated in Figure 7, for example, where the same devices (Inv 4 and Inv 7) are compared for a single day. The matrix temperature profiles are highly variable. In particular, the difference in cooling intensity is striking: while inverter 4 shows fewer but larger cooling ramps, inverter 7 exhibits many smaller and shorter cooling phases. These significant differences in high-frequency behavior will be examined further.

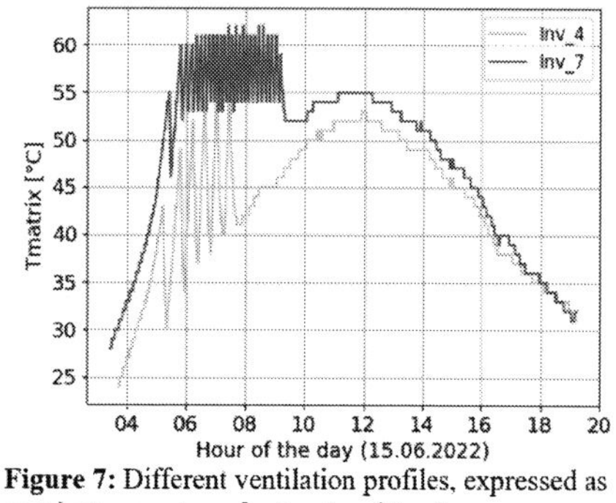

Figure 7: Different ventilation profiles, expressed as matrix temperature, for Inv 4 and Inv 7

To describe a possible decrease in ventilation intensity in high-frequency ranges, the local extreme points were determined. Subsequently, the difference between corresponding local minima and local maxima was calculated as Δ for each cooling process, removed by changes smaller 2 °C. The resulting frequency densities are shown in Figure 8 for five different years.

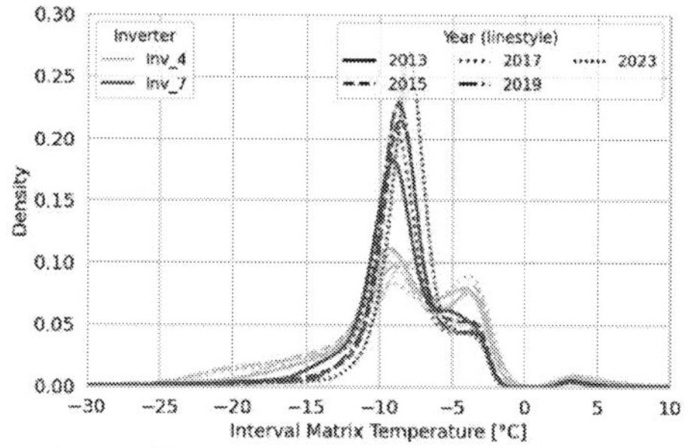

Figure 8: Difference of cooling impact Δ on matrix temperature for Inv 4 and Inv 7

It is apparent that cooling processes change slightly year to year. For example, the density curve for Inv 7 shifts to the right, indicating a change from higher to smaller absolute Δ temperatures (2013 to 2023).

3.2 Measured and predicted inverter efficiency

The measured–predicted comparison contrasts modeled and measured inverter efficiencies. The goal is to identify systematic deviations and possible causes.

Inverter efficiency is shown as a function of the inverter output power P_{AC} in Figure 9. Efficiency increases with increasing load. Inverters are optimized for specific load and voltage ranges in which they achieve their highest efficiency. At lower loads, they often operate outside their optimal range, so losses (e.g., switching and conversion losses, self-consumption by control electronics and cooling, and standby losses) carry greater weight in relative terms

This characteristic inverter efficiency curve is obtained by computing, over a given period, the median of efficiency values within separate power bins of several kilowatts each. The bin width depends on the inverter capacity; in this case, 10 kW (1.5% of rated capacity).

The curves shown in Figure 9 (measured and predicted) are based on an ANN model trained on inverter data shortly after commissioning and show close agreement. Figure 10 shows again the inverter efficiency as a function of the inverter's output power P_{AC} for the measured and predicted values but for 2023. Comparing efficiencies over the years of operation (2014 vs. 2023), increasing differences are evident. In the 40–50 kW range, efficiency differs by about 1.7 percentage points. Considering the model's accuracy in determining efficiency, a MAPE of 1.2% for the modeling year, this deviation exceeds the model error and should be regarded as relevant.

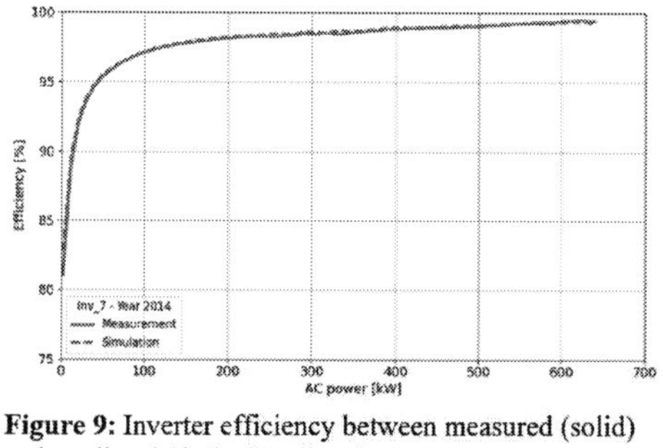

Figure 9: Inverter efficiency between measured (solid) and predicted (dashed) values for Inv 7, 2014

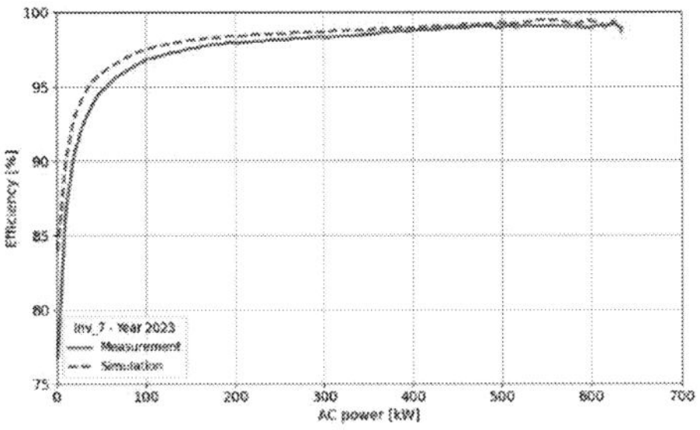

Figure 10: Inverter efficiency between measured (solid) and predicted (dashed) values for Inv 7, 2023

For comparison with Inv 7, Inv 4's efficiencies as a function of P_{AC} for 2014 (see Figure 11) and 2023 (see Figure 12) are also shown, respectively. In 2014 (the modeling year), measured and modeled efficiencies align almost perfectly, as they do for Inv 7. For 2023, Inv 4 shows smaller deviations than Inv 7; in the 40–50 kW range, the deviation is 0.8 percentage points.

In a previous publication [8], we examined in more detail whether the PV generator degraded in terms of its voltage level, which could have affected inverter operating by shifting it into less efficient regions. However, this was ruled out: the DC-side voltage level remained very stable over the period considered. We therefore conclude that a genuine change has occurred at the inverter level.

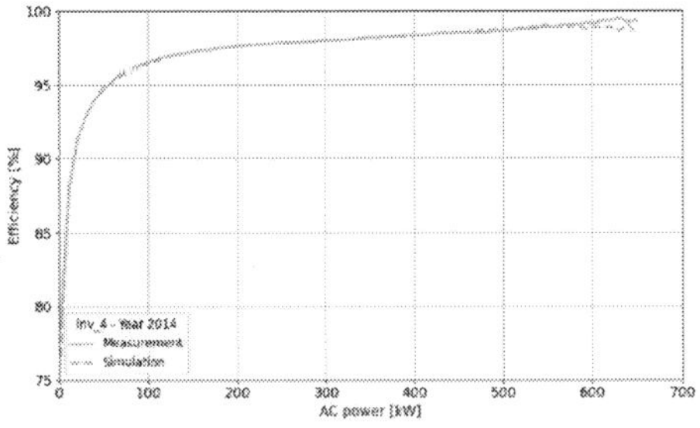

Figure 11: Comparison of inverter efficiency between measured (solid) and predicted (dashed) values, for Inv 4, 2014

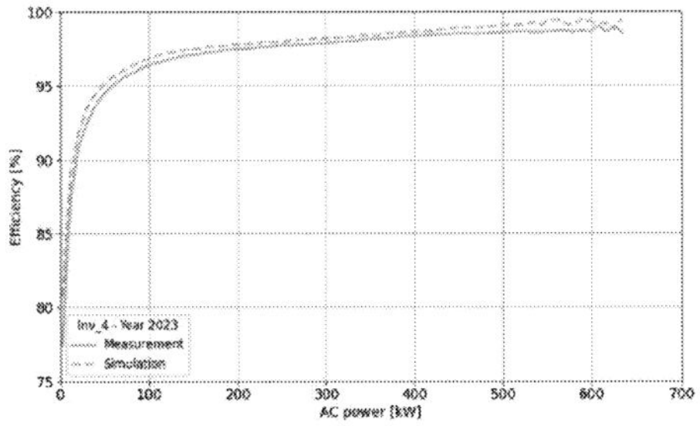

Figure 12: Comparison of inverter efficiency between measured (solid) and predicted (dashed) values, for Inv 4, 2023

4 DISCUSSION

The analysis reveal pronounced thermal heterogeneity (see Figure 2 & Figure 3). Despite being nominally identical and operating within the same plant, inverters exhibit markedly different matrix temperature distributions, with mean offset of up to 4 °C. These persistent differences translate into non-uniform thermal stress and aging, underscoring the need for device-level diagnostics rather than plant-level averages.

A second key observation is ventilation drift (see Figure 8). Cooling profiles vary significantly across devices, and the intensity of cooling ramps changes over time, indicating that fan behavior and thermal management changes gradually with age. This effect contributes to additional stress and explains part of the heterogeneity in temperature behavior.

Device-level stress also varies widely in frequency and intensity within the same plant. Factors such as clipping, shutdowns, and partial-load operation create distinct stress signatures, which can only be captured by constructing individual load and stress profiles for each inverter.

Over the long term, a systematic efficiency decline is evident. Across 11 years, efficiency decreased by approximately 1.7 percentage points (~0.2 %pt./a), with the strongest deviation occurring under partial-load conditions (around 10% P_{AC}, see Figure 10). This highlights the importance of monitoring low-P_{AC} regions, which are particularly sensitive to efficiency drift and often overlooked in conventional performance metrics. It is assumed that inverters are optimized for high power ranges in order to minimize conversion losses at high power levels. Small power ranges, as discussed, which are primarily used in the morning and evening hours, may be more susceptible to thermal loads.

Finally, these findings depend strongly on data quality. High-resolution monitoring data must be accompanied by rigorous plausibility checks, validation of sensor accuracy, and awareness of the inverter's operational state. Without such preprocessing, results risk being biased or misinterpreted.

5 CONCLUSION

The present study provides key insights into analyzing inverter efficiency losses in PV systems. By applying artificial neural networks (ANN), complex nonlinear relationships between operating parameters and environmental conditions were modeled with high precision. This enabled the identification and quantification of systematic efficiency losses that are highly relevant to PV plant operators.

The model accuracy depends strongly on the quality, completeness, and plausibility of operational data; faulty or incomplete data can impede the detection of efficiency losses. In this study, the trained ANN models achieved high predictive accuracy, with a mean absolute percentage error (MAPE) of 1.2% for inverter efficiency. This level of accuracy allows even small deviations between measured and modeled reference values to be detected reliably.

10.4229/EUPVSEC2025/4CV.1.52

Over time, we observed a systematic decrease in inverter efficiency of about 1.7 percentage points over ten years for a representative inverter, indicating long-term degradation mechanisms that are insufficiently monitored in current practice. In addition, a comprehensive assessment of operational stress factors, including clipping and ventilation, revealed their strong influence on inverter matrix temperature. There is pronounced thermal heterogeneity across apparently identical inverter, with temperature distributions differing by several degrees. These differences result in non-uniform thermal stress, accelerated aging, and diverging ventilation behaviors, with some inverters requiring progressively more cooling effort. Stress exposure also varies widely in frequency and intensity within the same plant, underscoring the need for device-specific stress and load profiles rather than plant-level averages.

These insights offer a valuable foundation for optimizing operation and maintenance strategies. Based on the identified efficiency losses and stress patterns, operators can implement targeted measures to extend inverter lifetimes, reduce unplanned downtime, and enhance overall PV system performance, by reducing or mitigating detected stresses and their potential causes. Early detection of deviations enables proactive responses and risk-based maintenance planning, ultimately supporting higher system reliability, improving profitability, and more accurate lifetime forecasting.

6 ACKNOWLEDGEMENT

Research was partially funded by the German Federal Bank Investitionsbank Sachsen-Anhalt, the German Federal State Saxony-Anhalt and the European Regional Development Fund (EFRE) in the project "KliMaTE" (ref.: 8377/1758) and „3D-Prove" (ref.: I 193) as well as by project "robStROM" (ref.: 03EE1163B) by the Federal Ministry for Economic Affairs and Climate Action in Germany.

7 REFERENCES

[1] S. Malik, D. Daßler, D. Patel, C. Klute, R. Klengel, A. Dietrich, K. Kaufmann, C. Hennig, D. Wehnert, M. Ebert. Analysis of Fault Detection and Defect Categorization in Photovoltaic Inverters for Enhanced Reliability and Efficiency in Large-Scale Solar Energy Systems. EPJ Photovoltaics 16, 25 (2025). Accepted 27.03.2025. Published 27.05.2025. DOI: https://doi.org/10.1051/epjpv/2025011

[2] S. Malik, D. Daßler, D. Patel, R. Klengel, C. Klute, M. Ebert. robStROM: Zuverlässiger Betrieb von PV-Wechselrichtern. PV Days – PV-Systeme: Optimierte Betriebsführung und Risikobewertung. 28. November 2024. Halle

[3] Gupta, P., & Singh, R. (2021). PV power forecasting based on data-driven models: a review. International, Journal of Sustainable Engineering, 14(6), 1733–1755. DOI: https://doi.org/10.1080/19397038.2021.1986590

[4] Martin János Mayer, Gyula Gróf. Extensive comparison of physical models for photovoltaic power forecasting. Applied Energy. Volume 283. 2021. DOI: https://doi.org/10.1016/j.apenergy.2020.116239.

[5] IEA-PVPS. Task 13 Report "The Use of Advanced Algorithms in PV Failure Monitoring". Report T13-19:2021. 2021. ISBN 978-3-907281-07-9

[6] D. Daßler, S. Malik, R. Gottschalg, M. Ebert. Effect of Availability and Quality of Data on the Detection of Defects Utilizing Artificial Neural Networks in PV System's Monitoring Data. 8th World Conference on Photovoltaic Energy Conversion. Milan. September 2022. DOI: https://10.4229/WCPEC-82022-4DO.1.5.

[7] D. Daßler, S.B. Kuppanna, S. Malik, R. Schmidt, M. Ebert. Training and Evaluation for Yield-Driven Detection of Losses in PV Systems Utilizing Artificial Neural Networks. IEEE 47th Photovoltaic Specialists Conference (PVSC). Virtual. 2020. DOI: https://10.1109/PVSC45281.2020.9300490

[8] D. Daßler, S. Malik, D. Patel, A. Dietrich, J. Spihola, K. Kaufmann, C. Hennig, R. Klengel, C. Klute, M. Ebert. Analyse der Effizienzverluste von Wechselrichtern in PV-Portfolios durch Auswertung von Betriebsdaten. 40. PV-Symposium. 2025.

42nd European Photovoltaic Solar Energy Conference and Exhibition

This presentation was selected by the Sc. Committee of the EU PVSEC 2025 for submission of a full paper to one of the EU PVSEC's collaborating peer-reviewed journals.

ENHANCING AUTONOMOUS AERIAL MONITORING OF LARGE-SCALE PHOTOVOLTAIC PLANTS USING A DEEP REINFORCEMENT LEARNING APPROACH FOR MULTI-AERIAL ROBOT SYSTEMS

A. Aghamohammadi [1], S.M. Esmaeilifar [1], M. Kolahi [2], A. Moradi Sizkouhi [3], and M. Aghaei[4,5*]

[1] Department of Aerospace Engineering, Amirkabir University of Technology, Tehran 15119-43943, Iran
[2] Department of Mechanical Engineering, Faculty of Engineering, University of Isfahan, 81746-73441, Isfahan, Iran
[3]Department of Electrical and Computer Engineering, Concordia University, Montreal, QC H3G 1M8, Canada
[4]Department of Ocean Operations and Civil Engineering, Norwegian University of Science and Technology (NTNU), 6009 Ålesund, Norway
[5]Department of Sustainable Systems Engineering (INATECH), University of Freiburg, 79110 Freiburg, Germany

*mohammadreza.aghaei@ntnu.no

ABSTRACT: Efficient inspection of large-scale photovoltaic (PV) power plants can be achieved using a multi-aerial robot system powered by Deep Reinforcement Learning (DRL). This study introduces an innovative algorithm for online coverage path planning to optimize the efficiency, scalability, and adaptability of multi-aerial robot systems. By dynamically adapting to real-time environmental changes, the algorithm ensures comprehensive inspection coverage while reducing computational overhead. Simulations conducted in both grid-based and realistic environments demonstrate the algorithm's robustness and its potential to revolutionize inspection tasks in dynamic and complex scenarios.

Keywords: Photovoltaic (PV) plants; Autonomous aerial monitoring (AAM), Artificial intelligence (AI), Deep Reinforcement Learning (DRL), Dueling Deep Q-network

1. INTRODUCTION

Large-scale photovoltaic (PV) power plants are anticipated to be a dominant renewable energy source by mid-century, playing a significant role in meeting the world's electricity needs. Ensuring their efficiency and reliability requires advanced monitoring strategies that can detect defects early, optimize energy yield, and reduce operational costs [1]. Aerial robots have emerged as an effective means of conducting inspections more quickly, accurately, and cost-effectively than conventional methods, significantly lowering monitoring expenses and labor requirements [2, 3]. This study presents a deep reinforcement learning (DRL)-based multi-aerial robot inspection framework that enables real-time coverage path planning, dynamic coordination, and collision avoidance for large-scale PV installations. The approach leverages Dueling Double Deep Q-Network (D3QN) architecture enhanced with Prioritized Experience Replay (PER), NoisyNets, and n-step returns, providing robust decision-making capabilities under high variability in environmental and operational conditions.

A Voronoi relaxation-based method is introduced to ensure balanced sub-area allocation, distributing inspection workloads evenly among multiple drones regardless of the solar field's irregular geometry. To maintain safe operation during multi-robot missions, a physics-based repulsive-force model dynamically adjusts flight paths to prevent collisions.

The system's RoboNN architecture integrates convolutional layers with batch normalization and fully connected layers, enabling stable and efficient learning while handling both abstract spatial representations and photorealistic visual inputs.

The framework supports online path planning, allowing aerial robots to adapt in real time to environmental changes such as variable lighting, wind effects, and unexpected obstacles. Furthermore, the scalable coordination mechanism allows efficient deployment of any number of drones to cover vast and irregularly shaped PV arrays without sacrificing inspection completeness or efficiency.

The proposed system is evaluated in both a simplified grid-world environment for algorithmic validation and a high-fidelity PV inspection simulation built on "Digital-PV" [4-7], modeling realistic aerodynamics, environmental disturbances, and camera-based defect detection scenarios. Experimental results demonstrate high coverage efficiency, low inspection redundancy, and real-time adaptability to dynamic conditions, verifying the system's suitability for operational deployment.

By integrating advanced DRL-based decision-making with scalable multi-robot coordination and intelligent collision avoidance, this study contributes to a flexible and high-performance solution that has the potential to reduce inspection time, lower operational costs, and ensure sustained energy yield reliability in the next generation of large-scale PV power plants.

2. SCIENTIFIC INNOVATION AND RELEVANCE

This study presents several innovations that address key challenges in multi-aerial robot systems:

- Dynamic Adaptability: Unlike conventional pre-planned paths, the proposed algorithm enables robots to adapt dynamically to environmental changes, such as obstacles or new area boundaries.
- Generalization: The algorithm generalizes to diverse environmental shapes and conditions, ensuring its applicability to a wide range of real-world scenarios.

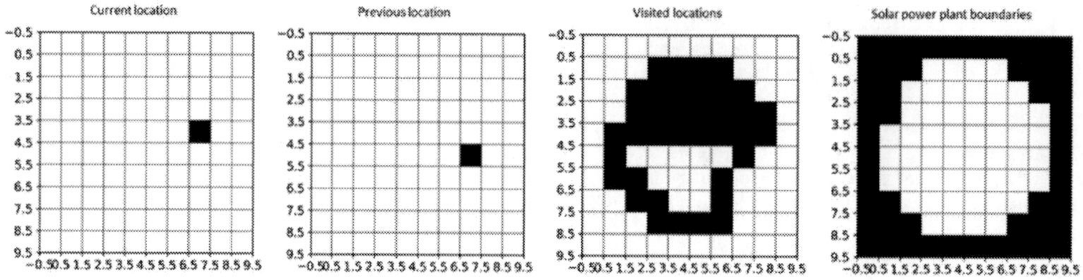

Figure 1 Space state description

- Collision Avoidance Mechanism: The repulsive force model integrates seamlessly into the system, ensuring safe and conflict-free navigation in multi-agent systems.
- Neural Network Advancements: The RoboNN architecture incorporates advanced DRL techniques, such as Dueling DQN and Prioritized Experience Replay, for better policy learning and decision-making efficiency.

The relevance of this work lies in its potential to improve the inspection of large-scale photovoltaic plants, reducing time, costs, and risks associated with manual methods. Its scalability and adaptability make it suitable for a variety of industrial applications.

3. DEEP REINFORCEMENT LEARNING

In the proposed framework, the environment is represented as a matrix that encodes four key elements: the distinction between visited and unvisited cells, the current and previous aerial robot position, and the location of obstacles as shown in Fig. 1. This spatial encoding ensures that the learning agent perceives both its operational context and the progress of its coverage task. The aerial robot operates within a discrete action space consisting of five possible maneuvers: moving forward, moving backward, rotating left, rotating right, or remaining stationary. The learning process is guided by a carefully designed reward function that combines positive incentives with penalties to encourage efficient and safe navigation. The aerial robot receives a positive reward when it successfully explores new cells and an additional terminal bonus when full coverage is achieved. Conversely, redundant revisits to already explored regions, unnecessary or excessive turning maneuvers, and collisions or near-miss events incur penalties, discouraging inefficient or unsafe behavior.

To approximate the optimal policy, a dueling deep Q-network (DQN) architecture is employed. The state matrix is processed by a convolutional neural network composed of four successive 3×3 convolutional layers, each followed by batch normalization to stabilize training. The resulting feature maps are flattened and concatenated with auxiliary information, forming a comprehensive feature vector. This vector is then split into two parallel streams: the value stream, which estimates the overall quality of a state, and the advantage stream, which evaluates the relative benefit of each action. Their outputs are recombined to produce the final Q-values, enabling more robust learning and faster convergence compared to traditional DQN formulations.

4. COORDINATION AND COLLISION AVOIDANCE

To ensure efficient multi-aerial robot operations, the environment is first partitioned into sub-areas using Voronoi diagrams constructed from the initial deployment positions of the agents. This geometric approach guarantees non-overlapping regions of responsibility while minimizing redundant coverage. Since differences in flight capacity may lead to workload imbalances, an iterative boundary relaxation procedure is applied to adjust dthe partitions dynamically. Through this process, the workload is redistributed according to the endurance and capabilities of each aerial robot, improving overall mission efficiency.

Collision avoidance is addressed through a decentralized strategy that combines local sensing and control. Each aerial robot continuously monitors the presence of neighboring agents within a predefined communication radius. When potential conflicts are detected, a smooth repulsive force function is applied to generate corrective avoidance maneuvers, thereby preventing abrupt or unstable deviations. This repulsive mechanism is integrated with a PID-based trajectory controller, which maintains adherence to the planned coverage path while ensuring safe separation between agents. The result is a coordinated system in which aerial robots achieve complete area coverage collaboratively while dynamically avoiding collisions.

5. SIMULATION AND EVALUATION

The proposed framework was first validated in a grid-world environment consisting of randomly generated 16×16 cell boundaries. Through training, the policy achieved a mean coverage rate of 99.6% with less than 9% redundancy, demonstrating both efficiency and completeness of area exploration. The learning process exhibited stable convergence, as reflected by a steadily decreasing loss curve over successive training episodes.

To further evaluate the system under realistic operating conditions, high-fidelity simulations were conducted using the "Digital-PV" environment. This platform accurately models environmental dynamics such as wind, gravity, and heterogeneous terrain, providing a physically grounded testbed for aerial robot coordination. Within this setting, the deep reinforcement learning policy was able to sustain real-time decision-making with an average action latency below 100 ms, ensuring responsiveness during flight. Across multiple cooperative aerial robot trials, the system consistently maintained safe separation, and no collision events were observed, confirming the robustness of the proposed coordination and collision avoidance strategies.

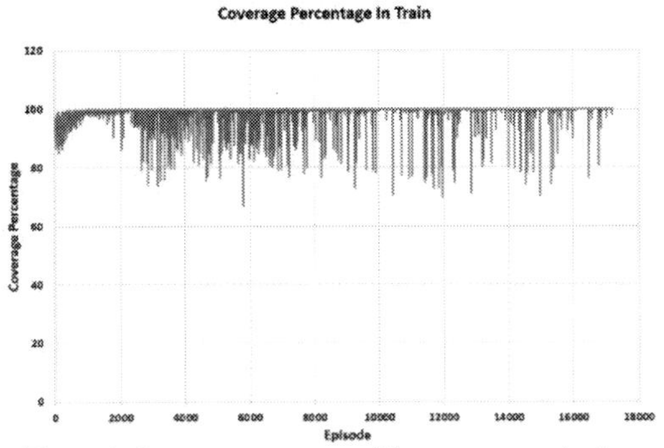

Figure 3: Coverage percentage of the agent over episodes.

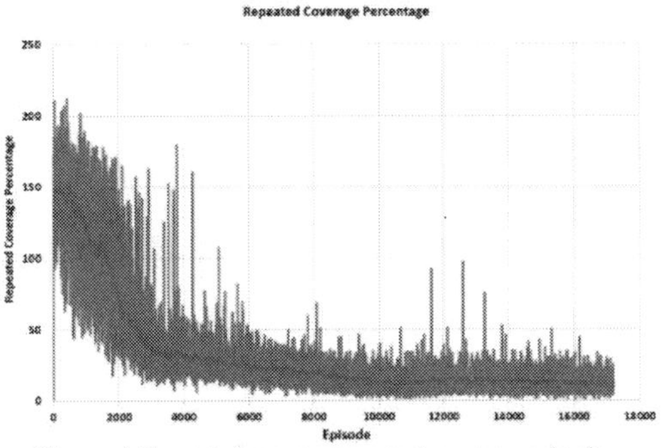

Figure 4: Repeated coverage percentage over episodes.

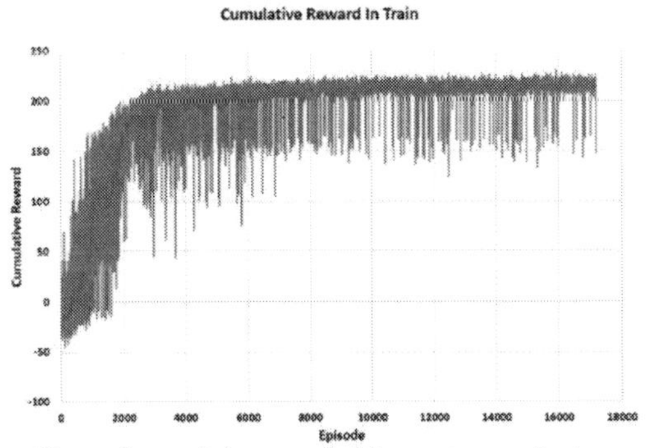

Figure 5: cumulative reward of the agent over episodes.

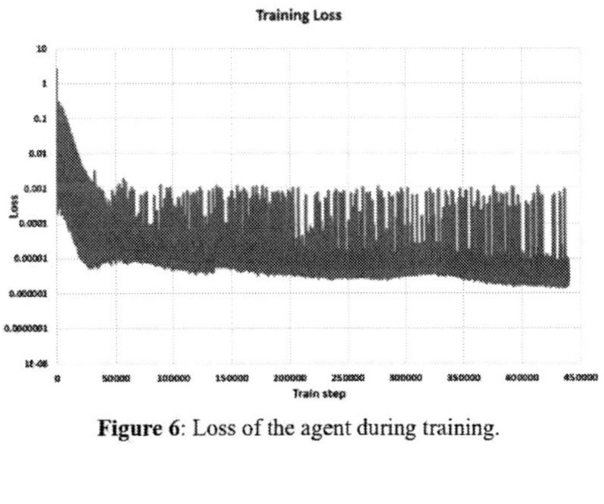

Figure 6: Loss of the agent during training.

6. RESULTS

The evaluation of the DRL-based coverage path planning algorithm was conducted through simulations in both grid-based and realistic environments, with the following key findings:

- Coverage Efficiency: The agent achieved a coverage rate of approximately 99.6% across randomly generated environments as shown in Fig. 2, showcasing its ability to handle diverse boundary shapes effectively.
- Repeated Coverage: The percentage of repeated coverage was minimized to 8.6%, demonstrating efficient navigation with minimal redundancy the results are shown in Fig. 3.

Figure 2: Simulated PV power plant in Digital-PV platform demonstrating algorithm adaptability in 3D environments.

- Total Reward: The cumulative rewards per episode stabilized, indicating the convergence of the agent's policy and consistent performance in achieving coverage objectives as shown in Fig. 4.
- Loss Reduction: Training loss decreased significantly over episodes, reflecting effective learning and optimization of the agent's policy (see Fig. 5).
- Realistic Simulation Performance: Integration with the Digital-PV platform revealed the algorithm's applicability to real-world scenarios, where it successfully adapted to 3D environmental constraints, such as wind and varied terrain, the simulation environment is shown in Fig. 6.

7. CONCLUSIONS

The proposed DRL-based approach demonstrates the following contribution:

1. Robustness in handling irregular area shapes and dynamic conditions.
2. Scalability, enabling coordination of multiple robots to efficiently cover large areas.
3. Safe operation through its integrated collision avoidance mechanism, ensuring conflict-free navigation.
4. Advanced learning efficiency via the RoboNN architecture, which provides stable and adaptable decision-making capabilities.

These results highlight the potential of DRL to revolutionize inspection processes in PV power plants and other industrial settings. Future work will explore multi-modal sensing, environmental condition adaptations, and broader applications for autonomous inspection systems.

8. REFERENCES

1. M. Aghaei et al., "Autonomous Intelligent Monitoring of Photovoltaic Systems: An In-depth Multidisciplinary Review," Progress in Photovoltaics: Research and Applications, 2024.
2. P. Nooralishahi et al., "Drone-based non-destructive inspection of industrial sites: A review and case studies," Drones, vol. 5, no. 4, p. 106, 2021.
3. A. Moradi Sizkouhi, M. Aghaei, and S. M. Esmailifar, "A deep convolutional encoder-decoder architecture for autonomous fault detection of PV plants using multi-copters," Solar Energy, vol. 223, pp. 217–228, 2021.
4. M. Kolahi, S. M. Esmailifar, A. M. M. Sizkouhi, and M. Aghaei, "Digital PV: A digital twin-based platform for autonomous aerial monitoring of large-scale photovoltaic power plants," Energy Conversion and Management, vol. 321, p. 118963, 2024.
5. Sizkouhi, A.M.M., et al. Autonomous Path Planning by Unmanned Aerial Vehicle (UAV) for Precise Monitoring of Large-Scale PV plants. in 2019 IEEE 46th Photovoltaic Specialists Conference (PVSC). 2019.
6. Moradi Sizkouhi, A.M., et al., RoboPV: An integrated software package for autonomous aerial monitoring of large scale PV plants. Energy Conversion and Management, 2022. 254: p. 115217.
7. Sizkouhi, A.M.M., et al., Automatic Boundary Extraction of Large-Scale Photovoltaic Plants Using a Fully Convolutional Network on Aerial Imagery. IEEE Journal of Photovoltaics, 2020. 10(4): p. 1061-1067.

Preprocessing I-V curve data for enhanced CNN-based fault diagnosis in Photovoltaic strings

*Woo Gyun Shin[1], Young Chul JU[1], Hye Mi HWANG[1], Jin-Seok Lee[1], **Suk Whan Ko[1]

Korea Institute of Energy Research, Korea

***presenting author** (swghero@kier.re.kr)*

Abstract

To respond to climate change and carbon neutrality, each country is actively investing in renewable energy sources. Among them, photovoltaic (PV) is a technology that converts light energy into electricity using solar cells, and is the fastest and most widely used. As of 2024, the cumulative PV installation worldwide is about 2TW, and it is expected to continue increasing. As PV installations increase, the PV plant maintenance and operation (O&M) market is also increasing. The solar O&M market size in 2024 is estimated to be approximately between $3.2 billion and $3.5 billion. PV O&M activity refers to a series of processes that ensure the stability of energy production goals of PV systems from efficient operation during their lifespan. Traditional PV O&M activities were PV module cleaning, vegetation management, and simple electrical inspection of PV modules and inverters. Such O&M activities make it difficult to diagnose power generation performance deterioration and failure. Recently, PV O&M companies and researchers are adopting digital technology in terms of asset management.

In this study, we propose a preprocessing method based on an I–V curve simulation model to improve the performance of convolutional neural network (CNN) trained with I–V curve data. The simulation is conducted using a single-diode model, which incorporates the number of series-connected modules within a PV string. By utilizing the irradiance and module temperature measured at the time of data acquisition, the model generates a simulated I–V curve representing the expected behavior of the PV string. The measured I–V curve is then preprocessed in two steps using the simulated curve, effectively minimizing discrepancies arising from variations in PV string capacity and measurement conditions. Comparative analysis shows that while the CNN trained on unprocessed I–V curve data tended to misclassify fault types, the model trained on preprocessed data accurately identified the actual faults, thereby demonstrating enhanced diagnostic accuracy.

Background

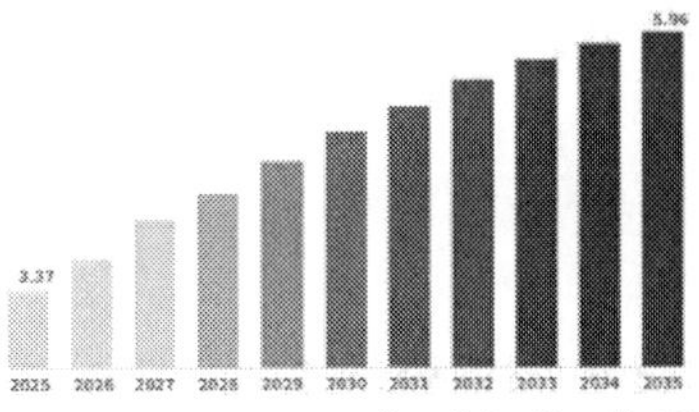

Source: Business Research Insight

Increase in PV O&M Market

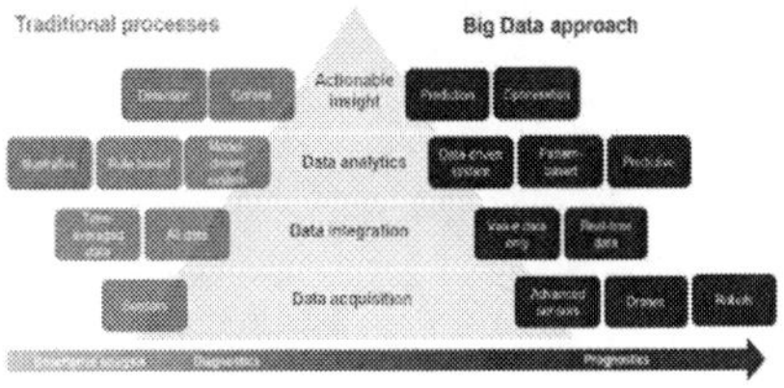

Source: Wood mackenzie

Evolution of PV O&M Technology: Past and Present

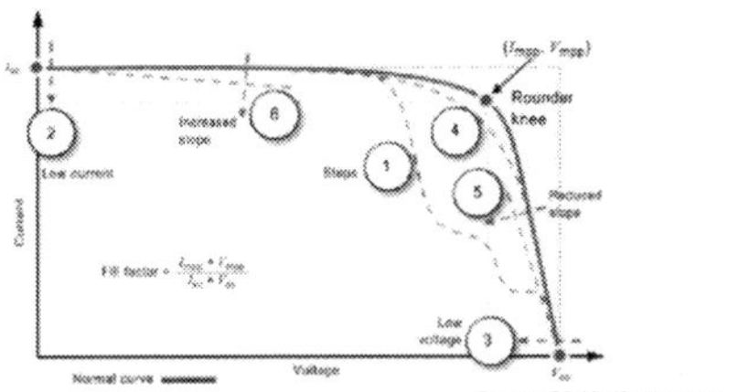

Source: IEC-62446-1(Annex D)

Electrical parameters derived from the I-V curve

Experiment and Result

◆ Necessity of Preprocessing I-V Curve Data for AI Training

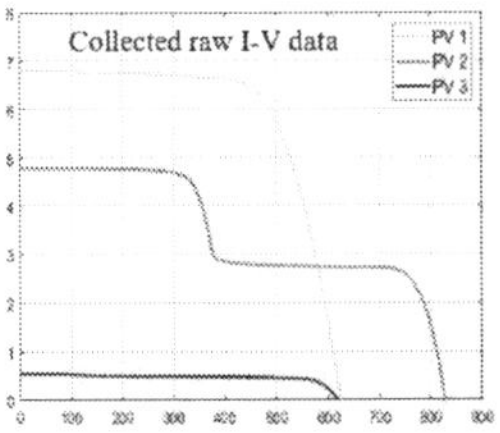

1. The rated capacity of PV strings differs among power plants due to variations in PV module types.
2. The I-V curves measured in the field do not correspond to those under Standard Test Conditions (STC).
3. It is not feasible to collect I-V curves under identical fault states, rated capacities, irradiance, and module temperature conditions.

Therefore, preprocessing is indispensable for fault diagnosis of I-V curves using artificial intelligence models.

◆ I-V Curve Data Before and After preprocessing

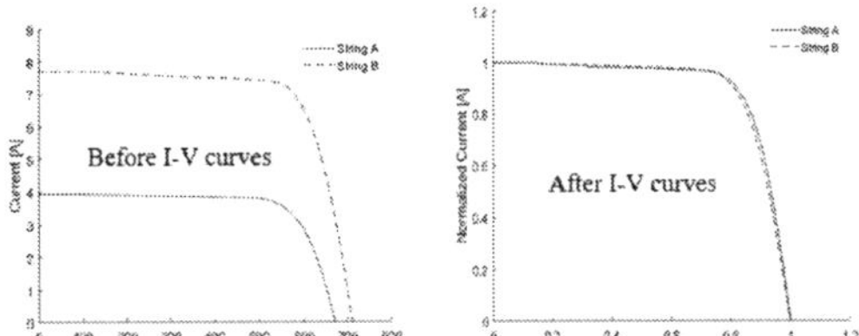

◆ Impact of Data Preprocessing on AI Model Training and Validation Results

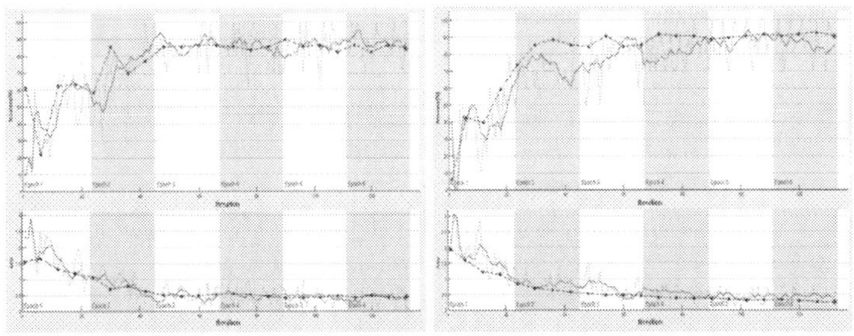

Training and Validation Results of I-V Curve Data (Left: Before Preprocessing, Right: After Preprocessing)

- The preprocessing of I-V curves consists of two steps. First, the I-V curve is normalized to the 0–1 range using the rated open-circuit voltage and short-circuit current of the PV string. Second, the measured I-V curve is adjusted based on the simulated I-V curve, which represents the normal condition under the given irradiance and temperature. This allows comparison of I-V curves under equivalent conditions despite differences in string capacity and measurement environment.
- The impact of data preprocessing on the accuracy of a CNN model was compared. The CNN model used for training was GoogLeNet, and transfer learning was performed with both preprocessed and non-preprocessed data. As shown in the figure above, the left side presents the training and validation results of GoogLeNet using non-preprocessed data, while the right side shows the results with preprocessed data. The validation accuracy of the model trained with non-preprocessed data was 84.38%, whereas that of the model trained with preprocessed data reached 90.63%. Thus, data preprocessing improved the accuracy by more than 6%.

Conclusion

- As the PV O&M market expands, new O&M technologies that combine data and artificial intelligence are being developed instead of traditional approaches.
- Among the various data collected from PV power plants, I-V curve data not only reflects the electrical performance of PV systems but also enables fault identification based on curve patterns.
- However, it is practically very difficult to collect faulty I-V curves while considering the rated capacity of PV strings and the environmental conditions at the time of measurement.
- In this study, a two-step preprocessing method was applied to measured I-V curves to minimize differences in rated capacity and environmental conditions of PV strings.
- It was verified that training with preprocessed data improved the accuracy of the CNN model by 6% compared with training on non-preprocessed data.
- Additionally, we plan to collect more data and train on a wider range of faulty I-V curve datasets to further validate our proposed approach.

This work was conducted under the framework of the research and development program of the Korea Institute of Energy Research(Project No: C5-2427).

SOLAR-ASP TOOL FOR EARLY FAULT DETECTION AND REMOTE DIAGNOSIS IN PHOTOVOLTAIC GENERATORS

Sandra Riaño[a] (sandra.riano@tecnalia.com), Ricardo Alonso[a], Jose Domingo Santos[a], Miguel Esteras[a], Ainhoa Pereda[a], Antonio Salvador[b], Jose Antonio Osuna[b], Javier Del Ser[c]

[a]TECNALIA, Basque Research & Technology Alliance (BRTA), 48160 Derio, Spain
[b] MAGTEL, P.E. Las Quemadas, Gabriel Ramos Bejarano, N.114, 14014 Córdoba
[c] University of the Basque Country (UPV/EHU), 48940 Leioa, Spain

ABSTRACT: This work presents results of SOLAR-ASP, a novel early Fault Detection ad Diagnosis (FDD) tool developed by TECNALIA and validated on a MAGTEL-operated photovoltaic (PV) plant. It combines data-driven analysis from SCADA measurements with domain-specific physical knowledge to assess PV asset health. This hybrid approach reduces reliance on labelled historical datasets (a common limitation observed in purely data-centric methods) while maintaining interpretability for PV experts. Field trials at a MAGTEL plant demonstrated its ability to estimate main characterization parameters, called Array State Parameters (ASPs), such as Maximum Power Point (MPP) current and voltage normalized to Standard Test Conditions (STC). SOLAR-ASP shows comparable performance to I-V curve measurements in the field, with errors lower than 3%. while enabling the earlier identification of performance degradation. This detection capability can inform proactive maintenance scheduling strategies, allowing for the reduction of in-field inspection campaigns and unnecessary preventative maintenance. This directly lowers OPEX costs while increasing performance by addressing issues before they increase.
Keywords: Photovoltaics, Operation and Maintenance, Hybrid Models, LCOE Reduction, Anomaly Detection

1 INTRODUCTION

The exponential rise of PV capacity installed in principal markets has recently surpassed the 2.2 TW threshold [1], while the Levelized Cost Of Energy (LCOE) of Solar PV utilities is kept on a sustained declining trend [2]. However, this rapid expansion has introduced significant operational challenges, particularly in the management of increasingly large and geographically dispersed PV systems. Modern solar farms now require monitoring vast component networks, while operators must adapt to the rapid deployment of evolving technologies in cells, modules, and system architectures [3]. These factors underscore the critical need for new approaches to support operational and maintenance (O&M) strategies, which represent 10–20% of the LCOE [7].

Traditional O&M practices used for this purpose, such as periodic I-V curve measurements, face limitations in scalability and cost-efficiency [5]. Alternatives like thermography delivered by drones or electroluminescence offer detailed diagnostics, but their high costs restrict their use to sporadic interventions [6]. This gap highlights the demand for real-time, automated monitoring solutions capable of detecting early degradations and faults.

In this regard, recent industry trends emphasize the growing adoption of Artificial Intelligence (AI) and Machine Learning (ML) to enable Condition-Based Maintenance (CBM) in PV systems [7]. By leveraging the Supervisory Control and Data Acquisition (SCADA) data and data-based models, AI-driven platforms can autonomously generate maintenance workflows, optimize resource allocation, and reduce reliance on reactive interventions [8]. Dynamic risk assessment frameworks further enhance this approach by combining historical failure data with real-time degradation indicators to prioritize critical assets [9]. Despite these advancements, the practical implementation of AI/ML tools in PV O&M is still emerging, with few operators achieving full integration of automated fault detection systems relying on this technology.

As the PV sector moves toward a 9% annual growth rate over the next three decades [10], the development of cost-effective, AI-powered CBM solutions will be decisive in O&M economic and technical sustainability. This paper aligns with this statement by presenting a hybrid framework for early fault detection and predictive maintenance. By integrating domain-specific physical models with data-driven machine learning, this hybrid framework enhances both accuracy and interpretability, ensuring that expert knowledge directly informs the patterns extracted from operational data. Our methodology leverages SCADA data and ML algorithms to bridge the gap between theoretical advancements and real-world implementation in large-scale PV systems.

The detection performance of SOLAR-ASP is validated over real-world data towards answering with empirical evidence 3 Research Questions (RQs):

- *RQ1: Can the MPP voltage (Vmp) and current (Imp) of PV arrays be accurately estimated using exclusively SCADA data?*
- *RQ2: What are the minimum data volume needed to achieve accurate and statistically stable estimates of Vmp and Imp?*
- *RQ3: Do the estimated Vmp and Imp values exhibit sufficient stability and low statistical dispersion to be comparable with the temperature-corrected Performance Ratio (PR)?*

The rest of the manuscript is organized as follows: Section 2 describes the diagnosis. The experimental setup is detailed in Section 3, whereas results are presented and discussed in Section 4. Finally, Section 5 summarizes the main conclusions and future research.

2 SOLAR-ASP TOOL

Whereas Section 2.1 provides a theoretical foundation for PV monitoring tool, Section 2.2 introduces SOLAR-ASP tool. Focusing on the practical implementation of the tool, Section 2.3 outlines the input data needed by

10.4229/EUPVSEC2025/4CV.1.60

SOLAR-ASP, while Section 2.4 details the output data.

2.1 Categorization of monitoring tools for PV systems

PV system monitoring tools are broadly categorized into three groups based on their methodological foundations: physical models, data-driven models, and hybrid/digital twin models [11].

Physical models simulate the ideal behaviour of PV systems using optical, thermal, and electrical equations derived from technical specifications [12]. By comparing theoretical outputs with real-time data, the identified deviations are declared to be indicative of anomalies. However, physical models often fail to automate root-cause diagnostics due to mismatches with real-world system behaviour.

Data-driven models leverage statistical relationships without requiring theoretical assumptions [13]-[17]. Their core strength lies in modelling the normal performance of asset as reflected in its operational data, bypassing the need for explicit knowledge of the underlying physics. Nevertheless, effective implementation demands large, high-quality datasets, and their ability to identify fault origins depends on expert-labelled training data—though emerging explainable AI techniques are lately addressing this limitation [18].

Hybrid and digital-twin models combine physical principles with data-driven calibration to improve sensitivity and enable automated diagnostics [19]. They estimate energy losses associated with faults without requiring extensive historical records but demand precise operational measurements and may struggle with unforeseen failures. Digital twins not only integrate physical principles and data, but also extend this integration to simulate design or operational. This makes them a specific application of hybrid models.

2.2 SOLAR-ASP: overall design and features

Presented tool exemplifies a hybrid approach, integrating data-driven analysis and modelling with embedded physical knowledge of PV systems for early-stage fault detection.

As a result of its hybrid nature, the parameters estimated by SOLAR-ASP are specifically designed to be compared against design/operational benchmarks established during commissioning. This enables the early detection of performance deviations, such as gradual degradations in module efficiency or sudden faults in electrical components.

Moreover, the physics-informed nature of SOLAR-ASP models enables generalizability across diverse PV systems without requiring extensive historical datasets for training. Notably, a key advantage of this framework is that the tool can be calibrated and validated using only a few months (e.g. 1 or 3 months), contrasting with data-driven methods that often demand larger datasets for reliable performance.

2.3 Input data needed by SOLAR-ASP

Data sources needed by SOLAR-ASP could be categorized into two main groups: system design parameters and real-time operational data. These inputs are critical for ensuring the accuracy and adaptability of the SOLAR-ASP monitoring framework. On the one hand, key design parameters include:

- Geographical and environmental context: Latitude, longitude, and altitude.
- PV system design: main electrical and physical characteristics of PV system.
- Electrical configuration: arrangement of modules in series and parallel within each inverter input channel.

On the other hand, the continuous monitoring through SCADA systems provides dynamic operational data. The following variables are necessary inputs for SOLAR-ASP:

- Electrical measurements: operating voltage and current from inverter input channels.
- Environmental conditions: plane-of-array (POA) irradiance and module temperature.

2.4 Output data provided by SOLAR-ASP

The tool estimates ASPs, which perform as core indicators for fault detection and degradation analysis. ASPs can be compared to electrical parameters of PV system normalized at Standard Test Conditions (STC). Key ASPs include:

- MPP voltage at STC
- MPP current at STC

By isolating whether a performance loss is primarily voltage-driven or current-driven, SOLAR-ASP has the potential to guide more targeted O&M strategies.

3 EXPERIMENTAL SETUP

Real-world data from a large-scale PV plant in southern Spain is used to validate SOLAR-ASP.

3.1 PV system setup

The PV system is a commercial installation which includes six PV arrays, labelled as Inverter1 to Inverter6. This installation has been operational for over a decade with a total nominal capacity of approximately 626 kWp. Each array is configured with 32 strings connected in parallel per inverter channel, whereas each string consists of 20 monocrystalline PV modules. Notably, two PV arrays have modules with distinct power ratings compared to the remaining four. The key electrical specifications of the system components are summarized in Table I. The system is in a CSA area (hot-summer Mediterranean climate) as per the Köppen climate classification [20].

Table I: Electrical characteristics of PV system at STC, obtained through PV modules characteristics and the electrical connections.

Component	Imp [A]	Vmp [V]
Inverter1, Inverter2	147.84	692
Inverter3 to Inverter6	154.24	706

Data for the validation period spans from April to October 2024. The SCADA system of the plant provides irradiance and module temperature measurements at the inverter level, with a shared sensoring system covering all six PV arrays.

3.2 PV system IV curve characterization

IV curve tracing was conducted using an HT Instruments IV-400W tracer (Serial No. 11091591) at string level, in October 2024. The IV characterization includes for each of the 32 strings across the six PV arrays:

- Full IV curve operating points.
- Full IV curve points translated to STC.
- Instantaneous irradiance ranged from approximately 670 to 930 W/m².

10.4229/EUPVSEC2025/4CV.1.60

- Instantaneous module temperature ranged from 35 to 50 °C.
- Measured and STC-translated values of open-circuit voltage (Voc), maximum power voltage (Vmp), short-circuit current (Isc), and maximum power current (Imp).

An aggregation process is implemented to align the string-level IV curve data with the SCADA-based SOLAR-ASP inputs, measured at inverter level. Firstly, individual string STC curves are aligned to a common array voltage via linear interpolation. The resolution of the array voltage-string is the one corresponding to 2000 points between minimum and maximum voltage at STC curves of each string. This ensures consistent voltage values across all strings. Secondly, the currents are aggregated at array-level. For parallel-connected strings, translated currents are summed at each voltage point. This methodology enabled direct comparison between the estimation values from SOLAR-ASP and empirical measurements.

4 RESULTS AND DISCUSSIONS

The empirical validation of SOLAR-ASP is structured around the presented RQ, each one addressing a distinct aspect of its hybrid modelling internals:

- Firstly, the accuracy of its estimation is evaluated by comparing them against the STC normalized values of measured IV curves. This assessment uses hybrid models trained on SCADA data from September 2024, a month preceding the measurement campaign, to address RQ1.
- Secondly, the influence of input data volume on estimation accuracy is investigated by applying different training windows to SCADA data. This analysis determines the minimum data requirements for achieving statistically stable and accurate estimates of Vmp and Imp, directly addressing RQ2.
- Finally, the seasonal variability of SOLAR-ASP estimations is evaluated by analysing its performance across multiple months. Hybrid models are trained using 30-day windows ending at the conclusion of each month. Nominal values normalized estimations are compared to the temperature-corrected PR, considering only Direct Current (DC) side. Temperature-corrected PR is a widely adopted standard metric [21][22] for assessing PV system efficiency. This comparison assesses whether the estimated Vmp and Imp values exhibit sufficient stability and low statistical dispersion to serve as reliable alternatives to PR for diagnostic purposes, addressing RQ3.

4.1 RQ1: SOLAR-ASP estimations against STC normalized IV curve measurements

The accuracy of the SOLAR-ASP tool is evaluated by comparing the estimations obtained from operational data collected in September 2024 with experimental IV curve measurements normalized to STC. 30-day training windows are used. Errors are gauged as relative percentage deviations, calculated as:

$$Error = 100\left(\frac{Estimation - Measurement}{Measurement}\right) \quad (1)$$

Figure 1 illustrates the estimation error across individual components, with current errors depicted in green and voltage errors in orange. Except from Inverter4, relative errors are ranging from -4 % to 1%. Across all six components, the error distribution could be represented by the mean and standard deviation (STD), −0.521%±2.984%, indicating a slight underestimation of magnitudes. However, the mean and STD may not fully capture the characteristics of distribution, particularly in the presence of outliers or skewness. Notably, Inverter4 exhibits a pronounced overestimation of Imp. To address this, the median error and interquartile range (IQR) are also computed. The IQR is defined as the difference between the 75th and 25th percentiles, complementing the median by quantifying the spread of the middle 50% of the data. In this case, the median of the errors is -0.893%, with a IQR of 3.11%. Therefore, the central tendency aligns with acceptable tolerances with industry benchmarks (±3%).

This analysis directly addresses RQ1: the ability of SOLAR-ASP to estimate voltage and current with accuracy comparable to I-V curve measurements, even when relying solely on SCADA data.

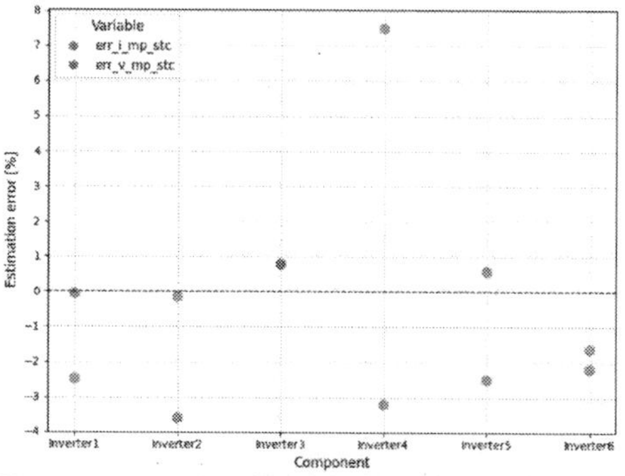

Figure 1: September 2024 SOLAR-ASP estimation error vs IV curve measurements normalized to STC.

4.2 RQ2: Impact of Training Window Duration on Estimation Accuracy

In response to this second RQ, windows of 15, 30, 45, 60 and 90 days, all ending in September 2024, are used to train hybrid models. The analysis is aimed to determine the minimum data volume required for accurate and reproducible prediction. Estimation errors are evaluated by comparing model outputs to STC-normalized I-V curves measurements. The results are summarized in Figures 2 and 3, and Tables II and III.

Intermediate windows (30-60 days) yield the lowest mean and median errors for both Imp and Vmp. Shorter and longer training windows exhibit greater variability. In case of Vmp estimation, training with 15 days causes the greatest errors: mean: −2.406%; median: −2.759%. In contrast, training with 90 days obtains the lowest errors: mean: −1.390%; median: −1.830%. Figure 2 shows that Inverter1 and Inverter3 deviates from this trend. However, their errors across all training-windows are under ±1%, which is comparable to the inherent measurement uncertainties in SCADA data. Regarding to Imp estimation, the 90-day window, while reducing median error (−3.405%), introduced higher mean error (−2.705%), suggesting that Imp is more sensitive to recent data.

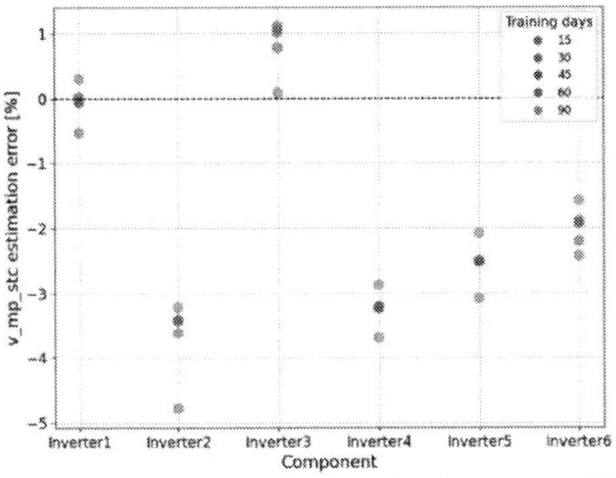

Figure 2: Comparison of Vmp estimation error vs IV curve measurements normalized to STC for varying training windows.

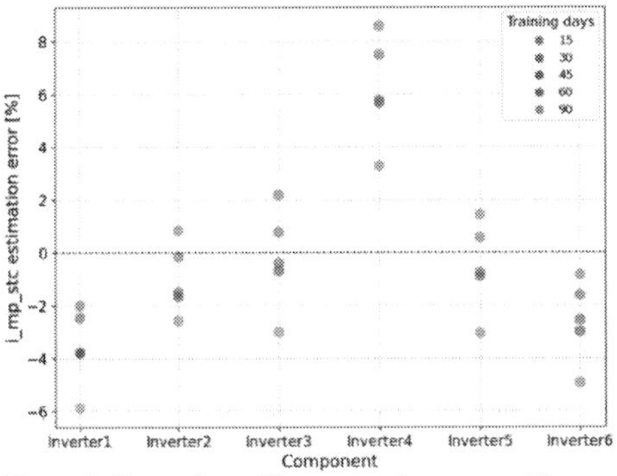

Figure 3: Comparison of Imp estimation error vs IV curve measurements normalized to STC for varying training windows.

Table II: Statistics of Imp estimation error.

Training days	MEAN	STD	MEDIAN	IQR
15	1.692	3.706	1.131	2.420
30	0.762	3.536	0.208	1.990
45	-0.540	3.333	-1.127	1.830
60	-0.739	3.335	-1.290	1.930
90	-2.705	3.198	-3.405	1.780

Table III: Statistics of Vmp estimation error.

Training days	MEAN	STD	MEDIAN	IQR
15	-2.406	1.873	-2.759	2.540
30	-1.804	1.770	-2.358	2.440
45	-1.664	1.831	-2.206	2.600
60	-1.686	1.795	-2.225	2.530
90	-1.390	1.743	-1.830	2.510

In response to RQ2, the obtained results identify 30-day window as the optimal compromise for estimation, balancing accuracy, data volume and operational feasibility. Although Vmp estimation benefits from longer windows, the 30-day window avoids excessive data smoothing and allows detecting short-term performance deviations.

4.3 RQ3: Long-Term Stability Analysis

The stability of SOLAR-ASP estimation for Imp and Vmp is evaluated by comparing their monthly variations to the temperature-corrected PR. The PR quantifies the ratio of actual energy production to the theoretical maximum achievable under given environmental conditions. Actual energy production is obtained as the product of measured current and voltage from available SCADA data. The theoretical production P_{ref} is derived using [21]:

$$P_{ref}(G,T) = \left(\frac{G}{1000}\right) P_{STC}\left(1 + \frac{\alpha_p(T-25)}{100}\right) \quad (2)$$

where G is the Global Tilted Irradiance (GTI) in W/m^2, T is the module temperature in °C, P_{STC} is the nominal power of PV array in W, and α_p is the power temperature coefficient in %/ °C. Data below a defined irradiance threshold ($G < 150$ W/m^2) are excluded to mitigate the impact of low-irradiance noise on accuracy [23].

The estimations are normalized dividing them by design values from Table I, obtaining per unit (pu) magnitudes. The normalized estimations are compared to the PR across six available months of SCADA data to assess the reliability of SOLAR-ASP as a diagnosis framework. Table IV shows the Imp and Vmp estimations for each month. Table V reports the statistical variability of the estimated metrics and PR through STD, coefficient of variation (CV) and IQR. As can be seen in these tables, Vmp exhibits the lowest variability in all metrics, while Imp demonstrates slightly lower variability than PR.

Figure 4 illustrates the monthly evolution of normalized Imp and Vmp estimations and PR for Inverter6, as a graphical representation of one component of Table IV. Data in his figure reveal that while the PR decreases from 0.89 pu in April to 0.83 pu in September, this decline might be driven by a reduction in Imp (from 0.88pu to 0.85 pu) rather than Vmp, which remains almost stable around 0.97–0.99 pu. This fact suggests that current-limiting factors are the dominant contributors to performance loss in the analysed PV system.

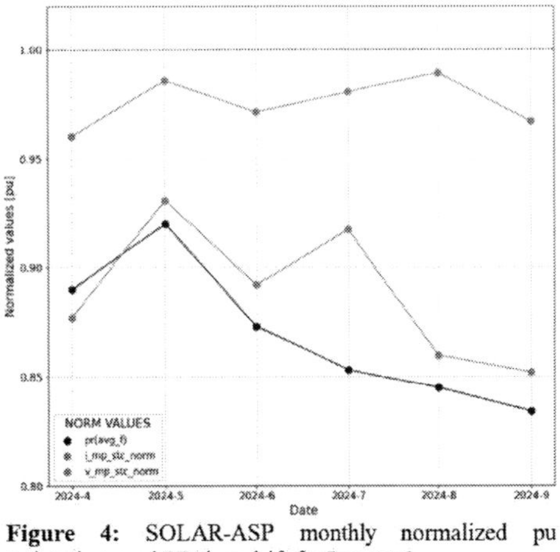

Figure 4: SOLAR-ASP monthly normalized pu estimations and PR time-drift for Inverter6.

The analysis directly answers RQ3 by demonstrating that estimations provided by SOLAR-ASP exhibit similar or lower variability than the temperature-corrected PR, validating their utility as stable and interpretable metrics for PV O&M. Moreover, SOLAR-ASP offers granular insights into the root causes of performance degradation, separating current and voltage instead of aggregating

10.4229/EUPVSEC2025/4CV.1.60

losses into a single metrics as PR. This distinction is critical for optimizing maintenance strategies, as it allows operators to prioritize interventions based on the specific nature of the fault

Table IV: Monthly normalized estimations and PR.

Date	Component	PR[pu]	Imp[pu]	Vmp[pu]
2024-4	Inverter1	0.877	0.859	0.988
	Inverter2	0.813	0.802	0.962
	Inverter3	0.828	0.825	0.957
	Inverter4	0.865	0.892	0.939
	Inverter5	0.872	0.887	0.959
	Inverter6	0.890	0.877	0.960
2024-5	Inverter1	0.904	0.912	1.017
	Inverter2	0.839	0.854	0.988
	Inverter3	0.853	0.880	0.979
	Inverter4	0.895	0.947	0.964
	Inverter5	0.913	0.957	0.986
	Inverter6	0.920	0.931	0.986
2024-6	Inverter1	0.780	0.878	0.996
	Inverter2	0.728	0.833	0.971
	Inverter3	0.810	0.851	0.970
	Inverter4	0.866	0.904	0.948
	Inverter5	0.858	0.915	0.970
	Inverter6	0.873	0.892	0.971
2024-7	Inverter1	0.842	0.894	1.018
	Inverter2	0.723	0.812	0.990
	Inverter3	0.793	0.869	0.977
	Inverter4	0.831	0.926	0.966
	Inverter5	0.853	0.936	0.989
	Inverter6	0.853	0.918	0.981
2024-8	Inverter1	0.834	0.860	1.022
	Inverter2	0.776	0.809	0.994
	Inverter3	0.784	0.844	0.972
	Inverter4	0.822	0.888	0.963
	Inverter5	0.845	0.890	0.993
	Inverter6	0.845	0.860	0.989
2024-9	Inverter1	0.826	0.841	1.001
	Inverter2	0.765	0.786	0.970
	Inverter3	0.778	0.813	0.974
	Inverter4	0.812	0.871	0.950
	Inverter5	0.832	0.876	0.971
	Inverter6	0.834	0.852	0.967

Table V: Statistics of estimated metrics and PR.

Variable	MEAN	STD	CV	IQR
PR	0.834	0.047	0.057	0.050
Imp	0.873	0.042	0.048	0.050
Vmp	0.978	0.019	0.020	0.020

5 CONCLUSIONS

The results of this study have demonstrated the effectiveness of SOLAR-ASP to assess the health of PV assets. SOLAR-ASP is a hybrid FDD tool that combines data-driven analytics from SCADA systems with domain-specific physical knowledge. SOLAR-ASP achieves estimation errors for operation current and voltage below 3%, which are comparable to those of traditional I-V curve measurements. This level of accuracy enables early identification of performance degradation, supporting proactive maintenance strategies in large-scale PV systems. Furthermore, its hybrid architecture ensures interpretable outputs for PV domain experts, eliminating the need for labelled historical datasets. Additionally, its minimal data requirements make it particularly suitable for newly commissioned systems or assets with limited historical operational data.

Our analysis of the results obtained over real data further revealed that SOLAR-ASP estimations exhibit lower variability than the temperature-corrected PR, while providing a granular diagnosis beyond the decline in performance. By separating current and voltage trends, SOLAR-ASP provides practical guidance for targeted maintenance, enhancing the cost-effectiveness of CBM strategies in large-scale PV plants.

In the future we will focus on quantifying the intrinsic uncertainty of hybrid models to establish robust thresholds that distinguish between estimation inaccuracies and real degradations. Moreover, we plan to evaluate the performance of SOLAR-ASP on diverse PV plants with varying configuration to assess its generalizability and scalability.

i

6 ACKNOWLEGMENTS

This work has been supported by SUNRISE-PV project (New Generation of Photovoltaic Technologies for energy cost reduction through circularity strategies), funded by The Centre for the Development of Industrial Technology (CDTI). "Science and Innovation Missions Program", of the State Program to Catalyze Innovation and Business Leadership of the State Plan for Scientific and Technical Research and Innovation 2021-2023 within the framework of the Recovery, Transformation and Resilience Plan. J. Del Ser also acknowledges funding support from the Basque Government through the consolidated research group MATHMODE (IT1456-22).

7 REFERENCES

[1] SolarPower Europe (2025): Global Market Outlook for Solar Power 2025-2029 https://www.solarpowereurope.org/insights/outlooks/global-market-outlook-for-solar-power-2025-2029/detail. Accessed August 2025.

[2] Lazard. (June 2024). LCOE+ (Levelized Cost of Energy)

[3] UNECE, "Carbon Neutrality in the UNECE Region: Integrated Life-cycle Assessment of Electricity Sources", 2022, Report.

[4] A. Walker et all, Model of Operation-and-Maintenance Costs for Photovoltaic Systems, National Renewable Energy Laboratory, 2020. https://docs.nrel.gov/docs/fy20osti/74840.pdf. Accessed August 2025.

[5] IEA-PVPS (2014): *Review of Failures of Photovoltaic Modules*, ISBN 978-3-906042-16-9.

[6] A. K. Vidal de Oliveira et al. (2019): *Automatic fault detection of photovoltaic array by convolutional neural networks during aerial infrared thermography*, European PV Solar Energy Conference.

[7] IEA\PVPS. Task 13. (2021) The use of advanced algorithms in PV failure monitoring. URL https://iea-pvps.org/key-topics/theuse-of-advanced-algorithms-in-pv-failure-monitoring/. Accessed August 2025.

[8] P.-C. Hwang et al. (2021). Detection of malfunctioning photovoltaic modules based on machine learning algorithms. 9:37210–37219. ISSN 2169-3536. doi: 10.1109/ACCESS. 2021.3063461.

URL https://ieeexplore.ieee.org/document/9367143
[9] Z. Zeng & E. Zio (2018): Dynamic Risk Assessment Based on Statistical Failure Data and Condition-Monitoring Degradation Data, IEEE Trans Reliab, 67(2):609–622.
[10] IRENA (2019): *Global Energy Transformation: A Roadmap to 2050*, ISBN 978-92-9260-122-8.
[11] A. Mellit, G. M. Tina, and S. A. Kalogirou, "Fault detection and diagnosis methods for photovoltaic systems: A review," Renewable and Sustainable Energy Reviews, vol. 91, pp. 1–17, 2018, doi: 10.1016/j.rser.2018.03.062.
[12] M. J. Mayer and G. Grof, "Extensive comparison of physical models for photovoltaic power forecasting," Applied Energy, vol. 283, p. 116239, 2021.
[13] K. S. Garud, S. Jayaraj, and M.-Y. Lee, "A review on modeling of solar photovoltaic systems using artificial neural networks, fuzzy logic, genetic algorithm and hybrid models," Int J Energy Res., 2020.
[14] C.-C. H. et al., "Real-time fault detection in massive multi-array PV plants based on machine learning techniques," 36th European Photovoltaic Solar Energy Conference and Exhibition, 2019.
[15] H. A. M. et al., "Real Time Fault Detection in Photovoltaic Systems," Energy Procedia, vol. 111, pp. 914–923, 2017.
[16] Å. Skomedal et al., "General, Robust and Scalable Methods for String Level Monitoring in Utility Scale PV Systems," 36th European Photovoltaic Solar Energy Conference and Exhibition, 2019.
[17] M. Carpentieri and S. Vergura, "Statistics to Detect Low-Intensity Anomalies in PV Systems," Energies, vol. 11, no. 30, pp. 1–12, 2018.
[18] C. Utama et al., "Explainable artificial intelligence for photovoltaic fault detection: A comparison of instruments," Solar Energy, vol. 249, pp. 139–151, 2023, doi: 10.1016/j.solener.2022.11.018.
[19] A. Jain, "How might data analytics help advance solar PV research?" DURAMAT consortium Webinar, 2020.
[20] Kottek M, Grieser J, Beck C, Rudolf B, Rubel F. World Map of the Köppen-Geiger climate classification updated. Meteorologische Zeitschrift. 2006 Jul;15(3):259–263. Available from: https://www.schweizerbart.de/papers/metz/detail/15/55034/World_Map_of_the_Koppen_Geiger_climate_classificat?af=crossref. Accessed August 2025.
[21] IEC 61724-1:2021, Photovoltaic system performance – Part 1: Monitoring, International Electrotechnical Commission, Geneva, Switzerland, 2021.
[22] B. Marion et al., "Performance parameters for grid-connected PV systems," Conference Record of the Thirty-first IEEE Photovoltaic Specialists Conference, 2005., Lake Buena Vista, FL, USA, 2005, pp. 1601-1606, doi: 10.1109/PVSC.2005.1488451.
[23] IEA-PVPS Task 13-22: Assessment of Performance Loss Rate of PV Power Systems. 2021. https://iea-pvps.org/wp-content/uploads/2021/04/IEA-PVPS-T13-22_2021-Assessment-of-Performance-Loss-Rate-of-PV-Power-Systems-report.pdf. Accessed July 2025.

FIRE PERFORMANCE OF POWER OPTIMIZERS IN PHOTOVOLTAIC SYSTEMS

Lasse Halle[1], David Joss[1], Christof Bucher[1]
[1] Bern University of Applied Sciences (BFH), School of Engineering and Computer Science (TI), Institute for Energy and Mobility Research (IEM), Laboratory for Photovoltaic Systems (PV-Lab)
[1]lasse.halle@bfh.ch, [1]christof.bucher@bfh.ch

ABSTRACT: This study investigates the behaviour of photovoltaic (PV) systems with power optimizers under externally induced fire exposure, with a particular focus on facade-mounted installations. The objective is to determine whether power optimizers increase fire risk due to energy absorption at various abnormal operating temperatures and how the system behaviour of a PV installation with power optimizers responds to elevated external temperatures. Experimental investigations were conducted on grid-connected PV systems consisting of inverters, power optimizers, and PV module simulation sources. Devices from three manufacturers were analysed: Huawei, SolarEdge, and Tigo. Two types of experiments were performed: (I) non-destructive heating up to 140 °C, and (II) destructive flame exposure at temperatures of at least 800 °C. In both cases, one optimizer within the PV system was exposed to abnormal temperature. The results show that power optimizers detect overtemperature, stop energy conversion, and switch to bypass mode on the string side while opening the module side. After cooling, devices resume operation even with visible damage. Under destructive flame tests, burning droplets, enlarged flames, smoke, and moving burning parts were observed due to melting brackets. No Rapid Shutdown of system voltage occurred, although string current was interrupted by the inverter. Overall, PV systems with power optimizers exhibit similar behaviour to systems without optimizers during fire, but additional material increases the fire load.
Keywords: PV Fire Performance, Rapid Shutdown, Fire Safety, Facade-mounted PV, Power Optimizers

1 INTRODUCTION

Photovoltaic (PV) facade systems are gaining increasing importance in Europe and worldwide. In addition to the energetic utilisation of building surfaces, the integration of PV modules into the building envelope also offers architectural advantages [1]. At the same time, the installation of PV systems on facades is subject to stringent requirements for preventive fire protection. In Switzerland, the fire safety requirements for facades are subject to regulations, as these building elements usually extend across the entire building height and can significantly contribute to fire spread. PV facade systems therefore lie at the intersection of ambitious energy policy objectives for the expansion of renewable energies and strict building and fire safety regulations. At the European level, test procedures and standards exist, for example within the framework of EN standards on the fire performance of construction products, but their national implementation differs significantly [2].

While the fire behaviour of PV modules and their mounting structures has been the subject of extensive research, the behaviour of PV systems with power optimizers under fire conditions has so far hardly been investigated [3]. For these power electronic components, there are currently no specific standards or testing procedures in the context of fire testing. This results in a regulatory gap that creates uncertainty for designers, manufacturers, and fire safety authorities. In particular, it remains unclear whether power optimizers increase the fire load due to their additional material content or whether their protective functions, such as overtemperature detection, may contribute positively to safety in the event of fire.

The objective of this study is therefore to systematically analyse the fire behaviour of PV systems with power optimizers. The central research question is whether power optimizers increase the fire risk due to energy absorption at abnormal operating temperatures and how the system behaviour responds to externally induced temperature increases. For this purpose, representative market products from major manufacturers – Huawei, SolarEdge, and Tigo – were selected, in order to provide results with high practical relevance and applicability.

2 METHODOLOGY

The experimental investigations were conducted at the Photovoltaics Laboratory (PV-Lab) of the Bern University of Applied Sciences (BFH). The systems consisted of 16 simulated PV modules connected to one Maximum Power Point Tracker (MPPT) of a grid-connected inverter. As module sources, programmable PV simulators of the type Delta Elektronika SM330-AR-22 were used, each configured to a nominal power of 330 W (≈ 33 V, 10 A) with STC (1000 W/m^2, 25 °C). The electrical parameters of the simulated modules were $V_{oc} \approx 40$ V and $I_{sc} \approx 11$ A, resulting in a total installed DC capacity of ≈ 5.28 kWp. The current-voltage characteristics were software-controlled to ensure reproducible and comparable operating conditions across all test series.

The investigated power optimizers were operated in combination with the corresponding manufacturer-specific inverters. Devices from Huawei, SolarEdge, and Tigo were tested, each together with a compatible inverter. In each test series, a single optimizer was subjected to targeted thermal stress, while the rest of the system remained in regular operation.

Table I: Tested device configurations:

Power Optimizers with	Inverter
Huawei: SUN2000-450W-P2	Huawei SUN2000-10KTL-M1
SolarEdge: S440	SolarEdge: SE10K
Tigo: TS4-A-O	Fronius: SYMO 6.0-3-M

2.1 Test Procedure

The investigations were divided into two main series. In the first experimental series (I), non-destructive heating tests were carried out in a climate chamber. The aim was

10.4229/EUPVSEC2025/4CV.1.61

to determine the temperature thresholds at which the optimizers detect overheating and to characterize their switching behaviour under controlled conditions. For each manufacturer, three independent test runs were performed. Each run followed a stepwise heating protocol with four plateaus at 80 °C, 100 °C, 120 °C, and 140 °C. Each plateau was maintained for 30 minutes to ensure a steady thermal state. After each heating step, the device was cooled down to 25 °C and held for an additional 30 minutes to guarantee complete thermal recovery before the next heating sequence. The subsequent plateau was then reached by a controlled ramp starting from 25 °C. This cycle of heating and cooling was repeated four times within each run, thereby provoking multiple overtemperature detections per device. To further increase the stress on the tested optimizer, the irradiance applied to its simulated PV module was pulsed between 1000 W/m² for two minutes and 300 W/m² for six minutes. This pulsed irradiance profile was applied only to the stressed optimizer, while all remaining simulated modules were operated at constant irradiance. Functional control sequences were performed before and after each full heating cycle to confirm correct system operation and to document any changes in device behaviour.

The second experimental series (II) consisted of destructive flame tests in which a single optimizer was exposed to an open flame generated by a burner. The objective was to reproduce a realistic fire scenario within the ventilated cavity of a PV facade system, with local surface temperatures reaching at least 800 °C. The test stand was designed to represent typical mounting conditions of a ventilated facade, enabling observation of both electrical and mechanical effects under external fire exposure [4]. In contrast to series (I), the irradiance profile was simplified for these tests: after an initial control sequence, a constant irradiance of 1000 W/m² was applied throughout the entire experiment to reduce complexity and to facilitate the analysis of the electrical response under dynamic fire conditions.

For this series, three flame tests were planned per manufacturer. For Huawei and Tigo, all three runs were successfully completed and documented. In the case of SolarEdge, however, only two experiments could be carried out, as the third planned test had to be cancelled due to a defect in the inverter.

2.2 Measurement and Monitoring

Across both experimental series, the system response was recorded with regard to string current, voltage, and power absorption, while the switching behaviour of the optimizers was monitored, including overtemperature detection, transition of the PV input side to open circuit, transition of the string output side to bypass, and possible reactivation after cooling. During the flame tests, visual observations were made systematically, including flame propagation, smoke emission, formation of burning droplets, and movement or detachment of components. Error and warning messages in the manufacturer monitoring portals were logged according to the firmware versions installed on the devices at the time of testing (November 2024 to January 2025), ensuring that the analysis reflects the actual operational states of the products.

3 RESULTS

The results are presented in two parts, corresponding to the experimental design: (I) controlled temperature increases in a climate chamber and (II) destructive flame tests representing external fire exposure in ventilated facade systems. In both series, the electrical response of the PV system, the switching behaviour of the optimizers, and the observed fire phenomena were evaluated. Manufacturer-specific monitoring data were additionally analysed with respect to fault detection and reporting.

3.1 Non-destructive temperature increase (Series I)

In the controlled heating experiments in the climate chamber, the PV-string voltage and current remained stable throughout the runs. The only electrical deviation was the interruption of power absorption by the thermally stressed optimizer once its overtemperature threshold was reached. Upon detection of excessive temperature, the optimizer disconnected its PV input side to open circuit and simultaneously placed the string output in bypass. This ensured that the overall PV system remained operational and that total power output was reduced only by the contribution of the affected device.

After cooling to normal operating conditions, the optimizers reactivated automatically and resumed normal operation, even when visible deformation of the housings was present. The switching response consistently exhibited a hysteresis effect: the restart temperature was lower than the shutdown temperature, preventing oscillatory switching behaviour while allowing the devices to return to operation after cooling.

Across all Series I experiments, the manufacturers' monitoring systems consistently issued fault or warning messages corresponding to the detected overtemperature condition. These messages were automatically cleared once the devices cooled down, leaving no persistent entries in the portals.

The applied irradiance pulsing sequence, consisting of short-term alternations between 1000 W/m² for two minutes and 300 W/m² for six minutes, did not trigger additional switching events. However, it confirmed that the optimizers maintained stable functionality under combined thermal and electrical stress, with no additional deviations observed in the string performance.

Figure 1 presents a representative measurement from Series I, showing the temperature trajectory and the corresponding switching response of one device, with shutdown and restart thresholds marked to highlight the hysteretic behaviour. Figure 2 summarizes the shutdown and restart temperatures for all test runs by optimizer type.

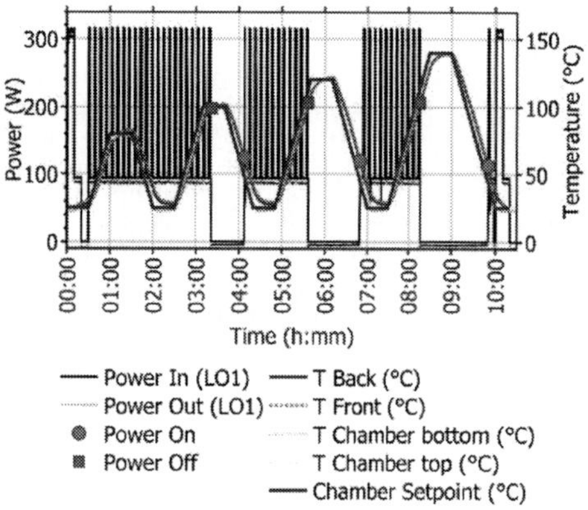

Figure 1: Electrical and thermal response of a representative optimizer under thermal stress in the climate chamber (Series I). Left axis: power; right axis: temperatures. Green and red markers indicate optimizer switching events (on/off).

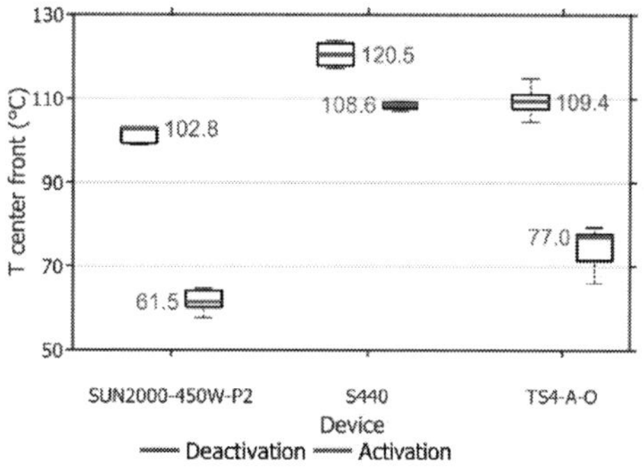

Figure 2: Boxplot of shutdown and restart temperatures for all tested optimizers (Series I) with median values.

3.2 Destructive flame tests (Series II)

In the flame exposure experiments, the thermal and mechanical behaviour of the optimizers under extreme external heating was markedly different from the controlled climate chamber tests. Local surface temperatures of at least 800 °C were reached, and in several cases, peak temperatures exceeded 1000 °C.

The electrical response of the systems varied depending on manufacturer and test conditions. In multiple experiments, the inverters disconnected the string within a few minutes of ignition, typically as a result of residual current device (RCD) tripping. In other cases, however, no system shutdown occurred and the PV string continued operating despite the burning optimizer. In none of the tested devices did the fire trigger a Rapid Shutdown or a complete reduction of system voltage. Instead, the optimizers exhibited either open-circuit or short-circuit behaviour on the PV input side, depending on the mode of failure.

The mechanical consequences of flame exposure were significant. In nearly all cases, the mounting structures of the optimizers melted, resulting in detachment of the devices from the test stand and, in some instances, swinging or falling components still partially connected by cables. Burning droplets were frequently observed, sometimes combined with molten metal residues.

The visual fire behaviour was characterized by strong flame formation and dense black smoke in most tests, with noticeable variability between devices. A representative frontal view of flame growth is shown in Figure 3, highlighting the rapid development of tall flames above the optimizer. To capture the side perspective, Figures 4 document the same experiment before and after the optimizer detached from its mounting.

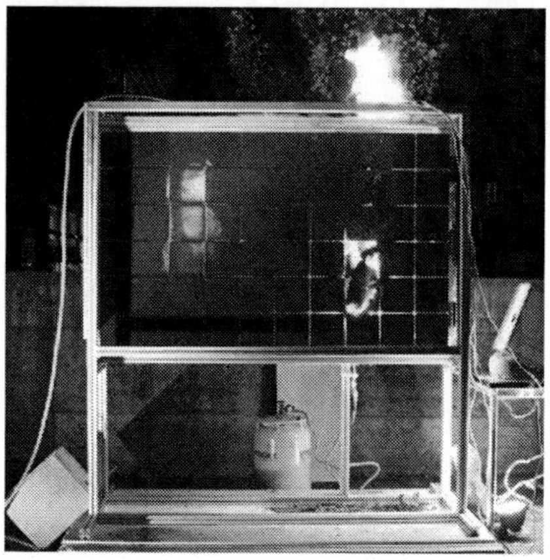

Figure 3: Frontal view of flame formation during Series II test.

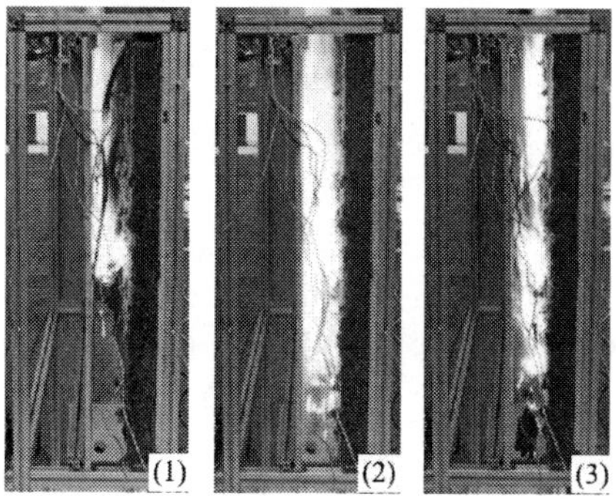

Figure 4: Side view of flame formation during Series II test with (1) optimizer still attached, (2) optimizer partially detaching, and (3) optimizer fully detached.

The chaotic burning behaviour made systematic comparisons difficult, as the fire dynamics differed strongly even between repeated runs of the same optimizer type. In total, error or warning messages were issued only in two out of six flame exposure tests, although an overtemperature-related switching response was observed in three of the six runs. In contrast, during Series I experiments consistently produced corresponding fault messages in the monitoring systems depending on optimizer typ.

While the electrical contribution of the burning optimizers was eliminated in all cases, the added fire load of the optimizer materials contributed significantly to flame growth, smoke production, and the spread of burning droplets. The chaotic behaviour observed under fire exposure limits the possibility of systematic evaluation, but the overall trend indicates that the presence of power optimizers increases the fire load in facade systems without providing a corresponding benefit in terms of system shutdown or voltage reduction.

10.4229/EUPVSEC2025/4CV.1.61
020359-003

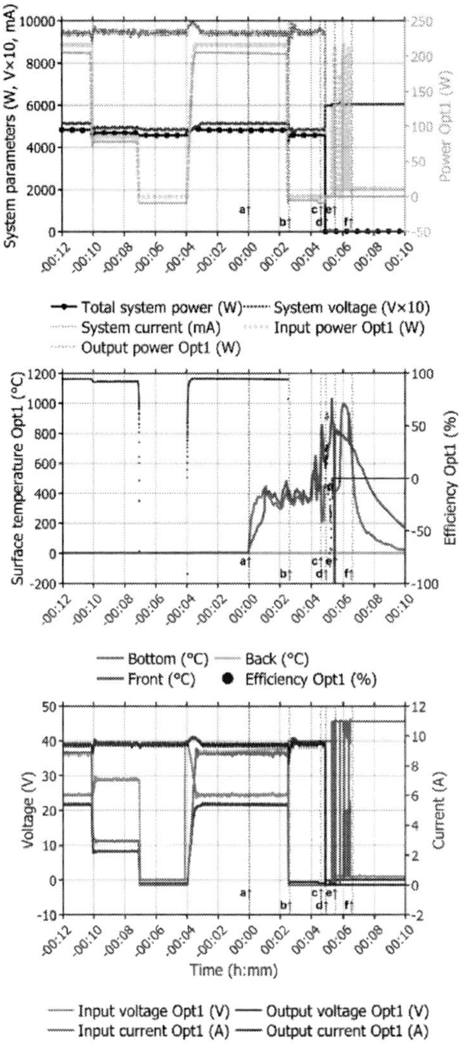

Figure 5: Exemplary evaluation chart with electrical and thermal response of a representative optimizer under thermal stress during a flame test in the ventilated facade cavity (Series II). Top: system power/voltage/current (left) and Optimizer-1 input/output power (right). Middle: module surface temperatures (left) and Optimizer-1 efficiency (right). Bottom: Optimizer-1 voltages (left) and currents (right). Letters a–f mark key events.

Table II: Event summary for the flame test in the ventilated facade cavity (Series II). Listed are lettered events a–f (as in Fig. 5) with synchronized electrical values at the event time: System current/voltage, Optimizer-1 Output current/voltage, Optimizer-1 Input current/voltage, and a brief Remark.

Event	Parameter	Measured value
a↑	System current (A)	9.2921
	System voltage (V)	516.2000
	Output current Opt1 (A)	9.2884
	Output voltage Opt1 (V)	22.0065
	Input current Opt1 (A)	8.8260
	Input voltage Opt1 (V)	24.4532
	Remark: Ignition	
b↑	System current (A)	8.5631
	System voltage (V)	506.7600
	Output current Opt1 (A)	8.5582
	Output voltage Opt1 (V)	-0.4368
	Input current Opt1 (A)	0.0114
	Input voltage Opt1 (V)	39.9679
	Remark: Overtemperature detection Opt1	
c↑	System current (A)	9.4476
	System voltage (V)	483.6700
	Output current Opt1 (A)	9.4430
	Output voltage Opt1 (V)	-0.9398
	Input current Opt1 (A)	-0.0017
	Input voltage Opt1 (V)	39.9818
	Remark: Detachment Opt1	
d↑	System current (A)	0.0225
	System voltage (V)	598.2700
	Output current Opt1 (A)	0.0160
	Output voltage Opt1 (V)	-0.1431
	Input current Opt1 (A)	-0.0002
	Input voltage Opt1 (V)	39.9802
	Remark: String disconnection inverter	
e↑	System current (A)	0.0289
	System voltage (V)	604.7400
	Output current Opt1 (A)	0.0222
	Output voltage Opt1 (V)	0.0835
	Input current Opt1 (A)	10.9662
	Input voltage Opt1 (V)	1.2567
	Remark: Chaotic input behaviour Opt1	
f↑	System current (A)	0.0284
	System voltage (V)	604.4800
	Output current Opt1 (A)	0.0217
	Output voltage Opt1 (V)	0.0330
	Input current Opt1 (A)	10.9667
	Input voltage Opt1 (V)	0.8262
	Remark: Input short circuit Opt1, burner off	

4 CONCLUSION

The experimental results provide a differentiated picture of the fire-related behaviour of PV systems with power optimizers. In the non-destructive heating tests (Series I), all tested devices reliably detected overtemperature and switched into a defined state, thereby ensuring that the affected optimizer stopped power absorption without interrupting the current flow of the string. The switching thresholds and hysteresis behaviour were reproducible, and the reactivation after cooling was consistently observed across all manufacturers. Even in cases where visible damage to the housings occurred, the optimizers resumed operation after cooling. System warnings and error messages, when generated, were automatically archived once the temperature returned to normal, leaving no persistent indication in the portals.

In the destructive flame exposure tests (Series II), the behaviour was markedly less systematic. The devices contributed to increased fire load through additional material, leading to intensified flame formation, smoke development, burning droplets, and in some cases detachment of components. The system reaction under these conditions varied considerably, with chaotic and non-reproducible patterns that limited systematic evaluation. In several cases, the PV system continued to operate until interrupted by inverter protection mechanisms, typically triggered by residual current device (RCD) tripping. Importantly, the electrical response of the PV systems with optimizers did not differ significantly from systems without optimizers, as shutdowns were initiated mainly by the inverter rather than by the optimizers themselves.

A central finding of this study is that, despite reliable overtemperature detection in controlled conditions, no full system shutdown with reduction of string voltage was observed in either test series. This contradicts the expectation that abnormal temperature events would trigger rapid-shutdown-like behaviour, a feature often assumed to enhance safety in facade-integrated PV systems. Instead, the results show that optimizers provide only local protection by halting energy absorption, while at the same time adding combustible material that increases the fire load. Nevertheless, catastrophic malfunctioning such as continued power absorption at high temperature, bursting, or explosive failure was not observed in any of the experiments.

The results highlight a regulatory gap, as no standards currently exist that address the fire behaviour of power optimizers in PV facade applications [2] [3]. For safety-critical building integration, this underscores the need for further research and potential adaptation of testing protocols to account for both the electrical and fire-related contributions of these devices. At the same time, the findings must be interpreted with caution, as the number of test runs was limited and the experimental conditions cannot fully reproduce the complexity of real facade fire scenarios. A structured overview of the identified advantages and disadvantages is provided in Table III.

Table III: Summary of advantages (+) and disadvantages (–) of power optimizers regarding electrical and fire-related behaviour.

Category	Behaviour
Electrical	(+) Detection of overtemperature
	(+) No electrical power absorption
	(–) No reduction of system voltage
	(–) Poor / missing alarm functionality
Fire	(–) Additional fire load
	(–) Detachment of burning parts
	(–) Burning droplet formation

5 OUTLOOK

The conducted investigations provide a first systematic insight into the thermal and fire-related behaviour of PV power optimizers. However, the limited number of tested devices and the simplified laboratory conditions restrict the general validity of the findings. Future work should therefore include large-scale facade fire tests under more realistic boundary conditions, as well as long-term cycling experiments to assess the effects of repeated overtemperature exposure on the reliability and safety of optimizers. In addition, further research is needed to evaluate the interaction of optimizers with defective PV modules and to define standardized procedures for testing and classifying their fire behaviour. Regulatory developments should particularly address requirements for fault reporting and system-level shutdown functionality in building-integrated PV applications.

6 ACKNOWLEDGMENT

The authors acknowledge the financial support of the Building Insurance of the Canton of Bern (GVB). Experimental work was conducted at the Photovoltaics Laboratory (PV-Lab) of the Bern University of Applied Sciences (BFH).

7 REFERENCES

[1] C. Bucher, (2025). Photovoltaic Systems: Planning, Installation, Operation (2nd rev. ed.). Zürich: Faktor Verlag.

[2] F. Fjaerestad, et al., Fire performance of building-integrated photovoltaics: A review, Fire Safety Journal 113 (2020) 102978.

[3] J. Benick, et al., Fire safety testing of PV modules: Current status and future needs, Proceedings of the 36th European Photovoltaic Solar Energy Conference (EU PVSEC), (2019) 1741–1746.

[4] L. Klintberg, et al., Experimental studies on fire safety of PV modules in façades, Solar Energy Materials and Solar Cells 220 (2021) 110851.

42nd European Photovoltaic Solar Energy Conference and Exhibition

Fire Behaviour of PV Power Optimizers

EU PVSEC 2025, 22.-26. September 2025 Bilbao (Spain)
Lasse Halle[1], David Joss[1], Christof Bucher[1]
[1]Bern University of Applied Sciences (BFH), School of Engineering and Computer Science (TI), Institute for Energy and Mobility Research (IEM), Laboratory for Photovoltaic Systems (PV-Lab), Burgdorf (Switzerland)
christof.bucher@bfh.ch

This project investigates the fire performance of facade-integrated photovoltaic (PV) systems with power optimizers. Experiments show that optimizers detect overtemperature and switch into bypass mode, ensuring continued system operation without module power absorption. After cooling, optimizers resumed operation even when visible damage was present. During flame tests, however, optimizers contributed to additional fire load, burning droplets, and smoke. The electrical behaviour of PV systems with optimizers was similar to systems without optimizers: no shutdown or system voltage reduction was triggered. The results allow for a critical assessment of the overall system behaviour.

Methodology

The behaviour of optimizers was examined experimentally using simulated PV modules (16 × 330 Wp ≈ 5.28 kWp). Two test series were carried out to investigate both controlled overtemperature behaviour and fire exposure:

- **Series I:** Controlled heating in a climate chamber up to 140 ° C.
- **Series II:** Flame exposure in a ventilated façade setup with burner temperatures > **800 ° C.**

Devices from three manufacturers were tested with their compatible inverters:

- **Huawei:** SUN2000-450W-P2 with SUN2000-10KTL-M1 inverter
- **SolarEdge:** S440 with SE10K inverter
- **Tigo:** TS4-A-O with Fronius SYMO 6.0-3-M inverter

Figure 1: Test setup in PV-Lab with climate chamber heating.

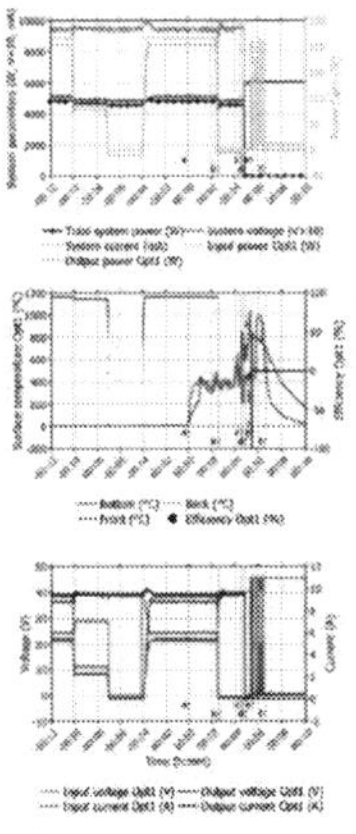

Event	Parameter	Measured value
a)	System current (A)	9.29
	System voltage (V)	**516.22**
	Output current Opt1 (A)	9.29
	Output voltage Opt1 (V)	22.01
	Input current Opt1 (A)	8.83
	Input voltage Opt1 (V)	24.45
	Remark: Ignition	
b)	System current (A)	8.56
	System voltage (V)	**506.76**
	Output current Opt1 (A)	8.56
	Output voltage Opt1 (V)	-0.44
	Input current Opt1 (A)	0.01
	Input voltage Opt1 (V)	39.97
	Remark: Overtemperature detection Opt1	
c)	System current (A)	9.45
	System voltage (V)	**483.67**
	Output current Opt1 (A)	9.44
	Output voltage Opt1 (V)	-0.04
	Input current Opt1 (A)	-0.00
	Input voltage Opt1 (V)	39.98
	Remark: Detachment Opt1	
d)	System current (A)	0.02
	System voltage (V)	**598.27**
	Output current Opt1 (A)	0.02
	Output voltage Opt1 (V)	-0.14
	Input current Opt1 (A)	0.00
	Input voltage Opt1 (V)	39.98
	Remark: String disconnection inverter	
e)	System current (A)	0.03
	System voltage (V)	**604.74**
	Output current Opt1 (A)	0.02
	Output voltage Opt1 (V)	0.08
	Input current Opt1 (A)	10.97
	Input voltage Opt1 (V)	1.26
	Remark: Chaotic input behaviour Opt1	
f)	System current (A)	0.03
	System voltage (V)	**604.48**
	Output current Opt1 (A)	0.02
	Output voltage Opt1 (V)	0.03
	Input current Opt1 (A)	10.97
	Input voltage Opt1 (V)	0.83
	Remark: Input short circuit Opt1, burner off	

Figure 2 and Table I: Exemplary evaluation of Series II flame test with system behaviour and event summary (a-f).

Behaviour with Overtemperature

Optimizers reliably detected overtemperature and switched to bypass, removing only their own contribution while the string continued operation. After cooling, they reactivated automatically even when visibly deformed. Switching thresholds showed consistent hysteresis, and monitoring warnings were only temporary.

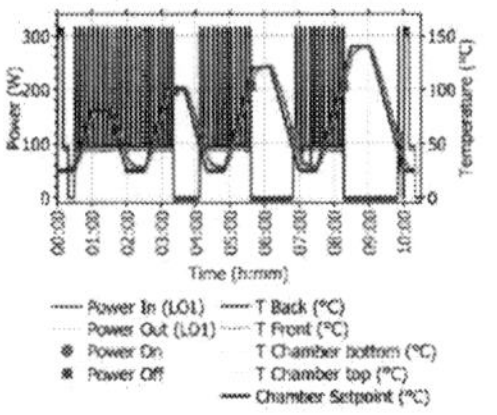

Figure 3: Exemplary switching behaviour of a thermally stressed optimizer (Series I)

Monitoring portals differed: Huawei gave position warnings, SolarEdge general errors, Tigo none. After cooling, all messages were archived, leaving no active faults or records, even when visible device damage was present.

A boxplot (Fig. 4) summarizes shutdown and restart temperatures by optimizer type.

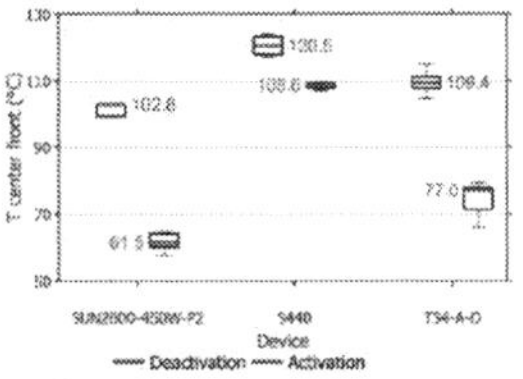

Figure 4: Shutdown and restart temperatures of optimizers (Series I) with hysteresis.

Behaviour under Fire Conditions

Evaluation was based on visual and electrical analysis (example in Fig. 2 and Tab. I). The flame process was highly chaotic, leading to non-reproducible system behaviour between runs.

In most cases, the inverter interrupted the string current within minutes, typically due to RCD tripping, while system voltage remained unaffected. In other tests, no shutdown occurred and the string kept operating despite the burning optimizer. Rapid Shutdown was never triggered due to the Fire Conditions.

Mechanically, brackets melted, causing optimizers to detach or swing while connected by cables. Burning droplets, strong flames, and dense smoke were frequently observed, showing that optimizers increase the fire load.

Figure 4 & 5: Flame tests in facade setup (front, side)

Conclusions and Outlook

In this research project it was observed that optimizers can detect overtemperature, but they do not trigger a complete system shutdown. From the flame test observations, the following fire safety–relevant behaviours can be derived:

Table II: Assessment of electrical (+) and fire-related (-) behaviour of PV systems with optimizers.

Category	(+) Pro	(-) Contra
Electrical behaviour	Detection of overtemperature	No reduction of system voltage
	No electrical power absorption	Poor / missing alarm functionality
Fire behaviour		Additional fire load
		Detachment of burning parts
		Burning droplet formation

The impact on fire safety should be discussed. The findings are shared openly, and the results should be critically questioned.

In further research projects, possible fire spread caused by optimizers should be investigated.

Acknowledgment

This research project was supported by the Building Insurance of the Canton of Bern (GVB).

References

[1] C. Bucher, (2025). *Photovoltaic Systems: Planning, Installation, Operation* (2nd rev. ed.). Zürich: Faktor Verlag.
[2] F. Fjaerestad et al., *Fire performance of building-integrated photovoltaics: A review*, Fire Safety Journal 113 (2020) 102978.

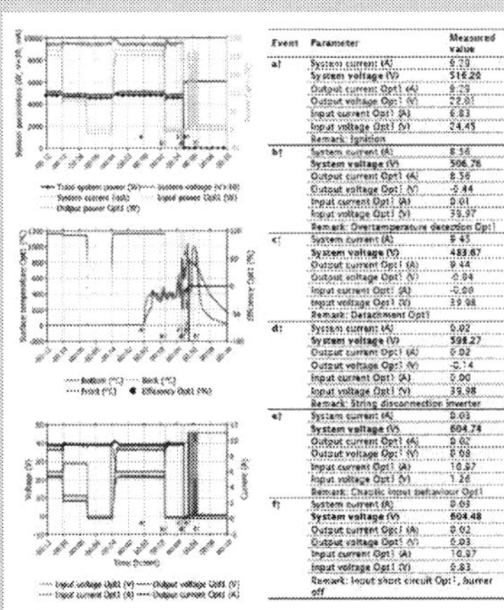

ONLINE CHARACTERIZATION OF PV STRINGS BY SMART INVERTERS USING A SELF REFERENCING ALGORITHM

Maximilian Schönau[1,2], Darwin Daume[3], Sasikumar Krishnan[1], Marius Weiß[1], Alexander Kusch[1], Christian Knausdorf[1], Sahereh Obeidavi[1], Achim Schulze[3,4], Dieter Landes[1], Bernd Hüttl[1]
[1]Coburg University of Applied Sciences, Dept. of Electrical Engineering and Computer Sciences, Coburg, Germany,
[2]smartblue AG, Kistlerhofstraße 75, Munich, Germany
[3]pvnode UG, Gabelsbergerstr. 9, 83022 Rosenheim
[4]Rosenheim Technical University of Applied Sciences, Germany,
Maximilian.Schoenau@smartblue.de, darwin@pvnode.com

ABSTRACT: We present a remote diagnostic method that uses the IV measurement function of smart inverters and a so called self-referencing procedure to represent the performance of the PV generator vs. operating conditions irradiance and temperature (*G* and *T*). We have recorded 200 IV-curves of a PV string within a period of six months using a smart inverter. A deep autoencoder detected disturbed or IV measurements so that these were not included in the evaluation. The effective irradiance G_{eff} at the PV string was determined, which was included in the evaluation instead of the measured irradiance. In addition, the cell temperature of the PV generator T_{eff} was determined using physical models for the evaluation. As a result, we create smooth power-surfaces over G_{eff} and T_{eff} conditions in the range of 100–1100 W/m² and 15–90 °C. For validation, the performance data of the PV string were compared by indoor measurements with a calibrated flasher at standard test conditions. The approach offers a remote and real-time diagnostic by smart inverters. It is well suited for accurate power monitoring of PV generators or degradation or soiling tracking without the need for additional sensor capabilities.
Keywords: Smart inverter IV tracing, IEC 61853-1, G–T performance matrix, Degradation monitoring, Soiling

1 INTRODUCTION

It is desirable for operators of PV systems to have continuous remote diagnostic performance monitoring for PV generators to detect degradation effects or soiling at an early stage. Performance determinations are possible by measuring current-voltage characteristics (IV-curves). The applicable standards IEC 60904, IEC 61829 and IEC 61853-1 define the procedures for measuring the IV-curves under controlled conditions of irradiance *G* and temperature *T* in order to create a performance matrix for G-T conditions [1].

However, very accurate performance determination of PV modules is only possible in measurement laboratories by means of calibrated solar simulators. Outdoor performance determinations on site often do not meet these accurate requirements and are also very costly. As a result, plant operators often lack a reliable, continuous overview of the performance of PV generators.

Smart inverters feature IV measurement capabilities that enable IV-curves of PV strings to be tracked directly without significantly interrupting the energy supply at the maximum power point (MPP). This function has opened promising possibilities for remote performance diagnostics of PV generators. Several studies have investigated the measurement uncertainties of IV measurements by inverters and their suitability for condition monitoring [2], [3]. In addition, self-referencing algorithms (SRA) have recently been developed that reduce the uncertainty of outdoor power ratings [4], [5].

In this article, we present a fully remote-controlled diagnostic measurement method for determining the power of PV generators based on the recording of IV-curves with smart inverters and on SRA.

To test and validate the measurement method, approximately 200 IV measurements were performed over a period of 6 months. The measurements were performed within a wide range of measurement conditions, *G* and *T*. IV measurements recorded under unsuitable measurement conditions are sorted out by means a deep autoencoder operating as a filter [6].

The result of the outdoor analysis was compared and verified with laboratory measurements under standard test conditions (STC) on PV modules of the string using a calibrated solar simulator.

2 SETUP

We used a smart inverter of SMA (Sunny Boy Smart Energy 5.0 inverter, type SBSE5.0-50) for energy harvesting and outdoor measuring the IV-curves of the connected string. By means of a well oriented pyranometer of Kipp & Zonen (SMP 10-A) and a temperature sensor, the global tilted irradiation (G_{mod}) and ambient temperature (T_{amb}) was measured.

In addition to that, we used satellite weather data of pvnode, to acquire the ambient temperature and the global tilted irradiation [7], to evaluate the need of accurate but costly on site sensors. In the future, it will also be possible to determine the measurement conditions by using machine learning based on data of satellites and of reference PV systems [8].

In total, we collected 200 IV-curves of a PV string consisting of six modules from supplier IBC: MonoSol 320 VL5-HC. These modules have a rated output of $P_{\mathrm{MPP,STC}} = 320\,\mathrm{W}$. To eliminate IV measurements recorded under unsuitable measurement conditions (e.g., with shadowing scenarios or with non-constant irradiance), a deep autoencoder was used as a filter [6]. The autoencoder was trained using "good" or "usable" IV curves so that IV curves from unsuitable conditions could be easily identified and sorted out.

The weather conditions of G_{mod} and T_{mod} varied over a wide range of measurement conditions. The SRA or referencing methodology developed in earlier work for on-site characterizations [4, 5] replaces the measured conditions G_{mod} and T_{mod} by the conditions G_{eff} and T_{eff}, which effectively affect the PV generator [4]. For realizing the remote concept, the SRA was modified regarding the determination of the temperature T_{eff} to reduce the number of electrical measurements required. We used the thermal

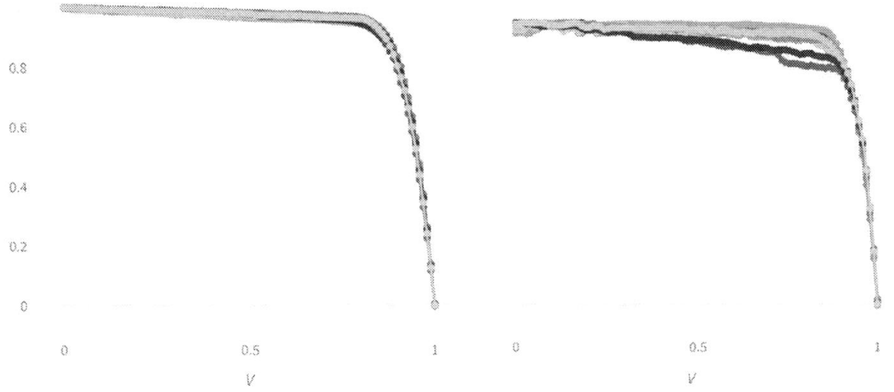

Figure 1: Examples of normalized deformed and undeformed IV-curves of our measurement campaign

model auf Sandia [9], [10] developed for physical modelling of cell temperature, using the ambient temperature T_{amb}, G_{eff} and some well-chosen parameters.

The power of PV string ($P_{mpp,\, string}$) is presented by our software concept as a surface versus the measurement conditions G_{eff} and T_{eff} to specify the nominal power ratings in accordance with the power matrix of the IEC 61853-1 standard [1].

For final validation of our remote performance determination concept, the outdoor P_{mpp} of the PV string at STC was compared with results of STC measurements on PV modules of the string by calibrated solar simulator cetisPV-XF-M of the company h.a.l.m.

3 ONLINE CHARACTERIZATIONS OF PV STRINGS USING SMART INVERTERS

Our remote measurement concept, which was described in the previous chapter, is mapped in our software and it is processed in three steps: (1): IV-curve filtering, (2): determination of the effective measurement conditions, and (3) adjusting the power surface by parameter fitting

3.1 IV-Curve Filtering

Typically, outdoor IV measurements suffer considerably from uncertainty regarding regular test conditions. For example, complete or partial shading or fluctuations in irradiance during the measurement lead to distorted IV curves, which are unusable for performance determinations [5].

To ensure that only undeformed IV-curves are used in performance analysis, we use a deep autoencoder as a monitoring filter: An autoencoder is an unsupervised neural network that learns a compact, nonlinear embedding of high-dimensional inputs by being trained to reproduce its own inputs at the output. In our implementation, each measured IV-curve was first normalized by it short-circuit current and open-circuit voltage and then passed through an encoder E that encodes the curve I_V into a seven-dimensional latent code,

$$E: I_V \to \mathbb{R}^7 \tag{1}$$

as well as a decoder D that reconstructs the complete curve [6]:

$$D: \mathbb{R}^7 \to I_V{}' \tag{2}$$

We trained the autoencoder network exclusively with "good" (undeformed), labeled in previous work [6]. After that, the model was used to decode and encode all IV curves,

$$I_V{}' = (D \circ E)(I_V) \tag{3}$$

which were then compared with the original:

$$\mathrm{RMSE} = \sqrt{\frac{1}{n_V} \cdot \sum_{V}^{n_V} (I_V - I_V{}')^2} \tag{44}$$

Deformed IV-curves show significant reconstruction deviations as a result. Since the autoencoder has never seen a deformed IV curve in the training process, these curves have significantly different encodings when given to the model due to their deformation. Reconstruction deviations can be quantified by the RMSE between reconstructed and ideally undeformed IV-curves. With the help of a sensibly defined threshold value, IV-curves with unacceptable deformations can be sorted out.

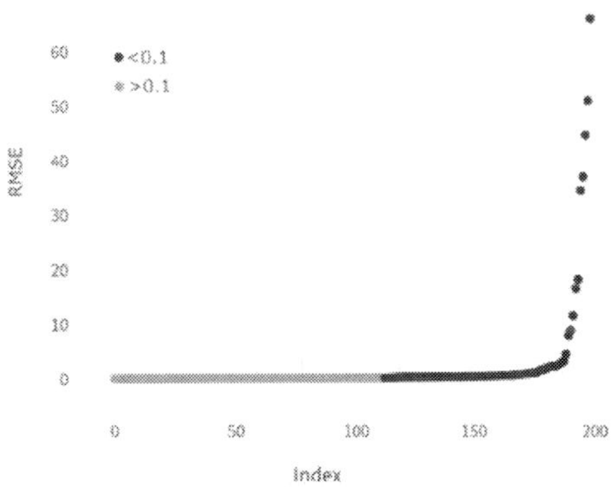

Figure 2: RMSE of autoencoder reconstruction uncertainty of measured IV-curves

Figure 2 shows the RMSE of the reconstruction deviations of all measured IV curves. We set a threshold

10.4229/EUPVSEC2025/4CV.1.62

value of 10 % for the RMSE of the reconstruction deviation, so that 90 IV-curves were sorted out from further analysis.

Figure 1 shows normalized usable and undistorted and distorted IV curves from our measurement campaign, that were filtered using the reconstruction error of the autoencoder.

3.2 Determination of the Effective Measurement Conditions

Using the measured IV-curves, the effective irradiance and the effective temperature are calculated from the module irradiance G_{mod} and the ambient temperature T_{amb}. The effective cell temperature T_{eff} is calculated using the thermal model of PV lib [10]:

$$T_{\text{mod}} = G_{\text{mod}} \cdot e^{a} \cdot \frac{\text{m}^2 \cdot ^\circ\text{C}}{\text{W}} + T_{\text{amb}} \tag{5}$$

$$T_{\text{eff}} = T_{\text{mod}} + \frac{G_{\text{mod}}}{G_{\text{STC}}} \cdot \Delta T \tag{6}$$

With a and ΔT being empirical parameters, and G_{STC} being $1000\ \frac{\text{W}}{\text{m}^2}$. Windspeed correction was not applied. For the glass/polymer open-rack PV modules the fit parameters were -3.56 and 3 °C for a and ΔT, respectively.

Moreover, the effective irradiation G_{eff} is calculated by means the short current at STC $I_{\text{SC,STC}}$ taken from the datasheet and the measured short circuit $I_{\text{SC, mod}}$ according to [4]:

$$G_{\text{eff}} = \frac{G_{\text{STC}}}{I_{sc.\text{STC}}} \cdot \frac{I_{\text{sc, mod}}}{1 + \alpha_{I_{sc}} \cdot (T_{\text{cell}} - 25\ ^\circ\text{C})} \tag{7}$$

The temperature coefficient α_{sc} was taken from datasheet too. Note, G_{eff} is the irradiance reaching the photovoltaic cell in the module and considering any AOI losses and losses of soiling or shadowing by degradation.

For our modelling we calculate theoretical power P_{model} and short circuit current $I_{\text{SC,model}}$ of the PV string for given irradiance G_{eff} and temperatures T_{eff} according with:

$$P_{\text{model}} = n_{\text{mod}} \cdot P_{\text{mpp,STC}} \cdot \frac{G_{\text{eff}}}{G_{\text{STC}}} \left(1 + \gamma_{P_{\text{mpp}}} \cdot (T_{eff} - 25\ ^\circ\text{C})\right) \tag{8}$$

In equation (8) $\gamma_{P_{\text{mpp}}}$ is the temperature coefficient of power and n_{mod}, is the quantity of modules of the string. The accuracy of our methodology will be further improved in the future by considering illumination-dependent modeling of the temperature coefficient [11].

3.3 Adjusting the Power Surface by Parameter Fitting

Using data of i IV-curves ($P_{\text{mpp, string},i}$, $I_{\text{sc, mod},i}$) vs. effective conditions $G_{\text{eff},i}$ and $T_{\text{eff},i}$ we can calculate $P_{\text{mpp,STC}}$ and $\gamma_{P_{\text{mpp}}}$ of equation (8) by minimizing the summed quadratic deviation of P_{model} and $P_{\text{mpp, string}}$ for all i measurements:

$$\left(P_{\text{mpp,STC}}, \gamma_{P_{\text{mpp}}}\right) = \arg\min_{x} \sum_{i} \left(P_{\text{model},i}(x) - P_{\text{mpp, string},i}\right)^2 \tag{9}$$

with $\boldsymbol{x}$ being the fit parameter set:

$$\boldsymbol{x} = \left(P_{\text{mpp,STC}}, \gamma_{P_{\text{mpp}}}\right) \tag{10}$$

By using the derived parameters $P_{\text{mpp,STC}}$ and $\gamma_{P_{\text{mpp}}}$ and equation (8) the power matrix vs. test conditions according to standard IEC 61853-1 can be calculated as shown in table 1.

4 RESULTS

Our measurement method was fed with data from a period of six months, during all 200 IV curves were measured. According to chapter 3 and figure 2, 115 measurements were chosen to be useful and were considered for analysis. Figure 4 shows the presentation of string power $P_{\text{mpp, string}}$ vs. effective measurement conditions, closely based on the performance matrix in accordance with the IEC 61853-1 standard. Please note that the effective conditions in use are based on our on-site measurements of G_{mod} and T_{mod}.

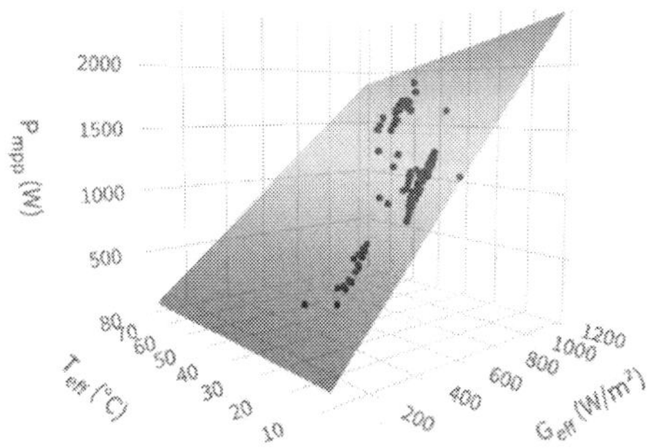

Figure 3: String power $P_{\text{mpp, string}}$ vs. effective irradiance G_{eff} and effective cell temperature T_{eff}, based on experimental data of smart inverter.

Table 1 was calculated by using equation (8), like the performance matrix of the IEC 61853-1 standard.

Table 1: String power $P_{\text{mpp, string}}$ vs. effective module temperature T_{eff} and irradiance G_{eff} derived from electrical measurements with smart inverter and based on on-site data T_{amb} and G_{mod}.

P_{mpp} in W	15 °C	25 °C	45 °C	50 °C	75 °C
100 W/m²	196	190	178	175	159
200 W/m²	393	380	355	349	318
400 W/m²	785	760	711	698	636
500 W/m²	981	950	888	873	795
600 W/m²	1178	1140	1066	1047	954
800 W/m²	1570	1521	1421	1396	1272
1000 W/m²	1963	**1901**	1777	1745	1590
1100 W/m²	2159	2091	1954	1920	1749

For comparison with calibrated solar simulator, we have determined the STC power of all modules of the string. The six modules of the string were performing $P_{\text{mpp, module, STC}} = 312\ \text{W} \pm 2\ \text{W}$ resulting in a string power of $P_{\text{mpp, string, STC}} = 1872\ \text{W}$, representing a loss of 1.39 % from the nominal 6-module rating of 1920 W. The outdoor performance rating using on-site data shows for STC a $P_{\text{mpp, string}}$ which is approximately 29 W or 1.5% higher than that of the indoor reference measurement.

Finally, we have used the complete remote concept for outdoor power rating, using satellite data of pvnode for determination of the temperature T_{amb} and irradiation G_{mod}. The results of the remote concept are very similar to the data of on-site measurements, as shown in table 2. Table 2 represents the measurement deviation of the two concepts. For all operating conditions, the string power $P_{mpp,\,string}$ based on remote data are typically lower by around 2 % in comparison to on-site data. For STC $P_{mpp,\,string,\,remote}$ is 1855 W, close to the reference level of calibrated indoor measurement.

Table 2: Deviation of the two analysis concepts using measured on-site and remote satellite data with: $\Delta P_{mpp} = P_{mpp,\ string,on\text{-}site} - P_{mpp,\ string,\ remote}$

ΔP_{mpp} in W	15 °C	25 °C	45 °C	50 °C	75 °C
100 W/m²	4	5	6	7	9
200 W/m²	8	10	12	13	17
400 W/m²	16	19	24	26	33
500 W/m²	20	23	30	32	41
600 W/m²	23	28	36	38	49
800 W/m²	31	37	48	51	65
1000 W/m²	39	46	60	64	81
1100 W/m²	43	50	66	70	90

5 CONCLUSIONS

We have demonstrated that modern smart inverters in combination with an intelligent evaluation concept, based on self-referencing and machine learning methods, are well suited to determine the performance behavior of PV strings across a wide range of measurement conditions in accordance with the performance matrix of the IEC 61853-1 standard.

The methodology can be set up entirely for remote diagnostics if reliable satellite data are available to determine the measurement conditions. The method is suitable for real-time diagnostics and degradation analysis.

Future work may continue with the validation and determination of uncertainty of the methodology. In addition to that, the methodology may be utilized for the detection of degradation and soiling.

ACKNOWLEDGEMENTS

The authors gratefully acknowledge the Bavarian Research Foundation for their financial support of the project Kick-PV: "AI-based characterization and classification of PV-plants for predictive maintenance" under reference number AZ-1564-22.

Portions of the manuscript text were drafted or edited with assistance from large language models. The authors reviewed, revised, and took full responsibility for the content.

LITERATURE

[1] *IEC 60904-1:2020, Photovoltaic devices. Part 1, Measurement of photovoltaic current-voltage characteristics*, Edition 3.0. Geneva, Switzerland: International Electrotechnical Commission, 2020.

[2] Alexander Kusch *et al.*, "Validierung von Smart-Wechselrichtern für die Leistungsferndiagnose von PV-Strängen," presented at the RET.Con, Nordhausen, Feb. 2025.

[3] M. Bartholomäus, L. Morino, P. B. Poulsen, and S. V. Spataru, "Evaluating the Accuracy of Inverter Based String IV Measurements," *40th European Photovoltaic Solar Energy Conference and Exhibition*, pp. 020370-001-020370–005, 2023, doi: 10.4229/EUPVSEC2023/4CV.1.4.

[4] B. Hüttl, L. Gottschalk, S. Schneider, D. Pflaum, and A. Schulze, "Accurate performance rating of photovoltaic modules under outdoor test conditions," *Solar Energy*, vol. 177, pp. 737–745, Jan. 2019, doi: 10.1016/j.solener.2018.12.002.

[5] M. Scheler *et al.*, "Precise On-Site Power Analysis of Photovoltaic Arrays by Self-Reference Algorithm," *8th World Conference on Photovoltaic Energy Conversion; 1070-1073*, p. 4 pages, 28190 kb, 2022, doi: 10.4229/WCPEC-82022-4DO.1.4.

[6] M. Schönau, D. Daume, B. Hüttl, and D. Landes, "Improving IV Curve Classification by Machine Learning Methods Using Deep Autoencoders," *40th European Photovoltaic Solar Energy Conference and Exhibition*, pp. 020410-001-020410–004, 2023, doi: 10.4229/EUPVSEC2023/4CV.1.53.

[7] "pvnode: Your partner for the new generation of precise PV data." Accessed: Feb. 18, 2025. [Online]. Available: https://www.pvnode.com/

[8] M. Schönau *et al.*, "Hindcasting Solar Irradiance by Machine Learning using Photovoltaic Data," *41st European Photovoltaic Solar Energy Conference and Exhibition*, pp. 020400-001-020400–005, 2024, doi: 10.4229/EUPVSEC2024/4CV.1.4.

[9] K. S. Anderson, C. W. Hansen, W. F. Holmgren, A. R. Jensen, M. A. Mikofski, and A. Driesse, "pvlib python: 2023 project update," *JOSS*, vol. 8, no. 92, p. 5994, Dec. 2023, doi: 10.21105/joss.05994.

[10] J. Kratochvil, W. Boyson, and D. King, "Photovoltaic array performance model.," SAND2004-3535, 919131, Aug. 2004. doi: 10.2172/919131.

[11] S. M. F. Zhang *et al.*, "Illumination-dependent temperature coefficients of the electrical parameters of modern silicon solar cell architectures," *Nano Energy*, vol. 98, p. 107221, Jul. 2022, doi: 10.1016/j.nanoen.2022.107221.

42nd European Photovoltaic Solar Energy Conference and Exhibition

Online Characterization of PV Strings by Smart Inverters Using a Self Referencing Algorithm

Maximilian Schönau, Darwin Daume, Sasikumar Krishnan, Marius Weiß, Alexander Kusch, Christian Knausdorf, Sahereh Obeidavi, Achim Schulze, Dieter Landes, Bernd Hüttl

Introduction

- **Challenge:** Creation of a remote performance diagnosis system for PV strings for early detection of performance degradation or soiling
- **Approach:** Application of the IV-measurement function of smart inverters for determination of a string-power matrix vs. operating conditions irradiance (G) and temperature (T).
- **Data Processing:** Improvement of measurement accuracy by using a self-referencing algorithm (SRA) and a deep autoencoder for sorting out distorted I-V curves.

Experimental Setup

- **Device under Test:** PV string of 6 monocrystalline PV modules with STC power of 320 W
- **IV-Tracer:** Sunny Boy Smart Energy 5.0 inverter
- **Operating Conditions:** G and T were measured on-site or were acquired by data service providers using satellite weather data
- **Measurement Campaign:** approximately 200 IV curves were collected within 6 months for varying operating conditions

IV Curve Evaluation by Autoencoder

- Shading or fluctuating irradiances during IV measurements result in deformed IV curves which are not useful for power rating
- Machine Learning by training of autoencoders can be used to recognize deformed IV curves
- Autoencoder was used to filter or non-deformed IV-curves (right hand side figure) and measurements with useless deformed IV curves (left hand side figure)

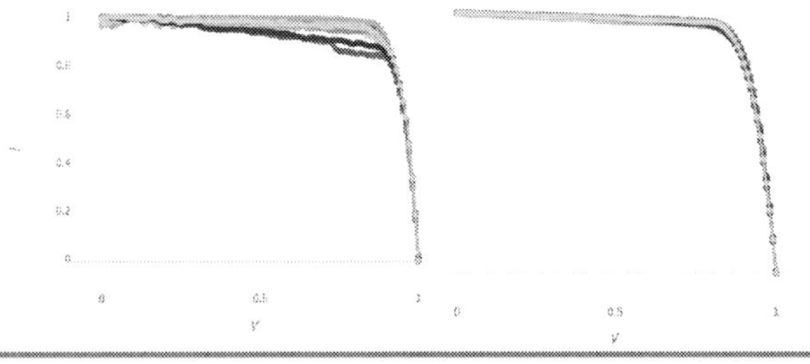

Determination of the Effective Measurement Conditions

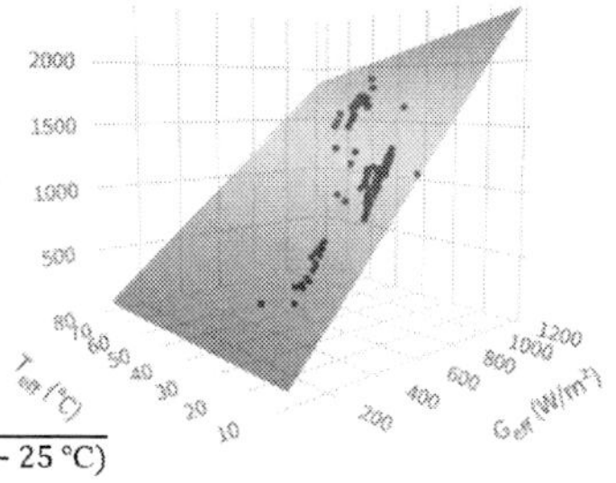

- The module temperature is modeled from the ambient temperature using pvlib
- The effective irradiance is calculated by:

$$G_{\mathrm{eff}} = \frac{G_{\mathrm{STC}}}{I_{sc,\,\mathrm{STC}}} \cdot \frac{I_{\mathrm{sc,\,mod}}}{1 + \alpha_{I_{sc}} \cdot (T_{\mathrm{cell}} - 25\,°\mathrm{C})}$$

- For all operating conditions, the power can be modeled with:

$$P_{\mathrm{model}} = n_{\mathrm{mod}} \cdot P_{\mathrm{mpp,STC}} \cdot \frac{G_{\mathrm{eff}}}{G_{\mathrm{STC}}} \left(1 + \gamma_{P_{\mathrm{mpp}}} \cdot (T_{\mathrm{eff}} - 25\,°\mathrm{C})\right)$$

- P_{mpp} is fitted as a surface over the temperature and irradiance over all measurements

By fitting all IV-curves at once to the performance matrix, the accuracy of the characterization is drastically increased.

Results

- A performance matrix similar to the IEC 61853-1 standard can be calculated
- At STC, the measurement deviation between the outdoor campaign and an indoor reference measurement is only 1.5 %
- Using satellite data instead of on-site sensors lead to the same results
  → Deviations in inaccurate satellite data are corrected by the fitting process

String Power over Module Temperature and Irradiance

P_{mpp} in W	15 °C	25 °C	45 °C	50 °C	75 °C
100 W/m²	196	190	178	175	159
200 W/m²	393	380	355	349	318
400 W/m²	785	760	711	698	636
500 W/m²	981	950	888	873	795
600 W/m²	1178	1140	1066	1047	954
800 W/m²	1570	1521	1421	1396	1272
1000 W/m²	1963	1901	1777	1745	1590
1100 W/m²	2159	2091	1954	1920	1749

Modern smart inverters in combination with an intelligent evaluation concept, are well suited to determine the performance behavior of PV strings in accordance with the performance matrix of the IEC 61853-1 standard

EU PVSEC Bilbao
22nd to 26th September 2025

Download
Full Paper

smartblue
smartblue AG, Kistlerhofstraße 75, Munich, Germany
COBURG UNIVERSITY of applied sciences and arts
Coburg University of Applied Sciences, Dep. of Electrical Engineering and Computer Sciences, Coburg, Germany
PVNODE
pvnode UG, Gabelsbergerstr. 9, 83022 Rosenheim
Technische Hochschule Rosenheim
Rosenheim Technical University of Applied Sciences, Germany
Bayerische Forschungsstiftung

020362-001

42nd European Photovoltaic Solar Energy Conference and Exhibition

This presentation was selected by the Sc. Committee of the EU PVSEC 2025 for submission of a full paper to one of the EU PVSEC's collaborating peer-reviewed journals.

BRIDGING THE GAP: INSIGHTS INTO BACKTRACKING-ANGLE RELATED DISCREPANCIES BETWEEN ESTIMATES AND ACTUAL PERFORMANCE IN LARGE-SCALE PHOTOVOLTAIC PLANTS

Juan Santamaría-Sancho, Javier Martín-Rueda, Eduardo Lorenzo Pigueiras, Javier R. Ledesma
Instituto de Energía Solar, Universidad Politécnica de Madrid
C/ Nikola Tesla, s/n
juan.santamariasan@upm.es, javier.martin@upm.es, antonio.lorenzo@upm.es, javier.ledesma@upm.es

ABSTRACT: Energy yield overestimation in large-scale photovoltaic (PV) simulations is a recurring issue that affects the accuracy of performance predictions. Analysis of SCADA data from four single-axis PV plants in different regions revealed systematic deviations between simulated and measured tracker angles during backtracking periods, prompting an investigation into the role of the estimated tracking irradiation gain (TIG) in these discrepancies. These deviations seemed to be linked to empirical corrections implemented to mitigate shading caused by terrain unevenness, which introduces elevation differences between tracker rows. While these adjustments reduce shading losses, they also modify the trackers' optimal tilt, lowering incident irradiance and ultimately reducing energy yield. A reverse-engineering approach was used to derive an equivalent correction model, based on a theoretical reduction in the effective inter-row spacing. When implemented in simulation tools, this correction produced TIG values 7–10% lower than those predicted under ideal flat-terrain conditions, leading to annual energy yield overestimations of around 3%. The results underscore the importance of accounting for realistic tracking behavior in energy yield simulations to improve both technical accuracy and the financial predictability of PV projects.
Keywords: energy yield overestimation, tracking irradiation gain, backtracking, terrain unevenness effects, PV simulation.

1 INTRODUCTION

In recent years, the growth of installed PV capacity and the increasing relevance of solar energy have drawn attention to the persistent overestimation of expected energy yields in large-scale PV plants [1] [2]. Within these discrepancies between actual and simulated results, the tracking irradiation gain (TIG) emerges as a key performance indicator (KPI), as it directly influences the energy yield.

Reports and consultations received at the Instituto de Energía Solar (IES) of the Universidad Politécnica de Madrid (UPM) frequently indicate that the TIG observed in large commercial single-axis tracking PV plants is systematically lower than the values predicted by simulations performed during the project design phase for bankability purposes. TIG, defined as the relative increase in irradiation collected by single-axis tracking systems compared to horizontal (zero-tilt) configurations, plays a central role in energy yield modelling and is given by

$$\mathrm{TIG}_T(\omega) = \frac{G_T(\omega) - G_T(0)}{G_T(0)}, \quad (1)$$

where $G_T(\omega)$ and $G_T(0)$ represent the solar irradiation accumulated during a period T on a plane tilted at angle ω and on a horizontal plane, respectively. It must be noted that a reduction in TIG does not affect the performance ratio (PR) or the availability indicators of the PV plants. For this reason, despite its relevance, this phenomenon has so far received little attention in the open literature.

This work investigates the causes of the lower-than-expected TIG through the analysis of four PV plants equipped with different tracker models installed on horizontal terrain. The study shows that terrain irregularities, often ignored in simulation models, produce small but systematic deviations in tracker alignment. These deviations require corrective adjustments in tracking operation to mitigate shading and the appearance of hot spots, but such adjustments come at the cost of reducing the amount of captured irradiance.

By focusing on TIG itself, this study aims to improve the understanding of the gap between simulated and actual values of this KPI and to emphasize the need to incorporate these effects into future energy yield assessments, leading to more accurate and financially reliable PV project evaluations.

2 MODELLING THE TRACKING ANGLES

This work focuses on quantifying the impact of tracker positioning during backtracking periods on the TIG in utility-scale PV plants equipped with horizontal single-axis trackers. This configuration is projected to represent nearly 40% of the market share in utility solar PV installations by 2030 [3]. To that end, the geometric framework underlying the computation of tracker rotation angles is introduced, as implemented in SISIFO, a simulation software developed by IES-UPM. SISIFO was developed within the European projects PVCROPS [4], MASLOWATEN [5] and PVOP [6] . It supports the simulation of grid-connected and pumping PV systems, including features such as mutual shading modeling [7] [8], multiple tracking strategies [9], and bifacial operation on sloped terrain [10]. The models for irradiance distribution, decomposition, transposition, and spectral correction are detailed in [11] [12] [13].

The physical domain is modeled as a three-dimensional affine space $\mathcal{A}_0 \equiv (\mathbb{R}^3, \mathbb{R}^3, \phi)$, where $\phi\colon \mathcal{A}_0 \times \mathcal{A}_0 \to \mathbb{R}^3$ denotes the vector difference, and the associated vector space $(\mathbb{R}^3, \|\cdot\|)$ is equipped with the standard Euclidean norm derived from the usual scalar product. The natural Euclidean distance $d_0\colon \mathcal{A}_0 \times \mathcal{A}_0 \to \mathbb{R}$ is used to compute physical distances in this space.

A right-handed Cartesian coordinate system-(x, y, z) is introduced, with origin $O \in \mathcal{A}_0$ located on the rotation axis of a reference tracker, at a height H_0 above ground level. The x-axis points East–West, the y-axis points North–South, and the z-axis is aligned with the zenith direction.

Trackers are assumed to be arranged in equidistant,

parallel rows indexed by $n \in \mathbb{Z}$, where $n = 0$ corresponds to the reference tracker. Rows to the right (respectively, left) are indexed by consecutive positive (respectively, negative) integers.

The solar position is calculated using the standard solar position equations [11] and is characterized by two standard angles: the solar azimuth γ_S, defined as the angle between the projection of the Sun onto the horizontal plane and the geographic North (positive eastwards), and the solar zenith angle θ_S, defined as the angle between the Sun and the vertical direction.

Tracker rotation is described by its tilt angle ω, measured with respect to the horizontal plane, and its azimuth angle, corresponding to the orientation of the rotation axis. In typical utility-scale configurations, including the ones considered in this work, trackers are aligned along the North–South direction, corresponding to azimuth $\alpha = 0$.

To simplify the analysis, SISIFO adopts a two-dimensional geometric representation in which the working domain is defined as the vertical plane orthogonal to the tracker rotation axis. For North–South-aligned trackers, this plane is orthogonal to the local meridian and is modeled as an affine plane $\mathcal{A} \subset \mathcal{A}_0$, endowed with the Euclidean distance $d: \mathcal{A} \times \mathcal{A} \to \mathbb{R}$ induced from d_0. An affine frame $\mathcal{R} = \{O; \mathcal{B}\}$ is fixed in $\mathcal{A}$, where $\mathcal{B}$ is the standard orthonormal basis of $\mathbb{R}^2$. Coordinates in this plane are denoted by (x, z). Within this working plane, the projection of the Sun's position is represented by the point $P_S \equiv (x_S, z_S)$, where $x_S = \cos\gamma_S \sin\theta_S$ and $z_S = \sin\theta_S$.

For subsequent analysis, the Euclidean distance in $\mathcal{A}$ is normalized so that the projected width of a tracker cross-section equals one unit. Specifically, if the projected endpoints of the n-th tracker cross-section in $\mathcal{A}$ are denoted by $E_{1,n}$ and $E_{2,n}$, for every $n \in \mathbb{Z}$ it is imposed the following condition,

$$d(E_{1,n}, E_{2,n}) = 1. \quad (2)$$

As a result, trackers are assumed to be evenly spaced by a normalized distance L_{EW} (East–West spacing) between consecutive rotation axes.

Figure 1 shows an schematic of the model implemented where blue segments represent the cross-sections of the trackers on the working domain. The baseline corresponds to the intersection between the working plane and the ground, assumed to be a perfectly horizontal plane. Yellow segments indicate illuminated ground areas, and black segments correspond to shaded ground regions. The trace of the Sun's ray is shown as a dashed black line. These colour conventions will be maintained in all subsequent figures, unless explicitly stated otherwise.

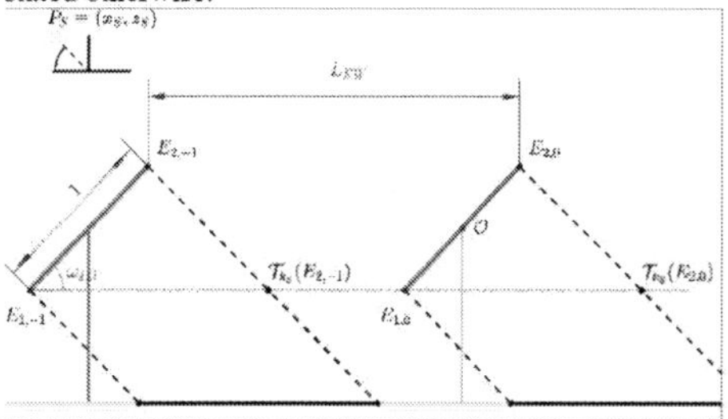

Figure 1: Simplified layout of the model. Trackers are shown in blue, and the ground is a horizontal line at height $-H$, with sunlit (yellow) and shaded (black) regions. The sun path appears as a dashed black line. The colour code employed for the notation corresponds to the colour of the respective elements it denotes.

2.1 Backtracking angles

In configurations with horizontal single-axis trackers, the rotation angle of each tracker is dynamically adjusted according to the position of the Sun. The ideal tracking condition corresponds to orienting the active surface of each generator such that the projection of the incident solar rays onto the working plane is orthogonal to the generator's cross-section. Equivalently, the normal vector to the tilted surface becomes collinear with the projection of the solar rays within this plane, thereby maximizing the irradiance collected by the active surface.

From simple trigonometric considerations, the corresponding ideal tracking angle ω_{ID} with respect to the horizontal is given by

$$\omega_{ID} = atan\frac{x_S}{z_S}. \quad (3)$$

However, this ideal configuration is not always feasible. At low solar altitudes, insufficient inter-row spacing may lead to one tracker row casting a shadow over the adjacent one, as schematically illustrated in **Figure 2**.

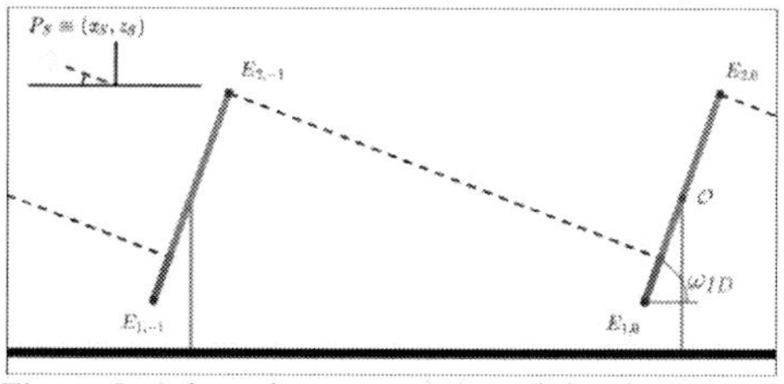

Figure 2: Schematic representation of the shadow cast between adjacent tracker rows at low solar altitudes, represented as red segments. The notation uses the same colour as the element it represents.

To avoid mutual shading between rows under these conditions, trackers are intentionally rotated away from the ideal direction, this strategy is known as backtracking.

To formalize the backtracking condition, the direction of sunlight projected onto the working domain $\mathcal{A} \subset \mathbb{R}^3$ is considered. Let

$$k_S = \frac{(x_S, z_S)}{\sqrt{x_S^2 + z_S^2}}, \quad (4)$$

denote the unit vector indicating the solar ray direction in the working plane, and $\pi_z: \mathbb{R}^3 \to \mathbb{R}$ the projection onto the vertical axis, that is, for any point $(x, y, z) \in \mathbb{R}^3$, $\pi_z(x, y, z) = z$. Based on the vector in Equation (4), an oblique projection operator $\mathcal{T}_{k_S}: \mathcal{A} \to \mathcal{G}$ is defined, mapping each point $P \in \mathcal{A}$ to the intersection of the ray emitted from P in the direction of k_S with the horizontal line $\mathcal{G} = \{(x, -H) \in \mathcal{A} | x \in \mathbb{R}\}$, where $H = \left(H_0 + min\left(\pi_z(E_{1,n}), \pi_z(E_{2,n})\right)\right) / d_0(E_{1,n}, E_{2,n})$ for any $n \in \mathbb{Z}$. That is,

$$\mathcal{T}_{k_S}(P) = (P + \lambda \cdot k_S) \cap \mathcal{G}, \quad (5)$$

for some $\lambda \in \mathbb{R}$. Formally, backtracking is triggered when the distance between the points $\mathcal{T}_{k_S}(E_{2,n})$ and $E_{1,n}$ or between the points $\mathcal{T}_{k_S}(E_{1,n})$ and $E_{2,n}$ exceeds the normalized inter-row spacing L_{EW}, for any $n \in \mathbb{Z}$. During the morning backtracking period, simple geometric analysis yields

$$d\left(E_{1,n}, \mathcal{T}_{k_S}(E_{2,n})\right) = sec(\omega_{ID}). \quad (6)$$

10.4229/EUPVSEC2025/4DO.1.2

It should be noted that this equation is well-defined, since during backtracking it always holds that $\omega_{ID} \neq 0$.
Hence, the condition for activating backtracking becomes

$$sec(\omega_{ID}) \geq L_{EW} \Leftrightarrow L_{EW} cos(\omega_{ID}) \leq 1. \quad (7)$$

An analogous condition applies symmetrically during the afternoon backtracking period.

To avoid shading, the tracker angle is corrected from the ideal value ω_{ID} by applying a backtracking correction angle ω_C^{BT} such that [14]

$$cos(\omega_C^{BT}) = L_{EW} cos(\omega_{ID}). \quad (8)$$

Accordingly, the resulting angle ω_{IDC} of the generator with respect to the horizontal during backtracking is given by

$$\omega_{IDC} = \omega_{ID} - \omega_C^{BT}. \quad (9)$$

This correction is the minimum required to prevent shading while minimizing energy losses due to deviation from the optimal angle. Therefore, the trackers are not rotated further than necessary, and under ideal conditions, the ground between rows remains completely shaded during backtracking periods, as illustrated in **Figure 3**.

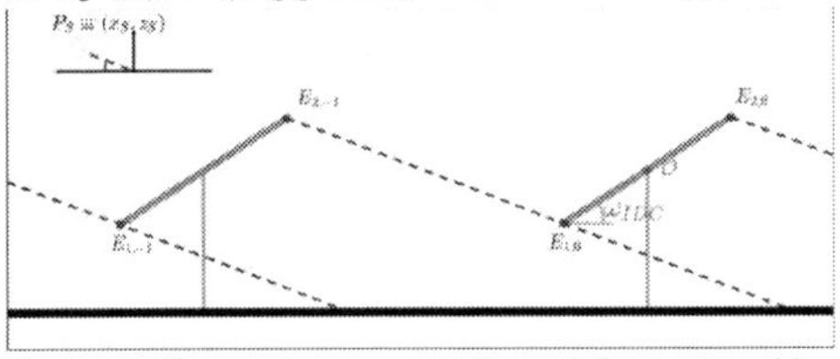

Figure 3: Schematic representation of the backtracking configuration. Colours in the notation match the corresponding elements they refer to.

2.2 Unevenness effect on backtracking

An essential assumption in the geometric model introduced above is the flatness of the terrain, whereby all tracker axes are assumed to lie on the same horizontal plane. While this simplification facilitates simulation and analytical treatment, it does not accurately reflect the conditions of real-world utility-scale PV plants. In practice, field inspections conducted during backtracking periods consistently revealed the presence of illuminated strips of ground between adjacent tracker rows, as illustrated in **Figure 4**. This empirical observation contradicts the theoretical prediction of complete ground shading during backtracking, indicating that additional factors must be influencing the actual behavior.

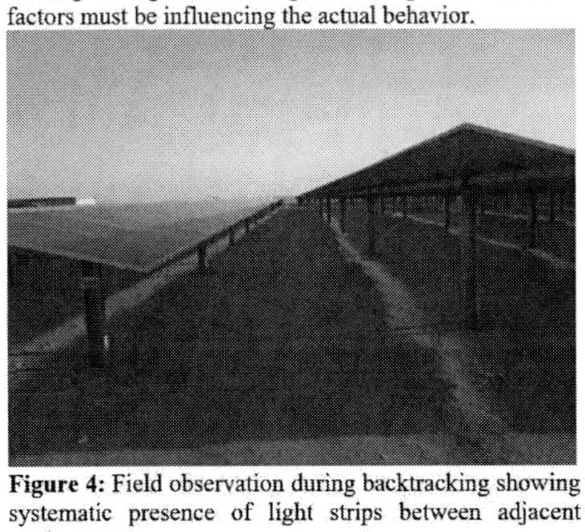

Figure 4: Field observation during backtracking showing systematic presence of light strips between adjacent tracker rows.

One of the contributors to this discrepancy is terrain unevenness, which introduces small but significant elevation differences between tracker rows. These vertical misalignments give rise to two possible shading scenarios. Focusing on the morning backtracking period, though the same reasoning applies in the afternoon, if a given tracker row $n \in \mathbb{Z}$ is situated at a slightly higher elevation than its preceding row $n-1$, its shadow fails to reach the adjacent row, resulting in a light strip on the ground. Conversely, if row n is at a lower elevation than row $n-1$, the shadow extends beyond the intended spacing, causing inter-row shading losses, the very outcome that backtracking algorithms are designed to avoid. These effects are illustrated schematically in **Figure 5**.

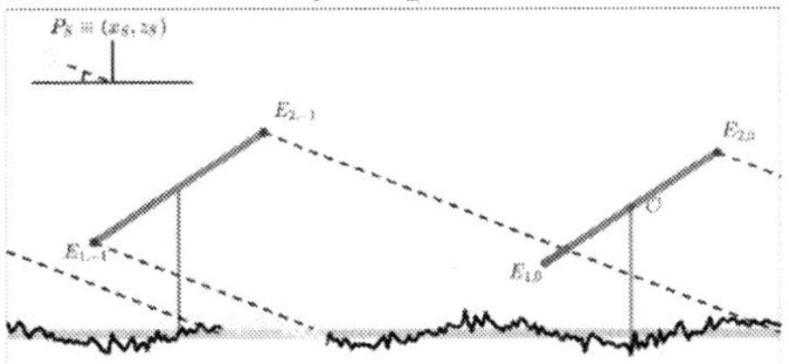

Figure 5: Schematic representation of the effects of terrain-induced elevation differences between tracker rows. The first generator row illustrates the appearance of light strips on the ground when the preceding row lies at a lower elevation. The second row depicts unintended shading (represented as a red segment) caused by a higher preceding row. The notation of each element is directly associated with its representative colour.

Interestingly, in actual PV plants, only the first of these scenarios, i.e. light strips between rows, was commonly observed. A plausible explanation is that shading between rows is undesirable not only due to its impact on energy yield but also because it generates hotspots that must be addressed during maintenance, and it is visually conspicuous. Consequently, it is hypothesized that the theoretical tracker positioning is deliberately adjusted in practice to prioritize the elimination of inter-row shading, even at the cost of reduced irradiance capture. This adjustment explains the systematic presence of ground illumination during backtracking periods, even on seemingly flat terrains.

3 APPROACH AND RESULTS

To validate the hypothesis proposed at the end of the previous section, SCADA data from the four PV plants under consideration were analyzed. These datasets included the angular position of each tracker, recorded as the empiric inclination angle ω_E with respect to the horizontal. To assess whether the angular position differs significantly across trackers within each PV plant, a pre-selection of trackers was performed based on data availability and quality. After this filtering, it was observed that the angular behavior of the selected trackers within each plant remained largely consistent over time. This observation supports the assumption that a single representative tracker per PV plant can reliably characterize the overall tracking behavior. Accordingly, the subsequent analysis focuses on one tracker per PV plant.

Table I summarizes the main characteristics of the analyzed PV plants, including their geographical location and the normalized inter-row spacing L_{EW} of each configuration. The second Mexican plant corresponds to a separate parcel within the same facility as the first and is therefore labeled 1.2, while the original is labeled 1.1 for clarity.

Table I: Some relevant technical specifications of the studied PV plants.

PV Plant	Location	L_{EW}/ []
1.1	Mexico	3.00
1.2	Mexico	3.00
2	Chile	2.26
3	Chile	2.56
4	Spain	2.74

Figure 6 illustrates, for PV plant 1.1 located in Mexico, the evolution of the generator's inclination angle throughout a full day, specifically on the spring equinox. The orange curve corresponds to the simulated tracker angle ω_{IDC}, while blue dots represent the experimental SCADA data ω_E. The difference between both values, shown as a dashed purple line (referenced to the right axis), reveals a sharp increase during backtracking intervals, highlighted with a white background. This confirms the deviation of real tracker behavior from the theoretical prediction specifically during those periods.

It should also be noted that the purple curve experiences a sudden change in trend at the end of the first daily backtracking period and at the beginning of the second. This behavior can be explained by the trackers reaching their mechanical saturation position, typically fixed around 55°. In the orange curve of **Figure 6**, this saturation is clearly visible as a flat region, reflecting the fact that, beyond this limit, the trackers can no longer follow the theoretical trajectory.

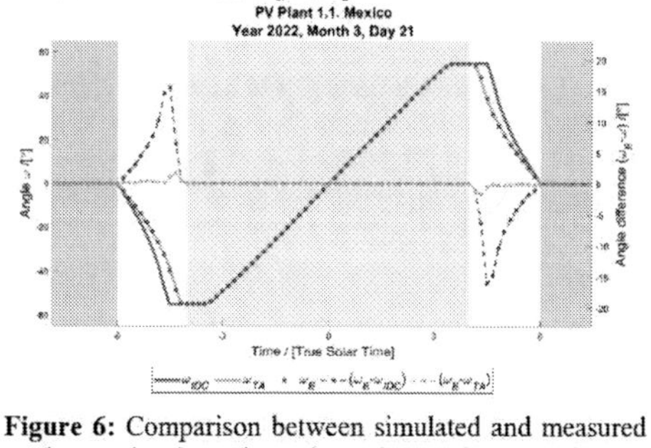

Figure 6: Comparison between simulated and measured tracker angles throughout the spring equinox day for PV plant 1.1, located in Mexico. The orange curve represents the theoretical inclination angle ω_{IDC} obtained from the ideal backtracking model, while the dark blue dots correspond to the experimental SCADA data ω_E. The dashed purple line, referenced to the right axis, quantifies the deviation between both values, which becomes particularly pronounced during backtracking intervals, highlighted with a white background. To account for this effect, a corrected simulation ω_{TA} was performed by introducing a reduced effective row-to-row distance $\tilde{L}_{EW}$. This correction, shown in dark yellow, results in a noticeable improvement, as reflected in the reduced discrepancy displayed in light blue, also , referenced to the right axis.

Figure 7 presents analogous results for the remaining PV plants located in Spain, Chile, and the second parcel in Mexico (PV plant 1.2), focusing exclusively on the first backtracking interval of the same day. Owing to the symmetry of the tracker motion with respect to solar noon, the analysis of this initial interval is sufficient, since the behavior observed during the second backtracking period mirrors that of the first.

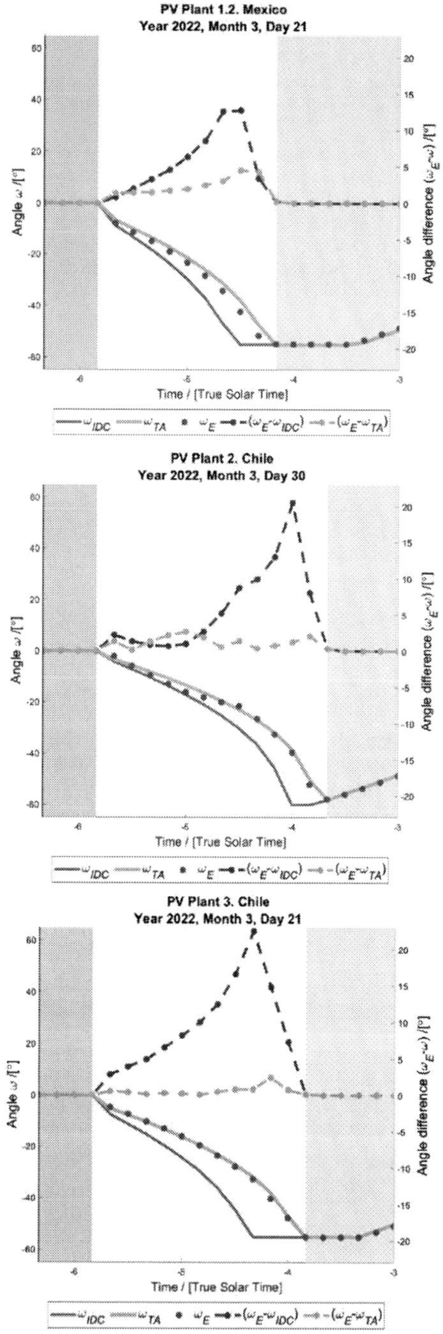

10.4229/EUPVSEC2025/4DO.1.2

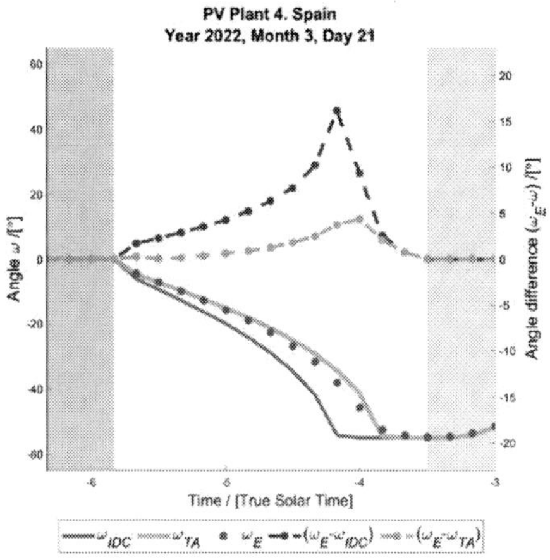

Figure 7: Simulated and measured tracking angles during the morning backtracking interval on the spring equinox for four PV plants. Each plot shows the original simulation ω_{IDC} (orange curve), the measured SCADA data ω_E (blue dots), and the initial discrepancy between them (dashed purple line, referenced to the right axis). The corrected simulated ω_{TA} using a reduced normalized spacing $\tilde{L}_{EW}$ is shown in dark yellow, while the resulting new discrepancy with ω_E is plotted in light blue (also referenced to the right axis). The backtracking interval is highlighted with a white background, where angular deviations are more pronounced and the correction significantly improves agreement.

In response to these observations, the angular configuration of the trackers at the PV plants was not modified. Instead, a correction was introduced within the simulation algorithm to replicate the observed deviations. This correction consists of recalculating the backtracking angle ω_{IDC} by assuming a reduced normalized inter-row spacing $\tilde{L}_{EW}$ in Equation (8), while preserving the actual physical configuration. In other words, a lower L_{EW} is used as an input to the backtracking algorithm, which forces a slightly smaller tracking angle, thereby generating light strips on the ground in the idealized model that mimic those observed in the field.

Focusing on the morning backtracking period, this correction accounts for terrain unevenness: if a row is slightly lower than its predecessor, the margin introduced by the modified angle allows it to remain illuminated, provided the elevation difference remains within acceptable bounds. Conversely, if the row is slightly higher than the preceeding one, the light strip widens, leading to reduced irradiance capture, but without introducing shading and, thus, maintaining one of the fundamental objectives of backtracking.

It is also worth noting that outside the backtracking periods, the tracker angle is independent of L_{EW}, making this correction easily implementable in practice by simulating the tracking angles for an entire day with a modified L_{EW}. However, as shown in Equation (7), the limits of the backtracking period do depend on L_{EW}. In practice, this effect is not observed in the analyzed plants, since the saturation angle of the trackers is reached before the theoretical backtracking periods end (or begin, in the case of the afternoon backtracking intervals).

The same figures discussed in this section also include, in dark yellow, the results of the simulation with the corrected angle ω_{TA}, obtained using $\tilde{L}_{EW}$. The light blue curve (again referenced to the right axis) represents the new discrepancy with respect to the measured values ω_E, which is now reduced by several orders of magnitude compared to the original simulation.

Finally, the relative annual variation $\Delta(\mathrm{TIG}_A)$ in tracking irradiation gain (TIG) between the ideal and corrected configurations is computed as

$$\Delta(\mathrm{TIG}_A) = \frac{\mathrm{TIG}_A(\omega_{IDC}) - \mathrm{TIG}_A(\omega_{TA})}{\mathrm{TIG}_A(\omega_{IDC})} \cdot 100, \quad (10)$$

where the explicit dependence of TIG on the tracking angle used in the simulation has been indicated in brackets. Moreover, to reflect the annual nature of the analysis, the temporal subscript T previously used is replaced by A. It should be noted that the simulation results obtained with SISIFO are computed using a Typical Meteorological Year (TMY) as input. Furthermore, the applied correction is conceptually analogous to introducing an artificial East–West slope on the terrain, thereby modifying the effective geometry of the PV plant [10]. This scenario can be easily simulated in SISIFO, which natively supports simulations on sloped terrain, representing a major improvement over most existing PV simulation tools. The resulting values of $\Delta(\mathrm{TIG}_A)$ for each PV plant are summarized in **Table II**, together with the corresponding normalized spacing $\tilde{L}_{EW}$ used in the corrected simulations.

Table II: Normalized inter-row spacing $\tilde{L}_{EW}$ and relative annual tracking irradiation gain variation $\Delta(TIG_A)$ for the analyzed PV plants.

PV Plant	$\tilde{L}_{EW}$/ []	$\Delta(\mathrm{TIG}_A)$/ [%]
1.1	2.50	7.3
1.2	2.50	7.3
2	1.96	9.4
3	2.24	9.2
4	2.16	7.8

4 CONCLUSIONS

The widespread overestimation of energy production in PV simulations can be partly attributed to an overvaluation of the tracking irradiation gain. Experimental data from four PV plants across different countries show that systematic angle corrections are applied in the field to prevent mutual shading caused by terrain unevenness. A reverse-engineering approach, based on considering a reduced inter-row spacing, reveals that these corrections lead to TIG values 7–10% lower than theoretical estimates. This results in an average annual energy yield overestimation of about 3%, roughly half of the typical discrepancy between simulated and actual performance [10].

5 ACKNOWLEDGEMNETS

The authors express their sincere appreciation for the financial support provided through the project PVOP, funded by the European Union. Views and opinions expressed are however those of the authors only and do not necessarily reflect those of the European Union or CINEA. Neither the European Union nor the granting authority can be held responsible for them.

The authors are also grateful to EU PVSEC for the opportunity to present their work at the 2025 edition held in Bilbao, Spain. Special thanks go to the research staff at the Instituto de Energía Solar of the Universidad Politécnica de Madrid for their valuable contributions.

REFERENCES

[1] kWh Analytics, "Solar Risk Assessment 2024," 2024. Accessed: Sep. 17, 2025. [Online]. Available: https://kwhanalytics.com/wp-content/uploads/2025/02/2023-Solar-Risk-Assessment.pdf

[2] Solar Power World, "Solar projects are underperforming by 6.3%, new report suggests better assessment standards." Accessed: Sep. 17, 2025. [Online]. Available: https://www.solarpowerworldonline.com/2020/10/solar-projects-are-underperforming-by-6-3-new-report-suggests-better-assessment-standards/

[3] D. Keiner, L. Walter, M. ElSayed, and C. Breyer, "Impact of backtracking strategies on techno-economics of horizontal single-axis tracking solar photovoltaic power plants," *Solar Energy*, vol. 267, p. 112228, Jan. 2024, doi: 10.1016/j.solener.2023.112228.

[4] European Commission, "PhotoVoltaic Cost reduction, Reliability, Operational performance, Prediction and Simulation," 2015. Accessed: Sep. 17, 2025. [Online]. Available: https://cordis.europa.eu/project/id/308468

[5] European Commission, "MArket uptake of an innovative irrigation Solution based on LOW WATer-ENergy consumption," Sep. 01, 2015. doi: 10.3030/640771.

[6] European Commission, "Digitalising the PV sector for the era of Terawatts." Accessed: Sep. 17, 2025. [Online]. Available: https://cordis.europa.eu/project/id/101147000

[7] F. Martínez-Moreno, J. Muñoz, and E. Lorenzo, "Experimental model to estimate shading losses on PV arrays," *Solar Energy Materials and Solar Cells*, vol. 94, no. 12, pp. 2298–2303, Dec. 2010, doi: 10.1016/j.solmat.2010.07.029.

[8] L. Narvarte and E. Lorenzo, "Tracking and ground cover ratio," *Progress in Photovoltaics: Research and Applications*, vol. 16, no. 8, pp. 703–714, Dec. 2008, doi: 10.1002/pip.847.

[9] E. Lorenzo, L. Narvarte, and J. Muñoz, "Tracking and back-tracking," *Progress in Photovoltaics: Research and Applications*, vol. 19, no. 6, pp. 747–753, Sep. 2011, doi: 10.1002/pip.1085.

[10] J. R. Ledesma, E. Lorenzo, and L. Narvarte, "Single-Axis Tracking and Bifacial Gain on Sloping Terrain," *Progress in Photovoltaics: Research and Applications*, vol. 33, no. 2, pp. 309–325, Feb. 2025, doi: 10.1002/pip.3847.

[11] E. Lorenzo, "Energy Collected and Delivered by PV Modules," in *Handbook of Photovoltaic Science and Engineering*, Wiley, 2003, pp. 905–970. doi: 10.1002/0470014008.ch20.

[12] N. Martín and J. M. Ruiz, "A new method for the spectral characterisation of PV modules," *Progress in Photovoltaics: Research and Applications*, vol. 7, no. 4, pp. 299–310, Jul. 1999, doi: 10.1002/(SICI)1099-159X(199907/08)7:4<299::AID-PIP260>3.0.CO;2-0.

[13] J. Muñoz; N. Tyutyundzhiev; L. Marroyo; M. Collares-Pereira; M. Conlon; B. Wilkin, *AN OPEN-SOURCE SIMULATION TOOL OF GRID-CONNECTED PV SYSTEMS*. Paris, 2013. Accessed: Sep. 17, 2025. [Online]. Available: https://www.researchgate.net/publication/338047197_AN_OPEN-SOURCE_SIMULATION_TOOL_OF_GRID-CONNECTED_PV_SYSTEMS

[14] E. Lorenzo and M. H. Macagnan, "Considerations in the design of a one-axis tracking photovoltaic system," *Progress in Photovoltaics: Research and Applications*, vol. 2, no. 1, pp. 45–55, Jan. 1994, doi: 10.1002/pip.4670020107.

Bridging the Gap:

Insights into Backtracking-Angle Related Discrepancies Between Estimates and Actual Performance in Large-Scale Photovoltaic Plants

Juan Santamaría Sancho

Fco. Javier Ramírez Ledesma, Javier Martín Rueda, Eduardo Lorenzo Pigueiras

Instituto de Energía Solar

Universidad Politécnica de Madrid

Problem:

Overestimation of energy yield in utility-scale PV simulations.

Approach:

Assess how tracker positioning during backtracking contributes to the overestimation of Tracker Irradiation Gain (TIG),

$$\mathrm{TIG}_A(\omega) = \frac{G_A(\omega) - G_A(0)}{G_A(0)},$$

where $G_A(\omega)$ and $G_A(0)$ are the annual irradiation per square meter on a plane tilted at an angle ω and on a horizontal plane, respectively.

Model features

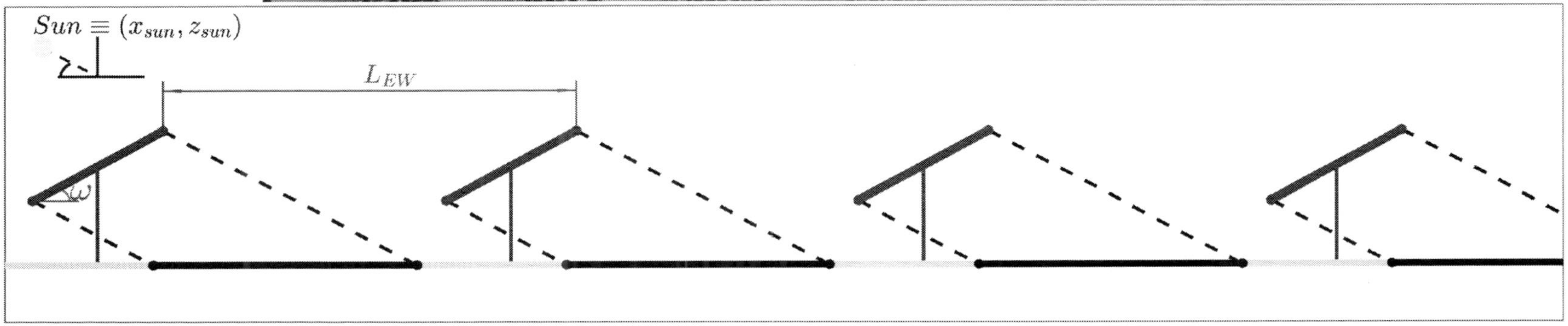

Non-backtracking behaviour

$$\omega_{ID} = \operatorname{atan}\frac{x_{sun}}{z_{sun}}$$

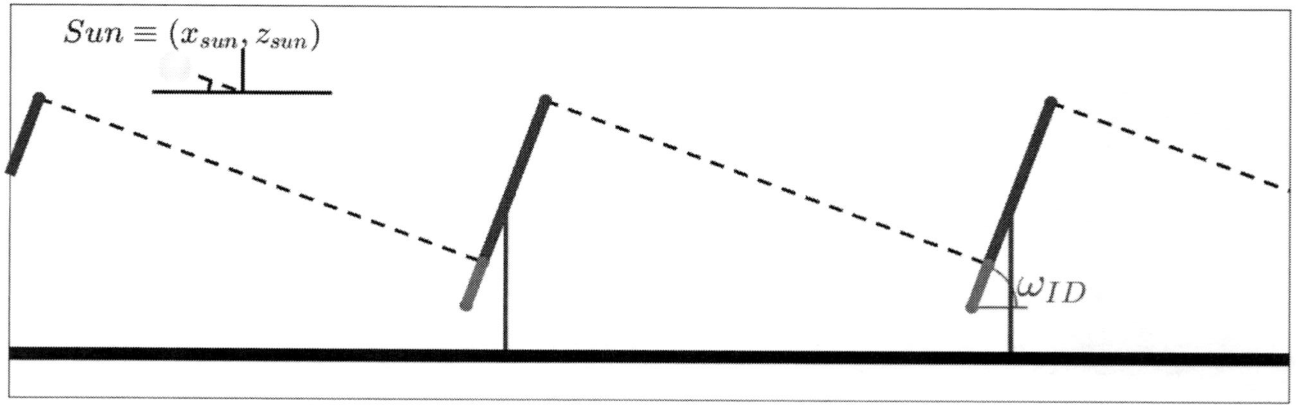

Backtracking behaviour for flat terrains

$$\omega_{IDC} = \omega_{ID} - \text{acos}\left[L_{EW}\cos(\omega_{ID})\right]$$

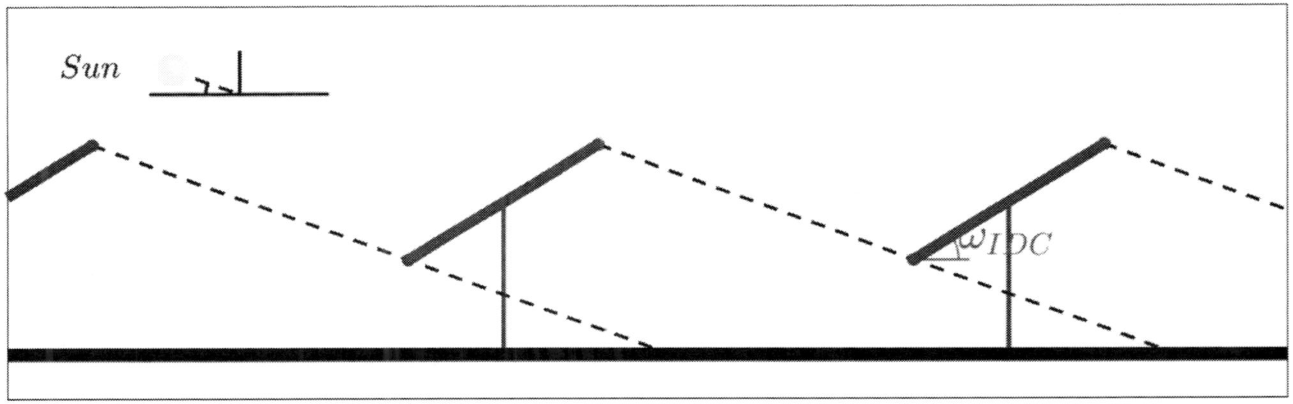

Sun
Time/[a.u.]
Angle/[a.u.]

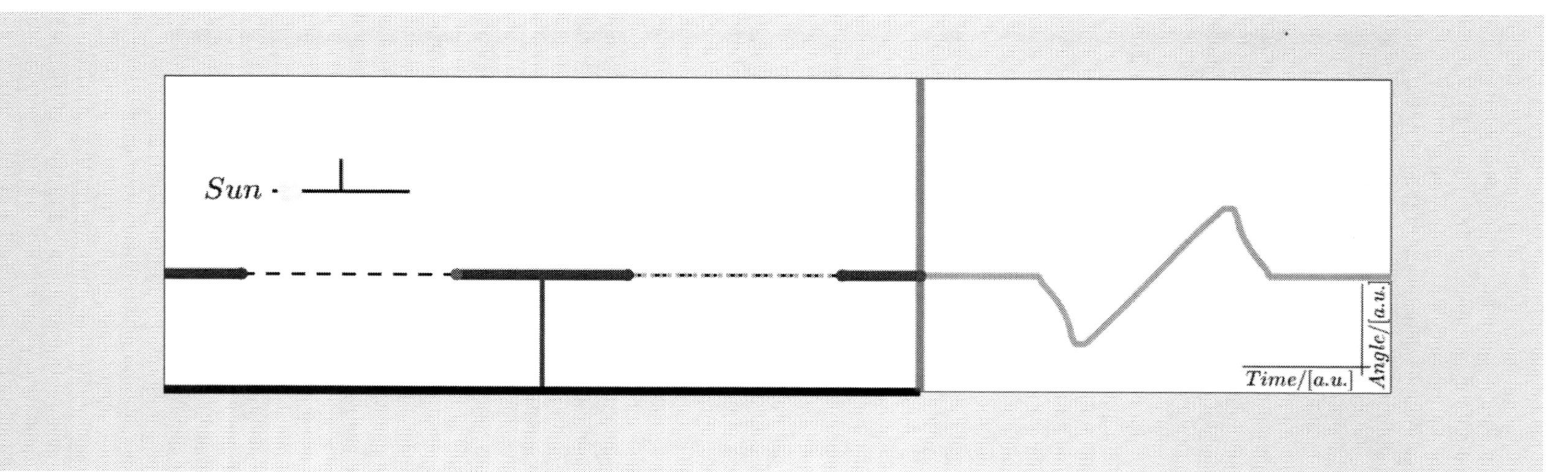

PV plants during the backtracking period

Effect of terrain unevenness

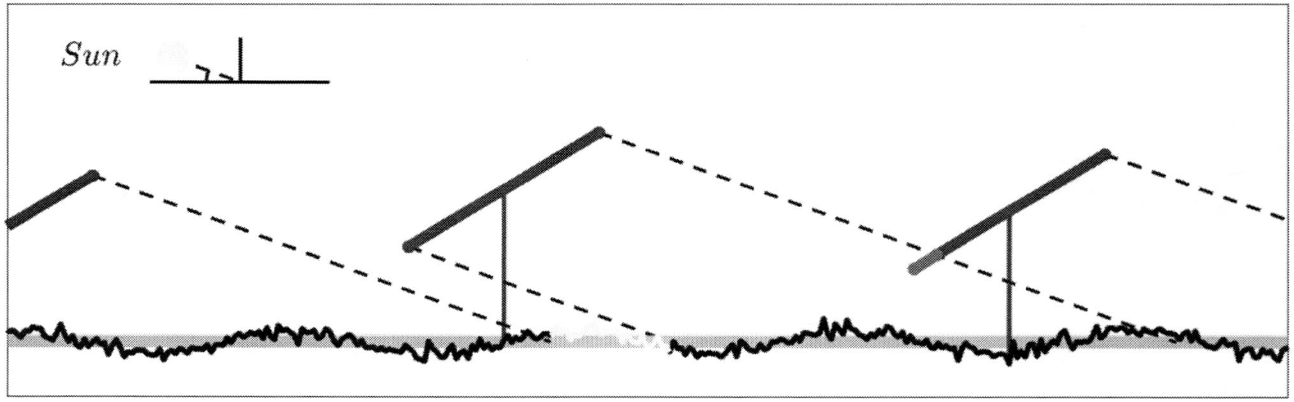

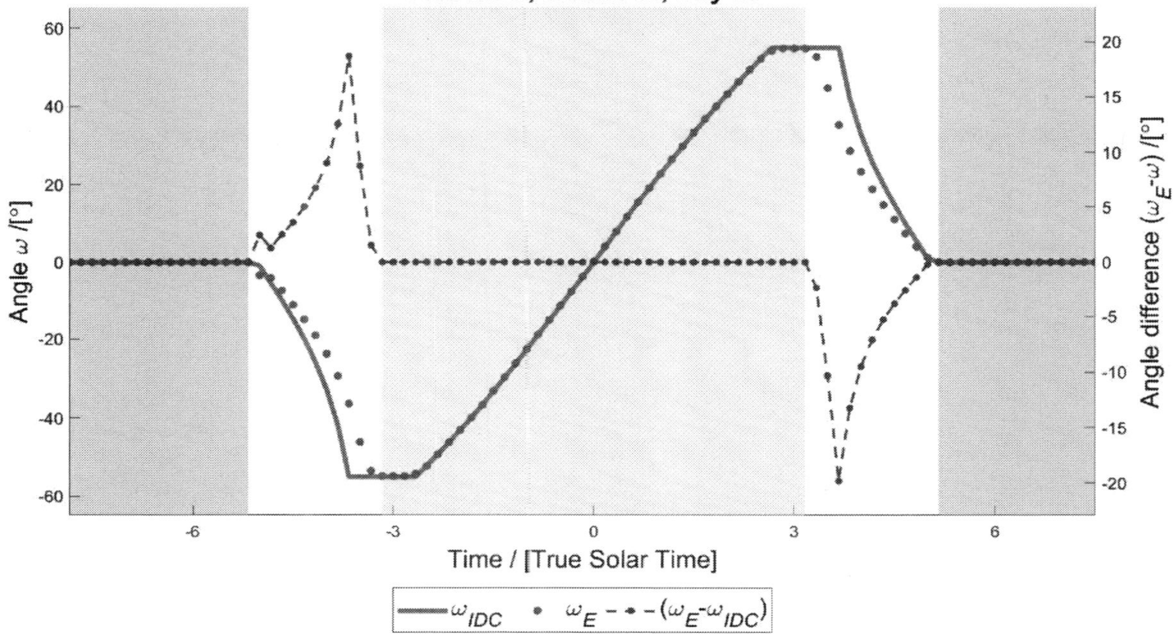
PV Plant 1.1. Mexico
Year 2022, Month 12, Day 21
Angle ω /[°]
60
40
20
0
-20
-40
-60
Angle difference (ω_E-ω) /[°]
20
15
10
5
0
-5
-10
-15
-20
-6
-3
0
3
6
Time / [True Solar Time]
ω_IDC
ω_E
(ω_E-ω_IDC)

- Compute the backtracking angles using a row spacing $\tilde{L}_{EW}$ different from L_{EW}.

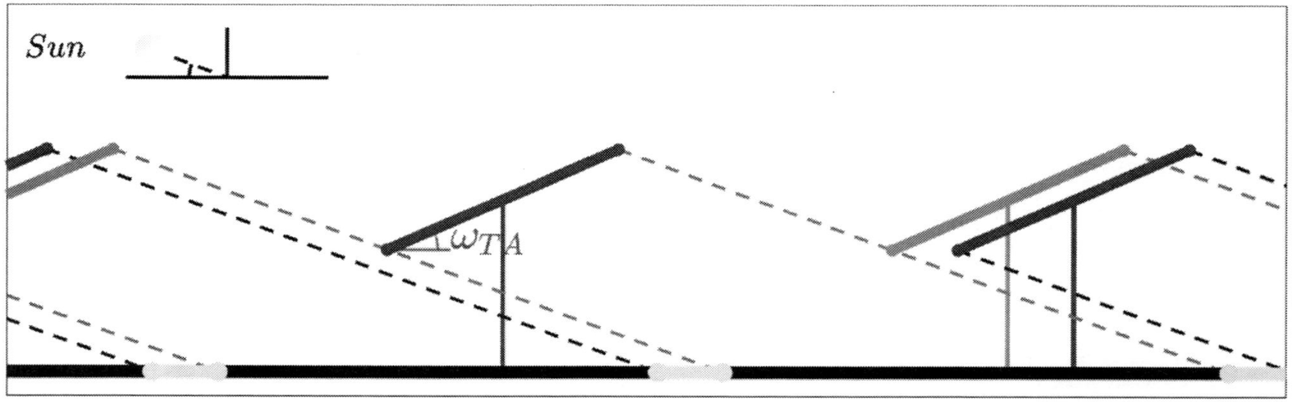

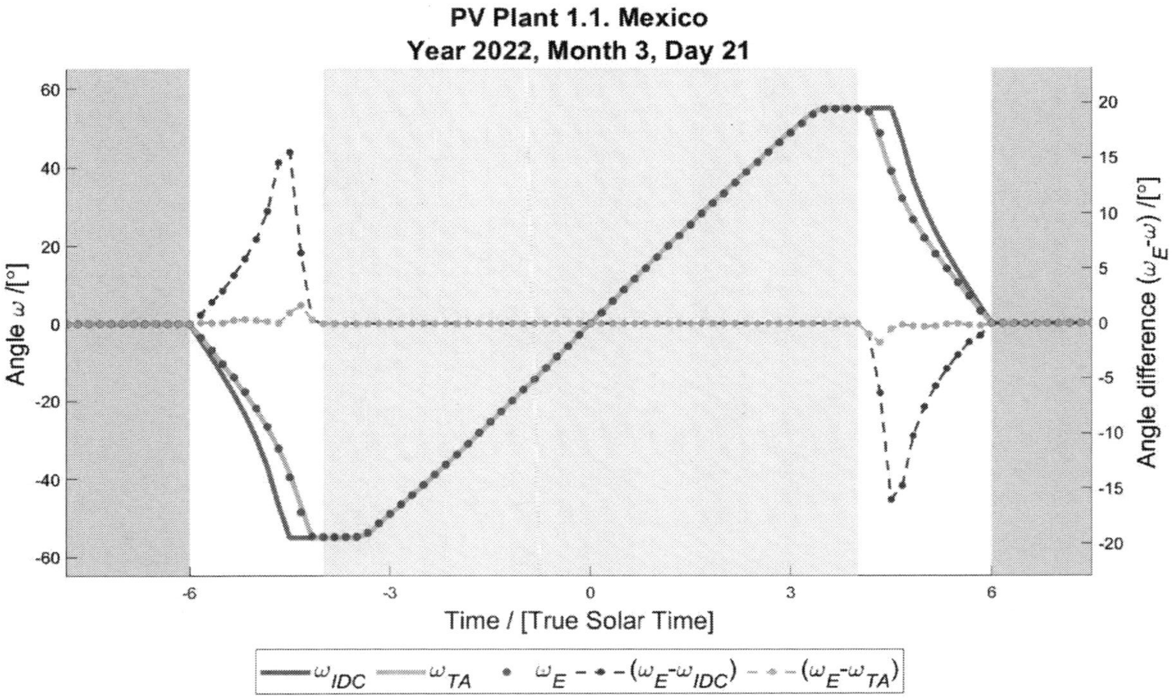
PV Plant 1.1. Mexico
Year 2022, Month 3, Day 21
Angle ω /[°]
Angle difference (ω_E-ω) /[°]
Time / [True Solar Time]
60
40
20
0
-20
-40
-60
20
15
10
5
0
-5
-10
-15
-20
-6
-3
0
3
6
ω_IDC
ω_TA
ω_E
(ω_E-ω_IDC)
(ω_E-ω_TA)

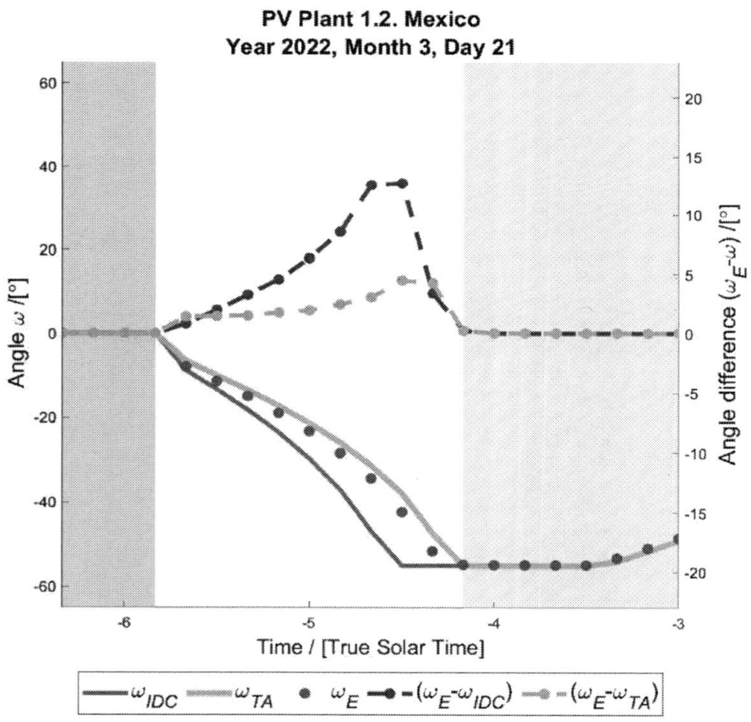
PV Plant 1.2. Mexico
Year 2022, Month 3, Day 21
Angle ω /[°]
Angle difference (ω_E-ω) /[°]
Time / [True Solar Time]
ω_IDC
ω_TA
ω_E
(ω_E-ω_IDC)
(ω_E-ω_TA)

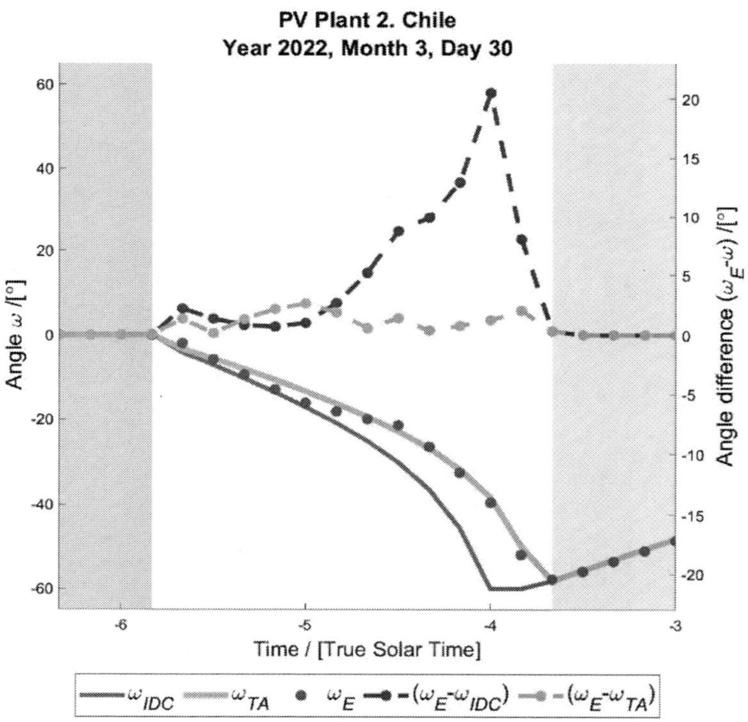
PV Plant 2. Chile
Year 2022, Month 3, Day 30
Angle ω /[°]
Angle difference (ω_E-ω) /[°]
Time / [True Solar Time]
ω_IDC
ω_TA
ω_E
(ω_E-ω_IDC)
(ω_E-ω_TA)

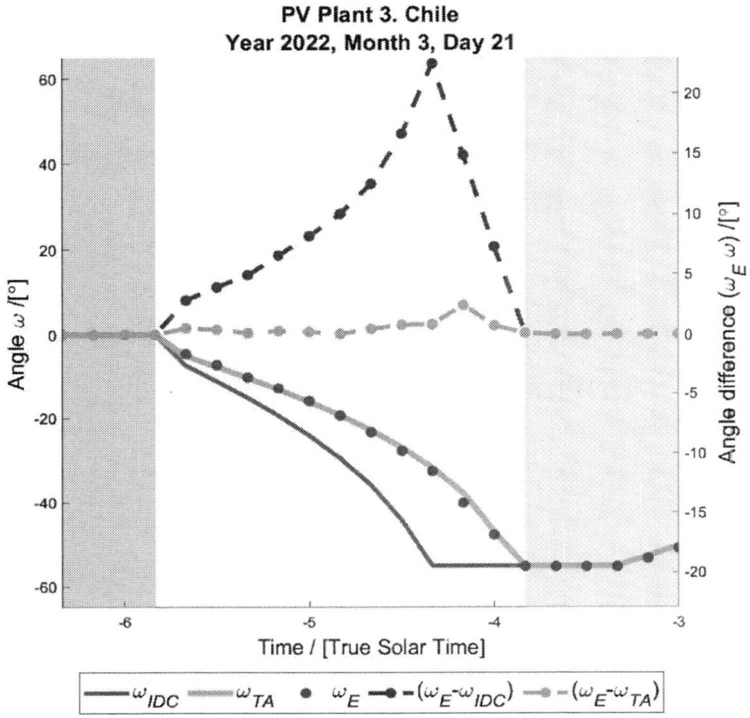
PV Plant 3. Chile
Year 2022, Month 3, Day 21
Angle ω /[°]
Angle difference (ω_E ω) /[°]
Time / [True Solar Time]
ω_IDC
ω_TA
ω_E
(ω_E-ω_IDC)
(ω_E-ω_TA)

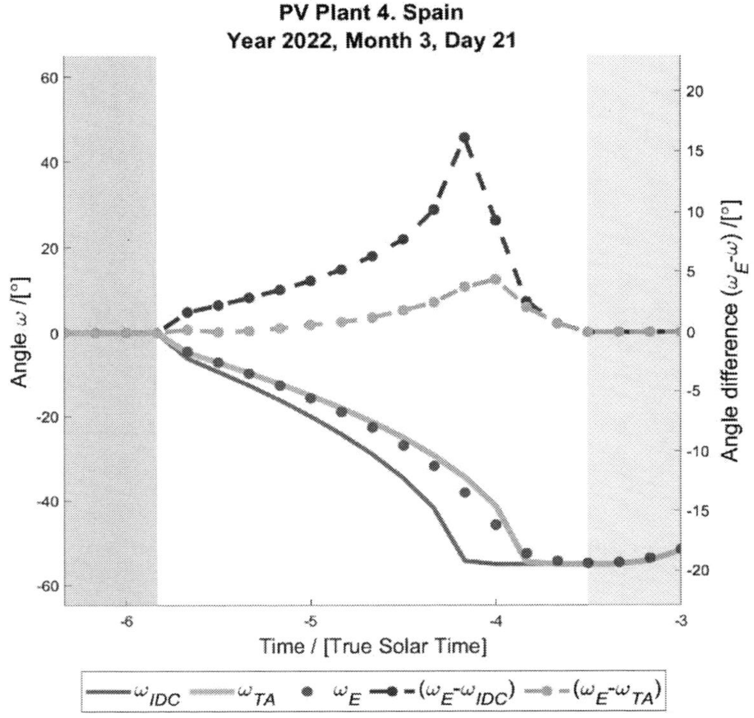
PV Plant 4. Spain
Year 2022, Month 3, Day 21
Angle ω /[°]
Angle difference (ω_E-ω) /[°]
Time / [True Solar Time]
ω_IDC
ω_TA
ω_E
(ω_E-ω_IDC)
(ω_E-ω_TA)

TIG overestimation analysis

$$\Delta(\mathrm{TIG}_A) = \frac{\mathrm{TIG}_A(\omega_{IDC}) - \mathrm{TIG}_A(\omega_{TA})}{\mathrm{TIG}_A(\omega_{IDC})} \cdot 100$$

PV Plant	Location	L_{EW} / []	$\widetilde{L}_{EW}$ / []	$\Delta(\mathrm{TIG}_A)$ / [%]
1.1	Mexico	3.00	2.50	7.3
1.2	Mexico	3.00	2.50	7.3
2	Chile	2.26	1.96	9.4
3	Chile	2.56	2.24	9.2
4	Spain	2.74	2.16	7.8

Tracking irradiation losses between 7-10%

↓

Losses in energy production of approximately 3%

Thank you for your time!

https://www.sisifo.info

CONTACT ME: juan.santamariasan@upm.es

The authors express their sincere appreciation for the financial support provided through the project PVOP, funded by the European Union. Views and opinions expressed are however those of the authors only and do not necessarily reflect those of the European Union or CINEA. Neither the European Union nor the granting authority can be held responsible for them.

Funded by the European Union

PVOP

EUPVSEC 2025 – Bilbao

42nd EUROPEAN PHOTOVOLTAIC SOLAR ENERGY CONFERENCE AND EXHIBITION

EXPERIMENTAL VALIDATION OF HORIZONTAL SINGLE-AXIS SOLAR TRACKER ALGORITHMS IN TERMS OF ENERGY PRODUCTION AND OPERATIONAL PERFORMANCE

Ildefonso Muñoz, Gregorio Olivares, Sara Díaz, Aritz Legarrea, Ana Gracia

Solar Energy Technologies & Storage Dept. - CENER

CENER | CENTRO NACIONAL DE ENERGÍAS RENOVABLES

Gobierno de Navarra
Nafarroako Gobernua

INTRODUCTION & MOTIVATION

CURRENT STATUS

- **Horizontal single axis:** the most widely used solar tracker system in large utility-scale PV plants
- **Astronomical algorithm:** the most used solar tracking strategy, based on minimizing the angle of the normal vector of the POA and the solar vector

CHALLENGERS & OPPORTUNITIES

- Astronomical algorithm, **is not always the optimal** tracking algorithm
- Electronic control system of solar tracker **allows an easy implementation of new solar tracking algorithms**

4DO.1.3 - EXPERIMENTAL VALIDATION OF HORIZONTAL SINGLE-AXIS SOLAR TRACKER ALGORITHMS IN TERMS OF ENERGY PRODUCTION AND OPERATIONAL PERFORMANCE

CENER | CENTRO NACIONAL DE ENERGÍAS RENOVABLES

Gobierno de Navarra Nafarroako Gobernua

BACKGROUND (1)

Simulation study presented in 40th EUPVSEC (Lisbon) and paper published in SolarRRL: "***Evaluation of Horizontal Single-Axis Solar Tracker Algorithms in Terms of Energy Production and Operational Performance***" (DOI: 10.1002/solr.202300507) based on:

- **In–depth comparative and evaluation** in terms of energy production and operational performance of solar tracking algorithms for a horizontal single axis solar tracker with monofacial PV modules
- Comparison of performance with Astronomical algorithm **based on high temporal resolution data (1 minute)** taking into account:
  - Atmospheric conditions (radiation and temperature)
  - Mechanical constrains of horizontal solar tracker (non-continuous movement)
  - Disposition of PV modules on the solar tracker
- Solar tracking algorithms proposed for this study:
  - **DIFFUSE RADIATION ALGORITHMS**
  - **ANALYTICAL ALGORITHM** (new development by CENER)

BACKGROUND (2)

DIFFUSE RADIATION ALGORITHM

- On cloudy day, diffuse component of radiation can be higher than beam component
- Diffuse Radiation Algorithm criteria:
  - *GHI* > G_{POA} → *Horizontal Position*
  - *GHI* ≤ G_{POA} → *Astronomical Tracking*

ANALYTICAL ALGORITHM (Developed by CENER)

- Diffuse Radiation algorithm only consider as optimal position the one according to Astronomical algorithm or the horizontal position.
- In multiple situations and locations, beam and diffuse radiation components may not be so different → **Optimal angle could be an intermediate position between horizontal and Astronomical**.

$$\frac{\partial G_{POA}}{\partial \beta} = \frac{\partial G_B}{\partial \beta} + \frac{\partial G_D}{\partial \beta} + \frac{\partial G_G}{\partial \beta} = 0$$

Max. Irradiance condition, as function of β

DIFFUSE RADIATION ALG.

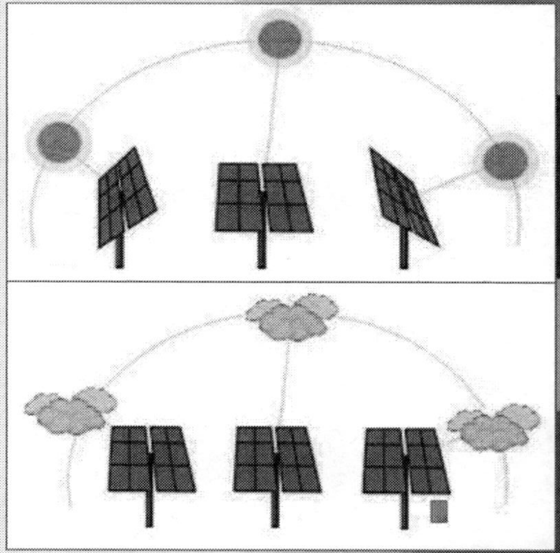

ANALYTICAL ALG.

CENER | CENTRO NACIONAL DE ENERGÍAS RENOVABLES

Gobierno de Navarra
Nafarroako Gobernua

PREVIOUS WORK SUMMARY AND OBJECTIVES

PREVIOUS WORK: Simulation study carried out for six locations with different climates and GHI/DHI ratios (diffuse radiation fraction)

PREVIOUS RESULTS:

- In all cases, studied algorithms present a gain compared with the Astronomical algorithm
- The higher diffuse fraction, the higher gain
- Astronomical & Analytical algorithms present highest values of number of movements per year
- Diffuse Radiation Algorithm presents the highest value of accumulated angular displacement and risk of oscillating positions on days with cloudy intervals

OBJECTIVES FOR THE PRESENT WORK:

- ***Validation of previous simulation results by applying algorithms to real solar trackers***

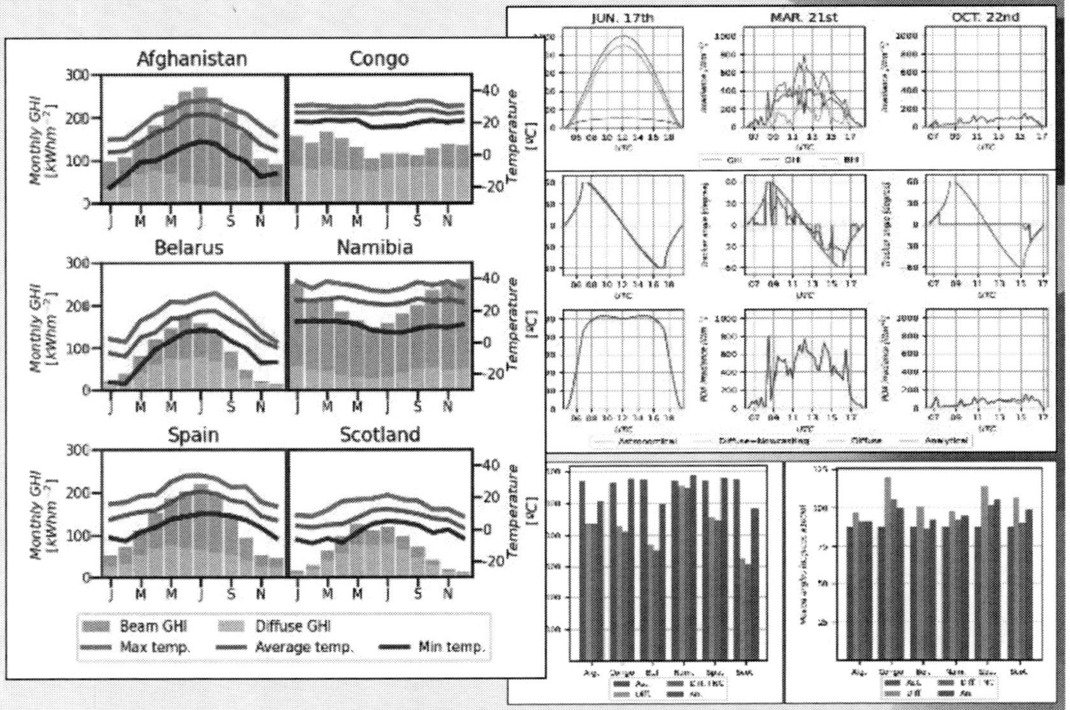

ANALYTICAL ALGORITHMS – NEW DEVELOPMENTS

SOLAR RADIATION TRASPOSITION MODELS

ISOTROPIC (LIU-JORDAN)
HAY-DAVIES
PEREZ

$$\frac{\partial G_{POA}}{\partial \beta} = \frac{\partial G_B}{\partial \beta} + \frac{\partial G_D}{\partial \beta} + \frac{\partial G_G}{\partial \beta} = 0$$

Max. Irradiance condition, as function of β

$$\beta_{opt} = arctan\left(\frac{DNI \cdot sin\,\theta_s \cdot cos(\gamma_s - \gamma)}{\frac{DHI - GHI \cdot a}{2} + DNI \cdot cos\,\theta_s}\right)$$

Isotropic

$$\beta_{opt} = arctan\left(\frac{DNI \cdot sin\,\theta_s \cdot cos(\gamma_s - \gamma)}{\frac{DHI - GHI \cdot a}{2} + DNI \cdot cos\,\theta_s}\right)$$

Hay-Davies

$$\beta_{opt} = arctan\left(\frac{sin\,\theta_Z \cdot cos(\gamma_s - \gamma) \cdot \left[DNI + DHI \cdot \frac{F_1}{f_b}\right] + DHI \cdot \frac{F_1 \cdot F_2}{f_b}}{DNI \cdot cos\,\theta_Z + DHI\left[\left(\frac{F_1 - 1}{2}\right) \cdot \frac{F_1}{f_b} \cdot cos\,\theta_Z\right] - \frac{1}{2} \cdot GHI \cdot a}\right)$$

Perez

4DO.1.3 - EXPERIMENTAL VALIDATION OF HORIZONTAL SINGLE-AXIS SOLAR TRACKER ALGORITHMS IN TERMS OF ENERGY PRODUCTION AND OPERATIONAL PERFORMANCE

CENER | CENTRO NACIONAL DE ENERGÍAS RENOVABLES

Gobierno de Navarra
Nafarroako Gobernua

EXPERIMENTAL SET-UP

Test carried out in Experimental PV installation of CENER (CENIFER)

Main Set-Up equipment:

- Solar Trackers and electronic controllers (EC)
  - Solar Tracker 1, with EC Prototype 1
  - Solar Tracker 2, with EC Prototype 2
  - Solar Tracker Control, with commercial EC
- Meteo station (GHI, albedo, Tamb & Wind)
- G_{POA} sensors on each solar tracker

4DO.1.3 - EXPERIMENTAL VALIDATION OF HORIZONTAL SINGLE-AXIS SOLAR TRACKER ALGORITHMS IN TERMS OF ENERGY PRODUCTION AND OPERATIONAL PERFORMANCE

CENER | CENTRO NACIONAL DE ENERGÍAS RENOVABLES

Gobierno de Navarra Nafarroako Gobernua

ELECTRONIC CONTROLLER PROTOTYPE

CENER hardware developments

In-house hardware for implementing tracking algorithms, based on:

- Raspberry Pi 5 8Gb
- Inclinometer ifm EC2045
- A-D Converter ADS1115 16 bits (8 inputs)

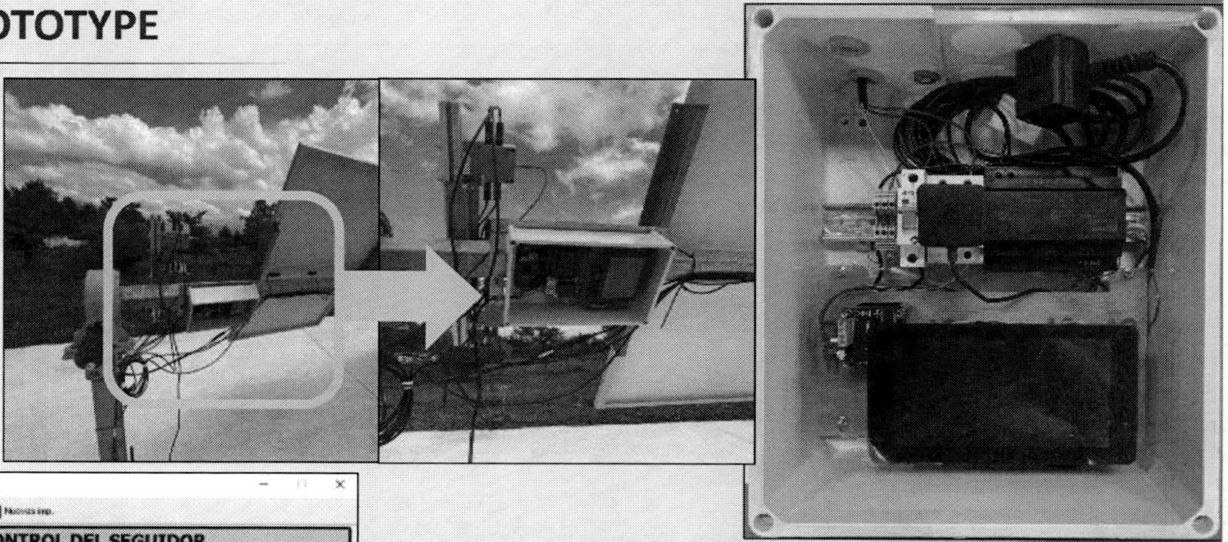

python

CENER software developments

- Tracking algorithms designed and programmed in open source code (Python)
- User-friendly communication and GUI systems to select tracking algorithm and download measured data

4DO.1.3 - EXPERIMENTAL VALIDATION OF HORIZONTAL SINGLE-AXIS SOLAR TRACKER ALGORITHMS IN TERMS OF ENERGY PRODUCTION AND OPERATIONAL PERFORMANCE

CENER | CENTRO NACIONAL DE ENERGÍAS RENOVABLES

Gobierno de Navarra Nafarroako Gobernua

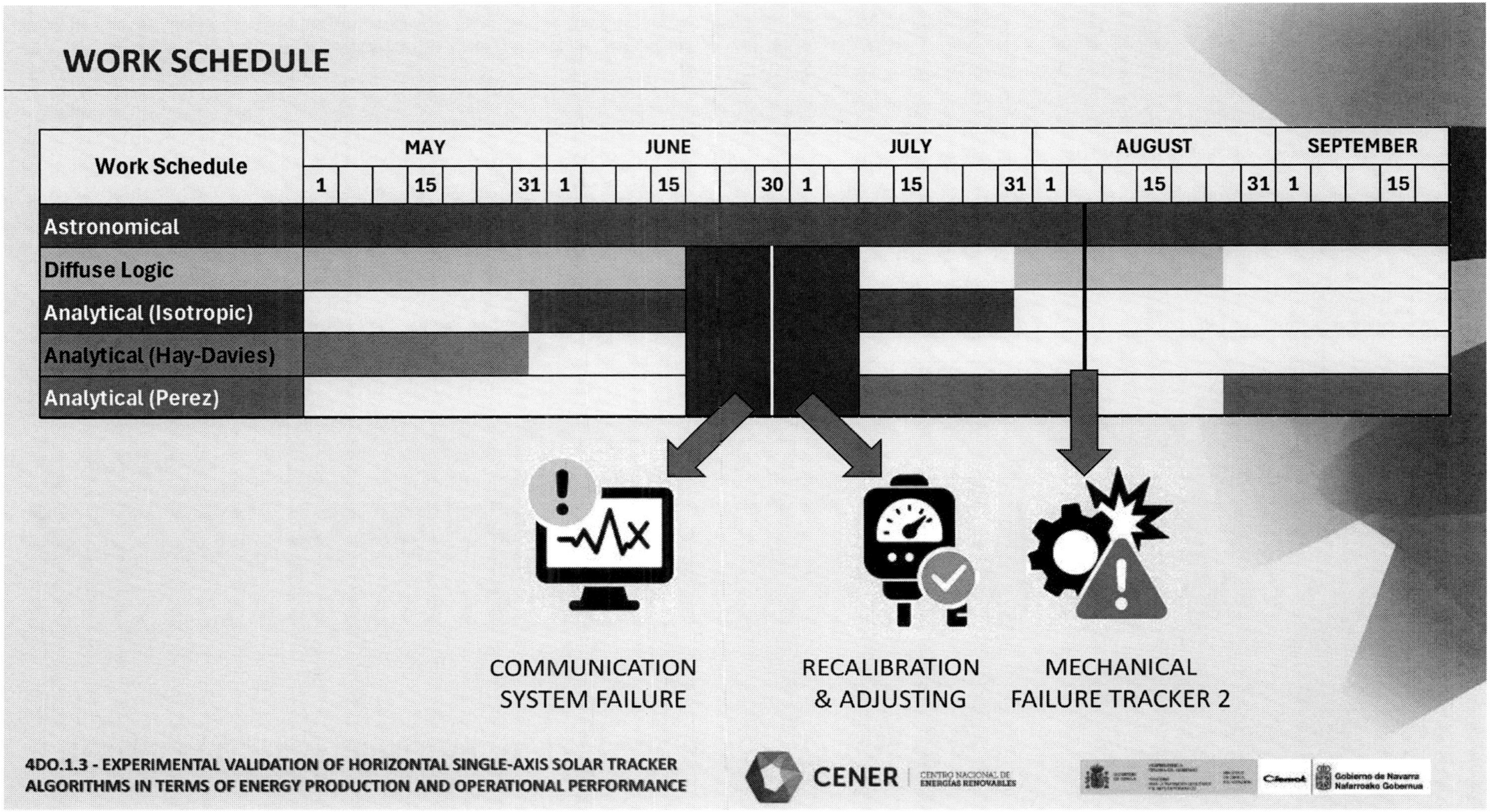
WORK SCHEDULE
Work Schedule
MAY
JUNE
JULY
AUGUST
SEPTEMBER
1
15
31
1
15
30
1
15
31
1
15
31
1
15
Astronomical
Diffuse Logic
Analytical (Isotropic)
Analytical (Hay-Davies)
Analytical (Perez)
COMMUNICATION SYSTEM FAILURE
RECALIBRATION & ADJUSTING
MECHANICAL FAILURE TRACKER 2
4DO.1.3 - EXPERIMENTAL VALIDATION OF HORIZONTAL SINGLE-AXIS SOLAR TRACKER ALGORITHMS IN TERMS OF ENERGY PRODUCTION AND OPERATIONAL PERFORMANCE
CENER
CENTRO NACIONAL DE ENERGÍAS RENOVABLES
Gobierno de Navarra
Nafarroako Gobernua

RESULTS (1) – ASTRONOMICAL, DIFFUSE & ANALYTICAL (HAY-DAVIES)

Cloudy Day Condition	ASTR.	DIFFUSE	ANALYTICAL (HAY-D)
G_{POA} (W/m²/day)	186.9	209.1	209.9
# Movements	108	92	84
Angular displacement (°)	252	609	454

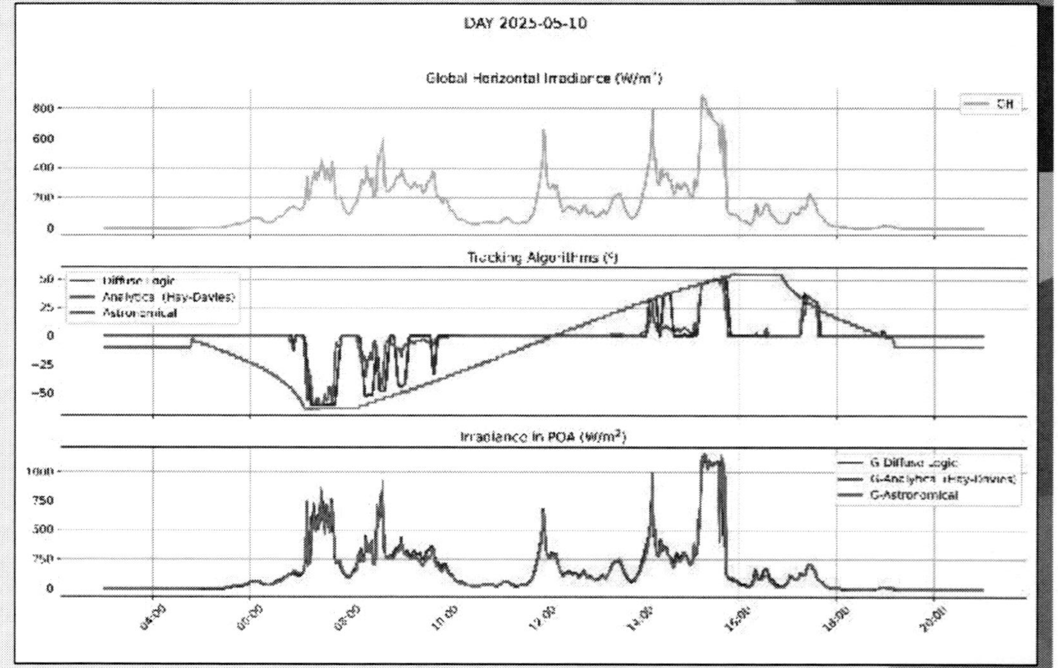

4DO.1.3 - EXPERIMENTAL VALIDATION OF HORIZONTAL SINGLE-AXIS SOLAR TRACKER ALGORITHMS IN TERMS OF ENERGY PRODUCTION AND OPERATIONAL PERFORMANCE

CENER | CENTRO NACIONAL DE ENERGÍAS RENOVABLES

Gobierno de Navarra Nafarroako Gobernua

RESULTS (2) – ASTRONOMICAL, DIFFUSE & ANALYTICAL (ISOTROPIC)

Sunny-Cloudy Day Condition	ASTR.	DIFFUSE	ANALYTICAL (ISOTROPIC)
G_{POA} (W/m²/day)	408.9	447.8	460.3
# Movements	106	120	133
Angular displacement (°)	251	274	689

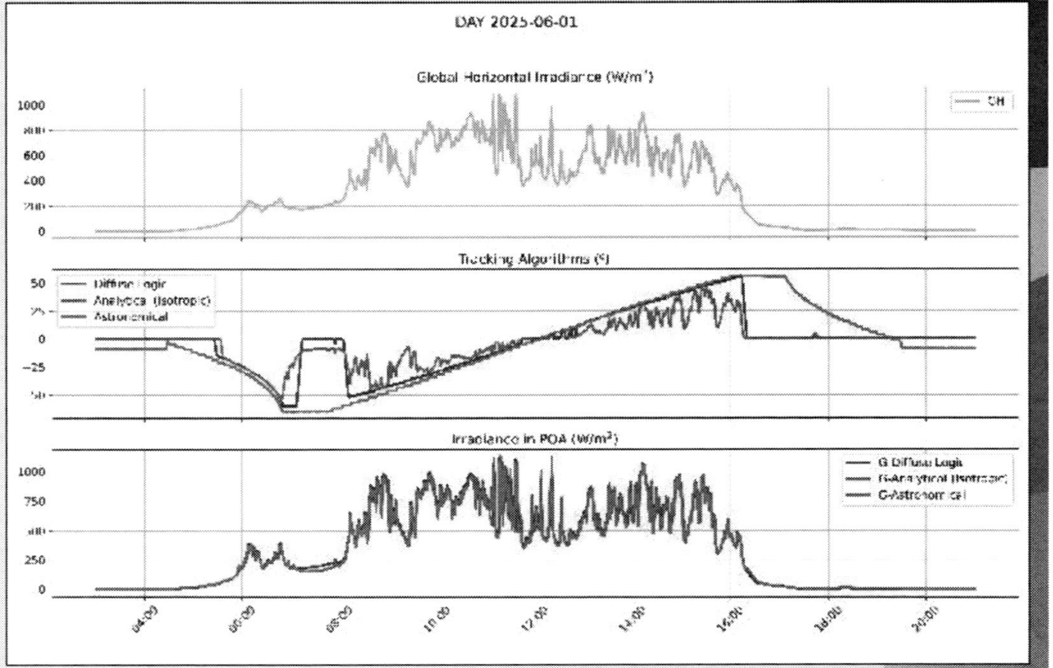

4DO.1.3 - EXPERIMENTAL VALIDATION OF HORIZONTAL SINGLE-AXIS SOLAR TRACKER ALGORITHMS IN TERMS OF ENERGY PRODUCTION AND OPERATIONAL PERFORMANCE

CENER | CENTRO NACIONAL DE ENERGÍAS RENOVABLES

Gobierno de Navarra / Nafarroako Gobernua

RESULTS (3) – ASTRONOMICAL, A.(ISOTROPIC) & A.(PEREZ)

Sunny-Cloudy Day Condition	ASTR.	ANALYTICAL (ISOTROPIC)	ANALYTICAL (PEREZ)
G_{POA} (W/m²/day)	295.7	309.5	319.4
# Movements	106	135	123
Angular displacement (°)	251	274	398

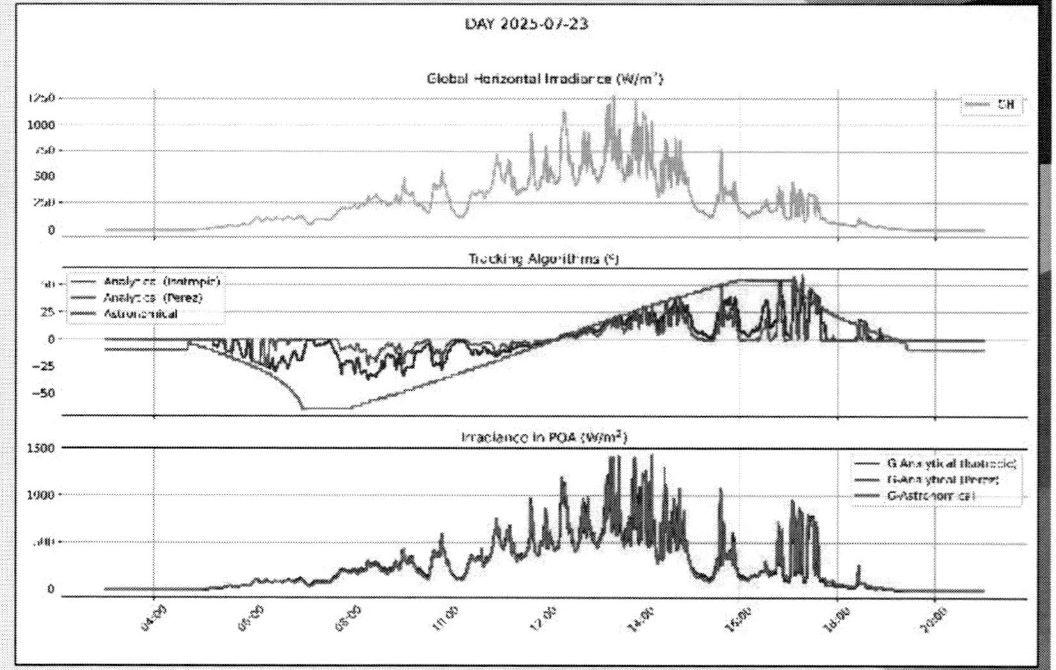

4DO.1.3 - EXPERIMENTAL VALIDATION OF HORIZONTAL SINGLE-AXIS SOLAR TRACKER ALGORITHMS IN TERMS OF ENERGY PRODUCTION AND OPERATIONAL PERFORMANCE

CENER | CENTRO NACIONAL DE ENERGÍAS RENOVABLES

Gobierno de Navarra
Nafarroako Gobernua

RESULTS (4) – ASTRONOMICAL, DIFFUSE & ANALYTICAL (PEREZ)

Sunny-Cloudy Day Condition	ASTR.	DIFFUSE	ANALYTICAL (PEREZ)
G_{POA} (W/m²/day)	597.7	621.2	638.1
# Movements	106	144	151
Angular displacement (°)	251	518	623

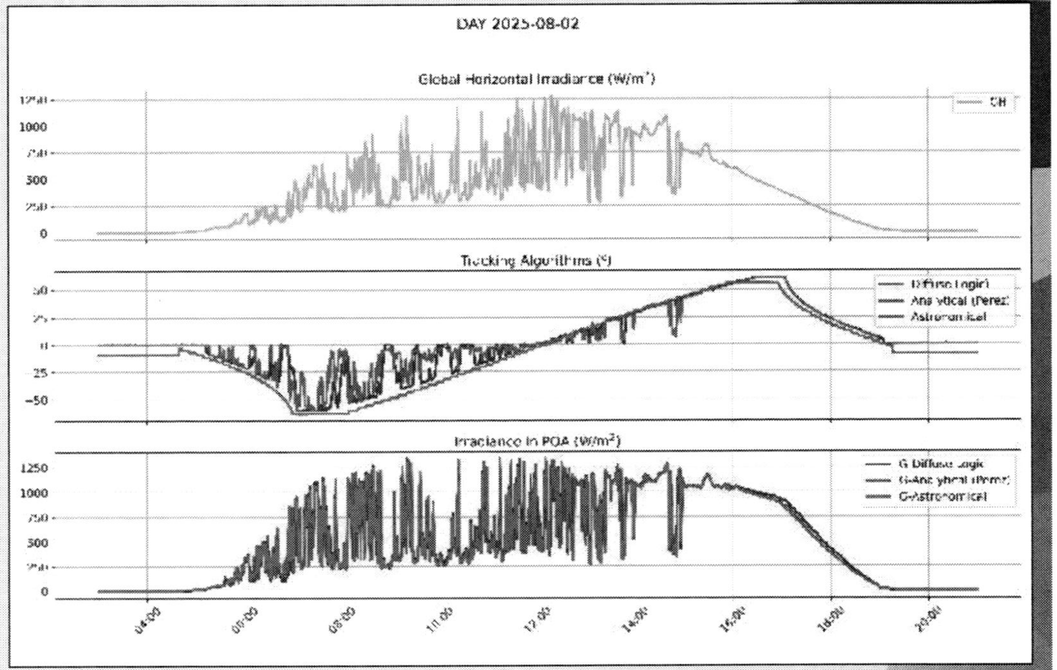

4DO.1.3 - EXPERIMENTAL VALIDATION OF HORIZONTAL SINGLE-AXIS SOLAR TRACKER ALGORITHMS IN TERMS OF ENERGY PRODUCTION AND OPERATIONAL PERFORMANCE

CENER | CENTRO NACIONAL DE ENERGÍAS RENOVABLES

Gobierno de Navarra
Nafarroako Gobernua

RESULTS (5) – BEHAVIOUR IN SUNNY-CLOUDY DAYS

- Sunny and cloudy days: most days recorded
- Effect of not setting the angle demanded by the algorithm in the event of rapid cloud movement → Oscillating positions (as expected in previous work)
- Effect registered in all new tracking algorithms, but especially in Diffuse Radiation Algorithm
- No application of Hysteresis or delays techniques for checking this effect in experimental results

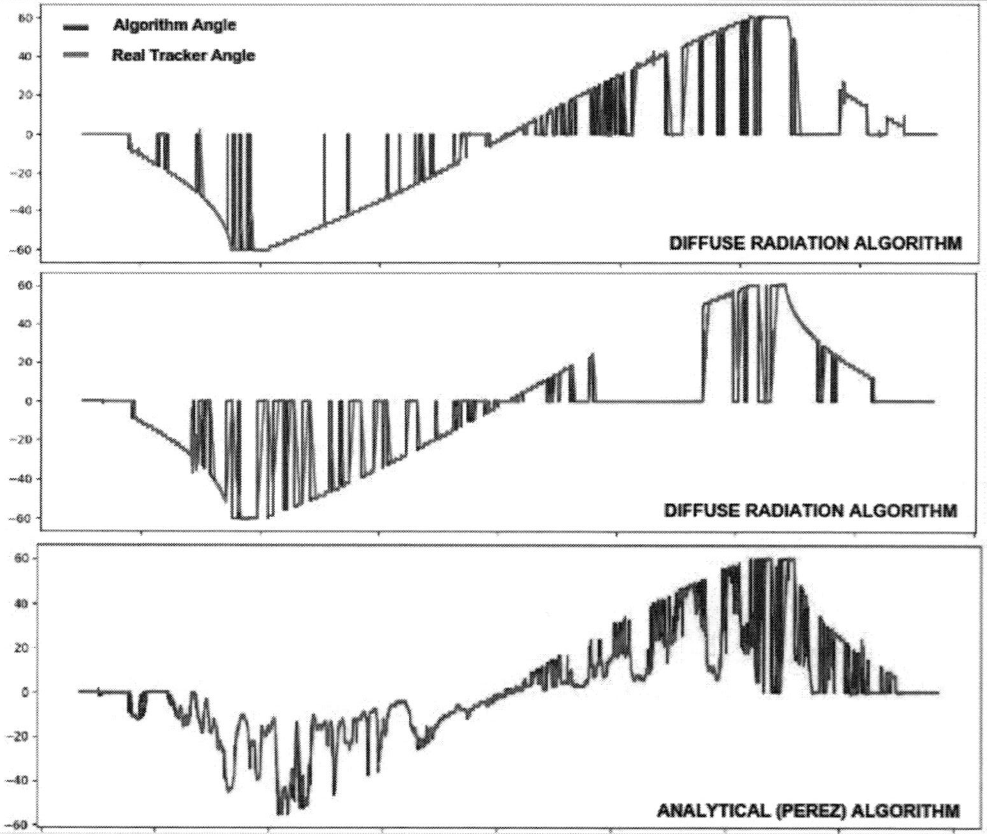

4DO.1.3 - EXPERIMENTAL VALIDATION OF HORIZONTAL SINGLE-AXIS SOLAR TRACKER ALGORITHMS IN TERMS OF ENERGY PRODUCTION AND OPERATIONAL PERFORMANCE

CENER | CENTRO NACIONAL DE ENERGÍAS RENOVABLES

Gobierno de Navarra Nafarroako Gobernua

SUMMARY & CONCLUSIONS

- CENER has developed new tracking algorithms and their application in open-source software (Python).
- CENER has created a prototype of electronic controller (two units) and the appropriate software to run any solar tracker algorithm. It has been applied with real solar trackers.
- Main results of the previous work have been confirmed in real tests:
  - Increase of G_{POA} of new algorithms compared to Astronomical algorithm
  - The higher diffuse fraction, the higher gain (lack of enough measurement days with high diffuse fraction)
  - Increase of number of movements and angle displacement (consideration of reliability and energy consumption aspects)
  - Effect of sunny-cloudy days confirmed (oscillating positions)
- CENER's ability to test any tracking algorithm (whether its own or that of an external developer) has been confirmed and is available to future clients.

4DO.1.3 - EXPERIMENTAL VALIDATION OF HORIZONTAL SINGLE-AXIS SOLAR TRACKER ALGORITHMS IN TERMS OF ENERGY PRODUCTION AND OPERATIONAL PERFORMANCE

CENER | CENTRO NACIONAL DE ENERGÍAS RENOVABLES

Gobierno de Navarra / Nafarroako Gobernua

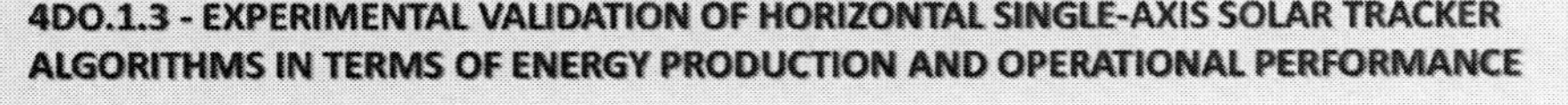

ONGOING & FUTURE WORKS

- Complete the study for all cases of day types and algorithms developed (tests conducted between spring and summer).
- Study of algorithm modification in situations of rapid cloud movement (hysteresis techniques), evaluation, and real-test validation.
- Consideration of bifacial PV modules for the modification or design of new solar tracker algorithms → **Non-homogeneous condition** of the radiation on the back side of PV modules
- Evaluation of new solar tracker algorithms, designing and adapted for specific systems (e.g. agriPV)

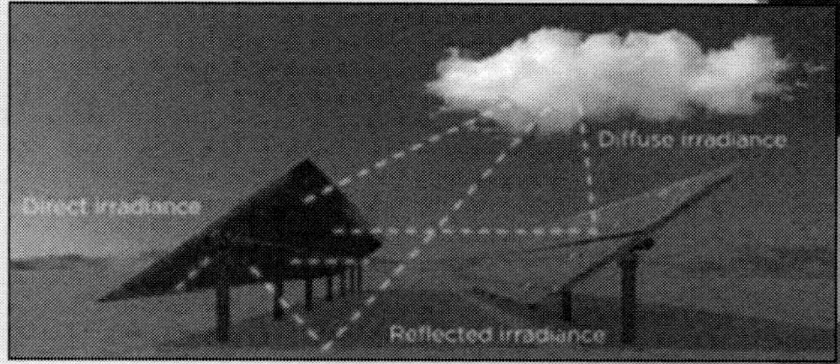

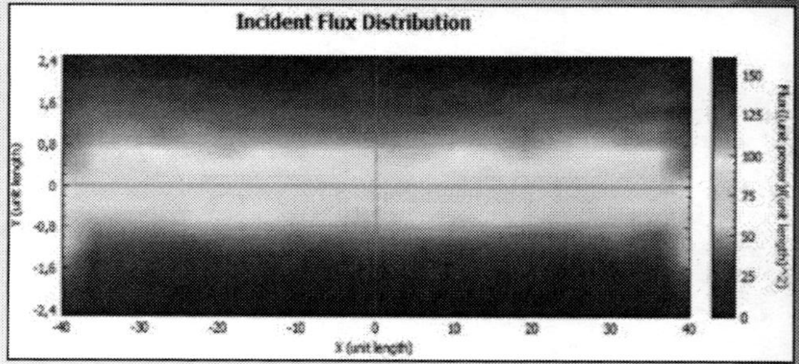

4DO.1.3 - EXPERIMENTAL VALIDATION OF HORIZONTAL SINGLE-AXIS SOLAR TRACKER ALGORITHMS IN TERMS OF ENERGY PRODUCTION AND OPERATIONAL PERFORMANCE

CENER | CENTRO NACIONAL DE ENERGÍAS RENOVABLES

Gobierno de Navarra Nafarroako Gobernua

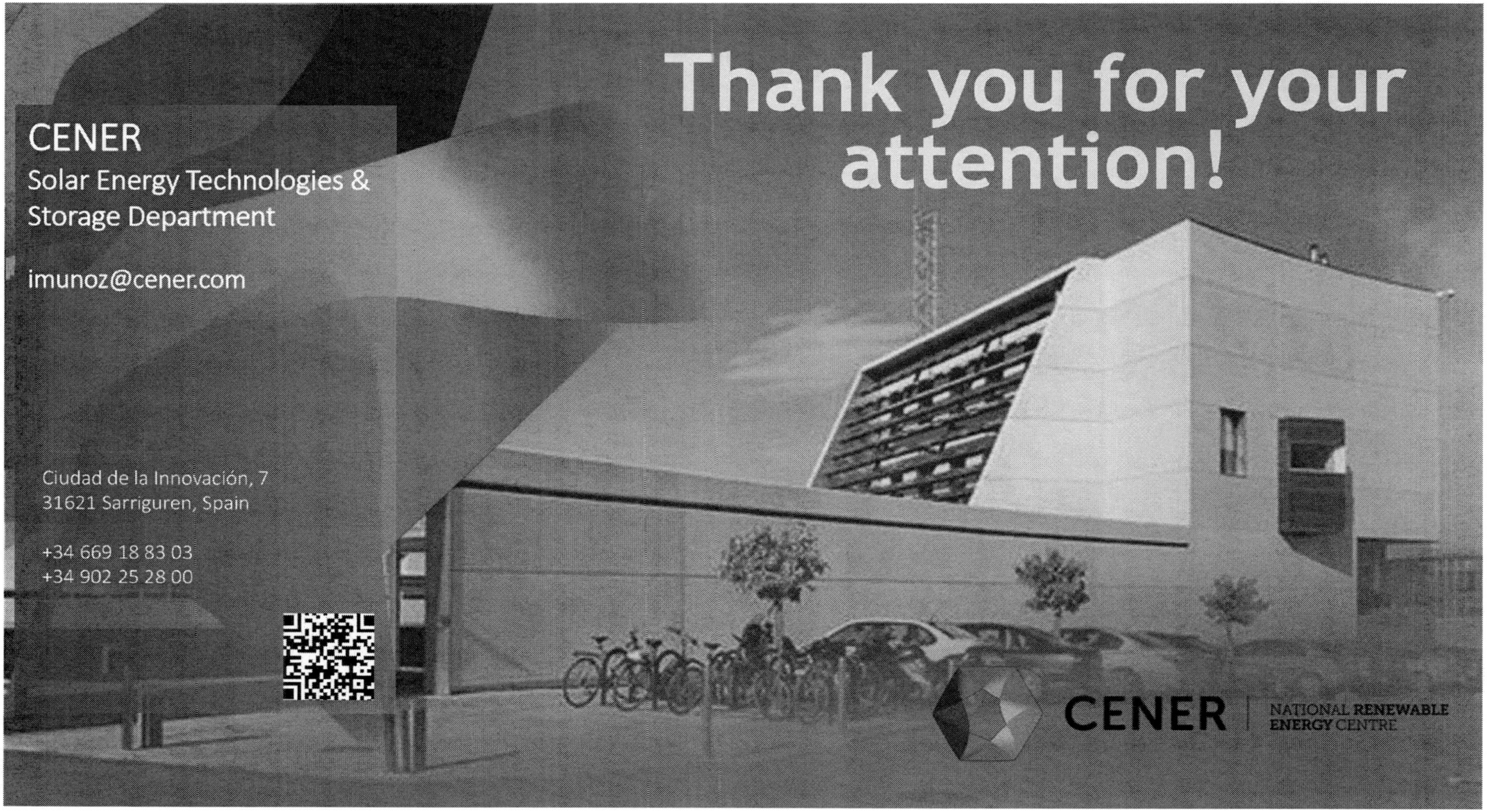
Thank you for your attention!
CENER
Solar Energy Technologies & Storage Department
imunoz@cener.com
Ciudad de la Innovación, 7
31621 Sarriguren, Spain
+34 669 18 83 03
+34 902 25 28 00
CENER | NATIONAL RENEWABLE ENERGY CENTRE

2025 EU PVSEC
22-26 September 2025
Bilbao (Spain)

4DO.1.4:
DEVELOPMENT AND EVALUATION OF NEW BACKTRACKING STRATEGIES (N-BT AND IRR-BT) FOR HORIZONTAL SINGLE-AXIS SOLAR TRACKERS

Gregorio Olivares, Ildefonso Muñoz, Sara Díaz, Ana Gracia

Solar Energy Technologies & Storage Dept. – CENER

CENER | CENTRO NACIONAL DE ENERGÍAS RENOVABLES

GOBIERNO DE ESPAÑA | VICEPRESIDENCIA TERCERA DEL GOBIERNO | MINISTERIO PARA LA TRANSICIÓN ECOLÓGICA Y EL RETO DEMOGRÁFICO | MINISTERIO DE CIENCIA E INNOVACIÓN | Ciemat | Gobierno de Navarra Nafarroako Gobernua

INTRODUCTION & MOTIVATION (1)

CURRENT STATUS

- **Horizontal single axis** → most widely used solar tracker system.
- **Astronomical algorithm with Backtracking strategy** is the most basic and usual algorithm in single axis trackers.

CHALLENGERS & OPPORTUNITIES

- Classic backtracking strategy is calculated **using ground coverage ratio** (GCR) as input[1].
- These strategies **could use other inputs** in order to increase production during sunrise and sunset time.

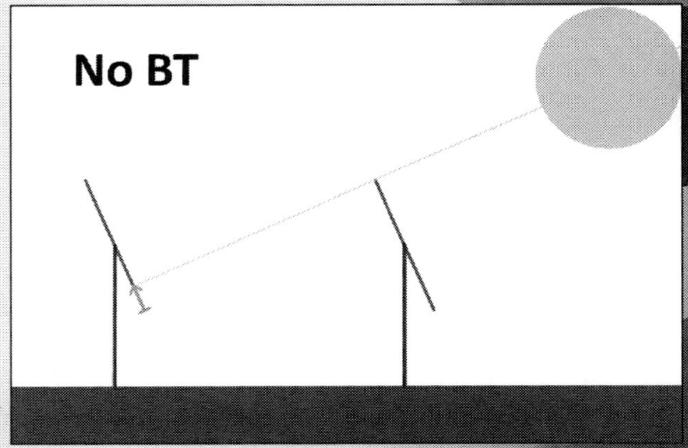

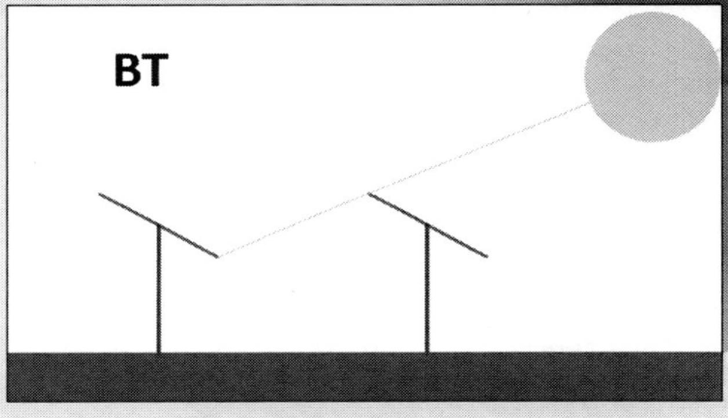

[1] K. Anderson, M. Mikofski. *Slope-Aware Backtracking for Single-Axis Trackers*. NREL, Jul. 2020.

CENER | CENTRO NACIONAL DE ENERGÍAS RENOVABLES

Gobierno de Navarra Nafarroako Gobernua

INTRODUCTION & MOTIVATION (2)

- Study presented: **Evaluation** in terms of energy production of three different backtracking strategies
- Solar backtracking strategies proposed for this study:
  - **Classical/Standard backtracking (BT)**
  - **Layout-adapted backtracking (N-BT)**
  - **Terrain-adapted backtracking (Irr-BT)**
- Comparison based on **high temporal resolution TMY (1 minute)** considering:
  - **Disposition of PV modules** on the solar tracker
  - **Terrain complexity** and height difference between trackers

CENER | CENTRO NACIONAL DE ENERGÍAS RENOVABLES

Gobierno de Navarra
Nafarroako Gobernua

METHODOLOGY – SOLAR BACKTRACKING STRATEGIES (1)

Standard BT strategy

- Avoid shading in the entire structure
- Only GCR as input

N - Backtracking

- **Adapt shading** to structure layout
- Repeat backtracking N times to apply shading to **module subdivisions**
- A **modification of the standard BT** eq. is used

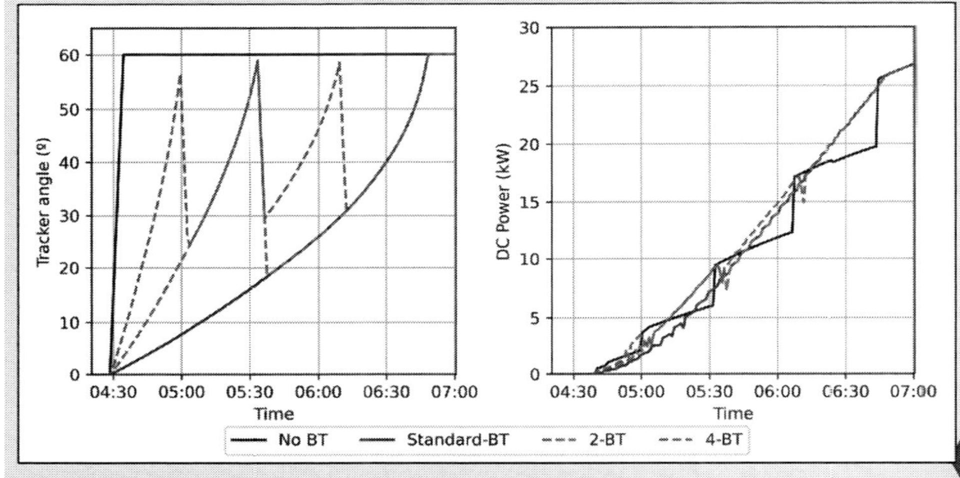

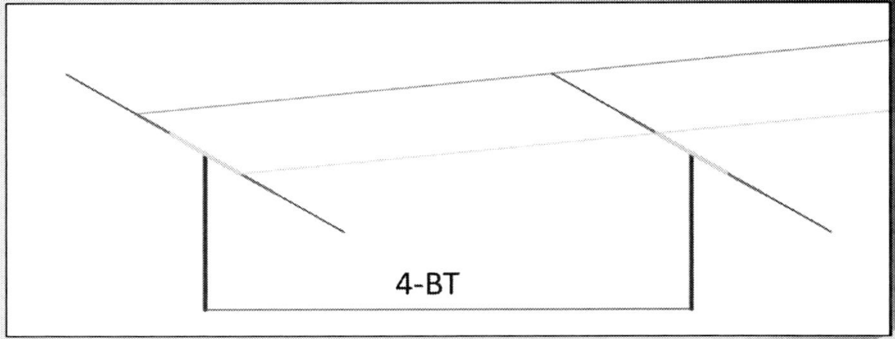

CENER | CENTRO NACIONAL DE ENERGÍAS RENOVABLES

Gobierno de Navarra
Nafarroako Gobernua

METHODOLOGY – SOLAR BACKTRACKING STRATEGIES (2)

Irr - Backtracking

- Adapt tracker angle in order to **avoid inter-row shadings on complex terrains**
- Each tracker angle are **individually-calculated**.
- Tracking angle is adapted based **only on the tracker at the front** (2D considered)
    - If no angle can avoid shading, the front tracker angle is modified

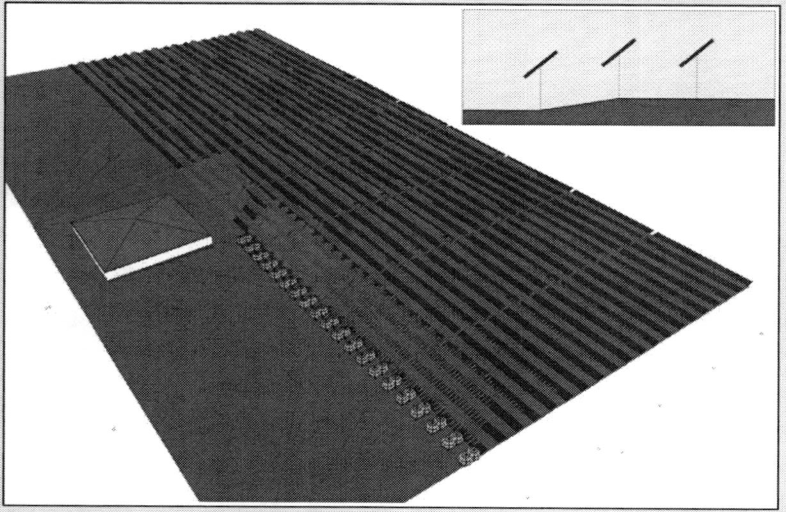

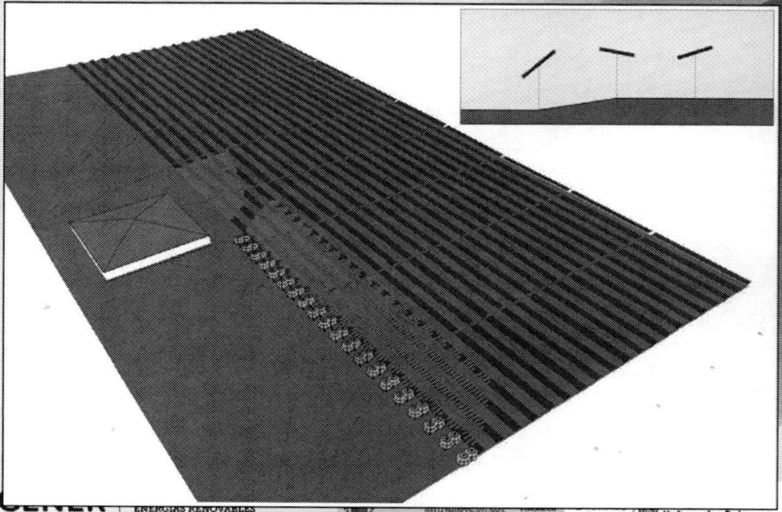

METHODOLOGY – SOLAR BACKTRACKING STRATEGIES (3)

- Backtracking strategies are **independent of the tracking algorithm** applied.
- While the algorithm keep avoiding inter-row shading, **it can override the strategy**.
- **Astronomical algorithm will be applied** on all strategies of this study to avoid false gains.

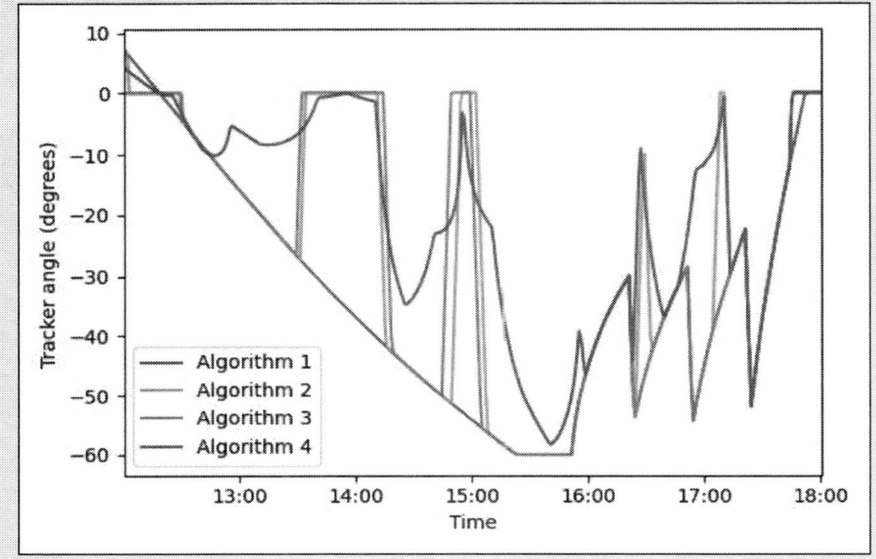

CENER | CENTRO NACIONAL DE ENERGÍAS RENOVABLES

Gobierno de Navarra / Nafarroako Gobernua

METHODOLOGY – STUDY SCENARIOS

N - Backtracking

- Simulations in Pamplona, Sevilla (Spain) and Libya
- **1P and 2P** (portrait) module disposition.

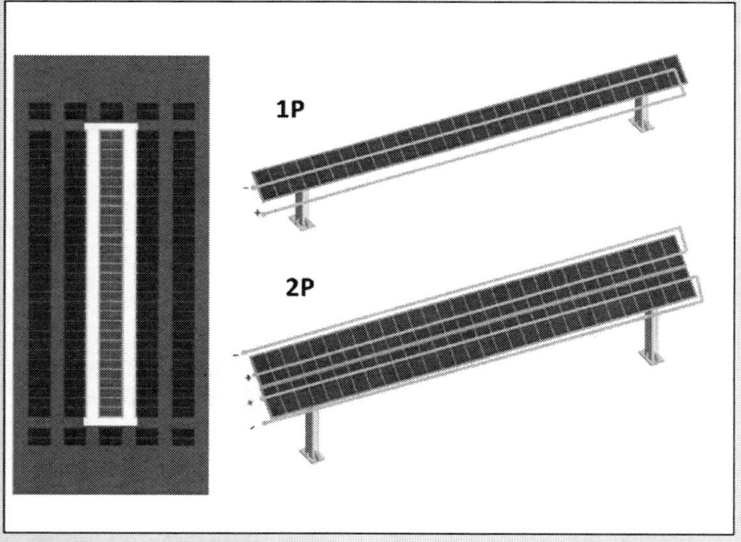

Irr - Backtracking

- Simulation of terrain close to Zamora (Spain)
- Up to 10% slope between trackers

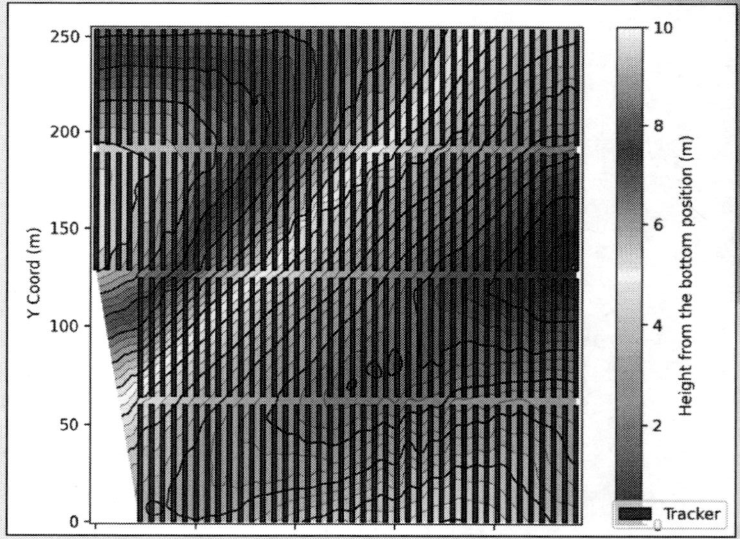

CENER | CENTRO NACIONAL DE ENERGÍAS RENOVABLES

Gobierno de Navarra
Nafarroako Gobernua

METHODOLOGY – SOLAR RADIATION & METEOROLOGICAL DATA

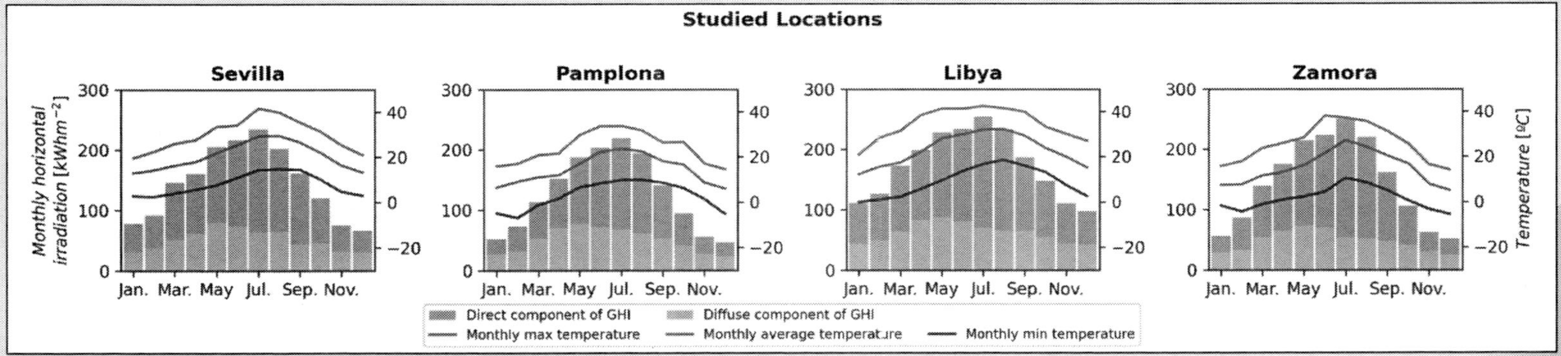

Strategy	Location	LAT. [º]	LON. [º]	H_{GHI} [kWh·m⁻²]	H_{DHI} [kWh·m⁻²]
N-BT	Spain 1 (Pamplona)	42.80	-1.60	1527	600
	Spain 2 (Sevilla)	37.38	-5.98	1755	609
	Libya	31.31	13.4	2100	746
Irr-BT	Spain 3 (Zamora)	41.5	-5.75	2072	572

- Generation of **one-minute resolution TMY** based on:
  - CAMS & MERRA-2 one-minute resolution data (SoDa platform): 19 years of data (Feb 2004 – Jan 2023)
  - Generation of TMY according to CENER methodology [2] implemented in UNE 206013:2017 standard [3]

[2] C.M. Fernández-Peruchena, et al. *Renewable Sustainable Energy Rev*. 2018, 91, 802.
[3] UNE 206013:2017. *Solar thermal electric plants. Procedure for the generation of solar radiation percentiles years*. UNE:Normalización Española, 2017.

CENER | CENTRO NACIONAL DE ENERGÍAS RENOVABLES

Gobierno de Navarra Nafarroako Gobernua

METHODOLOGY – ESTIMATION OF ENERGY PRODUCTION (1)

Evaluation demands a software tool that enables:

- **High resolution** data (1 minute)
- Programming **any solar backtracking strategy**
- Calculating **derate factors** on each tracker individually

SI.MP.V

pvlib python

SIMPV: PV plant simulation software developed by CENER with the ability of simulate behaviour and production of a complete photovoltaic installation.

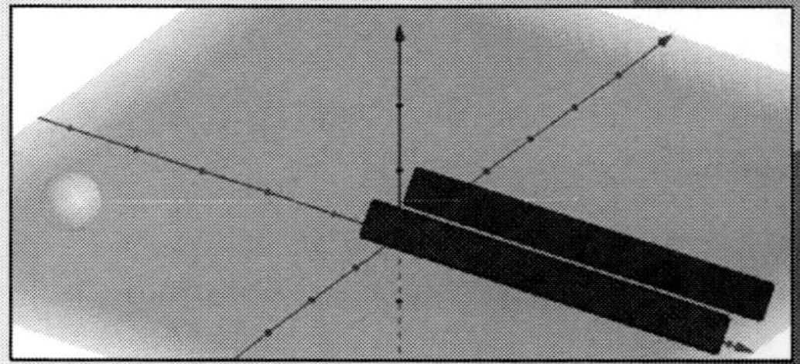

Some of the considered effects:

- **Real solar tracker movement** (non-continuous movement) .
- **Inter-row shadings** (self-shading) by trigonometrical relations between PV modules*.
- **Transient effects** considered.
- **Full I-V curve** at the MPPT input.
- **Electrical effect of shadings** applied on I-V curve.

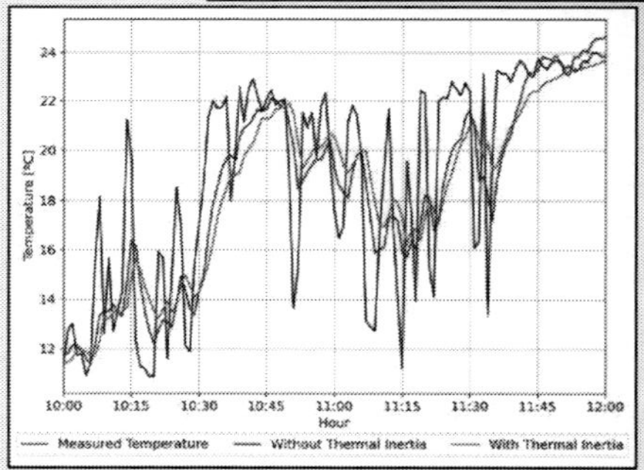

CENER | CENTRO NACIONAL DE ENERGÍAS RENOVABLES

Ciemat

Gobierno de Navarra
Nafarroako Gobernua

METHODOLOGY – ESTIMATION OF SHADING POSITION

Complex terrains difficult use of trigonometrical relations for shading estimation

- Also applied to near shadings (buildings, trees…)
- This method is **not suitable** for shading estimations in complex terrains or roof installations.

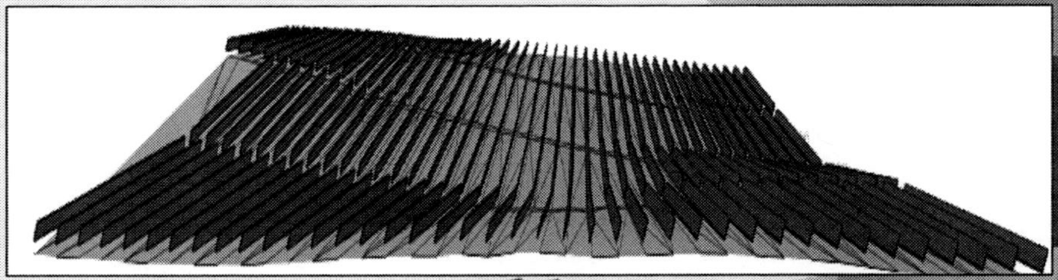

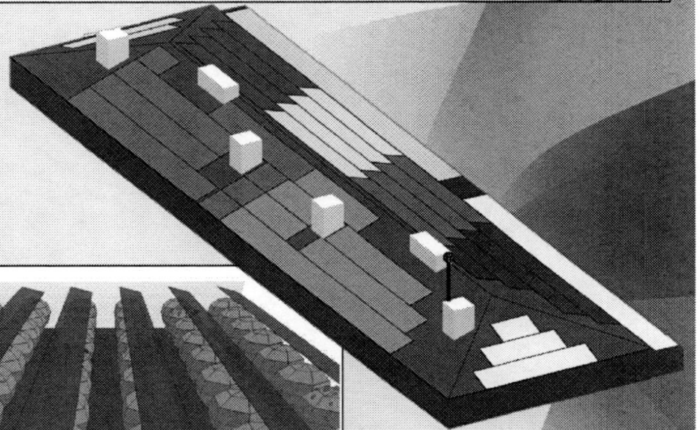

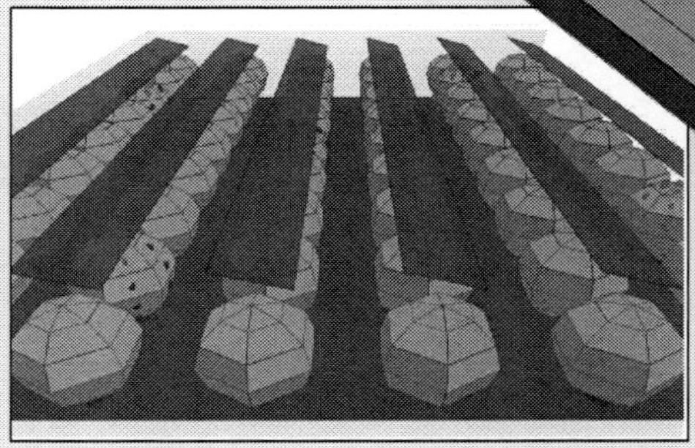

SIMPV Shading Tool: Shading simulation tool developed by CENER to estimate the shading position on photovoltaic structures, obtaining a **high-precision shading profile**.

The program evaluates if an element is shaded by the surrounding elements, with the precision defined by the user.

The tool can be used for calculate shading position in trees, making suitable its use as an agrivoltaic tool:

- ***4DO.5.4***: *Development and Evaluation of an Agrivoltaic System in Olive Groves based on a Novel Smart Tracking Algorithm.*
  Thursday 25th, 17:00, Room 1B.

CENER | CENTRO NACIONAL DE ENERGÍAS RENOVABLES

Gobierno de Navarra
Nafarroako Gobernua

RESULTS – N-BACKTRACKING STRATEGY (N-BT)

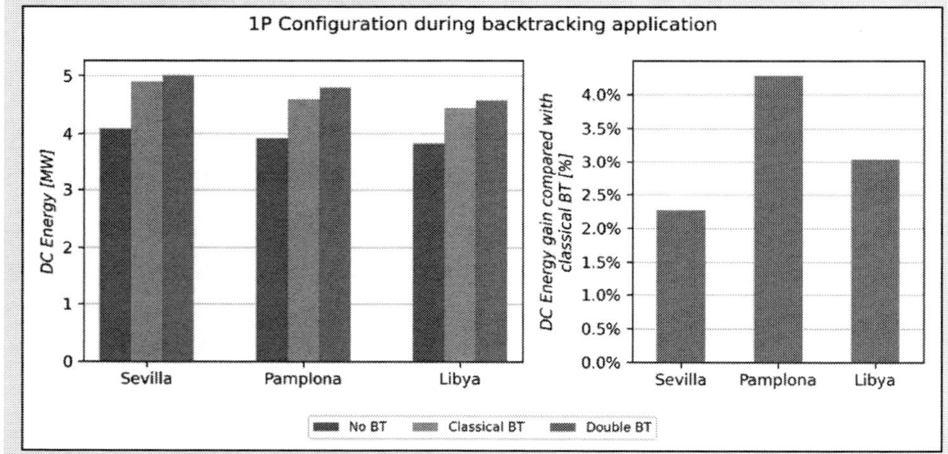

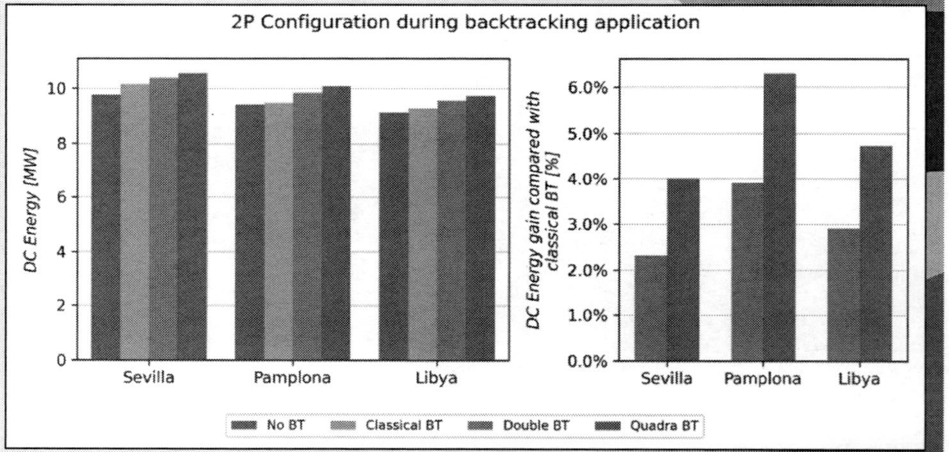

- N-Backtracking strategy **increase the energy generated** compared with classical BT:
  - **1P**: 0.32% - 0.67% with Double-BT
  - **2P**: 0.34% - 0.62% with Double-BT, 0.56%-1% with Quadra-BT
- During backtracking application, gain could reach **up to 4% in 1P** configuration and **6% in 2P** configuration.
- **All N-BT strategies override classical BT.**

CENER | CENTRO NACIONAL DE ENERGÍAS RENOVABLES

Ciemat | Gobierno de Navarra Nafarroako Gobernua

RESULTS – IRR-BACKTRACKING STRATEGY (Irr-BT) (1)

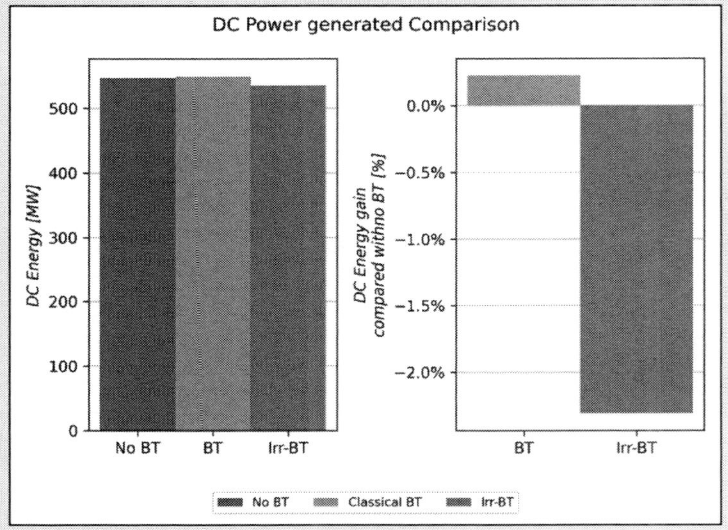

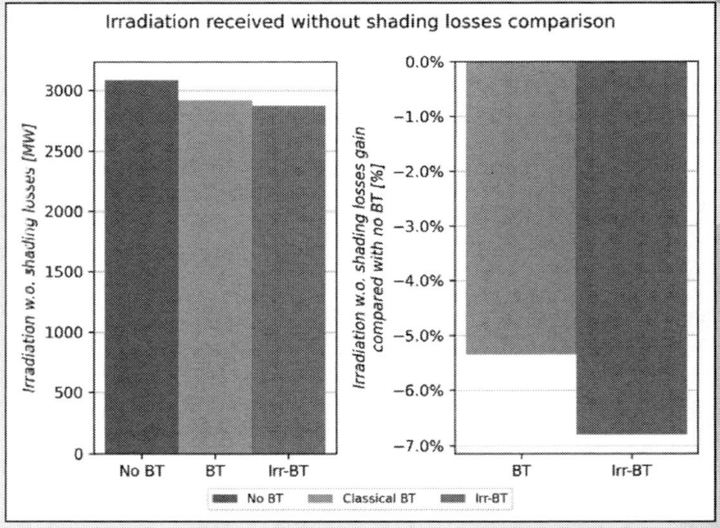

- Application of Irr-BT strategy **does not imply a gain** in DC energy production.
- **Two** main reasons:
  - Loss due to misalignment of modules during backtracking (even if not shading is applied) **is higher than gain** by avoiding shading.
  - **Undesired shadings** are applied by other surrounding trackers.

CENER | CENTRO NACIONAL DE ENERGÍAS RENOVABLES

Gobierno de Navarra Nafarroako Gobernua

RESULTS – IRR-BACKTRACKING STRATEGY (Irr-BT) (2)

Irr-BT vs classical BT

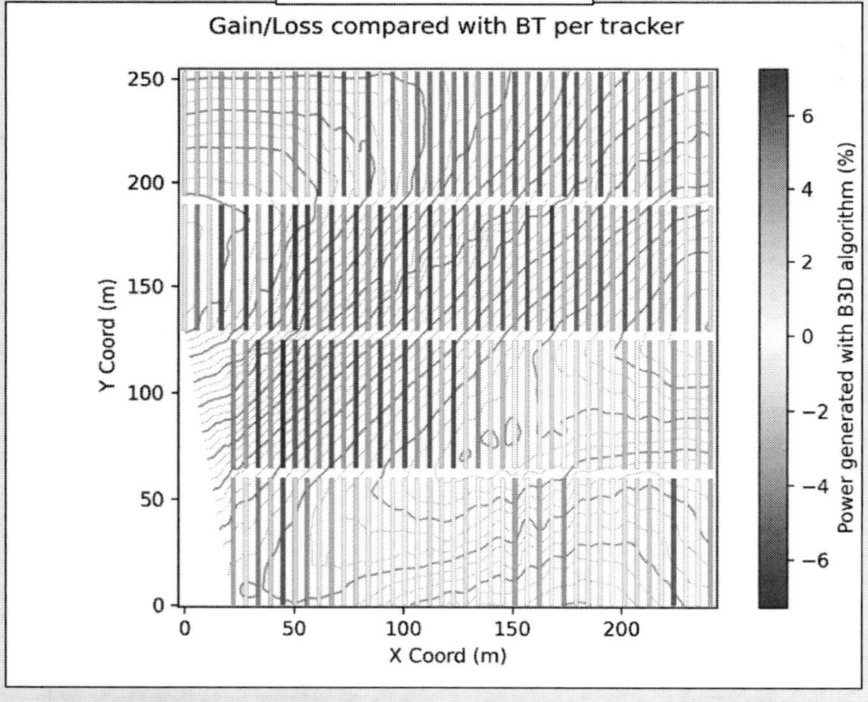

Classical BT vs No BT

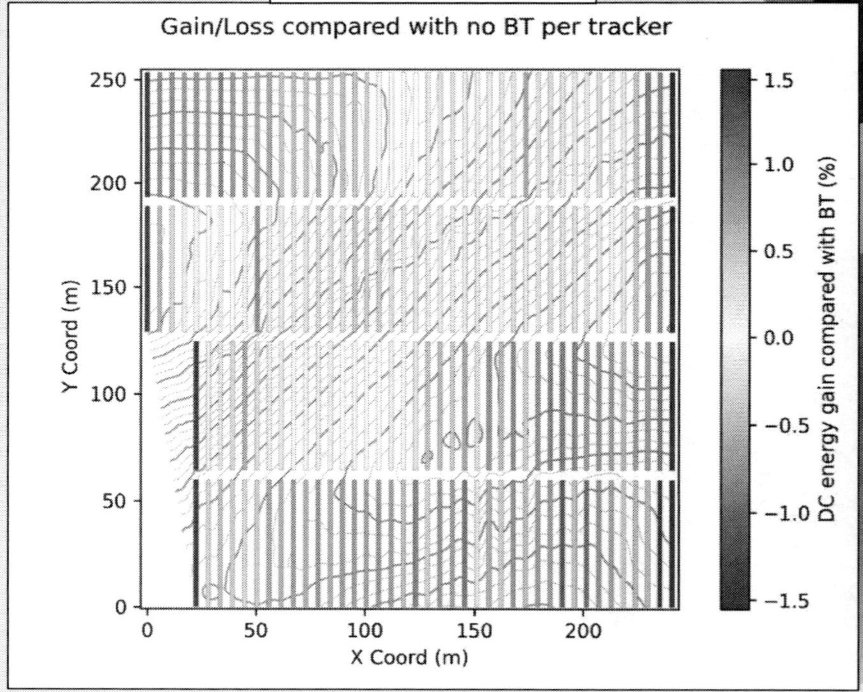

CENER | CENTRO NACIONAL DE ENERGÍAS RENOVABLES

Gobierno de Navarra
Nafarroako Gobernua

SUMMARY & CONCLUSIONS

SUMMARY

- In-depth & **high-resolution study** performed for **three different backtracking strategies**
- Proposed **two new backtracking strategies called N-BT and Irr-BT**.

CONCLUSIONS

- **Backtracking strategies are necessary** on all solar tracking algorithms.
- **Higher backtracking adaptation to** installation could improve performance.
- **N-BT strategy:**
  - Adapt backtracking repetitions to structure layout could reach up to 6% gain during BT application time compared with classical backtracking.
- **Irr-BT strategy:**
  - Terrain-dependent backtracking strategy has not increased PV generation compared with classical backtracking.
  - A full study of surrounding trackers could be considered in high-slope zones

CENER | CENTRO NACIONAL DE ENERGÍAS RENOVABLES

Gobierno de Navarra
Nafarroako Gobernua

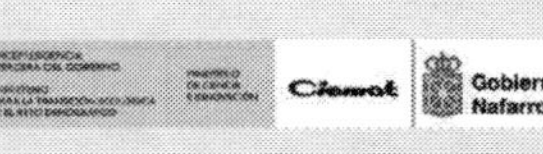

ONGOING & FUTURE WORKS

- Both strategies could be complementary: **Merge of N-BT and Irr-BT.**
- Study of backtracking strategies with **other module cell technologies** (bifacial, back contact…)
- **Clearing works** (cuttings and embankments) could be considered to bring the tracking angle closer to the astronomical angle.
- Validation of strategies on a real PV installation.

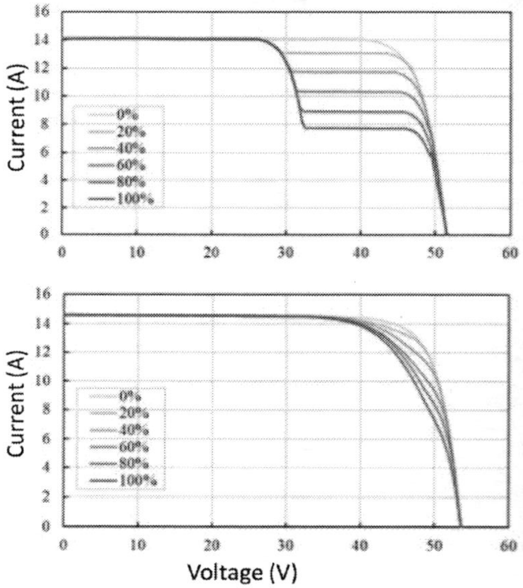

[4] LI, Zhiwei, et al. *Power output performance analysis of back-contact photovoltaic module under actual field shading conditions: A comparison with TOPCon photovoltaic module. Solar Energy*, 2025, vol. 300, p. 113818.

CENER | CENTRO NACIONAL DE ENERGÍAS RENOVABLES

Gobierno de Navarra Nafarroako Gobernua

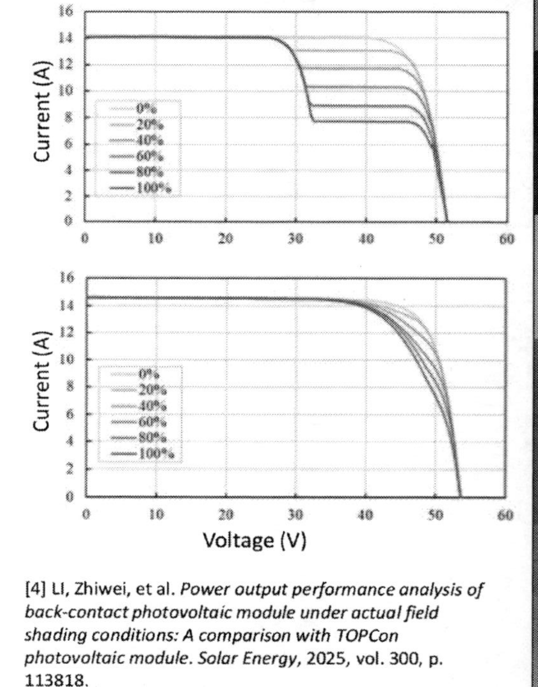

CENER
Solar Energy Technologies &
Storage Department
golivares@cener.com
Ciudad de la Innovación, 7
31621 Sarriguren, Spain
+34 669 18 83 03
+34 902 25 28 00
Thank you for your attention!
CENER
NATIONAL RENEWABLE ENERGY CENTRE

42nd European Photovoltaic Solar Energy Conference and Exhibition

This presentation was selected by the Sc. Committee of the EU PVSEC 2025 for submission of a full paper to one of the EU PVSEC's collaborating peer-reviewed journals.

Terrain-Following Single-Axis Tracking PV Systems: Civil Work Reduction, Performance Impact, and Lifetime Financial Analysis

Abhinav Ratnagiri[1], Shrey Bhatnagar[1], Angel Velasco[1], Viktor Kapetanovic[1], Claire Puttock[1], Amir Asgharzadeh Shishavan[1]

[1] Nextracker, Inc. Fremont, CA, USA 94555

[*]Corresponding Author – email: aratnagiri@nextracker.com – phone number: +1(302) 660–1105
Address:
Nextracker, Inc.
ATTN: Abhinav Ratnagiri
6200 Paseo Padre Pkwy
Fremont, CA 94555
USA

Keywords: Terrain-Following Trackers, Performance Impact, Lifetime Financial Analysis

Abstract: Single-axis tracking (SAT) systems have quickly become the most deployed photovoltaic systems at the utility-scale. Conventional SAT systems were designed originally for flat and semi-flat terrain, utilize a straight torque tube around which the modules rotate. However, availability of as flat and semi-flat terrain continues to dwindle, PV system developers are looking to utilize increase undulating land for development. In undulating conditions, conventional SAT systems require either additional grading to level the terrain or a variably adjusted pile height along the tracker to maintain a straight torque tube. However, both approaches incur high costs—either from increased civil work or the additional steel required for piers. As an alternative, terrain-following trackers have been introduced, allowing the tracker to adapt to the natural terrain while maintaining consistent pier heights. While this can induce significant cost savings, the nominal concern with terrain-following systems is the potential for increased electrical mismatch due to variations in the angle of incidence (AOI) across a string, as well as the risk of higher shading losses. Any performance loss will lead to decreased lifetime revenue, a contrasting financial force to the civil work savings incurred in a terrain-following system. While this performance loss has previously been studied in synthetic conditions, we are extending this analysis to a real selection of SAT sites in this work. We have paired this performance analysis with an evaluation of the reduction in civil work at the same set of sites. Using a real-site case study structure, a variety of site conditions were analyzed, seeking to quantify the financial impacts of both the reduction in civil work and the potential performance loss due to terrain-following trackers. Across this selection of sites, the use of terrain-following trackers reduced the need for civil work by an average of over 80%, constituting a significant benefit to the developer of the PV system. In contrast, even the most significant performance loss was just 0.65%, contributing to a minimal impact on lifetime revenue. As a result, across all sites in the selection, the use of terrain-following tracking systems had a positive financial impact, reducing the levelized cost of energy (LCOE) by up to 1.51$/MWh.

1. Introduction

Increasing the financial viability of photovoltaic (PV) systems has been a driving force for innovation across the industry, with particular focus on adapting technology to a growing variety of environmental conditions. As part of this innovation, single-axis tracking (SAT) systems have become the preferred choice for utility-scale PV deployment [1]. The earliest SAT systems—referred to as conventional SAT systems—were designed with a single tube around which the modules rotated, mounted on piles of uniform height. While effective on flat ground, these systems lack the adaptability needed for all site conditions. As flat land becomes increasingly saturated with PV projects and access to such terrain declines, developers are turning to more undulating topographies. To adapt conventional SAT systems to uneven terrain, extensive earthwork or variable pile heights are required. Both solutions, however, come at significant cost and can hinder project development. To address this challenge, terrain-following systems have been introduced. These systems allow the torque tube—the axis of module rotation—to conform to the ground, thereby reducing the need for grading. This approach can dramatically decrease civil work requirements, but it has also raised concerns about system performance. Unlike conventional SAT systems, terrain-following trackers can introduce varying angles of incidence (AOI) across a single row of modules, leading to greater electrical mismatch. Additionally, these systems may create complex shading patterns that standard tracking algorithms are not designed to manage. Consequently, performance losses remain a concern with terrain-following designs. Previous research has examined these potential losses under synthetic conditions; the present work extends that analysis to a real-site case study. Any performance loss in a PV system directly translates into reduced revenue for the asset owner, a financial risk that could prevent project development. Therefore, a holistic financial evaluation of terrain-following systems must weigh both the savings from reduced grading requirements and the potential revenue loss from decreased energy production.

2. Civil Work Approach

The potential savings from installing terrain-following systems stem directly from the reduced need for civil work. Leveling existing ground requires two opposing processes, cut (removing earth material) and fill (inserting earth material). Terrain-following trackers greatly reduce the need for both processes due to their ability to adapt to the existing topography.

Given an existing site topography, the grading necessary to implement both tracking systems were analyzed using the earthwork tool TerrainPro from Terabase Energy [3]. In performing this analysis, both the original ground topography and the mechanical characteristics of the tracker configuration, either conventional SAT or terrain-following, were considered. In the terrain-following case, the maximum deflection angle between bays of a tracker is a key consideration, while in both cases the allowable variation in pier reveal height is a necessary input to determine the total amount of grading necessary. In this analysis, real sites with two different terrain-following systems were used – using a maximum deflection angle of 0.75 or 1.5 degrees between each bay. The variation in pier reveal height constitutes the maximum allowable range in distance from the ground to the tracker. Varying this distance allows the tracker to remain closer to flat on undulating terrain, once again affecting the amount of change necessary to the original topography. For the sake of our tracker configurations, both conventional SAT and terrain-following systems, the maximum pier reveal height was assumed to be 18 inches, consistent with current tracking system standards. To quantify the necessary civil work for a given site, the metric Balanced Earthwork (BE) was used, defined as twice the larger of the necessary cut and necessary fill in cubic yards, representing the total volume of earth altered. This metric was used because it allows for a reasonable cost model to be applied by determining a price per cubic meter of earth moved. By analyzing the difference in the required BE between conventional and terrain-following tracker systems, a quantitative measure of the civil work avoided with the terrain-following system was determined. Figure 1 shows the areas of a site where grading was necessary, with Fig. 1a showing the numerous locations throughout the site where earthwork was necessary, with sharper colors indicating larger amounts of work. In Fig. 1b, many of these colored patches disappear, clearing demonstrating that the need for earthwork has reduced significantly because of a terrain-following system.

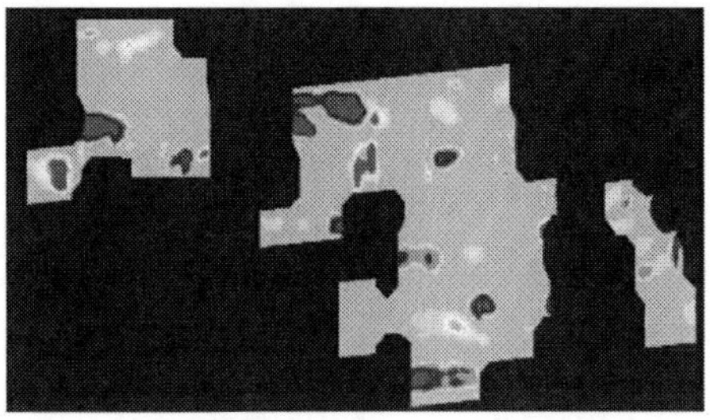

a) Cut/Fill Map with Conventional Trackers

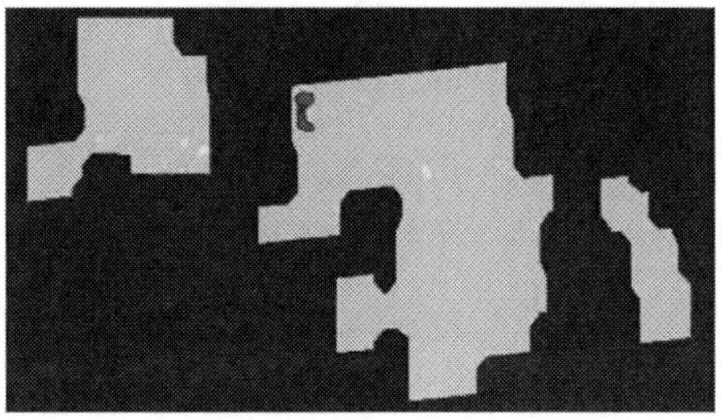

b) Cut/Fill Map with Terrain-Following Trackers

Cut/Fill Legend		
Range (feet)		Color
Maximum Cut	-2.00	
-2.00	-1.50	
-1.50	-1.00	
-1.00	-0.50	
-0.50	-0.10	
0.10	0.50	
0.50	1.00	
1.00	1.50	
1.50	2.00	
2.00	Maximum Fill	

Figure 1: Reduction in Cut/Fill Requirements with use of Terrain-Following Trackers (b) as opposed to Conventional Trackers (a)

3. Energy Performance Modeling

To accurately quantify the differences in energy performance between a conventional SAT system and a terrain-following one, Nextracker's performance modeling engine, TrueSim [4], was used. This model is built on foundations from open-source PV performance modeling tools including pvlib [5], System Advisor Model (SAM) [6], and PVMismatch [7]. Using the physical configuration of a PV project, TrueSim performs cell-level irradiance and shade calculations given a set of tracking angles for the SAT system. Cell-level calculations are essential to accurately account for the potential additional mismatch and shading loss in terrain-following systems. TrueSim's 3D shading model calculates shade polygons for each module along a tracker. In conjunction, plane-of-array (POA) irradiance is computed for both front and back sides of the module using the infinite-sheds model [8], which itself considers both ground and diffuse shading. Due to the 3D nature of the TrueSim shading model, the same methodology was applicable for all tracker configuration solutions. Using the shading pattern and the calculated POA, the resulting total effective

10.4229/EUPVSEC2025/4DO.1.5

irradiance is computed for each module cell. Cell IV curves are then calculated based on the single-diode model [9], using both effective irradiance and cell temperature as inputs. These cell-level IV curves are aggregated to module-level IV curves while considering the module's bypass diodes. Similarly, module IV curves are aggregated to produce string-level and system-level IV curves from which the maximum power point is used to determine the total DC output of the site as whole. For the purposes of this study, DC power output calculations were performed according to this process over the course of a typical meteorological year (TMY), interpolated to 15-minute intervals. To derive an AC power output better suited for downstream revenue calculations, an assumed AC conversion factor of 98% was used.

4. Economic Analysis

The civil work reduction and the performance impact of utilizing a terrain-following system often fall on opposing sides of a cost-benefit analysis. To perform this contrasting analysis, cost and revenue models were necessary to convert the BE and AC energy output metrics into a dollar value that was relevant over the lifetime of the project.

The earthwork cost savings model was derived from historical cost data collected across Nextracker's fleet. The cost per cubic meter of earthwork required was calculated as shown in Equation (1):

$$\text{Unit Cost (\$/cu.m.)} = (43.7 \times \text{BE})^{-0.185} \quad (1)$$

to account for the diminishing marginal costs of additional cut and fill. This was used to determine the cost per cubic yard of BE, which was used to calculate the total gross savings due to terrain-following trackers. For the purposes of this analysis, further cost differences between tracker types were ignored to isolate the impact of civil work reduction. With this being an upfront capital expenditure (CAPEX), no discount was necessary to account for the potential future implications on total cashflow.

However, estimating the present value of revenue loss due to the performance impact required a more complex model. To quantify the annual financial impact over the lifetime of the project, degradation, inflation, and price per MWh were necessary assumptions. Degradation because of standard site conditions was assumed to be 1% year-to-year, whereas inflation was assumed to be 3% to best account for the value of future revenue. Regarding the price per MWh, this can vary significantly from project to project, heavily dependent on the region where the project is located. Across the selection of sites chosen for analysis, the power purchase agreement (PPA) price varied from $40-80/MWh. In regions such as Texas and the southern US, lower PPA prices were considered, whereas European sites and northern US sites often had higher PPA prices [10]. Once the annual revenue was calculated for each year in the project lifetime, a discount rate of 7% was applied to calculate the net present value (NPV) of the lifetime project revenue. An established financial modeling concept, NPV was calculated using the following formula:

$$NPV = \sum_{t=0}^{30} \frac{R_t}{(1 + 0.07)^t} \quad (2)$$

where t is the year and R_t is the revenue for that year over the full, 30-year lifetime of the project. This NPV allowed for a reasonable comparison with the upfront, CAPEX savings from earthwork reduction. Calculating the difference between these values resulted in the lifetime financial impact (LFI) and dividing this value by the total discounted lifetime production in MWh resulted in the impact on the levelized cost of energy in terms of $/MWh.

5. Case Study Structure

Fourteen real sites were chosen to best analyze the trade-off between performance loss and civil work reduction in a variety of conditions. It was important to vary each facet of analysis, both related to civil work reduction as well as performance analysis. The varied tracker technologies combined with a range of site land areas and topographies caused differences across the selection in civil work reduction. In terms of performance analysis, choosing sites with different capacities, different regions, and different layouts was essential. As a result, different electrical configurations, weather conditions, and shading patterns were modeled. Varying these important factors, allowed for conclusions that could be applicable to a wide range of site conditions.

6. Results and Discussion

Comparative analysis demonstrates that terrain-following tracker systems consistently deliver substantial reductions in civil work requirements while maintaining nearly identical energy performance relative to conventional designs. Figure 2 shows that, across the portfolio of case studies, earthwork volumes reduce by 65–92%, with most projects clustered above 80% reduction. This large decrease in cut/fill activity represents a significant practical benefit to the developer of the PV plant.

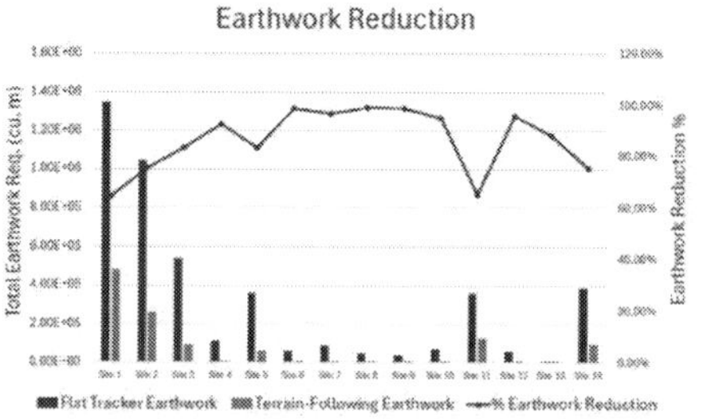

Figure 2: Balanced Earthwork reduction with terrain-following trackers at a selection of real PV sites.

In contrast, energy production differences between flat and terrain-following configurations were found to be negligible. As shown in Fig. 3, performance loss was at an average of 0.34%, with even the most severe case having a loss of just 0.65% per year. These results confirm that concerns about mismatch or shading penalties associated with terrain-following systems are minimal.

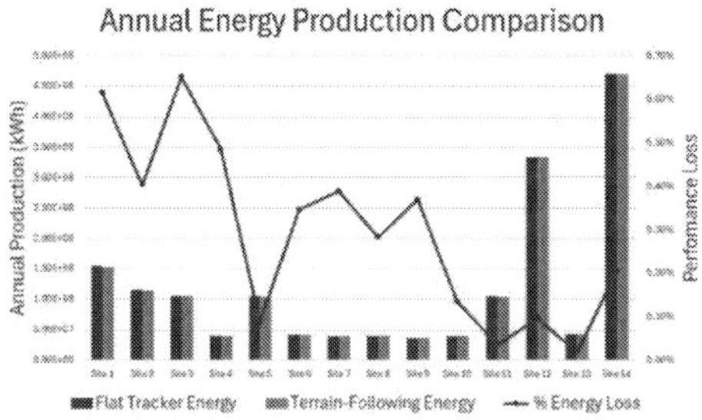

Figure 3: Energy production comparison between terrain-following systems and their conventional SAT counterparts.

Analyzed as financial forces, the avoided earthwork expenditures outweighs the minor revenue losses from reduced performance in every case evaluated, as shown in Figure 4. Net cost effects are uniformly positive, reaching hundreds of thousands to several million dollars, while even smaller projects demonstrate clear gains. This translates into consistent improvements in the LCOE, with savings between $0.03/MWh and $1.51/MWh with a mean value of $0.50/MWh across the selection. Considering the scale of production over the full lifetime of a project, these savings are significant.

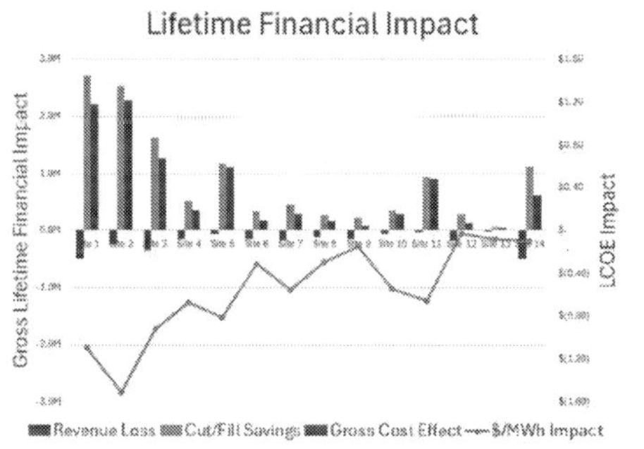

Figure 4: Lifetime financial analysis for terrain-following and conventional SAT systems.

7. Conclusions

Terrain-following trackers have an overall positive impact on the financial viability of a PV project over its lifetime across a variety of given site conditions. Across the selection of sites chosen, terrain-following systems led to an 80% reduction in civil work. When this reduction was contrasted with a maximum terrain loss of 0.65% the result was a significant reduction in LCOE and lifetime financial impact, up to $1.51/MWh at utility-scale production. Beyond the direct cost savings, these improvements have practical real-world implications. By minimizing grading requirements, terrain-following trackers expand the pool of viable project sites, shorten construction timelines, and reduce environmental disruption. Together, these benefits strengthen the economic case for adopting terrain-following designs, representing a scalable strategy to improve the competitiveness and feasibility of PV deployment across diverse landscapes.

7. REFERENCES

[1] J. [Lawrence B. N. L. (LBNL) Seel Berkeley CA (United States)] et al., "Utility-Scale Solar, 2024 Edition: Empirical Trends in Deployment, Technology, Cost, Performance, PPA Pricing, and Value in the United States [Slides]."

[2] A. A. Shishavan, V. R. Abbaraju, A. Dobos, and F. Borrelli, "Terrain-Following Single-Axis Tracking PV Systems: Advantages and Performance Analysis," 38th European Photovoltaic Solar Energy Conference and Exhibition; 1060-1064, 2021, doi: 10.4229/EUPVSEC20212021-5DO.3.3.

[3] Terabase Energy, "Terrain Pro," https://plantpredict.com/.

[4] Nextracker, Inc., "TrueSim Version 4.2.4."

[5] K. S. Anderson, C. W. Hansen, W. F. Holmgren, A. R. Jensen, M. A. Mikofski, and A. Driesse, "pvlib python: 2023 project update," J Open Source Soft, vol. 8, no. 92, p. 5994, 2023, doi: 10.21105/joss.05994.

[6] National Renewable Energy Laboratory, "System Advisor Model (SAM) Version 2023.12.17."

[7] M. Mikofski, B. Meyers, and C. Chaudhari, "PVMismatch Project: https://github.com/SunPower/PVMismatch," 2018, SunPower Corporation, Richmond, CA.

[8] Mikofski, M., Darawali, R., Hamer, M., Neubert, A., and Newmiller, J. "Bifacial Performance Modeling in Large Arrays". 2019 IEEE 46th Photovoltaic Specialists Conference (PVSC), 2019, pp. 1282-1287.

[9] W. De Soto et al., "Improvement and validation of a model for photovoltaic array performance", Solar Energy, vol 80, pp. 78-88, 2006

[10] LevelTen Energy, *PPA Price Index Report: North America Q1 2024*, LevelTen Energy, 2024

10.4229/EUPVSEC2025/4DO.1.5
020367-004

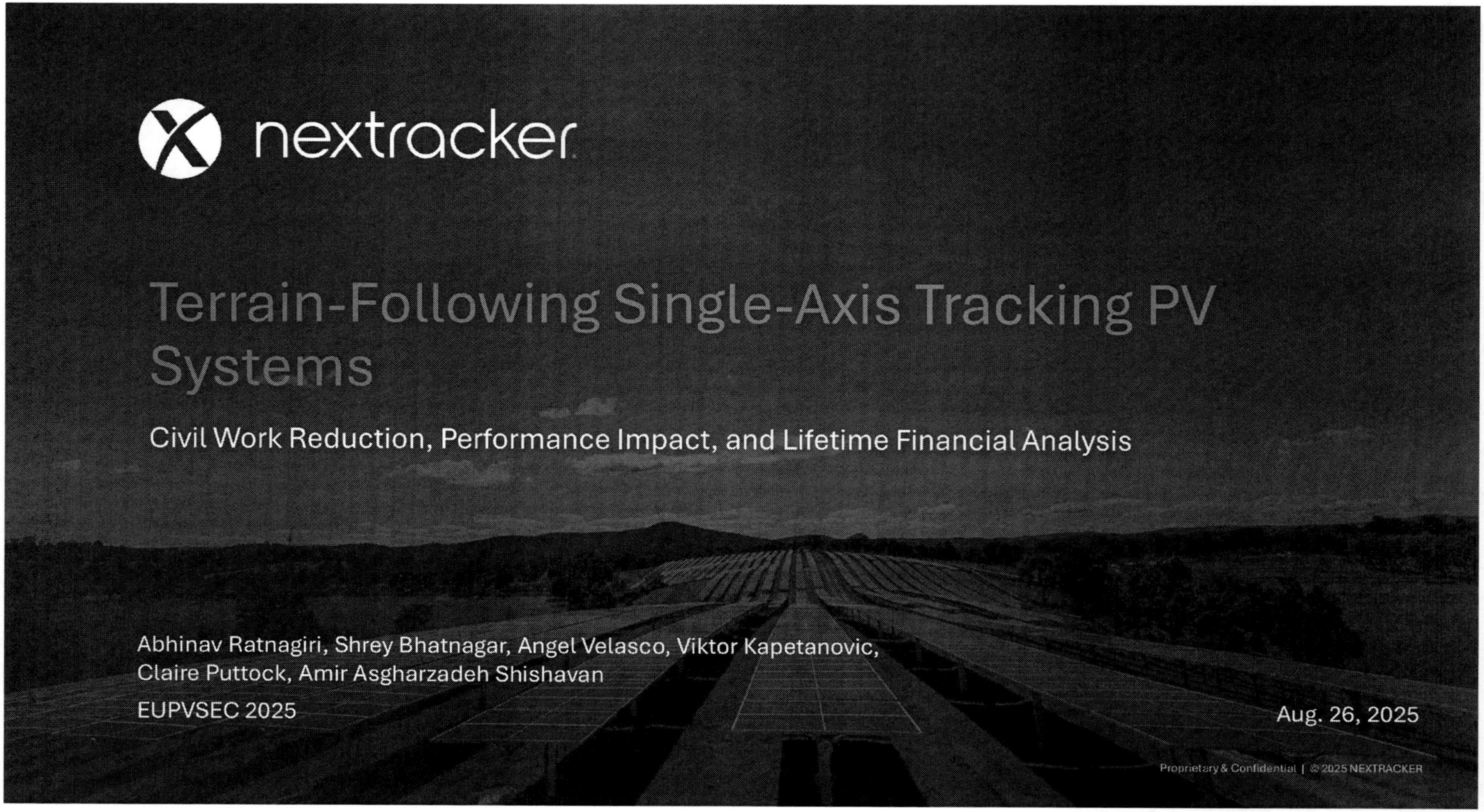
nextracker
Terrain-Following Single-Axis Tracking PV Systems
Civil Work Reduction, Performance Impact, and Lifetime Financial Analysis
Abhinav Ratnagiri, Shrey Bhatnagar, Angel Velasco, Viktor Kapetanovic,
Claire Puttock, Amir Asgharzadeh Shishavan
EUPVSEC 2025
Aug. 26, 2025
Proprietary & Confidential | © 2025 NEXTRACKER

Terrain-Following PV Systems: Background

Flat Tracker System

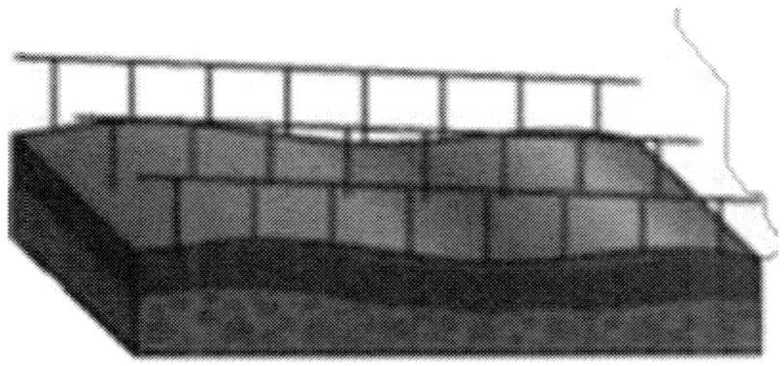

Terrain-Following System

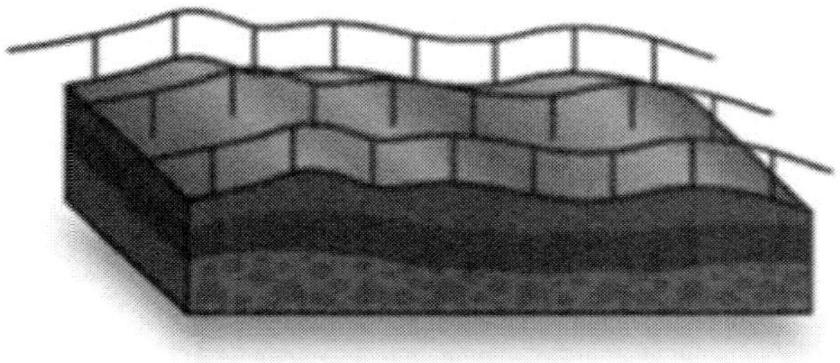

nextracker

Terrain-Following PV Systems: Implementation

Motivations

- Can be installed on undulating terrain
- Significantly less earthwork required

Concerns

- Increased irradiance mismatch across single tracker
- Operation at a lower MPP
- Complex shading patterns
- Potential resultant performance loss

Do the savings due to earthwork reduction outweigh the potential performance loss when considering terrain-following systems?

nextracker

 3

Methodology

Provide Quantitative Financial Analysis of Terrain-Following System

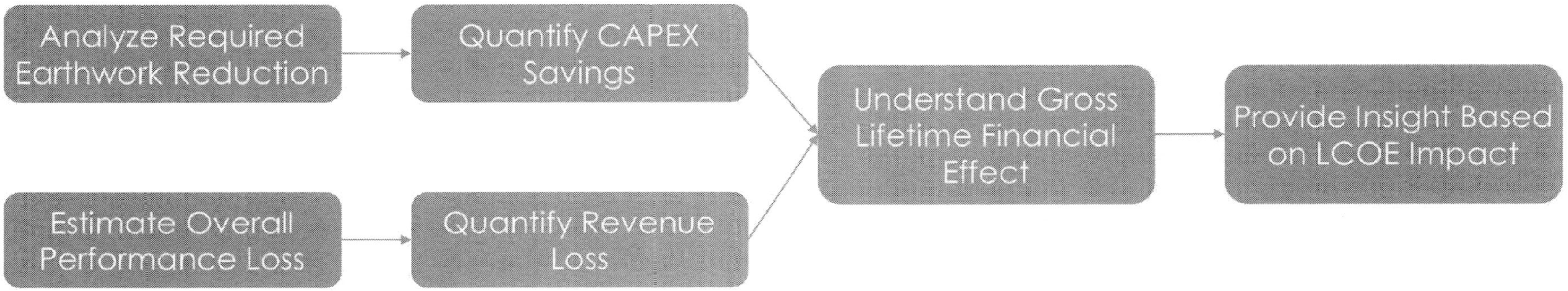

nextracker

Earthwork Analysis

Quantify Earthwork Reduction due to Terrain-Following Systems

- Comparison between Flat Trackers & Terrain Following
- Grading analysis performed by Terabase Terrain Pro
  - Required Cut/Fill based on original topography
  - Mechanical assumptions based on **NX Horizon** and **NX XTR 0.75, NX XTR 1.5**
  - Proposed Final Grading Metric:

$$\boldsymbol{BE = 2 \times \max(C, F)}$$

BE -- Balanced Earthwork
C -- Required Cut (cu. m)
F -- Required Fill (cu. m)

nextracker.

Terrain Pro Grading Maps

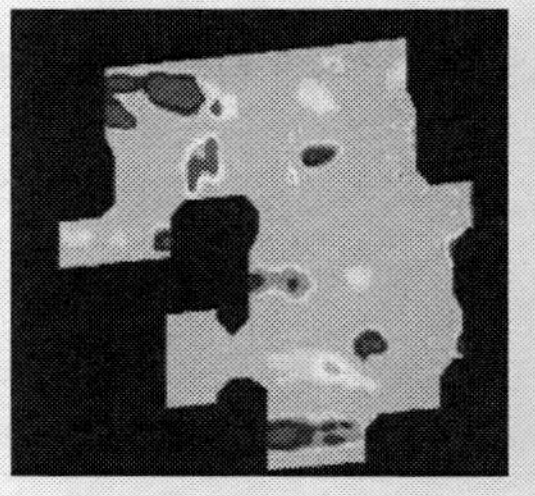

Flat Tracker Grading Map

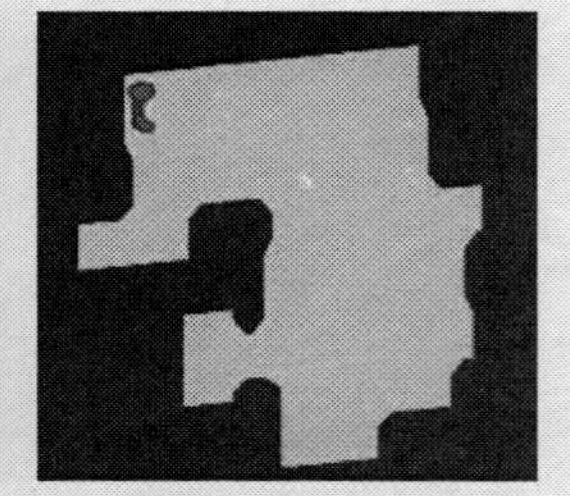

Terrain-Following Grading Map

Cut/Fill Legend		
Range (feet)		Color
Maximum Cut	-2.00	
-2.00	-1.50	
-1.50	-1.00	
-1.00	-0.50	
-0.50	-0.10	
0.10	0.50	
0.50	1.00	
1.00	1.50	
1.50	2.00	
2.00	Maximum Fill	

Energy Yield Analysis

Estimate Performance Differences due to Irradiance Mismatch

- TrueSim Performance Modeling Engine
  - High-Fidelity tool to model Terrain-Following Systems
  - 3D shade model to determine cell-level shading losses
  - Infinite-Sheds, Single Diode models determine cell-level irradiance, IV curves
  - PVLIB based DC mismatch calculations for string level IV curve, MPPT estimation
  - Performed with 15-min time resolution with typical meteorological year (TMY) data for increased accuracy
  - Fixed AC Conversion factor of 98% for financial comparison
- Total Energy Loss (kWh), Energy Loss Percentage Calculated

nextracker

TrueSim 3D Shade Model

Terrain-Following Solution

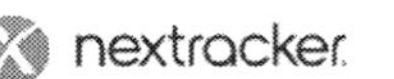

Flat Tracker Solution

Financial Impact Analysis

Understand Lifetime Financial Impact of Terrain-Following System

- Quantify CAPEX savings
  - Exponential formula based on empirical data applied to account for diminishing marginal cost

$$\mathrm{BEC} = (43.7 \times \mathrm{BE})^{-0.185} \times \mathrm{BE}$$

BEC -- Balanced Earthwork Cost ($)
BE -- Balanced Earthwork (cu. m)

- Quantify performance-related revenue loss
  - Net Present Value (NPV) of cashflow calculated
    - Region Specific PPA price applied ($/kWh)
    - Inflation rate: **3%**, Discount rate: **7%**
- Lifetime Financial Impact Measured:
  - $\mathrm{LFI} = \mathrm{Cost\ Savings} - \mathrm{NPV\ Revenue\ Loss}$
- LCOE Impact Calculated:
  - $\mathrm{LCOE\ Impact} = \mathrm{LFI} / \mathrm{Discounted\ Energy\ Production}$

nextracker

Real Site Case Study

14 total sites analyzed across North America and Europe

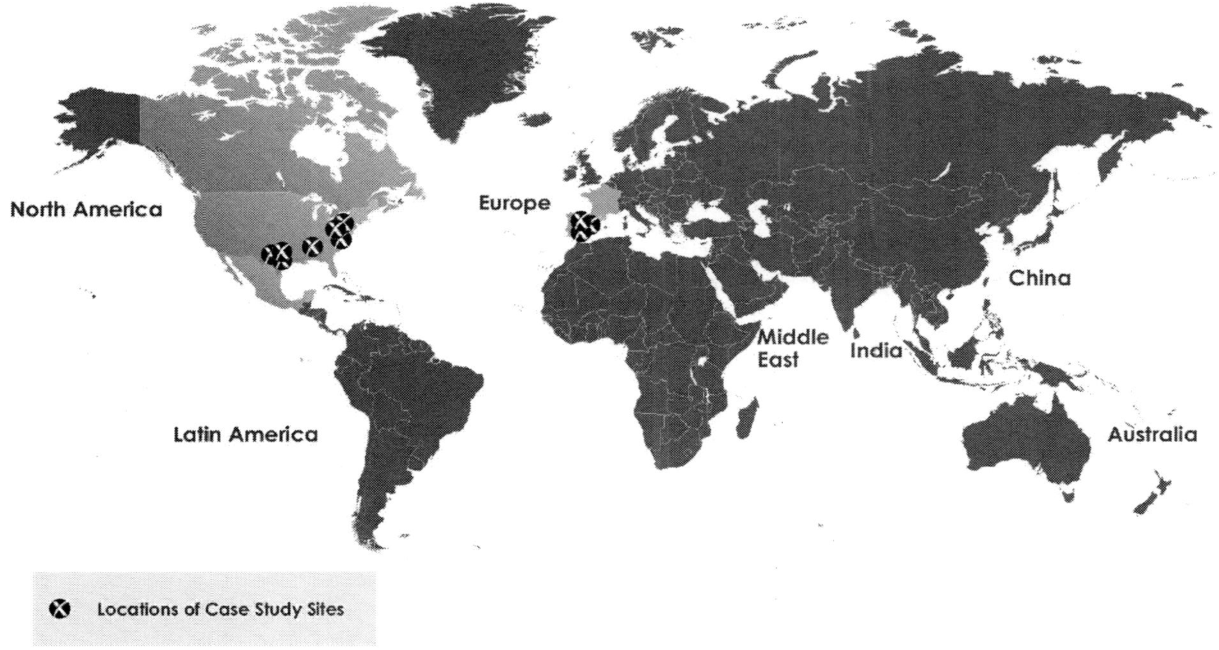

nextracker

Varied Site Capacity
Up to 200 MW

Varied Terrain-Following Systems
Multiple Tracker Configurations

Varied Energy Markets
PPA prices: $40 – $80 / kWh

Earthwork Analysis Results

Significant Reduction in Necessary Grading Across All Sites

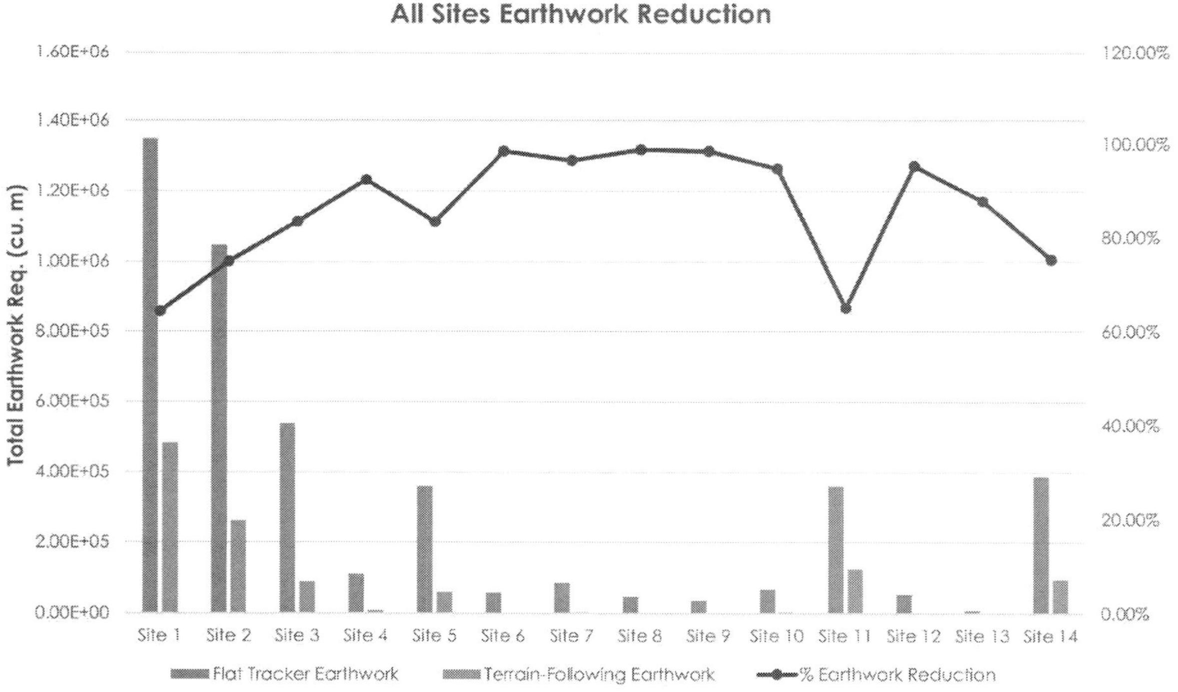

nextracker.

303,260 cu. m

Average Flat Tracker BE required

75,633 cu. m

Average Terrain-Following BE required

87.28%

Average Earthwork Reduction

Performance Analysis Results

Minimal Performance loss due to Terrain-Following Systems

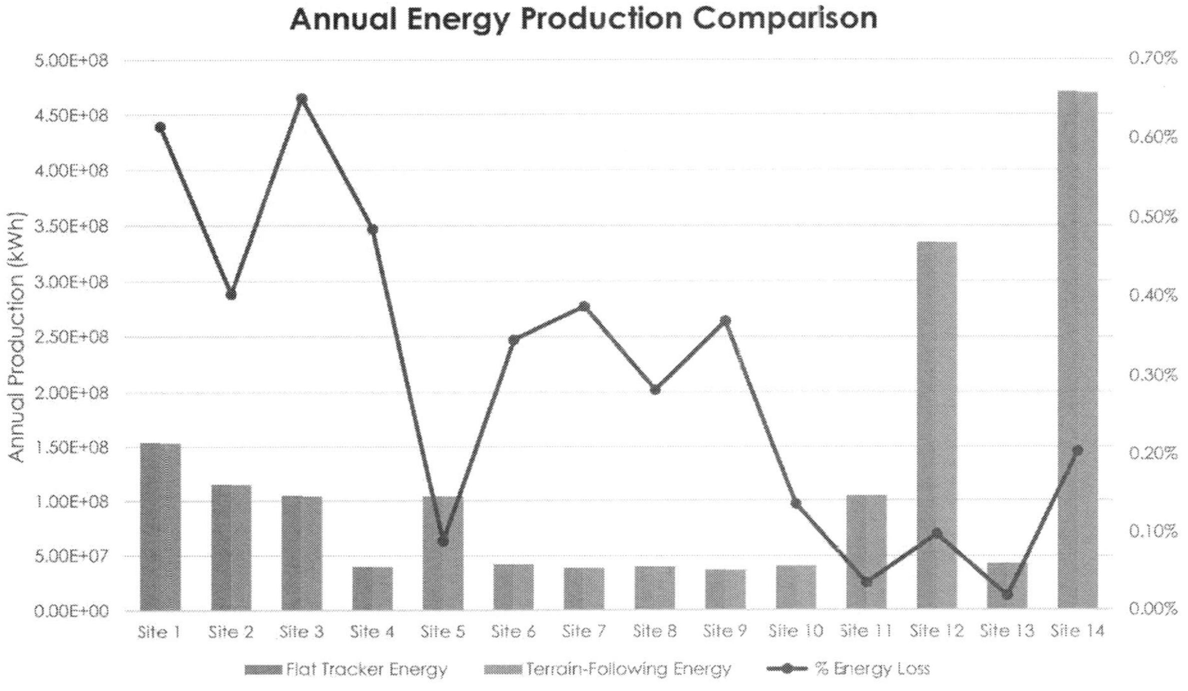

nextracker

0.65%

Maximum Annual Performance Loss

0.02%

Minimum Annual Performance Loss

0.34%

Average Annual Performance Loss

Lifetime Financial Impact

Cost savings, LCOE decrease observed due to Terrain-Following Systems

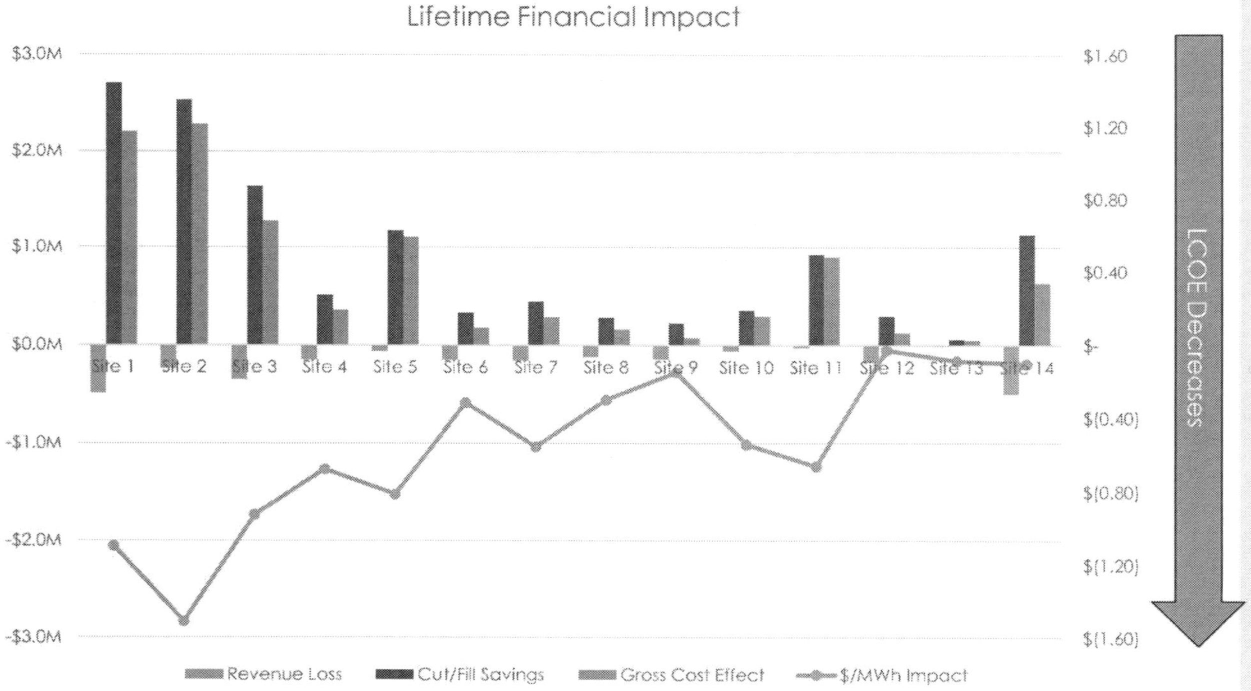

nextracker

$200,732
Average Discounted Revenue Loss

$853,470
Average Cost (CAPEX) Savings

$652,737
Average Overall Cost Impact

($0.50)
Average LCOE Reduction per MWh

Conclusions & Outlook

Terrain-Following Trackers have a <u>POSITIVE</u> Financial Impact Across a Variety of Site Conditions

Future Studies

- Increased range of regions/sites in case study
- Comparison of different Terrain-Following Solutions
- Analysis of OPEX/O&M costs, Installation times
- Inclusion of dynamic pricing for increasingly accurate revenue calculations

nextracker

64-99% Earthwork Reduction

0.02 - 0.65% Annual Energy Loss

~$650,000 Cost Savings

Up to $1.51 Saved per MWh

Thank you

aratnagiri@nextracker.com

nextracker

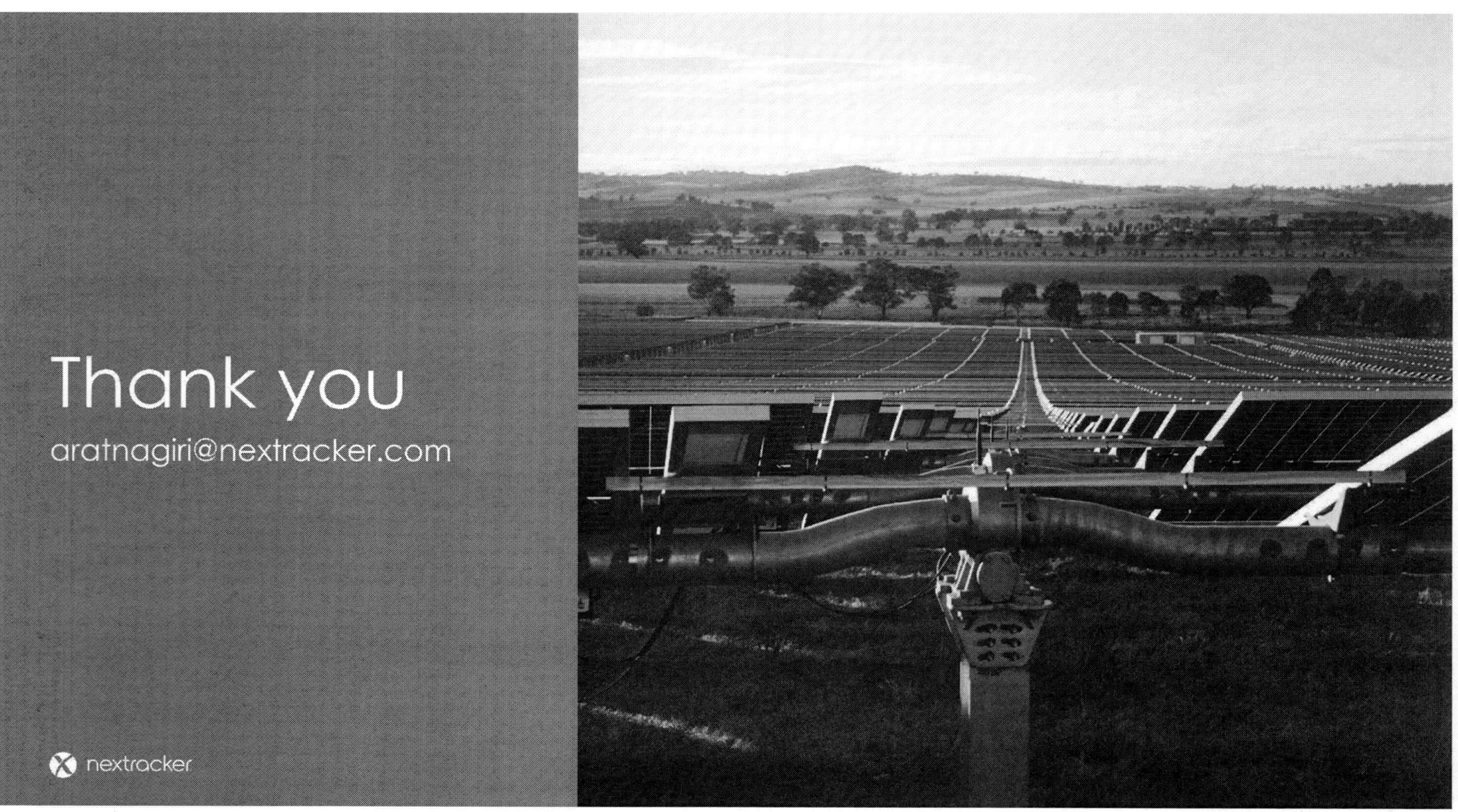

References

- J. [Lawrence B. N. L. (LBNL) Seel Berkeley CA (United States)] et al., "Utility-Scale Solar, 2024 Edition: Empirical Trends in Deployment, Technology, Cost, Performance, PPA Pricing, and Value in the United States [Slides]."
- A. A. Shishavan, V. R. Abbaraju, A. Dobos, and F. Borrelli, "Terrain-Following Single-Axis Tracking PV Systems: Advantages and Performance Analysis," 38th European Photovoltaic Solar Energy Conference and Exhibition; 1060-1064, 2021, doi: 10.4229/EUPVSEC20212021-5DO.3.3.
- Terabase Energy, "Terrain Pro," https://plantpredict.com/.
- Nextracker, Inc., "TrueSim Version 4.2.4."
- K. S. Anderson, C. W. Hansen, W. F. Holmgren, A. R. Jensen, M. A. Mikofski, and A. Driesse, "pvlib python: 2023 project update," J Open Source Soft, vol. 8, no. 92, p. 5994, 2023, doi: 10.21105/joss.05994.
- National Renewable Energy Laboratory, "System Advisor Model (SAM) Version 2023.12.17."
- M. Mikofski, B. Meyers, and C. Chaudhari, "PVMismatch Project: https://github.com/SunPower/PVMismatch," 2018, SunPower Corporation, Richmond, CA.
- W. De Soto et al., "Improvement and validation of a model for photovoltaic array performance", Solar Energy, vol 80, pp. 78-88, 2006

42nd European Photovoltaic Solar Energy Conference and Exhibition

This presentation was selected by the Sc. Committee of the EU PVSEC 2025 for submission of a full paper to one of the EU PVSEC's collaborating peer-reviewed journals.

STANDARDIZED ASSESSMENT OF PV ARRAY SIMULATORS

Theo Zwahlen[1], David Joss[1], Christian Messner[2], Christof Bucher[1], Luciano Borgna[1], Michael Gafert[2], Steffen Eyhorn[3] and Roland Bründlinger[2]
[1] Laboratory for Photovoltaic Systems (PV-Lab) - Bern University of Applied Sciences (BFH), Jlcoweg 1, 3400 Burgdorf, Switzerland
[2]AIT – Austrian Institute of Technology GmbH, Giefinggasse 2, 1210 Vienna, Austria
[3] Fraunhofer Institute for Solar Energy Systems ISE, Heidenhofstr. 2, 79110 Freiburg, Germany
[1]christof.bucher@bfh.ch

ABSTRACT: PV array simulators are used for testing PV and PV battery inverters. A test procedure has been developed to evaluate these simulators, ensuring realistic PV module and array behavior. It provides laboratories with uniform test conditions and helps developers optimise their devices. The proposed procedure includes three phenomenological tests with random PV inverters and three potentially standardisable tests examining properties like accuracy and frequency response.
Keywords: PV array simulator assessment / solar array simulator evaluation / photovoltaic inverter testing / I–V curve emulation / SAS quality

1 INTRODUCTION

Correct functionality of photovoltaic inverters is vital for renewable energy expansion, requiring extensive testing. Standards such as EN50530 [1], the BVES/BSW Efficiency Guideline [2], and various grid codes define inverter testing. Beyond grid-connection standards [3–5], precise characterisation of grid-support functions will become increasingly important [6].

Testing laboratories need AC grid simulators and PV array simulators, which must accurately mimic grid behaviour and PV module strings, including inverter-induced DC ripple [7,8]. A review in [9] outlines PV array simulator architectures and their I-V reproduction characteristics. While IEC provides a specification for DC source performance [10], no guideline exists for testing the simulators themselves, and current requirements remain vague. Literature shows only one prior publication on PV array simulator assessment [11], proposing tests for steady-state and dynamic performance under load changes and irradiance fluctuations.

Recent tests at AIT revealed that some advanced simulators produce excessive DC ripple or oscillations. These oscillations led to MPPT efficiency values above 100%. To address such issues, BFH and AIT developed a dedicated test procedure for PV array simulator evaluation, later joined by Fraunhofer ISE for additional expertise. The full work presents the procedure and anonymised results from completed assessments.

2 TEST METHOD AND BACKGROUND

Most modern PV array simulators emulate I-V curves using digital switching power supplies without linear output stages. Their small-signal behaviour depends on power electronics and control software. Compared to real PV modules, the tested simulators show slower dynamics, especially with inverters: current output lags voltage changes, delaying PV dynamics and impairing MPPT accuracy. This often causes oscillations between simulator and inverter.

Existing criteria are necessary but insufficient for realistic inverter operation, particularly in grid-support mode. Individual tests are required to determine simulator–inverter compatibility. The authors propose two categories Each category includes three tests, summarised in Table I (Phenomenological Tests) and Table II (Standard Tests).

2.1 Phenomenological tests

The tests offer limited repeatability but can quickly reveal issues when simulators are used with PV inverters. However, the results depend strongly on the chosen inverter, and since no pass–fail criteria are defined, standardisation remains difficult.

Table I. Phenomenological Tests

Category	Cat. 1: Phenomenological Tests		
Test No	Phen 1	Phen 2	Phen 3
Test Name	I-V Curve Stability	Current Ripple	MPPT Efficiency Difference
Short description	Slow I-V curve tracing. Plotting the I-V curve.	Connected to a PV inverter. Measurement of current ripple.	Comparison of array simulator internal measurement with external measurement.
Pass-Fail criterion (remarks)	n. a. (no oscillations should be seen)	n. a. (current ripple should be small)	n. a. (difference should be small)

2.2 Standard tests

In these tests, the array simulator is operated under defined conditions and without a PV inverter. Pass-fail criteria are defined for these tests.

Table II. Standard Tests

Category	Cat. 2: Standard Tests		
Test No	Std 1	Std 2	Std 3
Test Name	MPP Accuracy and Drift	Frequency Response	Irradiance Variation
Short description	Manual MPP tracing after startup and after 10 minutes. Power measurement.	Superimpose an AC signal at a given DC operating point. Measure phase shift.	Measure difference between setpoint (ramp) and actual value (step function).
Pass-Fail criterion (remarks)	MPP accuracy be below 1 %	Frequency shift shall be below 30° from 0 Hz to 150 Hz	RMSE shall be below 1 %

3 TEST SETUP

Four setups were used, with largely identical measurement equipment. For accuracy-focused tests (Phen 3, Std 3), a high-precision power analyser records voltage, current, and power. If it provides raw data >50 kHz, these values can support further analysis. Otherwise, an oscilloscope with appropriate probes must be added.

3.1 Setup 1:

The PV array simulator is loaded with a DC power supply able to sink power across the full operating range and perform simple functions (e.g., ramps) (***Figure 1***).

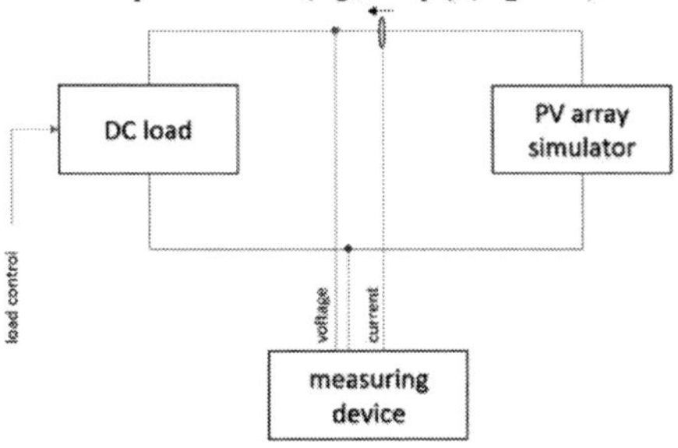

Figure 1. Test Setup 1: PV array simulator loaded with a bidirectional DC power supply.

3.2 Setup 2:

The simulator is tested with at least two different PV inverters. Using the same reference inverters across assessments ensures comparability (***Figure 2***).

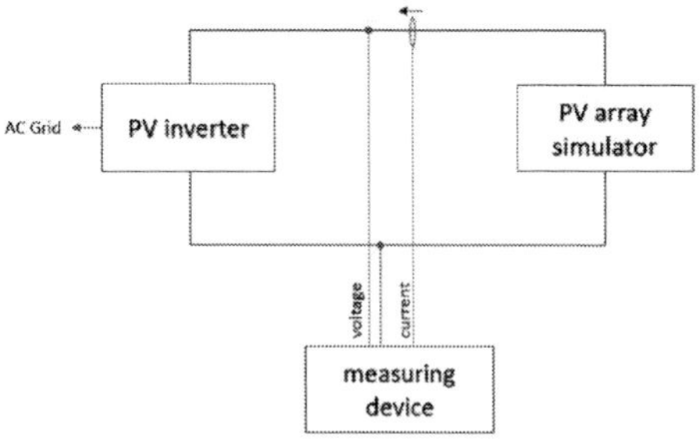

Figure 2. Test Setup 2: PV array simulator loaded with a common PV inverter.

3.3 Setup 3:

As in Setup 1, but with an added AC power supply to apply dynamic signals. A single device may provide both DC load and AC modulation if capable (***Figure 3***).

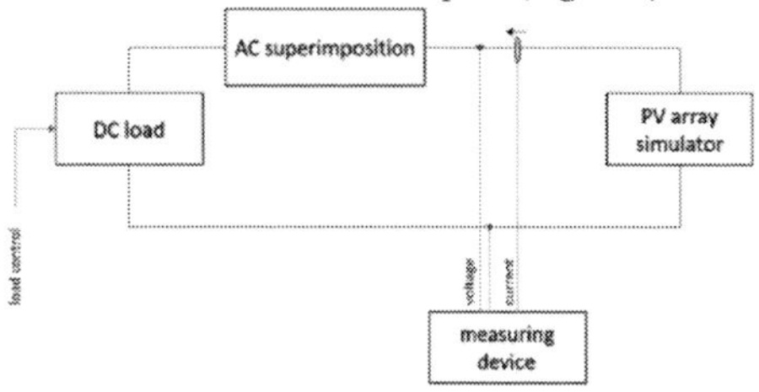

Figure 3. Test Setup 3: PV array simulator loaded with a bidirectional DC power supply and an additional AC source to superimpose an alternating voltage.

3.4 Setup 4:

Simplest configuration, with the simulator short-circuited to observe irradiance variation effects via short-circuit current. Voltage measurement is unnecessary (***Figure 4***).

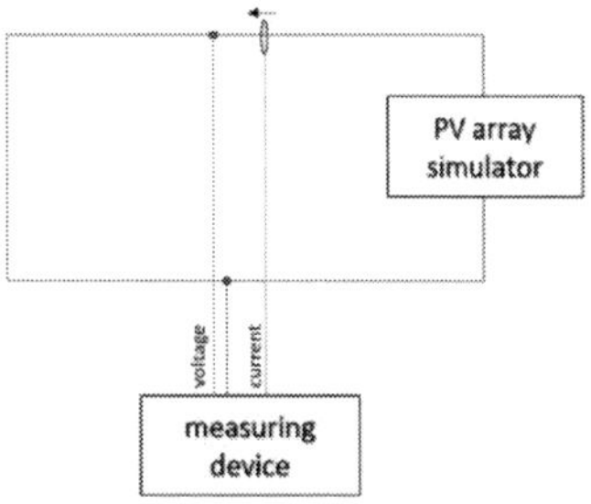

Figure 4. Fig. 4. Test Setup 4: PV array simulator with short-circuited output

4 OPERATING POINTS

For tests with a static I-V curve, the PV array simulator is parametrised as described here. Characterisation follows EN50530 with crystalline silicon (cSi) cells [1]. Four operating points (OP) are defined (Table III) for simulators up to 1500 V output. OP1 represents a single PV module, while OP2–OP4 cover a broader output range.

10.4229/EUPVSEC2025/4DO.1.6

Table III. Operating point parameters for tests with static I-V curve

Operating point (OP)	V_{MPP} [V]	I_{MPP} [A]
1	40	15
2	100	25
3	500	20
4	1000	15

To adapt for simulators with different ratings, OP1 remains fixed, while OP2–OP4 use V_{MPP} values scaled relative to the simulator's maximum output voltage $V_{PVAS,MAXV}$. Operating currents can either follow the absolute values in Table III or be scaled from relative power as in Table IV.

Table IV. Operating point parameters for tests with static I-V curve, relative to the output specifications of the PV array simulator under test

Operating point (OP)	VMPP	PMPP
2	7 % of $V_{PVAS,MAX}$	10 % of $P_{PVAS,MAX}$
3	33 % of $V_{PVAS,MAX}$	40 % of $P_{PVAS,MAX}$
4	66 % of $V_{PVAS,MAX}$	60 % of $P_{PVAS,MAX}$

4.1 PV inverters used in Setup 2

In Setup 2, at least two PV inverters serve as reference devices. Table V lists those used in the Results and Discussion. Since the aim is not to evaluate inverter quality, the devices are not anonymised.

Table V. PV inverter used in Test Setup 2

Designation	Manufacturer	Model name
SMA	SMA Solar Technology AG	STP6.0-3AV-40
Huawei	Huawei Digital Power Technologies Co., Ltd.	SUN2000-10KTL-M1

5 DEVICE UNDER TEST (DUT)

The proposed test procedure was developed alongside PV array simulator evaluations. Most devices were tested at BFH, with some at AIT.

A distinction is made between bidirectional and unidirectional simulators. Unless noted, both types use nonlinear switched-mode power supplies.

In some tests, a real PV system was also used as reference.

At this stage PV array simulators are referred anonymously to protect manufacturer interests. The results aim to support overall progress, not critique specific devices.

6 PHENOMENOLOGICAL TESTS

Test laboratories often encounter unexpected phenomena, which may arise from the DUT or its interaction with lab infrastructure. For PV array simulators, some phenomena can be induced with simple tests. These tests have no strict pass-fail criteria but help verify the accuracy of subsequent evaluations.

6.1 Phen 1: I-V Curve Instability

PV array simulators can exhibit instabilities at certain I-V curve operating points, dependent on the load. The proposed test uses Setup 1: the simulator operates at each operating point, while the load is swept from 0 V to U_{OC} in 5 seconds, then back to 0 V in 5 seconds. This slow, semi-static sweep avoids intentionally triggering oscillations or secondary distortions. ***Figure 5*** shows expected data without instabilities, calculated in MATLAB from the EN50530 I-V model for OP3 settings.

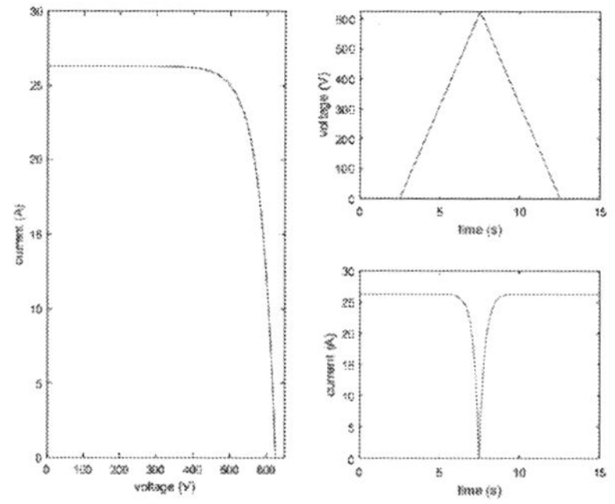

Figure 5. Theoretical simulation result of an I-V curve instability test without any instabilities. Left: X-Y plot corresponding to the I-V curve. Right: time series of voltage (top in blue) and current (bottom in orange). The calculation follows an I-V model according to EN50530.

6.2 Phen 2: Current Ripple

Some PV array simulators generate high current ripple, which can affect inverter MPPT and efficiency measurements. Ripple magnitude depends on load and varies between inverters. ***Figure 6*** shows measured current during an EN50530 MPP tracking test: the red trace is raw current (100 kHz), the green trace is a 10 ms moving average.

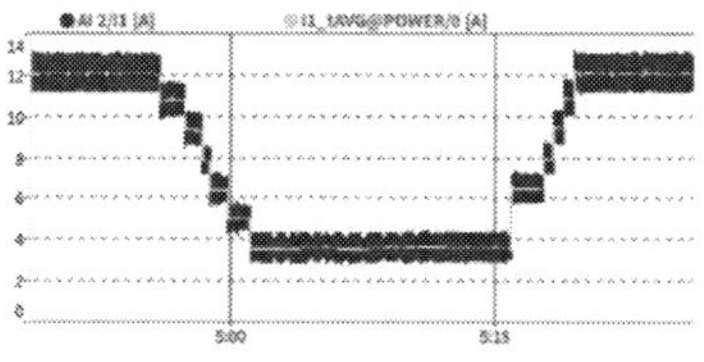

Figure 6. Part of an MPP tracking efficiency measurement with raw current values (red) and averaged current values (green). Screenshot is taken from Dewetron power analyser.

10.4229/EUPVSEC2025/4DO.1.6

Ripple can be reduced with a series inductance, though this affects other behaviours, such as dynamics.

Phen 2 compares current ripple across simulators using a partly dynamic MPP tracking test with at least two inverters. The test follows the last line of Table B.3 in EN50530 [1] with parameters in

Table *VI*. High-frequency ripple (>20 kHz) from inverter switching is filtered using a 10 kHz, fourth-order

n [Number]	10
Slope [W/m2/s]	1000
Ramp UP [s] t1	7
Dwell time[s] t2	10
Ramp DN [s] t3	7
Dwell time [s] t4	10
Duration [s]	640

low-pass filter.

Table VI. Parameters of the irradiance sequence part according to EN50530 [1]

n [Number]	10
Slope [W/m²/s]	1000
Ramp UP [s] t_1	7
Dwell time[s] t_2	10
Ramp DN [s] t_3	7
Dwell time [s] t_4	10
Duration [s]	640

Ripple is quantified by peak-to-peak values over 200 ms of the filtered signal, for both high and low static current levels (3.8 A and 12 A, ***Figure*** *7*), expressed relative to the current setpoint.

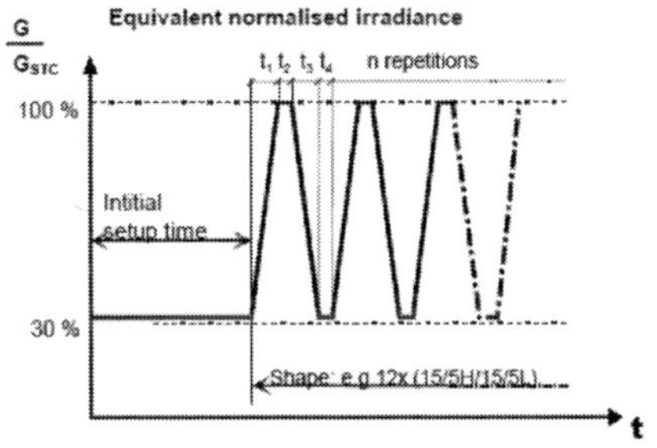

Figure 7. Test sequence with a 30 % - 100 % ramp according to EN50530 [1]

6.3 Phen 3: MPPT Efficiency Difference

This test evaluates whether measured MPPT efficiency of an inverter varies with different PV array simulators.

The evaluation is not discussed further in this short report.

7 STANDARD TESTS

While phenomenological tests provide a general overview, standard tests offer detailed, reproducible assessment of PV array simulators. They highlight deviations from real PV module behaviour and suitability for inverter testing. Tests can be used with pass/fail criteria or to compare simulators.

7.1 Std 1: MPP Accuracy and Drift

The accuracy drift provides information on the operational accuracy of the source and the extent to which it varies due to heating during operation. A detailed discussion of the measurement or the results is not included in this short report.

7.2 Std 2: Frequency Response

PV inverters can impose oscillations or rapidly changing loads on PV array simulators, e.g., 100 Hz ripple from single-phase inverters [1,3] or minor fluctuations from three-phase inverters [10].

To evaluate simulator response, Test Setup 3 is used at all operating points. The simulator is loaded at MPP with a DC load, while an AC signal (±2% V_{MPP}) is superimposed. The AC frequency is swept 0–1000 Hz, and the phase shift between voltage and current is measured. Ideally, voltage increases cause current decreases, giving a 180° phase shift.

Figure 8 shows a theoretical current response (amplitude ±3% for clarity). The pass criterion is 180° ± 30° phase shift up to at least 150 Hz. This accounts for typical inverter-induced loading and allows some lab measurements despite minor deviations. Many commercial PV array simulators fail this conservative requirement.

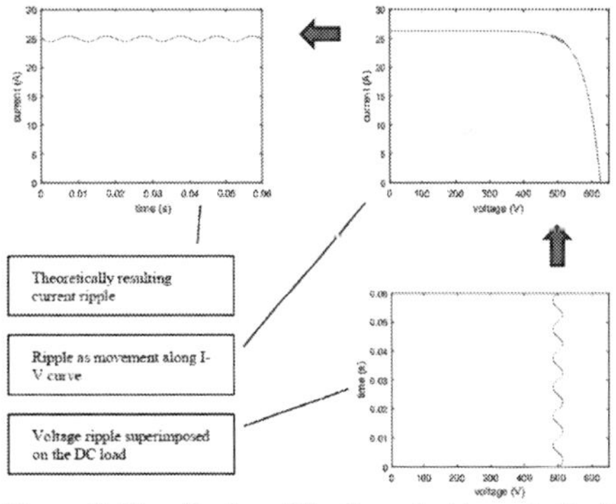

Figure 8. Visualization of the theoretical impact of a 100 Hz voltage ripple on the current, generated by simulation.

7.3 Std 3: Irradiance Variation

PV array simulators are often required to follow irradiance ramps, e.g., for dynamic MPP tracking tests (EN50530). Most simulators adjust power in discrete steps rather than continuously. A basic evaluation measures the minimum step interval, while a detailed assessment calculates the RMSE between the expected continuous ramp and the simulator's step response.

Since irradiance changes directly affect short-circuit current, the simulator is tested with the output short-circuited (Setup 4), and performance is assessed from the measured current.

8 RESULTS AND DISCUSSION

This chapter presents results from an exemplary test series with several PV array simulators. The first part highlights phenomenological test outcomes, showing varying simulator behaviour and unexpected responses. The second part covers standardized tests, illustrating performance ranges.

10.4229/EUPVSEC2025/4DO.1.6

8.1 Phen 1: I-V Curve Stability

Several simulators showed unstable I-V behaviour. ***Figure 9*** displays I-V curves of four devices across all operating points. Three devices are classified as unstable; PVAS2 shows minor oscillations only at the lowest voltage. Oscillation magnitude and occurrence vary between simulators and tend to increase at lower voltages. For OP4, a second series load ensured full voltage coverage, which may affect stability.

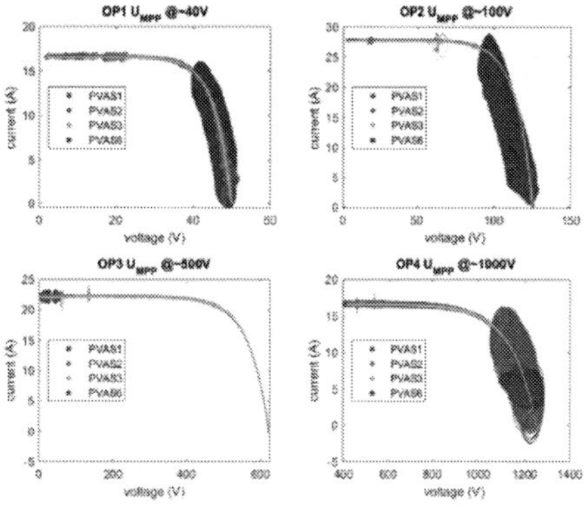

Figure 9. Measured I-V curves of four PV array simulators at all four operating points

Figure 10 illustrates the impact on a real inverter: PV current of an SMA inverter (Table V) supplied by PVAS1 shows clear oscillations at ~13 s and ~23 s during startup.

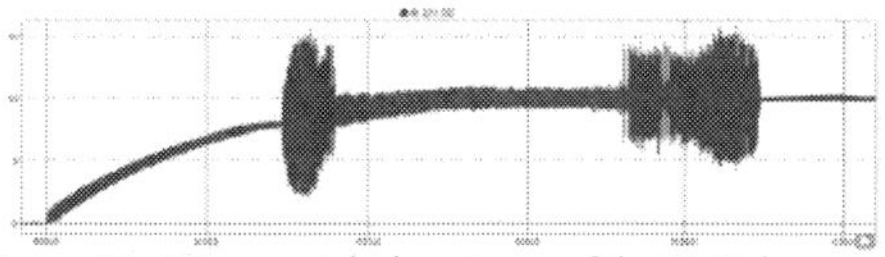

Figure 10. PV current during startup of the SMA inverter supplied by PVAS1 (Dewetron screenshot).

8.2 Phen 2: Current Ripple

Current ripple was assessed for PVAS1–PVAS3. **Figure *11*** shows a segment of measured and filtered currents, with peak-to-peak values and a 4-second moving average as a reference during steady irradiance.

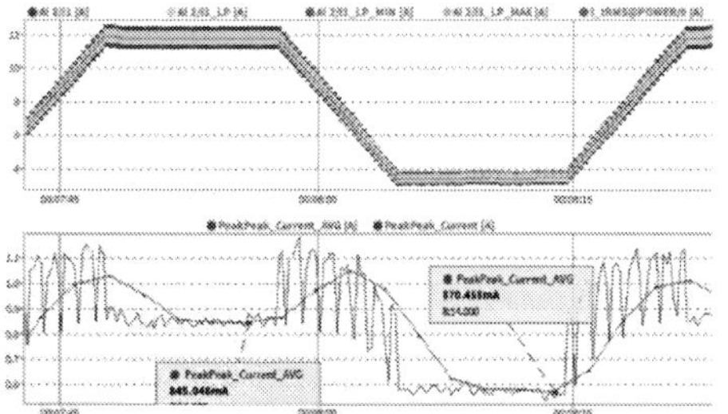

Figure 11. Current waveform including filtered signal (top) and resulting peak-to-peak current (bottom) from the ripple test. (Dewetron screenshot)

Figure *12* presents ripple normalized to average current. Results show the connected inverter strongly influences ripple: all simulators exhibit higher ripple with the SMA inverter. The method is consistent, as lower ripple with one inverter correlates with lower ripple on another.

Even at 3.5 A, ripple above 20% is excessive; the best simulator reached ~16% at worst. Ripple remains significant at other operating points or with the second inverter, though under higher power conditions, two simulators achieved <5% ripple.

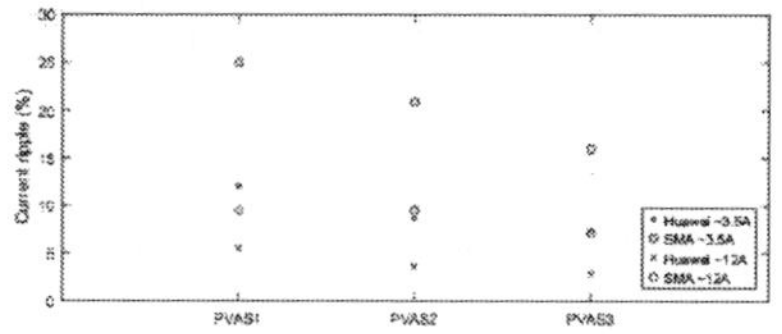

Figure 12. Comparison of current ripple normalized to the average current at the respective power level.

8.3 Std 2: Frequency Response

Frequency response was tested for multiple PV array simulators. Some could be tested at all operating points (OP1–OP4), while others were limited, e.g., PVAS7 and PVAS8 lack OP4 data, and PVAS4 was tested at 800 V instead of 1000 VMPP due to its voltage limit.

Figure *13* shows measured phase shifts for all devices, compared with real PV modules (RealPV) at OP1–OP3. Phase response varies significantly. Many simulators show considerable phase shift at low frequencies, especially at higher voltages (OP3–OP4).

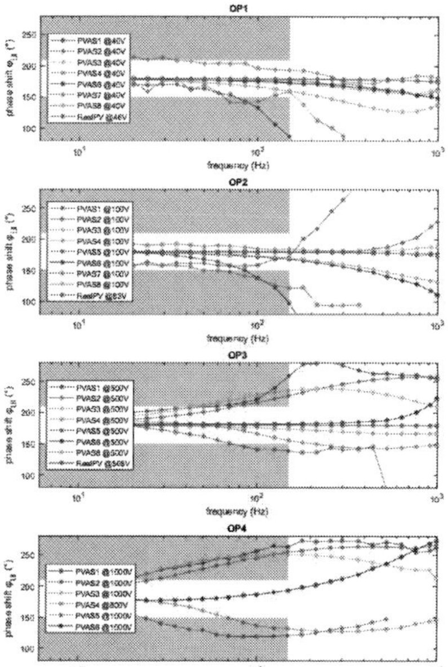

Figure 13. Phase shift across frequency for all measured PV array simulators

8.4 Std 3: Irradiance Variation

The following plot shows the dynamics of each DUT (***Figure 14***).

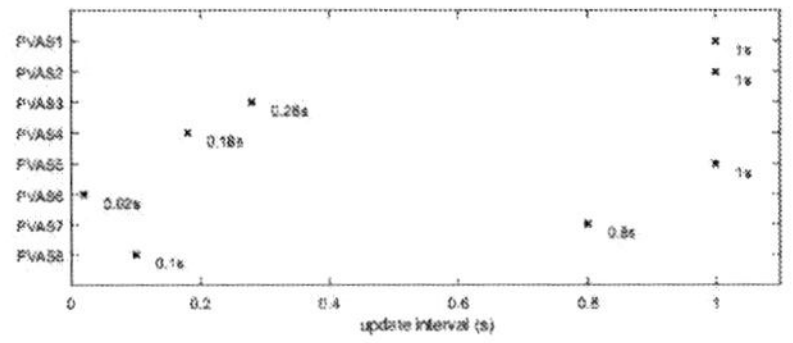

Figure 14. Minimum I-V curve update interval measured for PVAS1 to PVAS8

Instead of the intended ramp, a 100–500 W/m² MPPT efficiency profile (5 s ramp, 100 W/m²/s) was used, with current normalized to account for differing I-V characteristics. ***Figure 15*** shows measured currents, with the red trace as the reference ramp.

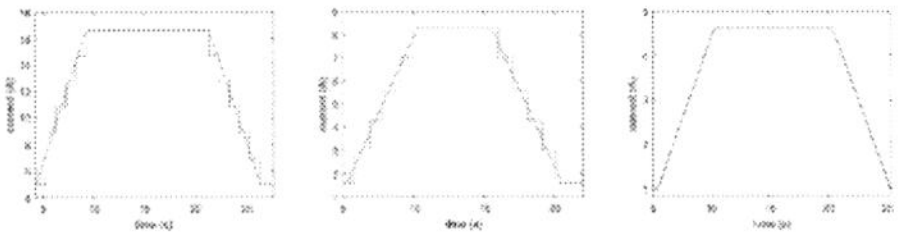

Figure 15. Current profiles of PVAS1 (left), PVAS2 (middle), PVAS8 (right) with reference ramp (red).

Figure *16* presents current errors and RMSE over each ramp. Upward ramps show decreasing error, downward ramps increasing error, indicating deviations from the intended slope.

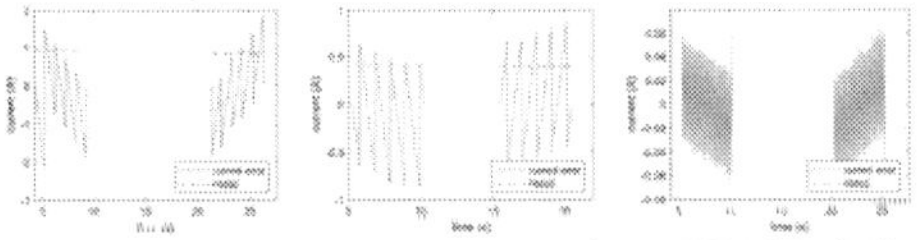

Figure 16. Current error measured on PVAS1 (left), PVAS2 (middle), and PVAS8 (right), including the respective calculated RMSE value.

Table VII reports normalized RMSE for ramp-up and ramp down. PVAS1 and PVAS2 have similar errors (1 s transition), while PVAS8 has lower RMSE due to a 100 ms transition set by external SCPI commands.

Table VII. Relative RMSE (as a percentage of the current at maximum irradiance) for three simulators during ramp-up and ramp-down.

	PVAS1	**PVAS2**	**PVAS8**
Relative RMSE during ramp-up	5.55 %	4.96 %	0.51%
Relative RMSE during ramp-down	5.11 %	4.81 %	0.54%

9 CONCLUSION

The full work presents a test procedure for evaluating PV array simulators, with results from varying numbers of devices from different manufacturers. Not all tests include every simulator, limiting generalisability.

The results reveal substantial differences in output characteristics, affecting inverter tests. For example, MPPT efficiency (Phen 3) varies between simulators, questioning its reliability as a comparative metric. I-V curve instabilities are particularly critical, especially under power curtailment where voltage exceeds MPP, a region prone to oscillations, potentially invalidating tests.

The proposed tests provide a comprehensive assessment framework, but some behaviours remain unaddressed, such as synchronised control of multiple simulator outputs. Many simulators offer limited multi-channel support, with observable time delays. Future updates could include a dedicated multi-channel synchronisation test.

ACKNOWLEDGMENTS

Many of the measurement data originate from PV array simulators that were provided by distributors or manufacturers for testing purposes. Thank goes out to them for their cooperation.

FUNDING

This research received no external funding.

CONFLICTS OF INTEREST

BFH has a paid consulting agreement with a manufacturer aimed at improving their PV array simulator. However, the data used in this study was collected prior to this collaboration and is therefore not considered a conflict of interest. The other authors have nothing to disclose

DATA AVAILABILITY STATEMENT

For reasons of manufacturer confidentiality, the data associated with this article cannot be shared.

AUTHOR CONTRIBUTION STATEMENT

Conceptualization, Theo Zwahlen, Luciano Borgna, David Joss and Christof Bucher.; Methodology, Theo Zwahlen, Luciano Borgna, David Joss and Christof Bucher.; Validation, Christian Messner, Steffen Eyhorn and Michael Gafert.; Data Curation, Theo Zwahlen and Michael Gafert.; Writing – Original Draft Preparation, Theo Zwahlen.; Writing – Review & Editing, Theo Zwahlen, David Joss, Christof Bucher, Christian Messner, Michael Gafert and Steffen Eyhorn.; Visualization, Theo Zwahlen, David Joss.; Supervision, Christof Bucher and Roland Bründlinger.; Project Administration, Theo Zwahlen and David Joss

REFERENCES

[1] EN 50530:2010, Overall efficiency of grid connected photovoltaic inverters, (2010).

[2] BVES Bundesverband Energiespeicher Systeme, BSW-solar Bundesverband Solarwirtschaft, Efficiency guideline for PV storage systems, (n.d.). https://solar.htw-berlin.de/wp-content/uploads/Efficiency-guideline-for-PV-storage-systems-2.0.pdf (accessed June 30, 2025).

[3] SN EN 50549-1:2019(E) - DV-31964/1 - Electrosuisse, (n.d.). https://shop.electrosuisse.ch/de/SN-EN-50549-1_2019_E_-48355.html (accessed July 16, 2025).

[4] SN EN 50549-2:2019+AC:2019(D) - DV-34426/1 - Electrosuisse, (n.d.). https://shop.electrosuisse.ch/de/SNEN-50549-

2_2019_AC_2019_D_-54247.html (accessed July 16, 2025).
[5] SN EN 50549-10:2022(E) - DV-45035/1 - Electrosuisse, (n.d.). https://shop.electrosuisse.ch/de/SN-EN-50549-10_2022_E_-397612.html (accessed July 16, 2025).
[6] TC 82, Project: IEC 63409-6 ED1, IEC (International Electrotechnical Commission) (n.d.). https://www.iec.ch/dyn/www/f?p=103:38:601780107873093::::FSP_ORG_ID,FSP_APEX_PAGE,FSP_PROJECT_ID:1276,23,105972 (accessed July 16, 2025).
[7] R. Ayop, C.W. Tan, A comprehensive review on photovoltaic emulator, Renewable and Sustainable Energy Reviews 80 (2017) 430–452. https://doi.org/10.1016/j.rser.2017.05.217.
[8] Spitzenberger & Spies, Necessity for high speed PV Simulators, n.d. www.spitzenberger.de/weblink/1005 (accessed January 24, 2025).
[9] J.P. Ram, H. Manghani, D.S. Pillai, T.S. Babu, M. Miyatake, N. Rajasekar, Analysis on solar PV emulators: A review, Renewable and Sustainable Energy Reviews 81 (2018) 149–160. https://doi.org/10.1016/j.rser.2017.07.039.
[10] IEC TS 63106-2, Simulators used for testing of photovoltaic power conversion equipment - Recommendations - Part 2: DC power simulators, (2022).
[11] V.M. Cavalcante Junior, R.C. Neto, E.J. Barbosa, F. Bradaschia, M.C. Cavalcanti, G.M. de S. Azevedo, Evaluation of the Effectiveness of Solar Array Simulators in Reproducing the Characteristics of Photovoltaic Modules, Sustainability 16 (2024) 6932. https://doi.org/10.3390/su16166932.

Standardised Assessment of PV Array Simulators

EUPVSEC, 22.-26. September 2025, Bilbao

▸ Organisationseinheit oder Leistungsbereich

Background

- Maximum power point trackers (MPPT) are tested using solar array simulators (SAS).
- Other inverter functions (e.g. grid connection functions) can also be tested using SAS.
- Two types of simulators
  - Switching power supply
  - Linear power supply
- Advances in power electronics: linear power supplies are no longer necessary (at least according to manufacturers' claims)

But…

- … then why do we see such behaviour?

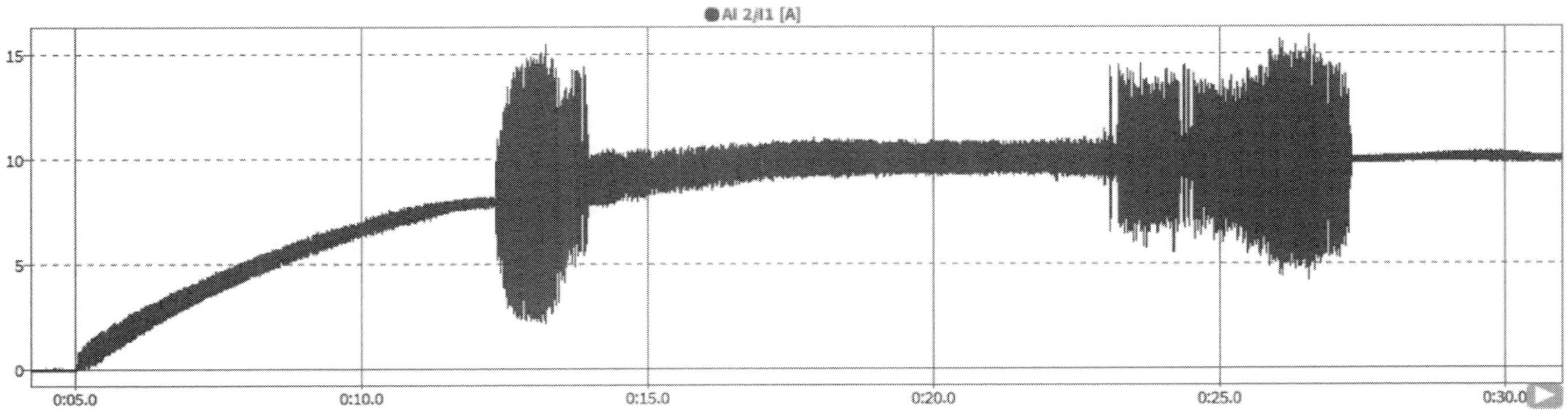

Array simulator DC current during inverter startup

But…

- … then why do we see such behaviour?

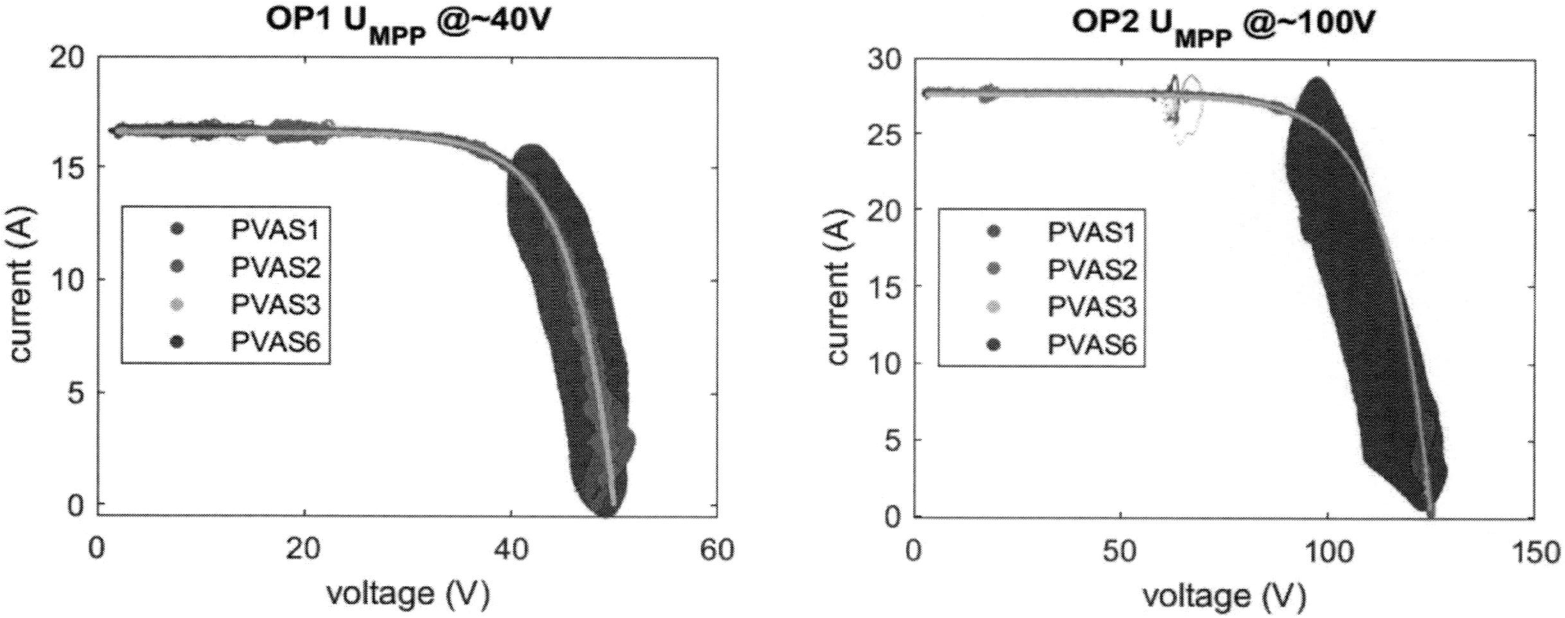

Berner Fachhochschule | Haute école spécialisée bernoise | Bern University of Applied Sciences

...and this?

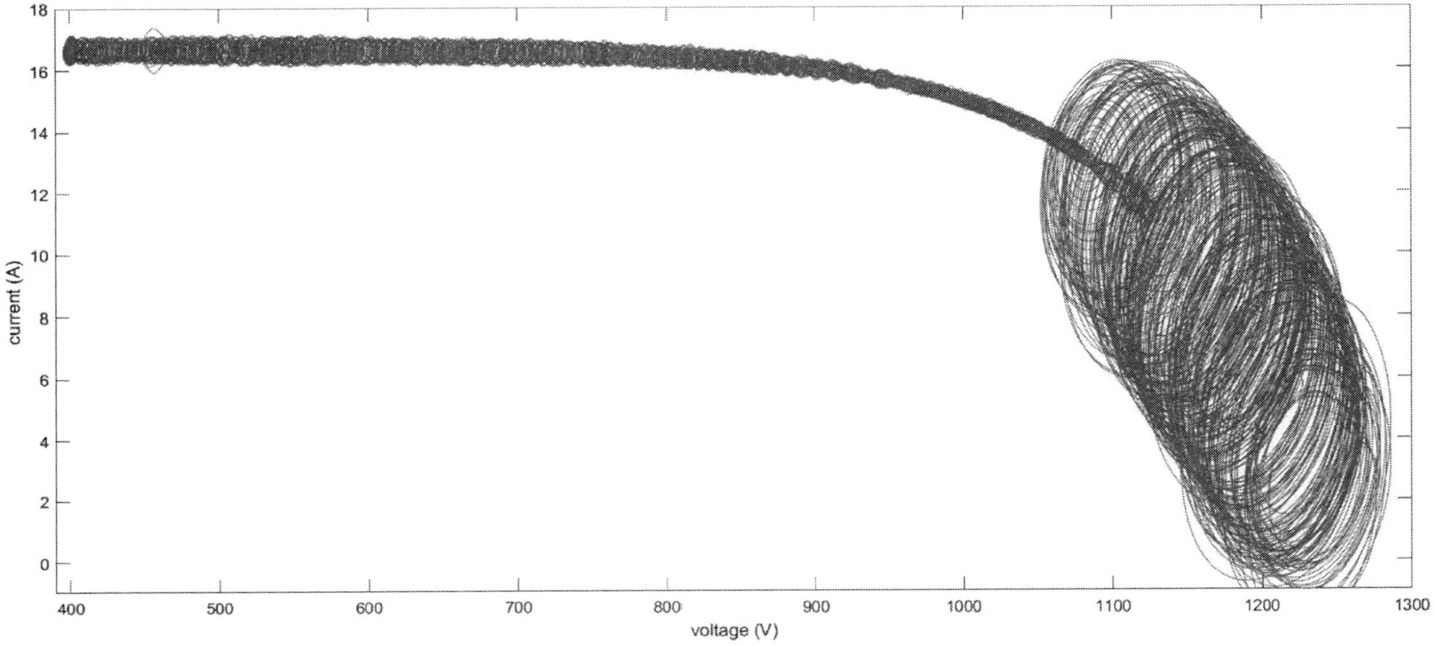

Berner Fachhochschule | Haute école spécialisée bernoise | Bern University of Applied Sciences

Initial situation PV laboratory

- Budget for procurement of approx. 150 kW DC array simulators
- 8 devices from 6 manufacturers delivered and tested
- Stability problems
  - Too slow (does not follow the IV curve during MPPT)
  - Unstable, especially at U > Umpp
- Consultation with manufacturers leads to minor improvements
- Contact with AIT and Fraunhofer ISE
- Joint development of test routines
- Procurement cancelled, in-house development of an array simulator with linear output stage

Development of 6 tests

Cat 1: Phenomenological tests

- Phen 1: I-V curve stability → "manual, visual curve inspection"
- Phen 2: Current ripple → connected to an inverter
- Phen 3: MPPT eff. difference → internal vs. external measurement

Cat 2: Standard tests

- Std 1: MPP accuracy and drift → MPPT after 10 minutes
- Std 2: Frequency response → DC with AC superposition
- Std 3: Irradiance variation → step functions

Test Setup Std 2: Frequency response

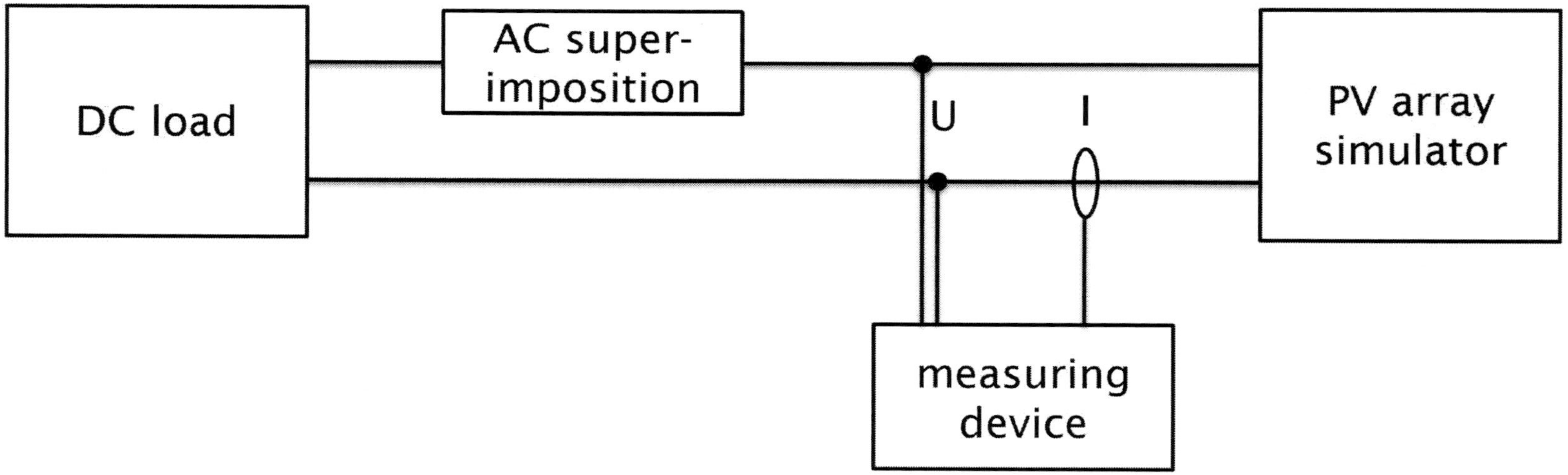

Std 2: Frequency Response

Expected behaviour

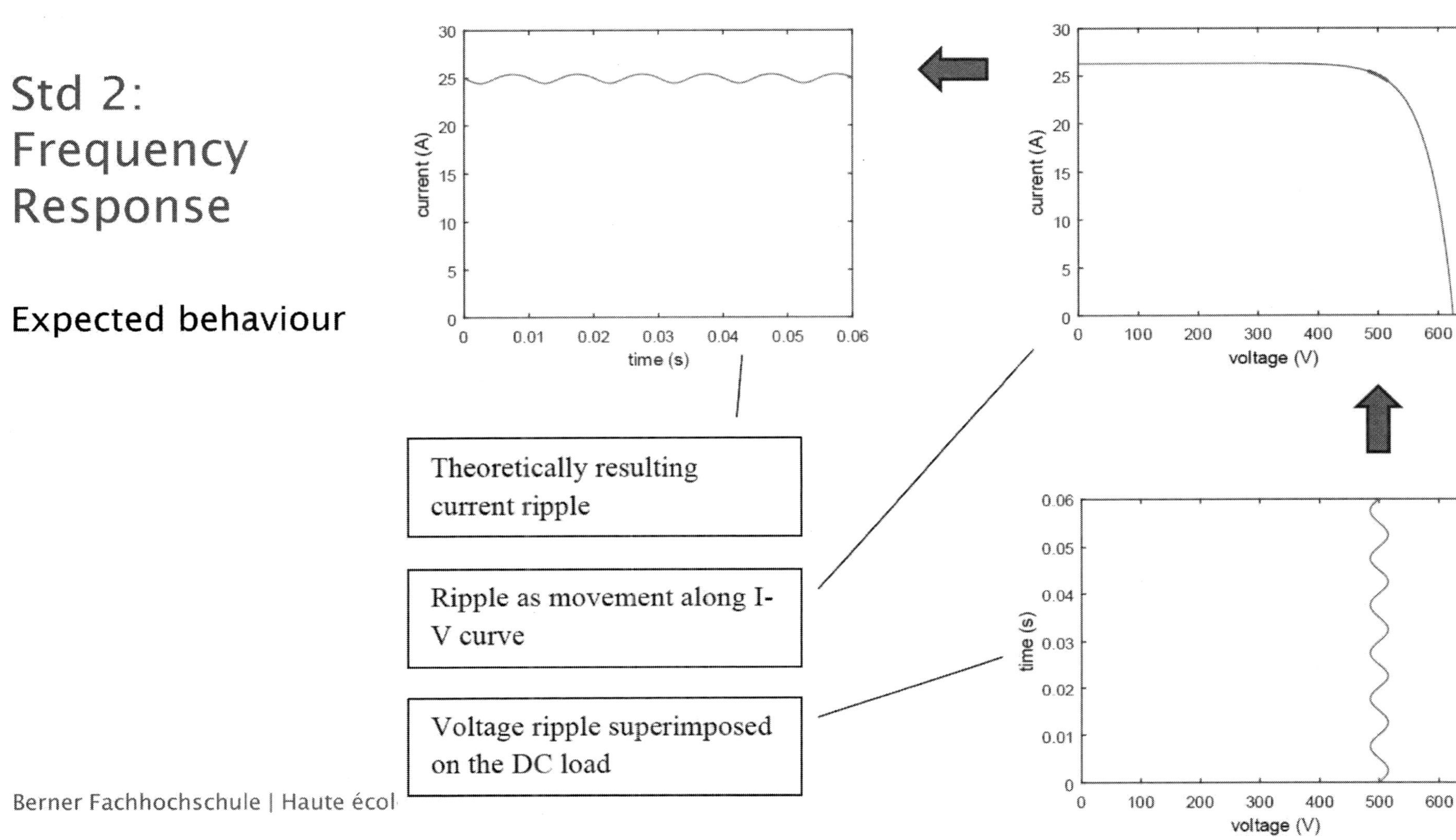

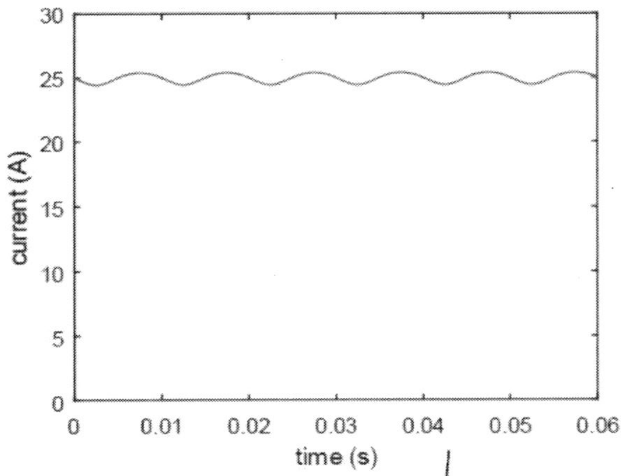

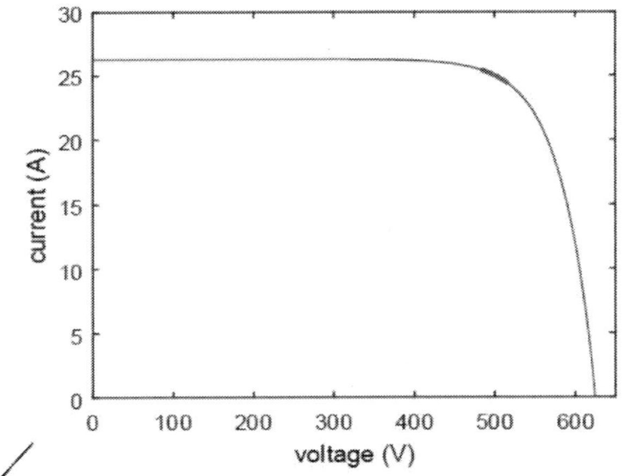

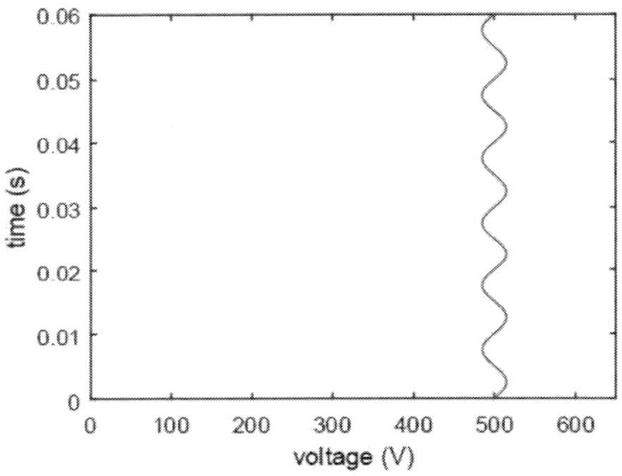

Theoretically resulting current ripple

Ripple as movement along I-V curve

Voltage ripple superimposed on the DC load

Berner Fachhochschule | Haute écol

But instead of this…

Expe

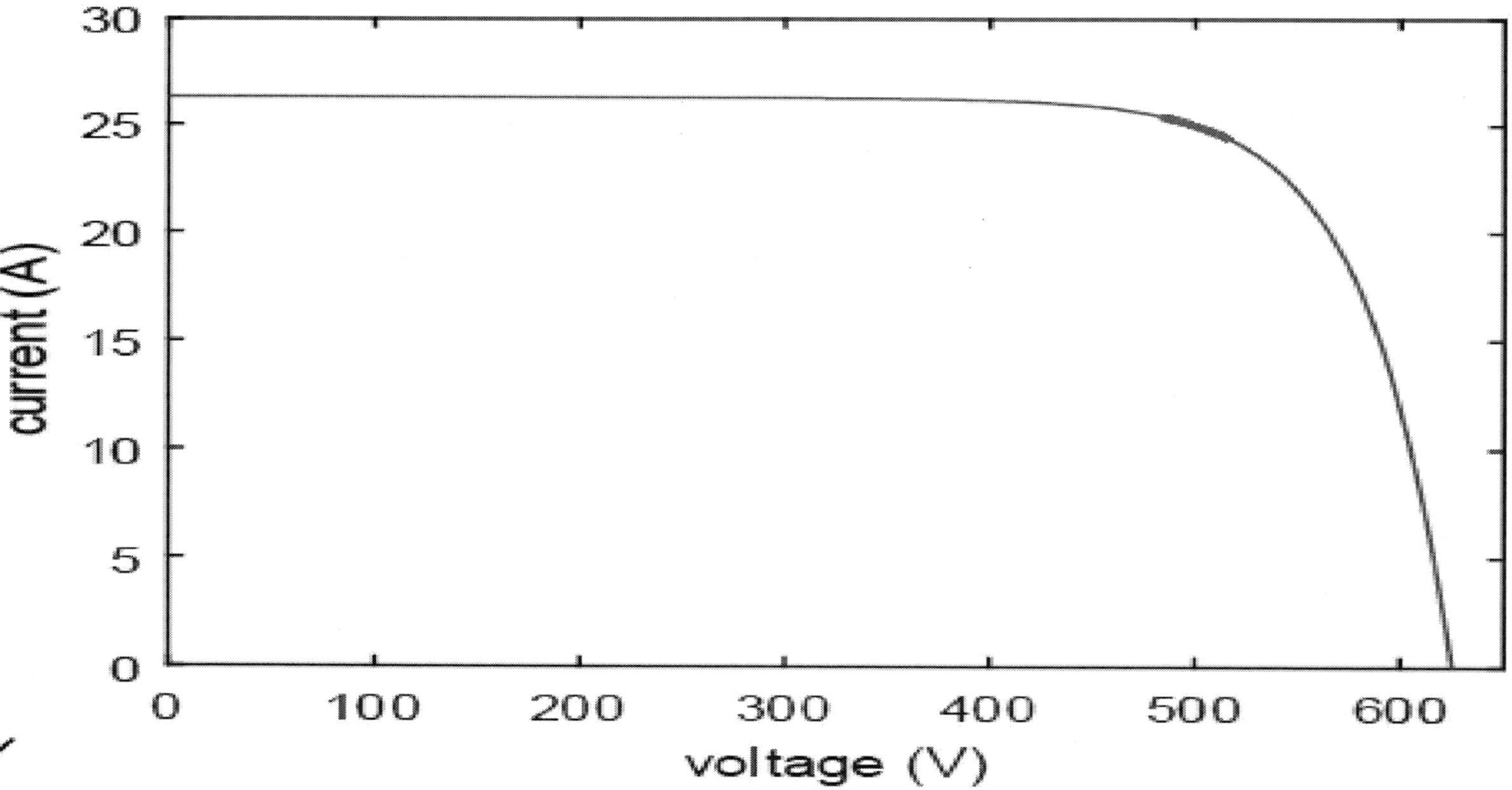

Berner

...we get this. (100 Hz AC ripple on MPP voltage)

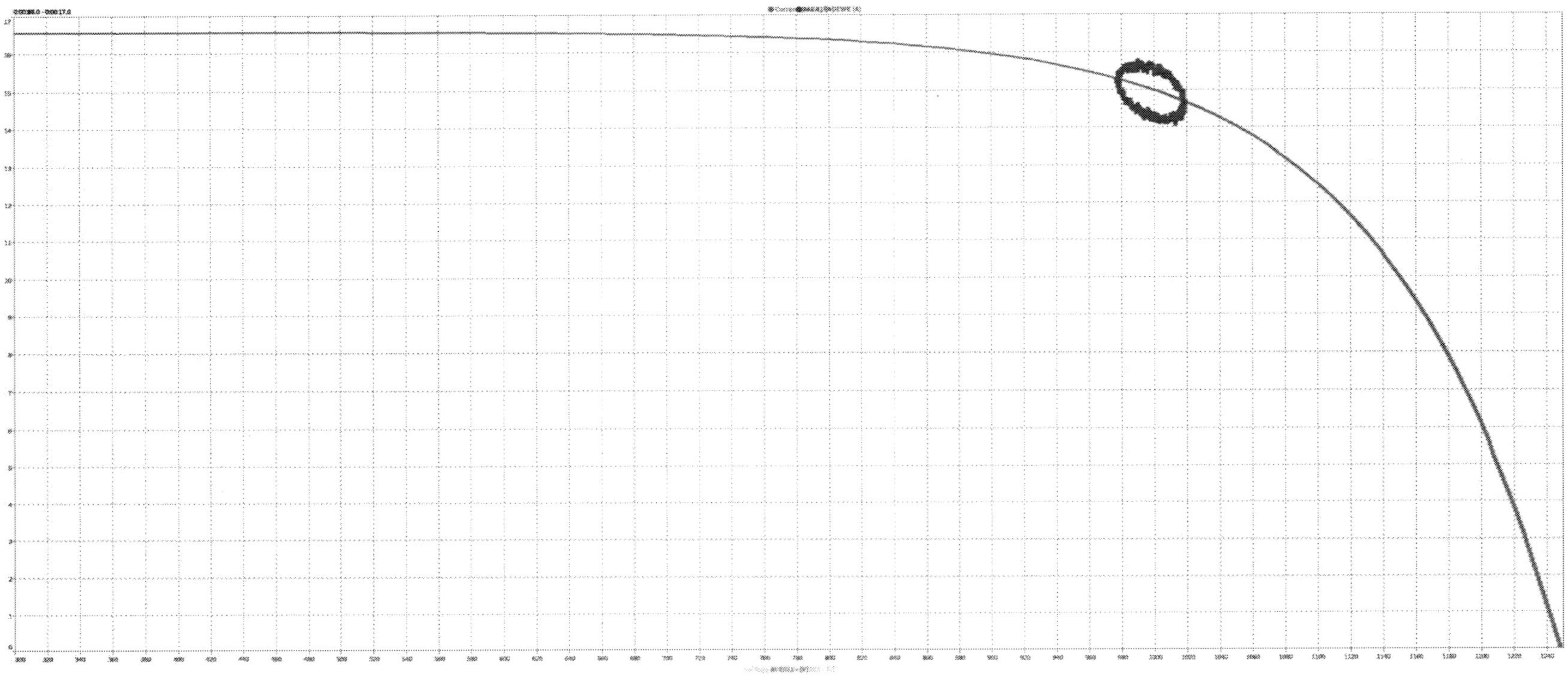

Proposed pass / fail criteria

Max. 30° phase shift

- At MPP
- Between 0 Hz and 150 Hz ripple
- Given an amplitude of 2%

All AS
Operating
Point 1: 40 V
phase shift φUI (°)
250
200
150
100
PVAS1 @40V
PVAS2 @40V
PVAS3 @40V
PVAS4 @40V
PVAS6 @40V
PVAS7 @40V
PVAS8 @40V
RealPV @46V
10^1
10^2
10^3
frequency (Hz)
Operating
Point 1: 1000 V
PVAS1 @1000V
PVAS2 @1000V
PVAS3 @1000V
PVAS4 @800V
PVAS5 @1000V
PVAS6 @1000V
Berner Fachhochschule | Hau

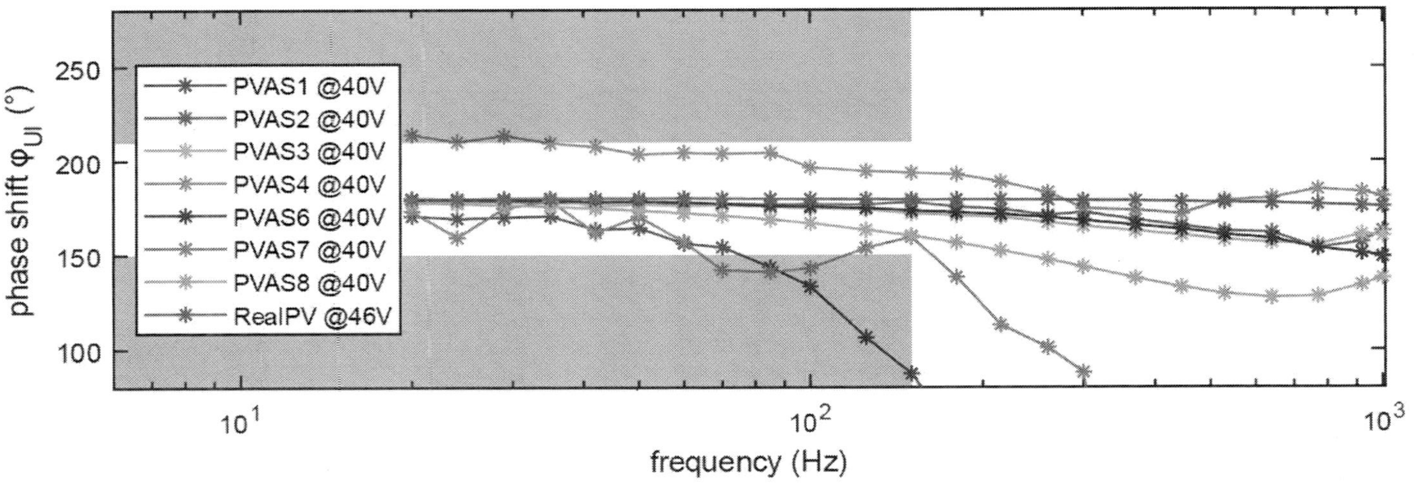

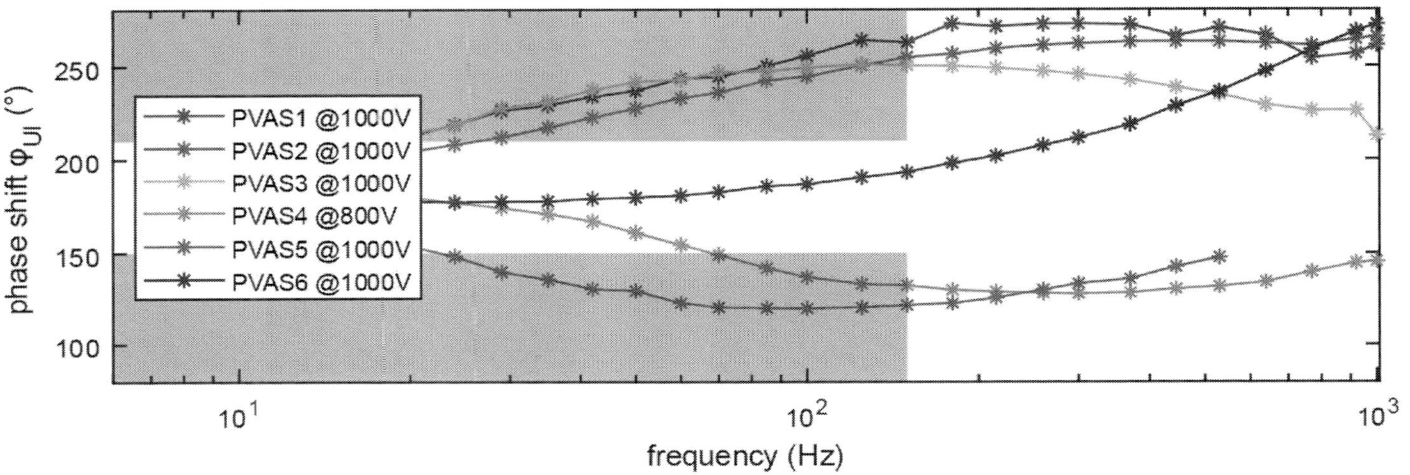

Best AS

Operating Point 1: 40 V

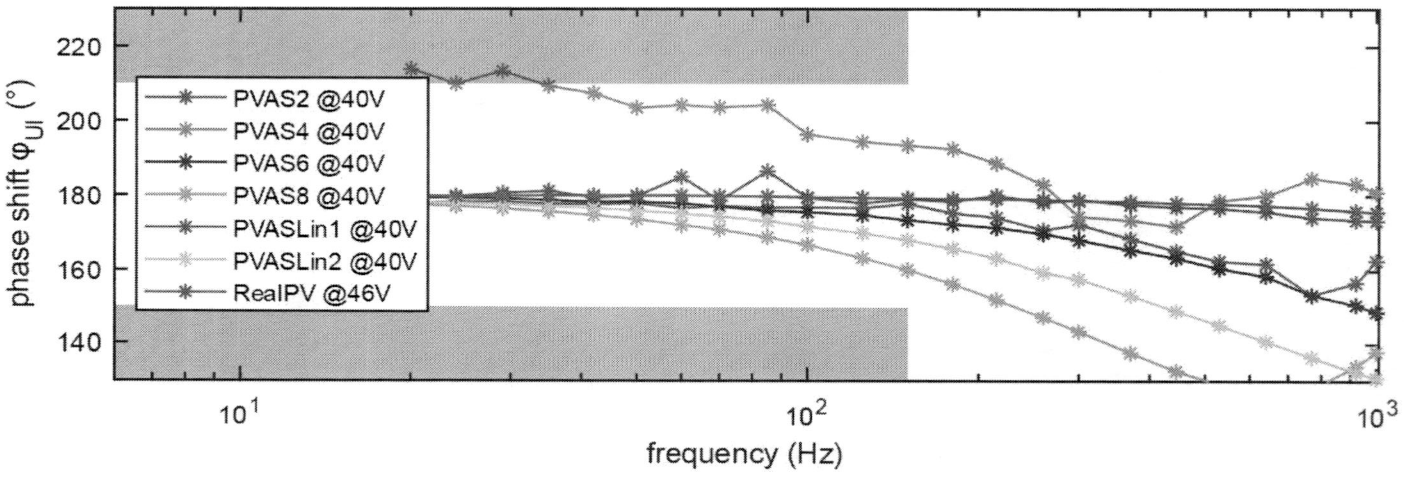

Operating Point 1: 1000 V

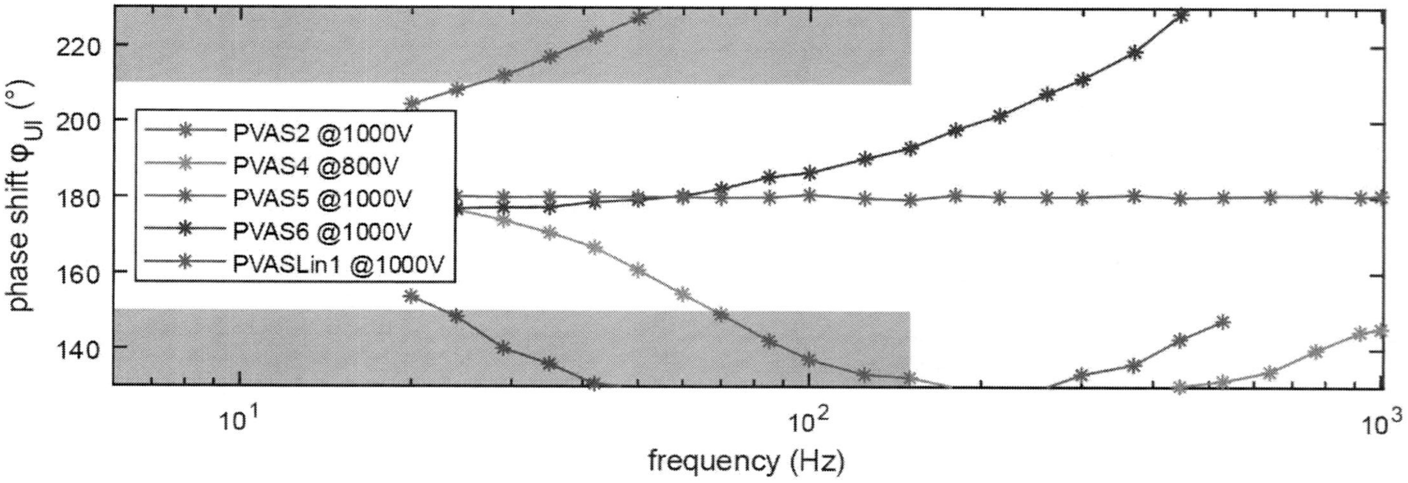

Conclusion

- It is difficult to equip laboratories with bidirectional, high quality DC sources.
- We have not found any array simulator on the market that meet all our criteria out of the box. Adjustments and trial and error setup are often needed.
- Manufacturers of DC sources to be used in Solar Array Simulator (SAS) application seem not to be aware of the challenges present in this field of application.
- Linear power amplifiers have almost completely disappeared from the mass market although their SAS simulation is still more promising.
- Thus, we think it is important to have a new set of standardized test sequences to compare SAS on an international level.

Prototype of Linear Solar Module Simulator of BFH

Berner Fachhochschule | Haute école spécialisée bernoise | Bern University of Applied Sciences

Berner Fachhochschule
Haute école spécialisée bernoise
Bern University of Applied Sciences

Thank you for your attention!

christof.bucher@bfh.ch

Table 1. Overview of the proposed tests for evaluating array simulators.

Category	**Cat. 1: Phenomenological Tests**			**Cat. 2: Standard Tests**		
Test No	Phen 1	Phen 2	Phen 3	Std 1	Std 2	Std 3
Test Name	I-V Curve Stability	Current Ripple	MPPT Efficiency Difference	MPP Accuracy and Drift	Frequency Response	Irradiance Variation
Short description	Slow I-V curve tracing. Plotting the I-V curve.	Connected to a PV inverter. Measurement of current ripple.	Comparison of array simulator internal measurement with external measurement.	Manual MPP tracing after startup and after 10 minutes. Power measurement.	Superimpose an AC signal at a given DC operating point. Measure phase shift.	Measure difference between setpoint (ramp) and actual value (step function).
Pass-Fail criterion (remarks)	n. a. (no oscillations should be seen)	n. a. (current ripple should be small)	n. a. (difference should be small)	MPP accuracy be below 1 %	Frequency shift shall be below 30° from 0 Hz to 150 Hz	RMSE shall be below 1 %

Table 2. Operating point parameters for tests with static I-V curve

Operating point (OP)	**V_{MPP} [V]**	**I_{MPP} [A]**
1	40	15
2	100	25
3	500	20
4	1000	15

Table 4. PV inverter used in Test Setup 2

Designation	Manufacturer	Model name
SMA	SMA Solar Technology AG	STP6.0-3AV-40
Huawei	Huawei Digital Power Technologies Co., Ltd.	SUN2000-10KTL-M1

Table 5. PV array simulators included in any of the tests.

No	Manufacturer	Model name	Device type	Tested by
α	Chroma	62180D	Bidirectional	BFH
β	Elektro-Automation (EA)	PSB11500	Bidirectional	BFH
γ	ET System	N35500	Bidirectional	BFH
δ	Itech	IT6018C	Bidirectional	BFH
ε	Itech	IT6642C	Bidirectional	BFH
ζ	Keysight	PV8922A	Unidirectional	AIT
η	Keysight	RP7982A	Bidirectional	BFH
θ	Regatron	G5.UNV	Bidirectional	BFH
ι	AIT	PVS	Linear Unidir.	AIT
κ	BFH	MSS	Linear Unidir.	BFH
λ	Siemens	SM55	Real PV Modules	BFH

Berner F

Test Setup Phen 1: I-V curve stability

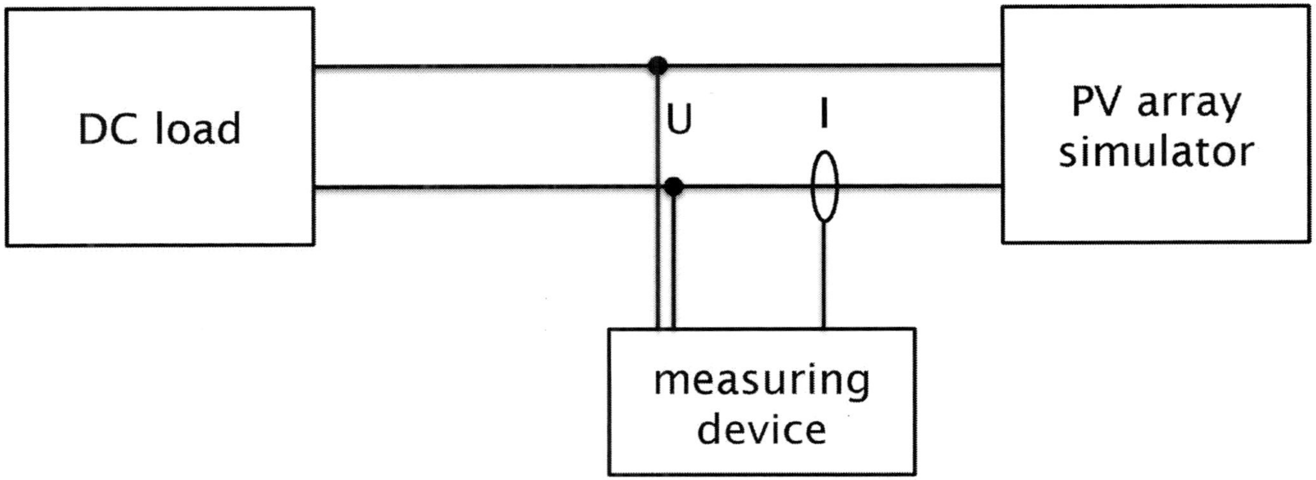

Berner Fachhochschule | Haute école spécialisée bernoise | Bern University of Applied Sciences

Test Setup Phen 2: Current ripple

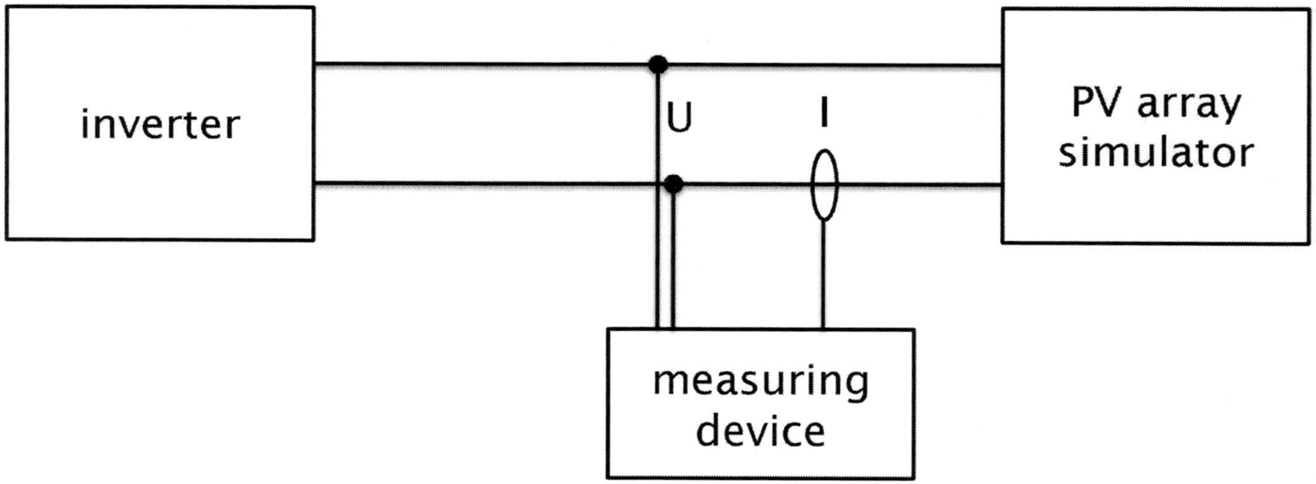

42nd European Photovoltaic Solar Energy Conference and Exhibition

This presentation was selected by the Sc. Committee of the EU PVSEC 2025 for submission of a full paper to one of the EU PVSEC's collaborating peer-reviewed journals.

DEVELOPING A NOVEL SENSOR HEALTH KPI FOR EVALUATING IRRADIANCE SENSOR PERFORMANCE

Sascha Lindig, Spyros Theocharides, Julián Ascencio-Vásquez
Univers SAS
1 Passerelle des Reflets, 92400 Courbevoie, France
sascha.lindig@univers.com

ABSTRACT: Reliable irradiance measurements are essential for accurate performance analysis in PV systems, influencing everything from system health diagnostics to financial forecasting and energy modeling. However, irradiance sensors such as pyranometers or reference cells can be impacted by a range of issues including miscalibration, soiling, misalignment, and data corruption. To address this challenge, we introduce the **Sensor-Health KPI**—a data-driven metric designed to evaluate and rank the data quality and reliability of each irradiance sensor in a PV system daily. The proposed KPI incorporates six evaluation parameters encompassing general data quality metrics and irradiance related performance attributes. Each parameter is individually scored, weighted, and aggregated to yield a normalized KPI score ranging from 0 to 100. This framework is integrated into the photovoltaic analytics software Solar -AI Analytics Univers. The method fills a gap in current PV monitoring standards such as IEC 61724-1:2021 by providing a structured methodology for sensor selection in performance assessments. Ultimately, the Sensor-Health KPI enables more robust downstream calculations, leading to improved performance evaluation and operational decision-making in PV systems.
Keywords: photovoltaic performance, weather station, data quality, operation and maintenance

1 INTRODUCTION

Accurate and reliable irradiance measurements are a cornerstone of photovoltaic (PV) system performance evaluation. From expected power estimation and performance ratio calculations to loss estimations, irradiance data are a critical input. Despite its importance, ensuring the quality and reliability of irradiance measurements over the operational life of a PV plant remains a considerable challenge, both from a technical and a computational point of view.

Irradiance sensors such as pyranometers and reference cells can be affected by multiple sources of error, including calibration drift, dirt accumulation, physical misalignment, and data communication issues. These problems can distort downstream performance indicators, potentially leading to inaccurate diagnostics, misinformed decisions, or even financial losses. Notably, current PV monitoring guidelines, such as IEC 61724 [1, 2, 3], cover basic data quality practices but fall short in providing a methodology for disregarding irradiance sensors or selecting among different irradiance sources.

To address this gap, we present a novel metric—the **Sensor-Health Key Performance Indicator (SH-KPI)**—developed to assess and rank irradiance sensors based on data quality and data accuracy. The SH-KPI evaluates several aspects of sensor behavior, including compliance with existing data boundaries, and correlation with other sources. It combines the individual aspects with a single score, ranging from 0 to 100, thereby enabling an automated sensor selection on a daily. This is combined with a strict prioritization scheme of irradiance sources including plane-of-array (POA) and global horizontal (GHI) sensors as well as satellite data.

In this paper, we describe the structure and scoring logic of the SH-KPI and provide examples of its application to real-world PV data. We demonstrate how the SH-KPI can improve operational performance assessments by dynamically selecting the most trustworthy irradiance data source, especially in systems with multiple sensors or varying data quality. To the best of our knowledge, there are no directly comparable approaches in the literature; most related work focuses on weather-corrected performance ratios or insolation-based adjustments. This highlights the novelty of our method and its potential to complement existing performance assessment techniques.

2 HIGH LEVEL ARCHITECTURE

The sensor-health KPI is a newly established key performance indicator which is used to evaluate and compare individual irradiance sensors with one another. The aim is to decide which sensor is the most reliable for each day. The SH-KPI rates each individual sensor based on individual factors to make an informed decision which of the available sensors is most suited to be used for all downstream calculations.

The KPI ranges from 0 to 100 with higher values indicating high-quality sensor readings. An SH-KPI of -99 represents a disregarded sensor which did not pass one or several of the data reliability tests. The SH-KPI is an aggregate across several data quality and reliability related parameters:

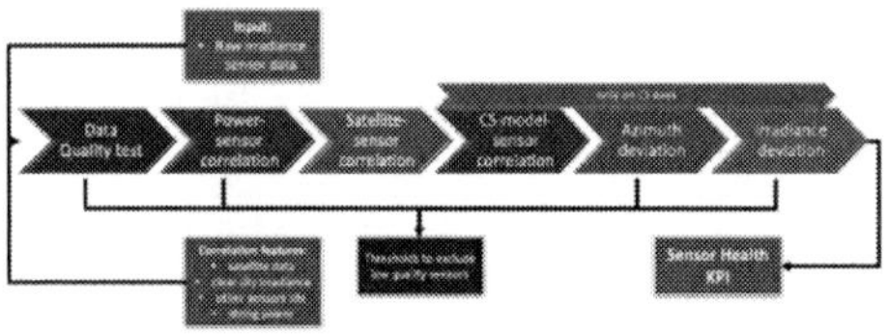

Figure 1: Sensor-health KPI structure with individual rating parameters

The individual rating parameters are discussed in chapter 3. The sensor health KPI is calculated daily for every ground-based irradiance sensor to select the best suited sensor per inverter for downstream calculations.

3 SENSOR HEALTH KPI - DETAILS

As introduced in **Figure 1**, the SH-KPI is constructed based on several parameters. In this section, the individual parameters will be introduced and described in detail. All correlation steps use the Pearson correlation parameter [4]. The KPI is constructed daily. The data are evaluated in five-minute resolution but practically it can be applied to all resolutions up to 15 minutes.

3.1 Data quality

The first set of parameters are data quality (DQ) parameters. Thereby, the following DQ parameters are being considered:

- **Missing data**: NaN values
- **Corrupt data**: corrupt values are commonly one of the following:
  [-99, -999, -9999, -99999, -999999, -9999999]
- **Stuck data**: Stuck or unchanging values are identified by checking whether data points vary as expected over time
- **Outlier data**: outlier data are defined as values out of pre-defined bounds

The definitions of stuck values as well as outlier bounds are in line with standard IEC 61724-3:2016 [3].

Every datapoint during daytime is subject to data quality tests. If the daily amount of datapoints affected by DQ issues amounts to more than 20%, that day is flagged and the sensor will be excluded. Data quality data are aligned based on the Univers Solar-AI data quality page:

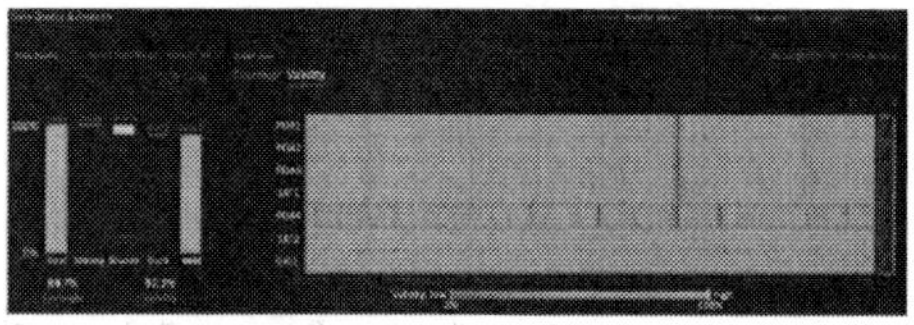

Figure 2: Data quality overview of irradiance sensors

3.2 Power-sensor correlation parameter

Under normal operating conditions, PV power output shows a string, approximately linear correlation with irradiance. That is why this correlation parameter was introduced and has a high weight in the determination of the SH-KPI. The difficulty is to select a suitable power parameter which is used for the power-irradiance correlation. Given the position of the SH-KPI algorithm within the processing pipeline (following data ingestion and basic quality control, but preceding KPI calculation and loss categorization), the power readings available were only subject to basic quality checks but not yet to extended quality testing regarding reliability and IEC states. The objective is to select the most reliable DC string reading per irradiance orientation, if available. It is important to select one string per orientation so that the POA orientation (tilt & azimuth) of the DC string is aligned to the orientation of the irradiance sensor.

The parameter is prepared in three steps:

a. Inverter string selector: Select the highest-yielding DC string per inverter after filtering out strings with data quality issues, curtailment, or anomalous daily patterns.

b. Racking string selector: From the pre-selected strings, group by onboarded orientation and choose the highest daily energy yield string.

c. Inverter racking string builder: Combine the selected strings from step b to create the final dataset for power-irradiance correlation calculation.

3.3 Satellite-sensor correlation parameter

For satellite correlation, transposed global horizontal irradiance (GHI) satellite data are used. Before calculating the satellite correlation, the satellite data are tested against the reference irradiance. To compute the reference irradiance, the median value of all POA sensors with the same specified orientation is calculated. In the next step, the Pearson correlation of the selected satellite irradiance and the reference irradiance is computed. If the correlation value exceeds 0.75, the satellite data are included in the SH-KPI calculation. If it is below, the satellite correlation is not being executed. The reason for this is to avoid using "poor" satellite data.

An example can be seen in **Figure 3**. This site experienced a day of extremely low irradiation. Especially under such conditions, it is not unusual for satellite data to divert from the irradiance/power profile on site. The reference irradiance parameter is the median value across the POA sensors 1 to 5, and the correlation between the selected satellite data sat_poa_1 and the reference irradiance is 0.56. So, the parameter did not meet the quality threshold and is excluded for this particular day.

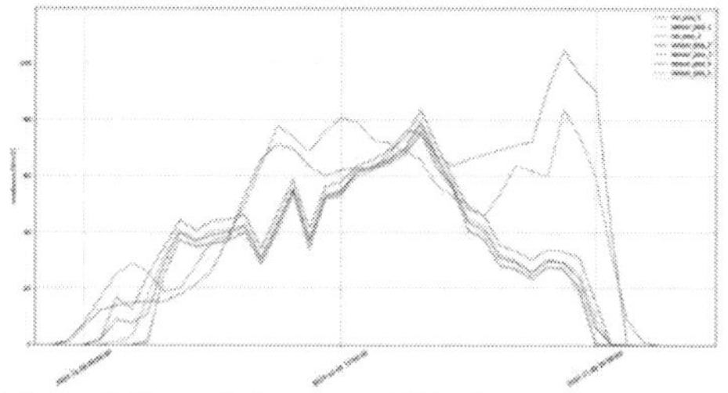

Figure 3: Example for poor satellite data quality

3.4 Transposed clear-sky model-sensor correlation parameter

The clear-sky (CS) model is modelled based on the Ineichen and Perez clear sky model [5, 6] available in the Python package pvlib [7]. To transform the global horizontal clear-sky model into clear-sky POA [8, 9, 10]. The parameter is only being used on clear-sky days. A clear-sky day is defined as a day in which at least 80% of the datapoints are clear-sky instances.

3.5 Azimuth deviation

The azimuth alignment check is performed only on fixed tilt systems with a tilt greater than (or equal to) 10° and only on clear-sky days. Azimuth analysis for lower tilt systems is not sufficiently reliable.

First, the true sensor azimuth is determined from the time series data. This is done using an azimuth fitting subroutine. The objective is to find the azimuth parameter for the clear-sky POA model that minimizes the root-mean-square-error (RMSE) between the magnitude-scaled clear-sky POA and measured POA. The minimization is implemented via the scipy.optimize.minimize method [11, 12]. The azimuth value that minimizes RMSE is the "observed" azimuth. If the POA sensor's observed azimuth is more than 12° different from the specified sensor azimuth in the site configuration, the sensor is flagged as "misaligned" and is eliminated from use in further analysis.

3.6 Irradiance deviation

Irradiance deviation is based on the reference irradiance introduced in section 3.3. The irradiance deviation parameter is only used on clear sky days. At each timestamp, the median value of all POA sensors with the same specified orientation is calculated. Then, for each sensor, the percentage error between the total daily irradiance measured and the medium value is determined:

$$poa_{error} = \frac{\sum poa_{meas} - \sum irr_{ref}}{\sum irr_{ref}}$$

The aggregation step is daily. Here, poa_{meas} are the sensor readings and irr_{ref} is the reference irradiance. If poa_{error} is greater than 12% for a sensor, the sensor is flagged and excluded from further use.

3.7 Sensor-health KPI calculation

The SH-KPI is an aggregated KPI based on the results from the quality test parameters described above.

The parameters 1) data quality, 2) power–irradiance correlation, 5) azimuth deviation, and 6) irradiance deviation have fail-thresholds. If one of them is surpassed, the SH-KPI is set to −99 and the sensor excluded from the sensor selection for that day. These fail-thresholds are intentionally defined as conservative cut-off values: they serve to eliminate sensors whose data is very likely unreliable rather than to capture subtle deviations. This approach ensures that severely erroneous or inconsistent measurements do not bias the subsequent scoring and selection process, while less critical deviations are still reflected through the gradual scoring scale.

Each parameter has score levels between 1 and 5. The SH-KPI is calculated according to:

$$SH - KPI\,[\%] = \frac{\sum score * 100}{\sum score_{max}}$$

Here, $score_{max}$ is the maximum reachable sum if all parameters under consideration are returning the highest possible score. $score$ is the sum of all individual scores of the parameters considered.

The final SH-KPIs across a PV site and for each day can be seen exemplarily in **Figure 4**. It is visible that also GHI sensors are being evaluated, but without considering power-irradiance correlation as well as azimuth deviation. If any of the parameters seen in **Figure 1** are not available, the SH-KPI is computed excluding this specific parameter (for instance CS-irradiance correlation, irradiance deviation and azimuth deviation on clear-sky days).

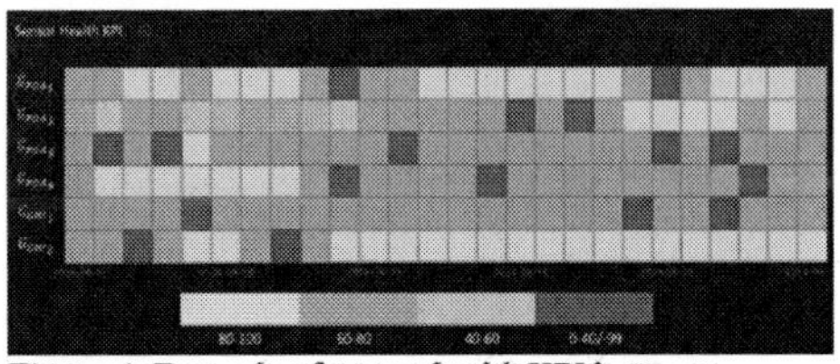

Figure 4: Example of sensor-health KPI heatmap

4 IRRADIANCE SENSOR SELECTION

The final step is to pass the SH-KPI information to the irradiance source selection. Here, the best-performing irradiance source (sensor or satellite) is selected for each day and for each inverter. The selection follows a strict prioritization scheme (see Table 1) which can be adjusted by the user if required. The process consists of three steps:

Figure 5: Sensor selection decision making

After, calculating the SH-KPI for each individual sensor, the user-defined sensor prioritization scheme is loaded, anf the irradiance source selected based on these inputs. Based on the prioritization and the SH-KPI values, one irradiance source is chosen for downstream calculations. Assigned and backup sensors are specifically assigned sensors for individual inverters (set by the user). Such manual assignment may be required in cases where a particular sensor must be used to meet contractual obligations, for regulatory reporting, or to align with existing operational procedures, even if other sensors might show better data quality.

In addition to directly assigned sensors, two further strategies are available. The average sensor combines data from all reliable irradiance sensors with the same orientation, while the highest-rated sensor is the sensor with the highest SH-KPI within a given racking group/orientation. The prioritization gives preference to POA sensors, followed by GHI sensors transposed to POA.

For quality control, sensors are first considered only if their SH-KPI exceeds 90. If no sensor passes this threshold, a second selection round includes sensors above a lower threshold. If none of the ground-mounted sensors achieve at least 60, the system falls back on satellite data, since it must be assumed that all sensors are either corrupt or of insufficient quality.

Table 1: Default sensor prioritization

Priority	Irradiance Source	Description
1	Assigned POA sensor	**User-defined** preferred choice
2	Backup POA sensor	**User-defined** 2nd preferred choice
3	Average POA	Mean across all well-functioning POA sensors
4	Highest rated POA sensor	POA sensor with highest sensor health KPI
5	Transposed assigned GHI sensor	**User-defined** preferred GHI choice
6	Transposed average GHI	Transposed irradiance of mean across all well-functioning GHI sensors
7	Transposed highest rated GHI sensor	Transposed GHI sensor with highest sensor health KPI
8	Satellite POA	Irradiance from onboarded satellite POA source
9	Transposed satellite GHI	Transposed irradiance from onboarded satellite GHI source

5 CONCLUSIONS

This work presents the Sensor-Health Key Performance Indicator (SH-KPI), a comprehensive data-driven metric designed to evaluate and rank irradiance sensor reliability in photovoltaic systems. The SH-KPI addresses a critical gap in current PV monitoring standards by providing an automated methodology for daily sensor selection and quality assessment, thereby building upon the IEC 61724 framework. The proposed SH-KPI not only standardizes sensor evaluation but also directly improves the reliability of downstream PV analytics, by supporting more accurate performance assessments and operational decisions.

The SH-KPI incorporates six evaluation parameters that encompass both general data quality metrics and irradiance-specific performance attributes: 1) data quality, 2) string-power correlation, 3) satellite-sensor correlation, 4) clear-sky model-sensor correlation, 5) azimuth deviation, and 6) irradiance deviation.

The methodology successfully addresses common irradiance measurement challenges including calibration drift, soiling effects, physical misalignment, and data corruption. The normalized scoring system (0-100) with fail-safe thresholds ensures consistent evaluation across diverse PV installations and varying environmental conditions. The hierarchical sensor selection process, ranging from assigned POA sensors to satellite fallback options, provides resilience against sensor failures while maintaining data continuity for critical performance assessments.

In the future, we want to explore several opportunities for enhancement and validation of the methodology. First, the current framework requires extension to accommodate tracking systems, where sensor orientation dynamics and tracking accuracy significantly impact irradiance measurements. Future iterations will incorporate tracking error detection algorithms and develop specialized correlation metrics that account for the temporal alignment challenges inherent in tracking systems. Second, comprehensive bias analysis is essential to identify potential blind spots in the SH-KPI evaluation framework. Additionally, machine learning approaches could enhance the methodology by enabling adaptive weighting of the six evaluation parameters based on site-specific characteristics and seasonal variations. Finally, expanding the framework to incorporate emerging sensor technologies, such as silicon photodiodes and low-cost pyranometers, will ensure the methodology remains relevant as PV monitoring technology evolves. Long-term field validation studies across diverse geographical locations and plant configurations will be crucial for establishing the robustness and universal applicability of the SH-KPI methodology.

6 REFERENCES

[1] International Electrotechnical Commission, "IEC 61724-1:2021 Photovoltaic system performance, Part 1: Monitoring Standard," Geneva, 2021.

[2] International Electrotechnical Commission, "IEC 61724-2:2016: Photovoltaic system performance - Part 2: Capacity evaluation method," Geneva, 2016.

[3] International Electrotechnical Commission, "IEC 61724-3:2016: Photovoltaic system performance, Part 3: Energy evaluation method," Geneva, 2016.

[4] I. Cohen, Y. Huang, J. Chen and J. Benesty, Noise Reduction in Speech Processing, Springer, 2009.

[5] R. Perez and P. Ineichen, "A new airmass independent formulation for the Linke turbidity coefficient," *Solar Energy,* vol. 73, pp. 151-157, 2002.

[6] R. Perez et al., "A new operational model for satellite-derived irradiances: description and validation," *Solar Energy,* vol. 73, pp. 307-317, 2002.

[7] W. F. Holmgren, C. W. Hansen and M. A. Mikofski, "pvlib python: a python package for modeling solar energy systems," *Journal of Open Source Software,* vol. 3, no. 29, 2018.

[8] R. Perez, P. Ineichen, E. Maxwell, R. Seals and A. Zelenka, "Dynamic Global-to-Direct Irradiance Conversion Models," *ASHRAE Transactions-Research Series,* pp. 354-369, 1992.

[9] R. Perez, R. Seals, P. Ineichen, R. Stewart and D. Menicucci, "A new simplified version of the perez diffuse irradiance model for tilted surfaces," *Solar Energy,* vol. 39, no. 3, pp. 221-232, 1987.

[10] M. Mikofski and K. Anderson, "Slope-Aware Backtracking for Single-Axis Trackers," NREL, 2020.

[11] R. H. Byrd, P. Lu, J. Nocedal and C. Zhu, "A Limited Memory Algorithm for Bound Constrained Optimization," *SIAM Journal on Scientific and Statistical Computing,* vol. 16, no. 5, pp. 1190-1208, 1995.

[12] C. Zhu, R. H. Byrd and J. Nocedal, "L-BFGS-B: Algorithm 778: L-BFGS-B, FORTRAN routines for large scale bound constrained optimization," *ACM Transactions on Mathematical Software,* vol. 23, no. 4, pp. 550-560, 1997.

10.4229/EUPVSEC2025/4DO.10.1

A novel Sensor Health KPI for evaluating irradiance sensor performance

Dr. Sascha Lindig

Senior Solar Performance Engineer

EUPVSEC, Bilbao, 25.09.2025

univers Proprietary and Confidential

Univers AS (former Bazefield)

- Global software company within renewables. Roots back to 1991 as an industrial IT company
- OEM independent offering within renewable since 2010
- Market leading Bazefield® Operations Management System. Based on the same foundation that has shown its scalability, performance, reliability and robustness for many clients over many years in different industries
- Offer off-the-shelf support for solar, wind, battery storage, hydro, biomass and other renewable technology sources
- Univers AS operates fully independent regarding governance, data confidentiality, cybersecurity etc.

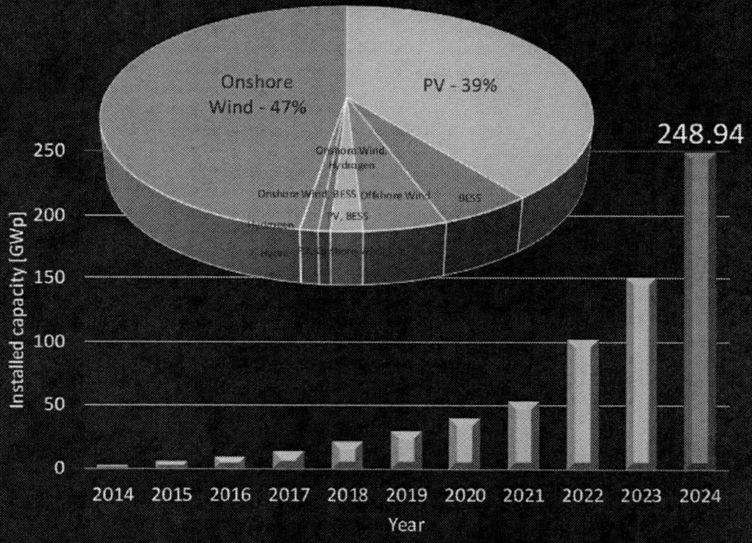

Kingfield Solar Portfolio (Excelsior Energy, Minnesota , US)

Fallago Rig (Natural Power, UK)

Hornsdale Power Reserve (Australia)

Sheringham Shoal (Equinor, UK)

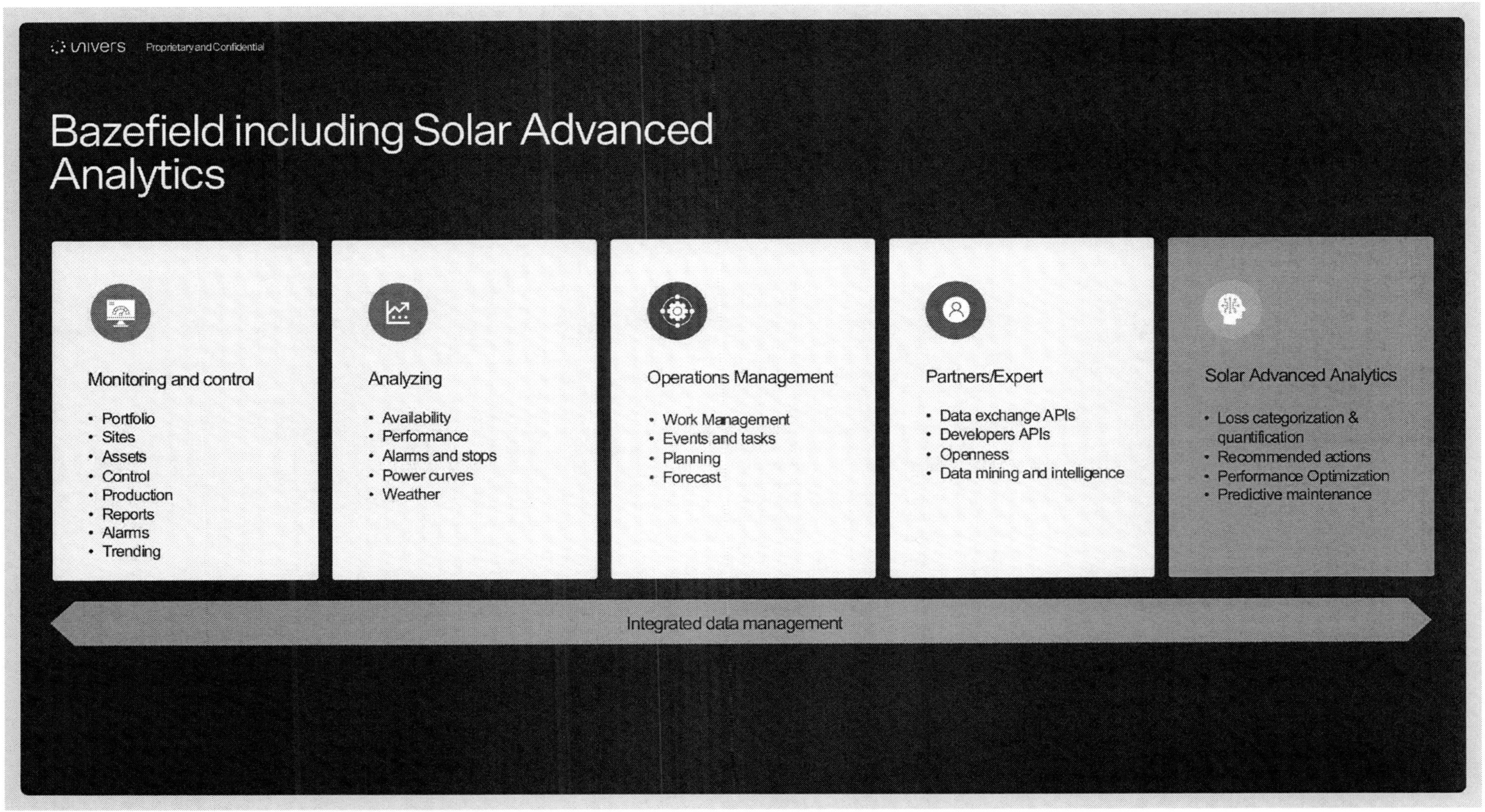
univers Proprietary and Confidential
Bazefield including Solar Advanced Analytics
Monitoring and control
• Portfolio
• Sites
• Assets
• Control
• Production
• Reports
• Alarms
• Trending
Analyzing
• Availability
• Performance
• Alarms and stops
• Power curves
• Weather
Operations Management
• Work Management
• Events and tasks
• Planning
• Forecast
Partners/Expert
• Data exchange APIs
• Developers APIs
• Openness
• Data mining and intelligence
Solar Advanced Analytics
• Loss categorization & quantification
• Recommended actions
• Performance Optimization
• Predictive maintenance
Integrated data management

univers Proprietary and Confidential

What do we do?

Transform raw data coming from PV plants into human readable key information about:

- Economic viability
- Sustainability aspects
- Technical viability

- System performance
- Compare different PV projects
- **Detection of potential problems**
- **Actionable/data-driven insights**

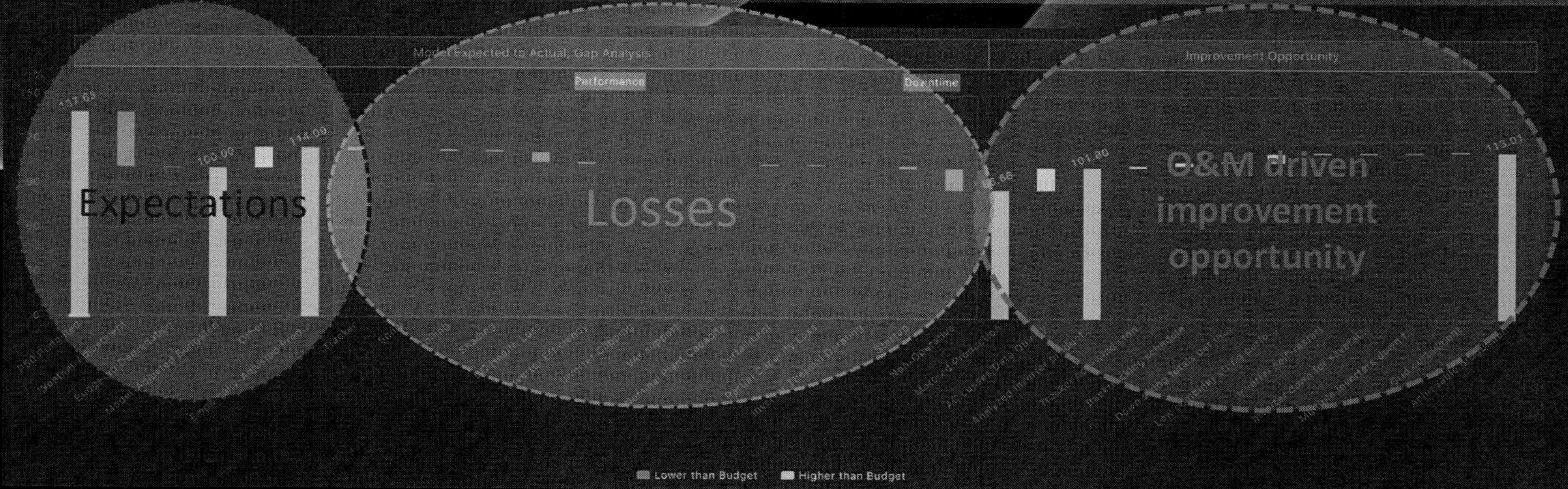

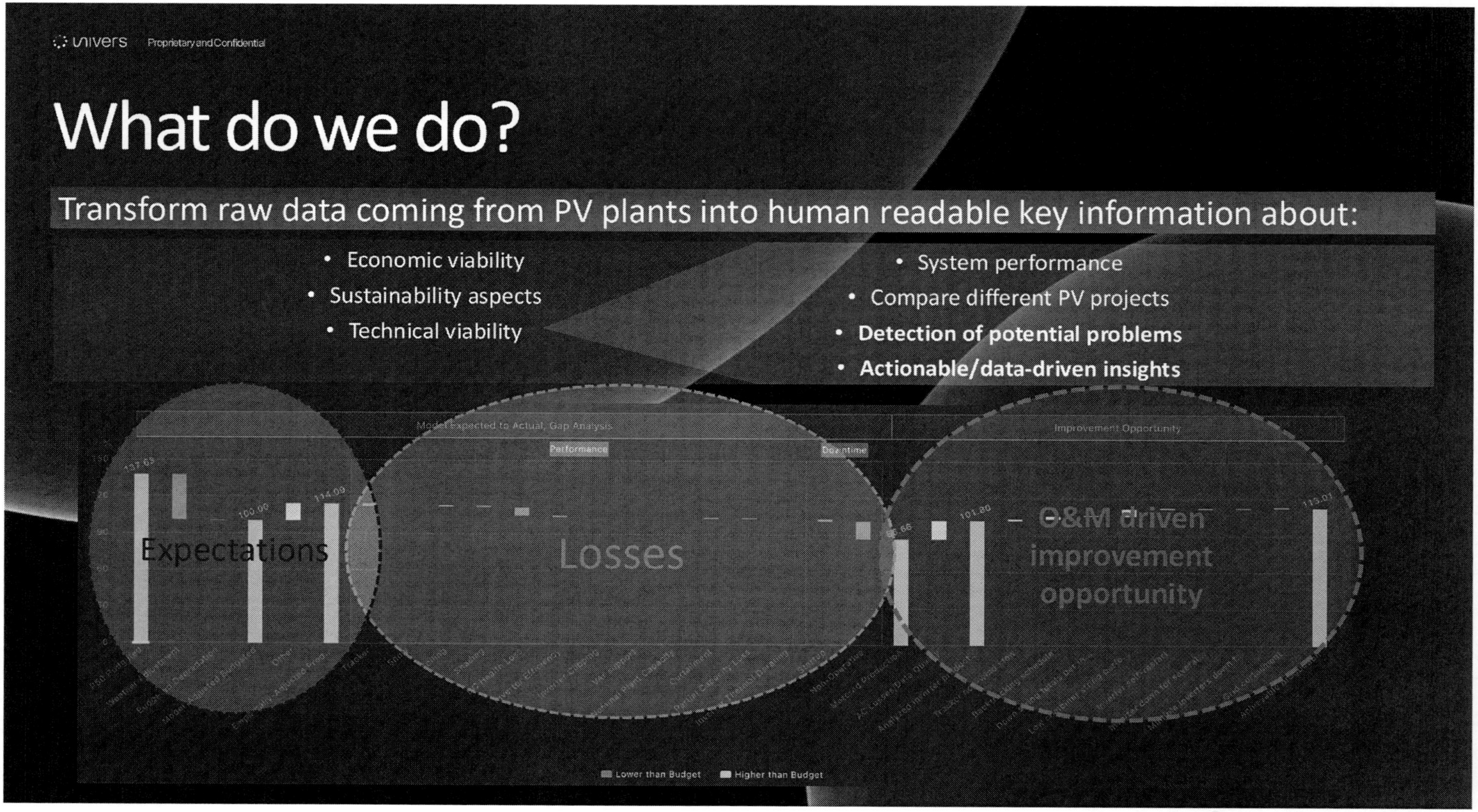

univers Proprietary and Confidential

Data usage, calculations

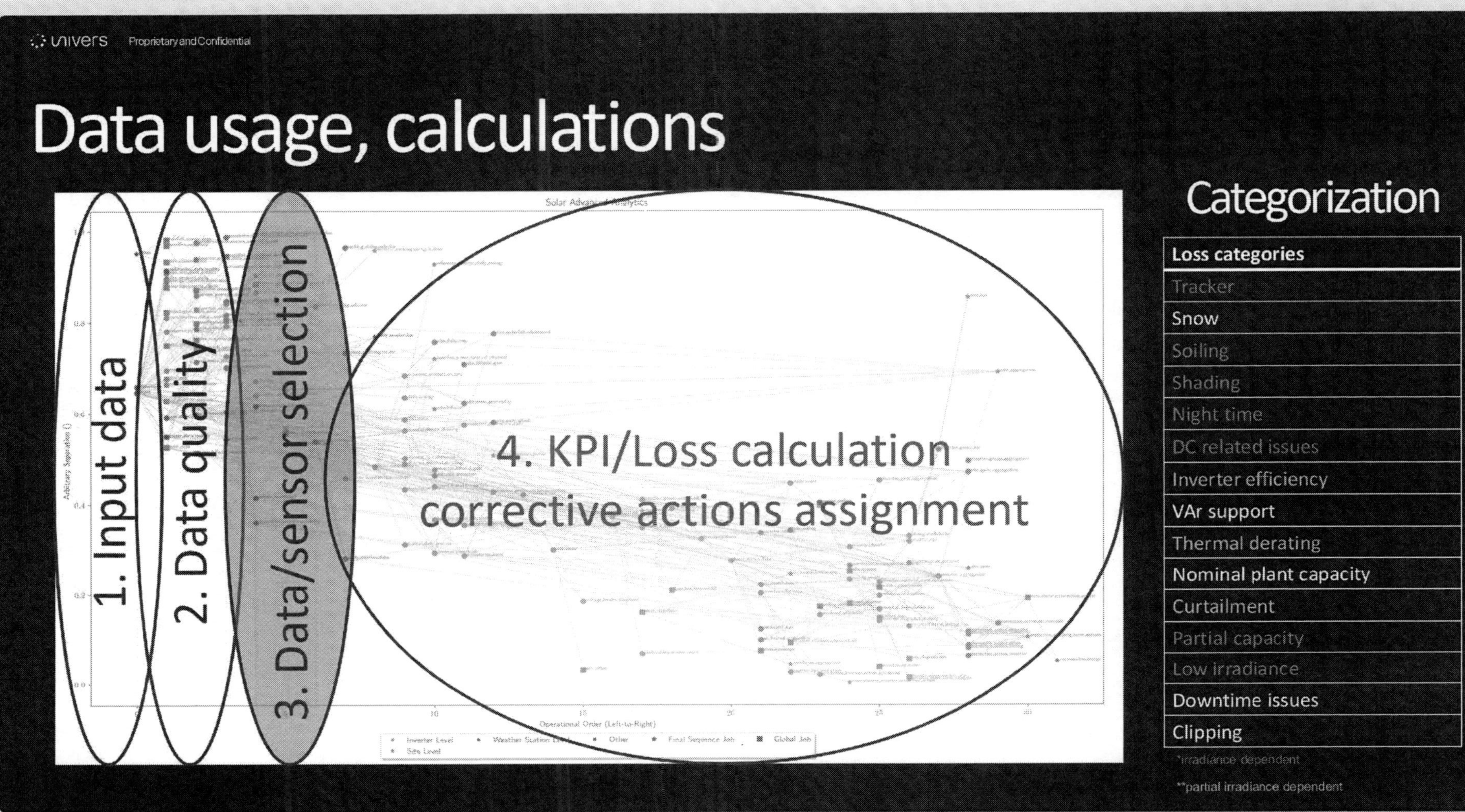

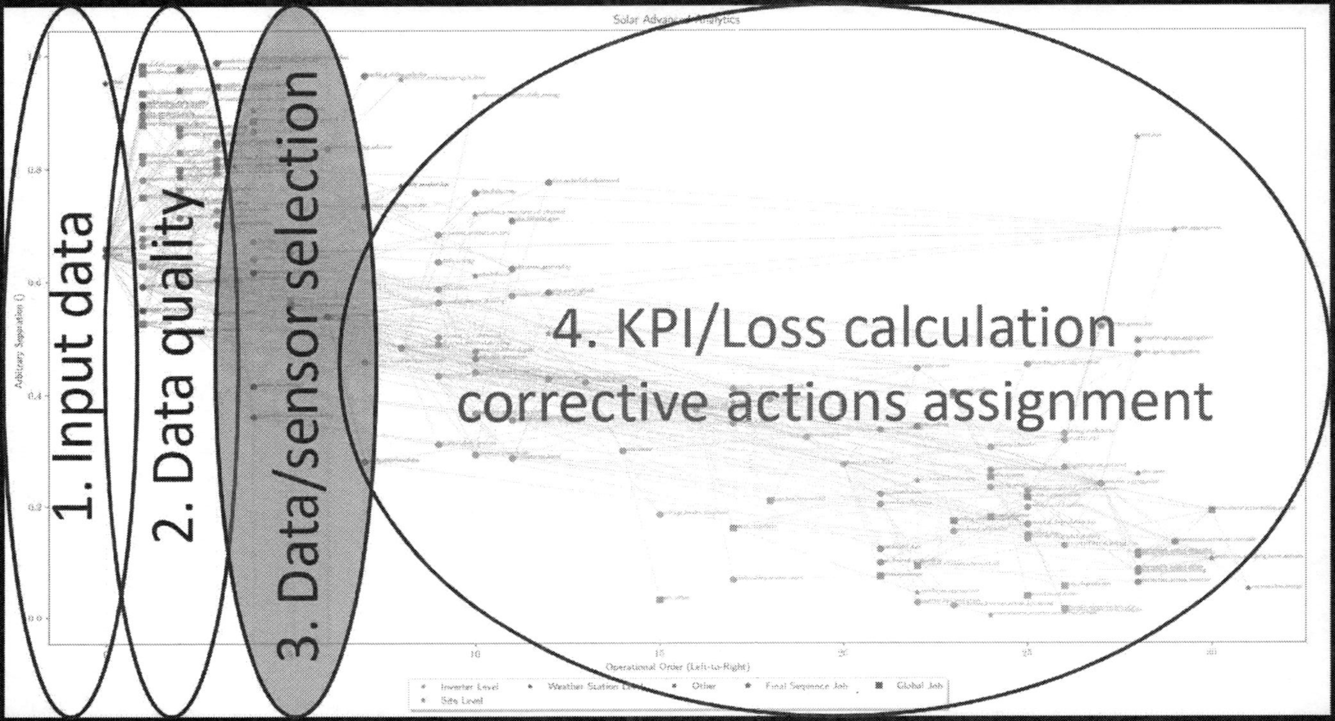

Categorization

Loss categories
Tracker
Snow
Soiling
Shading
Night time
DC related issues
Inverter efficiency
VAr support
Thermal derating
Nominal plant capacity
Curtailment
Partial capacity
Low irradiance
Downtime issues
Clipping

*irradiance dependent

**partial irradiance dependent

univers Proprietary and Confidential

Which irradiance sensor to choose?

- plane-of-array sensors
- global horizontal sensors
- satellite

IEC 61724-1:2021 [1]

- requires class A pyranometers
- provides # of sensors per plant
- location shall be selected representative
- sensor shading shall be avoided
- GHI sensors leveled within 0.5°
- POA sensors leveled within 0.5° tilt and 1° azimuth

[1] International Electrotechnical Commission, "IEC 61724-1:2021 Photovoltaic system performance - Part 1: Monitoring, Standard", Geneva, CH 2021.

univers Proprietary and Confidential

Which irradiance sensor to choose?

- Data quality
- Data logging, communication
- Orientation
- Correlation with power
- Correlation vs other available sensors/satellite
- Affected by soiling?
- long-term stability & calibration drift
- ....

EURAC Research – ABD Plant

Daily job – select irradiance source → Across 1000+ sites → For each inverter → Input to more than 90% of downstream jobs

Trade-off: Accuracy vs Computational performance

univers Proprietary and Confidential

Sensor Health KPI

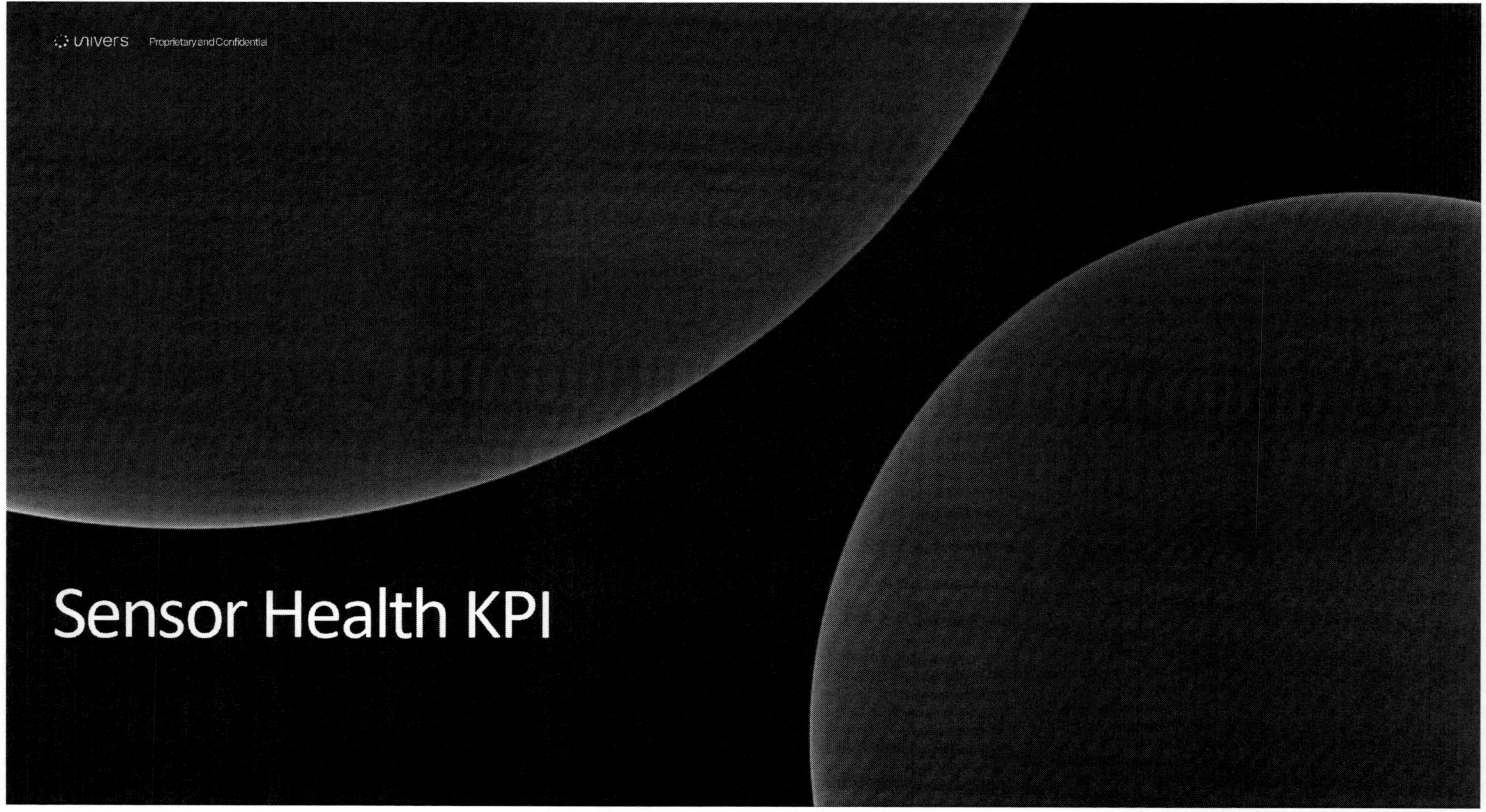

univers Proprietary and Confidential

Definition

- in-house developed daily KPI (0–100) that rates the data quality and reliability of individual irradiance sensors
- used to select the most reliable sensor per inverter for downstream calculations

• 90 – 100	Very good	The sensor is perfoming optimally, with high data quality, validity, and accuracy.
• 80 – 90	Good	The sensor is functioning well, though there may be minor issues.
• 60 – 80	Average	The sensor's peformance is adequate, but closer attention is needed.
• Below 60 / -99	Failing	The sensor's performance is subpar and requires attention.

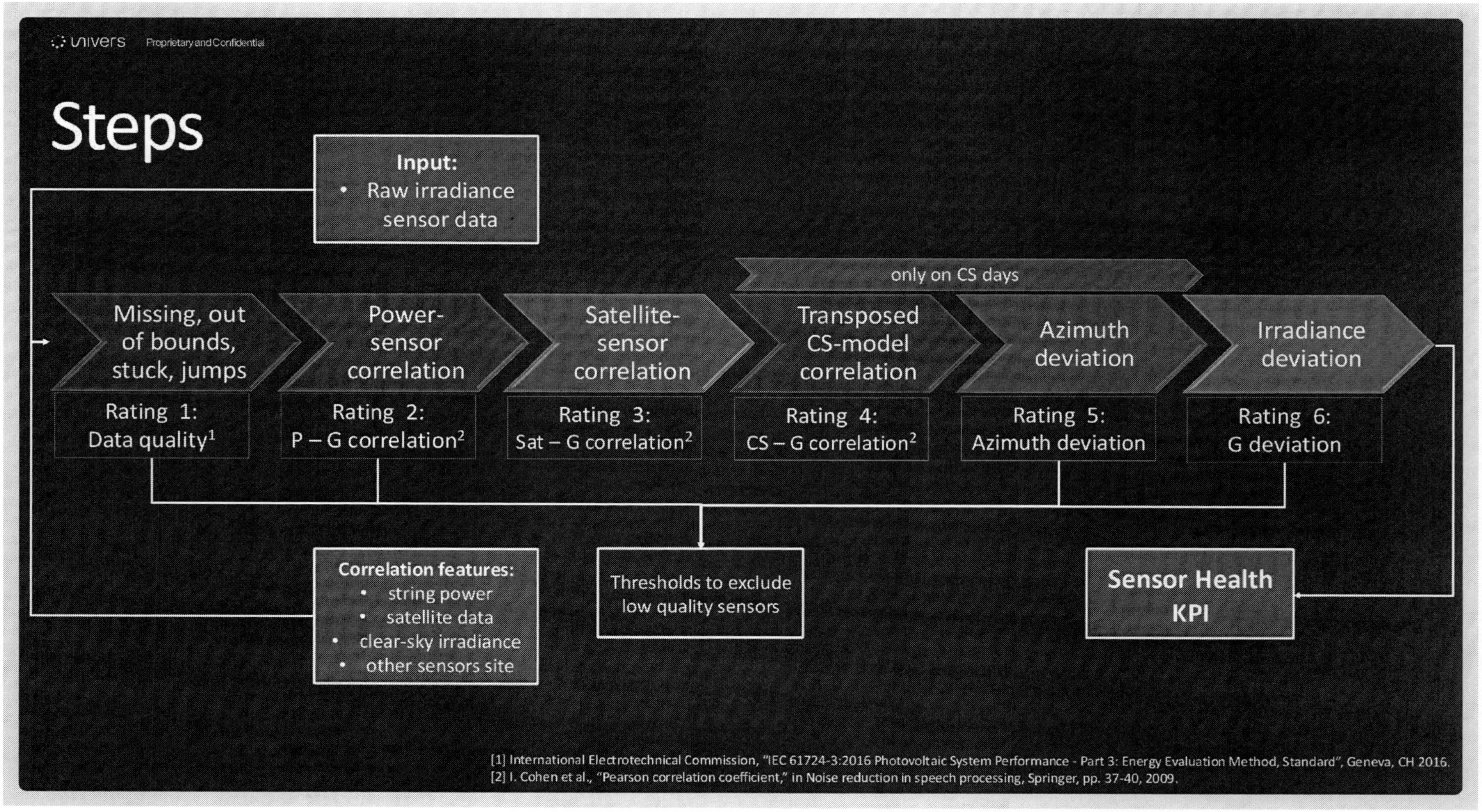
univers Proprietary and Confidential
Steps
Input:
• Raw irradiance sensor data
only on CS days
Missing, out of bounds, stuck, jumps
Power-sensor correlation
Satellite-sensor correlation
Transposed CS-model correlation
Azimuth deviation
Irradiance deviation
Rating 1: Data quality1
Rating 2: P – G correlation2
Rating 3: Sat – G correlation2
Rating 4: CS – G correlation2
Rating 5: Azimuth deviation
Rating 6: G deviation
Correlation features:
• string power
• satellite data
• clear-sky irradiance
• other sensors site
Thresholds to exclude low quality sensors
Sensor Health KPI
[1] International Electrotechnical Commission, "IEC 61724-3:2016 Photovoltaic System Performance - Part 3: Energy Evaluation Method, Standard", Geneva, CH 2016.
[2] I. Cohen et al., "Pearson correlation coefficient," in Noise reduction in speech processing, Springer, pp. 37-40, 2009.

univers
Proprietary and Confidential
Steps – Data Quality
Data Quality & Analysis
Sensor Point: Weather Statio...
Devices:
Plant Level
Data Quality
Period 2023-01-01 - 2023-06-30
Detail View
Coverage
Validity
Period 2023-01-02 - 2023-06-30
100%
0%
100%
-0.33%
-6.94%
-0.67%
92.16%
Total
Missing
Bounds
Stuck
Valid
99.7%
Coverage
92.2%
Validity
POA1
POA2
POA3
SAT1
POA4
SAT2
GHI1
Validity: low
0%
high
100%

univers
Proprietary and Confidential
Steps – Power-Irradiance deviation
Active Power Analysis
Date 2024-08-05 - 2024-08-11
POA
Early Morning
Morning
Late Morning
Early Afternoon
Early Night
Late Night
Correlation = 0.96
Active Power Analysis
Date 2025-06-21 - 2025-06-22
POA
111.08
Morning: 138.32kW
Early Morning
Morning
Late Morning
Early Afternoon
Early Night
Late Night
Strong curtailment – not usable

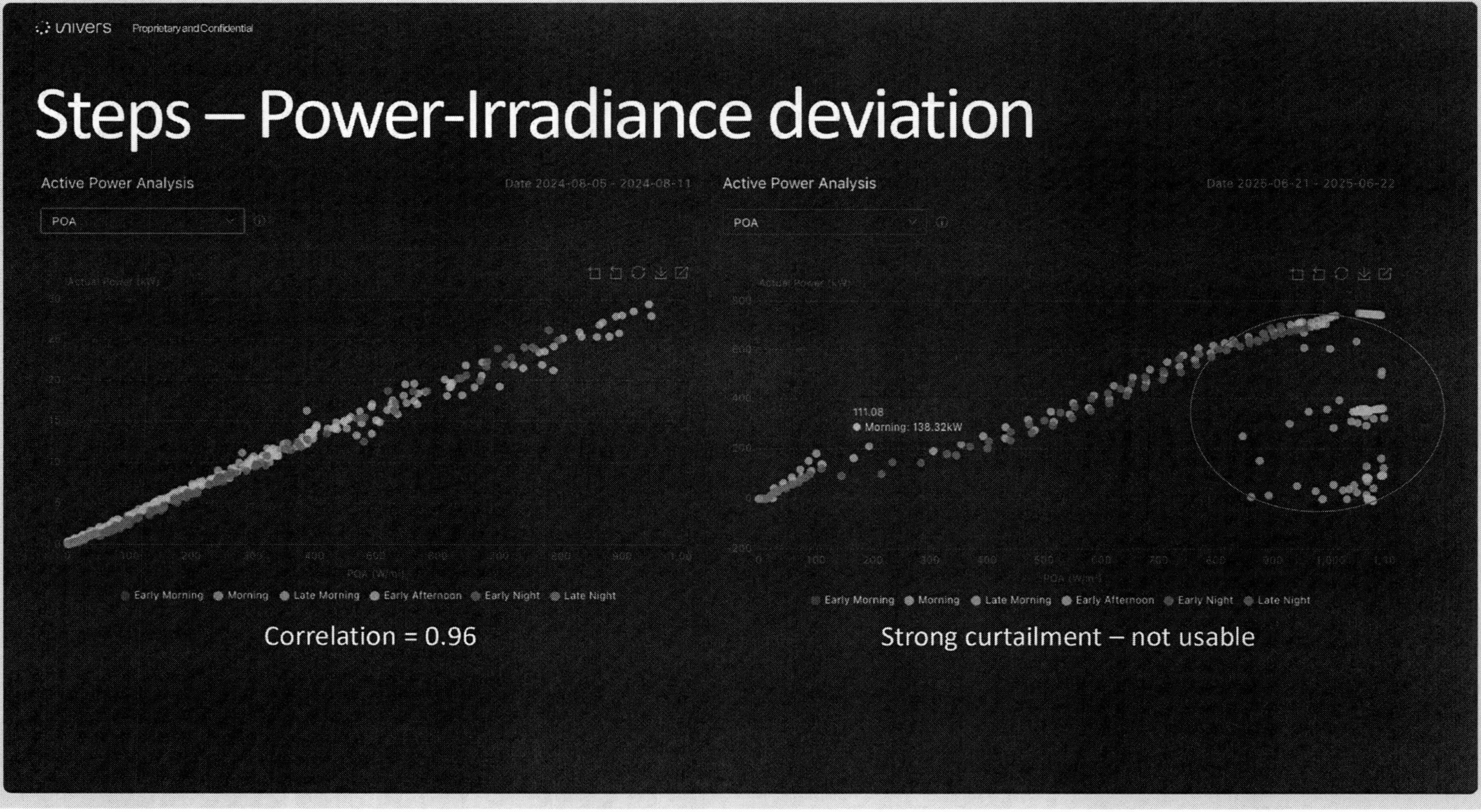

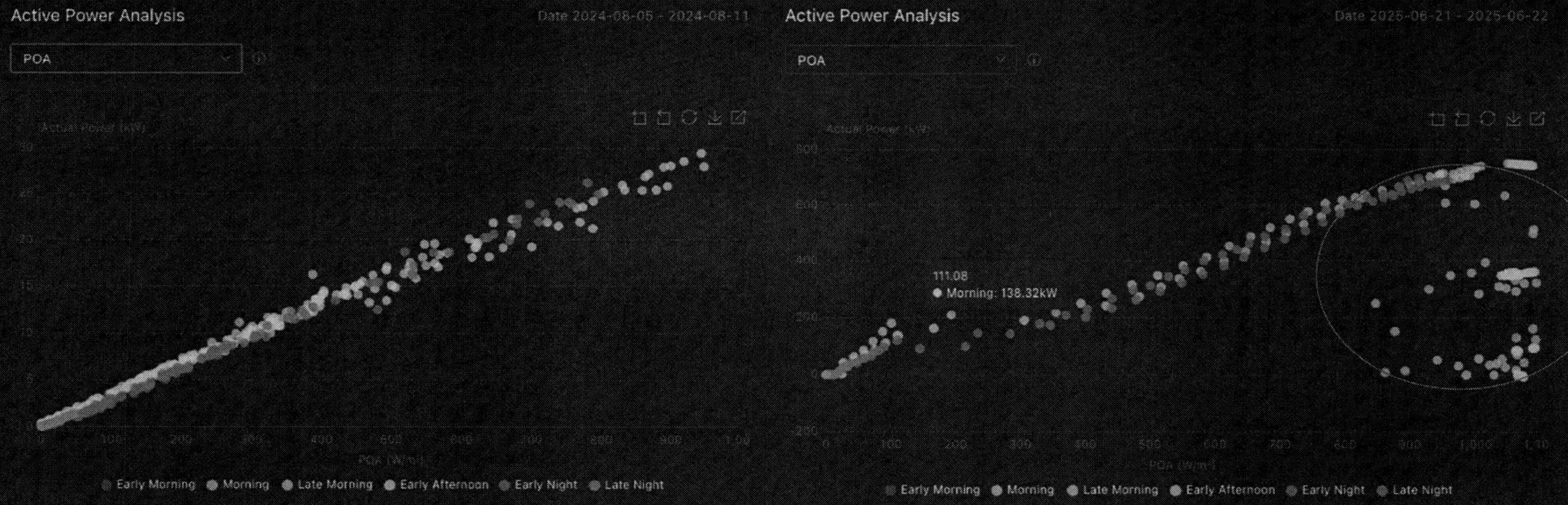

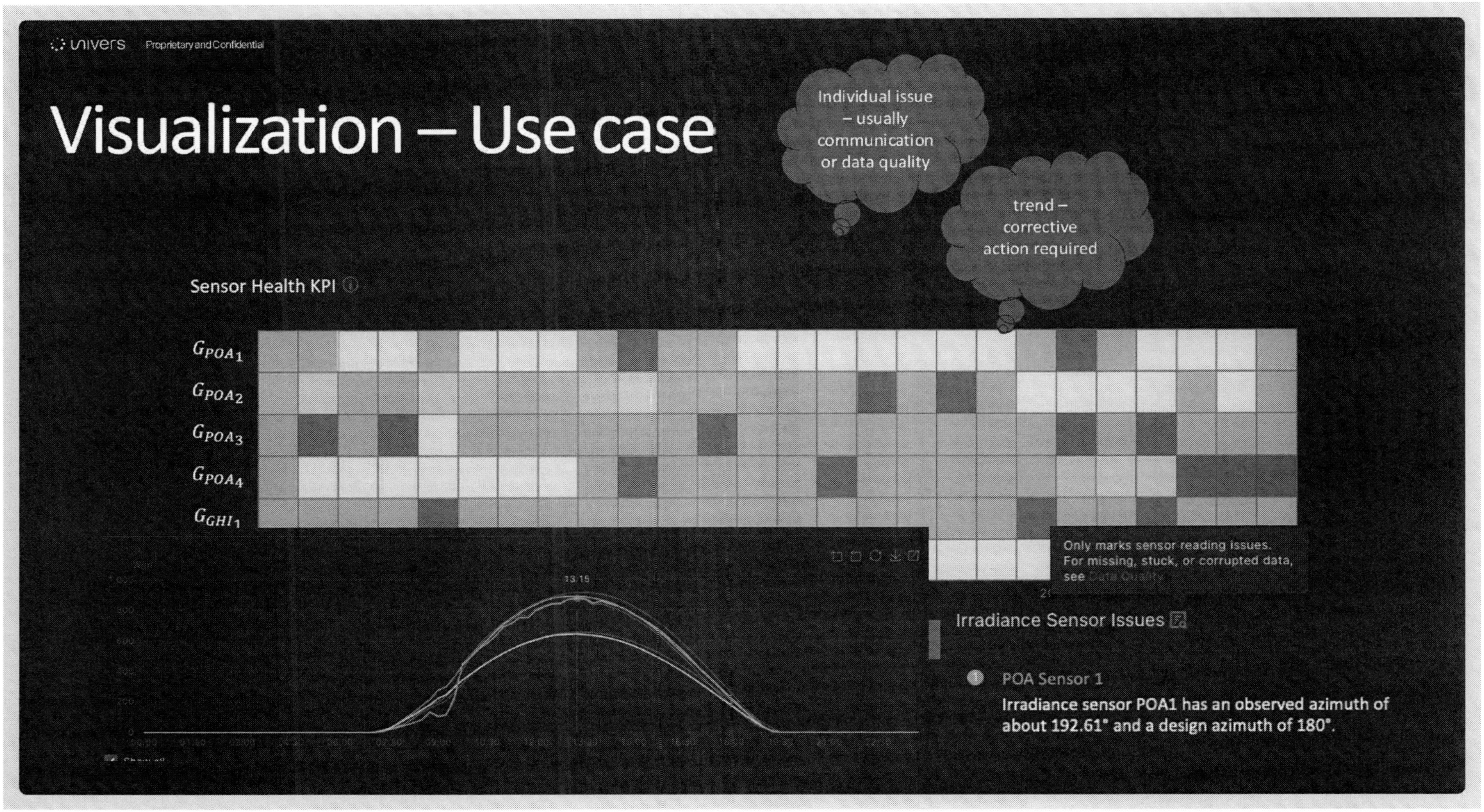
univers
Proprietary and Confidential
Visualization – Use case
Individual issue – usually communication or data quality
trend – corrective action required
Sensor Health KPI
G_{POA_1}
G_{POA_2}
G_{POA_3}
G_{POA_4}
G_{GHI_1}
Only marks sensor reading issues. For missing, stuck, or corrupted data, see Data Quality
13:15
Irradiance Sensor Issues
POA Sensor 1
Irradiance sensor POA1 has an observed azimuth of about 192.61° and a design azimuth of 180°.

univers Proprietary and Confidential

Sensor Selection

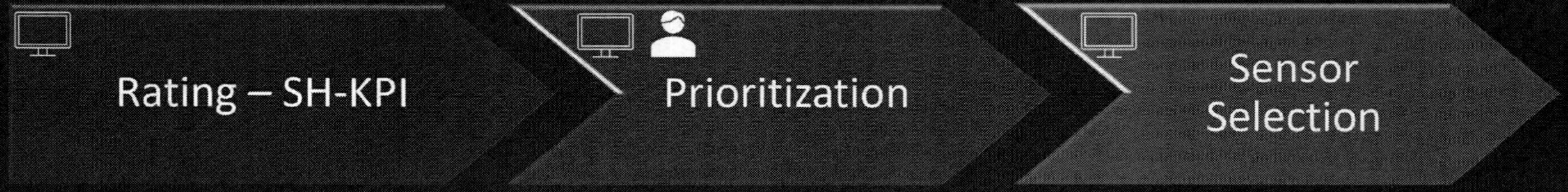

Priority	Irradiance Source	Description
1	Assigned POA sensor	**User-defined** preferred choice
2	Backup POA sensor	**User-defined** 2nd preferred choice
3	Average POA	Mean across all well functioning POA sensors
4	Highest rated POA sensor	POA sensor with highest sensor health KPI
5	Transposed assigned GHI sensor	**User-defined** preferred GHI choice
6	Transposed average GHI	Transposed irradiance of mean across all well functioning GHI sensors
7	Transposed highest rated GHI sensor	Transposed GHI sensor with highest sensor health KPI
8	Satellite POA	Irradiance from onboarded satellite POA source
9	Transposed satellite GHI	Transposed irradiance from onboarded satellite GHI source

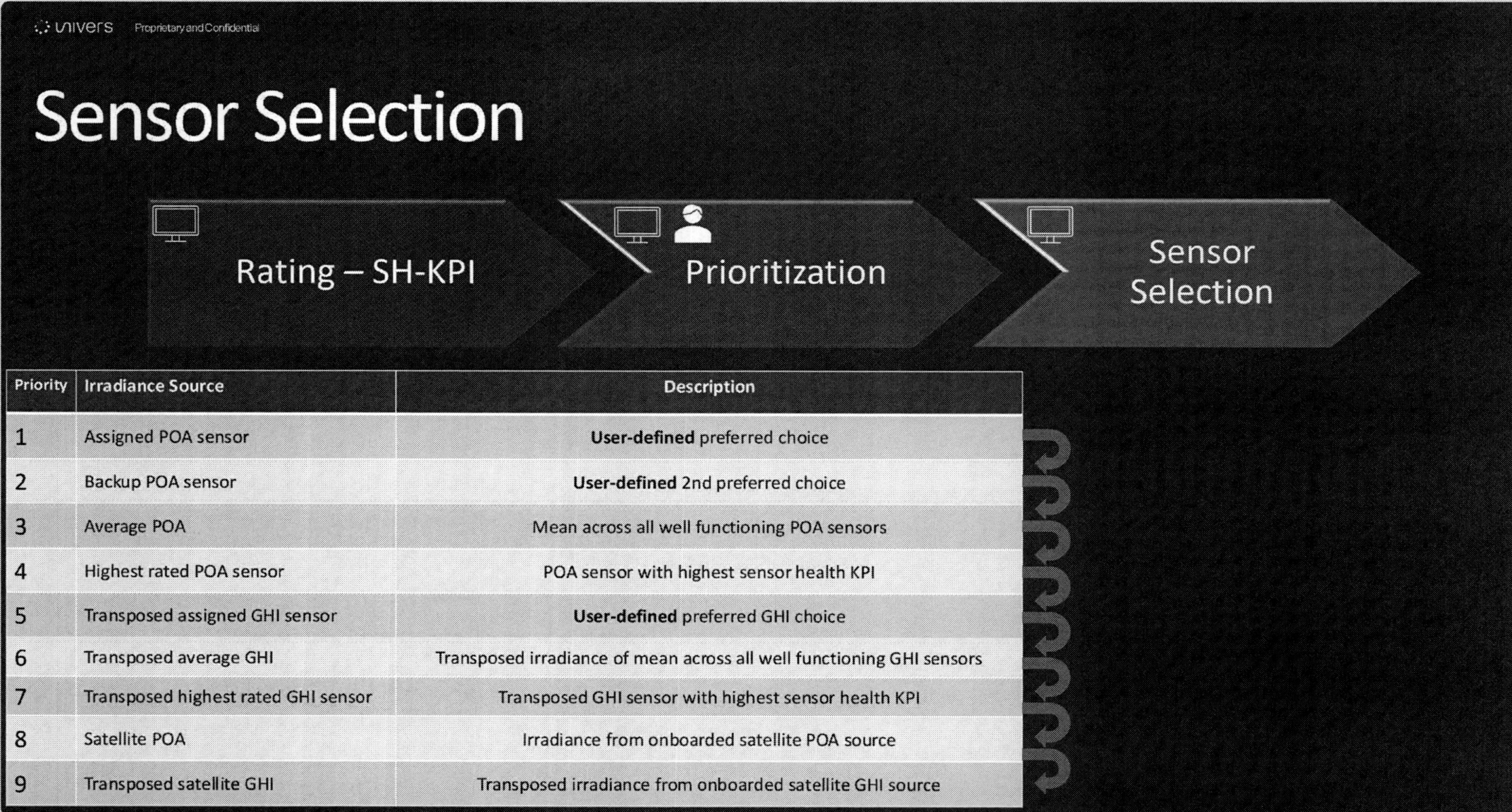

univers Proprietary and Confidential

Wrong assignment

	Well assigned sensor	Poorly assigned sensor
Example	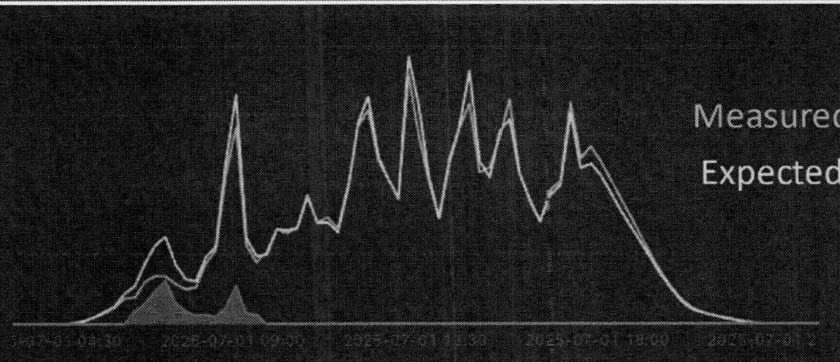	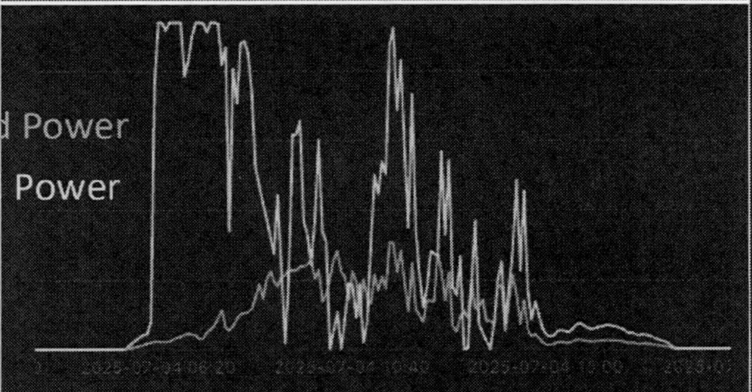
Expected power	Follows power (under normal circumstances) well – required indicator for loss identification	Due to erroneous irradiance reading expected power is faulty
Loss assignment	Accurate based on logics relying on accurate expected power estimation	Many categories difficult to detect & quantify
Recommended actions	Potential misclassification might lead to faulty recommendations	Require accurate loss assignment to improve system performance

univers Proprietary and Confidential

Conclusions

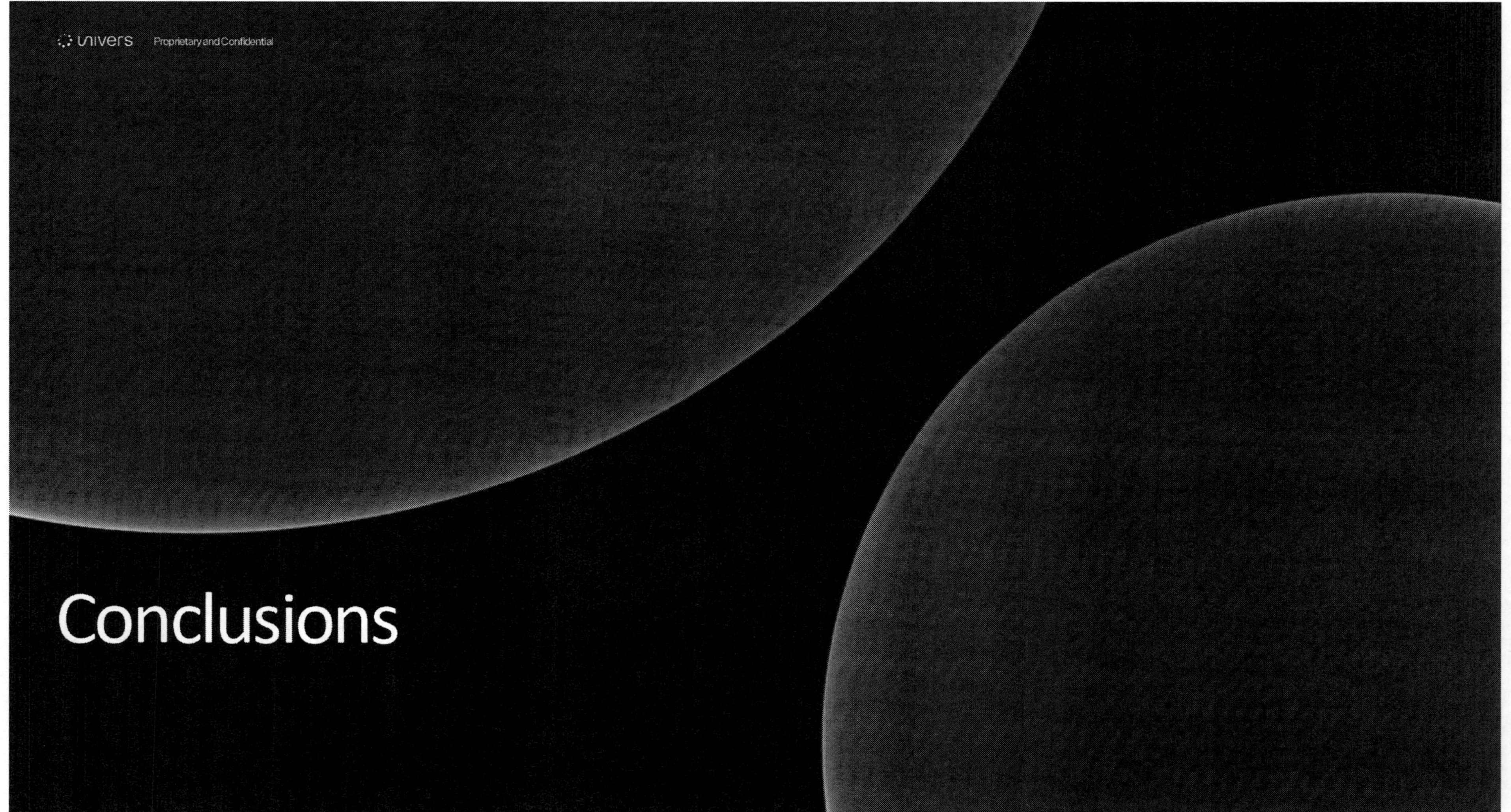

Conclusions

- development of a new KPI to rate irradiance sensor data
  - ➢ accuracy-efficiency trade-off to find best possible source
  - ➢ On-site sensor care will go a long way!!!
- Why not employing “more sophisticated” AI methodologies?
  - ➢ computational speed
  - ➢ universal applicable – edge cases
  - ➢ transparency -> reporting to stakeholder
    - ➢ justification of why specific sensors are selected

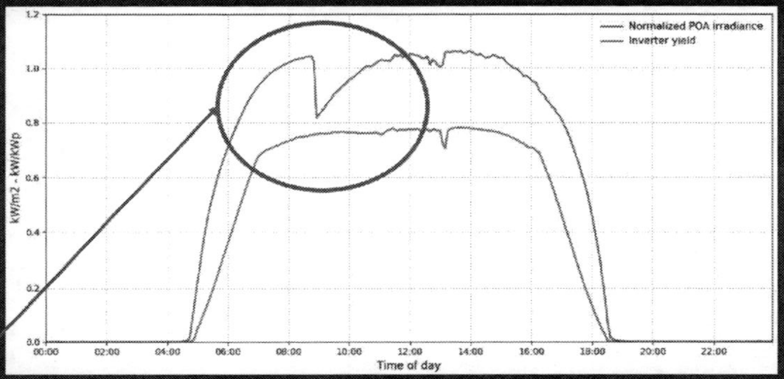

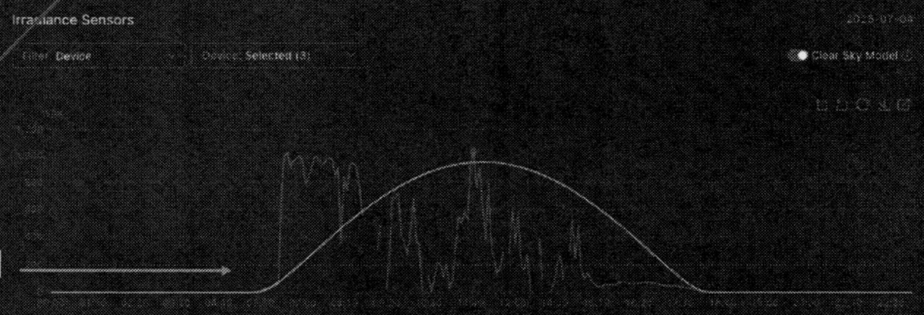

- Future improvements
  - ➢ account for tracking issues in SAT sites
  - ➢ ensure SH-KPI has no bias or blind spots
  - ➢ additional fail-safe logic for small & strongly curtailed sites with low amount of sensors

univers

Thank you for your attention!

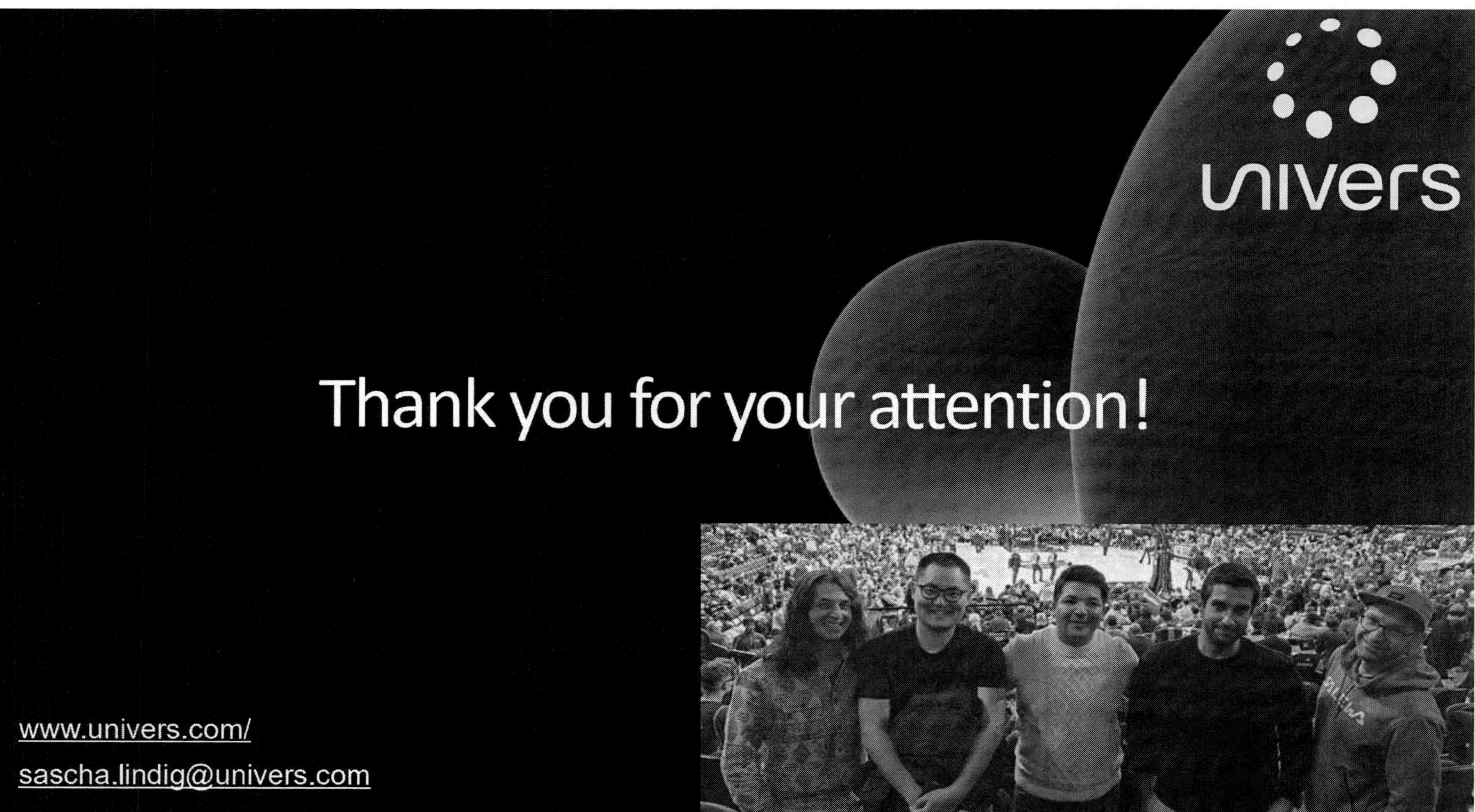

www.univers.com/

sascha.lindig@univers.com

EU PVSEC 2025

INES INSTITUT NATIONAL DE L'ENERGIE SOLAIRE

cythelia ENERGY

trace software

Measurement and Analysis of Bifacial Gain for Commercial & Industrial PV Systems: Impact of Building Structure and Environmental Factors

-

Pierre Besson[1], Jean-Francois Lelièvre[1], Antoine Dizier[1], Ismael Lokhat[2], Benoit Lelong[3]
[1] INES Training and Expertise Department; [2] Trace Software; [3] Cythelia Energy

Jean-François LELIEVRE – jf.lelievre@ines-solaire.org

25/09/2025

PLATEFORME FORMATION & ÉVALUATION

ines
INSTITUT NATIONAL
DE L'ENERGIE SOLAIRE
ines

Bifacial Gain for Commercial & Industrial PV Systems

INSTITUT NATIONAL DE L'ENERGIE SOLAIRE

PLATEFORM

3

The Promise vs. Reality

INSTITUT NATIONAL DE L'ENERGIE SOLAIRE

- Simulations & lab tests: 5 to 25% energy gain (!)

- Theoretical benefits well known
  but local conditions can reduce or cancel them
  → Real installations face shadows, non uniform albedo, **rear irradiance and temperature inhomogeneities**

- Simulation tools oversimplify albedo & rear irradiance
  → *Field data is key to refine models*

- Lack of detailed field data for C&I systems
  → Help for **better design** and **improve energy yield**

A Real-World Laboratory

INSTITUT NATIONAL DE L'ENERGIE SOLAIRE

- **70 kW_p bifacial PV system**
- 214 Soluxtec bifacial PV modules (330 W_p)
- Enphase IQ7+ Micro-inverters on each module
- 10 front & rear irradiance sensors + 3 thermocouples + meteorologial station
- 10-min resolution, **2-year period monitoring**

A Real-World Laboratory

INES INSTITUT NATIONAL DE L'ENERGIE SOLAIRE

- 2 representative C&I PV sub-systems

- **Flat Rooftop: 28 kW$_p$**
  3 PV modules converted to monofacial

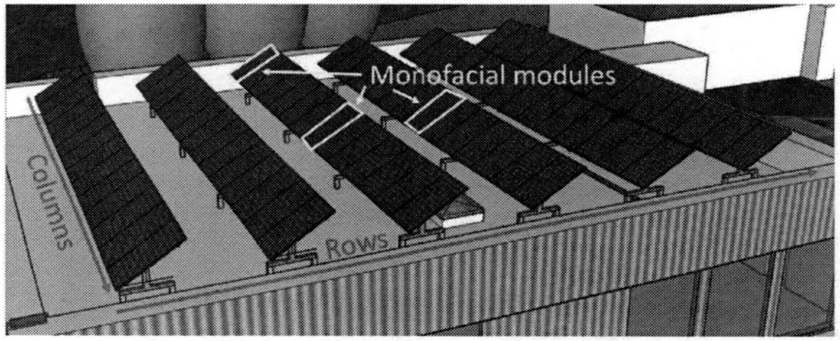

- **Carport: 43 kW$_p$**
  Impact of the carport structure and building

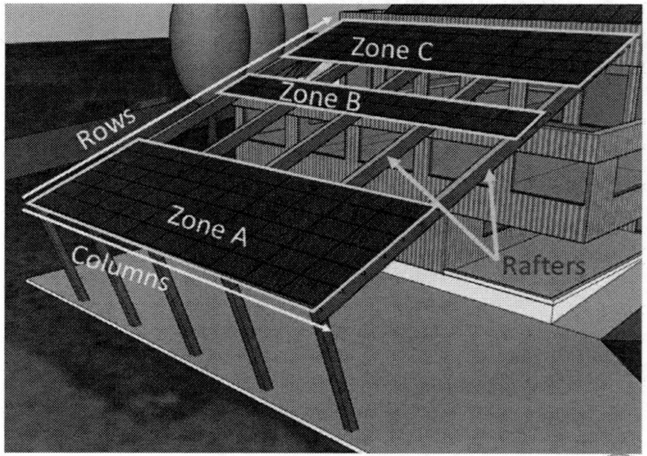

- *Nearby shading due to vegetation and neighbouring buildings has been modelled and the data filtered accordingly*

Flat rooftop – 28 kW_p : the simple case

- 1.5m height – 20° Tilted – Albedo= 30%
- Soluxtec 330W_p bifacial modules
  PERC+ solar cells – BiFi=70%
- *3 PV modules converted to monofacial*
  → **Real bifacial gain**

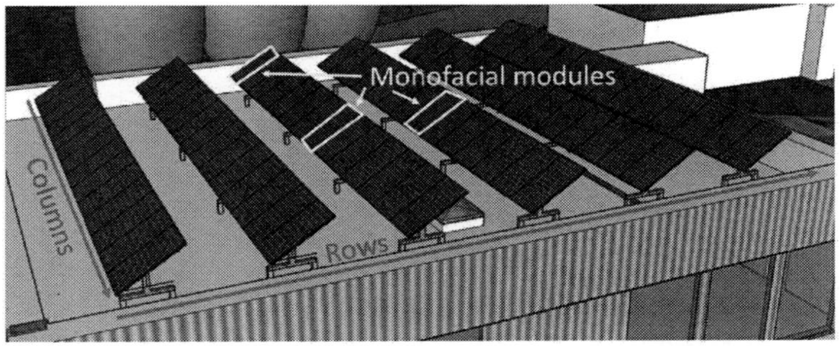

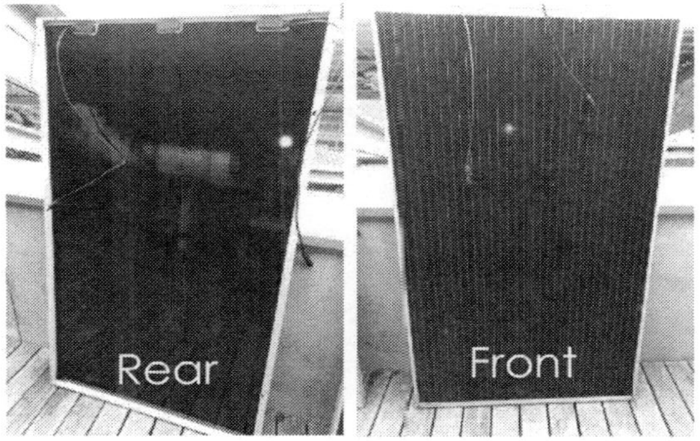

Rear-side irradiance & irradiation

INES INSTITUT NATIONAL DE L'ENERGIE SOLAIRE

Hourly irradiance – Front & Rear

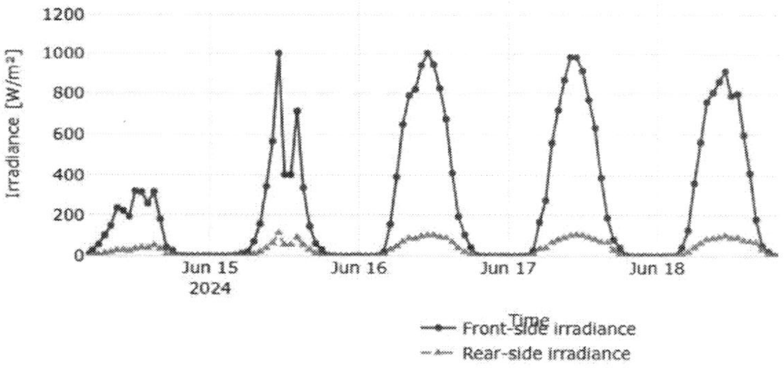

Irradiation and Rear/Front ratio

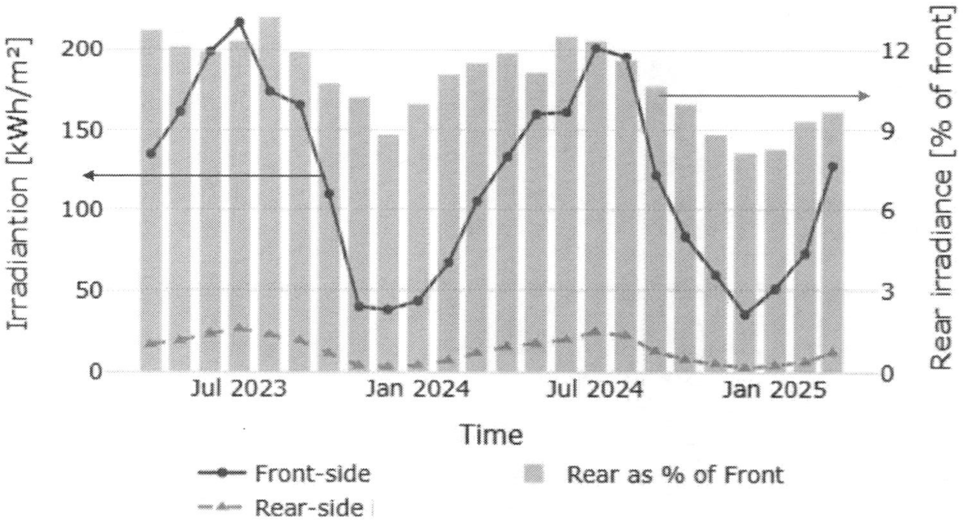

- 8-12% rear irradiation gain
  → *Favourable albedo and height*
- Seasonal effects

Energy distribution & Bifacial gain

INSTITUT NATIONAL DE L'ENERGIE SOLAIRE

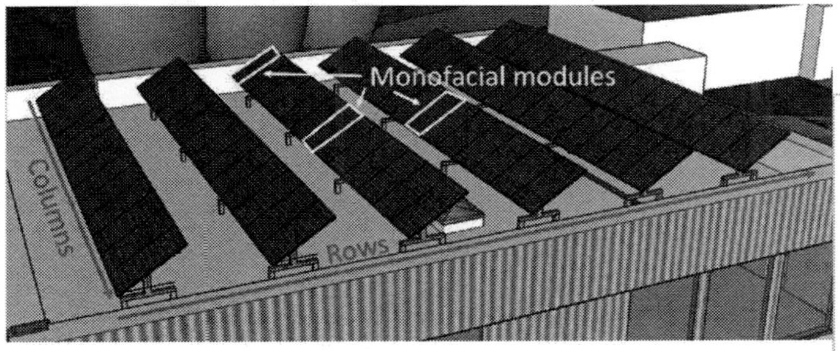

- *Homogeneous installation conditions*
- **Significant but not fully uniform bifacial energy gain**
- Higher relative gain at PV system edges (S & E)

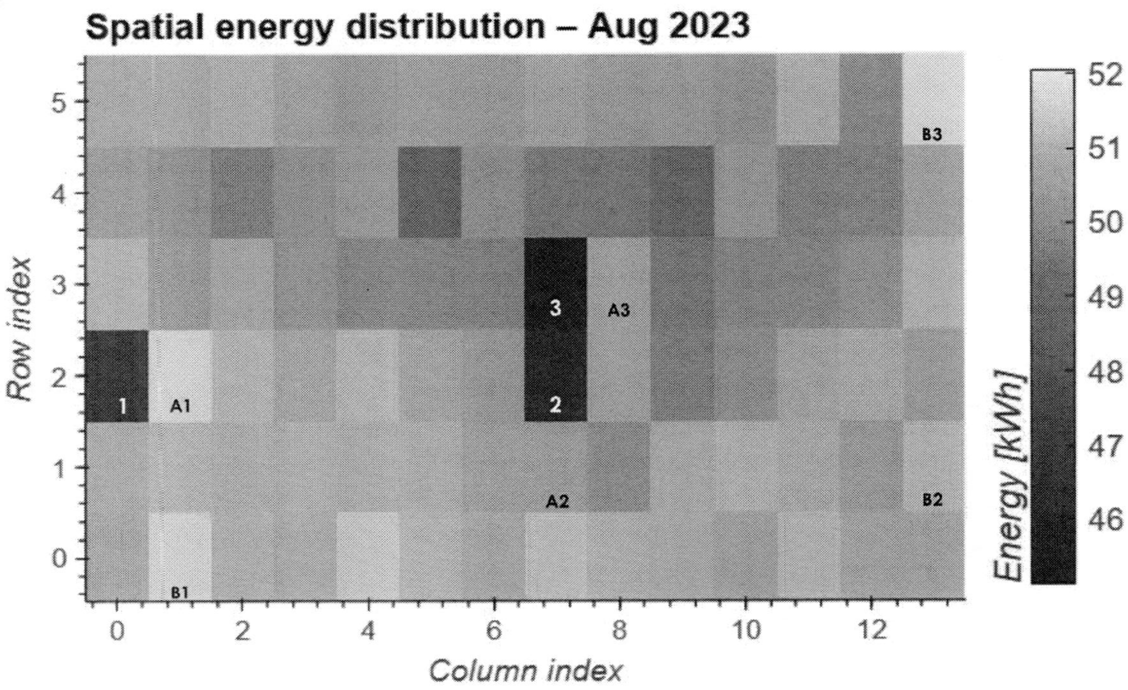

Energy distribution & Bifacial gain

INSTITUT NATIONAL DE L'ENERGIE SOLAIRE

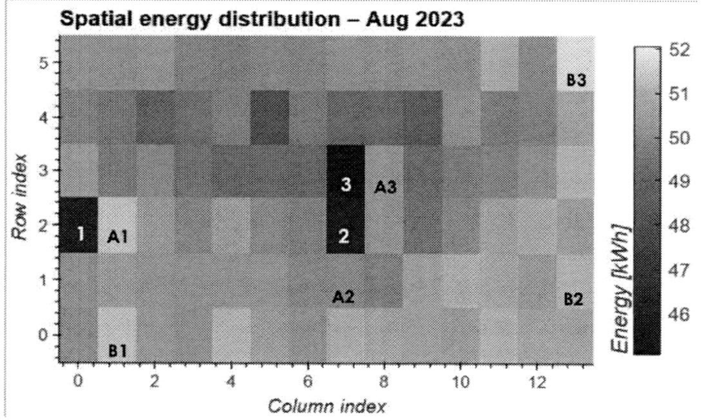

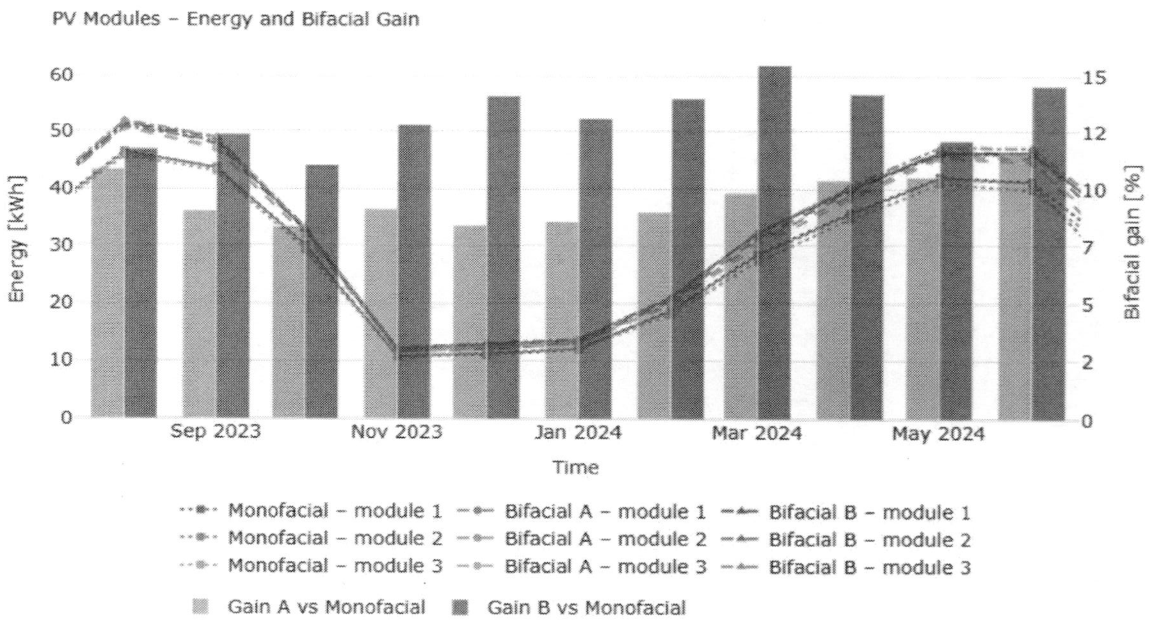

- **8 to 11% real absolute bifacial gain**
- Higher relative gain at PV system edges
- Small but non negligeable **3% current mismatch** in such homogeneous installation conditions → *cabling*

PLATEFORME FORMATION & ÉVALUATION

P. Besson et al. – EUPVSEC 2025

Carport – 43 kW_p : Rear Side Heterogeneity

INSTITUT NATIONAL DE L'ENERGIE SOLAIRE

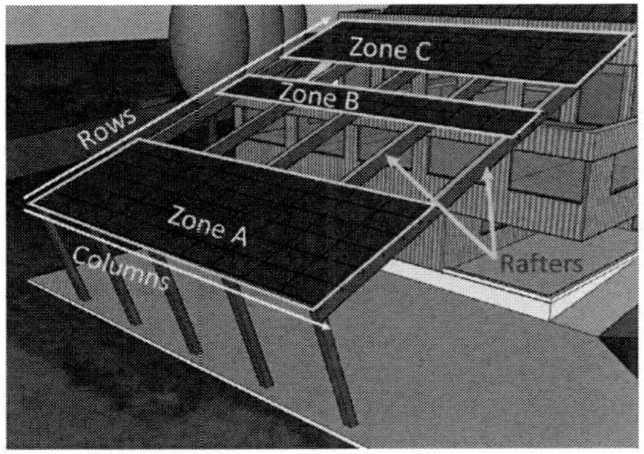

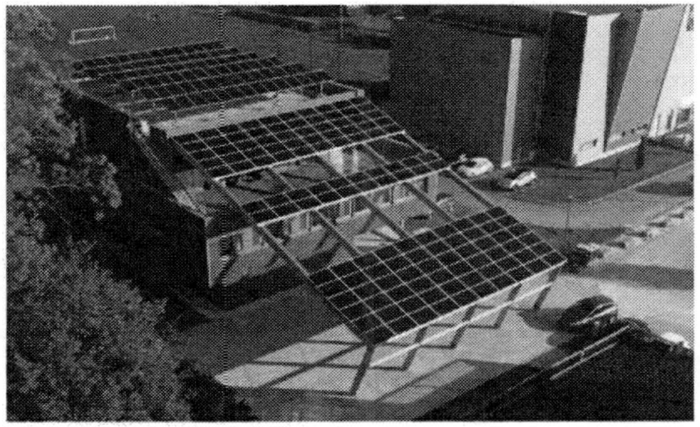

- Design phase vs. Reality

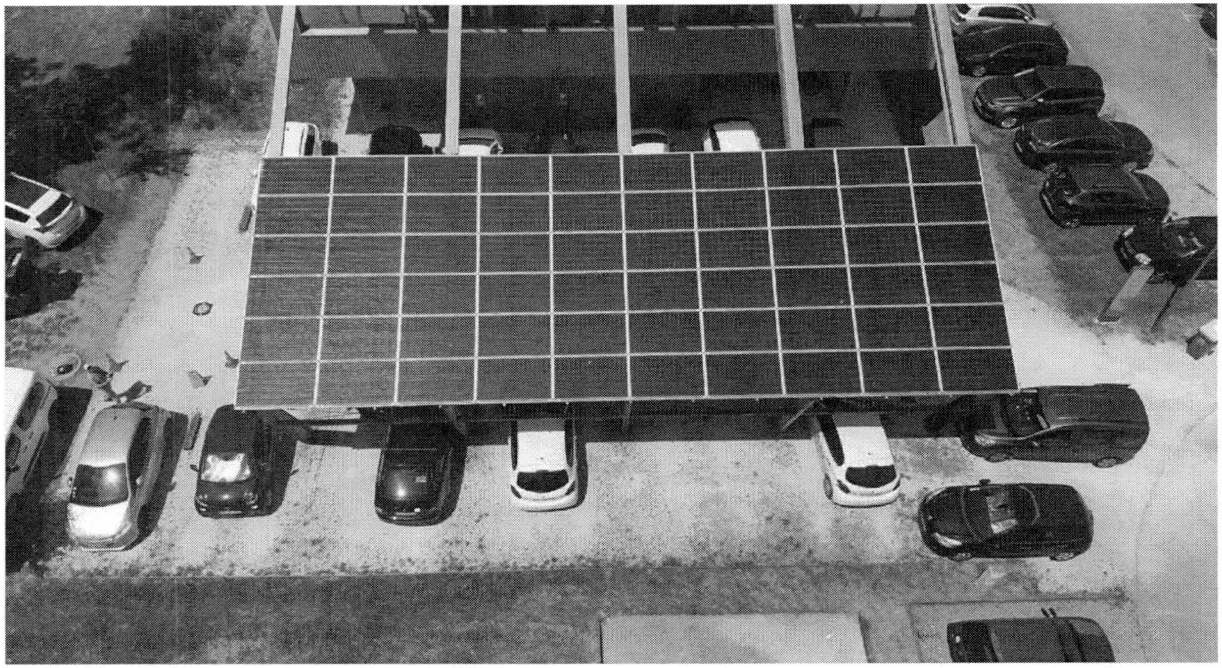

Carport – 43 kW_p : Rear Side Heterogeneity

INSTITUT NATIONAL DE L'ENERGIE SOLAIRE

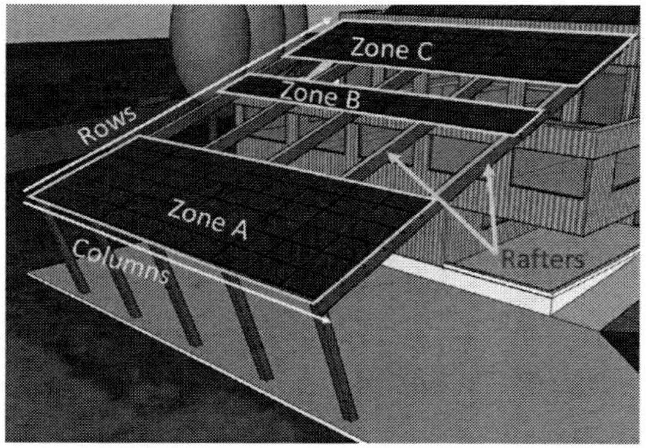

Carport – 43 kW_p : Rear Side Heterogeneity

INES INSTITUT NATIONAL DE L'ENERGIE SOLAIRE

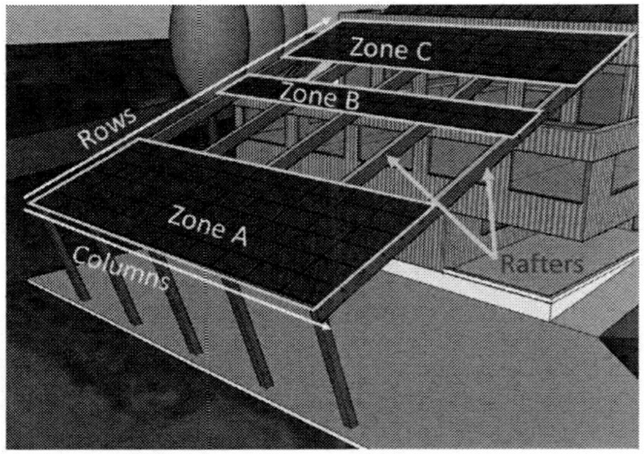

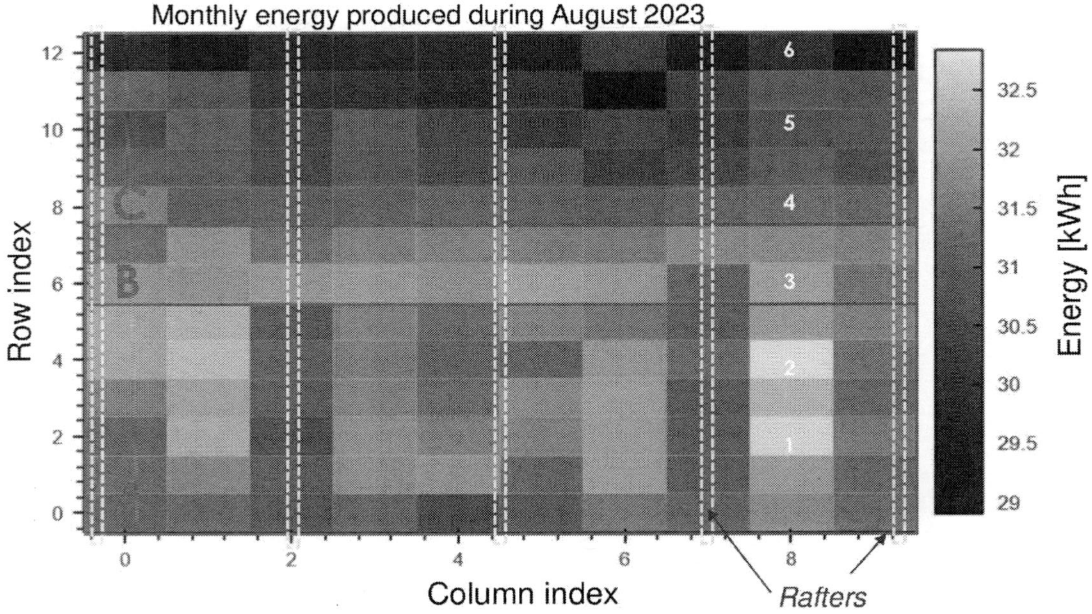

- **Impact of the carport/shading structure**
  → *up to 5% current mismatch along a row*
- Combined effect of **reduced rear side irradiance** and **higher temperature** near building

Carport – 43 kW_p : Rear Side Heterogeneity

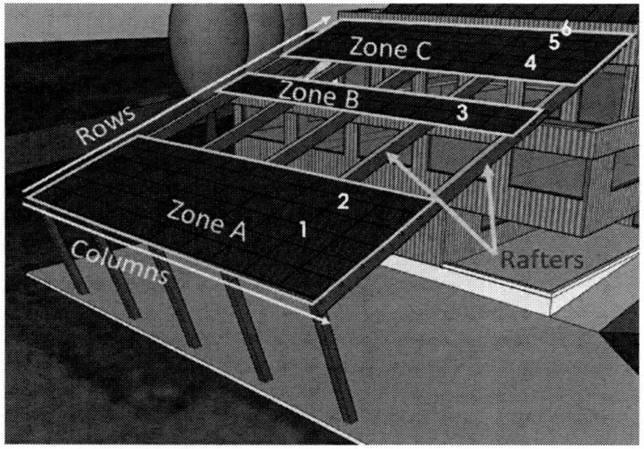

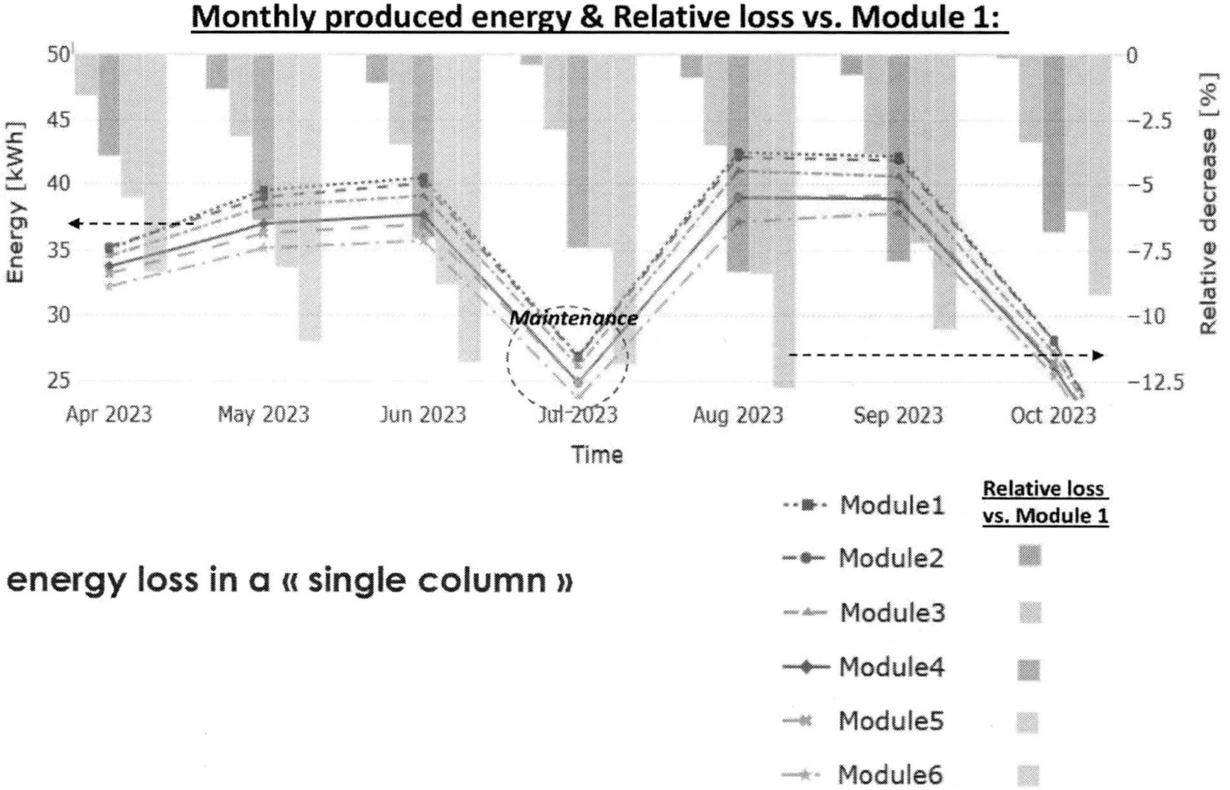

- Up to -12.5% relative monthly energy loss in a « single column »

When Temperature Cancels the Gain

INES INSTITUT NATIONAL DE L'ENERGIE SOLAIRE

Modules – Current over time

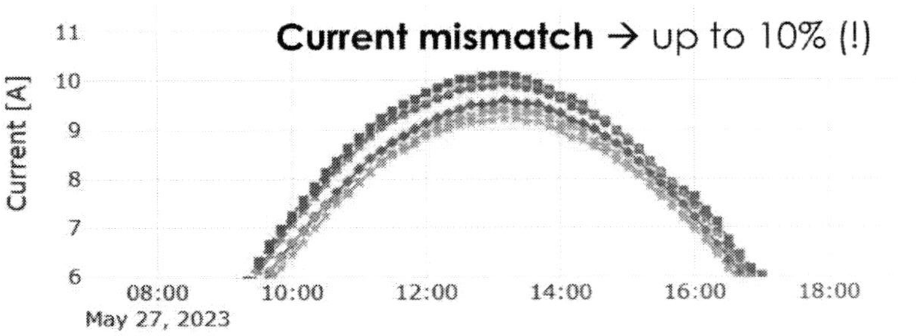

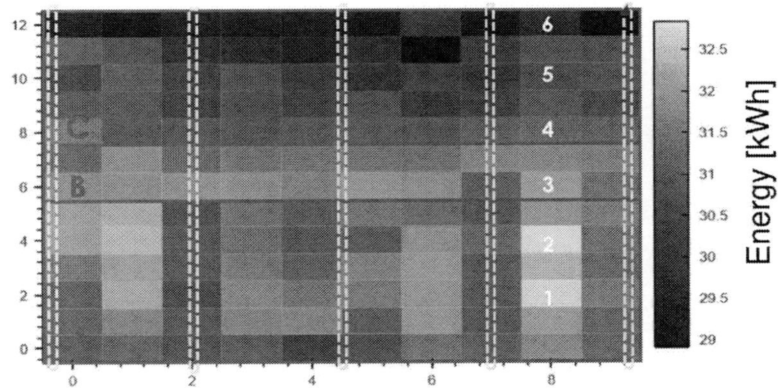

Modules – Voltage over time

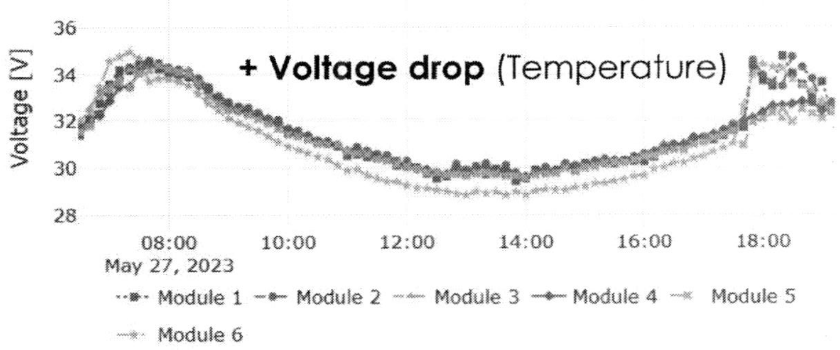

Module temperature (estimated from V & I)

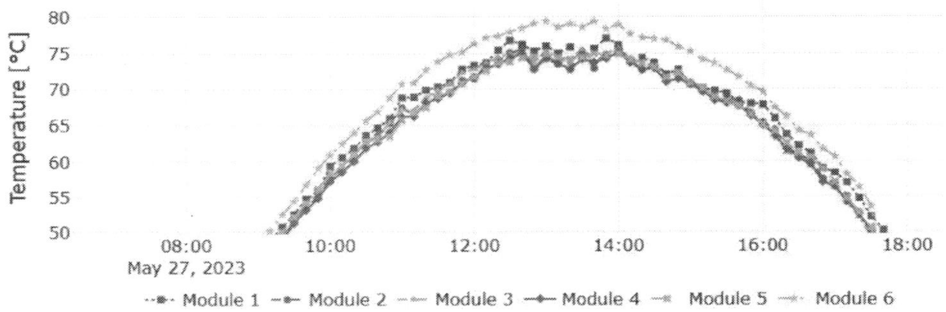

Conclusion

INES
INSTITUT NATIONAL DE L'ENERGIE SOLAIRE

- Flat Rooftop: reliable bifacial gain (8 to 11%)
  → Edge effect lead to additional 3% relative bifacial gain (and current mismatch)

- Carport: rear side irradiance heterogeneity + temperature increase near building
  → Up to 10% relative **current mismatch**
  → Difficult to simulate overall bifacial gain
- Non-uniform PV module degradation (T) may increase current mismatch

- *Points to watch out for when designing PV systems for C&I buildings:*
  → **Cabling** according to specific configurations (string inverters)
  → Micro-inverters and power-optimizers may be beneficial
- Simulation tools (PVlib, PVsyst, Archelios PRO) must handle **heterogeneity** *and rear-side shading losses*
  → Bridge the gap between models & reality

EU PVSEC 2025

ines INSTITUT NATIONAL DE L'ENERGIE SOLAIRE

cythelia ENERGY

trace software

Thanks for your attention

Jean-François LELIEVRE | jf.lelievre@ines-solaire.org

www.ines-solaire.org

PV Training Catalogue

- Consulting, sizing, design, installation, operation and maintenance
  - **35 PV training courses in the catalogue** (face-to-face, 100% online or hybrid)
  - **1 900 m² technical and teaching facilities**
  - **Short, long, certifying and tailor-made trainings**

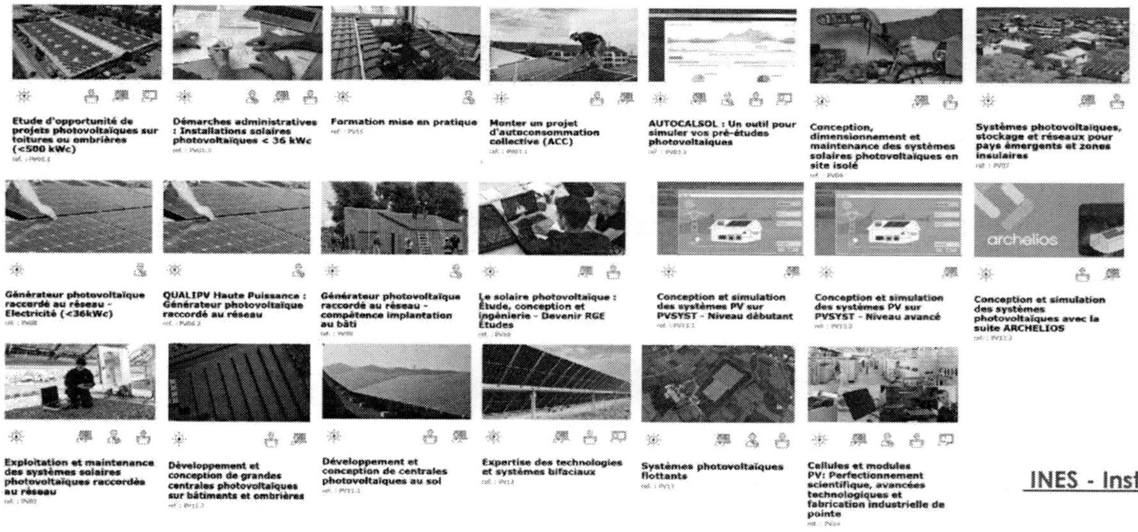

⇨ Our trainings
INES - Institut National de l'Énergie Solaire

Photovoltaic Expertise services

INES INSTITUT NATIONAL DE L'ENERGIE SOLAIRE

Consulting & Audits for professionals

- Review of technical documentation
- Study of innovative markets (technologies, economic models, etc.)
- Analysis on design or production (due diligence)
- Data analysis, specific R&D work

Installators | Design office | Developers | Energy unions | Chamber of Agriculture

Contracting authority support

- Solarization strategies, advice on regulatory requirements
- Global feasibility study
- Support for consulting with companies, critical review of bids
- Field performance audits for operating facilities

Local authorities | Industrials | Lenders | C&I

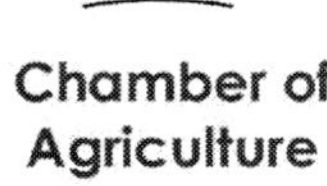

MODEL OPTIMIZATION FOR MULTI-CLASS REAL TIME UAV THERMAL ANOMALY DETECTION IN SOLAR PV SYSTEMS

G. Taghipour Kani [1], S.M. Esmailifar [1], A. Ghahremani[1], and M. Aghaei[2,3*]

[1] Department of Aerospace Engineering, Amirkabir University of Technology, Tehran 15119-43943, Iran
[2]Department of Ocean Operations and Civil Engineering, Norwegian University of Science and Technology (NTNU), 6009 Ålesund, Norway
[3]Department of Sustainable Systems Engineering (INATECH), University of Freiburg, 79110 Freiburg, Germany

* mohammadreza.aghaei@ntnu.no

ABSTRACT: This study investigates an intelligent UAV-based thermal inspection framework for photovoltaic (PV) modules, aiming to improve fault detection accuracy while ensuring suitability for real-time aerial deployment. Utilizing deep learning techniques, the system evaluates and compares multiple Convolutional Neural Network (CNN) architectures and YOLO classifiers for multi-class thermal anomaly detection. A comprehensive dataset of 20,000 aerial infrared images, categorized into nine distinct fault classes, was used to assess each model's classification performance and computational efficiency. CNNs such as EfficientNet and ResNet50 achieved strong classification results, with EfficientNet reaching an accuracy of 84%. However, their high inference latency and large model sizes pose challenges for onboard processing in UAV-based systems, particularly under power and memory constraints. Alternatively, the YOLO family of models demonstrated a compelling balance of speed, compactness, and accuracy. Among them, YOLOv8n offered exceptional runtime performance with an inference time of just 8 ms and a model size of 2.94 MB, making it ideal for lightweight deployment. At the same time, YOLOv8l achieved a Top-1 accuracy of 83.02% after hyperparameter tuning. The study highlights how YOLO classifiers can outperform traditional CNNs in practical UAV deployment scenarios, maintaining high accuracy while significantly reducing computational costs. The findings underscore YOLO's viability as a scalable and efficient solution for real-time PV anomaly detection, supporting the main goal of autonomous and cost-effective solar farm maintenance.

Keywords: UAV-based monitoring; thermal anomaly detection; photovoltaic modules; convolutional neural networks (CNNs); YOLO classifiers; real-time inspection; PV fault detection

1 INTRODUCTION AND MOTIVATION

The growing demand for renewable energy has led to a rapid expansion of photovoltaic (PV) installations globally. As solar farms scale up, maintaining their performance and detecting faults in a timely manner becomes increasingly critical. Undetected anomalies such as hot spots, diode failures, or module cracking can significantly reduce energy output, impacting the overall system efficiency and lifespan. Traditional inspection methods including manual walk-throughs, infrared thermography using handheld devices, and electroluminescence imaging, are labor-intensive, time-consuming, and often impractical for large-scale solar farms. These approaches fail to provide the responsiveness required for real-time maintenance, particularly when instant anomaly detection is essential to minimize operational downtime [1-5].

The convergence of UAV (Unmanned Aerial Vehicle) technology, infrared imaging systems, and machine learning has introduced promising alternatives for automated PV monitoring. UAVs equipped with thermal cameras can perform rapid, non-contact inspections across vast areas, also, machine learning models can process thermal imagery to identify and classify a wide range of PV anomalies [6-8].

One notable system, RoboPV, developed by Moradi Sizkouhi et al. [9], exemplifies this integration by combining autonomous UAV navigation with fault detection capabilities. However, despite its strengths in visual inspection and automation, existing solutions often fall short in terms of real-time responsiveness when deployed onboard UAVs. Specifically, the challenge lies in selecting a model that balances classification accuracy with computational efficiency, ensuring deployment feasibility within the hardware constraints of UAVs.

To address this challenge, the present study proposes a comprehensive framework for model optimization tailored to UAV-based thermal anomaly detection in PV farms. We conduct a comparative evaluation of Convolutional Neural Networks (CNNs) and YOLO (You Only Look Once) classifiers using a dataset of 20,000 aerial infrared images spanning nine PV fault categories. While CNNs like EfficientNet offer high classification accuracy, their deployment is hindered by inference latency and model size. In contrast, YOLO models demonstrate substantial promises for real-time onboard deployment due to their lightweight architecture and high-speed inference. The key contributions of this work are as follows:

- A multi-class thermal image dataset comprising diverse PV anomalies is curated and preprocessed for model training.
- A comparative study is conducted across several CNN architectures and YOLO classifiers, considering both classification and computational metrics.
- A hyperparameter tuning process is employed to improve model efficiency and accuracy, especially for real-time UAV operations.
- The best-performing models are analyzed for practical integration into UAV-based inspection workflows, highlighting the trade-offs and deployment strategies.

10.4229/EUPVSEC2025/4DO.17.2

By optimizing both detection performance and operational efficiency, this study provides actionable insights for developing intelligent UAV-based inspection platforms in large-scale solar energy systems.

1.2 Dataset Description

The dataset used in this study comprises 20,000 aerial infrared images, each labeled into one of nine distinct classes representing various PV module conditions. Eight of these classes correspond to common anomalies found in operational solar farms, such as diode failures, vegetation obstruction, or surface cracking, while one class represents normal, defect-free modules. This diverse composition ensures that the dataset closely reflects real-world scenarios encountered during solar PV farm inspection [10, 11]. All images were captured using UAVs equipped with high-resolution mid-wave and long-wave infrared sensors, covering wavelengths between 3 and 13.5 μm. Depending on the sensor and altitude, the ground sampling distance (GSD) varied between 3.0 and 15.0 cm per pixel, ensuring adequate thermal granularity for detecting subtle anomalies.

Figure 1. Representative sample images from each of the nine classes in the dataset, showcasing the variety of thermal anomalies and the no-anomaly condition in PV modules.

Class distribution was intentionally imbalanced to reflect operational conditions in large PV farms, where most modules function nominally. The "No-Anomaly" class, comprising half of the dataset (10,000 images), helps the model generalize effectively by exposing it to a wide range of normal patterns. The remaining 10,000 images are distributed among the eight anomaly classes, each representing critical conditions that may lead to performance degradation.

Representative sample images for each class are shown in Figure 1, illustrating the diversity of thermal features across the dataset. For better visual clarity, thermal colormaps were applied to the originally grayscale infrared images, allowing more intuitive observation of temperature differences and localized heat signatures.

Table 1. Dataset Description

Class Name	Number of Images	Description
Hot-Spot	3,663	High-temperature regions indicating faults.
Cracking	941	Surface cracks visible through thermal imaging.
Shadowing	1,056	Obstructions caused by vegetation or structures.
Diode	1,499	Activation of bypass diodes, reducing module efficiency.
Diode-Multi	175	Multiple activated bypass diodes.
Vegetation	1,639	Panels blocked by vegetation.
Soiling	205	Dirt or debris affecting energy generation.
Offline-Module	828	Entire modules disconnected from the circuit.
No-Anomaly	10,000	Defect-free modules.

2. IMPLEMENTING ANOMALY MODELS

2.1 CNN Models

This study evaluated a variety of convolutional neural network (CNN) architectures to identify thermal anomalies in PV modules using aerial infrared imagery. The models were selected based on their popularity in image classification tasks and their diversity in depth, complexity, and computational requirements. Evaluation focused not only on classification performance measured by metrics such as test accuracy and F1 score but also on computational aspects like inference time and model size, which are critical for UAV deployment.

All CNNs were implemented using the TensorFlow framework, chosen for its extensive support for deep learning development and its compatibility with both GPU and embedded hardware environments. To ensure a fair comparison, all models were trained under consistent conditions. The dataset was split into training, validation, and test sets, using an 80–10–10 ratio, and standardized image input sizes of 96×96 pixels were applied across all networks.

Training was performed for up to 600 epochs with a batch size of 32, utilizing the early stopping technique with a patience threshold of 100 epochs to prevent overfitting. This allowed training to stop once validation performance stopped improving, saving computation time and preserving generalizability. Furthermore, data augmentation techniques such as random rotations, horizontal and vertical flips, brightness variation, and zooming, were employed to simulate real-world variations in UAV flight conditions and environmental factors, thus enhancing model robustness.

10.4229/EUPVSEC2025/4DO.17.2

The evaluated CNN architecture ranged from lightweight custom-designed models to well-established deep networks, including:

- Simple CNN: A baseline model with minimal convolutional and dense layers.
- Deep CNN: A deeper variant of the baseline with increased layers and complexity.
- VGG16: A widely used deep model characterized by a fixed set of 3×3 convolution filters and large parameter count.
- DenseNet: An architecture utilizing dense connectivity for improved feature propagation.
- EfficientNet: A compound-scaled network that balances accuracy and efficiency.
- InceptionV3: A multi-scale processing architecture for diverse feature extraction.
- MobileNet: A lightweight model utilizing depthwise separable convolutions, well-suited for resource-limited applications.
- ResNet50: A residual learning network that enables deep model training by mitigating gradient vanishing.

Each of these models offers distinct trade-offs in terms of depth, parameter count, and memory footprint, allowing a comprehensive evaluation of their feasibility for deployment in UAV-based PV inspection platforms. The following section details the performance of each model and their implications for real-time anomaly detection.

2.2 YOLO Classification Models

YOLO (You Only Look Once) classifiers are modern deep learning models engineered for high-speed computer vision tasks such as object detection, classification, and segmentation. Unlike traditional multi-stage pipelines, YOLO performs all tasks in a single forward pass, making it exceptionally fast and suitable for real-time applications such as UAV-based thermal monitoring of solar farms.

In this study, we utilized YOLO models for pure classification purposes by employing classification-specific versions of YOLOv8 and YOLO11. These variants are designed to handle multi-class classification efficiently. This architectural modification reduces computational load while retaining the core benefits of YOLO's backbone and feature extraction layers.

The YOLO models were implemented using the Ultralytics framework, which offers a high-level, modular interface for training and deployment. This framework supports rapid prototyping, GPU acceleration, and straightforward conversion for edge inference, aligning well with the constraints of UAV onboard processing.

A total of 14 YOLO models including .pt-based pre-trained models and .yaml-based custom configurations were trained and evaluated. Consistent training parameters were used across all models:

- Input resolution: 96×96 pixels (to match CNN training)
- Training epochs: Up to 600
- Batch size: 32
- Early stopping: Patience of 100 epochs

Data augmentation was also applied during YOLO training using random horizontal flips, scaling, HSV augmentation, and mosaic augmentation. These augmentations help improve model generalization, especially under variable UAV altitudes, lighting conditions, and vegetation interference.

YOLO classifiers were evaluated based on classification performance (Top-1 and Top-5 accuracy), as well as computational efficiency (inference time and model size). Given that UAV platforms often rely on embedded hardware or edge AI accelerators with limited memory and processing power, inference latency and memory footprint were critical metrics in our selection process.

The results, discussed in later sections, demonstrate that YOLO architectures, particularly YOLOv8n and YOLOv8l, offer a promising balance between high classification accuracy and minimal computational demand. This makes them strong candidates for real-time, onboard fault detection in UAV-based PV inspection systems.

3. TRAINING RESULTS AND MODEL OPTIMIZATION

3.1 CNN Models Results

As summarized in Table 2, the performance of CNN architectures varied significantly in terms of both classification accuracy and computational efficiency. Among the evaluated models, EfficientNet achieved the highest test accuracy (84%) and F1 score (0.837), making it the top-performing CNN for identifying PV module anomalies. Its compound-scaling strategy, which simultaneously balances depth, width, and input resolution, allows it to extract highly discriminative features, contributing to its superior classification performance.

Table 2. Performance Report of CNN Models

CNN Model	Test Accuracy	F1 Score	Inference Time (ms)	Model Size (MB)
Simple CNN	0.751	0.736	76	23.4
Deep CNN	0.620	0.598	144	126.7
VGG16	0.500	0.333	410	186.4
DenseNet	0.791	0.789	2121	110.7
EfficientNet	0.840	0.837	2522	82.4
InceptionV3	0.779	0.770	1200	262.2
MobileNet	0.807	0.808	886	61.3
ResNet50	0.822	0.816	1012	331.9

However, this accuracy came at a computational cost: EfficientNet's inference time was measured at 2522 ms, and its model size reached 82.4 MB. These figures indicate significant processing and memory requirements, making EfficientNet less suitable for real-time deployment on UAV platforms where latency and power efficiency are critical.

ResNet50, another high-performing architecture, attained a test accuracy of 82.2% and an F1 score of 0.816. Its residual learning framework facilitates deeper networks by avoiding vanishing gradients, enabling robust learning even with complex data like thermal anomalies. While ResNet50 demonstrated faster inference compared to EfficientNet (1012 ms), its model size of 331.9 MB poses a significant limitation for embedded deployment.

In contrast, MobileNet emerged as the most balanced CNN for real-time applications. With a test accuracy of 80.7%, an F1 score of 0.808, and an inference time of 886 ms, MobileNet offers reasonable classification performance while maintaining a compact model size of 61.3 MB. Its

use of depthwise separable convolutions significantly reduces computational complexity, making it well-suited for lightweight deployment on UAVs.
Other models such as DenseNet, InceptionV3, and VGG16 demonstrated moderate to low classification performance or suffered from high computational costs. Notably, DenseNet achieved a decent accuracy of 79.1%, but required 2121 ms for inference and 110.7 MB of memory. The VGG16 model, while historically impactful, performed poorly in this study, highlighting the limitations of older architectures in real-time aerial thermal classification tasks.

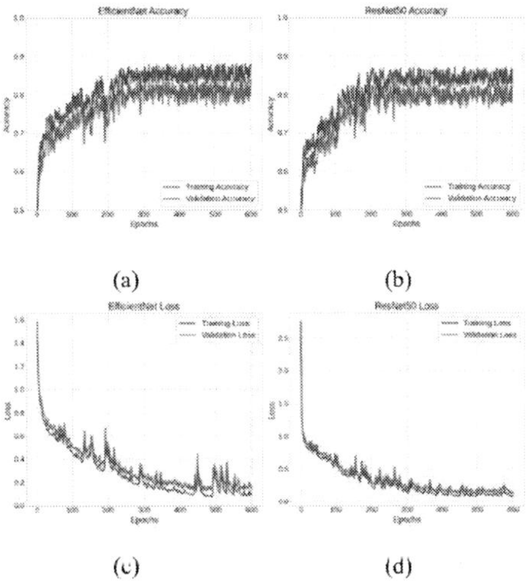

Figure 2. Loss and accuracy curves for two best-performing CNN models: a) EfficientNet accuracy curve, b) ResNet50 accuracy curve, c) EfficientNet loss curve and d) ResNet50 loss curve.

Training and validation learning curves for EfficientNet and ResNet50 (shown in Figure 2) further confirm the robustness of these models. Both displayed steady convergence during training. EfficientNet exhibited consistently higher validation accuracy and lower validation loss across epochs, indicating stronger generalization.
Overall, while CNNs excel at anomaly classification when computational resources are not a constraint, their use in real-time UAV-based monitoring is limited unless compressed or accelerated variants are deployed. In such scenarios, MobileNet offers a feasible trade-off, enabling on-board inference with acceptable accuracy and latency.

3.2 YOLO Classifiers Results

The YOLO classification models were assessed based on their Top-1 and Top-5 classification accuracy, inference time, and model size. These metrics are critical when evaluating model suitability for real-time UAV-based deployment, where processing speed and memory usage must be tightly controlled without sacrificing detection precision.

Table 3. YOLO Model Performance

YOLO Classifier	Top-1 Accuracy	Top-5 Accuracy	Inference Time (ms)	Model Size (Mb)
yolov8l-cls.pt	0.815	0.991	11.0	70.92
yolov8l-cls.yaml	0.817	0.990	12.07	70.93
yolov8m-cls.pt	0.808	0.992	10.0	30.97
yolov8m-cls.yaml	0.807	0.993	10.0	30.98
yolov8n-cls.pt	0.807	0.992	8.0	2.94
yolov8n-cls.yaml	0.804	0.991	14.0	2.95
yolov8s-cls.pt	0.809	0.990	8.95	10.06
yolov8s-cls.yaml	0.808	0.992	8.0	10.05
yolov8x-cls.pt	0.814	0.993	21.0	109.88
yolov8x-cls.yaml	0.811	0.993	12.0	109.89
yolo11l-cls.pt	0.806	0.991	17.06	25.37
yolo11m-cls.pt	0.802	0.989	14.96	20.44
yolo11n-cls.pt	0.792	0.991	10.0	3.15
yolo11s-cls.pt	0.800	0.990	11.00	10.81
yolo11x-cls.pt	0.810	0.992	16.04	55.71

As shown in Table 3, YOLOv8n-cls.pt stood out for its exceptional computational efficiency. With an inference time of 8 ms and a compact model size of 2.94 MB, it offers ultra-fast processing and minimal memory footprint, ideal characteristics for embedded systems on UAVs. Despite its compact size, it maintained strong classification accuracy with Top-1: 0.807 and Top-5: 0.992, highlighting its robustness even in lightweight configurations.
Meanwhile, YOLOv8l-cls.pt emerged as the most accurate classifier among the tested YOLO variants, achieving a Top-1 accuracy of 0.815 and Top-5 accuracy of 0.991. Its inference time of 11 ms and moderate model size of 70.92 MB place it comfortably within the operational limits of many UAV hardware setups, especially those equipped with edge AI accelerators. Its balance of accuracy and efficiency makes it particularly suitable for large-scale PV farm monitoring where real-time decision-making is essential.
The larger model YOLOv8x-cls.pt also delivered competitive results, with a Top-1 accuracy of 0.814 and Top-5 of 0.993. However, its inference time of 21 ms and model size of 109.88 MB limit its applicability to higher-end platforms, where computational capacity is more abundant.
The performance of YOLO11 models was slightly lower across the board, although YOLO11l-cls.pt provided the best trade-off in this group with 0.806 Top-1 accuracy and 17.06 ms inference time. These models still demonstrated reliable performance but did not surpass their YOLOv8 counterparts in either speed or accuracy.

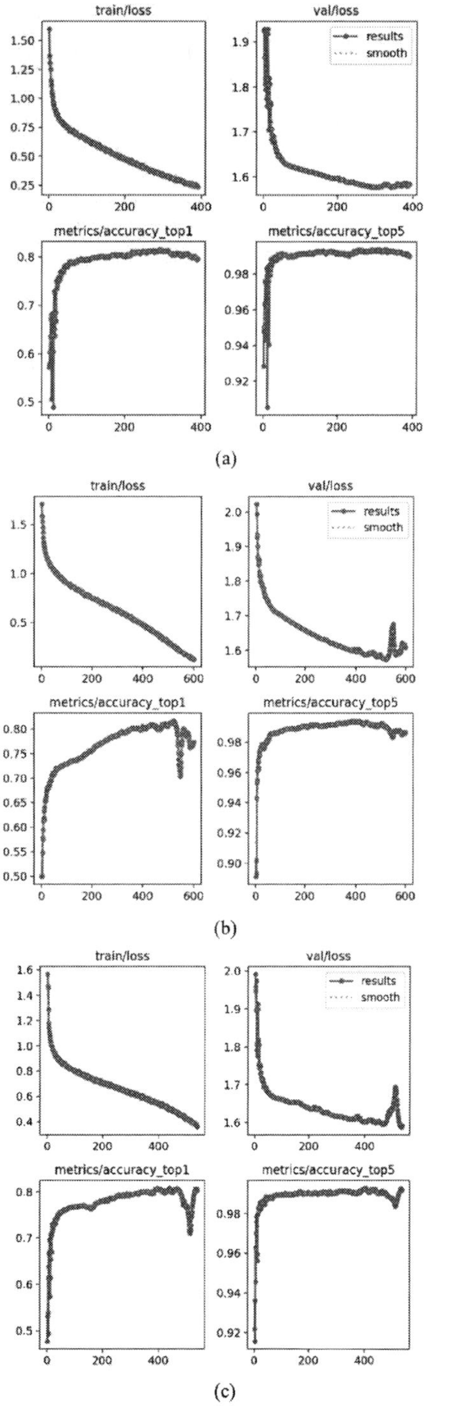

Figure 3. Loss and accuracy curves for best-performing YOLO classifiers: a) yolov8x-cls.pt training process, b) yolov8l-cls.yaml and c) yolov8n-cls.pt during the training process.

The training and validation curves shown in Figure 3 (for YOLOv8x, YOLOv8l, and YOLOv8n) illustrate consistent convergence patterns and highlight the impact of the built-in early stopping mechanism in the Ultralytics framework. This strategy effectively prevented overfitting by stopping the training once validation metrics stopped improving, thereby saving computational resources and promoting generalization.

Key insights from this evaluation are as follows:

- Performance Trade-offs: YOLOv8l offers the best overall accuracy, while YOLOv8n achieves the lowest inference latency and model size, making each suitable for different UAV deployment scenarios.
- High Top-5 Accuracy: All models consistently exceeded 99% Top-5 accuracy, indicating that even when misclassifications occurred, the correct class remained among the top candidates.
- Real-Time Feasibility: The combination of fast inference times and compact model footprints confirms the YOLOv8 series' viability for real-time thermal anomaly detection on UAVs.

In summary, the YOLO models, particularly those from the v8 series, demonstrate strong classification performance and superior computational efficiency compared to traditional CNN architectures. These traits make them well-suited for deployment in UAV-based PV inspection systems where speed, reliability, and hardware constraints are critical factors.

3.3 Performance Optimization and Model Tuning

To enhance the real-time applicability of YOLO models for UAV-based thermal anomaly detection, a comprehensive hyperparameter tuning was conducted. The aim was to boost classification performance, particularly Top-1 accuracy, while preserving computational efficiency for large-scale solar monitoring. Three models (YOLOv8n, YOLOv8l, and YOLOv8x) were selected due to their strong pre-tuning accuracy and manageable footprints. A grid search explored 30 hyperparameter combinations per model, including learning rates (lr0, lrf), momentum, weight decay, warmup epochs, and augmentation factors (HSV range, scale, mosaic probability). The objective was to improve the fitness score, a composite of accuracy and loss convergence, without increasing inference time or size.

Post-tuning results (Tables 4 and 5) showed clear gains:

- **YOLOv8x:** Fitness 0.902, Top-1 82.13%, Top-5 99.37%. Validation loss decreased with smoother convergence, enhancing generalization. Though still computationally heavy, it is better suited for precision-critical use.
- **YOLOv8n:** Fitness 0.90238, Top-1 82.25%, Top-5 99.23%. Maintained 8 ms inference and 2.94 MB size, reinforcing its role as the best trade-off for resource-limited UAVs.
- **YOLOv8l:** Highest fitness 0.9055, Top-1 83.02%, Top-5 99.17%. Its larger capacity improved detection of subtle anomalies, making it ideal where accuracy and real-time performance must both be met.

Table 4. Tuned Hyperparameter Configurations

Model	lr0	lrf	Momentum	Weight Decay	Warmup Epochs	HSV-H	Scale	Mosaic
YOLOv8x	0.01	0.01	0.937	0.0005	3.0	0.015	0.5	1.0
YOLOv8n	0.0101	0.01112	0.91359	0.00047	2.78907	0.015	0.6	0.99306
YOLOv8l	0.00939	0.01112	0.92606	0.00044	3.01336	0.014	0.488	0.977

Table 5. Tuning Results

Model	Pre-Tuning Accuracy	Post-Tuning Accuracy	Inference Time (ms)	Model Size (MB)
YOLOv8n	0.807	0.822	8.0	2.94
YOLOv8l	0.817	0.830	12.07	70.92
YOLOv8x	0.814	0.821	21.0	109.88

The tuned hyperparameter configurations (Table 4) and resulting performance metrics (Table 5) clearly illustrate the impact of tuning on model effectiveness. Visualizations of normalized confusion matrices (Figure 4) further confirm that class-level misclassifications were reduced post-tuning, especially in minority classes such as "Soiling" and "Diode-Multi," which are often difficult to distinguish in thermal images.

By optimizing these YOLO models, the framework not only achieved better predictive accuracy but also ensured that deployment feasibility on UAV platforms remained intact. This tuning process plays a vital role in closing the gap between high-performance classification and the practical requirements of real-world aerial inspection systems.

(a)

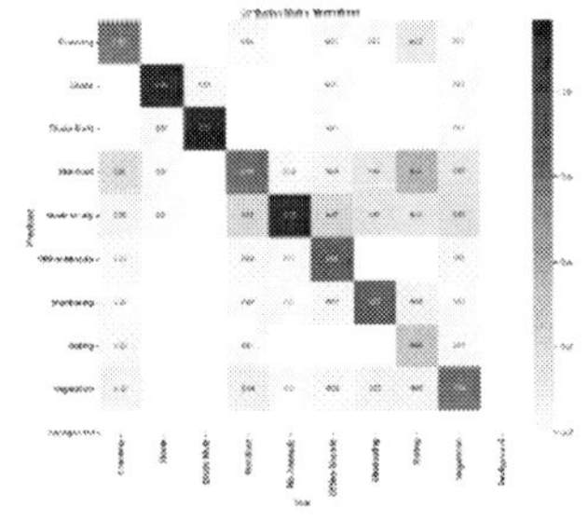

(b)

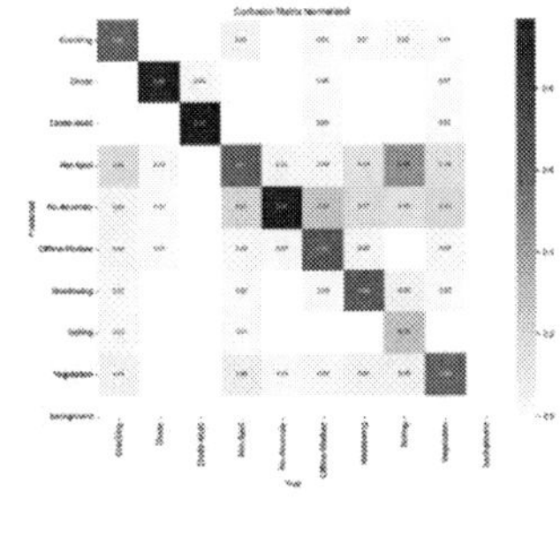

(c)

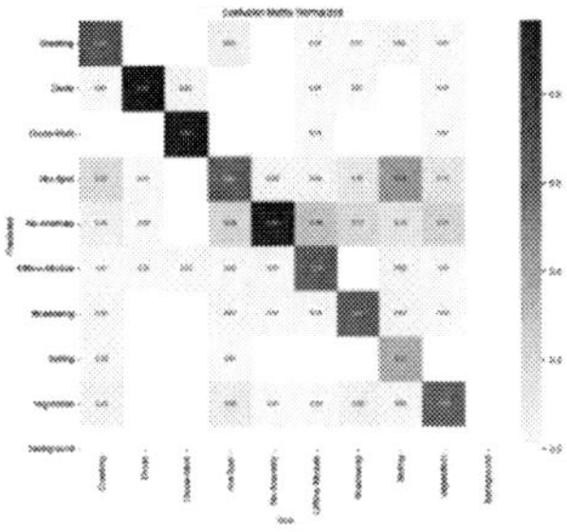

Figure 4. Normalized confusion matrices for tunned YOLO models: a) YOLOv8x, b) YOLOv8n, and c) YOLOv8l.

4 CONCLUSIONS

This study compared CNN and YOLO architectures for UAV-based thermal anomaly detection in PV systems, highlighting the trade-off between accuracy and computational efficiency. CNNs like EfficientNet and ResNet50 achieved strong Top-1 accuracies (84% and 82.2%) but suffered from high inference times (2522 ms and 1012 ms) and large sizes (82.4 MB and 331.9 MB), limiting real-time UAV deployment.

YOLO models proved far more practical. YOLOv8n achieved 82.25% Top-1 accuracy (post-tuning) with just 8 ms inference and a 2.94 MB size, ideal for UAV hardware constraints. YOLOv8l offered the best balance, with 83.02% Top-1 accuracy and 11 ms inference, suitable for missions requiring both precision and speed. All YOLO variants maintained Top-5 accuracies above 99%, confirming robustness in complex solar environments.

Hyperparameter tuning further improved detection, especially for minority classes, without raising computational costs. Overall, YOLO-based classifiers, particularly lightweight and tuned variants, represent a scalable solution for autonomous real-time PV inspection. Their efficiency and adaptability enable intelligent fault detection at scale, reducing downtime, streamlining maintenance, and supporting renewable energy optimization.

5 REFERENCES

1. Sriraman, D. and R. Ramaprabha. *Application of Machine Learning and Convolutional Neural Networks for the Fault Detection and Classification Monitoring System in PV Plants*. in *2023 9th International Conference on Electrical Energy Systems (ICEES)*. 2023.
2. Deitsch, S., et al., *Automatic classification of defective photovoltaic module cells in electroluminescence images*. Solar Energy, 2019. **185**: p. 455-468.
3. Fonseca Alves, R.H., et al., *Automatic fault classification in photovoltaic modules using Convolutional Neural Networks*. Renewable Energy, 2021. **179**: p. 502-516.
4. Nie, J., T. Luo, and H. Li, *Automatic hotspots detection based on UAV infrared images for large-scale PV plant*. Electronics Letters, 2020. **56**(19): p. 993-995.
5. Sinap, V. and A. Kumtepe, *CNN-based automatic detection of photovoltaic solar module*

anomalies in infrared images: a comparative study. Neural Computing and Applications, 2024.
6. Aghaei, M., A. Esksndari, and A. Reinders, *Autonomous Monitoring and Analysis of PV Systems by Unmanned Aerial Vehicles, Internet of Things and Big Data Analytics*. 2020.
7. Eskandari, A., et al., *Autonomous Monitoring of Line-to-Line Faults in Photovoltaic Systems by Feature Selection and Parameter Optimization of Support Vector Machine Using Genetic Algorithms.* Applied Sciences, 2020. **10**(16): p. 5527.
8. Moradi Sizkouhi, A., M. Aghaei, and S.M. Esmailifar, *A deep convolutional encoder-decoder architecture for autonomous fault detection of PV plants using multi-copters.* Solar Energy, 2021. **223**: p. 217-228.
9. Moradi Sizkouhi, A.M., et al., *RoboPV: An integrated software package for autonomous aerial monitoring of large scale PV plants.* Energy Conversion and Management, 2022. **254**: p. 115217.
10. Millendorf, M., E. Obropta, and N. Vadhavkar. *Infrared solar module dataset for anomaly detection.*
11. M. Aghaei, et al, *Autonomous Intelligent Monitoring of Photovoltaic Systems: An In-Depth Multidisciplinary Review,* Progress in Photovoltaics: Research and Applications, 2024, https://doi.org/10.1002/pip.3859.

OPTIMIZING AUTONOMOUS AERIAL MONITORING OF PHOTOVOLTAIC POWER PLANTS VIA AN INTEGRATED SOFTWARE PACKAGE AND A DIGITAL TWIN BASED SIMULATION ENVIRONMENT

M. Kolahi[1], S.M. Esmaeilifar[2], A. Moradi Sizkouhi[3], and M. Aghaei[4,5*]

[1] Department of Mechanical Engineering, Faculty of Engineering, University of Isfahan, 81746-73441, Isfahan, Iran
[2] Department of Aerospace Engineering, Amirkabir University of Technology, Tehran 15119-43943, Iran
[3]Department of Electrical and Computer Engineering, Concordia University, Montreal, QC H3G 1M8, Canada
[4]Department of Ocean Operations and Civil Engineering, Norwegian University of Science and Technology (NTNU), 6009 Ålesund, Norway
[5]Department of Sustainable Systems Engineering (INATECH), University of Freiburg, 79110 Freiburg, Germany

*mohammadreza.aghaei@ntnu.no

ABSTRACT: This paper presents an advanced embedded software package tailored for the autonomous aerial monitoring (AAM) of photovoltaic (PV) plants. It employs an encoder-decoder deep learning model to accurately pinpoint the boundary points of the PV plants. Additionally, a unique path-planning algorithm guarantees comprehensive coverage of the monitoring area. A highly precise neural network is also utilized to analyze images in real time, enabling automatic fault detection. To improve performance during inspections, custom decision-making, and maneuvering algorithms are designed to adapt to various flight conditions. To showcase and optimize the software's performance and test autonomous PV monitoring flights and missions, a virtual environment is also presented. This innovative platform allows for the examination of different scenarios and configurations of PV power plants, assessing their impact on the AAM process. It features tools for generating data that enable the development of intelligent monitoring and inspection models. The creation of this platform involved building a digital twin of a PV plant using Unreal Engine, simulating drone flight with AirSim, and expanding the application programming interfaces (APIs) to adapt to various scenarios for evaluating smart monitoring models and collecting datasets. Additionally, a dataset of aerial images was compiled from this platform to train a segmentation model aimed at identifying bird droppings on PV panels.

Keywords: Photovoltaic (PV) plants; Autonomous aerial monitoring (AAM), Artificial intelligence (AI); Digital twin (DT); Fault detection.

1 AIM AND APPROACH

The rapid growth of large-scale photovoltaic (PV) power plants is projected to supply over one-third of global electricity by 2050 [1]. To ensure energy performance and reliability, efficient monitoring strategies are essential as the number and size of PV plants continue to grow [2]. The use of AI and drones for inspections has transformed traditional monitoring methods, offering faster, more accurate assessments while reducing costs [3]. In this regard, we present an advanced embedded software package tailored for the autonomous aerial monitoring (AAM) of PV plants.

This software package is designed to revolutionize PV plant monitoring and inspection by providing an autonomous, efficient, and intelligent aerial inspection solution. It uses advanced deep learning and drones to facilitate real-time analysis during aerial inspections. It aims to improve the reliability and speed of detecting faults in large-scale PV plants, overcoming the limitations of traditional human-operated methods and significantly reducing inspection time.

When utilizing AI techniques for monitoring PV plants, one of the main challenges is the difficulty in obtaining a substantial set of annotated data [4]. Public datasets are often limited [3], [5], and conducting field flights to gather data or testing autonomous flights with intelligent models can be both costly and risky, as errors might lead to damage to either the drone or the PV panels. To address these challenges, this paper also introduces a digital twin (DT)-based environment designed for developing, simulating, and evaluating different smart monitoring models in the context of AAM of PV plants. This virtual testing environment is essential for evaluating our autonomous flight missions, incorporating aspects such as boundary detection, path planning, and fault detection, thus offering an important understanding of their abilities and possible efficiency in practical situations. Additionally, this framework enables efficient augmentation of our dataset with labeled images, which is useful for training a robust intelligent fault detection model.

Our approach for developing this environment involved first creating a virtual model of a utility-scale PV plant using the Unreal Engine. Subsequently, we conducted drone flight simulations with AirSim, expanding its Python APIs to test various monitoring models in defined scenarios. Through these contributions, our work aims to advance monitoring applications for PV systems, with a focus on optimizing the AAM of large-scale PV plant monitoring.

2 SCIENTIFIC INNOVATION AND RELEVANCE

2.1 Integrated Software Package

The proposed software automates inspections, path planning, image acquisition, fault detection, and decision-making. As Figure 1 provides, the software consists of four key units: i) A boundary detection module that Uses an encoder-decoder network to define the PV plant's boundaries before inspection. ii) A path planning module that generates an optimal flight path, ensuring full coverage of the PV area, is tailored to the drone's capabilities, such as endurance and maneuverability. iii) A dynamic processing unit that monitors flight data, allowing for real-time decision-making and remedial actions during inspections. Additionally, it allows the drone to maneuver closer to detected faults for detailed

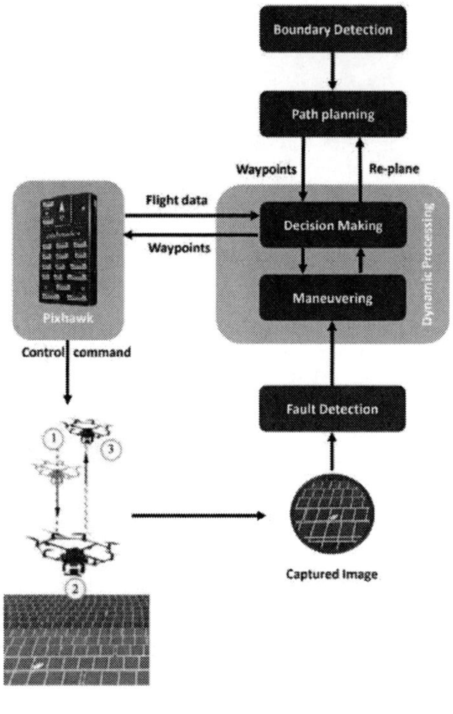

Figure 1: An overview of the proposed software package in AAM of a PV plant.

analysis and adjusts the flight plan based on battery levels, ensuring efficient operation. iv) A fault detection module that Processes video streams from PV modules to identify defects and locate their positions accurately [6].

Boundary Detection: Boundary detection is achieved using a modified encoder-decoder network built on a Fully Convolutional Network (FCN) backbone, which can identify the pixel-level boundaries of PV plants. The architecture of the proposed network can be seen in Figure 2.

To develop a robust image segmentation model, a comprehensive dataset of aerial images of large-scale photovoltaic plants, was utilized [7]. This dataset comprises a total of 3,584 aerial images of PV plants sourced from twelve different countries. For the purpose of training and validation, 80% of the dataset was randomly allocated for training, while the remaining 20% was set aside for validation.

Path Planning: The proposed software features an autonomous path-planning method designed to create the shortest, most efficient "lawn mower" path for monitoring PV plants. It uses data like camera field of view (FoV) and imaging height to calculate waypoints, ensuring full coverage of the plant. Waypoints are determined by intersecting the plant boundary with guidelines based on plant width, flight altitude, and camera FoV. This optimal path ensures drone effectively covers all areas, including corners.

Dynamic Processing: A dynamic algorithm that adjusts the route to capture closer images of identified anomalies enhances the proposed path planning method. An in-built control block establishes waypoints based on flight conditions. In Home Mode, the drone is at the home position and should take off and fly to the first waypoint. During Flight Mode, it follows a predetermined path, constantly updating its target waypoint as it approaches the current one. In Maneuver Mode which would be activated if a fault is detected, the drone descends to a height of 5 meters and hovers for 60 seconds to assess the situation. After this monitoring period, it will determine whether to continue on its current path or alter its trajectory based on the remaining battery life.

Fault Detection: This study proposes an encoder-decoder-based architecture for automatic fault detection in PV panels. A dataset of 2,400 synthetic aerial images was collected from the virtual PV plant in the DT-based simulation environment, to train an end-to-end segmentation model. This model is designed to detect bird droppings on PV panels without the need to separately extract individual modules from aerial images that feature multiple PV installations. The encoder, a modified VGG16, downsamples the input image and extracts feature maps, with the first 14 layers initialized using pre-trained ImageNet weights to improve training accuracy. The decoder upsamples the features via deconvolution, mapping low-resolution features to full-resolution images for pixel-level segmentation

2.2 DT-Based Simulation Environment

Our DT-based simulation environment comprises a dashboard that features a visualization interface, a flight simulation module, and a back-end system involving intelligent decision-making models and Python APIs designed for monitoring scenarios [8]. For the visualization interface, we have utilized Unreal Engine to build a highly realistic virtual PV plant, employing advanced graphics and physics simulations to closely replicate real-world conditions. The development process included modeling a 4-square-kilometer terrain and

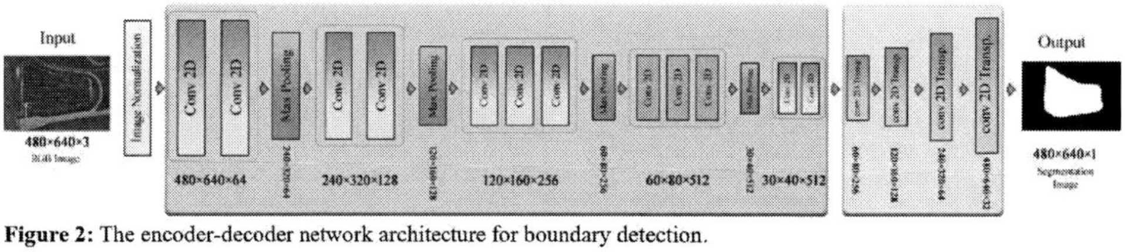

Figure 2: The encoder-decoder network architecture for boundary detection.

integrating various 3D assets such as vegetation, environmental features, and PV panels, all optimized for enhanced performance and realism.

Additionally, we crafted custom meshes to simulate faults on the PV panels. To simulate drone dynamics in the virtual PV plant environment, we use AirSim, which includes a quadrotor model, a physics engine for drag and collisions, and an environment model with magnetic fields, gravity, and air pressure. It also features sensors like barometers, gyroscopes, accelerometers, GPS, and RGB and depth cameras [9]. The camera settings were configured to a resolution of 480×640 with a 90-degree view, motion blur was disabled, and auto exposure speed was increased to 100 for improved image quality. Finally, to interact with the drone during simulations, the Airsim Python APIs were expanded to perform different tasks like tracking the generated flight path for monitoring, capturing images of PV arrays along the path, and executing maneuvers for detailed inspections when faults or anomalies are detected.

3 PERFORMANCE EVALUATION AND SIMULATION RESULTS

The performance of the proposed software package can be evaluated using two approaches: qualitative and quantitative assessments. Qualitative evaluations are performed in the computer simulation environment, while quantitative analyses are conducted using AI metrics like precision, F1-score, recall, accuracy, the Dice coefficient, and Intersection over Union (IoU), to measure the monitoring model's performance.

To quantitatively assess the performance of fault detection and boundary detection models, pixel accuracy is utilized. The boundary detection model achieved a training accuracy of 97.61% and a testing accuracy of 96.99%. Also, the fault detection model attained a training accuracy of 98.31% and a testing accuracy of 95.20%. Additionally, the fault detection model achieved a precision rate of 76.44% and a recall rate of 84.89%.

To qualitatively demonstrate the accuracy of the developed software package in performing AAM of a PV plant, it is essential to simulate the entire aerial monitoring process in real-world conditions.

For this purpose, All functions of the software package are simulated in real time within the developed DT-based simulation environment. A predefined scenario will be followed in the simulation environment which begins by extracting the boundaries of the virtual PV plant using a trained deep neural network. As illustrated in Figure 3, after the boundary of the PV plant is identified, a convex curve is drawn around it.

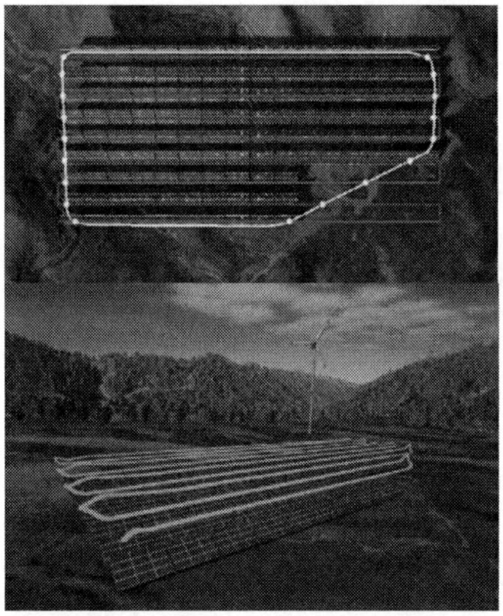

Figure 4: The designed trajectory for a PV plant (up) and trace line of the drone after passing the given waypoints (down).

The curve is input into the path planning algorithm, which creates the waypoints for aerial monitoring. The drone then proceeds to the first waypoint to begin its monitoring mission. During monitoring, the drone aims for the next waypoint in its path. It switches to the following waypoint when it gets close to the current one, and it continues this procedure until it successfully reaches the last waypoint (see Figure 4).

The drone flies along the planned path and takes pictures of the panels' surfaces with its camera. The fault detection model analyzes these images as shown in Figure 5, to find faults and sends a "fault flag" to a decision-making unit. Images also are tagged with locations, allowing the drone to investigate detected issues off its path. If the drone finds a faulty panel, it lowers itself to the problem's location for a closer look, taking detailed images of its modules and analyzing them (see Figure 6). After the investigation, the fault flag is reset, and the drone returns to its original height to continue its mission. Upon reaching the final waypoint, the drone is instructed to return home and lands back at the take-off location to complete the simulation.

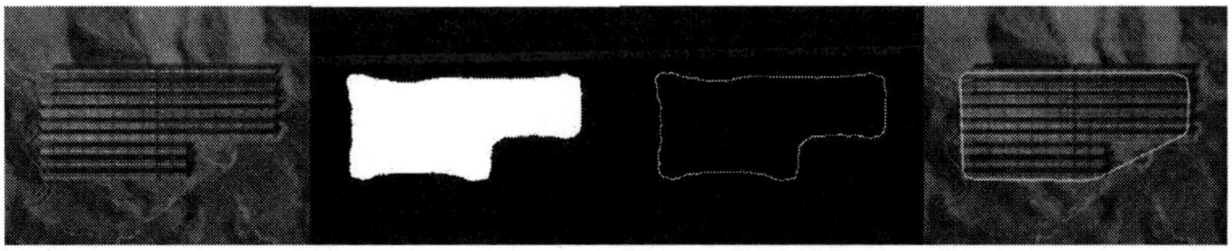

Figure 3: Boundary detection and convex closure drawing steps, employing the proposed model.

10.4229/EUPVSEC2025/4DO.17.3

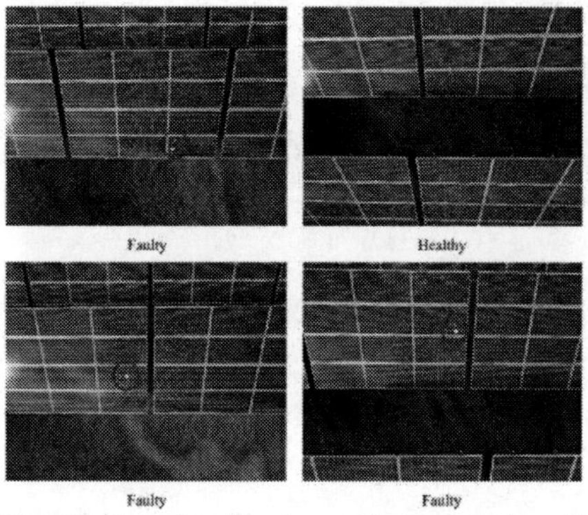

Figure 5: Examples of the images from monitoring with their predicted labels.

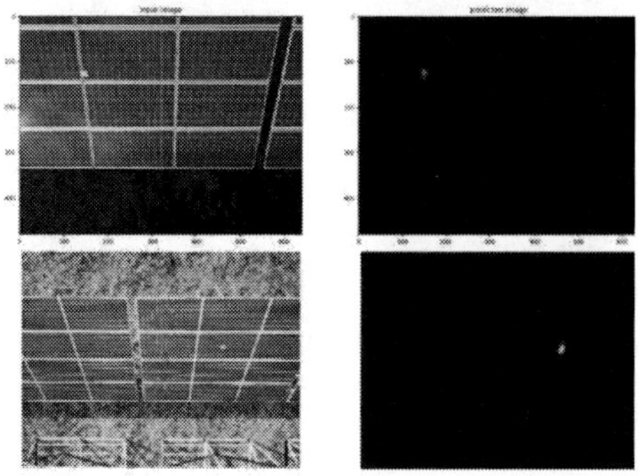

Figure 6: Examples of the images of the affected modules and their predicted masks.

4 CONCLUSIONS

This study proposed an embedded software package designed for managing drones in large-scale AAM of PV plants. Both qualitative and quantitative assessments have validated the software's performance. Additionally, functionalities such as path planning and dynamic processing are simulated in real time using a DT-based realistic simulation environment. The results indicate that the software achieves a high level of accuracy in conducting autonomous aerial inspections. Furthermore, this study demonstrates how innovative technologies, such as AI and DT integration, can enhance the accuracy of PV monitoring.

5 REFERENCES

[1] IRENA, "Future of Solar Photovoltaic: Deployment, investment, technology, grid integration and socio-economic aspects (A Global Energy Transformation: paper)," Abu Dhabi, 2019. doi: 978-92-9260-156-0.

[2] M. Aghaei *et al.*, "A Holistic Study on Failures and Diagnosis Techniques in Photovoltaic Modules, Components and Systems," in *2023 International Conference on Future Energy Solutions (FES)*, IEEE, 2023, pp. 1–6.

[3] M. Aghaei *et al.*, "Autonomous Intelligent Monitoring of Photovoltaic Systems: An In-depth Multidisciplinary Review," *Progress in Photovoltaics: Research and Applications*, 2024.

[4] A. K. V. de Oliveira, M. Aghaei, and R. Rüther, "Automatic Inspection of Photovoltaic Power Plants Using Aerial Infrared Thermography: A Review," *Energies*, vol. 15, no. 6, p. 2055, 2022.

[5] B. Li, C. Delpha, D. Diallo, and A. Migan-Dubois, "Application of Artificial Neural Networks to photovoltaic fault detection and diagnosis: A review," *Renewable and Sustainable Energy Reviews*, vol. 138, p. 110512, 2021.

[6] A. M. Moradi Sizkouhi *et al.*, "RoboPV: An integrated software package for autonomous aerial monitoring of large scale PV plants," *Energy Conversion and Management*, vol. 254, p. 115217, 2022, doi: https://doi.org/10.1016/j.enconman.2022.115217.

[7] A. M. M. Sizkouhi, M. Aghaei, S. M. Esmailifar, M. R. Mohammadi, and F. Grimaccia, "Automatic boundary extraction of large-scale photovoltaic plants using a fully convolutional network on aerial imagery," *IEEE Journal of Photovoltaics*, vol. 10, no. 4, pp. 1061–1067, 2020.

[8] M. Kolahi, S. M. Esmailifar, A. M. M. Sizkouhi, and M. Aghaei, "Digital-PV: A digital twin-based platform for autonomous aerial monitoring of large-scale photovoltaic power plants," *Energy Conversion and Management*, vol. 321, p. 118963, 2024.

[9] S. Shah, D. Dey, C. Lovett, and A. Kapoor, "Airsim: High-fidelity visual and physical simulation for autonomous vehicles," in *Field and Service Robotics: Results of the 11th International Conference*, Springer, 2018, pp. 621–635.

42nd European Photovoltaic Solar Energy Conference and Exhibition

This presentation was selected by the Sc. Committee of the EU PVSEC 2025 for submission of a full paper to one of the EU PVSEC's collaborating peer-reviewed journals.

INFLUENCE OF IRRADIANCE AND DRONE ALTITUDE IN INFRARED THERMOGRAPHY INSPECTIONS OF PHOTOVOLTAIC PLANTS

Rodrigo del Prado Santamaría, Gisele A. dos Reis Benatto, Mahmoud Dhimish, Timurhan Koc, Rizal Friansyah, Thøger Kari, Aysha Mahmood, Peter B. Poulsen and Sergiu V. Spataru
Technical University of Denmark, Department of Electrical and Photonics Engineering
Frederiksborgvej 399, 4000 Roskilde, Denmark

ABSTRACT: This study evaluates the effectiveness of drone-based infrared thermography (IRT) for detecting photovoltaic (PV) module defects under varying drone altitudes and irradiance levels. Several PV modules were artificially degraded to induce common faults, including cell cracks, cell interconnect disconnections and short-circuited bypass diodes. IRT images were acquired under irradiances ranging from 200 W/m^2 to 1000 W/m^2 and at four different drone altitudes (8 m, 10 m, 14 m, and 20 m). A detailed temperature pattern analysis at both the module and cell level was performed to characterize the thermal signatures of each fault type under the different imaging conditions. Results show that modules with cell cracks are difficult to distinguish from healthy modules while disconnected interconnects display distinct elongated thermal patterns that remain detectable at a minimum irradiance of 600 W/m^2 and are robust to detect even at higher imaging altitudes. Modules with short-circuited bypass diodes caused prominent hotspots of around 80°C which remained clearly detectable even at low irradiance levels (200 W/m^2) and elevated drone altitudes. To support further research, the complete IRT image dataset generated in this study will be made publicly available.
Keywords: Infrared Thermography, Photovoltaics, Defects, Drone Inspections

1 INTRODUCTION

Regular and efficient operation and maintenance (O&M) procedures are critical for ensuring the longevity and efficiency of PV plants. Among the available diagnostic tools, infrared thermography (IRT) is widely employed due to its non-contact, non-destructive nature. IRT enables the rapid detection of hotspots in PV modules and strings, which may indicate underlying degradation [1, 2, 3]. These thermal anomalies can be caused by various fault types, including cell cracks, potential-induced degradation (PID), defective bypass diodes, cell interconnect faults, and external stressors such as soiling—each exhibiting a characteristic thermal signature [4, 5].
IRT has gained popularity in utility-scale PV plants because it offers a fast and cost-effective inspection solution, particularly when deployed via drone-mounted thermal cameras. However, the accuracy of IRT-based fault detection is highly dependent on environmental conditions. Optimal performance typically requires a plane-of-array (POA) irradiance above 600 W/m^2, wind speeds below 28 km/h, and minimal cloud cover or soiling according to current inspection practices, as described in the IEC TS 62446-3 [6]. Such conditions are not consistently present in all regions; for example, in Nordic countries, where IRT inspections are often restricted to summer months.
In addition to weather conditions, the relative position of the thermal camera significantly influences the accuracy of temperature measurements and defect visibility. Previous research has shown that non-optimal imaging angles, particularly in drone-based inspections, can lead to temperature errors of up to 10°C [7]. Several studies have addressed the challenges of IRT under non-ideal scenarios, such as partial shading [8, 9], and have proposed best practices for the inspection setup and procedure.
This work aims to provide a comprehensive evaluation of IRT images under varying irradiance levels and drone altitudes. We analyzed the thermal behavior of PV modules subjected to different types of degradation, namely, cell cracks, cell interconnect degradation and short-circuited bypass diodes. The experiments were conducted across irradiance levels ranging from 200 to 1000 W/m^2 and drone altitudes from 8 m to 20 m. The influence of windspeed was not evaluated in this work due to constraints for drone flying safety.
The key contribution of this study is to identify the conditions under which IRT remains a reliable diagnostic tool beyond the standard recommendations and to outline its limitations for specific fault types. These findings have practical implications for improving inspection protocols, optimizing drone-based inspection strategies, enhancing the robustness of automated defect detection algorithms, and estimating which failures are happening in the plants, knowing their temperature ranges and signatures.
All the data acquired in this study is released as an open dataset containing IRT images of the studied modules at all irradiances and drone altitudes, EL images and I-V curves.

2 MATERIAL AND METHODS

2.1 Background

PV modules in the field can be subject to different types of degradation mechanisms that can affect their performance and potentially cause reliability issues and safety risks.
Cell cracks can appear in PV modules as a result of mechanical stress, for example during transport and installation, due to extreme weather conditions or through extended thermal cycling and field exposure [10]. These cracks can develop at any point in the module's lifetime; although often considered an early-life failure, they may propagate over time, leading to significant power losses and the formation of hotspots. When hotspots appear, cell cracks pose a safety risk to the installation. Moreover, cracks are not visually detectable, making characterization techniques such as EL or IRT essential for their identification. Cell cracks have been extensively studied in literature. They increase the module's series resistance, which, under illumination and operation at the maximum power point, causes additional losses to dissipate as heat. This thermal behavior forms the basis for using IRT imaging to characterize and detect this defect [11-15].
Cell interconnect disconnections or degradations refer to a physical or electrical break of the tab ribbons between cells in the PV modules. This defect can appear due to thermo-mechanical stress or during manufacturing as a problem with the soldering process. This degradation causes an

increase in series resistance of the cells, because of a current mismatch between the cells [16]. As shown in Table I, this defect can affect up to 15% of the module power production based on the severity of the disconnections, and if severe enough, it could trigger the bypass diodes leading to a larger power loss contribution.
Modules with short-circuited bypass diodes pose a significant problem in PV plants. Defective bypass diodes are often reported after a few years of field exposure; however, they have a large impact on power generation, as a short circuit in a PV module bypass diode can lead to power losses ranging from 33% to the full module being bypassed if all diodes fail. This is one of the most common targets of IRT inspections due to their characteristic thermal signal, which is a complete or partial PV module substrings heating with very high temperatures [5].

2.2 Experimental Setup and Methodology

Table I summarizes the types of defects, number of affected modules and estimated power loss ranges. The study includes both monofacial and bifacial Passivated Emitter Rear Cell (PERC) modules with nominal powers of 295 W and 305 W.

Table I. Summary of defective modules in this study.

Defect Type	Module #	Power Loss	Details
Cell cracks	8	4 - 5%	Cells cracked by mechanical stress test. Total of 69 cells affected.
Cell interconnections	8	3-14%	Cell ribbon interconnection cut from the back sheet. Total of 98 cells affected.
Short-circuited bypass diode	7	33-66%	4 modules with 1 Shorted diode and 3 with 2 Shorted diodes

All these defect types have been induced through accelerated stress testing or replicating common failures that modules experience in the field. Thereafter, the modules were installed in different PV strings at DTU's PV plant in Risø.
Every stress-tested module was characterized before and after degradation by I-V flashing at Standard Test Conditions (STC) (1000 W/m², 25°C, and AM 1.5) using a class AAA solar simulator; EL images were recorded at 100 and 10% I_{sc} bias with a NIKON D3500 CMOS camera. After installing the stress-tested modules in the plant, IRT inspections were carried out. A DJI Mavic M3T drone with a thermal camera of 640x480 px and a sensitivity <40 mK was used. The inspections were conducted under four irradiance conditions, monitored by an in-plane reference cell: 200 W/m², 600 W/m², 800 W/m² and >800 W/m². For each irradiance, the drone acquired images at four flight altitudes: 8 m, 10 m, 14 m and 20 m.
Image processing consisted of module corner detection and perspective correction. For each of the modules, statistical parameters such as the average and maximum module temperature have been calculated.

3 RESULTS

3.1 Cell cracks
Fig. 1 shows a selected module with cell cracks EL image and its corresponding IRT images. The module presents several cracked cells with different degrees of severity. At 200 W/m² the temperature difference within the module between cracked and healthy cells is very small, between 0.2 and 0.3°C, however, as the temperature increases the cells on the left start heating up, indicating the cracks location. Under high irradiance, where the temperature differences are more significant, the temperature difference between a cracked cell and the healthy one is between 1 and 2°C.

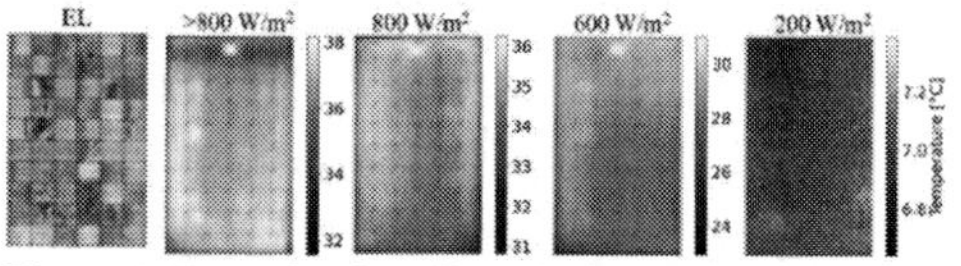

Figure 1. Example of a cell cracked module IRT images at different irradiances. EL image as a reference.

3.2 Cell interconnect degradation
Fig. 2 shows an example of a module with cell interconnection failures EL image and the resulting IRT images under different irradiances. This defect shows significantly under high irradiances with temperature differences in affected cells of up to 4°C; furthermore, imaging at irradiances of 600 W/m² can effectively distinguish this degradation mode, whose thermal characteristic resembles the pattern of the EL image.

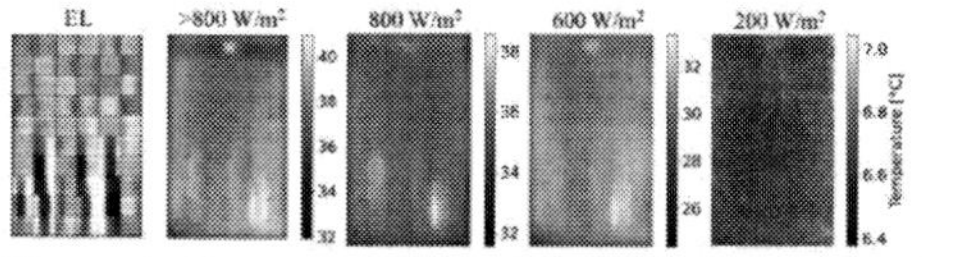

Figure 2. Example of a module with damaged cell interconnects where the IRT images were taken at different irradiances. EL image as a reference.

3.3 Shot-circuited bypass diodes

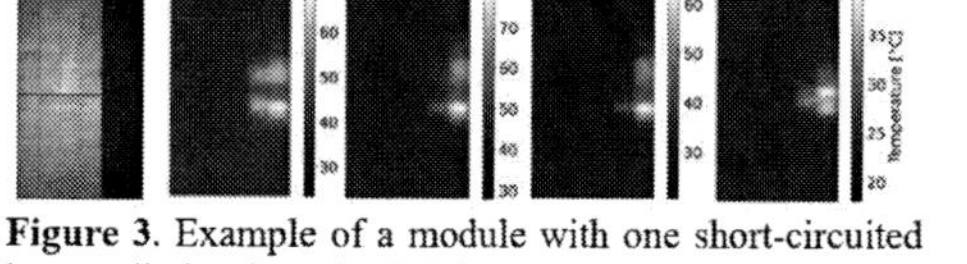

Figure 3. Example of a module with one short-circuited bypass diode where the IRT images were taken at different irradiances. EL image as a reference.

In this study, PV modules were artificially degraded by short-circuiting either one or two bypass diodes per module. Fig. 3 shows an example of a module with one shorted bypass diode and the evolution of the thermal patterns as the irradiance increases. Notably, the cells surrounding the middle section of the module, where the defective diode is located, are where the hot spots appear, with temperature differences of up to 20 °C. The maximum temperature difference is reduced as irradiance goes down; however, the patterns are still visible even at 200 W/m². These defective modules were always identifiable under all conditions and, certainly, low

10.4229/EUPVSEC2025/4DO.17.4

irradiance imaging is possible for this defect, as the observed average module temperature difference at low irradiance was 10 °C or larger.
Modules with short-circuited bypass diodes were also shown to be detectable under high drone altitudes.

4 DISCUSSION

Drone altitude is a critical parameter in IRT inspections, as it significantly influences image quality and diagnostic accuracy. As drone altitude increases, the spatial resolution of thermal images decreases; each pixel covers a larger surface area of the PV module, resulting in a lower pixel density per cell. This reduction in resolution compromises the detectability of small or localized defects, potentially hindering reliable fault detection.
Fig. 4 illustrates this effect by comparing thermal images of a module with cell cracks and another with cell interconnect failure, captured at 8 m and 20 m drone altitude. A substantial degradation in image detail is observed with increasing altitude, particularly at the cell level. The camera used in this study has a resolution of 640x512 pixels with a focal length of 40 mm. As a result, the detectability of small-area defects such as cell cracks is significantly impaired. While interconnect failures remained partially detectable at higher altitudes in severe cases, their characteristic elongated thermal patterns became indistinct at 20 m. This loss of pattern fidelity complicates root-cause analysis, as the defect-specific thermal signature is no longer discernible.
However, not all fault types are equally sensitive to reduced spatial resolution. Large-area defects such as short-circuited bypass continued to produce prominent and easily identifiable thermal anomalies at high altitudes.
Consequently, for the reliable detection of small, localized faults, lower drone altitudes—preferably between 8 m and 10 m—are recommended. In contrast, for large-area defects, inspections can still be effectively conducted at higher altitudes without substantial loss of diagnostic capability.

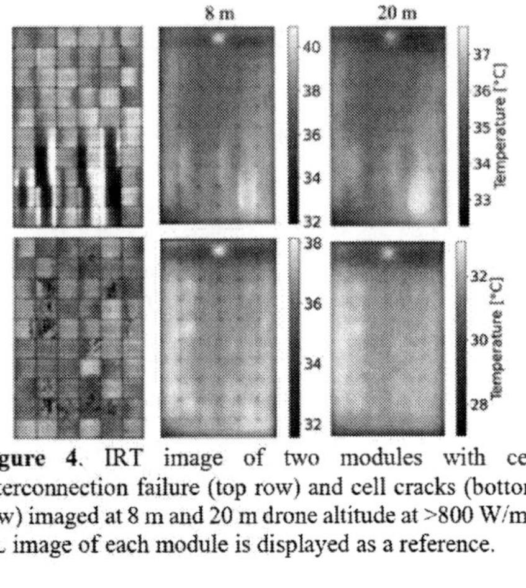

Figure 4. IRT image of two modules with cell interconnection failure (top row) and cell cracks (bottom row) imaged at 8 m and 20 m drone altitude at >800 W/m^2. EL image of each module is displayed as a reference.

In addition to drone altitude, solar irradiance is one of the most influential parameters affecting IRT reliability. At higher irradiance levels, modules operating at maximum power dissipate more heat at defect sites, enhancing thermal contrasts and improving defect visibility. As recommended by current technical specifications, irradiance levels above 600 W/m^2 are optimal for accurate IRT inspections. The results from this study confirm that most defect types exhibited increased thermal contrast under high irradiance compared to healthy modules. Conversely, under low irradiance, thermal gradients were minimal, and most defects were difficult or impossible to detect. Notably, short-circuited bypass diodes remained detectable even at low irradiance levels (e.g., 200 W/m^2), further confirming their robust thermal signature.

Table II. Maximum temperature difference of each defect severity vs the average healthy cell or module. Data taken from the inspections at 8 m altitude and over 800 W/m^2 irradiance.

Module Type	Max. cell T [°C]
Healthy	38
Cell cracks	38.7
Defective cell interconnects	44.17
Shorted bypass diodes	84.37

These qualitative trends are supported by the quantitative results presented in Table II. Under optimal imaging conditions (8 m drone altitude and >800 W/m^2 irradiance), modules with cell cracks exhibited temperature differences of less than 1 °C compared to healthy modules. In contrast, defective cell interconnects exhibited higher thermal anomalies, with hotspot temperatures reaching 44.2°C depending on degradation severity. This corresponds to a 6.2°C increase over the healthy module baseline.
The largest thermal anomalies were observed for shorted bypass diodes with hotspot temperatures exceeding 40°C relative to healthy modules. This defect generates large-area heating that remains visible even under suboptimal irradiance and at high drone altitudes, demonstrating IRT's robustness for detecting such failures.
Taken together, these results emphasize that IRT detectability is strongly dependent on both the size and severity of the defect, as well as inspection conditions. While IRT is effective for large or severe faults, it has notable limitations in identifying small-scale or subtle defects, especially when inspections are conducted at high altitudes or under low irradiance.

5 CONCLUSIONS

Drone-based infrared thermography is widely employed to assess the operational state of PV power plants. It enables the identification of hotspots in PV modules and strings, which may result from defects, shading, or soiling. While IRT is a valuable diagnostic tool for plant operators, its limitations under non-optimal weather conditions are often overlooked. Current IRT standards recommend that IRT inspections be conducted under irradiance levels above 600 W/m^2, low wind speeds, and minimal cloud cover. However, these ideal conditions are not always achievable all year round in many regions, particularly in northern climates.
Although the thermal signatures of common PV module defects have been previously studied under standard conditions, the behavior of these signatures under sub-

10.4229/EUPVSEC2025/4DO.17.4

optimal weather conditions remains poorly understood. This study investigated the influence of irradiance and drone altitude on the visibility and characteristics of thermal anomalies in IRT images, aiming to assess whether typical PV failures remain detectable under varying inspection scenarios.

A comprehensive thermal analysis was performed on defective PV modules under controlled field conditions, with irradiance levels ranging from 200 W/m^2 to 1000 W/m^2 and drone altitudes between 8 m and 20 m. The modules exhibited various defect types, including cell cracks, defective cell interconnects and short-circuited bypass diodes. Defects were introduced via stress testing, and modules were operated under realistic conditions in a PV farm environment.

Our findings show that drone altitude significantly affects image resolution and, consequently, diagnostic accuracy. At low altitudes (8 to 10 m), spatial resolution is sufficient to capture cell-level temperature inhomogeneities, enabling the identification of small or localized defects. However, at higher altitudes, spatial resolution degrades, obscuring subtle thermal patterns such as those caused by interconnect failures or cell cracks. In contrast, large-area defects like shorted bypass diodes remain clearly detectable even at higher altitudes due to their broad and intense thermal signatures.

Solar irradiance was also found to be a critical parameter for reliable fault detection. While current standards recommend irradiance levels above 600 W/m^2, our results show that certain large-area faults can still be detected at 200 W/m^2.

Cell cracks, which showed temperature differences below 1°C, were largely undetectable even under optimal imaging conditions. Interconnect failures exceeded this threshold in severe cases, while shorted bypass diodes and soiling produced the most pronounced hotspots.

These results have direct practical implications. For accurate fault localization, especially in diagnostic or warranty contexts, drone flights should be conducted at low altitudes during periods of high irradiance. For general condition monitoring or the detection of severe, high-impact faults, higher-altitude inspections may suffice, making such strategies more viable in regions with limited solar availability or access constraints.

To further support future efforts in developing and benchmarking automated defect detection algorithms, the IRT image dataset produced in this work has been made publicly available.

REFERENCES

[1] G. Schirripa Spagnolo, P. Del Vecchio, G. Makary, D. Papalillo, and A. Martocchia, "A review of IR thermography applied to PV systems," in 2012 11th International Conference on Environment and Electrical Engineering, IEEE, May 2012, pp. 879–884. doi: 10.1109/EEEIC.2012.6221500.

[2] A. K. V. de Oliveira, M. Aghaei, and R. Rüther, "Automatic Inspection of Photovoltaic Power Plants Using Aerial Infrared Thermography: A Review," Energies (Basel), vol. 15, no. 6, p. 2055, Mar. 2022, doi: 10.3390/en15062055.

[3] A. W. Kandeal et al., "Infrared thermography-based condition monitoring of solar photovoltaic systems: A mini review of recent advances," Solar Energy, vol. 223, pp. 33–43, Jul. 2021, doi: 10.1016/j.solener.2021.05.032.

[4] M. Köntges et al., "Review of Failures of Photovoltaic Modules," International Energy Agency (IEA) PVPS Task 13, Subtask 3.2, 978-3-906042-16–9, Mar. 2014.

[5] U. Jahn et al., "Review on Infrared and Electroluminescence Imaging for PV Field Applications," International Energy Agency (IEA) PVPS Task 13, Subtask 3.3, 978-3-906042-53–4, Mar. 2018.

[6] "IEC Technical Specification 62446-3. Photovoltaic (PV) systems - Requirements for testing, documentation and maintenance - Part 3: Photovoltaic modules and plants - Outdoor infrared thermography," 2017.

[7] S. Vergura, "Criticalities of the Outdoor Infrared Inspection of Photovoltaic Modules by Means of Drones," Energies (Basel), vol. 15, no. 14, p. 5086, Jul. 2022, doi: 10.3390/en15145086.

[8] O. E. Ikejiofor, Y. E. Asuamah, H. O. Njoku, and S. O. Enibe, "Detection of Hotspots and Performance Deteriotations in PV Modules under Partial Shading Conditions Using Infrared Thermography," in 7th International Electronic Conference on Sensors and Applications, Basel Switzerland: MDPI, Nov. 2020, p. 71. doi: 10.3390/ecsa-7-08201.

[9] G. Álvarez-Tey, J. A. Clavijo-Blanco, Á. Gil-García, R. Jiménez-Castañeda, and C. García-López, "Electrical and Thermal Behaviour of Crystalline Photovoltaic Solar Modules in Shading Conditions," Applied Sciences, vol. 9, no. 15, p. 3038, Jul. 2019, doi: 10.3390/app9153038.

[10] M. Köntges, I. Kunze, S. Kajari-Schröder, X. Breitenmoser, and B. Bjørneklett, "The risk of power loss in crystalline silicon based photovoltaic modules due to micro-cracks," Solar Energy Materials and Solar Cells, vol. 95, no. 4, pp. 1131–1137, Apr. 2011, doi: 10.1016/j.solmat.2010.10.034.

[11] M. Dhimish, V. d'Alessandro, and S. Daliento, "Investigating the Impact of Cracks on Solar Cells Performance: Analysis Based on Nonuniform and Uniform Crack Distributions," IEEE Trans Industr Inform, vol. 18, no. 3, pp. 1684–1693, Mar. 2022, doi: 10.1109/TII.2021.3088721.

[12] A. Morlier, F. Haase, and M. Kontges, "Impact of Cracks in Multicrystalline Silicon Solar Cells on PV Module Power—A Simulation Study Based on Field Data," IEEE J Photovolt, vol. 5, no. 6, pp. 1735–1741, Nov. 2015, doi: 10.1109/JPHOTOV.2015.2471076.

[13] J. I. van Mölken et al., "Impact of Micro-Cracks on the Degradation of Solar Cell Performance Based On Two-Diode Model Parameters," Energy Procedia, vol. 27, pp. 167–172, 2012, doi: 10.1016/j.egypro.2012.07.046.

[14] M. Dhimish, V. Holmes, B. Mehrdadi, and M. Dales, "The impact of cracks on photovoltaic power performance," Journal of Science: Advanced Materials and Devices, vol. 2, no. 2, pp. 199–209, Jun. 2017, doi: 10.1016/j.jsamd.2017.05.005.

[15] M. Dhimish and P. I. Lazaridis, "An empirical investigation on the correlation between solar cell cracks and hotspots," Sci Rep, vol. 11, no. 1, p. 23961, Dec. 2021, doi: 10.1038/s41598-021-03498-z.

[16] R. Asadpour, D. B. Sulas-Kern, S. Johnston, J. Meydbray, and M. A. Alam, "Dark Lock-in Thermography Identifies Solder Bond Failure as the Root Cause of Series Resistance Increase in Fielded Solar Modules," IEEE J Photovolt, vol. 10, no. 5, pp. 1409–1416, Sep. 2020, doi: 10.1109/JPHOTOV.2020.3003781.

42nd European Photovoltaic Solar Energy Conference and Exhibition

This presentation was selected by the Sc. Committee of the EU PVSEC 2025 for submission of a full paper to one of the EU PVSEC's collaborating peer-reviewed journals.

STRATEGY FOR SIMPLE, ON-SITE FAILURE ANALYSIS: INVESTIGATING BUBBLES AND BURN MARKS IN BACKSHEETS OF PV MODULES

C. Buerhop[1], A. Kirsten Vidal de Oliveira[2], O. Mashkov[1], L. Nascimento[2], R. Rüther[2], M. I. Peters[1]
[1] Forschungszentrum Jülich GmbH, Helmholtz-Institute Erlangen-Nürnberg, HI ERN, 91058 Erlangen, Germany
[2] Solar Energy Research Laboratory Fotovoltaica/ UFSC, Florianópolis, Brazil

ABSTRACT: This study investigates localized degradation in PV modules, focusing on bubbles and burn/scorch marks on the backsheet. These defects were discovered in 3.4% of 714 inspected modules at a multi-MWp PV plant in Brazil after three years of operation on a single-axis tracker system. High-throughput methods—visual inspection, serial number scanning, UV fluorescence imaging, and selective methods like current-voltage measurements, near-infrared spectroscopy, and electroluminescence imaging —were applied. The defects were concentrated at specific areas, occurring predominantly at the edges of the top and bottom cell rows, particularly at the contact points and corners. IV measurements and insulation measurements showed no impact on electrical properties. The study concludes that the localized degradation is likely caused by partial shading from adjacent tracker rows, inducing reverse bias, localized heating, and polymer breakdown. Additionally, the proposed method for on-site fault detection proved to be an effective, high-throughput approach for identifying degradation patterns in operational PV plants, offering a practical strategy for early fault detection and proactive maintenance.
Keywords: Field measurements, defect detection, backsheet degradation

1 INTRODUCTION

Photovoltaic (PV) power plants are subject to various degradation mechanisms that can compromise long-term performance and safety. While electrical testing is commonly used to assess system health, many defects first manifest as anomalies in module materials. These anomalies can serve both as indicators of malfunction and as root causes of accelerated degradation, making their early detection critical for reliable operation.

In this study, we investigate bubbles (blisters) and burn marks found on the backsheets of PV modules that were reported by operators. To analyze their origin and potential risks, we applied a structured inspection approach combining high-throughput on-site methods with more targeted techniques. This integrated methodology provides insight into both the material-level degradation and its correlation with electrical performance. It also establishes a practical framework for large-scale failure inspection in operational PV plants, enabling early fault detection and proactive maintenance.

2 AIM AND APPROACH

The aim of this paper is to propose a strategy for failure inspection in PV power stations, utilizing straightforward methods for on-site testing. It recognizes that observed anomalies can serve both as root causes of system weaknesses and as indicators of malfunction or poor component interaction. Using the example of modules with bubbles (blisters) and burn marks observed on their rear side by the operators, whose cause is unknown (see **Fehler! Verweisquelle konnte nicht gefunden werden.**), we present our measurement strategy. This degradation phenomenon was studied in multi-MWp PV power plant in the northeast region of Brazil, installed on a single-axis tracking system operating for four years. A total of 714 PV modules were analyzed using simple, high throughput on-site methods on site, including visual inspection (VIS), serial number (SN) scanning to build a comprehensive database, and UV fluorescence imaging (UVF) with a UV lamp and camera during nighttime to detect polymer degradation. More targeted methods, requiring additional effort, were applied to a subset of modules. These included current-voltage (IV) measurements for electrical properties, near-infrared spectroscopy (NIRA) for polymer identification in the encapsulant and backsheet, and electroluminescence (EL) imaging to detect cell defects.

3 RESULTS AND DISCUSSION

Our inspection revealed that 3.4% of the inspected modules exhibit bubbles (blisters) and burn marks on the backsheet. Typical characteristics of these defects are illustrated in **Figure 1**. It is striking, that these anomalies occur in very specific locations, rather than randomly across the module, and are confined to either the bottom or top row of cells along the module's edge (**Figure 2**). The faults consistently appear at critical points such as cell

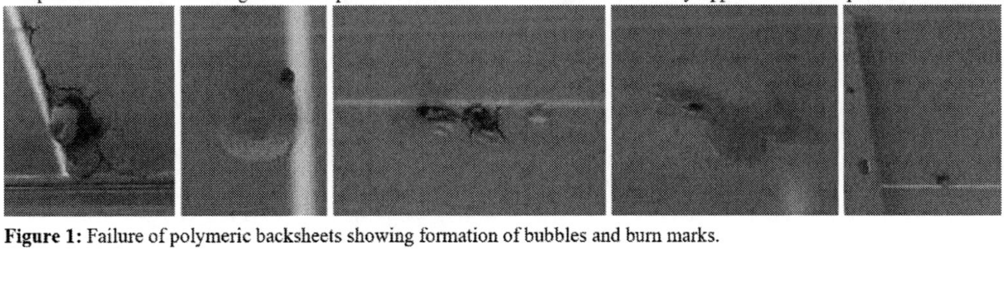

Figure 1: Failure of polymeric backsheets showing formation of bubbles and burn marks.

edges, corners, contact points, or between the contact points.

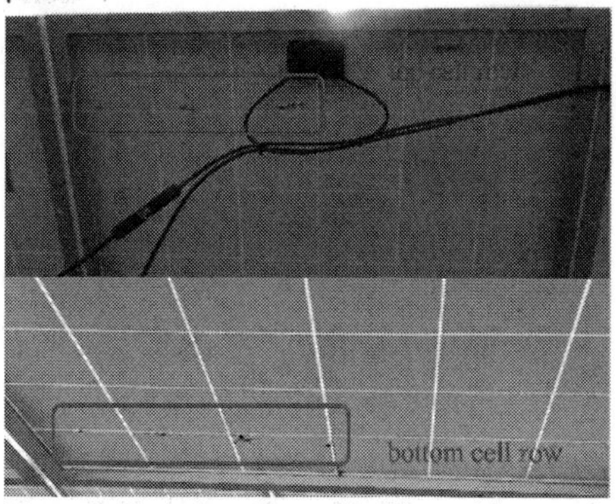

Figure 2: Typical positions of bubbles and burn marks: top cell row on junction box side and bottom cell row opposite junction box side.

To document/map the findings, we scanned the serial numbers of the modules. The SN were categorized into eight distinct groups (A-H). Modules with blisters and burn marks were exclusively found in SN group D, which accounted for approx. 34% of the inspected modules. Within this group, 9.8% of the modules exhibited these anomalies. The distribution of the SN groups and the positions of the anomalies are visualized in the map in **Figure 3**.

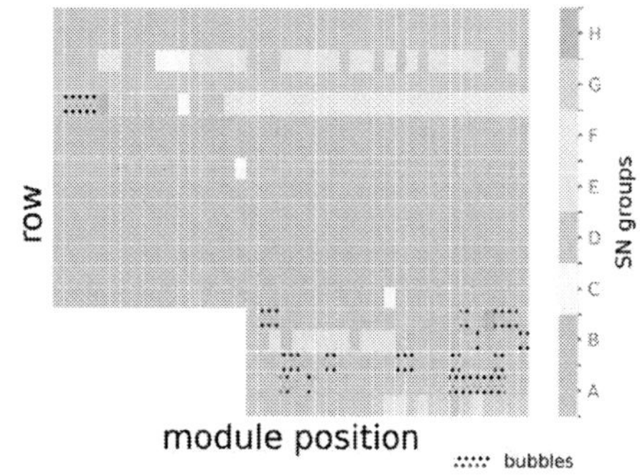

Figure 3: Typical positions of bubbles and burn marks: mapping of batches and marking modules with bubbles.

From the front, the defects were relatively inconspicuous. However, with prior knowledge of the rear side anomalies, the anomalies became identifiable from the front as well, see **Figure 4**. Close-up images reveal clear signs of delamination, corrosion, and scorch marks.

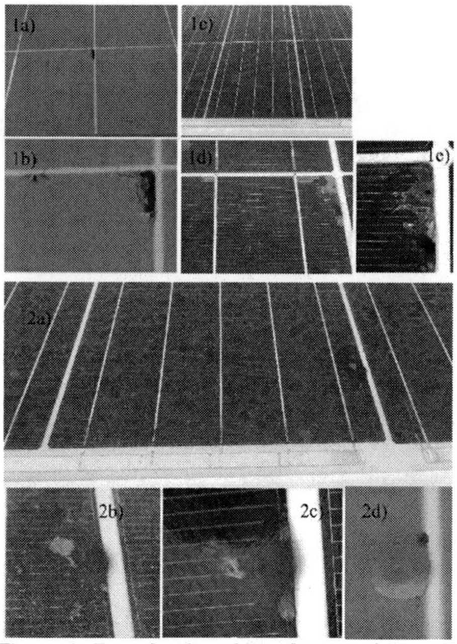

Figure 4: Examples (1 and 2) of two modules with bubbles and burn marks including close-ups (1c-1e, 2b-2-d), rear side (images vertically flipped).

Additionally, EL images of the affected modules showed electrically inactive cell areas. In **Figure 5**, the edges of the peripheral cells appear dark, indicating deactivated regions. This phenomenon is absent in the central cells, as confirmed by EL images of two sample modules. These defects are highly concentrated in specific areas.

Figure 5: Front (a) and back (b) VIS and EL (c) images of a module highlighting defects in specific areas.

UVF images highlight signs of polymer ageing. For instance, the module in **Figure 6** displays typical square-shaped ring patterns in the lower row of cells. Irregularities with intense UVF intensity are visible at the upper cell edge. These patterns are typically caused by high temperatures degrading polymers [1]. These positions align with the dark areas in EL images and the bubbles and burn marks observed in VIS inspection.

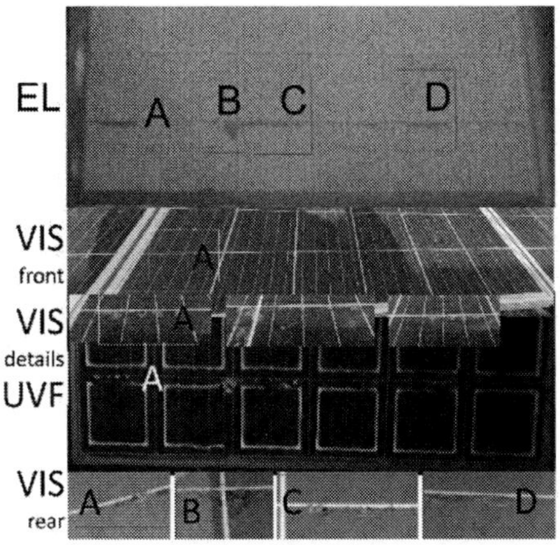

Figure 6: Module with bubbles and burn marks: VIS (front and rear), EL, and UVF. Aeras marked A-D guide the eye to the same spots in different image.

The polymer materials identified through NIRA measurements include EVA as the encapsulation material and a symmetric double-fluoropolymer backsheet, namely PVDF-PET-PVDF [2]. This backsheet comprises polyvinylidene fluoride (PVDF) and polyethylene terephthalate (PET), both of which were consistently identified in the inspected modules. A literature review was carried out to investigate the decomposition behavior of the polymers. PVDF is thermally stable up to approx. 150°C, with a melting temperature of 170°C. PET remains stable up to 80°C, although its melting temperature is higher at 260°C. The decomposition of these polymers produces gases such as carbon monoxide CO and carbon dioxide CO_2 [3]. The decomposition characteristics of EVA for thermal degradation are according to Norrish I process, which begins at 150- 200°C, with the formation of methane CH_4, CO, CO_2, and acetaldehyde [4,5]. - The IV measurements show no significant impact on the electrical parameters.

Statistical analysis highlights that the formation of bubbles and scorch marks is a highly concentrated phenomenon. These defects occur exclusively at the top or bottom cell rows and appear to be caused by temperature-induced damage. We hypothesize that adjacent tracker rows create partial shading of these cells, either early in the morning or late in the afternoon. Partial shading induces reverse bias in the affected cells, concentrating current density at the weakest points, such as cell edges and soldering points. This leads to localized temperature increases, forming hot spots that damage the solar cells. The heat accelerates the deterioration and decomposition of the polymers, resulting in gas formation, bubbles, embrittlement (cracking), burn marks on the polymer, and delamination. Additionally, burn marks on the front side and a loss of adhesion may occur. While the immediate implications for module performance are negligible, cracks and open bubbles create pathways for moisture ingress, potentially leading to electrical hazards and safety concerns [6]. In conclusion, the issue of bubbles and burn marks arises from a superposition of system design factors and variations in module batch quality. The risk of bubbles and burn marks is estimated to affect between 2% and 4.7% of the modules across the entire PV power station.

4 SUMMARY

Localized defects, including bubbles and scorch marks, were found in 3.4% of the inspected PV modules, primarily in the top and bottom cell rows at contact points, edges, and corners. Statistical analysis revealed that 9.8% of modules in one SN group exhibited these anomalies. Partial shading from adjacent tracker rows, occurring early morning or late afternoon, is believed to cause reverse bias, creating hot spots that locally degrade polymers.

Key findings include: 1) EL images showed electrically inactive areas at the edges of affected cells, 2) UV fluorescence imaging revealed polymer degradation, with strong UVF signals correlating with visible defects, and 3) NIRA analysis identified EVA encapsulants and PVDF-PET-PVDF backsheets as the degraded polymers.

Although IV measurements show no immediate performance impact, these defects pose a potential risk of accelerated degradation. Key concerns include vulnerabilities to moisture ingress, which could significantly increase the likelihood of electrical hazards.

The proposed method of high-throughput, on-site inspection using visual inspection, UV fluorescence, EL imaging, and NIRA analysis has proven effective in identifying degradation patterns early, providing a practical and efficient approach for fault detection in operational PV plants. This method facilitates proactive maintenance, allowing operators to identify weak points and mitigate potential risks before they impact system performance.

5 ACKNOWLEDGEMENTS

We gratefully thank the Alexander von Humboldt Stiftung for funding the collaboration between UFSC and HI ERN. HI ERN thanks for the support of the ZIM Project RobInspec FKN: 16KN083044, dig4morE," FKZ: 03EE1090B, "REMBup" FKZ: 03WR021F by the Federal Ministry for Economic Affairs and Climate Action on the basis of a decision by the German Bundestag, and the Helmholtz Association in the framework of the innovation platform "Solar TAP" (No. 714-62150-3/1 (2023)).

6 REFERENCES

[1]D. J. Colvin, et al.; IEEE Journal of Photovoltaics (2025).

[2]O. Stroyuk, et al.; Progress in Photovoltaics: Research and Applications (2022).

[3]S. Uličná, et al.; Scientific Reports 12 (2022) 14399.

[4]M. Oliveira, et al.; Renewable and Sustainable Energy Reviews (2017).

[5]S. Jiang, et al.; Macromolecular Reaction Engineering (2015).

[6]O. K. Segbefia, et al.; Solar Energy (2021).

42nd European Photovoltaic Solar Energy Conference and Exhibition

This presentation was selected by the Sc. Committee of the EU PVSEC 2025 for submission of a full paper to one of the EU PVSEC's collaborating peer-reviewed journals.

DESIGN AND TESTING OF AN INNOVATIVE CLOSED AGRIVOLTAIC SYSTEM: "ALGAEVOLTAICS™"

Alessandra Scognamiglio*[1], Aniello Borriello[1], Carmine Cancro[1], Mariam De Blasi[2], Maria Genovese[2], Marcello Diano[3], Stefano Mazzoleni[4], Fabrizio Carteni[4], Paola Delli Veneri[1]
[1]ENEA - Energy Technologies and Renewable Sources Department, Portici Research Center
[2]Enel Green Power (EGP), Environment and Impacts Mitigation Unit
[3]M2M Engineering
[4]Dept. of Agricultural Sciences, University of Naples Federico II
***Corresponding author: alessandra.scognamiglio@enea.it**

ABSTRACT: Agrivoltaics (agri-PV) is acknowledged an optimal way to combine energy generation from photovoltaics (PV) and crop production on the same land unit. In general, the economic value of the crops generated is significantly lower than the economic value of energy, and therefore the energy component of the system design and performance is better evaluated than the plants (agri) one. Nevertheless, the seek for optimal light transmission conditions through or underneath the PV modules, suitable for the plants growth, leads to spatial designs that can lower the energy production from PV as the density of power is lower than in a standard PV layout (e.g. increased distance between the modules stripes). This project experiments with an optimized energy and economic combination between a standard PV layout and a crop characterized by a high photosynthesis efficiency and a high market value. The result is an innovative integrated design that combines PV and micro algae generation, with several advantages with respect to current PV designs and crop selections for agrivoltaics. The name of this system is Algaevoltaics™.
The paper presents and discusses preliminary data (energy and micro algae) from the monitoring of the pilot realized at the ENEA facilities in Portici, in October 2023. This is made of two 3.4kW$_p$ PV systems, integrating two identical circuits of tubular photobioreactors. These two units differ because of the use of mono facial (glass-tedlar technology) or bifacial (glass-glass technology) PV modules.
Keywords: agrivoltaics: microalgae; photobioreactors; innovative agrivoltaics.

1 "LAND FOR ENERGY OR LAND FOR FOOD?"

As it is well known, the scarcity of land compared to our ecological footprint is nowadays an urgent issue, especially in high densely inhabited areas, or with limited agricultural land. Therefore, the use of land, i.e. agricultural land, for installing renewable energy generation systems, such as Photovoltaics (PV), is often a concern, especially for local communities. This low acceptance generates limitations to the use of PV on ground. For example, in some countries there is a ban to the implementation of PV in agricultural area.

Given this framework, agrivoltaics (APV), that is the combined use of land for agriculture and for energy is becoming increasingly common. The combined efficiency of such systems is still under investigation; as the reduction of daylight (due to PV) affects the growth rate of crops, through changes in air, ground and crop temperature with respect to traditional crop systems. Studies are ongoing on the selection of the most suitable crops for such uses, and on optimal arrangements of PV modules to meet the best lighting conditions. In several countries guidelines exist on the design of agrivoltaics to meet the national definitions.

Despite being agrivoltaics still a field for innovation and research, a rich literature already acknowledges the many advantages of this approach, besides the combined use of land, such as the beneficial effects of the shadow from the PV modules on the crops, especially in terms of water requirements, the mechanical protection of the crops.

This paper reports about the design and experimentation of an innovative agrivoltaic systems, whose design is aimed to maximise the energy and economic efficiency of both PV and crops. This is made by combining a traditional layout of on-ground PV (energy density maximisation for the lowest energy cost) and a high photosynthetic efficient, and high market value crop, which benefits from the shadow of the PV modules.

The proposed innovative agrivoltaic system is a combination of PV and microalgae (Chlorella) integrated into a unique design, which maximizes the energy generation per single land unit, by combining the electricity production and the biomass production into one integrated, engineered PV system. The typical dilemma "land for energy or land for food" is here overcome by an optimised design which merges the two approaches.

2 INTRODUCTION

Current approaches integrate the energy production and the food production in the so called "agrivoltaic concept", where PV modules and crops are placed in the same land unit. In this case, to find a good balance between the PV and the crop needs, the light transmission is a key element of the design: the crop yield can be in fact decreased because of the shading effect of PV.

In general, the standard layout of on ground mounted PV (which is corresponding to the optimal energy and economic performance for PV) requires some spatial adjustments in order to ensure the optimal light transmission balance to allow a satisfying crop production, i.e. the distance in between the stripes of modules is increased, the height of the modules from the ground is higher compared to standard on ground PV (Figure 1).

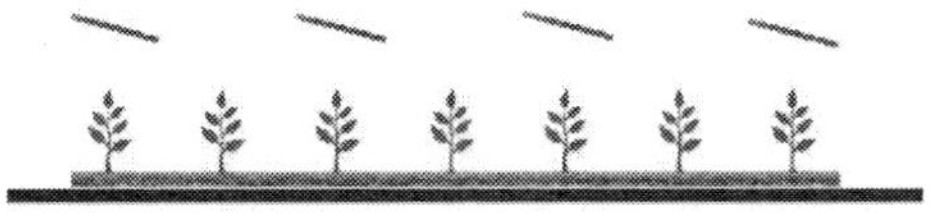

Figure 1: To ensure an optimal light transmission, allowing for a satisfying crop yield, in a typical agrivoltaic layout the height of the modules from the ground is bigger than the standard height to be considered for the standard on ground photovoltaic pattern, with an increased cost related to the materials of the supporting structure. Image from the Italian guidelines for agrivoltaic plants, June 2022, Ministry of Ecological Transition.

Consequently, APV systems are in general less energy effective and more expensive than standard PV systems.

A possible alternative approach is limiting the area for crops to the area in between the photovoltaic modules, which is interested only by a dynamic shading from the PV modules (Figure 2). Nevertheless, in this case, the area underneath the modules surface is not useful for crops because of the insufficient height. This is known as "intercropped agrivovoltaics".

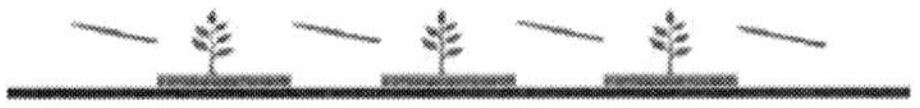

Figure 2: The typical agrivoltaic layout that use the standard patterns of on ground photovoltaics allow the crop production only in between the stripes of photovoltaic modules. The area corresponding to the projection of the photovoltaics modules on ground remains unused. Image from the Italian guidelines for agrivoltaic plants, June 2022, Ministry of Ecological Transition.

In this project the starting point is the willingness to experiment with standard PV layout (orientation of the modules, distance between the stripes of the modules, and height of the modules from the ground) with the purpose of finding solutions for using the unused area of the PV field in the best possible way from an energy and economical point of view.

3 GENERAL OBJECTIVES

The specific objectives that have driven the design of the algaevoltaic system are: a) keeping the standard layout of on ground PV; 2) maximizing the PV power generation (on a land unit); 3) improving the yield of the biomass by means of an appropriate design.

Specific key performance parameters for such objectives are: a) the market value of the produced biomass; b) the PV energy yield (KWh/kWp/year); c) the biomass yield (t/year)

To maximize the performance related to the specific biomass related design objectives, microalgae (Chlorella) have been selected because of their low light requirements (highest photosynthesis efficient among vegetable species) and because of their high economic market value.

More in detail, microalgae present several advantages, if compared with other crops or algae: they need low levels of solar radiation; their market value is high as they are used as food and as integrators (e.g. Chlorella market value ranges from 100 to 200€ per kg); do have low water requirements.

Microalgae cultivation techniques are essentially based on the use of open and closed systems.

Open systems use large tanks, ponds, canals, low-water circulation units in the form of panels or circuits consisting of polycarbonate pipes with forced circulation as the culture environment.

Closed systems, on the other hand, use large polyethylene systems or cylindrical, helical, annular or panel photobioreactors as the culture environment, which are supplied with semi-continuous radiant energy in order to maximise algal growth. Among closed systems, photobioreactors stand out, with tubular and plate reactors being the most widely used.

This equipment can achieve high cell density and facilitate the maintenance of monocultures of algal species, thanks to its closed structure and relatively controllable environment with consequent better contamination control.

Figure 3: Example of vertical tubular photobioreactors. The tubes are typically oriented horizontally or vertically and are supplied from a central unit with pump, sensors, nutrients and CO_2.

Among the different forms of photobioreactors the use of tubular, vertical photobioreactors was chosen (Figure 3). This allows for a complete engineered design, including a closed system, with an optimal control of the growth features of the microalgae.

Photobioreactors are closed systems in which a single species is inoculated to keep a clean colture operation.

Since the tubes behave as solar collectors, overheating is detrimental; in this sense, the shading offered by the PV modules can advantage the efficiency of the system. Furthermore, the engineering of photobioreactors offers a good opportunity for experiencing with the integration of the PV system and the photobioreactor, if an appropriate engineering design is performed.

The photobioreactors are made of closed circuits including a circulation pump, a system for releasing oxygen into the atmosphere (degasser) and a centrifuge, which is used to collect the algae. The advantages of this approach concern: a) the possibility of creating a dynamic culture in continuous recirculation and with a single control point; b) low water consumption; c) the complete automation of the plant.

10.4229/EUPVSEC2025/4DO.2.1

4 THE PILOT @ENEA RESEARCH CENTER FACILITY IN PORTICI

4.1 The system design

The algaevoltaic pilot plant @ENEA Portici is the result of an accurate design and simulation work conducted by a multi-disciplinary team. Combining since the very early design both the competences in several fields of PV and in microalge allowed for a design able to optimize the integrated energy performance. In this sense, the final design of the project into a unique, integrated system the results of simulations made both for PV and for the microalgae.

Figure 4: The pilot algaevoltaic plant @ENEA Research Center in Portici (IT).

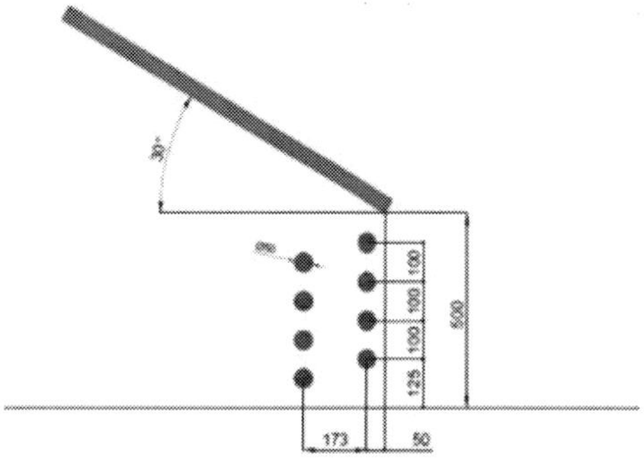

Figure 5: Cross section of the algaevoltaic plant.

The light transmission optimisation (finding the optimal balance between the shade from PV and the microalgae growth) oriented the geometry of the system and therefore the mounting position of the tubular photobioreactors with respect to the PV array; i.e. identifying a geometric configuration that determines partial shading of the photobioreactors when the sun is particularly high on the horizon, but which still allows sufficient irradiation for the growth of the microalgal culture.

Several combinations of PV and microalgae photobioreactors have been considered for meeting all the above-mentioned requirements. Several simulations have been run by using PVSyst for different integrated solutions in order to: 1) calculate the solar radiation on the surfaces of the PV tubes (which is not immediate due to the circular section of the tubes), and evaluating the corresponding biomass yield; 2) calculate the solar radiation on the photovoltaic modules surface (Figure 6), and evaluating the corresponding energy yield.

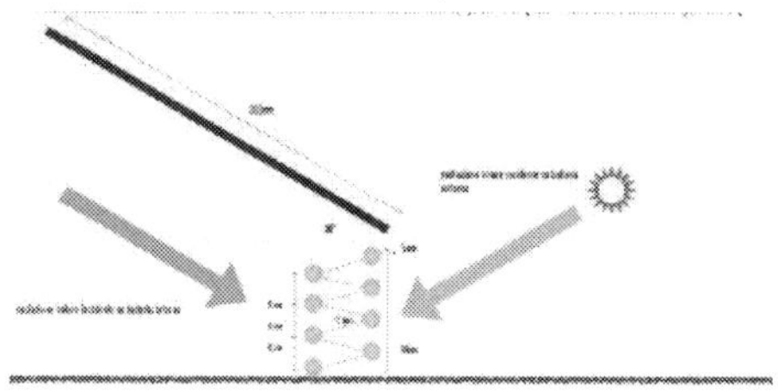

Figure 6: The incident radiation on both internal and external tubes has been evaluated along with the diffuse radiation from the North and the beam radiation from the South.

The final configuration corresponds to a typical on ground PV layout, being the modules organized in stripes East-West oriented and facing the South with a tilt angle of 30° (optimised on the site latitude), which allow also for the use of bifacial PV modules. The positioning of the photobioreactors has been chosen to ensure an optimal irradiation value on the tubes' surface (Figure 5 and Figure 6).

Figure 7: General view of the algaevoltaic plant @ENEA. The two sub-field are made with monofacial and bifacial PV modules, respectively.

The algaevoltaic field is divided into two sub-fields, that are exactly the same but built one with standard photovoltaic modules (glass-tedlar), and the other one with bifacial PV modules (glass-glass). These systems are equipped with two perfectly equal circuits of photobioreactors each with a capacity about of 450l, connected to a centrifuge used for the separation of microalgae from the culture water.

Figure 8: The degasser.

Figure 9: Samples of Chlorella, collected @the algaevoltaic pilot in Portici.

4.2 The monitoring system

Both the electrical production data and the microalgae parameters, such as temperature, pH, oxygen concentration, are continuously monitored. From these data it is possible to control the grope of microalgae and to regulate parameters affecting the growth such as CO_2 rate (automatically injected by the degasses). The microalgae solution is periodically analysed using a spectrophotometer to measure the light absorption @720nm: when this parameter becomes particularly high, the algae harvesting proceeds, connecting the circuit to the centrifuge.

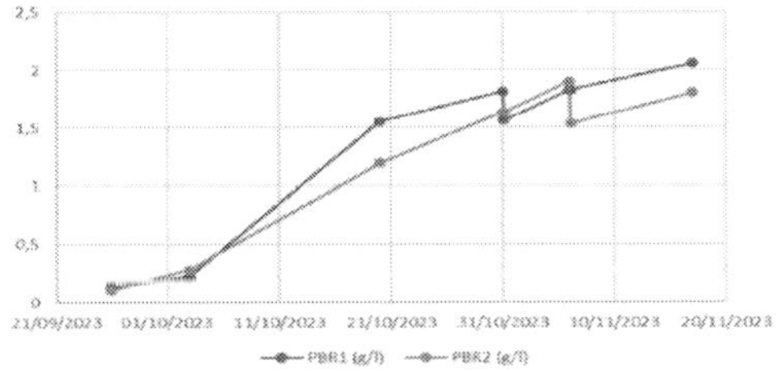

Figure 10: Growth curves of the microalgal cultivation: in blue double-sided PV plant, in orange single-sided PV plant (the steps observed in the curves are in correspondence with the algae harvesting).

4.3 Microalgae growth optimisation

Regarding the microalage growth optimisation, once the geometrical configuration of the system has been defined, the work involved the development of a mathematical model for the growth of microalgae in photobioreactors.

In particular, the optimization of irradiance utilization by microalgae grown in photobioreactors is a topic of great interest, and its mathematical modelling can be crucial for the commercial exploitation of microalgae. The microalgal photosynthesis model studied for this work is a modular model, in which various phenomena regulating algal growth are reproduced. The modules can be activated or deactivated depending on the simulation to be performed and possibly combined. The modules integrated into the microalgae growth model concern the various photoadaptation responses to excess light, which, if channelled into the photosynthetic process, could damage the cells through oxidative.

The phenomena at play include the reduction of pigments involved in photo-capture and the damage and repair of the D1 protein in photosystem II, known as "photoinhibition" both of which result in a reduction in photosynthetic efficiency in cells grown under high light.

A third module, based on previous work on plants reproduces two more relevant processes, i.e. the activation of the Rubisco enzyme after exposure to light (night-day cycle), and the dissipation of excess energy in the form of heat through the process called Non-Photochemical Quenching (NPQ).

The parameters of the developed simulation model, composed of a set of Ordinary Differential Equations (ODE), has been calibrated using data from the pilot algal bioreactor. Specifically, data of O2 concentration (expressed in ppm) in the growth solution has been used to calibrate the simulated photosynthetic flow at daily scale

The potential of this approach if of high importance. In fact, once the model is validate (through experimental data), this can be applied to a system in any location. For this reasons, in order to make the model easily applicable to different locations, the main inputs of the model are solar radiation measured as global horizontal irradiance (GHI expressed in W m-2) and air temperature (oC).

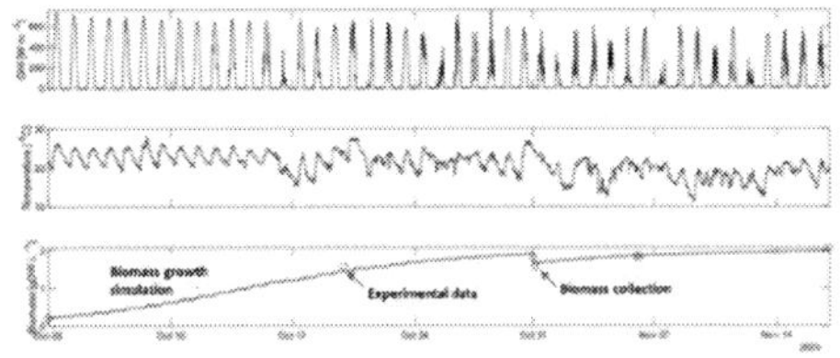

Figure 11: Comparison between simulated growth curves and experimental data.

4.4 Field experimental data

Starting from October 2023 to June 2024, the plant was continuously monitored, obtaining the first experimental results.

Regarding the PV section, there are no significant differences in electricity production between the system with monofacial PV modules and the one with bifacial modules: both have a Performance Ratio about of 84%.

Several microalgae collections were performed, growth curves were obtained (Figure 10), and growth rates were calculated for both plants. The data shows that the system with bifacial modules has growth rate that is approximately 20% higher than those of the single-facial system. This is probably due both to the partial transparency of the bifacial modules and to the better reflection of the incident light on the back-sheet of the module, the latter being made of glass, while that of the standard module is made of Tedlar. These effects produce better irradiation of the photobioreactors placed under the bifacial modules, compared to those placed under the monofacial ones.

The microalgae growth model was used to simulate their production using the real horizontal incident global radiation and ambient temperature as input data. The experimental data show a very good correspondence between the simulated and the experimental data (Figure 11).

5 PRELIMINARY NUTSHELL CONCLUSIONS

In terms of implementation possibility, the potential of the proposed approach is very high, as the study considered can be applied in several cases such as

10.4229/EUPVSEC2025/4DO.2.1

revamping and repowering of standard PV layouts, or, also, improvements of existing power PV plants, though increased energy production and economic efficiency.

It is worth notice that the cultivation of microalgae is carried out through an almost completely automatic process which requires much less manpower than conventional open agrivoltaic systems. Lastly, the market value of microalgae is very high, and this could significantly reduce the break-even point of the investment.

EXPERIMENTAL INVESTIGATION OF AN AGRIVOLTAIC COLLECTOR WITH PLANAR SPECTRAL BEAM SPLITTING

Inga Krasilnikov[1,3], Abraham Kribus[1]*, Gur Mittelman[2], Liad Reshef[3], Shay Ozer[3], Lavi Rosenfeld[3], Helena Vitoshkin[3]

[1]School of Mechanical Engineering, Faculty of Engineering, Tel Aviv University, Tel Aviv, Israel
[2]Afeka Tel-Aviv Academic College of Engineering, Tel Aviv, Israel
[3]Institute of Agricultural Engineering, Agricultural Research Organization, Rishon LeZion, Israel
* Corresponding author: kribus@tauex.tau.ac.il

ABSTRACT: Spectrum splitting agrivoltaic collectors allow photosynthetic radiation to pass through the collectors in contrast to conventional collectors that produce full shading. The rest of the solar spectrum is redirected for electricity generation. The current study presents experimental results for the optical and electrical performance of a laboratory-scale prototype of a spectrum splitting collector, aimed at validating the theoretical performance predictions. Commercially available architectural Low-E window glass panes were used as spectral splitters. An off-the-shelf bifacial PV module was illuminated equally on both sides with modified sunlight reflected from the splitters, containing a reduced share of visible light. Measurements included incident fluxes on the PV module from both sides, module temperature, and electrical output as well as the radiation flux reaching the ground. The experimental results were compared against theoretical predictions and demonstrated good agreement for both the radiation fluxes and electrical output. The results confirm the potential of collectors with spectrum splitting to significantly increase the ground-level PAR flux compared to full shading, thus reducing the impact of agrivoltaics on shade-sensitive crops, while maintaining a high level of electricity production.
Keywords: Agrivoltaics, Spectrum splitting, Hor mirror, Bifacial module

1 INTRODUCTION

Agrivoltaics (or agri-photovoltaics, APV), with photovoltaic (PV) modules installed over cropland, can open vast agricultural land resources for renewable electricity generation. However, conventional PV modules are opaque and create significant shading, which can reduce photosynthesis and the crop yield [1]. Some crops are insensitive or even benefit from partial shading, but most of the agricultural area globally (about 70% according to FAO database) is allocated to crops that are sensitive to shading. Therefore, solutions that minimize the damage to crop yield are essential.

Spectrum splitting of sunlight is one such solution: APV collectors that transmit the photosynthetic part of sunlight to the crop, while using the rest of the solar spectrum for electricity generation [2], [3]. Dichroic mirrors that transmit either the entire visible light range (hot mirror), or the red and blue parts only (dual bandpass mirror), while reflecting the rest of the spectrum, can be used as splitters. While some published concepts use curved surfaces and concentration, a simpler design was proposed with flat splitter mirrors and a bifacial solar module receiving equal illumination from both sides as shown in Figure 1 [3], [4]. The photosynthetically active radiation (PAR, 400 nm – 700 nm) part of incident sunlight is transmitted through the splitters towards the crop. The rest of the sunlight spectrum containing near infrared (NIR, 700 nm – 1100 nm), and possibly also green light (500 nm – 570 nm) in the case of a dual bandpass mirror, is reflected to the PV module to generate electricity. The bifacial module is illuminated equally on both sides, in contrast to conventional use where the back side receives only a small amount of reflected radiation. The spaces among collector rows allow full sunlight to reach the crop. During east-west daily tracking the regions of full and filtered sunlight move across the crop field, minimizing the variations in illumination during the day and promoting uniform crop growth.

Our previous work focused on modeling the performance of this collector [4] and showed that the loss of PAR on the crop can be reduced from about 20% in a conventional APV field that uses opaque modules, to approximately 10%. At the same time, electricity generation per unit land area can be about the same or even higher. However, these results are based on a theoretical model of the spectrum splitting and of the module performance, which needs experimental validation. In particular, the illumination of the bifacial PV module with a modified spectrum of sunlight, and under equal flux on both sides, is an unusual set of conditions that needs validation. The current study provides the needed experimental demonstration with a comparison to the theoretical predictions.

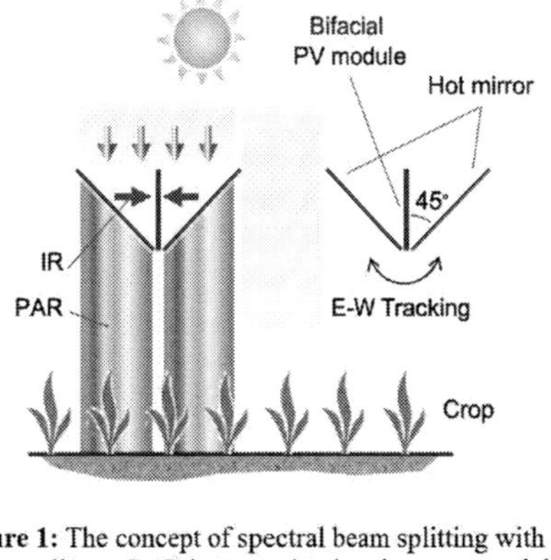

Figure 1: The concept of spectral beam splitting with planar splitters: PAR is transmitted to the crops, and the rest of the spectrum is reflected to both sides of a bifacial PV module.

2 EXPERIMENTAL METHODS

Figure 2 shows the experimental setup located at the Institute of Agricultural Engineering in Beit-Bagan, Israel.

Commercially available hot mirror spectral splitters were used (Low-E glass SN-75 by Guardian Glass). These were selected for their availability at reasonable cost, even though their spectral selectivity is only moderate and their absorptance is too high as shown in Figure 3. The splitters are at 45° angle to a bifacial PV module (LR5-72HBD, LONGi, China). An additional identical module was installed facing the direction of the sun as reference. A single axis tracking mechanism rotates the collector from east to west following the daily apparent motion of the sun, guided by a sun sensor.

Figure 2: Experimental setup: 1- hot mirrors, 2 - PV module, 3 - single axis tracking mechanism and sun sensor, 4 – reference PV module.

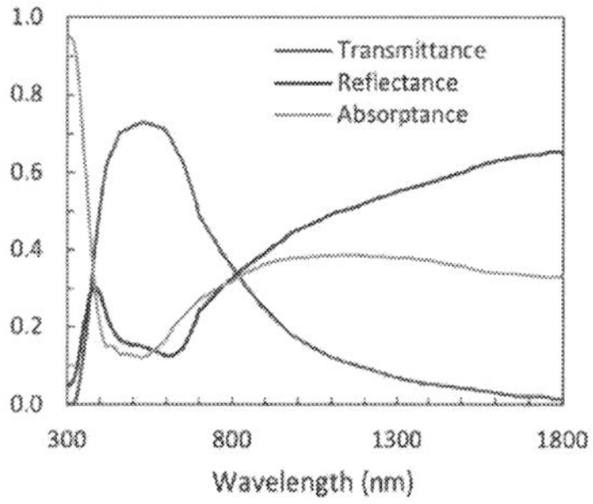

Figure 3: SN-75 hot mirror optical properties.

The setup was equipped with global irradiation pyranometers (Apogee Instruments, USA) installed on both sides of the module, and global and PAR sensors (LI-COR Biosciences, USA) on the ground in the filtered radiation area below the test setup. The module temperature was monitored using T-type thermocouples (XF-1166-FAR Labfactory) attached to the back side of each module using thermally conductive foil. Ambient conditions were obtained by the local meteorological station (METOS by Pessl, Austria). The data was logged in a Campbell Scientific Inc datalogger (model 21X Micrologger) with a 1-minute sampling interval. The electrical power output was recorded every 10 minutes by a EKO MP-11 Solar Module Analyzer.

3 RESULTS

3.1 Incident radiation on module

Figure 4(a) shows the radiation flux measurements taken during several hours on August 30. The global horizontal insolation (GHI) data taken from a nearby meteorological station indicates clear day behavior. The tracking pyranometer installed near the reference module shows almost constant incident flux of about $980\,W/m^2$. The fluxes reflected by the splitters and incident on both sides of the PV module are similar and are lower due to the transmission of part of the light towards the ground. The sum of radiation fluxes incident on the module from both sides is also nearly constant at about $1070\,W/m^2$.

The radiation flux reaching the module contains contributions of direct radiation reflected from the splitters, diffuse radiation from the sky, and radiation reflected from the ground which mostly passes through the splitters on its way up. These contributions were calculated assuming standard reference spectra (ASTM G173 standard) for each solar radiation component, the measured values of direct and diffuse radiation fluxes, the optical properties of the splitters, and the reflectance of the ground surface (0.4, measured separately).

Figure 4(b) shows the calculated spectrum reaching the module, accounting for both sides. The large deficit in the visible range compared to the spectrum of GHI is due to the selective reflectance of the splitters, where much of the visible light is transmitted. In the NIR, there is a smaller reduction compared to GHI due to higher reflectance of the splitters in this range. The total incident flux (integral over the spectrum) on the two sides of the module according to the theoretical prediction is $977\,W/m^2$, about 6% lower than the actual measurement. This is a good match considering the measurement uncertainty and the modeling inaccuracy.

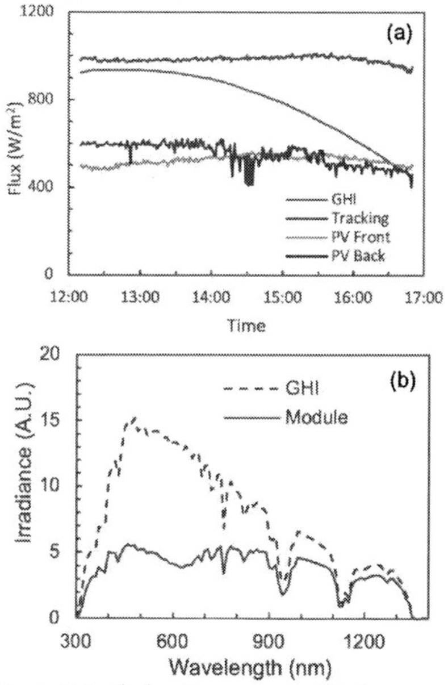

Figure 4: (a) Radiation fluxes measured during Aug. 30: global horizontal, tracking (reference), and both sides of the PV module. (b) Calculated spectrum of radiation incident on the module at 12:50, in comparison to the spectrum of GHI.

3.2 Module temperature

Figure 5 shows the measured temperature of the PV module in comparison to that of the reference module which received full sunlight while tracking. There is a small difference until about 14:00 and then the two

10.4229/EUPVSEC2025/4DO.2.2

modules have approximately the same temperature (46°C ±1.5°C). This qualitative change can be understood by considering the wind: its speed was generally constant during the day, but around 14:00 the wind direction changed from west to north-west. The western wind was largely blocked by the splitters which are aligned in the north-south direction, leading to higher module temperature compared to the reference module. The later appearance of a north wind component increased the airflow and the convection heat transfer in the space enclosed by the splitters, leading to module temperature comparable to the conventional tracking reference module.

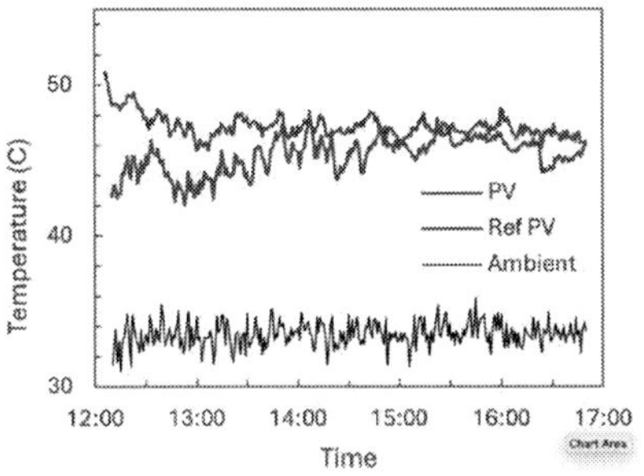

Figure 5: Module temperature in comparison to reference module.

3.3 Electrical output

Figure 6 shows the power output of the module compared to the reference module during the test day. There is a large difference even though the two modules are subject to similar total incident flux and are at similar temperatures. However, the spectra of incident radiation on the two modules are different, and therefore a more detailed analysis is needed to understand the different performance.

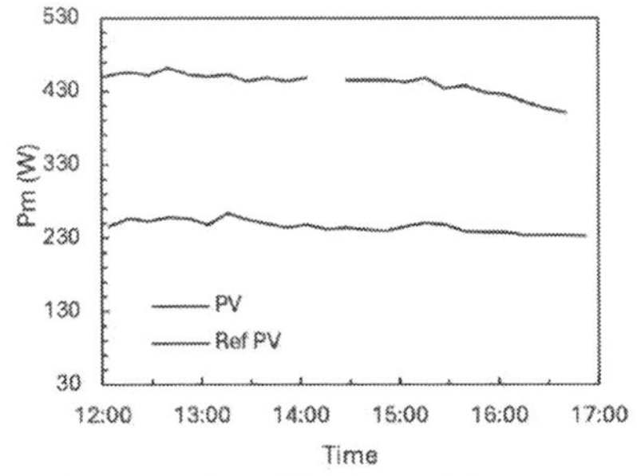

Figure 6: Power output of the two modules.

The electrical performance of the module was modeled using the CEC six-parameter single-diode equivalent circuit model [5] that provides the relation of current and voltage:

$$I(V) = 2A_c J_L - I_o\left[exp\left(\frac{V + IR_s}{a}\right) - 1\right] - \frac{V + IR_s}{R_{sh}} \quad (1)$$

A_c is the area of a half-cell, multiplied by 2 to represent two parallel strings of half-cells in the module. I_o, a, R_s and R_{sh} are the module parameters that are derived from the manufacturer's data of the module and corrected to the temperature measured in the experiment [4]. The photogeneration (light) current density J_L is determined by the modified spectrum incident on the module and is calculated using the spectral response SR of a typical silicon cell [6]:

$$J_L = (1 + BF) \cdot \int_{300}^{2500} q_{in}(\lambda)\, \tau_m\, SR(\lambda)\, d\lambda \quad (2)$$

q_{in} is the spectral flux incident on one side of the module as shown in Figure 4(b). τ_m is the transmittance of the module glass, and BF is the module bifaciality factor.

Figure 7 shows the measured and predicted current-voltage and power-voltage at solar Noon. The measured value of the short-circuit current is lower than the prediction by 4.3%, and the open-circuit voltage matches to within 1.1%. However, the measured curve shows a drop in current as the voltage increases, which can represent a current mismatch behavior attributed to flux non-uniformity. This leads to a large difference of 23% between the predicted and measured maximum power. Some cells were indeed partially shaded on the back side by the module frame due to imperfect tracking, and by the tracking mechanism shaft. These effects can be eliminated by changes in the mechanical design.

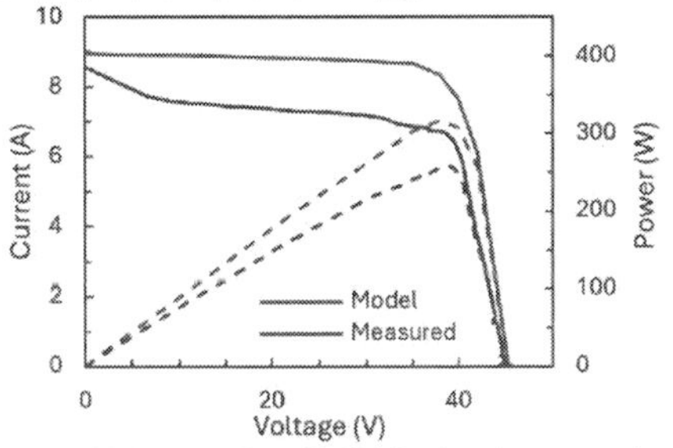

Figure 7: Current-voltage (solid lines) and power-voltage (dashed lines) model predictions vs. measured values.

3.4 Incident radiation of the ground

Figure 8(a) shows incident total flux and PAR flux of filtered radiation incident on the ground during the experiment, measured locally in the shaded area. Also shown are the corresponding fluxes for full shade, i.e., diffuse radiation only, representing the situation in the shaded area under conventional PV collectors. The amount of PAR reaching the ground under the collector is about 3.3 times higher than the amount that would reach the ground under the full shade. The short time intervals of low flux in Figure 8(a) correspond to times when the sensor is shaded by a structural element. The PAR fraction in the filtered light is 65% - 70%, much higher than about 45% in normal sunlight.

The calculated spectrum of filtered radiation on the ground corresponding to the experimental conditions at 12:50 is shown in Figure 8(b). The visible or PAR section is high while the NIR part is much lower as can be seen by comparison the GHI spectrum. This is due the preferential transmission of visible light and reflection of NIR by the splitters. Comparison the spectrum of diffuse radiation representing full shade shows the much higher PAR content of the filtered light. The integrals of the calculated spectra over wavelength result in total flux and PAR flux of $393\,W/m^2$ and $276\,W/m^2$, both about 12% higher than the measured values. This reasonable difference can be partly attributed to measurement uncertainty and the rest to simulation inaccuracy.

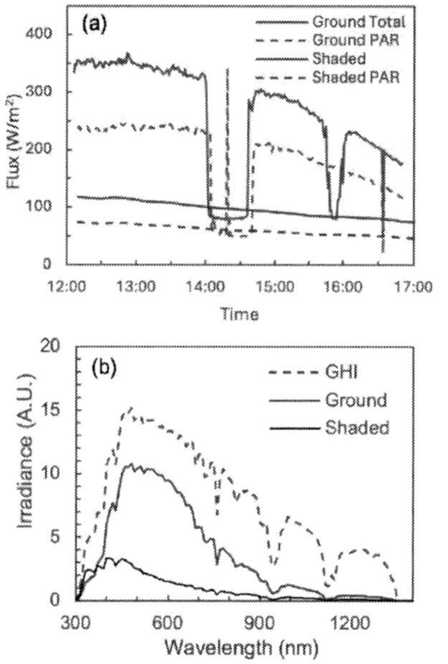

Figure 8: (a) Total and PAR fluxes of filtered radiation incident on the ground compared to full shade, (b) calculated spectrum of radiation incident on the ground, in comparison to GHI and to full shade.

3.4 Prediction for an improved splitter

The splitter used in this work is not optimized for agrivoltaics and its spectral selectivity is quite low. It is possible to produce much better dichroic mirrors using thin-film technologies such as vapor deposition and polymer film co-extrusion [7] having the potential to achieve very low cost when mass-produced. To consider the potential of such splitters and their impact on performance, we define a high-quality splitter specifically designed for the agrivoltaic application. The following optical properties (which can be achieved with dichroic mirrors) are used: transmittance 0.9 for red (600 nm – 700 nm) and blue (400 nm – 500 nm) wavelengths, reflectance 0.9 for the rest of the spectrum, and negligible absorptance. The expected performance of our test setup was recalculated for this splitter using the same test conditions.

Figure 9(a) shows the calculated spectra of radiation incident on the module and on ground in the presence of the improved splitter. Clearly, both the radiation reaching the module (including most of the green light), and the red and blue photosynthetic radiation reaching the ground, are higher compared to the low-performance splitter as shown in Figure 4 and Figure 8. Figure 9(b) shows the predicted current-voltage curve for the improved splitter, with much higher current due to the increase of incident radiation on the module.

Table I shows a comparison of module performance as measured, as calculated by our model for the experiment conditions (eliminating the effect of flux non-uniformity), and as calculated for the improved splitter. The current and the power output with the improved splitter are significantly higher due to the improved reflectance of the splitter at the relevant wavelengths, and the additional reflection of green light to the module. The maximum power is close to the nominal rating of the module adjusted for temperature: 483 W. The loss of red and blue light reaching the ground is only 12% with the improved splitter compared to 35% with the low-grade splitter that was used in the experiment. Considering that each location on the ground receives alternately filtered light and full sunlight, the average loss of photosynthetic light should be significantly less than 10%.

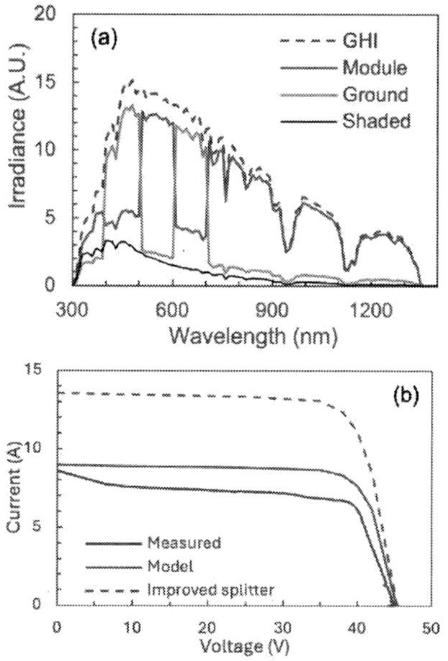

Figure 9: (a) Calculated spectra of radiation incident on the module and on the ground with the improved splitter, compared to GHI and full shade. (b) modeled current-voltage curve of the module with the improved splitter, compared to the actual experimental measurement and corresponding model.

Table I: Open circuit voltage, short circuit current, maximum power, and flux of red and blue (RB) radiation on the ground, for the experiment, the model of the experiment, and model with an improved splitter

	V_{OC} (V)	I_{SC} (A)	P_m (W)	RB (W/m²)
Experiment	44.80	8.58	257.1	
Model	45.30	8.95	316.6	175.9
Improved splitter	45.37	13.56	470.1	237.1

4 CONCLUSIONS

A bifacial PV module was tested under the unusual conditions of spectrum-splitting collector, including a modified spectrum and equal illumination of both sides of the module. The measured optical and electrical performance was in reasonable agreement with the prediction based on the properties of the splitter and a standard single-diode equivalent circuit model. A deviation of the measured maximum power from the prediction was observed, and this is due to the non-uniformity of the incident flux which can be improved with better mechanical design. Measurements of the photosynthetic radiation incident on the ground showed a significant advantage over conventional collectors that create full shade.

A comparison of the experimental results vs. a theoretical prediction of performance with improved high-quality splitters showed a potential for significant improvements in both the module electrical performance and the photosynthetic radiation reaching the ground. This should be therefore a major avenue for future development and optimization.

The current experimental results allow the model validation and refining required to predict the performance of large-scale APV fields based on the proposed concept of spectrum splitting collectors.

ACKNOWLEDGMENTS

Funding for this work was provided by the Israel Ministry of Energy and Infrastructure, grant 219-11-125, and by the US-Israel binational agricultural research and development fund (BARD), grant US-5236-20.

REFERENCES

[1] Z. Tahir and N. Z. Butt, "Implications of spatial-temporal shading in agrivoltaics under fixed tilt & tracking bifacial photovoltaic panels," *Renew Energy*, vol. 190, pp. 167–176, 2022, doi: 10.1016/j.renene.2022.03.078.

[2] W. Huang *et al.*, "A dish-type high-concentration photovoltaic system with spectral beam-splitting for crop growth," *Journal of Renewable and Sustainable Energy*, vol. 9, no. 6, 2017, doi: 10.1063/1.5009319.

[3] G. Mittelman, H. Vitoshkin, B. Lew, H. Mamane, and A. Kribus, "Innovative Solar Spectral Beam Splitting Concepts: Cogeneration and Photochemistry," in *35th European Photovoltaic Solar Energy Conference and Exhibition*, Brussels, 2018, pp. 203–207. doi: 10.4229/35thEUPVSEC20182018-1CV.4.75.

[4] B. A. Shalom, G. Mittelman, A. Kribus, and H. Vitoshkin, "Optical and electrical performance of an agrivoltaic field with spectral beam splitting," *Renew Energy*, vol. 219, Dec. 2023, doi: 10.1016/j.renene.2023.119438.

[5] A. P. Dobos, "An improved coefficient calculator for the california energy commission 6 parameter photovoltaic module model," *Journal of Solar Energy Engineering, Transactions of the ASME*, vol. 134, no. 2, pp. 1–6, 2012, doi: 10.1115/1.4005759.

[6] M. A. Green, K. Emery, Y. Hishikawa, W. Warta, and E. D. Dunlop, "Solar cell efficiency tables (version 48)," *Progress in Photovoltaics: Research and Applications*, vol. 24, no. 7, pp. 905–913, Jul. 2016, doi: 10.1002/pip.2788.

[7] W. Liu *et al.*, "A novel agricultural photovoltaic system based on solar spectrum separation," *Solar Energy*, vol. 162, no. June 2017, pp. 84–94, 2018, doi: 10.1016/j.solener.2017.12.053.

Agri-PV Potential in Northern Climates An Experimental Study on Panel Transparency, and Leafy Vegetable Productivity

M. Rudzikas[1], G. Samuolienė[2], J. Raginskis[3], P. Dubravskij[4], A. Baležentis[1], S. Baležentienė[1]

[1] The Applied Research Institute for Prospective Technologies, Vismaliukų str. 34, Vilnius LT-10243, Lithuania;

[2] The Lithuanian Research Centre for Agriculture and Forestry, Instituto av. 1, LT-58344 Kėdainiai distr., Lithuania

[3] Kaunas University of Technology, K. Donelaicio st. 73, 44249 Kaunas, Lithuania

[4] JSC "Modern E-Technologies", Vismaliukų str. 34, Vilnius LT-10243, Lithuania;

matas.rudzikas@protechnology.lt

EU PVSEC 2025, Bilbao

PROTECH

Outline

- About PROTECH;
- Motivation;
- Methodology;
- Results;
- Conclusions;

2

About PROTECH

PROTECH - The Applied Research Institute for Prospective Technologies is an Industrial Research Institute of renewable energy technologies research in Lithuania since 2005. In-depth research, patent and infrastructure the following topics for industrial applications in:

- Photovoltaic technologies;
- Thermal and energy storage technologies;
- Measurement technologies and devices;
- Digital solutions;

Motivation

- Agrivoltaic systems combine solar energy production with agriculture, more sustainable solution, reduction of CO_2 footprint.
- A barrier to renewable energy adoption in Agriculture - fear of potential yield losses.
- Widely studied in temperate/arid regions (for example Italy, Greece, Almeria, Agadir).
- This study addresses the gap of northern climates by evaluating the potential of agrivoltaics in Lithuania (northern climates), focusing on the impact of different PV panel transparencies on the growth of leafy vegetables.

4

Mothodology – PV modules and shading

- 4 sites without and with PV panels with transparencies: 76%, 56%, 43%;
- PV module power: 77.7 W, 56.9 W, 29W;
- Each site of 3x4 = 12 of PV modules with area of: 2.77 x 3.27 m;
- Lightweight PV panels made with PERC bifacial solar cells, PET backsheets, EVA encapsulation, aluminum frame.frontsheets and

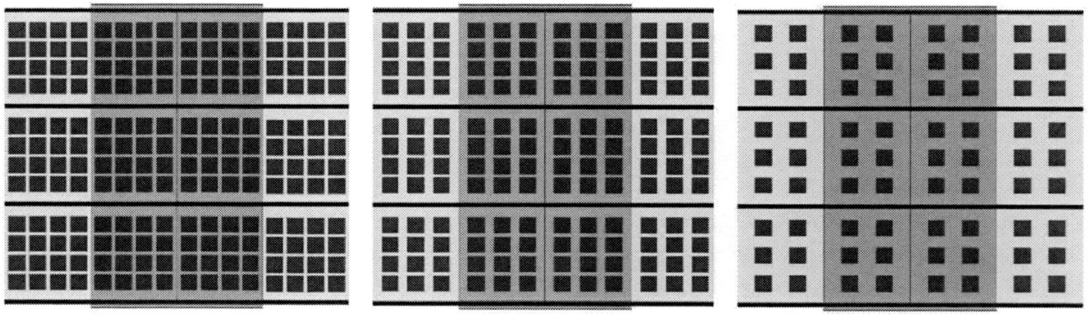

Methodology – plant characterization and growth cycles

PROTECH

- Four different vegetables: lettuce (*Lactuca sativa*), spinach (*Spinacia oleracea*), mustard (*Brassica juncea*), and purslane (*Portulaca oleracea*);
- The plants were cultivated for around 3 weeks before analysis;
- First trial: September 12 – October 2 (no additional lightning);
- Second trial: October 9 – October 30 (additional lightning using high-pressure sodium lamps daily from 6AM to 8AM and from 4PM to 6PM). Included in sensor loggings;
- Fructose and glucose measured using UPLC (Shimdazu) ELSD-LTII detector with NUCLEOSIL Carbohydrate chromatography column (250 x 4mm);
- Leaf area measured using leaf area measurement device: AT Delta –T Devices.

Methodology – Greenhouse and Irradiance measurement

- Venlo type greenhouse made from glass;
- Irradiance sensors placed in each of 4 zones: Si-V-1.5TC;
- Measured irradiance in AM1.5g solar spectrum;
- DLI – daily light integral;
- PAR - Photosynthetically Active Radiation from 400 to 700 nm;
- Conversion from AM1.5g to Photosynthetically Active Radiation (PAR) was done by coefficient of 0.48 [1];

[1] J. Schallenberg-Rodriguez et al., Energy Reports. 9 (2023) 5420–5431.

Results – Measured DLI of PAR per Zone

- Balanced DLI for Spinach: ≈ 10 mol/day·m^2;
- Balanced DLI for Mustard: ≈ 12 mol/day·m^2;
- Balanced DLI for Salad and Portulaka: ≈17 mol/day·m^2;

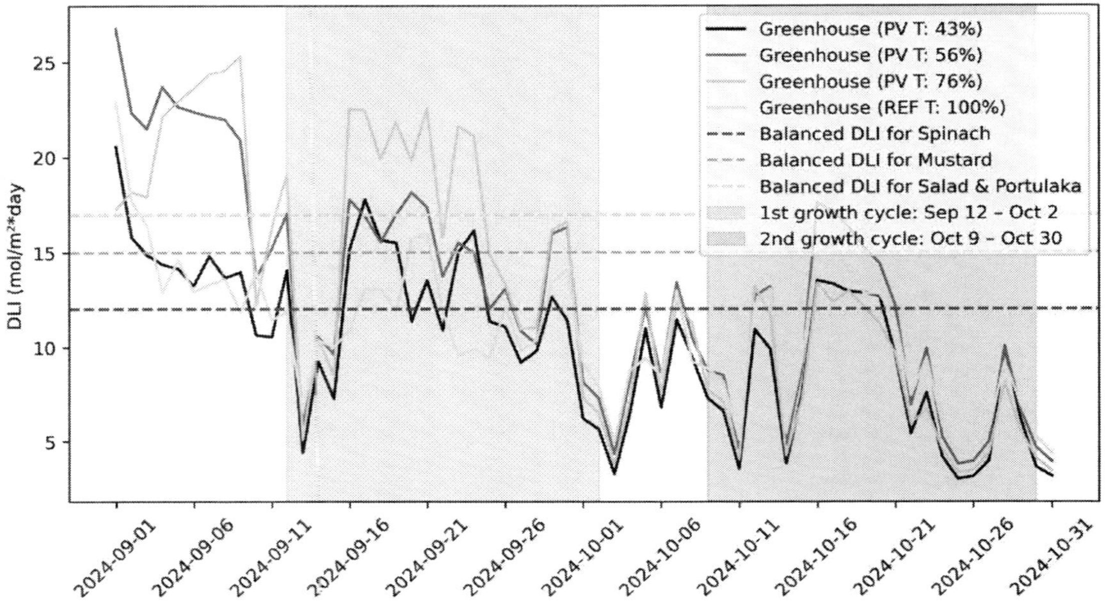

8

Results – Measured DLI of PAR per Zone for growth cycle 1

- Balanced DLI for Spinach: ≈ 10 mol/day·m²;
- Balanced DLI for Mustard: ≈ 12 mol/day·m²;
- Balanced DLI for Salad and Portulaka: ≈17 mol/day·m²;

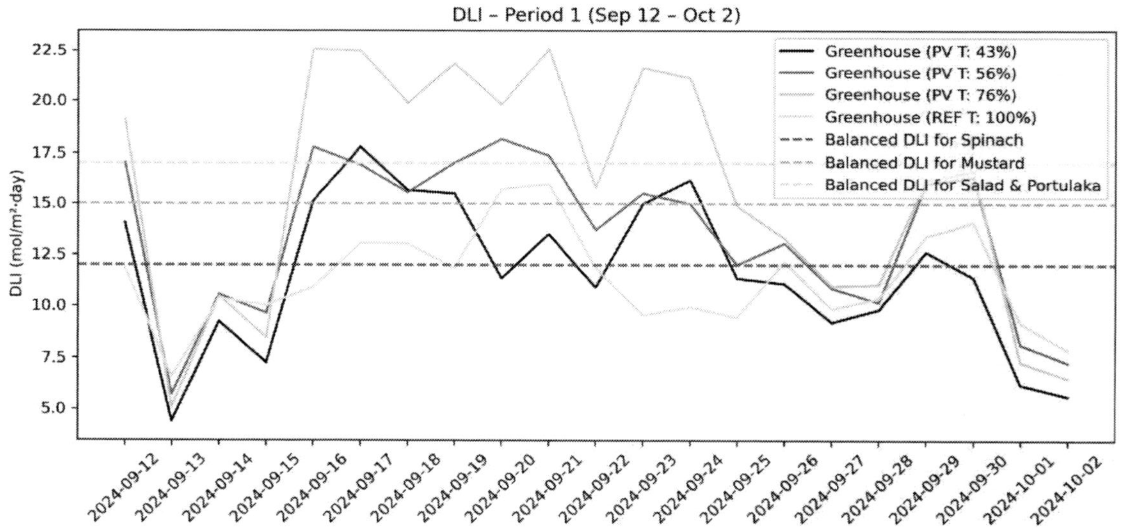

Results – Measured DLI of PAR per Zone for growth cycle 2

- Balanced DLI for Spinach: ≈ 10 mol/day·m^2;
- Balanced DLI for Mustard: ≈ 12 mol/day·m^2;
- Balanced DLI for Salad and Portulaka: ≈17 mol/day·m^2;

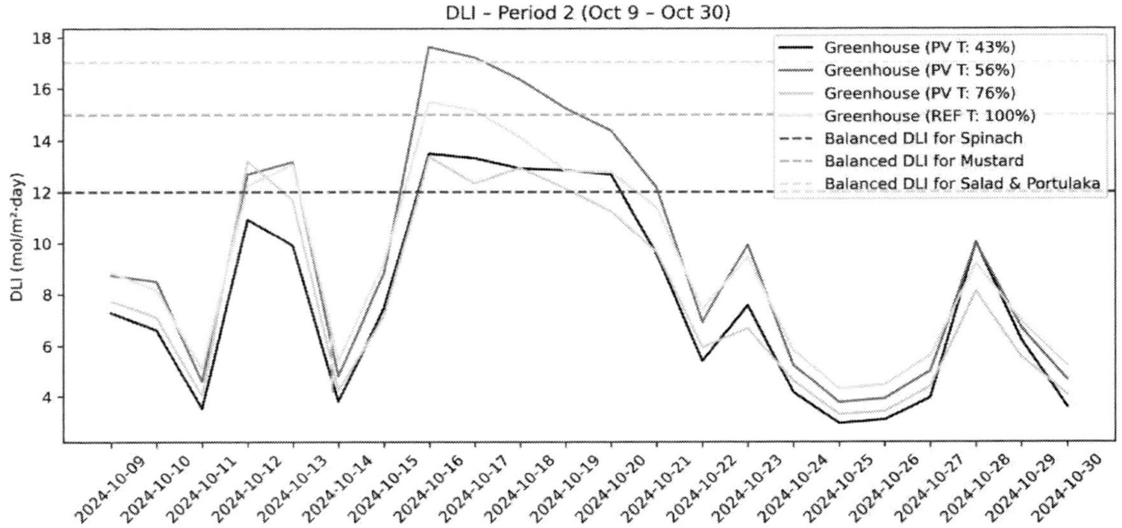

Results – monthly average DLI PAR values per Zone

Period:	Greenhouse (PV T: 43%)	Greenhouse (PV T: 56%)	Greenhouse (PV T: 76%)	Greenhouse (REF T: 100%)
1st growth cycle: Sep 12 – Oct 2	11.59	13.51	15.60	11.28
2nd growth cycle: Oct 9 – Oct 30	7.78	9.56	7.86	9.19

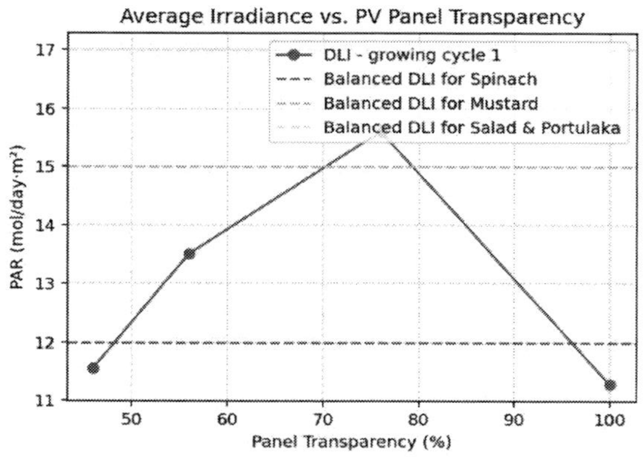

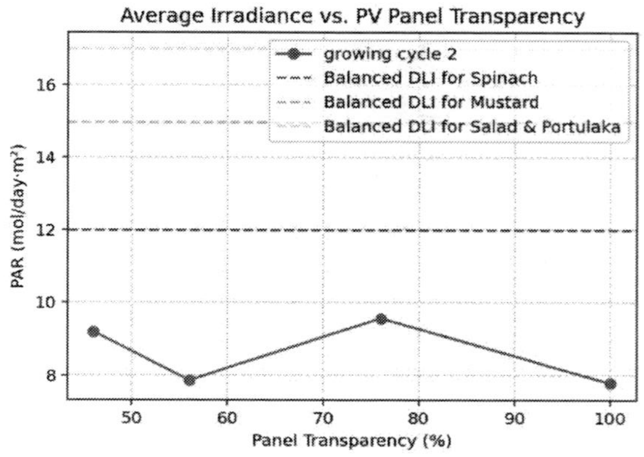

11

Results – monthly average DLI PAR values per Zone

- Figure of merit for the analysis: actual DLI / required DLI.

Period:	Greenhouse (PV T: 43%)	Greenhouse (PV T: 56%)	Greenhouse (PV T: 76%)	Greenhouse (REF T: 100%)
1st growth cycle: Sep 12 – Oct 2	11.59	13.51	15.60	11.28
2nd growth cycle: Oct 9 – Oct 30	7.78	9.56	7.86	9.19

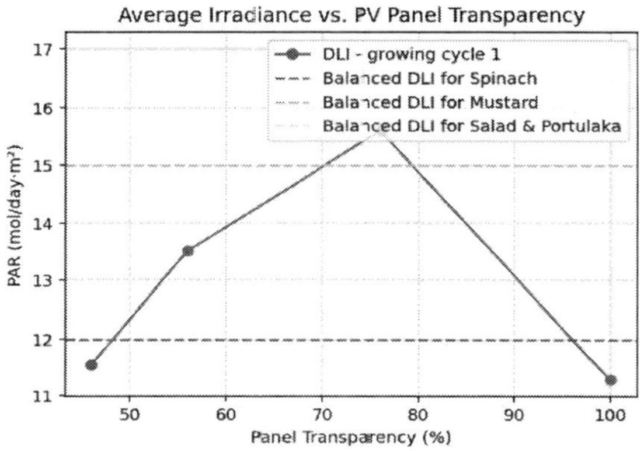

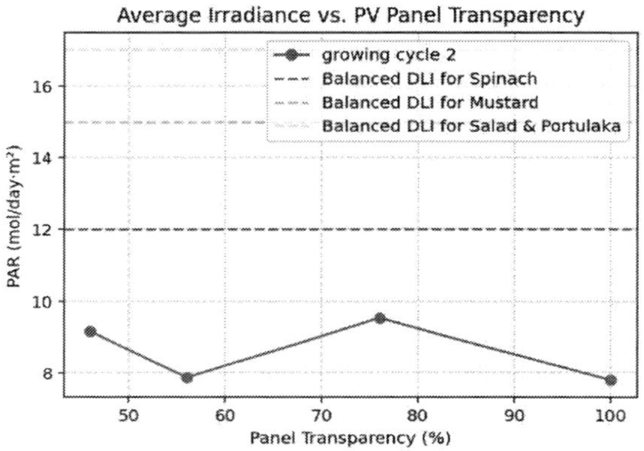

Results – Fructose and Glucose content

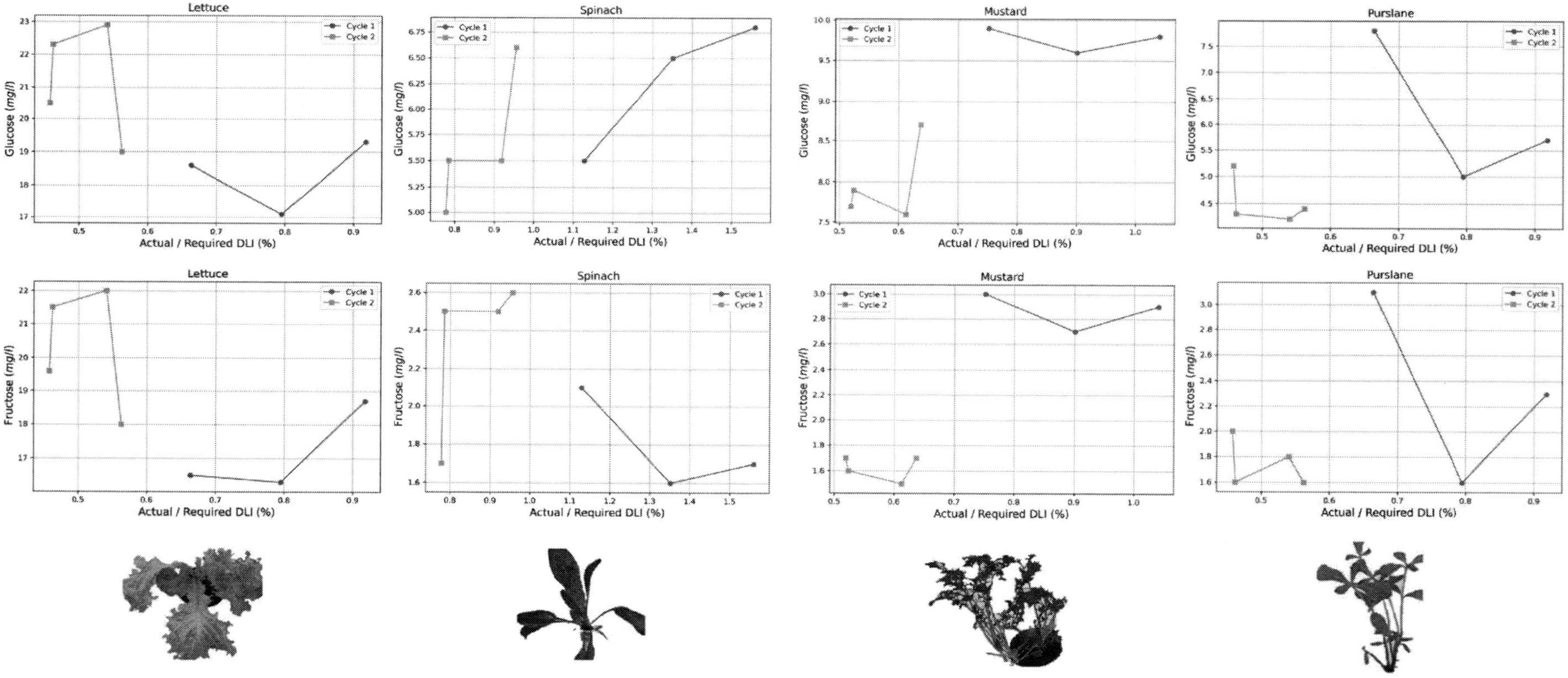

Lettuce
Glucose (mg/l)
Actual / Required DLI (%)
Cycle 1
Cycle 2

Spinach
Glucose (mg/l)
Actual / Required DLI (%)
Cycle 1
Cycle 2

Mustard
Glucose (mg/l)
Actual / Required DLI (%)
Cycle 1
Cycle 2

Purslane
Glucose (mg/l)
Actual / Required DLI (%)
Cycle 1
Cycle 2

Lettuce
Fructose (mg/l)
Actual / Required DLI (%)
Cycle 1
Cycle 2

Spinach
Fructose (mg/l)
Actual / Required DLI (%)
Cycle 1
Cycle 2

Mustard
Fructose (mg/l)
Actual / Required DLI (%)
Cycle 1
Cycle 2

Purslane
Fructose (mg/l)
Actual / Required DLI (%)
Cycle 1
Cycle 2

13

Results – Fructose and Glucose content

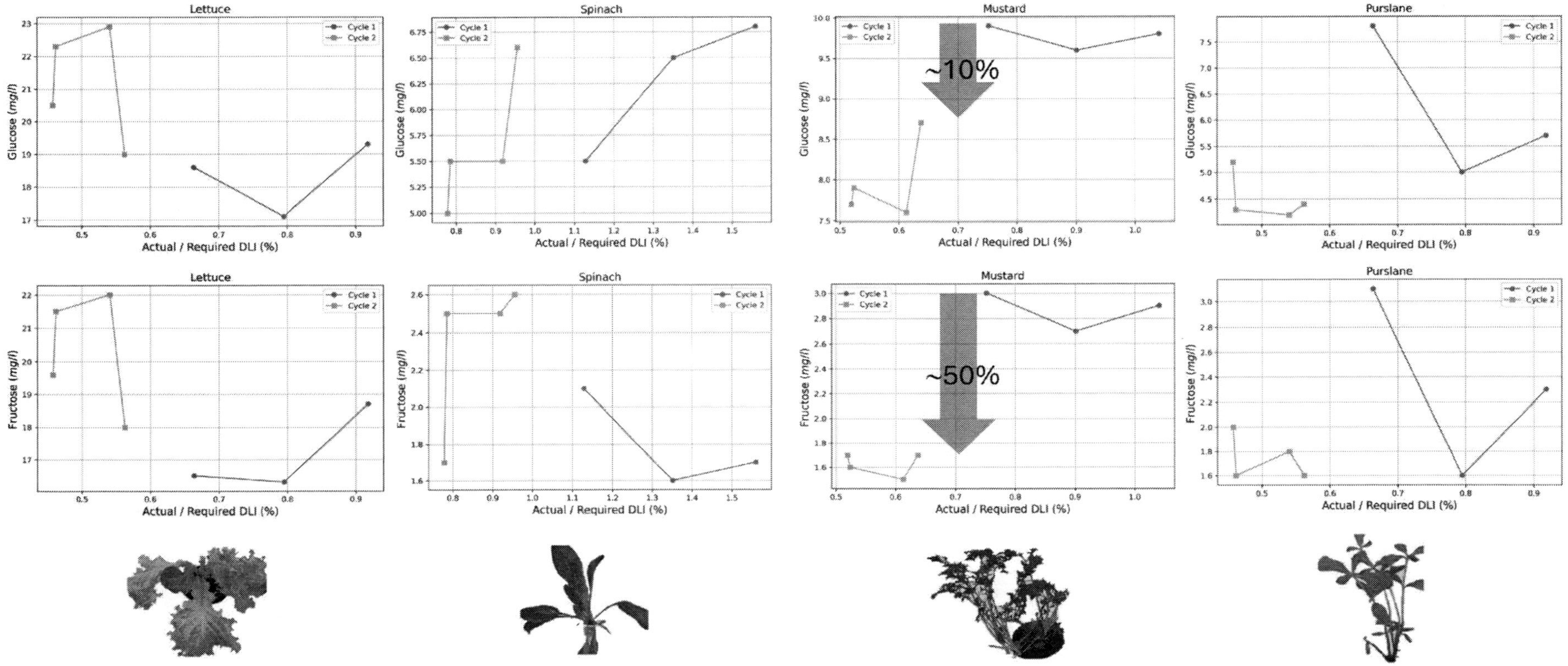

14

Results – leaf size and green mass

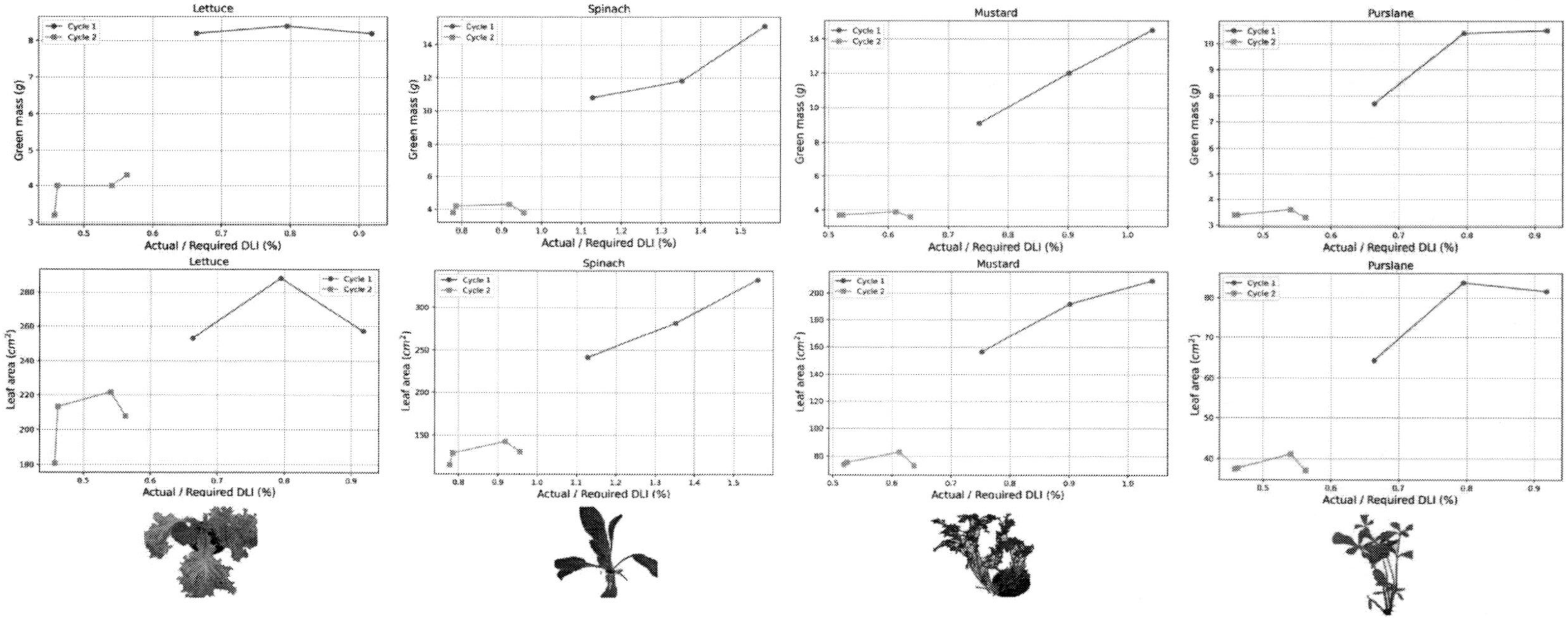

- Green mass declined 50–65% or more for all plant species at DLI ratios below 0.6–0.65, except spinach, which showed similar reductions only below 1;
- Leaf area reduced for 15-50% below 0.6-0.65 except for, where spinach reduction observed below 1.

15

Results – leaf size and green mass

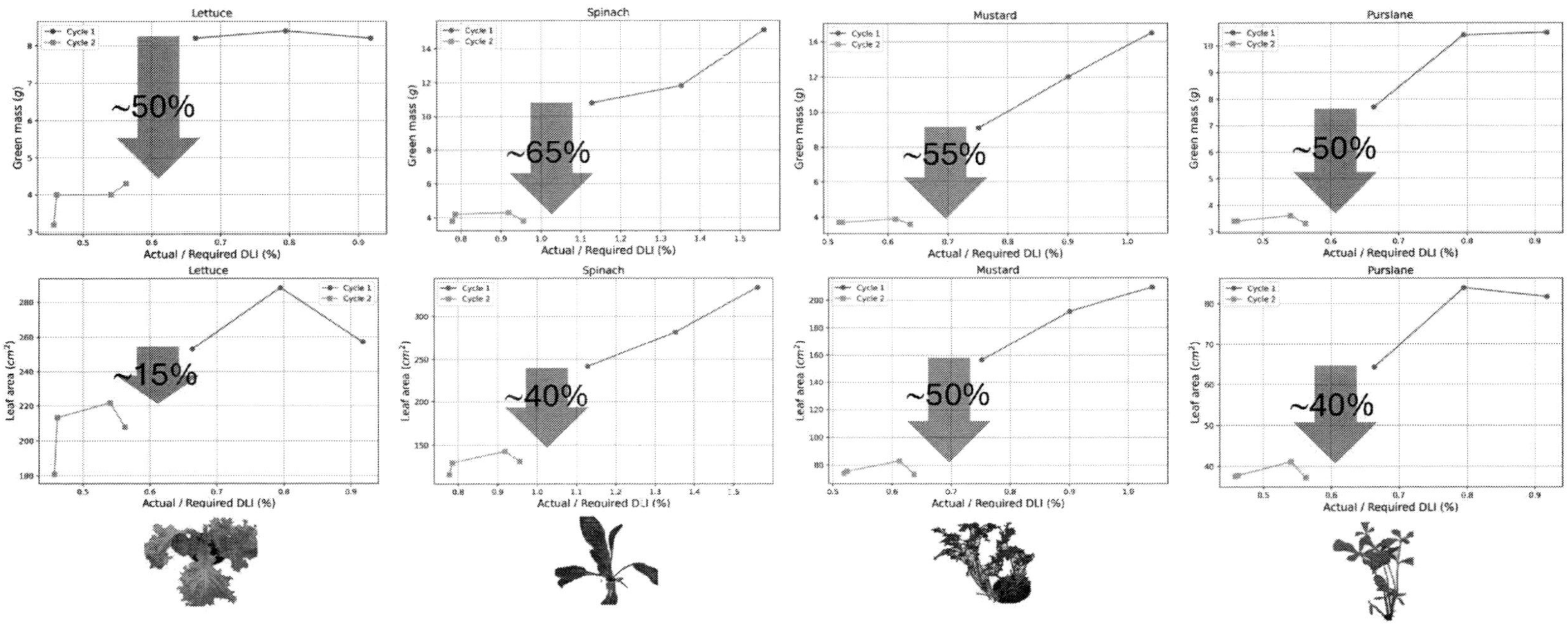

- Green mass declined 50–65% or more for all plant species at DLI ratios below 0.6–0.65, except spinach, which showed similar reductions only below 1;
- Leaf area reduced for 15-50% below 0.6-0.65 except for, where spinach reduction observed below 1.

16

Results – leaf size and green mass

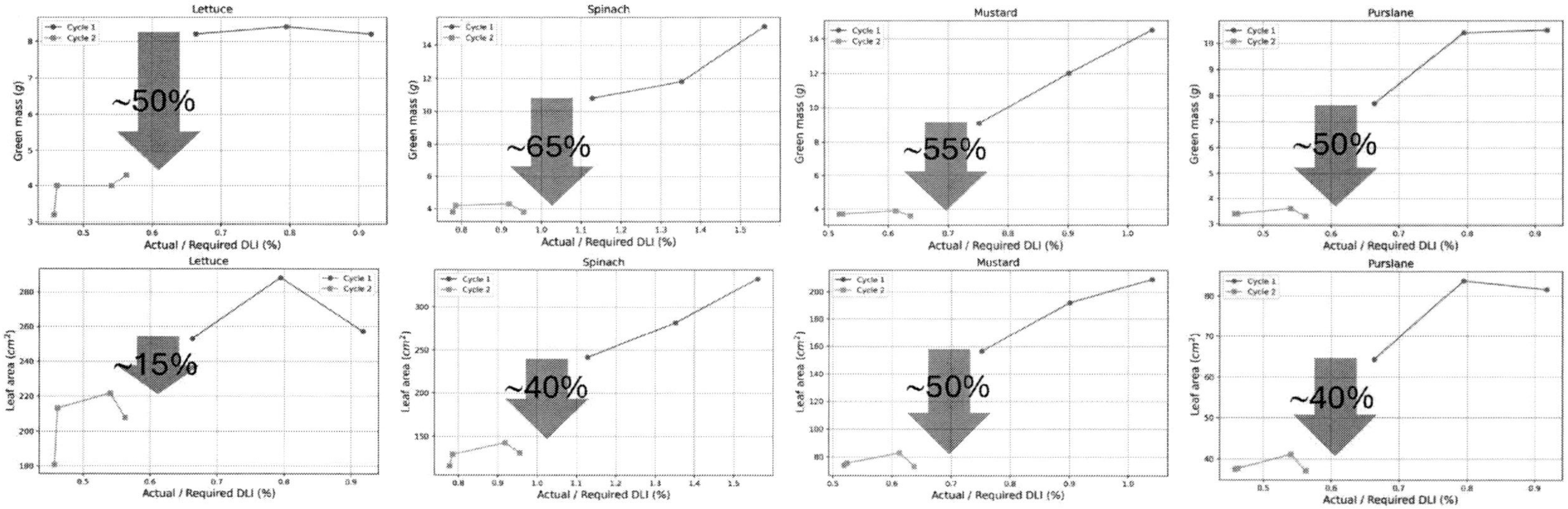

Cycle 1:

Cycle 2:

protech

Conclusions

- **Experimental design:** The plot size (2.77 × 3.27 m) was too small, and daily/ regional solar variability (and possibly greenhouse construction elements) made direct comparisons of PV shading effects unreliable. Analysis was therefore based on actual irradiance relative to required DLI.
- **Sugar content:** Glucose and fructose showed no clear pattern across species, except in mustard, where glucose decreased 10–20% and fructose nearly 50% when actual/required DLI fell below 0.6–0.65.
- **Biomass:** Green mass declined 50–65% or more for all plant species at DLI ratios below 0.6–0.65, except spinach, which showed similar reductions only below 1. Leaf area reduced for 15-60% below 0.6-0.65 except for, where spinach reduction observed below 1.
- **Supplemental lighting:** Four extra hours of high-pressure sodium lighting (Oct 9–30) still left irradiance 35–55% below required DLI for most species, and 5–22% for spinach.

Thank you for your attention!

met. protech ktu 1922 LAMMC

19

Coloured Semi-Transparent CdTe PV Module in Agrivoltaics:
A 2-Year Study on Broccoli Growth and System Potential

Silvia Ma Lu[1], Xiaolin Wang[1], Arash Khosravi[1] and Pietro Elia Campana[1]
[1]Mälardalen University, Västerås, Sweden

25 September 2025 – Session 4DO.2: Agrivoltaic Technologies
The 42nd European Photovoltaic Solar Energy Conference and Exhibition
22 – 26 September 2025, Bilbao, Spain

EUPVSEC
European Photovoltaic Solar Energy Conference and Exhibition

Mälardalen University

Background

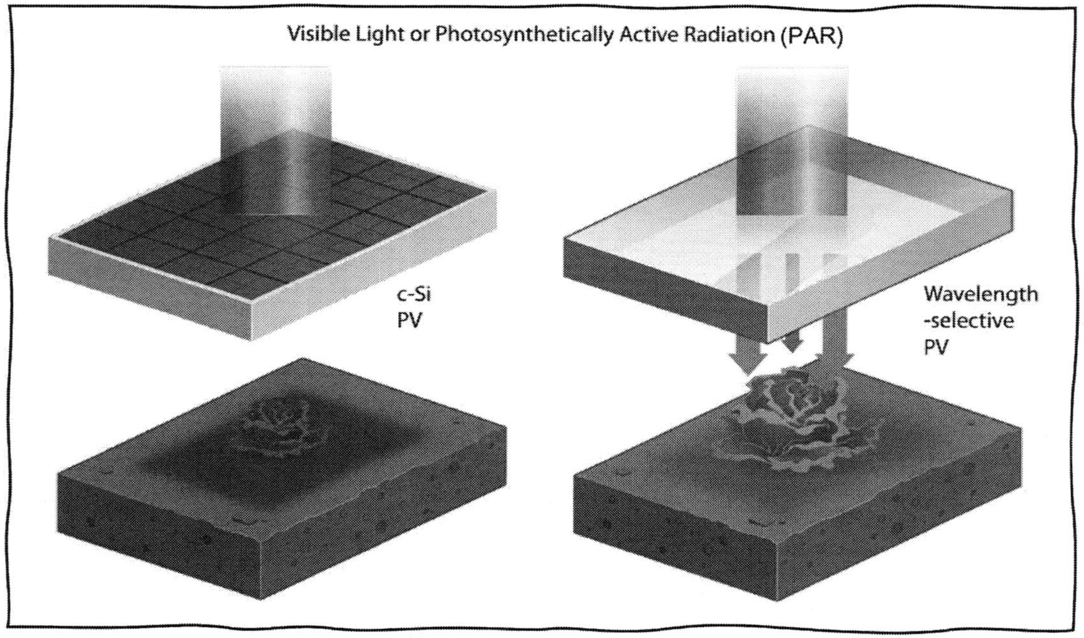

- Plants require a specific spectrum of solar irradiance to perform photosynthesis and grow: photosynthetically active radiation (PAR).
- Excessive high light intensity can harm plant growth by causing photo-inhibition.
- Severe shading is generally detrimental to plant growth.

S. Zhen, M. van Iersel and B. Bugbee. (2021) Why Far-Red Photons Should Be Included in the Definition of Photosynthetic Photons and the Measurement of Horticultural Fixture Efficacy. Front. Plant Sci. 12:693445.
N. R. Baker. (1996). "Photoinhibition of Photosynthesis," in Light as an Energy Source and Information Carrier in Plant Physiology, eds R. C. Jennings, G. Zucchelli, F. Ghetti, and G. Colombetti (New York, NY: Plenum Press), 89–97.
S. Touil, A. Richa, M. Fizir et al. (2021). Shading effect of photovoltaic panels on horticulture crops production: a mini review. Rev Environ Sci Biotechnol 20, 281–296.
Illustrations: S. Ma Lu, S. Amaducci, S. Gorjian et al. (2024). Wavelength-selective solar photovoltaic systems to enhance the spectral sharing of sunlight in agrivoltaics. Joule, 8, 2483–2522.

Background

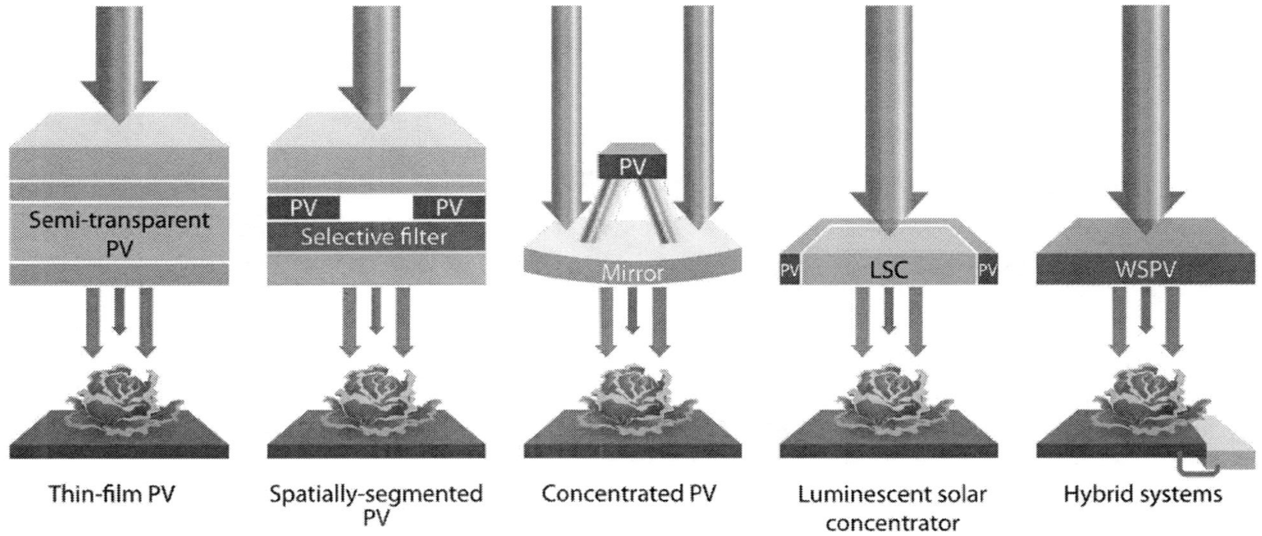

Wavelength-selective solar photovoltaic (WSPV) technologies consider the absorption profiles of plants and enable the transmission of light at wavelengths that are beneficial for photosynthesis.

H. Shi, R. Xia, G. Zhang et al. (2019). Spectral engineering of semitransparent polymer solar cells for greenhouse applications. Adv Energy Mater, 9 : 1803438.
S. Ma Lu, S. Amaducci, S. Gorjian et al. (2024). Wavelength-selective solar photovoltaic systems to enhance the spectral sharing of sunlight in agrivoltaics. Joule, 8, 2483–2522.

Spatially-segmented PV: Semi-transparent coloured cadmium telluride (CdTe) solar photovoltaic panels

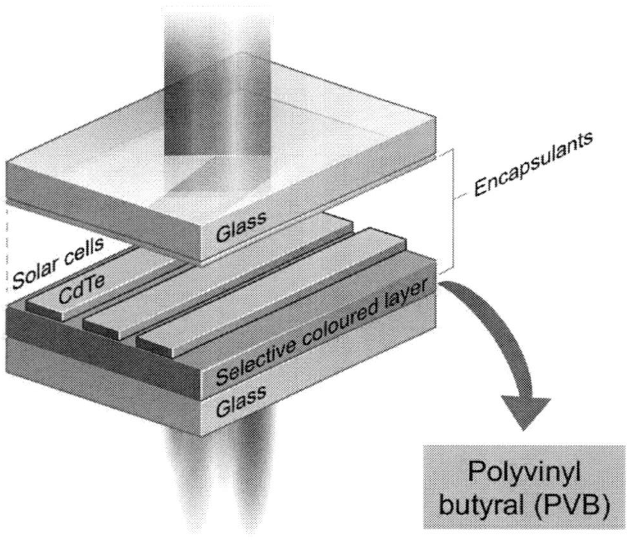

Advanced Solar Power (ASP-LAM2)

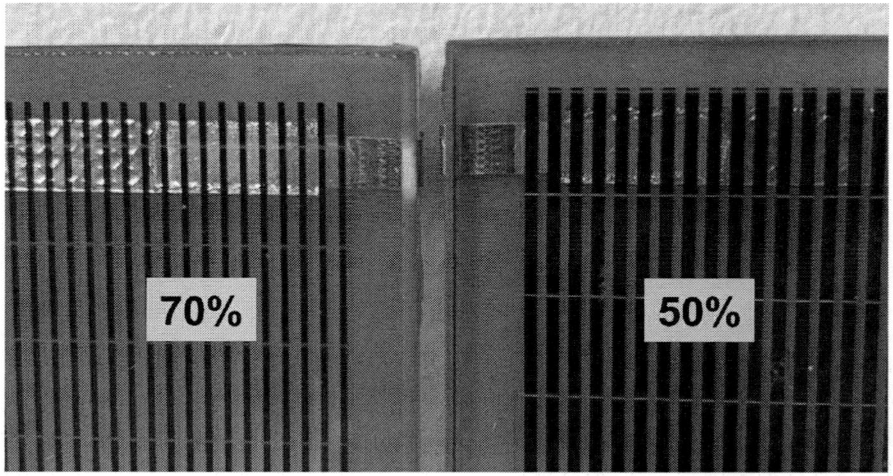

Illustration adapted from: S. Ma Lu, S. Amaducci, S. Gorjian et al. (2024). Wavelength-selective solar photovoltaic systems to enhance the spectral sharing of sunlight in agrivoltaics. Joule, 8, 2483–2522.

Experimental setup 2023: Kärrbo Prästgård, Sweden

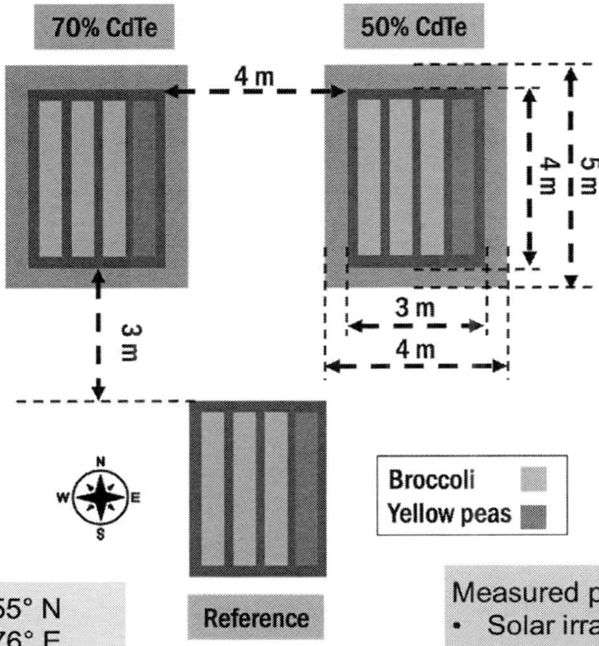

59.55° N
16.76° E
Jul-Oct 2023

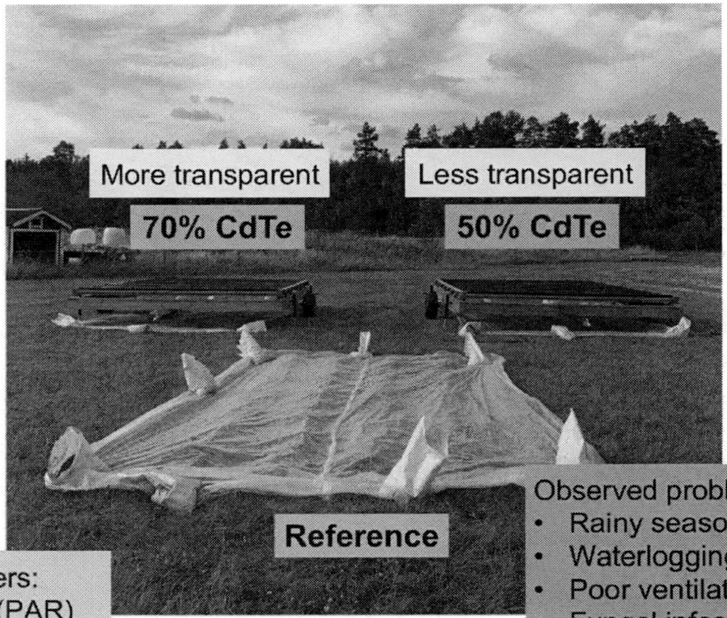

Height 0.7 m

Measured parameters:
- Solar irradiation (PAR)
- Air temperature, RH, … (site's weather station)

Observed problems:
- Rainy season
- Waterlogging
- Poor ventilation
- Fungal infestation (yellow peas)
- Limited light availability

Experimental setup 2024: Kärrbo Prästgård, Sweden

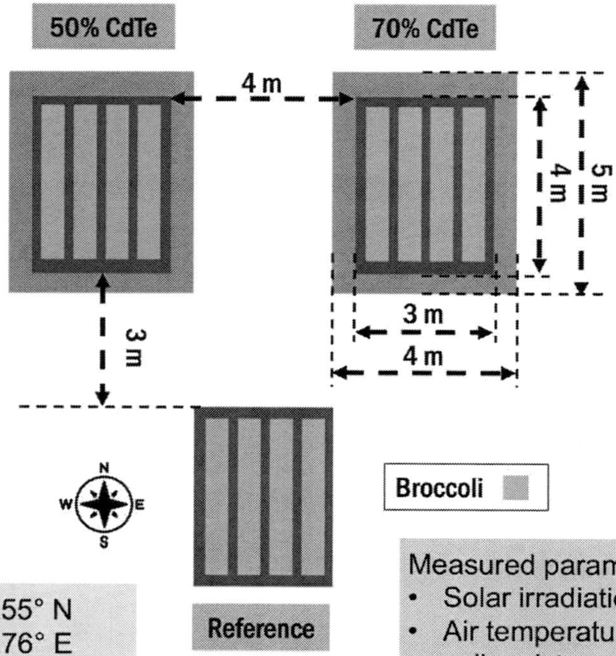

59.55° N
16.76° E
Jul-Oct 2024

Measured parameters:
- Solar irradiation (PAR)
- Air temperature, RH, soil moisture and temperature

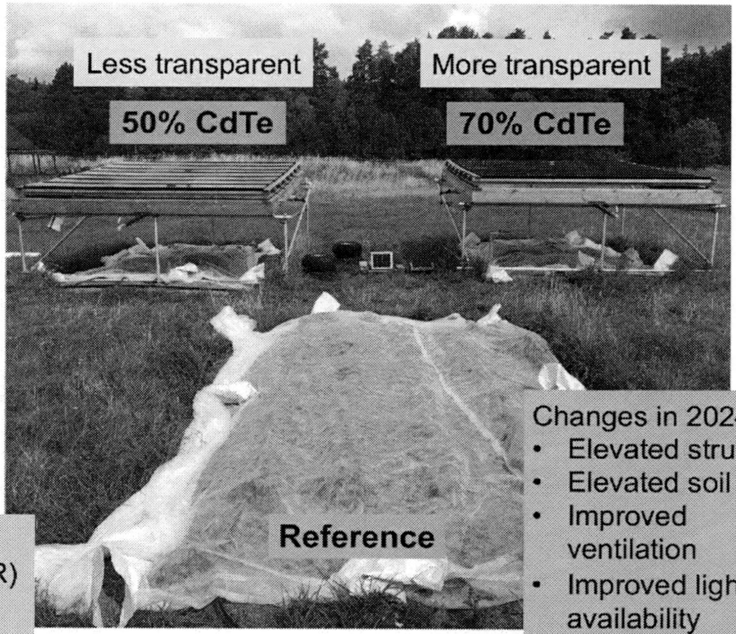

Height 1.5 m

Changes in 2024:
- Elevated structure
- Elevated soil
- Improved ventilation
- Improved light availability
- More edge effects

Comparison daily light integral levels* 2023 vs. 2024

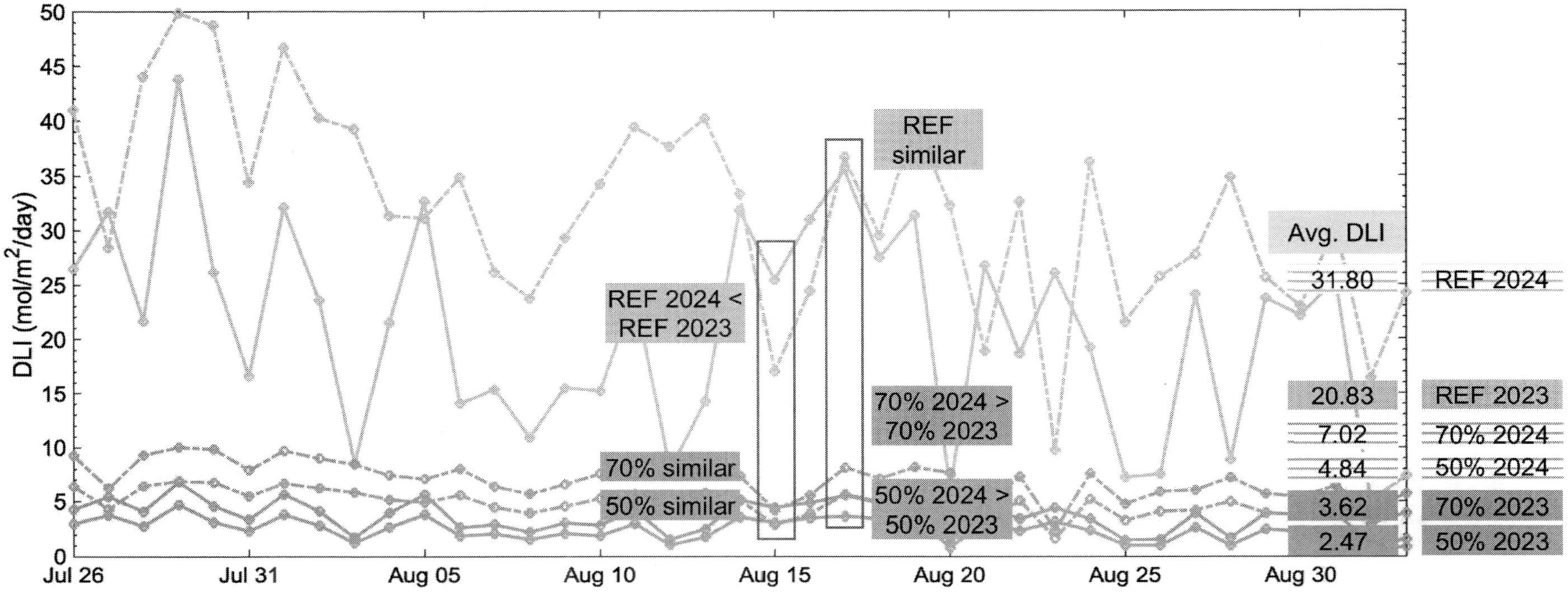

*White insect net light reduction not shown (further -14% of transmitted light is estimated)
DLI = total number of photosynthetic photons received by plants per m² during a 24 h period

Comparison daily light integral levels* 2023 vs. 2024

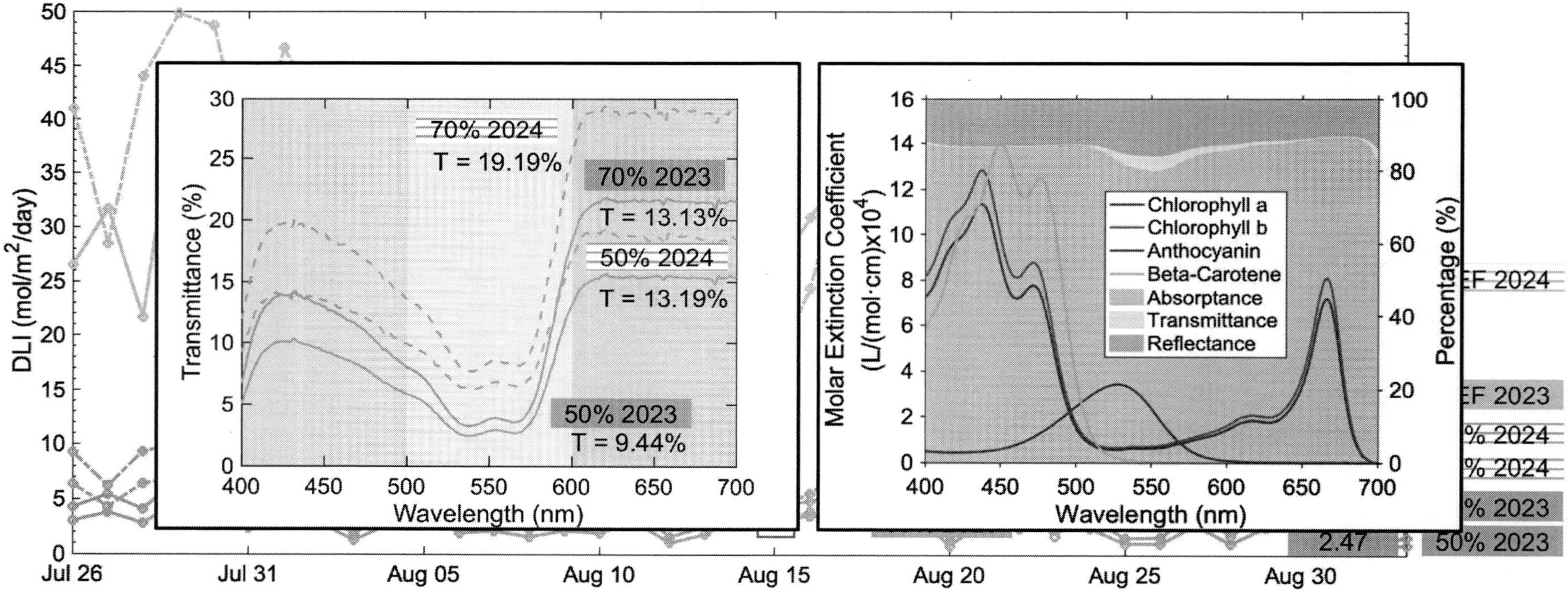

*White insect net light reduction not shown (further -14% of transmitted light is estimated)
DLI = total number of photosynthetic photons received by plants per m² during a 24 h period

Peters, R. D. & Noble, S. D. (2014) Spectrographic measurement of plant pigments from 300 to 800nm. Remote Sens. Environ. 148, 119–123.
Average absorptance, transmittance and reflectance data from of 8 fully-expanded broccoli leaves (Ramoso Calabrese) grown under white LED light and measured using an integrated sphere.

Comparison broccoli head yield 2023 vs. 2024

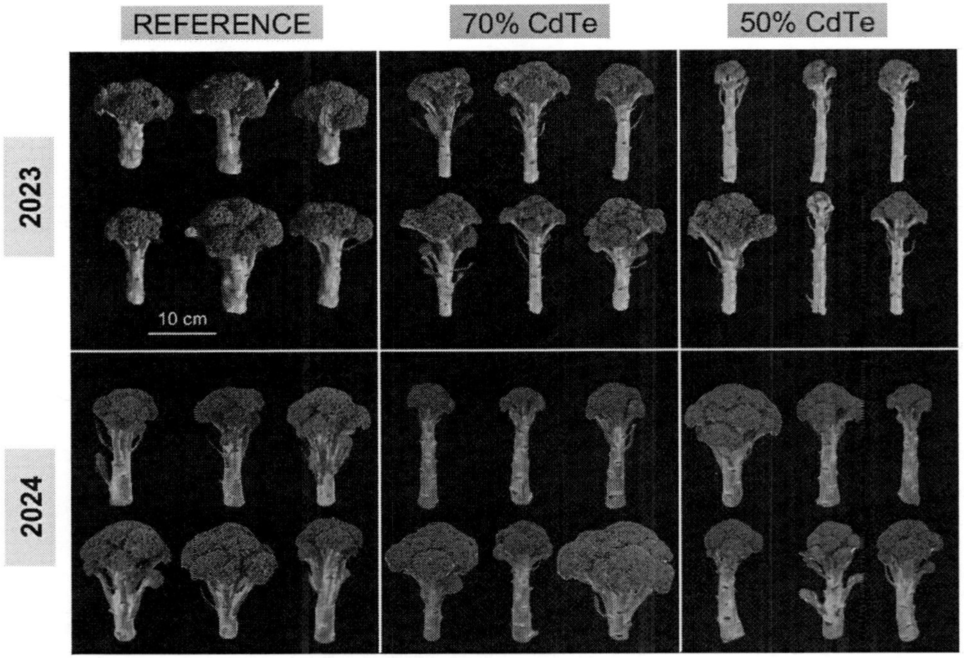

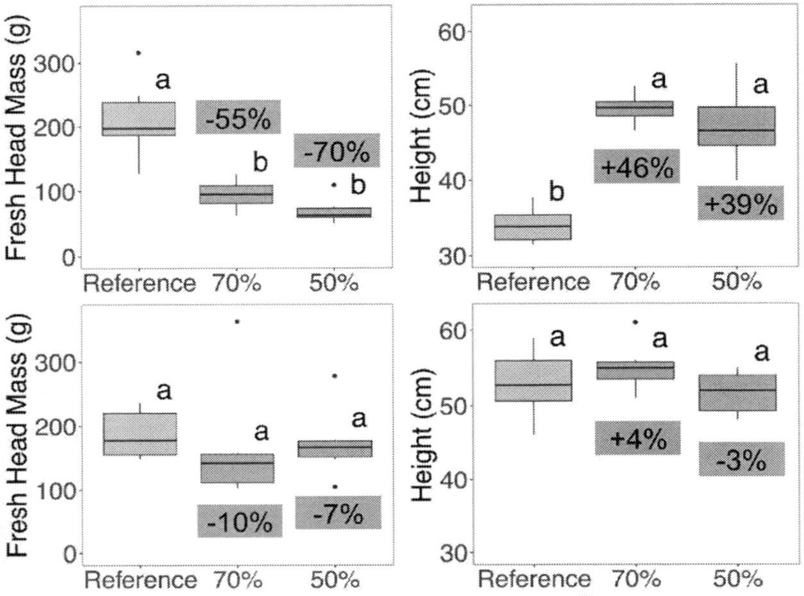

Brassica oleracea L. var. italica, cv. Marathon
Seedling dates: May 20 (2023), June 15 (2024)
Transplanting dates: Jul 2 (2023), Jul 2 (2024)
Harvest dates 2023: Aug 29 (Reference), Sep 26 (70%), Oct 13 (50%)
Harvest dates 2024: Sep 19 (Reference), Oct 14 (70% and 50%)

One-way ANOVA and Tukey Post hoc test at significance threshold of 5% ($P < 0.05$) (n=6).

Delayed harvest of 1 month under WSPVs

S. Ma Lu, A. Khosravi, X. Wang et al. Increasing land productivity with semi-transparent colored CdTe thin-film photovoltaics and broccoli cultivation in agrivoltaic systems. (Submitted)

9

Microclimate 2023 vs. 2024

Unfortunately, we did not have a proper monitoring system but we noticed the following observations:
- Poor ventilation
- High moisture levels and waterlogging

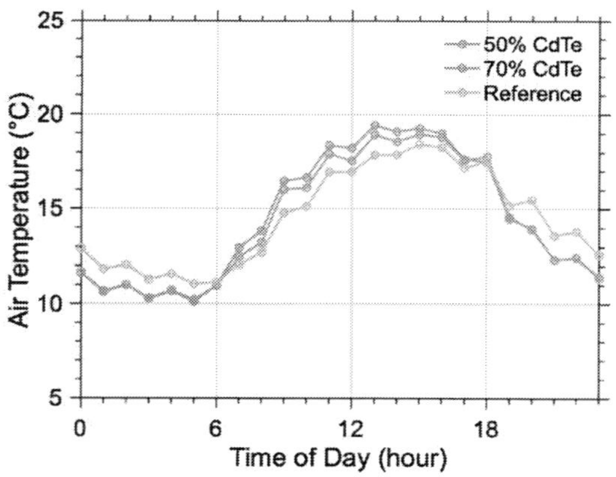

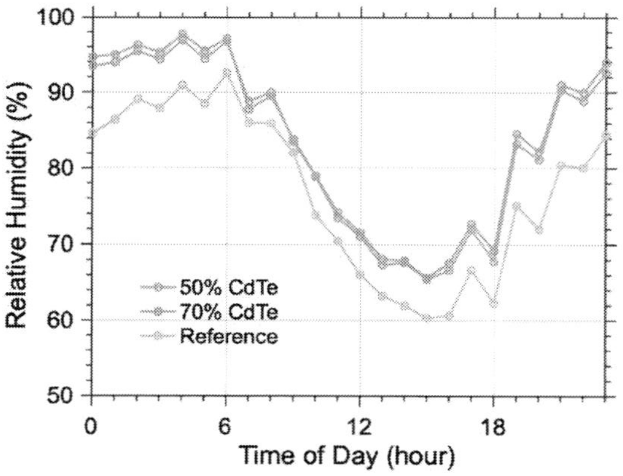

S. Ma Lu, A. Khosravi, X. Wang et al. Increasing land productivity with semi-transparent colored CdTe thin-film photovoltaics and broccoli cultivation in agrivoltaic systems. (Submitted)

Microclimate 2023 vs. 2024

Unfortunately, we did not have a proper monitoring system but we noticed the following observations:

- Poor ventilation
- High moisture levels and waterlogging

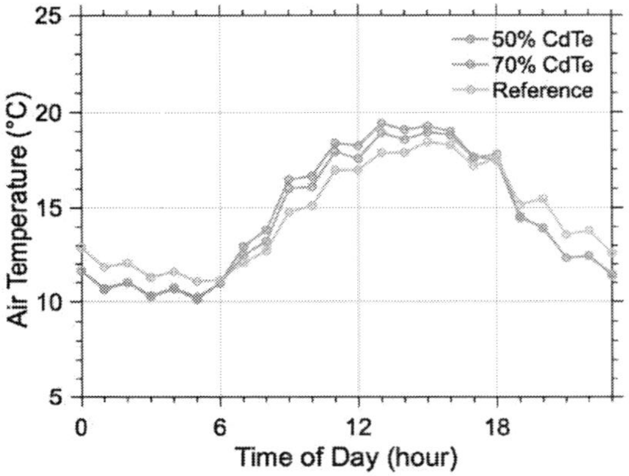

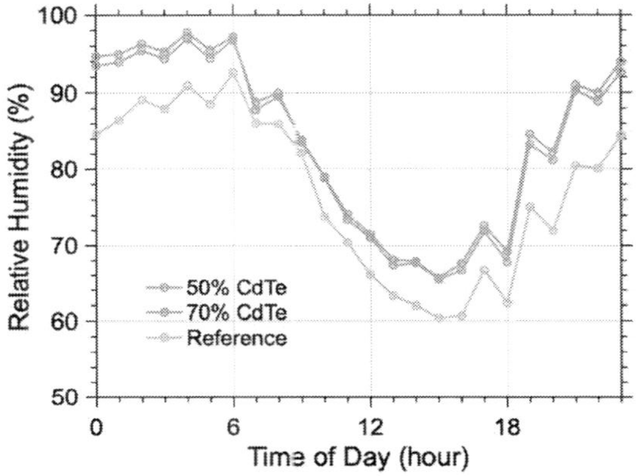

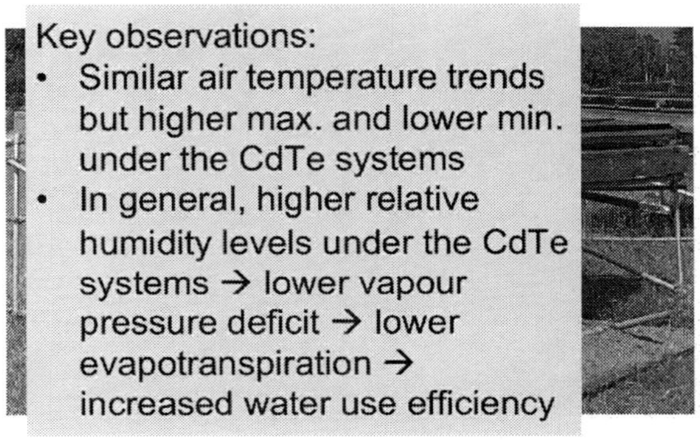

Key observations:

- Similar air temperature trends but higher max. and lower min. under the CdTe systems
- In general, higher relative humidity levels under the CdTe systems → lower vapour pressure deficit → lower evapotranspiration → increased water use efficiency

S. Ma Lu, A. Khosravi, X. Wang et al. Increasing land productivity with semi-transparent colored CdTe thin-film photovoltaics and broccoli cultivation in agrivoltaic systems. (Submitted)

Light-response curves 2024

No LRCs measurements performed in 2023. Only instantaneous leaf-gas exchange measurements and not respresentative (too late) → Lessons learned

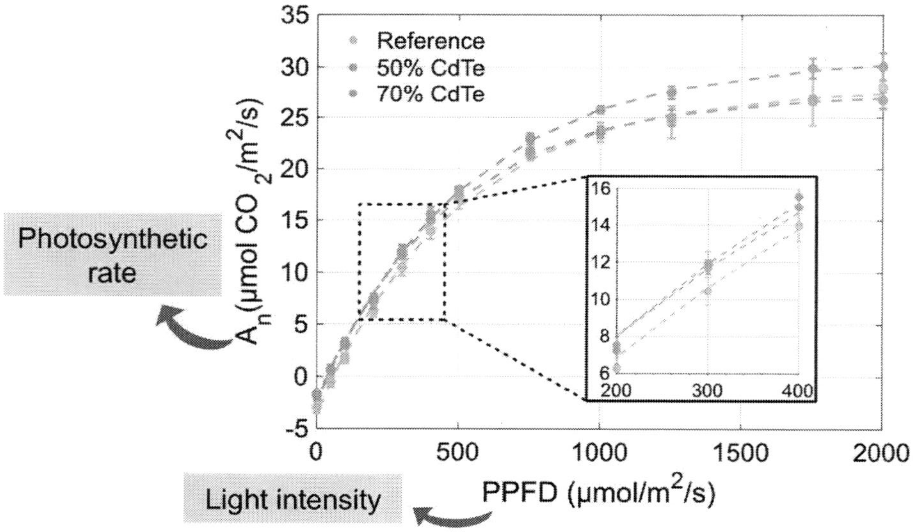

Average of three measurements at different dates: Aug 13, Sep 2 and Sep 19. Fully-expanded leaves at the second upper levels, one leaf-one plant per treatment). Average leaf temperature 21.4 ± 2.8°C std dev.

1 W/m² = 4.57 µmol/m²/s

S. Ma Lu, A. Khosravi, X. Wang et al. Increasing land productivity with semi-transparent colored CdTe thin-film photovoltaics and broccoli cultivation in agrivoltaic systems. (Submitted)

Light-response curves 2024

No LRCs measurements performed in 2023. Only instantaneous leaf-gas exchange measurements and not respresentative (too late) → Lessons learned

Photosynthetic rate

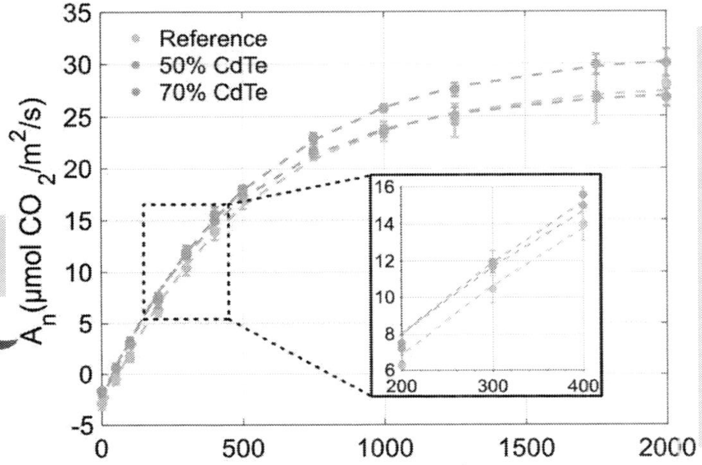

Light intensity

Average of three measurements at different dates: Aug 13, Sep 2 and Sep 19. Fully-expanded leaves at the second upper levels, one leaf-one plant per treatment). Average leaf temperature 21.4 ± 2.8°C std dev.

Key observations:

- Growth at lower PPFD under WSPVs likely induced biochemical and morphological response to enhance light capture and utilisation in broccoli plants
- Higher photosynthesis under WSPVs could be linked with higher N content and likely higher chlorophyll (not measured)

1 W/m² = 4.57 µmol/m²/s

S. Ma Lu, A. Khosravi, X. Wang et al. Increasing land productivity with semi-transparent colored CdTe thin-film photovoltaics and broccoli cultivation in agrivoltaic systems. (Submitted)

Preliminary calculations on system potential

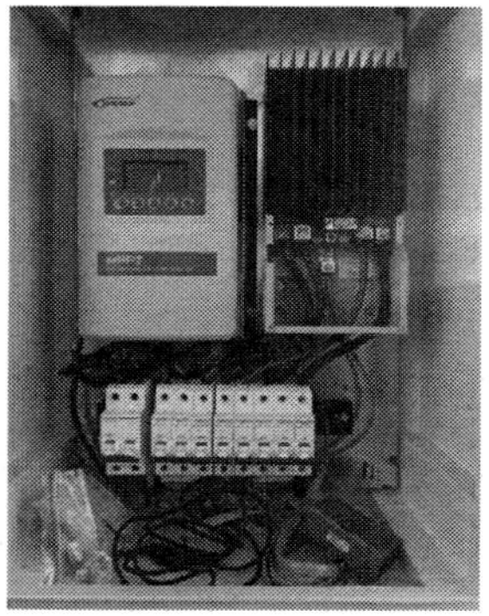

Off-grid PV system:
- 3 CdTe PV modules connected in parallel for each 50% and 70%
- Battery
- Dumping Load
- 2 MPPT Solar Controller
- 2 Dataloggers

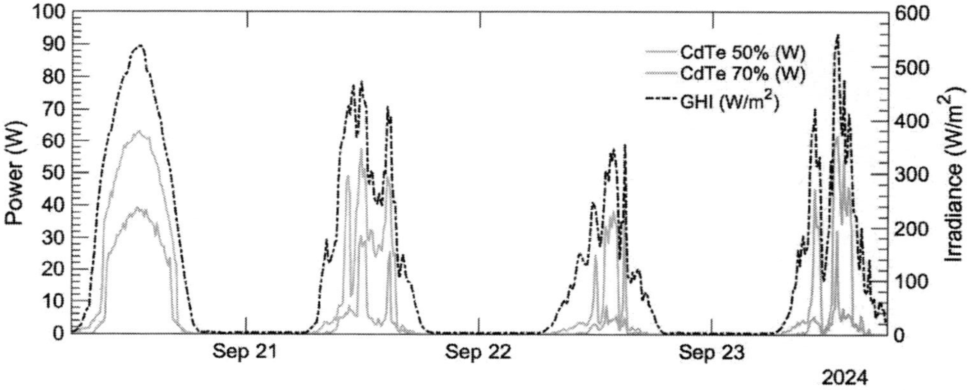

Monitoring data roughly 2-months (Sep 17 - Nov 19 2024)

50% CdTe PV system: 21 panels → 655.2 W_p
70% CdTe PV system: 21 panels → 390.6 W_p

Input weather data (Jul 2– Oct 14)

calibration

Agri-OptiCE® (in-house modelling and simulation tool)

50% CdTe:
- 311.7 kWh_{DC}
- PCE = 4.3%

70% CdTe:
- 185.8 kWh_{DC}
- PCE = 2.6%

PCE = power conversion efficiency

Specific yield (Jul 2 – Oct 14):
- 475.7 kWh/kWp

Land equivalent ratio (LER) 50% CdTe:
- LER = 1.24

$$LER = \frac{Y_{crop\ APV}}{Y_{monocrop}} + \frac{Y_{electricity\ APV}}{Y_{electricity\ PV}}$$

In line with other WSPVs technologies, despite modest PCE vs. c-Si

Loik, M. E. et al. (2017) Wavelength-Selective Solar Photovoltaic Systems: Powering Greenhouses for Plant Growth at the Food-Energy-Water Nexus. 10
Vasiliev, M. et al. (2023). High-transparency clear window-based agrivoltaics. Sustain. Build. 6, 5 (2023)

Conclusions and future work

Broccoli yield in 2023 was reduced under WSPVs, but in 2024 design improvements led to **yields comparable** to the reference showing the feasibility of the magenta panels despite lower overall light transmitted.

Light-response curves showed **improved light utilisation** under WSPVs indicating an **adaptive response** to modified light quantity and quality.

CdTe panels have **lower power conversion efficiencies** than c-Si, but advanced WSPVs technologies like organic PVs with similar light transmittance profiles could narrow the gap in the near future.

Related work

Ma Lu et al. (2025). **Selective light transmission in agrivoltaics: Modeling light spectra and photosynthetic rate.** Nexus, 2(3), 100074. https://doi.org/10.1016/j.ynexs.2025.100074

- Development of 2 spectrum-aware models for light transmission and photosynthesis
- Assessment of crop suitability under different WSPVs technologies globally
- Optimization method to guide ideal light transmittance of WSPVs for optimum plant growth

16

SOLVE Swedish Energy Agency EUPVSEC European Photovoltaic Solar Energy Conference and Exhibition STIFTELSEN J. GUST. RICHERT Mälardalen University

Thank you for your attention!

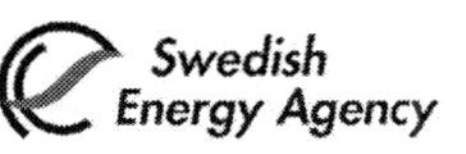

Silvia Ma Lu
PhD Candidate
silvia.ma.lu@mdu.se
25 September 2025

LinkedIn

Let's connect!

42nd European Photovoltaic Solar Energy Conference and Exhibition

This presentation was selected by the Sc. Committee of the EU PVSEC 2025 for submission of a full paper to one of the EU PVSEC's collaborating peer-reviewed journals.

A CASE STUDY: QUANTIFYING THE IMPACT OF MINOR DESIGN CHANGES ON LARGE-SCALE SOLAR PV PLANTS

Ayesha Jacobs[1], Keanu Damon[2] and Paul Nel[2]
[1]Zutari (Pty) Ltd, Cape Town, South Africa, ayesha.jacobs@zutari.com
[2]7SecondSolar (Pty) Ltd, Cape Town, South Africa

ABSTRACT: Utility-scale solar photovoltaic (PV) plants continue to expand globally, with overall performance depending not only on module and inverter technologies but also on early-stage design choices such as equipment placement and cable configuration. This paper highlights the specific impact of minor changes in layout design and equipment placement on the direct current (DC) cable network, as well as the resulting effects on capital expenditure, power loss, and energy yield. A base case scenario PV plant is defined, and nine design variations are assessed. Results indicate that the positioning of combiner boxes and inverters has the strongest influence on both cable costs and associated power losses. The study demonstrates that relatively minor adjustments to equipment layout and other key design decisions can result in significant reductions in costs without compromising energy yield. These findings underline the importance of layout-driven design decisions during early project stages and provide practical guidance for developers seeking cost-effective PV plant development.
Keywords: Cable layout optimisation, PV system design, utility-scale solar PV

1 INTRODUCTION

Solar Photovoltaic (PV) is one of the most widely utilised forms of renewable technologies worldwide and continues to expand rapidly, with an additional 4,000 GW of solar capacity predicted to be added to the global grid by 2030. Utility-scale projects are expected to drive the majority of this expansion [1]. As projects grow larger in capacity, the design of these plants becomes more complex and constrained, requiring careful trade-offs between cost, performance, and constructability.

Research on PV plant optimisation has primarily focused on module improvements, tracking systems, and control strategies. Relatively fewer studies have examined how system-level design choices, such as equipment selection, placement, and cable routing, can influence overall system efficiency and cost.

In practice, these design choices are often overlooked or simplified during the early stages of a project; yet they can be a significant driver of plant performance. Small changes in cable sizing, length, or array layout can impact resistive losses, voltage drop, and capital expenditure (CAPEX).

This study explores how minor variations in the layout of utility-scale PV plants affect the DC cable network and, in turn, impact the energy yield, power losses, and costs. By linking design decisions to measurable technical and economic outcomes, it highlights the importance of cable and layout optimisation in the early stages of project development.

2 LOSSES IN PV SYSTEMS

The losses in a PV system refer to the difference between a plant's theoretical maximum output and the actual energy generated under real conditions. These losses can result from both environmental factors and technical inefficiencies. The accurate estimation and management of these losses is essential for reliable yield prediction and financial assessment.

In utility-scale systems, losses typically include shading, soiling, thermal effects, module mismatch, and electrical resistances, primarily due to resistive losses in cables [2]. While the losses due to the site location or environment are partially unavoidable, electrical losses – particularly those in the DC subsystem – can be managed through detailed design considerations. Cable losses occur due to the inherent resistance of conductors, resulting in part of the transmitted energy being dissipated as heat. These losses are proportional to the current, area, and length of the conductor.

As the capacities of PV plants grow and equipment ratings increase, cabling will account for a larger share of overall system losses. Decisions on cable sizing, routing, and equipment placement, therefore, play an important role in minimising resistive losses while balancing capital costs.

3 OPTIMISATION APPROACHES IN PV SYSTEMS

A wide range of approaches to improving PV system efficiency have been investigated, with much of the existing research focusing on module-level improvements or control-based strategies. Examples include tracking systems, module cooling methods, and Maximum Power Point Tracking (MPPT) control strategies [3]. These approaches can significantly increase energy yield, with dual-axis tracking achieving gains of up to 45% and module cooling providing improvements of 3-7.5% [4,5]. However, losses that result from inefficient system-level layout and electrical design are generally overlooked.

Recent research highlights the importance of cable optimisation. Khan et al. present a comparative assessment of six cable configurations for a PV array. Their analysis highlights the trade-offs between performance and cost, demonstrating that the lowest-loss designs are not always the most cost-effective [6]. Gan et al. present an optimisation framework for DC cable sizing in a PV system over its lifetime. They demonstrate that oversizing cables, although having a higher initial cost, can reduce the associated cost of resistive energy losses [7].

Other studies present holistic optimisation approaches that integrate module layout and tilt angle, inverter placement, cabling, and other key design decisions to minimise shading and electrical losses while reducing the levelised cost of energy [8,9]. These studies demonstrate that system-level design choices – namely, cable sizing, routing, and equipment placement – can substantially affect both performance and cost. However, even with these more recent studies, the combined technical and economic impacts of DC cable design remain relatively unexplored. This study evaluates how array layout and equipment placement influence cable losses, cost, and energy yield in utility-scale PV plants.

4 SYSTEM ARCHITECTURE AND SCOPE OF ANALYSIS

Utility-scale PV plants combine structural, electrical, and civil design to deliver power to the grid. Arrays of PV modules, mounted onto fixed-tilt structures or tracking systems, are connected in series to form strings. These strings are then grouped into sub-arrays. The DC power from these sub-arrays is routed through a cable network to inverters, where it is converted to alternating current (AC) and stepped up by a transformer for grid integration.

Two inverter architecture types are typically used in large-scale PV plants: string inverters and central inverters. String inverters are rated up to 350 kW and offer greater design flexibility, multiple MPPTs, and improved performance under varying operating conditions [10]. Central inverters, often housed within a Power Conversion Unit (PCU), are rated up to 5 MW. These inverters aggregate multiple PV strings through DC combiner boxes. Although less flexible, central inverters can be more cost-effective, as a single high-capacity unit replaces many smaller inverters. Additionally, a central inverter architecture simplifies installation and reduces maintenance requirements [11,12].

In central inverter systems, cable design plays a critical role. As shown in Figure 1, DC string cables connect modules to combiner boxes, and sub-array cables connect the combiner boxes to the PCU. Their sizing and routing have a direct impact on electrical losses and capital expenditure. This study focuses on the central inverter architecture to quantify the impacts of DC layout design on performance and cost.

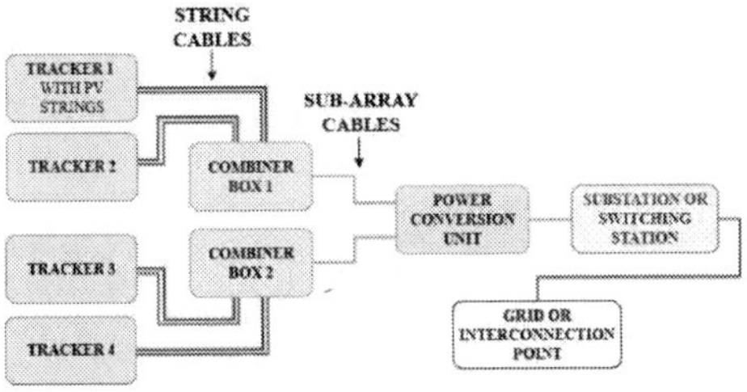

Figure 1: Central inverter system architecture for a PV plant

5 METHODOLOGY

To evaluate the impact of minor design changes on the PV system and its DC cable network, a base case scenario and several design variations were developed. The scenarios focused on three key areas where trade-offs are expected to occur:

1. Equipment selection and placement
2. Civil considerations
3. Electrical considerations

A single-axis tracking 330MWp solar PV facility, using a central inverter architecture, was developed using a single development area. Nine design variations were applied. The plant capacity, DC sub-array cable selection, development area, and general overall layout were kept constant. A complete low-voltage cable design, including accurate cable routing, was developed for each scenario using AUTOPV™, a software platform that automates the electrical design of solar plants. The output from AUTOPV™ is used to calculate the cable losses, voltage drop, and cable cost.

5.1 Base Case

The base case scenario was designed in accordance with engineering best practices, based on a real PV project currently being developed in South Africa. Figure 2 shows the typical equipment placement for the base case scenario. The combiner boxes are placed in the centre of the sub-array on the edge of the trackers closest to the PCU. This spacing between the trackers is referred to as the minor corridor. The PCU is placed in the centre of the groups of sub-arrays, in the major corridor. The plant has the following parameters:

Table I: Base case scenario parameters

Parameter	Value
Plant DC Power	331.51 MWdc
Plant AC Power	316.80 MWac
DC/AC Ratio	1.046
Pitch	6.2 m
Major corridor width	21 m
Minor corridor width	5 m
Quantity of PV Blocks	36
Quantity of DC Combiner Boxes	1080

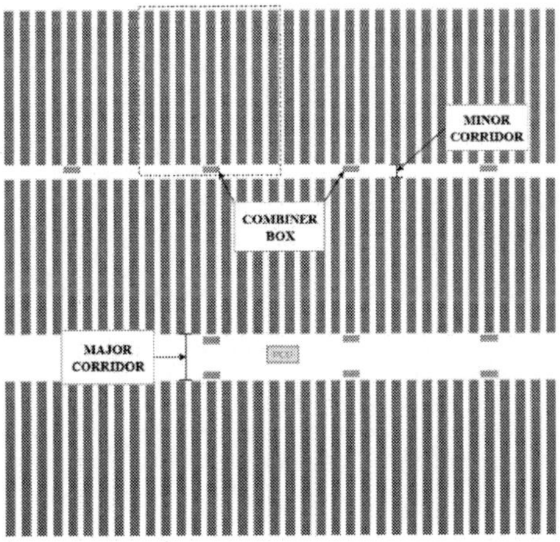

Figure 2: Typical equipment placement in a PV block for the base case scenario

5.2 Scenarios varying equipment selection and placement

Variations in equipment selection and placement can significantly impact cable design. For this paper, the scenarios were designed as follows:

- Scenario 1: Increasing the quantity of combiner boxes
- Scenario 2: Placing combiner boxes in the major corridor closer to the PCU
- Scenario 3: Placing combiner boxes in the minor corridors closer to the PCU

- Scenario 4: Reducing the size of the PCU from 8.8 MVA to 4.4 MVA and increasing the quantity

5.3 Scenarios varying civil considerations

The width of the corridors between the trackers, where combiner boxes and PCUs are often placed, is typically determined by logistical and civil engineering constraints. The following variations were applied to the base case to assess the impact of these assumptions:

- Scenario 5: Reducing the minor corridor width from 5 m to 3 m
- Scenario 6: Reducing the minor corridor width from 5 m to 1 m
- Scenario 7: Adjusting the minor corridor width to 9 m and the major corridor to 15 m

5.4 Scenarios varying electrical considerations

The power loss of a cable is directly affected by its size, as a smaller cable will have higher electrical resistance. Scenarios 8 and 9 consider the impact of varying the string cable sizes to 4 mm² and 10 mm², respectively.

5.5 Financial Assumptions

The financial assumptions used in this analysis are shown in Table II. The cost of DC cables was based on standard industry pricing at the time of this study. While the exact prices may vary regionally and over time, the values used are representative of the current industry and provide a reasonable basis for a comparative analysis.

Table II: Financial assumptions used in analysis

Parameter	Value
4mm² DC Solar Cable	1.30 USD/m
6mm² DC Solar Cable	1.60 USD/m
10mm² DC Solar Cable	2.00 USD/m
400mm² XLPE Aluminium Cable	15.00 USD/m

6 RESULTS

Figure 3 presents the simulation results for all scenarios, illustrating cable cost and power loss across all design scenarios. Given that the optimisation focuses on cable performance and the interplay between cable quantities, Figure 4 represents the results in terms of the ratio of DC string to sub-array cable lengths.

The results indicate that equipment placement, particularly of combiner boxes and PCUs, has the greatest influence on cable lengths, costs, and losses. While scenario 1 – increasing the quantity of combiner boxes – has the second-lowest power loss, it also has the highest cost due to the increased length of the sub-array cables. Using a smaller PCU results in the lowest cable cost and a relatively lower power loss when compared to the other scenarios; however, this does not consider the cost of additional PCUs. Adjusting corridor widths has a minimal impact on cost and losses, indicating that constructability considerations should guide these parameters. Larger DC cable sizes effectively reduce losses, but at the expense of a significantly higher cable cost.

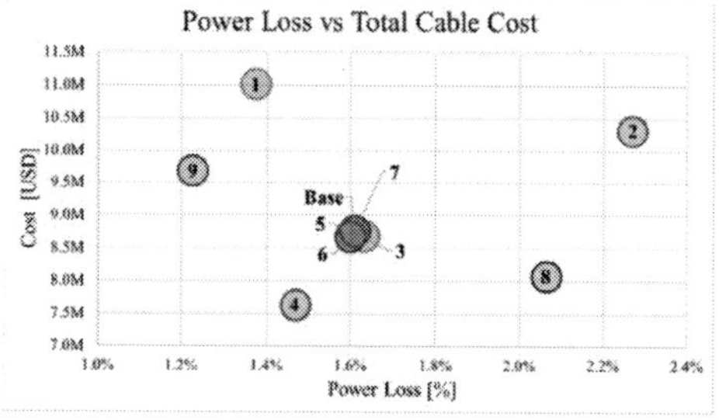

Figure 3: Cable cost and power loss for all scenarios

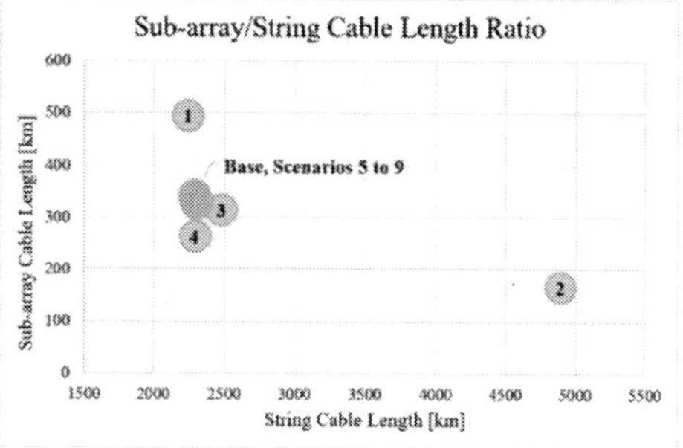

Figure 4: Sub-array versus String cable length for all scenarios

7 CONCLUSION

This study demonstrates that DC cable layout and sizing decisions can significantly impact power losses and capital costs in utility-scale PV systems, and that even minor variations in equipment selection or system layout can influence the DC design in ways that affect overall efficiency. Across the scenarios assessed, substantial differences were observed in both cable costs and power loss, driven primarily by the placement of combiner boxes and size of the PCU. Corridor width adjustments had minimal effect, suggesting that constructability considerations should be the main factor for this design decision.

There are two distinct findings in this investigation: first, that relatively small changes in design assumptions can lead to meaningful differences in both power loss, which impacts annual energy revenue, and CAPEX; and second, that a design optimised for lowest cost will not necessarily align with one optimised for lowest power loss or maximum yield.

Future work should extend the scope beyond DC cabling to include the cost of inverters, AC-side infrastructure, and assess the impact of adopting a string-inverter architecture for the system. A techno-economic analysis over the lifetime of the plant would provide a more comprehensive understanding of the long-term impact of using different DC cable sizes.

A well-designed PV plant should balance both economic return and technical performance. Projects should optimise layout configurations in alignment with the relevant design and financial objectives. This study highlights the importance of an iterative design approach in the early stages of project development to ensure that these seemingly minor design changes and their impact are considered, as they can have a significant impact on power loss, CAPEX, and energy yield.

8 REFERENCES

[1] International Energy Agency, "Renewables 2024: Analysis and forecast to 2030," IEA Publications, 2024. [Online]. Available: https://iea.blob.core.windows.net/assets/45704c88-a7b0-4001-b319-c5fc45298e07/Renewables2024.pdf

[2] S. Ekici and M. A. Kopru, "Investigation of PV System Cable Losses," *International Journal of Renewable Energy Research*, vol. 7, no. 2, 2017. [Online]. Available: https://www.researchgate.net/publication/317701311_Investigation_of_PV_System_Cable_Losses

[3] D. T. Cotfas, P.A. Cotfas, Multiconcept Methods to Enhance Photovoltaic System Efficiency, *International Journal of Photoenergy*, 1905041, 14 pages, 2019. doi: 10.1155/2019/1905041

[4] A. Glick, N. Ali, J. Bossuyt et al. "Utility-scale solar PV performance enhancements through system-level modifications," *Scientific Reports*, vol. 10, p. 10505, 2020. doi: 10.1038/s41598-020-66347-5

[5] L. Idoko, O. Anaya-Lara and A. McDonald, "Enhancing PV modules efficiency and power output using multi-concept cooling technique," *Energy Reports*, vol. 4, pp. 357-369, 2018. doi: 10.1016/j.egyr.2018.05.004

[6] F. U. Khan, A. F. Murtaza, H. A. Sher, K. Al-Haddad and F. Mustafa, "Cabling Constraints in PV Array Architecture: Design, Mathematical Model and Cost Analysis," in *IEEE Access*, vol. 8, pp. 182742-182754, 2020. [Online]. Available: https://ieeexplore.ieee.org/abstract/document/9214484

[7] C. K. Gan, Y. M. Lee, D. Pudjianto and G. Strbac, "Role of Losses in Design of DC Cable for Solar PV Applications", Australasian Universities Power Engineering Conference, (AUPEC 2014 – Proceedings). 1-5. doi: 10.1109/AUPEC.2014.6966594.

[8] T. Kerekes, E. Koutroulis, D. Séra, R. Teodorescu and M. Katsanevakis, "An Optimization Method for Designing Large PV Plants," in *IEEE Journal of Photovoltaics*, vol. 3, no. 2, pp. 814-822, 2013. doi: 10.1109/JPHOTOV.2012.2230684.

[9] T. E. K. Zidane, A. S. Aziz, Y. Zahraoui, H. Kotb, K. M. AboRas, Kitmo, Y. B. Jember, "Grid-Connected Solar PV Power Plants Optimization: A Review," *in IEEE Access*, vol. 11, pp. 79588-79608, 2023, doi: 10.1109/ACCESS.2023.3299815.

[10] L. Miller, "Comparing Central vs String Inverters for Utility-Scale PV Projects," Mayfield Renewables, May 14, 2024. Accessed Jul. 3, 2025. [Online]. Available: https://www.mayfield.energy/technical-articles/comparing-central-vs-string-inverters-for-utility-scale-pv-projects/.

[11] J. Vickerman and A. Pajares, "What are central and string solar inverters and how do they compare?", RatedPower, Mar. 14, 2024. Accessed Jul. 3, 2025. [Online]. Available: https://ratedpower.com/glossary/solar-inverters/.

[12] Essentra Components, "What is a solar inverter and how does it work?," Jan. 17, 2024. Accessed Jul. 12, 2025 [Online]. Available: https://www.essentracomponents.com/en-us/news/industries/renewable-energy/what-is-a-solar-inverter-and-how-does-it-work?srsltid=AfmBOooMfldM180w_w2D5KO8fIw8r71YPeTESAqRg6UZOT-_H2MFdmfg.

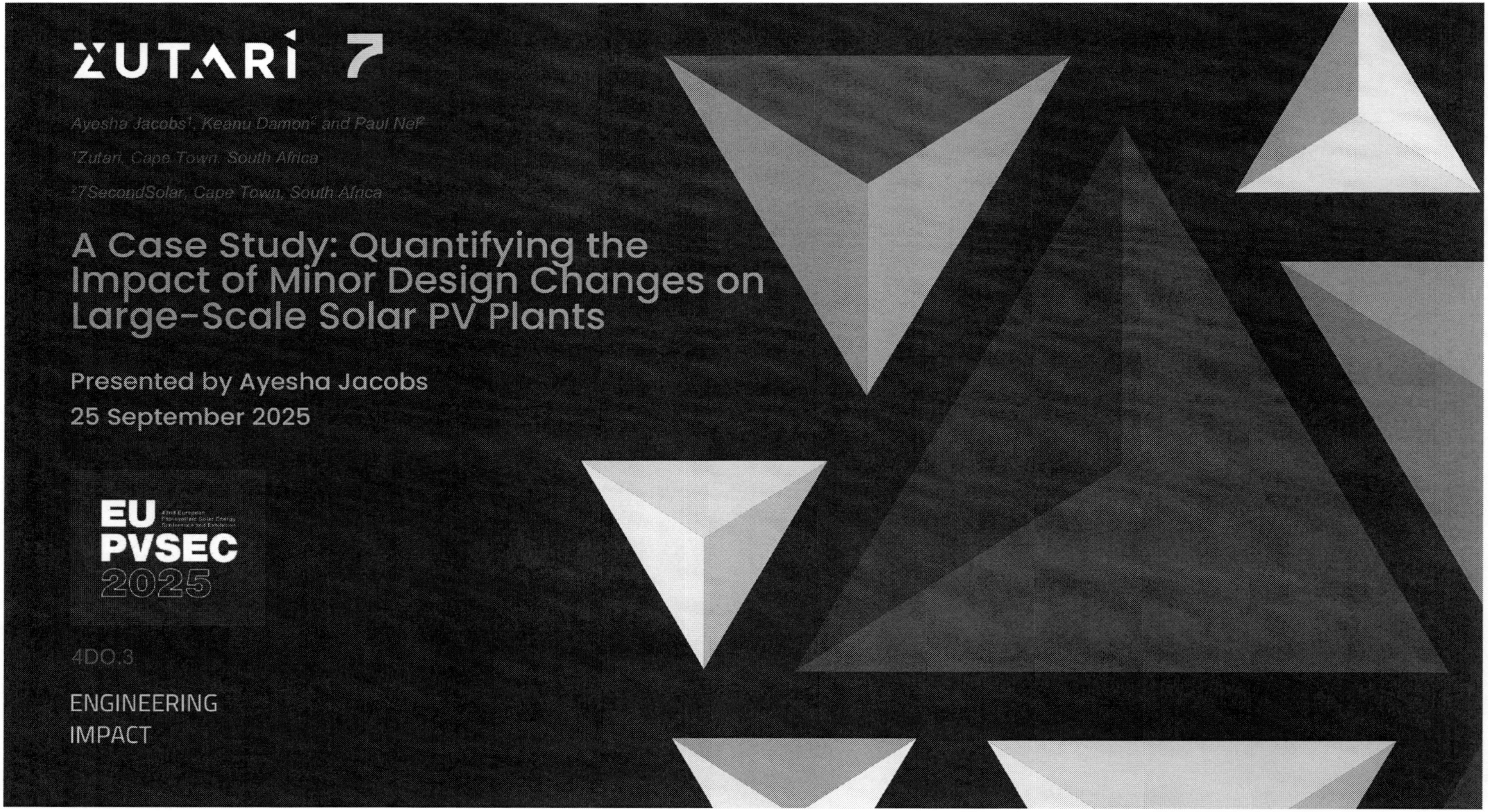
ZUTARI 7
Ayesha Jacobs[1], Keanu Damon[2] and Paul Nel[2]
[1]Zutari, Cape Town, South Africa
[2]7SecondSolar, Cape Town, South Africa
A Case Study: Quantifying the Impact of Minor Design Changes on Large-Scale Solar PV Plants
Presented by Ayesha Jacobs
25 September 2025
EU PVSEC 2025
4DO.3
ENGINEERING
IMPACT

SOLAR PV OPTIMISATION: WHAT HAS BEEN DONE BEFORE?

Module improvements & innovations

Cable route optimisation – shortest path algorithms

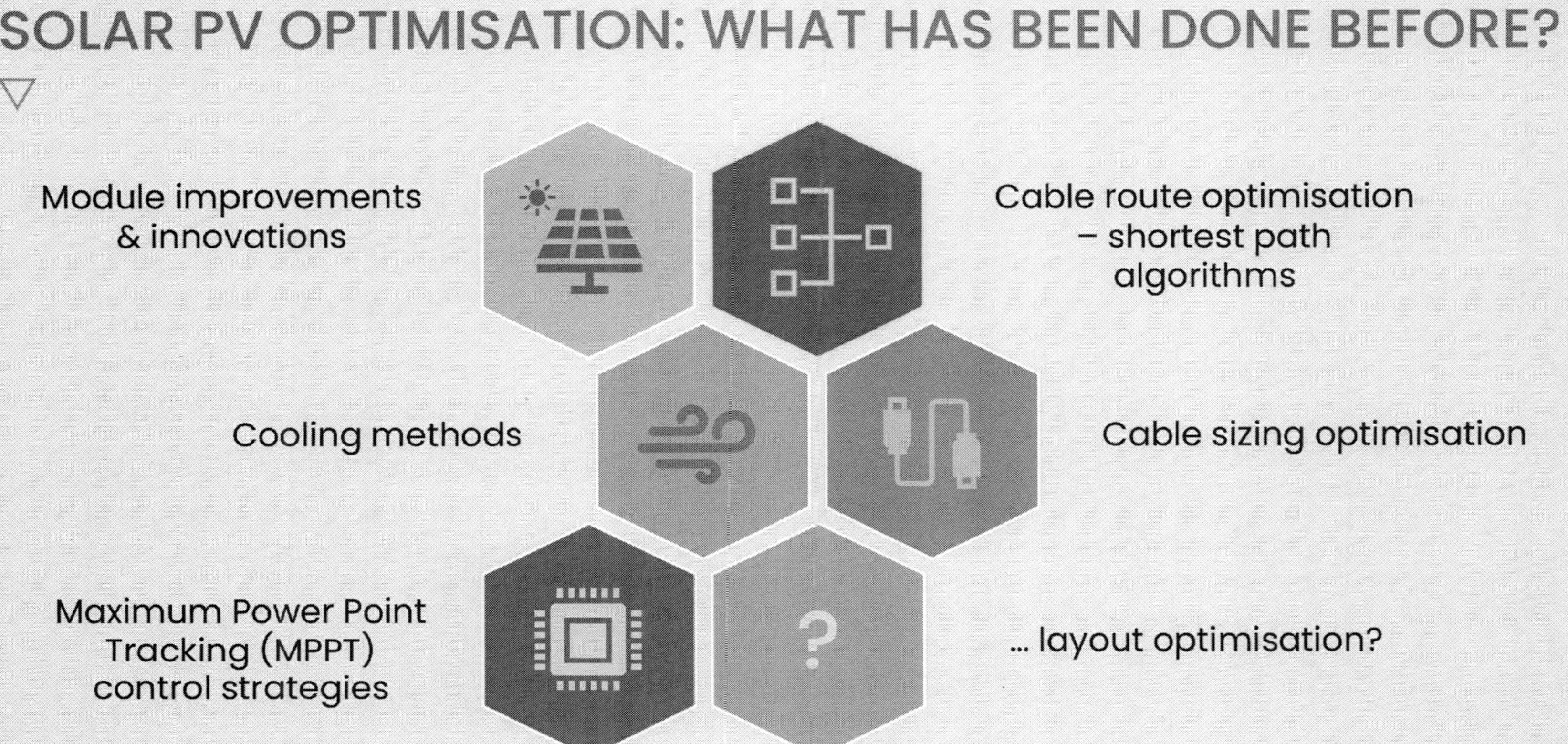

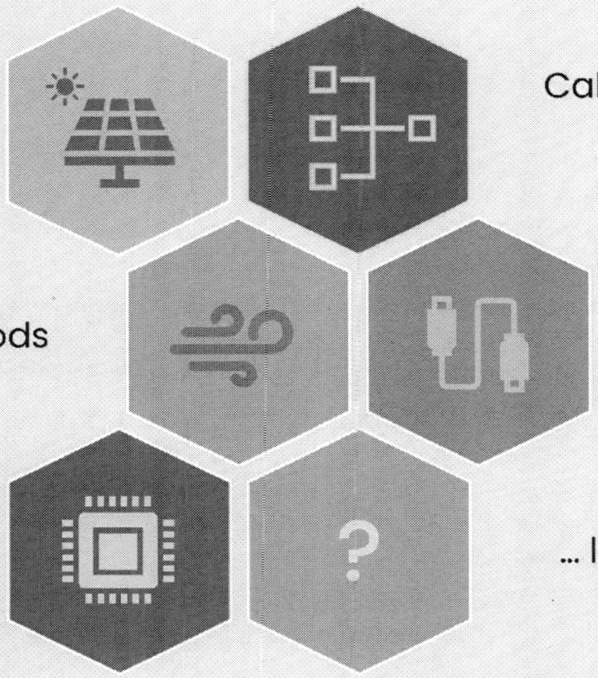

Cooling methods

Cable sizing optimisation

Maximum Power Point Tracking (MPPT) control strategies

... layout optimisation?

WHY OPTIMISE PV CABLE DESIGN?

- Cost of cables can be a significant portion of capital costs
- Longer cables have higher cost and losses, lowers yield
- **Our Question: How does the design of PV plants affect the DC cable network in plants using Central Inverters?**
  - → Strategic array layout
  - → Equipment placement
  - → Ratio of string vs subarray cable length

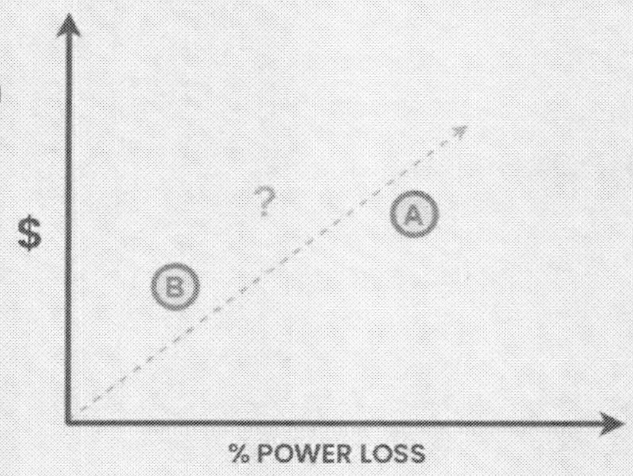

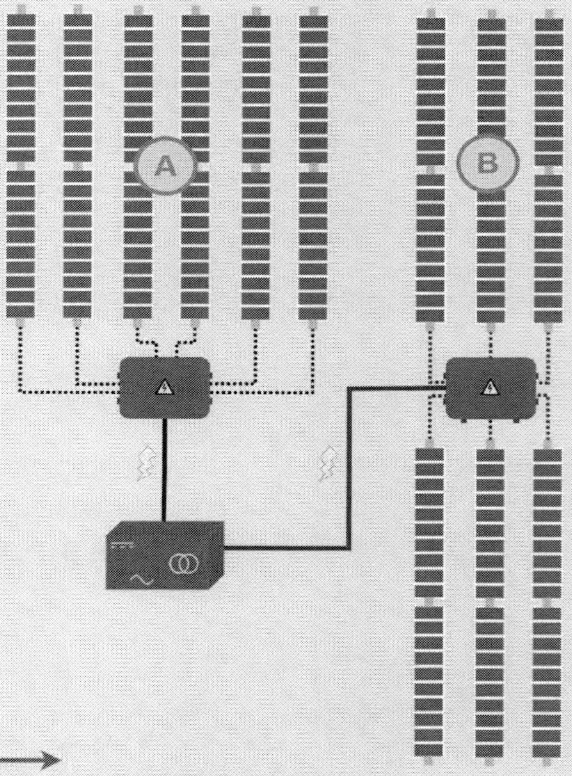

ZUTARI

EU PVSEC 2025 Bilbao • 4DO.3

METHODOLOGY

▽ Parametric analysis

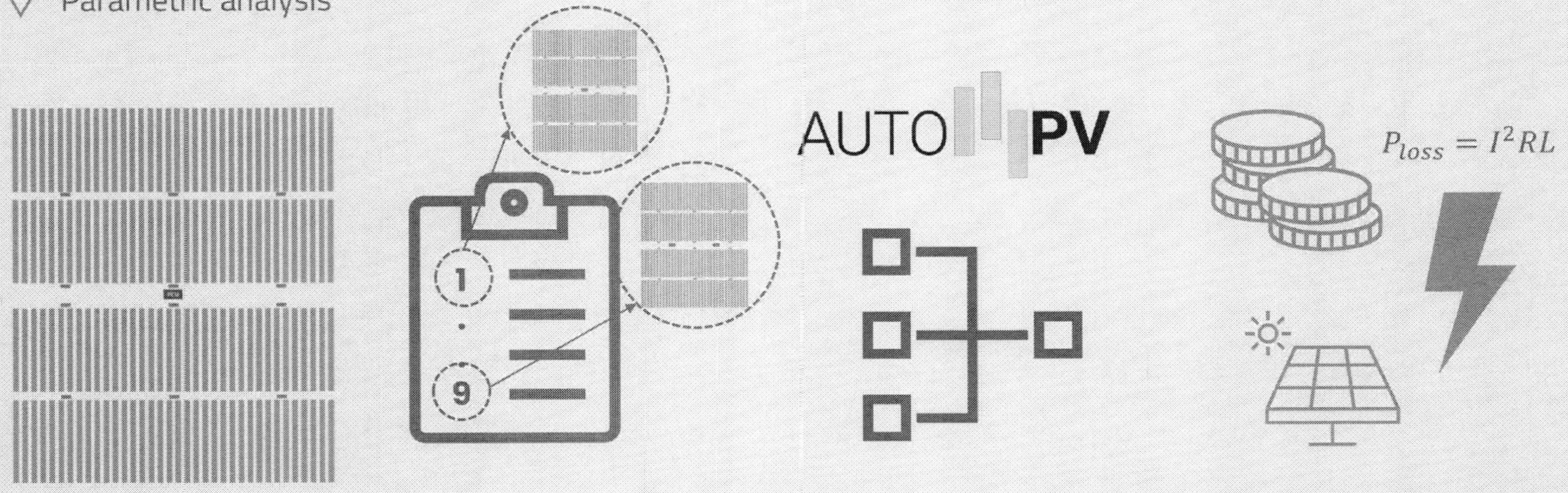

Base Case

9 Design Variations

Design DC Cable Network

Calculate cable cost, power loss & yield

ZUTARI

EU PVSEC 2025 Bilbao • 4DO.3

METHODOLOGY

▽ Financial Assumptions

Parameter	Value	Unit
4mm^2 DC Solar Cable	1.30	USD/m
6mm^2 DC Solar Cable	1.60	USD/m
10mm^2 DC Solar Cable	2.00	USD/m
400mm^2 XLPE Aluminium cable	15.00	USD/m
Energy tariff (BW 7)	25.64	USD/MWh

METHODOLOGY

▽ Parametric analysis

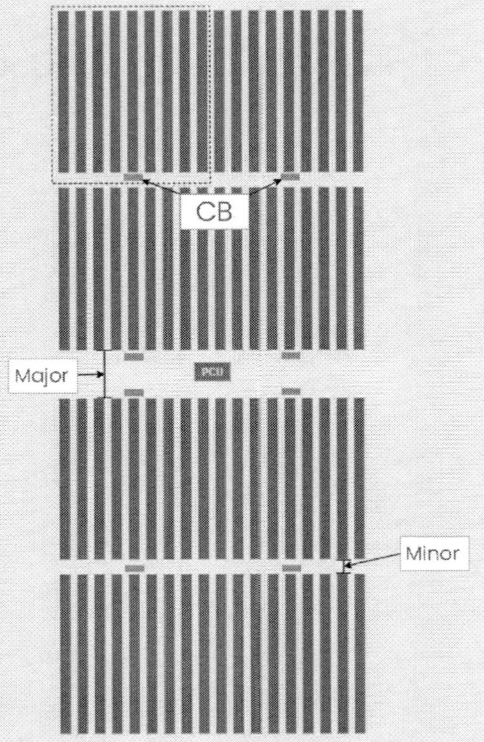

Base Case

- 300MWp, using latest technology
- Central inverter architecture
- Single-axis tracking
- 6mm^2 PV string cable
- Designed with standard engineering practices and assumptions
  → Minor corridor – 5m
  → Major corridor – 20m

ZUTARI

EU PVSEC 2025 Bilbao • 4DO.3

6

9 DESIGN VARIATIONS

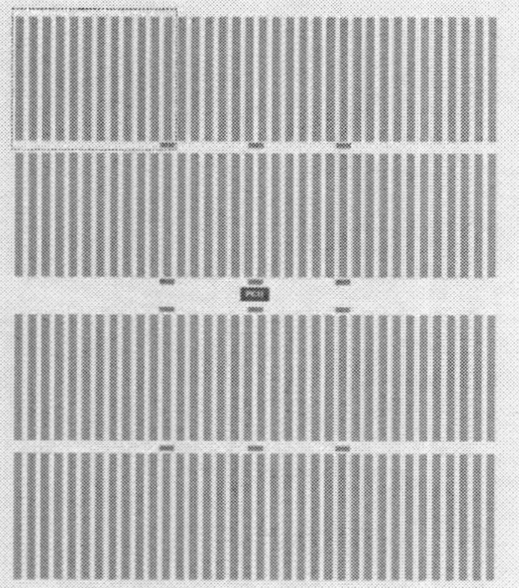

Combiner Box Layout
Scenario 1 to 3

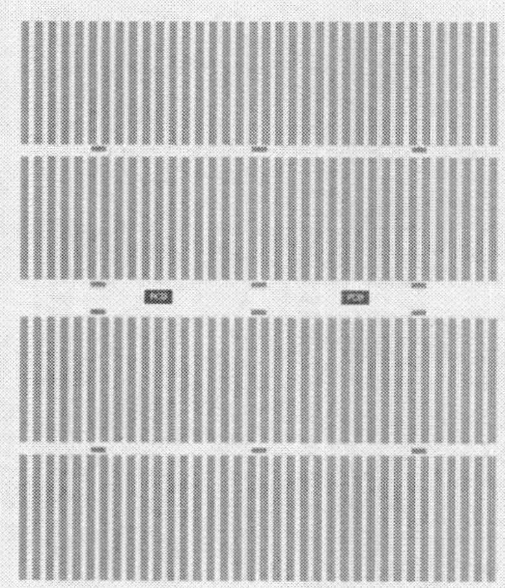

PCU Configuration
Scenario 4

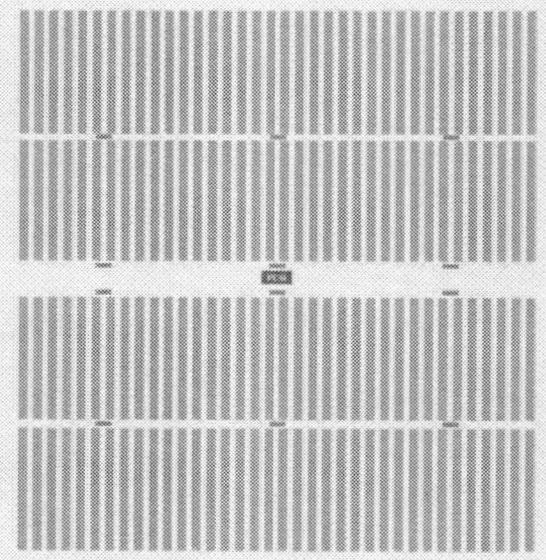

Corridor Widths
Scenario 5 to 7

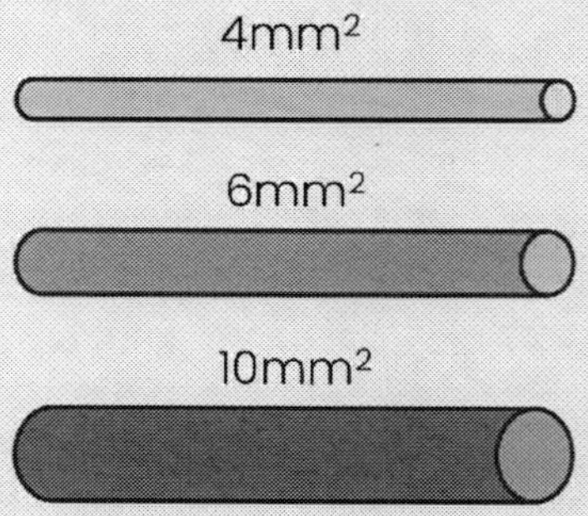

DC String Cable Size
Scenario 8 & 9

ZUTARI

RESULTS
Scenarios 1 to 4
Power Loss vs Total Cable Cost
(Varying Combiner Box/PCU Configuration)
Total cable cost [USD]
12.0M
11.5M
11.0M
10.5M
10.0M
9.5M
9.0M
8.5M
8.0M
7.5M
7.0M
Scenario 1
Scenario 2
Base
Scenario 3
Scenario 4
1.00%
1.20%
1.40%
1.60%
1.80%
2.00%
2.20%
2.40%
Power Loss [%]
Impact of Sub-array/String Cable Length Ratio on Cable Cost
Sub-array Cable Lenth [km]
600
500
400
300
200
100
0
$11,016,715
$8,766,444
$8,684,422
$7,630,770
$10,316,312
1,500
2,500
3,500
4,500
5,500
String Cable Length [km]
Impact of Sub-array/String Cable Length Ratio on Power Loss
1.37%
1.61%
1.63%
1.47%
2.27%
ZUTARI
EU PVSEC 2025 Bilbao • 4DO.3
8

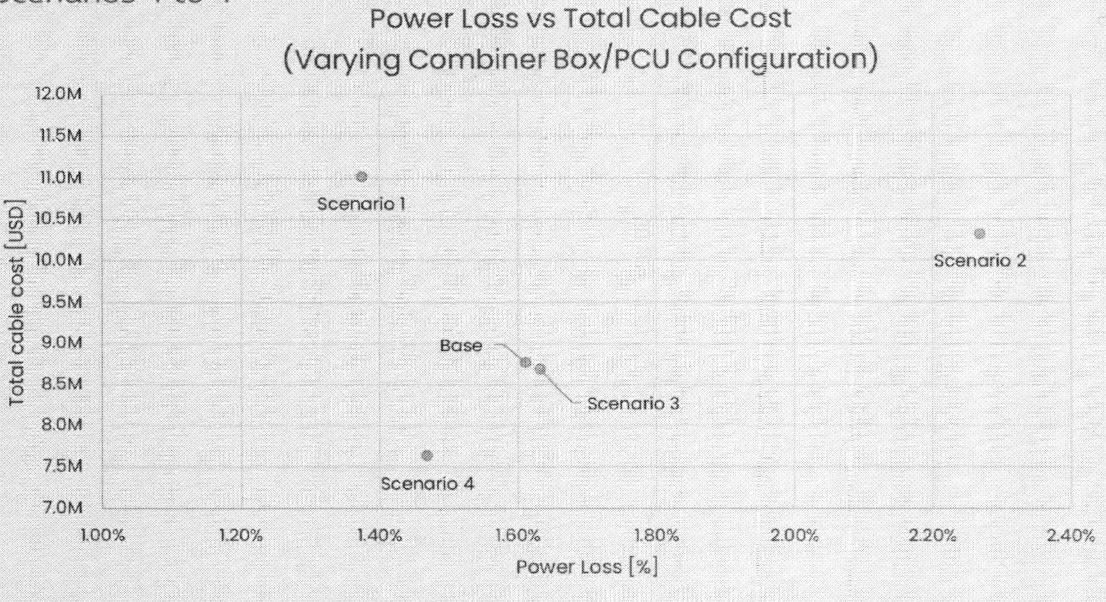

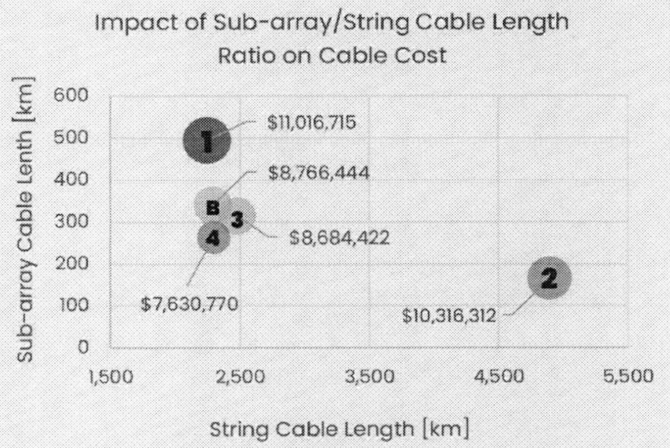

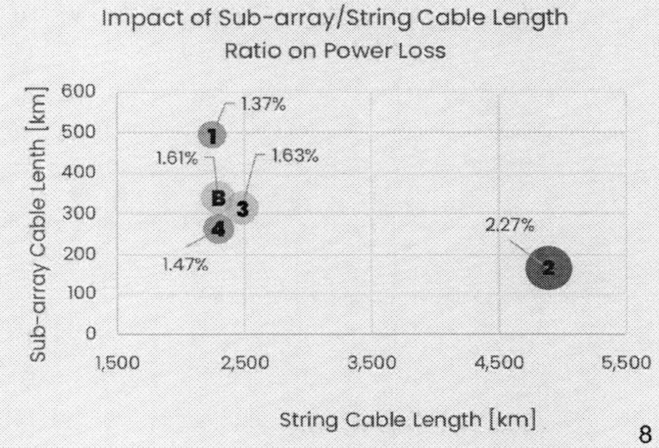

RESULTS

Scenarios 5 to 7

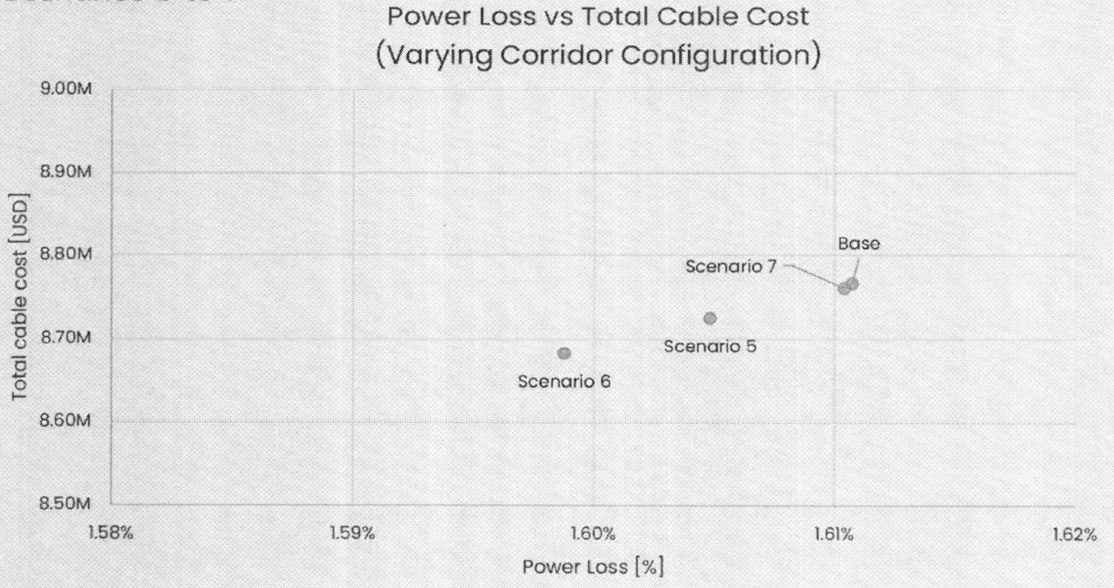

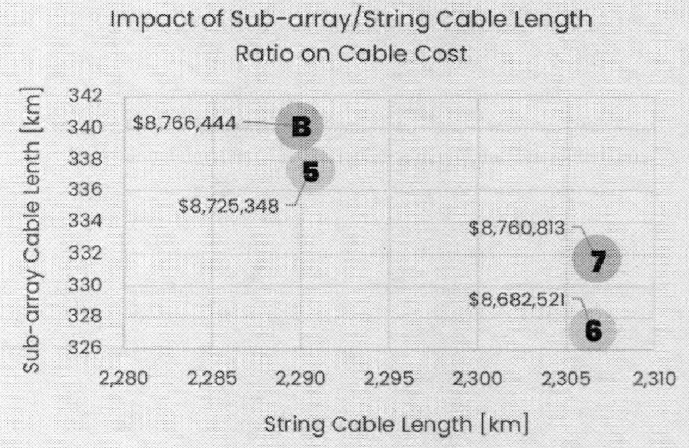

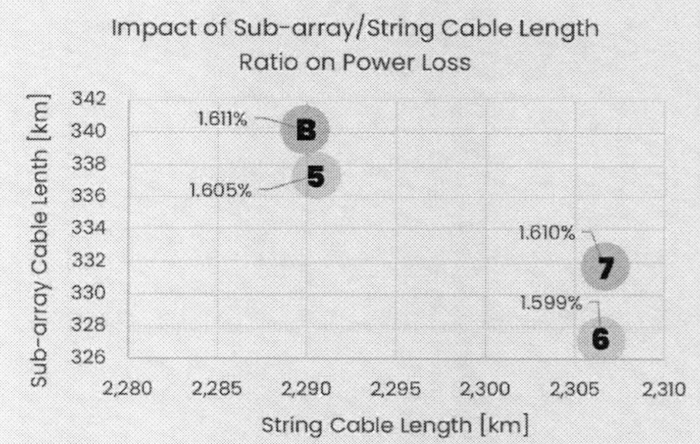

ZUTARI

EU PVSEC 2025 Bilbao • 4DO.3

9

RESULTS

Scenarios 8 & 9

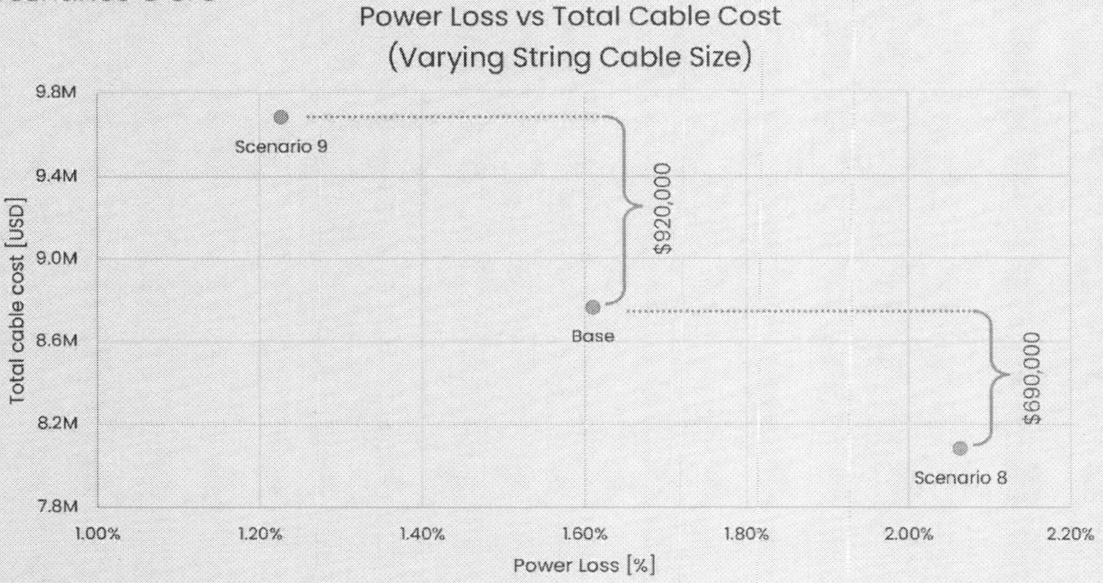

This result is intuitive

- $10mm^2$
  - Additional revenue of $72,500 (lowers loss by 0.38%)
  - Additional $920,000 cost
  - Payback period of 13 years
- $4mm^2$
  - Cost saving of $690,000
  - Revenue loss of $85,200 due to losses
  - Cost savings surpassed by lost revenue after 8 years
  - Voltage drop exceeds 5.46%

RESULTS

▽

All Scenarios

Power Loss vs Total Cable Cost
(All Scenarios)

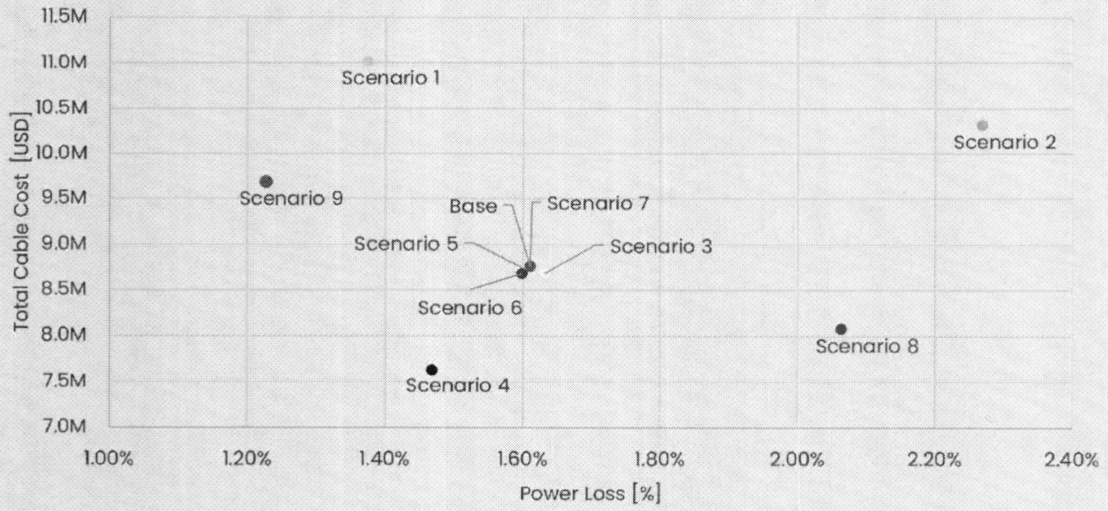

Impact of Sub-array/String Cable Length
Ratio on Cable Cost

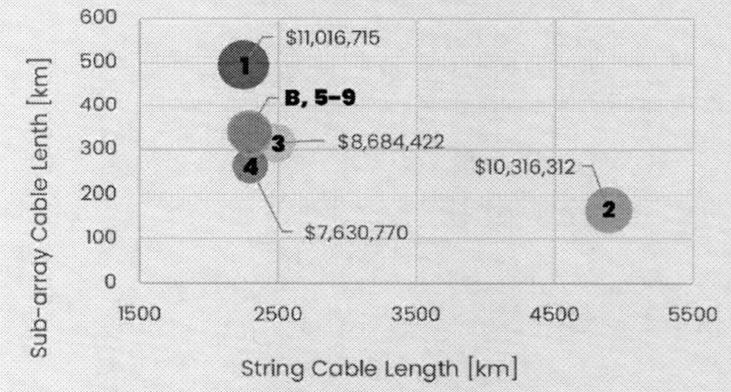

Impact of Sub-array/String Cable Length
Ratio on Power Loss

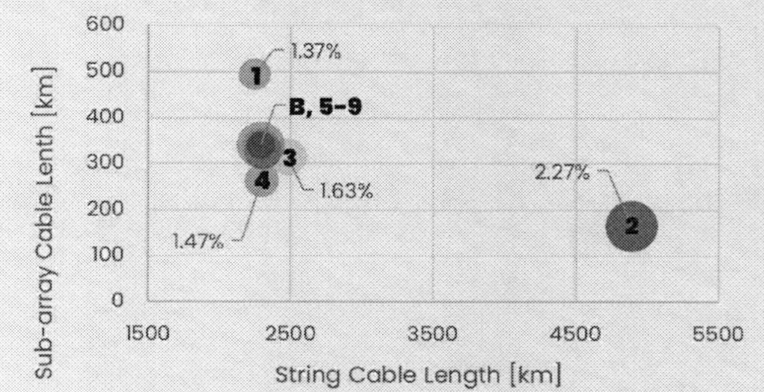

ZUTARI

EU PVSEC 2025 Bilbao • 4DO.3

CONCLUSION

▽

Key Take-Aways

- Strategic array layout and early design decisions can have a significant impact on DC cable power loss and capital cost
- Trade-off between yield, cost, design flexibility and constructability
- Adjusting corridor widths has minimal impact on losses – constructability should be priority
- Using smaller PCU's decreases cable lengths significantly
- CAPEX-optimised design differs from yield-optimised design – lowest cost option does not always equal shortest cable length or lowest power loss

FUTURE WORK

How can we expand on this?

- Scope should be expanded to include other system components including cost of inverters and AC infrastructure
- String inverter configuration assessment – is one architecture better than the other?
- Complete techno-economic analysis across lifetime of plant to assess long term impact of different DC string cable sizes

THANK YOU!

Ayesha.Jacobs@zutari.com

paul@7secondsolar.com

keanu@7secondsolar.com

SEVEN SECOND SOLAR
empowered@7SecondSolar.com

AUTO PV™
VALUE ENGINEERING

zutari.com

EU PVSEC 2025 Bilbao • 4DO.3

ZUTARI
zutari.com

DURABLE BONDING OF LIGHTWEIGHT CRYSTALLINE SILICON PV MODULES

Guy Beaucarne[1], Tobias Hopp[2], Dominique Culot[1], Jonathan Curon[1]

[1]Dow Silicones Belgium SRL, Rue Jules Bordet Parc Industriel Zone C, B-7180 Seneffe, Belgium
[2] Sunman Energy (Deutschland) GmbH

ABSTRACT: Lightweight semi-flexible crystalline silicon photovoltaic modules have been introduced in the market for several years and provide an appealing possible alternative to conventional modules. In particular they are well suited for flat industrial or commercial roofs with limited load bearing capacity. An appropriate method to install such lightweight modules is to bond them to the roof structures using a suitable adhesive. This bonding approach actually needs special attention and care because the joints will undergo frequent high loads while being exposed to all possible weather conditions for many years. We introduce the use of silicone structural adhesives in this application, leveraging the large and long experience with creating durable structural bonds in the field of structural glazing for facades. The right joint dimensions are calculated taking into account wind load and design strength of the adhesive. Adhesion is tested not only in the as-bonded state, but also after stringent accelerated aging tests (long-term immersion in water, UV exposure, damp heat treatment, thermal cycling), which is a mix of tests developed for structural glazing and for the photovoltaic industry. We show that strong and durable adhesion can be reached.

Keywords: silicone, adhesive, sealant, adhesion, lightweight, semi-flexible, module

1 INTRODUCTION

To achieve the massive PV generation that is needed for the energy transition, very large areas need to be covered by photovoltaic modules. It is therefore important to make use of all available space that is suitable and socially acceptable for PV installation. Commercial and Industrial (C&I) flat rooftops are of particular interest as they cover large areas and are usually not used for any other activity. Moreover, the proximity of power generation and consumption makes such systems very appealing as they avoid problems with grid congestion and benefit from low 'behind-the-meter' power costs. However, there are challenges to install PV systems on such rooftops. Modern traditional PV modules are heavy, typically 30 kg or even more, because of the use of front and rear covers made of glass and an aluminum frame. Additionally, they need to be fixed on metal mounting structure, increasing the weight. Finally, because of the high wind load, the mounting structure needs to either be screwed into the rooftop, or maintained firmly on the rooftop using heavy ballast. Some roofs simply cannot take this weight, while watertightness of the roof may be lost if mechanical fixation is used.

Lightweight semi-flexible crystalline silicon photovoltaic modules, which feature a thin front cover and do not feature an Al frame, have been introduced in the market for several years and provide an appealing possible alternative to conventional modules. An appropriate method to install such lightweight modules is to bond them to the roof structures using a suitable adhesive, as it is simple and low cost. However, special attention and care is needed to ensure that the bonding and the system as a whole has the level of durability that is expected of a PV system.

2 DESIGN

2.1 Substructure

To avoid moisture accumulation and/or excessive heating of the modules, a space is needed between the roof and the PV laminate, enabling proper ventilation. Some roofs have a corrugated form and provide ventilation channels without any additional component. However, most C&I roofs do not have such profile, and therefore a substructure consisting of extruded profiles is used, ensuring that the module lies a few centimeters above the roof surface. This substructure consists in pieces of tube with rectangular cross-section made of weather-resistant plastic or metal. Two adhesive joints are needed to connect the substructure to the roof on one hand and the PV module to the substructure on the other hand.

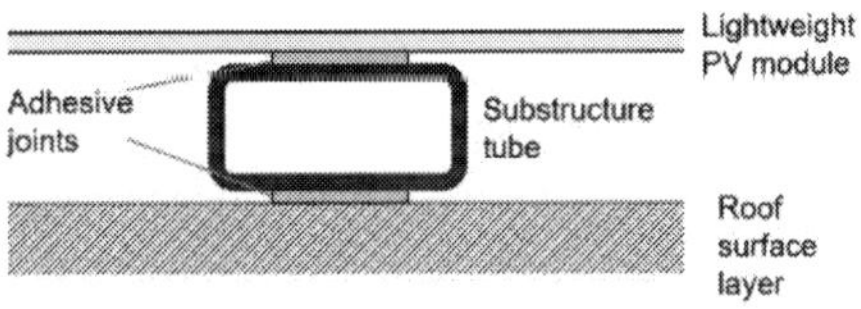

Figure 1: Cross-section schematic of installation of lightweight PV module

2.2 Geometry of the joints

Linear adhesive joints are used, parallel to the short edge of the module. The maximum spacing between the substructure tubes/joints is determined by the properties of the semi-flexible modules and is given by the module manufacturer. Depending on the size of the modules, the number of substructure tubes vary between five and eight. To avoid any overhanging of module parts, the outer joints are placed right at the edges of the module.

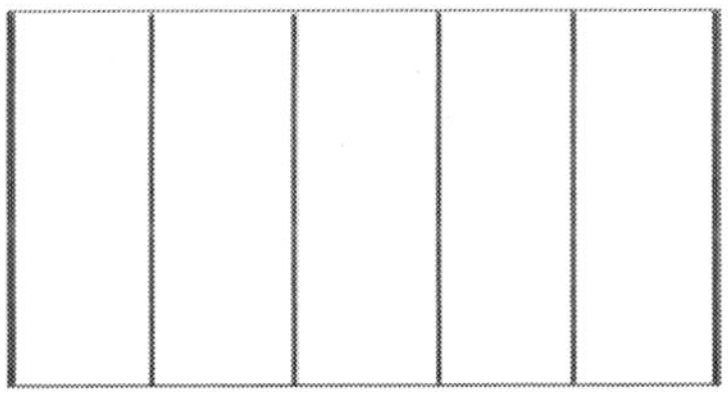

Figure 2: Example of geometry of the joints

Figure 3: Photo of lightweight semi-flexible module and installation structure including substructure and adhesive

2.3 Joint calculation

The determination of the final planar geometry of the joints translates into the adhesive width (the 'bite'), as the number and length of joints are fixed by previous considerations. The bite needs to be determined by calculations taking into account expected loads, the mechanical and physical properties of the various materials, the dimensions of the solar panels and the strength of the adhesive. The dimensioning takes certain safety factors into account to make sure the strength of the adhesive is never exceeded.

The main load to consider to calculate the bite is wind load. In the calculations, a design wind load W_d is used. In Europe, this design wind load has to be determined following the methodology prescribed by Eurocode EN 1991-4 [1] which takes into account the location of the building, its height and edge effects.

Once the design wind load is determined, the minimum bite can be calculated using this formula:

$$bite = \frac{Sp \times W_d}{R_d} \quad (1)$$

Where S_p is the spacing between two joints and R_d is the design strength R_d. This value, which is provided by the manufacturer of structural adhesives, is determined by extensive testing of the material in standard test sequences including accelerated aging, applying statistical considerations and safety factors, and confirmed by external testing in an independent test laboratory. This rigorous procedure was introduced for structural glazing (ETAG002, now known as EAD 090010-00-0404 [2]) and comes in useful in this application that similarly requires a very high level of reliability and durability.

2.4 Calculator

A digital tool was developed by Sunman Energy Deutschland in collaboration with renowned structural engineering firm Arup, which incorporates the Eurocode standard and carries out calculations resulting in the desired geometry and design of the joints. As wind effects are larger close to the corners or edge of the roof, the calculated bite depends on the location on the roof. Figure 4 gives an example calculation.

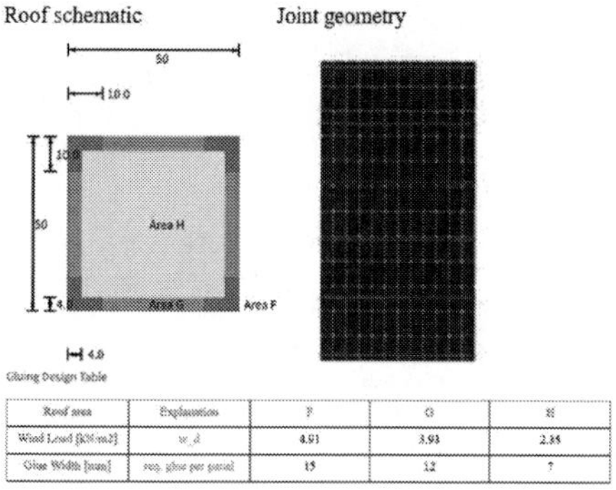

Roof area	Explanation	F	G	H
Wind Load [kN/m2]	w_d	4.91	3.93	2.35
Glue Width [mm]	req. glue per panel	15	12	7

Figure 4: Example of outcome of joint dimensioning calculation

3 SELECTION OF APPROPRIATE ADHESIVE

3.1 Durability requirements

As the lifetime of PV systems is 30 years or more, it is obvious that the adhesive to be used should have a durability that can provide this kind of lifetime. There are in fact not many adhesives that can fulfill their function even after many years while exposed to sometimes harsh weather conditions including heavy rain, high winds, frost, very cold temperature, UV exposure and summer heat.

This type of reliability is also required in the field of structural glazing, which is a technology to bond glass panels to metal frames and which enables glass curtain wall facades, very common in modern commercial and high rise buildings. Introduced more than 50 years ago, structural glazing has been made possible thanks to silicone structural sealants, providing the required combination of strength, elasticity and durability [3]. By selecting silicone structural adhesives for the lightweight PV module application, the experience and outstanding track record of the structural silicone glazing is leveraged.

Figure 5: Example of glass façade enabled by silicone structural glazing

In the early introduction of bonding for the installation of lightweight modules, different adhesive types were used that have turned out ill-suited for the application, either because of insufficient durability or incompatible material properties. An example of this is the use of visco-plastic adhesives, which are materials that can deform easily and achieve adhesion through a high tackiness. In Figure 6 we schematically compare the response of materials upon an imposed cyclic stress. After a force is applied, elastic materials return to their original shape while visco-plastic materials have some remaining plastic deformation. This might be a small deformation, but it builds up as the material is subjected to further cyclic loads. Such behavior finally leads to failure of the material. As the lightweight module bonding application implies cycling loads (e.g. through the effect of wind), adhesives showing this type of behavior are undesirable.

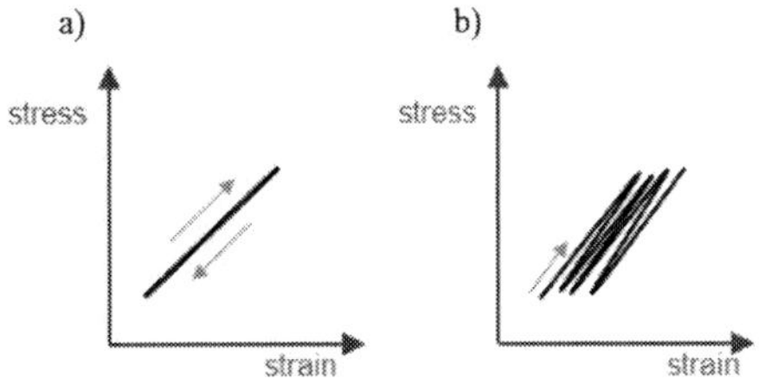

Figure 6: Schematic illustrating stress-strain behavior upon cyclic load for a) elastic materials, b) visco-plastic materials

3.2 Failure mode

Although the goal of the bonding technology is to create connections that never break in the application, it is necessary to consider which failure mode is preferred in case there is failure, as it is needed for the proper design of the joint. Figure 7 shows the three possibilities that can occur when the applied force exceeds the force that the bonded structure can take.

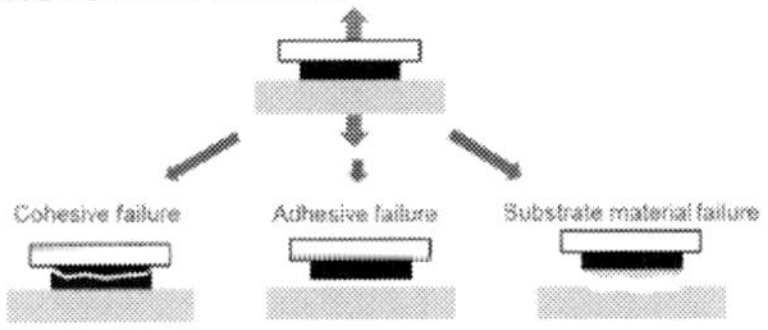

Figure 7: Potential failure modes of a bonded structure

In the cases of adhesive or substrate material failure, the force at which the structure fails depends not only on the properties of the adhesive, but on other factors such as surface properties and substrate material properties. A parameter characterizing the strength of the adhesive is therefore not enough and may not even be relevant to evaluate the force to which the structure may safely be subjected to. The dimensioning of the joint is then complex and inconvenient. That is why the situation where breakage occurs within the adhesive is preferable. In that case the design strength of the material can be used for joint dimensioning. Therefore, the target is to achieve adhesion on the substrate that is so strong that, if failure were to occur, it would be cohesive failure in the adhesive.

4 TESTING

A key component of the bonding technology for applications where reliability is paramount is testing. Because bonding of lightweight modules is a relatively new application, there are no standards yet that prescribe the tests to carry out, and there is no decades-long experience. A safe approach at this stage is therefore to carry out extensive testing on all substrates involved, leverage procedures developed in adjacent fields, and to do both lab testing and on-site testing.

4.1 Testing in the laboratory

Adhesion has to be tested on all substrates involved in the bonding structure, including the back of the lightweight solar panels, the substructure tube materials and the roof top surface. Similar to the practice in structural glazing, peel tests are made, where the adhesive is applied on a substrate with a strong mesh embedded in it. When testing, the mesh is pulled at 180°. The major parameter that is looked at during testing is the failure mode. If the adhesive comes clean off the substrate, this means that there is poor adhesion and no chemical bonds between adhesive and substrate. We are looking for a cohesive failure mode, with adhesive material remaining on the whole surface after pulling, which indicates that the adhesion between adhesive joint and substrate is strong. Sometimes the failure mode is mixed, with some regions failing adhesively and others cohesively. The percentage of the area of cohesive failure is noted down as the outcome of the measurement.

The peel tests should not only be done after curing of the adhesive, but importantly also after aging in various conditions. The set of tests we apply makes use of aging procedures that combine typical aging protocols used in the construction testing (e.g. water immersion and direct exposure to intense UV) and IEC testing standards (damp heat at 85°C-85% RH, thermal cycling between – 40°C and 85°C and a combination of thermal cycling and humidity freeze).

Testing in water immersion for a long period, while usually not practiced in the PV world, is very important in this application because many types of adhesives do not perform well in such conditions while there is a risk that the adhesive joint will be in contact with water for a significant period of time.

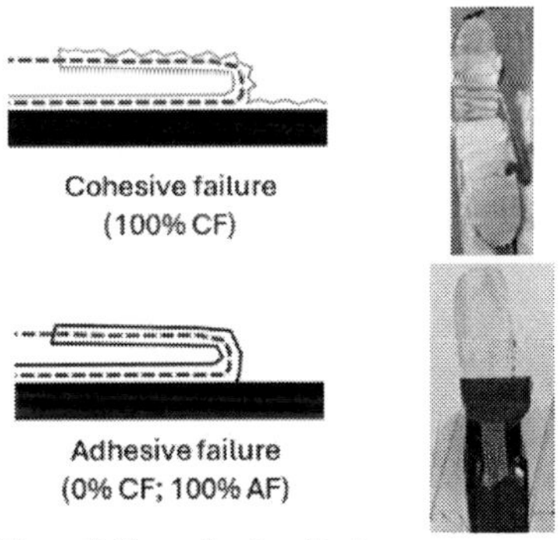

Figure 8: Example of peel tests

The results of a peel test campaign on various substrates using adhesive DOWSIL™ 895 Structural Glazing Sealant are given as an example in Table 1. DOWSIL™ 895 is a one part silicone adhesive which is applied as a paste with a caulking gun and cures into an elastomer upon reaction with moisture present in the ambient air.

Table 1: Peel test results

	PVC tube A	Backsheet of Sunman module SMF 520 12 x 12 UW	Roof membrane A (no primer)	Roof membrane A (with primer)	Roof membrane B
After curing	100 % CF	100 % CF	100 % CF	100 % CF	100 % CF
After 1 week water immersion	100 % CF	100 % CF	30 % CF	100 % CF	100 % CF
After 3 weeks UV exposure	100 % CF	100 % CF	100 % CF	100 % CF	100 % CF
After 1000 h damp heat	100 % CF	100 % CF	100 % CF	100 % CF	100 % CF
After 200 thermal cycles	100 % CF	100 % CF	100 % CF	100 % CF	100 % CF
After 50 TC + 10 humidity freeze cycles	100 % CF	100 % CF	100 % CF	100 % CF	100 % CF

In this example, we see that good adhesion is achieved on all substrates in the as-cured state. For the type of the PVC tube tested and the backsheet of the lightweight module, we see that good adhesion is maintained after the various accelerated aging procedures. For roof membrane A however, some adhesion was lost after 1 week immersion in water, resulting in 30% cohesive failure. However, when a primer (DOWSIL™ 1200 OS Primer) had been used prior to adhesive application, 100% cohesive failure was maintained even after one week water immersion. The need of primer depends on the specific types of roof membranes. In the example above, it can be seen that roof membrane B showed good adhesion after aging without priming.

4.2 Testing on-site

Apart from lab testing, some on-site testing is required. When a project is planned and a specific adhesive is anticipated to be used, a preliminary adhesion test should be performed on the roof surface, either a peel test or a tensile adhesion test. It is further recommended to carry out regular tests during the module installation campaign for quality control purposes.

Such on-site testing is complementary to lab testing but cannot replace it. Tests in the laboratory with accelerated aging are essential to check if the bonding will hold over time when permanently exposed to weather and climate.

5. CONCLUSIONS

Lightweight semi-flexible crystalline silicon photovoltaic modules provide an appealing possible alternative to conventional modules, in particular for flat industrial or commercial roofs with limited load bearing capacity. We investigate the direct bonding of those lightweight modules to the roof structures using an adhesive. This is a critical application because the joints will undergo frequent high loads while being exposed to all possible weather conditions for the whole lifetime of the PV system. Silicone structural adhesives are found to be well-suited in this application, thanks to the very stable and durable nature of silicone materials and the long experience with creating durable structural bonds in the field of structural glazing for facades. The right joint dimensions are calculated taking into account the local wind load and the adhesive's design strength. Adhesion is tested not only in the as-bonded state, but also after stringent accelerated aging tests which include tests developed both for structural glazing and photovoltaics. We show that strong and durable adhesion can be reached.

8 REFERENCES

[1] EN 1991-4: Eurocode 1: Actions on structures - Part 1-4: General actions – Wind actions

[2] European Assessment Document (EAD): EAD 090010-00-0404 Bonded glazing kit and bonding sealants

[3] Wolf A.; Recknage C.; Wenzel, N.; Sitte S; Structural Silicone Glazing:Life Expectancy of more than 50 Years? in Proceedings GPD Glass Performance Days 2017, 338-345.

zh aw

School of Engineering

MEASURES TO ADAPT THE POWER OUTPUT ON DEMAND BY SYSTEM DESIGN ON ROOFTOP PV SYSTEMS

Hartmut Nussbaumer, Lona Tulinski, Gian-Luca Bühlmann, Maximilian Eidtmann, Pascal Vögeli*, Markus Klenk

Zurich University of Applied Science, SoE
Institute of Energy Systems and Fluid Engineering, Technikumstrasse 9, 8401 Winterthur, Switzerland
*Institute for Sustainable Developement, Technoparkstrasse 2, 8406 Winterthur, Switzerland

41th European Photovoltaic Solar Energy Conference, 4DO.3

From static to dynamic tariffs – what are the consequences?

- In several European countries, dynamic feed-in tariffs are introduced
- Especially in summer at midday, the market price of electricity drops to zero or below
- In the winter months, the average price of electrical energy is higher
- What are the economic implications for photovoltaic systems on flat roofs, and which design is the most economically efficient?

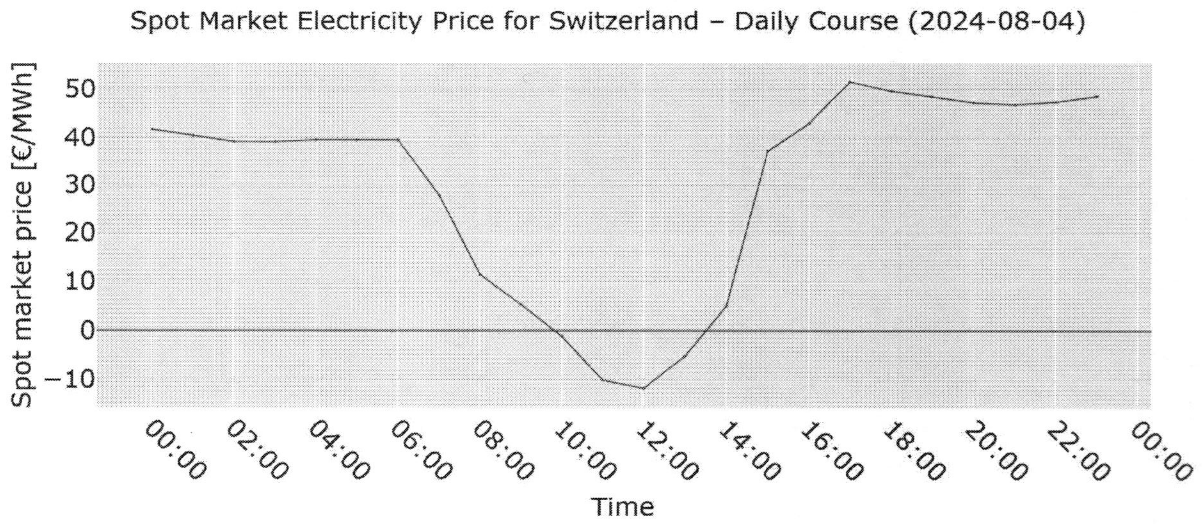

Typical PV system for flat roofs

East/west orientation
Low tilt angles in example 10°
Ground Cover Ratio **GCR** of ~90%
In our study: **The Reference**

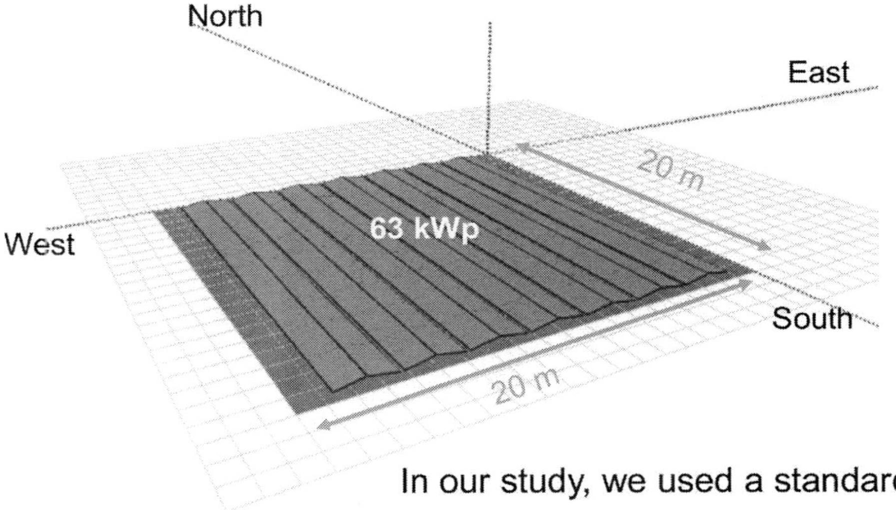

In our study, we used a standard roof area of 20 x 20 m²

⇒ For static feed-in tariffs currently the most economic design

Will this design still be the most economical option once dynamic grid feed-in tariffs are introduced?

Alternative designs of PV systems on flat roofs

South orientated, tilt angle 35°

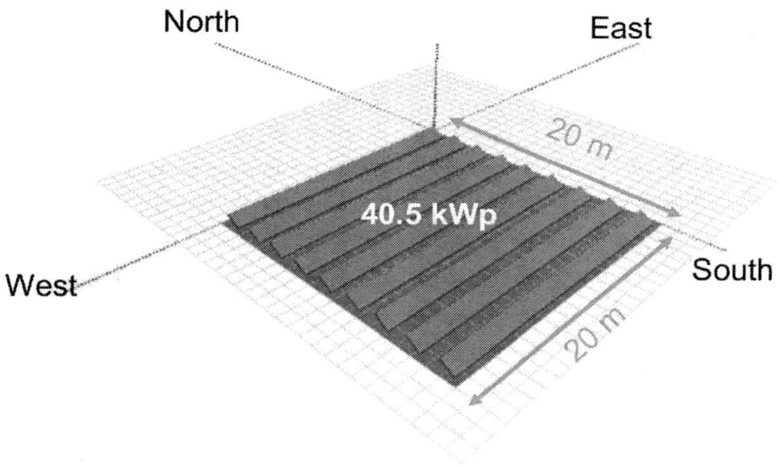

East/west oriented, vertically installed

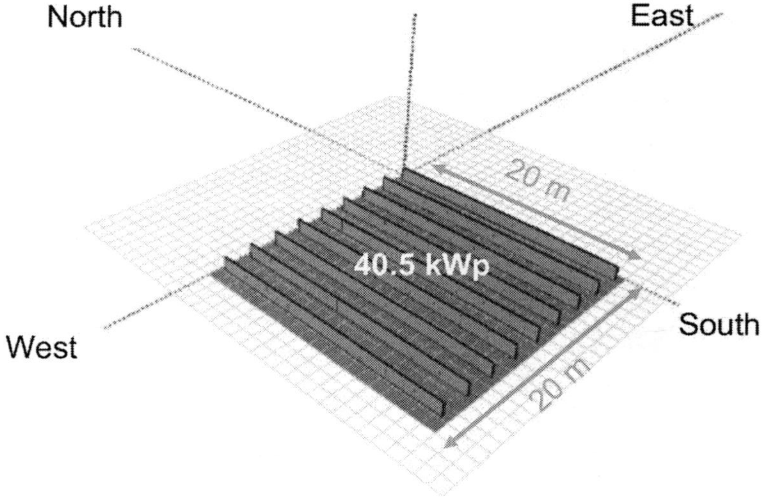

Lower GCR ⇒ lower rated power ⇒ lower yearly energy yield compared to the reference

Investment and maintenance costs

PV Systems with higher rated power generally show lower specific investment costs

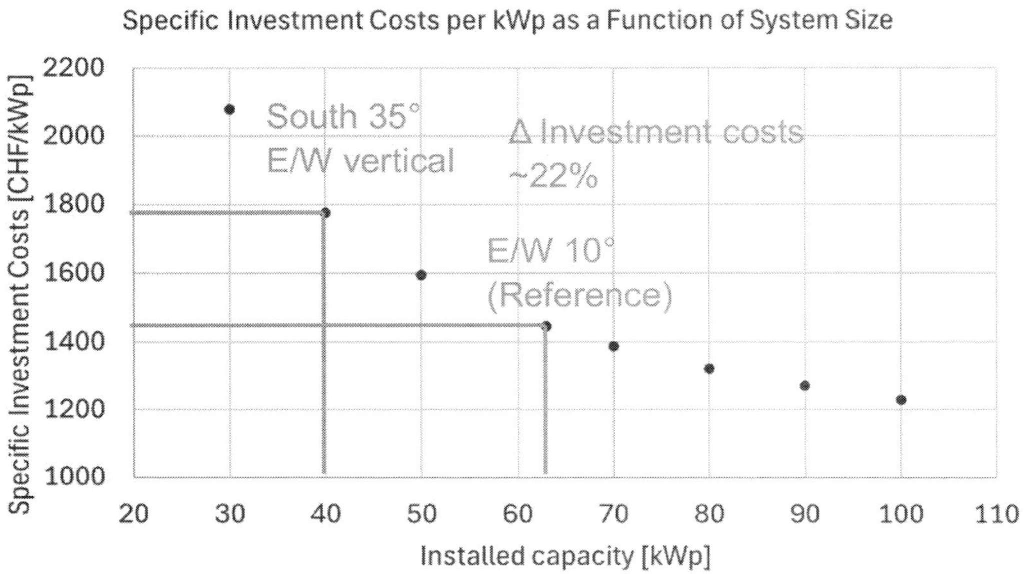

Source: Photovoltaics Market: Price Monitoring Study by SFOE (2024), p. 17

Analysed systems 20 x 20 m^2

System	Investment costs [CHF]	Maintenance costs [CHF/ a]
E/W 10°	90'972	1'260
South 35°	71'478	1'001
E/W vertical	71'478	1'001

Annual maintenance costs were assumed to be 1.4% of the investment costs
Source: Operating costs of photovoltaic systems by EnergieSchweiz (2017)

1 CHF = 1.05 EUR (2024)

Simulation of the economic efficiency

Net Present Value NPV

- Electricity prices for Winterthur in 2024
  - Day Ahead Stock Market Electricity Prices
  - 0.359 CHF/kWh fixed price (consumption)
  - 0.10 CHF/kWh fixed feed-in tariff
  - 0.025 CHF/kWh GO (guarantee of origin)
- 25 years operational lifetime of the PV system
- 0.4% yearly degradation of module
- 2.5% discount rate

Simulation of energy yield

- Location: Winterthur, Switzerland
- Weather data 2024 (irradiance)

Not considered

- Dynamic supply tariffs
- Batteries
- Demand-side management

1 CHF = 1.05 EUR (Ø 2024)

Seasonal dependencies

Monthly energy yield of the different designs versus average monthly electricity prices

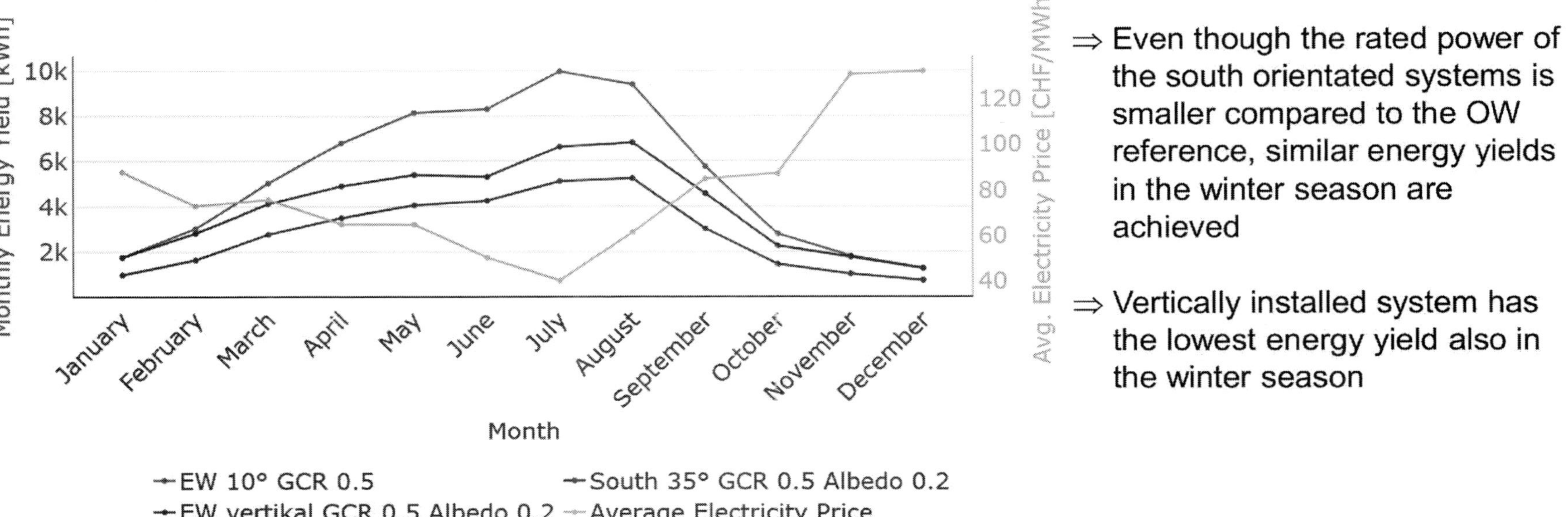

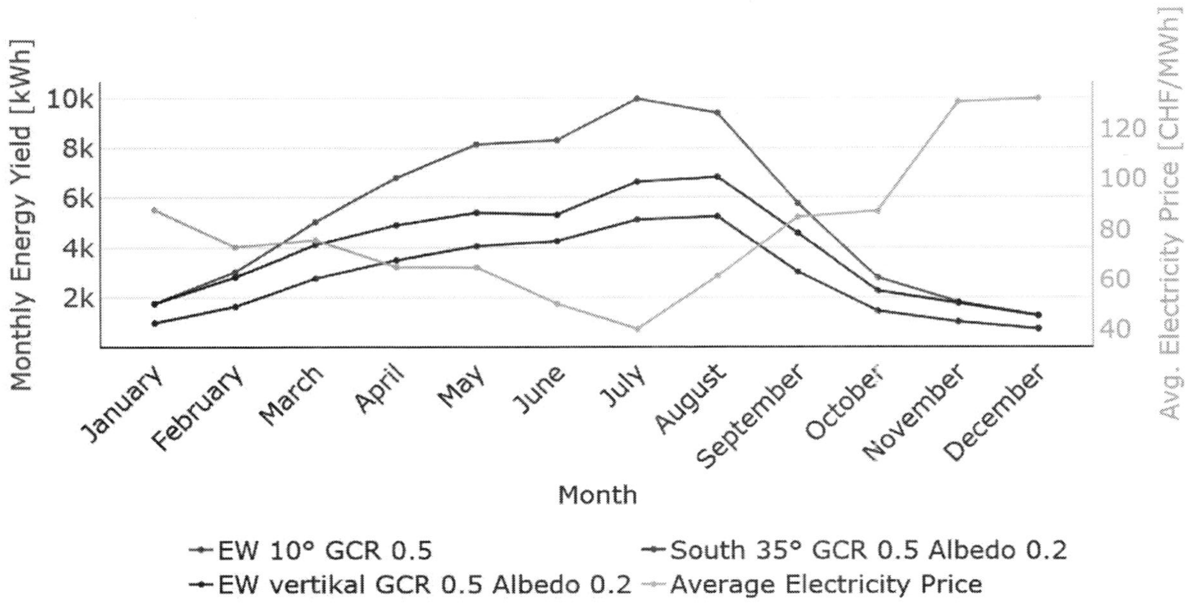

⇒ Even though the rated power of the south orientated systems is smaller compared to the OW reference, similar energy yields in the winter season are achieved

⇒ Vertically installed system has the lowest energy yield also in the winter season

1 CHF = 1.05 EUR (Ø 2024)

Hourly energy yield, self- consumption, feed-in tariffs

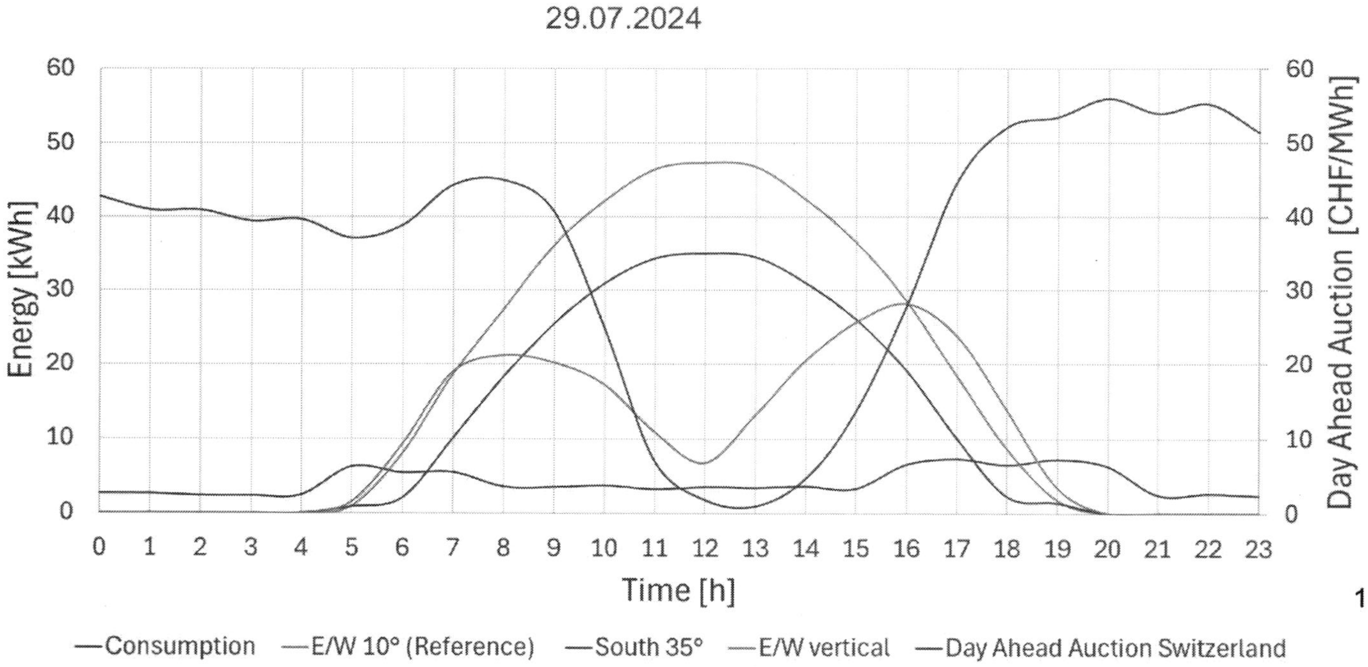

1 CHF = 1.05 EUR (2024)

Assumption: Consumption 30’000 kWh/y (multi-family household)
Resulting **Self-Consumption SC rates**: **19% (EW), 23% (S), 32% (V)**

NPV for static and dynamic feed in tariffs
With self-consumption

NPV [CHF] - Considering Partial Self-Consumption

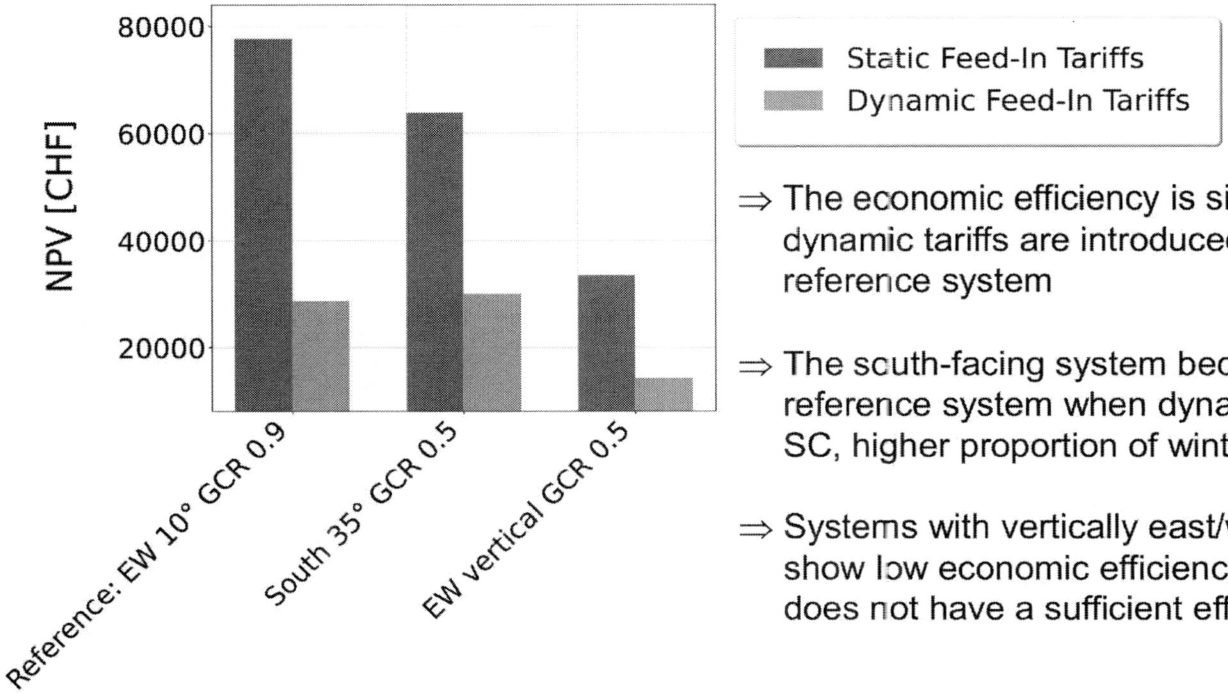

1 CHF = 1.05 EUR (Ø 2024)

⇒ The economic efficiency is significantly reduced when dynamic tariffs are introduced; highest impact on the E/W reference system

⇒ The south-facing system becomes more economical than the reference system when dynamic tariffs are introduced (higher SC, higher proportion of winter yield)

⇒ Systems with vertically east/west-facing modules generally show low economic efficiency. The "better" generation profile does not have a sufficient effect

NPV for static and dynamic feed in tariffs – Two different consumptions and self-consumption rates

Static Feed-in Tariff

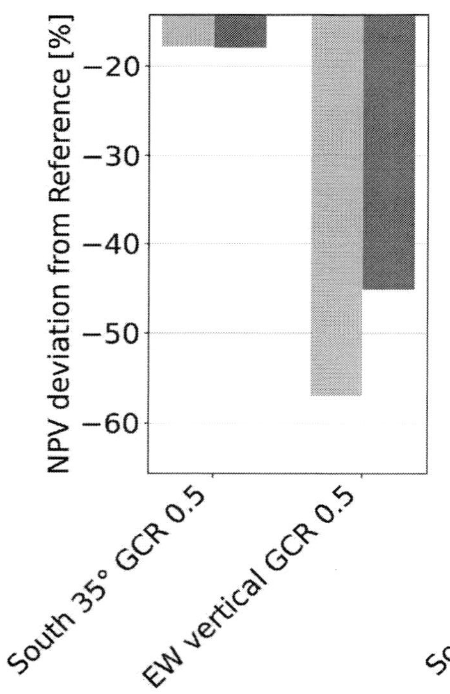

Dynamic Feed-in Tariff

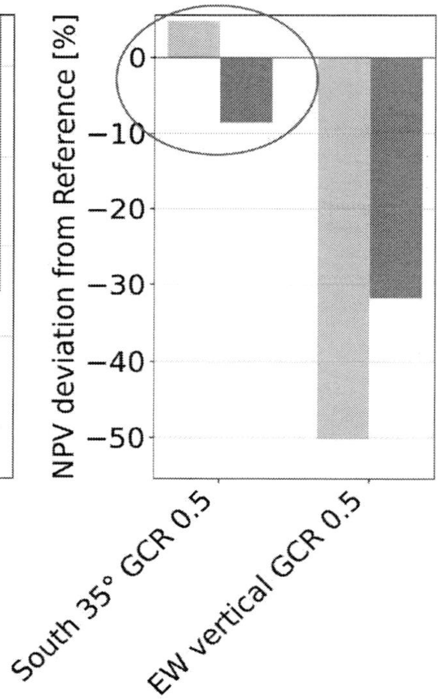

System	SC Rate [%]	SC Rate [%]
EW 10° GCR 0.9	19	33
South 35° GCR 0.5	23	39
EW 90° GCR 0.5	32	53

Low Consumption
High Consumption

SC = Self-Consumption

- Depending on the SC rate, south orientated systems with lower rated power can be economically more efficient than the reference
- With increasing SC-rate the reference E/W oriented system remains most economically efficient.

NPV for static and dynamic feed-in tariffs
Full feed-in systems (No self-consumption)

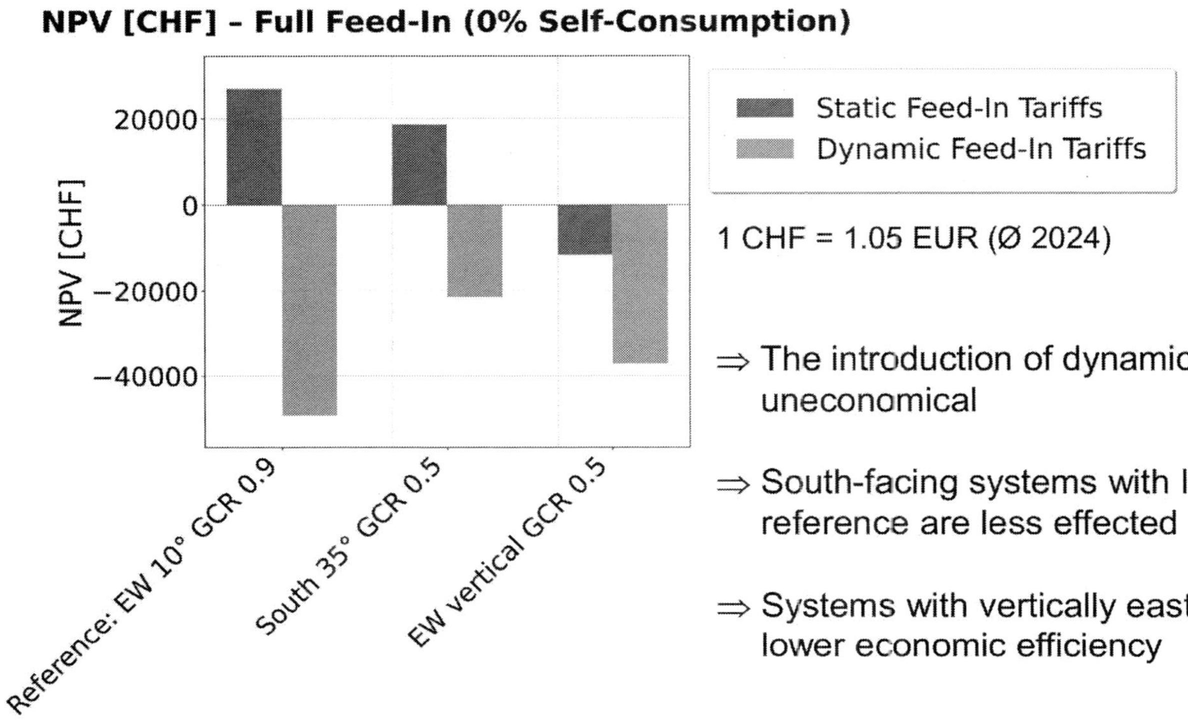

1 CHF = 1.05 EUR (Ø 2024)

⇒ The introduction of dynamic feed-in tariffs makes full feed-in systems uneconomical

⇒ South-facing systems with lower rated power compared to the reference are less effected

⇒ Systems with vertically east/west-facing modules generally show lower economic efficiency

Summary and conclusion

- The transition from static to dynamic feed-in tariffs generally reduces the economic efficiency of PV systems significantly.
- South-facing systems with lower rated power become more economically attractive compared to east/west systems when dynamic feed-in tariffs apply.
- For PV systems in combination of green roofs where the GCR is anyway lower, south orientated modules with higher tilt angels become more economically attractive when dynamic feed-in tariffs apply.
- Each PV project must be assessed individually. Designs with south-facing modules and steeper tilt angles should be considered.

Outlook

- In further investigations the influence of **batteries** and **energy management systems** need to be considered.
- **Horizontal Axis Tracking** might be an option in regions with high direct radiation.
- **Additional reflectors** at the edges of collector fields could enhance annual energy yield and change the generation profiles of flat-roof PV systems.

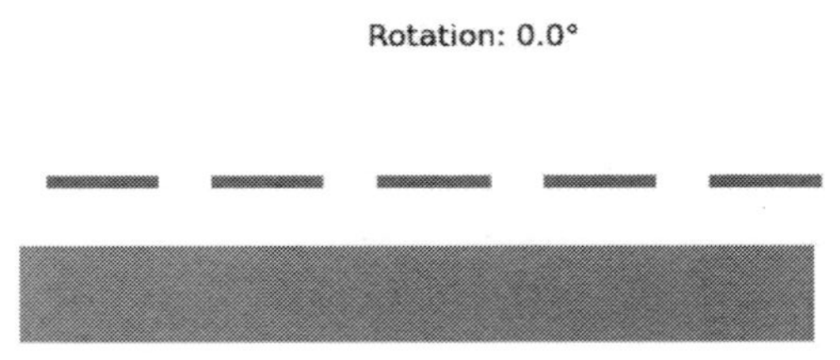

Thank you for your attention!

Zürcher Hochschule für
Angewandte Wissenschaften

ZHAW School of Engineering
Organisationseinheit

Prof. Dr. Hartmut Nussbaumer
Technikumstrasse 9 | Postfach
8401 Winterthur
Tel. +41 58 934 4799
Hartmut.nussbaumer@zhaw.ch
www.zhaw.ch/engineering

ZHAW School of Engineering | IEFE | 42th European Photovoltaic Solar Energy Conference, 4DO.3

42nd European Photovoltaic Solar Energy Conference and Exhibition

This presentation was selected by the Sc. Committee of the EU PVSEC 2025 for submission of a full paper to one of the EU PVSEC's collaborating peer-reviewed journals.

ASSESSMENT OF PERSONAL SAFETY CONCERNS OF PLUG AND PLAY PHOTOVOLTAIC INVERTERS USING A BLACK BOX APPROACH AND LABORATORY MEASUREMENTS

Alexander Erber[1], David Joss[1], Christof Bucher[1]*
[1] Bern University of Applied Sciences (BFH), School of Engineering and Computer Science (TI), Institute for Energy and Mobility Research (IEM), Laboratory for Photovoltaic Systems (PV-Lab)
Jlcoweg 1, 3400 Burgdorf, Switzerland
Corresponding author: Christof Bucher, christoph.bucher@bfh.ch

ABSTRACT: The rising utilization of plug and play photovoltaic systems has sparked safety concerns, particularly when installed by non-professionals, as current standards only partially address these issues. This paper introduces a black box testing method to evaluate the personal safety of plug and play inverters. 25 microinverters are assessed using three tests: (1) residual voltage behavior at the mains plug following disconnection, (2) current increase with low grid voltage, and (3) maximum touch temperature during operation. Results indicate 56% of inverters comply with the proposed German plug and play standard, performing comparably to other electrical devices. Further investigation is necessary to determine if exceeding this threshold poses a direct safety threat. A correlation has been identified between the output parameters of the inverters (resistance and capacitance) in the unplugged state and the duration required to reach safe voltage levels for most devices. The integration of a relay, however, can ensure compliance across all devices. During low voltage conditions, current surges are recorded, which could strain non-dedicated circuits. The temperature test reveals a positive correlation between the power density of inverters and their touch temperature. The outcomes of this study offer insights and guidance for future standardization and product improvements.

Keywords: plug and play photovoltaics, plug-in photovoltaics, microinverter, safety assessment, laboratory measurements

1 INTRODUCTION

Plug and play photovoltaic (PV) systems – often called balcony or plug-in PV – have seen rapid growth among end consumers, notably in Germany, the current largest market. By June 2025, over one million systems (>1 GWp) were registered in Germany, with actual numbers considerably higher due to unreported installations [1] [2]. These systems use microinverters, typically limited to a maximum output power depending on the national regulation (e.g. 600 or 800 VA) and are connect to the grid with standard household mains plugs (e.g., Typ F).

In terms of personal safety, the installation of plug and play PV systems by end users is more critical compared to professionally installed PV systems, as most of the microinverters were designed to be connected to the grid through a fixed connection. Presently debated safety issues include the residual voltage at the mains plug after the grid disconnection, the potential overloading of distribution circuits, and the effects on the functionality of RCD (residual current device) [3]. Current inverter safety standards, such as IEC 62109-1 [4], only partly address these issues, and comprehensive regulation is still evolving. The German draft standard E DIN VDE V 0126-95 [5] aims to close regulatory gaps but requirements for grid connections via household plugs remain under discussion. This draft is currently in its second revision and outlines requirements for all components of a plug and play PV system, such as module mounting frame, inverter, PV modules, DC connectors, and grid connection. For the connection to the grid through a standard mains plug, new requirements are defined that would legalize this type of connection, as current standards [6] do not allow it yet. For this new requirement, limited information and experience is available on the behavior of plug and play PV inverters regarding their residual voltage behavior.

Previous studies on plug and play microinverters used in plug and play systems primarily addressed efficiency and yield assessments [7] [8]. In 2017, the photovoltaic institute (PI) Berlin investigated RCD interference and overload situations of cable sections for 600 VA systems through lab tests [9]. In 2025, HTW Berlin extended the PI's methodology to 800 VA systems [10]. The 2017 PI study also considered electric shock protection related to residual voltage after unplugging, although without lab tests. A recent US study examined plug and play PV system barriers and three safety features (touch-safe plugs, breaker masking, bidirectional residual circuit devices) [11]. Both studies claim anti-islanding functions and relay interfaces ensure safety, but this is misleading, as these features are intended mainly for system and grid protection, not personal safety. While they offer a galvanic separation, non-switchable capacitors may still leave residual voltage levels non-compliant, as noted in the German plug and play draft standard.

The mentioned publications show the lack of data on the behavior of microinverters used for plug and play systems concerning the grid connection through standard household hold plugs (e.g. Typ F in most of the EU and T13 in Switzerland). This could lead to overregulation's and additional bureaucratic procedures in testing and installation, thus causing higher costs for consumers.

This paper addresses these challenges by analyzing a set of microinverters used in plug and play systems, with a focus on three safety concerns: (1) analyzing the residual voltage at the mains plug following disconnection, (2) the current increase under low grid voltage conditions and (3) the maximum touch temperature during operation. Laboratory-based black box testing is employed, using only components accessible in normal operation. Results are discussed in the context of current standardization gaps and guidance for future standard and product development is given. In this paper, "microinverters used in plug and play systems" and "plug and play inverters" are used interchangeably.

2 METHODS AND MATERIAL

2.1 DEVICES UNDER TEST

To assess relevant safety concerns, 25 commercially available inverters from 11 manufacturers are analyzed (see Table 1). The devices nominal AC outputs span from 300 VA to 2000 VA and are selected to represent the current plug and play inverter market. Although not all units fall within national plug and play system limits (600 VA for Switzerland; 800 VA for most EU countries), most can be software-limited to comply with these regulations. The test set includes 23 single-phase and 2 three-phase inverters, allowing both standard and potential future (three-phase) scenarios to be considered.

The devices can be grouped according to typical national power limits in three categories: 16 devices in category A (≤600 VA), 5 in category B (>600 VA & <=800 VA), and 4 in category C (>800 VA).

Table 1: Overview of the tested inverter categories. A detailed overview of the tested devices is given in Erber et al. [12].

Power category	Power range of category [VA]	Power range of invertrs	Number of inverters
A	<=600	300-600	16
B	>600 & <=800	601-800	5
C	>800	801-2000	4

2.2 SAFETY TESTS

Based on currently discussed safety concerns for plug and play PV inverters and a review of relevant standards, three laboratory tests are defined. The test conditions are set according to a black box approach, in which only parts and connectors accessible during normal operation are utilized. No additional communication gateways, monitoring equipment, or firmware updates are used, reflecting typical consumer usage where regular updates are often neglected. The tests and their origins are outlined as follows:

- **Residual voltage after disconnection:** Plug and play inverters contain capacitors that may retain voltage after grid disconnection. The test method is adapted from the draft German plug and play PV standard (E DIN VDE V 0126-95:2024-6) in line with the black box approach, voltage is measured at directly before the mains pins, rather than directly at the capacitors. The same compliance limit from IEC 60335-1 (maximum 34 V touch voltage after one second) as in the German draft standard is applied. The product standard draft mandates that the residual voltage test be conducted at various power levels – nominal power, 50% of nominal power, and the lowest feasible rated power – but due to the number of inverters under test, this paper conducts the test only at nominal power, assuming it represents the worst-case condition.
- **Maximum touch temperature:** As convection-cooled inverters can develop potentially hazardous surface temperatures, touch temperatures are measured under two defined conditions (1:1 and 1:1.5 AC-DC-Ratio) and assessed against the IEC 62109-1 limit for touch temperatures.
- **Feed-in current limitation at reduced grid voltage:** To prevent overloads in household wiring, inverters are tested for current limitation at low grid voltages as described in the German standard draft and DIN VDE V 0124-100 [13]. The draft standard requires an additional testing voltage at 0.85 Vn. During testing the feed-in current must not exceed 3.5 A (+2%). In this paper the holding time per voltage step is reduced, due to the number of devices, and additional voltages are included for further insights in the inverter behavior at low voltage levels.

The purpose of these tests is not to declare devices as unsafe, but rather to identify situations where more specific requirements for plug and play operation may be necessary. Microinverters designed for rooftop use may need additional specifications when applied in plug and play systems. For instance, capacitors implemented for electromagnetic compatibility can influence residual voltage and may require pre- or post-manufacturing adaptations.

All tests are conducted at the Laboratory for Photovoltaic Systems (PV Lab) of the Bern University of Applied Sciences in Burgdorf (BFH), where a dedicated test bench has been developed especially for the test "Residual voltage after disconnecting". The measurements are conducted within the SFOE funded project "Plug & Play Photovoltaic Systems" [14].

2.2.1 RESIDUAL VOLTAGE AFTER DISCONNECTION

The measurement setup for the residual voltage test is shown in Figure 1a. The plug and play inverter under test (DUT) are connected to the PV module simulator(s) (Modul Sim; Delta Elektronika SM330-AR-22 and Delta Elektronika SM100-AR-75) on the DC side and to the plug side of the socket connection at the mechanical disconnector on the AC side. The power analyzer (Dewetron DEWE3-PA8-RM with 3x TRION3-1810M-Power-4 measurement cards) measures the current and the voltages ($V_{L\text{-}N}$, $V_{PE\text{-}L}$, $V_{PE\text{-}N}$) shortly before the plug side. To ensure the same grid conditions for each measurement and prevent interferences from other grid connected devices, the setup uses a grid simulator. the grid simulator Due to space reasons, the used grid Simulator (Regatron TC.ACS.50.528.4WR.HC.LC) is not shown.

Figure 1b illustrates the function of the automated mechanical disconnection through the linear motor. The parallel configuration of three Swiss T13 sockets on the grid side, alongside three measurement cards on the power analyzer, enables the concurrent measurement of three inverters. This setup also permits measurements of three-phase inverters, as a T15 socket (three-phase) occupies the same amount of space as a T13 socket (one-phase).

Due to the number of inverters the residual voltage test is only conducted at nominal power and repeated 30 to 50 times, depending on the start time of the inverter, to ensure measurements at different phase angles. The required DC power is not determined iteratively and the I-V curve parameters are set with the conditions described in Erber et al. [12].

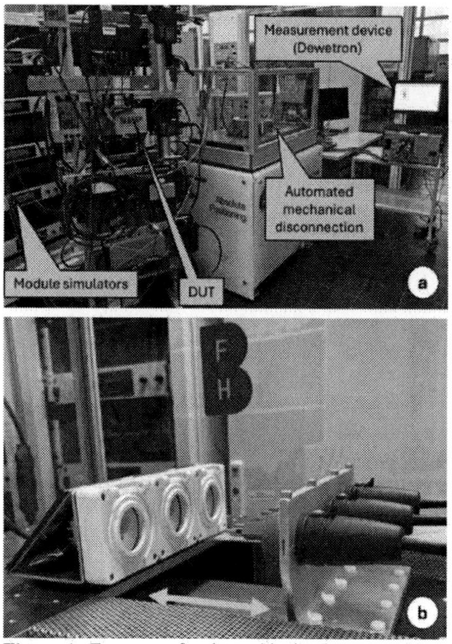

Figure 1: Test setup for the residual voltage test (a) and detail of the automated mechanical disconnection (b)

The residual voltage test is conducted with the following procedure: First, the AC connection to the grid is closed with the linear motor and the corresponding I-V curves are activated on the module simulator(s). When the inverter reaches the nominal power the AC connection is opened through the linear motor and the measurement is triggered by the power analyzer. A trigger pre- and post-time of 1 s is used. The process is repeated automatically with the same unplug conditions in context of velocity and acceleration.

In addition to plug and play inverters, other electrical household devices are analyzed with the same test procedure for a comparison of the residual voltage behavior.

The selected configuration, in contrast to a setup utilizing a (solid-state-) relay, accurately simulates actual conditions, ensuring that measurements are unaffected by switch bounce or parasitic capacitance phenomena. However, the limitation of this configuration is the inability to establish a precise phase angle for grid disconnection.

The measurement files are processed in Python after the measurements. As the measurement is triggered at the middle socket connection it is possible that the disconnection occurred earlier or later at the other two sockets. For this reason, an individual disconnect time is calculated for each socket. The disconnection for this paper is defined, where the voltage $V_{PE\text{-}N}$ exceeds 1.35 times the mean values of the first 0.5 s in the pre-time window. In the second step, the timestep is determined, where the maximum touch voltage falls below 34 V, and the time for the voltage decline is calculated. In the last step, the voltage at the point of disconnection is determined for the analysis. Figure 4 shows the current and voltage curves of a plug and play inverter after disconnection from the mains. Upon disconnection, the current reduces to 0 A due to the absence of a load on the plug (such as a body resistor), and the voltage displays the characteristic discharge curve of a capacitor. At t=130 ms, a shift in the voltage gradient signifies a switching event. The peak touch voltage decreases below the 34 V threshold after 793 ms, thereby adhering to the 1-second duration limit specified in E DIN VDE V 0126-95:2024-6.

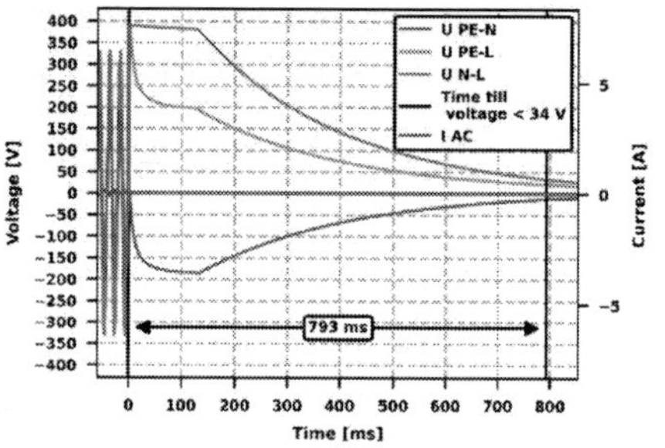

Figure 2: Current and voltage after disconnection from the mains of a plug and play inverter (600 W)

2.2.2 MAXIMUM TOUCH TEMPERATURE

The measurement setup for the maximum touch temperature test is shown in Figure 3, where three inverters are tested in parallel. The inverters are supplied on the DC side by the module simulators (Delta Elektronika SM330-AR-22 and Delta Elektronika SM100-AR-75) and are connected to the laboratory grid – no grid simulator is used. At every inverter the temperature is measured in the middle of both sides of the inverter with y typ T thermocouple. For the temperature measurement of the surface and ambient temperature (typ K thermocouple) the Keithley DAQ6510 with a 7700 measurement card is used. The power measurement is conducted with a Yokogawa WT3000 power analyzer. Both measurement devices acquired the temperature and power data in a 10s interval.

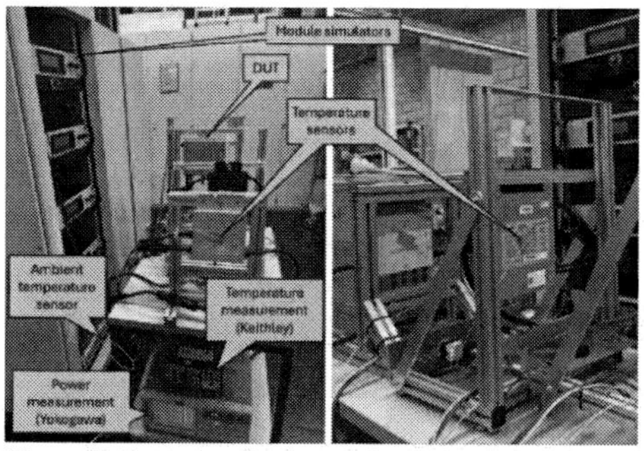

Figure 3: Test setup for the maximum touch temperature test

IEC 62109-1 [4] mandates that the maximum touch temperature must remain within a specified limit even in the most severe-rated operating conditions. For testing, the limit outlined in Table 3 of IEC 62109-1 for "Enclosure parts accessible to user by casual contact" is applied. These limit is 70 °C for metal parts and 95 °C for plastic and rubber parts. All plug and play inverters being tested have metal enclosures, except for the two Enphase® inverters with polymer enclosures.

Given that microinverters rely on convection cooling, the most severe operating conditions are thus present at high ambient temperatures, small cooling surfaces, high input powers, low efficiencies and/or limited convection (i.e. low heat transfer coefficient). For the test, it is assumed that the microinverters have mounting conditions with sufficient convection. In this setup, the input power – defined as a function of irradiance – is the only variable actively adjusted. The effects of ambient temperature can be considered retrospectively by calculation. The irradiance profile features a 2-minute ramp time and a 3.5-hour step time to achieve steady-state conditions. Two irradiance level are set in the profile. An irradiance of 1000 W/m², aligning with standard test condition (STC), indicates the nominal power operating point. Conversely, 1500 W/m² simulates increased input power to the inverter (i.e., overpaneling). This irradiance profile serves as a basis for the adjustment of the I-V curves at the module simulators for each inverter. The calculation of the I-V curve parameters is described in Erber et al. [12].

The analysis of the measurement files focuses on identifying the maximum touch temperature and its corresponding timestamp for each inverter, to assess the influence of heightened input power on temperature behavior. With the maximum touch temperature and the ambient temperature at that time, it is concluded at what ambient temperature the maximum allowable touch temperature will be surpassed.

2.2.3 LIMITATION OF FEED-IN CURRENT AT LOW GRID VOLTAGE

In this test, the setup and equipment are identical to those in the residual voltage test, with the exclusion of mechanical AC disconnection. Voltage consistency at the grid connection for each inverter is maintained using a sense cable. The testing is conducted with one inverter per measurement. For the low voltage grid scenarios, a voltage profile featuring a 5-second ramp time and a 30-second step duration is utilized, decreasing the voltage to 0.7 V_N. This profile diverges from the DIN VDE V 0124-100 [13] standard and E DIN VDE V 0126-95:2024-6, so an additional compliant profile (ramp time: 1 minute; step time: 15 minutes; voltages: 1.09, 0.9, and 0.85 VN) is implemented to verify the inverter behavior, such as stabilization time. Three inverters are selected for the validation. For the analysis, it is assessed whether the inverter raises the feed-in current (recorded as a 20 ms true RMS value) during testing relative to the initial current and the voltage at which inverter shutdown occurs.

3 RESULTS AND DISCUSSION

The results of the laboratory measurements are presented in the following subchapters. Two inverters from the same manufacturer were not restarting after the residual voltage test (WVC-300) and the maximum touch temperature test (WVC-600). The inverters showed error states via the LED indicator but were not reachable via the monitoring App. Therefore, not all three tests could be conducted on these two inverters.

3.1 RESIDUAL VOLTAGE AFTER DISCONNECTION

Figure 4 shows the results of the residual voltage test for 25 microinverters operating at nominal power and five consumer devices under various loads. The time to reach 35 V spans from 100 ms to over 12 seconds. None of the inverters consistently maintained a 230 V_{RMS} AC output after disconnection. Among the assessed inverters, 14 (56%) complied with the E DIN VDE V 0126-95 residual voltage limit, while 11 surpassed it in at least one test. Inverters DS3-S and EZ1-M had a 2.5% and 2.3% probability, respectively, of exceeding the limit. For seven other inverters, discharge times hovered around the 1 s threshold, with 39.5% to 95.7% exceeding it. All measurements for the three-phase inverters (YC1000-EU and HMT-2000) surpassed the limit, with discharge times differing by over four times. Grouping inverters by power – A: <=600 VA, B: <=800 VA & >600 VA, C: >800 VA – shows that 44% of group A (n=16), 20% of group B (n=5), and 75% of group C (n=4) exceeded the limit. Classification by manufacturer reveals minor impact: 40% (A), 20% (B), and 67% (C) of manufacturers had at least one inverter with discharge times over 1 s. Caution is advised as differing population sizes affect the sensitivity. Based on the analyzed inverter set, no correlation between the inverter power and number of limit-exceeding inverters can be determined.

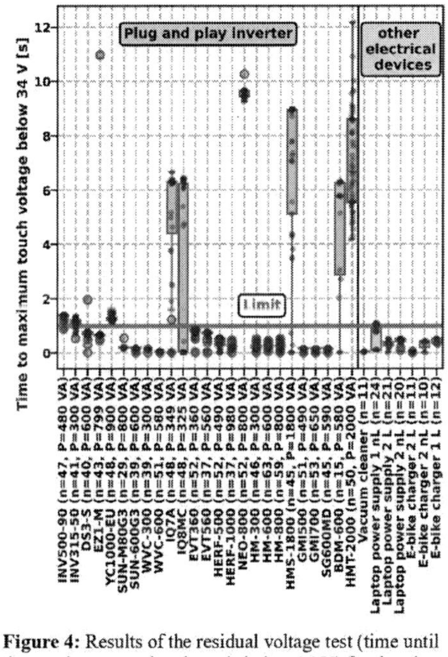

Figure 4: Results of the residual voltage test (time until the maximum touch voltage is below 34 V) for the plug and play inverters and other typical electrical devices. (nL = no load; L = load). The red "Limit" line is the residual voltage limit of E DIN VDE V 0126-95:2024-6.

The tests with household devices reveals one device exceeding the limit at least once, while compliant inverters and devices show similar discharge times.

Since no inverter sustained a stable 230 V_{RMS} AC output voltage following disconnection and a typical discharge voltage curve was observed across most measurements, the resistance and capacitance between L and N were assessed in the unplugged state using a Philips PM6304 RCL meter. It should be noted that the measured capacitance does not directly correspond to the X-capacitance installed between L and N in the devices, as additional Y-capacitances to earth (PE) may be present for EMC purposes, which can influence the overall measurement results. However, assuming that the Y-capacitances are two orders of magnitude smaller than the X-capacitance, their influence on the measurement is considered negligible.

Table 2 shows the results of this measurement with the share of the limit exceeding measurements in the residual voltage test. Inverters characterized by measurable capacitance and non-measurable resistance surpass the 1 s limits in all or the majority of the residual voltage measurements, due to the prolonged discharge duration of the capacitance. Therefore, the measured resistance in the limit complying inverter acts as a discharge resistor for the capacitance. The reason for the long discharge times of the two Enphase® inverters with low resistance values is most likely the absence of the Q-Relay which contains the interface protection relay. Even though the inverters (DS3-S and EZ1-M have no measurable resistance, one measurement each exceed the limit. This indicates that the capacitance is low enough to ensure a discharge time to 34 V in nearly all measurements. The two exceeding discharge times, which are more than twice as long as the calculated times (see Figure 4), illustrate that under certain conditions (e.g. phase time dependency) longer discharge times are possible although with a small likelihood. In contrary to the previous stated finding the two inverters INV500-90 and INV315-50 have more than 50% of the measurements exceeding the limit, but their resistance differs by a factor of 10 and the resistance as well as the capacitance of INV500-90 are in the range of the limit complying inverters. Due to the black box approach, no reasons other than inverter or manufacturer-specific behavior can be stated.

Table 2. Resistance and Capacitance between L and N for all tested inverters with share of values exceeding the residual voltage limit. Measured in the unplugged state (OL = open load)

Inverter	R_{L-N} [kOhm]	C_{L-N} [nF]	share of values exceeding the VDE limit
INV500-90	140	380	95.7%
INV315-50	1300	416	73.2%
DS3-S	OL	98	2.5%
EZ1-M	OL	100	2.3%
YC1000-EU	OL	400	100%
SUN-M80G3	900	90	-
SUN600G3	950	89	-
WVC-300	OL	OL	-
WVC-600	OL	OL	-
IQ7A	120	924	89.6%
IQ8MC	55	980	39.6%
EVT360	810	587	-
EVT560	712	487	-
HERF-500	198	433	-
HERF-1000	194	440	-
NEO-800	OL	1455	100%
HM-300	200	435	-
HM-600	196	424	-
HM-800	197	438	-
HMS-1800	OL	1100	88.9%
GMI500	OL	OL	-
GMI700	OL	OL	-
SG600MD	OL	OL	-
BDM-600	OL	1800	86.7%
HMT-2000	OL	1872	100%

In category A (≤ 600 VA), some inverters have power values nearing 50% of the limit, allowing the use of two inverters for a plug and play setup. Figure 5 presents the residual voltage test results with two inverters in parallel on the same grid connection compared to single operation. For two of the three tested inverters, there is no difference between single and parallel setups. This can be explained with the parallel connection of two R-C circuits, with the same resistance and capacitance values. The total resistance halves, and the capacitance doubles, maintaining the original time constant. However, for the two INV315-50 inverters, the time nearly doubled compared to single operation, which is an unexplained behavior likely specific to this model. The subtests indicate that for systems with multiple inverters, residual voltage tests should be conducted on the entire setup to ensure safety.

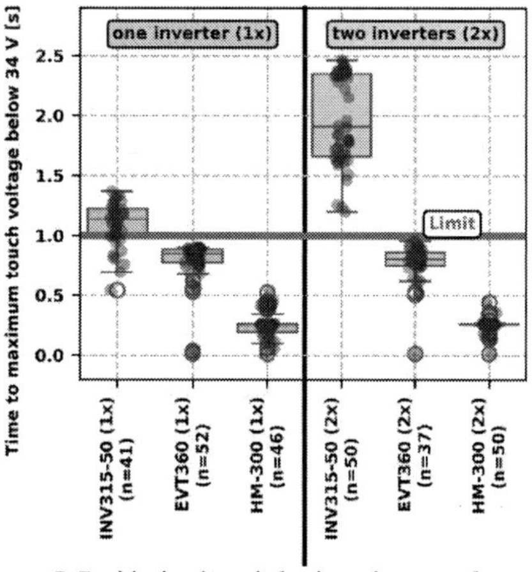

Figure 5: Residual voltage behavior, when two plug and play inverters are operated in parallel to the grid and disconnected. The red "Limit" line is the residual voltage limit of E DIN VDE V 0126-95:2024-6.

The exemplary measurement in Figure 6 shows, which body current would flow, when the pins of L and N are touched after 1 s of unplugging. A resistor with 1 kOhm is used for this measurement. When both pins are touched a charged energy of around 52 mJ is discharged over 3.2 ms with a peak current of 465 mA. Due to the fact that only one single test was conducted no final conclusion in this context can be state. Although a future analysis on this aspect, assessing touch combinations and current path, while also including secondary effects, could determine if a time dependent charge limit in addition to the voltage limit could be introduced.

10.4229/EUPVSEC2025/4DO.3.6

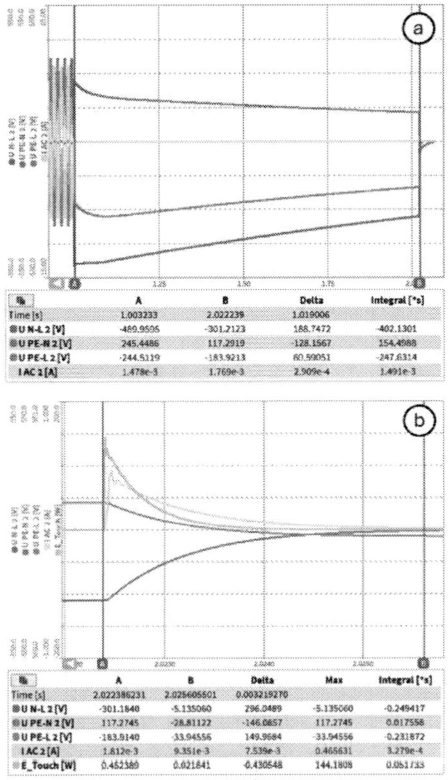

	A	B	Delta	Integral [*s]
Time [s]	1.003233	2.022239	1.019006	
U N-L 2 [V]	-489.9505	-301.2123	188.7472	-402.1301
U PE-N 2 [V]	245.4486	117.2919	-128.1567	154.4988
U PE-L 2 [V]	-244.5119	-183.9213	60.59051	-247.6314
I AC 2 [A]	1.478e-3	1.769e-3	2.909e-4	1.491e-3

	A	B	Delta	Max	Integral [*s]
Time [s]	2.022386231	2.025605501	0.003219270		
U N-L 2 [V]	-301.1840	-5.135060	296.0489	-5.135060	-0.249417
U PE-N 2 [V]	117.2745	-28.81122	-146.0857	117.2745	0.017558
U PE-L 2 [V]	-183.9140	-33.94556	149.9684	-33.94556	-0.231872
I AC 2 [A]	1.812e-3	9.351e-3	7.539e-3	0.465631	3.279e-4
E_Touch [W]	0.452389	0.021841	-0.430548	144.1808	0.061733

Figure 6. Measurement results (HMS-1800), when L and N are connected to a 1 kOhm body resistance after 1s of unplugging (a). Details of touch current and energy are shown in (b).

As 44% of the tested inverters surpass the proposed threshold of E DIN VDE V 0126-95:2024-6 in at least one measurement, the potential application of a safety adapter to meet compliance is examined. The primary role of a safety adapter is to maintain a conforming residual voltage level after 1 s and ensure touch safety when unplugged. This function might be achieved via a two-pole relay that disconnects the inverter's phase and neutral conductors from the power outlet, thus eliminating voltage at the plug terminals. Another approach involves a mechanical touch-safe mechanism paired with a discharge resistor to link phase and neutral post-grid disconnection, discharging capacitors to reach compliant residual voltage levels. Due to the novelty of this safety application, it can be assumed that other implementation concepts for the required security function will be developed and that the aforementioned implementation variants serve as examples. The above listing of potential realizations was assembled without checking whether these concepts are under patent protection.

An exemplary test on an HMS-1800 inverter using a SEP 1.16 adapter from the company "Seplugs", which employs the last described voltage reduction method, was conducted. Figure 7 displays the residual voltage test results with and without the safety adapter. Incorporating the safety adapter enables the system to meet the residual voltage limit, which supports the statement that the entire system should be evaluated rather than the inverter alone. Inverters exceeding the limits without additional AC side components can achieve compliance by adding a safety adapter. In addition, inverter manufacturers might consider integrating the safety adapter's functionality into the internal design during product updates.

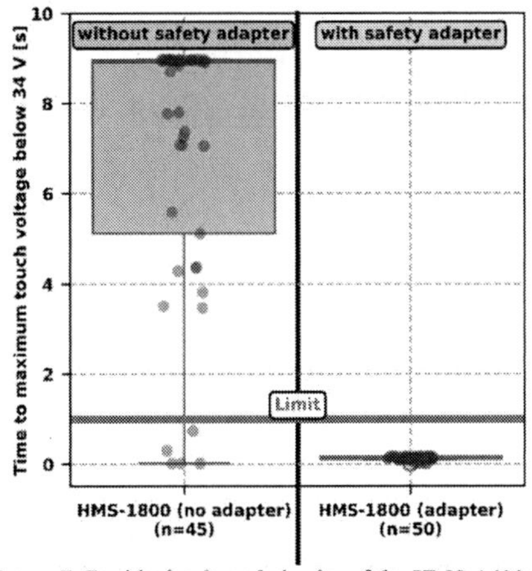

Figure 7: Residual voltage behavior of the HMS-1600 inverter with and without a safety adapter (SEP 1.16). The red "Limit" line is the residual voltage limit of E DIN VDE V 0126-95:2024-6.

During the visual validation of the used disconnection condition, the behavior presented in Figure 8 was found. Among the 52 measurements conducted on this inverter, this behavior was observed a single time. In this measurement, the inverter starts to generate a 50 Hz voltage of approximately 173 V_{RMS} (0.75 V_N) at the AC output 5 ms after the mains plug is pulled out. This behavior is most likely due to the inverter assuming that a grid fault has occurred and that it must not disconnect from the grid during the fault ride-through procedure. The voltage output continues for 3 s until the interface protection relay disconnects the inverter from the grid due to the voltage drop protection time as mandated in VDE-AR-N 4105 [15] (<0.8 V_N for 3 s). Such a behavior is compliant with VDE-AR-N 4105 as the islanding detection and grid disconnection under dynamic grid supporting measures must happen within 9 s (normal 2 s). For the previously mentioned safety adapter such a behavior might be challenging to distinguish from a normal grid condition in the context of the residual voltage behavior. On the one hand, it could be argued that, if the safety adapter maintains a touch protection even though the discharge functionality is not activated, there is still an additional safety layer due to the touch safety. On the other hand, it should be discussed if plug and play inverters must not provide fault ride-through functionality, considering the small system power. The later argument would result in a separate grid profile with reduced requirements for plug and play inverters, if applied. As plug and play inverters can also be used in larger PV systems, the distributor would have to ensure that the plug and play inverter is configured with the right profile or application code respectively.

10.4229/EUPVSEC2025/4DO.3.6

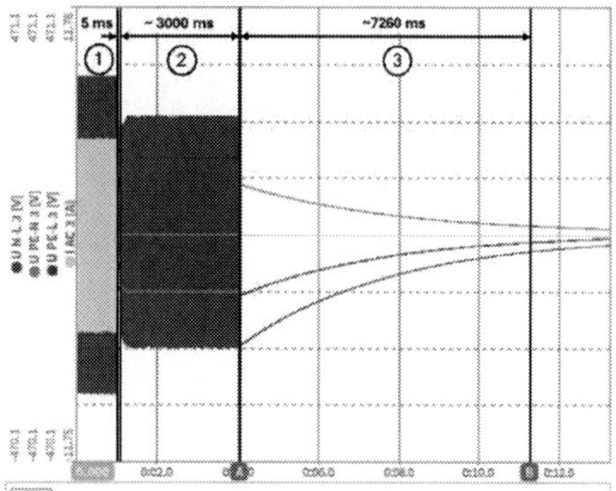

	A	B	Delta
Time [s]	4.04699	0:11.26454	7.21755
U N-L 3 [V]	-228.3714	-33.97536	194.3960
U PE-N 3 [V]	104.3599	19.81878	-84.54109
U PE-L 3 [V]	-123.9855	-14.13059	109.8549
I AC 3 [A]	4.556e-4	1.600e-4	-2.956e-4

Figure 8: Measurement results of an inverter (NEO-800) after unplugging (1), with an islanding and fault-ride-through behavior (2). The interface protection relay stops this behavior after 3 s and the normal discharge phase starts (3). This behavior was observed in one out of the 52 residual voltage measurements on this inverter

3.2 MAXIMUM TOUCH TEMPERATURE

The recorded touch temperatures span from 43.40 °C to 80.33 °C. Among the 24 tested inverters, 18 (75%) adhere to the limit of IEC 62109-1. Most inverters maintain a stable temperature and consistent power output, demonstrating efficient thermal management. Conversely, models like GMI500, GMI700, and SG600MD show temperature and power variability, suggesting active thermal derating most probably due to internal temperature constraints. In addition, the WVC-600 inverter showed an early power drop, potentially due to protective shutdown or inadequate thermal performance. These observations highlight that, while many inverters perform reliably under thermal stress, some devices experience limitations related to thermal protection strategies or insufficient cooling capabilities. Such thermal derating can further decrease the system yield.

The reason why microinverters that have valid IEC 62109-1 certificates (e.g. SUN-M80G3) would still exceed the touch temperature limit in a configuration with sufficient available DC power and at certain ambient temperatures is most likely due to the considerate mounting situation in the certification test. The usual mounting situation for most of the systems, which are not purely designed for plug and play systems, is behind the module. Therefore, no inverter surfaces are accessible during the operation and high temperatures are only a concern for the component lifetime and not in terms of safety. This aspect should be considered in the safety standard for plug and play PV systems.

Given that the touch temperature is dependent on the ambient temperature, Figure 9 shows the maximum allowable power-dependent temperature rise (maximum touch temperature minus ambient temperature) (x-axis) to comply under a 35 °C ambient temperature condition. 11 out of 24 inverters (46%) would exceed the temperature limit. The figure further depicts a positive correlation between maximum power-dependent temperature rise and power density (nominal inverter power/datasheet volume) of the tested inverters. Inverters with lower power, like those in category A, show a reduced power density and temperature rise. Variation in data arises partly from power density calculations based on datasheet dimensions, sometimes excluding mounting dimensions. Efficiency and heat transfer area (cooling fin design) are also impactful. Barring two outliers in category A, the findings suggest the use of smaller inverters with lower power density over a single high-density inverter to reduce the touch temperature risk. This could further prolong inverter lifespan, acknowledging that component aging (e.g. capacitors) is temperature depending.

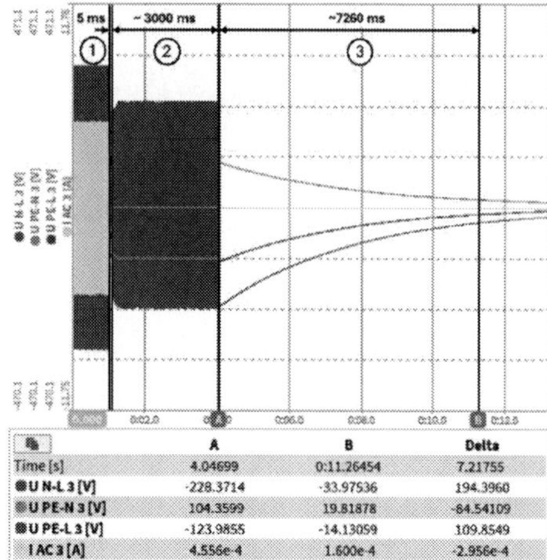

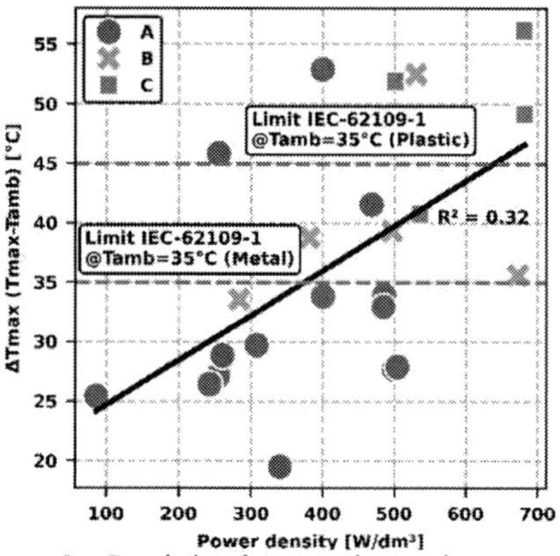

Figure 9: Correlation between the maximum power-dependent temperature increase (maximum touch temperature minus ambient temperature) and the power density (nominal inverter power/datasheet volume). Both red "Limit"-lines indicate the maximum allowable power-dependent temperature rise at 35°C for two enclosure materials. The categories A, B and C are the previously mentioned power categories (A: <=600 VA, B: <=800 VA & >600 VA and C: >800 VA).

3.3 LIMITATION OF FEED-IN CURRENT AT LOW GRID VOLTAGE

Figure 10 shows the test results for analyzing whether inverters boost their feed-in current at low grid voltage. All tested inverters show a current increase ranging from 1.7% to 26.3% of their nominal current. Of the three inverters (HM-800, NEO-800, SUN-M80G3) with a nominal power of 800 VA, two surpassed the 3.5 A limit (including the 2% tolerance), which is non-compliant with E DIN VDE V 0126-95:2024-6. Although other category A and B inverters increased their feed-in currents, they stayed within the absolute limit. To uniform the feed-in current regulation for plug and play systems a relative current limit, e.g. "The maximum feed-in current must not exceed 2% of the nominal feed-in current", could be proposed to preplace the absolute limit. This would ease the configuration of plug and play systems for with multiple inverters of the same type and one mains plug, if the inverter is known to meet the 2% limit. An absolute limit introduces more complexity. With a relative limit, only one tested inverter would comply.

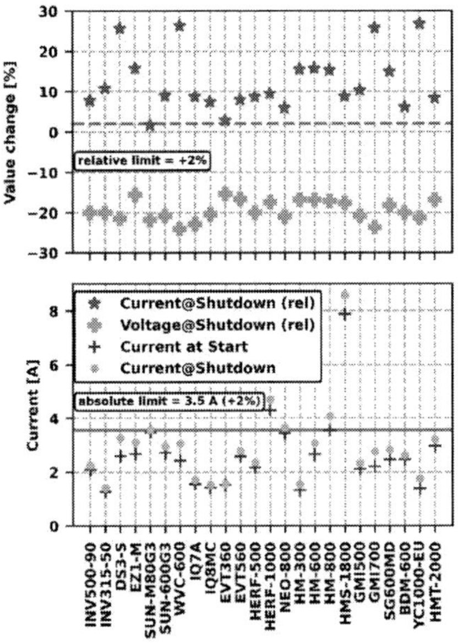

Figure 10: Results of the feed-in current test a low grid voltage at nominal power. Top figure: Values at inverters shutdown (top figure) referenced to the starting values at normal (230 V_{RMS} grid conditions). Bottom figure: absolute current values (test start and shutdown). The limit lines indicate the absolute and relative limit.

4 SUMMARY AND CONCLUSION

This paper assesses three safety concerns of plug and play inverters using a black box method, creating a data basis for discussions on safety standards. The methods are also applicable for future compliance tests. In the residual voltage testing 56% of the analyzed inverters did comply with the proposed limit of the latest official draft of E DIN VDE V 0126-95. Regarding the 11 non-compliant inverters, it must be stated, that an exceedance of the residual voltage limit should not be directly linked to a safety risk without taking the severity of the exceedance (time and number of occasion) into account and conducting further assessments. An exemplary measurement showed the body current and duration that can be expected when the power plug of non-compliant inverters is touched.

The test highlights that system testing is recommended for setups with multiple inverters, as they may exhibit extended residual voltage durations compared to single inverter systems. An exemplary test illustrated that integrating a safety relay, which actively lowers residual voltage post-disconnection, can bring non-compliant inverters into compliance. This adaptation might serve as a cost-efficient solution to mitigate the risks posed by residual voltage, given that discharge times vary significantly with different devices, necessitating numerous repeated tests, which could increase both test duration and cost.

Additionally, one out of 52 measurements for an individual inverter indicates a need to discuss grid support functions, such as fault ride-through, concerning the residual voltage behavior of plug-and-play inverters.

In future research on residual voltage testing, emphasis could be placed on validating our analysis with triggered relay tests and exploring ways to minimize testing duration. Additionally, tests at varied power levels (50% of nominal power or minimal operating power, as required in the draft of E DIN VDE V 0126-95), should be performed to investigate their impact on residual voltage behavior.

The second test reveals that several inverters surpass the feed-in limit at low grid voltages, with variance in non-compliance numbers depending on the use of an absolute or relative limit. Implementing a relative limit is advised to harmonize regulations across different power-rated devices. Although this safety issue is the least likely due to infrequent low voltages during sunny hours, the limitation of the feed-in current to a maximum of 3.5 A (800 VA or 2.6 A (600 VA) remains crucial for plug and play PV inverters due to the connection on non-dedicated distribution circuits. It can be assumed that the observed feed-in behavior can be corrected via a firmware update and hence a verification of those updates should be carried out in the future.

The final test indicates that at a high DC supply scenario and high ambient temperatures, the tested inverters may exceed the IEC 62109-1 touch temperature limit. To reduce thermal issues, the use of multiple smaller inverters instead of one large unit is recommended for the system design. Future studies assessing the thermal behavior of power-limited inverters (e.g. category C inverters limited to 800 VA) may offer guidance for system design, as their larger housing volume could enhance heat dissipation.

The results and findings of this paper show that safety risks may be present at certain plug and play inverters under the tested conditions and should be considered for market entry and surveillance. However, these issues can be addressed with technical adaptations and system engineering adjustments leading to a save use of plug and play PV systems.

ACKNOWLEDGEMENT

This research was carried out in the project "Plug & Play Photovoltaic Systems" funded by the Swiss Federal Office of Energy (Project number SI/502662). The responsibility for the content and conclusions lies solely with the authors.

REFERENCES

[1] Bundesnetzagentur für Elektrizität, Gas, Telekommunikation, Post und Eisenbahnen, "Marktstammdatenregister." Accessed: Jun. 18, 2025. [Online]. Available: https://www.marktstammdatenregister.de/MaStR/Einheit/Einheiten/ErweiterteOeffentlicheEinheitenuebersicht

[2] J. Bergner, R. Hoelger, and B. Praetorius, "Der Markt für Steckersolargeräte," Hochschule für Technik und Wirtschaft HTW Berlin, 2022. Accessed: May 21, 2025. [Online]. Available: https://solar.htw-berlin.de/studien/marktstudie-steckersolar-2022/

[3] H. Laukamp *et al.*, "Entwicklung einer Produktnorm für Steckersolargeräte," in *37. PV-Symposium/BIPV-Forum 2022*, Jan. 2022. doi: 10.24406/publica-1243.

[4] IEC 62109-1, *Safety of power converters for use in photovoltaic power systems - Part 1: General requirements*, 2010.
[5] E DIN VDE V 0126-95, *Steckersolargeräte für Netzparallelbetrieb - Sicherheitsanforderungen und Prüfungen*, Berlin., 2024.
[6] VDE Verband der Elektrotechnik Elektronik Informationstechnik e.V., "Steckerfertige PV-Anlagen: Anschluss & Anmeldung." Accessed: Aug. 26, 2025. [Online]. Available: https://www.vde.com/fnn-pv-stecker
[7] S. Krauter and J. Bendfeld, "PV Microinverters: Latest Efficiency Rankings, Energy Yield Assessments, Firmware Issues," *40th European Photovoltaic Solar Energy Conference and Exhibition*, pp. 020267-001-020267–005, 2023, doi: 10.4229/EUPVSEC2023/3EO.1.2.
[8] S. Krauter and J. Bendfeld, "PV Microinverters: Balcony Power Plants, Latest Efficiency Rankings, Yield Calculation for Overpowered Mini PV Systems," *41st European Photovoltaic Solar Energy Conference and Exhibition*, pp. 020162-001-020162–007, 2024, doi: 10.4229/EUPVSEC2024/3AV.1.37.
[9] Marcus Vietzke, "Untersuchung der Beeinflussung der Schutzkonzepte von Stromkreisen durch Stecker-Solar-Geräte," Jan. 2017. [Online]. Available: https://www.pvplug.de/wp-content/uploads/2017/05/pi-berlin.testreport.20170520.pdf
[10] J. Bergner, "Kurzbericht: Steckersolar 800 W," 2025. Accessed: Mar. 12, 2025. [Online]. Available: https://solar.htw-berlin.de/publikationen/kurzbericht-steckersolar-800-w/
[11] D. L. Gerber, A. Ginsberg-Klemmt, L. Stoler, J. Shackelford, and A. Meier, "Barriers to Balcony Solar and Plug-In Distributed Energy Resources in the United States," *Energies*, vol. 18, no. 8, p. 2132, Jan. 2025, doi: 10.3390/en18082132.
[12] A. Erber, D. Joss, and C. Bucher, "Assessment of Personal Safety Concerns of Plug and Play Photovoltaic Inverters using a Black Box Approach and Laboratory Measurements [Manuscript submitted for publication]," *Solar RRL*, 2025.
[13] DIN VDE V 0124-100, *Niederspannung – Prüfanforderungen an Erzeugungseinheiten, vorgesehen zum Anschluss und Parallelbetrieb am Niederspannungsnetz*, 2020.
[14] Bern University of Applied Sciences, "Plug & Play Photovoltaic Systems." Accessed: Jun. 19, 2025. [Online]. Available: https://www.bfh.ch/en/research/research-projects/2023-764-629-419/
[15] VDE-AR-N 4105, *VDE-AR-N 4105 Anwendungsregel:2018-11 Erzeugungsanlagen am Niederspannungsnetz*, 2018.

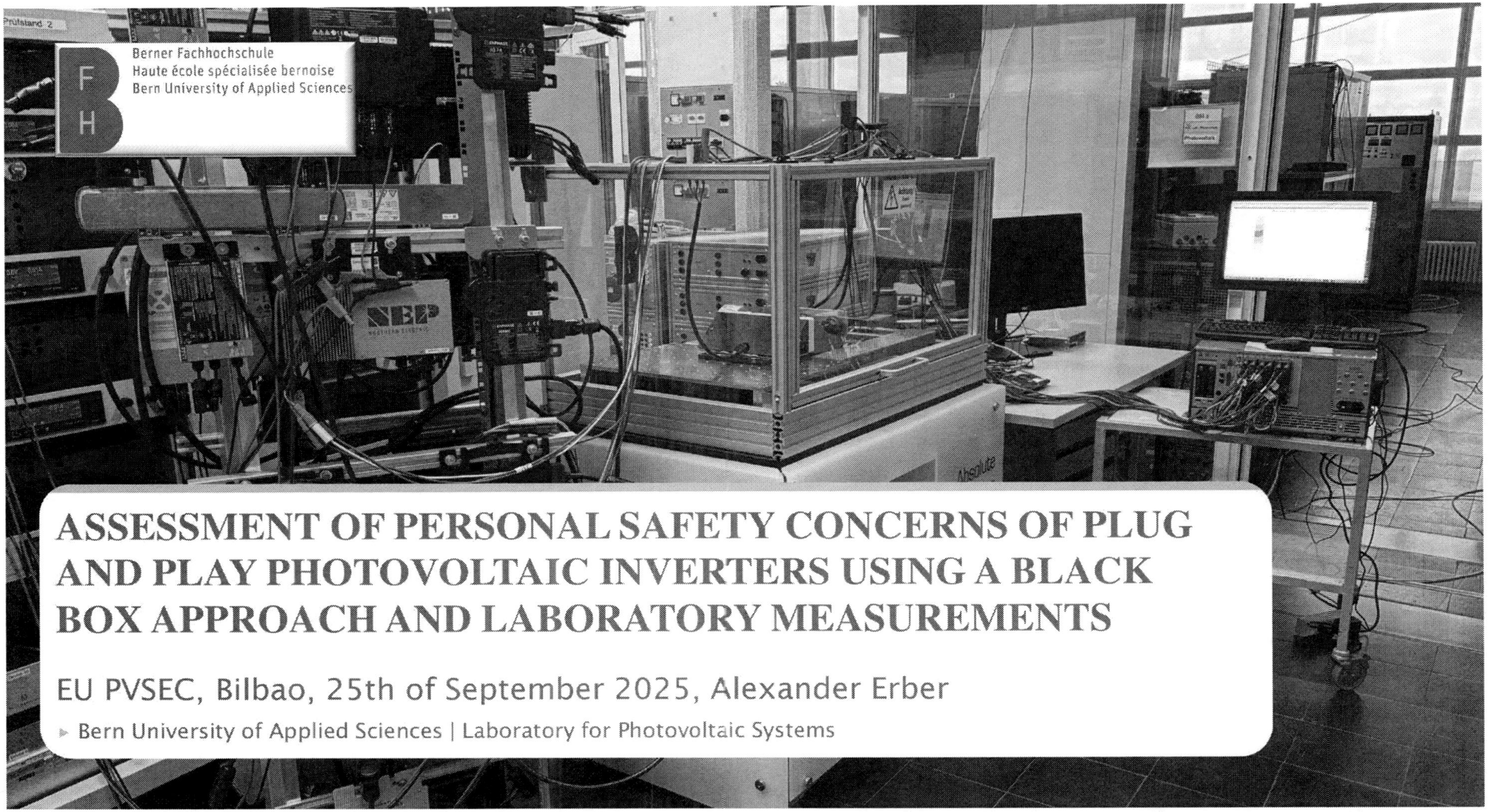
Berner Fachhochschule
Haute école spécialisée bernoise
Bern University of Applied Sciences
ASSESSMENT OF PERSONAL SAFETY CONCERNS OF PLUG AND PLAY PHOTOVOLTAIC INVERTERS USING A BLACK BOX APPROACH AND LABORATORY MEASUREMENTS
EU PVSEC, Bilbao, 25th of September 2025, Alexander Erber
Bern University of Applied Sciences | Laboratory for Photovoltaic Systems

Situation of plug and play PV systems

- Rapid growth, notably in Germany
  - June 2025: 1 million registered systems (>1 GWp)
  - Total system numbers considerably higher
  - Most systems sold with Type F plug [1]
- Safety concerns of these systems [2]
  - Installation and personally safety
- Inverter standards (e.g. IEC 62109) only partly cover the inverter concerns
- **Limited data/studies available**
- **Plug and play PV inverters $\stackrel{?}{=}$ microinverter**

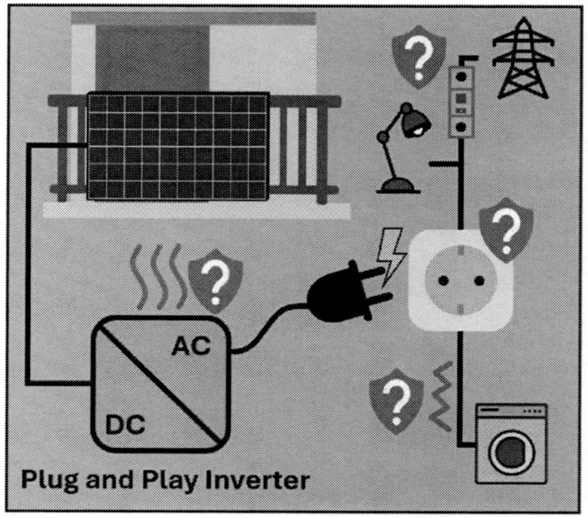

[1] J. Bergner et al, 2022,"Der Markt für Steckersolargeräte", https://solar.htw-berlin.de/studien/marktstudie-steckersolar-2022/
[2] H. Laukamp et al.,2022, "Entwicklung einer Produktnorm für Steckersolargeräte," in 37. PV-Symposium/BIPV-Forum 2022

Safety Test in the Laboratory

Literature and standard research

- exchange with experts and standard groups
- Condensed test plan to three main tests

Test approach

- Black box approach
- 25 inverters to test

Power category	Power range of category [VA]	Power range of invertrs	Number of inverters
A	<=600	300-600	16
B	>600 & <=800	601-800	5
C	>800	801-2000	4

1.Test: Residual voltage test

- Realistic conditions and repeated measurements (30-50 per inverter)
- Compliancy limit of E DIN VDE V 0126-95:2024-6 (<34 V after 1s)

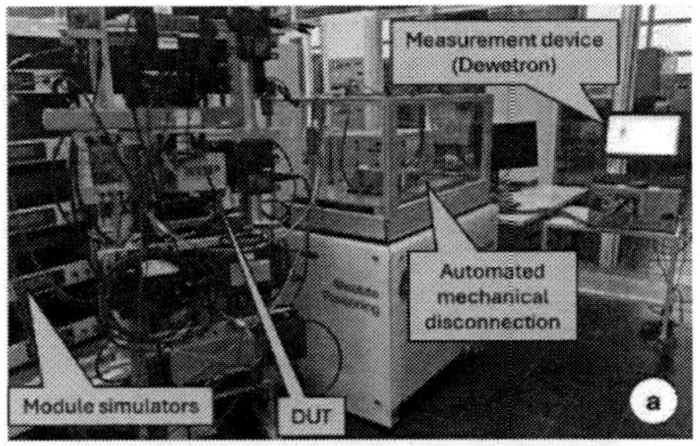

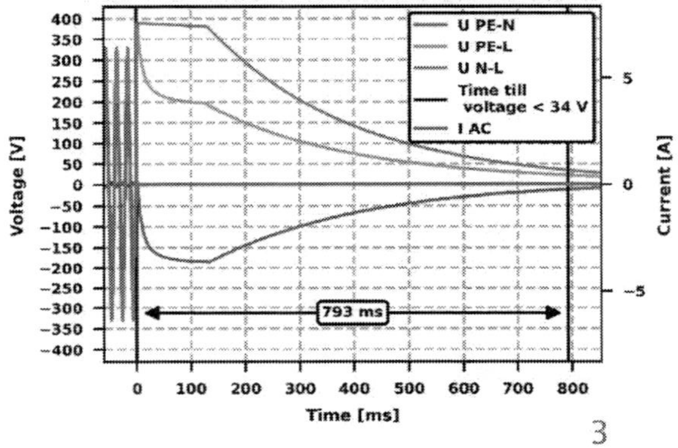

Safety Test in the Laboratory

2. Test: Maximum Touch Temperature

- Determine max. stationary touch temperature @ nominal DC power & overpanelling (150%)
- Limits of IEC 62109-1 (70 °C/95 °C)

3. Test: Limitation of Feed-in Current at Low Grid Voltage

- Determine the max. increase of current
- Voltage profile with reduced testing time (30s steps to 0.7 p.u)
- Limit (E DIN VDE V 0126-95:2024-6): 3.5 A +2%

A detailed measurement steps can be found in the supporting information of our Solar RRL Article (in production)

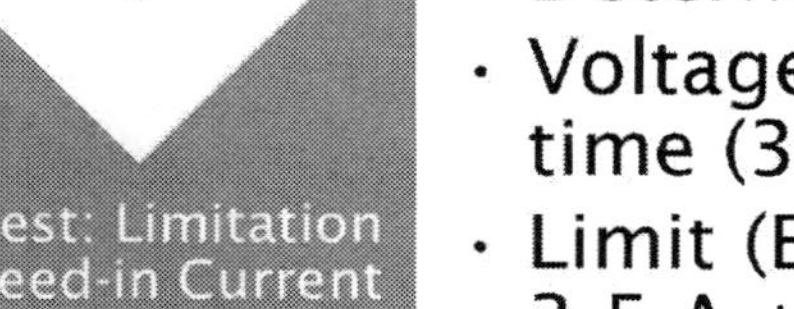

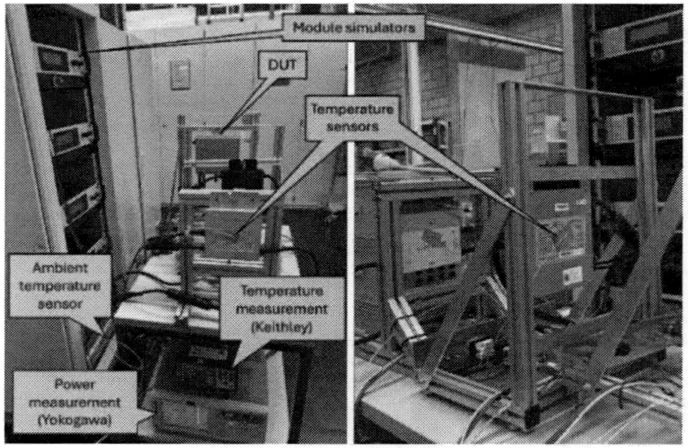

AI generated

Further "hot" research → 4CV.1.61

Residual Voltage Test

- Times to 34 V: 15 ms to 12 s
- 56% compliancy of tested inverters

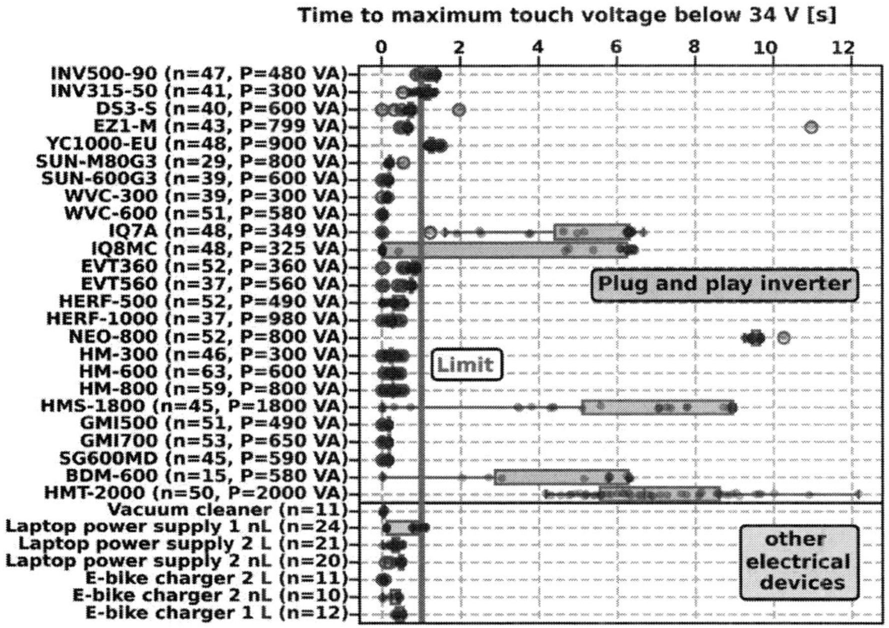

- Phase-angle dependency could be partly confirmed
- System testing for systems with more than one inverter is recommended

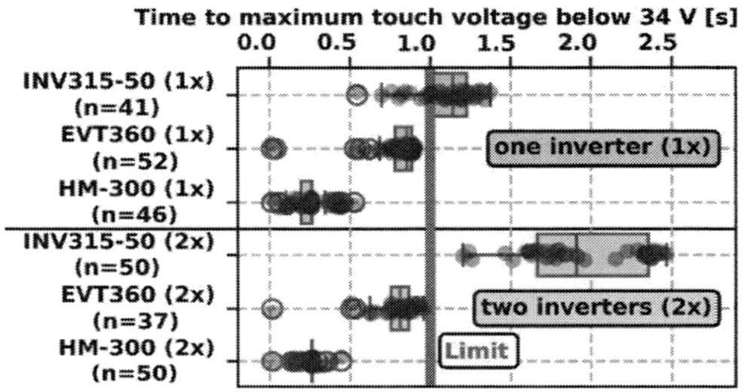

Residual Voltage Test

- Safety adapter (touch safety + optional discharge functionality) for a compliant system

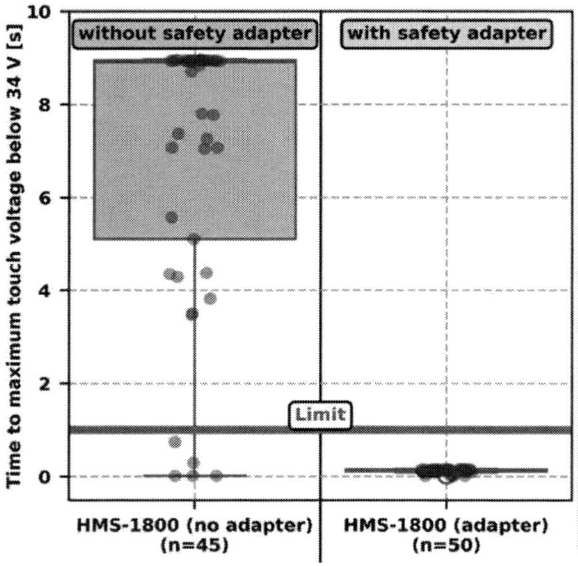

- Exemplary measurement: Touching L and N (finger to finger) after 1s with a 1 kOhm body resistance
  - 1 non-compliant inverter
  - Energy: 52 mJ
  - Peak current: 465 mA
  - Time: 3.2 ms

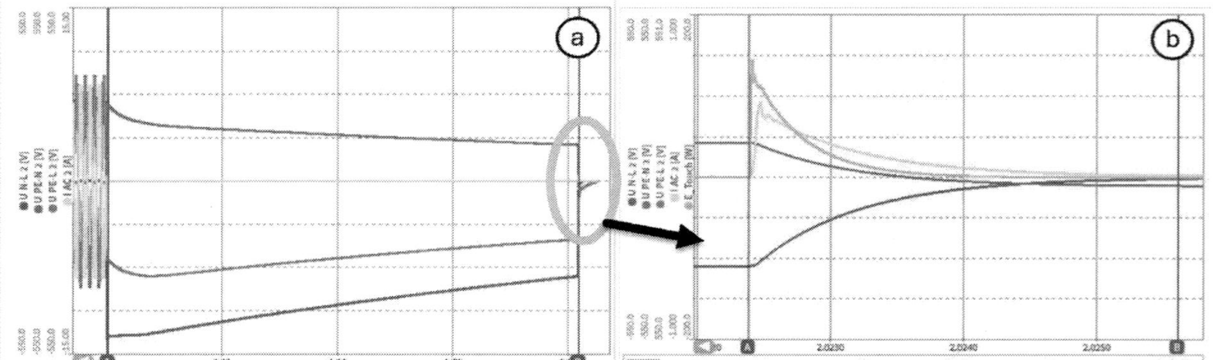

	A	B	Delta	Integral [*s]
Time [s]	1.003233	2.022239	1.019006	
U N-L 2 [V]	-489.9595	-301.2123	188.7472	-402.1301
U PE-N 2 [V]	245.4486	117.2919	-128.1567	154.4988
U PE-L 2 [V]	-244.5119	-183.9213	60.59051	-247.6314
I AC 2 [A]	1.478e-3	1.769e-3	2.909e-4	1.491e-3

	A	B	Delta	Max	Integral [*s]
Time [s]	2.022386231	2.025605501	0.003219270		
U N-L 2 [V]	-301.1840	-5.135060	296.0489	-5.135060	-0.249417
U PE-N 2 [V]	117.2745	-28.81122	-146.0857	117.2745	0.017558
U PE-L 2 [V]	-183.9140	-33.94556	149.9684	-33.94556	-0.231872
I AC 2 [A]	1.812e-3	9.351e-3	7.539e-3	0.465631	3.279e-4
E_Touch [W]	0.452389	0.021841	-0.430548	144.1808	0.051733

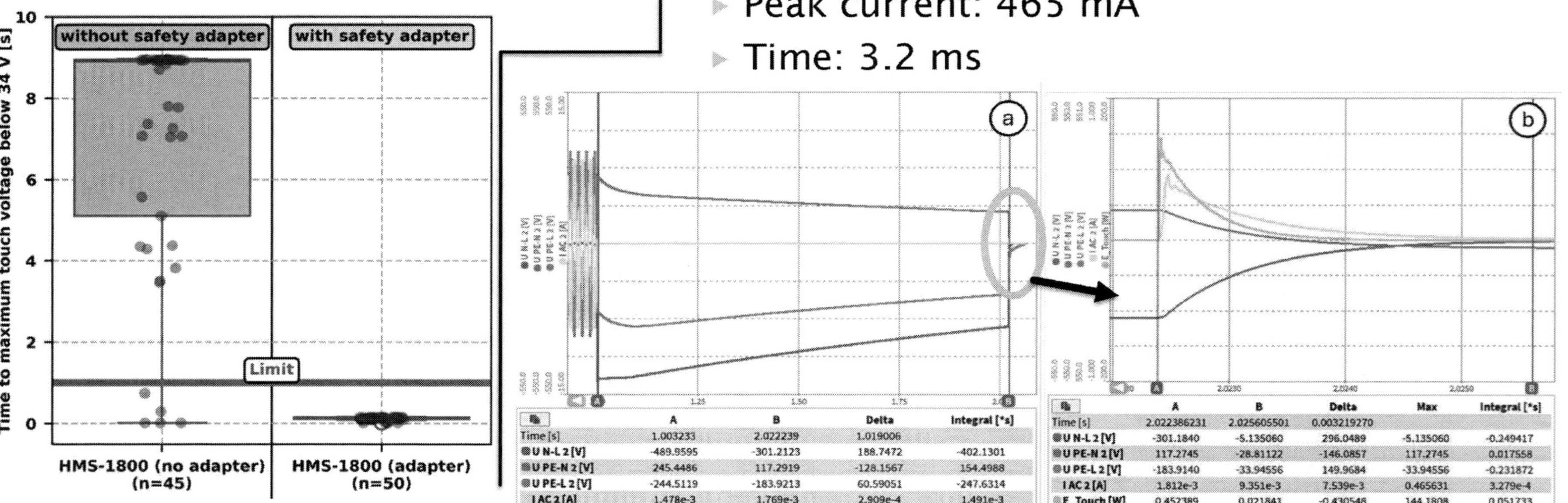

Residual Voltage Test

- Problematic behaviour of complaint device
  - 1 out of 52 measurements
  - Islanding after grid disconnection
  - Fault-ride through for 3 s
  - Disconnection through voltage drop protection time (<0.8 V_N for 3 s)

- **Reduced grid profile/code for plug and play inverters**

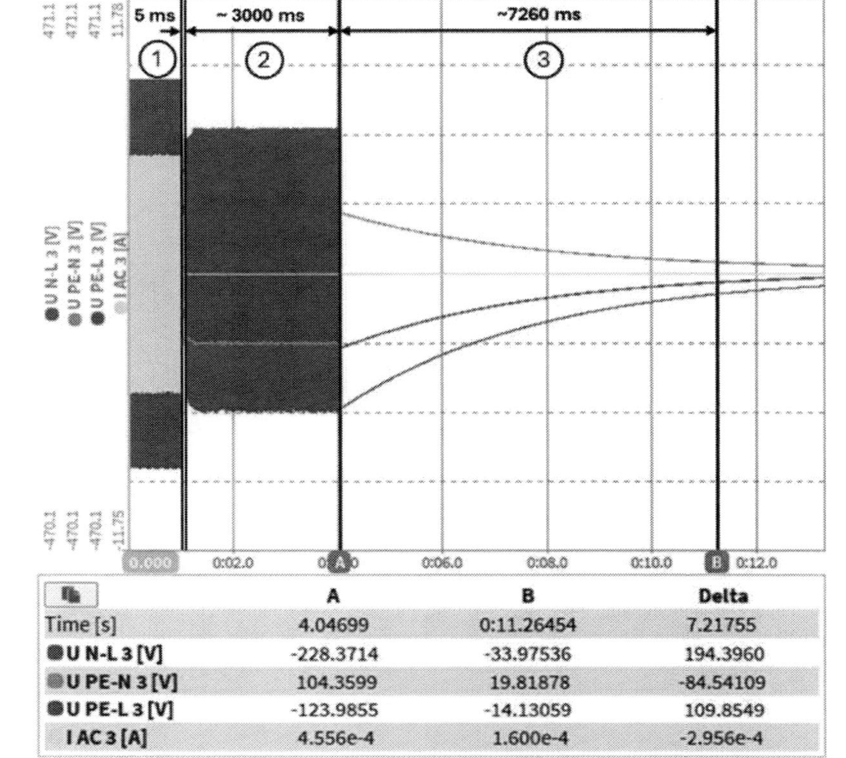

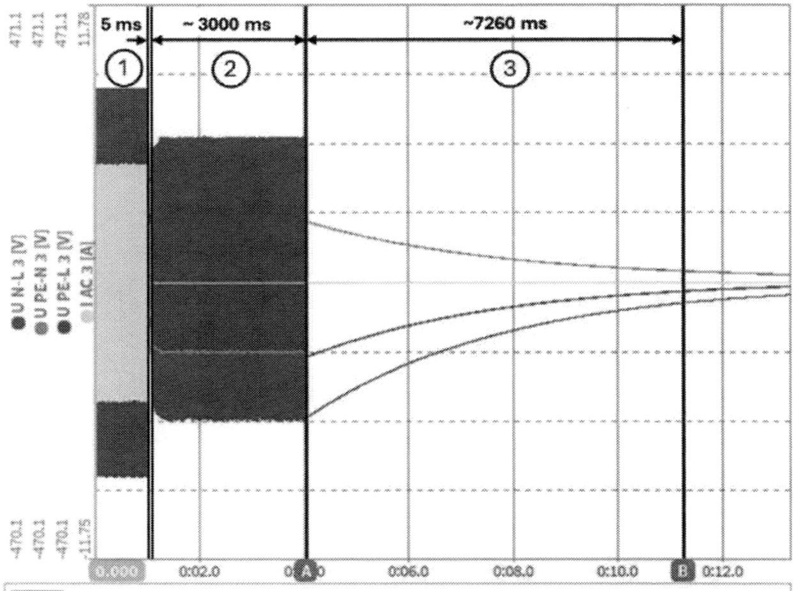

	A	B	Delta
Time [s]	4.04699	0:11.26454	7.21755
U N-L 3 [V]	-228.3714	-33.97536	194.3960
U PE-N 3 [V]	104.3599	19.81878	-84.54109
U PE-L 3 [V]	-123.9855	-14.13059	109.8549
I AC 3 [A]	4.556e-4	1.600e-4	-2.956e-4

Maximum Touch Temperature

- Maximum touch temperatures:
  43.40 °C to 80.33 °C (~23 °C ambient temp)
- 18 inverter (75%) comply with limits
- Ambient temperature dependency
- Correlation between power density and power dependent temperature increase
- **A microinverters is a non-touchable system part, a plug and play inverter is touchable**

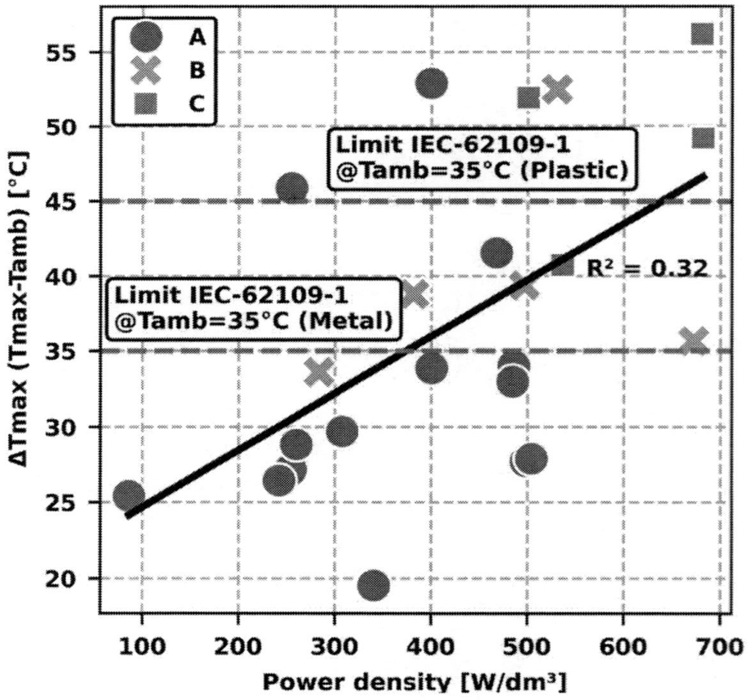

Limitation of Feed-in Current at Low Grid Voltage

- Current increase between 1.7% to 26.3%
- Absolute limit (3.5 A +2%)
  - 4 non-compliant inverters
- Relative limit (+2%)
  - Only 1 compliant inverter
- Absolute vs relative limit?
  - Relative limit for uniform requirements

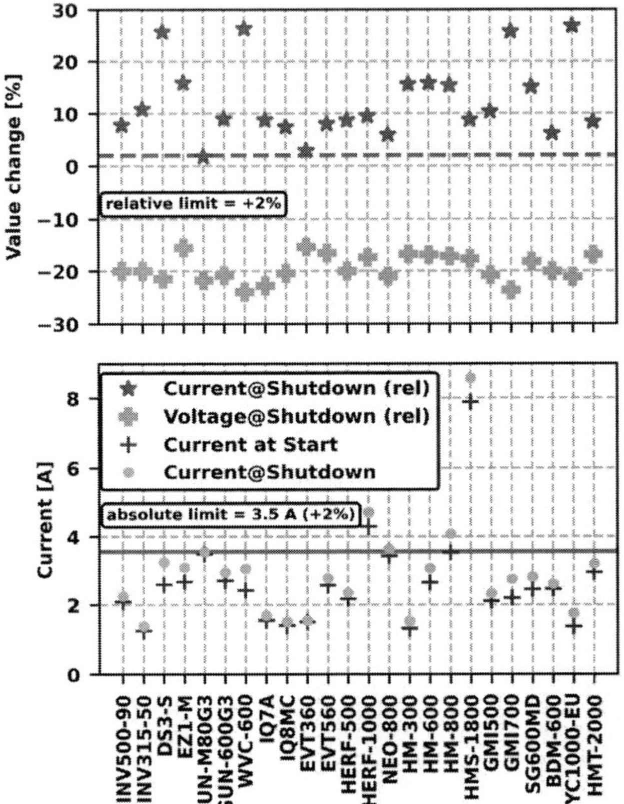

Conclusions and Recommendations

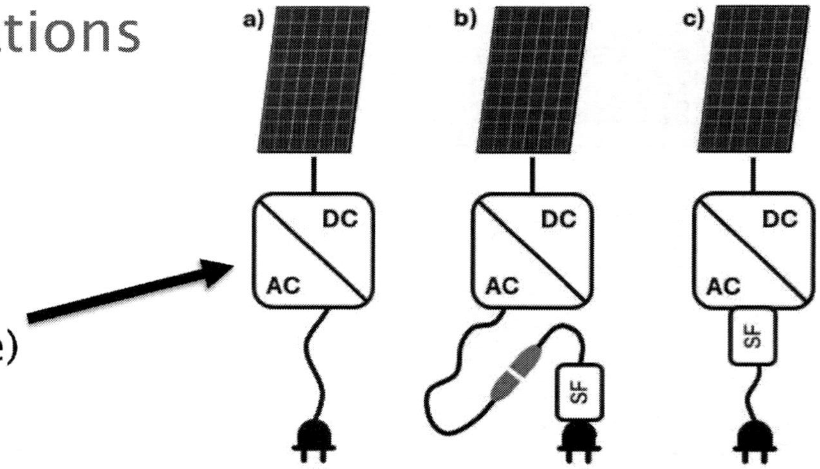

- Residual voltage
  - 56% compliancy rate of tested set
  - System testing is recommended
  - Different solutions for this concern (without and with additional hardware)
  - Separate and reduced grid profile
- Touch temperature
  - Inclusion in plug and play system standard(s) and note in IEC 62109-1
  - More smaller inverters are better than one single inverter
  - Larger power limited inverter(?)
- Limitation of Feed-in Current
  - Fix through software update(?)
- **Plug and play PV inverters ≠ microinverter**

Berner Fachhochschule
Haute école spécialisée bernoise
Bern University of Applied Sciences

Merci PV-Lab and thank you for your attention!

Project information and contact

ACKNOWLEDGEMENT
This research was carried out in the project "Plug & Play Photovoltaic Systems" funded by the Swiss Federal Office of Energy (Project number SI/502662). The responsibility for the content and conclusions lies solely with the authors.

▸ Bern University of Applied Sciences | Laboratory for Photovoltaic Systems

Residual Voltage Test

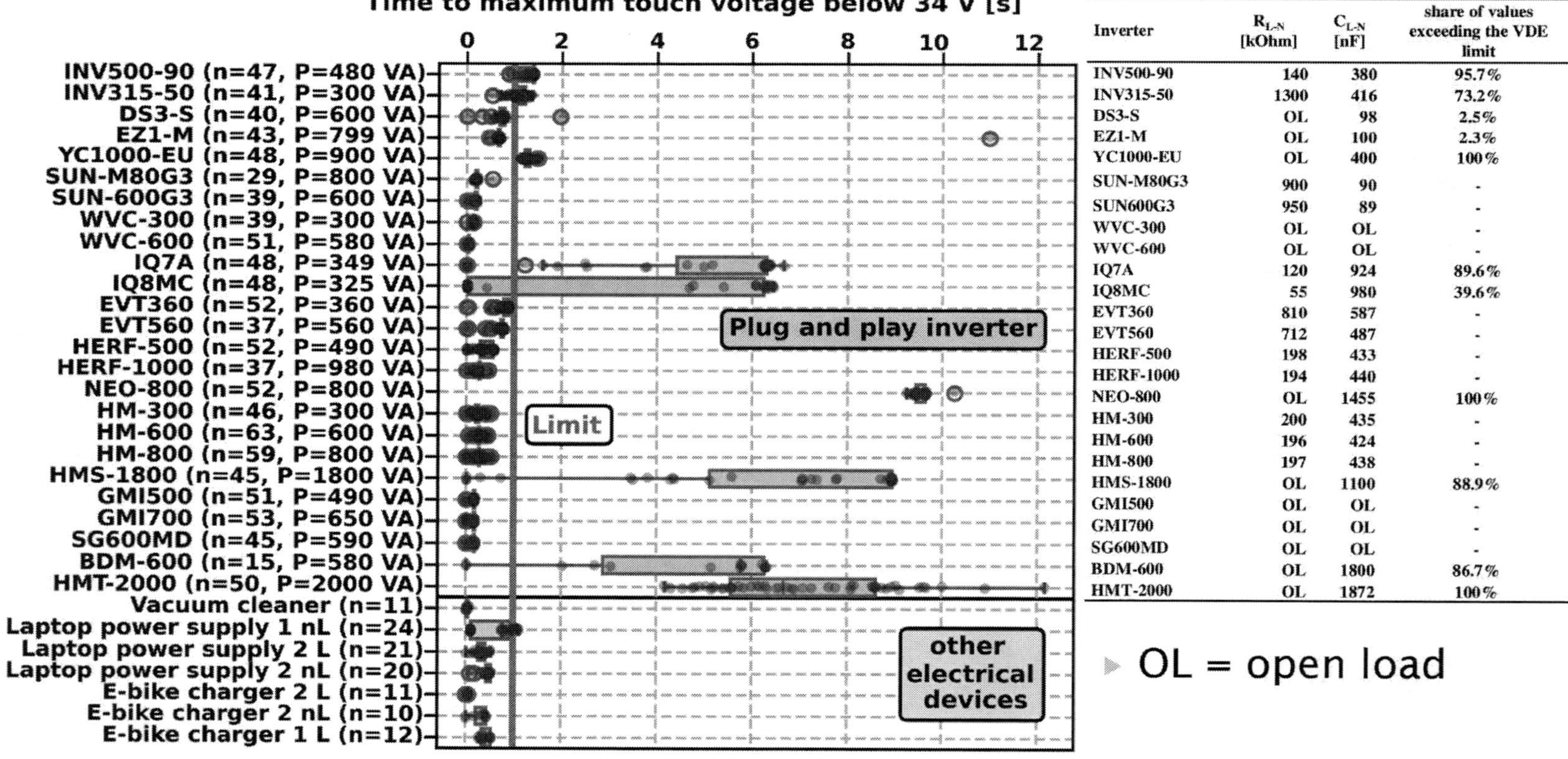

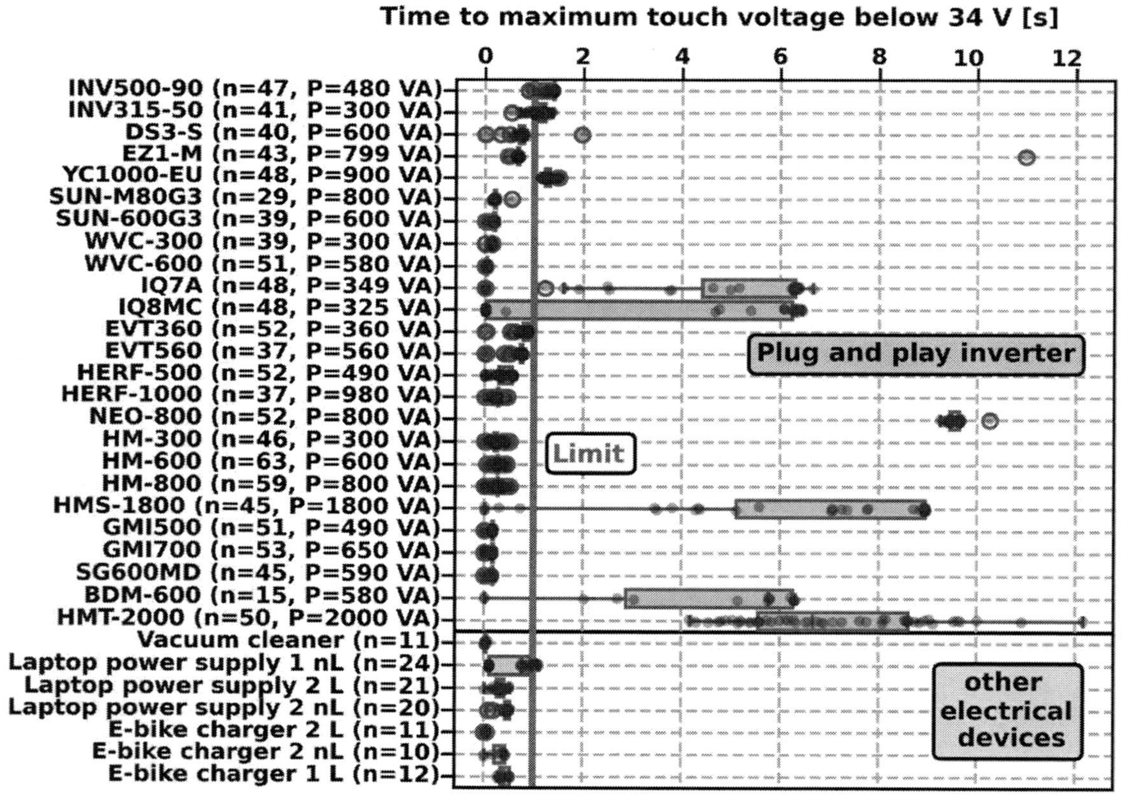

Inverter	$R_{L\text{-}N}$ [kOhm]	$C_{L\text{-}N}$ [nF]	share of values exceeding the VDE limit
INV500-90	140	380	95.7%
INV315-50	1300	416	73.2%
DS3-S	OL	98	2.5%
EZ1-M	OL	100	2.3%
YC1000-EU	OL	400	100%
SUN-M80G3	900	90	-
SUN600G3	950	89	-
WVC-300	OL	OL	-
WVC-600	OL	OL	-
IQ7A	120	924	89.6%
IQ8MC	55	980	39.6%
EVT360	810	587	-
EVT560	712	487	-
HERF-500	198	433	-
HERF-1000	194	440	-
NEO-800	OL	1455	100%
HM-300	200	435	-
HM-600	196	424	-
HM-800	197	438	-
HMS-1800	OL	1100	88.9%
GMI500	OL	OL	-
GMI700	OL	OL	-
SG600MD	OL	OL	-
BDM-600	OL	1800	86.7%
HMT-2000	OL	1872	100%

- OL = open load

Measurement Setup

- Residual Voltage Test

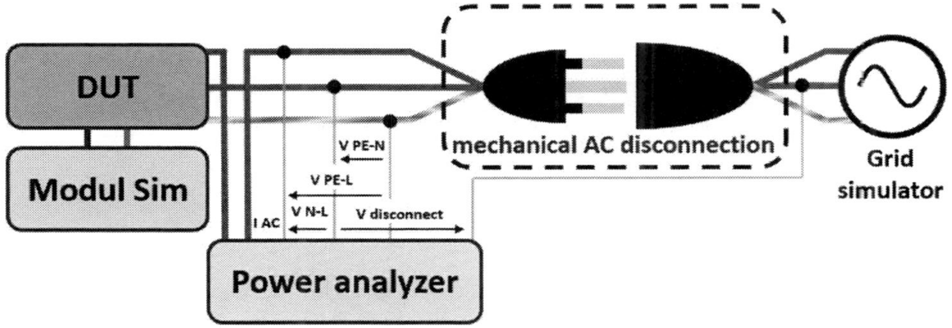

- Limitation of Feed-in Current at Low Grid Voltage

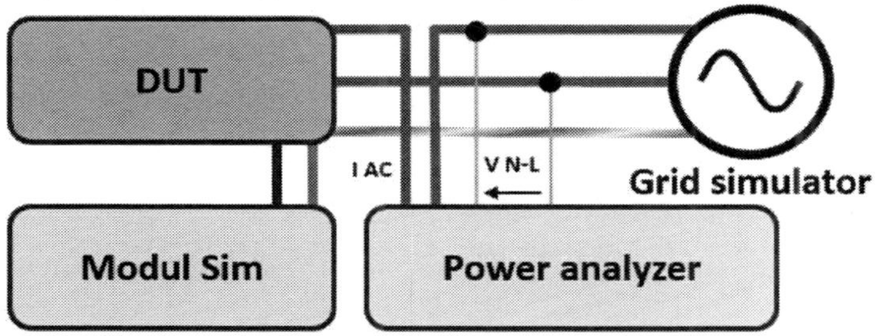

- Maximum Touch Temperature

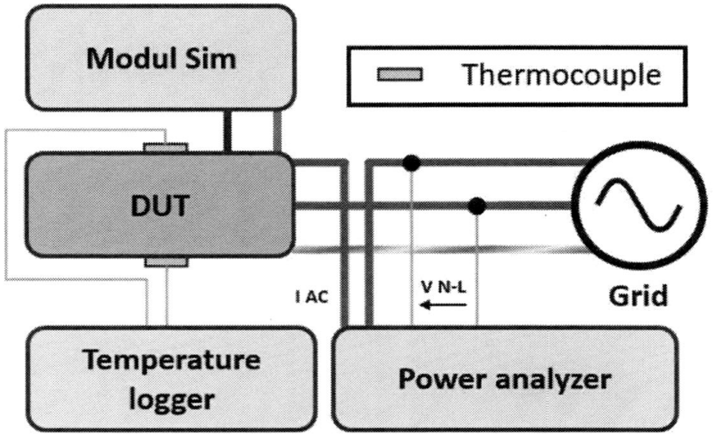

BOOSTING PROFITABILITY: THE POWER OF VERTICAL BIFACIAL PV IN MODERN AGRIVOLTAICS

Marc Andre Schüler[1], Peter Bendix [1], Simon Lahr [1], Aysim Schäfer [1] and Anna Morales Vilches [1]

[1]Research office at Next2Sun AG. Franz-Meguin-Str. 10a, 66763 Dillingen (Germany)
ma.schueler@next2sun.de.

ABSTRACT: This study investigates the potential of fixed tilt **vertical bifacial** (VB) photovoltaic (PV) systems in agrivoltaics (APV), focusing on their **economic viability** rather than its agricultural benefits. Unlike traditional PV installations, vertical bifacial systems allow for more uniform light and rainwater distribution to crops and offer protection against strong winds. Moreover, this work states the profitability and grid integration of these systems, demonstrating **energy production profiles of vertical bifacial APV** in Germany. In contrast to the state of technology of south-tilted PV, vertical systems can mitigate negative midday electricity prices, making them a promising alternative for the future energy market. Simulation results comparing the Next2Sun System incorporating Huasun SHJ modules to traditional TOPCon and PERC modules indicate a **significant energy yield advantage** in the vertical bifacial system, if driven by precise module selection and racking system design. The production profile of the Next2Sun system in Wellingen, Germany, shows two production peaks, with **minimal self-shading** effects and **high bifaciality**. Additionally, financial analysis of vertical bifacial PV plants in Donaueschingen/Aasen and Dirmingen reveals **up to 45% surplus** performance over the market price, highlighting the economic potential of these systems in the context of increasing PV capacity and negative midday electricity prices. This work suggests that vertical bifacial PV installations can be a profitable and sustainable solution for integrating renewable energy into the agricultural sector.

Keywords: Agrivoltaics, grid-friendly PV generation, vertical PV, profitability

1 INTRODUCTION

Various solutions exist for installing PV modules in agrivoltaics (APV), such as tilted but spaced (fixed or tracked) ground-mounted systems or elevated systems (fixed or tracked). This study focuses on fixed vertical bifacial (VB) systems, as depicted in Figure 1. The multiple benefits of VB systems for agriculture, as described in the literature, include uniform light and rainwater distribution to crops and protection against strong winds from directions perpendicular to the PV module orientation [1]. In addition to these agricultural benefits, the profitability and grid serviceability of vertical bifacial PV systems, discussed in [2], are confirmed in this work.

Figure 1: Vertical Bifacial Power Plant built by Next2Sun in Epfendorf (Germany)

In line with the prognosis in [3], we demonstrate the profitability of east–west (E/W) oriented vertical bifacial PV (VBPV) systems, which outperform south-oriented PV in Germany. With the ongoing increase in predominantly south-tilted PV which is expected to face low or negative midday electricity prices, alternative layouts are needed to better match grid demand. Recent studies recommend integrating vertical E/W systems or combining them with south-tilted PV [4]. With this work, we state the installation can be profitable with the system approach designed by Next2Sun already today marking a significant step towards integrating these systems into future energy markets.

2 RELEVANCE OF NEGATIVE ELECTRICITY PRICES TO PROFITABILITY IN PV

Photovoltaics (PV) have become a key driver of renewable power generation in Germany. With rising deployment, however, oversupply increasingly occurs during midday in summer, leading to lower capture rates. Historically above 80%, capture rates have recently declined. Figure 2 shows monthly and yearly capture rates for the PV Portfolio from 2022 to 2024, with the latest value at ~58% or 46.24 €/MWh.

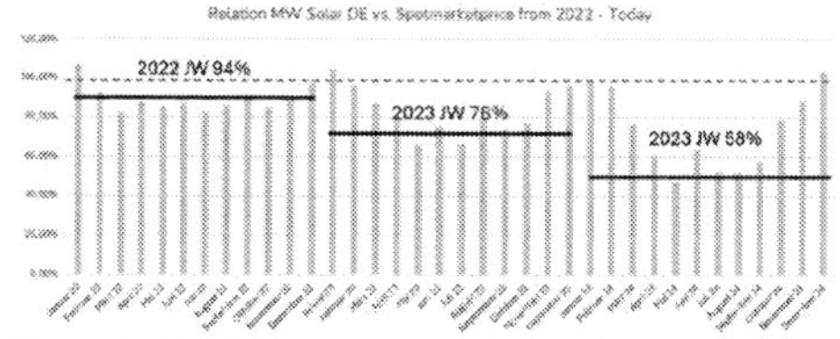

Figure 2: Monthly capture rates for MW Solar Germany in relation to EEX spot market from January 2022 to December 2024

One important factor in the decline of capture rates, is the rise in negative electricity prices in recent years, which has accompanied the growing deployment of solar power, especially during midday hours [5]. Figure 3 illustrates the spread of negative prices in the Ger/Lux EEX spot market, with positive prices capped at 200 €/MWh to highlight negative price events. The X-axis shows the days of the year, while the Y-axis indicates the hourly resolution.

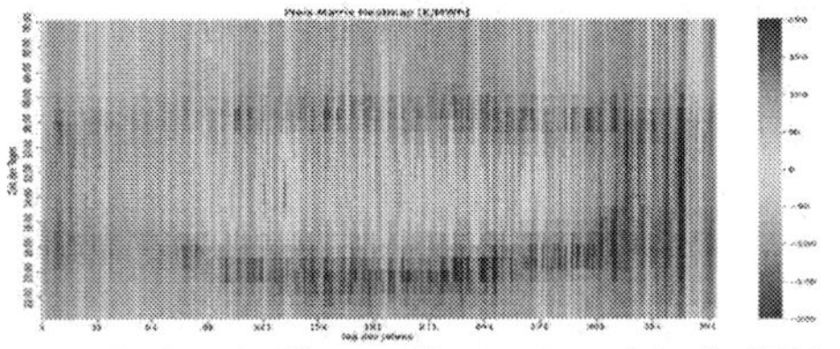

Figure 3: Spread of hours with negative pricing in 2024 EEX Germany/Luxembourg

3 DEMAND-ORIENTED ENERGY PRODUCTION IN AGRI-PV

Traditional agriculture and sophisticated forms of energy generation are not mutually exclusive. Next2Sun's vertical Agri-PV concept, as seen in (**Figure 4**), represents a combined solution with high land usage ratio and renewable energy production which is mostly demand-oriented by design. The installation is based on a robust racking structure with pile-driven steel posts, which can support up to three vertically stacked PV modules, reaching system heights of up to 4.5 m. The vertical arrangement minimizes shading on adjacent agricultural areas while ensuring structural stability against wind loads. Agricultural usability is preserved through wide crop rotation strips, typically ranging from 8 to 15 m, resulting in agricultural land-usage ratios above 85 %.

From an energy generation perspective, the system employs high-efficiency bifacial PV modules, which are optimally suited to capture diffuse irradiation as well as direct sunlight from both east and west directions. This design leads to a generation profile with a broader distribution of electricity production throughout typical days, better aligning with local consumption patterns and enhancing grid integration. Combined with the preserved agricultural productivity, this dual-use approach increases overall land-use efficiency and can contribute in parallel to both food and energy security.

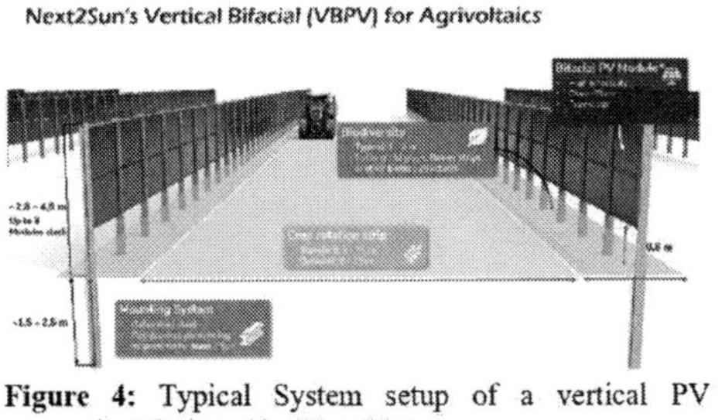

Figure 4: Typical System setup of a vertical PV powerplant designed by Next2Sun

4 COMPARISONS OF CAPTURE RATES IN VERTICAL BIFACIAL vs. CONVENTIONAL PV

In accordance with the assumptions in [2], a production profile for south-oriented and vertical bifacial fixed tilt PV inverters of the power plant in Wellingen (Germany) is shown in **Figure 5**. As can be seen, the production profile of vertical bifacial PV has two production peaks, arising during morning and late afternoon. Note, while the equipped inverter type and nominal power are the same for the data provided (Huawei SUN2000-60KTL), the installed module capacity in the E/W strings is possible to be set at 1.5 for the DC/AC Ratio (about 89.23 kWp) without limitation while the south-oriented strings are installed with 71.04 kWp with a common DC/AC Ratio of 1.2.

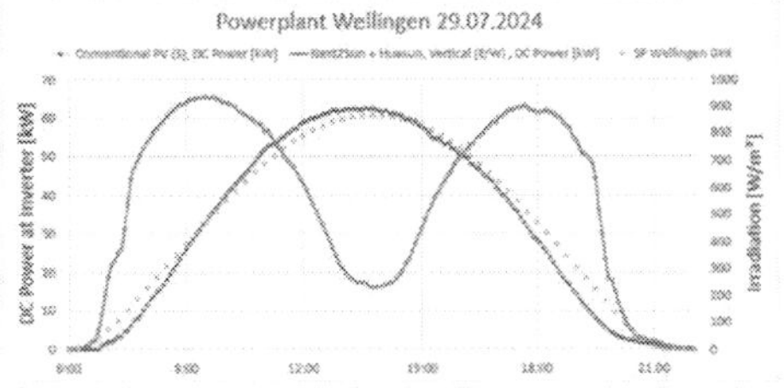

Figure 5: Power Production Profile of the South-facing PV and Vertical Bifacial PV in Next2Sun Powerplant Wellingen (Germany) on the 29-07-2024 – 5 minutes resolution for power generation, 15 minutes for GHI.

The results presented in **Figure 5** prove, when designed precisely, the self-shade effects are neglectable and combined with a high bifaciality on module level, the energy peaks are somewhat of a similar height and enhanced when compared to early adaptors of vertical PV [1]. This energy profile verifies the simulation results in [6], respectively that the Next2Sun System generates significantly more energy when compared to competitors with same nominal power, due to precise racking system design and profound module selection.

Figure 6 presents a comparison of the monthly surplus in market electricity prices for vertical bifacial PV plants in Donaueschingen/Aasen and Dirmingen, Germany, from August 2020 to August 2024. The monthly benefit, measured against the market electricity price ("Marktwert Solar"), showed that the power plants reached **up to 45% asset performance**, with most months being positive. The continuous growth in PV capacity in Germany (+15.6 GWp in 2023 and +15.9 GWp in 2024) has increased the midday surplus, contributing to more frequent negative electricity prices. [7] Likewise in 2024, the VBPV plants of Next2Sun in Dirmingen and Aasen achieved a 24.0% and 25.3% benefit over the market price, respectively. Wellingen Ost achieved an even higher benefit of 27.8%.

From the graph in **Figure 6** for nearly every month between August 2020 and December 2024 the atypical production led to significant added value. Only 2 months resulted in an exception as SP Aasen recorded slightly negative profile when compared to MW Solar Germany in December 2021 and December 2024.

10.4229/EUPVSEC2025/4DO.4.1

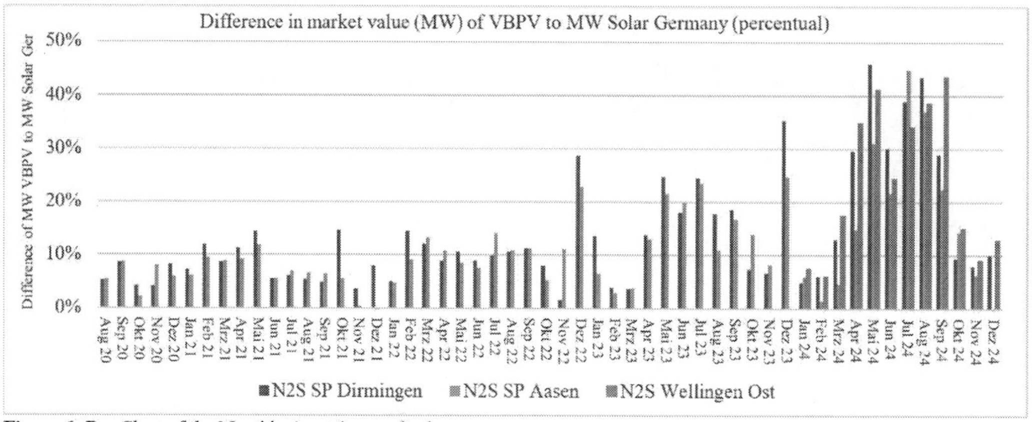

Figure 6: Bar-Chart of the Monthly Asset (percent) when Comparing Vertical Bifacial Power Plants in Donaueschingen/Aasen, Dirmingen and Wellingen (Germany) with "Marktwert Solar"

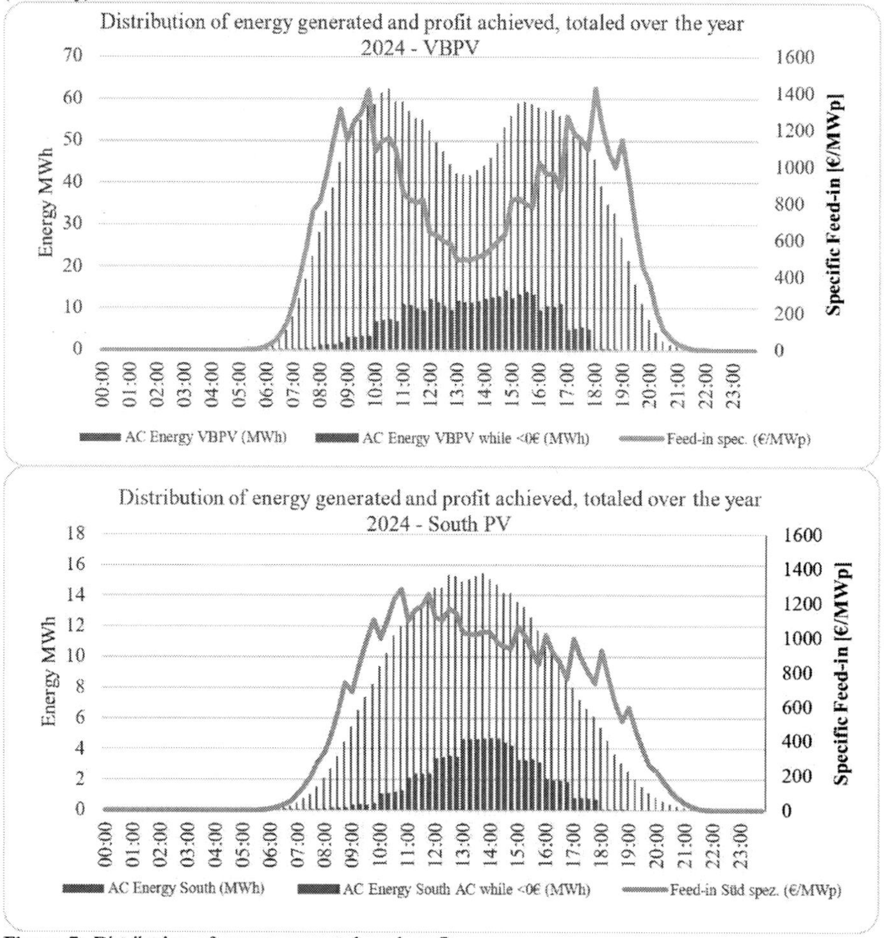

Figure 7: Distribution of energy generated, and profit achieved for VBPV and conventional south PV at SP Wellingen (Germany), totalled over the year 2024 and accounted to the timestamp of production

A comparison of vertical bifacials profile against a conventional south PV system is presented for the year 2024. Both are located at the powerplant in Wellingen (Germany). The respective power of the VBPV is 3 MWp while the conventional south is 532 kWp. The azimuth is: ±90° for the 90°Tilt East/West facing system and ~0° for the 20° tilted south PV. Both production profiles present the accumulated energy as distribution to the production timestamp with a resolution of 15 minutes. At the same time the power-specific feed-in part $R_{spec\,(t)}$ (in €/MWp) is accumulated for the total year and shown as distribution to the timestamp in **Figure 7**. The revenue is calculated as energy $E_{AC(t)}$ times market price $p_{(t)}$ as presented in Equation:

$$R_{spec\,(t)} = p_{(t)} \cdot \frac{E_{AC(t)}}{P_{NOM}}$$

When observing the distribution of AC energy generated during times of negative prices with the total AC energy produced, the effected amount of energy in VBPV equals 14.2% or 112.4 MWh/MWp, while south PV was affected by 19.1% or 166.7 MWh/MWp. At the same time, the market profile differs more drastic, as VBPV recorded a price of 59.09 €/MWh while 50.76 €/MWh for the conventional part. In 2025, Next2Sun's module design has been optimized further regarding the vertical AgriPV System, so the specific energy yield in upcoming power plants will likely perform even higher.

Comparing the capture rates recorded in this work with prognosis made in 2022s Literature, indicate the economic perspectives have fallen more drastic than prognosed. The study from 2022 assumes capture rates will continue to diverge until 2045. Although, the benefit for atypical generation profiles have been prognosed as significantly higher than the capture rates of the PV portfolio with differences of around 12% between VBPV and conventional south profiles from beginning of 2025. [8]

As early as 2024 (Presented in **Figure 8**), the median value of Next2Sun's vertical power plants was around 16% higher, when comparing the capture rates of VBPV with the market value of PV portfolio (MW Solar Germany). Referring to the numbers as 7.95 ct/kWh as average price of electricity at EEX in 2024, while the PV portfolio accounted for 4.62 ct/kWh (58%) and 5.88 ct/kWh as Median for VBPV of Next2Sun's Powerplants which equalled a capture rate of 74%.

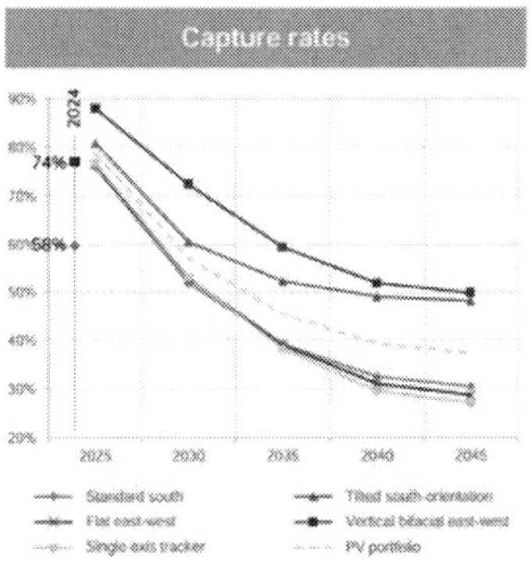

Figure 8: Capture rates prognosis by Enervis in 2022, adjusted with capture rates seen in 2024 [8]

CONCLUSIONS

This work demonstrates the economic attractiveness of vertical bifacial AgriPV systems from an energy production perspective. As shown, the yearly benefit of the two power plants in Germany outperformed conventional PV systems. Furthermore, the analysis of the production profiles for both south-oriented and vertical bifacial fixed-tilt PV systems at the Next2Sun power plant in Wellingen (Germany) confirm its competitiveness. Considering the similar achieved specific yield when comparing E/W with South orientation in the same power plant on the exemplary test day in July, along with a higher market electricity price of over 30%, the economic benefit is substantial. Further, the recorded difference in capture rates for VBPV and conventional PV indicate a correlation to negative prices seen at the spot market. While actual studies prognose the number of negative hours will continuously increase until meaningful grid flexibility is present, this indicates the profitability of VBPV over conventional solar without batteries. The results align with previous simulations and indicate, aside from the agricultural benefits mentioned, profitability as a key factor is making them a promising solution for land conflicts in modern agricultural and future energy demand.

REFERENCES

[1] M. Victoria and et.al, "Vertical Agrivoltaics in a Temperate Climate: Exploring Technical, Agricultural, Meteorological, and Social Dimensions," 2024.

[2] R. Kopecek and J. Libal, "Bifacial Photovoltaics 2021: Status, Opportunities and Challenges," *Creative Commons Attribution 4.0 International*, 2021.

[3] M. Baricchio, M. Korevaar, P. Babal and H. Ziar, "Modelling of bifacial photovoltaic farms to evaluate the profitability of East/West vertical configuration," *Solar Energy*, vol. 272, no. ISSN 0038-092X, 2024.

[4] S. Reker, J. Schneider and C. Gerhards, "Integration of vertical solar power plants into a future German energy system," *Smart Energy*, vol. Volume 7, no. ISSN 2666-9552, 2022.

[5] K. D. Vos, "Negative Wholesale Electricity Prices in the German, French and Belgian Day-Ahead, Intra-Day and Real-Time Markets," *The Electricity Journal*, vol. 28, no. 4, 2015.

[6] J. Libal and J. Eickelmann, 06 06 2023. [Online]. Available: https://isc-konstanz.de/wp-content/uploads/2023/06/ISC-white-paper-Next2Sun_2023_DE-1.pdf.

[7] B. Burger, "Energy Charts," Fraunhofer ISE, 01 01 2025. [Online]. Available: https://www.energy-charts.info/downloads/Stromerzeugung_2024.pdf.

[8] Enervis-Energy-Advisors, "Analysis of innovative system designs for a power market optimised PV portfolio in Germany," Dezember 2022. [Online]. Available: https://thegreenroofs.com/wp-content/uploads/2024/07/Analysis-of-innovative-system-designs-06.2023.pdf. [Accessed 08 08 2025].

10.4229/EUPVSEC2025/4DO.4.1
020388-004

Energy Yield Analysis and Performance Monitoring of Three Photovoltaic Noise Barriers in Belgium and the Netherlands

Sara Bouguerra, Richard de jong, Santhosh Ramesh, Tine Engelen, Marta Casasola Paesa, Jan Mertens, Fallon Colberts, Ismail Kaaya, Patrizio Manganiello, Georgi Yordadov, Arnaud Morlier, Michaël Daenen

EU PVSEC 2025: 4DO.4.4

25/09/2025

fwo IMO-IMOMEC UHASSELT imec

Outline

Introduction

Methodology

- IIPV Demonstrators
  - DEMO1: Vertical built-on concrete PVNB with different module technologies
  - DEMO2: Semi-transparent PVNB with different module technologies
  - DEMO3: Cassette built-on PVNB with a zigzag design and c-Si modules
- Temperature monitoring
- Energy Yield Simulation

Results

Conclusion and Outlook

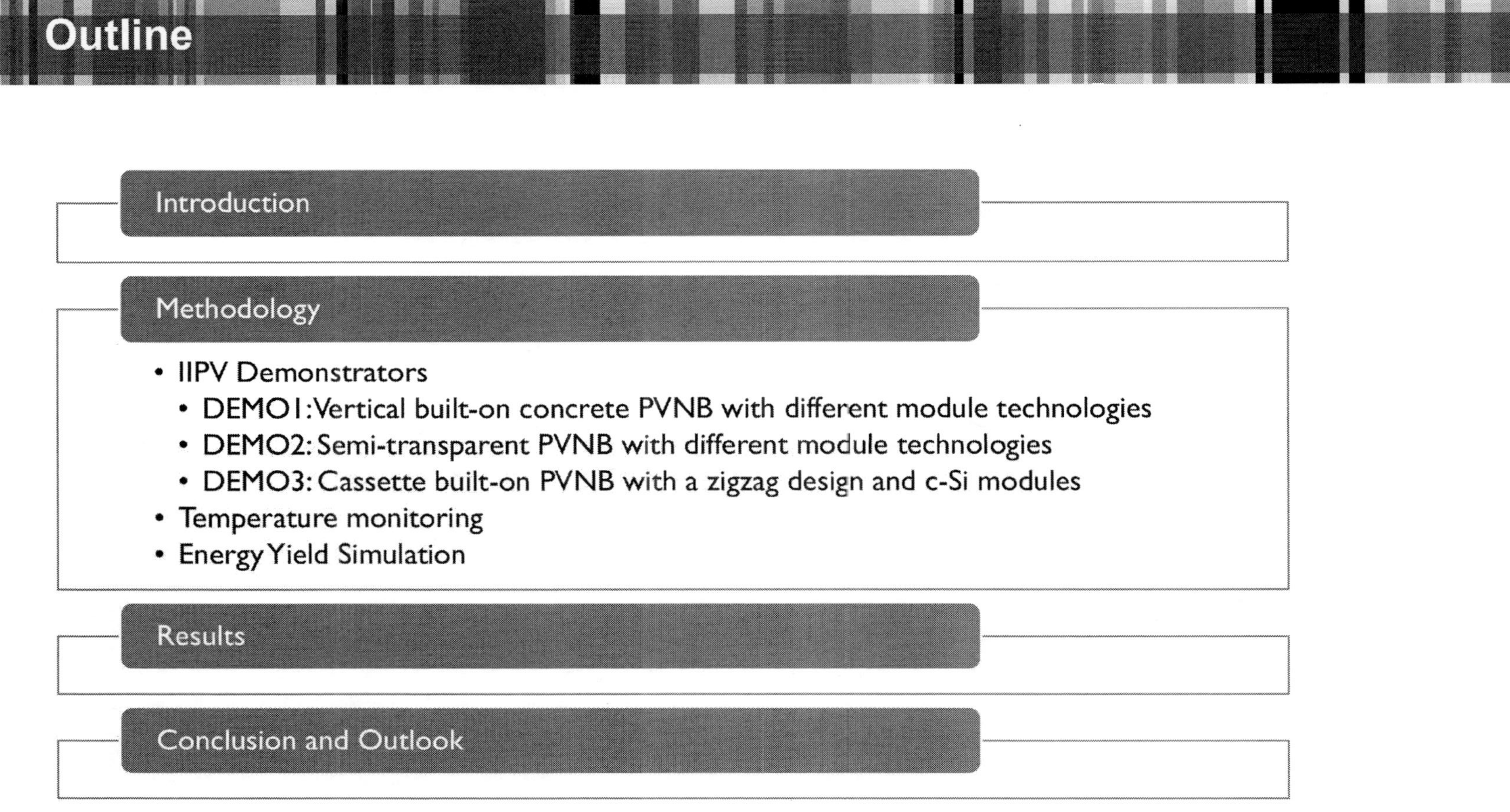

Introduction

- EU's Zero Pollution Action Plan (2021)➔ decrease the share of people chronically disturbed by transport noise by 30% [1].
- Noise barriers are vital in reducing the harmful effects of traffic-related sound pollution.
- PVNBs optimize land use for sustainable energy production.
- PVNBs can be implemented either by retrofitting existing ones or integrating modules into new designs.

Traditional and PV Noise barriers on roads [2]-[3]

[1] Zero Pollution Action Plan - European Commission
[2] The Importance of Noise Barriers in City Life – Hatko Sound Barrier
[3] Photovoltaic Noise Barriers (PVNBs) | SoliTek

Objectives

- Validate the electrical and thermal models of three PVNB demonstrators through on-site measurements
- Compare the energy performance using different integration methods.

Methodology

IMO-IMOMEC

UHASSELT imec

Methodology

DEMO 1: Vertical built-on PVNB with different module technologies

Location: Thor Park, Genk, Belgium

Structure:

- 13m-wide, 5m-high , East-facing concrete wall

Solar Panels:

- 2 c-Si PERC PV modules
- 2 thin film CdTe modules on rails attached to a concrete wall, both mounted with an air gap of 5 cm between them and the wall
- 4 CIGS modules glued directly to the wall

Power and Temperature monitoring:

- Each of the modules in this system were connected to an individual MPP tracker
- No temperature measurement

Data collection Period:

- August 2021 to present

DEMO1:Vertical built-on PVNB with different module technologies

Methodology

DEMO 2: Semi-transparent PVNB with different module technologies

Location: Thor Park, Genk, Belgium

Structure:

- 8m-long and 5m-high vertical East-facing metal frame

Solar Panels:

- 8 bifacial c-Si PERC PV modules (top-lower row)
- 4 CIGS modules (middle row)

Power and Temperature monitoring:

- Each of the modules is connected to an individual MPP tracker.
- Temperature measurement: FBG sensors (M1 and M2)

Data collection Period: August 2021 to present.

DEMO2: Semi-transparent PVNB with different module technologies

Methodology

DEMO 3: Cassette built-on PVNB with a zigzag design

Location: Chemelot Campus in Geleen, Netherlands

Structure:

- South-facing concrete wall
- Two zigzag configurations with four cassettes each

Cassettes filled with noise-absorbing material

Solar Panels:

- 8 customized glass/glass PERC PV modules from Soltech (103 Wp)
- PV Modules connected in series, forming two strings (A, B)

Power and Temperature monitoring:

- Power: QEED QI-power-485-LV
- Temperature: DS18B20 (back of panels), FBG sensors (lower left & right panels).

Data collection Period: May 2023 to present.

DEMO3: Cassette built-on PVNB with a zigzag design

Methodology

Temperature Monitoring (FBG-based sensors)

- Real-time monitoring of mechanical strain and temperature within PV modules.
- Optical fibres with fibre Bragg gratings (FBGs) using different packaging.

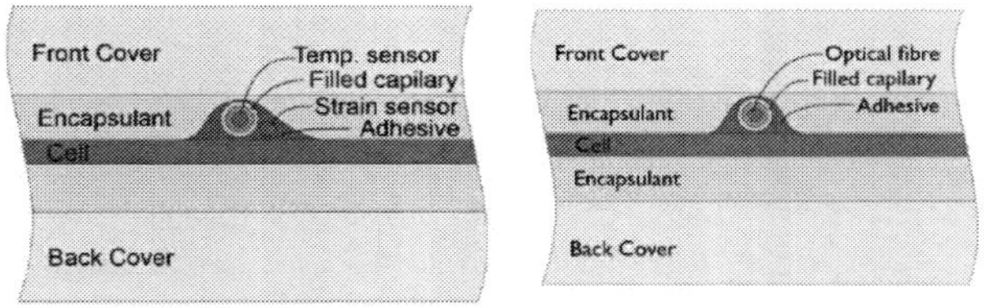

FBG-based sensing solution [5]

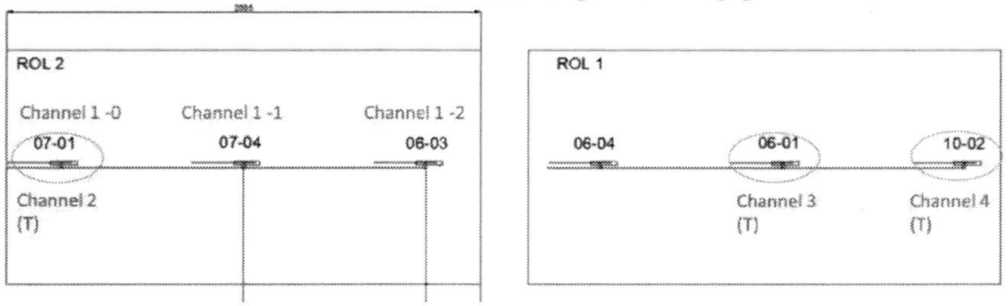

FBG sensor location in DEMO 2

Module I in DEMO2 with sensors

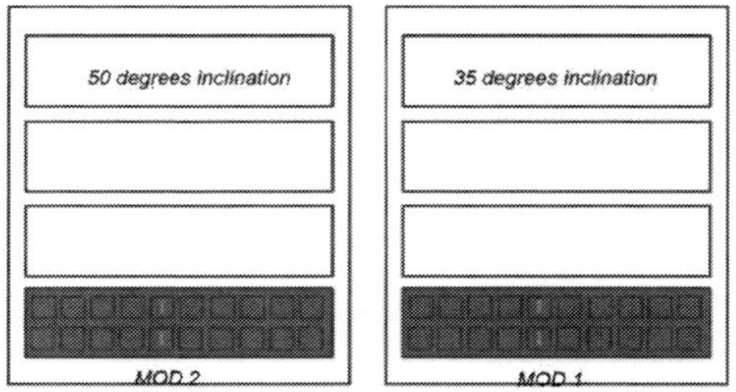

FBG sensor location in DEMO 3

[5] https://doi.org/10.1002/pip.3622.

Methodology

Energy Yield Simulation

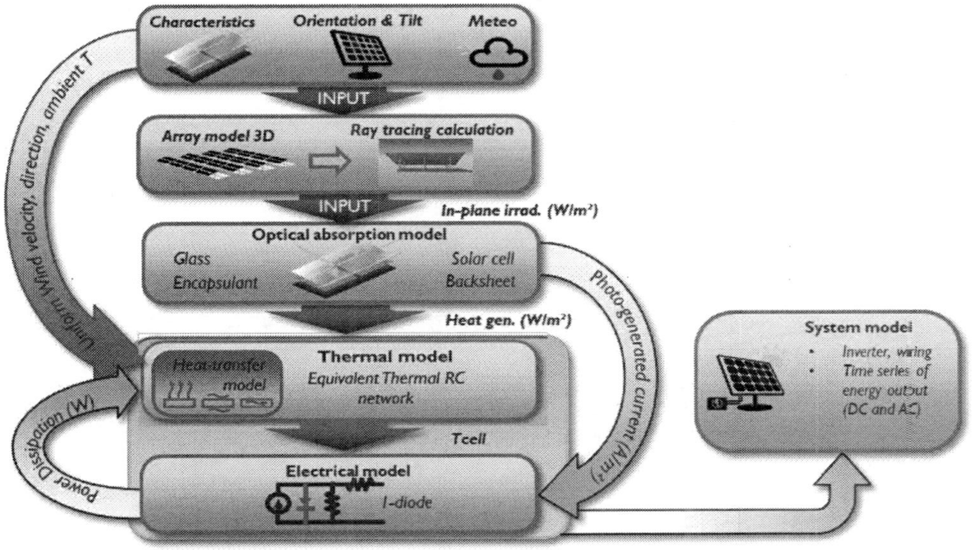

Imec's energy Yield Simulation Framework [6]

DEMO 1

DEMO 2

DEMO 3

Geometrical model in the E-Yield Framework

[6] https://doi.org/10.4229/EUPVSEC20192019-5DP.2.2.

Results

IMO-IMOMEC

Results

DEMO 1: Vertical built-on concrete PVNB with different module technologies

Module Type	RMSE (Capacity Factor, Sep–Oct 2021) [7]
c-Si	14% – 17%
CdTe	20% – 23%
CIGS	13% – 31%

[7] https://doi.org/10.1038/s41598-024-78862-w

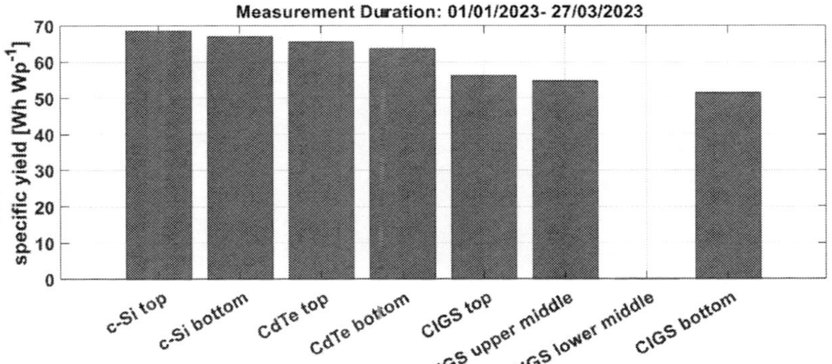

Measured Specific Yield of DEMO1 over a three-month period.

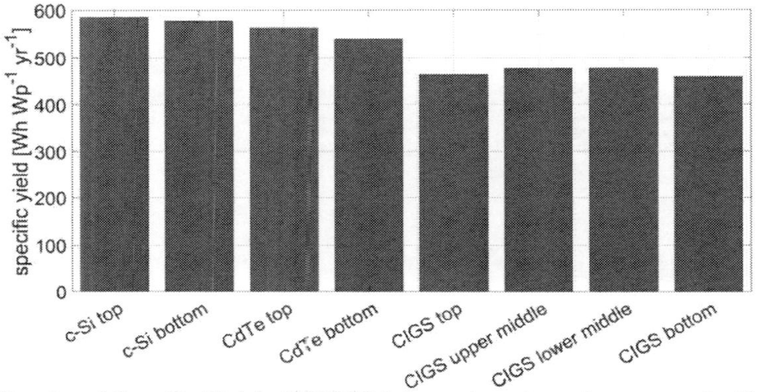

Simulated Specific Yield of DEMO1 for a duration of one year in Genk using TMY.

Results: DEMO1

Thermal Effects

CIGS modules attached to the concrete wall

SketchUp 3D model of DEMO1 (unventilated)

- Irradiance-weighted annual average cell temperature: 18.6°C
- Annual specific yield: 470 kWh/kWp

CIGS modules separated from the concrete wall

SketchUp 3D model of DEMO1 (ventilated)

$$\overline{T}_{\text{cell,iw}} = \frac{\sum_{i=1}^{N} T_{\text{cell},i} \cdot G_i \cdot \Delta t_i}{\sum_{i=1}^{N} G_i \cdot \Delta t_i}$$

- Irradiance-weighted annual average cell temperature: 16.4°C (↓2.2°C)
- Annual specific yield: 474 Wh/Wp (↑0.8%)

Results: DEMO2

Electrical and Thermal model Validation (hourly resolution)

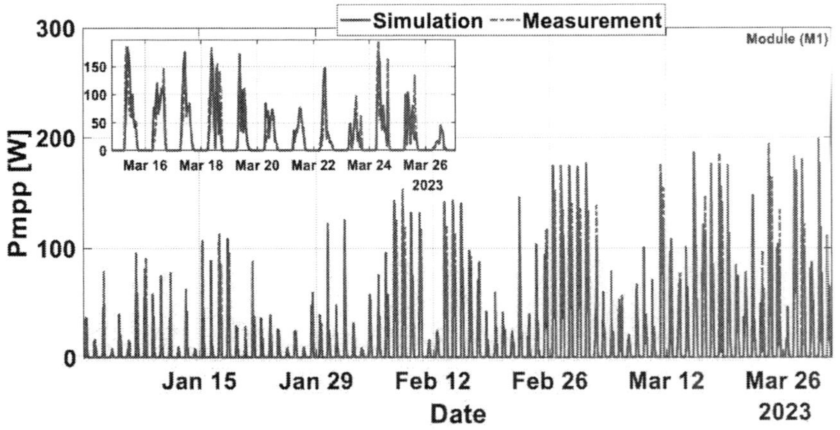

Power at PMPP with 10-Minute Resolution in Genk.

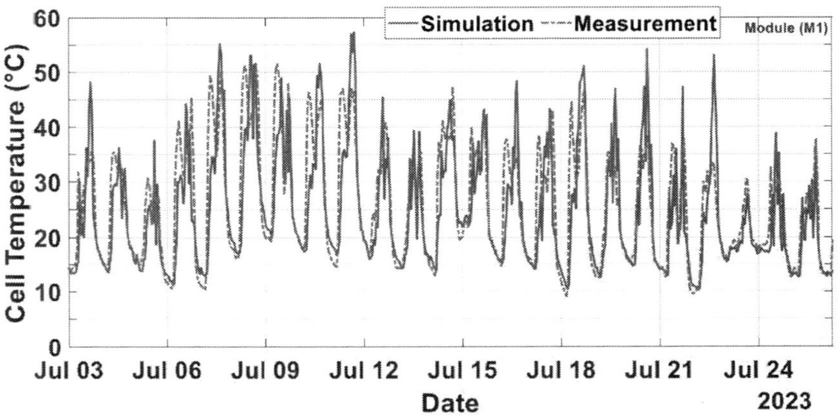

Cell temperature for the (M1) module in Genk.

RMSE =17W, 5.8% of Pmax

RMSE =6.5°C

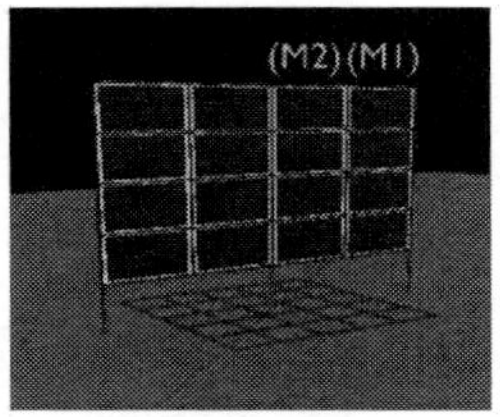

Results: DEMO3

Electrical model Validation (10-min resolution)

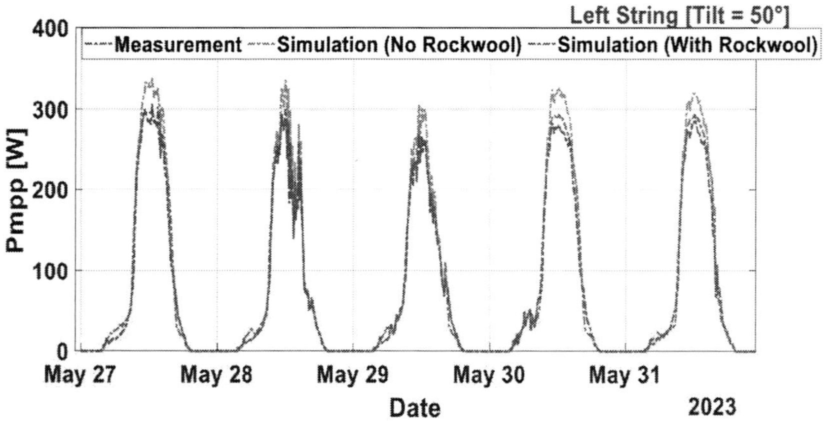

Power at MPP for the left string in Geleen, the Netherlands.

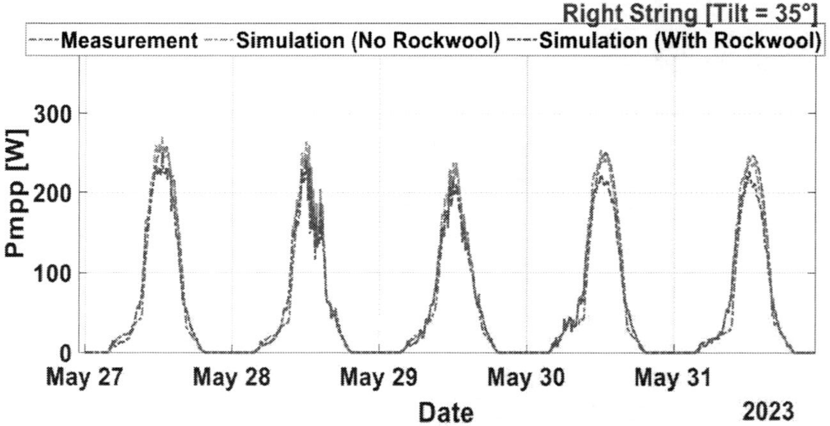

Power at MPP for the right string in Geleen, the Netherlands.

RMSE (No Rockwool) = 14W(3.5% of Pmax)

RMSE (With Rockwool) =10 W, (2.5% of Pmax)

RMSE (No Rockwool) = 12W (3% of Pmax)

RMSE (With Rockwool) =13W (3% of Pmax)

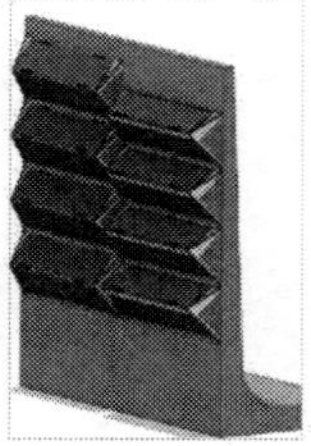

Results: DEMO3

Thermal model Validation (10-min resolution)

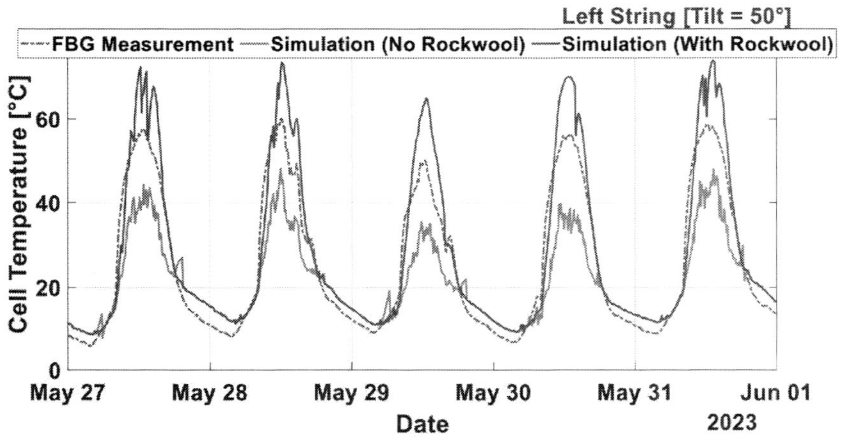

Cell temperature in the bottom modules of the left string in Geleen.

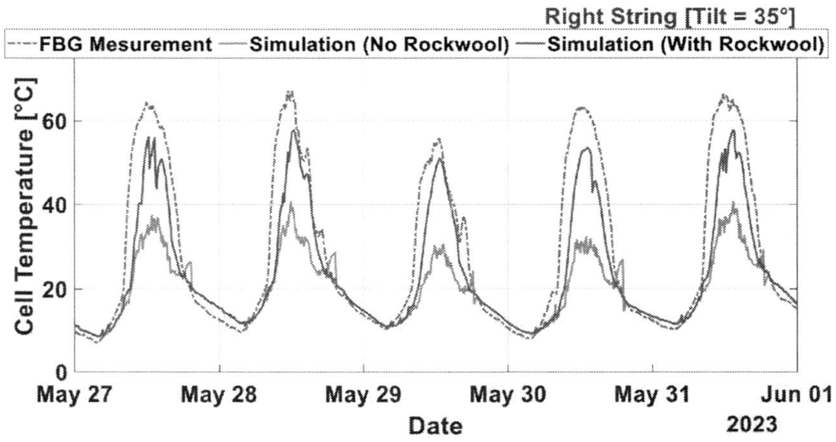

Cell temperature in the bottom modules of the right string in Geleen.

RMSE (No Rockwool) =9°C
RMSE (With Rockwool) =6°C

RMSE (No Rockwool) = 15°C
RMSE (With Rockwool) = 9°C

[8] https://doi.org/10.1016/j.apenergy.2024.124724

IMO-IMOMEC UHASSELT imec

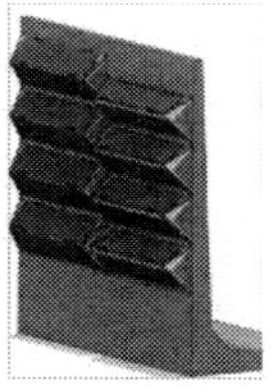

Results: DEMO2 VS DEMO3

Module Temperature (TMY Genk, hourly resolution)

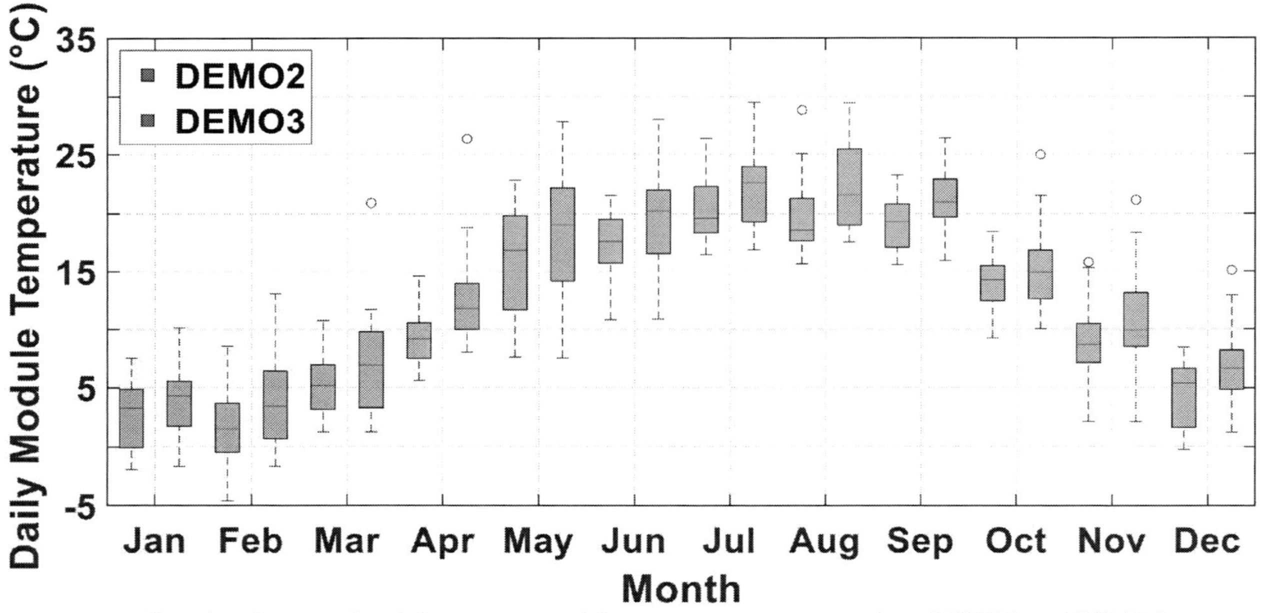

Boxplot showing the daily average module temperature per month in DEMO2 and DEMO3.

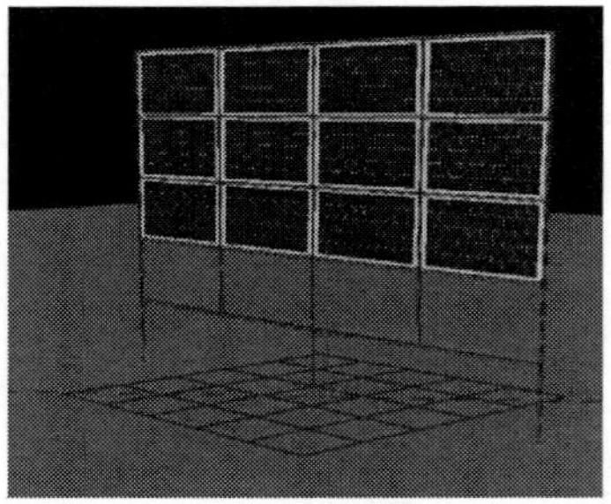

DEMO 2

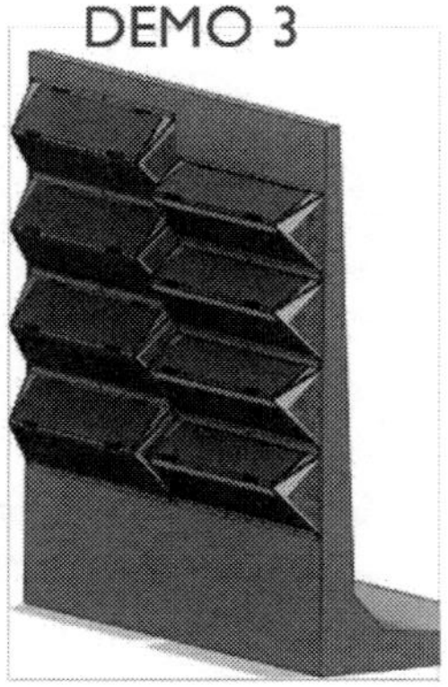

DEMO 3

Lower module temperature in DEM2 (↓ 2°C)

Results: DEMO2 VS DEMO3

Yearly Energy Yield (hourly resolution)

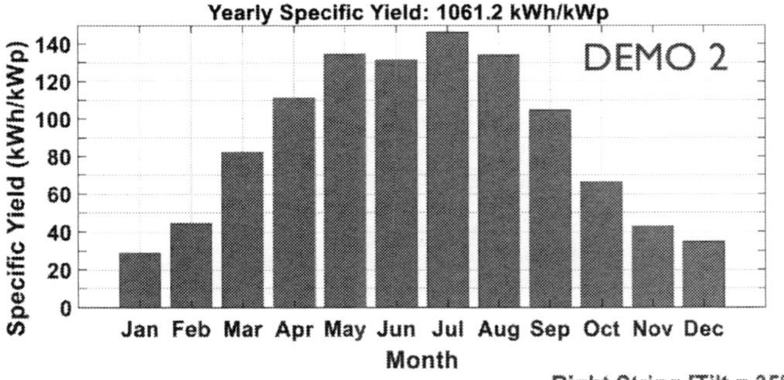

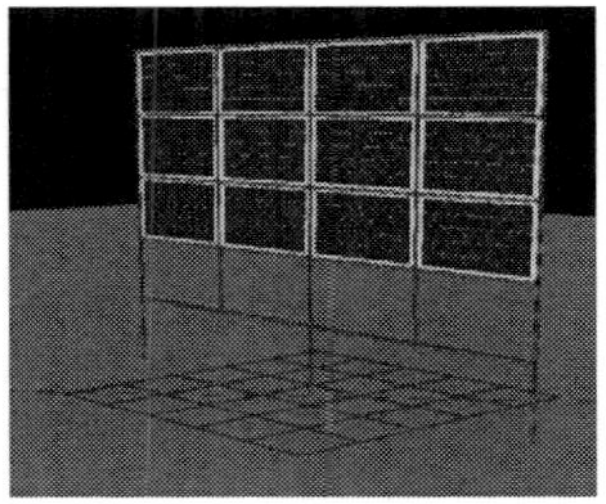

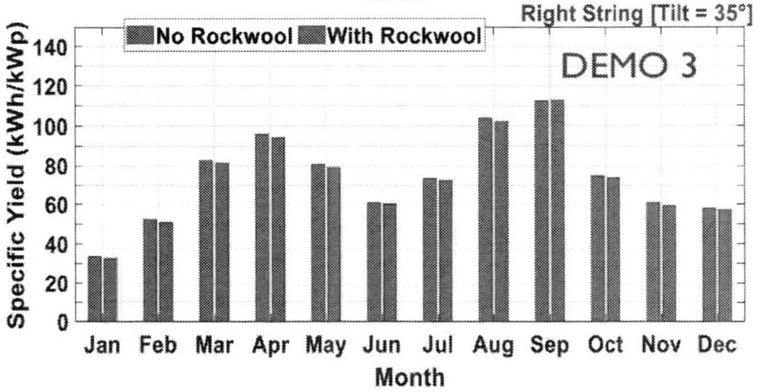

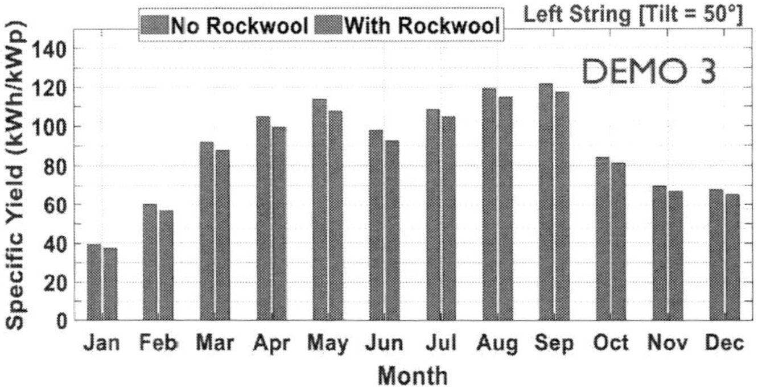

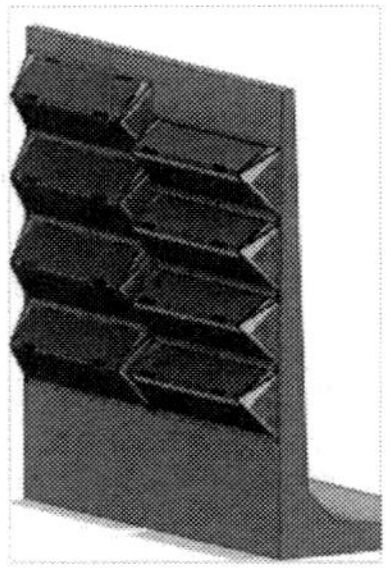

Simulated Specific Yield of DEMO2 and DEMO3 using TMY data in Genk.

Yearly Yield (No Rockwool) =890 kWh/kWp

Yearly Yield (With Rockwool) =877 kWh/kWp (↓ 1.5%)

Yearly Yield (No Rockwool) =1079 kWh/kWp

Yearly Yield (With Rockwool) =1032 kWh/kWp (↓ 4.4%)

Conclusion & Outlook

- Noise-absorbing layers raise module operating temperatures by 10–20 °C➔ performance reduction

➔must be carefully addressed in design.

- In-laminate sensors ➔ enhanced thermal modelling of PVNB systems➔ accurate power prediction.
- East–west oriented bifacial PVNBs operate at cooler temperatures and achieve higher yields compared with monofacial counterparts.
- Direct bonding or gluing of PV modules to concrete barriers ➔ low heat dissipation and increased module temperature
- Chimneys and ventilation gaps ➔low operating temperatures, enhanced long-term performance.

Outlook

- Acoustic pressure simulations for the different PVNB configurations
- Exploring novel integration methods to enhance the cooling and mitigate noise (coupled Multiphysics modelling)
- Assessment of PVNB performance at the infrastructure scale (through upscaling)

Acknowledgements

This work is conducted within the Solar Energy Made Regional (SolarEMR) and Rolling Solar projects, within the Interreg V-A Euregio MeuseRhine, with support from the European Regional Development Fund. The authors thank Wim Van De Wall from ZigZagSolar, Eindhoven, Netherlands and Tatjana Vavilkin from Soltech, Genk, Belgium.

I wish to formally acknowledge the financial support provided by Fonds Wetenschappelijk Onderzoek (FWO) through the travel grant, which enabled my participation in EUPVSEC 2025

Interreg Euregio Maas-Rijn
Europees Fonds voor Regionale Ontwikkeling
EUROPESE UNIE

Thank you for the attention!

sara.bouguerra@uhasselt.be

Energy Ville ENERGY IN TRANSITION IMO-IMOMEC UHASSELT imec

EUPVSEC
22 — 26
September
BEC —
Bilbao Exhibition Centre
Bilbao —
Spain
EU
PVSEC
2025
42nd European
Photovoltaic Solar Energy
Conference and Exhibition

C30001-001

Conference Highlights

Robert Kenny
European Commission Joint Research Centre
EU PVSEC Technical Programme Chair

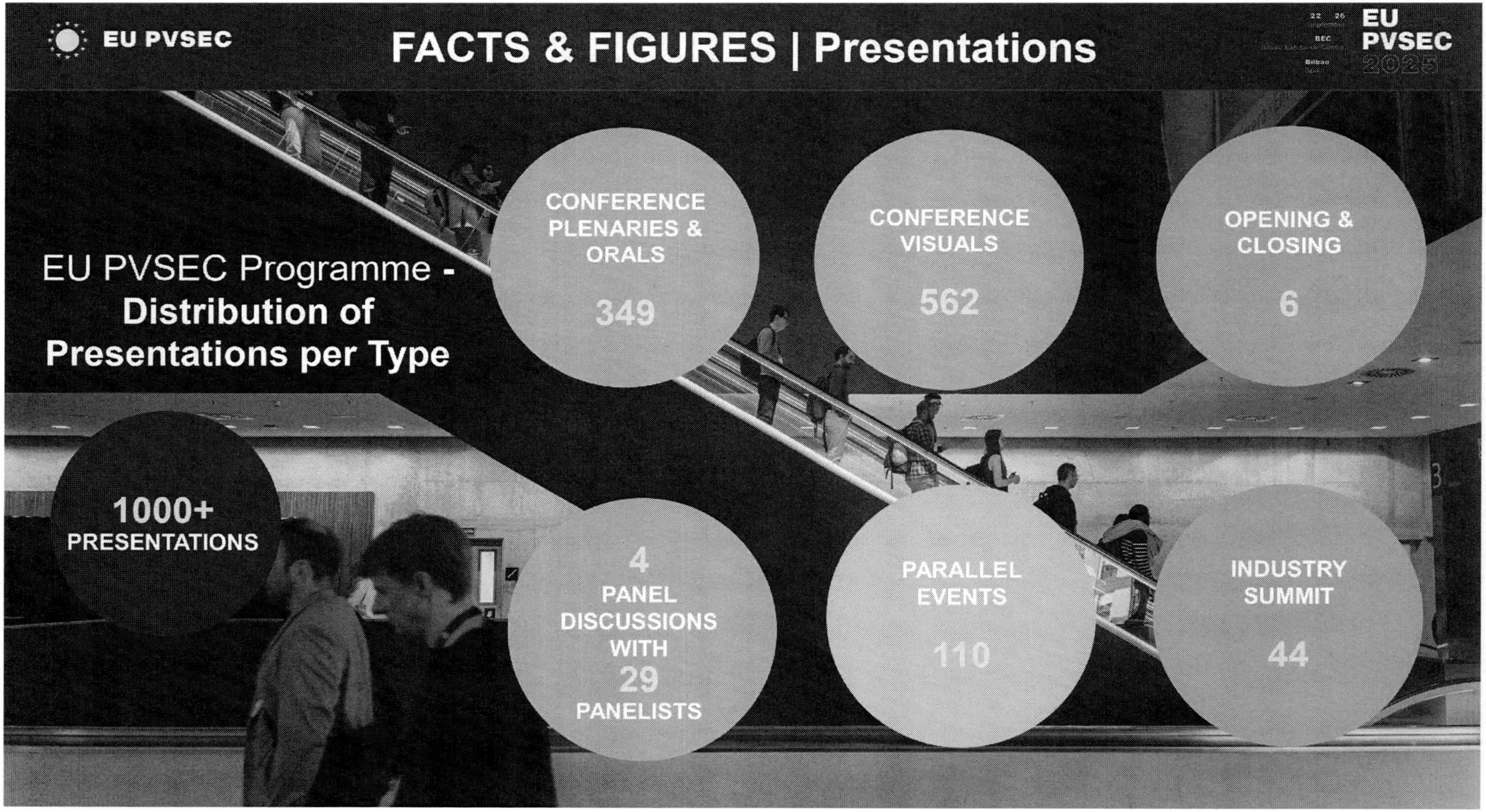
EU PVSEC
FACTS & FIGURES | Presentations
22 26
BEC
Bilbao
EU
PVSEC
2025
EU PVSEC Programme -
Distribution of
Presentations per Type
CONFERENCE
PLENARIES &
ORALS
349
CONFERENCE
VISUALS
562
OPENING &
CLOSING
6
1000+
PRESENTATIONS
4
PANEL
DISCUSSIONS
WITH
29
PANELISTS
PARALLEL
EVENTS
110
INDUSTRY
SUMMIT
44

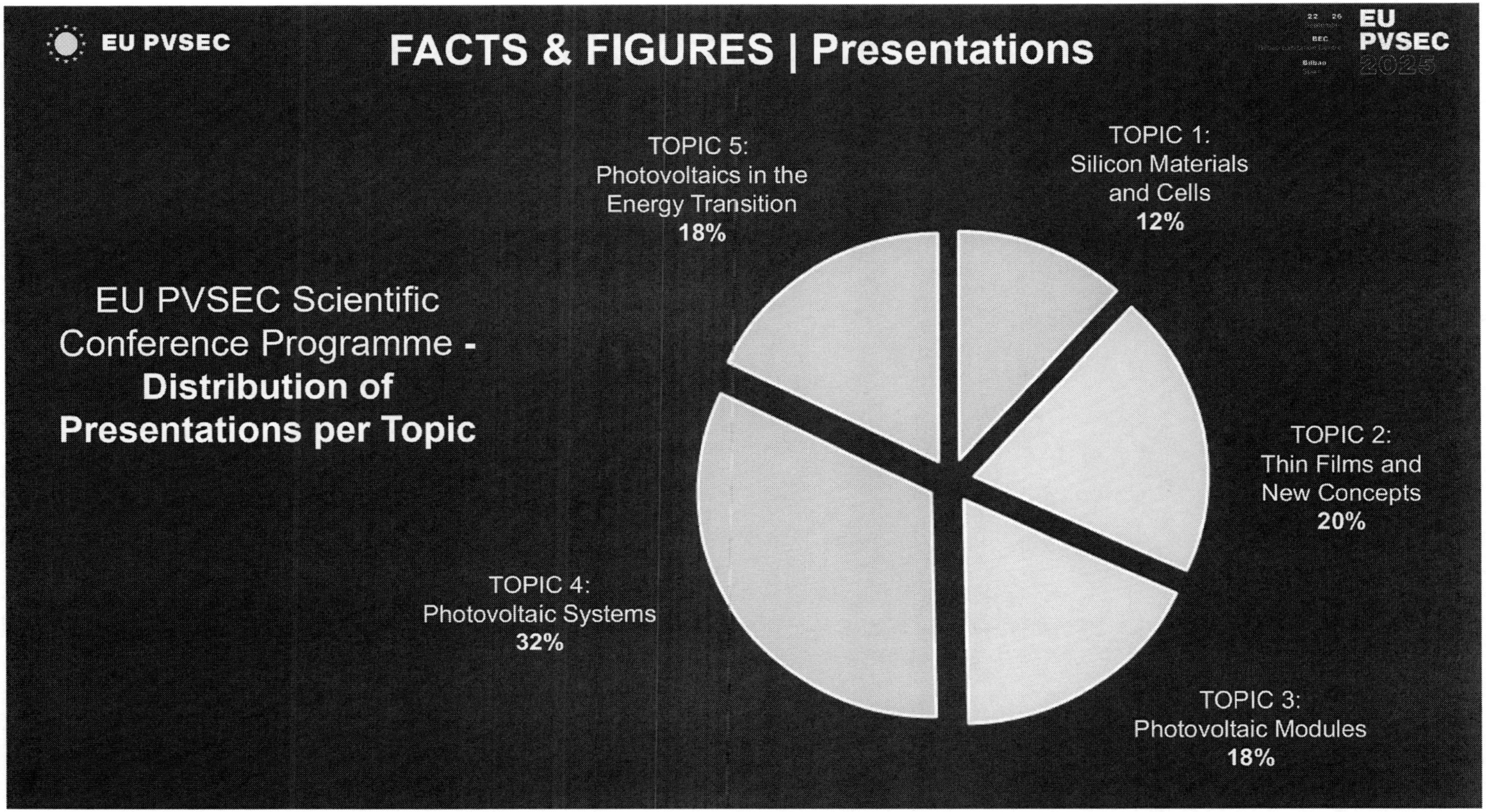
EU PVSEC
FACTS & FIGURES | Presentations
EU PVSEC 2025
EU PVSEC Scientific Conference Programme - Distribution of Presentations per Topic
TOPIC 1: Silicon Materials and Cells 12%
TOPIC 2: Thin Films and New Concepts 20%
TOPIC 3: Photovoltaic Modules 18%
TOPIC 4: Photovoltaic Systems 32%
TOPIC 5: Photovoltaics in the Energy Transition 18%

EU PVSEC

FACTS & FIGURES | Participants

22 26 September
BEC
Bilbao
EU PVSEC 2025

Participants by Countries
Top 10

No	Country	Participants
1	Germany	310
2	Spain	270
3	France	108
4	Italy	90
5	The Netherlands	76
6	South Korea	67
7	Switzerland	62
8	Japan	55
9	Belgium	44
10	Norway	35

TOTAL PARTICIPANTS
1600+
FROM 61
COUNTRIES

Plenary Session "PV Everywhere"
OPENING
Monday, 22 Sept. 2025
Becquerel Prize Ceremony
Welcome Messages
Jon DE GREGORIO
Moderated Panel Discussion "Solar in Turbulent Times: Global Dynamics and the Way Forward"
Key Note Speech "The Dual Face of Global Solar Growth"
EU PVSEC 2025
www.eupvsec.org
Bilbao Exhibition Centre

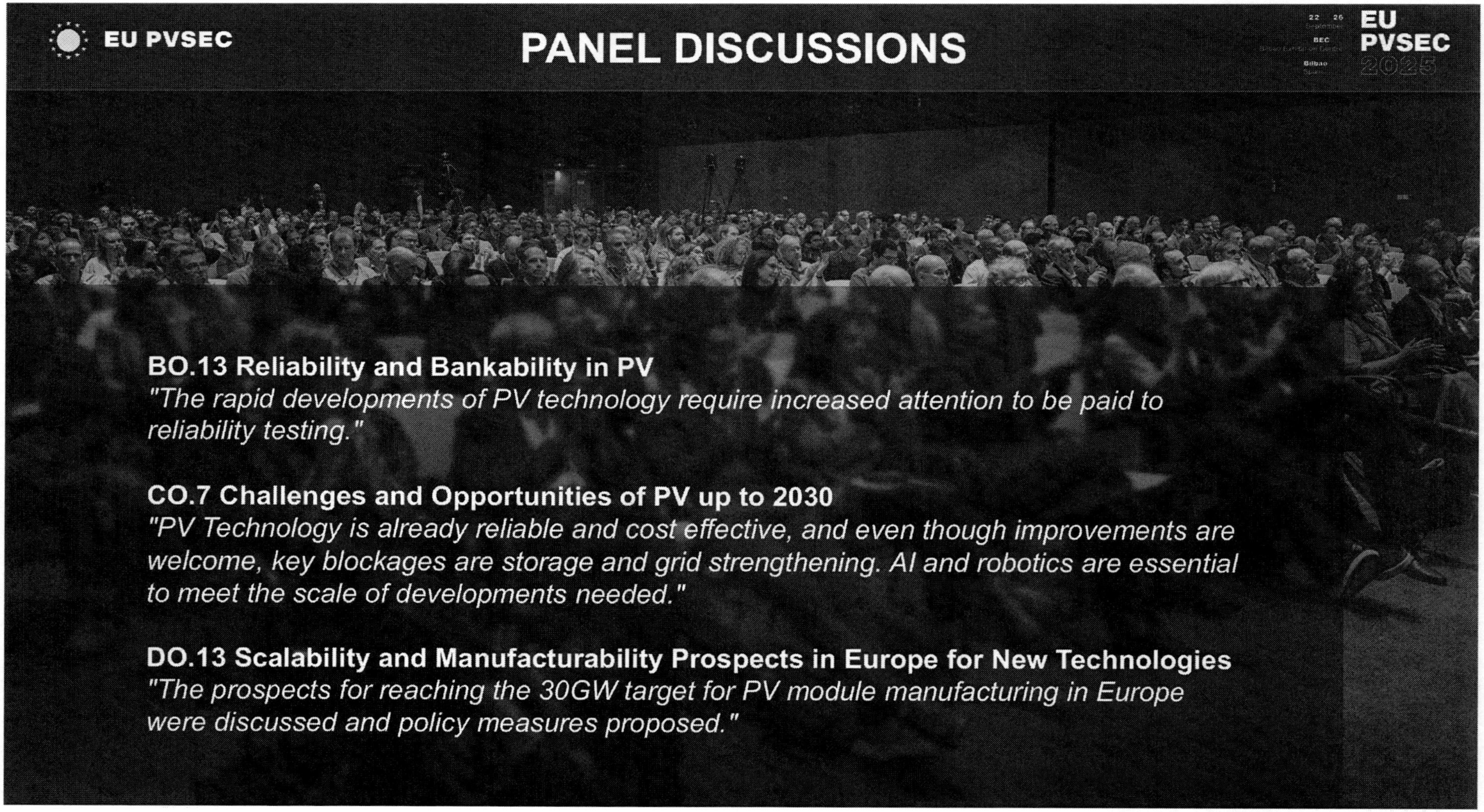
EU PVSEC
PANEL DISCUSSIONS
22 26 September
BEC
Bilbao
EU PVSEC 2025
BO.13 Reliability and Bankability in PV
"The rapid developments of PV technology require increased attention to be paid to reliability testing."
CO.7 Challenges and Opportunities of PV up to 2030
"PV Technology is already reliable and cost effective, and even though improvements are welcome, key blockages are storage and grid strengthening. AI and robotics are essential to meet the scale of developments needed."
DO.13 Scalability and Manufacturability Prospects in Europe for New Technologies
"The prospects for reaching the 30GW target for PV module manufacturing in Europe were discussed and policy measures proposed."

EU PVSEC

22 26 September BEC Bilbao Exhibition Centre Bilbao Spain

EU PVSEC 2025

CONFERENCE

KEY MESSAGES

Cross-cutting themes emerged throughout the programme, showcasing how solar technologies can be applied everywhere, from traditional to emerging fields.

- Sustainability and circularity remain central, with research focused on reducing material use, such as replacing silver with copper, and advancing end-of-life management of modules.
- Ensuring long-term stability and predictable energy yield is equally essential, with studies of degradation mechanisms such as UVID carried out.
- The role of AI across the PV value chain is rapidly expanding, from design to operations and maintenance, including drone applications.

EU PVSEC

22 26 September

BEC Bilbao Exhibition Centre

Bilbao Spain

EU PVSEC 2025

CONFERENCE

TOPIC 1: SILICON MATERIALS AND CELLS

Enhancements in IV measurement procedures

- Michael Rauer, Fraunhofer ISE: 1AO.4.5 *Universal Contacting Approaches for the Characterization of Solar Cells*
- Shuai Nie, UNSW: 1AO.4.6 *Contact-Free J-V: a Simple Technique for Universal State-of-the-Art Solar Cells*

Replacement of critical by sustainable materials:

- Reduced Ag consumpion e.g. by replacing by Cu (plating)
- In-free SHJ solar cells and Pero-Si tandems

EU PVSEC

EU PVSEC 2025

CONFERENCE

TOPIC 1: SILICON MATERIALS AND CELLS

Great advance in understanding of UV induced degradation and Hydrogen related degradation

- Excellent PLENARY by Bram Hoex (presenting for Muhammad Umair Khan), UNSW: 1CP.3.5 *Understanding the Root Cause of UV-Induced Degradation in TOPCon and PERC Solar Cells*

Further high quality orals:

- Christina Hollemann, ISFH: 1AO.4.2 *Mitigating UV-Induced Degradation: Impact of PECVD and PEALD AlOx Layers Deposited in a Tube-Type Direct Plasma-Enhanced Chemical Vapor Deposition System*
- Hugo Lajoie, CEA: 1AO.4.3 *New Insights on UV-Induced Degradation of SHJ Solar Cells*
- Byungsul Min, ISFH: 1BO.3.6 *UV Stable Passivation Stack with Plasma-Enhanced Atomic Layer Deposition of Aluminum Oxide from an Industrial Tube-Type Direct Plasma-Enhanced Chemical Vapor Deposition System*
- Wolfram Kwapil, Fraunhofer ISE: 1AO.5.6 *Impact of Illumination on Solar Cell Properties: Insights into Atomic Hydrogen Release*

EU PVSEC

EU PVSEC 2025

CONFERENCE

TOPIC 1: SILICON MATERIALS AND CELLS

Advances in TOPCon and SHJ technology → Pushing the Limits of Performance

- Fantastic keynote lecture (PLENARY) on heterojunction solar cells by Dr. Guangtao Yang, Trina: 1CP.1.1 *Silicon Surface and Interface Study for >27% Efficient SHJ Solar Cell*
    - Deep insight into technological aspects eg. influence of rear side polishing on cell performance
    - Very high efficiencies for both-sides contacted HJT > 27%
    - Issues with CAPEX, sustainibility (Ag, In)
    - Pero-Si tandem cells on large area and modules

Late News Presentation on 27.8% efficient back contact silicon solar cells by Hua Wu, Longhi: 1DO.9.1 *Hybrid Interdigitated Back Contact Silicon Solar Cells with Superior Efficiency*

Late News Presentation as TOPCon for Bottom Solar Cells in Pero-Si Tandem devices by Jana Polzin-Isabelle Polzin, Fraunhofer ISE: 1DO.9.3 *Silicon Solar Cells – From High Efficiency Single-junction to Bottom Cells in Two-Terminal Perovskite-Silicon Tandem Devices*

EU PVSEC

EU PVSEC 2025

CONFERENCE

TOPIC 1: SILICON MATERIALS AND CELLS

Further high quality orals:

- Hua Wu, Longhi: 1DO.9.1 *Hybrid Interdigitated Back Contact Silicon Solar Cells with Superior Efficiency*
- Daming Chen, Trina: 1AO.5.1 *Large Area i-TOPCon Solar Cells with 25.9% Record Efficiency*
- Maysa Sarsour, UNSW: 1AO.6.1 *Evaluating Silicon Heterojunction Solar Cell Stability under Industrial Illuminated Hydrogenation Conditions*

Bottom cell optimization for Pero-Si tandems

EU PVSEC

22 26 BEC Bilbao EU PVSEC 2025

CONFERENCE

TOPIC 2: THIN FILMS AND NEW CONCEPTS

A lot of focus on the long-term stability improvement and upscaling of tandem devices based on a variety of materials (hence not only pero-Si).

Many companies (e.g. Hanwha Q-cells, Oxford PV, Microquanta Seminconductor, Jinko Solar, Longi, etc. non-exhaustive list) presented impressive results on industrial size single-junction pero modules and pero-based tandem modules. A highlight here was the plenary talk from Hanwha Q-cells showing a record large area (M10) pilot-scale Pk/Si tandem cell of 28.6% efficiency.

EU PVSEC

22 26 September BEC Bilbao Exhibition Centre Bilbao Spain

EU PVSEC 2025

CONFERENCE

TOPIC 2: THIN FILMS AND NEW CONCEPTS

In the field of pero-Si tandems, there is clearly more focus on improving the stability of the tandem devices than before with many contributions doing in-depth investigations into the different degradation mechanisms that can occur in pero-Si tandems.

In this respect, 2DO9.5 presented a consensus statement about reliability testing of perovskite-based tandems that is endorsed by specialists worldwide from both industry and research and presents a kind of minimum that should be done in terms of testing and reporting concerning the stability and lifetime of perovskite-based tandem devices.

More and more advanced characterization methods for perovskite and perovskite - silicon tandem solar cells are being used, hyperspectral imaging methods identify non-uniformities by layer for processing development.

EU PVSEC

22 26 BEC Bilbao

EU PVSEC 2025

CONFERENCE

TOPIC 2: THIN FILMS AND NEW CONCEPTS

Another clear trend is that pero-TOPCon cells are nearing the same record efficiencies as pero-Heterojunction cells. A highlight talk here was the certified 34.22% efficiency perovskite/ topcon tandem solar cell(1cm2) by Jinko Solar 2CO2.1

Another highlight was the 30.5% triple junction pero/pero/silicon cell by EPFL (2CO2.3)

In the field of perovskite single junction devices, 2DO.7.3 showed perovskite devices with remarkable reliability, withstanding 4 years of outdoor exposure. The degradation mechanism is attributed to the diurnal behaviour, also verified and replicated with indoor experiments.

2AO3.6 investigated experimental degradation and recovery of perovskite solar cells, improving the comprehension of instability's dynamics, to extend the lifetime of devices.

EU PVSEC

22 26

BEC

Bilbao

EU PVSEC 2025

CONFERENCE

TOPIC 2: THIN FILMS AND NEW CONCEPTS

In the field of compound semiconductors, there were many presentations on alternative materials for perovskite in tandems. In this way, first monolithic (AgCu)(InGa)Se2 on Si tandem cells were demonstrated as well as 16.1% semitransparent Ag doped Cu(InGa)S2 sulfide top cells.

An exciting highlight in this field was 2BO8.2 in which UPC Barcelona achieved 18% efficiency under indoor lighting for kesterite solar cells with alkali doping

EU PVSEC

22 26 September

BEC

Bilbao

EU PVSEC 2025

CONFERENCE

TOPIC 3: PHOTOVOLTAIC MODULES

"Reliable packaging to Maximize the energy yield from high efficiency cells"

big theme: Optimizing module materials and packaging for long lifetime and predictable energy yield from high efficiency cells. The industry and research community are moving quickly to assess and improve reliability.

- Understanding, accelerated testing, and mitigating UV-ID in n-type cells and modules
- How do you develop accelerated tests for constantly changing BOMs - new encapsulants, new metallization, thinner glass, and high efficiency cells

EU PVSEC

22 26 EU PVSEC 2025 BEC Bilbao

CONFERENCE

TOPIC 3: PHOTOVOLTAIC MODULES

- Degradation and metastability in packaged perovskite tandems - understanding energy yield and realistic degradation rates
- Characterization out of the lab and into the field and factory - accurate outdoor performance, online quality control measurements for encapsulant cross linking
- Reducing silver content and metallization temperatures - reliability of low temperature and low silver metallization
- Developing glass qualification requirements to minimize breakage

EU PVSEC

EU PVSEC 2025

CONFERENCE

TOPIC 4: PHOTOVOLTAIC SYSTEMS

Advances in O&M of PV systems

(4CV.1) focuses on fault detection, cleaning optimization, soiling (and snow 4CO.8), UAV for autonomous monitoring and digital twin.

Data driven and AI based O&M (4CO.9) including a medicine-like workflow in Autonomous multi-AI agent system for health monitoring: a fully automated O&M pipeline with field robotics (4CO.9.4 D. Moser, EURAC)

PV Everywhere from space to agricultural applications like integration in vineyards (Mo, Opening plenary) and many other **integrated options** as we have seen throughout the week. On Thursday (4DO.4) agriPV, noise barriers and floating integrated systems. AgriPV technologies (4DO.2), BIPV

PV needs solar energy. **Solar resource and forecasting** (Mo, 4AO.7-9 & Tu 4BV.3). Shortly IEA PVPS T16 will publish minute irradiance data, some including GT over 220 stations worldwide with. Same format and quality controlled. (*Worldwide solar radiation measurement database with quality-control added value*, Anne Forstinger CSP Services, 4AO.7.1)

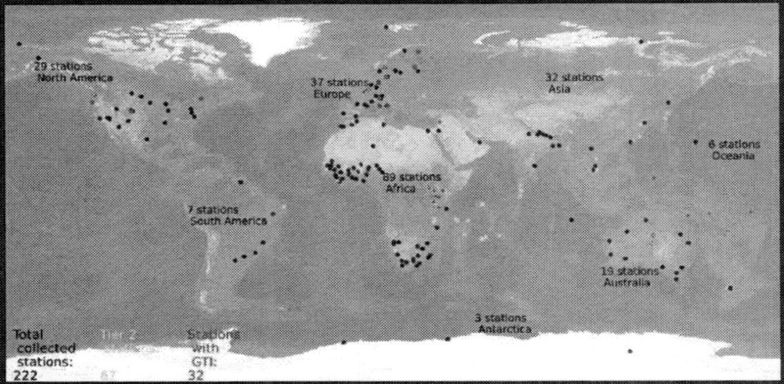

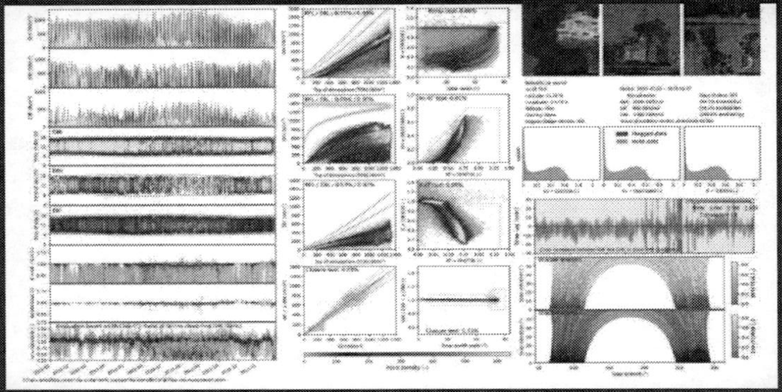

(4BV.3). Poster winner 4BV.3.12 *Advancing Very Short-Term Solar Irradiance Forecasting in Africa: A Low-Cost Sky Imaging and Machine Learning-Based Approach*, implications for PV deployment and grid integration (Martin Ansong, KIT). Runner-up 4BV.3.25 *Evaluating the Suitability of Köppen-Geiger Climate Classifications for Photovoltaic Systems: Micro-climate Analysis and Risk Assessment Maps,* with worldwide distribution of humidity related risk assessment for PV performance (Pavan Kumar Panda, Anhalt University of Applied Sciences).

TOPIC 4: PHOTOVOLTAIC SYSTEMS

Integrated PV

BIPV (4BO.16) examples of coloured modules (which was main topic of the poster session along with fire concerns of BIPV, 4BV.4), lightweight solutions (4BO.5) and modelling partial shading effects 4BO.17.1, *Modelling partial shading at the cell level on PV modules,* Jean-Paul Calin, ENSTA) and 4BO.17.3, *Comparing the energy yield and degradation rates of smart PV modules compared to conventional PV system designs in shaded urban scenario's,* Youri Blom, TU DELF.

AgriPV 4DO.2 the room was fully packed showing the interest in the topic. 5 talks were on new ways of sharing light (2 spectral splitting before the PV conversion, 2 semitransparent PV modules both c-Si and CdTe, 1 on downshifting encapsulate) + 1 new AgrivPV like application with Algae instead of crops.

4DO.4 also included AgriPV and **Others types of integration like noise barriers and floating.** In addition to performance other aspects like (*Hydrological and ecological effects on floating PV,* Konstantin Ilgen, FHO ISe) have been highlighted this week

4DO4.2

BOS and tracking systems (4DO.1) focused on backtracking strategies and terrains with complex topography.

4DO.1.4

EU PVSEC

EU PVSEC 2025

CONFERENCE

TOPIC 4: PHOTOVOLTAIC SYSTEMS

Reliability of PV systems

Several presentations focused long-term monitored degradation, failure modes and degradation modes identification techniques (non-destructive, aerial images, AI-based)

4BO.6.1 *Three decades, three climates: insights and lessons on PV reliability*. Good BOM offer very high reliability in power production, with 30-35 years old modules showing 0.24% degradation rate per year.

4BO.6.3 *Non-destructive detection of water ingress in solar modules using NIR spectroscopy* (Oleksandr Mashkow HI ERN) proved near-infrared absorption (NIRA) technique to detect water ingress in modules in the field, which correlated with the module degradation.

4BO.7.2 *Robust PV performance loss rate calculation for high latitudes* (Lauri Karttunen, Meteo Inst Helsinki) and 4BO.7. 3 *Detailed analysis of degradation rates of operating PV assets in tropical climate conditions* (Xioaqi Xu, Seris Singapore) Performance loss rates reported for high latitudes and tropics based on solid data sets. PLR in the tropics -1.4%/year

4DO.3.6 PV system design and assessment highlighted how inverter safety issues are extremely important and how more research about inverter safety and reliability is needed.

EU PVSEC

EU PVSEC 2025

CONFERENCE

TOPIC 5: PHOTOVOLTAICS IN THE ENERGY TRANSITION

Main topics of interest :

- Flexibility
- Artificial intelligence
- EoL management

EU PVSEC

22 26 BEC Bilbao EU PVSEC 2025

CONFERENCE

TOPIC 5: PHOTOVOLTAICS IN THE ENERGY TRANSITION

5.1 Grid Integration and Flexibility Enablers (2 sessions)

- Smoothing effect related to different orientations of PV systems in a given area allows 10 to 15% additional hosting capacity of the distribution grid compared to the conservative calculation that consists in summing the AC power. Such accurate calculation enabled by high resolution large area images and LIDAR and induces therefore very low costs.

5.2 Sustainability of PV (4 sessions)

- New inventories LCI and LCA for emerging technologies even though lack of data for perovskites, LCA showing a way for low environmental Impacts with technology improvement and localisation. / Technological improvements will contribute to the reduction of environmental Impact / Grid Efficiency has an Impact on the environmental Footprint.
- Manufacturing optimization / Reuse & recycling: results from the perspective of economic performance – would it convince manufacturer to consider it if economic benefit ?
- EoL Management /recycling -> emerging field attracting lots of activities / mainly EU projects (EVERPV / ICARUS / QASAR) – highlight on polymer, interesting question came up and to be debated for the next decade: is it worth it to consider polymer (EVA/ backsheet) recycling ?
- Major progress in methodology and indicators to assess sustainable design & circularity and improve transparency recyclability index, technical recyclability, digital passport)

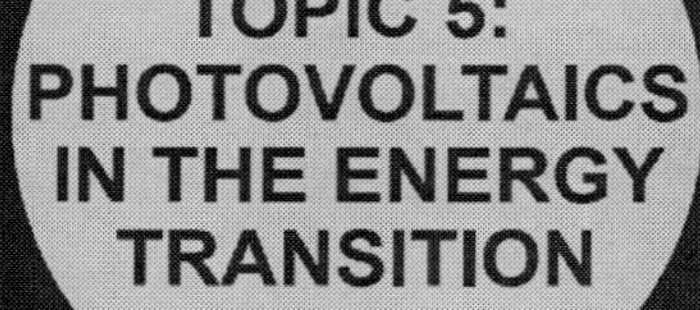

CONFERENCE

5.3 Scenarios for Renewables, Policy, Global Challenges (1 session)

- wide scope of contributions on the way to massive, medium- to long-term PV deployment -> should not be taken for granted despite positive projections since there can be limiting factors such as public acceptance / regulatory restrictions and effect of climate change

5.4 Costs, Economics, Finance and Markets (1 session)

- Annual installed capacity over 400 GWp / total cumulative installed capacity worldwide over 2.1 TWp / Clear mismatch between PV module installations rate worldwide and PV module production rate leading to bunch of inventories and drastically reduced prices.

5.6 Societal Challenges; Citizens' Participation, Awareness (1 session)

- data and analysis in gender aspects are emerging in PV! (poster session) + Highlight on innovation in education! On example that targets students & skilled workers -> mobile Lab for advanced experimental training PV-related to bring skills and characterization tools everywhere.

PARALLEL
EVENTS
Collaborat° Network
Diversity
Prejudice
Justificat°
Change
Needs - Profile Match
Avoid blind spots
Job loss?
Integration
Resilience (people + company)
Creativity
Different communicat°
Internal friction

EU PVSEC

22 26

BEC

Bilbao

EU PVSEC 2025

PARALLEL EVENTS

- Perovskite Innovation Roundtable: Driving EU Leadership in Perovskite Innovation
- Women in PV presents: Leading with Inclusion – Embracing the 6 Traits of Inclusive Leadership
- Unlocking the Potential of Integrated Photovoltaic Systems - European R&D Approach
- Why Do PV Plants Perform Lower than Expected? (Estimating losses by backtracking algorithms in undulating terrain & Analysis of the loss chain and identification of deviations from initial expectations)
- PV Made in the EU: How Do Companies Die and How Can They Thrive?

22 — 26
September
BEC —
ilbao Exhibition Centre
Bilbao — Spain
EU
PVSEC
2025
GEOPOLITICS & PV MANUFACTURING CHALLENGES
EXHIBITION
FORUM
INDUSTRY
SUMMIT

The road to a

EU PVSEC

22 26 BEC Bilbao EU PVSEC 2025

INDUSTRY SUMMIT

Industry Summit Opening (session I)

Session Title: Solar PV production in Europe - the way forward

Moderators: Begoña Molinete, Walburga Hemetsberger

Key Takeaway:

This session discussed the state of play of European manufacturing projects and whether there is enough European support. It was clear that political support is further lacking – only 3 Member States have developed schemes to support European manufacturing. While the Net Zero Industry Act is helpful to diversify supplies, it will not particularly support European manufacturing.

All panellists agreed that apart from further policy support (financing, derisking) collaboration is the way forward.

EU PVSEC

EU PVSEC 2025

INDUSTRY SUMMIT

Session II
Session Title: International corporations in the light of changing geopolitics
Moderators: Radovan Kopecek, Puzant Baliozian

Key takeaway:
EU machine builders are still supporting mostly Indian but also US and EU projects with their technology and expertise. The major arguments for choosing EU tech are quality, training, support and low OPEX.

Session III
Session Title: PV Systems: How do we get the produced electricity in Europe into the grid?
Moderators: Catarina Augusto, Peter Fath

Key Takeaway:
Hybrid PV + storage systems (co-located or distributed) are essential for integrating PV into electricity grids. Storage adds flexibility and stabilizes the grid, making it a cornerstone of resilient energy systems; while the technology is mature, scalable and bankable revenue models remain the key gap for widespread deployment.

LIST OF EXHIBITORS
(in alphabetical order)

Company name	Country
2nd Cycle FlexCo	Austria
9-Tech	Italy
Avalon ST / Pasan	Switzerland
BASQUENERGY Cluster	Spain
Becquerel Institute	Belgium
ECOPROGETTI	Italy
EKIENERGY	Spain
ESMC Pavilion	Belgium
Eternal Sun I WAVELABS	The Netherlands
EU PVSEC Startup Pavilion	
European Commission JRC	Italy
exateq	Germany
FLUXiM AG	Switzerland
G2V Optics	Canada
GALEA	Spain
halm elektronik	Germany
HighLine Technology	Germany
IEA PVPS	
Innovations in Optics, Inc.	United States of America
ISC Konstanz	Germany
LAB14	Germany
MBJ Solutions	Germany
Mondragon Assembly	Spain
Nagase Chemtex America	United States of America
NEO Messtechnik Holding	Austria
ODTÜ GÜNAM	Türkiye
Phoenixolar	China
PSE Instruments	Germany
PVsyst	Switzerland
RCT Future	Germany
RCT Solutions	Germany
RENA	Germany
ReNewPV-CA21148 / 5GSOLAR	Estonia
SALD B.V.	The Netherlands

SCIPRIOS	Germany
SEMILAB	Hungary
SINGULUS TECHNOLOGIES	Germany
Sinton Instruments	United States of America
SOLAR MATERIALS	Germany
SolarNL	The Netherlands
Soli Tek R&D	Lithuania
TAMURA ELSOLD	Germany
TECNALIA	Spain
The Netherlands Pavilion	The Netherlands
TNO	The Netherlands
University of the Basque Country	Spain
Vector Energy	Spain
VON ARDENNE	Germany
WCPEC-9	South Korea
WIP Renewable Energies	Germany
ZSW	Germany

EU PVSEC 2025
42nd European Photovoltaic Solar Energy Conference and Exhibition

We thank the EU PVSEC 2025 Sponsors

Platinum

MONDRAGON ASSEMBLY

Gold

ENERGIAREN EUSKAL ERAKUNDEA
ENTE VASCO DE LA ENERGÍA

G2V ENGINEER THE SUN

halm.

RCT solutions

Silver

Sinton instruments

Bronze

AESOLAR

AUTHORS OF EU PVSEC 2025 PROCEEDINGS PAPERS

A. dos Reis Benatto, Gisele — 020028, 020037, 020039, 020191, 020265, 020376, 020477
DTU, Roskilde, Denmark

Aaltonen, Lauri — 020537
Tampere University, Tampere, Finland

Abad Alcaraz, Verónica — 020336
University of Almería, La Cañada de San Urbano, Spain

Abbott, Malcolm D. — 020396
PV Lighthouse, Coledale, Australia

Abbotto, Alessandro — 020077
University of Milano-Bicocca, Milan, Italy

Abdallah, Amir A. — 020146, 020166
QEERI, Doha, Qatar

Abdel Nour, Christine — 020188
EDF R&D, Moret Loing Orvanne, France

Abdelrahim, Mohamed — 020166
QEERI, Doha, Qatar

Abdou-Tankari, Mahamadou — 020562
Paris-East Créteil University, Créteil, France

Abrego, Gillen — 020392
ALLOTARRA, Allo, Spain

Acciarri, Maurizio — 020087
University of Milano Bicocca, Milan, Italy

Acevedo Devoto, M. Ignacia — 020220
ISC Konstanz, Konstanz, Germany

Achenbach, Jannik — 020522
University of Applied Science Cologne, Cologne, Germany

Acinas, Victor — 020019
Applied Materials, Dublin, Ireland

Adachi, Satoru — 020436
NIED, Shinjo, Japan

Aden, Samira — 020513
HZB, Berlin, Germany

Adinolfi Borea, Riccardo — 020314
University of Bologna, Bologna, Italy

Adnan Hameed, Mohammed — 020156
Martin-Luther-University Halle-Wittenberg, Halle, Germany

Adothu, Baloji — 020229
DEWA, Dubai, United Arab Emirates

Aghaei, Mohammadreza — 020335, 020356
NTNU, Aalesund, Norway

Aghaei, Mohammadreza — 020374, 020375
NTNU, Ålesund, Norway

Aghamohammadi, Amirhossain 020356
Amirkabir University of Technology, Tehran, Iran
Aguirre, Aranzazu 020064
Hasselt Unversity, Genk, Belgium
Ahmadi, Mehdi 020066
CNR-IMM, Catania, Italy
Aiello, Andrea 020255
ACCA Software, Cosenza, Italy
Aimé, Jérémie 020217, 020311
CEA / INES, Le Bourget-du-Lac, France
Aissa, Brahim 020042, 020075, 020108, 020109, 020146, 020147
QEERI, Doha, Qatar
Aizpurua, Jon 020139
Tecnalia, Donostia - San Sebastián, Spain
Akbayrak, Serdar 020020
Necmettin Erbakan University, Konya, Türkiye
Akram, M. Waqar 020164
Hohai University, Changzhou, China
Al Katrib, Mirella 020116
IPVF, Palaiseau, France
Alam, Habeel 020394
Lancaster University, Lancaster, United Kingdom
Alberts, Vivian 020229
DEWA, Dubai, United Arab Emirates
Albuquerque, Daniel P. 020464
Centre for New Energy Technologies, Sacavém, Portugal
Alet, Pierre-Jean 020238, 020544
CSEM, Neuchâtel, Switzerland
Alexandris, Nikos 020210
European Commission JRC, Ispra, Italy
Alfieri, Felice 020497
Viegand Maagøe, Copenhagen, Denmark
Ali, Adnan 020147
QEERI, Doha, Qatar
Allen, Vince 020048
SunDrive Solar, Kurnell, Australia
Alloji, Esma 020020
Necmettin Erbakan University, Konya, Türkiye
Almeida Silva, José 020565
University of Évora, Évora, Portugal
Almuneau, Guilhem 020074
LAAS-CNRS, Toulouse, France
Alonso, Ricardo 020197, 020198, 020353, 020358
TECNALIA, Derio, Spain
Alonso-Montesinos, Joaquín 020100
University of Almeria, Almeria, Spain

Alonso-Montesinos, Joaquín 020336
University of Almería, La Cañada de San Urbano, Spain
Álvarez Hervás, José Domingo 020336
University of Almería, La Cañada de San Urbano, Spain
Alvarez, José 020040, 020058
CNRS, Gif-sur-Yvette, France
Álvarez, Marta 020300
CENER, Sarriguren, Spain
Álvarez-Pérez, Guillem 020062
IPVF, Palaiseau, France
Alvaro Høye, Ingar 020443
Solkraft Sør, Øyslebø, Norway
Alves e Silva, Kiane 020439, 020535, 020567, 020575
UPM, Madrid, Spain
Amaro e Silva, Rodrigo 020490
University of Lisbon, Lisbon, Portugal
Amatriain, Irati 020392
CENER, Sarriguren, Spain
Anamiati, Gaetana 020448, 020481
GreenPowerMonitor a DNV company, Barcelona, Spain
Anaya, Julian 020191, 020205
University of Valladolid, Valladolid, Spain
Ancillao, Andrea 020079
Polytechnic University of Turin, Turin, Italy
Anderlini, Alessandro 020155
Coveme, Gorizia, Italy
Andersen, Nanna L. 020250
DTU, Roskilde, Denmark
Andersen, Nanna Lysgaard 020306
DTU, Roskilde, Denmark
Andrade-Arvizu, Jacob 020094
IREC, Barcelona, Spain
Andreozzi, Federico 020494
University of Rome Tor Vergata, Rome, Italy
Anefnaf, Ikram 020093
University of Verona, Verona, Italy
Ansong, Martin 020272
KIT, Eggenstein-Leopoldshafen, Germany
Antognini, Luca 020196
PVsyst, Geneva, Switzerland
Antoine, C. 020508
IMDEA Nanoscience Institute, Madrid, Spain
Antón, Ignacio 020209, 020246, 020257, 020453, 020459
UPM, Madrid, Spain
Antonucci, Daniele 020551
Eurac Research, Bolzano, Italy

Apostoleris, Harry 020487
EPRI, Dubai, United Arab Emirates

Arakawa, Hayato 020436
NIED, Shinjo, Japan

Aranguren, Gerardo 020289, 020353
UPV/EHU, Bilbao, Spain

Arbaretaz, Sebastien 020317
CEA INES, Le Bourget-du-Lac, France

Ardissone, Bastien J. J. 020396
PV Lighthouse, Coledale, Australia

Arduino, Daniele 020079
Polytechnic University of Turin, Turin, Italy

Ariolli, Daniela Maria Godinho 020325
BayWa r.e, Rome, Italy

Ariza Camacho, Maria Jesus 020100
University of Almeria, Almería, Spain

Armstrong, Alona 020394
Lancaster University, Lancaster, United Kingdom

Arribat, Mathieu 020074
LAAS-CNRS, Toulouse, France

Arrizabalaga, Igor 020139
Tecnalia, Donostia - San Sebastián, Spain

Artegiani, Elisa 020057, 020089, 020093
University of Verona, Verona, Italy

Arumughan, Jayaprasad 020569
ISC Konstanz, Konstanz, Germany

Asaa, Shu-Ngwa 020393
imo-imomec, Genk, Belgium

Ascencio-Vásquez, Julián 020371
Univers, Courbevoie, France

Askins, Steve 020209, 020257
UPM, Madrid, Spain

Assaid, El Mahdi 020171
University of Chouaib Doukkali, El Jadida, Morocco

Aste, Niccolò 020249
Polytechnic University of Milan, Milan, Italy

Astigarraga, Alexander 020226
Eurac Research, Bolzano, Italy

Athienitis, Andreas 020248
Concordia University, Montreal, Canada

Aurrekoetxea, Olaia 020302
TECNALIA, Saint Sebastian, Spain

Awadallah, Carlos 020536
Wattkraft, Madrid, Spain

Azkona, Nekane 020055, 020097, 020153, 020287
UPV/EHU, Bilbao, Spain

Azzopardi, Brian 020318, 020334, 020520
FIR, Birkirkara, Malta

Azzopardi, Carmel 020334
FIR, Birkirkara, Malta

Babich, Francesco 020551
Eurac Research, Bolzano, Italy

Babics, Maxime 020217
CEA / INES, Le Bourget-du-Lac, France

Babin, Markus 020249, 020250, 020306, 020477
DTU, Roskilde, Denmark

Bachour, Dunia A. 020275, 020278
QEERI, Doha, Qatar

Bachour, Dunia 020291
QEERI, Doha, Qatar

Baderiya, Naman 020390
MARIN, Wageningen, The Netherlands

Badosa Franch, Jordi 020214
Polytechnic Institute of Paris, Palaiseau, France

Baeck, Pieter-Jan 020511
Flemish Institute for Technological Research (VITO), Genk, Belgium

Bai, Jianbo 020164
Hohai University, Changzhou, China

Bailache, Simon 020303
CSTB, Marne-la-Vallée, France

Bakhtiari, Afshin 020121
AESOLAR, Koenigsbrunn, Germany

Balafoutis, Athanasios T. 020464
CERTH, Athens, Greece

Bald, Juan 020514
AZTI, PASAIA, Spain

Baldacchino, Alex J. 020065
UNSW, Sydney, Australia

Baležentienė, Skirmantė 020380
The Applied Research Institute for Prospective Technologies, Vilnius, Lithuania

Baležentis, Algirdas 020380
The Applied Research Institute for Prospective Technologies, Vilnius, Lithuania

Ballif, Christophe 020467
CSEM, Neuchâtel, Switzerland

Ballif, Christophe 020251
EPFL, Neuchâtel, Switzerland

Bandaru, Narendra 020039, 020043, 020104
Aarhus University, Aarhus, Denmark

Bang, Ole 020043
Technical University of Denmark, Copenhagen, Denmark

Barakel, Damien 020188
Toulon University, Marseille, France

Baraket, Mira 020039
ATLANT 3D, Taastrup, Denmark

Baranek, Philippe 020060
EDF R&D, Palaiseau, France

Barchi, Grazia 020485, 020489, 020544
Eurac Research, Bolzano, Italy

Bardizza, Giorgio 020181
TÜV Rheinland Italia, Milan, Italy

Bardizza, Giorgio 020208
TÜV Rheinland Solar, Cologne, Germany

Bardizza, Giorgio 020144
TÜV Rheinland, Cologne, Germany

Barguès, Anna 020505
Becquerel Institute France, Lyon, France

Barguès, Anna 020558
Becquerel Institute, Brussels, Belgium

Barnscheidt, Verena 020063, 020114
ISFH, Emmerthal, Germany

Barretta, Chiara 020325
PCCL, Leoben, Austria

Barrionuevo, Bruno 020464
CERTH, Athens, Greece

Barroso, João 020565
University of Évora, Évora, Portugal

Barrou, Alexis 020467
CSEM, Neuchâtel, Switzerland

Barrutia, Laura 020446, 020536
UPM, Madrid, Spain

Barth, Vincent 020134
CEA / INES, Le Bourget-du-Lac, France

Barth, Vincent 020019
CEA, Le Bourget-du-Lac, France

Barth, Vincent 020226
CEA/ INES, Le Bourget-du-Lac, France

Bartholomäus, Martin 020346
DTU, Roskilde, Denmark

Bartolo, Brian 020334
FIR, Birkirkara, Malta

Basta, Beata 020068
Roltec, Poznań, Poland

Basta, Marek 020068
Roltec, Poznań, Poland

Battisti, Kurt A-Null Development, Vienna, Austria	020255
Bauhuis, Gerard Radboud University, Nijmegen, The Netherlands	020067
Baumann, Kerstin bifa Umweltinstitut, Augsburg, Germany	020470
Baumann, Sara ISFH, Emmerthal, Germany	020063
Baumann, Ulrike ISFH, Emmerthal, Germany	020006
Baur, Carsten European Space Agency, Noordwijk, The Netherlands	020246
Beaucarne, Guy Dow Silicones Belgium, Seneffe, Belgium	020384
Becker, Carl DLR, Almería, Spain	020331
Behrensdorff Poulsen, Peter DTU, Lyngby, Denmark	020037
Beinert, Andreas J. Fraunhofer ISE, Freiburg, Germany	020123
Bejat, Timea CEA, Le Bourget-du-Lac, France	020225, 020500
Belawadi, Aditya Girish Fraunhofer ISE, Freiburg, Germany	020231
Belferkous, Brahim Anis PCCL, Leoben, Austria	020325
Bellmann, Martin SINTEF, Trondheim, Norway	020495, 020510
Bellvert, Eduard Tecnalia, Donostia - San Sebastián, Spain	020139
Beltran-Condori, Sonia University of Antofagasta, Antofagasta, Chile	020129, 020417
Belzunce, María Jesús AZTI, PASAIA, Spain	020514
Bendix, Peter Next2Sun Technology, Dillingen, Germany	020388
Bengoechea, Jaione CENER, Sarriguren, Spain	020181, 020300
Bermudez Benito, Veronica QEERI, Doha, Qatar	020146
Bermudez-Garcia, Anderson Thales Alenia Space, Cannes, France	020246
Berrian, Djaber Belectric, Kolitzheim, Germany	020492
Berson, Solenn CEA / INES, Le Bourget-du-Lac, France	020134

Besson, Pierre 020373
INES, Le Bourget-du-Lac, France

Betak, Juraj 020241
Solargis, Bratislava, Slovakia

Bettucci, Ottavia 020077
University of Milano-Bicocca, Milan, Italy

Bhardwaj, Shashank 020515
TU Delft, Delft, The Netherlands

Bhatnagar, Shrey 020367
Nextracker, Fremont, United States of America

Biard, Yves 020303
SemperStyl, Eragny, France

Bieber, Lisa-Marie 020195
Fraunhofer ISE, Freiburg, Germany

Bilitu, Eddie 020393
Hasselt University, Hasselt, Belgium

Binani, Ashish 020225
TNO, Petten, The Netherlands

Binetti, Simona 020093
University of Milano Bicocca, Milan, Italy

Binetti, Simona 020087
University of Milano-Bicocca, Milan, Italy

Blakesley, James 020293
National Physical Laboratory, Teddington, United Kingdom

Blanc, Philippe 020291
MINES Paris, Nice, France

Blanco Aguiar, Adrián 020243
ieco.io, Vigo, Spain

Blieske, Ulf 020141
University of Applied Science Cologne, Cologne, Germany

Blieske, Ulf 020140
University of Applied Sciences Cologne, Cologne, Germany

Blstak Catlosova, Katarina 020274
Solargis, Bratislava, Slovakia

Blum, Niklas 020235, 020237, 020239
DLR, Almería, Spain

Boccardi, Roberto 020039
DTU, Copenhagen, Denmark

Boccardi, Roberto 020037
DTU, Lyngby, Denmark

Boccardi, Roberto 020028
DTU, Roskilde, Denmark

Boddaert, Simon 020302, 020303
CSTB, Marne-la-Vallée, France

Bokalič, Matevž 020047, 020319
University of Ljubljana, Ljubljana, Slovenia

Bolink, Henk J. 020226
University of Valencia, Paterna, Spain

Bonal, Victor 020085
UAM, Madrid, Spain

Bonnet, Martin 020141
University of Applied Science Cologne, Cologne, Germany

Bonnet-Eymard, Bénédicte 020251
CSEM, Neuchâtel, Switzerland

Borgers, Tom 020225
IMEC, Genk, Belgium

Borgna, Luciano 020369
BFH, Burgdorf, Switzerland

Borie, Benjamin 020039
ATLANT 3D, Taastrup, Denmark

Borowski, Peter 020307
Avancis, Munich, Germany

Borriello, Aniello 020378
ENEA, Portici, Italy

Borzi, Giovanni 020019
Enginsoft, Padua, Italy

Bosch, Elina 020252, 020543, 020564, 020573
Becquerel Institute, Brussels, Belgium

Bosma, Theo 020571
DNV, Arnhem, The Netherlands

Bothe, Karsten 020236
ISFH, Emmerthal, Germany

Bou-Nassif, Liliane 020338
CETHIL, Villeurbanne, France

Bouchier, Daniel 020058
CNRS, Palaiseau, France

Bouguerra, Sara 020156, 020294, 020389, 020393
imec, Genk, Belgium

Bourdin, Vincent 020406
CNRS, Paris, France

Bourgeois, Antoine 020102
SERIS, Singapore, Singapore

Bovesecchi, Gianluigi 020494
University of Rome Tor Vergata, Rome, Italy

Brabec, Christoph J. 020117
HI ERN, Erlangen, Germany

Bradford, David Roy 020077
Newcastle University, Newcastle upon Tyne, United Kingdom

Brailovsky, Peter Henri 020475
Fraunhofer ISE, Freiburg, Germany

Braña, Alejandro F. 020508
Autonomous University of Madrid, Madrid, Spain

Brandstätter, Andreas 020227
Lenzing Plastics, Lenzing, Austria

Braun, Christian 020457
Luxembourg Institute of Science and Technology, Esch-sur-Alzette, Luxembourg

Brecl, Kristijan 020269, 020319
University of Ljubljana, Ljubljana, Slovenia

Bredemeier, Dennis 020240
Leibniz University Hannover, Hannover, Germany

Breitenbücher, Marian 020225
Highline Technologies, Freiburg, Germany

Brendel, Rolf 020006, 020008, 020236, 020240, 020260, 020482
ISFH, Emmerthal, Germany

Brendstrup Møller, Clara Bolette 020028
DTU, Roskilde, Denmark

Bretzel, Tamara 020195
Fraunhofer ISE, Freiburg, Germany

Breyer, Christian 020479
LUT University, Lappeenranta, Finland

Brito, Miguel 020457
University of Lisbon, Lisbon, Portugal

Brivio, Elisabetta 020462
RSE, Milan, Italy

Brockmann, Lukas 020063
ISFH, Emmerthal, Germany

Brodnicke, Linda 020296
ETH, Zurich, Switzerland

Brueckner, Emanuel 020063
ISFH, Emmerthal, Germany

Bründlinger, Roland 020369
AIT, Vienna, Austria

Brun, Gonzalo 020414, 020517
ENDEF, Zaragoza, Spain

Bruno, Maddalena 020452
Fraunhofer ISE, Freiburg, Germany

Buceta, Alicia 020300
CENER, Sarriguren, Spain

Bucher, Christof 020179, 020322, 020359, 020369, 020386
BFH, Burgdorf, Switzerland

Buchholz, Florian 020035, 020225, 020569
ISC Konstanz, Konstanz, Germany

Buchmann, Johanna 020309
Berlin University of Applied Sciences, Berlin, Germany

Buck, Thomas 020033
ISC Konstanz, Konstanz, Germany

Buckland, Daniel 020119, 020218
Henkel, Düsseldorf, Germany

Buddana, Viswa Harinath 020482
DLR, Oldenburg, Germany

Bühlmann, Gian-Luca 020385
ZHAW, Winterthur, Switzerland

Buerhop, Claudia 020149, 020150, 020377
HI ERN, Erlangen, Germany

Buerhop-Lutz, Claudia 020185, 020230
HI ERN, Erlangen, Germany

Burgers, Antonius R. 020405
TNO, Petten, The Netherlands

Burri, Matthias 020179
BFH, Burgdorf, Switzerland

Busto, Chiara 020521
Eni, Novara, Italy

Butrichi, Fabio 020087
University of Milano-Bicocca, Milan, Italy

Butt, Nauman 020394
Lahore University of Management Sciences, Lahore, Pakistan

C. Tavares, Fabiele 020090
Federal University of Rio de Janeiro, Duque de Caxias, Brazil

Cabal, Raphael 020034
University Grenoble Alpes, Le Bourget-du-Lac, France

Caballero, Luis Jaime 020501, 020508
UPM, Madrid, Spain

Caballero, Raquel 020094
CSIC, Madrid, Spain

Caballero, Raquel 020085
IO-CSIC, Madrid, Spain

Cabecinha, Vasco 020565
Nova University Lisbon, Lisbon, Portugal

Cabello, Fatima 020085
IO-CSIC, Madrid, Spain

Caçapietra Pires da Silva, Lucas Teixeira 020025
PUCRS, Porto Alegre, Brazil

Caccavelli, Dominique 020551
CSTB, Bussy-Saint Georges, France

Caccivio, Mauro 020204, 020574
SUPSI, Mendrisio, Switzerland

Caffari, Francesca 020551
ENEA, Ispra, Italy

Calabrese, Nicolandrea 020551
ENEA, Ispra, Italy

Calin, Jean-Paul 020251
ENSTA Paris, Palaiseau, France

Çalışkan Arslan, Meriç 020006, 020135
Kalyon PV, Ankara, Türkiye

Caluori, Philip 020455
Virtual Vehicle, Graz, Austria

Camara, Assa 020274
Solargis, Bratislava, Slovakia

Cambarau, Werther 020139
Tecnalia, Donostia-San Sebastián, Spain

Campana, Pietro Elia 020381
Mälardalen University, Västerås, Sweden

Campos Guzman, Laura 020331
DLR, Almería, Spain

Cancro, Carmine 020378
ENEA, Naples, Italy

Canesse, Auriane 020196
PVsyst, Geneva, Switzerland

Cañizo, Carlos 020097
IES-UPM, Madrid, Spain

Cano, Francisco J. 020139
Tecnalia, Donostia - San Sebastián, Spain

Cano, Lucía 020127
ENDEF, Zaragoza, Spain

Cánovas, Enrique 020508
IMDEA Nanoscience Institute, Madrid, Spain

Cao, Han 020263
SERIS, Singapore, Singapore

Capitaine, Anna 020116
IPVF, Palaiseau, France

Cappelle, Jan 020329, 020351
KU Leuven, Ghent, Belgium

Capron, Guillaume 020217
CEA / INES, Le Bourget-du-Lac, France

Carballo López, José Antonio 020336
University of Almería, La Cañada de San Urbano, Spain

Cardenas, Luis Alejandro 020339, 020546
National University of Colombia, Bogotá, Colombia

Carmo, Paulo 020304, 020420
University of Évora, Évora, Portugal

Carrasco, Luis Miguel 020439, 020535, 020567
UPM, Madrid, Spain

Carrillo Mejía, Luis 020279
District University of Bogotá, Bogotá, Colombia

Carrillo, Rafael E. 020238
CSEM, Neuchâtel, Switzerland

Carroy, Perrine 020226
CEA/ INES, Le Bourget-du-Lac, France

Carstens, Justus 020003
ISC Konstanz, Konstanz, Germany

Cartenì, Fabrizio 020378
University of Naples Federico II, Naples, Italy

Casappa, Michele 020087
National Research Council, Parma, Italy

Casasola Paesa, Marta 020389
Hasselt University, Diepenbeek, Belgium

Castilla Nieto, María del Mar 020336
University of Almeria, La Cañada de San Urbano, Spain

Castillo Patton, Daniel Jason 020326
Enertis Applus+, Madrid, Spain

Castro, Luis Guilherme 020530
Casa dos Ventos, Fortaleza, Brazil

Castro, Rui 020464
University of Lisbon, Lisbon, Portugal

Castro-Gallardo, Fernando 020417, 020422
University of Antofagasta, Antofagasta, Chile

Cavaco, Afonso 020304, 020565
University of Évora, Évora, Portugal

Cebecauer, Tomas 020274
Solargis, Bratislava, Slovakia

Çekerek, Gamze 020006
Kalyon PV, Ankara, Türkiye

Celik, Duygu 020551
WIP Renewable Energies, Munich, Germany

Çeliktaş, Melih Soner 020559
Ege University, İzmir, Türkiye

Centazzo, Massimo 020006
EnPV, Karlsruhe, Germany

Centeno Brito, Miguel 020421, 020490
University of Lisbon, Lisbon, Portugal

Cereceda, Eneko 020055, 020097, 020153, 020287
UPV/EHU, Bilbao, Spain

Ceretti, Mattia 020204
SUPSI, Mendrisio, Switzerland

Cesar, I. 020405
TNO, Petten, The Netherlands

Ceuppens, Ignas 020302
BUILD`UP, Aarschot, Belgium

Chatterji, Nithin 020071
SVNIT, Surat, India

Chen, Daniel 020048
SunDrive Solar, Kurnell, Australia

Chen, Syh-Homg 020161
ITRI, Hsinchu, Taiwan

Chen, Xiang 020111
Hohai University, Changzhou, China

Cheung, Kak Pong 020313
Kiel University of Applied Sciences, Kiel, Germany

Chhapia, Gaurang 020492
Belectric, Kolitzheim, Germany

Chiba, Takahiro 020436
Hokkaido University of Science, Sapporo, Japan

Chichignoud, Guy 020495
13Institut Polytechnique De Grenoble, Grenoble, France

Chicote, Beatriz 020289
Mondragon University, Arrasate-Mondragon, Spain

Chiesa, Matteo 020487
Khalifa University, Abu Dhabi, United Arab Emirates

Chini de Freitas, Felipe 020023
PUCRS, Porto Alegre, Brazil

Cho, Yunae 020045
KIER, Daejeon, South Korea

Choi, Kwan Bum 020102
SERIS, Singapore, Singapore

Chouder, Aissa 020301
University of M'sila, M'sila, Algeria

Chowdhury, Gofran 020276, 020544
3E, Brussels, Belgium

Christ, Anja 020063
ISFH, Emmerthal, Germany

Chrkavy, Daniel 020262
Solargis, Bratislava, Slovakia

Chueh, Wei-Lo 020021
TSEC, Hsinchu, Taiwan

Ciesla, Alison 020065
UNSW, Sydney, Australia

Cirimele, Vincenzo 020314
University of Bologna, Bologna, Italy

Clausing, Roland 020063, 020114
ISFH, Emmerthal, Germany

Clochard, Laurent 020031
Nines Photovoltaics, Dublin, Germany

Clochard, Laurent 020007
Nines Photovoltaics, Dublin, Ireland

Clyncke, Jan 020472, 020513
PV CYCLE, Brussels, Belgium

Coşkun, Özlem 020006, 020027, 020225
Kalyon PV, Ankara, Türkiye

Colberts, Fallon 020389
Zuyd University, Heerlen, The Netherlands

Colin, Hervé 020217, 020262
CEA / INES, Le Bourget-du-Lac, France

Collin, Stéphane 020074
C2N, Palaiseau, France

Colwell, Jack 020048
SunDrive Solar, Kurnell, Australia

Comak, Mertcan 020003
ISC Konstanz, Konstanz, Germany

Connolly, James Patrick 020058, 020060
CNRS, Gif-sur-Yvette, France

Cordeiro, Diogo 020464
EDP, Lisbon, Portugal

Cornago, Iñaki 020392
CENER, Sarriguren, Spain

Cornaro, Cristina 020494
University of Rome Tor Vergata, Rome, Italy

Correa, Guillermo 020412
Gonvarri MS R&D, Corvera - Asturias, Spain

Correia, Joana 020565
University of Évora, Évora, Portugal

Couderc, Romain 020217, 020311, 020546
CEA / INES, Le Bourget-du-Lac, France

Coutel, John 020244
SOLAÏS, Valbonne, France

Cowan, Don 020230
Kiwa PI Berlin, Hudson, United States of America

Cox, Joel D. 020250
SDU Climate Cluster, Odense, Denmark

Cox, Joel D 020306
SDU Climate Cluster, Odense, Denmark

Coz, Pier Luigi 020246
European Space Agency, Noordwijk, The Netherlands

Crespo, Carolina 020490
University of Lisbon, Lisbon, Portugal

Cristiane Pan, Aline 020548
UFRGS, Tramandaí, Brazil

Cristóbal, Ana Belén 020491, 020535, 020575
UPM, Madrid, Spain

Crozier McCleland, Jacqueline 020185, 020344
Nelson Mandela University, Port Elizabeth, South Africa

Cuadra, Juan Manuel 020318
CENER, Sarigurren, Spain

Cui, Jindan 020320, 020525
Tokyo University of Science, Tokyo, Japan

Culot, Dominique 020384
Dow Silicones Belgium, Seneffe, Belgium
Curon, Jonathan 020384
Dow Silicones Belgium, Seneffe, Belgium
Cusenza, Maria Anna 020466
RSE, Milan, Italy

D. Pinto, Luciana 020090
Federal University of Rio de Janeiro, Rio de Janeiro, Brazil
Daenen, Michael 020156, 020389, 020393
imec, Genk, Belgium
Dagla, Anastasia 020276
3E, Brussels, Belgium
Dahle, Arne 020225, 020495
Norsun, Oslo, Norway
Dahlioui, Dounia 020443
University of Agder, Grimstad, Norway
Dalibor, Thomas 020307
Avancis, Munich, Germany
Dalla Maria, Enrico 020485
Eurac Research, Bolzano, Italy
Dalla Torre, Francesco 020010
Applied Materials, Treviso, Italy
Dalmazzone, Didier 020251
ENSTA Paris, Palaiseau, France
Damon, Keanu 020382
7SecondSolar, Cape Town, South Africa
Danelli, Andrea 020462, 020466
RSE, Milan, Italy
Darsene Dimd, Berhane 020270
SINTEF, Trondheim, Norway
Das, Gourab 020005, 020222, 020463
RCT Solutions, Konstanz, Germany
Dasilva-Villanueva, Nerea 020014, 020501, 020508
UPM, Madrid, Spain
Daßler, David 020313
Fraunhofer CSP, Halle, Germany
Daßler, David 020355
Fraunhofer IMWS, Halle, Germany
Daume, Darwin 020361
pvnode, Rosenheim, Germany
Davidsen, Rasmus Schmidt 020028, 020039, 020043
Aarhus University, Aarhus, Denmark
De Almeida, Laura 020074
LAAS-CNRS, Toulouse, France

De Biasio, Martin 020504
Silicon Austria Labs, Villach, Austria
De Blasi, Mariam 020378
Enel Green Power, Pisa, Italy
de Graaf, Gertjan J. 020405
TNO, Petten, The Netherlands
de Groot, Koen M. 020405
TNO, Petten, The Netherlands
De Gruijter, Alvaro 020254
Eurac Research, Bolzano, Italy
de Jong, Minne M. 020169, 020425
TNO, Eindhoven, The Netherlands
De Jong, Richard 020156, 020294, 020389
imec, Genk, Belgium
de l'Epine, Mélodie 020252, 020505, 020543, 020564
Becquerel Institute France, Lyon, France
de l'Epine, Melodie 020225, 020334, 020520, 020558
Becquerel Institute, Brussels, Belgium
de l'Epine, Melodie 020570
IEA PVPS Task 1, Lyon, France
de la Casa Higueras, Juan 020269
University of Jaén, Jaén, Spain
de la Viuda, Eva 020205
University of Valladolid, Valladolid, Spain
de Meatza, Iratxe 020495
CIDETEC, San Sebastián, Spain
De Rose, Angela 020123
Fraunhofer ISE, Freiburg, Germany
De Rose, Jonas 020010
Fraunhofer ISE, Freiburg, Germany
Debastiani Benato, Betina 020019
AMIRES, Prague, Czech Republic
Deepti, 020563
SRM University, Sonipat, India
Del Campo, Valeria 020311
Federico Santa María Technical University, Valparaiso, Chile
del Cañizo, Carlos 020014, 020501, 020507, 020508
UPM, Madrid, Spain
Del Pero, Claudio 020249
Polytechnic University of Milan, Milan, Italy
Del Pozo, Alberto 020197, 020198
TECNALIA, Derio, Spain
del Prado Santamaria, Rodrigo 020191, 020376
DTU, Roskilde, Denmark
del Ser, Javier 020358
UPV/EHU, Bilbao, Spain

Delgado-Sanchez, Jose Maria 020089
University of Seville, Seville, Spain

Delli Veneri, Paola 020378
ENEA, Naples, Italy

Denafas, Julius 020225, 020353
Solitek, Vilnius, Lithuania

Deniz, Engin 020559
Ege University, İzmir, Türkiye

Denke, Sebastian 020236
ISFH, Emmerthal, Germany

Dentz, Laurie 020058
CNRS, Palaiseau, France

Derin Gure, Pinar 020513, 020521, 020556
ODTU GUNAM, Ankara, Türkiye

Derj, Anyssa 020116
IPVF, Palaiseau, France

Dessì, Alessio 020077
CNR-ICCOM, Sesto Fiorentino, Italy

Devenson, Jan 020157
Center for Physical Sciences and Technology (FTMC), Vilnius, Lithuania

Dhimish, Mahmoud 020346, 020376
DTU, Roskilde, Denmark

Di Matteo, Alfredo 020010
Enel Green Power, Catania, Italy

Diab, Mohanad 020203
Eurac Research, Bolzano, Italy

Diano, Marcello 020378
M2M Engineering, Naples, Italy

Diaz, Roberto 020300
Notio Association, Toledo, Spain

Díaz, Sara 020365, 020366
CENER, Sarriguren, Spain

Dietrich, Andreas 020355
DiSUN Deutsche Solarservice, Werder, Germany

Díez Alcántara, Eduardo 020501
UCM, Madrid, Spain

Díez, Eduardo 020508
UCM, Madrid, Spain

Dimd, Berhane Darsene 020495, 020510
SINTEF, Trondheim, Norway

Ding, Kaining 020233
FZJ, Jülich, Germany

Ding, Kung 020111
Hohai University, Changzhou, China

Dittmann, Sebastian 020318
Anhalt University of Applied Sciences, Köthen, Germany

Dittrich, Arne 020240
ISFH, Emmerthal, Germany

Dizier, Antoine 020373
INES, Le Bourget-du-Lac, France

Djeukeu, Ivanol Jaurece 020050
halm elektronik, Frankfurt am Main, Germany

Dobreva, Petja 020193
University of Namibia, Windhoek, Namibia

Dörenkämper, Maarten 020169
TNO, Eindhoven, The Netherlands

Dörn, Markus 020255
A-Null Development, Vienna, Austria

Doi, Minh Thong 020317
CEA INES, Le Bourget-du-Lac, France

Domínguez, César 020209, 020246, 020257
UPM, Madrid, Spain

Donadello, Alessandro 020485, 020489
Edyna, Bolzano, Italy

Donėlienė, Jolanta 020157
Applied Research Institute for Prospective Technologies, Vilnius, Lithuania

Donoso, José 020570
UNEF, Madrid, Spain

Doppler, Christian 020455
Virtual Vehicle, Graz, Austria

dos Reis, Givaldo 020348
University of São Paulo, São Paulo, Brazil

dos Santos, Jeremias 020409
University of Évora, Évora, Portugal

Doucet, Jean-Baptiste 020074
LAAS-CNRS, Toulouse, France

Dovesi, Roberto 020060
Academy of Sciences of Turin, Torino, Italy

Driesse, Anton 020211, 020293, 020452
PV Performance Labs, Freiburg, Germany

Duarte, Dorivaldo 020418, 020565
University of Evora, Évora, Portugal

Dubois, Sebastien 020034
University Grenoble Alpes, Le Bourget-du-Lac, France

Dubravskij, Piotr 020157
Applied Research Institute for Prospective Technologies, Vilnius, Lithuania

Dubravskij, Piotr 020380
Modern E-Technologies, Vilnius, Lithuania

Duerinckx, Filip 020064, 020225
Hasselt Unversity, Genk, Belgium

Düz, Cansel 020135
Kalyon PV, Ankara, Türkiye
Dullweber, Thorsten 020006, 020007, 020008, 020225
ISFH, Emmerthal, Germany
Dunlop, Ewan D. 020173, 020210, 020213
European Commission JRC, Ispra, Italy
Dupon, Olivier 020294
imec, Genk, Belgium
Dupuis, Julien 020188
EDF R&D, Moret Loing Orvanne, France
Dutykh, Denys 020338
Khalifa University, Abu Dhabi, United Arab Emirates
Duzellier, Sophie 020073
University of Toulouse, Toulouse, France
Dypvik Sødahl, Elin 020340
IFE, Kjeller, Norway

Ebert, Matthias 020426
Fraunhofer CSP, Halle, Germany
Ebert, Matthias 020355
Fraunhofer IMWS, Halle, Germany
Ebner, Rita 020318, 020334, 020521
AIT, Vienna, Austria
Echeverria, Oihane 020139
Tecnalia, Donostia - San Sebastián, Spain
Eder, Gabriele C. 020160, 020162, 020249, 020500, 020504
OFI, Vienna, Austria
Eelma, Tonis 020302
IBS, Tartu, Estonia
Efthymiou, Venizelos 020544
EPL Technology Frontiers, Dhali, Cyprus
Egan, Renate 020048
UNSW, Sydney, Australia
Egido, Miguel-Ángel 020407
UPM, Madrid, Spain
Eidtmann, Maximilian 020385
ZHAW, Winterthur, Switzerland
Eijgelaar, Marcel 020571
DNV, Arnhem, The Netherlands
Eikelboom, Erik 020225
Futurasun, Citadella, Italy
Einhaus, Roland 020312
ZSW, Stuttgart, Germany
Eisenacher, Matthias 020141
University of Applied Science Cologne, Cologne, Germany

Eiternick, Stefan — 020004, 020052
Fraunhofer CSP, Halle (Saale), Germany

Ekins-Daukes, Nicholas J. — 020065
UNSW, Sydney, Australia

El Ainaoui, Khadija — 020171
Green Energy Park, Benguerir, Morocco

El mrabet, Yasmine — 020171
Green Energy Park, Benguerir, Morocco

Elgaili, Mohamed — 020166
QEERI, Doha, Qatar

Elhamaoui, Said — 020171
Green Energy Park, Benguerir, Morocco

Ellis, Hanna — 020213
European Commission JRC, Ispra, Italy

Engelen, Tine — 020389
Hasselt University, Diepenbeek, Belgium

Erber, Alexander — 020386
BFH, Burgdorf, Switzerland

Eryılmaz, Hande — 020521
ODTÜ-GÜNAM, Ankara, Türkiye

Escudero, Ana — 020414
IaSol, Zaragoza, Spain

Esmailifar, Seyyed Majid — 020335, 020356, 020374, 020375
Amirkabir University of Technology, Tehran, Iran

Espinosa, Nieves — 020497, 020506
University of Murcia, Murcia, Spain

Essam T. Mohammed, Sarah — 020546
EU SOLARIS, Almeria, Spain

Esteras, Miguel — 020358
TECNALIA, Derio, Spain

Eyhorn, Steffen — 020369
Fraunhofer ISE, Freiburg, Germany

Fabel, Yann — 020235, 020237, 020239
DLR, Almería, Spain

Fabris, Francesca — 020225
Futurasun, Citadella, Italy

Faes, Antonin — 020251
CSEM, Neuchâtel, Switzerland

Falangas, Alexandros — 020210
TRASIS International, Brussels, Belgium

Fang, Xue — 020525
Tokyo University of Science, Tokyo, Japan

Fano, Vanesa — 020055, 020097, 020153, 020287
UPV/EHU, Bilbao, Spain

Farhat, Mohammad 020428
Australian University, Kuwait City, Kuwait

Farina, Andrea 020066
CNR-IFN, Milan, Italy

Farrias-Basulto, Guillermo 020101
HZB, Berlin, Germany

Fath, Moritz 020463
RCT Solutions, Konstanz, Germany

Fath, Peter 020005, 020463
RCT Solutions, Konstanz, Germany

Fava, Henrique 020565
University of Évora, Évora, Portugal

Feichtner, Markus 020255
Sonnenkraft Energie, St. Veit/Glan, Austria

Feichtner, Markus 020160
Sonnenkraft Energy, St. Veit/Glan, Austria

Feldbacher, Sonja 020136, 020500
PCCL, Leoben, Austria

Feldhof, Anne Maren 020522
University of Applied Science Cologne, Cologne, Germany

Fernandes, Cláudia 020464
Centre for New Energy Technologies, Sacavém, Portugal

Fernández Solas, Álvaro 020331
DLR, Almería, Spain

Ferrando, Jorge 020226
University of Valencia, Paterna, Spain

Ferreira, Catarina G. 020250
SDU Climate Cluster, Odense, Denmark

Ferreira, Catarina 020306
SDU Climate Cluster, Odense, Denmark

Ferrero, Sergio 020079
Polytechnic University of Turin, Turin, Italy

Feuerherdt, Niels 020309
Berlin University of Applied Sciences, Berlin, Germany

Fialho, Luis 020203, 020254, 020261, 020304, 020403, 020409, 020418, 020420, 020565
Eurac Research, Bolzano, Italy

Figueroa, Andrés 020339
National University of Colombia, Bogotá, Colombia

Fischer, Stefan 020495
SGL Carbon, Meitingen, Germany

Fleischanderl, Martin 020136
voestalpine Stahl, Linz, Austria

Fleury, Perine 020513, 020521
Biosphere Solar, Delft, The Netherlands

Flouchi, Imane 020171
Green Energy Park, Benguerir, Morocco

Fodor, Nikoletta — 020521
SolarPower Europe, Brussels, Belgium

Fontani, Daniela — 020066
CNR-INO, Florence, Italy

Forster, Jacob — 020135
Fraunhofer ISE, Freiburg, Germany

Forstinger, Anne — 020331
CSP Services, Cologne, Germany

Franch, Jordi Badosa — 020406
Ecole Polytechnique, Palaiseau, France

Franchi, Daniele — 020077
CNR-ICCOM, Sesto Fiorentino, Italy

Franquet, Erwin — 020259, 020428
Côte d`Azur University, Nice, France

Frasson, Nicola — 020019
Applied Materials, San Biagio di Callalta, Italy

Freer, Solomon — 020396
PV Lighthouse, Coledale, Australia

Freitag, Marina — 020077
Newcastle University, Newcastle upon Tyne, United Kingdom

Freund, Timo — 020312
EnBW, Karlsruhe, Germany

Friansyah, Rizal — 020376
DTU, Roskilde, Denmark

Friesen, Gabi — 020160, 020249, 020574
SUPSI, Mendrisio, Switzerland

Friesen, Thomas — 020249
Megasol Energie, Deitingen, Switzerland

Fritz Muñoz, Benjamín — 020099
UPV, Valencia, Spain

Froebel, Jens — 020121, 020142, 020192, 020223
Fraunhofer CSP, Halle, Germany

Frontini, Francesco — 020249, 020253
SUPSI, Mendrisio, Switzerland

Fuentealba-Vidal, Edward — 020129, 020311, 020342, 020417, 020422
University of Antofagasta, Antofagasta, Chile

Füreder-Kitzmüller, Friedrich — 020136
voestalpine Stahl, Linz, Austria

Fuertes Marrón, David — 020014, 020501, 020507, 020508
UPM, Madrid, Spain

Fuertes, David — 020097
IES-UPM, Madrid, Spain

Furnari, Alessandro — 020010
Enel Green Power, Catania, Italy

Fuß, Michael — 020206
MBJ Solutions, Ahrensburg, Germany

Gabor, Andrew M. 020166
BrightSpot Automation, Boulder, United States of America

Gaete, Martin 020311
University of Antofagasta, Antofagasta, Chile

Gafert, Michael 020369
AIT, Vienna, Austria

Gageot, Tristan 020040
CEA / INES, Le Bourget-du-Lac, France

Gainza, Eusebio 020392
ALLOTARRA, Allo, Spain

Galarza, Alejandra 020461
IPVF, Palaiseau, France

Galbiati, Giuseppe 020119, 020218
Henkel, Düsseldorf, Germany

Galdikas, Algirdas 020157
Applied Research Institute for Prospective Technologies, Vilnius, Lithuania

Galiana, Beatriz 020085
Charles III University of Madrid, Madrid, Spain

Galiazzo, Marco 020019
Applied Materials, San Biagio di Callalta, Italy

Gall, Stefan 020101
HZB, Berlin, Germany

Gallmetzer, Sandra 020261, 020509
Eurac Research, Bolzano, Italy

Galparsoro, Ibon 020514
AZTI, PASAIA, Spain

Gamarra, Ana Rosa 020502
CIEMAT, Madrid, Spain

Ganter, Alissa 020296
ETH, Zurich, Switzerland

Gaona García, Elvis Eduardo 020279
District University of Bogotá, Bogotá, Colombia

Garabetian, Thomas 020551
SolarPower Europe, Brussels, Belgium

García Campos, Enrique 020336
University of Almería, La Cañada de San Urbano, Spain

García, Fernando 020326
UC3M, Madrid, Spain

García, Sonia 020139
Tecnalia, Donostia - San Sebastián, Spain

García-Cañas, Alejandro 020257
IMDEA Nanoscience, Madrid, Spain

García-Salinas, María José 020100
University of Almeria, Almería, Spain

Garcia-Sanchez, Almudena 020246, 020257
UPM, Madrid, Spain

Garg, Vivek 020069, 020071, 020081
SVNIT, Surat, India

Garraín, Daniel 020502
CIEMAT, Madrid, Spain

Gasse, Hugues 020073
University of Toulouse, Toulouse, France

Gassner, Anika 020160, 020162, 020500, 020504
OFI, Vienna, Austria

Gatti, Cesare 020541
PedersoliGattai, Milan, Italy

Gattu, Apoorva 020003
ISC Konstanz, Konstanz, Germany

Gautier, Damien 020505
Becquerel Institute, Brussels, Belgium

Gauvin, Xavier 020302
Bouygues Construction, Saint-Quentin-en-Yvelines, France

Ge, Hua 020249
Concordia University, Montreal, Canada

Gebhardt, Paul 020195
Fraunhofer ISE, Freiburg, Germany

Geerligs, L. J. 020030
TNO, Petten, The Netherlands

Gehrlein, Janek 020522
University of Applied Science Cologne, Cologne, Germany

Geier, Jutta 020234
PCCL, Leoben, Austria

Geml, Fabian 020031
University of Konstanz, Constance, Germany

Genovese, Maria 020378
Enel Green Power, Pisa, Italy

Georghiou, George E. 020534
University of Cyprus, Nicosia, Cyprus

Germani, Simone 020302
CEI, Milan, Italy

Getsiou, Maria 020181
Directorate General for Research and Innovation, Brussels, Belgium

Geymayer, Lukas 020136
voestalpine Stahl, Linz, Austria

Ghahremani, Amirreza 020335, 020374
Amirkabir University of Technology, Tehran, Iran

Ghennioui, Abdellatif 020171
Green Energy Park, Benguerir, Morocco

Ghosh, Saptak 020519
CSTEP, Bengaluru, India

Girardi, Pierpaolo 020462, 020466
RSE, Milan, Italy

Giroux-Julien, Stephanie 020338
CNRS, Villeurbanne, France

Gissler, Antoine 020060
EDF R&D, Palaiseau, France

Göckeritz, Robert 020119
Fraunhofer CSP, Halle, Germany

Gohil, Hardik 020222
RCT Solutions, Konstanz, Germany

Gomes de Venuto, Vitor 020025
PUCRS, Porto Alegre, Brazil

Gomez Trillos, Juan Camilo 020482
DLR, Oldenburg, Germany

Gomez-Lazaro, Emilio 020562
University of Castilla-La Mancha, Albacete, Spain

Gonnella, Gabriella 020249, 020254
Eurac research, Bolzano, Italy

González Pérez, Sara 020151
ULL, San Cristóbal de La Laguna, Spain

González Rodríguez, Brais 020243
University of Vigo, Vigo, Spain

González, Miguel Ángel 020205
University of Valladolid, Valladolid, Spain

González-Díaz, Benjamín 020151
ULL, San Cristóbal de La Laguna, Spain

Goraya, Baljeet Singh 020475
Fraunhofer ISE, Freiburg, Germany

Gordillo, Gerardo 020110
National University of Colombia, Bogotá, Colombia

Gordon, Ivan 020521
imec, Genk, Belgium

Gottschalg, Ralph 020158
Anhalt University of Applied Sciences, Köthen, Germany

Gottschalg, Ralph 020056, 020201, 020229, 020233, 020284, 020574
Fraunhofer CSP, Halle, Germany

Govaerts, Jonathan 020019
imec, Genk, Belgium

Gracia Amillo, Ana María 020211
CENER, Pamplona, Spain

Gracia Amillo, Ana María 020318
CENER, Sarigurren, Spain

Gracia Amillo, Ana María 020181, 020365, 020366, 020497
CENER, Sarriguren, Spain

Gregory, Geoffrey 020006
EnPV, Karlsruhe, Germany

Greslou, Olivier 020551
CSTB, Bussy-Saint Georges, France

Grommes, Eva-Maria 020522, 020523
University of Applied Science Cologne, Cologne, Germany

Grosser, Stephan 020119, 020142, 020218
Fraunhofer CSP, Halle, Germany

Grünsteidl, Stefan 020307
Avancis, Munich, Germany

Gruginskie, Natasha 020067
Radboud University, Nijmegen, The Netherlands

Guedea, Isabel 020127, 020517
ENDEF, Zaragoza, Spain

Gülsoy, Eren Cihan 020521
METU, Ankara, Türkiye

Gümüs Çiftci, Burcu 020027
Kalyon PV, Ankara, Türkiye

Guerra, Gerardo 020448, 020481
GreenPowerMonitor a DNV company, Barcelona, Spain

Guidetti, Giulia 020541
Green Horse Advisory, Milan, Italy

Guillemoles, Jean François 020062
IPVF, Palaiseau, France

Guillevin, Nicolas 020225
TNO, Petten, The Netherlands

Gunbas, Gorkem 020113
ODTÜ-GÜNAM, Ankara, Türkiye

Gupta, Akshit 020551
Eurac Research, Bolzano, Italy

Gutierrez, Jose Ruben 020055, 020097, 020153, 020287
UPV/EHU, Bilbao, Spain

Gutjahr, Astrid 020030
TNO, Petten, The Netherlands

Haaland, Petry Kristine Nøttum 020476
NTNU, Trondheim, Norway

Haase, Felix 020063
ISFH, Emmerthal, Germany

Hadiwidjaja, Stella 020102
SERIS, Singapore, Singapore

Hadjipanayi, Maria 020064
University of Cyprus, Nicosia, Cyprus

Haedrich, Ingrid 020195, 020231
Fraunhofer ISE, Freiburg, Germany

Hämmer, Matthias 020470
bifa Umweltinstitut, Augsburg, Germany

Hafidi, Elias 020511
Inflights BV, Brussels, Belgium

Hagemann, Elizabeth M. 020416
Nelson Mandela University, Port Elizabeth, South Africa

Hallais, Géraldine 020058
CNRS, Palaiseau, France

Halle, Lasse 020359
BFH, Burgdorf, Switzerland

Hallensleben, Carina 020220
TAMURA-ELSOLD, Ilsenburg, Germany

Halm, Andreas 020218, 020220, 020221
ISC Konstanz, Konstanz, Germany

Halme, Janne 020249
Aalto University, Espoo, Finland

Hamada, Toshiyuki 020190
Osaka Electro-Communication University, Osaka, Japan

Hammer, Annette 020239
DLR, Oldenburg, Germany

Hamouda, Frederic 020058
CNRS, Palaiseau, France

Hanifi, Hamed 020121, 020125, 020137, 020223
AESOLAR, Koenigsbrunn, Germany

Hansen, Per-Anders 020017, 020503
Institute for Energy Technology, Kjeller, Norway

Harit, Amit Kumar 020064
Hasselt Unversity, Genk, Belgium

Harrison, Samuel 020225
CEA, Le Bourget-du-Lac, France

Hashem, Ahmad 020056, 020201
Anhalt University of Applied Sciences, Köthen, Germany

Hategan, Sergiu Mihai 020283
West University of Timisoara, Timisoara, Romania

Hauch, Jens 020117, 020149, 020150
HI ERN, Erlangen, Germany

Hauer, Martin 020255
Bartenbach, Vienna, Austria

Haverkamp, Helge 020008
centrotherm international, Blaubeuren, Germany

Hee Lee, Sang 020045
KIER, Daejeon, South Korea

Heidrich, Robert 020233
Fraunhofer CSP, Halle, Germany

Heikkinen, Kyösti 020423
VTT Technical Research Centre of Finland, Oulu, Finland

Heiser, Moritz 020230
Kiwa PI Berlin, Berlin, Germany

Helbig, Matthias 020220
ISC Konstanz, Konstanz, Germany

Helten, David 020331
CSP Services, Cologne, Germany

Hennig, Carsten 020313, 020355
saferay holding, Berlin, Germany

Hennig, Patrick 020313
Kiel University of Applied Sciences, Kiel, Germany

Heras, Jesús 020536
Wattkraft, Madrid, Spain

Hermle, Martin 020475
Fraunhofer ISE, Freiburg, Germany

Hernández Mora, Johann Alexander 020279, 020441
District University of Bogotá, Bogotá, Colombia

Hernández, Jaime J. 020257
IMDEA Nanoscience, Madrid, Spain

Hernández, Johann 020526
Francisco José de Caldas District University, Bogota, Colombia

Herodotou, Panayiotis 020534
University of Cyprus, Nicosia, Cyprus

Herrera Leon, Fernando Augusto 020339, 020546
National University of Colombia, Bogotá, Colombia

Herrero, Leire 020139
Tecnalia, Donostia - San Sebastián, Spain

Herrero, Rebeca 020209, 020453, 020459
UPM, Madrid, Spain

Herrmann, Werner 020208
TÜV Rheinland Solar, Cologne, Germany

Herteleer, Bert 020329, 020351
KU Leuven, Ghent, Belgium

Herteleer, Bert 020574
SUPSI, Mendrisio, Switzerland

Hessler-Wyser, Aïcha 020251
EPFL, Neuchâtel, Switzerland

Heydari, Azim 020485
Eurac Research, Bolzano, Italy

Hinken, David 020236
ISFH, Emmerthal, Germany

Hladys, Bertrand 020010
CEA, Grenoble, France

Hoex, Bram 020065
UNSW, Sydney, Australia

Hofer, Leo 020322
BFH, Burgdorf, Switzerland

Hoffmann, Erik 020006
EnPV, Karlsruhe, Germany

Hogan Almeida, Rita UPM, Madrid, Spain	020535, 020567
Hollemann, Christina ISFH, Emmerthal, Germany	020008
Holovský, Jakub Czech Technical University, Prague, Czech Republic	020107
Honrubia-Escribano, Andrés University of Castilla-La Mancha, Albacete, Spain	020562
Hopp, Tobias Sunman Energy, Frankfurt, Germany	020384
Horn, Jonas halm elektronik, Frankfurt am Main, Germany	020050
Horta, Pedro University of Évora, Évora, Portugal	020304, 020403, 020409, 020418, 020420, 020565
Hosatte, Mikaël SEGTON Advanced Technology, Versailles, France	020068
Hoß, Jan ISC Konstanz, Konstanz, Germany	020004, 020035
Hossain, Mohammad Istiaque QEERI, Doha, Qatar	020042, 020075, 020108, 020109, 020146, 020147
Hou, Yi SERIS, Singapore, Singapore	020102
Hsiao, Pei-Chieh UNSW, Sydney, Australia	020048
Hsieh, Cho Fan ITRI, Hsinchu, Taiwan	020083, 020161, 020163
Hu, Shuaifeng University of Oxford, Oxford, United Kingdom	020226
Huang, Chris SunDrive Solar, Kurnell, Australia	020048
Huang, Gan KIT, Eggenstein-Leopoldshafen, Germany	020272
Huang, Lu-Jan TNO, Leiden, The Netherlands	020425
Huang, Tzu-Yen National Synchrotron Radiation Research Center, Hsinchu, Taiwan	020096
Hügi, Matthias BFH, Burgdorf, Switzerland	020322
Huemer, Martin University of Linz, Linz, Austria	020227
Huerta, Hugo E. TUAS, Turku, Finland	020286, 020400
Hüttl, Bernd Coburg University of Applied Sciences, Coburg, Germany	020361

Hulik Jansova, Marketa 020274
Solargis, Bratislava, Slovakia

Hung, Tzu Han 020552
ITRI, Taipei City, Taiwan

Hutterer-Tik, Thomas 020347
Watt Analytics, Vienna, Austria

Hwang, Hye-Mi 020324, 020357, 020561
KIER, Daejeon, South Korea

Iglesias, Unai 020139
Tecnalia, Donostia - San Sebastián, Spain

Ikeda, Kazuaki 020436
AIST, Koriyama, Japan

Infante, Paulo 020420
University of Évora, Évora, Portugal

Isabella, Olindo 020515
TU Delft, Delft, The Netherlands

Ishikawa, Ryousuke 020106, 020115
Tokyo City University, Setagaya, Japan

Iwaszko, Victorien 020495
ROSI Solar, Saint-Martin-d'Hères, France

Izquierdo-Roca, Victor 020094
IREC, Barcelona, Spain

J. N. Soares, Guillermo 020090
Federal University of Rio de Janeiro, Duque de Caxias, Brazil

Jacob, Julieu 020302
METABUILD, Berlin, Germany

Jacobs, Ayesha 020382
Zutari, Cape Town, South Africa

Jaeckel, Bengt 020056, 020119, 020121, 020140, 020142, 020175, 020192, 020201, 020223, 020229
Fraunhofer CSP, Halle, Germany

Jäger Waldau, Arnulf 020570
European Commission, Rome, Italy

Jäger, Philip 020006
ISFH, Emmerthal, Germany

Jäggi, Adrian 020179
BFH, Burgdorf, Switzerland

Järventausta, Pertti 020445
Tampere University, Tampere, Finland

Jaffré, Alexandre 020058
CNRS, Gif-sur-Yvette, France

Jahn, Ulrike 020521, 020574
Fraunhofer CSP, Halle, Germany

Jahn, Ulrike Fraunhofer IMWS, Halle, Germany	020355
Jahreis, Sophia Fraunhofer CSP, Halle, Germany	020142, 020192
Jakomin, Roberto Federal University of Rio de Janeiro, Duque de Caxias, Brazil	020090
Jakubik, Martin Solargis, Bratislava, Slovakia	020274
Jakuza, Paola University of Padova, Padova, Italy	020089
Jalkh, Judy Virtual Vehicle, Graz, Austria	020455
Jandl, Ralf FFHS, Zurich, Switzerland	020204
Jankovec, Marko University of Ljubljana, Ljubljana, Slovenia	020197
Jaworczak, Kamil Technology Innovation Institute, Abu Dhabi, United Arab Emirates	020402
Jensen, Adam R. DTU, Kongens Lyngby, Denmark	020267
Jeong, Jungi K-water, Daejeon, South Korea	020323
Jeong, Kyung Taek KIER, Daejeon, South Korea	020045
Jeong, Minsoo KIER, Daejeon, South Korea	020045
Jeronimo, Pedro CEA, Grenoble, France	020010
Jiang, Zonghan Anhalt University of Applied Sciences, Köthen, Germany	020158, 020201
Jimenez, Maria Onyx Solar, Avila, Spain	020302
Jimeno, Juan Carlos UPV/EHU, Bilbao, Spain	020055, 020097, 020153, 020287, 020289, 020353
Jo, Hyunsik K-water, Daejeon, South Korea	020323
Job, Enzo Fraunhofer ISE, Freiburg, Germany	020231
Johnson, Mark Robert Institut Laue-Langevin (ILL), Grenoble, France	020546
Joo, Dongmyoung KETI, Wonmi-gu, South Korea	020449
Jooss, Wolfgang RCT Solutions, Konstanz, Germany	020005, 020222, 020463

Joseph, Daniel Christopher 020123
Fraunhofer ISE, Freiburg, Germany
Joshi, Deepak 020069, 020081
SVNIT, Surat, India
Joss, David 020359, 020369, 020386
BFH, Burgdorf, Switzerland
Jouini, Anis 020034
ECM Technologies, Grenoble, France
Jouttijärvi, Sami 020286, 020298, 020398
University of Turku, Turku, Finland
Joziak, Roman 020230
Kiwa PI Berlin, Berlin, Germany
Ju, Young-Chul 020324, 020357, 020561
KIER, Daejeon, South Korea
Jugo, Josu 020437
UPV/EHU, Leioa, Spain
Junge, Sebastian 020008, 020482
ISFH, Emmerthal, Germany

Kaaya, Ismail 020156, 020294, 020389, 020393
imec, Genk, Belgium
Kähler, Jan-Dirk 020482
Centrotherm International, Blaubeuren, Germany
Kahraman, Mert 020027
Kalyon PV, Ankara, Türkiye
Kainz, Konrad 020430
AIT, Vienna, Austria
Kaiser, Martin 020215
Fraunhofer ISE, Freiburg, Germany
Kaizuka, Izumi 020570
RTS Corporation, Tokyo, Japan
Kajari-Schröder, Sarah 020063
ISFH, Emmerthal, Germany
Kallioharju, Kari 020444, 020445
TUAS, Tampere, Finland
Kalliojärvi, Heidi 020194
Tampere University, Tampere, Finland
Kalshetty, Mahesh 020519
CSTEP, Bengaluru, India
Kaltenbach, Thomas 020195
Fraunhofer ISE, Freiburg, Germany
Kamphues, Joshua 020031
University of Konstanz, Constance, Germany
Kandiyoti-Eskenazi, Selin 020467
CSEM, Neuchâtel, Switzerland

Kang, Min Gu 020045
KIER, Daejeon, South Korea

Kapetanovic, Viktor 020367
Nextracker, Fremont, United States of America

Karhu, Juha 020286
Finnish Meteorological Institute, Helsinki, Finland

Kari, Thøger 020191, 020376
DTU, Roskilde, Denmark

Karimy, Hedayatullah 020052
Fraunhofer CSP, Halle (Saale), Germany

Karttunen, Lauri 020298, 020398
University of Turku, Turku, Finland

Kasper, Ruth 020167, 020232
University of Applied Sciences Cologne, Cologne, Germany

Katouli, Tannaz 020195
Fraunhofer ISE, Freiburg, Germany

Kaufmann, Kai 020355
DENKweit, Halle, Germany

Kawabata, Rudy 020092
PUC-Rio, Rio de Janeiro, Brazil

Kemp, Linda 020390
MARIN, Wageningen, The Netherlands

Kenchington, Ian 020225, 020474, 020558
Becquerel Institute, Brussels, Belgium

Kenny, Robert 020210
European Commission JRC, Ispra, Italy

Khan, Abeer Ali 020513
First Solar, Mainz, Germany

Khosravi, Arash 020381
Mälardalen University, Västerås, Sweden

Kikkert, Benjamin W. J. 020405
TNO, Petten, The Netherlands

Kilickaya, Seda 020020
ODTÜ-GÜNAM, Ankara, Türkiye

Kim, Jin-Hong 020449
KETI, Wonmi-gu, South Korea

Kim, Jun-Tae 020249
Kongju National University, Chungnam, South Korea

Kim, Kihwan 020112
KIER, Daejeon, South Korea

Kim, Seok Won 020449
KETI, Wonmi-gu, South Korea

Kim, Yong-Jin 020045
KIER, Daejeon, South Korea

Kinge, Sachin 020117
Toyota Motors Europe, Brussels, Belgium

Kitamura, Ibuki 020190
Osaka Electro-Communication University, Osaka, Japan

Kitzberger, Gregor 020136
voestalpine Stahl, Linz, Austria

Kivambe, Maulid 020166
QEERI, Doha, Qatar

Kizukuri, Rihoko 020220
TAMURA-ELSOLD, Ilsenburg, Germany

Kladas, Anastasios 020329, 020351
KU Leuven, Ghent, Belgium

Kleider, Jean-Paul 020040, 020058
CNRS, Gif-sur-Yvette, France

Kleissl, Jan 020528
University of California, San Diego, United States of America

Klengel, Robert 020355
Fraunhofer IMWS, Halle, Germany

Klenk, Markus 020385
ZHAW, Winterthur, Switzerland

Klos, Christine 020510
Buhck Re.Energy, Hamburg, Norway

Kluska, Sven 020019
Fraunhofer ISE, Freiburg, Germany

Klute, Carola 020355
Fraunhofer IMWS, Halle, Germany

Knausdorf, Christian 020361
Coburg University of Applied Sciences, Coburg, Germany

Ko, Seok-whan 020561
KIER, Daejeon, South Korea

Ko, Suk Whan 020324, 020357
KIER, Daejeon, South Korea

Koc, Timurhan 020376
DTU, Roskilde, Denmark

Koduvelikulathu, Lejo Joseph 020035, 020068
ISC Konstanz, Konstanz, Germany

Koduvelikulathu, Lejo 020003
ISC Konstanz, Konstanz, Germany

Köntges, Marc 020206
ISFH, Emmerthal, Germany

Koepge, Ringo 020142, 020192
Fraunhofer CSP, Halle, Germany

Koester, Lukas 020203, 020261, 020325
Eurac Research, Bolzano, Italy

Kohlenberg, Heike 020063
ISFH, Emmerthal, Germany

Kohno, Tohru 020186
Hitachi, Tokyo, Japan

Kolahi, Mohammad 020356, 020375
University of Isfahan, Isfahan, Iran

Konagai, Makoto 020106, 020115
Tokyo City University, Setagaya, Japan

Kono, Toru 020484
Hitachi, Kokubunji, Japan

Konu, Christopher Bruce 020132
HTW Berlin, Berlin, Germany

Kopecek, Radovan 020569
ISC Konstanz, Konstanz, Germany

Kopp, Nils 020220
TAMURA-ELSOLD, Ilsenburg, Germany

Korkmaz Arslan, Melisa 020020
ODTÜ-GÜNAM, Ankara, Türkiye

Korpås, Magnus 020476
NTNU, Trondheim, Norway

Kortetmäki, Aki 020444, 020445
TUAS, Tampere, Finland

Koskela, Juha 020444, 020445, 020554
Tampere University, Tampere, Finland

Kossen, Eric J. 020030
TNO, Petten, The Netherlands

Kowalski, Julia 020237
RWTH, Aachen, Germany

Kräling, Ulli 020215
Fraunhofer ISE, Freiburg, Germany

Kraft, Thomas M. 020423
VTT Technical Research Centre of Finland, Oulu, Finland

Krainer, Diana Maria 020430
AIT, Vienna, Austria

Krasilnikov, Inga 020379
Tel Aviv University, Tel Aviv, Israel

Krever Lopes, Bruno 020023
PUCRS, Porto Alegre, Brazil

Kribus, Abraham 020379
Tel Aviv University, Tel Aviv, Israel

Krishnan, Sasikumar 020361
Coburg University of Applied Sciences, Coburg, Germany

Kroon, Jan 020225
TNO, Petten, The Netherlands

Kuan, Ta-Ming 020021, 020053
TSEC, Hsinchu, Taiwan

Kubicek, Bernhard 020281, 020318, 020334, 020347, 020430
AIT, Vienna, Austria

Kucuk, E. Busra 020030
TNO, Petten, The Netherlands

Kuczyńska-Łażewska, Anna 020498, 020499
Gdansk University of Technology, Gdansk, Poland

Kühne, Philip 020240
Leibniz University Hannover, Hannover, Germany

Kuhrmann, Bernd 020206
MBJ Solutions, Ahrensburg, Germany

Kujansivu, Eino 020554
Solarigo Systems, Pirkkala, Finland

Kumar, Gaurav 020563
MERI College of Engineering and Technology, Bahadurgarh, India

Kumar, Sagarika 020402
Technology Innovation Institute, Abu Dhabi, United Arab Emirates

Kumar, Saurabh 020563
PTB, Braunshweig, Germany

Kuo, Cheng-Wen 020021, 020053
TSEC, Hsinchu, Taiwan

Kurtulus, Gunes 020556
ODTU GUNAM, Ankara, Türkiye

Kuruganti, Vaibhav V. 020033
ISC Konstanz, Konstanz, Germany

Kurz, Hannes 020136
voestalpine Stahl, Linz, Austria

Kusch, Alexander 020361
Coburg University of Applied Sciences, Coburg, Germany

Kuzhagaliyeva, Nursulu 020402
Technology Innovation Institute, Abu Dhabi, United Arab Emirates

Kuznicki, Zbigniew T. 020013, 020068
SEGTON Advanced Technology, Versailles, France

Kwiatkowski, Jerzy 020551
NAPE, Warsaw, Poland

Kyranaki, Nikoleta 020156
Hasselt University, Genk, Belgium

Kyranaki, Nikoleta 020393
Hasselt University, Hasselt, Belgium

Kyranaki, Nikoleta 020294
imec, Genk, Belgium

Kyratsi, Theodora 020495
University of Cyprus, Nicosia, Cyprus

L. Andersen, Nanna 020477
DTU, Roskilde, Denmark

L. Souza, Patrícia 020090
Federal University of Rio de Janeiro, Rio de Janeiro, Brazil

Lachowicz, Agata 020039
CSEM, Neuchâtel, Switzerland

Lahr, Simon 020388
Next2Sun Technology, Dillingen, Germany

Lahr, Simon 020411
Next2Sun, Dillingen, Germany

Lajunen, Antti 020400
University of Helsinki, Helsinki, Finland

Lambertz, Andreas 020233
FZJ, Jülich, Germany

Lamblot, Hervé 020302
Sunstyle, Paris, France

Lamghari, Fouad 020402
Fujairah Research Centre, Fujairah, United Arab Emirates

Lamminaho, Jani 020250, 020306
SDU Climate Cluster, Odense, Denmark

Landaas, Christian 020495
Northern Silicon, Meråker, Norway

Landberg, Lars 020448
DNV Denmark, Hellerup, Denmark

Landberg, Lars 020481
DNV Denmark, Hellerup, Spain

Landes, Dieter 020361
Coburg University of Applied Sciences, Coburg, Germany

Landová, Lucie 020107
Czech Technical University, Prague, Czech Republic

Lansade, David 020073
University of Toulouse, Toulouse, France

Lappalainen, Kari 020194, 020528, 020537
Tampere University, Tampere, Finland

Lara, Yolanda 020127, 020414, 020517
ENDEF, Zaragoza, Spain

Larionova, Yevgeniya 020006, 020007, 020225
ISFH, Emmerthal, Germany

Låstad, Jonas 020011
NTNU, Trondheim, Norway

Laurens-Berge, Clarisse 020034
University Grenoble Alpes, Le Bourget-du-Lac, France

Laurikėnas, Paulius 020353
Solitek, Vilnius, Lithuania

Lauwaert, Johan 020064
Ghent University, Ghent, Belgium

Lazaro-Castrillon, Luna 020085
IO-CSIC, Madrid, Spain

Le Bossenec, Hugo 020116
IPVF, Palaiseau, France

Le Brun, Anton 020096
Australian Nuclear Science and Technology Organisation, Lucas Heights, Australia

Lechón, Yolanda 020502
CIEMAT, Madrid, Spain

Ledesma, Javier R. 020337
UPM, Madrid, Spain

Ledesma, Javier 020446
UPM, Madrid, Spain

Lee, Chun-Wei 020021
TSEC, Hsinchu, Taiwan

Lee, Hyunju 020046
Meiji University, Kanagawa, Japan

Lee, Jieun 020323
K-water, Daejeon, South Korea

Lee, Jin-Seok 020324, 020357, 020561
KIER, Daejeon, South Korea

Legarrea, Aritz 020365
CENER, Sarriguren, Spain

Lelievre, Jean-Francois 020373
INES, Le Bourget-du-Lac, France

Lelong, Benoit 020373
Cythelia Energy, La Motte-Servolex, France

Leloux, Jonathan 020262
LuciSun, Villers-la-Ville, Belgium

Lenain, Philippe 020495
benkei, Lyon, France

Lennon, Alison 020048
UNSW, Sydney, Australia

Lenz, Markus 020226
School of Life Sciences FHNW, Muttenz, Switzerland

Lenzmann, Frank 020019
TNO Energy Transition, Petten, The Netherlands

Leone, Sander 020405
Novar, Rotterdam, The Netherlands

Leonforte, Fabrizio 020249
Polytechnic University of Milan, Milan, Italy

Leopold, Ulrich 020457
Luxembourg Institute of Science and Technology, Esch-sur-Alzette, Luxembourg

Levrat, Jacques 020251, 020467
CSEM, Neuchâtel, Switzerland

Levtchenko, Alexandra 020116
IPVF, Palaiseau, France

Lewandowski, Simon 020073
University of Toulouse, Toulouse, France

Leza, Baurin Gonvarri MS R&D, Corvera - Asturias, Spain	020412
Lezaca, Jorge DLR, Oldenburg, Germany	020239
Li, Xinyang RCT Solutions, Konstanz, Germany	020222
Li, Yung-Chih TSEC, Hsinchu, Taiwan	020021
Li, Yuxuan East China University of Science and Technology, Shanghai, China	020001
Libal, Joris ISC Konstanz, Konstanz, Germany	020218, 020474
Lichtenberger, Janine AIT, Vienna, Austria	020430
Lițiu, Andrei Vladimir EPB Center, Rotterdam, The Netherlands	020551
Lin, Shih-Chieh TSEC, Hsinchu, Taiwan	020021
Lindahl, Johan Becquerel Sweden, Knivsta, Sweden	020486, 020532
Linder, Johannes Belectric, Kolitzheim, Germany	020492
Lindfors, Anders Finnish Meteorological Institute, Helsinki, Finland	020286
Lindig, Sascha Univers, Courbevoie, France	020371
Linke, Jonathan ISC Konstanz, Konstanz, Germany	020004, 020035, 020225
Linß, Volker VON ARDENNE, Dresden, Germany	020033
Lipovšek, Benjamin University of Ljubljana, Ljubljana, Slovenia	020047
Lippke, Benjamin Kiwa PI Berlin, Berlin, Germany	020180, 020230
List-Kratochvil, Emil HZB, Berlin, Germany	020101
Litrico, Grazia Enel Green Power, Catania, Italy	020010
Liu, Cui East China University of Science and Technology, Shanghai, China	020001
Liu, Dongyang ISFH, Emmerthal, Germany	020063
Liu, Han-Chang ITRI, Tainan, Taiwan	020350

Liu, Huiping 020495
GRÄNGES, Finspång, Sweden

Liu, Mengdi 020144, 020208
TÜV Rheinland, Shanghai, China

Liu, Yung-Tsung 020053, 020083
ITRI, Hsinchu, Taiwan

Livera, Andreas 020534
University of Cyprus, Nicosia, Cyprus

Lizin, Sebastien 020513, 020521
UHasselt, Hasselt, Belgium

Llarena, María Elena 020151
ITER, Granadilla de Abona, Spain

Loeckenhoff, Ruediger F. 020416
AZUR SPACE Solar Power, Heilbronn, Germany

Löhning, Martha 020063
ISFH, Emmerthal, Germany

Löhr, Johannes 020063, 020114
ISFH, Emmerthal, Germany

Lokhat, Ismaël 020262
Cythelia Energy, La Motte-Servolex, France

Lokhat, Ismael 020373
Trace Software, Saint-Romain-de-Colbosc, France

Lombardo, Salvatore 020066
CNR-IMM, Catania, Italy

Long, Yean-San 020053, 020083
ITRI, Hsinchu, Taiwan

Longo, Giulia 020099
UPV, Valencia, Spain

Lopes Gomes, Carlos Javier 020432, 020434
Sunveon, Madrid, Spain

Lopes, Ana Patrícia 020464
University of Lisbon, Lisbon, Portugal

López Cuéllar, Juan Manuel 020501
UCM, Madrid, Spain

López Dalmau, Daniel 020432, 020434
Sunveon, Madrid, Spain

López, Nuria 020451
DTU, Roskilde, Denmark

Lorenz, Dieter 020206
MBJ Solutions, Ahrensburg, Germany

Lorenzo Pigueiras, Eduardo 020363
UPM, Madrid, Spain

Lorenzo, Celena 020337, 020536
UPM, Madrid, Spain

Lorenzo, Eduardo 020439, 020446
UPM, Madrid, Spain

Lossen, Jan ISC Konstanz, Konstanz, Germany	020003, 020035
Louwen, Atse Eurac Research, Bolzano, Italy	020203, 020226, 020261, 020509, 020546
Louwen, Atse RISE, Boras, Sweden	020316
Lu, Huan-Wu ITRI, Hsinchu, Taiwan	020161
Lu, Matthew Kiwa PI Berlin, Shanghai, China	020230
Lucea, Aingeru TECNALIA, Derio, Spain	020197, 020198
Lüdemann, Marius Fraunhofer CSP, Halle, Germany	020233
Luís, Margarida University of Lisbon, Lisbon, Portugal	020421
Lustoza de Souza, Patricia UFRJ, Rio de Janeiro, Brazil	020092
Ly, Moussa PUCRS, Porto Alegre, Brazil	020023, 020025
Lyubenova, Teodora European Commission JRC, Ispra, Italy	020210
M. Bazilio, Willian PUC-Rio, Rio de Janeiro, Brazil	020092
M. S. Kawabata, Rudy Pontifical Catholic University of Rio de Janeiro, Rio de Janeiro, Brazil	020090
M. Torelly, Guilherme Pontifical Catholic University of Rio de Janeiro, Rio de Janeiro, Brazil	020090
Ma Lu, Silvia Mälardalen University, Västerås, Sweden	020381
Ma, Xiang SINTEF, Oslo, Norway	020011
Macé, Philippe Becquerel Institute, Brussels, Belgium	020225, 020252, 020474, 020505, 020543, 020558, 020573
Mack, Sebastian Fraunhofer ISE, Freiburg, Germany	020031
Madsen, Morten SDU Climate Cluster, Odense, Denmark	020250, 020306
Mahmood, Aysha DTU, Roskilde, Denmark	020265, 020376
Maixner, Andreas AESOLAR, Koenigsbrunn, Germany	020121, 020125, 020137, 020223

Maiz, Alexander 020437
UPV/EHU, Vitoria-Gasteiz, Spain

Majak, Martyna 020068
Roltec, Poznań, Poland

Makrides, George 020534
University of Cyprus, Nicosia, Cyprus

Malarkannan, Lavanya 020210
National Physical Laboratory, Teddington, United Kingdom

Malcorps, Philippe 020276
3E, Brussels, Belgium

Malik, Stephanie 020313
Fraunhofer CSP, Halle, Germany

Malik, Stephanie 020355
Fraunhofer IMWS, Halle, Germany

Maliutina, Kristina 020141
University of Applied Science Cologne, Cologne, Germany

Malo, Javier 020209
UPM, Madrid, Spain

Mancini, Simone 020425
TNO, Eindhoven, The Netherlands

Mandiola, Gotzon 020514
AZTI, PASAIA, Spain

Manganiello, Patrizio 020389
Hasselt University, Diepenbeek, Belgium

Manganiello, Patrizio 020294
imec, Genk, Belgium

Manito, Alex 020348
University of São Paulo, São Paulo, Brazil

Manochehrian, Rasoul 020539
Frankfurt University of Applied Sciences, Frankfurt am Main, Germany

Manzolini, Giampaolo 020261
Polytechnic University of Milan, Milan, Italy

Maqsood, Ayman 020101
HZB, Berlin, Germany

Marangis, Demetris 020534
University of Cyprus, Nicosia, Cyprus

Marcos-Castro, Ana 020297
CIEMAT, Madrid, Spain

Marechal, Philippe 020217
CEA / INES, Le Bourget-du-Lac, France

Marí Soucase, Bernabé 020099
UPV, Valencia, Spain

Markert, Jochen 020231
Fraunhofer ISE, Freiburg, Germany

Marquardt, Cornelia 020063
ISFH, Emmerthal, Germany

Marteau, Baptiste 020034
ECM Technologies, Grenoble, France

Martín Rueda, Javier 020535
UPM, Madrid, Spain

Martín, Francisco José 020459
UPM, Madrid, Spain

Martín, Francisco 020209
UPM, Madrid, Spain

Martín-Chivelet, Nuria 020297
CIEMAT, Madrid, Spain

Martín-Rueda, Javier 020337, 020363
UPM, Madrid, Spain

Martínez González, Mario 020326
Enertis Applus+, Madrid, Spain

Martinez, Juan Ignacio 020252
Becquerel Institute Spain, San Sebastian, Spain

Martinez, Oscar 020191, 020205
University of Valladolid, Valladolid, Spain

Martínez-Barbeito, María 020243
ieco.io, Vigo, Spain

Maruyama, Rodrigo P. 020154, 020348
University of São Paulo, São Paulo, Brazil

Marzo, Aitor 020311, 020546
University of Granada, Granada, Spain

Mashkov, Oleksandr 020149, 020150, 020377
HI ERN, Erlangen, Germany

Massaro, Lorenzo 020541
PedersoliGattai, Milan, Italy

Masson, Gaëtan 020474, 020558, 020564, 020573
Becquerel Institute, Brussels, Belgium

Masson, Gaëtan 020570
IEA PVPS Task 1, Brussels, Belgium

Mateos, Yeray 020055, 020153
UPV/EHU, Bilbao, Spain

Maturi, Laura 020249, 020254, 020551
Eurac Research, Bolzano, Italy

Mayer-Ullmann, Philipp 020430
AIT, Vienna, Austria

Mazzoleni, Stefano 020378
University of Naples Federico II, Naples, Italy

McIntosh, Keith R. 020396
PV Lighthouse, Coledale, Australia

McNab, Shona 020065
UNSW, Sydney, Australia

Meereboer, Martijn 020225
Energyra, Westknollendam, The Netherlands

Meier, Rico 020132
HTW Berlin, Berlin, Germany

Meixner, Michael 020050
halm elektronik, Frankfurt am Main, Germany

Mekhaldi, Bouchra 020406
Ecole Polytechnique, Palaiseau, France

Melges de Andrade, Adnei 020154
University of São Paulo, São Paulo, Brazil

Melino, Francesco 020314
University of Bologna, Bologna, Italy

Mellone, Celeste 020541
Green Horse Advisory, Rome, Italy

Menard, Lionel 020291
MINES Paris, Nice, France

Mencaraglia, Denis 020058
CNRS, Gif-sur-Yvette, France

Menchaca, Iratxe 020514
AZTI, PASAIA, Spain

Mendes Ferreira Gomes, Amanda 020548
UFSC, Florianopolis, Brazil

Mendikoa, Iñigo 020514
Tecnalia, BRTA, Derio, Spain

Meneghini, Matteo 020089
University of Padova, Padova, Italy

Ménézo, Christophe 020317
LOCIE, Le Bourget-du-Lac, France

Menghini, Mariela 020508
IMDEA Nanoscience Institute, Madrid, Spain

Mercade Ruiz, Pau 020448, 020481
GreenPowerMonitor a DNV company, Barcelona, Spain

Merino, Amanda 020040
CEA / INES, Le Bourget-du-Lac, France

Merino, José Manuel 020085
UAM, Madrid, Spain

Mermoud, André 020196
PVsyst, Geneva, Switzerland

Merodio, Pablo 020337
UPM, Madrid, Spain

Mertens, Jan 020389
imec, Genk, Belgium

Mertens, Verena 020006, 020008
ISFH, Emmerthal, Germany

Meßmer, Marius 020031
Fraunhofer ISE, Freiburg, Germany

Messmer, Tobias 020218, 020221, 020225
ISC Konstanz, Konstanz, Germany

Messner, Christian 020369
AIT, Vienna, Austria
Mettner, Larissa 020063, 020114
ISFH, Emmerthal, Germany
Meusel, Manuel 020052
Fraunhofer CSP, Halle (Saale), Germany
Meyer, Kevin 020260
ISFH, Emmerthal, Germany
Meza, Carlos 020318, 020334, 020426, 020520
Anhalt University of Applied Sciences, Köthen, Germany
Mezzasalma, Frédéric 020217
CEA / INES, Le Bourget-du-Lac, France
Micha, Daniel 020092
CEFET/RJ, Petrópolis, Brazil
Michael, Poland 020193
Nelson Mandela University, Port Elizabeth, South Africa
Miclea, Paul-Tiberiu 020233
Fraunhofer CSP, Halle, Germany
Midtgård, Ole-Morten 020476
NTNU, Trondheim, Norway
Miettunen, Kati 020286, 020298, 020398
University of Turku, Turku, Finland
Migan-Dubois, Anne 020406
CNRS, Gif-sur-Yvette, France
Mignonac, Alexandre 020217
CEA / INES, Le Bourget-du-Lac, France
Mignonac, Alexandre 020334
CEA, Cadarache, France
Mignonac, Alexandre 020318
CEA, Saint-Paul-Lez-Durance, France
Miguel Laborda, María 020414
IaSol, Zaragoza, Spain
Mihailetchi, Valentin Dan 020033
ISC Konstanz, Konstanz, Germany
Mihailetchi, Valentin 020225
ISC Konstanz, Konstanz, Germany
Mihaylov, Blago 020210
European Commission JRC, Ispra, Italy
Milani, Emanuele 020495
Marelli Europe, Venaria Reala, Italy
Milesi, Frédéric 020068
CEA, Grenoble, France
Min, Byungsul 020008, 020482
ISFH, Emmerthal, Germany
Mirandona López, Haritz 020432, 020434
Sunveon, Madrid, Spain

Miró-Llorente, Marta 020094
IREC, Barcelona, Spain

Misra, Prashant 020429
NISE, Gurugram, India

Miszczuk, Andrzej 020068
Roltec, Poznań, Poland

Mittag, Max 020137
Fraunhofer ISE, Freiburg, Germany

Mittal, Ankit 020318
AIT, Vienna, Austria

Mittelman, Gur 020379
Afeka Tel-Aviv Academic College of Engineering, Tel Aviv, Israel

Mizushima, Io 020028
IPU P/S, Virum, Denmark

Mizushima, Io 020037
IPU, Virum, Denmark

Mngomezulu, Ndumiso 020344
PVinsight, Port Elizabeth, South Africa

Mo, Alvin 020065
UNSW, Sydney, Australia

Mockeviciute-Azzopardi, Austeja 020334
FIR, Birkirkara, Malta

Moe Nygård, Magnus 020340
IFE, Kjeller, Norway

Moehlecke, Adriano 020023, 020025
PUCRS, Porto Alegre, Brazil

Mohammadi, Mohammad Hossein 020037, 020104
Aarhus University, Aarhus, Denmark

Mollier, Stéphane 020262
CEA / INES, Le Bourget-du-Lac, France

Moltke, Asbjørn 020043
Technical University of Denmark, Copenhagen, Denmark

Mondaca-Cuevas, Gino 020422
University of Antofagasta, Antofagasta, Chile

Monokroussos, Christos 020181
TÜV Rheinland Shanghai, Shanghai, China

Monokroussos, Christos 020144, 020208
TÜV Rheinland, Shanghai, China

Monteiro Martins, Filipa 020317
Galp Energia, Lisbon, Portugal

Montes, Carlos 020151
ITER, Granadilla de Abona, Spain

Montoya, Josefa 020311
University of Antofagasta, Antofagasta, Chile

Morabito, Floriana 020066
CNR-IFN, Milan, Italy

Moradi Sizkouhi, Amirmohammad 020356, 020375
Concordia University, Montreal, Canada

Moradi Zavie Kord, Soroush 020400
University of Helsinki, Helsinki, Finland

Morales, Sergio 020491
UPM, Madrid, Spain

Morantes Quintana, Giobertti Raul 020551
Eurac Research, Bolzano, Italy

Mordvinkin, Anton 020233
Fraunhofer CSP, Halle, Germany

Moreda, Guillermo P. 020407
UPM, Madrid, Spain

Morin, Claire 020551
SolarPower Europe, Brussels, Belgium

Morisset, Audrey 020068
CSEM, Neuchâtel, Switzerland

Morlier, Arnaud 020156
Hasselt University, Genk, Belgium

Morlier, Arnaud 020294, 020389
imec, Genk, Belgium

Mortazavifar, Leila 020056, 020158, 020201, 020284
Anhalt University of Applied Sciences, Köthen, Germany

Moruno, Ricardo 020209, 020453
UPM, Madrid, Spain

Mosel, Frank 020015
PVA TePla, Wettenberg, Germany

Moser, David 020573
Becquerel Institute Italy, Trento, Italy

Moser, David 020316
Becquerel Institute, Bolzano, Italy

Moser, David 020254
Bequerel Institute, Trento, Italy

Moser, David 020203, 020226, 020261, 020325, 020485, 020489, 020546
Eurac Research, Bolzano, Italy

Mouhoubi, Felicia 020134
CEA / INES, Le Bourget-du-Lac, France

Müllejans, Harald 020208, 020213
European Commission JRC, Ispra, Italy

Müller, Alexander 020119
Fraunhofer CSP, Halle, Germany

Müller, Larissa 020523
University of Applied Sciences Cologne, Cologne, Germany

Mugica, Maikel 020139
Tecnalia, Donostia - San Sebastián, Spain

Mujovi, Fahradin 020251
CSEM, Neuchâtel, Switzerland

Mukherjee, Srijani 020338
CEA / INES, Le Bourget-du-Lac, France

Mukhtar, Mariyam 020057
University of Verona, Verona, Italy

Mulder, Peter 020067
Radboud University, Nijmegen, The Netherlands

Muller, Matthew 020314
NREL, Denver, United States of America

Munkhammar, Joakim 020532
Uppsala University, Uppsala, Sweden

Muñoz Cerón, Emilio 020269
University of Jaén, Jaén, Spain

Muñoz, Delfina 020040, 020311, 020546
CEA / INES, Le Bourget-du-Lac, France

Muñoz, Delfina 020521
CEA, Le Bourget-du-Lac, France

Muñoz, Delfina 020226
CEA/ INES, Le Bourget-du-Lac, France

Muñoz, Ildefonso 020365, 020366, 020392
CENER, Sarriguren, Spain

Muñoz, Jesús Ángel 020508
UCM, Madrid, Spain

Muñoz-García, Miguel-Ángel 020407
UPM, Madrid, Spain

Murano, Giovanni 020551
ENEA, Ispra, Italy

Murillo, Asier 020497
CENER, Sarriguren, Spain

Musembi, Robinson J. 020272
University of Nairobi, Nairobi, Kenya

Nabipouor, Mohammad 020426
Anhalt University of Applied Sciences, Köthen, Germany

Nagel, Henning 020475
Fraunhofer ISE, Freiburg, Germany

Nakamura, Kyotaro 020046
Toyota Technological Institute, Nagoya, Japan

Nanno, Ikuo 020190
Nanno Energy Research Center, Yamaguchi, Japan

Nargelienė, Viktorija 020157
Center for Physical Sciences and Technology (FTMC), Vilnius, Lithuania

Narsi Patel, Hitarth 020069
SVNIT, Surat, India

Narvarte, Luis 020337, 020446, 020491, 020535, 020536, 020567, 020575
UPM, Madrid, Spain

Nascimento, Lucas 020377
Solar Energy Research Laboratory Fotovoltaica/ UFSC, Florianópolis, Brazil

Nasebandt, Lasse 020063
ISFH, Emmerthal, Germany

Nasser, Hisham 020226
ODTÜ-GÜNAM, Ankara, Türkiye

Naveiro, José Manuel 020414
ENDEF, Zaragoza, Spain

Nazififard, Mohammad 020259, 020428
Côte d`Azur University, Nice, France

Nejim, Ahmed 020058
SILVACO, St. Ives, United Kingdom

Nel, Paul 020382
7SecondSolar, Cape Town, South Africa

Nelson, Jenny 020394
Imperial College London, London, United Kingdom

Neuba, Adam 020114
Paderborn University, Paderborn, Germany

Neuber, Viola 020031
Fraunhofer ISE, Freiburg, Germany

Neuhaus, Holger 020123, 020140
Fraunhofer ISE, Freiburg, Germany

Neumaier, Lukas 020504
Silicon Austria Labs, Villach, Austria

Neussl, Vassilissa 020318, 020430
AIT, Vienna, Austria

Neykova, Neda 020107
Czech Technical University, Prague, Czech Republic

Nezhad, Mahyar 020230
Kiwa PI Berlin, Hudson, United States of America

Nguyen, Viet Xuan 020008
centrotherm international, Blaubeuren, Germany

Nicolet-dit-Félix, Kléber 020251
EPFL, Neuchâtel, Switzerland

Nicot-Senneville, Zoltan 020102
SERIS, Singapore, Singapore

Nielsen, Michael P. 020065
UNSW, Sydney, Australia

Nissen, Hauke 020313
Wattmanufactur, Galmsbüll, Germany

Nitsche, Tobias 020119, 020218
Henkel, Düsseldorf, Germany

Nobre, André M. 020263
PV Doctor, Singapore, Singapore

Noels, Serge 020472
PV CYCLE, Brussels, Belgium

Noh, Yong-Su 020449
KETI, Wonmi-gu, South Korea

Nold, Sebastian 020461
Fraunhofer ISE, Freiburg, France

Nold, Sebastian 020475
Fraunhofer ISE, Freiburg, Germany

Nordboe, Eirik 020495
Fiven Norge, Lillesand, Norway

Norde Santos, Fernanda 020331
DLR, Almería, Spain

Nouri, Bijan 020235, 020237, 020239
DLR, Almería, Spain

Nova, David 020339
National University of Colombia, Bogotá, Colombia

Núñez, Rubén 020209, 020453
UPM, Madrid, Spain

Núñez-Osorio, Alessia 020100
University of Almeria, Almeria, Spain

Nurmesjärvi, Antti 020423
VTT Technical Research Centre of Finland, Oulu, Finland

Nussbaumer, Hartmut 020385
ZHAW, Winterthur, Switzerland

Nyang'onda, Thomas N. 020272
University of Nairobi, Nairobi, Kenya

Obeidavi, Sahereh 020361
Coburg University of Applied Sciences, Coburg, Germany

Oberbeck, Lars 020461
TotalEnergies OneTech, Paris, France

Oberegger Filippi, Ulrich 020551
Eurac Research, Bolzano, Italy

Ocaña, Luis Manuel 020151
ITER, Granadilla de Abona, Spain

Ockert, Ajka 020312
EnBW, Karlsruhe, Germany

Odilio dos Santos, Daniel 020548
UFSC, Florianopolis, Brazil

Öhgren, Gustav 020532
Becquerel Sweden, Knivsta, Sweden

Öttl, Christian 020347
Watt Analytics, Vienna, Austria

Öz, Aksel Kaan 020135
Fraunhofer ISE, Freiburg, Germany

Özden, Talat 020226
ODTÜ-GÜNAM, Ankara, Türkiye

Özkalay, Ebrar 020160, 020204
SUPSI, Mendrisio, Switzerland

Ogura, Atsushi 020046
Meiji University, Kanagawa, Japan

Ohdaira, Keisuke 020131
JAIST, Ishikawa, Japan

Ohshita, Yoshio 020046
Toyota Technological Institute, Nagoya, Japan

Ojala, Aleksi 020554
Solarigo Systems, Pirkkala, Finland

Okawa, Hayato 020115
Tokyo City University, Setagaya, Japan

Okel, Lars A. G. 020030
TNO, Petten, The Netherlands

Oksanen, Jani 020067
Aalto University, Espoo, Finland

Oliosi, Michele 020196
PVsyst, Geneva, Switzerland

Olivares, Douglas 020311
University of Antofagasta, Antofagasta, Chile

Olivares, Gregorio 020365, 020366, 020392
CENER, Sarriguren, Spain

Oliveira Santos, João Victor 020188
EDF R&D, Moret Loing Orvanne, France

Oliveira, Helena 020420
University of Évora, Évora, Portugal

Oller Westerberg, Amelia 020570
Becquerel Sweden, Knivsta, Sweden

Ollo, Olatz 020139
Tecnalia, Donostia - San Sebastián, Spain

Oozeki, Takashi 020436, 020525
AIST, Koriyama, Japan

Opatovsky, Martin 020241, 020262
Solargis, Bratislava, Slovakia

Oreski, Gernot 020136, 020234, 020325, 020500, 020574
PCCL, Leoben, Austria

Ortega, Eneko 020055, 020153, 020287, 020353
UPV/EHU, Bilbao, Spain

Ortega, Eneko 020289, 020437
UPV/EHU, Leioa, Spain

Ortega, Pascal 020214
University of French Polynesia, Faa'a, French Polynesia

Ortiz-Pena, Aaron 020562
University of Castilla-La Mancha, Albacete, Spain

Ory, Daniel 020188
EDF R&D, Palaiseau, France

Ory, Daniel 020116
EDF, Palaiseau, France

Osman, Alaa 020006
ISFH, Emmerthal, Germany

Osuna, Jose Antonio 020358
MAGTEL, Córdoba, Spain

Osvald, Oliver 020274
Solargis, Bratislava, Slovakia

Otaegi, Aloña 020055, 020097, 020153, 020287
UPV/EHU, Bilbao, Spain

Otnes, Gaute 020169
Institute for Energy Technology, Kjeller, Norway

Otto, Nicolas 020101
HTW, Berlin, Germany

Otto, William 020390
MARIN, Wageningen, The Netherlands

Ou, Chao-Wei 020350
National Chin-Yi University of Technology, Taichung, Taiwan

Ovaitt, Silvana 020314
NREL, Denver, United States of America

Ovaitt, Silvana 020574
NREL, Golden, United States of America

Oviedo Hernandez, Guillermo 020325
BayWa r.e, Rome, Italy

Ozer, Shay 020379
Agricultural Research Organization, Rishon LeZion, Israel

P. Pires, Maurício 020090
Federal University of Rio de Janeiro, Rio de Janeiro, Brazil

Pabiou, Herve 020338
CETHIL, Villeurbanne, France

Pabst, Elena 020312
ZSW, Stuttgart, Germany

Paiva, Lúcio 020530
Casa dos Ventos, Fortaleza, Brazil

Palais, Olivier 020188
Toulon University, Marseille, France

Palitzsch, Wolfram 020225, 020495
LuxChemTech, Freiberg, Germany

Palomino, Laura 020491, 020535
UPM, Madrid, Spain

Pamir Aly, Shahzada 020229
DEWA, Dubai, United Arab Emirates

Pamula, Bindu 020069
SVNIT, Surat, India

Panda, Pavan Kumar 020284
Anhalt University of Applied Sciences, Köthen, Germany

Pandar, Matthias 020229
Fraunhofer CSP, Halle, Germany

Pander, Matthias 020121, 020142, 020175, 020192, 020218, 020223, 020232
Fraunhofer CSP, Halle, Germany

Panduri, Fabio 020322
BFH, Burgdorf, Switzerland

Pantoja, Jaime 020526
Francisco José de Caldas District University, Bogota, Colombia

Papantoni, Veatriki 020482
DLR, Oldenburg, Germany

Paraficz, Danuta 020204
FFHS, Zurich, Switzerland

Paraskeva, Vasiliki 020064
University of Cyprus, Nicosia, Cyprus

Pardo, Eduardo 020414
Tecnova, Almeira, Spain

Parfeniukas, Karolis 020039
ATLANT 3D, Taastrup, Denmark

Parion, Jonathan 020064
Hasselt Unversity, Genk, Belgium

Park, Hyeonwook 020112
KENTECH, Naju-Si, South Korea

Parmar, Richa 020429
NISE, Gurugram, India

Parra, Johan 020406
Ecole Polytechnique, Palaiseau, France

Parra, Johan 020214
Polytechnic Institute of Paris, Palaiseau, France

Parrilla, Carlos G. 020402
Fujairah Research Centre, Fujairah, United Arab Emirates

Pascual Gallego, Valero 020407
UPM, Madrid, Spain

Pasquier, Mathis 020451
DTU, Roskilde, Denmark

Passaro, Marcello 020513
Sunzest Solar, Rotterdam, The Netherlands

Patel, Dharm 020355
Fraunhofer IMWS, Halle, Germany

Paul, Ananta 020250, 020306
SDU Climate Cluster, Odense, Denmark

Paulescu, Marius 020283
West University of Timisoara, Timisoara, Romania

Paviet-Salomon, Bertrand 020068, 020467
CSEM, Neuchâtel, Switzerland

Payno, David 020085, 020094
UAM, Madrid, Spain

Pearce, Pheobe 020065
UNSW, Sydney, Australia

Peche, René 020468, 020495
bifa Umweltinstitut, Augsburg, Germany

Pehlivanli, Ezgi 020521
METU, Ankara, Türkiye

Peibst, Robby 020006, 020063, 020114
ISFH, Emmerthal, Germany

Pelfort Ojer, Marta 020241
Solargis, Bratislava, Slovakia

Pelland, Sophie 020211
Natural Resources Canada, Varennes, Canada

Pelle, Martina 020249, 020254
Eurac Research, Bolzano, Italy

Peña-Bermudez, Julian 020110
University of the Caribbean, Santo Domingo, Dominican Republic

Peng, Cheng-Yu 020350
National Chin-Yi University of Technology, Taichung, Taiwan

Pera, David 020457
Luxembourg Institute of Science and Technology, Esch-sur-Alzette, Luxembourg

Perani, Martina 020204
FFHS, Zurich, Switzerland

Peraticos, Elias 020064
University of Cyprus, Nicosia, Cyprus

Pereda, Ainhoa 020198, 020358
TECNALIA, Derio, Spain

Pereira Fialho, Luis Andre 020509
Eurac Research, Bolzano, Italy

Pereira, Sara 020403, 020418, 020565
University of Évora, Évora, Portugal

Pérez García, Manuel 020336
University of Almería, La Cañada de San Urbano, Spain

Pérez, Ernesto 020339
National University of Colombia, Bogotá, Colombia

Pérez, Jairo 020412
Gonvarri AgroTech, Corvera - Asturias, Spain

Pérez, Jorge 020412
Gonvarri AgroTech, Corvera - Asturias, Spain

Pérez, Luis 020412
Gonvarri MS R&D, Corvera - Asturias, Spain

Perez, Richard 020494
University at Albany, Albany, United States of America

Perez-Astudillo, Daniel 020275, 020278, 020291
QEERI, Doha, Qatar

Pérez-García, Manuel 020100
University of Almeria, Almería, Spain

Pérez-Rodríguez, Alejandro 020085, 020094
IREC, Barcelona, Spain

Pernas, Tomás 020412
Gonvarri AgroTech, Corvera - Asturias, Spain

Pernau, Thomas 020008
centrotherm international, Blaubeuren, Germany

Perrin, Marion 020544
Energy Pool, Le Bourget-du-Lac, France

Pervan, Nikolina 020136, 020234
PCCL, Leoben, Austria

Peter Amalathas, Amalraj 020107
University of Jaffna, Jaffna, Sri Lanka

Peter, Kristian 020569
ISC Konstanz, Konstanz, Germany

Peters, Ian Marius 020230, 020263
Forschungszentrum Jülich, Erlangen, Germany

Peters, Ian Marius 020149, 020150, 020377, 020574
HI ERN, Erlangen, Germany

Petersons, Karlis 020250, 020306
Stensborg, Roskilde, Denmark

Petkovski, Emil 020571
DNV, Arnhem, The Netherlands

Petzschmann, Jonas 020312
ZSW, Stuttgart, Germany

Pfau, Jan Hendrik 020240
Leibniz University Hannover, Hannover, Germany

Pfeiffer, Oliver 020141
University of Applied Science Cologne, Cologne, Germany

Pfeiffer, Oliver 020140
University of Applied Sciences Cologne, Cologne, Germany

Philipp, Daniel 020215, 020231
Fraunhofer ISE, Freiburg, Germany

Pierro, Marco 020489, 020494
Eurac Research, Bolzano, Italy

Pieters, Bart E. 020180
FZJ, Jülich, Germany

Pieterse, Marco 020495
Chemconserve, Bussum, The Netherlands

Pietralunga, Silvia Maria 020066
CNR-IFN, Milan, Italy

Pietsch, Veith 020331
Aquila Capital, Hamburg, Germany

Pilat, Eric 020311
CEA / INES, Le Bourget-du-Lac, France

Pilat, Eric 020317
CEA INES, Le Bourget-du-Lac, France

Pillai, Akhildev 020558
Becquerel Institute, Brussels, Belgium

Pinheiro, Philippe 020457
Luxembourg Institute of Science and Technology, Esch-sur-Alzette, Luxembourg

Pinho Almeida, Marcelo 020348
University of São Paulo, São Paulo, Brazil

Pinto, Cristina Leyre 020497
CENER, Sarriguren, Spain

Pinto, Luciana 020092
UFRJ, Rio de Janeiro, Brazil

Pitaval, Sébastien 020244
SOLAÏS, Valbonne, France

Pitz-Paal, Robert 020237, 020331
DLR, Cologne, Germany

Plakhotnyuk, Maksym 020039
ATLANT 3D, Taastrup, Denmark

Platero Gaona, Carlos A. 020332
UPM, Madrid, Spain

Plaza, Caroline 020543, 020564, 020573
Becquerel Institute France, Lyon, France

Polacchi, Cristina 020509, 020513
Eurac Research, Bolzano, Italy

Polo, Jaime 020300
CENER, Sarriguren, Spain

Polo, Jesús 020297
CIEMAT, Madrid, Spain

Polverini, Davide 020181
Directorate General for Internal Market, Industry, Entrepreneurship and SMEs, Brussels, Belgium

Polverini, Davide 020497
European Comission, Brussels, Belgium

Pongthanacharoenkul, Nattapark 020230
Kiwa PI Berlin, Berlin, Germany

Poortmans, Jef 020064
Hasselt Unversity, Genk, Belgium

Popescu, Lacramioara 020068
ISC Konstanz, Konstanz, Germany

Pospischil, Maximilian 020225
Highline Technologies, Freiburg, Germany

Poulsen, Peter B. 020039
DTU, Copenhagen, Denmark
Poulsen, Peter B. 020250, 020265, 020267, 020376, 020451
DTU, Roskilde, Denmark
Poulsen, Peter Behrensdorff 020028, 020306, 020346
DTU, Roskilde, Denmark
Pourshafi, Pouya 020121, 020125, 020137
AESOLAR, Koenigsbrunn, Germany
Pozza, Cristian 020551
Eurac Research, Bolzano, Italy
Prakash, Jai 020429
NISE, Gurugram, India
Prando, Davide 020485, 020489
Edyna, Bolzano, Italy
Prasad, Manjunath 020225
ISC Konstanz, Konstanz, Germany
Pravettoni, Mauro 020402
Technology Innovation Institute, Abu Dhabi, United Arab Emirates
Preis, Pirmin 020003
ISC Konstanz, Konstanz, Germany
Preu, Ralf 020475
Fraunhofer ISE, Freiburg, Germany
Preuschoff, Jonas 020101
HTW, Berlin, Germany
Protti, Alexander Aguilar 020140
Fraunhofer ISE, Freiburg, Germany
Protti, Alexander 020137
Fraunhofer ISE, Freiburg, Germany
Provost, Marion 020116
IPVF, Palaiseau, France
Puel, Jean Baptiste 020062
IPVF, Palaiseau, France
Puertas López, Antonio Manuel 020100
University of Almeria, Almeria, Spain
Puttock, Claire 020367
Nextracker, Fremont, United States of America

Queste, Samuel 020068
Marie and Louis Pasteur University, Besançon, France
Quiroz, Mónica 020328
Qualifying Photovoltaics, Madrid, Spain

R. Ledesma, Javier 020363
UPM, Madrid, Spain

Rabanal Arabach, Jorge 020183
University of Antofagasta, Antofagasta, Chile
Rabanal-Arabach, Jorge 020129, 020342, 020417, 020422
University of Antofagasta, Antofagasta, Chile
Rabiei, Hossein 020063
ISFH, Emmerthal, Germany
Rachdi, Lazhar 020035, 020068
ISC Konstanz, Konstanz, Germany
Radzevicius, Aurimas 020225
Valoe Cells, Vilnius, Lithuania
Rafiee, Hossein 020539
Frankfurt University of Applied Sciences, Frankfurt am Main, Germany
Raginskis, Justinas 020380
Kaunas University of Technology, Kaunas, Lithuania
Raievska, Oleksandra 020117, 020149
HI ERN, Erlangen, Germany
Rajan, S. Prithivi 020262
LuciSun, Villers-la-Ville, Belgium
Rajkiewicz, Katarzyna 020551
NAPE, Warsaw, Poland
Rakotoniaina, Jean Patrice 020311
CEA / INES, Le Bourget-du-Lac, France
Ramachandran Nair, Jishnu 020233
Fraunhofer CSP, Halle, Germany
Ramesh, Santhosh 020389
imec, Genk, Belgium
Ramírez Ledesma, Javier 020535
UPM, Madrid, Spain
Ramirez, S. 020396
PV Lighthouse, Coledale, Australia
Rampino, Stefano 020087
National Research Council, Parma, Italy
Ramspeck, Klaus 020050
halm elektronik, Frankfurt am Main, Germany
Ranisch, Tadeus 020101
HTW, Berlin, Germany
Ranta, Samuli 020286, 020400
TUAS, Turku, Finland
Ranta, Samuli 020298, 020398
Turku University of Applied Sciences, Turku, Finland
Raposo, Mauro 020565
University of Évora, Évora, Portugal
Ratnagiri, Abhinav 020367
Nextracker, Fremont, United States of America
Raugewitz, Annika 020063, 020114
ISFH, Emmerthal, Germany

Raval, Mehul 020005, 020222, 020463
RCT Solutions, Konstanz, Germany
Razanajao, Aina 020244
SOLAÏS, Valbonne, France
Razi, Umair 020085
IREC, Barcelona, Spain
Recart, Federico 020097
UPV/EHU, Bilbao, Spain
Redondo Cuevas, Marta 020332
UPM, Madrid, Spain
Redondo, Juan Manuel 020209
UPM, Madrid, Spain
Rehan, Muhammad 020112
KIER, Daejeon, South Korea
Rehman, Anees ur 020111, 020164
Hohai University, Changzhou, China
Reichart, Hannah 020167, 020232
University of Applied Sciences Cologne, Cologne, Germany
Reichel, Christian 020123, 020137, 020140
Fraunhofer ISE, Freiburg, Germany
Reichle, Julian 020005, 020222, 020463
RCT Solutions, Konstanz, Germany
Reinders, Angele 020253
TU Eindhoven, Eindhoven, The Netherlands
Reindl, Thomas 020263
SERIS, Singapore, Singapore
Reis, Luiz Filipe 020530
Casa dos Ventos, Fortaleza, Brazil
Rémondeau, Paul 020251
EPFL, Neuchâtel, Switzerland
Renard, Charles 020058
CNRS, Palaiseau, France
Rende, Fedele 020255
ACCA Software, Cosenza, Italy
Rennhofer, Marcus 020180, 020281, 020318, 020334, 020347,
AIT, Vienna, Austria 020430
Rentsch, Jochen 020475
Fraunhofer ISE, Freiburg, Germany
Rerat, Michel 020060
IPREM, Pau, France
Reshef, Liad 020379
Agricultural Research Organization, Rishon LeZion, Israel
Revol, Inès 020074
LAAS-CNRS, Toulouse, France
Reyal, Jean-Pierre 020303
SemperStyl, Eragny, France

Riaño, Sandra 020197, 020358
TECNALIA, Derio, Spain

Richards, Bryce S. 020272
KIT, Karlsruhe, Germany

Riechelman, Stefan 020181
PTB, Braunschweig, Germany

Riechelmann, Stefan 020177, 020199, 020211
PTB, Braunschweig, Germany

Riedel-Lyngskær, Nicholas 020451
DTU, Roskilde, Denmark

Rienäcker, Michael 020063
ISFH, Emmerthal, Germany

Rindert, Sören 020230
Kiwa PI Berlin, Berlin, Germany

Ríos Moral, Lucía 020501
UCM, Madrid, Spain

Ríos-Ledesma, Felipe 020446
UPM, Madrid, Spain

Ripke, Melanie 020006
ISFH, Emmerthal, Germany

Riva, Roland 020495
CEA, Le Bourget-du-Lac, France

Rivas Rodríguez, José Manuel 020326
Enertis Applus+, Madrid, Spain

Robledo, Jesús 020262
LuciSun, Villers-la-Ville, Belgium

Rodríguez Lucas, Delia 020407
EkiLabs, Boston, United States of America

Rodríguez Plaza, José Luis 020508
Autonomous University of Madrid, Madrid, Spain

Rodríguez Rodríguez, Araceli 020501
UCM, Madrid, Spain

Rodríguez Salazar, David Leonardo 020441
District University of Bogotá, Bogotá, Colombia

Rodríguez, Araceli 020508
UCM, Madrid, Spain

Rodríguez, Diego Julián 020526
Francisco José de Caldas District University, Bogota, Colombia

Rodríguez, Isabel 020257
IMDEA Nanoscience, Madrid, Spain

Rodriguez, Sonia Maria 020289
UPV/EHU, Leioa, Spain

Rodríguez, Velia 020097
UPV/EHU, Bilbao, Spain

Rodríguez-Conde, Sofía 020326
Enertis Applus+, Madrid, Spain

Rodríguez-Gallegos, Carlos D. 020149, 020150
SERIS, Singapore, Singapore

Rodríguez-Romero, Sebastián 020342, 020417, 020422
University of Antofagasta, Antofagasta, Chile

Rodziewicz, Hanna 020498
Gdansk University of Technology, Gdansk, Poland

Römer, Udo 020006, 020063
ISFH, Emmerthal, Germany

Röver, Ingo 020225
LuxChemTech, Freiberg, Germany

Rojas, Christian A. 020422
Federico Santa María Technical University, Valparaíso, Chile

Rojas-Henríquez, Katalina 020129
University of Antofagasta, Antofagasta, Chile

Román, Eduardo 020139
Tecnalia, Donostia - San Sebastián, Spain

Romeo, Alessandro 020057, 020089, 020093
University of Verona, Verona, Italy

Romer, Pascal 020231
Fraunhofer ISE, Freiburg, Germany

Roodt, Roelof 020185
Nelson Mandela University, Port Elizabeth, South Africa

Roosloot, Nathan 020169
Institute for Energy Technology, Kjeller, Norway

Rosca, Victor 020030
TNO, Petten, The Netherlands

Rosen, Isaac 020225
Copprint, Jerusalem, Israel

Rosenfeld, Lavi 020379
Agricultural Research Organization, Rishon LeZion, Israel

Rosina, Konstantin 020241
Solargis, Bratislava, Slovakia

Rossa, Carlos 020432, 020434
Sunveon, Madrid, Spain

Rouffie, Brice 020068
SEGTON Advanced Technology, Versailles, France

Roulleau, Lea 020303
CSTB, Marne-la-Vallée, France

Rousset, Jean 020116
EDF, Palaiseau, France

Roy, Shantanu 020519
CSTEP, Bengaluru, India

Rudolph, Dominik 020003, 020068
ISC Konstanz, Konstanz, Germany

Rudzikas, Matas 020380
The Applied Research Institute for Prospective Technologies, Vilnius, Lithuania

Rüther, Ricardo 020377
Solar Energy Research Laboratory Fotovoltaica/ UFSC, Florianópolis, Brazil

Rüther, Ricardo 020548
UFSC, Florianopolis, Brazil

Ruf, Manuel 020455
Robert Bosch, Stuttgart, Germany

Ruiz Donoso, Elena 020331
DLR, Almería, Spain

S. Sousa, Graciana 020090
Federal University of Rio de Janeiro, Rio de Janeiro, Brazil

Safarian, Jafar 020011
NTNU, Trondheim, Norway

Sah, Dheeraj 020039
Aarhus University, Aarhus, Denmark

Sahin, Hasret 020479
LUT University, Lappeenranta, Finland

Saito, Kimihiko 020106
Tokyo City University, Setagaya, Japan

Salem, Mohammad 020428
Australian University, Kuwait City, Kuwait

Salerno, Giorgia 020077
University of Milano-Bicocca, Milan, Italy

Salis, Fabio 020541
Iberdrola, Rome, Italy

Salvador, Antonio 020358
MAGTEL, Córdoba, Spain

Sample, Tony 020213
European Commission JRC, Ispra, Italy

Samuolienė, Giedrė 020380
The Lithuanian Research Centre for Agriculture and Forestry, Kaunas, Lithuania

San José, Luis Javier 020209, 020453
UPM, Madrid, Spain

Sánchez de León Peque, Miguel 020243
ieco.io, Vigo, Spain

Sanchez Garcia, Alfredo 020270
SINTEF, Trondheim, Norway

Sanchez, Hugo 020056, 020158, 020284
Anhalt University of Applied Sciences, Köthen, Germany

Sanchez, Jesus 020437
UPV/EHU, Vitoria-Gasteiz, Spain

Sanchez, Laura 020437
UPV/EHU, Leioa, Spain

Sánchez, Yudania 020085
IREC, Barcelona, Spain

Sanchez-Friera, Paula 020412, 020513, 020521
Solkeys, Gijón, Spain

Sanchez-Ruiz, Alain 020437
UPV/EHU, Vitoria-Gasteiz, Spain

Sansavini, Giovanni 020296
ETH, Zurich, Switzerland

Sansoni, Paola 020066
CNR-INO, Florence, Italy

Santamaría Fernández, Susanna 020249
TECNALIA, Derio, Spain

Santamaría-Sancho, Juan 020363
UPM, Madrid, Spain

Santos, Jose Domingo 020197, 020198, 020358
TECNALIA, Derio, Spain

Santos, Rodrigo 020530
Casa dos Ventos, Fortaleza, Brazil

Sanz Martinez, Asier 020546
Tecnalia, Bilbao, Spain

Sanz, Asier 020514
Tecnalia, BRTA, Derio, Spain

Sanz, Asier 020197
TECNALIA, Derio, Spain

Sanz-Cuadrado, Cristina 020575
UPM, Madrid, Spain

Sanz-Saiz, Carlos 020297
CIEMAT, Madrid, Spain

Sarafijanovic-Djukic, Natasa 020204
FFHS, Regensdorf, Switzerland

Saretti, Angelica 020301
Polytechnic University of Bari, Bari, Italy

Sarkadi, Monika 020569
ISC Konstanz, Konstanz, Germany

Sauer, Thomas 020140
EXXERGY, Gräfelfing, Germany

Saura, Juan Antonio 020506
University of Murcia, Murcia, Spain

Savisalo, Tuukka 020225
Valoe, Mikkeli, Finland

Saw, Min Hsian 020402
Technology Innovation Institute, Abu Dhabi, United Arab Emirates

Saxena, Anmol Ratan 020429
NIT, Delhi, India

Sayed, Abdullah Abu 020180, 020230
Kiwa PI Berlin, Berlin, Germany

Scaltrito, Luciano 020079
Polytechnic University of Turin, Turin, Italy

Scerri, Kenneth 020334
University of Malta, Msida, Malta

Schading, Steve 020443
University of Agder, Grimstad, Norway

Schäfer, Aysim 020388
Next2Sun Technology, Dillingen, Germany

Schäfer, Sebastian 020539
Frankfurt University of Applied Sciences, Frankfurt am Main, Germany

Schenk, Paul 020192
Fraunhofer CSP, Halle, Germany

Schermer, John 020067
Radboud University, Nijmegen, The Netherlands

Scherret, Jacqueline 020255
A-Null Development, Vienna, Austria

Schifferegger, Raffael 020162
OFI, Vienna, Austria

Schimanke, Sabrina 020006
ISFH, Emmerthal, Germany

Schirmer, Yoko 020101
HTW, Berlin, Germany

Schläger, Christian 020240
Leibniz University Hannover, Hannover, Germany

Schlatmann, Rutger 020101
HTW, Berlin, Germany

Schmidt Davidsen, Rasmus 020037, 020104
Aarhus University, Aarhus, Denmark

Schnaus, Dominik 020237
TUM, Garching, Germany

Schneider, Andreas 020129, 020183
University of Applied Sciences Gelsenkirchen, Gelsenkirchen, Germany

Schneider, Astrid 020255
TU Wien, Vienna, Austria

Schneider, Friedrich 020482
LPKF SolarQuipment, Suhl, Germany

Schneider, Marc Gabriel 020522
University of Applied Science Cologne, Cologne, Germany

Schneiderlöchner, Eric 020033
VON ARDENNE, Dresden, Germany

Schnierer, Branislav 020262
Solargis, Bratislava, Slovakia

Schönau, Maximilian 020361
Coburg University of Applied Sciences, Coburg, Germany

Schönau, Maximilian 020544
smartblue, Munich, Germany

Schönheits, Markus 020468, 020470
bifa Umweltinstitut, Augsburg, Germany

Schranz, Christian 020255
TU Wien, Vienna, Austria

Schrempf, Michael 020199
PTB, Braunschweig, Germany

Schrijvers, Patrick 020390
MARIN, Wageningen, The Netherlands

Schröter, Nick 020142
Fraunhofer CSP, Halle, Germany

Schubert, Martin C. 020475
Fraunhofer ISE, Freiburg, Germany

Schubnel, Baptiste 020238
CSEM, Neuchâtel, Switzerland

Schüler, Marc Andre 020388
Next2Sun Technology, Dillingen, Germany

Schüler, Marc Andre 020411
Next2Sun, Dillingen, Germany

Schueler, Nadine 020015
Freiberger Instruments, Freiberg, Germany

Schulte-Huxel, Henning 020008, 020260
ISFH, Emmerthal, Germany

Schultz, Christof 020101
HTW, Berlin, Germany

Schulz, Philip 020060
IPVF, Palaiseau, France

Schulze, Achim 020361
Rosenheim Technical University of Applied Sciences, Rosenheim, Germany

Schulze, Patricia S.C. 020475
Fraunhofer ISE, Freiburg, Germany

Schwenke, Almut 020495
SGL Battery Solutions, Meitingen, Germany

Sciuto, Marcello 020010
Enel Green Power, Catania, Italy

Scognamiglio, Alessandra 020541
ENEA, Naples, Italy

Scognamiglio, Alessandra 020378
ENEA, Portici, Italy

Sedaghat, Ahmad 020428
Australian University, Kuwait City, Kuwait

Seiffert, Christoph 020169
Institute for Energy Technology, Kjeller, Norway

Seiffert, Daniela 020008
centrotherm international, Blaubeuren, Germany

Seitz, Matthias 020468
bifa Umweltinstitut, Augsburg, Germany

Selj, Josefine H. 020169
Institute for Energy Technology, Kjeller, Norway

Senno, Maximiliano Alejandro 020226
University of Valencia, Paterna, Spain

Senturk, Bilge 020556
ODTU GUNAM, Ankara, Türkiye

Setien, Eneko 020198
TECNALIA, Derio, Spain

Šetkus, Arūnas 020157
Center for Physical Sciences and Technology (FTMC), Vilnius, Lithuania

Shaaban, Ahmed 020402
Technology Innovation Institute, Abu Dhabi, United Arab Emirates

Shah, Syed Fawad Ali 020112
KENTECH, Naju-Si, South Korea

Shanmugam, Raphael 020218, 020220
ISC Konstanz, Konstanz, Germany

Sharma, Rajesh Kumar 020071, 020081
SVNIT, Surat, India

Sharma, Sushma 020563
SRM University, Sonipat, India

Shen, Xinyi 020226
University of Oxford, Oxford, United Kingdom

Shen, Zhenjue 020001
YIST, Jiangyin, China

Shin, Donghyeop 020112
KIER, Daejeon, South Korea

Shin, Woo Gyun 020324, 020357
KIER, Daejeon, South Korea

Shin, Woo-gyun 020561
KIER, Daejeon, South Korea

Shirai, Yasuhiro 020115
NIMS, Tsukuba, Japan

Shirazi, Elham 020544
University of Twente, Enschede, The Netherlands

Shishavan, Amir Asgharzadeh 020367
Nextracker, Fremont, United States of America

Shishido, Hirotaka 020106
Tokyo City University, Setagaya, Japan

Shochet, Ofer 020225
Copprint, Jerusalem, Israel

Shyong, Yung-Jen 020163
ITRI, Hsinchu, Taiwan

Sicot, Lionel 020217
CEA / INES, Le Bourget-du-Lac, France

Sidler, Anika 020226
School of Life Sciences FHNW, Muttenz, Switzerland

Siebert, Michael 020206
ISFH, Emmerthal, Germany

Siefer, Gerald 020246
Fraunhofer ISE, Freiburg, Germany

Sierra, Daniel 020491
UPM, Madrid, Spain

Sigounis, Anna-Maria 020248, 020249
Concordia University, Montreal, Canada

Søiland, Anne-Karin 020495
ReSiTec, Kristiansand, Norway

Silva, José A. 020304, 020409, 020420
University of Évora, Évora, Portugal

Silva, José 020403
University of Évora, Évora, Portugal

Silvestre, Santiago 020301
UPC, Barcelona, Spain

Simeunovic, Jelena 020238
CSEM, Neuchâtel, Switzerland

Simón-Allué, Raquel 020127, 020414, 020517
ENDEF, Zaragoza, Spain

Singh, Ravi 020571
DNV, Arnhem, The Netherlands

Sinha, Amish Kumar 020463
RCT Solutions, Konstanz, Germany

Sinopoli, Alessandro 020042
QEERI, Doha, Qatar

Sivaramakrishnan Radhakrishnan, Hariharsudan 020064
Hasselt Unversity, Genk, Belgium

Sivaramakrishnan, Hariharsudan 020225
IMEC, Genk, Belgium

Snaith, Henry 020226
University of Oxford, Oxford, United Kingdom

Søndenå, Rune 020503
Institute for Energy Technology, Kjeller, Norway

Sobajima, Yasushi 020131
Gifu University, Gifu, Japan

Soler Toledo, Denet 020509
University of Antofagasta, Antofagasta, Chile

Solomon, Asfaw A. 020479
LUT University, Lappeenranta, Finland

Solórzano, Jorge 020328
Qualifying Photovoltaics, Madrid, Spain
Sondoqah, Mousa 020316
Becquerel Institute, Bolzano, Italy
Sondoqah, Mousa 020261
Eurac Research, Bolzano, Italy
Song, Hee-eun 020045
KIER, Daejeon, South Korea
Spagnolo, Sofia 020462, 020466
RSE, Milan, Italy
Spataru, Sergiu V. 020265, 020267, 020283, 020376, 020451
DTU, Roskilde, Denmark
Spataru, Sergiu Viorel 020346
DTU, Roskilde, Denmark
Spera, Fabian 020411
Next2Sun, Dillingen, Germany
Spihola, Jan 020355
DiSUN Deutsche Solarservice, Werder, Germany
Sraisth, 020005, 020222
RCT Solutions, Konstanz, Germany
Sraisth, Sraisth 020463
RCT Solutions, Konstanz, Germany
Staňková, Tereza 020107
Czech Technical University, Prague, Czech Republic
Steckenreiter, Verena 020063
ISFH, Emmerthal, Germany
Stegemann, Bert 020309
Berlin University of Applied Sciences, Berlin, Germany
Stegemann, Bert 020101
HTW, Berlin, Germany
Stellbogen, Dirk 020312
ZSW, Stuttgart, Germany
Stensborg, Jan F. 020250
Stensborg, Roskilde, Denmark
Stensborg, Jan 020306
Stensborg, Roskilde, Denmark
Stieldorf, Karin 020255
TU Wien, Vienna, Austria
Stierstorfer, Johannes 020225
WIP - Renewable Energies, Munich, Germany
Stierstorfer, Johannes 020551
WIP Renewable Energies, Munich, Germany
Stivanello, Juan José 020226
Eurac Research, Bolzano, Italy
Stoicescu, Liviu 020198
Solarzentrum Stuttgart, Stuttgart, Germany

Stowhas-Villa, Alejandro 020422
Federico Santa María Technical University, Valparaiso, Chile

Stoyanova Lyubenova, Teodora 020173
European Commission JRC, Ispra, Italy

Sträter, Hendrik 020211
PTB, Braunschweig, Germany

Strey, Jessica 020063, 020114
ISFH, Emmerthal, Germany

Strömberg, Rich 020472
University of Alaska, Fairbanks, United States of America

Stroyuk, Oleksander 020185
HI ERN, Erlangen, Germany

Stroyuk, Oleksandr 020117, 020149, 020150
HI ERN, Erlangen, Germany

Suárez Sánchez, Sergio 020326
Enertis Applus+, Madrid, Spain

Subasi, Dilara Maria 020475
Fraunhofer ISE, Freiburg, Germany

Sudbury, Ben A. 020396
PV Lighthouse, Coledale, Australia

Suemitsu, Issei 020484
Hitachi, Kokubunji, Japan

Suhonen, Riikka 020423
VTT Technical Research Centre of Finland, Oulu, Finland

Sulca, Kabir Paúl 020191, 020205
University of Valladolid, Valladolid, Spain

Svatos, Jan 020250
DTU, Roskilde, Denmark

Sylla, David 020063
ISFH, Emmerthal, Germany

Syre Wiig, Marie 020340
IFE, Kjeller, Norway

Szarek, Magda 020298, 020398
University of Turku, Turku, Finland

Taghipour Kani, Ghaem 020335, 020374
Amirkabir University of Technology, Tehran, Iran

Takahashi, Kanji 020106
Tokyo City University, Setagaya, Japan

Talvi, Micke 020528
Tampere University, Tampere, Finland

Tanahashi, Tadanori 020436
AIST, Koriyama, Japan

Tang, Kai 020011
SINTEF, Trondheim, Norway

Tang, Torben 020028
IPU P/S, Virum, Denmark

Tang, Torben 020037
IPU, Virum, Denmark

Tayebjee, Murad J. Y. 020065
UNSW, Sydney, Australia

Taylor, Nigel 020210
European Commission JRC, Ispra, Italy

Tellez Rodriguez, Eduardo 020230
Kiwa PI Berlin, Berlin, Germany

Teppe, Andreas 020005
RCT Solutions, Konstanz, Germany

Terheiden, Barbara 020031
University of Konstanz, Constance, Germany

Terrados, Cristian 020205
University of Valladolid, Valladolid, Spain

Thakur, Dhruv Singh 020071, 020081
SVNIT, Surat, India

Theocharides, Spyros 020371
Univers, Courbevoie, France

Thomas, Jean 020169
Ciel et Terre, Lille, France

Thorning, Jacob K. 020267, 020283
DTU, Roskilde, Denmark

Thorsteinsson, Sune 020039
DTU, Copenhagen, Denmark

Thorsteinsson, Sune 020037
DTU, Lyngby, Denmark

Thorsteinsson, Sune 020028, 020249, 020250, 020265, 020306, 020477
DTU, Roskilde, Denmark

Timofte, Tudor 020218, 020221
ISC Konstanz, Konstanz, Germany

Ting, San-Yu 020161, 020163
ITRI, Hsinchu, Taiwan

Tissier, Corentin 020238
CSEM, Neuchâtel, Switzerland

Tönies, Alexandra 020523
University of Applied Sciences Cologne, Cologne, Germany

Tomšič, Špela 020047
University of Ljubljana, Ljubljana, Slovenia

Tong, Yongfeng 020108, 020109
QEERI, Doha, Qatar

Topič, Marko 020047, 020269, 020319
University of Ljubljana, Ljubljana, Slovenia

Torabi, Narges 020089
University of Verona, Verona, Italy

Torelly, Guilherme 020092
PUC-Rio, Rio de Janeiro, Brazil
Torre, Gorka 020437
UPV/EHU, Leioa, Spain
Torres Aguilar, Moira Itzel 020214
CentraleSupélec, Gif-sur-Yvette, France
Torres Aguilar, Moira Itzel 020406
CNRS, Gif-sur-Yvette, France
Torres Silva, Nicole 020546
ATAMOSTEC, Santiago, Chile
Torres, Oscar 020110
National University of Colombia, Bogotá, Colombia
Tosi, Irene 020037
IPU, Virum, Denmark
Tran Caliste, Thu Nhi 020546
European Synchrotron Radiation Facility (ESRF), Grenoble, France
Treberspurg, Christoph 020255
Treberspurg und Partner Ziviltechniker, Vienna, Austria
Treberspurg, Martin 020255
Treberspurg und Partner Ziviltechniker, Vienna, Austria
Trefzer, Aaron 020135
Fraunhofer ISE, Freiburg, Germany
Trifiletti, Vanira 020087
University of Milano-Bicocca, Milan, Italy
Trigo-Gonzalez, Mauricio 020342, 020422
University of Antofagasta, Antofagasta, Chile
Tsai, Min-An 020053, 020083, 020161, 020163
ITRI, Hsinchu, Taiwan
Tsanakas, Ioannis (John) A. 020262
CEA / INES, Le Bourget-du-Lac, France
Tsanakas, Ioannis (John) A. 020544
CEA, Le Bourget-du-Lac, France
Tsanakas, Ioannis (John) 020546
CEA / INES, Le Bourget-du-Lac, France
Tsanakas, Ioannis (John) 020317
CEA INES, Le Bourget-du-Lac, France
Tsanakas, Ioannis (John) 020513, 020521
CEA, Le Bourget-du-Lac, France
Tsanakas, Ioannis 020217, 020338
CEA / INES, Le Bourget-du-Lac, France
Tsanakas, Ioannis 020500
CEA, Le Bourget-du-Lac, France
Tsanakas, John A. 020311
CEA / INES, Le Bourget-du-Lac, France
Tseberlidis, Giorgio 020093
University of Milano Bicocca, Milan, Italy

Tseberlidis, Giorgio 020087
University of Milano-Bicocca, Milan, Italy

Tsoi, Konstantin 020113
ODTÜ-GÜNAM, Ankara, Türkiye

Tsombou, Francois M. 020402
Fujairah Research Centre, Fujairah, United Arab Emirates

Tsuno, Yuki 020436
AIST, Koriyama, Japan

Tsunoda, Jun 020484
Hitachi, Kokubunji, Japan

Tsunoda, Jun 020186
Hitachi, Tokyo, Japan

Tulinski, Lona 020385
ZHAW, Winterthur, Switzerland

Tune, Daniel 020220, 020221, 020225
ISC Konstanz, Konstanz, Germany

Turcu, Mircea 020063
ISFH, Emmerthal, Germany

Turek, Marko 020004, 020052
Fraunhofer CSP, Halle (Saale), Germany

Ueda, Yuzuru 020320, 020525
Tokyo University of Science, Tokyo, Japan

Ujvari, Gusztav 020318, 020430
AIT, Vienna, Austria

Ulbikaitė, Vaidvilė 020157
Applied Research Institute for Prospective Technologies, Vilnius, Lithuania

Ulbikas, Juras 020225
Protechnology, Vilnius, Lithuania

Ulyashin, Alexander G. 020011
SINTEF, Oslo, Norway

Unsur, Veysel 020020
ODTÜ-GÜNAM, Ankara, Türkiye

Urban, Harald 020255
TU Wien, Vienna, Austria

Useni, Yannick 020393
University of Lubumbashi, Lubumbashi, Congo (DRC)

Uzuner, Bahri Eren 020113
ODTÜ-GÜNAM, Ankara, Türkiye

Väisänen, Kaisa-Leena 020423
VTT Technical Research Centre of Finland, Oulu, Finland

Vaicikauskas, Viktoras 020157
Center for Physical Sciences and Technology (FTMC), Vilnius, Lithuania

Valaski, Rogério 020090
National Institute of Metrology Quality and Technology, Rio de Janeiro, Brazil

Valencia, Felipe 020342, 020546
AtamosTec, Santiago, Chile

Vallerotto, Guido 020209, 020246, 020257
UPM, Madrid, Spain

van Aken, Bas B. 020405
TNO, Petten, The Netherlands

van der Heide, Arvid 020472
imec, Genk, Belgium

van der Zee, Friso F. 020405
Wageningen University and Research, Wageningen, The Netherlands

Van Dyck, Rik 020225
IMEC, Genk, Belgium

van Dyk, E. Ernest 020193, 020416
Nelson Mandela University, Port Elizabeth, South Africa

van Dyk, Ernest E. 020344
Nelson Mandela University, Port Elizabeth, South Africa

Van Overstraeten, Julien 020543
Becquerel Institute France, Lyon, France

Van Overstraeten, Julien 020252
Becquerel Institute, Brussels, Belgium

vanBaal, Rene 020492
Belectric, Kolitzheim, Germany

Vanhanen, Tuomas 020225
Valoe, Mikkeli, Finland

Vargas, Renzo 020348
University of São Paulo, São Paulo, Brazil

Varney, Valérie 020522
University of Applied Science Cologne, Cologne, Germany

Varney, Valérie 020523
University of Applied Sciences Cologne, Cologne, Germany

vas Dyk, Ernest 020185
Nelson Mandela University, Port Elizabeth, South Africa

Vasconcelos, Letícia 020530
Casa dos Ventos, Fortaleza, Brazil

Vavilkin, Tatjana 020302
Soltech, Genk, Belgium

Vázquez Adán, Alejandra 020501
UCM, Madrid, Spain

Vázquez, A. 020508
UCM, Madrid, Spain

Veas, Christian 020136, 020234
PCCL, Leoben, Austria

Vecino, Fernando Román 020346
DTU, Roskilde, Denmark
Veerman, Sebastian 020035
ISC Konstanz, Konstanz, Germany
Vega de Seoane, José Maria 020252
Becquerel Institute Spain, San Sebastian, Spain
Vega de Seoane, Jose 020546
Becquerel Institute, Brussels, Belgium
Vega-Herrera, Jorge 020342
University of Antofagasta, Antofagasta, Chile
Vehus, Tore Sandnes 020443
University of Agder, Grimstad, Norway
Veirman, Jordi 020203, 020226, 020254
Eurac Research, Bolzano, Italy
Velasco, Angel 020367
Nextracker, Fremont, United States of America
Veludo, Jorge 020317
Galp Energia, Lisbon, Portugal
Veneri, Alessandro 020093
University of Verona, Verona, Italy
Vergura, Silvano 020301
Polytechnic University of Bari, Bari, Italy
Verlinden, Pierre 020001
YIST, Jiangyin, China
Vermang, Bart 020064
Hasselt Unversity, Genk, Belgium
Vernay, Christophe 020244
SOLAÏS, Valbonne, France
Vero, Giuseppe 020301
Polytechnic University of Bari, Bari, Italy
Veronese, Elisa 020513
Eurac Research, Bolzano, Italy
Veurman, Welmoed 020063
ISFH, Emmerthal, Germany
Viani, Lucas 020326
Enertis Applus+, Madrid, Spain
Vicente-Laiglesia, Pablo 020181
European Climate, Infrastructure and Environment Executive Agency, Brussels, Belgium
Vidal de Oliveira, Aline 020377
Solar Energy Research Laboratory Fotovoltaica/ UFSC, Florianópolis, Brazil
Vidal, Beatriz Muñoz 020414
IaSol, Zaragoza, Spain
Vidal-Fuentes, Pedro 020094
IREC, Barcelona, Spain

Videla-Magnata, Natalia 020129
Universidad de Antofagasta, Antofagasta, Chile
Videla-Magnata, Natalia 020417
University of Antofagasta, Antofagasta, Chile
Vilches, Anna Morales 020388
Next2Sun Technology, Dillingen, Germany
Villalonga Palou, Joan Tomás 020432, 020434
Sunveon, Madrid, Spain
Villén, Raúl 020127, 020414, 020517
ENDEF, Zaragoza, Spain
Villodas, Aritz 020198
TECNALIA, Derio, Spain
Vincent, Laetitia 020058
CNRS, Palaiseau, France
Vincent, Robin 020196
PVsyst, Geneva, Switzerland
Viorel Spataru, Sergiu 020191
DTU, Roskilde, Denmark
Viriyaroj, Bergpob 020298
Aalto University, Espoo, Finland
Viti, Valeria 020541
Legance, Milan, Italy
Vitoshkin, Helena 020379
Agricultural Research Organization, Rishon LeZion, Israel
Vögeli, Pascal 020385
ZHAW, Winterthur, Switzerland
Vogt, Malte R. 020515
TU Delft, Delft, The Netherlands
Vogt, Thomas 020482
DLR, Oldenburg, Germany
Vollbrecht, Joachim 020063, 020114
ISFH, Emmerthal, Germany
Voltan, Alessandro 020010
Applied Materials, Treviso, Italy
von Friedeburg, Christoph 020557
CF Energy Research-Consulting-Operation, Berlin, Germany
Voronko, Yuliya 020162, 020249
OFI, Vienna, Austria
Vorster, Frederik J. 020193, 020344, 020416
Nelson Mandela University, Port Elizabeth, South Africa
Vorster, Frederik 020185
Nelson Mandela University, Port Elizabeth, South Africa
Vuillon, Laurent 020338
CNRS, Chambery, France

Vulic, Natasa 020296
Univesity of Applied Arts and Sciences Northwestern Switzerland, Muttenz, Switzerland

Vumbugwa, Monphias 020185, 020193, 020344
Nelson Mandela University, Port Elizabeth, South Africa

Waibel, Christoph 020511
Flemish Institute for Technological Research (VITO), Genk, Belgium

Wakabayashi, Ryo 020484
Hitachi, Kokubunji, Japan

Wakazono, Kouzen 020131
Gifu University, Gifu, Japan

Wallner, Gernot M. 020227
University of Linz, Linz, Austria

Walpita, Harsha 020169
University of Oslo, Kjeller, Norway

Walsh, Yoselyn 020520
Costa Rica Institute of Technology, Cartago, Costa Rica

Wambach, Karsten 020468, 020470
bifa Umweltinstitut, Augsburg, Germany

Wang, Chia-Chen 020549
ITRI, Hsinchu, Taiwan

Wang, Shuo 020286, 020400
TUAS, Turku, Finland

Wang, Tzuya 020549
ITRI, Hsinchu, Taiwan

Wang, Xiaolin 020381
Mälardalen University, Västerås, Sweden

Wannenwetsch, Jann 020312
EnBW, Karlsruhe, Germany

Wargocki, Pawel 020551
DTU, Roskilde, Denmark

Waschl, Alfred 020255
buildingSMART, Vienna, Austria

Weber, Thomas 020180, 020230
Kiwa PI Berlin, Berlin, Germany

Weeber, Arthur W. 020515
TU Delft, Delft, The Netherlands

Wei, Wenpeng 020484
Hitachi, Kokubunji, Japan

Weihs, Philipp 020281
BOKU, Vienna, Austria

Weinrich, Frank 020177
PTB, Braunschweig, Germany

Weiß, Marius 020361
Coburg University of Applied Sciences, Coburg, Germany

Wellens, Christine 020135
Fraunhofer ISE, Freiburg, Germany

Whyatt, Duncan 020394
Lancaster University, Lancaster, United Kingdom

Wienands, Karl 020218, 020220, 020221
ISC Konstanz, Konstanz, Germany

Wiesenfarth, Maike 020246
Fraunhofer ISE, Freiburg, Germany

Wietler, Tobias 020063
ISFH, Emmerthal, Germany

Wilbert, Stefan 020235, 020237, 020239, 020331
DLR, Almería, Spain

Willers, Guido 020201
Fraunhofer CSP, Halle, Germany

Wilson, Helen R. 020249
Fraunhofer ISE, Freiburg, Germany

Winter, Renate 020063
ISFH, Emmerthal, Germany

Winter, Stefan 020177, 020181
PTB, Braunschweig, Germany

Wirtz, Wiebke 020260
ISFH, Emmerthal, Germany

Witkowska, Agnieszka 020498
Gdansk University of Technology, Gdansk, Poland

Wittmer, Bruno 020196
PVsyst, Geneva, Switzerland

Wolf, Andreas 020031
Fraunhofer ISE, Freiburg, Germany

Wong, Craig 020230
Kiwa PI Berlin, Berlin, Germany

Wu, Li-Guo 020021
TSEC, Hsinchu, Taiwan

Wu, Yu 020030
TNO, Petten, The Netherlands

Wyss, Philippe 020068
CSEM, Neuchâtel, Switzerland

Xiong, Weizhen 020320
Tokyo University of Science, Tokyo, Japan

Xu, Jiahui 020001
YIST, Jiangyin, China

Xu, Wenhao 020144, 020208
TÜV Rheinland, Shanghai, China

Xu, Xiaoqi 020263
SERIS, Singapore, Singapore

Xu, Yu 020263
SERIS, Singapore, Singapore

Xuereb, Steven 020180, 020230
Kiwa PI Berlin, Berlin, Germany

Yadav, Shivendra 020071, 020081
SVNIT, Surat, India

Yamaguchi, Yosuke 020484
Hitachi, Kokubunji, Japan

Yanagida, Masatoshi 020115
NIMS, Tsukuba, Japan

Yanar, T. Meriç 020027
Kalyon PV, Ankara, Türkiye

Yang, Donggeon 020323
K-water, Daejeon, South Korea

Yang, Hyoung-Kyu 020449
KETI, Wonmi-gu, South Korea

Yde, Leif 020250, 020306
Stensborg, Roskilde, Denmark

Ye, JiaYi 020102
SERIS, Singapore, Singapore

Yerci, Selcuk 020113
ODTÜ-GÜNAM, Ankara, Türkiye

Ylikunnari, Mari 020423
VTT Technical Research Centre of Finland, Oulu, Finland

Ylinen, Marko 020444
Satakunta University of Applied Sciences, Pori, Finland

Ylipaino, Juho 020444, 020445, 020554
TUAS, Tampere, Finland

Yılmaz, Büşra 020521
Kameleon Solar, Roosendaal, The Netherlands

Yordadov, Georgi 020389
imec, Diepenbeek, Belgium

Younes, Kareem 020487
Khalifa University, Abu Dhabi, United Arab Emirates

Yu, Cheng-Yeh 020021, 020053
TSEC, Hsinchu, Taiwan

Yu, Shusen 020406
Ecole Polytechnique, Palaiseau, France

Yuan, Xiao 020001
YIST, Jiangyin, China

Yun, Jae Ho 020112
KENTECH, Naju-si, South Korea

Zaimi, Mhammed 020171
University of Chouaib Doukkali, El Jadida, Morocco

Zanatta Britto, João Victor 020025
PUCRS, Porto Alegre, Brazil
Zanesco, Izete 020023, 020025
PUCRS, Porto Alegre, Brazil
Zaror, Yasmin 020225
WIP - Renewable Energies, Munich, Germany
Zarzalejo, Luis F. 020237, 020331
CIEMAT, Madrid, Spain
Zekri, Atef 020146
QEERI, Doha, Qatar
Zerafa, Steve 020334
PIXAM, Msida, Malta
Zhang, Geng 020001
Jolywood (ShanXi) Solar Technology, Taiyuan, China
Zhang, Jingwei 020111
Hohai University, Changzhou, China
Zhang, Kai 020233
FZJ, Jülich, Germany
Zhang, Wenjing 020001
YIST, Jiangyin, China
Zhang, Wuai 020101
HZB, Berlin, Germany
Zhang, Yating 020144, 020208
TÜV Rheinland, Shanghai, China
Zhou, Qilin 020102
SERIS, Singapore, Singapore
Zhu, Junjie 020017
Institute for Energy Technology, Kjeller, Norway
Ziaullah, Abdul Wahab 020278, 020291
QEERI, Doha, Qatar
Zilles, Roberto 020154, 020348
University of São Paulo, São Paulo, Brazil
Zimmermann, Iwan 020116
IPVF, Palaiseau, France
Zubillaga, Oihana 020139
Tecnalia, Donostia - San Sebastián, Spain
Zugasti, Eugenia 020334
CENER, Pamplona, Spain
Zugasti, Eugenia 020300
CENER, Sarriguren, Spain
Zwahlen, Theo 020369
BFH, Burgdorf, Switzerland

KEYWORDS OF EU PVSEC 2025 PROCEEDINGS PAPERS

42nd European Photovoltaic Solar Energy Conference and Exhibition (EU PVSEC 2025)

Bilbao, Spain
22-26 September 2025

Volume 5 of 6

ISBN: 979-8-3313-2987-7

Printed from e-media with permission by:

Curran Associates, Inc.
57 Morehouse Lane
Red Hook, NY 12571

Some format issues inherent in the e-media version may also appear in this print version.

WIP – Renewable Energies
Sylvensteinstr. 2
81369 Munchen
Germany

Phone: +49 89 72012735
Fax: +49 89 72012791

wip@wip-munich.de

Additional copies of this publication are available from:

Curran Associates, Inc.
57 Morehouse Lane
Red Hook, NY 12571 USA
Phone: 845-758-0400
Fax: 845-758-2633
Email: curran@proceedings.com
Web: www.proceedings.com

42nd European Photovoltaic Solar Energy Conference and Exhibition

Proceedings of the International Conference

22 September – 26 September 2025

Edited by:

C. DEL CAÑIZO
Solar Energy Institute
UPM
Spain

R. KENNY
European Commission
Joint Research Centre
Italy

J. BERGMILLER
WIP Renewable Energies
Germany

J. DE GREGORIO
WIP Renewable Energies
Germany

Edition Team:

B. Yildiz
L. Großhans
A. Michaelsen
U.E. Birgi
WIP Renewable Energies
Germany

Photos at:

Coordination of the Technical Programme:

European Commission Joint Research Centre
Via E. Fermi 1
21020 Ispra (VA)
Italy

Institutional Support:

European Commission

Institutional PV Industry Cooperation:

SolarPower Europe

ESMC – European Solar Manufacturing Council

Supporting Organisations:

AUSTRALIAN PV INSTITUTE

ASOM – Alliance for Solar Mobility

BASQUE ENERGY CLUSTER

BILBAO CONVENTION BUREAU

EASE – European Association for Storage of Energy

ETIP PV – European Technology & Innovation Platform PV

GÜNDER – Turkish Solar Energy Society

IEA PVPS - IEA Photovoltaic Power Systems Programme

INSTITUTO SOLAR DE ENERGÍA SOLAR

LDES – Long Duration Energy Storage Council

NSEFI – National Solar Energy federation of India

NUS /SERIS – National University of Singapore / Solar Energy Research Institute of Singapore

UPM - Polytechnic University of Madrid

Supporting Associations:

EERA – European Energy Research Aliance

EREF – European Renewable Energies Federation

EUREC – The Association of European Renewable Energy Research Centres

VDMA Photovoltaic Equipment

Local Support:
ENTE VASCO DE LA ENERGÍA
EUH – University of the Basque Country

EU PVSEC 2025 realised by:

WIP Renewable Energies
Sylvensteinstr. 2, 81369 Munich, Germany
Tel: +49 89 720 12 735, Fax: +49 89 720 12 791
Email: pv.conference@wip-munich.de
www.eupvsec.org
www.wip-munich.de

Proceedings produced and published by:

WIP Renewable Energies
Sylvensteinstr. 2, 81369 Munich, Germany
Tel: +49 89 720 12 735, Fax: +49 89 720 12 791
Email: pv.conference@wip-munich.de
www.eupvsec.org
www.wip-munich.de

42nd EUROPEAN PHOTOVOLTAIC SOLAR ENERGY CONFERENCE AND EXHIBITION
22 SEPTEMBER – 26 SEPTEMBER 2025

EU PVSEC 2025 COMMITTEES

INTERNATIONAL SCIENTIFIC ADVISORY COMMITTEE (ISAC)

Chair

P. Szymanski, European Commission Joint Research Centre, Director of Energy, Transport and Climate, Petten, The Netherlands

Committee Members

V. Bermúdez Benito, Founder & Principal Consultant, Berbetin, Antibes, France
G.C. Eder, OFI, Vienna, Austria
P. Frankl, Head of the Renewable Energy Division, International Energy Agency, France
M. Getsiou, European Commission, DG RTD, Brussels, Belgium
S.W. Glunz, Head of Division Photovoltaics - Research, Fraunhofer ISE, Freiburg, Germany
N.M. Haegel, Director of the National Center for Photovoltaics, NREL, Golden, USA
R. Kenny, European Commission Joint Research Centre, Directorate for Energy and Transport and Climate, Ispra, Italy
S. Nowak, Managing Director of NET Nowak Energy & Technology, St. Ursen, Switzerland
R. Schlatmann, Chairman of ETIP PV, Head of the Solar Energy Division at Helmholtz-Zentrum Berlin, Germany
W.C. Sinke, TNO Energy Transition, The Netherlands
M. Topič, Head of Laboratory of Photovoltaics and Optoelectronics of the University of Ljubljana, Slovenia
P. Verlinden, Director at Amrock, Visiting Professor at Sun Yat-Sen University, Guangzhou, China
E. Voroshazi, Head of PV module process laboratory, CEA, Le Bourget-du-Lac, France
J. Bergmiller, Managing Director Events & Knowledge Transfer, WIP Renewable Energies, Munich, Germany
J. de Gregorio, Head of Unit, Scientific Services and Cooperation, WIP Renewable Energies, Munich, Germany

CONFERENCE EXECUTIVE COMMITTEE

Conference General Chair

C. del Cañizo, UPM, Madrid, Spain

Technical Programme Chair

R. Kenny, European Commission Joint Research Centre, Directorate for Energy and Transport and Climate, Ispra, Italy

Committee Members

W.C. Sinke, Program Development Manager, TNO Energy Transition, The Netherlands
S. Nowak, Managing Director of NET Nowak Energy & Technology, St. Ursen, Switzerland
M. Topič, Head of Laboratory of Photovoltaics and Optoelectronics of the University of Ljubljana, Slovenia
V. Bermúdez Benito, BERBETIN, France
E. Voroshazi, Head of PV Module Process Laboratory, CEA, Le Bourget-Du-Lac France
H. Ossenbrink, Former European Commission Joint Research Centre, Germany
J. Bergmiller, Managing Director Events & Knowledge Transfer, WIP Renewable Energies, Munich, Germany
J. de Gregorio, Head of Unit, Scientific Services and Cooperation, WIP Renewable Energies, Munich, Germany

2025 SCIENTIFIC COMMITTEE

Programme Technical Chair

R. Kenny, European Commission, Joint Research Centre, Italy

Topic Chairs

Topic 1: Silicon Materials and Cells
F. Schindler, Fraunhofer ISE, Germany

Topic 2: Thin Films and New Concepts
I. Gordon, imec, Belgium

Topic 3: Photovoltaic Modules and BoS Components
T. Barnes, NREL, USA

Topic 4: PV Systems Engineering, Integrated/Applied PV
A.M. Gracia Amillo, FUNDACION CENER, Spain

Topic 5: PV in the Energy Transition
C. Agraffeil, CEA / INES, France

Topic Organisers and Paper Review Experts

Topic 1: Silicon Materials and Cells
F. Schindler, Fraunhofer ISE, Germany
C. Fischer, Wacker Chemie, Germany
G. Hahn, University of Konstanz, Germany
K. Ding, Forschungszentrum Jülich, Germany
P. Roca i Cabarrocas, CNRS-LPICM, France
A. W. Weeber, TNO Energy Transition, The Netherlands
D. Muñoz, CEA / INES, France
S. W. Glunz, Fraunhofer ISE, Germany
K. Bothe, ISFH, Germany
M. Topic, University of Ljubljana, Slovenia
P. Fath, RCT-Solutions, Germany
S. Peters, Hanwha Q CELLS, Germany

M.P. Bellmann, SINTEF, Norway
A. Ciesla, UNSW, Australia
C. Hagendorf, Freiberg Instruments, Germany
X. Yu, Zhejiang University, China
J.S. Lee, KIER, South Korea
R. Brendel, ISFH, Germany
T. Dullweber, ISFH, Germany
J. Horzel, Fraunhofer ISE, Germany
W. Nemeth, NREL, United States of America
R. Turan, METU, Türkiye
F. Menchini, ENEA, Italy
W. Favre, CEA, France

J. Meier, Meier Technologies, Switzerland
J. Schmidt, ISFH, Germany
M. Wright, University of Oxford, United Kingdom
J. Zhao, CSEM, Switzerland
A. Morisset, CSEM, Switzerland
A. Richter, Fraunhofer ISE, Germany
J. Linke, ISC Konstanz, Germany
B. Geerligs, TNO Energy Transition, The Netherlands
S. Dubois, CEA, France
M. Hermle, Fraunhofer ISE, Germany
B. Terheiden, University of Konstanz, Germany
P. Delli Veneri, ENEA, Italy
T. Matsui, AIST, Japan
Y. Ohshita, Toyota Technological Institute, Japan
E. Bruhat, HOLOSOLIS, France
A. Augusto, Dalarna University, Sweden
F. Ferrazza, ENI S.p.A., Italy
A. Otaegi, UPV/EHU, Spain
M.C. Schubert, Fraunhofer ISE, Germany
H. Duman, KalyonPV, Türkiye
N. Usami, Nagoya University, Japan
Y. Zhu, UNSW, Australia
D. Brunner, RENA Technologies, Germany
A. Danel, CEA, France
C. Gerardi, 3Sun, Italy
H.J. Nonnenmacher, Meyer Burger, Germany
P. Verlinden, AMROCK, Australia
Q. Wang, Wang, Qi, China
W. Zhang, Zhang, Weiming, China
Y. Chen, Trina Solar Energy, China
E. Krassowski, CE Cell Engineering, Germany
M. Foti, 3Sun, Italy
D.L. Bätzner, Meyer Burger Research, Switzerland

Topic 2: Thin Films and New Concepts
I. Gordon, imec, Belgium
J.C. Goldschmidt, Marburg University, Germany
F. Schoofs, Oxford PV, United Kingdom
N. Kyranaki, Hasselt University, Belgium
S. Veenstra, TNO Energy Transition, The Netherlands
T. Aernouts, imec, Belgium
A.N. Tiwari, SOLTIWA, Switzerland
G. Siefer, Fraunhofer ISE, Germany
M. Edoff, Uppsala University, Sweden
A. Martí Vega, UPM, Spain
J. Poortmans, imec, Belgium
I. Ramiro, UPM, Spain
T. Magorian Friedlmeier, ZSW, Germany

S. Albrecht, HZB, Germany
S. Berson, CEA, France
P. Carroy, CEA, France
C. Case, Oxford PV, United Kingdom
G. Coletti, FuturaSun, Italy
S. De Wolf, KAUST, Saudi Arabia
U.W. Paetzold, KIT, Germany
H. Sivaramakrishnan Radhakrisnan, imec, Belgium
P. Schulze, Fraunhofer ISE, Germany
L. Wang, Technology Innovation Institute, United Arab Emirates
Y. Smirnov, Applied Materials, United States of America
B. Stannowski, HZB, Germany
F. Fertig, Hanwha Q CELLS, Germany
L. Lancellotti, ENEA, Italy
S. Cros, CEA, France
S. Hayase, The University of Electro-Communications, Japan
S. Huang, Macquarie University, Australia
M. Khenkin, HZB, Germany
C. Lin, National Taiwan University, Taiwan
M.S.H. Norton, University of Cyprus, Cyprus
P. Pistor, Pablo de Olavide University, Spain
W. Tress, Zurich University of Applied Sciences, Switzerland
A. Aguirre, imec, Belgium
D. Lan, UNSW Sydney, China
M. Saliba, University of Stuttgart, Germany
P. Manshanden, TNO Energy Transition, The Netherlands
L. Vesce, University of Rome II, Italy
I. Dogan, TNO Solliance, The Netherlands
Y. Kuang, imec, Belgium
M. Al Katrib, IPVF, France
M.I. Hossain, QEERI, Qatar
W.H. Chiu, Chang Gung University, Taiwan
C. Chen, Ming Chi University of Technology, Taiwan
C. Fell, CSIRO Energy Technology, Australia
G. Brammertz, imec, Belgium
T. Dalibor, Avancis, Germany
S. Ishizuka, AIST, Japan
A. Redinger, University of Luxembourg, Luxembourg
A. Romeo, University of Verona, Italy
V. Sittinger, Fraunhofer IST, Germany
M. Theelen, TNO/Solliance, The Netherlands
G. Timò, RSE, Italy
A. Kanevce, ZSW, Germany
A. Pérez-Rodríguez, IREC, Spain
R. Gutzler, ZSW, Germany
W. Witte, ZSW, Germany
T. Nishimura, Tokyo Institute of Technology, Japan
C. Qian, University of New South Wales, Australia
J.P. Connolly, CentraleSupelec, France
J.P. Kleider, CNRS/GeePs, France
I. Konovalov, University of Applied Sciences Jena, Germany
Y. Okada, University of Tokyo, Japan
M. Rusu, HZB, Germany
H. Meddeb, DLR, Germany
E. Saucedo, Universitat Politècnica de Catalunya (UPC), Spain
P. Vidal-Fuentes, FUNDACIÓ INSTITUT DE RECERCA EN ENERGIA DE CATALUNYA, Spain
C. Malerba, ENEA, Italy
C. Becker, HZB, Germany
D. Kuciauskas, NREL, United States of America
M. Ochoa, University of Cantabria, Spain
T. Tayagaki, AIST, Japan
S. Wasmer, WAVELABS Solar Metrology Systems, Germany
S. Zandi, UNSW, Australia
C. Messmer, University of Freiburg, Germany
J.B. Puel, Institut Photovoltaïque d'Ile de France (IPVF), France
S. Ternes, University of Rome II, Italy

Topic 3: Photovoltaic Modules and BoS Components
V. Bermúdez Benito, BERBETIN, France
R. Preu, Fraunhofer ISE, Germany
R. Gottschalg, Fraunhofer CSP, Germany
T. Barnes, NREL, United States of America
G. Friesen, SUPSI, Switzerland
G. Bardizza, TÜV Rheinland Solar, Italy

V. Barth, CEA, France
A. Faes, CSEM, Switzerland
A. Lennon, Sundrive Solar, Australia
M. Mittag, Fraunhofer ISE, Germany
M.A. Muñoz-García, UPM, Spain
H. Nagel, Fraunhofer ISE, Germany
S. Pietralunga, CNR, Italy
T. Timofte, ISC Konstanz, Germany

S. Feldbacher, PCCL, Austria
A. Halm, ISC Konstanz, Germany
H. Hanifi, AESOLAR, Germany
E. Warren, NREL, United States of America
S. Zhang, Trina Solar Energy, China
X. Zhen, Canadian Solar, China
G. Beaucarne, Dow Silicones Belgium, Belgium
T. Bejat, CEA, France
C. Camus, LayTec, Germany
U. Jahn, Fraunhofer CSP, Germany
G. Oreski, PCCL, Austria
M. Pander, Fraunhofer CSP, Germany
T. Sample, European Commission JRC, Italy
A. Morlier, imo-imomec, Belgium
C. Barretta, PCCL, Austria
P. Gebhardt, Fraunhofer ISE, Germany
C. Sen, UNSW, Australia
O. Arriaga Arruti, CSEM, Switzerland
X. Gu, NIST, United States of America
C. Xiao, Chinese Academy of Sciences, United States of America
R. Aninat, TNO/Solliance, The Netherlands
S. Mitterhofer, NIST, United States of America
B. Hoex, UNSW, Australia
E. Özkalay, SUPSI, Switzerland
M. Bokalič, University of Ljubljana, Slovenia
S. Bordihn, ISFH, Germany
M. Despeisse, CSEM, Switzerland
J. Govaerts, imec, Belgium
J. Lopez-Garcia, STS-Certified, Spain
M. Pravettoni, Technology Innovation Institute, United Arab Emirates
T. Stoyanova Lyubenova, Joint Research Centre, Italy
C. Ulbrich, HZB, Germany
J. Moereke, Avancis, Germany
Y.S. Long, ITRI, Taiwan
D. Pavanello, European Commission JRC, Italy
A.K. Vidal de Oliveira, UFSC, Brazil
J. Bengoechea, CENER, Spain
M. Ernst, ANU, Australia
H. Ellis, European Commission JRC, Italy
B. Mihaylov, European Commission JRC, Italy
G. Chowdhury, 3E, Belgium
B. Aissa, QEERI - Qatar Environment and Energy Research Institute, Qatar

Topic 4: PV Systems Engineering, Integrated/Applied PV
A. Gracia Amillo, CENER, Spain
W.G.J.H.M. van Sark, Utrecht University, The Netherlands
K. Lappalainen, Tampere University, Finland
J.M. Almeida Serra, University of Lisbon, Portugal
I. Tsanakas, CEA, France
C. Buerhop-Lutz, HI ERN, Germany
D. Moser, Becquerel Institute Italia, Italy
F. Frontini, SUPSI, Switzerland
G.C. Eder, OFI, Austria
A. Scognamiglio, ENEA, Italy
A. Chatzipanagi, European Commission JRC, Italy
I. Antón Hernández, UPM, Spain
R.M.E. Valckenborg, TNO, The Netherlands
T. Reindl, SERIS, Singapore
J.R. Gonzalez, European Space Agency, The Netherlands
G. Mütter, Gerhard Mütter e.U., Austria
T. Merdzhanova, Forschungszentrum Jülich, Germany

V. Lara-Fanego, Solargis, Spain
A. Louwen, Eurac Research, Italy
A. Martinez Fernandez, European Commission JRC, Italy
T. Oozeki, AIST, Japan
J. Remund, Meteotest, Switzerland
M. Sengupta, NREL, United States of America
M. Zehner, Rosenheim Technical University of Applied Sciences, Germany
B. Nouri, German Aerospace Center, Spain
S. Poddar, UNSW, Australia
D. Bachour, HBKU/ Qatar Foundation, Qatar
J. Yang, NREL, United States of America
S. Bouguerra, imo-imomec, Belgium
C. Alonso-Tristán, UBU, Spain
M. Carbone, ENEL Green Power, Italy
M. Dennenmoser, BayWa r.e. Solar Projects GmbH, Germany
C.W. Hansen, Sandia National Laboratories, United States of America
A. Neubert, DNV Maritime Software GmbH, Germany
D. Berrian, Belectric, Germany
M. Oliosi, PVsyst, Switzerland
J. Moschner, KU Leuven / EnergyVille, Belgium
C. Bucher, BUAS, Switzerland
B. Wittmer, PVsyst SA, Switzerland
M. Bolen, SB Energy, United States of America
D. Daßler, Fraunhofer CSP, Germany
R. Einhaus, ZSW, Germany
P. Hacke, NREL, United States of America
A. Heimsath, Fraunhofer ISE, Germany
J. Lin, PV Guider, Taiwan
A. Migan-Dubois, GeePs, France
M. Rinio, University of Karlstad, Sweden
J.S. Stein, Sandia National Laboratories, United States of America
D. Stellbogen, ZSW, Germany
M. Theristis, Sandia National Laboratories, United States of America
A. Virtuani, CSEM, Switzerland
A. Driesse, PV Performance Labs, Germany
M. Øgaard, IFE, Norway
A. Nobre, SERIS, Singapore
T. Trupke, UNSW, Australia
C. Cornaro, University of Rome II, Italy
G. A. dos Reis Benatto, DTU, Denmark
S. Malik, Fraunhofer CSP, Germany
S. Lindig, Univers SAS, France
M.M. Nygård, Institute for Energy Technology, Norway
P. Alonso Gomez, BayWa r.e., Germany
Y. Assoa, CEA, France
P. Bonomo, SUPSI, Switzerland
V. D'Ambrosio, University of Naples Federico II, Italy
E. Román Medina, Tecnalia, Spain
L.H. Slooff, TNO Energy Transition, The Netherlands
S. Villa, TNO, The Netherlands
M. La Rosa, Glass to Power, Italy
T. Del Caño, Onyx Solar Energy, Spain
X. Zhihao, AIST, Japan
P. Sharif, ODTU-GUNAM, Türkiye
K. Umeda, TAISEI CORPORATION, Japan
S. Boddaert, CSTB, France
N. Lysgaard Andersen, DTU, Denmark
K. Meyer, ISFH, Germany
T. Biel, NET Nowak Energy & Technology, Switzerland
F. Colucci, ENEA, Italy
A. Pascaris, NREL, United States of America
C. Dupraz, INRAE, France
C. Alonso-García, CIEMAT, Spain
A. Lefort, BayWa, Germany
H.N. Riise, IFE, Norway
M.A. Schüler, Next2Sun Technology GmbH, Germany
P.J. Pérez-Higueras, University of Jaén, Spain
K. Oda, Agritree,

M. Berwind, Fraunhofer ISE, Germany
M. Dörenkämper, TNO, The Netherlands
M. Heinrich, Fraunhofer ISE, Germany
B. Newman, Lightyear, The Netherlands
A. Reinders, Eindhoven University of Technology, The Netherlands
T. Tanahashi, AIST, Japan
J. Leloux, LuciSun, Belgium
E. Shirazi, University of Twente, The Netherlands
K. Araki, University of Miyazaki, Japan
K. Nishioka, University of Miyazaki, Japan
R. Campesato, CESI, Italy
V. Khorenko, Azur Space, Germany
G. Kakoulaki, European Commission Joint Research Centre, Italy
H. Toyota, JAXA, Japan
P. Garcia-Linares, UPM, Spain
I. Weiss, Weiss, Ingrid, Germany
A. Hensel, Fraunhofer ISE, Germany
J.S. da Fernandes, Hochschule Offenburg, Germany
Y. Ueda, Tokyo University of Science, Japan
J. Braid, Sandia National Laboratories, United States of America

Topic 5: PV in the Energy Transition
J. Stierstorfer, WIP Renewable Energies, Germany
R. Pestana, R&D Nester, Portugal
P.J. Alet, CSEM, Switzerland
C. Agraffeil, CEA, France
K. WAMBACH, Wambach-Consulting, Germany
C. del Cañizo, UPM, Spain
L. Großhans, WIP Renewable Energies, Germany
M. Getsiou, European Commission DG RTD, Belgium
S. Nowak, NET Nowak Energy & Technology, Switzerland
C. Breyer, LUT University, Finland
I. Kaizuka, RTS Corporation, Japan
G. Masson, Becquerel Institute, Belgium
P. Baliozian, VDMA, Germany
L. Großhans, WIP Renewable Energies, Germany
C. Candelise, Bocconi University, Italy
S. Caneva, WIP Renewable Energies, Germany

G. Barchi, Eurac Research, Italy
R. Bründlinger, AIT, Austria
V. Efthymiou, University of Cyprus, Cyprus
M. Centeno Brito, University of Lisbon, Portugal
F. Carigiet, ZHAW, Switzerland
B. Gaiddon, HESPUL, France
F.Z. Ouchani, Green Energy Park, Morocco
M. Rennhofer, AIT, Austria
G. Adinolfi, ENEA, Italy
W. Schaffer, Salzburg Netz, Austria
A. Haber, e-control, Austria
G. Heilscher, Technische Hochschule Ulm, Germany
A. Anctil, Michigan State University, United States of America
S. Arancón, Plug and Play, Spain
S. Capaccioli, ETA - Florence Renewable Energies, Italy
V. Fthenakis, Columbia University, United States of America
G. Heath, NREL, United States of America
K. Komoto, Mizuho Research & Technologies, Ltd., Japan
W. Palitzsch, LuxChemtech, Germany
S. Ovaitt, NREL, United States of America
M. de Wild-Scholten, SmartGreenScans, The Netherlands
S. Herceg, Fraunhofer ISE, Germany
C. Polacchi, Eurac Research, Italy
N. Espinosa, Universidad de Murcia, Spain
E. Drahi, TotalEnergies OneTech, France
S. Guastella, RSE, Italy

H. Ossenbrink, Band Gap, Germany
D. Polverini, European Commission DG GROW, Belgium
N. Taylor, European Commission JRC, Italy
K.A. Weiß, Fraunhofer ISE, Germany
I. Kafedjiska, Helmholtz Zentrum Berlin, Germany
P. Malbranche, Solar Action, France
S. De Iuliis, ENEA, Italy
T. Haarberg, BNW-Energy, Norway
A. Nayfeh, Khalifa University, United Arab Emirates
E. Vartiainen, Fortum Renewables Oy, Finland
E. Veronese, Eurac Research, Italy
P. Sanchez-Friera, Solkeys, Spain
N. Cherradi, Desert Technologies, Saudi Arabia
S. Nold, Fraunhofer ISE, Germany
H.J.J. Yu, CEA, France
M. Beck, U.S. Department of Energy, United States of America
M. Woodhouse, NREL, United States of America
A.B. Cristóbal, UPM, Spain
G. Ruggieri, Insubria University, Italy
S. Tay, NUS, Singapore

Awards Coordinators

Student Awards Coordinator
A.H.M. Smets, Delft University of Technology, The Netherlands

Student Awards Committee
R. Kenny, EU PVSEC Technical Programme Chair, Italy
C. del Canizo, Conference Chair, UPM, Spain
E. Voroshazi, CEA, France
J. Poortmans, imec, Belgium
P.J. Alet, CSEM, Switzerland
S. Caneva, WIP Renewable Energies, Germany
A. Romeo, University of Verona, Italy
G. Friesen, SUPSI, Switzerland
F. Schindler, Fraunhofer ISE, Germany
J.C. Goldchmidt, Marburg University, Germany
D. Moser, Becquerel Institute, Italy
K. Ding, FZJ, Germany
W.C. Sinke, TNO Energy Transition, The Netherlands
M. Topic, University of Ljubljana, Slovenia
R. Schlatman, HZB, Germany
S. Glunz, Fraunhofer ISE, Germany
A.M. Vega, UPM, Spain
I. Kaizuka, RTS, Japan
P.D. Veneri, ENEA, Italy
J. Bengoechea, CENER, Spain

Poster Awards Coordinator
P. Malbranche, Solar Action, France

Poster Awards Committee
R. Kenny, European Commission JRC, Italy
C. del Canizo, UPM, Spain
W. van Sark, Utrecht University, The Netherlands
I. Tsanakas, CEA INES, France
L. Miranda, Oxford PV, United Kingdom
D. Munoz, CEA INES, France
I. Gordon, imec, Belgium
E. Roman, Tecnalia, Spain
G. Eder, OFI, Austria
I. Antón, UPM, Spain
S. Veenstra, TNO, The Netherlands
J.M. Almeida Serra, University of Lisbon, Portugal
T. Magorian Friedlmeier, ZSW, Germany
J. Stierstorfer, WIP Renewable Energies, Germany

G. Kakoulaki, European Commission JRC, Italy
T. Barnes, NREL, USA
T. Merdzhanova, Forschungszentrum Jülich, Germany

Highlights Committee
C. del Cañizo, UPM, Madrid, Spain
R. Kenny, European Commission Joint Research Centre, Directorate for Energy and Transport and Climate, Ispra, Italy
W.C. Sinke, TNO Energy Transition, The Netherlands
S. Nowak, Managing Director of NET Nowak Energy & Technology, St. Ursen, Switzerland
M. Topič, Head of Laboratory of Photovoltaics and Optoelectronics of the University of Ljubljana, Slovenia
V. Bermúdez Benito, BERBETIN, France
E. Voroshazi, Head of PV Module Process Laboratory, CEA, Le Bourget-Du-Lac France
H. Ossenbrink, Band Gap, Germany
J. Bergmiller, Managing Director Events & Knowledge Transfer, WIP Renewable Energies, Munich, Germany
J. de Gregorio, Head of Unit, Scientific Services and Cooperation, WIP Renewable Energies, Munich, Germany
S. Leanza, Marketing and PR Manager, WIP Renewable Energies, Munich, Germany
B. Yildiz, Project Manager Events & Knowledge Transfer, WIP Renewable Energies, Munich, Germany
F. Schindler, Fraunhofer ISE, Freiburg, Germany
I. Gordon, imec, Leuven, Belgium
T. Barnes, NREL, Evergreen, USA
A.M. Gracia Amillo, FUNDACION CENER, Sarriguren, Spain
C. Agraffeil, CEA / INES, Le Bourget-du-Lac, France

SUBJECT INDEX

Topic Code	Session Type	Day Codes
1 Silicon Materials and Cells	P = Plenary Session	A = Monday, 22 September 2025
2 Thin-Films and New Concepts	O = Oral Session	B = Tuesday, 23 September 2025
3 Photovoltaic Modules	V = Visual Session	C = Wednesday, 24 September 2025
4 Photovoltaic Systems		D = Thursday, 25 September 2025
5 Photovoltaics in the Energy Transition		E = Friday, 26 September 2025

e.g. 1AO.4 ⇒ 1= Silicon Materials and Cells, A=Monday, O=Oral session, 4=Session 4

FOREWORD

The European Photovoltaic Solar Energy Conference and Exhibition (EU PVSEC) stands as the World's leading and most renowned forum for PV research and development and the biggest conference on PV solar energy. In 2025, celebrating its 42nd edition, the EU PVSEC was the essential meeting and exchanging point for global PV experts from research, development, and industry.

Held from 22–26 September 2025 in Bilbao, Spain, the EU PVSEC 2025 was a resounding success, showcasing a wide range of cutting-edge research results. Bringing together both the Conference and the Exhibition, this edition attracted more than 1600 participants from 61 countries who contributed over 1000 presentations across various fields of science and technology. The event provided an essential platform for the exchange of knowledge and ideas on photovoltaic research, innovations, and applications. In the exhibition area 51 companies from all parts of the world welcomed visitors and presented their products and services.

Conference Highlights

The EU PVSEC covered a broad range of topics with an extensive programme that offers an opportunity for workers from across the entire field of photovoltaics to share their findings, as well as an opportunity for multidisciplinary learning. Rapid advances in materials, designs, and manufacturing processes reflect the accelerating expansion of the global PV market. The programme was arranged into 5 topics as follows:

- Silicon Materials and Cells;
- Thin Films and New Concepts;
- Photovoltaic Modules and Balance of System Components;
- PV Systems Engineering, Integrated/Applied PV;
- PV in the Energy Transition.

Communicating the key messages from the conference, not only to participants, but also to other researchers, key stakeholders, policy makers and the general public was an important added value. We thank the Highlights Committee, composed of selected members of the Scientific Committee, as well as the Session Chairs, for providing a comprehensive summary of the findings and state of the art research that were delivered during this year´s event. Some key highlights are listed below, while further details may be found in the dedicated highlights presentation in the annex of these proceedings.

Cross-cutting themes:

- Demonstrated the versatility of solar technologies, spanning traditional and emerging application areas.
- Sustainability and circularity remain central, with research focused on reducing material use, such as replacing silver with copper, and advancing end-of-life management of modules.
- Ensuring long-term stability and predictable energy yield is equally essential, with many examples of studies on degradation mechanisms and efforts to elucidate their root-causes, such as in the case of UVID.
- The role of artificial intelligence across the PV value chain is rapidly expanding, from design to operations and maintenance, including among many others drone applications.

Latest Solar Innovations in Materials, Cells, Modules and PV Systems:

While silicon solar cells remain the cornerstone of PV technology, perovskite solar cells continue to stand out as the leading complementary technology to silicon, both as standalone devices and in tandem configurations. Research efforts are increasingly focused on enhancing stability, understanding degradation mechanisms, improving durability and scalability, and ensuring full industrial compatibility.

Many companies presented impressive results on industrial-size single-junction perovskite modules as well as perovskite-based tandem modules, and several new efficiency records were announced during the event. The rapid pace of innovation in cell and module architecture underscores the need for accelerated and more robust testing and qualification methodologies. Both the industry and the research community are moving swiftly to assess and improve reliability in this fast-evolving PV landscape.

A major focus in module research remains the optimisation of materials and packaging to ensure long lifetimes and predictable energy yields from high-efficiency cells. In parallel, many innovative advances in the operation and maintenance (O&M) of PV systems were presented and discussed.

Applications, Grid Integration and Storage

"PV can be deployed everywhere": from space applications to agrivoltaics, PV noise barriers, building-integrated photovoltaics (BIPV), floating PV systems, and even vehicles. Among these, agrivoltaics is gaining momentum as a promising dual land use approach, offering economic benefits for farmers while increasing resilience to climate change.

Flexibility solutions, particularly through battery storage, were recognised in many technical presentations as essential to accommodate higher PV penetration levels and to reduce energy curtailment. At the same time, strengthening grid infrastructure and enhancing grid management capabilities remain critical to enable the next phase of large-scale PV integration.

Photovoltaics in the Energy Transition

Options for re-establishing competitive module manufacturing in Europe were extensively analysed, including detailed policy recommendations for industrial support and market growth. Currently, a mismatch persists between global PV module installation rates and production rates, resulting in growing inventories and sharply reduced prices.

Finally, inclusiveness, diversity, citizen participation, awareness, education, and social engagement were

underlined as vital dimensions of the sector's long-term sustainability and innovation capacity.

EU PVSEC 2025 Proceedings

Selection for inclusion in the conference was made by the Scientific Committee's paper review experts and topic organisers (see the listing on pages 010002-001-005), to whom we express our sincere gratitude for their comprehensive review work and overall contribution to the success of the conference.

The EU PVSEC 2025 Proceedings contain the full papers covering most of the highlights described above and more. The Proceedings provide a comprehensive overview of the PV solar sector, its current status and future prospects in science, research, innovation, development and deployment extending to 3,750 pages. In addition to the 299 submitted papers, the proceedings include 101 presentations (slides) shown during the plenary and oral presentations as well as 176 poster files of the visual presentations. In total this amounts to 576 publications.

The Conference Proceedings are published as downloadable files and are also fully accessible online. A DOI code (Digital Object Identifier) has been assigned to each paper. This ensures unequivocal and permanent identification and full citability. The EU PVSEC 2025 papers can be viewed and downloaded in a full free open access from the EU PVSEC's Proceedings website https://userarea.eupvsec.org/proceedings.

The proceedings of the EU PVSEC 2025 strengthen the commitment to providing quick and open access to high quality scientific results. This is a powerful source for targeted and quick information search and retrieval, enabling you to search by topic, keywords, paper title, DOI, author, or organization.

We are confident that these Proceedings will play an important role in providing a comprehensive overview of the current actors and activities in the global PV sector and that they will disseminate information on the state-of-the-art of technologies and applications. This can generate further research, add momentum to innovation and promote interest in PV worldwide.

We would like to cordially thank all authors and participants of the EU PVSEC 2025 for their contributions and look forward to welcoming you in Rotterdam, The Netherlands from 14 – 18 September 2026 at the EU PVSEC 2026, the 43rd European Photovoltaic Solar Energy Conference and Exhibition

The Editors

TABLE OF CONTENTS OF EU PVSEC 2025 PROCEEDINGS PAPERS

Oral SESSION 1AO.5 Si TOPCon Solar Cells and Related Processing Steps

Oral SESSION 1BO.2 Characterisation and Modelling of Si Solar Cells

Oral SESSION 1BO.3 Si Solar Cell Manufacturing Processes

Visual SESSION 1CV.2 Si Solar Cells | Characterisation & Modelling of Silicon Cells and Their Building Blocks

[1] *Anhalt University of Applied Sciences, Köthen, Germany;* [2] *Fraunhofer CSP, Halle, Germany*

Oral SESSION 2AO.2 Advances in Chalcogenide Devices

2AO.2.3 A New Method for Sb-doped CdSeTe/CdTe Devices with Superior Stability 020057
Elisa Artegiani[1], *Mariyam Mukhtar*[1], *Alessandro Romeo*[1]
[1] *University of Verona, Verona, Italy*

Oral SESSION 2AO.3 III-V Based Devices | Tandem and Perovskite Solar Cells

2AO.3.3 Micro-Crystal GaAs Array Sub-Cells for Si Tandem Solar Cells 020058
James Patrick Connolly[1], *Ahmed Nejim*[2], *Alexandre Jaffré*[1], *José Alvarez*[1], *Jean-Paul Kleider*[1], *Denis Mencaraglia*[1], *Laurie Dentz*[3], *Géraldine Hallais*[3], *Frederic Hamouda*[3], *Laetitia Vincent*[3], *Daniel Bouchier*[3], *Charles Renard*[3]
[1] *CNRS, Gif-sur-Yvette, France;* [2] *SILVACO, St. Ives, United Kingdom;* [3] *CNRS, Palaiseau, France*

2AO.3.5 Multiscale Models for Perovskite Optimisation 020060
Philippe Baranek[1], *James Patrick Connolly*[2], *Antoine Gissler*[1], *Philip Schulz*[3], *Michel Rerat*[4], *Roberto Dovesi*[5]
[1] *EDF R&D, Palaiseau, France;* [2] *CNRS, Gif-sur-Yvette, France;* [3] *IPVF, Palaiseau, France;* [4] *IPREM, Pau, France;* [5] *Academy of Sciences of Turin, Torino, Italy*

2AO.3.6 Modelling Recovery in Perovskite Solar Cells under Light and Dark to Address Stability Challenges 020062
Guillem Álvarez-Pérez[1], *Jean Baptiste Puel*[1], *Jean François Guillemoles* [1]
[1] *IPVF, Palaiseau, France*

Oral SESSION 2BO.10 Advanced Modelling and Characterisation of Perovskite Solar Cells

2BO.10.2 On Perimeter Losses in Perovskite Top- and Poly-Si-Passivated Silicon Bottom Cells – Do Small Area Tandems Reveal the Full Efficiency Potential? 020063
Felix Haase[1], *Lukas Brockmann*[1], *Annika Raugewitz*[1], *Verena Steckenreiter*[1], *Verena Barnscheidt*[1], *Roland Clausing*[1], *Sara Baumann*[1], *Joachim Vollbrecht*[1], *Welmoed Veurman*[1], *Johannes Löhr*[1], *Dongyang Liu*[1], *Mircea Turcu*[1], *Lasse Nasebandt*[1], *Udo Römer*[1], *David Sylla*[1], *Jessica Strey*[1], *Martha Löhning*[1], *Larissa Mettner*[1], *Renate Winter*[1], *Anja Christ*[1], *Heike Kohlenberg*[1], *Cornelia Marquardt*[1], *Emanuel Brueckner*[1], *Hossein Rabiei*[1], *Michael Rienäcker*[1], *Sarah Kajari-Schröder*[1], *Tobias Wietler*[1], *Robby Peibst*[1]
[1] *ISFH, Emmerthal, Germany*

2BO.10.5 In-depth Characterization and Simulation Approach for the Understanding of In- and Outdoor Degradation of Perovskite Solar Cells 020064
Jonathan Parion[1], *Amit Kumar Harit*[1], *Elias Peraticos*[2], *Vasiliki Paraskeva*[2], *Maria Hadjipanayi*[2], *Aranzazu Aguirre*[1], *Filip Duerinckx*[1], *Hariharsudan*

Sivaramakrishnan Radhakrishnan[1], Jef Poortmans[1], Johan Lauwaert[3], Bart Vermang[1]
[1] Hasselt Unversity, Genk, Belgium; [2] University of Cyprus, Nicosia, Cyprus; [3] Ghent University, Ghent, Belgium

Oral SESSION 2BO.8 Advanced Conversion Devices

2BO.8.1 Singlet Fission Route for >30% Efficient Solar Cells: Silicon Cell Requirements 020065
Shona McNab[1], Alex J. Baldacchino[1], Pheobe Pearce[1], Alvin Mo[1], Alison Ciesla[1], Bram Hoex[1], Nicholas J. Ekins-Daukes[1], Murad J. Y. Tayebjee[1], Michael P. Nielsen[1]
[1] UNSW, Sydney, Australia

2BO.8.5 Performance of a 4-Terminals Spectral Splitting Asymmetric Solar Concentrator in Diffuse Sunlight: a Numerical Study 020066
Floriana Morabito[1], Daniela Fontani[2], Paola Sansoni[2], Mehdi Ahmadi[3], Salvatore Lombardo[3], Andrea Farina[1], Silvia Maria Pietralunga[1]
[1] CNR-IFN, Milan, Italy; [2] CNR-INO, Florence, Italy; [3] CNR-IMM, Catania, Italy

2BO.8.6 GaAs for Thermophotonics: From Thin-Film Solar Cells to Highly Efficient LEDs 020067
Natasha Gruginskie[1], Peter Mulder[1], Gerard Bauhuis[1], Jani Oksanen[2], John Schermer[1]
[1] Radboud University, Nijmegen, The Netherlands; [2] Aalto University, Espoo, Finland

Visual SESSION 2BV.1 New Materials, Devices and Conversion Concepts | New Modelling and Characterisation Techniques

2BV.1.4 Low-Energy Electron Multiplication on Nanostructured Solar Cells: a Novel Route to Overcome Si-PV Efficiency Limits 020068
Mikaël Hosatte[1], Brice Rouffie[1], Zbigniew T. Kuznicki[1], Frédéric Milesi[2], Bertrand Paviet-Salomon[3], Audrey Morisset[3], Philippe Wyss[3], Lejo Joseph Koduvelikulathu[4], Lazhar Rachdi[4], Lacramioara Popescu[4], Dominik Rudolph[4], Marek Basta[5], Andrzej Miszczuk[5], Martyna Majak[5], Beata Basta[5], Samuel Queste[6]
[1] SEGTON Advanced Technology, Versailles, France; [2] CEA, Grenoble, France; [3] CSEM, Neuchâtel, Switzerland; [4] ISC Konstanz, Konstanz, Germany; [5] Roltec, Poznań, Poland; [6] Marie and Louis Pasteur University, Besançon, France

2BV.1.5 Tailoring CBTSSe Solar Cells for Indoor Photovoltaic Applications 020069
Hitarth Narsi Patel[1], Bindu Pamula[1], Deepak Joshi[1], Vivek Garg[1]
[1] SVNIT, Surat, India

2BV.1.6 Theoretical Insights through DFT into $AgBiS_2$ Thin Films Absorber for Photovoltaic Applications 020071
Dhruv Singh Thakur[1], Rajesh Kumar Sharma[1], Nithin Chatterji[1], Vivek Garg[1], Shivendra Yadav[1]
[1] SVNIT, Surat, India

Visual SESSION 2BV.2 Compound and Organic Semiconductors

Gerardo Gordillo[1], Oscar Torres[1], Julian Peña-Bermudez[2]
[1] National University of Colombia, Bogotá, Colombia; [2] University of the Caribbean, Santo Domingo, Dominican Republic

2CV.3.71 Comparative Analysis and Efficiency Optimization of Sulfur-based Chalcogenide Perovskites ($MgHfS_3$, $CaZrS_3$, $BaZrS_3$) via Interface Engineering for High-Performance Solar Cells 020111
Anees ur Rehman[1], Kung Ding[1], Jingwei Zhang[1], Xiang Chen[1]
[1] Hohai University, Changzhou, China

2CV.3.72 Development of Inorganic Perovskite $CsPbI_3$ with Heterojunction Engineering at the Buried Interface for Enhanced Stability and Performance 020112
Syed Fawad Ali Shah[1], Hyeonwook Park[1], Muhammad Rehan[2], Donghyeop Shin[2], Kihwan Kim[2], Jae Ho Yun[3]
[1] KENTECH, Naju-Si, South Korea; [2] KIER, Daejeon, South Korea; [3] KENTECH, Naju-si, South Korea

Oral SESSION 2DO.6 Industrially Scalable Processes to Manufacture Perovskite Solar Cells and Modules

2DO.6.2 Eliminating P2 Scribes: A New Interconnection Design for Efficient Perovskite Solar Modules Under Indoor Lighting 020113
Bahri Eren Uzuner[1], Konstantin Tsoi[1], Gorkem Gunbas[1], Selcuk Yerci[1]
[1] ODTÜ-GÜNAM, Ankara, Türkiye

2DO.6.5 Evaporated Self Assembled Monolayer (SAM) Hole Transport Layers for Scalable Perovskite Solar Cells 020114
Joachim Vollbrecht[1], Verena Barnscheidt[1], Roland Clausing[1], Johannes Löhr[1], Larissa Mettner[1], Adam Neuba[2], Annika Raugewitz[1], Jessica Strey[1], Robby Peibst[1]
[1] ISFH, Emmerthal, Germany; [2] Paderborn University, Paderborn, Germany

Oral SESSION 2DO.7 Insights Into the Stability of Perovskite Solar Cells and Modules

2DO.7.1 Outdoor Performance and Degradation Analysis of Inverted Perovskite Solar Cells 020115
Makoto Konagai[1], Hayato Okawa[1], Ryousuke Ishikawa[1], Masatoshi Yanagida[2], Yasuhiro Shirai[2]
[1] Tokyo City University, Setagaya, Japan; [2] NIMS, Tsukuba, Japan

Oral SESSION 2DO.8 Multiple Aspects of Perovskite PV Research

2DO.8.2 Strategies for Quasi-2D Perovskite Integration in p-i-n Solar Cells 020116
Anna Capitaine[1], Hugo Le Bossenec[1], Marion Provost[1], Alexandra Levtchenko[1], Daniel Ory[2], Jean Rousset[2], Iwan Zimmermann[1], Anyssa Derj[1],

Mirella Al Katrib[1]
[1] *IPVF, Palaiseau, France;* [2] *EDF R&D, Palaiseau, France*

2DO.8.3 Innovative Approach to Bismuth-Antimony-Iodide Double Perovskite PV Absorbers via Anion Exchange and Solide-State Reactions 020117
Oleksandr Stroyuk[1]*, Oleksandra Raievska*[1]*, Sachin Kinge*[2]*, Jens Hauch*[1]*, Christoph J. Brabec*[1]
[1] *HI ERN, Erlangen, Germany;* [2] *Toyota Motors Europe, Brussels, Belgium*

Visual SESSION 3AV.1 PV Module Design and Manufacturing

3AV.1.1 Investigating the 3-Dimensional Structure of Metallic Filler Particles in Electrically Conductive Adhesives 020119
Stephan Grosser[1]*, Alexander Müller*[1]*, Robert Göckeritz*[1]*, Tobias Nitsche*[2]*, Daniel Buckland*[2]*, Giuseppe Galbiati*[2]*, Bengt Jaeckel*[1]
[1] *Fraunhofer CSP, Halle, Germany;* [2] *Henkel, Düsseldorf, Germany*

3AV.1.6 Investigation on Different Bypass Diodes for Shade Resistant PV-Modules 020121
Jens Froebel[1]*, Matthias Pander*[1]*, Bengt Jaeckel*[1]*, Andreas Maixner*[2]*, Pouya Pourshafi*[2]*, Afshin Bakhtiari*[2]*, Hamed Hanifi*[2]
[1] *Fraunhofer CSP, Halle, Germany;* [2] *AESOLAR, Koenigsbrunn, Germany*

3AV.1.7 Optimization of Infrared Soldering Process to Reduce the Temperature Inhomogeneity in Silicon Solar Cells Using Finite Element Methods 020123
Daniel Christopher Joseph[1]*, Angela De Rose*[1]*, Christian Reichel*[1]*, Andreas J. Beinert*[1]*, Holger Neuhaus*[1]
[1] *Fraunhofer ISE, Freiburg, Germany*

3AV.1.10 Performance Evaluation of a New Design Photovoltaic Module with Reduced Self-Shading 020125
Pouya Pourshafi[1]*, Andreas Maixner*[1]*, Hamed Hanifi*[1]
[1] *AESOLAR, Königsbrunn, Germany*

3AV.1.11 Materials Assessment for PV-T Modules Thermal Performance Improvement 020127
Lucía Cano[1]*, Raquel Simón-Allué*[1]*, Raúl Villén*[1]*, Yolanda Lara*[1]*, Isabel Guedea*[1]
[1] *ENDEF, Zaragoza, Spain*

3AV.1.12 Evaluating Repair Techiniques for c-Si PV Modules: Spot-Welding 020129
Jorge Rabanal-Arabach[1]*, Sonia Beltran-Condori*[1]*, Natalia Videla-Magnata*[1]*, Katalina Rojas-Henriquez*[1]*, Andreas Schneider*[2]*, Edward Fuentealba-Vidal*[1]
[1] *University of Antofagasta, Antofagasta, Chile;* [2] *University of Applied Sciences Gelsenkirchen, Gelsenkirchen, Germany*

3AV.1.13 Thermally Conductive Filler Particle Mixed Silicone Layer to Provide Heat Dissipation Functionality to c-Si Solar Cell Modules without Encapsulants 020131
Yasushi Sobajima[1]*, Kouzen Wakazono*[1]*, Keisuke Ohdaira*[2]
[1] *Gifu University, Gifu, Japan;* [2] *JAIST, Ishikawa, Japan*

3AV.1.16 Ultrasonic Characterization of Ethylene-Vinyl Acetate in Glass-Glass-Modules 020132
Christopher Bruce Konu[1]*, Rico Meier*[1]
[1] *HTW Berlin, Berlin, Germany*

Visual SESSION 3AV.2 PV Module Durability and Reliability

Nathan Roosloot[1], Harsha Walpita[2], Christoph Seiffert[1], Jean Thomas[3], Maarten Dörenkämper[4], Minne M. de Jong[4], Josefine H. Selj[1], Gaute Otnes[1]
[1] Institute for Energy Technology, Kjeller, Norway; [2] University of Oslo, Kjeller, Norway; [3] Ciel et Terre, Lille, France; [4] TNO, Eindhoven, The Netherlands

Visual SESSION 3AV.3 PV Modules Characterisation and Performances Assessment

3AV.3.1 A New Method for Comprehensive Power Rating and Performance Analysis of PERC Modules based on Half-Cut Cell Technology 020171
Khadija El Ainaoui[1], Mhammed Zaimi[2], Imane Flouchi[1], Said Elhamaoui[1], Yasmine El mrabet[1], Abdellatif Ghennioui[1], El Mahdi Assaid[2]
[1] Green Energy Park, Benguerir, Morocco; [2] University of Chouaib Doukkali, El Jadida, Morocco

3AV.3.2 Energy Rating Analysis of Heterojunction PV Modules 020173
Teodora Stoyanova Lyubenova[1], Ewan D. Dunlop[1]
[1] European Commission JRC, Ispra, Italy

3AV.3.3 Trend of Temperature Coefficients of c-Si Module Technologies from the past 15 Years 020175
Bengt Jaeckel[1], Matthias Pander[1]
[1] Fraunhofer CSP, Halle, Germany

3AV.3.6 Angle of Incidence Measurements on Bifacial PV Modules 020177
Frank Weinrich[1], Stefan Riechelmann[1], Stefan Winter[1]
[1] PTB, Braunschweig, Germany

3AV.3.8 Plug & Play IV Curve Tracer for PV Modules 020179
Adrian Jäggi[1], Christof Bucher[1], Matthias Burri[1]
[1] BFH, Burgdorf, Switzerland

3AV.3.9 Seasonal and Location-Dependent Temperature Coefficients for Thin-Film PV Modules: Enhancing Yield Prediction Accuracy 020180
Thomas Weber[1], Abdullah Abu Sayed[1], Benjamin Lippke[1], Steven Xuereb[1], Marcus Rennhofer[2], Bart E. Pieters[3]
[1] Kiwa PI Berlin, Berlin, Germany; [2] AIT, Vienna, Austria; [3] FZJ, Jülich, Germany

3AV.3.10 Standardisation Methods for Bifacial Energy Yield Estimation and PV Module Long-Term Performance Degradation Estimation: Potential Policy Implications 020181
Jaione Bengoechea[1], Ana Maria Gracia Amillo[1], Stefan Riechelmann[2], Stefan Winter[2], Giorgio Bardizza[3], Christos Monokroussos[4], Davide Polverini[5], Pablo Vicente-Laiglesia[6], Maria Getsiou[7]
[1] CENER, Sarriguren, Spain; [2] PTB, Braunschweig, Germany; [3] TÜV Rheinland Italia, Milan, Italy; [4] TÜV Rheinland, Shanghai, China; [5] Directorate General for Internal Market, Industry, Entrepreneurship and SMEs, Brussels, Belgium; [6] European Climate, Infrastructure and Environment Executive Agency, Brussels, Belgium; [7] Directorate General for Research and Innovation, Brussels, Belgium

3AV.3.11 Shaalke: Development of a MATLAB Software Tool for Advanced Statistical Outdoor Data Evaluation 020183

Cristian Terrados[1], Eva de la Viuda[1], Kabir Paul Sulca[1], Julian Anaya[1], Miguel Ángel González[1], Oscar Martínez[1]
[1] University of Valladolid, Valladolid, Spain

3BO.11.6 Luminescence Measurements of PV Modules with a Cost-Effective and Small-Sized Hood-Based Tool under Daylight Conditions 020206
Marc Köntges[1], Michael Siebert[1], Dieter Lorenz[2], Bernd Kuhrmann[2], Michael Fuß[2]
[1] ISFH, Emmerthal, Germany; [2] MBJ Solutions, Ahrensburg, Germany

Oral SESSION 3BO.12 Characterisation and Energy Rating of PV Modules

3BO.12.1 Developing a New I-V Translation Methodology in Accordance with IEC 60891:2021 Correction Procedure 1 and 2 020208
Wenhao Xu[1], Yating Zhang[1], Mengdi Liu[1], Christos Monokroussos[1], Werner Herrmann[2], Giorgio Bardizza[2], Harald Müllejans[3]
[1] TÜV Rheinland, Shanghai, China; [2] TÜV Rheinland Solar, Cologne, Germany; [3] European Commission JRC, Ispra, Italy

3BO.12.2 Characterization of Vehicle Integrated Photovoltaic Modules 020209
Ricardo Moruno[1], Francisco José Martín[1], Juan Manuel Redondo[1], Javier Malo[1], Luis Javier San José[1], Guido Vallerotto[1], Steve Askins[1], Rubén Núñez[1], César Domínguez[1], Ignacio Antón[1], Rebeca Herrero[1]
[1] UPM, Madrid, Spain

3BO.12.4 Estimating the Energy Yield of Bifacial Photovoltaics with the JRC's Photovoltaic Geographic Information System 020210
Nigel Taylor[1], Teodora Lyubenova[1], Lavanya Malarkannan[2], Nikos Alexandris[1], Alexandros Falangas[3], Robert Kenny[1], Ewan D. Dunlop[1], Blago Mihaylov[1]
[1] European Commission JRC, Ispra, Italy; [2] National Physical Laboratory, Teddington, United Kingdom; [3] TRASIS International, Brussels, Belgium

3BO.12.5 An Update on Energy Rating Amendments – Integration of Bifacial Modules 020211
Stefan Riechelmann[1], Hendrik Sträter[1], Ana María Gracia Amillo[2], Sophie Pelland[3], Anton Driesse[4]
[1] PTB, Braunschweig, Germany; [2] CENER, Pamplona, Spain; [3] Natural Resources Canada, Varennes, Canada; [4] PV Performance Labs, Freiburg, Germany

Oral SESSION 3BO.14 Characterisation and Outdoor Monitoring of Perovskite-based PV Modules

3BO.14.1 Outdoor Measurements of Perovskite Modules 020213
Hanna Ellis[1], Harald Müllejans[1], Ewan D. Dunlop[1], Tony Sample[1]
[1] European Commission JRC, Ispra, Italy

Oral SESSION 3BO.15 Outdoor Performances and Degradation Analysis of PV Modules

3CO.11.5 Indoor Characterization and Analysis of Reverse Breakdown Behavior of Solar Cells with Different Cell Architectures 020223

Bengt Jaeckel[1], Jens Froebel[1], Matthias Pander[1], Andreas Maixner[2], Hamed Hanifi[2]
[1] Fraunhofer CSP, Halle, Germany; [2] AESOLAR, Koenigsbrunn, Germany

Plenary SESSION 3CP.1 Si PV Manufacturing: Pushing the Limits of Performance

3CP.1.2 IBC4EU: European Back Contact Technology 020225

Florian Buchholz[1], Daniel Tune[1], Tobias Meßmer[1], Jonathan Linke[1], Manjunath Prasad[1], Valentin D. Mihailetchi[1], Juras Ulbikas[2], Arne Dahle[3], Martijn Meereboer[4], Francesca Fabris[5], Erik Eikelboom[5], Tom Borgers[6], Rik Van Dyck[6], Filip Duerinckx[7], Hariharsudan Sivaramakrishnan Radhakrishnan[7], Timea Bejat[8], Samuel Harrison[8], Ashish Binani[9], Nicolas Guillevin[9], Jan Kroon[9], Yevgeniya Larionova[10], Thorsten Dullweber[10], Ofer Shochet[11], Isaac Rosen [11], Ingo Röver [12], Wolfram Palitzsch[12], Yasmin Zaror[13], Johannes Stierstorfer[14], Aurimas Radzevicius[15], Julius Denafas[16], Tuomas Vanhanen [17], Tuukka Savisalo[17], Maximilian Pospischil [18], Marian Breitenbücher [18], Özlem Coşkun[19], Melodie de l'Epine [20], Philippe Macé[20], Ian Kenchington[20]
[1] ISC Konstanz, Konstanz, Germany; [2] Protechnology, Vilnius, Lithuania; [3] Norsun, Oslo, Norway; [4] Energyra, Westknollendam, The Netherlands; [5] Futurasun, Citadella, Italy; [6] IMEC, Genk, Belgium; [7] Hasselt Unversity, Genk, Belgium; [8] CEA, Le Bourget-du-Lac, France; [9] TNO, Petten, The Netherlands; [10] ISFH, Emmerthal, Germany; [11] Copprint, Jerusalem, Israel; [12] LuxChemTech, Freiberg, Germany; [13] WIP Renewable Energies, Munich, Germany; [14] WIP - Renewable Energies, Munich, Germany; [15] Valoe Cells, Vilnius, Lithuania; [16] Solitek, Vilnius, Lithuania; [17] Valoe, Mikkeli, Finland; [18] Highline Technologies, Freiburg, Germany; [19] Kalyon PV, Ankara, Türkiye; [20] Becquerel Institute, Brussels, Belgium

Plenary SESSION 3CP.3 Perovskite – Silicon Tandems: Towards Commercialisation | PV Stability in the Field

3CP.3.4 Outdoor Performance and Reliability of Perovskite (Pk)-Silicon (Si) Tandems: >1 year of Monitoring in the NEXUS Project 020226

Atse Louwen[1], Jordi Veirman[1], Alexander Astigarraga[1], Juan José Stivanello[1], David Moser[2], Perrine Carroy[3], Vincent Barth[3], Delfina Muñoz[3], Markus Lenz[4], Anika Sidler[4], Jorge Ferrando[5], Maximiliano Alejandro Senno[5], Henk J. Bolink[5], Talat Özden[6], Hisham Nasser[6], Shuaifeng Hu[7], Xinyi Shen[7], Henry Snaith[7]
[1] Eurac Research, Bolzano, Italy; [2] Becquerel Institute Italy, Trento, Italy; [3] CEA / INES, Le Bourget-du-Lac, France; [4] School of Life Sciences FHNW, Muttenz, Switzerland; [5] University of Valencia, Paterna, Spain; [6] ODTÜ-GÜNAM, Ankara, Türkiye; [7] University of Oxford, Oxford, United Kingdom

Oral SESSION 3DO.12 Innovative Encapsulation Materials

Nikolina Pervan[1], Jutta Geier[1], Christian Veas[1], Gernot Oreski[1]
[1] PCCL, Leoben, Austria

Oral SESSION 4AO.7 Solar Resource Assessment

4AO.7.4 Potential of Decimeter-Resolution Ground Albedo Data for Bifacial Photovoltaics 020235
Niklas Blum[1], Bijan Nouri[1], Yann Fabel[1], Stefan Wilbert[1]
[1] DLR, Almeria, Spain

4AO.7.5 Method for the Determination of Spectral Responsivity of Digital Solar Irradiance Sensors 020236
David Hinken[1], Sebastian Denke[1], Karsten Bothe[1], Rolf Brendel[1]
[1] ISFH, Emmerthal, Germany

Oral SESSION 4AO.8 Solar Irradiance Forecasting

4AO.8.2 Cutting-Edge Generative AI for Intra-Hour Solar Forecasting 020237
Yann Fabel[1], Dominik Schnaus[2], Bijan Nouri[1], Stefan Wilbert[1], Niklas Blum[1], Luis F. Zarzalejo[3], Julia Kowalski[4], Robert Pitz-Paal[5]
[1] DLR, Almeria, Spain; [2] TUM, Garching, Germany; [3] CIEMAT, Madrid, Spain; [4] RWTH, Aachen, Germany; [5] DLR, Cologne, Germany

4AO.8.4 Integrating Satellite Imagery and GNNs for Improving Day-Ahead Solar Irradiance Forecasting 020238
Baptiste Schubnel[1], Jelena Simeunovic[1], Corentin Tissier[1], Pierre-Jean Alet[1], Rafael E. Carrillo[1]
[1] CSEM, Neuchâtel, Switzerland

4AO.8.5 Enhancing Intra-Hour Solar Irradiance Forecasting for Solar Applications: A Blended Model of Satellite, Sky Imager and Persistence 020239
Bijan Nouri[1], Jorge Lezaca[2], Yann Fabel[1], Annette Hammer[2], Niklas Blum[1], Stefan Wilbert[1]
[1] DLR, Almeria, Spain; [2] DLR, Oldenburg, Germany

Oral SESSION 4AO.9 Irradiance for PV Design | Shading and Glare Mitigation

4AO.9.1 Reflective Properties of Urban Materials and Their Impact on PV Yield 020240
Christian Schläger[1], Dennis Bredemeier[1], Arne Dittrich[2], Jan Hendrik Pfau[1], Philip Kühne[1], Rolf Brendel[2]
[1] Leibniz University Hannover, Hannover, Germany; [2] ISFH, Emmerthal, Germany

4AO.9.3 Understanding Short-Term PV Power Variability Based on Solargis Time Series Data and Simulations 020241
Martin Opatovsky[1], Marta Pelfort Ojer[1], Juraj Betak[1], Konstantin Rosina[1]
[1] Solargis, Bratislava, Slovakia

4AO.9.5 Accelerating Photovoltaic System Simulations via Statistical Data Aggregation 020243

Adrián Blanco Aguiar[1], Brais González Rodríguez[2], María Martínez-Barbeito[1], Miguel Sánchez de León Peque[1]
[1] ieco.io, Vigo, Spain; [2] University of Vigo, Vigo, Spain

4AO.9.6 Addressing Glare Problematics for Photovoltaic Projects in the Immediate Proximity of Roads and Railways through the Use of Accurate Digital Surface Models 020244
Christophe Vernay[1], John Coutel[1], Aina Razanajao[1], Sébastien Pitaval[1]
[1] SOLAÏS, Valbonne, France

Plenary SESSION 4AP.1 PV Everywhere

4AP.1.3 Micro-Concentrator Photovoltaics for Deep Space Missions: Overcoming LILT Challenges with High-Specific-Power Solar Arrays 020246
Guido Vallerotto[1], Anderson Bermudez-Garcia[2], Gerald Siefer[3], Maike Wiesenfarth[3], Almudena Garcia-Sanchez[1], Ignacio Antón[1], Carsten Baur[4], Pier Luigi Coz[4], César Domínguez[1]
[1] UPM, Madrid, Spain; [2] Thales Alenia Space, Cannes, France; [3] Fraunhofer ISE, Freiburg, Germany; [4] European Space Agency, Noordwijk, The Netherlands

Oral SESSION 4BO.16 Color in Photovoltaics

4BO.16.1 Experimental Investigation of Colored BIPV/T Systems for Wood-Framed Roofs 020248
Anna-Maria Sigounis[1], Andreas Athienitis[1]
[1] Concordia University, Montreal, Canada

4BO.16.3 How to Perform Accurate Colour Measurements for BIPV Module Glass Covers: an IEA PVPS Task 15 Round-Robin Measurement Campaign 020249
Markus Babin[1], Gabriele C. Eder[2], Thomas Friesen[3], Martina Pelle[4], Gabriella Gonnella[5], Fabrizio Leonforte[6], Yuliya Voronko[2], Helen R. Wilson[7], Sune Thorsteinsson[1], Laura Maturi[4], Niccolò Aste[6], Claudio Del Pero[6], Janne Halme[8], Jun-Tae Kim[9], Susanna Santamaría Fernández[10], Anna-Maria Sigounis[11], Hua Ge[11], Gabi Friesen[12], Francesco Frontini[12]
[1] DTU, Roskilde, Denmark; [2] OFI, Vienna, Austria; [3] Megasol Energie, Deitingen, Switzerland; [4] Eurac Research, Bolzano, Italy; [5] Eurac research, Bolzano, Italy; [6] Polytechnic University of Milan, Milan, Italy; [7] Fraunhofer ISE, Freiburg, Germany; [8] Aalto University, Espoo, Finland; [9] Kongju National University, Chungnam, South Korea; [10] TECNALIA, Derio, Spain; [11] Concordia University, Montreal, Canada; [12] SUPSI, Mendrisio, Switzerland

4BO.16.6 Predicting Light Scatter in Structural Colored BIPV Modules and Textured Glass Using Radiance 020250
Nanna Lysgaard Andersen[1], Markus Babin[1], Jan Svatos[1], Karlis Petersons[2], Leif Yde[2], Jan F. Stensborg[2], Catarina G. Ferreira[3], Ananta Paul[3], Jani Lamminaho[3], Joel D. Cox[3], Morten Madsen[3], Peter B. Poulsen[1], Sune Thorsteinsson[1]
[1] DTU, Roskilde, Denmark; [2] Stensborg, Roskilde, Denmark; [3] SDU Climate Cluster, Odense, Denmark

Oral SESSION 4BO.17 Performance of PV on/in Buildings

4BO.17.1 Modeling Partial Shading at the Cell Level on Photovoltaic Modules 020251
Jean-Paul Calin[1], Jacques Levrat[2], Antonin Faes[2], Fahradin Mujovi[2], Paul Rémondeau[3], Kléber Nicolet-dit-Félix[3], Bénédicte Bonnet-Eymard[2], Didier Dalmazzone[1], Aïcha Hessler-Wyser[3], Christophe Ballif[3]
[1] ENSTA Paris, Palaiseau, France; [2] CSEM, Neuchâtel, Switzerland; [3] EPFL, Neuchâtel, Switzerland

4BO.17.2 Market Potential of Building-Integrated Photovoltaics: a Granular Analysis of the European Building Stock 020252
Juan Ignacio Martinez[1], Julien Van Overstraeten[2], Philippe Macé[2], José Maria Vega de Seoane[1], Elina Bosch[2], Mélodie de l'Epine[3]
[1] Becquerel Institute España, San Sebastian, Spain; [2] Becquerel Institute, Brussels, Belgium; [3] Becquerel Institute France, Lyon, France

4BO.17.3 Photovoltaics in the Built Environment – an Overview of Timely Topics for Research and Development 020253
Francesco Frontini[1], Angele Reinders[2]
[1] SUPSI, Mendrisio, Switzerland; [2] TU Eindhoven, Eindhoven, The Netherlands

4BO.17.5 Advancing BIPV: Shingled HJT Technology for High-Efficiency and Aesthetic Solar Integration 020254
Gabriella Gonnella[1], Alvaro De Gruijter[1], Jordi Veirman[1], Martina Pelle[1], Laura Maturi[1], David Moser[2], Luis Fialho[1]
[1] Eurac Research, Bolzano, Italy; [2] Bequerel Institute Italy, Trento, Italy

4BO.17.6 PV-Planning and Simulation, Daylight Simulation and Energy-Certificate Calculation based on an Open-BIM-Building-Model 020255
Astrid Schneider[1], Karin Stieldorf[1], Christian Schranz[1], Harald Urban[1], Alfred Waschl[2], Markus Feichtner[3], Fedele Rende[4], Andrea Aiello[4], Martin Hauer[5], Kurt Battisti[6], Markus Dörn[6], Jacqueline Scherret[6], Martin Treberspurg[7], Christoph Treberspurg[7]
[1] TU Wien, Vienna, Austria; [2] buildingSMART, Vienna, Austria; [3] Sonnenkraft Energie, St. Veit/Glan, Austria; [4] ACCA Software, Cosenza, Italy; [5] Bartenbach, Vienna, Austria; [6] A-Null Development, Vienna, Austria; [7] Treberspurg und Partner Ziviltechniker, Vienna, Austria

Oral SESSION 4BO.5 PV-Products for Buildings

4BO.5.1 Fabrication of a Novel Semi-Translucent BIPV Module Providing High Power Density and Active Daylight Management 020257
Almudena Garcia-Sanchez[1], Guido Vallerotto[1], Jaime J. Hernández[2], Alejandro García-Cañas[2], Steve Askins[1], Ignacio Antón[1], Isabel Rodríguez[2], César Domínguez[1]
[1] UPM, Madrid, Spain; [2] IMDEA Nanoscience, Madrid, Spain

4BO.5.3 A Comparative Study of Photovoltaic Shading Devices for Net Zero Energy Buildings across French Climates 020259

Visual SESSION 4BV.4 BIPV

Visual SESSION 4CV.1 Advances in Operation, Performance and Maintenance of PV Systems

Oral SESSION 4DO.1 PV Tracking and Simulation

4DO.5.4 Development and Evaluation of Agrivoltaic System in Olive Groves based on a Novel Smart Tracking Algorithm 020392
Ildefonso Muñoz[1], Irati Amatriain[1], Gregorio Olivares[1], Gillen Abrego[2], Eusebio Gainza[2], Iñaki Cornago[1]
[1] CENER, Sarriguren, Spain; [2] ALLOTARRA, Allo, Spain

4DO.5.5 Adoption and Optimisation Analysis of Agrivoltaic Systems for Horticultural Production and Energy Autonomy in Lubumbashi/DR Congo 020393
Eddie Bilitu[1], Shu-Ngwa Asaa[2], Sara Bouguerra[3], Nikoleta Kyranaki[3], Ismail Kaaya[3], Yannick Useni[4], Michael Daenen[3]
[1] Hasselt University, Hasselt, Belgium; [2] imo-imomec, Genk, Belgium; [3] imec, Genk, Belgium; [4] University of Lubumbashi, Lubumbashi, Congo (DRC)

Visual SESSION 4DV.1 Agrivoltaics Approaches, Experiences, Results | Integrated and Innovative PV Applications

4DV.1.5 Maximizing Economic Performance of Agrivoltaic Systems through Module Array Design 020394
Habeel Alam[1], Jenny Nelson[2], Alona Armstrong[1], Duncan Whyatt[1], Nauman Butt[3]
[1] Lancaster University, Lancaster, United Kingdom; [2] Imperial College London, London, United Kingdom; [3] Lahore University of Management Sciences, Lahore, Pakistan

4DV.1.7 Bifacial and Mismatch Factors of Agri-Photovoltaics Systems 020396
Keith R. McIntosh[1], Solomon Freer[1], Bastien J. J. Ardissone[1], S. Ramirez[1], Ben A. Sudbury[1], Malcolm D. Abbott[1]
[1] PV Lighthouse, Coledale, Australia

4DV.1.10 Performance Analysis of Agrivoltaic System Configurations in Nordic Conditions 020398
Magda Szarek[1], Sami Jouttijärvi[1], Lauri Karttunen[1], Samuli Ranta[2], Kati Miettunen[1]
[1] University of Turku, Turku, Finland; [2] TUAS, Turku, Finland

4DV.1.11 Irradiance Management in Agrivoltaic Systems with Varying Designs Across Latitudes: Toward Finland's First Significant Demonstration 020400
Shuo Wang[1], Soroush Moradi Zavie Kord[2], Hugo E. Huerta[1], Antti Lajunen[2], Samuli Ranta[1]
[1] TUAS, Turku, Finland; [2] University of Helsinki, Helsinki, Finland

4DV.1.12 An Innovative Agrivoltaic System for Desert Climates with Anti-Soiling, Irradiance Control, and Water Management 020402
Sagarika Kumar[1], Min Hsian Saw[1], Ahmed Shaaban[1], Kamil Jaworczak[1], Nursulu Kuzhagaliyeva[1], Carlos G. Parrilla[2], Francois M. Tsombou[2], Fouad Lamghari[2], Mauro Pravettoni[1]
[1] Technology Innovation Institute, Abu Dhabi, United Arab Emirates; [2] Fujairah Research Centre, Fujairah, United Arab Emirates

4DV.1.15 Review of Sensor Technologies for Monitoring Agrivoltaic Systems 020403
Sara Pereira[1], José A. Silva[1], Luís Fialho[2], Pedro Horta[1]
[1] University of Évora, Évora, Portugal; [2] Eurac Research, Bolzano, Italy

Visual SESSION 4DV.4 PV System Engineering

[1] Luxembourg Institute of Science and Technology, Esch-sur-Alzette, Luxembourg; [2] University of Lisbon, Lisbon, Portugal

4EO.2.6 Optimizing Angular Performance of Curved VIPV Modules 020459
Francisco José Martín[1], Rebeca Herrero[1], Ignacio Antón[1]
[1] UPM, Madrid, Spain

Oral SESSION 5CO.4 Life Cycle Assessment of Silicon and Perovskite-based Cells and Modules

5CO.4.1 Towards Low-Impact Triple-Junction Perovskite/Silicon Tandem Modules: LCA of Precursor Materials to Describe the Influence of Background Data Sources 020461
Alejandra Galarza[1], Sebastian Nold[2], Lars Oberbeck[3]
[1] IPVF, Palaiseau, France; [2] Fraunhofer ISE, Freiburg, Germany; [3] TotalEnergies OneTech, Paris, France

5CO.4.3 Sustainability Assessment of Perovskite/Silicon Tandem Solar Modules: from Laboratory Scale to Industrial Implementation 020462
Elisabetta Brivio[1], Andrea Danelli[1], Sofia Spagnolo[1], Pierpaolo Girardi[1]
[1] RSE, Milan, Italy

5CO.4.4 LCA Learning Curve for Crystalline Silicon Solar Technologies based on Technology Improvements 020463
Julian Reichle[1], Moritz Fath[1], Sraisth[1], Amish Kumar Sinha[1], Mehul Raval[1], Wolfgang Jooss[1], Peter Fath[1], Gourab Das[1]
[1] RCT Solutions, Konstanz, Germany

Oral SESSION 5CO.5 Life Cycle Assessment of New PV Applications and Recycling

5CO.5.1 Optimizing AgriPV: A Comprehensive Assessment Framework for Sustainable Energy and Agriculture 020464
Ana Patrícia Lopes[1], Bruno Barrionuevo [2], Daniel P. Albuquerque[3], Diogo Cordeiro[4], Cláudia Fernandes[3], Athanasios T. Balafoutis [2], Rui Castro[1]
[1] University of Lisbon, Lisbon, Portugal; [2] CERTH, Athens, Greece; [3] Centre for New Energy Technologies, Sacavém, Portugal; [4] EDP, Lisbon, Portugal

5CO.5.2 Environmental Sustainability Assessment of Agrivoltaic Systems: a Life Cycle Approach 020466
Maria Anna Cusenza[1], Andrea Danelli[1], Pierpaolo Girardi[1], Sofia Spagnolo[1]
[1] RSE, Milan, Italy

5CO.5.4 Closing the Circle: Integrating the Circular Footprint Formula into Photovoltaic System Life Cycle Assessment 020467
Alexis Barrou[1], Selin Kandiyoti-Eskenazi[1], Jacques Levrat[1], Bertrand Paviet-Salomon[1], Christophe Ballif[1]
[1] CSEM, Neuchâtel, Switzerland

5CO.5.6 Environmental Benefits of Silicon Kerf Secondary Products in Pilot Processes over Conventional Production of Equivalent Products with Primary Raw Materials in China and Europe 020468

René Peche[1], Matthias Seitz[1], Markus Schönheits[1], Karsten Wambach[1]
[1] bifa Umweltinstitut, Augsburg, Germany

Oral SESSION 5CO.6 PV Recycling and Circularity

5CO.6.4 Quantification of Technical Recyclability of PV Modules for Different Recycling Scenarios 020470

Matthias Hämmer[1], Kerstin Baumann[1], Karsten Wambach[1], Markus Schönheits[1]
[1] bifa Umweltinstitut, Augsburg, Germany

5CO.6.5 IEC Technical Report 63525 on the Reuse of PV Modules: Final Result 020472

Arvid van der Heide[1], Serge Noels[2], Jan Clyncke[2], Rich Strömberg[3]
[1] imec, Genk, Belgium; [2] PV CYCLE, Brussels, Belgium; [3] University of Alaska, Fairbanks, United States of America

Plenary SESSION 5CP.1 Si PV Manufacturing: Pushing the Limits of Performance

5CP.1.4 Business Model Optimization for European Solar PV: A Study on Costs and Commercial Strategies 020474

Ian Kenchington[1], Philippe Macé[1], Gaëtan Masson[1], Joris Libal[2]
[1] Becquerel Institute, Brussels, Belgium; [2] ISC Konstanz, Konstanz, Germany

Plenary SESSION 5CP.2 Perovskite – Silicon Tandems: Towards Commercialisation | PV Stability in the Field

5CP.2.3 Total Cost of Ownership, LCA and LCOE Analysis of Perovskite-Silicon Tandems Compared to Single Junction Crystalline Silicon PV Technologies 020475

Baljeet Singh Goraya[1], Dilara Maria Subasi[1], Peter Henri Brailovsky[1], Henning Nagel[1], Patricia S.C. Schulze[1], Martin C. Schubert[1], Jochen Rentsch[1], Martin Hermle[1], Ralf Preu[1], Sebastian Nold[1]
[1] Fraunhofer ISE, Freiburg, Germany

Oral SESSION 5DO.11 The Road to Massive PV Deployment

5DO.11.1 Integration of Solar PV in a Norwegian Energy System, Navigating the Trade-offs between Land Use and Solar Power Production 020476

Petry Kristine Nøttum Haaland[1], Ole-Morten Midtgård[1], Magnus Korpås[1]
[1] NTNU, Trondheim, Norway

Oral SESSION 5DO.18 PV Recycling and Material Demand

Visual SESSION 5DV.2 Life Cycle Analysis and PV Recycling | Citizens Participation and Awareness

Visual SESSION 5DV.3 Grid Integration and Flexibility Enablers | Global, Country- and Application-Specific Analysis of PV Deployment Aspects | Costs, Economics, Finance and Markets

Oral SESSION 5EO.1 Citizens Participation and Awareness

MODEL TESTS ON WATERLILY SHAPED OFFSHORE PV SYSTEM

Linda Kemp[1], Patrick Schrijvers, Naman Baderiya, William Otto
Maritime Research Institute Netherlands (MARIN)
(1) l.j.kemp@marin.nl

ABSTRACT: The European Union funded NATURSEA-PV project aims to develop a lily-inspired PV substructure solution to meet the specific needs for Offshore Floating PV. The substructure will be manufactured of a flexible, light and ecofriendly type of concrete which will give the substructure the advantages of flexibility and lightness to withstand offshore conditions. As part of the project, model scale tests on the flexible substructure are performed to capture the behavior of the substructure to waves. These basin tests are conducted in the MARIN shallow water basin at scale 1:30. To allow for numerical model validation, the tests are conducted using two sets of soft-mooring system to ensure that there is no interaction between the natural periods of the mooring system and wave frequencies. During irregular wave tests, different vertical behavior is observed at the outer ring of the substructure compared to the inner ring. Wave response is more extreme in high frequency ranges (smaller wave length) for the outer ring, which is related to the number of beams connected to the floater constraining the vertical motion. Strain measurements perpendicular to the longitudinal axis show the largest deformations, but this is not observed along the longitudinal axis. There is no exceedance of the air gap for the tested wave conditions. These basin tests demonstrate the validity of the original design, and serve as input for future numerical model validation.
Keywords: floating PV, basin test, validation, flexibility

1 INTRODUCTION

The European Union funded NATURSEA-PV project aims to develop a lily-inspired PV substructure solution to meet the specific needs for Offshore Floating PV. The lily's concept of radial and tangential girders is researched and engineered using flexible eco-Ultra High Performance Concrete (eco-UHPC) elements. The concrete girders will provide support to a lightweight sheet, which spans the construction like an umbrella. This sheet will have openings to ensure sufficient sunlight reaches the water surface, and it will provide sufficient carrying capacity for the PV panels as well as maintenance technicians [1].

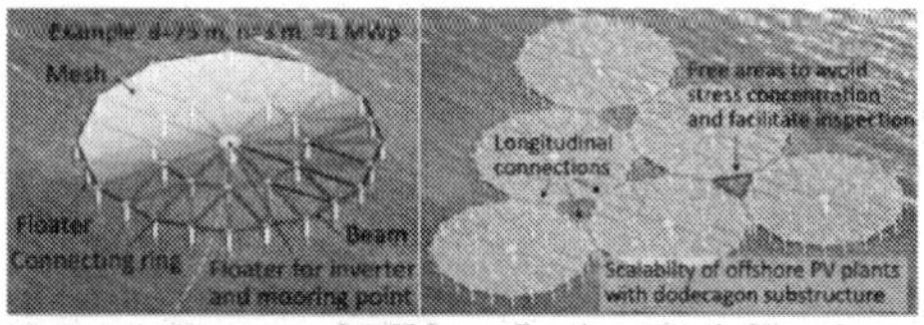

Figure 1: Conceptual Offshore floating PV (left) and scalability of the solution (right)

A conceptual and global design of the substructure was made, which serves as starting point of the prototype that is tested in a wave basin test campaign [2].

The main objectives of the test campaign are to validate the overall concept's performance, model the dynamic and flexible response of the floater and provide validation data for numerical tools [3].

Within the floating offshore PV different technologies are used, to harvest solar energy in harsh wave environments and strong winds [4]. To better understand the floating PV technologies, the concepts can be roughly distinguished into flexible membrane type concepts and hinge connected fixed floaters as well as into floating PV at the water surface or PV panels elevated above the water surface level. For example, the Solar@Sea concept consists of flexible floaters, where the PV panels are glued on top of the floaters [5]. Another membrane type floating PV on the water level is installed by company Ocean Sun in Norway inspired by fish farms [6]. The tested NATURSEA-PV concept is a combination of the a flexible structure by the use of UHPC as the main material and an elevated shield of solar panels. The eco-UHPC is considered as an effective material with improved reliability and maintainability for offshore floating PV substructures [1].

2 EXPERIMENTAL SET-UP

2.1 Flexible model and instrumentation

The basin tests are conducted at a scale of 1:30, based on the general dimensions of the floater and the wave maker capabilities. The structure is a combination of 21 floaters, connected with two layers of beams to create an orthogonal design. The numbering of the floaters, and location of instrumentation is shown in Figure 2.

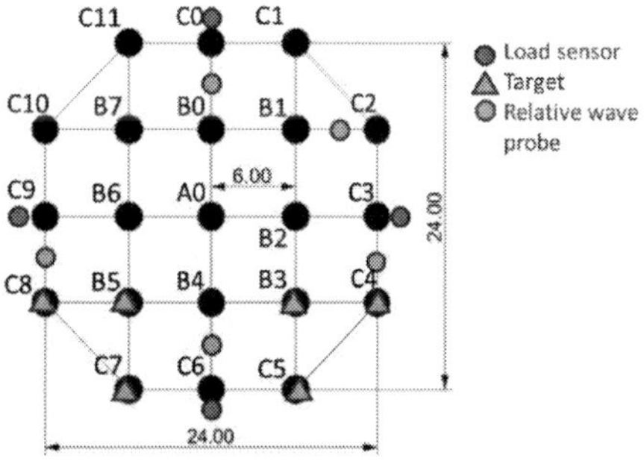

Figure 2: Floater numbering used for the substructure layout

The scale model is designed based on the required flexibility, dimensions and weight distribution of the prototype substructure. The material and dimensions of the beams are carefully selected to match the bending stiffness. PVC beams are used with a slightly smaller width at model scale, as this provided the closest match in the desired bending stiffness. The small deviation of 0.03m in beam width is considered acceptable at this stage of the project, since it is expected that modelling the correct bending stiffness is vital to the objectives of this project.

10.4229/EUPVSEC2025/4DO.4.5

Bending tests are conducted on the individual beams to document the corresponding stiffness, which is used as input for the numerical modelling. In addition, a bending test on the complete substructure has been performed for numerical model validation (see Figure 3). The global flexibility of the model in the basin is shown in Figure 4.

Figure 3: Bending test on the global substructure

Figure 4: Flexibility of the global substructure shown in the basin (still from model test video, available at https://youtu.be/DLAIcCs89J8?si=1_RINsoFnwlfCwAV)

The instrumentation on the model consisted of motion measurement on 6 floaters, depicted by the green triangles in Figure 2. The NDI contact-less optical measurement system is used. Since the floater is flexible, the motions are measured at multiple locations. Resistance type wave probes are used to directly measure the airgap, and ring-shaped strain gauge force transducers are used to measure the loads from the soft-mooring system.

An optical fiber is used to directly measure strain differences on the flexible model. These optical fiber sensors have brass gratings at a specific position along the fiber, which reflects a specific wavelength of the incoming light. The remaining light travels to the next bragg grating with a slightly different bragg grating wave length. Since the wavelength changes when the fiber is stressed or compressed, this allows for a direct measurement of the strain.

2.2 Mooring system

During the model tests, a so-called horizontal soft spring mooing system was used to keep the model in position and at the specified heading. The system consists of 4 steel wired including linear springs. The lines are identical to avoid undesired coupling effects between modes of motion. The lines are oriented horizontally to a pulley and vertically up to the mooing points.

Two sets of springs are used. Set 1 has a theoretical horizontal stiffness of 41.5 kN/m and pretention of 271.5kN (surge and sway), which results in natural periods of 14.0s. These periods are within the wave period for a white noise wave and two irregular waves. Therefore, the drift forces on the model may not be captured well.

A second set of springs has been used with stiffness of 7.5kN and a pretension of 135.7kN. These softer springs increase the natural periods to 24.1s, which is outside the wave frequency range and therefore won't affect the motion behavior of the model.

In order to achieve different model headings, the model is rotated. Two relative wave headings are considered during the tests.

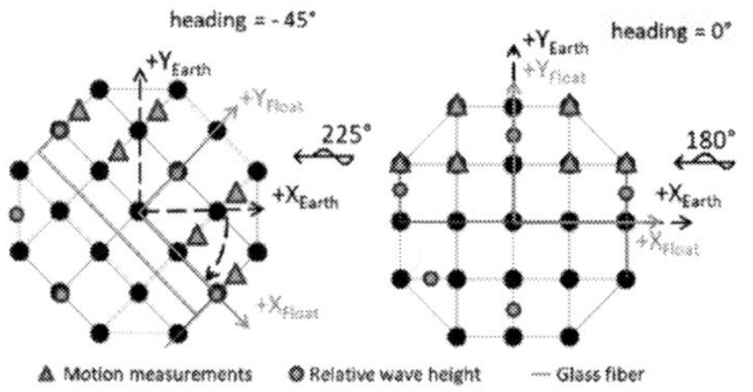

Figure 5: Floater with heading of -45 and 0 degrees.

2.3 MARIN's shallow water basin

Tests are conducted in the MARIN shallow water basin. The basin is 220m long, 15,8m wide and has a water depth of 1.0m. Waves can be generated from one side using a wave board. Both regular and irregular waves can be generated. The experiments are conducted at a fixed location, 30m from the wave generators. More information on the shallow water basin can be found at https://www.marin.nl/en/about/facilities-and-tools/basins/shallow-water-basin

2.4 Environmental conditions

Seven (7) regular waves are generated, ranging from H = 3.5m with period T of 5.7s to H=7.0m with T = 8.6s. Five (5) irregular JONSWAP waves are calibrated for a duration of 3½ hour, ranging from Hs = 0.8m with Tp = 4.5s to Hs = 5.3m with Tp = 12.50s. In addition, two white noise tests are generated with Hs = 2.0 and 4.0m

Table I: Calibrated Regular and Irregular waves

Environment	Duration	Wave characteristics		
Regular waves		H [m]	T [s]	
Reg. wave 5	~20 oscillations	3.52	5.7	
Reg. wave 6		4.50	6.4	
Reg. wave 7		5.40	7.0	
Reg. wave 8		6.26	7.6	
Reg. wave 9		7.06	8.1	
Reg. wave 10		6.86	9.0	
Reg. wave 11		7.04	8.6	
Irregular waves		H_s [m]	T_P [s]	γ [-]
Irreg. wave 1	½ + 3 hr	5.416	12.566	3.3
Irreg. wave 2		3.329	12.566	3.3
Irreg. wave 3		3.807	10.472	3.3
Irreg. wave 4		1.824	8.490	3.3
Irreg. wave 5		0.771	4.525	3.3
White noise 1	½ + 1 hr	1.965	5-20	1.0
White noise 2		3.987	5-20	1.0

10.4229/EUPVSEC2025/4DO.4.5

The calibrated regular and irregular wave conditions (see Table I) are calibrated prior to the actual model tests, without the model in the basin. The wave elevations are measured by means of resistance wire wave probes, placed at the centre of the test set-up and at one additional reference position. The reference wave probe remains at its location in the test set-up for the entire duration of the model test project. The deviations between requested and measured wave height was less than 2% for all waves.

3 BASIN TEST RESULTS

3.1 Verification tests

The mooring stiffness was verified using static pull out tests, where a surge offset is applied to the substructure in three distinct steps. The applied external load, loads in the mooring lines and global translation and rotation are measured. The measured inline mooring forces and pull out force magnitudes are reported in figure 6. The mooring forces show linear trends with increasing external load, and the theoretical stiffness of 41.5 kN/m is matching well with the as-build mooring system.

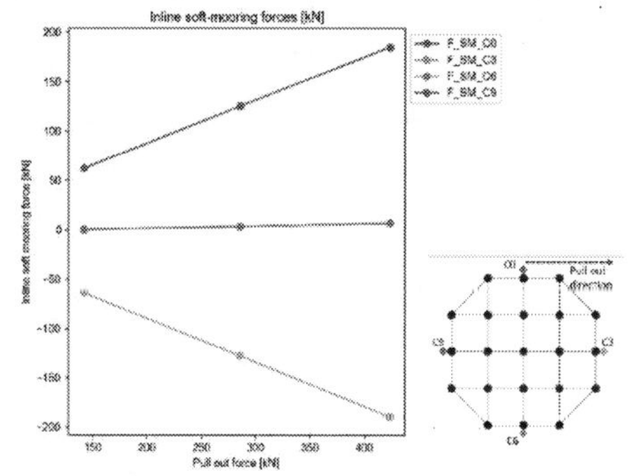

Figure 6: Soft-mooring forces during pull-out tests.

Decay tests were conducted to verify the natural periods. Two free floating heave decays were conducted, surge, sway and heave decay tests are conducted for the moored system. From these tests, the natural periods and where possible the linear and quadratic damping were analyzed. The free floating heave decays show a clear damped oscillation for the first four to five oscillations, after which non-linear response of the system affects the heave oscillations at the floaters in the first ring (B3 and B5) around the initial position of the decay.

During the decay tests, the oscillations of the different instrumented targets do not show clear differences. Figure 7 shows the heave response of the 6 instrumented floaters in one of the performed heave decay tests. The natural heave periods of the individual floaters are within 2% of the average value of the floaters. Also, the linear damping (P) and quadratic damping (Q) coefficients show a clear relation to the floater positions or motions. The heave decays are initialized by a positive heave offset, applied to the middle floater (A0). This initial offset causes a high strain value at the optical fiber measurement locations close to the attachment point. The strain magnitude decreases for measurement points further from the attachment point. No clear bending eigenmodes of the substructure are observed during the heave decay tests.

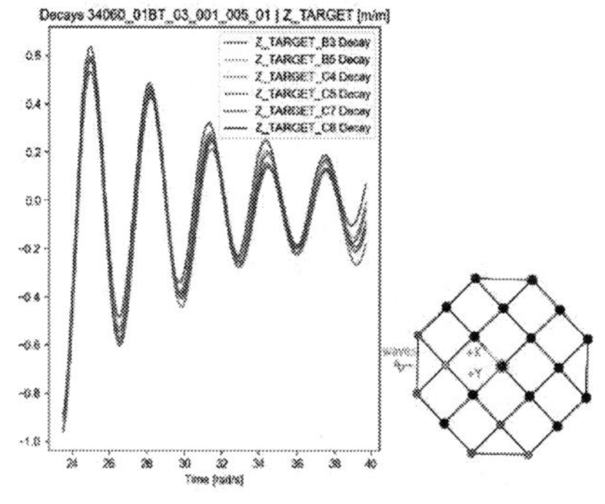

Figure 7: Heave decay measured at 6 floater positions, heave applied to floater C0 with a +Z offset

3.1 Motions and deformation

The Response Amplitude Operator (RAO) of the different floaters within one test are compared. For a model heading of 0 degrees, the substructure shows rigid body pitch, surge and yaw response. For heave, there is a clear distinction between the outer ring floaters and inner ring floaters (see figure 8). For low frequencies, the RAO is approximately 1 m/m, but increases for the higher frequency range for floaters C4 and C8 in the outer ring. This difference is related to the beam layout of the individual floaters. The floaters in the outer ring are restrained by 3 beams, while the floaters in the inner ring are restrained by 4 beams, limiting the vertical motion of these floaters

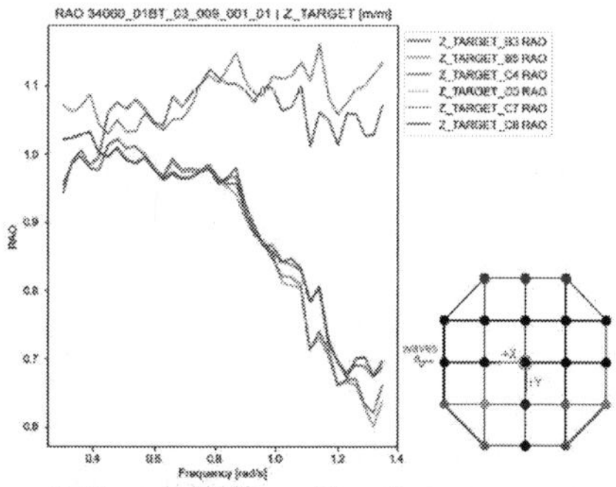

Figure 8: Heave RAO for a white noise test.

10.4229/EUPVSEC2025/4DO.4.5

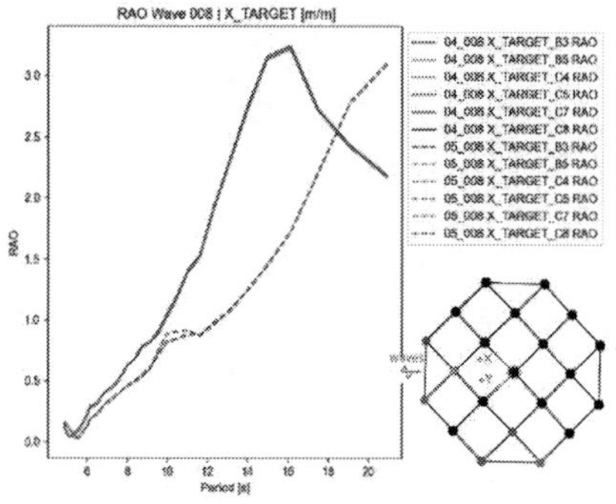

Figure 9: Surge RAO for a white noise test as a result of different soft mooring systems. The solid line represents the soft mooring system with eigen period of 14.0 s, while the dashed line represents the system with eigen period of 24.1s.

In Figure 9 the RAO of body surge is compared for two different set of soft mooring spring systems. The natural period for surge of the original soft mooring system with a stiffness of 41.5 kN/m (indicated by solid lines) shows a clear response around 14.0 seconds. The second set of springs with surge stiffness of 17.0 kN the natural period is outside the wave frequent period, around 24.1 seconds and is therefore not visible in Figure 9.

3.2 Relative wave elevations

One of the design constraints was a positive air gap, meaning that there is no impact or green water event on the solar panel system. For each irregular wave test, the airgap is calculated, which shows a positive value for each tests. The smallest recorded airgap was 1.32m at the leading side of the substructure. A still of the video recording is shown in Figure 10.

Figure 10: still of wave test recording with smallest positive airgap.

3.3 Measured strain

The FBG optical fiber is used to measure microstrain in the centerline of the substructure. The strain response is converted to a RAO along this centerline per meter incoming wave. The overall strain response on the top beam is higher for 0 degree heading, when the bending strain is in-line with the wave direction (see Figure 11). The highest strain is measured at the waveward side of the substructure (the 'bow'), and decreases further for the locations further towards the 'stern'. Based on the motion response in regular waves, no clear resonance in bending motions is observed.

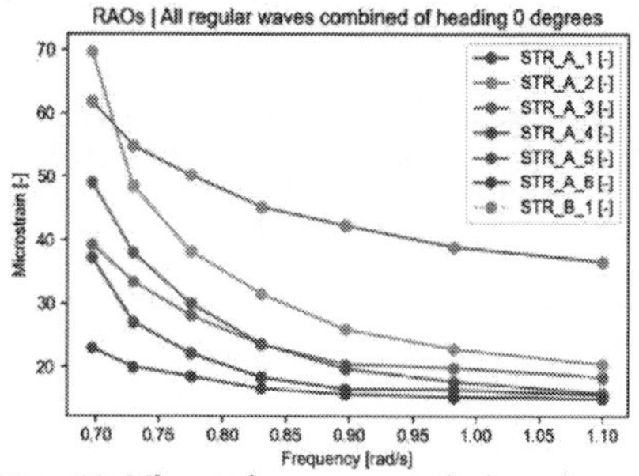

Figure 11: Microstrain response to the incoming regular wave at 7 different positions.

4 CONCLUDING REMARKS

Basin tests were executed to test and validate the lily-shaped floating offshore PV system in relevant environmental conditions. A flexible model-scale substructure was engineered, closely representing the overall concept. The beams were build from PVC with a slightly smaller width at model-scale, such that the bending stiffness of the beams matched between model-scale and prototype scale.

The basin tests demonstrated that the overall concept performance is as expected from the general design. The flexible model-scale substructure did not experience any wave impact loads on the solar deck, with a positive airgap of at least 1.3m. The dynamic beam loads remained below the capacity of the beam - in other words: the substructure did not break.

Emphasis was placed during the basin tests on verification tests, to ensure that the obtained dataset can be used for numerical model calibration and validation. In addition to multiple motion sensors, a novel fiber optical measurement system was used to directly measure the strain in the substructure. This high quality dataset allows to further improve the numerical model that was used for the first design. This work is ongoing.

FUNDING

This work is part of the NATURSEA-PV project, funded by the HORIZON-CL5-2021-D3-03-10 program with grant agreement number 101084348. MARIN would like to thank all parties in the NATURSEA-PV project for their valuable contributions and discussions in the design and testing of the substructure.

DATA AVAILIBITY STATEMENT

The full dataset of the model tests can be accessed through https://doi.org/10.5281/zenodo.17047051 (accessed on 4/9/2025).

5 REFERENCES

[1] Fundación Tecnalia Research and Innovation, "Proposal NATURSEA-PV - Part B," Derio, 2022.

[2] N. Baderiya and W. Otto, "D1.2 Design of Substructure," NATURSEA-PV, Wageningen, 2024.

[3] L. Kemp, N. Baderiya, R. Heijmen and E. Linnartz, "D4.1 Substructure Model Tests," NATURSEA-PV, Wageningen, 2024.

[4] E. Solomin, E. Sirotkin, E. Cuce, S. Selvanathan and S. Kumarasamy, "Hybrid Floating Solar Plant

Designs: A Review," *Energies,* vol. 14, no. 2751, 2021.

[5] W. Otto, T. Bunnik and L. Kaydihan, "Hydro-Elastic Behavior of an Inflatable Mattress in Waves," in *9th International Conference on Hydroelsticity in Maritime Technology*, Rome, 2022.

[6] Ocean Sun, "About Ocean Sun," Ocean Sun, [Online]. Available: https://oceansun.no/about/. [Accessed 22 08 2025].

NATURSEA-PV

NOVEL ECO-CEMENTITIOUS MATERIALS AND COMPONENTS FOR DURABLE, COMPETITIVE, AND BIO-INSPIRED OFFSHORE FLOATING PV SUBSTRUCTURES

EU PVSEC | Session 4DO.4

25th September 2025 | Bilbao, Spain

Linda Kemp
(MARIN)

"Funded by the European Union. Views and opinions expressed are however those of the author(s) only and do not necessarily reflect those of the European Union or the European Climate Infrastructure and Environment Executive Agency (CINEA). Neither the European Union nor the granting authority can be held responsible for them."

Funded by the European Union

NATURSEA-PV

Partners

tecnalia
MEMBER OF BASQUE RESEARCH & TECHNOLOGY ALLIANCE

MARIN

université de BORDEAUX

UCC | MaREI

TECHNISCHE UNIVERSITÄT DARMSTADT

UPV EHU
POLYMAT

CSIC

PREFFOR
PREFABRICADOS FORMEX

Warrant Hub
TINEXTA GROUP

RDC

CENTEC
Centro de Engenharia e Tecnologia Naval e Oceânica

IST-ID
Associação do Instituto Superior Técnico para a Investigação e Desenvolvimento

Funded by the European Union

"Funded by the European Union. Views and opinions expressed are however those of the author(s) only and do not necessarily reflect those of the European Union or the European Climate Infrastructure and Environment Executive Agency (CINEA). Neither the European Union nor the granting authority can be held responsible for them."

Victoria Amazonica (left) showing underside of a leaf (right)

Conceptual Offshore Floating PV sideview

NATURSEA-PV

Our approach

The substructures will be built using newly developed environmentally friendly low carbon **ultra-high performance concrete**, and it will be coated with new biobased antifouling and anticorrosive coatings.

The lily's concept of radial and tangential girders will take advantage of the **flexibility and lightness** of the new eco-concretes to withstand the harsh offshore metocean conditions.

The computational toolkit will serve to optimize materials properties and plan timely maintenance operations.

Funded by the European Union

"Funded by the European Union. Views and opinions expressed are however those of the author(s) only and do not necessarily reflect those of the European Union or the European Climate Infrastructure and Environment Executive Agency (CINEA). Neither the European Union nor the granting authority can be held responsible for them."

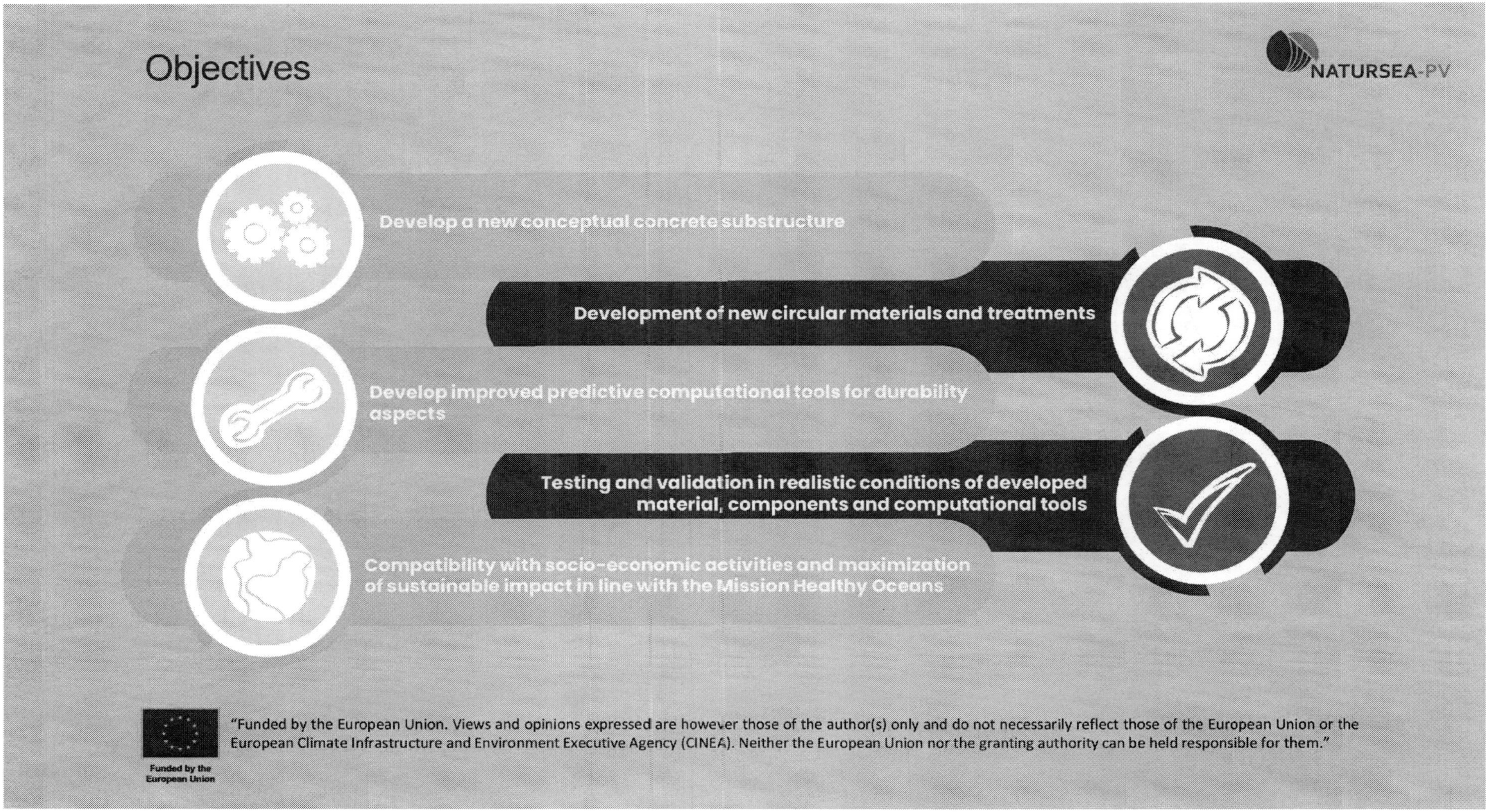
Objectives
NATURSEA-PV
Develop a new conceptual concrete substructure
Development of new circular materials and treatments
Develop improved predictive computational tools for durability aspects
Testing and validation in realistic conditions of developed material, components and computational tools
Compatibility with socio-economic activities and maximization of sustainable impact in line with the Mission Healthy Oceans
"Funded by the European Union. Views and opinions expressed are however those of the author(s) only and do not necessarily reflect those of the European Union or the European Climate Infrastructure and Environment Executive Agency (CINEA). Neither the European Union nor the granting authority can be held responsible for them."
Funded by the European Union

Experimental setup
Model and instrumentation

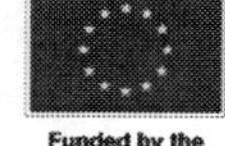

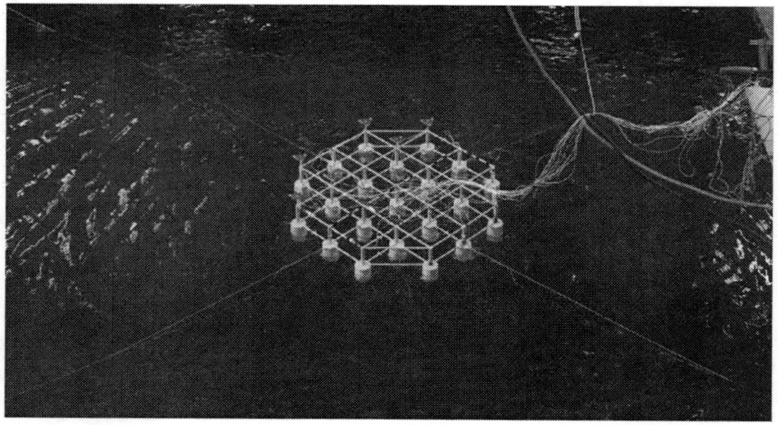

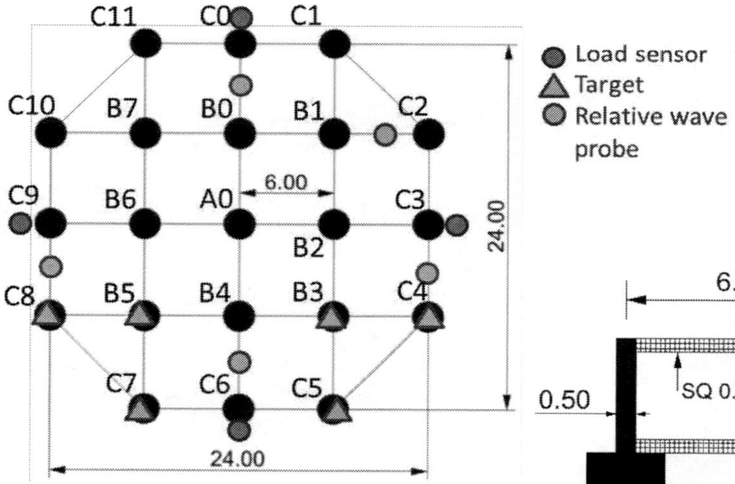

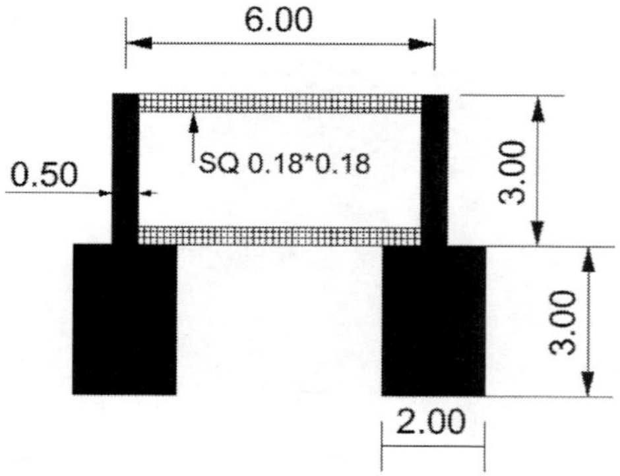

Funded by the European Union

"Funded by the European Union. Views and opinions expressed are however those of the author(s) only and do not necessarily reflect those of the European Union or the European Climate Infrastructure and Environment Executive Agency (CINEA). Neither the European Union nor the granting authority can be held responsible for them."

Experimental setup
Flexibility modelling

NATURSEA-PV

(Dry) Flexibility Test

(Wet) Flexibility demonstration

Funded by the European Union

"Funded by the European Union. Views and opinions expressed are however those of the author(s) only and do not necessarily reflect those of the European Union or the European Climate Infrastructure and Environment Executive Agency (CINEA). Neither the European Union nor the granting authority can be held responsible for them."

Experimental setup
Test Basin & Wave Conditions

NATURSEA-PV

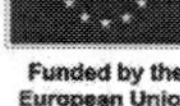

Shallow water basin
220 m x 15.8 m x 1 m (L x B x T)

Environment	Duration	Wave characteristics		
Regular waves		H [m]		T [s]
Reg. wave 5	~20 oscillations	3.52		5.7
Reg. wave 6		4.50		6.4
Reg. wave 7		5.40		7.0
Reg. wave 8		6.26		7.6
Reg. wave 9		7.06		8.1
Reg. wave 10		6.86		9.0
Reg. wave 11		7.04		8.6
Irregular waves		H_s [m]	T_p [s]	γ [-]
Irreg. wave 1	½ + 3 hr	5.416	12.566	3.3
Irreg. wave 2		3.329	12.566	3.3
Irreg. wave 3		3.807	10.472	3.3
Irreg. wave 4		1.824	8.490	3.3
Irreg. wave 5		0.771	4.525	3.3
White noise 1	½ + 1 hr	1.965	5-20	1.0
White noise 2		3.987	5-20	1.0

Funded by the European Union

"Funded by the European Union. Views and opinions expressed are however those of the author(s) only and do not necessarily reflect those of the European Union or the European Climate Infrastructure and Environment Executive Agency (CINEA). Neither the European Union nor the granting authority can be held responsible for them."

MARIN
NATURSEA-PV

NATURSEA-PV

Basin Test Results
System verification & Decays

Mooring system verification – Pull out tests

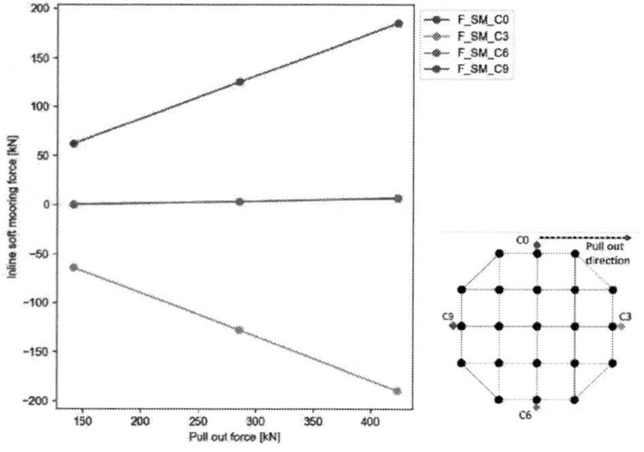

Heave decay tests – Offset applied to floater A0 (+Z)

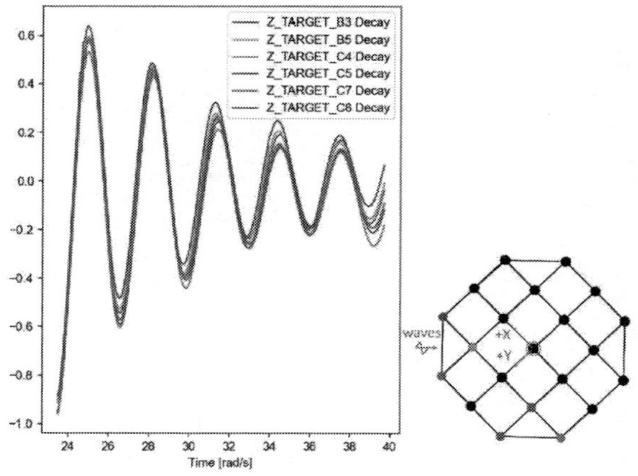

Funded by the European Union

"Funded by the European Union. Views and opinions expressed are however those of the author(s) only and do not necessarily reflect those of the European Union or the European Climate Infrastructure and Environment Executive Agency (CINEA). Neither the European Union nor the granting authority can be held responsible for them."

NATURSEA-PV

Basin Test Results
Motions & Deformations

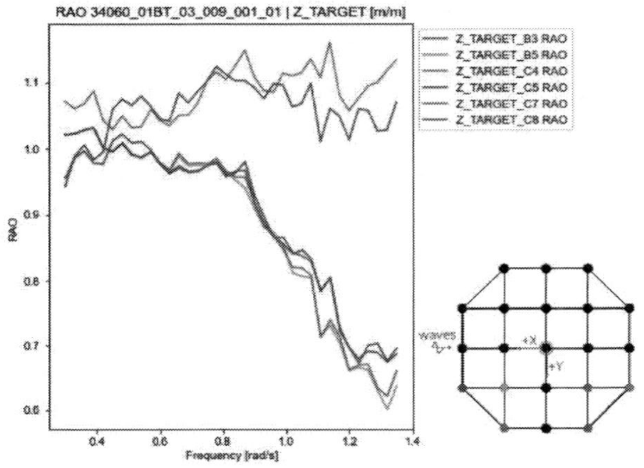

Relative Amplitude Operator – Vertical motions (heave)

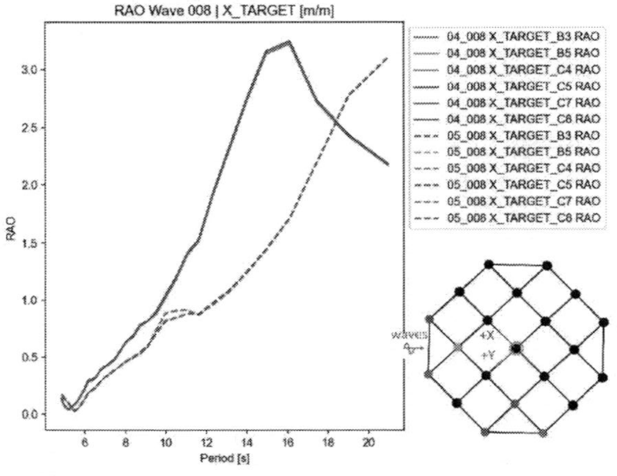

Relative Amplitude Operator – Horizontal motions (surge) in two different mooring systems

"Funded by the European Union. Views and opinions expressed are however those of the author(s) only and do not necessarily reflect those of the European Union or the European Climate Infrastructure and Environment Executive Agency (CINEA). Neither the European Union nor the granting authority can be held responsible for them."

Funded by the European Union

NATURSEA-PV

Basin Test Results
Relative wave elevations & Strain

Still from model test with airgap minimum

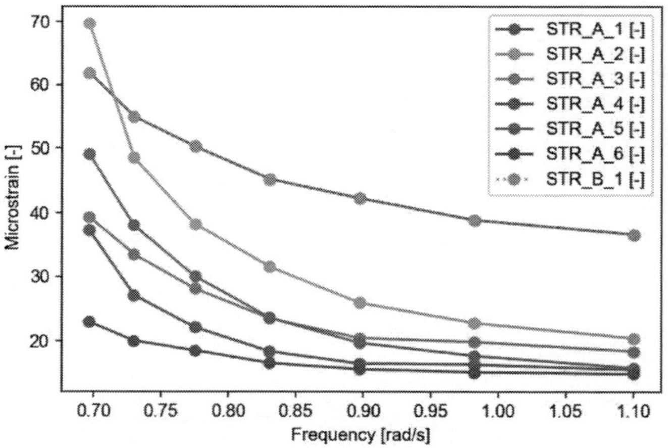

Strain measurements in Regular Wave tests

Funded by the European Union

"Funded by the European Union. Views and opinions expressed are however those of the author(s) only and do not necessarily reflect those of the European Union or the European Climate Infrastructure and Environment Executive Agency (CINEA). Neither the European Union nor the granting authority can be held responsible for them."

Concluding remarks

NATURSEA-PV

- A flexible model-scale substructure was engineered, closely representing the overall concept.
- The basin tests demonstrated that the overall concept performance is as expected from the general design.
- Emphasis was placed during the basin tests on verification tests, to ensure that the obtained dataset can be used for numerical model calibration and validation. This high-quality dataset allows to further improve the numerical model that was used for the first design. This work is ongoing.

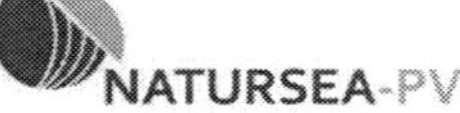

Funded by the European Union

"Funded by the European Union. Views and opinions expressed are however those of the author(s) only and do not necessarily reflect those of the European Union or the European Climate Infrastructure and Environment Executive Agency (CINEA). Neither the European Union nor the granting authority can be held responsible for them."

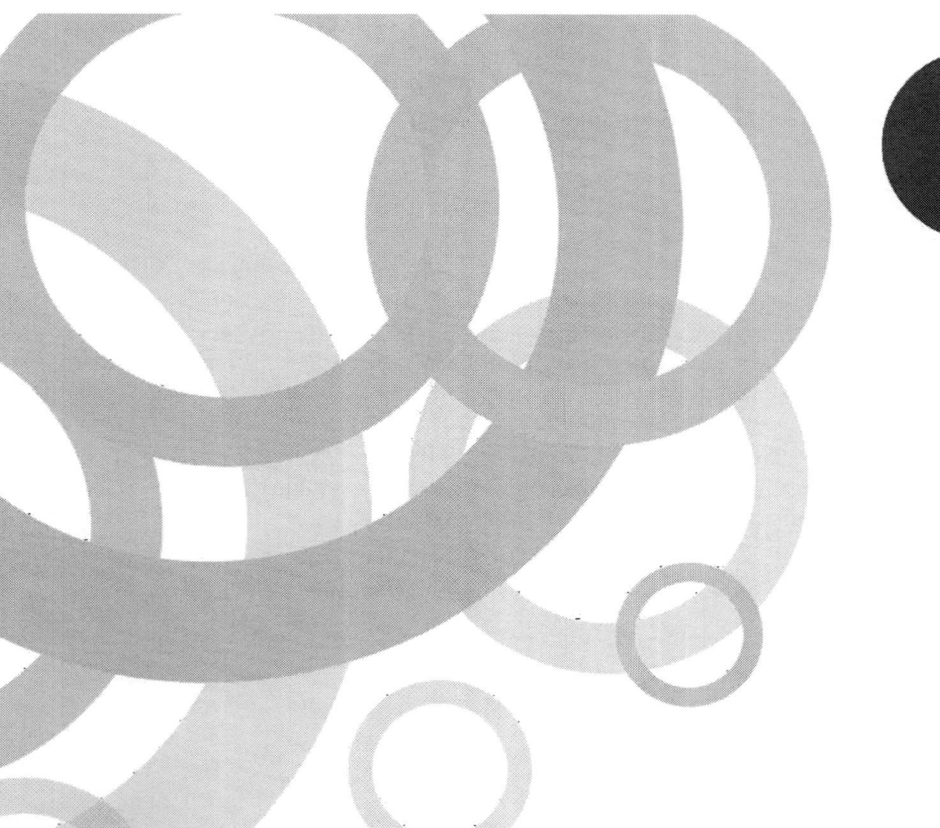

NATURSEA-PV

NOVEL ECO-CEMENTITIOUS MATERIALS AND COMPONENTS FOR DURABLE, COMPETITIVE, AND BIO-INSPIRED OFFSHORE FLOATING PV SUBSTRUCTURES

THANKS FOR YOUR ATTENTION

Visit our website!

www.natursea-pv.eu

Funded by the European Union

"Funded by the European Union. Views and opinions expressed are however those of the author(s) only and do not necessarily reflect those of the European Union or the European Climate Infrastructure and Environment Executive Agency (CINEA). Neither the European Union nor the granting authority can be held responsible for them."

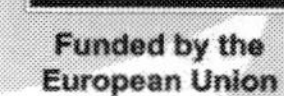

DEVELOPMENT AND EVALUATION OF AGRIVOLTAIC SYSTEMS IN OLIVE GROVES BASED ON A NOVEL SMART TRACKING ALGORITHM

Ildefonso Muñoz[1], Irati Amatriain[1], Gregorio Olivares[1], Gillen Abrego[2], Eusebio Gainza[2], Iñaki Cornago[1]

[1] *CENER, National Renewable Energy Centre*
[2] *ALLOTARRA, Association for Organic Agriculture and Livestock*

42nd European Photovoltaic Solar Energy Conference and Exhibition
25.09.2025

CENER | NATIONAL RENEWABLE ENERGY CENTRE

Allotarra

GOBIERNO DE ESPAÑA · VICEPRESIDENCIA TERCERA DEL GOBIERNO · MINISTERIO PARA LA TRANSICIÓN ECOLÓGICA Y EL RETO DEMOGRÁFICO · MINISTERIO DE CIENCIA E INNOVACIÓN · Ciemat · Gobierno de Navarra · Nafarroako Gobernua

OUTLINE

01 CLIMATE CHANGE THREATS

02 IGUZKITZA PROJECT

03 TWO DIFFERENT FIELDS/CONFIGURATIONS

04 SENSOR SYSTEM

05 CROP MODEL

06 SMART TRACKING ALGORITHM

07 PRODUCTION ESTIMATIONS

08 CONCLUSIONS & ONGOING WORK

CENER | NATIONAL RENEWABLE ENERGY CENTRE

Ciemat | Gobierno de Navarra Nafarroako Gobernua

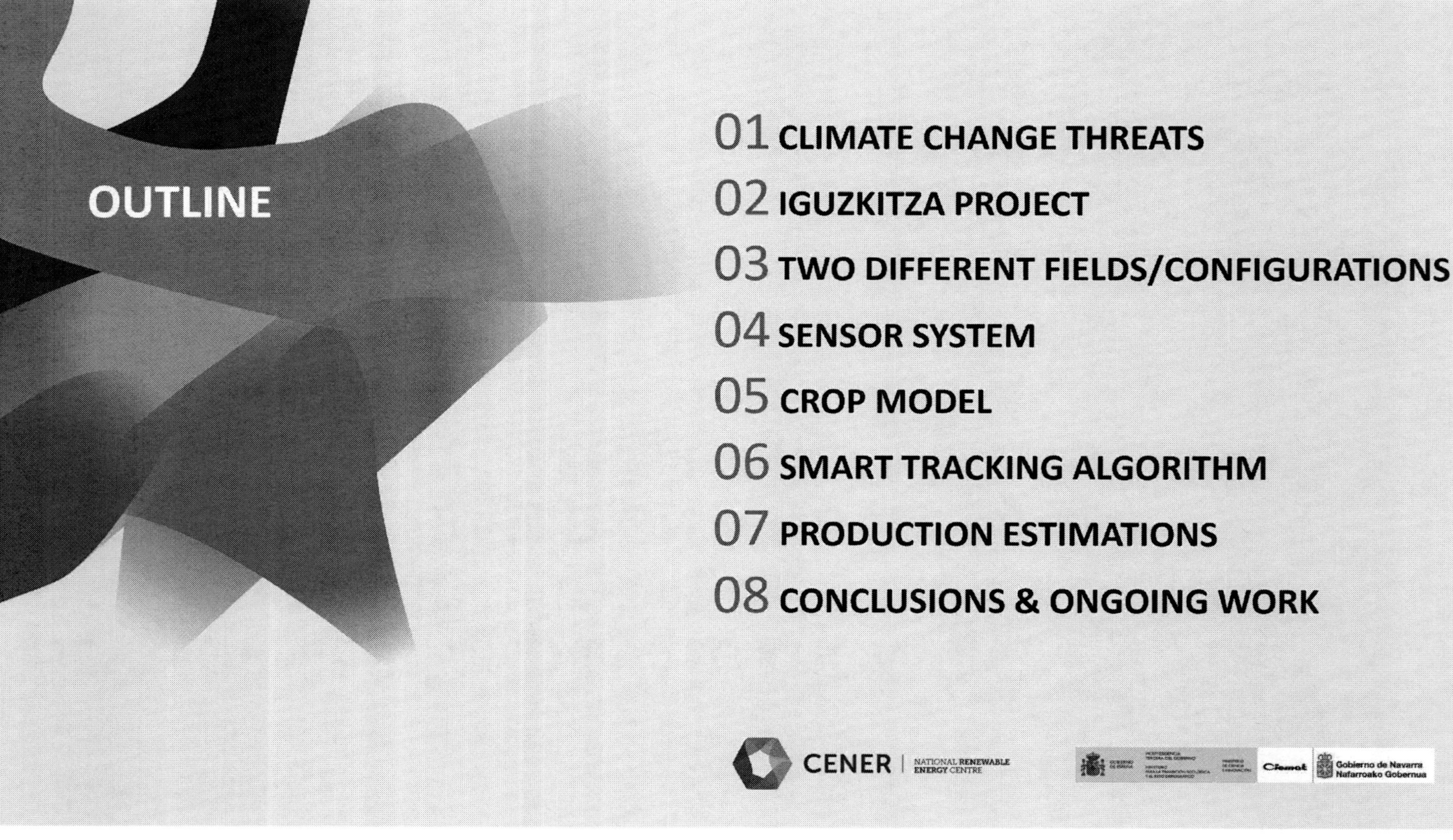

SOLAR ENERGY TECHNOLOGIES AND STORAGE

01 CLIMATE CHANGE THREATS

- Olive Groves: Well adapted to Mediterranean climate and resilience to water scarcity
- However, olives trees are being affected by effects of climatic change:
  - Increase of solar irradiance
  - Higher temperatures
  - Extreme weather events (droughts, heavy rainfall, hailstorms)

- AgriPV techniques could mitigate this effects

CENER | NATIONAL RENEWABLE ENERGY CENTRE

Ciemat Gobierno de Navarra Nafarroako Gobernua

02 IGUZKITZA PROJECT

SOLAR ENERGY TECHNOLOGIES AND STORAGE

IGUZKITZA PROJECT
Navarra Regional Strategic Project of Circular Economy focused on Olives Groves

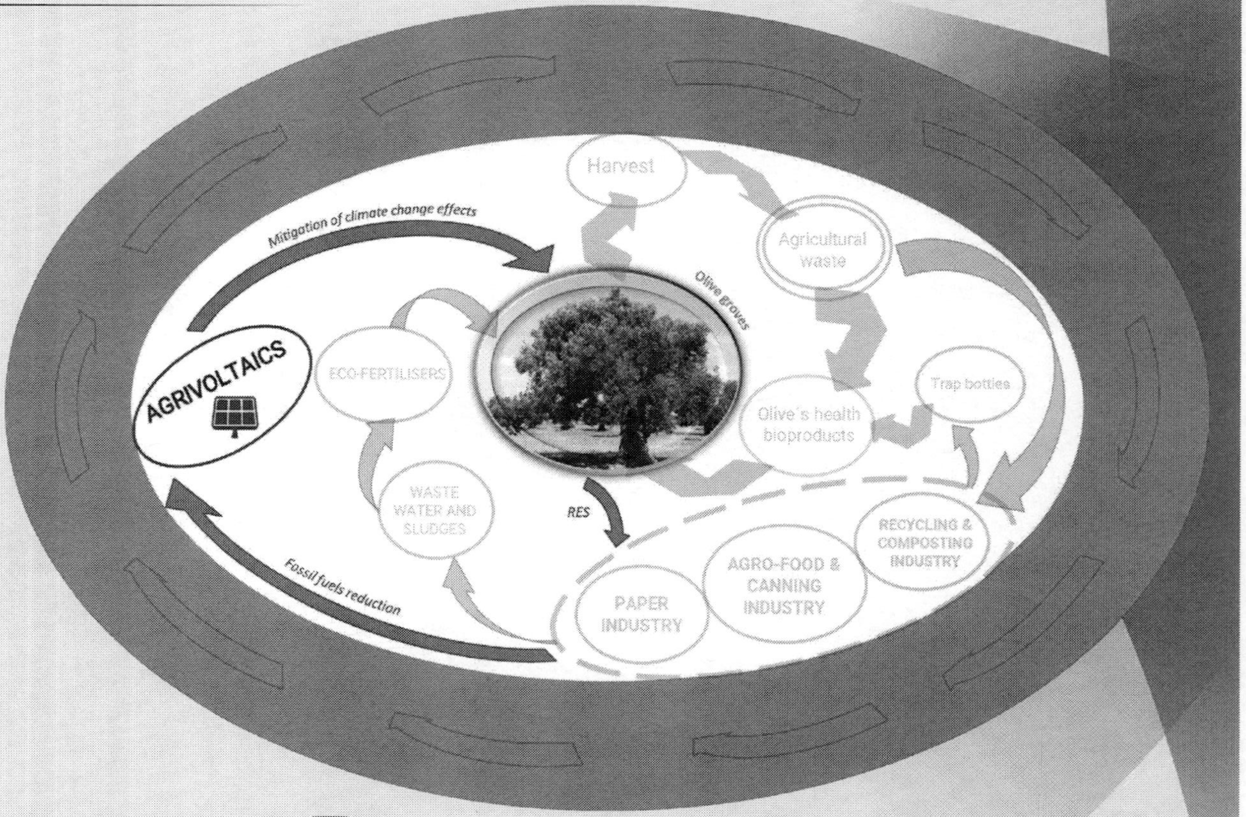

CENER | NATIONAL RENEWABLE ENERGY CENTRE

Gobierno de Navarra
Nafarroako Gobernua

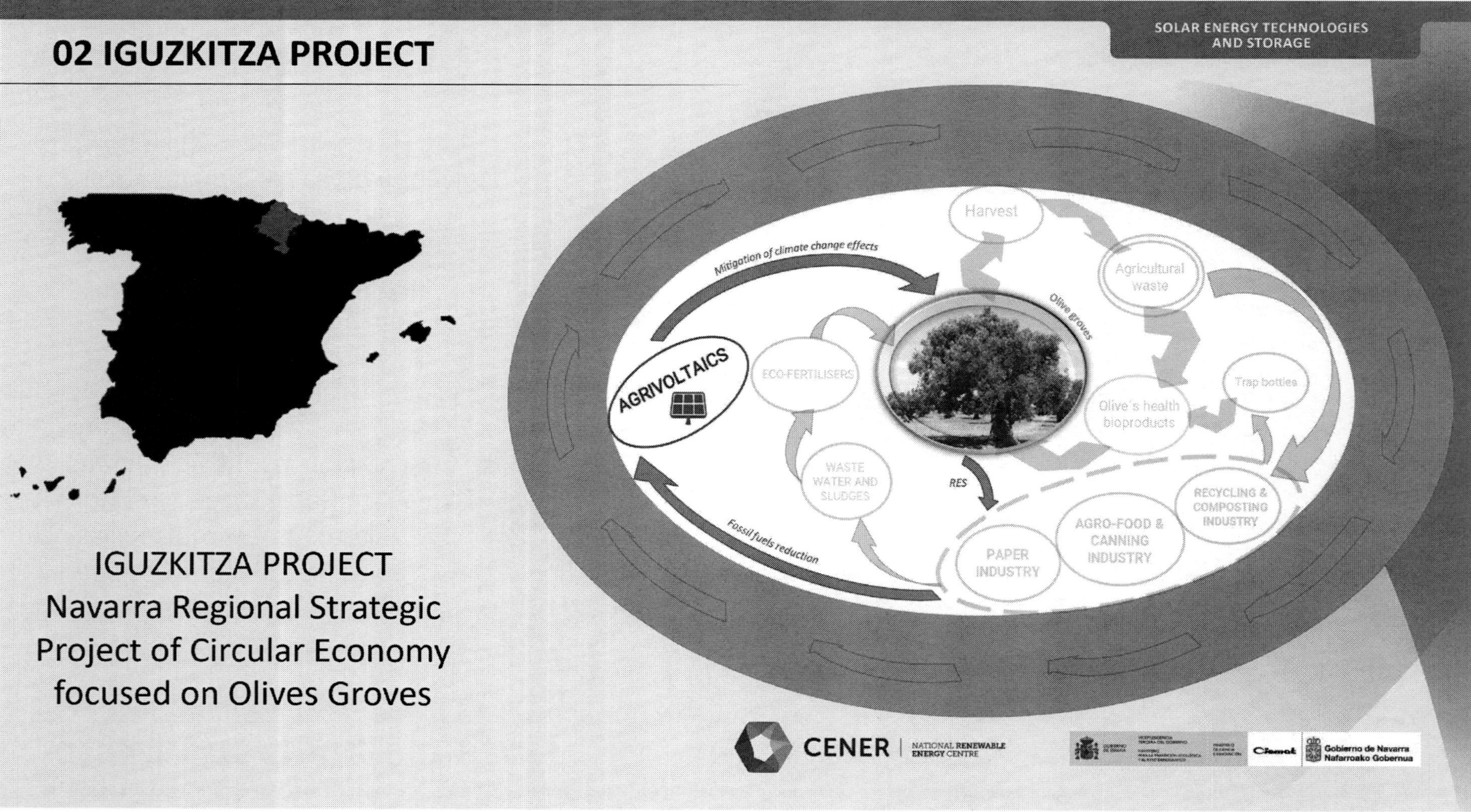

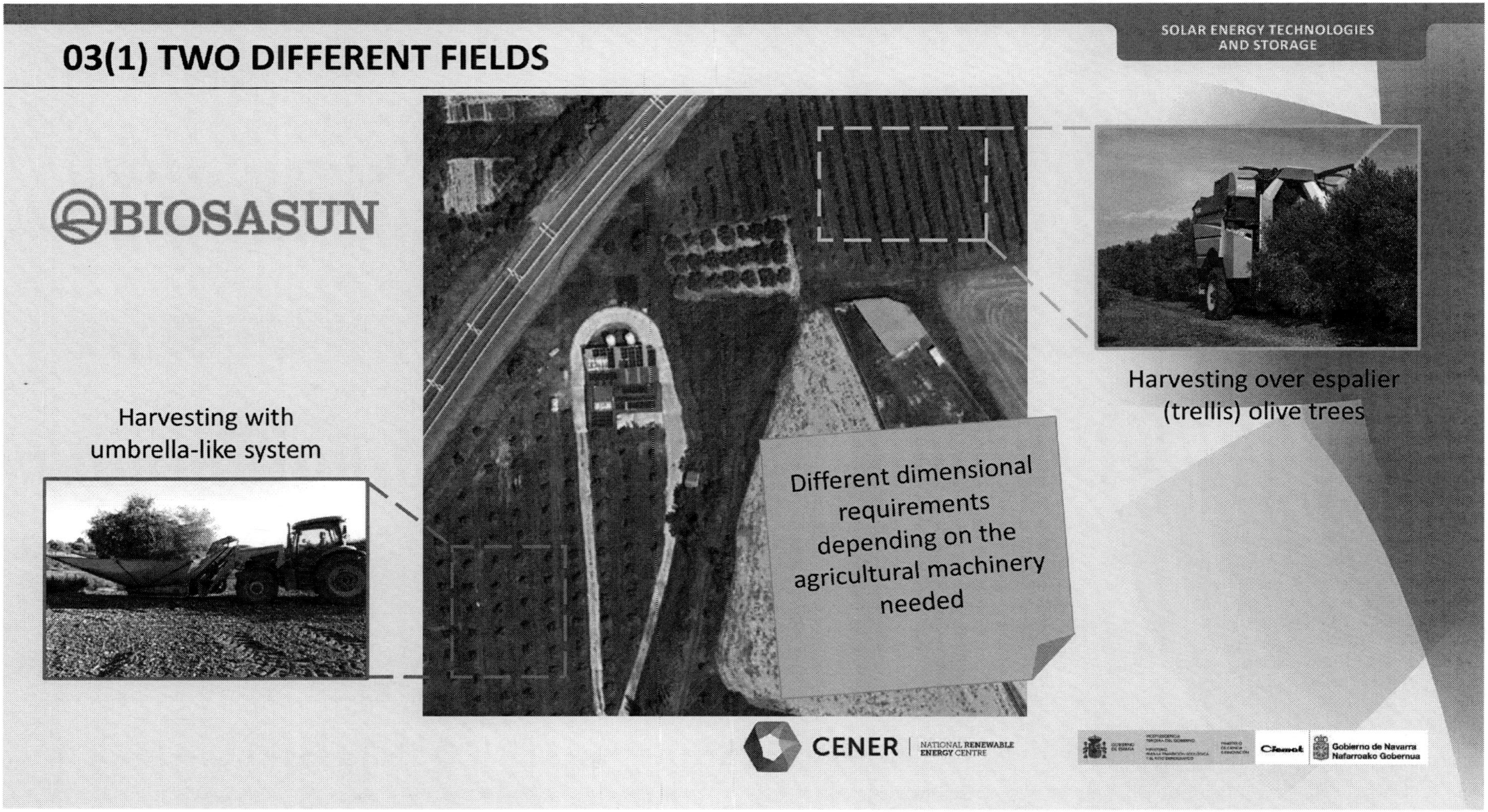
03(1) TWO DIFFERENT FIELDS
SOLAR ENERGY TECHNOLOGIES AND STORAGE
BIOSASUN
Harvesting with umbrella-like system
Harvesting over espalier (trellis) olive trees
Different dimensional requirements depending on the agricultural machinery needed
CENER | NATIONAL RENEWABLE ENERGY CENTRE
Ciemat
Gobierno de Navarra
Nafarroako Gobernua

SOLAR ENERGY TECHNOLOGIES AND STORAGE

03(2) TWO DIFFERENT CONFIGURATIONS

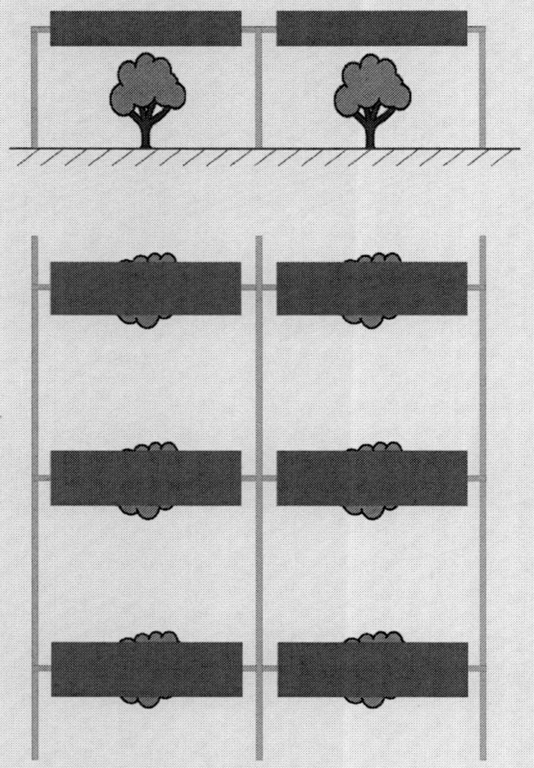

South

Horizontal single-axis solar trackers:

- N-S tracking
- E-W tracking

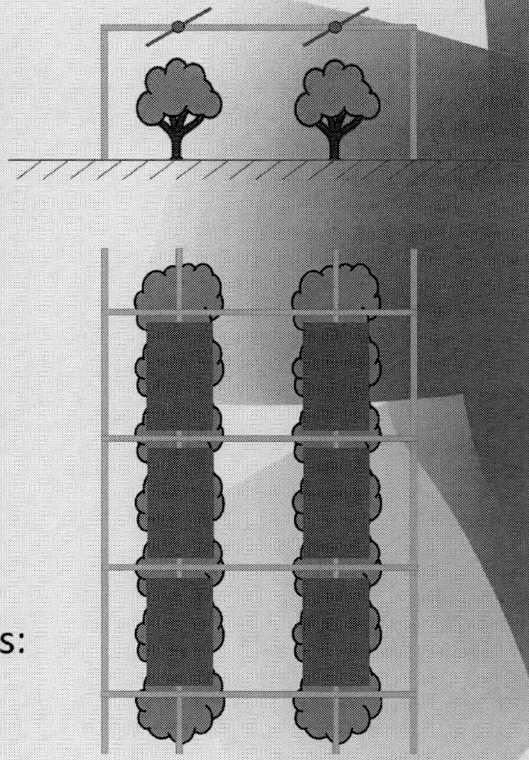

South

CENER | NATIONAL RENEWABLE ENERGY CENTRE

Gobierno de Navarra
Nafarroako Gobernua

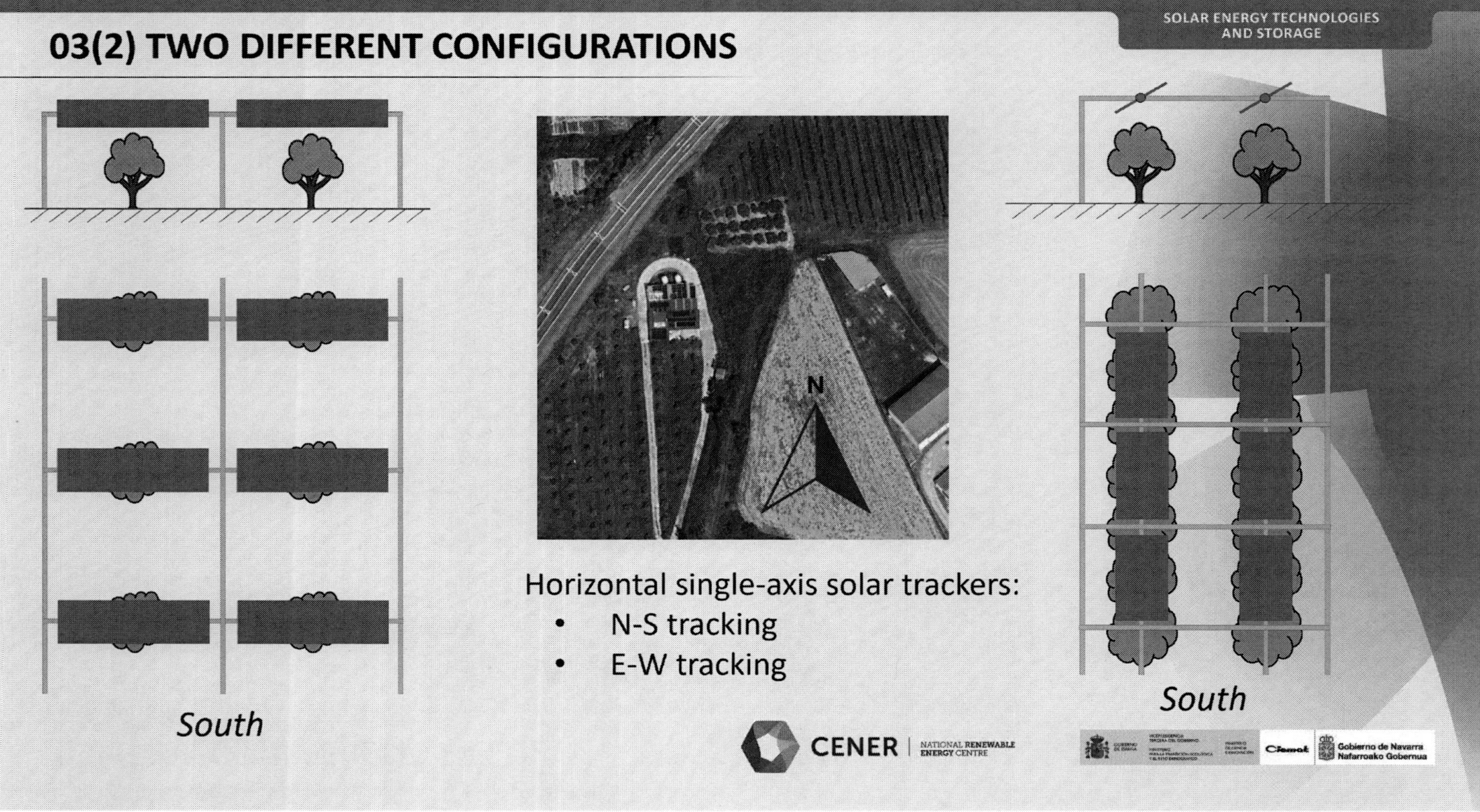

03(3) TWO DIFFERENT MECHANICAL DESIGNS

SOLAR ENERGY TECHNOLOGIES AND STORAGE

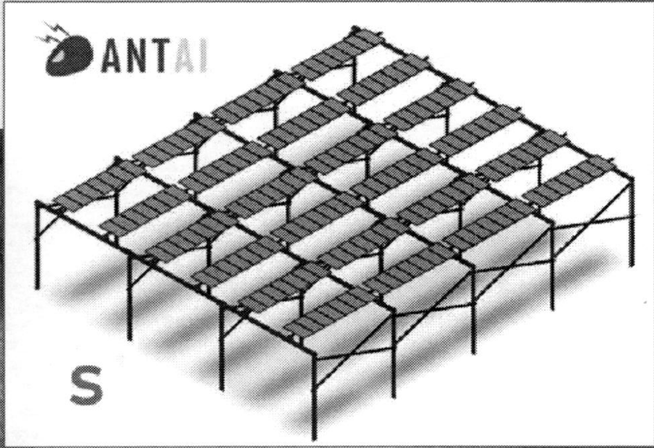

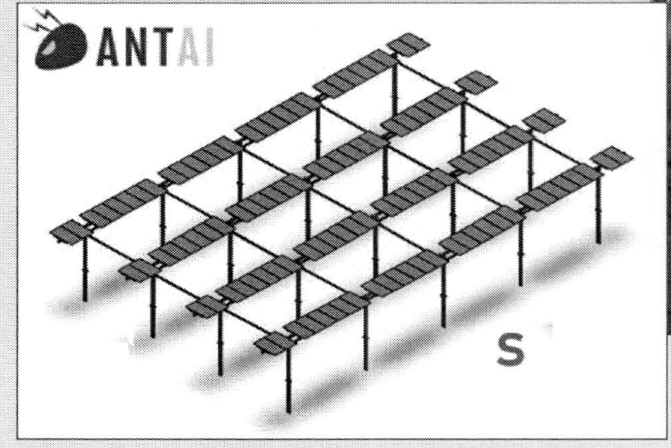

CENER | NATIONAL RENEWABLE ENERGY CENTRE

Gobierno de Navarra
Nafarroako Gobernua

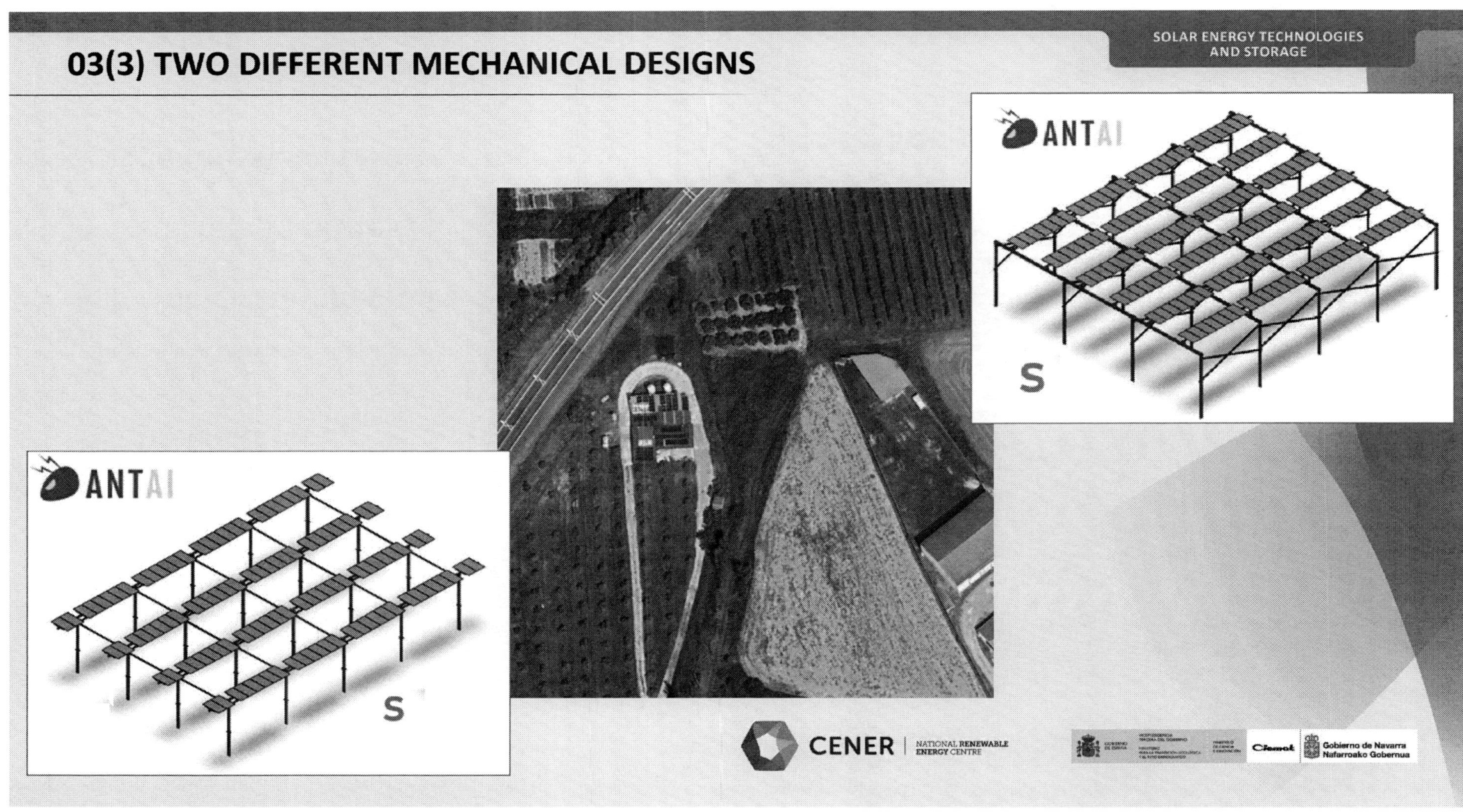

SOLAR ENERGY TECHNOLOGIES AND STORAGE

04 SENSOR SYSTEM

- 5 pyranometers
- 5 PAR
- 2 wind speed and direction
- 1 precipitation
- 1 snow
- 5 ambient temperature & RH
- 6 soil temperature & RH
- 8 dendrometers

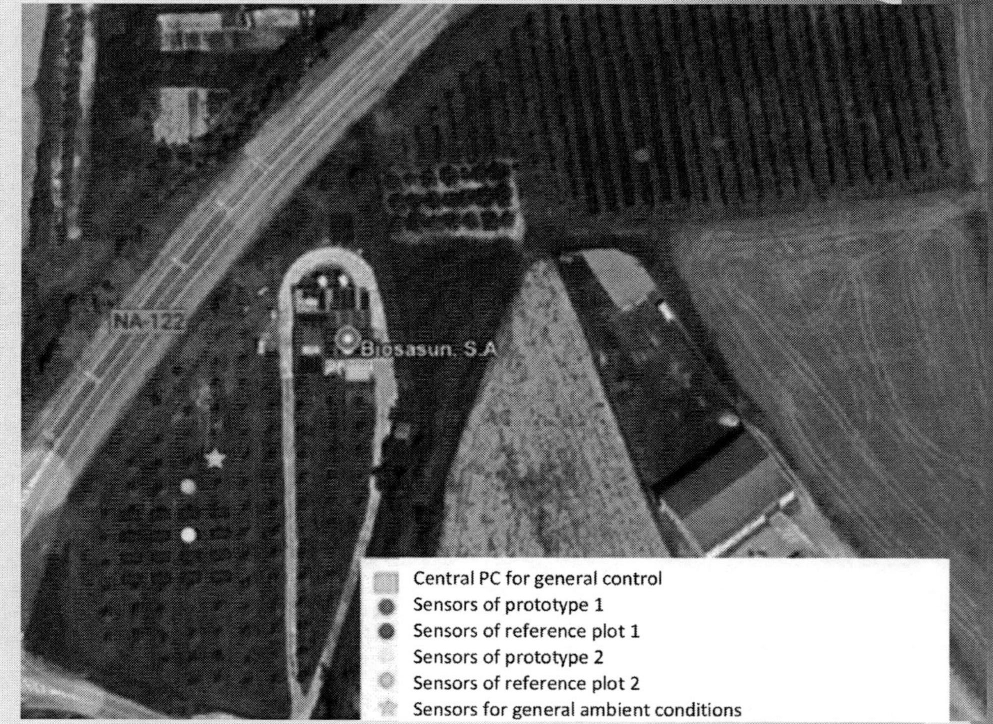

CENER | NATIONAL RENEWABLE ENERGY CENTRE

Gobierno de Navarra
Nafarroako Gobernua

05(1) CROP MODEL

SIMPLE model (C. Zhao et al. 2019) adapted to project needs

$$Biomass_{rate} = Radiation \cdot fSolar \cdot RUE \cdot f(CO_2) \cdot f(Temp) \cdot \min[f(Heat), f(Water)]$$

- PAR → A. García-Rodríguez methodology
- $fSolar$ → F. Orgaz model
- RUE → F. J. Villalobos proposal
- $f(Temp)$ → SIMPLE model from C. Zhao et. Al.
- $\min[f(Heat), f(Water)]$ → SIMPLE model from C. Zhao et. Al.
- $f(PAR)$ → IdAB-CSIC (project partner)

$$Biomass_{rate} = PAR \cdot fSolar \cdot RUE \cdot f(Temp) \cdot \min[f(Heat), f(Water)] \cdot f(PAR)$$

CENER | NATIONAL RENEWABLE ENERGY CENTRE

Ciemat | Gobierno de Navarra Nafarroako Gobernua

05(2) CROP MODEL

Olive trees shading approach (PAR collected by olive tree surface)

1. Geometric representation of polygonal spheres
2. Calculation of shading for every polygon, which are considered different planes
3. Weighted sum of all planes

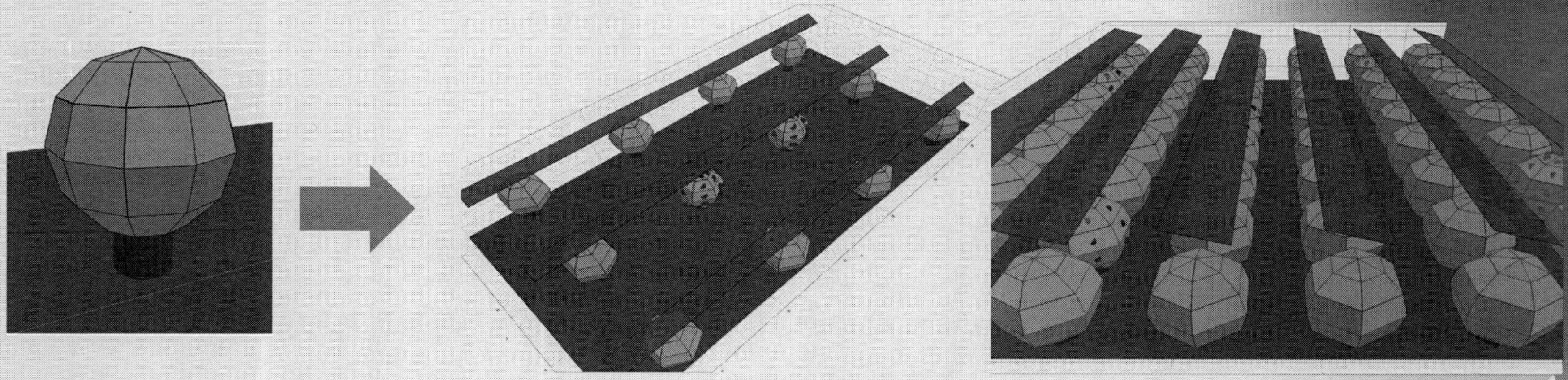

CENER | NATIONAL RENEWABLE ENERGY CENTRE

Ciemat | Gobierno de Navarra Nafarroako Gobernua

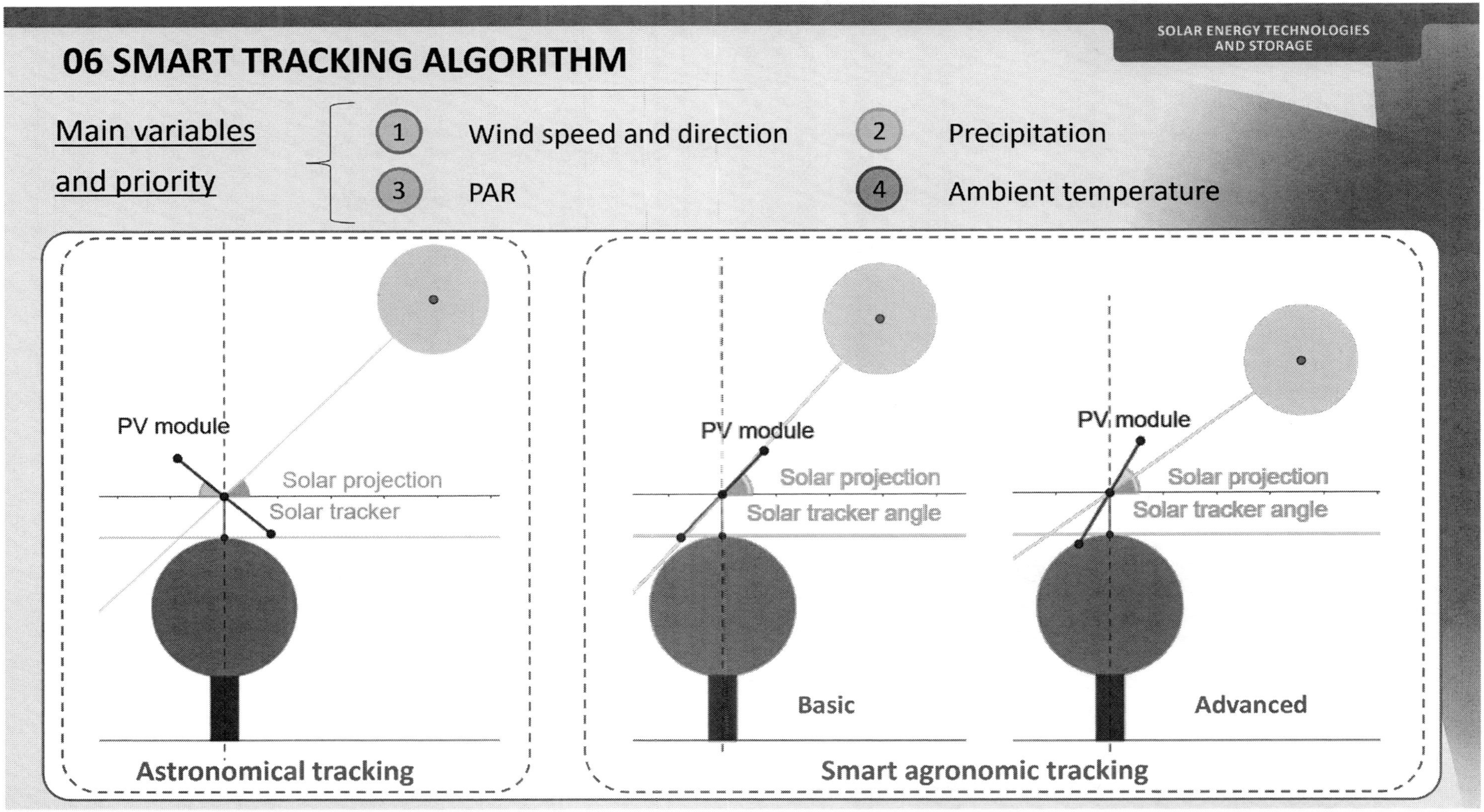
SOLAR ENERGY TECHNOLOGIES AND STORAGE
06 SMART TRACKING ALGORITHM
Main variables and priority
1 Wind speed and direction
2 Precipitation
3 PAR
4 Ambient temperature
PV module
Solar projection
Solar tracker
Astronomical tracking
PV module
Solar projection
Solar tracker angle
Basic
PV module
Solar projection
Solar tracker angle
Advanced
Smart agronomic tracking

07 PRODUCTION ESTIMATIONS

SOLAR ENERGY TECHNOLOGIES
AND STORAGE

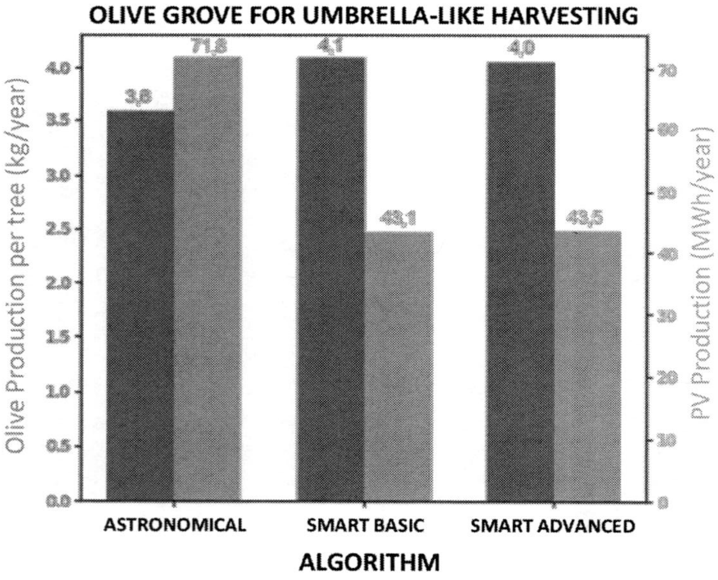

Prototype of 50 kWp

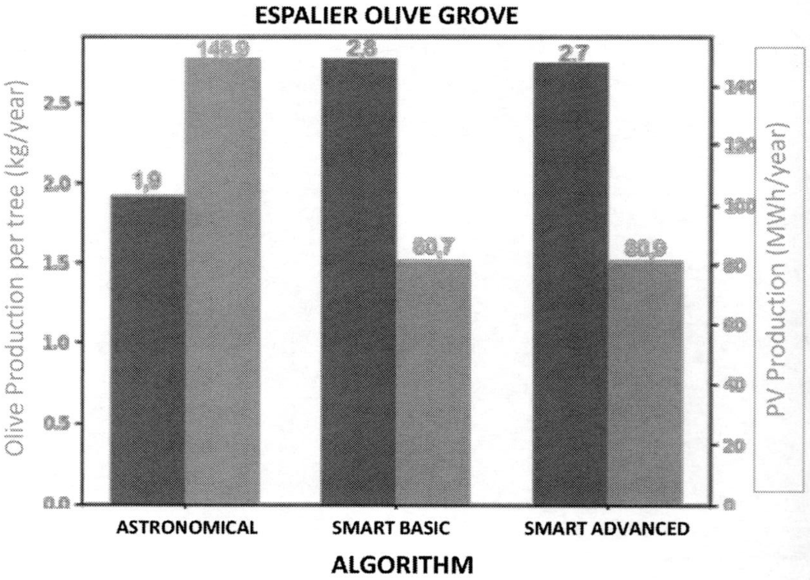

Prototype of 100 kWp

CENER | NATIONAL RENEWABLE ENERGY CENTRE

Gobierno de Navarra
Nafarroako Gobernua

08 CONCLUSIONS & ONGOING WORK

- Two overhead 1-axis tracking agrivoltaic systems designed according to the needs of two different olive groves.
- Two agrivoltaic prototypes to be installed in the upcoming weeks, including a comprehensive sensor system to assess their performance.
- Crop growing model adapted to project needs.
- Development of two smart tracking algorithms (N-S & E-W), prioritising olive trees needs over PV production in terms of light and protection.
- Preliminary production estimations. Need to fine-tune crop model and tracking algorithm after prototype implementation and experimentation.

CENER | NATIONAL RENEWABLE ENERGY CENTRE

Gobierno de Navarra Nafarroako Gobernua

DEVELOPMENT AND EVALUATION OF AGRIVOLTAIC SYSTEMS IN OLIVE GROVES BASED ON A NOVEL SMART TRACKING ALGORITHM

THANKS A LOT.

www.cener.com
info@cener.com
T +34 948 25 28 00

Ildefonso Muñoz
imunoz@cener.com

Iñaki Cornago
icornago@cener.com

42nd European Photovoltaic Solar Energy Conference and Exhibition

Université de Lubumbashi

Adoption and Optimisation Analysis of Agrivoltaic Systems for Horticultural Production and Energy Autonomy in Lubumbashi/DR Congo

Eddie Bilitu[1,2,3], **Shu-Ngwa Asaa**[3], **Sara Bouguerra**[2,3], **Nikoleta Kyranaki**[2,3], **Ismail Kaaya**[3], **Yannick Useni**[4], **Michael Daenen**[2,3]

[1] University of Lubumbashi, Electrical Engineering Department, Lubumbashi P.O. Box 1825, Democratic Republic of the Congo;
[2] Hasselt University, Institute for Materials Research (imo-imomec), Martelarenlaan 42, B-3500 Hasselt, Belgium;
[3] Energyville, imo-imomec, Thor Park 8320, B-3600 Genk, Belgium;
[4] University of Lubumbashi, Faculty of Agronomic Sciences, Ecology, Ecological Restoration and Landscape Unit, Lubumbashi P.O. Box 1825, Democratic Republic of the Congo;

020393-001

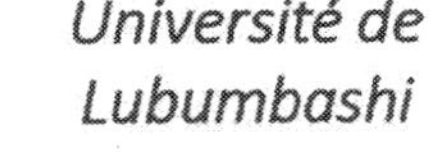

OUTLINE

1. Context
2. Objectives
3. Methodology
4. Preliminary Results
5. Conclusions

1 Context: Rapid and unplanned urbanisation in Lubumbashi

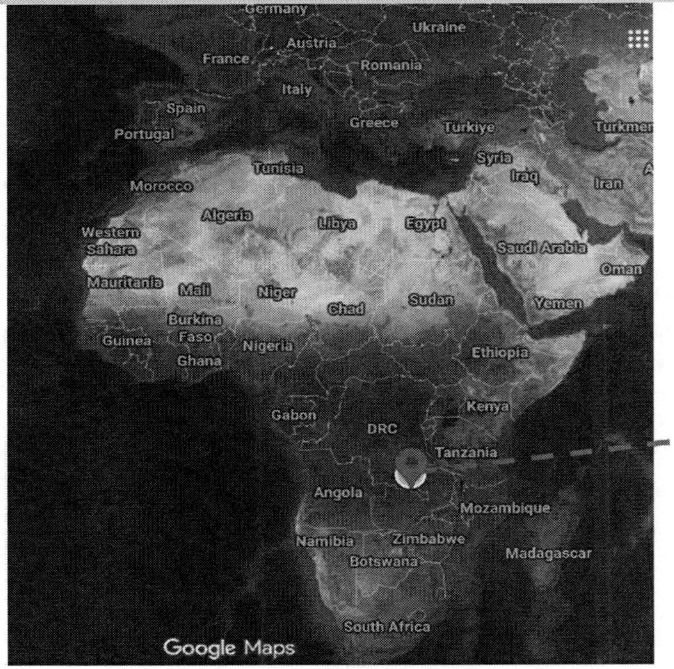

City of Lubumbashi

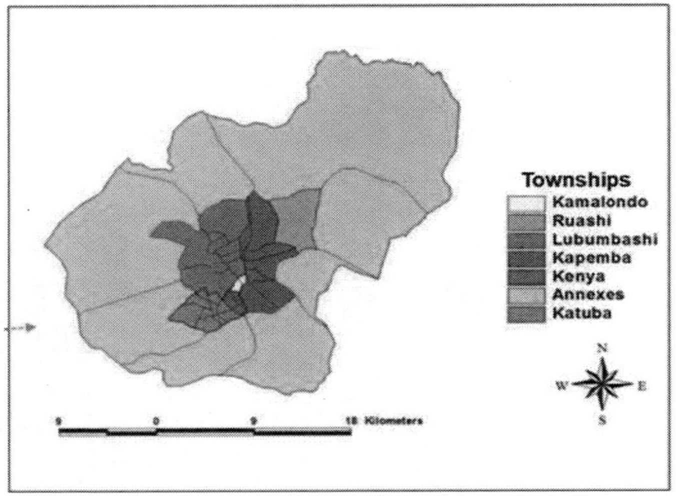

Irradiance level :~ $6\text{kWh}/m^2 d$

PV potential: 1753 kWh/kWp *(solagis.com)*

Lubumbashi is facing rapid and unplanned urban spatial growth (more than 5% / year)

(Useni et al., 2020, Khoji et al., 2022)

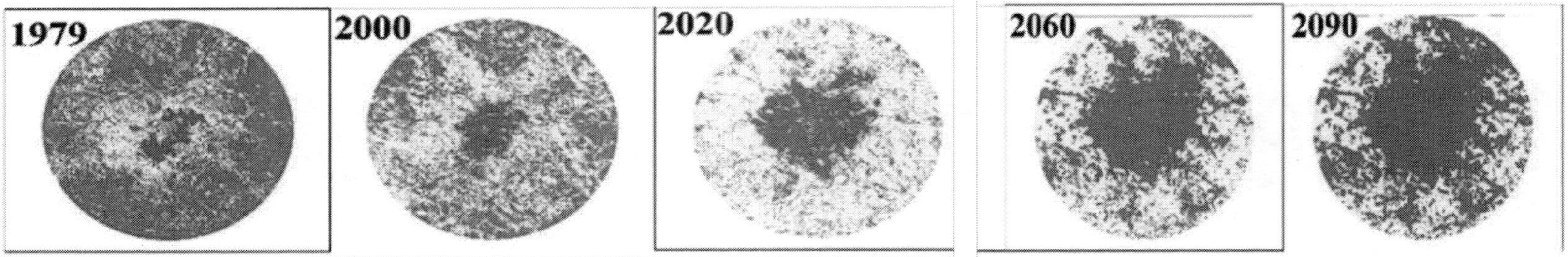

Legend
- Water
- Natural land cover
- Agriculture and energy production
- Built up area

020393-003

IMO-IMOMEC UHASSELT imec Energy Ville

1 Context: Energy deficit and Food insecurity in Lubumbashi

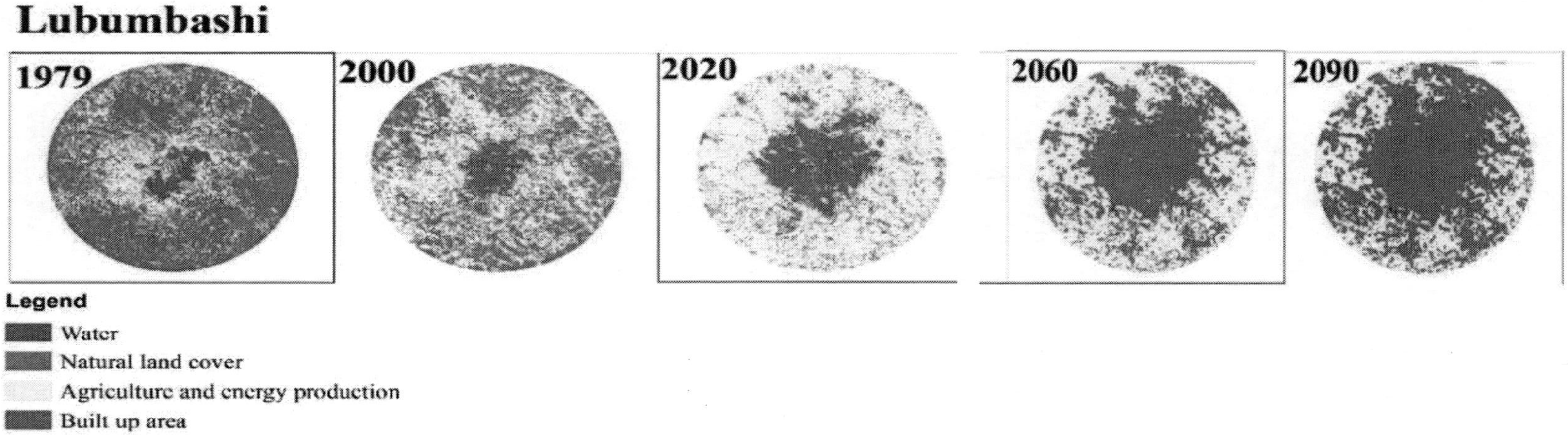

Challenges →

Energy deficit
(Currently estimated at **24.8%** and projected to reach **73.3%** by 2050)

(Nkulu et al., 2022)

Food insecurity
(28million or 25.5% of people in DR Congo)

(WFP, 2025; Nghonda et al., 2024

IMO-IMOMEC UHASSELT imec EnergyVille

1 Context: The Population of Lubumbashi facing the challenges arising from urbanisation.

Challenges

Energy deficit
(Currently estimated at **24.8%** and projected to reach **73.3%** by 2050)

(Nkulu et al., 2022)

Food Insecurity
(28million or 25.5% of people in DR Congo)

(WFP, 2025; Nghonda et al., 2024)

Population solutions

Intensive use of generators

Market gardening

Consequences

Atmospheric and noise pollution

Main survival activity hampered by rainfall deficit
(Kesonga, 2024)

Low crop yield

Manual irrigation
(Kesonga, 2024)

IMO-IMOMEC UHASSELT imec EnergyVille

1 Conext:

These two problems are traditionally addressed separately, whereas an integrated and innovative approach could offer a synergistic solution. ***Agrivoltaics (AVS) represents such an opportunity.***

?

Agrivoltaic systems

Despite the **high irradiance level (~ 6kWh/$m^2 d$) in the city**, AVS application, effectiveness, and specific impacts within the socio-economic and climatic context of Lubumbashi have not been studied and remain unknown.

Research question:

*"**How** can PV modules **be integrated into market gardening** to **optimally** produce both **electrical energy and vegetable crops** under the farming practices, climatic and socio-economic context of Lubumbashi?"*

IMO-IMOMEC UHASSELT imec Energy Ville

2 Objectives:

Examining the **potential** for the synergistic **integration of AVS** into market gardening practices to address the **interconnected challenges of energy crisis** and **low crop yield** in the local socioeconomic and climatic context of Lubumbashi.

Specifically, we:

1. Evaluate urban agriculture (UA) stakeholder perceptions on AVS benefits and adoption barriers.
2. Simulate optimal AVS configurations for main crops within the local climatic conditions of Lubumbashi.

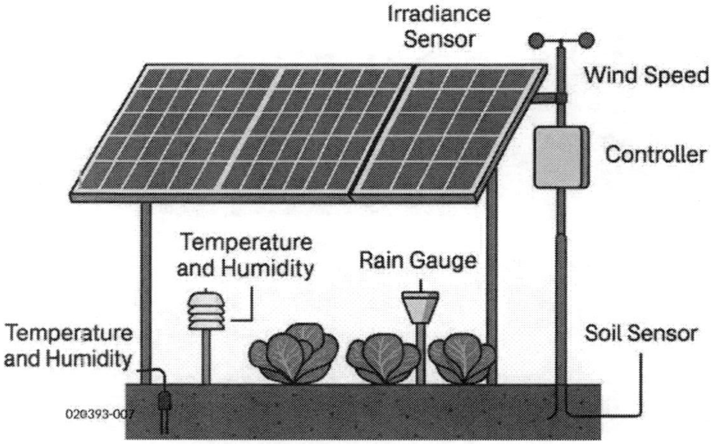

3 Methodology

3.1. Stakeholders perception analysis

Random & convenience sampling of stakeholders:

- **157 farmers from 7 main sites**
- **26 experts from Energy, Research & UA sectors**

→ Surveys on AVS adoption by interviews from April to July 2025 using **Kobo Collect**

→ Multiple Correspondence Analysis (MCA) of Survey Data using **SPSS**

→ Identification of farming practices, factors influencing AVS adoption, drivers and barriers in Lubumbashi

3.2. Identification of optimal configurations of AVS

Energy yield modelling of bifacial tilted & vertical modules (455Wp) (Simplified SAM model)

***Input**: Meteorological data of Lubumbashi, site size, cultivar, etc.*

Crop yield modelling of cabbage (Stress-based DSSAT model)

→ Multi-objective optimisation using **NSGA-II method**

→ Analysis of the irradiation distribution using the **imec Framework**

→ Identification & comparison of **Optimal solutions**

***Output:** Tilt, height, spacing, nr. of modules, energy & crop yields, LER, shading, PAR*

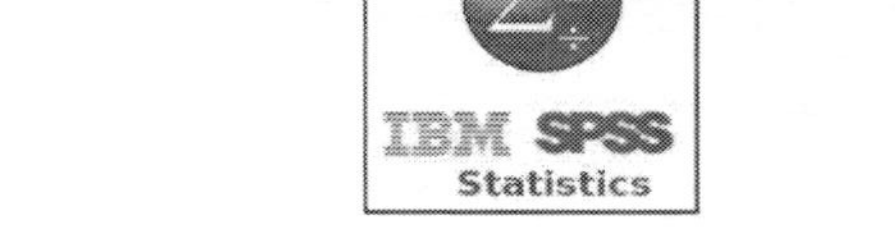

4 Results : Stakeholders' perception analysis

IMO-IMOMEC UHASSELT imec EnergyVille

4.1. Farming practices

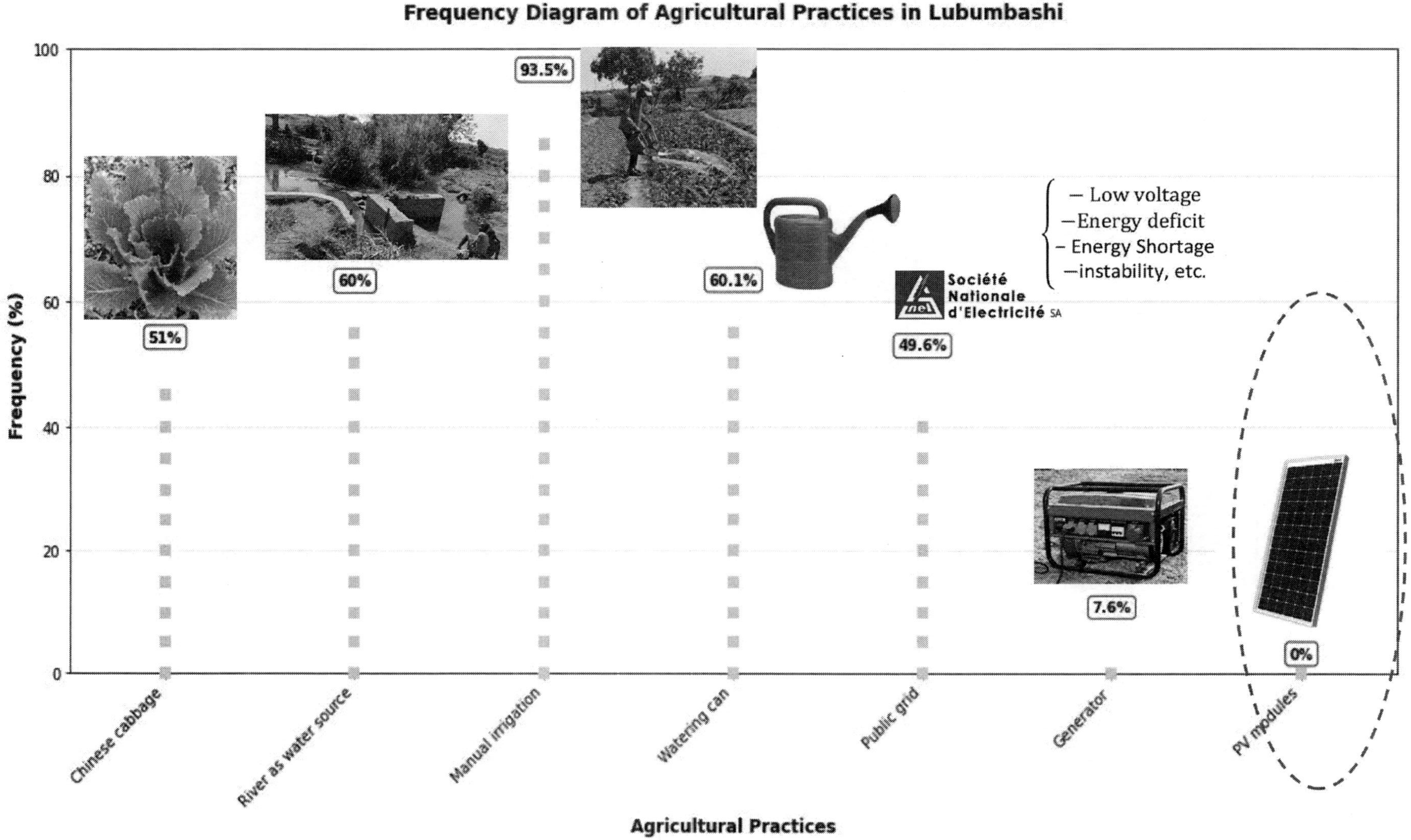

4 Results : Stakeholders' perception analysis

IMO-IMOMEC UHASSELT imec EnergyVille

4.2. Cross-Comparison of stakeholders' views on the adoption of AVS (Response variable)

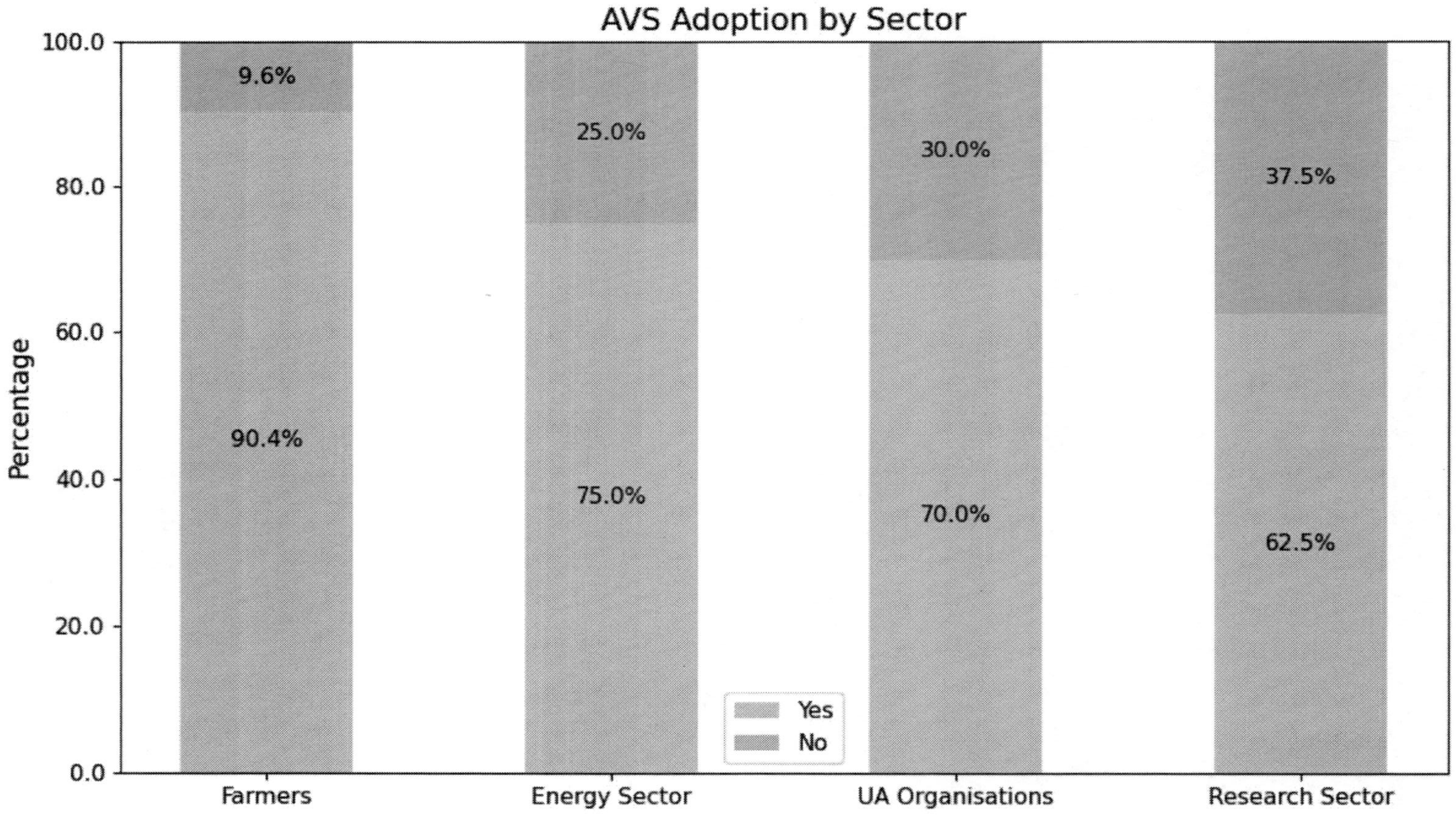

4 Results : Stakeholders' perception analysis

IMO-IMOMEC UHASSELT imec EnergyVille

4.3. Motivations & barriers to AVS adoption

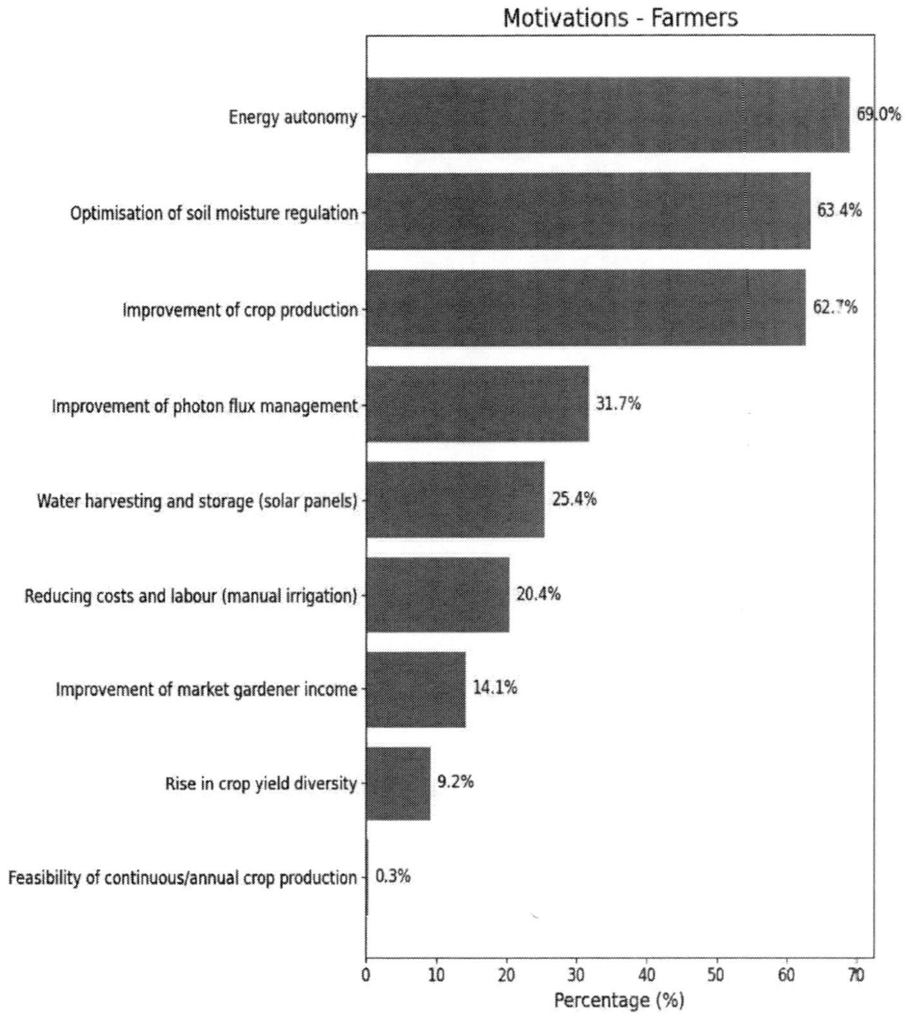

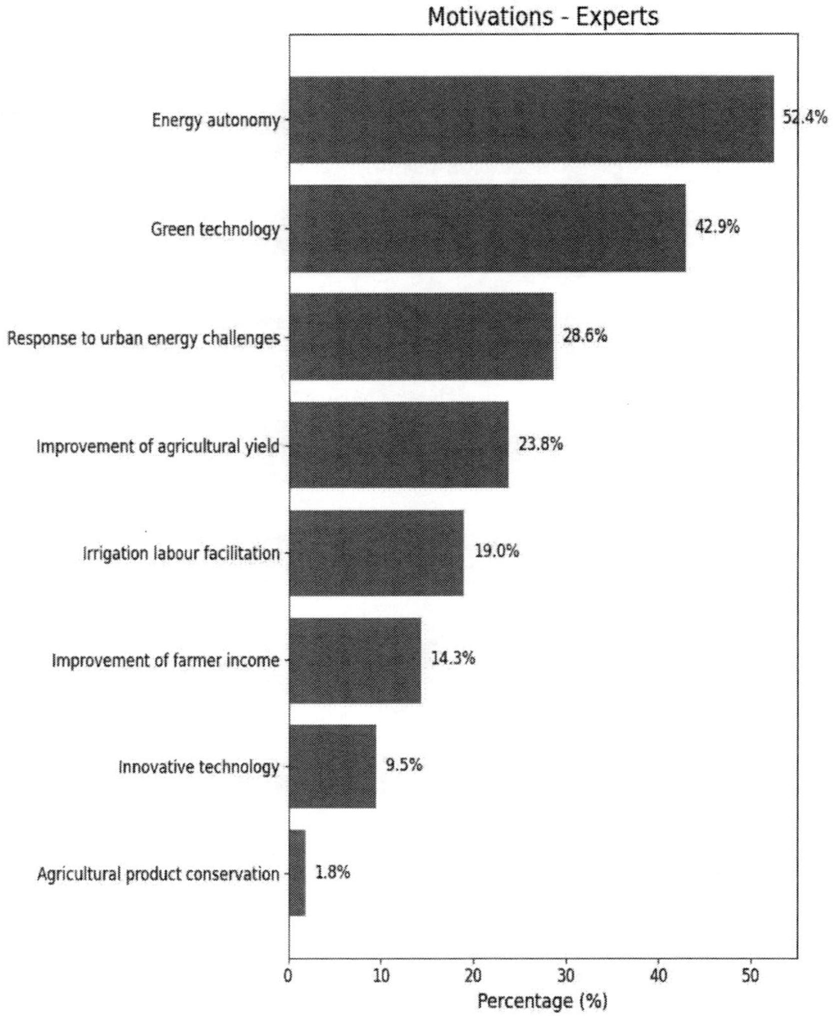

4 Results : Stakeholders' perception analysis

IMO-IMOMEC UHASSELT imec EnergyVille

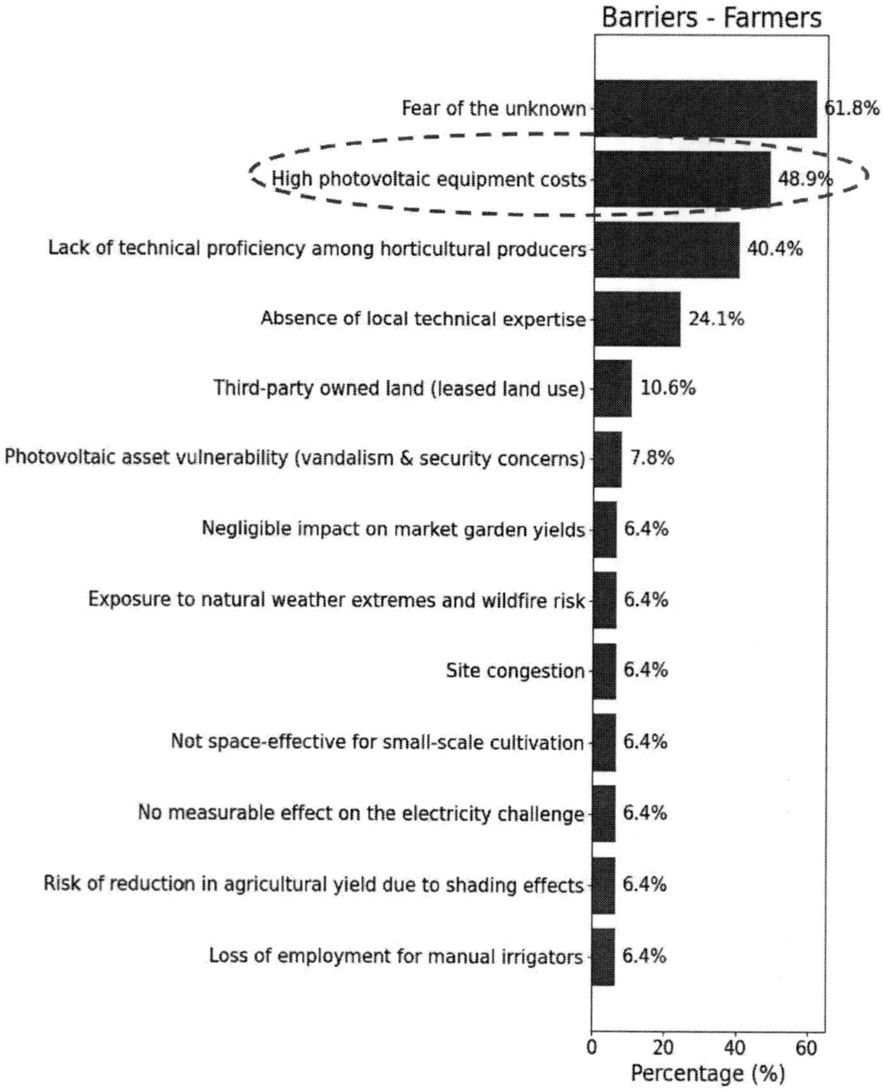

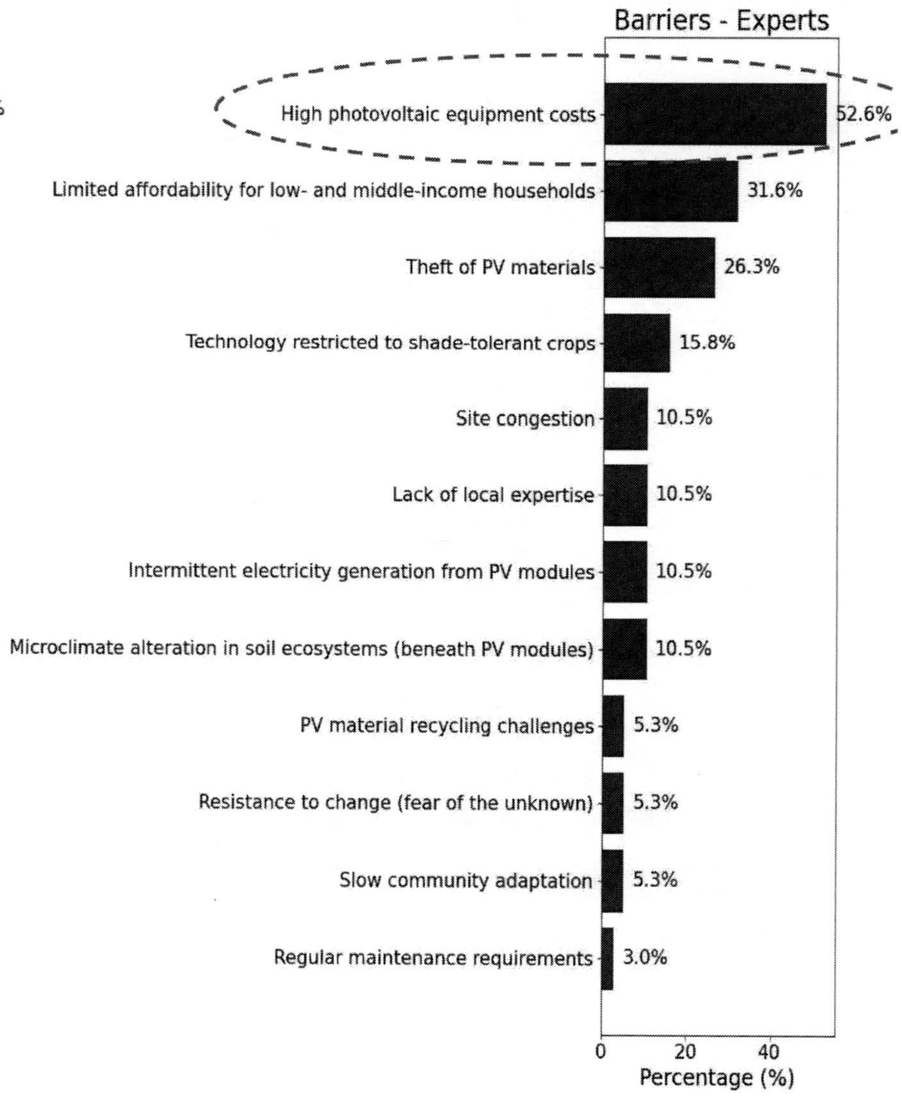

4 Results : Stakeholders' perception analysis

IMO-IMOMEC UHASSELT imec Energy Ville

4.4. Factors influencing AVS adoption by farmers

Discrimination diagram

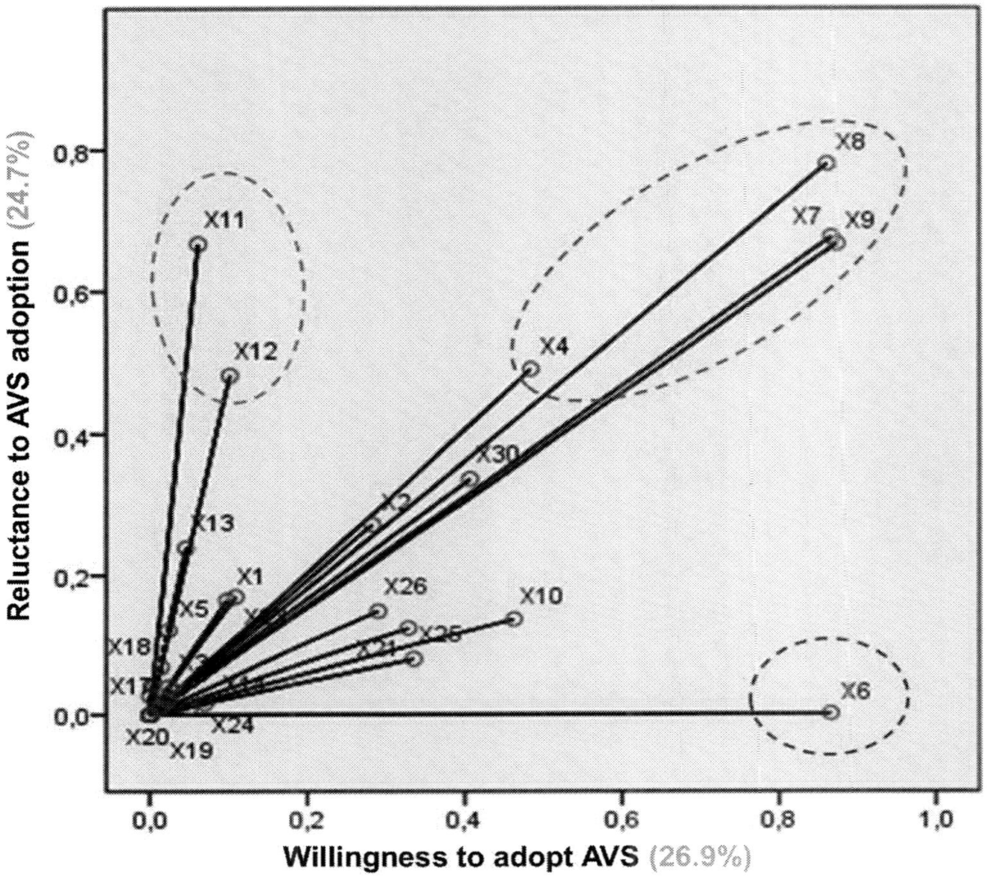

Most influential explanatory variables

Variable	Label
X4	Difficulties_faced
X6	Availability_Power_Supply
X7	Electricity_Source_Type
X8	Usefulness_Power_source
X9	Reason_Lack_Power_Source
X11	Irrigation_Type
X12	Means_of_manual_irrigation

4 Results : Stakeholders' perception analysis

IMO-IMOMEC UHASSELT imec EnergyVille

4.5. Key levers and public policies to encourage AVS Adoption

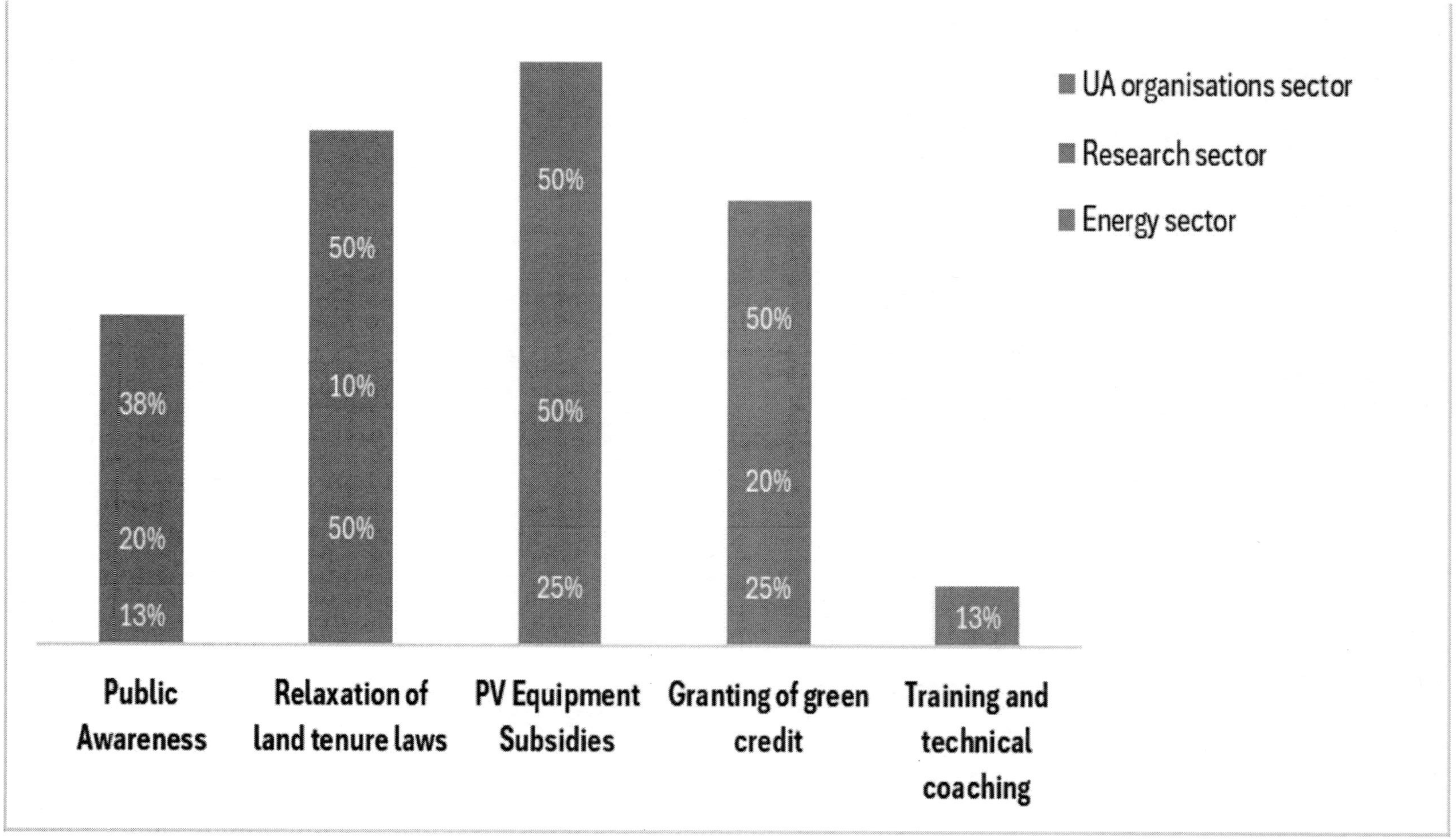

42nd European Photovoltaic Solar Energy Conference and Exhibition

4.6. IRRADIATION DISTRIBUTION

Tilted modules (12° facing north)

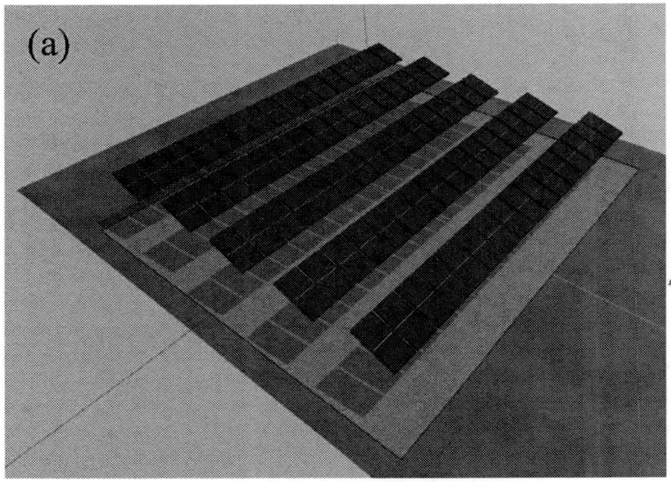

Vertical modules (East-West)

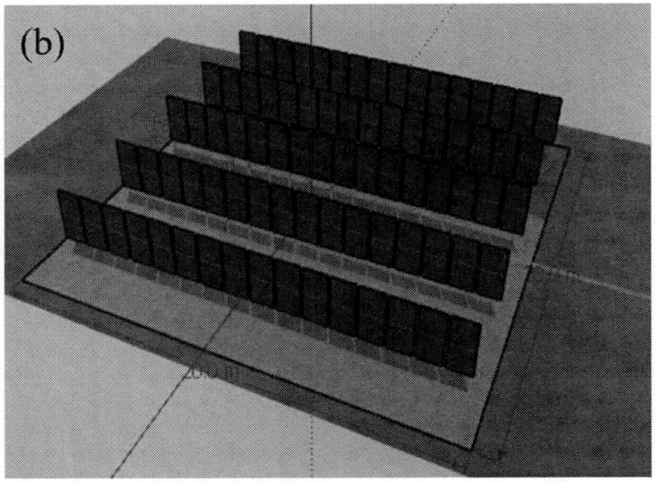

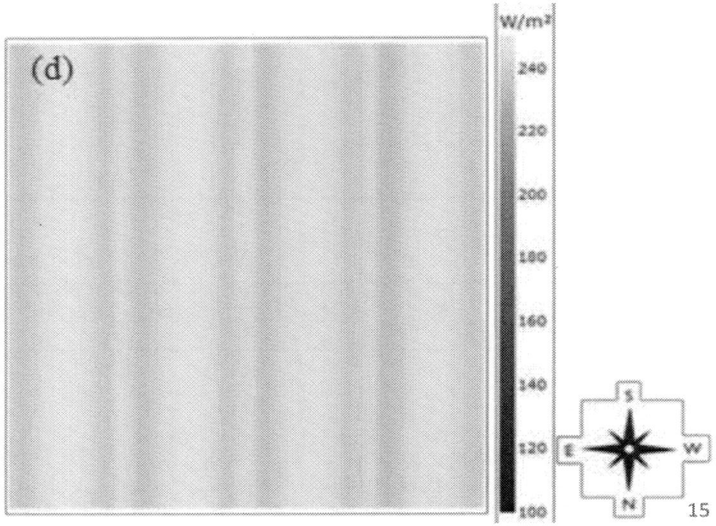

4 Results : Identification of optimal configurations of AVS

IMO-IMOMEC UHASSELT imec EnergyVille

	Optimal confugurations	
Parameters	Tilted modules	Vertical modules
Electricity production (kWh/year)	63395	51221
Energy yield (kWh/kWp)	**1741**	**1407**
Agricultural yield (kg/m^2)	**1.79**	**1.9**
Modules(455Wp)	80(5 rows × 16 modules)	80 (5 rows × 16 modules)
Installed capacity (kWp)	36.4	36.4
Tilt angle (°)	12	90
Mounting height (m)	2	1
Shading ration (%)	40	6
LER	**1.32**	**1.29**

4 Results : Identification of optimal configurations of AVS

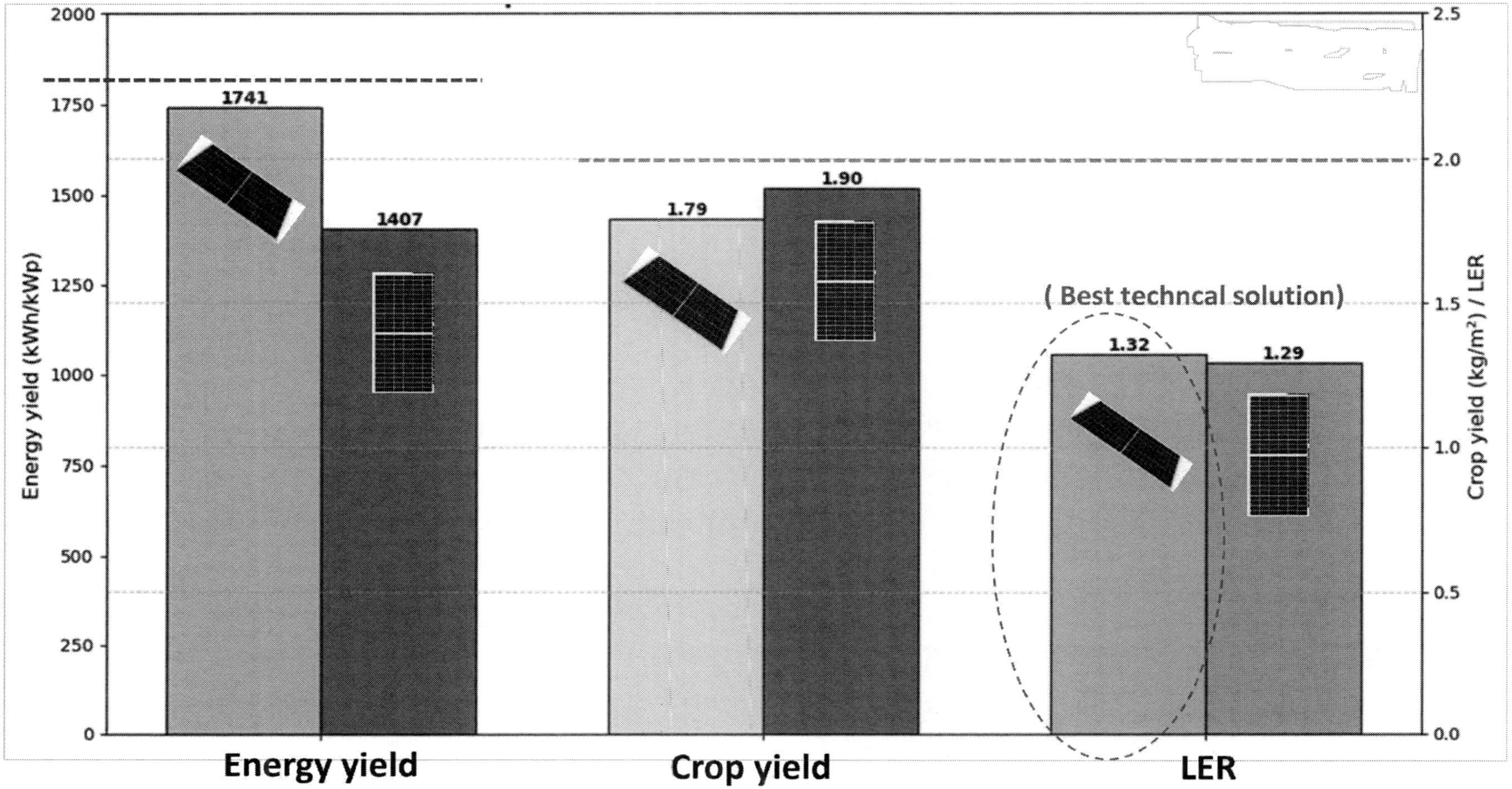

Average yearly energy yield in Lubumbashi: **1753 kWh/kWp** *(solagis.com)*

Average cabbage yield in Lubumbashi: **2 kg/m²** *(https://agrovolaille.com)*

5 Conclusions

- **Stakeholder Support:** **Strong support** from stakeholders, driven by the prospect of **energy autonomy.**
- **Identified Barriers:** The main perceived obstacles are the **high initial cost, fear of the unknown** and the **lack of local expertise**.
- **Policies to encourage AVS Adoption:** The majority of experts advocate for **PV equipment subsidie and granting green credit**
- **Optimal Configuration:** Simulations identify **tilted configuration at 12° facing the north as the better technical solution** to optimise both energy and Chinese cabbage production by a **LER of 1.32**, demonstrating a **32% increase** in the overall land productivity.

Agrivoltaics (AVS) → **Possible solution** to **simultaneously** address the energy deficit and food insecurity in Lubumbashi.

→ Further research: **Economic analysis**

MAXIMIZING ECONOMIC PERFORMANCE OF AGRIVOLTAIC SYSTEMS THROUGH MODULE ARRAY DESIGN

Habeel Alam[1,2,3]*, Jenny Nelson[2], Alona Armstrong[3], Duncan Whyatt[3] and Nauman Butt[1]
[1]Department of Electrical Engineering, Lahore University of Management Science, Lahore, Pakistan
[2]Department of Physics, Imperial College London, London, United Kingdom
[3]Lancaster Environment Centre, Lancaster University, United Kingdom
Tel: +923132251333, *h.alam@lancaster.ac.uk

ABSTRACT: Growing demand for food and energy has prompted the need for an efficient utilization of the land resources which are globally under increasing stress due to climate change and population growth. Agrivoltaics (***AV***) offers a dual use of land for harvesting food and solar energy. The design of module arrays in ***AV*** must achieve an optimal balance between food and energy production while ensuring an economic viability. We explore techno-economic effects of module array density, hardware infrastructure cost, land specific soft costs, and the net crop income on the AV system design. A variety of module technologies including fixed tilt and tracking modules with standard tracking (***ST***) and anti-tracking (***AT***) are explored. We show that both fixed tilt and tracking systems can be designed for an optimal yield and economic viability, the latter provides best flexibility for various types of crops. While ***ST*** maximizes the energy conversion, agriculture yield may significantly decrease. ***AT*** on the other hand, maximizes agricultural production, but the energy conversion can drop by ~60% making it economically infeasible. An optimal tracking system for ***AV*** can therefore use a combination of ***ST*** and ***AT*** to meet the yield and economic targets.
Keywords: agrivoltaics, food-energy yield, economic feasibility, module array design

1 INTRODUCTION

The adverse effects of climate change have prompted the utilization of renewable sources to meet global energy demand. The issue with renewables, specifically solar, is the huge land requirement for adequate generation which leads to conflict of land usage between agriculture (food) and energy production. Agrivoltaics (*AV*) is a type of dual land usage system which solves this conflict by elevating the *PV* panels above ground (for maneuvering of agricultural machinery) and utilizing the same land for both energy and crop(food) production [1-3]. The crop cultivation under the *PV* modules can provide economic benefits including increased revenue and higher land usage efficiency[4]. It can also enable favorable microclimatic conditions including protection of crops from heat stress via shading and water savings by reducing evapotranspiration under *PV* modules in hot arid and semi-arid regions [2]. In some cases, *AV* can provide protection to vulnerable crops from hail, wind, heavy rainfall and snow. Favorable microclimate resulting in reduction in temperatures due to crop cultivation underneath the modules can also result in increased performance of *PV* during hot temperatures [5]. The energy production from *AV* can meet local agricultural demands, increase self-consumption and diversify farmers income through additional revenue stream. [3].

The economic viability is highly dependent on the module array design optimization which is crucial for maximizing solar *PV* and agricultural production. Several factors including the tilt angle, orientation, row to row distance, crop selection and elevation of the modules play a vital role in determining both the crop and energy yield. Optimizing these design parameters is essential to maximize the overall benefits and achieve economic feasibility for *AV* systems. The economic feasibility also dependent on high initial capital costs associated with *AV* in comparison with Ground mounted Photovoltaics (*GMPV*) due to mounting structure and customization requirements[6]. Thus, optimization of *AV* design and careful selection of crops which can tolerate shading without significantly reducing the yield is crucial as its revenue can offset the initial capital costs. The additional revenue can also provide an opportunity to invest in automation of agricultural machinery which will further increase their revenue [7].

Despite many commercial and academic installations having demonstrated the promising potential of *AV* across various global locations, comprehensive modeling quantifying economic aspects for a variety of module array configurations, crops, and associated impacts has not been reported. Here, we present a techno-economic framework to evaluate the relative economic performance of *AV* farms relative to ground mounted *PV* for different bifacial *AV* systems including a) conventional North/South faced b) East/West faced vertical, c) Standard solar tracking and d) Anti-tracking modules. We have used the location of Lahore (31.5204° N, 74.3587° E) for illustration throughout the simulations. We used the crop rotation of tomato, cauliflower, and garlic over a complete year. The rest of the paper includes mathematical modeling in Section II, results and discussion describing relative food-energy productivity, and economic trends in Section III. Finally, conclusions are presented in Section IV.

2 MODELING APPROACH

2.1 *PV* Energy and incident *PAR* over crops

The modelling framework for food-energy yields and economics have been discussed in detail in [8] and [9]. A view factor approach validated by field experiments is used [8], [10-11]. *PV* yield is calculated by sunlight interception by *PV* panels including the contributions from direct beam, diffused light and albedo. We evaluate the shading for the direct beam and diffused light caused by the solar panels to calculate the available *PAR* at any horizontal surface on the ground or at an elevation underneath the panel arrays. Diffuse and direct components of global horizontal irradiation are estimated by using typical meteorological conditions [12]. An isotropic model is assumed for diffused light. Computations are carried out on 1-minute resolution. Fig 1. shows the *AV* systems for which the analysis is

10.4229/EUPVSEC2025/4DV.1.5

Nomenclature

AT	Anti-tracking	M_L	Module hardware to soft cost ratio
AV	Agrivoltaics	n	Number of solar tracking hours
CGR	Crop growth rate	p	Pitch between the module rows
$CAPEX$	Capital expenditure	p_r	Price
CT	Customized tracking	pb	Performance
FIT	Feed in tariff	P_C	Normalized crop profit
$GMPV$	Ground mounted photovoltaics	ppr	Price performance ratio
h	Height	PV	Photovoltaics
κ_L	Normalized soft cost ratio	ST	Standard tracking
κ_M	Hardware cost ratio	Y_{Crop}	Biomass/crop yield
$LCOE$	Levelized cost of electricity	Y_{PAR}	PAR yield
		Y_{PV}	Energy ratio

performed which includes (a) fixed tilt 40° N/S faced, $(b) E/W$ faced vertically installed, (c) standard solar tracking (ST) and (d) anti/back (AT) tracking systems. AT is opposite of ST in such a way that in AT, module face is kept parallel to direct beam throughout the day prioritizing agricultural production rather than maximizing electricity generation.

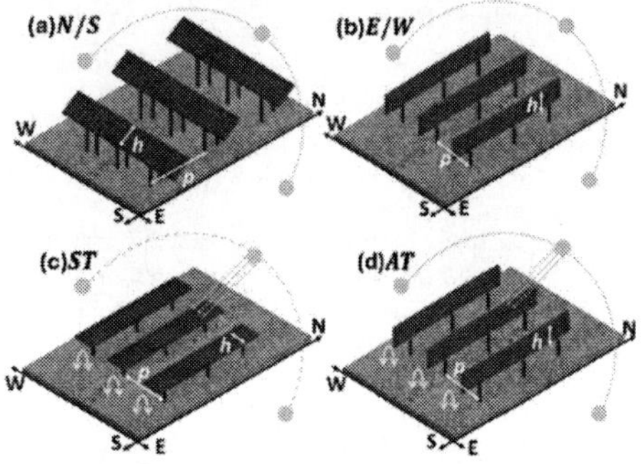

Figure 1: Schemetic of modelled agrivoltaic systems including a) $\boldsymbol{N/S}$ facing fixed tilt b) $\boldsymbol{E/W}$ facing vertical bifacial c) Standard solar tracking ($\boldsymbol{ST}$) and d) Anti-tracking ($\boldsymbol{AT}$) systems. Row to row distance ($\boldsymbol{p}$) which is an important design parameter along with height ($\boldsymbol{h}$) of modules is also shown.

2.2 Useful PAR & Relative Crop Yield

While the incident PAR intensity over crops can provide an indication of the shading related impact due to modules, the actual impact depends on the shade sensitity of the specific crop as defined by the threshold PAR (PAR_{th}) above which the PAR intensity does not contribute to photosynthesis. The crop dependent useful PAR at any point (y) across the pitch is calculated across the day as:

$$PAR_{u,open}(y) = \int_{tr}^{ts} PAR_0(x,t)\,dt;\; PAR_0 \leq PAR_{th} \qquad (1)$$

where t_r and t_s are the times for sunrise and sunset, respectively, and PAR_0 is the incident PAR under open sun. The PAR underneath the panel shades is smaller relative to the open farm. PAR_u for AV is calculated as:

$$PAR_{u,AV}(y) = \int_{tr}^{ts} PAR_{AV}(x,t)\,dt; PAR_{AV} \leq PAR_{th} \qquad (2)$$

where PAR_{AV} is the incident PAR on ground.

2.3 Relative Crop-Energy Yields

The relative crop yield (Y_{PAR}) for a given crop over its cycle and the relative AV energy yield (Y_{PV}) are calculated as [8]:

$$Y_{PAR} = \frac{PAR_{u,AV}}{PAR_{u,open}} \qquad (3)$$

$$Y_{PV} = \frac{I_M(AV)}{I_M(GMPV)} \qquad (4)$$

where I_M is energy output. Y_{PAR} and Y_{PV} can be useful metrics for the early assessment of the crop-energy yields and overall farm productivity. Using these, [5] provides a holistic view of the AV performance for various module configurations.

2.4 Economic Performance

We explore when a module configuration, designed for an AV system, could be profitable relative to a standard ground mounted PV ($GMPV$) system. The answer depends on the quantitative balance between a higher CAPEX needed for an elevated mounting and the net income from the crops. The economic performance for an AV system is evaluated by comparing the profits from energy and crops of an AV system with individual profits from $GMPV$ and that for an open agricultural farm. The model is described in detail in [9],[13]. For a better economic performance as compared to $GMPV$:

$$P_{AV} + P_{c,AV} \geq Max\,(P_{GMPV}, P_{c,full\,sun}) \qquad (5)$$

where P_{AV}, P_{GMPV} are the annual energy profit from AV and $GMPV$, respectively, and $P_{c,AV}$ and $P_{c,full\,sun}$ denote the crop profits for AV and full sun, respectively. We assume that the energy profit per unit land area is higher as compared to that from crop. For AV, an economic performance equivalent or better than $GMPV$ requires:

$$(FIT_{GMPV} - FIT_{AV} + LCOE_{AV} - LCOE_{GMPV}) \times YY_T \leq P_{C,AV} \qquad (6)$$

where YY_T is the total annual energy production taken to be the same for AV and $GMPV$ and $P_{c,AV}$ is assumed to be scale linearly with Y_{PAR}.

After solving and re-arranging (6), for the same FIT for AV and $GMPV$, the condition to have economic equivalence or improvement over $GMPV$ can be written as:

$$\kappa_M + \kappa_L - Y_{PV}' \leq (Y_{Crop} \times P_C) \qquad (7)$$

where the 1st two terms (κ_M & κ_L) on the left-hand side represent difference in hardware and soft costs for AV modules relative to ground mounted PV representing customized module technology for land preservation. Y_{PV}' represents normalized annual energy produced per unit module area for AV relative to that for $GMPV$. P_C is the normalized crop profit, and Y_{crop} denotes crop yield. The terms on left hand side of (7) can be termed as price(p_r) while the right-hand side terms can be termed as performance(p_b), thus making economic viability condition for AV as

$$ppr \stackrel{\text{def}}{=} \frac{\mathrm{p_r}}{\mathrm{p_b}} \leq 1 \quad (8)$$

A price performance ratio of less than one ($ppr \leq 1$) is desirable for economic feasibility.

3 RESULTS AND DISCUSSION

3.1 Food-energy yield for different module configurations.

Fig. 2 shows the effect of module density ratio (p/h) on food (Y_{PAR}) and energy (Y_{PV}) yields for bifacial modules under the 4 different configurations. A tradeoff between the module collected light and the PAR incident to the ground can be seen on the plots. It can be noted that the result for different configurations deviates strongly at higher density ($p/h \leq 2$) but come closer at higher array densities. Both Y_{PV} and Y_{PAR} tends to saturate at lower module densities (p/h~6).

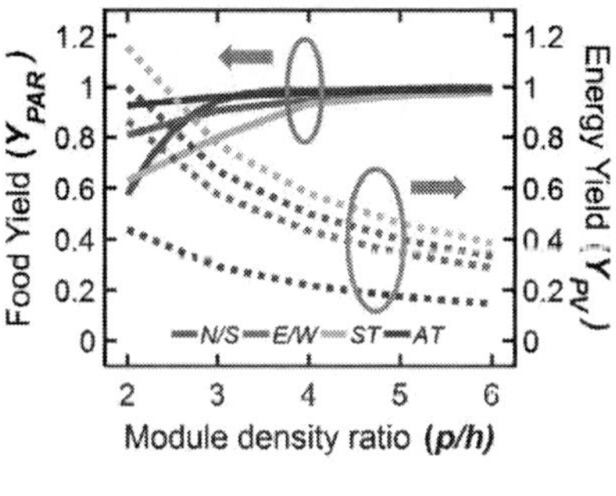

Figure 2: Normalized food ($\boldsymbol{Y_{PAR}}$) and energy yield ($\boldsymbol{Y_{PV}}$) is plotted as a function of module array density for fixed tilt (***N/S***), vertical (***E/W***) faced, solar tracking (***ST***) and anti-tracking (***AT***) orientations. Food yield decreases while energy yield increases by reducing the module density.

3.2 Effect of module density ratio on techno-economics.

Fig. 3 shows the effect of module density ratio (p/h) on different parameters in (7) which makes price, performance and ppr. Capital cost ratio is highest for ST and AT followed by N/S and vertical E/W faced orientations. Energy yield ratio is highest for ST and lowest for AT as it prioritizes food over energy production. Crop profit ratio increase with increase in p/h due to increased sunlight availability to crops translating into higher yield and thus higher profits.

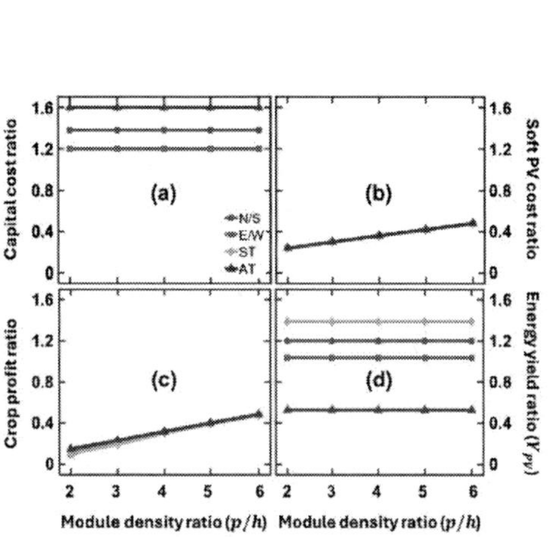

Figure 3: Effect of module density ratio($\boldsymbol{p/h}$) on various techno-economic parameters including a) capital cost ratio, b) soft ***PV*** cost ratio, c) Crop profit ratio and d) energy yield ratio. Crop profit ratio increase with increase in $\boldsymbol{p/h}$ due to increased sunlight availabilty to crops.

Fig. 4 shows the effect of module density ratio (p/h) on price, performance and ppr. For high row to row distance ($p/h \geq 6$), the economic feasibility is achieved for N/S, E/W and ST orientations. The economic feasibility is not achieved for AT and it might require policy intervention to achieve economic equivalence.

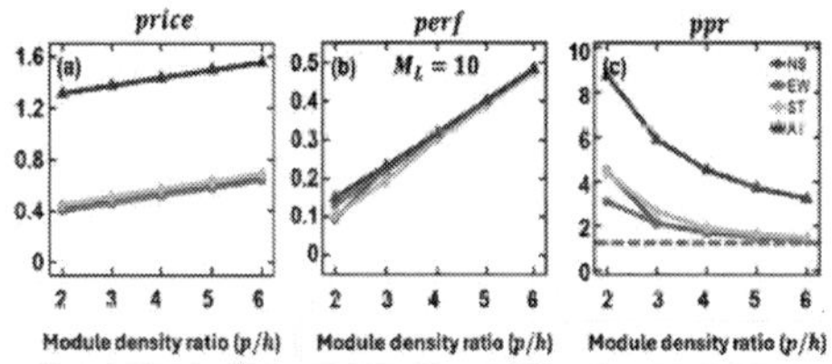

Figure 4. Effect of module density ratio ($\boldsymbol{p/h}$) on price ($\boldsymbol{p_r}$), performance($\boldsymbol{p_b}$) and price performance ratio ($\boldsymbol{ppr}$) for $\boldsymbol{N/S, E/W}$, ***ST*** and ***AT***. The horizontal dotted line represents economic feasibilty condition ($\boldsymbol{ppr = 1}$). For high $\boldsymbol{p/h(p/h \geq 6)}$, the economic feasibilty is achieved for $\boldsymbol{N/S, E/W}$ and ***ST*** orientations.

3.3 Customized tracking for Agrivoltaics

Fig. 5 shows the conceptual schematic of customized tracking (CT) scheme which can be defined by multiplexing ST, which maximizes the energy, with anti-tracking (AT) which maximizes the agricultural yield. CT incorporates both ST and AT such that ST is implemented for n hours with $n/2$ number of hours on each side of midday (noon) while AT is implemented.

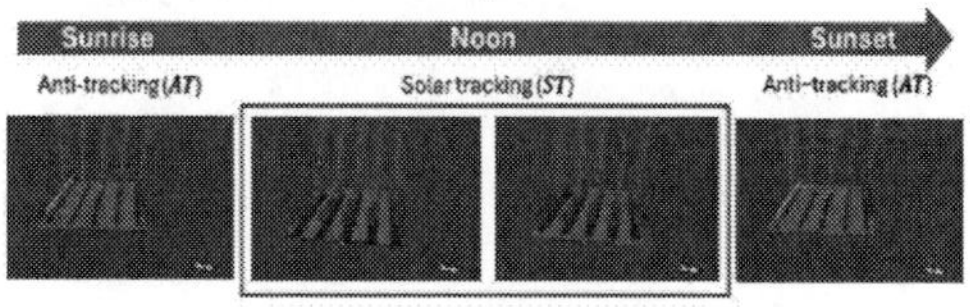

Figure 5. Schematic of customized tracking (CT) which time multiplexes ST and AT by performing ST at noon and AT for the remaining hours.

Fig. 6 shows the number of standard tracking hours on price, performance and ppr for $p/h = 3$ and $M_L = 10$. As we go from anti tracking (ST hours=0) to standard tracking (ST hours=12), price decreases which results in reduction in ppr. The economic feasibility is not achieved for this case and policy intervention might be required.

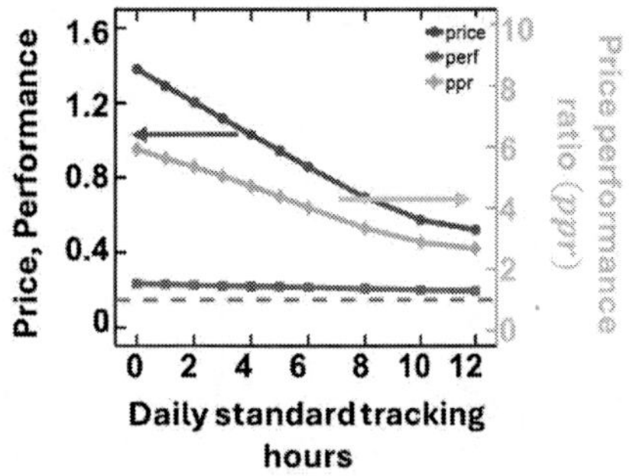

Figure 6. Effect of daily standard tracking hours on price ($\boldsymbol{p_r}$), performance($\boldsymbol{p_b}$) and price performance ratio ($\boldsymbol{ppr}$) for $\boldsymbol{N/S, E/W}$, $\boldsymbol{ST}$ and $\boldsymbol{AT}$. The horizontal dotted line represents economic feasibilty condition ($\boldsymbol{ppr = 1}$).

3.4 Effect of feed-in-tariff

F To make AV economically feasible, policy interventions in the form of subsidies or feed in tariff (FIT) might be needed. Fig. 7 shows the threshold feed-in tariff requirements for different AV orientations for $M_L = 10$. Due to its lowest energy contribution, AT requires the highest FIT. N/S fixed tilt, E/W vertical bifacial and ST require additional FIT between 7-13% relative to ground mounted PV.

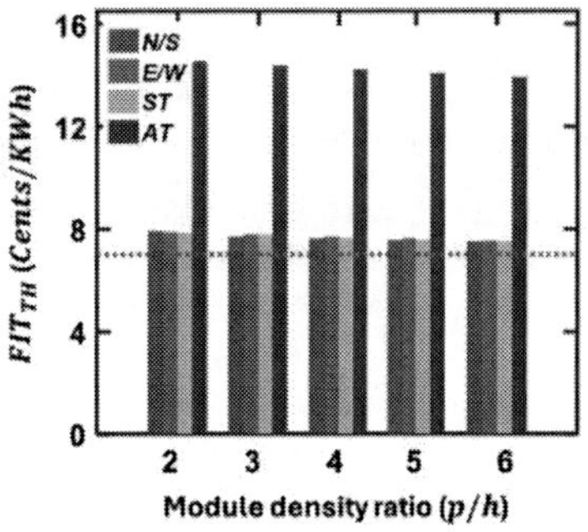

Figure 7: Effect of module density ratio ($\boldsymbol{p/h}$) on threshold feed in tariff ($\boldsymbol{FIT}$) requirement for $\boldsymbol{N/S, E/W, ST}$ and $\boldsymbol{AT}$ orientations. The horizontal dotted line shows the $\boldsymbol{FIT}$ for ground mounted $\boldsymbol{PV}$. $\boldsymbol{AT}$ requires highest $\boldsymbol{FIT}$ due to lowest energy contribution and highest CAPEX requirements.

4 CONCLUSIONS

Food-energy yield and economic performance for agrivoltaics are evaluated using a techno-economic framework. For high module density (p/h~2), anti-tracking bifacial modules can provide highest crop yield but at a reduced energy generation while standard solar tracking modules can provide highest energy yield but at reduced crop yield. The economic equivalence for AV relative to ground mounted PV was evaluated in terms of price performance ratio. The economic competitiveness for AV relative to ground mounted PV requires a module array design at a reduced array density. At a lower module density ($p/h \geq 6$) related to land acquisition, taxes, and overheads along with a significant crop income, E/W faced vertical bifacial, N/S faced, and standard solar tracking systems can have an equivalent or economic feasibility relative to ground-mounted PV. Anti tracking systems produce the lowest energy and hence require the highest feed-in tariff to achieve economic equivalence. A customized approach where the standard tracking is applied only for a selected number of hours before and after the noon can provide a high flexibility in terms of food-energy yield and can be designed to obtain best economic trade-offs while satisfying minimum crop yield threshold. The proposed framework can be utilized to facilitate economic assessments and guide policy formulation across various global locations.

5 REFERENCES

[1] Sacchelli, S., Garegnani, G., Geri, F., Grilli, G., Paletto, A., Zambelli, P., Ciolli, M. and Vettorato, D., 2016. Trade-off between photovoltaic systems installation and agricultural practices on arable lands: An environmental and socio-economic impact analysis for Italy. *Land Use Policy*, *56*, pp.90-99.

[2] Barron-Gafford, G.A., Pavao-Zuckerman, M.A., Minor, R.L., Sutter, L.F., Barnett-Moreno, I., Blackett, D.T., Thompson, M., Dimond, K., Gerlak, A.K., Nabhan, G.P. and Macknick, J.E., 2019. Agrivoltaics provide mutual benefits across the food–energy–water nexus in drylands. *Nature Sustainability*, *2*(9), pp.848-855.

[3] Schindele, S., Trommsdorff, M., Schlaak, A., Obergfell, T., Bopp, G., Reise, C., Braun, C., Weselek, A., Bauerle, A., Högy, P. and Goetzberger, A., 2020. Implementation of agrophotovoltaics: Techno-economic analysis of the price-performance ratio and its policy implications. *Applied Energy*, *265*, p.114737.

[4] Giri, N.C. and Mohanty, R.C., 2022. Agrivoltaic system: Experimental analysis for enhancing land productivity and revenue of farmers. *Energy for Sustainable Development*, *70*, pp.54-61.

[5] Weselek, A., Ehmann, A., Zikeli, S., Lewandowski, I., Schindele, S. and Högy, P., 2019. Agrophotovoltaic systems: applications, challenges, and opportunities. A review. *Agronomy for sustainable development*, *39*(4), p.35.

[6] Feuerbacher, A., Herrmann, T., Neuenfeldt, S., Laub, M. and Gocht, A., 2022. Estimating the economics and adoption potential of agrivoltaics in Germany using a farm-level bottom-up approach. *Renewable and Sustainable Energy Reviews*, *168*, p.112784.

[7] Lowenberg-DeBoer, J., Huang, I.Y., Grigoriadis, V. and Blackmore, S., 2020. Economics of robots and automation in field crop production. *Precision Agriculture*, *21*(2), pp.278-299.

[8] Riaz, M.H., Imran, H., Alam, H., Alam, M.A. and Butt, N.Z., 2022. Crop-specific optimization of bifacial PV arrays for agrivoltaic food-energy production: The light-productivity-factor approach. *IEEE Journal of Photovoltaics*, *12*(2),

pp.572-580.
[9] Alam, H., Alam, M.A. and Butt, N.Z., 2022. Techno economic modeling for agrivoltaics: Can agrivoltaics be more profitable than ground mounted PV?. *IEEE Journal of Photovoltaics*, *13*(1), pp.174-186.
[10] Riaz, M.H., Imran, H., Younas, R., Alam, M.A. and Butt, N.Z., 2021. Module technology for agrivoltaics: Vertical bifacial versus tilted monofacial farms. *IEEE Journal of Photovoltaics*, *11*(2), pp.469-477.
[11] Patel, M.T., Khan, M.R., Sun, X. and Alam, M.A., 2019. A worldwide cost-based design and optimization of tilted bifacial solar farms. *Applied Energy*, *247*, pp.467-479..
[12] PV performance modeling collaborative | an industry and national laboratory collaborative to improve photovoltaic performance modeling, https:// pvpmc.sandia.gov/2016
[13] Alam, H. and Butt, N.Z., 2024. How does module tracking for agrivoltaics differ from standard photovoltaics? Food, energy, and technoeconomic implications. *Renewable Energy*, *235*, p.121151.

Maximizing Economic Performance of Agrivoltaic Systems through Module Array Design

Habeel Alam[1,2,3*], Jenny Nelson[2], Alona Armstrong[3], Duncan Whyatt[3] and Nauman Z. Butt[1] *(h.alam@lancaster.ac.uk)

[1] Department of Electrical Engineering, Lahore University of Management Sciences, Pakistan
[2] Department of Physics, Imperial College London, United Kingdom
[3] Lancaster Environment Centre, Lancaster University, United Kingdom

Introduction

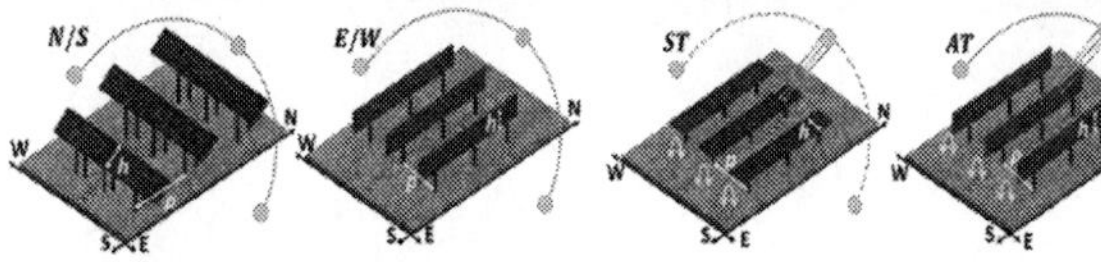

- Selection of an optimal module array density (**p/h**) for agrivoltaics (AV) can be non-trivial
- Various performance metrics and constraints may need to be met
  - **Food-energy yields, available land area, and economics**
- North/South faced fixed tilt, vertical East/West faced bifacial, standard tracking and anti tracking orientations are studied
- Economic constraints are explored for high and low value crops.

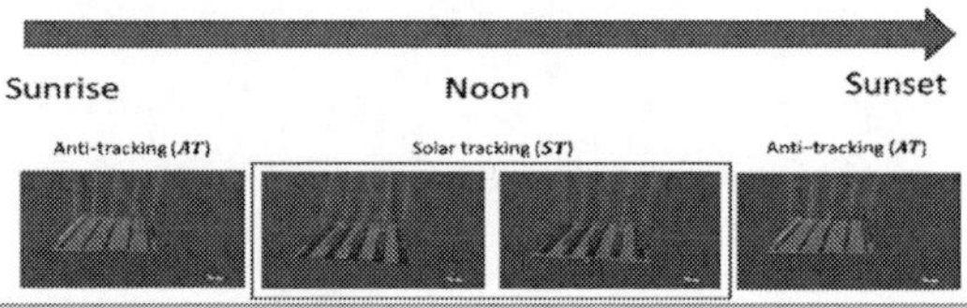

Performance Metrics & Economic Constraints

- Energy yield ratio [1]:
$$= \frac{Annual\ energy/\ unit\ farm\ area\ for\ AV}{Annual\ energy/\ unit\ farm\ area\ for\ standard\ PV}$$
- Sunlight availability to crops (PAR ratio) [1]:
$$= \frac{PAR\ available\ to\ crop\ for\ a\ given\ AV\ system}{PAR\ available\ to\ crop\ for\ the\ reference\ full\ sun\ condition}$$
- Crop(biomass) yield ratio (Y_{PAR}) [2]:
$$= \frac{Biomass\ yield\ for\ a\ crop\ in\ AV\ system}{Biomass\ yield\ for\ the\ same\ crop\ in\ full\ sun\ condition}$$
- Economic constraints [2]:
$$price(p_r') = Hardware\ costs + Soft\ PV\ costs - Energy\ yield\ ratio$$
$$performance\ benefit(pb') = crop\ profit$$
$$price\ performance\ ratio(ppr) = \frac{price\ (p_r')}{performance\ benefit\ (pb')}$$
$$\mathbf{ppr \leq 1}\ is\ desired\ for\ economic\ feasibility$$
- In case of feed in tariff, performance benefit becomes:
$$performance\ benefit(pb') = crop\ profit + \Delta FIT$$

Food-Energy Yield for different crops

(i) **shade susceptible** (S) ⇒ highly susceptible to shade
(ii) **shade tolerant** (T) ⇒ moderately affected by shade
(iii) **shade benefiting** (B) ⇒ mildly affected by shade

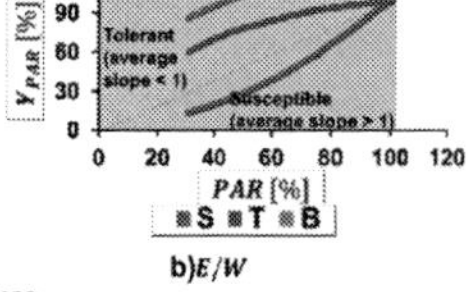

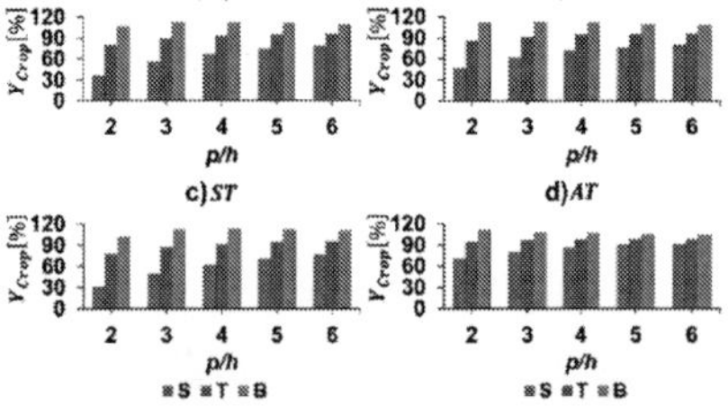

- Y_{Crop} increases with increasing p/h which is most evident in the crop type S.
- ST is not recommended for crop type S at $p/h \leq 4$.

CT for various crop types and seasons.

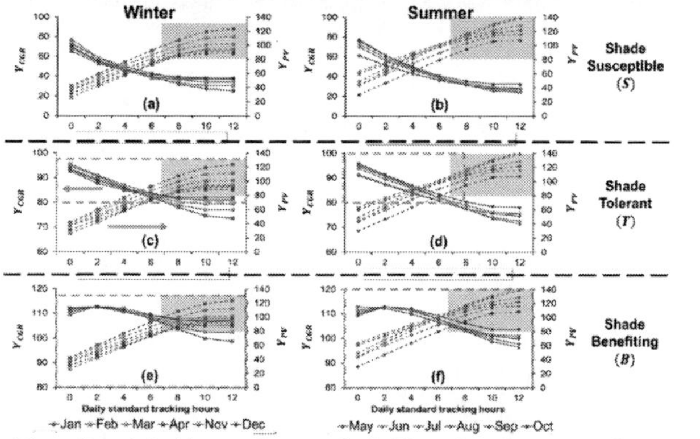

- The yellow dotted box and green shaded box show the space where the value of ST hours can meet 80% value for Y_{CGR} and Y_{PV}, respectively.
- For shade sensitive crops, the assumed threshold limit of Y_{CGR} = 80% is not met at any value for ST hours.
- The required yield limits are met for the crop type T and B for a range of ST hours.

Economic Feasibility Relative to Standard PV

- Lower ppr (lower module density) requires more land for the same energy capacity but reduces crop shading losses..
- Except for AT, all other module configurations become economically viable for $\Delta FIT \geq 10\%$.

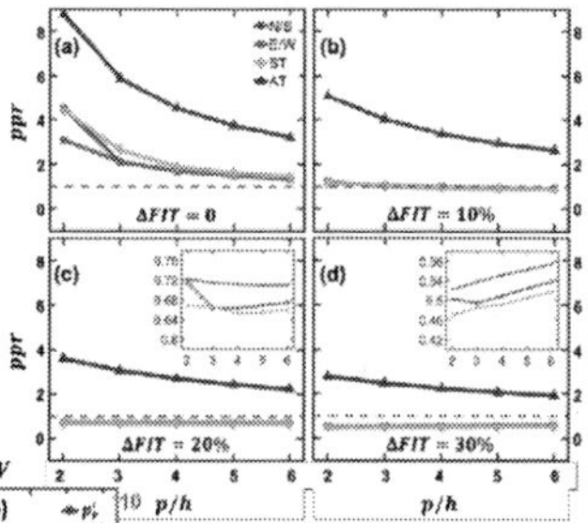

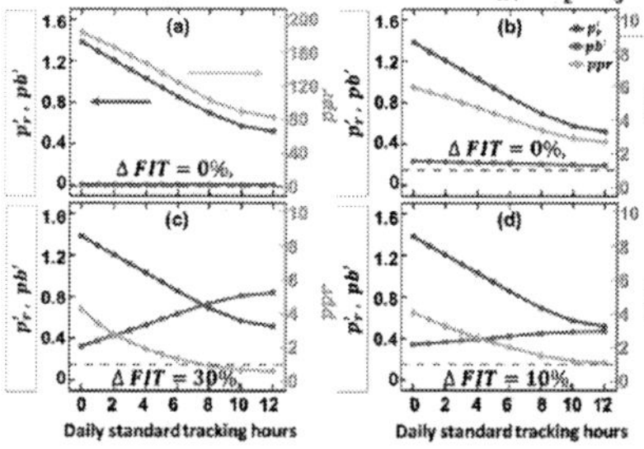

- p_r', $pb'$and ppr shows decreasing trend with increasing ST hours when $\Delta FIT = 0$.
- At higher ΔFIT, pb' increases with increasing p/h.

Conclusions

- Requirements for lower ppr and higher land equivalent ratio (LER) often contradict each other.
- Economic scenario shown assumes single ownership of energy and crop revenues; partnerships require mutual contracts to ensure feasibility for each stakeholder

References

[1] H. Alam *et al., IEEE Journal of Photovoltaics* (2023)

[2] H. Alam *et al., Renewable Energy* (2024)

[3] M. Laub, *et al. Agronomy for Sustainable Development (2022).*

SCAN ME

BIFACIAL AND MISMATCH FACTORS OF AGRI-PHOTOVOLTAICS SYSTEMS

Keith R. McIntosh, Solomon Freer, Bastien J.J. Ardissone, S. Ramirez, Ben A. Sudbury and Malcolm D. Abbott
PV Lighthouse
Coledale, NSW, Australia

ABSTRACT: We use ray tracing and circuit simulation to examine bifacial and mismatch factors in three very different types of Agri-PV systems: (A) east–west waves with semi-transparent modules above crops; (B) single-axis trackers with greenhouses between the rows; and (C) east–west facing vertical modules. We determine the annual bifacial gain to be 6%, 4% and 70%, respectively, where the gain for Systems A and B is considerably reduced by crop absorption, and where the gain for System C is close to the bifaciality of the modules. We quantify the shading and transmission factors of the Agri-PV systems, finding them to be significantly higher than for equivalent conventional systems, largely due to extra shading from crops and greenhouses, extra spacing between modules and bays, and, in the case of System A, semitransparent modules. We also quantify the electrical mismatch loss that arises from non-uniform irradiance, finding it to be moderate for System A (0.8%), small for System B (0.3%) and very high for System C (3.9%), primarily due to row-to-row shading when the sun is low in the sky. In addition to quantifying their annual values, we show that these factors depend strongly on the solar position and the diffuse fraction (cloudiness), and we quantify the error introduced into forecasts of output power when this dependence is neglected.
Keywords: agri-photovoltaics, bifacial, yield, mismatch, ray tracing, systems

1 INTRODUCTION

The development of an Agri-PV system requires an understanding of its energy gains and losses, both for the PV modules and the crops. This understanding is assisted by simulation tools that are fast and accurate at quantifying system parameters that cannot easily be measured or calculated. Such parameters include module yield Y_{mod}, bifacial gain g_B, and factors that are used in yield forecasting software: the rear-side shading f_S, the transmission factor f_T, and the electrical mismatch factor f_M, which some split into front f_{MF} and rear f_{MR} components.

The determination of these system parameters tends to be more difficult for Agri-PV than for regular utility-scale systems—especially for bifacial modules—because Agri-PV often includes one or more of the following complications: semitransparent modules, large spacing between modules, custom configurations, additional shading from structural supports or greenhouses, and crops that grow below and between the modules [e.g., 1–4].

The most common way to determine Y_{mod} and g_B involves modelling the optics of the system with a view-factor approach. It solves the optical behavior of an ideal system and then modifies the rear irradiance by the three factors, f_S, f_T and f_{MR}. PVsyst [5] is the best-known software that follows this approach. One of its drawbacks is that it requires the user to know (or guestimate) values for f_S, f_T and f_{MR}, which are exceedingly difficult to measure.

The bifacial factors for Agri-PV systems tend to be quite different from those for conventional utility-scale systems. For example, f_S can be much higher due to shading from crops, greenhouses, or additional structural supports; f_T can be much higher due to the use of semitransparent modules or additional spacing to allow light to pass through to the crops; and f_M can be much higher due greater non-uniformity of the rear irradiance, both in terms of cell-to-cell non-uniformity and module-to-module non-uniformity. These parameters are very different again for Agri-PV systems with vertically mounted modules. Thus, one cannot simply assume default or typical values of f_S, f_T and f_M when forecasting the yield of bifacial Agri-PV systems.

Another way to determine Y_{mod} and g_B is to model the optics with ray tracing, and the mismatch with SPICE modelling. This accounts directly for the complicated geometry of the system, avoiding any need to determine f_S, f_T and f_M.

Moreover, ray tracing and SPICE modelling can used to determine f_S, f_T and f_M for the view-factor programs [6–15]. This is achieved by solving simulations with and without structural supports, with and without transmission through and between modules, and with and without stringing the cells within the module and the modules within the system.

In this work, we determine the system parameters for three very different Agri-PV systems shown in Fig. 1: (a) an east–west wave orientation with semitransparent modules above tall crops, (b) a single-axis tracker (SAT) with greenhouses between its rows, and (c) vertically mounted modules facing east–west and supported by vertical posts.

With the assistance of irradiance maps generated by ray tracing, and with plots of g_B, f_S, f_T and f_M against solar position, day of year, and diffuse fraction, we describe and quantify the major trends for these Agri-PV systems. The results illustrate how the factors for Agri-PV systems differ markedly from those of conventional utility-scale systems, both in terms of magnitude and variability. We also compute the subsequent error that arises in yield forecasting when constant values of f_S, f_T and f_M are used in conventional view-factor programs.

The approach and procedure contained in this paper can be applied to determine the parameters for any Agri-PV configuration and location.

2 SIMULATION DETAILS

Fig. 1 presents the three types of Agri-PV systems examined in this work. The left-hand images are photos of real systems, and the right-hand images show the results of simulations at one timestep during the year, where the color of each solar cell represents its generation current J_G, and where redder/bluer cells indicate a higher/lower J_G.

The colored modules in Fig. 1 are within the simulated unit-system; that is, the set of modules that represents a repeatable unit within the full system. Thus, the simulations account for local edge effects like the spacing

Figure 1: **(a)** Actual and **(b)** simulated view of System A: Bifacial semitransparent modules (with 50% cell area) installed in a fixed east-west wave configuration above tall crops.

Figure 2: **(a)** Actual and **(b)** simulated view of System B: Bifacial modules installed on a two-in-portrait single axis tracker with semi-cylindrical greenhouses between rows. At the example timestep, a strip of cells has a higher J_G (i.e., the redder cells) due to reflection from the top of the greenhouse onto the modules.

Figure 3: **(a)** Actual and **(b)** simulated view of System C: Bifacial modules installed in a vertical north-south configuration. Tractor omitted from yield simulations. Shading from neighboring rows is evident. Fig. 3(a) reprinted with permission from Raphael Faschang.

between bays, but not the global edge effects at the boundaries of the system.

We simulate the systems with SunSolve Yield [18], which harnesses 600 parallel cores in the cloud to solve the annual yield within minutes (see Table I). The assigned computing power makes this endeavor much less time-consuming than prior studies [6–11] and capable of accounting for more effects, like spectral dependencies, frames, cell optics, crops, large unit systems, and stringing.

Moreover, for System A, the ray tracing extends into the module, accounting for the complicated optics of modern cells and modules (anti-reflection coatings, surface texture, etc.), as well as the cell layout, permitting light to pass between the cells. Their inputs are very similar to those listed in [6] except that the cells are

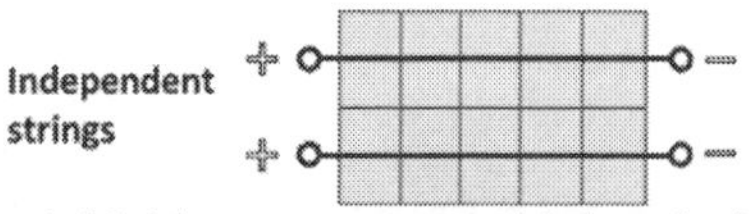

Figure 4: Module rows are connected independently in this study to minimize module-to-module mismatch within strings.

separated such that they encompass 50% of the module area. For Systems B and C, we emulate a Longi LR5 530 W bifacial module with 144 half-cut cells but the raytracing extends only to the surface of the module. It has a bifaciality of 70%.

The wavelength-dependent optical behavior of the albedo (green grass) and galvanized steel is identical to that shown in Fig. 3 of [15]; the crops of System A assume the reflectance of green grass, and the greenhouses of System B assume the reflectance of glass.

After the ray tracing has computed J_G in every cell of the unit system, the electrical circuit is solved with a SPICE model. This circuit accounts for the conventional stringing of cells within the module (including bypass diodes), as well as the stringing of the modules within the unit system as shown in Fig. 4. The electrical calculations account for thermal effects as described in [6].

We situate all three systems in the same location: Santiago do Cacém, Portugal (38° N, 8.7° E), where Europe's largest PV power plant (1.2 GW) is planned [16]. We use the same weather and atmospheric conditions as described in [15]. The tracking algorithm for the SATs includes conventional backtracking.

10.4229/EUPVSEC2025/4DV.1.7

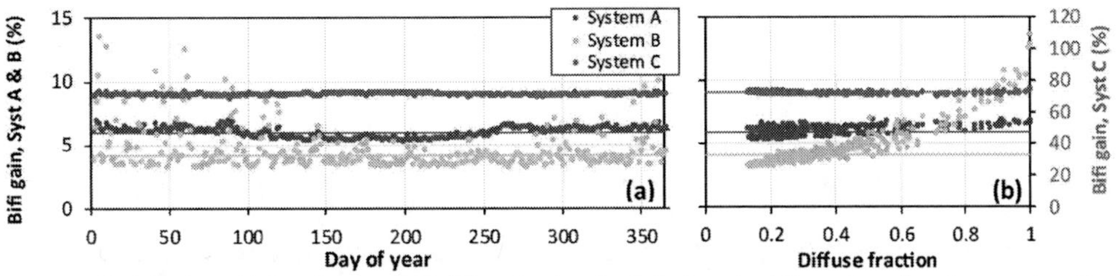

Figure 5: Bifacial gain vs (a) day of year and (b) diffuse fraction. Symbols show the daily g_B, lines show the annual g_B. Data for System C plotted on the right-hand y-axis, whose scale 10× larger than the left-hand y-axis.

3 RESULTS

The results of the simulations are summarized as follows: Table I lists the annual results, Fig. 5 plots the daily bifacial gain against day of year and diffuse fraction, Fig. 6 plots the shading factor f_S at every timestep against the solar zenith angle θ_s, Fig. 7 plots daily factors against day of year, and Fig. 8 plots the factors at each timestep on a single day that contains periods of clear, cloudy and overcast skies. We now describe the major conclusions from the simulations.

3.1 Annual yield

Table I indicates that the energy yield per module Y_{mod} is highest for System B (SAT) because it tracks the sun, and its cells have a high packing density. The yield is the lowest for System A (waves) because its modules are semi-transparent and widely spaced.

TABLE I

ANNUALISED SIMULATION RESULTS

System	A	B	C
N_{mod}	8	80	16
Sim time (min)	3	7	1
Y_{mod} (kWh)	317	1239	815
g_B	6.0%	4.1%	72.8%
f_S	46.9%	52.70%	2.4%
f_T	174.2%	8.6%	0.9%
f_{MR}	0.5%	1.2%	−1.3%
f_M	0.8%	0.3%	3.9%

3.2 Bifacial gain

The bifacial gain g_B is determined by comparing the yield of the full simulation Y_1 to the yield of a simulation that neglects any rays that impinge on the rear-side of the module Y_2. The gain is then given by $g_B = Y_1/Y_2 - 1$. Being the gain in yield, rather than irradiance, it considers the effects of temperature and mismatch.

Table I indicates that g_B of Systems A and B is small but sufficiently large that it should be accounted for in any energy-yield calculation. A gain of 4.1% for System B is smaller than the 5–9% typical of SATs with moderate albedo because the greenhouses absorb some of the light that would otherwise have reflected from the ground onto the rear of the modules. The greenhouses also reflect some light away from the modules.

By contrast, g_B for System C is very large because its modules are vertically mounted and facing east–west [2], and thus, direct sunlight impinges on the rear of the modules after midday. Moreover, like practical vertical PV systems, the module orientation is alternated for each row in the system (i.e., the front side is alternated from being east-facing to west-facing); thus, in the simulated scene, there must be the same irradiance on the front and rear of all modules combined. We find that the bifacial gain in yield is 73%, close to the bifaciality of the modules (70%), but a little higher due to the non-linear dependence of module power on irradiance.

Fig. 5 plots the daily g_B vs day of year and diffuse fraction, exhibiting informative trends that would be difficult to determine experimentally:

System A displays weak dependencies of g_B on season and diffuse fraction, where g_B is higher in winter than summer, and higher in cloudy skies than in clear skies.

System B exhibits almost no dependence on season, but a strong dependence on diffuse fraction. In fact, g_B is 13% when completely overcast and 3.5% under clear skies. That is, the fraction of diffuse sunlight that reaches the rear of the module is much greater than the fraction of direct light. Thus, the value of bifacial modules is much greater on days with low irradiance, when solar electricity is more valuable.

System C exhibits no dependence on season or diffuse fraction, and little scatter in g_B. This is due to the alternating orientation of the front-side of the module

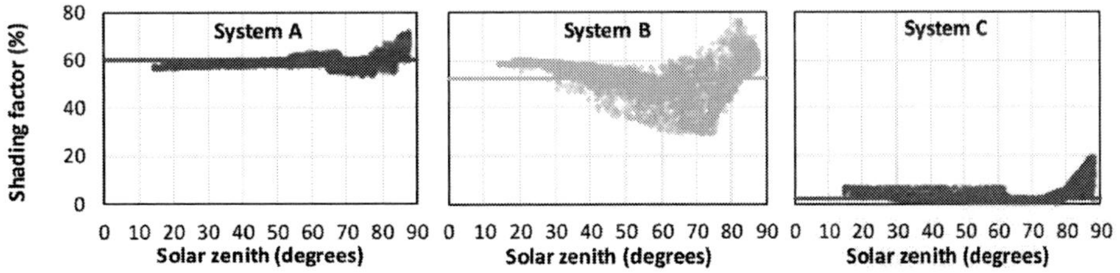

Figure 6: Shading factor vs solar zenith. Symbols show the hourly f_S, lines show the annual f_S.

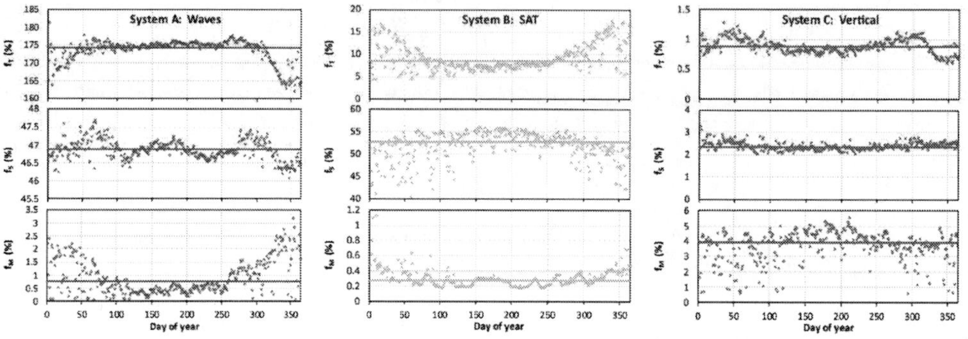

Figure 7: Bifacial factors, f_T, f_S and f_M, for Systems A, B and C. Symbols show daily factors, lines show annual factors.

3.3 Shading factor

The irradiance impinging on the rear surface of the modules is attenuated by shading from structural supports, crops and greenhouses. As in [9, 10], we quantify that shading by solving the rear irradiance I_R with and without those features that shade the rear, $f_S = 1 - I_{R3}/I_{R1}$, where I_{R1} represents the full simulation and I_{R3} represent the simulation without the features. (As described in the appendix, an alternative approach must be applied for wave configurations in PVSyst V8, but we maintain this equation here because it is more informative when comparing configurations.)

The results in Table I indicate the following: In System A, the structural supports and crops approximately halve the rear-side irradiance. In System B, the annual f_S is 47%, which is much higher than f_S for a regular SAT (about 5–10%) [9], indicative of the large impact of the greenhouses. In System C, f_S is much smaller but non-zero, where the shading arises primarily from the posts, which shade the modules when the sun is due south.

We learn more with Fig. 6, which plots f_S vs solar zenith θ_s at every timestep. The large variations in f_S, particularly for System B, indicate that the rear-side irradiance depends strongly on solar position and other factors like the diffuse fraction. Thus, although an energy-weighted annual value of f_S can be determined for simple yield forecasts of Agri-PV (i.e., the lines in Figs. 6 and 7), it introduces error, as quantified in Section 4.

Finally, Fig. 7 shows that f_S is relatively constant over the course of a day for System A. By contrast, for System B, f_S varies strongly since the fraction of light shaded by the greenhouses depends on how much direct light falls between the rows.

3.4 Transmission factor

The transmission factor defines the extra light that reaches the ground due to the semi-transparent nature of modules, or due to spacing between modules—both of which are omitted from idealized view-factor calculations. Thus, those calculations account for these effects by multiplying their ground irradiance by f_T (neglecting any spatial dependence to the light). As in [9, 10], we calculate the factor as $f_T = 1 - I_{R4}/I_{R3}$, where I_{R4} represents the simulation without module spacing and with opaque gaps between the cells of the module (as well as without the features that shade the rear).

Table I indicates that f_T differs greatly between systems. It is very high (174%) for System A because it contains large gaps between semi-transparent modules, making f_T a very important correction factor for view-factor models (see appendix regarding the calculation of f_T for waves in PVsyst). For System B, the value of f_T is greater than is typical of SATs due to the large bay spacing, and for System C, f_T is very small because the gaps between the posts and modules is small.

We observe in Figs. 7 and 8 that f_T varies with season and time of day, indicating that f_T depends strongly on the

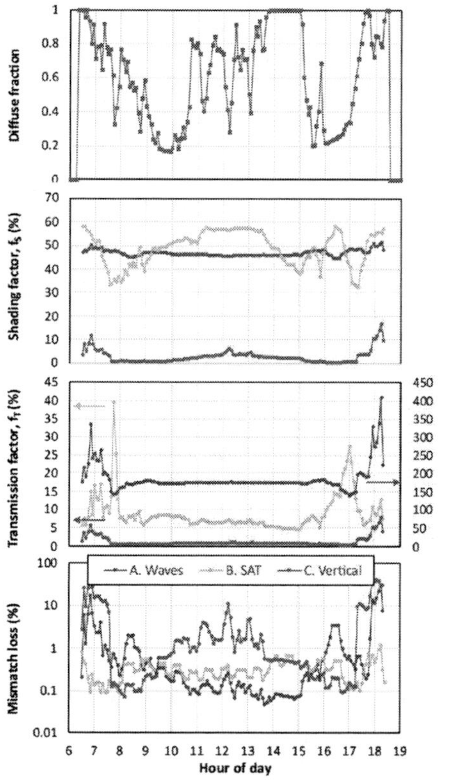

Figure 8: One of day data with 5-minute intervals showing (a) diffuse fraction, (b) f_M (c) f_T and (d) f_S for Systems A, B and C. As evident from the diffuse fraction, the sky is clear during the periods 9h–10.5h and 16h–17h, overcast at 14h–15h, and otherwise partly cloudy.

10.4229/EUPVSEC2025/4DV.1.7

position of the sun in the sky. Interestingly, f_T is lowest in the winter for System A but highest in the winter for System B. This arises due to the systems having very different dependencies on direct and diffuse light.

Once again, there is a large amount of variation in the data, suggesting that the use of annual values (lines) introduce significant error into yield simulations—as will be quantified in Section 4.

3.5 Mismatch factor

The factor f_M quantifies the relative reduction in yield caused by the electrical mismatch arising from non-uniform irradiance. In this work, f_M includes both cell-to-cell and module-to-module mismatch and does not distinguish between front and rear non-uniformity. (It is determined in the manner described in [6, 14].)

Table I indicates that f_M is small for System B, moderate for System A, and very large for System C. It is highest for System C due to the row-to-row shading of direct light that occurs when the sun is low in the sky, and to a lesser extent from the non-uniformity arising from ground reflection.

Fig. 7 shows that there are strong seasonal dependencies in all factors for all systems—moreso than for conventional utility-scale systems [13]. They arise primarily from changes in the solar position and the resulting introduction of row-to-row shading of direct light for Systems A and C, and also due to changes in non-uniformity on the rear. The scatter about those trends is mostly due to variation in diffuse fraction.

4 ERROR WHEN ASSUMING CONSTANT VALUES OF f_S, f_T and f_M DURING A YIELD FORECAST

Many yield forecasting programs (e.g., PVSyst, SAM, Solar Farmer) solve the system optics with a view-factor model. The model computes the irradiance on the front and rear of the modules for the ideal scenario of opaque modules, no space between modules, and no structural supports. The programs then modify the rear irradiance by multiplying it by $(1 + f_T)$ and $(1 - f_S)$ to account for additional light impinging on the ground and shading from structural supports. These programs also account for electrical mismatch due to non-uniformity by multiplying the yield by $(1 - f_M)$. This approach provides a fast optical model but requires the user to input values of f_T, f_S and f_M, which can either be guesstimated or determined by ray tracing.

Current versions of these programs restrict the user to entering constant values of f_T, f_S and f_M to represent all timesteps. As evident above, however, these values can vary substantially over the course of the day and year, whether due to their dependence on the position of the sun, or on the atmosphere (changing the diffuse fraction or, to a lesser extent, the incident spectra). Thus, the 'constant-factor' assumption introduces error into yield forecast.

We now investigate the error at each timestep introduced by the constant-factor assumption. Fig. 9 presents the results, plotting the absolute error in module power at every timestep for each of our example agri-PV systems. To put the error into context, the average output power per module during daylight hours $P_{mod\ av}$ is (a) 70 W, (b) 276 W and (c) 172 W. (Note that the sum of the absolute errors of each plot in Fig. 9 is zero because the constant value of f_S, f_T and f_M are energy-weighted averages that ensure there is no error in the annual yield.)

Fig. 9 demonstrates that the error (i) is not insignificant and (ii) exhibits very different trends for each system, indicative of very different dependencies on the position of the sun in the sky.

For System A (waves, $P_{mod\ av}$ = 70 W), the yield from each module is underestimated by between 0 and 1 W when $\theta_s < 65°$, and overestimated by as much as 6 W when $\theta_s > 65°$ (i.e., when the sun is low in the sky). In short, the forecast of System A tends to be significantly overestimated at the shoulders of the day.

System B (SAT, $P_{mod\ av}$ = 276 W) follows a different trend. Its error is within ±5 W, where it tends to overestimate when $\theta_s < 50°$ and overestimate when $\theta_s >$ 55°.

System C (vertical, $P_{mod\ av}$ = 172 W) exhibits the greatest error and the greatest scatter. It overestimates the yield by as much as 50 W, particularly when the sun is low in the sky (primarily due to an underestimation of electrical mismatch due to row-to-row shading) and underestimates by as much as 30 W, particularly when the sun is high in the sky. Unlike the other systems, the error also depends strongly on the diffuse fraction.

For both System A and B, the error is predominantly due to the variation in structural shading that is not captured when assuming a constant f_S. For System C, the error is predominantly due to the variation in electrical mismatch.

5 CONCLUSION

With ray tracing and SPICE solving, we calculated the bifacial and mismatch factors of three types of Agri-PV systems. We found the factors vary greatly for each system and exhibit markedly different trends. We demonstrated that the factors depend strongly on the position of the sun in the sky and cloud cover—more than is typical for utility-scale non-Agri-PV systems. We found that the application of the 'constant-factor assumption'

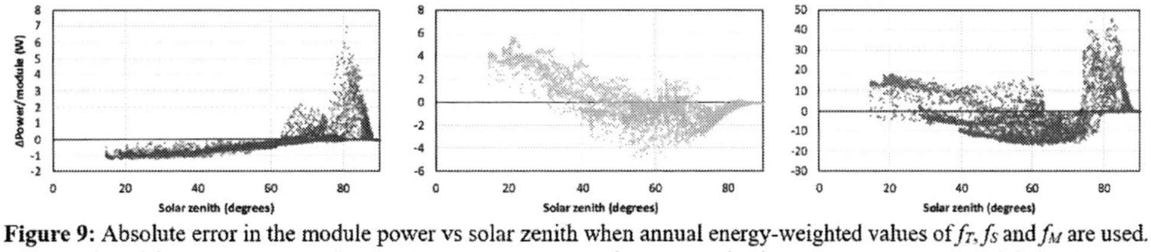

Figure 9: Absolute error in the module power vs solar zenith when annual energy-weighted values of f_T, f_S and f_M are used. Results plotted for Systems (a) A, (b) B and (c) C. For context, the average daytime output power per module is (a) 70 W, (b) 276 W and (c) 172 W.

leads to significant errors, particularly during the shoulders of the day for wave systems due to structural shading, and in vertical systems due to electrical mismatch.

These results underscore the complexity of simulating bifacial Agri-PV systems and demonstrate how insights can be gained by studying the systems with a combination of ray tracing and SPICE modelling.

6 APPENDIX

At the time of writing, the simulation of bifacial wave systems with PVsyst necessitates a complicated procedure. Although PVsyst (V 8.0.15) contains the option to simulate 'domes' (a waves system), it does not permit the modules to be bifacial. Consequently, a bifacial wave system must create two separate 'infinite-shed' systems—one for the east-facing and another for the west-facing modules—where the bifacial option is selected for both.

PVsyst's optical model then computes the irradiance on the rear of the module as if (i) there are no lateral gaps between modules, (ii) the modules are opaque, and (iii) the neighbouring rows of modules are exclusively of the same type of system. Thus, to simulate the east–west waves structure of Figure 1(a), PVsyst simulates the rear optics of the east-facing modules as if the west-facing modules were not present as shown in Figure 4(b), and the equivalent case for the west-facing.

The procedure for determining f_S and f_T must therefore change to accommodate this approach. Remember that the purpose of f_S and f_T is to modify the optics such that the configuration simulated by PVsyst emulates the actual configuration as simulated by the ray tracing.

In the new procedure, the approach to determine the baseline current I_{R1} remains the same, and the full simulation is solved as normal. However, I_{R3} and I_{R4} must be determined by removing the structures *and* the neighbouring row; thus to determine f_S and f_T for the east-facing modules, the west-facing modules are omitted from the ray tracing simulation; and vice versa. The determination of I_{R4} also requires (i) the removal of the spacing between modules and (ii) converting any semi-transparent regions in the module to be opaque.

Finally, we note that the recommended procedure to determine the bifacial factors for PVsyst might have to adapt to future versions of PVsyst. Refer to [18] for updates.

TABLE II

ANNUALISED SIMULATION RESULTS FOR SYSTEM A

	Standard approach	**Modified approach for PVsyst V8**
f_S	46.9%	60.3%
f_T	174.2%	34.8%

7 ACKNOWLEDGEMENT

This project received funding from the Australian Renewable Energy Agency (ARENA) as part of ARENA's Advancing Renewables Program. The views expressed herein are not necessarily the views of the Australian Government, and the Australian Government does not accept responsibility for any information or advice contained herein.

8 REFERENCES

[1] B. Staie, Agrivoltaics Technical Assistance in the United States, NREL Report PR-6A20-90143 (2024).

[2] S. Ovaitt, A. Kinzer, M. Boyd, J. Jones, C. Deline, J. Macknick, "Viewfactor and Raytracing for AgriPV Modeling", NREL Report PR-5K00-86631 (2023).

[3] M. H. Riaz, H. Imran, N. Z. Butt, "Optimization of PV Array Density for Fixed Tilt Bifacial Solar Panels for Efficient Agrivoltaic Systems," IEEE PVSC, 2020, pp. 1349–1352.

[4] Y. Hu, X. Zhang, X. Ma, "Agrivoltaics with semitransparent panels can maintain yield and quality in soybean production," Solar Energy 282 (2024) 112978.

[5] PVSyst, http://pvsyst.com/

[6] K. R. McIntosh, M. D. Abbott, B. A. Sudbury, J. Meydbray, "Mismatch loss in bifacial modules due to nonuniform illumination in 1-D tracking systems," IEEE Journal of PV 9 (2019) 1504.

[7] S. A. Pelaez, C. Deline, J. S. Stein, B. Marion, K. Anderson, M. Muller, "Effect of torque-tube parameters on rear-irradiance and rear-shading loss for bifacial PV performance on single-axis tracking systems," Proceedings 46th IEEE PVSC (2019).

[8] C. Deline, S. A. Pelaez, S. MacAlpine, C. Olalla, "Estimating and parameterizing mismatch power loss in bifacial photovoltaic systems," Progress in Photovoltaics 28 (2020) 691.

[9] K. R. McIntosh, M. D. Abbott, B. A. Sudbury, "How the PVSyst inputs for bifacial systems depend on conditions," Bifacial Workshop 2020, Virtual Proceedings.

[10] C. Zhao, J. Xiao, Y. Yu, J. N. Jaubert, "Accurate shading factor and mismatch loss analysis of bifacial HSAT systems through ray-tracing modeling," Solar Energy Advances 1 (2021) 100004.

[11] G. Raina, S. Sunanda, "A comprehensive assessment of electrical performance and mismatch losses in bifacial PV module under different front and rear side shading scenarios," Energy Conversion and Management 261 (2022) 115668.

[12] A. C. Russell, C. E. Valdivia, C. Bohémier, J. E. Haysom, K. Hinzer, "DUET: A Novel Energy Yield Model With 3-D Shading for Bifacial Photovoltaic Systems," IEEE Journal of PV 12 (2022) 1576.

[13] A. Calcabrini Andres, R. Cardosso, D. Gribnau, P. Babal, P. Manganiello, M. Zeman, O. Isabella, "Time-varying, ray tracing irradiance simulation approach for photovoltaic systems in complex scenarios with decoupled geometry, optical properties and illumination conditions," Progress in Photovoltaics 31 (2023) 134–148.

[14] PV Lighthouse, "Step-by-step guide to determine PVSyst bifacial inputs with SunSolve," 2024.

[15] K. R. McIntosh, M. D. Abbott, B. A. Sudbury, "Quantifying Inherent Sources of Electrical Mismatch in Utility-Scale Bifacial Systems," Proceedings 40th EU PVSEC, Lisbon (2023).

[16] https://taiyangnews.info/markets/europes-largest-solar-power-farm-planned-in-portugal/, Taiyang News, 1-Feb-2023.

[17] Pelaez, S.A., C. Deline, P. Greenberg, J. Stein, and R.K. Kostuk. 2018. "Model and Validation of Single-Axis Tracking with Bifacial Photovoltaics: Preprint." NREL/CP-5K00-72039.

[18] https://sunsolve.com/
[19] Mahim, T.M., Rahim, A.H.M.A, Mosaddequr Rahman, M., "Review of Mono- and Bifacial Photovoltaic Technologies: A Comparative Study," IEEE Journal of Photovoltaics 14 (2024) 375.
[20] Toqueboeuf, C., "Comparative Modeling And Validation Of Bifacial Gains In PV Power Plants", Dissertation, 2025.
[21] Benbba, R., Akhsassi, M., El mouden, H., Wifaya, A., and Outzourhit, A., "View Factors Approach for Bifacial Photovoltaic Array Modeling: Bifacial Gain Sensitivity Analysis." J. Sol. Energy Eng., 147 (2025) 021008.

PV LIGHTHOUSE

42nd European Photovoltaic Solar Energy Conference and Exhibition

SunSolve

Bifacial factors for AgriPV

K.R. McIntosh, S. Freer, B. Ardissone, S. Ramirez, B.A. Sudbury and M.D. Abbott

An optical challenge

Bifacial modules provide a significant boost to the electrical yield from AgriPV.

What is the bifacial gain? How does it depend on time of day, time of year, weather?

View-factor (VF) approaches struggle to answer those questions due to the complexity of AgriPV. E.g.,

- semitransparent modules,
- large spacing between modules,
- shading from supports or greenhouses,
- crops that grow below and between modules.

VF programs account for complexity with correction factors for the bifacial irradiance, like transmission f_T, shading f_S, and mismatch due to non-uniformity f_M.

Findings

Ray tracing (RT) can solve complex systems to give:

- electrical yield — annual, daily, hourly;
- bifacial gain;
- bifacial factors for VF programs like PVsyst.

Modern RT programs solve those systems in 1–10 mins, using cloud processing and tuned algos. We find:

AgriPV bifi factors depend greatly on configuration.

Results give useful insights. E.g., for our location, f_M is

- 10× higher for vertical PV than SATs,
- Variability for vertical PV is due mostly to cloud,
- Variability for waves, SATs due more to season.

The paper quantifies the error from assuming f_S, f_T and f_M are constants. It depends strongly on zenith angle.

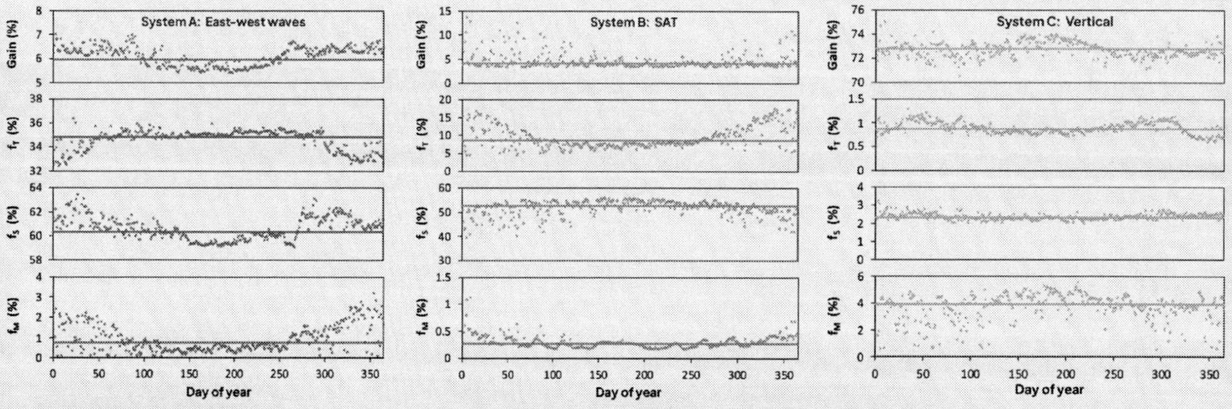

Conclusions

- AgriPV systems are optically complex.
- Modern ray tracers can solve their bifacial gain and annual yield in 1–10 minutes.
- RT can also determine the bifacial factors (f_S, f_T and f_M) required by PVsyst and other VF programs.
- The factors vary with site, weather, time of day and year.

020397-001

Learn how to determine bifacial factors for PVsyst at sunsolve.com/news/agripv_factors_2025

PERFORMANCE ANALYSIS OF AGRIVOLTAIC SYSTEM CONFIGURATIONS IN NORDIC CONDITIONS

Magda Szarek[1], Sami Jouttijärvi[1], Lauri Karttunen[1], Samuli Ranta[2], Kati Miettunen[1]
[1]Department of Mechanical and Materials Engineering, University of Turku, Vesilinnantie 5, 20500 Turku, Finland
[2]Turku University of Applied Sciences, Joukahaisenkatu 7, 20520 Turku, Finland

ABSTRACT: This study compares the energy yields, ground shading, and financial impacts of several agrivoltaic (APV) system layouts in high-latitude conditions. APV systems allow farmland to be combined with energy production, thus reducing the land-use conflict between photovoltaic systems and food production. APVs have been gaining popularity worldwide, including in Nordic countries and other high-latitude locations where solar energy has received little attention until recently. High latitude locations face different conditions than low latitude locations because of different sun elevation angles, day length, and weather patterns. Because of this, system configurations must be optimized for these conditions. We analyzed three APV configurations of 1 MW that include 1) vertically mounted east-west facing bifacial panels, 2) a single-axis tracker system, and 3) a south-facing overhead system at separations of 8, 10, 15, and 30 m. The tracker system had the highest specific yield (1.26–1.39 kWh/kW). However, the two production peaks of the vertical system more closely matching high spot prices of electricity resulted in the highest capture price of electricity produced by the vertical system (43.77–43.83 EUR/MWh).
Keywords: photovoltaic, agrivoltaic, land use

1 INTRODUCTION

The need for renewable technologies continues to grow as the environment and society change. Cheap renewable energy offers opportunities for economic gain, resilience through local energy production, and reduced emissions. To compound, solar photovoltaic (PV) technologies have become cheaper, making them attractive prospects in a wide range of applications and climates. Until recently, wide-scale implementation of solar installations in the Nordic countries has been limited compared to other regions of the world. This was, in part, due to the solar energy conditions being less favorable at high latitudes. In recent years, this trend has shifted, and solar installations have seen rapid growth in the Nordic countries [1].

Until recently, investments were primarily in small personal installations; however, a significant number of large-scale installations are currently in various stages of planning and implementation [2]. This booming interest has created an opportunity and a need for research on the suitability of various system designs in high latitude conditions. Differences between high and low-to-mid latitude conditions entail a need for different design approaches and types of systems analyses. Lower temperatures, typical of higher latitudes, result in reduced heat loss. However, the highly variable yearly irradiance, low sun elevation angles, and snow cover pose challenges to creating optimal systems [3]. In addition, electricity prices in the Nordic countries are typically low, especially during the summer months. As a result, efficient designs tailored to local conditions are needed to ensure the profitability of solar energy production [4]. For example, bifacial panels, especially when combined with vertical placements that allow both sides direct access to irradiance, may be particularly well suited to high latitudes, as they can make use of long periods of low solar elevation [5].

One of the challenges of PV energy production is ensuring the efficient use of available land. A potential solution is to place solar panels in actively used locations. Agrivoltaics (APVs), which combine agricultural land with PV installations, are a notable form of dual land use. APVs have been implemented in many locations around the world and have already been successfully tested in high-latitude locations, though in a limited capacity [6], [7]. Because APV land can produce more combined value than dedicated agricultural or PV land, it is attractive as both a means of supplementary income for farmers and a means of preserving land for other uses, including biodiversity [8], [9]. APV can also decrease evaporation, improving crop yield during drought years [10], though this positive effect is likely limited in typical high-latitude conditions.

Our previous studies have already shown how bifacial technologies can be efficiently utilized in high latitude conditions [5] and the benefits of east-west facing vertical bifacial (VBPV) systems in APV applications [11] and the higher value for self-consumption of produced electricity [12]. This study expands on previous research by analyzing tracker systems and comparing three types of systems using bifacial panels in a high-latitude location. Specifically, a VBPV system, a tracker system, and a south-facing overhead (SO) system are compared in terms of their total produced energy, ground shading, revenue, and the value of produced electricity based on Nordpool spot prices. Several row separations (8, 10, 15, and 30 m) were analyzed to compare the impact of varying row separation. The albedo values used in simulations are typical of crops grown in high-latitude conditions.

2 METHODOLOGY

2.1 Meteorological and environmental data

The study was conducted in high latitude Nordic conditions, specifically in southwestern Finland in the area of Turku at 60° N. To determine the systems' performance in that area's meteorological and solar conditions, satellite weather data and measured albedo from a site at a similar latitude were used. Satellite data were obtained from Copernicus Atmosphere Monitoring Service (CAMS), and the output was analyzed for the 2024 calendar year [13]. Barley is the most common crop grown in Finland, and planting in the spring is the most common method. Thus, the albedo for the system surroundings was chosen from a measured spring barley albedo. The location at which it was measured is situated at a similar latitude in Sweden

[14]. The albedo in high latitudes, especially cropland, is highly varied, as it can go from as low as 0.08 in October to as high as 0.74 in December when snow cover is significant.

2.2 Spot price data

The electricity price in Finland is updated on an hourly basis, so the value of the electricity produced at any given hour is determined by the current market price. That price depends on multiple factors, including the variable renewable electricity production in Finland as well as prices in neighboring electricity markets. To determine the profitability of the different configurations, the Nordpool tax-free spot price in the day-ahead market for the 2024 calendar year was used [12], [15]. Finland is covered by a single price zone, with no price differences for different regions. The electricity value was determined as the total revenue divided by the production of the given system. The total revenue was calculated using the following formula:

$$revenue = \sum_{t=1}^{n}(p_{spot,t} \cdot E_{PV,t}), \quad (1)$$

where p_{spot} is the spot price, t is the hour of the year, and $E_{PV,t}$ is the energy output of the PV system at t.

2.3 System design

The simulations were completed using PVsyst® [16] software, which was previously found to be capable of creating accurate simulations for high latitude locations [9]. A generic bifacial panel offered by the program was used for all system types, with the built-in bifaciality function of "unlimited sheds" for the SO and VBPV systems and "unlimited trackers" for the tracker system. The panel parameters are depicted in Table I.

Table I: Selected generic bifacial solar panel parameters

Parameter	Mono 700 Wp Twin half-cells bifacial
Rated power (W)	700
Rated voltage (V)	42.60
Rated current (A)	16.43
Open circuit voltage (V)	50.59
Short circuit current (A)	17.33

The nominal power of the created systems was 1 MW. A generic "1,000 kWac central inverter" was used. Ground shading is the difference between irradiance reaching the agriculturally usable ground between solar rows and the total GHI. The formula for ground shading is as follows:

$$irradiance = \frac{\sum_{t=1}^{n}(GHI_{,t} - I_{ground,t})}{\sum_{t=1}^{n}(GHI_{,t})} \cdot 100\%, \quad (2)$$

where GHI is the global horizontal irradiance, t is the hour of the growing season in Southern Finland (27.04–17.10), and $I_{ground,t}$ is the irradiance at ground level at t.

The unused space around PV panel rows is 0.5 m on each side of the VBPV and SO panels. The ground shading of the tracker system was omitted due to program limitations. The effects of snow cover, which primarily affect SO systems, were omitted [17]. Due to snow being present during low irradiance months, the effect is limited, especially for vertical and tracker systems, as their tilt significantly reduces the likelihood of snow cover. All systems were created in a configuration of 19 rows of 40 × 2 panels.

The VBPV system is placed 1 m above ground level and consists of two horizontally situated solar panels, and 0.5 m of clearance space is left unused on each side of solar rows, resulting in 1 m of unused land per row (see Fig. 1).

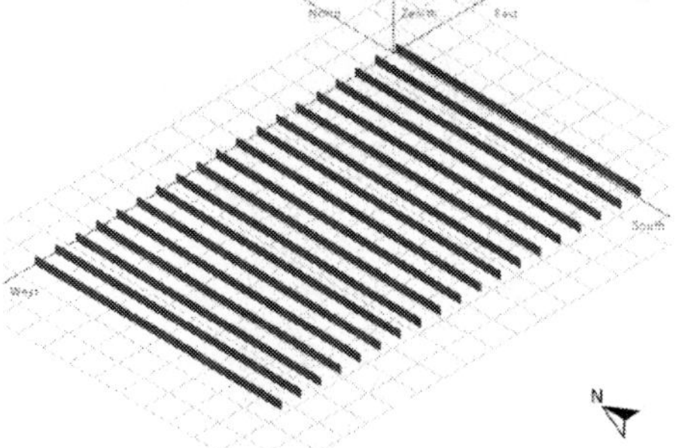

Figure 1: VBPV system (created with PVsyst®)

The tracker system was designed as a standing ground system raised 1 m above ground level (see Fig. 2).

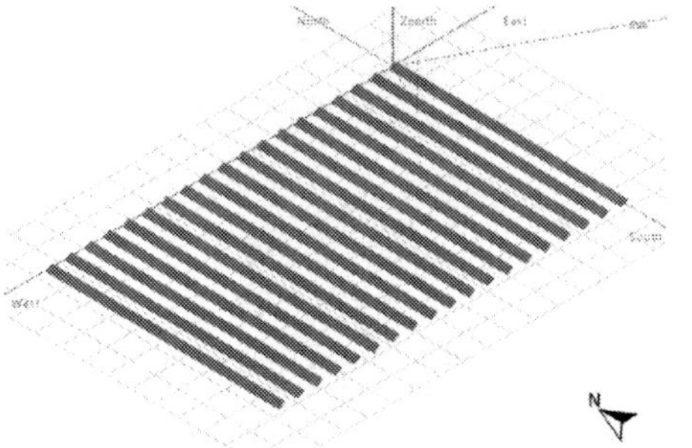

Figure 2: North-south axis bifacial tracker system (created with PVsyst®)

The SO system was designed as an overhead system placed 5 m above ground level to leave space for agricultural activity (see Fig. 3). To account for the large beams typically used in overhead systems, 0.5 m of unused space was left as clearance on each side.

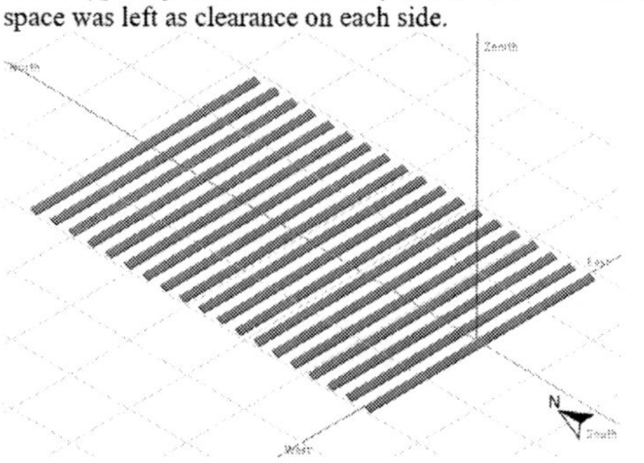

Figure 3: Bifacial south-facing overhead (SO) system (created with PVsyst®)

For each system, four different row separations (8, 10, 15 and 30 m), and for the ground shading three row separations (8, 10 and 15 m) were analyzed as large-scale farming equipment may necessitate significant clearance. The PV systems at a 30 m separation were assumed to be a case with minimal self-shading. In the case of very large farming vehicles, even over 20 m of clearance could be necessary; however, APV systems with such a scale are not currently utilized at high latitudes and thus were not taken into consideration. The 8 m separated variant occupied 14,112 m^2, the 10 m separated variant occupied 17,640 m^2, and the 15 m variant occupied 26,460 m^2.

3 RESULTS

Three types of PV systems were analyzed to compare their outputs, production times, value of produced electricity, and ground shading. A comparison of the average power production in each month of 2024 is shown in Fig. 4. The SO installation performed best at noon when electricity prices are typically lower. The tracker system performed well throughout the day and was characterized by the most consistent energy production as well as the highest performance overall. The VBPV system had two production peaks, one in the morning and one in the evening, which matches energy use peaks than the other systems[18].

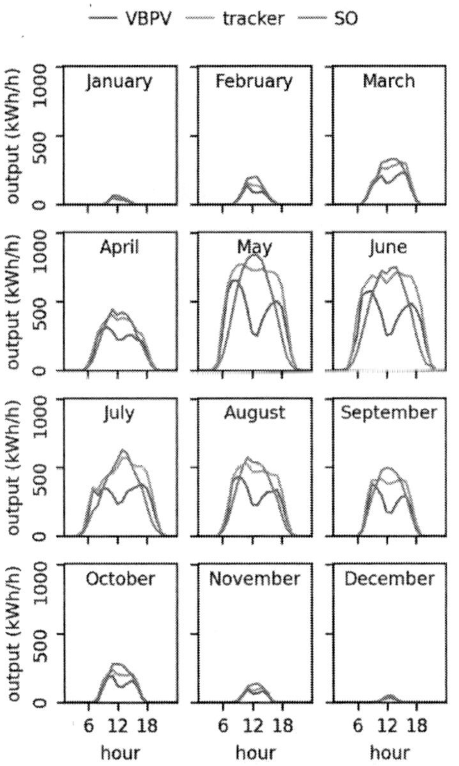

Figure 4: Average power production of the VBPV, SO, and tracker systems for each month in Turku, Finland in 2024 at a row distance of 15 m

The total energy production in 2024 for each system at 8, 10, 15 and 30 m separations is shown in Fig. 5. In all cases, increasing row separation in the analyzed range resulted in increased energy output. Tracker panels had the highest output in all cases. The SO systems outperformed the VBPV system at the analyzed row distances. However, the performance of the SO panels remained constant at above 10 m separation, and they received no further benefit from increasing row separation, while the VBPV system's output continued to increase.

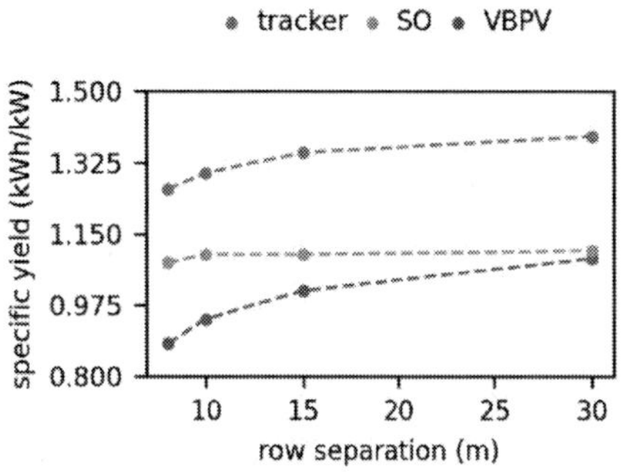

Figure 5: Specific yield of three agrivoltaic systems utilizing trackers, a VBPV configuration, and an SO installation in Finland in 2024

A comparison of the hourly energy output and spot price for selected summer days containing both sunny and cloudy conditions is shown in Fig. 6.

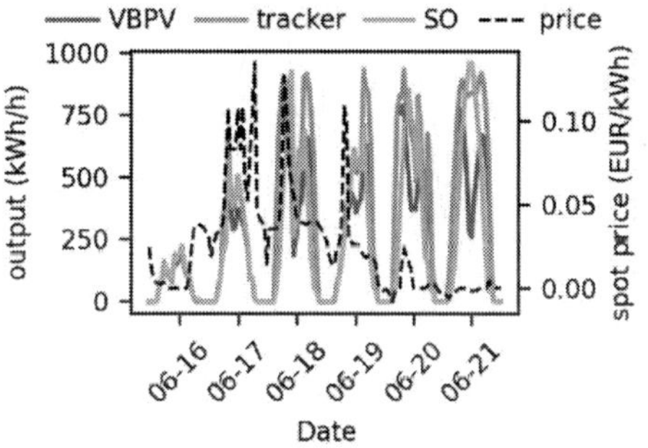

Figure 6: Output of the analyzed systems at a 15 m separation and spot price in 2024. Chosen days are summer days with both sunny and cloudy conditions as well as varied spot-price

The irradiance reaching the ground in the analyzed systems for row separations of 8, 10, and 15 m is depicted in Fig. 7. In the cases of both the VBPV and SO systems, the irradiance reaching the ground increased rapidly with increased row separation, which resulted in reduced crop impact. It is estimated that a roughly 25% reduction in irradiance reaching crops results in minor losses only [2]. The exact value depends on both the exact growth conditions and the crop; thus, the threshold is only a generalized estimate. At low row separations, VBPV allows more light to reach the ground, resulting in a lower crop impact than an SO system. At large row separations, shading from both types of systems is minimal and should have no significant impact on the crops.

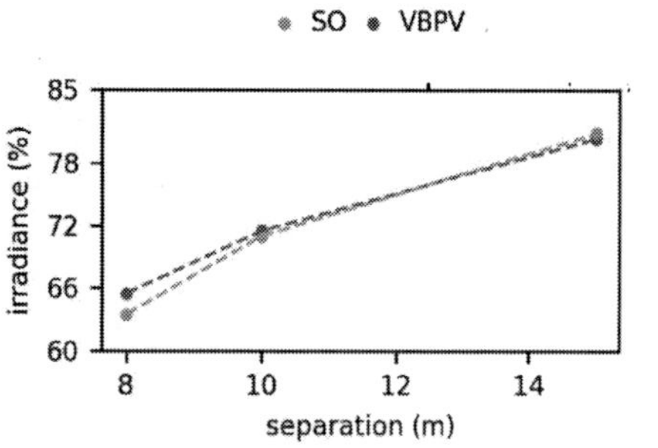

Figure 7: Irradiance reaching the ground for an SO system and a VBPV installation in Finland in 2024

The revenue and value of electricity based on the Nordpool spot price for each system are depicted in Fig. 8. Revenue increases with an increase in PV energy output. The tracker system had the highest revenue and energy yield per panel. Although the VBPV system had a higher revenue than the SO system at high row separations, at low separations, the SO system had a higher revenue. However, electricity prices from 2024 are still only affected by existing PV systems to a small degree due to a small number of PVs in the Finnish energy grid. In the future south facing PV systems will drive the electricity prices down, which can be seen in countries like Germany where PV adoption is much further ahead. By contrast, the value of the energy in the VBPV system was the highest due to the difference in price between different times of day and two-peak production profiles of the VBPV systems [4].

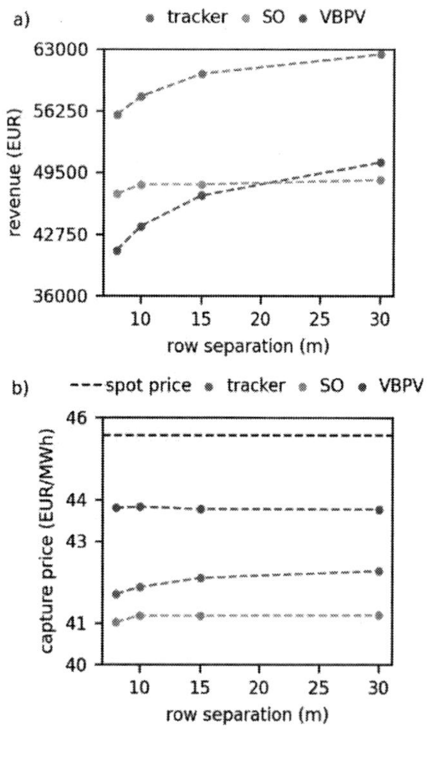

Figure 8: Graphs showing a) revenue (EUR) and b) capture price (EUR/MWh) for tracker, SO, and VBPV installations based on Nordpool spot prices for Finland in 2024

4 CONCLUSIONS

This study compared the performance of three types of high-latitude APV systems. All the systems had an equal number of bifacial panels to ensure comparability. The total yearly output based on meteorological data from 2024 was determined for VBPV, SO, and tracker systems at three row separations (8, 10, and 15 m) with an additional comparison of PV output of a 30 m separated system for an unshaded scenario. Ground shading for the SO and VBPV systems was comparable at larger row distances; however, at 8 m, the VBPV installation was favored because it shaded the ground less than the SO system, and a PV system's negative impact on crop yield is primarily due to shading. The tracker system had the highest production and revenue. Although the VBPV system notably had the highest value of electricity produced, in terms of output, it was outperformed by the tracker and SO systems.

While the VBPV system had the highest capture price per MWh, it only resulted in a higher revenue at very large row separation. The difference in revenue stemming from increased production in the case of the tracker and SO systems at this time outpaces the difference in capture price between the systems at lower row separations. However, as the share of solar energy in the energy market continues to grow, the value of electricity produced around noon is expected to drop further, which can put SO systems at a greater disadvantage, which would favor VBPV systems, which are expected to be less affected due to different peak production times matching demand and thus daily price peaks. Additionally, SO systems are the most vulnerable to snow cover during winter, when electricity prices are typically higher than in the summer months, which can further decrease the value of the electricity they produce. Note that, although these calculations omitted snow cover losses, vertical and tracker systems are less prone to snow cover, which gives them an advantage in snow-heavy regions.

Overhead and tracker systems are more expensive than VBPV systems; although, SO systems can also be installed directly on the ground, giving VBPV an advantage in the form of lower investment costs and increased resilience to the effects of the growing share of PV in the energy market. Based on 2024 prices, the VBPV systems require large row separation to result in higher revenue than an SO system due to their lower energy production. Designs that reduce self-shading can result in a higher specific yield, but the main draw of a vertical system remains its synergy in dual land-use scenarios. While the revenue from SO systems is likely to plummet in the future, which will favor vertical systems, the most valuable system type is still likely to be the one that produces energy at times when it can be self-consumed on site rather than sold.

ACKNOWLEDGMENTS

This project was funded by the Strategic Research Council established within the Research Council of Finland Decision No. 358542 (KM, SJ, MS, LK), Decision No. 359141 (SR), University of Turku Graduate School (LK) and the city of Salo and University of Turku HEMS-project (LK).

REFERENCES

[1] V. Olkkonen, A. Lind, E. Rosenberg, L. Kvalbein, "Electrification of the agricultural sector in Norway in an effort to phase out fossil fuel consumption," Energy 276 (2023) 127543, doi: 10.1016/J.ENERGY.2023.127543.

[2] "RENEWFM: EUR 27.5 million supporting 7 solar power plants in Finland - European Commission", [Online]. Available: https://cinea.ec.europa.eu/news-events/news/renewfm-eur-275-million-supporting-7-solar-power-plants-finland-2024-05-29_en.

[3] J. Viitanen, A. Amogpai, M. Puolakka, L. Halonen, "Photovoltaic production possibilities and its utilization in office buildings in Finland," Int. J. Eng. Appl. IREA 2 (2011), doi: 10.15866/irea.v7i1.17186.

[4] S. Jouttijärvi et al., "Sensitivity of electricity price in the Finnish market conditions with increasing solar energy production," doi: 10.4229/EUPVSEC2024/5DV.3.27.

[5] S. Jouttijärvi, G. Lobaccaro, A. Kamppinen, K. Miettunen, "Benefits of bifacial solar cells combined with low voltage power grids at high latitudes," Renew. Sustain. Energy Rev. 161 (2022) 112354–112354, doi: 10.1016/J.RSER.2022.112354.

[6] S. Völler, M.D. Sabatino, R.J. Randle-Boggis, G. Stokkan, "AgriPV in Norway: evaluating the initial performance and lessons learned," EU PVSEC (2024), doi: 10.4229/EUPVSEC2024/4DV.1.10.

[7] P.E. Campana et al., "Experimental results, integrated model validation, and economic aspects of agrivoltaic systems at northern latitudes," J. Clean. Prod. 437 (2024) 140235–140235, doi: 10.1016/J.JCLEPRO.2023.140235.

[8] A.K. Schneider et al., "Drawing transformation pathways for making use of joint effects of food and energy production with biodiversity agriphotovoltaics and electrified agricultural machinery," J. Environ. Manage. 335 (2023) 117539, doi: 10.1016/J.JENVMAN.2023.117539.

[9] P.E. Campana, B. Stridh, S. Amaducci, M. Colauzzi, "Optimisation of vertically mounted agrivoltaic systems," J. Clean. Prod. 325 (2021), doi: 10.1016/J.JCLEPRO.2021.129091.

[10] S. Touil, A. Richa, M. Fizir, B. Bingwa, "Shading effect of photovoltaic panels on horticulture crops production: a mini review," Rev. Environ. Sci. Biotechnol. 20, no. 2 (2021) 281–296, doi: 10.1007/S11157-021-09572-2/FIGURES/10.

[11] M. Szarek, S. Jouttijärvi, L. Karttunen, T. Hynnä, S. Ranta, K. Miettunen, "Performance evaluation of high-latitude agrivoltaic systems with vertically mounted bifacial panels.," under Review for Applied Energy (2025).

[12] S. Jouttijärvi, L. Karttunen, S. Ranta, K. Miettunen, "Techno-economic analysis on optimizing the value of photovoltaic electricity in a high-latitude location," Appl. Energy 361 (2024) 122924, doi: 10.1016/J.APENERGY.2024.122924.

[13] "CAMS solar radiation time-series", [Online]. Available: https://ads.atmosphere.copernicus.eu/datasets/cams-solar-radiation-timeseries?tab=overview.

[14] P. Sieber, S. Böhme, N. Ericsson, P.A. Hansson, "Albedo on cropland: field-scale effects of current agricultural practices in Northern Europe," Agric. For. Meteorol. 321 (2022) 108978, doi: 10.1016/J.AGRFORMET.2022.108978.

[15] "Nord Pool | Data Portal", [Online]. Available: https://data.nordpoolgroup.com/auction/day-ahead.

[16] "PVsyst – Photovoltaic software", [Online]. Available: https://www.pvsyst.com/.

[17] S. Tsuchida, Y. Tsuno, D. Sato, T. Oozeki, N. Yamada, "Power generation characteristics of vertical bifacial photovoltaic arrays in heavy snow regions," EPJ Photovolt. 15 (2024) 32, doi: 10.1051/EPJPV/2024029.

[18] A. Meriläinen, P. Puranen, A. Kosonen, J. Ahola, "Optimization of rooftop photovoltaic installations to maximize revenue in Finland based on customer class load profiles and simulated generation," Sol. Energy 240 (2022) 422–434, doi: 10.1016/J.SOLENER.2022.05.057.

PERFORMANCE ANALYSIS OF AGRIVOLTAIC SYSTEM CONFIGURATIONS IN NORDIC CONDITIONS

Magda Szarek[1*], Sami Jouttijärvi[1], Lauri Karttunen[1], Samuli Ranta[2], Kati Miettunen[1]
[1]Department of Mechanical and Materials Engineering, University of Turku, Vesilinnantie 5, 20500 Turku, Finland
[2]Turku University of Applied Sciences, Joukahaisenkatu 7, 20520 Turku, Finland
*email: magda.szarek@utu.fi

Our group

Tracker systems have the highest output, vertical systems have the highest energy value in high-latitudes

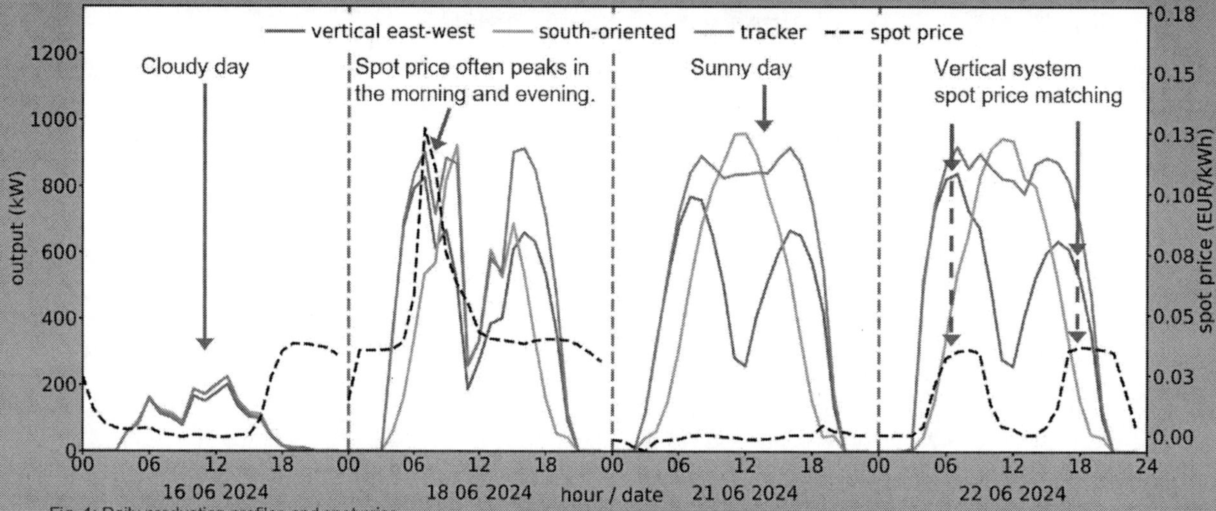

Fig. 1: Daily production profiles and spot price.

Aim and context

- **Comparing performance of three types of bifacial systems in high-latitude conditions in Turku, Finland.**
- Solar energy in the Nordics is developing rapidly, local energy market has a high fraction of renewables and high-latitude conditions.

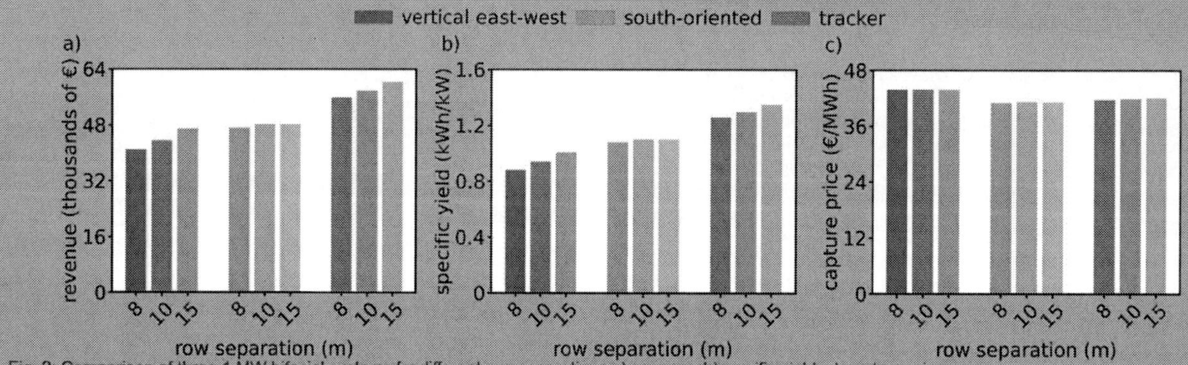

Fig. 2: Comparison of three 1 MW bifacial systems for different row separations a) revenue, b)specific yield, c) capture price.

Tracker systems
- Highest yield and revenue.
- Capture price is less sensitive to low spot prices at noon than south oriented panels.
- High system cost.

Vertical east-west systems
- Highest benefit from increased row distance.
- Resilient to low spot prices at noon.
- High capture price due to a better spot-price match [1].
- Lower output than other types.

South-oriented systems
- Higher yield and revenue than vertical for closely situated rows.
- Little benefit from increased row distance.
- Lowest capture price, expected to drop even further as the share of PV in the market grows [2].

References

[1] S. Jouttijärvi, L. Karttunen, S. Ranta, and K. Miettunen, "Techno-economic analysis on optimizing the value of photovoltaic electricity in a high-latitude location," Appl. Energy, vol. 361, p. 122924, May 2024
[2] S. Jouttijärvi et al., "SENSITIVITY OF ELECTRICITY PRICE IN THE FINNISH MARKET CONDITIONS WITH INCREASING SOLAR ENERGY PRODUCTION", 41st EU-PVSEC, Vienna (2024)

UNIVERSITY OF TURKU

strategicRESEARCH

020399-001

Acknowledgements

The work was funded by the Strategic Research Council Finland Decision No. 358542 (project RealSolar).

IRRADIANCE MANAGEMENT IN AGRIVOLTAIC SYSTEMS WITH VARYING DESIGNS ACROSS LATITUDES: TOWARD FINLAND'S FIRST SIGNIFICANT DEMONSTRATION

Shuo Wang[1*], Soroush Moradi Zavie Kord[2], Hugo E Huerta[1], Antti Lajunen[2], Samuli Ranta[1]
1. New Energy Research Group, Turku University of Applied Sciences, 20520 Turku, Finland
2. Department of Agricultural Sciences, University of Helsinki, 00790 Helsinki, Finland
*Corresponding author: shuo.wang@turkuamk.fi

ABSTRACT: This study performs irradiance management in AgriPV systems with varying design parameters to support the development of Finland's first significant AgriPV demonstration project. Using ray-tracing simulations at three locations with distinct latitudes, we analyzed annual solar insolation on PV modules and ground level. Within the azimuth-tilt iterations, maximum module insolation occurs with a southwest orientation, corresponding to minimal ground insolation. Due south orientation induces the strongest non-uniformity in ground irradiance. For more balanced distribution between PV modules and crops, a southeast-facing configuration is preferred. Height-GCR iterations show that increasing installation height or reducing GCR enhance both module and ground insolation. Height controls the shading extent beneath the mounting structure, whereas GCR modulates the spacing between shaded regions. Accordingly, two different optimization strategies can be suggested for overhead and vertical configurations. Overhead systems benefit primarily from optimizing installation height, enabling more uniform irradiance distribution under the PV modules, while vertical systems require low mounting height and tuned GCR to achieve shading-free areas between PV arrays. Latitude-dependent effects have also been identified. For overhead systems, higher latitudes allow lower installation heights to achieve a given ground uniformity, while for vertical systems, lower latitudes tolerate higher GCRs without sacrificing the uniformity.
Keywords: Agrivoltaics, irradiance management, vertical PV, overhead PV, high latitude

1 INTRODUCTION

Solar energy plays an important role in the transition to a sustainable energy system, reducing dependence on fossil fuels, and lowering CO_2 emissions in Finland. It requires innovative solutions to balance renewable energy production with land use efficiency. Agrivoltaics (AgriPV), which combines solar energy generation with agricultural activities, presents a promising approach to optimizing land use while supporting climate goals. Given Finland's high latitude, seasonal variations in solar irradiance, and challenging weather conditions, research on AgriPV is crucial to understanding its feasibility, productivity, and potential benefits for farmers and energy producers. One of the biggest challenges is to understand how the crops are influenced by the shading effect from PV modules and how to balance or optimize the irradiance distribution between crops and PV modules.

To address this challenge, several simulation models and methods have been proposed, such as decomposition models [1], transposition models [2], view-factor analysis [3], and ray-tracing techniques [4]. In this study, we investigated the irradiance distribution for both PV modules and crops in high-latitude AgriPV systems using ray-tracing modeling tools. The shading effects of PV modules at ground level were analyzed in detail under different system parameters. A comparison was also made between Helsinki, where the first significant AgriPV demonstration project in Finland is planned, and lower-latitude locations with different irradiance conditions. The findings will support the design of the upcoming demonstration project, with validation to follow once the system is operational.

2 METHODOLOGY

2.1 Pilot site and solar irradiance

The planned AgriPV pilot site is located in Viikki, Helsinki, Finland, covering an area of 3.5 hectares. It is adjacent to the Viikki campus of the University of Helsinki. Detailed onsite crop assessments will be conducted in the future. Two types of AgriPV configurations, overhead and vertical PV, will be implemented and tested on two approximately equal portions of the site, labeled Areas A and B in Figure 1, respectively. Area C will be maintained as a reference area without any PV arrays.

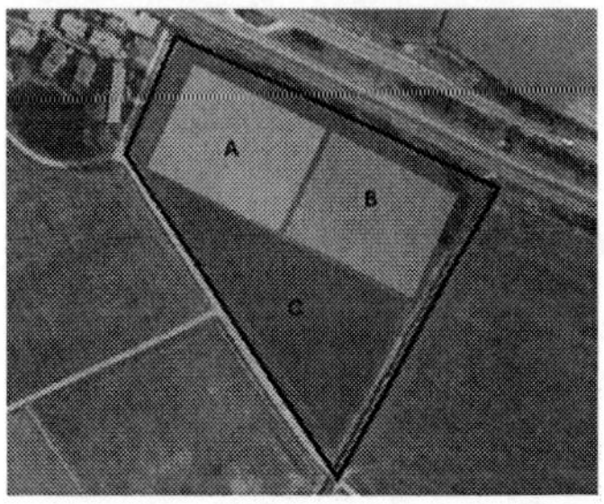

Figure 1: Satellite photo of the pilot site in planning in Viikki Helsinki. Area A and B are planned to host overhead and vertical PV arrays, respectively. Area C will be kept free of PV as a reference.

Solar irradiance data were obtained from the SARAH3 dataset via the PVGIS platform [5]. In addition to Helsinki (60.222° N, 25.026° E), the primary site for high-latitude analysis, this study considered two other locations: Murcia, Spain (37.917° N, 1.478° W), and Katibougou, Mali (12.501° N, 8.091° W). These lower-latitude sites provide a broad range for comparative analysis. AgriPV pilot systems have been established in these regions, offering opportunities to potentially validate the modeling results.

2.2 Irradiance modeling

The irradiance modeling was performed using the bifacial_radiance toolkit [6], which is a peer-reviewed open-source Python wrapper based on the ray-tracing software Radiance [7]. The tool was further developed to enable efficient irradiance sampling on both the surface of PV modules and ground level. With the solar irradiance as the input data, five rows of PV modules were created in the model with different system configurations. The irradiance on both sides of PV modules and at ground level was simulated within one run of simulation. Accumulative simulations were used for the annual insolation modelling. The key parameters and their default values used for modeling are summarized in Table 1. Azimuth is defined as the angle clockwise from north and Ground Covering Ratio (GCR) is calculated by dividing the array width by the row pitch.

Table 1: Key parameters and the default values for modeling

Item	Value	Item	Value
Azimuth	135°	Module length	2.38 m
Tilt	40°	Module width	1.3 m
Hub height	5 m	Row number	5
Pitch	15 m	Module per row	20×2
GCR	0.18	Ground albedo	0.2

2.3 Evaluation indicator

The irradiance harvested by PV modules is evaluated by the annual average solar insolation on both sides of the modules, $\bar{I}_m$.

$$\bar{I}_m = \frac{\sum_{i=1}^{M} I_{mi}}{M} \quad (1)$$

where I_{mi} is the sum of annual front- and back-side insolation on module i. M is the total number of PV modules in the simulation.

To illustrate the solar irradiance at ground level, Figure 2 (a) shows a heat map of annual ground insolation within the AgriPV system as described in Table 1. Shading from the PV modules reduces irradiance available for crop growth, with the worst-affected areas experiencing losses of up to about 25% in this case. The detailed profile along the central line can be found in Figure 2(b).

Peaks in ground insolation occur between the rows, while valleys can be observed near the PV module mounting positions. This variation is qualified using two indicators. $\bar{I}_{gn}$ evaluates the solar irradiance that is reserved for crops at ground level in AgriPV systems.

$$\bar{I}_{gn} = \frac{\sum_{i=1}^{N} I_{gi}}{N\, I_{gmax}} \quad (2)$$

where $\bar{I}_{gn}$ is defined as the average ground insolation over the central sampling positions, normalized to the maximum value of the sampling points I_{gmax} (the reference ground insolation clear of shading). I_{gi} is the annual insolation at ground position i. N is the total number of the sampling positions along the central line.

Another indicator σI_{gn} is used to evaluate the variation of irradiance at ground level over the central line as shown in Figure 2(a).

$$\sigma I_{gn} = \frac{1}{\bar{I}_g}\sqrt{\frac{\sum_{i=1}^{N}\left|I_{gi}-\bar{I}_g\right|^2}{N}} \quad (3)$$

where σI_{gn} is defined as the root mean square deviation (RMSE) of the annual ground insolation, normalized to the average value over the sampling positions. $\bar{I}_g$ is the average ground insolation over the central sampling positions without normalization.

With these indicators, the optimization of an AgriPV system aims to high $\bar{I}_m$, high $\bar{I}_{gn}$, and low σI_{gn}, though in practice a compromise between these factors is often required.

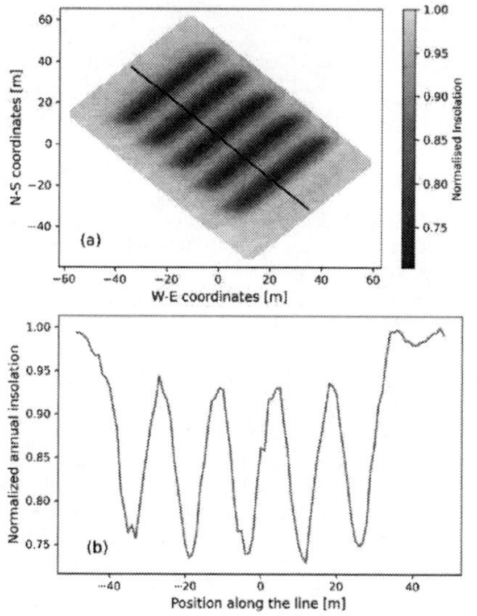

Figure 2: Exemplary results of annual ground-level insolation with the parameters as listed in Table 1. (a) heat map of the ground-level insolation normalized to the maximum, (b) normalized annual insolation profile along the central line as labeled in (a).

3 RESULTS

The AgriPV system was modeled by varying key parameters, including azimuth, tilt angle, GCR, and hub height of the PV arrays. Unless otherwise specified, the values listed in Table 1 were used for the simulations.

3.1 Azimuth – tilt angle evaluation

To determine the proper orientation of PV arrays, the influence of azimuth and tilt angle were investigated for Helsinki, as shown in Figure 3.

Figure 3 (a) shows the variation of $\bar{I}_m$ for different azimuth and tilt combinations, normalized to the maximum value within the investigated range to highlight deviations from the locally optimized. The optimization for module irradiance occurs at an azimuth of 225° (southwest) and a tilt of 50°. Correspondingly, as more sunlight is captured by the PV modules, the minimal ground irradiance for crops is observed at this configuration, with about 15% of solar energy lost compared to the unshaded reference, as shown in Figure 3(b). Figure 3(c) indicates that the highest ground irradiance variation (σI_{gn}) occurs at an azimuth of 180° (due south), suggesting that south-facing modules produce the most non-uniform ground irradiance, potentially leading to the greatest deviation in crop quality.

Simulations for the other two locations with lower latitudes produced results similar to those for Helsinki. AgriPV system optimization can vary depending on objectives, such as maximizing profit, solar generation, or crop yield. In this study, to achieve a more balanced irradiance between PV modules and crops and minimize the nonuniformity of ground irradiance, an azimuth of 135° and a tilt angle of 40° were selected for the overhead

10.4229/EUPVSEC2025/4DV.1.11

AgriPV system in the following simulations. For the vertical AgriPV system, the same azimuth of 135° was used, with the tilt angle fixed at 90°.

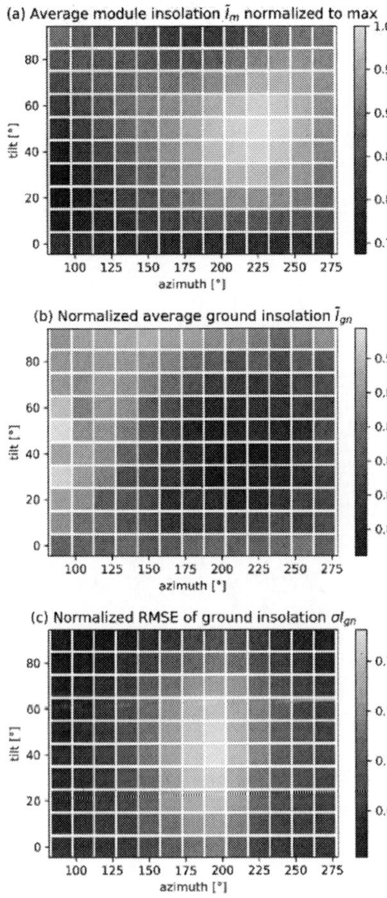

Figure 3: Evaluation of the three indicators with different combinations of the azimuth and tilt angle of the PV arrays. (a) average annual insolation on PV modules $\bar{I}_m$ normalized to the maximum value within the investigated range, (b) normalized average annual insolation at ground level $\bar{I}_{gn}$, and (c) normalized RMSE of ground-level insolation σI_{gn}.

3.2 GCR – hub height evaluation

Figure 4 illustrates the influence of GCR and hub height on the evaluation indicators. The results show that lower GCR consistently improves system performance, yielding higher $\bar{I}_m$, higher $\bar{I}_{gn}$, and lower σI_{gn}. A similar, though less pronounced, improvement is observed with increasing hub height.

However, note that in practice these parameters need to be balanced with installation constraints. Low GCR reduces land-use efficiency, while high hub height increases structural costs. Therefore, the ground irradiance distribution is further analyzed under varying GCR and hub height.

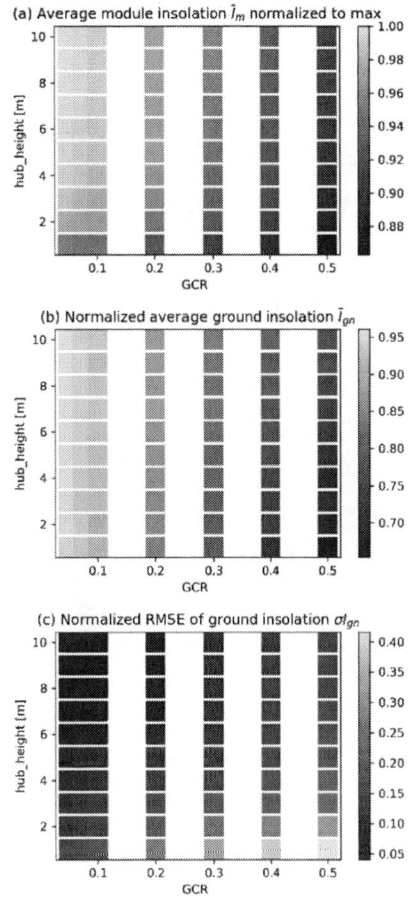

Figure 4: Evaluation of the three indicators with different combinations of the hub height and GCR of the PV arrays. (a) average annual insolation on PV modules $\bar{I}_m$ normalized to the maximum value within the investigated range, (b) normalized average annual insolation at ground level $\bar{I}_{gn}$, and (c) normalized RMSE of ground-level insolation σI_{gn}.

3.2.1 Effect of hub height on ground-level irradiance profile

The annual ground insolation along the central line was simulated for varying hub heights in both overhead and vertical systems. In overhead systems, as shown in Figure 5(a), the area between PV rows can clearly be identified as shaded and unshaded zones at low hub heights. Shading is confined to a narrow band near the module mounting position, with irradiance reduced to about 20% of the reference value, while the unshaded areas retain insolation comparable to the reference. As hub height increases, the shaded zone broadens, but irradiance within it also improves. Beyond 7 m hub height in this case, the ground insolation becomes nearly uniform, with no clear distinction between shaded and unshaded areas, averaging the insolation around 80% of the reference value.

The vertical system, shown in Figure 5(b), exhibits similar trends with increasing hub height as the overhead system. However, at low heights the contrast between

10.4229/EUPVSEC2025/4DV.1.11

shaded and unshaded areas is less pronounced, and irradiance losses in shaded zones are significantly smaller than in the overhead configuration.

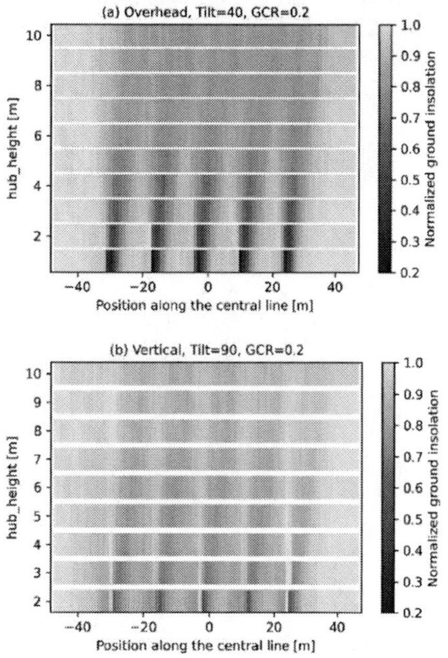

Figure 5: Detailed ground-level insolation profiles along the central line of systems with varying hub height of PV arrays. (a) overhead system with tilt angle of 40° and GCR of 0.2, (b) vertical system (tilt angle of 90°) and GCR of 0.2.

3.2.2 Effect of GCR on ground-level irradiance profile

The influence of GCR on ground irradiance profile is similar for both system types, as shown in Figure 6. At high GCR, the row spacing is small, causing extensive shading under the PV array. As GCR decreases, unshaded areas emerge between the PV rows, with annual insolation approaching that of the reference area, while confining shaded areas near the module rows.

3.3 Optimization strategies for different types of systems

Based on these observations, different optimization strategies can be suggested for different AgriPV system configurations.

For overhead systems, the supporting structure must be sufficiently high to allow agricultural activities beneath, with optimization favored on achieving uniform ground irradiance across the area. This makes hub height the critical parameter, while GCR remains relatively flexible. For example, Figure 7(a) shows the annual ground-level insolation profile at a hub height of 8 m and GCR of 0.2. In this case, ground insolation remains within 80-100% of the reference across the entire area, ensuring uniform crop quality and yield. Such conditions are suitable for crops requiring slightly less irradiance than open-field reference.

For vertical systems, agricultural activities are arranged between PV module rows, requiring a relatively low GCR. In this configuration, optimization could aim to confine shading close to the module rows, which necessitates a low hub height. At the same time, an appropriate GCR ensures that the inter-row space remains largely free from shading. Figure 7(b) illustrates such a case with a hub height of 2 m and GCR of 0.1. Here, areas receiving less than 80% of the reference insolation are restricted to within ±2 m of the mounting position, while the remaining space maintains sufficient irradiance, with most of it completely free from shading. This case is particularly suitable for crops sensitive to irradiance.

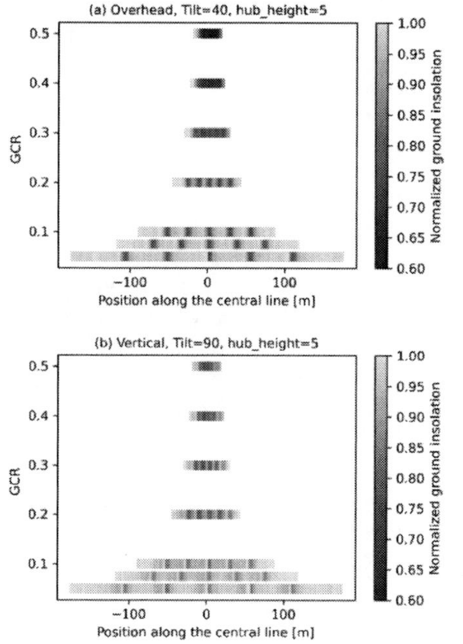

Figure 6: Detailed ground-level insolation profiles along the central line of systems with varying GCR of PV arrays. (a) overhead system with tilt angle of 40° and hub height of 5 m, (b) vertical system (tilt angle of 90°) and hub height of 5 m.

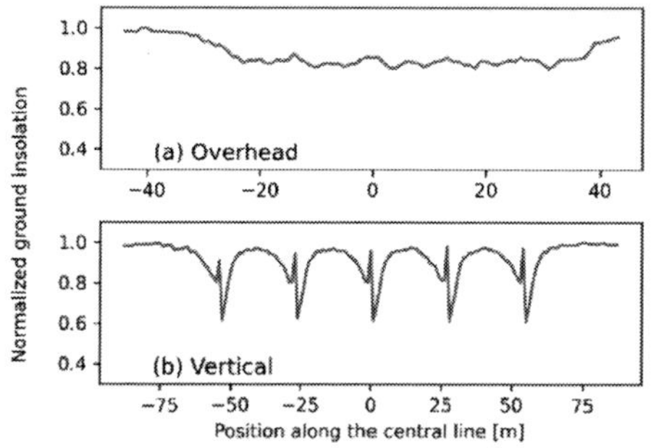

Figure 7: Ground-level insolation profile along the central line optimized following different strategies for (a) overhead system with hub height of 8m and GCR of 0.2, (b) vertical system with hub height of 2m and GCR of 0.1.

3.4 Comparison of different locations

Since the low latitude location usually has better solar radiation than the high latitude area for PV production, the comparison on absolute PV generation among different locations is not critical. The discussion in this section focuses on the influence of various locations on ground-level irradiance distribution.

As demonstrated in the previous sections, hub height is the critical parameter in the overhead system. To minimize the influence of PV shading on crops and achieve balance between energy production and crop yield, one needs to find compromise among ground irradiance, agricultural requirements and construction costs. Low height is preferred if it ensures good ground irradiance distribution to save costs. Figure 8 (a) and (b) show the influence of hub height on the $\bar{I}_{gn}$ and σI_{gn} in different locations. The low latitude locations show higher $\bar{I}_{gn}$ in the investigated range of hub height. However, high-latitude areas achieve lower σI_{gn} at relatively modest hub heights, indicating more uniform ground irradiance with less structural height.

The investigation on GCR in vertical systems is shown in Figure 9. Low-latitude locations outperform high latitudes again in terms of $\bar{I}_{gn}$. At the same GCR, they also exhibit lower σI_{gn}, demonstrating both higher ground irradiance and greater uniformity.

These findings can be explained by differences in solar position across latitudes. At high latitudes, the lower solar elevation enables sunlight to reach beneath overhead arrays more effectively, reducing ground irradiance variation. At low latitudes, the higher solar elevation keeps shading closer to the modules, producing more uniform ground irradiance.

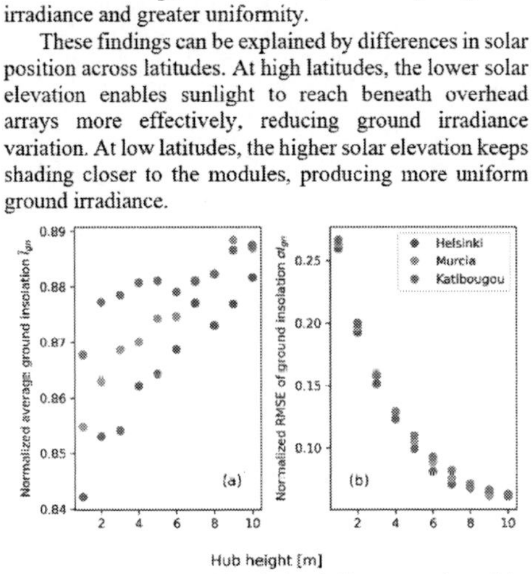

Figure 8: Ground-level insolation indicators evaluated for overhead systems with varying hub heights across different locations. (a) normalized average annual insolation at ground level $\bar{I}_{gn}$, and (b) normalized RMSE of ground-level insolation σI_{gn}.

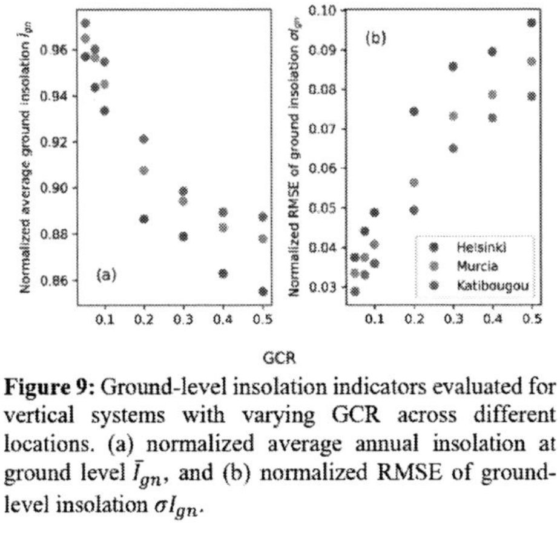

Figure 9: Ground-level insolation indicators evaluated for vertical systems with varying GCR across different locations. (a) normalized average annual insolation at ground level $\bar{I}_{gn}$, and (b) normalized RMSE of ground-level insolation σI_{gn}.

4 CONCLUSION

In this work, we performed irradiance management in AgriPV systems with varying design parameters, providing guidance for the design of the first significant AgriPV demonstration system in Finland. Using ray-tracing simulations at three locations with different latitudes, we analyzed the distribution of annual solar insolation on both PV modules for power generation and ground for crop growth.

From the azimuth-tilt iteration, we identify a trade-off between module and ground insolation. Maximum module insolation is achieved with a southwest azimuth and a tilt angle of around 50°, which corresponds to minimal ground insolation. However, the greatest non-uniformity in ground insolation does not occur under this configuration, but instead with a due south orientation. A southeast-facing configuration emerges as a compromise, offering a more balanced distribution between PV modules and crops.

From the height-GCR iteration, we find that higher installation heights and lower GCRs increase insolation for both modules and ground. However, their effects on ground irradiance distribution differ. Height determines the breadth of shading area beneath the mounting position, while GCR modulates the spacing between adjacent shaded zones. The findings suggest two different optimization strategies for overhead and vertical configurations. For overhead systems, optimizing the installation height is more critical for achieving uniform insolation beneath the modules. For vertical systems, a low mounting height is essential to confine the shading area near the installation point. At the same time, optimizing the GCR is crucial to obtain shading-free zones between adjacent PV arrays.

Finally, comparison among the three locations reveals latitude-dependent effects. Low-latitude location offers higher average ground insolation in all cases. However, the uniformity of ground insolation varies by system type. For overhead systems, higher latitudes allow lower installation heights to achieve a given uniformity, while for vertical systems, lower latitudes tolerate higher GCRs without sacrificing the uniformity.

ACKNOWLEDGEMENTS

The work is funded by the Strategic Research Council (SRC) established within the Research Council of Finland under project RealSolar 359141, and European Regional Development Fund (ERDF) under the project Aurinkoenergiapelto A81526.

REFERENCES

[1] Y. Elamri, B. Cheviron, A. Mange, C. Dejean, F. Liron, and G. Belaud, "Rain concentration and sheltering effect of solar panels on cultivated plots," Hydrology and Earth System Sciences, vol. 22, no. 2, pp. 1285–1298, Feb. 2018, doi: 10.5194/hess-22-1285-2018.

[2] P. E. Campana, B. Stridh, S. Amaducci, and M. Colauzzi, "Optimisation of vertically mounted agrivoltaic systems," Journal of Cleaner Production, vol. 325, Nov. 2021, doi: 10.1016/j.jclepro.2021.129091.

[3] P. E. Campana et al., "Solar irradiance distribution under vertically mounted agrivoltaic systems-Model development, validation, and applications for microclimate assessment," EarthArXiv, 2022. doi: 10.31223/X5G07D
[4] O. A. Katsikogiannis, H. Ziar, and O. Isabella, "Integration of bifacial photovoltaics in agrivoltaic systems: A synergistic design approach," Applied Energy, vol. 309, Mar. 2022, doi: 10.1016/j.apenergy.2021.118475.
[5] "Photovoltaic Geographical Information System." Accessed: Sep. 17, 2025. [Online]. Available: https://re.jrc.ec.europa.eu/pvg_tools/en/
[6] S. Ayala Pelaez and C. Deline, "bifacial_radiance: a python package for modeling bifacial solar photovoltaic systems," Journal of Open Source Software, vol. 5, no. 50, p. 1865, Jun. 2020, doi: 10.21105/joss.01865.
[7] G. J. Ward, "The RADIANCE Lighting Simulation and Rendering System," in 21st Annual Conference on Computer Graphics and Interactive Techniques, 1994, pp. 459–472. doi: 10.1145/192161.192286.

IRRADIANCE MANAGEMENT IN AGRIVOLTAIC SYSTEMS WITH VARYING DESIGNS ACROSS LATITUDES:

TOWARD FINLAND'S FIRST SIGNIFICANT DEMONSTRATION

TURKU AMK

HELSINGIN YLIOPISTO

Shuo Wang[1*], Soroush Moradi Zavie Kord[2], Hugo E Huerta[1], Antti Lajunen[2], Samuli Ranta[1]

1. New Energy Research Group, Turku University of Applied Sciences, 20520 Turku, Finland
2. Department of Agricultural Sciences, University of Helsinki, 00790 Helsinki, Finland

Contact: shuo.wang@turkuamk.fi

Objective

- Perform irradiance management for bifacial AgriPV systems using ray-tracing modeling
- Various system design parameters
- Different latitude locations
- Provide design guidance for demo site

Methodology

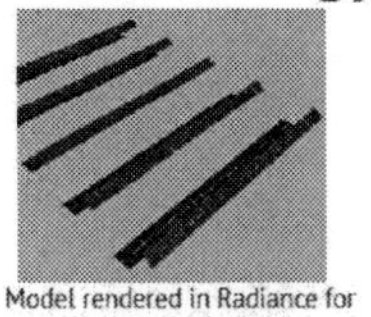

Model rendered in Radiance for ray-tracing modelling

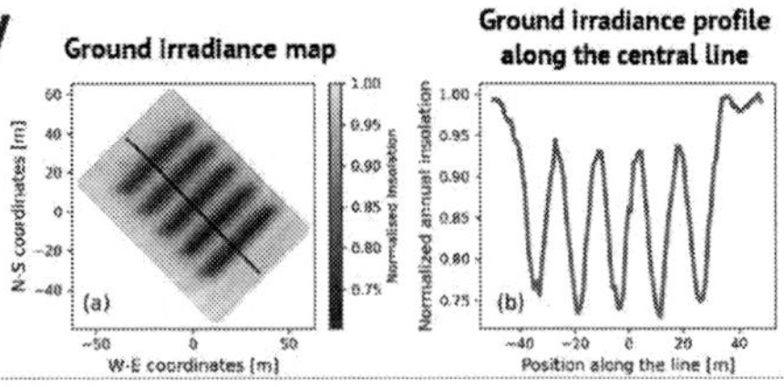

Evaluation Indicators

(a) Average PV insolation

$$\bar{I}_m = \frac{\sum_{i=1}^{M} I_{mi}}{M}$$

(b) Average ground insolation

$$\bar{I}_{gn} = \frac{\sum_{i=1}^{N} I_{gi}}{N\, I_{gmax}}$$

(c) RMSE of Ground insolation

$$\sigma I_{gn} = \frac{1}{\bar{I}_g}\sqrt{\frac{\sum_{i=1}^{N}\left|I_{gi}-\bar{I}_g\right|^2}{N}}$$

Azimuth – Tilt

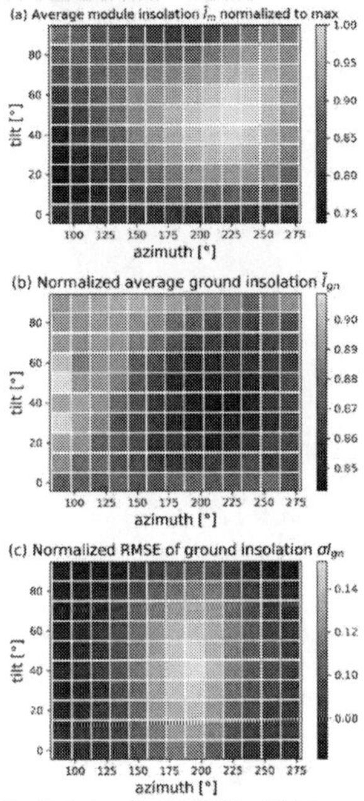

Southeast → Better PV-Crop Balance & Lower Ground RMSE

GCR – Hub height

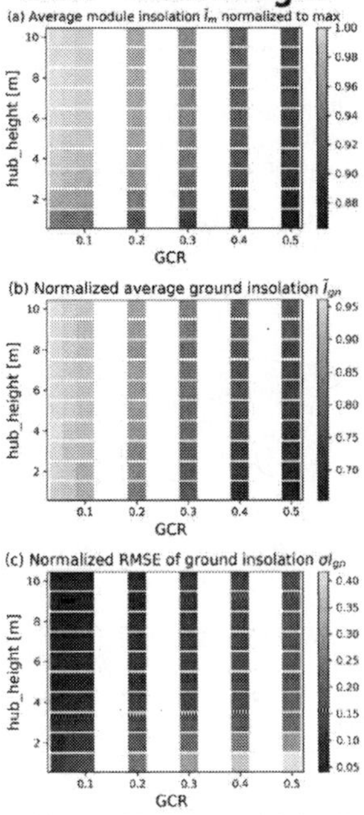

↑Height, ↓GCR → Better Performance

Detailed ground-level irradiance profile

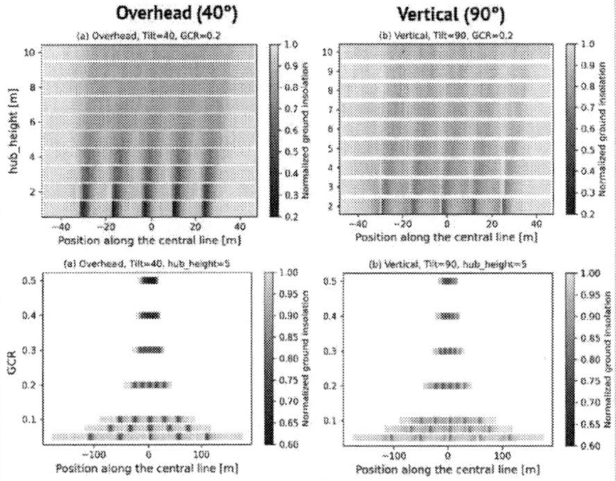

Different optimization strategies: critical parameter

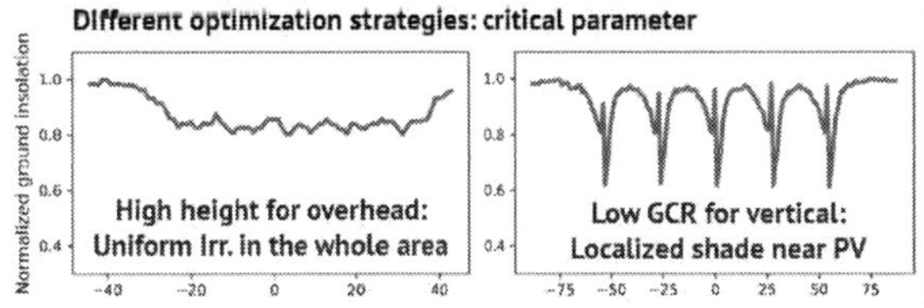

Different latitude locations

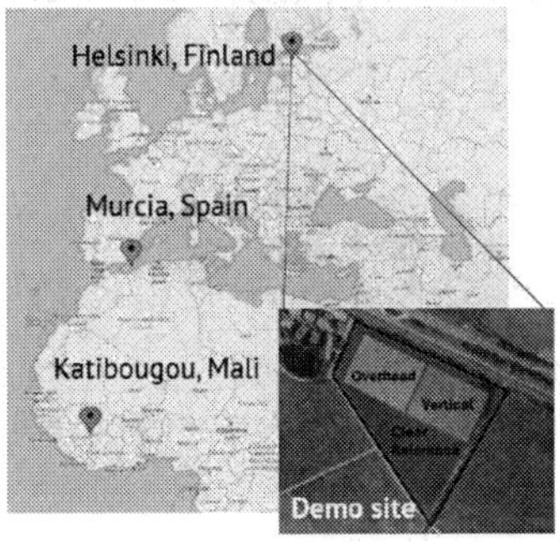

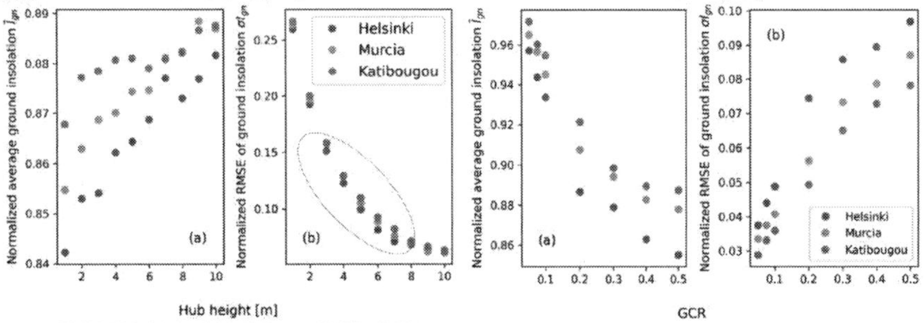

High latitude: lower height needed for better ground irradiance uniformity

Low Latitude: better in both indicators

Conclusion

- Panels facing southeast help with the irradiance balance between PV and crops, as well as the ground irradiance uniformity
- Considering the ground irradiance, different strategies for GCR-hub height optimization for overhead and vertical system: hub height for overhead system and GCR for vertical system are more critical for the optimization
- High latitudes favor overhead systems, where lower height is sufficient for uniform ground irradiance, while low latitudes favor vertical systems, providing higher ground irradiance with more uniform distribution.

RealSolar

Aurinkoenergiapelto

Euroopan unionin osarahoittama

Elinkeino-, liikenne- ja ympäristökeskus

Acknowledgement

The work is funded by the Strategic Research Council (SRC) established within the Research Council of Finland under project RealSolar 358141, and European Regional Development Fund (ERDF) under the project Aurinkoenergiapelto A81526.

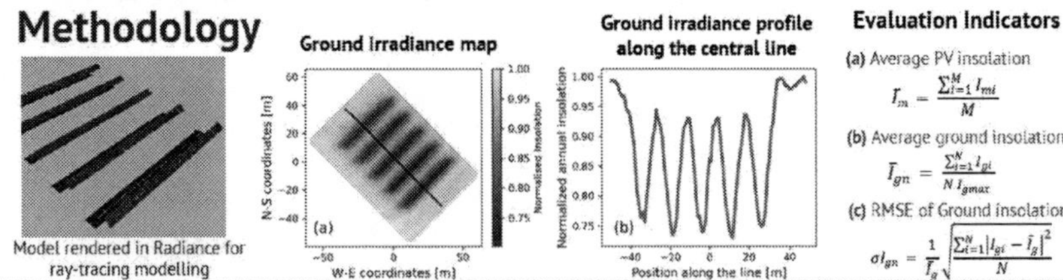

AN INNOVATIVE AGRIVOLTAIC SYSTEM FOR DESERT CLIMATES WITH ANTI-SOILING, IRRADIANCE CONTROL, AND WATER MANAGEMENT

Sagarika Kumar[1], Min Hsian Saw[1], Ahmed Shaaban[1], Kamil Jaworczak[1], Nursulu Kuzhagaliyeva[1], Carlos G. Parrilla[2], Francois M. Tsombou[2], Fouad Lamghari[2], and Mauro Pravettoni[1]
[1]Technology Innovation Institute, Renewable and Sustainable Energy Research Centre, Abu Dhabi, UAE
[2]Fujairah Research Centre, Fujairah, UAE
Sagarika.Kumar@tii.ae

ABSTRACT: The need to balance renewable energy generation and sustainable agriculture in arid regions is of global interest, due to water scarcity in many regions, and intensified heat by climate change. Conventional agrivoltaic (agri-PV) systems fall short under desert conditions. GROOViD (Green, Robust & Optically-Optimised agriVoltaics in Deserts) was conceived to overcome some of these limits by integrating conventional solar tracking with dual-use water systems for irrigation and module cleaning. The aim is to reduce water demand, enhance solar efficiency, and protect crops, supporting the UAE's Food Security 2051, Water Security 2036, and Net Zero 2050 goals while creating a scalable model for desert agriculture. In this paper, the authors focus on the concept of the GROOViD solution, introducing the methodology, and presenting the performance and preliminary reliability findings after the first 6 months of operation. They also present a quantitative analysis of the shading benefit to the photosynthetically active radiation (PAR) and to the crops evapotranspiration. They finally show the advantages of the combined cleaning-irrigation system in terms of antisoiling.
Keywords: agrivoltaics, climate change, arid regions, antisoiling, tracking systems

1 INTRODUCTION

The increasing global demand for renewable energy and sustainable food production has intensified the competition for land resources, particularly in arid and semi-arid regions. Climate change further exacerbates these challenges, driving higher temperatures, more frequent extreme weather events [1], and severe water scarcity. Conventional agrivoltaic (agri-PV) systems, originally designed for temperate climates, often fail to deliver optimal performance under desert conditions [2], where high irradiance, dust accumulation (soiling), and limited freshwater availability constrain both solar and agricultural outputs. In the United Arab Emirates (UAE), these challenges are critical, given the country's reliance on food imports and limited arable land [3]. National initiatives such as the Food Security Strategy 2051, the Water Security Strategy 2036, and the Net Zero by 2050 commitment highlight the need for innovative, climate-resilient solutions.

The GROOViD project (an acronym for Green, Robust and Optically-Optimised agriVoltaics in Deserts) was conceived to address this gap by combining advanced photovoltaic (PV) technologies with smart agricultural practices. The system integrates the PV energy production of bifacial modules on single-axis trackers with crop shading and a dual-use water system for irrigation and PV cleaning, and complimentary water generation via atmospheric water harvesting (AWH). This holistic approach aims at reducing water consumption, improving crop resilience, and sustaining solar efficiency in extreme desert environments.

This paper presents the first results from the prototype deployed at Masdar City in Abu Dhabi, UAE. The efficacy of the system against soiling is illustrated, comparing the performance of GROOViD modules with that of modules exposed to natural soiling. The study also illustrates the benefit of the prototype in terms of reduced crop evapotranspiration, and a preliminary analysis of few reliability indicators, thus providing a basis for scaling up the system in rural and agricultural settings.

2 THE GROOVID PROJECT

2.1 The prototype at Masdar City

The GROOViD prototype (Fig. 1) was designed to test an integrated agri-PV system optimized for desert conditions. The small-scale prototype consists of four bifacial *n*-type TOPCon PV modules (144 M10 half-cut cells, with nominal 570 W and >80% bifaciality, see Tab. I) mounted on a single-axis tracker, operating within an angular range of −60° to 60° over the day with a GPS-time-based control system. The modules are installed in 2-P (portrait, 2×2 modules) configuration.

Figure 1: The GROOViD prototype at Masdar City, Abu Dhabi.

Table I: Technical specifications of the tested modules.

Parameter	Tech. Spec.	Tech. drawing
Cell type	TOPCon	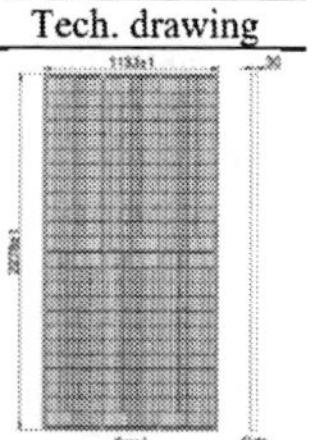
Cell size [mm]	182 (M10), half-cut	
Cell number	144	
Dimensions [mm]	2278×1113	
Weight [kg]	30	
Bifaciality [%]	>80	
P_{max} [W]	570	
δ [%/K]	−0.30	

10.4229/EUPVSEC2025/4DV.1.12

A dual-use water distribution system was implemented, serving both crop irrigation and module cleaning. In parallel, a condensation-based AWH unit was integrated to supplement irrigation in water-scarce conditions.

In the 2.28 kWp system, modules have been divided into two pairs, labelled as:

- AA02 and AA03 (east side of the tracker), uncleaned (benchmark);
- AA04 and AA05 (west side), with GROOViD integrated cleaning and irrigation system.

The system also incorporates light diffusing panels to protect the crops from direct irradiance, thus creating a microclimate with reduced evapotranspiration and heat stress while ensuring adequate photosynthetically active radiation (PAR). Crops tested included mint and basil, selected for shade tolerance and relevance to UAE agriculture.

Irradiance and temperature sensors for PV yield analysis; thermistor probes and infrared (IR) thermometers to monitor the crop evapotranspiration (ET_C); a volume meter for measurements of water-use efficiency; a 4-quadrant bipolar power supply for current-voltage (IV) characterization of the PV modules; IR thermography to detect hotspots; and UV fluorescence imaging for early signs of encapsulant degradation form the comprehensive monitoring system of the testbed.

2.2 Operating principle

Fig. 2 illustrates the operating principle of GROOViD.

During the day (Fig. 2a), the single-axis solar tracker follows the sun, allowing the system to maximize solar power generation while simultaneously protecting the crops from direct irradiance in most of the time, while a portion of the directly sunlight only occasionally enters the crops area to enhance photosynthesis.

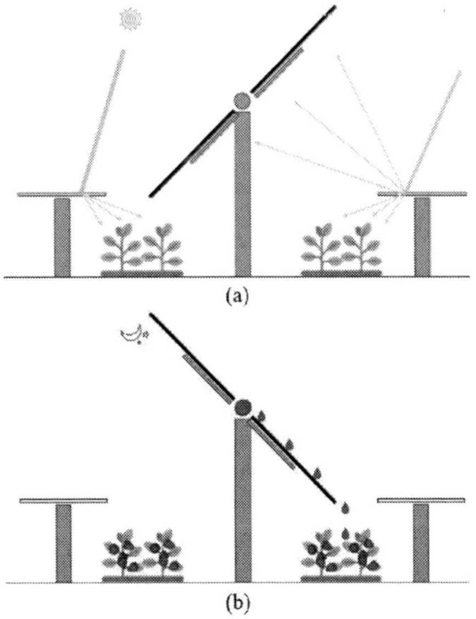

Figure 2: Concept diagrams of: (a) day and (b) night operations.

A system of white diffusers positioned to the east and west side of the installation enhances albedo, thus helping to improve solar power generation. Overall, the shading effect reduces crop heat stress and water evaporation, lowering evapotranspiration rates (see section 4). The design ensures that plants receive sufficient photosynthetically active radiation (PAR) for healthy growth, while the PV system delivers enhanced albedo-driven energy yield.

At night (Fig. 2b), the tracker repositions the modules first to stow, then to east, while a battery-powered system pumps water through the irrigation system on the top of the module and in axis with the tracker: the system serves both irrigation of crops and cleaning of PV modules. This process ensures uniform water distribution across the agricultural rows while removing accumulated dust and soiling from the panels, which is a major performance concern in desert regions. In addition, the integration of AWH provides a supplementary water source, reducing water consumption in water-scarce areas.

3 ELECTRICAL AND CLEANING PERFORMANCE

3.1 Electrical measurement setup

IV measurements of the PV modules were performed with a 4-quadrant programmable bipolar power supply by Kepco (BOP-ME 1000W).

Plane-of-array, GHI irradiance and albedo was monitored by EKO MS-80SH Class A pyranometers (response time: <0.5 s; 285-3000 nm responsivity; <0.7% calibration uncertainty).

Module temperature was recorded at the centre, at the sides and at the corner of the testing module by Pt100 probes sticked at the rear side. An offset temperature of 5 °C was derived from measured temperature and cell temperature, based on IR thermographic imaging measurements.

No spectral correction was performed on measurements that were always performed at approximately AM1.5 conditions and in clear-sky. No irradiance correction was performed; temperature correction was performed based on the nameplate relative temperature coefficient for maximum power, reported in Tab. I.

3.2 Results

The four PV modules were measured at various tilt angles, corresponding to various in-plane irradiances from 700 to 1100 W/m^2. IV measurements were performed after installation. After a pre-conditioning period of about 1 month, modules were deeply cleaned and remeasured; successively, modules were remeasured 1, 4, 5 and 6 weeks after cleaning, respectively.

Maximum power (P_{max}, in W), temperature corrected to 25 °C, are reported in Fig. 3 as a function of the plane-of-array irradiance G_{POA} (in W/m^2): T-corrected P_{max} measurements of the two benchmark modules AA02 and AA03 are reported in Fig. 3a and 3b, respectively; the performance of the GROOViD-treated modules AA04 and AA05 are shown in Fig. 3c and 3d, respectively. The charts show also the isolines corresponding to a module efficiency η_{mod} of 12%, 17% and 22% respectively.

Fig. 4 summarises the module efficiency trend: data at each measurement condition are distributed in box-and-whiskers and plotted as a function of time.

10.4229/EUPVSEC2025/4DV.1.12

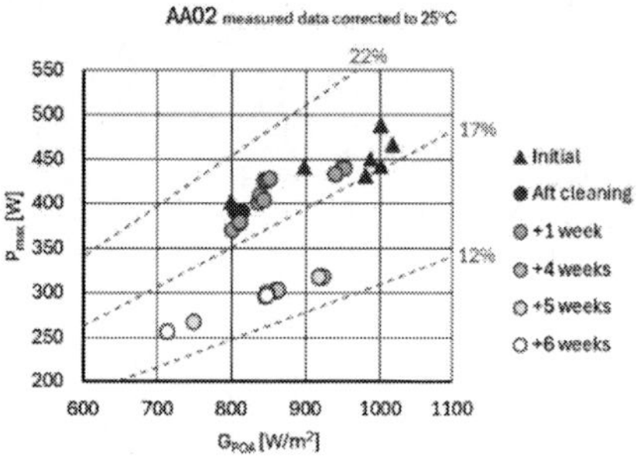

(a)

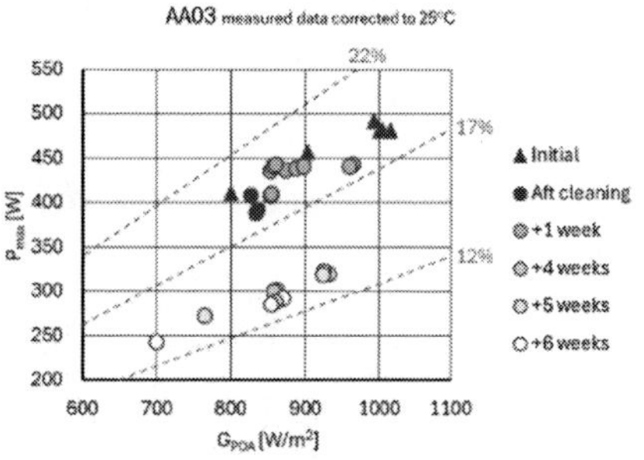

(b)

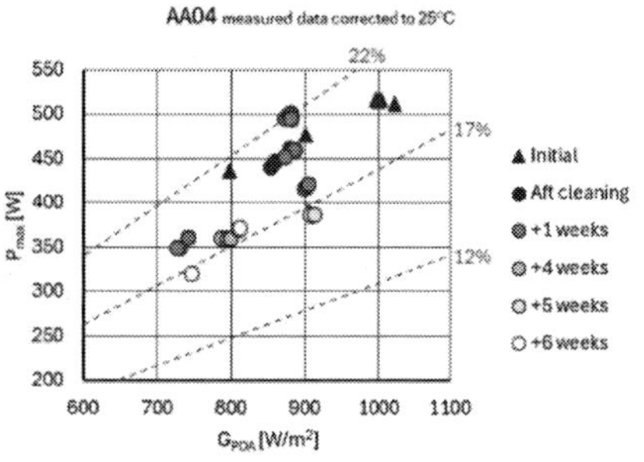

(c)

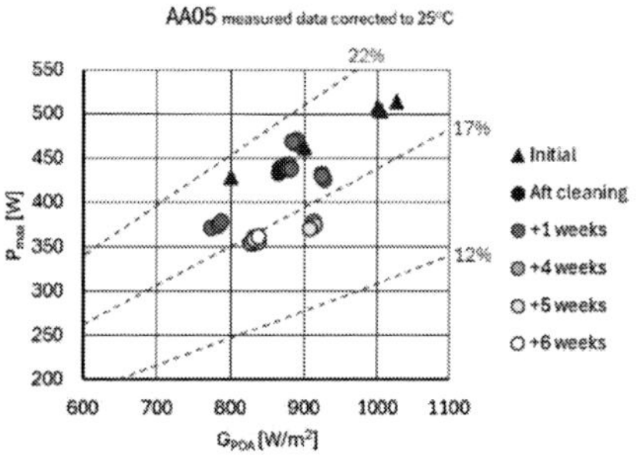

(d)

Figure 3: Electrical performance of the benchmark modules: (a) AA02, and (b) AA03; and of the GROOViD treated modules: (c) AA04 and (d) AA05. Maximum power (P_{max}) data have been corrected to 25 °C and plotted as a function of the plane-of-array irradiance G_{POA}. Measurements were performed after installation (dark-coloured triangles), after cleaning (dark-coloured circles) and 1, 4, 5 and 6 weeks after cleaning, respectively (lighter-coloured circles).

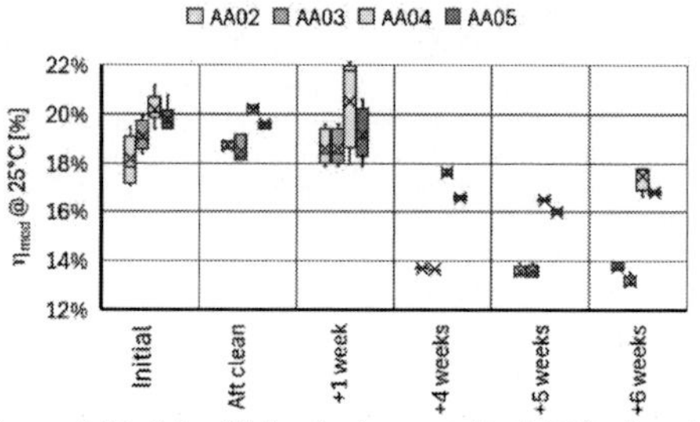

Figure 4: Module efficiencies (corrected to 25 °C), plotted as a function of time for benchmark modules (AA02 and AA03) and for GROOViD-treated modules (AA04 and AA05).

3.3 Discussion

The measurement results shows that the initial performance of modules AA02 and AA03 (benchmark modules not connected to the GROOViD cleaning and irrigation system, Fig. 3a and 3b, respectively) lay in an efficiency range 17-20%: considering measurement uncertainty and the module technology this is broadly consistent with the nameplate efficiency. After the first week of exposure, no significant reduction in P_{max} was observed. By week 4 and until week 6, however, the temperature-corrected P_{max} points felt in the 12-14% efficiency region, indicating substantial power losses due to soiling accumulation, primarily dust and organic deposits, which are known to be severe in desert environments.

Modules AA04 and AA05 (Fig. 3c and 3d, respectively) showed initial performance in line with modules AA02 and AA03. However, maintained under the GROOViD cleaning-irrigation solution, they sustained efficiencies in the 16-18% module efficiency range, confirming that the integrated cleaning and irrigation solution is functional to ensure stable, long-term operation of solar arrays in the desert environments.

4 EVAPOTRANSPIRATION AND CROP HEALTH MONITORING

4.1 Crop selection and measurement approach

Basil and mint were selected for the GROOViD prototype as shade-tolerant, fast-growing, and water-sensitive crops, making them ideal indicators of microclimate effects in agri-PV systems. Their moderately high commercial value in the UAE, combined with measurable responses in evapotranspiration and yield stability, makes them excellent pilot crops for evaluating GROOViD's dual benefits in desert farming.

The crop evapotranspiration value ET_C was estimated using the FAO-56 Penman-Monteith equation [4], which incorporates temperature, wind speed, humidity, and solar radiation to derive a reference evapotranspiration ET_0, which later was corrected to ET_C with a crop-specific correction factor.

Site-specific climatic data were used to simulate the effect of different shading levels – with direct irradiance reduction from 10% to 100%. Measurements of spectral irradiance were used for the solar irradiation input in an unshaded scenario and in the shaded case of GROOViD system. These measurements and simulations were crucial in predicting water needs for the crops under varying levels of solar exposure.

Fig. 5 shows the results for the calculated ET_C (in mm/d, equivalent to l/m^2/d) for mint (Fig. 5a) and basil (Fig. 5b) in 4 crop growing phases: initial, development, mid-season and late season. The cases of 100% (unshaded) irradiance, 25% irradiance (partial shading) and GROOViD measured data (indicated by stars) are shown.

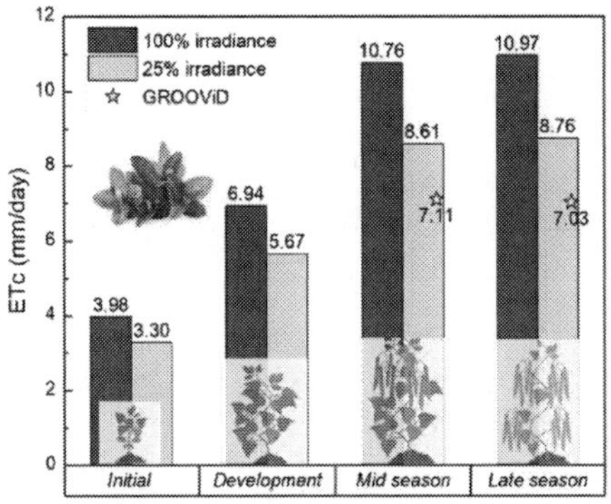

(a)

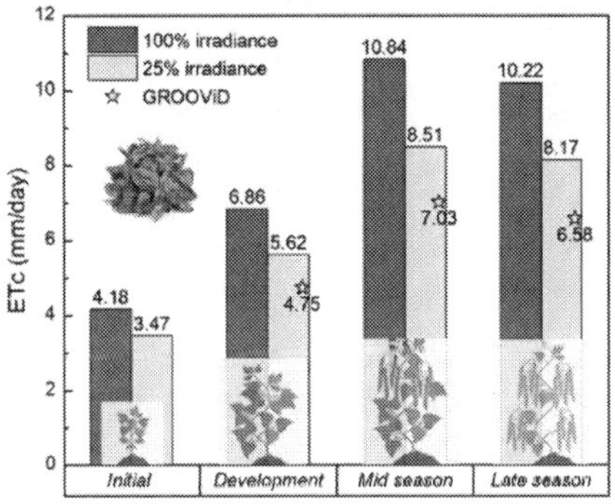

(b)

Figure 5: Crop evapotranspiration for: (a) mint, and (b) basil. Shown data (in mm/d) are based on site-specific climatic data, with 100% and 25% irradiance, and with the directly measured irradiance under GROOViD system.

4.2 Results

GROOViD shaded irradiance generates ~30% decrease in crop evapotranspiration ET_C down to about 7 mm/day in the mid and late seasons for the two case studies (mint and basil). The microclimate created by the GROOViD solution has been confirmed by observed crop resilience during the hottest season, as presented by M. H. Saw et al. in [5].

5 PRELIMINARY RELIABILITY RESULTS

5.1 Visual inspection

The 4 modules have been regularly inspected during the first 6 weeks of monitoring after cleaning. Tab. II shows the visual aspect of the modules in the various phases.

The visual inspection of benchmark modules AA02 and AA03 highlighted significant soiling accumulation, both sand dust and bird droppings, more evident after week four. These deposits reduced optical transmission and contributed to efficiency losses over time, as observed in section 3 above.

Table II: Visual inspection of the 4 tested modules: after cleaning, and after 1, 4 and 6 weeks, respectively.

	Aft cleaning	+1 w	+4 w	+6 w
AA02 AA03 AA04 AA05	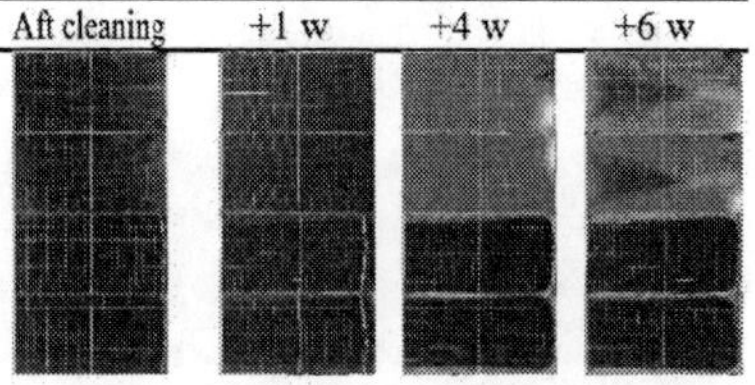			

After 6 weeks of exposure, the repeated accumulation and subsequent wash-off of morning dew resulted in a distinct arrow-shaped deposition pattern on benchmark modules AA02 and AA03.

In contrast, GROOViD-treated modules AA04 and AA05, leveraging on the integrated cleaning-irrigation system, showed consistent reduction of soiling, which sustained the higher and more stable performance highlighted in section 3. Evidence of non-uniform cleaning can be observed in AA04 and AA05, due to the non-optimised position of water sprinklers: this has left stains of dirt particularly accumulated to the long sides of the modules that increased the risk of hot-spot.

5.2 IR thermography

Tab. III shows IR thermography imaging after 6 weeks of exposure. Measurements were performed at 900 ± 100 W/m^2 plane-of-array irradiance and with the testing module kept in short-circuit conditions for 5 minutes.

Table III: Visual inspection of the 4 tested modules: after cleaning, and after 1, 4 and 6 weeks, respectively.

	+6 weeks
Benchmark GROOViD	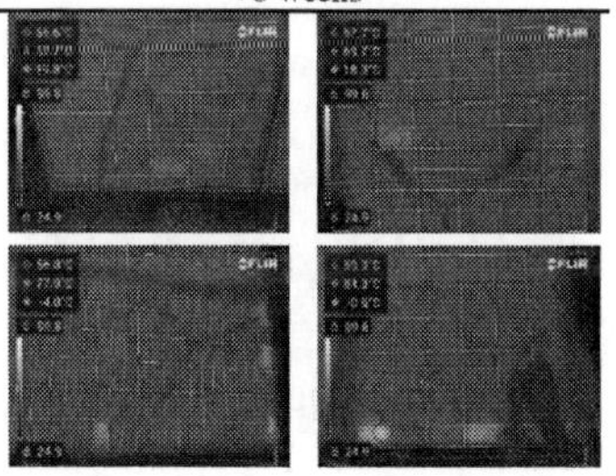

The benchmark modules AA02 and AA03 presented mild hot-spot findings, with up to +12 °C deviations between the coldest and the hottest area in the modules. GROOViD modules AA04 and AA05, instead, presented more distinct hot spots in correspondence to the partial shading areas caused by non-uniform cleaning. In this case, the deviations between the coldest and the hottest areas in the modules raised to +25 °C, with hottest areas in the range of 80-90 °C. Hot spots caused by non-uniform cleaning require more attention in the future development of GROOViD solution.

5.3 UV fluorescence imaging

UV fluorescence imaging highlighted organic soiling deposits and bird droppings (Fig. 6a) and fluorescent streaks along cell edges in the shortest side of the modules, with no significant difference between the modules treated with GROOViD irrigation-cleaning system and the benchmark modules. This may indicate an early EVA encapsulant degradation, exacerbated by UV exposure and extreme heat. Oxygen and moisture ingress, likely enhanced by thermomechanical stresses, are under investigation as possible causes.

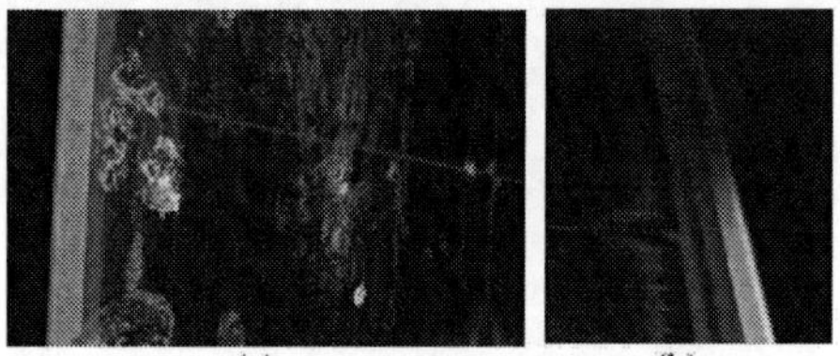

(a) (b)

Figure 6: UV fluorescence imaging: (a) organic deposits and bird drops; (b) fluorescence streaks along cell edges.

6 FUTURE WORKS

A 4-times scaled-up GROOViD pilot system is under development in collaboration with the Fujairah Research Centre at its Honey Park in Dibba, Fujairah (UAE), with a nominal capacity of 9.12 kWp . The system will consist of sixteen bifacial TOPCon modules of Tab. I, arranged in one string, extending the design of the Masdar City prototype, with diffuser and water management systems that are scaled up based on insights gained from observations and measurements conducted at Masdar City.

7 CONCLUSIONS

GROOViD project demonstrates that agri-PV can be effectively adapted to desert conditions by integrating PV tracking, dual-use of water management, and optimized shading. Results showed reduced evapotranspiration with improved crop health, and stable power performance of the solar modules against soiling. This integrated approach can support the UAE's food, water, and energy security strategies, while offering a scalable model for arid regions worldwide. Future work will focus on improved cleaning uniformity, the pilot expansion in Fujairah, and long-term reliability studies, reinforcing GROOViD's role as a climate-resilient solution for sustainable agriculture in arid regions.

REFERENCES

[1] S. Kumar, M. H. Saw, S. L. Heng, A. Sinha, S. W. Leow, L. Wang, M. Pravettoni, Proceedings of the 52nd IEEE Photovoltaic Specialist Conference (PVSC), (2024) 1487-1492.

[2] B. Adothu, S. Kumar, J. J. John, G. Oreski, G. Mathiak, B. Jäckel, V. Alberts, J. Bin Jahangir, M. A. Alam, R. Gottschalg Prog. Photovolt: Res. Appl., 32(8) (2024) 495-527.

[3] US-UAE Business Council, "The U.A.E.'s Food Security Vision: Innovation, Investment, and Partnerships", policy reports (2024).

[4] R. G. Allen, L. S. Pereira, D. Raes, M. Smith, Crop evapotranspiration - Guidelines for computing crop water requirements, FAO Irrigation and drainage paper 56 (1998).

[5] M. H. Saw, S. Kumar, S. Singh, C. G. Parrilla, F. Lamghari, M. Pravettoni, Proceedings of the Agrivoltaics World Conference (2025).

10.4229/EUPVSEC2025/4DV.1.12

REVIEW OF SENSOR TECHNOLOGIES FOR MONITORING AGRIVOLTAIC SYSTEMS

Sara Pereira[1], José A. Silva[1], Luís Fialho[2], Pedro Horta[1]
[1]Applied Research in Solar Energy for the Energy Transition (SOL4R), University of Évora, Polo da Mitra da Universidade de Évora, Edificio Ário Lobo de Azevedo, 7000-083 Nossa Senhora de Tourega, Portugal.
[2]Eurac Research-Institute for Renewable Energy, 39100 Bolzano, Italy

ABSTRACT: Agrivoltaics (AgriPV) co-locates photovoltaic generation with crops, coupling microclimate, plant physiology and power conversion. This paper assembles an empirical baseline of current monitoring practice via a systematic review of 123 experimental studies (2014–2024). It presents what is measured across meteorological, energy-performance and agricultural domains, how measurements are acquired (manual, automated, hybrid), and how research themes co-occur. The literature shows a higher volume of papers addressing agronomic/environmental effects, frequently studied alongside system integration/design and energy performance. Meteorological sensing is most prevalent (102 papers), followed by energy-performance (53) and agricultural variables (41). Acquisition is predominantly hybrid: 65.0% combine automated logging (weather/power) with targeted plant measurements; 21.1% are automated-only; 13.8% manual-only. Documentation gaps cluster in operational metadata, such as maintenance/durability, power supply/autonomy, data transmission and calibration/accuracy. Where PAR/PPFD is explicitly measured or robustly derived and co-reported with module temperature and inverter telemetry on a shared time base, studies can trace causal chains from forcing to conversion and crop response, enabling quantitative, design-relevant comparisons. By consolidating what AgriPV studies actually measure and pinpointing concise, high-impact co-measurements and reporting items (timekeeping, calibration, placement, power/telemetry), this review provides the practical foundation for portable, cross-site synthesis and supports emerging data-driven analysis and control in AgriPV.
Keywords: agrivoltaics, sensors, monitoring, microclimate, soil

1 INTRODUCTION

The rapid expansion of photovoltaic (PV) capacity is intensifying pressure on land, particularly where food production and energy security are both strategic priorities. Agrivoltaics (AgriPV), which is the co-location of PV generation and crop cultivation, offers a path to dual productivity per unit area and has been repeatedly proposed as a land-sharing solution with agronomic and energetic co-benefits [1], [2]. By altering the radiation field, wind exposure, and surface energy balance, AgriPV structures can moderate heat and water stress and create distinctive microclimates that influence canopy function and soil–plant water fluxes. Evidence spans greenhouse and open-field contexts: spatial photosynthetic photon flux density (PPFD) mapping under PV roofs quantifies light gradients that guide planting geometry and crop placement [3], while instrumented open-field pilots couple plane-of-array or global irradiance, air temperature/humidity and power telemetry to link microclimate with energy conversion in situ [4]. Crop responses are system and species dependent. Multi-crop field studies document both neutral and beneficial outcomes for shade-tolerant vegetables under moderate coverage and more stringent thresholds for cereals [5].

The measurement challenge is therefore central to AgriPV research and practice. Physiological monitoring in perennial systems has demonstrated how shading alters leaf temperature and gas exchange, reinforcing the need to synchronize plant with meteorological data [6]. Sensor-rich tomato deployments show how coordinated monitoring of atmosphere, soil and canopy enables mechanistic interpretation of yield and quality outcomes [7]. Beyond agronomy, optical and spectral design choices can produce hydrological co-benefits, plot-scale experiments report measurable reductions in surface evaporation under tailored PV/glazing configurations [8]. At the water–energy–food nexus, integrated pilots highlight how harmonized data collection supports operational control and policy-relevant assessment [9].

In this work we assemble and organize the experimental AgriPV literature into an empirical baseline of current monitoring practice, mapping which variables are measured across meteorological, energy-performance and agricultural domains, how they are acquired and documented, and highlighting concise, high-impact reporting items and co-measurements that make studies portable across crops, layouts and climates enabling for researchers and practitioners to move from isolated case studies to reproducible, design-relevant synthesis and, in turn, to more credible evidence for AgriPV deployment and management.

2 METHODOLOGY

This study follows a systematic review protocol tailored to experimental AgriPV research. The objective was to map how sensors are used to monitor meteorological conditions, agricultural variables, and energy-performance metrics in AgriPV deployments, and to assess the degree of automation, time synchronization, and reporting completeness.

2.1 Literature selection

Scientific papers were extracted from Scopus, Google Scholar, and IEEE Xplore using keyword combinations such as "agrivoltaics", "monitoring", "sensors", "soil", "IoT", "case study" and "pilot" published from 2014 to 2024. Only peer-reviewed conference and journal papers published in English and explicitly describing AgriPV systems with identifiable sensor-based monitoring were considered. Purely simulation-based or review papers, and studies lacking experimental data were excluded. Records were deduplicated, screened by title/abstract, and full texts assessed for eligibility. 123 studies met the criteria and were retained for analysis.

2.2 Data extraction and classification

Studies were systematically examined using a structured data extraction protocol. For each publication, metadata and descriptive information when available were compiled into a database, including research questions addressed, system characteristics, deployment scale, sensor categories, automation and control mechanisms, sensor accuracy and calibration methods, IoT and machine learning use, sensor power supply details, data collection and transmission details, frequency and duration of data collection, as well as maintenance and durability aspects of the monitoring system.

Monitoring variables were systematically classified into three key categories: meteorological, energy performance, and agricultural monitoring. Particular care was taken to distinguish between fully automated sensor-based monitoring and manual field data collection, with the latter categorized separately to maintain consistency. Information was only included when explicitly mentioned in the source document.

Each paper was tagged against six research questions: RQ1—meteorological impacts on PV shading; RQ2—energy generation performance; RQ3—AgriPV impacts on environment or agriculture; RQ4— the roles of digital and automated technologies (IoT/control/ML); RQ5—economic and policy considerations; RQ6— system integration and design strategies. Papers could map to multiple RQs.

Given the heterogeneity of systems and metrics, this classification methodology was designed to allow for cross-study comparison and to highlight both the technological heterogeneity and reporting gaps in AgriPV monitoring research.

3 RESULTS AND DISCUSSION

The systematic literature review analyzed 123 peer-reviewed studies on AgriPV, with a specific focus on monitoring systems.

3.1 Thematic focus of AgriPV Studies

The reviewed AgriPV studies span a broad range of research objectives. As shown in Fig. 1, RQ3 (the impacts of AgriPV on the environment and agriculture) appears in 105 papers, followed by 87 for RQ6 (system integration/design) and 63 for RQ2 (energy performance), while RQ1 (impacts of meteorological factors on PV), RQ4 (digital/automation) and RQ5 (economics/policy) are comparatively less represented. Studies frequently straddle multiple RQs (Fig. 2): the most common pairing is RQ3 + RQ6 (31 papers), reflecting the tight coupling between crop outcomes and design/layout choices, and a substantial number of RQ2 + RQ3 + RQ6 (17 papers) mirrors the need to evaluate energy yield, agronomy and geometry together.

The emphasis on RQ3 is evident in field and greenhouse experiments that quantify how partial shading modulates microclimate and plant function, often linking soil moisture dynamics, gas exchange and biomass or quality metrics. Rice studies explore yield responses across coverage regimes and altered light fields, highlighting threshold behavior and the need for crop-specific photosynthetically active radiation (PAR) targets [10]. In greenhouses, tomato experiments track microclimate and plant performance under PV roofing, demonstrating how localized radiation and humidity patterns translate into physiology and quality traits [11]. These investigations place measurement at the center of interpretation: without time-synchronized meteorological and plant data, it is difficult to distinguish beneficial microclimate control from unintended stress.

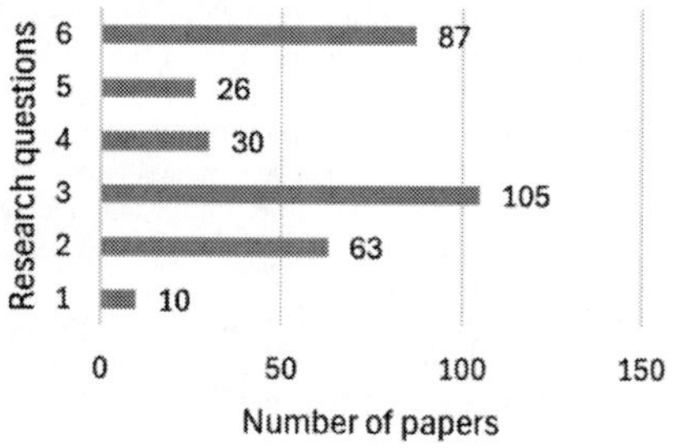

Figure 1: Number of papers addressing each research question.

Under RQ6, researchers increasingly treat layout as a control knob. Algorithmic approaches for semi-transparent or patterned PV optimize shading geometry and spectral transmission to stabilize plant light regimes through the season, connecting optical design with agronomic targets [12]. This design lens extends into open fields, where geometry (row spacing, tilt, vertical vs tilted) is treated as part of an agronomic–energetic trade-off, with instrumentation used to capture wind shelter, shade dynamics and their implications for both plants and power (the latter often appearing under RQ2) [13].

Energy performance (RQ2) in AgriPV is typically assessed through inverter telemetry coupled with module temperature and irradiance proxies, either in situ or inferred for the plane-of-array. Studies that co-report agricultural outputs and AC generation are particularly informative because they expose the simultaneity of benefits and trade-offs—e.g., rice–PV configurations that quantify electricity production alongside yield stability under different layouts [14].

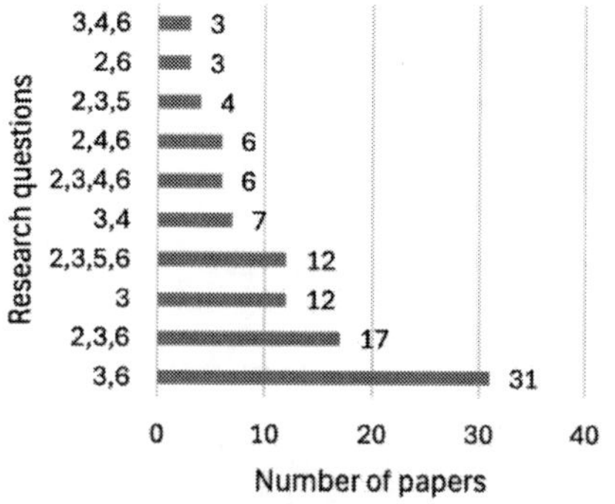

Figure 2: Most frequent combinations of research questions addressed in individual papers.

10.4229/EUPVSEC2025/4DV.1.15

Digital and automated technologies (RQ4) are emerging. IoT-based fertigation platforms demonstrate how soil-moisture-driven control loops and low-power telemetry can stabilize water status while creating reproducible data streams for agronomic analysis, but such implementations remain the exception rather than the rule [15]. Finally, RQ5 (economics/policy) appears in techno-economic assessments that relate module transparency/coverage and crop response to levelized metrics and payback, providing a first link between sensor-evidenced agronomy and investment logic [16].

Taken together, the pattern in Fig. 1–2 suggests a maturing field that already recognizes the need to co-measure energy, environment and crop physiology.

3.2 Categories of sensors

Across literature, meteorological monitoring dominates (Fig. 3) with 102 studies reporting meteorological variables, typically global or plane-of-array irradiance and PAR/PPFD, air temperature and humidity, wind and precipitation. Open-field pilots that log plane-of-array irradiance alongside air temperature and humidity provide the basic scaffold for linking microclimate to agronomy and power, typically with dataloggers appropriate for long-term deployments [4]. Where geometry itself is the treatment, multi-station layouts capture gradients in wind, radiation components and PAR across vertical versus tilted arrays, enabling design-level inference [13].

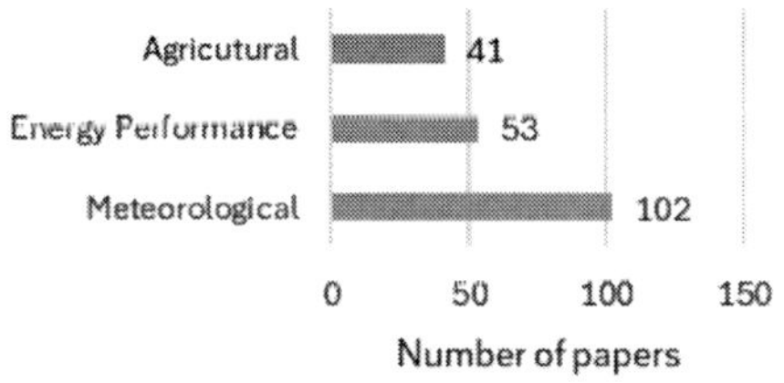

Figure 3: Number of papers with automated sensors by monitoring category.

Energy-performance sensing appears in 53 papers and most often comprises inverter telemetry coupled with back-of-module temperature, with occasional string-level current/voltage or I–V traces for detailed diagnostics. Greenhouse-integrated studies often access AC output through manufacturer platforms, which are helpful for continuity even when internal climate is sparsely documented [17]. Studies that time-align the electrical stream with radiation and temperature offer clearer attribution of transient behavior (e.g., cloud-edge events), a practice increasingly visible in geometry-comparison pilots that record power at short intervals [13] and in field trials where PV–crop co-location is evaluated with concurrent weather logging [4].

Papers using automated agricultural sensors are the fewest in number (41 papers) yet they ultimately validate AgriPV's agronomic value. The most common variables are soil moisture and temperature at depth, soil pH/EC/NPK, and leaf or canopy indicators such as chlorophyll indices or NDVI. Where physiological mechanisms matter, campaigns with portable gas-exchange (e.g., LI-6400) are used to connect microclimate to photosynthesis and stomatal control, generally layered onto the automated weather baseline [7]. Chlorophyll-a fluorescence is also applied to track photo-physiological status in crop-specific contexts (e.g., tomatoes or cereals), tying light regime and plant performance to yield and quality outcomes [11], [14]. Greenhouse and semi-transparent configurations, in particular, show how spectral control reshapes plant light budgets and physiology, underscoring the need to report sensor placement and heights relative to canopy [11], [18].

Acquisition modes mirror field reality (Fig. 4): 65.0% of studies combine manual and automated measurements, 21.1% are automated-only, and 13.8% remain manual-only. This hybrid pattern works provided two basics are met: time-synchronization across streams and explicit metadata on sensor siting (heights, within vs inter-row, above/below canopy). Where calibration or accuracy is reported (particularly for PAR/PPFD or soil moisture) comparability improves substantially. Recent IoT-enabled systems document calibration steps, telemetry, and low-power autonomy, illustrating a reproducible template for field deployments [15].

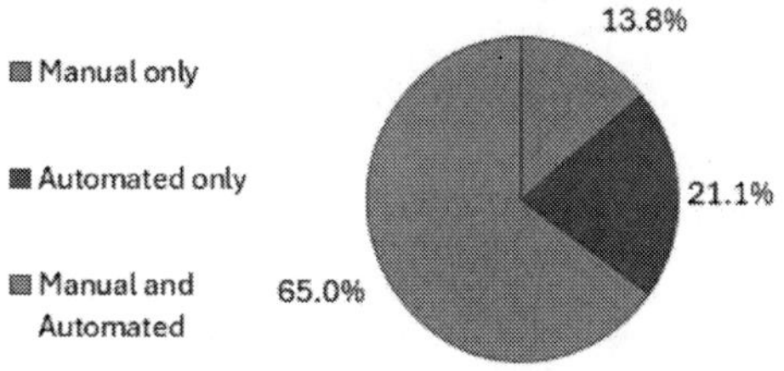

Figure 4: Percentage of papers by acquisition method.

Taken together, Fig. 3–4 indicate a field that already measures the dominant forcing (meteorology) and the electrical conversion stream, but still under-instruments continuous plant-side responses and under-reports the metadata that make results transferable.

3.3 Data acquisition practices

Fig. 5 reports gaps (number of papers lacking each item) across the 123 studies. The largest omissions are maintenance/durability (missing in 116 papers) and power supply/autonomy (105), followed by data-transmission method (102) and sensor accuracy/calibration (93). By contrast, only 28 papers fail to describe data-acquisition/processing, indicating that most studies now state sampling and basic processing, whereas operational metadata remain under-reported.

These omissions matter for reproducibility: without maintenance logs or power/telemetry descriptions, drift, dropouts and soiling effects are hard to interpret. Positive exemplars show what helps: explicit soiling/cleaning records alongside short-interval power and microclimate logging in geometry trials [13]; clear PAR to PPFD conversion and calibration notes where the photosynthetic light environment is central [19]; and concise statements of logger cadence and channels in pilot deployments [4]. Where telemetry is used, a one-line "how data leave the field" (e.g., LoRaWAN to cloud or inverter portal) plus time-synchronization notes makes datasets portable and auditable [15]. In short, most studies already state how they sampled, what is still missing, and most useful to add, are the operational details (power, transmission,

10.4229/EUPVSEC2025/4DV.1.15

calibration, maintenance), that make AgriPV monitoring comparable across sites and seasons.

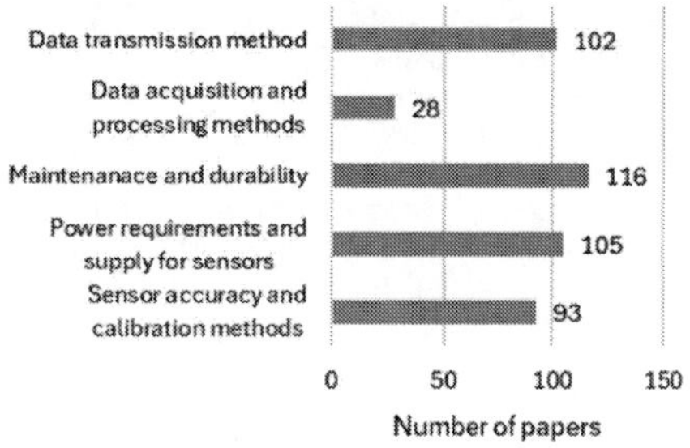

Figure 5: Number of papers missing information on key aspects of data acquisition.

4 CONCLUSIONS

This review of 123 experimental AgriPV studies shows a field converging on an integrated treatment of crops, climate and power. Most studies prioritize agronomic effects while layout and energy performance are co-determinants, and the prevailing hybrid acquisition model (continuous logging of weather and electrical variables complemented by targeted plant measurements) now enables causal chains from forcing to conversion and crop response to be traced with increasing confidence. Where photosynthetic light is explicitly resolved through PAR/PPFD sensing or robust irradiance-to-PPFD conversions, crop outcomes are interpretable in terms of the light budget rather than generic "shade," and geometry can be evaluated as a control parameter in its own right, from vertical/tilted rows in open fields to spectral tailoring in protected cultivation [3], [13], [19]. The literature also reveals that operational details such as timekeeping, calibration/uncertainty, placement relative to canopy and rows, and simple notes on power/telemetry and maintenance, remain the information most likely to be omitted, yet they are precisely the details that make results portable across sites and seasons.

Consolidating the evidence across studies, three elements of current practice consistently underpin credible AgriPV inference. First, co-reporting PAR/PPFD, inverter telemetry and module temperature on a shared time base provides a direct bridge from light environment to electrical conversion and plant response. When this triad is present, attribution improves, and design comparisons become quantitatively defensible. Second, pairing microclimate with soil-water information (at minimum, soil moisture at two or more depths and simple irrigation volumes) connects radiation and wind to water status and yield, enabling the interpretation of crop outcomes beyond instantaneous weather. Third, when layouts are the experimental treatment, multi-station measurements that resolve spatial gradients in wind and illumination across rows or panel orientations capture the heterogeneity that drives both physiology and power.

To make results truly portable, the most effective step is not more instrumentation but concise, high-impact documentation that standardizes what studies already do. At minimum, papers should specify logger clocks and time zones, sampling and aggregation intervals for each stream, sensor models and stated accuracies, exact placement relative to canopy height, row position and panel geometry, and one-line statements on power supply, telemetry and cleaning/maintenance. Providing these items in a machine-readable appendix with consistent variable names and SI units allows cross-site synthesis without reinterpretation. With such documentation and the co-measurement choices outlined above, the community can progress from coverage counts to transferable response functions that inform positioning, geometry and optical choices by crop and climate, and assess when simple automation (e.g., moisture-triggered fertigation) delivers operational benefit.

ACKNOWLEDGMENTS

This research was partly funded by the PRR Mobilizing Agendas, project Alliance for Energy Transition (ATE) with Grant agreement ID C644914747-00000023.

REFERENCES

[1] H. J. Williams, K. Hashad, H. Wang, and K. Max Zhang, "The potential for agrivoltaics to enhance solar farm cooling," *Appl Energy*, vol. 332, p. 120478, Feb. 2023, doi: 10.1016/j.apenergy.2022.120478.

[2] M. Jordan *et al.*, "Sonoran Desert Photovoltaics Laboratory and Growing Green: A Networked Regional Approach to Agrivoltaics Citizen Science," in *2024 IEEE 52nd Photovoltaic Specialist Conference (PVSC)*, IEEE, Jun. 2024, pp. 1465–1467. doi: 10.1109/PVSC57443.2024.10749646.

[3] S. Castellano, P. Santamaria, and F. Serio, "Solar radiation distribution inside a monospan greenhouse with the roof entirely covered by photovoltaic panels," *Journal of Agricultural Engineering*, vol. 47, no. 1, p. 1, Mar. 2016, doi: 10.4081/jae.2016.485.

[4] P. Gese, F. M. Martínez-Conde, G. Ramírez-Sagner, and F. Dinter, "Agrivoltaic in Chile - Integrative solution to use efficiently land for food and energy production and generating potential synergy effects shown by a pilot plant in Metropolitan region," in *Proceedings of the ISES Solar World Congress 2019 and IEA SHC International Conference on Solar Heating and Cooling for Buildings and Industry 2019*, International Solar Energy Society, 2020, pp. 1016–1024. doi: 10.18086/swc.2019.19.04.

[5] H. J. Lee, H. H. Park, Y. O. Kim, and Y. I. Kuk, "Crop Cultivation Underneath Agro-Photovoltaic Systems and Its Effects on Crop Growth, Yield, and Photosynthetic Efficiency," *Agronomy*, vol. 12, no. 8, p. 1842, Aug. 2022, doi: 10.3390/agronomy12081842.

[6] G. Ferrara, M. Boselli, M. Palasciano, and A. Mazzeo, "Effect of shading determined by photovoltaic panels installed above the vines on the performance of cv. Corvina (Vitis vinifera L.)," *Sci Hortic*, vol. 308, p. 111595, Jan. 2023, doi: 10.1016/j.scienta.2022.111595.

[7] S. Mohammedi, G. Dragonetti, N. Admane, and A. Fouial, "The Impact of Agrivoltaic Systems on Tomato Crop: A Case Study in Southern Italy," *Processes*, vol. 11, no. 12, p. 3370, Dec. 2023, doi: 10.3390/pr11123370.

[8] A. Ali Abaker Omer *et al.*, "Water evaporation reduction by the agrivoltaic systems development," *Solar Energy*, vol. 247, pp. 13–23, Nov. 2022, doi: 10.1016/j.solener.2022.10.022.
[9] J. Fleischmann *et al.*, "Guiding the data collection for integrated Water-Energy-Food-Environment systems using a pilot smallholder farm in Costa Rica," *Energy Nexus*, vol. 13, p. 100259, Mar. 2024, doi: 10.1016/j.nexus.2023.100259.
[10] S. S. Joy, I. Khan, and A. M. Swaraz, "A non-traditional Agrophotovoltaic installation and its impact on cereal crops: A case of the BRRI-33 rice variety in Bangladesh," *Heliyon*, vol. 9, no. 7, 2023, doi: 10.1016/j.heliyon.2023.e17824.
[11] R. Bulgari, G. Cola, A. Ferrante, G. Franzoni, L. Mariani, and L. Martinetti, "Micrometeorological environment in traditional and photovoltaic greenhouses and effects on growth and quality of tomato (Solanum lycopersicum L.)," *Italian Journal of Agrometeorology*, vol. 20, no. 2, pp. 27–38, 2015, [Online]. Available: https://www.scopus.com/inward/record.uri?eid=2-s2.0-84942313617&partnerID=40&md5=c0475f81f29e22209ba8305f7a69710f
[12] T. Petrakis, V. Thomopoulos, and A. Kavga, "Algorithmic advancements in agrivoltaics: Modeling shading effects of semi-transparent photovoltaics," *Smart Agricultural Technology*, vol. 9, p. 100541, Dec. 2024, doi: 10.1016/j.atech.2024.100541.
[13] K. A. Khan Niazi and M. Victoria, "Field Characterization of Vertical and Tilted Agrivoltaic Installations," in *2024 IEEE 52nd Photovoltaic Specialist Conference (PVSC)*, IEEE, Jun. 2024, pp. 410–410. doi: 10.1109/PVSC57443.2024.10749577.
[14] S.-W. Park, S.-M. Yun, D.-G. Seong, J. J. Lee, and J.-S. Chung, "Rice yield and electricity production in agro-photovoltaic systems," *Chil J Agric Res*, vol. 84, no. 5, pp. 674–685, Oct. 2024, doi: 10.4067/s0718-58392024000500674.
[15] F. Zito, N. I. Giannoccaro, R. Serio, and S. Strazzella, "Analysis and Development of an IoT System for an Agrivoltaics Plant," *Technologies (Basel)*, vol. 12, no. 7, p. 106, Jul. 2024, doi: 10.3390/technologies12070106.
[16] U. R. Patel, G. A. Gadhiya, and P. M. Chauhan, "Techno-economic analysis of agrivoltaic system for affordable and clean energy with food production in India," *Clean Technol Environ Policy*, vol. 26, no. 7, pp. 2117–2135, Jul. 2024, doi: 10.1007/s10098-023-02690-1.
[17] M. Torres *et al.*, "The Photovoltaic Greenhouse as Energy Hub for a More Sustainable Agriculture," in *2022 IEEE International Conference on Automation/25th Congress of the Chilean Association of Automatic Control: For the Development of Sustainable Agricultural Systems, ICA-ACCA 2022*, Institute of Electrical and Electronics Engineers Inc., 2022. doi: 10.1109/ICA-ACCA56767.2022.10006135.
[18] T. Hickey, M. Uchanski, and J. Bousselot, "Vegetable crop growth under photovoltaic (PV) modules of varying transparencies," *Heliyon*, vol. 10, no. 16, p. e36058, Aug. 2024, doi: 10.1016/j.heliyon.2024.e36058.
[19] D. Yajima, T. Toyoda, M. Kirimura, K. Araki, Y. Ota, and K. Nishioka, "Agrivoltaic system: Estimation of photosynthetic photon flux density under solar panels based on solar irradiation data using all-climate solar spectrum model," *Clean Eng Technol*, vol. 12, p. 100594, Feb. 2023, doi: 10.1016/j.clet.2022.100594.

Review of Sensor Technologies for Monitoring Agrivoltaic Systems

Sara Pereira[1], José A. Silva[1], Luís Fialho[2], Pedro Horta[1]
[1]Applied Research in Solar Energy for the Energy Transition (SOL4R), University of Évora, Portugal
[2]Eurac Research-Institute for Renewable Energy, 39100 Bolzano, Italy

Introduction

Agrivoltaics (AgriPV) co-locates PV generation with crops, coupling microclimate, plant physiology, and power conversion. Robust, time-aligned monitoring is central to interpreting crop–climate–power interactions and to comparing layouts across sites and crops.

Objectives

- Systematically review sensor types and monitoring strategies used in research on AgriPV.
- Identify and analyze **current practices and gaps in AgriPV monitoring setups.**

Methods

- Literature search: IEEE Xplore, Scopus, Google Scholar (2014–2024).
- Criteria: AgriPV-specific, included sensor use, peer-reviewed, English. Resulted in the **selection of 123 studies.**
- Classify sensors by manual vs automated and by monitoring objectives: environmental, energy performance, and agricultural.
- Data extracted: system type, deployment scale, sensor type, calibration, data acquisition, data transmission, power supply, etc.

Results

Research questions addressed

RQ1	Impact of the environment on AgriPV systems [1].	RQ4	Roles of digital and automated technologies [4].
RQ2	Energy generation performance [2].	RQ5	Economic and policy consideration [5].
RQ3	Impact of the AgriPV system on the environment or agriculture [3].	RQ6	System integration and design strategies [6].

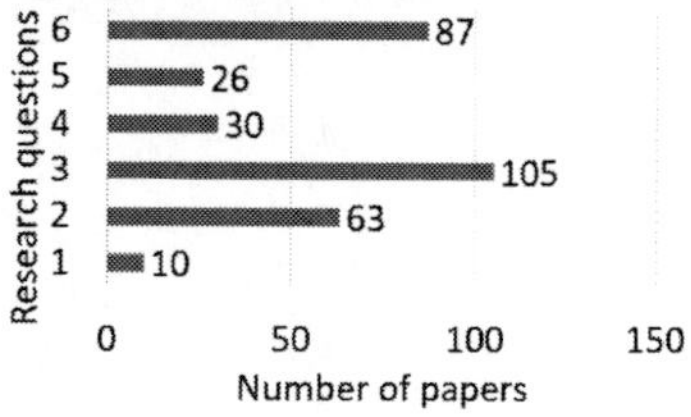

Categories of sensors

Number of papers mentioning automated sensors by category:

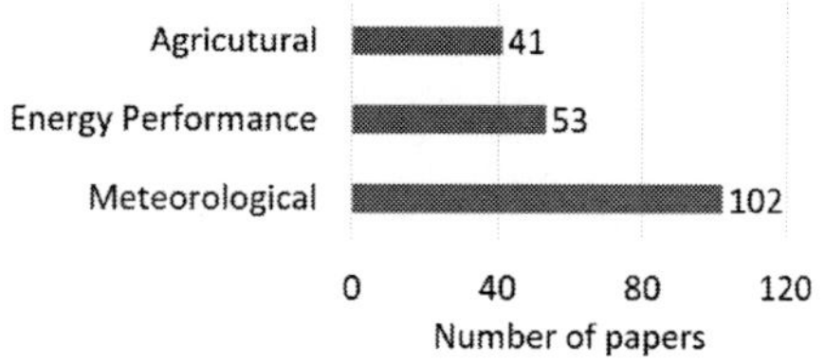

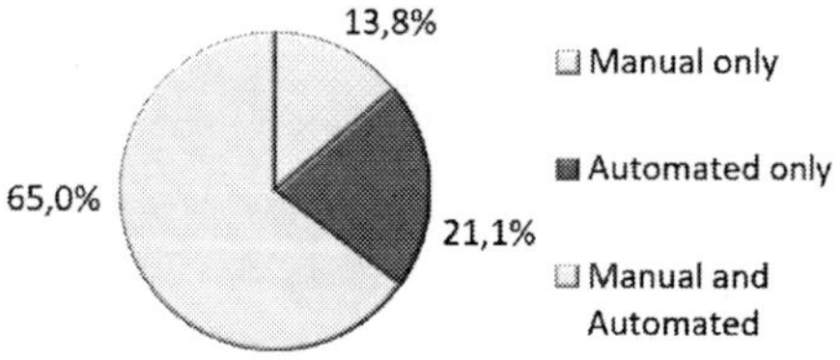

Category	Measured Variable	Sensors reported
Meteorological	Global / plane-of-array irradiance	Pyranometers: Kipp & Zonen CMP11, CMP22, CMP3; Hukseflux SR20, SR11; EKO
	PAR / PPFD (crop height)	Quantum sensor
	Spectral distribution	Spectroradiometer: Ocean Optics USB2000+
	Air temperature / relative humidity	Shielded thermo-hygrometer
	Wind speed/direction	Cup/ultrasonic anemometers: RM Young 05103
	Precipitation	Tipping-bucket rain gauge
Energy Performance	Inverter AC power / telemetry	Inverter-based loggers
	String DC / I-V	I–V curve tracer; string monitoring unit (Hall-effect or shunt); DC power analyzer
	Module temperature	T/K thermocouples, PT100
Agricultural	Soil moisture / temperature	TDR/FDR/capacitance probes: Campbell CS650/CS655
	Leaf temperature	Thermography: Apogee SI-111/IRT; FLIR cameras
	Gas exchange	IRGA-based portable photosynthesis system: LI-COR LI-6400/LI-6800
	Chlorophyll-a fluorescence	PAM fluorometer: Walz MINI-PAM / PAM-2500
	Canopy indices (chlorophyll/NDVI/PRI)	Chlorophyll meter / proximal multispectral sensor: SPAD-502, GreenSeeker
	LAI / light interception	Ceptometer / canopy analyzer: LI-COR LAI-2200, AccuPAR LP-80, Delta-T SunScan

Critical research gaps

Number of studies lacking information on key aspects of data collection:

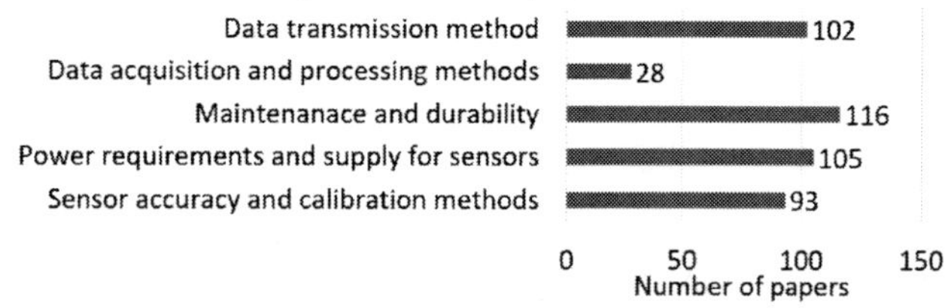

- Operational metadata underreported, timekeeping and precise sensor placement seldom specified.
- PAR/PPFD often absent or conversions undefined.
- Plant-soil responses under-instrumented, irrigation volumes frequently missing.
- Spatial under-sampling and limited automation.

Conclusion

This review turns a scattered literature into a usable baseline of how AgriPV is actually monitored. By quantifying what is measured, how it is acquired, and where key operational metadata are missing, it enables portable, cross-site comparisons of crop–climate–power interactions. The results point to simple, high-impact practices: **co-reporting PAR/PPFD, module temperature, and inverter telemetry on a shared clock and documenting timekeeping, calibration, placement, power and telemetry.** This transforms isolated case studies into design-relevant evidence for geometry, optics, and emerging data-driven control.

References

[1] H. J. Williams et al., (2023). doi: 10.1016/j.apenergy.2022.120478

[2] K. A. Khan Niazi and M. Victoria, *(2024)*. doi: 10.1109/PVSC57443.2024.10749577

[3] H. J. Lee et al., (2022). doi: 10.3390/agronomy12081842

[4] F. Zito et al., (2024). doi: 10.3390/technologies12070106

[5] U. R. Patel et al., (2024). doi: 10.1007/s10098-023-02690-1

[6] T. Petrakis et al. (2024). doi: 10.1016/j.atech.2024.100541

Contact me:

TNO innovation for life

Commercially viable solar parks with improved soil quality

A.R. Burgers, B.B. Van Aken, K.M. de Groot, G.J. de Graaff, B.W.J. Kikkert, I. Cesar, TNO solar energy, Petten
F.F. van der Zee, Wageningen University and Research
S. Leone, Novar

E/W facing systems and soil quality

- Typical E/W solar parks NL: high ground coverage ratio (>90%)
- Vegetation:
  - in aisles, extending 50-100 cm under lower edges
  - Very little vegetation elsewhere
- **Idea**: concentrate crest opening light to create central zone with conditions viable for plant growth

Funnel view 08-2025

Experiment

- Optical element installed Sep-2024
  - So far been in-place for about 1 ½ grow season
- Irradiance on ground measured with sensor arrays
- Vegetation assessment squares
  - Monitoring by Wageningen University
  - Assess vegetation at intervals, statistical evaluation.
  - requires time, maybe multiple growth seasons

key

funnel
Normal crest opening, little vegetation
below reflecting funnel, potentially more vegetation
Hairline
Irradiance sensor

regular crest, crest with funnel

Design of optical elements

- Funnel limiting spread of light entering through crest opening
  - Non-imaging concentration of light
  - Parameters such as tilt of mirror, height of mirror.
- bigeye view factor approach extended with ray tracing.
- Calculations validated with on-site measurements
- Comparing measured and simulated irradiance on a clear day:
  - Sun rays: direct, 1 reflection (E-face or W-face), detectors registering sun multiple times
  - Each color: time series per sensor.

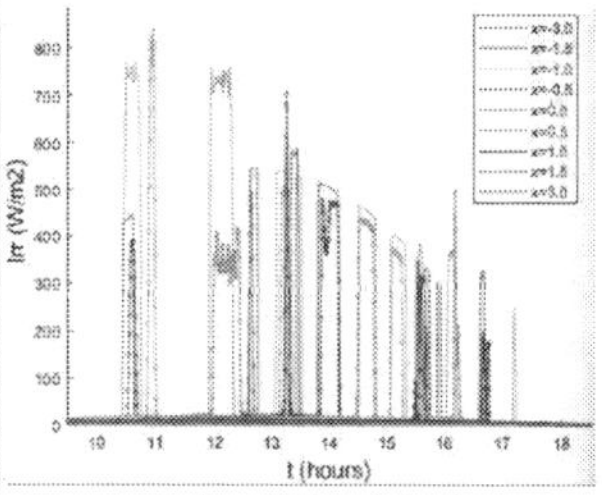

measured and simulated irradiance on a clear day.

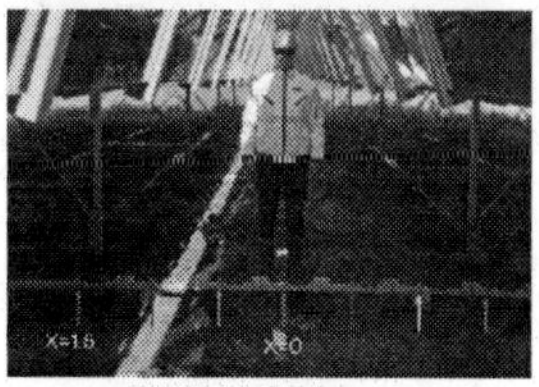

sensor array (wet circumstances 09-2024)

Carbon fixation model calibration and "hairline"

- Vegetation present from aisle up to"hairline"
- steep decrease in irradiance below lower edge of table
- Realise conditions below crest opening better than "hairline" to extend vegetation coverage
- Funnel: more peaked irradiance profile than open crest reference case

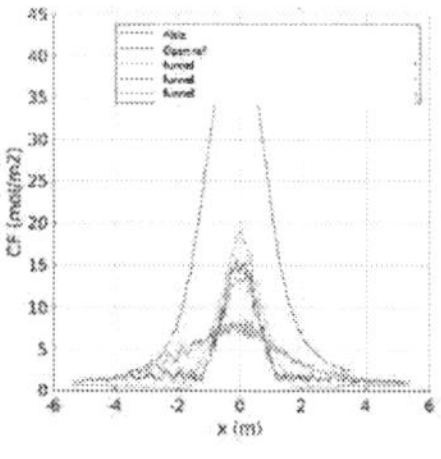

Calculated crop yield: open ref, aisle, funnel

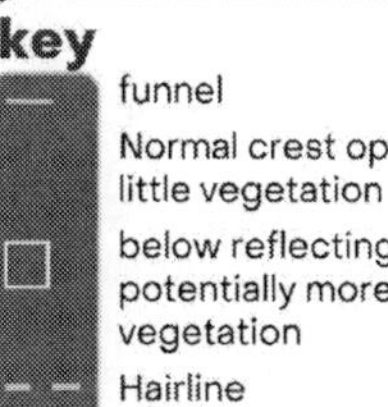

Grass growth in aisle extending below PV

Conclusions

- Designed and realized optical elements to boost the vegetation growth conditions below densely packed PV
- Validated the irradiance with and without these elements below the tables and in the aisle
- Improved irradiance conditions below the crest: should lead to more vegetation growth, but needs longer observation period

- Mirrors have withstood near 2 years of operation well.
- Comprehensive approach: optical elements, irradiance measurements, vegetation assessment
- Geometry of this system (narrow crest opening) was critical with respect to gains

PROGRAMME DE RECHERCHE
FRANCE 2030
SYSTÈMES ÉNERGÉTIQUES & ÉNERGIES RENOUVELABLES

AgriPV

Meira Itzel Torres Aguilar[1], Shusen YU[2], Anne MIGAN-DUBOIS[1,3], Vincent BOURDIN[3,4], Jordi Badosa FRANCH[2], Johan PARRA[2], Bouchra MEKHALDI[2]

[1] Université Paris-Saclay, CentraleSupélec, CNRS, Laboratoire de Génie Électrique et Électronique de Paris, 91192 Gif-sur-Yvette, France
[2] LMD/IPSL, Ecole Polytechnique, IP Paris, Sorbonne Université, ENS, PSL University, CNRS – 91128 – France
[3] Sorbonne Université, CNRS, Laboratoire de Génie Électrique et Électronique de Paris, 75252 Paris, France
[4] CNRS, LISN, Bâtiment 507, Rue du Belvédère, 91405 Orsay, France

Power Output Modelling of a Single-Axis Backtracking Bifacial Module in an Agrivoltaic System in Palaiseau, France

Introduction (1)

In recent years, the use of land for both agricultural crop production and photovoltaic (PV) solar energy conversion has gained considerable attention, leading to an accelerated growth of agrivoltaics.
New bifacial technologies and larger utility-scale PV arrays result in a growing need for models that can more accurately account for the multiple diffuse light components and reflections incident on various surfaces of a PV array. For this reason, integrated modelling, simulation, and optimisation of systems are fundamental.
Together, new bifacial technologies and models, aim to develop a better understanding of how the shading produced by PV modules impacts solar irradiation distribution on the ground, the microclimate beneath the PV modules, how this microclimate influences crop growth, and, in turn, how microclimate and crop growth affects PV production.
This work presents initial results of a modelling chain starting from tracker angles up to power output while considering the impact of a variable albedo due to the presence of plants under the PV installation.

Installation (2)

Figure 1 Layout of agripv installation located on the campus of Ecole Polytechnique in Palaiseau, France.

- North-South orientation with single-axis tracking (East-West)
- 72 TOPCon half-cell bifacial modules (555 Wp, 560 Wp, 565 Wp)
- 36 modules equipped with individual optimizers
- 4 inverters (1 per row)
- Meteorological variables: wind, air temperature, precipitation, among others

Methodology (3)

- 4 c-Si reference cells on module A8 (2 front/2 back)
- 4 temperature probes (2 on A8)

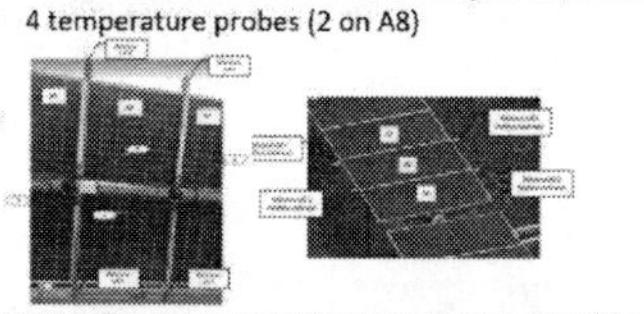

Figure 2 Location of temperature probes (left) and of reference cells on module A8 (right).

- 2 periods of PV tracking: fixed horizontal and backtracking

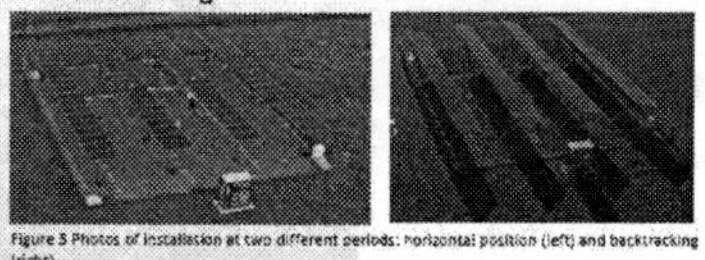

Figure 3 Photos of installation at two different periods: horizontal position (left) and backtracking (right)

- 3 alfalfa cycles:
  - June 10th – August 29th 2024
  - August 30th – November 12th 2024
  - November 14th– May 27th 2025

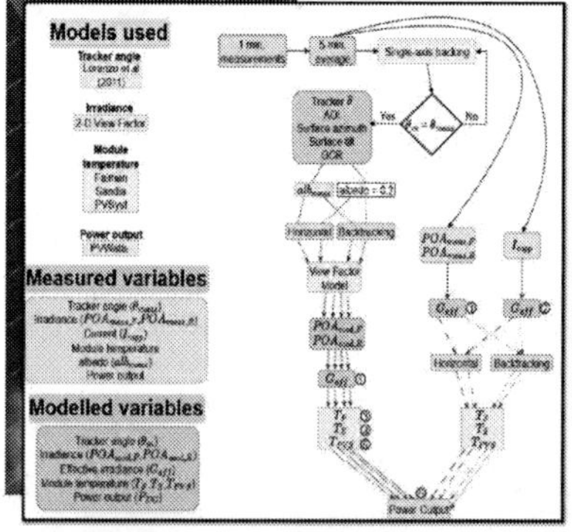

Models (4)

$$G_{eff} = POA_{front} + (POA_{back} * \varphi_{Pmax}) \quad (1)$$

$$G_{eff} = \frac{I_{MPP}}{I_{mpp,STC}} \quad (2)$$

$$T_F = T_a + \frac{POA}{U_0 + U_1 * WS} \quad (3)$$

$$T_S = POA * \exp(U_0 + U_1 * WS) + T_a \quad (4)$$

$$T_{PVS} = T_a + \frac{\alpha\, POA\, (1-\eta)}{U_0 + U_1 * WS} \quad (5)$$

$$P_{DC} = \frac{POA}{G_{STC}} P_{STC}(1 + \gamma(T_m - T_{STC})) \quad (6)$$

α: absorption coefficient
γ: power temperature coefficient
η: module efficiency
Φ: bifaciality factor
I_{mpp}: current at maximum power point
$I_{mpp,STC}$: current at maximum power point under STC
P_{STC}: power output at STC
POA: plane-of-array irradiance
T_a: air temperature
T_m: measured module temperature
T_{STC}: module temperature at STC
U_0: heat loss factor
U_1: heat loss factor influenced by wind
WS: wind speed

Results (5)

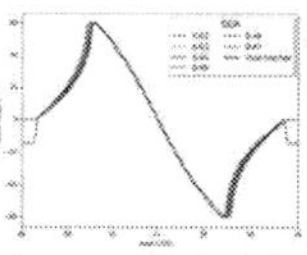

Figure 4 Modeling of module A8's angle tracker. Each colored line represents a different GCR, the black line represents measured angle.

- GCR that best models measured tracker angle is 0.44
- Falls within the 10% tolerance of module size with respect to the GCR value provided by the installer of 0.407

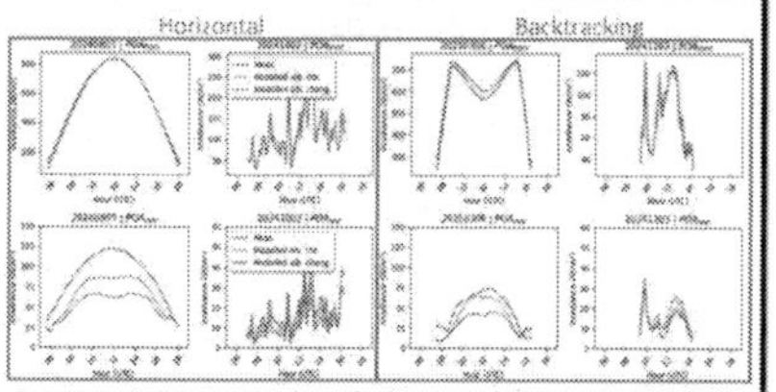

Figure 5 Comparison between measured and modeled front and rear irradiance for sunny and cloudy days during period in horizontal position and backtracking. Blue corresponds to measured value, orange to modeled value considering a fixed albedo of 0.2, and green to a modeled value considering a variable albedo

- There is a maximum relative mean bias error (rMBE) of 2.22% for the front side irradiance and of -40.91% for the back.
- The large error is suspected to be partly due to spectral and engle-of-incidence effects not being considered by the model
- The presence of plants results in a an albedo variation of ~4%

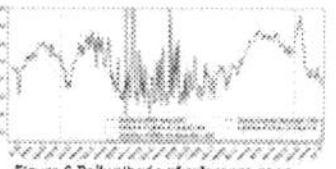

Figure 6 Daily albedo of reference zone Brown lines represent sowing of plant and golden represent recollection

(1) (2)

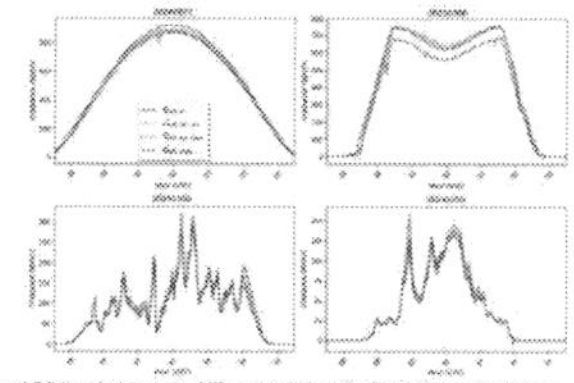

Figure 7 Comparison between different calculated G_{eff}. For the blue curve, on-site measurements were used. For orange, modeled values considering a fixed albedo, for green a variable albedo was considered. The brown curve was calculated using only the module's I_{mpp}

(3) (4) (5)

- The uncertainty associated to the modeled rear irradiance does not have a strong impact on the calculated effective irradiance (G_{eff}) due to the bifaciality factor (75%) and low irradiance values
- The most impactful factor is the front irradiance measurements used
- Calculated G_{eff} using the module's current at maximum power point (I_{mpp}), is lower than the others because it corresponds to the irradiance truly absorbed by the module.

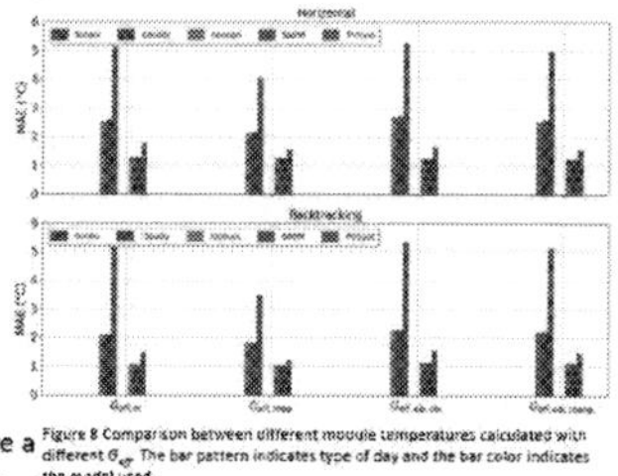

Figure 8 Comparison between different module temperatures calculated with different G_{eff}. The bar pattern indicates type of day and the bar color indicates the model used.

(6)

- There is good agreement between modeled and measured module temperature (T_p), specially for the Faiman and Sandia models
- Large errors for the PVSyst model are due to low values of U_0 and U_1 estimated with local wind measurements
- The free air flow due to module rotation in backtracking mode keeps the modules cooler
- The smaller difference for cloudy days is due to overall lower temperatures.

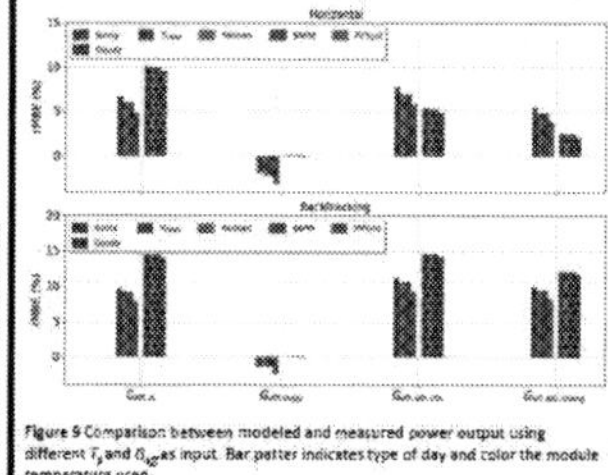

Figure 9 Comparison between modeled and measured power output using different T_p and G_{eff} as input. Bar patter indicates type of day and color the module temperature used.

- Even large errors when modeling T_p have a negligible impact on the modeled power output
- The determining factor is the irradiance used
- Utilizing measured instead of fixed albedo for modelling irradiance provides an improvement of up to 2.88%
- For cloudy conditions all temperature models give similar results, for sunny days there is a difference of up to 1.82%
- The best result is obtained when using a G_{eff} calculated from the module's own I_{mpp}.

Conclusions (6)

- Even though a model is capable of accurately modelling incident irradiance on the front side of modules, there is increased difficulty for a moving surface
- Adding a changing albedo due to the presence of plants in the model for the back irradiance is complex and will require furrther work
- Despite large errors when using a specific temperature model, the defining factor is the irradiance data used for modelling
- The best power output modelling results are obtained when using an effective irradiance calculated with the module's I_{mpp}

Acknowledgements

This work is part of the AgriPV-ER project (22-PETA-0007), which contributes to the "Pole National de Recherche sur l'Agriphotovoltaïsme" from INRAE. The project is supported by France 2030, the PEPR TASE (https://www.pepr-tase.fr/), as well as the 3rd Programme d'investissements d'Avenir (ANR-18-EUR-006-02), and the Foundation of Ecole polytechnique (Chaire "Défis Technologiques pour une Energie Responsable") financed by TotalEnergies

RÉPUBLIQUE FRANÇAISE
Liberté
Égalité
Fraternité

GeePS Génie électrique et électronique de Paris
LISN LABORATOIRE INTERDISCIPLINAIRE DES SCIENCES DU NUMÉRIQUE
IPSL
LMD
ÉCOLE POLYTECHNIQUE
IP PARIS
îledeFrance

YIELD AND PR ESTIMATION FOR VERTICAL AGRIVOLTAICS SYSTEMS

[1]Guillermo P. Moreda (gullermo.moreda@upm.es, [2]Miguel Ángel Egido (egido@ies-def.upm.es) , [3]Valero Pascual Gallego (valero.pascual@upm.es), [4]Delia Rodriguez Lucas, (delia@ekilabs.com), [1*]Miguel A. Muñoz-García (miguelangel.munoz@upm.es)
[1] Dep. Ing. Agroforestal. ETSIAAB. Universidad Politécnica de Madrid. R&D group: LPF-Tagralia. Av. Puerta de Hierro, 2. 28040. Madrid, Spain. Tel.: +34 91 06 70968.
[2] Instituto de Energía Solar. Universidad Politécnica de Madrid.
[2] Dep. Estructuras y Física de la Edificación. Universidad Politécnica de Madrid.
[3] EkiLabs CORP.

ABSTRACT: Photovoltaic systems interspersed with cropland are gaining ground. Since both elements compete for radiation, determining the amount of light that reaches each of them is of great interest. Vertical agrivoltaic systems are an alternative to other systems installed in crop fields, which interfere less with tillage and machinery. When these systems consist of bifacial panels, energy capture is almost twice that of monofacial system. To determine profitability, measurements of both actual production and expected output or performance ratio (PR) must be obtained. Likewise, if the system is agrivoltaic, agricultural production must not be substantially reduced, and regulations set different limits depending on the country, with an extended objective of not assuming a reduction greater than 20%. The calculation of the PR in a vertical system is something that is still open to debate when the panels are bifacial. In addition, when the system is oriented with a north-south axis, the maximum radiation can be strongly affected by nearby shadows, both from other parallel strings and from nearby obstacles. Given the sensitivity of a vertical system to these aspects, in this work we address the elements that will affect the correct understanding and design of vertical agrivoltaic plants.
Keywords: Photovoltaic, bifacial, performance ratio, agrivoltaic

1 INTRODUCTION

Agrivoltaics (AV), the dual use of agricultural land to produce crops and photovoltaic (PV) power in the same plot, is a hot topic of research. A key aspect in AV is that both the crop and the PV plant can mutually benefit if the materials are adequately selected, and the geometry of the system is well designed. The crop can be inside a greenhouse or in open-field, what gives rise to different designs of the PV plant.

In the last years, two open-field AV geometries have been proposed: The South-facing tilted static panels arranged on a gantry-type shed structure and the static vertical East-West facing bifacial panels assembled on a fence-type structure. The research reported here is in the context of how well vertical bifacial AV will serve as the generator for electric-powered pump irrigation.

The calculation of the performance ratio (PR) in a vertical system is something that is still open to debate when the panels are bifacial. In addition, when the system is oriented with a north-south axis, the maximum radiation can be strongly affected by nearby shadows, both from other parallel strings and from nearby obstacles. Given the sensitivity of a vertical system to these aspects, in this work we address the elements that will affect the correct understanding and design of vertical agrivoltaic plants.

In this regard, the following points should be discussed:

- Is the peak power indicated by the manufacturer or should both sides be taken into account?
- If both sides are included, what bifaciality coefficient should be applied?

The objective of this work is to compare the model-based estimates of incident solar radiation on the active faces of bifacial solar panels placed vertically, with the actual radiation received by them. In this way, it will be possible to determine which parameters come into play when using radiation databases.

2 MATERIALS AND METHODS

To carry out this task, a real vertical installation (Figure 1, Figure 2) was instrumented with bifacial panels, with the intention of measuring the real radiation on both sides and at different heights. On the other hand, the electrical production on both sides was monitored.

Figure 1: Agrivoltaic system with vertical bifacial PV panels

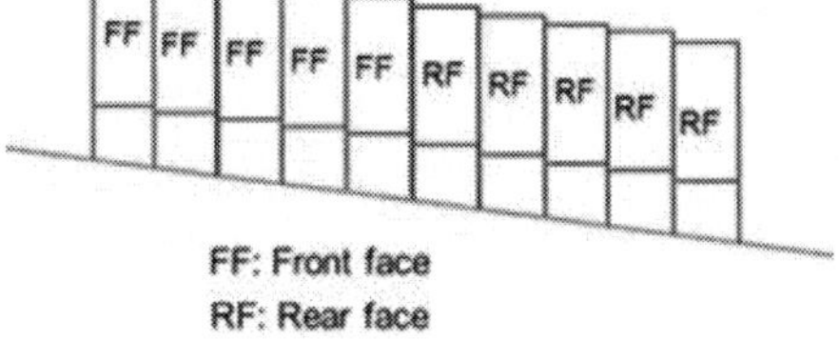

Figure 2: Vertical bifacial PV panels, where FF is the main side and RF is the rear side.

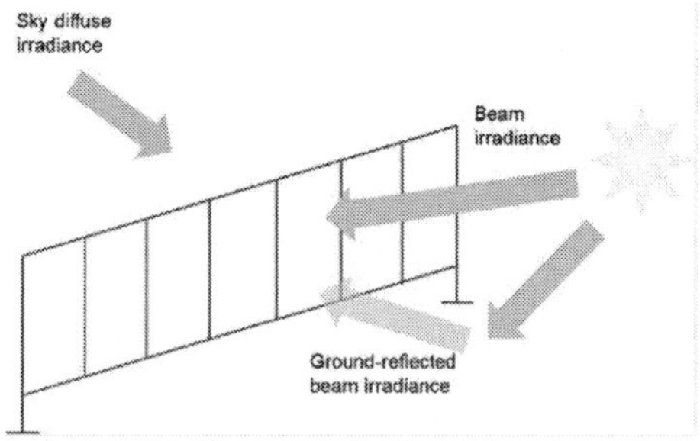

Figure 3: Main radiation sources for bifacial PV panels

Determining the quality of the data obtained from databases such as CAMS, PVGIS SARAH-2, or Solargis is of vital importance to calculate the yield of agrivoltaic plants with vertical installation.

On the other hand, the Performance Ratio (PR) would be the most commonly used parameter to determine the proper functioning of a conventional plant. However, if we look at the formula for obtaining it (Eq. 1), in a bifacial panel there would be a discussion about whether the radiation to be measured should be taken from the most exposed side, as well as whether the peak power should include both sides.

Eq. 1:

$$PR = \frac{Yield\,(kWh)}{PSH\left(\frac{kWh}{1\,kW}\right)\cdot P_p\,(kW)}$$

The bifaciality of a bifacial PV panel is measured with the bifaciality coefficients. The bifaciality coefficient prescribed by the technical specification IEC 60904-1-2: 2024 is the bifaciality of current, φ_{Isc}, defined as the ratio between the short-circuit current (I_{sc}) generated exclusively by the rear face of the panel and the I_{sc} generated exclusively by the front face, with the condition that both currents are measured at STC (irradiance of 1000 $W\cdot m^{-2}$, panel temperature of 25 °C, and with the IEC 60904-3 reference solar spectral irradiance distribution). To determine the φ_{Isc}, bifacial PV panels can be tested as showcased in Figure 4.

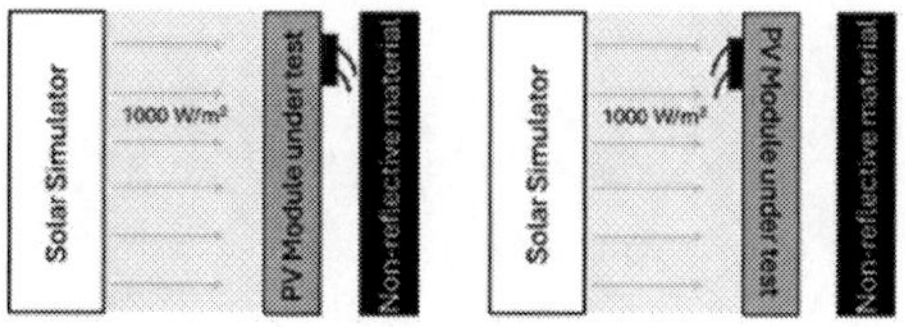

Figure 4: Single-side illumination test method for bifacial PV panels.

To qualify bifacial panels, the so-called bifacial standard test condition (BSTC) applies, characterized by a front irradiance of 1000 W/m^2, a rear irradiance of 135 W/m^2 and an equivalent irradiance G_E defined [1] in Eq.2, where $\varphi_{Isc} = I_{sc,rear} / I_{sc,front}$

Eq. 2:

$$G_E = (1000 + \varphi_{Isc}\cdot 135)\ W/m^2$$

If our solar simulator can only illuminate the tested panel from one side, then the rear irradiance is transferred to the front by using an G_E higher than 1000 $W\cdot m^{-2}$ (Eq. 1). The bifacial power gain or BiFi [2] is determined from solar simulator test as the slope of the linear fit that corresponds to plotting $P_{max.}$ against G_{rear}.

The conventional PR is given by Eq.1, where PSH is the Peak Solar Hours (kWh/m^2) on the generator's plane and Pp is the generator peak power.

In the case of vertical system, with main axis North-South and two parallel rows (strings), connected to independent MPPT, where one row has the main face oriented to the East and the other one to the West, we propose the PR expression of Eq.3, where the index 1 or 2 represents the Yield, PSH, Pp and bifaciality coefficient (φ_{Isc}) for each string.

Eq. 3:

$$PR = \frac{\frac{Yield_{(1)}}{PSH_{(1)}\cdot P_{p1}\cdot(1+\varphi_{Isc(1)})} + \frac{Yield_{(2)}}{PSH_{(2)}\cdot P_{p2}\cdot(1+\varphi_{Isc(2)})}}{2}$$

3 RESULTS AND DISCUSSION

IEC 61724-1:2021 proposes to calculate PR of a bifacial array by Eq. 4:

$$PR_{BIF} = \sum \frac{P}{\sum \frac{C\cdot P_0\cdot G_{front}\cdot BIF}{1000\,W\cdot m^{-2}}}$$

where P is the system AC power output, P_0 is the system DC power rating at STC, C is a temperature correction factor and BIF, that stands for bifacial irradiance factor, is equal to $1 + \varphi\cdot(G_{rear} / G_{front})$

Karttunen et al. (2023) proposed a temperature-corrected PR [5].

Little information is available on the measurement of

bifaciality coefficient under real operating conditions. An exception is the work by Muñoz-Cerón et al. (2024), who for outdoor conditions found that the bifaciality coefficient increases with increasing irradiance. They recommended assessing the bifaciality coefficient preferably in the central hours of sunny days. But in our case the greatest impact would be at the beginning and end of the day, so we propose a more direct method, which applies different coefficients to each string depending on its orientation (Eq.).

Starting from the estimated radiation data, both for clear and average days (Figure 5), and measuring the real radiation, it will be possible to validate the method for the real calculation and minimize the error applied in the estimation of bifacial vertical agrivoltaic systems.

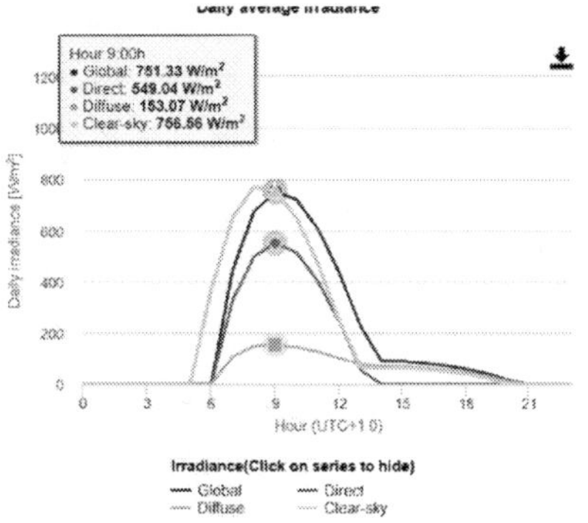

Figure 5: PVGIS estimated radiation on one side of a vertical east-oriented PV panel.

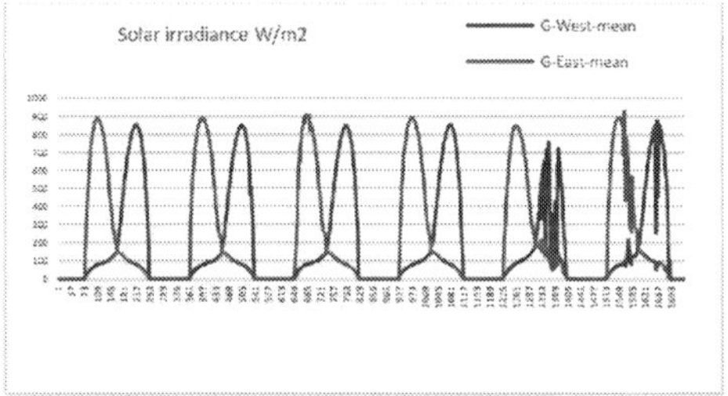

Figure 6: Radiation measured on both sides (east and west) of a vertical mounted solar panel.

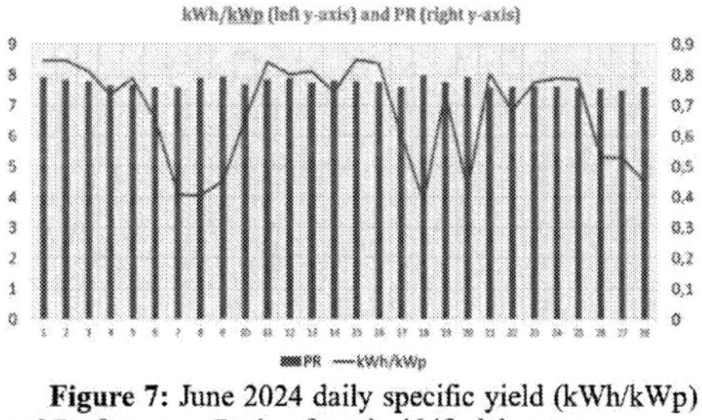

Figure 7: June 2024 daily specific yield (kWh/kWp) and Performance Ratio of vertical bifacial system.

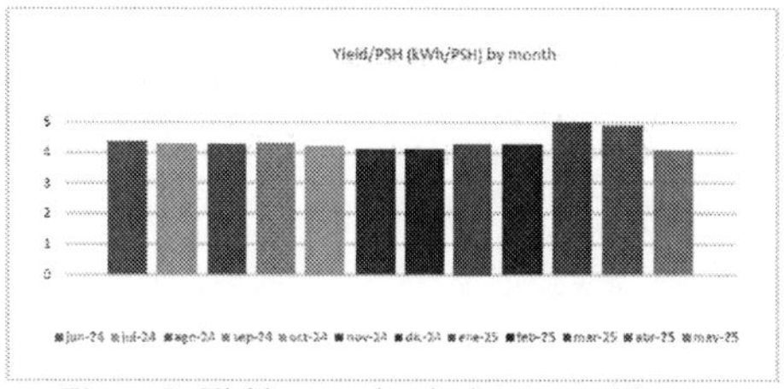

Figure 8: Yield per peak solar hour, monthly average, from June 2024 to May 2025.

For a vertical bifacial array of HJT photovoltaic panels, Badran and Dhimish [3] found that increased diffuse irradiance correlated with higher bifacial gain. Nonetheless, Muñoz-Cerón et al. [4] reported lower bifaciality coefficient for cloudy day (more diffuse irradiance) with respect to sunny day (less diffuse irradiance), although the bifacial panels in [4] were not vertical.

4 CONCLUSIONS

The following conclusions can be drawn:

- Diffuse irradiance plays a major role in vertical bifacial PV systems.
- A vertical system presents the question of radiation to be taken into account. In this work, we considered that radiation should be the sum of that captured on both sides, but applying a bifaciality coefficient.
- More research is needed on outdoor characterization of bifaciality, especially for vertical bifacial systems.

5 Acknowledgements

This work is partially funded by the grant 'PID2023-147841OB-C22' of Spain MCIN/AEI (10.13039/501100011033): Studies on emerging photovoltaic technologies for pumping hydrants adapted to irrigation needs and distribution network characteristics. (EMERPVPUMP), and by European Union 'NextGeneration'.

6 References

[1] X. Zhang, C. Monokroussos, M. Schweiger, M. Heinze. (2018). Power rating and qualification of bifacial PV modules. *Photovoltaics International*, 40: 90- 96.

[2] International Energy Agency-Photovoltaic Power Systems Programme. (2021). Bifacial photovoltaic modules and systems: Experience and results from international research and pilot applications.

[3] G. Badran & M. Dhimish. (2024). Comprehensive study on the efficiency of vertical bifacial photovoltaic systems: a UK case study. *Scientific Reports*, 14: 18380.

[4] E. Muñoz-Cerón, S. Moreno-Buesa, J. Leloux, J.

Aguilera, D. Moser. (2024). Evaluation of the bifaciality coefficient of bifacial photovoltaic modules under real operating conditions. *Journal of Cleaner Production*, 434: 139807.

[5] Karttunen et al. (2023). Comparing methods for the long-term performance assessment of bifacial photovoltaic modules in Nordic conditions. *Renewable Energy*, 219: 119473.

10.4229/EUPVSEC2025/4DV.1.22
020407-004

42nd European Photovoltaic Solar Energy Conference and Exhibition

EU PVSEC European PV Solar Energy Conference and Exhibition

YIELD AND PR ESTIMATION FOR VERTICAL AGRIVOLTAICS SYSTEMS

G.P. Moreda[1], Miguel Ángel Egido[2], Valero Pascual Gallego[3] D. Rodríguez-Lucas[4], M.A. Muñoz-García[1] *

1 Dep. Ing. Agroforestal. ETSIAAB. Universidad Politécnica de Madrid. R&D group: LPF-Tagralia. Av. Puerta de Hierro, 2. 28040. Madrid, Spain. Tel.: +34 91 06 70968.
2 Instituto de Energía Solar. Universidad Politécnica de Madrid.
3 Dep. Estructuras y Física de la Edificación. Universidad Politécnica de Madrid.
4 EkiLabs CORP.
*Corresponding author. E-mail: miguelangel.munoz@upm.es

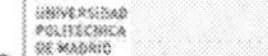

Introduction

Photovoltaic systems interspersed with cropland are gaining ground. Given that both elements compete for radiation, determining the amount of light that reaches each of them is a matter of great interest. Vertical agrivoltaic systems (Figure 1) are presented as an alternative to other systems installed in crop fields, which interfere less with tillage and the passage of machinery. When these systems are composed of bifacial panels (Figure 2, Figure 3), energy capture increases to almost double that of a non-bifacial system.

To determine the profitability of a photovoltaic system, measurements of both actual production and expected output or performance ratio (PR) must be obtained. Likewise, if the system is agrivoltaic, agricultural production must not be substantially reduced. In this case, regulations set different limits depending on the country, with an extended objective of not assuming a reduction of agricultural production greater than 20%.

The calculation of the PR in a vertical system is something that is still open to debate when the panels are bifacial. In addition, when the system is oriented with a north-south axis, the maximum radiation can be strongly affected by nearby shadows, both from other parallel strings and from nearby obstacles. Given the sensitivity of a vertical system to these aspects, in this work we address the elements that will affect the correct understanding and design of vertical agrivoltaic plants.

Materials and Methods

The bifaciality of a bifacial PV panel is measured with the bifaciality coefficients. The bifaciality coefficient prescribed by the technical specification IEC 60904-1-2: 2024 is the bifaciality of current, φ_{Isc}, defined as the ratio between the short-circuit current (I_{sc}) generated exclusively by the rear face of the panel and the I_{sc} generated exclusively by the front face, with the condition that both currents are measured at STC (irradiance of 1000 $W \cdot m^{-2}$, panel temperature of 25 °C, and with the IEC 60904-3 reference solar spectral irradiance distribution). To determine the φ_{Isc}, bifacial PV panels can be tested as showcased in Figure 4.

To qualify bifacial panels, the so-called bifacial standard test condition (BSTC) applies, characterized by a front irradiance of 1000 W/m², a rear irradiance of 135 W/m² and an equivalent irradiance G_E defined [1] in Eq.1, where $\varphi_{Isc} = I_{sc\,rear} / I_{sc\,front}$

$$\text{Eq.1. } G_E = (1000 + \varphi_{Isc} \cdot 135)\ W/m^2$$

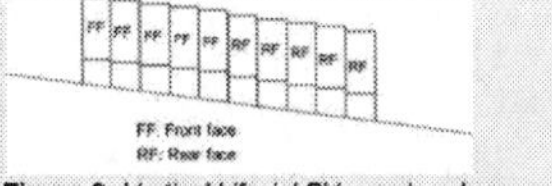

Figure 2: *Vertical bifacial PV panels, where FF is the main side and RF is the rear side.*

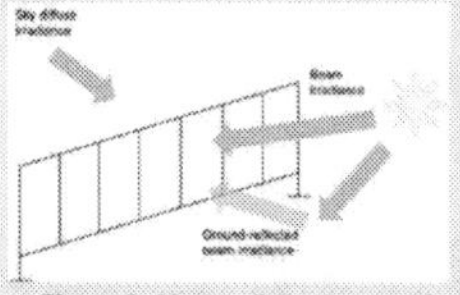

Figure 3: *Main radiation sources for bifacial PV panels.*

If our solar simulator can only illuminate the tested panel from one side, then the rear irradiance is transferred to the front by using an G_E higher than 1000 $W \cdot m^{-2}$ (Eq. 1). The bifacial power gain or BiFi [2] is determined from solar simulator test as the slope of the linear fit that corresponds to plotting P_{max} against G_{rear}

The conventional PR is given by Eq.2, where PSH is the Peak Solar Hours (kWh/m²) on the generator's plane and Pp is the generator peak power.

$$\text{Eq.2. } PR = \frac{Yield\ (kWh)}{PSH\left(\frac{kWh}{1\ kW}\right) \cdot P_p\ (kW)}$$

In the case of vertical system, with main axis North-South and two parallel rows (strings), connected to independent MPPT, where one row has the main face oriented to the East and the other one to the West, we propose the PR expression of Eq.3, where the index 1 or 2 represents the Yield, PSH, Pp and bifaciality coefficient (φ_{Isc}) for each string.

$$\text{Eq.3. } PR = \frac{\frac{Yield_{(1)}}{PSH_{(1)} \cdot P_{p1} \cdot (1+\varphi_{Isc(1)})} + \frac{Yield_{(2)}}{PSH_{(2)} \cdot P_{p2} \cdot (1+\varphi_{Isc(2)})}}{2}$$

Note that in Eq.3., PSH is the daily irradiation in kWh/m² but taking into account both sides of the solar panel (main and rear), for each string.

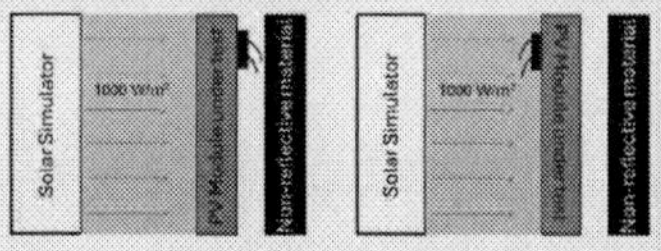

Figure 4: *Single-side illumination test method for bifacial PV panels.*

Figure 1: *Agrivoltaic system with vertical bifacial PV panels.*

Results and Discussion

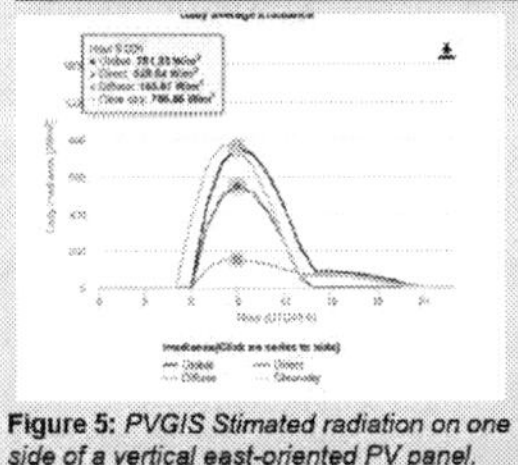

Figure 5: *PVGIS Stimated radiation on one side of a vertical east-oriented PV panel.*

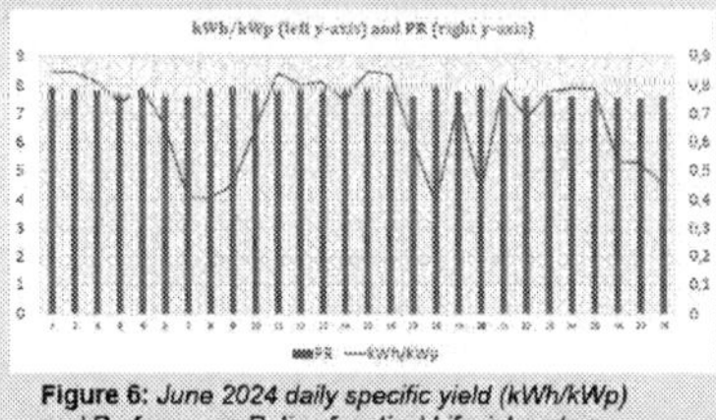

Figure 6: *June 2024 daily specific yield (kWh/kWp) and Performance Ratio of vertical bifacial system.*

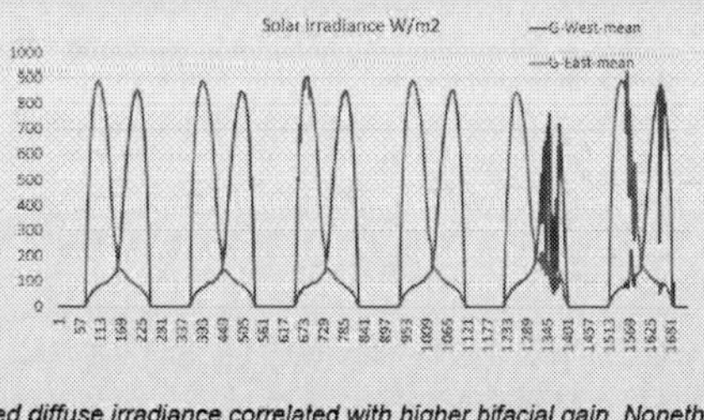

Figure 7: *Radiation measured on both sides (east and west) of a vertical mounted solar panel.*

For a vertical bifacial array of HJT photovoltaic panels, Badran and Dhimish [3] found that increased diffuse irradiance correlated with higher bifacial gain. Nonetheless, Muñoz-Cerón et al. [4] reported lower bifaciality coefficient for cloudy day (more diffuse irradiance) with respect to sunny day (less diffuse irradiance), although the bifacial panels in [4] were not vertical.

IEC 61724-1:2021 proposes to calculate PR of a bifacial array by Eq. 4:

$$\text{Eq.4. } PR_{BIF} = \sum \frac{P}{\sum \frac{C \cdot P_0 \cdot G_{front} \cdot BIF}{1000\ W \cdot m^{-2}}}$$

, where P is the system AC power output, P_0 is the system DC power rating at STC, C is a temperature correction factor and BIF, that stands for bifacial irradiance factor, is equal to $1 + \varphi \cdot (G_{rear} / G_{front})$

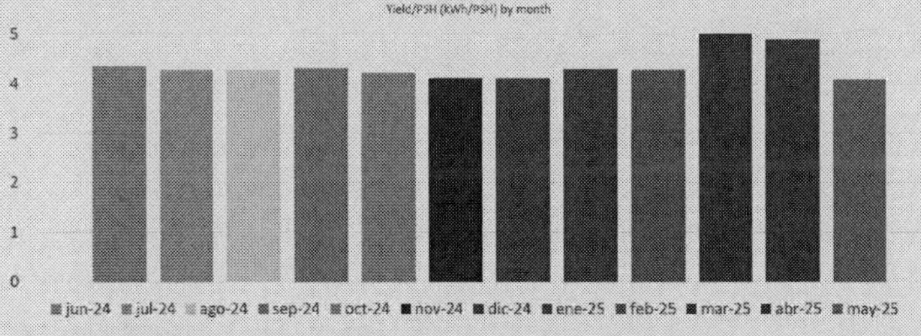

Figure 8: *Yield per peak sun hour, monthly average, from June 2024 to May 2025.*

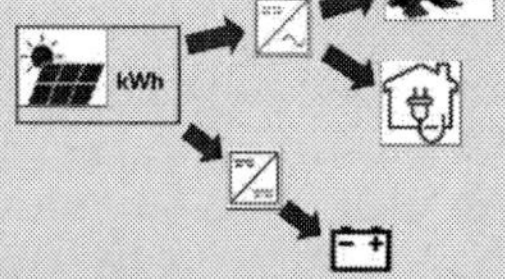

Figure 9: *Diurnal (daylight) electric energy flow of power produced by PV generator.*

Conclusions

- *Diffuse irradiance plays a major role in vertical bifacial PV systems.*
- *A vertical system presents the question of radiation to be taken into account. In this work, we considered that radiation should be the sum of that captured on both sides, but applying a bifaciality coefficient.*
- *More research is needed on outdoor characterization of bifaciality, specially for vertical bifacial systems.*

References

[1] X. Zhang, C. Monokroussos, M. Schweiger, M. Heinze. (2018). Power rating and qualification of bifacial PV modules. Photovoltaics International, 40: 90- 96.
[2] International Energy Agency-Photovoltaic Power Systems Programme. (2021). Bifacial photovoltaic modules and systems: Experience and results from international research and pilot applications.
[3] G. Badran & M. Dhimish. (2024). Comprehensive study on the efficiency of vertical bifacial photovoltaic systems: a UK case study. Scientific Reports, 14: 18380.
[4] E. Muñoz-Cerón, S. Moreno-Buesa, J. Leloux, J. Aguilera. D. Moser. (2024). Evaluation of the bifaciality coefficient of bifacial photovoltaic modules under real operating conditions. Journal of Cleaner Production, 434: 139807.

4DV.1.22. Topic: 4DV.1: Agrivoltaics Approaches, Experiences, Results / Integrated and Innovative PV Applications

020408-001

Acknowledgements

This work is partially funded by the grant 'PID2023-147841OB-C22' of Spain MCIN/AEI (10.13039/501100011033): Studies on emerging photovoltaic technologies for pumping hydrants adapted to irrigation needs and distribution network characteristics (EMERPVPUMP), and by European Union "NextGeneration".

AGRIVOLTAIC – STUDY OF THE POTENTIAL IN PORTUGAL CONTINENTAL

Jeremias dos Santos [1], José A. Silva[1], Luís Fialho [2], Pedro Horta[1]
[1]Renewable Energies Chair, University of Évora. Pólo da Mitra da Universidade de Évora, Edifício Ario Lobo de Azevedo, 7000-083 Nossa Senhora da Tourega, Portugal
[2]Institute for Renewable Energy, Eurac Research, Via Alessandro Volta, 13ª, 39100 Bolzano BZ, Itália

ABSTRACT: The objective for the share of renewable energy in Portugal's total energy consumption was raised from 47% to 51% in the revised National Energy and Climate Plan for 2030, highlighting Portugal's commitment to reducing emissions, enhancing renewable energy usage, and improving energy efficiency. Agrivoltaics systems can be one of the strategies to accomplish this goal. These systems allow the combination of food and energy production in the same space in a synergistic way, avoiding land-use competition between PV and agriculture. This study analyzes the technical potential of agrivoltaics in mainland Portugal, a country particularly suitable for its implementation due to its high solar potential and diversified agriculture. The study used public geographic information system databases to perform systematic mapping of the viable areas. The methodology used was based on a multicriteria geospatial analysis, which included the identification of agricultural and pasture areas (based on the 2023 Land Use Charter), the exclusion of zones with legal restrictions such as National Agricultural Reserve (RAN), National Ecological Reserve (REN), and Natura 2000 Network, and the areas with a terrain slope >10%. The analysis revealed that the Alentejo region has the greatest technical potential, due to its predominantly flat topography, high solar radiation, and low density of environmental restrictions. The study estimated the potential for installed photovoltaic (PV) power through overhead configuration.
Keywords: agrivoltaics; photovoltaic energy; agriculture; sustainable development; territorial planning

1 INTRODUCTION

Over the last few decades, the ongoing climate changes, combined with the increasing need for energy production and growing pressure on natural resources, has imposed considerable challenges on the sustainability of economic, social, and environmental systems. While the energy sector seeks to transition to clean and renewable sources, the agricultural sector faces challenges such as water scarcity, soil degradation, reduction of biodiversity, and the search for greater resilience and efficiency in production systems [1].

In this scenario, agrivoltaics or AgriPV presents itself as a promising solution, allowing for the combined use of the same area of land for agricultural production and electricity generation through photovoltaic solar panels. By combining energy and food production in the same location, this strategy fosters a more efficient use of rural land, reducing land-use conflicts and promoting synergies between strategic sectors [2].

The adoption of agrivoltaics has increased in European countries with a Mediterranean climate, such as France, Italy, and Spain. In Southern Europe, the high levels of solar radiation and the strong agricultural traditions make this technology particularly promising [3,4]. In addition, countries with more temperate climates, such as Germany and the Netherlands, are also developing agrivoltaic solutions adapted to their specific climatic conditions. In these countries, public policies, incentive programs, and specific regulations have helped to consolidate the agrivoltaic model as a viable option for achieving climate goals and strengthening food security [5, 6, 7, 8].

In Portugal, the outlook is also promising: the country has high levels of solar radiation (>1,800 kWh/m²/year in most of the territory), extensive coverage of agricultural areas, and solid commitments to decarbonization, established in the National Energy and Climate Plan (PNEC 2030), which foresees a significant increase in the contribution of photovoltaic (PV) energy to the country's energy matrix [9]. However, there are still important gaps to be solved at the national level, such as the lack of specific regulations for the agrivoltaic sector, the scarcity of applied technical-scientific studies, and the lack of a systematic mapping of the territory to identify areas with technical, legal, and environmental viability for the implementation of this type of system.

Identifying these areas is essential to boost the adoption of agrivoltaics in Portugal, contributing to more sustainable territorial energy planning that considers legal constraints of the lands, as well as their potential to be used in AgriPV projects. Thus, this study aims to fill this gap through a multicriteria geospatial analysis that examines the agrivoltaic viability of the territory in the different regions of mainland Portugal, considering criteria such as legal constraints on land use, as well as its current use and slope.

2 METHODOLOGY

2.1 Definition of Criteria for the Selection of Potential Areas.

To define the areas suitable for the installation of agrivoltaic systems, it's necessary to consider criteria that encompass agronomic, environmental, and technical-spatial dimensions [2, 10, 11].

In this analysis, the selection criteria were divided into three main categories:

- Current land use: The selection of eligible areas was based on vector data from the Land Use Map of 2023 (COS 2023), where classes with the greatest compatibility with agrivoltaic systems were selected: agricultural use and pasture [12].
- Legal and environmental restrictions: Areas that intersect with the Natura 2000 Network, the National Agricultural Reserve (RAN), and the National Ecological Reserve (REN) were excluded due to legal restrictions that make the installation of energy infrastructures unfeasible [13, 14, 15].

10.4229/EUPVSEC2025/4DV.1.25

- Topographic conditions: Two slope categories were analyzed (≤10% and >10%) based on the methodology for assessing agricultural suitability and the installation of photovoltaic panels [16, 17].
- The analysis consisted of:
- Intersection between agricultural and pasture areas (COS 2023) with the restriction layers (Natura 2000, RAN, and REN).
- Topographic filtering to retain areas within slopes categories ≤10%.
- Calculation of the potential photovoltaic energy installation capacity in the identified useful areas, based on simulations using the PVSyst 8.0.13 software [18].

2.1.1 Land Use: Classification by COS 2023

The first spatial selection criterion used in this analysis was the current land use designation. Areas designated for agriculture and pasture were selected, as recorded in the 2023 Land Use Map (Carta de Ocupação do Solo, COS) [12]. This map represents the most recent cartographic database for mainland Portugal. Figure 1 presents the land use classification map, which shows the spatial distribution of the main land use and land cover categories for mainland Portugal.

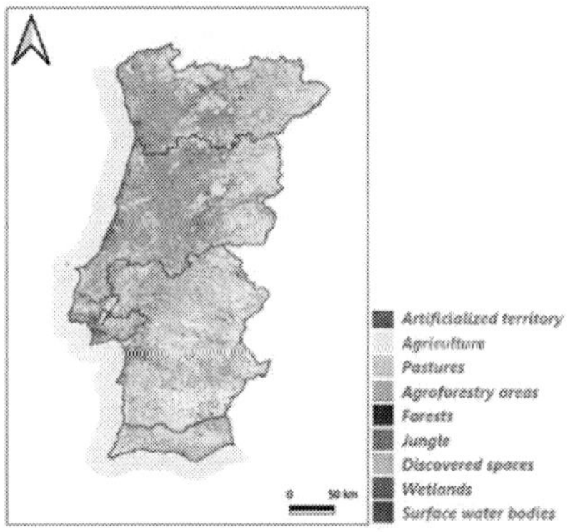

Figure 1: Land Use and Land Cover Map according to COS 2023.

The land use categories selected for agrivoltaic use in this project were:

- Agriculture: This class or category of land use and cover includes the crop regions shown on this land use and land cover map.
- Pasture: This class or category includes all regions occupied by pasture.

Figure 2 shows the eligible areas for pasture and agriculture in mainland Portugal.

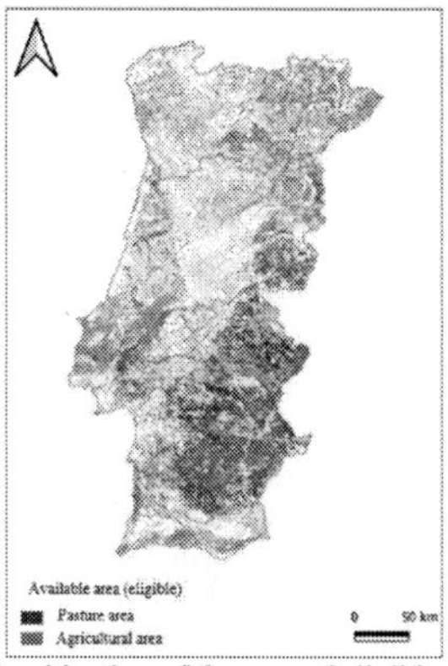

Figure 2: Combination of the map of eligible areas (pasture and agriculture)

The selection of these land use classes was based on their technical and ecological feasibility for integration with photovoltaic systems. These uses allow for the continuation of agricultural or livestock activities with controlled levels of shading, without significantly affecting productivity [10, 19].

2.1.2 Map of areas with legal restrictions.

The second step involved removing areas that intersect with zones of legal restrictions (Rede Natura 2000, REN, RAN) to ensure that the agrivoltaic systems comply with land-use planning regulations. This removal is essential for the development of agrivoltaic systems to comply with the legislation governing environmental preservation and sustainable land use, ensuring territorial compatibility with current public policies.

Figure 3 shows the areas occupied by each of these protection zones.

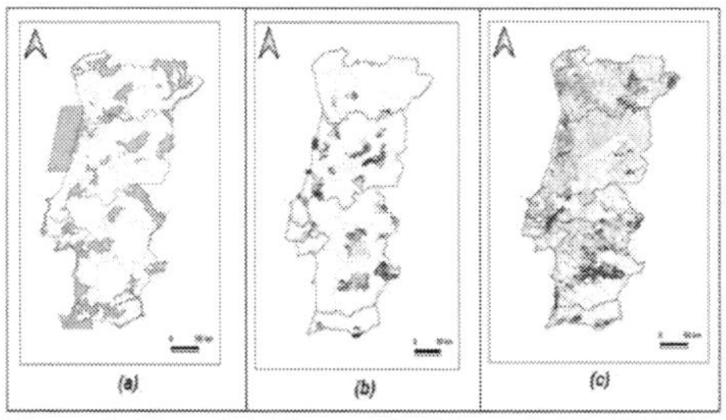

Figure 3: Map of the Natura 2000 Network (a); REN (b); and RAN (c).

2.1.3 Slope of the Land.

Land slope was the third criterion evaluated to identify suitable areas for agrivoltaic systems. The energy and economic sustainability of agrivoltaic installation is heavily affected by the terrain's inclination. Land with steep slopes presents technical challenges for both the installation of photovoltaic panels with ideal orientation and for agricultural activity.

The exclusion of regions with a slope above 10% is intended to ensure:

- That the orientation and inclination of the photovoltaic modules are ideal to maximize solar radiation capture [16].

- A decrease in system installation costs, by reducing the need for earthmoving and land leveling services.
- Improved accessibility and safety during operations, facilitating the movement of agricultural machinery and the maintenance of the energy infrastructure [19].

This technical criterion is essential to ensure the technical and economic viability of agrivoltaic projects, especially when implemented on a large scale in rural regions. There are various technical and scientific studies that discuss the definition of a slope threshold for land slopes. Some studies indicate that land with slopes up to 3% are ideal for agrivoltaic projects with high agro-productive integration, as it reduces the need for earthworks and maximizes land use [2, 20]. According to the U.S. Environmental Protection Agency and the National Renewable Energy Laboratory, conventional ground-mounted photovoltaic solar plants can accommodate slopes up to 10%, although this increases project costs and complexity [16]. In this study, a threshold of 10% slope was used to determine whether land is suitable for AgriPV projects or not. Figure 4 presents the map with areas with slopes ≤10 and >10% in mainland Portugal.

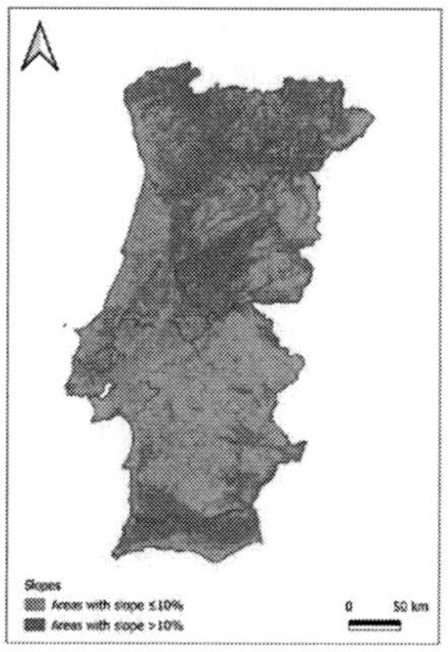

Figure 4: The map of the areas with the two different slopes ≤10% and >10% in mainland Portugal.

2.2 Estimation of the potential for PV installation capacity.

Determining the potential for photovoltaic energy installation capacity is a fundamental step in analyzing the economic potential of agrivoltaic systems. This allows for the quantification of the installed potential capacity of the areas considered technically viable. In this sub-chapter, we present the methodology used to determine the photovoltaic installation potential, expressed in kilowatt-peak (kWp), based on the useful area identified in each region.

2.3.1 Technical Reference Parameters

The potential for photovoltaic energy installation capacity was calculated based on a standard configuration of a monocrystalline Trina Solar microcrystalline silicon bifacial module with a nominal power of 655 Wp and a total area of 3.106 m² [21]. This value indicates the ground area required for each panel, excluding additional structural spaces.

The potential for photovoltaic energy installation capacity was calculated using the following equations:

$$Nm = Int\frac{Au}{Am} \quad \text{(Eq1)}$$

$$PPV = Nm * Pm \quad \text{(Eq2)}$$

Where: Nm is the number of modules, which is given by the integer quotient between the useful area, Au (m2), and the module area, Am (m2).
PPV is the total photovoltaic potential (kWp).
Pm is the nominal power of each module (kWp).

This calculation was performed for all analyzed regions, based on the useful area values obtained after applying the geospatial criteria previously mentioned. The results are presented in gigawatt-peak (GWp).

2.3.2 Structural Configurations

In this analysis an agrivoltaic plant with an overhead configuration was considered.

Overhead configuration: In this setup, the modules are raised relative to the ground typically > 3 m, allowing for agricultural or grazing activities to take place underneath the photovoltaic systems. Figure 6 shows the PVsyst design of the elevated configuration analyzed in this study, which considered the following parameters:

- Alignment and Orientation: The photovoltaic array was oriented to the south (azimuth = 0°).
- Module Tilt: A fixed tilt of 25° was adopted.
- Installation Height: The modules were installed at a height of 4.0 m above the ground, and the spacing between rows is 5 m.
- Bifacial Photovoltaic Module: A dual-glass monocrystalline silicon bifacial PV Trina Vertex module with a nominal power of 655 Wp an area of 3.106 m² per module [21].
- Total Area Occupied: The simulation considered a plot of 1 hectare (10,000 m²).
- A reference location in the Central region of mainland Portugal was selected for the simulations in the PVsyst software. This location was chosen to adequately represent the average solar irradiation and climate conditions of mainland Portugal.

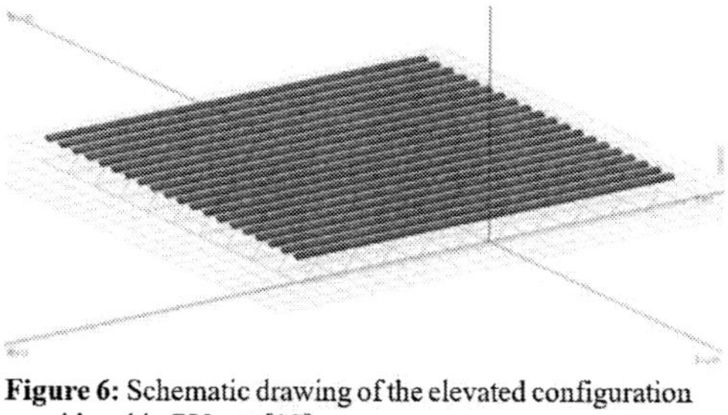

Figure 6: Schematic drawing of the elevated configuration considered in PVsyst [18].

3 RESULTS AND DISCUSSION

The geospatial analysis showed that a total of 1263 kha area suitable to be used for AgriPV, the analysis evidenced significant regional variations in the distribution of suitable areas between the different regions.

3.1 Area affected by legal restrictions.

Figure 7 presents the fractions of the agricultural and pasture areas affected by legal limitations in each region of Portugal's mainland.

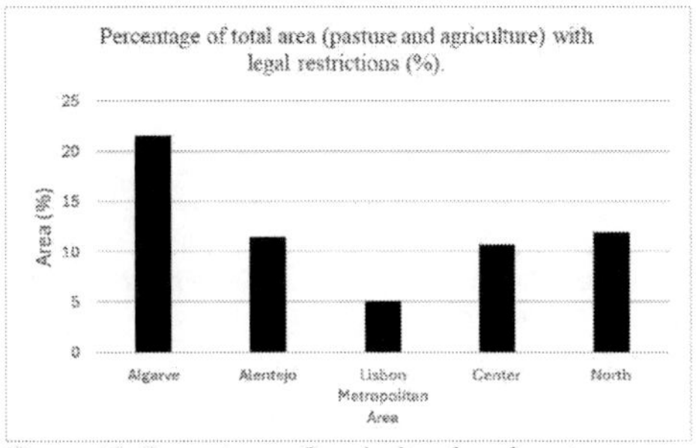

Figure 7: Percentage of agricultural and pasture areas affected by legal restrictions in each region.

It can be observed that Algarve has the highest percentage of areas impacted by legal restrictions with 22% areas intercepting protected zones, while the Lisbon Metropolitan Area has the lowest percentage, with only 5% of its agricultural and pastureland subject to legal restrictions.

3.2 Pasture and agricultural area with a slope >10%.

The analysis of agricultural and pasture areas excluded due to slopes greater than 10% indicates that there are significant topographical restrictions for implementing agrivoltaic systems in mainland Portugal.

Figure 8 shows the percentages of the total agricultural and pasture area excluded for having slopes >10% in each region of mainland Portugal.

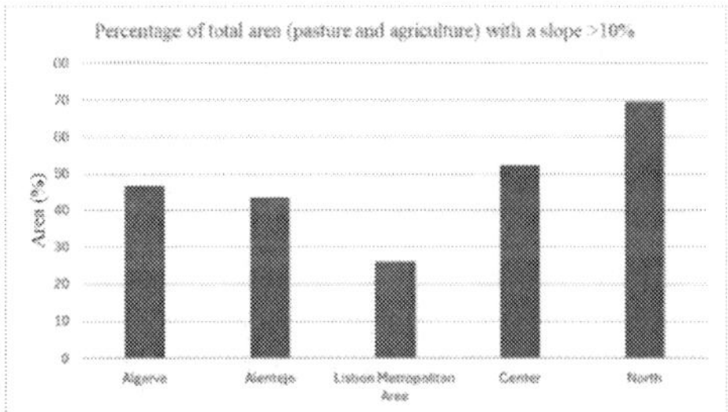

Figure 8: Percentage of total agricultural and pasture areas excluded due to a slope >10% in each region.

It's observed that the North region has the largest area excluded (69.9%), reflecting the strong presence of steep terrains. Center (51%) and the Algarve (46.6%) regions also have very significant areas excluded due to their high slope. The Alentejo registers 43.0% of area excluded, while the Lisbon Metropolitan Area has the lowest percentage of area excluded due to the slope with 26%.

3.3 Analysis of the useful areas.

Figure 9 shows the regional distribution areas (agricultural and pasture) which are considered suitable for agrivoltaic projects in mainland Portugal.

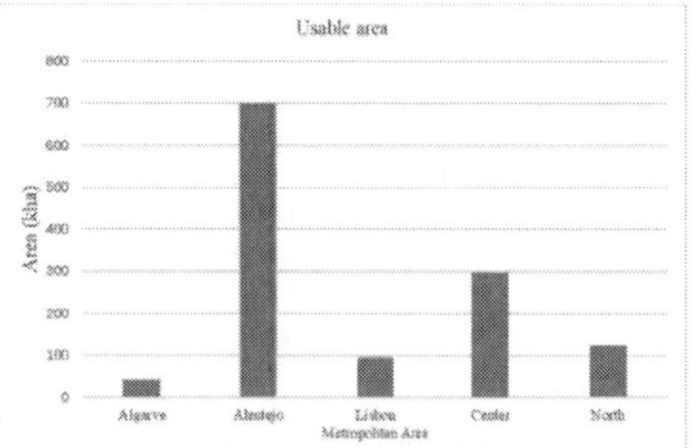

Figure 9: Areas of agriculture and pasture are usable for AgriPV.

Figure 9 indicates that, in the Algarve, the availability of area for agrivoltaic implementation is quite restricted compared to other regions, having 44 kha considered usable for AgriPV. Alentejo stands out as the region with the greatest potential, with a total area of 700 kha. This result is particularly interesting due to the high solar potential available in this region. In Lisbon Metropolitan Area, there are 96 kha considered usable for AgriPV, while Center and North regions of respectively 299 kha and 124 kha are usable for agrivoltaic projects.

3.4 Estimation of Photovoltaic Installation Potential

The analysis focused on the overhead configuration, considering the usable areas previously determined for each region.

3.4.1 Calculation of the potential for photovoltaic energy installation capacity in the useful areas.

- Calculation of the potential for photovoltaic energy installation capacity of the elevated configuration.

To determine the number of PV panels and PV power that can be installed on a specific plot of land, equations 1 and 2 were used.

Considering the bifacial PV panels above described, and assuming a maximum ground coverage ratio (GCR) of 35%, it was concluded that it is possible to install 1,125 modules on a 10,000 m2 area, which results in a total installed capacity of 736.9 kWp. Using this feature and considering the usable area for each region, the respective potential for PV capacity installation was obtained.

Table 1 shows the distribution of the potential for PV capacity installation with overhead configuration (GCR=35%) by region. The results show the significant differences in the potential available in the different regions.

Table 1: Potential for PV capacity installation in each region.

Region	**PV capacity (GWp)**
Algarve	32
Alentejo	515
Lisbon Metropolitan Area	71
Center	220
North	92

10.4229/EUPVSEC2025/4DV.1.25

As expected, Algarve shows lowest potential, while concentrates the largest PV installation potential reaching 515 GWp, which reflects both the vast available area and favorable topographic conditions. The Center region stands out as the second most relevant in terms of PV installation potential with 220 GWp. While Lisbon Metropolitan Area and North region have a moderate potential for the installation of PV capacity.

4 CONCLUSIONS

The analysis of the energy production potential proved to be a fundamental step to evaluate the technical potential of agrivoltaic systems in mainland Portugal. The integration of geospatial criteria, such as land use, slope, and legal restrictions, and considering an overhead structure with a GCR=35%, enabled a detailed regional analysis of the potential for PV capacity installation. This approach also allowed for an assessment of the impact of the legal constrains and terrain slopes, on the usability of agricultural and pasture areas for agrivoltaics.

The Alentejo region stood out, the region with highest potential with 515 GWp, confirming its leadership potential for large-scale agrivoltaic deployment. The Center region followed with 220 GWp, while the North and Lisbon Metropolitan Area registered 92 GWp and 71 GWp, respectively. The Algarve presented the lowest value, with 32 GWp. These results show that the Alentejo and Center together account for the largest share of the national potential, making them key territories for the expansion of overhead agrivoltaic systems in Portugal.

5 REFERENCES

[1] Intergovernmental Panel on Climate Change (IPCC), *Climate Change 2022 – Impacts, Adaptation and Vulnerability: Working Group II Contribution to the Sixth Assessment Report of the Intergovernmental Panel on Climate Change*. Cambridge: Cambridge University Press, 2023. doi: 10.1017/9781009325844.

[2] S. Amaducci, X. Yin, e M. Colauzzi, «Agrivoltaic systems to optimize land use for electric energy production», *Appl. Energy*, vol. 220, pp. 545–561, jun. 2018, doi: 10.1016/j.apenergy.2018.03.081.

[3] Agenzia per le Erogazioni in Agricoltura [AGEA], "Guida agli incentivi agrivoltaici in Italia", Agenzia per le Erogazioni in Agricoltura, 2023. Accessed: 8 August 2025. [Online]. Available at: https://www.agea.gov.it/portale-agea/

[4] IDAE – Instituto para la Diversificación y Ahorro de la Energía, "Estrategia de energias renovables y uso del suelo agrícola". Accessed: 8 August 2025. [Online]. Available at: https://www.idae.es/

[5] Bundesnetzagentur, Renewable Energy Sources Act (EEG). Accessed: 8 August 2025. [Online]. Available at: https://www.bundesnetzagentur.de/

[6] Fraunhofer ISE, "Agrivoltaics - Electricity and Agriculture", Fraunhofer Institute for Solar Energy Systems ISE. Accessed: 8 August 2025.

[7] RVO – Netherlands Enterprise Agency, "Stimulation of sustainable energy production and climate transition (SDE++)", RVO.nl. Accessed: 8 August 2025. [Online]. Available at: https://english.rvo.nl/en/subsidies-financiering/sde

[8] C. Jjls. C. S. Wageningen University & Research, Wageningen Solar Research Programme, WUR. Accessed: 8 August 2025. [Online]. Available at: https://www.wur.nl/en/research-results/research-institutes/environmental research/projects/wageningen-solar-research-programme.htm

[9] "PNEC 2030." Accessed: Aug. 13, 2025. [Online]. vailable: https://www.dgeg.gov.pt/pt/destaques/pnec-2030/

[10] C. Dupraz, H. Marrou, G. Talbot, L. Dufour, A. Nogier, e Y. Ferard, «Combining solar photovoltaic panels and food crops for optimizing land use: Towards new agrivoltaic schemes», *Renew. Energy*, vol. 36, n.º 10, pp. 2725–2732, oct. 2011, doi: 10.1016/j.renene.2011.03.005.

[11] A. Weselek, A. Ehmann, S. Zikeli, I. Lewandowski, S. Schindele, e P. Högy, «Agrophotovoltaic systems: applications, challenges, and opportunities. A review, *Agron. Sustain. Dev.*, vol. 39, n.º 4, p. 35, Aug 2019, doi: 10.1007/s13593-019-0581-3.

[12] Direção-Geral do Território (DGT), "COSc2023 – Carta de Ocupação do Solo Conjuntural de 2023 | DGT." Accessed: Aug. 13, 2025. [Online]. Available: https://www.dgterritorio.gov.pt/COSc2023-Carta-de-Ocupacao-do-Solo-Conjuntural-de-2023

[13] Comissão Nacional do Território (CNT), "Reserva Ecológica Nacional (REN)." Accessed: Aug. 13, 2025. [Online]. Available: https://cnt.dgterritorio.gov.pt/ren-pagina

[14] Direção-Geral de Agricultura e Desenvolvimento Rural (DGADR), "Reserva Agrícola Nacional (RAN)." Accessed: Aug. 13, 2025. [Online]. Available: https://www.dgadr.gov.pt/pt/reserva-agricola-nacional-ran

[15] Instituto da Conservação da Natureza e das Florestas (ICNF), "Rede Natura 2000." Accessed: Aug. 13, 2025. [Online]. Available: https://www.icnf.pt/conservacao/redenatura2000/aredenatura2000

[16] EPA & NREL, Best practices for siting solar photovoltaics on municipal solid waste landfills. Accessed: August 13, 2025.

[17] S. G. Simões, T. Simões, J. Barbosa, *et al.*, "Estimativa de potenciais técnicos de energia renovável em Portugal…," LNEG, Amadora, Portugal. Accessed: August 13, 2025.

[18] PVsyst SA. "PVsyst 8." Accessed: August 19, 2025. [Online]. Available: https://www.pvsyst.com

[19] G. A. Barron-Gafford *et al.*, «Agrivoltaics provide mutual benefits across the food–energy–water nexus in drylands», *Nat. Sustain.*, vol. 2, n.º 9, pp. 848–855, set. 2019, doi: 10.1038/s41893-019-0364-5.

[20] T. Sekiyama e A. Nagashima, Solar Sharing for Both Food and Clean Energy Production: Performance of Agrivoltaic Systems for Corn, A Typical Shade-Intolerant Crop, *Environments*, vol. 6, n.º6, p.65, jun. 2019, doi: 10.3390/environments6060065.

[21] Trina solar TSM-XXXDEG21C.20 product datasheet, URL:https://static.trinasolar.com/sites/default/files/Vertex_DEG21C.20_EN_2021_Aus_A_web_1.pdf

AGRIVOLTAIC – STUDY OF THE POTENTIAL IN PORTUGAL CONTINENTAL

RENEWABLE ENERGIES CHAIR
UNIVERSITY OF ÉVORA
SOL4R

Jeremias dos Santos[1], José Silva[1], Luís Fialho[2], Pedro Horta[1]
[1]Renewable Energies Chair, University of Évora, Portugal
[2]Eurac Research-Institute for Renewable Energy, 39100 Bolzano, Italy

ABSTRACT

The objetive for the share of renewable energy in Portugal's total energy consumption was raised from 47% to 51% in the revised National Energy and Climate Plan for 2030, highlighting Portugal's commitment to reducing emissions, enhancing renewable energy usage, and improving energy efficiency. Agrivoltaics systems can be one of the strategies to accomplish this goal. These systems allow the combination of food and energy production in the same space in a synergistic way, avoiding land-use competition between PV and agriculture. This study analyzes the technical potential of agrivoltaics in mainland Portugal, a country particularly suitable for its implementation due to its high solar potential and diversified agriculture. The study used public geographic information system databases to perform a systematic mapping of the viable areas. The methodology used was based on a multicriteria geospatial analysis, which included the identification of agricultural and pasture areas (based on the 2023 Land Use Charter), the exclusion of zones with legal restrictions such as National Agricultural Reserve (RAN), National Ecological Reserve (REN), and Natura 2000 Network, and the areas with a terrain slope >10%.

METHODOLOGY

1. Identification of eligible areas using the Land Use chart (COS 2023)
2. Application of legal restrictions to eligible areas (Natura 2000 Network, RAN and REN)
3. Intersection of eligible areas with slope ≤10%
4. Definition of useful areas for slope ≤10%
5. Calculation of the potential FV (photovoltaic) installation capacity in the identified useful areas

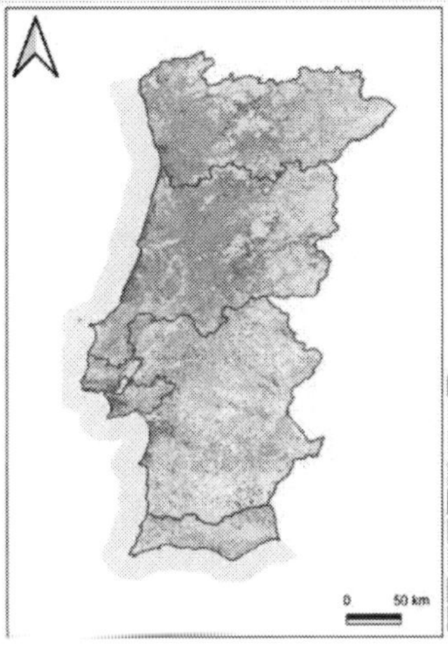

Land Use and Land Cover Map according to COS 2023.

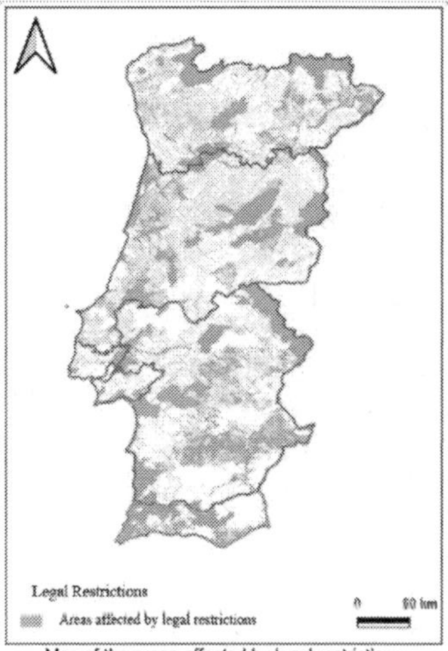

Map of the areas affected by legal restrictions (Natura 2000 Network, REN and RAN)

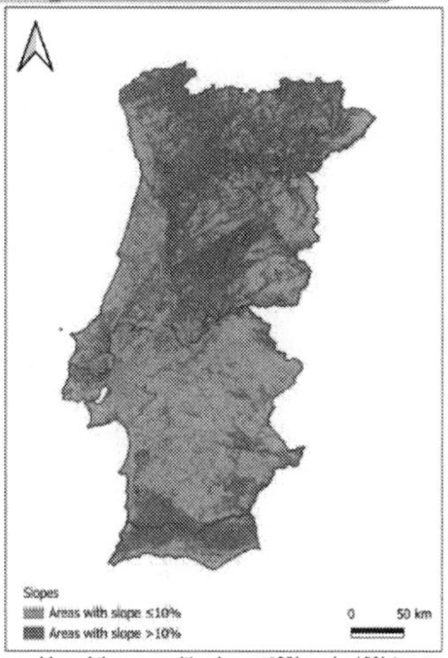

Map of the area with slope ≤10% and >10% in mainland Portugal

RESULTS

Total area (pasture and agriculture) with area affected by legal restrictions, the area with slope >10% and the total usable area

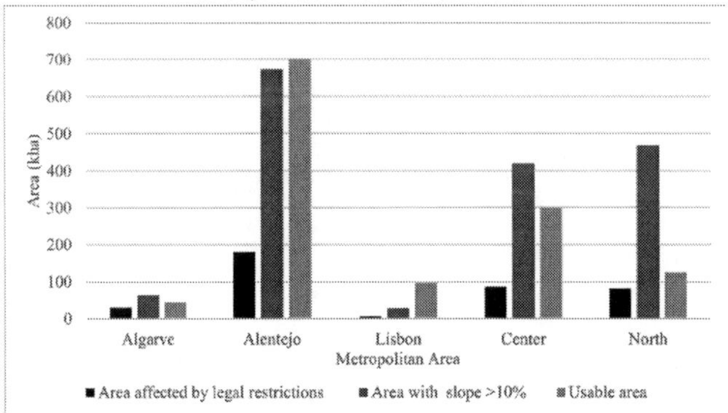

Potential for photovoltaic energy installation capacity of each region in the useful areas with an overhead configuration

Region	Potential for PV energy installation capacity in useful areas (GWp)
Algarve	32
Alentejo	515
Lisbon Metropolitan Area	71
Center	220
North	92

Conclusion

- Integration of geospatial criteria (land use, slope, legal restrictions) enabled the assessment of agrivoltaic technical potential in mainland Portugal.
- Alentejo: largest potential, 515 GWp, confirming national leadership.
- Center: second highest, 220 GWp
- North: 92 GWp.
- Lisbon Metropolitan Area: 71 GWp.
- Algarve: lowest potential, 32 GWp.
- Alentejo and Center together account for the majority of the national potential, making them priority regions for the expansion of agrivoltaic systems.

Acknowledgements

The authors would like to thank the project AGROVOLTEP for supporting and funding this project.

AGROVOLTEP

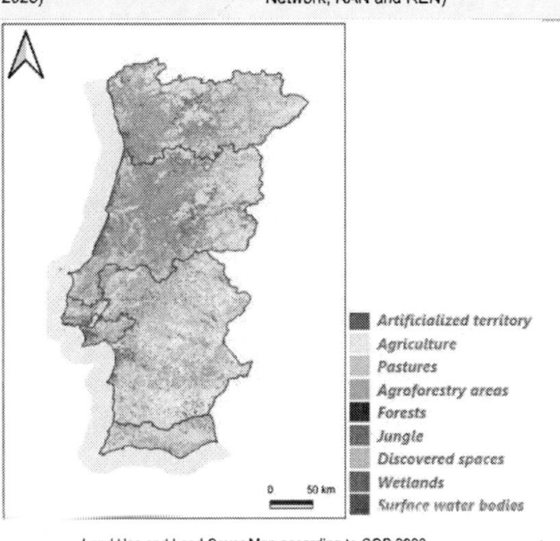

42nd European Photovoltaic Solar Energy Conference and Exhibition

Levelized Cost of Electricity

and its limitations to consider the value of electricity

Fabian Spera[1], Simon Lahr[1] and Marc Andre Schüler[1]
[1] Department of Research Next2Sun Technology GmbH. Franz-Meguin-Str. 10a, 66763 Dillingen (Germany)

Introduction

European climate targets drive a steady expansion of PV capacity. With increasing PV penetration, day-ahead market prices around midday decrease and even turn negative [1]. Conventional PV (C-PV) mainly generate electricity during these low-price hours. Vertical PV (VB-PV) shifts generation to the morning and evening, when higher prices are usually achieved. The aim of this study is to highlight that LCOE neglects generation profile characteristics. Hence, market revenues are evaluated as a complementary indicator reflecting the real value of different PV approaches.

Assumptions

Seven locations were analyzed. An overview of the sites is provided in Table 1 and Figure 1.

Table 1: Overview of the analyzed sites including their latitudes

Site	Latitude
Oulu (Finland)	64.9468
Kärrbo (Sweden)	59.5525
Milkowice (Poland)	51.2552
Aasen (Germany)	47.9949
Bologna (Italy)	44.5352
Toulouse (France)	43.5968
Valencia (Spain)	39.5021

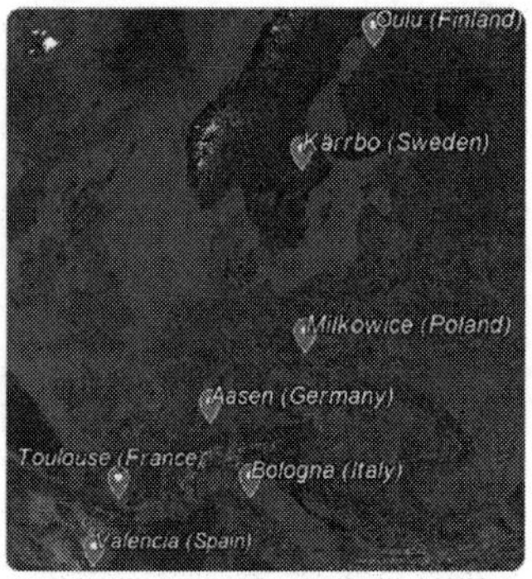

Figure 1: Geographical distribution of the analyzed sites

Table 2 shows the system parameters for VB-PV and C-PV. Both systems were simulated with the same installed capacity of 15 MWp. Due to the lower power density of the VB-PV system (384 kWp/ha) compared to the C-PV system (1050 kWp/ha), the required land area differs significantly. For the given capacity, VB-PV requires ca. 39 ha, while C-PV requires 14 ha. Operational costs are split into fixed OPEX, representing standard operational PV expenses, and variable OPEX, describing land related costs.

Table 2: Overview of the considered system and investment parameters

System	Tilt (°)	Orientation	Module	Pitch (m)	GCR (%)
Vertical-PV	90°	East/West	560 Wp Bifacial (95%)	12	18
Conventional-PV	25°	South	565 Wp Monofacial	-	50

System	CAPEX (€/kWp)	OPEX fix (€/kWp*a)	OPEX var. (€/kWp*a)
Vertical-PV	565 1*	15 [2]	2,000
Conventional-PV	450	16.5 2*	3,000

Results

The VB-PV system was simulated using the in-house simulation tool from Next2Sun, based on Python and pvlib, while the C-PV system was modeled in PVsyst. Specific yield and LCOE were determined using TMY data. Market revenues for 2024 were simulated with historical weather data, considering hourly spot market prices. Negative hours were included, with no curtailment applied to the systems.

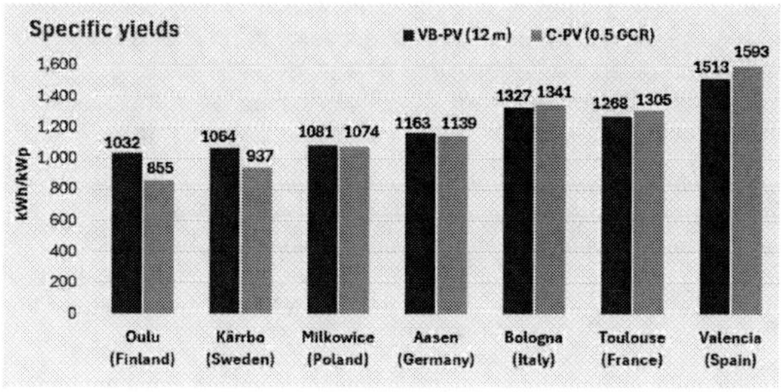

- VB-PV shows higher specific annual yields than C-PV at all locations north of a transition point between Aasen and Bologna, which aligns with findings from other scientific studies [3].

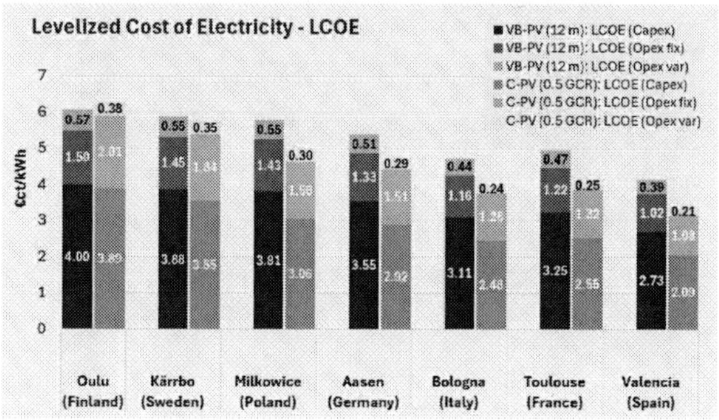

- While CAPEX optimizations have reduced the LCOE gap between VB-PV and C-PV, higher variable OPEX - driven by land related costs due to lower specific installed capacity - remain a key economic drawback.

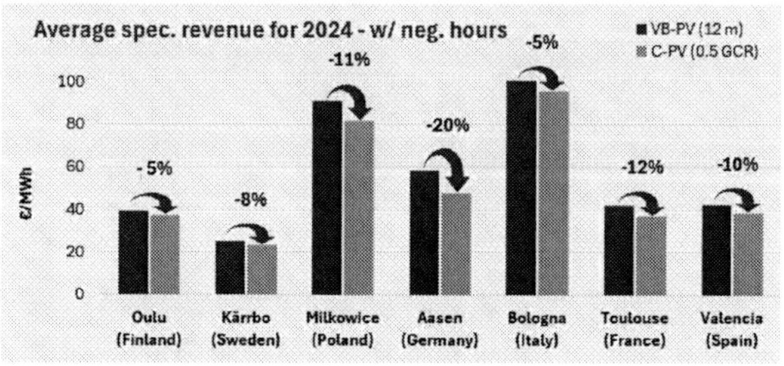

- VB-PV generates significantly higher spec. revenues than C-PV at all studied locations due to its grid friendly generation profile. Disadvantages in terms of LCOE can thus be at least partially offset over the lifetime of the plant even in southern latitudes, while at the same time reducing the risk of producing renewable electricity at negative electricity prices.

Summary

- **LCOE** will **underestimate** the **economic performance** of systems with grid friendly generation profiles like **VB-PV**
- To make an informed investment decision, the achievable **market revenue**, considering the **specific generation profile**, should be **taken into account**.
- Land related **variable OPEX** remain a **key challenge** for **VB-PV** due to the lower power density

Outlook

- **Future assessment** of **C-PV** should be done with **bifacial module** deployment
- **VB-PV** is expected to **achieve** even **higher market revenue in the future** in EU states due to increasing PV penetration & negative electricity prices

1* Assumption: CAPEX VB-PV = CAPEX C-PV + 25.5%; 2* Assumption: OPEX fix C-PV = OPEX fix VB-PV + 10%

[1] Fraunhofer ISE (2025). Aktuelle Fakten zur Photovoltaik in Deutschland. Fraunhofer Institute for Solar Energy Systems ISE, Freiburg, Germany. https://www.ise.fraunhofer.de/de/veroeffentlichungen/studien/aktuelle-fakten-zur-photovoltaik-in-deutschland.html

[2] Böhm (2024). Wirtschaftlichkeit verschiedener Agri-PV Konzepte Impuls aus der Forschung. Presentation at the 2nd National Agri-PV Forum, Leibniz Centre for Agricultural Landscape Research (ZALF), Müncheberg, Germany.

[3] Chudinzow, D., Nagel, S., Güsewell, J., & Eltrop, L. (2020). Vertical bifacial photovoltaics – A complementary technology for the European electricity supply? Applied Energy, 264. https://doi.org/10.1016/j.apenergy.2020.114782

020411-001

Next2Sun
www.next2sun.com

Fabian Spera
Next2Sun Technology GmbH
Franz-Meguin-Str. 10a,
66763 Dillingen (Germany)
f.spera@next2sun.de

DEVELOPMENT OF A SIMPLE TOOL FOR ESTIMATING IRRADIATION REDUCTION IN AGRIVOLTAIC GREENHOUSES

Paula Sánchez-Friera[1], Guillermo Correa[2], Luis Pérez[2], Baurin Leza[2], Tomás Pernas[3], Jairo Pérez[3], Jorge Pérez[3]
[1] Solkeys, Mar Cantábrico 16, 33204 Gijón, Spain
[2] Gonvarri MS R&D, PI Cancienes, 33470 Corvera de Asturias, Spain
[3] Gonvarri AgroTech, PI Cancienes, 33470 Corvera de Asturias, Spain
e-mail: paula@solkeys.com

ABSTRACT: Agrivoltaic greenhouses combine photovoltaic (PV) energy production with horticultural cultivation, but their success depends on maintaining sufficient light transmission to crops. Current modelling tools provide accurate projections of PV performance yet are often too complex for early-stage design or regulatory assessments. This work presents PASSIFLORA, a simplified but physically consistent framework for estimating both crop-level irradiation and PV energy yield in greenhouses. The model reuses and adapts geometric ray-casting and hemispherical sampling algorithms originally developed in PASE, enabling efficient calculation of direct and diffuse irradiance beneath PV-covered roofs. A graphical interface allows users to configure greenhouse geometry, roof layouts and cover properties, with automatic module placement and an option to sweep module coverage to achieve a target irradiation reduction factor. Validation against PVsyst was carried out for a Gothic tunnel greenhouse in the region of Toledo (Spain). The results showed excellent agreement in crop-level irradiation (<0.5% difference) and close agreement in PV yield (within 3%). Case studies further demonstrated the application of the tool to assess different factors such as tunnel configuration, layout patterns, and greenhouse orientation. PASSIFLORA provides a fast, transparent and regulation-oriented approach for pre-design of agrivoltaic greenhouses, complementing detailed engineering software in later project stages.
Keywords: agrivoltaics; greenhouses; solar irradiation; shading analysis; PV simulation.

1 INTRODUCTION

The accelerating deployment of renewable energy systems and the parallel demand for sustainable food production have placed agrivoltaics (AV)—the combined use of land for photovoltaic (PV) energy generation and agriculture—at the center of current research and policy agendas. First proposed by Goetzberger and Zastrow in 1982 [1], the concept has since evolved from an academic idea into a recognized strategy for addressing the food–energy–land nexus, with pilot projects emerging across Europe, Asia, and North America. By co-locating PV with crops, AV systems promise higher overall land productivity and resilience against climate change. Their success, however, hinges on the careful distribution of solar radiation between energy and agriculture.

A central challenge in AV research is the accurate quantification of the solar irradiation reaching the crop zone. While the calculation of plane-of-array irradiance on PV modules is well established in design tools such as PVsyst, PV*SOL, or SAM, these tools were developed primarily for energy applications and are not specifically designed to simulate ground-level shading or the complex distribution of transmitted light. As a result, specialized models or adaptations are required to evaluate the availability of light for crops in AV settings.

Over the past decade, a wide spectrum of approaches has been proposed to address this need [2]. On one side, empirical or semi-empirical indicators such as the ground coverage ratio (GCR) or shading factors have been used as proxies for crop irradiation. These allow quick assessment of average irradiation reduction and have been incorporated into design guidelines, but they provide limited insight into the heterogeneity of light distribution. More recent work has refined these approaches by introducing dedicated shading-factor models, based on analytical projections of regular module geometries [3].

At the opposite end of the spectrum are high-accuracy frameworks [4]. Ray-tracing methods, such as radiance-based, have long been applied to PV system analysis, and in the AV field they are increasingly used to resolve 3D light distribution with spatial and temporal detail. GPU-accelerated approaches such as LuSim [5], [6] extend this capability by providing fast and accurate calculations of light interception in large, heterogeneous scenes, enabling applications to complex AV scenes [7]. Module-level multi-physics detailed models [8], illustrate the depth of resolution achievable when intra-module shading and temperature effects are explicitly considered. These methods capture the full angular structure of diffuse irradiance and complex module geometries, but their computational and/or data and design requirements make them more suitable for advanced engineering studies than for early project exploration.

Greenhouse-based AV has attracted specific attention, as roof-integrated PV modifies not only light availability but also the microclimate within the enclosure. A number of studies [9], [10], [11], [12], [13] have examined how PV integration affects transmitted light and crop performance within greenhouses, addressing aspects such as maximum feasible cover ratios, the effects of shading on yield and quality, and the use of coupled light–climate–crop models to validate growth responses. These works highlight both the opportunities and agronomic risks of PV greenhouse integration, and underline the importance of reliable light-distribution modelling for design and regulation.

Despite this progress, the field continues to face a trade-off between accuracy and usability. The current gap lies in tools that are user-friendly, transparent, fast, physically consistent, and able to deliver reliable estimates of crop-level irradiation without requiring extensive modelling expertise—particularly at the early stages of project development.

This need is reinforced by the evolving regulatory context. In Catalonia, technical guidelines issued in 2023 [14] stipulate that agricultural yield in AV systems must be at least 60% of reference levels, supported by studies quantifying irradiation reduction inside the protected cultivation area. In France, the April 2024 national decree on agrivoltaics [15] requires agricultural yields to remain above 90% of comparable control zones. Similar regulatory frameworks are being debated in other European regions. Such rules necessitate practical modelling tools that can quickly inform design decisions, support compliance assessments, and facilitate dialogue between developers, farmers, and regulators.

In this study, we introduce the streamlined tool PASSIFLORA for estimating the reduction of solar irradiation under PV-covered greenhouses. Our tool builds on validated algorithms to compute direct and diffuse irradiance on the ground, reusing modules from the open-source framework Python Agrivoltaic Simulation Environment (PASE) [16], which has been adapted to integrate specific features for PV greenhouses. By abstracting material properties into global transmission coefficients (e.g., [17]), the approach minimizes input requirements while retaining sufficient physical realism.

The main objectives of this work are therefore: i) to develop a computationally efficient and user-friendly tool for estimating irradiation reduction under PV greenhouse configurations; ii) to validate its predictions against more advanced modelling approaches and reference scenarios; iii) to demonstrate its applicability as a pre-design decision-support tool for regulatory compliance and project development.

By addressing the need for a balance between accuracy and simplicity, this work aims to complement the suite of available AV models, providing a practical solution that supports the early design and approval phases of greenhouse-based agrivoltaic projects.

2 METHODOLOGY

2.1 General approach

The framework developed in this work is designed to provide a fast and user-friendly means of estimating the reduction in solar irradiation reaching the crop zone under photovoltaic (PV) greenhouse systems.

The modelling strategy is based on algorithms developed within the open-source Python Agrivoltaic Simulation Environment (PASE) [16]. Rather than employing full optical ray-tracing—which can capture every reflection and scattering event within the greenhouse system but at significant computational cost—the tool relies on efficient geometric ray-casting algorithms. For each point on the crop zone, rays are traced toward incoming light directions and tested for obstruction by PV modules. The direct component corresponds to the sun vector at each timestep, while the diffuse component is obtained by sampling multiple directions across the sky dome and scaling the diffuse irradiance according to the unobstructed fraction.

In addition to these PASE-based algorithms, PASSIFLORA also makes extensive use of the open-source pvlib Python library [18], which ensures consistency with widely used PV modelling practices.

By integrating these modules into a streamlined workflow (see Figure 1), the tool requires only a limited number of user inputs yet produces physically meaningful outputs that are directly interpretable in the context of agrivoltaic regulation. The primary model output is the transmitted irradiation available to crops, provided both as an hourly time series and as aggregated seasonal or annual totals.

2.2 Set-up of the 3D scene: greenhouse and PV module layout

The first step in the workflow is the definition of the physical scene, which establishes the geometry of the greenhouse and the placement of the photovoltaic (PV) modules. To make the process accessible to non-specialist users, the tool provides automated routines that generate realistic greenhouse models and PV layouts from a limited number of high-level inputs.

Greenhouse geometry: The tool can represent both single-tunnel and multi-tunnel structures, reflecting the two main categories of commercial greenhouses. Each tunnel can be defined with a flat sloped roof or a curved roof, as shown in Figure 2. In the curved case, the radius or curvature factor can be adjusted by the user, enabling the representation of roof types ranging from shallow arcs to sharply vaulted profiles such as Gothic or parabolic designs. Roof height, window gap, span, tunnel length and number of parallel tunnels are also user-defined, which allows the geometry to be scaled to match commercial dimensions.

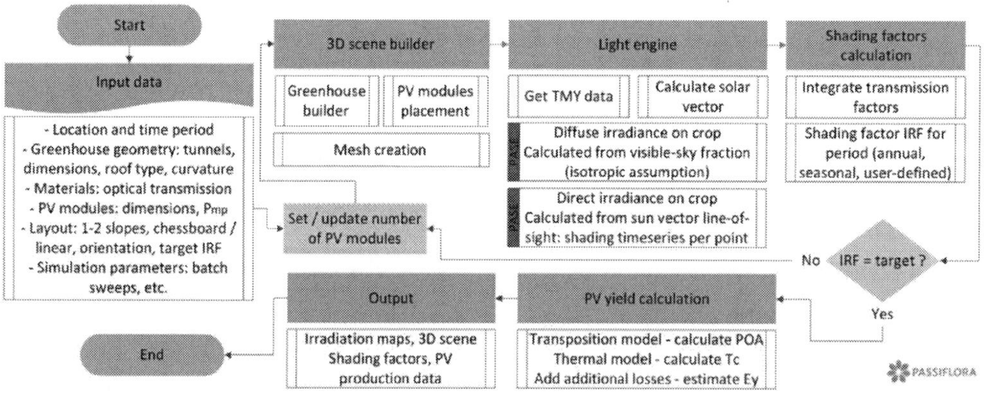

Figure 1: Simulation workflow for the determination of optimal PV capacity on a greenhouse roof to reach the target irradiation reduction factor (IRF)

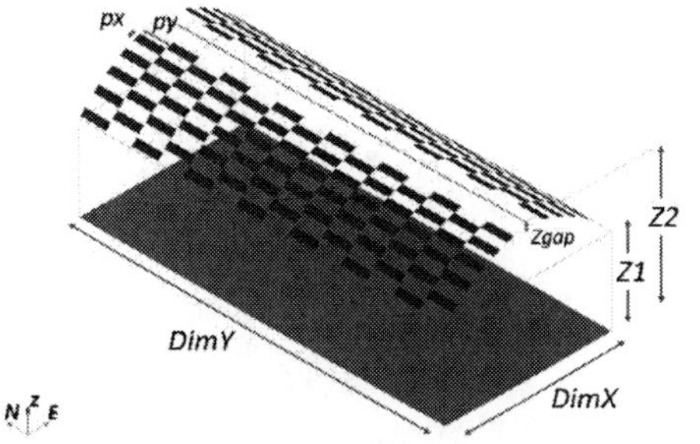

Figure 2: Example of a 3D scene with single-tunnel gothic-arc greenhouse and relevant geometry variables

The orientation of the greenhouse is another key parameter, as it determines how both PV generation and crop light distribution align with the sun's path. The tool allows users to set the azimuth of the greenhouse's longitudinal axis, enabling the simulation of common north–south or east–west orientations as well as any arbitrary angle required by local site constraints.

PV module properties: the type of PV module is defined by its dimensions, peak power and weight. This enables detailed shading calculations as well as the determination of the energy production during the time period specified by the user. The total additional weight of the PV system is also calculated.

PV module layout: The tool automatically generates a PV module arrangement on the roof surface. Several layout strategies are implemented to capture typical design options. In particular, modules can be installed on one slope only (e.g. the south-facing side of an east–west oriented greenhouse) or on both slopes simultaneously. The modules can be arranged in linear rows or in chessboard patterns, the latter often used to improve spatial homogeneity of transmitted light on the crop zone. Finally, the fraction of the roof covered with modules can be adjusted by the user, either directly by specifying the desired ground coverage ratio (GCR) or indirectly by setting a target shading factor on the crops. The tool then determines the appropriate number and spacing of modules to meet this specification.

The output of the scene set-up stage is a fully defined 3D representation of the greenhouse and PV system, which serves as the geometric basis for the subsequent irradiance calculations.

2.3 Weather and irradiance data

Accurate weather inputs are essential for quantifying both the reduction of irradiation in the crop zone and the potential photovoltaic output. In PASSIFLORA, the default workflow retrieves a Typical Meteorological Year (TMY) dataset from PVGIS using the default database for the site (usually SARAH3 for most European locations). The user specifies the geographical location, and the file is automatically downloaded through the pvlib interface. Alternatively, the user may provide a local weather file in CSV format, which is read by the same routines. This dual option ensures that the tool can be applied both in early design stages, when site-specific measurements may not yet be available, and in detailed analyses where local meteorological records are accessible.

In all cases, the model expects the standard irradiance components—global horizontal irradiance (GHI), diffuse horizontal irradiance (DHI), and direct normal irradiance (DNI)—to be explicitly included in the dataset. Solar position parameters, namely zenith and azimuth angles, are calculated with pvlib's astronomical routines to guarantee consistency across irradiance processing and geometric evaluation of shading and sky obstruction.

2.4 Calculation of irradiation on the crop zone

For each timestep, the model evaluates both the direct and diffuse contributions of solar radiation reaching the ground beneath the PV structure.

The direct beam irradiance is determined by tracing a virtual line from the sun's position to the ground plane and checking whether this line intersects any PV module. If the point is shaded, the direct component is set to zero; if unshaded, the component is calculated as the product of DNI and the cosine of the solar zenith angle. This binary shading logic, adapted from PASE's ray-casting module, provides a computationally efficient means of generating shading masks without requiring full 3D rendering.

The diffuse irradiance is estimated with an isotropic sky model in combination with a hemispherical sampling approach. For each point in the crop zone, a set of uniformly distributed rays is generated over the upper hemisphere using a Fibonacci-sphere method, which ensures a nearly even angular coverage. Each ray is then tested for visibility: if it exits unobstructed to the sky it contributes to the diffuse component, whereas rays that intersect a PV module are counted as blocked. The ratio of visible to total rays provides a numerical estimate of the sky view factor, which is used to scale the diffuse horizontal irradiance to the ground level. Although the model assumes isotropic diffuse conditions and therefore neglects anisotropic effects such as horizon or circumsolar brightening, the method offers a good compromise between accuracy and computational efficiency for agrivoltaic applications.

The global irradiance at the crop zone is obtained as the sum of the direct and diffuse components. Finally, the effect of the greenhouse covering material is represented by a single transmission factor (τ). In the reference case, based on literature values for multilayer polyethylene–EVA films, a transmission of 90% in the photosynthetically active radiation (PAR) range is assumed [17]. The transmitted irradiance is then calculated as the product of τ and the global irradiance beneath the modules.

Finally, to quantify the impact of the PV installation, the tool computes the irradiation reduction factor (IRF) for the specified time period, defined as the relative difference between the transmitted irradiation under PV coverage and the reference irradiation without modules (but including cover transmission). This ratio directly expresses the fraction of light lost to the crops due to PV integration, and can be compared against regulatory thresholds. Note that this ratio in our model is independent of the global optical transmission coefficient.

2.5 Photovoltaic energy production

In addition to estimating the irradiance available to crops, the PASSIFLORA tool calculates the energy yield of the installed PV system. This step makes use of the irradiance components (GHI, DNI, DHI) from the weather dataset together with the geometric layout of the modules defined in the scene.

The first step is the computation of irradiance on the plane of array (POA) for each module. The tool makes use of the Reindl transposition model, as implemented in pvlib. Compared to purely isotropic approaches, the Reindl model provides a more realistic representation of diffuse irradiance under a wide range of sky conditions and is widely used in PV performance modeling.

Once the POA irradiance is determined, the module operating temperature is estimated using the SAM temperature model implemented in pvlib, which relates cell temperature to ambient conditions and incident irradiance. The effective POA irradiance and cell temperature are then combined with the module's electrical parameters to compute the energy output in the defined time period. To approximate additional losses not explicitly modelled, a global loss factor is applied. This term accounts for effects such as angular losses, spectral variations, mismatch, soiling, cabling resistance, and inverter conversion, thereby yielding the final system energy production. Results are generated as hourly time series and aggregated into annual or seasonal indicators such as total yield and performance ratio. These outputs are presented alongside the crop-level irradiation reduction, enabling an integrated assessment of agrivoltaic system performance.

2.6 Framework and user interface

A distinctive feature of this modelling framework is its emphasis on accessibility. The computational routines are implemented in Python, but they are embedded within a graphical user interface (GUI) that allows users to configure greenhouse dimensions, PV layout, and material properties without requiring programming skills. Input parameters are organised in simple forms, and results are displayed both as numerical values (annual irradiation totals, reduction percentages) and as graphical outputs such as time series plots and shading maps.

By default, the tool can be run in an automatic sweep mode where the number of PV modules is varied until the simulated irradiation reduction factor matches, as closely as possible, a user-defined target. This feature is particularly relevant in contexts where regulatory frameworks prescribe a maximum allowable reduction in transmitted light, as it enables the user to directly identify a compliant configuration without trial-and-error adjustments.

This design choice serves two purposes. First, it makes the tool usable by a broad range of stakeholders—including farmers, project developers, and regulators—who may not have expertise in simulation software. Second, it facilitates potential deployment as a web-based application, where the GUI could be adapted into an online interface enabling interactive design studies. By combining simplified but validated algorithms with a user-friendly interface, the framework ensures that reliable irradiation reduction assessments can be carried out quickly and consistently at the earliest stages of project planning.

3 VALIDATION

3.1 Case definition

The reference system is a commercial Gothic-tunnel greenhouse supplied by Gonvarri AgroTech, located in the region of Toledo (Spain). The site has no PV cover at present; the PV layout described below is a controlled configuration used for validation.

Although the greenhouse is multitunnel, for the validation we have focused on a single-span Gothic tunnel, with dimensions 30 m length and 9.6 m span, channel height 5.0 m, and ridge height 7.8 m. The impact of multiple tunnels is analysed in section 4. The curved roof is represented by circular arcs of 10 m radius, yielding a mean roof slope of ~30°. The greenhouse longitudinal axis is north–south, so the roof slopes face east and west. A vent opening at the top is modelled by using a maximum z value for the positioning of the modules. Other elements such as the greenhouse structure are neglected.

The enclosure is treated as a typical multilayer LDPE/EVA greenhouse film; a PAR transmission factor of 0.90 is adopted for the baseline, consistent with values reported for commercial films.

For roof integration we consider narrow crystalline-Si modules of 1.00 m × 0.25 m and 35 Wp, aligned with the roof arcs. These lightweight units were selected because they had been used previously in a small laboratory prototype test, and their reduced width facilitates uniform coverage along the curved roof geometry. Although their efficiency is lower than that of standard PV modules, they provide a representative case for evaluating the modelling framework.

3.2 PASSIFLORA and PVsyst configuration

For the geometry of the greenhouse described above and the type of PV module, PASSIFLORA was used to generate automatically PV modules on the roof with a target of 20% irradiation reduction factor. The positions, tilts and azimuths of the PV modules were exported to a file for later use in PVsyst. The weather data was ingested from PVGIS.

In PVsyst, the roof-mounted modules are modelled in the 3D scene for the energy-yield run, employing the same reference PV module as in the PASSIFLORA simulation. The positions, tilts and azimuths of the PV modules are input in the 3D scene using the exported values from PASSIFLORA. The electrical model includes standard PVsyst loss mechanisms (IAM, temperature, wiring/mismatch, soiling, inverter behaviour).

To obtain crop-level irradiation under the canopy, a second variant is used: the roof modules are converted into opaque shading objects, and a horizontal "virtual array" is defined at crop height over the greenhouse floor. PVsyst's hourly shading engine (direct, diffuse sky, circumsolar) then returns transmitted ground irradiation and shading factors on that horizontal plane, while the regular variant provides the PV production of the roof array. This enables the calculation of the irradiation values on the crop area for direct comparison with PASSIFLORA.

3.3 Results

The results of this simulation with both modeling approaches are shown in Table I. The annual ground-level global irradiation agrees to better than 1 kWh m^{-2}. The irradiation reduction factors were essentially identical in both simulations (0.1775), which corresponds to a ratio of 0.52 for a ground cover ratio of 0.3448.

The annual energy delivered by the system differs by 1.38%. This is partially due to small differences in the plane-of-array irradiance, which arise from the different transition methods employed in the two simulations, and to the simplification of loss factors in PASSIFLORA.

The validation confirms that the easy-to-use approach in PASSIFLORA reproduces crop-level irradiation beneath a PV greenhouse with negligible bias relative to PVsyst. Differences in PV energy yield remain small ($\leq$ ~3%) and trace primarily to the distinct loss and

10.4229/EUPVSEC2025/4DV.1.29

transposition treatments. Taken together, these results support the use of PASSIFLORA for rapid, regulation-oriented pre-designs of solar PV greenhouses.

Table I: Comparison of PVsyst and PASSIFLORA for the simulation of a single-tunnel PV greenhouse

Variable	PASSI FLORA	PVsyst	Diff.
Irradiation reduction factor (IRF)	0.1775	0.1779	-0.22%
PV energy yield [kWh kWp^{-1}]	1382.1	1363.3	1.38%

4 CASE STUDIES

Following the validation against PVsyst, a series of case studies were conducted to illustrate the capabilities of PASSIFLORA in exploring different design options for agrivoltaic greenhouses. These examples are not intended as detailed engineering designs but rather as demonstrations of how the tool can be applied to support early-stage decisions and regulatory compliance. Each case highlights a different design variable and its impact on both crop-level irradiation and PV production.

4.1 Multi-tunnel configuration

The influence of adjacent tunnels on crop-level irradiation was analysed by simulating an increasing number of identical Gothic tunnel units placed side by side. Each tunnel retained the same geometry and PV layout as in the reference case; only the number of lateral repetitions was varied, as shown in Figure 3. Irradiation was then evaluated at the ground level in the central tunnel, so that the results reflect the effect of neighbour shading.

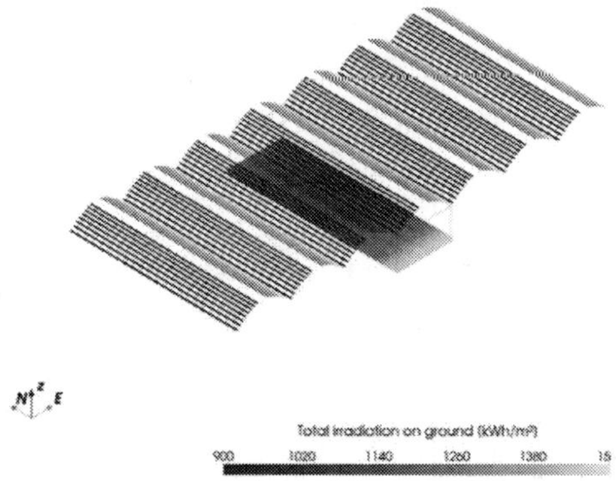

Figure 3: Representation of a 3D scene with 7 tunnels to assess the impact on the irradiation on crop for the central tunnel

Figure 4 shows the variation of the ratio of annual irradiation reduction to geometric cover (IRF/GCR_x) as a function of the total number of tunnels in the greenhouse. A sharp increase occurs when moving from an isolated tunnel to configurations with three or more tunnels. This is caused by lateral shading from neighbouring roofs, which diminishes both the visible fraction of sky and the direct beam component. Beyond approximately seven tunnels, the shading factor stabilises, indicating that the central tunnel has reached a "pseudo-infinite" condition where side effects become negligible. In this situation the value of IRF/GCR_x reaches 0.87, which is consistent with values reported in previous studies [9], [19]. This demonstrates that multi-tunnel arrangements accentuate shading effects and must be accounted for when modelling large-scale greenhouse blocks.

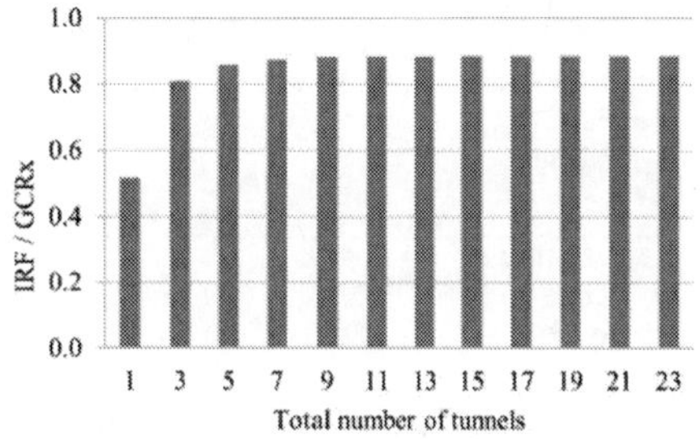

Figure 4: Impact of the number of tunnels on the irradiation on crop at a central tunnel

4.2 Alternative module arrangements

PASSIFLORA allows testing of different roof layouts beyond the baseline linear configuration. To illustrate this, two roof patterns were compared: linear rows and a chessboard arrangement. In both cases the number of modules per tunnel and the overall ground coverage ratio were kept identical. Results show that the chessboard pattern produces negligible changes in annual IRF and PV yield when compared to the linear layout. However, the irradiation distribution at crop level becomes slightly more homogeneous in the chessboard case, with lower contrasts between shaded and unshaded zones. This suggests that, while energy metrics remain unaffected, the chessboard pattern may provide agronomic benefits in terms of spatial light uniformity.

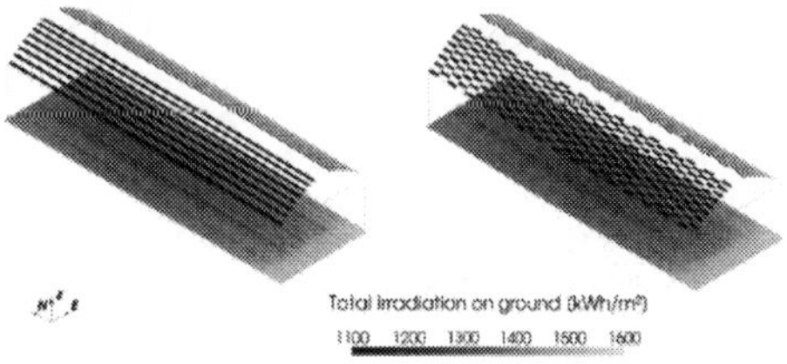

Figure 5: Comparison of linear (left) versus chessboard (right) patterns for the PV modules layout on the greenhouse roof

4.3 Impact of orientation

The effect of greenhouse orientation was evaluated by comparing a north–south (N–S) ridge, with PV modules placed on both roof slopes facing east and west, against an east–west (E–W) ridge, with PV modules placed only on the south-facing slope, as shown in Figure 6. Both configurations used the same greenhouse geometry and the same number of PV modules (300), corresponding to a total installed capacity of 10.5 kWp. The geometric ground cover ratio was 0.22 in both cases.

The results are shown in Table II. The crop-level irradiation is lower in the E-W case, with a nearly 30% higher irradiation reduction factor.

In terms of electricity generation, the E-W ridge PV greenhouse delivers around 20% more energy. Despite the lower production, the N-S greenhouse produces a more homogeneous daily output. Moreover, shading on the crop is more evenly distributed temporally and spatially in the N-S orientation, while the E-W orientation presents

10.4229/EUPVSEC2025/4DV.1.29

stronger asymmetries. These differences underline that orientation affects not only the balance between energy yield and crop irradiation but also the diurnal and seasonal light patterns experienced by crops, which may be critical depending on crop sensitivity.

Table II: Comparison of N-W vs E-W orientations for a PV greenhouse

Variable	N-S	E-W	Diff.
Irradiation reduction factor (IRF)	0.1118	0.1571	-28.8%
PV energy yield [kWh kWp^{-1}]	1391.3	1712.5	-18.8%

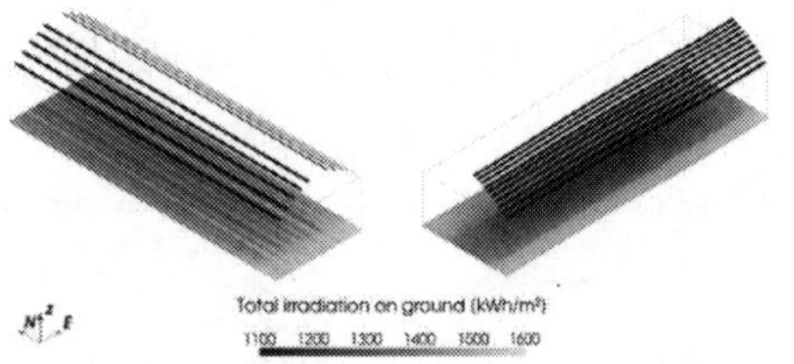

Figure 6: Comparison of N-S (left) versus E-W (right) greenhouse orientation with same total number of PV modules

5 CONCLUSIONS

This work presented the development and first validation of PASSIFLORA, a simplified modelling framework for estimating irradiation reduction and PV energy yield in agrivoltaic greenhouses. By adapting geometric shading and light-sharing algorithms originally developed in PASE, the tool provides physically consistent estimates of transmitted irradiation without relying on computationally intensive ray-tracing methods. A graphical interface and automated layout routines make the framework accessible for non-expert users, supporting early-stage design and compliance with emerging agrivoltaic regulations.

Validation against PVsyst for a real Gothic tunnel greenhouse at the region of Toledo (Spain) showed excellent agreement in crop-level irradiation, with annual differences below 0.5%, and close agreement in PV energy yield, within approximately 3%. These results confirm that the simplified ray-casting and hemispherical sampling approach implemented in PASSIFLORA can reproduce the outputs of a reference engineering tool with negligible bias, while requiring significantly less design effort.

The case studies further illustrated how the framework can be applied to explore practical design variables. Multi-tunnel arrangements introduced additional shading due to neighbouring tunnels reduced the light available in the central tunnel, while alternative layouts such as chessboard arrangements improved homogeneity without altering annual totals. The comparison between north–south and east–west ridge orientations showed that in this case the east-west orientation offers more homogeneity and more irradiation for the crops while lowering the PV yield.

Overall, PASSIFLORA demonstrates that simplified yet physically grounded methods can provide reliable and transparent estimates of both crop irradiation and PV performance. Its ease of use and ability to deliver regulation-oriented metrics position it as a valuable decision-support tool for developers, farmers and policymakers, complementing but not replacing detailed simulation software in later design stages.

ACKNOWLEDGEMENTS

This work has been partially funded by the Agencia SEKUENS through the FLORA project (reference IDE/2024/000462). The authors gratefully acknowledge the PASE development team for making their open-source algorithms publicly available, which provided the foundation for part of the modelling framework presented here.

REFERENCES

[1] A. Goetzberger and A. Zastrow, 'On the Coexistence of Solar-Energy Conversion and Plant Cultivation', *International Journal of Solar Energy*, vol. 1, no. 1, pp. 55–69, Jan. 1982, doi: 10.1080/01425918208909875.

[2] S. Zainali *et al.*, 'Modelling, simulation, and optimisation of agrivoltaic systems: a comprehensive review', *Applied Energy*, vol. 386, p. 125558, May 2025, doi: 10.1016/j.apenergy.2025.125558.

[3] S. Zainali *et al.*, 'Direct and diffuse shading factors modelling for the most representative agrivoltaic system layouts', *Applied Energy*, vol. 339, p. 120981, Jun. 2023, doi: 10.1016/j.apenergy.2023.120981.

[4] S. P. Rajan, S.-N. Asaa, A. Katsikogiannis, J. Robledo, J. Leloux, I. Kaaya, G. Bosco, 'Validation and benchmark of modelling tools for light assessment using ray-tracing and GPU-based method', Deliverable 2.2 - Symbiosyst - Horizon Europe EU project - Grant Agreement No. 101096352, Dec. 2024.

[5] J. Robledo, J. Leloux, E. Lorenzo, and C. A. Gueymard, 'From video games to solar energy: 3D shading simulation for PV using GPU', *Solar Energy*, vol. 193, pp. 962–980, Nov. 2019, doi: 10.1016/j.solener.2019.09.041.

[6] J. Robledo Bueno *et al.*, 'Lessons Learned from Simulating the Energy Yield of an Agrivoltaic Project with Vertical Bifacial Photovoltaic Modules in France', *38th European Photovoltaic Solar Energy Conference and Exhibition; 1588-1595*, p. 8 pages, 7533 kb, 2021, doi: 10.4229/EUPVSEC20212021-6CV.4.41.

[7] I. El Boujdaini *et al.*, '3D Modelling of Light-Sharing Agrivoltaic Systems for Orchards, Vineyards and Berries', *40th European Photovoltaic Solar Energy Conference and Exhibition*, pp. 020430001–020430010, 2023, doi: 10.4229/EUPVSEC2023/4DO.2.3.

[8] H. Goverde *et al.*, 'Energy Yield Prediction Model for PV Modules Including Spatial and Temporal Effects', *29th European Photovoltaic Solar Energy Conference and Exhibition; 3292-3296*, 2014, doi: 10.4229/EUPVSEC20142014-5CV.2.28.

[9] M. Cossu *et al.*, 'Assessment and comparison of the solar radiation distribution inside the main

commercial photovoltaic greenhouse types in Europe', *Renewable and Sustainable Energy Reviews*, vol. 94, pp. 822–834, Oct. 2018, doi: 10.1016/j.rser.2018.06.001.

[10] M. Cossu *et al.*, 'Agricultural sustainability estimation of the European photovoltaic greenhouses', *European Journal of Agronomy*, vol. 118, p. 126074, Aug. 2020, doi: 10.1016/j.eja.2020.126074.

[11] C. J. Torrente, J. Reca, R. López-Luque, J. Martínez, and F. J. Casares, 'Simulation model to analyze the spatial distribution of solar radiation in agrivoltaic Mediterranean greenhouses and its effect on crop water needs', *Applied Energy*, vol. 353, p. 122050, Jan. 2024, doi: 10.1016/j.apenergy.2023.122050.

[12] M. E. Evans, J. A. Langley, F. R. Shapiro, and G. F. Jones, 'A Validated Model, Scalability, and Plant Growth Results for an Agrivoltaic Greenhouse', *Sustainability*, vol. 14, no. 10, pp. 020430-001-020430–010, 2022, doi: https://doi.org/10.3390/su14106154.

[13] G. López-Díaz, A. Carreño-Ortega, H. Fatnassi, C. Poncet, and M. Díaz-Pérez, 'The Effect of Different Levels of Shading in a Photovoltaic Greenhouse with a North–South Orientation', *Applied Sciences*, vol. 10, no. 3, p. 882, Jan. 2020, doi: 10.3390/app10030882.

[14] Generalitat de Catalunya Departament d'Acció Climàtica, Alimentació i Agenda Rural Direcció General d'Agricultura i Ramaderia., *Instrucció tècnica que estableix els criteris d'agrovoltaisme a Catalunya*. 2023.

[15] Journal Officiel de la République Française, *Décret no 2024-318 du 8 avril 2024 relatif au développement de l'agrivoltaïsme et aux conditions d'implantation des installations photovoltaïques sur des terrains agricoles, naturels ou forestiers*. 2024.

[16] R. Bruhwyler *et al.*, 'Modelling light-sharing in agrivoltaics: the open-source Python Agrivoltaic Simulation Environment (PASE 1.0)', *Agroforest Syst*, vol. 98, no. 8, pp. 2747–2764, Dec. 2024, doi: 10.1007/s10457-024-01090-8.

[17] H.-J. Tantau *et al.*, 'Solar Transmittance of Greenhouse Covering Materials', *Acta Hortic.*, no. 956, pp. 441–448, Oct. 2012, doi: 10.17660/ActaHortic.2012.956.51.

[18] K. S. Anderson, C. W. Hansen, W. F. Holmgren, A. R. Jensen, M. A. Mikofski, and A. Driesse, 'pvlib python: 2023 project update', *Journal of Open Source Software*, vol. 8, no. 92, p. 5994, Dec. 2023, doi: 10.21105/joss.05994.

[19] N. Hanrieder, A. Kujawa, A. B. Seychelles, M. Blanco, J. Carballo, and S. Wilbert, 'Estimation of maximum photovoltaic cover ratios in greenhouses based on global irradiance data', *Applied Energy*, vol. 365, p. 123232, Jul. 2024, doi: 10.1016/j.apenergy.2024.123232.

Development of a simple tool for estimating irradiation reduction in agrivoltaic greenhouses

solkeys

R&D Gonvarri

Paula Sánchez-Friera[1], Guillermo Correa[2], Luis Pérez[2], Baurin Leza[2], Tomás Pernas[3], Jairo Pérez[3], Jorge Pérez[3]

[1] Solkeys, Mar Cantábrico 16, 33204 Gijón, Spain

[2] Gonvarri MS R&D, PI Cancienes, 33470 Corvera de Asturias, Spain

[3] Gonvarri AgroTech, PI Cancienes, 33470 Corvera de Asturias, Spain

E-mail: paula@solkeys.com

CONTEXT AND OBJECTIVES

- **Regulatory context:** constraints on maximum shading factors and/or maximum yield reduction inside the greenhouse due to PV
- **Challenge:** Standard PV simulation tools lack features to model in detail irradiation at the crop level, while more sophisticated tools exist but require a high-level of modeling expertise / cost
- **Need:** fast, accurate and transparent tool for early-stage design and regulation compliance

Key objectives:

- Development of a computationally efficient and user-friendly tool for estimating irradiation reduction under PV greenhouse configurations
- Validation against other modelling approaches
- Demonstration as a pre-design decision-support tool for regulatory compliance and project development

METHODOLOGY

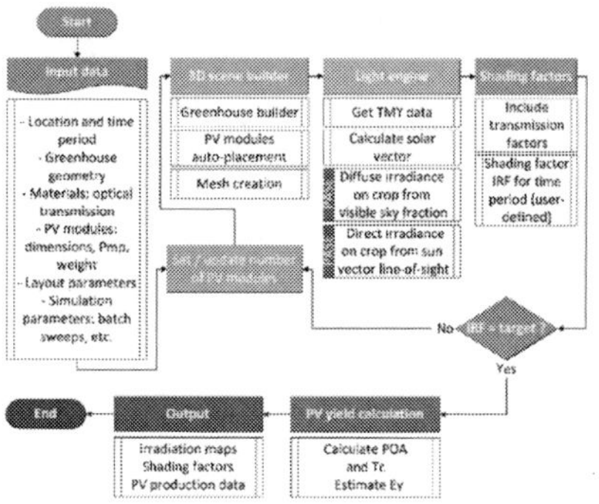

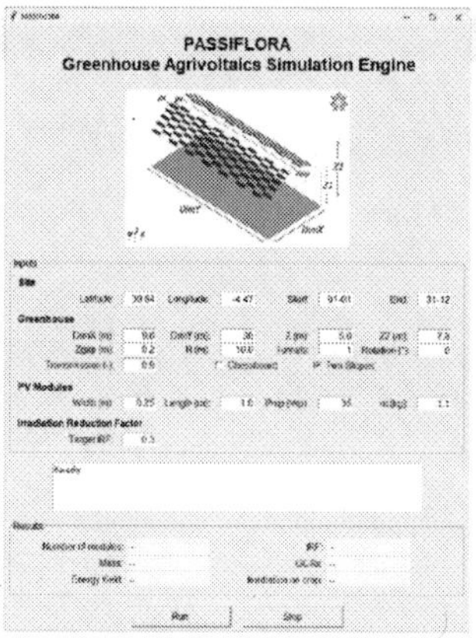

VALIDATION

- Comparison with PVsyst simulation results
- Gothic tunnel greenhouse (30 m × 9.6 m)
- Modules: linear layout, 8 rows per slope, 0.25 m
- PVsyst variants:
  A. PV roof: positions of tables input from PASSIFLORA
  B. Sensor field: PV modules transformed to objects and virtual PV field created at crop level

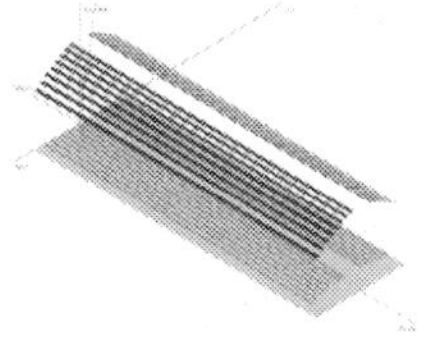

- Results show very good agreement

Variable	PASSIFLORA	PVsyst	Diff.
Irradiation reduction	0.1775	0.1779	-0.22%
PV energy yield [kWh/kWp]	1382.1	1363.3	1.38%

CASE STUDIES

Impact of number of parallel tunnels

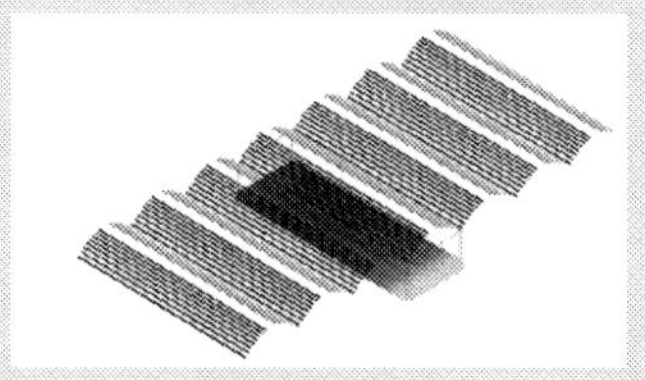

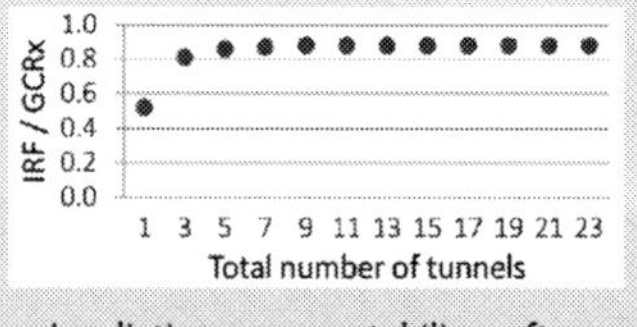

- Irradiation on crop stabilizes after 2-3 tunnels on each side

Impact of N-S vs E-W orientation

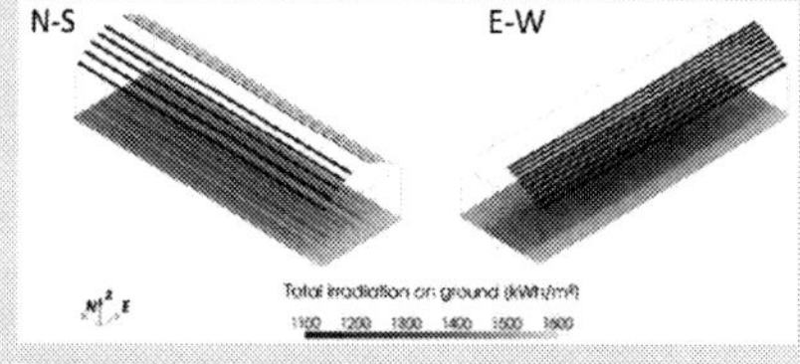

Variable	N-S	E-W	Diff.
Irradiation reduction [%]	0.1118	0.1571	-28.8%
PV energy yield [kWh/kWp]	1391.3	1712.5	-18.8%

- N-S ridge orientation favours higher irradiation on crop, more uniformity and better-balanced diurnal PV production

Impact of PV module layout

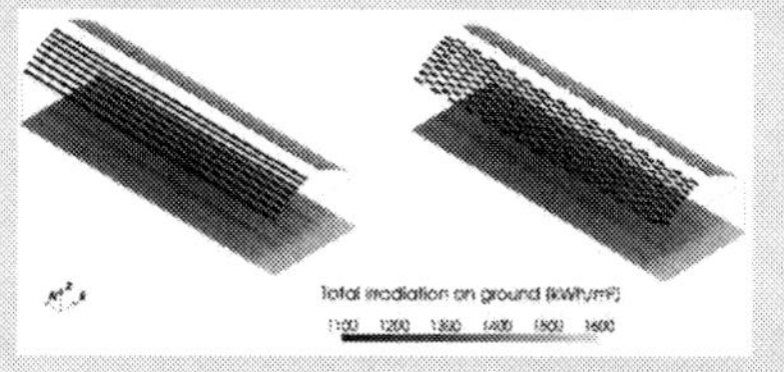

- Linear vs chessboard lay-out comparison
- IRF and PV yield almost unchanged
- Chessboard slightly more uniform light distribution

CONCLUSIONS AND OUTLOOK

- PASSIFLORA enables fast, regulation-oriented design of AV greenhouses
- Validated against PVsyst with excellent agreement
- Flexible for geometry, layout, orientation
- Accessible through GUI
- Minimal inputs needed

Future work:

- Integration of additional models
- Further validation including real greenhouse
- Online deployment for interactive design

This work has been partially funded by the Agencia SEKUENS through the FLORA project (reference IDE/2024/000462).
The authors gratefully acknowledge the PASE development team for making their open-source algorithms publicly available, which provided the foundation for part of the modelling framework.

Download full paper here →

PV AND PVT SYSTEMS DESIGN FOR "RASPA Y AMAGADO" GREENHOUSES

Author(s): José Manuel Naveiro[1,*], Beatriz Muñoz Vidal[2], Eduardo Pardo[3], María Miguel Laborda[2], Ana Escudero[2], Gonzalo Brun[1], Raquel Simón-Allué[1], Raúl Villén[1], Yolanda Lara[1]
Company / Institute(s): (1) Endef; (2) IaSol; (3) Fundación Tecnova
Address(es): josemanuel.naveiro@endef.com , beatrizmunoz@iasol.es , ingenieria@fundaciontecnova.com , mariamiguel@iasol.es , anaescudero@iasol.es , gonzalo.brun@endef.com, raquel.simon@endef.com, raul.villen@endef.com , yolanda.lara@endef.com

ABSTRACT: **Achieving symbiosis between agriculture and photovoltaic production** is one of the most critical aspects of developing agrivoltaic technology (Agri-PV), being the integration with greenhouses one of the main research lines. Among greenhouses, Almería's region, in Spain, shows a unique typology known as "raspa y amagado" (or Almería-type) characterized by lightweight removable plastic covers.

The present study is part of the Agrisol project; a Spanish-national project that seeks to implement Agri-PV in Almería-type greenhouses. Within this project, options for achieving an efficient and simple installation of solar systems in this type of greenhouses have been studied.

Innovation was also achieved with the integration of photovoltaic-thermal air-based solar panels, which generate hot air that can contribute to general heating, ventilation, or cooling consumption, depending on the greenhouse and crop requirements.

This paper presents the studies and designs developed for the Agri-PV system. **It is the first study conducted on "raspa y amagado" greenhouses with photovoltaic and hybrid (PVT) panels.**

1 INTRODUCTION

Agrivoltaics (Agri-PV), also known as agrophotovoltaics, involves harnessing a single area of land to produce both solar energy and agricultural products. In other words, solar panels coexist with crops on the same surface. This technique was originally conceived by Adolf Goetzberger and Armin Zastrow in 1981, but the concept only became popular in the last decade. According to a study published by Nature [1], if just 1% of arable land were dedicated to solar electricity production, it would be possible to meet global energy demand.

One of the aspects to be considered is the amount of shading provided by the solar panels that may be acceptable for the crops. Studies reported no significant effects of 20% coverage with photovoltaic panels on growth, yield, and quality in a greenhouse in Greece [2]. In Italy, pepper species were found to be compatible within photovoltaic greenhouses with a shading rate of 25%, causing limited yield reduction below this value [3].

The most characteristic greenhouse in Almería is the so-called "raspa y amagado" greenhouse (Figure 1), which occupies approximately 96% of the total greenhouse surface area [4]. This type of greenhouse consists of a wooden or steel structure covered by a lightweight plastic cover that is replaced every 2 years. These greenhouses have narrow windows in the roof to allow for ventilation, covered with a more durable plastic than the rest of the structure, which is replaced every 8 years.

Figure 1 "raspa y amagado" greenhouse.

The electricity consumption required by this type of greenhouse is around 15,000–30,000 kWh per hectare per year, being the highest consumption due to the water pumping systems and the motors for opening and closing windows. These characteristics of low-energy greenhouses represent, a priori, the potential to cover greenhouse demand with photovoltaic energy, improving the farmer's operating account and reducing the carbon footprint of Almería's products [5].

The purpose of the Agrisol project is to research and develop new methodologies, processes, and components for optimizing the implementation and operation of Agri-PV technology, resulting from the integration of photovoltaic generation facilities in greenhouse crops.

To achieve this objective, the project seeks to install photovoltaic modules adapted to the layout and structure of Almería-type greenhouses without affecting the development of the crops.

Agrisol incorporates two types of infrastructure innovation within the framework of Agri-PV technology: the support structure for the photovoltaic panels and the implementation of a hybrid system that generates both electricity and heat.

2 DESIGN PROCESS

For the design process, aspects such as the structural requirements, the weight of the system, and the replacement of the plastic cover needed to be considered together with global Agri-PV aspects such as shading.

The replacement of the plastic envelope was one of the limitations found during the study. After the assessment of several options, it was decided the most adequate location for the solar system was the greenhouse roof windows. This offered a standard and more solid structure, although narrow surface to work on, with lower replacement frequency of the plastic cover. Additionally, the windows are yet considered as shading area in these greenhouses, so the shading percentage is not increased.

There are two window orientations (East and West) and two main positions for the windows: closed (0% aperture, 11° tilt) or opened (100% aperture, 52° tilt). A

10.4229/EUPVSEC2025/4DV.1.33

representation of the East-faced window is shown in Figure 2.

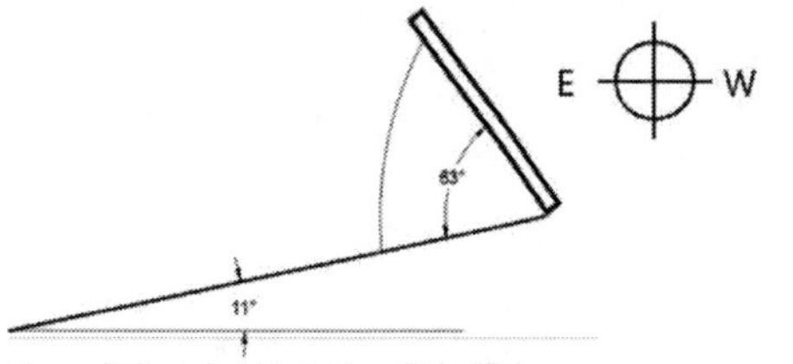

Figure 2 East-faced window tilt 100% aperture.

The evaluation and selection of photovoltaic modules to be used in the PV and PVT systems were framed by the windows area and the weight limitations. Thus, flexible photovoltaic modules were adopted for both systems.

2.1. PV Fastening system.

In a photovoltaic installation, the mounting structure is a mechanical component responsible for securing the modules by fixing them to the roof either through anchoring or ballast. The structure allows for setting the panel's orientation and tilt parameters and angles that determine the plant's final energy output.

The fastening system employed had to enable anchoring the modules to the window frame structure. To achieve this, a structural analysis of the components was performed using a FEM-based software and assembly tests were carried out on a replica of the greenhouse window where the modules would be installed.

For the photovoltaic system, two distinct anchoring methods were proposed:

1. Hook-type component; commonly used for anchoring lightweight modules on balconies. The proposed components are very lightweight, made of aluminium 5005-T5, and consist of three elements: (1) a small curved L-, (2) a larger flat rectangular (3) the joining mechanism. This three individual pieces interlock to create a hook-shaped structure.
2. Sheet Metal Threaded Profile; which involves attaching three very lightweight aluminium profiles per module to the window structure using sheet metal screws. The distribution of these profiles matches that of the hooks, as both are arranged according to the module's mounting holes.

For the structural assessment of each component under system loads, the Finite Element Method (FEM) was employed. The showed results are the ones from the final selected structure for the PV system: sheet metal threaded profile. The location of the threaded profiles is presented in Figure 3 below:

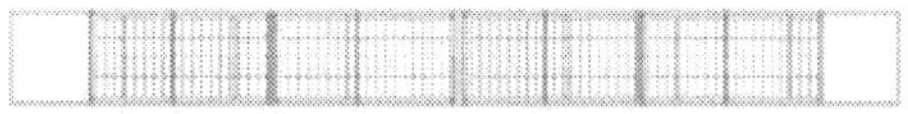

Figure 3 Structure design (threaded profiles in pink colour).

The sheet metal threaded profile method requires drilling the base window structure. The most relevant element for this method is the window structure itself and how the incorporation of these profiles and their corresponding drilled holes affect it. The distribution of 5.5 kg among six supports of the photovoltaic modules is accounted for in the FEM analysis. In addition, the weight of the profile between the two supports in the structure is considered, resulting in a point load of 9.77 N. This point load is transmitted through the 12 module mounting holes distributed along the longitudinal window profiles. The analysis indicates that the maximum resulting longitudinal displacement of the window is 0.422 mm.

In Figure 4 the result of the Finite Element Analysis (FEA) is shown. The FEA allows to dimension the critical points of the structure and to decide if it is necessary to reinforce the structure or change to another attaching system.

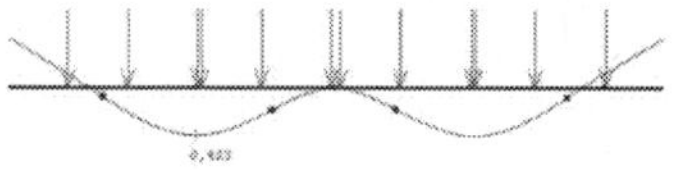

Figure 4 Finite Element Analysis applied to the longitudinal profile of the window.

The stress analysis performed yielded values that were practically negligible, indicating that the induced stresses do not significantly compromise the structural integrity of the window. Furthermore, the displacement results corroborate the minimal influence of this fastening method on the overall load-bearing behaviour of the system. Based on these findings, it can be concluded that the implementation of Sheet Metal Threaded Profiles provides sufficient stability, thereby eliminating the necessity for additional structural reinforcement.

As part of the validation process, a series of assembly tests were conducted at Endef's facilities. The objective of these tests was to evaluate the technical feasibility and compatibility of the two proposed structural systems for securing the photovoltaic panels on the greenhouse window under study. A photography of the assembly test appears in Figure 5.

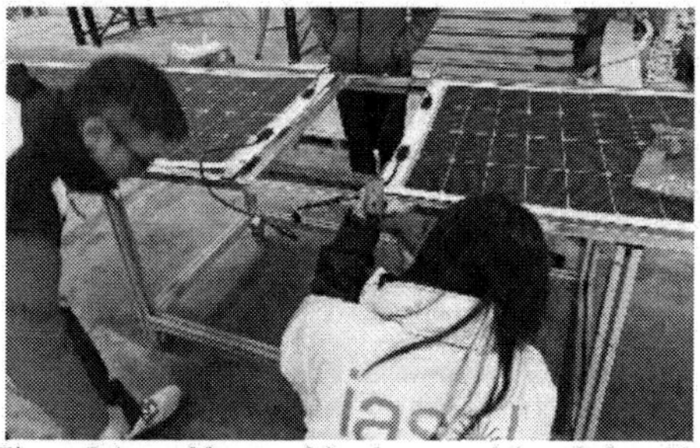

Figure 5 Assembly test of the sheet metal threaded profile method.

The tests enabled identification of potential design adjustments, confirmed the mechanical and functional suitability of the structures for future implementation, and allowed selection of the structure type with the simplest assembly. This, in turn, helps to reduce assembly times and associated costs. During assembly, the evaluated aspects included time required, personnel needed, and tools used.

For the sheet metal threaded profile method, only one installer was required, with an estimated assembly time of approximately 15 minutes per module. The assembly process was simpler and safer, and it reduced the buckling effect that was observed in the photovoltaic module when hook-type components were used.

2.2. PVT system

As for the integration of hybrid photovoltaic-thermal (PVT) panels into agricultural structures, this technology adds a unique and innovative element to the Agrisol project. These panels combine the production of thermal energy with the generation of electrical energy. This dual functionality enables the system's energy efficiency to be maximised.

The PVT-system requires the creation of a channel for the air to flow under the photovoltaic modules. This air, which passes between the photovoltaic modules and the plastic, comes from inside the greenhouse and returns to it at a higher temperature. In order to create this channel within the available surface, taking into account the weight and structural requirements, numerous hybrid system configurations and concepts were explored throughout the process in order to arrive at the final solution. Figure 6 shows the design's evolution regarding materials and distribution.

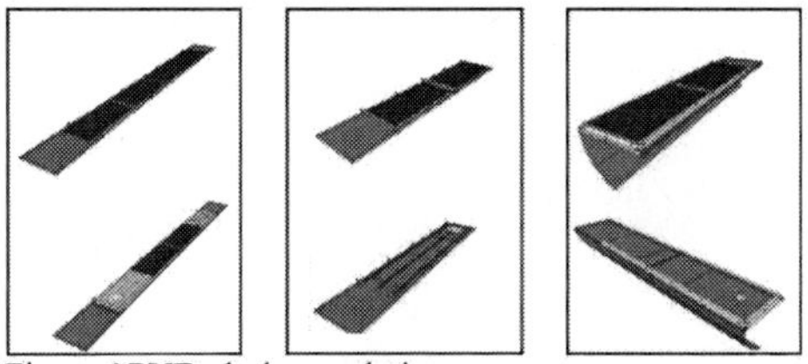

Figure 6 PVTs design evolution.

The final design presents the easiest mounting system of the explored concepts and is also the most resistant one thanks to the employed materials and structure.

An aluminium mounting structure bolted to the roof windows that creates a channel for the air flow between the photovoltaic modules and window surface was designed (Figure 7). This structure also underwent through the FEM analysis as well as through a series of assembly tests at Endef's facilities to check the technical feasibility of the process.

Figure 7 First assembled PVT system prototype at Endef's facilities.

The end result of the design process is a small, light, and effective system that maximizes the use of the available space, makes mounting easier, and minimizes the need for new structural elements.

3 INSTALLATION PROCESS AND TESTING

Both systems, PV and PVT, were installed in Almería during the spring-summer of 2025 on a "raspa y amagado" greenhouse. The installed systems were located over the greenhouse windows, as seen in Figure 8.

Figure 8 Photovoltaic modules installed on the "raspa y amagado" roof windows.

Two of the three available windows on the roof of the demonstrator greenhouse were used to install the PV system (East- and West-faced windows), while the remaining window was assigned to the PVT system (East-faced window).

The commissioning and first data acquisition were done on summer 2025. During this period, thermal performance data have been gathered in order to prepare for the final testing phase which will take place during the pepper planting season, in autumn.

The working hours for the initial testing were between 8 a.m. and 1 p.m. This initial testing allowed to analyse the performance and the hardiness of the PVT system as a preparation for the full testing.

Figure 9 shows temperature and irradiance data for July 28th. This situation is the worst-case scenario because the data were gathered with the window totally opened, facing the west orientation in the morning and with crops inside the greenhouse. In this scenario, an increment of 8.2 °C over the greenhouse internal temperature was observed.

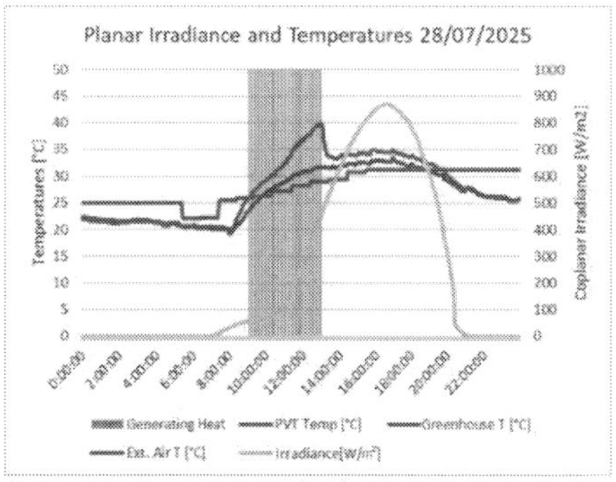

Figure 9 Temperatures and irradiance.

The blue background colour represents the working hours of the fan (from 8 a.m. to 1 p.m.). The blue line is the temperature of the air at the exit of the PVT system. As shown in the figure, while the fan is turned on, this temperature reaches a sharper increase than the greenhouse one (red line) as well as the ambient one (grey line). Once the fan is turned off the temperature of the PVT decreases and becomes similar to the temperature of the greenhouse.

The shape of the irradiance curve (yellow line) corresponds to the 100% opened window (52° tilt and west orientation), and does not reach the maximum values during the working time. Higher temperatures are expected during peak irradiation hours, and future test data will be used to clarify this expectation.

Data collection will be performed during autumn to determine performance during the crop season. Through that time the fan of the PVT system will be working all the day continuously.

4 CONCLUSSIONS

Two small, light, and effective structures for installing PV and PVT technologies in Almería-type greenhouses have been designed.

The designed configurations have been installed in Almería in spring-summer 2025. Performance data will be collected in autumn 2025.

The worst-case scenario during the summer obtained an increase of 8.2 °C in the PVT air temperature over the internal greenhouse temperature.

The project provides a previously unexplored component in Almería-type greenhouses. The developed systems allow to find more efficient and widespread applications of these technologies and reduce the CO_2 emissions.

5 ACKNOWLEDGEMENTS

This publication is part of the R&D&I project AGRISOL, funded by MCIN/AEI (CPP2021-008521) and the European Union Next Generation EU/PRTR.

6 REFERENCES

[1] Adeh, E. H., Good, S. P., Calaf, M., & Higgins, C. W. (2019). Solar PV power potential is greatest over croplands. Scientific reports, 9(1), 1-6.

[2] Kavga, A., Trypanagnostopoulos, G., Zervoudakis, G., & Tripanagnostopoulos, Y. (2018). Growth and physiological characteristics of lettuce (Lactuca sativa L.) and rocket (Eruca sativa Mill.) plants cultivated under photovoltaic panels. Notulae Botanicae Horti Agrobotanici Cluj-Napoca, 46(1), 206-212.

[3] Cossu, M., Yano, A., Solinas, S., Deligios, P. A., Tiloca, M. T., Cossu, A., & Ledda, L. (2020). Agricultural sustainability estimation of the European photovoltaic greenhouses. European Journal of Agronomy, 118, 126074.

[4] Céspedes, A. J., García, M. C., Pérez-Parra, J. J., & Cuadrado, I. M. (2010). Caracterización de la explotación hortícola protegida almeriense. Almería, España: FIAPA.

[5] López-Díaz, G., Carreño-Ortega, A., Fatnassi, H., Poncet, C., & Díaz-Pérez, M. (2020). The effect of different levels of shading in a photovoltaic greenhouse with a north–south orientation. Applied Sciences, 10(3), 882

PV and PVT systems design for "raspa y amagado" greenhouses

Author(s): José Manuel Naveiro[1,*], Beatriz Muñoz[2], Eduardo Pardo[3], María Miguel Laborda[2], Ana Escudero[2], Gonzalo Brun[1], Raquel Simón-Allué[1], Raúl Villén[1], Yolanda Lara[1]
Company / Institute(s): (1) ENDEF; (2) IASOL; (3) Fundación Tecnova
***corresponding e-mail address(es):** josemanuel.naveiro@endef.com

INTRODUCTION: AGRISOL Project

The work is part of the **Agrisol** project; a Spanish-national project that seeks to **implement agrivoltaics technology (Agri-PV) in Almería-type greenhouses.** Thus, we have designed the implementation of two technologies for this type of greenhouses: **photovoltaic (PV) and photovoltaic thermal (PVT)** for electricity (with PV and PVT) and heat generation (with PVT), to maintain the greenhouse temperature above 25 °C.

"Raspa y amagado" greenhouse

- The most characteristic greenhouse in Almería
- Wooden or steel structure .
- Lightweight plastic cover, replaced every 2 years.
- Narrow windows in the roof to allow for ventilation (their plastic is replaced every 8 years).

Design process: decisions

- To use narrow windows for solar installation due to its plastic cover replacement frequency.
- Narrow windows are already considered shaded space.
- Flexible PV modules are selected due to the structural requirements and the modules lightweight.

PVT SYSTEM

Objective: To create a channel below PV modules for enable forced air circulation and heat the greenhouse.

ANALYSIS

Solar energy: Estimation of electrical and thermal production

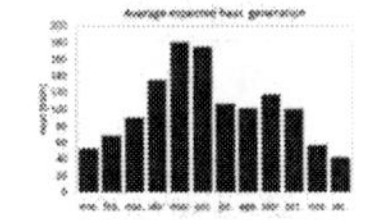

CONCEPT

Redesign: Generation of different designs that accomplishes the requirements

PROTOTYPE

Resulting system: Compact solution that is simpler to assemble. It recirculates the air from the greenhouse

PV FASTENING SYSTEM

Objective: To enable anchoring the modules to the window though a low weight and easy-to-install grip.

ANALYSIS

Structural: Strains and deformations

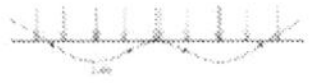

CONCEPT

Anchoring methods: two proposed :

- Hook-type component
- Sheet Metal Threaded Profile

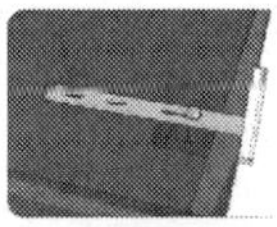

PROTOTYPE

Resulting system: Simpler and safer solution to install. Reduction of the buckling effect

INSTALLATION AND TESTING

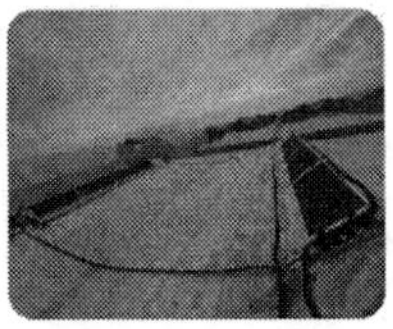

INSTALLATION PROCESS: 1 PVT and 2 PV systems were installed in Almería, during the spring-summer of 2025 on a "raspa y amagado" greenhouse.

- Commissioning and first data acquisition: summer, without crop.
- Two position for windows: open (11° tilt, east) / closed (52° tilt, west).
- Working hours for initial testing: 8 a.m. to 1 p.m.

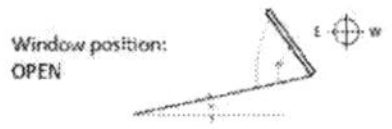

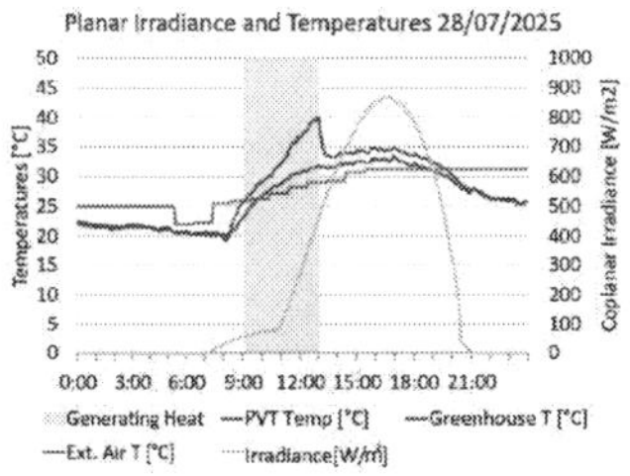

PRELIMINARY RESULTS: **Increase of 8.2 °C over internal temperature**, in the worst-case scenario (summer, open window facing west, morning operation and with crops)

Data collection will be performed **during autumn** to determine performance during the crop season.

CONCLUSIONS

- The designed configurations have been **installed in Almería** in spring-summer 2025. Thermal data will be collected in autumn 2025.
- The end result of the design process is a **small, light, and effective structure** for each technology, the PV and the PVT technologies.
- The worst-case scenario during the summer obtained **an increase of 8.2 °C over the internal greenhouse temperature**.
- The project provides a previously unexplored component in Almería-type greenhouses. The developed systems allow to find more efficient and widespread applications of these technologies and reduce the CO_2 emissions.

This publication is part of the R&D&I project AGRISOL, funded by MCIN/AEI (CPP2021-008521) and the European Union NextGenerationEU/PRTR.

INVESTIGATING SPECTRAL, THERMAL AND POSITIONAL EFFECTS ON THE PERFORMANCE OF 5-JUNCTION CPV CELLS

Elizabeth M Hagemann[1], Frederik J Vorster[1], E Ernest van Dyk[1], Ruediger F Loeckenhoff[2]
[1] Physics, Nelson Mandela University, University Way, Summerstrand, Port Elizabeth, 6031, South Africa
[2] AZUR SPACE Solar Power GmbH, Theresienstr. 2 74072 Heilbronn, Germany

Corresponding author e-mail address: s221440003@mandela.ac.za

ABSTRACT: Concentrator photovoltaic (CPV) cells are sensitive to environmental conditions, including solar spectral composition and operating temperature, as well as cell alignment relative to the Fresnel lens. Using a research-based CPV module, provided by AZUR SPACE Solar Power and deployed in South Africa, the study provides insights into the effects of spectral composition, operating temperature and cell misalignment on the performance of two variations of the 5C46 cell under operational conditions. Solar spectral data, using Average Photon Energy, indicated that Port Elizabeth is predominantly blue-rich relative to AM1.5d, with seasonal variations. Measurements revealed temperature differences of approximately 10 °C between cells along the edge and in the centre of the module, resulting in power variations of up to 0.328 W. Positional displacement showed that small lateral x–y misalignments had a limited effect on Voc and Isc, but a noticeable influence on power. Variations in cell height with respect to the Fresnel lens affected all electrical parameters. Spectral analysis confirmed that a version of the 5C46 cell performed as designed with improved performance in red-rich spectra. These findings emphasise the importance of spectral considerations, effective thermal management, and accurate optical alignment in the design of CPV modules.
Keywords: Concentrator Photovoltaics, Multi-junction Solar Cell, Spectral Composition, Thermal Effects, Positional Effects

1 INTRODUCTION

Most concentrator photovoltaic (CPV) systems utilise multi-junction solar cells (MJSCs) to efficiently convert solar energy to electricity. MJSCs are sensitive to a variety of factors, including environmental conditions and the cell's position within the module, which influence their behaviour under real-world operational conditions. Thus, to evaluate the MJSCs performance under realistic conditions, AZUR SPACE Solar Power developed and provided a research-based CPV test module, referred to as the Analysis Module [1].

The Analysis Module is deployed at the Outdoor Research Facility of Nelson Mandela University (NMU) in Port Elizabeth, South Africa. Mounted on a dual-axis tracker, the Analysis Module is adjacent to the modules it replicates. The baseline modules form part of a C3PV system which is a commercial 4 kW CPV system franchised by AZUR SPACE Solar Power [2], [3]. To provide a detailed comparative performance analysis of MJSCs, the Analysis Module contains sixty MJSCs manufactured by AZUR SPACE Solar Power, which vary in the number of junctions, subcell current balance and position within the module. This study focuses on the performance of two variations of the 5C46 CPV cell (5-Ja and 5-Jf) under varying spectral, temperature, and positional conditions.

MJSC performance depends on both the magnitude of the direct normal irradiance (DNI) and its spectral composition. Spectral composition, impacted by time of day, season and atmospheric conditions, influences the photon flux incident on each subcell and consequently affects overall MJSC power output.

Port Elizabeth is well-suited for studying the impact of solar spectrum on MJSCs due to its geographical position as a coastal town producing variability in the environmental conditions. Despite frequent cloud cover limiting the power production from CPV systems, the area experiences variations in temperature, aerosol concentrations and water vapour concentration, which make it ideal for MJSCs and CPV system testing.

In addition to the impacts of DNI and spectral composition, the operating temperature plays a critical role in determining MJSC performance. Although MJSCs are typically made from materials with larger band gaps than silicon cells, an increase in operating temperature causes a narrowing of the band gap in the semiconductor material and ultimately reduces the open-circuit voltage (Voc) of MJSCs [4]. Thus, higher operating temperatures lead to a loss of power for the MJSC.

Beyond environmental influencing factors, positional variations of the MJSCs relative to the Fresnel lens may occur during the assembly of the module and can impact the performance of the MJSCs. Misalignments of the enhanced Fresnel assembly (EFA), comprising the MJSC and secondary lens, can be both an x–y positional displacement on the module backsheet or a variation in the cell- Fresnel lens distance. Both types of displacement can alter the spectral and thermal conditions experienced by the cell, ultimately impacting its power.

Thus, the purpose of this study is to investigate the influence of environmental and positional conditions on the performance of two variations of the 5C46 cell. The research focuses on the influence of spectral composition, operational temperature variations, and cell position in the module during operational conditions.

2 THEORY

Average Photon Energy (APE), Equation 1, is a simple, single-unit measurement used to classify the solar spectral composition by comparing the integral of spectral composition $E(\lambda)$ to the integral of photon flux $\varphi(\lambda)$ [5]. Spectra can be compared to a reference spectrum, where spectra with higher APE values are considered blue-shifted, whilst lower APE values are considered red-shifted. A comparison can be IEC standard spectral composition AM1.5d, with APE = 1.545 eV for the wavelength range of 290-1800 nm.

$$APE = \frac{\int_{\lambda_a}^{\lambda_b} E(\lambda)\, d\lambda}{q \times \int_{\lambda_a}^{\lambda_b} \varphi(\lambda)\, d\lambda} \ (eV) \quad (1)$$

Although APE values provide a convenient single-value metric for complex spectral comparison and are indicative of spectral shifts, it does not directly translate to photovoltaic power output [6], [7]. This limitation arises because APE values average the spectral information, masking variability and ultimately obscuring the effects of features such as water vapor absorption and aerosol optical depth on the spectral composition. Consequently, APE values can be used as a qualitative measurement and must be complemented with detailed spectral and performance analyses.

APE values vary by region, reflecting the local atmospheric and environmental conditions. Desert locations often exhibit red-rich spectra with lower APE values, whereas high-altitude or low-aerosol regions, such as Lima, Peru, are characterised by blue-rich spectra with APE values as high as 1.920 to 1.930 eV [8].

The operating temperature of a solar cell has a well-established effect on performance. In single-junction solar cells, elevated temperatures reduce both the open-circuit voltage (Voc) and fill factor (FF) due to an increased intrinsic carrier concentration and enhanced recombination rates within the semiconductor material [4]. For MJSCs, these thermal effects are even more pronounced. Because each subcell operates at a different band gap, temperature-induced changes can lead to current mismatch among subcells, thereby adding to the overall power loss. Additionally, an increase in operating temperature results in an increase in the current at the maximum power point (Imp) of a solar cell.

Finally, positional displacement of MJSCs relative to the focal point can affect device performance. Displacement may occur during module assembly, from mechanical stress or from thermal warping of the module backsheet. Such misalignments can manifest either as x-y displacements on the module backsheet or as deviations in the cell–lens distance. In both cases, the spectral distribution on the cell surface and the cell's thermal conditions are altered, ultimately influencing its electrical output [9].

3 EXPERIMENTAL PROCEDURE

To evaluate the performance of the 5C46 cells, producing approximately 7 W of power under full concentrated sunlight, both electrical and environmental parameters were measured using the Analysis Module. The collected data were subsequently filtered and analysed to determine the impact of spectral composition, operational temperature and cell displacement on MJSC performance.

3.1 Analysis Module

Designed and provided by AZUR SPACE Solar Power, the Analysis Module replicates the base structure of a C3PV module, a commercial CPV system. It is a compound refractive module consisting of sixty EFAs, a Fresnel lens and an aluminium module housing [1]. Each MJSC varies in the number of junctions, subcell current balance and position within the module. This study focuses on 2 variations of the 5C46 illustrated in Figure 1. These are the 5-Ja and 5-Jf, adapted for AM1.5d and red-rich spectra according to AZUR SPACE Solar Power.

To monitor positional displacement of the MJSCs as a height variation from the Fresnel lens, the Analysis Module is constructed with 4 separate panels, which are indicated in Figure 1. The panels are 0 mm (no deviation from a C3PV module), -1.8 mm (decreased MJSC to Fresnel lens distance), +2.2 mm (increased MJSC to Fresnel lens distance), and +4.4 mm (further increased MJSC to Fresnel lens distance).

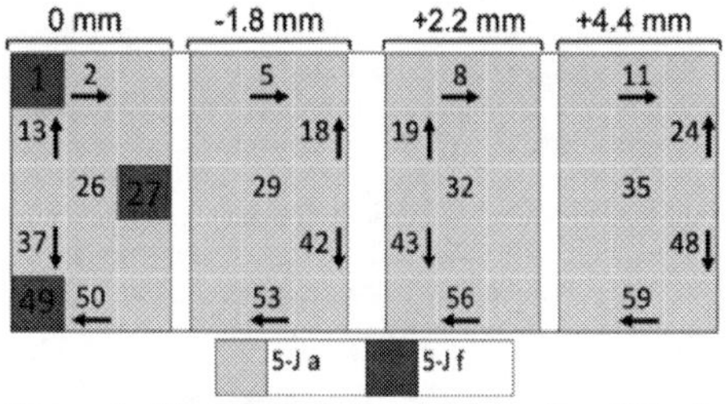

Figure 1: Simplified diagram of the cells within the Analysis Module.

Due to the construction of the Analysis Module, panels -1.8 mm and +2.2 mm are partially thermally isolated from the module housing, whereas the cells on panels Δ0 mm and +4.4 mm are secured directly to the backsheet of the aluminium housing and thus benefit from the heat-sinking capabilities of the surrounding housing. Additionally, unlike power-producing C3PV modules, the Analysis Module does not deliver electricity to a load. As a result, the MJSCs operate at different temperatures within the Analysis Module and operate at temperatures higher than those observed in the adjacent C3PV modules.

For the temperature analysis, the 5C46 cells, 5-Jf in Figure 1, are examined. The cells are located on the Δ0 mm panel and positioned on the outer edge (cells 1 and 49) and towards the centre (cell 27) of the panel.

For the cell displacement and spectral analysis, the 5C46 5-Ja cells, in Figure 1, are examined. The x-y-displacement consists of cells that have a ±2 mm shift, as well as a reference cell on the panel that has no shift from the position optimised during the design of the C3PV modules. Replicating possible variations that could occur in the placement of the MJSC in a CPV module during the assembly or due to a mechanical strain of the backsheet allows for an understanding of the tolerances of cell misalignment.

3.2. Experimental Method

Measured data was collected from the Analysis Module, including electrical measurements comprising Voc, short-circuit current (Isc), Imp and the voltage at the maximum power point (Vmp). Simultaneously, it records environmental parameters, such as backsheet temperature and, using a Spectrafy D2 sensor, it determines DNI and solar spectral composition.

Following data collection, APE was calculated for every solar spectrum, using equation 1, and the measurement data was then filtered to remove incorrect measurements and false readings. The data is limited to above 500 W/m^2, after 09h00 and before 15h00. Due to the placement of the Analysis Module at the bottom of the tracker, the data was limited to remove data entries with module or Spectrafy D2 sensor shading.

For the temperature analysis, thermal images were taken of the Analysis Module at 14h30 on 17 January 2025 under clear sky conditions. The three 5C46 cells, 1, 27, and 49, were identified, and the corresponding backsheet temperatures and electrical data were compared.

To evaluate positional misalignment effects, both lateral displacement and height variation to the Fresnel lens, 20 cells with 5 cells per panel were examined. The data was compared to understand the impact of positional tolerances on MJSC performance.

For the spectral analysis, two reference spectra, whose APE values are shown in Figure 2, were selected to represent red-shifted and blue-shifted spectral conditions in Port Elizabeth. These were defined as the median spectra of all data entries with APE values below and above AM1.5d, respectively. All measurement data were filtered relative to these reference spectra. Pmp normalised by DNI (a proxy for efficiency) was then compared against the cell performance at AM1.d.

4 RESULTS AND DISCUSSION

Port Elizabeth provides an ideal testing ground due to the wide range of solar spectral compositions experienced. In this section, the impacts of spectral composition, operating temperature, and positional displacement on MJSC performance are presented.

4.1 Solar Spectrum in Port Elizabeth

The distribution of APE values for Port Elizabeth, shown in Figure 2, was determined from January 2024 to August 2025, with data recorded between 09h00 and 15h00. The yearly APE values for Port Elizabeth are clustered around AM1.5d, with the yearly median APE slightly above the APE value of AM1.5d (1.545 eV). Thus, Port Elizabeth is a predominantly blue-rich region, for data entries above 500 W/m^2, when compared to AM1.5d. However, when compared to sites such as Lima, Peru, with APE values as high as 1.930 eV [8], Port Elizabeth appears relatively red-rich.

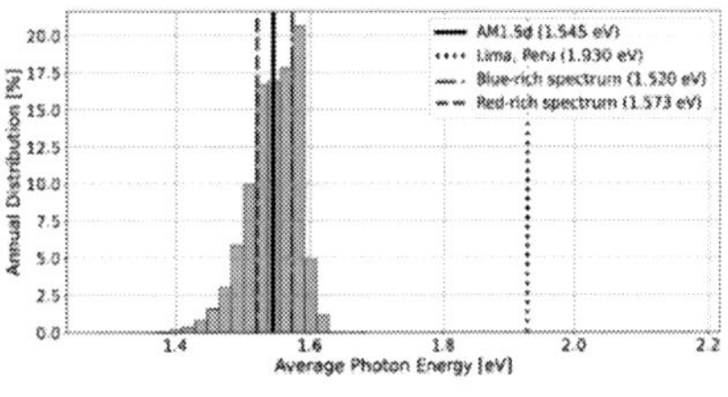

Figure 2: Distribution of APE values for Port Elizabeth. For comparison, the APE of AM1.5d, the maximum APE reported for Lima, Peru [8], and the representative red-rich and blue-rich spectra for Port Elizabeth are shown.

Table I provides a comparison of the median monthly APE values for Port Elizabeth. There is a seasonal variation with an APE difference of 0.063 eV between the highest and lowest months. This indicates measurable seasonal spectral shifts, making Port Elizabeth a suitable environment for the spectral analysis of MJSCs and CPV modules.

Table I. Median monthly APE values for Port Elizabeth, with comparison to AM1.5d.

Month	Median APE [eV]	Comparison to AM1.5d [%]
January	1.578	2.129
February	1.580	2.281
March	1.576	2.040
April	1.570	1.579
May	1.541	-0.269
June	1.525	-1.282
July	1.526	-1.237
August	1.517	-1.795
September	1.526	-1.223
October	1.532	-0.831
November	1.570	1.647
December	1.573	1.815

4.2 Temperature Variations on MJSC Performance

Temperature measurements of three 5C46 cells (cells 1, 27, and 49), on the Δ0 mm panel, revealed operating temperature differences. These differences are illustrated in the thermal image of the back of the Analysis Module, Figure 3, captured at 14h30 on 17 January 2025. The cells near the edges (cells 1 and 49) exhibited lower operating temperatures due to additional heat sinking from the module housing, while the central cell (cell 27) was approximately 10 °C hotter. This temperature distribution is noticed in the C3PV module, where the cells on the outer edge are cooler than the central cells.

Additionally, visible in Figure 3 is the increased temperature of the cells on the -1.8 mm panel. The -1.8 mm and +2.2 mm exhibited increased temperatures because of poor thermal contact with the aluminium housing. As such, the MJSCs on panel -1.8 mm operate at temperatures hotter than those on the Δ0 mm panel.

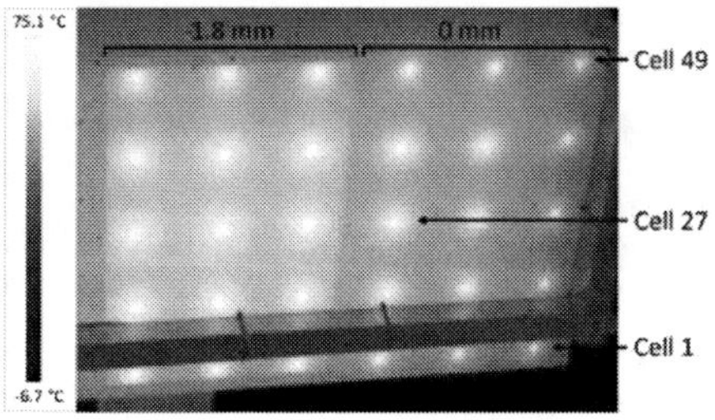

Figure 3: Thermal image of the Analysis Module taken at 14h30 on 17 January 2025. The investigated cells, 1, 27 and 49 are shown with temperatures of 66.5 °C, 76.7 °C and 66.1 °C respectively.

The operating temperatures are confirmed by the electrical performance of cells 1, 27, and 49. Table II summarises Isc, Voc, Imp, Vmp, and Pmp, expressed as a difference relative to cell 27. The edge cells, approximately 10 °C cooler, achieved significantly higher Voc values and improved Pmp.

The reduction in Imp for Cell 49 was within measurement uncertainty and is considered negligible compared to the strong impact of temperature on Voc and Vmp.

Furthermore, solar cells commonly increase in Imp with an increase in temperature, and the situation is more complex for MJSCs. In this case, the 5-Jf, adapted for red-rich spectra, was mostly used under blue-rich conditions.

10.4229/EUPVSEC2025/4DV.1.41
020416-003

Consequently, the uppermost solar cell, which benefits most from the bandgap shift at elevated temperatures, was seldom current limiting. Under red-rich spectra, the Imp and temperature relationship may show a strong positive relation.

Table II. Electrical parameters for cells 1, 27, 49 on the Δ0 mm panel. The parameters are given as a percentage difference to cell 27. Data was taken between 14h15 and 14h45 on the 17 January 2025 at a DNI of 886.59 W/m².

Parameter		Cell		
		1	27	49
Isc	[A]	0,014	0,000	0,014
Voc	[V]	0,180	0,000	0,187
Imp	[A]	0,015	0,000	-0,004
Vmp	[V]	0,186	0,000	0,190
Pmp	[W]	0,328	0,000	0,250
FF	[-]	0,006	0,000	-0,005

These results confirm the sensitivity of MJSC performance to operating temperature. Thus, emphasis must be placed on the importance of thermal management in CPV module design, as the location of the cell within the module can impact its performance.

4.2 Spectral and Positional Variations on MJSC Performance

To assess the effect of MJSC displacement, five cells were analysed on each panel corresponding to a 2mm shift up, right, down and left. The electrical characteristics, including Voc, Isc and Pmp were considered for the filtered data.

Positional displacement had minimal impact on Voc, as shown in Figure 4. The cells, on the 0 mm panel, showed maximum Voc variations of approximately 1 %. The altered panels showed a maximum variation of approximately 3 %. Additionally, the effect of an increased operational temperature is further illustrated for the Voc of cells 26, 32, 35. Situated in the middle of their respective panel, they performed worse than the surrounding cells.

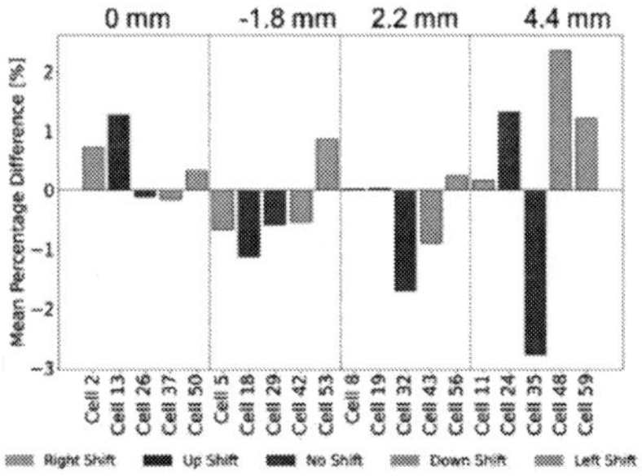

Figure 4: Voc of displaced 5-Ja cells at AM1.5d.

With an average Isc of approximately 1.3 A, the variations in current were varied across all panels. The cells on the 0 mm panel experienced the lowest variations in Isc, indicating the 0 mm panel has the best tolerance for misalignment. Additionally, the -1.8 mm panel showed an increased Isc for all cells indicating an improved performance for shorter variations of heights between the Fresnel lens and MJSC.

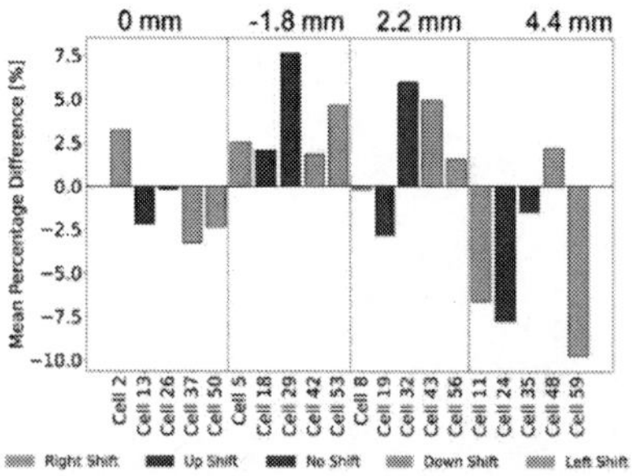

Figure 5: Isc of displaced 5-Ja cells at AM1.5d.

Pmp was sensitive to displacement as a combination of both Imp and Vmp. On the 0 mm panel, differences of less than 8 % were observed, whilst a maximum approximately 13 % was observed on the adjusted panels.

These findings highlight the importance of precise cell placement during module assembly. Small misalignments can cause significant performance variations and significant influences on electrical output.

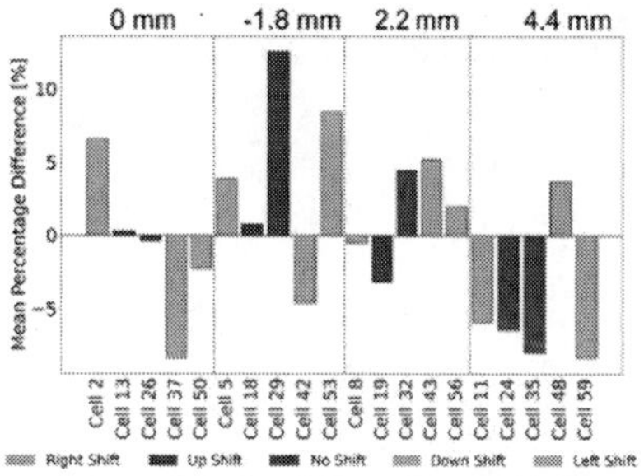

Figure 6: Pmp of displaced 5-Ja cells at AM1.5d.

Finally, the influence of the spectrum is shown for the Pmp normalised by DNI (a proxy for efficiency) of the displaced cells, 5-Ja, which are adapted for current matching at AM1.5, in Figure 7. As expected, the 5C46 generally performed well at AM1.5d, with little performance variation shown for any cell in the red-rich spectrum.

(a) Red-rich spectrum

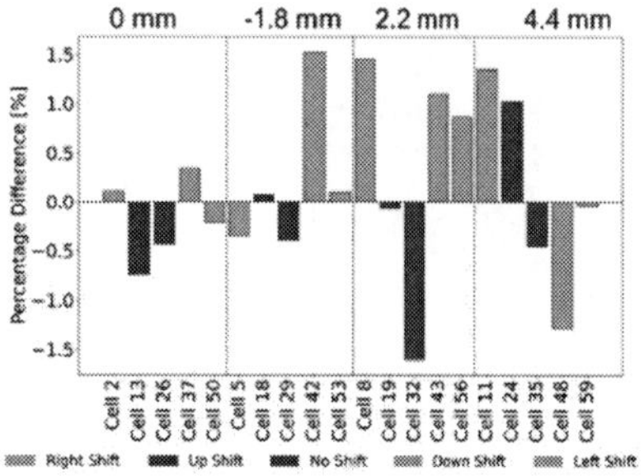

(b) Blue-rich spectrum

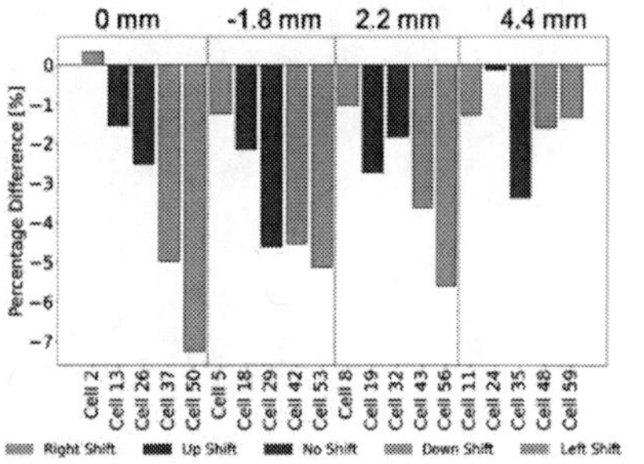

Figure 7: Impact of spectral composition Pmp normalised to DNI of the displaced 5-Ja cells under (a) red-rich and (b) blue-rich conditions as compared to AM1.5d.

5 CONCLUSION

Utilising the Analysis Module, built and provided by AZUR SPACE Solar Power and deployed in Port Elizabeth, the electrical and environmental parameters for the 5C46, an MJSC manufactured by AZUR SPACE Solar Power, were analysed. This study focused on the influence of spectral composition, operating temperature, and positional alignment on the performance of the 5C46 cell.

The solar spectral data and the respective APE values determined that Port Elizabeth is a blue-rich region compared to AM1.5d, however, when compared to other sites such as Lima, Peru, it tends to be quite red. Additionally, seasonal shifts in APE highlight the region's suitability for spectral studies.

Thermal imaging and electrical measurements confirmed the temperature dependence of an MJSC. A temperature difference of approximately 10 °C between central and edge cells led to power variations up to 0.328 W, primarily driven by changes in Voc. These results underline the importance of thermal management in CPV module design.

Positional displacement experiments revealed that small misalignments in the x–y plane had minimal influence on Voc and Isc, but more significant effects on power output (Pmp). Variations in cell-Fresnel lens distance also altered both spectral distribution and thermal conditions, resulting in electrical parameters varying across the panels in the Analysis Module. The results confirm that the C3PV module is well aligned.

Spectral effects showed that the 5-Ja variation of the 5C46 cell performed as expected. As it was adapted for AM1.5d, it performed well under these conditions. Additionally, little variation was shown for red-rich conditions, and a reduced performance is noted under blue-rich conditions.

Overall, this study underscores the importance of accounting for spectral composition during MJSC design, operating temperatures during the module design and the importance of accurate cell placement during assembly of the module.

6 ACKNOWLEDGEMENTS

The authors wish to acknowledge assistance from colleagues and financial support from Nelson Mandela University and AZUR SPACE Solar Power.

7 REFERENCES

[1] R. F. Loeckenhoff and P. Schroth, "Comprehensive analysis of the interactions between a concentrating photovoltaics (CPV) module and 5-junction solar cells: indoor and outdoor sub-cell current measurements," in *40th European Photovoltaic Solar Energy Conference and Exhibition*, 2023. doi: 10.4229/EUPVSEC2023/4CP.3.3.

[2] AZUR SPACE Solar Power GmbH, "C3PV Concentrator PV System - 5C37S," Feb. 2021.

[3] R. F. Loeckenhoff, A. Endress, and W. Bensch, "C3PV: Mass Produced EFA Receivers for a Franchised Module Technology," Mar. 2021. Accessed: Mar. 06, 2025. [Online]. Available: https://www.azurspace.com/index.php/en/company/company-publications

[4] V. M. Andreev, V. A. Grilikhes, and V. D. Rumyantsev, *Photovoltaic conversion of concentrated sunlight*. Chichester: John Wiley and Sons, 1997.

[5] L. A. Conde, J. R. Angulo, M. Sevillano-Bendezú, G. Nofuentes, J. A. Töfflinger, and J. de la Casa, "Spectral effects on the energy yield of various photovoltaic technologies in Lima (Peru)," *Energy*, vol. 223, May 2021, doi: 10.1016/j.energy.2021.120034.

[6] G. Nofuentes, C. A. Gueymard, J. Aguilera, M. D. Pérez-Godoy, and F. Charte, "Is the average photon energy a unique characteristic of the spectral distribution of global irradiance?" *Solar Energy*, vol. 149, pp. 32–43, 2017, doi: 10.1016/j.solener.2017.03.086.

[7] E. M. Hagemann, F. J. Vorster, and E. Ernest Van Dyk, "A methodology for evaluating the performance of a concentrator photovoltaic module," in *SASEC 2024 Proceedings*, SPRINGER Energy Proceedings, 2025.

[8] C. Cornaro and A. Andreotti, "Influence of Average Photon Energy index on solar irradiance characteristics and outdoor performance of photovoltaic modules," *Progress in Photovoltaics: Research and Applications*, vol. 21, no. 5, pp. 996–1003, Aug. 2013, doi: 10.1002/PIP.2194.

[9] F. Vorster, "On the evaluation of a photovoltaic concentrator system," Magister Scientiae, University of Port Elizabeth, 2001.

EPOXY RESIN AND FIBERGLASS TO INTEGRATE PV INTO TERRESTRIAL ELECTRIC VEHICLES

Fernando Castro-Gallardo[1, 2*] Jorge Rabanal-Arabach[1, 2], Sebastían Rodríguez-Romero[1, 2], Sonia Beltran-Condori[1, 2], Natalia Videla-Magnata[1, 2] and Edward Fuentealba-Vidal[1, 2]

[1] University of Antofagasta, Av. Angamos 601, 1270300 Antofagasta, Chile.
[2] Solar Energy Research Center, Tupper 2007, 8370451 Santiago, Chile.
* email: fernando.castro.gallardo@ua.cl

ABSTRACT: Epoxy–fiberglass laminates are evaluated as glass-free encapsulation for vehicle-integrated photovoltaics (VIPV). Two commercial epoxies were characterized on cured films (FT-IR, ASTM E96 WVTR at 40 °C, push-rod dilatometry CTE, and ASTM D638 tensile). Six back-contact c-Si cells (Maxeon Gen III) were encapsulated between epoxy layers on a fiberglass backing to build 2 × 3 mini-modules (MIMOs). Outdoor I–V and electroluminescence (EL) were recorded before and after single-axis vibration. MEPSOLARIS-1350 exhibited ~ 4× lower WVTR than MEPOX-441; MEPOX-441 showed a linear CTE of 48.2 ± 15.9 ppm K^{-1} (25–60 °C). The MEPOX-441 MIMO retained ≈97% of HALM-translated P_{MPP} post-vibration with unchanged EL maps, indicating no electrically active cracking at the tested excitation. Results support epoxy–fiberglass glass-free stacks as a viable path for VIPV prototypes and highlight barrier/thermomechanical trade-offs for scaling.
Keywords: VIPV, glass-free laminate, epoxy–fiberglass, I–V and EL, vibration durability

1 Introduction

Vehicle-integrated photovoltaics (VIPV) aims to harvest solar energy directly on the vehicle envelope (roof, hood, body panels) to extend range and reduce grid dependence [1, 2]. Unlike building-integrated modules, VIPV requires lightweight constructions, tight curvature conformity, and resistance to vibration and thermal cycling, eliminating the glass cover is attractive for mass and integration, but raises challenges in barrier performance, adhesion, and mechanical reliability [3].

Epoxy systems are promising encapsulants for glass free laminates due to their processability, adhesion and stiffness, especially when combined with fiberglass reinforcement [4]. However, moisture ingress (quantified by water vapor transmission rate, WVTR) and thermo-mechanical mismatch with crystalline silicon can limit durability through corrosion, debonding, and micro-cracking [5]. A materials stack must therefore balance: (i) low WVTR; (ii) compatible coefficients of thermal expansion (CTE) with c-Si; and (iii) adequate strength and stiffness under dynamic loads [6].

This work evaluates two epoxy formulations MEPOX 441 and MEPSOLARIS 1350. We first characterize moisture barrier via ASTM E96 water-cup test at 40 °C [7], and assess CTE [8] and tensile properties [9]. We then fabricate six-cell MIMOs with IBC cells and evaluate electrical performance (I–V, EL) before and after vibration. The results quantify trade-offs between barrier and mechanical behavior and demonstrate feasibility for VIPV prototypes.

The manuscript is structured as follows: Section 2 describes materials and methods, including WVTR testing; Section 3 presents results and discussions; Section 4 summarizes conclusions and implications for full-size panels.

2 Materials and Methods

This work comprises three methodological blocks. First, the encapsulation materials are characterized chemically and physico-mechanically (FT-IR, WVTR, CTE, uniaxial tensile) on cured epoxy specimens. Second, glass-free mini-modules (MIMOs) are fabricated by encapsulating six back-contact c-Si cells between epoxy layers with a fiberglass backing. Third, the MIMOs are evaluated electrically and for durability by pre- and post-vibration I–V and EL under controlled conditions.

2.1 Materials characterization

2.1.1 Materials and specimen preparation

Two commercial epoxy systems were investigated as encapsulants: MEPOX 441 Cristal and MEPSOLARIS 1350. Resins and hardeners were mixed according to the manufacturers' instructions, cast on flat glass molds and cured at 60 °C for 8 h, followed by >24 h at room temperature before machining. Unless otherwise noted, coupons were taken from the same cast sheets to ensure comparable thermal and curing history.

Specimens for each characterization were prepared as follows: (i) FT-IR (ATR): flat films (~1 mm) with smooth surfaces; contact area was cleaned with isopropyl alcohol prior to measurement. (ii) WVTR: circular discs (film thickness ~1 mm) sized to seal a 3D-printed ASTM E96 cup (effective inner diameter 50 mm) using a TPU gasket; an ABS polymer disc was used only as a methodological reference. (iii) CTE: cylindrical pins with flat, parallel ends (reference length L_0 measured to ±0.01 mm), suitable for push-rod dilatometry. (iv) Tensile: ASTM D638 type IV dog-bones cut from the cast sheets (thickness ~1 mm).

For prototype mini-modules, six back-contact c-Si cells (SunPower Maxeon Gen III) were encapsulated between epoxy layers with a fiberglass fabric backing acting as a glass-free structural substrate. All dimensions reported in the analysis correspond to the measured values of each specimen.

2.1.2 Fourier-transform infrared spectroscopy (FT-IR)

FT-IR spectra were recorded in attenuated total reflectance (ATR) on a Nicolet Avatar 330 (Thermo Electron). Cured epoxy films (flat surfaces, thickness ~1 mm) were pressed against a diamond ATR crystal (45°). For each resin, at least $n = 2$ spectra were measured and averaged (32 scans per spectrum, 4 cm^{-1} resolution) over 4 000 cm^{-1} to 600 cm^{-1}. A fresh background was acquired before each series; spectra were baseline-corrected and ATR-corrected. To enable between-material comparison, intensities were normalized to the aromatic ring band at 1 508 cm^{-1}.

10.4229/EUPVSEC2025/4DV.1.42

2.1.3 Water Vapor Transmission Rate (WVTR)

WVTR was measured according to ASTM E96/E96M [7] in the upright *water-cup*configuration. 3D-printed cups with an effective inner diameter of 50 mm ($A = 1.9635 \times 10^{-3}\ \mathrm{m}^2$) were used; the water level was kept 10–15 mm below the specimen. Epoxy films (thickness ~1 mm) were sealed with a TPU gasket and weighed on an analytical balance, with the assembly placed on a 40 °C hot plate. After discarding the initial transient, a linear model $m(t) = a+bt$ (least squares) was fitted to the steady regime; the slope $|b|$ ($\mathrm{g\,h^{-1}}$) was converted to

$$\mathrm{WVTR} = \frac{|b|}{A} \times 24 \quad \left[\mathrm{g\,m^{-2}\,day^{-1}}\right].$$

For each material we report WVTR and the fit coefficient R^2. An ABS polymer was included as a methodological reference.

2.1.4 Coefficient of thermal expansion (CTE)

Linear CTE was measured with a push-rod dilatometer (Orton DIL 1412 STD) according to ASTM E228 [8]. Cylindrical specimens with flat, parallel ends (reference length $L_0 \approx 25$ mm, measured to ±0.01 mm) were ramped at $3\,^\circ\mathrm{C\,min^{-1}}$. The instrument records ExpPLC (percent linear change) versus temperature. CTE was obtained from a least-squares fit of the linear region (25–60 °C, below T_g), converting percent to fraction as

$$\alpha\ [\mathrm{ppm/K}] = \frac{1}{100}\,\frac{d(\mathrm{ExpPLC})}{dT} \times 10^6.$$

Instrument performance was verified with the supplied reference. Results are reported as mean ± SD over n replicates.

2.1.5 Uniaxial tensile testing (ASTM D638)

Uniaxial tensile tests were performed according to ASTM D638 [9] on a Zwick/Roell Z50 universal testing machine (50 kN) with flat grips. Type IV dog-bone specimens were cut from cast sheets (thickness ~1 mm). Tests were run at a crosshead speed of $1\ \mathrm{mm\,min^{-1}}$ under laboratory conditions. Engineering stress–strain curves were computed from force and grip-to-grip displacement. Young's modulus E was obtained by a least-squares fit to the initial linear region (typically 0.05–0.25% strain), and the yield strength σ_y was determined by the 0.2% offset method. At least $n = 2$ replicates were tested per resin; outliers were screened with a median–absolute–deviation (MAD) criterion and discarded when $|z_{\mathrm{MAD}}| > 3$.

2.2 Mini-module fabrication

2.2.1 Stack architecture

Six back-contact c-Si cells (SunPower Maxeon Gen III; 125 × 125 × 0.175 mm) [10] were arranged in a 2 × 3 matrix with 1 mm inter-cell gaps and a 10 mm perimeter margin, giving an internal footprint of 273 × 401 mm. The glass-free laminate—from front (exposed side) to back—consisted of: epoxy encapsulant (front layer) / solar cells / epoxy encapsulant (rear layer) / fiberglass backing acting as a structural substrate and backsheet substitute. An RTV silicone casting mold with internal dimensions 273 × 401 × 5 mm (external 293 × 421 × 10 mm) controlled geometry, providing nominal epoxy cover layers of ~1 mm above and below the cell matrix and a fiberglass backing thickness of 1 mm (shown Fig.1).

2.2.2 Encapsulation process and curing

Only the epoxy system (MEPOX 441) was used for MIMO encapsulation. The RTV mold was conditioned with release wax and PVA. Resin and hardener were mixed at 2:1 (A:B) by weight, stirred for ~3 min while scraping the cup walls, and

Fig. 1: Exploded view of the glass-free MIMO

allowed to rest for 2–3 min to promote bubble release. A first ~1 mm epoxy layer was poured slowly (edge-to-center) to wet the surface; the pre-interconnected 2×3 cell matrix was aligned on the wet epoxy; a second ~1 mm epoxy layer was applied; and the pre-molded fiberglass backing (1 mm) was placed onto the rear wet layer to achieve bonding. Air entrapment was minimized by slow pouring and a short dwell before handling; critical surfaces were cleaned with isopropyl alcohol. Laminates were cured for **24 h at** 27 °**C** under laboratory conditions (20–25 °C, 40–60 % RH). After cure, modules were demolded, edge-trimmed and visually inspected (voids/delamination); thickness and mass were recorded for traceability. (show Fig. 2).

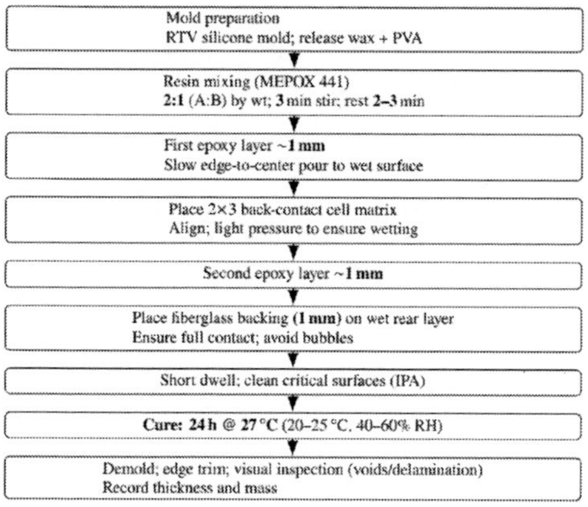

Fig. 2: Encapsulation process and curing workflow for epoxy–fiberglass MIMOs (MEPOX 441).

2.3 Performance and durability assessment

2.3.1 Electrical performance (I–V)

I–V curves were measured with a H.A.L.M. *cetisPV Outdoortest* tracer under natural sunlight in accordance with IEC 60904-1 [11]. Plane-of-array irradiance was monitored by a calibrated c-Si reference cell mounted coplanar with the MIMO, and the back-surface temperature T_{mod} by a PT1000 bonded at the laminate center. The module was connected in four-wire to the tracer. For each MIMO, three single sweeps were recorded within ≤1 min to limit irradiance drift (sweep time ≈0.1–0.2 s, ≥500 points). From each curve we obtained I_{SC}, V_{OC}, P_{MPP} and FF. The measurement setup is shown in Fig. 3.

2.3.2 Electroluminescence (EL) imaging

EL was recorded in a dark enclosure by forward-biasing the mini-modules. Each specimen was imaged *before* and *after* vibration at 2, 3, and 4 A using identical camera settings. Images were saved as 16-bit grayscale without tone mapping; only frames at matching current/exposure were compared.

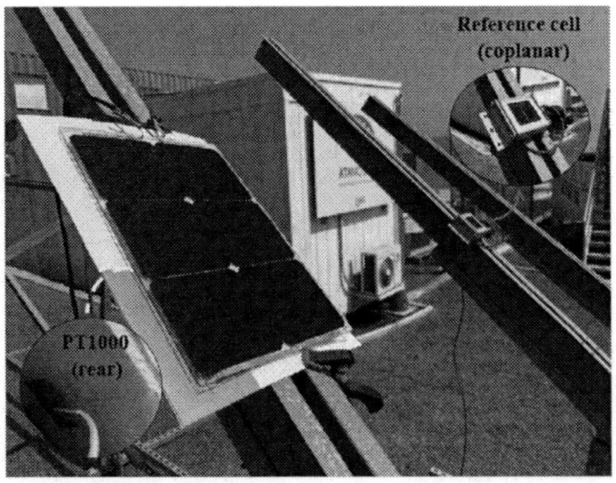

Fig. 3: Outdoor I–V setup with HALM tracer: coplanar reference cell and rear PT1000; four-wire connection to the mini-module.

2.3.3 *Vibration test*

Mechanical excitation was applied on a custom frame using an unbalanced-mass motor. A module-fixed coordinate system was used with X along the long edge (401 mm), Y along the short edge (273 mm), and Z normal to the laminate. A smartphone accelerometer (iPhone 13, phyphox) was rigidly fixed on the support plate and aligned with X (Table I).

At the selected dial setting, the dominant frequency was f_0 = 72.4 Hz with peak (RMS) acceleration a_{pk} = 1.01 g (a_{rms} = 0.68 g) along X; transverse and out-of-plane components were much smaller (Y: a_{rms} = 0.13 g; Z: a_{rms} = 0.068 g). Each specimen was exposed for 12 min under X excitation only. Immediately before and after the exposure, I–V and EL were recorded with identical settings.

Table I: Single-axis vibration measured with smartphone (phyphox, iPhone 13).

Axis	a_{rms} [g]	a_{pk} [g]	f_0 [Hz]
X	0.677	1.009	72.4
Y	0.130	0.215	72.4
Z	0.068	0.131	72.4

2.3.4 *Post-vibration re-evaluation and acceptance criteria*

Immediately after vibration, I–V and EL were repeated with the same protocols and settings. Acceptance was defined a priori as P_{MPP} retention ≥ 90% relative to baseline (same reporting basis: as-measured or IEC 60891-translated) [12]and absence of critical EL-visible defects (e.g., cell fragmentation, extensive dark areas crossing busbars). Statistics are reported as mean ± SD over available replicates.

3 Results and Discussion

3.1 Materials characterization

3.1.1 *WVTR at 40°C*

Mass–time series exhibited steady-state behavior (linear fits with $R^2 \geq 0.998$). Table II summarizes the slope and the area-normalized WVTR (film thickness ~1 mm).

Under identical conditions (40 °C, Ø 50 mm, $e \approx$ 1 mm), MEPSOLARIS 1350 shows the lowest WVTR (~86.7 g m^{-2} day^{-1}), about 4× lower than MEPOX 441, indicating a superior moisture barrier. ABS is reported only as a methodological control and not as an encapsulation candidate.

Table II: WVTR at 40 °C (water-cup, Ø 50 mm).

Material	e (mm)	n (–)	Slope (g h^{-1})	WVTR (g m^{-2} d^{-1})	R^2 (–)
MEPSOLARIS 1350	1.00	1	0.007 10	86.73	0.999 7
MEPOX 441	1.00	1	0.028 66	350.33	0.999 0
ABS (reference)	1.00	1	0.034 09	416.68	0.998 3

Note: ABS was used only as a methodological control (not an encapsulation candidate).

3.1.2 *FT-IR results*

Both resins exhibit the typical features of cured epoxy networks (Fig. 4). A broad O–H band at 3 200 cm^{-1} to 3 600 cm^{-1} is present in both materials, consistent with hydroxyl formation upon curing.

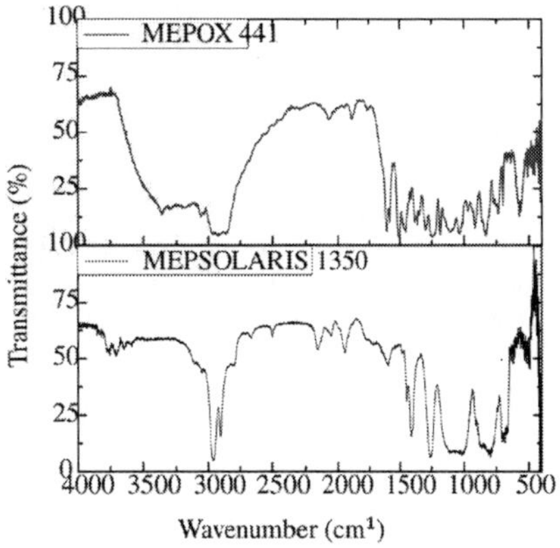

Fig. 4: FT-IR (ATR) of cured resins. Spectra baseline- and ATR-corrected, normalized to the aromatic band at 1508 cm^{-1}.

The ether-related C–O–C band near 1 240 cm^{-1} confirms epoxy ring opening. The epoxy-ring breathing at ~910 cm^{-1} shows low relative intensity in both spectra, indicative of a high degree of cure under the selected schedule. Compared with MEPOX 441, MEPSOLARIS 1350 displays stronger aliphatic C–H stretching at 2 9252 850 cm^{-1} and an additional carbonyl band near 1 720 cm^{-1}, suggestive of ester-containing modifiers. Selected bands and assignments are summarized in Table III.

Table III: Selected FT-IR bands (ATR) and assignments for cured resins. Spectra normalized at 1508 cm^{-1}.

Wavenumber (cm^{-1})	Assignment	Obs.[1]	Note
3200–3600	O–H stretching (hydroxyl, curing)	Both	Broad band.
2925 / 2850	Aliphatic C–H stretching	MS1350	Stronger vs. M441[2].
1720	C=O stretching (ester/additive)	MS1350	Present.
1600	Aromatic C=C stretching	M441	Higher aromatic content.
1508	Aromatic C–H bending (reference)	Both	Normalization band.
1240	C–O–C (ether linkages)	Both	Cure confirmation.
910	Epoxy ring breathing (residual)	Both	Weak in both[3].

[1] Obs.: M441 = MEPOX 441; MS1350 = MEPSOLARIS 1350.
[2] Relative intensity after normalization at 1508 cm^{-1}.
[3] Low 910 cm^{-1} indicates high degree of cure in both resins.

These qualitative differences indicate a more aromatic backbone in MEPOX 441 and a higher aliphatic/ester contribution in MEPSOLARIS 1350. While FT-IR confirms curing and

10.4229/EUPVSEC2025/4DV.1.42

network chemistry, moisture-barrier performance is addressed separately by the WVTR results in Section 3.

3.1.3 *CTE results*

Table IV summarizes the linear CTE of MEPOX 441 in the 25–60 °C window. The mean value is 48.2 ± 15.9 ppm/K (n = 3), which is in the expected range for unfilled epoxies and implies a positive mismatch of ≈46 ppm/K relative to c-Si (~2.6 ppm/K).

Table IV: Linear CTE of MEPOX 441 in 25–60 °C.

Specimen	α (ppm K^{-1})
MEPOX441#1	31.3
MEPOX441#2	50.5
MEPOX441#3	62.8
Mean ± SD (n = 3)	**48.2 ± 15.9**

3.1.4 *Tensile results*

Table V summarizes tensile metrics for the epoxy matrix. For MEPOX 441 (n = 2 after MAD screening) we obtained $E \approx 0.438$ GPa and $\sigma_y \approx 1.59$ MPa. MEPSOLARIS 1350 is not reported here because specimens failed at the grips prior to loading; new tests will be performed with soft jaw pads and end tabs to prevent pre-damage.

Table V: Tensile properties of cured epoxy matrix (ASTM D638).

Material	n	E (GPa)	σ_y (MPa)
MEPOX 441	2	0.438	1.59

In the context of the mini-module, these values are typical of unreinforced epoxy networks: the laminate stiffness will be dominated by the fiberglass backing, while the matrix provides adequate elastic response provided operational stresses remain well below ~1 MPa during vibration.

3.2 Mini-module performance

3.2.1 *Baseline I–V and EL (pre-vibration)*

Figure 5 (gold trace) shows the pre-vibration sweep. The EL map at 4 A (bottom-left panel of Fig. 6) is largely uniform; the consistently brighter top-right cell serves as a visual marker. A representative surface temperature during the acquisition is shown in the top-left panel of Fig. 6.

3.2.2 *Post-vibration I–V and EL; P_{MPP} retention*

The post sweep (blue in Fig. 5) was taken under different outdoor conditions, hence the as-measured current is lower; a fair comparison uses HALM's STC translation. Relative to baseline, P^*_{MPP} is retained at **97%** (14.76 W vs. 14.35 W). Small shifts appear in V^*_{OC} (+2.1%), I^*_{SC} (+3.2%), and FF^* (–2.4%). The post-vibration EL at 4 A (bottom-right panel of Fig. 6) remains qualitatively unchanged, indicating no electrically active cracks at the tested excitation. The corresponding surface temperature is shown in the top-right panel of Fig. 6.

4 Conclusions

We fabricated glass-free epoxy–fiberglass 2 × 3 IBC mini-modules and combined a simple materials screen with a pre/post vibration check using outdoor I–V and EL.

Materials screen (films ~1 mm, 40°C). MEPSOLARIS-1350 exhibited a markedly lower WVTR than MEPOX-441

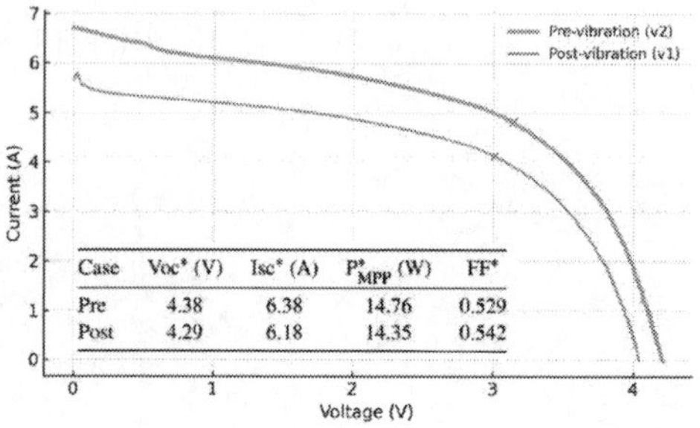

Fig. 5: Outdoor I–V, pre (gold) vs post (blue); *as measured* (no STC). Crosses mark the MPP of each sweep.

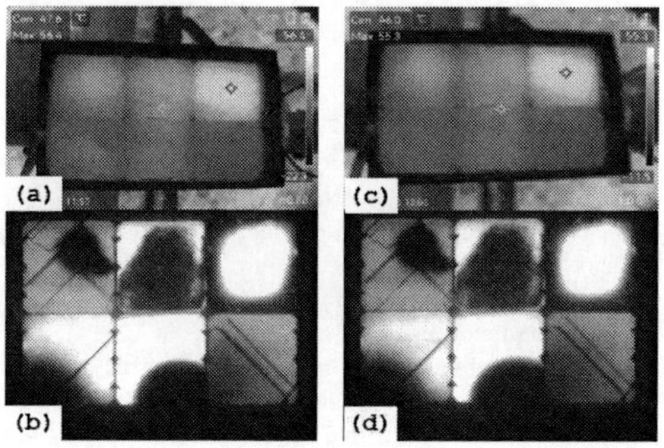

Fig. 6: Thermography (top row) and electroluminescence at 4 A (bottom row) acquired during I–V. Left: pre-vibration; right: post-vibration. Identical camera/current settings were used for pre/post EL.

(86.7 vs. 350.3 g m^{-2} d^{-1}, ~4× difference). MEPOX-441 showed a linear CTE of 48.2 ± 15.9 ppm K^{-1} (25–60°C) and tensile values typical of unfilled epoxies ($E \approx 0.438$ GPa, $\sigma_y \approx 1.59$ MPa).

Module response to vibration. After single-axis excitation (72.4 Hz, 0.68 g_{rms}, 12 min, X axis), the STC-translated power (IEC 60891) was **97%** of baseline and EL at 4 A remained unchanged, indicating no electrically active cracking at the tested level.

Implications. Epoxy–fiberglass stacks are a viable glass-free route for VIPV prototypes. Barrier performance favors MS1350 over M441, while the positive CTE mismatch to c-Si suggests that laminate design (backing thickness/lay-up) and perimeter sealing or barrier coatings will be key for durability.

Next steps. (i) Replace or hybridize the matrix to improve moisture barrier (e.g., MS1350 + edge seals/coatings); (ii) extend to standard reliability sequences (damp-heat 85/85, thermal cycling, UV/optical stability) and to automotive-relevant random vibration; (iii) quantify adhesion/peel and interfacial aging; and (iv) scale to curved demonstrators with energy-yield assessment for VIPV.

Acknowledgments

This work was supported by the Chilean Solar Energy Research Center (SERC Chile) under Grant ANID/FONDAP/1523A0006, the HEUMA ING2030 Project 16ENI2-71940, and the Power Electronics and Electromobility Laboratory (POWEREMLAB). We also acknowledge the Master's Program in Solar Energy at the University of Antofagasta.

References

[1] S. Rodríguez-Romero, J. Rabanal-Arabach, C. A. Rojas, M. Trigo-Gonzalez, G. Mondaca-Cuevas, D. Arias,

F. Castro-Gallardo, and E. Fuentealba-Vidal, "Analysis of advanced nonisolated topologies for vehicle-integrated photovoltaic (vipv) systems in urban electric transport buses," *IEEE Journal of Photovoltaics*, pp. 1–7, 2025.

[2] F. Castro-Gallardo, J. Rabanal-Arabach, S. Rodríguez-Romero, D. Olivares, and E. Fuentealba, "Enhancing electric vehicle autonomy with solar energy: A case study of the "takai urban" in northern chile," *SiliconPV Conference Proceedings*, vol. 2, 2 2025. [Online]. Available: https://www.tib-op.org/ojs/index.php/siliconpv/article/view/1307

[3] S. Kim, M. Holz, S. Park, Y. Yoon, E. Cho, and J. Yi, "Future options for lightweight photovoltaic modules in electrical passenger cars," *Sustainability*, vol. 13, p. 2532, 2021, review; published 26 Feb 2021. [Online]. Available: https://doi.org/10.3390/su13052532

[4] G. Espitia-Mesa, E. Hernández-Pedraza, S. Molina-Tamayo, and R. Mejía-Gutiérrez, "Design, analysis, and modeling of curved photovoltaic surfaces using composite materials," *TecnoLógicas*, vol. 25, no. 53, p. e2171, May 2022. [Online]. Available: https://doi.org/10.22430/22565337.2171

[5] C. Peike, I. Hädrich, K.-A. Weiß, and I. Dürr, "Overview of PV module encapsulation materials," *Photovoltaics International*, no. 19, pp. 85–92, Mar. 2013.

[6] J. Rabanal-Arabach, "Development of a c-si photovoltaic module for desert climates," Ph.D. dissertation, Universität Konstanz, Konstanz, 2019.

[7] ASTM International, "Standard test methods for water vapor transmission of materials," ASTM International, West Conshohocken, PA, ASTM Standard E96/E96M-16, Apr. 2016, historical version. [Online]. Available: https://www.astm.org/e0096_e0096m-16.html

[8] ——, "Standard test method for linear thermal expansion of solid materials with a push-rod dilatometer," ASTM International, West Conshohocken, PA, ASTM Standard E228-22, Dec. 2022, active version. [Online]. Available: https://www.astm.org/e0228-22.html

[9] ——, "Standard test method for tensile properties of plastics," ASTM International, West Conshohocken, PA, ASTM Standard D638-14, Apr. 2014, active version. [Online]. Available: https://www.astm.org/d0638-14.html

[10] R. Kopecek, F. Buchholz, V. D. Mihailetchi, J. Libal, J. Lossen, N. Chen, H. Chu, C. Peter, T. Timofte, A. Halm, Y. Guo, X. Qu, X. Wu, J. Gao, and P. Dong, "Interdigitated back contact technology as final evolution for industrial crystalline single-junction silicon solar cell," *Solar*, vol. 3, pp. 1–14, 2023, open Access (CC BY). [Online]. Available: https://doi.org/10.3390/solar3010001

[11] I. E. C. 60904-1:2020, "Photovoltaic devices. part 1, measurement of photovoltaic current-voltage characteristics," Tech. Rep., 2020.

[12] I. E. C. 60891:2021, "Photovoltaic devices - procedures for temperature and irradiance corrections to measured i-v characteristics," Tech. Rep., 2021.

DESIGN, SIZING, AND SENSORISATION OF AN FPV POWER PLANT AT THE MONTE NOVO DAM, PORTUGAL

Dorivaldo Duarte*[1], Luis Fialho[2], Pedro Horta[1], Sara Pereira[1]

*Corresponding author: duarte@uevora.pt
[1] Renewable Energies Chair, Polo da Mitra da Universidade de Évora, Edifício Ário Lobo de Azevedo, 7000-083 Nossa Senhora da Tourega, Portugal.
[2] Eurac Research, Viale Druso (Drususallee) 1, 39100 Bolzano, Italy

Abstract: This study presents the design for implementation of a floating photovoltaic (FPV) system on the Monte Novo reservoir in Évora, a potable water supply resource. The installation integrates multiple flotation technologies and structural layouts, combined with a dense sensor network for real-time monitoring of environmental parameters, water quality, and energy performance. The work focuses on assessing the mutual impacts between the FPV system and the aquatic ecosystem, while defining robust protocols for safe operation and long-term reliability. In addition, the study explores hybridisation with the electrical grid to strengthen water treatment processes. By addressing technical performance, environmental interactions, and operational integration, the study provides evidence-based insights to guide future FPV projects in sensitive freshwater environments and contributes to advancing sustainable solutions for the water–energy nexus.

Keywords: Floating PV, Water quality, Environmental impact, Aquatic ecosystem, Sensorisation

1. Introduction

FPV systems have attracted significant attention as an innovative and sustainable solution for renewable energy generation. In recent years, FPV systems have experienced rapid growth, both in terms of installed capacity and technological advancements. According to the International Renewable Energy Agency (IRENA), the global installed capacity of floating solar systems surpassed 3.5GW in 2021, with projections indicating an increase to over 27GW by 2030, driven by their cost-effectiveness and efficiency in utilising surfaces that would otherwise remain underutilised [1]. This growth is further supported by advancements in floating structures.

The installation of FPV systems in water bodies designated for human consumption represents a significant advancement in terms of innovation and sustainability, particularly for Portugal, as it requires a high level of sensorisation to continuously monitor several parameters. The results generated will give an important contribution for the development of testing protocols and safety standards for the installation of FPV systems in potable water bodies.

Furthermore, careful integration with sensor systems allows for continuous monitoring of water quality, ensuring that potable water standards are maintained [2] [3].

Continuous sensing of the water properties is crucial to ensure the safety and quality of the potable water supply. Studies have shown that the installation of FPV systems can affect parameters such as temperature, turbidity, and oxygen levels, making real-time monitoring essential to prevent adverse effects on water quality. The integration of FPV systems with advanced sensor and monitoring systems allows its safe and sustainable integration in the water bodies, and can contribute to boost the deployment of this technology in worldwide [4] [5].

2. Methodology

The diagram presents the methodology for implementing a pilot FPV plant in freshwater reservoirs. The process includes reservoir selection considering uses and restrictions, obtaining environmental and water domain permits, system design and sizing (floats, modules, sensors, anchoring, and data acquisition), and finally, energy licensing and plant construction. This approach ensures the technical, environmental, and legal feasibility of the installation, optimising energy utilisation without compromising the reservoir's original function.

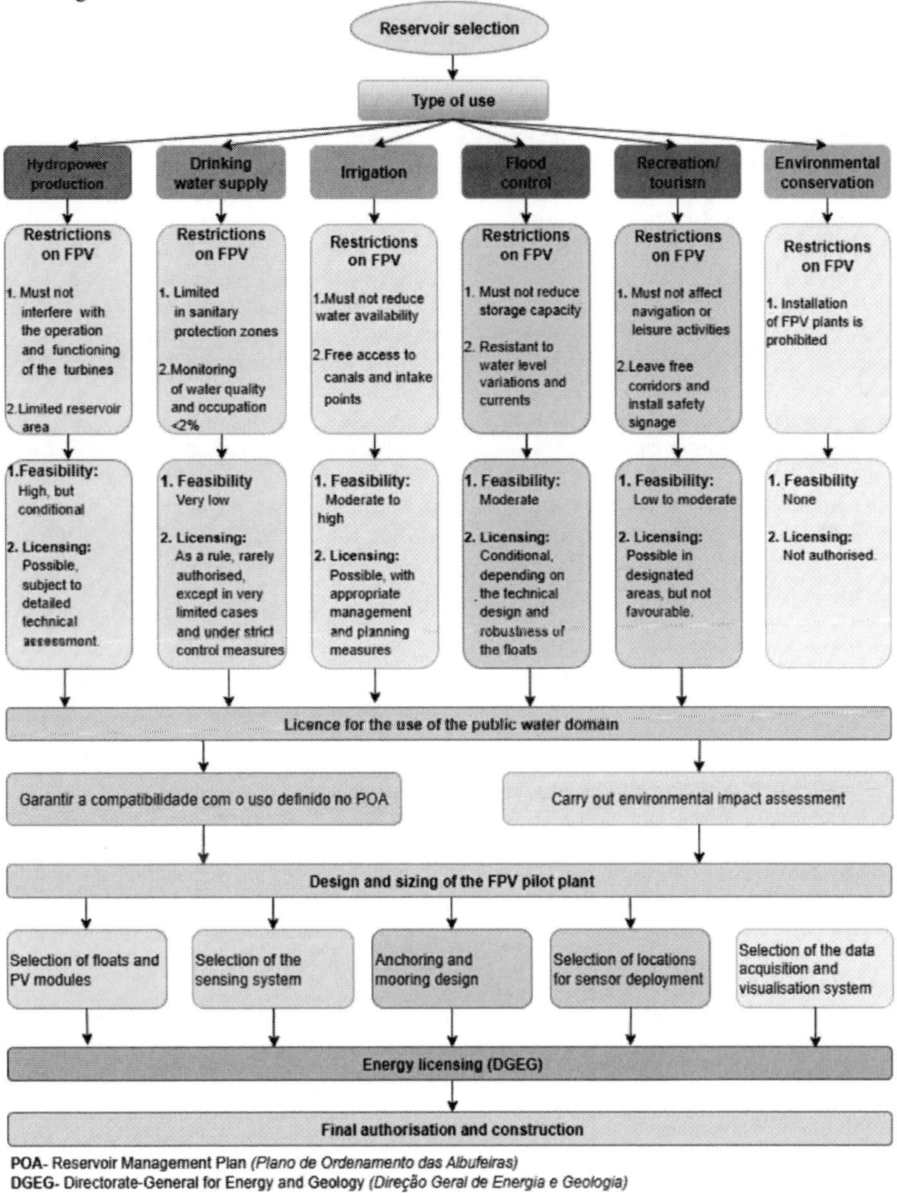

Figure 1. Methodology overview for implementing a pilot FPV plant

3. Description of the FPV system

3.1. Location and Characterisation of the Reservoir

The pilot system will be installed at the Monte Novo Dam (38.514, -7.712), a potable water reservoir whose primary uses include public water supply to the city of Évora, agricultural irrigation as part of the regional hydraulic management system, and flood control. Secondary uses, such as recreational activities and sport fishing, are also present but subject to restrictions. Due to its relative water level stability during the peak solar radiation period (spring and summer), an average depth exceeding 10 metres, and minimal interference with navigation or leisure activities, coupled with its proximity to existing electrical infrastructure, such as substations and medium-voltage lines, the site provides suitable conditions for the installation of the FPV pilot plant and its integration with the existing facilities [6] .

3.2. FPV system configuration

This FPV pilot plant was designed to systematically evaluate the performance of three distinct floating platform technologies across four structural configurations.

I. **System 1:** Features an East–West orientation, with modules arranged in a portrait layout and a fixed tilt between 12° and 15°.
II. **System 2:** Also follows an East–West orientation but utilises a landscape layout with a fixed tilt of 15°.
III. **System 3:** Comprises two variants:

a) *Variant 1* is south facing, with modules in a landscape layout and an adjustable tilt ranging from 10° to 40°.
b) *Variant 2* maintains an East–West orientation, landscape layout, and the same adjustable tilt range.

The selection of these configurations allows for a comprehensive assessment of the factors influencing FPV system performance. Variations in orientation and tilt enable the analysis of the effect of solar incidence angles on energy yield and the optimisation of module positioning. Simultaneously, the diversity of structural layouts facilitates the evaluation of platform stability under dynamic environmental conditions, including wind and water movement. Furthermore, the pilot configuration provides the opportunity to study water surface utilisation, contributing to an understanding of the spatial efficiency of FPV systems while minimising potential ecological and recreational impacts.
By integrating both fixed and adjustable tilt systems, as well as multiple orientations and module arrangements, the pilot establishes a robust experimental framework. This approach supports the investigation of interactions between structural design, environmental conditions, and energy performance, providing critical information to guide the design, optimisation, and deployment of larger-scale FPV installations in similar reservoirs.
The FPV system has been designed with an installed capacity of approximately 200 kW, remaining within the limits for low-voltage energy injection in accordance with Decree-Law No. 15/2022 and Regulation No. 815/2023 [7] [8]. This limitation ensures compatibility with the existing electrical grid and simplifies the licensing and operation procedures of the system.

3.3. Sensorisation

The sensor network was designed to assess the performance of the FPV system, taking into account environmental variables and the conditions of the aquatic environment in which the system is installed. In addition, it enables the monitoring of the FPV system's impacts on the ecosystem, including local fauna and flora, as well as water quality.

I. Reservoir bank meteorological Station

The installation of a meteorological station on the reservoir bank was designed to monitor environmental conditions, system performance, and impacts on the aquatic ecosystem. Solar radiation, wind, temperature, relative humidity, precipitation, and other meteorological parameters will be recorded using the sensors listed in **Table 1**.

Table 1. Set of sensors for the reservoir bank

Description	Qt.
Campbell Scientific CR310 Datalogger	1
Campbell NL241 Wi-Fi Transmitter	2
Solar Radiation Sensor	1
Gill WindSonic Wind Sensor	1
Campbell HyroVue10 Temperature and Relative Humidity Sensor	1
Lambrecht Precipitation Sensor	1
Campbell Present Weather Sensor	1

II. FPV platform sensor network

The monitoring system is organised into five main categories of sensors: environmental, energy, subsurface, water quality, and operational. Environmental sensors measure variables such as air temperature and humidity, wind speed and direction, and solar radiation. Within the energy component, sensors measuring incoming and reflected solar radiation enable the calculation of albedo and the analysis of the surface energy balance. Subsurface monitoring is conducted using temperature sensors distributed at various depths in the water, allowing the assessment of thermal gradients. For water quality, multiparameter probes measure pH, conductivity, dissolved oxygen, and turbidity. Additionally, inclinometers monitor potential movements of the floating platforms, while automated systems ensure continuous and integrated data acquisition The complete list of sensors and equipment is presented in **Table 2.**

Table 2. FPV platform sensor network

Description	Qt.
Campbell Scientific CR1000X Datalogger	2
Solar Radiation Sensor	7
Pyranometer Mounting Support	7
Solar Radiation Sensor (for albedo)	2
Albedo Kit	1
Wind Sensor with GPS	1
Campbell HyroVue10 Temperature and Relative Humidity Sensor	1
Campbell CS241 Module Temperature Sensor	7
Campbell 109 Depth Temperature Profile Sensors	11
Eureka Water Quality Probe	1
Rion Inclinometer	4

III. Upstream buoy sensor network relative to the FPV system

In addition to the meteorological and platform instrumentation, specific equipment was installed to characterise the thermal profile of the water column and assess water quality. This includes a Campbell Scientific CR1000X datalogger with a Campbell NL241 Wi-Fi transmitter for data acquisition and transmission, a set of 11 Campbell 109 temperature sensors at different depths, and an Eureka Manta+30a multiparameter probe for water quality monitoring. The complete list of equipment is provided in **Table 3**.

Table 3. Upstream buoy sensor network relative to the FPV system

Description	Qt.
Campbell Scientific CR1000X Datalogger	1
Campbell NL241 Wi-Fi Transmitter	1
Campbell 109 Depth Temperature Profile Sensors	11
Eureka Water Quality Probe	1

IV. Meteorological station at the water intake

To complement the monitoring system, a Campbell Scientific CR310 datalogger was installed for data acquisition and management, along with a UWT NR7200 level sensor to measure water level variations in the reservoir. The list of equipment is summarised in **Table 4**.

Table 4. Meteorological station at the water intake

Description	Qt.
Campbell Scientific CR310 Datalogger	1
Level Sensor	1

4. Results and Discussion

The selection of the reservoir represented the first fundamental step of this work, taking into account its geomorphological and environmental characteristics, as well as restrictions related to land and water use. This choice was made through an integrated approach, considering the specific requirements for water quality monitoring and

ensuring that the installation FPV system would not compromise the multiple uses of the water resource.
Following this selection, an analysis of the hydrographic characteristics was carried out, along with a bathymetric survey. These data proved essential not only for the design of the mooring and anchoring system but also for assessing the stability of the FPV installation. The analysis ensured that even under scenarios of reduced water levels, down to their minimum values, there would be no risk of structural or operational damage to the system. Based on these results, the design of the FPV pilot plant was developed, including the selection of floater types, module configurations and orientations, and the specification of the necessary instrumentation. This set of equipment addresses both the requirements of water quality monitoring and the assessment of the system's energy performance. The sensor network was designed in conjunction with a data acquisition and visualisation platform, ensuring a continuous flow of information and enabling real-time analysis. **Figure 2** presents a synthesis of these developments.

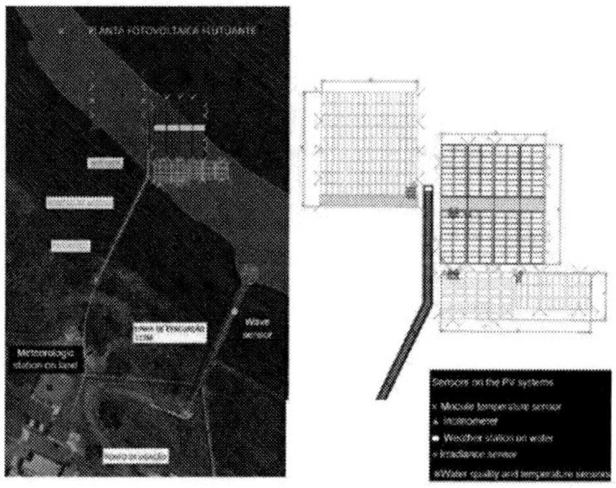

Figure 2. Configuration of the FPV pilot

In parallel with these technical developments, the licensing process was initiated, involving various local and national authorities, including municipalities, environmental conservation agencies, the bodies responsible for the National Agricultural Reserve and the National Ecological Reserve, as well as those with jurisdiction over the reservoir's water domain. It was found that no specific licensing framework currently exists for FPV systems, and as such, the project was categorised as a conventional photovoltaic power plant. This classification required full compliance with all legal and regulatory requirements applicable to the surrounding environment, making the process more complex and time-consuming. Another important outcome was the preparation of the technical specifications document, which consolidated all the requirements for both the FPV system and the associated instrumentation. This document serves as a key tool to align technical specifications with monitoring needs and to ensure the performance guarantees of the pilot installation.
Regarding the monitoring strategy, the integrated measurement of environmental, hydrological, and operational variables will be crucial for ensuring both the energy efficiency and environmental sustainability of the FPV system. The measurement of incoming and reflected solar radiation will be fundamental for evaluating the performance of the photovoltaic panels and understanding the system's impact on the surface energy balance of the reservoir. Atmospheric parameters such as air temperature, humidity, and wind will influence not only the efficiency of the modules but also the local environmental conditions, including evaporation dynamics.
Furthermore, thermal monitoring at various depths in the water column will allow the identification of temperature gradients that will be essential for assessing potential environmental impacts, such as changes in thermal stratification caused by the floating system. These changes may, in turn, affect water quality, which will be assessed through measurements of pH, dissolved oxygen, and turbidity. These data will provide insight into the possible consequences of shading and surface coverage by the FPV system on aquatic ecosystems.
Finally, operational sensors, such as inclinometers and water level sensors, will play a key role in the early detection of structural movements and variations, ensuring the safety and stability of the floating platforms. The continuous integration and acquisition of all monitoring data will support more efficient and proactive management of the system, serving as a critical tool for optimising operation while minimising environmental impacts.

5. Conclusions

The implementation of FPV systems in water supply reservoirs presents significant challenges, as it requires balancing energy efficiency, water security, and environmental protection. Currently, no licensing framework exists specifically for FPV installations, making each project subject to rigorous evaluation. In this context, the proposed installation demands a robust sensor network to continuously monitor the interactions between the pilot FPV plant and the surrounding ecosystem, including environmental parameters and water quality.

The comprehensive instrumentation and monitoring distinguish this project from commercial FPV installations, providing highly reliable scientific data. This enables a detailed understanding of the impacts of FPV systems on supply reservoirs and supports the development of best practices for design, operation, and maintenance. Ultimately, the project establishes a solid foundation for future FPV developments, promoting the safe, efficient, and scientifically grounded integration of floating photovoltaic systems in sensitive environments.

6. Future works

The next steps involve launching the tender for the acquisition of the FPV systems, the instrumentation, and the data acquisition and visualisation system, followed by their installation and commissioning. Once deployed, the sensors will operate continuously, enabling permanent monitoring of both energy performance and water quality, and thus supporting the assessment of bidirectional interactions between the FPV system and the surrounding ecosystem. The collected data will provide the basis for calculating energy indicators such as the performance ratio (PR) and the levelised cost of energy (LCOE), as well as for evaluating potential environmental impacts. This integrated analysis will provide the foundation for the development of a best-practice manual and dedicated testing and commissioning protocols, thus contributing to the standardisation and optimisation of future FPV installations.

7. Acknowledgements

This research was partly funded by the PRR Mobilizing Agendas, project Alliance for Energy Transition (ATE) with Grant agreement ID C644914747-00000023.

8. References

[1] International Renewable Energy Agency (IRENA), «Floating Solar: A Guide to the Technology, Applications and Markets,» IRENA, Abu Dhabi, 2021.

[2] R. L. Pedroso de Lima, K. Paxinou, F. C. Boogaard, O. Akkerman e L. Fen-Yu, «In-Situ Water Quality Observations under a Large-Scale Floating Solar Farm Using Sensors and Underwater Drones, https://doi.org/10.3390/su13116421,» *Sustainability*, 2021.

[3] «Large-scale floating photovoltaic systems impact the water quality of deep sand extraction lakes in the Netherlands,» Deltares, 2024.

[4] S. Gadzanku, N. Lee e A. Dyreson, «Enabling Floating Solar Photovoltaic (FPV) Deployment,» National Renewable Energy Laboratory (NREL), 2022.

[5] canalsolar. [Online]. Available: https://canalsolar.com.br/en/solar-flutuante-crescer-significativamente-mundo-woodmac/.

[6] Agência Portuguesa do Ambiente (APA), «Barrahens de Portugal," Sistema Nacional de Informação Hídricas.,» [Online]. Available: https://snirh.apambiente.pt/index.php?idMain=1&idItem=1.3. [Consultato il giorno 05 09 2025].

[7] Diário da República, «Decreto-Lei n.º 15/2022, de 14 de janeiro».

[8] Diário da República, «Regulamento n.º 815/2023, de 27 de julho».

42nd European Photovoltaic Solar Energy Conference and Exhibition

UNIVERSITY OF ÉVORA SOL4R

DESIGN, SIZING, AND SENSORISATION OF AN FPV POWER PLANT AT THE MONTE NOVO DAM, PORTUGAL

Dorivaldo Duarte*[1], Luis Fialho[2], Pedro Horta[1], Sara Pereira[1]
*Corresponding author: duarte@uevora.pt
[1]Renewable Energies Chair, Polo da Mitra da Universidade de Évora, Edifício Ário Lobo de Azevedo, 7000-083 Nossa Senhora da Tourega, Portugal.
[2]Eurac Research, Viale Druso (Drususallee) 1, 39100 Bolzano, Italy

ABSTRACT

This study presents the design and implementation of a floating photovoltaic (FPV) system on the Monte Novo reservoir in Évora, a potable water supply resource. The installation integrates multiple flotation technologies and structural layouts, combined with a dense sensor network for real-time monitoring of environmental parameters, water quality, and energy performance. The work focuses on assessing the mutual impacts between the FPV system and the aquatic ecosystem, while defining robust protocols for safe operation and long-term reliability. In addition, the study explores hybridisation with the electrical grid to strengthen water treatment processes. By addressing technical performance, environmental interactions, and operational integration, the study provides evidence-based insights to guide future FPV projects in sensitive freshwater environments and contributes to advancing sustainable solutions for the water–energy nexus.

OBJECTIVE

- ❑ Design and sizing of a pilot FPV plant at Monte Novo reservoir.
- ❑ Compare floating technologies and module configurations (orientation, tilt, layout) for stability and energy efficiency.
- ❑ Implement an advanced sensor network to monitor:
  1. Meteorological conditions
  2. Energy performance
  3. Water quality
- ❑ Assess interactions with the aquatic ecosystem, ensuring environmental protection and drinking water safety.
- ❑ Develop operation and maintenance protocols for safe, reliable, and durable system performance.
- ❑ Integrate with the low-voltage grid for legal and operational compatibility.
- ❑ Produce scientific and technical knowledge to support future FPV standards, best practices, and testing protocols.

METHODOLOGY

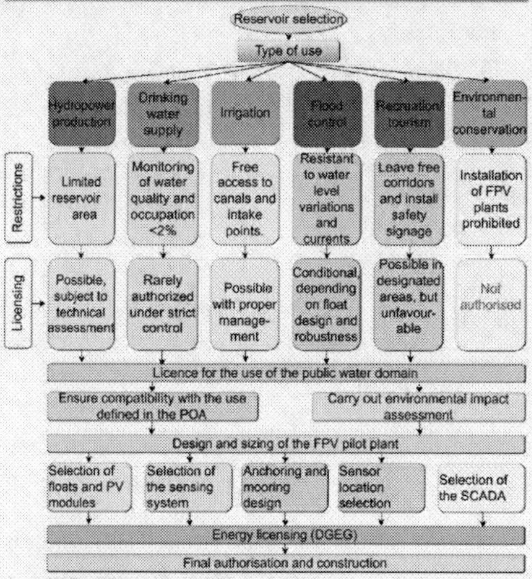

POA - Reservoir Management Plan (Plano de Ordenamento de Albufeira)
DGEG - Directorate-General for Energy and Geology ([illegible])
SCADA - Supervisory Control and Data Acquisition

DESCRIPTION OF FPV SYSTEMS

❑ **Location:**

- ➢ Monte Novo Dam, Évora (38.514, -7.712), drinking water reservoir used for public supply, irrigation, and flood control.
- ➢ Stable water levels and >10 m depth make it ideal for FPV installation.

❑ **Installed capacity:**

- ➢ 200 kW, compatible with low-voltage grid injection (DL 15/2022, Regulation 815/2023).

❑ **Floating platforms** (three technologies tested across four configurations):

- ➢ **System 1:**
  - East–West, portrait, fixed tilt 12–15°
- ➢ **System 2:**
  - East–West, landscape, fixed tilt 15°
- ➢ **System 3:**
  - a. South-facing, landscape, adjustable tilt 10–40°
  - b. East–West, landscape, adjustable tilt 10–40°

RESULTS

Description	Qt.
Set of 11 Campbell 109 Temperature Profile Sensors:	
– 1 sensor with 5 m cable	
– 2 sensors with 10 m cables	
– 3 sensors with 15 m cables	
– 2 sensors with 20 m cables	
– 3 sensors with 25 m cables	1
Eureka Manta+30a Water Quality Probe	1

Description	Qt.
Class A" Solar Radiation Sensor EKO MS-80SH	1
Gill WindSonic Wind Sensor	1
Campbell HyroVue10 Temperature and Relative Humidity Sensor	1
Lambrecht 15189 Precipitation Sensor	1
Campbell CS125 Present Weather Sensor	1

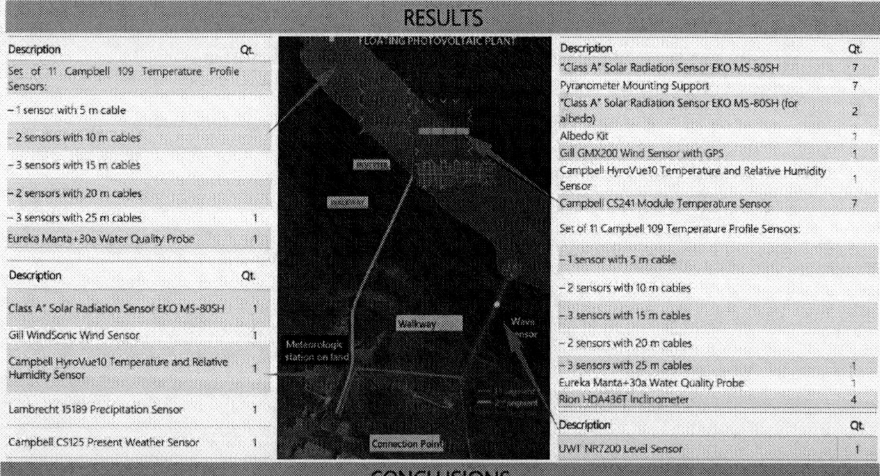

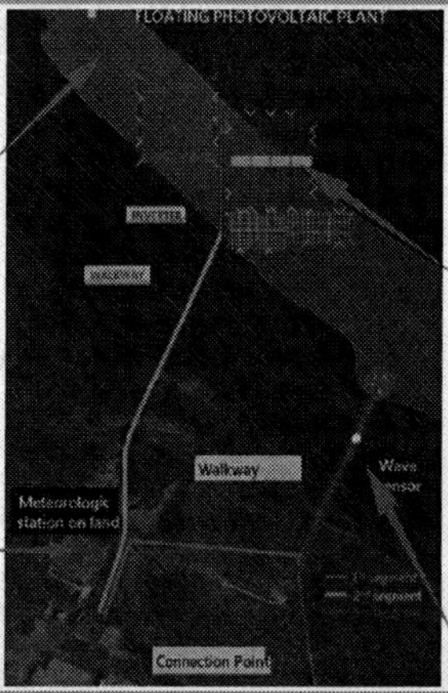

Description	Qt.
"Class A" Solar Radiation Sensor EKO MS-80SH	7
Pyranometer Mounting Support	7
"Class A" Solar Radiation Sensor EKO MS-80SH (for albedo)	2
Albedo Kit	1
Gill GMX200 Wind Sensor with GPS	1
Campbell HyroVue10 Temperature and Relative Humidity Sensor	1
Campbell CS241 Module Temperature Sensor	7
Set of 11 Campbell 109 Temperature Profile Sensors:	
– 1 sensor with 5 m cable	
– 2 sensors with 10 m cables	
– 3 sensors with 15 m cables	
– 2 sensors with 20 m cables	
– 3 sensors with 25 m cables	1
Eureka Manta+30a Water Quality Probe	1
Rion HDA436T Inclinometer	4

Description	Qt.
UWI NR7200 Level Sensor	1

FUTURE WORKS

- ❑ Launch tender for FPV systems, instrumentation, and data acquisition platform.
- ❑ Install and commission the plant with continuous sensor monitoring.
- ❑ Monitor energy performance (PR, LCOE) and water quality.
- ❑ Assess interactions between FPV and the ecosystem.
- ❑ Use data to develop best-practice guidelines and testing protocols.
- ❑ Contribute to the standardisation and optimisation of future FPV projects.

CONCLUSIONS

- ❑ FPV deployment in water supply reservoirs requires balancing energy efficiency, water security, and environmental protection.
- ❑ The lack of a specific licensing framework demands rigorous project evaluations.
- ❑ The sensor network enables continuous monitoring of water quality and environmental impacts.
- ❑ The project stands out from commercial FPV plants by generating highly reliable scientific data.
- ❑ Results support best practices for FPV design, operation, and maintenance.
- ❑ Contributes to the safe and efficient integration of FPV systems in sensitive environments.

ACKNOWLEDGEMENTS

This research was partly funded by the PRR Mobilizing Agendas, project Alliance for Energy Transition (ATE) with Grant agreement ID C644914747-00000023

PRR REPÚBLICA PORTUGUESA Financiado pela União Europeia NextGenerationEU

MOBILE E-BIKE SHARING SYSTEMS WITH INTEGRATED PHOTOVOLTAICS: ELECTRIC MOBILITY SOLUTIONS FOR LARGE EVENTS IN ÉVORA, PORTUGAL

Helena Oliveira [a], Paulo Carmo [a], José A. Silva [a], Luís Fialho [b], Paulo Infante [c], Pedro Horta [a]
a Renewable Energies Chair, University of Évora. Mitra Campus of the University of Évora, Edificio Ario Lobo de Azevedo, 7000-083 Nossa Senhora da Tourega, Portugal
b Eurac Research, Viale Druso (Drususallee) 1, 39100 Bolzano, Italy
c Department of Mathematics, University of Évora, Rua Romão Ramalho, 7000-671 Évora, Portugal
helena.oliveira@uevora.pt; paulo.carmo@uevora.pt; jose.silva@uevora.pt; luis.fialho@eurac.edu; pinfante@uevora.pt; phorta@uevora.pt

ABSTRACT: Mobile e-bike sharing stations integrated with photovoltaics are proposed for Évora to serve baseline urban demand and event-related surges while respecting heritage constraints. The system is powered primarily by photovoltaics, with optional grid-assist for resilience. We present a siting–sizing framework that (i) selects candidate locations via AHP and a p-median model based on origin–destination flows and travel times, and (ii) sizes PV and storage under two energy hypotheses: full-recharge of all e-bikes versus a usage-driven demand model (Wh/km × trip length × trips/bike). Using worst-month irradiance and aggregate conversion losses, a worked example shows that the full-recharge assumption yields higher capacities (≈6 kWp PV + 25 kWh storage per 10 bikes for event peaks), whereas the usage-driven model reduces sizing substantially while meeting service levels; both are reported to ensure robustness. This compact framework is directly applicable to heritage cities planning PV-micromobility for large events.
Keywords: Electric Mobility, Photovoltaic Energy, Smart City, Urban Planning

1 INTRODUCTION

This study proposes a practical and scalable solution for sustainable urban mobility in Évora, Portugal, through the implementation of mobile e-bike docking stations powered primarily by photovoltaic energy. These stations will be strategically distributed across the city and equipped with battery storage to enable 24-hour operation for both e-bike sharing and charging. The system will be supported by a digital monitoring application offering real-time data, user interface, and integrated security features.

The concept of mobile stations is particularly relevant given Évora's designation as the European Capital of Culture for 2027, which will attract large audiences to a historic urban environment recognized by UNESCO since 1986 [1]. The initiative aligns with Évora's smart city agenda and its participation in the EU-funded POCITYF project [2], which promotes climate-neutral innovation in heritage cities.

Portugal's National Strategy for Active Mobility sets ambitious targets for bicycle modal share in urban areas, 4% by 2025 and 10% by 2030 [3]. Évora already leads in electric public transport [4] and academic cycling initiatives [5], yet its transport sector remains the largest contributor to local GHG emissions (37.97%) [6]. This project aims to reduce emissions and foster long-term behavioral change by integrating clean energy and intelligent mobility infrastructure into the city's cultural and urban landscape.

The central region of the city of Évora (Figure 1) has a specific PV output of approximately 1652.0 kWh/kWp, as indicated by the data for annual and monthly average values of PV electricity (AC) supplied by a PV system and normalized to 1 kWp of installed capacity, from the Global Solar Atlas. This high output highlights the region's significant potential to harness solar energy, which can be effectively utilized to support sustainable mobility solutions. By leveraging this significant solar resource, Évora can improve its green infrastructure and contribute to reducing CO2 emissions in the domestic transportation sector [7].

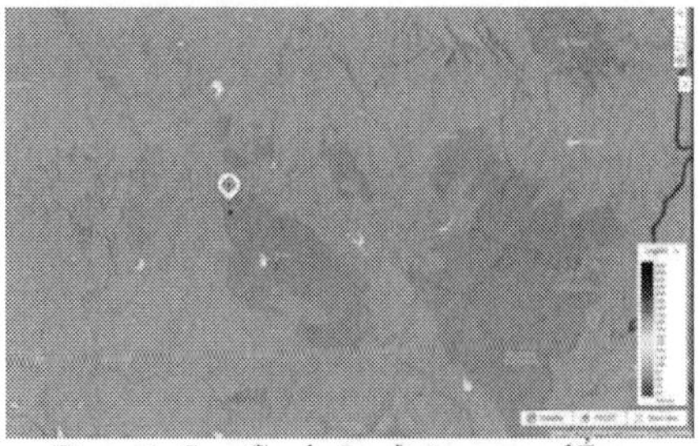

Figure 1: Specific photovoltaic power of Évora
Source: [7] (accessed: February 2025)

One of the objectives of this project is to gather recommendations for the implementation of a monitoring application that allows users to easily know the availability of e-bikes for rent, as well as available spaces for docking and charging, through an interactive map. This application should provide real-time monitoring of e-bikes, including location, battery status and availability.

The sharing stations will be strategically located to facilitate the daily routine of residents and users, integration with other existing means of public transport and the journey between different tourist attractions, events and nearby establishments.

2 RELATED WORKS

2.1 Integrated photovoltaic charging stations for electric micromobility

There are many examples of integrated photovoltaic charging stations for electric micromobility that inspire this work:

- An urban sharing platform in London, UK (2017), is a successful example of how data from a wide range of mobility measures, including e-bikes, e-cargo bikes, electric vehicle charging, smart parking and solar energy systems, can be combined and shared separately to inform policy decisions, generate financial savings and reduce CO2 emissions [8].
- The SUNPOD CYCLO charging station, from the French company MOBENDI, is an example of a

modular and scalable option, with solar energy production and integrated storage batteries, i.e. 100% self-sufficient in electricity [9].

- Swiftmile, a Californian company, is a complete charging and parking solution for e-bikes, e-scooters and e-mopeds, featuring advanced fleet management technology and available with integrated solar panels [10].

In Portugal, there are successful examples of electric bike sharing, such as Gira - Lisbon's Bicycle Sharing System, but only a few stations with modular infrastructure have the potential for solar power [11]. In contrast, there are companies in Portugal that develop and distribute mobile stations for electric bike sharing, with integrated charging, digital management, and solar solutions [12], and some even combine solar and wind power to ensure full autonomy in an off the grid setup [13].

Unlike fixed stations, mobile units can be deployed in smaller towns, rural areas, or university campuses with lower initial investment. These stations offer a high degree of spatial flexibility, allowing municipalities to adapt infrastructure to seasonal demand, temporary events, or urban renovations. In heritage cities like Évora, where permanent installations may face regulatory or aesthetic constraints, mobile units provide a non-invasive alternative that can be relocated or reconfigured as needed, as demonstrated by Beam Global's BeamBike system, which operates fully off-grid (Figure 2) and is designed for rapid deployment and relocation [14].

Figure 2: BeamBike system
Source: [14] (accessed: September 2025)

Given that the technology for mobile e-bike sharing stations powered by solar energy is already available and proven, this study focuses on the strategic planning of station placement. The effectiveness of the system depends largely on the selection of locations that ensure accessibility, user engagement, and integration with existing urban infrastructure.

3 METHODS

3.1 Demand modelling

To support the strategic deployment of solar-powered e-bike sharing stations in Évora, a demand modeling framework was developed to simulate usage patterns under different urban conditions. This model aims to inform station sizing, energy requirements, and operational flexibility, particularly in a city characterized by seasonal tourism, cultural events, and heritage constraints.

- Baseline Scenario: Typical Urban Day

The baseline scenario represents a standard weekday in Évora, capturing regular commuting flows, student mobility, and local errands. Key parameters include:

- Temporal distribution of trips by hour (morning/evening peaks), distinguishing between weekdays and weekends.
- Trip length percentiles (p50/p90), used to estimate average and upper-bound energy consumption per trip.
- OD (Origin–Destination) profiles across nine strategic points, including residential zones (e.g., Horta das Laranjeiras), commercial hubs (Évora Plaza), university areas, and heritage sites.

- Event Scenario: High-Demand Conditions

To account for fluctuations during cultural, academic, or seasonal events, a second scenario was modeled using a multiplicative factor applied to trip volumes and temporal peaks. This scenario reflects:

- Increased demand during festivals, conferences, and tourism surges.
- Shifted usage patterns, with extended evening activity and higher turnover rates at central stations.
- Stress testing of station capacity and solar generation adequacy under peak conditions.

- Application of the Model

The demand model supports:

- Station sizing: Estimating the number of bikes and charging docks required per location.
- Energy planning: Aligning solar generation profiles with usage peaks to optimize battery autonomy and reduce grid dependency.
- Operational logistics: Informing redistribution strategies, maintenance scheduling, and dynamic station placement (for mobile units).

- Origin–Destination Matrix

A simplified OD matrix was constructed to analyze trip flows between the nine proposed station sites. This matrix enables:

- Identification of high-demand corridors.
- Prioritization of intermodal integration zones.
- Validation of station placement based on real and projected mobility patterns.

3.2 Solar resource & system model[1]

To ensure autonomous operation of solar-powered e-bike sharing stations in Évora, a dimensioning model was developed based on local solar resource data, estimated daily energy demand per station, and system efficiency parameters. The goal is to guarantee energy availability even under worst-case conditions, such as low solar yield in winter and peak demand during urban events.

- Monthly Solar Yield ($Y[\frac{kWh}{kWp}.day]$)

According to PVGIS simulations for Évora [15], the average daily solar yield per installed kilowatt-peak (kWp) varies seasonally:

- Average 8.26 kWh/day in Summer.
- Average 4.51 kWh/day in Autumn.
- Average 2.62 kWh/day in Winter.
- Average 6.29 kWh/day in Spring.

These values reflect long-term averages and includes typical meteorological conditions, making it suitable for preliminary sizing.

[1] The system design follows applicable standards: EN 15194 (EPAC e-bikes), IEC 61215/61730 (PV modules), IEC 62109 (PV power converters), and IEC 62619/62133-2 (Li-ion stationary/portable batteries). Charging cabinets include thermal protection and ventilation; the EMS enforces SOC limits (20–90%) and rate control. Data handling complies with GDPR; the app/backend adopt privacy-by-design and standard cybersecurity controls.

- Estimated Daily Load per Station ($E_{load}[day]$)

Based on demand modeling (Section 3.1), each station is expected to support:

- Baseline load: ~2.5 kWh/day (charging 10 bikes with 250 Wh each)
- Event peak load: up to 7.5–12.5 kWh/day (factor 3–5× increase)

- System Efficiency and Losses

To account for real-world losses, a global system efficiency factor of 80–85% is applied, considering:

- MPPT (Maximum Power Point Tracking) and inverter losses
- Battery charge/discharge inefficiencies
- Cable and environmental losses

Thus, the effective solar yield becomes:

$$Y_{eff} = Y \times \eta_{sys}$$

- Robustness Criterion

To ensure robustness, the system must satisfy:

- Worst scenario: Winter ($Y \approx 2.62 \frac{kWh}{kWp}.day$)
- Peak event load: up to 12.5 kWh/day

Required installed capacity per station:

$$Required\ kWp = \frac{E_{load}}{Y_{eff}} = \frac{12.5}{2.62 \times 0.80} \approx 6.0\ kWp$$

Battery sizing (2 days autonomy):

$$Battery\ capacity = 2 \times 12.5 = 25\ kWh$$

- Design Implications

- Stations should be equipped with $\geq 6\ kWp$ solar panels and $\geq 25\ kWh$ battery storage to ensure full autonomy year-round.
- Modular configurations allow scaling based on location-specific demand.
- Hybrid systems (solar + wind) may be considered for enhanced resilience in low-radiation periods.

3.3 Energy sizing with two hypotheses (robustness check)

Let Y_m be the monthly specific PV yield (kWh/kWp·day) for Évora (worst case scenario value), and let η_{sys} be the aggregate system efficiency (MPPT/inverter/charge/distribution). The results are reported to $\eta_{sys} \in [0.80,0.85]$.

H1: Full-recharge (upper bound).

Daily load assumes full recharge of N_b bikes with battery capacity C_b(kWh):

$$E_{\text{load}}^{\text{H1}} = N_b\ C_b \times f_{\text{util}},$$

with $f_{\text{util}} \leq 1$(fraction of capacity replenished daily; baseline $f_{\text{util}} = 1$for a conservative upper bound). Required PV and storage for autonomy of Ddays:

$$P_{\text{PV}}^{\text{H1}} = \frac{E_{\text{load}}^{\text{H1}}}{Y_m\ \eta_{\text{sys}}}, E_{\text{BESS}}^{\text{H1}} = \frac{D\ E_{\text{load}}^{\text{H1}}}{\text{DoD}}.$$

H2: Usage-driven (demand model).

Daily load derives from travel demand:

$$E_{\text{load}}^{\text{H2}} = N_b \times c_{\text{Wh/km}} \times L_{\text{trip}} \times T_{\text{per bike}} \times (1 + \ell),$$

where $c_{\text{Wh/km}}$is the specific e-bike consumption, $L_{\text{trip}}$the average trip length, $T_{\text{per bike}}$trips/bike/day, and ℓaccounts for charging/distribution losses. Sizing:

$$P_{\text{PV}}^{\text{H2}} = \frac{E_{\text{load}}^{\text{H2}}}{Y_m\ \eta_{\text{sys}}}, E_{\text{BESS}}^{\text{H2}} = \frac{D\ E_{\text{load}}^{\text{H2}}}{\text{DoD}}.$$

Worked example (10 bikes, worst case scenario sizing).

- Baseline (typical day): $c_{\text{Wh/km}} = 10$, $L_{\text{trip}} = 3$ km, $T_{\text{per bike}} = 2$, $\ell \approx 0.15$, $Y_m = 2.62$kWh/kWp·day, $\eta_{\text{sys}} = 0.80$, DoD = 80%, $D = 2$days.
- $E_{\text{load}}^{\text{H2}} \approx 0.71$kWh/day $\Rightarrow$ $P_{\text{PV}}^{\text{H2}} \approx 0.34$kWp; $E_{\text{BESS}}^{\text{H2}} \approx$ 1.8kWh useful (~2.2 kWh nominal).
- Event peak (×5 trips): $E_{\text{load}}^{\text{H2}} \approx 3.5$kWh/day $\Rightarrow$ $P_{\text{PV}}^{\text{H2}} \approx$ 1.7kWp; $E_{\text{BESS}}^{\text{H2}} \approx 7.1$kWh useful (~8.9 kWh nominal).

For comparison, **H1** with full-recharge of 10×0.25 kWh/day under the same Y_m, η_{sys} yields ≈ **6 kWp PV** and **25 kWh** storage for 2-day autonomy in event conditions. Reporting **both** H1/H2 makes the design robust yet realistic and aligns with the "primarily PV" positioning.

The Table 1 below summarizes the results under worst-case PV yield conditions for Évora (Y_m = 2.62 kWh/kWp·day), system efficiency η_{sys} = 0.80, and depth of discharge DoD = 80%.

Table 1: Energy sizing results under H1 and H2 hypotheses

Scenario	Daily Load (kWh)	PV Required (kWp)	Storage Required (kWh useful)	Storage Nominal (~kWh)
H1: Full Recharge	2.50	1.19	6.25	7.81
H2: Baseline Demand	0.69	0.33	1.72	2.15
H2: Event Peak	3.45	1.65	8.62	10.78

3.4 Location optimisation

To ensure strategic placement of solar-powered mobile e-bike stations in Évora, a location optimisation framework was developed combining multi-criteria decision analysis (MCDA) and spatial allocation models. The goal is to balance operational efficiency, user accessibility, and urban constraints, particularly in heritage zones.

- Multi-Criteria Decision Analysis (MCDA)

An Analytic Hierarchy Process (AHP) was applied to evaluate candidate locations based on the following criteria (Table 2):

Table 2: Multicriteria Decision Analysis

Criterion	Description
Demand density	Estimated trip volume from demand modeling (Section 3.1)
Intermodality	Proximity to bus stops, parking lots, and pedestrian zones
Solar exposure	Average insolation and shading conditions (from PVGIS/GSA)
Heritage constraints	Restrictions on permanent infrastructure in protected urban areas
Safety and vandalism risk	Historical data on theft, vandalism, and nighttime visibility
Visual impact	Integration with urban aesthetics and minimization of visual clutter

Criteria were weighted via AHP (Demand 0.30, Intermodality 0.25, Solar exposure 0.10, Heritage constraints 0.10, Safety/Vandalism 0.10, Visual impact 0.15). The pairwise matrix yielded a Consistency Ratio (CR)=0.05, below the 0.10 threshold, indicating acceptable internal consistency.

Location–allocation used a p-median model with K=8 facilities to minimize demand-weighted travel time from OD pairs; we solved it with OR-Tools CP-SAT to optimality (gap 0%). A sensitivity sweep K ∈ [6,10] is provided in the supplement.

Each criterion was weighted based on stakeholder input and urban planning priorities. The resulting composite score guided the ranking of the nine proposed locations.

- Spatial Allocation Model

To refine the station network, a p-median model was applied to minimize the weighted average distance between origin–destination flows and station locations. The model uses:

- OD matrix from Section 3.1
- Flow weights based on simulated trip volumes
- Constraints on station mobility and solar exposure

This approach ensures that stations are placed where they serve the highest demand with minimal detour, while respecting urbanistic and patrimonial limitations.

- Seed Network and Refinement

The initial set of nine strategic points, including Évora Plaza, University of Évora, Centro Histórico, and peripheral residential zones, served as a seed network. These locations were refined using the MCDA-AHP scores and flow-weighted spatial allocation, resulting in a robust and context-sensitive station layout.

The Estimated Shading classification was inferred based on the criteria of visual impact and patrimonial sensitivity, according to the weights defined in the AHP model. The logic applied was:

- Low shadow: points with low visual impact (≤ 0.55) and lower heritage sensitivity (≤ 0.85), indicating a lower risk of aesthetic or cultural interference.
- High shade: points with high visual impact (≥ 0.90) or high heritage sensitivity (≥ 0.90), requiring greater care in urban integration.
- Medium shade: intermediate cases, where the criteria indicate neither high risk nor absence of restrictions.

4 CASE STUDY: ÉVORA

4.1 Cycle path network and opportunities for sustainable electric mobility in Évora

The existing and planned cycle paths in the city of Évora, in addition to meeting adequate urban conditions, motivate the purpose of this study. Évora has 4 cycle paths in operation, implemented on the outskirts of the historic center, plus the Ecopista route that starts in the urban center and crosses the entire city towards the city of Arraiolos (± 25 km). Furthermore, the project includes connecting these cycle paths to the wall of the Historic Center and extending them to the Évora Industrial and Technological Park (PITE). It also includes the development of a Cycle Path along Avenida Dr. Francisco Barahona, between the Rossio roundabout and the train station [16].

The Historic Center has limited paid parking, with designated areas for residents, visitors, and people with reduced mobility. Parking lots in Évora could be strategic assets for this electric mobility project with e-bike sharing, especially if integrated with solar infrastructure, docking stations, and urban intermodality.

Parking lots outside the city walls, such as Porta da Lagoa and Avenida Túlio Espanca, offer better accessibility and physical space. Two parks, Av. Túlio Espanca and Rua Eng. Arantes e Oliveira, are being equipped with photovoltaic systems for energy production as part of the European POCITYF project [17].

For the academic community and tourists, having bicycles at shared docking stations available with the ease of returning them after use at different points in the city often solves the problem of physical space in homes and accommodations. In addition, it is important to offer an e-bike in usable condition, with charging and green, safe and smart parking. This makes the option accessible to those who have difficulty driving on the terrain of the city, which is predominantly flat (Figure 3), but with gentle hills and elevations that require greater physical effort [18].

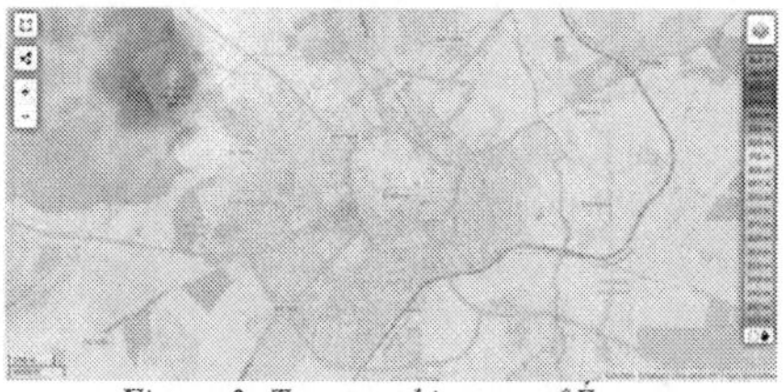

Figure 3: Topographic map of Évora
Source: [18] (accessed: January 2025)

4.2 Initial Investment Strategies for Solar-Powered E-Bike Sharing Stations in Évora

The initial investment required for installing solar-powered charging stations often represents a major barrier to large-scale implementation, particularly in cities with constrained public budgets and heritage-sensitive urban environments such as Évora.

To support the implementation of solar-powered e-bike sharing stations in Évora, the following table summarizes key financing alternatives, highlighting their mechanisms, benefits, and contextual relevance to the city's urban and heritage constraints (Table 3).

Table 3: Initial Investment Strategies for Solar-Powered E-Bike Sharing Stations in Évora

Financing Model	Description	Relevance to Évora
Public–Private Partnerships	Collaboration between local government and private sector for installation and maintenance, often via concession agreements.	Enables flexible deployment in heritage-sensitive areas; reduces municipal burden while ensuring service quality.
Green Financing Instruments	Includes tax incentives, low-interest loans, and dedicated credit lines for clean energy and mobility projects.	Aligns with Évora's sustainability goals and can support solar infrastructure in public parking areas (e.g., Água de Prata).
Public Sector Grants	Funding from municipal, regional, or EU programs (e.g., Horizon Europe, POCITYF) targeting renewable energy and smart mobility.	Can be leveraged for pilot stations near cultural hubs and university zones, especially during EU2027 events.

Financing Model	Description	Relevance to Évora
Crowdfunding & Donations	Community-based funding involving citizens, local businesses, and institutions to support station deployment.	Encourages civic engagement and ownership, particularly in residential areas like António Gedeão and Horta das Laranjeiras.
Corporate Sponsorship	Branding and co-investment by companies in exchange for visibility and social responsibility recognition.	Ideal for commercial zones like Évora Plaza; promotes private sector involvement in sustainable urban mobility.
Energy Cooperatives	Local energy communities invest in solar infrastructure and share benefits from energy generation and mobility services.	Could be explored in partnership with University of Évora and local stakeholders for long-term energy autonomy.

4.3 Maintenance and Operational Efficiency: Ensuring Long-Term System Performance in Évora

One of the key concerns in deploying solar-powered infrastructure for electric mobility, particularly in high-traffic urban areas such as charging stations, is ensuring sustained operational efficiency over time. In Évora, where heritage constraints and seasonal fluctuations in demand must be considered, maintenance strategies must be both technically robust and context sensitive:

a. **Preventive Maintenance and Remote:** Monitoring Modern technologies allow real-time monitoring of station performance, enabling early detection of faults and minimizing service disruptions. In Évora's historic center, where physical interventions must be minimal, remote diagnostics and predictive maintenance protocols are essential to preserve both infrastructure and urban aesthetics.

b. **Local Technical Training and Workforce Development:** To ensure sustained system availability, it is crucial to train local maintenance teams in solar and mobility technologies. This not only reduces downtime but also fosters local employment and strengthens Évora's technical capacity in renewable energy and sustainable transport, aligning with the city's long-term strategic goals.

c. **Long-Life Batteries and Modular Systems:** Using durable batteries and modular components (such as inverters and docking units) allows for phased upgrades and simplified replacements. In Évora, where flexibility is key due to frequent cultural events and spatial constraints, modularity supports rapid reconfiguration and ensures that the system evolves alongside technological advancements.

5 RESULTS

The study proposes prioritizing mobile stations within the Historic Center of Évora to ensure flexibility in the management of electric bike-sharing infrastructure, allowing for the relocation of facilities in response to temporary changes in the urban space resulting from major events. This approach respects the city's heritage and ensures the continuity of sustainable mobility services, even in contexts of high land use.

To ensure that the implementation of solar-powered e-bike sharing stations, with integrated batteries for uninterrupted docking, charging, rental, and monitoring, is compatible with the city's spatial and operational realities, the following locational criteria were considered essential:

- Historic Center prioritization: enabling relocation when major events require local adjustments.
- User-oriented planning: proximity to parking lots, schools, shops, markets, restaurants, and tourist attractions, supporting key traffic routes and ensuring pleasant, accessible journeys.
- Public transport integration: proximity to bus and train stations, stops, and taxi hubs, especially for events attracting large groups from nearby cities.
- Solar exposure optimization: preference for less shaded areas to maximize photovoltaic efficiency.

The AHP matrix was applied to the nine proposed station sites, generating a composite score for each location. These scores were then used to refine the initial seed network, prioritizing points with high demand density, strong intermodal connections, and favorable solar exposure, while respecting heritage constraints and minimizing visual impact.

In parallel, a p-median location-allocation model was implemented using the OD matrix from Section 3.1. This model minimizes the flow-weighted average distance between trip origins/destinations and station locations, ensuring operational efficiency and user accessibility.

The combination of MCDA and spatial optimization resulted in a robust, context-aware station layout, adaptable to seasonal variation and event-based demand. The mobile nature of the infrastructure allows for periodic reallocation based on updated demand profiles and urban dynamics.

From the nine candidate sites evaluated, eight were selected based on technical, urbanistic, and functional criteria. The selection of these eight points reflects a balance between spatial efficiency, heritage sensitivity and operational feasibility. The multicriteria approach allows for the technical justification of each inclusion and exclusion, aligning with the objectives of sustainable mobility and respect for the urban context of Évora. Table 4 presents the decision-making indexes:

Table 4: Summary Table:Strategic Point Evaluation

STRATEGIC POINT	AHP SCORE	ESTIMATED SHADING[2]	AVG. OD DISTANCE (M)	DECISION
António Gedeão	0.838	Low	1211.	Include
Évora Plaza	0.795	Low	2367.	Include
Porta de Aviz	0.863	High	1291.	Include

[2] Estimated Shading: inferred from visual impact and heritage sensitivity scores. Points with lower visual interference and reduced patrimonial constraints were classified as having low shading.

Água de Prata Parking Lot	0.89	High	1494.	Include
Horta das Laranjeiras	0.878	High	812.	Include
Giraldo Square	0.958	High	1033.	Include
Rodoviária do Alentejo	0.82	Low	1392.	Include
Évora Train Station	0.792	Low	1327.	Include
Fire service	0.73	Medium	1210.	Exclude

The resulting network is strategically balanced, encompassing high-traffic corridors, intermodal hubs, student residences, commercial zones, and green spaces, including the following points:

- António Gedeão University Residence (38.561199, -7.912974): A residential location with a large number of students. This station promotes daily e-bike use as an alternative to motorized transportation for the commuting of students, in addition to reducing pressure on local parking.
- Évora Plaza (38.548690, -7.905595): A commercial center with a large flow of visitors and workers. The presence of a station at this location favors short trips for shopping, leisure, and services, in addition to allowing integration with peripheral residential areas.
- Porta de Aviz (38.576884, -7.910092): A strategic entrance to the Historic Center, with the potential to serve as a transition point between heritage and modern areas. Electric mobility here helps reduce car traffic within the city walls.
- Água de Prata Parking Lot (38.576187, -7.914491): A park with solar infrastructure under development (POCITYF), ideal for installing green charging stations. It can function as an intermodal hub, especially during events or peak hours.
- Horta das Laranjeiras (38.567196, -7.907665): A green and recreational space, excellent for promoting the tourist and leisure use of e-bikes. The installation here reinforces the project's sustainable nature and expands access to low-density urban areas.
- Giraldo Square (38.570567, -7.908990): The symbolic and functional heart of the city. The presence of a station at this location ensures visibility, tourist engagement, and quick access to services, commerce, and heritage.
- Rodoviária do Alentejo, S.A. (38.567404, -7.917300): Bus terminal with high passenger turnover. Installing a station at this location favors intermodality and expands the reach of the shared system for those arriving from outside the city.
- Évora Train Station (38.560774, -7.907245): Railway entry point to the city. Integration with the e-bike system allows for quick travel to the historic center, universities, and shopping areas, promoting a fluid and sustainable mobility experience.

To assess the spatial coverage of the proposed e-bike system, we generated isochrones of 5, 10 and 15 minutes of travel time from a central location (38.5711, -7.9106, Serpa Pinto Street - Évora), using the OpenRouteService (ORS) API with the cycling-electric profile. This profile accounts for the specific performance of e-bikes, including acceleration and average speeds on the road network. The resulting polygons represent the maximum area that can be reached within each time threshold, providing a realistic measure of accessibility that complements the set of eight candidate stations previously identified. Isochrone generation was implemented in R with the openrouteservice, sf and leaflet packages, and the approach is fully reproducible. Figure 4 illustrates the 5/10/15-minute isochrones, which will be used to benchmark system coverage in both baseline and event scenarios [19].

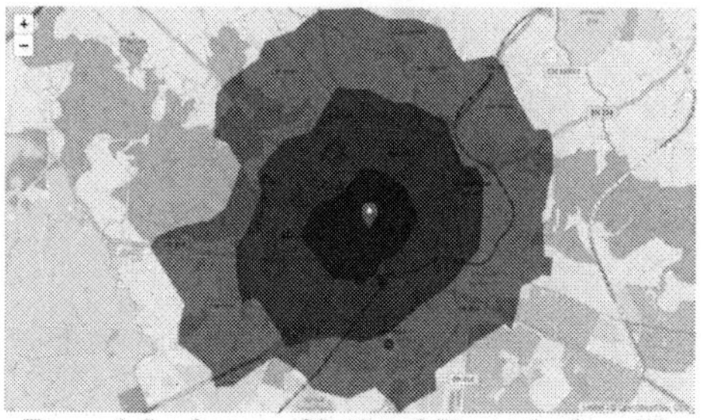

Figure 4: Isochrones of 5, 10 and 15 minutes for e-bike trips from the city centre (Serpa Pinto Street, Évora), generated with HeiGIT gGmbH, OpenRouteService[3]
Source: [19]; ORS, processed in R (openrouteservice, sf, leaflet packages) (accessed: September 2025)

Most of the eight selected candidate stations fall within the 10-minute isochrone, ensuring accessibility for daily commuting and intermodal trips, while the 15-minute coverage extends the system's reach to peripheral residential and leisure areas. This confirms that the proposed network provides adequate spatial coverage under both baseline and event scenarios.

To support the strategic deployment of solar-powered e-bike sharing stations in Évora, a demand simulation was conducted using synthetic data modeled in R. The results are presented in four visualizations (Figure 5a–5d) that inform key operational and locational decisions:

• Temporal Distribution of Trips Figure 5a illustrates the hourly distribution of trips across weekdays and weekends. Weekday demand shows pronounced peaks around 8:00 and 17:00, consistent with commuting patterns, while weekend usage is more evenly distributed throughout the day. These findings suggest that:

– Stations near residential and employment zones should prioritize early morning and late afternoon availability.

– Weekend demand may require broader coverage in leisure and tourism areas, with extended operational windows.

• Trip Length Percentiles Figure 5b presents the P50 and P90 percentiles of trip duration, estimated from a bimodal distribution modeled in R. The P50 value (~15 minutes) reflects typical intra-urban mobility, while the P90 (~30+ minutes) indicates outlier trips that may require higher battery autonomy or strategic redistribution. These metrics support:

– Sizing of battery capacity per station.

[3] HEIGIT - Heidelberg Institute for Geoinformation Technology. OpenRouteService (accessed: September 2025). From https://openrouteservice.org.

– Estimation of solar generation needs based on average energy consumption per trip.

• Origin–Destination Matrix Figure 5c shows the simulated OD flows between nine strategic points in Évora. The heatmap highlights asymmetric demand patterns, with certain nodes acting as major trip generators or attractors. This analysis informs:

– Prioritization of station placement in high-flow corridors.

– Identification of intermodal integration points (e.g., university ↔ historic center ↔ commercial zones).

– Dynamic reallocation strategies for mobile stations based on temporal and spatial demand.

• Estimated Travel Time Matrix Figure 5d presents the simulated travel times (in minutes) between the nine proposed station sites, calculated from geodesic distances and assuming an average e-bike speed of 15 km/h. This visualization complements the OD flow analysis by introducing a temporal dimension to spatial accessibility. Key insights include:

– Identification of time-efficient corridors, where short travel durations align with high trip volumes, reinforcing their suitability for station placement and redistribution logistics.

– Detection of peripheral nodes with longer travel times, which may require additional battery autonomy or serve as candidates for grid-assist fallback strategies.

– Support for dynamic routing and fleet balancing, especially during peak hours or event-driven demand shifts.

Together, these visualizations enhance the operational planning framework by linking spatial layout to real-world

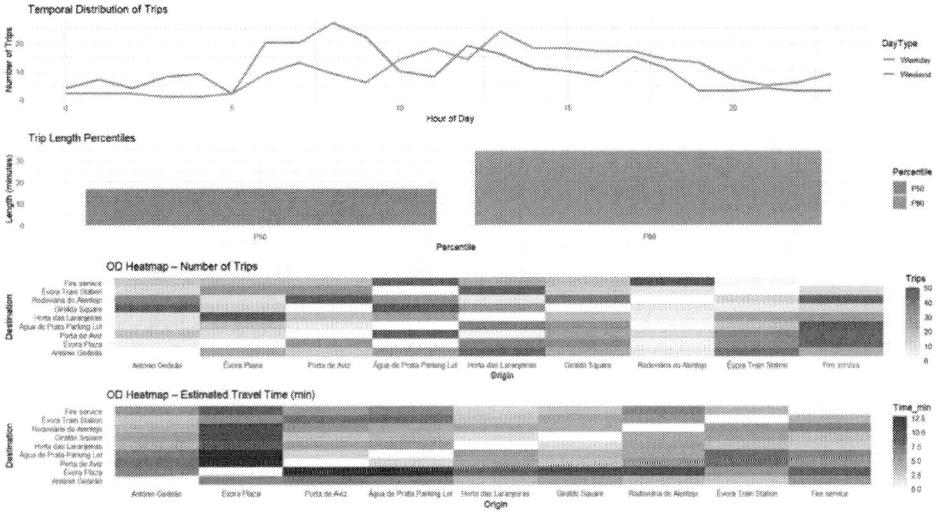

Figure 5: Demand modelling

travel behavior, ensuring that station deployment responds not only to demand intensity but also to temporal feasibility and urban dynamics.

From the nine candidate locations evaluated through the AHP matrix and spatial optimization, eight were selected for initial deployment. This decision reflects a balance between maximizing coverage and maintaining operational feasibility.

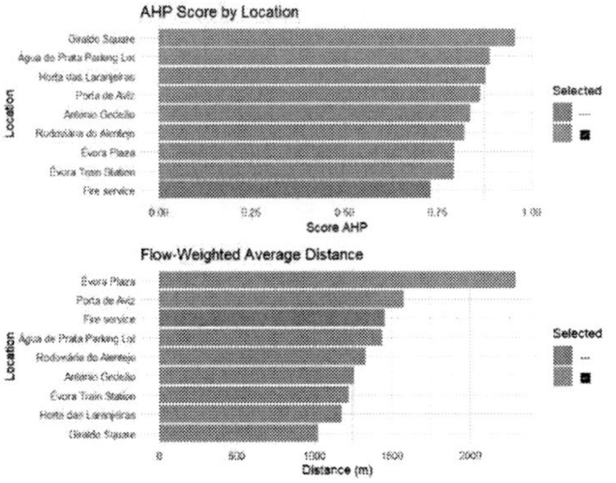

Figure 6: Station Selection Strategy

The exclusion of one site was based on its comparatively lower composite score and higher flow-weighted average distance, indicating reduced accessibility and strategic relevance within the current demand scenario (Figure 6).

The selection process prioritized locations that offer strong intermodal connectivity, favorable solar exposure, and proximity to high-demand corridors. The modular nature of the infrastructure allows for future inclusion or rotation of sites as demand patterns evolve, ensuring that the system remains responsive and scalable.

6 DISCUSSIONS

- **Trade-offs: "Primarily PV" vs. "Grid-Assist"**

The decision to operate stations primarily on photovoltaic energy reflects a commitment to full autonomy and carbon neutrality. However, this choice entails important trade-offs:

- Advantages of Primarily PV: Zero operational emissions and full energy independence; Simplified permitting in heritage zones (no grid connection or trenching); Symbolic value in showcasing clean energy leadership.
- Limitations: Vulnerability to seasonal variation and shading (especially in winter or dense urban areas);

10.4229/EUPVSEC2025/4DV.1.46

Need for oversizing PV and battery systems to meet peak demand, increasing cost and footprint; Limited fallback options during extreme weather or prolonged overcast periods.
- Grid-Assist Alternative: Allows for smaller PV arrays and batteries, reducing upfront investment; Ensures uninterrupted service during low-generation periods; Enables smart charging strategies (e.g., grid charging during off-peak hours).

The choice between these models depends on site-specific constraints, policy priorities, and operational resilience goals. In Évora, where heritage preservation and visual impact are critical, a mobile, PV-exclusive model may be preferable, but hybrid configurations could be considered for high-demand or shaded locations.

- **Operational Dynamics During Events**

Cultural, academic, and tourism events in Évora introduce temporary spikes in mobility demand, which challenge the static assumptions of baseline station sizing. Key considerations include:
- Temporal reallocation: Mobile stations can be repositioned to event zones (e.g., festival venues, university campuses) to absorb demand surges.
- Energy stress: Higher trip volumes increase charging cycles, requiring robust battery autonomy or temporary energy support.
- User behavior shifts: Events may alter trip timing (e.g., extended evening use), duration, and origin–destination patterns.

Operational strategies should include:
- Predictive modeling: Using historical event calendars and demand simulations to anticipate peak loads.
- Flexible logistics: Rapid deployment protocols, mobile maintenance units, and real-time monitoring.
- Fallback planning: Optional grid-assist or mobile powerbanks to ensure continuity without compromising the PV-first principle.

These dynamics reinforce the value of modularity and mobility in station design, allowing the system to adapt to urban rhythms without permanent infrastructure.

7 CONCLUSIONS

The combined analysis of AHP criteria, shading estimation and flow-weighted average distance reveals a robust selection of strategic points for the implementation of e-bike stations in Évora.

Giraldo Square has the highest AHP score (0.958), standing out as the most balanced point between demand, intermodality and low equity interference. Its average distance (1033 m) reinforces the operational centrality.

Horta das Laranjeiras combines a high AHP score (0.878) with the shortest average distance (812 m), suggesting strong coverage potential with low travel cost.

Água de Prata Parking Lot and Porta de Aviz have high scores ($\geq$ 0.86) and high shading, which requires attention to visual and heritage integration, but are compensated by good connectivity.

Évora Plaza, despite having the longest average distance (2367 m), was included due to its intermodal relevance and consistent demand, evidenced by the AHP score (0.795).

Fire Service, with the lowest AHP score (0.730) and average shading, was excluded from the final selection because it had lower relative performance in the combined criteria, despite its average distance being competitive (1210 m).

The innovative contribution of this study lies in its strategic approach to integrating solar-powered mobility infrastructure within the urban and heritage context of Évora. By focusing on the deployment of mobile and modular e-bike sharing stations powered by renewable energy, the project addresses critical challenges related to sustainable transport, energy transition, and urban planning in medium-sized cities with historical constraints.

Rather than emphasizing technological novelty alone, the study prioritizes contextual feasibility, identifying optimal station locations based on accessibility, solar exposure, and urban dynamics. This includes the use of public parking areas with photovoltaic potential, intermodal hubs, and flexible deployment zones within the historic center, ensuring that mobility solutions remain adaptable to seasonal events and spatial limitations.

The proposed model contributes to the broader goals of climate adaptation and decarbonization by promoting low-emission transport and efficient land use. It also reinforces the importance of interoperability, local workforce training, and preventive maintenance as pillars for long-term operational sustainability.

Ultimately, this study offers a replicable framework for other heritage cities seeking to balance environmental goals with mobility innovation. It aligns with national and European strategies for smart cities, energy efficiency, and inclusive urban development, positioning Évora as a reference in the integration of clean energy and sustainable transport systems.

8 FUTURE WORK

The potential of Évora to lead innovative actions in sustainable urban mobility and renewable energy integration is considerable and deserves further exploration. Building on the design and methodology proposed in this study, which prioritizes flexible, solar-powered e-bike sharing stations adapted to heritage and urban constraints, several avenues for future research and implementation are identified.

1. Energy and Infrastructure Enhancements
- Energy efficiency optimization: Investigate passive cooling systems and smart energy management for solar charging stations, especially in high-exposure zones such as public parking areas and intermodal hubs.
- Fallback energy strategies: Evaluate the feasibility of auxiliary power sources (e.g., grid connection, mobile power banks) for extreme weather conditions or justify exclusive PV operation through oversizing and autonomy modeling.
- Battery management protocols: Define operational thresholds for state-of-charge (SOC), thermal safety, and charge/discharge cycles to ensure system reliability.

2. Environmental and Operational Impact
- Carbon mitigation assessment: Quantify the modal shift from fossil-fueled transport to electric micromobility, supported by solar infrastructure and behavioral incentives.
- Performance indicators: Develop KPIs such as trips per bike per day, solar kWh delivered, CO_2 avoided, station uptime, and Levelized Cost of Charge

10.4229/EUPVSEC2025/4DV.1.46
020420-008

(LCOC) to evaluate system efficiency and cost-effectiveness.

- Resilience and adaptability: Analyze how modular stations respond to seasonal demand, urban events, and spatial reconfiguration needs within the historic center.

3. Urban Integration and Safety

- Heritage-sensitive deployment: Explore mobile, non-invasive station designs with concealed cabling, low-profile solar pallets, and no ground perforation to comply with heritage preservation standards.
- Shading and solar losses: Conduct photometric sampling or develop seasonal shadow maps to assess real-world solar exposure and optimize station placement.
- Electrical and fire safety: Include a technical review of Li-ion charging risks, ventilation requirements, thermal cutoff mechanisms, and applicable IEC/EN standards.
- Cybersecurity and data governance: Address privacy and security concerns related to geolocation, user tracking, and GDPR compliance within the app and backend systems.

4. Smart City and Socioeconomic Integration

- Platform interoperability: Investigate integration with public transport, energy grids, and digital mobility services to enhance user experience and operational intelligence.
- Community and workforce engagement: Study the socioeconomic impacts of solar mobility, including local job creation, inclusive access, and contributions to low-carbon urban development.

9 ACKNOWLEDGEMENTS

This work was supported by the project "NGS - Pacto de Inovação - New Generation Storage" Agenda, funded by the Portuguese Recovery and Resilience Plan (PRR), with reference C644936001-00000045.

10 REFERENCES

[1] UNESCO National Commission. Accessed on January 25, 2025, from https://unescoportugal.mne.gov.pt/pt/temas/proteger-o-nosso-patrimonio-e-promover-a-criatividade/patrimonio-mundial-em-portugal.

[2] Évora 2027 - Official Website (2025). Accessed on January 25, 2025, from https://www.evora2027.com.

[3] RCM – Council of Ministers Resolution No. 131/2019, National Strategy for Active Mobility. Accessed on January 25, 2025, from https://dre.pt/dre/en/detail/resolution-of-the-council-of-ministers/131-2019-123666113.

[4] TREVO - Urban Transport Network of the City of Évora. News. Accessed on January 29, 2025, from https://www.trevo.com.pt/

[5] UéUbike. University of Evora. Accessed on January 25, 2025, from https://www.ubike.uevora.pt/.

[6] MEM+, Municipal Emissions Monitoring. Emissions by sector - Évora. Accessed on January 29, 2025, from https://memmais.tecnico.ulisboa.pt/

[7] Global Solar Atlas. Specific photovoltaic power of Évora. Accessed on February 06, 2025, from https://globalsolaratlas.info/map

[8] BABLE. An E-Bike Loan Scheme Supporting Low-Carbon Shared Mobility (2017). Accessed on January 31, 2025, from https://www.bable-smartcities.eu/explore/use-cases/use-case/an-e-bike-loan-scheme-supporting-low-carbon-shared-mobility.html

[9] MOBENDI. SUNPOD CYCLO - Station de recharge solaire pour vélos électriques. Accessed on February 06, 2025, from https://mobendi.com/notre-station-solaire-pour-velos-electriques/

[10] Swiftmile. Micromobility Charging Stations. Accessed on February 06, 2025, from https://swiftmile.com/

[11] Gira - Bicicletas de Lisboa. Lisbon Bicycle Sharing System. Accessed on September 15, 2025, from https://www.gira-bicicletasdelisboa.pt/

[12] NIDTEC - Technology Solutions. Charging station for electric bicycles. Accessed on September 15, 2025, from https://nidtec.pt/

[13] BICIWAY. BiciCharger Sun+Wind. Accessed on September 15, 2025, from https://www.biciway.com/pt

[14] Beam Global. BeamBike. Accessed on September 16, 2025, from https://beamforall.com/product/beambike/

[15] European Commission, Joint Research Centre. (n.d.). Photovoltaic Geographical Information System (PVGIS). Accessed on September 16, 2025, from https://joint-research-centre.ec.europa.eu/pvgis_en

[16] Cycle path. Cycle paths in Évora. Accessed on January 28, 2025, from https://www.ciclovia.pt/ciclovias/4alentejo/2evora/evora/evora.php

[17] Câmara Municipal de Évora. Where to park. Accessed on January 28, 2025, from https://www.cm-evora.pt

[18] Topographic map. Topographic map of Évora. Accessed on January 28, 2025, from https://pt-pt.topographic-map.com/map-kfwkl/%C3%89vora/?center=38.57078%2C-7.9093 https://globalsolaratlas.info/detail?c=38.542258,-7.896423,11&s=38.590696,-7.957193&m=site

[19] Oliveira, H., 2025. Isochrones of 5, 10 and 15 minutes for e-bike trips from the city centre (Serpa Pinto Street, Évora), generated with ORS. Accessed on September 22, 2025, from https://rpubs.com/Hluisa/isochrones-evora

10.4229/EUPVSEC2025/4DV.1.46

THE SELF-CONSUMPTION POTENTIAL OF RAILWAY STATIONS: PORTUGAL AS A CASE STUDY

Margarida Luís, Miguel Centeno Brito
University of Lisbon, Faculty of Sciences, Lisbon, Portugal
fc54864@alunos.ciencias.ulisboa.pt, mcbrito@ciencias.ulisboa.pt

ABSTRACT: The European Union aims for climate neutrality by 2050. With transport being responsible for over one-third of carbon emissions, using transport infrastructure, such as rail, for renewable energy deployment can support decarbonisation while avoiding land-use conflicts. Solar Photovoltaics (PV) are particularly suited due to their availability, efficiency, and low maintenance. This study evaluates the solar potential of Portugal's railway infrastructure, with a focus on train station rooftops. It also examines the alignment between energy generation and consumption, exploring different PV system configurations to optimise the integration of renewable energy. The assessment of solar potential was based on estimates of physical and technical capacity, using tools such as Google Earth and PVGIS. Energy consumption at the railway stations does not match passenger flow, as it peaks during the night, and therefore does not coincide with PV generation hours. Adjusting PV system sizing at train stations to match their daytime energy demand can help minimise curtailment. If surplus generation persists, it can be managed through a collective self-consumption scheme or by integrating an energy storage system (ESS).
Keywords: Photovoltaic, Solar railways, Self-sufficiency, Self-consumption

1 INTRODUCTION

The European Climate Law sets the goal for the European Union (EU) to achieve climate neutrality by 2050 [1]. As the transport sector accounts for more than one-third of the CO_2 emissions from end-use sectors [2], decarbonisation is a pressing priority. Integrating renewable energy systems into the transport infrastructure offers a promising pathway, with rail emerging as a strong candidate given its existing reliance on electricity. Solar energy emerges as the most suitable renewable source due to the affordability, flexibility, and low maintenance of photovoltaic systems. While large-scale PV deployment is often linked to land-use conflicts, integrating PV into railway infrastructure offers a dual-use solution. This approach maximises space efficiency, adds value to an essential transport asset, and minimises additional environmental impacts.

Most studies on the solar potential of railways focus on geographical suitability and estimated energy output, often neglecting how the generated energy will actually be used [3], [4]. While they typically evaluate potential installed capacity and expected yield, few compare this generation to real energy consumption data [5], [6]. When such comparisons do occur, they are usually based on daily or monthly averages, which fail to reflect the hourly fluctuations in both energy demand and PV generation, overlooking the resulting supply-demand mismatch. This study addresses that gap by assessing the solar potential of the Portuguese railway network using real hourly energy consumption data, enabling a more comprehensive analysis of energy alignment.

This study assesses the physical and technical potential of integrating photovoltaic (PV) systems into railway infrastructure, more specifically, railway stations. Although traction substations and their respective consumption profiles were also analysed, they are the subject of a different publication. Focusing on mainland Portugal, this study evaluates various technical PV configurations on railway stations' rooftops. The estimated PV energy generation is then compared with railway station energy consumption to analyse the potential impacts on self-consumption and self-sufficiency across the national rail network.

2 METHODOLOGY

2.1 PV Configurations

The solar potential of the railway stations was assessed based on a diverse range of rooftop PV configurations that can be deployed on their rooftops to supply non-traction energy needs. Figure 1 shows the configurations analysed along with their respective specific installed capacities.

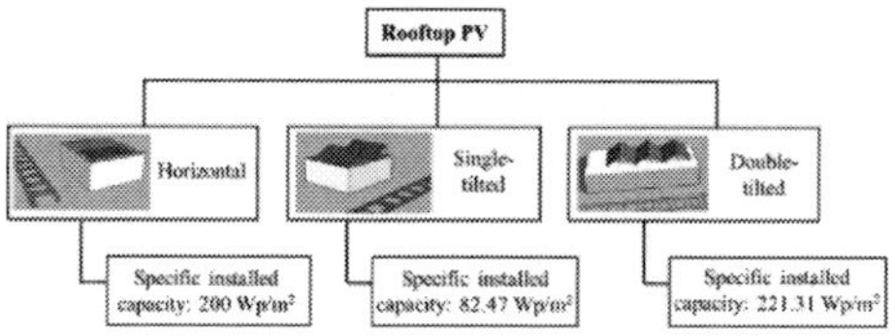

Figure 1: Technical PV configurations' schematics and respective specific installed capacities

The horizontal rooftop configuration consists of PV modules arranged co-planar with the roof of the train station. Assuming a 20% conversion efficiency, the specific installed capacity of this configuration is 200 W/m^2.

For the single-tilted and double-tilted configurations, the modules are south-facing with a 35° tilt, which is the optimal tilt angle for Portugal [7]. Using Equation 1, where D is the distance between modules, M is the module width (1 m), θ is the tilt angle (35°), and α is the solar elevation angle (28°) on the winter solstice day in Portugal [8], the minimum spacing between modules was calculated to be approximately 1.5 m. The specific installed capacity of the single tilted configuration is 82.47 W/m^2.

$$D = \frac{M \sin\theta}{\tan\alpha} \quad (1)$$

The double-tilted rooftop configuration is comprised of PV modules forming a triangle, oriented East and West. In this configuration, each PV module occupies less rooftop area than in the single-tilted configuration, since they are not installed to avoid self-shadowing losses. The area that each of the modules occupies was calculated according to equation 4, where A is the area occupied by the module, M is the module's width (1 m), and H is the module's height. Each module occupies 0.9 m^2 of rooftop

10.4229/EUPVSEC2025/4DV.1.48

space, meaning that the specific installed capacity of this configuration is 221.31 W/m^2.

$$A = \sqrt{M^2 - H^2} \times M \quad (2)$$

2.2 Case study: Portugal

As of 2024, the Portuguese railway network comprises 1,794 km of electrified tracks and 546 operating railway stations [9]. Given the impracticality of analysing the entire network, four representative railway lines were selected for this study: *Linha do Norte* (Line N), *Linha da Beira-Baixa* (Line BB), *Linha de Évora + Alentejo* (Line EA), and *Linha do Sul* (Line S). These lines provide broad geographical coverage, extending from north to south and east to west, while encompassing various types of rail services, including suburban, regional, and long-distance routes. This selection captures a diverse size and energy consumption range of railway stations, ensuring a representative assessment of the solar potential across the Portuguese railway system. The selected railway lines include a total of 196 train stations.

2.3 Geographical Potential

Geographical potential is mostly defined in literature as the incident irradiation on areas deemed suitable for PV deployment [10], [11], [12]. This study takes a different approach by defining geographical potential as the area deemed suitable for PV installation, rather than focusing on the solar irradiance received by that area.

The geographical potential of the railway stations pertains to their rooftop area. These areas were manually measured using satellite imagery and Google Earth's measuring tool [13]. Since the images are taken from a top-down perspective, the measurements are more accurate for stations with flat roofs than for those with sloped roofs.

2.4 Technical Potential

In the literature, technical potential is often defined as the portion of geographical potential that can be converted into electricity [10], [11], [14]. In this study, technical potential is divided into capacity potential and generation potential. The first regards the capacity (W_p) that is possible to install in the obtained geographical potential, and the second regards the amount of energy (kWh) that the capacity potential can effectively convert into electricity. The capacity potential refers to the maximum PV capacity that can be installed within the identified geographical potential, while the generation potential represents the amount of electricity that this installed capacity can realistically produce.

PV energy generation for the different technical configurations was estimated using PVGIS [15]. To automate this process, the *get_pvgis_hourly* function from the PVlib Python library was employed [16]. The energy output provided by the *get_pvgis_hourly* function is expressed in W/kWp. These values were then multiplied by the capacity potential of each technical PV configuration to determine the total energy generation (generation potential).

2.5 Energy Consumption Data

It is important to highlight the difference between traction and non-traction energy consumption in the railway system. Traction energy consumption covers the energy used to operate trains, including propulsion, lighting, air conditioning, and door mechanisms. Non-traction energy consumption refers to energy used by supporting infrastructure such as railway stations and maintenance centres. These two demand types differ significantly: traction loads are dynamic and subject to sudden peaks driven by train movement, while non-traction loads are more stable and predictable. This study focuses more strongly on the potential contribution of solar energy to meeting train station energy demands.

Non-traction energy consumption data for 2023 were supplied by Infraestruturas de Portugal. Originally recorded in 15-minute intervals, the data was aggregated into hourly intervals to match the PV energy production data and facilitate a consistent self-consumption analysis.

2.6 Self-Consumption Analysis

One of the main challenges of PV energy generation is its limited generation, being circumscribed to daylight hours. Similarly, energy consumption in the railway sector is variable and not evenly distributed throughout the day. To address these fluctuations, a self-consumption analysis was conducted to determine which of the proposed PV configurations best aligns with non-traction energy demands. Hourly PV generation data from the rooftop systems were matched with train station energy consumption. This hourly comparison allows the analysis to account for variations in both energy production and demand throughout the day. Self-sufficiency and self-consumption were obtained according to equations 3 and 4, where SS is self-sufficiency, SC is self-consumption, PV_C is the PV energy consumed, E_D is the energy demand of a given location, and PV_G is the PV energy generated. The analysis was carried out for each technical PV configuration and across multiple levels of installed capacity to assess performance under different deployment scenarios.

$$SS\ (\%) = \left(\frac{PV_C}{E_D}\right) \times 100 \quad (3)$$

$$SC\ (\%) = \left(\frac{PV_C}{PV_G}\right) \times 100 \quad (4)$$

3 RESULTS

3.1 Railway Stations' Solar Potential

The geographical potential of the railway stations in the selected railway lines amounts to 0.27 km^2. However, it is not evenly distributed throughout the 196 train stations, with 0.02 km^2 in Line BB, 0.15 km^2 in Line N, 0.02 km^2 in Line EA, and 0.08 km^2 in Line S. Regarding energy consumption data, it was only available for 84 train stations in the selected railway lines. The total geographical potential for the train stations with energy consumption data is 0.16 km^2, with 0.01 km^2 for Line BB, 0.12 km^2 for Line N, 0.02 km^2 for Line EA, and 0.01 km^2 for Line S. Line S has the biggest discrepancy between the actual rooftop area and the rooftop area of the train stations with energy consumption data. In comparison, the train stations along Line N are considerably larger than those on Line BB. Although Line N has only twice as many stations with available data, its total rooftop area is 11 times larger. The train stations on Line EA and Line S are similar in size, as both the number of stations and the total rooftop area are comparable.

10.4229/EUPVSEC2025/4DV.1.48

Figure 2 shows the annual PV energy generation from rooftop systems at train stations, assuming 50% of the available rooftop area is used for PV installation. As expected, the double-tilted configuration yields the highest energy output across all railway lines, due to its higher installed capacity. Conversely, the single-tilted configuration, having the lowest specific installed capacity, produces the least energy. Despite having fewer train stations with available data, Line S generates significantly more energy than Line BB in both the horizontal and double-tilted configurations.

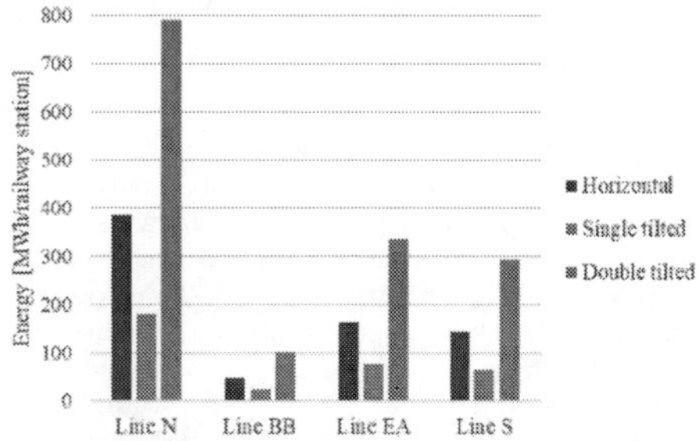

Figure 2: Annual PV generation of the railway stations in the selected railway lines when the PV system occupies 50% of their rooftop area

3.2 Self-consumption Analysis: Case Studies

To better understand how PV generation interacts with varying train station load profiles, two individual stations from different railway lines were discussed in detail. The selected stations are *Vila Franca de Xira* (VFX), located on Line N, and Pinhal Novo (PN), situated simultaneously in Line S and Line EA. VFX is located in the southernmost part of Line N and has a rooftop area of 589 m², while PN has a significantly larger rooftop with an area of 8,675 m² and is located on the westernmost part of Line S and the easternmost part of Line EA. Figure 3 presents the load profiles of these stations on June 3rd, 2023. PN stands out for its higher and more variable energy consumption, in contrast to VFX, which maintains an almost constant load throughout the day.

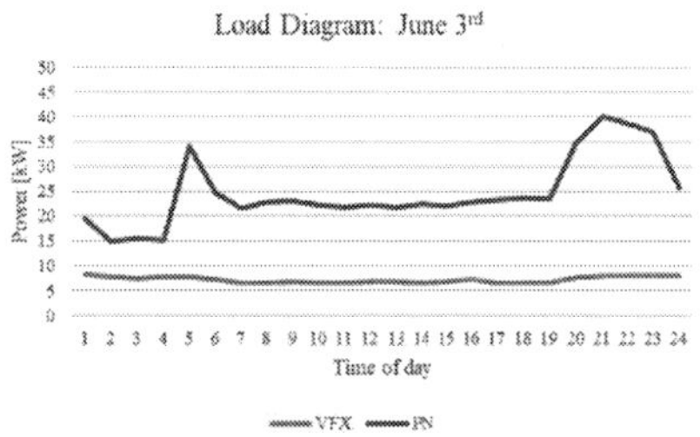

Figure 3: Load diagram of the railway stations VFX and PN, the case studies in the self-consumption analysis

Figure 4 illustrates the self-sufficiency and self-consumption rates of *Vila Franca de Xira* (VFX) as the rooftop occupancy increases, consequently increasing the installed capacity. The highest self-consumption rate, 100%, was achieved with the single-tilted configuration at 10% rooftop occupancy (4.86 kWp). Under the same conditions, the double-tilted configuration reached a self-consumption rate of 74%, with a slightly higher installed capacity of 13 kWp. The lowest self-sufficiency rate, at just 10%, was also recorded for the single-tilted configuration at 10% rooftop occupancy. The balance point between the metrics for this train station is around 40%.

Given the station's consumption profile, the horizontal configuration offers the best alignment between PV generation and energy demand. At 10% rooftop occupancy (4.86 kWp), it achieves 97% self-consumption and 21% self-sufficiency. While the self-sufficiency rate is moderate, this configuration provides the most balanced performance between the two metrics. Under the same conditions, the double-tilted setup reaches 74% self-consumption and 34% self-sufficiency, whereas the single-tilted configuration achieves full (100%) self-consumption but only 10% self-sufficiency.

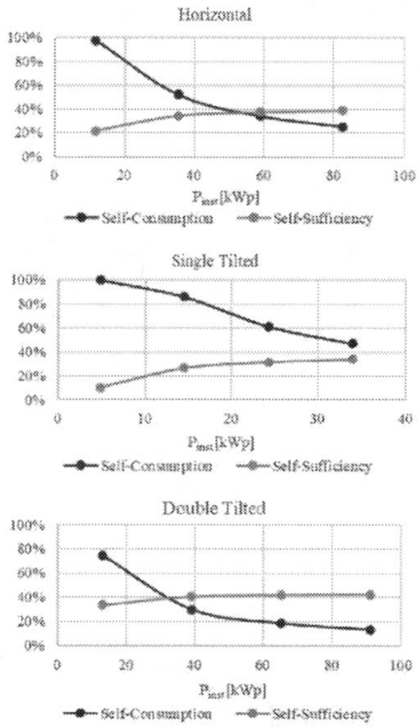

Figure 4: Self-sufficiency vs Self-consumption for the railway station VFX, located on Line N

In this scenario, if the goal is to maximise self-sufficiency, the double-tilted configuration with 50% rooftop occupancy emerges as the most suitable option. However, even at this level, it achieves only 42% self-sufficiency, accompanied by a low self-consumption rate of 19%. The data suggests that this system has reached its performance peak, self-sufficiency remains unchanged between 50% and 70% occupancy and increases by just 1% when rooftop use rises from 30% to 50%. Similarly, the horizontal and single-tilted configurations are nearing their saturation points, as evidenced by the minimal increases in self-sufficiency despite higher rooftop occupancy. This suggests that these PV systems are already producing as much energy as possible during daylight hours, while the remaining demand occurs at night, when solar generation is not available.

Figure 5 shows how self-consumption and self-sufficiency rates at the *Pinhal Novo* (PN) train station evolve with increasing rooftop occupancy and corresponding increases in installed capacity. The highest self-consumption rate is achieved with the single-tilted configuration at 10% rooftop occupancy, reaching 68%. In

10.4229/EUPVSEC2025/4DV.1.48

contrast, the lowest self-consumption occurs, consistently with other train stations, in the double-tilted configuration at 70% rooftop occupancy, yielding just 3%. The maximum self-sufficiency rate is 40%, attained by the double-tilted configuration at rooftop occupancies of 30%, 50%, and 70%, indicating a stagnation point beginning at 30% rooftop occupancy. The lowest self-sufficiency rate is 28% and coincides with the conditions that produce the highest self-consumption (single tilted configuration, 71.54 kWp of installed capacity).

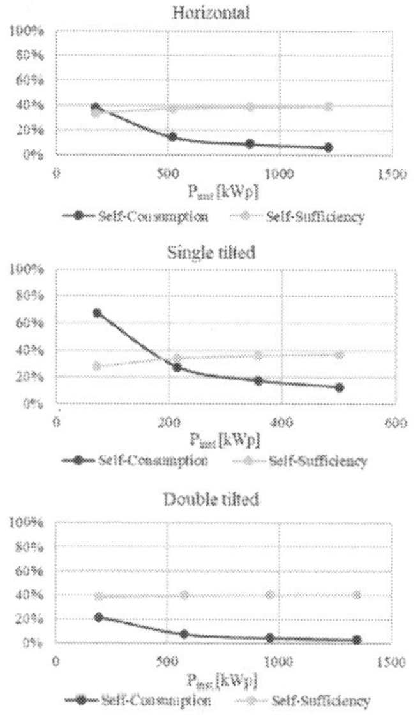

Figure 5: Self-sufficiency vs Self-consumption for the train station PN, located in Lines S and EA

At this railway station, the configuration and rooftop occupancy that best align PV generation with energy demand is the single-tilted setup at 10% rooftop occupancy, which yields the highest self-consumption. This configuration corresponds to an installed capacity of 72 kWp. Given that most of the station's energy demand occurs during nighttime hours, maximising self-consumption is the most effective way to utilise PV generation. However, 32% of the energy produced under this setup remains unused and must either be injected into the grid or curtailed.

3.3 Self-consumption analysis: Selected railway lines

Figure 6 shows the load profiles of train stations along the selected railway lines for a summer day. Line N stands out with the highest energy demand, while the other lines exhibit similar consumption patterns. Generally, energy use is slightly lower in the summer than in the winter. The demand across Lines BB, EA, and S is similar. All railway lines show lower demand during daylight hours, with noticeable peaks around 7 AM and 7 PM.

Figure 7 illustrates the self-sufficiency rate of the selected railway lines regarding the train stations' loads. When rooftop occupancy reaches 70%, self-sufficiency rates show little variation across different configurations within the same railway line. The highest self-sufficiency is recorded in Line N, where the double-tilted configuration at 70% rooftop coverage achieves a rate of 41%. Conversely, the lowest self-sufficiency is found in Line BB, with the single-tilted configuration covering just 10% of the rooftop area, resulting in only 10% self-sufficiency.

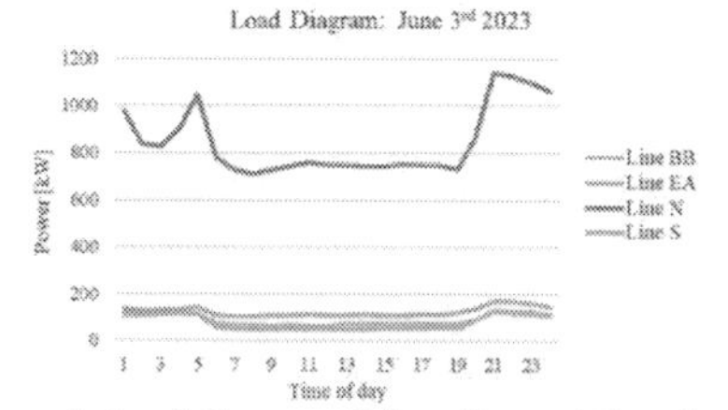

Figure 6: Load diagram of the railway stations located along the selected railway lines for June 3rd, 2023

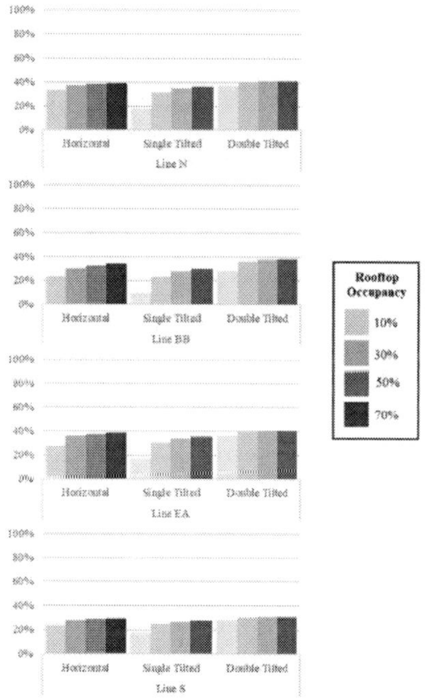

Figure 7: Evolution of the self-sufficiency rates at train stations of the selected railway lines as rooftop occupancy increases

Line S shows the smallest gains in self-sufficiency as rooftop occupancy increases, particularly with the double-tilted configuration. The most notable improvement occurs when rooftop coverage rises from 10% to 30% resulting in a 7% increase in self-sufficiency, significantly lower than the 13% to 14% gains observed on other lines for the same increase.

Beyond 30% rooftop occupancy, additional improvements in self-sufficiency become marginal across all configurations, with increases consistently under 5%. In some cases, such as the double-tilted configuration, self-sufficiency levels off entirely. This plateau effect is largely due to most energy occurring outside PV generation hours. Consequently, self-sufficiency in train stations tends to stabilise at around 40%, earlier than in traction substations, where physical space constraints, rather than time-of-use mismatches, limit the system size and performance.

Figure 8 shows the evolution of the self-consumption rates for the selected train stations as rooftop occupancy increases. Line S is the only line that does not reach 100% self-consumption at 10% rooftop occupancy, peaking instead at 94%. The highest self-consumption rate for the horizontal configuration is recorded in Line BB, also at 10% rooftop occupancy, reaching 80%. Likewise, the double-tilted configuration achieves its highest self-consumption in Line BB under the same conditions, at 72%. Overall, Line BB consistently exhibits the highest self-consumption rates across all configurations and occupancy levels.

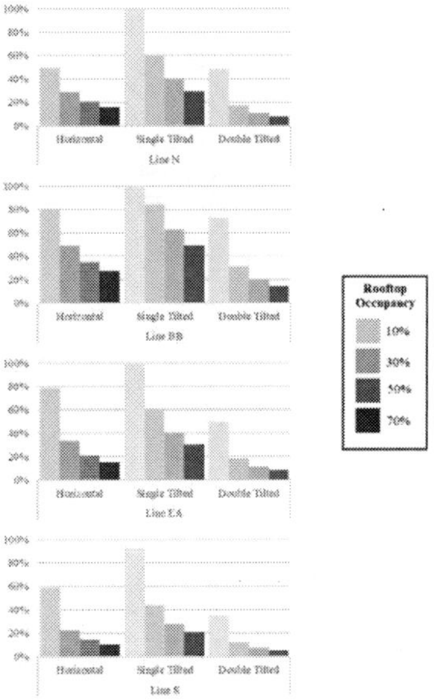

Figure 8: Evolution of the self-consumption rates at the train stations of the selected railway lines as rooftop occupancy increases

The largest increases in self-consumption generally occur when rooftop occupancy is reduced from 30% to 10% across all railway lines and configurations. The only exception is found in Line BB, where the single-tilted configuration shows the greatest increase when occupancy decreases from 50% to 30%.

4 DISCUSSION

Railway stations in Portugal exhibit their highest consumption at night, which suggests that station energy use is mostly due to lighting and largely independent of passenger traffic or train operations; as illustrated in Figure 4, energy demand at train stations drops during the morning rush hour (7 AM to 10 AM), despite high passenger flow. Similarly, in the evening, peak consumption occurs after the afternoon rush hour (5 PM to 7 PM) has ended. Some rural train stations barely have energy consumption during the day, only at night, presenting a total mismatch with PV energy generation.

Given the typical consumption profile of Portuguese train stations, characterised by high nighttime demand, achieving full self-sufficiency using only PV systems is unfeasible without the integration of energy storage systems (ESS) and demand-side management (DSM) strategies. However, PV systems can still effectively meet daytime energy needs. Since ESS significantly increases overall system costs, a more practical approach is to optimise PV generation for daytime consumption, maximising self-consumption during sunlight hours. DSM strategies, such as shifting non-essential nighttime loads to the day, can further improve PV utilisation. In stations with very low daytime demand, analysing nearby energy loads could help absorb surplus PV production, reducing curtailment and enabling efficient grid injection.

5 CONCLUSIONS

This work explores the solar potential of the Portuguese railway network, with a focus on integrating photovoltaic (PV) energy into railway station operations and identifying strategies to mitigate the mismatch between energy generation and consumption. With renewable sources already accounting for 71% of Portugal's energy mix, the railway sector is already benefiting from a substantial share of clean traction energy.

Four railway lines out of the Portuguese railway system were analysed regarding the mismatch between energy consumption and PV energy generation. Three rooftop technical configurations were evaluated: horizontal, single-tilted, and double-tilted.

Train stations exhibit a great mismatch between PV generation and energy demand due to their predominantly nighttime consumption. Consequently, no railway line achieves more than 41% self-sufficiency, and self-consumption rates are relatively low. Only the single-tilted configuration reaches 100% self-consumption, and even then, not across all railway lines. In contrast, the horizontal and double-tilted configurations consistently perform worse, with self-consumption rates always below 80% for the smaller systems analysed. To address this imbalance, PV systems should be sized based on daytime demand, as they cannot supply energy during the night. Integrating ESS offers another solution, enabling excess daytime generation to be stored for later use. Additionally, implementing DSM strategies, such as shifting or reducing non-essential nighttime loads, can enhance energy efficiency and better align demand with PV availability.

The Portuguese railway system has significant solar potential, offering a path to greater renewable energy use and improved environmental sustainability. Future research should analyse real rooftop areas and consumption profiles of train stations and assess how nearby energy needs could reduce curtailment. A detailed economic analysis, including the role of storage systems, is essential, and exploring hybrid solutions with wind or hydropower could ensure energy availability during low solar production periods.

6 ACKNOWLEDGEMENTS

We thank Infraestruturas de Portugal (IP) for providing load demand data and for their valuable advice.

This work is supported by the Portuguese Fundação para a Ciência e Tecnologia, FCT, I.P./MCTES through national funds (PIDDAC): UID/50019/2025 and LA/P/0068/2020 https://doi.org/10.54499/LA/P/0068/2020).

7 REFERENCES

[1] 'European Climate Law - European Commission'. Accessed: Jul. 31, 2025. [Online]. Available:

https://climate.ec.europa.eu/eu-action/european-climate-law_en
[2] 'Transport - Energy System', IEA. Accessed: Mar. 11, 2025. [Online]. Available: https://www.iea.org/energy-system/transport
[3] M. Herz, A. Sepanski, U. Hupach, B. Schönauer, and S. Ulrich, 'SOLAR FOR RAILWAYS - INVESTIGATION OF THE PV POTENTIAL ON THE GERMAN RAIL INFRASTRUCTURE'.
[4] F. Ding, J. Yang, and Z. Zhou, 'Economic profits and carbon reduction potential of photovoltaic power generation for China's high-speed railway infrastructure', *Renewable and Sustainable Energy Reviews*, vol. 178, p. 113272, May 2023, doi: 10.1016/j.rser.2023.113272.
[5] Z. Chen *et al.*, 'Using existing infrastructures of high-speed railways for photovoltaic electricity generation', *Resources, Conservation and Recycling*, vol. 178, p. 106091, Mar. 2022, doi: 10.1016/j.resconrec.2021.106091.
[6] L. Ji, Z. Yu, J. Ma, L. Jia, and F. Ning, 'The Potential of Photovoltaics to Power the Railway System in China', *Energies*, vol. 13, no. 15, p. 3844, Jul. 2020, doi: 10.3390/en13153844.
[7] M. Z. Jacobson and V. Jadhav, 'World estimates of PV optimal tilt angles and ratios of sunlight incident upon tilted and tracked PV panels relative to horizontal panels', *Solar Energy*, vol. 169, pp. 55–66, Jul. 2018, doi: 10.1016/j.solener.2018.04.030.
[8] 'OAL - Conjunções'. Accessed: May 30, 2025. [Online]. Available: https://oal.ul.pt/solsticio-de-inverno-2019/
[9] 'Rede Ferroviária | Infraestruturas de Portugal'. Accessed: Mar. 20, 2025. [Online]. Available: https://www.infraestruturasdeportugal.pt/pt-pt/infraestruturas/rede-ferroviaria
[10] Y. Zhang, J. Ren, Y. Pu, and P. Wang, 'Solar energy potential assessment: A framework to integrate geographic, technological, and economic indices for a potential analysis', *Renewable Energy*, vol. 149, pp. 577–586, Apr. 2020, doi: 10.1016/j.renene.2019.12.071.
[11] Monique Maria Hoogwijk, 'On the global and regional potential of renewable energy sources', Doctoral dissertation, 2004. [Online]. Available: https://np-net.pbworks.com/f/Hoogwijk+(2004)+Global+and+regional+potential+of+renewable+energy+sources+(Thesis+Utrecht).pdf
[12] S. Izquierdo, M. Rodrigues, and N. Fueyo, 'A method for estimating the geographical distribution of the available roof surface area for large-scale photovoltaic energy-potential evaluations', *Solar Energy*, vol. 82, no. 10, pp. 929–939, Oct. 2008, doi: 10.1016/j.solener.2008.03.007.
[13] 'Google Earth'. Accessed: Apr. 18, 2024. [Online]. Available: https://earth.google.com/web/@38.74537372,-9.19274542,80.09038843a,1243.56553885d,35y,0h,0t,0r/data=CgRCAggBOgMKATBCAggASg0I___ ________ARAA
[14] A. Gómez, M. Rodrigues, C. Montañés, C. Dopazo, and N. Fueyo, 'The potential for electricity generation from crop and forestry residues in Spain', *Biomass and Bioenergy*, vol. 34, no. 5, pp. 703–719, May 2010, doi: 10.1016/j.biombioe.2010.01.013.
[15] 'JRC Photovoltaic Geographical Information System (PVGIS) - European Commission'. Accessed: May 16, 2025. [Online]. Available: https://re.jrc.ec.europa.eu/pvg_tools/en/
[16] W. F. Holmgren, C. W. Hansen, and M. A. Mikofski, 'pvlib python: a python package for modeling solar energy systems', *JOSS*, vol. 3, no. 29, p. 884, Sep. 2018, doi: 10.21105/joss.00884.

PERFORMANCE ANALYSIS OF NON-ISOLATED DC-DC BOOST CONVERTER TOPOLOGIES IN VIPV SYSTEMS UNDER VARIABLE IRRADIANCE

Sebastían Rodríguez-Romero[1, 3,*], Jorge Rabanal-Arabach[1, 3], Mauricio Trigo-Gonzalez [1, 3], Gino Mondaca-Cuevas[1], Christian A. Rojas [2, 3], Alejandro Stowhas-Villa [2, 3], Fernando Castro-Gallardo[1, 3] and Edward Fuentealba-Vidal[1, 3]

[1] University of Antofagasta, Av. Angamos 601, 1270300 Antofagasta, Chile.
[2] Universidad Técnica Federico Santa María, Valparaíso 2390123, Chile.
[3] Solar Energy Research Center, Tupper 2007, 8370451 Santiago, Chile.

* Corresponding Author: sebastian.rodriguez@uantof.cl

ABSTRACT: The adoption of Vehicle-Integrated Photovoltaic (ViPV) systems into urban electric buses improves sustainability and reduces grid dependency in public transport. However, challenges such as variable irradiance and shading conditions limit their effectiveness. This study evaluates three advanced non-isolated DC-DC converter topologies (Boost Interleaved, Quadratic Boost, and Multi-Input/Single-Output) under MPPT control using the Perturb and Observe (P&O) algorithm. Simulations were conducted in Simulink using irradiance and temperature data collected in Antofagasta, Chile. The system assumed 600 PV cells forming a 350 V string connected to a 540 V DC-Link bus powered by a 50 kWh LiFePo4 battery bank. Key metrics analyzed include voltage gain, efficiency, stability, and current ripple under realistic urban conditions. Results demonstrate that Interleaved Boost exhibits high efficiency under uniform irradiance conditions, achieving stable current distribution with a low ripple of 2%. However, its performance is less robust during rapid irradiance changes. Quadratic Boost maintained a stable voltage gain in steady-state conditions and operated with a low duty cycle, reducing stress on switching components and enhancing long-term reliability. Nevertheless, it underperformed during abrupt transients due to the inherent complexity of its coupled stages, which impacted its ability to adapt to rapid system changes. The Multi-Input/Single-Output (MISO) topology effectively integrated multiple input sources and demonstrated strong performance under partial shading scenarios. However, its overall complexity and ripple management require optimization to improve efficiency in high irradiance conditions. These findings identify Interleaved Boost as the best option for stable conditions, while Quadratic Boost offers advantages in reducing component stress under steady-state operation. MISO emerges as a flexible alternative for scenarios with frequent shading. This research provides modeling insights for designing ViPV systems in urban electric buses, addressing the challenges of dynamic environments and improving sustainability in public transport.
Keywords: Vehicle-Integrated Photovoltaics (ViPV), DC-DC converters, MPPT, electric buses, partial shading, energy efficiency.

1 INTRODUCTION

The transportation sector contributes nearly 25% of global greenhouse gas (GHG) emissions [1], becoming one of the main drivers for the transition toward low-carbon technologies. Among renewable options, photovoltaic (PV) systems stand out due to their effectiveness in both grid-connected and off-grid applications, particularly in high-irradiance environments such as the Atacama Desert in northern Chile [2], [3], [4]. This region provides one of the most demanding natural laboratories for testing the performance and reliability of solar energy technologies.

Electric vehicles (EVs) represent a promising strategy to reduce fossil fuel dependency. However, challenges related to driving range and charging infrastructure remain [5]. In this context, Vehicle-Integrated Photovoltaics (ViPV) emerges as a complementary solution capable of delivering 10–30 km of daily range under favorable solar conditions [6], [7], while simultaneously reducing operating costs and carbon emissions. Yet, irradiance variability and partial shading in urban environments introduce significant uncertainties in converter operation and overall system efficiency [8], [7], [9], [10].

DC-DC converters are key to ensuring regulated energy transfer between PV arrays, batteries, and drivetrains [11]. However, comparative analyses of advanced non-isolated topologies under real irradiance conditions remain limited [12], [13]. This study addresses this gap by evaluating three high-gain non-isolated converters, namely Interleaved Boost, Quadratic Boost, and Multi-Input Single-Output (MISO), within a ViPV system designed for urban electric buses. The analysis employs real irradiance and temperature profiles collected in Antofagasta, Chile, to assess voltage regulation, efficiency, and input current ripple under dynamic operating conditions.

The main contribution of this work is to provide a comparative performance evaluation of advanced non-isolated DC-DC converters under real-world irradiance conditions, highlighting trade-offs in efficiency, stability, and current ripple. This offers design guidelines for

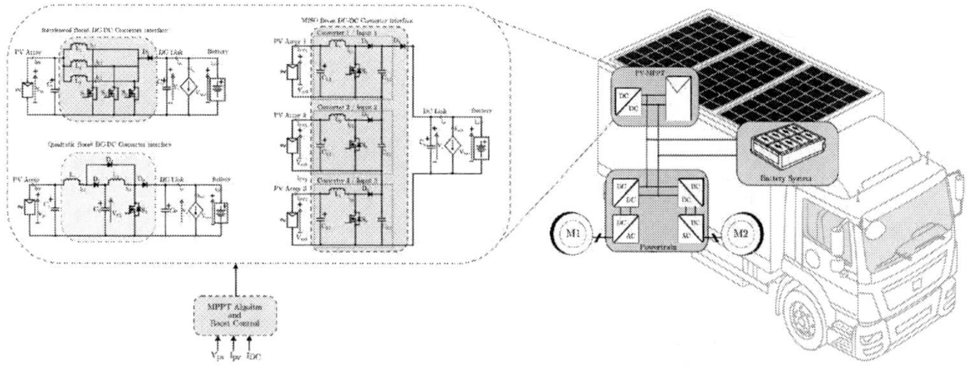

Fig. 1: Functional diagram of an integrated energy conversion and control system of ViPV powertrain systems.

selecting robust topologies in ViPV systems for urban electric transportation.

2 METHODOLOGY

2.1 PV System

The photovoltaic generator was modeled using experimental irradiance and temperature data obtained in the city of Antofagasta. A crystalline silicon reference cell mounted on the roof of a test vehicle provided the environmental inputs, which were implemented in Simulink using time-based lookup tables to replicate realistic operating conditions. The PV array consisted of 600 series-connected cells, delivering a nominal voltage of 350 V. This generator was coupled to a 540 V DC bus that supplied a 50 kWh $LiFePO_4$ battery bank. The storage system was represented by a $2RC$ equivalent circuit parameterized with experimental data and optimized through genetic algorithms, ensuring an accurate representation of voltage dynamics and state-of-charge evolution.

2.2 DC-DC Converters

Three non-isolated high-gain DC-DC converters were studied under identical operating conditions with a switching frequency of 10 kHz. The topologies considered were the Interleaved Boost converter, the Quadratic Boost converter, and the Multi-Input Single-Output (MISO) Boost converter. All of them were modeled in state-space representation and simulated in order to analyze their voltage gain, efficiency, and current ripple under dynamic solar conditions.

The electrical and simulation parameters used for the study are summarized in Table I. The component values were selected to maintain the inductor current ripple below 20% and to ensure settling times shorter than 100 ms, allowing consistent comparison across the three topologies.

Each converter was evaluated with a Maximum Power Point Tracking (MPPT) strategy based on the Perturb and Observe (P&O) algorithm. The algorithm flowchart is shown in Fig. 2, which illustrates the sequence of perturbation and decision steps to track the maximum power point. The control was implemented through a cascaded structure, where the outer voltage loop regulated the PV array voltage while the inner current loop controlled the inductor current. Proportional–integral controllers were applied to both loops in order to achieve stable tracking and adequate dynamic performance.

The control architectures of the Quadratic Boost, Interleaved Boost, and MISO Boost converters are illustrated in Fig. 3, highlighting their integration with the MPPT scheme. Furthermore, the performance of

Table I: Simulation Parameters.

Description	Symbol	Value
PV input	V_{PV}	350 V
Battery, output voltage	V_{batt}, V_o	540 V
Capacitors	C_1, C_2, C_3, C_o	200 μF
Inductors	L_1, L_2, L_3	2 mH
Output resistor	R_o	80-90 Ω
Switching frequency	f_{sw}	10 kHz
Max. Power	60 km/h	3.5 kW

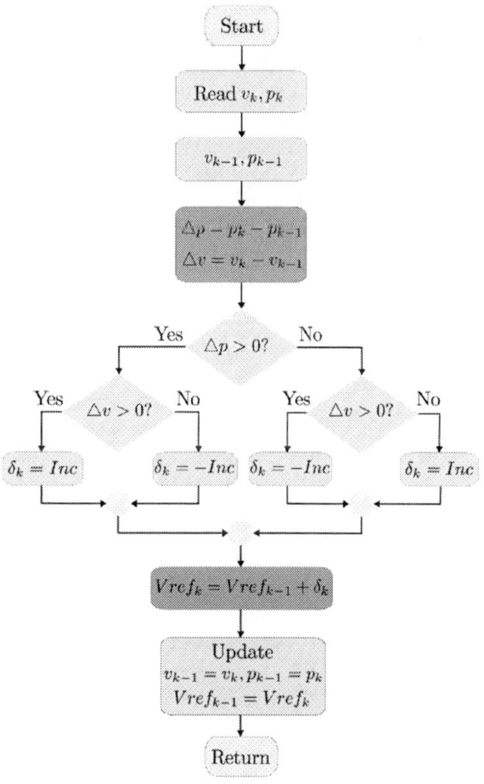

Fig. 2: Flowchart of the Perturb and Observe (P&O) MPPT algorithm

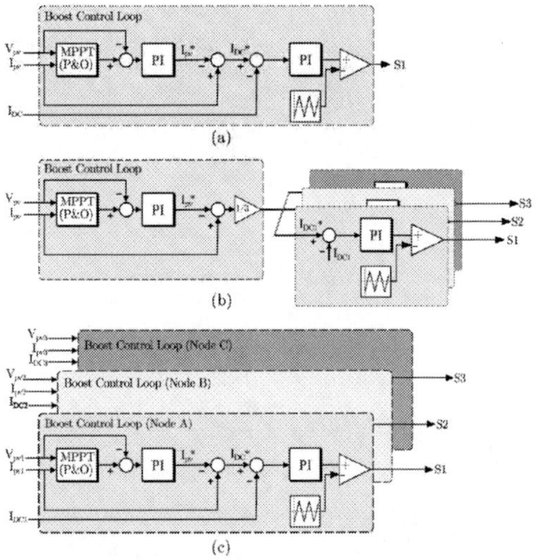

Fig. 3: MPPT control loop architectures for each converter topology: Quadratic (top), Interleaved (middle), and MISO (bottom).

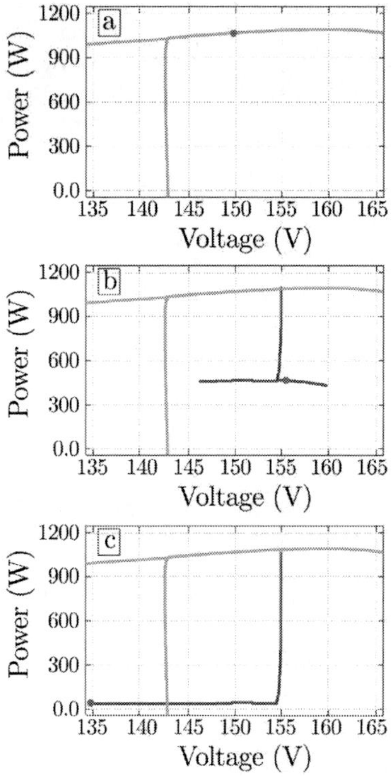

Fig. 4: MPPT algorithm response under different irradiance scenarios: (a) uniform irradiance of 1000 W/m^2, (b) transition from 1000 W/m^2 to 500 W/m^2 (partial shading), and (c) transition from 1000 W/m^2 to below 100 W/m^2 (severe shading).

the P&O algorithm under different irradiance profiles was analyzed to validate its use within the study. The results are presented in Fig. 4, where three scenarios are depicted: (a) operation under uniform irradiance of 1000 W/m^2 without shading, (b) a transition from 1000 W/m^2 to 500 W/m^2 corresponding to partial shading, and (c) a severe shading event with irradiance dropping from 1000 W/m^2 to below 100 W/m^2. This evaluation demonstrates the ability of the algorithm to maintain tracking across rapid irradiance changes, although oscillations around the maximum power point become more evident under shading.

3 RESULTS AND DISCUSSION

The three converter topologies delivered more than 3.2 kW with efficiencies higher than 98.4% under uniform high-irradiance conditions. Nevertheless, significant differences emerged when the system was subjected to variable and critical solar scenarios, which revealed the trade-offs between efficiency, current ripple, and voltage stability.

The Interleaved Boost converter exhibited strong steady-state performance and fast recovery during irradiance transients. These characteristics were achieved at the cost of elevated current peaks and increased thermal stress on the semiconductor devices, which may affect long-term reliability.

The Quadratic Boost converter reached the required voltage gain at relatively low duty cycles, reducing the stress on switching components. However, it was more sensitive to rapid irradiance variations, showing pronounced ripple in both duty cycle and current waveforms. This behavior indicates that, although suitable under stable conditions, its performance deteriorates significantly under dynamic scenarios.

The MISO Boost converter consistently maintained voltage regulation and sustained efficiency across all operating conditions. Its ability to operate with low input current ripple, even during severe shading events where irradiance dropped below 100 W/m^2, demonstrated its robustness. This topology minimized the stress on components and ensured reliable energy transfer across the full operating range.

The comparative qualitative performance is summarized in Table II, which highlights voltage stability, efficiency, and input current ripple for each topology. According to the table, the Interleaved Boost provides medium efficiency and stability, the Quadratic Boost shows lower robustness under disturbances, and the MISO configuration achieves high efficiency with superior stability and minimal current ripple. These

Table II: Comparative qualitative performance of non-isolated DC-DC topologies under real irradiance

Criterion	Interleaved Boost	Quadratic Boost	MISO
Voltage stability	Medium	Low	High
Efficiency	Medium–High	Medium	High
Input current ripple	Medium	High	Low

results are further illustrated in Fig. 5, where the temporal responses of the converters are presented under different irradiance and temperature conditions.

Subfigures (a) to (g) depict the irradiance profiles, FET currents, output voltages, and output currents across two test intervals. The figure evidences that while the Interleaved Boost responds rapidly, it induces higher current peaks; the Quadratic Boost suffers from ripple amplification during transitions; and the MISO Boost maintains stable operation even under partial and severe shading.

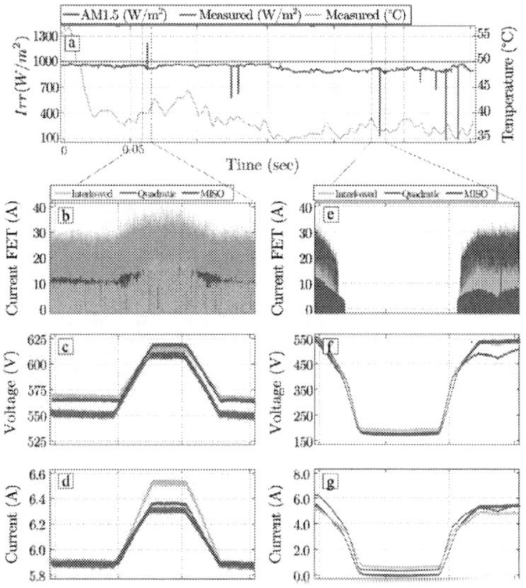

Fig. 5: Comparative performance of Interleaved, Quadratic, and MISO converters under variable irradiance and temperature conditions: (a) solar irradiance (AM1.5 and measured) and measured temperature; (b) FET current during the first interval; (c) output voltage during the first interval; (d) output current during the first interval; (e) FET current during the second interval; (f) output voltage during the second interval; (g) output current during the second interval.

4 CONCLUSIONS

This study analyzed the performance of three advanced non-isolated DC-DC converter topologies for Vehicle-Integrated Photovoltaic (ViPV) systems in urban electric buses, using real irradiance and temperature profiles collected in northern Chile. The Interleaved Boost, Quadratic Boost, and MISO Boost converters were simulated under identical conditions to assess their voltage stability, efficiency, and current ripple.

The results demonstrated that, although all converters achieved efficiencies above 98% under high irradiance, their behavior diverged under dynamic conditions. The Interleaved Boost exhibited rapid transient recovery but with elevated current peaks and thermal stress. The Quadratic Boost operated with reduced stress on switching devices due to low duty cycles, but its performance degraded during abrupt irradiance variations. In contrast, the MISO Boost consistently maintained stable output voltage, low input current ripple, and sustained efficiency even under severe shading events, making it the most robust and reliable alternative for urban scenarios with highly variable solar conditions.

The main contribution of this work lies in providing a comparative evaluation of advanced non-isolated DC-DC converters under realistic irradiance variations, highlighting the trade-offs between efficiency, stability, and current ripple. These results establish technical guidelines for selecting suitable topologies in ViPV systems, particularly in environments characterized by rapid and frequent solar fluctuations.

Future research should focus on experimental validation of the converters and the integration of adaptive or predictive MPPT strategies to further enhance tracking accuracy and dynamic robustness. Such developments will strengthen the role of ViPV systems in reducing grid dependency and improving sustainability in public transportation.

ACKNOWLEDGMENTS

This work was supported by the Chilean Solar Energy Research Center (SERC Chile) under Grant ANID/FONDAP/1523A0006 and the Chilean National Agency for Research and Development (ANID) through the National Doctorate Program under Grant ANID/Subdirección de Capital Humano/Doctorado Nacional/2024-21241192. Special thanks to the Consortium of Engineering Faculties of the Antofagasta Region, the HEUMA ING2030 16ENI2-71940 Project for their unparalleled fundings, Power Electronics and Electromobility Laboratory (POWEREMLAB) and the Doctoral Program in Solar Energy of the Universidad de Antofagasta for their invaluable support and research environment.

References

[1] D. W. Cunningham, E. P. Carlson, J. S. Manser, and I. C. Kizilyalli, "Impacts of wide band gap power electronics on photovoltaic system design," *IEEE Journal of Photovoltaics*, vol. 10, pp. 213–218, 1 2020.

[2] J. D. Clarke, "Antiquity of aridity in the chilean atacama desert," *Geomorphology*, vol. 73, no. 1, pp. 101–114, 2006. [Online]. Available: https://www.sciencedirect.com/science/article/pii/S0169555X05002023

[3] A. Marzo, P. Ferrada, F. Beiza, P. Besson, J. Alonso-Montesinos, J. Ballestrín, R. Román, C. Portillo, R. Escobar, and E. Fuentealba, "Standard or local solar spectrum? implications for solar technologies studies in the atacama desert," *Renewable Energy*, vol. 127, pp. 871–882, 2018.

[4] J. Rabanal-Arabach, "Development of a c-si photovoltaic module for desert climates," Ph.D. dissertation, Universität Konstanz, Konstanz, 2019.

[5] D. R. E. Trejo, S. Taheri, J. L. Saavedra, P. Vázquez, C. H. D. Angelo, and J. A. Pecina-Sánchez, "Nonlinear control and internal stability analysis of series-connected boost dc/dc converters in pv systems with distributed mppt," *IEEE Journal of Photovoltaics*, vol. 11, pp. 504–512, 3 2021.

[6] M. Yamaguchi, K. Nakamura, R. Ozaki *et al.*, "Analysis for the potential of high-efficiency and low-cost vehicle-integrated photovoltaics," *Solar RRL*, vol. 7, no. 1, 2022.

[7] P. Hoth, A. Dannenberg, E. Lüpfert *et al.*, "Vehicle-integrated photovoltaics—a case study for berlin," *World Electric Vehicle Journal*, vol. 15, no. 3, p. 113, 2024.

[8] M. C. Brito, T. Santos, F. Moura, D. Pera, and J. Rocha, "Urban solar potential for vehicle integrated photovoltaics,"

Transportation Research Part D: Transport and Environment, vol. 94, p. 102810, 2021.
[9] L. S. José, R. González, R. Ortega, E. Gutiérrez *et al.*, "Performance evaluation of mppt algorithm of vipv systems in realistic urban routes using image processing," *Solar Energy Materials and Solar Cells*, vol. 276, p. 113061, 2024.
[10] S. Rodríguez-Romero, J. Rabanal-Arabach, C. A. Rojas, M. Trigo-Gonzalez, G. Mondaca-Cuevas, D. Arias, F. Castro-Gallardo, and E. Fuentealba-Vidal, "Analysis of advanced nonisolated topologies for vehicle-integrated photovoltaic (vipv) systems in urban electric transport buses," *IEEE Journal of Photovoltaics*, pp. 1–7, 2025.
[11] A. Asadi, M. S. Karimzadeh, X. Liang, M. S. Mahdavi, and G. B. Gharehpetian, "A novel control approach for a single-inductor multi-input single-output dc-dc boost converter for pv applications," *IEEE Access*, vol. 11, pp. 114 753–114 764, 2023.
[12] R. Daxini, K. S. Anderson, J. S. Stein, and M. Theristis, "Photovoltaic module spectral mismatch losses due to cell-level eqe variation," *IEEE Journal of Photovoltaics*, 2025.
[13] P. H. S. B. Loureiro and A. M. S. S. Andrade, "Single switch asymmetrical high step-up dc-dc converter based on differential connection," *IEEE Transactions on Power Electronics*, 2024.

3D INTEGRATED PHOTOVOLTAIC SURFACES FOR PORTABLE APPLICATIONS

Thomas M. Kraft*, Riikka Suhonen, Kaisa-Leena Väisänen, Kyösti Heikkinen, Antti Nurmesjärvi, and Mari Ylikunnari
VTT Technical Research Centre of Finland Ltd., Kaitoväylä 1, Oulu 90590, Finland
*thomas.kraft@vtt.fi

ABSTRACT: To enable the use of portable, and potentially wearable, 3D molded autonomous energy modules the applicability of high pressure injection overmolded flexible solar cells was investigated [1]. The goal was to find commercially available flexible amorphous Si photovoltaic (PV) modules, test their overmolding possibilities and to investigate overmolding materials of the PV as a baseline for future studies. The devices' electrical behavior was measured under different conditions and in an outdoor test environment. Based on processing and testing, the goal was to evaluate the manufacturing possibilities of a 3D integrable autonomous energy module for wearable plastic/composite equipment.

The investigation was divided into three sub-tasks: 1) material design, 2) PV device overmolding, and 3) testing. Regarding materials, commercial solar cells made of amorphous silicon were used in the project due to their easy availability, and two materials were tested for overmolding: polycarbonate (PC) and thermoplastic polyurethane (TPU). For the overmolding process, various parameters were evaluated, with the TPU being a more suitable material for the selected PV devices. Finally, the overmolded cells were tested under different lighting conditions, bending stress, accelerated ageing, and the effect of scratching and dirt on the cell's operation was studied.

Keywords: structural electronics, injection molding, flexible PV

1 AIM AND APPROACH

Traditional solar panels aren't always practical for off-grid electronics users' gear. What's needed are lightweight, attachable, and detachable modules that include a solar cell, battery, and fasteners. These modules can be quickly integrated into gear, making it easier to stay powered up without extra weight. They can also be carried in multiples, shared among users, and placed close to where the power is needed.

Current wearable solar solutions often involve sewing solar cells onto fabrics, which can't be detached or replaced easily. Pre-shaped, detachable modules offer better durability and protection against wear and tear. They ensure off-grid electronics users have reliable power without compromising mobility or equipment weight.

The criterion for selecting the solar cell was its commercial availability, flexibility, and thin structure. Three different power solar cells were used in the work: MPT3.6, MPT4.8, and MPT6, purchased from PowerFilm Inc (Table I).

Table I: Power, and voltage, and current values provided by the manufacturer.

Cell	Power [mW]	Operating Voltage [V]
MPT3.6	180	3.6
MPT4.8	240	4.8
MPT6	300	6.0

2 RESULTS

The requirements for the overmolding material were flexibility, and suitability to be injection overmolded. Based on these criteria, two materials were selected for molding: polycarbonate (PC) and thermoplastic polyurethane (TPU). An Engel victory 120 overmolding device was used in the work and done on either the illuminated or non-illuminated side of the solar cell.

The electrical performance of the solar cells was measured using the AM1.5 artificial sunlight measurement device, which provided a current-voltage curve. Based on the obtained curve, the measurement program calculated the maximum power of the solar cell. The artificial sunlight was restricted with steel meshes, reducing the incoming sunlight power (100 mW/cm²) to 1/3 (33 mW/cm²) and 1/9 (11 mW/cm²) of its original value. Further studies done at various different bending radii: 4.55 cm, 3.30 cm, and 2.80 cm and measured in different positions relative to the incoming light.

The overmolded cells were stressed in a weather cabinet under various accelerated conditions. There were four different stress tests:

•ISOS protocol for solar cells: 100 mW/cm² light, 50% humidity, 65°C temperature
•IEC protocol with standardized high temperature and humidity: 85% RH, 85°C
•IEC protocol with temperature cycling: -40°C to +85°C
•Mechanical stress: scratching the cell, scratching the overmolding material, contamination

2.1 Injection over-molding of PV modules

During the overmolding process, suitable process parameters for the materials and the solar cell were determined. Despite adjusting the parameters, all the cells broke during the PC overmolding process due to layer incompatibility and high processing temperature required for PC.

Figure 1: Flat overmolding of the PV module with TPU.

10.4229/EUPVSEC2025/4DV.1.55

Figure 2: Curved TPU over-molding of the PV module.

Figure 3: Domed TPU over-molding of the PV module.

When molding with TPU, the solar cells withstood the overmolding process well, and moldings were made with three different molds: flat surface, curved surface, and dome-shaped surface (Figure 1, Figure 2, Figure 3). When molding into a curved shape, the cell easily detached from the overmolding material during mold removal. When molding into a dome shape, the cell did not stretch into the shape during molding, resulting in folds in the cell.

2.2 PV performance

By adjusting the illumination power of the simulated sunlight, various shaded conditions could be tested. Each overmolded solar cell was evaluated before and after overmolding, with parallel samples for accuracy. Weather cabinets simulated outdoor conditions, exposing cells to moisture and temperature changes.

Effect of Bending Radius

The angle of light significantly affects power output. As shown in Figure 4, for large cells like the MPT6, power drops by over 80% from 0° to 90°. Smaller bending radius and larger cell size further reduce power due to shading. For instance, MPT6's power dropped from 400 mW (flat at 1 SUN) to 50 mW with a 2.80 cm bending radius.

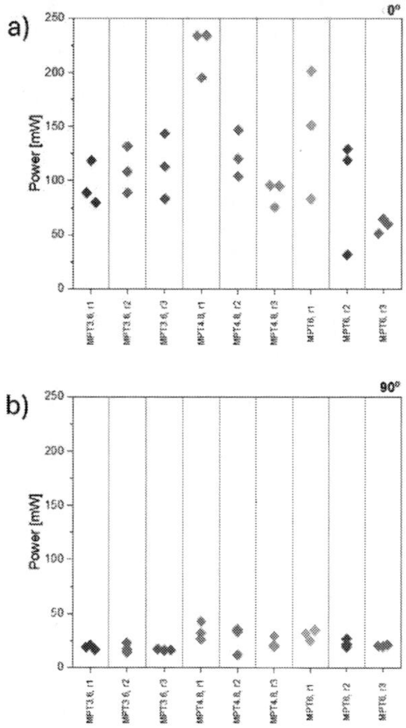

Figure 4. The effect of bending radius to cell performance. The bending radius used were r1 = 4.55 cm, r2 = 3.30 cm and r3 = 2.80 cm. At two angles of incident light a) 0° and b) 90°.

Effect of Overmolding

The performance of cells molded into flat or curved shapes remained unchanged, and the measured power values matched the manufacturer's specified values at 1SUN illumination (Figure 5). Additionally, the side of overmolding did not affect the cells' performance. Figure 5 shows the measured power values of MPT3.6 cells molded with a flat mold before and after overmolding.

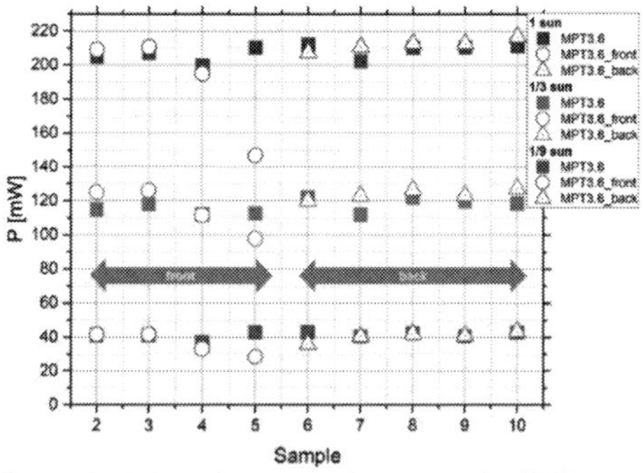

Figure 5: Cell performance before and after TPU over-molding measured at 1 sun, 1/3 sun and 1/9 light intensities. The filled symbols are power values before overmolding and "front" and "back" refer to the side of TPU overmolding.

Stress Tests of Overmolded Cells

Overmolded and non-overmolded cells were subjected to various accelerated conditions to assess their performance under stress. The cells were measured regularly outside the weather cabinet.

In Figure 6, the cell performance test of the overmolded and reference (no overmold) cells during ISOS-L-3 stability test is shown. After ~1500h of stress, the performance of reference cells starts to decrease which is mainly due to a decrease in voltage, caused by internal defects in the cell. Promisingly, the overmolded cells show stable performance even after 2500h of stress indicating that overmolding protects the flexible solar cells from degradation.

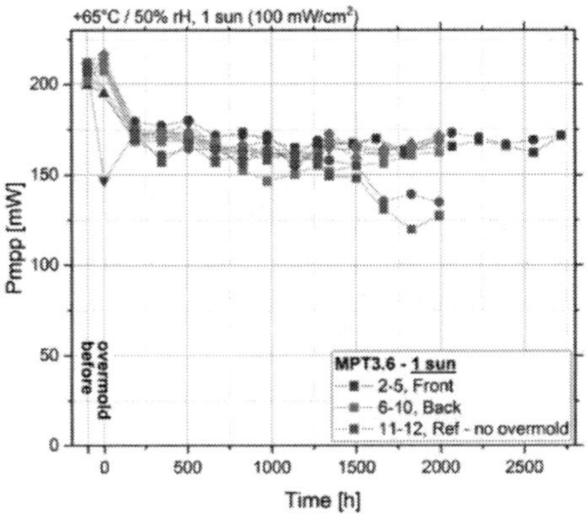

Figure 6. Performance of overmolded samples over time when stressed according the ISOS-L-3 stability test.

In the high temperature and humidity test, cells were kept at 85% humidity and 85°C temperature whereas in the temperature cycling test, cells were kept between -40°C and +85°C. As shown in Figure 7a, some variation in the cell performance was measured but with most of the cells, the output power was still > 90% of the original after 26 days of stressing. Whereas in the temperature cycling test, the performance did not change during cycling (Figure 7b). The overmolding material TPU became opaque (Figure 7c) but, surprisingly, this did not affect the electrical performance.

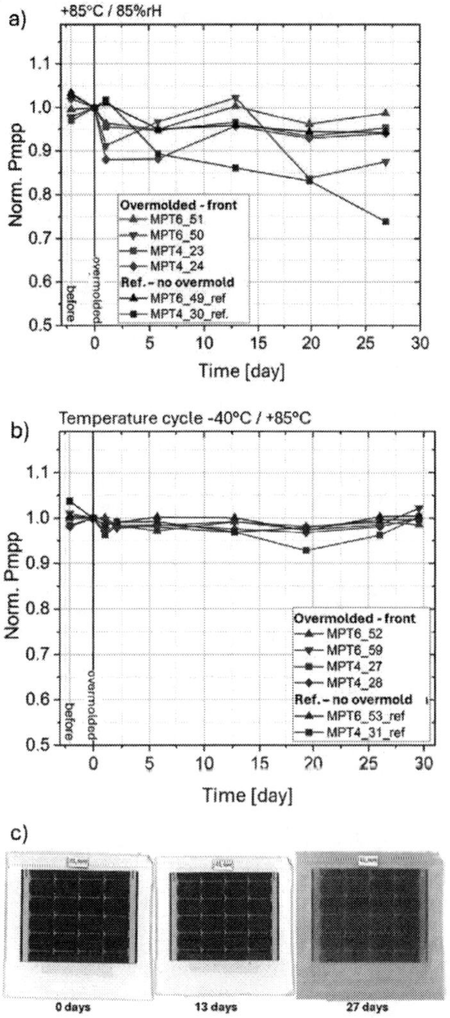

Figure 7. Cell performance during the IEC tests at a) +85°C and 85% rH and b) temperature cycling from -40°C to +85°C. In c) photographs of the overmolded samples after temperature cycling tests.

Mechanical Stress

Under mechanical stress, the surface of the cell was scratched with P60 sandpaper. When scratching the illuminated side of the front-molded TPU, the cell's electrical performance remained the same as the overmolded, non-scratched cell. Without the TPU protection, the cell stopped functioning when the illuminated side was scratched. The contamination of the cell surface was simulated by covering three cells (Table II) with a clear plastic film printed with partially covering patterns. Shadow A's coverage area was 37%, and Shadow B's coverage area was 56%, with the entirely black film covering 100%. Contamination significantly affects the current produced by the cell, thereby reducing the cell's power.

Table II: Power, voltage, and current of one MPT6 cell illuminated through covering films.

Film	Coverage	P [mW]	V [V]	I [mA]
Clear	0%	351	7	53
Shadow A	37%	157	7	24
Shadow B	56%	58	6	9
Black	100%	0	0	0

Outdoor Testing

The test site is located at VTT Oulu (N65.0564, E25.4580), where the temperature range during a one year period can fluctuate from –34.0 °C to +33.0 °C. The daylight duration varies from 3 hours 34 minutes in winter to 22 hours 3 minutes in summer. For this study, the testing period spans from 29 April 2025 to 28 July 2025 (Figure 8). The modules were fixed to a south facing stand and monitored with I-V sweeps every 30 minutes. Between I-V sweeps the modules were kept under a constant bias at maximum power point voltage of the previous I-V sweep. The test site also includes a weather station monitoring humidity, air pressure, wind speed and direction, precipitation, and solar irradiance.

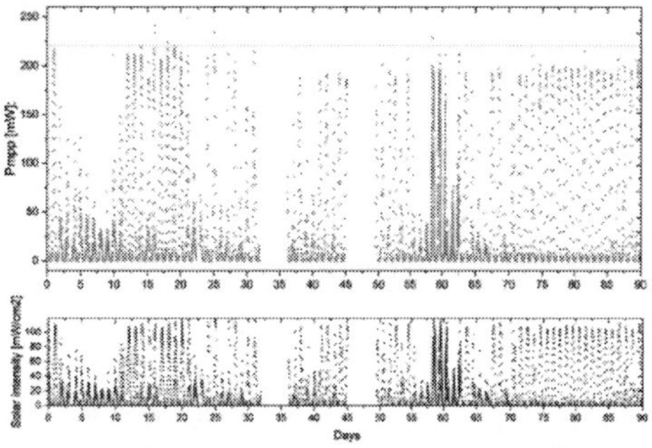

Figure 8: Outdoor Maximum Power Point (Pmpp) of over-molded PV modules (top) and corresponding measured solar intensity (bottom) over three months. Horizontal line at 220 mW corresponds to P_{MPP} measured with AM 1.5 prior to outdoor testing.

3 CONCLUSIONS

This study evaluated the suitability and primary considerations for integrated PV applications such as wearable devices and curved surfaces. It examined several key factors affecting performance after devices were injection overmolded with TPU.

The relationship between bending radius and cell area was explored, demonstrating that a smaller bending radius combined with a larger cell area leads to reduced power output. Additionally, it was found that the power output of the cell decreases by more than 80% when the illumination angle shifts from 0° to 90°.

Temperature and humidity effects were investigated, showing that overmolded cells possess strong resistance to accelerated stress environments; nonetheless, the overmolding material itself may undergo state changes when exposed to elevated temperature and relative humidity. Mechanical stress, such as scratching, was also considered: direct scratches on the cell surface result in performance failure, whereas scratches on the overmolded surface do not impact cell performance, highlighting the importance of protecting the cell surface from mechanical damage. Finally, contamination was addressed, with results indicating that when 56% of the cell area is obstructed, only 15–17% of the original power is produced.

In summary, this study highlights the crucial factors influencing the performance of flexible solar cells, including irradiance, bending radius, angle of illumination, temperature, humidity, mechanical stress, and contamination. These findings emphasize the importance of optimizing both material selection and environmental protection to ensure reliable operation in real-world applications. Furthermore, TPU overmolding, both flat and curved, was suitable for the selected solar cells and that the overmolded modules performed well outdoors and showed little degradation.

4 AKNOWLEDGEMENTS

This research was funded by the Scientific Advisory Board for Defence (MATINE) and the CETPartnership (REFORM, CETP-2022-00348), the European Partnership under Joint Call 2022 for research proposals, co-funded by the European Commission (GA N°101069750) and with funding by Business Finland, decision number 2876/31/2023.

Further support provided by the Research Council of Finland (RCF), Printed intelligence infrastructure funding, decision 358621 and the RCF Flagship Programme, Photonics Research and Innovation (PREIN), decision number 346545.

5 REFERENCES

[1] Ylikunnari, "Aurinkokennoenergiamoduulit 3D-pintojen integrointiin". Valtioneuvoston hallintoyksikkö, Julkaisutuotanto, Helsinki 2024

3D Integrated Photovoltaic Surfaces For Portable Applications

Authors Thomas M. Kraft*, Riikka Suhonen, Kaisa-Leena Väisänen, Kyösti Heikkinen, Antti Nurmesjärvi, Mari Ylikunnari

Ambition

Development of 3D integrated photovoltaic (PV) surfaces for portable and potentially wearable applications [1]

- Focused on three main tasks:
  - mold cavity designs
  - solar cell overmolding process
  - testing and integration

Commercially available flexible amorphous silicon solar cells were used, and two materials, polycarbonate (PC) and thermoplastic polyurethane (TPU), were tested as overmolding materials.

Injection Over-Molded PV modules

Amorphous Si-PV modules were overmolded at VTT. Three mold cavities were designed for the study to investigate the effect of:

- TPU vs. PC
- curved stress
  - shapes: flat, curve, dome

Figure 1: Injection overmolding equipment at VTT

Figure 2: Injection overmolded PV modules from PowerFilm Inc. with TPU: (left) flat; (middle) curved; (right) domed forms.

When overmolding with TPU, the solar cells withstood the molding process well, however, all the modules were damaged during the PC overmolding process (due to elevated T and P in the mold cavity).

The performance of modules molded into flat or curved shapes remained unchanged, and the measured power values matched the manufacturer's specified values at 1SUN illumination. Domed forms had low yield.

Additionally, side of overmolding (front or back) did not affect the cells' performance. Figure 3 shows the measured power values of moldules molded with a flat mold before and after overmolding.

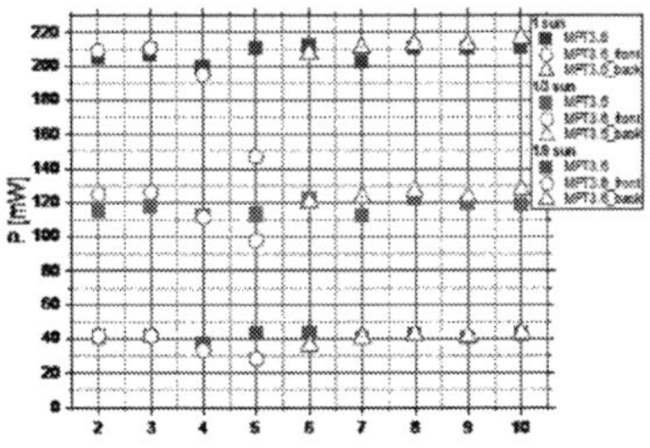

Figure 3: PV performance before (solid) and after (line) TPU overmolding flat form.

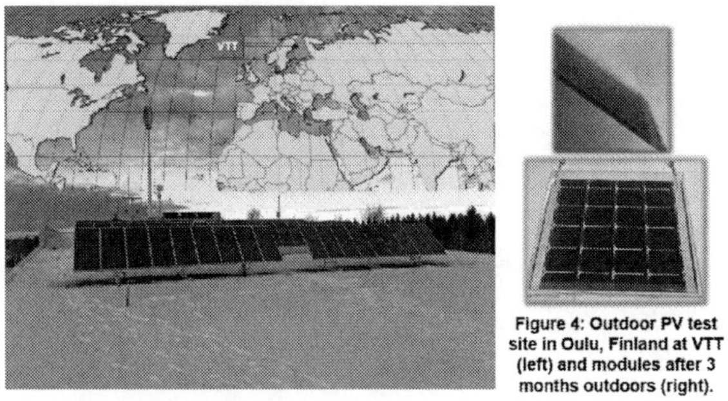

Figure 4: Outdoor PV test site in Oulu, Finland at VTT (left) and modules after 3 months outdoors (right).

Sub-Arctic Outdoor PV Testing

- Test site: VTT Oulu (N65.0564, E25.4580)
- Temperatures: –34.0 °C to +33.0 °C
  - Daylight: 3 h 34 min (winter) to 22 h 3 min (summer)
- I-V sweeps and correlating with humidity, air pressure, wind speed & direction, precipitation, solar irradiance. 29.04.25 to 28.07.25

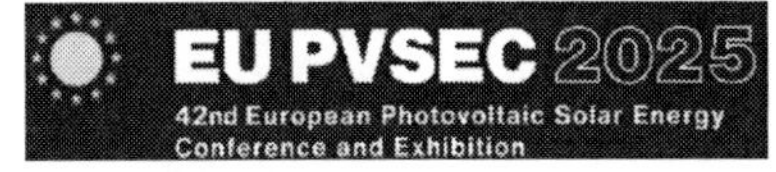

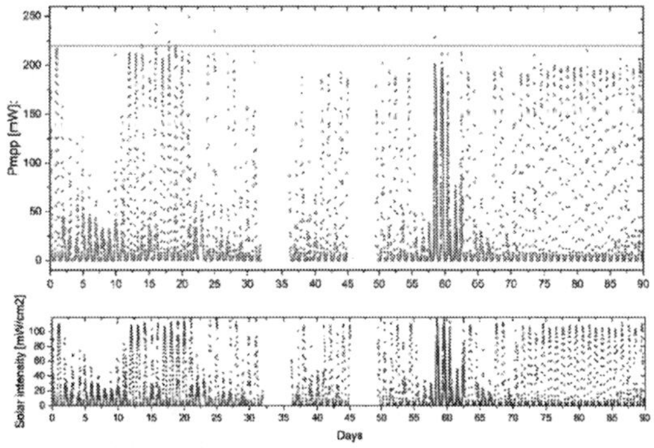

Figure 5: Outdoor Maximum Power Point (Pmpp) of over-molded PV modules (top) and corresponding measured solar intensity (bottom) over three months. Horizontal line at 220 mW corresponds to P_{MPP} measured with AM 1.5 prior to outdoor testing.

Conclusion

- **TPU overmolding was suitable for the selected solar cells.**
- **Overmolded modules performed well outdoors and showed little degradation.**
- **The performance of modules molded into flat or curved shapes remained unchanged**

Acknowledgements

This research was funded by the Scientific Advisory Board for Defence (MATINE) and the CETPartnership (REFORM, CETP-2022-00348), the European Partnership under Joint Call 2022 for research proposals, co-funded by the European Commission (GA N°101069750) and with funding by Business Finland, decision number 2876/31/2023.

Further support provided by the Research Council of Finland (RCF), Printed intelligence infrastructure funding, decision 358621 and the RCF Flagship Programme, Photonics Research and Innovation (PREIN), decision number 346545.

PREIN Photonics Research and Innovation

cet Partnership

Research Council of Finland

BUSINESS FINLAND

EU PVSEC 2025 42nd European Photovoltaic Solar Energy Conference and Exhibition

Contact: Thomas Kraft, PhD
Senior Scientist, Project Manager
Tel. +358 20 722 2070, thomas.kraft@vtt.fi

020424-001

beyond the obvious
www.vttresearch.com

[1] Ylikunnari, "Aurinkokennoenergiamoduulit 3D-pintojen integrointiin". Valtioneuvoston hallintoyksikkö, Julkaisutuotanto, Helsinki 2024

42nd European Photovoltaic Solar Energy Conference and Exhibition

EU PVSEC 2025

4DV.1
T4.6

TNO innovation for life

Modelling of marine assembly logistics for an offshore floating photovoltaic (OFPV) plant subject to weather dependencies

Lu-Jan Huang, Simone Mancini, Minne de Jong

louis.huang@tno.nl

Full details in our recent journal paper:

METHODOLOGY

This study applies a **discrete-event simulation** approach (*TNO UWiSE*), modelling operations such as transit, loading, and installation as time-based events. Each task is governed by **weather thresholds** (e.g. wave limits), with delays logged when conditions exceed those limits. Some events must occur **consecutively without interruption**, requiring a continuous weather window. The model uses **multi-year hourly weather data** to capture uncertainty in installation outcomes.

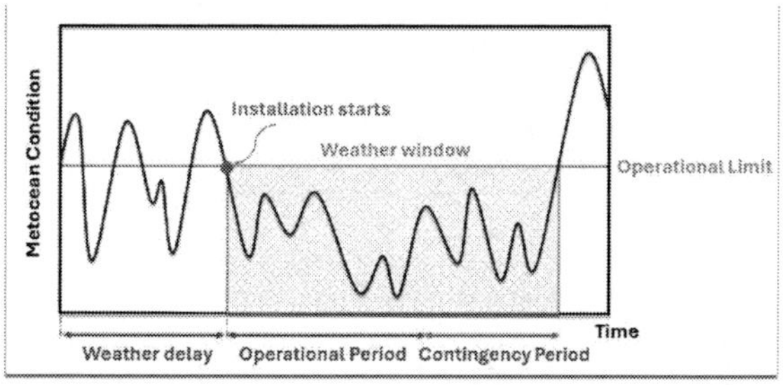

CASE STUDY: MODULAR OFPV

The 5 MWp OFPV plant consists of **54 triangular floating platforms** arranged into a large hexagonal array (left). Each platform (right) is based on a **truss-type prototype**, elevated ~10 m above sea level to withstand harsh wave conditions. Buoyancy and damping are provided by aluminum floats and gas cylinders, with **anchoring via 35 mooring lines and seabed anchors**.

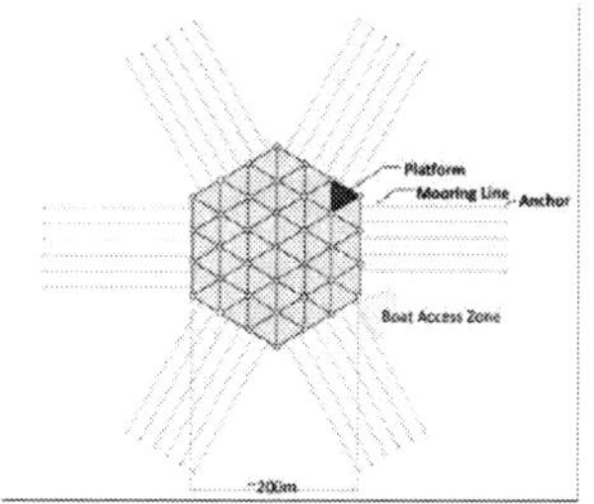

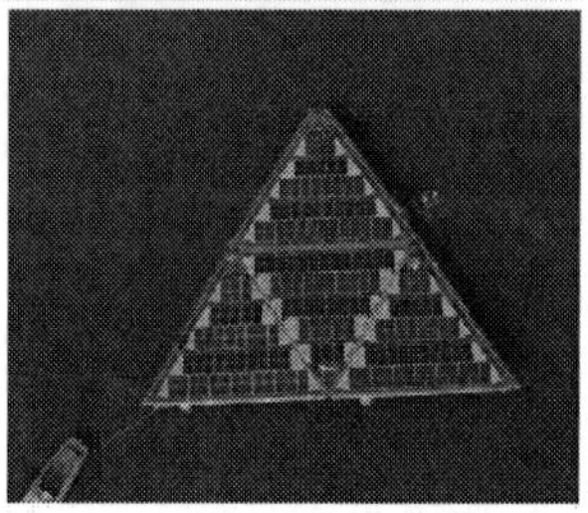

Reference: SolarDuck

MARINE ASSEMBLY LOGISTICS

Platforms are towed in **pre-assembled sets of six** using tugboats, then coupled offshore and secured with 35 mooring lines using a multicat vessel. All operations are modeled with vessel requirements, weather limits, and method statements defined per campaign.

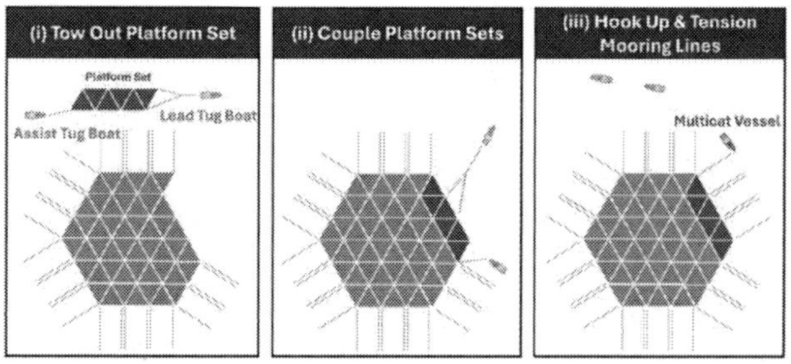

SCENARIOS

Three scenarios were modeled to assess how **weather risk** impacts installation planning. The key difference is whether a **continuous weather window** is enforced for interdependent steps. Comparison of scenarios shows how these policies affect timing and weather delay risks for critical operations.

Scenario	Risk Level	Risk Management Policy
1	High	No weather window is reserved to secure continuity between highly inter-dependent operational steps
2	Medium	Weather window of **Hs = 1.5 m with 50% margin** is reserved to reduce risks of discontinuity between highly inter-dependent operational steps.
3	Low	Weather window of **Hs = 1.0 m with 50% margin** is reserved to reduce risks of discontinuity between highly inter-dependent operational steps.

FINDINGS

- **Seasonal impact:** Installation during autumn/winter takes on average 160% longer than in spring/summer, driven by harsher wave conditions.
- **Risk policy impact:** Across all months, increasing policy strictness raises average duration from 70 days (high risk) to 130 days (low risk), due to added weather window requirements for interdependent tasks.
- **Anchor pre-laying** and **platform & mooring installation** account for >75% of all weather delays
- These campaigns are most sensitive to risk policies due to **task interdependencies** and tight weather thresholds.
- Mitigation should target these phases via faster operations, relaxed constraints, or modular methods that reduce weather exposure.

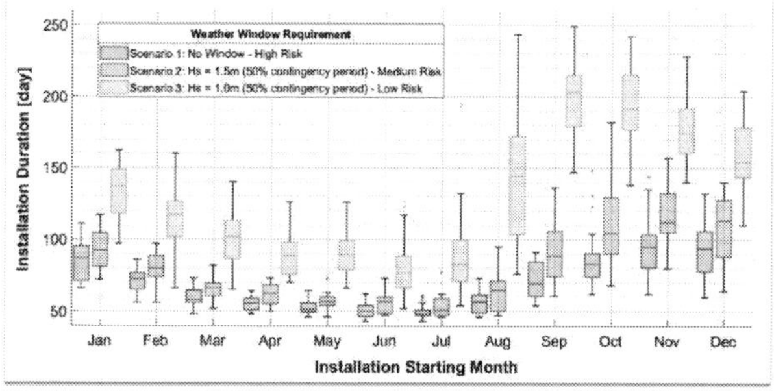

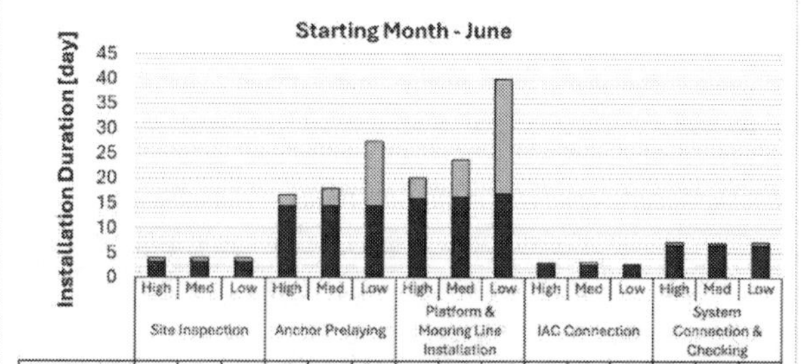

	Site Inspection			Anchor Prelaying			Platform & Mooring Line Installation			IAC Connection			System Connection & Checking		
	High	Med	Low	High	Med	Low	High	Med	Low	High	Med	Low	High	Med	Low
Weather Delay	1	1	1	2	3	13	4	7	23	0	1	0	1	0	1
Core Duration	3	3	3	14	14	14	16	16	17	3	3	3	7	7	7

020425-001

This research was partially financed by the Netherlands Enterprise Agency within the DEI+ Merganser project.

Rijksdienst voor Ondernemend Nederland

Sizing Strategy for Green Hydrogen Production: Maximizing PV Utilization and Electrolyzer Efficiency

Carlos Meza[1,2], Mohammad Nabipour[1,2], Matthias Ebert[1]

[1] *Fraunhofer Center for Crystalline Silicon Photovoltaics CSP, Halle (Saale), Germany*
[2] *Hochschule Anhalt University of Applied Sciences, Köthen, Germany*

carlos.meza@hs-anhalt.de

Abstract

ABSTRACT: Green hydrogen production from solar photovoltaic (PV) power is central to decarbonization strategies. European regulations mandate a temporal correlation between renewable energy generation and electrolyzer operation, currently on a monthly basis. This paper presents a sizing methodology to determine the optimal power ratio between a PV plant and an electrolyzer to comply with these regulations. This sizing ratio is defined by the month with the lowest solar resource availability. A techno-economic analysis for a case study demonstrates that the ratio derived from this energy balance approach is closely aligned with the ratio that minimizes the Levelized Cost of Hydrogen (LCOH) under various electricity pricing scenarios. The methodology provides a robust framework for designing economically viable and compliant green hydrogen systems. Operational strategies involving real-time estimation algorithms are identified as a necessary next step for future work but are beyond the scope of this paper.

Keywords: Green Hydrogen, PV Sizing, Electrolyzer, LCOH, System Design

1 Introduction

Green hydrogen, produced via water electrolysis powered by renewable energy sources, is a key component in global efforts to decarbonize the industrial and transportation sectors[4], [5], [3]. The European Union has established a regulatory framework to ensure that hydrogen labeled as "green" genuinely contributes to reducing greenhouse gas emissions. A central requirement of this framework is the principle of temporal correlation, which mandates that the production of hydrogen is closely linked in time with the generation of the renewable electricity used to power it [6].

This correlation is assessed monthly, meaning that the total renewable energy generated within a calendar month must be equal to or greater than the energy consumed by the electrolyzer in that same month. This provision allows for some flexibility, enabling producers to use grid electricity to stabilize electrolyzer operation as long as the monthly energy balance is met.

The intermittent nature of solar photovoltaic (PV) power makes sizing photovoltaic hydrogen systems a complex task. An oversized photovoltaic plant can lead to significant power clipping during the summer months, while an undersized plant can require substantial and costly electricity imports from the grid during winter months.

This work presents a sizing methodology for photovoltaic-based hydrogen production systems designed to meet the current monthly green hydrogen certification criteria. The objective is to define the power ratio between the PV plant and the electrolyzer in such a way that all the energy generated by the photovoltaic power is consumed by the electrolyzer on a monthly basis, thus preventing energy waste. This approach is then compared with an economic optimization that seeks to minimize the Levelized Cost of Hydrogen (LCOH) [2].

2 Methodology

The methodology is based on a simulation framework developed in Python that incorporates hourly weather data from a typical meteorological year (TMY) to estimate the PV power and hydrogen generation for a given site. Figure 1 shows a block diagram of the developed model. The proposed sizing strategy is based on meeting the monthly temporal correlation requirement stipulated by the EU regulations [6]. The core principle is to establish a monthly energy balance between the PV generation and the electrolyzer's consumption.

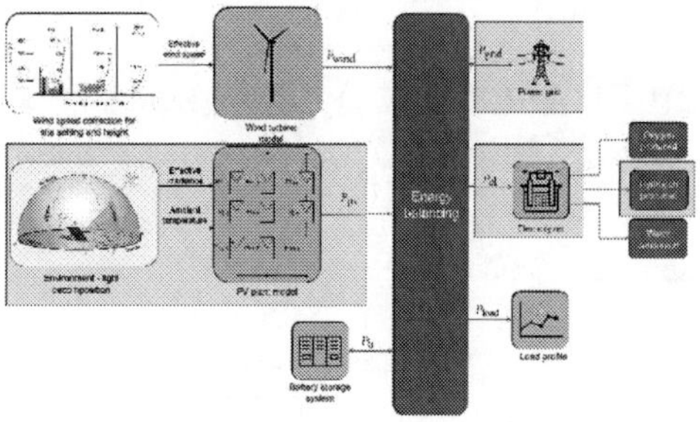

Figure 1: Scheme of the power to hydrogen system configuration (The gray box indicates the elements we focus on in this article.)

2.1 Sizing Based on Energy Balance

The temporal correlation for a given month, m, can be expressed as an integral equation where the total energy produced by the PV plant equals the total energy consumed by the electrolyzer:

$$\int_{t_m}^{t_m+T_m} P_{pv}(t)dt = \int_{t_m}^{t_m+T_m} P_{el}(t)dt = E_m \quad (1)$$

Here, $P_{pv}(t)$ is the PV power at time t, $P_{el}(t)$ is the power consumed by the electrolyzer at time t, and E_m is the total energy for month m. Notice that E_m is both the energy generated by the PV plant and the energy consumed by the electrolyzer in month m.

To avoid the detrimental effects of variable power operation on the electrolyzer, such as reduced efficiency and accelerated degradation, this methodology assumes that the electrolyzer operates at a constant optimal power level, P^*_{el}. Under this condition, the energy balance depends on the total operating hours of the electrolyzer each month, given that

$$\int_{t_m}^{t_m+T_m} P^*_{el}(t)dt = T_{m_{max}} P^*_{el} \quad (2)$$

The key sizing parameter is the ratio, $r_{pv/el}$, defined as the PV plant's nominal power at Standard Test Conditions (STC), P^*_{pv}, to the electrolyzer's nominal operating power, P^*_{el}:

$$r_{pv/el} = \frac{P^*_{pv}}{P^*_{el}} \quad (3)$$

This ratio can be calculated for each month by relating the monthly specific PV yield, Y_m (in kWh/kWp), to the maximum number of hours in that month, $T_{m_{max}}$:

$$r_{pv/el,m} = \frac{T_{m_{max}}}{Y_m} \quad (4)$$

This calculation results in 12 distinct values for $r_{pv/el}$, one for each month of the year. To ensure that PV energy is not curtailed in any month, the sizing strategy adopts the minimum of these 12 values as the definitive system ratio, $r^*_{pv/el}$:

$$r^*_{pv/el} = \min(r_{pv/el,1}, ..., r_{pv/el,12}) \quad (5)$$

This conservative approach guarantees that even in the month with the lowest solar irradiation (typically a winter month), all the generated PV energy can be consumed by the electrolyzer operating for all available hours. In all other months, the electrolyzer will operate for fewer than the maximum available hours to match the higher PV energy output.

2.2 Case study

The analysis was carried out for a case study located in Sombor, Serbia (latitude: 45.7° N, longitude: 19.7° E). We have used PVGIS TMY data for this location as input weather data for the model. Three different PV structures were analyzed, namely, fix-tilted, single-axis tracker and vertical. Additionally, the following assumptions were made:

- For the fix-tiled mounting structure: Azimuth: 180°.
- For the tracker and vertical PV, Azimuth angle 90°.
- Height above ground: 1 meter (standard for bifacial ground-mounted systems to enable rear-side irradiance capture).
- Mutual shading: Not considered; pitch between rows is assumed to be infinite to isolate the effect of tilt. This allows full irradiance to reach each row without shading losses, simplifying performance comparison.
- Albedo: 0.14 (typical for natural grassland or bare soil conditions in the Vojvodina region).
- Module type: Bifacial PV modules, with the following characteristics:
  - Bifaciality factor: 0.80 (i.e., the rear side produces 80% of what the front side does under the same irradiance).
  - Rated power at STC: 600 W
  - Module efficiency: 22.2 %

2.3 Utilization Factor

A key metric used in this document is the electrolyzer utilization factor shown in (6), which represents the ratio of electricity consumed by the electrolyzer to the total electricity produced by the PV system:

$$U_{el} = \frac{E_{el}}{E_{pv}} \quad (6)$$

A U_{el} below 0.5 indicates that the electrolyzer is significantly under-utilizing the available solar energy. In

10.4229/EUPVSEC2025/4DV.1.75
020426-002

such configurations, the PV plant is either oversized or the electrolyzer is undersized, often resulting in excess energy being exported to the grid or curtailed. This behavior signals a shift away from a Power-to-Hydrogen (PtH) business model toward a more electricity-driven configuration, where grid sales dominate the revenue structure.

2.4 Techno-Economic Analysis

To evaluate the economic viability of the proposed sizing ratio, a techno-economic analysis was performed using the Levelized Cost of Hydrogen (LCOH) as the primary metric following the approaches of [2], [1] [7]. The LCOH calculation includes Capital Expenditures (CAPEX) for the PV plant (I_{pv}) and electrolyzer (I_{el}), Operational Expenditures (OPEX) of the PV plant (O_{pv}) and the electrolyzer (O_{el}), stack replacement costs (C_s), and costs related to grid interaction (C_{grid}), i.e.,

$$LCOH = \frac{I_{el} + I_{pv} + C_s + \sum_{y=1}^{N} (O_{el}(y) + O_{pv}(y) + C_g(y))}{m_{H2}} \quad (7)$$

where y is an specific year, N is total number of years used for the economical analysis and m_{H2} is the total hydrogen produced over the service lifetime of the PV-based green hydrogen plant. In this work, hydrogen production was estimated from the PV plant's energy output for a typical meteorological year, adjusted for PV degradation across the entire project lifetime.

The economic parameters used for the calculation of the LCOH are presented in the following table.

Parameter	Value	Unit
PV plant CAPEX (fixed tilt)	800	€/kW
PV plant CAPEX (single axis tracking)	1007	€/kW
PV plant OPEX (fixed tilt)	13.3	€/kW p.a.
PV plant OPEX (single axis tracking)	20	€/kW p.a.
PV inverter cost	75	€/kW
AEM electrolyzer CAPEX	1285	€/kW
AEM electrolyzer OPEX	2	% of CAPEX p.a.
Stack replacement cost	15	% of CAPEX
Water cost	0.005	€/L
Electricity sale price	0.06	€/kWh
Electricity purchase price	0.06	€/kWh
WACC (equal to discount rate)	6	%
Plant life	25	years

3 Results and discussion

The sizing methodology was applied using Typical Meteorological Year (TMY) data for the selected location.

First, the specific monthly PV yield (Y_m) was simulated for the three PV systems, i.e., fixed-tilt, single-axis tracker and vertical. Using (4), the required $r_{pv/el}$ for each month was calculated. Figure 2 shows the resulting Utilization Factor and LCOH vs. the sizing parameter ratio for the fixed-tilt, tracker and vertical structures, respectively.

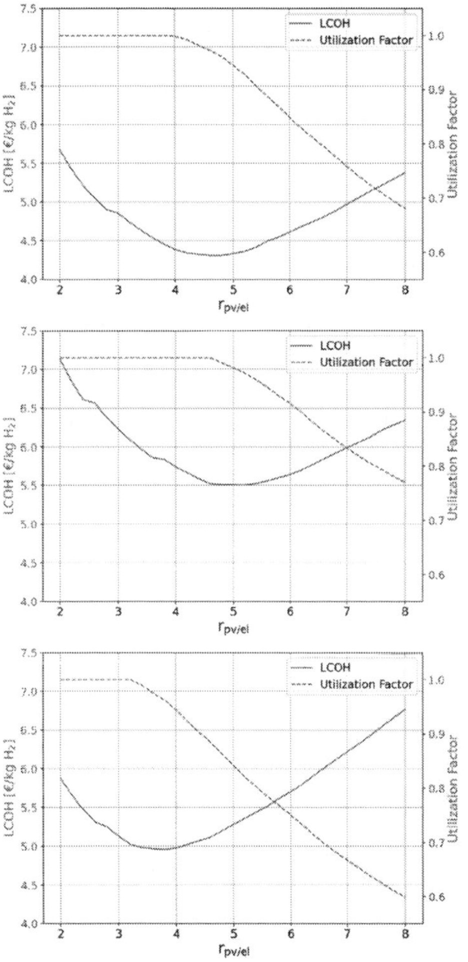

Figure 2: Variation of LCOH and electrolyzer utilization factor as a function of $r_{pv/el}$. The three subplots correspond to different PV system structures from top to bottom: fixed-tilt structure, vertical structure, and single-axis tracker.

The minimum ratio was determined to be approximately 4 for the fix-tilted structure. According to the methodology, this value is selected as $r^*_{pv/el}$ to ensure no PV energy is clipped throughout the year. The results show a clear U-shaped curve for the LCOH. As the ratio increases, the system becomes more self-sufficient, reducing the need for grid imports and thus lowering the LCOH. However, beyond an optimal point, the LCOH begins to rise again. This is because a very high $r_{pv/el}$ ratio implies a large investment in PV capacity (high CAPEX) that is not fully utilized, as the electrolyzer size remains fixed. The optimal $r_{pv/el}$ ratio that minimizes the LCOH is close to 4.6. This value is close to the 4 ratio determined by the energy balance methodology. This alignment demonstrates that sizing the system to avoid PV energy clipping based on a monthly balance is not only compliant with regulations but is also an economically sound strategy. The small difference between the energy-based ratio (4) and the cost-optimal ratio (4.6) indicates that a slight oversizing beyond the no-clipping limit provides a marginal economic benefit by further reducing reliance on grid electricity imports during less sunny periods.

4 Conclusion

This paper presented a sizing methodology for PV-hydrogen systems aimed at fulfilling the monthly temporal correlation requirements for green hydrogen certification in the EU. The methodology defines the PV-to-electrolyzer power ratio by ensuring that all PV energy generated in any given month can be fully utilized by the electrolyzer. This is achieved by selecting the minimum monthly ratio, which corresponds to the month with the highest solar energy yield.

A techno-economic analysis confirmed that the sizing ratio determined by this energy-balance approach is closely aligned with the ratio that minimizes the Levelized Cost of Hydrogen (LCOH) under different electricity market prices. The optimal economic ratio was found to be consistently around 4.6 for a fixed-tilt system, near the calculated no-curtailment ratio of 4 This finding validates the proposed method as a robust and practical tool for the initial design of economically viable and regulation-compliant green hydrogen projects.

It is important to highlight that this work focuses on a high-level sizing methodology. The actual operation of such a system requires dynamic strategies to manage the fluctuating PV power in real-time. Therefore, future work should focus on the development and integration of estimation and control algorithms to manage the energy flows between the PV plant, electrolyzer, and the grid on an operational basis. These aspects were considered out of the scope of the present paper.

Acknowledgments

This work was supported by the German Federal Ministry of Education and Research under the HyDS project (grant number 03SF0697B). We would like to thank our project partners at Leipziger Energiegesellschaft mbH & Co. KG, in particular Mr. Andriy Baranochnyk and Mr. Fabian Severing, as well as Dr. Klemens Ilse and Mr. Sebastian Schindler from Fraunhofer IMWS, for their valuable support.

References

[1] Abdin, Z., Khalilpour, K., Catchpole, K.: Projecting the levelized cost of large scale hydrogen storage for stationary applications. Energy Conversion and Management **270**, 116241 (2022). https://doi.org/10.1016/j.enconman.2022.116241, `https://www.sciencedirect.com/science/article/pii/S0196890422010184`

[2] Hönig, F., Rupakula, G.D., Duque-Gonzalez, D., Ebert, M., Blum, U.: Enhancing the levelized cost of hydrogen with the usage of the byproduct oxygen in a wastewater treatment plant. Energies **16**(12) (2023). https://doi.org/10.3390/en16124829

[3] Odenweller, A., Ueckerdt, F.: The green hydrogen ambition and implementation gap. Nature Energy **10**(1), 110–123 (2025). https://doi.org/10.1038/s41560-024-01684-7

[4] Oliveira, A.M., Beswick, R.R., Yan, Y.: A green hydrogen economy for a renewable energy society. Current Opinion in Chemical Engineering **33**, 100701 (2021). https://doi.org/10.1016/j.coche.2021.100701, `https://www.sciencedirect.com/science/article/pii/S2211339821000332`

[5] Squadrito, G., Maggio, G., Nicita, A.: The green hydrogen revolution. Renewable Energy **216**, 119041 (2023). https://doi.org/10.1016/j.renene.2023.119041, `https://www.sciencedirect.com/science/article/pii/S0960148123009552`

[6] Union, E.: Commission delegated regulation (eu) 2023/1184 of 10 february 2023 supplementing directive 2018/2001 of the european parliament and of the council by establishing a union methodology setting out detailed rules for the production of renewable fuels of non-biological origin. Official Journal **L 157**, 11–19 (2023-06-20)

[7] Wolf, N., Tanneberger, M.A., Höck, M.: Levelized cost of hydrogen production in northern africa and europe in 2050: A monte carlo simulation for germany, norway, spain, algeria, morocco, and egypt. International Journal of Hydrogen Energy **69**, 184–194 (2024). https://doi.org/10.1016/j.ijhydene.2024.04.319, `https://www.sciencedirect.com/science/article/pii/S0360319924016318`

42nd European Photovoltaic Solar Energy Conference and Exhibition

Sizing Strategy for Green Hydrogen Production: Maximizing PV Utilization and Electrolyzer Efficiency

Fraunhofer CSP

Fraunhofer IMWS

Carlos Meza[1,2], Mohammad Nabipour[1,2], Matthias Ebert[1]

[1] Fraunhofer Center for Crystalline Silicon Photovoltaics CSP , Walter-Hulse-Straße 1, 06120 Halle, Germany

[2] Anhalt University of Applied Sciences, Bernburger Str. 55, 06366 Kothen, Germany

Motivation and objectives

- Transition to green hydrogen using photovoltaic (PV) systems as a sustainable pathway to decarbonize energy-intensive processes.
- Strategy for sizing and operating PV water electrolysis systems based on a monthly correlation, compliant with European green hydrogen certification; focus on grid-connected solutions.
- Assessment of the impact of PV layouts on the levelized cost of hydrogen (LCOH) and the role of grid interactions in system performance.

Methodology

- According to European regulations, hydrogen produced by 31. December 2029, is to be produced in the same calendar month as the renewable electricity from the PPA or from a new storage facility directly connected to the renewable generator or electrolyser.
- The hydrogen produced is considered green, even if energy is exchanged with the electricity grid during the calendar month.
- Parameter $r_{pv/el}$: ratio between the nominal power (STC) of the PV system and the nominal power of the electrolyzer.

$$r_{pv/el} = \frac{PV capacity}{El\ capacity}$$

- The value of that maximizes the utilization of PV power while satisfying the energy balance condition for monthly time correlation depends on the monthly PV energy production and the number of available hours in each month.
- LCOH is used as an economic metric to compare different hydrogen production strategies.

$$LCOH = \frac{\sum\ Cost}{\sum\ Hydrogen\ production}$$

- To be economically attractive, green hydrogen must have costs compatible with those that potential off-takers are willing to pay. Maximizing hydrogen production while minimizing the cost of the system, means providing the lowest LCOH is crucial. Therefore, the optimal combination of sizes for PV-electrolyzer system is investigated to yield the lowest LCOH.
- A key metric used in this study is the electrolyzer utilization factor U_{EL}:

$$U_{EL} = \frac{\text{Electricity consumed by electrolyzer}}{\text{Total electricity produced by PV}}$$

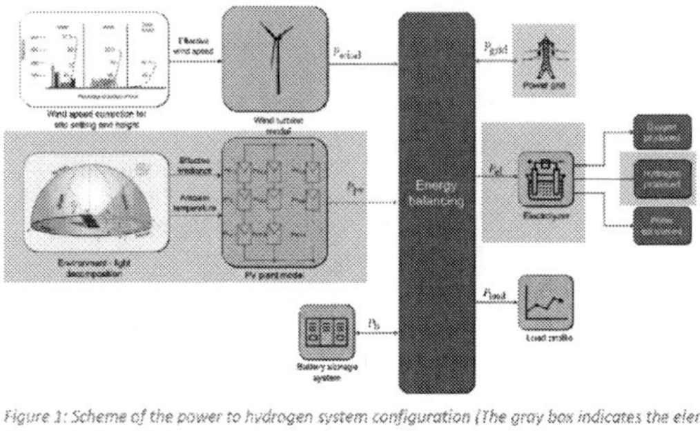

Figure 1: Scheme of the power to hydrogen system configuration (The gray box indicates the elements we focus on in this article.)

Case study

- Green hydrogen production in Sombor, Serbia by hourly simulations using PVGIS TMY data
- Electrolyzer size: 1000 kW, efficiency curve
- Bifacial PV modules (bifaciality factor = 0.8) and monofacial PV modules, nominal power at STC = 600 W

Results and discussion

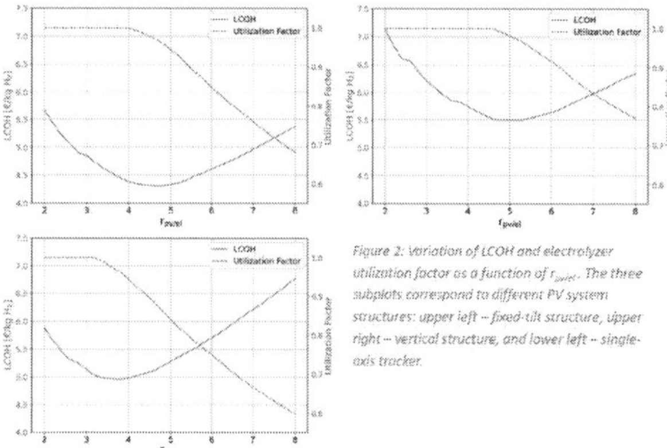

Figure 2: Variation of LCOH and electrolyzer utilization factor as a function of $r_{pv/el}$. The three subplots correspond to different PV system structures: upper left – fixed-tilt structure, upper right – vertical structure, and lower left – single-axis tracker.

- The minimum U_{EL} ratio was determined to be approximately 4 for the fixed-tilt structure. According to the methodology, this value is selected as optimal $r_{pv/el}$ to ensure no PV energy is clipped throughout the year.
- As the ratio $r_{pv/el}$ increases, the system becomes more self-sufficient.
- Beyond an optimal point, the LCOH begins to rise again. This is because a very high $r_{pv/el}$ implies a large investment in PV capacity that is not fully utilized, as the electrolyzer size remains fixed.
- The optimal $r_{pv/el}$ for fixed-tilt structure that minimizes the LCOH is close to 4.6 which is close to the ratio determined by the energy balance methodology equal to 4.
- This alignment demonstrates that sizing the system to avoid PV energy clipping based on a monthly balance is not only compliant with regulations but is also an economically sound strategy.

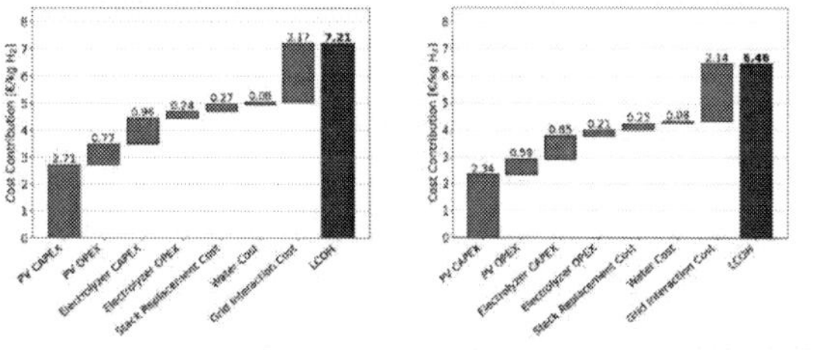

Figure 3: Cost components contributing to the LCOH for tracker structure with $r_{pv/el}$ = 3.6 (left) and for fixed-tilt structure with $r_{pv/el}$ = 4.6 (right). In this case, the PV system interacts with the grid in a monthly correlation with electricity sale price of 6 ¢/kWh and electricity purchase price of 10 ¢/kWh.

- Grid interaction cost impacts on LCOH with the cost contribution of 2.14 €/kg H_2 for fixed-tilt structure and 2.17 €/kg H_2 for single-axis tracker structure, and stands after the PV CAPEX cost.

Conclusions and outlook

- Proposes a sizing methodology for PV-hydrogen systems that meets current EU green hydrogen certification requirements.
- Techno-economic analysis shows by this energy-balance approach that sizing ratio ($r_{pv/el}$) closely matches the ratio that minimizes LCOH.
- Future work: develop and integrate estimation and control algorithms to manage PV-electrolyzer-grid energy flows during operation (out of scope of this study).

ACKNOWLEDGMENT

The work in the "HyDS" project is funded by the Federal Ministry of Education and Research (grant number: 03SF0697B). We thank the project partners of Leipziger Energiegesellschaft mbH & Co. KG, Mr. Andriy Baranochnyk and Mr. Fabian Severing as well as Dr. Klemens Ilse and Mr. Sebastian Schindler from Fraunhofer IMWS for supporting the work.

020427-001

Federal Ministry of Research, Technology and Space

HOCHSCHULE ANHALT University of Applied Sciences

RETROFITTING SHIPPING CONTAINERS INTO POSITIVE ENERGY BUS STATIONS WITH PHOTOVOLTAIC LVDC MICROGRIDS FOR SUSTAINABLE TRANSPORT IN RENEWABLE RESOURCE-RICH, HARSH ENVIRONMENTS

Mohammad Nazififard [1], Erwin Franquet [1], Ahmad Sedaghat [2], Mohammad Salem [3], Mohammad Farhat [4]
[1] Université Côte d'Azur, Polytech'Lab, France
[2] Dep. of Mechanical Engineering, College of Engineering, Australian University, West Mishref, Safat 13015, Kuwait [3] Dep. of Civil Engineering, College of Engineering, Australian University, West Mishref, Safat 13015, Kuwait
[4] Dep. of Electrical and Electronics Engineering, College of Engineering, Australian University, West Mishref, Safat 13015, Kuwait
mohammad.nazififard@univ-cotedazur.fr erwin.franquet@univ-cotedazur.fr a.sedaghat@au.edu.kw msalem@au.edu.kw m.farhat@au.edu.kw

ABSTRACT: This study evaluates the performance of a stand-alone photovoltaic (PV) system designed to power a bus stop constructed from recycled shipping containers under Kuwait's hot and arid climate conditions. The design aims to reduce construction costs and promote environmental sustainability through the implementation of a positive energy building. The system operates independently from the municipal grid, with all generated energy stored in batteries to ensure complete energy autonomy. Energy consumption was simulated using DesignBuilder software, assuming an average occupancy of two people. The station's annual energy demand was estimated at approximately 3660.1 kWh. The PV system comprises four fixed 670 W panels, installed at a 29° tilt angle and oriented south to optimize solar energy capture. Energy storage is provided by a 36 V lead-acid battery bank with a total capacity of 3671 Ah. PVsyst simulation results indicate that the system can generate approximately 4494.82 kWh annually, with 3385.33 kWh delivered to the useful load—covering about 92.5% of the station's total energy demand. This demonstrates a high level of energy self-sufficiency and significantly reduces dependence on external power sources. However, around 895.75 kWh per year (19.27% of the generated energy) is lost, primarily due to storage limitations and a temporal mismatch between energy generation and consumption. This excess energy could be utilized for supplementary applications, such as charging electric vehicles. Installing EV charging stations near bus stops offers a practical and sustainable solution to enhance overall system efficiency and environmental benefits.
Keywords: Energy storage, EV charging, Renewable energy, clean transportation, Sustainable cities, Sustainable mobility, Photovoltaic charging station.

1 INTRODUCTION

Green environmental policies aimed at reducing carbon emissions from energy sources are currently being implemented worldwide. Cities play a critical role in mitigating energy consumption and carbon dioxide emissions. Accordingly, the European Council's 2030 Climate and Energy Framework sets a target to increase the share of renewable energy to at least 27% of total energy consumption [1]. Similarly, the United Nations' 2030 Agenda for Sustainable Development includes 17 Sustainable Development Goals (SDGs), two of which directly support energy efficiency and sustainable urbanization: SDG 7 (Affordable and Clean Energy) and SDG 11 (Sustainable Cities and Communities) [2].

European Union (EU) member states have introduced several measures to reduce emissions from the energy sector. In December 2019, the European Union set a target to lower its net greenhouse gas emissions by a minimum of 55% by the year 2030, relative to 1990 levels, and to become climate-neutral by 2050 [3], [4]. The EU's updated development strategy includes actions to lower CO_2 emissions, transform transport and industrial sectors, reduce emissions from buildings, overhaul food production systems, and protect biodiversity [5].

At the international level, agreements such as the Kyoto Protocol, the Paris Agreement, and more recent initiatives like the Glasgow Climate Pact and the outcomes of COP28 emphasize the reduction of greenhouse gas emissions. These accords promote the transition to cleaner energy technologies and the development of sustainable transport systems to address the escalating climate crisis. Key challenges in promoting sustainable mobility include improving public transportation services, integrating urban planning, encouraging shared mobility, and promoting cycling. These efforts aim to reduce the growing reliance on private vehicles in cities worldwide [6], [7].

Public transportation, including buses, trains, and trams, is a vital component of sustainable urban mobility [8]. It plays a key role in reducing both traffic congestion and environmental pollution. Developing clean and efficient transit networks is essential for smart and sustainable urban planning [9]. However, urban sprawl has increased dependence on private vehicles [10]. Consequently, there is an urgent need to develop modern, clean, and intelligent public transit systems to achieve environmental and social sustainability goals.

The transportation sector is currently the fastest-growing contributor to energy consumption and greenhouse gas emissions [11]. Primary energy sources used in electricity generation and transport account for approximately 60% of global energy use. Integrating renewable energy sources into the transport sector presents a significant opportunity to transition to a low-carbon energy system [12] [13]. In cities such as Kuwait, where traffic congestion is severe, public transportation can reduce private vehicle use, alleviate traffic density, and improve the environment [14]. One promising strategy is to increase the share of renewable energy in the electricity mix [15]. Among renewable technologies, photovoltaic (PV) systems are considered one of the most viable options for achieving a carbon-neutral energy sector [16] [17]. PV applications have expanded significantly in urban environments, now supporting residential power and heating needs. Additional uses include street lighting, electric vehicle (EV) charging stations, digital signage, traffic signals, and solar-powered infrastructure.

However, not all urban areas are suitable for solar panel installations [18], [19]. Urban planners and policymakers must therefore assess local solar potential to implement effective PV-based solutions [20]. While rooftop and façade solar potential have been widely studied, exploring unconventional urban surfaces for PV deployment represents a new frontier in urban energy research. Future efforts should focus on expanding usable surface areas for solar energy systems. Ground-mounted PV (GPV), rooftop PV (RPV), and building-integrated PV (BIPV) have been extensively analyzed. The next step is to design solar-oriented infrastructure as part of holistic urban energy systems.

Bus stops, essential infrastructure in public transport systems, can benefit significantly from solar-powered technologies that enhance both service and quality of life. This supports broader smart city objectives. Traditional bus stops typically provide only basic shelter from weather conditions; however, their functionality can be expanded to include PV-powered amenities such as internet connectivity, device charging stations, digital advertising displays, and real-time information screens [21].

Improved lighting is another opportunity. Adequate illumination enhances passenger safety during nighttime hours [22]. While conventional bus stop lighting systems are typically grid-connected, solar-powered lighting is a viable alternative in areas with high solar exposure. Furthermore, weather-protected bus stop designs have been shown to increase public transport use by providing comfort and protection in adverse climates [23]. In extreme climates, enclosed bus stops have been proposed as a way to further promote public transport usage. When integrated with clean energy systems, such designs can reduce emissions by supplying power and heat sustainably [24]. Despite advances in geospatial tools and energy modeling, the effective integration of renewable energy into public infrastructure such as bus stops remains limited in many urban areas. This study aims to address this gap by evaluating solar-powered solutions specifically for bus stop infrastructure.

In response to growing energy demands in the transport sector and the need for sustainable urban systems, this study assesses the feasibility of converting recycled shipping containers into energy-positive bus stops in regions with high solar potential and harsh climates. These bus stops are designed to operate independently from the main grid by utilizing DC microgrids powered by photovoltaic systems [25], [26]. Prefabricated shipping containers offer several advantages, including reduced construction costs and rapid deployment of clean, smart infrastructure. The main objectives of this study are to:

- Assess the feasibility of using recycled shipping containers for constructing bus stops suitable for extreme weather conditions.
- Design a photovoltaic system and low-voltage DC (LVDC) infrastructure capable of supporting lighting, heating, mobile device charging, and EV charging.
- Analyze the solar potential of public spaces and identify optimal locations for implementation based on technical and climatic factors.

2 LITERATURE REVIEW

Sedaghat et al. [27] evaluated off-grid PVsystems for cooling portable cabins in Kuwait's extreme heat, achieving a 24.1% reduction in energy use and cutting CO_2 emissions by 129.4 kg over nine months. Similarly, Ding et al. [28] assessed solar-powered bus parking lots in Tianjin, China, integrating drone imaging and solar modeling tools. Their system could power 50% of the electric bus fleet and reduce CO_2, SO_2, and NO_x emissions.

AlKheder et al. [14], [29] investigated public transportation optimization in Kuwait, showing that increased bus use could reduce emissions by up to 46%, and numerical models improved bus scheduling to enhance efficiency and service quality.

Vossos et al. [30] examined DC distribution in U.S. homes with PV systems, showing energy savings of up to 14% with battery storage. Building on this, Chauhan et al. [31] demonstrated that DC microgrids reduce energy consumption and conversion losses compared to AC systems due to fewer conversion stages. Similarly, Gerber et al. [32] found DC systems in commercial buildings saved up to 18% energy under optimal conditions. Gelani et al. [33] further reported that DC systems outperform AC systems, especially during high load periods, due to improved converter performance.

In tropical regions, Dahiru and Tan [34] optimized grid-connected nanogrids combining renewables and storage, achieving high renewable supply and significant greenhouse gas reductions. Ammous et al. [35] highlighted the efficiency advantage of LVDC systems over conventional PV architectures, attributing gains to reduced conversion stages. Villacorta et al. [36] confirmed these benefits through an LVDC system at the Technical University of Ecuador, which lowered energy losses via DC-to-DC converters.

Alsaedi et al. [37] and Ammous et al. [38] independently reported LVDC systems offer 15–20% higher efficiency than AC systems in residential PV applications, emphasizing local consumption and fewer conversion steps as key factors. Finally, Ollas et al. [39] showed that DC distribution in a Swedish home reduced annual energy losses by 15.8% compared to AC systems with PV and battery storage, reinforcing the superior efficiency of DC systems.

Al-Thani et al. [40] provided a comprehensive review of renewable energy systems integrated with electric vehicle (EV) charging infrastructure in urban environments. Their work emphasizes the need to reduce emissions from combustion vehicles and improve urban air quality. The study shows that EV charging stations can operate either on-grid or off-grid using sources such as solar, wind, hydropower, and alternative carriers like hydrogen and ammonia. Supplementary energy storage, particularly batteries, is essential to manage fluctuations in renewable generation. The results indicate that integrating EVs with renewable energy sources can reduce carbon emissions, stabilize energy supply, and increase user adoption of green vehicles. However, the study also highlights challenges, including the need for advanced smart charging algorithms and improved storage systems.

Barman et al. [41] analyzed global charging infrastructure, energy storage technologies, smart grids, and industrial strategies to assess the role of renewable energy in EV charging. Their study reviewed international experiences with solar, wind, and hydropower as energy sources for EV charging. The findings underscore the importance of integrating smart charging with renewables to achieve sustainable transportation. This integration reduces costs and improves efficiency through load management and time-based tariffs. However, challenges remain, such as the need for infrastructure standardization, cybersecurity, and stronger governmental support through financial and educational incentives.

Cavalcante et al. [42] proposed a novel framework for using surplus solar energy from photovoltaic systems to charge EVs, introducing a decentralized energy exchange model between institutions and vehicle owners via blockchain technology. Their case study, conducted at an educational institution in Portugal, demonstrated that a 724 kW-peak PV system could charge more than 3,213 vehicles annually and generate over €45,000 in revenue. The system achieved a payback period of approximately two years and an internal rate of return of 61%, along with a 20% reduction in greenhouse gas emissions compared to conventional grid charging. Despite these benefits, the study identified challenges related to the scalability of blockchain, its energy consumption, the variability of solar energy, and the lack of regulatory frameworks for decentralized energy markets.

3 METHODOLOGY

3.1 Case study

This study evaluates the potential of converting a 20-foot SCF decommissioned shipping container into a photovoltaic-powered, positive-energy bus station in Kuwait through a series of systematic steps addressing both functional design and environmental considerations. First, the functional requirements of the bus station in Kuwait's hot and dry climate are determined, taking into account climatic challenges and passenger needs. The station must provide shelter for waiting passengers, offering adequate seating and protection from solar radiation as well as extreme hot and cold weather. To achieve this, structural modifications are made to the shipping container, including the installation of a window and a transparent door on the container side (Fig. 1-a). Additionally, to maintain interior comfort under Kuwait's extreme temperatures, an air conditioning system is installed. A model was developed to predict the energy performance of the bus station and validated with experimental data from a prototype. After validation, simulations were conducted under average passenger occupancy conditions to evaluate the station's net-zero energy performance and assess its feasibility at the city scale [44].

DesignBuilder software was used to model the station's energy load. The software estimates annual energy demand by accounting for the building's thermal characteristics, ventilation, lighting, and internal equipment. Energy consumption was simulated based on actual passenger occupancy data. Previous studies report an average occupancy of 1.8 passengers in the morning and 1.7 in the afternoon, indicating a relatively uniform distribution throughout the day. For modeling purposes, the average occupancy was rounded to two passengers to define a consistent daily usage pattern in DesignBuilder [29], [45].

This consumption scenario was used to simulate daily energy use, as shown in Figure 1-b. Based on this model, the station's total annual energy consumption was calculated to be 3,660.1 kWh. In the next step, the shipping container was converted into the bus station. An innovative photovoltaic low-voltage direct current (LVDC) microgrid system was designed and implemented to supply the required electricity.

The PV system consists of four 670W PV module installed on the container's roof. The PV panels are mounted at a tilt angle of 29° and oriented due to maximize solar radiation capture. The system is configured as a stand-alone unit, with no connection to the national electricity grid. All of the station's energy needs are supplied exclusively through solar power generation and on-site energy storage. The fabricated bus station is shown in Figure 1-c.

This study proposes an innovative sustainable solution for public transportation in Kuwait by transforming of decommissioned shipping containers into positive energy bus stations. A comparison between the energy consumption across different scenarios and the energy generation from the PV LVDC microgrid is performed to assess the bus station's potential for energy self-sufficiency and its ability to generate surplus energy for return to the grid (Fig. 2).

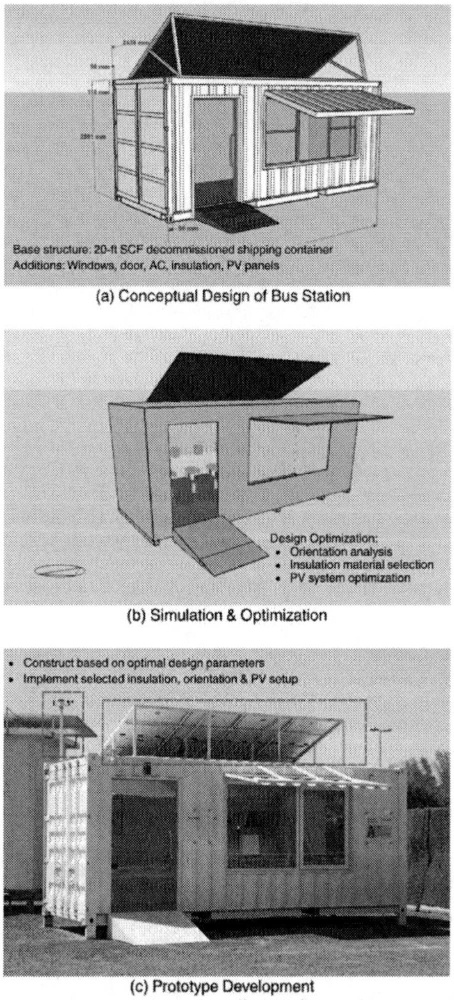

(c) Prototype Development

Figure 1: (a) Schematic of a 20-foot solar-powered, ventilated bus station with PV panels installed on the roof; (b) model of the bus station used for energy simulations; (c) photograph of the constructed bus station.

3.2 Validation

According to ASHRAE Standard 55-2023, the appropriate indoor temperature range for light activities and typical clothing levels is generally between 20 °C and 26 °C. However, this range may vary slightly depending on clothing insulation and the metabolic rate of individuals [46]. Under summer conditions, thermal comfort is typically defined within a narrower range of 23 °C to 26 °C [47]. Additionally, the recommended relative humidity range for maintaining comfort is between 30% and 60% [48]. To improve simulation accuracy, real weather data were collected from a weather station installed at the bus stop. These data include parameters such as dry-bulb temperature, dew point temperature, relative humidity, wind speed and direction, total horizontal solar radiation, and other relevant variables [49]. This dataset replaced the default EPW (EnergyPlus Weather) file, which typically provides 10-year average values that may not accurately reflect site-specific conditions. Using real-time data significantly reduces simulation errors and aligns the output more closely with actual performance. Figure 2 presents the hourly energy consumption pattern of the bus stop from August 4 to 18, 2025. The simulation results for the base scenario (without occupants) are compared with measured data, providing a clear assessment of model performance under standard operating conditions. The results show strong agreement between the simulation and experimental data, validating the modeling approach.

Figure 3 further demonstrates this agreement by comparing simulated and measured thermal comfort conditions inside the bus stop during the same period. Figure 4 presents the hourly energy consumption patterns at the bus station between August 4 and August 18, 2025, comparing simulated results with measured data under the first occupancy scenario. This comparison offers insight into model performance under baseline operating conditions. The simulation results closely match the empirical data, validating the modeling approach. The simulation's accuracy was evaluated using various statistical performance indicators, as presented in Table I. A Mean Bias Error (MBE) of −0.0187 kWh and a Normalized MBE of −1.89% suggest a slight underestimation of energy consumption. The coefficient of determination (R^2) is 0.9507, indicating that the model accounts for about 95.07% of the variation in the observed data. Furthermore, the Coefficient of Variation of the Root Mean Square Error (CV(RMSE)) is 11.78%, which complies with the acceptable limits outlined in ASHRAE guidelines [50].

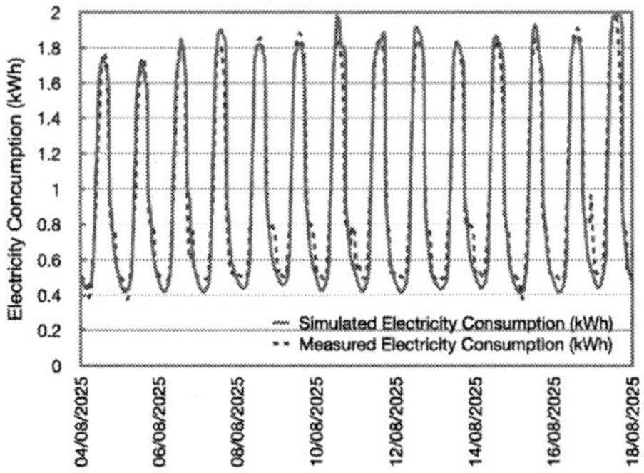

Figure 2: The hourly energy consumption patterns at the bus station from August 4 to August 18, 2025.

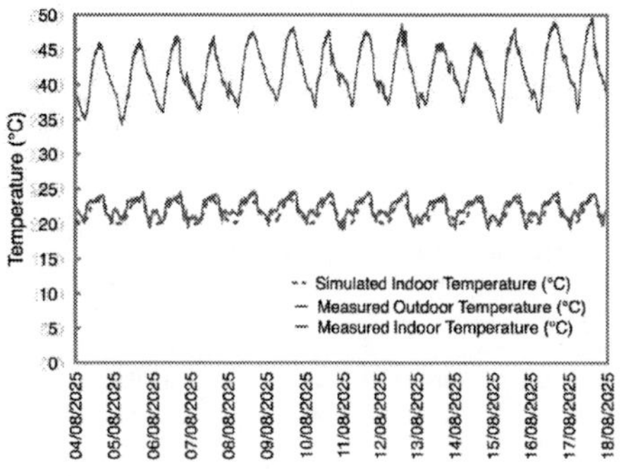

Figure 3: Comparison of simulated comfort temperatures and measured numbers.

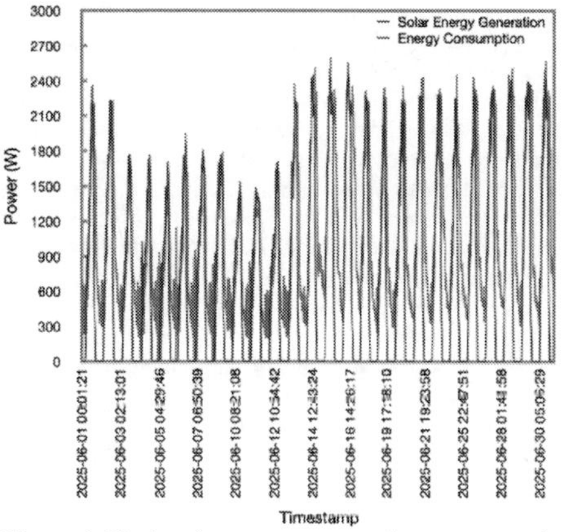

Figure 4: The hourly energy consumption patterns at the bus station from August 4 to August 18, 2025.

Table I: Model Evaluation Metrics

Metric	Value
R^2 Score	0.9629
Adjusted R^2	0.9627
MAE	0.0728
MSE	0.0102
RMSE	0.1012

4 RESULTS

The simulated consumption profile was exported as average power (kW) and imported into PVsyst, where it served as the user-defined load. The system's total annual energy consumption was estimated at 3,660.1 kWh. The PV system configuration includes four south-facing fixed PV modules rated at 670 W each, installed at a tilt angle of 29° to optimize year-round solar capture. Energy storage is provided by a 36 V lead-acid battery bank with a total capacity of 3,671 Ah. PVsyst simulation results indicate that the system can generate approximately 4,494.82 kWh per year. Of this, 3,385.33 kWh per year is delivered as useful energy to the load, covering approximately 92.49% of the bus stop's annual energy demand. This demonstrates a high degree of energy self-sufficiency and significantly reduces reliance on external power sources. However, not

10.4229/EUPVSEC2025/4DV.1.76

all generated energy is utilized. Approximately 895.75 kWh per year, or 19.27% of the available energy, is lost primarily due to battery storage limitations and temporal mismatches between energy generation and consumption. Additionally, 274.76 kWh per year of energy demand remains unmet, referred to as "Missing Energy," which indicates that auxiliary sources may be necessary to ensure continuous operation during peak demand periods.

Key performance indicators further validate system efficiency. The specific yield was calculated as 1,263 kWh/kWp/year, reflecting favorable performance under Kuwait's solar irradiance conditions [49]. The performance ratio (PR) was 61.42%, indicating good operational efficiency under real environmental conditions. Figure 5 presents the system's loss diagram, identifying various sources of energy loss. The most significant loss is due to unused energy (19.27%), followed by thermal losses (10.75%), which highlight the impact of Kuwait's high ambient temperatures. Other losses include inverter inefficiencies (4.05%), ohmic losses in cabling (1.60%), and module mismatch losses (2%). Battery performance, expressed as state of charge (SOC), is illustrated in Figure 6. The SOC profile reveals a seasonal pattern: during winter and early spring, energy production exceeds demand, resulting in fully charged batteries and an energy surplus. Conversely, during the summer months (June to September), high ambient temperatures reduce PV efficiency while demand increases due to cooling and ventilation loads. This leads to significant battery discharge and lower SOC levels, contributing to the recorded "Missing Energy" and highlighting a critical challenge in maintaining a stable energy supply during peak demand periods. Overall, the PVsyst simulations confirm that the standalone PV system is effective, achieving 92.49% energy self-sufficiency for the bus stop. However, two major challenges remain: performance degradation due to high temperatures and energy wastage caused by limited battery capacity. The analysis revealed that a significant portion of the energy generated, 895.75 kWh per year, remains unused because the batteries become fully charged, particularly during peak solar periods. This surplus energy offers an opportunity for alternative applications. One promising solution is to redirect the excess energy toward charging electric vehicles (EVs) [42], [41]. Given the bus stop's location, installing one or more EV charging stations near the PV array would be a practical and sustainable enhancement, further increasing the system's utility and environmental benefits. The results of this study align with previous research emphasizing the importance of utilizing renewable energy sources to minimize carbon emissions and enhance energy sustainability. Consistent with the findings of Al-Thani [40] and Barman [41], this study demonstrates that integrating energy storage systems with renewable sources can improve energy self-sufficiency and enable the use of surplus energy for charging electric vehicles. Similarly, Cavalcante [42] reported that surplus energy generated by photovoltaic systems provides significant economic and environmental benefits. In agreement with Jain and Bhullar [43], the findings highlight the need to optimize system performance and effectively manage energy storage to maintain overall efficiency and sustainability. Furthermore, the operational challenges identified in this study, including energy loss, limited battery capacity, and reduced photovoltaic performance under high temperatures, correspond to concerns raised in earlier research.

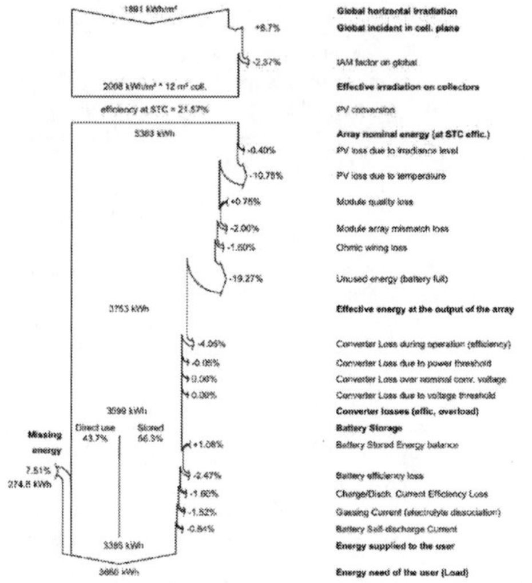

Figure 5: Energy loss diagram.

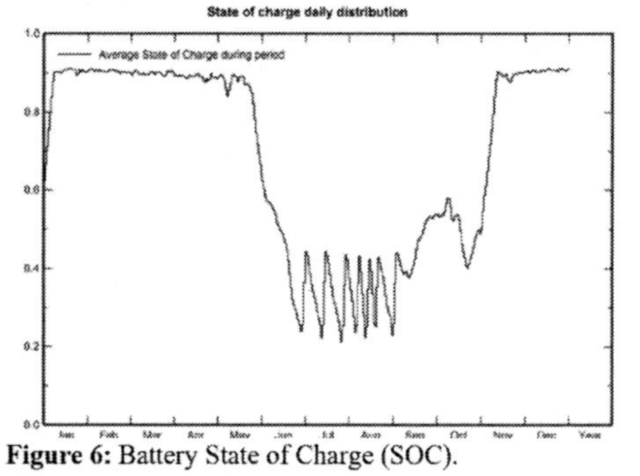

Figure 6: Battery State of Charge (SOC).

5 CONCLUTION

This study investigates the feasibility of converting a recycled shipping container into a positive energy bus stop suitable for the hot and arid climate of Kuwait. The station's energy demand was simulated using DesignBuilder software, based on actual passenger occupancy patterns. Subsequently, the performance of a stand-alone PV system was evaluated using PVsyst software. Simulation results indicate that the PV system can meet over 92% of the station's annual energy demand. However, approximately 895.8 kWh per year of the generated energy remains unused due to storage limitations and a mismatch between energy production and load demand.

Conversely, only 274.8 kWh per year of the load is left unmet, demonstrating the high efficiency and reliability of the system in stand-alone operation. These findings suggest that solar-powered bus stops offer a viable and sustainable solution for urban public transport infrastructure. In addition to meeting internal energy needs, the excess energy can be utilized for ancillary applications like charging electric vehicles, thereby contributing to the development of clean and integrated transportation systems.

Declaration of AI-assisted technologies in the writing process
The authors used AI-assisted English editing tools to improve readability and language, and they reviewed and revised the manuscript, taking full responsibility for the final version.

6 REFERENCES

[1] Eurostat, *Sustainable development in the European Union: Monitoring report on progress towards the SDGs in an EU context*. Publications office of the European Union, 2020.

[2] "SDGs: Sustainable Development Knowledge Platform. Available online: https://sustainabledevelopment.un.org/sdgs (accessed on 15 July 2024)."

[3] "EU's Plan for a Green Transition—Consilium. Available online: https://www.consilium.europa.eu/en/policies/green-deal/eu-plan-for-a-green-transition/ (accessed on 15 July 2025)."

[4] "A European Green Deal | European Commission. Available online: https://ec.europa.eu/info/strategy/priorities-2019-2024/european-green-deal_en (accessed on 15 July 2025)."

[5] G. Climate, "Decision-/CMA.3 Glasgow Climate Pact." [Online]. Available: https://www.ipcc.ch/report/ar6/wg1/.

[6] J. Vepsäläinen, K. Kivekäs, K. Otto, A. Lajunen, and K. Tammi, "Development and validation of energy demand uncertainty model for electric city buses," *Transp Res D Transp Environ*, vol. 63, pp. 347–361, Aug. 2018.

[7] M. Rupp, N. Handschuh, C. Rieke, and I. Kuperjans, "Contribution of country-specific electricity mix and charging time to environmental impact of battery electric vehicles: A case study of electric buses in Germany," *Appl Energy*, vol. 237, pp. 618–634, Mar. 2019.

[8] R. Goodspeed, T. Xie, T. R. Dillahunt, and J. Lustig, "An alternative to slow transit, drunk driving, and walking in bad weather: An exploratory study of ridesourcing mode choice and demand," *J Transp Geogr*, vol. 79, p. 102481, 2019.

[9] I. Lopez-Carreiro and A. Monzon, "Evaluating sustainability and innovation of mobility patterns in Spanish cities. Analysis by size and urban typology," *Sustain Cities Soc*, vol. 38, pp. 684–696, 2018.

[10] S. C. Kwan, R. Sutan, and J. H. Hashim, "Trip characteristics as the determinants of intention to shift to rail transport among private motor vehicle users in Kuala Lumpur, Malaysia," *Sustain Cities Soc*, vol. 36, pp. 319–326, 2018.

[11] R. Sims *et al.*, "IPCC Fifth Assessment Report (AR5)-Chapter 8: Transport," 2014.

[12] S. A. Sadat and M. Nazififard, "Introducing a Novel Hybrid Mobile Energy Storage System for Vulnerable Community Resilience Support," *Proceedings - 2020 6th International Conference on Electric Power and Energy Conversion Systems, EPECS 2020*, pp. 46–51, Oct. 2020.

[13] L. G. González, D. Cordero-Moreno, and J. L. Espinoza, "Public transportation with electric traction: Experiences and challenges in an Andean city," *Renewable and Sustainable Energy Reviews*, vol. 141, p. 110768, May 2021.

[14] S. AlKheder, "Promoting public transport as a strategy to reduce GHG emissions from private vehicles in Kuwait," *Environmental Challenges*, vol. 3, p. 100075, 2021.

[15] M. A. Green, "How did solar cells get so cheap?," *Joule*, vol. 3, no. 3, pp. 631–633, 2019.

[16] S. Zeynali and M. Nazififard, "Integrating Photovoltaic Systems into Urban Infrastructure: A Case Study of Tehran International Tower," *2024 11th Iranian Conference on Renewable Energy and Distribution Generation, ICREDG 2024*, 2024.

[17] M. Nazififard and E. Franquet, "Systematic analysis of roof-mounted photovoltaic systems for achieving net-zero energy in urban historic buildings in hot and arid climates: Potential and challenges," *Energy Build*, vol. 348, p. 116394, Dec. 2025.

[18] S. Ali Sadat, J. Faraji, M. Nazififard, and A. Ketabi, "The experimental analysis of dust deposition effect on solar photovoltaic panels in Iran's desert environment," *Sustainable Energy Technologies and Assessments*, vol. 47, Oct. 2021.

[19] M. Nazififard and N. Torabi, "Experimental Analysis of Dust Accumulation on the Panels of a Microgrid-Connected Photovlitaic System in an Arid Climate," *2023 13th Smart Grid Conference, SGC 2023*, 2023.

[20] T. Santos, N. Gomes, S. Freire, M. C. Brito, L. Santos, and J. A. Tenedório, "Applications of solar mapping in the urban environment," *Applied Geography*, vol. 51, pp. 48–57, 2014.

[21] T. Santos, K. Lobato, J. Rocha, and J. A. Tenedório, "Modeling Photovoltaic Potential for Bus Shelters on a City-Scale: A Case Study in Lisbon," *Applied Sciences*, vol. 10, no. 14, 2020.

[22] B. Kooi, "Security concerns at hot-spot bus stop locations," *Journal of Applied Security Research*, vol. 10, no. 3, pp. 277–307, 2015.

[23] Q. Miao, E. W. Welch, and P. S. Sriraj, "Extreme weather, public transport ridership and moderating effect of bus stop shelters," *J Transp Geogr*, vol. 74, pp. 125–133, 2019.

[24] D. A. Hensher, "Climate change, enhanced greenhouse gas emissions and passenger transport–What can we do to make a difference?," *Transp Res D Transp Environ*, vol. 13, no. 2, pp. 95–111, 2008.

[25] A. Imanloozadeh, M. Nazififard, and S. A. Sadat, "A new stochastic optimal smart residential energy hub management system for desert environment," *Int J Energy Res*, vol. 45, no. 13, pp. 18957–18980, Oct. 2021.

[26] A. Imanloozadeh, M. Nazififard, and H. Hashemi-Dezaki, "Optimal technoeconomic reliability-oriented design of islanded multicarrier microgrids with electrical and hydrogen energy storage systems considering emission concerns," *Energy Sci Eng*, vol. 12, no. 6, pp. 2702–2745, Jun. 2024.

[27] A. Sedaghat *et al.*, "Integrating solar PV systems for energy efficiency in portable cabins: A case study in Kuwait," *Solar Energy*, vol. 277, p. 112715, 2024.

10.4229/EUPVSEC2025/4DV.1.76

[28] X. Ding, Z. Zhang, W. Zhang, X. Yue, and Y. Zhang, "Evaluation of the energy-economic-environment potential of urban-scale photovoltaic bus parking lots: The case of Tianjin, China," *J Clean Prod*, vol. 425, p. 138983, 2023.

[29] S. AlKheder, F. AlRukaibi, and A. Zaqzouq, "Optimal bus frequency for Kuwait public transportation company: A cost view," *Sustain Cities Soc*, vol. 41, pp. 312–319, 2018.

[30] V. Vossos, K. Garbesi, and H. Shen, "Energy savings from direct-DC in U.S. residential buildings," *Energy Build*, vol. 68, no. PARTA, pp. 223–231, Jan. 2014.

[31] R. Chauhan, F. Gonzalez-Longatt, B. S. Rajpurohit, and S. Singh, "DC Microgrid in Residential Building," 2018, pp. 367–387.

[32] D. L. Gerber, V. Vossos, W. Feng, C. Marnay, B. Nordman, and R. Brown, "A simulation-based efficiency comparison of AC and DC power distribution networks in commercial buildings," *Appl Energy*, vol. 210, pp. 1167–1187, Jan. 2018,

[33] H. E. Gelani, F. Dastgeer, K. Siraj, M. Nasir, K. A. K. Niazi, and Y. Yang, "Efficiency Comparison of AC and DC Distribution Networks for Modern Residential Localities," *Applied Sciences*, vol. 9, no. 3, 2019.

[34] A. T. Dahiru and C. W. Tan, "Optimal sizing and techno-economic analysis of grid-connected nanogrid for tropical climates of the Savannah," *Sustain Cities Soc*, vol. 52, p. 101824, Jan. 2020.

[35] A. Ammous, A. Assaedi, A. Alahdal, and K. Ammous, "Energy efficiency of a novel low voltage direct current supply for the future building," *Int J Energy Res*, vol. 45, May 2021.

[36] A. Rios Villacorta, J. Guamán-Molina, F. Mayorga, and D. Taipe, "Platform of Intelligent Control of Indoor Lighting integrated into LVDC Distribution System: A Case Study in the Technical University of Ambato," *Technology and Economics of Smart Grids and Sustainable Energy*, vol. 7, p. 26, Jul. 2022.

[37] A. Alsaedi, F. Alharbi, A. Alahdal, A. Alahmadi, A. Ammous, and K. Ammous, "Low Voltage Direct Current Supplies Concept for Residential Applications," *Energy Exploration & Exploitation*, vol. 40, p. 014459872110728, May 2022.

[38] A. Ammous, A. Alsaedi, A. Alahmadi, F. Alharbi, and K. Ammous, "Efficiency Performances of LVDC Supplies for Residential Building," *Computer Systems Science and Engineering*, vol. 45, pp. 2171–2186, Nov. 2022.

[39] P. Ollas, T. Thiringer, M. Persson, and C. Markusson, "Energy Loss Savings Using Direct Current Distribution in a Residential Building with Solar Photovoltaic and Battery Storage," *Energies (Basel)*, vol. 16, no. 3, 2023.

[40] H. Al-Thani, M. Koç, R. J. Isaifan, and Y. Bicer, "A Review of the Integrated Renewable Energy Systems for Sustainable Urban Mobility," *Sustainability*, vol. 14, no. 17, 2022.

[41] P. Barman *et al.*, "Renewable energy integration with electric vehicle technology: A review of the existing smart charging approaches," *Renewable and Sustainable Energy Reviews*, vol. 183, p. 113518, 2023.

[42] I. Cavalcante *et al.*, "Electric Vehicles Charging Using Photovoltaic Energy Surplus: A Framework Based on Blockchain," *Energies (Basel)*, vol. 16, no. 6, 2023.

[43] A. Jain and S. Bhullar, "Operating modes of grid integrated PV-solar based electric vehicle charging system- a comprehensive review," *e-Prime - Advances in Electrical Engineering, Electronics and Energy*, vol. 8, p. 100519, 2024.

[44] M. Nazififard and S. Zeynali, "Analysis of Photovoltaic Panel Integration for Achieving Net-Zero Energy in French Residential Retrofits in a Mediterranean Climate," *E3S Web of Conferences*, vol. 545, p. 02006, Jul. 2024.

[45] F. AlRukaibi and S. AlKheder, "Optimization of bus stop stations in Kuwait," *Sustain Cities Soc*, vol. 44, pp. 726–738, 2019.

[46] "ASHRAE 55-2023".

[47] M. Koheji, "On Cooling and Comfort: The Engineering of Thermal Spaces in Bahrain," *Engineering Studies*, vol. 17, no. 1, pp. 30–50, Jan. 2025.

[48] Y. K. Kim, Y. Abdou, A. Abdou, and H. Altan, "Indoor Environmental Quality Assessment and Occupant Satisfaction: A Post-Occupancy Evaluation of a UAE University Office Building," *Buildings*, vol. 12, no. 7, 2022.

[49] N. Ghareeb *et al.*, "Integrating experimental and theoretical approaches for enhanced machine learning modeling of solar radiation," *Engineering Science and Technology, an International Journal*, vol. 70, p. 102156, Oct. 2025.

[50] R. and A.-C. E. (ASHRAE) American Society of Heating, "ASHRAE Guideline 14-2002: Measurement of Energy and Demand Savings," Jul. 2002.

COMPARATIVE STUDY OF SOLAR PV WATER PUMPING SYSTEMS IN INDIA: TRANSFORMING AGRICULTURE

Richa Parmar[1*], A. R. Saxena[2], Prashant Misra[1], Jai Prakash[1]
[1]National Institute of Solar Energy (NISE), Gurugram, India,
[2]National Institute of Technology (NIT), Delhi, India
Email: richa.parmar@nise.res.in

ABSTRACT: This paper discusses the design and testing of Solar PV Water Pumping Systems (SPVWPS) in India, highlighting the advantages of solar water pumps, technical challenges, and potential to improve crop yield with a strong focus on the positive impact of such systems on Indian farmers. Additionally, the paper explores different types of pumps, including helical, centrifugal, and reciprocating piston pumps, and provides detailed information of SPVWPS working principles as well as various components and performance characteristics. Furthermore, this paper provides insights into the test protocols for solar water pumps, specifically for Indian climatic conditions. The study concludes by evaluating the performance of various pump types and demonstrating how solar water pumps contribute to improving agricultural productivity and economic stability for Indian farmers.
Keywords: PV modules, Solar Water Pumping System, Pump Controllers, Battery, Storage, Irradiance.

1 INTRODUCTION

India's agricultural sector faces significant water scarcity, with farmers relying heavily on unreliable grid power or diesel-powered pumps [1]. Solar Photovoltaic (PV) water pumping systems offer a sustainable and cost-effective solution by harnessing abundant solar resources. SPVWPS are particularly suitable for remote and off grid locations, where conventional water pumping solutions are either unavailable or economically unviable. Recognizing their potential, Government of India has promoted solar water pumps through policies such as Pradhan Mantri Kisan Urja Suraksha evam Utthaan Mahabhiyan (PM-KUSUM) scheme [2]. More than 2,00,000 solar pumps have already been deployed nationwide, and the scheme targets 3 million installations by 2025. This large scale adoption is driven by declining PV costs, increasing subsidies with improved system efficiencies.

Global trends also highlight the competitiveness of SPVWPS technologies, showing the advances in module efficiency, pump controller technology and energy storage have made them viable even in regions with limited grid access [3], In India key challenges includes high upfront costs, lack of technical expertise and limited after sales support. However, with favourable policies, increasing subsidies, upskilling and the decreasing cost of solar panels, solar water pumps are becoming more accessible to farmers in India.

The present study evaluates the design, components and testing protocols of SPVWPS under Indian climatic conditions, comparative performance analysis of centrifugal, helical, and reciprocating piston pumps is conducted using standardized testing at National Institute of Solar Energy (NISE), with emphasis on efficiency, water output, seasonal variation and economic viability for agricultural applications.

2 METHODOLOGY

The performance evaluation of SPVWPS was conducted at National Institute of Solar Energy (NISE), Gurugram, India (28.26°N, 77.08°E). Based on five years of onsite data (2018-2023), the site records an average of approximately 300 sunny days annually. Peak solar irradiance values can reach up to 1000W/m^2, although such levels are typically sustained only for short durations and are more prominently observed during the winter season, reflecting the sesonal variabilty in solar resource availability.

2.1 System Components: The three major components used for SPVWPS are as follows:

2.1.1 Solar PV array with Module Mounting Structures (MMTS): Photovoltaic PV array converts solar energy into electrical energy (Figure 1). The most widely used panel types are monocrystalline and polycrystalline. Monocrystalline panels generally provide higher efficiency and longer life but are comparatively more expensive. Depending on pump size and irrigation requirements, the power output of PV arrays generally varies up to 9kWp.

***2.1.2 Motor Pump Set*:** Pump sets used in solar water pumping systems are mainly classified into two categories: surface and submersible pumps. Surface pumps are installed on the ground surface and are suitable for lifting water from shallow sources (up to ~ 7m), whereas submersible pumps are placed in the borewell and are more appropriate for deeper water tables, typically ranging from 10m to over 150m, depending on irrigation demand and site conditions

Figure 1: PV Array for Solar Water Pumps

Furthermore, Solar water pumps are classified into dynamic and positive displacement types. Dynamic pumps, primarily centrifugal (axial flow or radial flow),

10.4229/EUPVSEC2025/4DV.1.77

are widely used for irrigation due to their ability to deliver large volumes of water at low to medium heads. Positive displacement pumps include rotary, helical rotor and reciprocating pumps as shown in Figure 2. In addition, various motor technologies such as Brushless DC (BLDC), Switched Reluctance (SRM), and AC Induction Motors are integrated with pumps to operate the system efficiently and enhance overall performance under varying operating conditions.

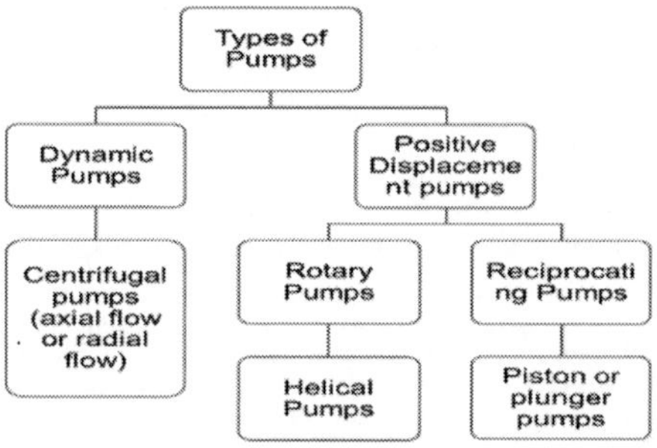

Figure 2: Types of Pumps

a) Centrifugal pumps: Centrifugal pumps are designed for continuous operation and are capable of delivering high flow rates, making them suitable for irrigation across larger-scale land holdings as shown in Figure 3. In this study, submersible type of centrifugal pump performance was evaluated under varying operating conditions. While centrifugal pumps offer advantages in terms of simplicity, cost-effectiveness, and ease of maintenance, their efficiency generally decreases when operating at higher heads or under low-flow conditions.

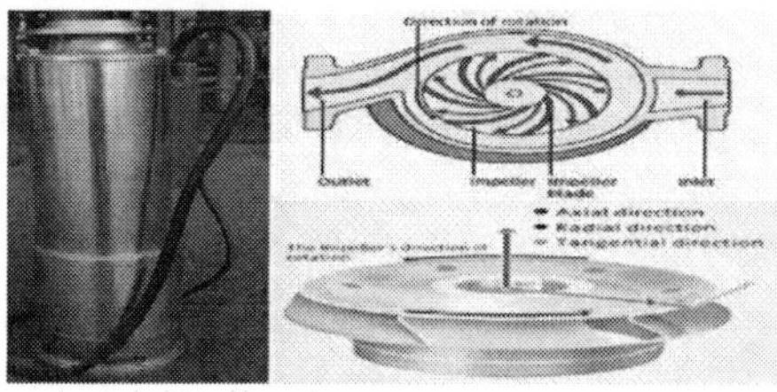

Figure 3: Centrifugal Solar Water Pump and Impeller mechanism

[1]**b) Helical rotor pumps:** Helical rotor pumps illustrated in Figure 4, are a class of positive displacement pumps designed to deliver moderate flow rates under comparatively higher heads.

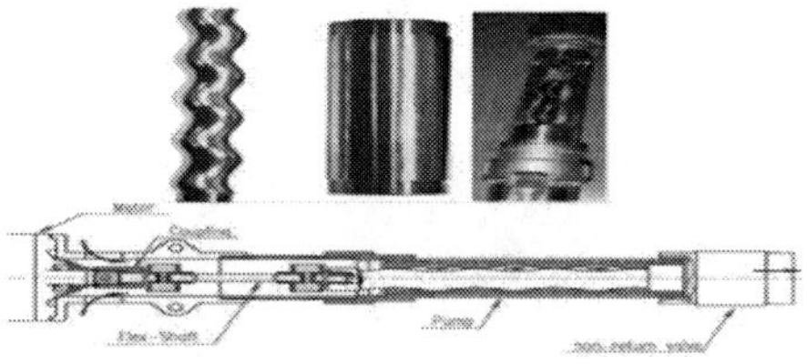

Figure 4: Helical Solar Water Pump and description of Screw gauge technology

c) Reciprocating piston pumps: Reciprocating piston pumps constitute low-power solutions, generally available in capacities of 0.1 hp, 0.25 hp, and 0.5 hp, and are primarily suited for shallow well applications with total dynamic heads in the range of 5–35 m. Owing to their small capacity and portability, these pumps are predominantly utilized by small marginal farmers with landholdings of up to 1 acre, as well as for kitchen gardens and livestock watering. In certain configurations, a battery backup of up to 20 minutes is integrated, enabling continued operation during periods of low solar irradiance or at night, thereby enhancing system operational hours for small-scale users. A reciprocating piston pump shown in Figure 5.

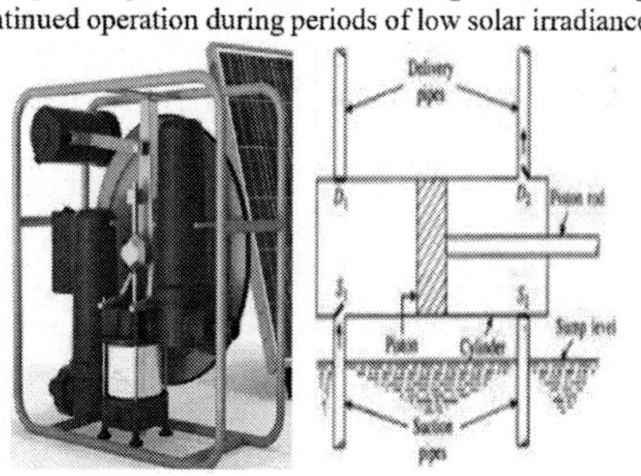

Figure 5: Reciprocating Piston Solar Pump

2.1.3 Pump Controllers: Pump controllers are essential components that regulate energy flow and convert DC output from solar panels into AC suitable for driving the pump set. They optimize system performance by dynamically adjusting pump speed according to solar irradiance, ensuring efficient operation under variable sunlight conditions [4]. Key features of a pump controller include a Maximum Power Point Tracker (MPPT), which continuously extracts the maximum available power from the PV array; a Variable Frequency Drive (VFD), which modulates pump speed to match water demand and solar input; and, in many cases, a Remote Monitoring System (RMS), enabling real-time monitoring and control of pump operation as illustrated in Figure 6.

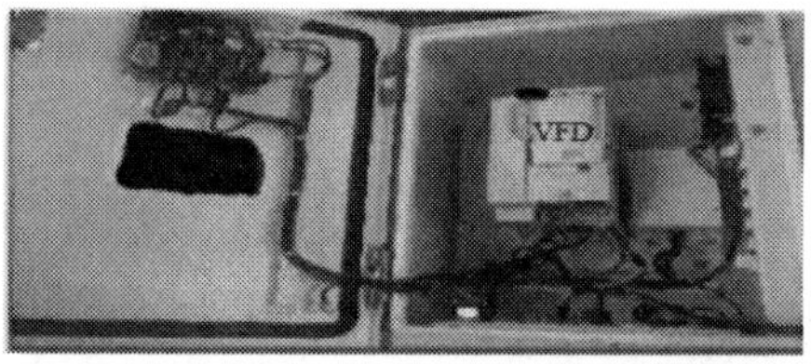

Figure 6: Solar PV Pump Controller with MPPT, VFD & RMS

2.2 Sizing Considerations: Proper sizing of a PV system for solar water pumping involves calculating the energy required to operate the pump for a specified duration [5].

[1] (adapted from Foster & Cota, 2013, ISES Solar World Congress, "Solar water pumping advances and comparative economics") and : Cross-section of typical helical rotor pump end (Foster & Cota, 2009)

A summarized description of the PV array requirements corresponding to different pump capacities and operating heads is given in Tables 1 and 2 as per Ministry of New and Renewable Energy (MNRE) updated SPVWPS F.No. 41/3/2018-SPV Division [2]. The pump capacity should be determined based on crop water requirements and end user demand, which are influenced by crop type, local climate, and irrigation practices. The system must be designed according to the available solar irradiance, which is typically 4–5 kWh/m²/day in most parts of India. In certain applications, water storage tanks and battery backups are incorporated to ensure uninterrupted operation during periods of low irradiance or after sunset [6].

Table 1: Technical Specifications of Solar Deep well (submersible) Pumping Systems with D.C. Motor Pump Set

Description	Model A	Model B	Model C	Model D	Model E	Model F
PV array (Wp)	1200	1800	3000	4800	6750	9000
Motor Pump-set capacity (hp)	1	2	3	5	7.5	10
Shut Off Head (meters)	45	45	100	150	150	150
Total Dynamic Head (TDH) (meters)	30	30	70	100	100	100
Water output * (Liters Per Day)	45600	68400	45000	50400	70875	94500

Table 2: Technical Specifications of Solar Deep well (submersible) Pumping Systems with A.C. Induction Motor Pump Set

Description	Model A	Model B	Model C	Model D	Model E	Model F
PV array (Wp)	1200	1800	3000	4800	6750	9000
Motor Pump-set capacity (hp)	1	2	3	5	7.5	10
Shut Off Head (meters)	45	45	100	150	150	150
Total Dynamic Head (TDH) (meters)	30	30	70	100	100	100
Water output * (Liters Per Day)	42000	63000	42000	43200	60750	81000

* Water output figures are on a clear sunny day with three times tracking of SPV panel, under the "Average Daily Solar Radiation" condition of 7.15 kWh/ sq.m. on the surface of PV array (i.e. coplanar with the PV Modules).

3 AIM AND APPROACH: TESTING OF SOLAR PV WATER PUMPING SYSTEMS

The primary objective of testing solar PV water pumping systems is to evaluate the performance and efficiency under different climatic conditions. This includes assessing energy conversion efficiency, water output, and overall system sustainability to ensure optimal design and functionality for agricultural and rural applications [7].

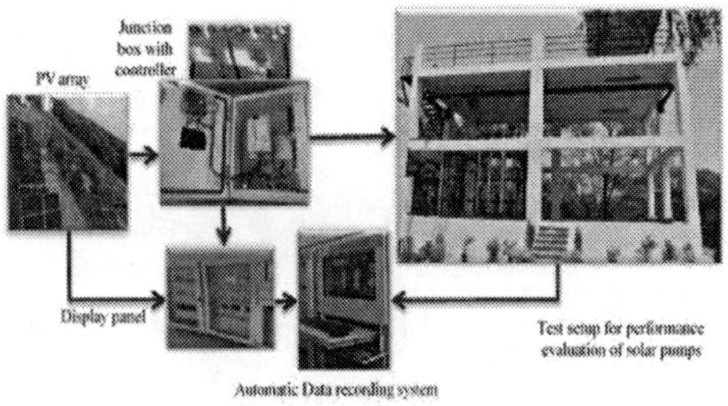

Figure 7 Solar Water Pump Test and R&D Facility at NISE (India)

3.1 ***Experimental setup and site details:*** All experiments were conducted at NISE test and R&D facility (Figure 7), which includes a 7-meter-deep sump well for water storage. The site is equipped with six test slots, slot details specified in Table 3, each fitted with a flow meter, pressure gauge, pressure sensor, and an automatic gate valve, facilitating controlled evaluation of different pump systems under different operating conditions (Outdoor Real time and simulated ideal conditions). A junction box with four terminals i.e. PV input, controller input, controller output, and pump output and connects the PV array to the pump system.

Table 3: Test Slot Specifications and Suitable Pump Capacities

Slot No.	Diameter	Suitable Pump Capacity
1	0.5 inch	< 1 hp
2	1 inch	0.5 hp – 2 hp
3	2 inch	3 hp – 7.5 hp
4	3 inch	7.5 hp – 10 hp
5	4 inch	10 hp – 25 hp
6	6 inch	25 hp – 50 hp

The PV array is also linked to a display panel to monitor array temperature and irradiance in real time. The display panel provides information on pump speed (RPM), water level, slip speed, and delivery pressures. Data acquisition is performed using a dedicated laboratory software connected to a laptop via Ethernet, which logs measurements at every 5 seconds interval. This setup allows precise monitoring and evaluation of system performance for different pump types and configurations. Details of laboratory instruments given in Table 4.

Table 4 Instruments used in the solar water pumping division at NISE

S.No.	Instrument	Make / Model	Function
1	Pyranometer	Kipp & Zonen / 163582	Measures solar irradiance
2	Solar Array Simulator	Chroma / 62150H-1000S	Enables precise control of voltage and current, simulating different environmental conditions such as solar radiation and temperature for accurate performance testing

S.No.	Instrument	Make / Model	Function
3	Power Analyzer	Yokogawa / WT1800	Measures electrical parameters including voltage, current, power, harmonics, and efficiency across system components
4	Pressure Gauge & Transmitter with Display	Yokogawa / EJA530E-JBS4N-012EL	Measures the head of pumps during operation
5	Electromagnetic Flow Meter	Yokogawa / S5W916138-AXG025	Measures water flow
6	Temperature Sensor	GCS / 15Bo57284	Measures the PV module surface temperature
7	Data Logging Software	Customized in LabView	Logs data at 5-second intervals
8	Digital Power Meter	Yokogawa / WT33E	Measures electrical parameters of the system

3.1.2 Testing Parameters: The performance of the solar PV water pumping systems was evaluated based on the following key parameters [7]:

- Pump performance metrics, including flow rate, total head, and energy consumption.
- System performance at variable heads, assessing pump output and efficiency under different total dynamic head (TDH) conditions to simulate real field conditions.

3.1.3 Data Collection: Continuous data on pump performance, PV panel efficiency, and weather conditions was collected over different operating conditions to assess long-term performance. Therefore, hot and cold profiles were designed to replicate real environmental conditions of an ideal summer day and ideal winter day.

The hot profile represents high solar irradiance and elevated module temperatures typically observed in peak summer day, leading to reduced PV module efficiency due to heat & thermal effects. Similarly, the cold profile corresponds to lower ambient temperatures and moderate irradiance levels typical of peak sunny winter day, resulting in higher module efficiency and stable power output. These profiles were incorporated into the DC programmable power supply to simulate realistic seasonal variations for performance evaluation, as illustrated in Figure 8.

Input data included irradiance, module temperature, and module efficiency, which were then fed to the pump controller. Water output measurements were recorded after the predefined head was established, ensuring consistency across all pump types and configurations.

4 RESULTS AND DISCUSSION

The performance of the tested SPVWPS was evaluated across centrifugal, helical rotor, and reciprocating piston pumps, considering under different operating conditions including variable total dynamic heads (TDH), seasonal irradiance variations in Hot & Cold Profile, and peak/off-peak sun hours.

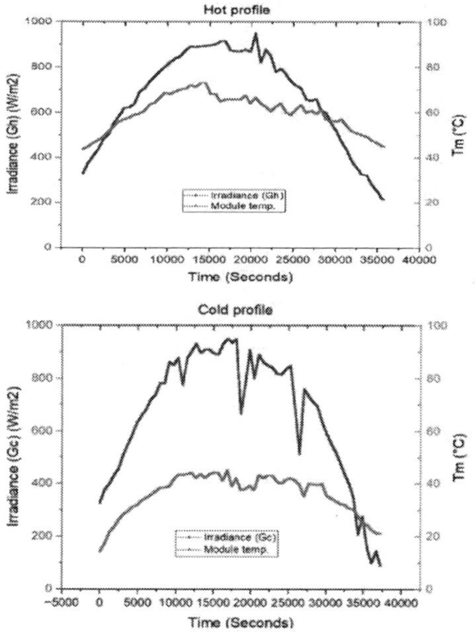

Figure 8: Hot profile and cold profile vs Irradiance graph

4.1 Pump Performance and Efficiency

4.1.1 Centrifugal Pumps: Submersible centrifugal pumps demonstrated robustness and delivered consistently high flow rates, making them suitable for large-scale irrigation applications. The 10 hp AC submersible pump tested at NISE, maintains high efficiencies across tested head levels, reflecting its robust electrical design. Among all measured heads, 100 meter head, i.e., the design head, distinctly stands out as the optimal operating point, balancing the system's WTW Eff. and hydraulic output for sustained, high-volume water delivery with minimal energy losses. The controller efficiency reaches 96.86% (Cold) and 96.61% (Hot), while the flow rate remains well-balanced under full-load conditions. Wire-to-water efficiency is highest at this head (100 m), at 53.97% (Hot) and 56.29% (Cold), indicating efficient energy transfer and system operation. And the average wire-to-water efficiency (WTW Eff.) was observed to be 49.32% under cold conditions and 46.11% under hot conditions. Water output decreases at higher total dynamic heads due to the inherent characteristics of centrifugal pumps, where increasing head results in higher system resistance and reduced flow rate. However, wire-to-water efficiency reaches its peak at the designed head (e.g., 100 m for the 10 HP pump), as this operating point represents the optimal balance between electrical input, hydraulic load, and pump performance, allowing maximum energy transfer from the PV array to the water. For instance, at a head of 150 m, the efficiency of a 10 hp pump was measured at 40.55% under cold conditions with a DC input power of 6.94 kW, and 31.23% under hot conditions at 6.20 kW DC power which is lowest as shown in Figure 9.

10.4229/EUPVSEC2025/4DV.1.77

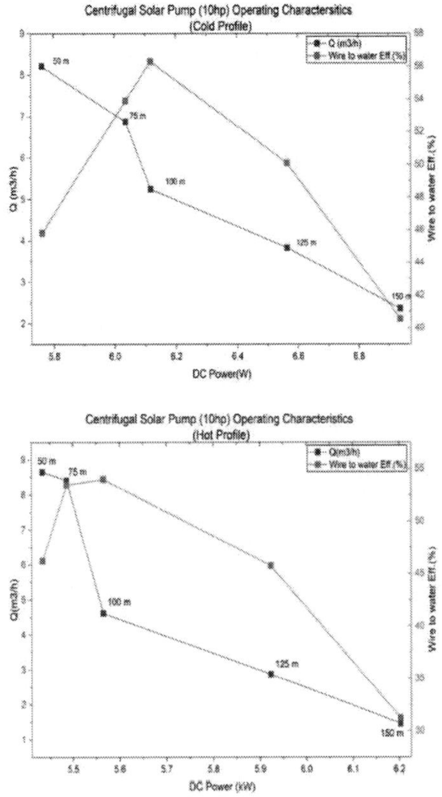

Figure 9: Hot profile and cold profile vs flow graph of 10hp Centrifugal Solar Water Pumps

4.1.2 Helical Rotor Pumps: Positive displacement helical pumps delivered moderate flow rates at higher total dynamic heads ranging from 30 to 90 m. As shown in Figure 10, a 1 hp configuration maintained steady operation and demonstrated average efficiencies of 36.60% under cold conditions and 35.16% under hot conditions.

The performance evaluation of the 1 hp DC helical submersible pump across various heads under hot and cold profiles provides critical insights into how environmental conditions and system parameters influence overall efficiency and output. Notably, at 60 meters, the design head, both WTW eff. and hydraulic performance are optimized. The controller efficiency peaks at 95.65% (Cold) and 95.54% (Hot), indicating excellent power conversion under real operating conditions. Wire-to-water efficiency at design head (60 m) is 41.2% (Cold) and 37.25% (Hot), demonstrating effective energy transfer from the PV panel to the pump. At the maximum tested head of 90 m, efficiency was observed at 31.19% with a DC input power of 0.74 kW in cold conditions, and 28.07% at 0.66 kW in hot conditions.

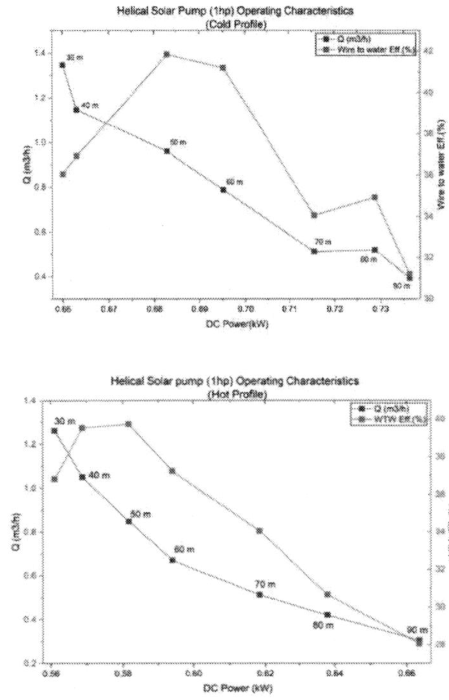

Figure 10: Hot profile and cold profile vs flow graph of 1hp Helical Solar Water Pumps

4.1.3 Reciprocating Piston Pumps: Reciprocating piston pump performance evaluated under real-time outdoor conditions, demonstrated effective performance for low-head, shallow-well applications. In the present evaluation, compact 1 hp pump configurations were tested across a total dynamic head range of 30–90 m. These systems demonstrate suitability for applications involving clean water, with particular relevance to potable water supply, community-level distribution networks, and smallholder irrigation practices.

The pump characteristics shown in Figure 11 indicate high wire-to-water efficiency, with maximum efficiency of 62.22% observed at the design head of 33 m. At higher heads, such as 38 m, efficiency decreased slightly to 57.12%, reflecting the behavior of reciprocating pumps where increased hydraulic resistance reduces flow. Flow rates varied from 0.86 to 1.29 m^3/h depending on the head. These results confirm that reciprocating piston pumps maintain efficient operation near the design head while offering a compact, low-power solution suitable for smallholder irrigation, kitchen gardens, and livestock watering..

4.2 Seasonal and Irradiance Effects: Hot and cold profiles, representing ideal summer (June) and winter (January) irradiance patterns, were used to evaluate system performance.

10.4229/EUPVSEC2025/4DV.1.77
020429-005

4.3 Variable Head Performance

- Testing at different Total Dynamic Head (TDH) values highlighted pump-specific characteristics: centrifugal pumps delivered maximum flow at design but saw reduced efficiency at non design heads.
- Data confirmed that selecting pump type according to required head and water volume is crucial for optimal performance and system efficiency.

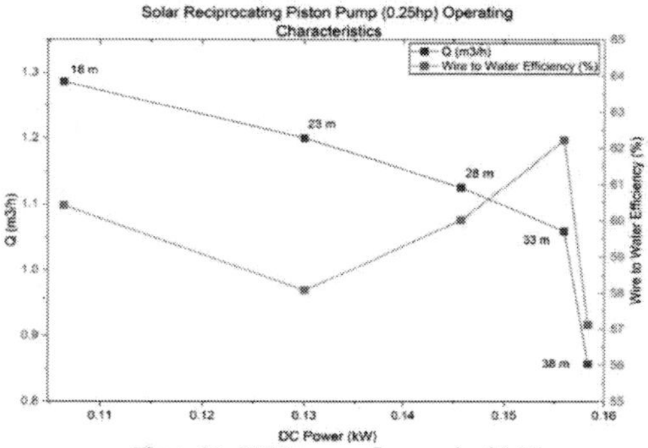

Figure 11: DC Power vs flow graph of 0.25hp Reciprocating Piston Solar Pump

5 CONCLUSION

The findings confirm that system performance is influenced by seasonal variations, with winter months yielding higher efficiency due to reduced thermal stress and improved PV module output. In hot profiles, the system consumes more DC power but delivers higher flow rates, that to reduced fluid resistance and improved pump dynamics. However, elevated temperatures tend to reduce voltage levels slightly, impacting overall energy conversion, also at higher head flow rate and water output drop significantly due to increased frictional and pressure losses, despite stable controller and MPPT efficiencies. The pump exhibits optimal performance at its designed head, with performance decrease at heads above or below this point. This analysis shows that choosing the right head is very important for getting the most water and best performance from a solar pump system.

The three evaluated pump technologies, centrifugal pumps were most effective for large-scale irrigation with moderate head requirements, while helical rotor pumps suitable for applications such as drinking water supply and community-level drinking water distribution. Reciprocating piston pumps emerged as a low-power (less than 1 hp) solution ideally suited for small marginal farmers, enabling efficient operation in shallow head ranges of 5–35 m.

Emerging reciprocating piston pump technologies currently under R&D exhibit promising potential for higher head applications, greater throughput capacity, and robust performance under low-irradiance conditions (160W/m^2). Such innovations represent a future pathway for advancing solar-based irrigation systems in India.

Overall, the results validate solar PV water pumps as technically robust, field-viable, and socio-economically impactful solutions for irrigation and drinking water needs, while highlighting opportunities for further integration, and policy-driven scaling.

References

1. Muralidhar K., & Rajasekar N., (2021), A review of various components of solar water-pumping system: Configuration, characteristics, and performance. International Transactions on Electrical Energy Systems, 31: e13002. https://doi.org/10.1002/2050-7038.13002.
2. Comprehensive guidelines for implementation of Pradhan Mantri Kisan Urja Suraksha Evam Utthaan Mahabhiyan (PM-KUSUM), Ministry of New and Renewable Energy (MNRE), 32/645/2017-SPV Division.
3. Rathore, P. K. S., Das, S. S., & Chauhan, D. S. (2018). Perspectives of solar photovoltaic water pumping for irrigation in India. Energy Strategy Reviews, 22, 385–395. https://doi.org/10.1016/j.esr.2018.10.009.
4. Gualteros, S., & Rousse, D. R. (2021). Solar water pumping systems: A tool to assist in sizing and optimization. Solar Energy, 225, 382–398. https://doi.org/10.1016/j.solener.2021.06.053.
5. Maity R., Sudhakar K., & Razak A. A. (2024). Agri-Solar Water Pumping design, energy, and environmental analysis: A comprehensive study in Tropical Humid climate. Heliyon, 10 (2024), e39604. https://doi.org/10.1016/j.heliyon.2024.e39604.
6. Ahmed N. M., Hassan A. M., Kassem M. A., Hegazi A. M., & Elsaadawi Y. F., (2023), Reliability and performance evaluation of a solar PV-powered underground water pumping system. Scientific Reports, 13:14174. https://doi.org/10.1038/s41598-023-41272-5.
7. Verma S., Mishra S., Chowdhury S., Gaur A., Mohapatra S., Soni A. & Verma P. (2021). Solar PV powered water pumping system – A review. Materials Today Proceedings, 46, 5601–5606. https://doi.org/10.1016/j.matpr.2020.09.434
8. Schüpbach, E., Muntwyler, U., Jost, M., Müller, A., & Urena, D. (2014). Introducing Solar Water Pumps to Female Farmers in India. European Photovoltaic Solar Energy Conference and Exhibition (EU PVSEC) 2014. https://doi.org/10.24451/arbor.7687.
9. Serbouh, Y., Benikhelef, T., Benazzouz, D., Chikh, M. a. A., Touil, S., Richa, A., & Mahmoudi, H. (2022). Performance optimization and reliability of solar pumping system designed for smart agriculture irrigation. Desalination and Water Treatment, 255, 4–12. https://doi.org/10.5004/dwt.2022.28316.
10. Dankoff, W., Foster, R., Cota, A., Lespin, E. (2022). Advances in Solar Powered Water Pumping: Providing for Energy Resiliency and Social Equity. In: Ghosh, A.K., Rixham, C. (eds) Proceedings of the American Solar Energy Society National Conference. ASES SOLAR 2022. Springer Proceedings in Energy. Springer, Cham. https://doi.org/10.1007/978-3-031-08786-8_3

PARTIAL LOAD EFFICIENCY OF PHOTOVOLTAICS IN DIRECT COUPLING TO HYDROGEN ELECTROLYSIS

M. Rennhofer[1], Ph. Mayer-Ullmann[1], D. Krainer[1,2], G. Ujvari[1], J. Lichtenberger[1], K. Kainz[1], V. Neussl[1,3]
[1]AIT Austrian Institute of Technology GmbH (AIT), Österreich
[2]TU Wien, Vienna University of Technology, Österreich
[3]Montanuniversität Leoben, Österreich
marcus.rennhofer@ait.ac.at

ABSTRACT: There are still many challenges to be overcome in order to achieve the goal of climate-neutral energy supply. On the one hand, there is a need for massive expansion of solar or wind energy and, on the other, further technological development in terms of performance, reliability and flexibility. Here, hydrogen (H2) can act as a central bridge between the volatile energy from sun or wind and the still dominant hydrocarbon-based energy system. Here we present two research initiatives (PH2ÖNIX and a mini-H2 technology demonstrator) investigating the use of photovoltaics and hydrogen production in direct DC coupling, one in a small set-up with research components and one with real components for industrial sites.

1 INTRODUCTION

In the PH2ÖNIX demonstrator, electricity from a nearby PV roof system (2x30 kWp) supplies two electrolysers. each 10 kW, PEM and the AEM technology, respectively. The hydrogen is stored in gas cylinders. A PEM fuel cell with 8 kW uses the stored hydrogen to generate electricity, thus completing the circuit of converting electricity from power to H2 into electricity (P2P). For the mini H2-technology demonstrator, 2 PV mini-modules with a total of 9 A and 4.8 V were directly connected to a small hydrogen electrolysis PEM cell with a nominal operating voltage of 4 V. Two topologies were investigated, one with high current (parallel modules) and one with high voltages (serial modules).

For the setups, different research questions were followed that investigate several components of the coupling of PV systems and H2 electrolysis systems. The paper focuses on PV self-consumption in real operation and the influence of direct system coupling on the efficiency levels and working points of the individual components, the partial load efficiencies and in particular, the influence of weather on the system working points.

While the direct DC coupling is not new, the approach here was to investigate systems of largely different power level to conclude on scaling factors. Further, for each system different modes of operation and diverse operation points allow to conclude on optimization potentials in design. Finally, PV-2-H2 scaling factors were investigated and are still under investigation. For PH2ÖNIX, a over dimensioning of PV power to H2 power is possible for investigating its impact on H2 production, ramp-up times and efficiencies. For the mini technology demonstrator different settings with low current and high voltage or high current low voltage were implemented and the impact on the H2 production was followed.

All this investigations are of relevance for of-grid PV-H2 systems. The system coupling without grid and direct DC might be in the minority of industrial application cases but it also brings in advantaged as minimum amount of technical components and investment and high reliability in operation. Understanding effects of mismatching electrical parameters as well as impact of weather is of high importance.

2 METHODOLOGY

2.1 Basic approach

The main aim of the studies was to investigate one typology of PV-H2 electrolysis coupling, which is special in the way that is has an absolute minimum of system components. The PH2ÖNIX project is investigating system scenarios for direct off-grid coupling of PV systems with water electrolysers, see Figure 1 the electrolysis of the research initiatives for hydrogen production exclusively draws electricity from a PV system. The variable energy is stored as hydrogen, but for PH2ÖNIX it is reenergized in times without generation via a fuel cell. Both systems have the same basic idea of coupling but at different system size, PH2ÖNIX with 60 KWp PV and 2x 10 kW electrolysis, the mini technology demonstrator 50 W PV with 36 W electrolysis. The approach was to investigate different operation modes in dependence of environmental conditions and conclude on system efficiency and longevity. In the following the system details for the two setups are given. They are also summarized in Table I.

2.2 Ph2önix – PV & Grid-Back-Up

In the PH2ÖNIX demonstrator at the AIT Seibersdorf campus, electricity from a nearby PV roof system (2x30 kWp) supplies two electrolyzers. Each electrolyzer has an electrical output of 10 kW. At night or late afternoon, a PEM fuel cell with 8 kW of electrical output uses the stored hydrogen.

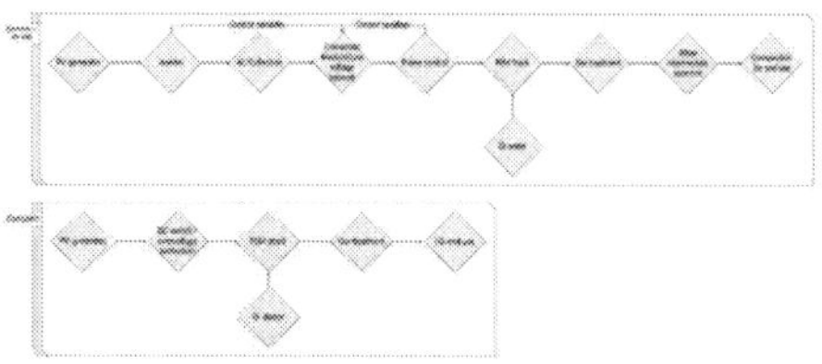

Figure 1: System diagrams for direct coupling types of PV-H2 electrolysis, (top) for PH2ÖNIX and (bottom) for the mini H2 demonstrator

Table I: Standing waves ratio

Equipment	Technology Demonstrator	PH₂ÖNIX
PV-system	50 Wp	63kWp
H2-electrolysis	36 W	2 x 10 kW
Storage	none	bundle 30bar
Fuel Cell	none	8kW
Coupling type	direct DC	direct DC or AC local grid

2.3 Technology demonstrator - Only PV-coupling

For the Mini-H2 demonstrator, 2x6-cell PV mini modules were selected, with a total maximum of 9 A ISC and 3.8 V open-circuit voltage on a small fuel cell store hydrogen electrolysis PEM cell with a nominal 4 V operating voltage and a maximum of 9 A input voltage, directly DC coupled.

3 RESULTS

As exemplary results here the system electrical efficiency is shown for the H2 mini technology demonstrator in the case of serial PV modules (too high voltage, too low current) and parallel PV modules (too low voltage, too high current).

The Figure 2 shows some operating points of the coupled system (orange-black) as well as ideal characteristic curve (black) and the STC characteristic curve of the 2 x 6 cell modules. The operating points show voltages that are too high and currents that are too low for the electrolyser. The main factors are the start time of the electrolyser, the temperature of the water and the compensation of the currents that are too low by high.

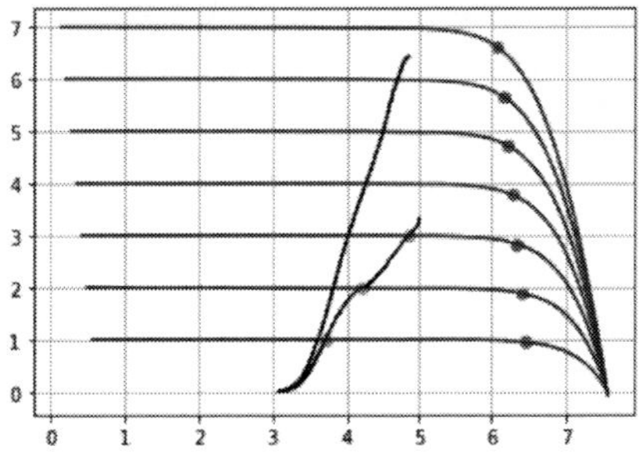

Figure 2: System efficiency dependency on operation conditions of the PV. Red points indicate joint operation point during heating up phase of the electrolyzer.

3.1 Partial load efficiencies

The influence of the position of the point where the systems are coupled at 1000 W relative to the MPP point of the PV shows clear when one makes the efficiency analysis of the used sunlight, see Figure 3. The pictures show the recorded proportions of sunlight at the respective irradiation. In Figure 3, top, for both modules in series (high voltages), and in Figure 3, bottom, for the scenario with the modules parallel (high currents).

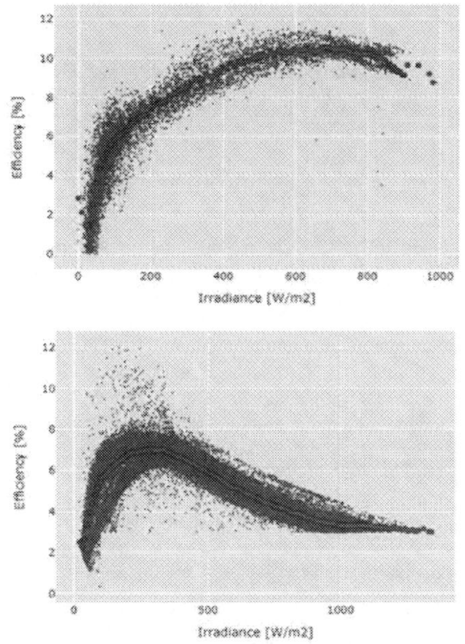

Figure 3: The influence of the position of the point where the systems at 1000 W regarding the efficiency analysis - absorbed shares of sunlight at the respective irradiation. Top: for both modules serial; Bottom: for both modules parallel

3.2 System behavior and degradation

While the efficiency of a PV module alone usually increases with the radiation, a clear maximum is pronounced for the coupled system. Figure 3 shows a significant decrease in efficiency above 700 W/m2, all working points are at voltages lower than the MPP voltage. For the parallel case, Figure 3, right, the maximum efficiency is smaller and the maximum is already about 300 W/m2. At 1000 W/m2 the system has almost no efficiency, all working points are higher than the MPP voltage.

For the serial connected modules, the hydrogen flow was investigated. Since all the working points are at voltages smaller than the MPP voltage, the relationship between irradiation and current is almost linear. The relationship between H2 flow of the electrolyser (H2 generation) and current is also linear, see Figure 4. The graph also shows that the H2 flow is temperature independent at constant voltage.

10.4229/EUPVSEC2025/4DV.1.78

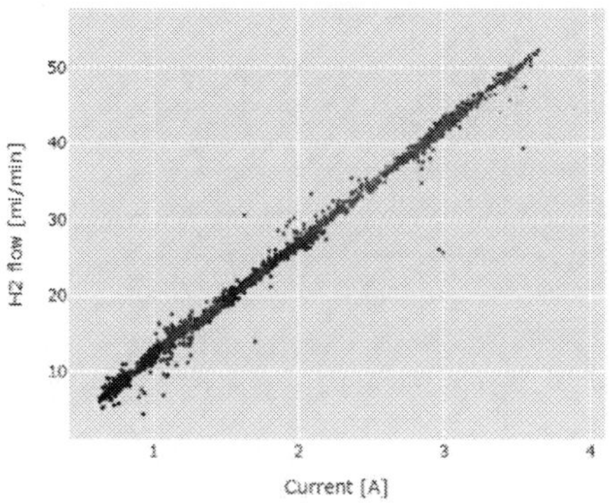

Figure 4: H2 flow of the electrolyser, the evaluation is shown for voltages of 4 V (nominal voltage).

Finally, an analysis was made to determine whether the non-optimal operating conditions affect the lifetime of the electrolyser. Figure 5 shows the related statistical analysis, showing all H2 flow values per month. It can be seen that there is a systematic decrease in the flow while the main cause is the system-coupling related high voltages larger than the nominal electrolysers voltage of 4V.

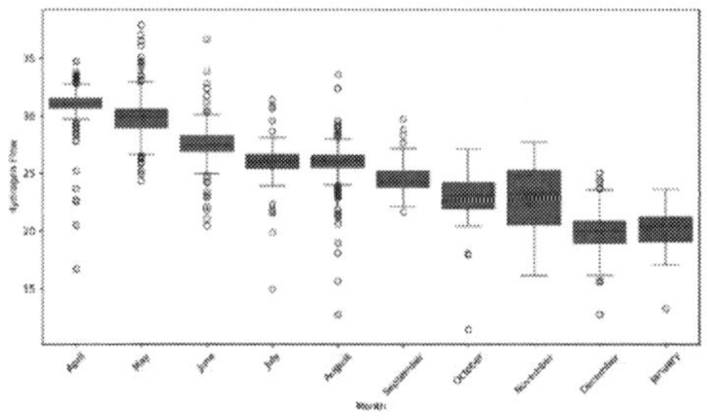

Figure 5: Statistical analysis of the aging of the system based on H2 flow values.

4 CONCLUSIONS

Concluding, two test systems for direct DC coupling of PV and H2-electric circuits were investigated, which differ in their system setup and size.

For the 50W system, the evaluations of the working points, system efficiencies and the time behavior of the H2 flow were evaluated and shown here. The analysis shows that although a directly coupled system is simple by number of components, but more know-how has to be put into the coordination and behavior of the working points. In detail, it was possible to deduce that:

- Directly coupled systems are functional and stable
- The choice of nominal voltages at STC for both systems is central to system efficiency
- Electrolysis systems allow working points outside the ideal characteristic
- The temperature influence on the functionality is very pronounced
- The hydrogen flow is approximately linear with the irradiation scalable
- The hydrogen flow decreases systematically through aging when high voltages are present.

10.4229/EUPVSEC2025/4DV.1.78

MARCUS RENNHOFER*[1] // PHIL... KUBICEK[1] // GUSZTAV UJVARI[1] // JANINE Lichtenberger[1]// BERNHARD KUBICEK[1] // KONRAD KAINZ[1]
1 AIT Austrian Institute of Technology GmbH, Center for Energy, Photovoltaic Systems, EnergyBase Vienna.
2 Montanuniversität Leoben, Österreich
3 TU Wien, Vienna University of Technology
* marcus.rennhofer@ait.ac.at

PARTIAL LOAD EFFICIENCY OF PHOTOVOLTAICS IN DIRECT COUPLING TO HYDROGEN ELECTROLYSIS

AUSTRIAN INSTITUTE OF TECHNOLOGY
TOMORROW TODAY

GOALS and METHODS

For the goal of a climate-neutral energy supply, the massive expansion of solar or wind energy is needed. For reliability, storage & flexibility, hydrogen (H2) can act as a central bridge. The coupling was tested in two systems of different sizing.

Methodological approach

- In contrast to conventional concepts in which the electrolyzer is connected to the power grid, the electrolysis of the research initiatives for hydrogen production draws electricity exclusively from a PV system.
- Both system included crystalline PV and PEM electrolysis
- For PH_2ÖNIX, it is converted back into electricity via a fuel cell in times when there is no generation
- PV related and hydrogen related parameters were monitored and evaluated
- Main focus was put on partial load behavior far away of the optimal operation points

Ph2önix – PV & Grid-Back-Up

- In the PH2ÖNIX demonstrator at the AIT Seibersdorf campus, electricity from a nearby PV roof system (2x30 kWp) supplies two electrolyzers. Each electrolyzer has an electrical output of 10 kW. At night or late afternoon, a PEM fuel cell with 8 kW of electrical output uses the stored hydrogen

Technology demonstrator - Only PV-coupling

- For the Mini-H2 demonstrator, 2x6-cell PV mini modules were selected, with a total maximum of 9 A ISC and 3.8 V open-circuit voltage on a small fuel cell store hydrogen electrolysis PEM cell with a nominal 4 V operating voltage and a maximum of 9 A input voltage, directly DC coupled.

Technical Details

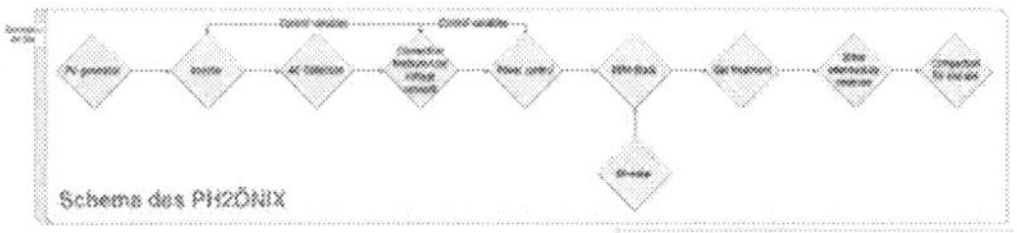
Schema des PH2ÖNIX

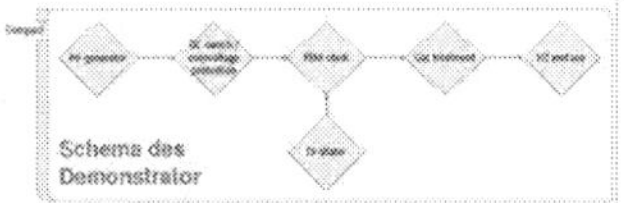
Schema des Demonstrator

Equipment	Technology demonstrator	PH2önix
PV-System	~50 Wp	63 kWp
H2-Elektrolysis	36 W	2 x 10 kWp
Storage	none	bundle storage at 30 bar
Fuel-cell	none	8 kWp
Coupling type	direct DC	direct DC or AC local grid

System set-up for the PH_2önix

- Construction of PH2ÖNIX with photovoltaic systems, electrolysers and reverse power generation at the AIT Seibersdorf campus.

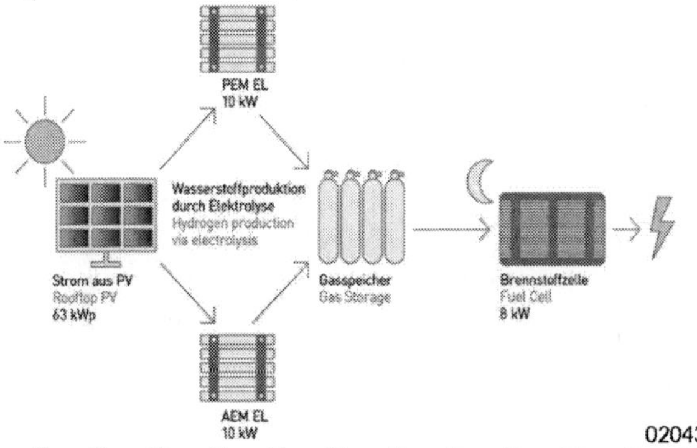

Joint Operation Points PV-electrolysis

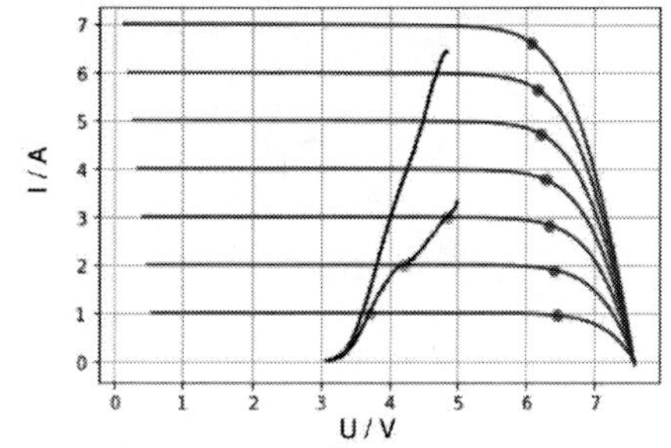

System efficiency depends on maintaining optimal operating points (MPP)

The figure shows some operating points of the coupled system (orange-black) as well as ideal characteristic curve (black) and the STC characteristic curve of the 2 x 6 cell modules. The operating points show voltages that are too high and currents that are too low for the electrolyser. The main factors are the start time of the electrolyser, the temperature of the water and the compensation of the currents that are too low by high voltages with the same PV output.

Coupling – Efficiency - Continuos Operation

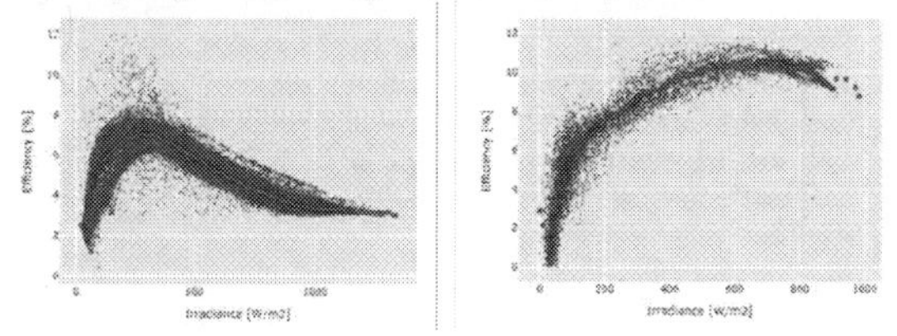

Coupling and Efficiency

Left: Efficiency analysis - recorded portions of sunlight during the respective irradiation for two modules in parallel. **Right:** Two Modules in series.

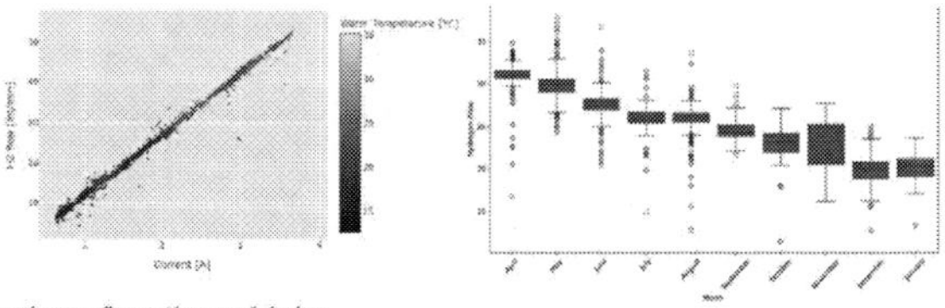

Continuos Operation and Aging

Left: H2 flow of the electrolyser. The evaluation is shown for voltages of 4 V (nominal voltage). The graph also shows that the H2 flux is temperature independent at constant voltage.

Right: Statistical analysis of the aging of the system using H2 flow values. The central cause of the decrease is the system coupling-related high voltages.

Goals Achieved & Conclusion

Two test systems for **direct DC coupling of PV and H2** electrolsysis were presented, which differ in their system performance. The **operating efficiency and durability** depend fundamentally on the component design. It was researched in detail that:

✓ Directly coupled systems are functional and stable
✓ The choice of nominal voltages at STC for both systems is central to system efficiency
✓ Electrolysis systems allow operating points away from the ideal characteristic curve
✓ Hydrogen flow systematically decreases through aging when there are over voltages.

The research was supported by the PH2ÖNIX (KPC photovoltaic lighthouses of the BMK Austria).

PREDICTING SHADING LOSSES IN PHOTOVOLTAIC PLANTS: A NOVEL APPROACH

D. López Dalmau[1], H. Mirandona López[1], C. Javier Lopes Gomes[1], J. Tomàs Villalonga Palou[1], C. Rossa[1]
[1]Sunveon
calle del Musgo, 2, 1B, Madrid, Spain. 28023

ABSTRACT: Accurately estimating shadow impact on large-scale photovoltaic (PV) plants is challenging due to the computational demands of traditional methods. This study introduces the Sunveon Model, a novel, efficient approach for simulating shading and mismatch losses without requiring complex I-V curve calculations. The model uses a hybrid methodology, combining a 2D irradiance model with a 3D submodule-level shading model. Its key innovation is the use of a regression model, whose accuracy was validated against over 500,000 I-V curves, to directly predict a string's Maximum Power Point (MPP), significantly reducing computational time. It also quantifies mismatch losses with a new 'Mixed Fill Factor' that establishes a direct quadratic relationship between losses, shadow percentage, and irradiance. Validated against real-world data, the Sunveon Model proved more accurate than two industry-standard models, showing substantially lower errors. A key finding is that mismatch losses for standard cells are about 64% higher than for half-cell modules. In summary, the Sunveon Model offers a precise and efficient tool for large-scale PV analysis.

Keywords: Shading-induced losses, mismatch losses, computational efficiency, 3D shading model

1 INTRODUCTION

Accurately estimating the impact of shadows on photovoltaic generation is significantly constrained by the current scale of photovoltaic (PV) plants and the complexity of the terrain. This challenge is compounded by the excessive computational cost associated with calculating complete I-V curves, which restricts their application in precisely estimating energy production from large-scale PV plants. For example, on a conventional PC, a typical 50 MW plant (about 3,000 strings) can be simulated in 30 seconds for shading table generation (12×13 positions per string) plus 50 seconds for yield simulation. This has motivated most standard production models available on the market to simplify yield estimations, working with statistical approaches to simulate the impact of shadows on current PV plants[1], [2], [3], which can be hundreds of megawatts in size. These models typically simulate only a few representative strings within the plant, leading to over or underestimating shading effects due to common loss factors. This, in turn, affects accurate assessment of mismatch losses.

This study proposes a novel approach to simulate shading-induced losses in PV plants without the need to compute complete I-V curves, thereby significantly reducing computational costs. Additionally, it proposes a method to estimate the mismatch losses due to different shade patterns throughout the strings.

2 METHODOLOGY

2.1 How the Sunveon Model works

Using a dataset of over 500,000 I-V curves from different manufacturers and spanning various shading and irradiance conditions, we developed linear regressions to accurately predict losses for standard and half-cell modules. This approach eliminates the need to calculate new I-V curves for every simulation, capturing the electrical effects in all possible shading scenarios in an actual PV plant. The impact of series and shunt resistances was very low in all cases and could be considered negligible.

From one of the classical transposition models[4], [5], the model uses a distinct approach to more precisely estimate diffuse and reflected irradiance on both the front and rear sides of modules. It estimates the shading effects on diffuse irradiance caused by surrounding structures, considering the shading state of the terrain[6], [7]. To achieve that, the model follows these steps:

1. The process begins by defining the basic parameters of a 2D scenario (Fig.1). This includes the characteristics of the structure (e.g., type, dimensions, axis height, pitch between rows, transparency, module spacing, number of modules, width, bifaciality), terrain characteristics (slope, albedo), and the location's latitude. The scenario sets the positions of the axes of five simulated rows of structures (either fixed-tilt or tracking). A constant slope is set for these five rows, as well as the terrain limits, and their normal and directional vectors. Latitude is important as it influences the sign of the slope angle, especially for fixed structures.
2. Since the scenario's composition is affected by the sun's position (structure rotation, projected shadows), some of its geometry must be recalculated at each interval. This involves calculating the solar ray vector in the 2D scenario by transforming its coordinates from a global reference system to the local 2D system. The position of the collectors and their segments are then calculated, attributing an index to each. For fixed structures, segment positions are constant, but for trackers, positions are calculated based on structure rotation, which depends on sun position and tracking strategy. The model also determines if segments are shaded or not.
3. Once segment locations and indices are calculated, view factors between them are determined. This involves calculating factors towards adjacent row segments, ground segments, and finally, the sky. Reciprocity is

used to avoid unnecessary calculations. Obstructions between segments are also accounted for when calculating lengths and diagonals.

4. Possible incident irradiance values are calculated for each segment type (front, back, ground) and shading scenario (illuminated/shaded), breaking it down into direct, circumsolar diffuse, and horizontal diffuse components. Isotropic diffuse component is treated differently, with its value inherently incorporating shadow effects, eliminating the need to differentiate between shaded and illuminated states. The model calculates direct irradiance for each segment type, considering the solar ray's incidence angles. The classical transposition methods[4], [5] are then applied, by removing the effect of coefficients dependent on inclination or incidence angle (Fig.2).
5. The model combines a 2D irradiance model with a 3D shadow calculation model. The 2D model discretises surfaces like structures and the ground into segments to calculate irradiance exchange using view factors. It provides the incident irradiance for two states: illuminated and shaded. These results are then combined with the 3D model, which provides information on the number of shaded submodules within a string. This new approach streamlines the process by focusing on the binary illumination states and the specific proportion of shaded submodules (Fig.3 and Fig.4).

Following these steps, the incident irradiance on both the front and rear of the central simulated row is estimated under illumination and shading conditions. This calculation, which is assumed to be the valid result, provides a detailed characterisation of incident irradiance in partially shaded rows. This results in a characteristic incident irradiance for each binary state of the submodules, either shaded (active bypass diode) or illuminated (no active bypass diode)[8], resulting in a characteristic I-V curve for the array formed by half-cell (Fig.5) or standard (Fig.6) modules. The output of the 2D irradiance model is then combined with a 3D submodule-level shading model, where individual strings exhibit different shadow patterns, and consequently, varying proportions of affected submodules. This analysis accounts for two key factors related to shading. First, the shading state is not a total absence of light; it specifically includes the amount of diffuse irradiance reaching shaded cells. Second, we consider edge effects, such as the minimum shadow cast by the module's frame, which would affect the entire submodule.

The Fig 1. depicts the 2D scenario defined by the model in the step 1. As a representative case of the model, the Fig. 2 depicts the global irradiation along a sunny day obtained from the Perez transposition model (grey line), and for both illuminated and shaded parts of the string calculated by the Sunveon model (blue and orange lines). Fig. 3 and Fig. 4 depict two 3D scenarios with their corresponding shading factor (% of shaded submodules) at each string of a PV Layout. The Fig. 5 and Fig. 6 depict, respectively, an I-V curve used to obtain the regression models from half-cell and standard modules.

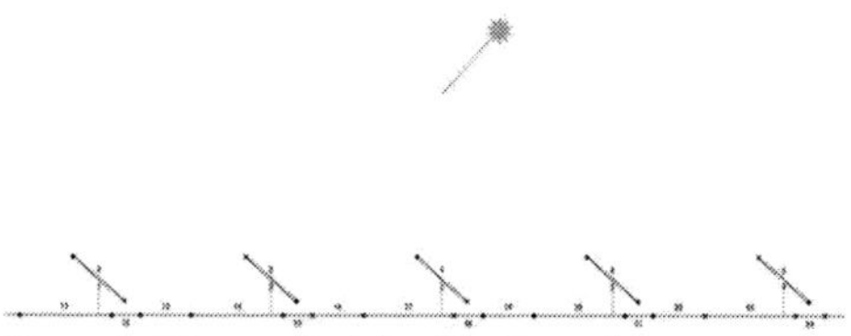

Figure 1: 2D scenario defined by the model

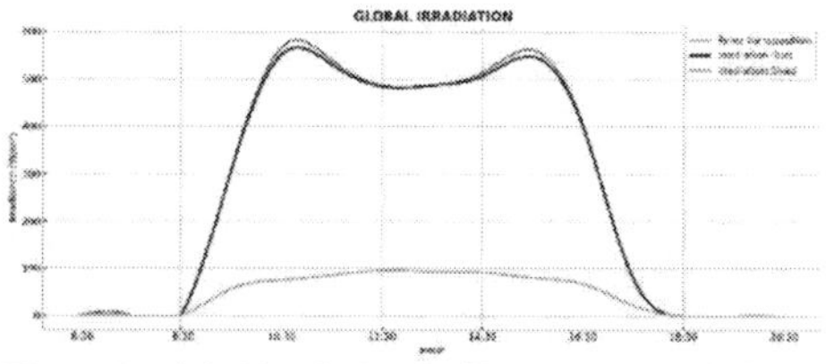

Figure 2: Global irradiation for illuminated and shades parts of a string, obtained from the Perez transposition model

Figure 3: 3D scenario depicting a front view of a PV plant illustrating the distribution of the shading factor. The darker the string's colour, the more shaded it is relative to the most illuminated string

Figure 4: 3D scenario depicting a diagonal view of a PV plant illustrating the distribution of the shading factor. The darker the string's colour, the more shaded it is relative to the most illuminated string

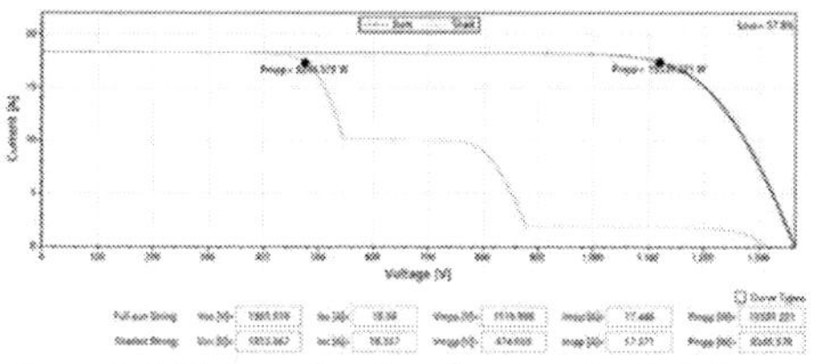

Figure 5: I-V curve of an illuminated and a shaded string of half-cell PV modules

10.4229/EUPVSEC2025/4DV.4.3

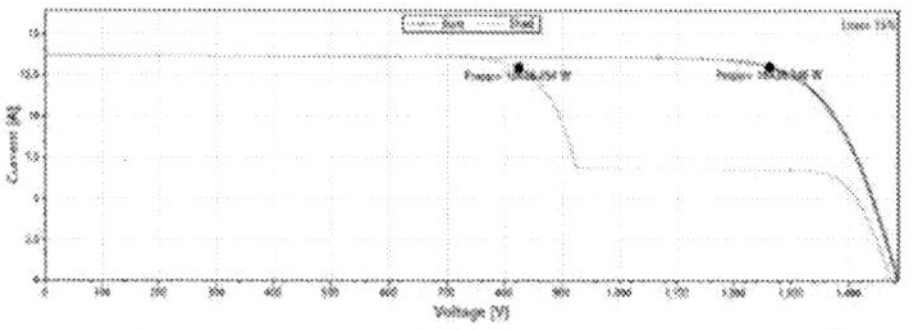

Figure 6: I-V curve of an illuminated and a shaded string of standard PV modules

The Sunveon Model is applicable to both standard and half-cell modules. It combines irradiance and shading models to estimate the Maximum Power Point (MPP) of each individual string within a solar plant, taking into account the mismatch losses induced by shadows. Unlike traditional methods, it doesn't require a full I-V curve calculation for every string. Instead, the regressions obtained from the over half a million I-V curves provide the necessary parameters to accurately estimate the energy production. We can extend the estimations to an entire PV plant by a precise calculation of input conditions for inverter MPPTs, allowing a granular production within any layout (Fig.7).

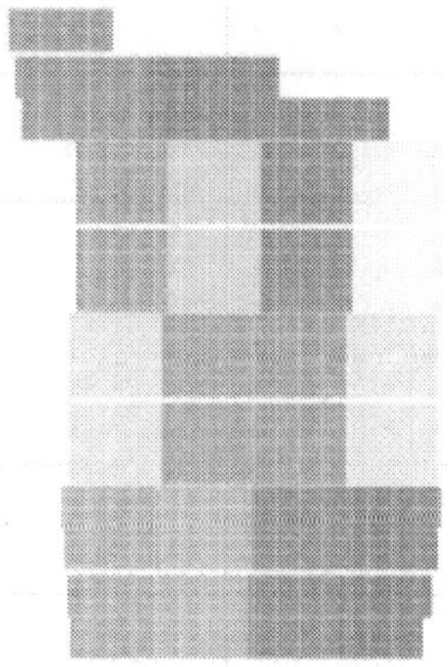

Figure 7: Electrical Layout (Power blocks) of a 70 MW_p plant

It is worth commenting that the model in its complete version also includes other types of losses, such as IAM, soiling and thermal losses induced by the wind[9], but their detailed description is beyond the scope of this article. Here we opted to make a description only for the ways to obtain a more precise irradiance reaching the modules. In this case, here we consider the intrinsic mismatch losses between the modules as null[10], [11].

3 RESULTS AND DISCUSSION

3.1 Benchmark validation

The model was validated against over 500,000 I-V curves, which resulted from shading patterns observed in real PV layouts (from five different PV plants, ranging from approximately 5 to 150 MW_p) under diverse incident irradiance conditions. The same analysis was also conducted using two other shadow models often used in the industry. The I-V curves derived from these various shading patterns are considered the 'real losses,' and the performance of all three models (the two industry-standard models and the Sunveon Model) is plotted against these real losses for comparison.

The models are described below:

- Model 1: it reduces the beam component of the incident irradiance according to percentage of shaded submodules, then it computes the MPP power (P_{MPP}) of the string (single-diode model)[12], [13].
- Model 2: it computes the P_{MPP} at illumination and shade conditions, then computes a new value that lies in-between both, depending on the shading factor[14].
- Sunveon Model: it uses a novel regression model with the following inputs: P_{MPP} at illumination, proportion of shaded submodules in the string and proportion of incident diffuse irradiance. A specific model is developed both for standard and half-cell modules.

3.2 The reliability of the Sunveon Model

As a representative case, Fig. 8 and Fig. 9 summarise the comparison between simulated I-V curves of a single string under various shading patterns and irradiance conditions. The results from the Sunveon Model (yellow squares) are presented alongside those from two industry-standard models, Model 1 (red diamonds) and Model 2 (blue triangles), for both standard and half-cell modules. The findings from large-scale numerical tests are detailed in Table I (Standard modules) and Table II (Half-cell modules), located below their respective figures.

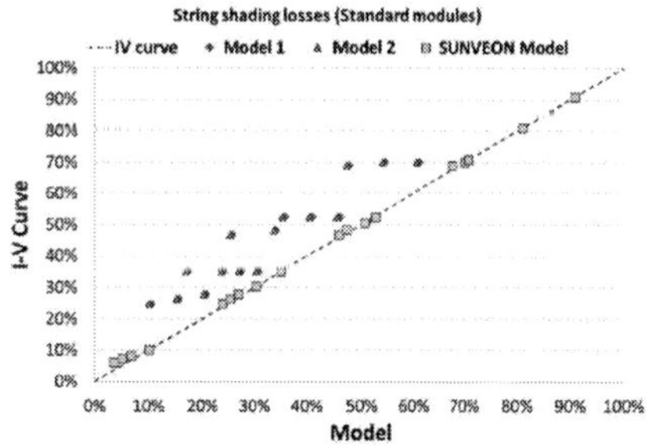

Figure 8: I-V Curve vs Shading loss models for Standard modules

Table I: Large-scale numerical testing (Standard modules)

	MAE [%]	STD [%]
Model 1	4.26	5.49
Model 2	6.48	4.76
Sunveon Model	0.79	1.53

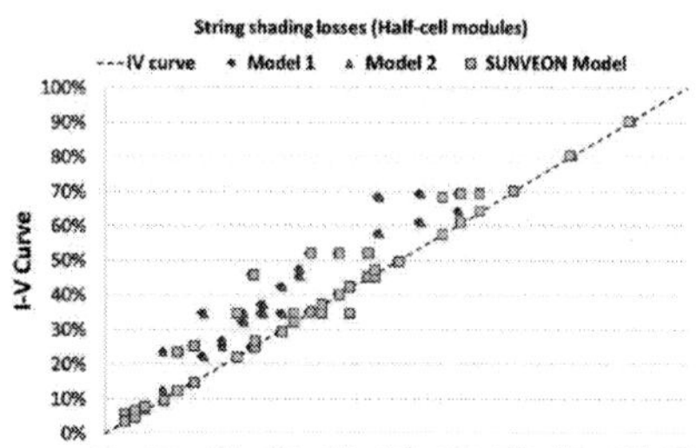

Figure 9: I-V Curve vs Shading loss models for Half-cell modules

Table II: Large-scale numerical testing (Half-cell modules)

	MAE [%]	STD [%]
Model 1	7.05	5.61
Model 2	6.99	5.62
Sunveon Model	1.36	2.28

The results from both Standard and Half-cell modules consistently demonstrate the superior accuracy and reliability of the Sunveon Model compared to Model 1 and Model 2, reflected both in their Mean Absolute Error (MAE) and Standard Deviation (STD). In both cases, the Sunveon Model aligns remarkably closely with the benchmark (the real I-V curve data), while the other models consistently underestimate losses, with their predictions typically falling above the diagonal when plotted against actual values. The following comments apply:

For Standard Modules:

- The Sunveon Model exhibits remarkably low error rates with an MAE of 0.79% and an STD of 1.53%. This precision is evident in its close alignment with the benchmark.
- Model 1 shows significantly higher errors with an MAE of 4.26% and an STD of 5.49%.
- Model 2 also presents elevated errors, with an MAE of 6.48% and an STD of 4.76%.

For standard modules, the Sunveon Model greatly outperforms the other models, with its MAE being approximately 5 to 8 times lower than that of the other two models and its STD approximately 3 times lower, indicating a far more precise and consistent prediction capability.

For Half-cell Modules:

- The Sunveon Model continues to show strong performance, with a MAE of 1.36% and a STD of 2.28%. While slightly higher than for standard modules, these values remain exceptionally low, confirming the model's robustness.
- Model 1 presents an MAE of 7.05% and an STD of 5.61%.
- Model 2 shows similar performance to Model 1, with an MAE of 6.99% and an STD of 5.62%.

A similar trend is observed in half-cell modules; though the Sunveon Model's errors are slightly higher (MAE 1.36%, deviation 2.28%), this is expected due to the more complex electrical topology of half-cell modules, consisting of six submodules arranged as two parallel strings of three submodules in series. Despite this, the estimation remains highly precise. Even in this more challenging scenario, the Sunveon Model maintains a substantially lower MAE (approximately 5 times lower) and STD (about 2.5 times lower) compared to Model 1 and Model 2. The trend of Model 1 and Model 2 consistently underestimating losses persists, albeit with some points deviating further from the diagonal, indicating less precision than for standard modules.

3.3 Mismatch losses due to different shading patterns

Each string, with its respective illumination and/or shading pattern, has a unique electrical characteristic and, consequently, an associated Fill Factor (FF). The parallel connection between these strings subsequently leads to instantaneous mismatch losses[15]. Based on the Sunveon Model, we were able to derive a new mismatch loss model that is applicable for estimating these losses in parallel strings due to different shading patterns. We describe this model below, step by step:

- Firstly, it is established a unique series of n modules, and then, 10 random different shading patterns (from about 0.5% to about 90%) are applied for each irradiance value, ranging from 100 W/m² to 900 W/m², in increments of 50 W/m².
- Each of these simulation conditions (shade and irradiance) generates an electrical response, and consequently, an individual FF. To assign an appropriate weight to both illuminated and shaded areas, we considered the FF here as the ratio between the maximum power in shade and the product of V_{oc} and I_{sc} in illumination. To differentiate this from the original concept of FF, we have termed this relation the 'Mixed Fill Factor,' calculated as:

$$FF_{mix} = \frac{I_{MPP,shd} V_{MPP,shd}}{I_{sc,illum} V_{oc,illum}} \quad (1)$$

where $I_{MPP,shd}$ and $V_{MPP,shd}$ are the current and voltage at the maximum power point in shading conditions and $I_{sc,illum}$ and $V_{oc,illum}$ are the short-circuit current and open-circuit voltage in illumination. It is worth commenting that the error in using the values in illumination rather than in shading conditions is no more than 3% in the worst cases.
- For each irradiance value, there are 10 different FF_{mix} values. The coefficient of variation of these values can now be calculated by the relation between the associated standard deviation and the mean value (Equation 2):

$$CV_{FF,mix} = \frac{\sigma_{FF_{mix}}}{\overline{FF_{mix}}} \quad (2)$$

- The ten strings combined in a single MPPT give rise to a characteristic I-V curve with its respective electrical patterns due to the different shades in each string. The ratio between the total power of this hypothetical shaded array and the sum of the individual power of each shaded string give rise to an electrical mismatch loss, i.e.:

$$EMM_{shd}(\%) = 1 - \frac{P_{total,array,shd}}{\sum_1^n P_{i,n\,string,shd}} \quad (3)$$

- A relationship between $EMM_{shd}(\%)$ and

$CV_{FF,mix}$ is then established (R^2>0.95). Equation 4 allows to calculate the mismatch losses directly from the method described in section 2.1 – i.e. for parallel connections-, now without the need to calculate any I-V curve. The relationship is also seen in Fig. 10.

$$EMM_{shd}(\%) = 0.0076\ CV_{FF,mix}(\%)^2 + 0.2445\ CV_{FF,mix}(\%) \quad (4)$$

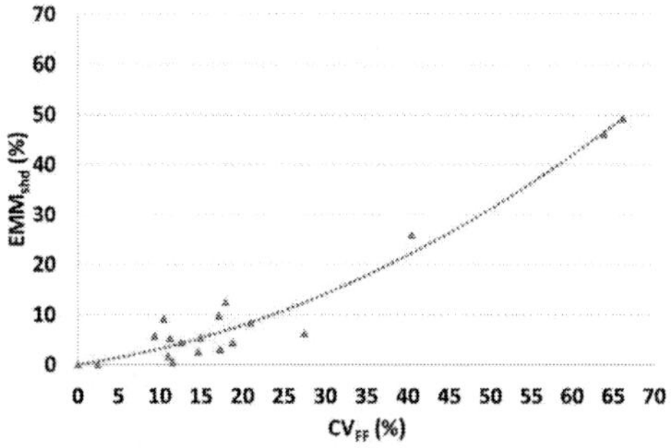

Figure 10: Relationship between the percentual values of Electrical Mismatch Losses (EMM_{shd}) and coefficient of variation of Mixed Fill Factor ($CV_{FF,mix}$)

Previous studies have also established a quadratic relationship for mismatch losses[11], [16], [17], [18], though mainly focused on series connections.

3.4 Mismatch losses for standard and half-cell modules

Mismatch losses between strings vary significantly depending on the shading conditions across different strings and also on the irradiance in the illuminated sections. One can intuitively infer that higher irradiances lead to greater mismatch losses, as the illumination gradient between shaded and illuminated areas becomes more pronounced. However, the precise magnitude of these losses is the key question. Equation 6 allows us to shed some light on these questions. Fig. 11 shows the mismatch losses for both standard and half-cell modules in a hypothetical case where n strings are connected in a single MPP, each one with its respective shading pattern. The losses are analysed for different shading patterns and subject to an in-illumination irradiance range of 100-1000 W/m². A direct comparison between both technologies shows that the standard modules are subject to about 64% more losses than the half-cell modules, or in other words, about two-thirds.

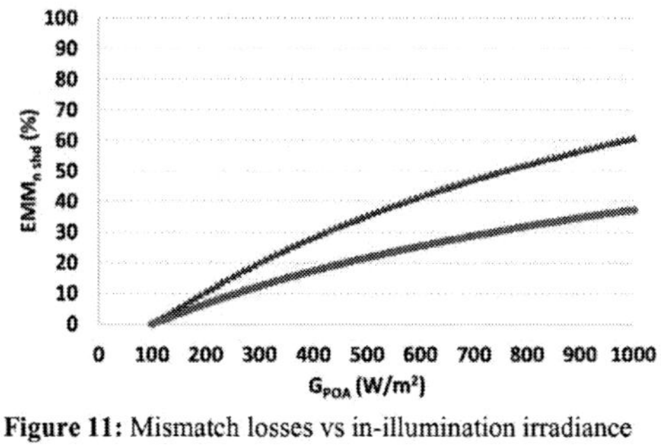

Figure 11: Mismatch losses vs in-illumination irradiance

over the PV panels

A quadratic relationship allows the estimation of mismatch losses for these cases, for different irradiance levels.

$$MML_G(\%) = a\ G_{POA}^2 + b\ G_{POA} - c \quad (6)$$

where G_{POA} is the plane-of-array irradiance. The values of each coefficient are shown in Table III.

Table III: Coefficients for mismatch losses estimations from shading casts and in-illumination irradiance

	Half-cell	Standard cell
a	-2.10^{-5}	-4.10^{-5}
b	0.067	0.111
c	-5.82	-9.84

It is worth noting that these models were developed specifically for parallel connections. Its accuracy for series connections remains to be verified.

3.5 From substrings to an entire PV plant

These estimates are calculated for the entire PV plant and accumulated over a full year. Figure 12 shows the maximum energy produced by each string over the year for the same 70 MWp PV plant as shown in Fig. 7. The output of each string is then proportionally compared to the highest-producing string, as indicated by the colour scheme. In this instance, the maximum energy accumulated by a single string is 51.4 MWh.

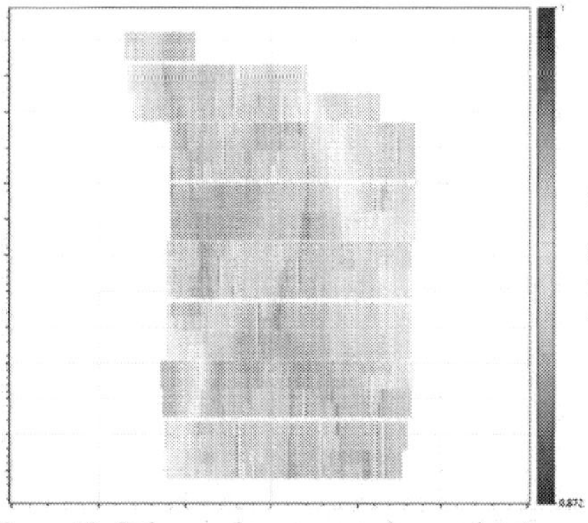

Figure 12: String maximum energy (accumulated) during a year for a 70 MW_p PV plant. The colours show the equivalent energy proportional to the string that produces the most energy

Fig. 13 depicts the maximum accumulated energy yielded by the inverters for the same PV plant and period. The total energy delivered in this case is 11.8 GWh.

10.4229/EUPVSEC2025/4DV.4.3

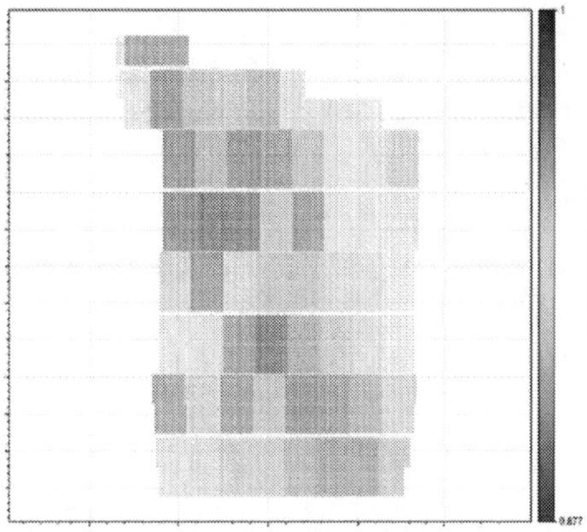

Figure 13: Inverter maximum energy (accumulated) during a year for a 70 MW_p PV plant. The colours show the equivalent energy proportional to the inverter that produces the most energy

For this PV plant, the combined Shading and Yield simulations ran about 43% faster than those based on I-V curves (40 min vs. 70 min). The yearly analysis considered roughly 85 transposition clusters and was carried out with a 15-minute time step. An interpolated simulation with the Sunveon model took 2.67 minutes in total, including per-string Shading Tables (0.32 min) and yield calculations (2.35 min). From this breakdown, it can be inferred that Shading calculations alone require 37.65 minutes. When isolating the yield component, the Sunveon model runs approximately 93% faster than full I-V curve simulations (2.35 min vs. 32.35 min). Although the extent of this computational gain depends on plant size, it remains highly significant even for smaller systems—for instance, around 75% faster for a 5 MW plant.

4 CONCLUSIONS

The challenge of accurately and efficiently estimating shading and mismatch losses in large-scale photovoltaic (PV) plants is a significant constraint for current production models. Conventional methods, which often rely on computationally expensive full I-V curve calculations or ray-tracing, can be slow. Conversely, simplified approaches may lead to substantial over- or underestimations of shading effects.

This study proposes the Sunveon Model, a novel and more efficient approach. It employs a hybrid transposition methodology, combining a 2D irradiance model with a 3D submodule-level shading model to accurately characterise incident irradiance on both standard and half-cell modules. A key advantage is its ability to estimate a string's Maximum Power Point (MPP) without requiring full I-V curve calculations, thus significantly reducing computational costs (between 75% and 93% for the yield calculation). The model also establishes a new method for quantifying mismatch losses using a 'Mixed Fill Factor,' allowing these losses to be calculated directly from a quadratic relationship.

The model's superior performance was validated against over 500,000 real I-V curves from five PV plants. The Sunveon Model consistently aligned more closely with this benchmark data compared to two industry-standard models, which were shown to systematically over or underestimate losses. Although errors for half-cell modules were slightly higher due to their more complex electrical topology, the model's performance remained highly precise, confirming its robustness.

A clear quadratic relationship was established between mismatch losses and both the percentage of cast shadow and the in-illumination irradiance. These equations allow for the direct estimation of losses. Notably, the analysis revealed that mismatch losses for standard cell modules are about two-thirds higher than for half-cell modules. It is important to note that these models were developed and validated specifically for parallel connections, with accuracy for series connections still to be verified.

In summary, the Sunveon Model offers a highly precise and robust tool for large-scale PV plant analysis, providing a valuable and computationally efficient alternative to existing methods by accurately modelling shading-induced and mismatch losses.

5 ACKNOWLEDGEMENTS

C.R. is partially supported by Torres Quevedo Grant No. PTQ2023-013183, funded by the Agencia Estatal de Investigación from the Spanish Ministry of Science. Most of the data used is available on the NREL web page, and the authors would like to thank them for it.

6 REFERENCES

[1] H. Rezk *et al.*, 'A novel statistical performance evaluation of most modern optimization-based global MPPT techniques for partially shaded PV system', *Renewable and Sustainable Energy Reviews*, vol. 115, Nov. 2019, doi: 10.1016/j.rser.2019.109372.

[2] O. Tsafarakis and W. G. J. H. M. van Sark, 'A density-based time-series data analysis methodology for shadow detection in rooftop photovoltaic systems', *Progress in Photovoltaics: Research and Applications*, vol. 31, no. 5, pp. 506–523, May 2023, doi: 10.1002/pip.3654.

[3] A. G. Olabi *et al.*, 'Artificial neural networks applications in partially shaded PV systems', *Thermal Science and Engineering Progress*, vol. 37, Jan. 2023, doi: 10.1016/j.tsep.2022.101612.

[4] R. Perez, P. Ineichen, R. Seals, J. Michalsky, and R. Stewart, 'Modeling daylight availability and irradiance components from direct and global irradiance', *Solar Energy*, vol. 44, no. 5, pp. 271–289, 1990, doi: 10.1016/0038-092X(90)90055-H.

[5] J. E. Hay, 'Calculation of monthly mean solar radiation for horizontal and inclined surfaces', *Solar Energy*, vol. 23, no. 4, pp. 301–307, 1979, doi: 10.1016/0038-092X(79)90123-3.

[6] M. A. Anoma, D. Jacob, B. C. Bourne, J. A. Scholl, D. M. Riley, and C. W. Hansen, 'View Factor Model and Validation for Bifacial PV and Diffuse Shade on Single-Axis Trackers', in *IEEE 44th Photovoltaic Specialists Conference (PVSC)*, Washington D.C., 2017, pp. 1549–1554. doi: 10.1109/pvsc.2017.8366704.

[7] D. Tschopp, A. R. Jensen, J. Dragsted, P. Ohnewein, and S. Furbo, 'Measurement and modeling of diffuse irradiance masking on tilted planes for solar engineering applications', *Solar Energy*, vol. 231, no. January, pp. 365–378, 2022, doi: 10.1016/j.solener.2021.10.083.

[8] A. Mermoud and T. Lejeune, 'Partial shading on PV arrays: by-pass diode benefits analysis', in *25th European Photovoltaic Solar Energy Conference*, Sep. 2010.

[9] C. Rossa, 'Energy losses in photovoltaic generators due to wind patterns', *Nature Communications Engineering*, vol. 2, no. 66, pp. 1–9, Sep. 2023, doi: 10.1038/s44172-023-00119-7.

[10] L. L. Bucciarelli, 'Power loss in photovoltaic arrays due to mismatch in cell characteristics', *Solar Energy*, vol. 23, no. 1, pp. 277–288, 1979.

[11] C. Rossa, F. Martinez-Moreno, and E. Lorenzo, 'Experimental observations in mismatch losses in monofacial and bifacial PV generators', *Progress in Photovoltaics: Research and Applications*, vol. 29, no. 12, pp. 1223–1235, Dec. 2021, doi: 10.1002/pip.3447.

[12] PVsyst, 'PVsyst shading calculation model - linear losses'. Accessed: Jul. 31, 2025. [Online]. Available: https://www.pvsyst.com/help-pvsyst7/shadings_model.htm

[13] M. Oliosi, B. Wittmer, and A. Mermoud, 'Analysis of Electrical Shading Effects in PV Systems', in *38th European PV Solar Energy Conference*, Sep. 2021, p. 2021.

[14] F. Martínez-Moreno, J. Muñoz, and E. Lorenzo, 'Experimental model to estimate shading losses on PV arrays', *Solar Energy Materials and Solar Cells*, vol. 94, no. 12, pp. 2298–2303, 2010, doi: 10.1016/j.solmat.2010.07.029.

[15] P. R. Satpathy and R. Sharma, 'Reliability and losses investigation of photovoltaic power generators during partial shading', *Energy Convers Manag*, vol. 223, Nov. 2020, doi: 10.1016/j.enconman.2020.113480.

[16] C. H. Rossa, E. Lorenzo, and F. Martinez-Moreno, 'Observations in PV module operation voltage distribution aling a PV array. An in-deep look on mismatch losses', in *35th European Photovoltaic Solar Energy Conference and Exhibition*, Brussels, 2018, pp. 2051–2055. doi: 10.4229/35thEUPVSEC20182018-6DV.1.38.

[17] R. Evans, M. Boreland, and M. A. Green, 'A holistic review of mismatch loss: From manufacturing decision making to losses in fielded arrays', *Solar Energy Materials and Solar Cells*, vol. 174, pp. 214–224, Jan. 2018, doi: 10.1016/J.SOLMAT.2017.08.041.

[18] C. Deline, S. Ayala Pelaez, S. MacAlpine, and C. Olalla, 'Estimating and parameterizing mismatch power loss in bifacial photovoltaic systems', *Progress in Photovoltaics: Research and Applications*, vol. 28, no. 7, pp. 691–703, Jul. 2020, doi: 10.1002/pip.3259.

42nd European Photovoltaic Solar Energy Conference and Exhibition

PREDICTING SHADING LOSSES IN PHOTOVOLTAIC PLANTS: A NOVEL APPROACH

D. López Dalmau, H. Mirandona López, C. Javier Lopes Gomes, J. Tomàs Villalonga Palou, C. Rossa*
Sunveon
Calle Musgo, 2, 1B, Madrid, Spain. 28023
*crossa@sunveon.com

Abstract

Accurately estimating shadow impact on large-scale photovoltaic (PV) plants is challenging due to the computational demands of traditional methods. This study introduces the Sunveon Model, a novel, efficient approach for simulating shading and mismatch losses without requiring complex I-V curve calculations. The model uses a hybrid methodology, combining a 2D irradiance model with a 3D submodule-level shading model. Its key innovation is the use of a regression model, based on over 500,000 I-V curves, to directly predict a string's Maximum Power Point (MPP), significantly reducing computational time. It also quantifies mismatch losses with a new 'Mixed Fill Factor' that establishes a direct quadratic relationship between losses, shadow percentage, and irradiance. Validated against real-world data, the Sunveon Model proved more accurate than two industry-standard models, showing substantially lower errors. A key finding is that mismatch losses for standard cells are about 70% higher than for half-cell modules. In summary, the Sunveon Model offers a precise and efficient tool for large-scale PV analysis.

Methodology

2D View factor Transposition

- Transposition model & view factors (front+rear).
- Accounts for terrain shadowing and diffuse shadings.
- Incident irradiance in 2 states: illumination + shade.

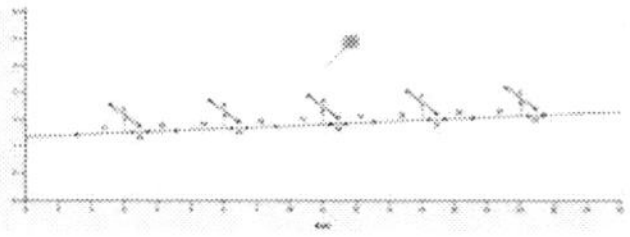

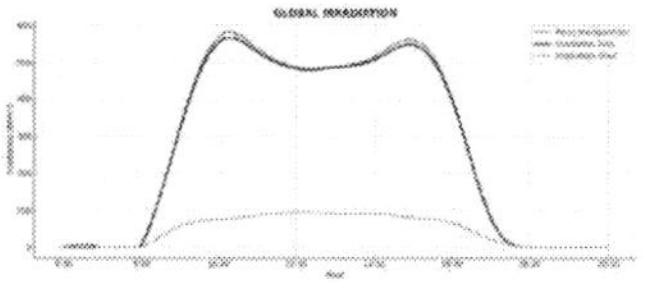

3D Shading Model

- 3D shadows: string level (% of submodules)

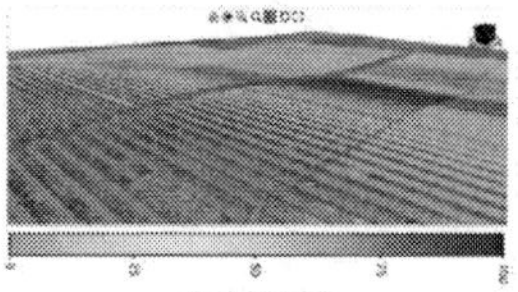

String Electrical Production (Sunveon Model)

- Regression model from I-V Curves
- High precision to estimate strings and arrays MPP

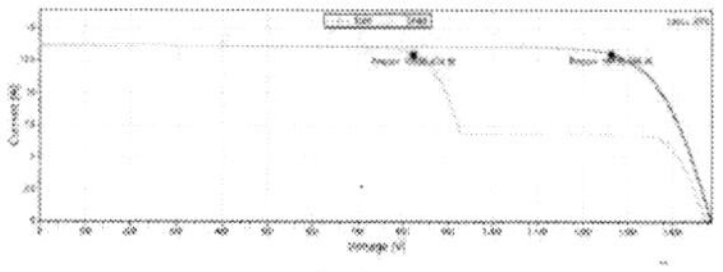

Standard Cell IV Curve

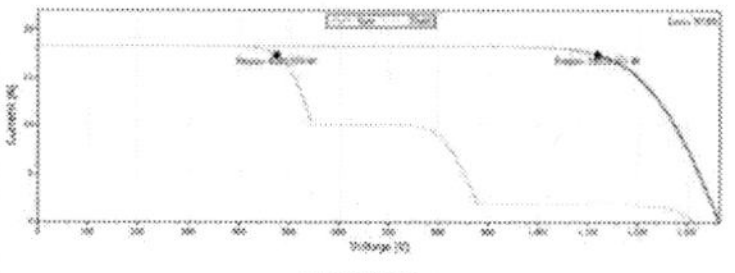

Half Cell IV Curve

Plant Production at inverter level

- Precise calculation of input conditions for inverter MPPTs
- Granular production data within the layout.
- "Mixed" fill factor: $FF_{mix} = \frac{I_{MPP,shd} V_{MPP,shd}}{I_{sc,STC} V_{oc,STC}}$
- Production according to PV plant Electrical Layout.

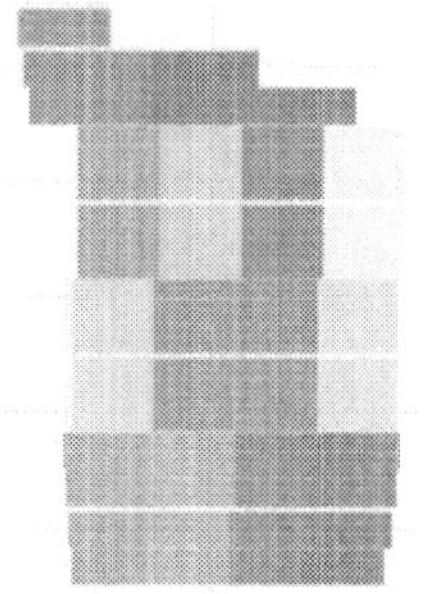

Results

String Losses estimation + Array Mismatch Losses = Energy Production

String Losses estimation

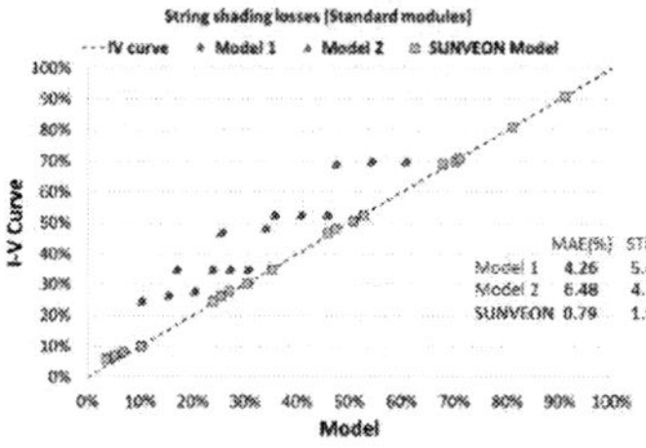

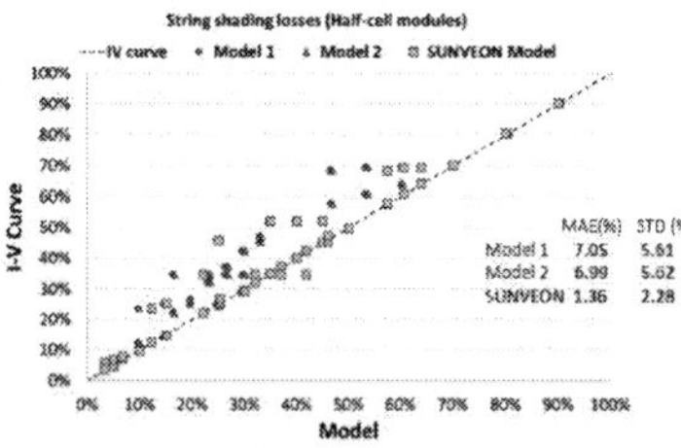

Array Mismatch Losses

$$EMM_{shd}(\%) = 1 - \frac{P_{total,array,shd}}{\sum_1^n P_{i,n\ string,shd}} \quad \text{VS} \quad CV_{FF,mix} = \frac{\sigma_{FF_{mix}}}{FF_{mix}}$$

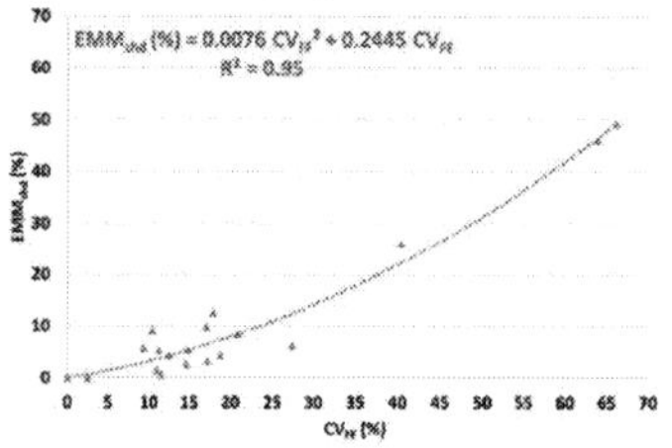

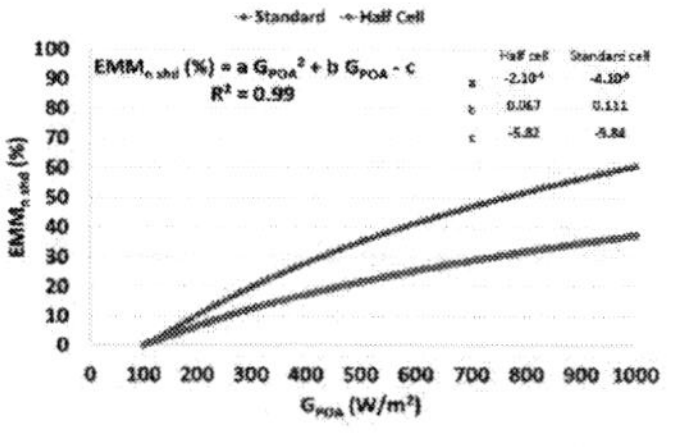

Energy Production

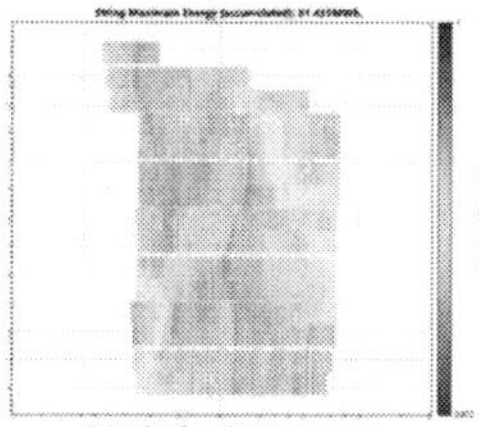

String level production per year

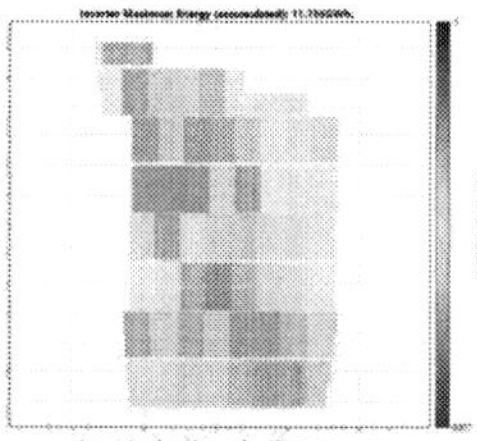

Inverter level production per year

Conclusions

- **New Model for Shading Losses**

The Sunveon Model is a novel, efficient tool that accurately estimates shading losses in large-scale PV plants. Unlike conventional methods that are slow or can be inaccurate, this model uses a hybrid approach to save computational time and provide precise results. Yield computation is between 75% faster for a 5 MW plant and up to 93% faster for a 70 MW plant compared to full I-V curve simulations.

- **Robustness of the Model**

The model's superior accuracy was proven by validating it against over 500,000 I-V curves. The Sunveon Model consistently performed better than the two other models.

- **Key Findings on Mismatch Losses**

The study established a direct, quadratic relationship between mismatch losses and the fill factor for parallel connections. It also found that standard cell modules have approximately 64% higher mismatch losses than half-cell modules, presenting a quadratic relationship with the irradiance.

Acknowledgements

MINISTERIO DE CIENCIA, INNOVACIÓN Y UNIVERSIDADES
AGENCIA ESTATAL DE INVESTIGACIÓN
NREL

SUNVEON

BACKTRACKING 3D: A NOVEL APPROACH TO CONVENTIONAL BACKTRACKING ALGORITHMS FOR IMPROVED PV PERFORMANCE IN COMPLEX TERRAINS

J. Tomás Villalonga Palou, D. López Dalmau, H. Mirandona López, C. Javier Lopes Gomes, C. Rossa
[1]SUNVEON
calle del Musgo, 2, 1B, Madrid, Spain. 28023

Backtracking strategies are widely used in photovoltaic (PV) plants to reduce shading, but they become ineffective on the irregular terrains typical of large-scale installations. Slope-aware approaches improve performance but rely on simplified terrain models, which fail to represent the diverse slopes of real PV layouts. As a result, current methods remain limited in mitigating shading losses, reducing irradiance capture, and lowering overall energy yield. To overcome these limitations, an innovative tracking strategy based on Machine Learning is proposed to optimize the performance of PV plants in complex terrains.

Keywords: backtracking strategies, irregular terrain, backtracking 3D, machine learning, shading losses

1 INTRODUCTION

Backtracking strategies are widely applied in tracking photovoltaic (PV) plants, to prevent mutual shadings between generators, especially during the early and late hours of the day[1]. In modern PV plants, which can cover areas as vast as a small city and reach installed powers in the gigawatt range[2], the inherent irregularity of the terrain makes conventional backtracking algorithms ineffective, as they fail to completely eliminate shading and consequently reduce the yield potential. In this sense, significant advancements have been made by incorporating slope-aware backtracking strategies[3], [4], [5], [6]. However, these tracking approaches assume a generalised terrain model, either flat or with a uniform slope, whereas real PV layouts are often installed in complex terrains made up of a wide variety of slopes, which limits the effectiveness of these methodologies in reducing the yield penalty due to near shadings. In this context, this work presents an innovative tracking strategy that accounts for the specificity of different zones within the plant site, based on a novel, multi-zonal clustering-based tracking strategy for photovoltaic plants in complex terrains (BT3D).

2 METHODOLOGY

2.1 The approach

The proposed methodology begins by dividing the plant site into distinct clusters, enabling a more granular and accurate representation of the landscape. This is achieved through machine learning techniques, specifically Ward's Hierarchical Clustering, which groups areas with similar terrain characteristics. The clustering is performed independently of the size or location of each zone within the plant—meaning that distant zones with comparable properties are treated similarly. This approach provides a precise characterization of the terrain, marking a significant departure from conventional methods that typically assume a uniform or gently sloping surface. Each cluster is assigned a specific transposition model (including bifaciality) and a coordinated tracker movement strategy, allowing for precise adaptation to local terrain slope and solar position. The rotation is determined by both the cross-axis slope of the terrain section and the representative axis tilt of the trackers in the selected cluster, as illustrated in Fig. 1

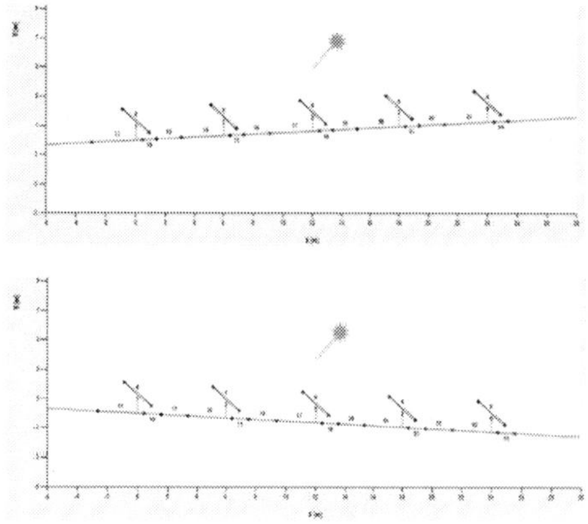

Figure 1: Cluster detail

This strategy optimizes tracker orientation according to the specific conditions of each zone, substantially reducing the negative impact of electrical shading on the PV plant's final energy yield. In addition, it improves irradiance capture and minimizes shading losses compared to conventional backtracking, which applies a single transposition model to the entire plant. In contrast, the proposed method assigns each cluster its own transposition value. This targeted approach is particularly relevant because it maximizes energy yield by adapting tracker orientation to local conditions, a key factor for efficient PV plant operation.

Under overcast conditions, the methodology further accounts for terrain heterogeneity at the cluster level. Within each cluster, the tracker rotation angle is optimized to maximize captured irradiance using Brent's method, a derivative-free numerical algorithm well suited for efficiently finding the optimal tilt. The search range spans from the standard tracking angle to the flat position (0°) and is adjusted by a slope-dependent margin, shown in equation 1:

$$\theta_{margin} = -\gamma \cdot \max(0, \cos\psi) \qquad (1)$$

where γ is the cross-axis slope angle and ψ is the angular difference between the solar azimuth and the slope aspect. This correction enables each cluster to progressively compensate for terrain slope when aligned with the solar vector. By allowing clusters to operate independently, the methodology contributes significantly to improving the overall energy yield of the plant.

2.2 Validation

The method is validated through simulations and compared with conventional backtracking, evaluating the increase in production in five real PV plants, located in Spain. Moreover, the predictability of the methodology, coupled with its significantly lower computational cost than other algorithms available in the market and literature (due to the group-based clustering behaviour), ensures compatibility with common simplifications in desktop software solutions, such as shading tables. The proposed approach offers a computationally efficient alternative to ray-tracing methods, which, while accurate, are computationally intensive (requiring 10,000 to 100,000 times more computing power) and impractical for conventional computers[7].

2.3 Brent's Algorithm

Brent's method [8] is a deterministic, derivative-free optimization algorithm designed to identify a local minimizer of a continuous function $f: [a,c] \to \mathbb{R}$ over a bounded interval $[a,c]$ known to contain at least one minimizer. The method achieves both efficiency and robustness by adaptively combining inverse quadratic interpolation (IQI) and golden-section search (GSS). At each iteration, three abscissae are maintained—x (the current best estimate), w (the second-best point), and v (the point before w)—which define a quadratic polynomial interpolating $(v, f(v))$, $(w, f(w))$, and $(x, f(x))$. The candidate minimizer x_p is obtained by solving $P'(q) = 0$, yielding the closed-form update:

$$x_p = x - \frac{(x-w)^2(f(x)-f(v))-(x-v)^2(f(x)-f(w))}{2[(x-w)(f(x)-f(v)-(x-v)(f(x)-f(w))]} \quad (2)$$

This step is accepted only if xp lies strictly within $[a,c]$ and is numerically stable, ensuring meaningful progress. Otherwise, the method reverts to a GSS step, in which the next candidate is computed as:

$$x_g = x \pm \varphi(c-x), \varphi = \frac{\sqrt{5}-1}{2} \approx 0.618 \quad (3)$$

This strategy shrinks the interval by a fixed ratio regardless of smoothness. After each new evaluation, the bracketing triplet (a,b,c) is updated to preserve the condition $a < b < c$ and $f(b) < min(f(a), f(c))$. Convergence is declared when the interval width satisfies $|c-a| < x_{tol}$ or when function values stagnate such that $|f(x\_new) - f(x)| < \varepsilon$. By blending the superlinear local convergence of IQI with the global reliability of GSS, Brent's method ensures robust minimization performance and is widely regarded as a standard in one-dimensional optimization.

2.4 Ward's Hierarchical Clustering Algorithm

Ward's method is an agglomerative hierarchical clustering [9] procedure that constructs a nested partition of a dataset by iteratively merging clusters. Unlike linkage criteria based on pairwise distances, Ward's method employs a minimum variance principle, selecting at each step the pair of clusters whose merger induces the smallest possible increase in the total within-cluster sum of squares. This criterion leads to compact and homogeneous clusters, making the method particularly suitable for exploratory data analysis.

Let clusters A and B contain nA and nB observations with centroids $\bar{x}_A$ and $\bar{x}_B$, respectively. The increase in the total within-cluster sum of squares resulting from their merger is:

$$\Delta(A,B) = \frac{nAnB}{nA+nB} \parallel \bar{x}_A - \bar{x}_B \parallel^2 \quad (4)$$

where $\|\cdot\|^2$ denotes the squared Euclidean norm. At each iteration, the pair (A,B) that minimizes $\Delta(A,B)$ is selected for fusion.

Algorithmic procedure

1. **Initialization:** Each of the N observations forms a singleton cluster.
2. **Iteration:** For all candidate pairs(A,B), compute $\Delta(A,B)$ and identify the minimizing pair.
3. **Update:** Replace clusters A and B by their union, update centroids and distances, and decrease the cluster count by one.
4. **Termination and interpretation:** The process continues until the desired number of clusters k is obtained, where k is specified according to the analytical objectives.

3 RESULTS AND DISCUSSION

Fig. 2 shows the distribution of the clusters considered at one of the analysed plants, which has an installed capacity of 51 MW. For this specific plant, the number of clusters is equal to 40.

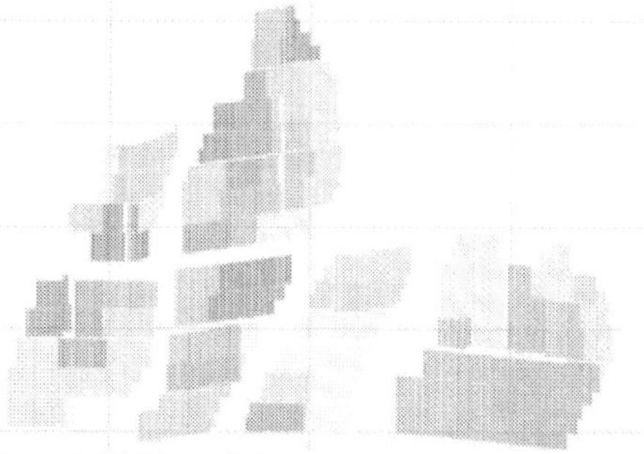

Figure 2: Multi-zonal cluster

Fig. 3 shows a heat map of the results for the same plant, comparing the 3D backtracking algorithm methodology (BT3D) with the traditional methodologies - standard tracking (ST) and conventional backtracking (BT) - during the early and late hours of the day, which are more prone to higher amounts of shading.

10.4229/EUPVSEC2025/4DV.4.4

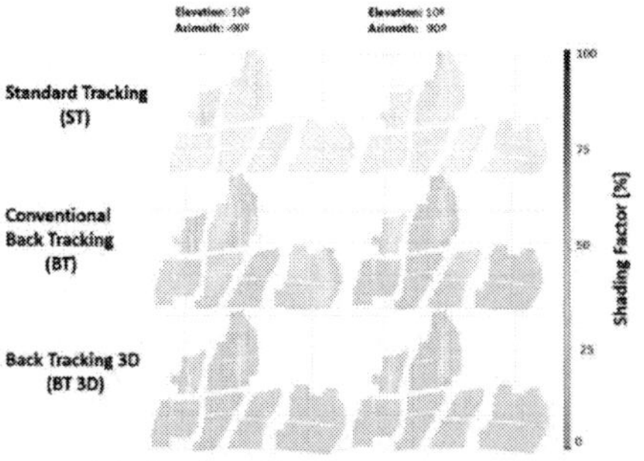

Figure 3: Shading factor heatmap

It should be noted that these specific results drawn from the analysed plant are equally representative of the other PV plants, without loss of generality. This is supported by the annual results for total energy accumulated by the strings, considering the different tracking strategies analyzed in Table I and Table II.

Table I: Strings total cumulative energy per plant. ST, BT and BT3D stands for standard tracking, conventional backtracking and backtracking 3D, respectively

		Total Cumulative Energy (Strings) per year [GWh]		
		Tracking Strategy		
Plant	**P[MW$_P$]**	**ST**	**BT**	**BT3D**
PV1	5.12	12.3	12.47	12.65
PV2	50.00	123.84	124.91	126.54
PV3	47.15	114.03	114.87	116.51
PV4	36.52	86.37	86.75	89.17

Table II: Comparison between standard strategies and the proposed strategy. ST, BT and BT3D stands for standard tracking, conventional backtracking and backtracking 3D, respectively

		Tracking Strategy Improvement	
Plant	**P[MW$_P$]**	**BT3D vs ST**	**BT3D vs BT**
PV1	5.12	2.85%	1.44%
PV2	50.00	2.18%	1.30%
PV3	47.15	2.17%	1.43%
PV4	36.52	3.24%	2.79%

The results indicate that the total energy accumulated by the strings using the BT3D strategy improves consistently, with an average gain of approximately 2.6% compared to ST and 1.7% compared to BT across the analysed plants. This increase in production is mainly attributed to the lower incidence of shading, which reduces both direct irradiance losses and the number of submodules affected by partial shading. As a representative case, Fig. 4 depicts the climate-dependence gain applying the proposed methodology for PV4.

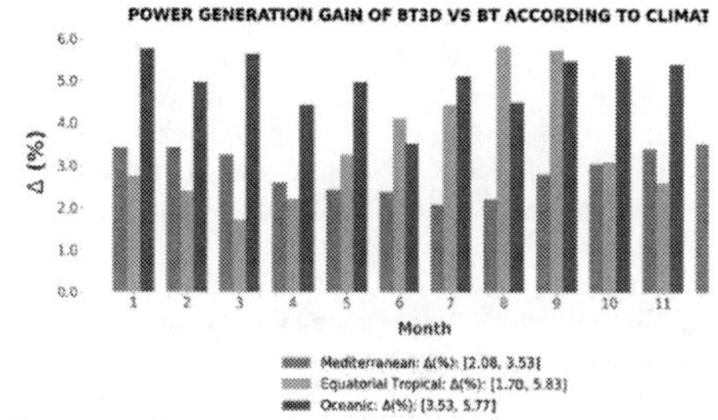

Figure 4: Climate-dependent power gain: BT3D vs BT

By analyzing the performance of the PV4 photovoltaic plant across diverse climates highlights the significant impact of geographical location on the energy output of the proposed algorithm. The results reveal substantial monthly gains in energy production, ranging from approximately 1.7% to 6%, depending on the climate. These improvements arise from the combination of detailed terrain modelling and the algorithm's ability to maximize captured irradiance under varying climate scenarios. This effect is further illustrated in the daily plots shown in Fig. 5, Fig. 6 and Fig. 7, which demonstrate the BT3D model's marked performance advantage over the BT model under specific weather conditions.

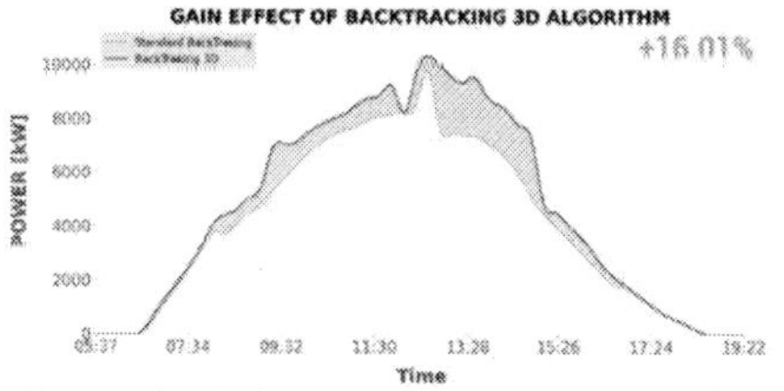

Figure 5: Typical overcast day – Equatorial tropical climate

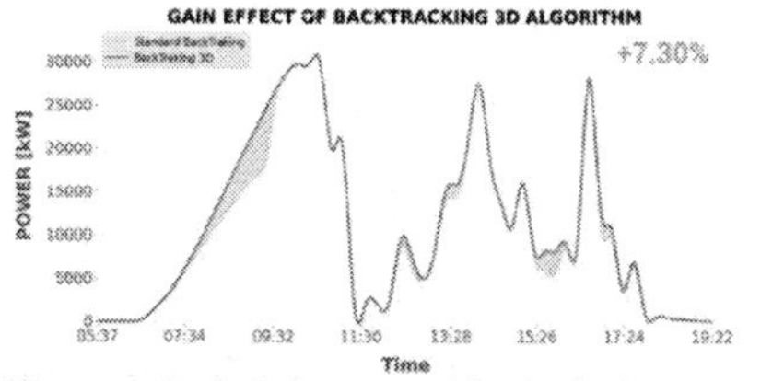

Figure 6: Typical clear to partialy cloudy day – Oceanic climate

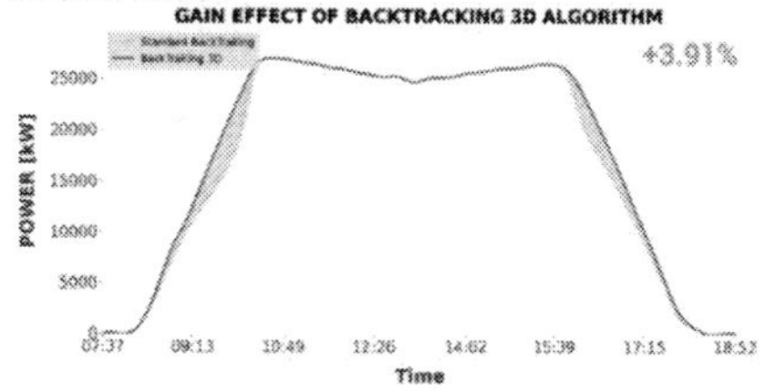

Figure 7: Typical sunny day – Mediterranean climate

10.4229/EUPVSEC2025/4DV.4.4

4 CONCLUSIONS

The detailed terrain representation achieved through clustering improves the accuracy of incident irradiance calculations, resulting in a 1.7% increase in string production compared to conventional backtracking (BT) and a 2.6% increase compared to standard tracking (ST). This improvement is particularly relevant, as accurate irradiance estimation is essential for optimizing PV plant design and operation, especially in challenging terrains.

In addition, the BT3D model demonstrates substantial performance improvements over the BT model under specific climatic scenarios, with gains ranging from 1.7% compared to BT to 6% compared to ST.

The predictable tracker behavior within each cluster also makes the proposed methodology compatible with commonly used simplified shading solutions, such as Shading Tables. This compatibility enables efficient integration with existing design tools while reducing computational burden, thereby facilitating the practical implementation of the method in real-world PV plant design and assessment.

Furthermore, the proposed method offers a computationally efficient alternative to traditional ray-tracing techniques, requiring 10,000 to 100,000 times less computing power. This efficiency not only overcomes significant computational limitations but also broadens accessibility, making the approach suitable for a wider range of users and projects.

5 ACKNOWLEDGEMENTS

C.R. is partially supported by Torres Quevedo Grant No. PTQ2023-013183, funded by the Agencia Estatal de Investigación from the Spanish Ministry of Science. Most of the data used is available on the NREL web page, and the authors would like to thank them for it.

6 REFERENCES

[1] E. Lorenzo, L. Narvarte, and J. Muñoz, 'Tracking and back-tracking', *Progress in Photovoltaics: Research and Applications*, vol. 19, no. 6, pp. 747–753, Sep. 2011, doi: 10.1002/pip.1085.

[2] V. Shaw, 'World's largest solar plant goes online in China', PV Magazine. Accessed: Jan. 29, 2025. [Online]. Available: https://www.pv-magazine.com/2024/06/06/worlds-largest-solar-plant-goes-online-in-china-2/

[3] K. S. Anderson and A. R. Jensen, 'Shaded fraction and backtracking in single-axis trackers on rolling terrain', *Journal of Renewable and Sustainable Energy*, vol. 16, no. 2, Mar. 2024, doi: 10.1063/5.0202220.

[4] K. Anderson and M. Mikofski, 'Slope-Aware Backtracking for Single-Axis Trackers', Golden, CO, 2020. [Online]. Available: https://www.nrel.gov/docs/fy20osti/76626.pdf.

[5] L. Perez *et al.*, 'Comparison of tracking algorithms for photovoltaic systems on irregular terrains', in *40th European Photovoltaic Solar Energy Conference and Exhibition (EU PVSEC)*, 2023, pp. 1–4. [Online]. Available: https://www.researchgate.net/publication/374387385

[6] E. Cooper, K. Anderson, and D. Riley, 'Performance Improvements Through Advanced PV Backtracking on Uneven Terrain', *IEEE J Photovolt*, pp. 1–7, 2025, doi: 10.1109/JPHOTOV.2025.3558254.

[7] A. Asgharzadeh *et al.*, 'A Benchmark and Validation of Bifacial PV Irradiance Models', *Conference Record of the IEEE Photovoltaic Specialists Conference*, no. July, pp. 3281–3287, 2019, doi: 10.1109/PVSC40753.2019.8981272.

[8] R. P. Brent, *Algorithms for Minimization without Derivatives*, vol. 1. Englewood Cliffs, New Jersey: Prentice-Hall, 1973.

[9] J. H. Ward, 'Hierarchical Grouping to Optimize an Objective Function', *J Am Stat Assoc*, vol. 58, no. 301, pp. 236–244, Mar. 1963, doi: 10.1080/01621459.1963.10500845.

BACKTRACKING 3D: A NOVEL APPROACH TO CONVENTIONAL BACKTRACKING ALGORITHMS FOR IMPROVED PV PERFORMANCE IN COMPLEX TERRAINS

J. Tomàs Villalonga Palou, D. López Dalmau, H. Mirandona López, C. Javier Lopes Gomes, C. Rossa
Sunveon
Calle Musgo, 2, 1B, Madrid, Spain. 28023
*crossa@sunveon.com

Abstract

Backtracking strategies are widely used in photovoltaic (PV) plants to reduce shading, but they become ineffective on the irregular terrains typical of large-scale installations. Slope-aware approaches improve performance but rely on simplified terrain models, which fail to represent the diverse slopes of real PV layouts. As a result, current methods remain limited in mitigating shading losses, reducing irradiance capture, and lowering overall energy yield. To overcome these limitations, an innovative tracking strategy based on Machine Learning is proposed to optimize the performance of PV plants in complex terrains.

Methodology

Clustering Strategy

- Apply Ward's Hierarchical Clustering
- Input: Geometrical parameters of PV structures
- Output: Multi-zonal segmentation of uneven terrain

Tracker coordination

- Each cluster enables grouped tracker rotation
- Rotation adapts to:
  - Local terrain slope
  - Solar position

Transposition Modeling

- Assign cluster-specific transposition
- Includes bifacial effects

Performance Optimization

- Under overcast conditions, clusters rotate to maximize irradiance capture by using an efficient numerical search (Brent's method).

Figure 1: Multi-zonal cluster **Figure 2:** Cluster detail

Figure 1 illustrates the proposed **terrain clustering** approach applied to a specific photovoltaic plant. Figure 2 shows how each **cluster** is assigned a **distinct solar transposition**, adapted to the local **cross-axis slope** and **axis tilt** conditions.

Results

Performance Comparison

- A heat map (Figure 3) compares three solar tracking methods: **3D backtracking (BT3D), standard tracking (ST), and conventional backtracking (BT).**
- The comparison focuses on performance during the early and late hours of the day when shading is most significant.
- Results for this plant are **representative of all other plants** analyzed, as supported by the annual energy data in Table I.

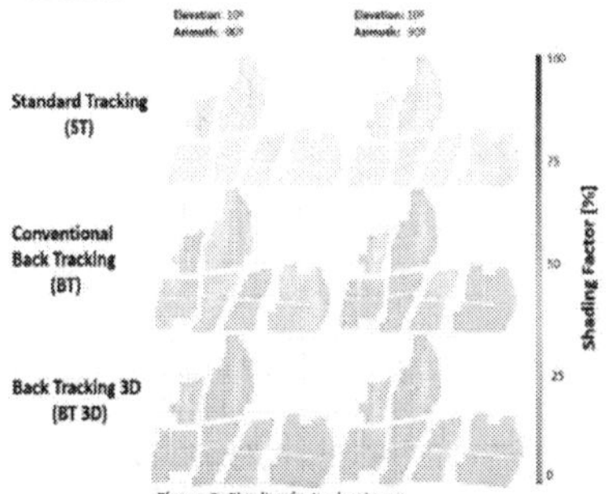

Figure 3: Shading factor heatmap

Plant	P [MW$_p$]	BT3D vs ST	BT3D vs BT
		Tracking Strategy Improvement	
PV1	5.12	2.85%	1.44%
PV2	50.00	2.18%	1.30%
PV3	47.15	2.17%	1.43%
PV4	36.52	3.24%	2.79%

Table I: Comparison between standard strategies and the proposed strategy

Impact of Location and Climate

- Figure 4 illustrates how the PV4 plant's energy performance changes with geographic location and climate.
- The study used **Typical Meteorological Year (TMY)** datasets for **Mediterranean, equatorial tropical, and oceanic climates.**
- The original plant geometry was maintained to isolate the effect of climate on the proposed algorithm's performance.

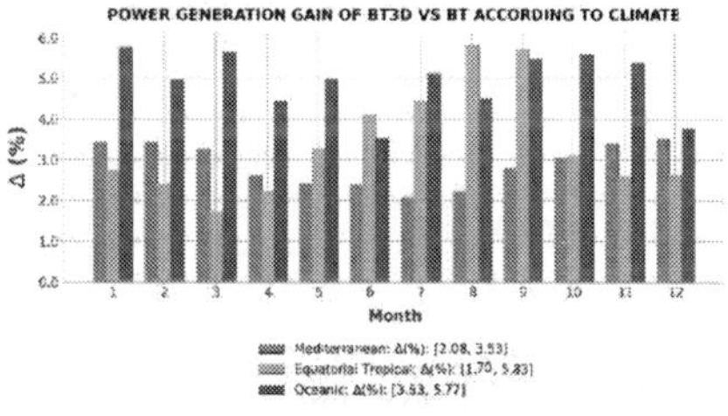

Figure 4: Climate-dependent power gain: BT3D vs BT

Energy Performance

- The proposed method shows significant monthly gains in energy production.
- This gain is due to the synergy between **terrain granularity** and **maximized irradiance.**
- Figures 5, 6, and 7 show that the **BT3D model** substantially outperforms the **BT model** on certain days and under specific weather conditions.

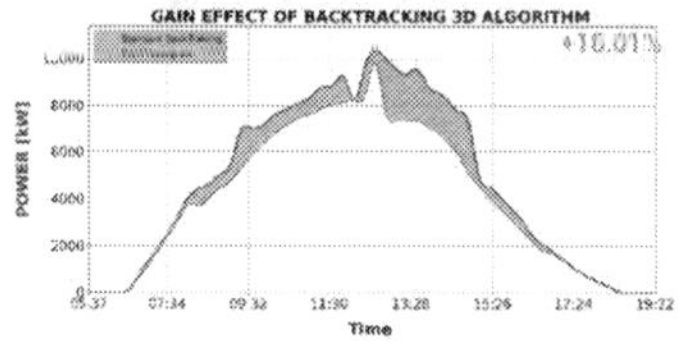

Figure 5: Typical overcast day – Equatorial tropical climate

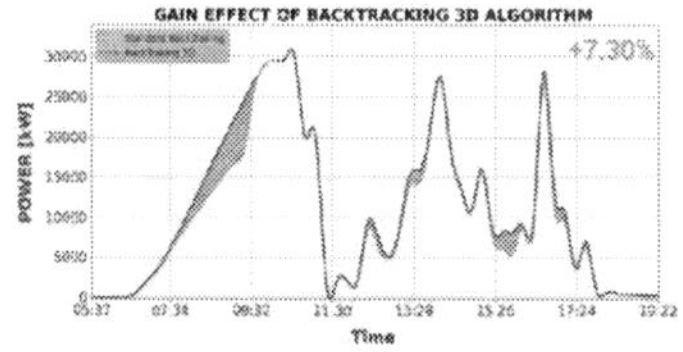

Figure 6: Typical clear to partially cloudy day – Oceanic climate

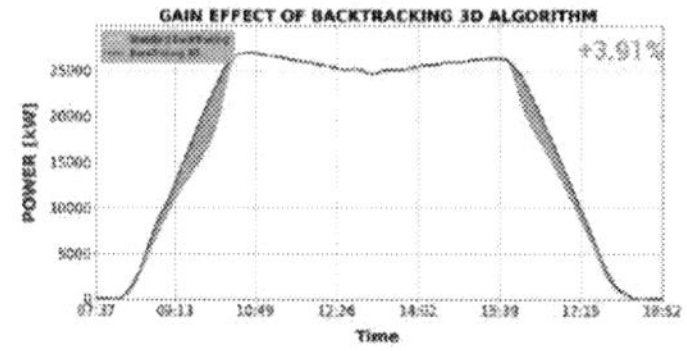

Figure 7: Typical sunny day – Mediterranean climate

Conclusions

- **Increased Production:** The new method, which uses terrain clustering, boosts electrical production by **1.7% over conventional backtracking (BT)** and **2.6% over standard tracking (ST).**
- **Efficient & Practical:** This approach is compatible with existing tools like **Shading Tables**, making it easy to integrate into current design workflows without a heavy computational burden.
- **Computational Power:** It is highly efficient, requiring **10,000 to 100,000 times less computing power** than traditional ray-tracing methods, making it widely accessible.

Acknowledgements

MINISTERIO DE CIENCIA, INNOVACIÓN Y UNIVERSIDADES
AGENCIA ESTATAL DE INVESTIGACIÓN
NREL

SUNVEON

Evaluation of Front Eave Load Caused by Snow Accumulation on Photovoltaic Array

Tadanori Tanahashi[1], Takahiro Chiba[2], Satoru Adachi[3], Hayato Arakawa[3], Yuki Tsuno[1], Kazuaki Ikeda[1], and Takashi Oozeki[1]

[1] National Institute of Advanced Industrial Science and Technology (AIST), Japan
[2] Hokkaido University of Science, Japan
[3] National Research Institute for Earth Science and Disaster Resilience (NIED), Japan

Background and Motivation

During the 2020-2021 snow season, the maximum snow depth on the ground exceeded 2 meters at the nearest meteorological station of the Japan Meteorological Agency (JMA).

Summary

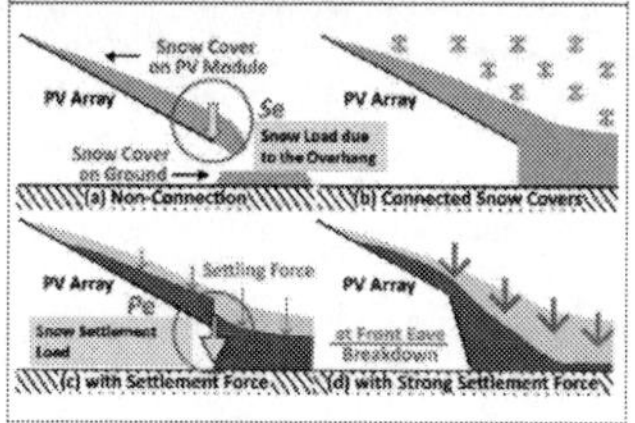

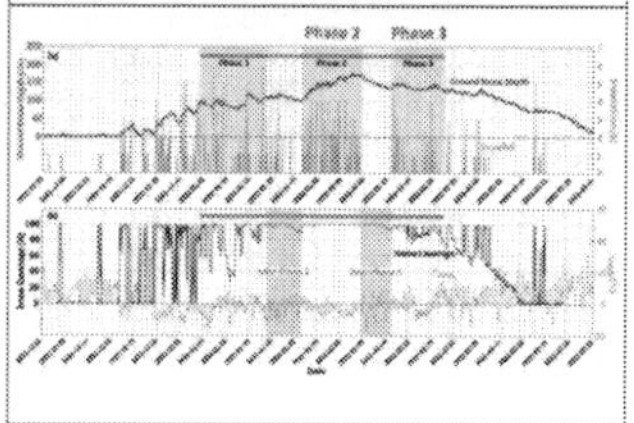

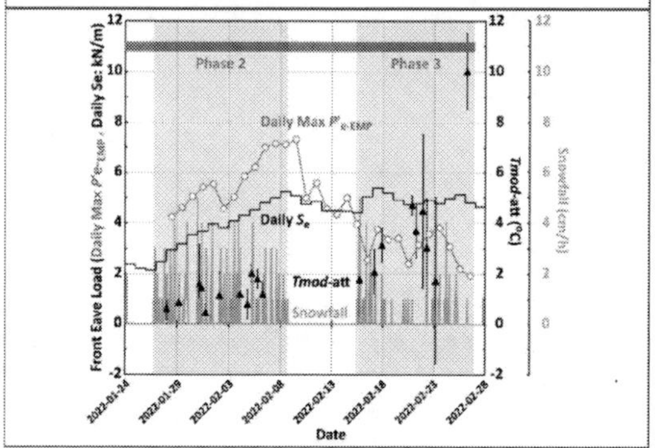

In snowy high-latitude and high-altitude regions, photovoltaic (PV) systems often experience heavy snow accumulation on their modules, which can cause significant damage to both the modules and their mounting structures. Such damage is largely attributed to the heavy snow load on the front eave of the PV array. This load increases due to (1) snow overhang at the front eave (S_e), (2) settlement forces generated by the connection between the snow on the modules and the snow accumulated on the ground (P_e), and not only (3) the direct snow load on the PV modules themselves. To date, the loads from direct snow accumulation on modules and snow overhang (S_e) have been addressed, and corresponding structural safety test procedures (IEC 61215 and IEC 62938) have been established as international standards. However, the additional load on the front eave caused by settlement of merged snow (P_e) has not been accurately evaluated. Furthermore, the relative strength of S_e and P_e has remained undetermined.

In this study, we estimated the linear load at the front eave (P'_e) and S_e during one snow season in a heavy-snow region and found that the intensity of P'_e greatly exceeded the load caused by snow overhang on the PV array (see the respective intensities during phase 2 in the left figure). This finding suggests that the structural safety requirements for snow load specified in the current IEC 62938 standard may be insufficient to mitigate the heavy snow loads observed in snowy high-latitude and high-altitude regions.

We also observed a distinctive evolution of snow loads in the front eave region [see the respective intensities during phase 3 in the left figure], which decreased due to heating of the PV modules. We expect that the heating of PV modules could serve as a potential measure to mitigate heavy snow loads in existing PV arrays installed in these areas.

Results

[Panel 01] Experimental Setup

Before Snowfall

Approx. Max Snow Accumulation

Vertical loads to the respective 4 pods were measured with load cells.

[Panel 02] Snow Load due to the Overhang

IEC 62938: 2020 Photovoltaic (PV) modules – Non-uniform snow load testing

$$S_e = \frac{(\mu_i \cdot S_k)^2}{\gamma}$$

S_e: Snow load due to the overhang (kN/m)
μ_i: Snow Load Shape Coefficient (depend on inclination)
　e.g. "0.8" at 10 degree
S_k: Characteristic Snow Load on the Ground (kN/m²)
γ: Specific Snow Weight (kN/m³)

[Panel 03] Estimation of Daily Se

Specific Snow Weight (γ: kN/m³)　　Snow Depth on the Ground (D: m)

Snow Water Equivalent (SWE: mm)　Snow Depth measured with Snow Stake (D: m)
Daily SWE measured at NIED (Shinjo, JP)　Daily D acquired at NIED (Shinjo, JP)

SWE (mm) → Daily Sp. Snow Weight (γ: kN/m³)

Characteristic Snow Load (S_k: kN/m²)

Daily S_k Can be Calculated!!

Snow Load due to the Overhang (Daily Se: kN/m)

$$Daily\ S_e = \frac{(\mu_i \cdot Daily\ S_k)^2}{\gamma}$$

Snow Pillow (Metal Wafer Type) for SWE Measurement

[Panel 04] Daily Trends on Snow Load

2021 - 2022 Snow Season (at NIED, Shinjo, JP)

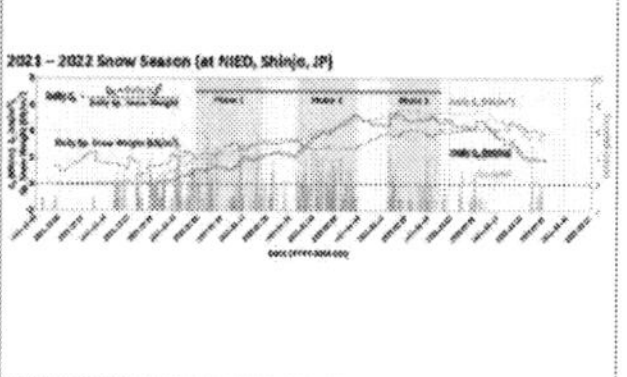

[Panel 05] Front Eave Load (P_e)

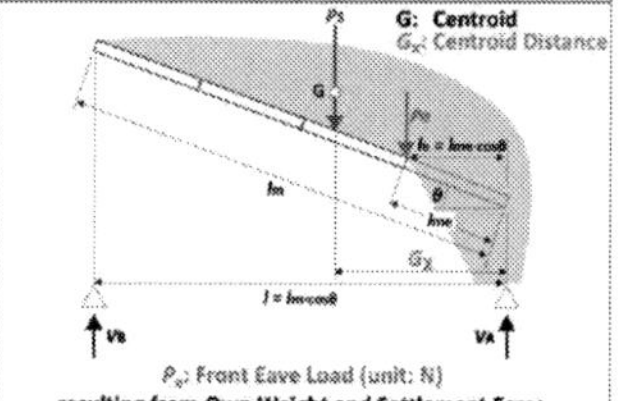

G: Centroid
G_x: Centroid Distance

P_e: Front Eave Load (unit: N)
resulting from Own Weight and Settlement Force

[Panel 06] Linear Load at Front Eave (P'_e)

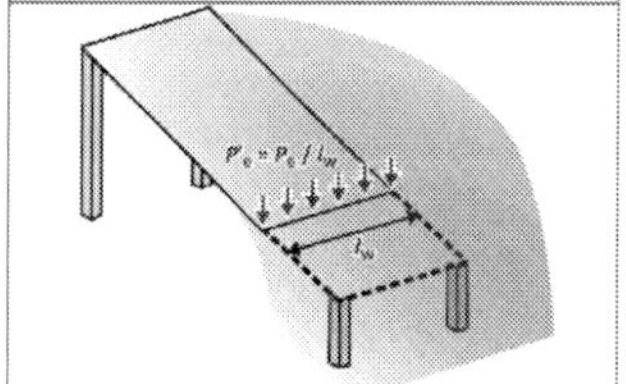

P'_e: Linear Load at Front Eave (unit: N/m)

[Panel 07] Calculation of Front Eave Load

P_e: Front Eave Load (unit: N)

$$P_e = \frac{V_A \cdot l - a}{b}$$

where

$$a = \frac{V_B \cdot l \cdot (l - G_X)}{G_X}$$

$$b = (l - lme \cdot \cos\theta) + \frac{lme \cdot \cos\theta \cdot (l - G_X)}{G_X}$$

P'_e: Linear Load at Front Eave (unit: N/m)

$$P'_e = \frac{P_e}{l_w}$$

[Panel 08] Estimation of Centroid Distance (G_x)

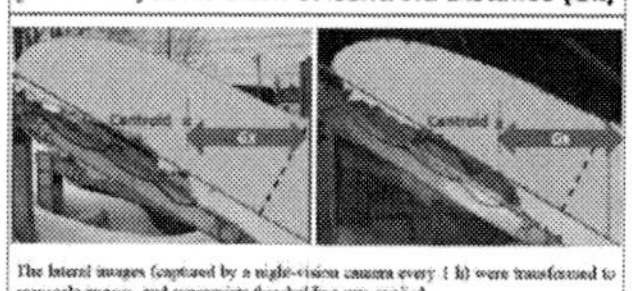

The lateral images (captured by a night-vision camera every 1 h) were transformed to grayscale images, and appropriate thresholding was applied.

Then, using the "Alucalic" package integrated into ImageJ software, the area of accumulated snow on the PV modules was extracted (Blue filled area), and the centroid of the snow accumulation (Red cross mark) was determined.

Centroid Distance (G_x) indicates the distance between the centroid and the bottom edge of PV modules.

[Panel 09] Evolution of $P'_{e\text{-GT}}$ and $P'_{e\text{-FIXED-GX}}$

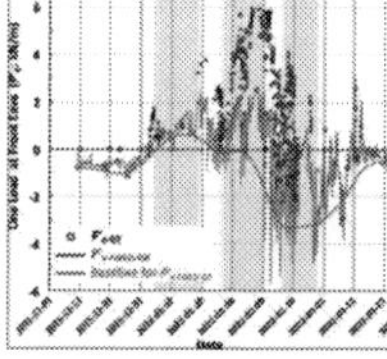

$P'_{e\text{-GT}}$: P'_e values calculated using the measured G_X.

$P'_{e\text{-FIXED-GX}}$: P'_e values calculated using a fixed G_X value of 1.4 m.

Baseline for $P'_{e\text{-GT}}$: Baseline determined using the Asymmetric Least Squares (ALS) Smoothing function, for $P'_{e\text{-FIXED-GX}}$.

[Panel 10] Correlations: $P'_{e\text{-GT}}$ & Corrected $P'_{e\text{-FIXED-GX}}$

(a) Phase 2

(b) Phase 3

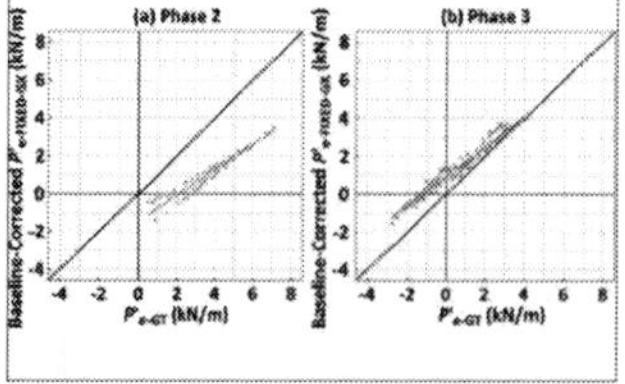

[Panel 11] Evolution of $P'_{e\text{-GT}}$ and $P'_{e\text{-EMP}}$

$P'_{e\text{-EMP}}$: Empirically Corrected Front Eave Load (kN/m)
= [$P'_{e\text{-FIXED-GX}}$] - [Baseline for $P'_{e\text{-FIXED-GX}}$]

Phase 2   Phase 3

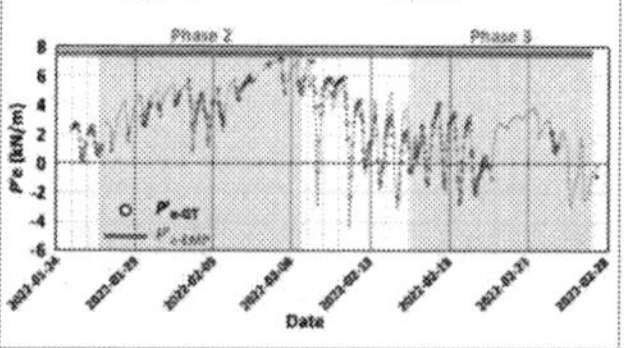

[Panel 12] T_{mod} Evolution with Panel Heating

$$T_{mod\text{-}obs} = \alpha \cdot exp(-\beta \cdot t) + T_{mod\text{-}att}$$

$T_{mod\text{-}obs}$: Observed Module Temperature
$T_{mod\text{-}att}$: Attained Module Temperature

Event ID: 41 (03 Area)
$T_{mod\text{-att}}$
$T_{mod\text{-obs}}$

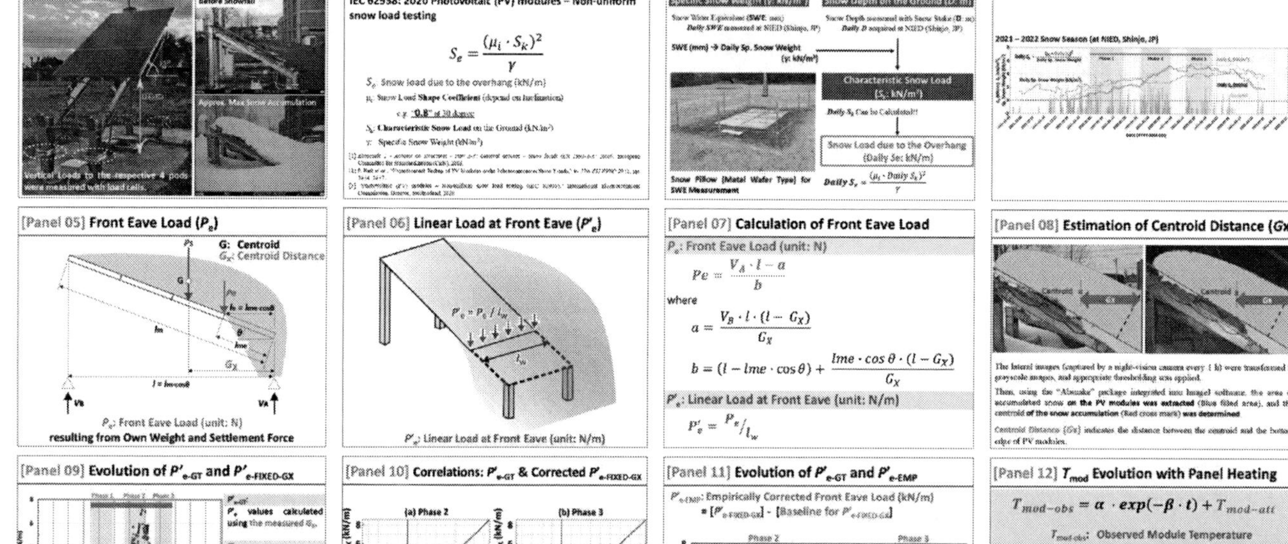

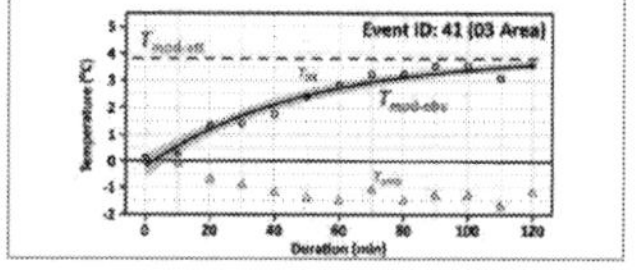

This work was supported in part by the "AIST Program for Promoting Technologies Invented by Industries in Disaster Areas in Tohoku (Seeds Support Program)".

EXPERIMENTAL SET-UP FOR VALIDATION OF MAXIMUM POWER POINT TRACKING ALGORITHMS FOR PHOTOVOLTAIC ARRAYS

Laura Sanchez[1], Gorka Torre[1],Jesus Sanchez[2],Alexander Maiz[2], Alain Sanchez-Ruiz[2], Josu Jugo[1] and Eneko Ortega[1,3]
[1] Electricity and Electronics Department, University of the Basque Country UPV/EHU, 48940, Leioa, Spain
[2] Department of Electronic Technology, University of the Basque Country UPV/EHU, 01006, Vitoria-Gasteiz, Spain
[3] Technological Institute of Microelectronics, University of the Basque Country UPV/EHU, 48013, Bilbao, Spain
eneko.ortegam@ehu.eus

ABSTRACT: The implementation of maximum power point tracking (MPPT) algorithms is essential for improving the performance ratio of photovoltaic (PV) systems. These algorithms optimize the energy generated by solar modules, ensuring maximum efficiency. Maximizing energy production becomes particularly important in sub-optimal conditions, such as partial shading, defects, and variable or diffuse irradiance. MPPT also mitigates the effects of mismatches between modules. This study developes a functional setup for testing and validating various MPPT algorithms. This setup will be developed in both a MATLAB-Simulink simulation environment and a laboratory setting and will be evaluated with two common MPPT algorithms: Perturb & Observe and Incremental Conductance under several scenarios, including changes in illumination, partial shading, and defects in the PV modules, such as variations in series and shunt resistance.
Keywords: photovoltaic systems, maximum power point tracking

1 INTRODUCTION

The growth of photovoltaic (PV) solar energy is increasing sharply during the last years, with a growth of more than 500 GW of installed PV capacity during 2024 [1]. Efficiency and performance of PV systems are growing in parallel. Performance is usually measured in terms of performance ratio (PR) [2], where performance losses, even for modern and well monitored PV systems can be up to 15 % [3]. Performance of PV systems may be affected by several causes such as high temperatures [4], shading of the PV modules [5], defects on the PV modules [6] or by system losses or inefficiencies.

PV arrays, composed by a variable number of PV modules connected in series and parallel, are in turn connected to an electronic circuit following different architectures as shown in [7]. When the PV modules feeds a DC bus, the used electronic circuit is a DC-DC converter. To ensure that the PV system is working at its maximum power, DC-DC converters can include maximum power point tracking (MPPT) algorithms. MPPT algorithms fix the PV modules operating current and voltage trough the control of the duty cycle of the DC-DC converter to ensure that the PV system power output is maximum.

The maximum power point (MPP) of the PV system depends on varying temperature and solar irradiation conditions. Recent studies have shown that solar irradiation conditions show high variability, of more than a 60% within the same day, being difficult to forecast [8], [9]. The use of an MPPT significantly improves the PR of a PV system by optimizing the use of the energy generated by the modules. The MPPT dynamically adjusts the voltage-current ratio so that the modules always operate at their MPP. This reduces electrical losses by preventing the PV modules from operating outside their optimal point, maximizing energy production even in suboptimal scenarios such as partial shading, presence of defects or diffuse and varying irradiance. The incorporation of this technology also mitigates the impact of mismatches between modules, improving overall system efficiency [10].

Several MPPT algorithms have been proposed by different authors to continuously recalculate the MPP of the PV system and obtain the maximum output power under varying operating conditions. Among the best known is the Perturb and Observe (P&O) algorithm, which is simple and effective under stable conditions, but it can exhibit oscillations under rapid changes in irradiance. The Incremental Conductance (IncCond), on the other hand is particularly useful in scenarios of varying irradiance. Recently, more sophisticated and accurate MPPT algorithms have been proposed based on Fuzzy Logic, optimization techniques or artificial neural networks [11], [12], reporting higher accuracies in achieving MPP with lower convergence times. However, they also require higher computational requirements, which may make it difficult to implement low-cost devices such as microcontrollers.

In this context, the aim of this work is to build a functional set-up in a simulation environment in MATLAB-Simulink, to deploy and validate different MPPT algorithms. The set-up will be validated with P&O and IncCond algorithms using a single PV module and a DC-DC Boost converter. The developed set-up will be used for the development and validation of new MPPT algorithms and for educational purposes.

2 DESCRIPTION OF THE SYSTEM

The basic diagram of the implemented system is shown in Fig.1. The system is composed by a PV system connected to a resistive load through a DC-DC Boost converter (to increase the output voltage). This resistive load represents the consumption of a load demanding the power generated by the PV system. The ratio between the input and output voltage in a Boost DC-DC converter is given by Eq. 1, where D is the duty cycle of the converter.

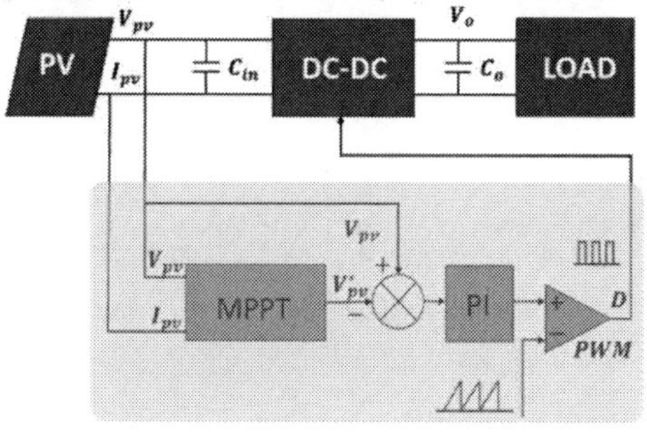

Figure 1: Schematic diagram of the implemented system

$$V_{out} = \frac{V_{PV}}{1-D} \quad (1)$$

The PV module operates at a working point, generating a current I_{pv} and a voltage V_{pv}. The MPPT algorithm controls the operating point by shifting it to the point where the output power of the PV module is at its maximum. For that I_{pv} and V_{pv} are measured and following different algorithms (P&O or IncCond) the MPPT algorithm determines the reference voltage $V_{pv}*$ that maximizes the power generated by the PV module. This value is compared with the actual voltage V_{pv}, generating an error signal that is minimized by a proportional-integral (PI) controller. The PI controller adjusts the duty cycle D, modulated by a pulse width modulation (PWM) signal, to control the DC-DC converter and maximize the power output. In fact, what is controlled by the DC-DC converter is its equivalent input impedance, adapting it to the dynamic resistance of the module at its MPP. This is done by modifying the duty cycle D that relates the input and output impedance of the converter, that is, the load impedance and the one seen by the module, as shown in Eq. 2.

$$R_{opt} = \frac{V_{MPP}}{I_{MPP}} = Z_{OUT}(1-D)^2 \quad (2)$$

The MPPT algorithm adjusts D dynamically as a function of the varying irradiance and temperature conditions, aiming to have the module operating at its MPP permanently.

The first algorithm to be implemented, P&O, is one of the simplest and most widespread MPPT techniques. It consists of periodically changing the PV module voltage in small increments proportional to the slope of the dP/dV curve, according to Eq. 3 and Eq. 4, where k is the current time instant, and observing the change in the generated power.

$$Vpv(k+1) = Vpv(k) \pm \Delta Vpv(k+1) \quad (3)$$

$$\Delta Vpv(k+1) = \Delta Vpm(k) \pm K\frac{P(k)-P(k-1)}{V(k)-V(k-1)} \quad (4)$$

If the power increases, the direction of the perturbation is maintained; if it decreases, the direction is reversed to approach the MPP. This process is repeated continuously, adjusting the voltage to maximize PV modules output power. Although simple and easy to implement, it can generate oscillations around the optimum point under stable conditions and respond slowly to rapid changes in irradiance or temperature.

The IncCond, unlike the P&O method, relies on calculating the derivative of power with respect to voltage (dP/dV). At the MPP, this derivative is zero. The algorithm computes the incremental conductance (ΔI/ΔV) and compares it to the instantaneous conductance (I/V). When both are equal, the system is operating at the MPP; if not, the voltage is adjusted in the appropriate direction to reach it. This method offers greater accuracy under rapidly changing irradiance conditions, although it is more complex to implement than P&O.

3 SIMULATION

Firstly, the proposed system has been implemented and validated on a simulation environment. For that, the model shown in Fig. 2 has been developed in MATLAB-Simulink.

The implemented model consists of a user-defined PV module connected to a DC-DC boost converter controlled by a PWM signal. The PV module used for the simulations was a commercial PV module of 120 cells and 3 bypass diodes with Isc = 14.26 A and Voc = 47.06 V .

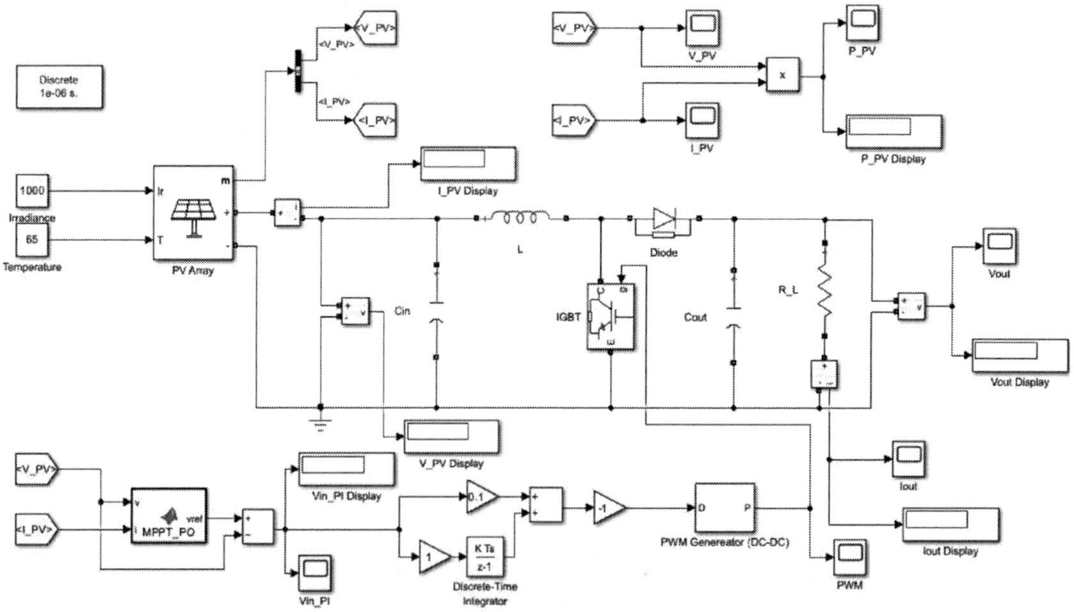

Figure 2: System model diagram developed in MATLAB-Simulink.

10.4229/EUPVSEC2025/4DV.4.9

Cin is a 150 µF capacitor connected between the PV string and the DC-DC converter to emulate the intrinsic capacitance of the PV modules as a consequence of the quick dynamic behavior of the system. The DC-DC boost converter has an inductor of 622 mH, a capacitor of 140 µF , a diode and a MOSFET as active switch with internal freewheeling diode. The boost converter is controlled by a PWM signal whose switching frequency is 20 kHz. The PWM signal is generated using a MPPT algorithm and a PI controller.

The developed system has been simulated and validated using both the MPPT P&O and IncCond algorithms, under different conditions. Four different scenarios are presented below. First, when the PV module is operating correctly and does not present any type of fault or degradation. For the purpose of the simulation, the following parameters were defined: Rsh = 228.42 Ω and Rs = 0.0016 Ω per PV module cell. Secondly, three different failure types were simulated: increment of series resistance (Rs) to 0.3Ω in one PV cell, decrease in shunt resistance (Rsh) to 0.2Ω and partial shadow on one PVcell (Iph = 6A activating the corresponding bypass diode. Fig. 3 shows the I-V curves of the PV module at 800W/m2 irradiation for a module without failure (blue), PVmodule with series resistance failure (orange), shunt resistance failure (green) and partial shadow (red). Fig. 4 shows the power-voltage (P-V) of the PV modules. For the case of partial shadow, with one bypass diode active, it can be observed that the P-V curve exhibits two local maxima, which complicates the performance of MPPT algorithms.

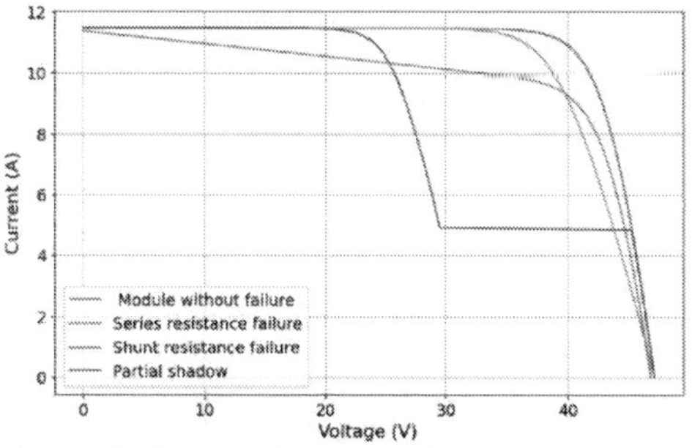

Figure 3: I-V curve of the PV modules operating without any failure, with an increment in series resistance, decrement in shunt resistance and shadow on a single PV cell (1 bypass diode activated).

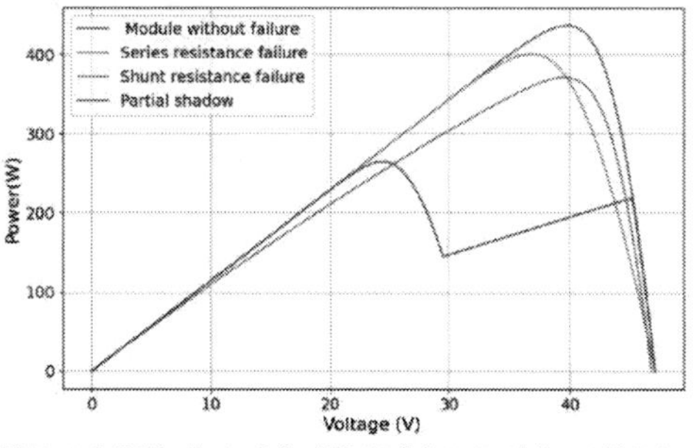

Figure 4: P-V curve of the PV modules operating without any failure, with an increment in series resistance, decrement in shunt resistance and shadow on a single PV cell (1 bypass diode activated).

For each case, the developed system has been simulated for different irradiance values. the irradiance is initially set to 800 W/m2 and later changed to 1000 W/m2 and 600 W/m2 respectively. The cell temperature is 65°C and remains constant throughout the simulation. For all simulations, the initial operating point of the PV module was set close to the MPP.

Fig. 5 shows the first simulation, using the MATLAB-Simulink model, with a PV module without any failure. As it can be seen, both MPPT algorithms present good performance, with very similar MPP values for the P&O and IncCond algorithm.

For PV modules with faults increasing Rs or decreasing Rsh, the maximum power output of a PV module decreases significantly when faults affecting the series resistance (Rs) or shunt resistance (Rsh) occur. An increase in Rs causes a greater drop in internal voltage as current flows, which reduces the voltage at the module terminals and, therefore, the power delivered. On the other hand, a decrease in Rsh allows part of the generated current to be diverted through non-useful paths (leakage currents), which reduces the current available at the load point. Both effects distort the I-V curve of the module and move its operating point away from the theoretical MPP, decreasing the efficiency of the system.

However, both MPPT algorithms proposed in this study are able to achieve the MPP of the new I-V curve of the PV module, obtaining slightly superior values for InCond algorithm in the case of Rs. Specially during non-constant irradiance periods (Fig. 6 and Fig. 7). This effect can be explained by the greater adaptability of the IncCond algorithm to variable conditions.

Similar experiments with partial shadows are being evaluated, achieving results equivalent to the previous ones.

4 LABORATORY IMPLEMENTATION

After validating the MPPT algorithms and the control system in a simulation environment, an experimental system is being developed to test the developed algorithms on a laboratory. For that, a PV module will be installed outdoor and connected to the DC-DC Boost converter shown in Fig.8.

The Boost DC-DC converter has been built using FDA38N30 MOSFET switched semiconductor, with an inherent freewheeling diode. External diode is STTH15R06. Equivalent inductance has been split in two toroidal inductors connected in series. The converter is sized to be able to work with 250 V input or output maximum voltage, and maximum 15 A current. Voltage and current measurements have been adapted to full-scale of the ADCs used in the microcontroller.

Ongoing work is focused on implementing the MPPT algorithms and the PI controller on an ESP32 microcontroller.

The developed system and algorithms will be validated in several scenarios, such as illumination changes, partial shadows or even defects on the PV module such as variations in series and shunt resistance.

5 CONCLUSIONS

A simulation set-up for the deployment and validation of MPPT algorithms has been developed and tested. The set-up consist of a simulation model developed on MATLAB-Simulink. A PI controller and P&O and

10.4229/EUPVSEC2025/4DV.4.9

IncCond MPPT algorithms have been evaluated obtaining good results for different PV modules failures. A laboratory set-up with a PV-module, a Boost DC-DC converter and an ESP32 microcontroller is being developed to test the algorithms on an experimental set-up. The set-up will be used for the development and validation of new MPPT algorithms and for educational purposes.

6 ACKNOWLEDGEMENTS

The European Union's Horizon Europe programme is acknowledged for financial support through the SUPERNOVA project (Grant Agreement No 101146883).

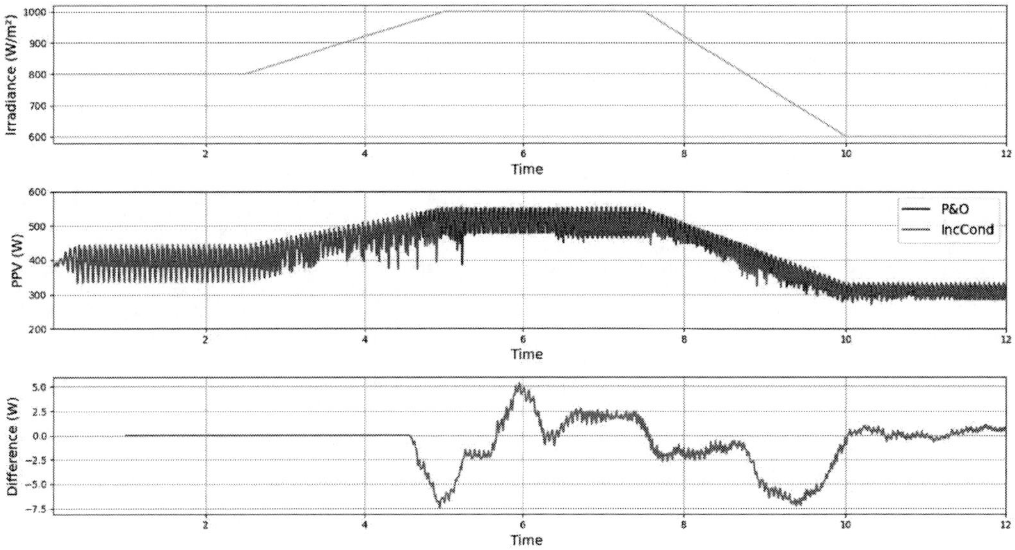

Figure 5: P&O and IncCond MPPT algorithms under variable irradiance conditions for PV modules withouth defects. Figure shows irradiance variations (top), MPPT algorithms achieved MPPT (middle) and power difference (P&O - IncCond).

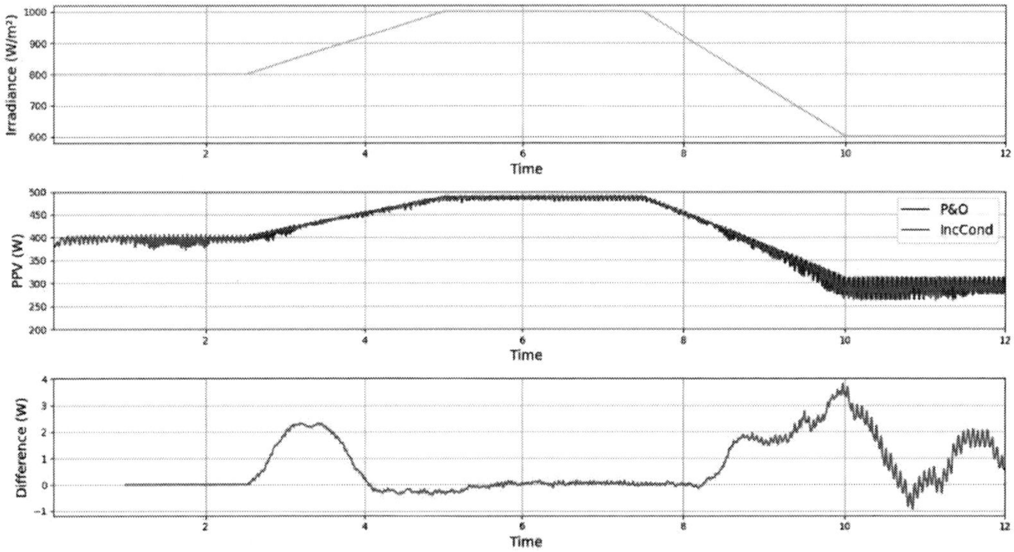

Figure 6: P&O and IncCond MPPT algorithms under variable irradiance conditions for PV modules with Rs increment. Figure shows irradiance variations (top), MPPT algorithms achieved MPPT (middle) and power difference(P&O - IncCond).

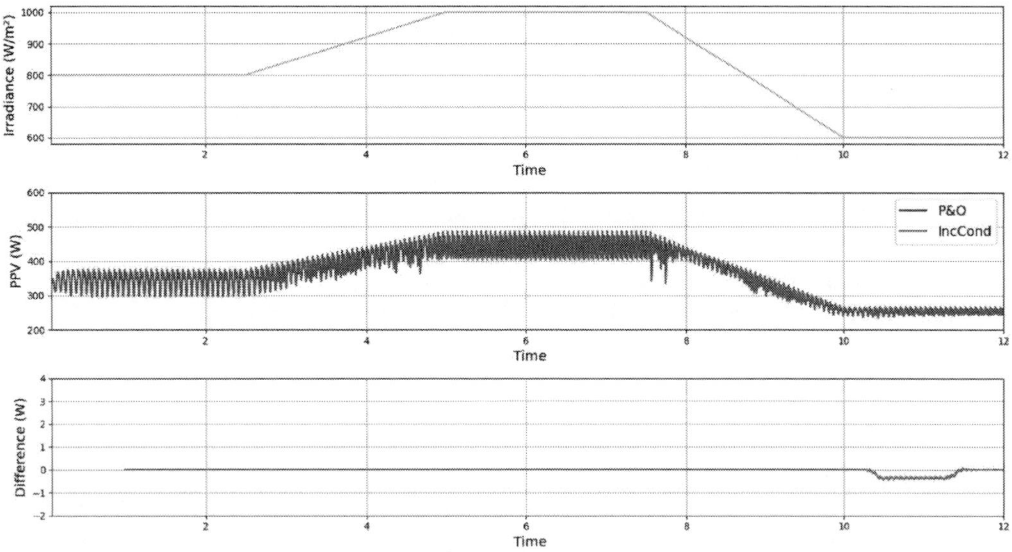

Figure 7: P&O and IncCond MPPT algorithms under variable irradiance conditions for PV modules with Rsh decrement. Figure shows irradiance variations (top), MPPT algorithms achieved MPPT (middle) and power difference(P&O - IncCond).

Figure 8: DC-DC Boost converter.

7 REFERENCES

[1] A. Jager-Waldau, Snapshot of photovoltaics - February 2024. EPJ Photovoltaics, vol. 15, p. 21, 2024.

[2] G. Blaesser, PV system measurements and monitoring the European experience. Solar Energy Materials, vol. 47, pp. 167-176, 1997.

[3] A. Louwen, S. Lindig, G. Chowdhury and D. Moser, Climate-and Technology-Dependent Performance Loss Rates in a Large Commercial Photovoltaic Monitoring Dataset. Solar RRL, vol. 8, p. 2300653, 2024.

[4] K. Hasan, S.B. Yousuf, M.S.H.K. Tushar, B.K. Das, P. Das and M.S. Islam, Effects of different environmental and operational factors on the PV performance: A comprehensive review. Energy Science and Engineering, vol. 10(2), p. 656-675, 2022.

[5] R.K. Pachauri, O.P. Mahela, A. Sharma, J. Bai, Y.K. Chauhan, B. Khan and H.H. Alhelou, Impact of partial shading on various PV array configurations and different modeling approaches: A comprehensive review. IEEE Access, vol. 8, p. 181375-181403, 2020.

[6] E. Ortega, G. Aranguren, M.J. Saenz, R. Gutierrez and J.C. Jimeno, Study of Photovoltaic Systems Monitoring Methods, in 44th IEEE Photovoltaic Specialist Conference (IEEE PVSC), 2017.

[7] H. Kim, G. Yu, J. Kim and S. Choi, PV String-Level Isolated DC–DC Power Optimizer with Wide Voltage Range, Energies, vol. 14(7), p. 1889, 2021.

[8] E. Ortega, S. Suarez, J.C. Jimeno, J.R. Gutierrez, V. Fano, A. Otaegi and S. Rodriguez-Conde, An statistical model for the short-term albedo estimation applied to PV bifacial modules, Renewable Energy, vol. 221, p. 119777, 2024.

[9] C.A. Gueymard, Cloud and albedo enhancement impacts on solar irradiance using high-frequency measurements from thermopile and photodiode radiometers. Part 1: Impacts on global horizontal irradiance, Solar Energy, vol. 153, pp. 755-765, 2017.

[10] C. Nataraj, G. Karthikeyan, G.J. Bharathi and S. Duraikannan, Comparative analysis of direct coupling and MPPT control in standalone PV systems for solar energy optimization to meet sustainable building energy demands, Scientific Reports, vol. 14(1), p. 22924, 2024.

[11] R. Sorensen and L. Mihet-Popa, Comparative Evaluation of Traditional and Advanced Algorithms for Photovoltaic Systems in Partial Shading Conditions, Solar, vol. 4(4), pp. 572-594, 2024.

[12] M. Derbeli, C. Napole, O. Barambones, J. Sanchez, I. Calvo and P. Fernández-Bustamante, Maximum power point tracking techniques for photovoltaic panel: A review and experimental applications, Energies, vol. 14(22), p. 7806, 2021.

Experimental set-up for Validation of Maximum Power Point Tracking Algorithms for Photovoltaic Arrays

Laura Sanchez[1], Gorka Torre[1], Jesus Sanchez[2], Alexander Maiz[2], Alain Sanchez-Ruiz[2], Josu Jugo[1] and Eneko Ortega[*,1,3]

*eneko.ortegam@ehu.eus

[1]Electricity and Electronics Department, UPV/EHU, 48940, Leioa, Spain

[2] Department of Electronic Technology, UPV/EHU, 01006, Vitoria-Gasteiz, Spain

[3]Technological Institute of Microelectronics, UPV/EHU, 48013, Bilbao, Spain

Introduction

- To maximize energy output, PV systems use DC-DC or DC-AC converters with MPPT algorithms, which adjust voltage and current to ensure operation at maximum power.
- MPPT algorithms: from simple ones like P&O or CondInc to advanced methods using Fuzzy Logic or neural networks.

Aim

Build a functional set-up in a simulation environment in MATLAB-Simulink, to deploy and validate different MPPT algorithms.

Description of the system

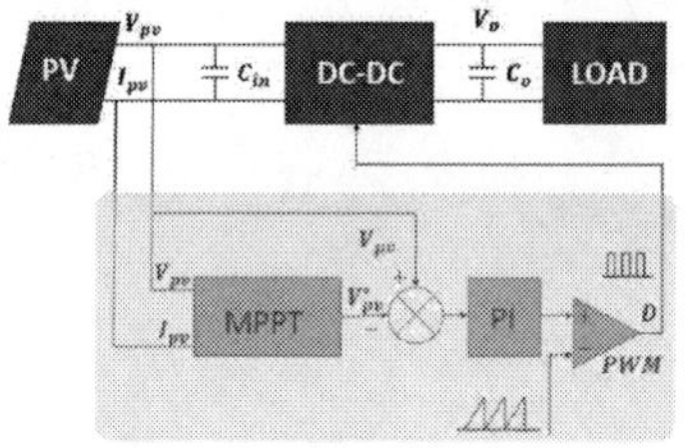

The system is composed by: PV system, resistive load and DC-DC Boost converter.

$$V_{out} = \frac{V_{pv}}{1-D} \quad (1)$$

The PI controller adjusts the duty cycle D, by a PWM signal, to control the DC-DC converter and maximize the power output.

The MPPT algorithm adjusts D to have the module operating at its MPP permanently.

P&O: periodically changes the PV module voltage in small increments proportional to the slope of the dP/dV curve and observing the change in the generated power. If the power increases, the direction of the perturbation is maintained; if it decreases, the direction is reversed to approach the MPP.

IncCond: calculates the derivative of power with respect to voltage (dP/dV)

Simulation and laboratory implementation

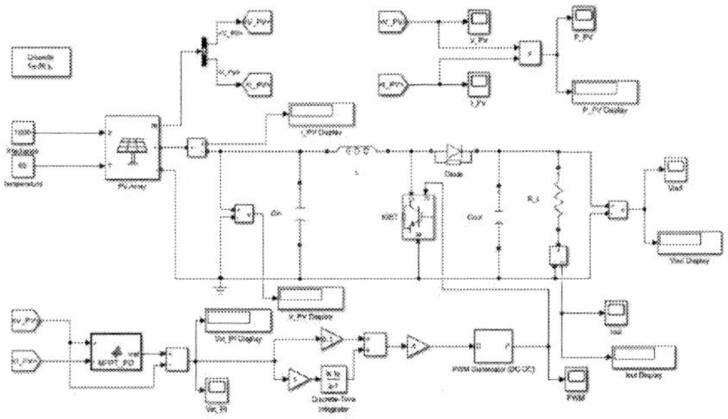

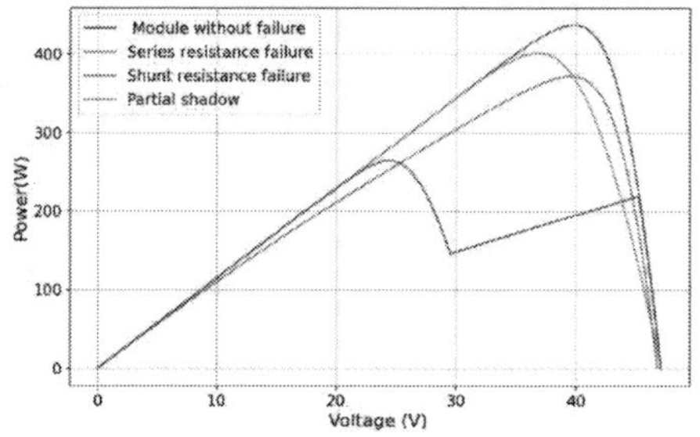

P-V curve of the PV modules under different operating conditions.

Simulation of P&O and CondInc MPPT algorithms:

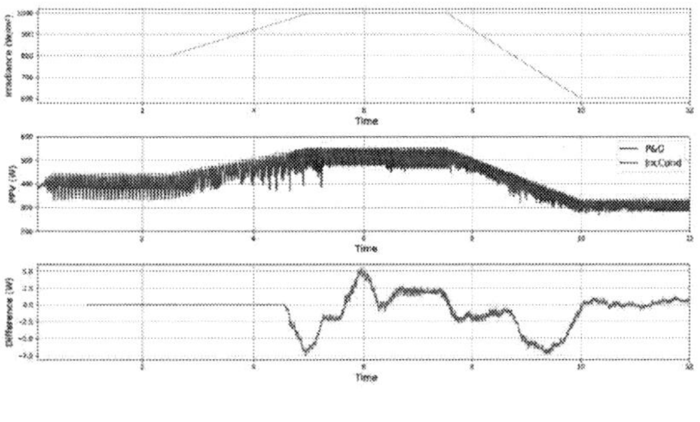

DC-DC Boost converter:

Acknowledgements

The European Union's Horizon Europe programme is acknowledged for financial support through the SUPERNOVA project (Grant Agreement No 101146883).

Conclusions

A simulation set-up for the deployment and validation of MPPT algorithms has been developed and tested. The set-up consist of a simulation model developed on MATLAB-Simulink. A PI controller and P&O and IncCond MPPT algorithms have been evaluated obtaining good results for different PV modules failures.

SIZING PHOTOVOLTAIC SELF-CONSUMPTION SYSTEMS THROUGH MISMATCH INDEX AND PROFITABILITY ANALYSIS

Kiane Alves e Silva, Luis Miguel Carrasco, Eduardo Lorenzo
Instituto de Energía Solar, Universidad Politécnica de Madrid
kiane.asilva@alumnos.upm.es, luismiguel.carrasco@upm.es, antonio.lorenzo@upm.es

ABSTRACT: This paper presents a methodology for evaluating and sizing photovoltaic self-consumption systems through a combined technical and economic approach. The analysis relies on hourly energy balance simulation and introduces the Mismatch Index (MI) to quantify the temporal alignment between energy availability and demand, enabling a more precise assessment of self-consumption performance. The financial analysis includes four indicators: Payback Period, Net Present Value, Internal Rate of Return, and Levelized Cost of Energy. The methodology has been applied to a real residential case using historical hourly data on consumption, irradiance, and electricity tariffs in Spain. As a result, the tool indicated a system size that achieves both technical alignment with demand and favorable economic outcomes. The proposed approach serves as a practical decision-support tool for residential PV system design, aligning energy behavior with realistic financial expectations.
Keywords: Photovoltaic systems; Self-consumption systems; Techno-economic analysis; Energy balance

1 INTRODUCTION

The increasing demand for sustainable energy solutions has made photovoltaic (PV) self-consumption systems an attractive option for residential, commercial, and institutional users. These systems offer several benefits, including environmental sustainability [1], savings on energy bills [2] and, in some cases, tax advantages [3]. However, their adoption is tied to their economic feasibility. While environmental concerns and energy independence are relevant motivators, financial returns are one of the main deciding factors in whether users choose to invest in a PV system or not [4].

According to the NREL technical report [5], for small-scale systems, the most commonly used economic indicators are those that are easy to understand by end users and directly tied to financial outcomes, highlighting Payback period (PBP), Monthly bill savings (MBS), and Net Present Value (NPV). Together, they represent investment recovery time, monthly cost reduction, and long-term economic value. However, in academic literature, particularly in techno-economic studies and comparative analyses of PV systems, Internal Rate of Return (IRR) and Levelized Cost of Energy (LCOE) are widely adopted due to their ability to standardize performance and compare different system configurations on equal terms [6], [7], [8], [9].

These financial considerations include not only the reduction of electricity bills and protection against rising energy prices, but also the stability and predictability of long-term savings. However, delivering these benefits requires more than just technical efficiency. The system must be property sized to match the user's specific consumption needs. A temporal mismatch between energy production and demand can significantly reduce self-consumption rates, diminishing overall returns.

Therefore, aligning energy generation with actual consumption behavior is as important as minimizing costs and maximizing output. By addressing both the financial expectations and the functional needs of the user can increase the viability of PV self-consumption systems.

Traditional performance indicators, such as self-consumption and self-sufficiency ratios, are commonly used to evaluate the effectiveness of PV systems [10]. These metrics provide valuable insights into how much of the generated energy is consumed locally and how independent the user is from the grid, respectively [11]. However, they do not account for the temporal alignment between energy generation and demand. This means that even a system with a high self-consumption rate may perform poorly from an economic perspective if most of the energy consumed does not coincide with periods of peak generation, especially under variable electricity tariffs. Studies in Spain show that load profile variations have a greater impact on system size and profitability than solar resource or electricity tariff [12].

Therefore, this paper presents a new metric, namely Mismatch Index (MI), designed to evaluate how well the distribution of energy availability aligns with the user's hourly consumption profile. Based on the Gini Coefficient [13] and Lorenz Curve [14], widely used in economics to measure social income inequality, the MI quantifies the temporal disparity between available energy and energy demand.

The MI was originally introduced in a previous study [15] as a metric to quantify the temporal mismatch between PV energy generation, based on irradiance data, and user consumption. While this initial work revealed the potential of adapting the Gini Coefficient and Lorenz Curve for PV applications, it had a limitation in scope: it did not consider how the addition of a storage system can affect the mismatch between energy availability and demand.

In this study, the MI has been adapted to include the effect of energy storage. This allows us to evaluate how different combinations of PV and battery sizes impact the alignment between generation and consumption. As a result, the index becomes more suitable for the design of real self-consumption systems, especially when combined with economic analysis.

The use of these two analyses allows identifying configurations that not only deliver financial returns but also align closely with the user's real energy behavior. In this way, the proposed approach promotes the development of PV self-consumption systems that are not just economically feasible, but also functionally optimized.

To support this methodology, a computational tool has been developed, integrating mathematical models of on-grid PV systems with energy storage, detailed meteorological data, and real hourly energy consumption profiles. The tool performs an energy balance analysis to

10.4229/EUPVSEC2025/4DV.4.11

achieve an optimal match between the distribution of energy availability and consumption. In addition to numerical outputs, it provides graphical visualizations to assist in decision-making during system sizing. These include: i) an isometric plot showing the calculated MI values for various combinations of PV and battery capacities, and ii) profitability curves that illustrate the relationship between system sizing and financial performance.

2 METHODOLOGY

The proposed methodology is applied to a typical on-grid PV self-consumption system with energy storage. The system is composed of a PV generator, an energy storage unit (battery), a load, and a connection to the grid. A schematic diagram of the system is shown in Figure 1 illustrating the energy flows between generation, storage, load, and grid exchange. The blue arrows indicate the energy outputs from the self-consumption system (PV generation and battery discharge).

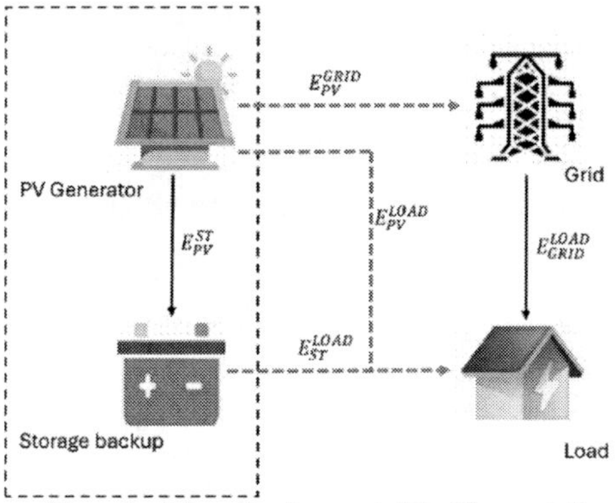

Figure 1 – Schematic of a generic PV self-consumption system with storage system.

The energy produced by the PV generator (E_{PV}) is first used to supply the demand (E_{PV}^{LOAD}). If there is surplus energy, it is stored in the battery (E_{PV}^{ST}) for later use. The battery's State of Charge (SOC) indicates the amount of energy currently stored, as a percentage of its total capacity. If the SOC is less than 100%, it charges when there is surplus energy and discharges when PV generation is not enough to meet the load demand (E_{ST}^{LOAD}). When the load is met and the battery is full, excess energy is sent to the grid (E_{PV}^{GRID}). If both PV and battery cannot meet the demand, energy is taken from the grid (E_{GRID}^{LOAD}).

A computational simulation tool has been developed to model this behavior using hourly data over one year. It calculates the energy balance for different PV and battery sizes, using real consumption profiles and typical meteorological year (TMY) data. The energy balance model used in this simulation has been introduced in a previous work [15], which details the interactions between PV generation, battery storage, and grid exchange under self-consumption conditions.

However, in the present study, the modeling framework is extended with three new elements:

- The use of the concept of System Energy Output (SEO), which is defined as the sum of the energy output from the PV generator and the battery.
- The application of the Mismatch Index (MI) to evaluate temporal alignment between energy availability and consumption.
- The integration of a profitability analysis to evaluate the economic performance of different system configurations.

A schematic representation of the methodological workflow is shown in Figure 2. The process begins with the integration of two main input datasets to simulate the hourly PV production – the hourly energy consumption profile and the hourly meteorological data (temperature and effective irradiation). Then, dynamic energy simulations are performed across multiple combinations of PV generator size (C_{PV}) and battery capacity (C_{ST}), defined as equation (1) and (2), respectively.

$$C_{PV} = \frac{E_{PV}}{E^{LOAD}} \quad (1)$$

$$C_{ST} = E_{ST} \times \frac{N_y}{E^{LOAD}} \quad (2)$$

where E_{PV} is the annual PV energy produced, E^{LOAD} is the annual demand of energy, E_{ST} is the energy storage capacity, and N_y is the number of days in the year.

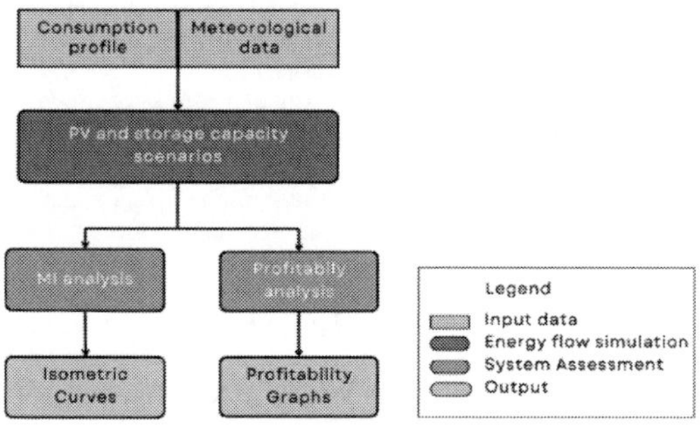

Figure 2 - Methodology flowchart.

Each simulation produces a different energy balance, which is then used to perform the MI and viability analysis.

2.1 Mismatch Analysis

To evaluate how well energy availability aligns with consumption over time, this study uses the MI, a temporal performance indicator based on the Lorenz curve and the Gini coefficient. Originally used to assess inequality in social economic inequality, these tools are adapted here to compare the distribution of energy availability with the distribution of user energy consumption.

In this analysis, the metric used to represent energy availability is the System Energy Output (SEO), defined as the total amount of energy made available by the system at each time step. The SEO includes all energy that passes through the self-consumption system: energy consumed directly from PV, energy exported to the grid, and energy discharged from the battery - that is, the energy flows represented by the dashed blue arrows in Figure 1. The SEO is defined as equation (3) and assumes an ideal system, with no losses considered.

$$SEO = E_{PV}^{Load} + E_{PV}^{Grid} + E_{ST}^{Load} \quad (3)$$

The SEO reflects all useful energy flows in from the

10.4229/EUPVSEC2025/4DV.4.11

PV system and serves as the reference distribution against which consumption is compared.

The MI is calculated by constructing a Lorenz curve that compares the cumulative distribution of energy consumption to that of the selected metric. To plot the Lorenz curve, the data has been sorted in ascending order of SEO, so that the relative cumulative distribution of each variable is represented.

An illustrative curve is shown in Figure 3. In this case, the hourly cumulative data over one year is sorted in increasing order of SEO. The cumulative share of consumption is plotted on the x-axis, while the cumulative share of SEO is plotted on the y-axis. A perfect alignment between the two distributions would result in a 45° diagonal line (red dashed line), and any deviation from this line represents temporal mismatch (gray area).

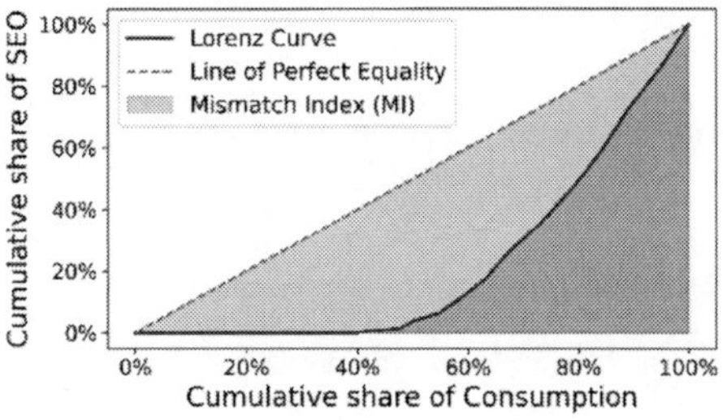

Figure 3 - Example of a Lorenz curve of SEO versus consumption.

Mathematically, the MI is defined as the normalized area between the Lorenz curve and the line of equality, represented as the gray area, and is calculated as presented in equation (4) [16].

$$MI = 1 - \sum_{k=1}^{N} (X_k - X_{k-1}) \cdot Y_k + Y_{k-1}) \tag{4}$$

where X_k is the cumulative share of energy consumption, Y_k is the cumulative share of SEO, and N is the number of time steps (8,760 for one year of hourly data).

MI values range from 0 (perfect temporal alignment) to 1 (maximum mismatch). A low MI indicates that energy is available when it is needed, while a high MI suggests that SEO and demand occur at different times.

Although the MI is applied here using SEO, the same method can be used with other PV system metrics, such as PV generation, effective irradiation, or energy cost, depending on the objective of the analysis. This flexibility makes the MI a powerful tool to support design decisions and improve system performance, especially in contexts where both energy and cost profiles vary significantly over time.

2.2 Profitability Analysis

In addition to the technical evaluation, the simulation tool includes an economic analysis to assess the financial performance of each simulated configuration.

In this study, we adopt a comprehensive approach by evaluating the economic performance of each configuration using the following four indicators: NPV, PBP, IRR, and LCOE.

The PBP (in years) estimates the time required to recover the initial investment (C_0) – also known as CAPEX – through accumulated savings [17] considering the project lifetime (LT), also expressed in years. In its simplest form, it is defined as equation (5).

$$PBP = \frac{C_0}{B - C} \tag{5}$$

where B is the annual financial benefit resulting from the PV system, including both the savings from self-consumed energy (based on the electricity import tariff) and revenues from excess energy exported to the grid (based on electricity export tariff). C represents the annual operational and maintenance costs (OPEX)

While PBP does not account for the time value of money, the NPV quantifies the profitability of an investment by bringing all projected future revenues and costs to present value using a discount rate and computing the net difference over the system's lifetime (LT) [9]. It is calculated as the difference between the present value of expected benefits and operational costs [18], as expressed in equation (6).

$$NPV = -C_0 + \sum_{t=1}^{LT} \frac{B_t - C_t}{(1+r)^t} \tag{6}$$

where B_t and C_t correspond to the benefits and OPEX in year t, respectively, and r is the discount rate.

Based on the NPV it is possible to calculate the IRR, since it is the discount rate (r) at which the NPV equals zero after the lifetime project [6], as expressed in equation (7)

$$0 = -C_0 + \sum_{t=1}^{LT} \frac{B_t - C_t}{(1+IRR)^t} \tag{7}$$

Lastly, the LCOE expresses the total cost of producing each kWh of energy over the system's lifetime, discounted to present value. Traditionally, LCOE calculation follows the ratio between the total discounted system costs and the total energy output [19], as presented in equation (8). This indicator provides an estimate of the cost of the generated energy, allowing the assessment of whether the system attains grid parity.

$$LCOE_{PV} = \frac{C_0 + \sum_{t=1}^{LT} C_t \times (1+r)^{-t}}{E_{PV}} \tag{8}$$

3 RESULTS AND DISCUSSIONS

The base case analyzed in this study corresponds to a real residential household located in La Coruña (43.63° N, -7.74° W), in northern Spain, to which the proposed tool has been applied. The annual consumption for 2022 has been 2,989 kWh [20], and the annual effective irradiance has been 1.25 MWh/m² [21]. Figure 4 shows the normalized values of the average hourly profile of energy consumption and the effective irradiation of the site over a 24-hour day period. Both energy consumption and effective irradiation have been normalized individually with respect to its total annual value, allowing for a direct comparison of their temporal patterns.

The PV generation profile was estimated on [21] based on typical module characteristics and local irradiance conditions, assuming a 30° tilt angle and 0° azimuth orientation. The base case considers a nominal capacity (P_n) of 6 kWp to match the annual energy demand (C_{PV} = 1), and a battery capacity (C_{bat}) of 8.19 kWh, equivalent to the average daily demand (C_{ST} = 1).

10.4229/EUPVSEC2025/4DV.4.11

This base case serves as the reference for all subsequent simulations and results discussed throughout the paper.

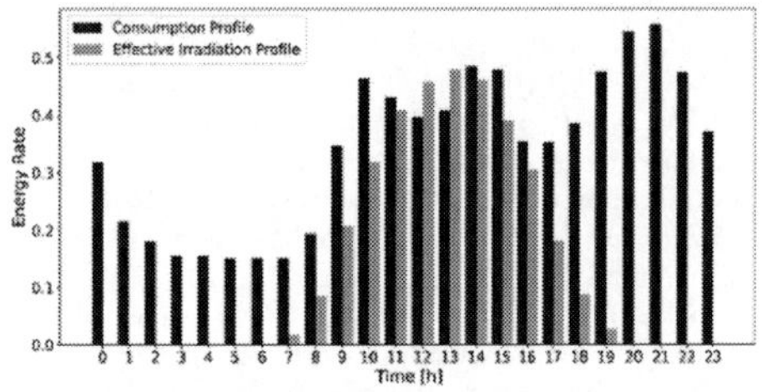

Figure 4 – Normalized average hourly consumption and irradiation profiles for the base case. Data obtained from [20] and [21], respectively. Each profile normalized to its own annual total.

3.1 Mismatch Results

The energy balance has been simulated with C_{PV} and C_{ST} ranging from 0 to 1, as fractions relative to the base case. To ensure accurate modeling of PV generation, the following technical assumptions have been considered: a Nominal Operating Cell Temperature (NOCT) of 41 °C and a power temperature coefficient of −0.26%/°C, both referring to the PV module; inverter efficiency of 98%; and overall system losses estimated at 15%, accounting for soiling, cabling, mismatching, and other typical effects.

The MI has been applied to each simulated configuration using the outputs from the energy balance. Figure 5 presents the resulting MI isometric curves over the range of C_{PV} and C_{ST} values. As expected, configurations with limited PV capacity or no storage have shown higher mismatch values, indicating reduced temporal alignment between availability and demand. The introduction of storage has significantly improved MI in most cases, particularly when combined with moderate PV generation levels.

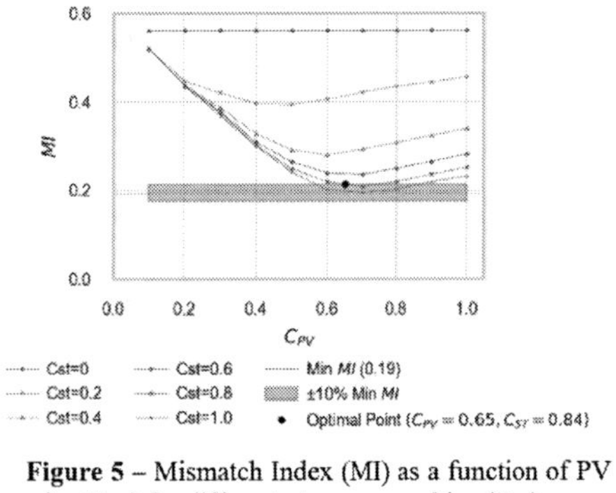

Figure 5 – Mismatch Index (MI) as a function of PV capacity (C_{PV}) for different storage capacities (C_{ST}).

According to the visual results presented in Figure 5, the minimum MI obtained is 0.19, which occurs when $C_{PV} = 0.7$ and $C_{ST} = 1.0$. Since designing a system based strictly on a single reference point may not be practical, a tolerance range instead accommodates configurations with similarly good performance. To support practical system design, a sensitivity range of ±10% around the minimum MI value (0.19) has been considered as an acceptable tolerance band for configurations with comparable MI-performance, represented in Figure 5 by the green shaded area.

Within this range, the smallest storage system that satisfies the tolerance criterion corresponds to $C_{ST} = 0.84$. For this storage size, the minimum PV capacity within the acceptable area is found at $C_{PV} = 0.65$. Therefore, this configuration can be considered the most suitable option from the perspective of this analysis.

3.2 Economic Results

For the financial evaluation, PVPC tariffs (*Precio Voluntario para el Pequeño Consumidor* in spanish) have been used for both energy imports and surplus exports. PVPC is the regulated time-of-use tariff structure applied in the Spanish electricity market for residential and small consumers, reflecting hourly wholesale market prices [22]. Hourly tariff data were obtained from the *Spanish Electricity System Operator Information Platform* (ESIOS) [23], which provides historical data on electricity purchase prices from the grid as well as compensation rates for surplus energy exported by self-consumption systems.

It is important to note that, under the current Spanish self-consumption regulation, there is a restriction on the economic compensation for surplus energy exported to the grid: the monthly compensation cannot exceed the billed amount for energy imported from the grid during the same billing period [24]. As a result, oversized systems or those with low self-consumption ratios may experience a reduction in economic benefits.

The financial simulations have been carried out considering a system lifetime of 10 years and a discount rate of 8% per year, consistent with typical assumptions for small-scale residential investments. An annual tariff growth of 8% has been applied to both buying and selling energy tariffs, combining expected inflation and market spread. PV system degradation has been modeled as a linear reduction of 0.5% per year in energy output.

CAPEX has been estimated based on recent market surveys. These data have been used to define PV and lithium-battery cost function according to system size, reflecting realistic price trends in the Spanish residential sector. Equation (9) shows the PV cost function where P_n is the PV capacity [kWp], and equation (10) refers to storage cost function where C_{bat} is the storage capacity [kWh]. Both equations were extracted using mathematical regression from current market studies.

$$CAPEX_{PV} = 2.577 \cdot (P_n)^{-0.303} \cdot P_n \quad (9)$$

$$CAPEX_{ST} = 45.0389 \cdot (e^{0.0798 \cdot C_{bat}} - 1) \quad (10)$$

The initial OPEX has been set at 2% of the total CAPEX and is assumed to increase annually by 2%, accounting for inflation and gradual maintenance adjustments over the system's lifetime.

Table **1** summarizes the main economic assumption used in the financial analysis.

Figure 6(a) shows that the shortest PBP values, around 6 years, occur for larger systems – since higher PV capacities generate more energy and therefore greater economic benefits. The inclusion of storage slightly improves the PBP, as storing energy for self-consumption is generally more profitable than selling the surplus to the grid. However, the relatively high cost of batteries limits this benefit, so that the impact on payback remains. In contrast, smaller systems present longer PBP values, which can reach up to 11 years. In these cases, the reduced PV capacity limits energy generation, keeping the system highly dependent on the grid and resulting in lower economic benefits. Consequently, investment recovery is slower and less attractive compared to larger configurations , but still corresponds to roughly half of the estimated system lifetime

Table 1 – Summary of economic assumptions used in the analysis.

Parameter	Value
System lifetime (LT)	20 years
Discount rate (r)	8% per year
Tariff annual growth	8 % per year
PV degradation	0.5% per year
CAPEX	$CAPEX_{PV} + CAPEX_{ST}$
Initial OPEX	2% of CAPEX
OPEX growth	2% per year
Tariff type	PVPC

Regarding NPV, the results in Figure 6(b) indicate economic viability in all scenarios, remaining positive throughout. Systems with $C_{PV} > 0.5$ show an average NPV of €4,673, reaching values above €6,000 in the most favorable cases. Although storage contributes to performance improvement, higher PV generation drives the financial return, consistent with the PBP trends.

The IRR results – Figure 6(c) – confirm the economic feasibility already indicated by the NPV, with values ranging from a minimum of 10% up to 18%. Since the lowest value remains above the 8% discount rate, all scenarios can be considered financially viable. Configurations with $C_{PV} > 0.5$ and $C_{ST} \geq 0.3$ show a slowdown in IRR growth, stabilizing around an average of 17.7%.

Finally, Figure 6(d) presents the LCOE$_{PV}$ results, which vary between €0.22 and €0.10/kWh, with an average of €0.13/kWh. Compared to the average electricity tariff in Spain of €0.21/kWh in 2022 [25], the PV system shows competitiveness. However, although market tariffs may fluctuate and even fall below the LCOE in certain periods, this indicator shows the stability of energy costs over the entire project lifetime, reinforcing the role of PV as a reliable long-term investment.

3.3 Techno-Economic Evaluation

Based on technical evaluations, a $C_{PV} = 0.65$ and $C_{ST} = 0.84$ configurations has been selected as it is the smallest system within the tolerance band relative to the minimun MI (0.19), as ilustrated in Figure 5. It represents a technically well-aligned system size, which can contribute to reducing investment costs.

A summary of the final techno-economical results for this system size are presented in Table 2. The system requires an initial investment of €3,610 and generates a net return of €16,474 over its lifetime, where net return corresponds to the difference between total benefits (€21,838) and the combined costs of CAPEX and OPEX (€5,364). When discounted to present value, this profit corresponds to an NPV of €4,516. The payback period of 6.6 years indicates that the investment is recovered well before the end of the 20-year project lifetime. This means that the system not only returns the initial capital within a safe margin, but also generates several years of net economic benefit during its operational horizon.

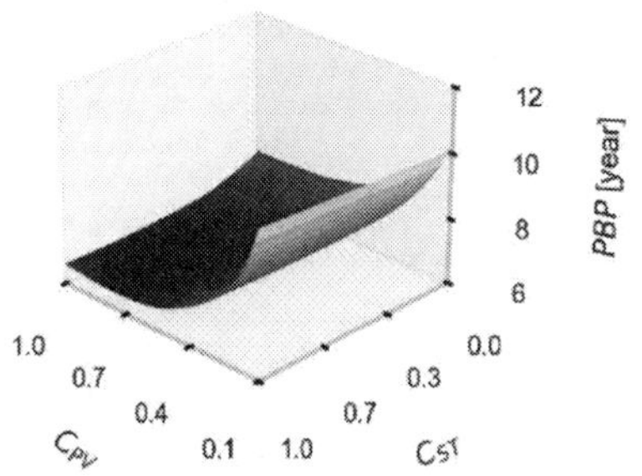

(a)

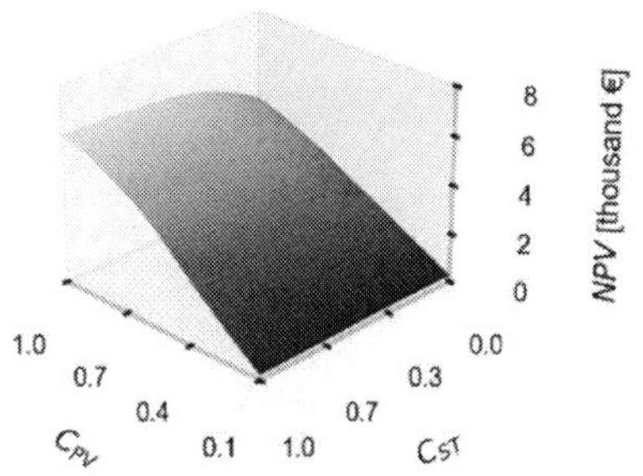

(b)

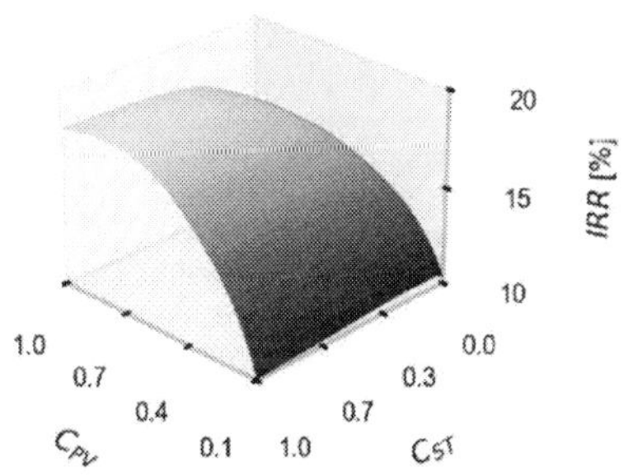

(c)

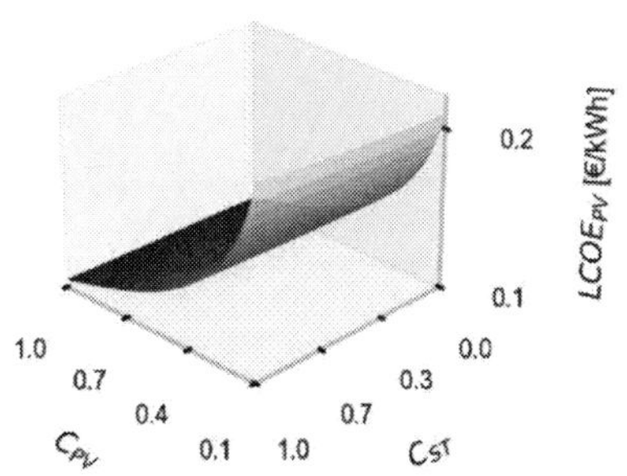

(d)

Figure 6 – Economic performance indicators for different PV and battery sizes (C_{PV} and C_{ST}, respectively): a) Payback Period (PBP); b) Net Present Value (NPV); c) Internal Rate of Return (IRR); d) Levelized Cost of Energy of the self-consumption system (LCOE$_{PV}$)

10.4229/EUPVSEC2025/4DV.4.11

In addition, the IRR reaches 18%, a value that largely surpasses the assumed discount rate of 8% and confirms the profitability of the investment. $LCOE_{PV}$ results in €0.12/kWh, placing the cost of self-generated electricity in a competitive range compared to market tariffs and ensuring stability over the project lifetime.

Table 2 – Summary of simulated results for the smallest system within the MI tolerance band

Parameter	Value
PV generator	3.90 kWp
Battery storage	6.55 kWh
MI	0.21
CAPEX	€ 3,610
OPEX	€ 1,754
Benefits	€ 21,838
PBP	6.6 years
NPV	€ 4,516
IRR	18%
LCOE	0.12 €/kWh

4 CONCLUSIONS

This study presents a methodology for evaluating and sizing PV self-consumption systems by combining technical performance and economic indicators based on hourly energy flow simulations. The simulation result shows that it is possible to identify configurations that offer a strong balance between energy availability and financial return.

The MI has been introduced and applied to the SEO to assess the temporal alignment between energy availability and demand. This approach captures not only how much energy is produced, but also when it is available relative to consumption. MI plays a key role in providing us with information about the performance of a self-consumption system and its dependence on the electricity grid. .

The economic evaluation included four economic indicators – PBP, NPV, IRR, and LCOE. These metrics togheter provide a comprehensive overview of financial performance, highlithing how different system sizes influence return on investment.

The methodology has been applied to a real case study using historic hourly data for energy demand, environmental inputs and electricity tariffs. Among the simulated scenarios, the optimized system ($C_{PV} = 0.65$ and $C_{ST} = 0.84$) has been identified as both technically efficient and economically viable, generating a net economic benefit more than three times higher than the associated costs, over its lifetime, equivalent to €4,516 NPV. The economic viability is supported by a PBP of 6.6 years, which ensures cost recovery well before the end of the 20-year lifetime. The IRR reaches 18%, more than double the assumed discount rate, thus confirming a strong profitability margin. In addition, $LCOE_{PV}$ of 0.12 €/kWh highlighting its competitiveness and long-term stability.

This practical example reinforces the potential of the tool as a decision-support resource for designing well-balanced and cost-effective residential PV self-consumption systems. With the results obtained from the tool, users can evaluate which configuration best fits their needs and constraints – whether prioritizing faster payback, higher long-term net benefits, greater annual returns, or stable generation costs.

Future work may explore the inclusion of demand-side management strategies, different tariff structures, as well as extending the methodology to other user profiles or climates. Overall, the approach showed here can support more informed and technically grounded decisions for sizing effective and cost-efficient PV systems.

5 ACKNOWLEDGEMENTS

This work has been possible thanks to the Project IND2022/AMB-23718 funded by Comunidad de Madrid and to the Project LIFE21-CET-ENERCOM-JALON funded by the European Union. Views and opinions expressed are, however, those of the author(s) only and do not necessarily reflect those of the European Union or CINEA. Neither the European Union nor the granting authority can be held responsible for them

REFERENCES

[1] I. Montero, MT. Miranda, F. Barrena, F. J. Sepúlveda, and J. I. Arranz, "Analysis of photovoltaic self-consumption systems for hospitals in southwestern Europe," *Energy Build*, vol. 269, p. 112254, Aug. 2022, doi: 10.1016/j.enbuild.2022.112254.

[2] J. M. Roldán Fernández, M. Burgos Payán, and J. M. Riquelme Santos, "Profitability of household photovoltaic self-consumption in Spain," *J Clean Prod*, vol. 279, p. 123439, Jan. 2021, doi: 10.1016/J.JCLEPRO.2020.123439.

[3] I. D'Adamo, M. Gastaldi, and P. Morone, "Solar collective self-consumption: Economic analysis of a policy mix," *Ecological Economics*, vol. 199, p. 107480, Sep. 2022, doi: 10.1016/j.ecolecon.2022.107480.

[4] V. Rai, D. C. Reeves, and R. Margolis, "Overcoming barriers and uncertainties in the adoption of residential solar PV," *Renew Energy*, vol. 89, pp. 498–505, Apr. 2016, doi: 10.1016/J.RENENE.2015.11.080.

[5] E. Drury, P. Denholm, and R. Margolis, "The Impact of Different Economic Performance Metrics on the Perceived Value of Solar Photovoltaics - NREL/TP-6A20-52197," Oct. 2011. Accessed: Jul. 03, 2025. [Online]. Available: https://docs.nrel.gov/docs/fy12osti/52197.pdf

[6] I. B. Carrêlo, R. H. Almeida, L. Narvarte, F. Martinez-Moreno, and L. M. Carrasco, "Comparative analysis of the economic feasibility of five large-power photovoltaic irrigation systems in the Mediterranean region," *Renew Energy*, vol. 145, pp. 2671–2682, Jan. 2020, doi: 10.1016/J.RENENE.2019.08.030.

[7] G. Liu, M. Li, B. Zhou, Y. Chen, and S. Liao, "General indicator for techno-economic assessment of renewable energy resources," 2018, *Elsevier*. [Online]. Available: https://www.sciencedirect.com/science/article/pii/S0196890417311068

[8] S. Quoilin, K. Kavvadias, A. Mercier, I. Pappone, and A. Zucker, "Quantifying self-consumption linked to solar home battery systems: Statistical analysis and economic assessment q," 2016, doi: 10.1016/j.apenergy.2016.08.077.

[9] C. H. Villar, D. Neves, and C. A. Silva, "Solar PV self-consumption: An analysis of influencing indicators in the Portuguese context," *Energy*

Strategy Reviews, vol. 18, pp. 224–234, Dec. 2017, doi: 10.1016/J.ESR.2017.10.001.

[10] A. Ciocia *et al.*, "Self-Consumption and Self-Sufficiency in Photovoltaic Systems: Effect of Grid Limitation and Storage Installation," *Energies 2021, Vol. 14, Page 1591*, vol. 14, no. 6, p. 1591, Mar. 2021, doi: 10.3390/EN14061591.

[11] R. Luthander, J. Widén, D. Nilsson, and J. Palm, "Photovoltaic self-consumption in buildings: A review," *Appl Energy*, vol. 142, pp. 80–94, Mar. 2015, doi: 10.1016/J.APENERGY.2014.12.028.

[12] B. Domenech, G. Calleja, and J. Olivella, "Residential Photovoltaic Profitability with Storage under the New Spanish Regulation: A Multi-Scenario Analysis," 2021, doi: 10.3390/en14071987.

[13] C. Gini, "On the measurement of concentration and variability of characters," *Metron - International Journal of Statistics*, vol. LXIII, no. 1, pp. 1–38, 2005.

[14] T. Sitthiyot and K. Holasut, "A simple method for estimating the Lorenz curve," *Humanit Soc Sci Commun*, vol. 8, no. 1, p. 268, Nov. 2021, doi: 10.1057/s41599-021-00948-x.

[15] K. A. Silva, L. M. Carrasco, and A. L. Mata, "ENERGY FLOW ALGORITHM TO THE OPTIMIZATION OF ON-GRID PV BUILDINGS WITH OR WITHOUT BACKUP STORAGE," in *EU PVSEC 2023*, Lisboa, 2023. doi: 10.4229/EUPVSEC2023/4BV.4.24.

[16] S. Karam and M. S. Ryerson, "Operating at the individual level: A review of literature and a research agenda to support needs-forward models of transport resource allocation," *Transp Res Interdiscip Perspect*, vol. 21, p. 100887, Sep. 2023, doi: 10.1016/J.TRIP.2023.100887.

[17] I. H. Ibrik and S. Cruz, "Techno-economic assessment of on-grid solar PV system in Palestine," *Cogent Eng*, vol. 7, no. 1, Jan. 2020, doi: 10.1080/23311916.2020.1727131.

[18] Q. Tushar, G. Zhang, F. Giustozzi, M. A. Bhuiyan, L. Hou, and S. Navaratnam, "An integrated financial and environmental evaluation framework to optimize residential photovoltaic solar systems in Australia from recession uncertainties," *J Environ Manage*, vol. 346, p. 119002, Nov. 2023, doi: 10.1016/J.JENVMAN.2023.119002.

[19] P. Kästel and B. Gilroy-Scott, "Economics of pooling small local electricity prosumers—LCOE & self-consumption," *Renewable and Sustainable Energy Reviews*, vol. 51, pp. 718–729, Nov. 2015, doi: 10.1016/J.RSER.2015.06.057.

[20] "E-distribuición Redes Digitales, S.L."

[21] Universidad Politécnica de Madrid, "SISIFO: An online simulator of PV systems," 2023, v3.2. Accessed: Jul. 31, 2023. [Online]. Available: https://www.sisifo.info/es/default

[22] "Precio Voluntario para el Pequeño Consumidor (PVPC)." Accessed: Jul. 07, 2025. [Online]. Available: https://www.miteco.gob.es/es/energia/energia-electrica/electricidad/contratacion-suministro/precio-voluntario.html

[23] "Análisis | ESIOS electricidad · datos · transparencia." Accessed: Dec. 05, 2024. [Online]. Available: https://www.esios.ree.es/es/analisis/1739?compare_indicators=1001&vis=1&start_date=23-02-2024T00%3A00&end_date=23-02-2024T23%3A55&compare_start_date=22-02-2024T00%3A00&groupby=hour&zoom=6&latlng=39.99395569397331%2C-3.021240234375

[24] Government of Spain, *Real Decreto 244/2019*. Spain: Boletín Oficial del Estado, 2019, pp. 35674–35719. Accessed: Dec. 05, 2024. [Online]. Available: https://www.boe.es/buscar/doc.php?id=BOE-A-2019-5089

[25] "EUPD Research Reveals Top European Residential Solar Markets and Most Impacting Installers Amidst Booming Market Growth – EUPD Group." Accessed: Jul. 21, 2025. [Online]. Available: https://eupd-group.com/eupd-research-reveals-top-european-residential-solar-markets-and-most-impacting-installers-amidst-booming-market-growth/

42nd European Photovoltaic Solar Energy Conference and Exhibition

INSTITUTO DE ENERGÍA SOLAR

SIZING PHOTOVOLTAIC SELF-CONSUMPTION SYSTEMS THROUGH MISMATCH INDEX AND PROFITABILITY ANALYSIS

POLITÉCNICA

Kiane Alves e Silva, Luis Miguel Carrasco, Eduardo Lorenzo

Instituto de Energía Solar – Universidad Politécnica de Madrid, Madrid Spain

kiane.asilva@alumnos.upm.es, luismiguel.carrasco@upm.es, antonio.lorenzo@upm.es

ABSTRACT

Context

The transition to clean energy has boosted the adoption of residential PV self-consumption systems. These systems contribute to reduce electricity bills, provide long-term energy price stability, and align with sustainability goals. However, system design is often based only on annual energy balance, ignoring the hourly match between PV generation and demand – a mismatch that reduces both self-consumption and profitability.

Objective

To develop a decision-support approach that identifies PV systems with storage configurations which are technically well-aligned with user demand and economically viable over their lifetime.

Challenge

Conventional indicators (self-consumption ratio, self-sufficiency) do not capture the temporal alignment between generation and demand. As a result, even technically efficient systems may underperform economically.

Contribution

- Introduces the Mismatch Index (MI) to evaluate hourly alignment between availability and demand.
- Integrates MI with profitability metrics (PBP, NPV, IRR, LCOE).
- Validates the approach with a real residential case study in Spain, demonstrating both technical and economic benefits.

Key Definitions

E_X^Y: *Energy flow from source x to destination y*

$$SEO = E_{PV}^{LOAD} + E_{PV}^{GRID} + E_{ST}^{LOAD}$$

$$C_{PV} = \frac{Annual\ PV\ production}{Annual\ energy\ demand}$$

$$C_{ST} = \frac{Energy\ Storage\ capacity}{Average\ daily\ demand}$$

METHODOLOGY

1 Hourly simulations of Energy Balanced

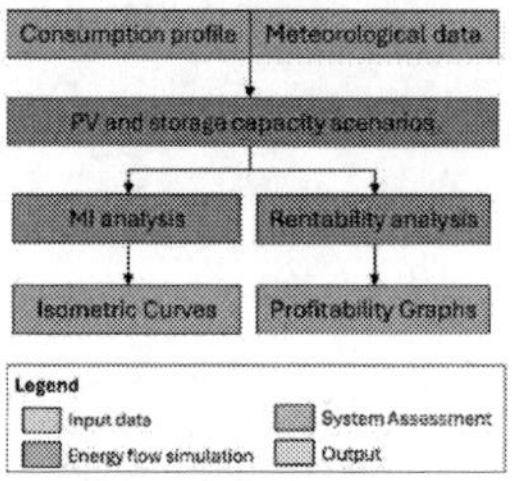

2 Representation of the PV Self-Consumption System

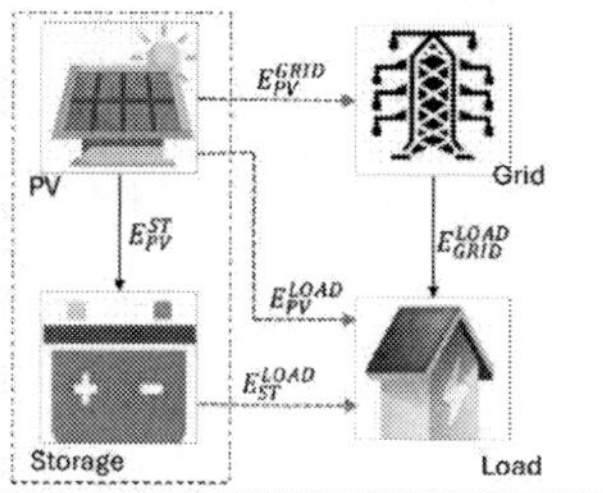

3 Mismatch Index (MI)

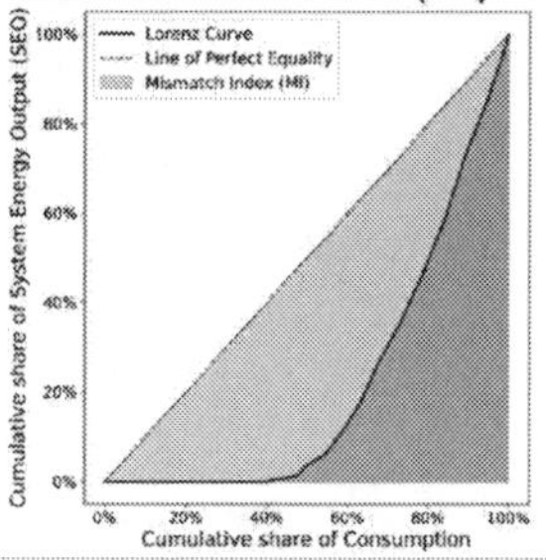

CASE STUDY

Methodology applied to a residential household in La Coruña, Spain:

$Annual\ Demand = 2.99\ MWh$

$Annual\ irradiance = 1.25\ MWh/m^2$

$PV\ system\ (C_{PV} = 1) = 6\ kWp$

$Storage\ Capacity\ (C_{ST} = 1) = 8.19\ kWh$

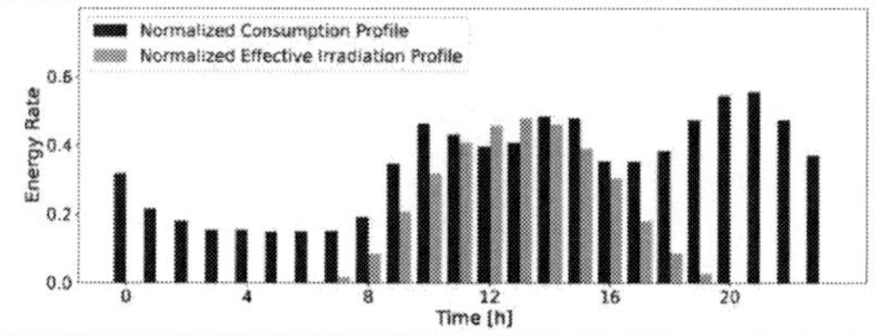

RESULTS

1 Temporal Alignment between Energy Generation and Demand (MI Analysis)

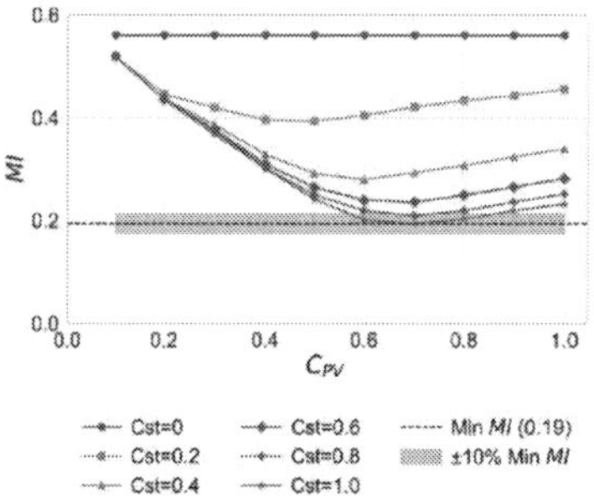

2 Economic Performance and Profitability Indicators (PBP, NPV, IRR, LCOE)

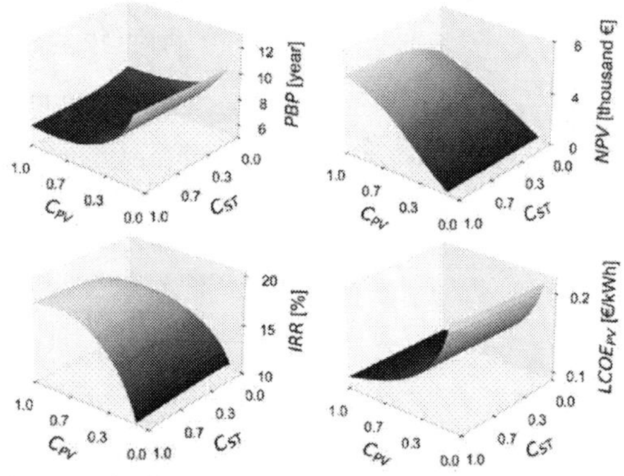

3 System Selection Based on Techno-Economic Criteria (20-years scenario)

The smallest configuration within the MI tolerance band (0.19 ± 10%) have been selected for detailed evaluation:

$PV\ system\ (C_{PV} = 0.65) \rightarrow 3.90\ kWp$

$Storage\ system\ (C_{ST} = 0.8) \rightarrow 6.55 kWh$

$MI = 0.21$

Parameter	Description	Value
CAPEX	Initial cost	€ 3,610
OPEX	Operation and maintenance cost	€ 1,754
Benefits	Savings and revenues	€ 21,838
PBP	Time to recover the initial investment	6.6 years
NPV	Present value of benefits minus costs	€ 4,516
IRR	Discount rate at which NPV = 0	18%
LCOE	Discounted cost per kWh produced	0.12 €/kWh

CONCLUSION

The proposed methodology combined temporal alignment (MI) and economic assessment to ensure reliable PV system sizing that are consistent with user demand while remaining financially viable.

This work has been possible thanks to the Project IND2022/AMB-23718 funded by the Comunidad de Madrid

Comunidad de Madrid

020440-001

This work has received funding from the European Union under grant agreement No 101076395

Funded by the European Union

METHODOLOGY FOR THE DESIGN OF OFF-GRID PHOTOVOLTAIC SYSTEMS FOR RESIDENTIAL ELECTRIC VEHICLE IN SHARED TRANSPORTATION SERVICES

David Leonardo Rodríguez Salazar, Johann Alexander Hernández Mora
Laboratorio de Investigación en Fuentes Alternativas de Energía (LIFAE), Faculty of Engineering, Universidad Distrital Francisco José de Caldas, Bogotá 110231, Colombia
rsdavidl@udistrital.edu.co, jahernandezm@udistrital.edu.co

ABSTRACT: The growing adoption of electric vehicles (EVs) in dense urban centers such as Bogotá, Colombia poses critical challenges for energy supply, particularly in shared transport schemes with intensive vehicle use. This paper presents a structured methodology to design and validate an off-grid photovoltaic (PV) system for residential EV charging, integrating probabilistic demand modeling and system simulation. A Monte Carlo approach was applied to capture stochastic variability in daily EV consumption, yielding critical percentiles such as P95 (77.4 kWh/day), used as a robust baseline for system sizing. The PV system was dimensioned considering solar resource availability, storage capacity, and conversion efficiencies, with a final configuration of 44 PV modules, a battery bank of 1,500 Ah at 48 V, and an 8 kW inverter. Validation in PV*SOL software confirmed an average daily generation of 74.8 kWh, with a performance ratio of 84.23 %. This value is approximately 3.4 % below the P95 demand. The results demonstrate the feasibility of deploying autonomous PV-based charging infrastructures for EVs in Bogotá, ensuring reliability even under adverse solar conditions and supporting the transition toward sustainable mobility in Latin American cities.
Keywords: Off-grid photovoltaic system, Electric vehicle charging, Monte Carlo simulation, Shared transportation, Bogotá

1 INTRODUCTION

As cities advance toward a greater penetration of electric mobility, the energy demand associated with electric vehicle (EV) charging acquires critical relevance. In dense urban environments such as Bogotá, where shared mobility services represent a growing share of the vehicle fleet, there is a pressing need for decentralized and sustainable energy solutions that enhance reliability while alleviating the burden on the conventional grid.

In parallel, recent developments in digital tools and simulation techniques enable the optimization of renewable energy system sizing. Monte Carlo simulation has proven to be a valuable resource for capturing the stochastic variability of electricity demand in both residential and industrial applications. Its application in the field of electric mobility allows for the estimation of critical consumption scenarios, represented by percentiles such as P95, which ensure system robustness.

Similarly, the deployment of stand-alone photovoltaic systems has shown to be a viable alternative to strengthening charging infrastructure in areas with limited grid availability [1]. When properly sized and evaluated under reliability and cost-efficiency criteria, these systems can meet the daily EV demand even under adverse conditions of solar radiation or high usage requirements.

This paper proposes a structured methodology in three stages: (1) probabilistic modeling of EV energy demand through Monte Carlo simulation, (2) sizing of a stand-alone photovoltaic system with storage and energy conversion components, and (3) performance validation through software analysis. The objective is to provide a replicable methodological framework that contributes to the consolidation of sustainable personal charging infrastructures in Bogotá and other cities facing similar mobility and energy challenges.

2 METHODOLOGY

The proposed methodology is developed in three integrated stages, enabling the progression from probabilistic demand modeling to the validation of a stand-alone photovoltaic system. To illustrate this process, a flow diagram (Figure 1) is included, summarizing the main phases: data collection, Monte Carlo simulation, system sizing, and software-based validation. This framework provides a clear overview of the sequence of steps and the iterative interactions between stages, ensuring that the final design achieves both robustness and efficiency.

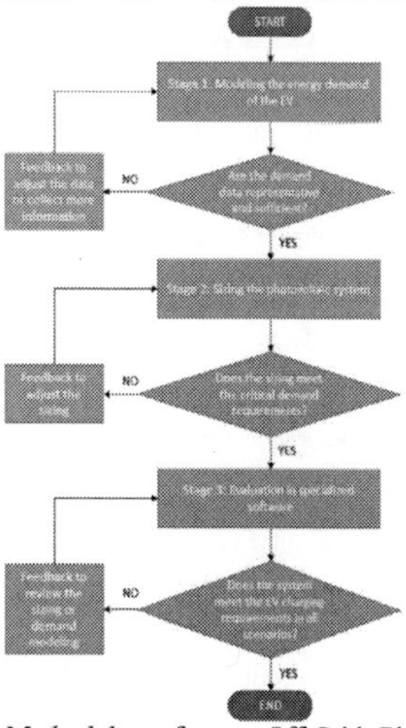

Figure 1. Methodology for an Off-Grid Photovoltaic System for Charging Residential EVs Used in Shared Transportation.

2.1 Energy demand estimation

The daily consumption of an EV can depend on random variables such as traveled distance, energy efficiency (kWh/km), and the use of auxiliary systems. To represent this variability, the Monte Carlo method is employed, as applied in energy studies such as [2], where it is used to assess the reliability of renewable-based systems. In that context, Monte Carlo simulation plays a crucial role in modeling probabilistic failure states and

10.4229/EUPVSEC2025/4DV.4.13

analyzing network capacity through power flow studies. Similarly, [3] applies Monte Carlo methods to demand estimation in charging stations, where random scenarios of connected vehicles and their state of charge are modeled to analyze the impact on the power grid, even under the integration of photovoltaic generation.

Accordingly, considering the variables mentioned above, the daily demanded energy is proposed to be modeled as:

$$E_d = \frac{D \cdot \eta_{EV} \cdot (1+\alpha)}{\eta_{ch} \cdot \eta_{bat} \cdot \eta_{inv}}$$

Where D is the daily traveled distance [km], η_{EV} is the EV efficiency [kWh/km], α is the auxiliary consumption factor, and η_{ch}, η_{bat}, η_{inv} represent the efficiencies of the charge controller, battery, and inverter, respectively.

For this study, the following probability distributions were considered:

- Daily distance (D): Based on a survey of 20 shared-mobility drivers, a truncated normal distribution with a mean of 230 km/day was estimated. For the purposes of this study, two standard deviations were considered: 50 km for EV X and 30 km for EV Y. This selection is justified because the traveled distance exhibits a symmetric behavior around a mean, but with natural limits (negative or excessively high values are unrealistic under typical urban use). Hence, a truncated normal distribution is suitable to capture both daily variability and the restriction of values outside the realistic range.

- Energy efficiency (η_{EV}): The energy efficiency of electric vehicles depends on factors such as vehicle weight, driving conditions, and the technology of the battery and powertrain. Based on specialized literature such as [4], a bounded range of specific consumption can be established (0.13–0.23 kWh/km). However, these studies do not provide sufficient data to estimate a normal distribution with robust parameters. Nevertheless, a more representative or modal value of 0.15 kWh/km has been identified under urban operating conditions, as proposed in [5]. Under these circumstances, a triangular distribution was adopted, as it allows capturing the highest probability of occurrence around the modal value while also reflecting uncertainty toward the extreme values of the range.

- Auxiliar factor (α): The energy consumption associated with EV auxiliary systems (air conditioning, ventilation, lighting, signaling, among others) depends on traffic and environmental conditions. International studies such as [6] have shown that, at low speeds, in congested traffic, or under extreme weather, auxiliaries can double the effective energy consumption and drastically reduce driving range, whereas at higher speeds their relative impact decreases due to aerodynamic drag dominance. In the Colombian context, an experimental study in Bogotá [7], based on the model of Fiori [8], considered a fixed auxiliary consumption of 700 W, equivalent to approximately 18% of the total EV consumption under urban conditions (≈35 Wh/km additional). Based on this evidence, a triangular distribution in the range 0.1–0.2, with a mode at 0.15, was adopted as the statistical representation of the auxiliary factor (α). This choice captures the higher probability of moderate consumption in typical Bogotá conditions, while reflecting the uncertainty and variability associated with dense traffic and adverse weather scenarios.

- Efficiency values (η_{ch}, η_{bat}, η_{inv}): To represent the losses in the charging and discharging chain, the product of partial efficiencies in series (controller/charger, battery, and inverter) was modeled. Empirical values from applied literature were adopted: battery efficiency (η_{bat}) = 0.90 [7], inverter efficiency (η_{inv}) = 0.98, and charge controller efficiency (η_{ch}) = 0.91 [9].

Consequently, 10,000 iterations of the Monte Carlo simulation were performed, obtaining daily demand distributions and critical percentiles (P50, P80, P95). These values are used in the next stage of system sizing.

2.2 Photovoltaic System Sizing

The system sizing is based on the energy demand estimated at the P95 percentile, following the methodology for stand-alone systems proposed in [9]. This procedure aims to ensure reliability under scenarios of maximum consumption demand. The process comprises the following stages:

- Solar resource assessment: The solar contribution is determined from the incident solar radiation characteristics of Bogotá. For this study, the geographical location corresponding to coordinates 4.61280100, -74.14294276 was considered as the reference point representing the specific case study site. The values of solar radiation obtained are presented in Table I of chapter 3, which allow estimating the required energy input for system sizing in the most unfavorable month.

- Peak power: The nominal power of the PV modules required to cover the daily energy demand under the least favorable solar conditions in Bogotá is calculated using the following equation:

$$P_{GEN} = 1.2 \cdot \frac{E_d}{HRS}$$

Where, E_d is the daily energy demand (resulting from the Monte Carlo simulation), and HRS represents the solar radiation hours (the value in hours equivalent to the incident solar radiation). On the other hand, the series configuration of the photovoltaic modules is defined by the following equation:

$$N_S = \frac{V_{oc-reg}}{V_{oc}}$$

Where, V_{oc-reg} is the maximum open-circuit voltage regulated by the charge controller, and V_{oc} is the open-circuit voltage of the selected photovoltaic module.

For the parallel configuration of the photovoltaic modules, the following equation is used:

$$N_P = \frac{P_{GEN}}{P_m \cdot N_S}$$

Where P_m is the panel power rating (as provided by the manufacturer).

Finally, the total number of panels is given by:

$$N_T = N_P \cdot N_S$$

- Battery capacity: The sizing of the battery bank is carried out under the criterion that it must be capable of supplying at least half a day of autonomy. This ensures coverage during periods when the photovoltaic modules do not generate sufficient energy, as well as during nighttime hours when shared transportation services are also in operation. For safety considerations, an additional 20% margin is included. Accordingly, the usable capacity of the battery bank is defined as:

$$C_u = \frac{1.2 \cdot E_d \cdot A}{V_n} \ [Ah]$$

Where A is the maximum number of consecutive days during which the installation will be able to meet the energy demand under unfavorable conditions, and V_n is the nominal voltage of the installation. It should be noted that E_d must be expressed in Wh. Once the usable capacity is defined, the nominal capacity of the battery bank is determined as:

$$C_n = \frac{C_u}{PD_{máx}} \ [Ah]$$

Where $PD_{máx}$ is the maximum allowable depth of discharge, established at 0.7.

- Charge controller: The selection of the charge controller is defined according to the following equation:

$$I_{reg} = 1.25 \cdot \sum_{i=1}^{n} I_{sci}$$

Where I_{sci} is the short-circuit current multiplied by the number of strings connected in parallel.

- Inverter: The sizing of the inverter must be based on the maximum power (kW) rather than the daily energy consumption (kWh). It is identified that the peak power required by the critical load—in this case, the internal EV charger—is in the range of 6–8 kW, according to slow-charging specifications for EVs.

With the above considerations, the general schematic of the photovoltaic system components is presented in Figure 2.

2.3 Evaluation of the Defined Photovoltaic System

The preliminary configuration is validated using PV*SOL software, with the objective of verifying that the proposed design meets the estimated energy demand at the P95 percentile under Bogotá's specific solar radiation and climatic conditions. However, PV*SOL does not provide a predefined topology for EVs in stand-alone systems. Therefore, the analysis is based on the general topology of an autonomous PV system, as shown in Figure 3.

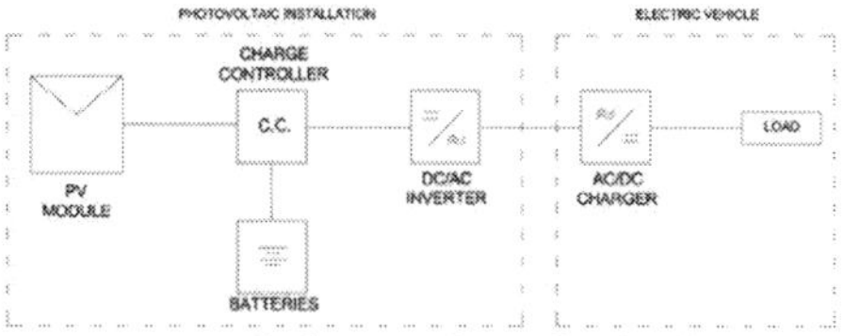

Figure 2. General diagram of an Off-Grid Photovoltaic System for charging residential EVs used in shared transportation.

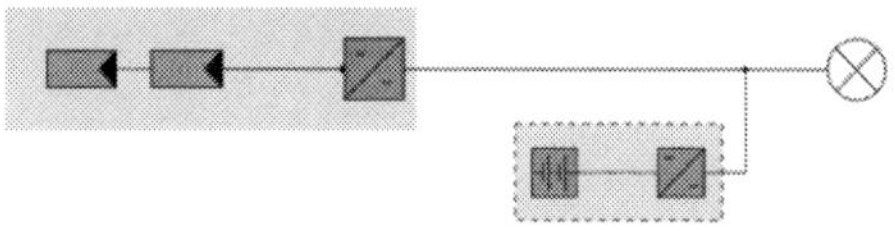

Figure 3. Topology in PV*SOL for a stand-alone system.

Although the theoretical scheme of the stand-alone system proposed in Figure 2 follows a DC-coupled topology—where a charge controller regulates the energy flow from the solar panels to the batteries—for the simulation in PV*SOL, it is necessary to adapt this design to the AC-coupled model (see Figure 3) employed by the software.

In this model, both the PV array and the battery bank are connected to a common AC bus through their respective inverters (a dedicated inverter for the PV modules and a bidirectional inverter/charger for the batteries).

This approach is conceptually different but functionally equivalent for evaluating the energy balance, system autonomy, and battery state of charge, which are the main objectives of the simulation. The overall system efficiency in PV*SOL accounts for the conversion losses of these inverters, providing results that are representative of real-world operation. In this way, the system is ensured to meet the robustness and reliability requirements prior to its actual implementation.

3 CASE STUDY: BOGOTÁ, COLOMBIA

The analysis focuses on Bogotá, Colombia, a city located at 2,640 m above sea level, with an average annual temperature of 13.6 °C, ranging between 4 °C and 21 °C. These climatic conditions are essential for applying temperature corrections to the photovoltaic modules.

Regarding the city's solar potential, the following table presents the estimated average values of solar radiation, based on different databases and analyzed over the twelve months of the year within a three-year period (2022–2024).

In terms of mobility, Bogotá shows a growing adoption of EVs in the private segment, although their presence in shared transport and remunerated services—such as electric taxis [10]— has gained relevance in recent years. Private EV usage has also begun to integrate into these schemes, as suggested by the Uber platform in [11], which adds value to this study by proposing a methodology to size stand-alone photovoltaic systems.

For the analysis, two random EV scenarios were defined, modeled under an intensive ride-sharing scheme with daily travel distances of approximately 230 km/day, emulating continuous usage patterns typical of collaborative services. This approach enables the estimation of EV energy consumption in high-turnover urban contexts. The technical parameters applied are based on surveys conducted with local EV users and manufacturer specifications.

Table I: Average Solar Radiation in Bogotá, Colombia

Month	Solar Radiation (KWh/m^2-day)		
	PVWATS	METEONORM	Average
Jan	6.22	5.00	5.61
Feb	5.53	4.86	5.19
Mar	4.77	4.65	4.71
Apr	4.16	5.10	4.63
May	4.07	5.19	4.63
Jun	4.07	5.17	4.62
Jul	4.25	4.94	4.59
Aug	4.57	4.84	4.70
Sep	4.82	4.67	4.74
Oct	4.97	4.45	4.71
Nov	5.02	4.53	4.78
Dec	5.63	5.06	5.35
Average	4.84	4.87	4.86

4 RESULTS AND DISCUSSION

4.1 Energy demand

The Monte Carlo simulation enabled the estimation of the daily charging demand of an EV operating under a ride-sharing scheme, considering an average travel distance of 230 km/day and the study parameters defined in Section 2.1.

Figure 4 presents the probability histogram of the daily energy demand, highlighting the relevant percentiles for the sizing of the photovoltaic system.

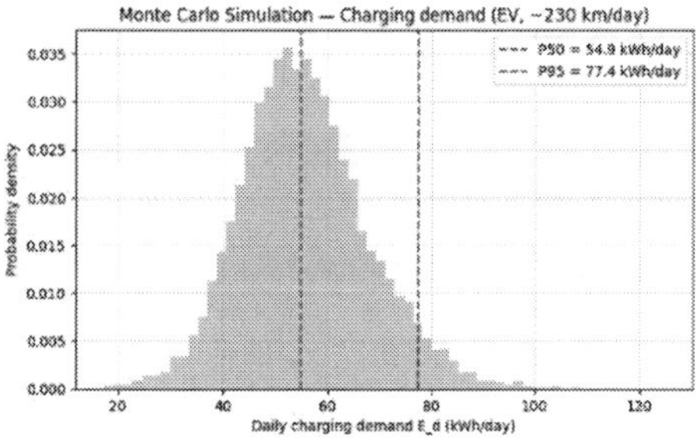

Figure 4. Monte Carlo simulation results to estimate the energy demand required for the EV.

The main statistical results obtained are summarized in the Table II.

Table II: Statistical Results of the Monte Carlo Simulation.

Indicator	Value [kWh/day]
Mean	55.7
Median (P50)	54.9
Standard Deviation	12.3
Percentile 80 (P80)	54.9
Percentile 95 (P95)	77.4

According to the distribution, the mean and the median are very close (55.7 and 54.9 kWh/day, respectively), indicating an approximately symmetric distribution around the central value. However, the presence of a right-hand tail reflects days with significantly higher consumption, reaching values of up to ~108 kWh/day in extreme scenarios.

In particular:

- P50 (54.9 kWh/day) represents the typical energy demand scenario.
- P80 (65.2 kWh/day) defines a more demanding scenario, with 80% reliability coverage.
- P95 (77.4 kWh/day) corresponds to a critical high-demand scenario, which is used for robust PV system sizing, since designing for this value ensures coverage of 95% of possible cases.

The variability in daily demand reflects the influence of factors such as travel distance, driving style, and vehicle efficiency, which justifies the use of probabilistic simulations to achieve a more realistic sizing of the energy system.

4.2 Photovoltaic System Sizing

Based on the average solar radiation values presented in Table I, and considering a daily energy demand of 77.4 kWh/day, the ratio between available solar radiation and energy demand is applied to identify the most unfavorable month in terms of solar resource. This month is then used as the reference for system sizing. The results of this ratio are presented in Table III.

Table III: Most unfavorable month for solar resource in Bogotá, Colombia.

Month	Solar Radiation (HRS)	Energy demand (E_d)	Ratio HRS/E_d
Jan	5.61	77.4	0.0725
Feb	5.19	77.4	0.0671
Mar	4.71	77.4	0.0608
Apr	4.63	77.4	0.0598
May	4.63	77.4	0.0598
Jun	4.62	77.4	0.0597
Jul	4.59	77.4	0.0593
Aug	4.70	77.4	0.0608
Sep	4.74	77.4	0.0613
Oct	4.71	77.4	0.0609
Nov	4.78	77.4	0.0617
Dec	5.35	77.4	0.0691

Accordingly, under the conditions of the most unfavorable month (July), the required peak power is calculated as:

$$P_{GEN} = 1.2 \cdot \frac{77.4\ kWh}{4.59\ h} = 20.235\ kW$$

Considering the use of EcoGreen photovoltaic modules rated at 550 Wp (Model EGE-550W-144M(M10)), with an open-circuit voltage V_{oc} de 49.68 V y and estimating a regulated open-circuit voltage V_{oc-reg} de 450 V, the required number of modules in series is obtained as:

$$N_S = \frac{450\ V}{49.68\ V} = 9.06\ \approx 9$$

10.4229/EUPVSEC2025/4DV.4.13

With the above, the distribution of photovoltaic modules in parallel is given by:

$$N_P = \frac{20.235}{(9 \cdot 0.550)} = 4.08 \approx 4$$

Thus, the total number of photovoltaic modules is calculated as:

$$N_T = 4 \cdot 9 = 36$$

However, 36 modules rated at 550 Wp yield only 19.8 kWp, which falls below the required P_{GEN}. Therefore, in order to ensure a sufficiently robust photovoltaic system configuration, the value was rounded up to 44 modules, arranged as four parallel strings of nine modules in series, plus one parallel string of eight modules in series.

$$N_T \approx 44$$

For the battery bank sizing, the usable capacity is defined as:

$$C_u = \frac{1.2 \cdot 77{,}400 \cdot 0.5}{48} = 967.5\ [Ah]$$

The nominal capacity of the battery bank is then defined as:

$$C_n = \frac{967.5}{0.7} = 1{,}382.1429\ [Ah]$$

If Maxpower 250-12 batteries are considered, the following configuration is required:

- Connection of four batteries in series to establish the system nominal voltage of 48 V.
- Connection of six parallel strings to attain a total capacity of 1,500 Ah.

To define the charge controller and the inverter for the proposed photovoltaic system, the following temperature correction for the selected photovoltaic module is considered.

The data required for these corrections are presented below:

- Tmin = 4 °C.
- Tmax = 21 °C.
- NOCT EGE-550W-144M(M10) = 45 °C.
- Voc EGE-550W-144M(M10) = 49.68 V.
- Isc EGE-550W-144M(M10) = 14.01 A.
- Temperature Coefficient of Isc EGE-550W-144M(M10) = 0.048 %/°C.
- Temperature Coefficient of Voc EGE-550W-144M(M10) = -0.28 %/°C.
- Temperature Coefficient of Pmax EGE-550W-144M(M10) = -0.35 %/°C.
- Pmax STC EGE-550W-144M(M10) = 550 W.
- G average for the study area = 1,197.79 W/m^2.

Thus, the temperature delta for the photovoltaic cell must first be defined. To this end, the cell temperature under site-specific conditions is determined and then subtracted from the standard test condition (STC) reference value of 25 °C.

$$T_{C_{amb}} = T_{amb} + \frac{NOCT - 20}{800} G_{avg}$$

- Case 1: Minimum temperature

$$T_{C_{amb}} = 4\ °C + \frac{45\ °C - 20\ °C}{800\ W/m^2} 1{,}197.79\ W/m^2$$
$$T_{C_{amb}} = 41.43\ °C$$

$$\Delta T_{min} = 41.43\ °C - 25\ °C = 16.43\ °C$$

- Case 2: Maximum temperature

$$T_{C_{amb}} = 21\ °C + \frac{45\ °C - 20\ °C}{800\ W/m^2} 1{,}197.79\ W/m^2$$
$$T_{C_{amb}} = 58.43\ °C$$

$$\Delta T_{max} = 58.43\ °C - 25\ °C = 33.43\ °C$$

Subsequently, the values of Isc, Voc, and Pmax are corrected for each temperature condition, also considering the adjustment for the average available irradiance. The general equations are as follows:

$$Isc_{Gavg} = \frac{G_{avg}}{G_{STC}} * Isc_{STC}$$

$$\Delta I = \Delta T * \text{temperature coefficient of Isc of PV module}$$

$$Isc_{new} = Isc_{Gavg} \pm \Delta I$$

$$Voc_{Gavg} \cong Voc_{STC}$$

$$\Delta V = \Delta T * \text{temperature coefficient of Voc of PV module}$$

$$Voc_{new} = Voc_{STC} \pm \Delta V$$

$$Pmax_{Gavg} = \frac{G_{avg}}{G_{STC}} * Pmax_{STC}$$

$$\Delta P = \Delta T * \text{temperature coefficient of Pmax of PV module}$$

$$Pmax_{new} = Pmax_{Gavg} \pm \Delta P$$

Consequently:

- Case 1.1: Isc correction for Tmin and G average:

$$Isc_{Gavg} = \frac{1{,}197.79\ W/m^2}{1{,}000\ W/m^2} * 14.01\ A = 16.78\ A$$

$$\Delta I = 16.43\ °C * 0.048\ \%/°C = 0.789\%$$

$$Isc_{new} = 16.78\ A + 0.789\% = 16.91\ A$$

- Case 1.2: Voc correction for Tmin and G average:

$$Voc_{Gavg} \cong 49.68\,V$$

$$\Delta V = 16.43\,°C * -0.28\%/°C = -4.6\%$$

$$Voc_{new} = 49.68\,V - 4.6\% = 47.39\,V$$

- Case 1.3: Pmax correction for Tmin and G average:

$$Pmax_{Gnew} = \frac{1{,}197.79\,W/m^2}{1{,}000\,W/m^2} * 550\,W = 658.78\,W$$

$$\Delta P = 16.43\,°C * -0.35\%/°C = -5.75\%$$

$$Pmax_{new} = 658.78\,W - 5.75\% = 620.89\,W$$

- Case 2.1: Isc correction for Tmax and G average:

$$Isc_{Gavg} = \frac{1{,}197.79\,W/m^2}{1{,}000\,W/m^2} * 14.01\,A = 16.78\,A$$

$$\Delta I = 33.43\,°C * 0.048\,\%/°C = 1.605\%$$

$$Isc_{new} = 16.78\,A + 1.605\% = 17.05\,A$$

- Case 2.2: Voc correction for Tmax and G average:

$$Voc_{Gavg} \cong 49.68\,V$$

$$\Delta V = 33.43\,°C * -0.28\%/°C = -9.36\%$$

$$Voc_{new} = 49.68\,V - 9.36\% = 45.03\,V$$

- Case 2.3: Pmax correction for Tmax and G average:

$$Pmax_{Gavg} = \frac{1{,}197.79\,W/m^2}{1{,}000\,W/m^2} * 550\,W = 658.78\,W$$

$$\Delta P = 33.43\,°C * -0.35\%/°C = -11.70\%$$

$$Pmax_{new} = 658.78\,W - 11.70\% = 581.7\,W$$

Based on the above, the selection of the charge controller is therefore conditioned by:

$$I_{reg} = 1.25 \cdot 5 \cdot 17.05\,A = 106.5625\,A$$

However, due to the five parallel strings, it is considered appropriate to use two controllers of the Victron SmartSolar MPPT RS 450/200-MC4 model, enabling the connection of four strings of nine modules in series with a maximum Voc of 426.51 V, and one string of eight modules in series with a Voc of 379.12 V.

Finally, to ensure the operation of the stand-alone photovoltaic system designed for EV charging, the Victron Energy MultiPlus-II 48/10000/140 inverter was selected. This unit, with an output power of 8 kW (10 kVA), is sized to meet the maximum demand of the EV onboard charger (estimated at 7.4 kW), thereby guaranteeing stable operation even during transient demand peaks. Its native integration with the previously selected Victron MPPT controllers allows for unified system management, maximizing energy efficiency and enabling remote monitoring.

All parameters corrected for temperature remain within the limits defined for both the charge controller and the inverter.

Based on the above, under the theoretical scheme of the dimensioned photovoltaic system, the daily energy production is:

$$E_{theo\ day} = HRS_{avg} \cdot N_T \cdot P_{máx\_mod}$$
$$E_{theo\ day} = 4.86\,h \cdot 44 \cdot 0.550\,kWp$$
$$E_{theo\ day} = 117.612\,kWh/day$$

4.3 Photovoltaic System Modeling in PV*SOL Software

To contrast the theoretical performance of the proposed photovoltaic installation with a practical scenario, the system was simulated in PV*SOL under the scheme presented in Figure 3. The objective was to determine the actual value of the energy generated by the system, which, according to the software, amounts to 27,112 kWh/year, equivalent to 74.78 kWh/day.

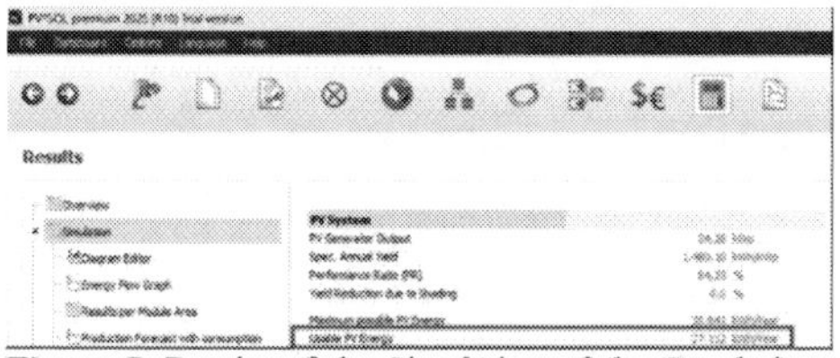

Figure 5. Results of the Simulation of the Stand-alone Photovoltaic System in PV*SOL Software.

The comparison between the theoretical results and the PV*SOL simulation reveals a significant difference in the energy generated by the photovoltaic system. In the theoretical model, without considering system losses, the estimated daily production was 117.612 kWh/day. In contrast, the PV*SOL simulation, which accounts for losses due to orientation, shading, temperature, component efficiency, wiring, and other real operating factors, reduced production to 74.8 kWh/day, representing approximately 36% less than the theoretical estimate.

The Performance Ratio (PR) of 84.23% obtained in PV*SOL is consistent with real values observed in photovoltaic installations under similar conditions, thereby validating the practical adjustment against the idealized calculation.

When comparing generation with the estimated demand:

- The theoretically designed system would comfortably cover the P95 percentile (77.4 kWh/day), with a margin of 52%.
- However, in the realistic PV*SOL scenario, the average daily generation of 74.8 kWh/day falls 3.4% short of the P95 demand, although it sufficiently covers the P50 (54.9 kWh/day) and P80 (65.2 kWh/day) percentiles.

This implies that the system, as currently sized, would reliably cover 80% of days; nevertheless, under critical P95 scenarios, energy deficits could occur, requiring either additional storage capacity (larger battery bank) or backup from an auxiliary source (e.g., grid or generator).

Thus, the PV*SOL simulation allows for a more accurate adjustment of performance expectations and highlights the importance of considering real operational losses in system sizing. If the objective is to ensure P95 coverage, the following measures are recommended:

- Moderate increase in the installed PV module capacity.
- Optimization of tilt and orientation configuration.
- Expansion of storage capacity to cover days with insufficient generation.

5 CONCLUSIONS

- The Monte Carlo simulation enabled the capture of part of the stochastic variability in electric vehicle (EV) demand under ride-sharing schemes, providing critical values (P50, P80, and P95) that strengthen the energy sizing process.
- The P95 percentile (77.4 kWh/day) was consolidated as the reference scenario for designing a robust photovoltaic (PV) system, ensuring 95% coverage of consumption situations for ride-sharing trips averaging 230 km/day.
- The comparison between the theoretical model (117.6 kWh/day) and the PV*SOL simulation (74.8 kWh/day) highlighted the importance of accounting for real-world losses associated with shading, orientation, component efficiency, and operational conditions.
- The Performance Ratio of 84.23% validated in PV*SOL demonstrates that the designed system is technically feasible and capable of meeting the critical EV demand, contributing to reduced dependence on the conventional grid.
- The installation of the system requires approximately 114 m² of available area, which represents a limitation in Bogotá, where households with this amount of space are typically located in multi-unit residential properties (condominiums). This restricts access for individual households to stand-alone systems of this scale.
- Given the spatial limitation, it is pertinent to consider grid-connected alternatives, which allow for surplus sharing, reduce the individual area requirement, and leverage existing electrical infrastructure as backup.
- The proposed methodology is replicable in other Latin American cities facing similar challenges in mobility and energy, contributing to the consolidation of sustainable and decentralized charging infrastructure solutions.

6 REFERENCES

[1] A. Villamarín Jácome, M. Saltos, and J. Echever, "Dimensionamiento Óptimo de Sistemas Fotovoltaicos y Baterías en Entornos Residenciales para Reducir la Dependencia de la Infraestructura Eléctrica Centralizada," *Revista Técnica "energía,"* vol. 21, no. 2, pp. 60–68, Jan. 2025, doi: 10.37116/revistaenergia.v21.n2.2025.685.

[2] A. C. Angulo Hurtado, " Análisis de la Penetración de Energías Renovables en la confiabilidad de los sistemas eléctricos utilizando simulación de Montecarlo," Artículos profesionales de alto nivel, Pontifica Universidad Católica del Ecuador, Esmeraldas - Ecuador, 2024.

[3] J. Lascano, L. Chiza, R. Saraguro, C. Quinatoa, and J. Tapia, "Estimación de la Demanda de una Estación de Carga para Vehículos Eléctricos Mediante la Aplicación de Métodos Probabilísticos," *Revista Técnica "energía,"* vol. 20, no. 1, pp. 52–64, Jul. 2023, doi: 10.37116/revistaenergia.v20.n1.2023.569.

[4] International Energy Agency, "Global EV Outlook 2024 Moving towards increased affordability," Apr. 2024.

[5] I. Sanz Arnaiz, "Análisis de la evolución y el impacto de los vehículos eléctricos en la economía europea," Trabajo final de grado, Universidad Pontificia Comillas Madrid, Madrid, 2015.

[6] I. Evtimov, R. Ivanov, and M. Sapundjiev, "Energy consumption of auxiliary systems of electric cars," *MATEC Web of Conferences*, vol. 133, p. 06002, Nov. 2017, doi: 10.1051/matecconf/201713306002.

[7] S. Torres Franco, M. M. Suárez Pradilla, I. C. Durán Tovar, and A. R. Marulanda Guerra, "Evaluation of the energy consumption of an electric vehicle in the city of Bogotá," *Revista de la Escuela Colombiana de Ingeniería*, vol. 120, 2020.

[8] C. Fiori, K. Ahn, and H. A. Rakha, "Power-based electric vehicle energy consumption model: Model development and validation," *Appl Energy*, vol. 168, pp. 257–268, Apr. 2016, doi: 10.1016/j.apenergy.2016.01.097.

[9] P. Pineda, "Guía de dimensionado simple de una instalación solar fotovoltaica Off-Grid," 2023.

[10] E. Mayorga Rincón, "Esta es la nueva flota de taxis eléctricos que llegó a Bogotá: se caracterizan porque su color no es amarillo como los convencionales," *El Tiempo*, Aug. 06, 2025.

[11] Uber Colombia, "Comfort Electric de Uber: Vehículos 100% eléctricos en Bogotá," Uber Newsroom.

42nd European Photovoltaic Solar Energy Conference and Exhibition
42nd European Photovoltaic Solar Energy Conference and Exhibition

Methodology for the Design of Off-Grid Photovoltaic Systems for Residential Electric Vehicle in Shared Transportation Services

David Leonardo Rodríguez and Johann Alexander Hernández
LIFAE, Faculty of Engineering, Universidad Distrital Francisco José de Caldas, Bogotá, Colombia.

Abstract

The increasing adoption of electric vehicles (EVs) in Bogotá poses significant energy challenges, particularly under shared transportation schemes. This study proposes a methodology for the design and validation of an off-grid photovoltaic (PV) charging system for residential EVs, integrating probabilistic demand modeling and simulation in PV*SOL. The methodology combines Monte Carlo simulations (10,000 iterations) with technical dimensioning of PV arrays, battery storage, and power electronics. The designed system, consisting of 44 PV modules, a 1,500 Ah battery bank (48 V), and 8 kW inverter, achieved an average simulated generation of 74.8 kWh/day, which is approximately 3.4 % below the critical demand level of 77.4 kWh/day (P95). The results confirm the technical feasibility of off-grid PV charging infrastructures to support sustainable mobility in urban contexts.

Methodology

The proposed methodology integrates probabilistic demand modeling with technical sizing and simulation of an off-grid photovoltaic system for residential EV charging. It is developed in three integrated stages that allow transitioning from demand modeling to the validation of the PV system. To illustrate this process, a flowchart (Figure 1) is included, summarizing the main phases: data collection, Monte Carlo simulation, system sizing, and software-based validation. This scheme provides a clear overview of the sequential steps and the iterative interactions between stages, ensuring robustness and efficiency in the final design.

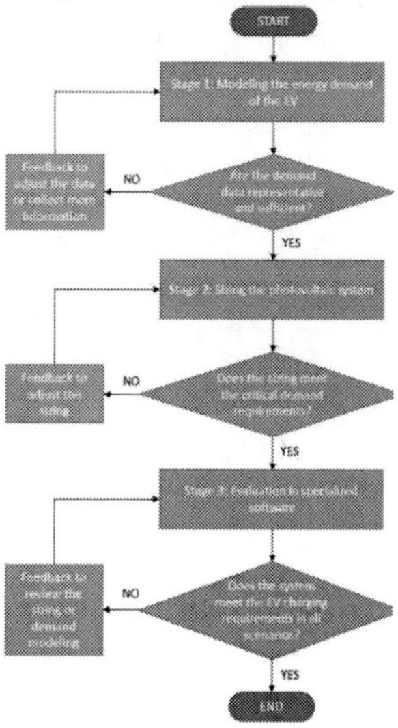

Figure. 1. Methodology for an Off-Grid Photovoltaic System for Charging Residential EVs Used in Shared Transportation.

Step 1. Energy Demand Estimation:

Daily EV charging demand was modeled through Monte Carlo simulations (10,000 iterations), based on urban driving profiles under shared-use conditions. Representative statistical percentiles (P50, P80, P95) were extracted to account for variability in vehicle usage.

The estimated daily charging energy E_d was calculated as:

$$E_d = \frac{D \cdot \eta_{EV} \cdot (1+\alpha)}{\eta_{ch} \cdot \eta_{bat} \cdot \eta_{inv}}$$

Where D is the daily driving distance [km], η_{EV} is the EV efficiency [kWh/km], α is the auxiliary systems consumption factor, and $\eta_{ch}, \eta_{bat}, \eta_{inv}$ are the efficiencies of the charge controller, battery, and inverter, respectively.

This formulation was extended using Monte Carlo simulation to generate a distribution of daily demand values, which were then used for system dimensioning.

Step 2. System Sizing:

The PV array, battery bank, charge controller and inverter capacity were dimensioned according to the P95 demand value (77.4 kWh/day), ensuring 95% supply reliability.

Step 3. Simulation and Validation:

The system was validated in PV*SOL using Bogotá's solar resource conditions. The effective performance ratio (PR) were obtained from the simulation.

Results

Energy Demand Estimation

Results showed an average of 55.7 kWh/day, with a typical scenario at P50 = 54.9 kWh/day, a more demanding case at P80 = 65.2 kWh/day, and a critical high-demand case at P95 = 77.4 kWh/day. Extreme situations reached up to ~108 kWh/day. For design purposes, the P95 value was selected to ensure 95% supply reliability.

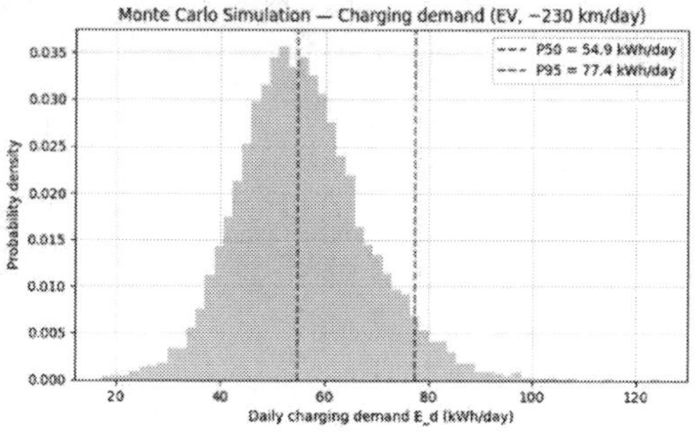

Figure. 2. Monte Carlo simulation results to estimate the energy demand required for the EV.

PV Sizing

The system was dimensioned using the P95 demand (77.4 kWh/day) to ensure 95% supply reliability. This resulted in a required peak power of 20.235 kWp, covered by 44 EcoGreen 550 Wp modules (≈24.2 kWp).The storage system consists of a 48 V, 1,500 Ah battery bank (Maxpower 250-12) arranged in 4S6P, providing sufficient autonomy. Charge regulation is achieved with two Victron SmartSolar MPPT 450/200 controllers, while a Victron MultiPlus-II 10 kVA inverter ensures stable operation of the EV charger (7.4 kW).

Simulation Output

- Theoretical PV generation: 117.6 kWh/day
- PV*SOL simulation output: 74.8 kWh/day
- Performance Ratio simulation output: 84.23%

The system configuration reliably meets P50 and P80 demand and nearly covers P95. Minor shortfalls are expected during low-solar months, mitigable through hybridization or demand management.

Summary

- Probabilistic modeling via Monte Carlo allowed incorporating demand uncertainty, ensuring a robust sizing approach under variable EV usage.
- The system configuration adequately meets average and high-demand scenarios (P50, P80). However, it fails to fully cover the P95 demand, exposing a limitation under peak consumption conditions.
- The achieved PR of 84.23% demonstrates the technical feasibility of the system under Bogotá's solar resource.
- The main constraint lies in the required installation area (~114 m²), which is rarely available in individual households, particularly in multifamily housing units.
- Considering these spatial and demand-coverage limitations, grid-connected or hybrid PV systems emerge as more viable alternatives. The methodology remains transferable to evaluate PV-based EV charging infrastructures in other urban contexts with similar energy and mobility challenges.

PERFORMANCE EVALUATION OF INSTALLED BIFACIAL PV MODULES: TOWARDS THE GROUND ALBEDO ENHANCEMENT

Dounia Dahlioui[1]*, Steve Schading[1], Ingar Alvaro Høye[2], Tore Sandnes Vehus[1]
[1]University of Agder, Department of Engineering Sciences, 4879 Grimstad, Norway
[2]Solkraft Sør AS, 4532 Øyslebø, Norway
*e-mail of corresponding author: dounia.dahlioui@uia.no

ABSTRACT: The growing deployment of bifacial photovoltaic (bPV) modules in large-scale utility PV power plants is driven by their potential to achieve higher energy output with minimal additional cost. The present study evaluates the performance of bPV modules installed in Grimstad, Norway, by analyzing their specific yield and assessing the impact of reflector integration on energy gains. A detailed review of ground reflectors used to enhance albedo and, consequently, bPV performance is presented. Reflectors were tested under real outdoor conditions to determine their effectiveness in improving bPV output. The installed system demonstrated substantial performance under Nordic conditions, achieving an annual specific yield of approximately 1282 kWh/kWp. The study evaluated two reflector types: white reflectors showed superior stability and consistent power gains, whereas semi-mirrored reflectors provided variable performance due to mismatch effects from uneven rear-side illumination. Experimental results indicated limited gains of 0.86-1.14% under optimal configurations, with some approaches yielding negative performance for semi-mirrored reflectors. These findings suggest that reflector implementation may not be economically viable for standard bPV installations until significant cost reductions are achieved. The study highlights the importance of experimental validation over simulation-based predictions, as optical interactions between reflective materials and atmospheric conditions may not be accurately captured by simulations. Future research should focus on utilizing larger areas for installation and exploring elevated configurations to fully validate the potential of reflector-enhanced bPV systems, while emphasizing their rentability.

Keywords: Bifacial photovoltaic, Nordic, energy yield, albedo, ground reflectors.

1 INTRODUCTION

The adoption of bifacial solar modules in large-scale utility PV power plants has grown, driven by the potential for increased energy output with minimal additional cost. An energy yield of 1300 kWh/kWp per year has been found for bifacial PV installed in low latitude areas [1], while 1000 kWh/kWp was calculated in high latitude locations such as Sweden [2]. However, a study in Norway reported 1342 kWh/kWp, though the authors noted this is exceptionally high for Norwegian PV installations [3].

Figure 1 shows the expected world market share on bifacial PV with an increase from less than 20% in 2019 to 70% in 2030 [4]. However, according to literature [5] two major limits exist when considering bifacial PV operation in high-latitude locations. First, there is a scarcity of confirmed field data particular to these places, limiting the ability to accurately evaluate and assess these systems. Second, present simulation methods for bPV systems do not provide enough accuracy to capture specific issues of high latitudes. According to TÜV Rheinland [6], many key factors influence the performance and energy output of bifacial PV modules. The energy gain is impacted by location and installation parameters, including ground albedo, tilt angle, mounting height, structural design, and row spacing, which play a role in shading and sunlight exposure.

The enhancement of ground albedo through the integration of reflectors with bifacial PV has been studied as a possible solution since decades [7]. Authors of [8] highlighted pioneering research on ground reflectors designed to enhance the reflected energy captured by the rear side of bifacial photovoltaic systems, including studies dating back to 1985.

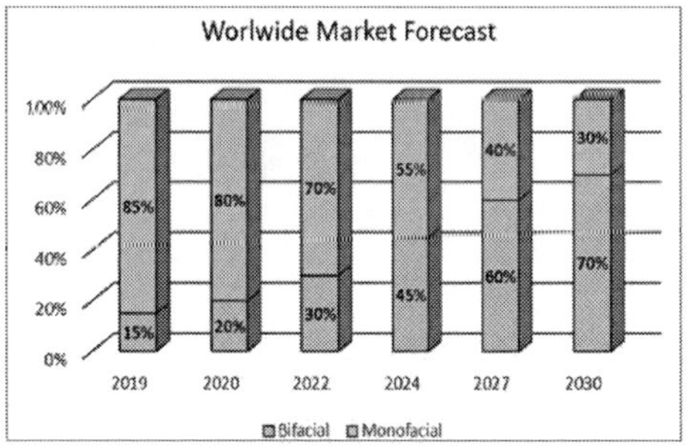

Figure 1: Prediction of the bifacial world market for the different cell technologies [4].

Based on the conducted literature detailed in appendix 1, reflector materials can be classified into three optical categories based on their scattering behavior [9] as shown in Fig. 2. Diffuse reflectors like white paint [10], [11] and gravel [1], [12] provide uniform rear-side illumination with minimal angle dependence. For specular reflectors like aluminum [13] and mirrors [14] that can create concentrated hotspots but may cause non-uniform irradiance patterns. Finally, glossy reflectors such as photopaper [9] and white tiles [15] represent an intermediate category with medium angle dependence, combining predominantly directional reflection with some diffuse scattering due to their smooth but slightly textured surfaces.The distribution of papers per reflectors type is presented in Figure 3, with 73% of research efforts focusing on diffuse reflectors. Ground reflectors show significant variation in performance gains, as detailed in Appendix 1. The gains are raning from 2.8% increases in bifacial performance as found for white tarps [16] to 59% energy increase compared to monofacial systems using

10.4229/EUPVSEC2025/4DV.4.16

diffuse reflectors [11]. It should be noted that most reported gains compare bifacial systems with monofacial PV, explaining their large amplitude. For fair comparison, the reference should be bifacial PV systems with different reflectors under identical exposure conditions

The objective of this study is to evaluate bPV module performance in Nordic climates, where field performance data remains limited, through specific yield analysis. The study also investigates energy gains achieved with different reflective ground surfaces to assess their effectiveness in enhancing bifacial PV performance.

Figure 2: Schematic of a (a) diffuse, (b) glossy, and (c) specular reflector (light incident from the right) [9].

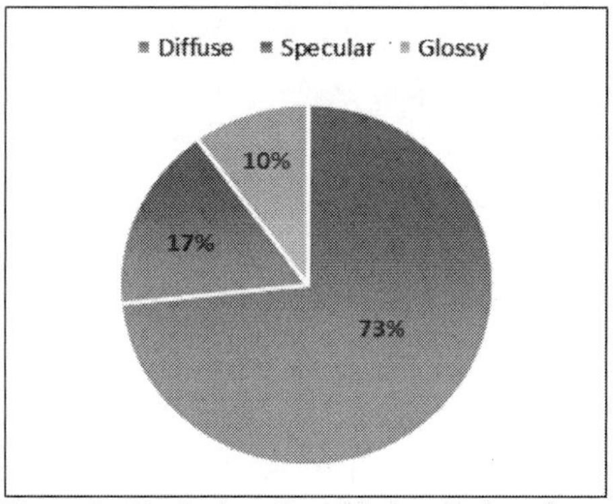

Figure 3: Distribution of published works by reflector types as reported in 18 papers (See Appendix 1).

2 EXPERIMENTAL APPROACHES

2.1 Study site and experimental Setup

Three bifacial PV modules, shown in Fig 4, have been installed on the rooftop of a building at the University of Agder's Grimstad campus in Norway (58.3345°N, 8.5755°E). The location falls under the Cfb climate classification according to the Köppen-Geiger system, characterized by mild temperatures, frequent rainfall (approximately 1,119 mm annually), and an average temperature of 9.7 °C. Each module is a 555 Wp N-type bifacial monocrystalline silicon half-cell with a double-glass design. The modules are equipped with microinverters, allowing real-time monitoring of individual energy production. The PV array is installed with a south-facing orientation at a 40° tilt angle.

2.2 Ground reflectors installation

Based on the results obtained from outdoor measurements of reflection properties, a selection of reflectors has been made. Among the tested materials, the white plates demonstrated the highest spectral albedo within the wavelength range of 300 nm to 1100 nm, with an albedo factor of approximately 0.7. In contrast, the semi-mirrored material exhibited the lowest spectral albedo, with a factor of 0.25. For comparison purposes, we selected white and semi-mirrored plates for installation.

These reflectors were installed beneath the PV panels to study the performance of the bPV system in an optimized configuaion. The nearby meteorological station provides measurements of Global Horizontal Irradiance (GHI) via Kipp & Zonen CMP11 pyranometers. Additionally, irradiance data is available from an albedometer, which consists of two Kipp & Zonen CMP11 pyranometers mounted to measure both upward and downward-facing irradiance. Missing albedo and GHI data were sourced from the NASA Power database [17], while cloud opacity data were obtained from Solcast [18].

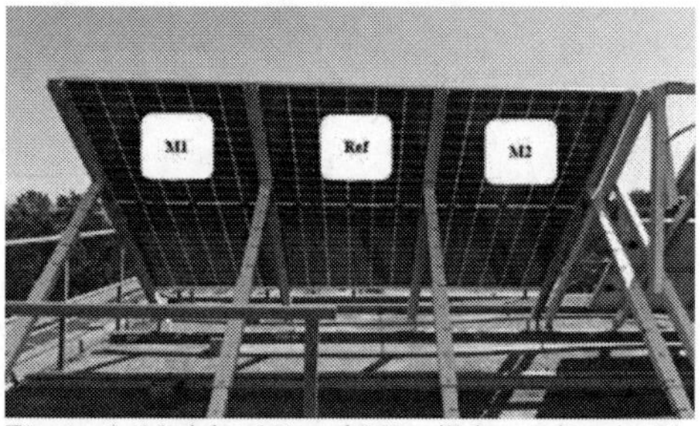

Figure 4: Modules M1 and M2 will be equipped with ground reflectors, while the reference module will remain without reflectors.

After the simultaneous exposure and due to space limitations, to avoid interference with the reference module, each reflector was exposed individually for one month as shown in Fig. 5. However, this sequential approach may introduce variability due to different irradiance conditions during each test period.

Figure 5: Bifacial PV with corresponding reflectors. (a) Simultaneous exposure, (b) Individual exposure.

3 RESULTS AND DISCUSSIONS

3.1 Yield assessment

Figure 6 shows the specific yield calculated based on the recorded production for the entire PV demonstrator presented with the corresponding global horizontal irradiance (GHI) and albedo. The bifacial PV demonstrates good seasonal performance with a total yield of 1183.25 kWh/kWp over 337 days of monitoring. Considering the average daily yield of 3.51 kWh/kWp, the estimated annual specific yield is around 1281.56 kWh/kWp. Peak performance occurs during spring and summer months (May-July) with daily yields frequently exceeding 7 kWh/kWp and reaching a maximum of 8.02 kWh/kWp. Winter months (December-January) show expected lower yields averaging below 1 kWh/kWp due to reduced daylight hours and solar irradiance. Wintertime is characterized by snow conditions which are clearly visible on the albedo values that reached 0.68 for example on 2nd January 2025 where the recorded snow depth was 18 cm according to [19].

10.4229/EUPVSEC2025/4DV.4.16

The overall correlation between energy yield and irradiance is high. However, some days, such as 17th February and 14th March 2025, show a high energy yield compared to the relatively low received irradiance. The daily average of GHI is calculated as the mean of hourly values, which may underestimate the results. These periods correspond mainly to missing data from our weather station, which were supplemented with data from weather databases.

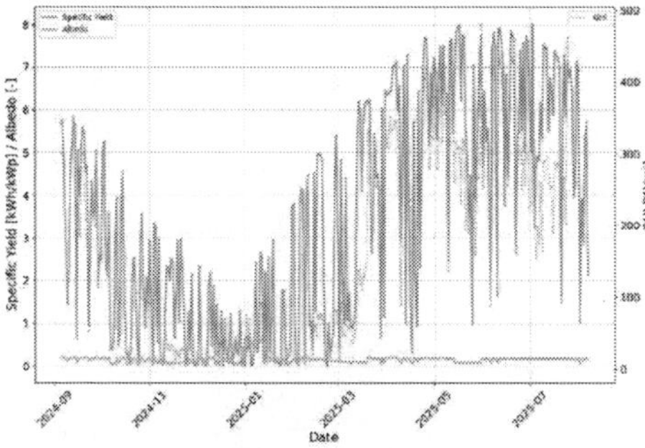

Figure 6: Daily specific yield for the period from 05 September 2024 to 07 August 2025, with the corresponding GHI and albedo.

3.2 Comparison of reflectors performance

To minimize the impact of rapidly changing irradiance conditions, such as during sunrise or sunset, we focused on 11:00, 13:00, and 15:00 hours for meaningful comparisons in power gain as shown in Fig. 7.

Based on the comprehensive almost one-year dataset, both white and semi-mirrored reflectors demonstrate positive mean performance throughout the day. White reflector provides superior consistency and reliability with peak performance at 13H (1.03% mean gain) and moderate variability manifested by a standard deviation interval of 1.41-2.36% while achieving maximum gains up to 20.74%. Semi-mirrored reflector showed mean performance between 0.71 and 1.09% gains with notably higher median values at 11H and 13H (0.71% and 0.91% respectively), lower overall variability and a maximum gain reaching 13%.

Daily negative gains in power production have been observed throughout the monitoring period for both reflector types, with semi-mirrored reflectors showing a higher frequency of negative values. The hypothesis for this unconventional result is that cross-interference between reflectors is affecting the reference panel measurements. Since both reflector systems were installed beneath adjacent bifacial PV panels with limited spacing, the reflected irradiance from the test reflectors is likely reaching the reference panel. This additional illumination of the reference panel may alter its performance baseline, causing the calculated gains to appear reduced or even negative.

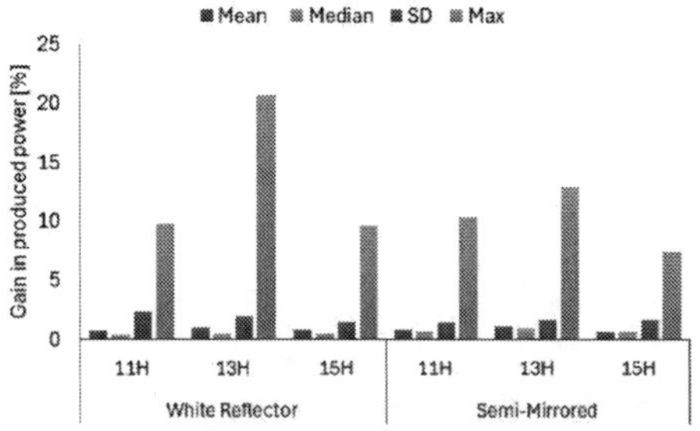

Figure 7: Average gain in produced power at times of the day during almost one year of monitoring for white and semi-mirrored plates.

It should be noted that [20] recommends that the reflective material should extend the module's width two times and four times the module's length to ensure that as much of the irradiance incident on the panel's rear surface is reflected off the foil. As the available installation area has limited space, this recommendation could not be implemented in the present work.

The semi-mirrored reflector, having higher reflectivity, generates more intense and directionally scattered reflected light, resulting in greater stray light effects on the corresponding PV module and more frequent negative gain calculations. To validate this hypothesis and obtain accurate reflector performance data, the following figure presents results from individual reflector exposure tests with increased spatial separation to prevent cross-interference effects.

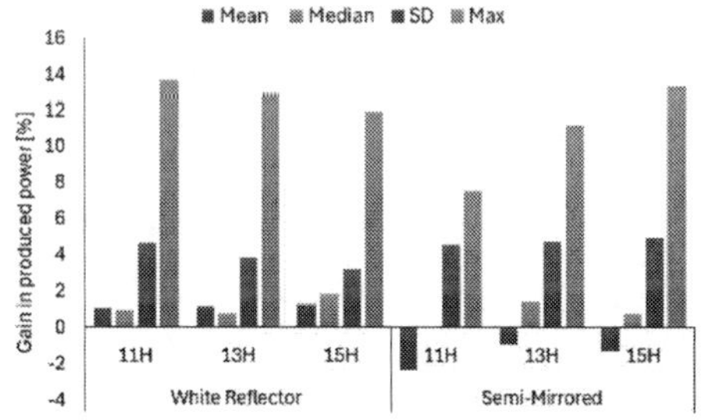

Figure 8: Bifacial gain enhancement from white reflectors and semi-mirrored at different times of the day for 1 month field study (Individual exposure).

Based data shown in Fig. 8, noticeable negative mean gain values are obtained for semi-mirrored reflector compared to white reflectors. It has been noticed that most of negative values in gain correspond to days with high irradiance and clear sky conditions. The system shows negative performance (-30 to -62W) during high irradiance conditions and clear sky where the cloud opacity was very low as shown in Fig. 9.

10.4229/EUPVSEC2025/4DV.4.16

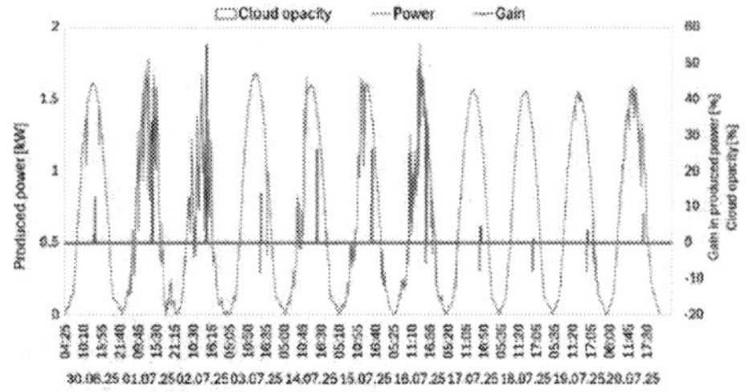

Figure 9: Produced power for entire system with corresponding gain from semi-mirrored reflector per PV module.

Figure 9 reveals that positive gains occur predominantly during cloudy conditions, as observed on July 15th where the coud opacity reached 26% [21]. Under diffuse lighting conditions, the semi-mirrored reflector effectively captures scattered light, enhancing rear-side illumination. Conversely, clear sky conditions may generate thermal effects that negate the optical benefits of the reflector. Therefore, using a thermal camera FLUKE Ti400, a series of thermal inspections has been conducted on sunny days where the temperatures of the module with semi-mirrored reflectors and the reference one did not exceed 38°C. No anomalies have been detected regarding the thermal effects. The study by [22] reveals that the ground albedo of concrete surfaces remains relatively stable, while the albedo of high-reflective surfaces can vary significantly on sunny days. This variation is attributed to the incident-angle dependence of ground reflections, particularly for reflectors with specular or mirror-like properties, which can result in mismatch loss in PV modules. Similarly, [23] investigates the behavior of both diffuse and specular reflectors. The study found that mirrors redirect more incoming irradiance, but only in specific reflection directions. Diffuse reflectors are more versatile as they redirect light with fewer angular restrictions, minimizing shading and maximizing light capture. In contrast, surfaces with diffuse reflections tend to maintain a stable albedo throughout the day

The white reflector demonstrated consistent positive performance throughout both daily cycles and the entire monitoring period. Variability was observed, particularly manifested by high standard deviation in morning measurements. However, the white reflector maintained optical benefits by enhancing both diffuse and direct irradiance reflection. Table 2 presents the overall gain for both simultaneous and individual exposure scenarios.

The slight gains observed suggest that reflector implementation may not be recommended for standard bifacial PV installations, consistent with other authors who advise against ground albedo enhancements until substantial cost reductions are realized [16]. However, significant improvements may be achievable with elevated panel configurations as recommended by [24], representing a promising direction for future work.

Table 1: Overall gain for simultaneous and individual exposure of reflectors.

Reflectors	White [%]	Semi-Mirrored [%]
Simultaneous	0.86	0.89
Individual	1.14	-1.56

4 SENSITIVITY ANALYSIS

The production modeling of 40 kWp of bifacial PV was conducted by SAM (Solar Advisor Model), considering the weather conditions of Grimstad. The installation consists of three subarrays, each containing one string, with two strings connected in parallel and oriented south. Each string has 18 PV modules of 555 W and 1 row, so a total of 4 rows is installed at a height of 0.5 from ground. The weather file has been obtained from the National Solar Radiation Database (NSRDB). For a typical GCR of 0.3, a height of 0.5 m as the experimental installation height, the parametric analysis of the energy yield to tilt angle and albedo is then carried out using SAM simulations. The number of possible run simulations is the product of the number of possible values for each factor, so a total of 25 runs. It should be noted that the albedo valued imputed based on the results of the experimental study conducted for the white and semi-mirrored plates.

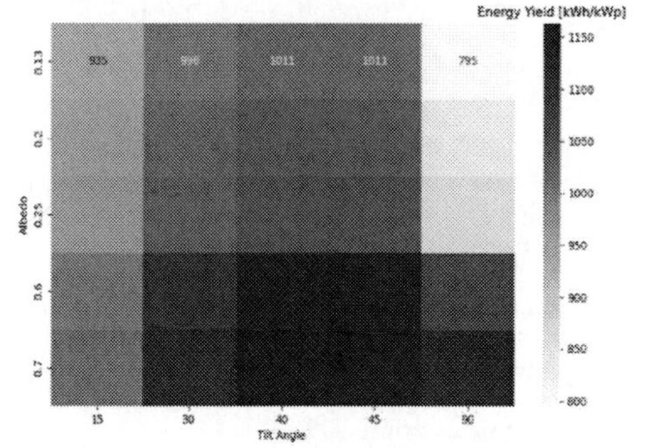

Figure 10: Results of 25 simulations for five different albedo values on the ground and four different tilt angles of PV modules shown in terms of annual specific performance for a fixed GCR.

The results of 25 simulations are presented in Fig. 10, showing annual energy yield versus tilt angle for different ground albedo values. The simulation results demonstrate a clear positive correlation between tilt angle and energy yield, with the exception of the 90° vertical configuration. Maximum energy yields of 1148 kWh/kWp and 1163 kWh/kWp were achieved at 40° and 45° tilt angles respectively, using the highest albedo value of 0.7. In contrast, the minimum energy yield of 795 kWh/kWp occurred with the lowest albedo of 0.13 and a vertical configuration.

While simulations consistently predict that higher albedo surfaces improve bifacial PV performance, the experimental results reveal important limitations of modeling software. Despite the semi-mirrored reflector having high reflectivity, it produced negative performance impacts under clear sky conditions; an effect not captured by standard simulation tools. This discrepancy highlights a gap between theoretical predictions and real-world performance, emphasizing that reflector material properties beyond simple albedo values significantly influence bifacial PV systems.

5 CONCLUSIONS

This study demonstrates that bifacial PV systems in Nordic conditions achieve substantial annual energy yields of 1281.56 kWh/kWp, confirming their viability in high-latitude environments. The experimental evaluation of ground reflectors under real outdoor conditions revealed distinct performance characteristics between reflector types. White reflectors demonstrated superior stability and consistent power gains, while semi-mirrored reflectors showed variable performance, likely due to mismatch loss that negatively impacted their reliability under the tested configurations.

The limited gains observed (0.86-1.14%) suggest that reflector implementation may not be economically justified for standard bifacial PV installations until substantial cost reductions are achieved. The potential for exploiting greater reflector surface areas, particularly with elevated modules, offers significant opportunities for improving bifacial PV performance.

This work highlights as well the critical importance of experimental validation over simulation-based predictions, as the complex optical interactions between reflective materials and varying atmospheric conditions cannot be accurately captured through modeling alone. Future investigations should focus on spatial adjustments and elevated configurations to fully realize the potential of reflector-enhanced bifacial PV systems.

6 ACKNOWLEDGEMENTS

This work has been funded partially by Forskningsmobilisering Agder in Norway and the Research Council of Norway in the framework of FME Solar (No 350244). The authors thank Prof. Anne Gerd Imenes from University of Agder for her valuable contribution to this work.

7 REFERENCES

[1] D. L. Dias, G. A. Rampinelli, G. N. Garrido, J. A. Tejero, M. S. de Cardona Ortín, and L. E. Bremermann, "Performance assessment of bifacial and monofacial PV systems on different types of soils in a low-latitude site," *Renew Energy*, vol. 246, Jun. 2025, doi: 10.1016/j.renene.2025.122868.

[2] E. Molin, B. Stridh, A. Molin, and E. Wackelgard, "Experimental yield study of bifacial PV modules in nordic conditions," *IEEE J Photovolt*, vol. 8, no. 6, pp. 1457–1463, Nov. 2018, doi: 10.1109/JPHOTOV.2018.2865168.

[3] H. N. Riise *et al.*, "Performance analysis of a BAPV bifacial system in Norway," in *Conference Record of the IEEE Photovoltaic Specialists Conference*, Institute of Electrical and Electronics Engineers Inc., Jun. 2021, pp. 1304–1308. doi: 10.1109/PVSC43889.2021.9518963.

[4] P. K. Sahu, J. N. Roy, and C. Chakraborty, "Performance assessment of a bifacial PV system using a new energy estimation model," *Solar Energy*, vol. 262, Sep. 2023, doi: 10.1016/j.solener.2023.111818.

[5] B. D. Dimd, A. S. Garcia, and M. Bellmann, "Empirical analysis of bifacial photovoltaic modules in high-latitude regions: Performance insights from a field laboratory in Norway," *Energy Convers Manag*, vol. 325, Feb. 2025, doi: 10.1016/j.enconman.2024.119396.

[6] V. Rodrigues, "Measurement and validation of bifacial modules' power output," 2019. Accessed: Feb. 04, 2025. [Online]. Available: https://www.pv-magazine.com/wp-content/uploads/2019/04/Vitor-Rodrigues-Presentation.pdf

[7] A. Luque, E. Lorenzo, G. Sala, and S. Lopez-Romero, "DIFFUSING REFLECTORS FOR BIFACIAL PHOTOVOLTAIC PANELS," 1984.

[8] R. Guerrero-Lemus, R. Vega, T. Kim, A. Kimm, and L. E. Shephard, "Bifacial solar photovoltaics - A technology review," Jul. 01, 2016, *Elsevier Ltd.* doi: 10.1016/j.rser.2016.03.041.

[9] S. S. Pal, F. H. C. Van Loenhout, J. Westerhof, and R. Saive, "Understanding and Benchmarking Ground Reflectors for Bifacial Photovoltaic Yield Enhancement," *IEEE J Photovolt*, vol. 14, no. 1, pp. 160–169, Jan. 2024, doi: 10.1109/JPHOTOV.2023.3319592.

[10] A. Basak, S. Chakraborty, and A. K. Behura, "Tilt angle optimization for bifacial PV module: Balancing direct and reflected irradiance on white painted ground surfaces," *Appl Energy*, vol. 377, Jan. 2025, doi: 10.1016/j.apenergy.2024.124525.

[11] A. Luque, E. Lorenzo, G. Sala, and S. Lopez-Romero, "DIFFUSING REFLECTORS FOR BIFACIAL PHOTOVOLTAIC PANELS," 1984.

[12] N. Riedel-Lyngskar *et al.*, "Spectral Albedo in Bifacial Photovoltaic Modeling: What can be learned from Onsite Measurements?," in *Conference Record of the IEEE Photovoltaic Specialists Conference*, Institute of Electrical and Electronics Engineers Inc., Jun. 2021, pp. 942–949. doi: 10.1109/PVSC43889.2021.9519085.

[13] K. Ganesan, D. P. Winston, S. Sugumar, and S. Jegan, "Performance analysis of n-type PERT bifacial solar PV module under diverse albedo conditions," *Solar Energy*, vol. 252, pp. 81–90, Mar. 2023, doi: 10.1016/j.solener.2023.01.020.

[14] P. Ooshaksaraei, K. Sopian, R. Zulkifli, M. A. Alghoul, and S. H. Zaidi, "Characterization of a bifacial photovoltaic panel integrated with external diffuse and semimirror type reflectors," *International Journal of Photoenergy*, vol. 2013, 2013, doi: 10.1155/2013/465837.

[15] M. Alam, M. S. Gul, and T. Muneer, "Performance analysis and comparison between bifacial and monofacial solar photovoltaic at various ground albedo conditions," *Renewable Energy Focus* , vol. 44, pp. 295–316, Mar. 2023, doi: 10.1016/j.ref.2023.01.005.

[16] N. Riedel-Lyngskær, P. B. Poulsen, M. L. Jakobsen, P. Nørgaard, and J. Vedde, "Value of bifacial photovoltaics used with highly reflective ground materials on single-axis trackers and fixed-tilt systems: A danish case study," *IET Renewable Power Generation*, vol. 14, no. 19, pp. 3946–3953, Dec. 2020, doi: 10.1049/iet-rpg.2020.0580.

[17] "NASA POWER | Data Access Viewer (DAV)." Accessed: Aug. 19, 2025. [Online]. Available: https://power.larc.nasa.gov/data-access-viewer/

[18] "Solcast API Toolkit." Accessed: Aug. 18, 2025. [Online]. Available: https://toolkit.solcast.com.au/

[19] "SeeNorway." Accessed: Aug. 13, 2025. [Online]. Available: https://www.senorge.no/

[20] A. Garrod, S. Neda Hussain, M. H. Intwala, A. Poudhar, S. Manikandan, and A. Ghosh, "Electrical and thermal performance of bifacial photovoltaics under varying albedo conditions at

temperate climate (UK)," *Heliyon*, vol. 10, no. 13, Jul. 2024, doi: 10.1016/j.heliyon.2024.e34147.
[21] F. W. Watt and P. A. Campbell, "The effects of solar insolation and cloud opacity on the optimum array size for a direct-coupled solar pumping system," *Renew Energy*, vol. 228, Jul. 2024, doi: 10.1016/j.renene.2024.120594.
[22] B. Sun, L. Lu, Y. Yuan, and P. Ocłoń, "Development and validation of a concise and anisotropic irradiance model for bifacial photovoltaic modules," *Renew Energy*, vol. 209, pp. 442–452, Jun. 2023, doi: 10.1016/j.renene.2023.04.012.
[23] S. Pal and R. Saive, "Output Enhancement of Bifacial Solar Modules under Diffuse and Specular Albedo," in *Conference Record of the IEEE Photovoltaic Specialists Conference*, Institute of Electrical and Electronics Engineers Inc., Jun. 2021, pp. 1159–1162. doi: 10.1109/PVSC43889.2021.9519093.
[24] U. A. Yusufoglu *et al.*, "Simulation of energy production by bifacial modules with revision of ground reflection," in *Energy Procedia*, Elsevier Ltd, 2014, pp. 389–395. doi: 10.1016/j.egypro.2014.08.111.
[25] P. Ooshaksaraei, K. Sopian, R. Zulkifli, M. A. Alghoul, and S. H. Zaidi, "Characterization of a bifacial photovoltaic panel integrated with external diffuse and semimirror type reflectors," *International Journal of Photoenergy*, vol. 2013, 2013, doi: 10.1155/2013/465837.
[26] N. Riedel-Lyngskaer *et al.*, "The effect of spectral albedo in bifacial photovoltaic performance," 2021, doi: 10.11583/DTU.14695437.v1.
[27] D. S. Braga, L. L. Kazmerski, D. A. Cassini, V. Camatta, and A. S. A. C. Diniz, "Performance of bifacial PV modules under different operating conditions in the State of Minas Gerais, Brazil," *Renewable Energy and Environmental Sustainability*, vol. 8, p. 23, 2023, doi: 10.1051/rees/2023021.
[28] T. Kaewnukultorn, S. B. Sepúlveda-Mora, R. Purnell, and S. Hegedus, "Electrical and Financial Impacts of Inverter Clipping on Oversized Bifacial Photovoltaic Systems," *Energies (Basel)*, vol. 17, no. 22, Nov. 2024, doi: 10.3390/en17225658.
[29] D. Fontani *et al.*, "Field optimization for bifacial modules," *Opt Mater (Amst)*, vol. 138, Apr. 2023, doi: 10.1016/j.optmat.2023.113715.
[30] E. Mouhib, P. M. Rodrigo, L. Micheli, E. F. Fernández, and F. Almonacid, "Quantifying the rear and front long-term spectral impact on bifacial photovoltaic modules," *Solar Energy*, vol. 247, pp. 202–213, Nov. 2022, doi: 10.1016/j.solener.2022.10.035.
[31] M. R. Lewis, S. Ovaitt, B. McDanold, C. Deline, and K. Hinzer, "Artificial ground reflector size and position effects on energy yield and economics of single-axis-tracked bifacial photovoltaics," *Progress in Photovoltaics: Research and Applications*, Oct. 2024, doi: 10.1002/pip.3811.
[32] J. Westerhof *et al.*, "Impact of grass retroreflection on bifacial solar panel electricity yield in agrivoltaics," *J Photonics Energy*, vol. 15, no. 03, Jan. 2025, doi: 10.1117/1.JPE.15.032702.

8 APPENDICES

APPENDIX 1: Summary of published works on ground reflectors for bPV performance enhancement.

Ref	Height [m]	Albedo [-]	Reflectors	Findings	Outperformance
[11]	1.55	-	White-painted ground	The use of high reflectivity of acrylic paint in white-painted planes in bifacial panels significantly increased energy collection.	White painted ground
[25]	0.115*	-	Semi-mirror White-painted	The study utilized an extended semimirror and a white-painted diffuse reflector for rear surface reflection, achieving maximum power generation at 30° and 10°, with 20% and 15% output power enhancements.	Semi-mirror
[2]	0.15	0.85 0.05	Snow Tar paper	Investigating higher albedo on sunny days with snow for bifacial east-west modules yielded a 48% increase in specific yield of 7.57 kWh/kWp compared to tar paper.	Snow
[16]	1.56	0.22 0.6	Grass White tarp	Using a white tarp provides a 2.8% bifacial increase. Bifacial systems with white tarp have a lower LCOE (0.1-0.4 EUR/MWh) compared to those without.	-
[26]	1.5	-	Green grass Dry grass Gravel Snow	Spectral gains are highest for bifacial systems, with 25% for green grass, 15% for dry grass, and 5% for gravel. Tracked systems show lower gains due to larger sky view factors.	Green grass
[27]	NA	0.50 0.20	White polymeric layer Natural ground cover	The Três Marias and Itaguara Solar Plants utilized a white polymeric layer, resulting in a 3.5% and 5.14% increase in bifacial gain respectively.	White polymeric layer
[28]	Elevated panels	0.1 0.35 0.7	Black Gravel White ground	The white ground in winter leads to the highest bifacial gain (13.1%) and daily DC efficiency (22.2%) due to the combination of high reflectivity with low solar angle.	White ground
[10]	0	-	White paint	This study highlights the critical role of tilt angle and ground reflectance when using white paint in maximizing energy output from bPV modules.	White paint
[15]	1	0.30–0.35 0.5–0.6 0.7–0.8 0.10–0.15	Concrete White pebbles White tiles Soil	The annual rear irradiance gains analysis revealed that white pebbles and tiles have the highest gain range (>30% gain), followed by soil surface and concrete.	White pebbles White tiles
[20]	0.50	0.21 0.90	Grass Reflective material	The experiments showed that bPV panel efficiency is lowest under direct irradiance and highest under diffuse light, with higher efficiency using reflective materials.	-
[13]	0.94	0.39 0.53 0.28 0.31 0.20	White paint Aluminum Sand Cement Grass	Aluminum surfaces produced more albedo, bifacial gain, and output power. The average bifacial gain is 21.4%. White paint coatings yield better results, with an average bifacial gain of 18.9%.	-
[29]	2.96	-	Retro-Reflective (RR) materials	RR materials are most effective at noon, optimizing the field, resulting in over 10% improved maximum power compared to traditional PV modules with only front-side cells.	-
[24]	0 0.5 2	0.2 0.5	Ground	The study reveals that bifacial modules perform better in diffuse irradiance regions, and higher ground installations are beneficial for all locations, with enhanced benefits in direct light region.	-

[30]	1	0.334 0.414 0.140 0.391	Light soil White sand Green grass Concrete slab	In terms of bifacial spectral energy gains, white sand is the most convenient among the ground types studied in this work.	-
[31]	1.5	0.7	High-density polyethylene geomembrane material (HDPE)	Tests showed reflector configurations can increase daily energy yield by up to 6.2%, with optimal placement directly underneath the module due to optimized rear irradiance increase.	-
[22]	1	0.54 0.15	Aluminum foil Concrete ground	Ground reflections' incident-angle dependence significantly affects ground-reflected irradiance modeling, with specular or mirror-like reflections causing mismatch loss in PV modules.	-
[32]	0.25	-	Grass	The study found that assuming diffuse grass can overestimate solar panel yield by up to 10.5%. Simulations suggest that long grass contributes minimally to yield, with short grass being more beneficial.	-
[9]	1	-	Mirror White paper Photopaper	The study compares simulated albedo-dependent short-circuit current density of bPV, highlighting that a good reflector should redirect more light, reduce mismatch, and be robust to changing sun positions.	White paper

**Panel separation from the reflector (parallel to the PV module).*

FIELD-BASED EVALUATION OF SMALL-SCALE PHOTOVOLTAIC SYSTEMS: COMPLIANCE AND INSTALLATION PRACTICES IN FINLAND

Juho Ylipaino[1, 2], Aki Kortetmäki[1, 2], Marko Ylinen[3], Kari Kalliohariu[1, 2], Juha Koskela[2]
[1] Tampere University of Applied Sciences, Tampere, Finland
[2] Tampere University, Tampere, Finland
[3] Satakunta University of Applied Sciences, Pori, Finland

ABSTRACT: This study evaluates the compliance of small-scale photovoltaic (PV) installations in Finland, focusing on 60 small-scale systems primarily installed between 2022 and 2024. The inspected systems were mainly located in detached houses, with participation based on voluntary recruitment. Using a systematic, field-based inspection methodology, the study examines adherence to standards throughout the installation process, including system design, installation practices, commissioning inspections, and documentation. Beyond identifying deficiencies, the analysis investigates installers' practices and interpretations of regulatory requirements. The findings reveal substantial variability in compliance, with only a small fraction of systems meeting all mandatory requirements. Common deficiencies include incomplete or missing commissioning inspection reports, inadequate system labeling, and deviations in safety-critical practices such as equipotential bonding. These issues emphasize the need for clearer guidance, enhanced installer training, and stricter oversight to ensure consistent adherence to standards. By offering a detailed evaluation of compliance challenges and highlighting examples of best practices, this study contributes to the development of safer, more reliable PV systems. It provides valuable insights for regulators, installers, and property owners, emphasizing the importance of standardization and professional expertise in supporting the successful adoption of PV technologies.
Keywords: Photovoltaic systems, Compliance, Installation practices, Safety and quality, Standards

1 INTRODUCTION

The installation of small-scale photovoltaic (PV) systems has increased rapidly in Finland in recent years, supported by falling component prices, favorable policy measures, and growing interest in self-generated renewable electricity [13]. While PV technology offers clear environmental and economic benefits, ensuring electrical safety and long-term reliability requires that systems are designed, installed, and commissioned in full compliance with binding standards and regulations.

All electrical installations in Finland, including PV systems, must comply with the Finnish Electrical Safety Act [4]. To fill enforcement of the Act, the national electrical safety authority maintains a mandatory list of standards, known as *Luettelo S10* [5]. Compliance with the standards on this list ensures that all statutory requirements are met. For PV systems, the list includes the SFS 6000 standard series, which applies to electrical installations up to 1000 V AC and 1500 V DC [6]. These standards are based on the European harmonization document CENELEC HD 60364 and the international IEC 60364 standards. In January 2023, Luettelo S10 was updated to include SFS-EN 62446-1:2016 + A1:2018, the Finnish adoption of EN 62446-1:2016, harmonized with IEC 62446-1:2016 [7], [8]. This standard specifies requirements for system documentation, commissioning tests, and inspection of grid-connected PV systems, thereby promoting consistent safety practices and regulatory compliance across all PV system installations.

In Finland, small-scale PV systems may be installed by any licensed electrical contractor [4]. There is no mandatory PV-specific certification, which can lead to differences in installers' knowledge of PV system's consistent application in practice. Contractor's supervisor of electrical works plays a central role in ensuring installation quality and safety. Their duties include guiding and managing the work, ensuring the competence of employees, instructing them in safety matters, and providing the necessary tools and working conditions [9]. They are responsible for ensuring that the Electrical Safety Act is complied with, that the condition of electrical installations meets statutory requirements before commissioning or handover, and that personnel performing the work possess adequate skills and receive sufficient instructions for their tasks [9]. The knowledge of the supervisor of electrical work and the extent and quality of supervision can vary in practice, potentially contributing to differences in compliance across installations.

Despite these binding requirements, previous investigation in Finland has shown considerable variation in installation quality, especially in commissioning inspections, documentation, and general installation practices [10]–[14]. Similar findings have been reported internationally, with faulty installations, deviations from manufacturer instructions, and inconsistent application of standards identified as recurring issues [15]–[17]. Earlier Finnish studies have mainly relied on self-reported information from contractors or customers, which may not fully reflect actual conditions. Systematic, on-site inspections enable a more accurate assessment of compliance by allowing direct verification of both technical implementation and documentation. They also provide insight into the practical effects of recent updates to national standards, such as the 2022 revision of SFS 6000, which became binding for installations in January 2023 after the update of the mandatory standard list [7], including the strong recommendation against unnecessary DC isolators and the requirement for non-combustible mounting surfaces.

This study addresses the lack of field-based compliance data by inspecting 60 small-scale PV systems primarily installed between 2022 and 2024 in Finland. The objective is to evaluate adherence to the Finnish Electrical Safety Act and relevant national and international standards, identify common deficiencies, and assess whether recent changes to the SFS 6000 standard are reflected in installation practices. The findings provide an evidence-based basis for improving PV installation quality through targeted training, clearer guidance, and effective application of standard requirements.

2 METHODOLOGY

This section describes the methodology used to investigate the compliance and safety of small-scale PV systems. The study involved the inspection of 60 small-scale PV systems using a standardized procedure. Figure 1 provides an overview of the full process from participant recruitment to data analysis. After an open call for participation, property owners submitted background information, based on which suitable sites were selected. On-site inspections were conducted using a predefined survey form, and the collected data were subsequently analyzed to assess compliance with applicable legislation and standards.

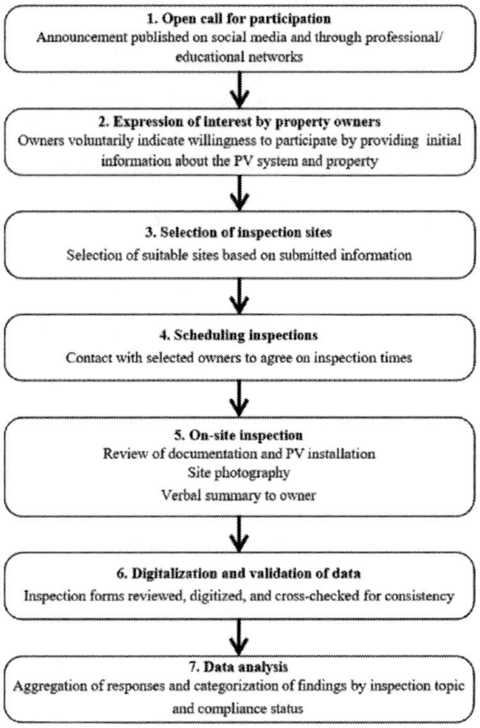

Figure 1: Process of site-recruitment, inspection, and data handling

2.1 Recruitment and selection of PV systems

The PV systems included in this study were selected on a voluntary basis. Property owners were invited to participate through open calls published on social media platforms and via professional and educational networks. The selection process was non-random and did not aim to create a statistically representative sample of all small-scale PV systems in Finland. Instead, the objective was to collect a diverse range of installations for a qualitative assessment of safety and compliance.

Interested participants signed up for the study by filling out a questionnaire about the property and PV system. Based on these responses, a selection of sites was made to represent the study group. For each selected site, a visit was scheduled, during which a standardized inspection was carried out and the available documentation was reviewed. No compensation was provided for participation, and each property owner gave informed consent for the site visit and data collection. The gathered data was anonymized for analysis and reporting purposes.

2.2 Characteristics of inspected PV systems

The inspected systems represented typical small-scale PV installations in Finland. The majority were commissioned in 2022 or 2023, allowing for an assessment of compliance with the latest applicable standards. Almost all were located in detached houses and connected with the common 3x25 A supply size. System sizes were most often between 6 and 10 kWp, which aligns with household self-consumption needs. In terms of technology, string inverters dominated, while microinverters and optimizers were used only occasionally. Across the 60 sites, installations have been carried out by 38 different electrical contractors, highlighting a fragmented installer base despite the relatively small market.

Table I presents an overview of key technical and procurement-related characteristics of the systems.

Table I: Technical and procurement-related characteristics of the inspected systems

Parameter	Distribution
Number of inspected systems	60
Installation year	2023 or later: 34 (57 %) 2022: 23 (38%) 2021 or earlier: 3 (5%)
PV system type	String inverter: 56 systems (93%) Microinverter: 3 systems (5%) String inverter with optimizer: 1 (2%)
Connection size	3x25 A: 50 sites (83%) 3x35 A: 9 sites (15%) 3x50 A: 1 site (2%)
Property type	Detached Houses: 57 (95%) Agricultural Buildings: 3 (5%)
PV system size (panel power)	Below 3 kWp: 1 (2%) 3-5 kWp: 15 (25%) 6-10 kWp: 39 (65%) 11-15 kWp: 1 (2%) Over 15 kWp: 3 (5%) Unknown: 1 (2%)
Number of panel strings	1 string: 32 (53%) 2 strings: 22 (37%) Over 2 strings: 3 (5%) No strings (micros): 3 (5%)
Number of electrical contractors	38 contractors across 60 systems

2.3 Inspection protocol

The data presented in this study were collected through a field survey of 60 small-scale PV systems. The systems were located primarily in detached houses in the Satakunta and Pirkanmaa regions and were selected on a voluntary basis through open calls via social media and professional networks. Each inspection followed a systematic protocol using a dedicated survey form developed for the research. The form was designed to assess compliance with the Finnish Electrical Safety Act (1135/2016), and relevant standards, including SFS 6000 and SFS-EN 62446-1. The inspection was structured into nine thematic sections, which are listed in Table II.

10.4229/EUPVSEC2025/4DV.4.17

Table II: Thematic sections of the inspection form

Section	Evaluation topic
0	General information on the PV system
1	Commissioning inspection and inspection report
2	System labeling and documentation
3	Electrical protection (e.g., overcurrent, shock protection)
4	Means of disconnection (AC and DC sides)
5	Selection and installation of electrical equipment
6	Cabling and routing
7	Equipotential bonding
8	Mechanical installation

During each site visit, the inspector first reviewed available documentation with the property owner. This was followed by a detailed inspection of the physical installation, with all findings recorded using the survey form. Each inspection concluded with a verbal summary of the findings and a later written summary report, including key observations and photographs.

Each inspected item was assessed for compliance with applicable legislation and mandatory standards. If deviations were identified, they were classified using a predefined scale. Minor deficiencies referred to deficiencies that had little or no immediate impact on safety but indicated non-compliance with formal requirements. Major deficiencies included cases where safety could be compromised or where legally mandated elements were missing altogether.

After each inspection, the completed forms were reviewed and digitized for analysis. Quantitative responses were analyzed according to predefined categories, and qualitative observations were transcribed. To ensure consistency, a review process was conducted to check for missing or inconsistent entries before compiling the data for further analysis.

All inspections were carried out with the explicit consent of the property owners. Participants were informed of the scope and purpose of the study, and no personal identifying information was published. Photographs taken during site visits were used solely for documentation and reporting purposes and were anonymized in all project materials.

3 RESULTS

The evaluation of 60 small-scale PV systems revealed significant variability in compliance with mandatory installation and safety standards. None of inspected systems were fully compliant, while 40 % exhibited minor deficiencies, and 60 % showed significant deficiencies in at least one area. The most frequent and severe deficiencies were observed in commissioning inspections and related documentation, system labelling, and certain protection arrangements. Missing or inadequate documentation and deviations in the selection and installation of equipment were also common findings.

Positive observations were also made. Many systems demonstrated good adherence to basic wiring practices, and recent installations more often placed inverters in non-combustible environments, improving fire safety. In addition, avoidance of unnecessary DC isolators has become more common in newer systems, reflecting evolving best practices. These trends were broadly similar in systems installed both before and after the 2023 update to national standards, although some recent improvements were noted in specific aspects of installation quality.

Next, the results are presented in detail under eight individual evaluation topics (sections 1-8).

3.1 Commissioning inspection and inspection report

None of the inspected systems had a commissioning inspection report that fully complied with the legal and standard requirements. In a total of ten sites (17%), the commissioning inspection report for the PV system was either unavailable or had not been handed over to the property owner. Therefore, the relative results presented in this section are based on the 50 sites where the commissioning inspection report was available. Among these, AC-side measurements were carried out in 49 sites (98%), and DC-side measurements in 40 sites (80%). However, both AC and DC measurement results were included in the report in only 39 sites (65%).

Among the sites where AC-side measurements had been performed, only 25% of the commissioning inspection reports met the content requirements specified in standard SFS 6000-6 for AC-side inspections. The most common deficiencies were the absence of phase sequence verification and failure to conduct functional tests. Of the sites with DC-side inspections provided, the requirements set out in standard SFS-EN 62446-1 were fully met in only 20% of the reports. In 72% of the sites (with DC-side inspections provided), the measurement results were not compared to the prevailing conditions at the time of measurement. Measurement results cannot be considered reliable unless they are assessed against the actual conditions during the measurement.

Table III summarizes the key findings related to the commissioning inspection and the associated documentation.

Table III: Summary of findings related to the commissioning inspection and inspection report (n = 60)

Indicator	Number of systems	Share (%)
Inspection report provided	50	83%
AC-side measurements provided	49	98% [1)]
Complete AC-side measurements	12	25% [2)]
DC-side measurements provided	39	78% [1)]
Complete DC-side measurements	8	20% [3)]
Summary:		
Fully compliant	8	13%
Minor deficiencies	24	40%
Major deficiencies	28	47%

[1] Value refers to sites with inspection report provided
[2] Value refers to sites with AC-measurements provided
[3] Value refers to sites with DC-measurements provided

3.2 System labeling and documentation

Standards governing PV installations set requirements for both system labeling and the provision of documentation to end users. The assessment revealed that while some basic labeling was typically in place, many systems lacked key safety-related markings, such as clear instructions for disconnection before maintenance. Label durability and readability were generally acceptable, though occasional issues were noted.

Documentation was often incomplete. Although basic system and installer information was commonly available, more detailed technical documents—such as component datasheets, wiring diagrams, and maintenance instructions—were frequently missing. In several cases, no documentation had been provided at all.

Overall, none of the systems reviewed fully met the labeling and documentation requirements. Most had minor deficiencies, while a significant number exhibited more serious deficiencies. Table IV summarizes the key findings concerning labeling and documentation.

Table IV: Summary of findings related to labeling and documentation (n = 60)

Indicator	Number of systems	Share (%)
Labeling:		
Required warning-labeling at distribution boards	54	90%
Required inverter disconnection instruction labeling	22	36%
Warning labels at DC-side components	44	73%
Compliant string cable labeling	23	38%
Documentation:		
Inverter datasheet provided	35	58%
Solar panel datasheet provided	27	45%
Mounting system datasheet provided	10	17%
Operating and maintenance instructions provided	20	33%
System specific wiring diagram provided	7	12%
Any document provided	5	8%
Summary:		
Fully compliant	0	0%
Minor deficiencies	38	63%
Major deficiencies	22	37%

3.3 Electrical protection

All inspected systems were equipped with appropriate protection measures against overcurrent and electric shock. On the AC side, overcurrent protection and automatic disconnection of supply were implemented consistently across all systems in accordance with applicable standards. No deficiencies were identified in these protections.

On the DC side, overcurrent protection was also implemented as required in all but one system. In that specific case, multiple panel strings were connected in parallel, which would have required separate string-specific overcurrent protection. However, this protection was missing. Despite this single shortcoming, all systems were assessed to have adequate protection against electric shock.

3.4 Means of disconnection

The assessment showed that AC-side disconnection was implemented appropriately in almost all sites, with only isolated deviations such as a missing disconnection switch or restricted access for the grid operator. This high compliance level is likely influenced by the requirements set by distribution system operators, who typically demand reliable AC isolation as part of the grid connection process, in addition to the national standards mandating it.

DC-side isolation was examined in systems without microinverters (57 sites). In line with the latest edition of SFS 6000 (published in 2022, binding from 2023), separate DC isolators should be avoided unless specifically required for maintenance or safety purposes. The updated requirement aims to reduce unnecessary components that could introduce additional failure points or increase maintenance needs. Most systems (approx. 80%) relied on the inverter's internal DC switch in combination with disconnectable plug connectors. A smaller share used external DC switches, some of which were considered redundant. In one case, there was no capability to perform DC isolation at all, as neither switches nor plug connectors were available. Overall, both AC and DC isolation methods generally met the standard requirements, though minor deviations and questionable design choices were observed in a limited number of systems.

Table V summarizes the key findings regarding means of disconnection on both the AC and DC sides.

Table V: Summary of findings on AC and DC side disconnection methods (n = 60)

Indicator	Number of systems	Share (%)
AC-side:		
Required AC-side isolator installed	59	98%
Lockable and DSO-accessible AC-side isolator	58	97%
DC side:		
Disconnection with inverter's internal DC-switch and disconnectable plug connectors	45	79% [1)]
Disconnection with separate DC-isolator (before 2023)	9	36% [2)]
Disconnection with separate DC-isolator (2023 or after)	3	9% [3)]
DC isolators considered redundant (before 2023)	3	12% [2)]
DC isolators considered redundant (2023 or after)	1	3% [3)]
No compliant disconnection	1	2% [1)]
Summary:		
Fully compliant	53	88%
Minor deficiencies	5	8%
Major deficiencies	2	3%

[1] Value refers to systems with string inverter configurations (n = 57).
[2] Value refers to systems with string inverter configurations installed before 2023 (n = 25).
[3] Values refers to systems with string inverter configurations installed 2023 or after (n = 32).

3.5 Selection and installation of electrical equipment

The assessment reviewed how appropriately system components had been selected and installed, with a particular focus on dimensioning, compatibility, and compliance with relevant standards and manufacturer instructions.

Most systems met the requirements, but various types of deficiencies were identified. In some cases, string voltages or currents exceeded inverter specifications, or component ratings were not fully adequate. Connector compatibility, especially among DC-side disconnectable plug connectors (commonly referred to as MC4), was often difficult to verify after installation. However, in several systems visible mismatches were observed, where connectors from different manufacturers had been joined together in contradiction to standard requirements

Installation practices around the inverter varied. While many inverters were properly mounted and had adequate clearance, some were installed on combustible surfaces or lacked the free space specified by the manufacturer. Although inverter manufacturers had already required non-combustible mounting surfaces in their installation instructions, this requirement was only later added to the updated SFS 6000 standard. This update is also reflected in the results, which are divided in Table VI between systems installed before and after 2023.

Table VI: Summary of findings related to selection and installation of electrical equipment (n = 60)

Indicator	Number of systems	Share (%)
Matched disconnectable plug connectors (MC4)	10	17%
Mismatched disconnectable plug connectors (MC4)	7	12%
Disconnectable plug connectors (MC4) compatibility unverifiable	43	72%
Inverter installed on non-combustible surface (before 2023)	14	53% [1]
Inverter installed on non-combustible surface (2023 or after)	2	6% [2]
Adequate inverter clearance	40	67%
Summary:		
Fully compliant	40	67%
Minor deficiencies	17	28%
Major deficiencies	3	5%

[1] Value refers to systems installed before 2023 (n = 26)
[2] Value refers to systems installed 2023 or after (n = 34)

3.6 Cabling and routing

This section reviewed whether AC and DC cables were selected in accordance with applicable standards and manufacturer instructions, and how mechanical protection along the cable routes was implemented.

Cable types and conductor sizes were generally appropriate for the application. On the AC side, standard installation cables with typical conductor diameters were commonly used, and most systems met the relevant requirements. DC-side cabling was also mostly implemented using suitable cable types and installation methods.

Mechanical protection of cables and cable routes varied. In a number of systems, observations included insufficient physical shielding, loose fastening, or exposed cable routes, particularly on rooftops and at structural penetrations. Minor deficiencies were relatively common, and a smaller number of systems showed more significant issues related to potential damage to cable insulation. Similar types of deficiencies were also noted in AC-side cabling, such as unprotected wall penetrations. The findings indicate variability in how mechanical protection was addressed across the assessed systems.

More detailed numerical results are not presented for this section, as installation practices and the related risks are difficult to compare directly against standard requirements or manufacturer instructions.

3.7 Equipotential bonding

The assessment reviewed whether potential equalization was implemented in accordance with applicable standards and inverter manufacturer requirements. In systems where specific equalization measures were required, most installations followed the instructions given. In microinverter-based systems (3 sites), where equalization was not required, implementation practices varied.

The extent and quality of the equalization could be confirmed in a portion of the sites. In many cases, rooftop accessibility limited verification, especially regarding connections to mounting structures and module frames. Where assessments were possible, implementation was generally appropriate, although some deficiencies were observed in the connections or coverage of bonded parts.

An overview of the findings is presented in Table VII.

Table VII: Summary of findings related to equipotential bonding (n = 60)

Indicator	Number of systems	Share (%)
Potential equalization required (by standard or manufacturer)	57	95%
System connected to potential equalization	52	87%
Connections made appropriately	29	56% [1]
All required parts connected	18	35% [1]
Summary:		
Fully compliant	37	62%
Minor deficiencies	14	23%
Major deficiencies	9	15%

[1] Values refer to systems with potential equalization implemented (n = 52).

3.8 Mechanical installation

This section examined the mechanical aspects of PV system installation, including module placement on the roof, mounting system attachments, shading conditions, and cable fastening between modules.

Most systems were installed with consistent distances between the array and roof edges. The positioning of arrays generally avoided significant external shading, though some minor shading from nearby structures was observed in a few cases.

Mounting systems and panel attachments were typically implemented using standard installation methods. Cable fastening between modules varied in quality, with deficiencies observed in a notable share of the systems. In several cases, the fastening solutions used could have been more robust or better suited to outdoor conditions.

10.4229/EUPVSEC2025/4DV.4.17

4 DISCUSSION

The inspection results confirm earlier findings on the prevalence of deficiencies in commissioning inspections and system documentation. In many cases, the commissioning inspection report was incomplete or missing, despite the requirement in the Finnish Electrical Safety Act (1135/2016) to perform and document the inspection. These deficiencies appear to be linked to limited knowledge of PV-specific requirements and insufficient ability to interpret test results. Without adequate competence, installers may struggle to prepare reports in accordance with SFS 6000-6 and SFS-EN 62446-1. In Finland, small-scale PV systems can be installed by any electrical contractor under the supervision of a qualified supervisor of electrical works, but PV-specific training is not mandatory. Improving the quality and completeness of commissioning inspections therefore requires targeted training on PV-related risks and test procedures, combined with effective supervision by the supervisor of electrical works.

System documentation was also generally poor. While basic system and installer details were usually available, many legally required items—such as wiring diagrams, datasheets, and operating and maintenance instructions—were missing. These deficiencies are common in small-scale electrical work, particularly when no separate designer is involved. As many of these documents are normally prepared during a design phase, their absence suggests that design and installation are often handled by the same contractor without dedicated design resources. One potential improvement would be to integrate the SFS-EN 62446-1 documentation requirements into building permit or grid-connection procedures. Several distribution system operators already require commissioning inspection reports as part of the connection process; extending this requirement to the full documentation package could strengthen compliance.

Some technical aspects showed consistently high levels of compliance. Electrical protection on both AC and DC sides was generally implemented correctly, with only one serious DC-side deficiency—missing string-specific overcurrent protection in a parallel configuration. This isolated case demonstrates that even uncommon errors can have significant safety implications and may remain undetected without systematic inspections. AC-side disconnection arrangements were almost universally compliant, which can be explained by the requirements set by DSOs, who typically demand reliable AC isolation as a condition for grid connection. However, a small number of questionable design choices were observed, such as redundant DC isolators or the absence of DC-side disconnection, that may reduce the system's fire safety or safety during maintenance operations

By contrast, mechanical protection of cable routes and compliance with inverter manufacturer installation instructions were less consistent. Frequent deficiencies included unprotected penetrations through walls or roofs and loosely fastened rooftop cables, increasing the risk of insulation damage over time. Panel placement was generally in line with good practice, but fastening of inter-module cables was in some cases insufficiently robust for long-term outdoor conditions. As these tasks represent relatively basic installation work, such deficiencies may reflect installer attitudes, oversight, or limited awareness of requirements rather than technical complexity.

Certain parts of the inspection process were subject to verification limitations. In many systems, the compatibility of DC-side disconnectable plug connectors could not be confirmed because manufacturer markings were no longer visible after installation. Similarly, the assessment of equipotential bonding was sometimes constrained by limited rooftop access, preventing full verification of connections to module frames or mounting structures. These limitations introduce some uncertainty into the reported compliance rates in these areas.

There are also signs of improvement over time. For example, installing inverters on non-combustible surfaces have become more common since this requirement was incorporated into the national SFS 6000 standard. This indicates that transferring manufacturer recommendations into binding national standards can have a measurable positive effect on installation quality. Likewise, the updated requirement to avoid unnecessary DC isolators is reflected in the lower share of such devices among systems installed in 2023 or later. While redundant isolators were still found in a small number of newer installations, their declining prevalence suggests that the revised guidance is beginning to influence practices. However, persistent non-compliance with other requirements, such as adequate inverter clearance, shows that standards and manufacturer guidelines alone are not sufficient without effective training, supervision, and enforcement.

The results of this study are well aligned with those of an earlier investigation conducted in Finland [11], which also identified frequent deficiencies in commissioning inspections, documentation, and installation practices. The overall picture is therefore very similar, indicating that the challenges observed are not isolated cases but recurring patterns in small-scale PV installations. Compared to the earlier investigation, however, the present work provides a more detailed basis for analysis, as the systematic inspection protocol and broader set of evaluation topics enable a closer examination of specific problems and areas in need of improvement.

It is important to note that the inspected PV systems were recruited on a voluntary basis and were mainly located in detached houses. The sample is not statistically representative of all small-scale PV installations in Finland, and results should therefore be interpreted as indicative of common compliance patterns rather than precise population-wide estimates. Nevertheless, voluntary recruitment allowed for a wide range of installation types, contractors, and commissioning years, providing valuable qualitative insight into recurring strengths and weaknesses in current practices.

Future research could focus on installations where a PV-related fire or near-miss incident has occurred. Comparing such cases with the compliance patterns identified in this study would allow for a more accurate assessment of the real-world safety implications of the observed deficiencies. This evidence could support the prioritization of regulatory updates, targeted training programs, and inspection practices in areas presenting the greatest actual risk.

5 CONCLUSION

This study conducted systematic on-site inspections of 60 small-scale photovoltaic systems installed in Finland primarily between 2022 and 2024 to assess compliance with the Finnish Electrical Safety Act and mandatory

10.4229/EUPVSEC2025/4DV.4.17

national and international standards. The evaluation covered all main aspects of PV installations, including commissioning inspections, documentation, labeling, electrical protection, means of disconnection, equipment selection and installation, cabling, equipotential bonding, and mechanical installation.

None of the inspected systems met all mandatory requirements, and all exhibited either minor or significant deficiencies. The most common issues were incomplete or missing commissioning inspection reports, inadequate documentation, and deficiencies in labeling. In contrast, electrical protection and AC-side disconnection were generally implemented correctly, and several installation practices have shown measurable improvement over time, such as wider adoption of non-combustible mounting surfaces for inverters and fewer unnecessary DC isolators in newer systems.

As the inspected systems were selected through voluntary participation and were mainly located in detached houses, the sample does not statistically represent all small-scale PV systems in Finland. The results should therefore be considered indicative of general compliance patterns rather than precise estimates for the entire installation base. Nevertheless, the study provides valuable insight into recurring strengths and weaknesses, as well as the visibility of recent national standard changes in practical installation work.

The results underline that standard updates can have a clear and positive effect on installation quality when requirements are specific and binding. However, persistent deficiencies in commissioning inspections, documentation, and certain installation details indicate that updated requirements alone are not sufficient. Improving compliance will require targeted training and education for installers, with emphasis on PV-specific risks, test procedures, and documentation obligations, supported by effective supervision from qualified supervisors of electrical work. Requiring commissioning inspection reports and related documentation as a condition for grid connection or building permit approval by authorities and DSOs could also strengthen compliance in practice. Strengthening both competence and oversight will contribute to safer, more reliable, and longer-lasting PV systems in Finland. Similar challenges and improvement needs have also been observed internationally, making the findings relevant beyond the Finnish context.

6 ACKNOWLEDGMENT

The authors would like to acknowledge the support of the Finnish Centre for Electrical Safety and Energy Efficiency (STEK).

7 DECLARATION OF GENERATIVE AI AND AI-ASSISTED TECHNOLOGIES IN THE WRITING PROCESS

During the preparation of this work the authors used ChatGPT-5 to improve readability and language. After using this tool, the authors reviewed and edited the content as needed and take full responsibility for the content of the publication.

8 REFERENCES

[1] Statistics Finland, "Altogether 95 per cent of Finland's electricity production was based on fossil-free energy in 2024." Accessed: Aug. 14, 2025. [Online]. Available: https://stat.fi/en/publication/cm1kktw8ualm207vwnzpsmpc8

[2] European Commission, "European Solar Charter," Brussels, 2024. Accessed: Aug. 14, 2025. [Online]. Available: https://energy.ec.europa.eu/topics/renewable-energy/solar-energy/european-solar-charter_en

[3] J. Ahola, "National Survey Report of PV Power Applications in Finland 2019," 2019. Accessed: Aug. 14, 2025. [Online]. Available: https://iea-pvps.org/wp-content/uploads/2020/09/NSR_Finland_2019.pdf

[4] *Electrical Safety Act 1135/2016*. 2016. [Online]. Available: https://www.finlex.fi/fi/laki/alkup/2016/20161135

[5] "Luettelo S10." Tukes, 2023. Accessed: Jan. 27, 2025. [Online]. Available: https://tukes.fi/teollisuus/standardit

[6] *SFS 6000-standard series: Low Voltage Electrical Installations*, 2022.

[7] Finnish Safety and Chemicals Agency (Tukes), "Luettelo S10 on päivitetty." Accessed: Jan. 13, 2025. [Online]. Available: https://tukes.fi/-/luettelo-s10-on-paivitetty

[8] *SFS-EN 62446-1: Photovoltaic (PV) systems – Requirements for testing, documentation and maintenance – Part 1: Grid connected systems – Documentation, commissioning tests and inspection*, 2016.

[9] Finnish Safety and Chemicals Agency (Tukes), "Duties of Supervisors of Electrical Works." Accessed: Aug. 14, 2025. [Online]. Available: https://tukes.fi/en/electricity/electrical-works-and-contracting/duties-of-supervisors-of-electrical-works

[10] J. Ylipaino, K. Kalliohatju, A. Kortetmäki, M. Ylinen, and J. Koskela, "Ensuring Compliance in the Installation of Residential Photovoltaic Systems: A Study of Standards and Practices in Finland," in *2025 21st International Conference on the European Energy Market (EEM)*, May 2025, pp. 1–5. doi: 10.1109/EEM64765.2025.11050297.

[11] S. Hatakka, E. Iivonen, and J. Välimaa, "Aurinkosähköjärjestelmien asennustyön vaatimustenmukaisuus," Turvallisuus- ja kemikaalivirasto, 2022. Accessed: Jan. 13, 2025. [Online]. Available: https://tukes.fi/-/aurinkosahkojarjestelmien-asennuksissa-tehdaan-paljon-virheita

[12] A. Rasinkoski, "Aurinkosähkön paloriskit ja sammutusturvallisuus," 2020. Accessed: Aug. 14, 2025. [Online]. Available: https://www.motiva.fi/ratkaisut/uusiutuva_energia/aurinkosahko/aurinkosahkon_paloturvallisuus/aurinkosahkon_paloturvallisuus_-projekti_2020-2021

[13] M. Pulkkinen, "Aurinkosähköjärjestelmien asentaminen, havaitut virheet sekä koulutus," 2023. Accessed: Aug. 14, 2025. [Online]. Available: https://lutpub.lut.fi/handle/10024/166708

[14] A. Kortetmäki, M. Ylinen, and J. Ylipaino, "Omatuotannon vaikutus pienkiinteistön sähköverkkoon," Tampereen ammattikorkeakoulu, publication, 2023. Accessed: Aug. 14, 2025. [Online]. Available: http://www.theseus.fi/handle/10024/804597

[15] M. Gradecka and Y. Lethbridge, "Fire and Solar PV Systems - Investigations and Evidence," BRE National Solar Centre, May 2018. Accessed: Aug. 14, 2025. [Online]. Available: https://assets.publishing.service.gov.uk/media/5c90a30840f0b633ff9a3537/Fires_and_solar_PV_systems-Investigations_Evidence_Issue_2.9.pdf

[16] L. Sloof-Hoek *et al.*, "Eindrapport Verbeteren monitoring en voorschriften brandveiligheid (BI)PV," TNO, Sept. 2025. Accessed: Aug. 14, 2025. [Online]. Available: https://www.tno.nl/en/newsroom/2024/11/building-fires-solar-panels-first-study/

[17] "Assessing Fire Risks in Photovoltaic Systems and Developing Safety Concepts for Risk Minimization," TÜV Rheinland Energie und Umwelt GmbH, 2018. Accessed: Aug. 14, 2025. [Online]. Available: https://www.ise.fraunhofer.de/en/research-projects/pv-brandschutz.html

THE IMPACT OF VIRTUAL NET-METERING ALLOCATION ON SELF-CONSUMPTION RATIOS IN MULTI-DWELLING BUILDING PHOTOVOLTAIC SYSTEMS

Aki Kortetmäki[1, 2], Juho Ylipaino[1, 2], Kari Kallioharju[1, 2], Juha Koskela[2], Pertti Järventausta[2]
[1]Tampere University of Applied Sciences
Kuntokatu 3, 33520 Tampere
[2]Tampere University
Korkeakoulunkatu 7, 33720 Tampere

ABSTRACT: Collective self-consumption (CSC) in multi-dwelling buildings (MDBs) became feasible in Finland following EU regulations through the Credit Calculation Model (CCM) with virtual net-metering integrated into the national Datahub system. This study evaluates self-consumption ratios (SCR) under three metering configurations—common-area consumption (CC), CCM, and behind-the-meter (BM)—using hourly consumption data (2019–2021) from 32 MDBs (14–168 apartments, built 1960s–2020s) in Pirkanmaa region. PV production was simulated with PVGIS-SARAH3 for 10–60 kWp systems at south, 45° east, and 45° west orientations (18° tilt). The goal was to quantify SCR gains from adopting CCM and to compare BM and CCM to guide simulations when only aggregated building-level data are available. CCM increased SCR by approximately 30% for 20–60 kWp systems compared with CC. BM–CCM differences averaged 6 to 9% (range 0 to 19.5%) for 20–60 kWp systems. West-oriented arrays achieved slightly higher SCR due to better load alignment. These findings provide quantitative tools for DSOs, housing companies, and PV designers to improve SCR estimation and PV project viability in MDBs. While results are based on Pirkanmaa, they offer guidance for broader contexts until higher-resolution metering and flexible loads are incorporated in future studies.
Keywords: Photovoltaic, Self-Consumption, Multi-dwelling buildings, Energy communities

1 INTRODUCTION

Collective renewable energy use across Europe now enables consumers to participate actively in local energy generation and sharing under EU directives promoting energy communities and collective self-consumption [1], [2]. Finland incorporated these concepts into its regulatory framework by defining groups of active customers and local energy communities in 2021, and by adding the definition of Citizen Energy Communities in 2023 [3], [4].

To operationalize collective self-consumption (CSC) in multi-dwelling buildings (MDBs), Finland introduced the Credit Calculation Model (CCM), known in Finnish as "hyvityslaskenta", in 2021 and subsequently integrated it into the national centralized data exchange system, Datahub [5]. CCM enables virtual net-metering, where photovoltaic (PV) production exceeding common-area consumption (CC)—such as corridor lighting, elevators, and ventilation—is redistributed on an hourly basis (or in 15-minute intervals where advanced smart metering is available) among shareholders according to a predefined sharing coefficient.

Before CCM was introduced, PV generation in MDBs could only offset CC—even when the surplus energy was consumed within the same building—and any excess was credited as sold energy. CCM thus represents a major step forward by allowing surplus production to be allocated to apartments. A third approach involves a single collective electricity contract with secondary apartment-level meters. In this so-called behind-the-meter (BM) system, the self-consumption ratio (SCR) is typically highest, as surplus energy is recorded only when PV production exceeds the total aggregated load during the metering period. However, Finland's Electricity Market Act grants residents the right to opt out of BM arrangements, making BM less common in housing-company structures and more typical in rental properties [6]. Figure 1 illustrates these metering configurations in MDBs, including separate CC meter (1), apartment-level meters (2), and separate BM meter in case of collective electricity contract (3).

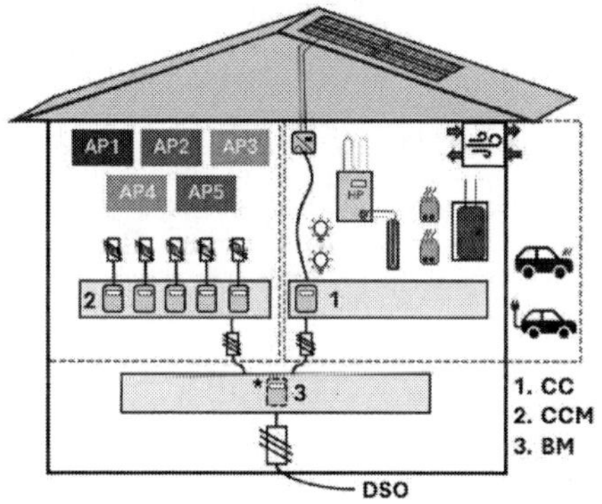

Figure 1: Metering arrangements in Finnish multi-dwelling buildings. BM is used only when a collective electricity contract is in place.

Internationally, extensive research has focused on optimizing PV self-consumption and sizing strategies under various sharing schemes and energy community models. For example, in Nordic countries, Berg et al. [7] studied how two static sharing keys affect cost distribution in a residential energy community in Norway. Similar studies in Spain [8], [9], France [10], and Austria [11] have examined both static and dynamic sharing coefficients under different energy community setups.

Our previous work also reported the effects on SCR of four different static sharing schemes, namely area-based allocation, equal allocation, ownership shares in the housing companies, and apartment floor area [12]. In Finland, allocation in MDBs is usually based on apartment ownership shares in the housing company, reflecting typical investment structures. Although hourly or quarter-hourly consumption data exist for optimal PV system size design, privacy rules often restrict DSOs to providing only aggregated building-level data or, in some cases, only common-area consumption data. Consequently, simulations of SCR can be performed for BM and CC cases but remain less accurate for CCM, where individual consumption profiles are unavailable.

Our earlier work on CCM's impact on SCR involved only two relatively large housing companies (114 and 224 apartments) and two PV system sizes, offering valuable but limited insight [13]. A broader, more diverse dataset is needed to understand how allocation methods and metering configurations affect SCR under real-world conditions.

This study addresses that gap by analyzing anonymized apartment-level hourly consumption data from 32 MDBs in the Pirkanmaa region, combined with PV production simulations for multiple system sizes and orientations. Using apartment floor area as a proxy for ownership shares—supported by prior findings from Ylipaino et al. [12], which show negligible SCR differences between area-based and ownership-based allocation—this work quantifies SCR under CCM and compares results to BM and CC cases. The findings provide practical guidance for stakeholders designing PV systems for MDBs, particularly under regulatory and data-access constraints.

2 METHODOLOGY

2.1 Data set

Data for this study were obtained from 32 multi-dwelling buildings (MDBs) located in the Pirkanmaa region of Finland. These buildings, constructed between the 1960s and 2020s, represent a diverse range of residential properties and include 14 to 168 apartments per property. Although the apartments are owned by a rental housing company, each apartment retains its own electricity meter, and residents pay for electricity based on their individual consumption.

Hourly electricity consumption data were collected for the period 2019–2021 for each apartment, together with common-area consumption. To ensure privacy, an anonymization process was conducted jointly with the property owner and the local DSO. Through this process, apartment-level consumption data were linked to each apartment's floor area and the property address without exposing identifiable personal information. This linkage enabled the aggregation of apartment consumption with common-area consumption for each building and the calculation of sharing coefficients based on apartment floor area. Figure 2 presents the total annual consumption of each building, showing both common-area consumption and total aggregated consumption.

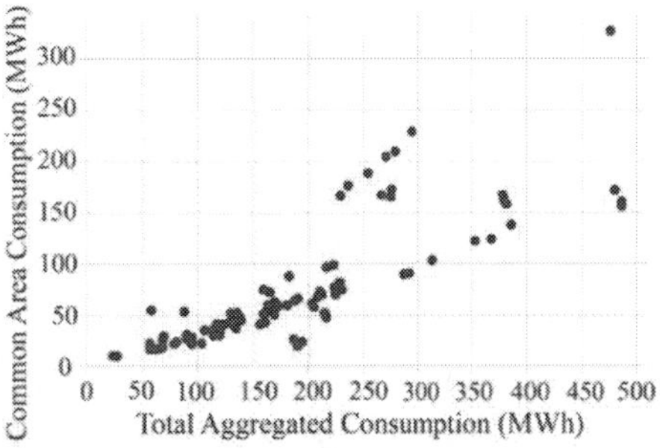

Figure 2: Annual common-area consumption in relation to total aggregated consumption in the building (n=32).

Hourly PV production was simulated using PVGIS for a range of system sizes (10, 20, 30, 40, 50, and 60 kWp) and orientations (south, 45° west, and 45° east), assuming a typical 18° roof tilt. The PVGIS-SARAH3 solar radiation database was employed [14].

2.2 Calculation models

The SCR was calculated for each property using three metering solutions—CC, CCM, and BM. Calculations were performed separately for each study year to capture annual variability, and all data handling, cleaning, and calculations were conducted in R.

In the first phase, surplus energy was calculated for common-area consumption. Annual surplus energy for the CC configuration was determined as shown in Equation 1.

$$S_{CC} = \sum_{\substack{t=1 \\ E_{PV}(t)>C_{CC}(t)}}^{a} E_{PV}(t) - C_{CC}(t) \qquad (1)$$

where a is the number of hours in a year, E_{PV} is the PV energy production at time t, and C_{CC} is the common-area consumption at time t. Surplus energy occurs at time t when PV production exceeds C_{CC}.

For the CCM configuration with virtual net-metering, the share of production exceeding C_{CC} was distributed among shareholders n according to the sharing coefficient, which were based on each apartment's floor area relative to the building's total living area. Surplus energy S_{CCM} was then calculated using Equation 2.

$$S_{CCM} = \sum_{t=1}^{a}\sum_{n=1}^{N} S_n(t,n) \Leftrightarrow \sum_{t=1}^{a} \sum_{\substack{n=1 \\ k(n)\cdot S_{CC}(t)>C_n(n,t)}}^{N} k(n)\cdot S_{CC}(t) - C_n(n,t) \qquad (2)$$

Where N is the total number of shareholders, S_n is the surplus energy of shareholder n, and C_n is the consumption of shareholder n. Surplus energy occurs at time t when the amount of shared energy allocated to a shareholder exceeds that shareholder's consumption.

Surplus energy under the BM configuration was calculated using Equation 3.

$$S_{BM} = \sum_{\substack{t=1 \\ E_{PV}(t)>C_B(t)}}^{a} E_{PV}(t) - C_B(t) \qquad (3)$$

Where C_B is the total aggregated consumption of the building.

After determining hourly surplus energy, the self-consumption ratio (SCR) for each metering scenario was calculated using Equation 4.

$$SCR = \sum_{t=1}^{a} \frac{E_{PV}(t) - S(t)}{E_{PV}(t)} \cdot 100\% \qquad (4)$$

Where S represents surplus energy for the CC, BM, or CCM configuration. Finally, the difference in SCR between BM and CCM configurations was calculated for each building and year, as this difference represents a key outcome for improving SCR simulations when only aggregated consumption data are available.

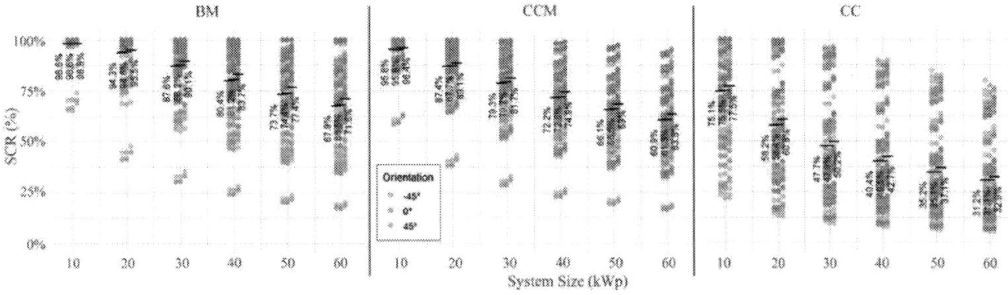

Figure 3: Results for SCR with BM, CCM, and CC configurations.

3 RESULTS

SCR were calculated for each building, each study year, each PV system size, and each metering configuration. Figures were first prepared to present these combinations individually. Figure 3 shows the SCR of each building for the study years using BM, CCM, and CC. For each configuration and system size, red points on the left represent systems oriented 45° east (south-east), green points in the middle represent south oriented systems, and blue points on the right represent systems oriented 45° west (south-west).

Across these configurations, substantial variation in SCR is observed between different buildings. A consistent trend emerges in which west-oriented systems show slightly higher SCR values. This reflects a better alignment with consumption profiles, though it is also partly attributable to the lower overall energy production of west-oriented systems compared with south-oriented systems.

As the differences between metering methods were a primary focus of this study, Figures 4 and 5 present the SCR differences for each individual point shown earlier, together with average values. Figure 4 illustrates the difference between CC and CCM configurations, while Figure 5 shows the difference between CCM and BM.

On average, adopting CCM in a building increased SCR by approximately 30% for system sizes between 20 kWp and 60 kWp across all orientations compared with the CC configuration. For 10 kWp systems, the increase ranged from 18.9% to 20.7%, depending on orientation.

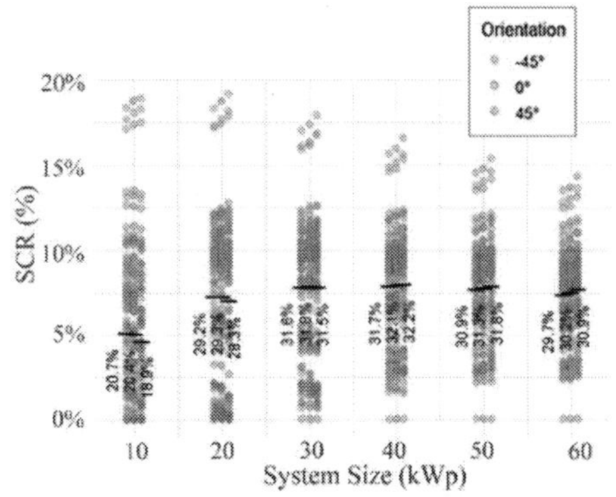

Figure 4: Difference in SCR between CC and CCM configurations.

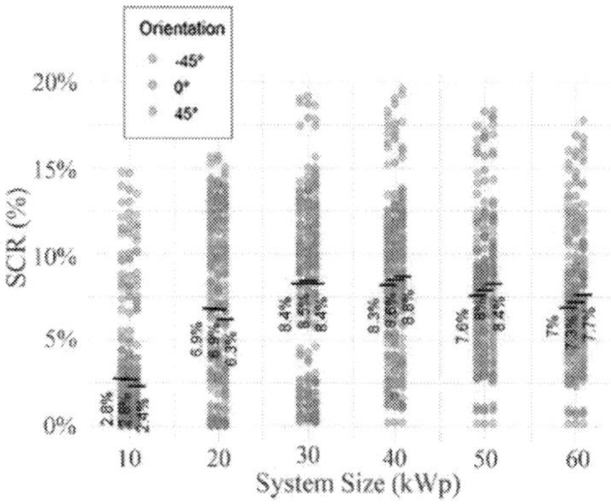

Figure 5: Difference in SCR between BM and CCM configurations.

When comparing average values between CCM and BM, clear differences were also observed. This occurred because some individual apartments did not consume their allocated share of production—even when total building consumption exceeded PV production—which caused SCR values under CCM to remain slightly lower. For 10 kWp systems, the difference between CCM and BM averaged 2.4–2.8%, reflecting the generally high SCR across all configurations at this small system size. For 20–60 kWp systems, the difference varied between 6.3% and 8.8% on average across orientations. However, high variability was present among buildings, with differences ranging from 0% up to 19.5%.

4 DISCUSSION

This study extends existing knowledge on self-consumption ratios (SCR) by incorporating a large and diverse dataset of multi-dwelling buildings (MDBs) and PV system configurations. In the first phase of analysis, real data–based calculations demonstrated how adopting the Credit Calculation Model (CCM) in MDBs has significantly increased viability through higher SCR compared with earlier situations where only common-area consumption (CC) was utilized. Although CCM has been available for several years, information dissemination to shareholders and housing companies has progressed gradually. These results provide quantitative evidence for professionals and stakeholders to communicate the benefits of CCM adoption. However, the wide range of differences between buildings and system sizes underscores the need for case-specific calculations to produce accurate SCR estimates.

The second major finding of this study concerns the difference in SCR between BM and CCM configurations. This comparison is critical for simulations where only aggregated building-level consumption data are available—data that inherently represent BM conditions. The results presented here offer a stronger empirical basis than our previous studies, which were limited to two large MDBs (114 and 224 apartments) with PV systems of 34 kWp and 59.3 kWp, respectively, oriented 71.3° east. While earlier work reported SCR differences of 5–15% [13], our new study—covering 32 buildings—revealed differences ranging from 0% to 19.5%. The variation suggests that PV size relative to total consumption, apartment numbers, occupancy behavior, and common-area load characteristics all influence how closely CCM-based SCR approaches BM results. These factors merit further exploration in future research.

Orientation and system size effects were also examined. On average, west-oriented systems achieved slightly higher SCR than comparable east-oriented systems, likely reflecting better temporal alignment with evening consumption patterns. However, this topic warrants dedicated studies to fully assess the profitability and performance trade-offs of orientation under different metering configurations and sensitivity parameters.

This study focused on SCR variation between different metering configurations. Nevertheless, while SCR is one of the main parameters in assessing the viability of PV systems, other factors also influence the overall feasibility of different setups. For example, orientation affects not only total production and alignment with consumption but also the average electricity market prices during production hours. Furthermore, as this study concentrated only on SCR differences between CCM and BM, it should be noted that collective electricity contracts may provide additional economic benefits through reduced DSO fees and potentially more favorable agreements with energy providers due to larger aggregated demand [13].

Several limitations should be considered when applying these findings. All studied buildings were located in Pirkanmaa, Finland, and owned by the same rental housing company. Consumption characteristics and PV production patterns may differ in other regions, climates, or ownership models such as limited liability housing companies, which are common in Finland. In addition, this study did not analyze differences arising from variation between buildings and apartments or from different electricity contract types. Nevertheless, because the CCM–BM difference is largely driven by probabilistic occupancy effects, and given the wide variation already observed, these results offer a robust basis for estimating SCR in PV simulations for MDBs in other contexts.

This study used hourly consumption data, consistent with current SCR calculation practices. However, Finland is rolling out new smart meters capable of 15-minute intervals, which could influence the difference between BM and CCM. Shorter interval would require individual apartments to match their allocated production more precisely within each interval, potentially increasing the CCM–BM gap observed here. Future studies should revisit these comparisons using higher-resolution metering data.

In this study, the sharing coefficient was based on apartment floor area, providing a close approximation of the typical situation in which coefficients are assigned according to ownership shares. However, there are no strict regulations on how the coefficient must be defined among customers, so in some cases it may differ—potentially influencing the SCR gap between CCM and BM configurations. In several European countries, studies have also explored dynamic coefficient strategies, particularly in larger and more complex energy communities, to identify methods for maximizing the total SCR within the community while simultaneously narrowing the gap between CCM and BM [8], [9], [10], [11].

5 CONCLUSION

The main motivation of this study was to improve understanding of the SCR gap between two metering methods—CCM and BM—because in practice, only aggregated building-level consumption data (representing BM conditions) are often available. At the same time, we evaluated the increase in SCR compared with the recent situation in Finnish MDBs, in which only common-area consumption (CC) was considered.

A key finding is that adopting CCM increases SCR by approximately 30% for medium-to-large PV systems (20–60 kWp) compared with the earlier situation where only CC was utilized. For the smallest 10 kWp systems, the average change was about 19–21%, primarily because SCR was already high under both metering configurations.

To support SCR simulations for CCM in MDBs using aggregated consumption data, we found that the difference between BM and CCM configurations averaged 6–9% for 20–60 kWp systems, with values ranging from 0% to 19.5% across all studied buildings, orientations, and years. For smaller 10 kWp systems, the difference was only 2–3% on average.

These results provide numerical tools for DSOs, housing companies, and PV designers to improve SCR estimation and PV project profitability assessments in MDBs. The findings are based on Pirkanmaa region buildings owned by a single rental housing company and on hourly consumption data, which should be considered as limitations. Nevertheless, they offer valuable insights for broader contexts until more advanced tools become available.

Future research could examine the effect of 15-minute metering intervals as new smart meters are rolled out, since stricter alignment between consumption and shared production may influence the CCM–BM gap. In addition, the transition from 60-minute to 15-minute market time units and imbalance settlement periods may affect customer consumption profiles as well as the value of self-consumed and surplus energy across different time periods. Flexible loads—such as EV charging and battery storage—also represent promising avenues for increasing total SCR in MDBs when optimized for self-consumption, and these were not yet included in the buildings analyzed in this study.

Given the wide range of results observed, future studies should replicate this analysis in other regions or ownership models to provide broader validation and to examine the parameters influencing SCR variability. As this study did not address overall economic feasibility or optimal PV system design, subsequent work could incorporate economic optimization to better link SCR performance parameters with financial viability.

6 ACKNOWLEDGMENT

The authors gratefully acknowledge the support of STEK – The Association for Electrical Technology and Energy Efficiency, Tampereen Energia Sähköverkko Oy (distribution system operator), and Tampereen Vuokratalosäätiö sr. Their contributions were essential to the successful completion of this study.

7 DECLARATION OF GENERATIVE AI AND AI-ASSISTED TECHNOLOGIES IN THE WRITING PROCESS

During the preparation of this work the authors used ChatGPT-5 to improve readability and language. After using this tool, the authors reviewed and edited the content as needed and take full responsibility for the content of the publication.

8 REFERENCES

[1] Directive (EU) 2018/2001 of the European Parliament and of the Council of 11 December 2018 on the promotion of the use of energy from renewable sources. 2018. [Online]. Available: http://data.europa.eu/eli/dir/2018/2001/oj/eng

[2] Directive (EU) 2019/944 of the European Parliament and of the Council of 5 June 2019 on common rules for the internal market for electricity and amending Directive 2012/27/EU (recast) (Text with EEA relevance.), amended by Directive (EU) 2023/2413. 2019. [Online]. Available: http://data.europa.eu/eli/dir/2019/944/oj/eng

[3] Valtioneuvoston asetus sähköntoimitusten selvityksestä ja mittauksesta 767/2021. Oikeusministeriö. [Online]. Available: https://finlex.fi/fi/laki/alkup/2021/20210767

[4] Laki sähkö- ja maakaasumarkkinoiden valvonnasta annetun lain muuttamisesta 499/2023. Oikeusministeriö, Edita Publishing Oy. [Online]. Available: https://www.finlex.fi/fi/laki/alkup/2023/20230499

[5] Fingrid, 'Datahub'. [Online]. Available: https://www.fingrid.fi/en/electricity-market/datahub/

[6] Sähkömarkkinalaki 588/2013. Oikeusministeriö, Edita Lakitieto Oy. [Online]. Available: https://www.finlex.fi/fi/laki/ajantasa/2013/20130588

[7] K. Berg, R. Rana, H. Taxt, and M. F. Dynge, 'Economic assessment and grid impact of different sharing keys in collective self-consumption', in 2024 IEEE PES Innovative Smart Grid Technologies Europe (ISGT EUROPE), Dubrovnik, Croatia: IEEE, Oct. 2024, pp. 1–5. doi: 10.1109/ISGTEUROPE62998.2024.10863813.

[8] A. J. Gil Mena, V. F. Nasimba Medina, A. Bouakkaz, and S. Haddad, 'Analysis and optimisation of collective self-consumption in residential buildings in Spain', Energy Build., vol. 283, p. 112812, Mar. 2023, doi: 10.1016/j.enbuild.2023.112812.

[9] E. Llera-Sastresa, J. Á. Gimeno, J. L. Osorio-Tejada, and P. Portillo-Tarragona, 'Effect of Sharing Schemes on the Collective Energy Self-Consumption Feasibility', Energies, vol. 16, no. 18, p. 6564, Sept. 2023, doi: 10.3390/en16186564.

[10] A. D. Mustika, R. Rigo-Mariani, V. Debusschere, and A. Pachurka, 'A two-stage management strategy for the optimal operation and billing in an energy community with collective self-consumption', Appl. Energy, vol. 310, p. 118484, Mar. 2022, doi: 10.1016/j.apenergy.2021.118484.

[11] A. Eisner, C. Neumann, and H. Manner, 'Exploring sharing coefficients in energy communities: A simulation-based study', Energy Build., vol. 297, p. 113447, Oct. 2023, doi: 10.1016/j.enbuild.2023.113447.

[12] J. Ylipaino, A. Kortetmäki, K. Kallioharju, J. Koskela, and P. Järventausta, 'Evaluating Allocation Methods for Collective Selfconsumption in Nordic Multi-Dwelling Buildings', in 2025 21st International Conference on the European Energy Market (EEM), Lisbon, Portugal: IEEE, May 2025, pp. 1–6. doi: 10.1109/EEM64765.2025.11050109.

[13] A. Kortetmäki, J. Ylipaino, J. Koskela, K. Kallioharju, and P. Järventausta, 'The Impact of Metering Methods on Collective Self-Consumption: Insights from Multi-Dwelling Buildings in Finland', 2024. doi: 10.2139/ssrn.4782201.

[14] EU Science Hub, 'Photovoltaic Geographical Information System (PVGIS)'. [Online]. Available: https://joint-research-centre.ec.europa.eu/photovoltaic-geographical-information-system-pvgis_en

IAM MODELS AND PHOTOVOLTAIC ENERGY YIELD SIMULATIONS

Felipe Ríos-Ledesma, Laura Barrutia, Javier Ledesma, Luis Narvarte and Eduardo Lorenzo
Instituto de Energía Solar, Universidad Politécnica de Madrid, Nikola Tesla s/n, Madrid, 28031, España
felipe.rios.ledesma@upm.es, laura.barrutia@upm.es, javier.ledesma@upm.es, luis.narvarte@upm.es,
antonio.lorenzo@upm.es

ABSTRACT: The Incidence Angle Modifier (IAM) in photovoltaic (PV) modules is a relationship between the incident ray on a surface and the normal to this module surface, which causes optical losses in PV modules and consequently in PV systems. There are different directional models that describe the behavior for different angles of incidence with an assigned normalized value. These models have been implemented in SISIFO, an open and free PV simulation software developed by the IES-UPM. A simulation exercise, extended to static and tracked PV arrays, has been carried out with the aim of understanding the impact of the IAM losses and the compatibility between the different models. To quantify the losses associated with IAM, spectral effects and the presence of soiling in the locations are ignored but they could be seamlessly incorporated into the current simulation tool. The annual IAM losses calculated with the different models allow us to find correspondences between the models studied in the impact of the annual losses on global irradiance and its components. Using these values, the annual IAM losses calculated with the different models are between 1 to 3.5% in static systems and less than 1% in tracking systems.
Keywords: IAM, Correction Factor, PV Simulation, open-source.

1 Introduction

The Photovoltaic (PV) modules suffer optical losses when the sun's rays are not incident perpendicular to the plane of the arrays (POA), mainly due to increased reflections. To avoid this, most commercial PV modules today employ anti-reflective (AR) coatings [1] to improve the performance of PV modules with high angles of incidence (AOI), in the range of 60 to 90°. These optical losses depend on the position, tilt and orientation of the module, as well as factors inherent to the geographical location of the PV system: latitude, longitude and climatic conditions.

The Incidence Angle Modifier (IAM), refers to additional optical losses that occur when the angle between the incidence light on a surface and the normal to the surface,θ, is not zero. The angular losses associated with IAM can be, in clean PV modules, due to reflection caused by changes in the optical properties as they pass through the PV module materials, while in dirty modules, volumetric properties of the dust are involved, leading to additional losses [2]. This work focuses on the implementation of photovoltaic modules under optimal cleanliness conditions within the simulations. The spectral effects associated with the photovoltaic modules have been deliberately eliminated [3] to simplify the calculations and achieve greater clarity and ease in the final estimation of the performance of the PV system under study. This methodology makes it possible to reduce the complexity of the parameters involved and to obtain more direct comparative results with respect to the ideal performance of the PV module.

Existing directional models for the calculation of reflection losses have been predominantly applied in the context of optimising photovoltaic performance under standard test conditions (STC), where accurate characterisation of the incidence angle dependence of optical losses is particularly relevant. These detailed models, which vary in complexity and applicability, are summarised in Table 1. Additional information can be found on this table regarding their mathematical formulation, underlying assumptions, and the specific fitting parameters on which their correct implementation ultimately depends.

Table I: IAM models

Names	IAM model
ASHRAE (1996) [4]	$1-b_0\left(\frac{1}{\cos\theta}\right)$
Air-glass (1996) [5]	$\frac{1-\frac{1}{2}\left[\frac{\sin^2(\theta_T-\theta)}{\sin^2(\theta_T+\theta)}+\frac{\tan^2(\theta_T-\theta)}{\tan^2(\theta_T+\theta)}\right]}{1-\left(\frac{n_1-n_2}{n_1+n_2}\right)^2}$
Martin Ruiz (2001) [6], [7]	$1-\frac{\exp\left(-\frac{\cos\theta}{a_r}\right)-\exp\left(-\frac{1}{a_r}\right)}{1-\exp\left(-\frac{1}{a_r}\right)}$
Sandia (2004) [8]	$a_0+a_1\theta+a_2\theta^2+a_3\theta^3+a_4\theta^4+a_5\theta^5$
Physical (2006) [9]	$\frac{1-\frac{1}{2}\left[\frac{\sin^2(\theta_T-\theta)}{\sin^2(\theta_T+\theta)}+\frac{\tan^2(\theta_T-\theta)}{\tan^2(\theta_T+\theta)}\right]}{1-\left(\frac{n_1-n_2}{n_1+n_2}\right)^2}\frac{\exp\left(-\frac{KL}{\cos\theta_T}\right)}{\exp(-KL)}$
Eye-sensitivity (2024) [10]	$1-\Gamma^{(\theta-90°)}$

Manufacturers often provide experimental IAM data through PAN files (with extension .PAN) for different angles of incidence, which allows comparative studies to be carried out. In addition, Figure 1 shows the IAM curve for ten different PV commercial modules with AR coating, whose experimental data have been provided by the manufacturers and extracted from the PVsyst software [11]. Differences depending on the type of PV module technology can be observed. These discrepancies might be considered, since they directly affect the optical reflection losses and, consequently, the overall energy yield of the PV system.

These IAM experimental results, which are essential for the parameterisation and accurate simulation of photovoltaic systems, make it possible to adjust the models of optical losses per angle of incidence and optimise the expected performance according to the constructive characteristics of the modules. Thus, the use of manufacturer-specific data, validated and hosted in tools, is vital to ensure that PV simulations reflect real-world conditions and provide reliable estimates of performance

10.4229/EUPVSEC2025/4DV.4.19

under different solar incidence conditions.

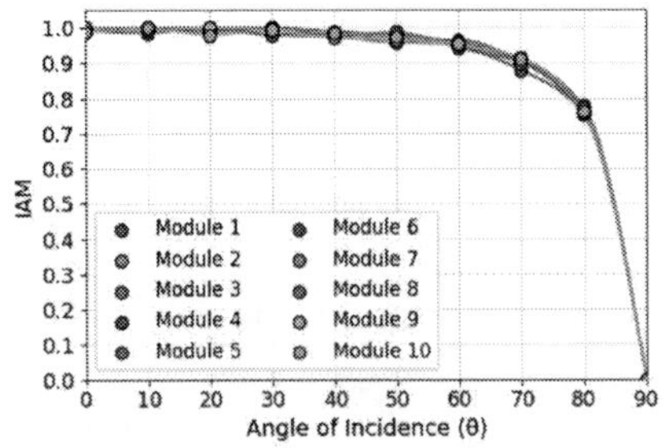

Figure 1: IAM values for different PV commercial modules with AR layers.

2 Correction factors for irradiance components

The calculation of the effective irradiance should be obtained with the lower uncertainty as possible. To reduce this uncertainty, both the effective irradiance corrected by the angle of incidence ($G_{\text{Front}}^{\text{AOI}}$) on the front surface of a photovoltaic module and the contribution of different solar components with their corresponding correction factors must be considered. Adjusted terms include direct solar irradiance (B_{Front}) together with circumsolar diffuse irradiance ($D_{\text{Front}}^{\text{CIR}}$), which are corrected by the factor $F_{\text{B,Front}} = IAM(\theta)$, reflecting the impact of the angle of incidence on the transmittance and reflection of the front glass. Diffuse isotropic diffuse irradiance ($D_{\text{Front}}^{\text{ISO}}$) is corrected by $F_{D,Front}$, while the diffuse component of the bright horizon ($D_{\text{Front}}^{\text{HB}}$) is associated with the factor $F_{\text{HB,Front}}$. In addition, the radiation reflected by the ground (R_{Front}) is considered by means of the factor $F_{\text{R, Front}}$. See Figure 2.

This formulation allows detailed and accurate modelling of the optical losses that affect the module's energy performance under real operating conditions, considering how the optical properties vary with solar geometry and module characteristics. Similar models are implemented and validated in simulation software such as PVsyst, and are based on the methodologies detailed in studies such as those by [8], which highlights the importance of incorporating angular corrections.

The consideration of these components and their correction factors is essential for a rigorous analysis in optimisation studies of photovoltaic systems, the design of new technologies and the evaluation of the field performance of PV systems. Specifically, these factors represent the sensitivity of each irradiance component to changes in angle of incidence and their effect on useful energy absorption, which directly influences loss modelling and the simulation of expected annual energy production.

$$G_{\text{Front}}^{\text{AOI}} = F_{\text{B,Front}}\left(B_{\text{Front}} + D_{\text{Front}}^{\text{CIR}}\right) + F_{\text{D,Front}}D_{\text{Front}}^{\text{ISO}} + F_{\text{HB,Front}}D_{\text{Front}}^{\text{HB}} + F_{\text{R,Front}}R_{\text{Front}}$$

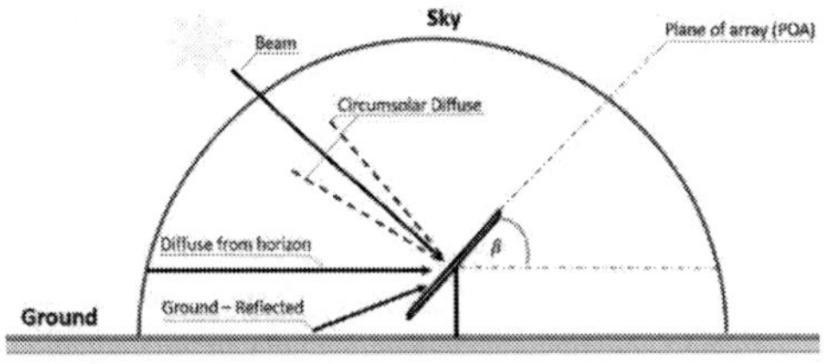

Figure 2: Components of irradiance in plane of array, POA.

The correction factors are applied to the equation that considers the solar resource components. In this work, we have corrected the directional component with the Martin-Ruiz IAM model recommended by the standard IEC-61853 [12]. This model is widely used because it fits a single experimental parameter *ar*.

To calculate the values of F_D, F_{HB} and F_R, the procedure for calculating the integral as proposed by [13]. Sweeping with typical *ar* values for widely studied PV modules.

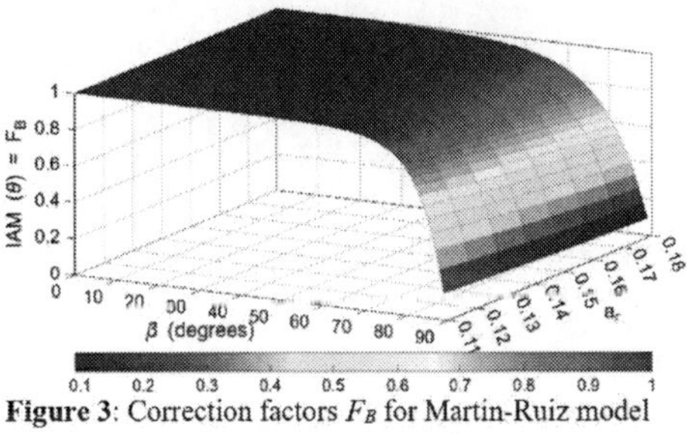

Figure 3: Correction factors F_B for Martin-Ruiz model

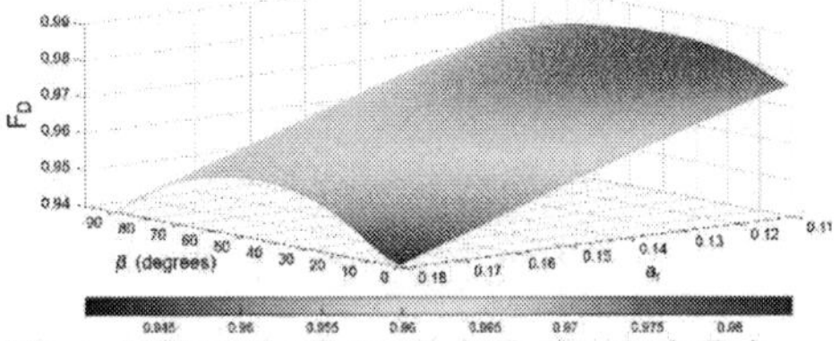

Figure 4: Correction factors F_D in sky for Martin-Ruiz model

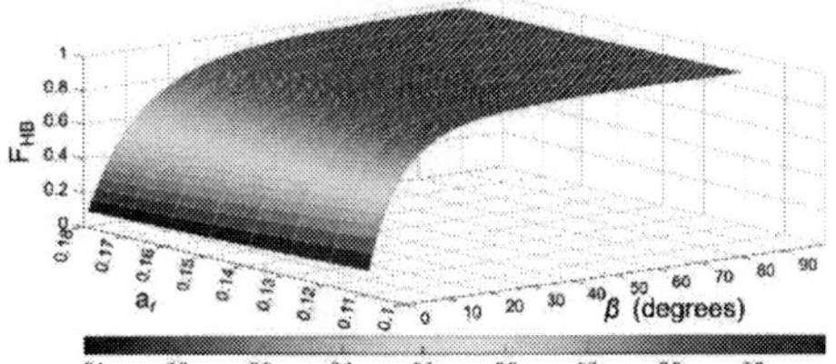

Figure 5: Correction factors F_{HB} in horizon for Martin-Ruiz mode

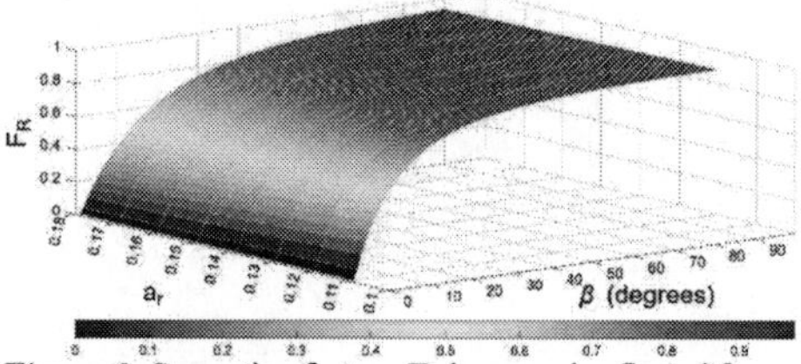

Figure 6: Correction factors F_R in ground-reflected for Martin-Ruiz model

These correction maps are available as metadata associated to previously defined matrices. As a result, the computational cost is significantly reduced, optimizing simulation time and allowing the available resources to be concentrated on the most relevant physical processes.

3 Implementation in SISIFO

The use of photovoltaic simulation software is a growing stage today with the emergence of simulation tools such as PVsyst and System Advisor Model (SAM) [11], [14]. The simulation stage is essential to analyse and optimise photovoltaic systems to estimate energy production with low uncertainty. In the case of this work, we have implemented the angular correction models for the study of IAM in SISIFO software (a free simulation tool developed at IES-UPM and freely available at www.sisifo.info) with the latest update—v3.3 (sisifoweb r503, sisifosvc r122, sisifomatlab r115)—the correction factors described in Section 2 have been implemented. It is available to simulate, under *Options – IAM model*, both for the front and rear face in bifacial modules in multirow PV arrays [15].

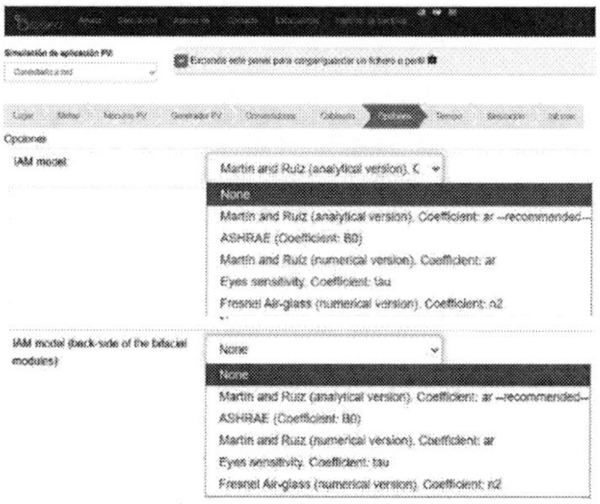

Figure 7: Drop-down menu in SISIFO to use IAM models on front and back side of a PV module.

4 Simulations Results and correspondences between the models

Annual Angular Losses (AAL) is defined as the difference between the global incident irradiance that would be obtained if no IAM losses were considered and the effective global irradiance after applying these angular factors, evaluated over a calendar year [10]. This parameter quantifies the cumulative energy reduction due to the angular dependence of the optical transmittance in the PV module and is a key value in the accurate modelling of the annual performance of PV systems when using simulation software.

$$AAL = \frac{\int_{year}[G - G^{AL}]\, dt}{\int_{year} G\, dt} \cong \frac{\sum_{year}[G - G^{AL}]}{\sum_{year} G}$$

The models have been implemented in the software SISIFO for static structures and for horizontal single-axis trackers. Thanks to this implementation, it has been possible to simulate a practical case that allows to quantify the difference between both static and with tracking on a horizontal axis system.

As a concrete example, the solar photovoltaic plant analysed in this work corresponds to a plant located in Chile, considering the following climatic characteristics.

Table II: Solar Climate Characteristics of PV Plant

Case study of a PV plant	
Latitude (°)	-24
Global horizontal irradiance (kWh/m²)	2680
Ratio D(0)/G(0)	0.14
Ground reflectivity	0.3
Tilt (°)	20
Ground coverage ratio (Static)	0.6
Ground coverage ratio (Tracking)	0.4

The results for each simulation are shown in Figure 8, showing a clear trend in the maximum annual overall loss values for each case with each IAM model parameter to be used to simulate.

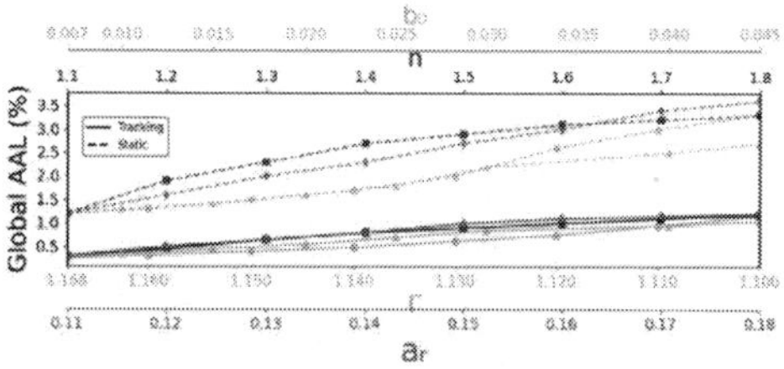

Figure 8: Annual Angular Losses Simulation Exercise for two different configurations (tracking and static).

The equivalence between parameters of each model in terms of annual yield is very important for simulation in PV software. This equivalence has been explored by other authors considering only the ASHRAE model and the physical model [16].

5 Conclusions

The angular correction factors implemented in SISIFO significantly improves the effective irradiance calculation and reduces the uncertainty in the simulation of PV systems, providing a robust and accurate tool for energy yield analysis. Available as open-source software, SISIFO facilitates access and transparency, allowing the research and professional community to perform reliable and reproducible simulations, contributing to the advancement and optimisation of PV projects.

The study of different IAM models and its implementation in this software has made possible to perform simulations with low uncertainty anywhere in the world where PV performance is to be studied.

10.4229/EUPVSEC2025/4DV.4.19

In this work, annual losses due to IAM in static PV systems typically range from 1% to 3.5%. These losses are significantly reduced in systems with solar tracking, where they typically remain below 1% due to better constant orientation of the module with respect to the sun. The reduction of angular losses through tracking contributes significantly to the improvement of the efficiency and annual energy yield of the PV system.

Acknowledgements

This work was supported by the Spanish State Research Agency through the project MORE-N (Proyectos de I + D + i Generación de Conocimiento 2023), with grants PID2023-148369OB-C41 and PREP2023-001767 funded by MICIU/AEI/10.13039/501100011033 and by ESF+.

References

[1] A. M. Law, L. O. Jones, and J. M. Walls, "The performance and durability of Anti-reflection coatings for solar module cover glass – a review," Sep. 01, 2023, *Elsevier Ltd.* doi: 10.1016/j.solener.2023.06.009.

[2] B. Guo and W. Javed, "Effect of incidence angle on PV soiling loss," *Solar Energy*, vol. 269, Feb. 2024, doi: 10.1016/j.solener.2023.112298.

[3] W. Sang *et al.*, "Spectral correction of photovoltaic module electrical properties," *Renew Energy*, vol. 237, Dec. 2024, doi: 10.1016/j.renene.2024.121907.

[4] A. F. Souka and H. H. Safwat, "Determination of the Optimum Orientations for the Double-Exposure, Flat-Plate Collector and Its Reflectors," *Solar Energy*, vol. 10, pp. 170–174, 1966, doi: https://doi.org/10.1016/0038-092X(66)90004-1.

[5] R. Preu, G. Kleiss, K. Bucher, R. Preu, G. Kleiss, and K. Reiche, K-Bucher, "PV-Module Reflexion Losses: Measurement, Simulation and Influence on Energy Yield and Performance Ratio," Nice: 13th European Photovoltaic Solar Energy Conference, 1995. [Online]. Available: https://www.researchgate.net/publication/282695694

[6] N. Martin and J. M. Ruiz, "Calculation of the PV modules angular losses under field conditions by means of an analytical model," *Solar Energy Materials & Solar Cells*, vol. 70, pp. 25–38, 2001, doi: https://doi.org/10.1016/S0927-0248(00)00408-6.

[7] N. Martin and J. M. Ruiz, "Corrigendum to 'Calculation of the PV modules angular losses under field conditions by means of an analytical model' [Sol. Energy Mater. Sol. Cells 70 (1) (2001) 25–38] (S0927024800004086) (10.1016/S0927-0248(00)00408-6))," Mar. 01, 2013, *Elsevier B.V.* doi: 10.1016/j.solmat.2012.11.002.

[8] D. L. King, W. E. Boyson, and J. A. Kratochvill, "Photovoltaic Array Performance Model," Alburquerque, NM, 2004. [Online]. Available: http://www.ntis.gov/help/ordermethods.asp?loc=7-4-0#online

[9] W. De Soto, S. A. Klein, and W. A. Beckman, "Improvement and validation of a model for photovoltaic array performance," *Solar Energy*, vol. 80, no. 1, pp. 78–88, 2006, doi: 10.1016/j.solener.2005.06.010.

[10] A. Goncalves, D. Rativa, and L. A. Gomez-Malagon, "Model-Based Assessment of the Incident Angle Modifier on the Annual Angular Losses and Gain of PV Modules in Tracking Systems," *IEEE J Photovolt*, vol. 14, no. 1, pp. 185–193, Jan. 2024, doi: 10.1109/JPHOTOV.2023.3323802.

[11] "PVsyst SA. (2025). PVsyst Photovoltaic System Software (Version 7.4) [Software]. https://www.pvsyst.com/."

[12] "IEC-61853-2, 'Photovoltaic (PV) module performance testing and energy rating-Part 2: Spectral response, incidence angle and module operating temperature measurements,'" Switzerland, 2012.

[13] B. Marion, "Numerical method for angle-of-incidence correction factors for diffuse radiation incident photovoltaic modules," *Solar Energy*, vol. 147, pp. 344–348, 2017, doi: 10.1016/j.solener.2017.03.027.

[14] "National Renewable Energy Laboratory. (2025). System Advisor Model (SAM) (Version 2025.6.30) [Software]. https://sam.nrel.gov/."

[15] J. R. Ledesma, E. Lorenzo, and L. Narvarte, "Single-Axis Tracking and Bifacial Gain on Sloping Terrain," *Progress in Photovoltaics: Research and Applications*, 2024, doi: 10.1002/pip.3847.

[16] Fatehi JH and Sauer KJ, "Modeling the Incidence Angle Dependence of Photovoltaic Modules in PVsyst," Denver: IEEE 40th Photovoltaic Specialist Conference, PVSC, 2014, pp. 1335–1338.

42nd European Photovoltaic Solar Energy Conference and Exhibition

INSTITUTO DE ENERGÍA SOLAR

IAM MODELS AND PHOTOVOLTAIC ENERGY YIELD SIMULATIONS

POLITÉCNICA

4DV.4.19

Felipe Ríos-Ledesma, Laura Barrutia, Javier Ledesma, Luis Narvarte and Eduardo Lorenzo

Instituto de Energía Solar, Universidad Politécnica de Madrid, Nikola Tesla s/n, Madrid, 28031, España

felipe.rios.ledesma@upm.es, laura.barrutia@upm.es, javier.ledesma@upm.es, luis.narvarte@upm.es, antonio.lorenzo@upm.es

IAM Models

ASHRAE $1 - b_0\left(\frac{1}{\cos\theta}\right)$

Air-glass $$\frac{1-\frac{1}{2}\left[\frac{\sin^2(\theta_T-\theta)}{\sin^2(\theta_T+\theta)}+\frac{\tan^2(\theta_T-\theta)}{\tan^2(\theta_T+\theta)}\right]}{1-\left(\frac{n_1-n_2}{n_1+n_2}\right)^2}$$

Martín-Ruíz $$1-\frac{\exp\left(-\frac{\cos\theta}{a_r}\right)-\exp\left(-\frac{1}{a_r}\right)}{1-\exp\left(-\frac{1}{a_r}\right)}$$

Sandia $a_0 + a_1\theta + a_2\theta^2 + a_3\theta^3 + a_4\theta^4 + a_5\theta^5$

Physical $$\frac{1-\frac{1}{2}\left[\frac{\sin^2(\theta_T-\theta)}{\sin^2(\theta_T+\theta)}+\frac{\tan^2(\theta_T-\theta)}{\tan^2(\theta_T+\theta)}\right]}{1-\left(\frac{n_1-n_2}{n_1+n_2}\right)^2}\cdot\frac{\exp\left(-\frac{KL}{\cos\theta_T}\right)}{\exp(-KL)}$$

Eye sensitivity $1 - \Gamma^{(\theta-90°)}$

Behaviour of the IAM curve for different commercial PV modules

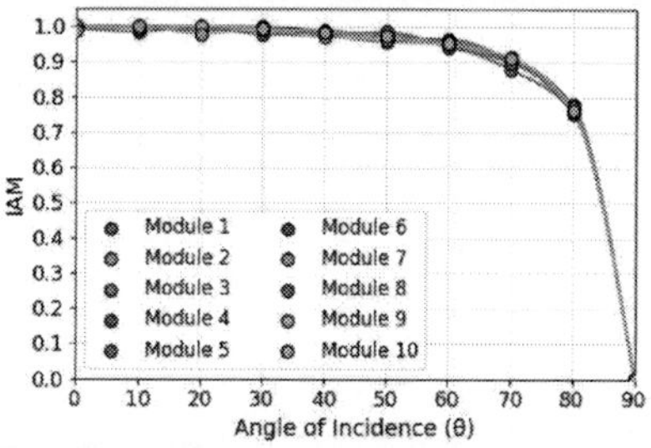

Correction Factors applied to SISIFO photovoltaic simulation software https://sisifo.info

To reduce the uncertainty in the calculation of the global to effective irradiance step.

$$G^{AOI}_{Front} = F_{B,Front}\left(B_{Front} + D^{CIR}_{Front}\right) + F_{D,Front}D^{ISO}_{Front} + F_{HB,Front}D^{HB}_{Front} + F_{R,Front}R_{Front}$$

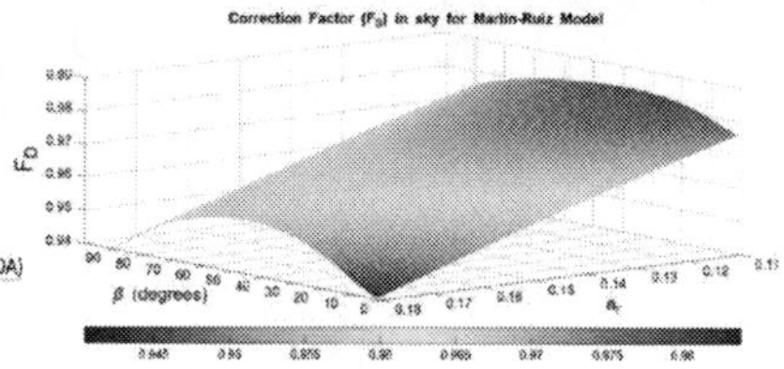

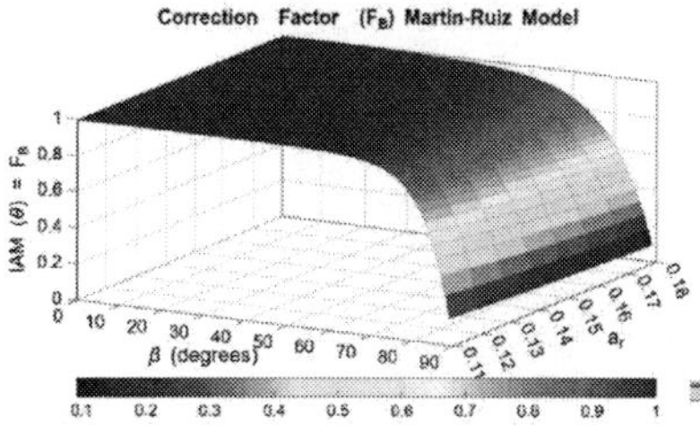

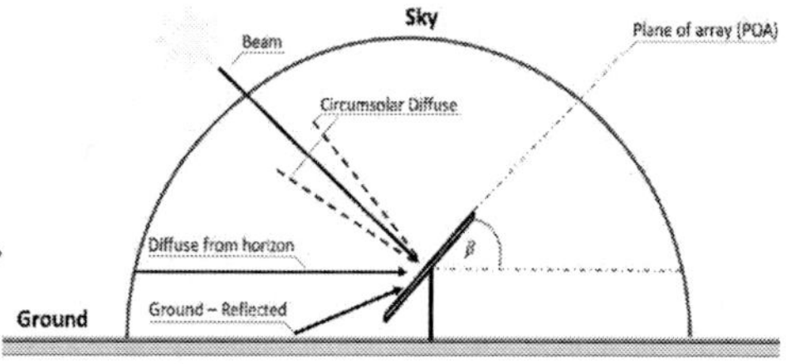

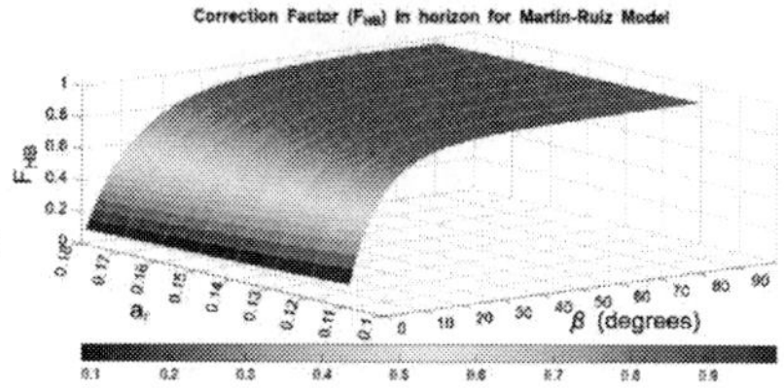

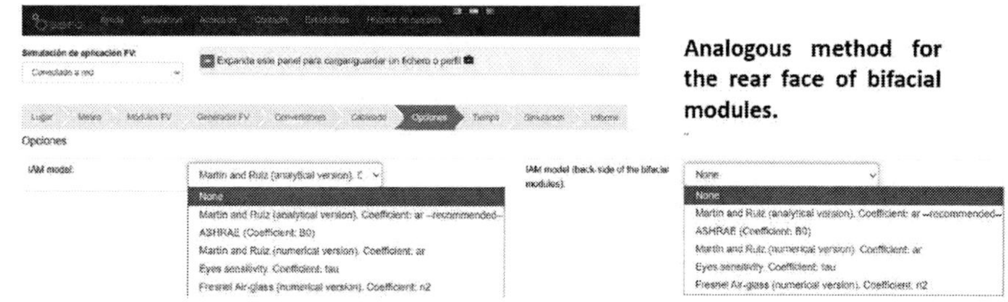

Analogous method for the rear face of bifacial modules.

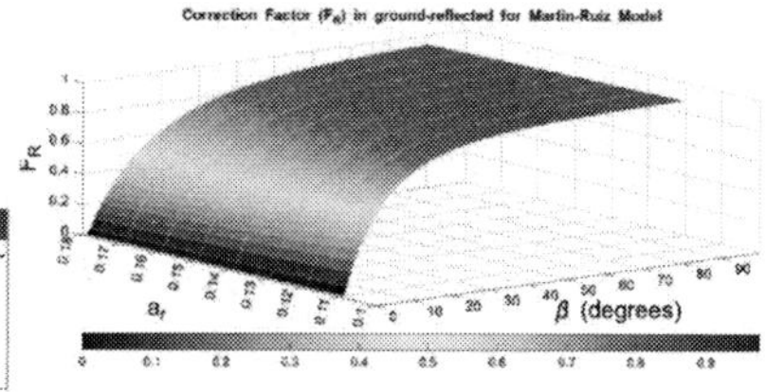

Results for a case study of a Photovoltaic System

Annual angular losses (AAL) due to IAM in static PV System and with tracking system in Chile.

Estimating real yearly energy yields and performance.

Allow us to find correspondences between the models.

$$AAL = \frac{\int_{year}[G - G^{AL}]\,dt}{\int_{year} G\,dt} \cong \frac{\sum_{year}[G - G^{AL}]}{\sum_{year} G}$$

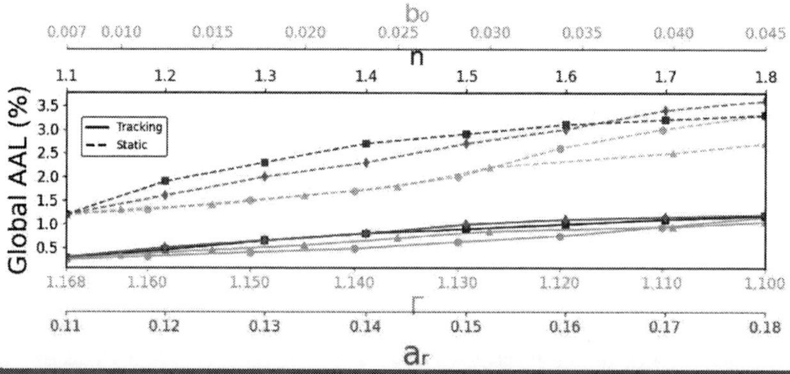

Conclusion

The annual IAM losses are between 1 and 3.5 % for static PV systems, which improve with tracking that is kept close to 1%.

The correction factors implemented in SISIFO reduce uncertainty and provide a valuable tool for PV simulations with OPEN software.

Grants PID2023-148369OB-C41 and PREP2023-001767 funded by MICIU/AEI/10.13039/501100011033 and by ESF+

MINISTERIO DE CIENCIA, INNOVACIÓN Y UNIVERSIDADES · Cofinanciado por la Unión Europea · AGENCIA ESTATAL DE INVESTIGACIÓN

ESTIMATING FUTURE SOILING LOSSES USING CLIMATE MODELS

Gerardo Guerra[1], Pau Mercade Ruiz[1], Gaetana Anamiati[1], Lars Landberg[2]
[1]GreenPowerMonitor a DNV company, Gran Via de les Corts Catalanes, 130, Barcelona, Spain; Email: gerardo.guerra@dnv.com, pau.mercade@dnv.com, gaetana.anamiati@dnv.com
[2]DNV Denmark, Tuborg Parkvej 8, Hellerup, Denmark; Email: lars.landberg@dnv.com

1. WHAT?

Perform an evaluation of future soiling losses for the 2021–2050 climate normal period [1] across 11 sites representative of the PV Köppen-Geiger climate zones [2]. The study will be based on the Kimber methodology [3] and precipitation data generated by a selection of CMIP6 model variants under the SSP245 and SSP585 scenarios [4].

3. HOW?

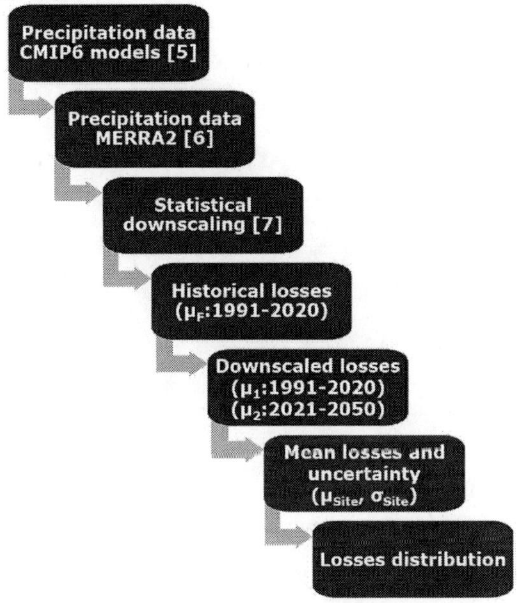

Fig 1. Estimation future losses

Future soiling losses are anchored to the real world using the delta method.

$$\Delta\mu = \mu_2 - \mu_1$$

$$\mu_F = \mu_H + \Delta\mu$$

$$\mu_{Site} = \frac{1}{N}\sum_{n=1}^{N} \mu_{F_n}$$

$$\sigma_{Site} = \sqrt{\sum_{n=1}^{N} \frac{\left(\mu_{F_n} - \mu_{Site}\right)^2}{N-1}}$$

2. WHY?

As climate change may alter precipitation patterns, reliance on historical data for planning purposes becomes increasingly uncertain. Consequently, estimating future soiling losses using climate projections is essential for informed decision-making.

4. RESULTS

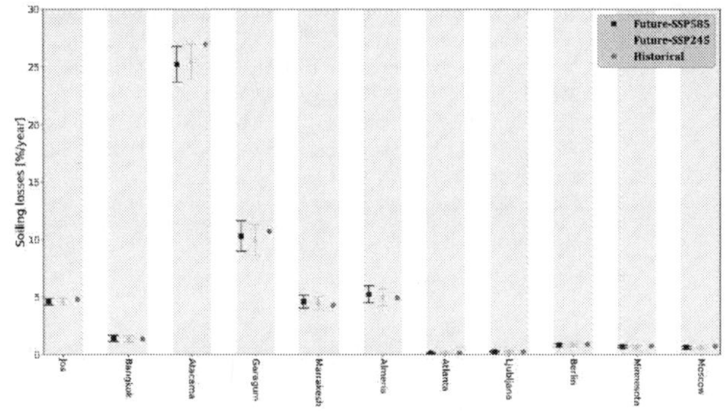

Fig 2. Test sites soiling losses.

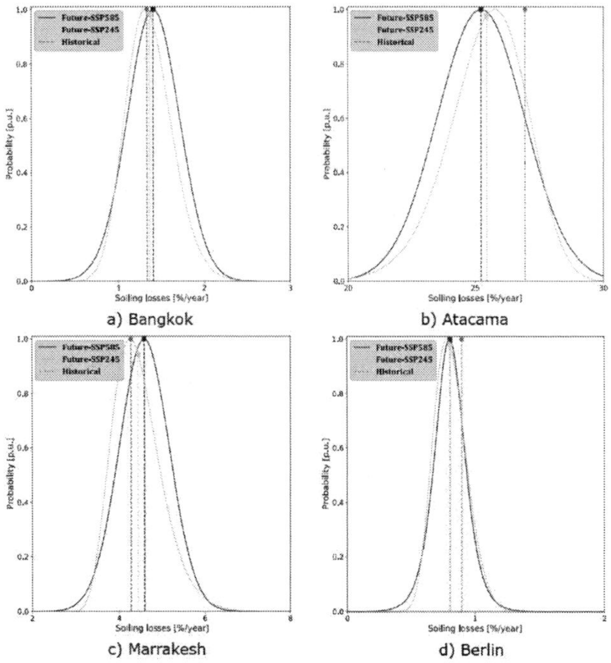

a) Bangkok b) Atacama

c) Marrakesh d) Berlin

Fig 3. Losses distribution sample sites

5. CONCLUSIONS

- Average soiling losses are projected to remain stable at most sites, but high-emission scenarios introduce greater uncertainty.
- The use of historical baselines for statistical downscaling may not fully capture evolving climate trends.
- The exclusion of precipitation intensity overlooks potential operational risks such as flooding or mechanical stress on PV infrastructure.

6. REFERENCES

[1] World Meteorological Organization. (2017). WMO Guidelines on the Calculation of Climate Normals.
[2] Ascencio-Vásquez, J. Brecl, K., & Topič, M. (2019). Methodology of Köppen-Geiger-Photovoltaic climate classification and implications to worldwide mapping of PV system performance. *Solar Energy*, 191, 672-685.
[3] Kimber, A., Mitchell, L., Nogradi, S., & Wenger, H. (2006). The Effect of Soiling on Large Grid-Connected Photovoltaic Systems in California and the Southwest Region of the United States. In *2006 IEEE 4th World Conference on Photovoltaic Energy Conference* (Vol. 2, pp. 2391-2395).
[4] O'Neill, B. C., Tebaldi, C., van Vuuren, D. P., Eyring, V., Friedlingstein, P., Hurtt, G., Knutti, R., Kriegler, E., Lamarque, J.-F., Lowe, J., Meehl, G. A., Moss, R., Riahi, K., & Sanderson, B. M. (2016). The Scenario Model Intercomparison Project (ScenarioMIP) for CMIP6. *Geoscientific Model Development*, 9(9), 3461-3482.
[5] Google cloud CMIP6
[6] NASA Power API
[7] Gudmundsson, L., Bremnes, J. B., Haugen, J. E., & Engen-Skaugen, T. (2012). Technical Note: Downscaling RCM precipitation to the station scale using statistical transformations – a comparison of methods. *Hydrology and Earth System Sciences*, 16(9), 3383-3390.

MAXIMUM POWER POINT TRACKING METHOD FOR GRID-CONNECTED PV SYSTEMS USING MAXIMUM POWER LINE

Hyoung-Kyu Yang, Seok Won Kim, Dongmyoung Joo, Yong-Su Noh, and Jin-Hong Kim
Korea Electronics Technology Institute (KETI) / Power System Research Center
14502, Bucheon, South Korea

ABSTRACT: In order to maximize energy production from a photovoltaic (PV) system, maximum power point tracking (MPPT) methods should rapidly track the maximum power point (MPP). This paper proposes an efficient MPPT method for grid-connected PV systems that can rapidly track the MPP while avoiding the power oscillations around the MPP. To achieve these, the proposed method employs output power control instead of PV array voltage control used in the conventional MPPT methods. The reference for the output power of PV systems is set to the maximum power line, which is the locus of MPPs under various irradiances at a given temperature. The proposed MPPT method forces the operating point of a PV array to rapidly converge to the MPP without the power oscillations. The simulation results clearly demonstrate that the proposed method can achieve a higher tracking efficiency than the conventional methods. Therefore, the proposed method helps foster the penetration level of PV generation in a cost-effective way.
Keywords: Maximum power line, maximum power point tracking, output power control, photovoltaic system.

1 INTRODUCTION

Photovoltaic (PV) generation has been playing a very important role in achieving high penetration levels of renewable energy because of its technical advances and enhanced economic viability during the last decade [1]–[3]. Generating more energy while reducing the production cost is inevitable so that the levelized cost of PV generation should be further reduced [4], [5]. To extract the maximum energy from the sun, a PV system should rapidly track the maximum power point (MPP), and the power oscillations should be avoided around the MPP.

Hence, a large number of maximum power point tracking (MPPT) methods have been proposed [6]–[24]. The perturbation and observation (P&O) method in [6]–[11], which has been widely used in the industry because of low cost and easy implementation, tracks the MPP by perturbing the PV array voltage (v_{pv}) with a fixed voltage step size and observing whether the power increases or not. A large v_{pv} step size can rapidly track the MPP, but cause the large power oscillations around the MPP. On the contrary, a small v_{pv} step size can avoid the power oscillations, but a slow tracking speed is inevitable. Thus, difficulties arise in determining the proper v_{pv} step size.

To overcome this, the variable step-size incremental conductance (VSSINC) method was suggested in [12]–[14]. The VSSINC method adjusts the v_{pv} step size by using the scaling factor depending on the gradient of the power-voltage (*P-V*) curve of a PV array. Thus, the VSSINC method can achieve a faster tracking speed while alleviating the power oscillations around the MPP. However, the VSSINC method is limited to improve the tracking speed because it should wait for the next perturbation step to check whether the power increases or not.

In [15]–[17], artificial-intelligence-based MPPT methods were suggested to decide the proper v_{pv} step size. However, the huge computational burden is inevitable, requiring more expensive processor. The model-predictive-control-based MPPT methods were reported in [18] and [19]. However, their performance is critically dependent on the converter topology and is very sensitive to converter parameter variations. The fuzzy-logic-based MPPT methods in [20] and [21] do not need to model the converter, but the closed-loop stability and performance issues are not guaranteed for various kinds of models. The authors of [22] suggested a direct MPPT method that tracks the MPP by estimating the ripples of the instantaneous PV array power and voltage. However, it was designed for single-phase inverters only, and the trade-off problem between the tracking speed and the power oscillations around the MPP still remains.

This paper proposes an efficient MPPT method for grid-connected PV systems that can rapidly track the MPP while avoiding the power oscillations around the MPP, thereby achieving a higher tracking efficiency. In the proposed method, output power control is employed instead of v_{pv} control used in the P&O and VSSINC methods. The proposed method does not perturb v_{pv}, but sets the reference for the output power as the maximum power line (MPL), which is the locus of MPPs with various irradiance conditions at a given temperature. The efficacy of the proposed MPPT method is investigated under various irradiance conditions using a PSIM software.

2 PROPOSED MPPT METHOD FOR PV SYSTEMS

2.1 PV Array Modeling

Fig. 1 shows a PV array represented as the single-diode equivalent circuit [25]–[27]. The ideal PV model consists of a current source and a diode in parallel. I_{ph} is the photocurrent generated by the incident light and I_D is the diode current. The equivalent series and parallel resistances, R_s and R_p, represent the contact resistance and leakage current in the practical PV model, respectively.

The current-voltage (*I-V*) characteristic of a PV array can be expressed as:

$$I = I_{ph} - I_D - \frac{V + R_s I}{R_p}. \qquad (1)$$

I_{ph} is a function of the irradiance and temperature as in:

$$I_{ph} = \left[I_{ph,n} + K_I \left(T - T_n \right) \right] \frac{G}{G_n} \qquad (2)$$

where G and G_n are the actual and nominal irradiances in W/m^2, respectively; T and T_n are the actual and nominal temperatures in K, respectively; K_I is the temperature coefficient of the short-circuit current, and $I_{ph,n}$ is the nominal photocurrent at the standard test condition (STC), which indicates that G_n = 1000 W/m² and T_n = 298.15 K (25 °C).

I_D is given by:

$$I_D = I_0\left[\exp\left(\frac{V+R_sI}{V_t a}\right)-1\right] \quad (3)$$

where $$I_0 = I_{0,n}\left(\frac{T}{T_n}\right)^3 \exp\left[\frac{qE_g}{ak}\left(\frac{1}{T_n}-\frac{1}{T}\right)\right] \quad (4)$$

and $$V_t = \frac{N_s k T}{q} \quad (5)$$

where I_0 is the saturation current, V_t is the thermal voltage, a is the diode ideality constant, $I_{0,n}$ is the nominal saturation current, q is the electron charge (1.602×10^{-19} C), E_g is bandgap energy (1.12 eV for the polycrystalline Si), k is the Boltzmann constant (1.380×10^{-23} J/K), and N_s is the number of cells connected in series. Fig. 2 shows the typical *I-V* (dotted) and *P-V* curves (solid) of a PV array.

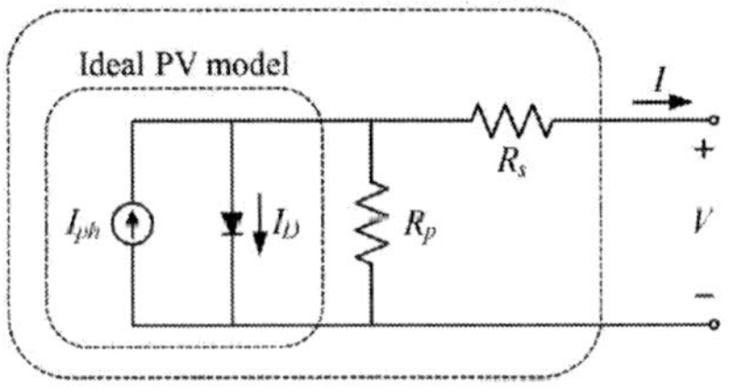

Figure 1: Single-diode equivalent circuit of a PV array.

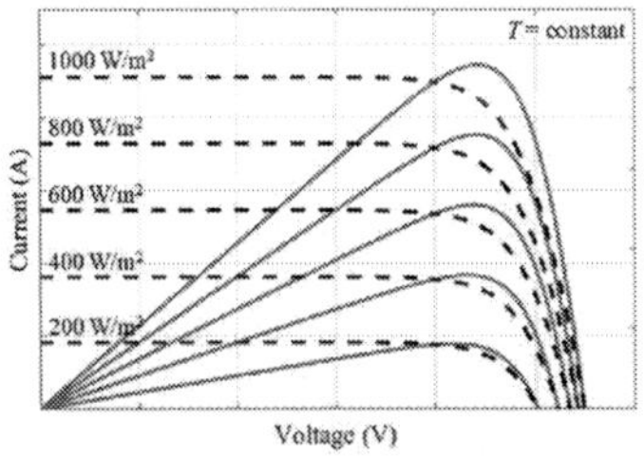

Figure 2: *I-V* and *P-V* curves of a PV array.

2.2 Derivation of the Maximum Power Line

The MPL is the locus of MPPs with various irradiances at a given temperature. The MPL can be obtained empirically. Alternatively, the MPL can be derived as follows. It can be assumed that R_s is very small and R_p is very large. Thus, these parameters can be neglected to obtain the simplified ideal model [28], [29]. Then, (1) can be simplified as:

$$I = I_{ph} - I_0\left[\exp\left(\frac{V}{V_t a}\right)-1\right]. \quad (6)$$

In the *P-V* curve, dP/dV can be represented as:

$$\frac{dP}{dV} = \frac{d}{dV}(VI) = I + V\frac{dI}{dV}, \quad (7)$$

dP/dV at the MPP becomes 0 and thus the current at the MPP thus (I_{mpp}) can be obtained as:

$$I_{mpp} = -V_{mpp}\left.\frac{dI}{dV}\right|_{V=V_{mpp},I=I_{mpp}} \quad (8)$$

where V_{mpp} is the voltage at the MPP.

dI/dV at the MPP in (8) can be obtained from (6).

$$\left.\frac{dI}{dV}\right|_{V=V_{mpp},I=I_{mpp}} = -\frac{I_0}{V_t a}\exp\left(\frac{V_{mpp}}{V_t a}\right). \quad (9)$$

Finally, the power at the MPP (P_{mpp}) can be obtained from (8) and (9), as in:

$$P_{mpp} = V_{mpp} I_{mpp} = \frac{I_0}{V_t a} V_{mpp}^2 \exp\left(\frac{V_{mpp}}{V_t a}\right) \quad (10)$$

As shown in (10), P_{mpp} is a function of V_{mpp} and V_t. In addition, P_{mpp} is not dependent on the solar irradiance. Fig. 3 shows a family of *P-V* curves for the irradiances from 200 W/m² to 1000 W/m² and the locus of P_{mpp} (MPL) obtained from the parameters of a PV cell in Table I.

Table I: Parameters of a PV Cell

Parameter	Symbol	Value
Nominal photocurrent	$I_{ph,n}$	3.80 A
Nominal saturation current	$I_{0,n}$	$2.16\cdot10^{-8}$ A
Thermal voltage	V_t	0.0257 V
Diode ideality constant	A	43.2
Temperature coefficient of short-circuit current	K_I	0.0024 A/K

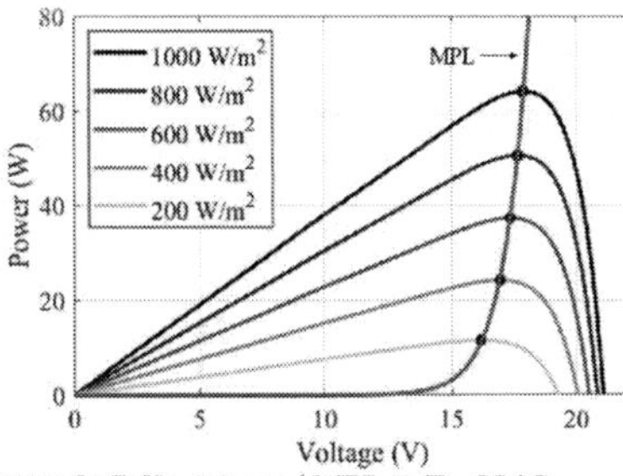

Figure 3: *P-V* curves and MPL at T = 25 °C.

2.2 Operating Principle of the Proposed MPPT Method

MPPT methods aim to track the MPP of the *P-V* curve whenever the irradiance changes. Fig. 4 shows the typical configuration of the single-stage grid-connected PV system. The power inverter, which can be either single- or three-phase depending on the grid type, is used to connect a PV array to the power grid. The MPPT controller generates I_g^* to maximize the PV array power (P_{pv}), by measuring v_{pv} and the PV array current (i_{pv}). The DC-link

10.4229/EUPVSEC2025/4DV.4.25
020449-002

capacitor is connected in parallel to the PV array to store P_{pv} while stabilizing v_{pv}.

Fig. 5 shows the main difference between the P&O method and proposed method. The proposed method regulates the power injected to the grid (P_g) while the P&O method regulates v_{pv}. This implies that the P&O method sets the reference for v_{pv} (v_{pv}^*), whereas the proposed method sets the reference for P_g (P_g^*). In addition, the P&O method requires v_{pv} and i_{pv}, whereas the proposed method requires only v_{pv}. The P&O method perturbs v_{pv}^* by the voltage step size to track the MPP. Then, the P&O method should wait for the predefined time step (T_s) between the consecutive steps to observe whether P_{pv} increases or not. This inevitably slows the tracking speed. In addition, even around the MPP, the P&O method keeps perturbing v_{pv} with a fixed step size and thus P_{pv} keeps oscillating, causing the power losses. Further, while the irradiance is changing, the P&O method might repeat consecutive confusions because P_{pv} is changed not by v_{pv} perturbation but by the irradiance change. This forces the operating point to deviate from the MPP, thereby further delaying the convergence and causing more power losses.

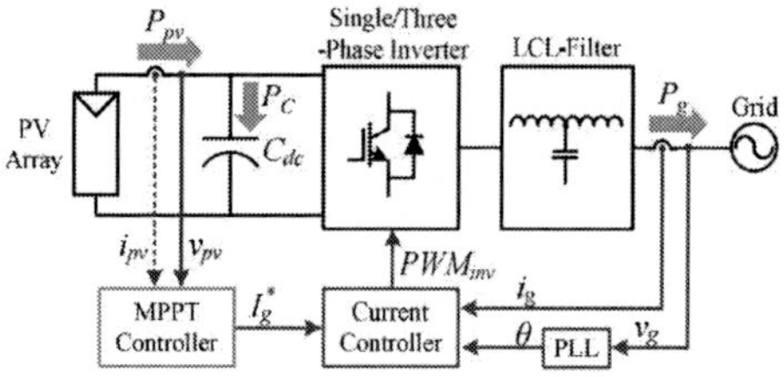

P_g, P_C: Power flowing into the grid and DC-link capacitor
P_{pv}, v_{pv}, i_{pv}: PV array power, voltage, and current
v_g, i_g: Grid voltage and current I_g^*: Reference for i_g
PLL: Phase-locked loop θ: Phase angle
PWM_{inv}: Pulse-width modulation C_{dc}: DC-link capacitance

Figure 4: Single-stage grid-connected PV system.

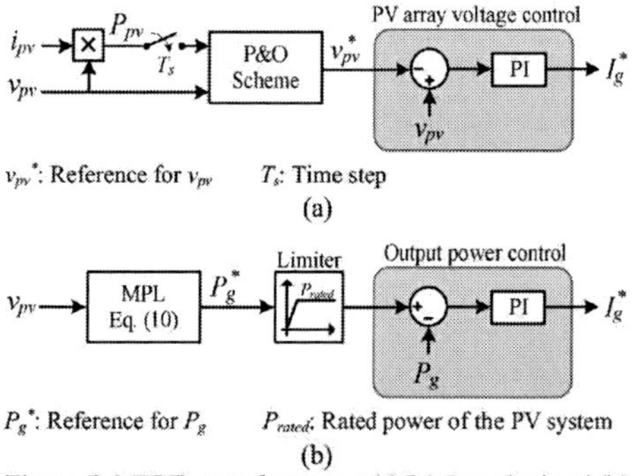

Figure 5: MPPT control structure (a) P&O method and (b) Proposed method.

To rapidly track the MPPs while avoiding the oscillations around the MPP, the proposed method regulates P_g instead of v_{pv}. Because P_g is calculated by the measured v_g and i_g, the proposed method does not need to measure i_{pv}. P_g^* is set to the MPL in (10) by inserting v_{pv} into V_{mpp}. To avoid the overcurrent in the PV system, P_g^* is limited by the rated power (P_{rated}). To generate I_g^*, a proportional-integral controller is used.

Assuming no loss in the single/three-phase inverter, the relationship between P_{pv} and P_g in Fig. 4 can be expressed as:

$$P_C = C_{dc} v_{pv} \frac{dv_{pv}}{dt} = P_{pv} - P_g \tag{11}$$

where P_C is the power flowing into the DC-link capacitor and C_{dc} is the DC-link capacitance.

Fig. 6 shows the typical MPL (red line) and P-V curve (black line) at an irradiance. The MPL is limited by P_{rated} to prevent damage to the hardware. We will show how the proposed method can rapidly track the MPP without oscillations around the MPP when an irradiance remains. The MPL and P-V curve intersect at the MPP. The P-V curve is divided into two parts: left-hand side (LHS) of the MPP, where the P-V curve is larger than MPL, and right-hand side (RHS) of the MPP, where the P-V curve is smaller than MPL.

Let us choose an initial operating point of v_{pv} at the LHS of the P-V curve. In this section, P_{pv} is larger than the MPL and thus dv_{pv}/dt becomes positive according to (11). As a result, v_{pv} increases. The increase rate of v_{pv} depends on $P_{pv} - P_g$. The increase in v_{pv} results in the increase in P_{pv} and P_g. In the LHS, P_{pv} is larger than P_g. Consequently, v_{pv} keeps increasing until v_{pv} reaches the MPP. At the MPP, P_{pv} equals P_g. v_{pv} does not move further because dv_{pv}/dt becomes zero.

Now let us choose an initial operating point of v_{pv} at the RHS of the P-V curve, where P_{pv} is smaller than the MPL. In this section, dv_{pv}/dt becomes negative and thus v_{pv} decreases. As a result, P_{pv} increases and P_g decreases. In the RHS, P_{pv} is smaller than P_g. Consequently, v_{pv} keeps decreasing until v_{pv} reaches the MPP. At the MPP, P_{pv} equals P_g and thus v_{pv} remains. Note that the proposed method does not wait for T_s used in the P&O method to determine the tracking direction. That is why the proposed method rapidly tracks the MPP without oscillations around the MPP.

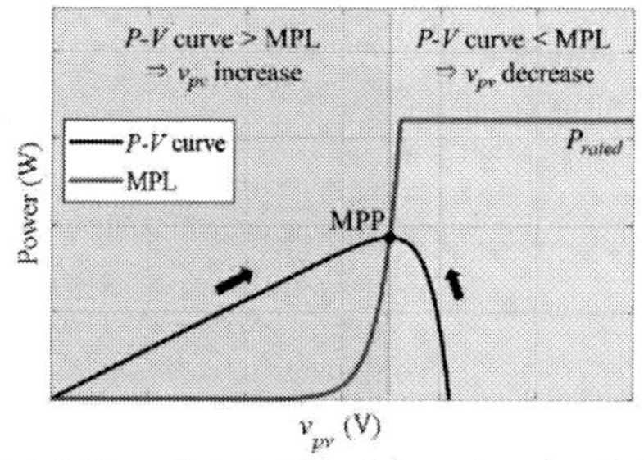

Figure 6: Operating principle of the proposed method.

3 SIMULATION RESULTS

This section investigates the performance of the MPPT methods based on a PSIM software. Table II shows the parameters of the PV system used in this paper. The performance of the proposed MPPT method is compared

10.4229/EUPVSEC2025/4DV.4.25

to the conventional MPPT methods: P&O method in [6]–[11] and VSSINC method in [12]–[14]. In this paper, the v_{pv} step size in the P&O method is set to 3 V. The v_{pv} step-size limit and scaling factor in the VSSINC method is set to 6 V and 0.2, respectively. T_s is set to 0.1 s in the P&O and VSSINC methods.

The key index of the comparison is the rise time (τ_{rise}), which indicates how rapidly MPPT methods track the MPP when the irradiance remains. In this paper, τ_{rise} is defined as the time for P_{pv} to reach 90% of the available maximum power (P_{max}), as in [30]. In addition, the tracking efficiency (η_{mppt}) indicates how much energy can be extracted from the sun during a time interval. As in [31], η_{mppt} is defined by:

$$\eta_{mppt} = \frac{\int_0^t P_{pv}(\tau)d\tau}{\int_0^t P_{max}(\tau)d\tau} \times 100 . \quad (12)$$

The performance of the MPPT methods is compared in the condition that the initial operating point is at the LHS or RHS of the MPP.

Table II: Parameters of the PV System

Parameter	Symbol	Value
PV array rated power	P_{rated}	10 kW
PV array MPP voltage	V_{mpp}	467 V
PV array MPP current	I_{mpp}	21.5 A
PV array open-circuit voltage	V_{oc}	548 V
PV array short-circuit current	I_{sc}	22.8 A
DC-link capacitor	C_{dc}	4.2 mF
LCL-filter	L_i, C_f, L_g	1 mH; 3.3 μF; 0.57 mH
Switching frequency	f_{sw}	10 kHz
Grid nominal voltage	V_g	190 V_{rms}
Grid nominal frequency	f_g	60 Hz

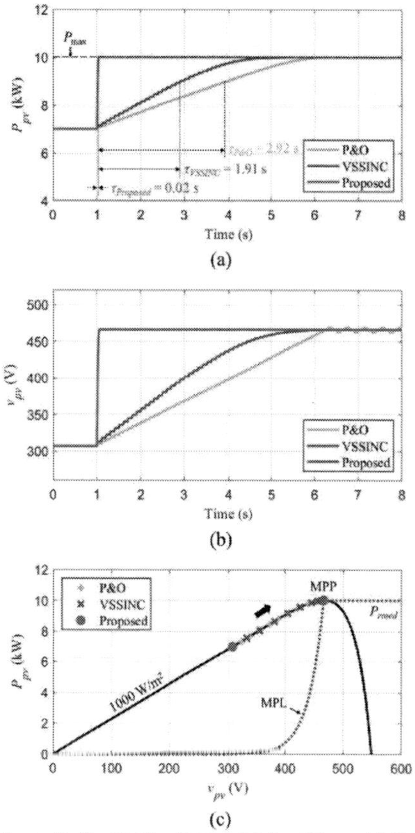

Figure 7: Results for *Case I*. (a) P_{pv}. (b) v_{pv}. (c) P_{pv}-v_{pv} locus.

3.1 *Case I*: Initial operating point at the LHS of the MPP

Fig. 7 illustrates the results for *Case I* with the operating point on the left side of the *P-V* curve under the STC at 1000 W/m^2 and 25 °C. The initial operating point is located on the left side of the *P-V* curve and the MPPT methods start to control at 1 s. Then, the operating point in all methods converges to the MPP along with the *P-V* curve (see Fig. 7(c)). As shown in Fig. 7(a), τ_{rise} in the proposed method is 0.02 s while τ_{rise} in the P&O and VSSINC methods are 2.92 s and 1.91 s, respectively. In addition, η_{mppt} in the P&O, VSSINC, and proposed methods are 86.97%, 91.29%, and 99.80%, respectively. This is because the proposed method can instantaneously track the MPP with the significant increase rate in v_{pv}, which has the maximum value of 5415 V/s. In contrast, the P&O and VSSINC methods track the MPP with T_s of 0.1 s, which causes the maximum value of the increase rate in v_{pv} to be 30 V/s and 60 V/s, respectively. That is why the proposed method provides much faster performance in tracking the MPP than the conventional methods. In addition, the VSSINC and proposed methods cause no oscillations around the MPP, whereas the P&O method causes the power oscillations. Therefore, the P&O method generates less energy than the VSSINC and proposed methods.

3.2 *Case II*: Initial operating point at the RHS of the MPP

Fig. 8 illustrates the results for *Case II* with the operating point on the right side of the *P-V* curve under the STC at 1000 W/m^2 and 25 °C. The initial operating point is on the open-circuit point and the MPPT methods start to control at 1 s. Then, the operating point in all methods converges to the MPP along with the *P-V* curve (see Fig. 8(c)). As shown in Fig. 8(a), τ_{rise} in the proposed method is 0.03 s while τ_{rise} in the P&O and VSSINC methods are 1.40 s and 0.70 s, respectively. In addition, η_{mppt} in the P&O, VSSINC, and proposed methods are 77.22%, 89.23%, and 99.07%, respectively. This is because the proposed method can instantaneously track the MPP with the significant decrease rate in v_{pv}, which has the maximum value of –4345 V/s. In contrast, the P&O and VSSINC methods track the MPP with T_s of 0.1 s, which causes the maximum value of the decrease rate in v_{pv} to be –30 V/s and –60 V/s, respectively. That is why the proposed method provides much faster performance in tracking the MPP than the conventional methods. In addition, there is no oscillations around the MPP in the VSSINC and proposed methods as in *Case I*. Therefore, the proposed method generates significantly a larger amount energy with a faster tracking speed than the conventional methods.

10.4229/EUPVSEC2025/4DV.4.25

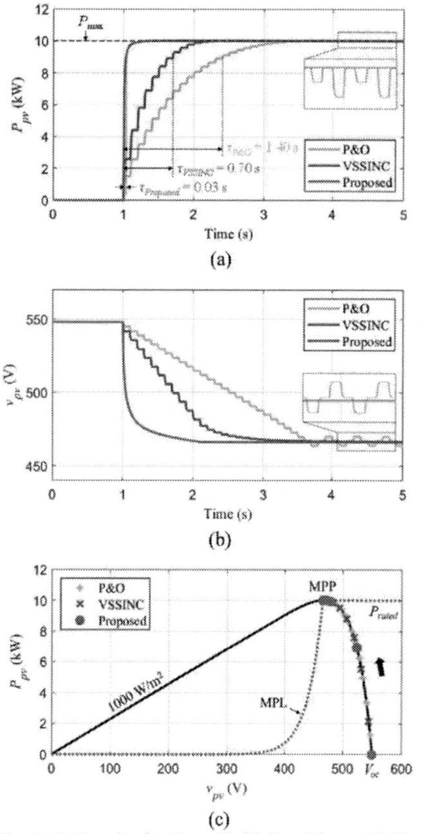

Figure 8: Results for *Case II*. (a) P_{pv}. (b) v_{pv}. (c) P_{pv}-v_{pv} locus.

4 CONCLUSIONS

This paper proposes an efficient MPPT method for grid-connected PV systems that uses output power control instead of PV array voltage control widely used in the conventional MPPT methods. The proposed method sets the output power reference as the MPL, thereby rapidly tracking the MPP while avoiding the oscillations around the MPP. The simulation results evidently demonstrate that the proposed method rapidly tracks the MPP, thereby achieving higher tracking efficiency. Further, no power oscillations are observed around the MPP in the steady-state. Hence, the proposed method helps provide a promising solution to foster the high penetration level of PV generation.

ACKNOWLEDGEMENT

This work was supported by Korea Institute of Energy Technology Evaluation and Planning(KETEP) grant funded by the Korea government(MOTIE)(RS-2023-00233148, Development of grid-forming topology and inverter core technology for grid access to distributed energy resources)

REFERENCES

[1] S. Kouro, J. I. Leon, D. Vinnikov, and L. G. Franquelo, "Grid-connected photovoltaic systems: an overview of recent research and emerging PV converter technology," *IEEE Ind. Electron. Mag.*, vol. 9, no. 1, pp. 47–61, Mar. 2015.

[2] E. Romero-Cadaval, B. Francois, M. Malinowski, and Q.-C. Zhong, "Grid-connected photovoltaic plants: an alternative energy source, replacing conventional sources," *IEEE Ind. Electron. Mag.*, vol. 9, no. 1, pp. 18–32, Mar. 2015.

[3] T. Stetz, J. von Appen, F. Niedermeyer, G. Scheibner, R. Sikora, and M. Braun, "Twilight of the grids: the impact of distributed solar on Germany's energy transition," *IEEE Power Energy Mag.*, vol. 13, no. 2, pp. 50–61, Mar./Apr. 2015.

[4] E. Koutroulis and F. Blaabjerg, "Design optimization of transformerless grid-connected PV inverters including reliability," *IEEE Trans. Power Electron.*, vol. 28, no. 1, pp. 325–335, Jan. 2013.

[5] Y. Yang, E. Koutroulis, A. Sangwongwanich, and F. Blaabjerg, "Pursuing photovoltaic cost-effectiveness: absolute active power control offers hope in single-phase PV systems," *IEEE Ind. Appl. Mag.*, vol. 23, no. 5, pp. 40–49, Sep./Oct. 2017.

[6] Y. H. Lim and D. C. Hamill, "Simple maximum power point tracker for photovoltaic arrays," *Electron. Lett.*, vol. 36, no. 11, pp. 997–999, May 2000.

[7] E. Koutroulis, K. Kalaitzakis, and N. C. Voulgaris, "Development of a microcontroller-based, photovoltaic maximum power point tracking control system," *IEEE Trans. Power Electron.*, vol. 16, no. 1, pp. 46–54, Jan. 2001.

[8] N. Femia, G. Petrone, G. Spagnuolo, and M. Vitelli, "Optimization of perturb and observe maximum power point tracking method," *IEEE Trans. Power Electron.*, vol. 20, no. 4, pp. 963–973, Jul. 2005.

[9] N. Kasa, T. Iida, L. Chen, "Flyback inverter controlled by sensorless current MPPT for photovoltaic power system," *IEEE Trans. Ind. Electron.*, vol. 52, no. 4, pp. 1145–1152, Aug. 2005.

[10] M. A. Elgendy, B. Zahawi, and D. J. Atkinson, "Assessment of perturb and observe MPPT algorithm implementation techniques for PV pumping applications," *IEEE Trans. Sustain. Energy*, vol. 3, no. 1, pp. 21–33, Jan. 2012.

[11] M. A. Elgendy, B. Zahawi, and D. J. Atkinson, "Operating characteristics of the P&O algorithm at high perturbation frequencies for standalone PV systems," *IEEE Trans. Energy Convers.*, vol. 30, no. 1, pp. 189–198, Mar. 2015.

[12] F. Liu, S. Duan, F. Liu, B. Liu, Y. Kang, "A variable step size INC MPPT method for PV systems," *IEEE Trans. Ind. Electron.*, vol. 55, no. 7, pp. 2622–2628, Jul. 2008.

[13] J. M. Enrique, J. M. Andújar, and M. A. Bohórquez, "A reliable, fast and low cost maximum power point tracker for photovoltaic applications," *Solar Energy*, vol. 84, no. 1, pp. 79–89, Jan. 2010.

[14] Q. Mei, M. Shan, L. Liu, and J. M. Guerrero, "A novel improved variable step-size incremental-resistance MPPT method for PV systems," *IEEE Trans. Ind. Electron.*, vol. 58, no. 6, pp. 2427–2434, Jun. 2011.

[15] N. Chettibi, A. Mellit, G. Sulligoi, and A. M. Pavan, "Adaptive neural network-based control of a hybrid AC/DC microgrid," *IEEE Trans. Smart Grid*, vol. 9, no. 3, pp. 1667–1679, May 2018.
[16] K. Yan, Y. Du, and Z. Ren, "MPPT perturbation optimization of photovoltaic power systems based on solar irradiance data classification," *IEEE Trans. Sustain. Energy*, vol. 10, no. 2, pp. 514–521, Apr. 2019.
[17] N. Kumar, B. Singh, B. K. Panigrahi, and L. Xu, "Leaky-least-logarithmic-absolute-difference-based control algorithm and learning-based InC MPPT technique for grid-integrated PV system," *IEEE Trans. Ind. Electron.*, vol. 66, no. 11, pp. 9003–9012, Nov. 2019.
[18] A. Lashab, D. Sera, J. M. Guerrero, L. Mathe, and A. Bouzid, "Discrete model-predictive-control-based maximum power point tracking for PV systems: overview and evaluation," *IEEE Trans. Power Electron.*, vol. 33, no. 8, pp. 7273–7287, Aug. 2018.
[19] A. Lashab, D. Sera, and J. M. Guerrero, "A dual-discrete model predictive control-based MPPT for PV systems," *IEEE Trans. Power Electron.*, vol. 34, no. 10, pp. 9686–9697, Oct. 2019.
[20] T. H. Kwan and X. Wu, "Maximum power point tracking using a variable antecedent fuzzy logic controller," *Solar Energy*, vol. 137, pp. 189–200, Nov. 2016.
[21] Y.-T. Chen, Y.-C. Jhang, and R.-H. Liang, "A fuzzy-logic based auto-scaling variable step-size MPPT method for PV systems," *Solar Energy*, vol. 126, pp. 53–63, Mar. 2016.
[22] F. E. Aamri, H. Maker, D. Sera, S. V. Spataru, J. M. Guerrero, and A. Mouhsen, "A direct maximum power point tracking method for single-phase grid-connected PV inverters," *IEEE Trans. Power Electron.*, vol. 33, no. 10, pp. 8961–8971, Oct. 2018.
[23] T. Esram and P. L. Chapman, "Comparison of photovoltaic array maximum power point tracking techniques," *IEEE Trans. Energy Convers.*, vol. 22, no. 2, pp. 439–449, Jun. 2007.
[24] B. Subudhi and R. Pradhan, "A comparative study on maximum power point tracking techniques for photovoltaic power systems," *IEEE Trans. Sustain. Energy*, vol. 4, no. 1, pp. 89–98, Jan. 2013.
[25] M. G. Villalva, J. R. Gazoli, and E. R. Filho, "Comprehensive approach to modeling and simulation of photovoltaic arrays," *IEEE Trans. Power Electron.*, vol. 24, no. 5, pp. 1198–1208, May 2009.
[26] E. I. Batzelis, G. E. Kampitsis, S. A. Papathanassiou, and S. N. Manias, "Direct MPP calculation in terms of the single-diode PV model parameters," *IEEE Trans. Energy Convers.*, vol. 30, no. 1, pp. 226–236, Mar. 2015.
[27] E. I. Batzelis and S. A. Papathanassiou, "A method for the analytical extraction of the single-diode PV model parameters," *IEEE Trans. Sustain. Energy*, vol. 7, no. 2, pp. 504–512, Apr. 2016.
[28] E. Saloux, A. Teyssedou, and M. Sorin, "Explicit model of photovoltaic panels to determine voltages and currents at the maximum power point," *Solar Energy*, vol. 85, no. 5, pp. 713–722, May 2011.
[29] Y. Mahmoud, W. Xiao, and H. H. Zeineldin, "A simple approach to modeling and simulation of photovoltaic modules," *IEEE Trans. Sustain. Energy*, vol. 3, no. 1, pp. 185–186, Jan. 2012.
[30] S. L. Brunton, C. W. Rowley, S. R. Kulkarni, and C. Clarkson, "Maximum power point tracking for photovoltaic optimization using ripple-based extremum seeking control," *IEEE Trans. Power Electron.*, vol. 25, no. 10, pp. 2531–2540, Oct. 2010.
[31] H. A. Sher, A. F. Murtaza, A. Noman, K. E. Addoweesh, K. Al-Haddad, and M. Chiaberge, "A new sensorless hybrid MPPT algorithm based on fractional short-circuit current measurement and P&O MPPT," *IEEE Trans. Sustain. Energy*, vol. 6, no. 4, pp. 1426–1434, Oct. 2015.

42nd European Photovoltaic Solar Energy Conference and Exhibition

Maximum Power Point Tracking Method for Grid-Connected Photovoltaic Systems Using Maximum Power Line

Hyoung-Kyu Yang, Seok Won Kim, Dongmyoung Joo, Yong-Su Noh, and Jin-Hong Kim
Korea Electronics Technology Institute (KETI)

I. Introduction

- ❖ MPPT needs to be improved to extract maximum energy from the sun
  - It should rapidly track the maximum power point (MPP)
  - It should avoid the power oscillations around the MPP
- ❖ This study proposes an efficient MPPT method for PV systems
  - The proposed MPPT method applies the output power controller with the maximum power line (MPL) to solve the issue.

II. Proposed MPPT Method for PV Systems

- ❖ Maximum power line (MPL) of PV array
  - MPL is the locus of MPPs with various irradiance conditions at a given temperature
  - MPL used in this study is derived from a single-diode equivalent circuit model
  - Note that Eq. (1) is not dependent on solar irradiance

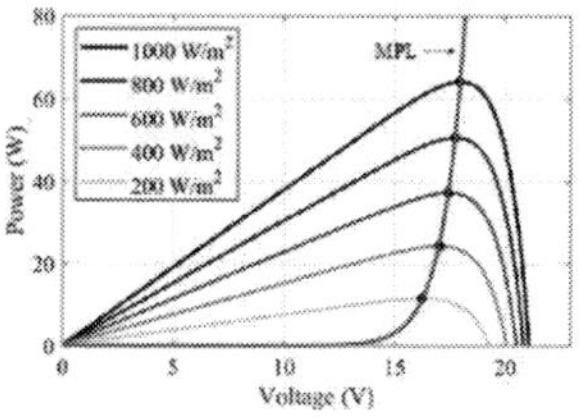

< Fig. 1. *P*-*V* curves and MPL >

$$P_{mpp} = V_{mpp} I_{mpp} = \frac{I_0}{V_t a} V_{mpp}^2 \exp\left(\frac{V_{mpp}}{V_t a}\right) \quad \cdots (1)$$

- P_{mpp} : Power at the MPP
- V_{mpp} : Voltage at the MPP
- I_0 : Saturation current
- V_t : Thermal voltage
- a : Diode ideality constant

- ❖ Operating principle of proposed MPPT method
  - The proposed method regulates P_g instead of v_{pv}
  - The reference of P_g (P_g*) is set to MPL in Eq. (1)
  - To avoid the overcurrent of PV system, P_g* is limited by the rated power
  - Then, the operating point of PV array converges to MPP by Eq. (2)

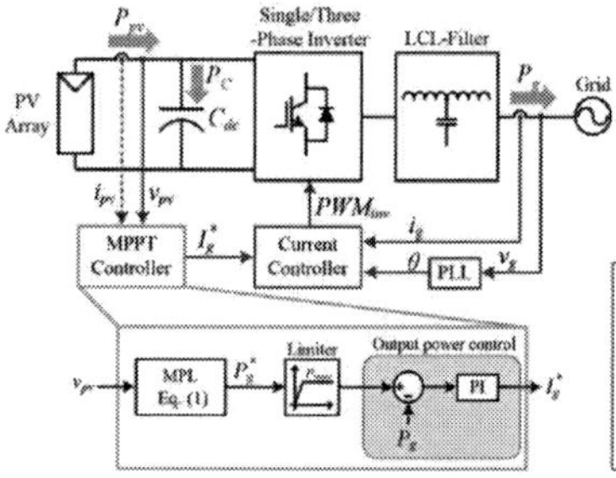

$$P_C = C_{dc} v_{pv} \frac{dv_{pv}}{dt} = P_{pv} - P_g \quad \cdots (2)$$

- P_C: Power flowing into the capacitor
- C_{dc}: DC-link capacitance
- v_{pv}: PV array voltage
- P_{pv}: PV array power
- P_g: Power flowing into the grid

< Fig. 2. Single-stage PV system and MPPT controller >

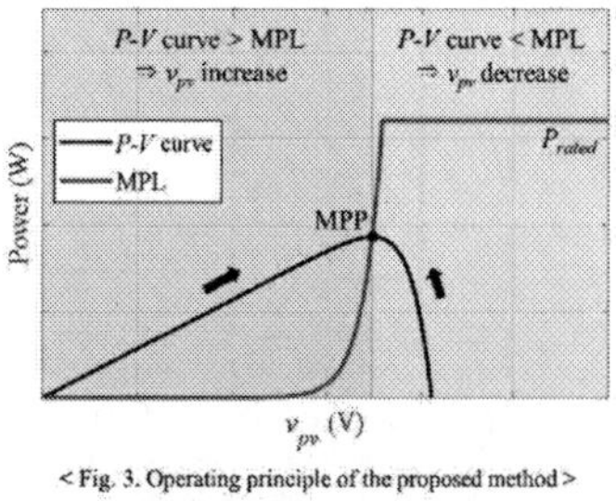

< Fig. 3. Operating principle of the proposed method >

III. Simulation Results

- ❖ Simulation conditions
  - The performance of the proposed MPPT method is compared to the conventional P&O and VSSINC methods
  - The test is conducted under irradiance 1000 W/m² and temperature 25 ℃
  - The rise time (τ_{rise}) is defined as the time for P_{pv} to reach 90% of the available maximum power (P_{max})

< Table 1. Parameters of the PV system >

Parameter	Symbol	Value
PV array rated power	P_{rated}	10 kW
PV array MPP voltage	V_{mpp}	467 V
PV array MPP current	I_{mpp}	21.5 A
PV array open-circuit voltage	V_{oc}	548 V
PV array short-circuit current	I_{sc}	22.8 A
DC-link capacitor	C_{dc}	4.2 mF
LCL-filter	L_c, C_f, L_g	1 mH; 3.3 μF; 0.57 mH
Switching frequency	f_{sw}	10 kHz
Grid nominal voltage	V_g	190 V_{rms}
Grid nominal frequency	f_g	60 Hz

- ❖ Case Studies
  - ***Case I*** : Initial operating point at the left hand side of MPP
  - ***Case II*** : Initial operating point at the right hand side of MPP

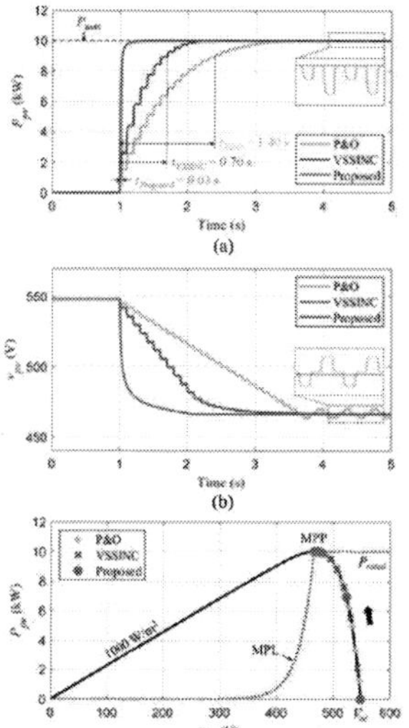

< Fig. 4. Simulation results for *Case I*. (a) P_{pv}. (b) v_{pv}. (c) P_{pv}-v_{pv} locus >

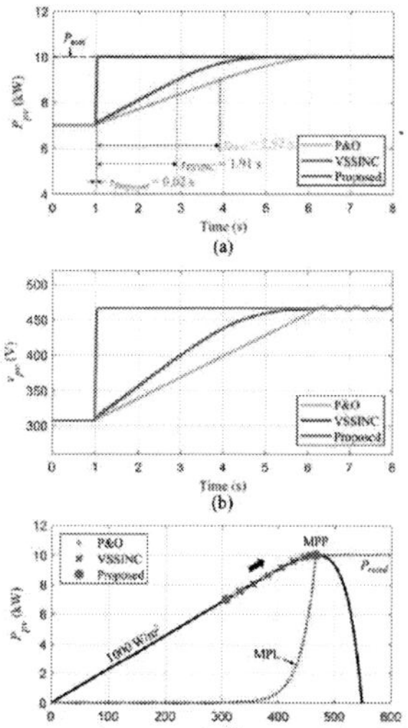

< Fig. 5. Simulation results for *Case II*. (a) P_{pv}. (b) v_{pv}. (c) P_{pv}-v_{pv} locus >

IV. Conclusion

- ❖ This study proposes the efficient MPPT method for PV systems that uses output power control
- ❖ The proposed method can rapidly tracking the MPP while avoiding the oscillations around the MPP

Acknowledgement

❖ This work was supported by Korea Institute of Energy Technology Evaluation and Planning(KETEP) grant funded by the Korea government(MOTIE)(RS-2023-00233148, Development of grid-forming topology and inverter core technology for grid access to distributed energy resources)

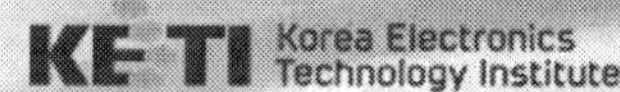

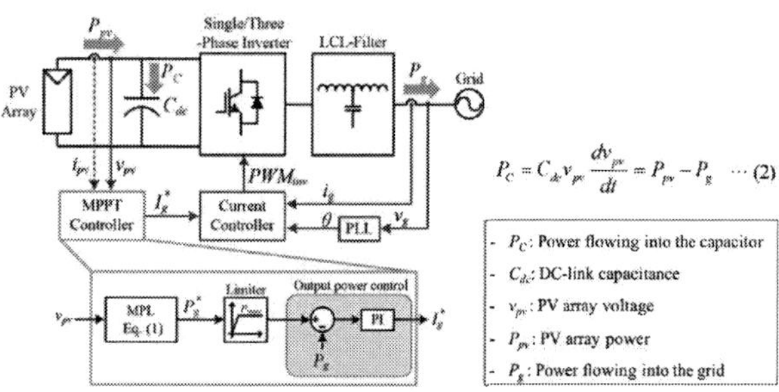

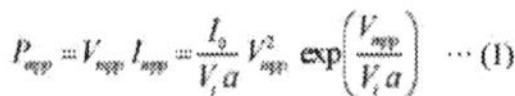

MODELLING, IMPLEMENTATION AND VALIDATION OF SOLAR TRACKING ALGORITHMS IN HORIZONTAL SINGLE AXIS TRACKERS

Nuria López, Mathis Pasquier, Nicholas Riedel-Lyngskær, Peter B. Poulsen and Sergiu V. Spataru
Technical University of Denmark (DTU), Department of Electrical and Photonics Engineering
Roskilde, Sjælland, 4000, Denmark

ABSTRACT: The increasing adoption of Horizontal Single-Axis Tracker (HSAT) systems in utility-scale solar farms has driven interest in tracking algorithms that optimize captured solar insolation. HSAT tracking algorithms calculate the optimal tracker angle to maximize incident solar irradiance at any given moment. However, many proposed algorithms lack experimental validation due to practical constraints and the proprietary nature of commercial HSAT controllers, and existing studies often neglect real-system implementation challenges. This work investigates the implementation of widely used tracking algorithms in HSAT systems, analyzing both simulated and measured plane-of-array (POA) irradiance and DC power production. A real-time HSAT model is proposed, incorporating tracker dynamics, including motor response time, rotational speed, and delays, as well as energy consumption. The model enables a realistic evaluation of tracker behavior and energy performance, highlighting discrepancies between idealized simulations and field measurements.

1 INTRODUCTION

New utility-scale PV plants are increasingly being equipped with trackers to maximize energy production, and the adoption of bifacial PV modules is also rising rapidly [1]. Trackers are devices designed to orient solar panels toward the optimal position of the sun, thus maximizing energy production. There are two main types of solar trackers: Single-Axis Trackers (SAT), which provide one degree of freedom, and Dual-Axis Trackers, which offer two degrees of freedom for greater adaptability to the sun's movement [2]. Single-axis trackers can have their axis of rotation oriented horizontally or at an incline. This study focuses on Horizontal Single-Axis Tracking (HSAT), where the axis of rotation is typically aligned along a north–south direction [3].

HSAT systems use motors and gear trains for precise movements. The optimal tracker tilt angle at any point in time is determined by a tracking algorithm, typically *Astronomical Tracking*, which minimizes the angle of incidence (AOI) between the solar panels and the sun's direct beam to maximize plane-of-array (POA) irradiance [4]. However, this method does not account for diffuse irradiance, which can be significant on cloudy days. Alternative algorithms, such as *Brute Force Search* and the *CENER Model*, attempt to maximize diffuse irradiance [5,6]. Most tracker manufacturers also have their own diffuse tracking algorithms, but these are proprietary.

Building on this context, the proposed HSAT model enables a direct comparison between real-field tracker performance and the predictions of implemented tracking algorithms, highlighting dynamic behaviors that are not fully captured by conventional models. By incorporating tracker dynamics, energy consumption, and additional measured parameters, the complete HSAT model provides more realistic simulations of tracker operation. This enhanced framework allows for improved evaluation of tracking strategies and their associated energy gains, supporting the development of more efficient and robust tracking algorithms for utility-scale solar plants.

2 OBJECTIVES

The primary objective of this work is to characterize the real operation of an HSAT and to develop a comprehensive HSAT model that goes beyond traditional energy production simulations by explicitly accounting for tracker dynamics and energy consumption. The model captures key operational characteristics such as motor response time, movement delays, and rotational speed, as well as the electrical energy required for tracking. This allows for a more realistic representation of the physical behavior of the tracker and its associated energy demands, and can be used to optimized new tracker designs and control.

Building on this model, the study aims to create a testing platform for the real-time implementation and evaluation of different tracking algorithms under real operating conditions. The platform integrates the HSAT model with field measurements from a full-scale PV tracker system, enabling side-by-side benchmarking of standard Astronomical Tracking against alternative diffuse tracking algorithms proposed in the literature.

A key goal is to validate the HSAT model and the testing platform by comparing the simulated results with sensor-based field measurements of irradiance, power output and tracker energy consumption. This comparison helps identify discrepancies between expected and actual performance, quantifies losses not captured by idealized models, and provides a robust framework for optimizing tracking algorithms under varying weather and operating conditions.

3 METHODOLOGY

Figure 1 illustrates the main inputs and outputs of the HSAT model following the *Astronomical Tracking* algorithm. The model had already been implemented; however, the tracker dynamics had not yet been included. During this study, these dynamics were analyzed and incorporated into the model, as shown in the red box labeled Tracker Control Unit (TCU).
The main outputs of the model are the optimal tracking angle θalgo in this case following the *Astronomical Tracking* algorithm, the front and rear plane of array irradiance *GPOA* and *RPOA* and the energy produced by the tracker (PDC).

The model was developed based on and validated at the Risø PV plant, previously described [7], which is equipped with eight Soltec SF7 HSATs, 295 Wp monofacial and bifacial module, and retrofitted with custom TCU's. Each HSAT operates with an independent TCU, as shown in Figure 2 allowing for side-by-side control and operation. The target angle is calculated through Python, and the command is transmitted from the central Network Control Unit (NCU) to each TCU. The TCU, an electronic device, applies voltage to the motor to rotate the tracker accordingly.

10.4229/EUPVSEC2025/4DV.4.26

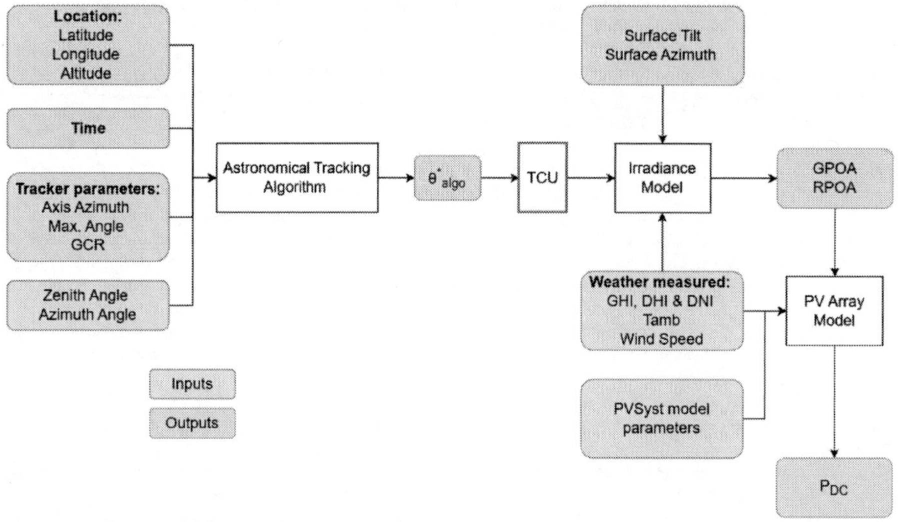

Figure 1:HSAT model following the Astronomical Tracking algorithm.

The solar irradiance components (DNI, DHI, GHI) used by the diffused tracking algorithm, are measured by a meteorological station located 250 m from the PV plant.

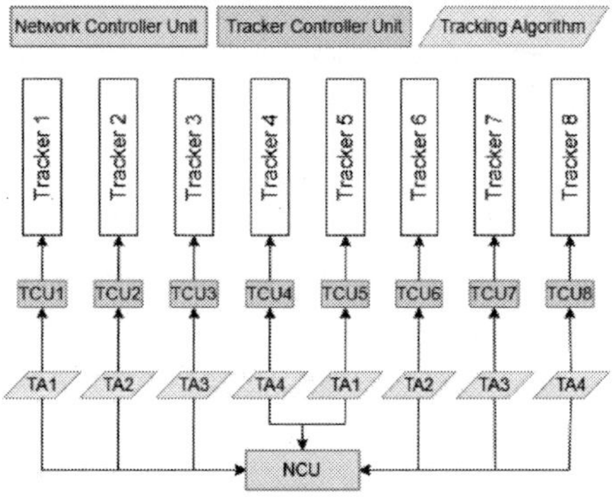

Figure 2: Overview of Trackers, TCUs, and Central NCU in Risø.

To measure and evaluate the actual captured insolation versus the model-simulated values, we deployed a few front plane-of-array (GPOA) sensors and one rear irradiance (RPOA) sensor on selected trackers during the summer of 2024, as illustrated in Figure 3.

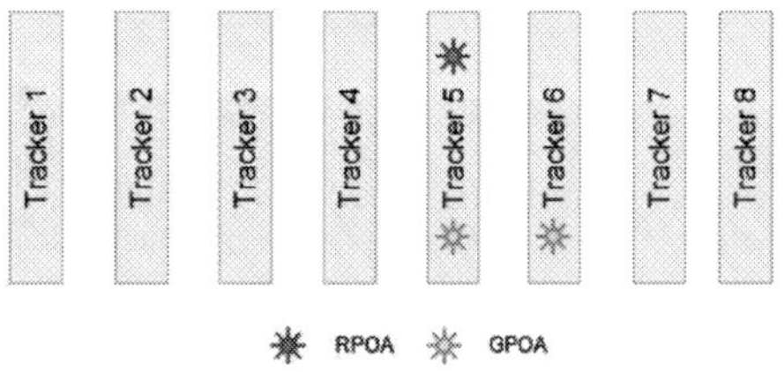

Figure 3: Placement of front and rear plane of array sensors on the HSATs.

Reference cells were used for this purpose, and the analysis focused on data from Tracker 5 and Tracker 6, which had fully operational sensors. Although additional reference cells have been installed on the remaining trackers, insufficient data were available for inclusion in this study.

3.1 Characterization of the trackers

The tracker dynamics were analyzed by evaluating the current and target angles in detail. On the 23rd of July, between 09:00 and 11:00, the tracker angles setpoints (denoted Target Angles) were manually controlled though the NCU/TCU to intentionally induce movements and observe the system's response, which was measured tracker tilt angle (denoted Current Angle) every 10 seconds, as shown in Figure 4. Two key performance indicators were defined: response time and delay.

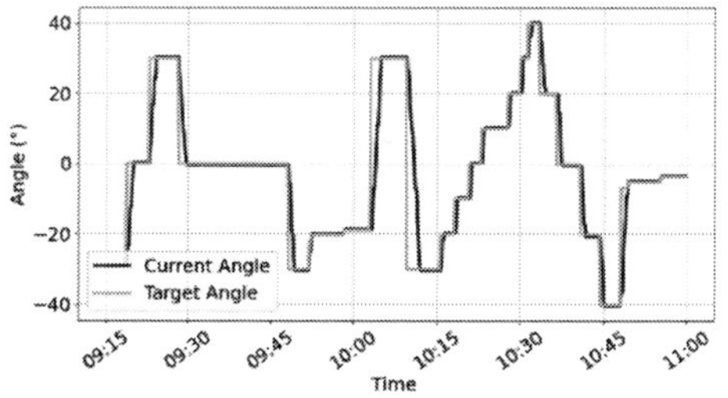

Figure 4: Current and Target Angles of Tracker 5 on the 23rd of July.

The **response time** represents the duration required for the motor to rotate the tracker from its initial position to the new target position, measured in seconds.
Because this time depends on the angular displacement, it was normalized by the response time and expressed as the Rotational Speed (RS), defined in Equation 1, in °/s.

$$RS = \frac{TargetAngle - CurrentAngle}{ResponseTime} \quad (1)$$

10.4229/EUPVSEC2025/4DV.4.26

The **delay** quantifies the time lag between the instant the target angle changes t_o and the moment the current angle starts deviating by more than a small threshold t_{delay}.
It is calculated in seconds, as shown in Equation 2, and represents the tracker's dead time before motion begins.

$$Delay = t_{delay} - t_o \tag{2}$$

The tracker energy consumption ($E_{tracker}$) in Wh is calculated from the motor runtime (t_{motor}), motor voltage (V_{motor}), and motor current (I_{motor}), shown in Equation 3. The motor operates at a constant drive voltage of 24 V for all trackers.

$$E_{tracker} = V_{motor} \cdot I_{motor} \cdot \frac{t_{motor}}{3600} \tag{3}$$

The tracker behavior was analyzed by comparing motor current with wind speed and direction to identify any correlations with wind conditions.

3.2 Improved HSAT Model and Validation

The HSAT model employs several *pvlib* implementations [8] to simulate system performance.
Optimal tracking angles are calculated using *pvlib.tracking.singleaxis*, module temperature is estimated with *pvlib.temperature*, and module electrical performance is modeled using *pvlib.pvsystem*. Plane-of-array (POA) irradiance, including bifacial effects, is obtained using *pvlib.bifacial.infinite_sheds*. Meteorological inputs (irradiance, temperature, and wind data) are sourced from on-site measurements retrieved from a dedicated database.
The DC power of each tracker (P_{DC}) is calculated using Equation 4 in W, where $P^{max}_{DC,module}$represents the module's maximum DC power as a function of module parameters, cell temperature, and total effective irradiance. Since each tracker consists of four strings, the module-level output is scaled by a factor of four to obtain the total tracker DC production.

$$P_{DC} = P^{max}_{DC,module} \cdot N_{mod,series} \cdot 4 \tag{4}$$

4 RESULTS

4.1 Rotational Speed and Delays

Figure 5 shows the rotational speed values recorded on 23rd July for Tracker 5, with an average rotational speed of 0.33°/s.
The speed remained relatively stable throughout the measurement period, indicating predictable and consistent tracker response behavior. This average rotational speed was used as a key input in the HSAT model to realistically simulate the dynamic behavior of the trackers, including response times and delays.

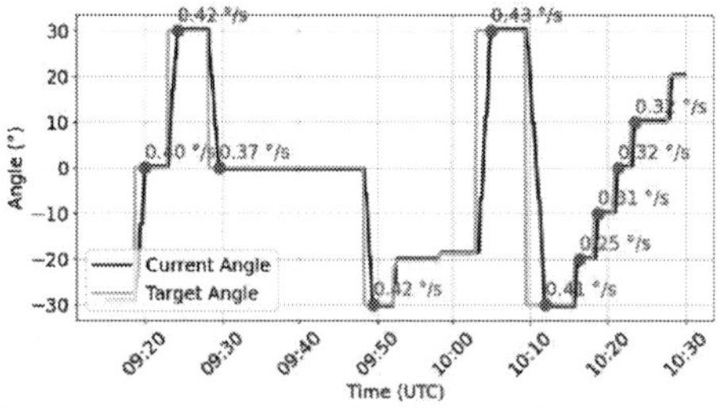

Figure 5: Rotational speeds, current angles, and target angles over the two-hour period.

Incorporating measured rotational speed ensures that the model closely reflects actual motor performance and tracker movements, providing a more accurate evaluation of tracking strategies. To better understand the distribution of tracker movements, Figure 6 presents a histogram of the recorded rotational speeds, showing that most values fall between 0.3 and 0.5 °/s highlighting the frequency at which different speeds occurred during the measurement period.

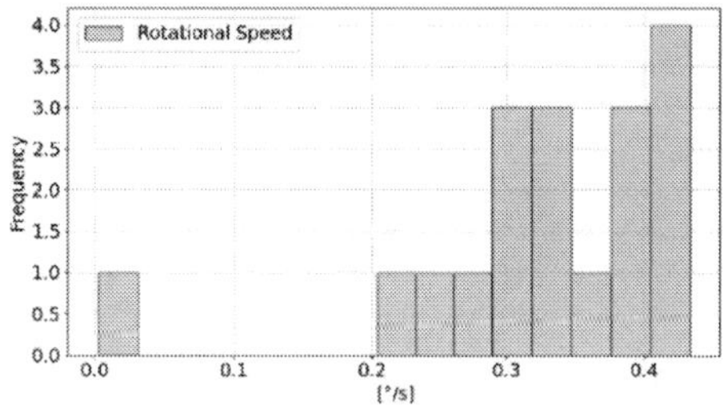

Figure 6: Histogram showing the distribution of rotational speeds measured during the two-hour period.

Figure 7 shows the distribution of the measured delays, with most values around 10 s, corresponding to the data timestamp resolution. The same values were observed for both trackers, even though the frequency is not the same. These delay measurements highlight the typical time lag between a target angle change and the actual tracker response, which should be considered in future HSAT model implementations to improve simulation realism.

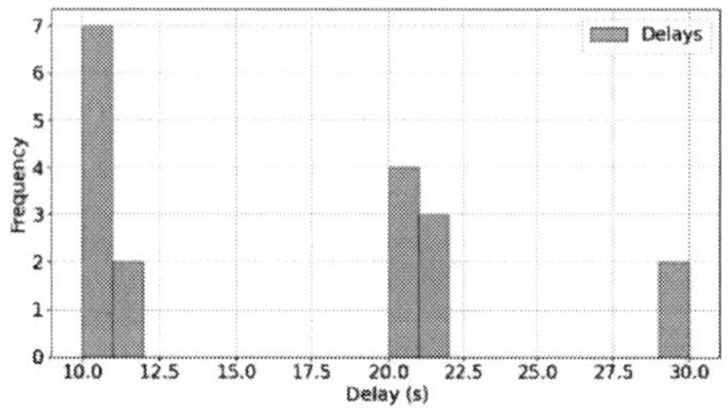

Figure 7: Histogram showing the distribution of delays during the two-hour period.

4.2 Energy consumption of the trackers

For characterizing the energy consumption of the trackers, the tracker average motor current was measured and reported by the TCUs, from different months and random days within the same month were analyzed. The consumption was also evaluated as a function of wind speed and wind direction, but no correlations were observed. Overall, the energy consumption of the trackers follows the same pattern across all analyzed days, as shown in Figure 8.

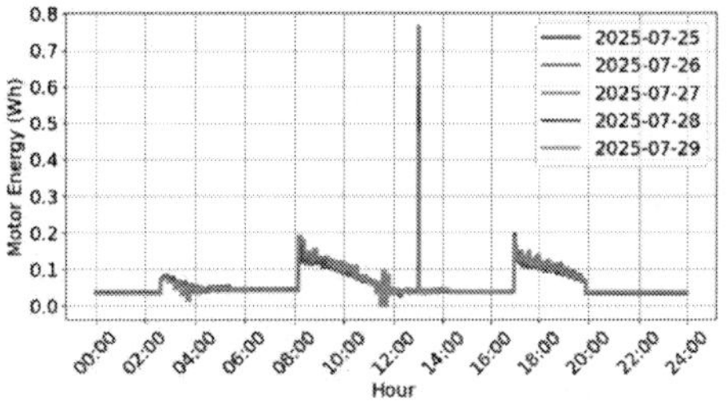

Figure 8: Motor energy consumption for four consecutive days in July.

4.3 Improved HSAT Model and Validation

To ensure the validity of comparing simulated values from the HSAT model with actual field data, the simulated tracking angles must match the measured angles. Figure 9 shows the measured angles of Tracker 5, which align with the simulated angles, as both use the *Astronomical Tracking* algorithm.

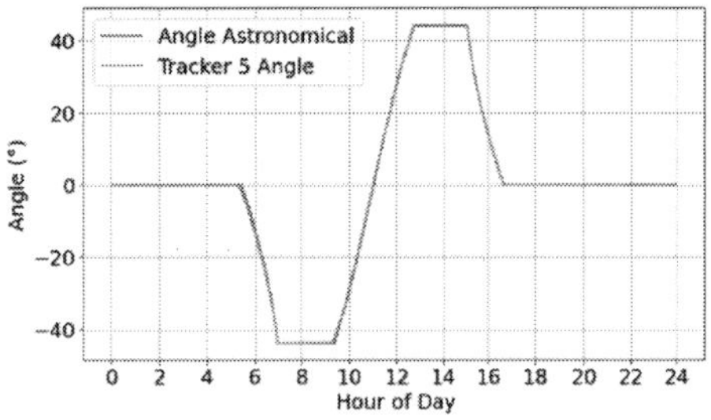

Figure 9: Simulated Astronomical Tracking Angles (blue line) and Actual Tracking Angles for Tracker 5 (orange line).

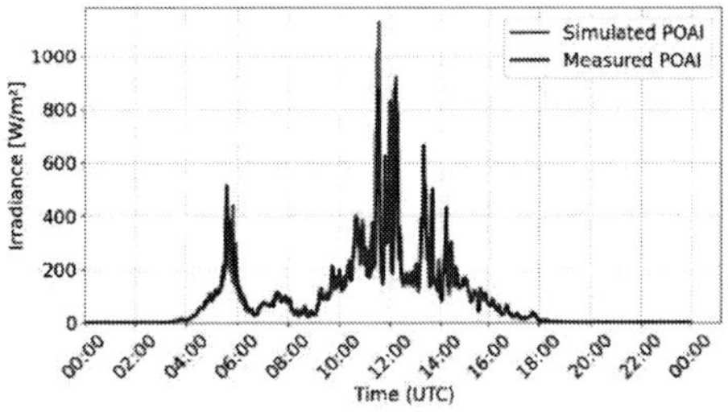

Figure 10: Comparison of simulated and measured POA irradiance for August 3rd.

The HSAT model was used to simulate POA irradiance (GPOA), which was then compared with field measurements. Figure 10 presents the results for a representative day. Similar trends were observed across several other days, with measured values consistently lower than simulated ones. This discrepancy reflects the idealized assumptions in the model, including the use of an isotropic sky model and the lack of operational losses such as shading, soiling, temperature effects, and electrical inefficiencies.

The DC production of the trackers was also simulated using the HSAT model and compared with measured production data. The simulated production was slightly higher than the measured values, largely due to the overestimation of POA irradiance and the absence of real-world tracker losses in the model. These results, shown in Figure 11, highlight the importance of incorporating operational losses and realistic irradiance assumptions to improve the accuracy of performance predictions.

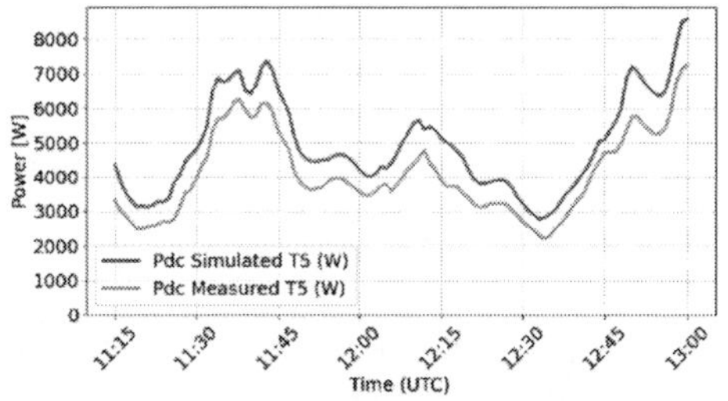

Figure 11: Comparison of simulated and measured tracker production over the two-hour period on July 23rd.

5. CONCLUSIONS AND FUTURE WORK

The analysis of the tracker system revealed several important insights. First, the energy consumption of the trackers remains largely constant across different days. This indicates that the motor operation and drive system behave consistently under normal conditionsand no significant influence from environmental factors such as wind speed or direction was observed.

Second, the POA irradiance simulated using the HSAT model was consistently slightly higher than the field measurements. This discrepancy arises from the modelling assumptions inherent in the simulation, such as the use of an isotropic sky model, idealized tracker alignment, and neglect of localized losses. These simplifications lead to a modest overestimation of the irradiance incident on the modules.

Finally, the DC energy production of the trackers was found to be lower than the simulated estimates. This reduction is primarily attributed to real-world effects not fully captured by the model, including inter-row shading, soiling of the module surfaces, elevated cell temperatures, and electrical losses within the module and system. These factors collectively reduce the effective energy output of the trackers compared to the idealized simulation, highlighting the importance of incorporating real-world performance factors when evaluating PV system behavior.

As future work, the HSAT model should be enhanced to incorporate all measured delays and rotational speeds, enabling a more realistic simulation of tracker dynamics and energy performance. Additionally, alternative diffuse tracking algorithms should be implemented and evaluated, using *Astronomical Tracking* as a reference. While Astronomical Tracking provides optimal performance under clear-sky conditions, it does not account for diffuse irradiance, which can lead to suboptimal energy capture on cloudy days. Diffuse tracking strategies, by contrast, incorporate real-time weather data such as solar irradiance, cloud cover, and atmospheric conditions to dynamically adjust the tracker angle for maximum energy yield. Ultimately, a full HSAT testing platform will be developed, which was the initial goal of this work.

[1] IEA PVPS, "Trends in Photovoltaic Applications 2024," International Energy Agency Photovoltaic Power Systems Programme (IEA PVPS), 2024. [Online]. Available: https://iea-pvps.org/wp-content/uploads/2024/10/IEA-PVPS-Task-1-Trends-Report-2024.pdf

[2] Solar Photovoltaic Energy, "Technology roadmap," Technical Report, IEA, 2014.

[3] M. S. A. Emon and M. Hasanuzzaman, "Solar thermal energy conversion," in *Technologies for Solar Thermal Energy*, Section 2.9.5: Single axis tracking, ScienceDirect, 2022.

[4] W. F. Marion and A. P. Dobos, "Rotation angle for the optimum tracking of one-axis trackers," Tech. Rep., National Renewable Energy Lab. (NREL), Golden, CO, USA, 2013.

[5] I. Muñoz, A. Guinda, G. Olivares, S. Díaz, A. M. Gracia-Amillo, and L. Casajús, "Evaluation of Horizontal Single-Axis Solar Tracker Algorithms in Terms of Energy Production and Operational Performance," *Solar RRL*, vol. 8, no. 1, p. 2300507, 2024.

[6] K. R. McIntosh, M. D. Abbott, and B. A. Sudbury, "The optimal tilt angle of monofacial and bifacial modules on single-axis trackers," *IEEE Journal of Photovoltaics*, vol. 12, no. 1, pp. 397–405, 2021.

[7] N. Riedel, A. C. de Aguilar Protti, M. L. Jakobsen, H. C. Pedersen, S. Thorsteinsson, P. B. Poulsen, A. A. Santamaria Lancia, G. A. dos Reis Benatto, G. Demurtas, F. Arrighi, D. Berrian, J. Libal, D. Barnard, and J. Vedde, "The Outdoor Bifacial Test Facility at Technical University of Denmark," in *Bifacial PV Workshop, BifiPV 2019*, 16–17 Sep. 2019, 2019.

[8] The pvlib Community, "pvlib Python User Guide," Accessed: Jan. 28, 2025. [Online]. Available: https://pvlib-python.readthedocs.io/en/stable/user_guide/index.html

10.4229/EUPVSEC2025/4DV.4.26

2025 EU-PVSEC, Bilbao

4DV.4.27

42nd European Photovoltaic Solar Energy Conference and Exhibition

Instrumentation to Evaluate Single-Axis Tracker Operation and Irradiance Transposition Calculations

Anton Driesse
PV Performance Labs, Freiburg, Germany
anton.driesse@pvperformancelabs.com

Maddalena Bruno
Fraunhofer ISE, Freiburg, Germany
maddalena.bruno@ise.fraunhofer.de

Reach out to us if you want to try this at your test site

Two Challenges

Clouds don't just reduce the available solar energy, they make everything much more **complicated**! It is hard to predict where and when they will appear, but even when they're already there, it's hard to know where to turn—if you're a single-axis tracker, that is.

To maximize power output, a single-axis tracker should in general be positioned so that its PV modules receive the **highest irradiance**. There are practical constraints why sometimes another position should be used, but the knowledge of the optimal position is still crucial.

In single-axis tracker systems, an algorithm decides what the position should be, and the manufacturer of the system usually claims it has the **best algorithm**.

The challenges:

1. How to **evaluate** their algorithms?
2. How to make your algorithm **even better**?

One Solution **

The POA-scan makes one rotation in only 2 seconds, while taking 400 POA irradiance measurements in all directions.

1. The maximum G_{POA} gives the optimal rotation angle, and the G_{POA} value measured at the PV tracker angle tells you how close a PV tracker controller came to that maximum.
2. PV tracker controllers use transposition models to estimate the irradiance at various angles and then identify the optimal one. Each POA-scan rotation provides unprecedented 400 validation points for fine-tuning transposition models.

Sample Tracking Algorithm Observations *

Using measured G_{POA} at all tracker angles, we can evaluate three tracking options

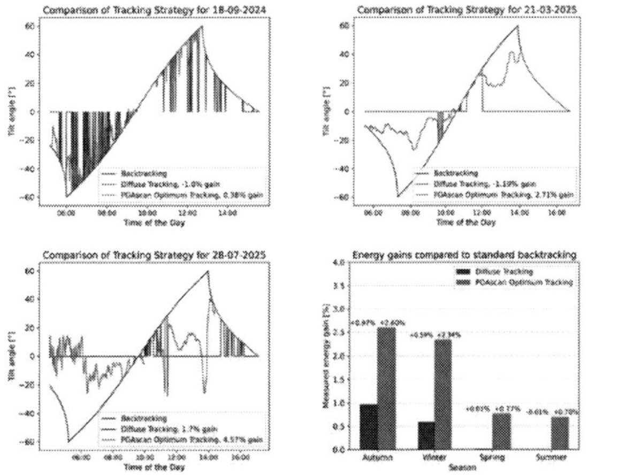

Compared to standard backtracking, moving to a horizontal position when the diffuse ratio (DHI/GHI) is high (blue) produces more energy in autumn and winter. But the POA-scan optimal angle measurements (red) show that further gains are possible with smarter algorithms during all four seasons (near Freiburg, Germany).

Sample Transposition Model Observations

A sunny afternoon, following a cloudy morning: sun azimuth 270 °, elevation 31°

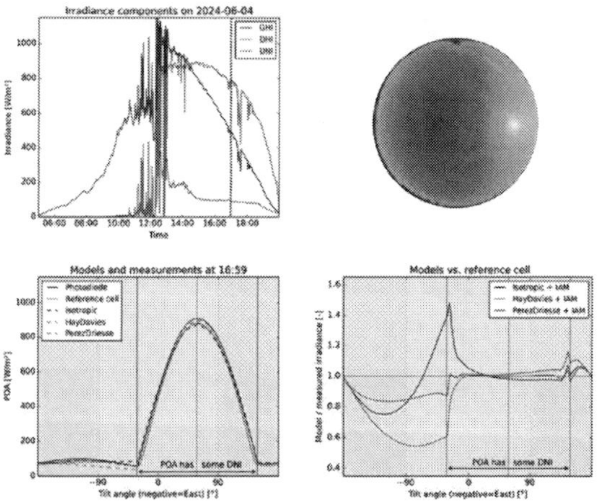

All three models under-predict tilted irradiance at the optimal tracker tilt angle. Over the full range of tilt angles, the Perez-Driesse model achieves the smallest relative error most of the time by capturing both horizon and circumsolar brightening of the non-isotropic sky, as seen in the sky image (at Fraunhofer ISE).

* Results from the DeepTrack Project ©Fraunhofer ISE.
M. Bruno et al., *"Field Insights on Optimizing Diffuse Light Tracking Performance"*, IEA PVPS Task 13 Bifacial Workshop, Rome, 2024. [Online]. Pat. pending EP25173791.1

** The POA-scan instrument is designed and built by PV Performance Labs. PV Performance Labs provides a range of services in support of PV system R&D and operations including planning, measurements, simulation and analysis.

920452-001

42nd European Photovoltaic Solar Energy Conference and Exhibition

This presentation was selected by the Sc. Committee of the EU PVSEC 2025 for submission of a full paper to one of the EU PVSEC's collaborating peer-reviewed journals.

PERFORMANCE ASSESSMENT OF VEHICLE-INTEGRATED PHOTOVOLTAIC MODULE DESIGNS UNDER DYNAMIC SHADING CONDITIONS

R. Moruno, L. San José, R. Núñez, R. Herrero, I. Antón
Instituto de Energía Solar-Universidad Politécnica de Madrid (IES-UPM), Madrid, Spain
Av. Complutense, 30, Moncloa - Aravaca, 28040 Madrid

ABSTRACT: This paper investigates the impact of module architecture, cell orientation and interconnection on the performance of vehicle-integrated photovoltaic (VIPV) systems under dynamic shading. High-frequency image acquisition and electrical simulations were conducted using realistic shading scenarios recorded from a vehicle's trajectory. Eight configurations, combining cell orientation, interconnection topology, and module partitioning, were analyzed through IV curve simulations and P&O-based MPPT evaluation. Results show that total cross-tied (TCT) connections consistently outperform series connections, while mini-modules offer marginal yield improvements. The energy losses due to different reasons were classified and quantified, finding mismatch losses between 12 and 8%. Findings highlight that shading patterns are evenly distributed across the PV surface, leading to similar MPPT behavior across modules, with high algorithm efficiencies at reasonable perturbation periods (95% with 100 ms perturbation periods). These insights provide a foundation for optimizing VIPV system design under realistic operating conditions.
Keywords: Vehicle-integrated photovoltaics, dynamic shading, MPPT, PV architecture, energy yield.

1 INTRODUCTION

Vehicle-integrated photovoltaics (VIPV) can significantly extend the driving range of electric vehicles, reduce grid demand, and lower operating costs. Unlike conventional PV modules, however, VIPV must operate under highly dynamic and irregular shading conditions. Previous research [1] has shown that increasing the number of bypass diodes and dividing the PV area into smaller modules with individual converters [2] may mitigate shading effects. Nevertheless, it remains unclear how these strategies perform under realistic dynamic vehicle shading.

To address this gap, a high-frequency image acquisition setup and electrical simulation framework were implemented, making use of a methodology previously developed and validated by researchers from IES-UPM [3], who also collaborated on this work. This work intends to evaluate different module configurations, focusing on energy yield and an ideal converter's MPPT behavior under realistic driving conditions.

2 METHODS

2.1 High-frequency image acquisition

The experimental setup employed a high-speed camera (240 fps) fixed to a vehicle roof (**Fig. 1**), capturing shading patterns projected on a calibrated white surface during a 17-minute urban route in Madrid (**Fig. 2**). Image frames were geometrically corrected, binarized using the Otsu method [4], and divided into grids representing different PV module architectures (**Fig. 3**). The proportion of shaded and illuminated pixels in each grid element was used to derive cell-level irradiance. Diffuse light was considered to affect the entire surface uniformly for simplification. A 0.75 Sky View Factor was assumed, as it represents a reasonable value for moderately building-dense urban areas [5]. The direct beam was considered to affect only the illuminated areas, affected by the cosine of the angle of incidence and the Incidence Angle Modifier (IAM). IAM was calculated using the physical model indicated in [6].

Figure 1: Image-acquisition setup. The camera is fixed to a mast attached by a suction cup to the vehicle's roof. The white plank was magnetized.

The video was recorded on a location in the proximity of the Moncloa Campus (Madrid, Spain) on a spring morning (23rd May 2025, 9:58 am) with a Global Horizontal Irradiance (GHI) of 360 W/m^2, with a duration of 17:20 minutes. The ambient temperature was 11°C, based on sensors located in the vicinity. The vehicle took a number of turns and directions, without a dominant orientation during the route.

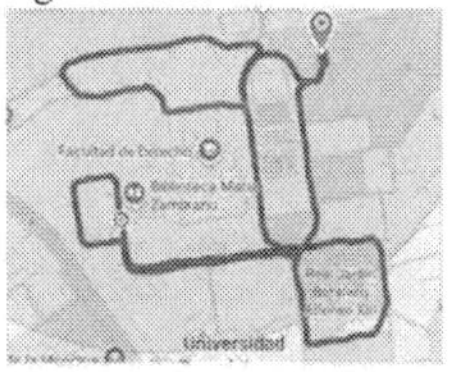

Figure 2: Trajectory of the recorded route, with an extension of approximately 5.6 km.

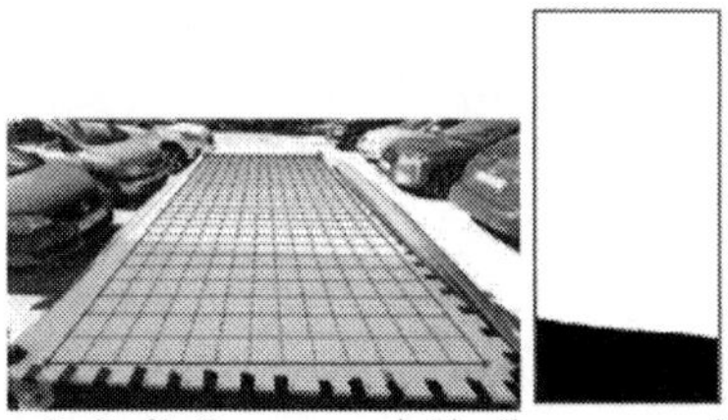

Figure 3: (Left). Frame recorded by the camera, with the grid representing the simulated module. (Right) Black and white binarization of the extracted area, after geometric transformations.

2.2 Electrical simulation

Eight configurations were simulated, combining:

10.4229/EUPVSEC2025/4EO.2.1

- **Cell orientation:** vertical / horizontal
- **Interconnection:** series / TCT
- **Layout:** single large module (SLM) / six mini-modules (6MM)

A total of 216 shingled silicon cells (141 W, 0.8 m²) were modeled. Illumination matrices were fed into a PVMismatch-based [7] script to generate IV curves (240 per second). The number of bypass diodes of the global PV surface is provided on **Table I.**

Table I: Number of bypass diodes

	SLM	6MM
Series-H	6	12
Series-V	12	36
TCT-H	6	12
TCT-V	12	36

2.3 MPPT simulation

A perturb and observe (P&O) [8] MPPT algorithm was applied on every case, sweeping across a range of the algorithm parameters: perturbation size and period. The basic operating principle of this algorithm consists on applying a variation (perturbation size) in the tension that polarizes the module with a certain periodicity (perturbation period). It incorporates a memory so it can measure the power variation between iterations, deciding the direction of the next perturbation (positive or negative) to try to increment power output. Efficiency trends were evaluated to assess the expected performance of realistic converters compared to idealized conditions.

3 RESULTS

3.1 Energy Yield

Shadows were found to reduce energy yield (EY) by 21% and SVF by 3%. Due to the changing angle of incidence, IAM losses amount to 7.5%, whereas curvature and temperature had nearly negligible effects, almost cancelling each other (-0.29% for curvature and +0.14% for temperature). Thermal effects actually improved energy yield thanks to the low ambient temperature and strong convective conditions on a moving vehicle. The maximum EY that a module could reach in those conditions was 68%. The gap between 68% and the actual EY corresponds to mismatch losses (**Fig. 4**). The EY on each case can be found on **Table II**.

Table II: Energy Yield of every configuration

	SLM EY [%]	6MM EY [%]
Series-H	56.1%	55.8%
Series-V	56.8%	57.3%
TCT-H	59.9%	60.1%
TCT-V	60.0%	60.4%

These results indicate that TCT interconnections outperform series connections by 3–4% in terms of EY. Vertical series configuration performs better than horizontal series due to the higher number of bypass diodes. The partition of the surface into Mini-modules showed only marginal improvements (<1%) in maximum available energy but maintained voltages below the 60 V safety threshold for EV auxiliary devices [9].

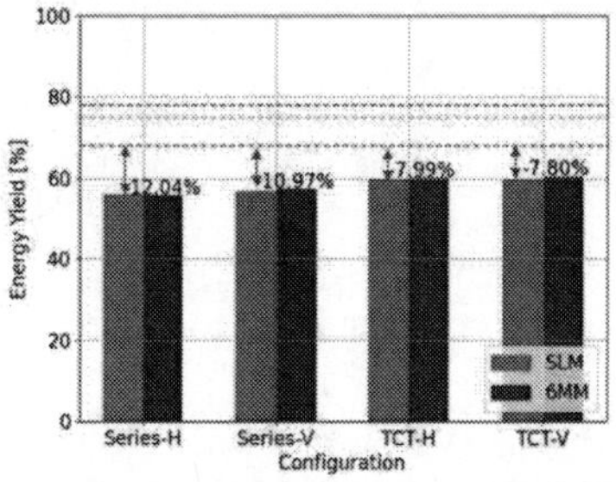

Figure 4: Maximum possible energy yield of each case of study, prior to the DC-DC converter. They are expressed as a percentage of the EY of the same module under the same GHI, which amounts to 13.68 Wh. The percentages indicate the mismatch losses of the average of both layouts (SLM and 6MM). The green dashed line represents the shading losses (-21%), the yellow one represents the SVF losses (-3%) and the turquoise one represents the IAM losses (-7.5%).

3.2 Shading Distribution

Shading was uniformly distributed across the PV surface, with an average shading factor of ~24% (**Fig. 5**). Slight deviations on MM5 and MM6 were caused by systematic artifacts (e.g., temporary camera shading).

The uniform shading can be explained by moving shadows: the same shadow moves from the front part of the PV surface to the back, as the vehicle moves forwards. This way, the same shadow covers frontal and rear modules, but at different instants, leaving similar IV curves across the Mini-Modules with a certain delay, depending on the vehicle's movement.

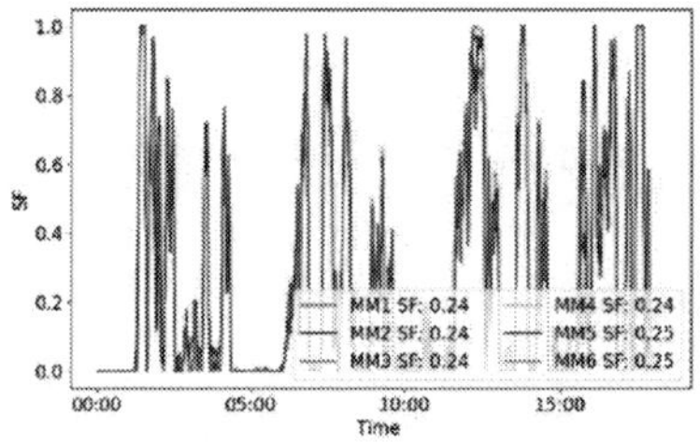

Figure 5: Temporal evolution of SF over each of the 6 Mini-Modules during the entire route. The legend indicates the average value on each case.

3.3 MPPT algorithm evaluation

Here, the P&O algorithm is evaluated on each collection of simulated IV curves. Several simulations are conducted on each case, each one with a certain value of step size and perturbation period. This analysis intends to explore efficiency trends related to the module's design parameters to provide an insight on the performance of a regular MPPT algorithm's efficiency.

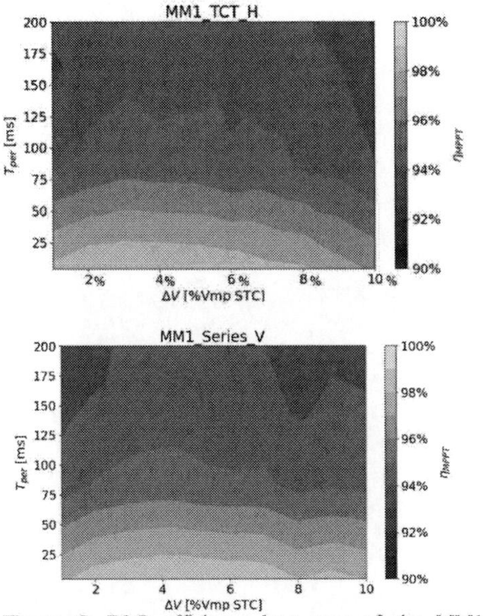

Figure 6: P&O efficiency heat map of the MM1 submodule. The X axis represents the perturbation size, expressed as a percentage of the maximum power voltage in Standard Test Conditions V_{MPSTC}. The Y axis represents the perturbation period. **Top)** TCT connection and horizontal cell orientation. **Bottom)** Series connection and Vertical cell orientation.

As they share similar shading profiles, according to the results described on the previous section, the performance of sub-modules with the same cell orientation and interconnection are almost identical. So, the findings obtained on one of them can be extrapolated to the rest.
98-99% efficiencies can be achieved when the perturbation period matches the timelapse between frames (**Fig. 6**), as that is the temporal resolution limit for these simulations. However, when more realistic perturbation periods are considered (100 ms) [10], these efficiencies drop down to 95-96%. It must be noted that this method does consider an ideal converter, without incorporating the dynamic effects due to the inner electronic components (capacitors, inductors, etc.), thus significantly impacting settling times.

TCT cell interconnection seems to be slightly more affected by perturbation size and series connection by perturbation period. This can be explained by the IV curves' shape. As TCT IV curves are steeper (higher currents, lower voltages), a similar perturbation produces larger current variations, affecting power extraction.
Similar behavior is found in the Single Large Module configuration (**Fig. 7**), reaching matching efficiency trends with the MM case. This means that the efficiency of the MPPT algorithm is almost independent of the layout, but strongly dependent on algorithm parameters (step size and perturbation period).

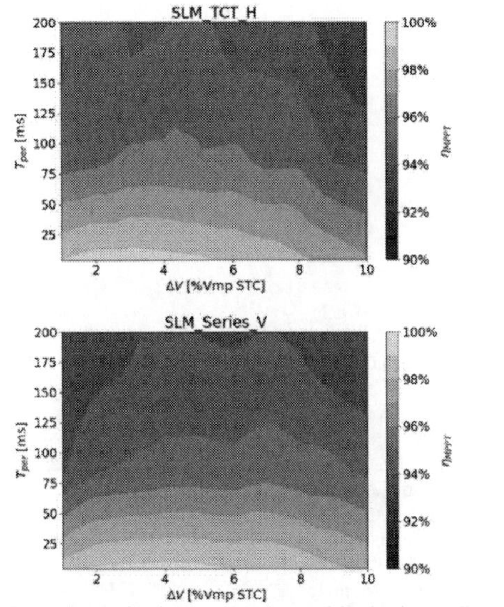

Figure 7: P&O efficiency heat map of the SLM case. The X axis represents the perturbation size, expressed as a percentage of V_{MPSTC}. The Y axis represents the perturbation period. **Top)** TCT connection and horizontal cell orientation. **Bottom)** Series connection and Vertical cell orientation.

4 CONCLUSIONS

This study demonstrates that mini-module partitioning offers limited energy yield benefits but may be valuable for compliance with EV auxiliary voltage limits. TCT connections consistently deliver better performance compared to series connections, although potential ohmic losses should be considered. The vertical cell disposition is preferable to the horizontal one in the series connection case, as it allows implementing a higher number of bypass diodes, improving performance under partial shading. However, with TCT connection, energy yield is almost unaffected by cell orientation, as current can flow more freely.

Average shading factor over the module, even with a low sun elevation (~20°) reached an average value of 24%. Combined with angle of incidence losses, it explains the low energy output compared to unshaded conditions. In addition, these shadows presented a uniform distribution over the studied surface. The moving shadows induce similar IV curves on the different sub-modules, although with a temporal delay.

This similarity in shading profiles upon each sub-module explains the matching MPPT algorithm efficiency trends among them. While in all cases high efficiencies can be obtained with low perturbation periods, equal to the recorded video fps rate, the algorithm still retains around 95-96% efficiency with higher, more realistic periods. The single large module behaves in a similar way, which combined with the similar energy yield, indicates that the potential gains of using the module partition strategy with various DC/DC converters are reduced.
All in all, further research including accurate thermal behavior models, realistic converter behavior and different MPPT algorithms might result in alternate findings.

10.4229/EUPVSEC2025/4EO.2.1

5 ACKNOWLEDGEMENTS

The authors gratefully acknowledge the DETEC-PV project, Grant PID2021-128853OB-I00, funded by MCIN/AEI/10.13039/501100011033 and "ERDF A way of making Europe."

R. Moruno thanks his grant "PID2021-128853OB-I00" funded by MCIN/AEI/ 10.13039/501100011033 and by "ERDF A way of making Europe".

6 REFERENCES

[1] J. Macías, R. Herrero, R. Núñez, and I. Antón, "On the effect of cell interconnection in Vehicle Integrated Photovoltaics: modelling energy under different scenarios," in *2021 IEEE 48th Photovoltaic Specialists Conference (PVSC)*, June 2021, pp. 1336–1339. doi: 10.1109/PVSC43889.2021.9518935.

[2] "Submodule Integrated Distributed Maximum Power Point Tracking for Solar Photovoltaic Applications | IEEE Journals & Magazine | IEEE Xplore." Accessed: Sept. 01, 2025. [Online]. Available: https://ieeexplore.ieee.org/abstract/document/6339082

[3] L. San José, R. Moruno, R. Núñez, R. Herrero, J. Macías, and I. Antón, "Performance evaluation of MPPT algorithm of VIPV systems in realistic urban routes using image processing," *Solar Energy Materials and Solar Cells*, vol. 276, p. 113061, Oct. 2024, doi: 10.1016/j.solmat.2024.113061.

[4] P. Puneet and N. Garg, "Binarization Techniques used for Grey Scale Images," *IJCA*, vol. 71, no. 1, pp. 8–11, June 2013, doi: 10.5120/12320-8533.

[5] K. Araki, Y. Ota, A. Nagaoka, and K. Nishioka, "3D Solar Irradiance Model for Non-Uniform Shading Environments Using Shading (Aperture) Matrix Enhanced by Local Coordinate System," *Energies*, vol. 16, no. 11, p. 4414, May 2023, doi: 10.3390/en16114414.

[6] W. De Soto, S. A. Klein, and W. A. Beckman, "Improvement and validation of a model for photovoltaic array performance," *Solar Energy*, vol. 80, no. 1, pp. 78–88, Jan. 2006, doi: 10.1016/j.solener.2005.06.010.

[7] "Quantification of System-Level Mismatch Losses using PVMismatch | IEEE Conference Publication | IEEE Xplore." Accessed: June 30, 2025. [Online]. Available: https://ieeexplore.ieee.org/abstract/document/8548107

[8] V. A. Martinez Lopez, U. Žindžiūtė, H. Ziar, M. Zeman, and O. Isabella, "Study on the Effect of Irradiance Variability on the Efficiency of the Perturb-and-Observe Maximum Power Point Tracking Algorithm," *Energies*, vol. 15, no. 20, p. 7562, Oct. 2022, doi: 10.3390/en15207562.

[9] "ISO 6469-3:2021," ISO. Accessed: July 28, 2025. [Online]. Available: https://www.iso.org/es/contents/data/standard/08/17/81746.html

[10] Y. Levron and D. Shmilovitz, "Maximum Power Point Tracking Employing Sliding Mode Control," *IEEE Trans. Circuits Syst. I*, vol. 60, no. 3, pp. 724–732, Mar. 2013, doi: 10.1109/TCSI.2012.2215760.

EUPVSEC 2025

Vehicle Integrated Photovoltaics module architecture optimization under dynamic shading

Ricardo Moruno Lobato, R. Núñez, R. Herrero, L. San José, and I. Antón

Instituto de Energía Solar, Universidad Politécnica de Madrid, Madrid (SPAIN)

INSTITUTO
DE ENERGÍA
SOLAR

POLITÉCNICA

Motivation

INSTITUTO DE ENERGÍA SOLAR

VIPV: Urban Dynamic Shading

Impact of shading on VIPV

1. Module's architecture mismatch losses
2. Shading distribution
3. DC/DC converters efficiency

POLITÉCNICA

Objectives

INSTITUTO DE ENERGÍA SOLAR

1. Optimize module design parameters
2. Study shading pattern distribution
3. MPPT VIPV parameter tuning

POLITÉCNICA

Methodology

INSTITUTO DE ENERGÍA SOLAR

IV Curves simulations

240 fps

1. RECORD VIDEO

2. SELECT AREA

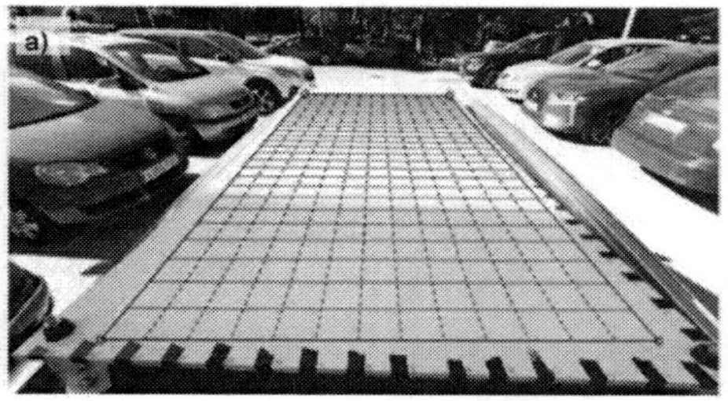

3. IMAGE PROCESSING

4. CONFIGURATION

Layout
- SLM OR 6MM

5. IV CURVE SIMULATION

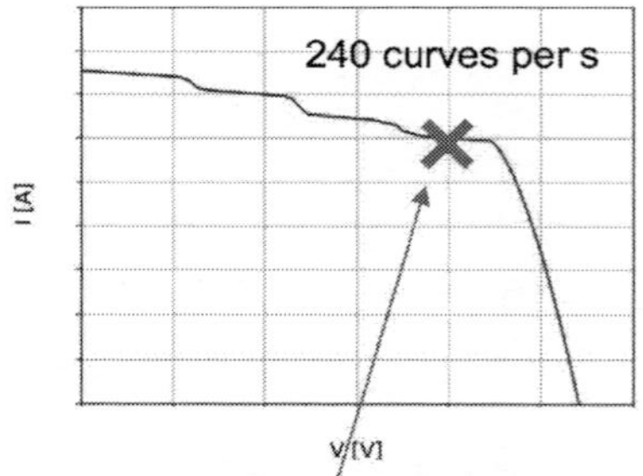

6. SIMULATE MPPT ALGORITHM

[1] L. San José et al. *Solar Energy Materials and Solar Cells,* [276], p. 113061 (2024)

Methodology

INSTITUTO DE ENERGÍA SOLAR

IV Curves simulations

240 fps

1. RECORD VIDEO

2. SELECT AREA

3. IMAGE PROCESSING

4. CONFIGURATION

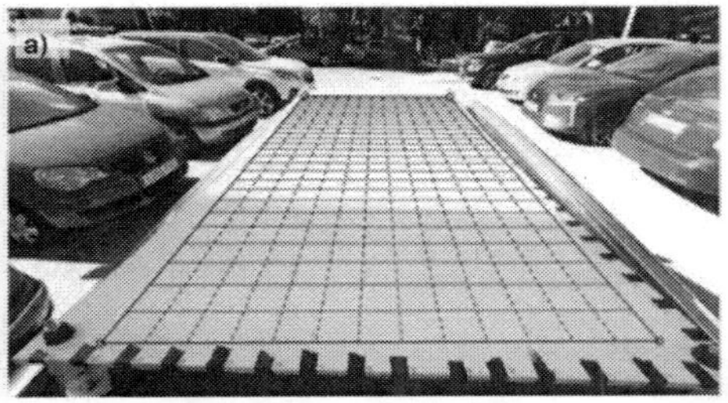

Layout

- SLM OR 6MM

[1] L. San José et al. *Solar Energy Materials and Solar Cells,* [276], p. 113061 (2024)

Methodology

INSTITUTO DE ENERGÍA SOLAR

IV Curves simulations

240 fps

1. RECORD VIDEO
2. SELECT AREA
3. IMAGE PROCESSING
4. CONFIGURATION

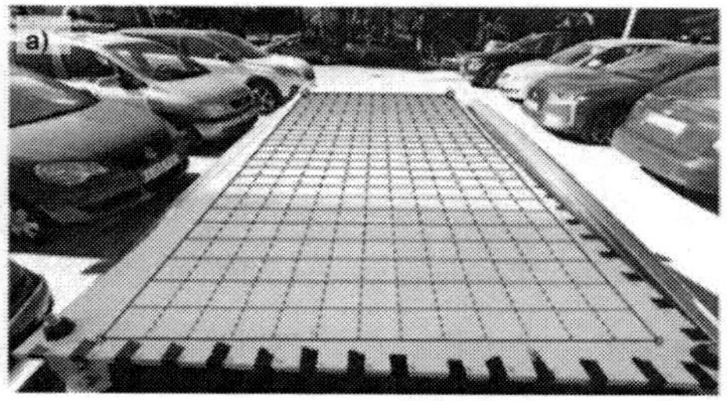

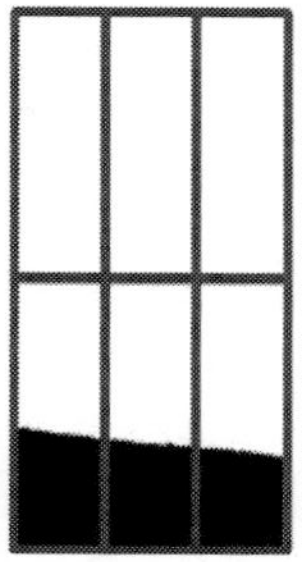

Layout

– SLM OR 6MM

[1] L. San José et al. *Solar Energy Materials and Solar Cells*, [276], p. 113061 (2024)

POLITÉCNICA

Methodology

INSTITUTO DE ENERGÍA SOLAR

IV Curves simulations

240 fps

1. RECORD VIDEO

2. SELECT AREA

3. IMAGE PROCESSING

4. CONFIGURATION

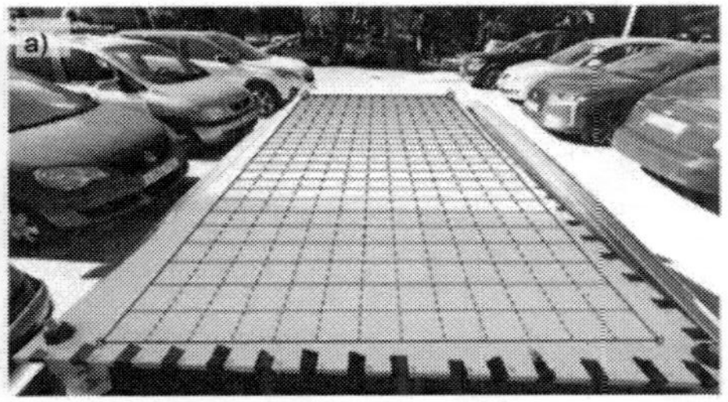

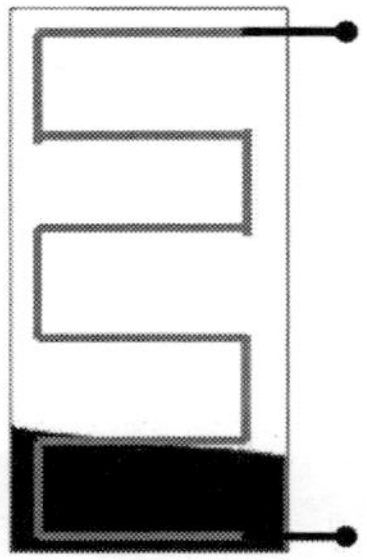

Layout
- SLM OR 6MM

Connection
- Series OR TCT

[1] L. San José et al. *Solar Energy Materials and Solar Cells*, [276], p. 113061 (2024)

Methodology

INSTITUTO DE ENERGÍA SOLAR

IV Curves simulations

240 fps

1. RECORD VIDEO

2. SELECT AREA

3. IMAGE PROCESSING

4. CONFIGURATION

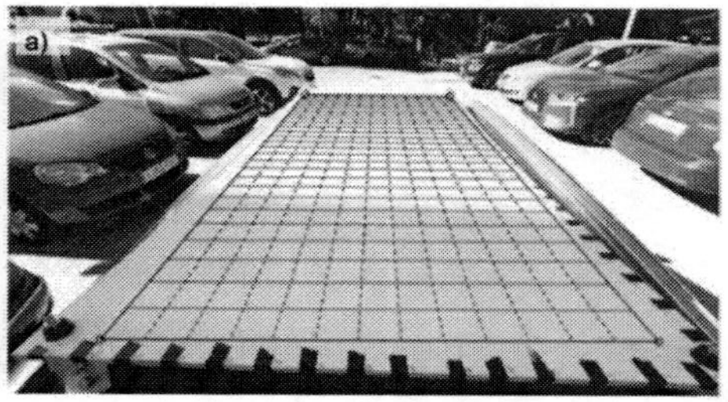

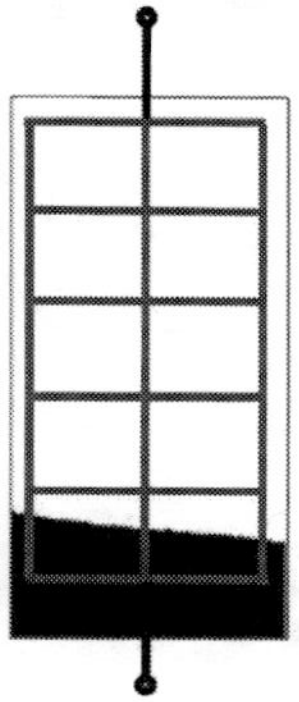

Layout
- SLM OR 6MM

Connection
- Series OR TCT

[1] L. San José et al. *Solar Energy Materials and Solar Cells,* [276], p. 113061 (2024)

Methodology

INSTITUTO DE ENERGÍA SOLAR

IV Curves simulations

240 fps

1. RECORD VIDEO
2. SELECT AREA
3. IMAGE PROCESSING
4. CONFIGURATION

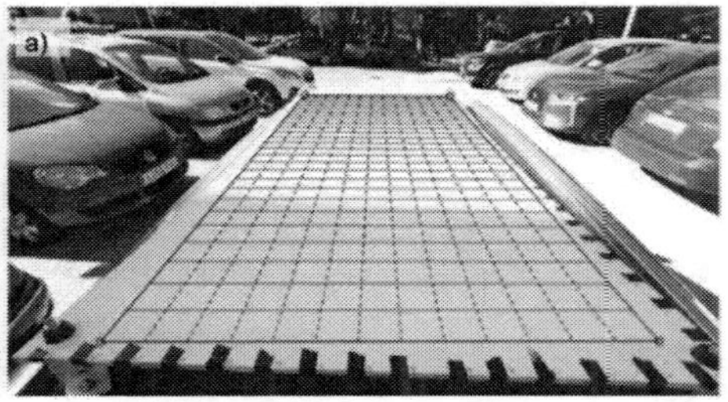

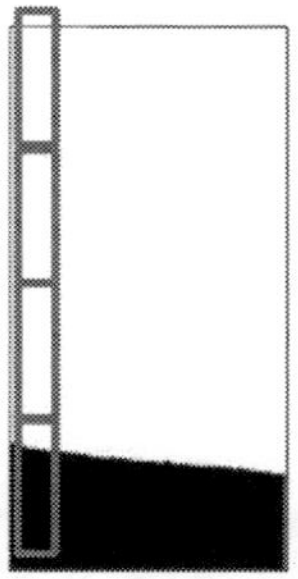

Layout
- SLM OR 6MM

Connection
- Series OR TCT

Cell Orientation
- V OR H

[1] L. San José et al. *Solar Energy Materials and Solar Cells*, [276], p. 113061 (2024)

Methodology

INSTITUTO DE ENERGÍA SOLAR

IV Curves simulations

240 fps

1. RECORD VIDEO
2. SELECT AREA
3. IMAGE PROCESSING
4. CONFIGURATION

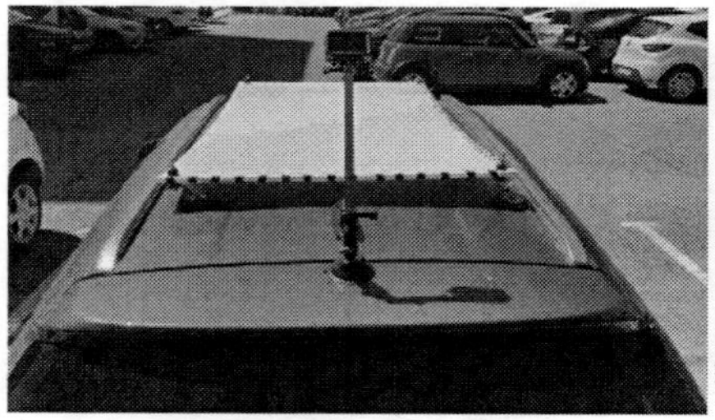

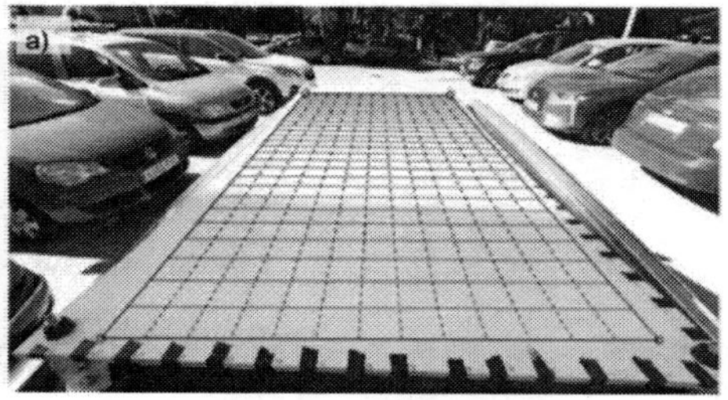

Layout
- SLM OR 6MM

Connection
- Series OR TCT

Cell Orientation
- V OR H

[1] L. San José et al. *Solar Energy Materials and Solar Cells,* [276], p. 113061 (2024)

POLITÉCNICA

Methodology

INSTITUTO DE ENERGÍA SOLAR

IV Curves simulations

240 fps

1. RECORD VIDEO

2. SELECT AREA

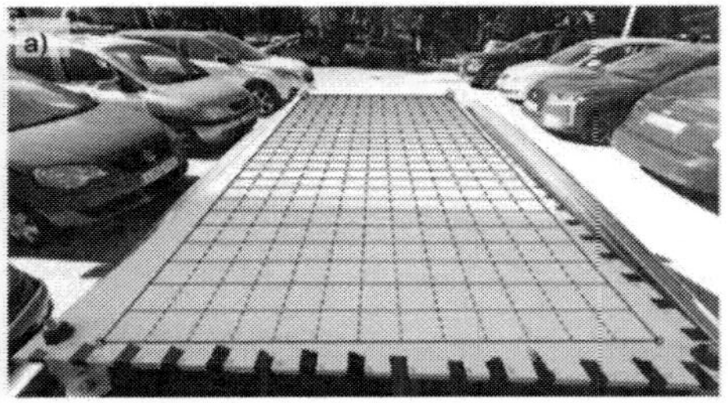

3. IMAGE PROCESSING

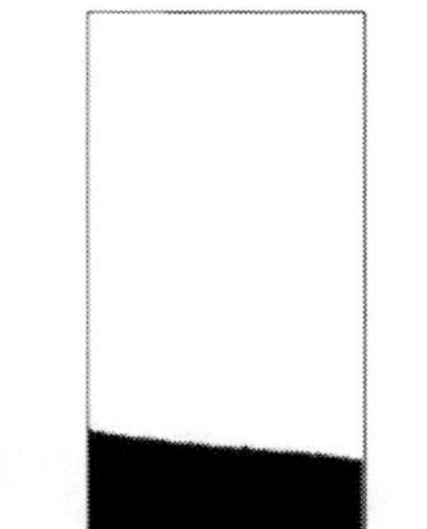

4. CONFIGURATION

Layout
- SLM OR 6MM

Connection
- Series OR TCT

Cell Orientation
- V OR H

5. IV CURVE SIMULATION

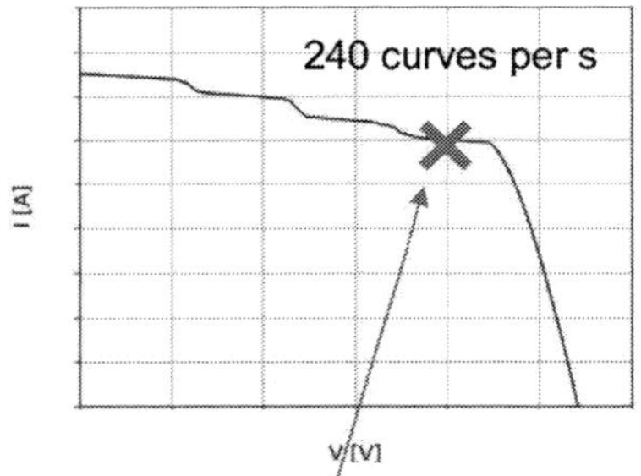

6. SIMULATE MPPT ALGORITHM

[1] L. San José et al. *Solar Energy Materials and Solar Cells*, [276], p. 113061 (2024)

Case of study

INSTITUTO DE ENERGÍA SOLAR

Route

- Extension: **~5.6 km**
- Time: **Spring morning (9:58 am)**
- Duration: **17:20 min**
- Conditions: **Clear sky**
  - **GHI** = 360 W/m^2
  - **Elevation** = 22 °
  - **Azimuth** = 81°

No predominant direction

Average Shading Factor:
24%

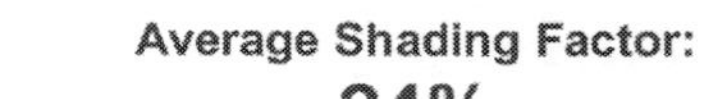

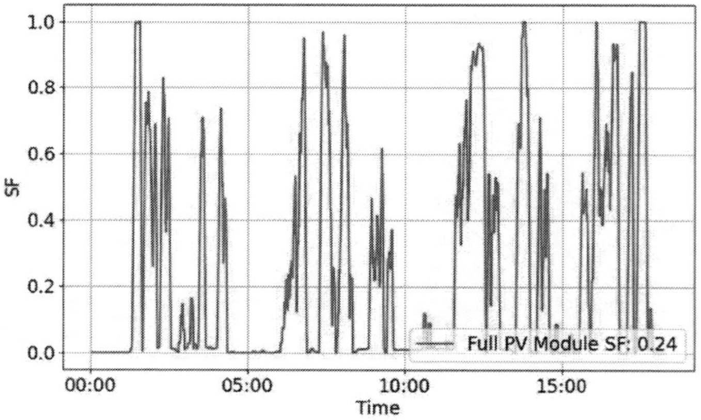

POLITÉCNICA

Case of study

INSTITUTO DE ENERGÍA SOLAR

Module

- PV active surface: **0.8 m²**
- Cells: **216 shingle silicon cells (10.5 x 3.5 cm)**

Layout:
- Single Large Module (SLM)
- 6 Mini Modules (6 MM)

Connection:
- TCT
- Series

Orientation:
- Vertical (V)
- Horizontal (H)

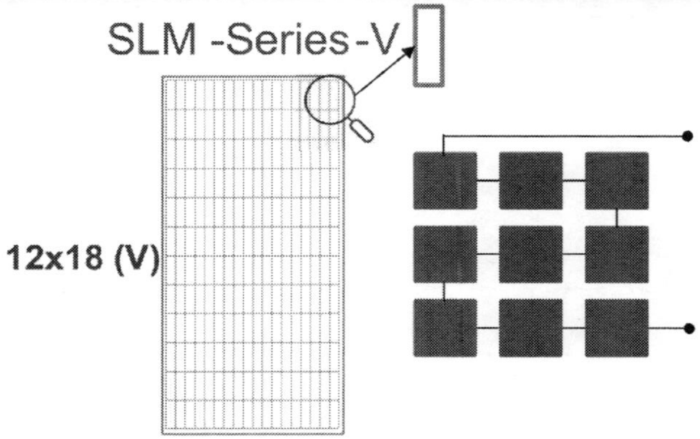

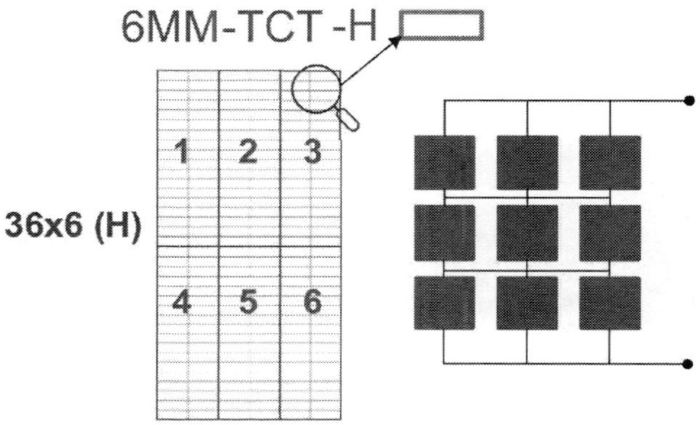

SLM

$P_{MP} = 141$ W

Configuration	Bypass diodes
SLM-Series-V	12
SLM-Series-H	6
SLM-TCT-V	12
SLM-TCT-H	6

6MM

$P_{MP\_MM} = 23.5$ W

$P_{MP\_GLOBAL} = 141$ W

Configuration	Bypass diodes (MM)	Bypass diodes (Global)
6MM-Series-V	6	36
6MM-Series-H	2	12
6MM-TCT-V	6	36
6MM-TCT-H	2	12

POLITÉCNICA

Results: PV System Energy Yield Comparison

INSTITUTO DE ENERGÍA SOLAR

1. Optimize module design parameters

Examine maximum available energy in entire route, **PRIOR TO THE DC/DC CONVERTER**

$$E_{max} = \int P_{MP}\, dt$$

SF: -21%

100% : Unshaded module at GHI= 360 W/m^2

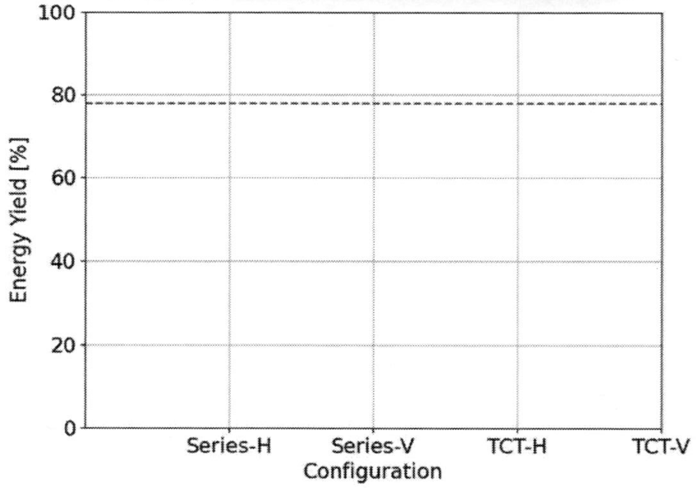

POLITÉCNICA

Results: PV System Energy Yield Comparison

INSTITUTO DE ENERGÍA SOLAR

1. Optimize module design parameters

Examine maximum available energy in entire route, **PRIOR TO THE DC/DC CONVERTER**

$$E_{max} = \int P_{MP}\, dt$$

SF: -21%

SVF: -3%

100% : Unshaded module at GHI= 360 W/m^2

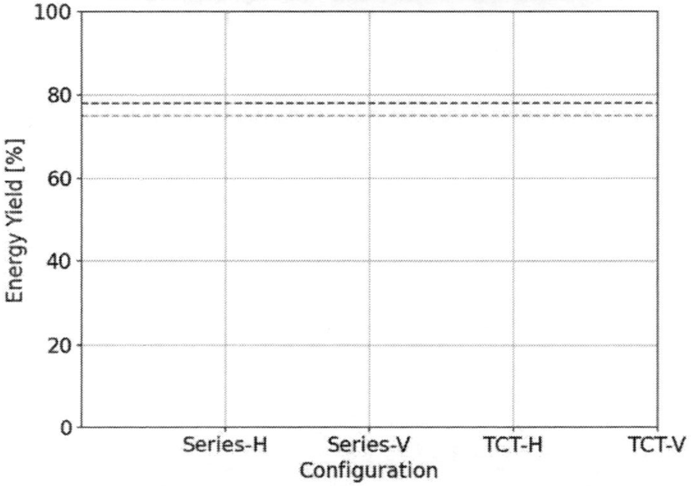

POLITÉCNICA

Results: PV System Energy Yield Comparison

INSTITUTO DE ENERGÍA SOLAR

1. Optimize module design parameters

Examine maximum available energy in entire route, **PRIOR TO THE DC/DC CONVERTER**

$$E_{max} = \int P_{MP}\, dt$$

SF: -21%
SVF: -3%
IAM: -7.5%

100% : Unshaded module at GHI= 360 W/m²

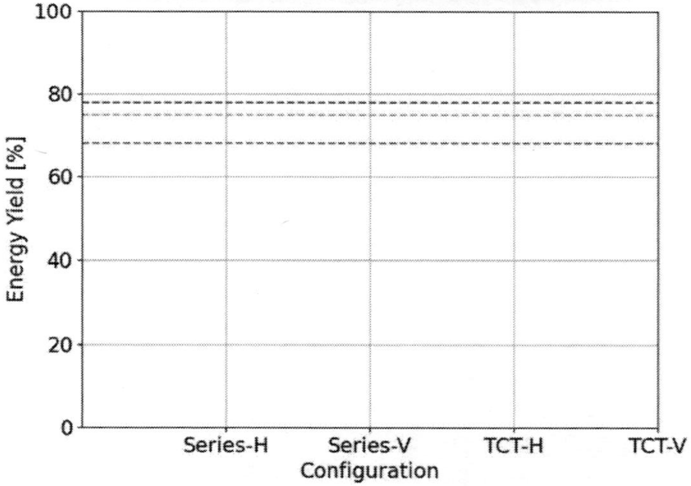

POLITÉCNICA

Results: PV System Energy Yield Comparison

INSTITUTO DE ENERGÍA SOLAR

1. Optimize module design parameters

Examine maximum available energy in entire route, **PRIOR TO THE DC/DC CONVERTER**

$$E_{max} = \int P_{MP}\, dt$$

SF: -21%

SVF: -3%

IAM: -7.5%

Curvature: -0.29%

T:+0.14%

100% : Unshaded module at GHI= 360 W/m²

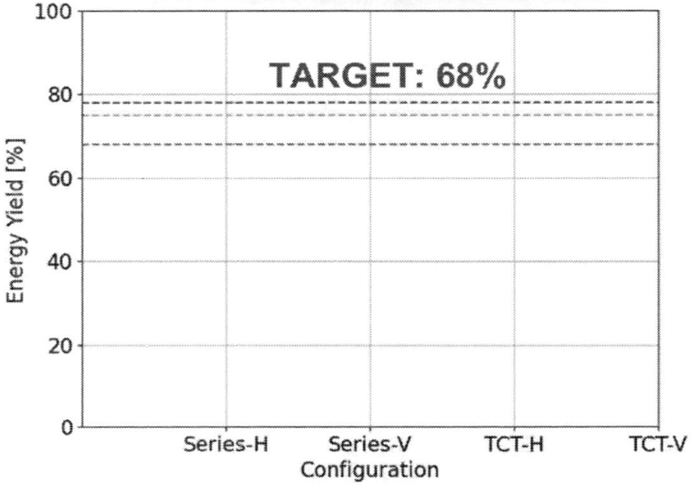

POLITÉCNICA

Results: PV System Energy Yield Comparison

INSTITUTO DE ENERGÍA SOLAR

1. Optimize module design parameters

Examine maximum available energy in entire route, **PRIOR TO THE DC/DC CONVERTER**

$$E_{max} = \int P_{MP}\, dt$$

SF: -21%

SVF: -3%

IAM: -7.5%

Curvature: -0.29%

T:+0.14%

– TCT outperforms series by ~3-4%.

100% : Unshaded module at GHI= 360 W/m^2

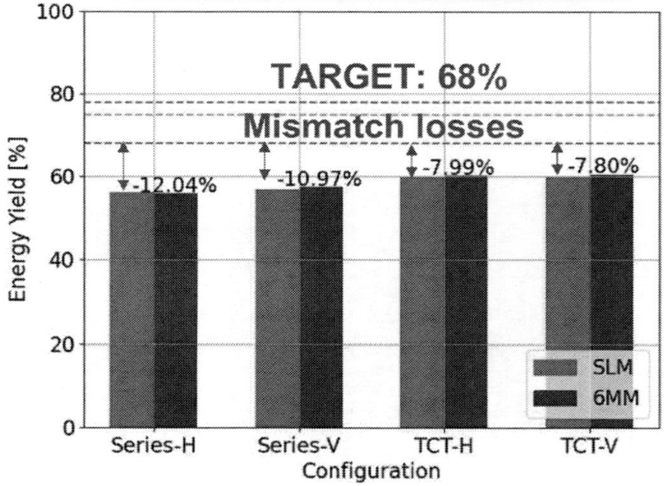

POLITÉCNICA

Results: PV System Energy Yield Comparison

INSTITUTO DE ENERGÍA SOLAR

1. Optimize module design parameters

Examine maximum available energy in entire route, **PRIOR TO THE DC/DC CONVERTER**

$$E_{max} = \int P_{MP}\, dt$$

SF: -21%

SVF: -3%

IAM: -7.5%

Curvature: -0.29%

T:+0.14%

– TCT outperforms series by ~3-4%.

100% : Unshaded module at GHI= 360 W/m²

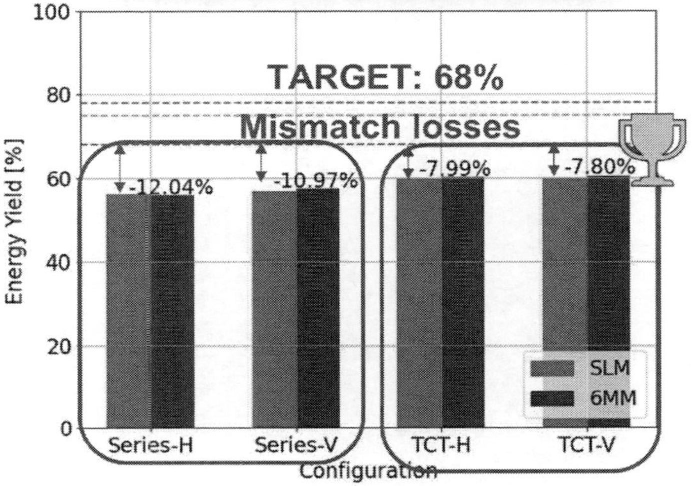

POLITÉCNICA

Results: PV System Energy Yield Comparison

INSTITUTO DE ENERGÍA SOLAR

1. Optimize module design parameters

Examine maximum available energy in entire route, **PRIOR TO THE DC/DC CONVERTER**

$$E_{max} = \int P_{MP}\, dt$$

SF: -21%

SVF: -3%

IAM: -7.5%

Curvature: -0.29%

T:+0.14%

– TCT outperforms series by ~3-4%.

– Series-V outperforms Series-H by ~1%.

100% : Unshaded module at GHI= 360 W/m²

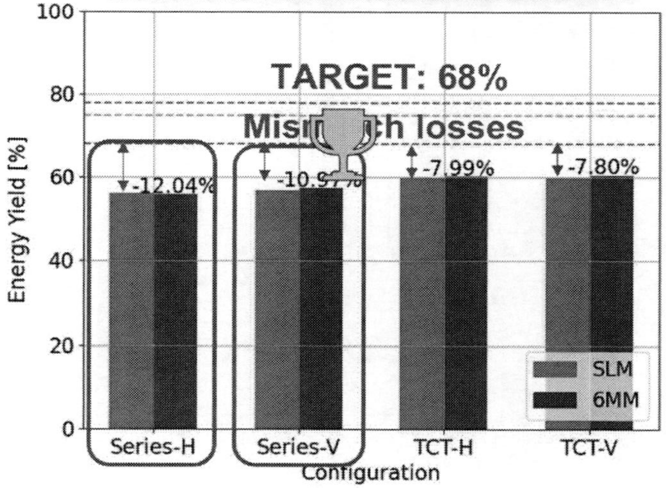

Vertical connection slightly better because of higher number of bypass diodes (long side interconnection)

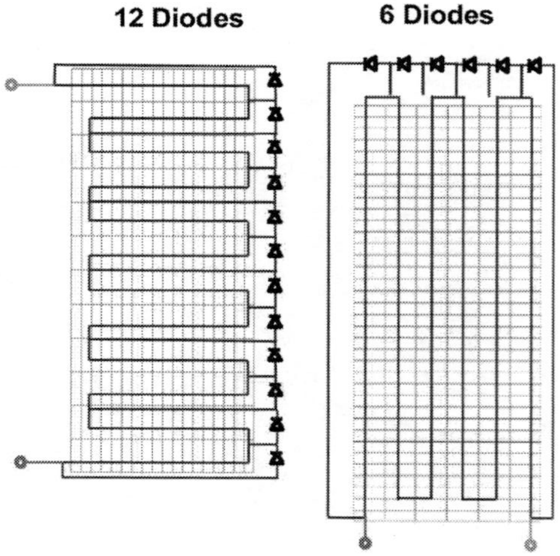

POLITÉCNICA

Results: PV System Energy Yield Comparison

INSTITUTO DE ENERGÍA SOLAR

1. Optimize module design parameters

Examine maximum available energy in entire route, **PRIOR TO THE DC/DC CONVERTER**

$$E_{max} = \int P_{MP}\, dt$$

SF: -21%
SVF: -3%
IAM: -7.5%
Curvature: -0.29%
T:+0.14%

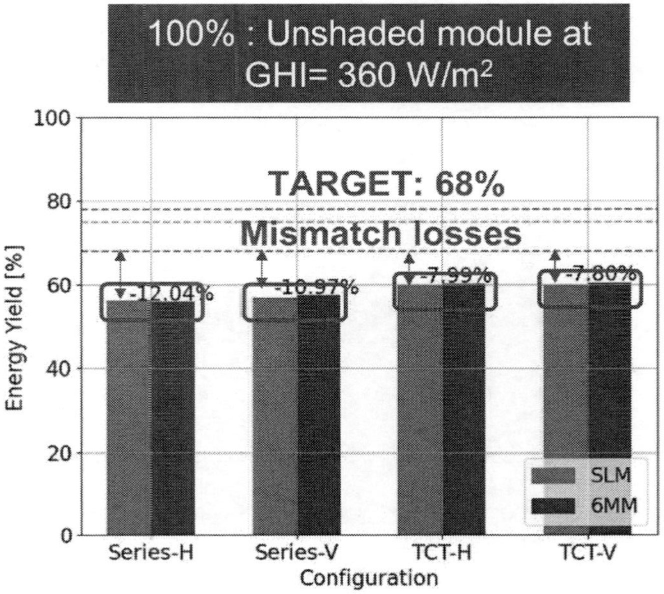

Vertical connection slightly better because of higher number of bypass diodes (long side interconnection)

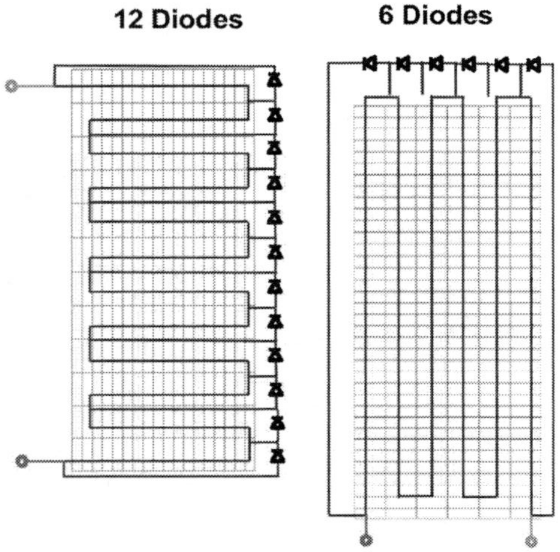

- TCT outperforms series by ~3-4%.
- Series-V outperforms Series-H by ~1%.
- Small variation of available energy with 6MM vs 1 SLM (<1%).

POLITÉCNICA

Results : Sub-module Energy Yield Analysis

INSTITUTO DE ENERGÍA SOLAR

2. Study shading pattern distribution

Sub-Module Energy Yield indicates presence of shadows

Small variation of available energy across all modules: similar shading patterns across the surface

Series → V slightly better (more bypass diodes)

TCT → negligible difference between V or H

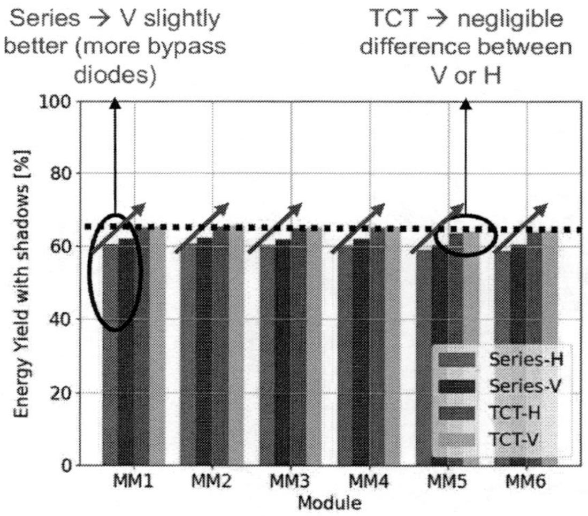

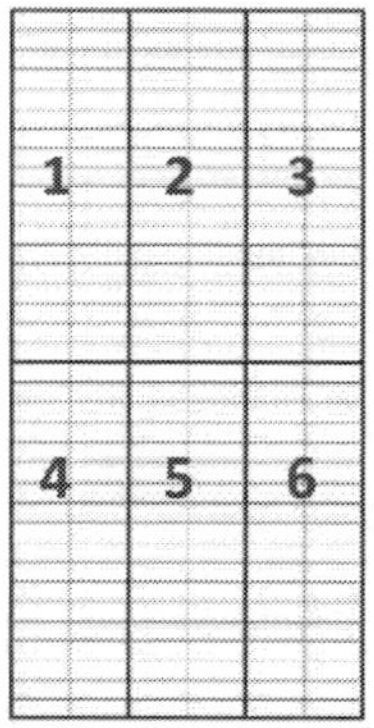

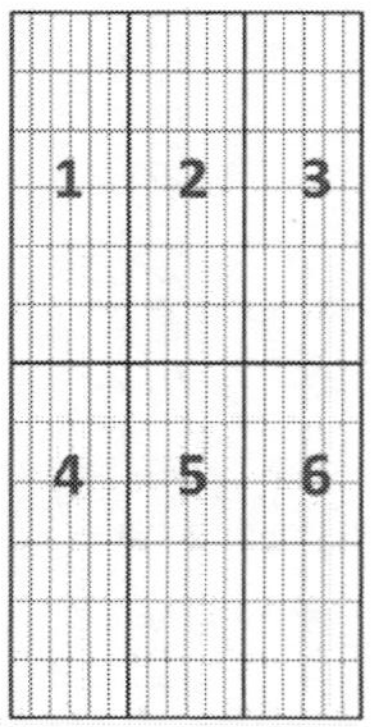

POLITÉCNICA

RESULTS: P&O sensitivity analysis

INSTITUTO DE ENERGÍA SOLAR

3. MPPT VIPV parameter tuning

$$\eta_{MPPT} = \frac{\int P_{MPPT}\,dt}{\int P_{MAX}\,dt}$$ [2]

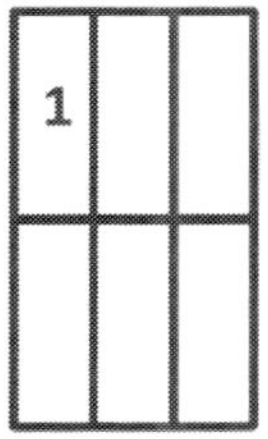

P&O algorithm tuning
(step size and perturbation period)

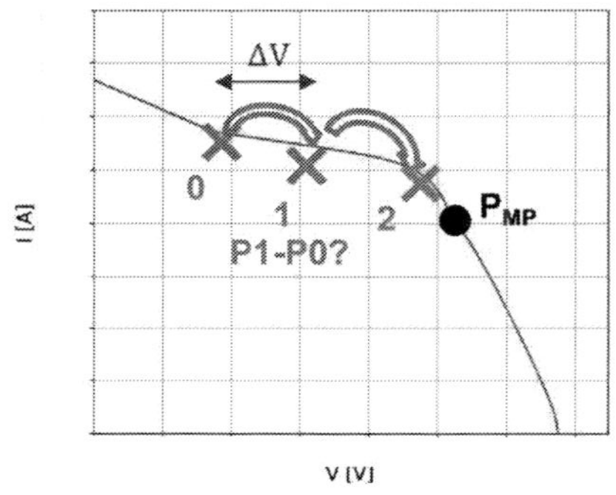

P&O dynamic effects:
Different V_{MP} → Confuse algorithm

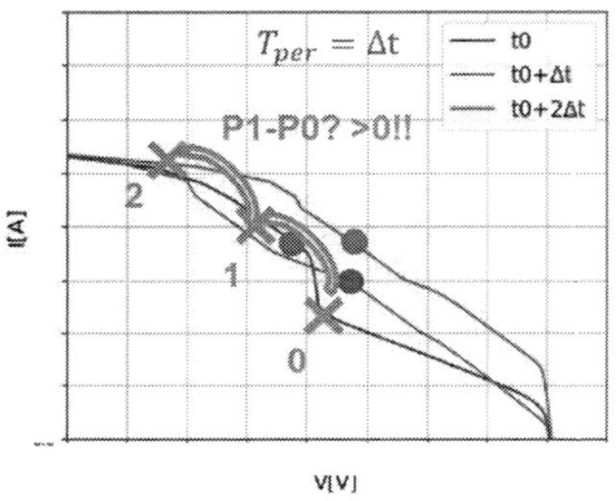

TCT → Diagonal trend, sensitive to step size because IV curve shape

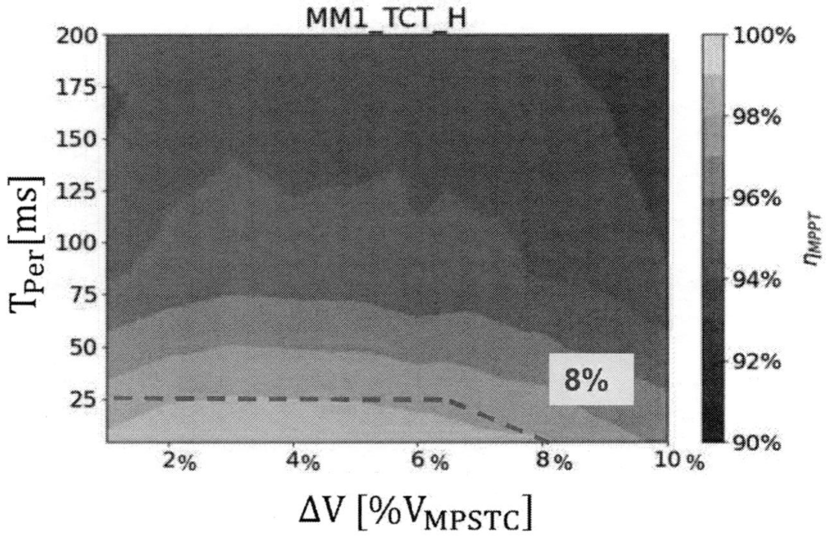

[2] "EVS-EN 50530:2010," EVS.

POLITÉCNICA

RESULTS: P&O sensitivity analysis

INSTITUTO DE ENERGÍA SOLAR

3. MPPT VIPV parameter tuning

$$\eta_{MPPT} = \frac{\int P_{MPPT}\, dt}{\int P_{MAX}\, dt} \text{ [2]}$$

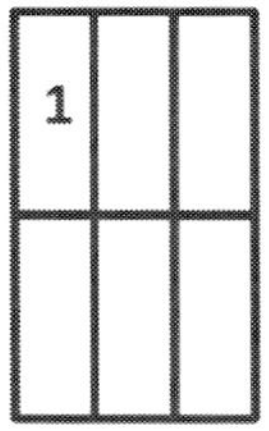

P&O algorithm tuning
(step size and perturbation period)

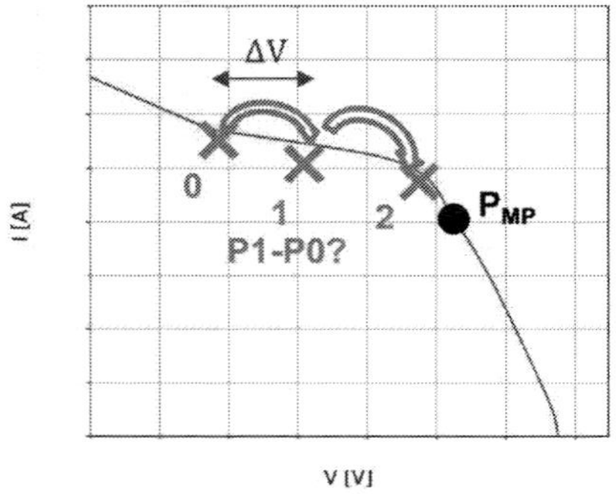

P&O dynamic effects:
Different V_{MP} → Confuse algorithm

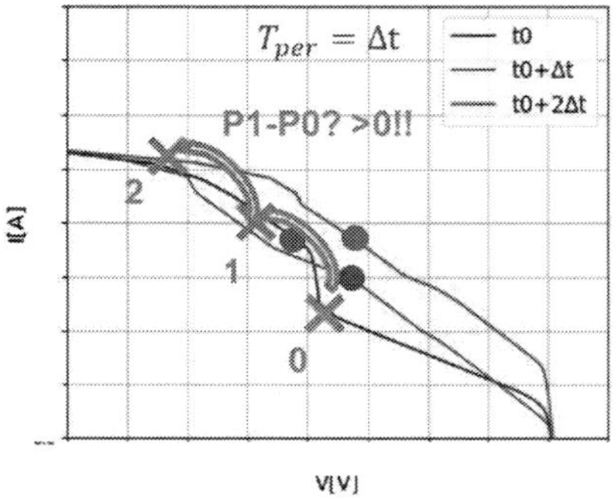

Series → Horizontal trend, sensitive to perturbation period

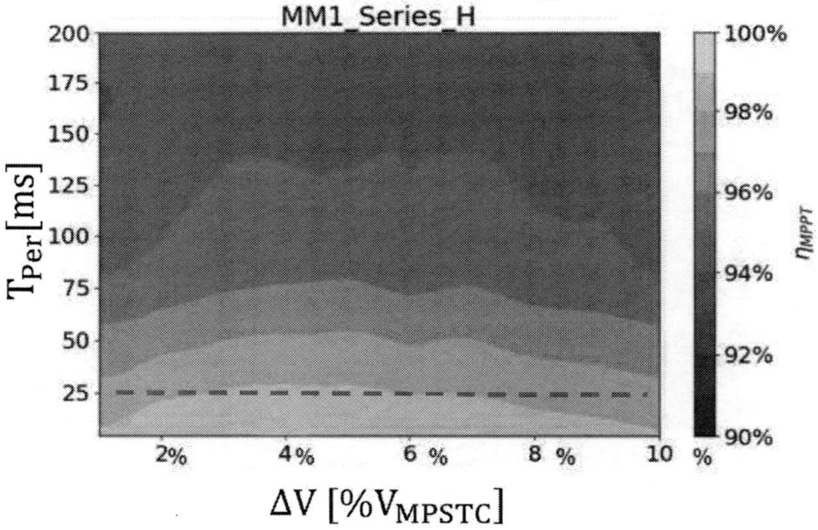

[2] "EVS-EN 50530:2010," EVS.

POLITÉCNICA

RESULTS: P&O sensitivity analysis

INSTITUTO DE ENERGÍA SOLAR

3. MPPT VIPV parameter tuning

$$\eta_{MPPT} = \frac{\int P_{MPPT}\, dt}{\int P_{MAX}\, dt}$$ [2]

Realistic P&O period: ~100 ms [3]

Low period eff: 98-99%

Very similar η among all sub-modules

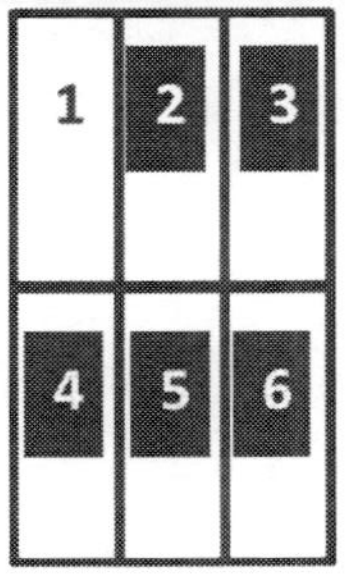

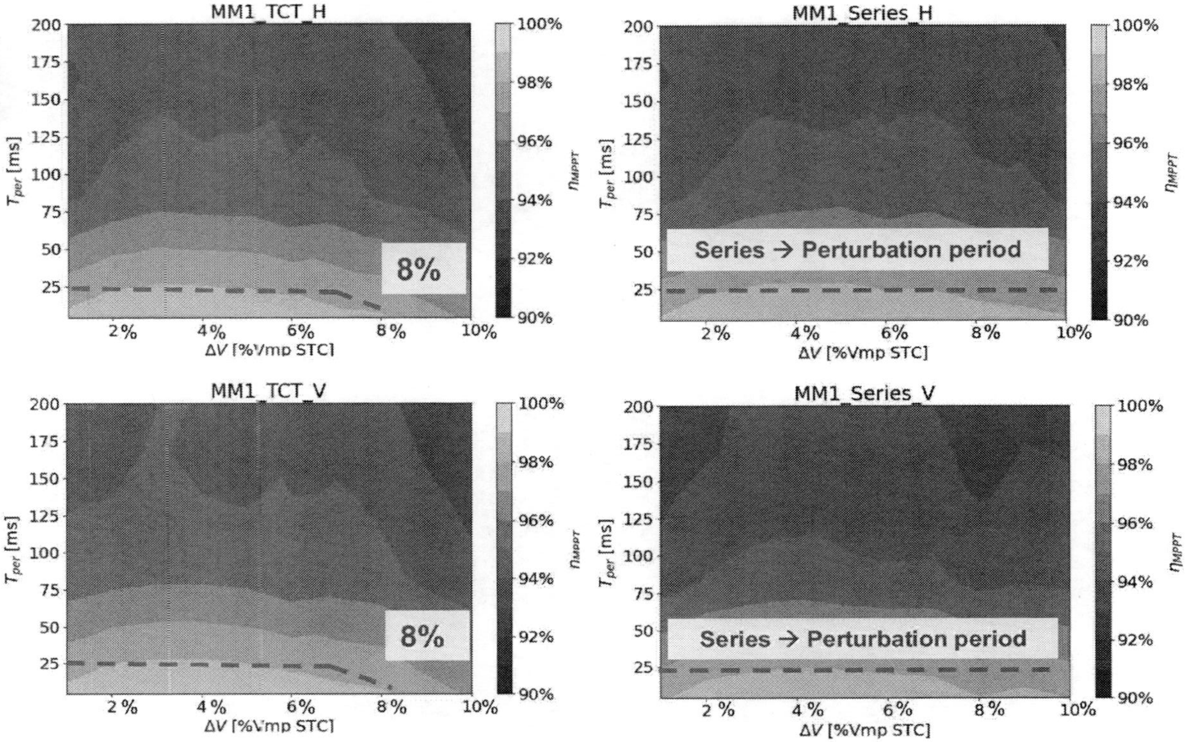

[2] "EVS-EN 50530:2010," EVS.
[3] Y. Levron et al. *IEEE Trans. Circuits Syst. I*, vol. 60, no. 3, pp. 724–732 (2013).

POLITÉCNICA

RESULTS: P&O sensitivity analysis

INSTITUTO DE ENERGÍA SOLAR

3. MPPT VIPV parameter tuning

$$\eta_{MPPT} = \frac{\int P_{MPPT}\,dt}{\int P_{MAX}\,dt}$$ [2]

Realistic P&O period: ~100 ms [3]

Very similar η among all sub-modules

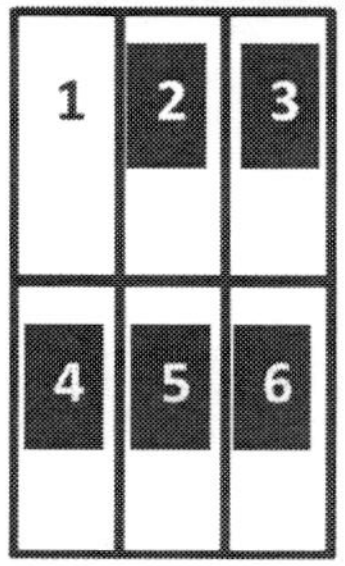

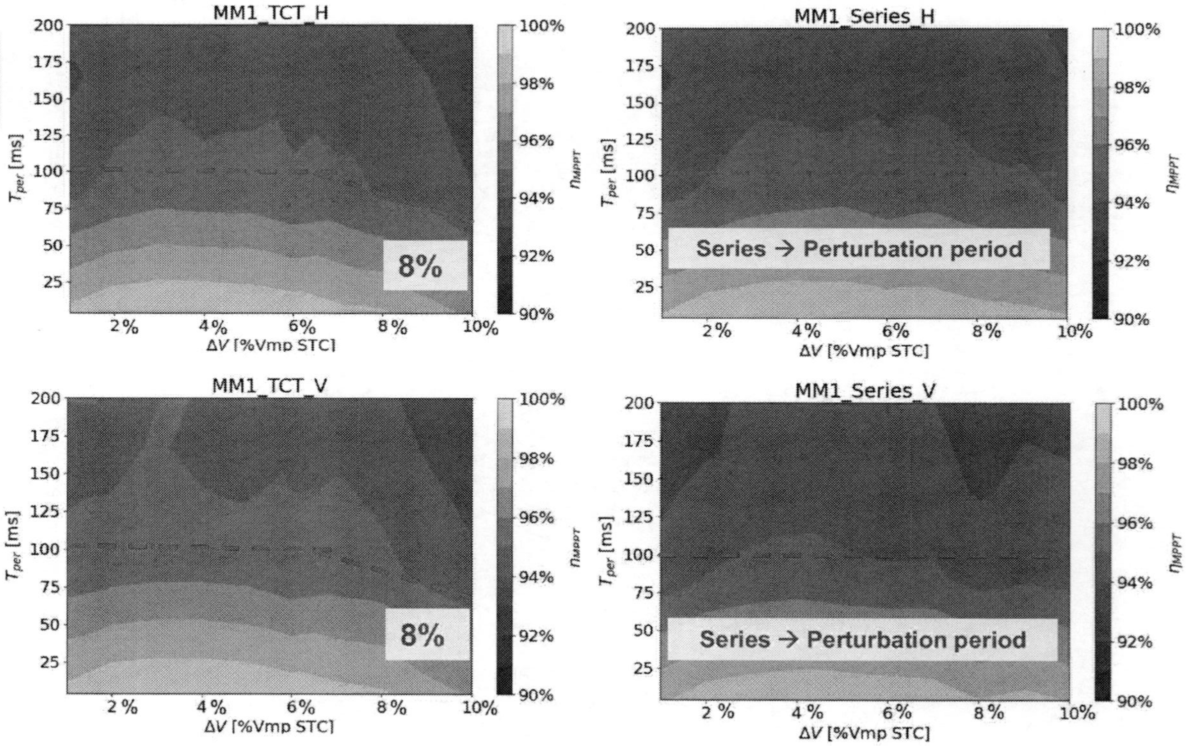

Low period eff: 98-99%

Realistic period eff: 95-96%

[2] "EVS-EN 50530:2010," EVS.
[3] Y. Levron et al. *IEEE Trans. Circuits Syst. I*, vol. 60, no. 3, pp. 724–732 (2013).

POLITÉCNICA

RESULTS: P&O sensitivity analysis

INSTITUTO DE ENERGÍA SOLAR

3. MPPT VIPV parameter tuning

$$\eta_{MPPT} = \frac{\int P_{MPPT}\,dt}{\int P_{MAX}\,dt}$$ [2]

Realistic P&O period: ~100 ms [3]

SLM

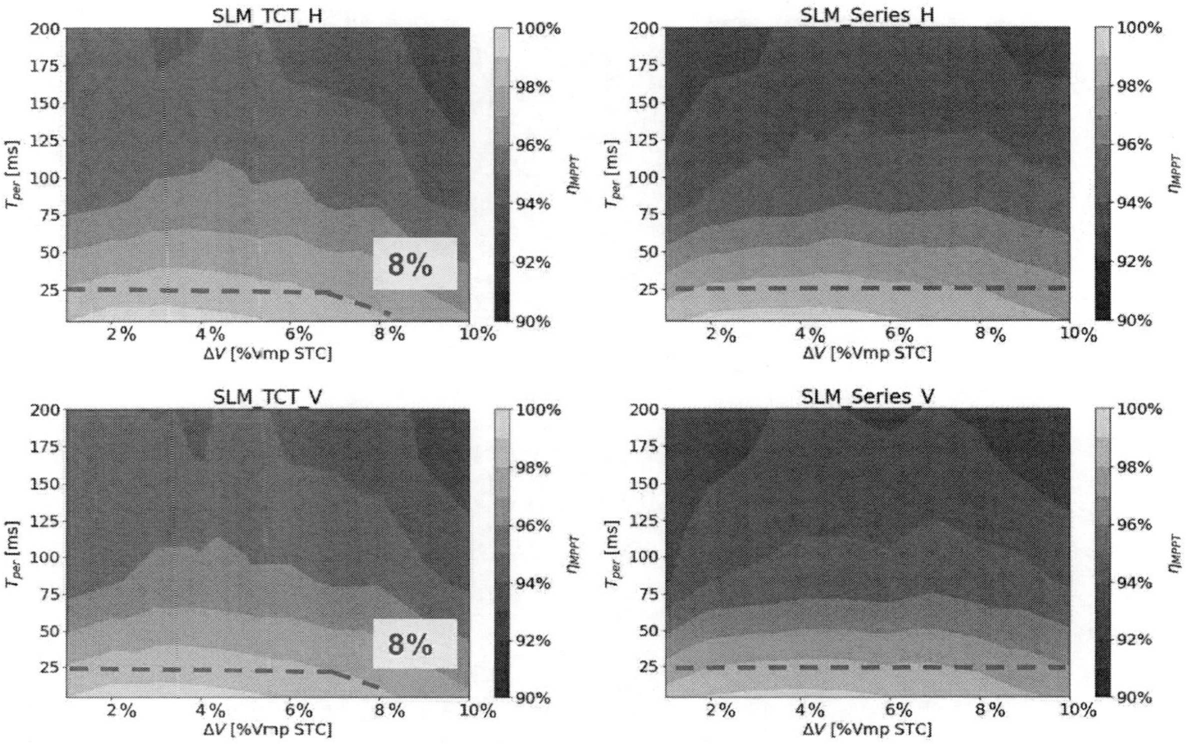

Same trends, similar efficiencies: 98-99% with 4.16 ms

[2] "EVS-EN 50530:2010," EVS.
[3] Y. Levron et al. *IEEE Trans. Circuits Syst. I*, vol. 60, no. 3, pp. 724–732 (2013).

RESULTS: P&O sensitivity analysis

INSTITUTO DE ENERGÍA SOLAR

3. MPPT VIPV parameter tuning

$$\eta_{MPPT} = \frac{\int P_{MPPT}\,dt}{\int P_{MAX}\,dt}$$ [2]

Realistic P&O period: ~100 ms [3]

SLM

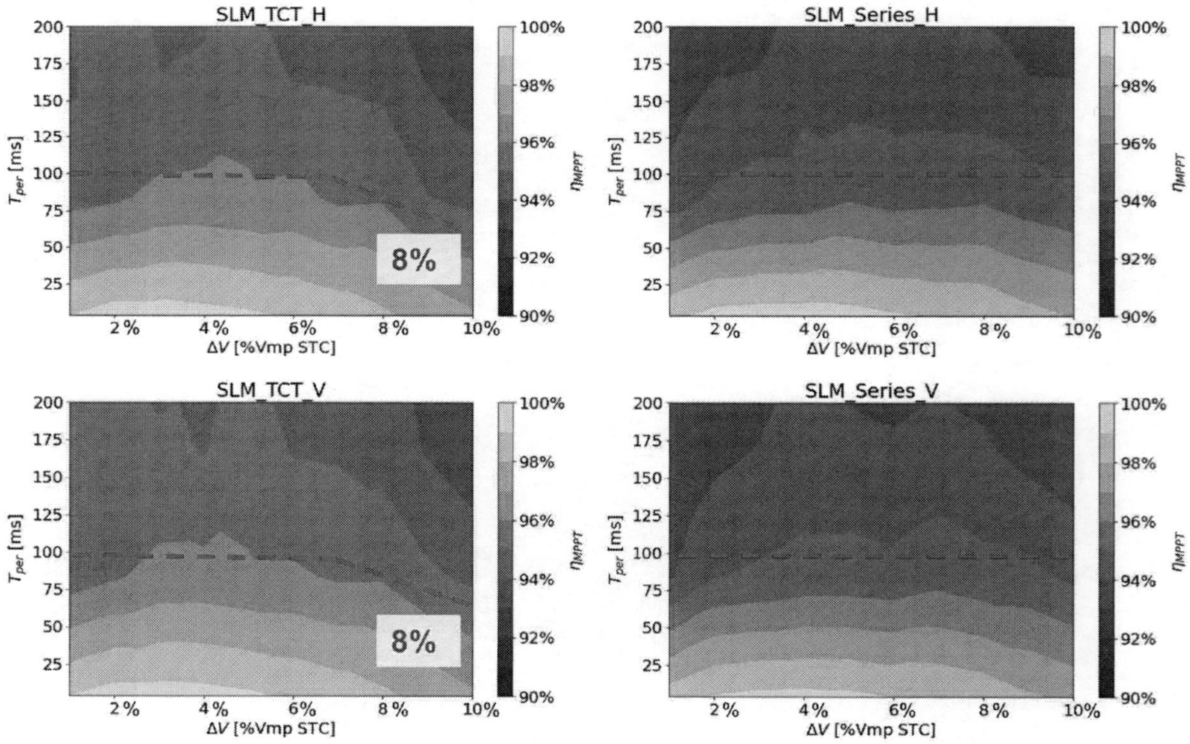

Same trends, similar efficiencies:
98-99% with 4.16 ms
95-96% with 100 ms

[2] "EVS-EN 50530:2010," EVS.
[3] Y. Levron et al. *IEEE Trans. Circuits Syst. I*, vol. 60, no. 3, pp. 724–732 (2013).

Conclusions

INSTITUTO DE ENERGÍA SOLAR

- Mini-Module strategy provides **marginal Energy Yield** improvement, prior to DC/DC **(<1%).**
- **Similar shading across all the roof**, but at different instants due to the **vehicle's movement**.
- **TCT** is the most productive connection, **independent** from cell orientation.
- **Series** connection performs **better** with **vertical** connection, due to the higher number of **bypass diodes**.
- **Almost identical efficiencies** with SLM or 6MM, very **similar trends**:
  - **98-99%** efficiency with lowest perturbation period possible (**4.16 ms**). However, might not be feasible.
  - **95-96 %** efficiency with realistic perturbation periods (**100 ms**).
  - **MPPT** efficiency strongly depends on MPPT parameters, not on module's architecture.
- Further studies are required to **validate** the Distributed MPPT strategy (better temperature, other surfaces, etc.). **Energy cost** of implementing various DC/DC converters should be considered.

POLITÉCNICA

Thank you for your attention

INSTITUTO DE ENERGÍA SOLAR

Ricardo Moruno

r.moruno@upm.es

Happy to take your questions

We gratefully acknowledge the DETEC-PV project, Grant PID2021-128853OB-I00, funded by MCIN/AEI/10.13039/501100011033 and “ERDF A way of making Europe”

R. Moruno thanks his grant “PID2021-128853OB-I00” funded by MCIN/AEI/ 10.13039/501100011033 and by “ERDF A way of making Europe”.

MINISTERIO DE CIENCIA E INNOVACIÓN

UNIÓN EUROPEA
FONDO EUROPEO DE DESARROLLO REGIONAL
"Una manera de hacer Europa"

AGENCIA ESTATAL DE INVESTIGACIÓN

POLITÉCNICA

INSTITUTO
DE ENERGÍA
SOLAR

Innovation in photovoltaics since 1979

INFLUENCE OF DIFFERENT DRIVING PATTERNS AND ELECTRICAL DESIGNS ON VIPV PERFORMANCE

Judy Jalkh[1], Christian Doppler[1], Philip Caluori[1], Manuel Ruf[2]
Virtual Vehicle GmbH[1], Robert Bosch GmbH[2]
[1]Inffeldgasse 21A, 8010 Graz, +433168738821, judy.jalkh@v2c2.at

ABSTRACT: This study evaluates the potential performance of Vehicle-Integrated Photovoltaics (VIPV) under varying driving and parking patterns across European locations, including Athens, Paris, and Helsinki. By analyzing distinct dynamic driver usage scenarios such as commuting, long-distance travel, short trips, and average yearly driving behaviors, this research provides a comprehensive understanding of usage patterns on VIPV efficiency. The target is to design a one single VIPV-system capable of covering the monthly electric vehicle HVAC (Heating Ventilation & Air Conditioning) energy requirements, for as many observed scenarios as possible. As a result, a PV size of 1.64m^2 was selected, sufficient to widely cover the regarded HVAC demands, especially with short-distance and commuter drive profiles. The study also examines the energy optimization during partial shading conditions by studying different electrical architectures, like varying bypass diodes and Maximum Power Point Trackers (MPPTs). This analysis shows that both the intensity and pattern of shading influence the optimal electrical configuration, with high-intensity shading favoring a configuration with 35 bypass diodes for a 1.64m^2 PV area. Overall, these findings demonstrate substantial variability in VIPV performance depending on geographic location, driving behavior, and system design, providing key insights for optimizing VIPV systems across diverse use cases.
Keywords: VIPV, partial shading, driving behavior, bypass diode, MPPT

1 INTRODUCTION

Recent studies have examined VIPV for commercial vehicles in Europe [1] and passenger cars in Germany, Spain, and California [2], but often under idealized conditions and without considering diverse usage patterns or parking environments. These gaps limit understanding of how VIPV performs in real-world contexts.

This work addresses this by analyzing VIPV across three European climates (Athens, Paris, and Helsinki) using four driver types (short, long, average, commuter) and three parking conditions (street, garage, shaded).

The study is conducted within the EFFEREST project [3], which develops user-centric control systems for electric vehicles. The TOGG electric vehicle (EV) serves as a demonstrator, where VIPV integration on the roof is simulated under diverse driving and climate scenarios. A key benchmark is whether VIPV can cover part of the vehicle's HVAC energy demand, linking solar generation directly to passenger comfort, an aspect often missing in previous analyses.

Optimized electric configuration under partial shading is also analyzed in terms of bypass diode (BPD) layouts and MPPT methods, building on findings that optimized BPDs can retain up to 69.2% of output under shading [4] and that advanced MPPT improves response to fluctuating irradiance [5]. A measurement campaign on bypass diodes was carried out to visualize and validate the effects of shading patterns on power output.

By combining climate, usage, parking, and system design, this study offers a more realistic assessment of VIPV, showing which driver–city combinations benefit most and supporting the broader adoption of solar-integrated EVs for reduced emissions and greater energy independence.

2 DRIVING PATTERNS

2.1 Exemplary reference week

BOSCH created exemplary driving weeks to represent real-world vehicle usage by combining internal, public, and purchased data. Four reference driving scenarios were defined: Short Distance Drive (SD), Long Distance Drive (LD), Average Drive (Avg), and Commute (Comm). These were mapped to three climatic regions: Helsinki (cold), Paris (average), and Athens (hot). The exemplary weeks were generated by enriching one year of real driving data (start/stop times, distance, GPS, velocity) with stochastic parking data (street, garage, shaded), charging models, and regional climate conditions. From this combination, a representative week was selected for each driving type and city using a least-squares method, ensuring that weekly patterns matched annual statistics as closely as possible. It was assumed that passenger cars in private European use with one year of driving reflect lifetime behavior if no major socio-economic changes occur. The final dataset includes GPS traces, velocity profiles, and parking types. For example, the short distance driver exemplary week is shown in Figure 1. Table I differentiates between the driver types in terms of parking type and monthly mileage.

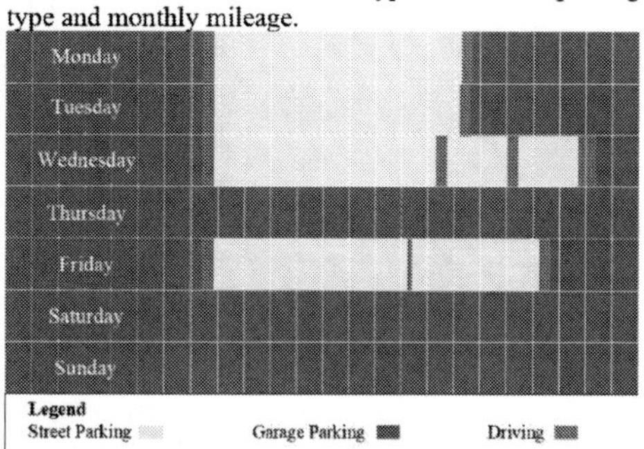

Figure 1: Exemplary week for short distance driver

Table I: Parameters of the four driver types

	Avg	SD	LD	Comm
Garage Parking	Yes	Yes	No	No
Street Parking [days/week]	3	4	7	7
Monthly Mileage [km]	~800	~300	~2600	~1250

2.2 SIC simulations

The in-house tool Solar Irradiance Calculator (SIC) has been used, which calculates dynamically the irradiation according to the changing driving profile of the moving TOGG EV. The model relies on several inputs to calculate the irradiance.

The main input is the weather data, namely GHI (Global Horizontal Irradiance), DNI (Direct Normal Irradiance), DHI (Diffuse Horizontal Irradiance), and the Temperature. This data is downloaded from the NSRDB database [6] for 365 days with 15 min interval for the year 2019 for the three studied cities. The "average" monthly day was elaborated for a more effective process to scale results.

The second input is the driving and parking cycle. The cycle is the 24-hr Bosch exemplary week for each city and driver type as discussed in the previous section. For simplification, the PV zone on the TOGG EV roof is assumed with a tilt of 0°.

Next, the SIC calculates the experienced shade on the entire roof. The irradiance already includes shadows from the clouds in the DHI. A Random Shading Generator (RSG) was developed to simulate irregular shading effects from environmental obstacles such as trees and buildings. Its purpose is to randomly vary the shading percentage across the cycle while ensuring that the overall average shading for the entire cycle meets a specified target. It is made up of two parameters, the shading factor and the number of sections. The shading factor is a value between 0 and 1, where 0 represents complete shade and 1 represents no shade. The number of sections represent time discretization. A reduced number of sections results in increased section dimensions, causing the vehicle to remain under the same shading level for longer periods. The "exemplary week" cycles are made up of four different periods: driving, street parking, shaded parking, and garage parking. During driving, the RSG driving is used with a shading factor of 0.6 and 120 sections. During street parking, the shading factor is increased to 0.8 while the number of sections is reduced to 60. This is because, during driving, the vehicle's higher velocity causes the shadows cast on its roof to shift more rapidly. In contrast, when the vehicle is stationary, shadow transitions occur at a much slower rate. Furthermore, the shading factor during driving is generally lower, as the vehicle frequently operates in closer proximity to buildings, other vehicles, and large trucks, resulting in more pronounced and transient shading compared to when it is parked in open areas. During shaded parking, the DHI irradiance is used, and finally during garage parking the irradiance is 0.

An example is portrayed in Figure 2. The "Final Export" is the final output of the SIC to the simulation model discussed in section 3.1. To interpret the figure, it is essential to first focus on the parking conditions, as the final output depends on this information to determine the appropriate irradiance profile. From time 0 until ~8:30, the vehicle is parked in a garage, resulting in an irradiance value of 0. Between roughly 08:30 and 09:00, there is a short driving period during which the RSG driving irradiance profile is applied. The vehicle is then parked in a shaded location, so the diffuse irradiance is used. At ~11:00, a 30-minute driving period occurs, during which the RSG driving irradiance is again applied. Finally, the vehicle returns home and is parked in the garage, where the irradiance value returns to 0.

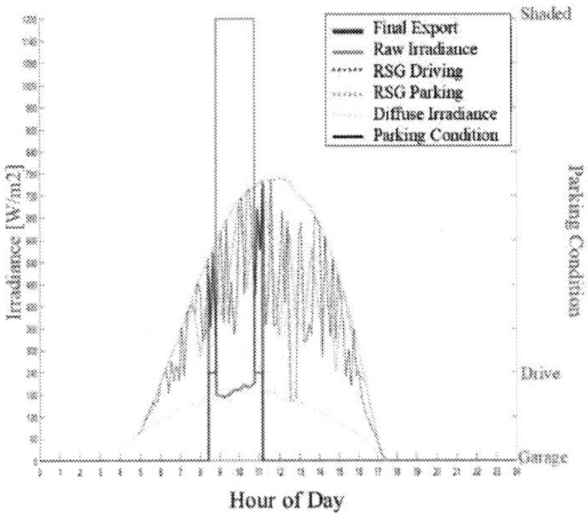

Figure 2: Different irradiance profiles [W/m^2] and parking conditions for the Average driver on Friday in Athens

Simulations for the 4 driving scenarios, the 3 cities, 12 months, 7 days a week were performed resulting in 1008 irradiance outputs in W/m^2.

At this point the SIC only calculates the environmental parameters acting on the vehicle to output the irradiance. The PV characteristics are then used to calculate the PV power. These include a PV area of 1.64m^2, PV cell efficiency of 23%, and a PE efficiency of 95%.

2.3 HVAC calculations

The required HVAC energy is calculated for each driver type, month, exemplary day of week, and city. The goal of this work is to cover all the required HVAC energy demand via PV. A pre-calculation led to the following required energy quantities mainly based on environmental temperature: 3 kWh/100km for hot (30 °C) and cold (0 °C), 0 kWh/100km for normal temperatures (15 °C), and 7 kWh/ 100km for very cold temperatures (-10 °C).

As a next step, the average frequency of temperature categories had to be identified. Therefore, daily temperature data was sourced from online meteorological databases which include recorded maximum, average, and minimum temperatures for each day [7]. The classification of thermal conditions is based on these values: Hot days are defined as days where the maximum temperature exceeds 25 °C, with the maximum temperature serving as an upper boundary indicator. Cold days are defined as days where the mean temperature ranges between −5 °C and 5 °C, as the minimum temperature dataset predominantly reflects nighttime temperatures, whereas the simulations are focused on daytime operating conditions. Very cold days are those with a mean temperature below −5 °C. The number of normal days per month is determined as the remainder of the total days in the month after subtracting the counts of hot, cold, and very cold days. Table II summarizes the number of days per year in each temperature category for the three cities.

Table II: Number of days for each temperature category

	Hot	Cold	Very cold	Normal
Athens	151	5	0	209
Paris	67	31	0	267
Helsinki	10	156	20	179

10.4229/EUPVSEC2025/4EO.2.2

Finally, monthly HVAC energy requirements are computed assuming operation only during driving. For each temperature category (hot, cold, very cold, and normal), the energy is obtained by multiplying percentage of days in each temperature category, the monthly driven distance, and the corresponding HVAC energy consumption per 100 km.

2.4 Results

In this section, the HVAC requirements and the produced PV energy are compared to understand the benefits of VIPV for each driver type and city.

Figure 3 summarizes in which months the PV production fully covers the HVAC requirements for all driver types and cities. For Athens, PV production is higher throughout the year, allowing it to satisfy HVAC demand for more months compared to Paris and Helsinki. For all cities, short distance and commuter drivers see similar coverage, with the prior gaining a few extra months in Athens and Paris, despite having a garage while the commuter parks on the street. Similarly, long distance and average drivers have comparable coverage, with the long distance driver slightly ahead, even though the average driver has a garage. This shows that having a garage does not necessarily reduce the benefits of PV. Driven distance is a key factor: the short distance driver covers only ~300 km/month and parks on the street during peak sunlight, whereas the average driver, with ~800 km/month and less street parking, experiences less PV contribution. The long distance driver, despite always parking on the street, has higher HVAC demand due to ~2600 km/month. In Helsinki, PV meets HVAC requirements from May to early October for all driver types, with short-distance and commuter drivers benefiting additionally in April.

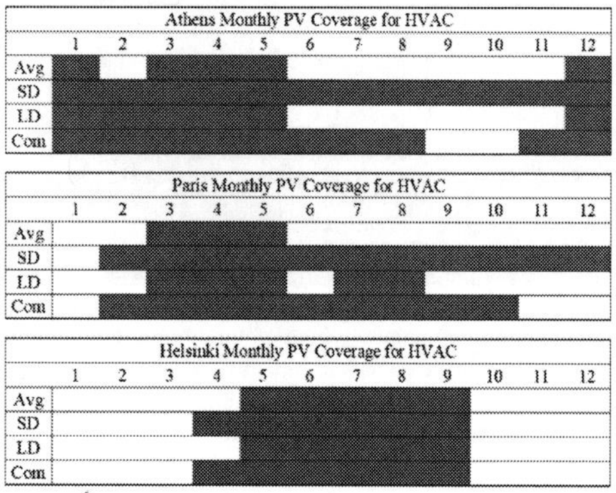

Figure 3: Months where PV output satisfies HVAC requirements (in blue)

In Table III, the yearly PV production and HVAC consumption energy values are presented. The short distance and commuter drivers in Athens and Paris have a surplus of PV energy that can be used for satisfying mileage (Red). Thus, one can conclude that VIPV is very beneficial for people driving a lower mileage living in southern regions of Europe.

Table III: Yearly PV output and HVAC requirements [kWh]

Cities	[kWh]	Avg	SD	LD	Comm
Athens	PV	78	152	313	356
	HVAC	127	49	397	199
Paris	PV	52	144	234	254
	HVAC	86	31	271	127
Helsinki	PV	45	123	196	219
	HVAC	167	76	553	259

In conclusion, VIPV performance depends on both garage availability and driven distance, which governs HVAC energy demand. Optimal utilization occurs for households with a garage under short distance driving and daytime street parking, whereas households without a garage benefit most from a commuter driving pattern with limited long trips.

3 ELECTRICAL ARCHITECTURES FOR PARTIAL SHADING

This section focuses on the effects of partial shading. The first sub-section focuses on finding the optimal bypass diode configuration to limit partial shading losses, while the second sub-section compares the behavior of two MPPT types under partial shading.

3.1 Simulation model

The simulation model is made in MATLAB/Simulink. The PV-cell technology modelled is based on the Maxeon Ne3 Cell [8]. Table IV lists all the parameters used to match the IV- and PV-curves between model and datasheet. The total PV area is made up of 15 by 7 PV cells, totaling 105 cells with 1.64m^2.

Table IV: PV cell simulation parameters

PV Cell Parameters	
Length [mm]	125
Width [mm]	125
Area [m^2]	0.015625
Voc [V]	0.7264
Isc [A]	6.123
Vmp [V]	0.61
Imp [A]	5.7
Pmax [W]	3.47
Efficiency [%]	22.3
N	1.05
Rs [Ω]	0.006
Rsh [Ω]	7

Next, the electrical circuit was studied. Therefore, BPDs and MPPTs are investigated.

3.2 BPD Simulations

BPDs are used to increase power output in shaded scenarios. Due to the limited available area on a vehicle roof, its precise design is crucial, to maximize PV power. To study which BPD configuration behaves best under partial shading, the PV simulation model discussed previously in section 3.1 were used The PV cells were connected in series to reach a higher voltage better aligning with the voltage levels of the EV battery.

10.4229/EUPVSEC2025/4EO.2.2

As for the varying parameters, these include the Shading Factor (SF), the Shading Pattern (SP), and the Electrical Configuration (EC). The SF indicates the shadows light intensity, where 0 means no light and 1 is no shadow. E.g. SF lower than 0.3 refer to intense shading. A range of 0 to 0.8 was investigated.

The shaded area itself is represented by the SP, which is the shading pattern, namely the location of the shadow on the roof. Five SPs are considered: diagonal beam, 20% random area shading, 60% random area shading, half-roof shading, and quarter-roof shading. The diagonal beam SP simulates a streetlight pole shadow extending from the front right to the back left of the roof. Each random SP includes three scenarios to assess shadow placement effects, while the half-roof and quarter-roof SPs each include four scenarios corresponding to shadows on different roof sections (front, back, left, right). Figure 4 portrays the different SPs on the TOGG roof, with the grey cells indicating shaded areas and the white cells representing unshaded ones. The small black arrow marks the front of the roof.

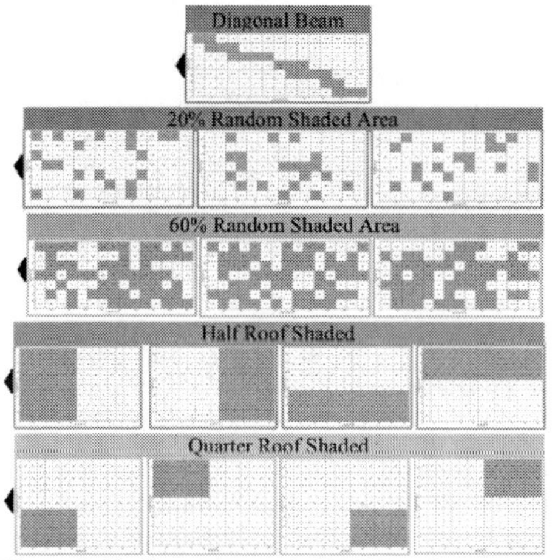

Figure 4: Shading patters on the TOGG roof

Finally, the electric configuration portrays the number of cells per BPD and thus the total number of BPDs. Table V shows the three scenarios used.

Table V: BPD simulation electric configuration scenarios

EC	1	2	3
Number of cells per BPD	3	7	15
Numbers of BPDs	35	15	7
Number of modules	35	15	7
Module dimensions [m^2]	0.047	0.11	0.23

For example, Figure 5 shows the SP front half-roof shaded combined with the 35 BPDs EC. Each dashed section refers to a module that is bypassed by 1 BPD.

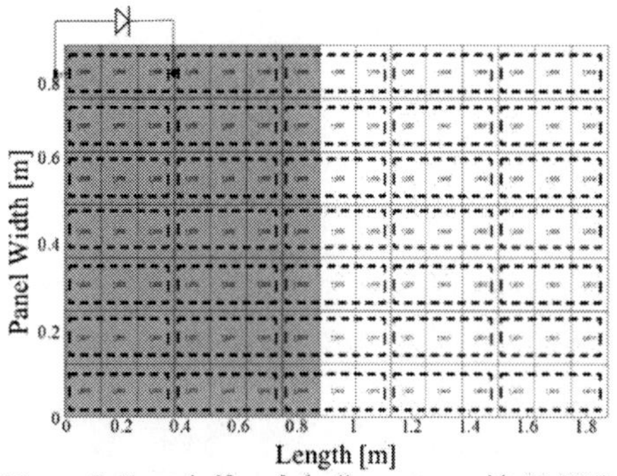

Figure 5: Front half-roof shading patter with 35 BPDs electric configuration

For each SP and SF, the three ECs were compared in terms of maximum power reached. Results indicate that under high-intensity shading (SF $\leq$ 0.3), ECs with 35 BPDs generally achieve higher power output. However, in half-roof shading scenarios, the 15 BPDs configuration performs better for front and rear shading, while the 7 BPDs configuration performs better for left and right shading. This is because with the half-roof shading, the orientation of the PV modules with respect to the shading location determines the EC preference. On the other hand, for lower intensity shading (SF >= 0.5), the EC does not matter.

For quarter-roof and 60% random shading patterns, SF has little influence on EC configuration preference. The 35 BPDs configuration consistently delivers the highest power, except at SF = 0.8 under all quarter-roof shading scenarios. In the 60% random shading cases, all scenarios produce similar power outputs, showing no clear EC preference regardless of SF, likely due to the extensive shading coverage across the roof.

The influence of shading patterns is evident when comparing the scenarios in Figure 6. Although each pattern (20% area shaded scenarios 1 and 2, any quarter-roof scenario, and the diagonal beam) covers 20% of the PV roof area, their power outputs vary for SF<0.5, demonstrating that shading distribution is as significant as the total shaded area. Nonetheless, all patterns consistently favor the 35 BPDs configuration under high intensity shading conditions.

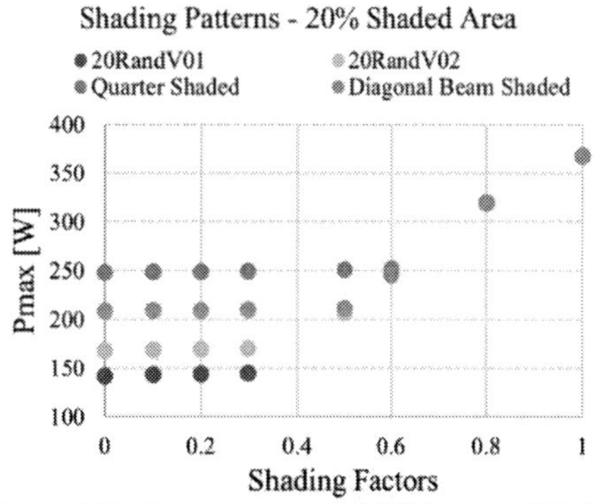

Figure 6: Maximum power reached [W] in terms of SF for four shading patterns with 20% shaded area

10.4229/EUPVSEC2025/4EO.2.2

3.3 BPD Measurement Campaign

To analyze the behavior of PV systems under real-world conditions, a measurement campaign was conducted focusing on partial shading effects on a PV string. Electrical characteristics, including IV- and PV-curves for different ECs, were recorded under various shading scenarios. The results were used to calibrate and refine the simulation model, ensuring a realistic representation of partial shading and its impact on system performance.

The test setup is shown in Figure 7 and includes light sources, infrared camera, PV-cells and bypass diodes. Not visible in the figure are the adjustable load and voltmeter, which were used to derive the IV curves. Pyranometers from EKO INSTRUMENTS, ML-02 [9] were used to measure the irradiance. The PV cells used were Copper Indium Gallium Selenide (CIGS) half cells from ISC-Konstanz with a size of 160x160mm. The BPDs used were of the type Schottky-Diode STPS1545D. The Virtual Vehicle inhouse system "DataBeam" was used for data collection. An infrared camera was used for temperature visualization.

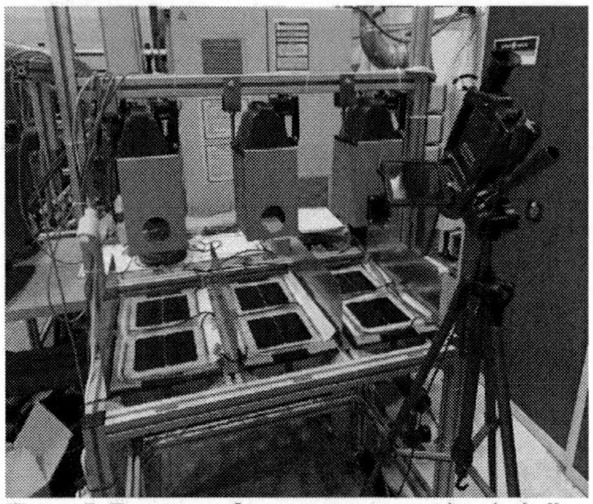

Figure 7: Test setup of measurement campaign, including light sources, infrared camera, PV-cells, bypass diodes

Figure 8 presents a schematic representation of the setup, highlighting the adjustable load, voltmeter, PV cells and their names. It also illustrates the four electrical configurations tested: no bypass diodes (EC-A), and configurations with 6 (EC-B), 3 (EC-C), and 2 (EC-D) bypass diodes.

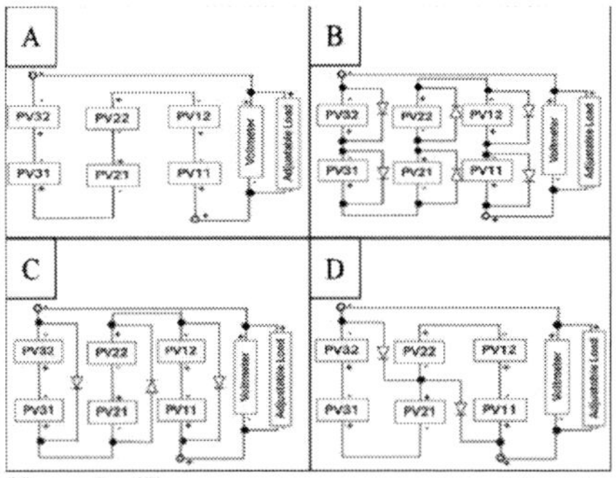

Figure 8: Measurement campaign setup with no bypass diodes, 6, 3, and 2 bypass diodes (A, B, C, and D respectively)

Table VI shows the average irradiance experienced on each of the PV cells at ~60ºC, which is assumed as the steady state temperature.

Table VI: Average irradiance [W/m²] on each PV cell

PV Cell	Irradiance [W/m²]
PV32	381
PV31	318
PV22	386
PV21	383
PV12	323
PV11	264

Different SPs and BPD configurations were tested. The shaded cells in these experiments were directly covered above their surface and therefore experienced zero irradiance. The first set of results is presented in Figure 9, showing the variation in output power across different EC and SP combinations. Shadowed cells are indicated by grayed-out PV labels in the lower part of the figure. For a fixed EC and varying SP, the results show that with no BPDs (EC-A), the power drop is already drastic with just 1 shaded cell. The power barely decreases with additional shaded cells. The highest power output can be achieved , as expected, when 6 BPDs (EC-B) are used. For EC-C or EC-D, identical power is observed at one and two shaded cell scenarios. This is because the BPD is already activated with conducts after the first shaded cell, bypassing the whole protected substring, so further shading within that substring does not further reduce output.

Although EC-B generally delivers the highest power output, EC-C slightly outperforms EC-B in the case of 2 shaded cells. This occurs because, within this shaded region, EC-B incorporates 2 BPDs in series, whereas EC-C only has one. The additional diode in EC-B increases resistance, resulting in reduced power.

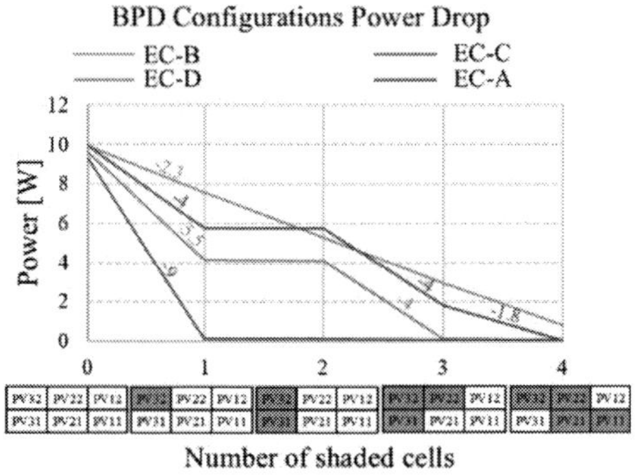

Figure 9: Power drop [W] for each SP and electric configuration

As a next step, the influence of the EC is investigated. Table VII compares the 3 EC cases previously shown in Figure 8 with 2 PV cells constantly shaded. With 1 cell per BPD (EC-B), the power is the same regardless of which cells are shaded. With more cells per BPD, the power depends on the SP and thus the number of strings affected. Case 2 vs case 3 with 2 cells/BPD (EC-C) is probably due to the distribution of the irradiance, even though the average is the same (Table VII).

Table VII: The average irradiance [W/m^2] and power [W] for each electric configuration

Case	Shaded Cells	Avg Irr [W/m^2]	Power [W]		
			EC-B	EC-C	EC-D
1	32 & 31	339	5.3	5.8	4.1
2	22 & 31	338	5.3	1.8	-
3	32 & 12	338	5.4	2.3	-
4	22 & 21	321	-	-	0.15

The results indicate that output power is governed by the fraction of strings affected by shading. Increasing the number of BPDs reduces this fraction. For instance, shading a single cell in a 1-cell-per-BPD configuration impacts only 1/6 of the strings, whereas in a 2-cells-per-BPD configuration, the same shading affects 1/3 of the strings, resulting in a greater power loss.

In general, it is valid that the more BPDs are used, the higher the power output of the whole system is. Configuration B in Figure 8 has the highest output, Configuration C still works well with only slightly lower power reduction but with significant less BPD used, hence this should be the favorite for future investigations.

3.4 MPPT comparisons

A second very big influence on the PV performance is made by the controller, the MPPT. It is used to set the modules to the voltage level with highest power output.

A previous study, which is a basis for this work was done with a so-called Perturbance and Observation (P&O) MPPT [10]. Due to slow stabilization times, also other possibilities like Particle Swarm Optimization (PSO) were investigated throughout this work.

For better understanding and optimizing power output under partial shading, this study includes the comparison of the P&O with the PSO MPPT. The P&O perturbs the voltage and then observes if the power response is positive or negative. Under partial shading, it can get stuck on the local instead of the global maximum power point (MPP) which leads to power loss. The PSO is bio-inspired (bird flocks/ fish swarms) and each particle is aware of its personal and global best. Under partial shading, it iteratively converges towards the global MPP.

To compare both MPPTs, a simulation model was set up with the PV model mentioned in section 3.1. The simulations include varying the SF (0.2, 0.5, and 0.8), the SP (mentioned in section 3.2), and the MPPT type. The following simulation parameters were used: an input irradiance of 1000 W/m2, a simulation time of 5 seconds, an MPPT time sample of 0.01 seconds, and an EC of 35 PV modules with 3 cells per BPD.

The results, as seen in Figure 10, show that the PSO MPPT reaches a higher maximum power than the P&O MPPT. In some cases, the added benefit (orange) is more pronounced than in others, but there is no clear trend. Due to the more favorable behavior of the PSO under partial shading, it will be integrated and used in future works.

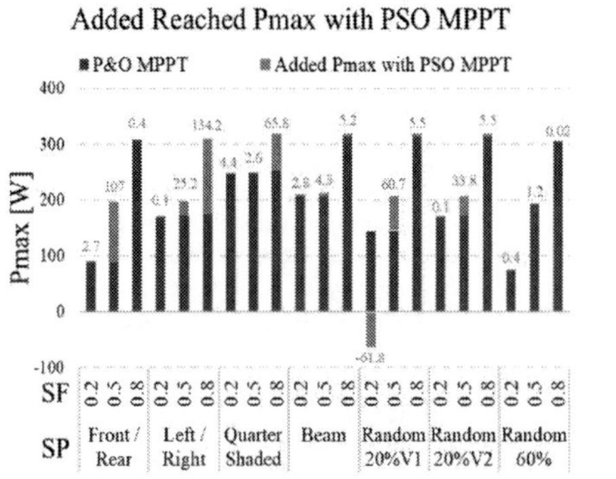

Figure 10: Maximum power [W] reached for the P&O and PSO MPPTs

4 CONCLUSIONS

In conclusion, four driving scenarios were analyzed for Athens, Paris, and Helsinki. PV energy production and HVAC coverage depend on both driven distance and parking location. Short trips with daytime street parking allow households, even with garages, to maximize VIPV benefits. For Short Distance and Commuter driving profiles, a PV area of 1.64m^2 is sufficient to fully cover the monthly HVAC energy demand in southern (Athens) and central (Paris) Europe. For Long Distance driving profiles, PV can supply the full HVAC demand for approximately half of the year. The lowest coverage occurs under Average Driving profiles due to the combination of infrequent street parking and high monthly mileage. In northern Europe (Helsinki), all driving profiles achieve full HVAC coverage from May to September, with Short Distance and Commuter drivers extending this coverage into April.

As for partial shading, the number of cells bypassed is important primarily with high intensity shading. The reached power is not only affected by the size of the shaded area, but also the distribution and location of the shadow. For a PV area of 1.64m^2 with a cell efficiency of 22.3%, a relatively low number of bypass diodes (~10) is sufficient under mild shading conditions, where the shaded cells receive 50 to 80% of their nominal irradiance. Under severe shading, with irradiance levels below 30% of the nominal value, a higher number of bypass diodes is required to maintain power output (~35 BPDs). Moreover, the PSO MPPT is better suited for partial shading than the P&O MPPT, even though there is no clear trend with respect to shading pattern or factor.

5 REFERENCES

[1] Kutter, C., Alanis, L.E., Neuhaus, D.H. and Heinrich, M. (2021) Yield Potential of Vehicle Integrated Photovoltaics on Commercial Trucks and Vans. 38*th European PV Solar Energy Conference and Exhibition* 2021, Online, 6-10 September 2021, 1412-1420. https://doi.org/10.4229/EUPVSEC20212021-6DO.8.2

[2] M. Heinrich, C. Kutter, F. Basler, M. Mittag, L. Alanis, D. Eberlein, A. Schmid, C. Reise, T. Kroyer,

D. H. Neuhaus and H. Wirth, "Potential and Challenges of Vehicle Integrated Photovoltaics for Passenger Cars," in *European Photovoltaic Solar Energy Conference and Exhibition (EU PVSEC)*, 2020.
[3] (n.d.). EFFEREST. https://efferest-project.eu/
[4] Klasen, N., Lux, F., Weber, J., Roessler, T., & Kraft, A. (2022). A Comprehensive Study of Module Layouts for Silicon Solar Cells Under Partial Shading. *IEEE Journal of Photovoltaics*, *12*(2), 546–556. https://doi.org/10.1109/jphotov.2022.3144635
[5] Abdulellah Aifan G. Alsulami, Abdullah Ali Alhussainy, Allehyani, A., Alturki, Y. A., Alghamdi, S. M., Alruwaili, M., & Alharthi, Y. Z. (2024). A comparison of several maximum power point tracking algorithms for a photovoltaic power system. *Frontiers in Energy Research*, *12*. https://doi.org/10.3389/fenrg.2024.1413252
[6] (n.d.). NSRDB. https://nsrdb.nrel.gov/
[7] *Weather data documentation*. (2025, July 2). Visual Crossing. https://www.visualcrossing.com/resources/documentation/weather-data/weather-data-documentation/
[8] Mateja, K., Skarka, W., & Drygała, A. (2022). Efficiency Decreases in a Laminated Solar Cell Developed for a UAV. *Materials*, *15*(24), 8774. https://doi.org/10.3390/ma15248774
[9] (n.d.). Solar Measurement and Environmental solutions | EKO Instruments. https://eko-instruments.com/
[10] Jalkh, J., Doppler, C., Spudat, C., Sammer, P., & Michelic, F. (2024). Energy harvesting potential for 3 EVs equipped with PV for the area of Graz in Austria. *Solar Energy Materials and Solar Cells*, *277*, 113116. https://doi.org/10.1016/j.solmat.2024.113116

6 ACKNOWLEDGEMENTS

This work was conducted in the EFFEREST project that has received funding from the European Union's Horizon Europe research and innovation programme under Grant Agreement No. 101138266. Views and opinions expressed are however those of the author(s) only and do not necessarily reflect those of the European Union or European Climate, Infrastructure and Environment Executive Agency (CINEA). Neither the European Union nor the granting authority can be held responsible for them. The publication was written at Virtual Vehicle Research GmbH in Graz and partially funded within the COMET K2 Competence Centers for Excellent Technologies by the Austrian Federal Ministry for Innovation, Mobility and Infrastructure (BMIMI), Austrian Federal Ministry for Economy, Energy and Tourism (BMWET), the Province of Styria (Dept. 12) and the Styrian Business Promotion Agency (SFG). The Austrian Research Promotion Agency (FFG) has been authorised for the programme management.

The authors would like to acknowledge ISC Konstanz for supplying their CIGS PV cells used is this study's measurement campaign.

Influence of Different Driving Patterns and Electrical Designs on VIPV Performance

Judy Jalkh[1], Christian Doppler[1], Philip Caluori[1], Manuel Ruf[2]

[1]Virtual Vehicle GmbH
[2]Robert Bosch GmbH

www.v2c2.at

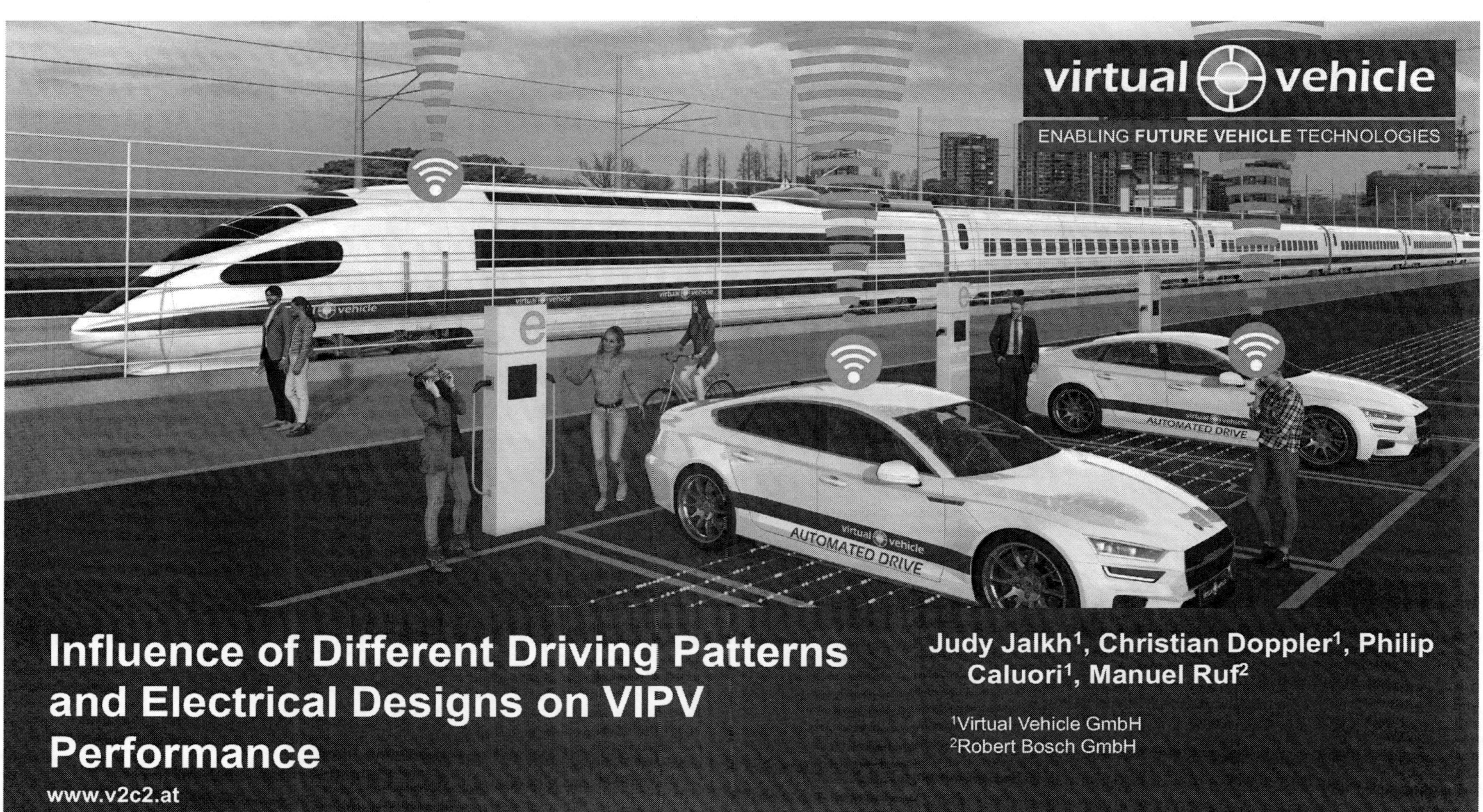

Outline

virtual vehicle

A. Introduction

B. Driving and Parking scenarios
   1. Exemplary Reference Week
   2. Solar Irradiance Calculator (SIC) simulations
   3. HVAC Calculation
   4. Results

C. Electrical architecture for partial shading
   1. Simulation Model
   2. Bypass diode (BPD) configurations and Results
   3. BPD Measurement Campaign
   4. MPPT comparisons

D. Conclusion

Introduction

- The **EFFEREST** project aims to boost energy efficiency in electric vehicles by developing user-centric control systems that optimize both powertrain and cabin comfort.

- It uses the TOGG electric vehicle as a demonstrator, including simulation scenarios with vehicle-integrated photovoltaics (VIPV) on the roof.

- The goal is investigating VIPV success wrt:
  1. The effect of driving and parking patterns across different geographical locations
  2. The influence of the electric configurations on partial shading

Exemplary Reference Week

virtual vehicle

- Preselection of of 4 distinct vehicle usage-profiles [Short – Long – Average Distance Driver – Commuter].
- According to daily and annual mileage and driving pattern identification from vehicles monitored for ~1 year.
- Enrichment of base journals with vehicle simulation model including stochastic parking data, charging models, and climatic data from regions [Cold: Helsinki / Average: Paris / Hot: Athens].
- Extraction of an exemplary week for each usage-profile with least-square deviation of most important indicators from a weekly extrapolation to actual annual values.

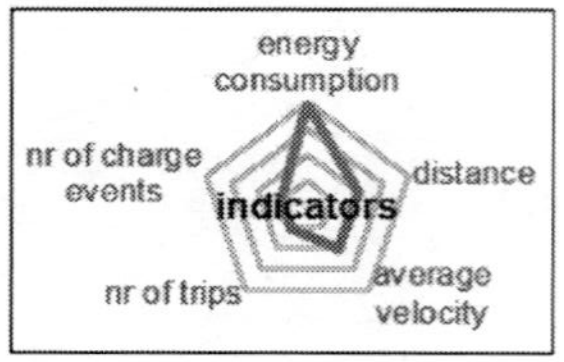

	Driver Type			
	Average Mileage (Avg)	**Short Distance (SD)**	**Long Distance (LD)**	**Commuter (Com)**
Garage Parking	Yes	Yes	No	No
Street Parking [days/week]	3	4	7	7
Monthly mileage [km]	~800	~300	~2600	~1250

Visualization of exemplary week for Short Distance Driver

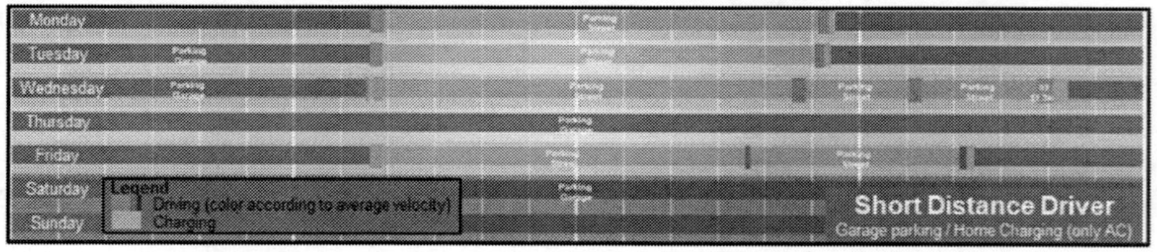

Which type of driver benefits the most from VIPV?

From Bosch

25/09/2025

© VIRTUAL VEHICLE 4

SIC Simulations

virtual vehicle

Weather
- GHI, DNI, DHI and Temperature
- **3 cities:** Athens, Paris, Helsinki
- Data for 365 days with 15 min interval for year 2019
- Calculation of **Monthly Average** weather conditions

from NSRDB: National Solar Radiation Database https://nsrdb.nrel.gov/

Cycles
- **Bosch Exemplary weeks** in 24-hr cycles joining parking and driving.
- Cycles include **4 driver types**: Long, short, commuter, average

Shading
- Random Shading Generator (RSG) is used.
- **When driving:** RSG with higher frequency.
- **When parking:**
  - Garage → irradiance = 0.
  - Shaded → only DHI considered.
  - Street → RSG lower frequency.

No Partial Shading at this point

PV characteristics
- Area of PV roof is 1.64 m^2.
- PV efficiency is 23%.
- PE efficiency is 95%.

Output
- **24-hr irradiance profiles** [W/m^2] for 3 cities x 4 driver types x12 months x different vehicle zones (roof, doors, hood, trunk)
- In .m format

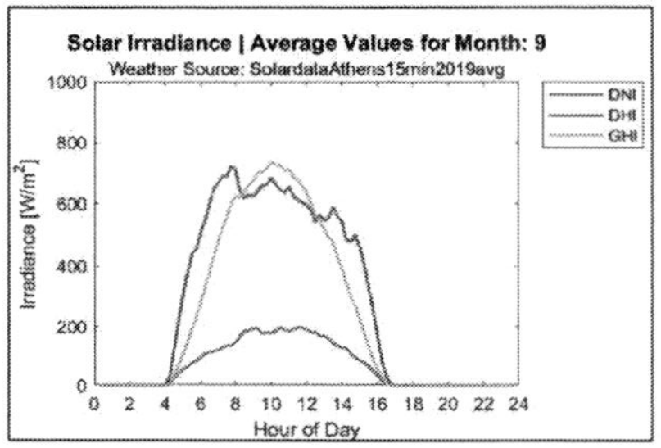

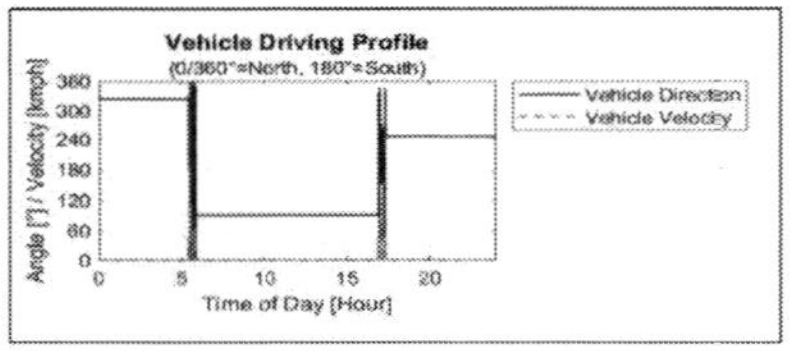

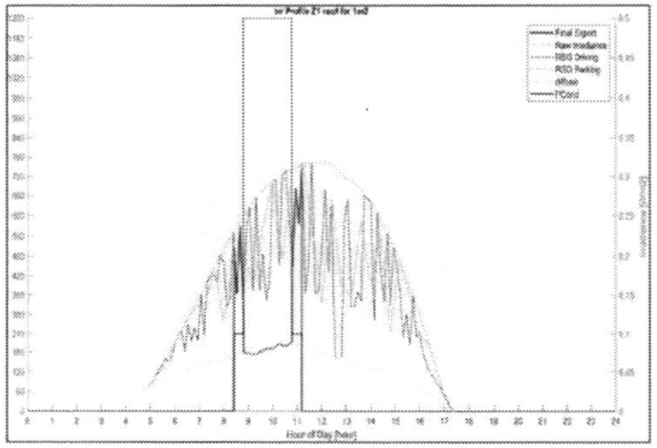

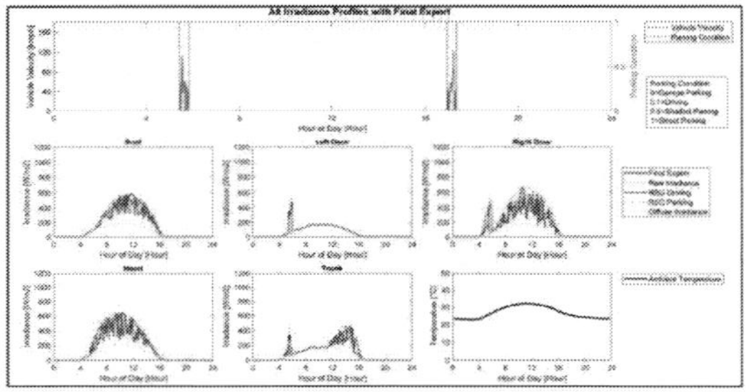

25/09/2025

© VIRTUAL VEHICLE

HVAC Calculations

virtual vehicle

HVAC energy consumption values
- From EFFEREST proposal

Distribution of Temperature Conditions
- Number of Hot/Cold/Normal/Very Cold days per month
- Using real temperature data for 2023 from online sources[1]

Monthly Driven Distance
- HVAC only used when driving

Result
- Example for Short Distance Driver in Athens

	HVAC/ThMgt EFFEREST [kWh/100km]
Hot / 30º	3
Normal / 15º	0
Cold / 0º	3
Very Cold / -10º	7

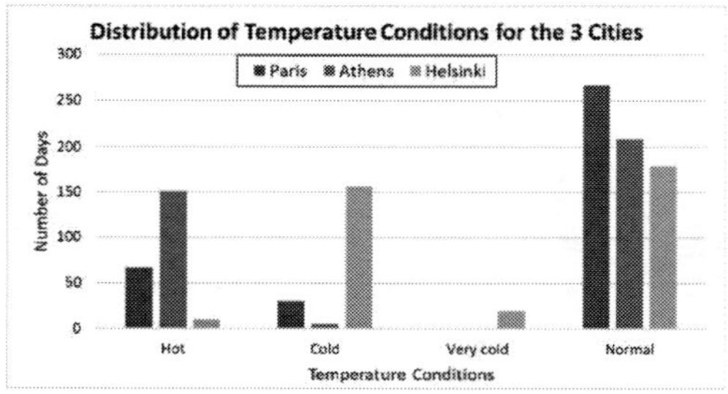

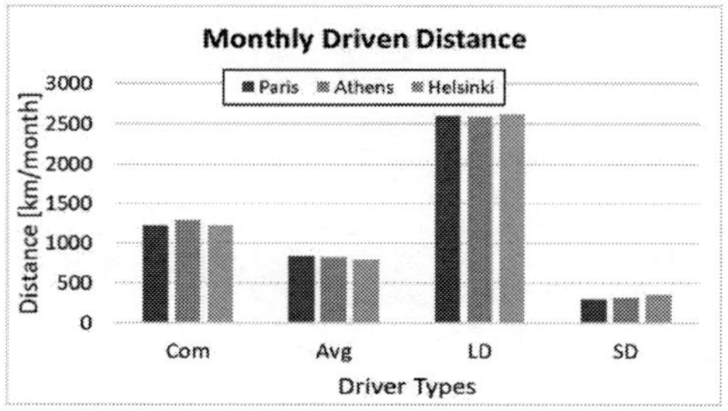

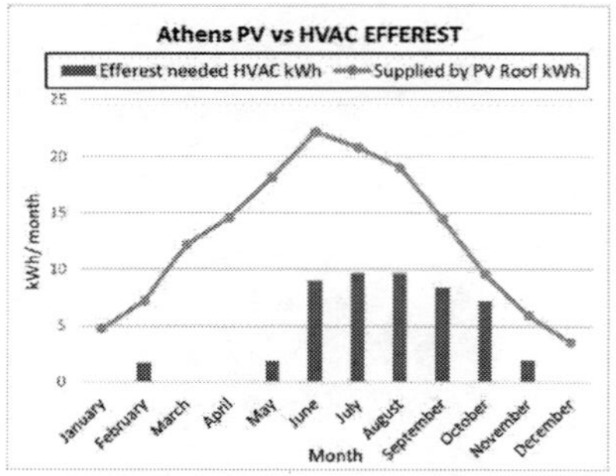

[1] https://www.visualcrossing.com/resources/documentation/weather-data/weather-data-documentation/

Results

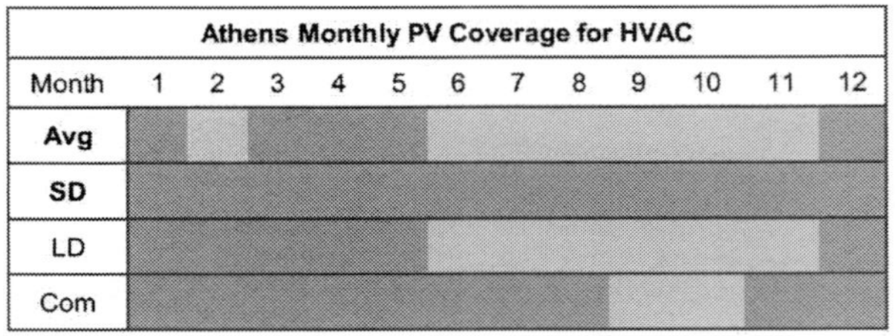

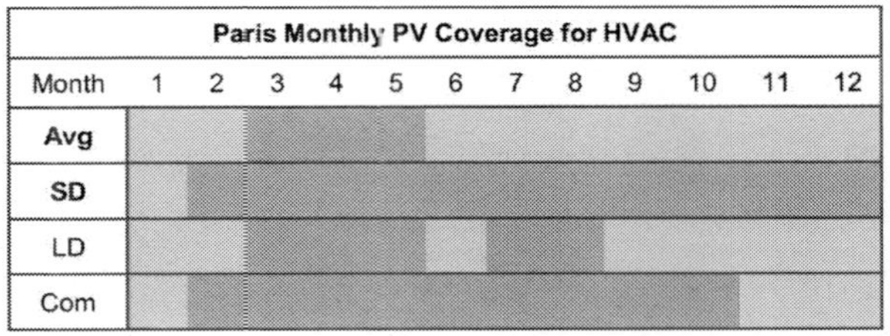

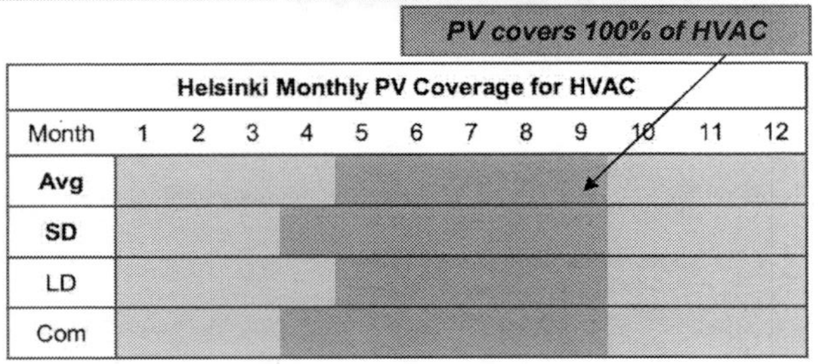

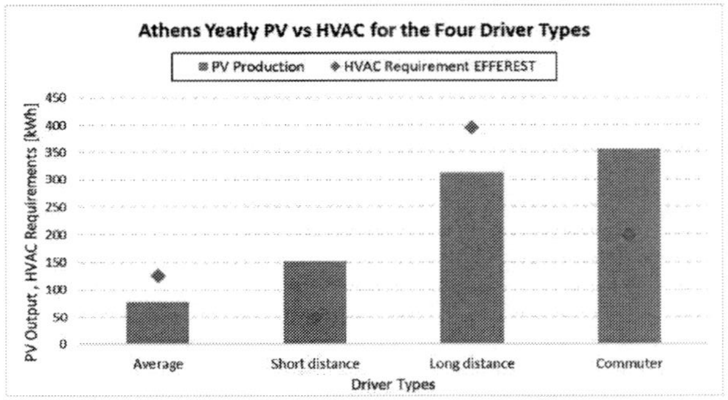

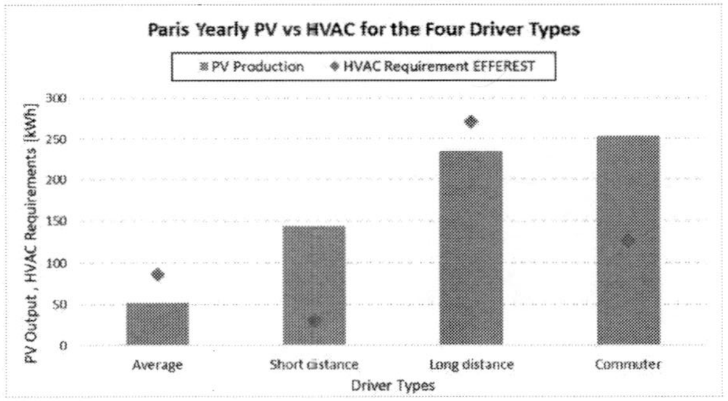

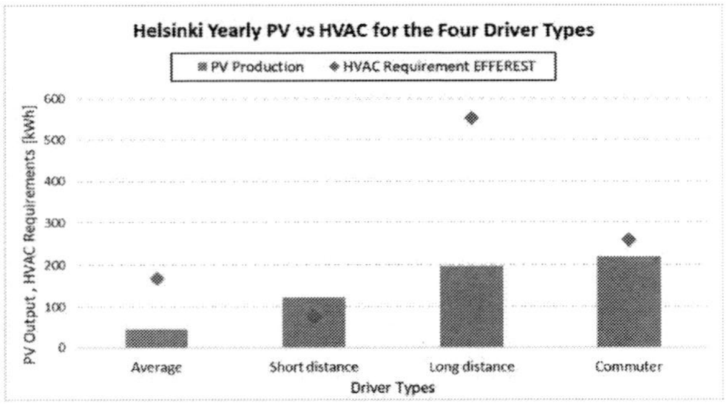

Conclusions:

- Both **garage presence** and **monthly driven distance** affect results.
- PV Surplus for commuter and SD driver can be used for mileage.

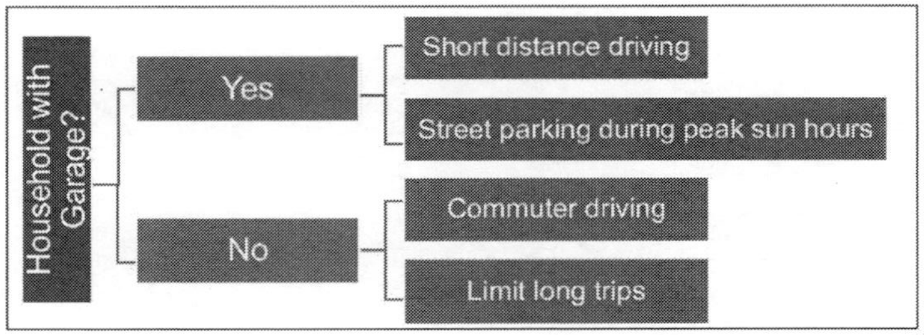

Simulation Model

virtual vehicle

PV Cell Model

- PV technology: Maxeon Ne3 Cell[2]
- To include roof integration, the laminated version was chosen.

	PV Cell
Number of Cells	1
Cells Series	1
Cells Parallel	1
Cell Length [mm]	125
Cell Width [mm]	125
Cell Area [m2]	0.015625
Voc [V]	0.7264
Isc [A]	6.123
Vmp [V]	0.61
Imp [A]	5.7
Pmax [W]	3.47
Efficiency [%]	22.3
N (Quality Factor)	1.05
Rs [Ω]	0.006
Rsh [Ω]	7

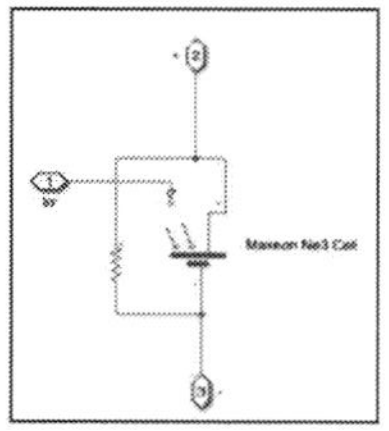

Matching simulated and datasheet curves

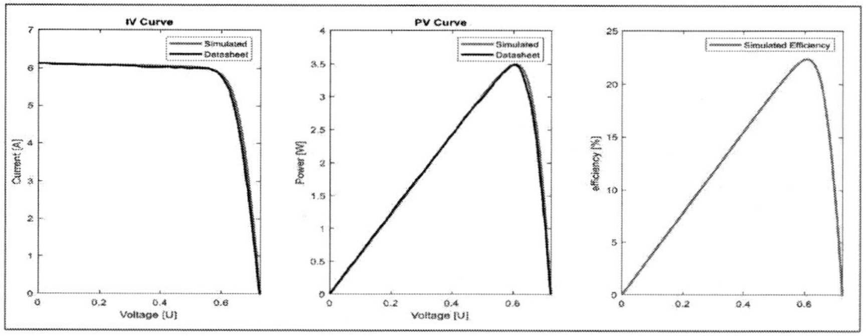

TOGG VIPV Model

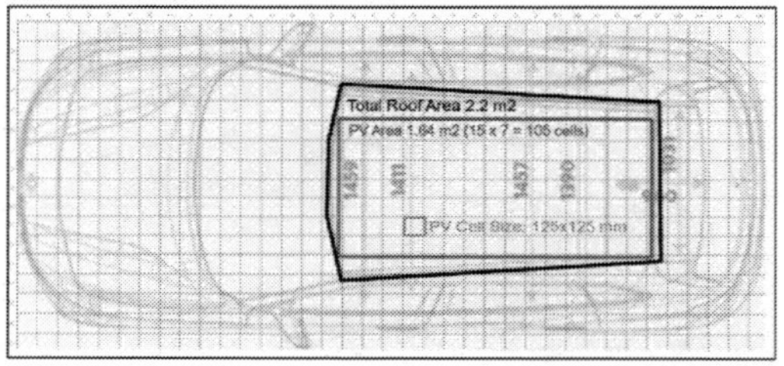

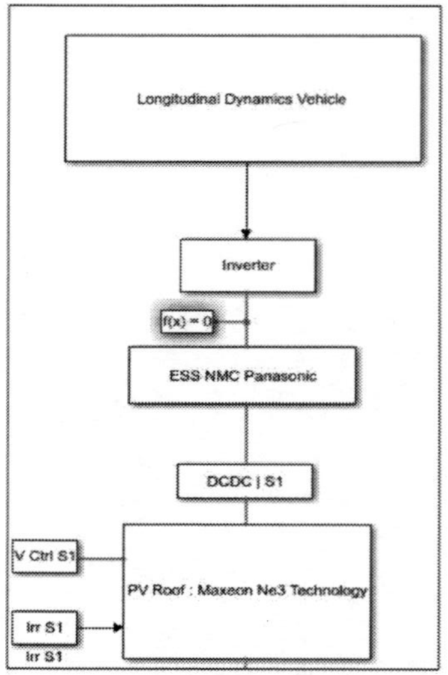

[2]Materials 2022, 15, 8774. https://doi.org/10.3390/ma15248774

BPD Simulations

virtual vehicle

- BPD simulations include varying the shading factor (SF), the electrical configuration (EC), and the shading pattern (SP).
- Simulation parameters:
  - Max. voltage = Voc
  - Simulation time: 300 s
  - Logarithmic increase to derive high resolution around Pmax
  - All PV cells connected in series

1. Shading Factor

- From 0 → 0.8
- Refers to the intensity of the shaded object
- The irradiance that reaches the PV cells in each case is: **Irradiance = SF x 1000 W/m2.**

2. Electrical Configuration

	Number of cells / BPD	Number of Modules	Module Dimensions [m2]
Option 1	3	35	0.047
Option 2	7	15	0.11
Option 3	15	7	0.23

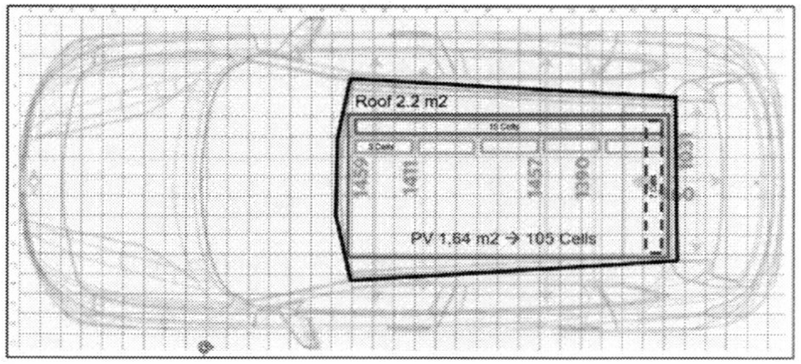

3. Shading Pattern

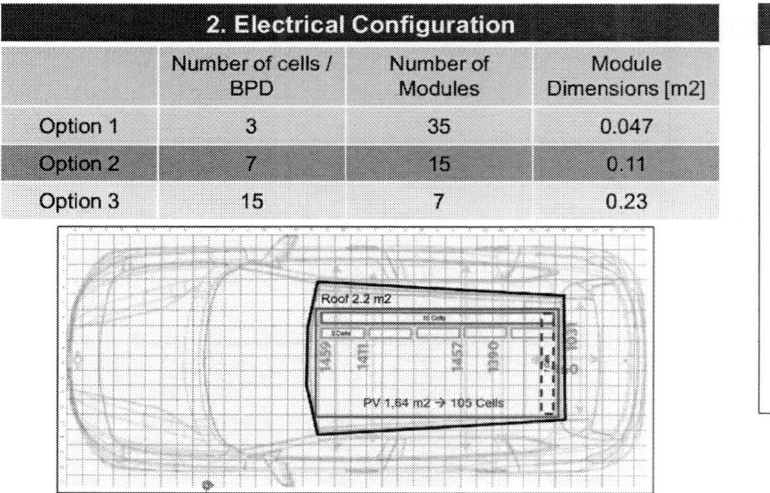

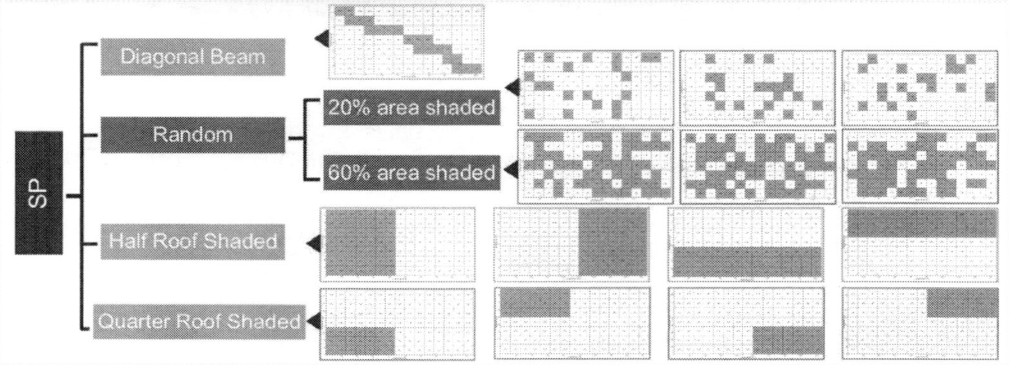

BPD TOGG Simulation Results

virtual vehicle

A- Which electrical configuration reaches the greatest Pmax?

For each SP and SF, the three ECs were compared in terms of maximum power reached.

- With high intensity shading (SF<= 0.3) ➔ 3 cells per BPD (35 BPDs)
- For lower intensity shading (SF >= 0.5) ➔ doesn't matter

Preferance of number of BPDs
35 15 7 No Preferance

	SF	20% area Random			60% area Random			Half Roof Shaded				Quarter Roof Shaded				Diagonal Beam
		V1	V2	V3	V1	V2	V3	Front	Rear	Left	Right	Front Left	Front Right	Rear Left	Rear Right	
High Intensity	0															
	0.1															
	0.2															
	0.3															
Low Intensity	0.5															
	0.6															
	0.8															

B- Effect of Shading Pattern

- Quarter Roof shaded ➔ the location of the shadow does not affect the power. The 3 cells per BPD gives the highest power (except with 0.8 SF).
- Half Roof Shaded ➔ the orientation of the PV modules wrt the shading location determines the EC preference (F + R vs L + Rt).
- 60% random shading ➔ No effect. All 3 scenarios achieve similar Pmax values with any of the ECs since the majority of the roof is shaded.
- 20% shaded area ➔ 4 different SP give different Pmax values, highlighting the effects of not only the amount of the shaded area, but its distribution. However, they all prefer the 3 cells/BPD EC for high intensity shading.

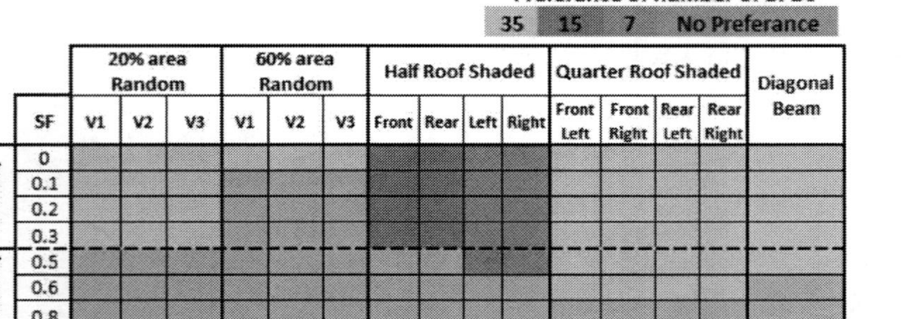

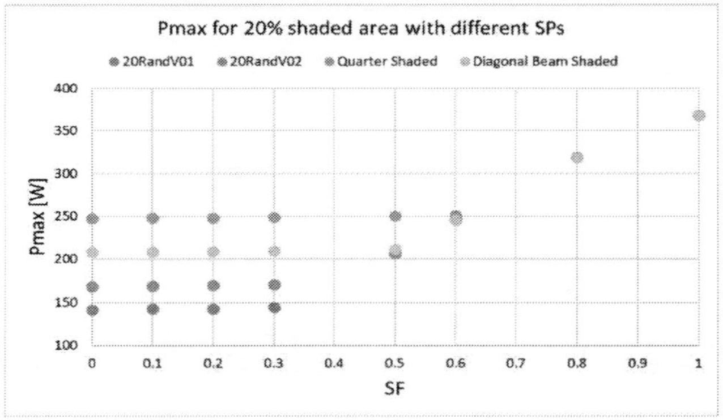

BPD Measurement Campaign

virtual vehicle

- Pyranometer: EKO INSTRUMENTS, ML-02
- Software: 'Data Beam'
- PV Cells: CIGS cells from ISC-Konstanz, 160x160 mm
- Bypass Diodes: Schottky-Diode STPS1545D
- Test-Bench provided by TU-Graz

Irradiance distribution

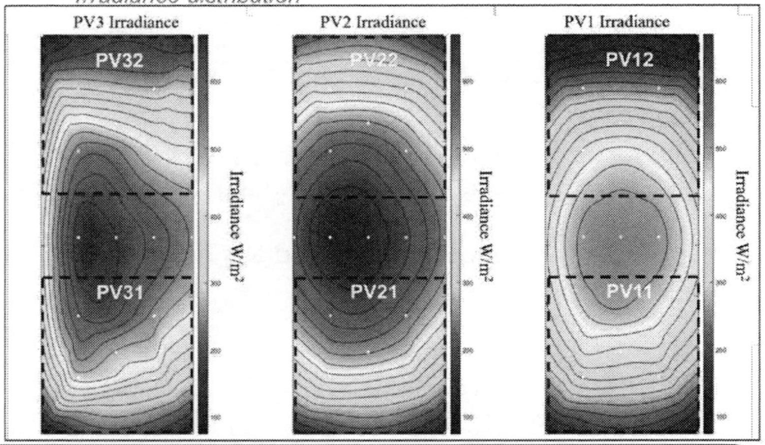

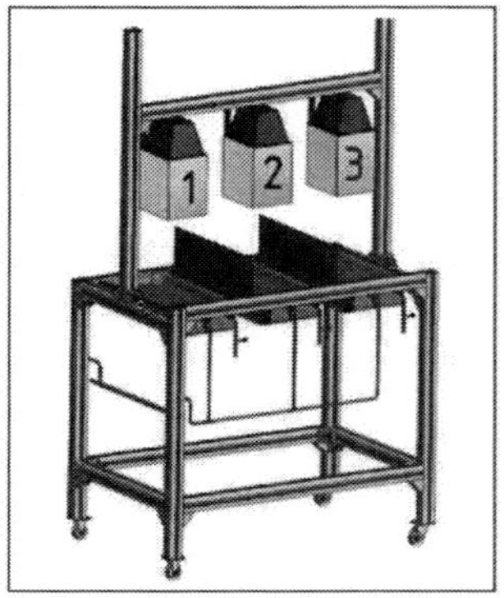

Strasser (2013)

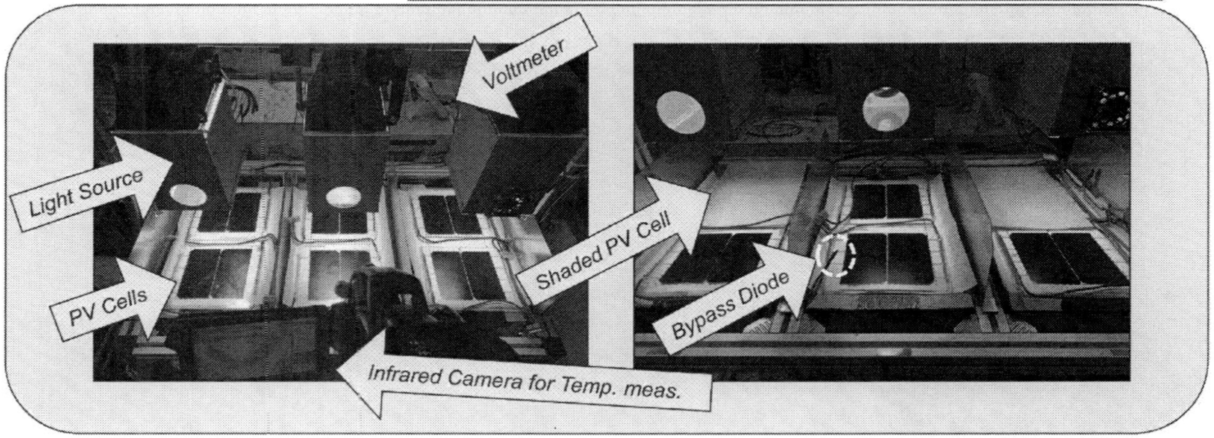

BPD Measurement Campaign Results

virtual vehicle

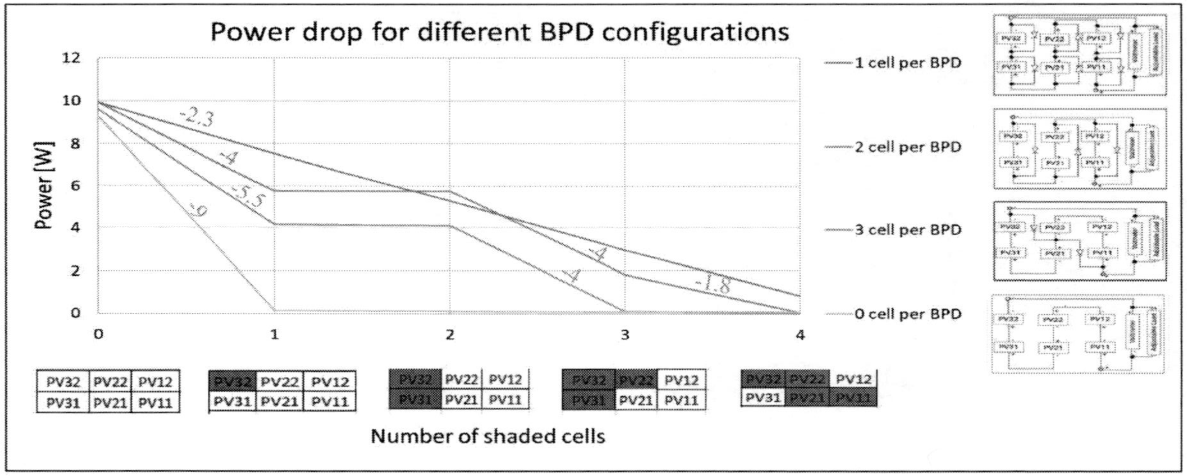

Fixed EC:

- <u>No bypass diodes:</u> Power drop is already drastic with just 1 shaded cell. The power barely decreases with additional shaded cells.
- <u>1 cell per BPD:</u> Power experiences a steady decline as the number of shaded cells increases.
- <u>2 and 3 cells per BPD:</u> Similar *non-steady* power drop trends. No change from 1 to 2 cells shaded because the same number of strings is affected.

Fixed SP:

- The 1 cell per BPD achieves the highest power except with 2 shaded cells. This is due the losses in the additional bypass diode.

BPD Measurement Campaign Results

Effect of shading pattern

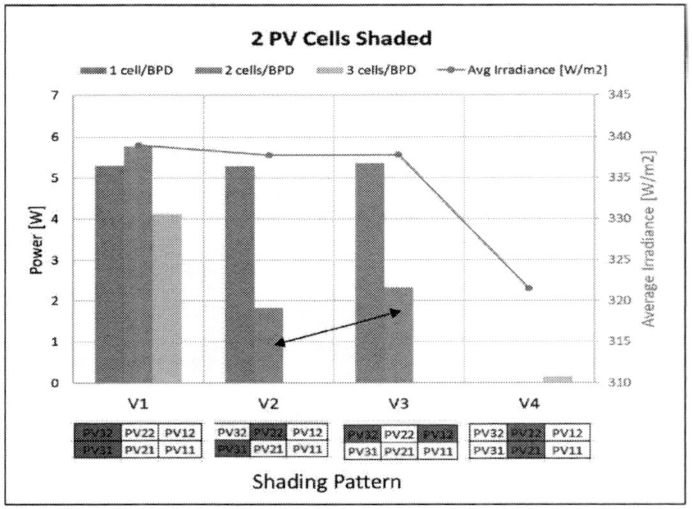

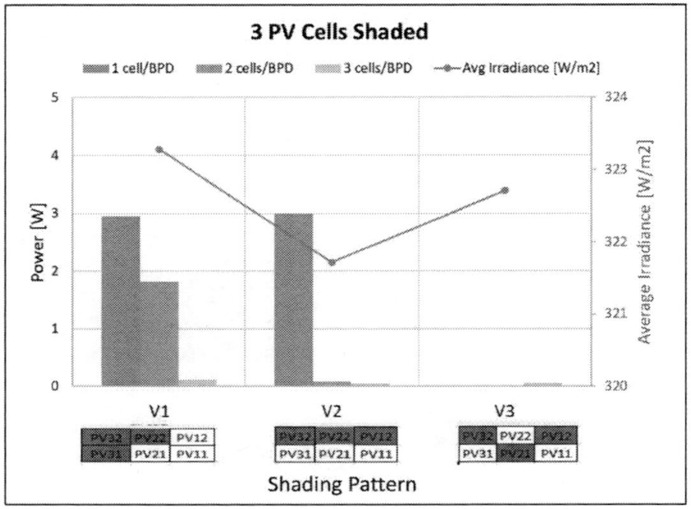

- With 1 cell/BPD, the power is the same independent of the SP.
- With more cells/ BPD, the power depends on the SP and thus the number of strings affected.
- V2 vs V3 for 2 PV cells shaded with 2 cells/BPD is probably due to the distribution of the irradiance, even though the average is the same. *(refer to prev slide with irradiance distribution)*

MPPT Comparisons

	Perturb and Observe (P&O)	Particle Swarm Optimization (PSO)
Working principle	• Perturbs the voltage • Observes if +ve or –ve power response	• Bio-inspired (bird flocks/ fish swarms) • Each particle is aware of its personal and global best
With partial shading	Can get stuck on local instead of global MPP which leads to power loss	Iteratively converges towards global MPP

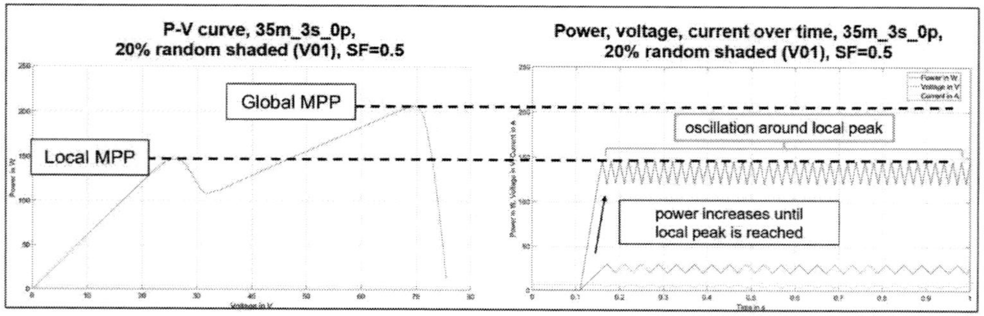

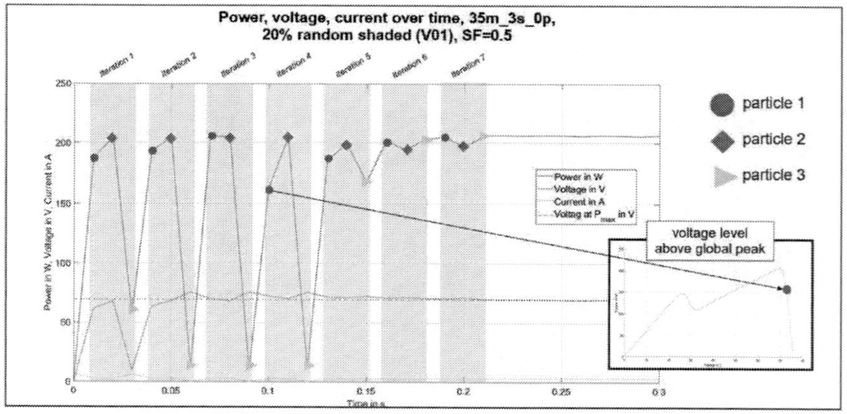

MPPT Comparisons

- MPPT simulations include varying the shading factor (SF), the shading pattern (SP), and the MPPT type.
- Simulation parameters:
  - Original irradiance = 1000 W/m2
  - Simulation time: 5 s
  - Time sample = 0.01 s
  - 35 modules, 3 cells per BPD

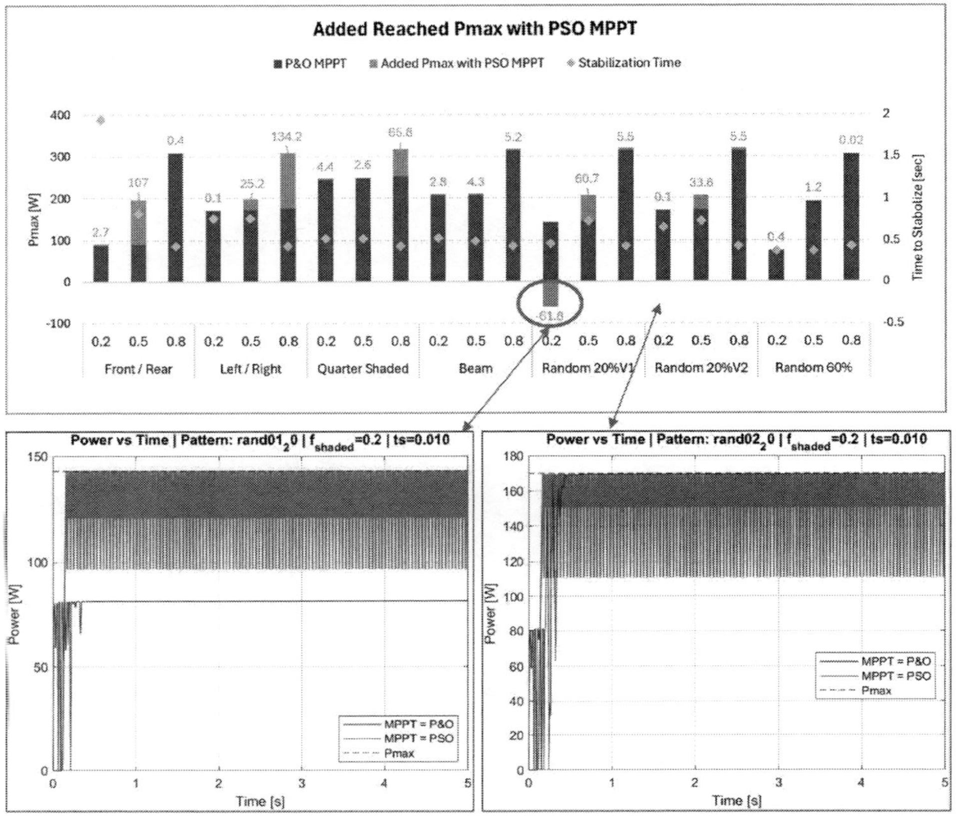

Results:

- PSO MPPT reaches a higher Pmax than the P&O.
- Some cases are better than others, but there is no clear trend.
- 1 exception is the R20V1 SF0.2 where the P&O behaves better.

Conclusion

virtual vehicle

- Four driver types with different driving and parking conditions were studied.
- The driven distance and parking location affect the produced PV energy.
- A household with a garage can still benefit from VIPV if its members take shorter trips and park outside during peak sun hours. This is why the Short Distance driver benefitted the most from VIPV.
- Driver type influences VIPV performance in Southern and Central Europe but has little impact in Northern Europe.

- The number of cells bypassed is important primarily with high intensity shading.
- The reached power is not only affected by the size of the shaded area, but also the distribution and location of the shadow.
- PSO is better suited for partial shading than P&O MPPT, even though there is no clear trend wrt shading pattern or factor.

Next Steps:
Simulate partial shading and temperature effects for all exemplary weeks

Acknowledgement

virtual vehicle

The authors would like to acknowledge ISC Konstanz for supplying their CIGS PV cells used in this study's measurement campaign.

This work was conducted in the EFFEREST project that has received funding from the European Union's Horizon Europe research and innovation programme under Grant Agreement No. 101138266. Views and opinions expressed are however those of the author(s) only and do not necessarily reflect those of the European Union or European Climate, Infrastructure and Environment Executive Agency (CINEA). Neither the European Union nor the granting authority can be held responsible for them. The publication was written at Virtual Vehicle Research GmbH in Graz and partially funded within the COMET K2 Competence Centers for Excellent Technologies by the Austrian Federal Ministry for Innovation, Mobility and Infrastructure (BMIMI), Austrian Federal Ministry for Economy, Energy and Tourism (BMWET), the Province of Styria (Dept. 12) and the Styrian Business Promotion Agency (SFG). The Austrian Research Promotion Agency (FFG) has been authorised for the programme management.

Funded by the European Union

Federal Ministry Republic of Austria Climate Action, Environment, Energy, Mobility, Innovation and Technology

Federal Ministry Republic of Austria Labour and Economy

FFG Promoting Innovation

Das Land Steiermark

SFG

virtual vehicle

ENABLING **FUTURE VEHICLE** TECHNOLOGIES

THANK YOU

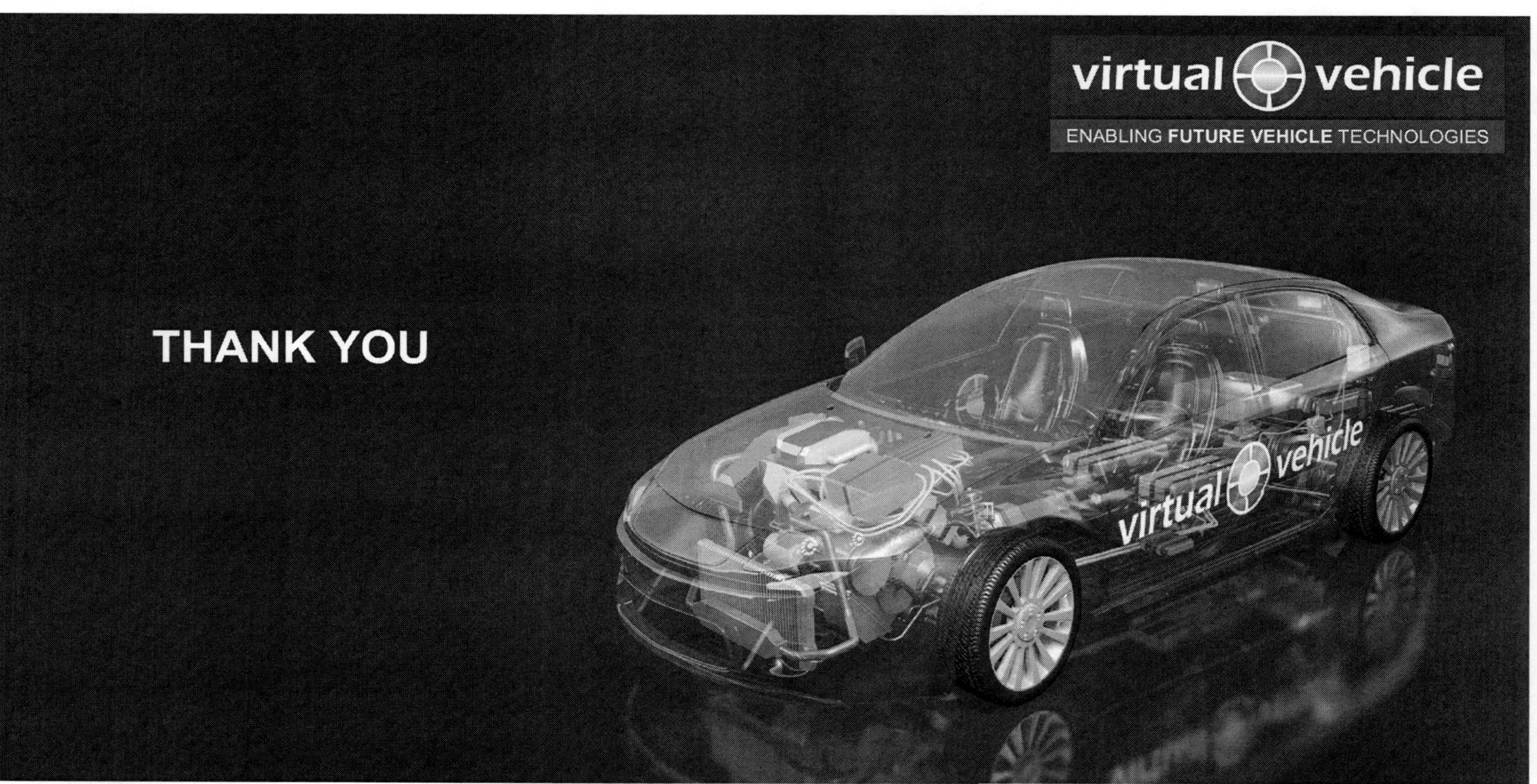

www.v2c2.at

25/09/2025

Bundesministerium Klimaschutz, Umwelt, Energie, Mobilität, Innovation und Technologie

Bundesministerium Arbeit und Wirtschaft

FFG

Das Land Steiermark

SFG

Virtual Vehicle Research GmbH wird im Rahmen von COMET Competence Centers for Excellent Technologies durch BMK, BMAW, Land Steiermark und Steirische Wirtschaftsförderung (SFG) gefördert. Das Programm wird durch die FFG abgewickelt.

42nd European Photovoltaic Solar Energy Conference and Exhibition

This presentation was selected by the Sc. Committee of the EU PVSEC 2025 for submission of a full paper to one of the EU PVSEC's collaborating peer-reviewed journals.

DYNAMIC GIS-BASED 3D SOLAR SIMULATION FRAMEWORK FOR ASSESSING VIPV IN URBAN PUBLIC TRANSPORT USING GTFS AND DRIVING CYCLES

David Pera[1], Christian Braun[1], Philippe Pinheiro[1], Miguel Brito[2] and Ulrich Leopold[1]
[1]Luxembourg Institute of Science and Technology, [2]Faculdade de Ciências da Universidade de Lisboa
david.pera@list.lu, philippe.pinheiro@list.lu, christian.braun@list.lu, mcbrito@fc.ul.pt, ulrich.leopold@list.lu

ABSTRACT: Vehicle-Integrated Photovoltaics (VIPV) represent a promising pathway to reduce the energy demand of electric bus fleets, particularly in urban environments where charging infrastructure constraints and operational costs are critical. This paper introduces a dynamic GIS-based 3D solar simulation framework that integrates General Transit Feed Specification (GTFS) data with advanced irradiation modeling to quantify VIPV potential along real-world bus routes. The methodology combines Copernicus Atmosphere Monitoring Service (CAMS) solar radiation datasets with hemispherical beam-projection shadow casting on standardized CityGML 3D city models, enabling detailed assessment of direct, diffuse, and reflected solar components under complex urban shadowing conditions. To assess the net impact of VIPV integration, GTFS-derived driving cycles are processed in conjunction with vehicle powertrain and consumption models, calibrated against experimental measurements from a field campaign in Luxembourg. This combined workflow provides time-resolved estimates of photovoltaic generation, energy consumption, and resulting battery state-of-charge, allowing direct comparison between baseline and VIPV-equipped operations.

In a case study of TICE Line 1 in Esch-sur-Alzette in Luxembourg, rooftop PV (3.5 kWp, PR = 75 %) covers 2.8–4.1 % of annual traction energy. Summer clear-sky operation reaches daily yields of about 3.9 kWh/kWp. This contribution avoids up to ~146 standard 20–80 % state-of-charge charging cycles per year (about 98 cycles under real-sky conditions) and offers simple payback of 7–10 years at current electricity tariffs. The open-data, standards-based workflow is transferable to other cities and provides a reproducible tool for assessing VIPV in public-transport electrification strategies.
Keywords: Vehicle-Integrated Photovoltaics, GTFS, 3D GIS, Urban Shadowing, Electric Buses

1 AIM AND APPROACH

The transition to electric mobility in public transport fleets introduces new challenges regarding charging demand, operational flexibility, and integration with energy systems. Vehicle-Integrated Photovoltaics (VIPV) have emerged as a complementary technology to reduce battery charging needs, but their deployment in complex urban contexts requires accurate assessment methods. The aim of this work is to present a dynamic GIS-based simulation framework that quantifies VIPV energy yield for buses under real operational conditions, explicitly considering urban shadowing, diffuse reflection, and route-specific driving cycles.

The novelty of this approach lies in the integration of General Transit Feed Specification (GTFS) data [6] with high-resolution 3D solar modeling. GTFS datasets, openly available for most cities worldwide, contain structured information on routes, timetables, and stops. In this framework, GTFS data are converted into continuous spatio-temporal driving cycles, capturing vehicle trajectories, speeds, gradients, and stop durations. These cycles serve as the basis for both solar irradiation and energy consumption simulations.

The irradiation model employs a multi-beam projection collision detection method [2], which computes the incident direct radiation for each time step along the route based on solar geometry. Diffuse radiation is corrected using the Sky View Factor (SVF) derived from a hemispherical viewshed analysis. This method propagates thousands of vectors in a 3D CityGML model [1] to identify visible sky fractions and surrounding surfaces. Each façade or obstacle is assigned an albedo coefficient according to its material properties, enabling the calculation of reflected diffuse components. The radiation datasets are accessed from the Copernicus CAMS Radiation Service (CRS) [3–5], ensuring realistic temporal resolution and spatial coverage for all radiative components.

Parallel to the irradiation estimation, a vehicle energy consumption module simulates the power demand of a battery-electric bus. This includes propulsion requirements, braking recovery, auxiliary systems such as HVAC and lighting, and road slope effects. The photovoltaic contribution is introduced by injecting the VIPV-generated power, corrected for maximum power point tracking and DC/DC conversion efficiencies, into the vehicle's energy balance. This enables a direct comparison between the baseline scenario and the VIPV-equipped case, expressed in terms of net energy demand, state-of-charge trajectories, and avoided charging cycles.

To enhance reliability, the simulation framework has been calibrated and validated with experimental measurements performed in Luxembourg during 2023–2024. The campaign included on-road monitoring with silicon irradiance sensors, GPS tracking, and 4G data transmission, complemented by reference meteorological data from national networks (LIST, ASTA, MeteoLux). These datasets were used to cross-check modelled solar components against ground-truth measurements, improving confidence in the shadow-casting and reflection algorithms.

By combining open GTFS datasets with standardized 3D city models, CAMS-derived solar radiation, and detailed vehicle physics, the framework offers a holistic and transferable workflow for assessing VIPV feasibility in public transport fleets. Its modular structure supports replication in cities with different urban morphologies, from dense canyons to suburban and rural areas. This work therefore provides a practical decision-support tool for transport operators and policymakers, enabling high-level techno-economic evaluations of VIPV deployment as part of fleet electrification strategies.

To clarify novelty versus existing approaches, this work differs from earlier VIPV or mobile PV studies that either extrapolate static rooftop yields or apply generic duty cycles. Here, GTFS-derived second-scale driving cycles are directly coupled to 3D radiative transfer and vehicle energy modelling, allowing every stop, gradient and dwell period to consider both irradiation and consumption. This tight coupling, together with automated façade-albedo attribution in a standardized CityGML context, enables route-level VIPV assessment that has not been possible with previous methods.

2 SCIENTIFIC INNOVATION AND RELEVANCE

Most solar potential assessment tools have been developed for static rooftop installations or rely on generalized assumptions about solar exposure. While these approaches are suitable for building-integrated photovoltaics, they fall short when applied to moving vehicles operating in dense urban environments. The framework proposed in this work advances the state of the art by linking real-world transport operations with detailed solar radiation modelling, thereby enabling a realistic quantification of VIPV applied to public transport fleets.

At the core of this innovation is the direct use of General Transit Feed Specification (GTFS) datasets [6], which describe the actual timetables, stops, and routes of public transport systems. By transforming these data into continuous spatial-temporal driving cycles, the methodology captures the specific motion and idling patterns of buses in daily operation. This allows the solar resource assessment to be tightly coupled with vehicle dynamics, rather than relying on simplified cycles or averaged duty profiles.

The accuracy of the solar model is enhanced through the integration of three-dimensional city representations based on the CityGML standard [1]. These models make it possible to calculate not only direct shading but also the hemispherical view of the sky at every point along the route (Figure 1).

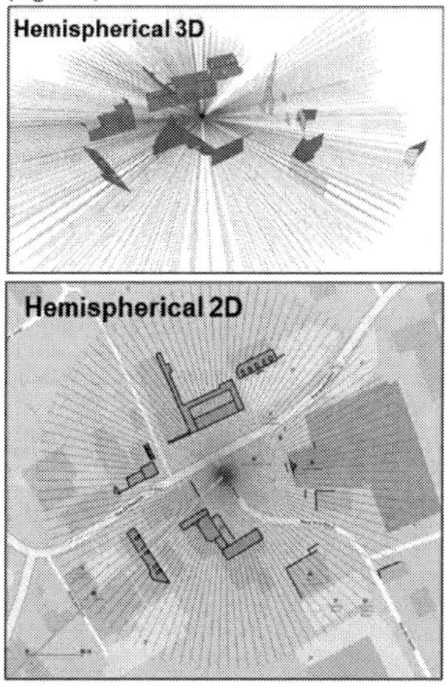

Figure 1: Example of hemispherical viewshed analysis using 3D CityGML models, showing calculation of Sky View Factor and façade reflections in dense urban areas. (top 3D view, bottom 2D view)

By embedding albedo information into the façades of surrounding infrastructure, the framework accounts for reflected diffuse radiation, which can play an important role in narrow streets and urban canyons. The radiation inputs themselves are obtained from the Copernicus CAMS Radiation Service [3–5], ensuring that cloud cover, atmospheric turbidity, and seasonal effects are consistently represented across different time scales and geographies (Figure 2).

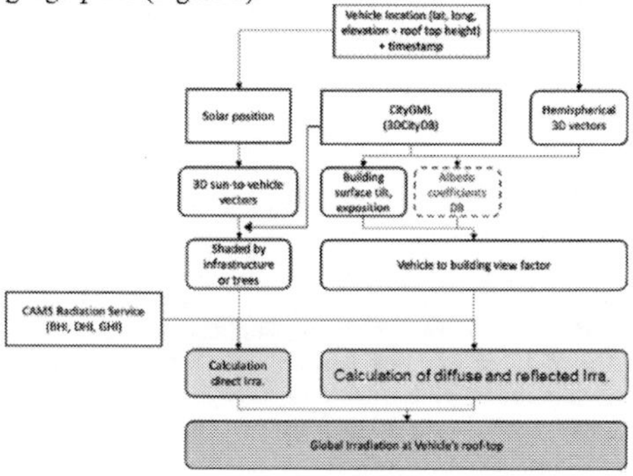

Figure 2: Workflow of the irradiation model integrating direct shading, diffuse sky fraction, and albedo-based façade reflections.

While the irradiation model provides a detailed estimation of the solar resource reaching the vehicle rooftop, a full assessment must also include how this energy interacts with the vehicle itself. This requires a robust description of vehicle power consumption, covering traction, regenerative braking, auxiliary systems, and state-of-charge evolution. For this purpose, the framework makes use of Vehicle Energy Consumption Calculation Tool (VECTO) [7], developed by EC/JRC, which has become the reference methodology for assessing CO_2 emissions and energy consumption in heavy-duty vehicles. Aligning with VECTO ensures that the results are comparable, reproducible, and consistent with European standards, while allowing the direct integration of GTFS-derived driving cycles into energy demand simulations.

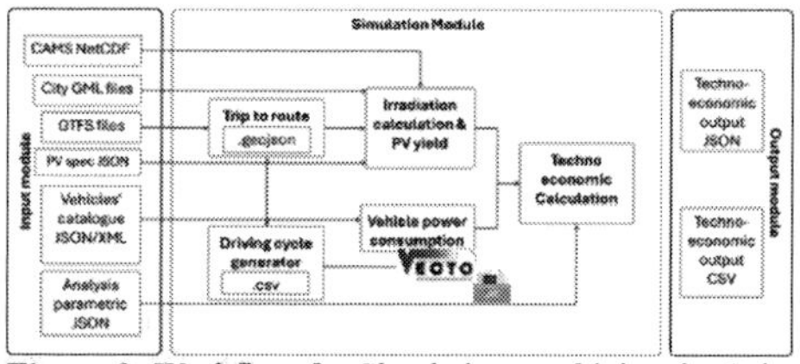

Figure 3: Workflow for Simulation combining the Solar potential assessment of the VIPV systems and the vehicles 'energy consumption.

Figure 3 summarizes how the solar and vehicle modules are combined into a unified workflow. Inputs include CAMS NetCDF irradiance products, CityGML files, GTFS feeds, PV specification JSON, a vehicles' catalogue (JSON/XML), and analysis parameters (JSON). GTFS data are converted in a Trip-to-Route stage to a geospatial trajectory (.geojson). A Driving-Cycle Generator then produces a time series (2-second resolution) representing

10.4229/EUPVSEC2025/4EO.2.5

speeds, stop times, and road gradients. These feed two computational branches: (i) Irradiation calculation & PV yield, and (ii) Vehicle power consumption using VECTO models. The vehicle energy consumption module determine the energy consumption of the vehicle considering, rolling resistance, aerodynamic drag, gear/axle ratios for e-axles, regenerative braking, auxiliary loads, and SoC evolution, providing comparable and reproducible energy baselines.The driving cycles derived directly from GTFS [6], ensure that both energy demand and PV contribution are evaluated under realistic service patterns.

The resulting workflow combines geospatial analysis, radiative transfer modelling, and vehicle physics into a single modular environment. This holistic design provides more than a simple estimation of annual photovoltaic yield; it delivers insights into the operational consequences of installing PV modules on buses, such as reductions in charging frequency, mitigation of peak demand, and potential impacts on battery life. By offering a method that is both transferable, thanks to the widespread availability of GTFS data, and scalable across different cities, the framework has direct relevance for transport operators and policymakers seeking to evaluate the techno-economic feasibility of VIPV adoption.

In this sense, the scientific contribution lies not only in the refinement of solar modelling techniques for mobile platforms, but also in the creation of a decision-support tool that bridges the domains of urban mobility, renewable energy integration, and fleet electrification.

3 RESULTS AND DISCUSSION

The developed framework was applied to TICE Line 1, a high-frequency bus corridor in southern Luxembourg connecting Esch-sur-Alzette and Lamadelaine. The line is particularly suitable for VIPV assessment due to its dense urban morphology, frequent service intervals, and regular operational schedule. Each direction of the route extends for approximately 17–18 km, with 25 and 30 stops and typical trip durations of 40 to 44 minutes, respectuvely. Up to 63 trips per day are performed in each direction, amounting to more than 41000 trips annually. This high service intensity provides an ideal case to evaluate both the energy yield of rooftop PV systems and their cumulative effect on fleet operations.

3.1 Irradiation and shadowing effects

Simulations performed with CAMS radiation data and 3D CityGML models indicate that the annual clear-sky irradiation potential on the bus rooftop reaches 1409 kWh/kWp. Under real-sky conditions, this value decreases to 944 kWh/kWp, corresponding to an overall reduction of about 33%.

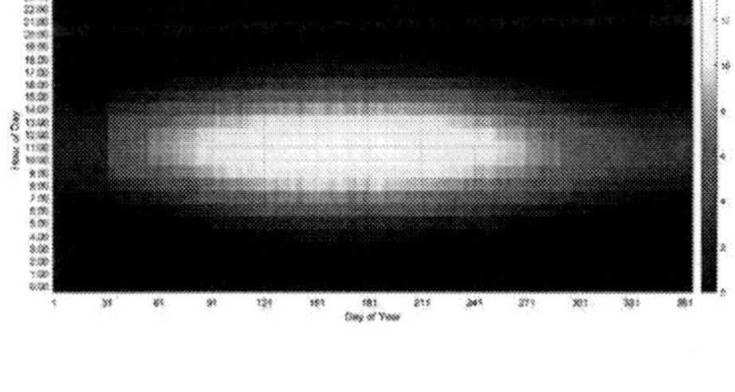

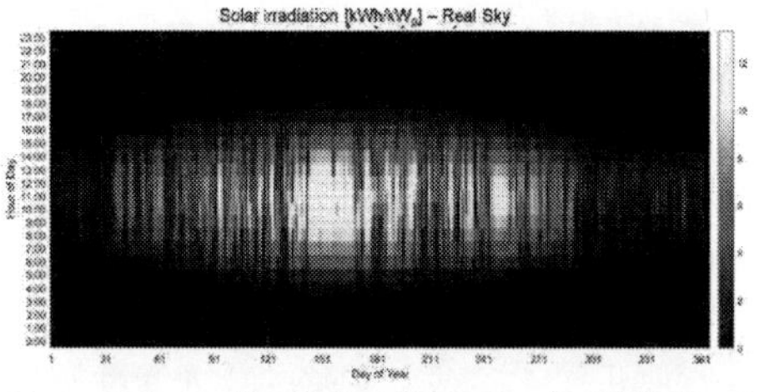

Figure 4: Annual irradiation distribution for TICE Line 1 under clear-sky (top) and real-sky (bottom), with shadowing losses.

The contribution of urban shadowing is non-negligible: losses of 20.5–20.8% were identified, depending on seasonal conditions. These results confirm that urban canyons, building heights, and orientation strongly affect VIPV feasibility and must be explicitly accounted for in yield estimations. Our internal sensitivity check shows that ignoring complex urban shading can overestimate annual production by more than one fifth.

3.2 Energy balance and fleet impact

The case study considered an 12 m Mercedes eCitaro K electric bus with two 125 kW motors, a 330 kWh battery system, and an average auxiliary load of 2–2.5 kW. For this configuration, the average energy demand per one way trip was ~23–24 kWh, corresponding to ~7% state-of-charge depletion. A charging event from 20% to 80% SoC requires ~198 kWh, meaning that multiple trips can be performed between recharges.

A "charging cycle" is counted whenever the cumulative net VIPV energy equals the energy required for a standard 20-80 % state-of-charge recharge (ΔSoC = 60 % of nominal battery capacity). Daily increments of VIPV energy are considered until this threshold is reached, after which the counter resets. This allows direct translation of PV yield into a number of full or partial charging events avoided over time.

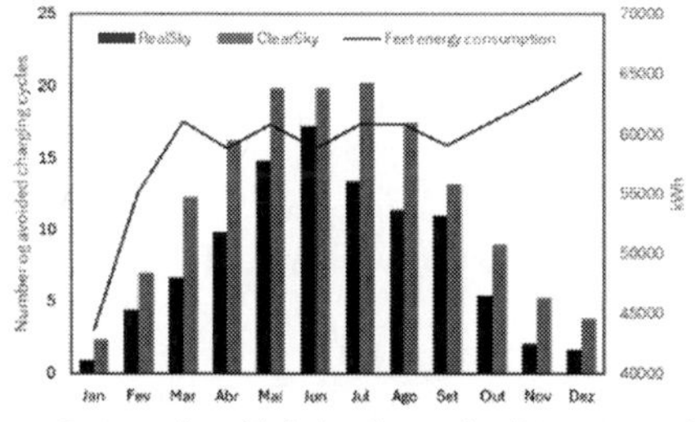

Figure 5: Annual avoided charging cycles (20–80% SoC) under clear-sky and real-sky conditions (bars, left axis) and monthly fleet energy consumption (line, right axis). Totals: 146 cycles (clear-sky), 98 cycles (real-sky), 707.8 MWh fleet demand.

Equipping the bus rooftop with 3.5kW$_P$ (considering 80% of the available area) of silicon PV modules and overall performance ratio of 75% (due to mismatch effects, temperature effects, and power conversion losses), yields an annual production covering between 2.8% and 4.1% of the total line energy demand. While modest in absolute terms, this contribution translates into tangible operational benefits. In the most favorable summer month, up to 17 cycles (June, real-sky), highlighting strong seasonality;

10.4229/EUPVSEC2025/4EO.2.5

annual totals are ~98 cycles (real-sky) versus ~146 cycles for clear-sky upper bound.

3.3 Techno-economic considerations

Considering the VIVP system costs (1.5 €/Wp) and a combined electricity tariff of 0.21 €/kWh, the simple payback time of the VIPV system is estimated to be between 7 and 10 years, depending on degradation, operational intensity, and shadowing conditions. This aligns with the expected service lifetime of bus fleets, indicating that VIPV can approach economic viability under favorable conditions. However, these payback times remain sensitive to several factors: higher installation costs, lower irradiation environments, or reduced vehicle utilization would significantly affect the business case.

While the presented results demonstrate the technical feasibility of VIPV for public transport fleets, the contribution to overall energy demand remains relatively small compared with the size of the traction battery. Ranging from 2.8 to 4.1% of the route's consumption will not fundamentally alter charging infrastructure requirements. Nevertheless, the ability to reduce charging frequency, extend battery lifetimes, and provide distributed generation at the fleet level should not be underestimated, especially in contexts where charging power is constrained.

Moreover, the methodology highlights the importance of urban morphology and shadowing in VIPV studies. The explicit representation of albedo and building façades shows that local geometry can significantly alter the irradiation balance. This suggests that VIPV deployment should be evaluated at the route level, rather than through general average assumptions.

A simple sensitivity analysis indicates that payback is most affected by electricity tariff and installation cost. At ±0.05 €/kWh around the baseline 0.21 €/kWh, payback varies by roughly ±1 year. Likewise, CAPEX shifts of ±20% change payback by approximately ±1.5 years.

From a broader perspective, the integration of GTFS data ensures that results are directly tied to realistic operating conditions, enhancing their relevance for decision makers. However, uncertainties remain. Future work should refine passenger load dynamics and auxiliary power variability (e.g., HVAC demand), which can alter the balance between demand and supply. In addition, further development of automated albedo attribution using open façade datasets could improve accuracy without increasing modeling complexity.

4 CONCLUSIONS

This study introduced a dynamic GIS-based simulation framework to evaluate the feasibility of VIPV for public transport fleets. By integrating GTFS-derived driving cycles, 3D CityGML shadow casting, and CAMS radiation datasets, the workflow delivers high-resolution irradiation profiles along operational bus routes and couples them with VECTO-based vehicle energy modelling. This combination quantifies photovoltaic yield and directly links it to state-of-charge evolution and avoided charging cycles, offering a clear metric for operational impact.

The broader contribution of this work lies in its transferability. GTFS datasets are openly available for most cities, and CityGML or equivalent 3D models are increasingly accessible through public repositories. The method's reliance on open/standardized data makes it well-suited for comparative planning across cities. As such, the framework can be readily applied to diverse geographic and operational contexts, supporting comparative studies across urban densities, climates, and fleet configurations.

Future work will refine passenger load dynamics and better capture seasonal and operational variability in auxiliary energy demand such as heating and cooling. In addition, automated façade albedo attribution will be enhanced to further reduce manual preprocessing. Together, these developments will improve the accuracy and robustness of VIPV yield estimates and energy balance assessments for bus operations.

5 References

[1] Open Geospatial Consortium (OGC), CityGML Standard, available at: https://www.ogc.org/standard/citygml, consulted in February 2025.

[2] Pera, D., Braun, C., Pinheiro, P., Leopold, U., (2023). GIS-based solar irradiance simulation for VIPV applications in a complex urban environment. 40th European Photovoltaic Solar Energy Conference and Exhibition.

[3] Lefèvre, M. et al., (2013). McClear: a new model estimating downwelling solar radiation at ground level in clear-sky conditions. Atmospheric Measurement Techniques, 6, 2403–2418. doi:10.5194/amt-6-2403-2013.

[4] Gschwind, B., et al., (2019). Improving the McClear model estimating the downwelling solar radiation at ground level in cloud-free conditions – McClear-V3. Meteorologische Zeitschrift.doi:10.1127/metz/2019/0946.

[5] Qu, Z. et al., (2017). Fast radiative transfer parameterisation for assessing the surface solar irradiance: The Heliosat-4 method. Meteorologische Zeitschrift, 26, 33–57. doi:10.1127/metz/2016/0781.

[6] GTFS, General Transit Feed Specification Documentation, available at: https://gtfs.org/documentation/,consulted July 2025.

[7] European Commission, Joint Research Centre (JRC). Vehicle Energy Consumption Calculation Tool (VECTO). Available at: https://web.jrc.ec.europa.eu/policy-model-inventory/explore/models/model-vecto/ (consulted July 2025).

Interreg North-West Europe — Co-funded by the European Union

STEER-NWE

Le Gouvernement du Grand-Duché de Luxembourg
Ministère de l'Environnement, du Climat et de la Biodiversité

DYNAMIC GIS-BASED 3D SOLAR SIMULATION FRAMEWORK FOR ASSESSING VIPV IN URBAN PUBLIC TRANSPORT USING GTFS AND DRIVING CYCLES

David Pera
ICES Unit, APG Group

david.pera@list.lu

David Pera[*1], C.Braun[1], P.Pinheiro[1], M.C.Brito[2] and U.Leopold[1]*

1Luxembourg Institute of Science and Technology

[2]Faculdade de Ciências da Universidade de Lisboa

Luxembourg Institute of Science and Technology LIST

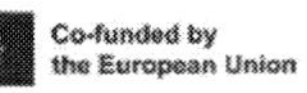

WHAT IS THE IMPACT OF URBAN SHADOWING ON VIPV?

A USE CASE ON BUSES FOR PUBLIC TRANSPORTATION

LUXEMBOURG INSTITUTE OF SCIENCE AND TECHNOLOGY | LIST

EXPERIMENTAL CAMPAIGN IN LUXEMBOURG 2023-2024

Nationwide coverage for a period of 2+ years and further continuation

In collaboration with:
6 acquisition systems on the road

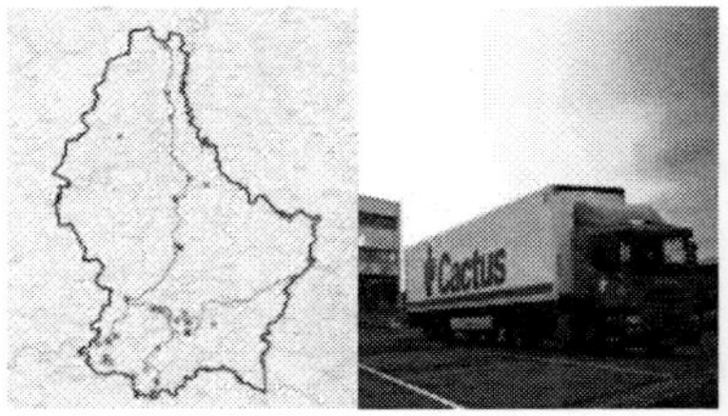

64 Stores and warehouses
- Freight transport
- National Distribution
- Home deliveries

Public transport company

Enerjin – Jinie sensor

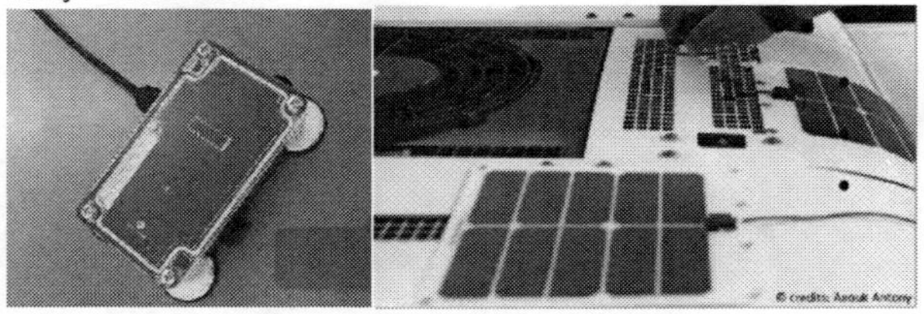

Fast response silicon sen
GPS tracking system
4G communication for dat
transmission

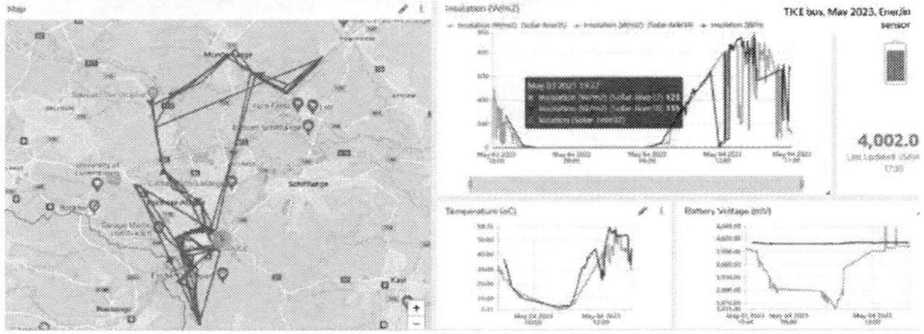

- Historical and real-time Irradiation monitoring
- Sensors' temperature
- Sensors' SoC

The data acquired experimentally, are used for comparison and calibration of the computational models.

LUXEMBOURG INSTITUTE OF SCIENCE AND TECHNOLOGY LIST

EXPERIMENTAL CAMPAIGN IN LUXEMBOURG 2023-2024

References measurements

Reference solar Irradiation data source: CAMS

Copernicus Europe's eyes on Earth — Atmosphere Monitoring Service

- Satellite derived
- GHI, DHI, DNI
- Up to 1 minute resolution
- Time coverage since 2004-02-01
- Spatial coverage: Europe, Africa, Atlantic Ocean, Middle East

Meteorological stations for additional ground validation

- LIST (red)
- ASTA – Admin. Services Tech. de l'Agriculture (green)
- MeteoLux (yellow)

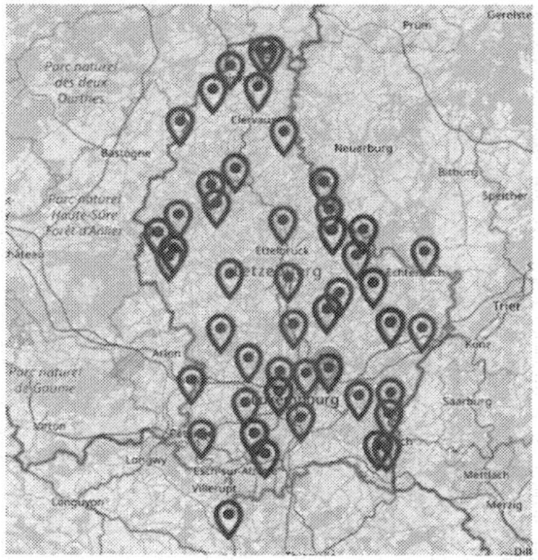

17 stations available
(GHI/DNI/DHI)

LUXEMBOURG INSTITUTE OF SCIENCE AND TECHNOLOGY LIST

SOLAR POTENTIAL ASSESSMENT

GIS approach using 3D City Models (City GML)in complex urban environments

The method allows to:

- Represent any urban infrastructure and other 3D objects (LoD 2 and LoD3)
- Attributes of surfaces:
  - Textures
  - Optical properties (e.g. albedo reflectivity, transmissivity)
  - other cadaster information…

LUXEMBOURG INSTITUTE OF SCIENCE AND TECHNOLOGY | LIST

5

SOLAR POTENTIAL ASSESSMENT

GIS approach using 3D City Models (City GML)in complex urban environments

Hemispherical viewshed

For each location

- Azimuth steps: 3º
- Zenith steps: 2.5º
- Length: 10000m
- 3D models under 100m radius
- Sum: 4320 hemispherical sectors

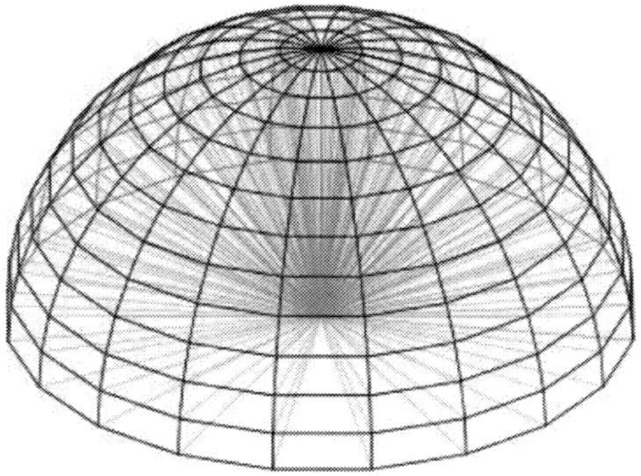

Hemispherical 3D

Hemispherical 2D

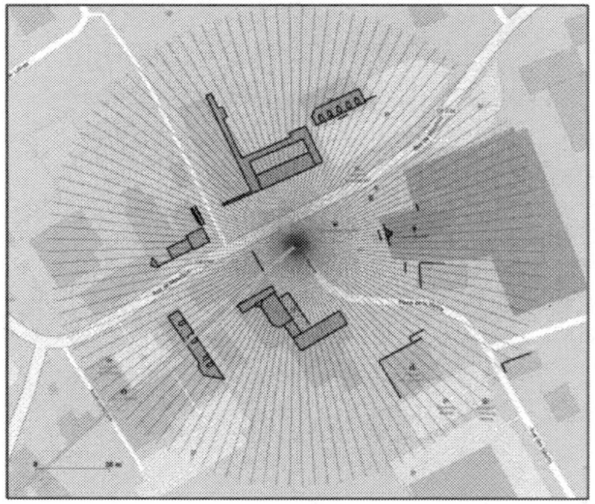

LUXEMBOURG INSTITUTE OF SCIENCE AND TECHNOLOGY | LIST

SOLAR POTENTIAL ASSESSMENT

GIS approach using 3D City Models (City GML)in complex urban environments

Processing workflow

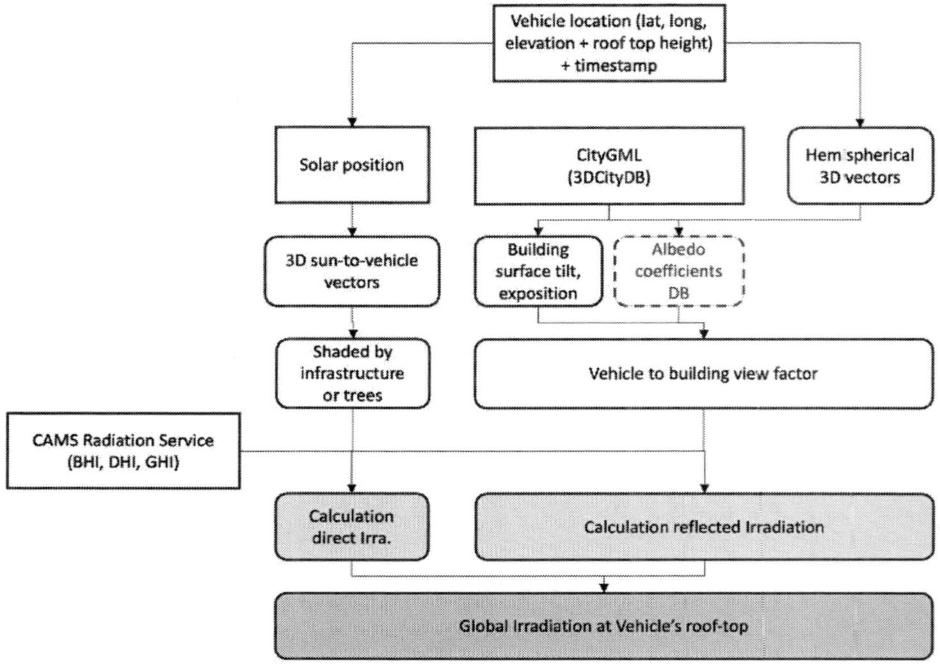

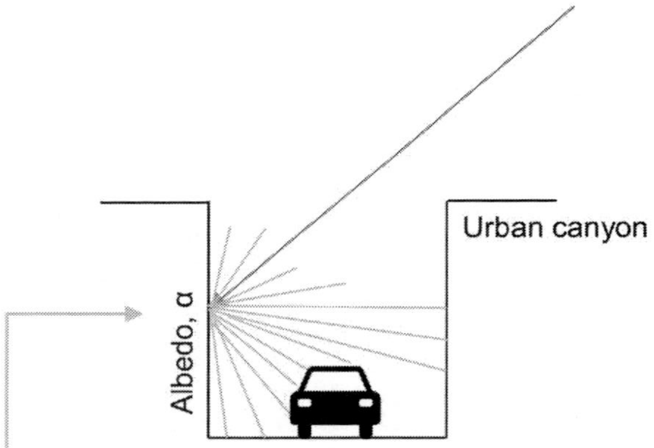

- Façades are considered Lambertian reflectors
- Same albedo coefficient along the surface
- Weighted sum of all hemispherical sectors

LUXEMBOURG INSTITUTE OF SCIENCE AND TECHNOLOGY LIST

SOLAR POTENTIAL ASSESSMENT

GIS approach using 3D City Models (City GML)in complex urban environments

Processing workflow

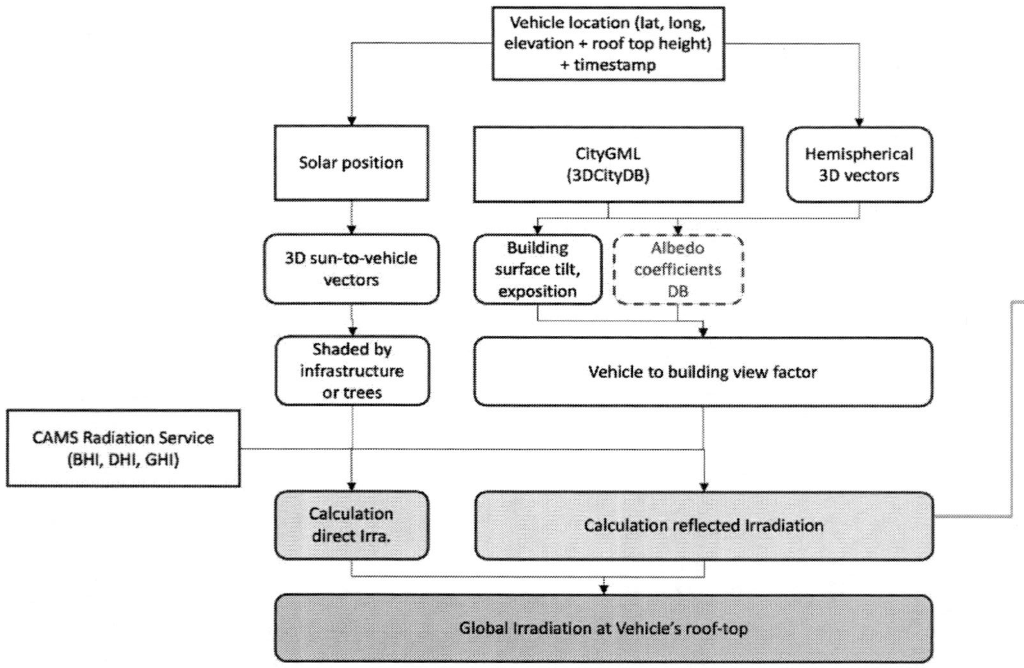

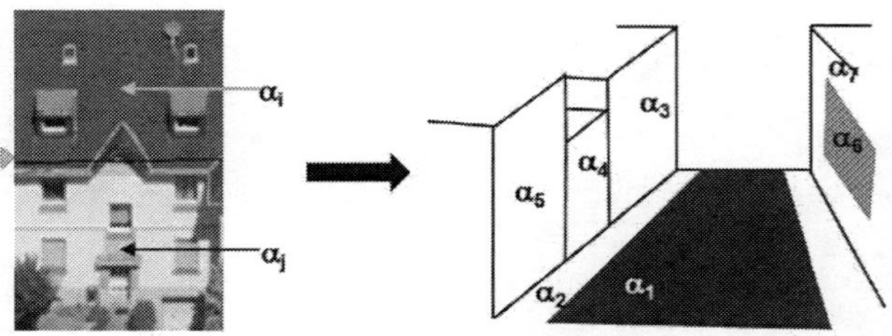

- Can Integrate varying albedo by using automated attribution to indexed surfaces , based on image recognition of materials (not yet deployed)

LUXEMBOURG INSTITUTE OF SCIENCE AND TECHNOLOGY LIST

SOLAR POTENTIAL ASSESSMENT

GIS approach using 3D City Models (City GML)in complex urban environments

Simulation Dashboard

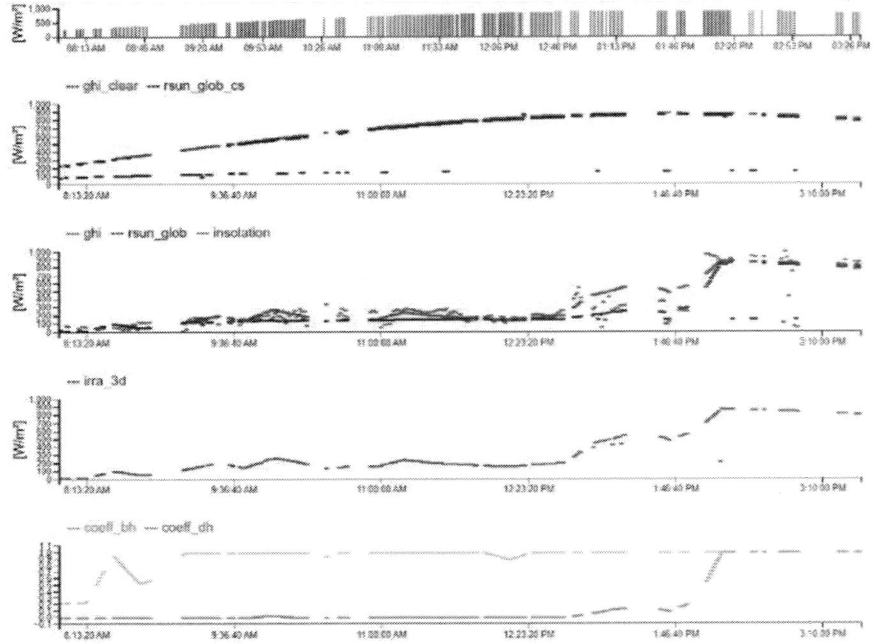

LUXEMBOURG INSTITUTE OF SCIENCE AND TECHNOLOGY | LIST

SOLAR POTENTIAL ASSESSMENT

GIS approach using 3D City Models (City GML)in complex urban environments

Results – Matching sensor and 3D simulations incl. local diffuse reflection and shading

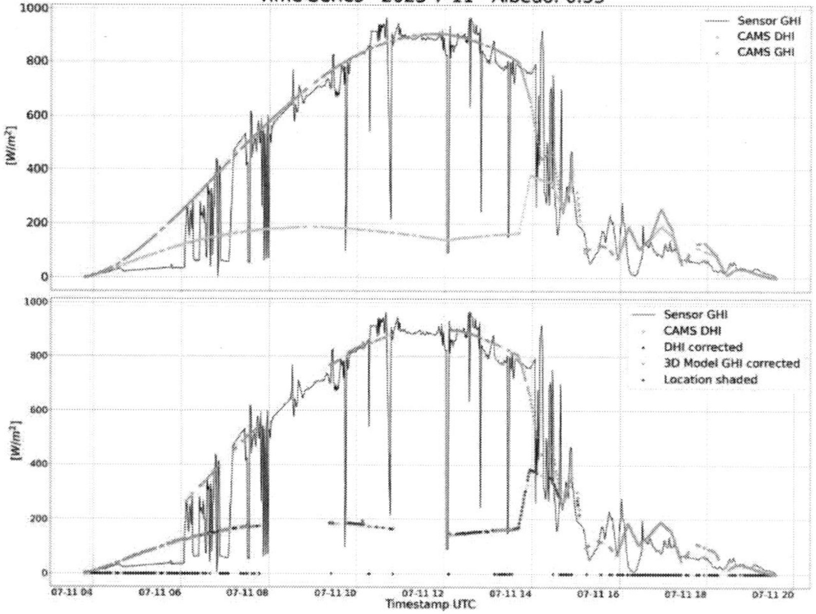

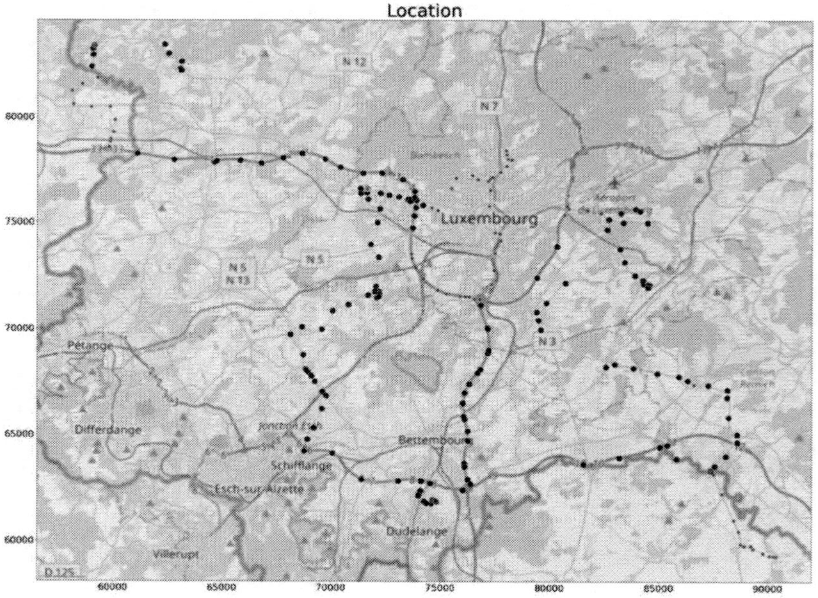

Obtained for a constant albedo coefficient of 0.35 (representative for façades)

LUXEMBOURG INSTITUTE OF SCIENCE AND TECHNOLOGY LIST

SOLAR POTENTIAL ASSESSMENT

GIS approach using 3D City Models (City GML)in complex urban environments

Results – Valleys, canyons with forested areas

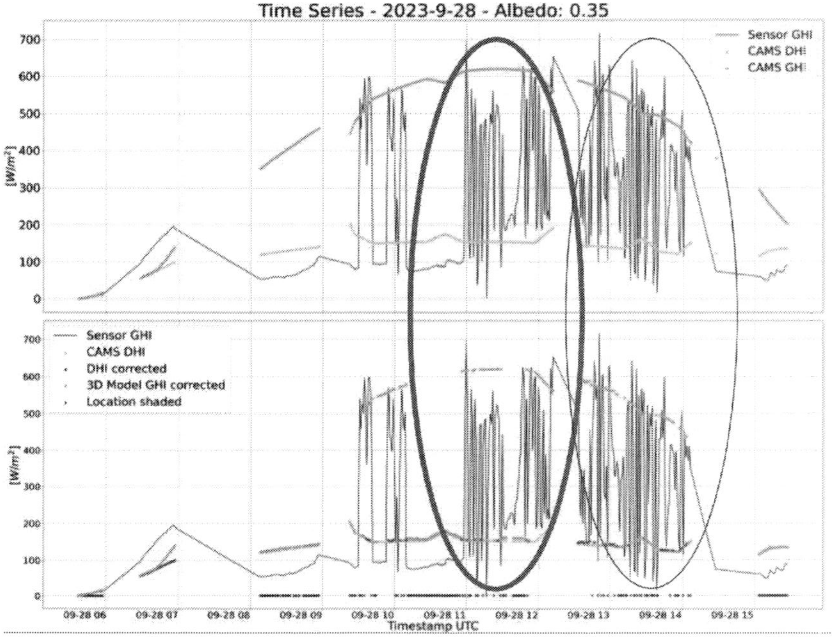

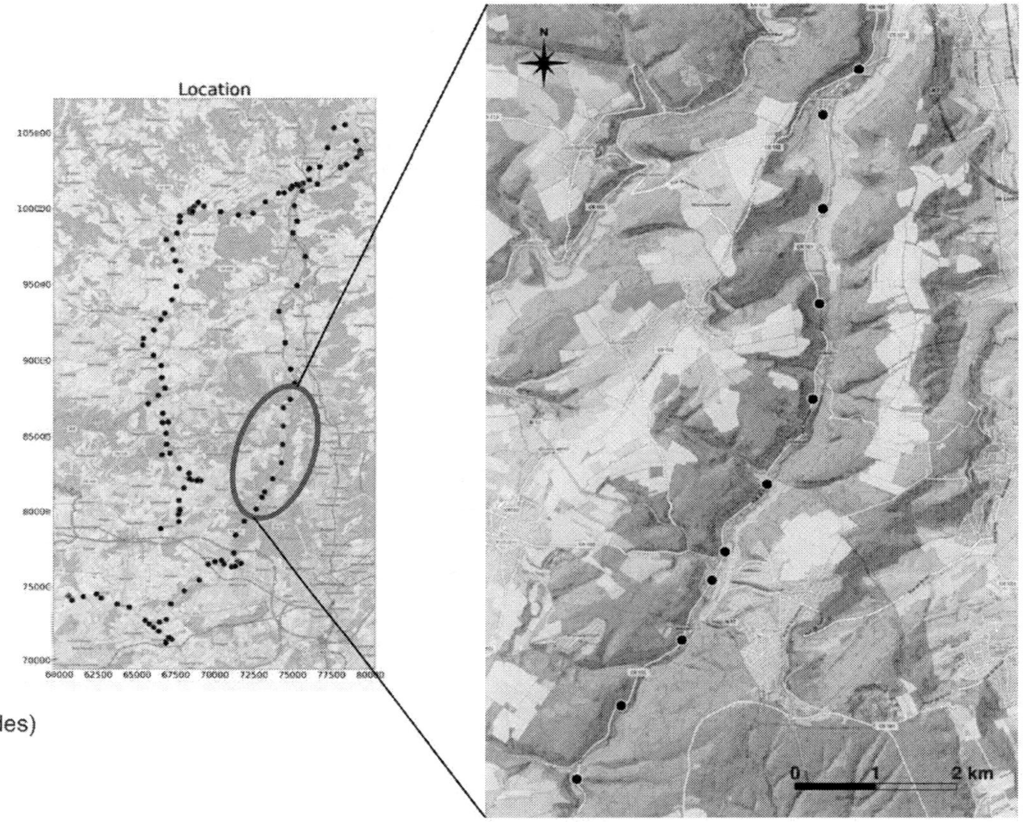

Obtained for a constant albedo coefficient of 0.35 (representative for façades)

SOLAR POTENTIAL ASSESSMENT

GIS approach using 3D City Models (City GML)in complex urban environments

Results – Valleys, canyons with forested areas

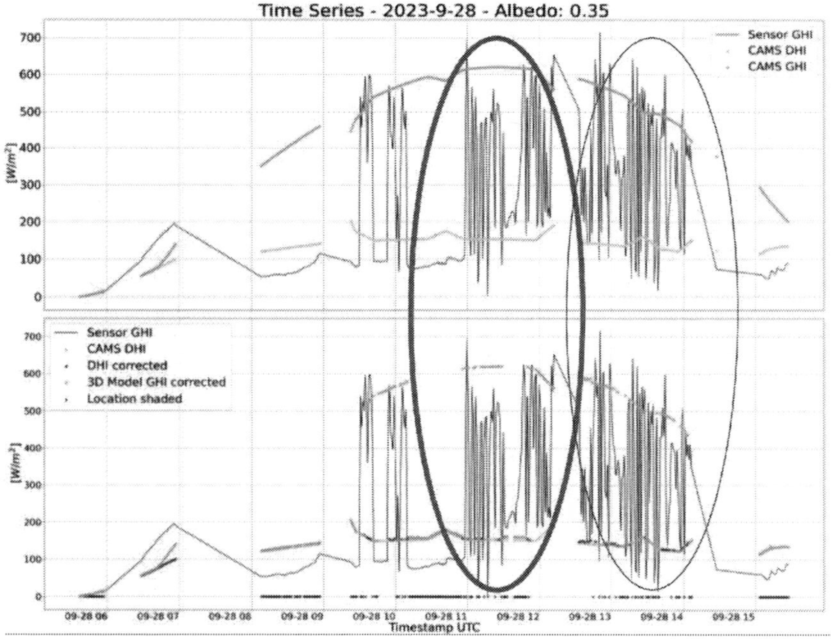

Obtained for a constant albedo coefficient of 0.35 (representative for façades)

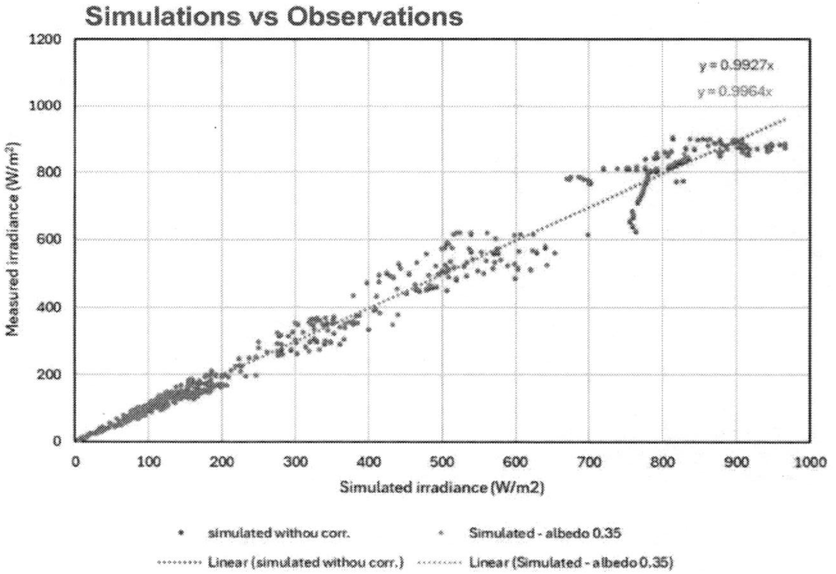

cleaned for >20% difference

LUXEMBOURG INSTITUTE OF SCIENCE AND TECHNOLOGY LIST

12

USING GTFS AND DRIVING CYCLES TO ASSESS VIPV POTENTIAL IN URBAN PUBLIC TRANSPORT

GTFS - General Transit Feed Specification, is an open standard adopted by thousands of public transport providers worldwide, containing information about routes, schedules, fares, and geographic transit details.

Documentation available at gtfs.org.

Use case – TICE Line 1

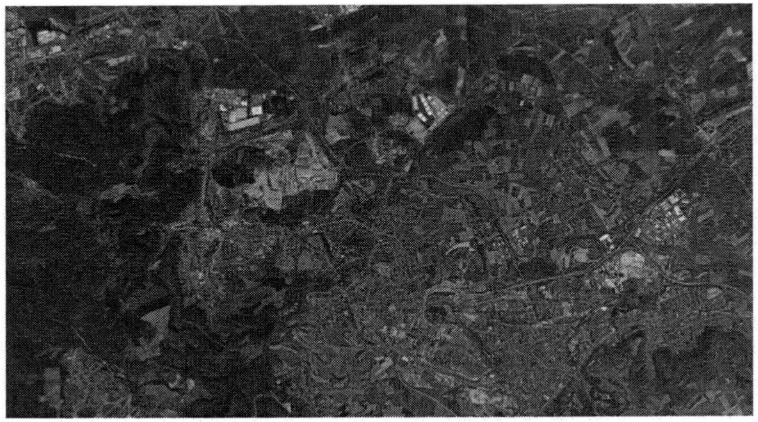

Direction 1 (D1) – Esch-sur-Alzette (Gare) – Lamadeleine (Pétange)
Distance: 17.4 km
Frequency: each 15 minutes
No stops: 25 (60s)
Typical time: 41 min
Up to 63 trips/day

Direction 2 (D2) –Lamadeleine (Pétange) - Esch-sur-Alzette (Gare)
Distance: 18.3 km
No stops: 30 (60s)
Typical duration: 43.7 min.
Up to 63 trips/day

41169 trips per year
2–8 vehicles simultaneously

LUXEMBOURG INSTITUTE OF SCIENCE AND TECHNOLOGY | LIST

USING GTFS AND DRIVING CYCLES TO ASSESS VIPV POTENTIAL IN URBAN PUBLIC TRANSPORT

GTFS based Simulation workflow

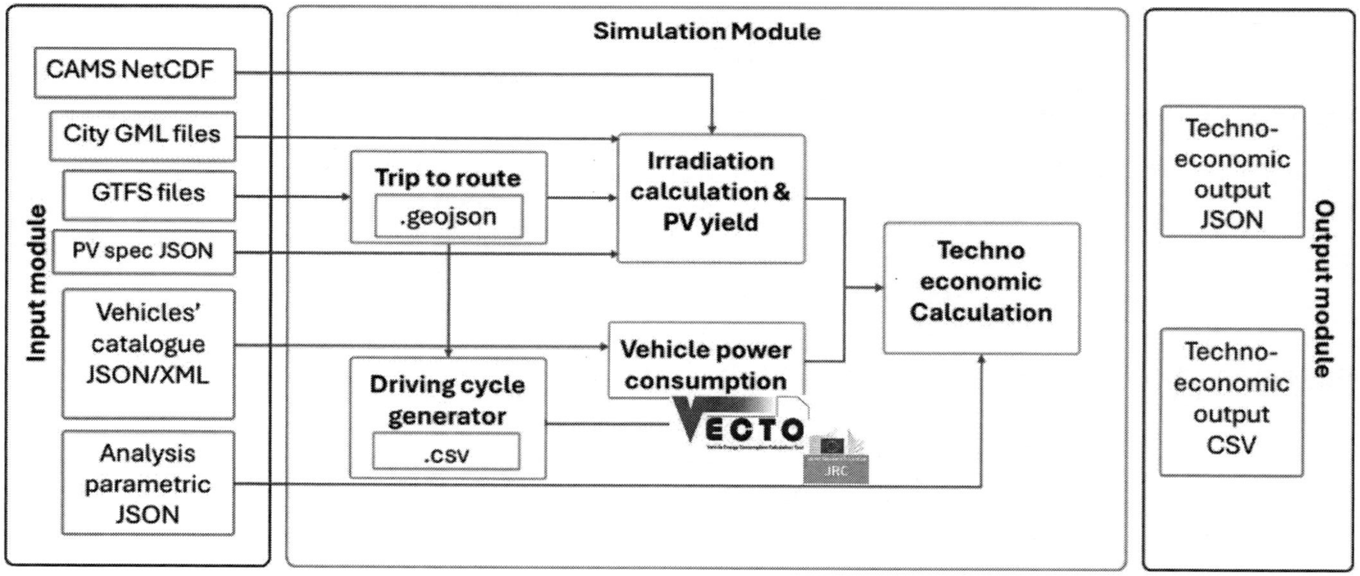

*VECTO is a simulation tool developed by the European Commission to determine CO2 emissions and fuel consumption from heavy-duty vehicles (HDVs).

LUXEMBOURG INSTITUTE OF SCIENCE AND TECHNOLOGY | LIST

USING GTFS AND DRIVING CYCLES TO ASSESS VIPV POTENTIAL IN URBAN PUBLIC TRANSPORT

Vehicle's Powertrain Components and Model

VECTO Accounts with 26 Powertrain Architectures available:

- ICE
- HEV (9 Parallel Hybrid Electric Vehicle Architectures)
- PEV (4 Pure Electric Vehicle Architectures)

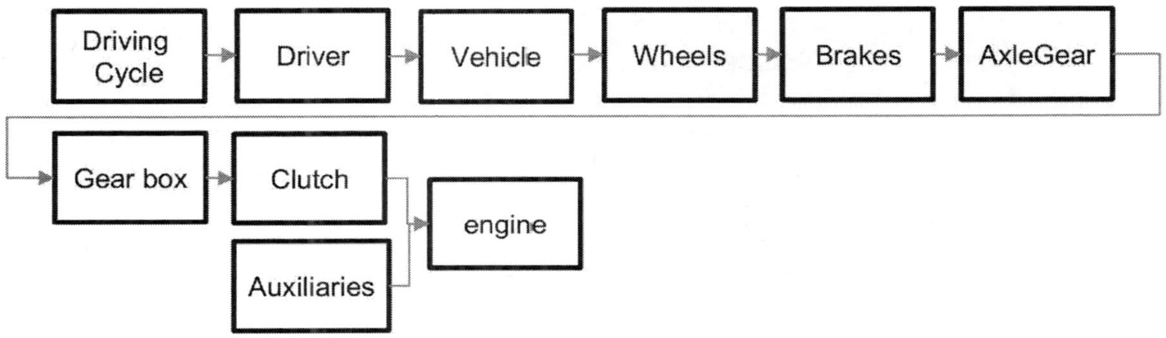

The engine tries to supply the requested power demand (including all power losses occurring in the powertrain and auxiliaries).
If the engine cannot meet the required power demand, the driver reduces acceleration.

LUXEMBOURG INSTITUTE OF SCIENCE AND TECHNOLOGY LIST

USING GTFS AND DRIVING CYCLES TO ASSESS VIPV POTENTIAL IN URBAN PUBLIC TRANSPORT

Driving cycle

t [s]	Timestep of the trip
v [km/h]	The target vehicle velocity. >= 0 km/h.
Stop [s]	Stopping Time. After this time, the vehicle tries to accelerate to v.
P_{add} [kW]	Additional auxiliary power demand.
Grad (%)	The road gradient.

Example of processed driving cycle for D1

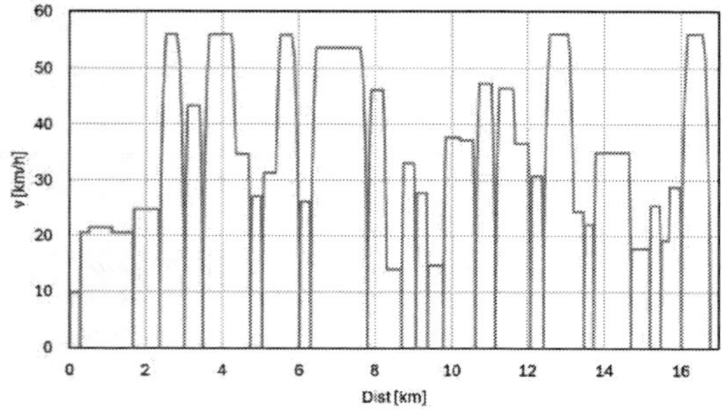

16

Simulation parameters : 2s frequency, 10 hypersegments

Vehicle's key parameterisation

- Mass and loading - Corrected Actual Curb Mass and loading
- Cross Sectional Area - Air Resistance and Cross Wind Correction Options
- Effective dynamic Wheel radius - engine speed calculation
- Relative axle load – Rolling resistance coefficient
- Electric machine – porwer and nr. of systems
- Rechargeable Electric Energy Storage System (RESS) parameters

Vehicle:

Mercedez eCitaro K:

- Category:12 m
- Powertrain: 2x 125 kW
- Torque: 2x 484 Nm
- RESS: 330 kWh
- Mass: 28500 kg
- Max occupancy: 158 pax.
- P.aux. 2kW (constant)

{ "Header": { "CreatedBy": "", "Date": "2025-02-02T14:18:02.0731125Z", "AppVersion": "3", "FileVersion": 10 }, "Body": { "SavedInDeclMode": false, "VehCat": "CityBus", "LegislativeClass": "M3", "CurbWeight": 13440.0, "CurbWeightExtra": 0.0, "MassMax": 11.99, "Loading": 6560.0, "rdyn": 459.0, "CdCorrMode": "CdofVdecl", "CdCorrFile": "", "AxleConfig": { "Type": "4x2", "Axles": [{ "Inertia": 6.5, "wheels": "275/70 R22.5", "AxleWeightShare": 0.38, "TwinTyres": false, "RRCISO": 0.0065, "FzISO": 20850.0, "Type": "VehicleNonDriven", "Steered": false }, { "Inertia": 6.5, "wheels": "275/70 R22.5", "AxleWeightShare": 0.62, "TwinTyres": true, "RRCISO": 0.0075, "FzISO": 20850.0, "Type": "VehicleDriven", "Steered": false }] }, "EngineStopStart": false, "EcoRoll": "None", "PredictiveCruiseControl": "None", "ATEcoRollReleaseLockupClutch": false, "CdA": 4.83, "VehicleHeight": 3.4, "InitialSoC": 80.0, "PowertrainConfiguration": "BatteryElectric", "ElectricMotors": [{ "Count": 2, "Ratio": 22.6, "Position": "E4", "MotorFile": "../GenericVehicleE4/GenericEMotor_125kW_485Nm.vem", "MechanicalEfficiency": 0.97 }], "Batteries": [{ "NumPacks": 2, "BatteryFile": "../GenericVehicleE4/GenericBattery_243kWh_750V.vbat", "StreamId": 0 }], "PTO": { "Type": "None", "LossMap": "", "Cycle": "", "CycleEPTO": "", "CycleDriving": "" } } }

- VIPV 80% rooftop – 3.5 kW_p/Bus
- PR – 75% (power losses in MPPT,
- voltage conversion, temperature, curvature, etc…)

LUXEMBOURG INSTITUTE OF SCIENCE AND TECHNOLOGY LIST

USING GTFS AND DRIVING CYCLES TO ASSESS VIPV POTENTIAL IN URBAN PUBLIC TRANSPORT

Results – TICE Line 1 solar potential

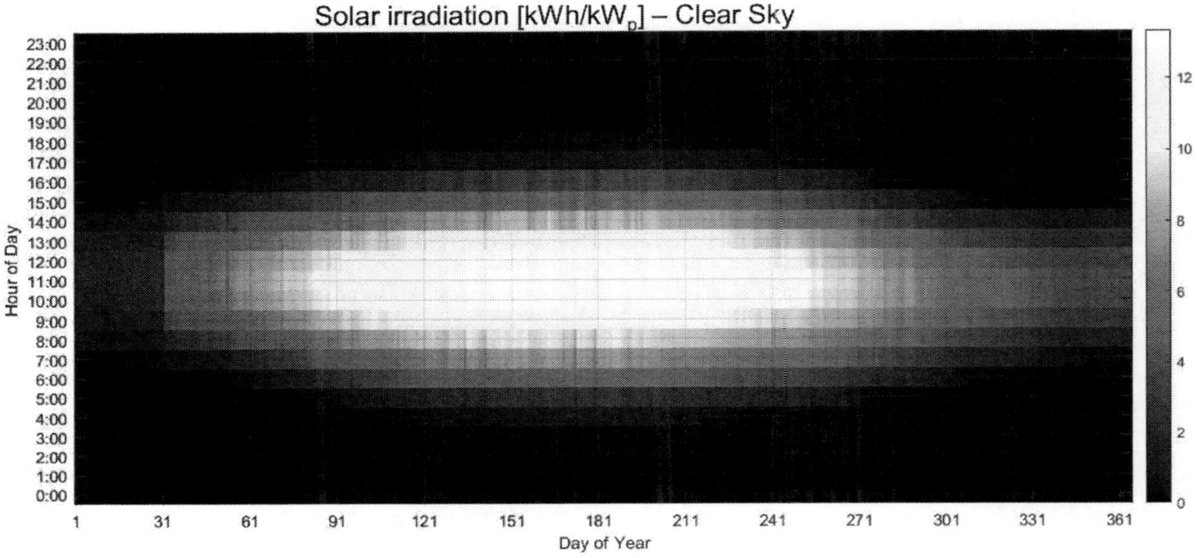

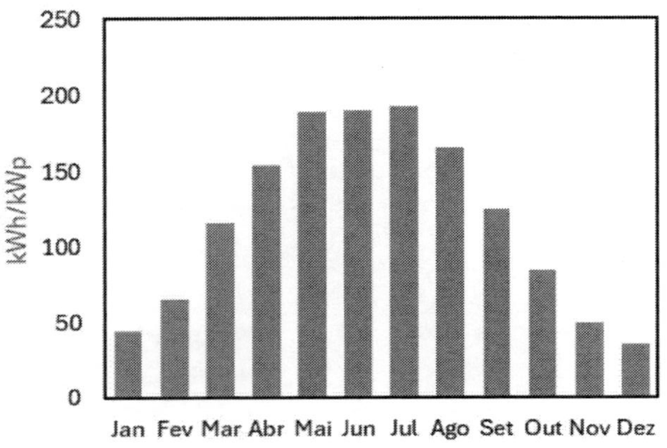

Yearly Total 1408.6 kWh/kW$_p$
E_{max} = *192.8 kWh/kW$_p$ July*
$E_{avg.}$ = *3.9 kWh/kW$_p$/day*

The shadow losses - 20.5%

LUXEMBOURG INSTITUTE OF SCIENCE AND TECHNOLOGY | LIST

17

USING GTFS AND DRIVING CYCLES TO ASSESS VIPV POTENTIAL IN URBAN PUBLIC TRANSPORT

Results – TICE Line 1 solar potential

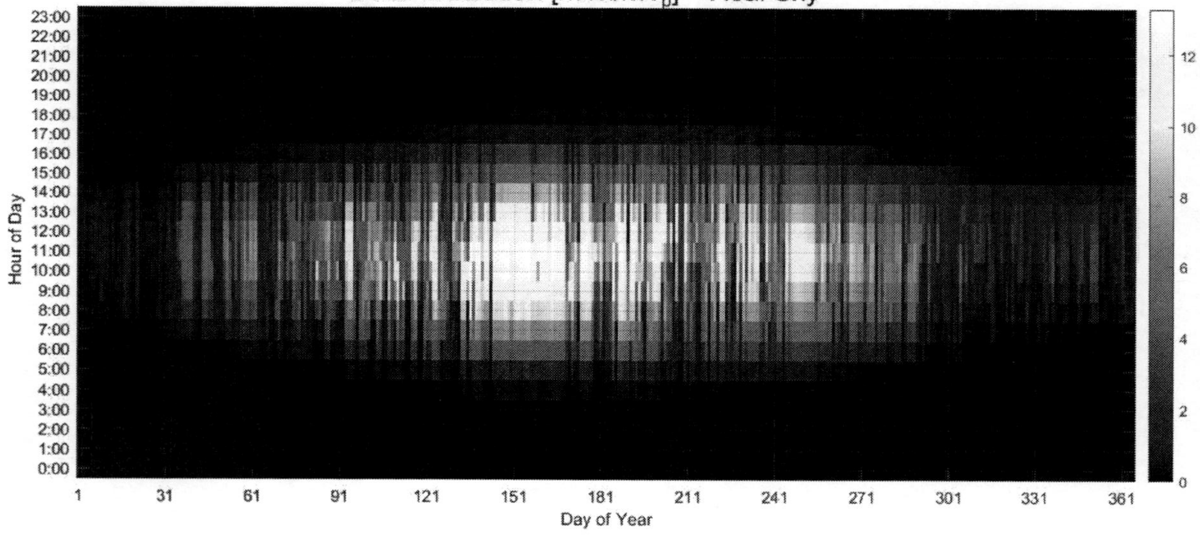

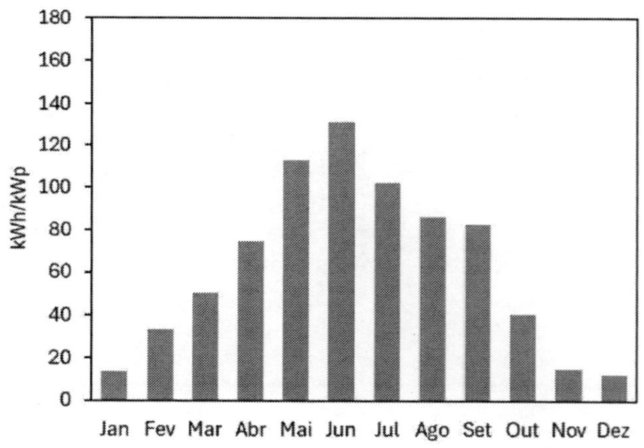

Yearly Total 943.5 kWh/kW$_p$
E_{max} = *164 kWh/kW$_p$ August*
$E_{avg.}$ = *2.58 kWh/kW$_p$/day*

The shadow losses - 20.8%

LUXEMBOURG INSTITUTE OF SCIENCE AND TECHNOLOGY | LIST

USING GTFS AND DRIVING CYCLES TO ASSESS VIPV POTENTIAL IN URBAN PUBLIC TRANSPORT

Results – TICE Line 1 VIPV Yield

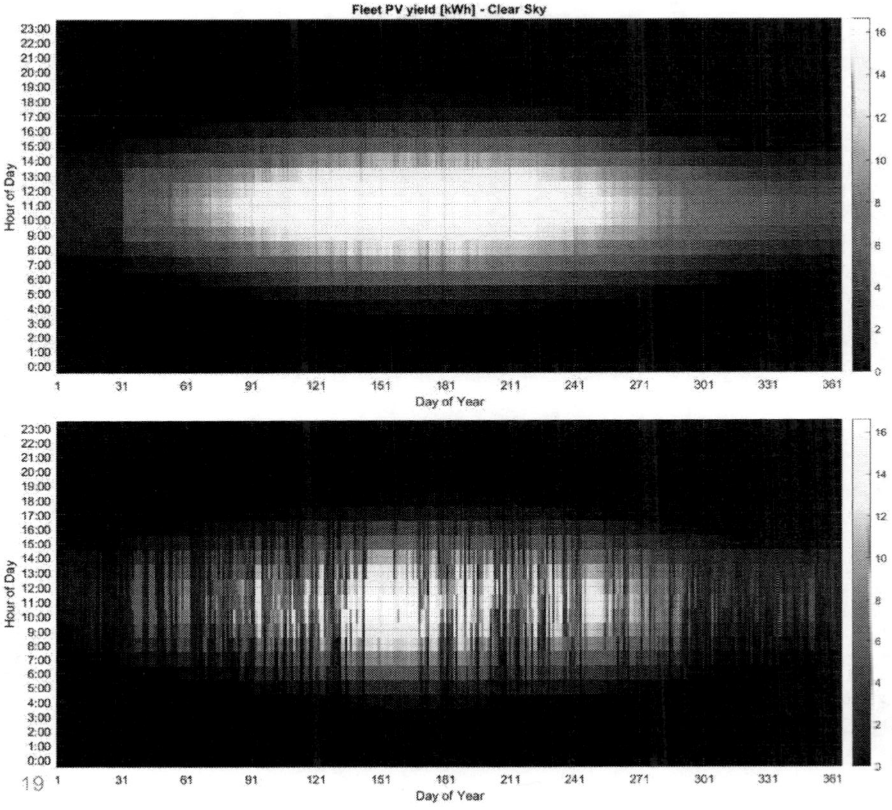

PR= 75 %
P= 3.5 kW_p (24 m^2)

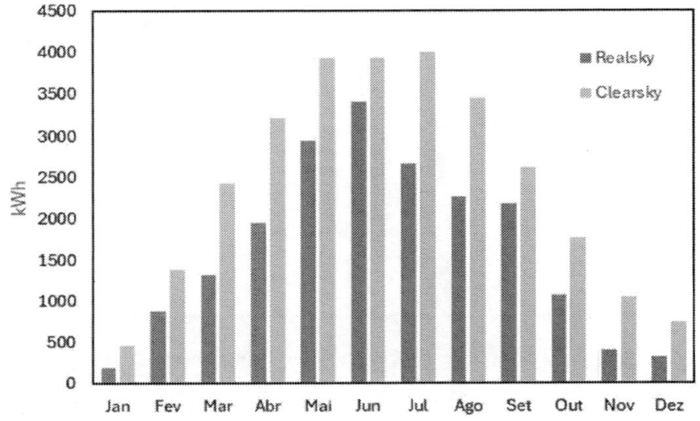

$E_{pv,clear} = 28948\ kWh$

$E_{pv,clear} = 19490\ kWh$

LUXEMBOURG INSTITUTE OF SCIENCE AND TECHNOLOGY | LIST

USING GTFS AND DRIVING CYCLES TO ASSESS VIPV POTENTIAL IN URBAN PUBLIC TRANSPORT Results – Energy balance

- Typical Battery discharge per trip:
    - D1 – 23.34 kWh (~7 %SoC)
    - D2 – 23.96 kWh (~ 7 %SoC)
- Charging 20% to 80% = 198 kWh

TICE line bus fleet energy consumption

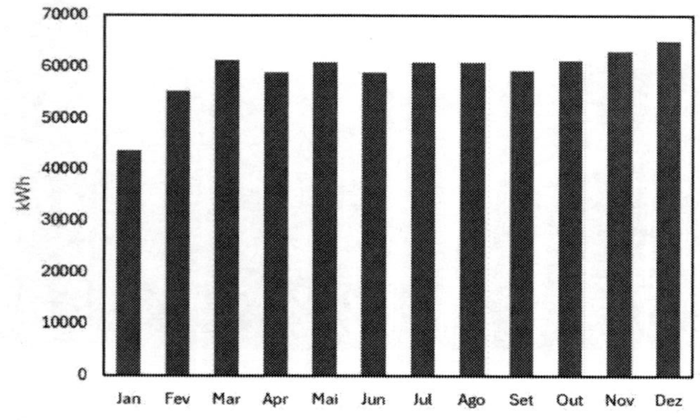

$E_{total} = 707.83 MWh$
$E_{month.avg} = 58.9 MWh$

VIPV system would cover 2.8 % - 4.1% of the TICE line 1 energy demand

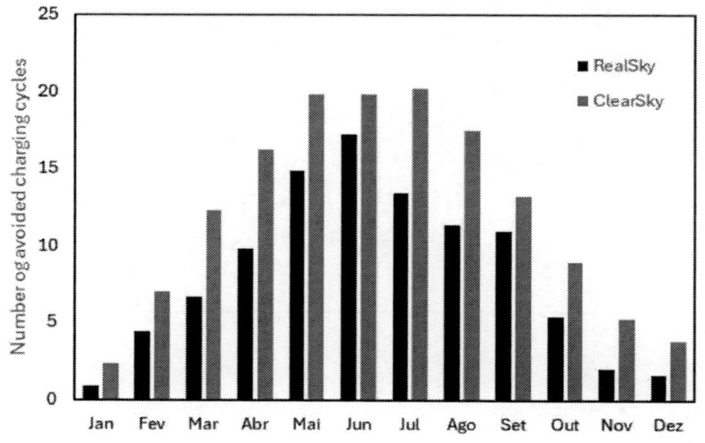

Simple payback time ranging 7 -10 years
Energy tariff – 0.21 €/kWh
VIPV cost – 1.5 €/kW$_p$

LUXEMBOURG INSTITUTE OF SCIENCE AND TECHNOLOGY LIST

USING GTFS AND DRIVING CYCLES TO ASSESS VIPV POTENTIAL IN URBAN PUBLIC TRANSPORT

Next Steps

- Complete the deployment of albedo coefficient indexing for solar the potential assessment, using open datasets based on façade textures.
- Evaluate trips across different urban density levels (low, medium, high), sub-urban, and rural areas.
- Improve vehicle operational parameterization, considering temporal variation of payload (passenger occupancy rates) and auxiliary power demand (e.g., impact on HVAC).

LUXEMBOURG INSTITUTE OF SCIENCE AND TECHNOLOGY LIST

thank you

For more info, please contact us

david.pera@list.lu
ulrich.leopold@list.lu

co-funded by:

LE GOUVERNEMENT
DU GRAND-DUCHÉ DE LUXEMBOURG
Ministère de l'Environnement, du Climat
et de la Biodiversité

Interreg
North-West Europe
Co-funded by the European Union
STEER-NWE

LUXEMBOURG
INSTITUTE OF SCIENCE
AND TECHNOLOGY
LIST

OPTIMIZING ANGULAR PERFORMANCE OF CURVED VIPV MODULES

F. Martín[1,2], R. Herrero[1], I. Antón[1]
[1]Instituto de Energía Solar – Universidad Politécnica de Madrid (IES-UPM), Madrid, Spain
[2]Solar Added Value (SAV), Madrid, Spain
f.martin.sanagustin@alumnos.upm.es

ABSTRACT: Vehicle-integrated photovoltaics (VIPV) typically operate under non-normal irradiance, making angular performance a critical metric for energy modeling. Because vehicle surfaces often require double curvature for aerodynamic and aesthetic purposes, their angular responses differ from those of flat modules. In addition, not only the curvature but also the electrical configuration influences the angular response. In this work, several electrical configurations of a curved VIPV module have been modeled, their electrical performance simulated, and their angular impact quantified.

The curvature and size of a curved module determine the angular variation across the surface. For this reason, the case study will focus on a large VIPV module of more than 2 m^2 integrated into a sedan, covering both the roof and rear window. Several electrical configurations were analyzed to assess power output under varying incidence angles, including cell orientation, bypass diode arrangements, and splitting the module into different MPPTs. Results indicate that half-cell orientation and diode parameters have negligible influence. In contrast, dividing the system into MPPT sections enhances overall generation, especially under varying angles of incidence.

For study validation, a commercial VIPV module of 0.87 m^2 was tested both indoors and outdoors with unique measurement capabilities. The experimental and simulated angular responses are compared, validating the developed model.

Keywords: curved photovoltaic modules, vehicle integrated photovoltaics (VIPV), characterization, relative angular response (RAR).

1 INTRODUCTION

The growth of electric vehicles (EVs) has increased interest in vehicle-integrated photovoltaics (VIPV), a technology that integrates solar panels into vehicle surfaces such as the roof, hood, doors, and windows [1]. These panels must be adapted to the vehicle's shape, which often involves curved and asymmetrical surfaces to maintain both design and aerodynamic needs.

The performance of VIPV systems is influenced by non-uniform light distribution due to these curved surfaces. Factors like shading and the changing angle of sunlight—affected by time of day, season, location, and vehicle position—result in variable energy generation.

The angle of incidence is critical for VIPV modules because it directly affects the irradiance reaching the cells. In flat modules, current is uniform across cells, but in curved modules, varying angles lead to differences in current. Therefore, VIPV module design is critical to reduce mismatch losses caused by both curvature and changing light conditions.

Curvature and shading in VIPV modules may require the integration of a higher number of by-pass diodes than in flat modules, potentially one per cell, to minimize power losses [2],[3]. While diodes are inexpensive, their increased use raises assembly costs, especially in larger modules. However, bypass diodes reduce shading losses and improve performance. The IV curves of VIPV modules show steps due to bypass diodes, indicating uneven illumination across cells. These curves depend on the angle of incidence and the module's electrical design, including cell connections and the number of diodes.

In this context, the objective of this study is to evaluate the angular performance of a sedan's rooftop, including the rear window as an active photovoltaic surface as shown in Fig.1. Specifically, we pointed to investigate potential energy gain of a VIPV module under optimized tilted irradiance conditions.

For this purpose, various electrical configurations were analyzed, including different cell orientations (portrait and landscape), number and breakdown voltage of by-pass diodes, number of MPPTs, etc.

Figure 1: VIPV module evaluated.

2 VALIDATION OF MODELLING TOOL

The validation of our modeling tool was carried out through indoor and outdoor characterization of a curved VIPV module as part of a round-robin activity within the PT600 working group. Further details can be found in [4]

Indoor measurements were performed under STC using a solar simulator designed and built for characterization of curved modules, equipped with a dual-axis rotation structure for varying module angles [5]. An image of the final design of the simulator and a picture of the VIPV module in the rotating structure is presented in Fig.2

Outdoor measurements were taken using a two-axis tracker at the Instituto de Energía Solar facilities in Madrid. VIPV module with its frame is shown in Fig.2.

10.4229/EUPVSEC2025/4EO.2.6

Figure 2: (up) Collimated solar simulator for curved modules; (left) module and rotating structure; (right) outdoor measurement of VIPV module.

Multiple indoor and outdoor measurements were carried out under various incident angles and compared against simulation results. To perform the angular characterization, the module was intentionally misaligned to the desired positions both in the solar simulator and on the two-axis tracker [6].

To validate the simulations, we also measured the angular response at the P_{mp} and compared it with the experimental data. Extensive validation was conducted across various scenarios, with simulations consistently matching experimental results.

Two representative cases are presented in Fig. 3, showing the excellent agreement between measured and simulated IV curves.

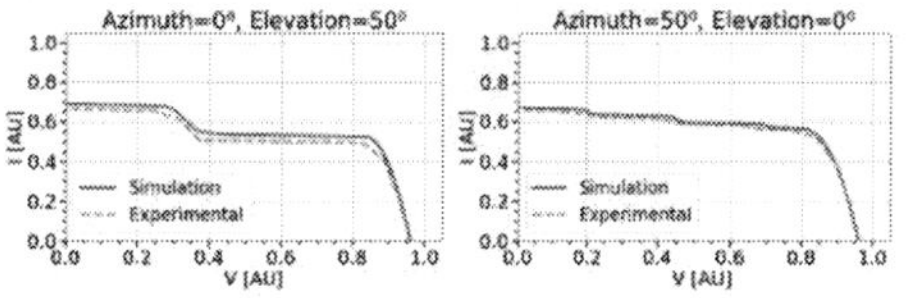

Figure 3: Comparison between measured and simulated IV curves under different angles of incidence.

3 CASE STUDY

This study focuses on the performance of a Vehicle-Integrated Photovoltaics (VIPV) module installed on the rooftop of a sedan, also utilizing the rear window as an active photovoltaic surface as shown in Fig.1. The main objective is to assess the potential energy gain of a VIPV system optimized for tilted irradiance.

It is important to distinguish the module used for experimental validation from the one analyzed in the case study. The validation module had an active area of less than 1 m² and a nominal power below 200 W, and was used to verify the accuracy of the simulation methodology with real data from indoor and outdoor measurements.

In contrast, the case study focuses on a full-scale VIPV module with an active area exceeding 2 m² and a nominal power of approximately 520 W, representative of a realistic integration in a production sedan vehicle.

To introduce the VIPV case study, we first are going to define the angular parameters used in the analysis. **α** is the incidence angle with respect to the normal at the center of the module, while **β** represents the azimuth angle as can be seen in Fig. 5.

For clarity in the angular response graphs, a sign convention is adopted for α where positive values indicate light incident from the front of the vehicle and negative values correspond to light from the rear direction.

Figure 5: (left) **α:** incidence angle relative to the normal at the center of the module; (right) **β:** azimuth.

Although α remains constant, different β values caused by the changing position of the sun and the movement of the vehicle, can produce significantly different irradiance distributions across the curved VIPV surface.

Due to the module's curvature and asymmetry, β has a significant effect on the irradiance distribution across the surface and cells.

Fig. 6 shows irradiance maps for identical α and varying β angles, highlighting the variation in irradiance patterns induced by β. This non-uniformity strongly impacts PV generation, making the electrical design and interconnection strategy a key aspect in the electrical configurations.

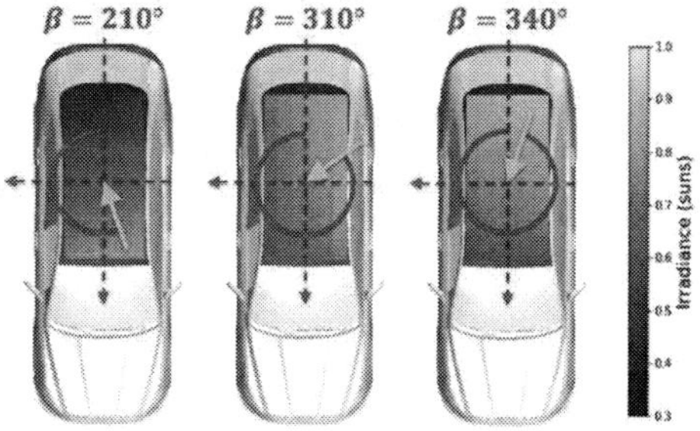

Figure 6: Irradiance variation on the VIPV surface for same α and different β angles.

To evaluate the influence of electrical design on angular performance, various combinations of electrical parameters were analyzed.

The analysis includes different cell orientations (portrait and landscape), bypass diode strategies (number and placement), a range of bypass diode breakdown voltages, and varying numbers of MPPTs per module.

Among the approaches studied, a particularly relevant case involves the use of one bypass diode per cell, not through external components but by leveraging the intrinsic behavior of Interdigitated Back Contact (IBC) cells [7]. These cells can be designed with a low and tunable breakdown voltage, allowing each cell to function as its own bypass element.

This complete analysis will help identify which of these design aspects have the most significant impact on performance and are therefore critical for the case study.

4 RESULTS AND CONCLUSIONS

Results obtained clearly indicate that the number of MPPT sections is the most critical factor for optimizing the angular performance of the VIPV module. Splitting the module into multiple MPPTs significantly improves power output, particularly at high tilted angles.

In contrast, other parameters such as cell orientation, the number of bypass diodes, and diode breakdown voltage have a minimal impact on overall performance.

To analyze these effects in detail, a step-by-step comparison of the angular responses of different configurations is presented in the following figures.

Fig 7. shows the angular response of two configurations where all cells are connected in series, with different orientations: portrait and landscape. The results reveal almost identical angular performance in both cases, with only slight differences at very tilted angles, where the power output is already low.

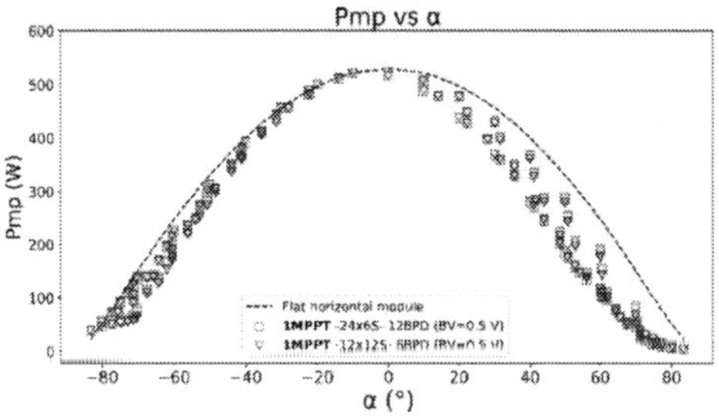

Figure 7: Angular response of VIPV module for different cell orientacion (landscape and portrait).

Fig.8 compares one of the previous configurations with three additional cases using 2 MPPTs. The new configurations are as follows:

- Portrait orientation with 6 bypass diodes (one per string).
- Landscape orientation with IBC cells and a diode breakdown voltage of 0.2 V.
- Same as the previous, but with a breakdown voltage of 1.5 V.

These cases show very similar angular responses. A slight performance improvement is observed in the configuration using IBC cells with 0.2 V breakdown voltage, particularly at highly tilted angles. This suggests that the diode is only activated under extreme angular conditions. Therefore, both the number of bypass diodes and their breakdown voltage provide only marginal benefits in such scenarios.

Additionally, Fig.8 confirms that cell orientation has no significant impact on the power output of the VIPV module under the tested conditions.

Above all, 2 MPPT configurations outperform the 1 MPPT case throughout the entire angular range. The improvement is especially noticeable for positive α angles, corresponding to light coming from the front of the vehicle.

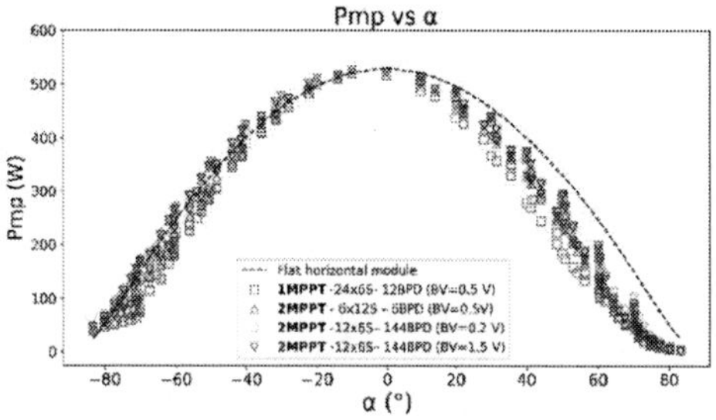

Figure 8: Angular response of VIPV module for different MPPT configurations.

To further validate the impact of MPPT segmentation, Fig.9 compares one of the previous 2 MPPT cases with a new configuration using 3 MPPTs. The results confirm that increasing the number of MPPTs enhances performance, especially at negative α angles, where light comes from the rear of the vehicle.

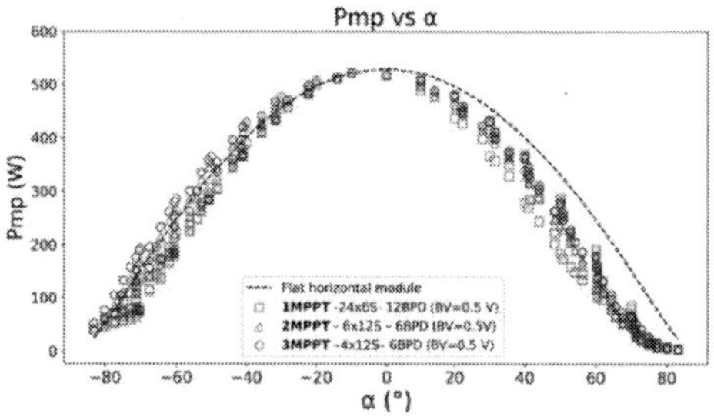

Figure 9: : Angular response of VIPV module for different MPPT configurations.

Overall, the results show distinct behaviors for positive and negative incidence angles:

- Negative α angles (light from the rear): Multi-MPPT configurations offer significant performance gains compared to a single MPPT setup.
- Positive α angles (light from the front): although all configurations perform below the flat module baseline, the single MPPT setup exhibits the greatest power loss. Multi-MPPT configurations mitigate this loss effectively.

In conclusion, optimizing the number of MPPT sections is the most effective strategy to maximize energy harvest in VIPV systems under variable angular and irradiance conditions.

5 ACKNOLEDGMENTS

The authors gratefully acknowledge the DETEC-PV project, Grant PID2021-128853OB-I00, funded by MCIN/AEI/10.13039/501100011033 and "ERDF A way of making Europe."

6 REFERENCES

[1] M. Yamaguchi *et al.*, 'Importance of Developing High-Efficiency Solar Cells for PV-Powered Vehicles', in *2020 47th IEEE Photovoltaic Specialists Conference (PVSC)*, Calgary, AB, Canada: IEEE, Jun. 2020, pp. 0221–0223. doi: 10.1109/PVSC45281.2020.9300413.

[2] Javier Macías,Rebeca Herrero, Luis Javier San José, Rubén Núñez, Ignacio Antón, 'On the optimization of the interconnection of photovoltaic modules integrated in vehicles', *in press*, iScience, 2024.

[3] J. Macias, R. Herrero, R. Nunez, and I. Anton, 'On the effect of cell interconnection in Vehicle Integrated Photovoltaics: modelling energy under different scenarios', in *2021 IEEE 48th Photovoltaic Specialists Conference (PVSC)*, Fort Lauderdale, FL, USA: IEEE, Jun. 2021, pp. 1336–1339. doi: 10.1109/PVSC43889.2021.9518935.

[4] F. Martín *et al.*, 'Relative angular response characterization in VIPV', *Sol. Energy Mater. Sol. Cells*, vol. 276, p. 113063, Oct. 2024, doi: 10.1016/j.solmat.2024.113063.

[5] G. Vallerotto *et al.*, 'Collimated solar simulator for curved PV modules characterization', *Sol. Energy Mater. Sol. Cells*, vol. 258, p. 112418, Aug. 2023, doi: 10.1016/j.solmat.2023.112418.

[6] D. Riley and C. Hansen, 'Sun-Relative Pointing for Dual-Axis Solar Trackers Employing Azimuth and Elevation Rotations', *J. Sol. Energy Eng.*, vol. 137, no. 3, p. 031008, Jun. 2015, doi: 10.1115/1.4029379.

[7] A. Calcabrini *et al.*, 'Low-breakdown-voltage solar cells for shading-tolerant photovoltaic modules', *Cell Rep. Phys. Sci.*, vol. 3, no. 12, p. 101155, Dec. 2022, doi: 10.1016/j.xcrp.2022.101155.

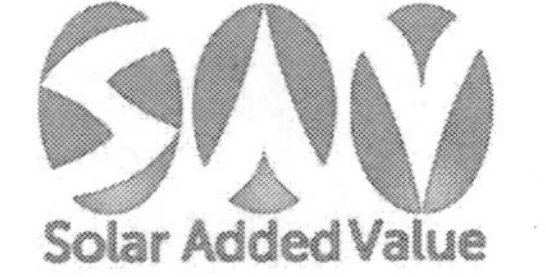

Optimizing angular performance of curved VIPV modules

F. Martín[1,2], R. Herrero[1], I.Antón[1]

[1]Instituto de Energía Solar, Universidad Politécnica de Madrid, Madrid (SPAIN)

[2] Solar Added Value (SAV), Madrid (SPAIN)

INSTITUTO DE ENERGÍA SOLAR

POLITÉCNICA

Solar Added Value

Motivation

INSTITUTO DE ENERGÍA SOLAR

- VIPV surfaces receive **non-normal sunlight**
- Curvature causes **non-uniform irradiance** distribution across cells
- Energy modeling must consider **varying angles of incidence**
- **Module design is critical** for efficient operation
  - Modules operate under **tilted irradiance allways**
  - **Partial shading** conditions only occur **occasionally**

POLITÉCNICA

Previous works

INSTITUTO DE ENERGÍA SOLAR

- Optimization of electrical VIPV module for partial shading (static)
  - Number and Breakdown Voltage of by-pass diodes matters!!
  - Increase the number of MPPTs also helps

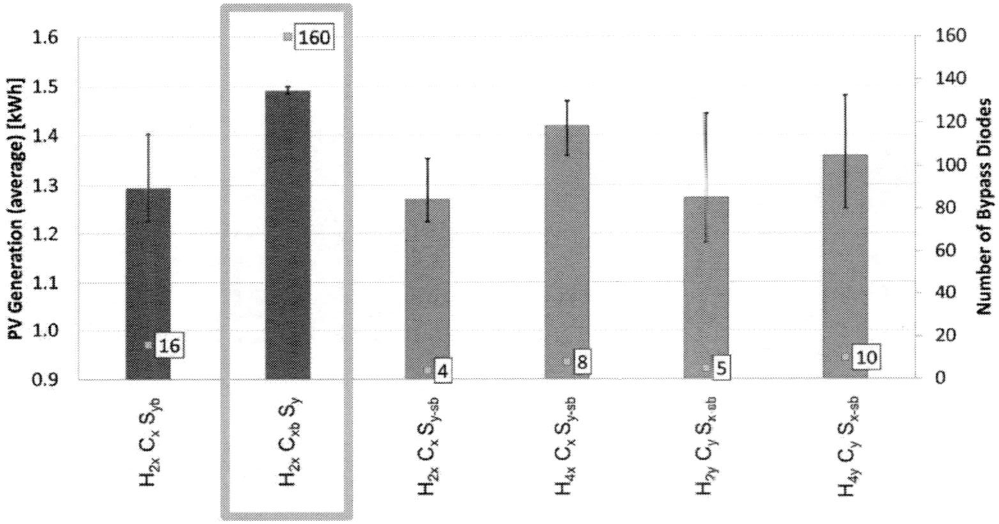

iScience

Volume 27, Issue 6, 21 June 2024, 110089

Article

On the optimization of the interconnection of photovoltaic modules integrated in vehicles

Javier Macías [1,2], Rebeca Herrero [1], Luis Javier San José [1], Rubén Núñez [1], Ignacio Antón [1]

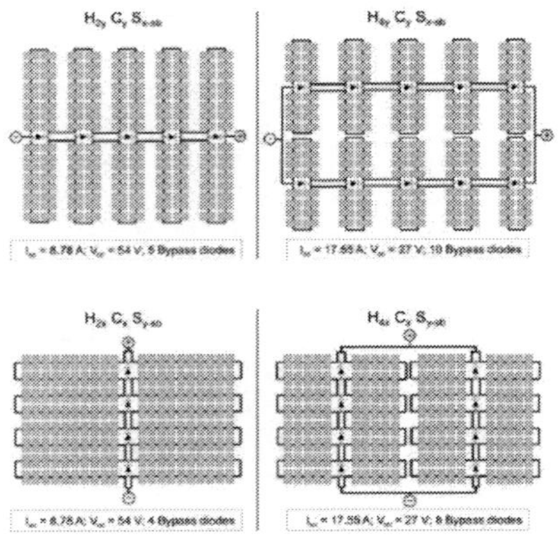

POLITÉCNICA

Objective

INSTITUTO DE ENERGÍA SOLAR

- What is the potential **gain** of **VIPV optimized** for tilted irradiance?

Parameter	Value	Units
Plan view area	2.13	m^2
PV area	2.30	m^2
Number of cells	144	Cells
Cell area	157.2	cm^2
Maximum power	520	W

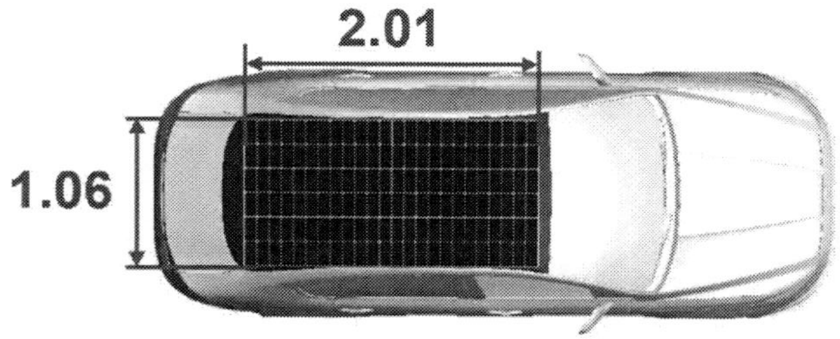

6 x 24 cells

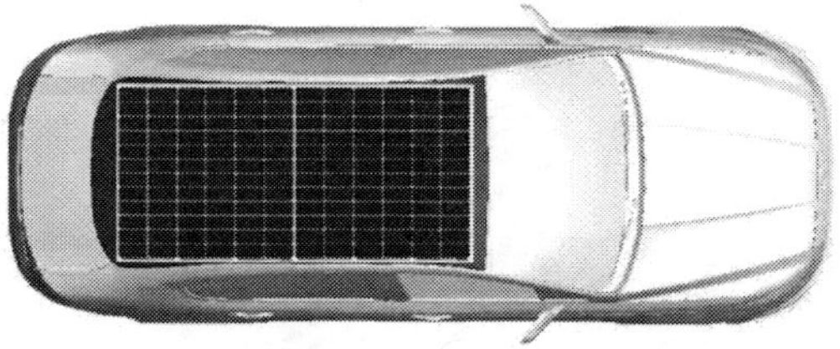

12 x 12 cells

POLITÉCNICA

Outline

INSTITUTO DE ENERGÍA SOLAR

- Validation of the Modelling Tool from experimental data
- Case Study – Angular performance VIPV integrated in sedan
- Electrical Interconnection Configurations
- Results
  - Tilted Irradiance Optimization.
  - Annual Energy Generation.
- Conclusions

Validation of the Modelling Tool from experimental data

INSTITUTO DE ENERGÍA SOLAR

Indoors

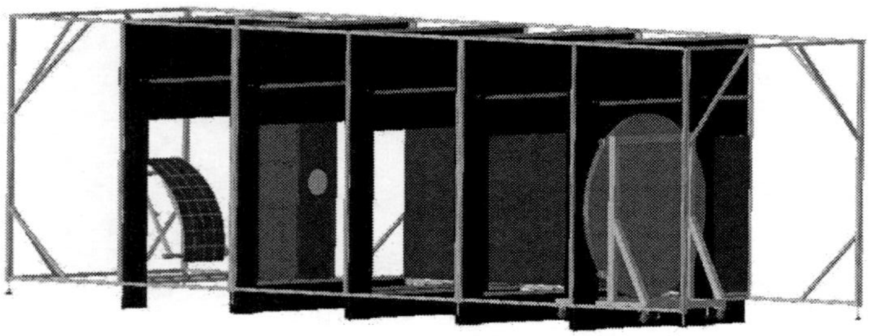

Outdoors

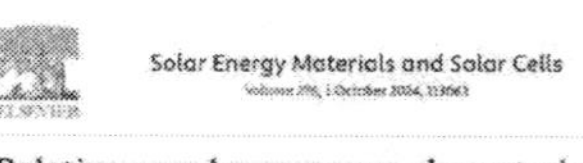

More information: 3BO.12.2 Testing VIPV Curved Modules: Methods and Challenges, Ricardo Moruno.

Articles

Solar Energy Materials and Solar Cells

Collimated solar simulator for curved PV modules characterization

Guido Vallerotto, Francisco Martín, Javier Macías, Rebeca Herrero, Luis J. San José, Steve Askins, Rubén Núñez, César Domínguez, Ignacio Antón

Solar Energy Materials and Solar Cells

Relative angular response characterization in VIPV

F. Martín, R. Moruno, L.J. San José, G. Vallerotto, J.M. Redondo, J. Melo, S. Askins, J. Macías, R. Núñez, R. Herrero, I. Antón

Solar Energy Materials and Solar Cells

Understanding the impact of sky diffuse irradiance on curved photovoltaic modules

R. Moruno, L. San José, F. Martín, R. Núñez, R. Herrero, I. Antón

POLITÉCNICA

Validation of the Modelling Tool from experimental data

INSTITUTO DE ENERGÍA SOLAR

Module	Active area $[m^2]$	Minimum curvature radius [m]	P_{mp} [W]
Commercial VIPV	0.875	3	<200
VIPV sedan	2.3	3	520

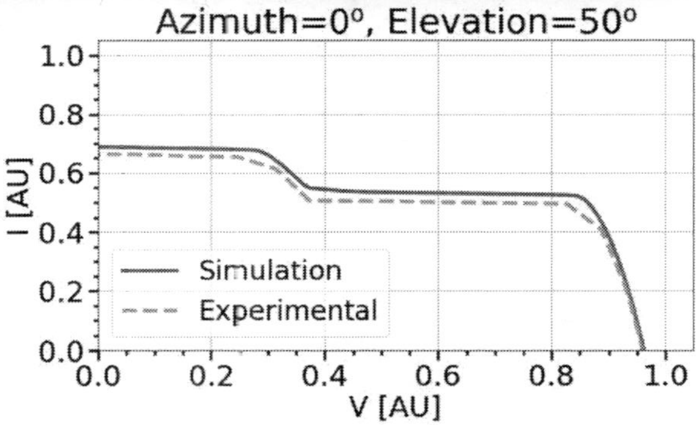

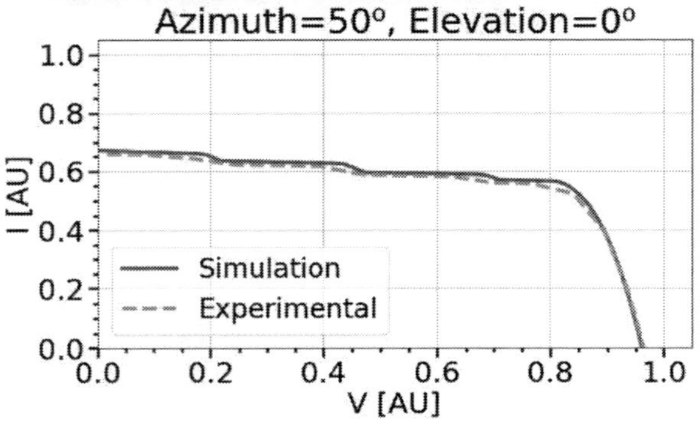

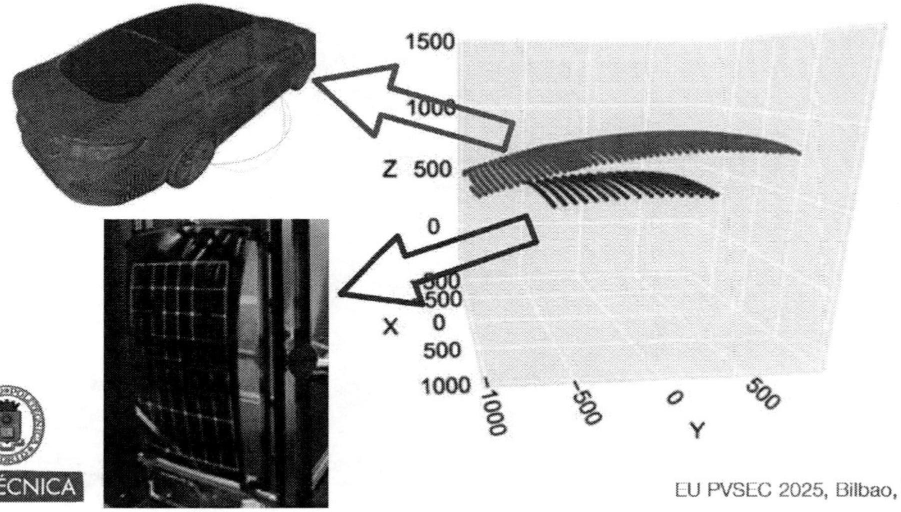

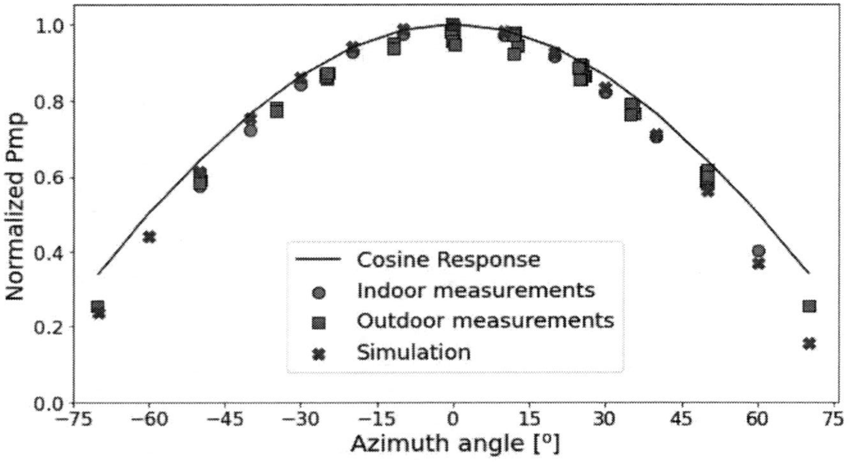

POLITÉCNICA

Case Study – Angular performance VIPV integrated in sedan

INSTITUTO DE ENERGÍA SOLAR

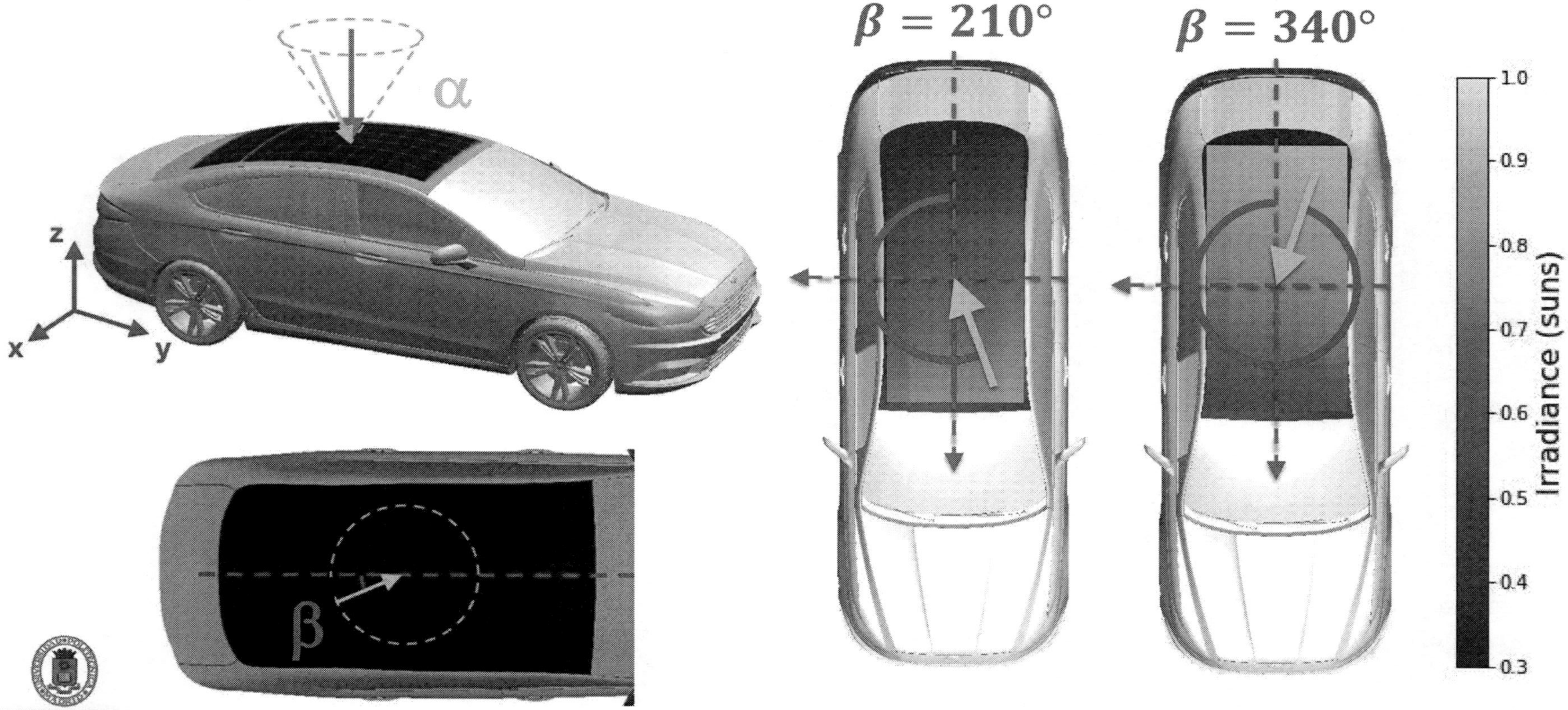

POLITÉCNICA

Case Study – Angular performance VIPV integrated in sedan

INSTITUTO DE ENERGÍA SOLAR

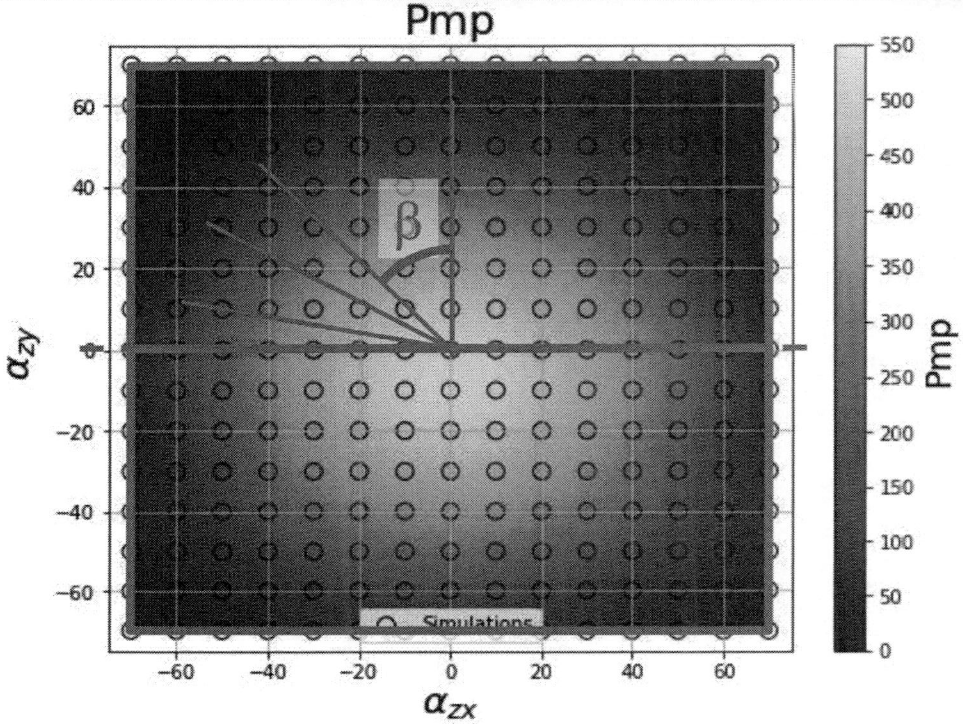

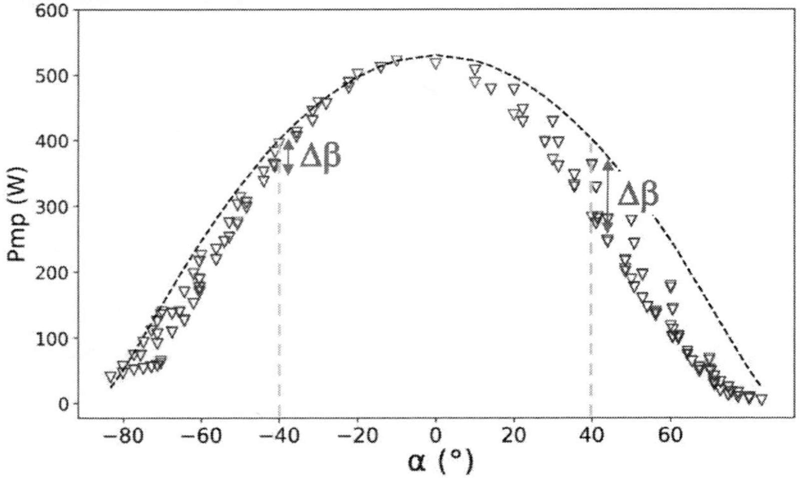

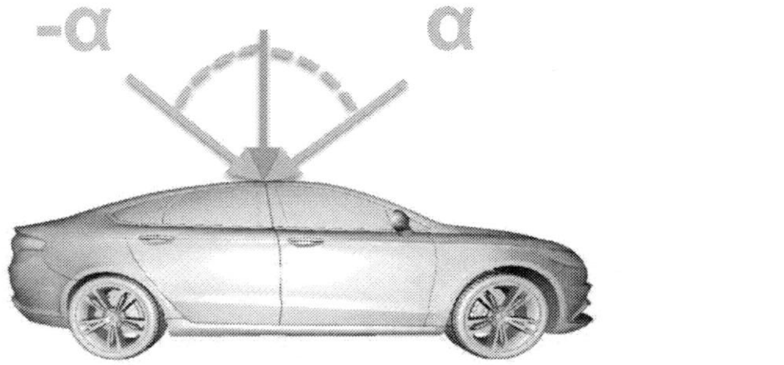

POLITÉCNICA

Application cases - Electrical Interconnection Configurations

INSTITUTO DE ENERGÍA SOLAR

6 x 24 cell matrix (landscape)

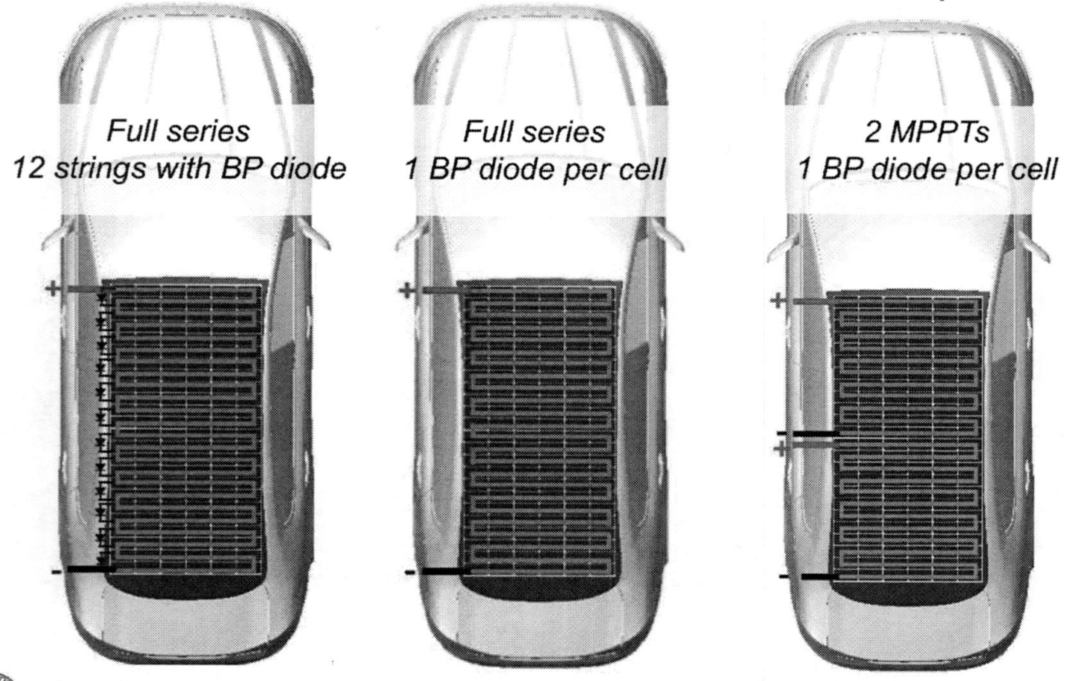

1MPPT - *24x6S - 12 BPD (BV=0.5V)*

1MPPT - *24x6S – 144 BPD (BV=0.2V)*

2MPPT - *12x6S – 144 BPD (BV=0.2 V)*
2MPPT - *12x6S – 144 BPD (BV=1.5 V)*

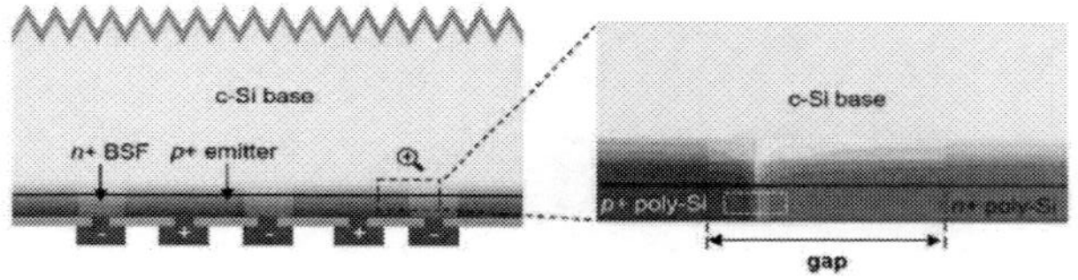

A. Calcabrini et Al, "Low-breakdown-voltage solar cells for shading-tolerant photovoltaic modules", Cell Reports Physical Science, Volume 3, Issue 12, 2022

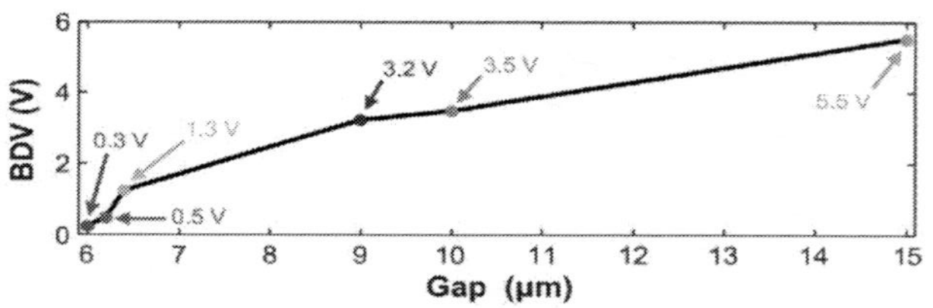

BDV of the IBC solar cells in dark at 2 A.

POLITÉCNICA

Application cases - Electrical Interconnection Configurations

INSTITUTO DE ENERGÍA SOLAR

12 x 12 cell matrix (portrait)

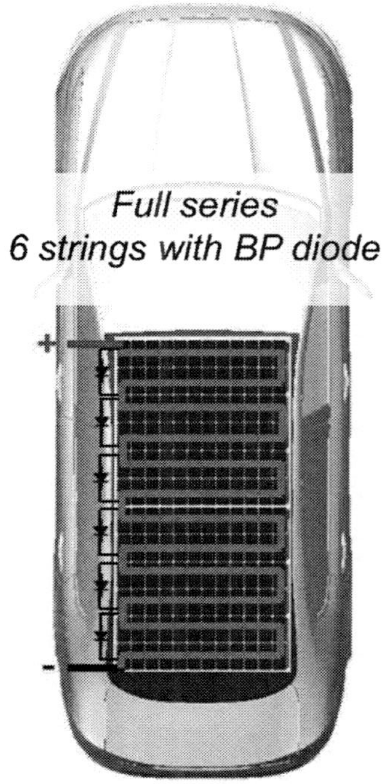

1MPPT - *12x12S – 6 BPD (BV=0.5V)*

2MPPT - *6x12S – 6 BPD (BV=0.5V)*

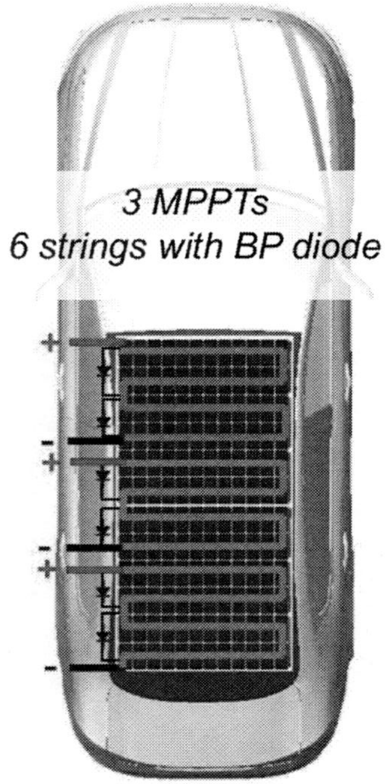

3MPPT – *4x12S – 6 BPD (BV=0.5 V)*

POLITÉCNICA

Results – Tilted Irradiance Optimization

INSTITUTO DE ENERGÍA SOLAR

Analysis	Result
Cell orientation	✗
Number of BP diodes	✗
BV of BP diodes	✗
Number of MPPTs	✓

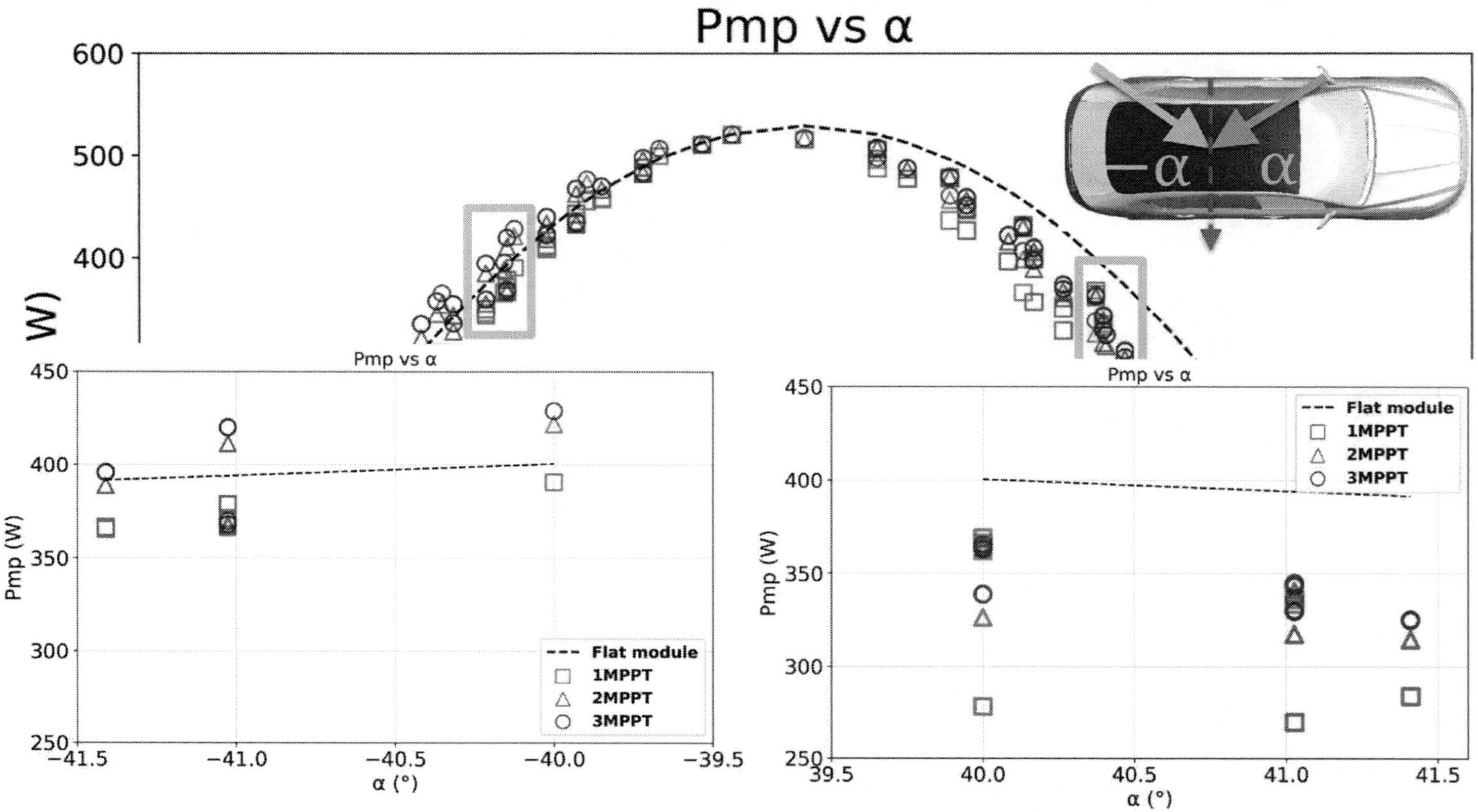

POLITÉCNICA

Results - Annual Energy Generation

INSTITUTO DE ENERGÍA SOLAR

- PV output for one typical meteorological year in Madrid (2005-2023)
- Direct, **diffuse solar radiation** and cells **temperature**
- 15-minute intervals for IV curves
- 8 car positions with azimuth variation of 45 degrees
- **135,596** cases for each electrical configuration

POLITÉCNICA

Results - Annual Energy Generation

INSTITUTO DE ENERGÍA SOLAR

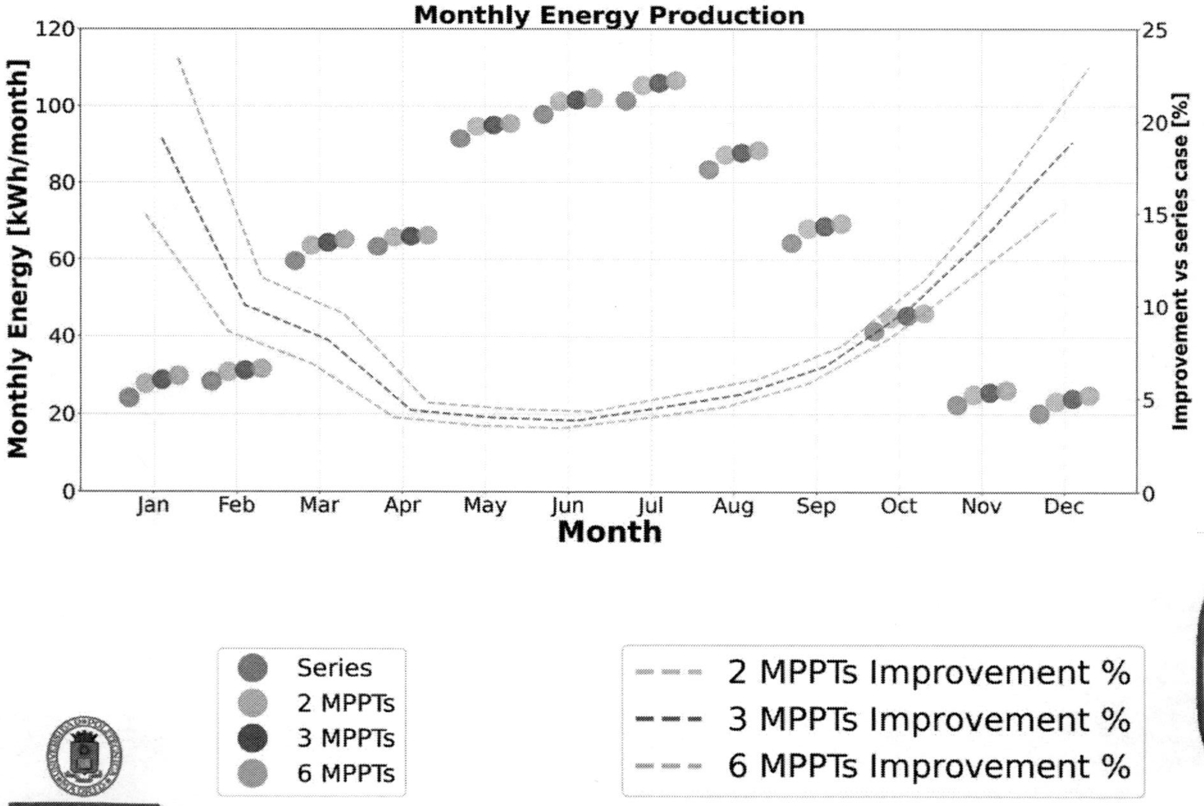

Case	Average Annual production [kWh/year]	Improvement from series [%]
Series	697.9	–
2 MPPTs	737.8	5.7%
3 MPPTs	744.6	6.7%
6 MPPTs	752.1	7.8%

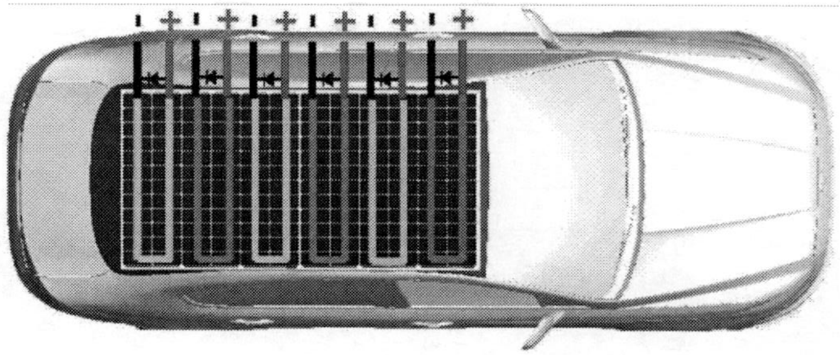

POLITÉCNICA

Conclusions

INSTITUTO DE ENERGÍA SOLAR

- Optimization for angular performance ≠ for partial shading. Do not provide an improvement:
  - Half cell orientation
  - Increasing number of bypass diodes (good for partial shading)
  - Breakdown voltage of bypass diodes (good for partial shading)
- Split module in MPPTs sections
  - 2 MPPTs significantly improves the series connection
  - 3 or 6 MPTTs show similar result, reaching maximum power output
- Energy generation
  - Optimized configuration increases annual yield by ~8% in Madrid climate

Thanks for your attention !

INSTITUTO DE ENERGÍA SOLAR

Francisco José Martín San Agustín

f.martin.sanagustin@alumnos.upm.es

Happy to take your questions

We gratefully acknowledge the DETEC-PV project, Grant PID2021-128853OB-I00, funded by MCIN/AEI/10.13039/501100011033 and "ERDF A way of making Europe"

The authors express sincere thanks to JEMA and JET program for sponsoring the activities, entrusted by METI (Japan) and carried out under the umbrella of the IEC TC82/PT600 group devoted to Vehicle Integrated Photovoltaic Systems

MINISTERIO DE CIENCIA E INNOVACIÓN

UNIÓN EUROPEA

FONDO EUROPEO DE DESARROLLO REGIONAL

"Una manera de hacer Europa"

AGENCIA ESTATAL DE INVESTIGACIÓN

POLITÉCNICA

INSTITUTO
DE ENERGÍA
SOLAR

Innovation in photovoltaics since 1979

TOWARDS LOW-IMPACT TRIPLE-JUNCTION PEROVSKITE/SILICON TANDEM MODULES

LCA OF PRECURSOR MATERIALS TO DESCRIBE THE INFLUENCE OF BACKGROUND DATA SOURCES

A. Galarza[1] , S. Nold[2] , L. Oberbeck[1,3]

1. *Institut Photovoltaïque d'Île-de-France (IPVF)*
2. *Fraunhofer Institute for Solar Energy Systems ISE*
3. *TotalEnergies OneTech*

EUPVSEC 2025 - 5CO.4 | Bilbao, Spain
September 24, 2025

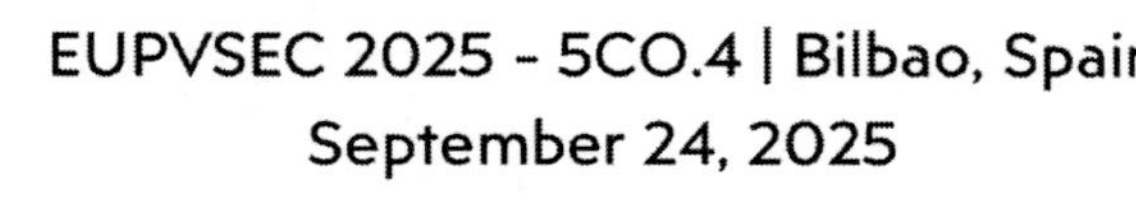

Outline

1. **Meet IPVF and the TRIUMPH project**
2. Life Cycle Assessment in the PV industry
3. Data availability for perovskite materials
4. Comparison between perovskite compositions
5. Summary

About IPVF

An initiative born from the French State's ambition to drive **scientific excellence** in support of an effective **European photovoltaic industry**, with active partners spanning most of the value chain and collaborating closely with leading academic institutions.

RESEARCH
PLATFORM
ENABLE
UNITE

TRIUMPH Quasar LAPERITIVO BRIGHT SIDE STAFF

About the TRIUMPH project
Triple Junction Solar Module

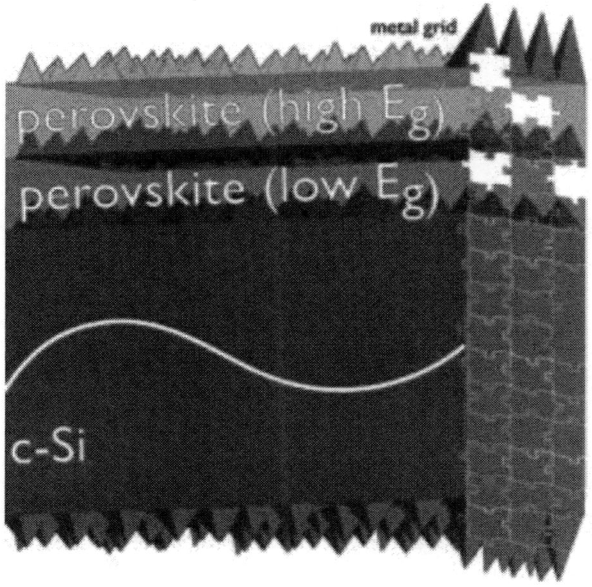

General objectives

1. High efficiencies and stability
   - Target efficiency **>33%** on 1 cm^2
   - Passing accelerated reliability testing.
2. Cost-effective and scalable technology (TRL = 5)
   - Target of **≥100 cm2** using cost-effective and scalable cell processes
3. Design for sustainability
   - Reduction of **critical raw materials** such as Indium and Silver
   - Circular concepts that allow easy recycling
4. Value chain buy-in
   - Establishing the **value chain** within **European Union** for future multi-junction modules.

Find more information →
- *Booth F6*
- *5EO.3: Markets, Costs and Economics (26th Sep – 8h30h-10h)*

TRIUMPH, IPVF, EDF, imec, SALD, TNO, Uni Freiburg, CNRS, Fraunhofer ISE, VON ARDENNE, dyenamo, EPFL, csem, RENA, Q CELLS

Outline

1. Meet IPVF and the TRIUMPH project
2. **Life Cycle Assessment in the PV industry**
3. Data availability for perovskite materials
4. Comparison between perovskite compositions
5. Summary

LCA in the PV industry

Life Cycle Assessment (LCA) is the systematic analysis of the potential environmental impacts of products or services during their entire life cycle (manufacturing, distribution, use and end-of-life phases) according to ISO 14040 and 14044

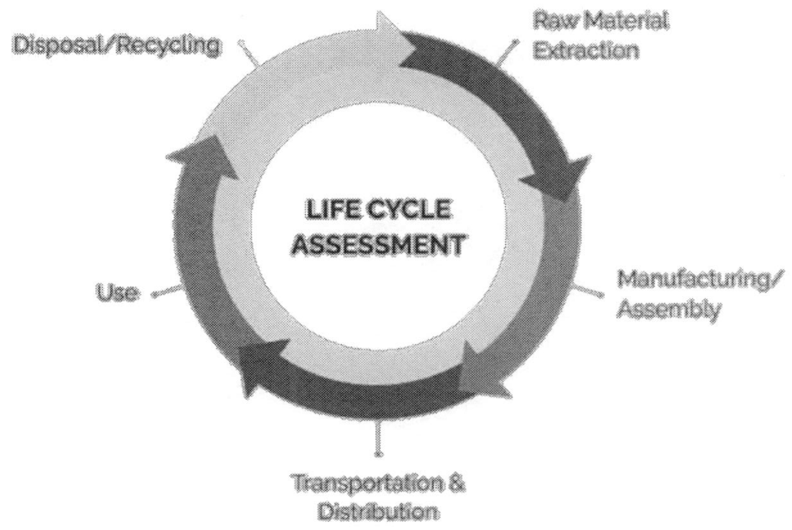

- Research and development
- Product design or improvement
- Process optimization
- Legislative compliance
- Market positioning

- **Minimization** of the environmental impact of PV technology developed in TRIUMPH
- **Focus** on categories of global warming potential, toxicity, and resource depletion
- **Strategic** material selection & energy use optimization

Where to find the data for an LCA
Background and Foreground data

Background Data

- Energy consumption
- Water consumption
- Reactants
- Source of the reactants
- Waste management (Emissions)

Foreground Data

Process input
- Materials
- Energy

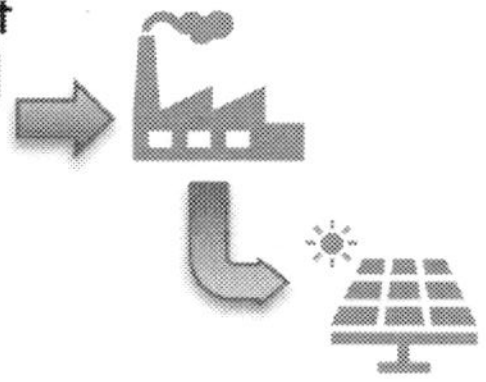

Process output
- PV
- Emissions

SPECIALIZED LCA DATABASES

+

LITERATURE REVIEW OR INDUSTRY INPUT

+

STOICHIOMETRY-BASED ESTIMATION

Outline

1. Meet IPVF and the TRIUMPH project
2. Life Cycle Assessment in the PV industry
3. **Data availability for perovskite materials**
4. Comparison between perovskite compositions
5. Summary

Availability of background data of precursor materials

TRIUMPH

Material	Specialized database	Industry (2024)	Alberola-Borras et al. (2018)	Khalifa et al. (2020)	Gong et al. (2015)	Espinosa et al. (2015)	Geisler et al. (2004)
PbBr2			●	●	●		●
PbCl2						●	
PbI2			●	●	●		
FABr		●					
FACl		●					
FAI		●	●	●			●
MABr			●				
MACl		●					
MAI		●	●	●	●	●	
CsBr		●					●
CsI		●	●	●			
DMF	●						
NMP	●						

- Most perovskite materials lack standard LCI datasets
- Available sources differ on the information provided and represent different production roads
- Critical gaps:
  - Organic salts
  - Cesium salts

Does the selection of the sources affect the LCA results?

IPVF

Implications of source variation

Environmental assessment for the production of precursors

Scope
- FU: Production 1 kg
- Cradle-to-gate

Methodology
- Simapro 9.5.0.2
- Ecoinvent 3.9.1
- Cut-off allocation
- Environmental Footprint 3.1 method

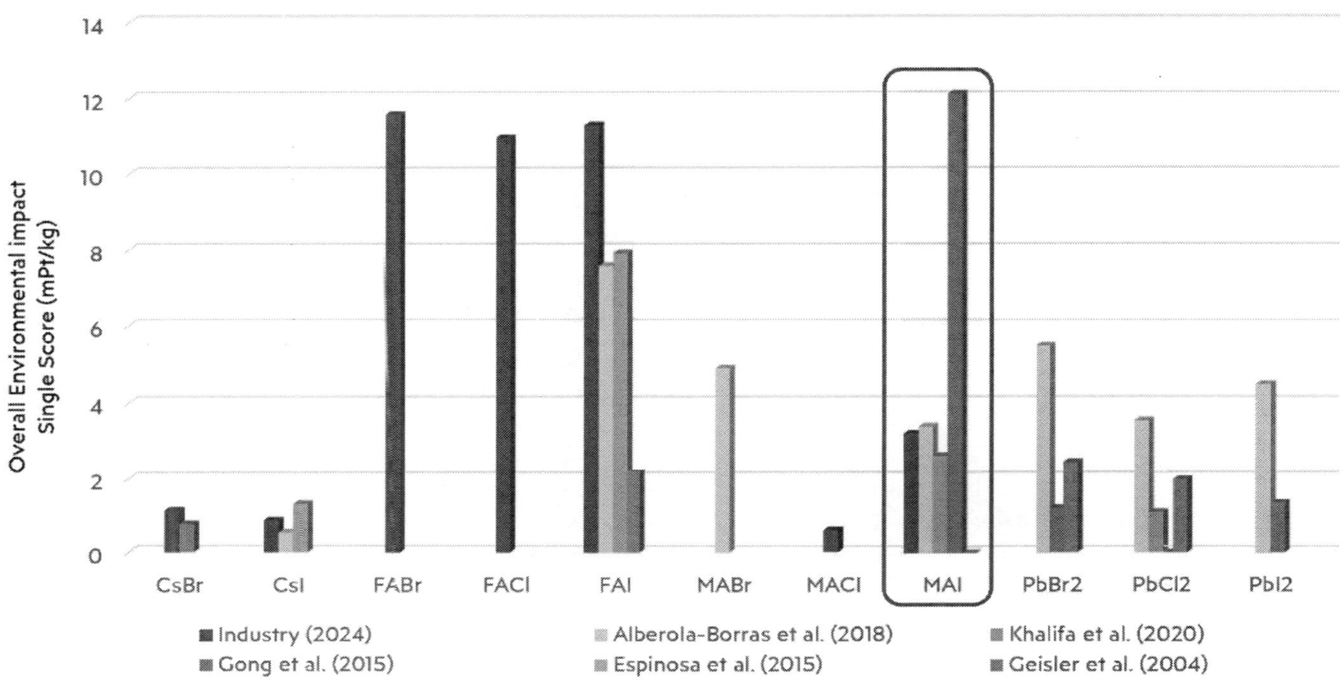

- Strong variations within materials
- No trends for global high/low impact sources
- Selection of source could be bias

IPVF

Case *Methylammonium Iodide* (MAI) *Distribution per category*

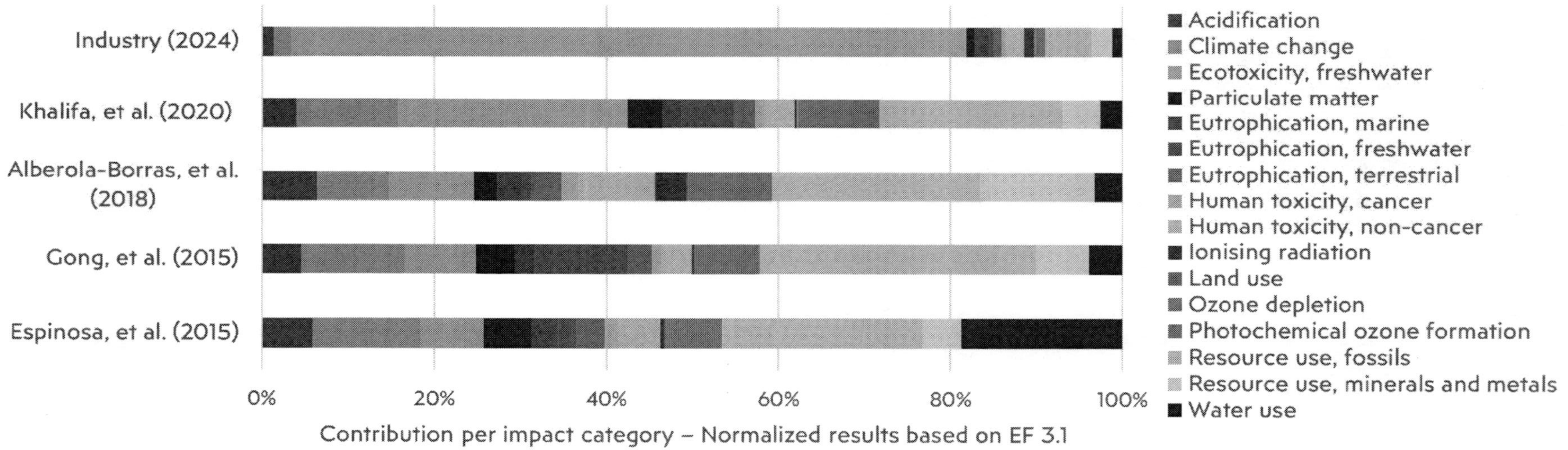

- Similar overall impacts could present different impact distribution
- Similar impact distribution could present different overall impact

- Variations in industrial processes influence the impact distribution
- High complexity for comparison and reliability determination
- Prioritization of data source selection remains challenging

Outline

1. Meet IPVF and the TRIUMPH project
2. Life Cycle Assessment in the PV industry
3. Data availability for perovskite materials
4. Comparison between perovskite compositions
5. Summary

Effects of source selection in perovskite layers

Process description
- 450 nm layer thickness
- Thermal evaporation
- M10 wafer size

Scope
- FU: Deposition 1 m^2
- Cradle-to-gate

Material	Alberola-Borras et al. (2018)	Khalifa et al. (2020)	Gong et al. (2015)
PbBr2			
PbI2	●	●	●
FAI			
MAI	●	●	●
CsI			

Selected Perovskites
- $MAPbI_3$ (3 sources)
- $FAPbI_3$ (2 sources)
- $MAPb(I_{0,8}Br_{0,2})_3$ (2 sources)
- $Cs_{0.15}FA_{0.85}PbI_3$ (2 sources)

Allow comparison of the effects of source variation for a perovskite layer

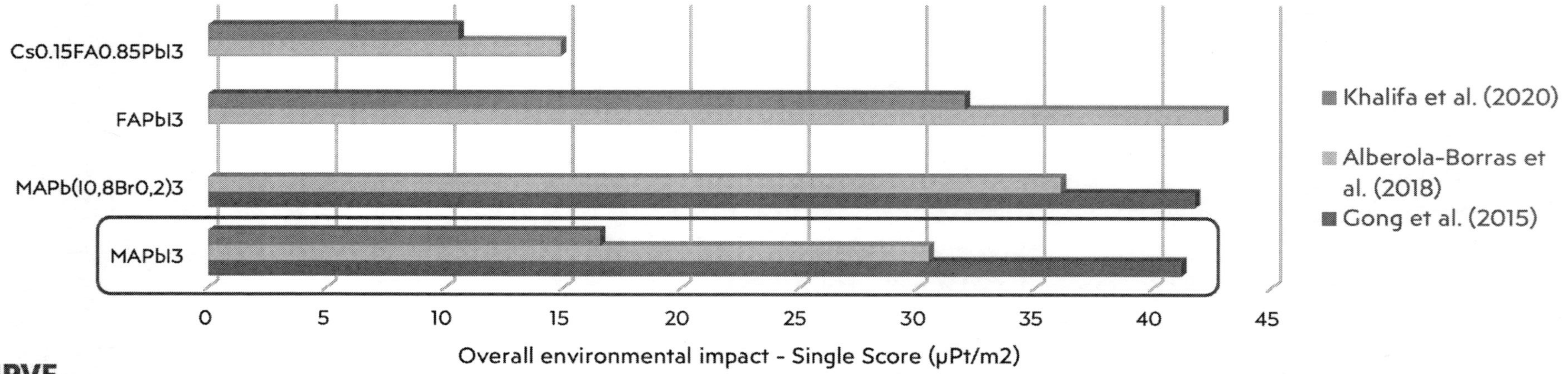

IPVF

Case MAPbI3 – *Comparison per category*

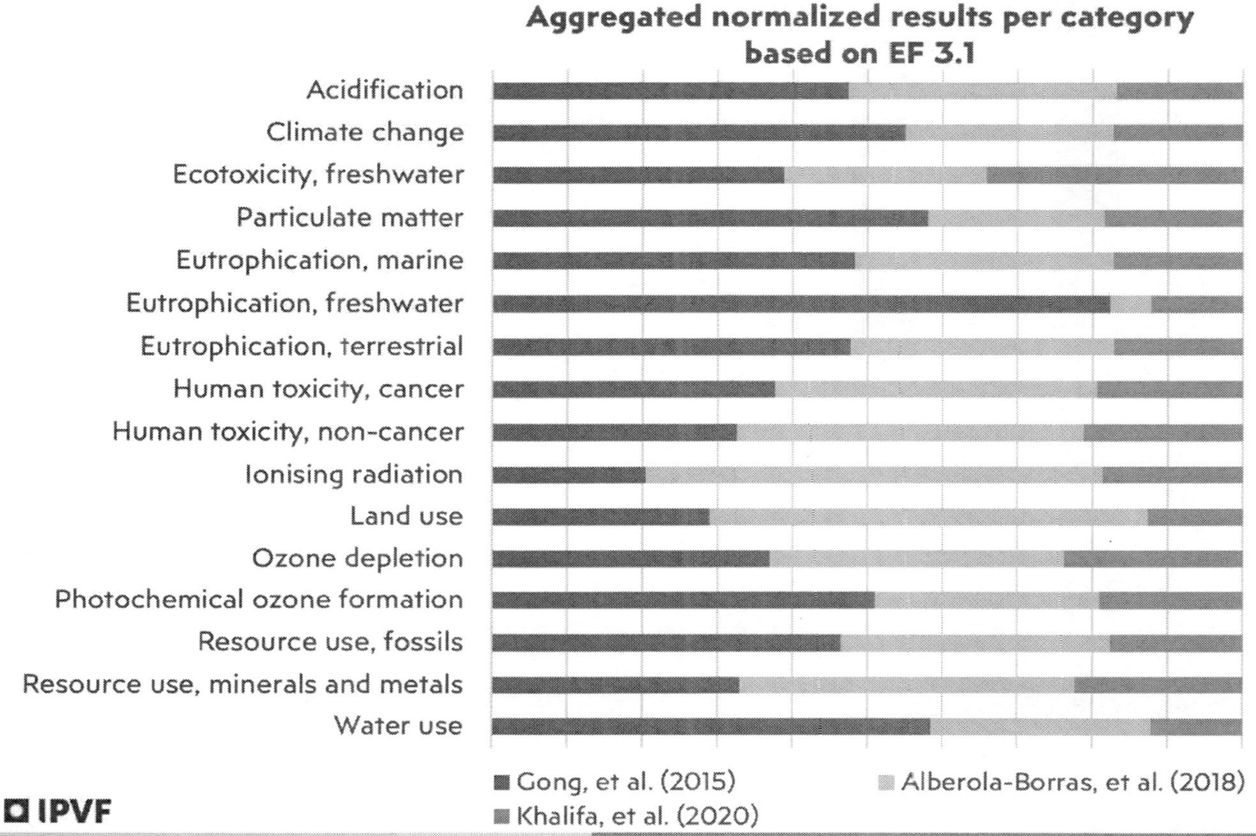

Gong et al. (2015):
406 g CO_2-eq/m^2

Alberola-Borras et al. (2018):
204 g CO_2-eq/m^2

Khalifa, et al. (2020):
127 g CO_2-eq/m^2

- Variations on the characterized result are significant
- Source selection could determine the hotspot categories and LCA conclusions

IPVF

Variation assessment

ACTIONS DONE FOR EACH PEROVSKITE

- Determine potential mix cases
- Characterization results under every case
- Calculation of mean and standard deviation per impact category
- Calculation of coefficient of variation (CV%)

$$CV\% = {}^{SD}/_{Mean} * 100$$

- Average of CV%

	MAPbI3	Cs0.15FA0.85PbI3	CsPbI2Br	FAPbI3	MAPb(I0.8Br0.2)3
Pure cases	3	2	-	2	2
Mixed cases	4	4	4	3	-
Total	**7**	**6**	**4**	**5**	**2**

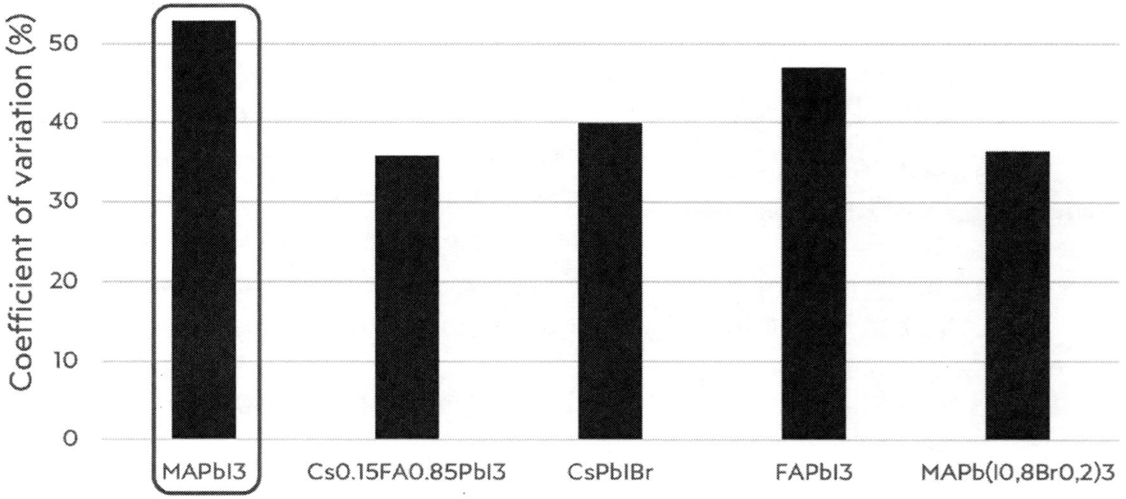

IPVF

Case $MAPbI_3$ – *Coefficient of variation per category*

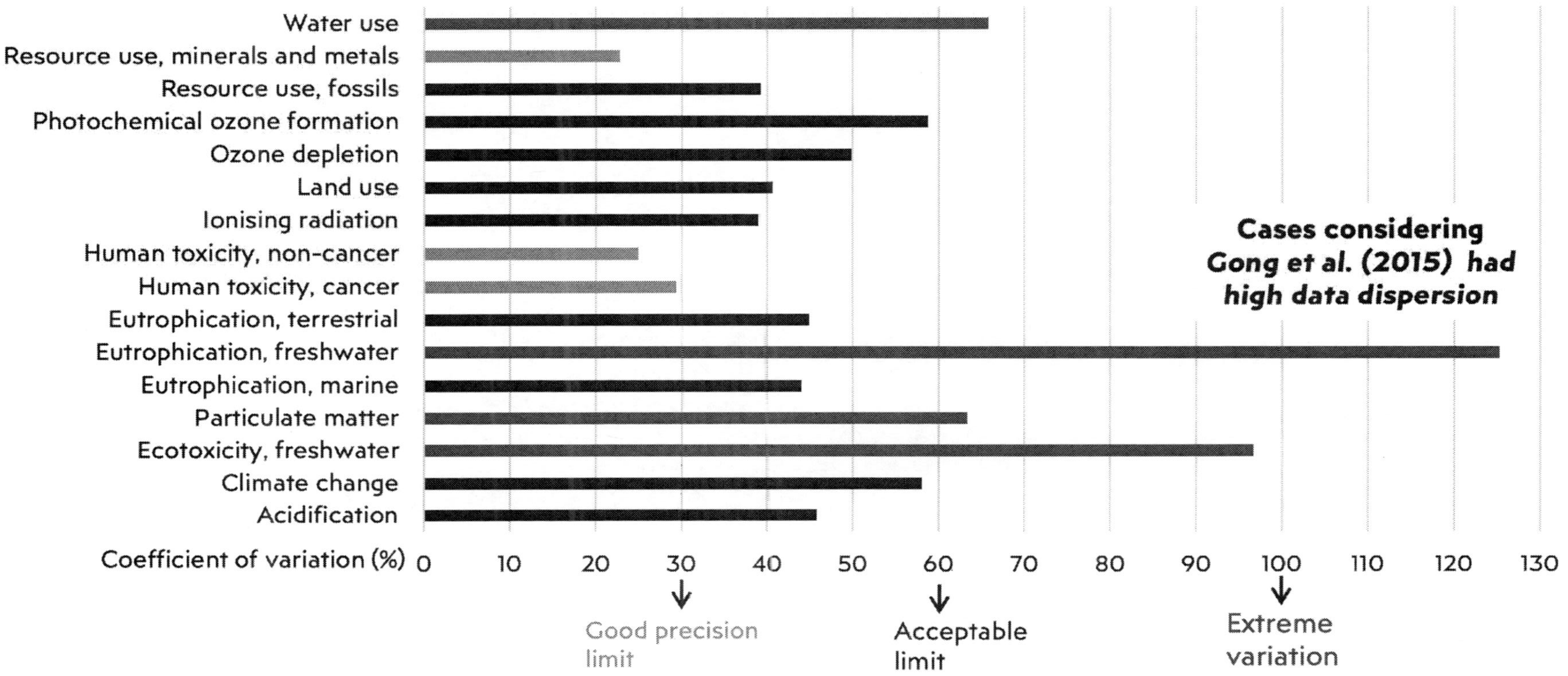

Outline

1. Meet IPVF and the TRIUMPH project
2. Life Cycle Assessment in the PV industry
3. Data availability for perovskite materials
4. Comparison between perovskite compositions
5. **Summary**

Conclusions

- **High variability in background data and no selection criteria:** Novel PV technologies (e.g., perovskites) show strong variation in material datasets due to lack of maturity and limited reporting.
- **Critical role of source selection:** Dataset selection influences the LCA outcomes. High coefficient of variation represent high LCA uncertainty and challenging comparisons. LCAs should incorporate a range of impact values from multiple sources to facilitate comparability
- **Research need:** Development of harmonized, high-quality LCI datasets for perovskite precursors is essential to improve reliability and comparability of LCAs.
- **Industry–science collaboration:** Closer collaboration is needed to generate trustworthy data and support robust environmental assessments of next-generation PV technologies.

Thank you for your attention

Further questions?

alejandra.galarza@ipvf.fr

This project is supported at IPVF by the French Government in the frame of the program of investment for the future (Programme d'Investissement d'Avenir - ANR-IEED-002-01)

This work has been co-funded by the European Union under the project TRIUMPH from the European Union's Horizon research and innovation program

TRIUMPH

Literature

- Alberola-Borras, J. A., Vidal, R., & Mora-Sero, I. (2018). *Evaluation of multiple cation/anion perovskite solar cells through life cycle assessment.*
- Khalifa, S. A., Spatari, S., Fafarman, A. T., & Baxter, J. B. (2020). *Environmental sustainability of mixed cation perovskite materials in photovoltaics manufacturing.*
- Gong, J., Darling, S. B., & You, F. (2015). *Perovskite photovoltaics: life-cycle assessment of energy and environmental impacts.*
- Espinosa, N., Serrano-Luján, L., Urbina, A., & Krebs, F. C. (2015). *Solution and vapour deposited lead perovskite solar cells: Ecotoxicity from a life cycle assessment perspective.*
- Geisler, G., Hofstetter, T. B., & Hungerbühler, K. (2004). *Production of fine and speciality chemicals: procedure for the estimation of LCIs*

RSE Ricerca Sistema Energetico / we move rsearch

Sustainability Assessment of Perovskite/Silicon Tandem Solar Modules: From Laboratory scale to Industrial implementation

Elisabetta Brivio, Andrea Danelli, Sofia Spagnolo, Pierpaolo Girardi

24/09/2025

EU PVSEC 2025
42nd European Photovoltaic Solar Energy Conference and Exhibition

Index

1. Introduction
2. What is an LCA
3. LCA of a lab-scale PVSK/Si tandem module
4. LCA of industrial-scale PVSK/Si tandem module
5. Potential application in a hypothetical PV plant

Introduction

EU solar energy strategy

aims to bring online over **700 GW by 2030.**

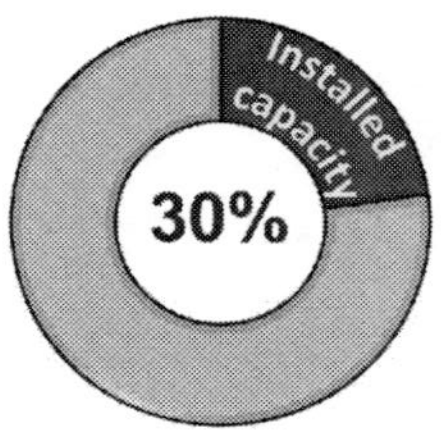

2022 vs 2030

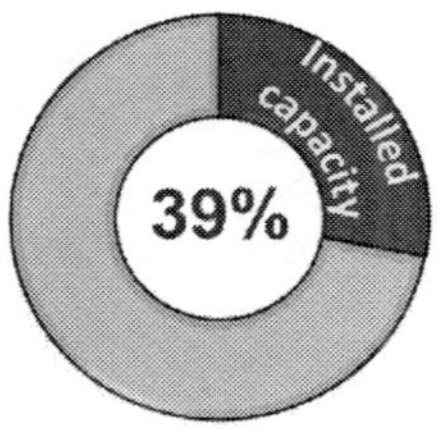

2023 vs 2030

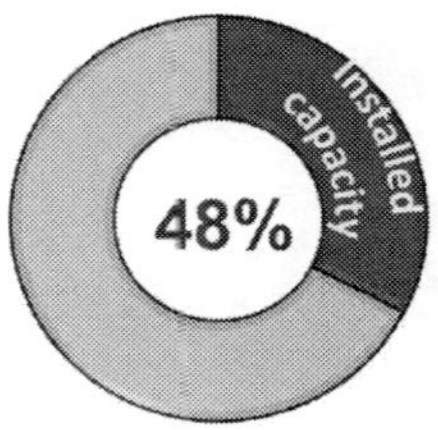

2024 vs 2030

IT National energy and climate plans (NECPs) 2030

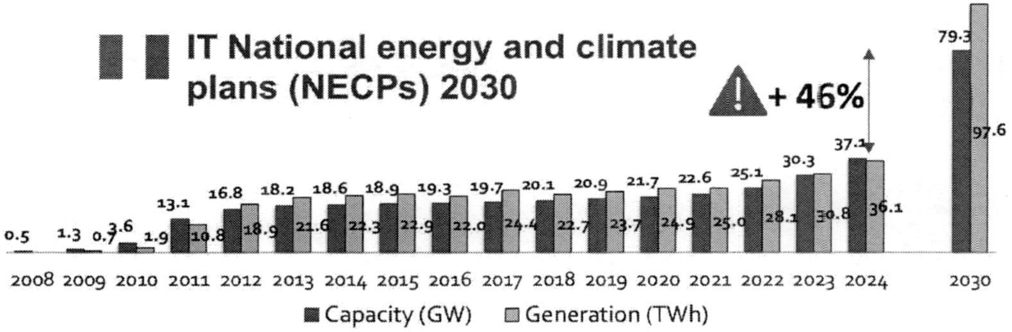

- Increase of the PV installed capacity
- Improving the efficiency of photovoltaic systems
- Mitigating CO_2-equivalent emissions related to the electricity system

Promote environmentally sustainable development of high-efficiency photovoltaic generation systems!

Life Cycle Assessment

Methodology description

- LCA is defined by the ISO 14040 as the compilation and evaluation of the inputs, outputs and the potential environmental impacts of a product or system throughout its life cycle.
- It consists in quantifying the **use of resources** ("inputs" such as energy, raw materials, water) and **emissions into the environment** ("outputs" in the air, water and soil) associated with a product, a process or an activity throughout its **life cycle** in order to evaluate the potential environmental impact.

ISO 14040

ISO 14044

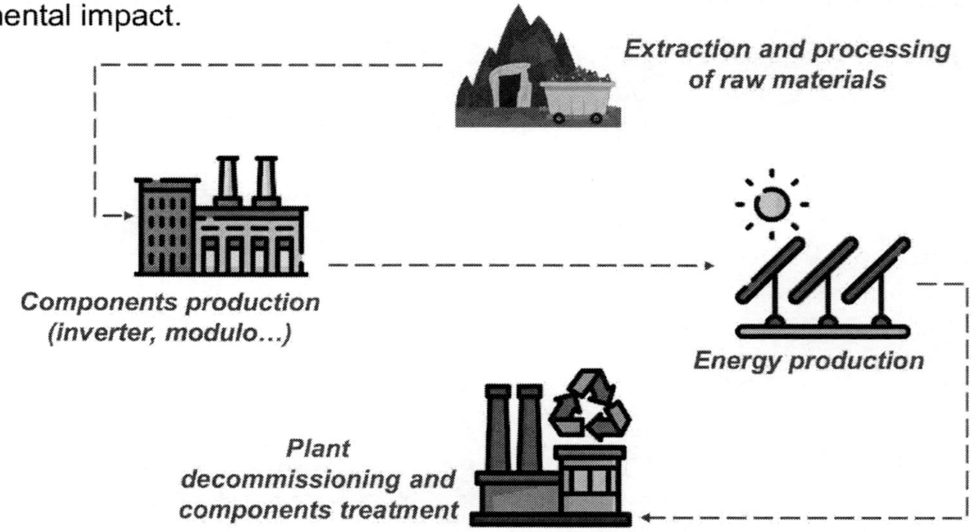

Life Cycle Assessment

Case study description

- The analysis aims to understand the **potential environmental benefit** generated by PVSK/Si tandem technology.
- The study focuses on its **future application**, assuming a system comparable to current silicon-based technologies

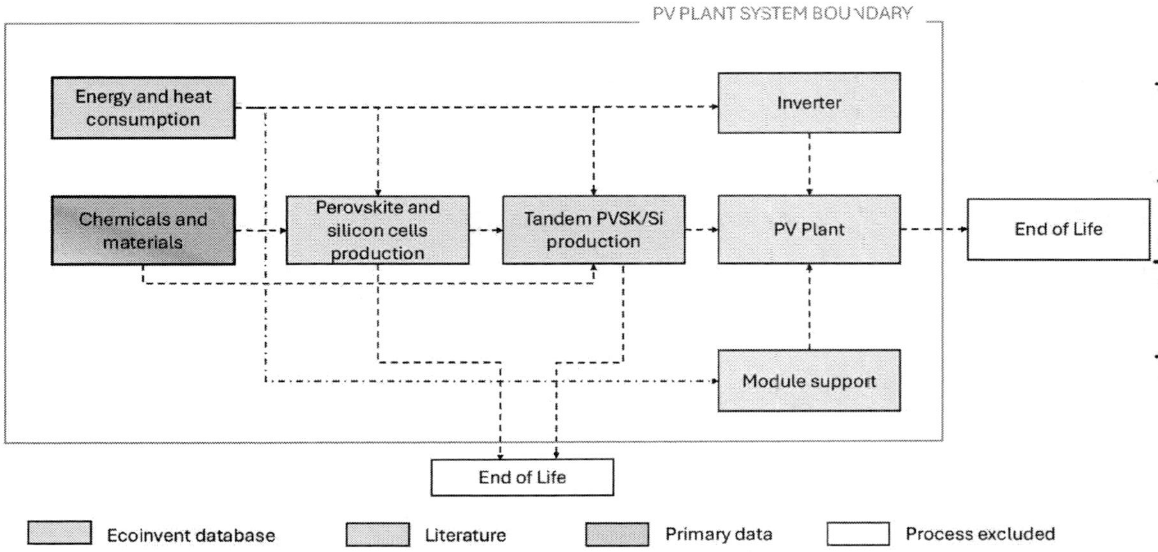

- The background processes are modelled by using the **Ecoinvent database.**
- Silicon cell and perovskite/silicon tandem cell and module production are based on **primary data**.
- Silicon solar grade and wafer are modelled according with **IEA PVPS Task 12 LCI**
- The analysis **considers all the life cycle phases,** from raw material extraction to energy production.
- The **wafer** and **silicon cell** are manufactured in **China**, whereas the **perovskite-silicon tandem module** is produced in **Italy**.

Life Cycle Assessment

PVSK cell production at laboratory scale

The production process includes **11 steps**:

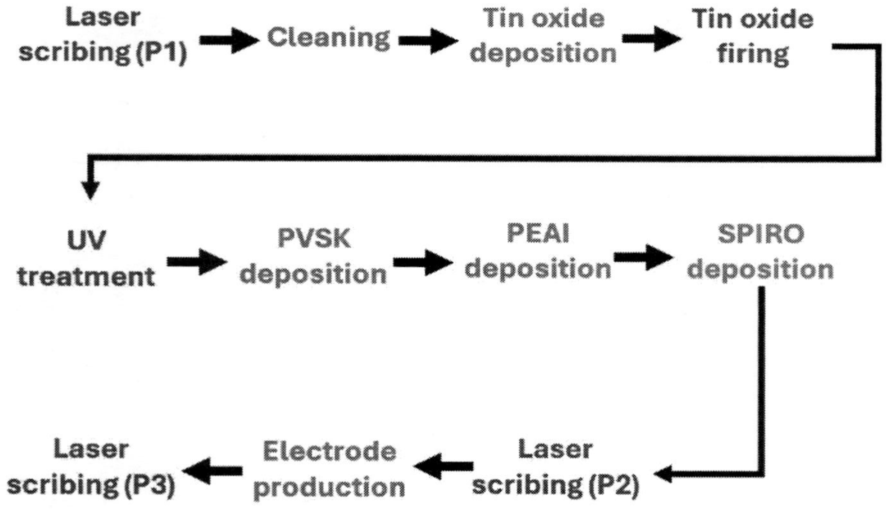

RED: this phase includes only energy consumption
BLUE: this phase includes the consumption of both energy and materials/chemicals

- The perovskite cell is modeled using primary laboratory-scale data
- The **muffle furnace** is used for tin oxide firing and perovskite (PVSK) deposition
- **Layer deposition** is carried out using the **slot-die coating technique**.

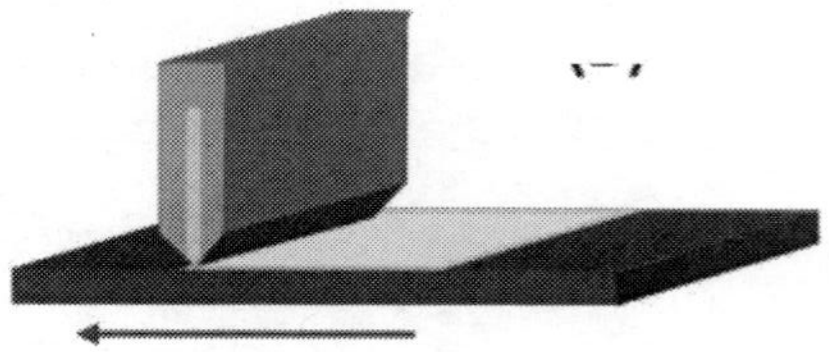

- The study considers **gold electrode**.

TOR VERGATA UNIVERSITÀ DEGLI STUDI DI ROMA

CHOSE POLO SOLARE ORGANICO REGIONE LAZIO

Life Cycle Assessment

PVSK cell production at industrial scale

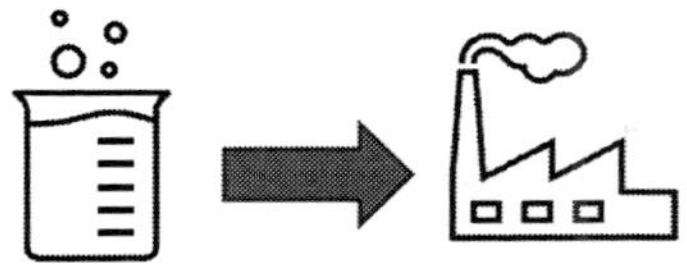

The laboratory-scale data have been adjusted to reflect a potential industrial-scale production scenario.

The **muffle furnace,** used for tin oxide firing and perovskite (PVSK) deposition, has been replaced with a **conveyor furnace.**

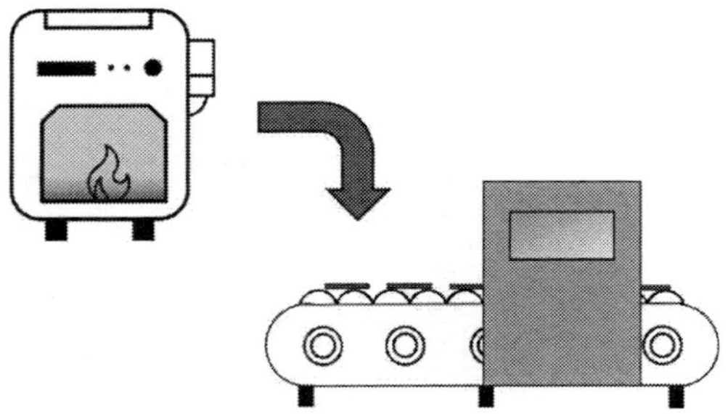

The study considers two possible electrode:

1. **SCENARIO A:** Gold/ITO electrode
2. **SCENARIO B:** MoOX/ITO electrode

The use of ITO implies the introduction of a sputtering process.

TOR VERGATA UNIVERSITÀ DEGLI STUDI DI ROMA

POLO SOLARE ORGANICO REGIONE LAZIO

Life Cycle Assessment

PVSK/Si tandem module production

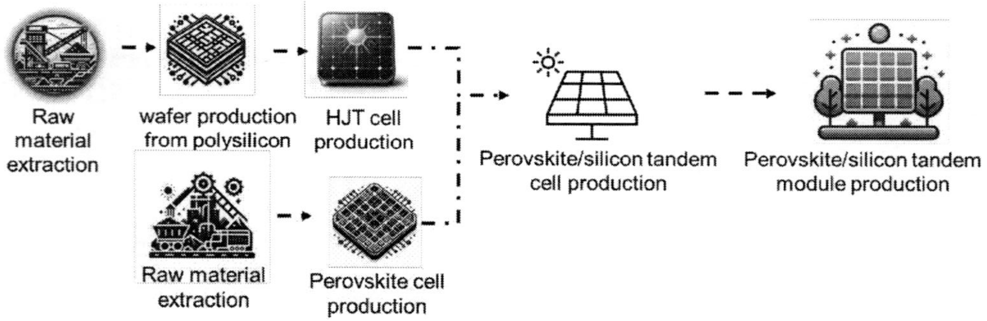

Silicon cell technical information

	HJT
Type	HJT n-Type
Dimension	156 mm x 156 mm
Thickness	185 µm
Efficiency	21.6 %
Power	5.3 W
Production site	China

Module technical information

Type of module	Mechanically stacked Perovskite/Silicon cell
Module efficiency	28.5%
Module power	563 W
Area	1.98 m^2
Type of Si-cell	N-type HJT cell

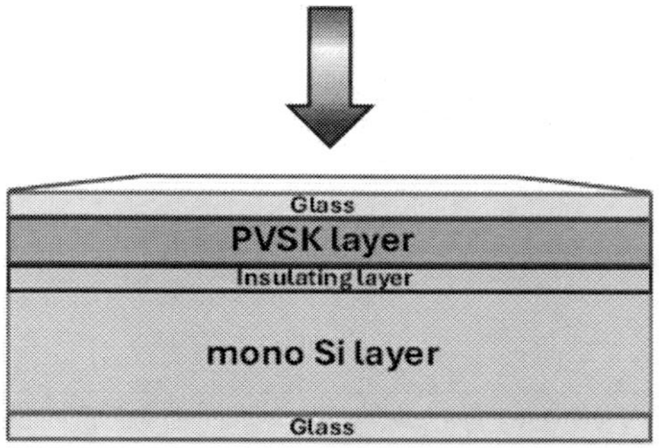

Perovskite/Silicon Tandem module structure

The study assumes a hypothetical **PVSK/Si tandem module comparable** to current **silicon modules** in terms of lifespan and degradation rate, in order to evaluate the technology at an industrial scale.

Life Cycle Assessment

Environmental impact of a tandem module at lab-scale

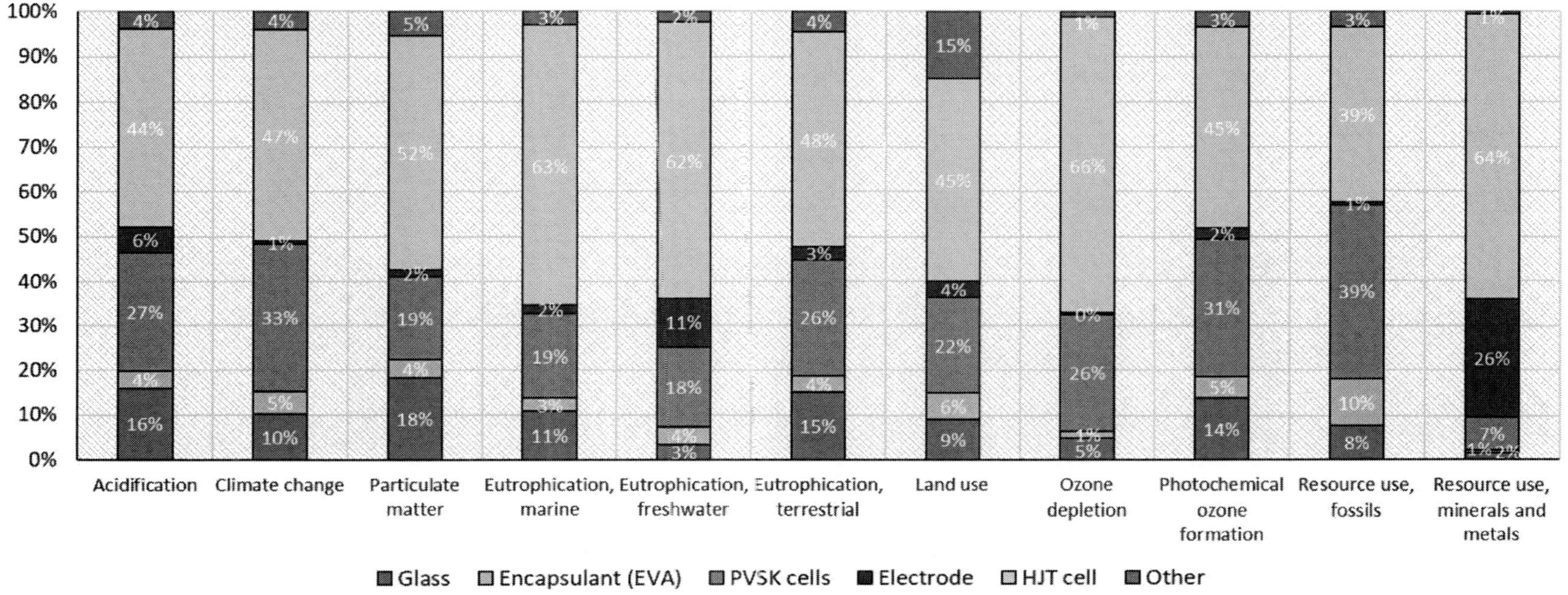

The results are referred to 1 W of module (A: 1.9 8m² and P: 563 W)

EF METHOD SimaPro

Life Cycle Assessment

Environmental impact of a PVSK cell at lab-scale

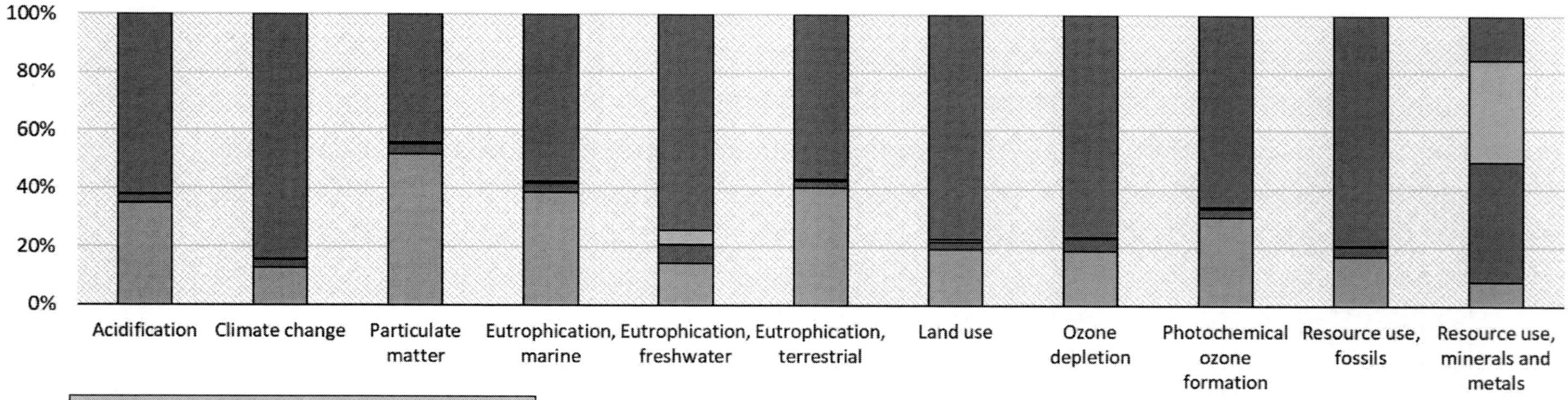

The results are referred to 1 cm^2 of PVSK cell

The impact associated with **energy consumption** is mainly due to the energy required for **the electrode deposition process**.
In the Resource use, mineral and metals category, the **electrode material** accounts for **40%** of the impacts.

EF METHOD SimaPro

Life Cycle Assessment

Comparison among different electrode scenarios

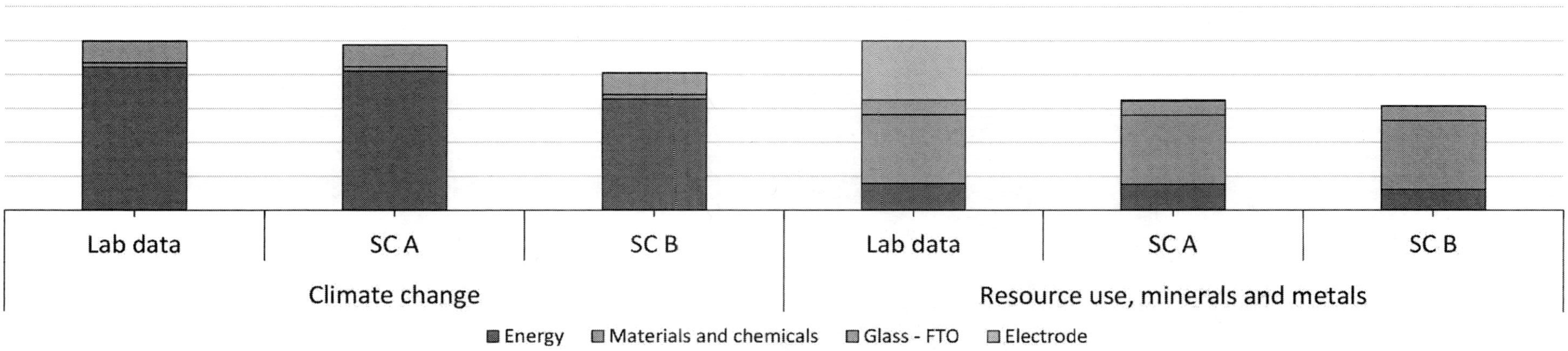

Electrode production accounts for **over 85%** of the total energy consumption

Scenarios A and B involve a **reduced material usage,** resulting in **lower environmental impacts** and a decreased contribution from the electrode

EF METHOD SimaPro

The results are referred to 1 cm^2 of perovskite cell. Lab data: PVSK cell modelled by using laboratory data; SC A: scale-up scenario with AU/ITO electrode; SC B: scale-up scenario with MoOx/ITO electrode.

RSE we move rsearch

Life Cycle Assessment

Comparison among different PVSK/Si module scenarios

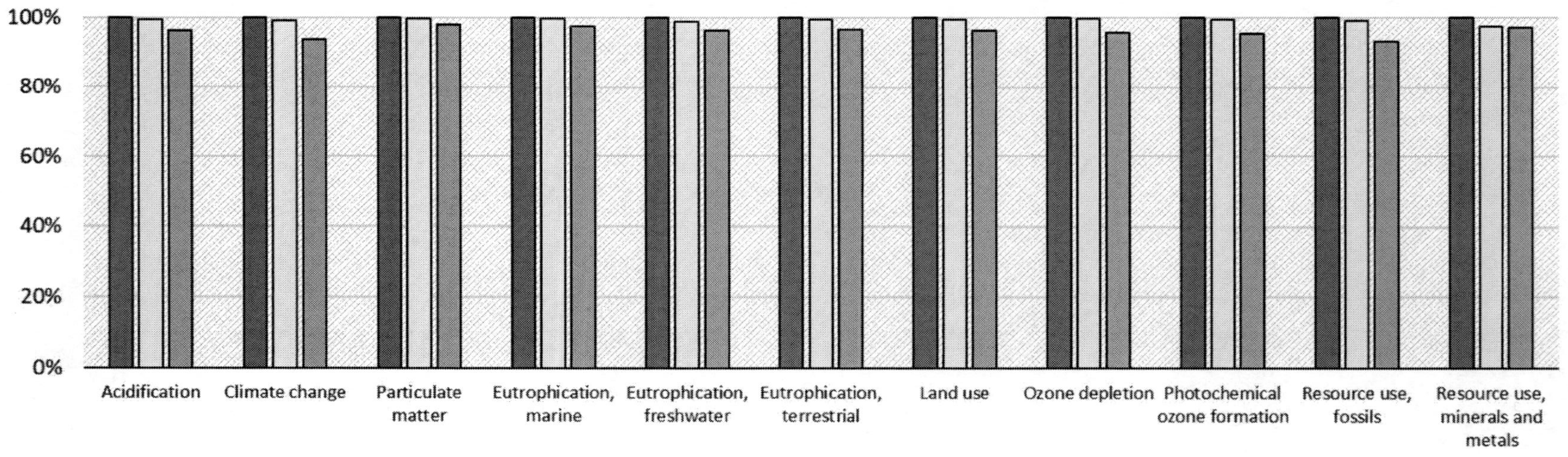

The use of fewer and **alternative materials**, combined with **lower energy consumption**, leads to a slight **reduction in environmental impact**.

EF METHOD SimaPro

The results are referred to 1 W of perovskite/Si module. Lab data: PVSK cell modelled by using laboratory data; SCA: scale-up scenario with AU/ITO electrode; SCB: scale-up scenario with MoOx/ITO electrode.

12

Life Cycle Assessment

PVSK/Si tandem application in a utility scale plant (Power 84.73 MW_{DC})

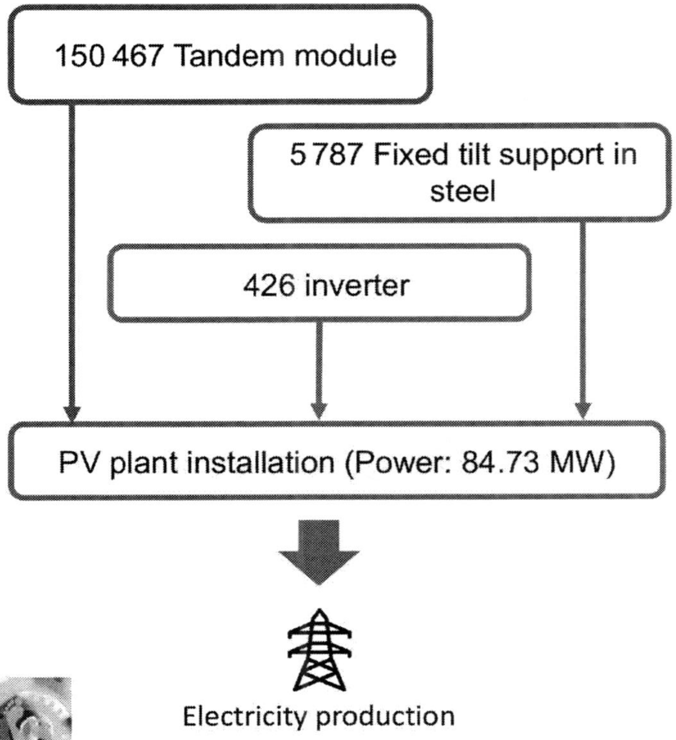

EF METHOD SimaPro

- The analysis considers the **Scenario B (MoOX/ITO electrode)** which is characterised by the lowest impact.
- The **module, module support and inverter** were modelled by using **primary data**.
- The analysis includes the **entire life cycle of the PV plant**, with the **exception** of the **end-of-life** (EOL) phase.
- **Electricity production** was assessed using the average equivalent hours in Italy, recorded as **1101 hours** according to the GSE reports.
- The plant has a **lifetime** of **25 years.**
- The **energy** produced over the lifetime is **2331 GWh**

Type of module	Mechanically stacked Perovskite/Silicon cell
Module efficiency	28.5%
Module power	563 W
Area	1.98 m^2

13

RSE Ricerca Sistema Energetico — we move rsearch

Life Cycle Assessment

PVSK/Si tandem application in a utility scale plant – contribution analysis

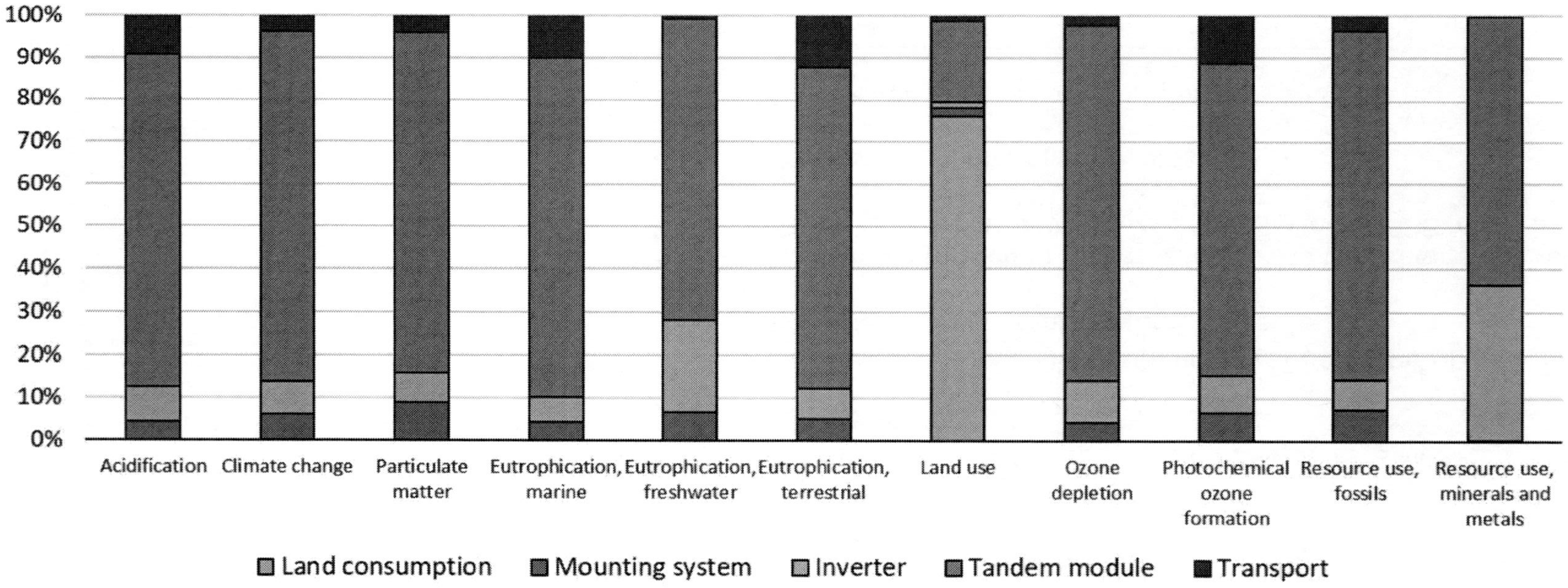

The **higher contribution** is associated to the production **of tandem module**, the only exception is **land use** categories in which the impact are generated to the **land consumption**.

EF METHOD SimaPro

The results are referred to 1 kWh produced – SC B: MoOX/ITO electrode is showed. Energy production over the lifetime: 2331 GWh

Life Cycle Assessment

PVSK/Si tandem application in a utility scale plant: a comparison with HJT technology

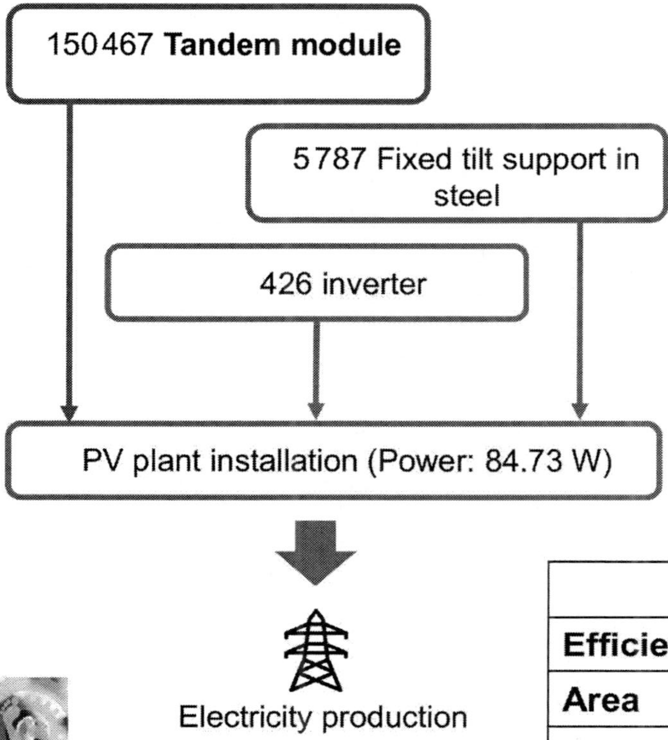

	Tandem	HJT
Efficiency	28.5%	21%
Area	1.98 m^2	1.98 m^2
Power	563 W	400 W

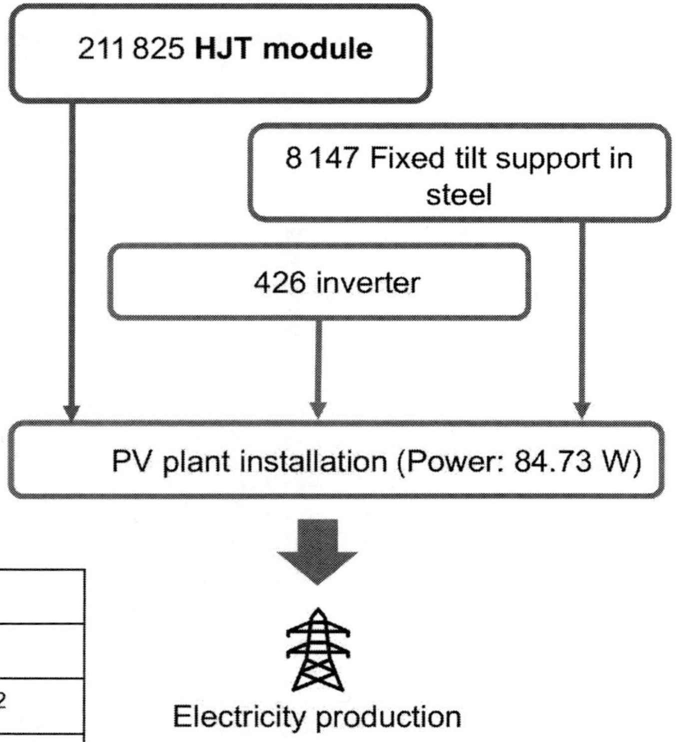

EF METHOD SimaPro

Life Cycle Assessment

PVSK/Si tandem utility scale plant VS HJT Plant

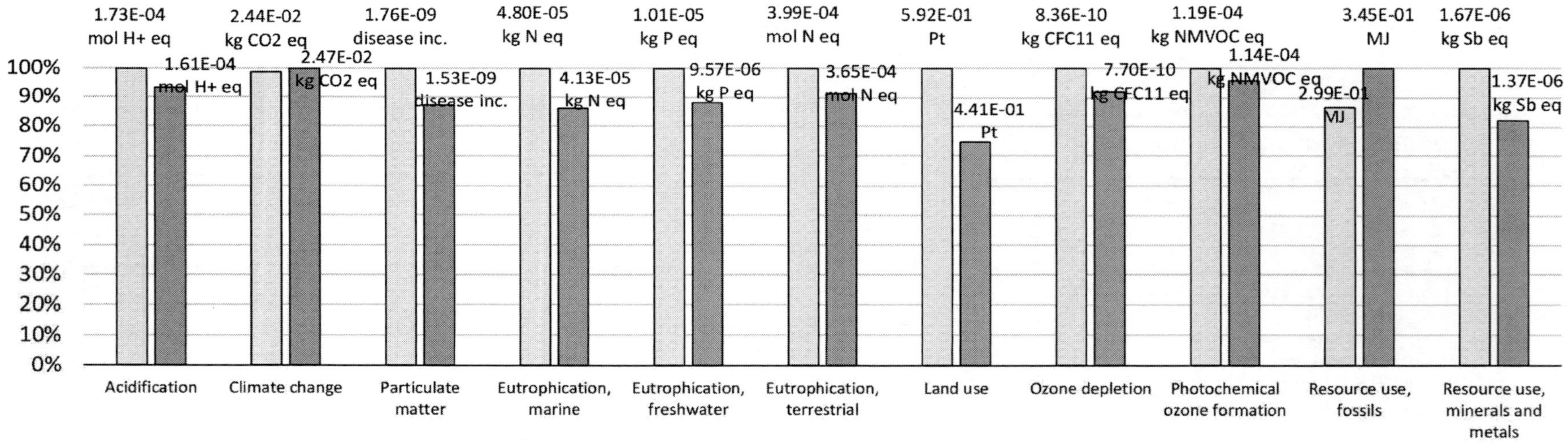

PVSK/Si tandem plant is characterised by **lower impacts** in **9 out of 11 categories**.

In the **Land use category**, the higher efficiency of the tandem module allows **for lower land consumption.**

In the resource use, fossil category, the impact of the tandem system is influenced by the **energy consumption** associated with the production of the **electrode.**

EF METHOD SimaPro

The results are referred to 1 kWh produced – SC B: MoOX/ITO electrode is showed. Energy production over the life: 2331 GWh

16

RSE Ricerca Sistema Energetico we move rsearch

Conclusion

- Focusing on the perovskite cell, the analysis highlights a **significant contribution** generated by the **energy consumed** during the **electrode production** phase in the climate change category.
- In the resource use, minerals and metals category, **Scenarios A and B** perform better than the Lab Scenario due to the **reduced quantity of electrode materials** required in the process. The result obtained emphasized the importance of proper material selection.
- The comparative analysis of the two PV plants (tandem and HJT) point out that the **higher efficiency** of the **PVSK/Si tandem** module compared to the HJT module enables the use of fewer modules, resulting in **reduced of land consumption**.
- In general, the photovoltaic is a promising technology that plays a key role in the energy transition process. For this reason, it is important to promote the development of high-efficiency photovoltaic characterized by lower environmental impact, like perovskite/silicon tandem module.

Contact

Stay tuned…

#wemoveresearch

Elisabetta Brivio

Elisabetta.brivio@rse-web.it

www.rse-web.it

@Ricerca sul Sistema Energetico - RSE SpA

@RSEnergetico

RSE SpA - Ricerca sul Sistema Energetico

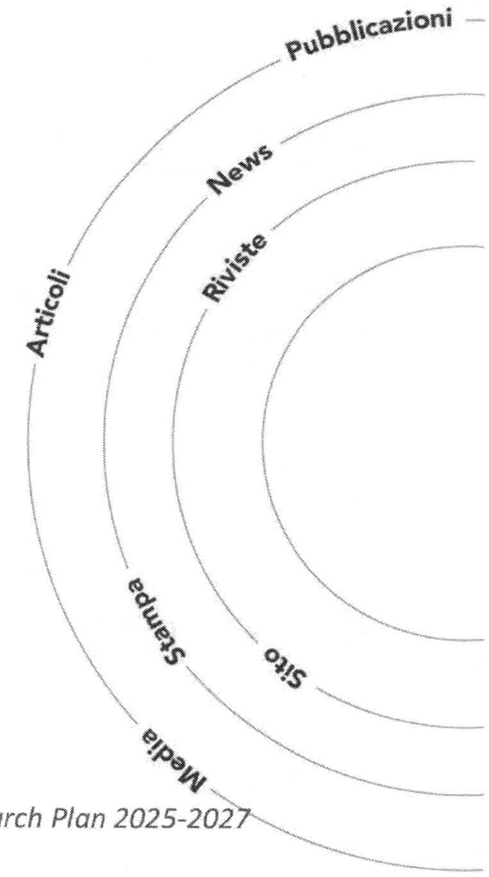

This work has been financed by the Research Fund for the Italian Electrical System under the Three-Year Research Plan 2025-2027 (MASE, Decree n.388 of November 6th, 2024), in compliance with the Decree of April 12th, 2024

RCT solutions
Photovoltaic
Services & Technology
Solutions Partner
LCA Learning Curve for Crystalline Silicon Solar
Technologies based on Technology Improvements
Group of companies
RCT
RCT power
RCT hydrogen
Julian Reichle*, Moritz Fath, Sraisth, Amish Kumar Sinha, Mehul Raval, Wolfgang Jooss and Peter Fath
RCT Solutions GmbH, Line - Eid - Str. 1, 78467 Konstanz, Germany
With support of Wolfgang Herbst from ViridisIQ GmbH, Germany
*E-mail: julian.reichle@rct-solutions.com

Motivation
Learning Rate of GWP for Crystalline Silicon Modules was at 10%

RCT solutions

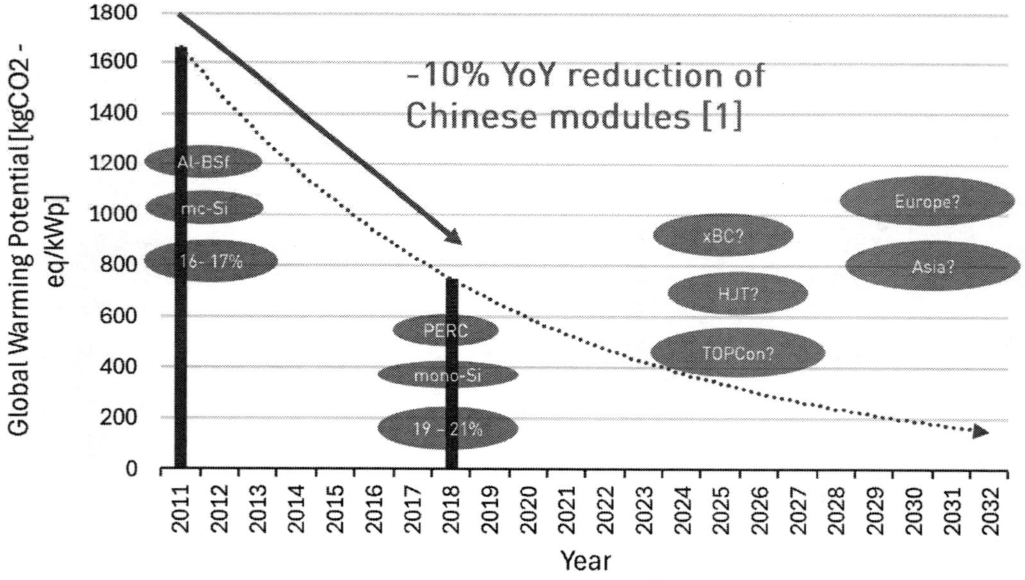

[1] L. Wang, T. Qiu, M. Zhang, Q. Cao, W. Qin and S. Wang, "Carbon emissions and reduction performance of photovoltaic systems," Renewable and Sustainable Energy Reviews, 2024.

- Reduction from **1660 to 750 kgCO_2-eq/kWp** between 2011 and 2018 [1].
- Technological improvements and deployment of renewables

What does the future hold?

- What **technological advancements** are expected?
- **Global Warming Potential (GWP)** of PV in the next years?
- Maintaining the recent **10% YoY reduction realistic?**
- How LCA guides us trough the engineering process?

Agenda for this LCA Study
KPIs for Learning Rate combined with LCA

Study Introduction
- Goal & Scope
- Functional Unit
- Boundary Conditions

KPIs for Modelling of Technological Improvements
- mgSi + PolySi
- Ingot & Wafer
- Cell
- Module

Life Cycle Impact Assessment - GWP
- Technology Improvements
- Technology Comparison
- Country Comparison

Summary and Outlook

The RCT Group at a Glance

RCT solutions

RCT solutions

Conceptual & Detailed Engineering

Training & On-site Installation

Financial & Business Modeling

2012
Founded, privately owned

≈ 100 GW
Supporting PV manufacturing capacity

26+
Countries

62
Factories worldwide

World's First
Fully integrated giga-scale factory installation

76 GW
Ingot & Wafer integration

RCT power

RCT Power Residential Batteries & inverters

RCT Power C&I/ Utility Battery Energy Storage

2015
Founded, privately owned

>15 GWh (5 GWh USA)
Total shipment

20GWh
production capacity, fully automated

Best Storage
Awarded in Germany

Fully EES manufacturing
Residential, commercial, utility scale (from kWh to MWh)

EU-China-USA Based
Battery production & Operations

RCT hydrogen

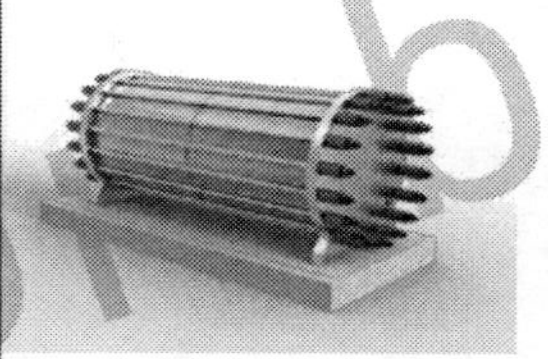

Electrolyser stack

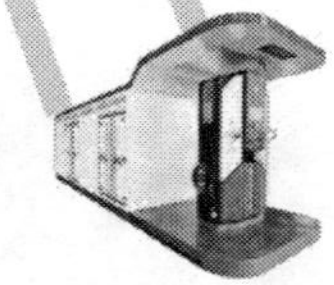

Re-fueling station

Gas Separation System

Hydrogen Purification System

Made/Engineered in Germany
Hydrogen equipment & engineering service

Factory Output
250MW (Target)

Typical Project Phases
RCT Services for PV Manufacturing Project and Detail of Life Cycle Assessment

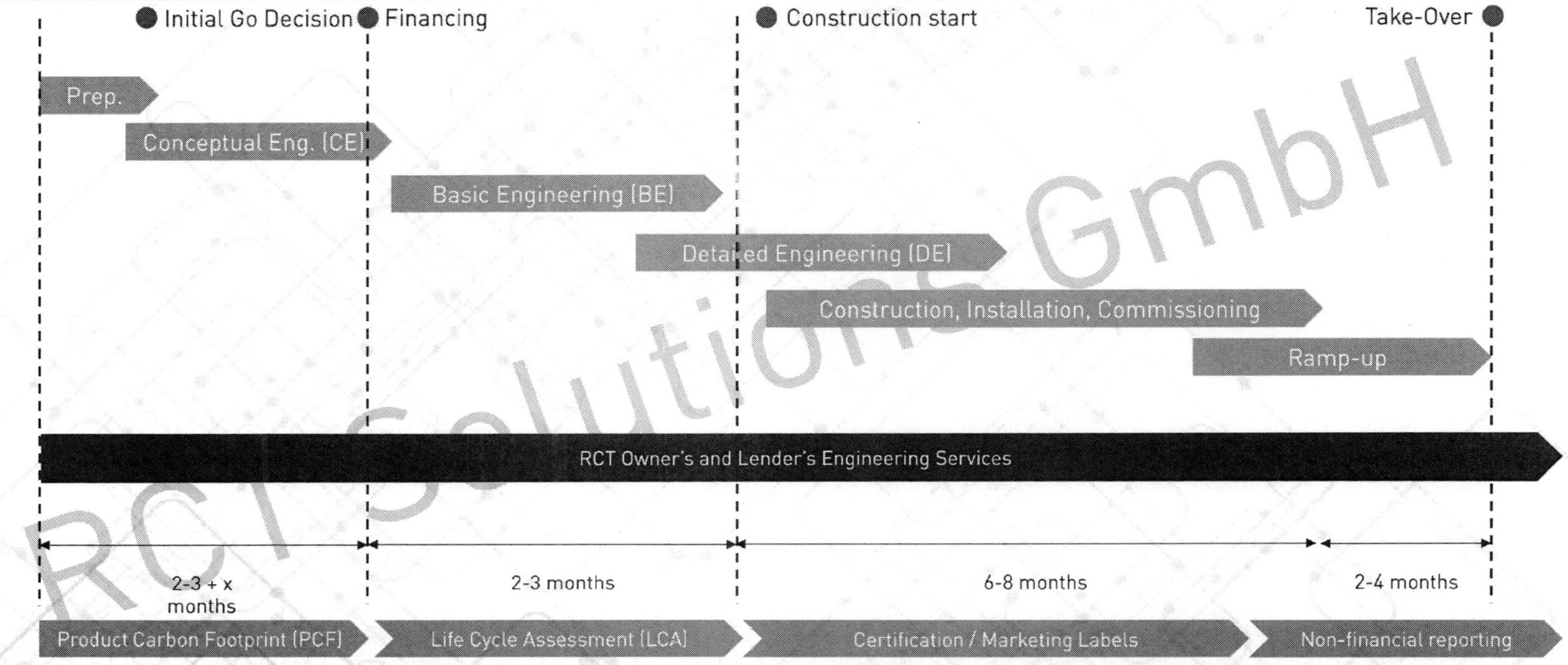

rct-solutions.com 5

Study Introduction
Goal and Scope: LCA Learning Curve Technologies and Regions

RCT solutions

- Life Cycle Assessment
  1. Technological advancements
  2. Different crystalline Silicon PV Module technologies
  3. Regional manufacturing
- Bottom-up and parametric model
- Incorporation of the extensive engineering experience

→ **Reliable and valid comparisons.**

→ **Reflects real-world PV manufacturing**

Technologies	TOPCon	HJT	TBC
Description	Tunnel Oxide Passivated Contact Solar Cell with LECO	Silicon Hetero Junction Solar Cell Technology	TOPCon Back Contact Solar Cell with Cu metallization
Cell Eff. (Fab-Theoretical)	25.5% → 27.6% [2]	25.7% → 26.9% [2]	26.0% → 28.0 [2]
Cell structure	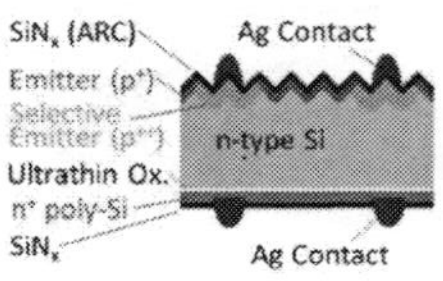	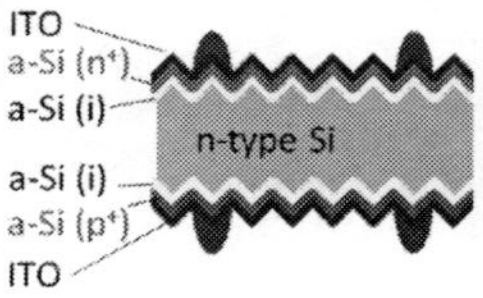	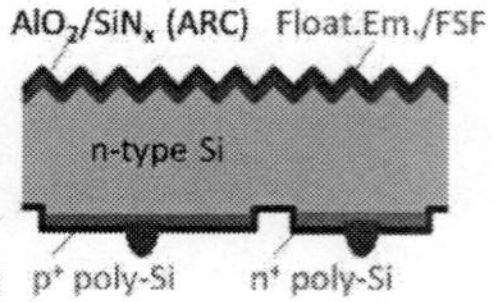

Locations	Germany	China	India
Flag			
Location details	Northern Germany	Inner Mongolia	Western India

[2] Solar Energy Materials & Solar Cells 231 (2021) 111291, - Solar Energy Materials & Solar Cells 238 (2022) 111560

Study Introduction
Functional Unit, Boundary Conditions & Methodology

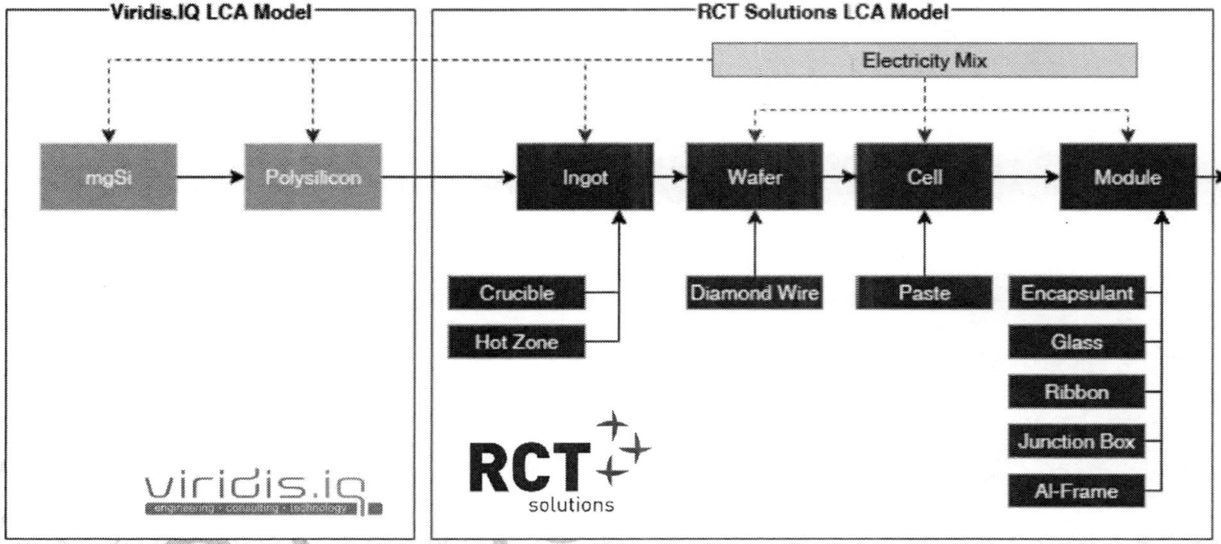

- 1 kilowatt-peak (kWp) photovoltaic (PV) module as functional unit
- Cradle-to-gate approach
- LCIA Method: EF 3.1
- Foreground data: RCT Solutions and Viridi.IQ
- Background data: Ecoinvent 3.11 Cutoff System-Processes
- Software used: openLCA 2.5

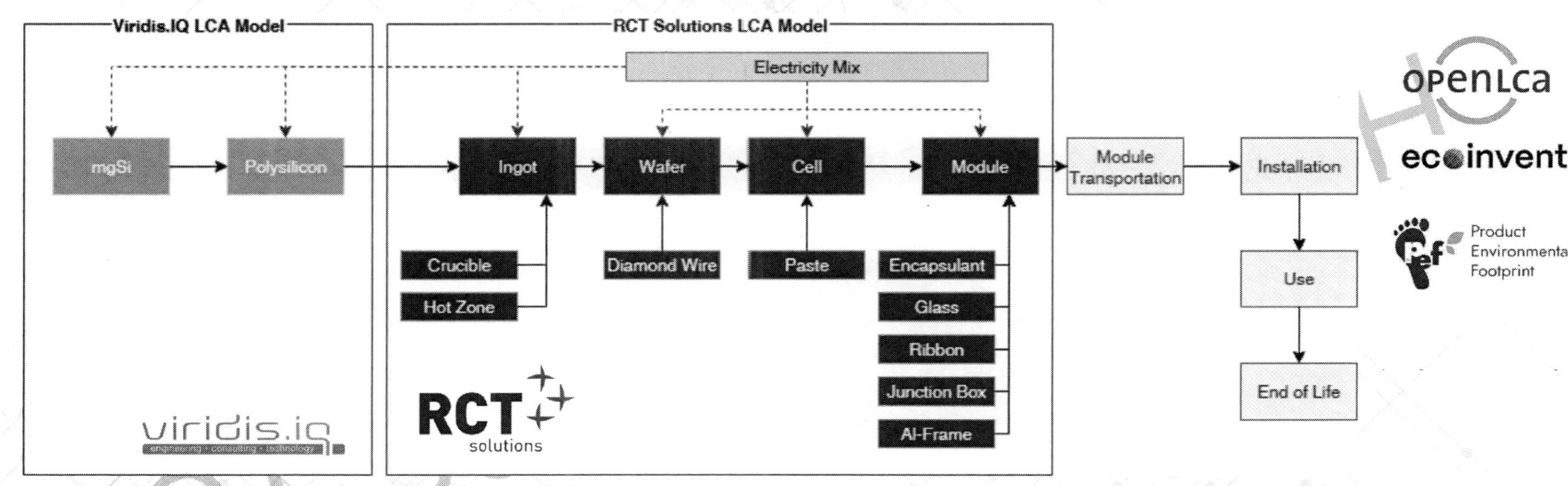

Global Parameters – Technological improvements
Process improvements considered and excluded

RCT solutions

	MG Si Production	Polysilicon Production	Ingot Production	Wafer Production	Cell Production	Module Production	Installation BoS	Storage system	End-Of Life
Incl.	• Electricity • Charcoal Share (Bio Mix) •Troughput	• Electricity • Yield	• Electricity • Cycle Load • Ingot Diameter	• Electricity* • Wafer Thickness • Kerf loss • Wafer Size	• Electricity* • Efficiency • Ag Paste Laydown • Water Consumption	• Electricity •Module Size • Ribbon thickness • Encapsulant thickness			
Excl. (selection, currentstill included in LCA)	• Yield		• Argon Demand	• Diamond Wire consumption		• Glass thickness			

*Electricity includes consumption + energy mix

*Technology depended parameters (also BOM differs)

Global Parameters– Technological improvements MgSi + Polysilicon - Projected trends

viridis.iq engineering · consulting · technology

Substituting the fossil-based materials in the charge mix

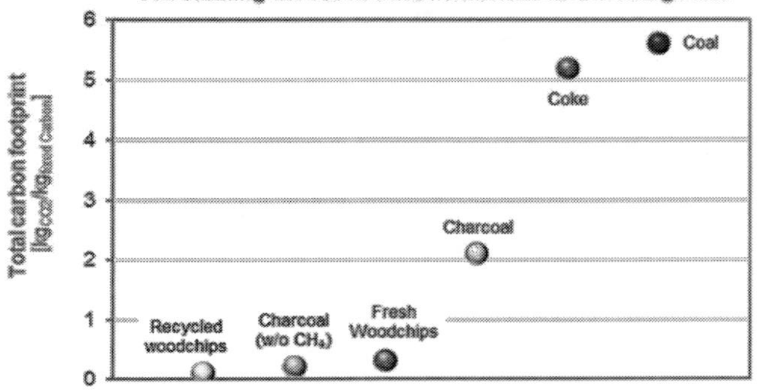

Improving the waste heat recovery in polysilicon production

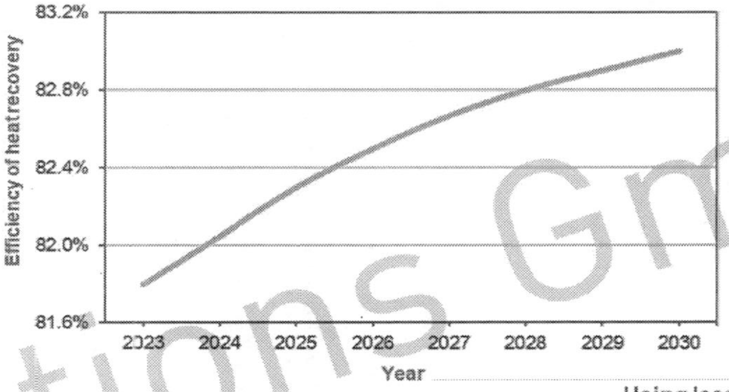

Polysilicon

- Improved TCS production
- Advanced CVD reactor design
- Higher waste heat recovery efficiency

Metallurgical Silicon

- Lower energy consumption
- Changing mix of reductants
- Using metallothermic reduction with the Mg or Al to increase the process yield and to reduce the silica content
- Carbon capture utilization from SAF off-gases

Using less electricity in the mgSi and polysilicon manufacturing

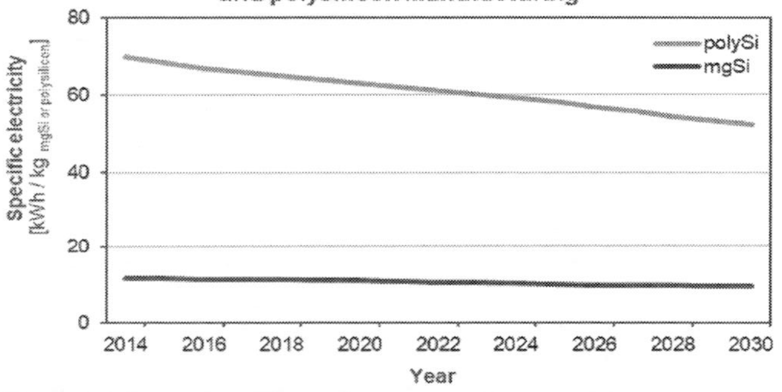

Global Parameters – Technological Improvements
Ingot and Wafering – Wafer Size Increase and Thickness Reduction

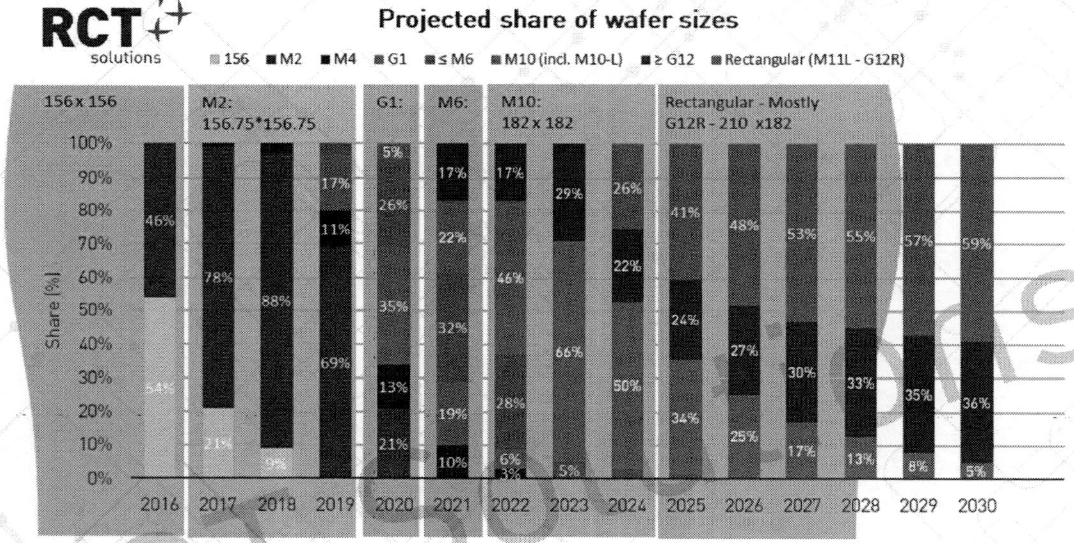

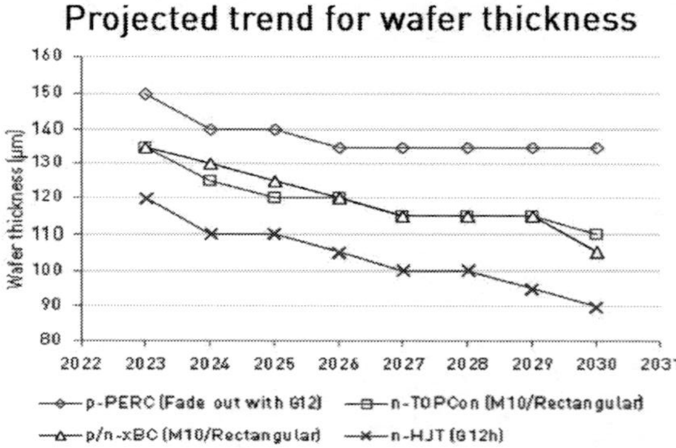

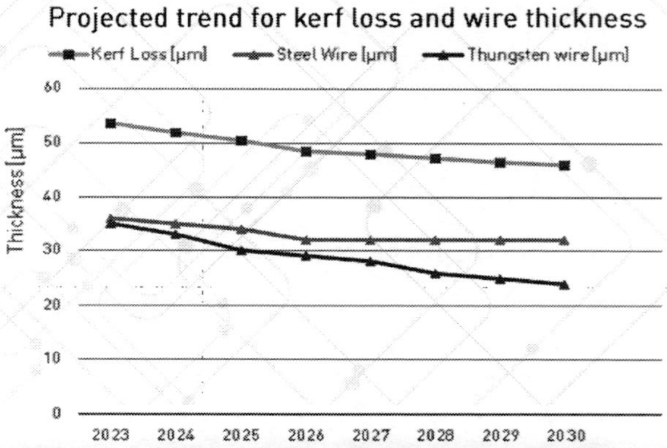

- TOPCon and xBC → G12R and G12 wafer size
- Wafer thickness is predicted to decrease to 110 µm.
- HJT stay at G12h
- Wafer thickness for HJT → reduce to 90 µm

Global Parameters – Technological improvements
Cell - Efficiency increase and paste consumptions

RCT solutions

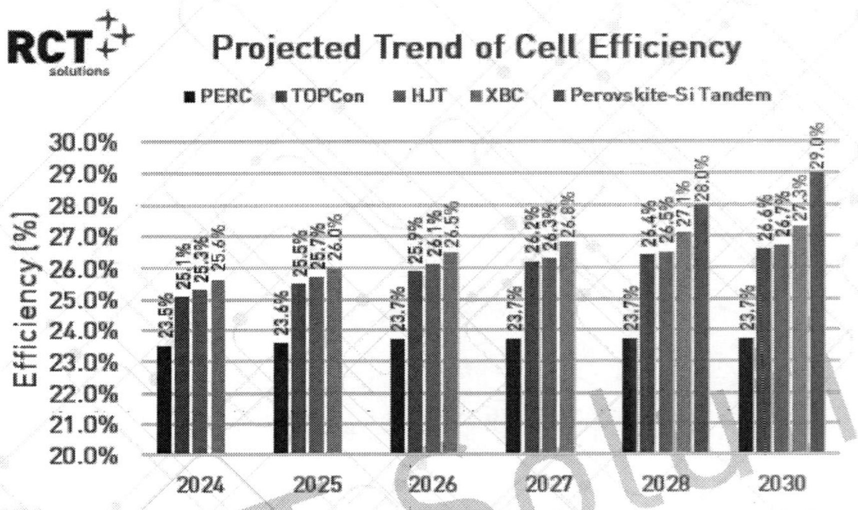

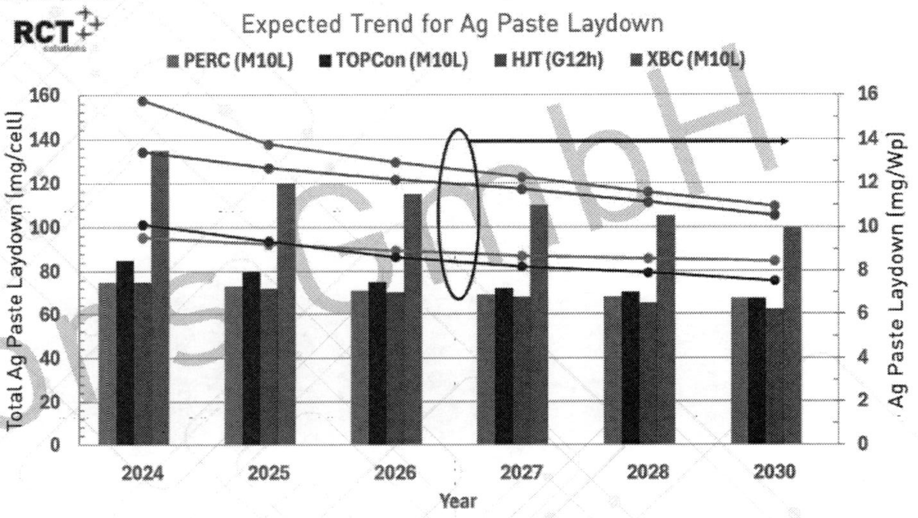

- Cell Efficiencies for TOPCon 25.5% (2025) up to 26.6% (2030)
- TBC from 26% to 27.3%, HJT from 25.7% to 26.7%

- Paste laydown expected to reduce
- Share of silver content changes

Global Parameters – Technological improvements
Module manufacturing – Glass thickness kept at 2mm

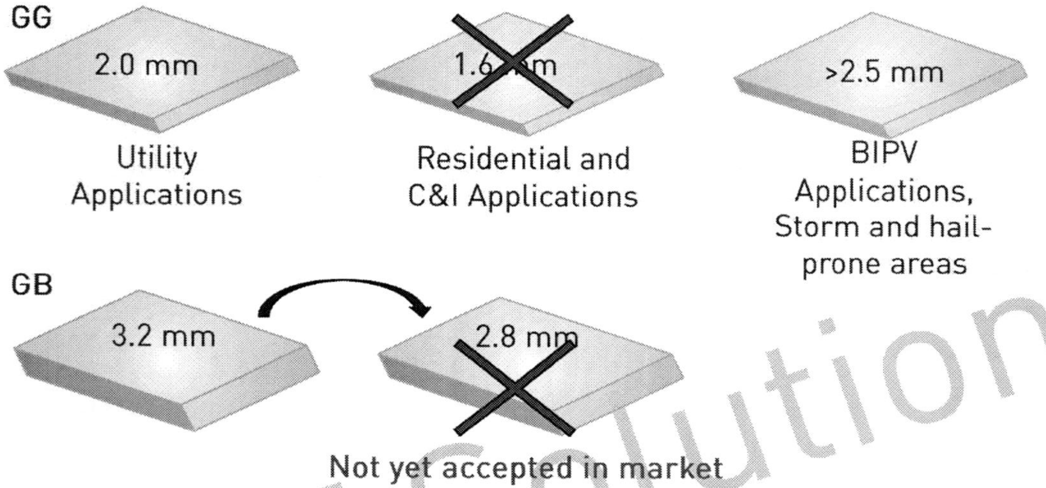

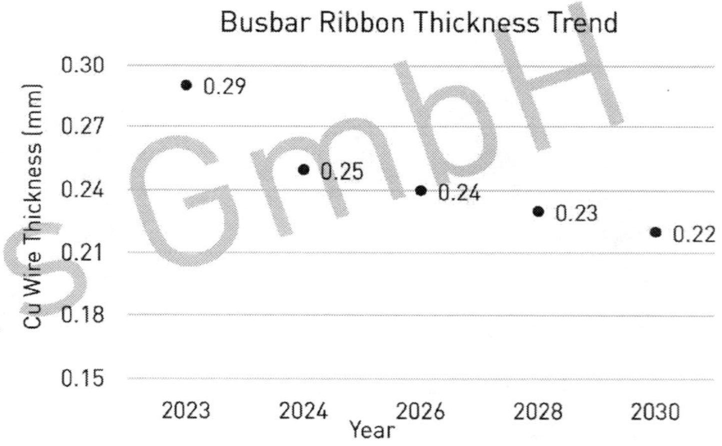

- More than 90% of modules Glass-Glass configuration for power plants
- Glass thinner than 2 mm not excepted for utility-scale power plants, particularly in hail-prone regions

→ The use of 2 mm glass is expected to continue until 2030

- Ribbon as another example for reduction in material use

Global Parameters – Technological improvements
General factory level KPIs take

RCT solutions

General KPIs

MgSi Yield	UOM	2025	2030
Process Yield	%	77.7%	76.5%
Polysilicon	**UOM**	**2025**	**2030**
MgSi Demand	%	1.08	1.07
Ingot	**UOM**	**2025**	**2030**
Cycle Load	kg/Cycle	3900	4600
Wafer	**UOM**	**2025**	**2030**
Kerf Loss	µm	50	44
Wafering Yield	µm	95%	95%

Tech. Rel. KPIs		TOPCon		HJT		TBC	
Ingot	**UOM**	**2025**	**2030**	**2025**	**2030**	**2025**	**2030**
Ingot Diameter	mm	258	300	305	300	258	300
Wafer	**UOM**	**2025**	**2030**	**2025**	**2030**	**2025**	**2030**
Wafer Thickness	µm	130	110	110	90	130	110
Wafer Size		M10L	G12	G12h	G12h	M10L	G12
Cell	**UOM**	**2025**	**2030**	**2025**	**2030**	**2025**	**2030**
Efficiency	%	25.5%	26.6%	25.7%	26.7%	26.0%	27.3%
Factory Yield	%	98%	98%	96%	96%	97%	97%
Module	**UOM**	**2025**	**2030**	**2025**	**2030**	**2025**	**2030**
Cells	pcs	72.0	66.0	66.0	66.0	72.0	66.0
CTM	%	98%	98%	98%	98%	98%	98%

Results – Technological improvements
Step breakdown for TOPCon (excl. E-mix change)

- TOPCon GWP 499 to 416 kgCO2 eq./kW in China → 3.7% YoY Improvement
- HJT lower GWP
    1. Low temperature processing
    2. Reduced upstream requirements
- TBC higher GWP
    1. More Process Steps → Higher electricity demand
    2. Increased supply chain volume and complexity
- Still **HJT and TBC** with nearly same YOY improvement of 3.5%/3.8%

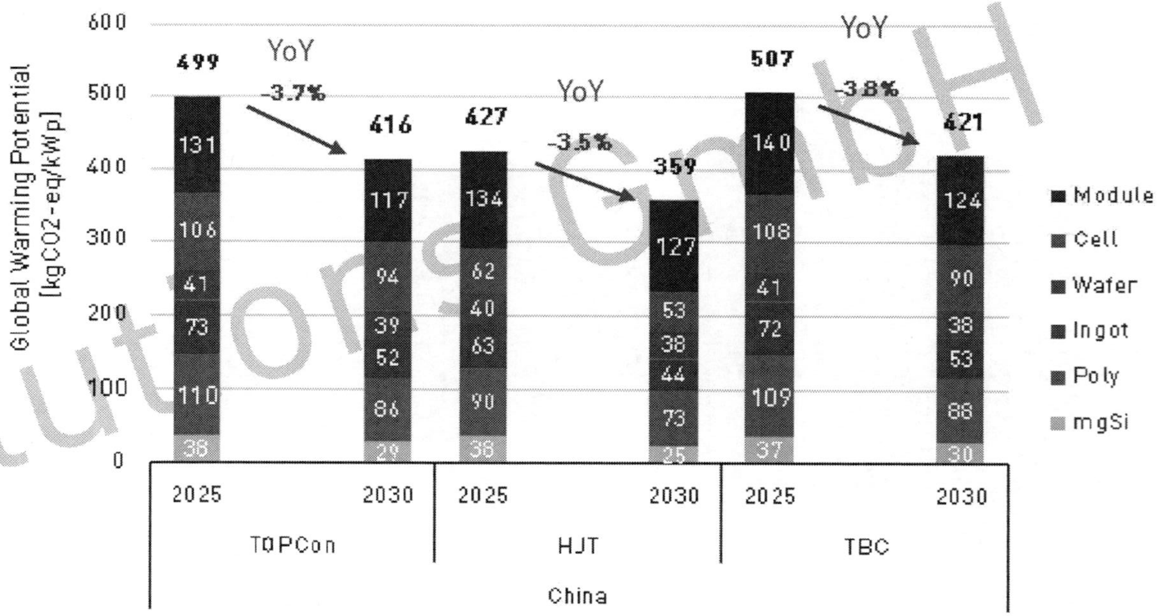

Results – Technological improvements
TOPCon, HJT and xBC @ different sites (excl. E-mix change)

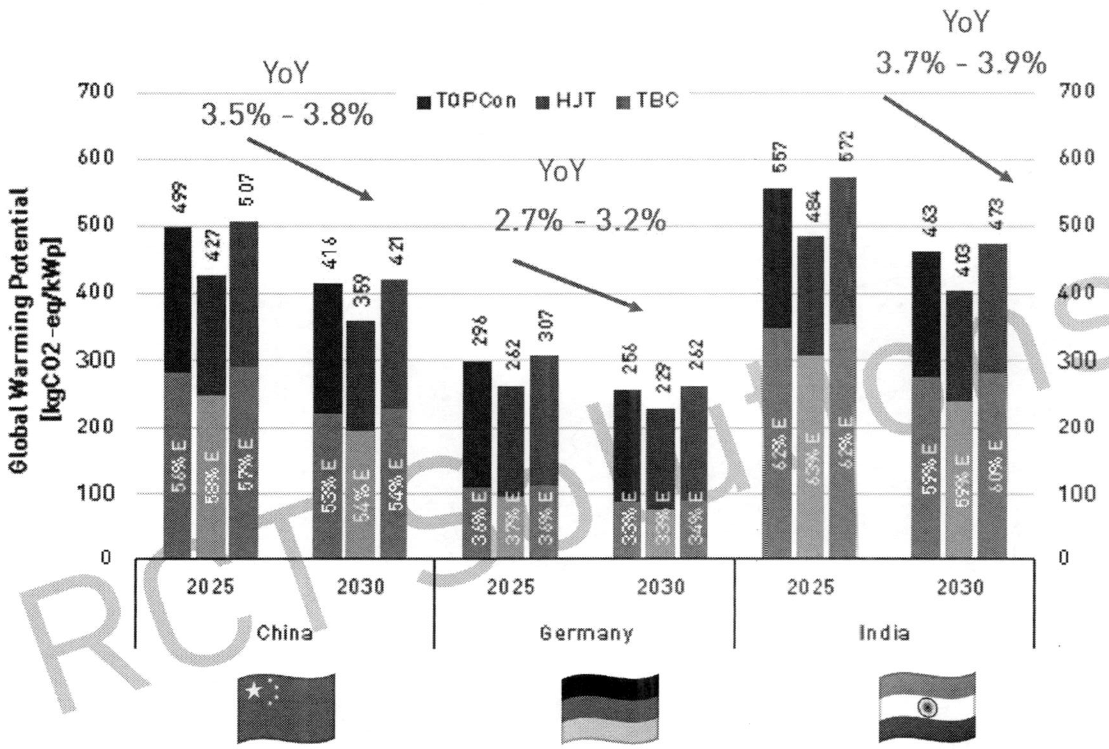

- GWP highest in India → high share of coal in grid mix
- Germany lowest → high share of renewable electricity
- German improvement lower → improvements in electricity have a lower overall impact
- TBC with highest per kWp emissions.
- TBC will get closer to TOPCon depending on the location.

Results – Technological improvements
Incorporating the influence of local electricity mix dynamics

- Integrate changes in electricity mix
- Main processes local and supply chain based on China
- 2024 data: BNetzA (DE), CEA & NPP (IN), and NEA (CN)
- The 2030 projections, from the IEA APS
- Germany Ren.-share 62% to 86%
- India Ren.-share 38% to 43%
- China Ren.-share 38% to 60%

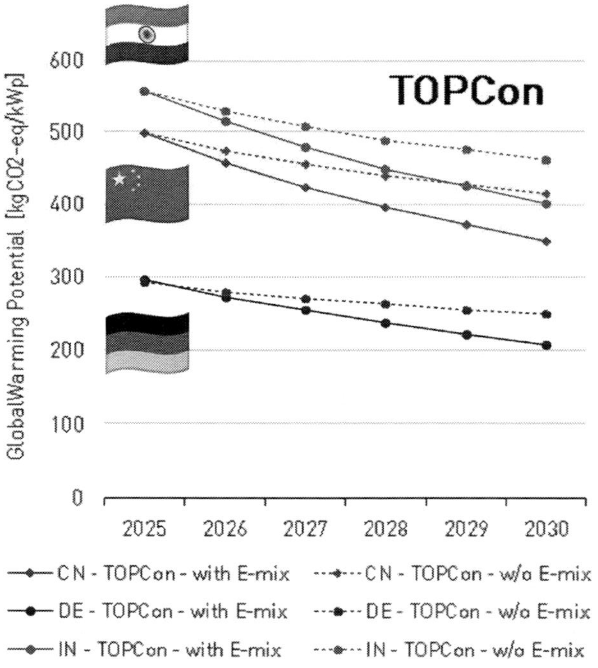

China (CN):

- Improvement 3.5% to 3.8% without E-mix and 7.4% to 7.6% with

→ doubling improvement

Germany (DE):

- Improvement is 2.7% to 3.2% without E-mix, lower impact of the electricity rising to 7.0% to 7.5% with E-mix

→ more than doubling

India (IN):

- Improvement shifts from 3.7% to 3.9% without E-mix, to 6.6% to 6.8% with it

→ only 70–80% higher

Results – Technological improvements
Closer look at TBC – GWP will get closer to TOPCon

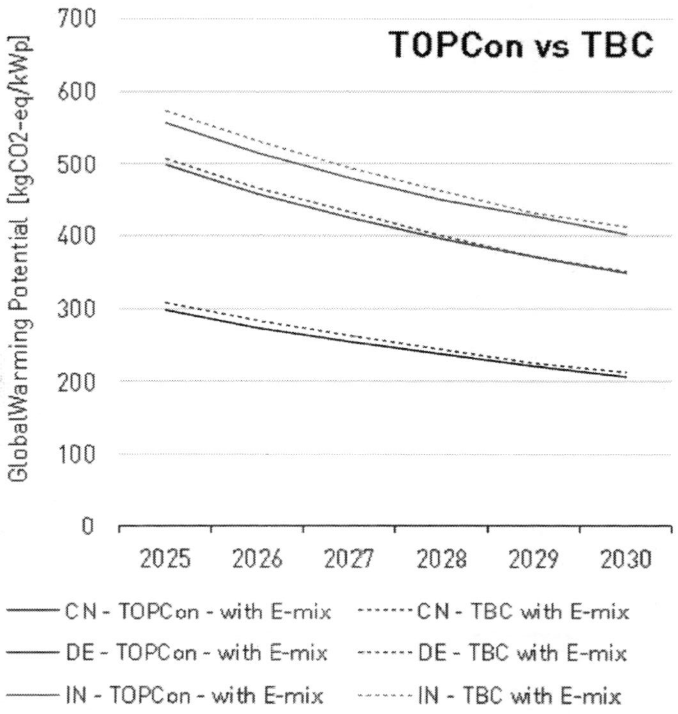

Summary
Expected development curves only at around 7% → Not 10% yet

- YOY improvement rate 7% (all countries)
- 3% to 4% without considering E-mix
- PV manufacturing benefits equal strong from technological improvements than from decarbonization of electricity supply
- HJT with lower and TBC with higher GWP
- TBC GWP will get closer to TOPCon
- India in country comparison high GWP - high global competitivity but disadvantage in environmental sensitive markets.
- German/EU with potential for manufacturing low carbon modules - competitiveness disadvantage in current market situation

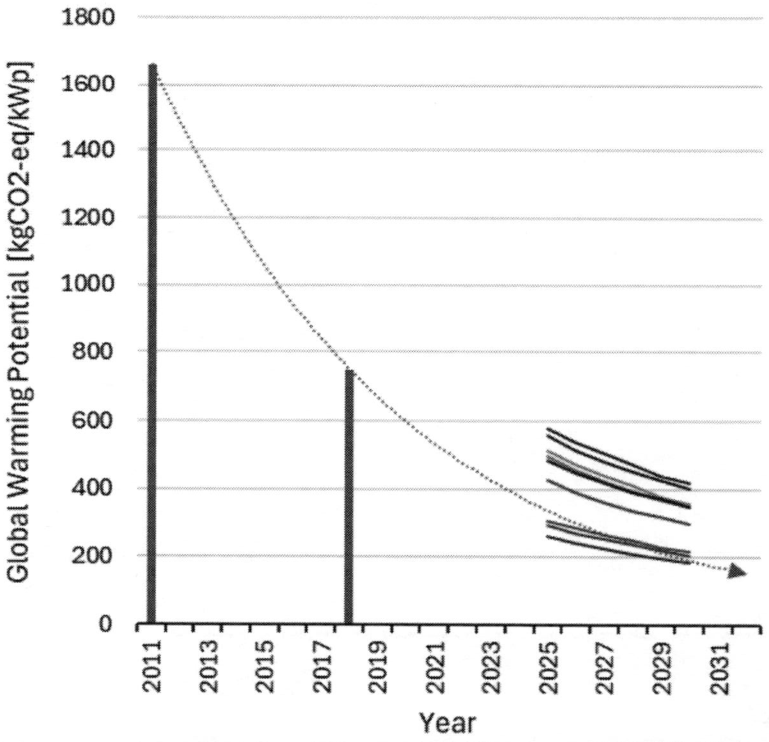

Outlook for low carbon modules
Hidden potential in upstream direct emissions and supply chain

- **Decarbonizing** of energy throughout **all steps**
  - Downstream placed in regions with lower share of renewables → Might lower the prediction of a 7% learning rate.
- Reduce **direct process related emissions**
  - e.g., emissions from silicon reduction process trough carbon capturing or non-fossil reductants
- Improving **yield** during production
- Improve the **supply chain**
  - Potential in background data
  - Technological improvements in supply chain
  - Localization

Thank you to all RCT Solution colleagues – Join us at Konstanz

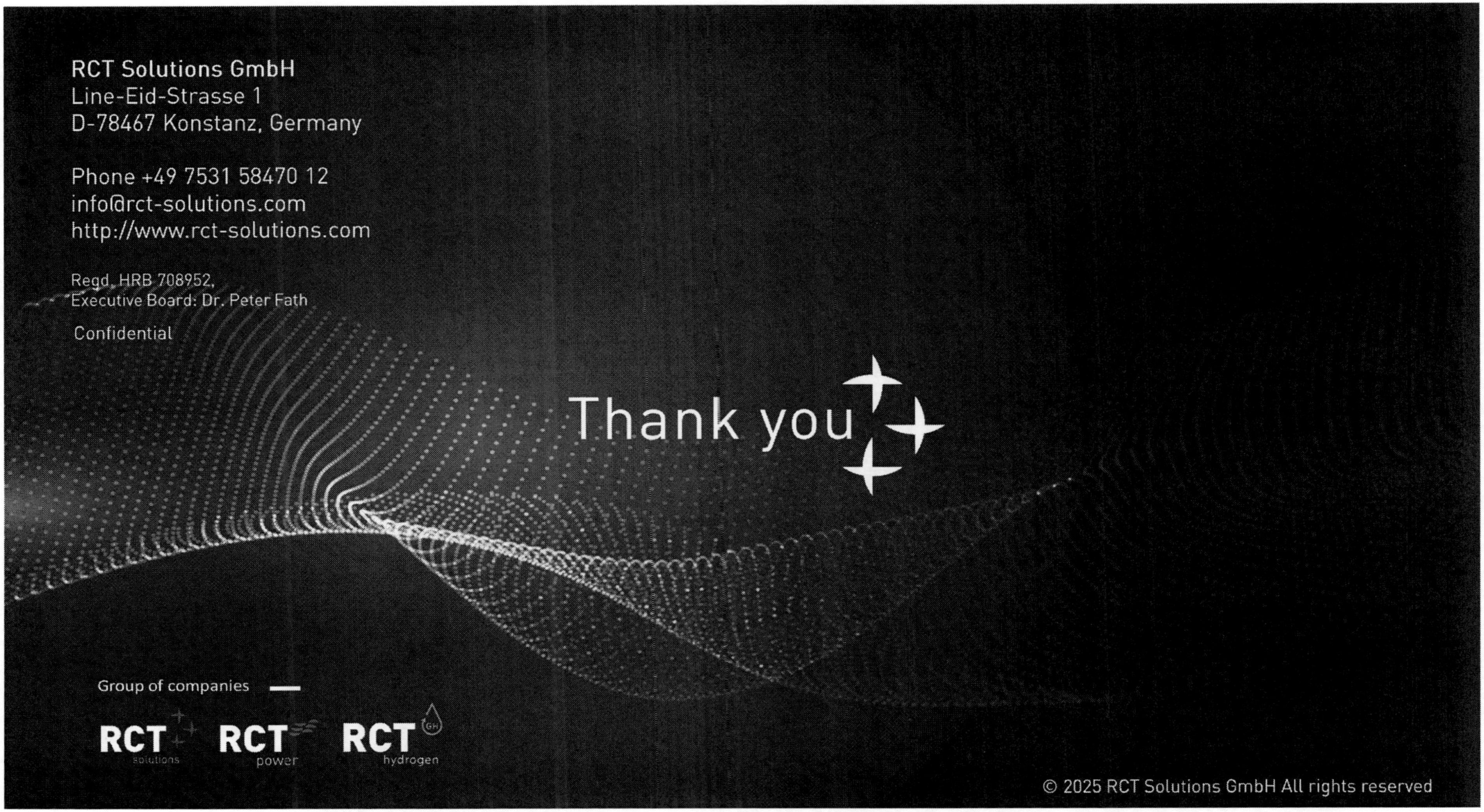
RCT Solutions GmbH
Line-Eid-Strasse 1
D-78467 Konstanz, Germany
Phone +49 7531 58470 12
info@rct-solutions.com
http://www.rct-solutions.com
Regd. HRB 708952,
Executive Board: Dr. Peter Fath
Confidential
Thank you
Group of companies
RCT solutions
RCT power
RCT hydrogen
© 2025 RCT Solutions GmbH All rights reserved

OPTIMIZING AGRIPV: A COMPREHENSIVE ASSESSMENT FRAMEWORK FOR SUSTAINABLE ENERGY AND AGRICULTURE

A. Lopes[1], B. Barrionuevo[2], D. P. Albuquerque[3], D. Cordeiro[4], C. Fernandes[3], A. T. Balafoutis[2], R. Castro[5]

[1] IST, University of Lisbon, Lisbon, Portugal
[2] Center for Research and Technology Hellas, Athens, Greece
[3] Centre for New Energy Technologies, SA, Sacavém, Portugal
[4] EDP Gestão da Produção de Energia, SA, Lisbon, Portugal
[5] INESC-ID/IST, University of Lisbon, Lisbon, Portugal

ABSTRACT: By integrating solar panels with agricultural activities, AgriVoltaics (AgriPV) optimizes land use while offering a solution to the increasing demand for food and renewable energy. This dual use approach not only enhances land productivity but also helps regulate microclimatic conditions, reduce water evaporation, and support biodiversity. AgriPV can improve soil conditions in areas with poor agricultural productivity and enable cultivation, transforming this type of land into productive farmland. This positions AgriPV as a promising strategy for the expansion of renewable energy and sustainable agriculture.

Despite its relatively recent emergence, AgriPV has shown significant advancements, though its implementation remains limited across Europe. To support its broader adoption, this study presents a Life Cycle Assessment (LCA) framework to analyze energy production, Greenhouse Gas (GHG) emissions and environmental impacts from raw material extraction to farm-gate, within the context of the EU-funded TALOS project. A comparative sustainability assessment also examines the trade-offs between AgriPV and conventional Photovoltaics (PV) in terms of energy generation, land use efficiency and agricultural productivity. By providing a structured evaluation framework, this research supports policymakers, researchers, and stakeholders in making informed decisions that enhance both energy production and agriculture.
Keywords: AgriPV, LCA, Sustainability

1 INTRODUCTION

AgriPV presents a dual land use strategy that enables the simultaneous generation of solar energy and agricultural production, addressing the increasing global demand for food and clean energy. Despite its potential, the widespread adoption of AgriPV remains constrained by several challenges, among which the absence of standardized and comprehensive sustainability assessment methodologies. This research seeks to overcome these barriers by developing an integrated sustainability assessment framework specifically designed for AgriPV systems.

The primary aim of this research is to establish a comprehensive approach that combines both qualitative and comparative analysis. The LCA framework evaluates GHG emissions, energy generation efficiency, and overall environmental impact across several stages of the lifecycle of the AgriPV systems. This is complemented by a comparative sustainability analysis that evaluates the advantages and trade-offs between AgriPV systems and conventional PV.

This dual functionality enhances the environmental performance and introduces a sustainable model that benefits a diverse range of stakeholders. The framework is designed to be a valuable tool not only for utility companies but also for farmers and other beneficiaries within AgriPV business models, providing additional energy production capabilities and promoting environmentally sustainable agricultural practices.

This work is divided into four parts. Section 2 present a qualitative LCA framework of AgriPV systems, analyzing the cradle-to-gate process to identify impacts, challenges and opportunities to improve. Section 3 a comparison is made between AgriPV systems and conventional PVs, analyzing the main differences in land use, energy production, environmental impacts, and economic factors. Lastly, Section 4 summarizes the key findings. limitations encountered and suggestions for future research.

2 AGRIPV Life Cycle Assessment

This LCA of AgriPV systems is based on the ISO 14040/14044 framework [1] and is divided into four main phases: Goal and Scope Definition, Life Cycle Inventory (LCI), Life Cycle Impact Assessment (LCIA) and Interpretation. These phases are interconnected and provide a structured basis for assessing environmental impacts. This study conducts a qualitative LCA, examining each phase in detail to identify challenges and opportunities for improvement.

2.1 Goal and Scope Definition

The first step in the LCA is to set the study's goal and scope. The goal is to qualitatively evaluate the environmental sustainability of AgriPV systems. The scope includes the entire life cycle of both PV and agricultural components, from raw material extraction to farm-gate. A cradle-to-gate approach is adopted, which includes the production and use phases but not the end of life. AgriPV projects are usually planned to last 25 to 30 years, but limited data exists regarding decommissioning. End of life for conventional PV is already known to be complicated and might need its own study [2], so focusing on the farm gate makes sure that the operational phase gets attention, while acknowledging the importance of disposal and recycling for future research.

Defining the functional unit is challenging because these systems produce both electricity and crops. ISO 14040/14044 [1] recommends functional unit that quantify system performance. From a methodological point of view, this problem of multifunctionality is dealt either through system subdivision, system expansion or allocation, depending on the characteristics of the system, the goals of the study and data availability. In the case of AgriPV, however, given its dual nature, having two different functional units could provide a clearer and more complete assessment of their full environmental impact than by using the methodological steps mentioned above. The units used are expressed in hectare year, including electricity output (kWh) and crop yield (kg). This method guarantees that both products are included, without favoring one output over the other, following recommendations to use multiple functional units for systems with more than one output [3]. Another metric is the Land Equivalent Ratio (LER) [1], which is also seen as a conceptual measure of how well land is used when both food and electricity are made in the same area.

This framework is meant to be useful for a wide range of people, including researchers, policymakers and project developers, as they could benefit from this by evaluating the advantages and disadvantages of their AgriPV projects.

2.2 Life Cycle Inventory

The LCI lists and quantifies all the inputs, outputs, emissions and waste flows of the AgriPV system, including materials and energy. It is organised in chronological order, from getting the raw materials to the use phase.

The first step in the PV subsystem is to get raw materials and turn them into a panel. In this type of systems is normal to use bifacial models and semi-transparent. They are mainly made of silicon for wafers and cells, aluminium and steel for structures, copper for wiring and glass for encapsulation. These processes release pollutants like CO_2, SO_2, Nox, as well as industrial waste[4]. The next step in the manufacturing process uses purified silicon, aluminium profiles, tempered glass and steel beams, requiring significant energy. Outputs include solid waste from cutting wafers, chemicals released during etching and cleaning and more emissions from processes that use a lot of heat. Overhead configurations require taller and stronger structures, so they can provide support and stability for the weight of panels. This increases the steel and aluminium usage relative to standard PV farms.

The environmental impact of making modules depends a lot on where they are made [5]. China is where most of the manufacturing happens and the electricity is mostly made of coal, which means that each module emits a high amount of greenhouse gases. In Europe, on the other hand, the energy is cleaner, which means that the emission of greenhouse gases are lower. One big problem with PV inventories is that Chinese manufacturers provide limited data, which proves to be a challenge regarding gathering information available about how much energy is used, how many chemicals are used and how efficient processes are. In this circumstances, secondary data from LCA databases can be obtained. This, however, can be challenging because datasets based on European averages may not accurately capture the actual environmental impacts of PV panels manufactured in regions like China, where production practices, energy sources, and supply chain may differ significantly, leading to potentially misleading or incomplete estimations.

When transporting PVs and their components, long distance shipping and subsequent land regional distribution via road or rail are required. Fossil fuel combustion during these processes results in more CO_2 emissions. Installation involves site preparation, assembly of mechanical structures and connection of electrical systems. This stage needs machines and transportation that run on diesel, which means that using the machines and workers travelling will create emissions, as well as waste from the packaging. During the use and maintenance phase, inputs include water and cleaning products for PVs, replacing electrical components if needed and moving people around for agricultural supervision, harvesting and maintenance of the PV system, which could be made by a farmer if provided with proper training, but which would require external services if not. The outputs are the amount of electricity produced per hectare year, the amount of electronic waste and the amount of wastewater from cleaning.

The agricultural subsystem uses seeds, fertilisers, pesticides, irrigation water and systems and energy to run pumps and machines. Outputs include the crop yield in kilogrammes per hectare year, any form of waste and the pollution that gets into the air, soil and water. Fertilisers release nitrous oxide (N_2O) directly, but they can also release it indirectly through volatilisation and nitrate leaching[6]. How minerals dissolve in soil, how much fertiliser is used and how much plants take in all affect how much nitrate leaches. Farm activities and soil management release CO_2. Crop residues increase the amount of organic matter in the soil and the amount of nitrogen that is released. Pesticides and heavy metals from inputs are considered as well as losses from leaching, erosion and harvesting. When nutrients are picked up depends on when they are planted and harvested.

Under AgriPV, these operations might have to change, for example by using smaller machines or changing how they rotate to make room for the PV infrastructure. Using pesticides and fertilisers, burning fuel and leaving organic matter in the field all create waste and emissions. Certain AgriPV systems use grazing animals to control the vegetation beneath or between the panels, which lowers the need for herbicides and diesel fuel for mowing while also producing manure that can partially replace synthetic fertilisers. Crop residues can be used as animal feed or soil amendments. These should be counted as flows that balance out outside inputs in the inventory.

Elevated structures for PV panels change the microclimate, which means that plants get less sunlight. This can slow down the rate of evapotranspiration and the amount of water needed for each unit of yield [7]. These changes can also change how much fertiliser is needed and how well crops grow. Additionally, the cover provided by PV panels can contribute to a reduction of overall moisture levels, which in turn leads to a reduction of fungicides application due to the creation of less favourable conditions for fungal growth.

This study excludes end of life processes due to insufficient data and livestock integration. However, these are significant domains for future investigation.

2.3 Life Cycle Impact Assessment

The LCIA transforms the inventory data for AgriPV systems into possible effects on the environment. ReCiPe model [8] and the EU Product Environmental Footprint (PEF)[7] are examples of standardised methods that give a structured way to measure these effects in many different areas. This is essential for AgriPV systems that can be used for energy and agriculture. ReCiPe uses midpoint indicators like eutrophication, acidification, toxicity, and resource depletion, as well as endpoint indicators that show adverse effects on human health, ecosystems, and

10.4229/EUPVSEC2025/5CO.5.1

resource availability. PEF on the other hand, provides a framework that is especially useful for European applications. Their use allows for a complete sustainability assessment by looking at not only climate change derived from GHG emissions but also pressures on water, soil and resources.

The production of PV modules, which accounts for the majority of the system's carbon footprint, is the main source of climate change consequences. The carbon payback period for PV systems is relatively short as operational energy offsets initial emissions.

Water related effects are also relevant due to the fact that PV modules need to be cleaned, and irrigation is needed for some crops. However, shading from panels can lower evapotranspiration, which can lower the amount of water needed, which is particularly relevant in arid and semi-dry regions where water scarcity is a major problem. Current LCIA methods do not fully capture these positive effects.

In addition to climate change and rising energy demand, other significant issues are based on the eutrophication and acidification from fertiliser use, water shortages from irrigation and cleaning panels and toxicity from pesticides or chemicals used in making PV panels.

Another important effect category for AgriPV is resource depletion. Increased material demand, especially for silicon, steel, aluminium, copper, and other materials, is caused by PV panels and structures manufacturer. There are ways to recycle glass and aluminium, but there is a lack inefficient ways to recover silicon. This indicates that mineral depletion should be prioritized when looking at long-term sustainability.

Using land efficiently is a key feature. The LER is a relevant metric, which shows that AgriPV produces more overall output than just farming or making energy.

2.4 Interpretation

Key findings, trade-offs and limitations are identified during the interpretation phase. The majority of impacts come from the production of PV modules, particularly the processing of silicon, while agriculture contributes using irrigation and fertilisers. AgriPV can improve the soil, save water, make it more resistant to drought and heat extreme events and make land use more efficient. It also gives farmers a new revenue source and lowers the risks of decreasing the crops production. Shading can lower the amount of crops that grow, but the value of electricity often makes up for this. These trade-offs must be considered because lower yields could cancel out environmental benefits.

AgriPV also helps fight climate change by producing renewable energy and helps crops adapt to extreme weather by keeping them safe. LCA indicators do not always show all the benefits, like creating microclimates, using less herbicide through grazing and creating jobs in rural areas, but they are still important.

There is still uncertainty related to the lack of long-term data for vertical and semi-transparent systems. Also, recycling options for PV parts are still under developed and LCA databases do not yet effectively capture the interactions between crops and regional conditions. Future research should be focused on enhanced data quality, demonstrations and investments. To fully unlock the potential of AgriPV as a sustainable alternative to traditional PV, it will be necessary to incorporate policy into land use and energy planning.

3 COMPARISON BETWEEN AGRIPV SYSTEMS AND CONVENTIONAL PV

Traditional PV farms and AgriPV systems represent two distinct approaches to solar installation. Conventional PV systems are only meant for producing electricity and they often take up a lot of land that cannot be used for anything else. AgriPV is made to be used for two things, producing renewable energy and growing crops on the same land. To understand the trade-offs between land use, energy output and agricultural value, as well as how design choices affect sustainability and resource efficiency, it is important to compare these different systems.

3.1 Land Use

The layout of traditional PV systems and AgriPV systems are very different, which affects how land is used. While traditional utility-scale PV commonly occupies cleared sites on low structures frequently with single-axis tracking, which the main objective is to capture as much sunlight as possible, with the aim of producing as much energy as possible. This leads to a high ground covering ratio (GCR), which means that most of the land surface is covered or shaded by panels, making it unsuitable for farming. On the other hand, AgriPV systems are made to be used for dual use of land. The PV panels are either raised several meters above the ground (overhead configuration) or arranged in rows (interspace configuration) with more space between them so that farming can take place underneath and between the panels respectively. For instance, overhead configurations use support structures that are between 2 and 5 meters high, which let tractors and other farm machinery pass through. In the other configuration, interspace, the panels are set up mostly vertically or with wide gaps between them, leaving strips of land open for farming. These configuration choices result in lower GCR, allowing sufficient sunlight to reach the ground for crop growth and development.

This dual use approach also makes it possible to produce solar energy in places where there limited land available for PV projects, since PV systems can coexist with farming instead of competing with it.

AgriPV systems can be adapted to various agricultural environments, such as vineyards, orchards, and greenhouses, facilitating energy production while preserving the land essential agricultural use. AgriPV mitigates the necessity to deforest, transform natural ecosystems or reserve arable land solely for energy generation by facilitating dual land use.

3.2 Energy Production

The way AgriPV is designed to allow farming also affects energy production. AgriPV systems have a lower installed capacity than traditional PV farms on the same area due to fewer panels being installed per hectare. More sunlight can reach crops with semi-transparent modules, but the part of the radiation that gets to plants is no longer available to be turned into electricity. This is why it is so important to find a balance in how radiation is spread out. Too much shade on crops lowers their yields and too much light on plants lowers their electricity output. An AgriPV project that works must make sure that neither energy production nor farming is harmed to the point where it becomes unsustainable. The goal is not to make one output more valuable than the other, but to find a way for both remain productive. Therefore, achieving an even distribution of solar radiation is crucial. Too much shade

10.4229/EUPVSEC2025/5CO.5.1

can stress the plants, which can slow their growth and productivity or even make it impossible to grow it in that place. It is also important to choose the right crops because some are more sensitive to shade, which can lower yields and make the project impossible. A successful AgriPV project must make sure that neither energy production nor farming is harmed that it becomes unviable. An additional factor to take into consideration is the microclimate created by the vegetation beneath the panels. The cultivation of crops decreases the ambient temperature near the modules, relieving thermal stress and enhancing panel efficiency. This cooling effect helps to mitigate the reduced energy produced in AgriPV configurations, which does not figure in conventional PV farms.

A way to increase the energy produced is to use tracking systems, but it remains a concern for keeping a balance between the distribution of the radiation between the panels and the crops, besides the higher Operational expenditure (OPEX) costs associated.

3.3 Material and Infrastructure Requirements

Common mounting methods used by traditional PV farms include fixed tilt racks and single axis trackers. Their designs are standardised and optimised for cost effectiveness and they often use a structural steel needed to support modules that are close to the ground. AgriPV systems, on overhead structures, on the other hand, need more complex structures. Structures that are higher up must be built to withstand wind loads and therefore in places where wind exposure is high, choosing the right site is very important. Because they are so high, they need special tools for cleaning and maintenance, which makes the materials needed and the work more complicated, increasing the overall costs.

Bifacial modules usually cost comparatively more than regular monofacial panels because they have two layers of glass and are more complex to produce. But their ability to capture both direct and reflected light increases the overall yield, which can be very helpful in AgriPV systems with lower density of panels. This higher energy output helps make up for the fact that there are fewer modules per hectare, which can make the system work better overall. Semi-transparent PV is an advanced technology that combines power generation with light transmission. However, the fact that it is more complex to manufacture, increases the costs while reducing energy production [8].

3.4 Environmental Impact

The production phase of regular PV systems has the largest impact on the environment, as module manufacturing requires significant energy and critical raw materials. This stage accounts for most CO_2 emissions over the course of the life cycle, while the operation itself generates almost no emissions. AgriPV systems share the same upstream effects, but add another dimension related to the crops cultivated under the panels. The vegetation cultivated under AgriPV systems absorbs CO_2 from the atmosphere through photosynthesis, temporarily storing biogenic carbon. While this process does not permanently offset the fossil-based emissions associated with PV module production, it may contribute to improving the overall carbon balance of the system, particularly if practices that promote longer-term carbon retention -such as soil carbon sequestration- are simultaneously implemented.

3.5 Economic Considerations

From an economic point of view, conventional PV systems are currently much cheaper to install. They are one of the most cost-effective sources of renewable energy because their design is standardised, their supply chains are well-established and large-scale deployment has lowered the cost per installed megawatt though the years. AgriPV systems, on the other hand, need more complex engineering, more building materials and more demanding maintenance. These factors increase the initial investment and running costs, which often means that capital expenditure (CAPEX) is higher than it is for regular PV farms [9].

In AgriPV, farmers can use the energy produced to meet their own needs, such as irrigation or others agricultural tasks. They can also sell the energy to the grid. Using electricity for personal consumption results in cost savings, while selling it to the grid generates revenue.

Despite these benefits, AgriPV continues to encounter significant regulatory obstacles. Although traditional PV systems benefit from robust legal protocols, dedicated regulations for AgriPV projects are limited in most European countries. This regulatory gap creates uncertainty for investors and blocks project development, frequently leading to protracted approval processes and less access to assistance programs. As legislation evolve to acknowledge AgriPV as a dual use solution, definitive rules will be crucial to achieve its complete economic and social potential.

4 CONCLUSION

Combining solar panels with farming is a promising way to combine renewable energy generation with food production. The LCA results show that producing PV modules, especially made in China, has the biggest impact on the environmental. On the other hand, agriculture has a smaller effect through the use of fertilisers. The analysis also highlights the problem of defining functional units in type of systems. Using both electricity output and crop yield per hectare-year, as well as the Land Equivalent Ratio (LER), gives a more balanced view. This study's LCA framework shows that it is better for land use efficiency and fighting climate change than traditional PV systems. There are still trade-offs to consider regarding, related to shading, lowering yields and lower energy produced compared with conventional PV farms. This means that system design needs to be extremely meticulous to achieve a balance between energy and agricultural production.

In addition to standard indicators, dual-use systems provide additional benefits, such as improved soil conditions, reduced irrigation requirements, greater resilience to extreme weather, and increased income opportunities for farmers. These synergies enhance the overall value of this land management approach for the environment, society, and the economy.

The study also found some important problems, such as lacking sufficient information on PV manufacturing, not having strong end-of-life scenarios, and current LCA databases not being able to include site-specific crop and regional interaction.

AgriPV systems provide a strategy to address the increasing demand for food and renewable energy on limited land. With advancements in solar technology, recyclable designs, and supportive policies, these systems have the potential to scale from individual projects to widespread implementation, enhancing both agricultural productivity and energy generation in the future.

5 ACKNOWLEDGEMENTS

Rui Castro was supported by national funds through FCT, Fundação para a Ciência e a Tecnologia, under project UIDB/50021/2020 (DOI: 10.54499/UIDB/50021/2020).

5 REFERENCES

[1] I. O. f. Standardization, "ISO 14040:2006. Environmental management — life cycle assessment — principles and framework," [Online]. Available: https://www.iso.org/standard/37456.html. [Acessed on 24 07 2025].

[2] R. Sanathi, S. Banerjee, S. Bhowmik, "A technical review of crystalline silicon photovoltaic module recycling", Solar Energy, Volume 281, 2024.

[3] Ai Leon, Keiichi N. Ishihara,"Assessment of new functional units for agrivoltaic systems", Journal of Environmental Management, Volume 226, 2018.

[4] T. Krexner, A. Bauer, A. Gronauer, C. Mikovits, J. Schmidt, I. Kral, "Environmental life cycle assessment of a stilted and vertical bifacial crop-based agrivoltaic multi land-use system and comparison with a mono land-use of agricultural land", Renewable and Sustainable Energy Reviews, Volume 196, 2024.

[5] A. Müller, L. Friedrich, C. Reichel, S. Herceg, M. Mittag, D. Neuhaus, "A comparative life cycle assessment of silicon PV modules: Impact of module design, manufacturing location and inventory", Solar Energy Materials and Solar Cells, Volume 230, 2021.

[6] W Moritz, J Lask, A. Kiesel, I. Lewandowski, A Weselek, P Högy, M Trommsdorff, M Schnaiker, A. Bauerle, "Agrivoltaics: The Environmental Impacts of Combining Food Crop Cultivation and Solar Energy Generation", Agronomy 13, 2023.

[7] G. Barron-Gafford, M. Pavao-Zuckerman, R. Minor, L. Sutter, I. Barnett-Moreno, D. Blackett, M. Thompson, K. Dimond, A. Gerlak, G. Nabhan, J. Macknick, "Agrivoltaics provide mutual benefits across the food–energy–water nexus in drylands", Nature Sustainability, Volume 2, 2019.

[8] S. Gorjian, E. Bousi, Ö. Özdemir, M. Trommsdorff, N. Manoj Kumar, A. Anand, K. Kant, S. Chopra, "Progress and challenges of crop production and
[9] electricity generation in agrivoltaic systems using semi-transparent photovoltaic technology", Renewable and Sustainable Energy Reviews, Volume 158, 2022.
S. Schindele, M. Trommsdorff, A. Schlaak, T. Obergfell, G. Bopp, C. Reise, C. Braun, A. Weselek, A. Bauerle, P. Högy, A. Goetzberger, E. Weber, "Implementation of agrophotovoltaics: Techno-economic analysis of the price-performance ratio and its policy implications", Applied Energy, Volume 265, 2020.

TALOS

AgriPV: A Comprehensive Assessment Framework for Sustainable Energy and Agriculture

Session 5CO.5.1

EU PVSEC Conference 2025

September 24, 2025

TÉCNICO LISBOA

Funded by the European Union

Introduction and Motivation

AgriPV presents a dual land use strategy **combining solar energy generation** and **agricultural production**

Addresses the increasing global **demand for food** and **clean energy**

Adoption remains limited due to lack of standardized sustainability assessment methodologies

This research proposes an **integrated framework** to evaluate energy generation, emissions and environmental impact. **Supports decision-making** for policymakers, researchers and farmers by providing a structured tool to evaluate the feasibility of AgriPV

1. The **Life Cycle Assessment (LCA)** methodology evaluates GHG emissions, energy generation efficiency and overall environmental impact across several stages
2. A **comparative sustainability analysis** between AgriPV and conventional PV complements the LCA

TALOS

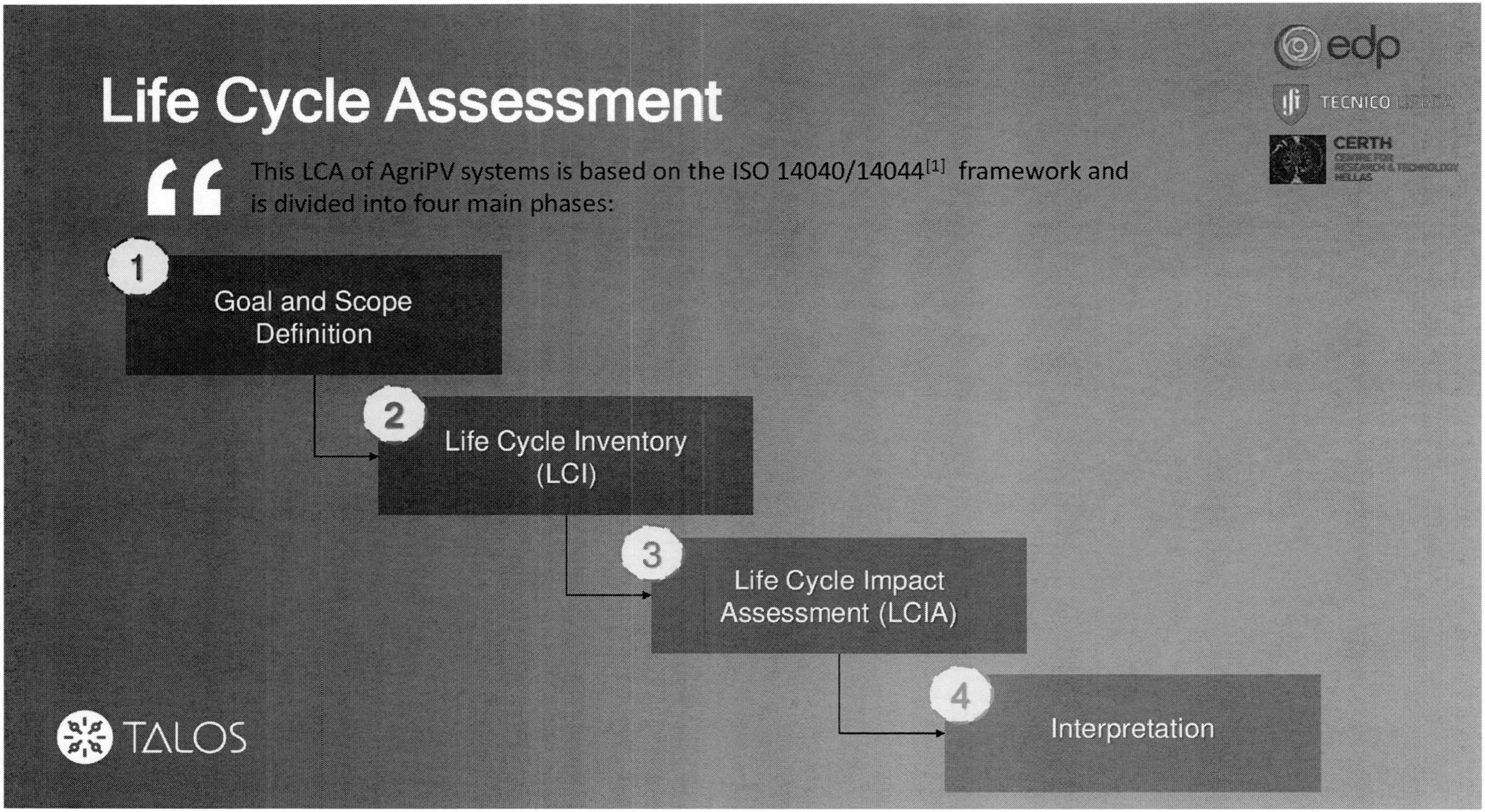
Life Cycle Assessment
This LCA of AgriPV systems is based on the ISO 14040/14044[1] framework and is divided into four main phases:
1
Goal and Scope Definition
2
Life Cycle Inventory (LCI)
3
Life Cycle Impact Assessment (LCIA)
4
Interpretation
TALOS
edp
TECNICO
CERTH

Life Cycle Assessment

This LCA of AgriPV systems is based on the ISO 14040/14044[1] framework and is divided into four main phases:

1. Goal and Scope Definition
- Life Cycle Inventory (LCI)
- Life Cycle Impact Assessment (LCIA)
- Interpretation

Objective
Evaluate environmental sustainability of AgriPV

Boundaries
Cradle-to-gate

Functional units
Electricity (kWh/ha·yr) and Crop yield (kg/ha·yr)
captures both outputs without favoring one

Another Metric
Land Equivalent Ratio (LER)

TALOS

Life Cycle Assessment

This LCA of AgriPV systems is based on the ISO 14040/14044[1] framework and is divided into four main phases:

- Goal and Scope Definition
- 2 Life Cycle Inventory (LCI)
- Life Cycle Impact Assessment (LCIA)
- Interpretation

	INPUTS	OUTPUTS
Raw materials For bifacial and semi-transparent PV modules and structures, and fertilisers and pesticides.	Silicon, aluminium, steel, copper, glass. Fertilisers and pesticides Steel and aluminium	Mining emissions and waste from extraction
Manufacturing	Energy-intensive processes and chemicals	Solid waste, CO_2, SO_2 and NOx
Transport	Fuel used for shipping	CO_2 from combustion
Installation	Diesel for agricultural machines and for transportation	Packaging waste and CO_2 emissions
Operation	Water, cleaning products and energy	Electricity, crop yield, wastewater and e-waste N_2O emissions from fertilisers, nitrate leaching, pesticides residues

TALOS

edp TECNICO LISBOA CERTH CENTRE FOR RESEARCH & TECHNOLOGY HELLAS

Life Cycle Assessment

This LCA of AgriPV systems is based on the ISO 14040/14044[1] framework and is divided into four main phases:

- Goal and Scope Definition
- Life Cycle Inventory (LCI)
- 3 Life Cycle Impact Assessment (LCIA)
- Interpretation

Methodologies

ReCiPe (midpoint & endpoint indicators)and EU Product Environmental Footprint (PEF)

Impact categories

- **Climate change**: CO_2 emissions, carbon payback time
- **Water related**: irrigation and panel cleaning, but a reduction from evapotranspiration
- **Eutrophication and acidification**: fertiliser use and runoff
- **Toxicity**: pesticides, chemical processes in PV manufacturing
- **Resource depletion**: silicon, steel, aluminium, copper demand

Key driver

PV module manufacturing dominates carbon footprint

TALOS

Life Cycle Assessment

This LCA of AgriPV systems is based on the ISO 14040/14044[1] framework and is divided into four main phases:

- Goal and Scope Definition
- Life Cycle Inventory (LCI)
- Life Cycle Impact Assessment (LCIA)
- 4 Interpretation

Main impacts
Manufacturing of PV modules is the dominant source

Agricultural share
Irrigation and fertilisers add emissions but at a smaller scale

Positive effects
- Improve soil quality
- Reduced water use
- Better resilience to extreme events, like heat and drought

Trade-offs
Balance between crop yield and electricity production critical to maintain overall sustainability

Knowledge gaps
Lack of transparent data from PV manufacturers

TALOS

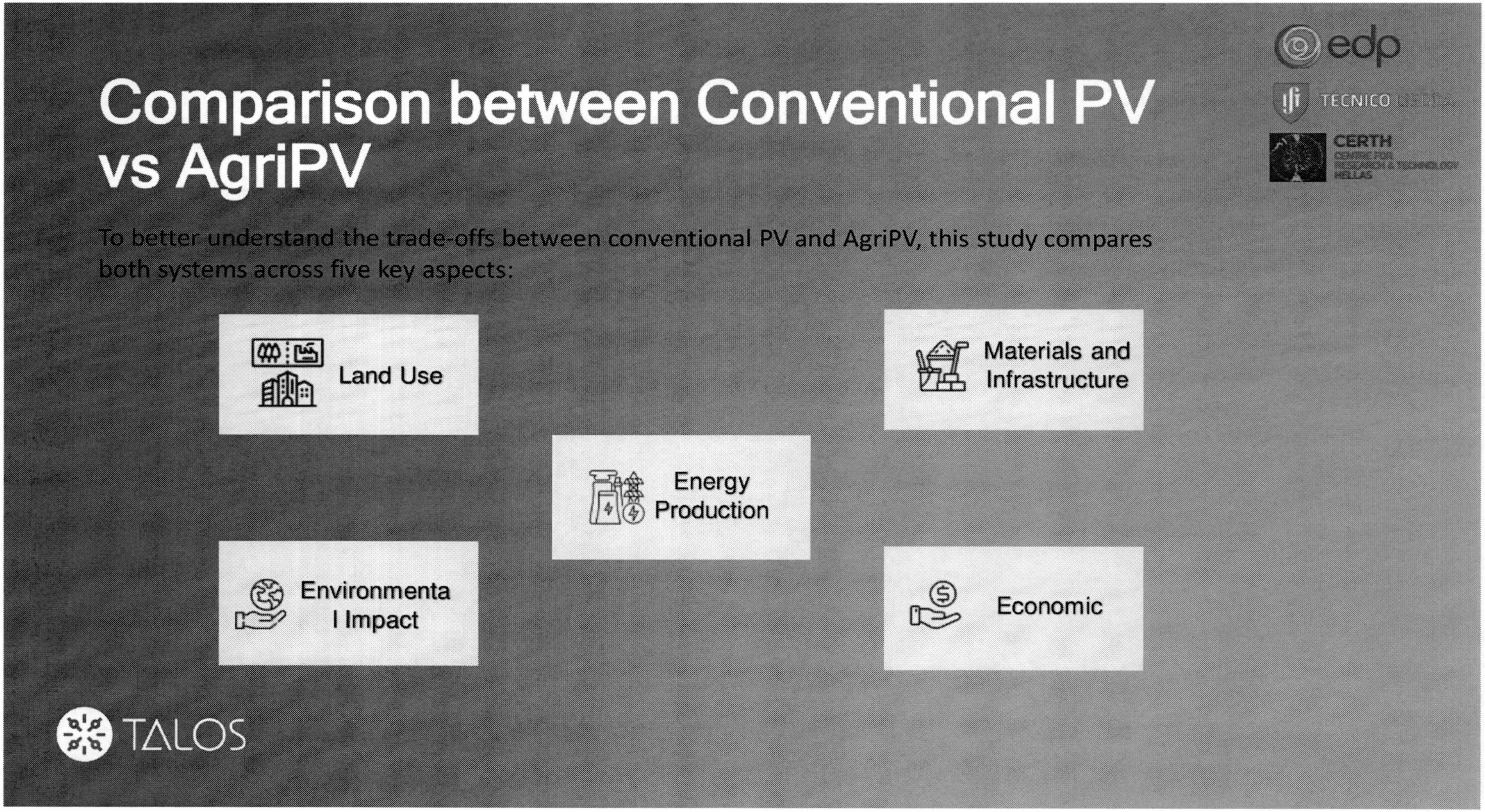
Comparison between Conventional PV vs AgriPV
To better understand the trade-offs between conventional PV and AgriPV, this study compares both systems across five key aspects:
Land Use
Energy Production
Materials and Infrastructure
Environmenta l Impact
Economic
TALOS
edp
TECNICO
CERTH
CENTRE FOR RESEARCH & TECHNOLOGY HELLAS

Comparison between Conventional PV vs AgriPV

To better understand the trade-offs between conventional PV and AgriPV, this study compares both systems across five key aspects:

Land Use	Energy Production	Materials and Infrastructure	Environmental Impact	Economic
AgriPV	Elevated structures or interspace layouts allow crop growth	Low Ground Coverage Ratio	Preserves soil, reduces erosion and enables dual land productivity	
Conventional PVs	Low-elevation, mainly with fixed-tilt or single-axis tracker	High Ground Coverage Ratio	Land is only used for the energy production purpose	

Comparison between Conventional PV vs AgriPV

To better understand the trade-offs between conventional PV and AgriPV, this study compares both systems across five key aspects:

Land Use	Energy Production	Materials and Infrastructure	Environmental Impact	Economic
AgriPV	Fewer panels per hectare: lower installed capacity	Vegetation can reduce temperature improves panel efficiency	Tracking systems can increase production, although they raise OPEX and may affect light distribution	Requires optimised design to balance shading and crop yields
Conventional PVs	Maximum panel density	Stable energy output unaffected by crops or shade	Optimised for only energy production	

Comparison between Conventional PV vs AgriPV

To better understand the trade-offs between conventional PV and AgriPV, this study compares both systems across five key aspects:

Land Use	Energy Production	Materials and Infrastructure	Environmental Impact	Economic
AgriPV	Overhead structures have stronger structures and need more material	Installation involves additional equipment (irrigation, sensors)	Special tools needed for cleaning and maintenance	Bifacial and semi-transparent modules add cost but improve performance
Conventional PVs	Standardised and cost-effective mounting systems		Lower consumption of steel and aluminium	

Comparison between Conventional PV vs AgriPV

To better understand the trade-offs between conventional PV and AgriPV, this study compares both systems across five key aspects:

	Land Use	Energy Production	Materials and Infrastructure	Environmental Impact	Economic
AgriPV		Creates microclimate that helps crops adapt to heat and drought	Improves soil quality and supports biodiversity under panels	Reduces water evaporation, potentially lowering irrigation needs	
Conventional PVs		Life Cycle Assessment dominated by module production impacts	Land use excludes agriculture and provides no biodiversity benefit	No contribution to soil quality	

edp
TÉCNICO LISBOA
CERTH CENTRE FOR RESEARCH & TECHNOLOGY HELLAS

Comparison between Conventional PV vs AgriPV

To better understand the trade-offs between conventional PV and AgriPV, this study compares both systems across five key aspects:

Land Use	Energy Production	Materials and Infrastructure	Environmental Impact	Economics
AgriPV	Higher CAPEX and OPEX due to taller structures and dual-use design	Additional revenue for farmers through crop production and energy sales	Potential cost savings from self-consumption	Regulatory frameworks still under development, leading to longer approval processes
Conventional PVs	Lower CAPEX, simpler design and installation		Fast permitting and standardised incentives	

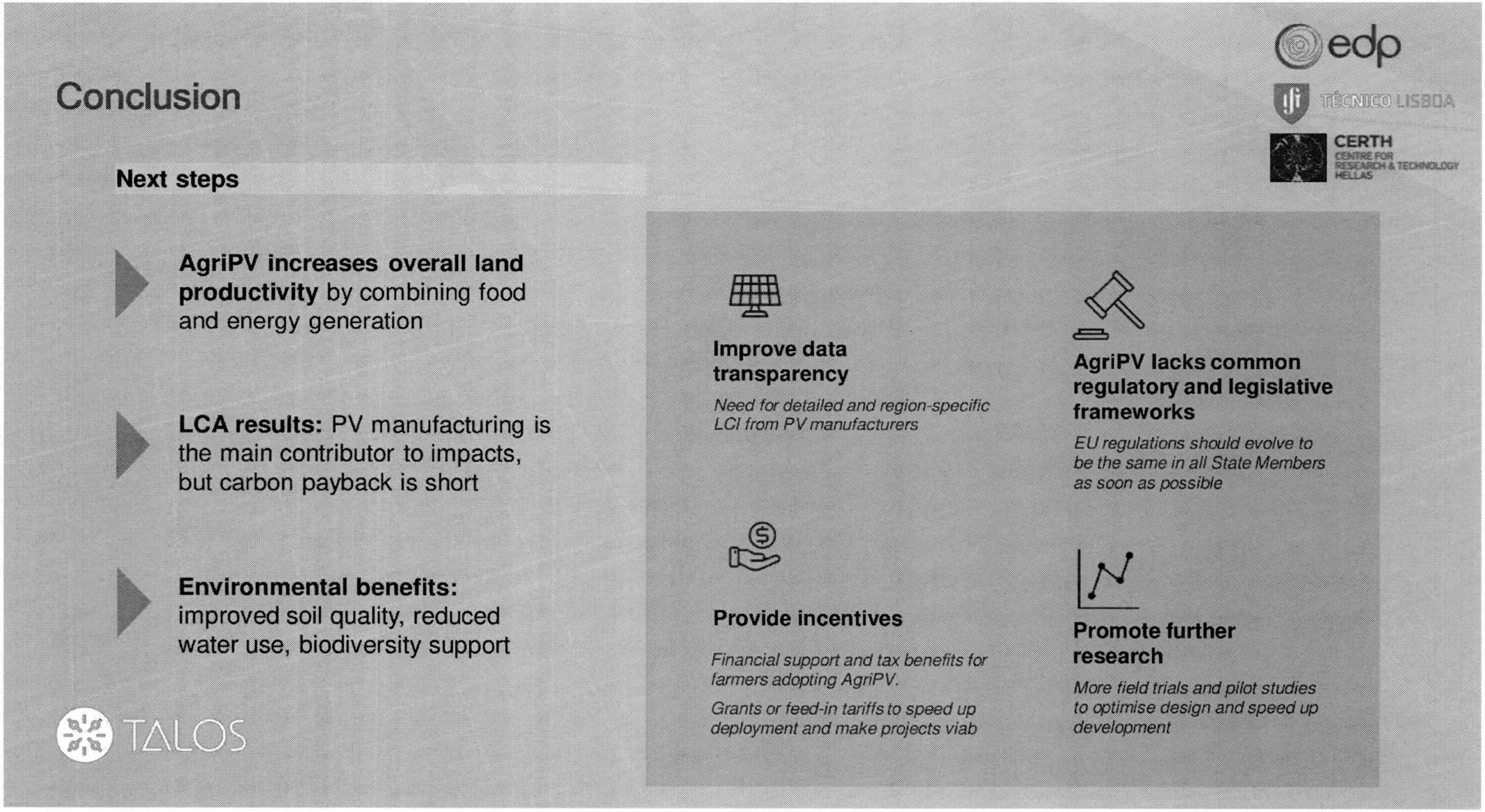
Conclusion
Next steps
AgriPV increases overall land productivity by combining food and energy generation
LCA results: PV manufacturing is the main contributor to impacts, but carbon payback is short
Environmental benefits: improved soil quality, reduced water use, biodiversity support
Improve data transparency
Need for detailed and region-specific LCI from PV manufacturers
AgriPV lacks common regulatory and legislative frameworks
EU regulations should evolve to be the same in all State Members as soon as possible
Provide incentives
Financial support and tax benefits for farmers adopting AgriPV.
Grants or feed-in tariffs to speed up deployment and make projects viab
Promote further research
More field trials and pilot studies to optimise design and speed up development
TALOS
edp
TÉCNICO LISBOA
CERTH
CENTRE FOR RESEARCH & TECHNOLOGY HELLAS

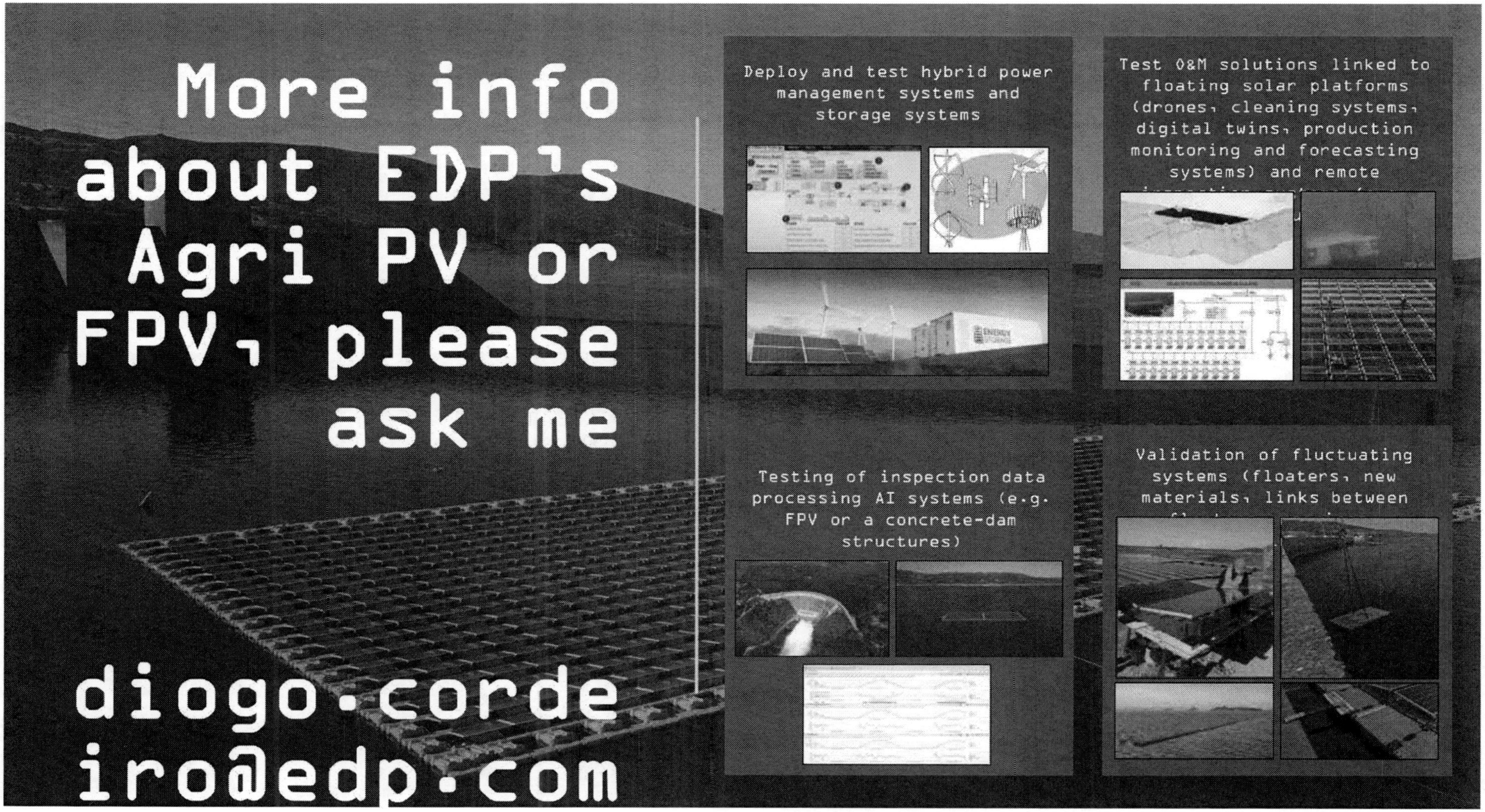
More info about EDP's Agri PV or FPV, please ask me
diogo.cordeiro@edp.com
Deploy and test hybrid power management systems and storage systems
Test O&M solutions linked to floating solar platforms (drones, cleaning systems, digital twins, production monitoring and forecasting systems) and remote
Testing of inspection data processing AI systems (e.g. FPV or a concrete-dam structures)
Validation of fluctuating systems (floaters, new materials, links between

TALOS
roboTics and Artificial intelligence Livinglabs improving Operations in PV Scenarios
Thank you
talosproject.eu
info@talosproject.eu
@Talos_EUproject
TALOS EU PROJECT
Funded by
the European Union

RSE Ricerca Sistema Energetico | we move research

Environmental Sustainability Assessment of Agrivoltaic Systems: A Life Cycle Approach

Maria Anna Cusenza, Andrea Danelli, Sofia Spagnolo, Pierpaolo Girardi

24.09.2025

This work has been financed by the Research Fund for the Italian Electrical System under the Three-Year Research Plan 2025-2027 (MASE, Decree n.388 of November 6th, 2024), in compliance with the Decree of April 12th, 2024.

EU PVSEC 2025

LCA applied to agrivoltaic system: methodological aspects and research gaps

Life Cycle Assessment(1,2)

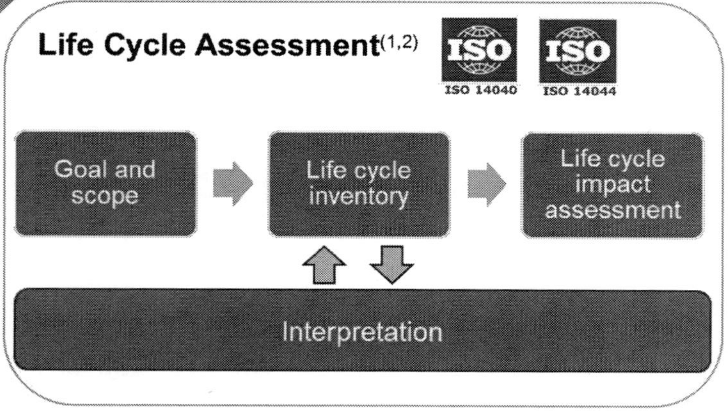

LCA applied to agrivoltaic systems

Agrivoltaic systems are **multifunctional** systems

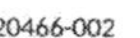

Key methodological aspects for the application of the LCA methodology to multifunctional systems in compliance with ISO 14040/14044

- Identification of the main function
- Selection of the appropriate functional unit
- Handling of multifunctionality

State of Research on Agrivoltaic LCA: research gaps(3)

1. *Few studies available*
2. *Main function not defined*
3. *Multifunctionality handling non ISO-compliant*
4. *Limited primary data on potential synergies and/or trade-offs*

Contribution to the research gaps

- *LCA fully compliant with ISO 14040/14044 → 1, 2 and 3* ☑
- *Scenario analysis to explore potential synergies and trade-offs → 4* ☑

LCA of an agrivoltaic system in Italy

Case study

Overhead agrivoltaic system installed in Robecco sul Naviglio (MI) near a wastewater treatment plant for electricity supply, by CAP Holding.

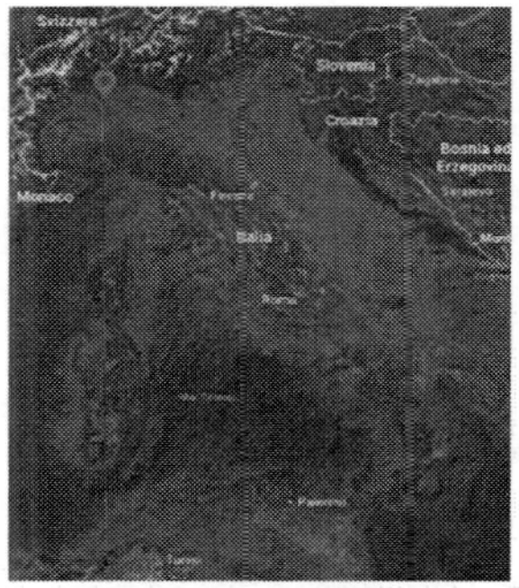

Main function: Electricity generation

Agrivoltaic system(3)

- Overhead agrivoltaic system
- Agricultural activity takes place underneath the PV modules
- Area (S_{AgriPV}): 15,000 m^2
- Modules at 5 m height from ground
- Row spacing (pitch): 16 m

Photovoltaic system

- Installed capacity: 540 kW
- Modules: 816 bifacial PERC monocrystalline (660 W)
- PV modules footprint (S_{PV}): 2,500 m^2
- 34 dual-axis trackers (24 PV modules/tracker), hot-dip galvanized steel
- 2 inverters (320 kW + 225 kW)
- Foundations: Screw piles, steel
- First-year generation: 1,533 kWh/(kW·yr)

Agricultural system

- Conventional maize cultivation
- Agricultural area (S_{Agr}): 13,900 m^2
- Yield reduction: -15% vs full-sun cultivation (literature)

$$S_{Agr} = 92{,}7\%\ of\ S_{AgriPV}$$

3

LCA of an agrivoltaic system in Italy – Goal and scope

Goal

Environmental sustainability assessment: agrivoltaic vs. conventional PV systems (**reference PV system**)

Scope definition

Functional unit: 1 kWh of electricity delivered to the grid over the plant's lifetime.

Key technical characteristics of the agrivoltaics and the reference PV systems for the comparative LCA

Parameter	Agrivoltaic system	Reference PV system(4)
Plant configuration	Overhead PV system, bi-axial solar tracker	Ground-mounted PV system, mono-axial solar tracker
Location	Robecco sul Naviglio (MI)	Piacenza (PC)
PV technology	PERC (bi-facial)	PERC (mono-facial)
Capacity (MW)	0.54	84.7
Equivalent operating hours (30-year average) (hours)	1,412	1,417

Agrivoltaic system

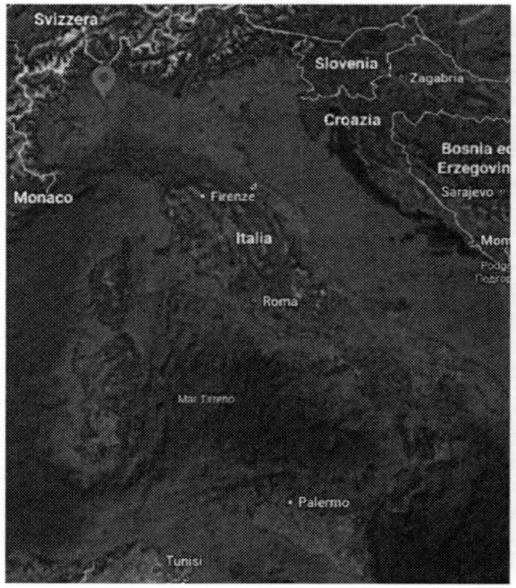

Reference PV system

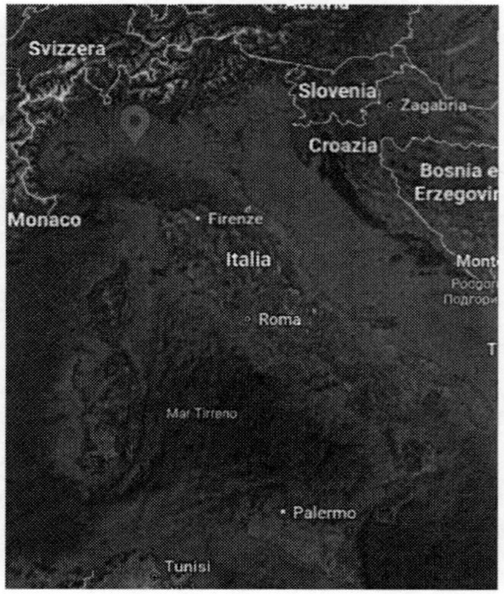

LCA of an agrivoltaic system in Italy – Goal and scope

Scope definition

Multifunctionality handling (to make systems functionally comparable): **System expansion**

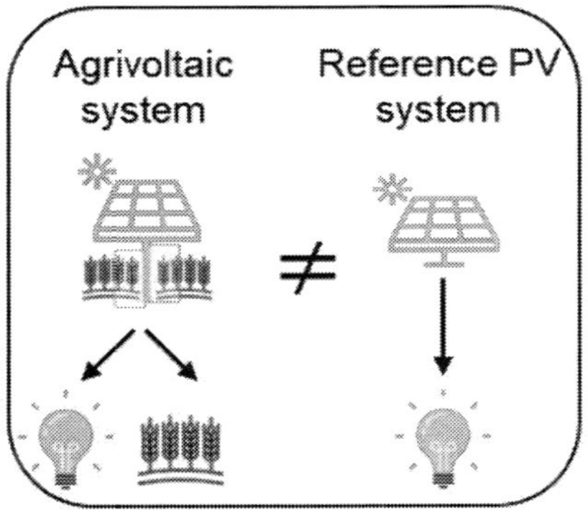

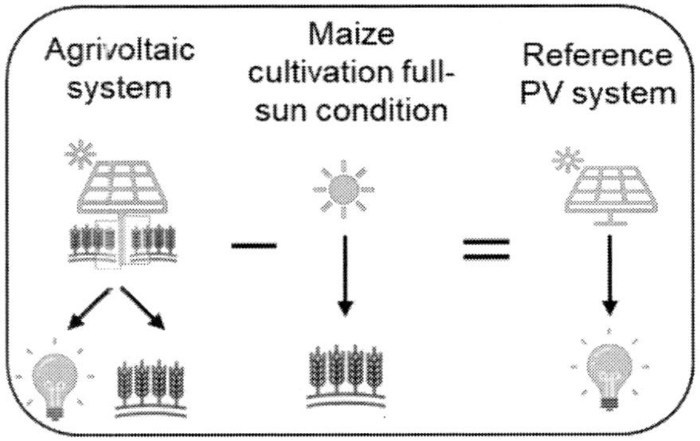

System boundaries

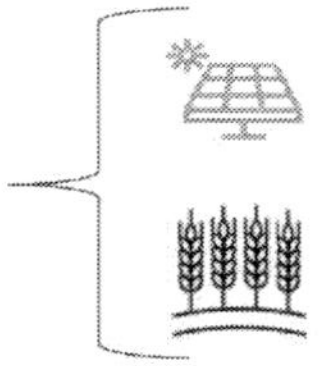

Life cycle impact assessement method

Environmental Footprint 3.1(5)

Impact category; (acronym); [robustness]	Unit
Acidification; (A); [II]	$molH^+eq$
Climate change; (CC); [I]	$kgCO_2eq$
Particulate matter; (PM); [I]	Disease incidence
Eutrophication marine; (EU_M); [II]	kgNeq
Eutrophication freshwater; (EU_{FW}); [II]	kgPeq
Eutrophication terrestrial; (EU_T); [II]	molNeq
Land use; (LU); [III]	Pt
Ozone depletion; (OD); [I]	kgCFC-11eq
Photochemical ozone formation human health; (POF); [II]	kgNMVOCeq
Resource use, minerals and metals; (RUMM) [III]	kgSbeq

RSE we move rsearch

LCA of an agrivoltaic system in Italy - LCI

Construction phase(3,4)

•**PV modules →** RSE dataset: PV datasheets + previous studies on PV modules based on PERC technology (European manufacturer primary data)

•**PV cell →** RSE dataset: based on PERC cell data from a European manufacturer

•**Overhead bi-axial tracker →** RSE dataset: project drawings (CAP holding) + tracker data (European manufacturer primary data).

•**Inverter →** RSE dataset created within the EU GoPV project, based on European manufacturer data

•**Other components →** Modelled consulting RSE experts and Ecoinvent database v. 3.9.1(6)

Operational phase

•**Lifetime electricity (30-years) →** calculated from net annual production provided by the system designer (1,533 kWh/kW/year), considering module degradation

End of Life

• **Inverters, trackers, foundations →** Assumed fully recyclable; recycling excluded from system boundary (cut-off approach) (5)

• **PV modules →** EoL model based on LCI data from IEA PVPS Task 12 activities(7,8,9)

IEA PVPS

Conventional maize cultivation in the Nothen Italy (Po Valley) – Full sun conditions

•**Yield →** Provided by Università Cattolica del Sacro Cuore – UNICATT (PhD program funded by RSE) (1.2 kg/m^2/year)

Main cultivation operations → Based on standard maize cultivation practices in the Po Valley, from UNICATT with support from literature

Conventional maize cultivation in the Po Valley, Italy – Agrivoltaic conditions

•**Yield →** ~15 % lower than full sun (based on literature)(10)

Upstream and downstream processes

Material and energy inputs, including raw materials, semi-finished products, auxiliary materials, electricity, and fuels, as characterised in Ecoinvent Database v3.9.1

ecoinvent

6

LCA of an agrivoltaic system in Italy - LCIA

Environmental impacts associated with the agrivoltaic system. All values are expressed per FU: 1 kWh of electricity.

Impact category	Agrivoltaic PV plant (A)	Maize cultivation - Agrivoltaic conditions (B)	Maize cultivation - Full sun condition (C)	FU (1 kWh of electricity) (A+B+C)/(A+B)
Acidification (Mol H^+eq)	$1.04 \cdot 10^{-4}$	$2.93 \cdot 10^{-4}$	$-2.48 \cdot 10^{-4}$	**$1.48 \cdot 10^{-4}$**
Climate change ($kgCO_2eq$)	$1.58 \cdot 10^{-2}$	$7.01 \cdot 10^{-3}$	$-5.95 \cdot 10^{-3}$	**$1.68 \cdot 10^{-2}$**
Particulate matter (disease inc.)	$1.18 \cdot 10^{-9}$	$1.97 \cdot 10^{-9}$	$-1.67 \cdot 10^{-9}$	**$1.48 \cdot 10^{-9}$**
Eutrophication marine (kgNeq)	$2.91 \cdot 10^{-5}$	$3.67 \cdot 10^{-3}$	$-3.12 \cdot 10^{-4}$	**$8.47 \cdot 10^{-5}$**
Eutrophication freshwater (kgPeq)	$7.24 \cdot 10^{-6}$	$7.02 \cdot 10^{-6}$	$-5.96 \cdot 10^{-6}$	**$8.30 \cdot 10^{-6}$**
Eutrophication terrestrial (mol Neq)	$2.33 \cdot 10^{-4}$	$1.26 \cdot 10^{-3}$	$-1.07 \cdot 10^{-3}$	**$4.23 \cdot 10^{-4}$**
Land use (Pt)	0,101	1.114	-1.197	**0,018**
Ozone depletion (kgCFC11eq)	$3.05 \cdot 10^{-10}$	$9.35 \cdot 10^{-11}$	$-7.94 \cdot 10^{-11}$	**$3.19 \cdot 10^{-10}$**
Photochemical ozone formation (kgNMVOCeq)	$7.07 \cdot 10^{-5}$	$2.38 \cdot 10^{-5}$	$-2.02 \cdot 10^{-5}$	**$7.43 \cdot 10^{-5}$**
Resource use, minerals and metals (kgSbeq)	$9.44 \cdot 10^{-7}$	$3.80 \cdot 10^{-8}$	$-3.23 \cdot 10^{-8}$	**$9.49 \cdot 10^{-7}$**

Shading effects on crop yield (limited primary data)

Percentage contribution of agrivoltaics PV plant, maize cultivation in the agrivoltaic system, and avoided impacts from conventional full-sun maize cultivation, relative to the total system impacts (A + B), set at 100%.

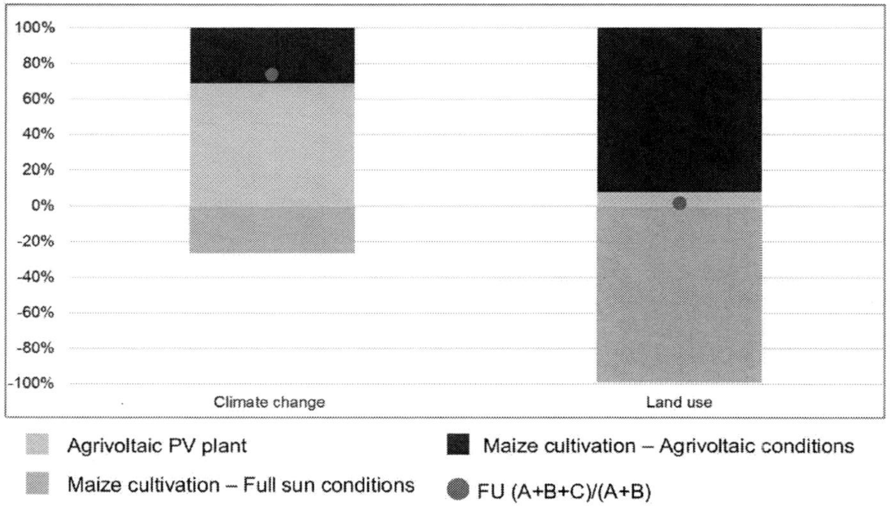

Key considerations:

- Land use efficiency: reduced land required per kWh generated
- Climate change: lack of synergy between electricity and agriculture systems can increase the overall environmental impact

7

LCA of an agrivoltaic system in Italy - LCIA

Comparative assessment with the reference PV system

Impact category	FU (1 kWh electricity into the grid form the agrivoltaic system)	1 kWh electricity into the grid from the reference PV system
Acidification (Mol H^+eq)	$1.48 \cdot 10^{-4}$	$1.00 \cdot 10^{-4}$
Climate change (kgCO_2eq)	$1.68 \cdot 10^{-2}$	$1.51 \cdot 10^{-2}$
Particulate matter (disease inc.)	$1.48 \cdot 10^{-9}$	$1.12 \cdot 10^{-9}$
Eutrophication marine (kgNeq)	$8.47 \cdot 10^{-5}$	$2.82 \cdot 10^{-5}$
Eutrophication freshwater (kgPeq)	$8.30 \cdot 10^{-6}$	$6.55 \cdot 10^{-6}$
Eutrophication terrestrial (mol Neq)	$4.23 \cdot 10^{-4}$	$2.23 \cdot 10^{-4}$
Land use (Pt)	$1.87 \cdot 10^{-2}$	$4.51 \cdot 10^{-1}$
Ozone depletion (kgCFC11eq)	$3.19 \cdot 10^{-10}$	$8.12 \cdot 10^{-10}$
Photochemical ozone formation (kgNMVOCeq)	$7.43 \cdot 10^{-5}$	$6.76 \cdot 10^{-5}$
Resource use, minerals and metals (kgSbeq)	$9.49 \cdot 10^{-7}$	$8.34 \cdot 10^{-7}$

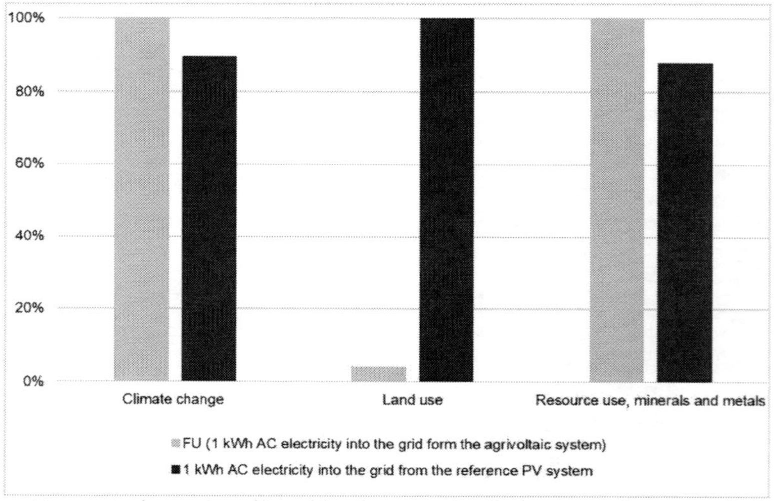

Life cycle impacts of 1 kWh from agrivoltaics vs. reference PV (normalized to 100).

Agrivoltaic systems vs reference PV systems

Land use: ☑ - 95% compared to reference PV system **Climate change:** ☑ impacts of the same order of magnitude

Beyond yield reduction, higher impacts linked to intrinsic features of the agrivoltaic configuration

- *e.g., more complex structures → higher resource use, minerals and metals* ➡ No additional supply risk

RSE Ricerca Sistema Energetico | we move rsearch

LCA of an agrivoltaic system in Italy – scenario analysis

Scenario analysis – impact of PV module shading on maize agricultural yield

Base case	Neutral yield scenario	Enhanced yield scenario
• *15% yield reduction vs. full light cultivation*	• *No yield reduction – shade-tolerant crops*	• *15% yield increase – vs full-light cultivation*

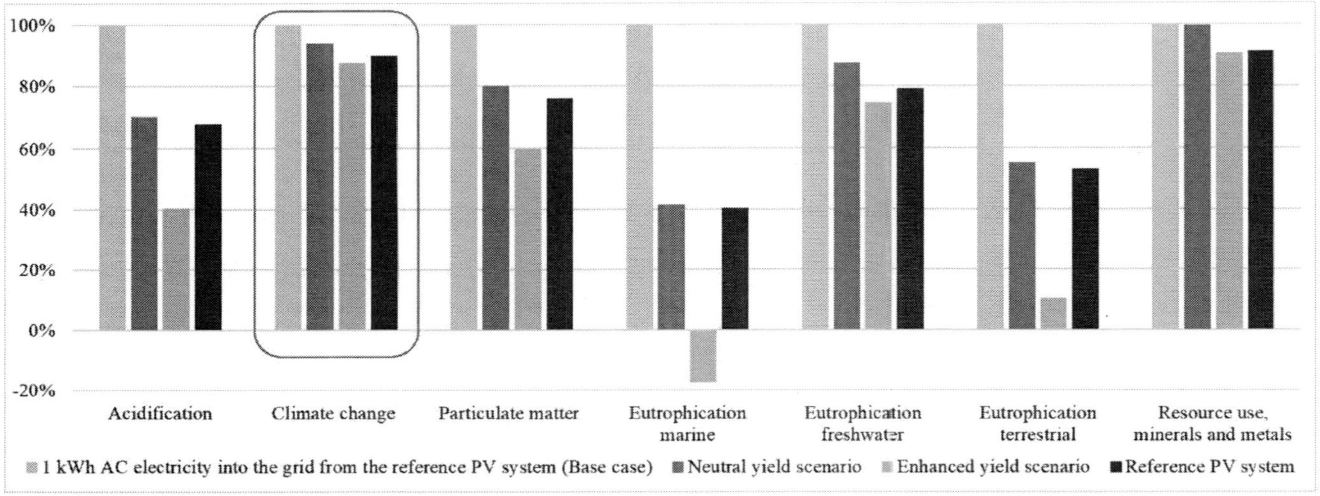

Life cycle impacts of 1 kWh from agrivoltaics vs. reference PV (normalized to 100)

Key considerations:

- Integrated system designs improve agrivoltaics' environmental performance
- Understanding interactions within agro-photovoltaic systems is crucial
- Site-specific data (different climates) support wider adoption

Conclusions and future reasearch

Research innovation

- *The study contributes to knowledge in an emerging field*

Environmental sustainability compared to conventional PV

- *Significant land use reduction, with comparable climate change impacts*
- *Integrated system design maximizes synergies between PV and crops, reducing trade-offs across impact categories*

Strategic implications

- *LCA results guide policymakers and industry; more data needed to support sustainable expansion across different climates*

Future research

- **LCA of agrivoltaic systems across diverse climates:** evaluation of different system configurations and crop varieties.
- **LCA of the RSE experimental agrivoltaic system in Piacenza:** based on primary data collected from the test field, both for the agrivoltaic system and for the corresponding single-use systems.

10

References

1. ISO 14040:2006/A1:2020, 2020. Environmental management - Life cycle assessment - Principles and framework - Amendment 1 (ISO 14040:2006/Amd 1:2020).
2. ISO 14044:2006/A1:2018, 2018. Environmental management - Life cycle assessment - Requirements and guidelines - Amendment 1 (ISO 14044:2006/Amd 1:2017).
3. Cusenza M.A., Danelli A., Spagnolo S., Girardi P. Comparative Life Cycle Assessment of an Overhead Agrivoltaic System: Environmental Impacts and Methodological Insights. Submitted to Journal of cleaner production (under review, JCLEPRO-D-25-23283)
4. Danelli, A., Brivio, E., Girardi, P., Baggio, N., Libal, J., 2024. Environmental Life Cycle Assessment of Passivated Emitter and Rear Contact (PERC) Photovoltaic Module Technology. Report IEA PVPS T12-26:2024. https://doi.org/10.69766/EEMP5995 ISBN: 978-3-907281-47-5.
5. Andreasi Bassi, S., Biganzoli, F., Ferrara, N., Amadei, A., Valente, A., Sala, S., Ardente, F., 2023. Updated characterisation and normalisation factors for the Environmental Footprint 3.1 method. Publications Office of the European Union, Luxembourg. https://doi.org/10.2760/798894.
6. Wernet, G., Bauer, C., Steubing, B., Reinhard, J., Moreno-Ruiz, E., Weidema, B., 2016. The ecoinvent database version 3 (part I): overview and methodology. Int J Life Cycle Assess 21, 1218–1230. https://doi.org/10.1007/s11367-016-1087-8.
7. Frischknecht, R., Heath, G., Raugei, M., Sinha, P., de Wild-Scholten, M., Fthenakis, V., Kim, H.C., Alsema, E., Held, M., 2016. Methodology Guidelines on Life Cycle Assessment of Photovoltaic Electricity, 3rd edition, IEA PVPS Task 12, International Energy Agency Photovoltaic Power Systems Programme. Report IEA-PVPS T12-06:2016.
8. Frischknecht, R., Stolz, P., Heath, G., Raugei, M., Sinha, P., de Wild-Scholten, M., 2020a. Methodology Guidelines on Life Cycle Assessment of Photovoltaic 2020. 4th edition, IEA PVPS Task 12, International Energy Agency Photovoltaic Power Systems Programme.
9. Frischknecht, R., Stolz, P., Krebs, L., de Wild-Scholten, M., Sinha, P., 2020b. Life Cycle Inventories and Life Cycle Assessments of Photovoltaic Systems. Report IEA-PVPS T12-19:2020.
10. Ramos-Fuentes, I.A., Elamri, Y., Cheviron, B., Dejean, C., Belaud, G., Fumey, D., 2023. Effects of shade and deficit irrigation on maize growth and development in fixed and dynamic AgriVoltaic systems. Agricultural Water Management 280, 108187. https://doi.org/10.1016/j.agwat.2023.108187.

Contacts

Thank you for the attention!

Stay informed about RSE

#wemoversearch

Maria Anna Cusenza

mariaanna.cusenza@rse-web.it

www.rse-web.it

@Ricerca sul Sistema Energetico - RSE SpA

@RSEnergetico

RSE SpA - Ricerca sul Sistema Energetico

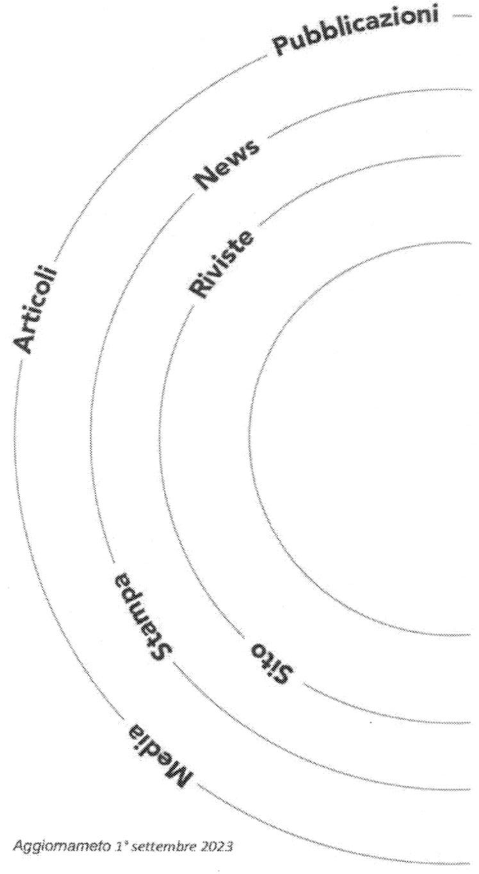

Aggiomameto 1° settembre 2023

CLOSING THE CIRCLE: INTEGRATING THE CIRCULAR FOOTPRINT FORMULA INTO PV SYSTEM LIFE CYCLE ASSESSMENT

Alexis Barrou, Selin Kandiyoti Eskenazi, Jacques Levrat, Bertrand Paviet-Salomon, Christophe Ballif

CSEM: Swiss Center of Electronic & Microtechnology, Neuchâtel, Switzerland

EU PVSEC 2025

OUTLINE

- What is the **circular footprint formula** and in which context it happens?
- How to implement the **CFF** for the **LCA** of PV modules and systems?
- What are the preliminary results? Can **CFF** show us how to improve the **environmental footprint** of PV modules and systems?
- What are the main **advantages**, **limitations** and **next steps**?
- Wrap-up

CONTEXT & MOTIVATIONS

EU policies

EU green deal: climate neutrality in **2050**

Circular economy plan: reuse, recycle, reduce waste

Ecodesign Sustainable Product Regulation:

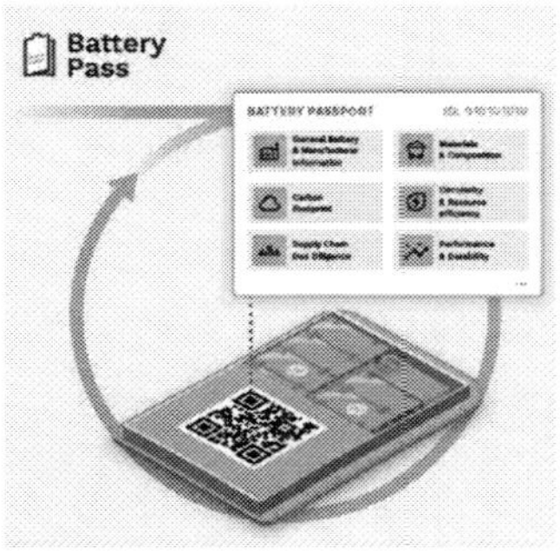

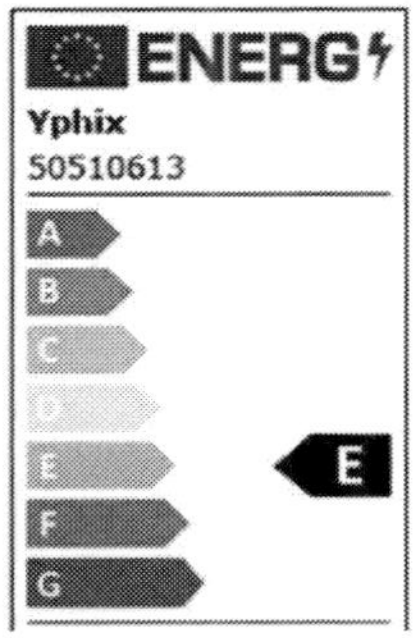

LCA standards for PV

ISO 14040:14044: international standards for LCA

IEA PVPS task 12: Acknowledged guidelines for PV LCAs

EN15804: EU standards for **Environmental Product Declaration (EPD)** for construction (including PV modules)

EU Product Environmental Footprint (PEF): official LCA methodology for EU products

Introduce the **Circular Footprint Formula (CFF)**

Understand & implement CFF for PV module & system LCAs

CIRCULAR FOOTPRINT FORMULA (CFF) IS A FORMULA USING PARAMETERS & PROCESSES

material	$(1-R_1)E_V + R_1 \times \left(AE_{recycled} + (1-A)E_V \times \frac{Q_{Sin}}{Q_P} \right) + (1-A)R_2 \times \left(E_{recyclingEoL} - E^*_V \times \frac{Q_{Sout}}{Q_P} \right)$
energy	$(1-B)R_3 \times \left(E_{ER} - LHV \times X_{ER,heat} \times E_{SE,heat} - LHV \times X_{ER,elec} \times E_{SE,elec} \right)$
disposal	$(1-R_2-R_3) \times E_D$

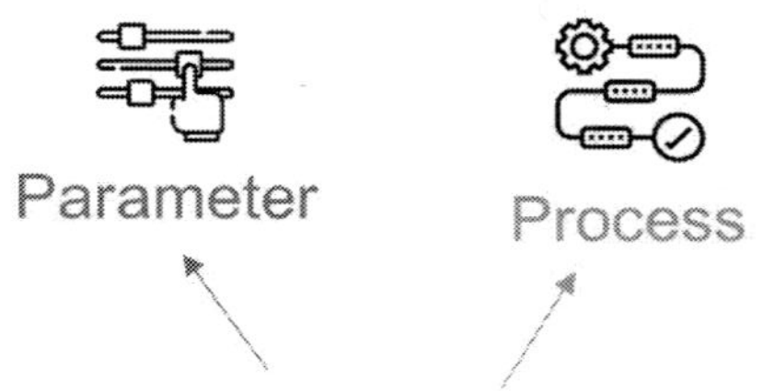

$$(1-R_1) * E_v$$

The parameters of the Circular Footprint Formula :

A: allocation factor of burdens and credits between supplier and user of recycled materials.
B: allocation factor of energy recovery processes: it applies both to burdens and credits.
Qs_{in}: quality of the ingoing secondary material, i.e. the quality of the recycled material at the point of substitution.
Qs_{out}: quality of the outgoing secondary material, i.e. the quality of the recyclable material at the point of substitution.
Q_p: quality of the primary material, i.e. quality of the virgin material.
R_1: it is the proportion of material in the input to the production that has been recycled from a previous system.
R_2: it is the proportion of the material in the product that will be recycled (or reused) in a subsequent system. R2 shall therefore take into account the inefficiencies in the collection and recycling (or reuse) processes. R2 shall be measured at the output of the recycling plant.
R_3: it is the proportion of the material in the product that is used for energy recovery at EoL.
$E_{recycled}$ (E_{rec}): specific emissions and resources consumed (per unit of analysis) arising from the recycling process of the recycled (reused) material, including collection, sorting and transportation process.
$E_{recyclingEoL}$ (E_{recEoL}): specific emissions and resources consumed (per unit of analysis) arising from the recycling process at EoL, including collection, sorting and transportation process.
E_v: specific emissions and resources consumed (per unit of analysis) arising from the acquisition and pre-processing of virgin material.
E^*_v: specific emissions and resources consumed (per unit of analysis) arising from the acquisition and pre-processing of virgin material assumed to be substituted by recyclable materials.
EER: specific emissions and resources consumed (per unit of analysis) arising from the energy recovery process (e.g. incineration with energy recovery, landfill with energy recovery, ...).
$E_{SE,heat}$ and $E_{SE,elec}$: specific emissions and resources consumed (per unit of analysis) that would have arisen from the specific substituted energy source, heat and electricity respectively.
ED: specific emissions and resources consumed (per unit of analysis) arising from disposal of waste material at the EoL of the analysed product, without energy recovery.
$X_{ER,heat}$ and $X_{ER,elec}$: the efficiency of the energy recovery process for both heat and electricity.
LHV: Lower Heating Value of the material in the product that is used for energy recovery.

CIRCULAR FOOTPRINT FORMULA (CFF) IS A FORMULA USING PARAMETERS & PROCESSES

material $$(1-R_1)E_V + R_1 \times \left(AE_{recycled} + (1-A)E_V \times \frac{Q_{Sin}}{Q_P}\right) + (1-A)R_2 \times \left(E_{recyclingEoL} - E^*_V \times \frac{Q_{Sout}}{Q_P}\right)$$

energy $$(1-B)R_3 \times (E_{ER} - LHV \times X_{ER,heat} \times E_{SE,heat} - LHV \times X_{ER,elec} \times E_{SE,elec})$$

disposal $$(1-R_2-R_3) \times E_D$$

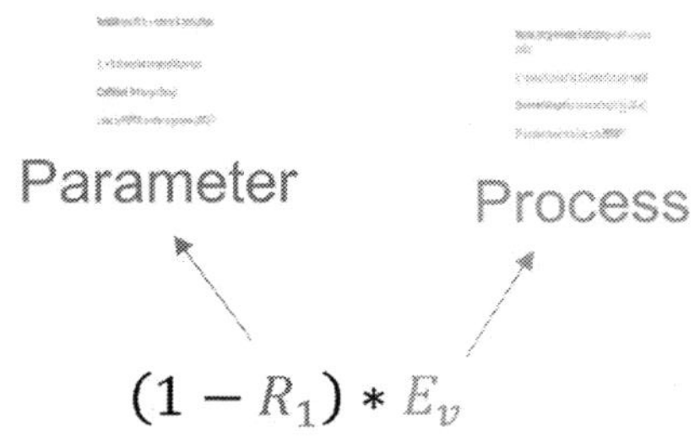

	Parameter	Process
Description	**Variable** specific to a material & product type	**Material, energy and waste & pollution** generated to create a product
Exemple	R_1 = % of recycled content of Aluminium	E_v = process to produce 1kg of aluminium from virgin material
Outcome data	**Coefficient** (**0-1** range oftenly)	**Environmental impact** such as carbon footprint [kg CO2-eq]
Source	Listed by PEFCR or other organisms (JRC) [1]	EF-compliant dataset, to be listed by the **PEFCR** [2]

[1] Joint Research Center, Ardente et al., Harmonised rules for the calculation of the carbon footprint of photovoltaic modules in the context of the EU Ecodesign Directive, 2025
[2] PEFCR for PV modules, 2020

:: csem

CIRCULAR FOOTPRINT FORMULA QUANTIFIES MATERIAL'S MANUFACTURING & END-OF-LIFE ENVIRONMENTAL IMPACTS

- Was created in the context of the **PEF methodology**
- Manages **end-of-life credits** and accounts material's **recycled share**

Parameter — Process

$(1 - R_1) * E_v$

Manufacturing

$1 - R_1$

R_1

End-of-life

R_2

R_3

$1 - R_2 - R_3$

Virgin/primary material

$(1 - R_1) * E_v$

Recycled/secondary material

$R_1 * (AE_{recycled} + (1 - A)E_v * \frac{Q_{Sin}}{Q_p})$

Recycling with benefits

$(1 - A)R_2 * (E_{recyclingEoL} - E_v^* * \frac{Q_{Sout}}{Q_p})$

Energy recovery

$(1 - B)R_3 * (E_{ER} - LHV * X_{ER,heat} * E_{SE,heat} - LHV * X_{ER,elec} * E_{SE,elec})$

Landfill/waste disposal

$(1 - R_2 - R_3) * E_D$

:: csem

HOW TO IMPLEMENT THE CFF FOR THE LCA OF PV MODULES & SYSTEMS?

13 Al Aluminium	$R_1, R_2, R_3, A, B, ...$	$E_v, E_v^*, E_D, E_{recycled}, E_{recyclingEoL}, ...$	...kg/PV module	...kg/PV BOS
47 Ag Silver	$R_1, R_2, R_3, A, B, ...$	$E_v, E_v^*, E_D, E_{recycled}, E_{recyclingEoL}, ...$	...kg/PV module	...kg/PV BOS
14 Si Silicon	$R_1, R_2, R_3, A, B, ...$	$E_v, E_v^*, E_D, E_{recycled}, E_{recyclingEoL}, ...$	...kg/PV module	...kg/PV BOS

Parameters [1]

Process environmental impact *, [2]

Weight PV module & system *

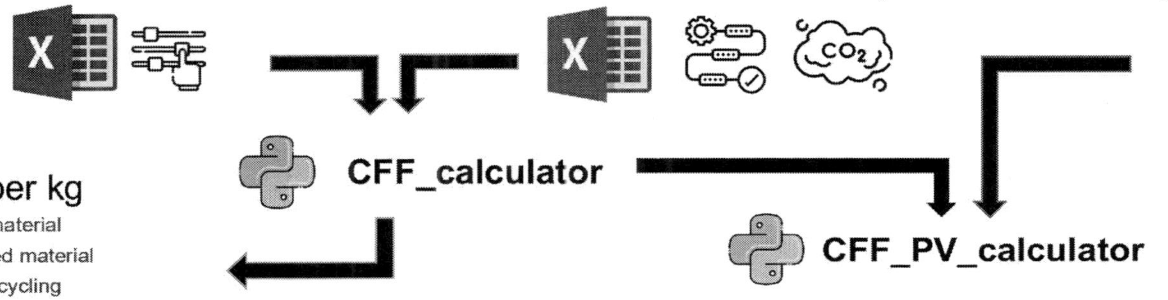

Impact per kg
- Virgin material
- Recycled material
- EoL Recycling
- EoL energy recovery
- EoL disposal

Impact per PV
- Virgin material
- Recycled material
- EoL Recycling
- EoL energy recovery
- EoL disposal

* Own calculations/sources

[1] Joint Research Center, Ardente et al , Harmonised rules for the calculation of the carbon footprint of photovoltaic modules in the context of the EU Ecodesign Directive, 2025

[2] PEFCR for PV modules, 2020

:: csem

SCOPE OF ANALYSIS

13 materials analyzed

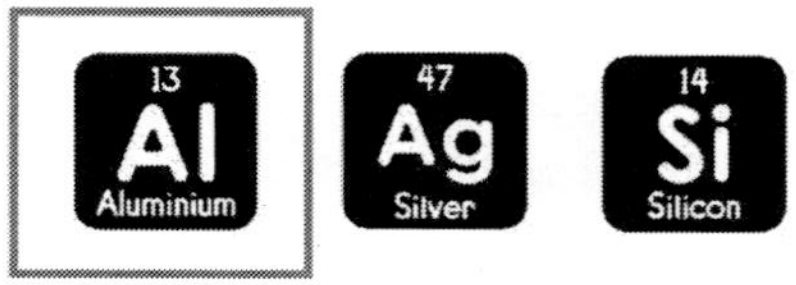

7 parameters $R_1, R_2, R_3, A, B, \dots$

16 environmental impact categories

4 PV module types:

- Glass-glass with alu frame
- Glass-glass without alu frame
- Glass-Backsheet with alu frame
- Lightweight without alu fame

Decomposition of the impact

- Virgin material
- Recycled material
- EoL Recycling
- EoL energy recovery
- EoL disposal

6 PV system configurations:

1. Slanted roof

2.A Flat roof (only racking)
2.B Flat roof (with ballast)
3.A Open-ground (no concrete)
3.B open-ground (with concrete)
4. Façade

:: csem

WEIGHT REPARTITION OF 4 TYPES OF PV MODULES

HJT technology
3.11 m², 132 ½ G12 cells, manufactured in China

- **Glass** = major **contributor** to module **weight** for GG and GBs
- For **lightweight module**: majority of impact is on **polymers**

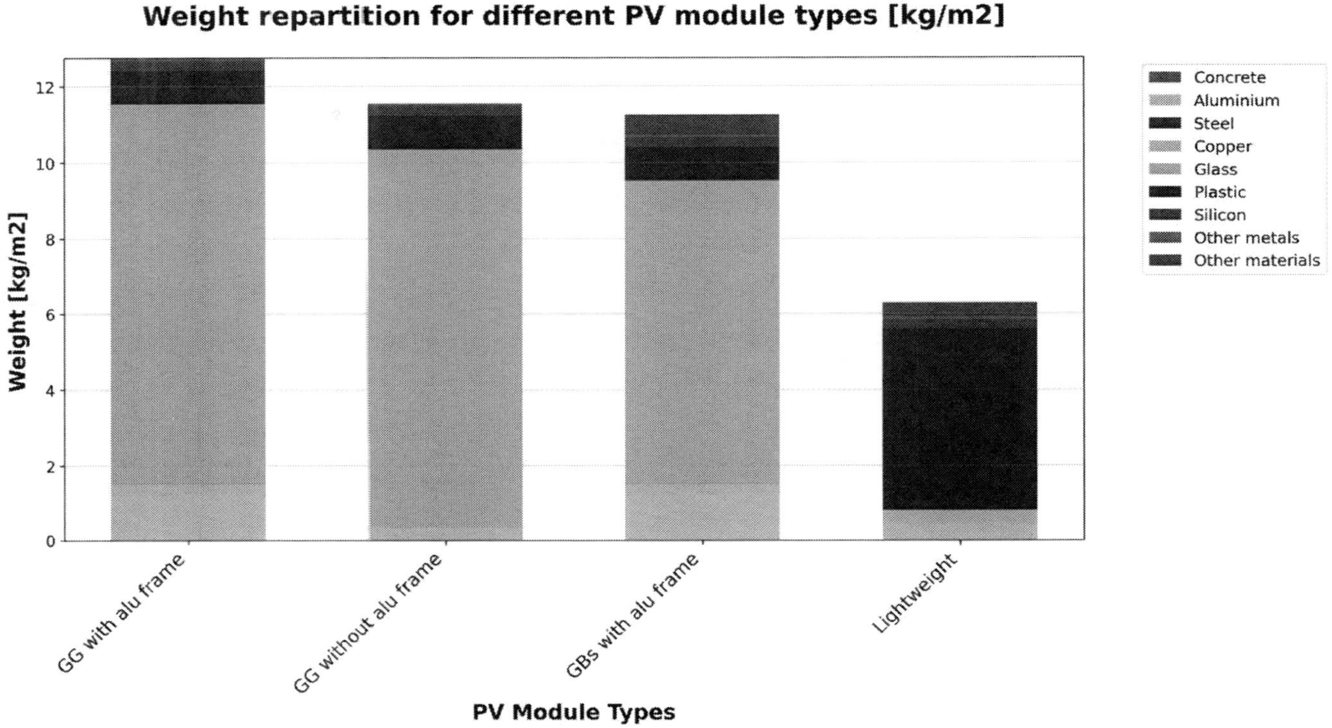

:: csem

PRELIMINARY RESULTS

~ 200 kgCO2-eq/kWp ←

Major impact:
- Silicon
- Glass (when present)
- Silver

Life cycle stages:
- Manufacturing (CN)
- End-of-life (EU)

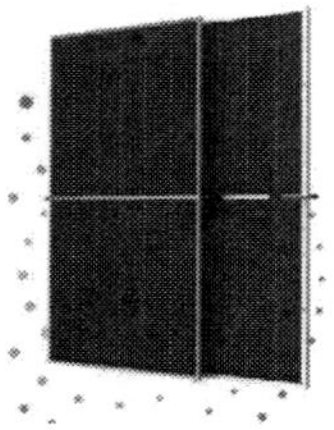

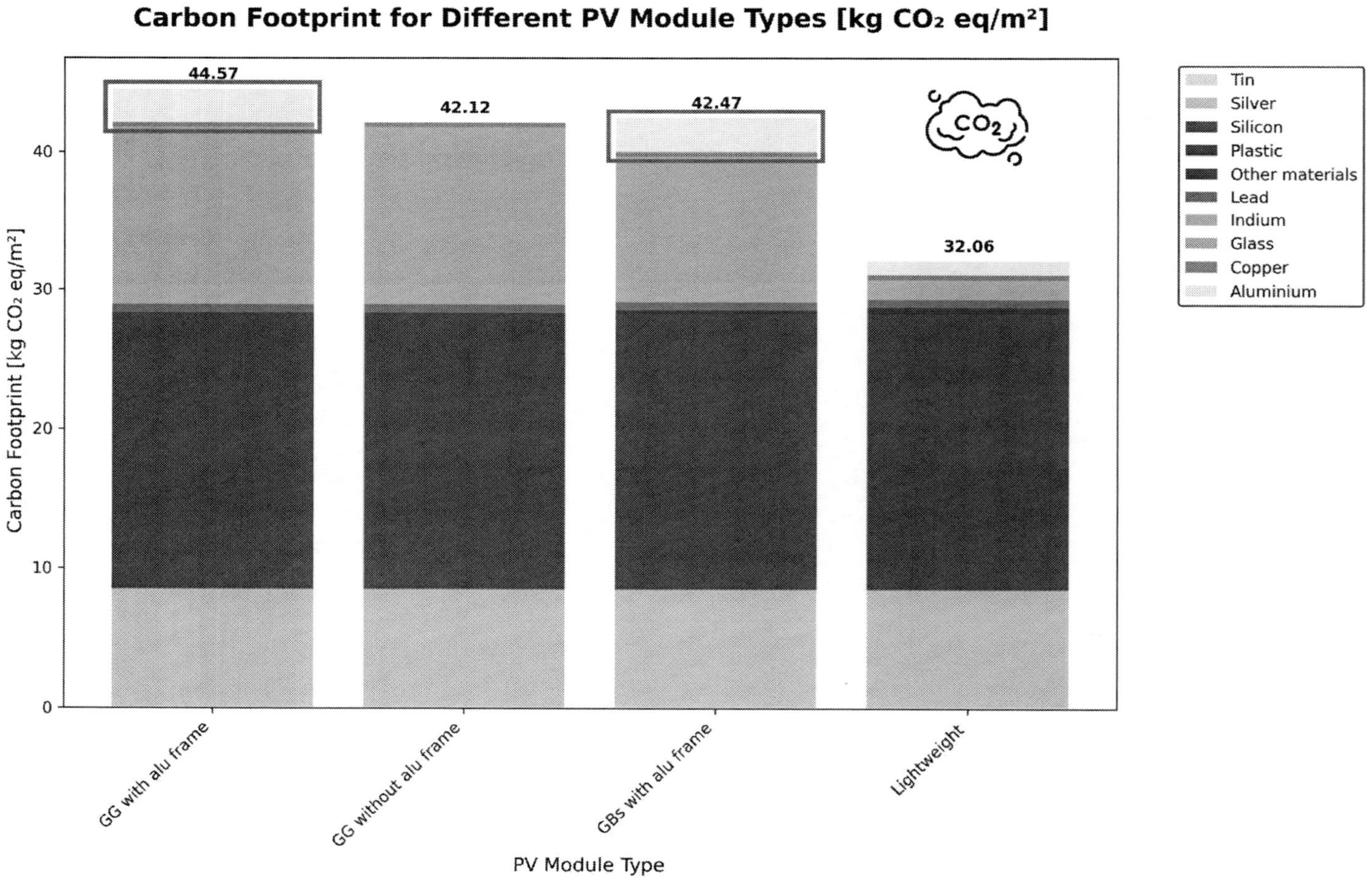

DECOMPOSITION OF ALUMINIUM CARBON FOOTPRINT

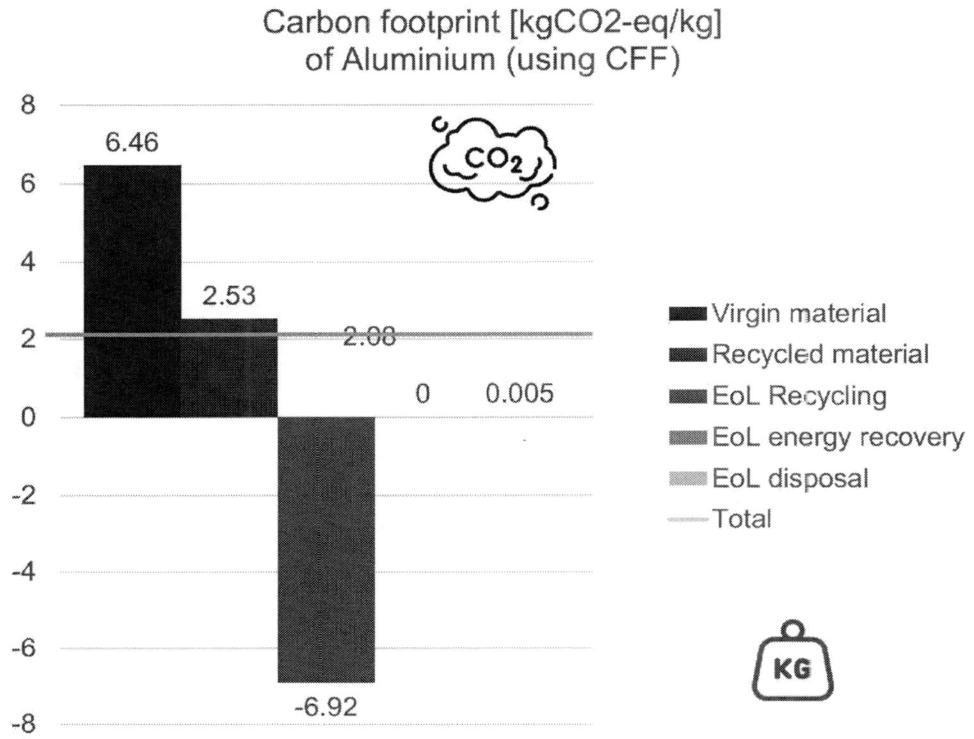

| EoL energy recovery | > Virgin material

- Important **recycled content** (R1 = 32%)
- **Massive recycling** (R2 = 95%)

- **Recycling has benefits (negative value)** by deleting the need of important quantities of virgin aluminium production

PARAMETER SENSITIVITY ANALYSIS WITH ALUMINIUM

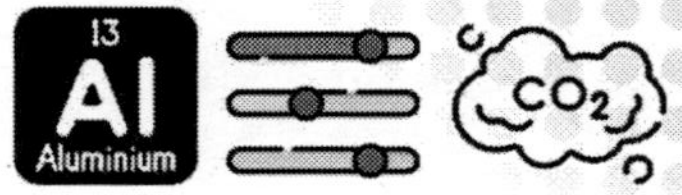

How the **carbon footprint** of 1kg of aluminium would change if **recycled content (R1) = 100%**?

What if **recycling rate (R2)** is reduced?

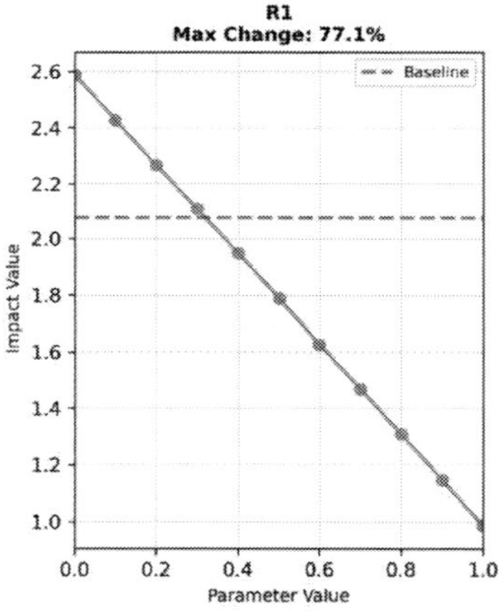

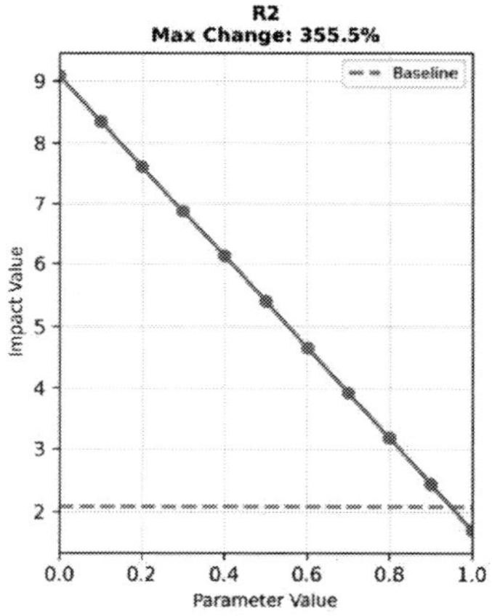

Baseline Parameters: A=0.20 | B=0.00 | R1=0.32 | R2=0.95
R3 (EU)=0.02 | Qs_in_Qp=1.00 | Qs_out_Qp=1.00

Sensitivity Analysis: Aluminum - Climate change (kg CO2 eq)
Baseline Impact: 2.076100

:: csem

PARAMETER SENSITIVITY ANALYSIS WITH ALUMINIUM

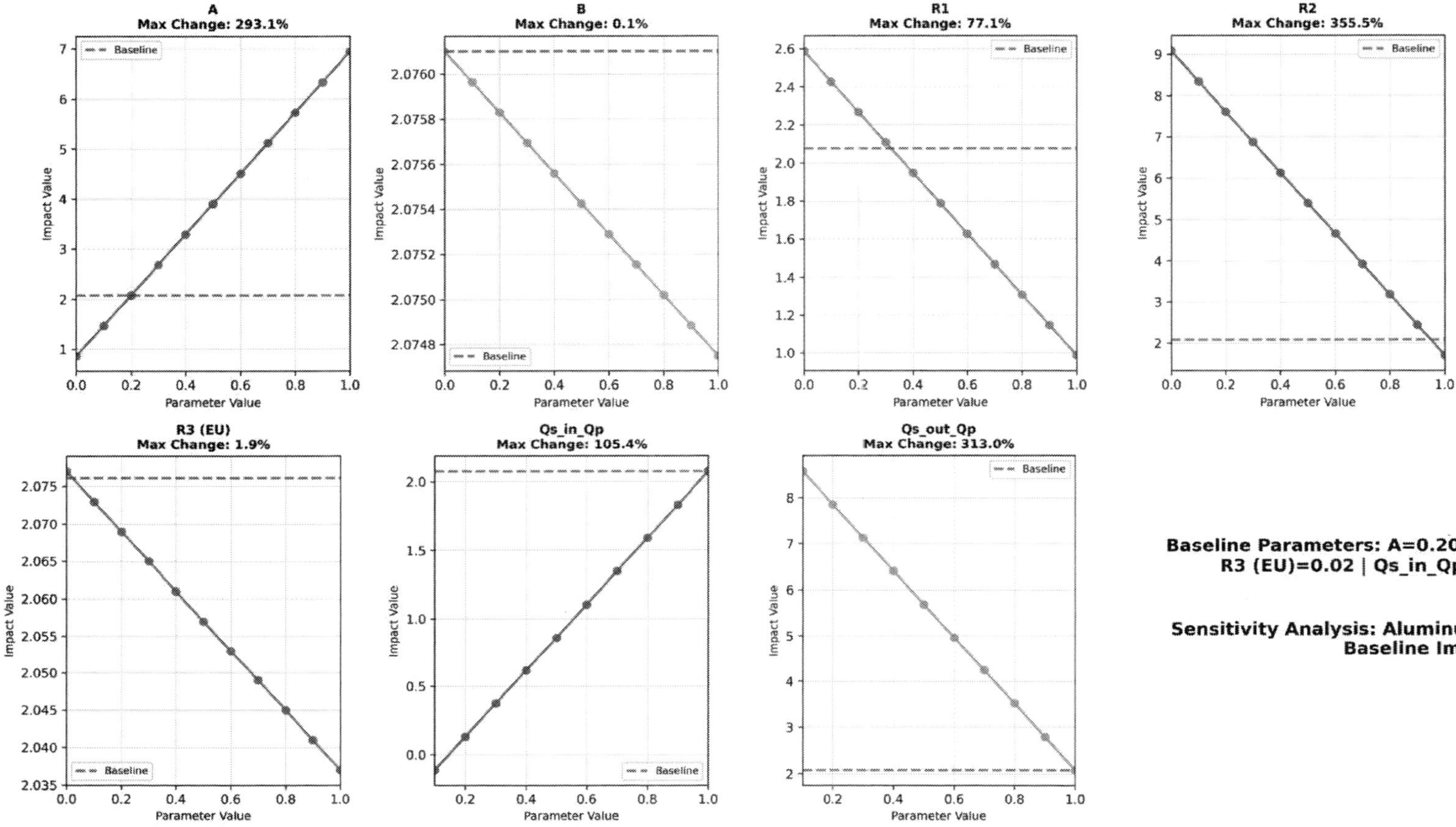

Baseline Parameters: A=0.20 | B=0.00 | R1=0.32 | R2=0.95
R3 (EU)=0.02 | Qs_in_Qp=1.00 | Qs_out_Qp=1.00

Sensitivity Analysis: Aluminum - Climate change (kg CO2 eq)
Baseline Impact: 2.076100

:: csem

ADVANTAGES, LIMITATIONS & NEXT STEPS

- **Advantages** of CFF:
  - Scenarios evaluation with parametric LCA
  - Decomposes material's environmental footprint along manufacturing & end-of-life
- **Inconvenients** of CFF:
  - Only focuses on materials' environmental footprint
  - Dependent of EF-compliant dataset for parameters & processes
  - LCA softwares do not always include parameters modelisation
- **Next steps & challenges**:
  - Implement the CFF in existing LCA software
  - Find up-to-date and accurate EF-compliant datasets
  - Establish link with other LCA methodologies: ex: EPD (EN15804) [1]

Parameter Process

$$(1 - R_1) * E_v$$

[1] Durao et al. Assessment and communication of the environmental performance of construction products in Europe

WRAP-UP

Circular footprint formula (CFF): $(1 - R_1) * E_v$

Parameter (R_1) — Process (E_v)

- **Is mandatory** to be PEF compliant, for **carbon footprint & ecodesign** regulations for PV [1]
- Has parameters & processes specific to a material used for a product
- Evaluates virgin and recycled materials **manufacturing** additionally to **end-of-life**
- Is useful to evaluate **circularity** or **recyclability** index for PV & how to reduce further the **environmental footprint of PV modules & systems**
- need **parameters** & **processes** EF-compliant datasets updates
- can be implemented in **LCA softwares** allowing parameters settings

[1] Joint Research Center, Ardente et al., Harmonised rules for the calculation of the carbon footprint of photovoltaic modules in the context of the EU Ecodesign Directive, 2025

Alexis Barrou , R&D Engineer, CSEM
alexis.barrou@csem.ch

EU PVSEC 2025
42nd European Photovoltaic Solar Energy Conference and Exhibition

42nd European Photovoltaic Solar Energy Conference and Exhibition

This presentation was selected by the Sc. Committee of the EU PVSEC 2025 for submission of a full paper to one of the EU PVSEC's collaborating peer-reviewed journals.

ENVIRONMENTAL BENEFITS OF SILICON KERF SECONDARY PRODUCTS IN PILOT PROCESSES OVER CONVENTIONAL PRODUCTION OF EQUIVALENT PRODUCTS WITH PRIMARY RAW MATERIALS IN CHINA AND EUROPE

René Peche, Matthias Seitz, Markus Schönheits, Karsten Wambach
bifa Umweltinstitut GmbH
Am Mittleren Moos 46, 86167 Augsburg, Germany

ABSTRACT: bifa Umweltinstitut GmbH is evaluating four pilot units newly developed in the ICARUS project for processing silicon kerf waste into secondary materials and marketable products and shows whether an ecological improvement compared to the conventional Chinese and European supply of functionally equivalent materials from primary raw material can be achieved. The evaluation is done using the method of life cycle assessment (LCA). The turning of PV waste silicon kerf into secondary raw materials or marketable products eliminates a large part of the environmental impact associated with the conventional production of equivalent raw materials or products. The reduction in environmental impact ranges from more than 85% for the production of secondary metallurgical grade and solar grade silicon compared to the conventional production in China over more than 75% for the production of secondary metallurgical grade and solar grade silicon compared to the conventional production in Europe to more than 30% for the production of hydrogen and water glass from silicon kerf waste compared to the conventional production in Europe. Thus, the newly developed processes in the ICARUS project not only reduce dependence on supplies from Asia, but also help to reduce harmful emissions into the environment during the production of raw materials.
Keywords: LCA; ecology index; secondary materials; silicon; recycling; PV modules

1 INTRODUCTION

In the ICARUS project, 17 European partners are collaborating to develop innovative methods for processing and refining secondary raw materials from silicon PV manufacturing. This involves transforming the process wastes Si-kerf waste, graphite waste and silica waste from silicon (Si)ingot and wafer production into valuable secondary resources (Figure 1).

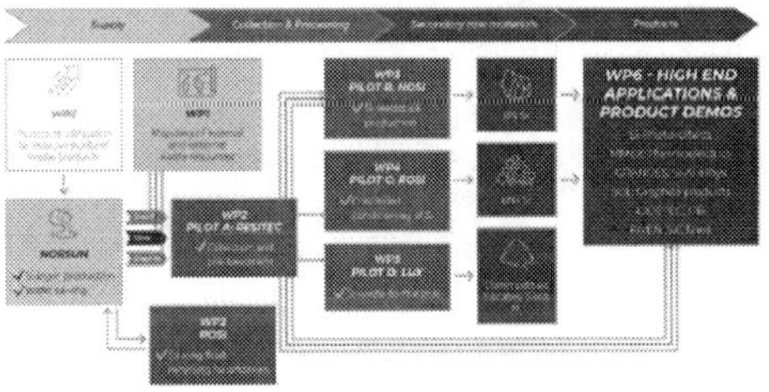

Figure 1: ICARUS project

For filtered Si-Kerf, which is produced during the diamond wire sawing of silicon blocks into wafers, four pilot processes have been developed and operated, demonstrating the relevance of the different technological options and bringing modularity in: (a) Si-kerf recycling and refining (PILOT A, B and C) considering different inputs and purity grades for diverse applications; and (b) revalorisation of Si (PILOT D), transforming Si-kerf into the valuable commodities green hydrogen and water glass. The energy intensity of silicon is strongly related to its purity. Therefore, the ICARUS project will take advantage of the silicon content of the kerf, invested with a lot of energy, and reuse it as secondary raw material. For example, reusing secondary silicon in wafer production can significantly reduce the high energy demands associated with processing primary raw Si into wafers, which accounts for about 75 % of the total energy used in PV module manufacturing.
The LCA conducted in the ICARUS project supports and quantifies the process developments.

2 METHOD

An LCA is a system analysis method for the integrated, media-wide acquisition and evaluation of environment-related matters in connection with products, processes and services. LCA are characterized by the analyses of environmental influences in association with prior or subsequent life cycle stages. Also considered here are inputs and withdrawals of raw materials and energy to and from environmental media, namely water, air and earth. Overall, LCA can make a comprehensive statement on the relevance to the environment of the systems investigated and are therefore optimally suited for environment-related comparison of various systems.

The LCA in the ICARUS project is carried out under the norm specifications for the execution of eco-balances DIN EN ISO 14040 [1] and DIN EN ISO 14044 [2], taken into account the Product Environmental Footprint Category Rules (PEFCR) for photovoltaic modules used in photovoltaic power systems for electricity generation [3,4]. Starting with the definition of goal and scope under the terms of the Life cycle inventory analysis, all relevant parameters are recorded and summarized in the life cycle impact assessment regarding their environmental impact. Figure 2 shows a schematic overview of the basic compilation of an LCA with fields of application.

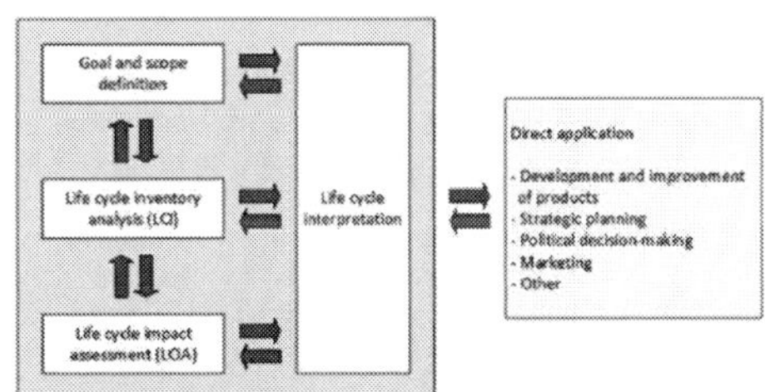

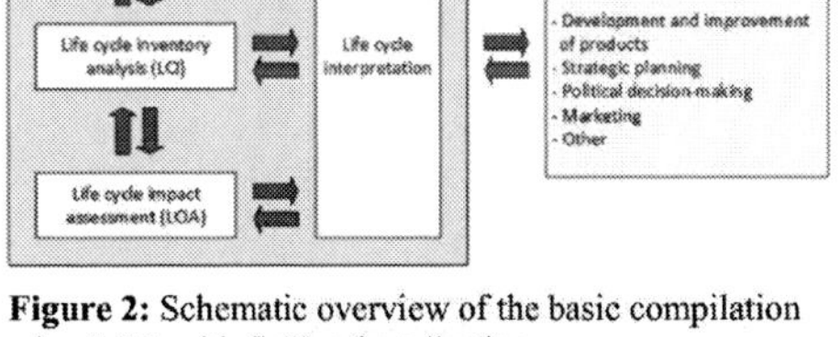

Figure 2: Schematic overview of the basic compilation of an LCA with fields of application

Table 1 shows the thirteen impact categories that are assessed and interpreted in the LCA of the ICARUS project.

Table 1: Applied environmental impact category used in the ICARUS project

Impact category	Unit
Climate change	kg CO_2 eq.
Ozon depletion	kg CF-11 eq.
Particulate matter	Disease Incidence
Ionizing radiation, human health	kBq U^{235} eq.
Photochemical ozone formation, human health	kg NMVOC eq.
Acidification	mole H^+ eq.
Eutrophication, terrestrial	mole N eq.
Eutrophication, freshwater	kg P eq.
Eutrophication, marine	kg N eq.
Land use	Pt
Water use	kg world eq. deprived
Resource use, minerals and metals	kg Sb eq.
Resource use, energy carriers	MJ

The individual results of the impact categories are combined using the normalization and weighting factors published by the European Commission's Joint Research Centre [5,6], to create a dimensionless single ecological indicator – the so-called ecology index.

3 RESULTS

Information and process data for the pilot processes are provided by the project partners. The Chinese and European production processes are modelled using data from IEA PVPS Task 12 [6] and ecoinvent database [7].

The data sets used together with the process data and information to create the LCA models also came from the ecoinvent database.

PILOT A process: Secondary dry silicon compared to conventional metallurgical grade silicon produced in China and Europe

The product of the pilot A process developed by project partner Resitec AS (Norway) is secondary dry silicon with less than 1% moisture. The starting material is filtered Si-kerf containing 47 % moisture from the silicon wafer sawing process.

The comparable conventional product is metallurgical grade silicon, produced from primary silica sand.

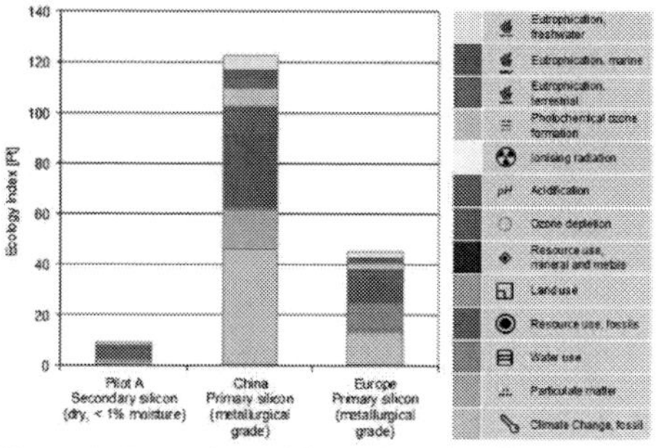

Figure 3: Comparison of the ecological indices of the pilot A process and the conventional production processes in China and Europe

Figure 3 demonstrates that secondary dry silicon has an ecological advantage of more than 90 % over conventional production of metallurgical grade silicon in China, and almost 80% compared to conventional production in Europe

The improved ecology index can be attributed primarily to the lower quantity of energy used in the pilot A process, and secondarily to the use of materials, which is significantly reduced compared to those used in the Chinese and European production processes.

For instance, the electricity consumption for the pilot A process is more than eight times lower than that required for the conventional production of metallurgical grade silicon. Furthermore, unlike the 2 conventional production processes the pilot A process does not require any thermal energy

PILOT B and PILOT C processes: Secondary silicon 6N+ and 8N compared to conventional solar grade silicon produced in China and Europe

The product of the pilot B process developed by project partner ROSI SAS (France) is secondary silicon of 8N purity and the product of the pilot C process developed by project partner Northern Silicon (Norway) is secondary silicon of 6N+ purity.

The comparable conventional product is solar grade silicon, produced from primary metallurgical grade silicon.

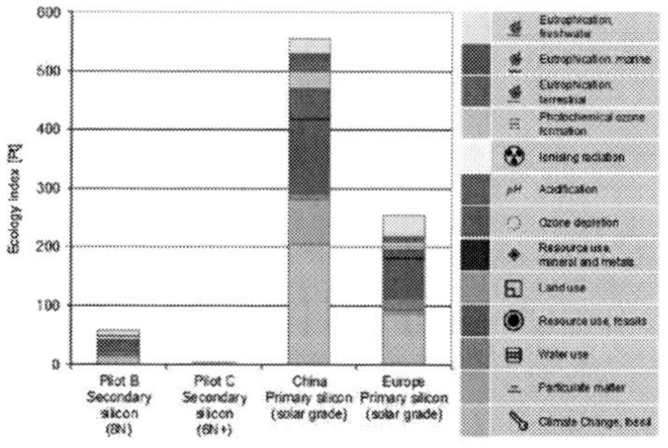

Figure 4: Comparison of the ecological indices of the pilot B and pilot C processes and the conventional production processes in China and Europe

Figure 4 shows that the secondary silicon 8N and 6N+ have an ecological advantage of more than 85 % over the conventional production of solar grade silicon in China and more than 75% over the conventional production in

10.4229/EUPVSEC2025/5CO.5.6

Europe.

The improved ecological indices are due to the same factors as described for pilot A process. The main reason is the lower quantity of energy used in the pilot processes. In addition, the consumption of primary materials is significantly lower compared to the conventional production processes because of the use of waste as a starting material.

PILOT D process: Hydrogen and water glass produced from silicon kerf compared to conventional hydrogen and sodium silicate produced in Europe

The products of the pilot D process developed by project partner LuxChemtech GmbH (Germany) are hydrogen and water glass. The starting material is the processed Si-kerf from the pilot A process.

In the conventional production processes of hydrogen (produced via the cracking of fossil fuels and chlor-alkali electrolysis) and water glass (produced from the furnace process), the starting materials are natural gas and the silica sand as well as soda ash, respectively.

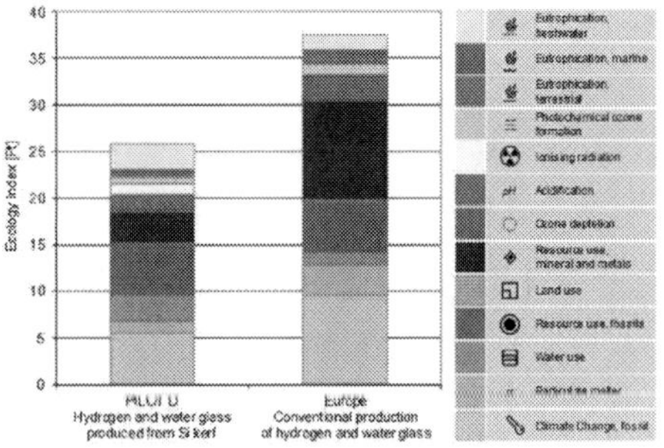

Figure 5: Comparison of the ecological indices of the pilot D process and the conventional production processes in Europe

Figure 5 shows that hydrogen and water glass produced from silicon kerf have an ecological advantage of more than 30 % over the conventional production of the two products in Europe.

The improved ecology index results from the reduction of primary raw materials and the lower consumption of fossil fuels, which are typically required for conventional hydrogen and water glass production.

4 DISCUSSION AND CONCLUSION

The turning of PV waste silicon kerf, which is energy-dense and rich in highly pure silicon, into secondary raw materials or marketable products eliminates a large part of the environmental impact associated with the conventional production of equivalent raw materials or products.

The reduction in environmental impact ranges from more than 85% for the production of secondary metallurgical grade and solar grade silicon compared to the conventional production in China over more than 75% for the production of secondary metallurgical grade and solar grade silicon compared to the conventional production in Europe to more than 30% for the production of hydrogen and water glass from silicon kerf waste compared to the conventional production in Europe.

Thus, the newly developed processes in the ICARUS project not only reduce dependence on supplies from Asia, but also help to reduce harmful emissions into the environment during the production of raw materials.

5 REFERENCES

[1] DIN EN ISO 14040:2021-02: Environmental management - Life cycle assessment - Principles and framework (ISO 14040:2006 + Amd 1:2020), Deutsches Institut für Normung DIN e.V.; 2021

[2] DIN EN ISO 14044:2021-02: Environmental management - Life cycle assessment - Requirements and guidelines (ISO 14044:2006 + Amd 1:2017 + Amd 2:2020), Deutsches Institut für Normung DIN e.V.; 2021

[3] Product Environmental Footprint Category Rules (PEFCR) for photovoltaic modules used in photovoltaic power systems for electricity generation. European Commission's Joint Research Centre - Institute for Environment and Sustainability; 2020

[4] JRC Technical Report - Updated characterisation and normalisation factors for the Environmental Footprint 3.1 method. European Commission's Joint Research Centre - Institute for Environment and Sustainability; 2023

[5] JRC Technical Reports - Development of a weighting approach for the Environmental Footprint. European Commission's Joint Research Centre - Institute for Environment and Sustainability; 2018

[6] Life Cycle Inventory and Life Cycle Assessments of Photovoltaic Systems. Report IEA-PVPS T12-19:2020, International Energy Agency; 2020

[7] Life cycle inventory database ecoinvent v3.8: https://www.ecoinvent.org, Zürich; 2021

6 ACKNOWLEDGEMENTS

This work has received funding from the European Union's Horizon 2020 research and innovation programme under grant agreement No 958365; project ICARUS.

Views and opinions expressed are however those of the authors only and do not necessarily reflect those of the European Union or CINEA. Neither the European Union nor the granting authority can be held responsible for them.

bifa
Umweltinstitut

EU PVSEC 2025

5CO.5.6

Bilbao, 24.09.2025

EU PVSEC 2025
42nd European Photovoltaic Solar Energy Conference and Exhibition

ICARUS project

Environmental Benefits of Silicon Kerf Secondary Products in Pilot Processes Over Conventional Production of Equivalent Products with Primary Raw Materials in China and Europe

René Peche, Matthias Seitz, Markus Schönheits, Karsten Wambach

www.bifa.de

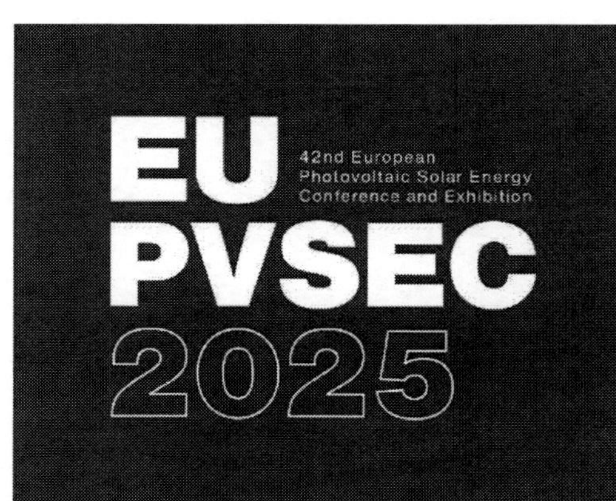

EU PVSEC 2025

bifa Umweltinstitut

bifa Umweltinstitut GmbH

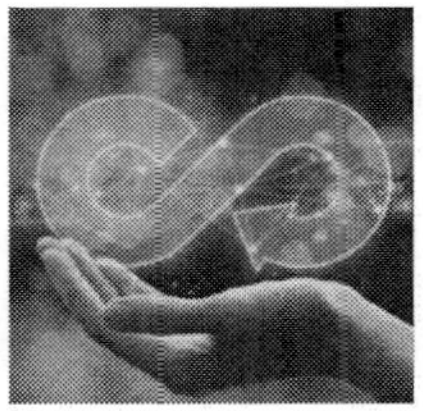

Application-orientated research, development and consulting facility

Our expertise:

- LCA, eco-efficiency analysis, LCC, TEA
- Recycling processes from laboratory to pilot plant scale
- Environmental Analytics
- Waste and circularity Assessment
- Recyclability and circularity Indices
- Ecodesign / design for recycling
- Social acceptance (workshops, surveys, interviews)

Recent and relevant EU Projects

ICARUS

smartline PV

PHOTORAMA

Quasar

24.09.2025

2

EU PVSEC 2025

bifa Umweltinstitut

Outline

1. **ICARUS project**
2. **Life Cycle Assessment (LCA)**
3. **Creation of the ecology index**
4. **Preliminary Results**
5. **Conclusion**

Source: https://www.icarus.eu.com

24.09.2025

3

EU PVSEC 2025

ICARUS project

bifa Umweltinstitut

Development of innovative methods for processing and refining secondary raw materials from silicon PV manufacturing

- 17 European partners
- ICARUS will demonstrate:
  - 3 innovative industrial pilots producing silicon, silica and graphite raw materials
  - 1 pilot converting silicon waste into full value industrial commodities
- **bifa's work package in the project:**
  - **Techno economic analysis**
  - **Life cycle assessment**
  - **Social acceptance**

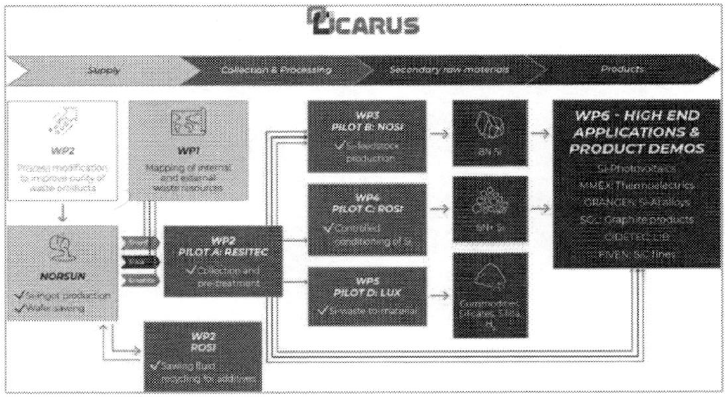

This project has received funding from the European Union's Horizon 2020 research and innovation programme under grant agreement No 958365

MARELLI, benkei, CHEMCONSERVE, LuxChemtech, ReSiTec, University of Cyprus, cea, NorSun, Grenoble INP UGA, bifa Umweltinstitut, GRÄNGES, SINTEF, FIVEN, cidetec energy storage, NORTHERN SILICON, sgl carbon, ROSI

24.09.2025

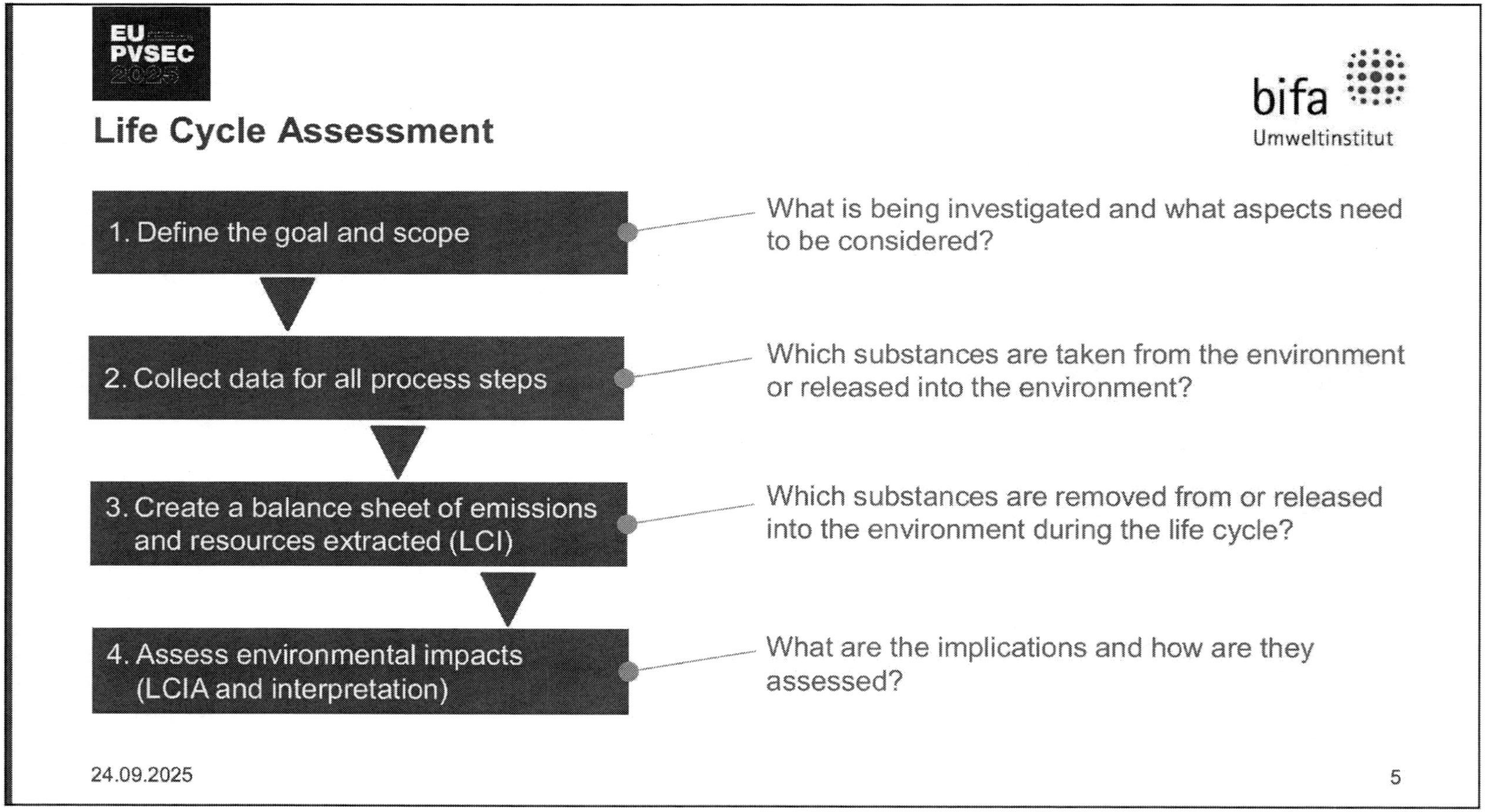
EU PVSEC 2025
Life Cycle Assessment
bifa Umweltinstitut
1. Define the goal and scope
What is being investigated and what aspects need to be considered?
2. Collect data for all process steps
Which substances are taken from the environment or released into the environment?
3. Create a balance sheet of emissions and resources extracted (LCI)
Which substances are removed from or released into the environment during the life cycle?
4. Assess environmental impacts (LCIA and interpretation)
What are the implications and how are they assessed?
24.09.2025
5

EU PVSEC 2025

Creation of the ecology index

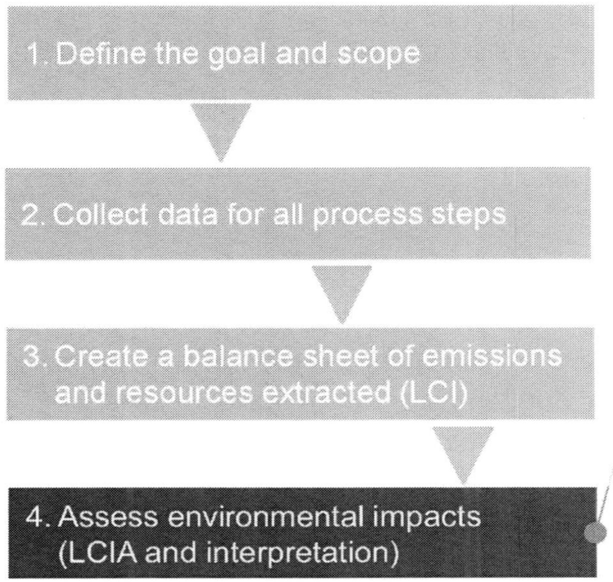

What are the implications and how are they assessed?

- Impact categories considered
  - Climate change
  - Resource use, energy carriers
  - Resource use, minerals and metals
  - Particulate matter
  - Acidification
  - Eutrophication, marine/freshwater and terrestrial
  - Photochemical ozone formation, human health
  - Land use
  - Water use
  - Ionizing radiation, human health
  - Ozon depletion

EU PVSEC 2025

bifa Umweltinstitut

Creation of the ecology index

Combination of individual LCA results (three-step process)

1. **Standardization:** Conversion of the individual results in the common reference unit of “population equivalents“
   - Basis → Normalisation factors in Environmental Footprint 3.1 (EF3.1)
   - Examples → Climate change: 7,550 kg CO_2 eq. / person
Acidification: 55.6 mol H^+ eq. / person
Resource use, fossils: 65 GJ / person
2. **Weighting:** Weighting of the individual impact categories
   - Basis → Weighting set for the standardized impact categories in EF3.1
   - Examples → Climate change: 22.19 %
Acidification: 6.64 %
Resource use, fossils: 8.92 %
3. **Combining:** Combining the weighted results to create the ecology index
   - Sum of the standardized, weighted impact indicator results to a dimensionless single value

24.09.2025 7

EU PVSEC 2025

bifa Umweltinstitut

PILOT A process: Secondary dry silicon

Comparison: ***Secondary*** *dry silicon with < 1% moisture from ICARUS vs.*
Conventional *metallurgical grade silicon (mg-Si) produced in China / Europe*

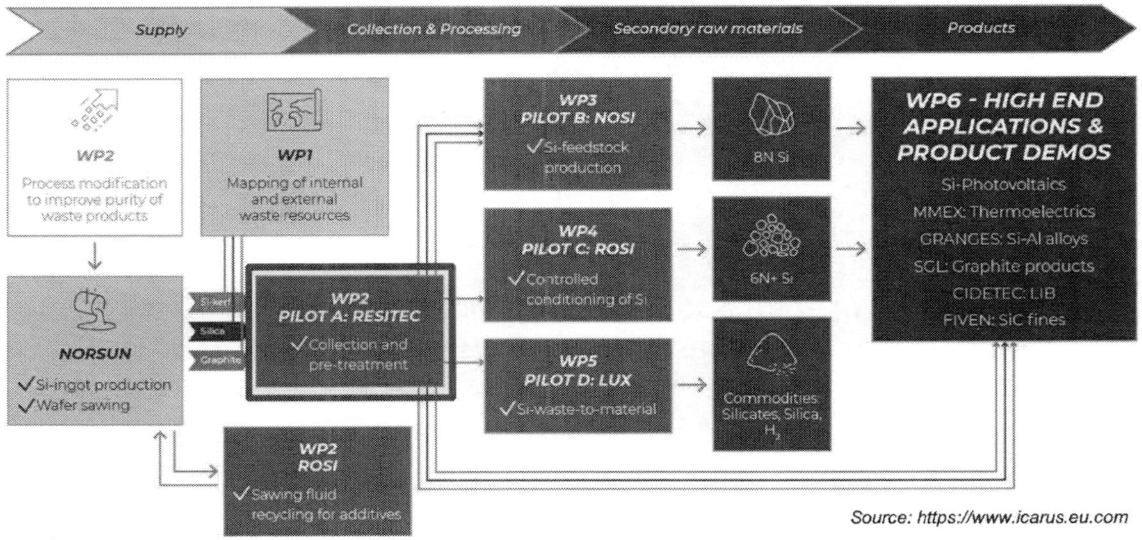

Source: https://www.icarus.eu.com

24.09.2025

8

EU PVSEC 2025

bifa Umweltinstitut

PILOT A process: Secondary dry silicon

Comparison: ***Secondary*** *dry silicon with < 1% moisture from ICARUS vs.*
Conventional *metallurgical grade silicon (mg-Si) produced in China / Europe*

PILOT A process:

- Starting material: filtered Si-kerf with 47% moisture from the wafer sawing process
- Process data: provided by project partner

Conventional processes in China/Europe:

- Starting material: primary silica sand
- Process data: IEA PVPS Task 12-19:2020 "LCI and LCA of Photovoltaic Systems"

24.09.2025

9

EU PVSEC 2025

bifa Umweltinstitut

PILOT A process: Secondary dry silicon

Comparison: ***Secondary*** *dry silicon with < 1% moisture from ICARUS vs.*
Conventional *metallurgical grade silicon (mg-Si) produced in China / Europe*

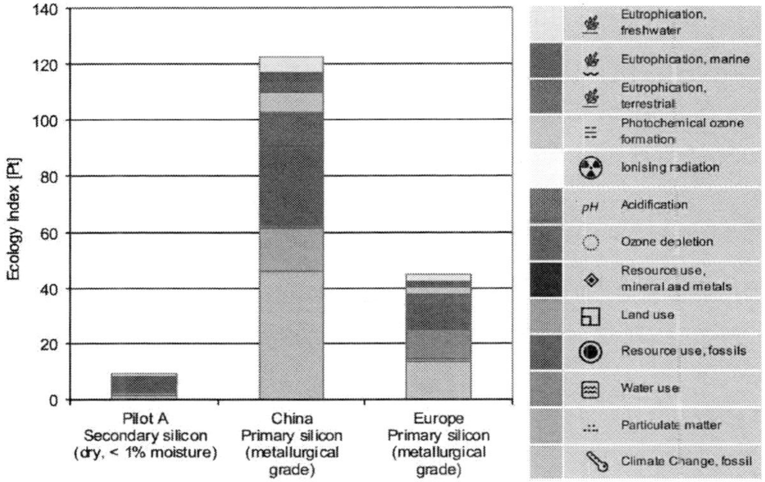

Ecological advantage of secondary dry silicon over primary mg-Si:

- China process: more than 90%
- Europe process: almost 80%

Main reasons for better result of Pilot A process:

- Electricity consumption is more than 8 times lower
- No thermal energy is required
- Starting material is the waste *silicon kerf* instead of the primary raw material *silica sand*

24.09.2025

10

EU PVSEC 2025

bifa Umweltinstitut

PILOT B/C processes: Secondary silicon 6N+ and 8N

Comparison: ***Secondary*** *silicon 6N+ and 8N from ICARUS vs.*
Conventional *solar grade silicon (sg-Si) produced in China / Europe*

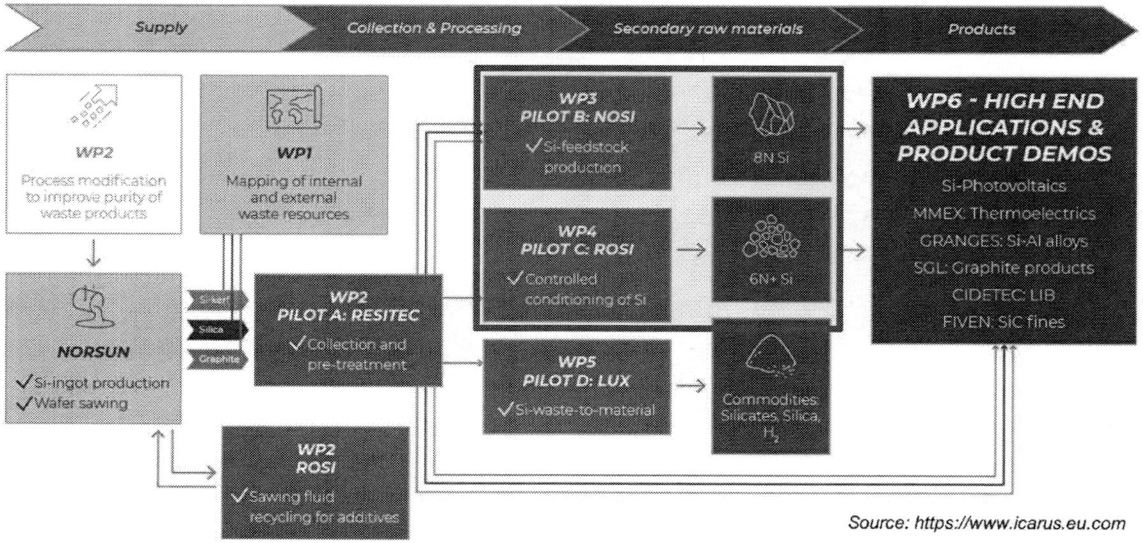

Source: https://www.icarus.eu.com

24.09.2025 11

EU PVSEC 2025

PILOT B/C processes: Secondary silicon 6N+ and 8N

bifa Umweltinstitut

Comparison: ***Secondary*** *silicon 8N and 6N+ from ICARUS vs.*
Conventional *solar grade silicon (sg-Si) produced in China / Europe*

PILOT B / PILOT C process:

- Starting material: secondary dry silicon with < 1% moisture from the Pilot A process
- Process data: provided by project partners

Conventional processes in China/Europe:

- Starting material: primary metallurgical grade silicon
- Process data: IEA PVPS Task 12-19:2020 "LCI and LCA of Photovoltaic Systems"

24.09.2025 12

EU PVSEC 2025

bifa Umweltinstitut

PILOT B/C processes: Secondary silicon 6N+ and 8N

Comparison: ***Secondary*** *silicon 6N+ and 8N from ICARUS vs.*
Conventional *solar grade silicon (sg-Si) produced in China / Europe*

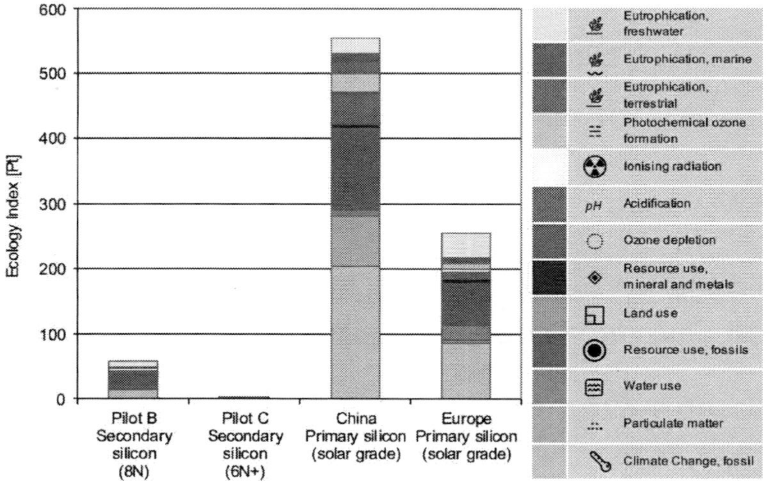

Ecological advantage of secondary silicon 6N+ and 8N over primary sg-Si:

- China process: more than 85%
- Europe process: more than 75%

Main reasons for better results of Pilot B/C processes:

- Electricity consumption is more than 4 times (Pilot B) or 46 times (Pilot C) lower
- No thermal energy is required
- Starting material is the waste *silicon kerf* instead of the primary raw material *mg-Si*

24.09.2025

13

EU PVSEC 2025

bifa Umweltinstitut

PILOT D process: Hydrogen and water glass

Comparison: ***Hydrogen and water glass*** *produced* ***from Si kerf*** *in ICARUS vs.*
Conventional hydrogen and sodium silicate *produced in Europe*

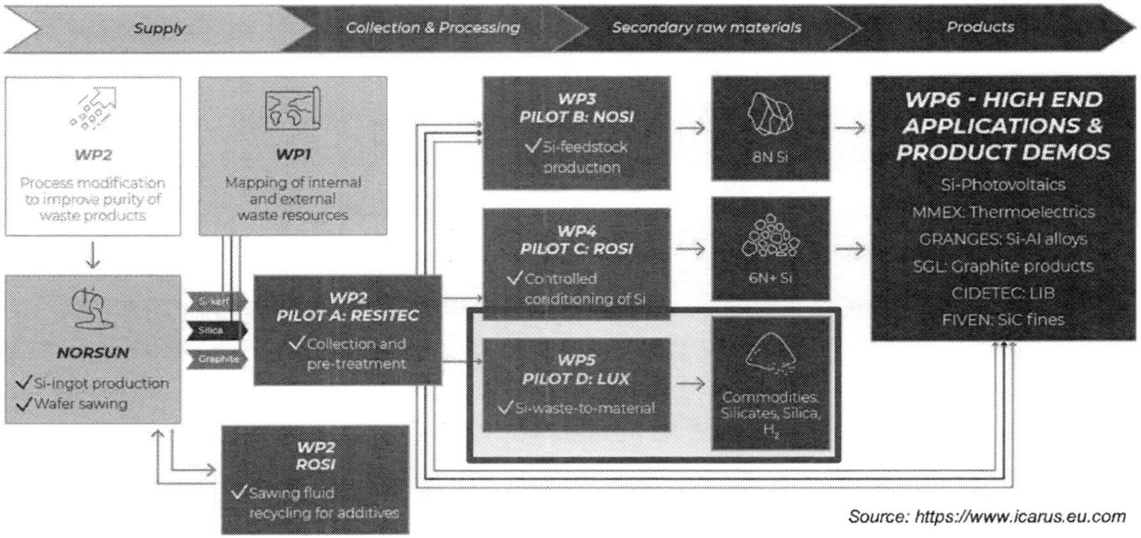

Source: https://www.icarus.eu.com

EU PVSEC 2025

bifa Umweltinstitut

PILOT D process: Hydrogen and water glass

Comparison: ***Hydrogen and water glass*** *produced* ***from Si kerf*** *in ICARUS vs.*
Conventional hydrogen and sodium silicate *produced in Europe*

PILOT D process:

- Starting material: secondary dry silicon with < 1% moisture from the Pilot A process
- Process data: provided by project partners

Conventional processes in Europe:

- Starting material: natural gas (hydrogen), silica sand and soda ash (water glass)
- Process data: ecoinvent data base v3.8

Detailed information about the process: **5DV.2.12 (25.09.2025 10:30-12:00 Poster Area)** *"Waste 2 Energy and Commodities – an Offbeat use of Silicon Kerf Loss and other Silicon-Based Waste with Amazing Side Effects"*

EU PVSEC 2025

bifa Umweltinstitut

PILOT D process: Hydrogen and water glass

Comparison: ***Hydrogen and water glass*** *produced* ***from Si kerf*** *in ICARUS vs.* ***Conventional hydrogen and sodium silicate*** *produced in Europe*

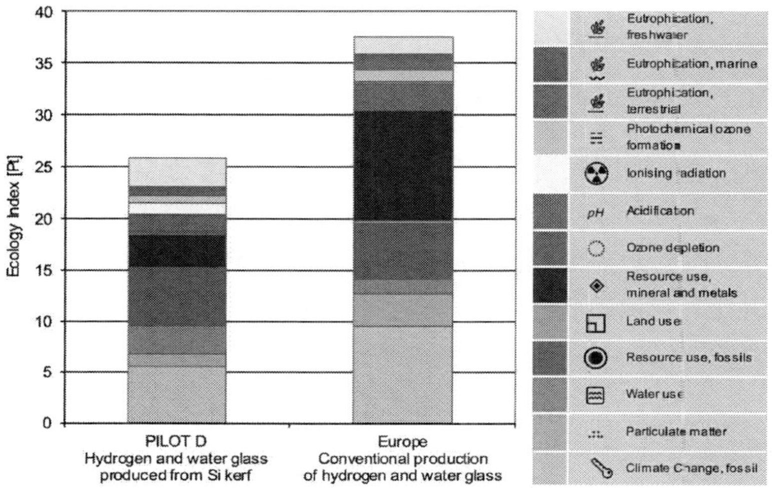

Ecological advantage of hydrogen and water glass produced from Si kerf:

- Europe process: more than 30%

Main reasons for better results of Pilot D process:

- Electricity consumption is more than 10 times lower
- Starting material is the waste *silicon kerf* instead of the primary raw materials *natural gas, petroleum* and *naphtha* (hydrogen) or *silica sand* and *soda ash* (water glass)

Detailed information about the process: **5DV.2.12 (25.09.2025 10:30-12:00 Poster Area)** *"Waste 2 Energy and Commodities – an Offbeat use of Silicon Kerf Loss and other Silicon-Based Waste with Amazing Side Effects"*

24.09.2025

EU PVSEC 2025

Conclusion

bifa Umweltinstitut

- The turning of PV waste, rich in highly pure Si and energy-dense, into a secondary raw material eliminates a large part of the environmental impact associated with the conventional production of equivalent primary raw materials.
- Compared to conventional production
  - → of mg- and sg-silicon in China by more than 85%
  - → of mg- and sg-silicon in Europe by more than 75%
  - → of hydrogen and water glass in Europe by more than 30%
- Thus, the newly developed processes in the ICARUS project not only reduce dependence on supplies from Asia, but also help to reduce harmful emissions into the environment during the production of raw materials.

24.09.2025 17

EU PVSEC 2025

Thank you for your attention!

bifa Umweltinstitut

This work has received funding from the European Union's Horizon 2020 research and innovation programme under grant agreement No 958365; project ICARUS. Views and opinions expressed are however those of the authors only and do not necessarily reflect those of the European Union or CINEA. Neither the European Union nor the granting authority can be held responsible for them.

Funded by the European Union

bifa Umweltinstitut GmbH
Am Mittleren Moos 46
86167 Augsburg

René Peche
Tel. +49 821 7000-186
rpeche@bifa.de
www.bifa.de

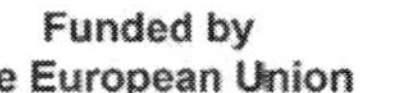

More info:

QUANTIFICATION OF TECHNICAL RECYCLABILITY OF PV MODULES FOR DIFFERENT RECYCLING SCENARIOS

Matthias Hämmer, Kerstin Baumann, Karsten Wambach, Markus Schönheits
bifa Umweltinstitut GmbH
Am Mittleren Moos 46, 86167 Augsburg, Germany

ABSTRACT: In the context of recyclability indices, the highest quality in calculating the recyclability values should be aimed for. Additionally, such high-quality calculations are also of fundamental interest in design for recycling in order to both quantify the status-quo and to monitor potential improvements. Calculations to quantify the recyclability of PV products are standardized by EN 45555. These calculations require detailed material specific recycling rate data for the relevant recycling processes. Frequently, there is lack of such data. Further, these calculations do not discriminate by the quality of recycling. Both challenges, the lack of recycling rate data and the lack of information about recycling quality, undermining the informative value of recyclability results are addressed in this paper. The recycling rate database recently presented by some of the authors is expanded and applied to PV module recycling. Moreover, the typical classification into "recycled" and "lost" is expanded by introducing four recycling categories including the assessment which recycled material can be used in the production of new PV modules. The technical recyclability of exemplary PV modules is calculated for five recycling scenarios ranging from 18% in worst-case mechanical recycling to 80% in advanced recycling facilities.
Keywords: recycling; recyclability; PV modules; ecodesign; circularity

1 INTRODUCTION

In the context of product labelling in EU ecodesign regulation and related aspects within the policy-making process in Europe, the labelling of a product's recyclability in the form of recyclability indices or as part of the digital product passport are extensively discussed [1]. This includes photovoltaic products, i.e. PV modules and inverters [2]. Right now, respective indices are being developed [3]. Naturally, for labelling, high-quality recyclability calculations should be aimed for. To quantify the recyclability of PV products, calculations can be made according to EN 45555 "General methods for assessing the recyclability and recoverability of energy related products" [4]. Yet, these calculations are hampered by the lack of material specific data for the relevant material recovery processes. EN 45555 allows the use of the so-called simplified method when data is missing. Then, unknown material recoverability factors are estimated to be either 1 or 0. Depending on the assumptions made during the simplified method, this yields recyclability values that are either much too small or much too high. Going from such potential recyclability to a more realistic assessment is often difficult due to a lack of data [5]. The recycling rates calculated according to EN 45555 can be considered technical recyclability [6]. Often, theoretical recyclability values are reported by PV module manufacturers. Theoretical recyclability is limited to the material choice and its recyclability properties. Technical recyclability also considers the practical waste quality and treatment, dismantling, size reduction and sorting and – most importantly - the existence of dedicated recycling processes. For the real recyclability, additionally, the aspect of collection as well as the market situation for the secondary raw output materials have to be considered. The differences between theoretical, technical and real recyclability are summarized in Fig. 1.

Besides recyclability indices and respective labelling, the calculation of technical recyclability of PV modules is also relevant as an ecodesign tool for comparison of various PV modules as well as for the quantitative comparison of recycling scenarios and technologies. Finally, such results enable realistic estimates of secondary raw material production per waste volume input – an essential part of any business plan for PV module recycling companies.

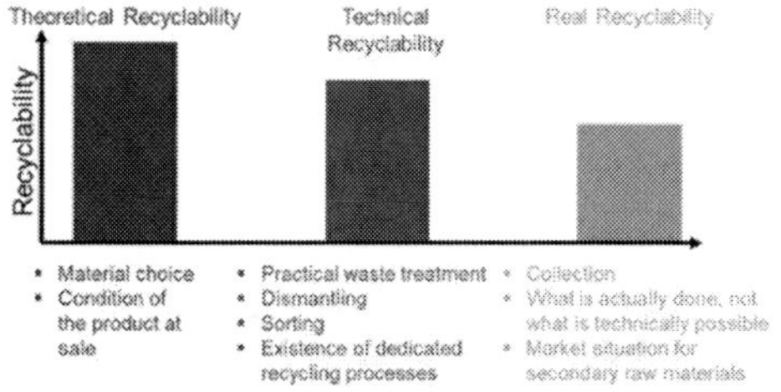

Figure 1: Comparison of the three types of recyclability according to [6]: Going from left to right the respective aspects are considered, additionally.

2 METHODS

Commonly, there are two challenges in calculating the technical recyclability according to EN 45555: the lack of (material specific) recycling rate data and the lack of consideration of recycling quality, e.g. downcycling, upcycling and other recycling varieties. Both challenges were addressed in our previous work [7]. Herein, the assessment is adjusted to PV modules using both literature data for various delamination [8-10] and downstream treatment options [7,8,10-12] and pilot line batch test data [10]. Available data for these calculations is scarce and its public availability is even more restricted. To the best of our knowledge, no similar recycling rate database for PV module recycling exists, so far.

Further, the four categories "circular", "recycled", "alternative material recovery" and "lost" are introduced discriminating by the quality of recycling. The "circular" recycling rate describes the rate of recovered material which can be used for the substitution of corresponding virgin material in the production of new PV modules. The "recycled" recycling rate describes the rate of recovered material which can substitute virgin material outside the PV industry. In other words, the category "circular" refers to closed-loop and the category "recycled" to open-loop recycling. The "alternative material recovery" rate describes the rate of material which can replace virgin materials that are not identical to the recovered materials. This includes so-called downcycling, e.g. solar glass recycled in the form of foam glass or slag in road construction. Materials are considered "lost" if they are used for energy recovery or landfilled. The recovery of ashes from waste incineration is neglected.

The discrimination by the quality of recycling enables the assessment which recycled material can be used in the production of new PV modules and, thus, the quantification of the circularity of the PV module value chain. At present, this applies only to recycled material assigned to the "circular" category. This highlights the relevance of the present work for circularity assessments for PV modules. For this study, the circular category's materials are Ag, Cu and Si.

As an example, an average c-Si Al-BSF glass-foil PV module [10] and five different recycling scenarios are considered for the technical recyclability calculations. Table I shows the bill-of-material for the PV module.

Table I: Bill of material for average c-Si Al-BSF glass-foil PV module [10]

Component	Material	wt.-%
Frame	Al	13.1
Cables	Cu	0.2
Cables	Polymer	0.4
Junction Box	Cu	0.3
Junction Box	Polymer	0.6
Glass	Glass	70.4
Encapsulant	EVA	6.5
Backsheet	PVF	2.8
Cells	Si	4.4
Cells	Ag	0.1
Cells	Al	0.3
Interconnectors	Cu	0.9

The five end-of-life scenarios are

S1: Worst-case recycling treatment by non-specialized glass recyclers [9]
S2: State-of-the-art dedicated mechanical recycling [8]
S3: Advanced recycling using pyrolysis delamination [8]
S4: Advanced recycling using water-jet delamination [8]
S5: PHOTORAMA pilot line recycling [10]

The respective flow charts for the five scenarios are shown in Fig. 2 to 6. All scenarios include dismantling, i.e. the removal of frame, cables and junction box prior to the processing of the PV module's laminate as mandatory in the EU according to the WEEE directive [13] and respective national or local legislation. The five scenarios differ as well in the used delamination technique and the downstream treatment as in their technology readiness levels (TRL). S1 and S2 include mechanical treatment for delamination and run at industrial scale (TRL 9). In S3, pyrolysis is used for delamination and S4 and S5 utilize the water-jet technology. The materials silicon and silver from the solar cells are recovered in S3, S4 and S5, only. All three, S3, S4 and S5, are at pilot scale (TRL 7). Further relevant differences in process steps are discussed with the results in the subsequent section. All five recycling scenarios comply with the WEEE directive. Further, waste inputs comprising solely of intact, i.e. non-broken PV modules is assumed. The set of recycling scenarios is not intended to be exhaustive representing exemplary end-of-life options.

In line with EN45555, the yields of downstream processes like smelting are included in the calculations as indicated by the system boundaries shown in dashed blue in Fig. 2 to 6.

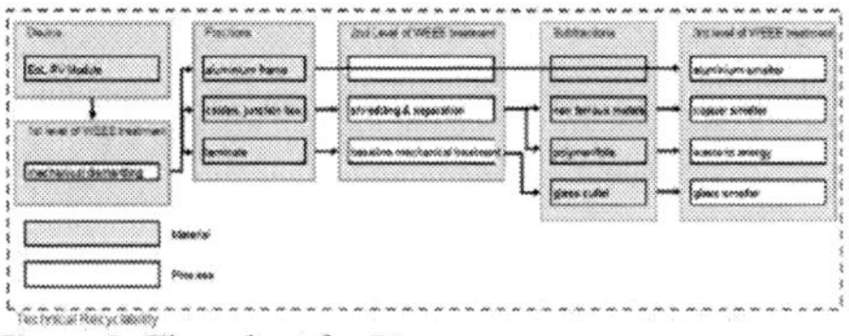

Figure 2: Flow sheet for S1

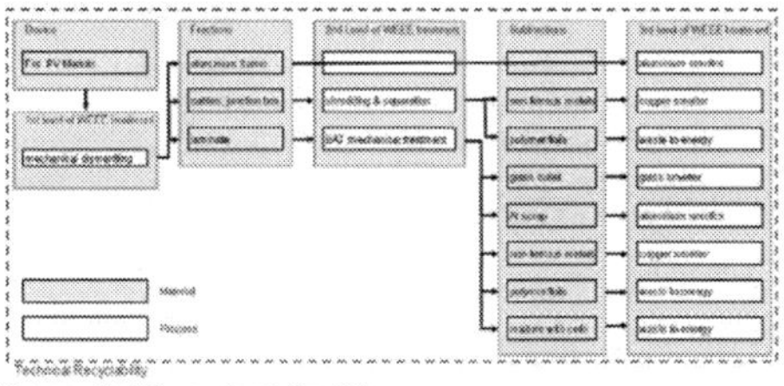

Figure 3: Flow sheet for S2

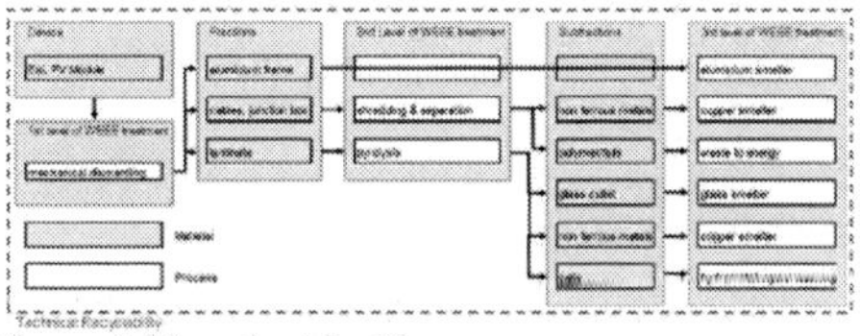

Figure 4: Flow sheet for S3

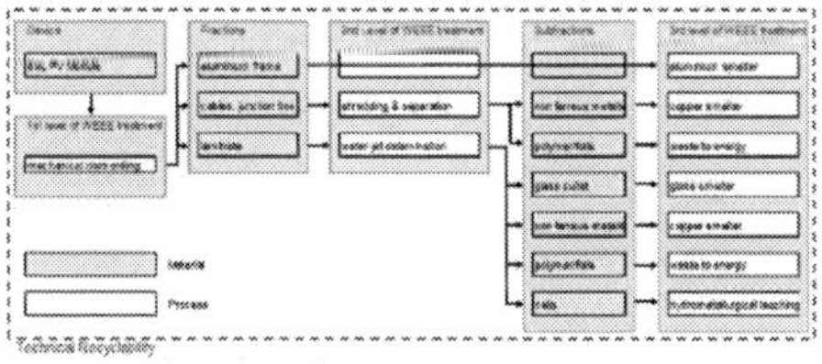

Figure 5: Flow sheet for S4

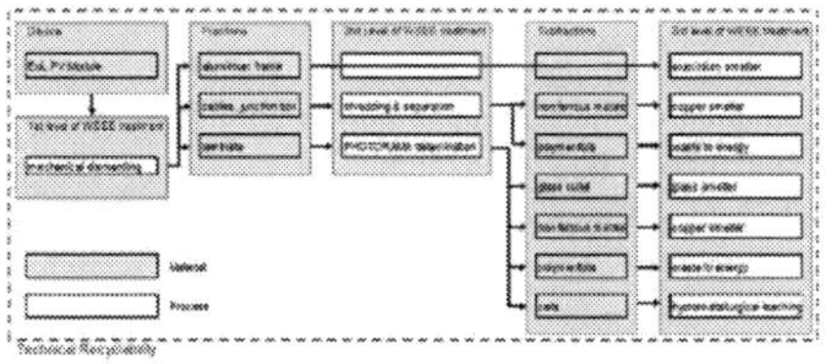

Figure 6: Flow sheet for S5

3 RESULTS

The technical recyclability results are shown in Fig. 7. They range from 18.1% for the worst-case scenario when the module is recycled by non-specialized glass recyclers to 80.2% for the PHOTORAMA pilot line.

In S1, following dismantling, the laminate is shredded and only glass is recovered. Thus, the materials aluminum from the frame, copper from the cables and junction box as well as glass from the laminate are recovered with rather

10.4229/EUPVSEC2025/5CO.6.4

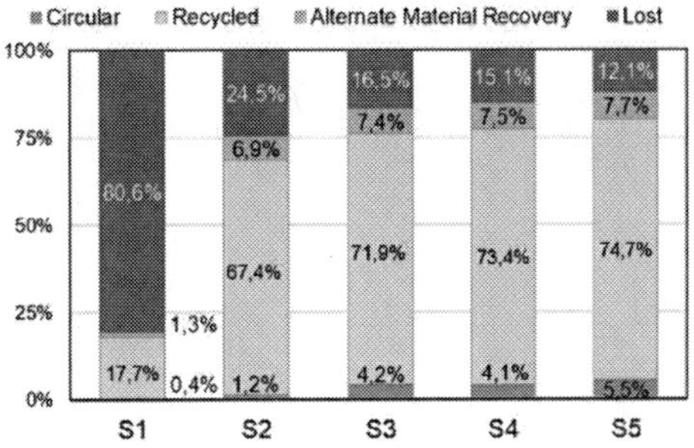

Figure 7: Technical recyclability results for five recycling scenarios for average c-Si Al-BSF glass-foil PV module on module level. For more details, see main text.

low process yields. In total, this results a technical recyclability of 18.1% with merely 0.4% in the circular category. S1 can be considered worst-case formal recycling of PV modules in the EU. In S2, mechanical delamination is performed, too. However, using state-of-the-art separation and sorting technology non-ferrous metals are recovered from the laminate fraction, too, and the mechanical treatment exhibits higher yields. In sum, this results in a technical recyclability of 68,6% with 1.2% in the circular category.

The remaining scenarios (S3-S5) include more advanced delamination techniques instead of mechanical treatment. However, this is accompanied by reduced - TRL. S1 and S2 can be considered industrial scale with TRL 9 while S3 to S5 reach TRL 7.

In S3, delamination using pyrolysis is performed. Further, dedicated hydrometallurgical downstream treatment enables the recovery of silicon and silver from the solar cells. Overall, the technical recyclability reaches 76.1% with 4.2% in the circular category. S4 utilizes water-jet delamination and state-of-the-art hydrometallurgical downstream treatment for silicon and silver recovery yielding a technical recyclability of 77.4% with 4.1% circular share. Finally, S5 representing the PHOTORAMA pilot line includes an improved combination of diamond wire and water-jet delamination together with optimized hydrometallurgical downstream treatment for silicon and silver extraction. In total, this results in a technical recyclability of 80.2% with 5.5% in the circular category.

The differences between the five recycling scenarios becomes even more obvious on the material (Fig. 8) or fraction level (Fig. 9).

Fig. 8 shows the material specific technical recyclability values for silicon and silver. These results emphasize the improvements in S5. Moreover, Fig. 9 depicts the technical recyclability values on the fraction level of the laminate fraction, i.e. excluding the frame, the cables and the junction box. The scenarios do not differ in the treatment of the excluded fractions. When comparing the technical recyclability results on the laminate fraction's level underlines the importance of delamination since the major differences in recyclability can be found in the laminate fraction.

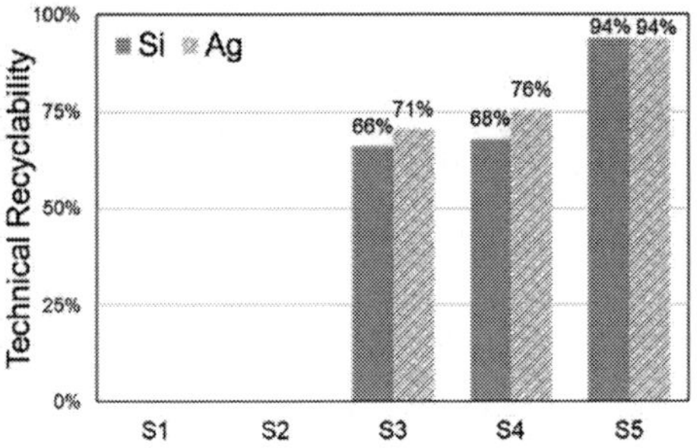

Figure 8: Technical recyclability results for five recycling scenarios for average c-Si Al-BSF glass-foil PV module on material level for silicon and silver. For more details, see main text.

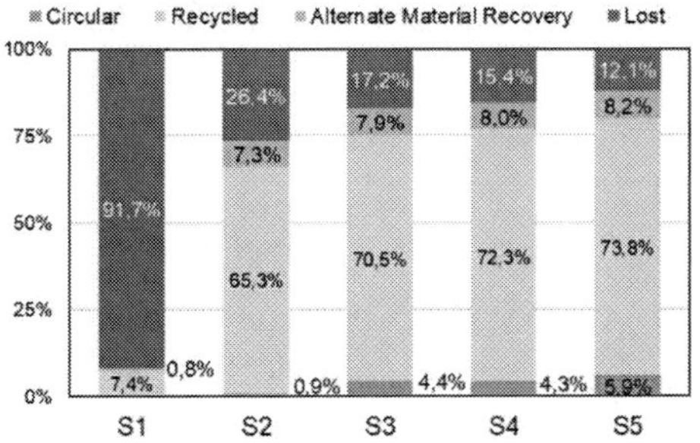

Figure 9: Technical recyclability results for five recycling scenarios for average c-Si Al-BSF glass-foil PV module on fraction level for the laminate fraction. For more details, see main text.

4 DISCUSSION AND CONCLUSION

As shown above, it is readily possible to quantitatively calculate the technical recyclability of PV modules using the database and methodology presented herein. Such calculations can be applied as an ecodesign tool to compare different PV modules, in recycling technology development to benchmark different recycling approaches as well as in economic assessments by realistically estimating secondary raw material production from PV module recycling.

Thus, it is possible to go from merely material-based theoretical recyclability values to more realistic technical recycling rates. When doing so, it is crucial to ensure the comparability of different results by disclosing the respective end-of-life scenario's details and to use identical system borders. Further, the discrimination between closed-loop and open-loop recycling via the categories "circular" and "recycled" is relevant for overall circularity assessments of PV modules. The result that even the best-case scenario barely exceeds 5% circular share - that means only 5% of the material reaching the end-of-life will have a "second life" in PV modules - highlights the room for improvements in the design for circularity and recycling infrastructure.

Beyond the current work, extended batch tests to be performed in the QUASAR project are expected to even further increase the recycling rate data quality for the two PV module recycling pilots in the QUASAR project using pyrolysis and water-jet delamination.

10.4229/EUPVSEC2025/5CO.6.4

5 REFERENCES

[1] Regulation (EU) 2024/1781, Ecodesign for Sustainable Products Regulation (ESPR): latest consolidated vers.: 2024-06-28, **2024**.
[2] D. Polverini, F. Alfieri, C. Spiliotopoulos, A. Arcipowska, *Prog Photovolt Res Appl.* **2024**, 1-9. doi: 10.1002/pip.3781.
[3] VIEGAND MAAGØE A/S, *Interim Report - Technical Support for the Development of a Recyclability Index for Photovoltaic Products Specific Contract No CINEA/2023/OP/0007/ SI2.906326*, **2024**.
[4] EN 45555:2020, *General methods for assessing the recyclability and recoverability of energy-related products*, **2020**.
[5] P. M. Mählitz, N. Korf, G. Chryssos, V. S. Rotter, *J of Industrial Ecology* **2022**, *26*, 1061–1077.
[6] R. Pomberger, A. Bezama, *Waste Manag Res* **2024**, *42*, 713–714.
[7] M. Hämmer, K. Wambach, *Sustainability* **2024**, *16*, 8726.
[8] K. Wambach, C. Libby, S. Shaw, *Advances in Photovoltaic Module Recycling: Literature Review and Update to Empirical Life Cycle Inventory Data and Patent Review*, Report IEA-PVPS T12-28:2024, **2024**.
[9] F. Ardente, C. E. L. Latunussa, G. A. Blengini, *Waste Management* **2019**, *91*, 156.
[10] M. Seitz, R. Steber, K. Baumann, M. Hämmer, PHOTORAMA Deliverable D5.5, **2025**, *unpublished.*
[11] C. E. Latunussa, F. Ardente, G. A. Blengini, L. Mancini, *Solar Energy Materials and Solar Cells* **2016**, *156*, 101.
[12] B. Huang, J. Zhao, J. Chai, B. Xue, F. Zhao, X. Wang, *Solar Energy* **2017**, *143*, 132.
[13] Directive 2012/19/EU; Waste Electrical and Electronic Equipment (WEEE): Latest Consolidated Vers.: 2024-04-08. European Union: Brussels, Belgium, **2024**.

6 ACKNOWLEDGEMENTS

This work has received funding from the European Union's Horizon 2020 research and innovation programme under grant agreement No 958223; project PHOTORAMA and from the European Union's Horizon Europe research and innovation programme under Grant Agreement No 101122298; project QUASAR. Views and opinions expressed are however those of the authors only and do not necessarily reflect those of the European Union or CINEA. Neither the European Union nor the granting authority can be held responsible for them.

EU PVSEC 2025

5CO.6.4

Bilbao, 24.09.2025

Quantification of Technical Recyclability of PV modules for different recycling scenarios

Matthias Hämmer, Kerstin Baumann, Karsten Wambach, Markus Schönheits

bifa Umweltinstitut

EU PVSEC 2025
42nd European Photovoltaic Solar Energy Conference and Exhibition

PHOTORAMA

Quasar

www.bifa.de

EU PVSEC 2025

bifa Umweltinstitut GmbH

bifa Umweltinstitut

Application-orientated research, development and consulting facility

Our expertise:

- LCA, eco-efficiency analysis, LCC, TEA
- Recycling processes from laboratory to pilot plant scale
- Environmental Analytics
- Waste and circularity Assessment
- Recyclability and circularity Indices (EN4555x and ISO590xx)
- Ecodesign / design for recycling
- Social acceptance (workshops, surveys, interviews)

Recent and relevant EU Projects

ICARUS

smartline PV

PHOTORAMA

Quasar

EU PVSEC 2025

bifa Umweltinstitut

Outline

1. Motivation
2. Methodology
3. Technical Recyclability Results
4. Conclusion

Ms Tech | Pixel Squid, https://www.technologyreview.com/2021/08/19/1032215/solar-panels-recycling/ (19.09.2022)

EU PVSEC 2025

Motivation

bifa Umweltinstitut

Technical recyclability of PV modules is relevant for

- Recyclability indices
- Ecodesign / design for recycling
- Comparison of PV modules (input)
- Comparison of PV module recycling technologies (output)
- Quantification of secondary raw material production

EU PVSEC 2025

bifa Umweltinstitut

Methodology

Theoretical Recyclability | Technical Recyclability | Real Recyclability

Theoretical Recyclability
- Material choice
- Condition of the product at sale

Technical Recyclability
- Practical waste treatment
- Dismantling
- Sorting
- Existence of dedicated recycling processes

Real Recyclability
- Collection
- What is actually done, not what is technically possible
- Market situation for secondary raw materials

Pomberger, R. *Österr Wasser- und Abfallw* **2021**, *73*, 24–35.
Pomberger, R.; Bezama, A. *Waste Manag.* Res. **2024**, *42*, 713–714.

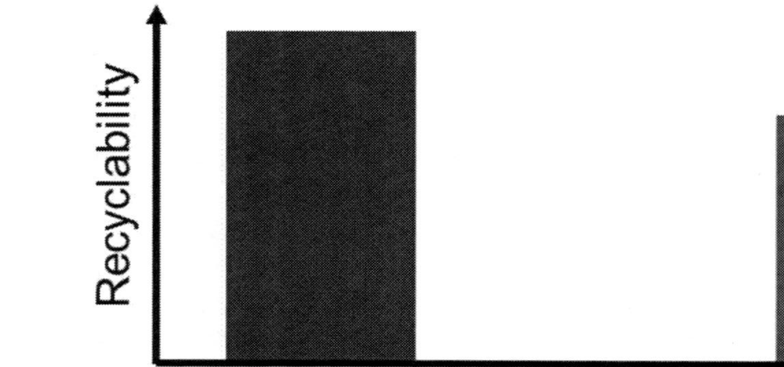

EU PVSEC 2025

Methodology

bifa Umweltinstitut

EN45555 describes calculation of technical recyclabilty

$$R = \frac{\sum_{k=1}^{n}(m_k \cdot R_k)}{m_{tot}}$$

n	number of materials
m_k	mass of material k
R_k	recyclability factor of material k
m_{tot}	total mass of device

Calculation for each step and each material.

EN 45555:2020, *General methods for assessing the recyclability and recoverability of energy-related products*, **2020**.

EU PVSEC 2025

Methodology

EN45555 describes calculation of technical recyclabilty

$$R = \frac{\sum_{k=1}^{n} (m_k \cdot R_k)}{m_{tot}}$$

n	number of materials
m_k	mass of material k
R_k	recyclability factor of material k
m_{tot}	total mass of device

Calculation for each step and each material.

EN 45555:2020, *General methods for assessing the recyclability and recoverability of energy-related products*, **2020**.

Challenges:

1. Lack of material-specific recycling rate data
2. No consideration of recycling quality

M. Hämmer, K. Wambach, *Sustainability* **2024**, *16*, 8726.

EU PVSEC 2025

Methodology

Quality of recycling

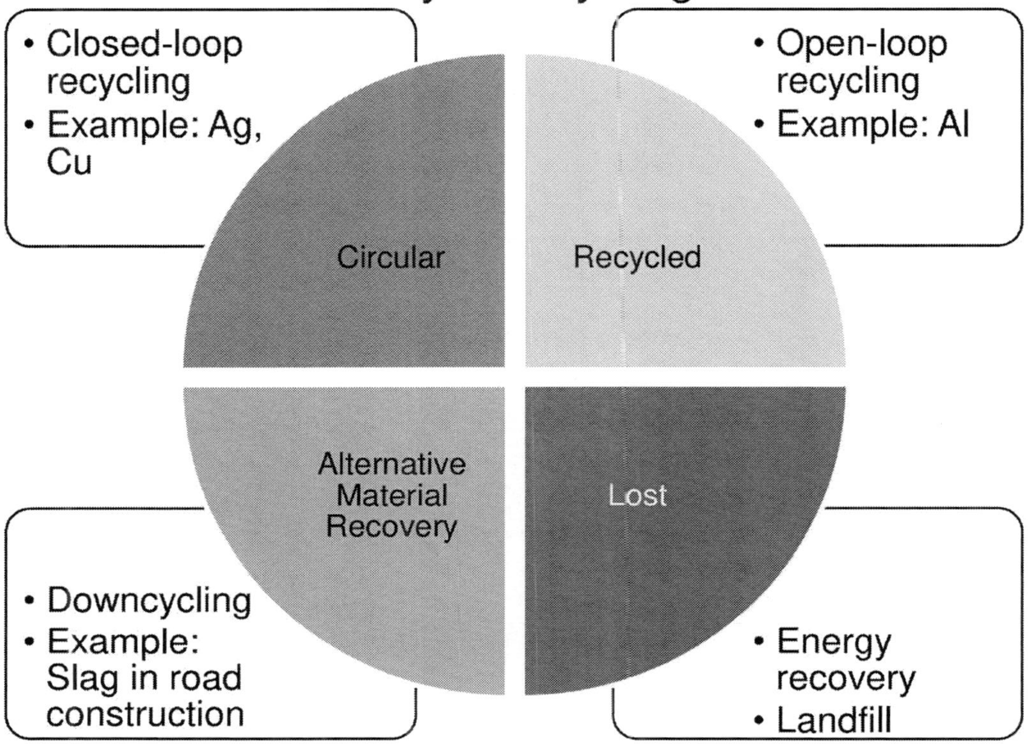

bifa Umweltinstitut

24.09.2025

M. Hämmer, K. Wambach, *Sustainability* **2024**, *16*, 8726.

EU PVSEC 2025

Methodology

bifa Umweltinstitut

System Boundaries

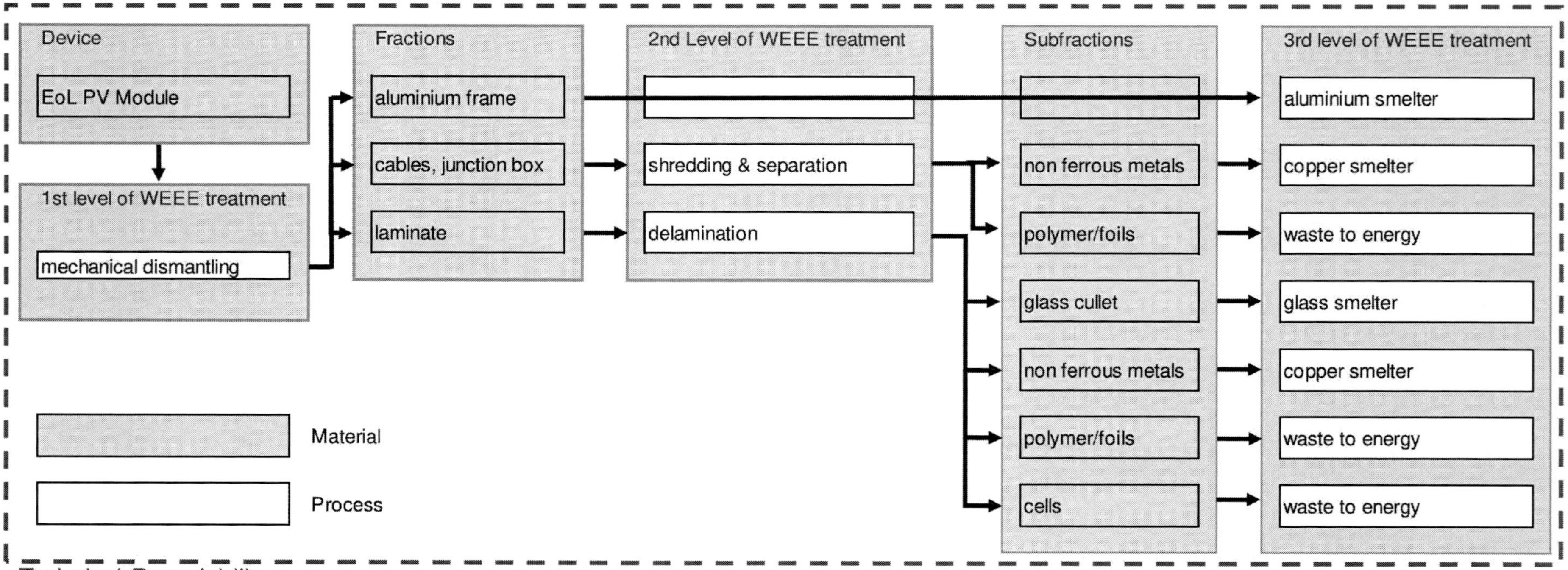

EU PVSEC 2025

bifa Umweltinstitut

Technical Recyclability Results

Example: Average c-Si Al-BSF glass-foil PV module

<u>End-of-life scenarios:</u>

S1: worst-case mechanical treatment
S2: BAT mechanical treatment
S3: pyrolysis
S4: water-jet delamination
S5: PHOTORAMA pilot

All scenarios include dismantling, i.e. the removal of frame, cables and junction box prior to the processing of the PV module's laminate.
→ Formal treatment as mandatory in the EU (WEEE directive)

Differences: delamination technique and downstream treatment

Technical Recyclability Results

Flow Chart, Scenarios and References

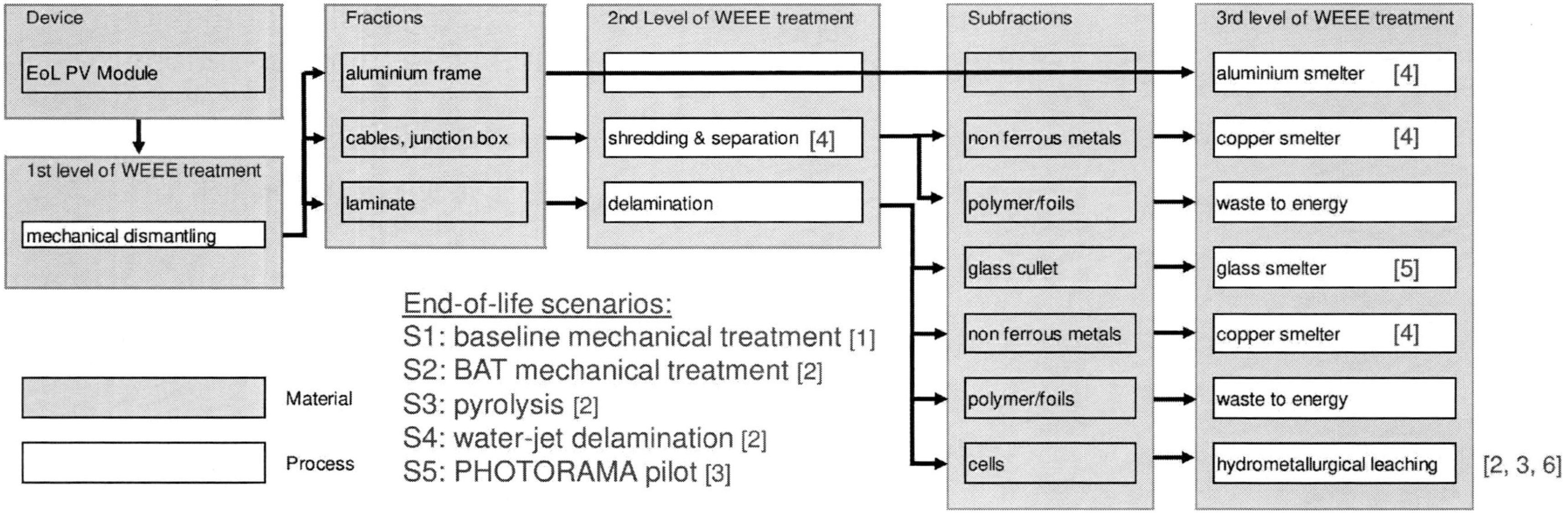

End-of-life scenarios:
S1: baseline mechanical treatment [1]
S2: BAT mechanical treatment [2]
S3: pyrolysis [2]
S4: water-jet delamination [2]
S5: PHOTORAMA pilot [3]

[1] F. Ardente, C. E. L. Latunussa, G. A. Blengini, *Waste Management* **2019**, *91*, 156.
[2] K. Wambach, C. Libby, S. Shaw, *Advances in Photovoltaic Module Recycling.* Report IEA-PVPS T12-28:2024, **2024**.
[3] M. Seitz, R. Steber, K. Baumann, M. Hämmer, PHOTORAMA Deliverable D5.5, **2025**.
[4] M. Hämmer, K. Wambach, *Sustainability* **2024**, *16*, 8726.
[5] C. E. Latunussa, F. Ardente, G. A. Blengini, L. Mancini, *Solar Energy Materials and Solar Cells* **2016**, *156*, 101.
[6] B. Huang, J. Zhao, J. Chai, B. Xue, F. Zhao, X. Wang, *Solar Energy* **2017**, *143*, 132.

Technical Recyclability Results

Worst-case recycling treatment by non-specialized glass recyclers (S1)

Recovered secondary raw materials
- ✓ Al (frame)
- ✓ Cu (cables and junction box)
- ✓ Glass cullet

End-of-life scenarios:
S1: baseline mechanical treatment
S2: BAT mechanical treatment
S3: pyrolysis
S4: water-jet delamination
S5: PHOTORAMA pilot

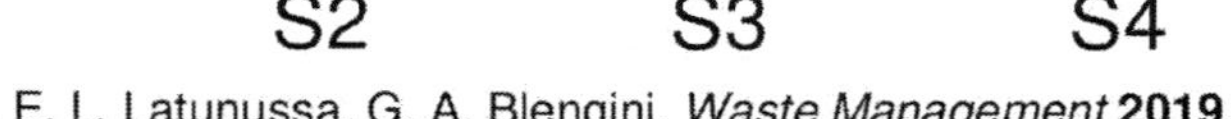

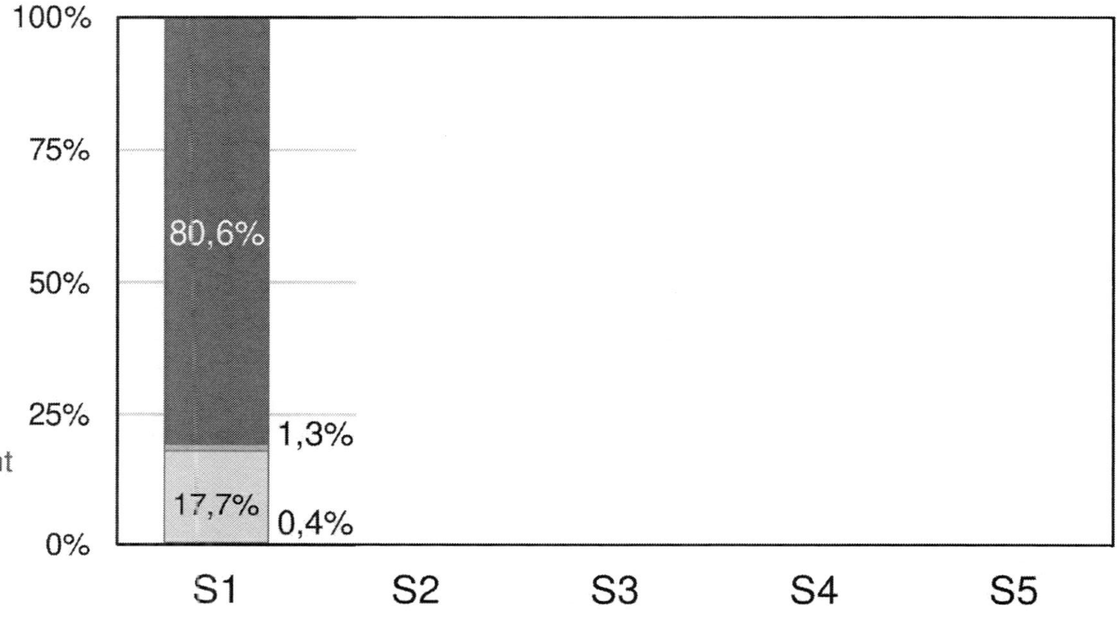

F. Ardente, C. E. L. Latunussa, G. A. Blengini, *Waste Management* **2019**, *91*, 156.

EU PVSEC 2025

Technical Recyclability Results

bifa Umweltinstitut

state-of-the-art dedicated mechanical recycling (S2)

Recovered secondary raw materials

- ✓ Al (frame)
- ✓ Cu (cables, junction box and ribbons)
- ✓ Glass cullet

End-of-life scenarios:
S1: baseline mechanical treatment
S2: BAT mechanical treatment
S3: pyrolysis
S4: water-jet delamination
S5: PHOTORAMA pilot

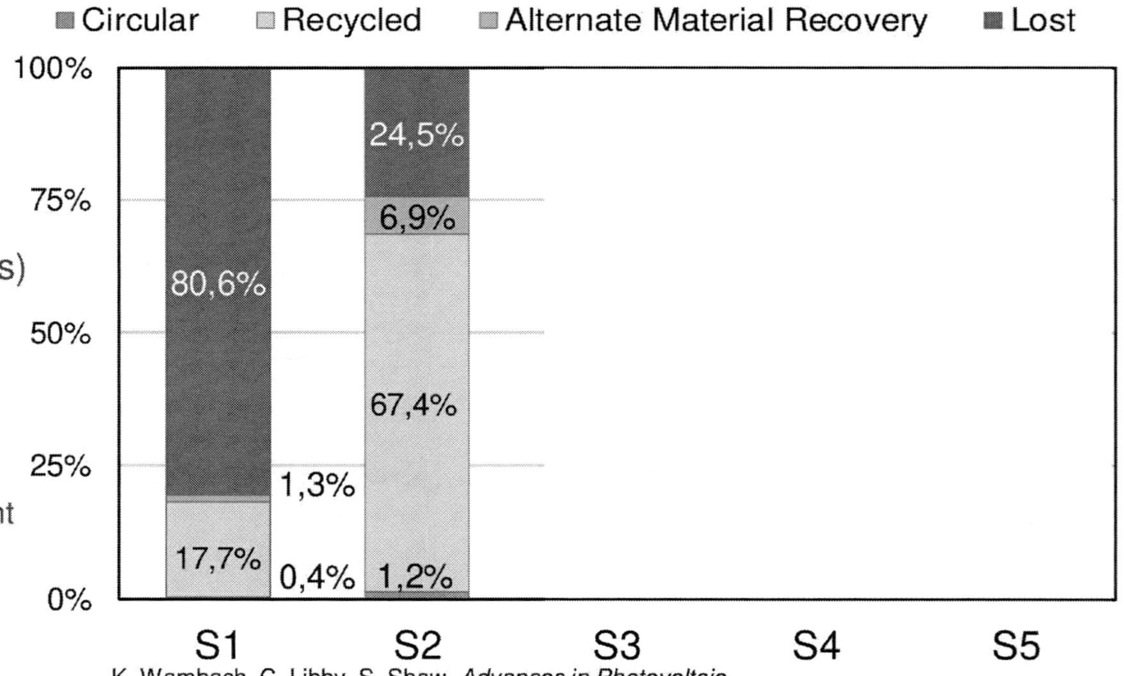

K. Wambach, C. Libby, S. Shaw, *Advances in Photovoltaic Module Recycling*. Report IEA-PVPS T12-28:2024, **2024**.

EU PVSEC 2025

bifa Umweltinstitut

Technical Recyclability Results

Advanced recycling pyrolysis (S3)

Recovered secondary raw materials
- ✓ Al (frame)
- ✓ Cu (cables, junction box and ribbons)
- ✓ Glass cullet
- ✓ Si
- ✓ Ag

End-of-life scenarios:
S1: baseline mechanical treatment
S2: BAT mechanical treatment
S3: pyrolysis
S4: water-jet delamination
S5: PHOTORAMA pilot

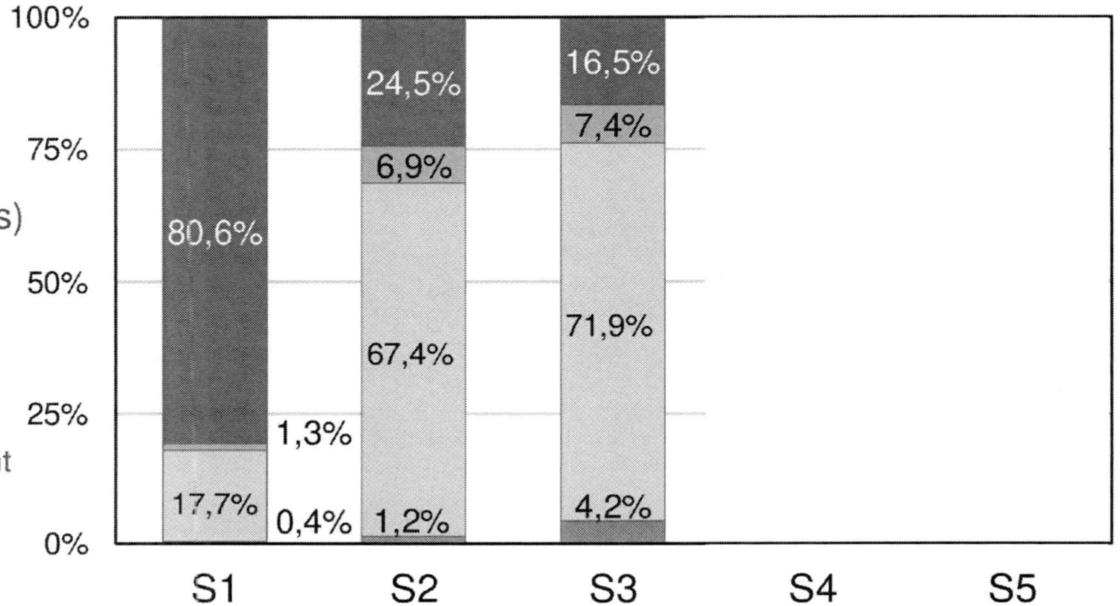

K. Wambach, C. Libby, S. Shaw, *Advances in Photovoltaic Module Recycling*. Report IEA-PVPS T12-28:2024, **2024**.

24.09.2025

EU PVSEC 2025

bifa Umweltinstitut

Technical Recyclability Results

Advanced recycling water-jet (S4)

Recovered secondary raw materials

- ✓ Al (frame)
- ✓ Cu (cables, junction box and ribbons)
- ✓ Glass cullet
- ✓ Si
- ✓ Ag

End-of-life scenarios:
S1: baseline mechanical treatment
S2: BAT mechanical treatment
S3: pyrolysis
S4: water-jet delamination
S5: PHOTORAMA pilot

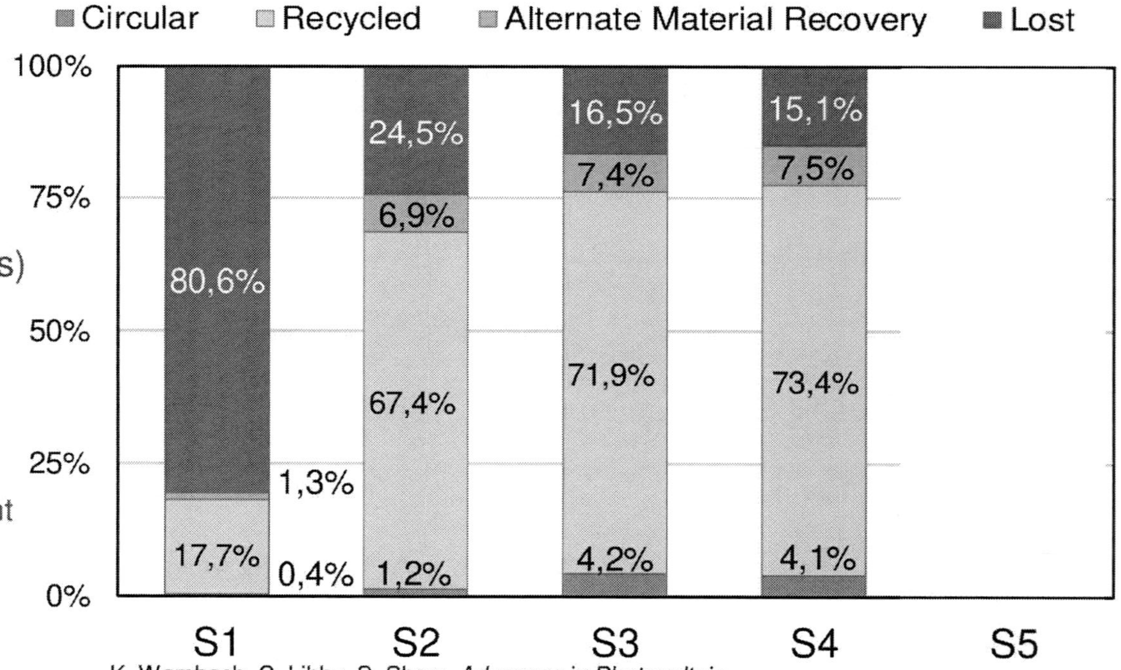

K. Wambach, C. Libby, S. Shaw, *Advances in Photovoltaic Module Recycling*. Report IEA-PVPS T12-28:2024, **2024**.

EU PVSEC 2025

bifa Umweltinstitut

Technical Recyclability Results

PHOTORAMA pilot line recycling (S5)

Recovered secondary raw materials
- ✓ Al (frame)
- ✓ Cu (cables, junction box and ribbons)
- ✓ Glass cullet
- ✓ Si
- ✓ Ag

End-of-life scenarios:
S1: baseline mechanical treatment
S2: BAT mechanical treatment
S3: pyrolysis
S4: water-jet delamination
S5: PHOTORAMA pilot

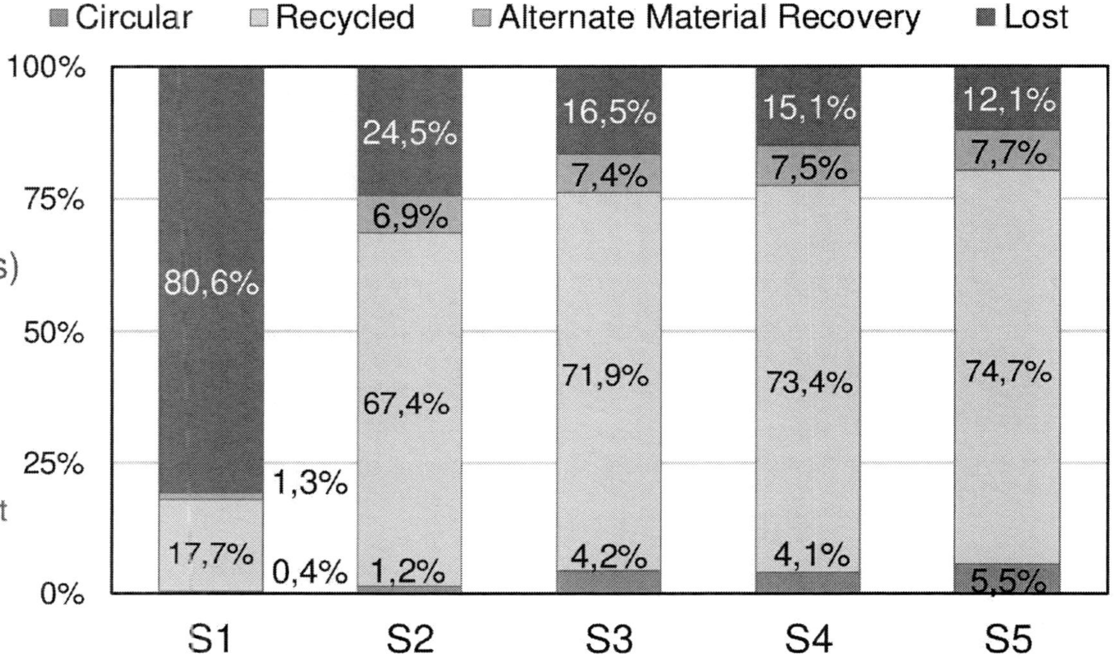

M. Seitz, R. Steber, K. Baumann, M. Hämmer, PHOTORAMA Deliverable D5.5, **2025**.

Technical Recyclability Results

Results on material and fraction level

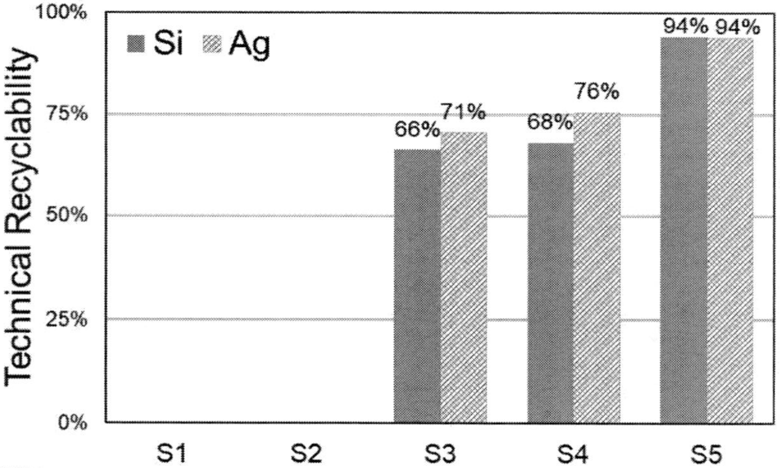

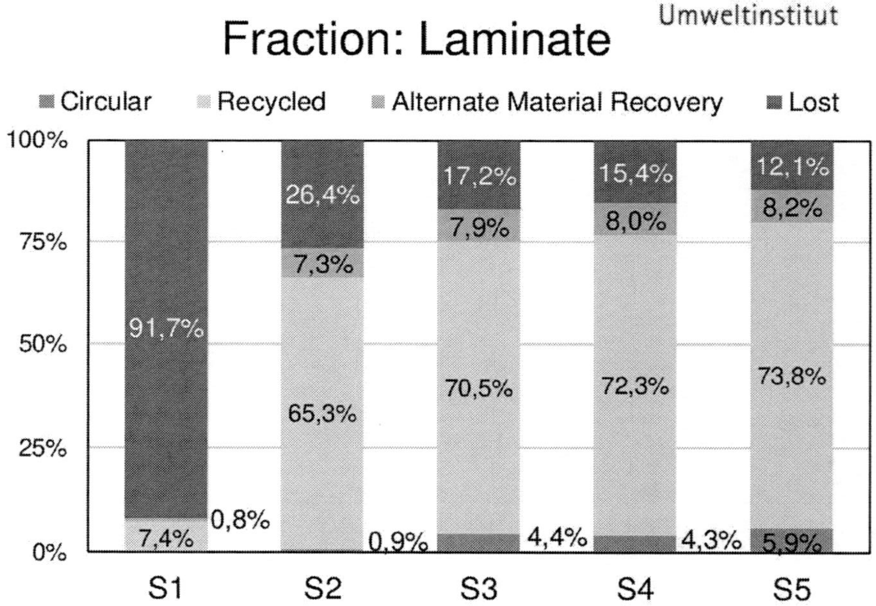

End-of-life scenarios:
S1: baseline mechanical treatment
S2: BAT mechanical treatment
S3: pyrolysis
S4: water-jet delamination
S5: PHOTORAMA pilot

24.09.2025

EU PVSEC 2025

Conclusion

bifa Umweltinstitut

- Quantification of technical recyclability for PV modules possible (with database and methodology)
- Application:
  - Ecodesign (comparison of different modules)
  - Recycling technology development (comparison of different recycling approaches)
  - Economic assessment (realistic quantitative secondary raw material production)
- Extended batch test QUASAR project for better data quality

EU PVSEC 2025

bifa Umweltinstitut

Thank you for your attention!

Funded by
the European Union

This work has received funding from the European Union's Horizon 2020 research and innovation programme under grant agreement No 958223; project PHOTORAMA and from the European Union´s Horizon Europe research and innovation programme under Grant Agreement No 101122298; project QUASAR. Views and opinions expressed are however those of the authors only and do not necessarily reflect those of the European Union or CINEA. Neither the European Union nor the granting authority can be held responsible for them.

bifa Umweltinstitut GmbH
Am Mittleren Moos 46
86167 Augsburg

Dr. Matthias Hämmer
Tel. +49 821 7000-297
mhaemmer@bifa.de
www.bifa.de

Mehr Infos:

19

Technical Recyclability Results

Scenarios:
S1: baseline mechanical treatment
S2: BAT mechanical treatment
S3: pyrolysis
S4: water-jet delamination
S5: PHOTORAMA pilot

bifa Umweltinstitut

Worst-case recycling treatment by not-specialized glass recyclers (S1)

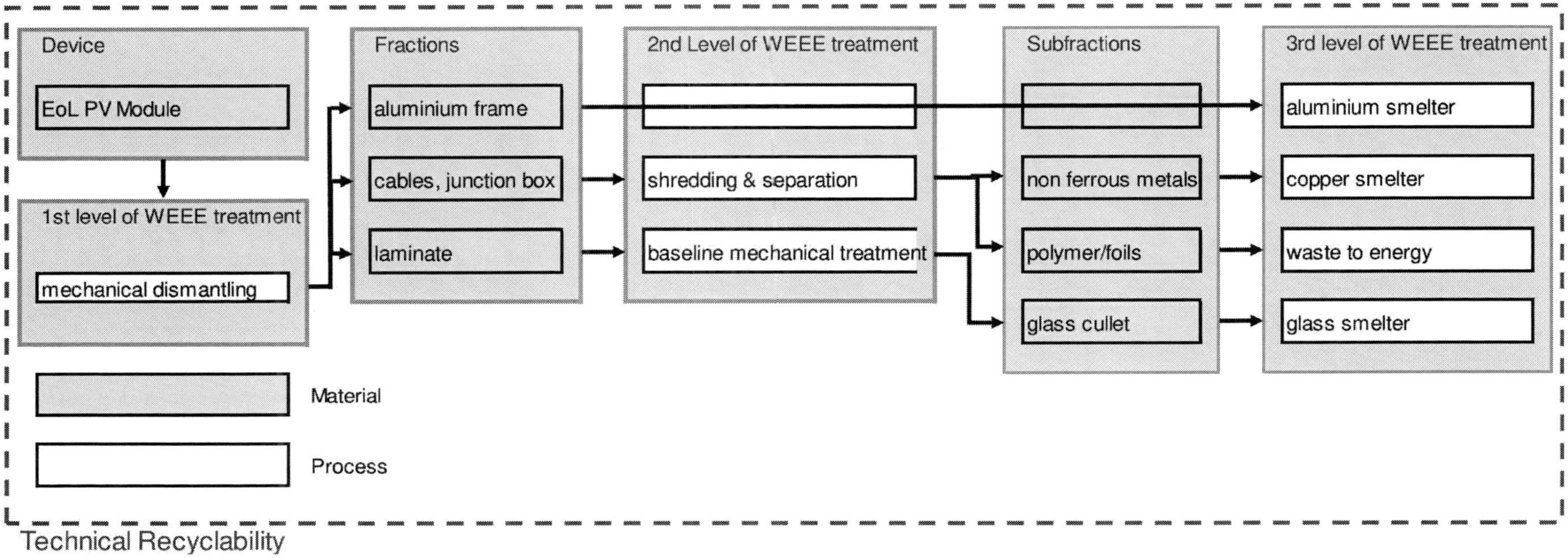

EU PVSEC 2025

Technical Recyclability Results

Scenarios:
S1: baseline mechanical treatment
S2: BAT mechanical treatment
S3: pyrolysis
S4: water-jet delamination
S5: PHOTORAMA pilot

bifa Umweltinstitut

state-of-the-art dedicated mechanical recycling (S2)

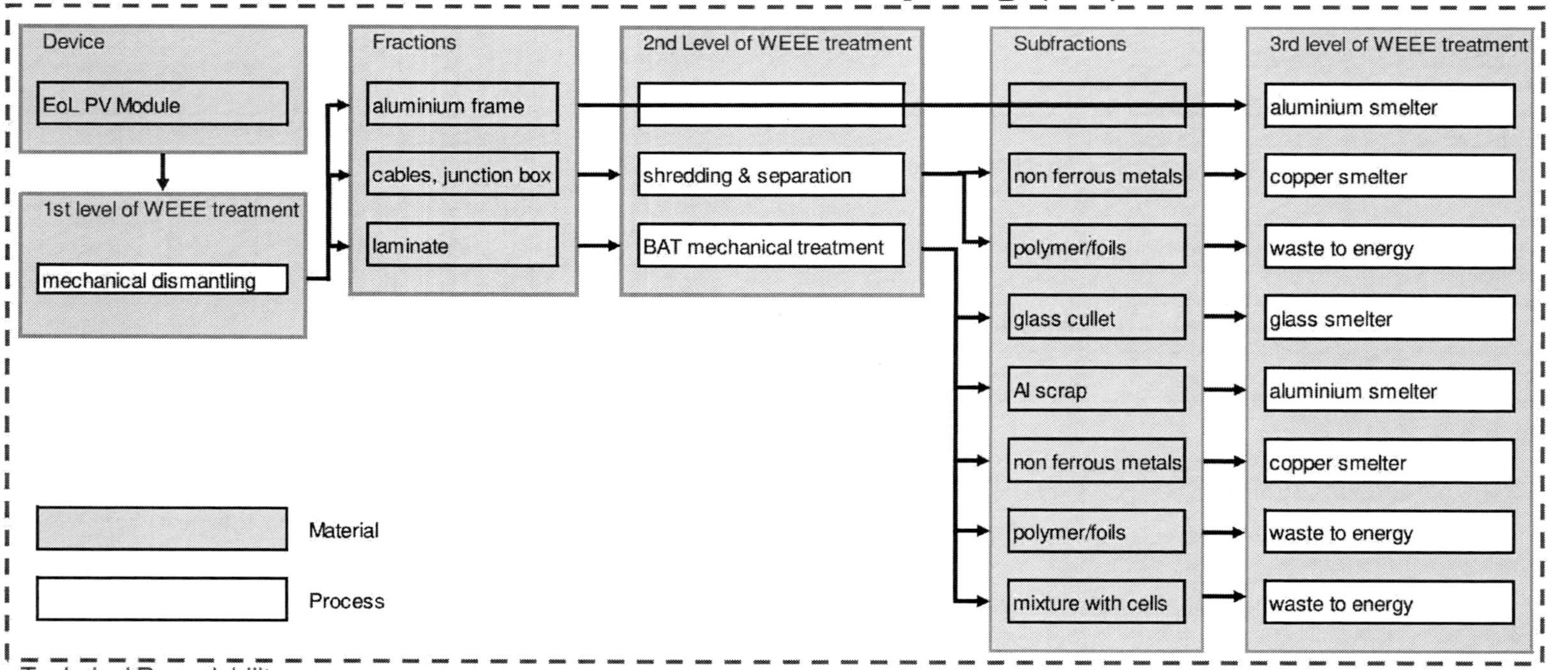

Technical Recyclability Results

Scenarios:
S1: baseline mechanical treatment
S2: BAT mechanical treatment
S3: pyrolysis
S4: water-jet delamination
S5: PHOTORAMA pilot

bifa Umweltinstitut

Advanced recycling pyrolysis (S3)

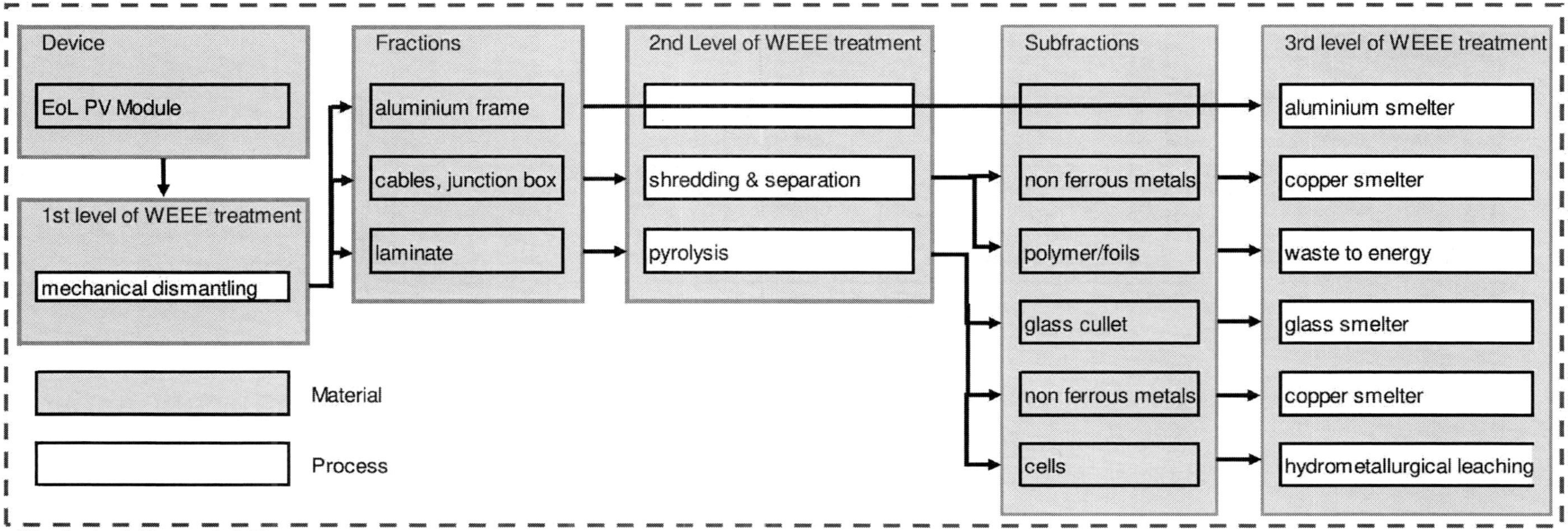

Technical Recyclability Results

Scenarios:
S1: baseline mechanical treatment
S2: BAT mechanical treatment
S3: pyrolysis
S4: water-jet delamination
S5: PHOTORAMA pilot

Advanced recycling water-jet (S4)

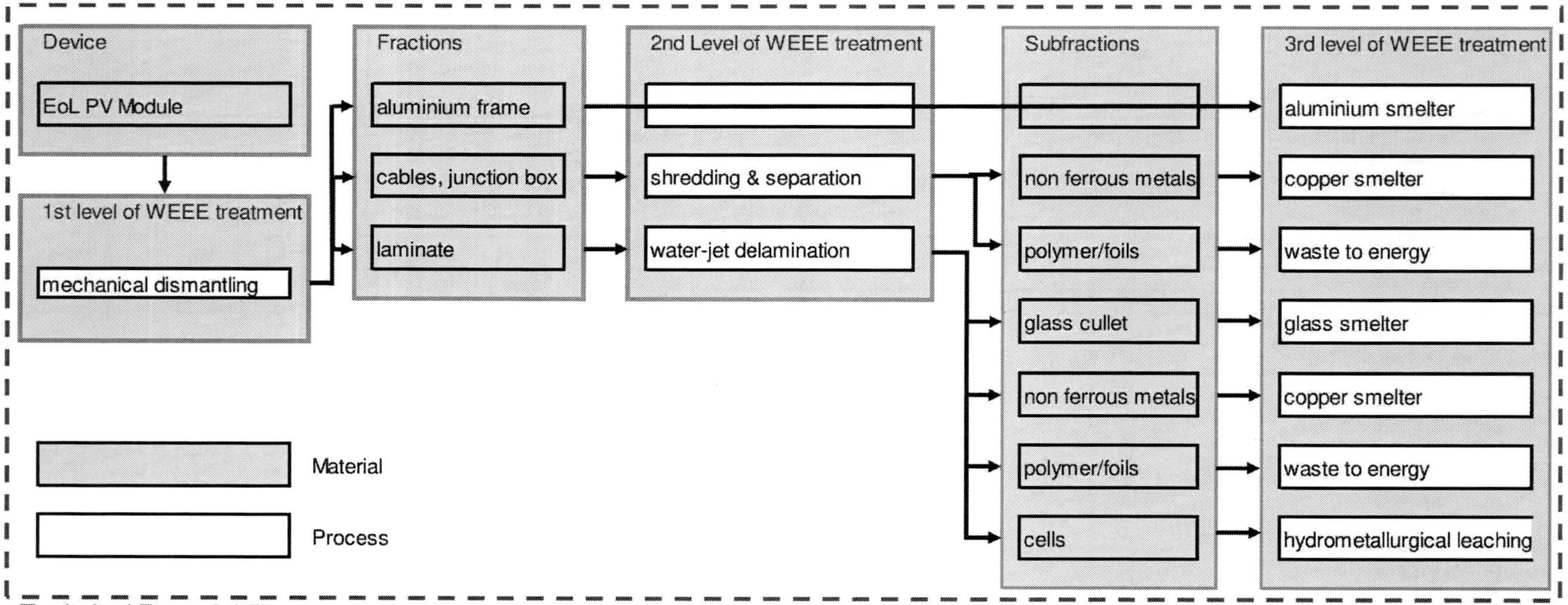

Technical Recyclability Results

Scenarios:
S1: baseline mechanical treatment
S2: BAT mechanical treatment
S3: pyrolysis
S4: water-jet delamination
S5: PHOTORAMA pilot

bifa Umweltinstitut

PHOTORAMA pilot line recycling (S5)

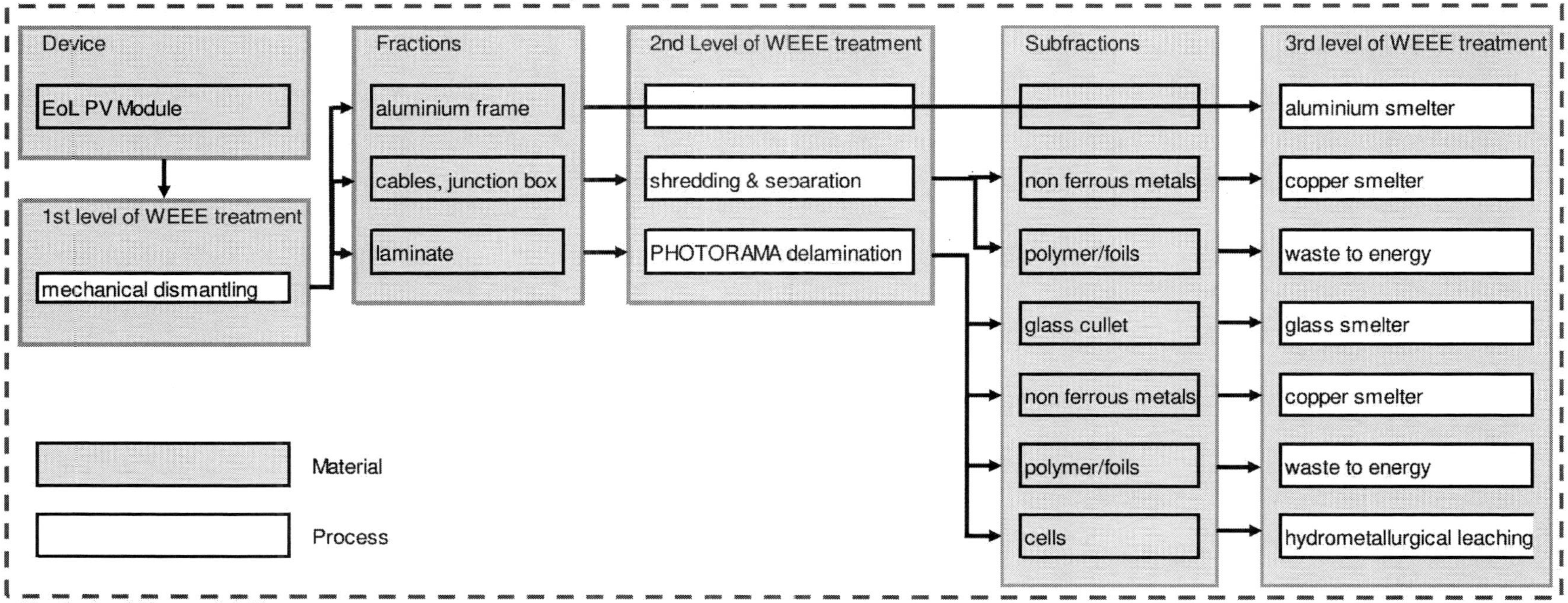

IEC TECHNICAL REPORT 63525 ON THE REUSE OF PV MODULES: FINAL RESULT

Arvid van der Heide[1,2,3], Serge Noels[4], Jan Clyncke[4], Rich Strömberg[5,6]
[1]imec, imo-imomec, Thor Park 8320, 3600 Genk, Belgium
[2]Hasselt University, imo-imomec, Martelarenlaan 42, 3500 Hasselt, Belgium
[3]EnergyVille, imo-imomec, Thor Park 8320, 3600 Genk, Belgium
[4]PV CYCLE, Brand Whitlocklaan 114/5, 1200 Brussels, Belgium
[5]ACEP, University of Alaska Fairbanks, 1764 Tanana loop, Fairbanks, AK 9975, USA
[6]Equitable Solar Solutions, P.O. Box 463, Gunnison CO 81230, USA
e-mail: arvid.vanderheide@imec.be

ABSTRACT: To promote PV sustainability, an IEC project team was created to prepare a Technical Report (TR) 63525 "PV module reuse and circular economy". The TR working draft has been finished recently and includes recommendations for PV module reuse, that can also serve as a basis for the future development of normative documents. The possibility of reducing the on-site inspection work by sampling of PV modules is discussed. Although this is a promising approach, the TR still recommends testing every PV module for possible reuse. The recommended tests (for PV modules without repair) are visual inspection, I-V, EL, bypass diode test and dry insulation test. Although the dry insulation test is not sensitive to all insulation defects, it is not recommended to do the wet insulation test for every PV module. It is only recommended after certain repairs, like junction box replacement or backsheet repair. The remaining power is recommended to be still above the guaranteed value, taking the age of the PV module into account. An additional label should be placed next to the original one, with the new maximum system voltage indicated (either the original or a reduced value when necessary).
Keywords: reuse, re-use, second life, circularity, standardisation

1 INTRODUCTION

Many PV modules will be decommissioned in the next years, either because they are near the end of their designed technical lifetime (20-30 years) or because they are replaced by new PV modules with higher efficiency ("repowering" of PV plants). According to IRENA, 78 million metric tons of PV module waste is expected worldwide by 2050 [1]. Because of this, it is very important to develop strategies to deal with these large numbers of decommissioned PV modules like reuse and recycling.

Currently, most decommissioned PV modules are either disposed of in landfills (but not in the European Union) or sent to waste treatment and recycling facilities [3,13,14]. Considering extending the lifetime of the products that are still functioning (through preparation for reuse) instead of sending them directly to recycling, this has proven to reduce the environmental impact and contributes to higher levels of circularity [2-3].

The main opportunities and advantages of reusing PV modules are listed below [2-12]:

- Prevent premature entry into the waste stream
- Reduce the PV module waste
- Reduce extraction of materials for new PV modules
- Reduce energy and water to produce new PV modules
- Decrease the environmental impact of the overall PV sector and enable wide-spread access to electricity, especially to poorly connected areas

Although the advantages of reusing PV modules are clear, it is a very complex subject. There are concerns about safety, performance, remaining lifetime, financial viability and possible export of PV modules to countries without (proper) waste treatment and recycling infrastructure in general. The first 3 concerns should be addressed by standardising the requirements for reuse of PV modules. For this reason, at the end of 2021, the IEC agreed to install a project team to start drafting a Technical Report (TR) on this subject. A TR is not normative but can give recommendations and can be used to develop future Technical Specifications and/or Standards. The preparation of the working draft has been completed, and it now moves to the committee stage "acceptance of draft". The main contents of the TR will be discussed in this paper.

2 THE CONTENTS OF THE TECHNICAL REPORT

In the TR, a PV module is considered to be fit for reuse only if it is still safe, has sufficient remaining power and a sufficient remaining lifetime. It should also be noted that the TR has been limited to the reuse of crystalline silicon PV modules, since other technologies have always been a small fraction of the installed capacity.

In the following, first the organisation of the TR will be described, followed by a description of the main issues discussed in the TR. These are:

- Testing via sampling or for every PV module
- Visual inspection
- I-V testing
- EL imaging
- Bypass diode testing
- Insulation tests (dry and wet)
- Relabelling
- Repair

2.1 Organisation of the TR

The TR starts with a general description of the technology to manufacture c-Si PV modules and the materials and components that are involved. Also, the reliability issues of PV modules are discussed, since it is an important subject in view of reusing PV modules. Then on-site inspection of PV plants and on-site evaluation methods are discussed including suggestions to select PV modules for reuse based on sampling instead of testing every PV module (although this way of working is considered to be not ready for implementation right now).

The concept of reduced maximum system voltage is introduced for PV modules that might have reduced insulation quality or PV modules that have undergone a certain repair. Then the actual tests for the evaluation of PV modules for reuse are presented. The subjects of repair and relabelling of the PV modules conclude the technical part of the report, and is followed by a few pages about other issues around the reuse of PV modules like legislation and policy. After this main part of the TR that contains 100 pages, several annexes have been added (containing for example some use cases but also pictures to support the visual inspection in the main document text). Including these annexes, the total number of pages in the TR adds up to 163.

2.2 Testing via sampling or testing every PV module

The project team for this TR has investigated the possibility of reducing the amount of effort for selection of PV modules for reuse by applying a sampling approach instead of testing every PV module. This would of course only be justified if the PV modules inside a plant can be assumed to be in similar condition, so not if the plant has been partly destroyed by a weather disaster, for example. For such cases it is suggested that such a sampling could be based on a similar approach as applied by Solar Power Europe for the inspection of newly installed PV plants [15]. Their approach is to use the Acceptable Quality Limit (AQL) sampling described in ISO 2859-1 with different inspection levels depending on the type of test. The idea would be to apply this also for the selection of PV modules for reuse, using the AQL sampling method with slightly stricter inspection levels. Especially in combination with energy yield data for the plant over the past years and drone inspection imaging, this could be an interesting and economically viable approach. However, for the moment it has not yet been determined under which circumstances and with which inspection levels this should be made, and it was decided that this will need to be described in a future technical specification or standard. For this reason, for the moment it is still recommended to test every PV module for its evaluation for reuse.

The recommended test sequence for the testing of every PV module for possible reuse is the following:

- Visual inspection
- I-V testing
- EL imaging
- Bypass diode testing
- Dry insulation test
- Wet insulation test, only in the case of certain repairs

For application in a reuse facility, all of these tests (except the wet insulation test that is not standard included anyway) can in principle be integrated in a "test unit".

2.3 Visual inspection

Before electrical testing, every PV module must be inspected visually since it does not make sense to spend more time on a PV module having unacceptable defects. Figure 1 shows the basic visual inspection.

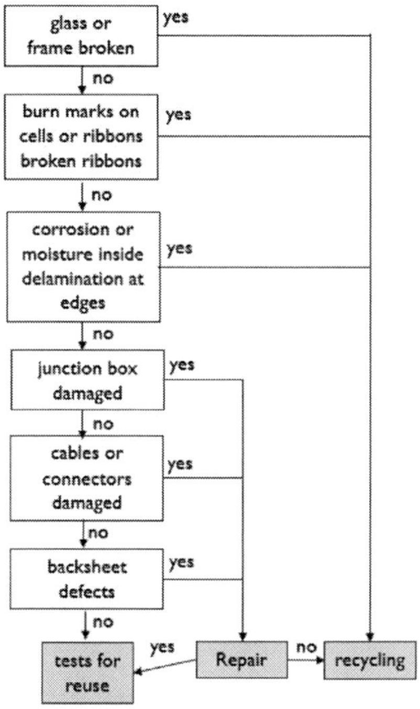

Figure 1: Basic visual inspection decision tree

In the TR, the visual inspection has been further detailed in a table containing recommended pass/fail/deliberate criteria for different components or materials of the PV module. In addition, example pictures to support the visual inspection are available in the annex C of the TR draft. The deliberation of a PV module means it could still be repaired or used at a reduced maximum system voltage.

2.4 I-V testing

Before I-V testing, PV modules have to be sufficiently clean (few % power loss due to soiling at most). The I-V measurement itself can be done outdoor or indoor, either on-site or at a reuse test facility.

The recommendation is to have a remaining measured P_{max} > guaranteed P_{max}, taking into account nameplate negative tolerance (if any), PV module age, guarantee curve from manufacturer and the measuring tolerance (default value 5%).

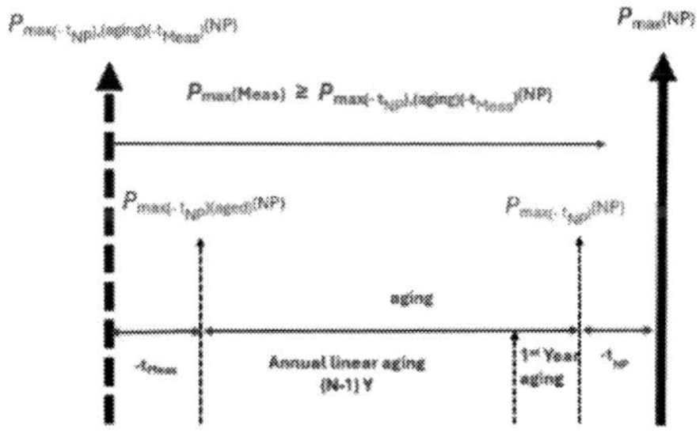

Figure 2: Determination of the remaining minimum power, starting on the right from $P_{max(NP)}$ and subtracting the tolerances and maximum allowed aging according to guarantee.

10.4229/EUPVSEC2025/5CO.6.5

In some cases, it might also be possible to agree with a lower P_{max}, but only when agreed beforehand with the end user.

2.5 EL imaging

EL imaging is useful to detect cell cracks inside the PV module. In IEC TS 60904-13, cell cracks of different severity have been classified into categories A, B and C. In Figure 3, a cell with cracks from all categories is shown:

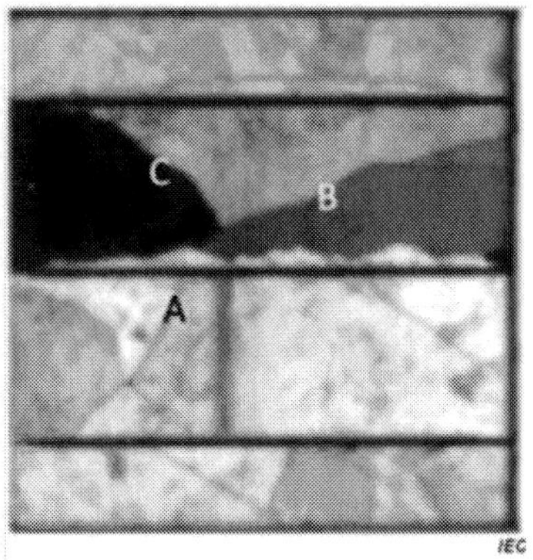

Figure 3: EL image of a cell having cell cracks of all three categories A, B, C used in IEC TS 60904-13

The cracks of the different classes are having the properties listed below:

- A: line defects not isolating cell area
- B: cracks causing partially disconnected regions
- C: cracks causing completely disconnected regions

Cracks of category B cause regions that are quite dark for an injected current that equals the short-circuit current I_{sc}, but that are not so dark for an injected current that equals only 10% of I_{sc}. For category C cracks, the disconnected region is black for any injected current.

The recommended rules for the acceptation of cracks in a PV module for reuse are the following:

- Only accept if $<$ 50% of cells are crack affected
- A cracks are allowed if affected cell area $<$ 1%
- B cracks are allowed if 1% $<$ affected cell area $<$ 20% and this occurs in $<$ 20% of cells
- C cracks are allowed if affected area $>$ 20% but $<$ 5% of the cells.

2.6 Bypass diode test

The recommended bypass diode test is the test named method A in IEC 61215-2. Since it involves reverse biasing of the PV module in the dark, it is recommended to perform this test after the EL test. The reverse current should be swept from 0 A to $1.25 I_{sc}$, while recording the required voltage. The expected voltage is now the number of diodes times the forward diode voltage required to pass the current through one diode (take the voltage at the highest current stated in the datasheet). If the total voltage is less (for 3 diodes typically by 1/3 or 2/3) it means that there are short-circuited bypass diodes. When no current can be passed in reverse for the expected forward bias voltage for 3 diodes, it means that one or more of the bypass diodes are open-circuited.

2.7 Dry insulation test

The dry insulation test that has been specified for new PV modules in IEC 61730 consists of two parts. First a voltage stress test of 4 times the maximum system voltage + 2000 V, with a dwell time of 1 minute. Afterwards, the voltage is reduced to the maximum system voltage (or 500 V at least), and after a dwell time of 2 minutes, the insulation resistance is determined. The voltage ramp rate should always remain $<$ 500 V/s. The criteria to pass this test in IEC 61730 are: no breakdown during the first part of the test, and a value of the insulation resistance times the PV module area $>$ 40 $M\Omega m^2$. In the TR, it is recommended to apply this dry insulation test also for testing PV modules for reuse, but with some adaptations to speed up the test: The dwell times are both reduced to only 1 s, and the voltage ramp rate may be $>$ 500 V/s. The recommended criteria for passing the test are the same, although it should be noted that it is possible to select a reduced maximum system voltage for the PV module when it will be reused, which means that the test requirements can now be lower than they had been when the PV modules were still new.

It is very important to realise that certain insulation defects might not lead to failing in the dry insulation test when the PV module is in well dried condition. For this reason, it is important to take care that no insulation defects like (deep) backsheet scratches are overlooked in the visual inspection. Although the research community is investigating ways of insulating testing for reuse that should be both practical and sensitive (for example using steam instead of liquid water), it was decided to not yet include such a method in the current TR draft.

2.8 Wet insulation test

In the first place, it has to be mentioned that the wet insulation test as described in IEC 61730 for new PV modules is very impractical for testing PV modules for reuse. In fact, it is not recommended to apply this test for every PV module, but only if for example the junction box has been replaced or a local back sheet repair has been made.

In IEC 61730, it is mentioned that the PV module has to be placed in a water tank with the front side facing down (water level still below frame height). The electrical test itself is exactly equal to the second part of the dry insulation test, including the criterion for passing. Also here, the recommended adaptations for testing for reuse are the same: dwell time of only 1 s and a voltage ramp rate that is allowed to be $>$ 500 V/s. Also here, the recommended criteria for passing the test are the same as for new ones. It should be noted again that it is possible to select a reduced maximum system voltage for the PV module when it will be reused, which means that the test requirements can now be lower than they had been when the PV modules were still new.

2.9 Relabelling

When a PV module has been found to be fit for reuse, the recommendation is to put an additional label on the PV module next to the original one. On this label, it is also required to specify the maximum system voltage from now on, which can be the original one or a reduced maximum system voltage. The proposed label is shown in Figure 4.

10.4229/EUPVSEC2025/5CO.6.5

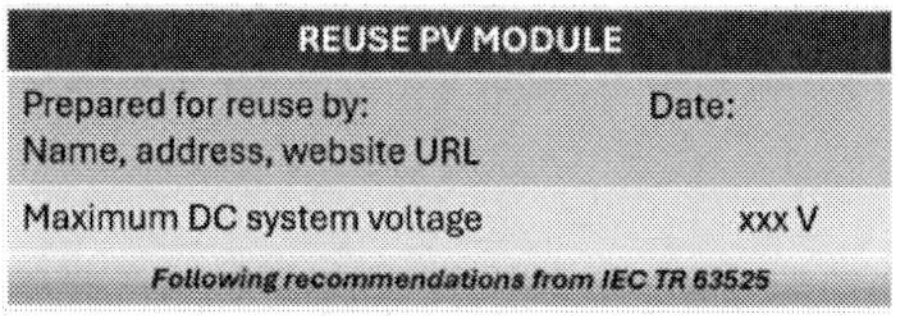

Figure 4: Proposed label to be placed next to the original one on a PV module that is fit for reuse.

Possible repairs should also be indicated on the label, as shown below.

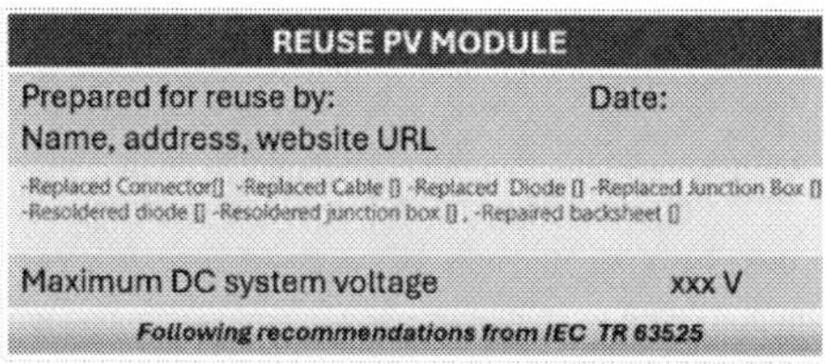

Figure 4: Proposed label to be placed next to the original one on a PV module that is fit for reuse, when the PV module has undergone one or more repairs

On another version of the label (not shown), it is also possible to add the newly measured electrical parameters. This is especially recommended when it has been agreed beforehand with the end user that the remaining power does not need to be higher than the minimum expected value based on the original power guarantee of the manufacturer.

2.10 Repair

Some of the options for repair have been discussed in the TR. While repair is relatively easy concerning liabilities and so on within an existing plant without change of ownership, it gets complicated when PV modules are offered to the market after repair. A simple replacement of connectors should not be a big issue, but replacing bypass diodes by other ones than the original ones is already something different, and certainly the replacement of a junction box is a major repair. In fact, it is a too complex subject to describe in detail in this paper, but different repair options for connectors, cables and backsheet are included in the TR, also recommending wet leakage testing and using the PV module at a reduced maximum system voltage where necessary.

3 CONCLUSIONS

The preparatory phase for the working draft of the IEC TR 63525 "Reuse of PV modules and circular economy" has been finished recently. Suggestions for future sampling of PV modules from large PV plants are given for future standardisation efforts, but for the moment it is recommended to still test every PV module on its properties. The tests that are recommended for every PV module are a visual inspection, I-V testing, EL, bypass diode testing and dry insulation testing. For the remaining power it is recommended to stay above the originally guaranteed power for the current age of the PV module, although it is possible to go below this value if the end user agrees with that beforehand. Concerning EL testing, criteria have been given for the acceptable presence of cracks for the different types A, B and C that have been specified in IEC 60904-13. The bypass diode testing is rather straightforward and can detect short-circuited or open-circuited diodes. For dry insulation testing, it is acknowledged that it is not perfect and some insulation defects like back sheet scratches can be missed, but it still has an added value for inspecting internal insulation issues. It also means that a good visual inspection is still very important, especially on (deep) back sheet scratches and possible junction box damage.

A new label has to be placed next to the original one and should mention the maximum system voltage, which can be reduced compared to the original value, for example because of a reduced insulation quality or certain repairs.

Repairing PV modules for reuse is in general still a complicated issue. While replacing connectors and cables is still rather straightforward, replacing a junction box or repairing a backsheet is a different thing, especially when the PV module is to be put on the market after the repair. However, since it is such an important topic, the TR does give some recommendations for repair options, including backsheet repair.

4 ACKNOWLEDGEMENTS

The authors thank all the IEC experts of the project team that have contributed to this final working draft.

The contribution to this IEC TR draft by Serge Noels as project team lead and editor of the draft has been funded:
- from Dec 2021 – Nov 2022 by CIRCUSOL. This project has received funding from the European Union's Horizon 2020 research and innovation programme under grant agreement number 776680.
- from Dec 2022 – Sep 2025 by PV CYCLE

The contribution to this IEC TR draft by Arvid van der Heide at imec has been funded in part by the CLOSER project. This project has received funding from the European Union's I3 instrument under grant agreement number 101161109.

5 REFERENCES

[1] IRENA, IEA-PVPS, 2016. End-of-life management: Solar Photovoltaic Panels. p.98.

[2] PVPS, I.E.A., 2021. Preliminary Environmental & Financial Viability Analysis of Circular Economy Scenarios for Satisfying PV System Service Lifetime. p.69 Report IEA-PVPST12-21:2021.

[3] Wim Van Opstal, Anse Smeets, 2022, Circular economy strategies as enablers for solar PV adoption in organizational market segments, Sustainable Production and Consumption, Volume 35, 2023, Pages 40-54, ISSN 2352-5509.

[4] G Oviedo Hernandez et al 2022. Trends and innovations in photovoltaic operations and maintenance. Prog. Energy 4 042002

[5] Majewski P et al 2021 Recycling of solar PV panels-product stewardship and regulatory approaches Energy Policy 149 112062

10.4229/EUPVSEC2025/5CO.6.5

[6] Tsanakas J A et al 2019 Towards a circular supply chain for PV modules: review of today's challenges in PV recycling, refurbishment and re-certification Prog. Photovolt. Res. Appl. 28 454–64

[7] Lempkowicz B et al 2021 RE-USE of PV modules, challenges and opportunities of the circular economy PV Cycle & IMEC (available at: https://pvcycle.be/wp-content/uploads/Press-Release-Reuse-08032021.pdf)

[8] Dodd N, Espinosa N, Van Tichelen P, Peeters K and Soares A 2020 Preparatory study for solar photovoltaic modules, inverters and systems: final report European Commission Publications Office (available at: https://data.europa.eu/doi/10.2760/852637)

[9] Godinho Ariolli D M 2021 Moving towards a circular photovoltaic economy in Europe: a system approach of the status, drivers, barriers, key policies and opportunities Master Thesis in the framework of the Erasmus Mundus Masters course in Environmental Sciences, Policy and Management (MESPOM)

[10] Hengky K S et al 2019 Drivers, barriers and enablers to end-of-life management of solar photovoltaic and battery energy storage systems: a systematic literature review J. Clean. Prod. 211 537–54

[11] van der Heide A et al 2021 Towards a successful re-use of decommissioned photovoltaic modules Prog. Photovolt. Res. Appl. 2021 1–11

[12] Strategic Research and Innovation Agenda Photovoltaics (SRIA), 2022.

[13] Farrell C C et al (2020). *Technical challenges and opportunities in realizing a circular economy for waste photovoltaic modules.* Renew. Sustain. Energy Rev. 128 109911

[14] Deng, R., Chang, N., Lunardi, M. M., Dias, P., Bilbao, J., Ji, J., & Chong, C. M. (2020). *Remanufacturing end-of-life silicon photovoltaics: Feasibility and viability analysis.* Progress in Photovoltaics: Research and Applications, pip.3376. https://doi.org/10.1002/pip.3376

[15] SolarPower Europe (2021)– *Engineering, Procurement & Construction Best practices guidelines version 2.0*
(https://www.solarpowereurope.org/insights/thematic-reports/epc-best-practice-guidelines-version-2-0

10.4229/EUPVSEC2025/5CO.6.5

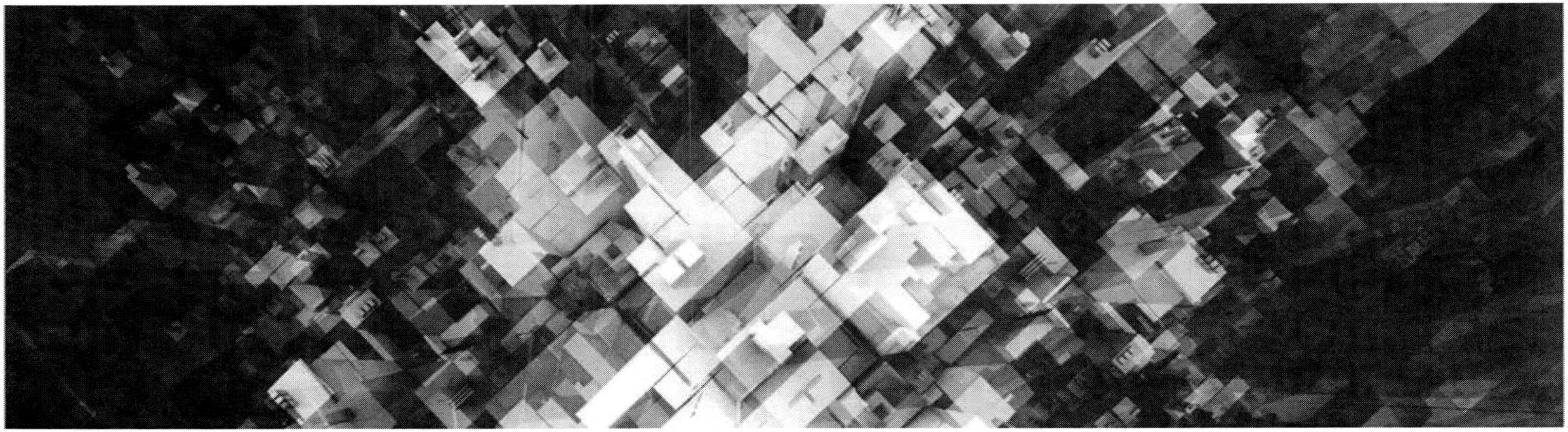

IEC Technical Report 63525 on the reuse of PV modules: final draft

Arvid van der Heide, Serge Noels, Jan Clyncke, Rich Strömberg

IMO-IMOMEC UHASSELT imec Energy Ville

PV CYCLE

UAF University of Alaska Fairbanks

Equitable Solar Solutions

ACEP Alaska Center for Energy and Power

IMO-IMOMEC UHASSELT imec

Technical Report (TR) on reuse of PV modules in IEC TC82 WG2

International Electrotechnical Commission

IEC TR 63525 : “Reuse of PV modules and circular economy”

- Project team started 2022, led by Serge Noels, ~ 30 IEC experts involved
- TR: **simplified** project flow but **cannot** be **normative**
- Draft has been completely finished last week
- IEC TC82 “mirror committees” now have to decide about acceptance
- This presentation: summary of the final TR contents

“Acceptance of draft”

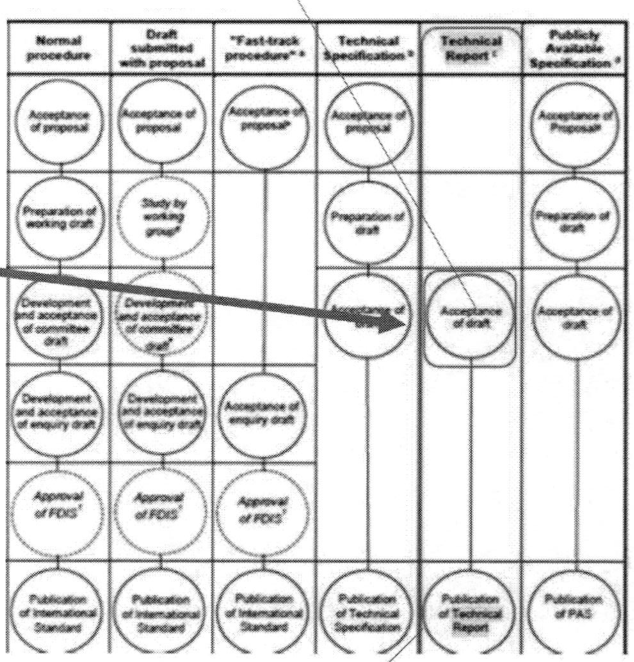

“Publication of Technical Report”

IMO-IMOMEC UHASSELT imec EnergyVille PV CYCLE UAF University of Alaska Fairbanks ACEP

Basic principles behind this TR

- Safe 
- Sufficient power 
- Enough remaining lifetime 

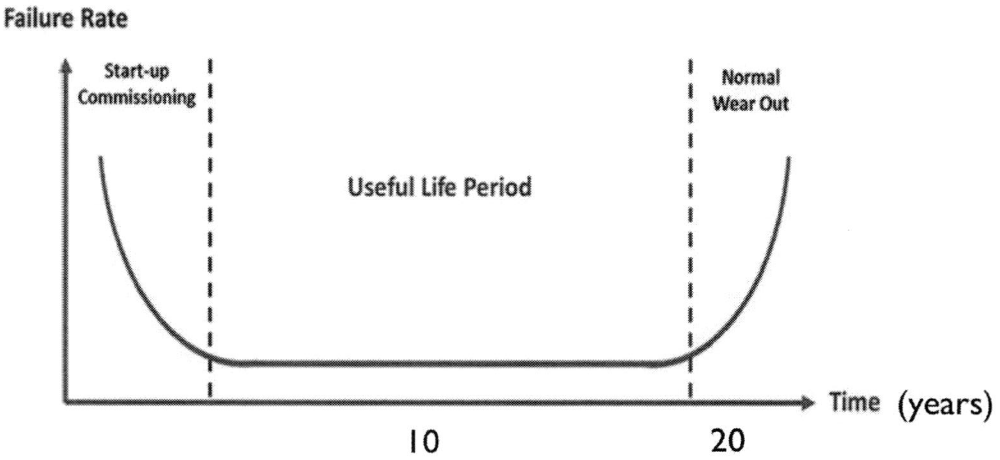

IMO-IMOMEC UHASSELT imec EnergyVille PV CYCLE UAF UNIVERSITY OF ALASKA FAIRBANKS ACEP

Main issues addressed in TR (100 pages, 163 pages with annexes)

- Testing **via sampling** or **testing every module**
- **Visual inspection** (and additional IR inspection in the field)
- **I-V test** and **remaining power**
- **EL** imaging and criteria on cell cracks
- Bypass diode testing
- **Insulation tests** (dry and wet) and possible reduction of maximum system voltage
- **Relabelling**
- Repair

Subjects in **bold**: will be discussed

IMO-IMOMEC UHASSELT imec Energy Ville PV CYCLE UAF UNIVERSITY OF ALASKA FAIRBANKS ACEP

4

Comparison testing based on sampling versus every module

Comparison subject	Sampling	Every module
Applicability	Only intact PV plants, preferably supported by O&M information like performance loss rate, drone images 	OK for testing all used modules  
Advantages	Fast, cheap and efficient	- Easier to standardise (more straightforward) - More guarantee for customer
Disadvantages	- Agreement required about justification for sampling and sampling rates	Slow and more expensive

IMO-IMOMEC UHASSELT imec EnergyVille PV CYCLE UAF UNIVERSITY OF ALASKA FAIRBANKS ACEP

5

Comparison testing based on sampling versus every module

Comparison subject	Sampling	Every module
Applicability	C… su… P…	OK for testing all used modules 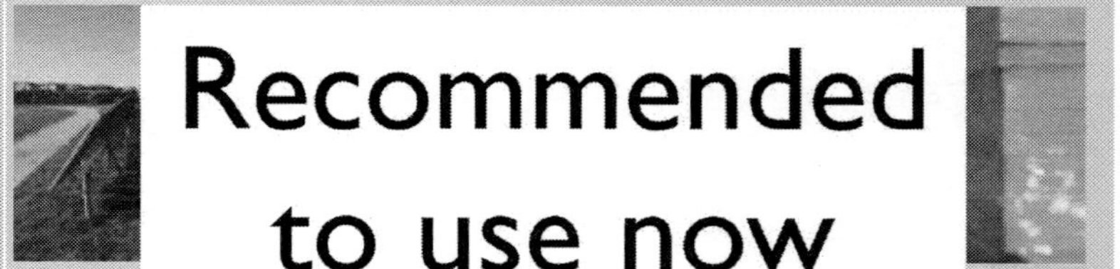
Advantages	F…	- Ea… …d) - M… guarantee for customer
Disadvantages	- … - …	Slow and more expensive

Not recommended for now, but for future standardisation efforts

Recommended to use now

IMO-IMOMEC UHASSELT imec EnergyVille PV CYCLE UAF UNIVERSITY OF ALASKA FAIRBANKS ACEP

Testing every module

- **Recommended tests** (after initial visual inspection):
  - I-V test
  - dry insulation test
  - (wet insulation test): only in case of certain replacements/repairs
  - bypass diode test (both shorted/open)
  - EL imaging

- Some companies in Germany already use such an approach in a factory line
- Typical speed per line: 60 modules/h
- On site testing typically ~ 20-30 modules/h

IMO-IMOMEC UHASSELT imec EnergyVille PV CYCLE UAF University of Alaska Fairbanks ACEP

Visual inspection

Basic principles of the visual inspection

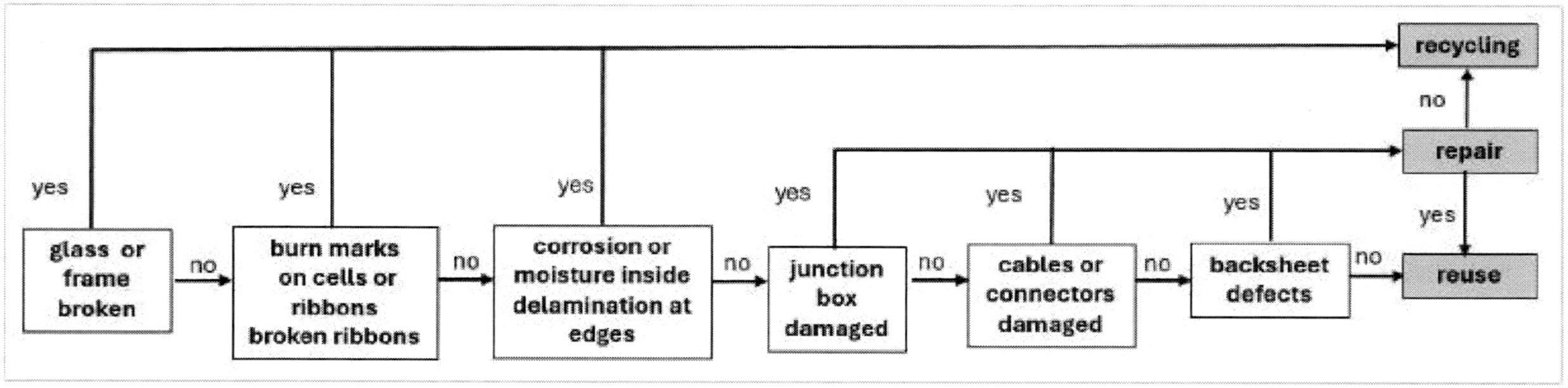

8

Visual inspection

Table with more detailed criteria on recommended pass/fail/deliberation of module

Example part of the table: →

Back-sheet: front & back view	Pass	Appearance and texture are like new.
Back-sheet: front & back view	Fail	Burn marks originating from internally. No repair (3.8) accepted.
Back-sheet: front & back view	Fail	Delamination that can occur from the edge to the centre, from the centre, or near a junction box, creating a void between the back-sheet and encapsulant, or between the layers of the back-sheet . No repair (3.8) accepted.
Back-sheet: front & back view	Fail	If cracks or chalking, along with corrosion visible from the front, are present.
Back-sheet: front & back view	Deliberate	Yellowing should be verified with an *I-V* test to assess performance at the batch level. PV modules should be free of burn marks or other anomalies.
Back-sheet: front & back view	Deliberate	Bubbles between the encapsulant and backsheet if the average bubble size is < 5 mm², the bubble is > 5 cm from the edge, and the total bubble area is < 1 % of the PV module area.
Back-sheet: front & back view	Deliberate	Superficial burn marks from an external source (e.g., grass fire) may require a polymer risk assessment for continued use. Individual patch repair (3.8) is possible based on technical and economic considerations. Wet insulation test depending on reuse application.

In **Annex C** also pictures have been included (back sheet chalking in this case)

↓

Defect Type	Representative Image
Chalking	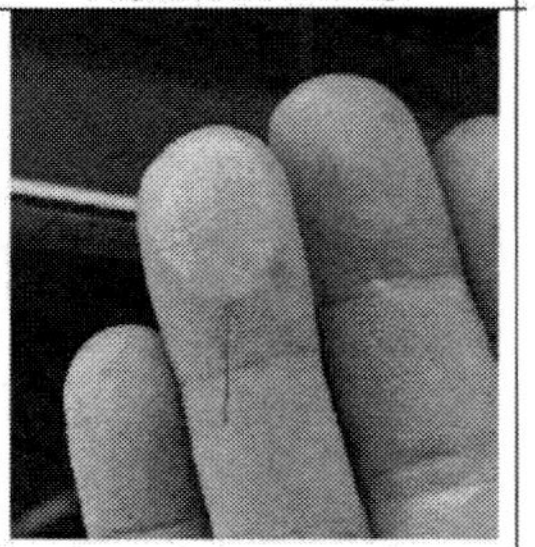

I-V test and remaining power

Recommendations:

- Modules have to be sufficiently clean
- I-V test can be done either **outdoor** or **indoor**, either **on-site** or at a **reuse test facility**
- **Remaining P_{max} > guaranteed P_{max}**, taking into account nameplate negative tolerance, module age and measuring tolerance (default value 5%). Lower P_{max} only when agreed with end user

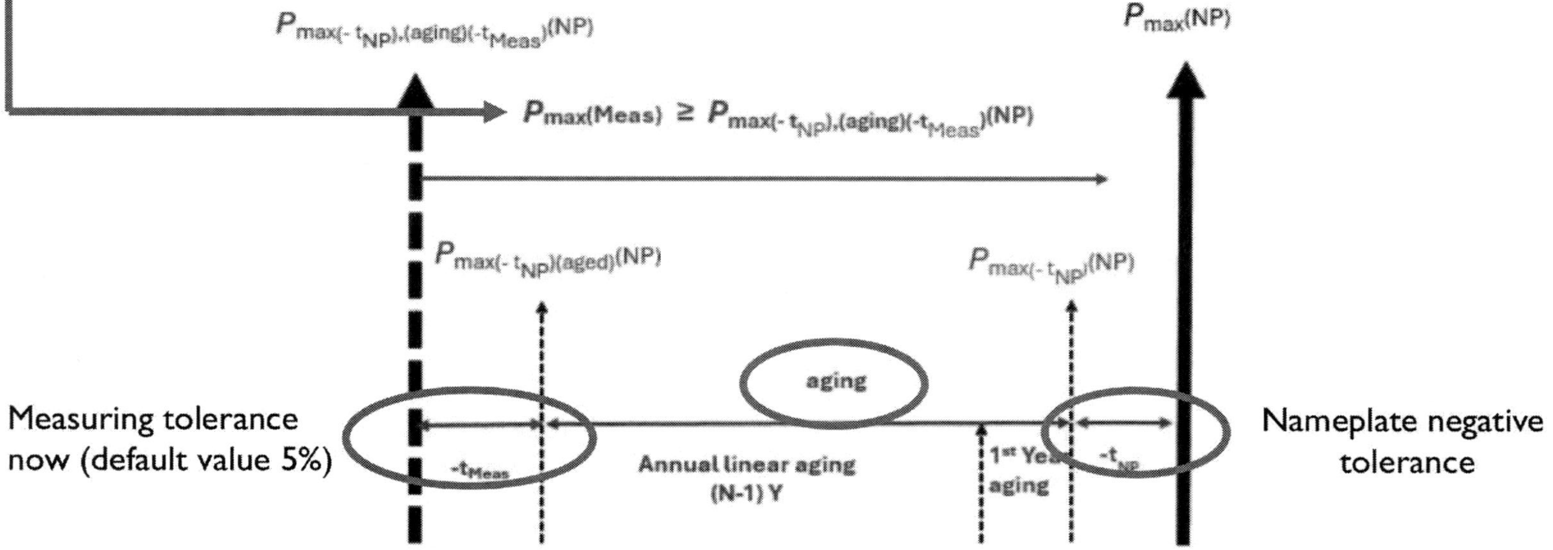

IMO-IMOMEC UHASSELT imec EnergyVille PV CYCLE UAF University of Alaska Fairbanks ACEP

EL imaging and criteria on cell cracks

- Cell crack classification A, B, C conform IEC TS 60904-13
  - A: line defects not isolating cell area
  - B: cracks causing partially disconnected regions
  - C: cracks causing completely disconnected regions

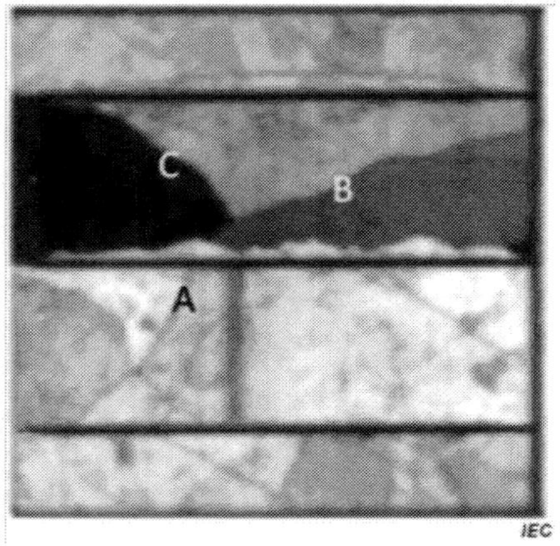

- Recommendation:

  To accept a module for reuse
  - Only if < 50% of cells are crack affected
  - Mode A cracks allowed if affected cell area < 1%
  - Mode B cracks allowed if 1% < affected cell area < 20% and in < 20% of cells
  - Mode C cracks allowed if affected area > 20% but < 5% of the cells

IMO-IMOMEC UHASSELT imec EnergyVille PV CYCLE UAF University of Alaska Fairbanks ACEP

Insulation testing

Insulation test	IEC 61730 (class II modules)	Recommended adaptations
Dry insulation test	2000 V + 4*$V_{sys,max}$ for 1 min (ramping up < 500 V/s) Followed by $V_{sys,max}$ for 2 min, then measuring R_{iso} Required: no breakdown & R_{iso}*area > 40 MΩm²	Dwell time 1 s, ramp up optional > 500 V/s Dwell time 1 s, then measuring R_{iso}
Wet leakage current test	Immersion of module in shallow water tank $V_{sys,max}$ for 2 min, then measuring R_{iso} Required: no breakdown & R_{iso}*area > 40 MΩm²	On site: water spraying (ASTM E2047-10) Indoor: water tank (or optional spraying) Dwell time 1 s, then measuring R_{iso}

Remarks:

Earlier determination R_{iso} : worst-case scenario, leakage current can be higher at start (capacitances)

Dry insulation test: for testing every module

Wet insulation test: not practical, only after certain repairs or sampling in PV plants

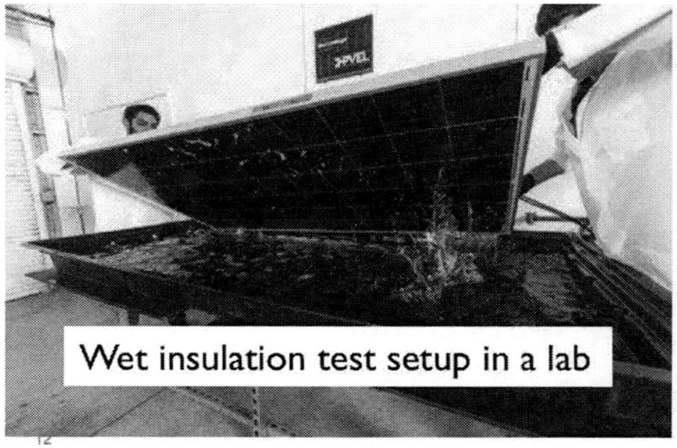

Wet insulation test setup in a lab

12

Detection limitations of insulation tests

Limitations dry insulation test:

- Result depends on storage condition (humidity) before testing: drying helps to pass
- “Dried modules” can still pass with damage (e.g. backsheet cracks): visual inspection also important

Limitation wet insulation test:

- Some defects not penetrated by liquid water, but sensitive to humid air

Alternative insulation tests for reuse have been proposed very recently, but too late for the TR*
However, can be useful for future standardisation

- *E.R.Anagha et. al, Solar Energy Materials and Solar Cells, Volume 292, 2025*
- *Maximilian Engel et.al, this conference 3AV.3.21*

IMO-IMOMEC UHASSELT imec EnergyVille PV CYCLE UAF University of Alaska Fairbanks ACEP Alaska Center for Energy and Power

Relabelling

- Next to original label
- Always with maximum system voltage (possibly reduced for reduced insulation quality)
- Label in the case of repair
- Also new electric parameters can be mentioned (below)

REUSE PV MODULE	
Prepared for reuse by: Name, address, website URL	Date:
Maximum DC system voltage	xxx V
Following recommendations from IEC TR 63525	

REUSE PV MODULE	
Prepared for reuse by: Name, address, website URL	Date:
-Replaced Connector[] -Replaced Cable [] -Replaced Diode [] -Replaced Junction Box [] -Resoldered diode [] -Resoldered junction box [] , -Repaired backsheet []	
Maximum DC system voltage	xxx V
Following recommendations from IEC TR 63525	

REUSE PV MODULE		
Prepared for reuse by: Name, address, website URL		Date:
Maximum power	P_{max}	xxx W
Maximum power voltage	V_{mp}	xxx V
Maximum power current	I_{mp}	xxx A
Open circuit voltage	V_{OC}	xxx V
Short circuit current	I_{SC}	xxx A
Maximum DC system voltage		xxx V
Following recommendations from IEC TR 63525		

IMO-IMOMEC UHASSELT imec EnergyVille PV CYCLE UAF University of Alaska Fairbanks ACEP

Summary

- TR working draft text finished
- Recommended to test every module until standard for sampling approach will be available
- Visual inspection list including example pictures in Annex provided
- Tests and criteria have been described for: I-V, (fast) dry/wet insulation test, bypass diode test, EL
- Minimum remaining P_{max}: based on age, still > guaranteed P_{max} , including nameplate tolerance and measuring uncertainty
- Reduced maximum system voltage for certain repairs and lower insulation quality

Acknowledgements

The authors thank **all the IEC experts of the project team** that have contributed to this final working draft

The contribution to this IEC TR draft by Serge Noels as project team lead and editor of the draft has been funded from

Dec 2021 – Nov 2022 : By **CIRCUSOL** - This project has received funding from the European Union's Horizon 2020 research and innovation programme under grant agreement number 776680

Funded by the European Union

Dec 2022 – Sep 2025 : By **PV CYCLE**

The contribution to this IEC TR draft by Arvid van der Heide at imec has been funded in part by the **CLOSER** project.

This project has received funding from the European Union's I3 instrument under grant agreement number 101161109

Funded by the European Union

16

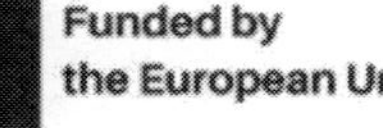

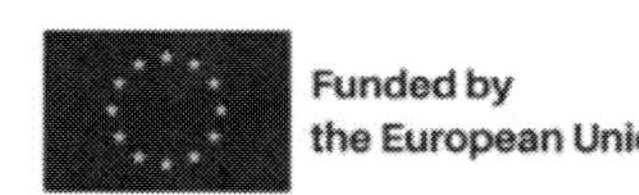

BECQUEREL INSTITUTE
Strategy Consulting in Solar PV

Business model optimization for European Solar PV: A study on costs & commercial strategies

Ian Kenchington[a], Philippe Macé[a], Gaëtan Masson[a], Joris Libal[b]

[a] Becquerel Institute (Belgium)
[b] ISC Konstanz (Germany)

ISC IBC4EU

This project has received funding from the European Union's Horizon Europe under grant agreement № 101084259

Funded by the European Union

BECQUEREL INSTITUTE
Strategy Consulting in Solar PV

Becquerel Institute at a Glance

- Est. 2014 in **Brussels, Belgium**
- Est. 2022 in **France**
- Est. 2023 in **Spain**
- Est. 2025 in **Italy**
- Focused on **solar PV**

Strategy Consulting

Technical Assistance

Applied Research

They Trust Us

Project Developers

TotalEnergies · EDF renouvelables · CNR · galp · AMARENCO

Manufacturers

VOLTEC solar · SAINT-GOBAIN · ArcelorMittal · CARBON · MONDRAGON ASSEMBLY

Associations

ETIP Photovoltaics · IEA PVPS · isa International Solar Alliance · eit InnoEnergy · giz Deutsche Gesellschaft für Internationale Zusammenarbeit (GIZ) GmbH

Researchers

tecnalia · eurac research · CENER · Fraunhofer ISE · cea · ines

BECQUEREL INSTITUTE

Table of Contents

1 | Context

2 | Research Questions

3 | Our Approach

4 | Main Results

5 | Takeaways

BECQUEREL INSTITUTE

Table of Contents

1 | Context

2 | Research Questions

3 | Our Approach

4 | Main Results

5 | Takeaways

1 | Context

BECQUEREL INSTITUTE

Prices of PV modules collapsed to unstainable levels as production has largely outpaced market demand and competition among Chinese manufacturers has been as fierce as ever

Weekly evolution of PV *modules* average spot prices (in USD/Wp)

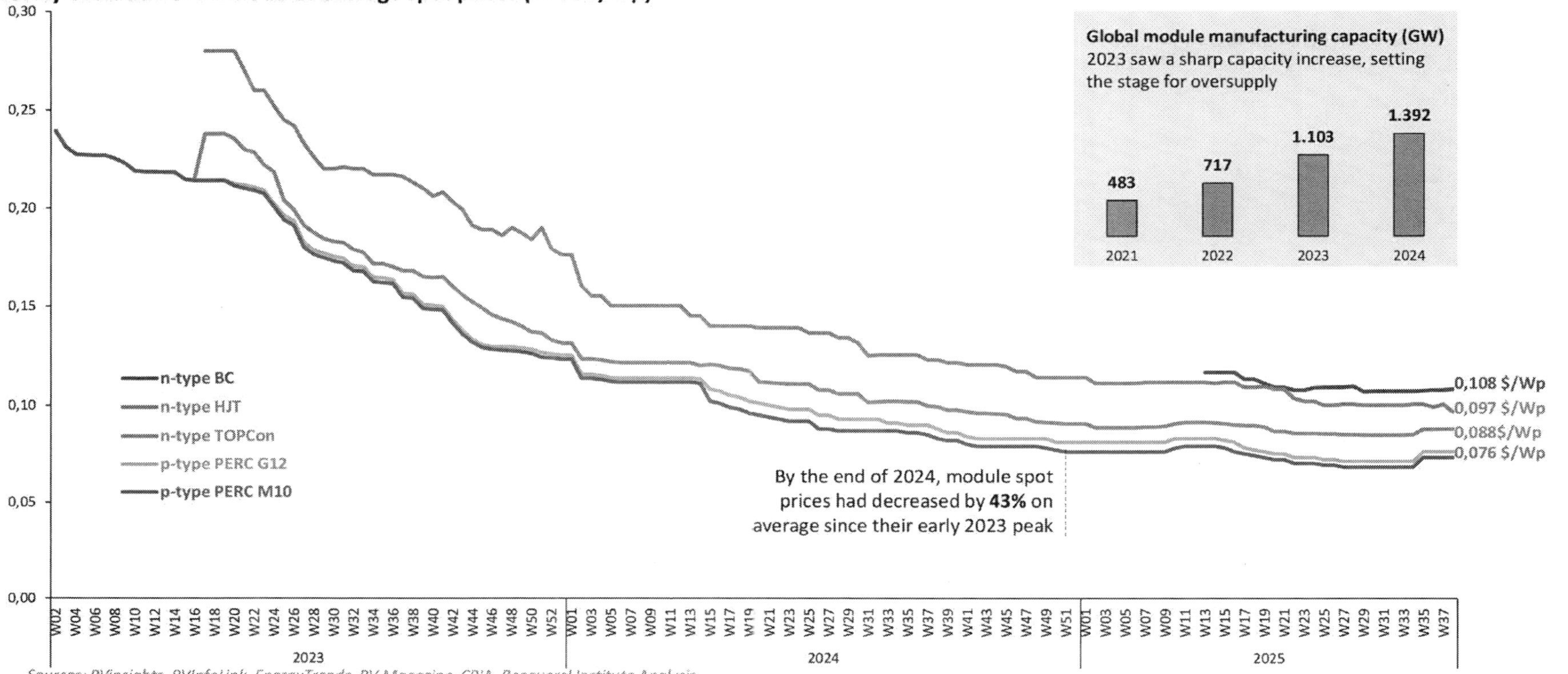

Sources: PVinsights, PVInfoLink, EnergyTrends, PV Magazine, CPIA, Becquerel Institute Analysis

1 | Context

BECQUEREL INSTITUTE

Spot prices seen since mid-2024 are below production costs, leading to heavy losses and threatening the existence of many actors, even the biggest ones

Average production cost* in FY 2024 (US$/Wp)

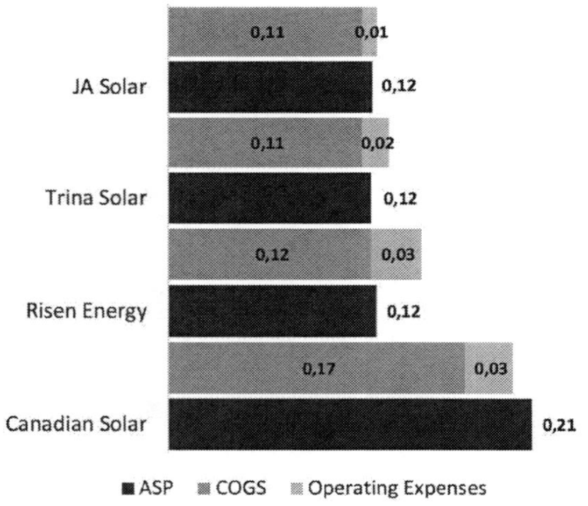

*Factory gate manufacturing cost, i.e. without margin and without transportation costs
**Canadian Solar calculations are made out of the revenues, COGS and operational expenses from the business unit CSI Solar that produces more than just solar PV modules.

Sources: Becquerel Institute analysis based on financial reports

1 | Context

BECQUEREL INSTITUTE

Spot prices seen since mid-2024 are below production costs, leading to heavy losses and threatening the existence of many actors, even the biggest ones

Average production cost* in FY 2024 (US$/Wp)

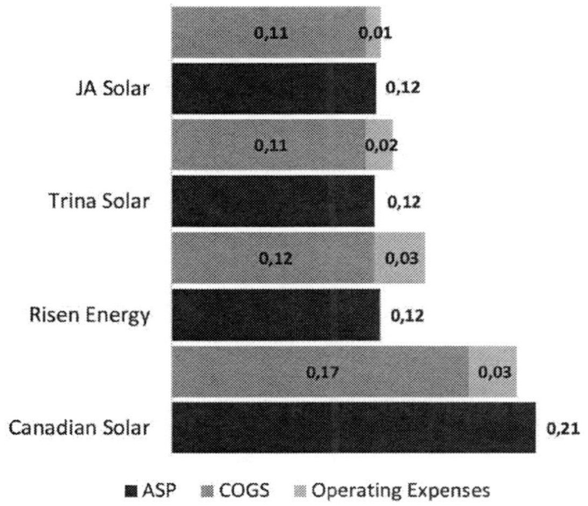

*Factory gate manufacturing cost, i.e. without margin and without transportation costs
**Canadian Solar calculations are made out of the revenues, COGS and operational expenses from the business unit CSI Solar that produces more than just solar PV modules.

Cumulative Losses FY 2024 + H1 2025 (US$ Million)

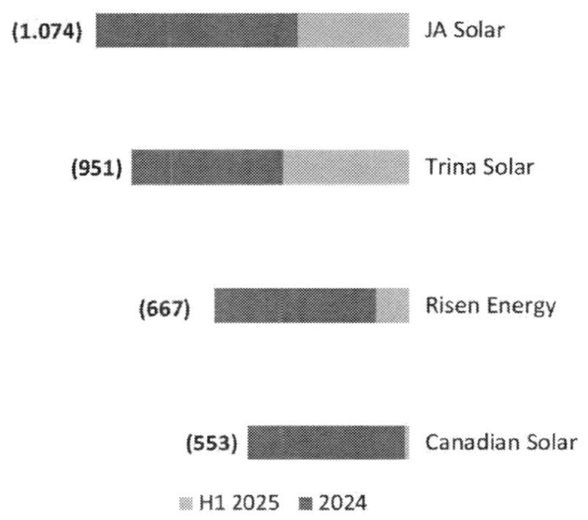

Sources: Becquerel Institute analysis based on financial reports

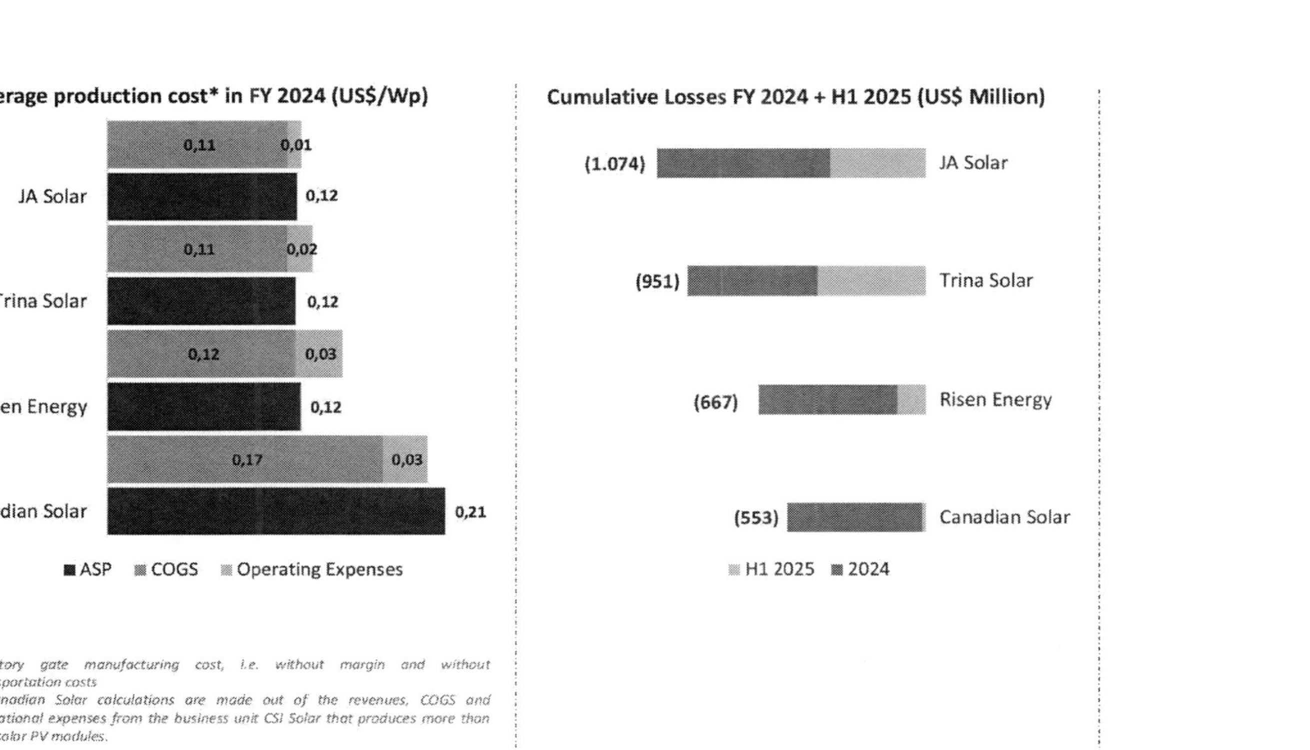

1 | Context

BECQUEREL INSTITUTE

Spot prices seen since mid-2024 are below production costs, leading to heavy losses and threatening the existence of many actors, even the biggest ones

Average production cost* in FY 2024 (US$/Wp)

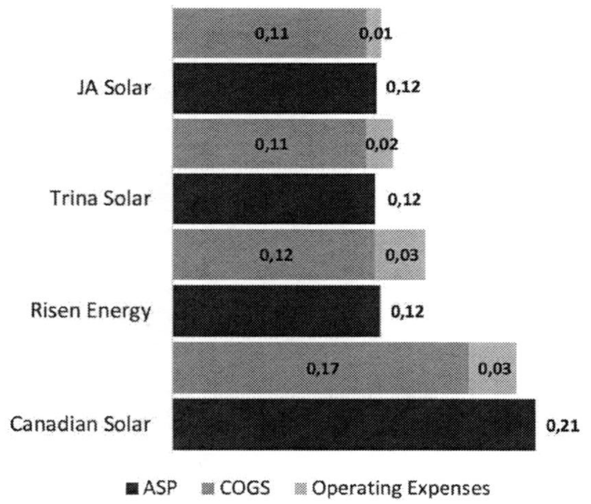

*Factory gate manufacturing cost, i.e. without margin and without transportation costs
**Canadian Solar calculations are made out of the revenues, COGS and operational expenses from the business unit CSI Solar that produces more than just solar PV modules.

Cumulative Losses FY 2024 + H1 2025 (US$ Million)

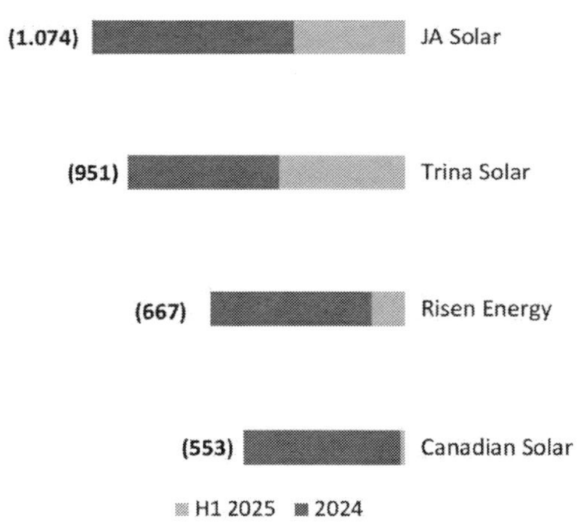

Cash Burn Rate* in H1 2025 (Months)

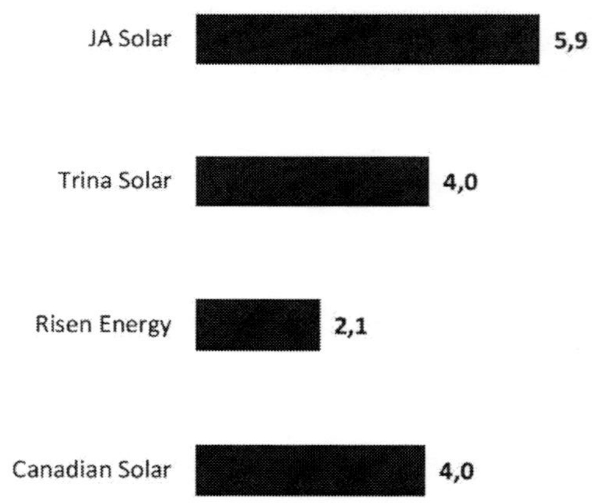

*Number of months during which Cash Balance could fund COGS + Operating Expenses

Sources: Becquerel Institute analysis based on financial reports

The European solar manufacturing sector suffers collateral damage from global overcapacity, with multiple closures in the last 18 months

Meyer Burger to cease PV module production in Germany

Meyer Burger, a Switzerland-based heterojunction cell and panel manufacturer, says it will stop making PV modules in Germany, but it will continue to produce solar cells in the country to support its panel production operations in the United States.

JANUARY 17, 2024 EMILIANO BELLINI

Exasun files for insolvency

Exasun, a Dutch manufacturer that specializes in building-integrated photovoltaics (BIPV), has blamed Chinese rivals for its decision to launch insolvency proceedings.

JANUARY 22, 2024 EMILIANO BELLINI

French PV module maker Systovi goes into liquidation

Systovi has gone into liquidation, as the commercial court in Nantes, France, has issued an order to do so, citing the solar panel manufacturer's failure to find new investors, despite its 80 MW of panel manufacturing capacity.

APRIL 18, 2024 GWÉNAËLLE DEBOUTTE

Aleo Solar to halt production at PV module factory in Germany

Aleo Solar says it will halt production at its solar panel factory in Prenzlau, Germany, affecting 110 employees. The manufacturer is a unit of Taiwan's Sino-American Silicon.

MARCH 10, 2025 SANDRA ENKHARDT

Solarwatt to close German solar module factory in August

The module manufacturing facility is located in Dresden, eastern Germany, and has an annual capacity of 300 MW.

APRIL 29, 2024 SANDRA ENKHARDT

BECQUEREL INSTITUTE

Table of Contents

1 | Context

2 | Research Questions

3 | Our Approach

4 | Main Results

5 | Takeaways

How to minimise the cost gap with Chinese competitors...

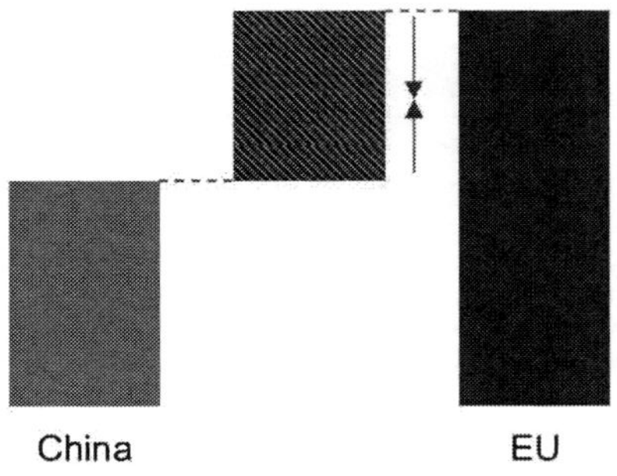

- *Location choice*
- *Bill of materials*
- *Level of integration*

How to minimise the cost gap with Chinese competitors…

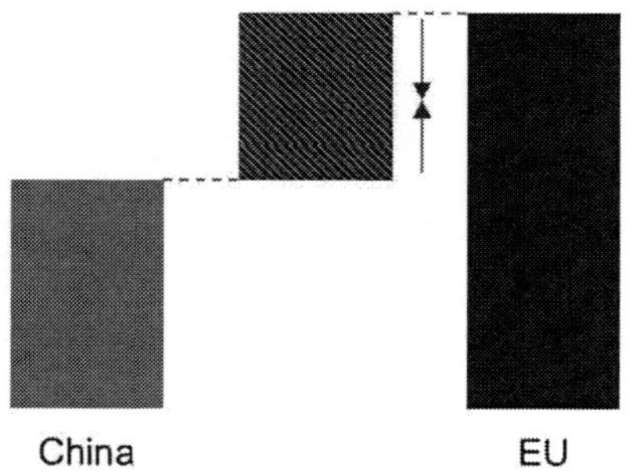

- *Location choice*
- *Bill of materials*
- *Level of integration*

…and maximise the chances of reaching a sustainable business…

- *Equipment procurement*
- *Supplier relationships*
- *Choice of market segments*

BECQUEREL INSTITUTE

How to minimise the cost gap with Chinese competitors...

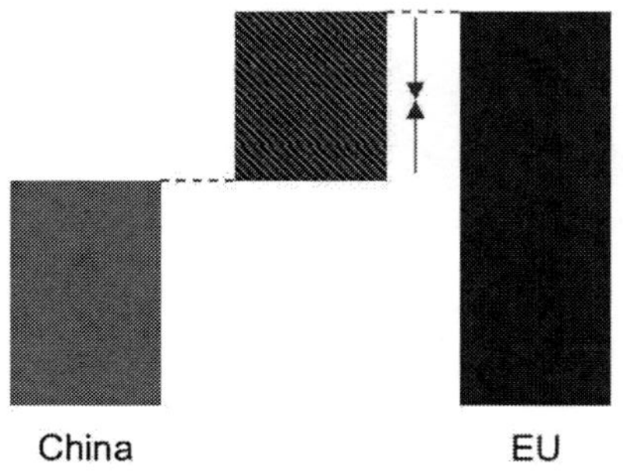

- *Location choice*
- *Bill of materials*
- *Level of integration*

...and maximise the chances of reaching a sustainable business...

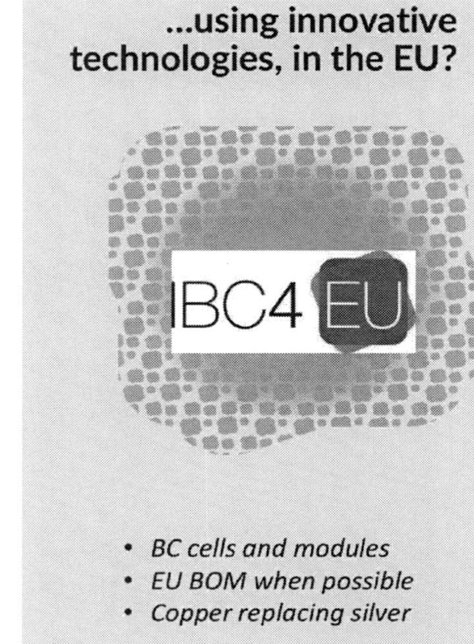

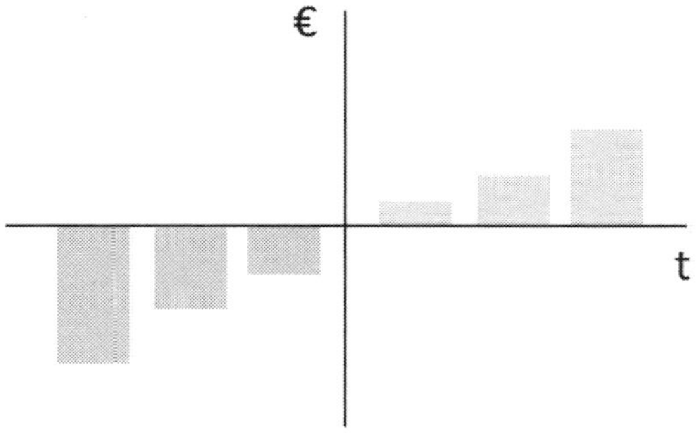

- *Equipment procurement*
- *Supplier relationships*
- *Choice of market segments*

...using innovative technologies, in the EU?

IBC4EU

- *BC cells and modules*
- *EU BOM when possible*
- *Copper replacing silver*

BECQUEREL INSTITUTE
Strategy Consulting in Solar PV

Table of Contents

1 | Context

2 | Research Questions

3 | **Our Approach**

4 | Main Results

5 | Takeaways

BECQUEREL INSTITUTE
Strategy Consulting in Solar PV

By using a Business Model Canvas approach, we can identify key business activities within manufacturing that affect business performance

Key Partnerships
- Material suppliers
- Equip. Manufacturers
- Distributors
- Research institutions
- Logistic companies

Key Activities
- Manufacturing
- R&D
- Quality control
- SC management
- Sales & marketing

Key Resources
- Manufacturing plants
- Tech & IP
- Skilled workforce
- Raw materials
- Financial capitals

Value Proposition
- High-efficiency modules
- Long-term warranties
- Sustainability
- Cost-effective solutions

Channels
- Distributors
- Direct sales
- Online platforms
- Trade shows & exhibitions

Customer Relationships
- B2B sales: EPC, contractors & utility companies
- After-sales service
- Customer support

Customer Segments
- Utility scale
- C&I
- Residential
- Distributors & EPC
- IPV

Cost Structure
- Raw materials costs
- Manufacturing costs
- R&D costs
- Sales & marketing expenses
- Logistics

Revenue Streams
- Module sales
- Licensing technology

We broke down the analysis into three analytical steps

Key Partnerships
- Material suppliers
- Equip. Manufacturers
- Distributors
- Research institutions
- Logistic companies

Key Activities
- Manufacturing
- R&D
- Quality control
- SC management
- Sales & marketing

Key Resources
- Manufacturing plants
- Tech & IP
- Skilled workforce
- Raw materials
- Financial capitals

Value Proposition
- High-efficiency modules
- Long-term warranties
- Sustainability
- Cost-effective solutions

Channels
- Distributors
- Direct sales
- Online platforms
- Trade shows & exhibitions

Customer Relationships
- B2B sales: EPC, contractors & utility companies
- After-sales service
- Customer support

Customer Segments
- Utility scale
- C&I
- Residential
- Distributors & EPC
- IPV

Cost Structure
- Raw materials costs
- Manufacturing costs
- R&D costs
- Sales & marketing expenses
- Logistics

Revenue Streams
- Module sales
- Licensing technology

1st Step

BECQUEREL INSTITUTE
Strategy Consulting in Solar PV

We broke down the analysis into three analytical steps

Key Partnerships
- Material suppliers
- Equip. Manufacturers
- Distributors
- Research institutions
- Logistic companies

Key Activities
- Manufacturing
- R&D
- Quality control
- SC management
- Sales & marketing

Key Resources
- Manufacturing plants
- Tech & IP
- Skilled workforce
- Raw materials
- Financial capitals

Value Proposition
- High-efficiency modules
- Long-term warranties
- Sustainability
- Cost-effective solutions

Channels
- Distributors
- Direct sales
- Online platforms
- Trade shows & exhibitions

Customer Relationships
- B2B sales: EPC, contractors & utility companies
- After-sales service
- Customer support

Customer Segments
- Utility scale
- C&I
- Residential
- Distributors & EPC
- IPV

Cost Structure
- Raw materials costs
- Manufacturing costs
- R&D costs
- Sales & marketing expenses
- Logistics

Revenue Streams
- Module sales
- Licensing technology

1st Step

2nd Step

BECQUEREL INSTITUTE

We broke down the analysis into three analytical steps

Key Partnerships
- Material suppliers
- Equip. Manufacturers
- Distributors
- Research institutions
- Logistic companies

Key Activities
- Manufacturing
- R&D
- Quality control
- SC management
- Sales & marketing

Key Resources
- Manufacturing plants
- Tech & IP
- Skilled workforce
- Raw materials
- Financial capitals

Value Proposition
- High-efficiency modules
- Long-term warranties
- Sustainability
- Cost-effective solutions

Channels
- Distributors
- Direct sales
- Online platforms
- Trade shows & exhibitions

Customer Relationships
- B2B sales: EPC, contractors & utility companies
- After-sales service
- Customer support

Customer Segments
- Utility scale
- C&I
- Residential
- Distributors & EPC
- IPV

3rd Step

Cost Structure
- Raw materials costs
- Manufacturing costs
- R&D costs
- Sales & marketing expenses
- Logistics

1st Step

2nd Step

Revenue Streams
- Module sales
- Licensing technology

BECQUEREL INSTITUTE

Our methodology combines ISC Konstanz technical expertise in upstream cost assessment, with Becquerel Institute's experience in module cost evaluation and business models

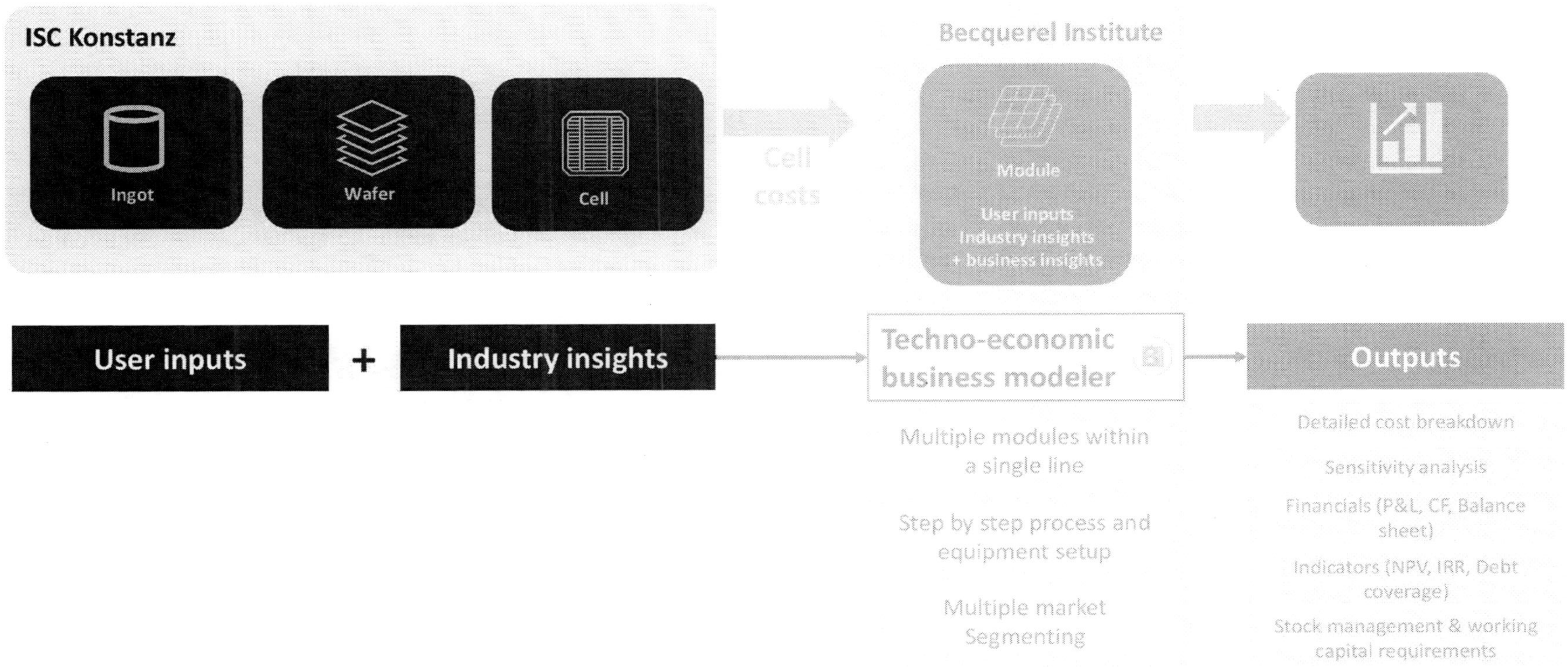

BECQUEREL INSTITUTE
Strategy Consulting in Solar PV

Our methodology combines ISC Konstanz technical expertise in upstream cost assessment, with Becquerel Institute's experience in module cost evaluation and business models

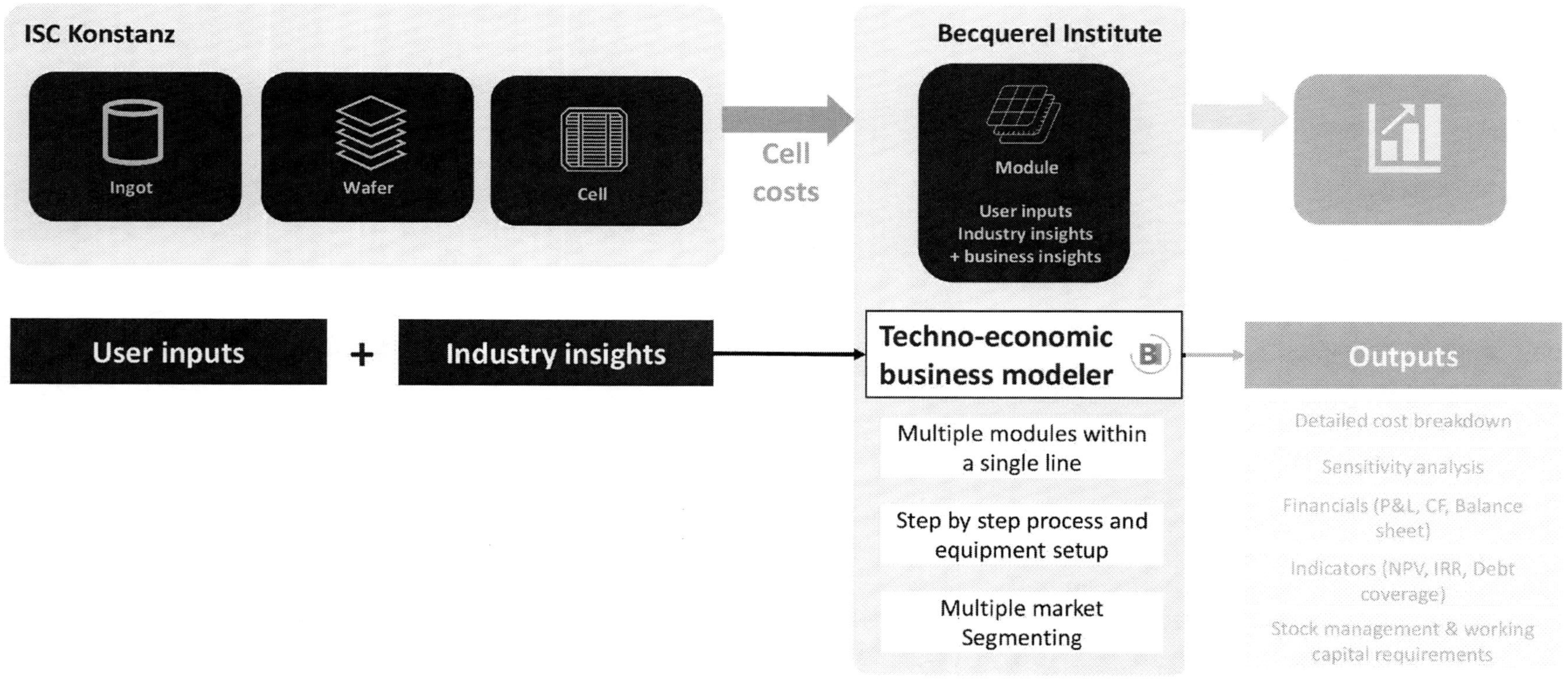

BECQUEREL INSTITUTE

Our methodology combines ISC Konstanz technical expertise in upstream cost assessment, with Becquerel Institute's experience in module cost evaluation and business models

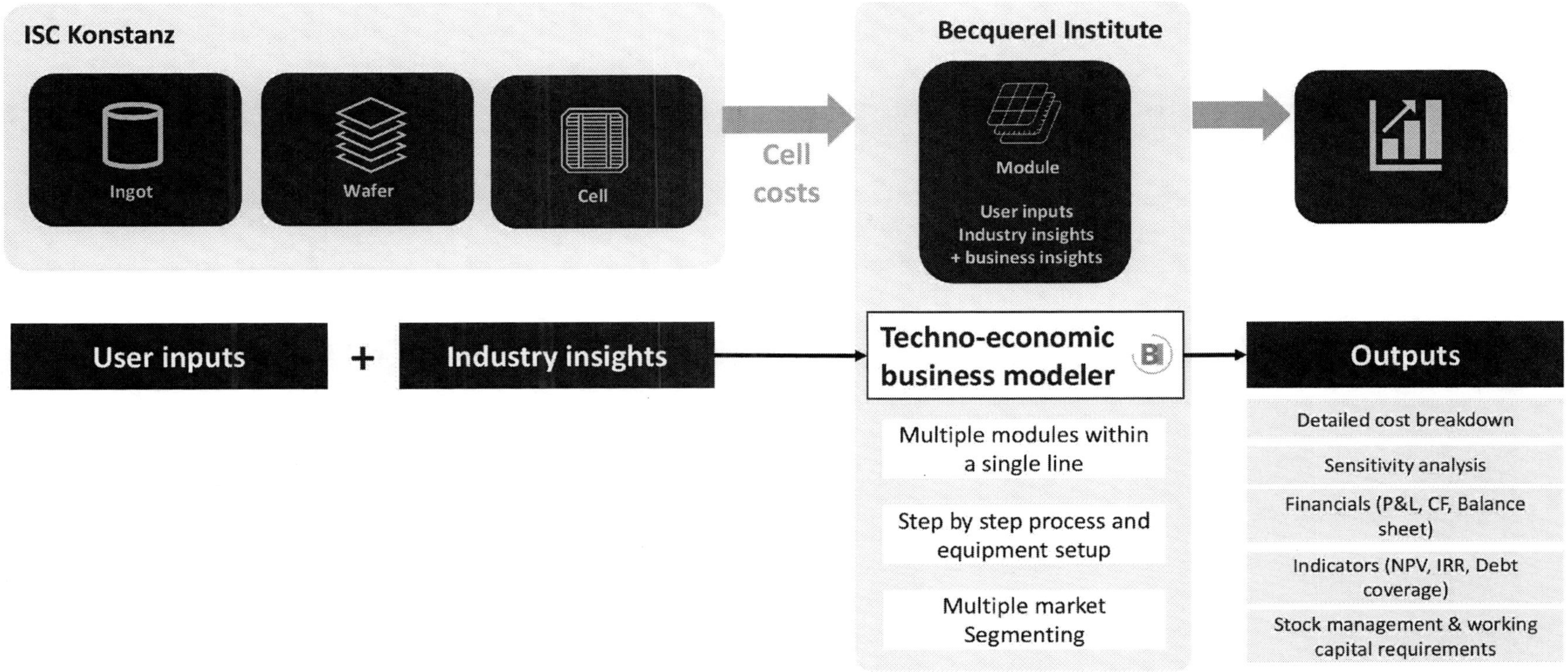

BECQUEREL INSTITUTE

Table of Contents

1 | Context

2 | Research Questions

3 | Our Approach

4 | **Main Results**

5 | Takeaways

BECQUEREL INSTITUTE

First step: What to make, where to make it

Before addressing the full business model, cost structures are first studied

- **Location choice**: EU low-cost or high-cost country
- **Materials used**: Mainstream Ag metallisation or innovative Cu alternative
- **Level of integration**: Importing cells from abroad, using EU-made cells, or fully EU-made value chain.

BECQUEREL INSTITUTE

First step: What to make, where to make it

Before addressing the full business model, cost structures are first studied

- **Location choice**: EU low-cost or high-cost country
- **Materials used**: Mainstream Ag metallisation or innovative Cu alternative
- **Level of integration**: Importing cells from abroad, using EU-made cells, or fully EU-made value chain.

Modules - Total Cost of Ownership (€cent /Wp) per level of integration and metallisation choice

Bars represent cost range between location

BECQUEREL INSTITUTE

First step: What to make, where to make it

Before addressing the full business model, cost structures are first studied

- **Location choice**: EU low-cost or high-cost country
- **Materials used**: Mainstream Ag metallisation or innovative Cu alternative
- **Level of integration**: Importing cells from abroad, using EU-made cells, or fully EU-made value chain.

Modules - Total Cost of Ownership (€cent /Wp) per level of integration and metallisation choice

Bars represent cost range between location

1. Operations must be in a low-cost location
2. Cell cost reductions are the main priority
3. Integration should be minimal at first to reach competitive costs

BECQUEREL INSTITUTE

First step: What to make, where to make it

Before addressing the full business model, cost structures are first studied

- **Location choice**: EU low-cost or high-cost country
- **Materials used**: Mainstream Ag metallisation or innovative Cu alternative
- **Level of integration**: Importing cells from abroad, using EU-made cells, or fully EU-made value chain.

Modules - Total Cost of Ownership (€cent /Wp) per level of integration and metallisation choice

Bars represent cost range between location

1 **Operations must be in a low-cost location**

2 **Cell cost reductions are the main priority**

3 **Integration should be minimal at first to reach competitive costs**

Second and Third step: We set out scenarios to test their impact in business performance

With starting strategy: Imported BC cells, low-cost EU location for modules' assembling

A. Cash management

A.1 **Equipment acquisition strategy**
Operational lease instead of purchase

A.2 **Just in Time manufacturing**
Reducing inventory levels

A.3 **Favourable payment conditions**
Deferring a fraction of payments

A.4 **Grants**
Reducing total CAPEX required

B. Sales optimisation

B.1 **Alternative market segments**
Carports, agrivoltaics, BIPV

B.2 **Downwards integration**
Direct end-user sales

B.3 **Aggressive diversified sales**
Alternative markets + end-user sales

B.4 **Sales de-risking**
Acting as OEM for third companies

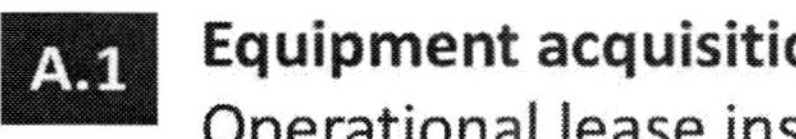

BECQUEREL INSTITUTE

Scenarios are developed through iterations from a defined business case

A.1

A.2

A.3

A.4

B.1

B.2

B.3

B.4

Base Case

NPV **0,4 M€**

IRR **7,5 %**

Targeting three segments:

Residential (Small 54 GB), **50% prod.**
- Channels: Distributors, installers

Commercial (Medium 60 GB), **30% prod.**
- Channels: Distributors, installers

Utility (Large 72 GG), **20% prod.**
- Channels: EPCs, developers

Yearly Cumulative Cash Flow after debt servicing (CFADS), in M€

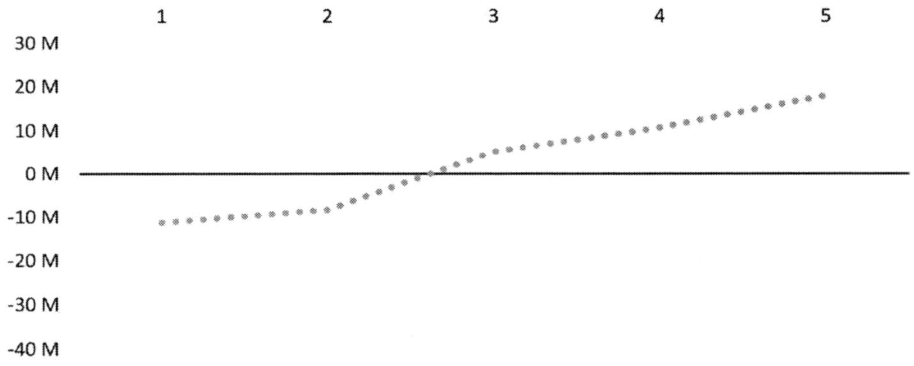

Segment	Channel	Selling price /Wp
Residential	Distributors	22,8 €ct
C&I	Distributors	20,7 €ct
C&I	Installers	23,0 €ct
Utility	EPC	20,0 €ct
Utility	Developers	20,7 €ct

BECQUEREL INSTITUTE

Operational leasing reduces CAPEX, but turns depreciation into cash expenses

A.1

A.2

A.3

A.4

B.1

B.2

B.3

B.4

A.1 Leased Equipment

NPV	IRR
▼(2,6 M€)	▼5,1 %

? Instead of **purchasing** equipment, it is acquired via **operational leasing**.

\+ Lower CAPEX (reduced early cash outflow, which can be crucial in a time of limited available financing)

\- Reduced total cash from operations (lease payments). Interests can be very high due to the high risk perception & limited number of actors

Yearly cumulative Cash Flow after debt servicing (CFADS), in M€

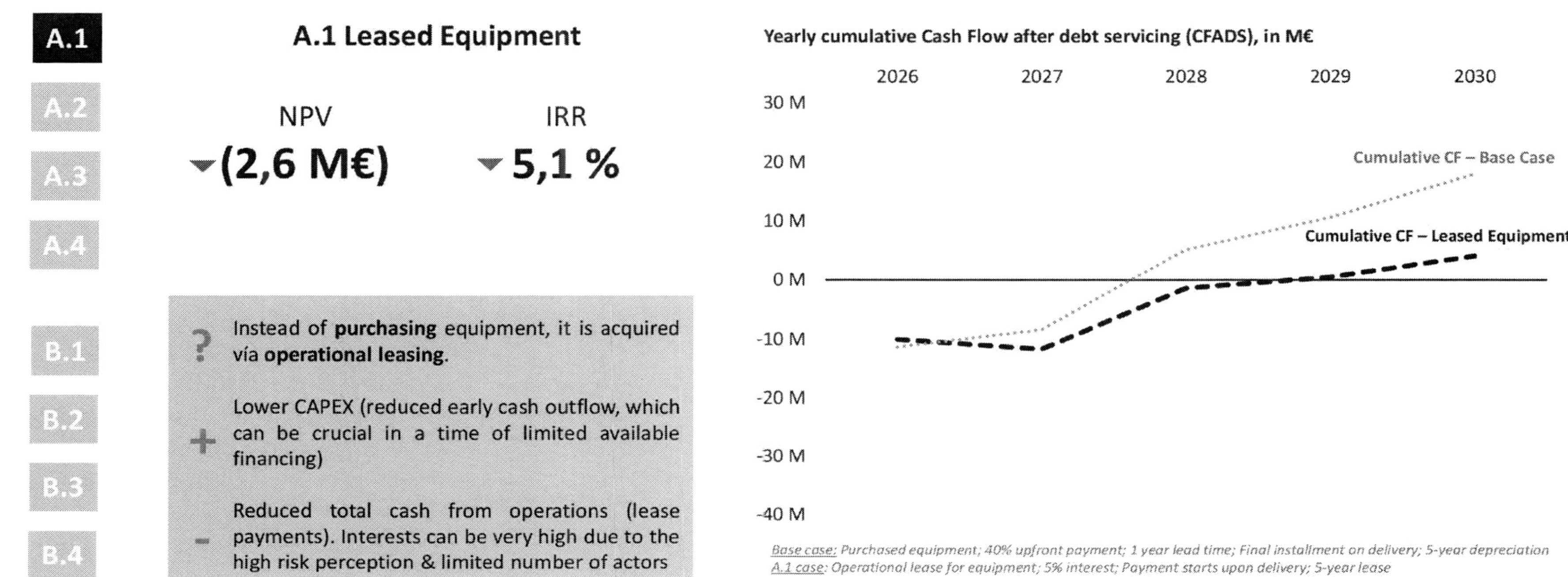

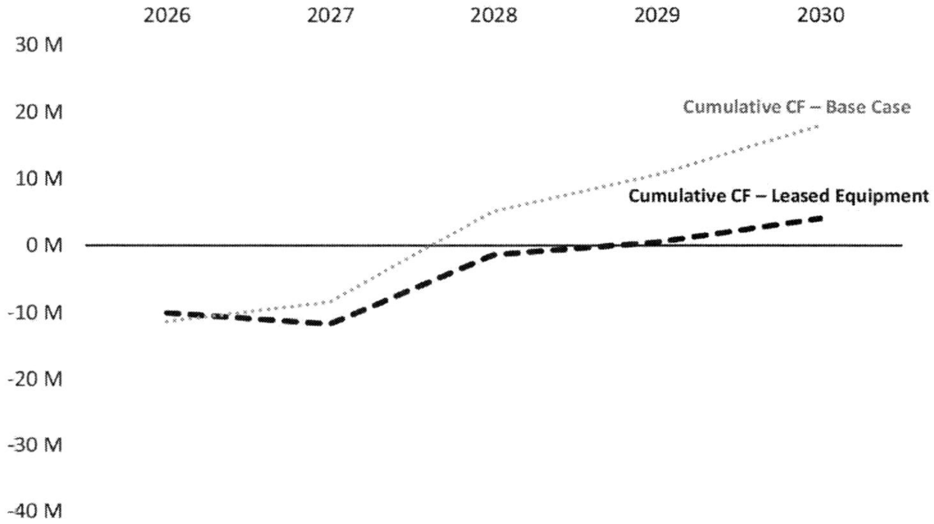

Base case: Purchased equipment; 40% upfront payment; 1 year lead time; Final installment on delivery; 5-year depreciation
A.1 case: Operational lease for equipment; 5% interest; Payment starts upon delivery; 5-year lease

Minimizing inventory levels keeps manufacturing costs lean on cash

A.1
A.2
A.3
A.4

B.1
B.2
B.3
B.4

A.2 Just-in-Time Manufacturing

NPV	IRR
▲ 10,7 M€	▲ 15,1 %

? Optimising value chain, minimising required inventories of raw materials.

\+ Lower working capital requirements (for the same manufacturing cost)

\- Higher supply chain risk

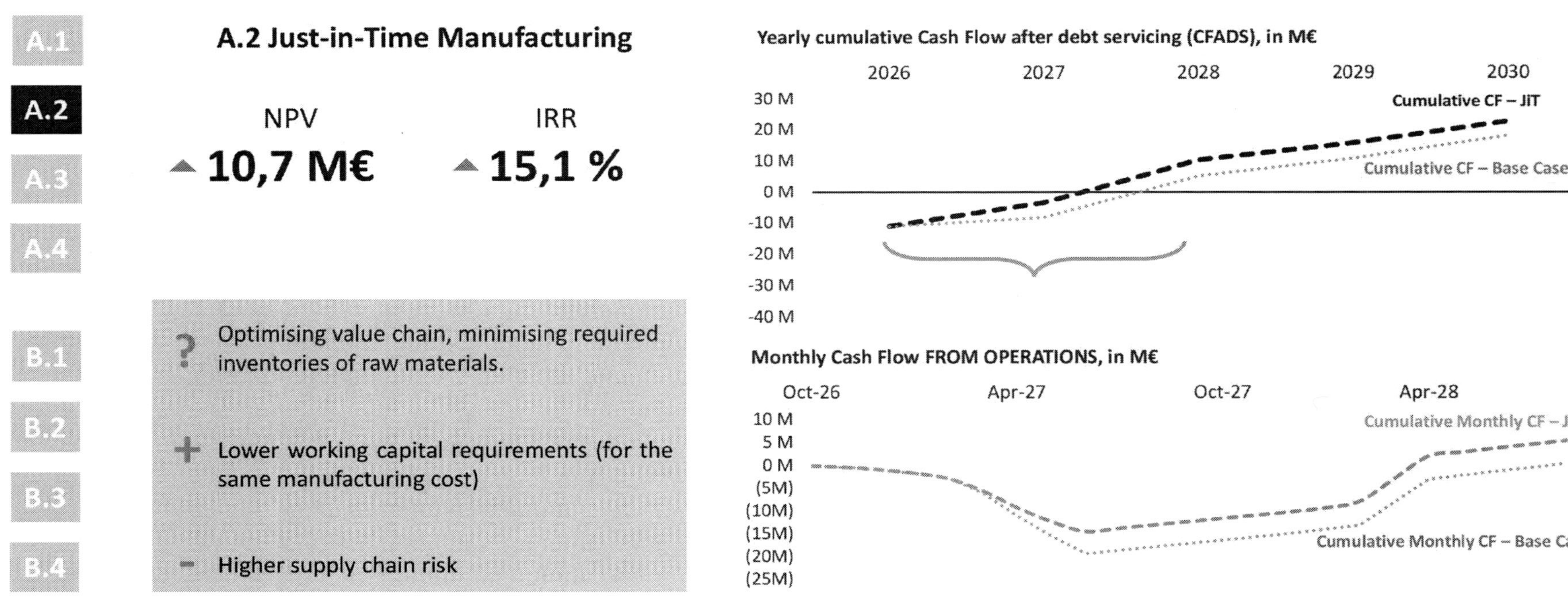

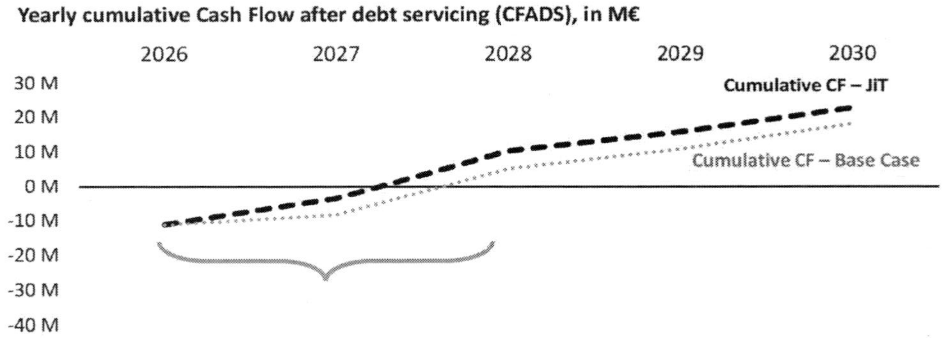

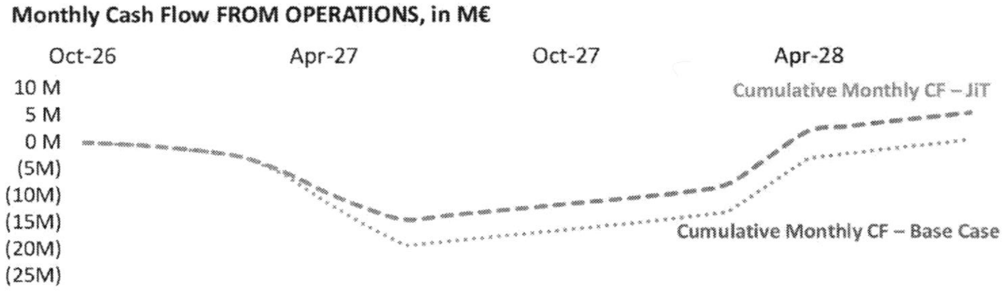

Base case: 2 months worth of inventories at the start of each month
A.2 case: 1 month of inventories at the start of each month

Better supplier relationships reduce working capital requirements

A.1
A.2
A.3
A.4

B.1
B.2
B.3
B.4

A.3 Favourable Payment Conditions

NPV	IRR
▲ 1,1 M€	▲ 8,2 %

? Initially, everything is paid upfront. After 4 months, 50% upfront only.

\+ Deferring payments reduces early BOM investments, increasing cash savings from operations (in blue)

\- Difficulties to find accepting suppliers, and it may come with a risk premium

Yearly cumulative Cash Flow after debt servicing (CFADS), in M€

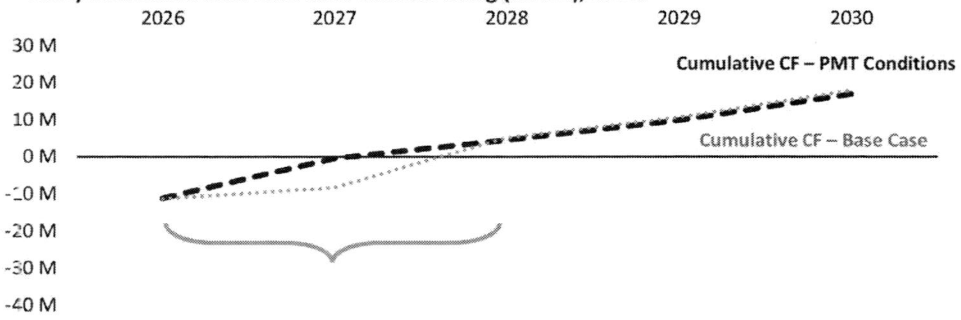

Monthly Cash Flow FROM OPERATIONS, in M€

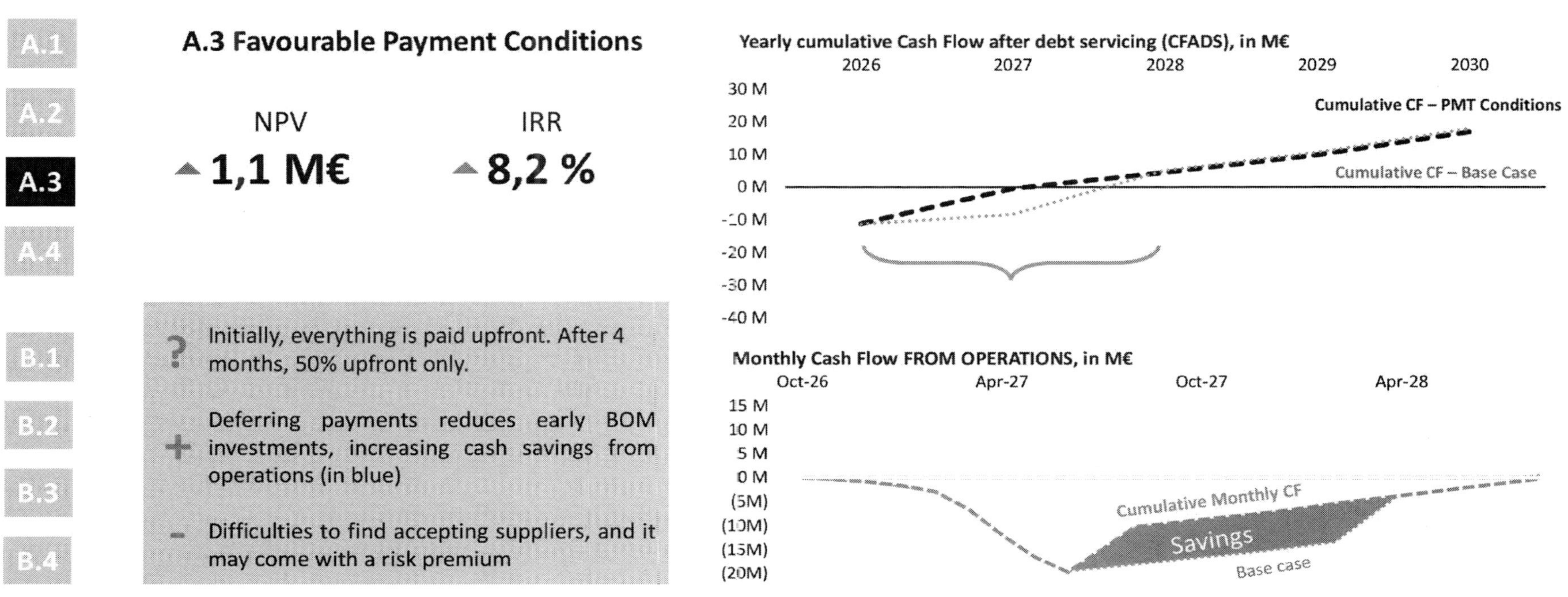

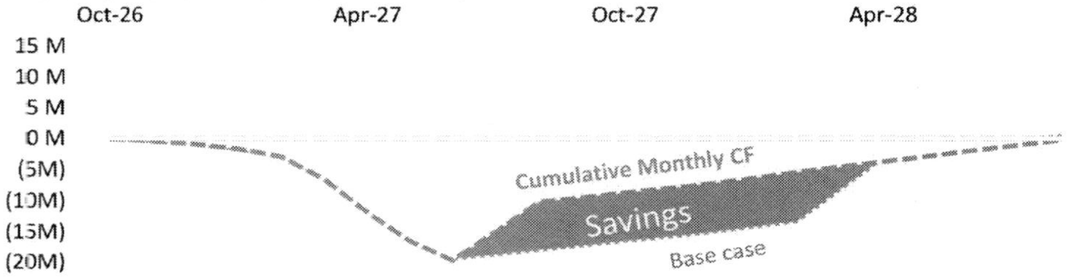

Base case: After 12 months, materials are paid 50% upfront and 50% on delivery
A.3 case: After 4 months, materials are paid 50% upfront and 50% on delivery

BECQUEREL INSTITUTE

CAPEX grants' benefits are twofold, with no drawbacks for manufacturers.

A.1
A.2
A.3
A.4
B.1
B.2
B.3
B.4

A.4 CAPEX Grants

NPV	IRR
▲ 0,8 M€	▲ 7,8 %

- ? 10% project financing via grants.
- \+ Early cash relief via direct CAPEX support.
- ↓ Reduce the need for early debt.
- \+ Late cash advantage via avoided interests from financing (OPEX effect)

Yearly cumulative Cash Flow after debt servicing (CFADS), in M€

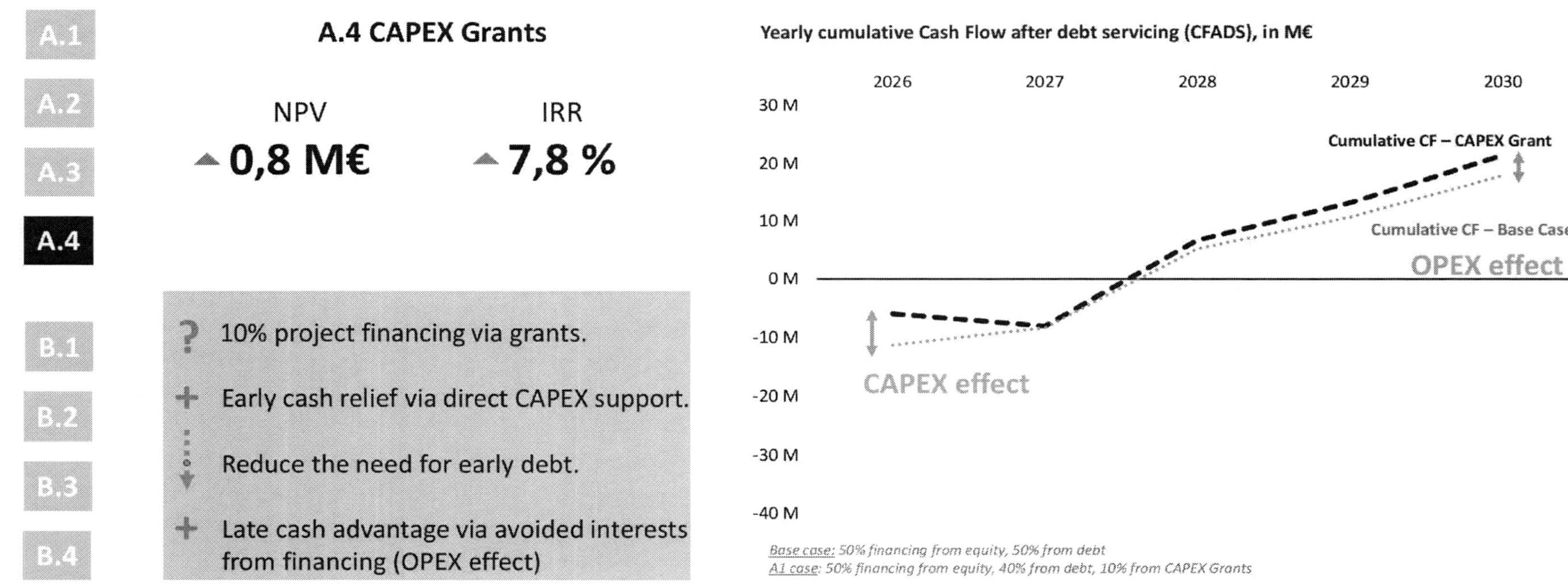

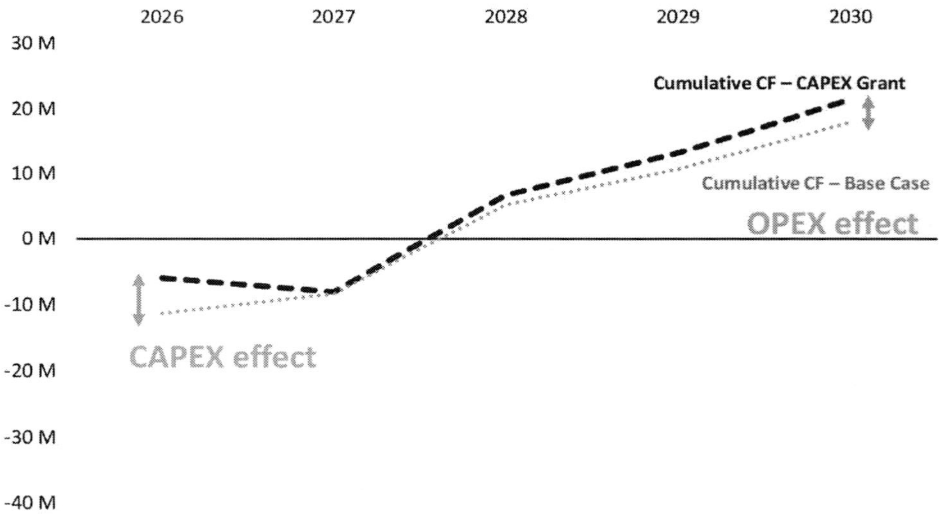

Base case: 50% financing from equity, 50% from debt
A1 case: 50% financing from equity, 40% from debt, 10% from CAPEX Grants

4 | Main Results

High-cost, premium alternative markets can yield better margins, but sales conversion cost almost offset the gains

A.1

A.2

A.3

A.4

B.1

B.2

B.3

B.4

B.1 Extended portfolio

NPV	IRR
▲ 1,4 M€	▲ 8,2 %

? Target **additional** alternative markets with greater potential margins:

Carports (Distributors, installers), **AgriPV** (Distributors), **BIPV** (Distributors)

\+ Higher margins, and diversified sales less prone to demand shocks

\- Higher sales conversion cost

Yearly cumulative Cash Flow after debt servicing (CFADS), in M€

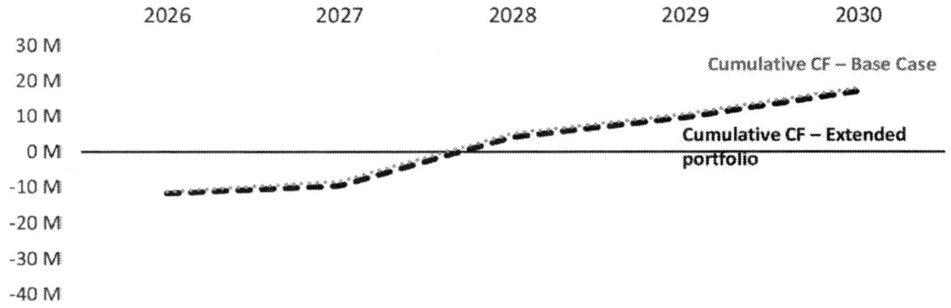

Module net production, in Million Units per year

Base case (left) v/s extended portfolio (right)

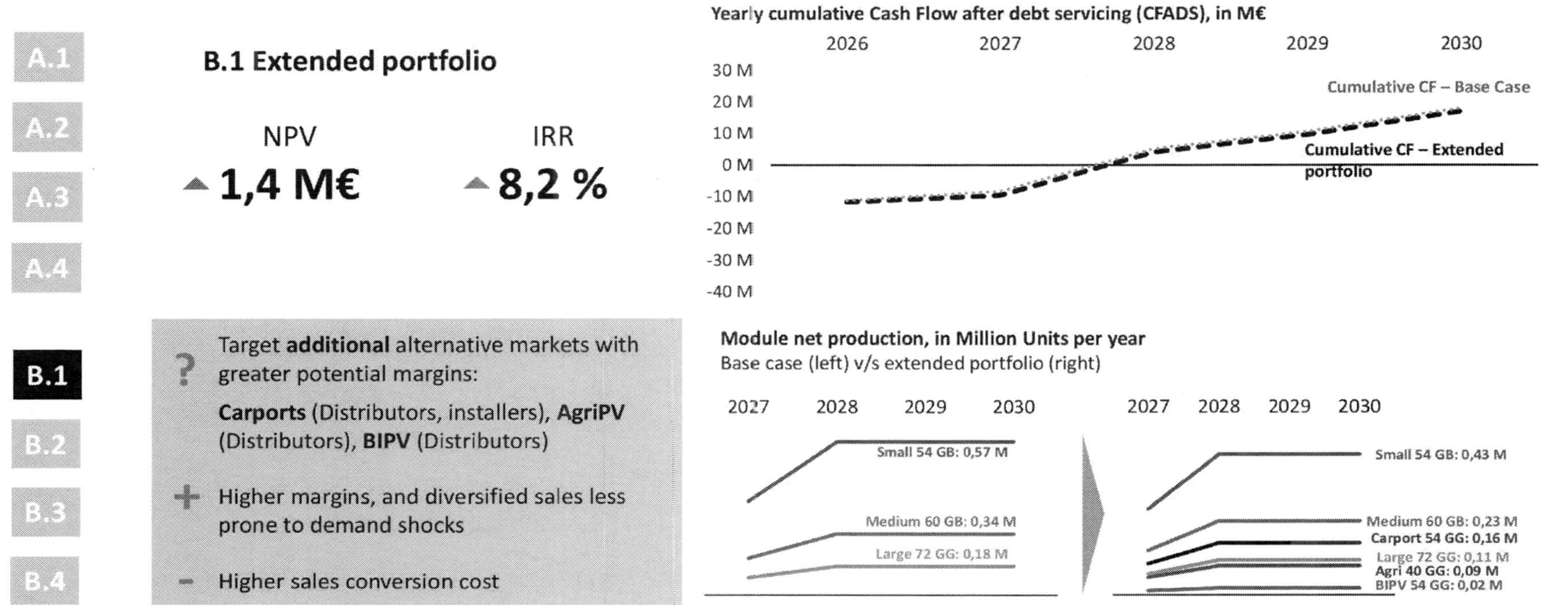

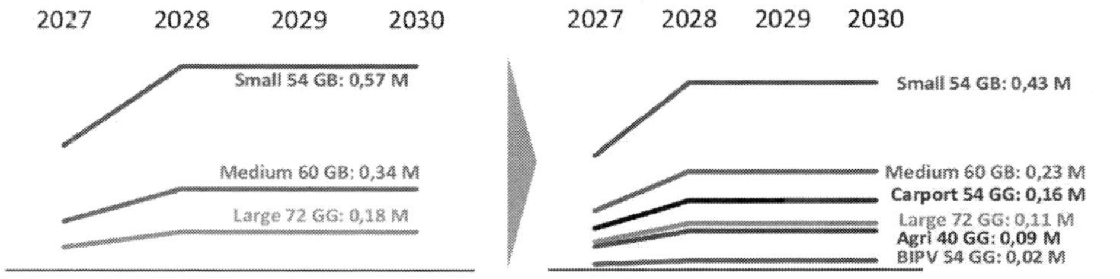

BECQUEREL INSTITUTE

Greater prices for end-users are outshined by high sales conversion costs

A.1
A.2
A.3
A.4

B.1
B.2
B.3
B.4

B.2 Downwards integration

NPV	IRR
▼ (5,0 M€)	▼ 4,1 %

? Products are also sold to end-users.

\+ Higher prices

\- Sales conversion costs have the potential to outweigh end-user pricings.

Yearly cumulative Cash Flow after debt servicing (CFADS), in M€

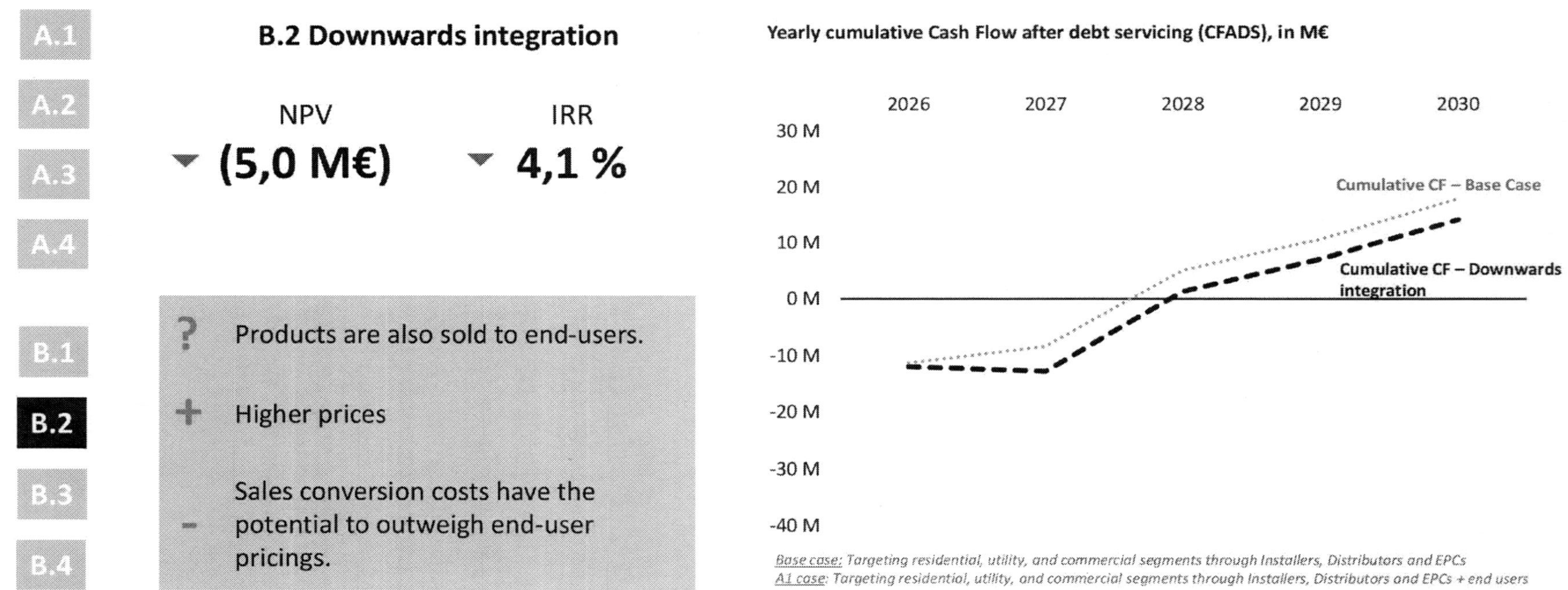

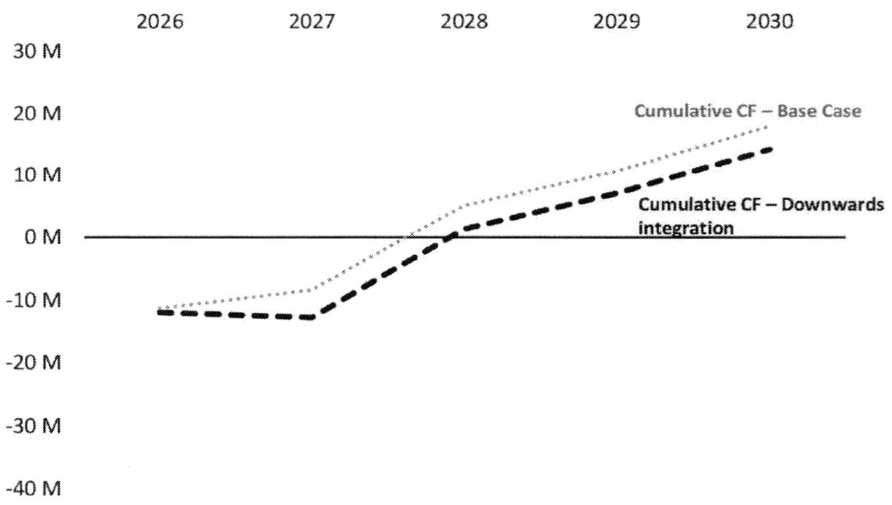

Base case: Targeting residential, utility, and commercial segments through Installers, Distributors and EPCs
A1 case: Targeting residential, utility, and commercial segments through Installers, Distributors and EPCs + end users

BECQUEREL INSTITUTE

Alternative markets with direct end-user sales are strategies that cannibalise each other

A.1

A.2

A.3

A.4

B.1

B.2

B.3

B.4

B.3 Extended portfolio (B.1)
+ Downwards integration (B.2)

NPV	IRR
▾ **(3,2 M€)**	▾ **5,2 %**

? Targeting all alternative markets and conducting downwards integration (target end-users for conventional markets, installers for alternative ones)

\- Alternative markets' extra income **cannot offset losses** from downstream integration.

Yearly cumulative Cash Flow after debt servicing (CFADS), in M€

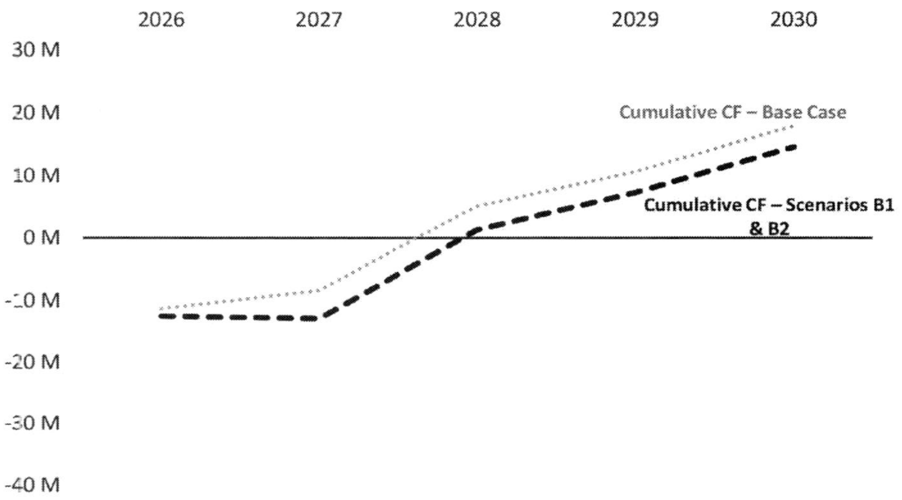

Base case: Targeting residential, utility, and commercial segments through Installers, Distributors and EPCs
A1 case: Targeting alternative markets (scenario B1) + downward integration (scenario B2)

Fully de-risking operative costs by acting as original equipment manufacturer (OEM)

A.1 A.2 A.3 A.4 B.1 B.2 B.3 **B.4**

B.4 Acting as OEM

NPV	IRR
▼ (7,6 M€)	▼ 1,8 %

? 1/3rd of each segment production is being sold as OEM.

\+ Lower risks on volumes

\- Savings from SG&A cannot compensate nearly at-cost selling.

Yearly cumulative Cash Flow after debt servicing (CFADS), in M€

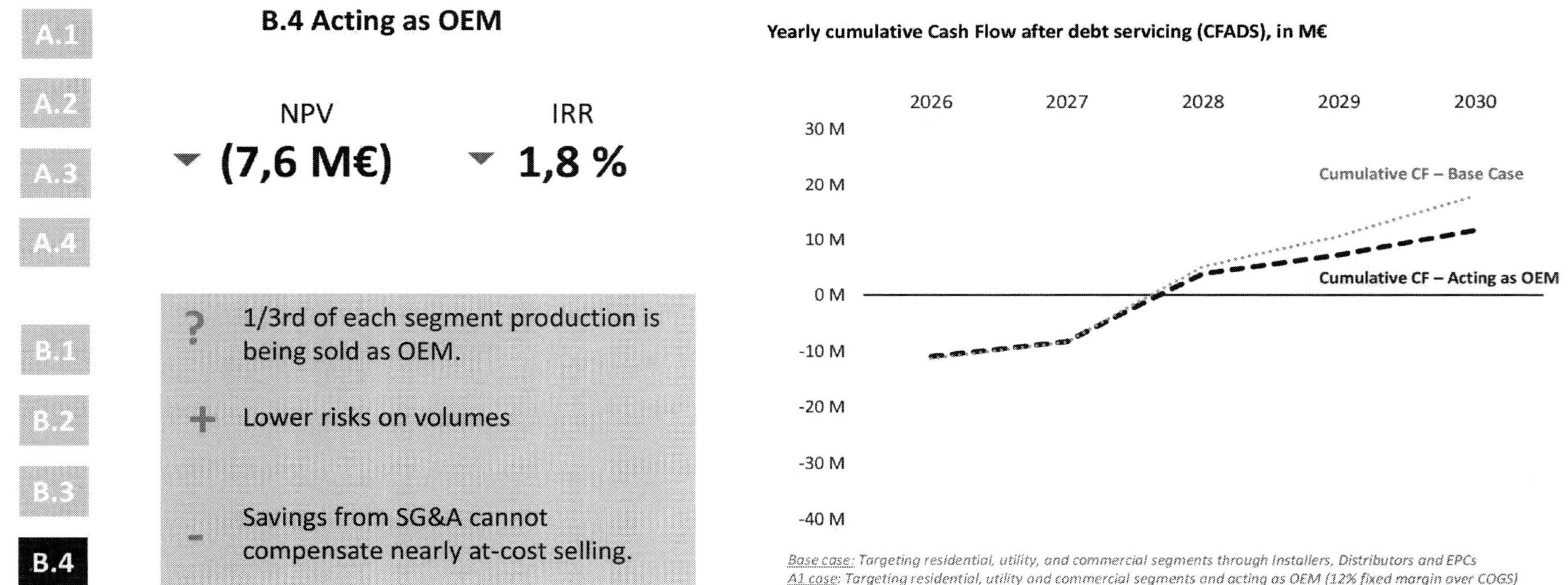

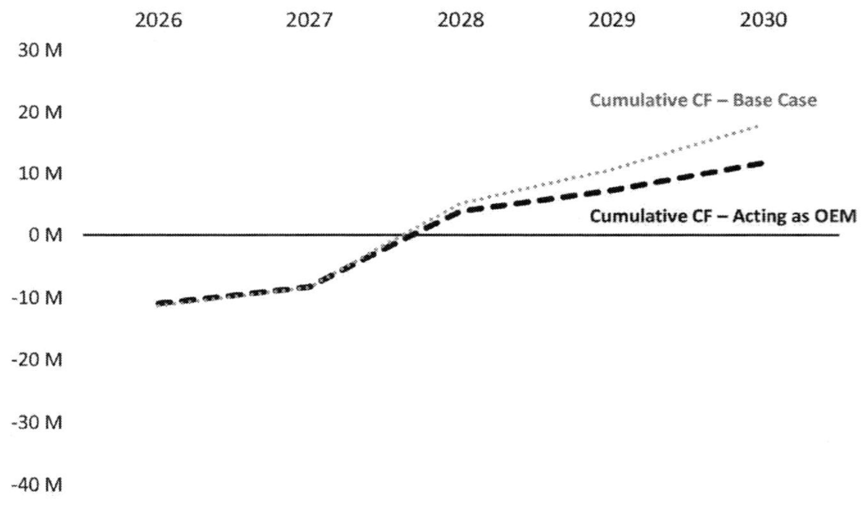

Base case: Targeting residential, utility, and commercial segments through Installers, Distributors and EPCs
A1 case: Targeting residential, utility and commercial segments and acting as OEM (12% fixed margin over COGS)

BECQUEREL INSTITUTE

Final stage: Choosing compatible strategies

By simultaneously implementing best strategies, companies can reduce risks

A. Cash management

- **A.1** **Equipment acquisition strategy**
  Operational lease instead of purchase
- **A.2** **Just in Time manufacturing**
  Reducing inventory levels
- **A.3** **Favourable payment conditions**
  Deferring a fraction of payments
- **A.4** **Grants**
  Reducing total CAPEX required

B. Sales optimisation

- **B.1** **Alternative market segments**
  Carports, agrivoltaics, BIPV
- **B.2** **Downwards integration**
  Direct end-user sales
- **B.3** **Aggressive diversified sales**
  Alternative markets + end-user sales
- **B.4** **Sales de-risking**
  Acting as OEM for third companies

BECQUEREL INSTITUTE

Strategy Consulting in Solar PV

Final stage: Choosing compatible strategies

Example: Efficient cash management & commercial strategies enable lower pricing

A.1 A.2 A.3 A.4

B.1 B.2 B.3 B.4

Optimised business strategy

NPV ▲ **0,5 M€**

IRR ▲ **7,7 %**

Effective cash management and **well-designed sales strategies** ease cash flow constraints, enabling manufacturers to **adjust pricing** and **strengthen competitiveness** in their target segments without sacrificing profitability, even when **manufacturing costs remain constrained.**

While these module prices may seem high compared to today's levels, they represent only a **minor increase at system price level**, allowing to reach **competitive LCOE.**

Yearly Cash Flow after debt servicing (CFADS), in M€

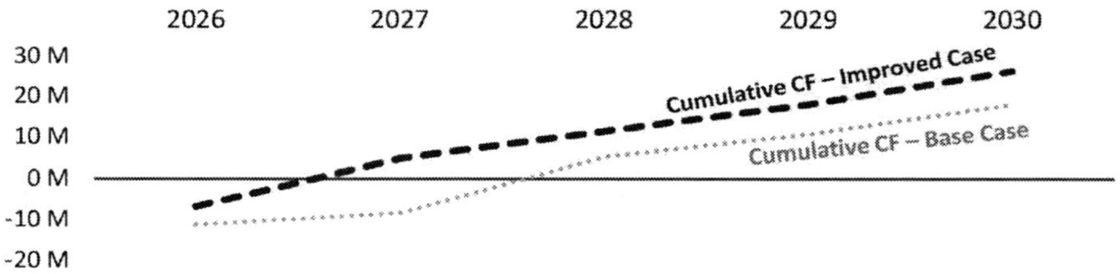

Segment	Channel	Base Price /Wp	New Price /Wp
Residential	Distributors	22,8 €ct	**22,1** ↓↓ 0,7 €ct
C&I	Distributors	20,7 €ct	20,7 €ct
C&I	Installers	23,0 €ct	**22,7** ↓↓0,3 €ct
Utility	EPC	20,0 €ct	20,0 €ct
Utility	Developers	20,7 €ct	20,7 €ct
Carports	Distributors	26,0 €ct	**25,3** ↓↓0,7 €ct
Carports	Installers	31,0 €ct	**29,8** ↓↓1,2 €ct
AgriPV	Distributors	31,0 €ct	**29,9** ↓↓1,1 €ct
BIPV	Distributors	44,0 €ct	**42,6** ↓↓1,4 €ct

Table of Contents

1 | Context

2 | Research Questions

3 | Our Approach

4 | Main Results

5 | **Takeaways**

BECQUEREL INSTITUTE

Once we understand how we can optimise our business models, we have to turn them into strategic and tactical activities

Key Partnerships

Supplier payment partnerships (A.3)

Logistic partners with reliable JiT delivery systems (A.2)

Key Activities

JiT logistics (A.2)

Key Resources

Flexible capital to optimize cash flow (A.1)

Financial support from grants (A.4)

Value Proposition

Offering customisable PV modules for emerging markets (B.1)

Channels

Specialised distributors and installers (B.1)

Customer Relationships

Building consultative and educational relationships with niche markets (B.1)

Customer Segments

Residential, C&I:
Distributors, installers
Agri, BIPV:
Distributors (B.1)

Cost Structure

Potentially higher negotiated costs for BOM flexibility (A.3)
JiT: Investment in real-time logistics systems and supplier coordination (A.2)

Revenue Streams

Premium pricing in niche markets with lower price elasticity (B.1)

BECQUEREL INSTITUTE

Profitability for the EU PV industry has become nearly impossible amid persistent market distortions

Urgent, ambitious policies are needed to break the "high risk, low reward" deadlock and create a level playing field

1. Cost-competitive manufacturing in the EU is currently **out of reach**, but the gap can be narrowed through smart **factory localization** and **phased vertical integration**, while leveraging current Asia's below-cost pricing

2. Adopting innovative technologies—such as back-contact cells, copper metallization instead of silver, or partial EU BOM—can **provide differentiation but does not necessarily enhance cost** competitiveness.

3. Strategic **levers beyond cost do exist**, but **not all are equally beneficial**; only by identifying the most effective and **combining those that are compatible** can economic sustainability be improved.

Even under optimized business strategies, the **path to success remains extremely narrow**, almost impossible, due to **persistent and severe market distortions**

Indeed, the **usual rules of economics seem no longer to apply to the PV sector** and have not for some time, as shown by the financial results of Asian players, who manage to survive regardless of market conditions.

How can we repair what is broken? **Political intervention is essential to break the 'high risk, low reward' deadlock**, especially in such a capital-intensive industry. Without it, private capital will remain unavailable, creating a **critical bottleneck with no solution**.

A. Cover risks that private actors cannot bear

- Guarantees, low to no interest loans
- Grants
- Production-linked incentives

B. Reduce risks by re-establishing fair rules

- Local content incentives or requirements, with quality and performance criteria
- Financial fairness criteria

BECQUEREL INSTITUTE

Your contact

Philippe Macé
p.mace@becquerelinstitute.eu

www.becquerelinstitute.eu

This project has received funding from the European Union's Horizon Europe under grant agreement № 101084259

Funded by the European Union

IBC4EU

ISC

EUPVSEC
22 — 26
September
BEC —
Bilbao Exhibition Centre
Bilbao —
Spain
EU
PVSEC
2025
42nd European
Photovoltaic Solar Energy
Conference and Exhibition

Conference Highlights

Robert Kenny

European Commission Joint Research Centre
EU PVSEC Technical Programme Chair

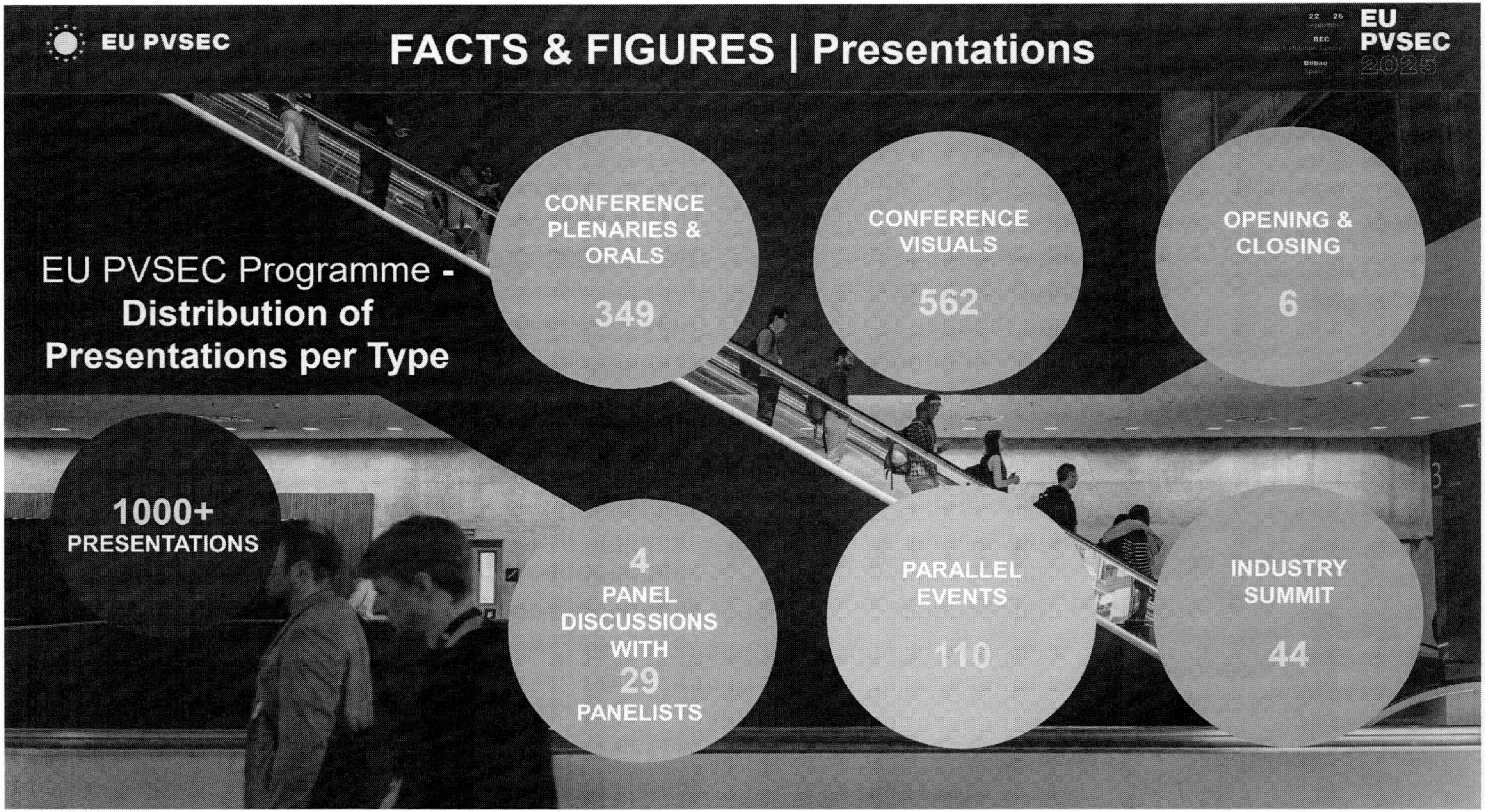
EU PVSEC
FACTS & FIGURES | Presentations
22 26
BEC
Bilbao
EU PVSEC 2025
EU PVSEC Programme - Distribution of Presentations per Type
CONFERENCE PLENARIES & ORALS
349
CONFERENCE VISUALS
562
OPENING & CLOSING
6
1000+ PRESENTATIONS
4 PANEL DISCUSSIONS WITH 29 PANELISTS
PARALLEL EVENTS
110
INDUSTRY SUMMIT
44

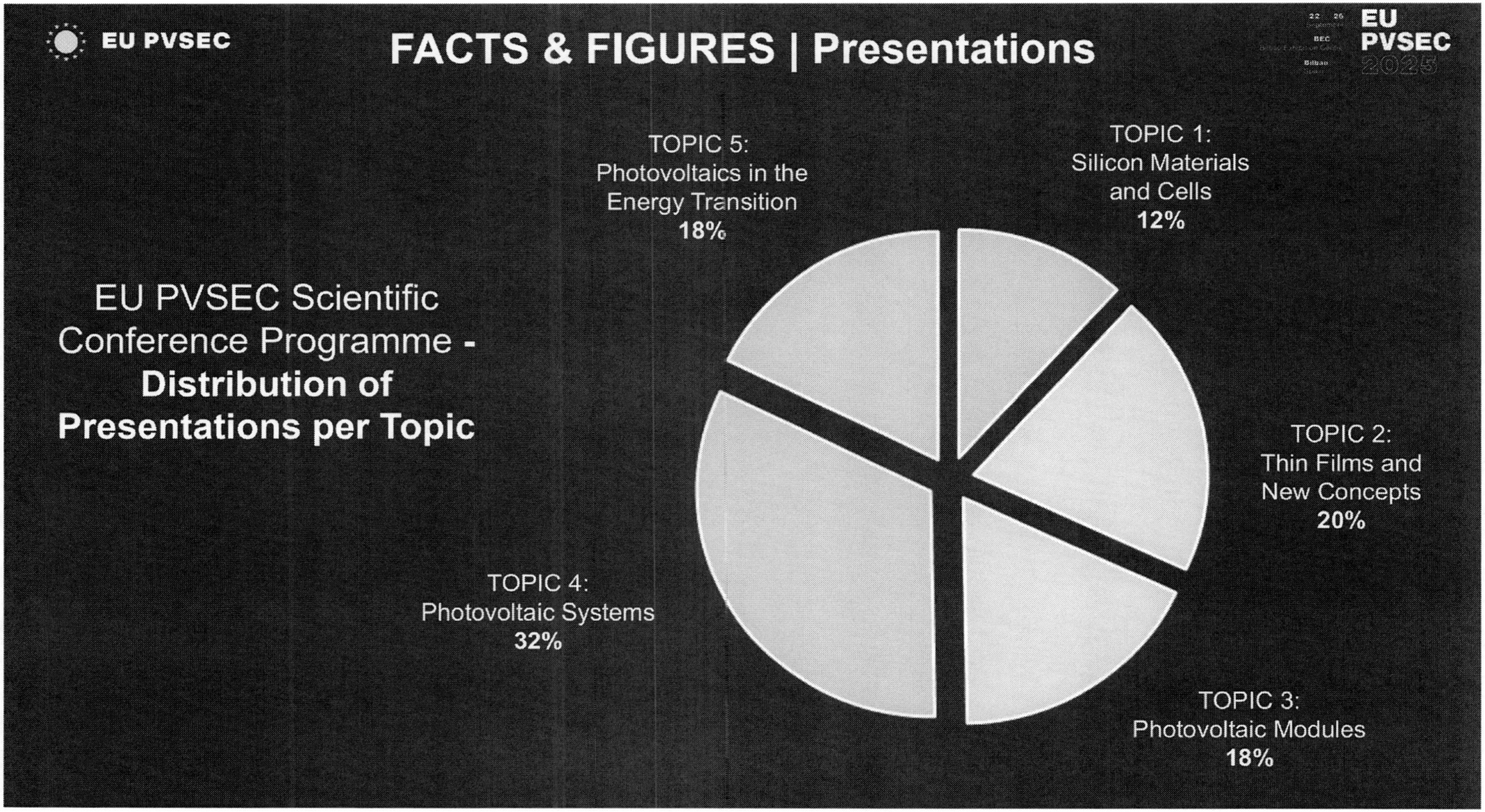
EU PVSEC
FACTS & FIGURES | Presentations
EU PVSEC 2025
EU PVSEC Scientific Conference Programme - Distribution of Presentations per Topic
TOPIC 5: Photovoltaics in the Energy Transition 18%
TOPIC 1: Silicon Materials and Cells 12%
TOPIC 2: Thin Films and New Concepts 20%
TOPIC 3: Photovoltaic Modules 18%
TOPIC 4: Photovoltaic Systems 32%

EU PVSEC

FACTS & FIGURES | Participants

EU PVSEC 2025

Participants by Countries
Top 10

No	Country	Participants
1	Germany	310
2	Spain	270
3	France	108
4	Italy	90
5	The Netherlands	76
6	South Korea	67
7	Switzerland	62
8	Japan	55
9	Belgium	44
10	Norway	35

TOTAL PARTICIPANTS
1600+
FROM 61
COUNTRIES

Plenary Session "PV Everywhere"
OPENING
Monday, 22 Sept. 2025
Becquerel Prize Ceremony
Welcome Messages
Jon DE GREGORIO
Moderated Panel Discussion "Solar in Turbulent Times: Global Dynamics and the Way Forward"
Key Note Speech "The Dual Face of Global Solar Growth"
EU PVSEC 2025
www.eupvsec.org
#EUPVSEC
22 — 26 September
BEC Bilbao Exhibition Centre
Bilbao — Spain

030001-007

EU PVSEC
PANEL DISCUSSIONS
22 26 September
BEC
Bilbao
EU PVSEC 2025
BO.13 Reliability and Bankability in PV
"The rapid developments of PV technology require increased attention to be paid to reliability testing."
CO.7 Challenges and Opportunities of PV up to 2030
"PV Technology is already reliable and cost effective, and even though improvements are welcome, key blockages are storage and grid strengthening. AI and robotics are essential to meet the scale of developments needed."
DO.13 Scalability and Manufacturability Prospects in Europe for New Technologies
"The prospects for reaching the 30GW target for PV module manufacturing in Europe were discussed and policy measures proposed."

EU PVSEC

EU PVSEC 2025

CONFERENCE

KEY MESSAGES

Cross-cutting themes emerged throughout the programme, showcasing how solar technologies can be applied everywhere, from traditional to emerging fields.

- Sustainability and circularity remain central, with research focused on reducing material use, such as replacing silver with copper, and advancing end-of-life management of modules.
- Ensuring long-term stability and predictable energy yield is equally essential, with studies of degradation mechanisms such as UVID carried out.
- The role of AI across the PV value chain is rapidly expanding, from design to operations and maintenance, including drone applications.

EU PVSEC

22 26 EU PVSEC 2025 BEC Bilbao

CONFERENCE

TOPIC 1: SILICON MATERIALS AND CELLS

Enhancements in IV measurement procedures

- Michael Rauer, Fraunhofer ISE: 1AO.4.5 *Universal Contacting Approaches for the Characterization of Solar Cells*
- Shuai Nie, UNSW: 1AO.4.6 *Contact-Free J-V: a Simple Technique for Universal State-of-the-Art Solar Cells*

Replacement of critical by sustainable materials:

- Reduced Ag consumpion e.g. by replacing by Cu (plating)
- In-free SHJ solar cells and Pero-Si tandems

EU PVSEC

EU PVSEC 2025

CONFERENCE

TOPIC 1: SILICON MATERIALS AND CELLS

Great advance in understanding of UV induced degradation and Hydrogen related degradation

- Excellent PLENARY by Bram Hoex (presenting for Muhammad Umair Khan), UNSW: 1CP.3.5 *Understanding the Root Cause of UV-Induced Degradation in TOPCon and PERC Solar Cells*

Further high quality orals:

- Christina Hollemann, ISFH: 1AO.4.2 *Mitigating UV-Induced Degradation: Impact of PECVD and PEALD AlOx Layers Deposited in a Tube-Type Direct Plasma-Enhanced Chemical Vapor Deposition System*
- Hugo Lajoie, CEA: 1AO.4.3 *New Insights on UV-Induced Degradation of SHJ Solar Cells*
- Byungsul Min, ISFH: 1BO.3.6 *UV Stable Passivation Stack with Plasma-Enhanced Atomic Layer Deposition of Aluminum Oxide from an Industrial Tube-Type Direct Plasma-Enhanced Chemical Vapor Deposition System*
- Wolfram Kwapil, Fraunhofer ISE: 1AO.5.6 *Impact of Illumination on Solar Cell Properties: Insights into Atomic Hydrogen Release*

EU PVSEC

22 – 26 September, BEC Bilbao — EU PVSEC 2025

CONFERENCE

TOPIC 1: SILICON MATERIALS AND CELLS

Advances in TOPCon and SHJ technology → Pushing the Limits of Performance

- Fantastic keynote lecture (PLENARY) on heterojunction solar cells by Dr. Guangtao Yang, Trina: 1CP.1.1 *Silicon Surface and Interface Study for >27% Efficient SHJ Solar Cell*
    - Deep insight into technological aspects eg. influence of rear side polishing on cell performance
    - Very high efficiencies for both-sides contacted HJT > 27%
    - Issues with CAPEX, sustainibility (Ag, In)
    - Pero-Si tandem cells on large area and modules

Late News Presentation on 27.8% efficient back contact silicon solar cells by Hua Wu, Longhi: 1DO.9.1 *Hybrid Interdigitated Back Contact Silicon Solar Cells with Superior Efficiency*

Late News Presentation as TOPCon for Bottom Solar Cells in Pero-Si Tandem devices by Jana Polzin-Isabelle Polzin, Fraunhofer ISE: 1DO.9.3 *Silicon Solar Cells – From High Efficiency Single-junction to Bottom Cells in Two-Terminal Perovskite-Silicon Tandem Devices*

CONFERENCE

TOPIC 1: SILICON MATERIALS AND CELLS

Further high quality orals:

- Hua Wu, Longhi: 1DO.9.1 *Hybrid Interdigitated Back Contact Silicon Solar Cells with Superior Efficiency*
- Daming Chen, Trina: 1AO.5.1 *Large Area i-TOPCon Solar Cells with 25.9% Record Efficiency*
- Maysa Sarsour, UNSW: 1AO.6.1 *Evaluating Silicon Heterojunction Solar Cell Stability under Industrial Illuminated Hydrogenation Conditions*

Bottom cell optimization for Pero-Si tandems

EU PVSEC

EU PVSEC 2025

CONFERENCE

TOPIC 2: THIN FILMS AND NEW CONCEPTS

A lot of focus on the long-term stability improvement and upscaling of tandem devices based on a variety of materials (hence not only pero-Si).

Many companies (e.g. Hanwha Q-cells, Oxford PV, Microquanta Seminconductor, Jinko Solar, Longi, etc. non-exhaustive list) presented impressive results on industrial size single-junction pero modules and pero-based tandem modules. A highlight here was the plenary talk from Hanwha Q-cells showing a record large area (M10) pilot-scale Pk/Si tandem cell of 28.6% efficiency.

CONFERENCE

TOPIC 2: THIN FILMS AND NEW CONCEPTS

In the field of pero-Si tandems, there is clearly more focus on improving the stability of the tandem devices than before with many contributions doing in-depth investigations into the different degradation mechanisms that can occur in pero-Si tandems.

In this respect, 2DO9.5 presented a consensus statement about reliability testing of perovskite-based tandems that is endorsed by specialists worldwide from both industry and research and presents a kind of minimum that should be done in terms of testing and reporting concerning the stability and lifetime of perovskite-based tandem devices.

More and more advanced characterization methods for perovskite and perovskite - silicon tandem solar cells are being used, hyperspectral imaging methods identify non-uniformities by layer for processing development.

EU PVSEC

22 26 BEC Bilbao EU PVSEC 2025

CONFERENCE

TOPIC 2: THIN FILMS AND NEW CONCEPTS

Another clear trend is that pero-TOPCon cells are nearing the same record efficiencies as pero-Heterojunction cells. A highlight talk here was the certified 34.22% efficiency perovskite/ topcon tandem solar cell(1cm2) by Jinko Solar 2CO2.1

Another highlight was the 30.5% triple junction pero/pero/silicon cell by EPFL (2CO2.3)

In the field of perovskite single junction devices, 2DO.7.3 showed perovskite devices with remarkable reliability, withstanding 4 years of outdoor exposure. The degradation mechanism is attributed to the diurnal behaviour, also verified and replicated with indoor experiments.

2AO3.6 investigated experimental degradation and recovery of perovskite solar cells, improving the comprehension of instability's dynamics, to extend the lifetime of devices.

EU PVSEC

22 26 September BEC Bilbao EU PVSEC 2025

CONFERENCE

TOPIC 2: THIN FILMS AND NEW CONCEPTS

In the field of compound semiconductors, there were many presentations on alternative materials for perovskite in tandems. In this way, first monolithic (AgCu)(InGa)Se2 on Si tandem cells were demonstrated as well as 16.1% semitransparent Ag doped Cu(InGa)S2 sulfide top cells.

An exciting highlight in this field was 2BO8.2 in which UPC Barcelona achieved 18% efficiency under indoor lighting for kesterite solar cells with alkali doping

EU PVSEC

22 – 26 September
BEC
Bilbao

EU PVSEC 2025

CONFERENCE

TOPIC 3: PHOTOVOLTAIC MODULES

"Reliable packaging to Maximize the energy yield from high efficiency cells"

big theme: Optimizing module materials and packaging for long lifetime and predictable energy yield from high efficiency cells. The industry and research community are moving quickly to assess and improve reliability.

- Understanding, accelerated testing, and mitigating UV-ID in n-type cells and modules
- How do you develop accelerated tests for constantly changing BOMs - new encapsulants, new metallization, thinner glass, and high efficiency cells

EU PVSEC

EU PVSEC 2025

CONFERENCE

TOPIC 3: PHOTOVOLTAIC MODULES

- Degradation and metastability in packaged perovskite tandems - understanding energy yield and realistic degradation rates
- Characterization out of the lab and into the field and factory - accurate outdoor performance, online quality control measurements for encapsulant cross linking
- Reducing silver content and metallization temperatures - reliability of low temperature and low silver metallization
- Developing glass qualification requirements to minimize breakage

EU PVSEC

EU PVSEC 2025

CONFERENCE

TOPIC 4: PHOTOVOLTAIC SYSTEMS

Advances in O&M of PV systems

(4CV.1) focuses on fault detection, cleaning optimization, soiling (and snow 4CO.8), UAV for autonomous monitoring and digital twin.

Data driven and AI based O&M (4CO.9) including a medicine-like workflow in Autonomous multi-AI agent system for health monitoring: a fully automated O&M pipeline with field robotics (4CO.9.4 D. Moser, EURAC)

PV Everywhere from space to agricultural applications like integration in vineyards (Mo, Opening plenary) and many other **integrated options** as we have seen throughout the week. On Thursday (4DO.4) agriPV, noise barriers and floating integrated systems. AgriPV technologies (4DO.2), BIPV

PV needs solar energy. **Solar resource and forecasting** (Mo, 4AO.7-9 & Tu 4BV.3). Shortly IEA PVPS T16 will publish minute irradiance data, some including GT over 220 stations worldwide with. Same format and quality controlled. (*Worldwide solar radiation measurement database with quality-control added value*, Anne Forstinger CSP Services, 4AO.7.1)

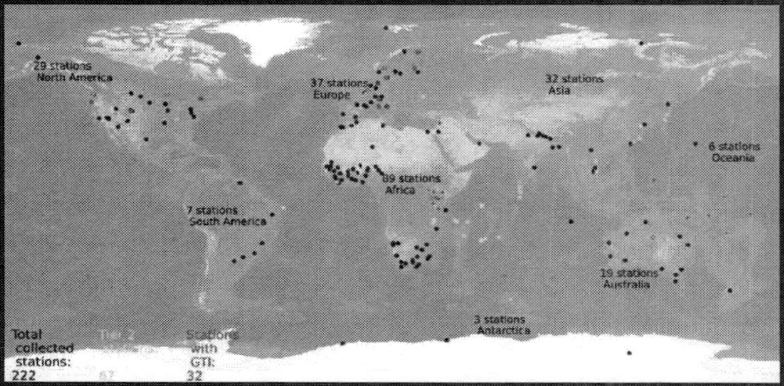

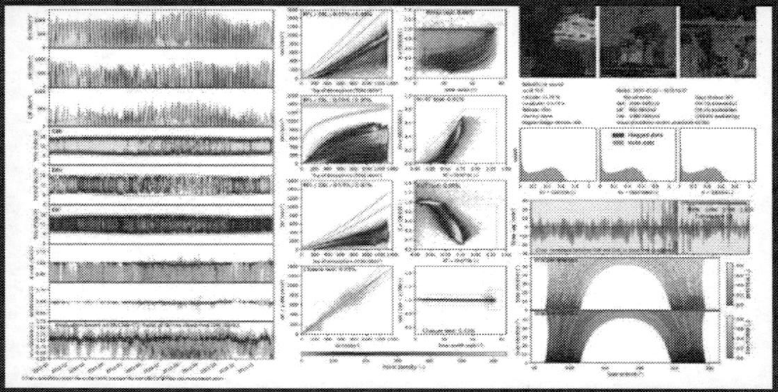

(4BV.3). Poster winner 4BV.3.12 *Advancing Very Short-Term Solar Irradiance Forecasting in Africa: A Low-Cost Sky Imaging and Machine Learning-Based Approach*, implications for PV deployment and grid integration (Martin Ansong, KIT). Runner-up 4BV.3.25 *Evaluating the Suitability of Köppen-Geiger Climate Classifications for Photovoltaic Systems: Micro-climate Analysis and Risk Assessment Maps*, with worldwide distribution of humidity related risk assessment for PV performance (Pavan Kumar Panda, Anhalt University of Applied Sciences).

Integrated PV

BIPV (4BO.16) examples of coloured modules (which was main topic of the poster session along with fire concerns of BIPV, 4BV.4), lightweight solutions (4BO.5) and modelling partial shading effects 4BO.17.1, *Modelling partial shading at the cell level on PV modules,* Jean-Paul Calin, ENSTA) and 4BO.17.3, *Comparing the energy yield and degradation rates of smart PV modules compared to conventional PV system designs in shaded urban scenario's,* Youri Blom, TU DELF.

AgriPV 4DO.2 the room was fully packed showing the interest in the topic. 5 talks were on new ways of sharing light (2 spectral splitting before the PV conversion, 2 semitransparent PV modules both c-Si and CdTe, 1 on downshifting encapsulate) + 1 new AgrivPV like application with Algae instead of crops.

4DO.4 also included AgriPV and **Others types of integration like noise barriers and floating.** In addition to performance other aspects like (*Hydrological and ecological effects on floating PV,* Konstantin Ilgen, FHO ISe) have been highlighted this week

4DO4.2

BOS and tracking systems (4DO.1) focused on backtracking strategies and terrains with complex topography.

4DO.1.4

EU PVSEC

EU PVSEC 2025

22 26 BEC Bilbao

CONFERENCE

TOPIC 4: PHOTOVOLTAIC SYSTEMS

Reliability of PV systems

Several presentations focused long-term monitored degradation, failure modes and degradation modes identification techniques (non-destructive, aerial images, AI-based)

4BO.6.1 *Three decades, three climates: insights and lessons on PV reliability*. Good BOM offer very high reliability in power production, with 30-35 years old modules showing 0.24% degradation rate per year.

4BO.6.3 *Non-destructive detection of water ingress in solar modules using NIR spectroscopy* (Oleksandr Mashkow HI ERN) proved near-infrared absorption (NIRA) technique to detect water ingress in modules in the field, which correlated with the module degradation.

4BO.7.2 *Robust PV performance loss rate calculation for high latitudes* (Lauri Karttunen, Meteo Inst Helsinki) and 4BO.7. 3 *Detailed analysis of degradation rates of operating PV assets in tropical climate conditions* (Xioaqi Xu, Seris Singapore) Performance loss rates reported for high latitudes and tropics based on solid data sets. PLR in the tropics -1.4%/year

4DO.3.6 PV system design and assessment highlighted how inverter safety issues are extremely important and how more research about inverter safety and reliability is needed.

EU PVSEC

22 26 September BEC Bilbao Exhibition Centre Bilbao Spain EU PVSEC 2025

CONFERENCE

TOPIC 5: PHOTOVOLTAICS IN THE ENERGY TRANSITION

Main topics of interest :

- Flexibility
- Artificial intelligence
- EoL management

EU PVSEC

EU PVSEC 2025

CONFERENCE

TOPIC 5: PHOTOVOLTAICS IN THE ENERGY TRANSITION

5.1 Grid Integration and Flexibility Enablers (2 sessions)

- Smoothing effect related to different orientations of PV systems in a given area allows 10 to 15% additional hosting capacity of the distribution grid compared to the conservative calculation that consists in summing the AC power. Such accurate calculation enabled by high resolution large area images and LIDAR and induces therefore very low costs.

5.2 Sustainability of PV (4 sessions)

- New inventories LCI and LCA for emerging technologies even though lack of data for perovskites, LCA showing a way for low environmental Impacts with technology improvement and localisation. / Technological improvements will contribute to the reduction of environmental Impact / Grid Efficiency has an Impact on the environmental Footprint.
- Manufacturing optimization / Reuse & recycling: results from the perspective of economic performance – would it convince manufacturer to consider it if economic benefit ?
- EoL Management /recycling -> emerging field attracting lots of activities / mainly EU projects (EVERPV / ICARUS / QASAR) – highlight on polymer, interesting question came up and to be debated for the next decade: is it worth it to consider polymer (EVA/ backsheet) recycling ?
- Major progress in methodology and indicators to assess sustainable design & circularity and improve transparency recyclability index, technical recyclability, digital passport)

EU PVSEC

EU PVSEC 2025

CONFERENCE

TOPIC 5: PHOTOVOLTAICS IN THE ENERGY TRANSITION

5.3 Scenarios for Renewables, Policy, Global Challenges (1 session)

- wide scope of contributions on the way to massive, medium- to long-term PV deployment -> should not be taken for granted despite positive projections since there can be limiting factors such as public acceptance / regulatory restrictions and effect of climate change

5.4 Costs, Economics, Finance and Markets (1 session)

- Annual installed capacity over 400 GWp / total cumulative installed capacity worldwide over 2.1 TWp / Clear mismatch between PV module installations rate worldwide and PV module production rate leading to bunch of inventories and drastically reduced prices.

5.6 Societal Challenges; Citizens' Participation, Awareness (1 session)

- data and analysis in gender aspects are emerging in PV! (poster session) + Highlight on innovation in education! On example that targets students & skilled workers -> mobile Lab for advanced experimental training PV-related to bring skills and characterization tools everywhere.

PARALLEL EVENTS
Collaborat° Network
Diversity
Prejudice
Change
Needs — Profile Match
Avoid Blind Spots
Job Loss?
Integration
Resilience (People + Company)
Creativity
Different Communicat°
Internal Friction

030001-027

EU PVSEC

22 26 BEC Bilbao EU PVSEC 2025

PARALLEL EVENTS

- Perovskite Innovation Roundtable: Driving EU Leadership in Perovskite Innovation
- Women in PV presents: Leading with Inclusion – Embracing the 6 Traits of Inclusive Leadership
- Unlocking the Potential of Integrated Photovoltaic Systems - European R&D Approach
- Why Do PV Plants Perform Lower than Expected? (Estimating losses by backtracking algorithms in undulating terrain & Analysis of the loss chain and identification of deviations from initial expectations)
- PV Made in the EU: How Do Companies Die and How Can They Thrive?

22 — 26
September
BEC —
ilbao Exhibition Centre
Bilbao — Spain
EU
PVSEC
2025
42nd European
Photovoltaic Solar Energy
Conference and Exhibition
GEOPOLITICS & PV MANUFACTURING CHALLENGES
EXHIBITION
FORUM
INDUSTRY
SUMMIT

The road to a
sustainable future

EU PVSEC

22 – 26 September BEC Bilbao Spain EU PVSEC 2025

INDUSTRY SUMMIT

Industry Summit Opening (session I)

Session Title: Solar PV production in Europe - the way forward

Moderators: Begoña Molinete, Walburga Hemetsberger

Key Takeaway:

This session discussed the state of play of European manufacturing projects and whether there is enough European support. It was clear that political support is further lacking – only 3 Member States have developed schemes to support European manufacturing. While the Net Zero Industry Act is helpful to diversify supplies, it will not particularly support European manufacturing.

All panellists agreed that apart from further policy support (financing, derisking) collaboration is the way forward.

INDUSTRY SUMMIT

Session II
Session Title: International corporations in the light of changing geopolitics
Moderators: Radovan Kopecek, Puzant Baliozian

Key takeaway:
EU machine builders are still supporting mostly Indian but also US and EU projects with their technology and expertise. The major arguments for choosing EU tech are quality, training, support and low OPEX.

Session III
Session Title: PV Systems: How do we get the produced electricity in Europe into the grid?
Moderators: Catarina Augusto, Peter Fath

Key Takeaway:
Hybrid PV + storage systems (co-located or distributed) are essential for integrating PV into electricity grids. Storage adds flexibility and stabilizes the grid, making it a cornerstone of resilient energy systems; while the technology is mature, scalable and bankable revenue models remain the key gap for widespread deployment.

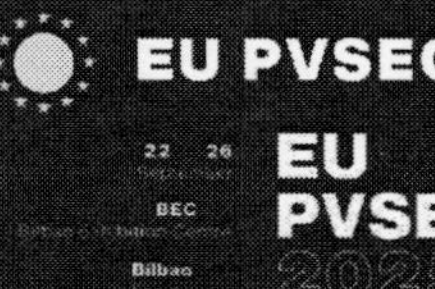

LIST OF EXHIBITORS
(in alphabetical order)

Company name	Country
2nd Cycle FlexCo	Austria
9-Tech	Italy
Avalon ST / Pasan	Switzerland
BASQUENERGY Cluster	Spain
Becquerel Institute	Belgium
ECOPROGETTI	Italy
EKIENERGY	Spain
ESMC Pavilion	Belgium
Eternal Sun I WAVELABS	The Netherlands
EU PVSEC Startup Pavilion	
European Commission JRC	Italy
exateq	Germany
FLUXiM AG	Switzerland
G2V Optics	Canada
GALEA	Spain
halm elektronik	Germany
HighLine Technology	Germany
IEA PVPS	
Innovations in Optics, Inc.	United States of America
ISC Konstanz	Germany
LAB14	Germany
MBJ Solutions	Germany
Mondragon Assembly	Spain
Nagase Chemtex America	United States of America
NEO Messtechnik Holding	Austria
ODTÜ GÜNAM	Türkiye
Phoenixolar	China
PSE Instruments	Germany
PVsyst	Switzerland
RCT Future	Germany
RCT Solutions	Germany
RENA	Germany
ReNewPV-CA21148 / 5GSOLAR	Estonia
SALD B.V.	The Netherlands

SCIPRIOS	Germany
SEMILAB	Hungary
SINGULUS TECHNOLOGIES	Germany
Sinton Instruments	United States of America
SOLAR MATERIALS	Germany
SolarNL	The Netherlands
Soli Tek R&D	Lithuania
TAMURA ELSOLD	Germany
TECNALIA	Spain
The Netherlands Pavilion	The Netherlands
TNO	The Netherlands
University of the Basque Country	Spain
Vector Energy	Spain
VON ARDENNE	Germany
WCPEC-9	South Korea
WIP Renewable Energies	Germany
ZSW	Germany

We thank the EU PVSEC 2025 Sponsors

Platinum

MONDRAGON ASSEMBLY

Gold

ENERGIAREN EUSKAL ERAKUNDEA
ENTE VASCO DE LA ENERGÍA

G2V

halm.

RCT solutions

Silver

Sinton instruments

Bronze

AESOLAR

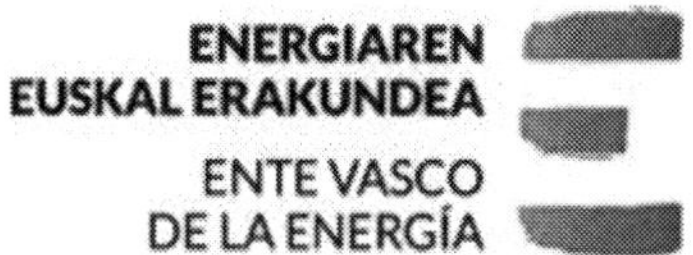

AUTHORS OF EU PVSEC 2025 PROCEEDINGS PAPERS

A. dos Reis Benatto, Gisele DTU, Roskilde, Denmark	020028, 020037, 020039, 020191, 020265, 020376, 020477
Aaltonen, Lauri Tampere University, Tampere, Finland	020537
Abad Alcaraz, Verónica University of Almería, La Cañada de San Urbano, Spain	020336
Abbott, Malcolm D. PV Lighthouse, Coledale, Australia	020396
Abbotto, Alessandro University of Milano-Bicocca, Milan, Italy	020077
Abdallah, Amir A. QEERI, Doha, Qatar	020146, 020166
Abdel Nour, Christine EDF R&D, Moret Loing Orvanne, France	020188
Abdelrahim, Mohamed QEERI, Doha, Qatar	020166
Abdou-Tankari, Mahamadou Paris-East Créteil University, Créteil, France	020562
Abrego, Gillen ALLOTARRA, Allo, Spain	020392
Acciarri, Maurizio University of Milano-Bicocca, Milan, Italy	020087
Acevedo Devoto, M. Ignacia ISC Konstanz, Konstanz, Germany	020220
Achenbach, Jannik University of Applied Science Cologne, Cologne, Germany	020522
Acinas, Victor Applied Materials, Dublin, Ireland	020019
Adachi, Satoru NIED, Shinjo, Japan	020436
Aden, Samira HZB, Berlin, Germany	020513
Adinolfi Borea, Riccardo University of Bologna, Bologna, Italy	020314
Adnan Hameed, Mohammed Martin-Luther-University Halle-Wittenberg, Halle, Germany	020156
Adothu, Baloji DEWA, Dubai, United Arab Emirates	020229
Aghaei, Mohammadreza NTNU, Aalesund, Norway	020335, 020356
Aghaei, Mohammadreza NTNU, Ålesund, Norway	020374, 020375

Aghamohammadi, Amirhossain 020356
Amirkabir University of Technology, Tehran, Iran

Aguirre, Aranzazu 020064
Hasselt Unversity, Genk, Belgium

Ahmadi, Mehdi 020066
CNR-IMM, Catania, Italy

Aiello, Andrea 020255
ACCA Software, Cosenza, Italy

Aimé, Jérémie 020217, 020311
CEA / INES, Le Bourget-du-Lac, France

Aissa, Brahim 020042, 020075, 020108, 020109, 020146, 020147
QEERI, Doha, Qatar

Aizpurua, Jon 020139
Tecnalia, Donostia - San Sebastián, Spain

Akbayrak, Serdar 020020
Necmettin Erbakan University, Konya, Türkiye

Akram, M. Waqar 020164
Hohai University, Changzhou, China

Al Katrib, Mirella 020116
IPVF, Palaiseau, France

Alam, Habeel 020394
Lancaster University, Lancaster, United Kingdom

Alberts, Vivian 020229
DEWA, Dubai, United Arab Emirates

Albuquerque, Daniel P. 020464
Centre for New Energy Technologies, Sacavém, Portugal

Alet, Pierre-Jean 020238, 020544
CSEM, Neuchâtel, Switzerland

Alexandris, Nikos 020210
European Commission JRC, Ispra, Italy

Alfieri, Felice 020497
Viegand Maagøe, Copenhagen, Denmark

Ali, Adnan 020147
QEERI, Doha, Qatar

Allen, Vince 020048
SunDrive Solar, Kurnell, Australia

Alloji, Esma 020020
Necmettin Erbakan University, Konya, Türkiye

Almeida Silva, José 020565
University of Évora, Évora, Portugal

Almuneau, Guilhem 020074
LAAS-CNRS, Toulouse, France

Alonso, Ricardo 020197, 020198, 020353, 020358
TECNALIA, Derio, Spain

Alonso-Montesinos, Joaquín 020100
University of Almeria, Almeria, Spain

Alonso-Montesinos, Joaquín 020336
University of Almería, La Cañada de San Urbano, Spain
Álvarez Hervás, José Domingo 020336
University of Almería, La Cañada de San Urbano, Spain
Alvarez, José 020040, 020058
CNRS, Gif-sur-Yvette, France
Álvarez, Marta 020300
CENER, Sarriguren, Spain
Álvarez-Pérez, Guillem 020062
IPVF, Palaiseau, France
Alvaro Høye, Ingar 020443
Solkraft Sør, Øyslebø, Norway
Alves e Silva, Kiane 020439, 020535, 020567, 020575
UPM, Madrid, Spain
Amaro e Silva, Rodrigo 020490
University of Lisbon, Lisbon, Portugal
Amatriain, Irati 020392
CENER, Sarriguren, Spain
Anamiati, Gaetana 020448, 020481
GreenPowerMonitor a DNV company, Barcelona, Spain
Anaya, Julian 020191, 020205
University of Valladolid, Valladolid, Spain
Ancillao, Andrea 020079
Polytechnic University of Turin, Turin, Italy
Anderlini, Alessandro 020155
Coveme, Gorizia, Italy
Andersen, Nanna L. 020250
DTU, Roskilde, Denmark
Andersen, Nanna Lysgaard 020306
DTU, Roskilde, Denmark
Andrade-Arvizu, Jacob 020094
IREC, Barcelona, Spain
Andreozzi, Federico 020494
University of Rome Tor Vergata, Rome, Italy
Anefnaf, Ikram 020093
University of Verona, Verona, Italy
Ansong, Martin 020272
KIT, Eggenstein-Leopoldshafen, Germany
Antognini, Luca 020196
PVsyst, Geneva, Switzerland
Antoine, C. 020508
IMDEA Nanoscience Institute, Madrid, Spain
Antón, Ignacio 020209, 020246, 020257, 020453, 020459
UPM, Madrid, Spain
Antonucci, Daniele 020551
Eurac Research, Bolzano, Italy

Apostoleris, Harry 020487
EPRI, Dubai, United Arab Emirates
Arakawa, Hayato 020436
NIED, Shinjo, Japan
Aranguren, Gerardo 020289, 020353
UPV/EHU, Bilbao, Spain
Arbaretaz, Sebastien 020317
CEA INES, Le Bourget-du-Lac, France
Ardissone, Bastien J. J. 020396
PV Lighthouse, Coledale, Australia
Arduino, Daniele 020079
Polytechnic University of Turin, Turin, Italy
Ariolli, Daniela Maria Godinho 020325
BayWa r.e, Rome, Italy
Ariza Camacho, Maria Jesus 020100
University of Almeria, Almería, Spain
Armstrong, Alona 020394
Lancaster University, Lancaster, United Kingdom
Arribat, Mathieu 020074
LAAS-CNRS, Toulouse, France
Arrizabalaga, Igor 020139
Tecnalia, Donostia - San Sebastián, Spain
Artegiani, Elisa 020057, 020089, 020093
University of Verona, Verona, Italy
Arumughan, Jayaprasad 020569
ISC Konstanz, Konstanz, Germany
Asaa, Shu-Ngwa 020393
imo-imomec, Genk, Belgium
Ascencio-Vásquez, Julián 020371
Univers, Courbevoie, France
Askins, Steve 020209, 020257
UPM, Madrid, Spain
Assaid, El Mahdi 020171
University of Chouaib Doukkali, El Jadida, Morocco
Aste, Niccolò 020249
Polytechnic University of Milan, Milan, Italy
Astigarraga, Alexander 020226
Eurac Research, Bolzano, Italy
Athienitis, Andreas 020248
Concordia University, Montreal, Canada
Aurrekoetxea, Olaia 020302
TECNALIA, Saint Sebastian, Spain
Awadallah, Carlos 020536
Wattkraft, Madrid, Spain
Azkona, Nekane 020055, 020097, 020153, 020287
UPV/EHU, Bilbao, Spain

Azzopardi, Brian 020318, 020334, 020520
FIR, Birkirkara, Malta

Azzopardi, Carmel 020334
FIR, Birkirkara, Malta

Babich, Francesco 020551
Eurac Research, Bolzano, Italy

Babics, Maxime 020217
CEA / INES, Le Bourget-du-Lac, France

Babin, Markus 020249, 020250, 020306, 020477
DTU, Roskilde, Denmark

Bachour, Dunia A. 020275, 020278
QEERI, Doha, Qatar

Bachour, Dunia 020291
QEERI, Doha, Qatar

Baderiya, Naman 020390
MARIN, Wageningen, The Netherlands

Badosa Franch, Jordi 020214
Polytechnic Institute of Paris, Palaiseau, France

Baeck, Pieter-Jan 020511
Flemish Institute for Technological Research (VITO), Genk, Belgium

Bai, Jianbo 020164
Hohai University, Changzhou, China

Bailache, Simon 020303
CSTB, Marne-la-Vallée, France

Bakhtiari, Afshin 020121
AESOLAR, Koenigsbrunn, Germany

Balafoutis, Athanasios T. 020464
CERTH, Athens, Greece

Bald, Juan 020514
AZTI, PASAIA, Spain

Baldacchino, Alex J. 020065
UNSW, Sydney, Australia

Baležentienė, Skirmantė 020380
The Applied Research Institute for Prospective Technologies, Vilnius, Lithuania

Baležentis, Algirdas 020380
The Applied Research Institute for Prospective Technologies, Vilnius, Lithuania

Ballif, Christophe 020467
CSEM, Neuchâtel, Switzerland

Ballif, Christophe 020251
EPFL, Neuchâtel, Switzerland

Bandaru, Narendra 020039, 020043, 020104
Aarhus University, Aarhus, Denmark

Bang, Ole Technical University of Denmark, Copenhagen, Denmark	020043
Barakel, Damien Toulon University, Marseille, France	020188
Baraket, Mira ATLANT 3D, Taastrup, Denmark	020039
Baranek, Philippe EDF R&D, Palaiseau, France	020060
Barchi, Grazia Eurac Research, Bolzano, Italy	020485, 020489, 020544
Bardizza, Giorgio TÜV Rheinland Italia, Milan, Italy	020181
Bardizza, Giorgio TÜV Rheinland Solar, Cologne, Germany	020208
Bardizza, Giorgio TÜV Rheinland, Cologne, Germany	020144
Barguès, Anna Becquerel Institute France, Lyon, France	020505
Barguès, Anna Becquerel Institute, Brussels, Belgium	020558
Barnscheidt, Verena ISFH, Emmerthal, Germany	020063, 020114
Barretta, Chiara PCCL, Leoben, Austria	020325
Barrionuevo, Bruno CERTH, Athens, Greece	020464
Barroso, João University of Évora, Évora, Portugal	020565
Barrou, Alexis CSEM, Neuchâtel, Switzerland	020467
Barrutia, Laura UPM, Madrid, Spain	020446, 020536
Barth, Vincent CEA / INES, Le Bourget-du-Lac, France	020134
Barth, Vincent CEA, Le Bourget-du-Lac, France	020019
Barth, Vincent CEA/ INES, Le Bourget-du-Lac, France	020226
Bartholomäus, Martin DTU, Roskilde, Denmark	020346
Bartolo, Brian FIR, Birkirkara, Malta	020334
Basta, Beata Roltec, Poznań, Poland	020068
Basta, Marek Roltec, Poznań, Poland	020068

Battisti, Kurt 020255
A-Null Development, Vienna, Austria

Bauhuis, Gerard 020067
Radboud University, Nijmegen, The Netherlands

Baumann, Kerstin 020470
bifa Umweltinstitut, Augsburg, Germany

Baumann, Sara 020063
ISFH, Emmerthal, Germany

Baumann, Ulrike 020006
ISFH, Emmerthal, Germany

Baur, Carsten 020246
European Space Agency, Noordwijk, The Netherlands

Beaucarne, Guy 020384
Dow Silicones Belgium, Seneffe, Belgium

Becker, Carl 020331
DLR, Almería, Spain

Behrensdorff Poulsen, Peter 020037
DTU, Lyngby, Denmark

Beinert, Andreas J. 020123
Fraunhofer ISE, Freiburg, Germany

Bejat, Timea 020225, 020500
CEA, Le Bourget-du-Lac, France

Belawadi, Aditya Girish 020231
Fraunhofer ISE, Freiburg, Germany

Belferkous, Brahim Anis 020325
PCCL, Leoben, Austria

Bellmann, Martin 020495, 020510
SINTEF, Trondheim, Norway

Bellvert, Eduard 020139
Tecnalia, Donostia - San Sebastián, Spain

Beltran-Condori, Sonia 020129, 020417
University of Antofagasta, Antofagasta, Chile

Belzunce, María Jesús 020514
AZTI, PASAIA, Spain

Bendix, Peter 020388
Next2Sun Technology, Dillingen, Germany

Bengoechea, Jaione 020181, 020300
CENER, Sarriguren, Spain

Bermudez Benito, Veronica 020146
QEERI, Doha, Qatar

Bermudez-Garcia, Anderson 020246
Thales Alenia Space, Cannes, France

Berrian, Djaber 020492
Belectric, Kolitzheim, Germany

Berson, Solenn 020134
CEA / INES, Le Bourget-du-Lac, France

Besson, Pierre 020373
INES, Le Bourget-du-Lac, France
Betak, Juraj 020241
Solargis, Bratislava, Slovakia
Bettucci, Ottavia 020077
University of Milano-Bicocca, Milan, Italy
Bhardwaj, Shashank 020515
TU Delft, Delft, The Netherlands
Bhatnagar, Shrey 020367
Nextracker, Fremont, United States of America
Biard, Yves 020303
SemperStyl, Eragny, France
Bieber, Lisa-Marie 020195
Fraunhofer ISE, Freiburg, Germany
Bilitu, Eddie 020393
Hasselt University, Hasselt, Belgium
Binani, Ashish 020225
TNO, Petten, The Netherlands
Binetti, Simona 020093
University of Milano Bicocca, Milan, Italy
Binetti, Simona 020087
University of Milano-Bicocca, Milan, Italy
Blakesley, James 020293
National Physical Laboratory, Teddington, United Kingdom
Blanc, Philippe 020291
MINES Paris, Nice, France
Blanco Aguiar, Adrián 020243
ieco.io, Vigo, Spain
Blieske, Ulf 020141
University of Applied Science Cologne, Cologne, Germany
Blieske, Ulf 020140
University of Applied Sciences Cologne, Cologne, Germany
Blstak Catlosova, Katarina 020274
Solargis, Bratislava, Slovakia
Blum, Niklas 020235, 020237, 020239
DLR, Almería, Spain
Boccardi, Roberto 020039
DTU, Copenhagen, Denmark
Boccardi, Roberto 020037
DTU, Lyngby, Denmark
Boccardi, Roberto 020028
DTU, Roskilde, Denmark
Boddaert, Simon 020302, 020303
CSTB, Marne-la-Vallée, France
Bokalič, Matevž 020047, 020319
University of Ljubljana, Ljubljana, Slovenia

Bolink, Henk J. 020226
University of Valencia, Paterna, Spain

Bonal, Victor 020085
UAM, Madrid, Spain

Bonnet, Martin 020141
University of Applied Science Cologne, Cologne, Germany

Bonnet-Eymard, Bénédicte 020251
CSEM, Neuchâtel, Switzerland

Borgers, Tom 020225
IMEC, Genk, Belgium

Borgna, Luciano 020369
BFH, Burgdorf, Switzerland

Borie, Benjamin 020039
ATLANT 3D, Taastrup, Denmark

Borowski, Peter 020307
Avancis, Munich, Germany

Borriello, Aniello 020378
ENEA, Portici, Italy

Borzi, Giovanni 020019
Enginsoft, Padua, Italy

Bosch, Elina 020252, 020543, 020564, 020573
Becquerel Institute, Brussels, Belgium

Bosma, Theo 020571
DNV, Arnhem, The Netherlands

Bothe, Karsten 020236
ISFH, Emmerthal, Germany

Bou-Nassif, Liliane 020338
CETHIL, Villeurbanne, France

Bouchier, Daniel 020058
CNRS, Palaiseau, France

Bouguerra, Sara 020156, 020294, 020389, 020393
imec, Genk, Belgium

Bourdin, Vincent 020406
CNRS, Paris, France

Bourgeois, Antoine 020102
SERIS, Singapore, Singapore

Bovesecchi, Gianluigi 020494
University of Rome Tor Vergata, Rome, Italy

Brabec, Christoph J. 020117
HI ERN, Erlangen, Germany

Bradford, David Roy 020077
Newcastle University, Newcastle upon Tyne, United Kingdom

Brailovsky, Peter Henri 020475
Fraunhofer ISE, Freiburg, Germany

Braña, Alejandro F. 020508
Autonomous University of Madrid, Madrid, Spain

Brandstätter, Andreas 020227
Lenzing Plastics, Lenzing, Austria
Braun, Christian 020457
Luxembourg Institute of Science and Technology, Esch-sur-Alzette, Luxembourg
Brecl, Kristijan 020269, 020319
University of Ljubljana, Ljubljana, Slovenia
Bredemeier, Dennis 020240
Leibniz University Hannover, Hannover, Germany
Breitenbücher, Marian 020225
Highline Technologies, Freiburg, Germany
Brendel, Rolf 020006, 020008, 020236, 020240, 020260, 020482
ISFH, Emmerthal, Germany
Brendstrup Møller, Clara Bolette 020028
DTU, Roskilde, Denmark
Bretzel, Tamara 020195
Fraunhofer ISE, Freiburg, Germany
Breyer, Christian 020479
LUT University, Lappeenranta, Finland
Brito, Miguel 020457
University of Lisbon, Lisbon, Portugal
Brivio, Elisabetta 020462
RSE, Milan, Italy
Brockmann, Lukas 020063
ISFH, Emmerthal, Germany
Brodnicke, Linda 020296
ETH, Zurich, Switzerland
Brueckner, Emanuel 020063
ISFH, Emmerthal, Germany
Bründlinger, Roland 020369
AIT, Vienna, Austria
Brun, Gonzalo 020414, 020517
ENDEF, Zaragoza, Spain
Bruno, Maddalena 020452
Fraunhofer ISE, Freiburg, Germany
Buceta, Alicia 020300
CENER, Sarriguren, Spain
Bucher, Christof 020179, 020322, 020359, 020369, 020386
BFH, Burgdorf, Switzerland
Buchholz, Florian 020035, 020225, 020569
ISC Konstanz, Konstanz, Germany
Buchmann, Johanna 020309
Berlin University of Applied Sciences, Berlin, Germany
Buck, Thomas 020033
ISC Konstanz, Konstanz, Germany

Buckland, Daniel — 020119, 020218
Henkel, Düsseldorf, Germany

Buddana, Viswa Harinath — 020482
DLR, Oldenburg, Germany

Bühlmann, Gian-Luca — 020385
ZHAW, Winterthur, Switzerland

Buerhop, Claudia — 020149, 020150, 020377
HI ERN, Erlangen, Germany

Buerhop-Lutz, Claudia — 020185, 020230
HI ERN, Erlangen, Germany

Burgers, Antonius R. — 020405
TNO, Petten, The Netherlands

Burri, Matthias — 020179
BFH, Burgdorf, Switzerland

Busto, Chiara — 020521
Eni, Novara, Italy

Butrichi, Fabio — 020087
University of Milano-Bicocca, Milan, Italy

Butt, Nauman — 020394
Lahore University of Management Sciences, Lahore, Pakistan

C. Tavares, Fabiele — 020090
Federal University of Rio de Janeiro, Duque de Caxias, Brazil

Cabal, Raphael — 020034
University Grenoble Alpes, Le Bourget-du-Lac, France

Caballero, Luis Jaime — 020501, 020508
UPM, Madrid, Spain

Caballero, Raquel — 020094
CSIC, Madrid, Spain

Caballero, Raquel — 020085
IO-CSIC, Madrid, Spain

Cabecinha, Vasco — 020565
Nova University Lisbon, Lisbon, Portugal

Cabello, Fatima — 020085
IO-CSIC, Madrid, Spain

Caçapietra Pires da Silva, Lucas Teixeira — 020025
PUCRS, Porto Alegre, Brazil

Caccavelli, Dominique — 020551
CSTB, Bussy-Saint Georges, France

Caccivio, Mauro — 020204, 020574
SUPSI, Mendrisio, Switzerland

Caffari, Francesca — 020551
ENEA, Ispra, Italy

Calabrese, Nicolandrea — 020551
ENEA, Ispra, Italy

Calin, Jean-Paul 020251
ENSTA Paris, Palaiseau, France
Çalışkan Arslan, Meriç 020006, 020135
Kalyon PV, Ankara, Türkiye
Caluori, Philip 020455
Virtual Vehicle, Graz, Austria
Camara, Assa 020274
Solargis, Bratislava, Slovakia
Cambarau, Werther 020139
Tecnalia, Donostia-San Sebastián, Spain
Campana, Pietro Elia 020381
Mälardalen University, Västerås, Sweden
Campos Guzman, Laura 020331
DLR, Almería, Spain
Cancro, Carmine 020378
ENEA, Naples, Italy
Canesse, Auriane 020196
PVsyst, Geneva, Switzerland
Cañizo, Carlos 020097
IES-UPM, Madrid, Spain
Cano, Francisco J. 020139
Tecnalia, Donostia - San Sebastián, Spain
Cano, Lucía 020127
ENDEF, Zaragoza, Spain
Cánovas, Enrique 020508
IMDEA Nanoscience Institute, Madrid, Spain
Cao, Han 020263
SERIS, Singapore, Singapore
Capitaine, Anna 020116
IPVF, Palaiseau, France
Cappelle, Jan 020329, 020351
KU Leuven, Ghent, Belgium
Capron, Guillaume 020217
CEA / INES, Le Bourget-du-Lac, France
Carballo López, José Antonio 020336
University of Almería, La Cañada de San Urbano, Spain
Cardenas, Luis Alejandro 020339, 020546
National University of Colombia, Bogotá, Colombia
Carmo, Paulo 020304, 020420
University of Évora, Évora, Portugal
Carrasco, Luis Miguel 020439, 020535, 020567
UPM, Madrid, Spain
Carrillo Mejía, Luis 020279
District University of Bogotá, Bogotá, Colombia
Carrillo, Rafael E. 020238
CSEM, Neuchâtel, Switzerland

Carroy, Perrine 020226
CEA/ INES, Le Bourget-du-Lac, France
Carstens, Justus 020003
ISC Konstanz, Konstanz, Germany
Carteni, Fabrizio 020378
University of Naples Federico II, Naples, Italy
Casappa, Michele 020087
National Research Council, Parma, Italy
Casasola Paesa, Marta 020389
Hasselt University, Diepenbeek, Belgium
Castilla Nieto, María del Mar 020336
University of Almeria, La Cañada de San Urbano, Spain
Castillo Patton, Daniel Jason 020326
Enertis Applus+, Madrid, Spain
Castro, Luis Guilherme 020530
Casa dos Ventos, Fortaleza, Brazil
Castro, Rui 020464
University of Lisbon, Lisbon, Portugal
Castro-Gallardo, Fernando 020417, 020422
University of Antofagasta, Antofagasta, Chile
Cavaco, Afonso 020304, 020565
University of Évora, Évora, Portugal
Cebecauer, Tomas 020274
Solargis, Bratislava, Slovakia
Çekerek, Gamze 020006
Kalyon PV, Ankara, Türkiye
Celik, Duygu 020551
WIP Renewable Energies, Munich, Germany
Çeliktaş, Melih Soner 020559
Ege University, İzmir, Türkiye
Centazzo, Massimo 020006
EnPV, Karlsruhe, Germany
Centeno Brito, Miguel 020421, 020490
University of Lisbon, Lisbon, Portugal
Cereceda, Eneko 020055, 020097, 020153, 020287
UPV/EHU, Bilbao, Spain
Ceretti, Mattia 020204
SUPSI, Mendrisio, Switzerland
Cesar, I. 020405
TNO, Petten, The Netherlands
Ceuppens, Ignas 020302
BUILD`UP, Aarschot, Belgium
Chatterji, Nithin 020071
SVNIT, Surat, India
Chen, Daniel 020048
SunDrive Solar, Kurnell, Australia

Chen, Syh-Homg 020161
ITRI, Hsinchu, Taiwan

Chen, Xiang 020111
Hohai University, Changzhou, China

Cheung, Kak Pong 020313
Kiel University of Applied Sciences, Kiel, Germany

Chhapia, Gaurang 020492
Belectric, Kolitzheim, Germany

Chiba, Takahiro 020436
Hokkaido University of Science, Sapporo, Japan

Chichignoud, Guy 020495
13Institut Polytechnique De Grenoble, Grenoble, France

Chicote, Beatriz 020289
Mondragon University, Arrasate-Mondragon, Spain

Chiesa, Matteo 020487
Khalifa University, Abu Dhabi, United Arab Emirates

Chini de Freitas, Felipe 020023
PUCRS, Porto Alegre, Brazil

Cho, Yunae 020045
KIER, Daejeon, South Korea

Choi, Kwan Bum 020102
SERIS, Singapore, Singapore

Chouder, Aissa 020301
University of M'sila, M'sila, Algeria

Chowdhury, Gofran 020276, 020544
3E, Brussels, Belgium

Christ, Anja 020063
ISFH, Emmerthal, Germany

Chrkavy, Daniel 020262
Solargis, Bratislava, Slovakia

Chueh, Wei-Lo 020021
TSEC, Hsinchu, Taiwan

Ciesla, Alison 020065
UNSW, Sydney, Australia

Cirimele, Vincenzo 020314
University of Bologna, Bologna, Italy

Clausing, Roland 020063, 020114
ISFH, Emmerthal, Germany

Clochard, Laurent 020031
Nines Photovoltaics, Dublin, Germany

Clochard, Laurent 020007
Nines Photovoltaics, Dublin, Ireland

Clyncke, Jan 020472, 020513
PV CYCLE, Brussels, Belgium

Coşkun, Özlem 020006, 020027, 020225
Kalyon PV, Ankara, Türkiye

Colberts, Fallon 020389
Zuyd University, Heerlen, The Netherlands

Colin, Hervé 020217, 020262
CEA / INES, Le Bourget-du-Lac, France

Collin, Stéphane 020074
C2N, Palaiseau, France

Colwell, Jack 020048
SunDrive Solar, Kurnell, Australia

Comak, Mertcan 020003
ISC Konstanz, Konstanz, Germany

Connolly, James Patrick 020058, 020060
CNRS, Gif-sur-Yvette, France

Cordeiro, Diogo 020464
EDP, Lisbon, Portugal

Cornago, Iñaki 020392
CENER, Sarriguren, Spain

Cornaro, Cristina 020494
University of Rome Tor Vergata, Rome, Italy

Correa, Guillermo 020412
Gonvarri MS R&D, Corvera - Asturias, Spain

Correia, Joana 020565
University of Évora, Évora, Portugal

Couderc, Romain 020217, 020311, 020546
CEA / INES, Le Bourget-du-Lac, France

Coutel, John 020244
SOLAÏS, Valbonne, France

Cowan, Don 020230
Kiwa PI Berlin, Hudson, United States of America

Cox, Joel D. 020250
SDU Climate Cluster, Odense, Denmark

Cox, Joel D 020306
SDU Climate Cluster, Odense, Denmark

Coz, Pier Luigi 020246
European Space Agency, Noordwijk, The Netherlands

Crespo, Carolina 020490
University of Lisbon, Lisbon, Portugal

Cristiane Pan, Aline 020548
UFRGS, Tramandaí, Brazil

Cristóbal, Ana Belén 020491, 020535, 020575
UPM, Madrid, Spain

Crozier McCleland, Jacqueline 020185, 020344
Nelson Mandela University, Port Elizabeth, South Africa

Cuadra, Juan Manuel 020318
CENER, Sarigurren, Spain

Cui, Jindan 020320, 020525
Tokyo University of Science, Tokyo, Japan

Culot, Dominique 020384
Dow Silicones Belgium, Seneffe, Belgium

Curon, Jonathan 020384
Dow Silicones Belgium, Seneffe, Belgium

Cusenza, Maria Anna 020466
RSE, Milan, Italy

D. Pinto, Luciana 020090
Federal University of Rio de Janeiro, Rio de Janeiro, Brazil

Daenen, Michael 020156, 020389, 020393
imec, Genk, Belgium

Dagla, Anastasia 020276
3E, Brussels, Belgium

Dahle, Arne 020225, 020495
Norsun, Oslo, Norway

Dahlioui, Dounia 020443
University of Agder, Grimstad, Norway

Dalibor, Thomas 020307
Avancis, Munich, Germany

Dalla Maria, Enrico 020485
Eurac Research, Bolzano, Italy

Dalla Torre, Francesco 020010
Applied Materials, Treviso, Italy

Dalmazzone, Didier 020251
ENSTA Paris, Palaiseau, France

Damon, Keanu 020382
7SecondSolar, Cape Town, South Africa

Danelli, Andrea 020462, 020466
RSE, Milan, Italy

Darsene Dimd, Berhane 020270
SINTEF, Trondheim, Norway

Das, Gourab 020005, 020222, 020463
RCT Solutions, Konstanz, Germany

Dasilva-Villanueva, Nerea 020014, 020501, 020508
UPM, Madrid, Spain

Daßler, David 020313
Fraunhofer CSP, Halle, Germany

Daßler, David 020355
Fraunhofer IMWS, Halle, Germany

Daume, Darwin 020361
pvnode, Rosenheim, Germany

Davidsen, Rasmus Schmidt 020028, 020039, 020043
Aarhus University, Aarhus, Denmark

De Almeida, Laura 020074
LAAS-CNRS, Toulouse, France

De Biasio, Martin 020504
Silicon Austria Labs, Villach, Austria
De Blasi, Mariam 020378
Enel Green Power, Pisa, Italy
de Graaf, Gertjan J. 020405
TNO, Petten, The Netherlands
de Groot, Koen M. 020405
TNO, Petten, The Netherlands
De Gruijter, Alvaro 020254
Eurac Research, Bolzano, Italy
de Jong, Minne M. 020169, 020425
TNO, Eindhoven, The Netherlands
De Jong, Richard 020156, 020294, 020389
imec, Genk, Belgium
de l`Epine, Mélodie 020252, 020505, 020543, 020564
Becquerel Institute France, Lyon, France
de l`Epine, Melodie 020225, 020334, 020520, 020558
Becquerel Institute, Brussels, Belgium
de l`Epine, Melodie 020570
IEA PVPS Task 1, Lyon, France
de la Casa Higueras, Juan 020269
University of Jaén, Jaén, Spain
de la Viuda, Eva 020205
University of Valladolid, Valladolid, Spain
de Meatza, Iratxe 020495
CIDETEC, San Sebastián, Spain
De Rose, Angela 020123
Fraunhofer ISE, Freiburg, Germany
De Rose, Jonas 020010
Fraunhofer ISE, Freiburg, Germany
Debastiani Benato, Betina 020019
AMIRES, Prague, Czech Republic
Deepti, 020563
SRM University, Sonipat, India
Del Campo, Valeria 020311
Federico Santa María Technical University, Valparaiso, Chile
del Cañizo, Carlos 020014, 020501, 020507, 020508
UPM, Madrid, Spain
Del Pero, Claudio 020249
Polytechnic University of Milan, Milan, Italy
Del Pozo, Alberto 020197, 020198
TECNALIA, Derio, Spain
del Prado Santamaria, Rodrigo 020191, 020376
DTU, Roskilde, Denmark
del Ser, Javier 020358
UPV/EHU, Bilbao, Spain

Delgado-Sanchez, Jose Maria 020089
University of Seville, Seville, Spain

Delli Veneri, Paola 020378
ENEA, Naples, Italy

Denafas, Julius 020225, 020353
Solitek, Vilnius, Lithuania

Deniz, Engin 020559
Ege University, İzmir, Türkiye

Denke, Sebastian 020236
ISFH, Emmerthal, Germany

Dentz, Laurie 020058
CNRS, Palaiseau, France

Derin Gure, Pinar 020513, 020521, 020556
ODTU GUNAM, Ankara, Türkiye

Derj, Anyssa 020116
IPVF, Palaiseau, France

Dessì, Alessio 020077
CNR-ICCOM, Sesto Fiorentino, Italy

Devenson, Jan 020157
Center for Physical Sciences and Technology (FTMC), Vilnius, Lithuania

Dhimish, Mahmoud 020346, 020376
DTU, Roskilde, Denmark

Di Matteo, Alfredo 020010
Enel Green Power, Catania, Italy

Diab, Mohanad 020203
Eurac Research, Bolzano, Italy

Diano, Marcello 020378
M2M Engineering, Naples, Italy

Diaz, Roberto 020300
Notio Association, Toledo, Spain

Díaz, Sara 020365, 020366
CENER, Sarriguren, Spain

Dietrich, Andreas 020355
DiSUN Deutsche Solarservice, Werder, Germany

Díez Alcántara, Eduardo 020501
UCM, Madrid, Spain

Díez, Eduardo 020508
UCM, Madrid, Spain

Dimd, Berhane Darsene 020495, 020510
SINTEF, Trondheim, Norway

Ding, Kaining 020233
FZJ, Jülich, Germany

Ding, Kung 020111
Hohai University, Changzhou, China

Dittmann, Sebastian 020318
Anhalt University of Applied Sciences, Köthen, Germany

Dittrich, Arne 020240
ISFH, Emmerthal, Germany

Dizier, Antoine 020373
INES, Le Bourget-du-Lac, France

Djeukeu, Ivanol Jaurece 020050
halm elektronik, Frankfurt am Main, Germany

Dobreva, Petja 020193
University of Namibia, Windhoek, Namibia

Dörenkämper, Maarten 020169
TNO, Eindhoven, The Netherlands

Dörn, Markus 020255
A-Null Development, Vienna, Austria

Doi, Minh Thong 020317
CEA INES, Le Bourget-du-Lac, France

Domínguez, César 020209, 020246, 020257
UPM, Madrid, Spain

Donadello, Alessandro 020485, 020489
Edyna, Bolzano, Italy

Donėlienė, Jolanta 020157
Applied Research Institute for Prospective Technologies, Vilnius, Lithuania

Donoso, José 020570
UNEF, Madrid, Spain

Doppler, Christian 020455
Virtual Vehicle, Graz, Austria

dos Reis, Givaldo 020348
University of São Paulo, São Paulo, Brazil

dos Santos, Jeremias 020409
University of Évora, Évora, Portugal

Doucet, Jean-Baptiste 020074
LAAS-CNRS, Toulouse, France

Dovesi, Roberto 020060
Academy of Sciences of Turin, Torino, Italy

Driesse, Anton 020211, 020293, 020452
PV Performance Labs, Freiburg, Germany

Duarte, Dorivaldo 020418, 020565
University of Evora, Évora, Portugal

Dubois, Sebastien 020034
University Grenoble Alpes, Le Bourget-du-Lac, France

Dubravskij, Piotr 020157
Applied Research Institute for Prospective Technologies, Vilnius, Lithuania

Dubravskij, Piotr 020380
Modern E-Technologies, Vilnius, Lithuania

Duerinckx, Filip 020064, 020225
Hasselt Unversity, Genk, Belgium

Düz, Cansel 020135
Kalyon PV, Ankara, Türkiye
Dullweber, Thorsten 020006, 020007, 020008, 020225
ISFH, Emmerthal, Germany
Dunlop, Ewan D. 020173, 020210, 020213
European Commission JRC, Ispra, Italy
Dupon, Olivier 020294
imec, Genk, Belgium
Dupuis, Julien 020188
EDF R&D, Moret Loing Orvanne, France
Dutykh, Denys 020338
Khalifa University, Abu Dhabi, United Arab Emirates
Duzellier, Sophie 020073
University of Toulouse, Toulouse, France
Dypvik Sødahl, Elin 020340
IFE, Kjeller, Norway

Ebert, Matthias 020426
Fraunhofer CSP, Halle, Germany
Ebert, Matthias 020355
Fraunhofer IMWS, Halle, Germany
Ebner, Rita 020318, 020334, 020521
AIT, Vienna, Austria
Echeverria, Oihane 020139
Tecnalia, Donostia - San Sebastián, Spain
Eder, Gabriele C. 020160, 020162, 020249, 020500, 020504
OFI, Vienna, Austria
Eelma, Tonis 020302
IBS, Tartu, Estonia
Efthymiou, Venizelos 020544
EPL Technology Frontiers, Dhali, Cyprus
Egan, Renate 020048
UNSW, Sydney, Australia
Egido, Miguel-Ángel 020407
UPM, Madrid, Spain
Eidtmann, Maximilian 020385
ZHAW, Winterthur, Switzerland
Eijgelaar, Marcel 020571
DNV, Arnhem, The Netherlands
Eikelboom, Erik 020225
Futurasun, Citadella, Italy
Einhaus, Roland 020312
ZSW, Stuttgart, Germany
Eisenacher, Matthias 020141
University of Applied Science Cologne, Cologne, Germany

Eiternick, Stefan — 020004, 020052
Fraunhofer CSP, Halle (Saale), Germany

Ekins-Daukes, Nicholas J. — 020065
UNSW, Sydney, Australia

El Ainaoui, Khadija — 020171
Green Energy Park, Benguerir, Morocco

El mrabet, Yasmine — 020171
Green Energy Park, Benguerir, Morocco

Elgaili, Mohamed — 020166
QEERI, Doha, Qatar

Elhamaoui, Said — 020171
Green Energy Park, Benguerir, Morocco

Ellis, Hanna — 020213
European Commission JRC, Ispra, Italy

Engelen, Tine — 020389
Hasselt University, Diepenbeek, Belgium

Erber, Alexander — 020386
BFH, Burgdorf, Switzerland

Eryılmaz, Hande — 020521
ODTÜ-GÜNAM, Ankara, Türkiye

Escudero, Ana — 020414
IaSol, Zaragoza, Spain

Esmailifar, Seyyed Majid — 020335, 020356, 020374, 020375
Amirkabir University of Technology, Tehran, Iran

Espinosa, Nieves — 020497, 020506
University of Murcia, Murcia, Spain

Essam T. Mohammed, Sarah — 020546
EU SOLARIS, Almeria, Spain

Esteras, Miguel — 020358
TECNALIA, Derio, Spain

Eyhorn, Steffen — 020369
Fraunhofer ISE, Freiburg, Germany

Fabel, Yann — 020235, 020237, 020239
DLR, Almería, Spain

Fabris, Francesca — 020225
Futurasun, Citadella, Italy

Faes, Antonin — 020251
CSEM, Neuchâtel, Switzerland

Falangas, Alexandros — 020210
TRASIS International, Brussels, Belgium

Fang, Xue — 020525
Tokyo University of Science, Tokyo, Japan

Fano, Vanesa — 020055, 020097, 020153, 020287
UPV/EHU, Bilbao, Spain

Farhat, Mohammad 020428
Australian University, Kuwait City, Kuwait

Farina, Andrea 020066
CNR-IFN, Milan, Italy

Farrias-Basulto, Guillermo 020101
HZB, Berlin, Germany

Fath, Moritz 020463
RCT Solutions, Konstanz, Germany

Fath, Peter 020005, 020463
RCT Solutions, Konstanz, Germany

Fava, Henrique 020565
University of Évora, Évora, Portugal

Feichtner, Markus 020255
Sonnenkraft Energie, St. Veit/Glan, Austria

Feichtner, Markus 020160
Sonnenkraft Energy, St. Veit/Glan, Austria

Feldbacher, Sonja 020136, 020500
PCCL, Leoben, Austria

Feldhof, Anne Maren 020522
University of Applied Science Cologne, Cologne, Germany

Fernandes, Cláudia 020464
Centre for New Energy Technologies, Sacavém, Portugal

Fernández Solas, Álvaro 020331
DLR, Almeria, Spain

Ferrando, Jorge 020226
University of Valencia, Paterna, Spain

Ferreira, Catarina G. 020250
SDU Climate Cluster, Odense, Denmark

Ferreira, Catarina 020306
SDU Climate Cluster, Odense, Denmark

Ferrero, Sergio 020079
Polytechnic University of Turin, Turin, Italy

Feuerherdt, Niels 020309
Berlin University of Applied Sciences, Berlin, Germany

Fialho, Luis 020203, 020254, 020261, 020304, 020403,
Eurac Research, Bolzano, Italy 020409, 020418, 020420, 020565

Figueroa, Andrés 020339
National University of Colombia, Bogotá, Colombia

Fischer, Stefan 020495
SGL Carbon, Meitingen, Germany

Fleischanderl, Martin 020136
voestalpine Stahl, Linz, Austria

Fleury, Perine 020513, 020521
Biosphere Solar, Delft, The Netherlands

Flouchi, Imane 020171
Green Energy Park, Benguerir, Morocco

Fodor, Nikoletta 020521
SolarPower Europe, Brussels, Belgium

Fontani, Daniela 020066
CNR-INO, Florence, Italy

Forster, Jacob 020135
Fraunhofer ISE, Freiburg, Germany

Forstinger, Anne 020331
CSP Services, Cologne, Germany

Franch, Jordi Badosa 020406
Ecole Polytechnique, Palaiseau, France

Franchi, Daniele 020077
CNR-ICCOM, Sesto Fiorentino, Italy

Franquet, Erwin 020259, 020428
Côte d`Azur University, Nice, France

Frasson, Nicola 020019
Applied Materials, San Biagio di Callalta, Italy

Freer, Solomon 020396
PV Lighthouse, Coledale, Australia

Freitag, Marina 020077
Newcastle University, Newcastle upon Tyne, United Kingdom

Freund, Timo 020312
EnBW, Karlsruhe, Germany

Friansyah, Rizal 020376
DTU, Roskilde, Denmark

Friesen, Gabi 020160, 020249, 020574
SUPSI, Mendrisio, Switzerland

Friesen, Thomas 020249
Megasol Energie, Deitingen, Switzerland

Fritz Muñoz, Benjamín 020099
UPV, Valencia, Spain

Froebel, Jens 020121, 020142, 020192, 020223
Fraunhofer CSP, Halle, Germany

Frontini, Francesco 020249, 020253
SUPSI, Mendrisio, Switzerland

Fuentealba-Vidal, Edward 020129, 020311, 020342, 020417, 020422
University of Antofagasta, Antofagasta, Chile

Füreder-Kitzmüller, Friedrich 020136
voestalpine Stahl, Linz, Austria

Fuertes Marrón, David 020014, 020501, 020507, 020508
UPM, Madrid, Spain

Fuertes, David 020097
IES-UPM, Madrid, Spain

Furnari, Alessandro 020010
Enel Green Power, Catania, Italy

Fuß, Michael 020206
MBJ Solutions, Ahrensburg, Germany

Gabor, Andrew M. 020166
BrightSpot Automation, Boulder, United States of America

Gaete, Martin 020311
University of Antofagasta, Antofagasta, Chile

Gafert, Michael 020369
AIT, Vienna, Austria

Gageot, Tristan 020040
CEA / INES, Le Bourget-du-Lac, France

Gainza, Eusebio 020392
ALLOTARRA, Allo, Spain

Galarza, Alejandra 020461
IPVF, Palaiseau, France

Galbiati, Giuseppe 020119, 020218
Henkel, Düsseldorf, Germany

Galdikas, Algirdas 020157
Applied Research Institute for Prospective Technologies, Vilnius, Lithuania

Galiana, Beatriz 020085
Charles III University of Madrid, Madrid, Spain

Galiazzo, Marco 020019
Applied Materials, San Biagio di Callalta, Italy

Gall, Stefan 020101
HZB, Berlin, Germany

Gallmetzer, Sandra 020261, 020509
Eurac Research, Bolzano, Italy

Galparsoro, Ibon 020514
AZTI, PASAIA, Spain

Gamarra, Ana Rosa 020502
CIEMAT, Madrid, Spain

Ganter, Alissa 020296
ETH, Zurich, Switzerland

Gaona García, Elvis Eduardo 020279
District University of Bogotá, Bogotá, Colombia

Garabetian, Thomas 020551
SolarPower Europe, Brussels, Belgium

García Campos, Enrique 020336
University of Almería, La Cañada de San Urbano, Spain

García, Fernando 020326
UC3M, Madrid, Spain

García, Sonia 020139
Tecnalia, Donostia - San Sebastián, Spain

García-Cañas, Alejandro 020257
IMDEA Nanoscience, Madrid, Spain

García-Salinas, María José 020100
University of Almeria, Almería, Spain

Garcia-Sanchez, Almudena 020246, 020257
UPM, Madrid, Spain

Garg, Vivek 020069, 020071, 020081
SVNIT, Surat, India

Garraín, Daniel 020502
CIEMAT, Madrid, Spain

Gasse, Hugues 020073
University of Toulouse, Toulouse, France

Gassner, Anika 020160, 020162, 020500, 020504
OFI, Vienna, Austria

Gatti, Cesare 020541
PedersoliGattai, Milan, Italy

Gattu, Apoorva 020003
ISC Konstanz, Konstanz, Germany

Gautier, Damien 020505
Becquerel Institute, Brussels, Belgium

Gauvin, Xavier 020302
Bouygues Construction, Saint-Quentin-en-Yvelines, France

Ge, Hua 020249
Concordia University, Montreal, Canada

Gebhardt, Paul 020195
Fraunhofer ISE, Freiburg, Germany

Geerligs, L. J. 020030
TNO, Petten, The Netherlands

Gehrlein, Janek 020522
University of Applied Science Cologne, Cologne, Germany

Geier, Jutta 020234
PCCL, Leoben, Austria

Geml, Fabian 020031
University of Konstanz, Constance, Germany

Genovese, Maria 020378
Enel Green Power, Pisa, Italy

Georghiou, George E. 020534
University of Cyprus, Nicosia, Cyprus

Germani, Simone 020302
CEI, Milan, Italy

Getsiou, Maria 020181
Directorate General for Research and Innovation, Brussels, Belgium

Geymayer, Lukas 020136
voestalpine Stahl, Linz, Austria

Ghahremani, Amirreza 020335, 020374
Amirkabir University of Technology, Tehran, Iran

Ghennioui, Abdellatif 020171
Green Energy Park, Benguerir, Morocco

Ghosh, Saptak 020519
CSTEP, Bengaluru, India

Girardi, Pierpaolo — 020462, 020466
RSE, Milan, Italy

Giroux-Julien, Stephanie — 020338
CNRS, Villeurbanne, France

Gissler, Antoine — 020060
EDF R&D, Palaiseau, France

Göckeritz, Robert — 020119
Fraunhofer CSP, Halle, Germany

Gohil, Hardik — 020222
RCT Solutions, Konstanz, Germany

Gomes de Venuto, Vitor — 020025
PUCRS, Porto Alegre, Brazil

Gomez Trillos, Juan Camilo — 020482
DLR, Oldenburg, Germany

Gomez-Lazaro, Emilio — 020562
University of Castilla-La Mancha, Albacete, Spain

Gonnella, Gabriella — 020249, 020254
Eurac research, Bolzano, Italy

González Pérez, Sara — 020151
ULL, San Cristóbal de La Laguna, Spain

González Rodríguez, Brais — 020243
University of Vigo, Vigo, Spain

González, Miguel Ángel — 020205
University of Valladolid, Valladolid, Spain

González-Díaz, Benjamín — 020151
ULL, San Cristóbal de La Laguna, Spain

Goraya, Baljeet Singh — 020475
Fraunhofer ISE, Freiburg, Germany

Gordillo, Gerardo — 020110
National University of Colombia, Bogotá, Colombia

Gordon, Ivan — 020521
imec, Genk, Belgium

Gottschalg, Ralph — 020158
Anhalt University of Applied Sciences, Köthen, Germany

Gottschalg, Ralph — 020056, 020201, 020229, 020233, 020284, 020574
Fraunhofer CSP, Halle, Germany

Govaerts, Jonathan — 020019
imec, Genk, Belgium

Gracia Amillo, Ana María — 020211
CENER, Pamplona, Spain

Gracia Amillo, Ana María — 020318
CENER, Sarigurren, Spain

Gracia Amillo, Ana María — 020181, 020365, 020366, 020497
CENER, Sarriguren, Spain

Gregory, Geoffrey — 020006
EnPV, Karlsruhe, Germany

Greslou, Olivier 020551
CSTB, Bussy-Saint Georges, France
Grommes, Eva-Maria 020522, 020523
University of Applied Science Cologne, Cologne, Germany
Grosser, Stephan 020119, 020142, 020218
Fraunhofer CSP, Halle, Germany
Grünsteidl, Stefan 020307
Avancis, Munich, Germany
Gruginskie, Natasha 020067
Radboud University, Nijmegen, The Netherlands
Guedea, Isabel 020127, 020517
ENDEF, Zaragoza, Spain
Gülsoy, Eren Cihan 020521
METU, Ankara, Türkiye
Gümüs Çiftci, Burcu 020027
Kalyon PV, Ankara, Türkiye
Guerra, Gerardo 020448, 020481
GreenPowerMonitor a DNV company, Barcelona, Spain
Guidetti, Giulia 020541
Green Horse Advisory, Milan, Italy
Guillemoles, Jean François 020062
IPVF, Palaiseau, France
Guillevin, Nicolas 020225
TNO, Petten, The Netherlands
Gunbas, Gorkem 020113
ODTÜ-GÜNAM, Ankara, Türkiye
Gupta, Akshit 020551
Eurac Research, Bolzano, Italy
Gutierrez, Jose Ruben 020055, 020097, 020153, 020287
UPV/EHU, Bilbao, Spain
Gutjahr, Astrid 020030
TNO, Petten, The Netherlands

Haaland, Petry Kristine Nøttum 020476
NTNU, Trondheim, Norway
Haase, Felix 020063
ISFH, Emmerthal, Germany
Hadiwidjaja, Stella 020102
SERIS, Singapore, Singapore
Hadjipanayi, Maria 020064
University of Cyprus, Nicosia, Cyprus
Haedrich, Ingrid 020195, 020231
Fraunhofer ISE, Freiburg, Germany
Hämmer, Matthias 020470
bifa Umweltinstitut, Augsburg, Germany

Hafidi, Elias 020511
Inflights BV, Brussels, Belgium

Hagemann, Elizabeth M. 020416
Nelson Mandela University, Port Elizabeth, South Africa

Hallais, Géraldine 020058
CNRS, Palaiseau, France

Halle, Lasse 020359
BFH, Burgdorf, Switzerland

Hallensleben, Carina 020220
TAMURA-ELSOLD, Ilsenburg, Germany

Halm, Andreas 020218, 020220, 020221
ISC Konstanz, Konstanz, Germany

Halme, Janne 020249
Aalto University, Espoo, Finland

Hamada, Toshiyuki 020190
Osaka Electro-Communication University, Osaka, Japan

Hammer, Annette 020239
DLR, Oldenburg, Germany

Hamouda, Frederic 020058
CNRS, Palaiseau, France

Hanifi, Hamed 020121, 020125, 020137, 020223
AESOLAR, Koenigsbrunn, Germany

Hansen, Per-Anders 020017, 020503
Institute for Energy Technology, Kjeller, Norway

Harit, Amit Kumar 020064
Hasselt Unversity, Genk, Belgium

Harrison, Samuel 020225
CEA, Le Bourget-du-Lac, France

Hashem, Ahmad 020056, 020201
Anhalt University of Applied Sciences, Köthen, Germany

Hategan, Sergiu Mihai 020283
West University of Timisoara, Timisoara, Romania

Hauch, Jens 020117, 020149, 020150
HI ERN, Erlangen, Germany

Hauer, Martin 020255
Bartenbach, Vienna, Austria

Haverkamp, Helge 020008
centrotherm international, Blaubeuren, Germany

Hee Lee, Sang 020045
KIER, Daejeon, South Korea

Heidrich, Robert 020233
Fraunhofer CSP, Halle, Germany

Heikkinen, Kyösti 020423
VTT Technical Research Centre of Finland, Oulu, Finland

Heiser, Moritz 020230
Kiwa PI Berlin, Berlin, Germany

Helbig, Matthias 020220
ISC Konstanz, Konstanz, Germany
Helten, David 020331
CSP Services, Cologne, Germany
Hennig, Carsten 020313, 020355
saferay holding, Berlin, Germany
Hennig, Patrick 020313
Kiel University of Applied Sciences, Kiel, Germany
Heras, Jesús 020536
Wattkraft, Madrid, Spain
Hermle, Martin 020475
Fraunhofer ISE, Freiburg, Germany
Hernández Mora, Johann Alexander 020279, 020441
District University of Bogotá, Bogotá, Colombia
Hernández, Jaime J. 020257
IMDEA Nanoscience, Madrid, Spain
Hernández, Johann 020526
Francisco José de Caldas District University, Bogota, Colombia
Herodotou, Panayiotis 020534
University of Cyprus, Nicosia, Cyprus
Herrera Leon, Fernando Augusto 020339, 020546
National University of Colombia, Bogotá, Colombia
Herrero, Leire 020139
Tecnalia, Donostia - San Sebastián, Spain
Herrero, Rebeca 020209, 020453, 020459
UPM, Madrid, Spain
Herrmann, Werner 020208
TÜV Rheinland Solar, Cologne, Germany
Herteleer, Bert 020329, 020351
KU Leuven, Ghent, Belgium
Herteleer, Bert 020574
SUPSI, Mendrisio, Switzerland
Hessler-Wyser, Aïcha 020251
EPFL, Neuchâtel, Switzerland
Heydari, Azim 020485
Eurac Research, Bolzano, Italy
Hinken, David 020236
ISFH, Emmerthal, Germany
Hladys, Bertrand 020010
CEA, Grenoble, France
Hoex, Bram 020065
UNSW, Sydney, Australia
Hofer, Leo 020322
BFH, Burgdorf, Switzerland
Hoffmann, Erik 020006
EnPV, Karlsruhe, Germany

Hogan Almeida, Rita UPM, Madrid, Spain	020535, 020567
Hollemann, Christina ISFH, Emmerthal, Germany	020008
Holovský, Jakub Czech Technical University, Prague, Czech Republic	020107
Honrubia-Escribano, Andrés University of Castilla-La Mancha, Albacete, Spain	020562
Hopp, Tobias Sunman Energy, Frankfurt, Germany	020384
Horn, Jonas halm elektronik, Frankfurt am Main, Germany	020050
Horta, Pedro University of Évora, Évora, Portugal	020304, 020403, 020409, 020418, 020420, 020565
Hosatte, Mikaël SEGTON Advanced Technology, Versailles, France	020068
Hoß, Jan ISC Konstanz, Konstanz, Germany	020004, 020035
Hossain, Mohammad Istiaque QEERI, Doha, Qatar	020042, 020075, 020108, 020109, 020146, 020147
Hou, Yi SERIS, Singapore, Singapore	020102
Hsiao, Pei-Chieh UNSW, Sydney, Australia	020048
Hsieh, Cho Fan ITRI, Hsinchu, Taiwan	020083, 020161, 020163
Hu, Shuaifeng University of Oxford, Oxford, United Kingdom	020226
Huang, Chris SunDrive Solar, Kurnell, Australia	020048
Huang, Gan KIT, Eggenstein-Leopoldshafen, Germany	020272
Huang, Lu-Jan TNO, Leiden, The Netherlands	020425
Huang, Tzu-Yen National Synchrotron Radiation Research Center, Hsinchu, Taiwan	020096
Hügi, Matthias BFH, Burgdorf, Switzerland	020322
Huemer, Martin University of Linz, Linz, Austria	020227
Huerta, Hugo E. TUAS, Turku, Finland	020286, 020400
Hüttl, Bernd Coburg University of Applied Sciences, Coburg, Germany	020361

Hulik Jansova, Marketa 020274
Solargis, Bratislava, Slovakia

Hung, Tzu Han 020552
ITRI, Taipei City, Taiwan

Hutterer-Tik, Thomas 020347
Watt Analytics, Vienna, Austria

Hwang, Hye-Mi 020324, 020357, 020561
KIER, Daejeon, South Korea

Iglesias, Unai 020139
Tecnalia, Donostia - San Sebastián, Spain

Ikeda, Kazuaki 020436
AIST, Koriyama, Japan

Infante, Paulo 020420
University of Évora, Évora, Portugal

Isabella, Olindo 020515
TU Delft, Delft, The Netherlands

Ishikawa, Ryousuke 020106, 020115
Tokyo City University, Setagaya, Japan

Iwaszko, Victorien 020495
ROSI Solar, Saint-Martin-d'Hères, France

Izquierdo-Roca, Victor 020094
IREC, Barcelona, Spain

J. N. Soares, Guillermo 020090
Federal University of Rio de Janeiro, Duque de Caxias, Brazil

Jacob, Julieu 020302
METABUILD, Berlin, Germany

Jacobs, Ayesha 020382
Zutari, Cape Town, South Africa

Jaeckel, Bengt 020056, 020119, 020121, 020140, 020142, 020175, 020192, 020201, 020223, 020229
Fraunhofer CSP, Halle, Germany

Jäger Waldau, Arnulf 020570
European Commission, Rome, Italy

Jäger, Philip 020006
ISFH, Emmerthal, Germany

Jäggi, Adrian 020179
BFH, Burgdorf, Switzerland

Järventausta, Pertti 020445
Tampere University, Tampere, Finland

Jaffré, Alexandre 020058
CNRS, Gif-sur-Yvette, France

Jahn, Ulrike 020521, 020574
Fraunhofer CSP, Halle, Germany

Jahn, Ulrike 020355
Fraunhofer IMWS, Halle, Germany

Jahreis, Sophia 020142, 020192
Fraunhofer CSP, Halle, Germany

Jakomin, Roberto 020090
Federal University of Rio de Janeiro, Duque de Caxias, Brazil

Jakubik, Martin 020274
Solargis, Bratislava, Slovakia

Jakuza, Paola 020089
University of Padova, Padova, Italy

Jalkh, Judy 020455
Virtual Vehicle, Graz, Austria

Jandl, Ralf 020204
FFHS, Zurich, Switzerland

Jankovec, Marko 020197
University of Ljubljana, Ljubljana, Slovenia

Jaworczak, Kamil 020402
Technology Innovation Institute, Abu Dhabi, United Arab Emirates

Jensen, Adam R. 020267
DTU, Kongens Lyngby, Denmark

Jeong, Jungi 020323
K-water, Daejeon, South Korea

Jeong, Kyung Taek 020045
KIER, Daejeon, South Korea

Jeong, Minsoo 020045
KIER, Daejeon, South Korea

Jeronimo, Pedro 020010
CEA, Grenoble, France

Jiang, Zonghan 020158, 020201
Anhalt University of Applied Sciences, Köthen, Germany

Jimenez, Maria 020302
Onyx Solar, Avila, Spain

Jimeno, Juan Carlos 020055, 020097, 020153, 020287, 020289, 020353
UPV/EHU, Bilbao, Spain

Jo, Hyunsik 020323
K-water, Daejeon, South Korea

Job, Enzo 020231
Fraunhofer ISE, Freiburg, Germany

Johnson, Mark Robert 020546
Institut Laue-Langevin (ILL), Grenoble, France

Joo, Dongmyoung 020449
KETI, Wonmi-gu, South Korea

Jooss, Wolfgang 020005, 020222, 020463
RCT Solutions, Konstanz, Germany

Joseph, Daniel Christopher 020123
Fraunhofer ISE, Freiburg, Germany

Joshi, Deepak 020069, 020081
SVNIT, Surat, India

Joss, David 020359, 020369, 020386
BFH, Burgdorf, Switzerland

Jouini, Anis 020034
ECM Technologies, Grenoble, France

Jouttijärvi, Sami 020286, 020298, 020398
University of Turku, Turku, Finland

Joziak, Roman 020230
Kiwa PI Berlin, Berlin, Germany

Ju, Young-Chul 020324, 020357, 020561
KIER, Daejeon, South Korea

Jugo, Josu 020437
UPV/EHU, Leioa, Spain

Junge, Sebastian 020008, 020482
ISFH, Emmerthal, Germany

Kaaya, Ismail 020156, 020294, 020389, 020393
imec, Genk, Belgium

Kähler, Jan-Dirk 020482
Centrotherm International, Blaubeuren, Germany

Kahraman, Mert 020027
Kalyon PV, Ankara, Türkiye

Kainz, Konrad 020430
AIT, Vienna, Austria

Kaiser, Martin 020215
Fraunhofer ISE, Freiburg, Germany

Kaizuka, Izumi 020570
RTS Corporation, Tokyo, Japan

Kajari-Schröder, Sarah 020063
ISFH, Emmerthal, Germany

Kallioharju, Kari 020444, 020445
TUAS, Tampere, Finland

Kalliojärvi, Heidi 020194
Tampere University, Tampere, Finland

Kalshetty, Mahesh 020519
CSTEP, Bengaluru, India

Kaltenbach, Thomas 020195
Fraunhofer ISE, Freiburg, Germany

Kamphues, Joshua 020031
University of Konstanz, Constance, Germany

Kandiyoti-Eskenazi, Selin 020467
CSEM, Neuchâtel, Switzerland

Kang, Min Gu 020045
KIER, Daejeon, South Korea

Kapetanovic, Viktor 020367
Nextracker, Fremont, United States of America

Karhu, Juha 020286
Finnish Meteorological Institute, Helsinki, Finland

Kari, Thøger 020191, 020376
DTU, Roskilde, Denmark

Karimy, Hedayatullah 020052
Fraunhofer CSP, Halle (Saale), Germany

Karttunen, Lauri 020298, 020398
University of Turku, Turku, Finland

Kasper, Ruth 020167, 020232
University of Applied Sciences Cologne, Cologne, Germany

Katouli, Tannaz 020195
Fraunhofer ISE, Freiburg, Germany

Kaufmann, Kai 020355
DENKweit, Halle, Germany

Kawabata, Rudy 020092
PUC-Rio, Rio de Janeiro, Brazil

Kemp, Linda 020390
MARIN, Wageningen, The Netherlands

Kenchington, Ian 020225, 020474, 020558
Becquerel Institute, Brussels, Belgium

Kenny, Robert 020210
European Commission JRC, Ispra, Italy

Khan, Abeer Ali 020513
First Solar, Mainz, Germany

Khosravi, Arash 020381
Mälardalen University, Västerås, Sweden

Kikkert, Benjamin W. J. 020405
TNO, Petten, The Netherlands

Kilickaya, Seda 020020
ODTÜ-GÜNAM, Ankara, Türkiye

Kim, Jin-Hong 020449
KETI, Wonmi-gu, South Korea

Kim, Jun-Tae 020249
Kongju National University, Chungnam, South Korea

Kim, Kihwan 020112
KIER, Daejeon, South Korea

Kim, Seok Won 020449
KETI, Wonmi-gu, South Korea

Kim, Yong-Jin 020045
KIER, Daejeon, South Korea

Kinge, Sachin 020117
Toyota Motors Europe, Brussels, Belgium

Kitamura, Ibuki 020190
Osaka Electro-Communication University, Osaka, Japan
Kitzberger, Gregor 020136
voestalpine Stahl, Linz, Austria
Kivambe, Maulid 020166
QEERI, Doha, Qatar
Kizukuri, Rihoko 020220
TAMURA-ELSOLD, Ilsenburg, Germany
Kladas, Anastasios 020329, 020351
KU Leuven, Ghent, Belgium
Kleider, Jean-Paul 020040, 020058
CNRS, Gif-sur-Yvette, France
Kleissl, Jan 020528
University of California, San Diego, United States of America
Klengel, Robert 020355
Fraunhofer IMWS, Halle, Germany
Klenk, Markus 020385
ZHAW, Winterthur, Switzerland
Klos, Christine 020510
Buhck Re.Energy, Hamburg, Norway
Kluska, Sven 020019
Fraunhofer ISE, Freiburg, Germany
Klute, Carola 020355
Fraunhofer IMWS, Halle, Germany
Knausdorf, Christian 020361
Coburg University of Applied Sciences, Coburg, Germany
Ko, Seok-whan 020561
KIER, Daejeon, South Korea
Ko, Suk Whan 020324, 020357
KIER, Daejeon, South Korea
Koc, Timurhan 020376
DTU, Roskilde, Denmark
Koduvelikulathu, Lejo Joseph 020035, 020068
ISC Konstanz, Konstanz, Germany
Koduvelikulathu, Lejo 020003
ISC Konstanz, Konstanz, Germany
Köntges, Marc 020206
ISFH, Emmerthal, Germany
Koepge, Ringo 020142, 020192
Fraunhofer CSP, Halle, Germany
Koester, Lukas 020203, 020261, 020325
Eurac Research, Bolzano, Italy
Kohlenberg, Heike 020063
ISFH, Emmerthal, Germany
Kohno, Tohru 020186
Hitachi, Tokyo, Japan

Kolahi, Mohammad 020356, 020375
University of Isfahan, Isfahan, Iran
Konagai, Makoto 020106, 020115
Tokyo City University, Setagaya, Japan
Kono, Toru 020484
Hitachi, Kokubunji, Japan
Konu, Christopher Bruce 020132
HTW Berlin, Berlin, Germany
Kopecek, Radovan 020569
ISC Konstanz, Konstanz, Germany
Kopp, Nils 020220
TAMURA-ELSOLD, Ilsenburg, Germany
Korkmaz Arslan, Melisa 020020
ODTÜ-GÜNAM, Ankara, Türkiye
Korpås, Magnus 020476
NTNU, Trondheim, Norway
Kortetmäki, Aki 020444, 020445
TUAS, Tampere, Finland
Koskela, Juha 020444, 020445, 020554
Tampere University, Tampere, Finland
Kossen, Eric J. 020030
TNO, Petten, The Netherlands
Kowalski, Julia 020237
RWTH, Aachen, Germany
Kräling, Ulli 020215
Fraunhofer ISE, Freiburg, Germany
Kraft, Thomas M. 020423
VTT Technical Research Centre of Finland, Oulu, Finland
Krainer, Diana Maria 020430
AIT, Vienna, Austria
Krasilnikov, Inga 020379
Tel Aviv University, Tel Aviv, Israel
Krever Lopes, Bruno 020023
PUCRS, Porto Alegre, Brazil
Kribus, Abraham 020379
Tel Aviv University, Tel Aviv, Israel
Krishnan, Sasikumar 020361
Coburg University of Applied Sciences, Coburg, Germany
Kroon, Jan 020225
TNO, Petten, The Netherlands
Kuan, Ta-Ming 020021, 020053
TSEC, Hsinchu, Taiwan
Kubicek, Bernhard 020281, 020318, 020334, 020347, 020430
AIT, Vienna, Austria
Kucuk, E. Busra 020030
TNO, Petten, The Netherlands

Kuczyńska-Łażewska, Anna 020498, 020499
Gdansk University of Technology, Gdansk, Poland

Kühne, Philip 020240
Leibniz University Hannover, Hannover, Germany

Kuhrmann, Bernd 020206
MBJ Solutions, Ahrensburg, Germany

Kujansivu, Eino 020554
Solarigo Systems, Pirkkala, Finland

Kumar, Gaurav 020563
MERI College of Engineering and Technology, Bahadurgarh, India

Kumar, Sagarika 020402
Technology Innovation Institute, Abu Dhabi, United Arab Emirates

Kumar, Saurabh 020563
PTB, Braunshweig, Germany

Kuo, Cheng-Wen 020021, 020053
TSEC, Hsinchu, Taiwan

Kurtulus, Gunes 020556
ODTU GUNAM, Ankara, Türkiye

Kuruganti, Vaibhav V. 020033
ISC Konstanz, Konstanz, Germany

Kurz, Hannes 020136
voestalpine Stahl, Linz, Austria

Kusch, Alexander 020361
Coburg University of Applied Sciences, Coburg, Germany

Kuzhagaliyeva, Nursulu 020402
Technology Innovation Institute, Abu Dhabi, United Arab Emirates

Kuznicki, Zbigniew T. 020013, 020068
SEGTON Advanced Technology, Versailles, France

Kwiatkowski, Jerzy 020551
NAPE, Warsaw, Poland

Kyranaki, Nikoleta 020156
Hasselt University, Genk, Belgium

Kyranaki, Nikoleta 020393
Hasselt University, Hasselt, Belgium

Kyranaki, Nikoleta 020294
imec, Genk, Belgium

Kyratsi, Theodora 020495
University of Cyprus, Nicosia, Cyprus

L. Andersen, Nanna 020477
DTU, Roskilde, Denmark

L. Souza, Patrícia 020090
Federal University of Rio de Janeiro, Rio de Janeiro, Brazil

Lachowicz, Agata CSEM, Neuchâtel, Switzerland	020039
Lahr, Simon Next2Sun Technology, Dillingen, Germany	020388
Lahr, Simon Next2Sun, Dillingen, Germany	020411
Lajunen, Antti University of Helsinki, Helsinki, Finland	020400
Lambertz, Andreas FZJ, Jülich, Germany	020233
Lamblot, Hervé Sunstyle, Paris, France	020302
Lamghari, Fouad Fujairah Research Centre, Fujairah, United Arab Emirates	020402
Lamminaho, Jani SDU Climate Cluster, Odense, Denmark	020250, 020306
Landaas, Christian Northern Silicon, Meråker, Norway	020495
Landberg, Lars DNV Denmark, Hellerup, Denmark	020448
Landberg, Lars DNV Denmark, Hellerup, Spain	020481
Landes, Dieter Coburg University of Applied Sciences, Coburg, Germany	020361
Landová, Lucie Czech Technical University, Prague, Czech Republic	020107
Lansade, David University of Toulouse, Toulouse, France	020073
Lappalainen, Kari Tampere University, Tampere, Finland	020194, 020528, 020537
Lara, Yolanda ENDEF, Zaragoza, Spain	020127, 020414, 020517
Larionova, Yevgeniya ISFH, Emmerthal, Germany	020006, 020007, 020225
Låstad, Jonas NTNU, Trondheim, Norway	020011
Laurens-Berge, Clarisse University Grenoble Alpes, Le Bourget-du-Lac, France	020034
Laurikėnas, Paulius Solitek, Vilnius, Lithuania	020353
Lauwaert, Johan Ghent University, Ghent, Belgium	020064
Lazaro-Castrillon, Luna IO-CSIC, Madrid, Spain	020085
Le Bossenec, Hugo IPVF, Palaiseau, France	020116

Le Brun, Anton 020096
Australian Nuclear Science and Technology Organisation, Lucas Heights, Australia
Lechón, Yolanda 020502
CIEMAT, Madrid, Spain
Ledesma, Javier R. 020337
UPM, Madrid, Spain
Ledesma, Javier 020446
UPM, Madrid, Spain
Lee, Chun-Wei 020021
TSEC, Hsinchu, Taiwan
Lee, Hyunju 020046
Meiji University, Kanagawa, Japan
Lee, Jieun 020323
K-water, Daejeon, South Korea
Lee, Jin-Seok 020324, 020357, 020561
KIER, Daejeon, South Korea
Legarrea, Aritz 020365
CENER, Sarriguren, Spain
Lelievre, Jean-Francois 020373
INES, Le Bourget-du-Lac, France
Lelong, Benoit 020373
Cythelia Energy, La Motte-Servolex, France
Leloux, Jonathan 020262
LuciSun, Villers-la-Ville, Belgium
Lenain, Philippe 020495
benkei, Lyon, France
Lennon, Alison 020048
UNSW, Sydney, Australia
Lenz, Markus 020226
School of Life Sciences FHNW, Muttenz, Switzerland
Lenzmann, Frank 020019
TNO Energy Transition, Petten, The Netherlands
Leone, Sander 020405
Novar, Rotterdam, The Netherlands
Leonforte, Fabrizio 020249
Polytechnic University of Milan, Milan, Italy
Leopold, Ulrich 020457
Luxembourg Institute of Science and Technology, Esch-sur-Alzette, Luxembourg
Levrat, Jacques 020251, 020467
CSEM, Neuchâtel, Switzerland
Levtchenko, Alexandra 020116
IPVF, Palaiseau, France
Lewandowski, Simon 020073
University of Toulouse, Toulouse, France

Leza, Baurin 020412
Gonvarri MS R&D, Corvera - Asturias, Spain

Lezaca, Jorge 020239
DLR, Oldenburg, Germany

Li, Xinyang 020222
RCT Solutions, Konstanz, Germany

Li, Yung-Chih 020021
TSEC, Hsinchu, Taiwan

Li, Yuxuan 020001
East China University of Science and Technology, Shanghai, China

Libal, Joris 020218, 020474
ISC Konstanz, Konstanz, Germany

Lichtenberger, Janine 020430
AIT, Vienna, Austria

Lițiu, Andrei Vladimir 020551
EPB Center, Rotterdam, The Netherlands

Lin, Shih-Chieh 020021
TSEC, Hsinchu, Taiwan

Lindahl, Johan 020486, 020532
Becquerel Sweden, Knivsta, Sweden

Linder, Johannes 020492
Belectric, Kolitzheim, Germany

Lindfors, Anders 020286
Finnish Meteorological Institute, Helsinki, Finland

Lindig, Sascha 020371
Univers, Courbevoie, France

Linke, Jonathan 020004, 020035, 020225
ISC Konstanz, Konstanz, Germany

Linß, Volker 020033
VON ARDENNE, Dresden, Germany

Lipovšek, Benjamin 020047
University of Ljubljana, Ljubljana, Slovenia

Lippke, Benjamin 020180, 020230
Kiwa PI Berlin, Berlin, Germany

List-Kratochvil, Emil 020101
HZB, Berlin, Germany

Litrico, Grazia 020010
Enel Green Power, Catania, Italy

Liu, Cui 020001
East China University of Science and Technology, Shanghai, China

Liu, Dongyang 020063
ISFH, Emmerthal, Germany

Liu, Han-Chang 020350
ITRI, Tainan, Taiwan

Liu, Huiping 020495
GRÄNGES, Finspång, Sweden
Liu, Mengdi 020144, 020208
TÜV Rheinland, Shanghai, China
Liu, Yung-Tsung 020053, 020083
ITRI, Hsinchu, Taiwan
Livera, Andreas 020534
University of Cyprus, Nicosia, Cyprus
Lizin, Sebastien 020513, 020521
UHasselt, Hasselt, Belgium
Llarena, María Elena 020151
ITER, Granadilla de Abona, Spain
Loeckenhoff, Ruediger F. 020416
AZUR SPACE Solar Power, Heilbronn, Germany
Löhning, Martha 020063
ISFH, Emmerthal, Germany
Löhr, Johannes 020063, 020114
ISFH, Emmerthal, Germany
Lokhat, Ismaël 020262
Cythelia Energy, La Motte-Servolex, France
Lokhat, Ismael 020373
Trace Software, Saint-Romain-de-Colbosc, France
Lombardo, Salvatore 020066
CNR-IMM, Catania, Italy
Long, Yean-San 020053, 020083
ITRI, Hsinchu, Taiwan
Longo, Giulia 020099
UPV, Valencia, Spain
Lopes Gomes, Carlos Javier 020432, 020434
Sunveon, Madrid, Spain
Lopes, Ana Patrícia 020464
University of Lisbon, Lisbon, Portugal
López Cuéllar, Juan Manuel 020501
UCM, Madrid, Spain
López Dalmau, Daniel 020432, 020434
Sunveon, Madrid, Spain
López, Nuria 020451
DTU, Roskilde, Denmark
Lorenz, Dieter 020206
MBJ Solutions, Ahrensburg, Germany
Lorenzo Pigueiras, Eduardo 020363
UPM, Madrid, Spain
Lorenzo, Celena 020337, 020536
UPM, Madrid, Spain
Lorenzo, Eduardo 020439, 020446
UPM, Madrid, Spain

Lossen, Jan 020003, 020035
ISC Konstanz, Konstanz, Germany
Louwen, Atse 020203, 020226, 020261, 020509, 020546
Eurac Research, Bolzano, Italy
Louwen, Atse 020316
RISE, Boras, Sweden
Lu, Huan-Wu 020161
ITRI, Hsinchu, Taiwan
Lu, Matthew 020230
Kiwa PI Berlin, Shanghai, China
Lucea, Aingeru 020197, 020198
TECNALIA, Derio, Spain
Lüdemann, Marius 020233
Fraunhofer CSP, Halle, Germany
Luís, Margarida 020421
University of Lisbon, Lisbon, Portugal
Lustoza de Souza, Patricia 020092
UFRJ, Rio de Janeiro, Brazil
Ly, Moussa 020023, 020025
PUCRS, Porto Alegre, Brazil
Lyubenova, Teodora 020210
European Commission JRC, Ispra, Italy

M. Bazilio, Willian 020092
PUC-Rio, Rio de Janeiro, Brazil
M. S. Kawabata, Rudy 020090
Pontifical Catholic University of Rio de Janeiro, Rio de Janeiro, Brazil
M. Torelly, Guilherme 020090
Pontifical Catholic University of Rio de Janeiro, Rio de Janeiro, Brazil
Ma Lu, Silvia 020381
Mälardalen University, Västerås, Sweden
Ma, Xiang 020011
SINTEF, Oslo, Norway
Macé, Philippe 020225, 020252, 020474, 020505, 020543, 020558, 020573
Becquerel Institute, Brussels, Belgium
Mack, Sebastian 020031
Fraunhofer ISE, Freiburg, Germany
Madsen, Morten 020250, 020306
SDU Climate Cluster, Odense, Denmark
Mahmood, Aysha 020265, 020376
DTU, Roskilde, Denmark
Maixner, Andreas 020121, 020125, 020137, 020223
AESOLAR, Koenigsbrunn, Germany

Maiz, Alexander 020437
UPV/EHU, Vitoria-Gasteiz, Spain

Majak, Martyna 020068
Roltec, Poznań, Poland

Makrides, George 020534
University of Cyprus, Nicosia, Cyprus

Malarkannan, Lavanya 020210
National Physical Laboratory, Teddington, United Kingdom

Malcorps, Philippe 020276
3E, Brussels, Belgium

Malik, Stephanie 020313
Fraunhofer CSP, Halle, Germany

Malik, Stephanie 020355
Fraunhofer IMWS, Halle, Germany

Maliutina, Kristina 020141
University of Applied Science Cologne, Cologne, Germany

Malo, Javier 020209
UPM, Madrid, Spain

Mancini, Simone 020425
TNO, Eindhoven, The Netherlands

Mandiola, Gotzon 020514
AZTI, PASAIA, Spain

Manganiello, Patrizio 020389
Hasselt University, Diepenbeek, Belgium

Manganiello, Patrizio 020294
imec, Genk, Belgium

Manito, Alex 020348
University of São Paulo, São Paulo, Brazil

Manochehrian, Rasoul 020539
Frankfurt University of Applied Sciences, Frankfurt am Main, Germany

Manzolini, Giampaolo 020261
Polytechnic University of Milan, Milan, Italy

Maqsood, Ayman 020101
HZB, Berlin, Germany

Marangis, Demetris 020534
University of Cyprus, Nicosia, Cyprus

Marcos-Castro, Ana 020297
CIEMAT, Madrid, Spain

Marechal, Philippe 020217
CEA / INES, Le Bourget-du-Lac, France

Marí Soucase, Bernabé 020099
UPV, Valencia, Spain

Markert, Jochen 020231
Fraunhofer ISE, Freiburg, Germany

Marquardt, Cornelia 020063
ISFH, Emmerthal, Germany

Marteau, Baptiste 020034
ECM Technologies, Grenoble, France

Martín Rueda, Javier 020535
UPM, Madrid, Spain

Martín, Francisco José 020459
UPM, Madrid, Spain

Martín, Francisco 020209
UPM, Madrid, Spain

Martín-Chivelet, Nuria 020297
CIEMAT, Madrid, Spain

Martín-Rueda, Javier 020337, 020363
UPM, Madrid, Spain

Martínez González, Mario 020326
Enertis Applus+, Madrid, Spain

Martinez, Juan Ignacio 020252
Becquerel Institute Spain, San Sebastian, Spain

Martinez, Oscar 020191, 020205
University of Valladolid, Valladolid, Spain

Martínez-Barbeito, María 020243
ieco.io, Vigo, Spain

Maruyama, Rodrigo P. 020154, 020348
University of São Paulo, São Paulo, Brazil

Marzo, Aitor 020311, 020546
University of Granada, Granada, Spain

Mashkov, Oleksandr 020149, 020150, 020377
HI ERN, Erlangen, Germany

Massaro, Lorenzo 020541
PedersoliGattai, Milan, Italy

Masson, Gaëtan 020474, 020558, 020564, 020573
Becquerel Institute, Brussels, Belgium

Masson, Gaëtan 020570
IEA PVPS Task 1, Brussels, Belgium

Mateos, Yeray 020055, 020153
UPV/EHU, Bilbao, Spain

Maturi, Laura 020249, 020254, 020551
Eurac Research, Bolzano, Italy

Mayer-Ullmann, Philipp 020430
AIT, Vienna, Austria

Mazzoleni, Stefano 020378
University of Naples Federico II, Naples, Italy

McIntosh, Keith R. 020396
PV Lighthouse, Coledale, Australia

McNab, Shona 020065
UNSW, Sydney, Australia

Meereboer, Martijn 020225
Energyra, Westknollendam, The Netherlands

Meier, Rico 020132
HTW Berlin, Berlin, Germany
Meixner, Michael 020050
halm elektronik, Frankfurt am Main, Germany
Mekhaldi, Bouchra 020406
Ecole Polytechnique, Palaiseau, France
Melges de Andrade, Adnei 020154
University of São Paulo, São Paulo, Brazil
Melino, Francesco 020314
University of Bologna, Bologna, Italy
Mellone, Celeste 020541
Green Horse Advisory, Rome, Italy
Menard, Lionel 020291
MINES Paris, Nice, France
Mencaraglia, Denis 020058
CNRS, Gif-sur-Yvette, France
Menchaca, Iratxe 020514
AZTI, PASAIA, Spain
Mendes Ferreira Gomes, Amanda 020548
UFSC, Florianopolis, Brazil
Mendikoa, Iñigo 020514
Tecnalia, BRTA, Derio, Spain
Meneghini, Matteo 020089
University of Padova, Padova, Italy
Ménézo, Christophe 020317
LOCIE, Le Bourget-du-Lac, France
Menghini, Mariela 020508
IMDEA Nanoscience Institute, Madrid, Spain
Mercade Ruiz, Pau 020448, 020481
GreenPowerMonitor a DNV company, Barcelona, Spain
Merino, Amanda 020040
CEA / INES, Le Bourget-du-Lac, France
Merino, José Manuel 020085
UAM, Madrid, Spain
Mermoud, André 020196
PVsyst, Geneva, Switzerland
Merodio, Pablo 020337
UPM, Madrid, Spain
Mertens, Jan 020389
imec, Genk, Belgium
Mertens, Verena 020006, 020008
ISFH, Emmerthal, Germany
Meßmer, Marius 020031
Fraunhofer ISE, Freiburg, Germany
Messmer, Tobias 020218, 020221, 020225
ISC Konstanz, Konstanz, Germany

Messner, Christian 020369
AIT, Vienna, Austria
Mettner, Larissa 020063, 020114
ISFH, Emmerthal, Germany
Meusel, Manuel 020052
Fraunhofer CSP, Halle (Saale), Germany
Meyer, Kevin 020260
ISFH, Emmerthal, Germany
Meza, Carlos 020318, 020334, 020426, 020520
Anhalt University of Applied Sciences, Köthen, Germany
Mezzasalma, Frédéric 020217
CEA / INES, Le Bourget-du-Lac, France
Micha, Daniel 020092
CEFET/RJ, Petrópolis, Brazil
Michael, Poland 020193
Nelson Mandela University, Port Elizabeth, South Africa
Miclea, Paul-Tiberiu 020233
Fraunhofer CSP, Halle, Germany
Midtgård, Ole-Morten 020476
NTNU, Trondheim, Norway
Miettunen, Kati 020286, 020298, 020398
University of Turku, Turku, Finland
Migan-Dubois, Anne 020406
CNRS, Gif-sur-Yvette, France
Mignonac, Alexandre 020217
CEA / INES, Le Bourget-du-Lac, France
Mignonac, Alexandre 020334
CEA, Cadarache, France
Mignonac, Alexandre 020318
CEA, Saint-Paul-Lez-Durance, France
Miguel Laborda, María 020414
IaSol, Zaragoza, Spain
Mihailetchi, Valentin Dan 020033
ISC Konstanz, Konstanz, Germany
Mihailetchi, Valentin 020225
ISC Konstanz, Konstanz, Germany
Mihaylov, Blago 020210
European Commission JRC, Ispra, Italy
Milani, Emanuele 020495
Marelli Europe, Venaria Reala, Italy
Milesi, Frédéric 020068
CEA, Grenoble, France
Min, Byungsul 020008, 020482
ISFH, Emmerthal, Germany
Mirandona López, Haritz 020432, 020434
Sunveon, Madrid, Spain

Miró-Llorente, Marta 020094
IREC, Barcelona, Spain

Misra, Prashant 020429
NISE, Gurugram, India

Miszczuk, Andrzej 020068
Roltec, Poznań, Poland

Mittag, Max 020137
Fraunhofer ISE, Freiburg, Germany

Mittal, Ankit 020318
AIT, Vienna, Austria

Mittelman, Gur 020379
Afeka Tel-Aviv Academic College of Engineering, Tel Aviv, Israel

Mizushima, Io 020028
IPU P/S, Virum, Denmark

Mizushima, Io 020037
IPU, Virum, Denmark

Mngomezulu, Ndumiso 020344
PVinsight, Port Elizabeth, South Africa

Mo, Alvin 020065
UNSW, Sydney, Australia

Mockeviciute-Azzopardi, Austeja 020334
FIR, Birkirkara, Malta

Moe Nygård, Magnus 020340
IFE, Kjeller, Norway

Moehlecke, Adriano 020023, 020025
PUCRS, Porto Alegre, Brazil

Mohammadi, Mohammad Hossein 020037, 020104
Aarhus University, Aarhus, Denmark

Mollier, Stéphane 020262
CEA / INES, Le Bourget-du-Lac, France

Moltke, Asbjørn 020043
Technical University of Denmark, Copenhagen, Denmark

Mondaca-Cuevas, Gino 020422
University of Antofagasta, Antofagasta, Chile

Monokroussos, Christos 020181
TÜV Rheinland Shanghai, Shanghai, China

Monokroussos, Christos 020144, 020208
TÜV Rheinland, Shanghai, China

Monteiro Martins, Filipa 020317
Galp Energia, Lisbon, Portugal

Montes, Carlos 020151
ITER, Granadilla de Abona, Spain

Montoya, Josefa 020311
University of Antofagasta, Antofagasta, Chile

Morabito, Floriana 020066
CNR-IFN, Milan, Italy

Moradi Sizkouhi, Amirmohammad 020356, 020375
Concordia University, Montreal, Canada
Moradi Zavie Kord, Soroush 020400
University of Helsinki, Helsinki, Finland
Morales, Sergio 020491
UPM, Madrid, Spain
Morantes Quintana, Giobertti Raul 020551
Eurac Research, Bolzano, Italy
Mordvinkin, Anton 020233
Fraunhofer CSP, Halle, Germany
Moreda, Guillermo P. 020407
UPM, Madrid, Spain
Morin, Claire 020551
SolarPower Europe, Brussels, Belgium
Morisset, Audrey 020068
CSEM, Neuchâtel, Switzerland
Morlier, Arnaud 020156
Hasselt University, Genk, Belgium
Morlier, Arnaud 020294, 020389
imec, Genk, Belgium
Mortazavifar, Leila 020056, 020158, 020201, 020284
Anhalt University of Applied Sciences, Köthen, Germany
Moruno, Ricardo 020209, 020453
UPM, Madrid, Spain
Mosel, Frank 020015
PVA TePla, Wettenberg, Germany
Moser, David 020573
Becquerel Institute Italy, Trento, Italy
Moser, David 020316
Becquerel Institute, Bolzano, Italy
Moser, David 020254
Bequerel Institute, Trento, Italy
Moser, David 020203, 020226, 020261, 020325, 020485, 020489, 020546
Eurac Research, Bolzano, Italy
Mouhoubi, Felicia 020134
CEA / INES, Le Bourget-du-Lac, France
Müllejans, Harald 020208, 020213
European Commission JRC, Ispra, Italy
Müller, Alexander 020119
Fraunhofer CSP, Halle, Germany
Müller, Larissa 020523
University of Applied Sciences Cologne, Cologne, Germany
Mugica, Maikel 020139
Tecnalia, Donostia - San Sebastián, Spain
Mujovi, Fahradin 020251
CSEM, Neuchâtel, Switzerland

Mukherjee, Srijani 020338
CEA / INES, Le Bourget-du-Lac, France
Mukhtar, Mariyam 020057
University of Verona, Verona, Italy
Mulder, Peter 020067
Radboud University, Nijmegen, The Netherlands
Muller, Matthew 020314
NREL, Denver, United States of America
Munkhammar, Joakim 020532
Uppsala University, Uppsala, Sweden
Muñoz Cerón, Emilio 020269
University of Jaén, Jaén, Spain
Muñoz, Delfina 020040, 020311, 020546
CEA / INES, Le Bourget-du-Lac, France
Muñoz, Delfina 020521
CEA, Le Bourget-du-Lac, France
Muñoz, Delfina 020226
CEA/ INES, Le Bourget-du-Lac, France
Muñoz, Ildefonso 020365, 020366, 020392
CENER, Sarriguren, Spain
Muñoz, Jesús Ángel 020508
UCM, Madrid, Spain
Muñoz-García, Miguel-Ángel 020407
UPM, Madrid, Spain
Murano, Giovanni 020551
ENEA, Ispra, Italy
Murillo, Asier 020497
CENER, Sarriguren, Spain
Musembi, Robinson J. 020272
University of Nairobi, Nairobi, Kenya

Nabipouor, Mohammad 020426
Anhalt University of Applied Sciences, Köthen, Germany
Nagel, Henning 020475
Fraunhofer ISE, Freiburg, Germany
Nakamura, Kyotaro 020046
Toyota Technological Institute, Nagoya, Japan
Nanno, Ikuo 020190
Nanno Energy Research Center, Yamaguchi, Japan
Nargelienė, Viktorija 020157
Center for Physical Sciences and Technology (FTMC), Vilnius, Lithuania
Narsi Patel, Hitarth 020069
SVNIT, Surat, India
Narvarte, Luis 020337, 020446, 020491, 020535, 020536, 020567, 020575
UPM, Madrid, Spain

Nascimento, Lucas 020377
Solar Energy Research Laboratory Fotovoltaica/ UFSC, Florianópolis, Brazil

Nasebandt, Lasse 020063
ISFH, Emmerthal, Germany

Nasser, Hisham 020226
ODTÜ-GÜNAM, Ankara, Türkiye

Naveiro, José Manuel 020414
ENDEF, Zaragoza, Spain

Nazififard, Mohammad 020259, 020428
Côte d`Azur University, Nice, France

Nejim, Ahmed 020058
SILVACO, St. Ives, United Kingdom

Nel, Paul 020382
7SecondSolar, Cape Town, South Africa

Nelson, Jenny 020394
Imperial College London, London, United Kingdom

Neuba, Adam 020114
Paderborn University, Paderborn, Germany

Neuber, Viola 020031
Fraunhofer ISE, Freiburg, Germany

Neuhaus, Holger 020123, 020140
Fraunhofer ISE, Freiburg, Germany

Neumaier, Lukas 020504
Silicon Austria Labs, Villach, Austria

Neussl, Vassilissa 020318, 020430
AIT, Vienna, Austria

Neykova, Neda 020107
Czech Technical University, Prague, Czech Republic

Nezhad, Mahyar 020230
Kiwa PI Berlin, Hudson, United States of America

Nguyen, Viet Xuan 020008
centrotherm international, Blaubeuren, Germany

Nicolet-dit-Félix, Kléber 020251
EPFL, Neuchâtel, Switzerland

Nicot-Senneville, Zoltan 020102
SERIS, Singapore, Singapore

Nielsen, Michael P. 020065
UNSW, Sydney, Australia

Nissen, Hauke 020313
Wattmanufactur, Galmsbüll, Germany

Nitsche, Tobias 020119, 020218
Henkel, Düsseldorf, Germany

Nobre, André M. 020263
PV Doctor, Singapore, Singapore

Noels, Serge 020472
PV CYCLE, Brussels, Belgium

Noh, Yong-Su 020449
KETI, Wonmi-gu, South Korea
Nold, Sebastian 020461
Fraunhofer ISE, Freiburg, France
Nold, Sebastian 020475
Fraunhofer ISE, Freiburg, Germany
Nordboe, Eirik 020495
Fiven Norge, Lillesand, Norway
Norde Santos, Fernanda 020331
DLR, Almería, Spain
Nouri, Bijan 020235, 020237, 020239
DLR, Almería, Spain
Nova, David 020339
National University of Colombia, Bogotá, Colombia
Núñez, Rubén 020209, 020453
UPM, Madrid, Spain
Núñez-Osorio, Alessia 020100
University of Almeria, Almeria, Spain
Nurmesjärvi, Antti 020423
VTT Technical Research Centre of Finland, Oulu, Finland
Nussbaumer, Hartmut 020385
ZHAW, Winterthur, Switzerland
Nyang'onda, Thomas N. 020272
University of Nairobi, Nairobi, Kenya

Obeidavi, Sahereh 020361
Coburg University of Applied Sciences, Coburg, Germany
Oberbeck, Lars 020461
TotalEnergies OneTech, Paris, France
Oberegger Filippi, Ulrich 020551
Eurac Research, Bolzano, Italy
Ocaña, Luis Manuel 020151
ITER, Granadilla de Abona, Spain
Ockert, Ajka 020312
EnBW, Karlsruhe, Germany
Odilio dos Santos, Daniel 020548
UFSC, Florianopolis, Brazil
Öhgren, Gustav 020532
Becquerel Sweden, Knivsta, Sweden
Öttl, Christian 020347
Watt Analytics, Vienna, Austria
Öz, Aksel Kaan 020135
Fraunhofer ISE, Freiburg, Germany
Özden, Talat 020226
ODTÜ-GÜNAM, Ankara, Türkiye

Özkalay, Ebrar 020160, 020204
SUPSI, Mendrisio, Switzerland

Ogura, Atsushi 020046
Meiji University, Kanagawa, Japan

Ohdaira, Keisuke 020131
JAIST, Ishikawa, Japan

Ohshita, Yoshio 020046
Toyota Technological Institute, Nagoya, Japan

Ojala, Aleksi 020554
Solarigo Systems, Pirkkala, Finland

Okawa, Hayato 020115
Tokyo City University, Setagaya, Japan

Okel, Lars A. G. 020030
TNO, Petten, The Netherlands

Oksanen, Jani 020067
Aalto University, Espoo, Finland

Oliosi, Michele 020196
PVsyst, Geneva, Switzerland

Olivares, Douglas 020311
University of Antofagasta, Antofagasta, Chile

Olivares, Gregorio 020365, 020366, 020392
CENER, Sarriguren, Spain

Oliveira Santos, João Victor 020188
EDF R&D, Moret Loing Orvanne, France

Oliveira, Helena 020420
University of Évora, Évora, Portugal

Oller Westerberg, Amelia 020570
Becquerel Sweden, Knivsta, Sweden

Ollo, Olatz 020139
Tecnalia, Donostia - San Sebastián, Spain

Oozeki, Takashi 020436, 020525
AIST, Koriyama, Japan

Opatovsky, Martin 020241, 020262
Solargis, Bratislava, Slovakia

Oreski, Gernot 020136, 020234, 020325, 020500, 020574
PCCL, Leoben, Austria

Ortega, Eneko 020055, 020153, 020287, 020353
UPV/EHU, Bilbao, Spain

Ortega, Eneko 020289, 020437
UPV/EHU, Leioa, Spain

Ortega, Pascal 020214
University of French Polynesia, Faa'a, French Polynesia

Ortiz-Pena, Aaron 020562
University of Castilla-La Mancha, Albacete, Spain

Ory, Daniel 020188
EDF R&D, Palaiseau, France

Ory, Daniel 020116
EDF, Palaiseau, France

Osman, Alaa 020006
ISFH, Emmerthal, Germany

Osuna, Jose Antonio 020358
MAGTEL, Córdoba, Spain

Osvald, Oliver 020274
Solargis, Bratislava, Slovakia

Otaegi, Aloña 020055, 020097, 020153, 020287
UPV/EHU, Bilbao, Spain

Otnes, Gaute 020169
Institute for Energy Technology, Kjeller, Norway

Otto, Nicolas 020101
HTW, Berlin, Germany

Otto, William 020390
MARIN, Wageningen, The Netherlands

Ou, Chao-Wei 020350
National Chin-Yi University of Technology, Taichung, Taiwan

Ovaitt, Silvana 020314
NREL, Denver, United States of America

Ovaitt, Silvana 020574
NREL, Golden, United States of America

Oviedo Hernandez, Guillermo 020325
BayWa r.e, Rome, Italy

Ozer, Shay 020379
Agricultural Research Organization, Rishon LeZion, Israel

P. Pires, Maurício 020090
Federal University of Rio de Janeiro, Rio de Janeiro, Brazil

Pabiou, Herve 020338
CETHIL, Villeurbanne, France

Pabst, Elena 020312
ZSW, Stuttgart, Germany

Paiva, Lúcio 020530
Casa dos Ventos, Fortaleza, Brazil

Palais, Olivier 020188
Toulon University, Marseille, France

Palitzsch, Wolfram 020225, 020495
LuxChemTech, Freiberg, Germany

Palomino, Laura 020491, 020535
UPM, Madrid, Spain

Pamir Aly, Shahzada 020229
DEWA, Dubai, United Arab Emirates

Pamula, Bindu 020069
SVNIT, Surat, India

Panda, Pavan Kumar 020284
Anhalt University of Applied Sciences, Köthen, Germany

Pandar, Matthias 020229
Fraunhofer CSP, Halle, Germany

Pander, Matthias 020121, 020142, 020175, 020192, 020218, 020223, 020232
Fraunhofer CSP, Halle, Germany

Panduri, Fabio 020322
BFH, Burgdorf, Switzerland

Pantoja, Jaime 020526
Francisco José de Caldas District University, Bogota, Colombia

Papantoni, Veatriki 020482
DLR, Oldenburg, Germany

Paraficz, Danuta 020204
FFHS, Zurich, Switzerland

Paraskeva, Vasiliki 020064
University of Cyprus, Nicosia, Cyprus

Pardo, Eduardo 020414
Tecnova, Almeira, Spain

Parfeniukas, Karolis 020039
ATLANT 3D, Taastrup, Denmark

Parion, Jonathan 020064
Hasselt Unversity, Genk, Belgium

Park, Hyeonwook 020112
KENTECH, Naju-Si, South Korea

Parmar, Richa 020429
NISE, Gurugram, India

Parra, Johan 020406
Ecole Polytechnique, Palaiseau, France

Parra, Johan 020214
Polytechnic Institute of Paris, Palaiseau, France

Parrilla, Carlos G. 020402
Fujairah Research Centre, Fujairah, United Arab Emirates

Pascual Gallego, Valero 020407
UPM, Madrid, Spain

Pasquier, Mathis 020451
DTU, Roskilde, Denmark

Passaro, Marcello 020513
Sunzest Solar, Rotterdam, The Netherlands

Patel, Dharm 020355
Fraunhofer IMWS, Halle, Germany

Paul, Ananta 020250, 020306
SDU Climate Cluster, Odense, Denmark

Paulescu, Marius 020283
West University of Timisoara, Timisoara, Romania

Paviet-Salomon, Bertrand 020068, 020467
CSEM, Neuchâtel, Switzerland

Payno, David 020085, 020094
UAM, Madrid, Spain

Pearce, Pheobe 020065
UNSW, Sydney, Australia

Peche, René 020468, 020495
bifa Umweltinstitut, Augsburg, Germany

Pehlivanli, Ezgi 020521
METU, Ankara, Türkiye

Peibst, Robby 020006, 020063, 020114
ISFH, Emmerthal, Germany

Pelfort Ojer, Marta 020241
Solargis, Bratislava, Slovakia

Pelland, Sophie 020211
Natural Resources Canada, Varennes, Canada

Pelle, Martina 020249, 020254
Eurac Research, Bolzano, Italy

Peña-Bermudez, Julian 020110
University of the Caribbean, Santo Domingo, Dominican Republic

Peng, Cheng-Yu 020350
National Chin-Yi University of Technology, Taichung, Taiwan

Pera, David 020457
Luxembourg Institute of Science and Technology, Esch-sur-Alzette, Luxembourg

Perani, Martina 020204
FFHS, Zurich, Switzerland

Peraticos, Elias 020064
University of Cyprus, Nicosia, Cyprus

Pereda, Ainhoa 020198, 020358
TECNALIA, Derio, Spain

Pereira Fialho, Luis Andre 020509
Eurac Research, Bolzano, Italy

Pereira, Sara 020403, 020418, 020565
University of Évora, Évora, Portugal

Pérez García, Manuel 020336
University of Almería, La Cañada de San Urbano, Spain

Pérez, Ernesto 020339
National University of Colombia, Bogotá, Colombia

Pérez, Jairo 020412
Gonvarri AgroTech, Corvera - Asturias, Spain

Pérez, Jorge 020412
Gonvarri AgroTech, Corvera - Asturias, Spain

Pérez, Luis 020412
Gonvarri MS R&D, Corvera - Asturias, Spain

Perez, Richard 020494
University at Albany, Albany, United States of America

Perez-Astudillo, Daniel 020275, 020278, 020291
QEERI, Doha, Qatar

Pérez-García, Manuel 020100
University of Almeria, Almería, Spain

Pérez-Rodríguez, Alejandro 020085, 020094
IREC, Barcelona, Spain

Pernas, Tomás 020412
Gonvarri AgroTech, Corvera - Asturias, Spain

Pernau, Thomas 020008
centrotherm international, Blaubeuren, Germany

Perrin, Marion 020544
Energy Pool, Le Bourget-du-Lac, France

Pervan, Nikolina 020136, 020234
PCCL, Leoben, Austria

Peter Amalathas, Amalraj 020107
University of Jaffna, Jaffna, Sri Lanka

Peter, Kristian 020569
ISC Konstanz, Konstanz, Germany

Peters, Ian Marius 020230, 020263
Forschungszentrum Jülich, Erlangen, Germany

Peters, Ian Marius 020149, 020150, 020377, 020574
HI ERN, Erlangen, Germany

Petersons, Karlis 020250, 020306
Stensborg, Roskilde, Denmark

Petkovski, Emil 020571
DNV, Arnhem, The Netherlands

Petzschmann, Jonas 020312
ZSW, Stuttgart, Germany

Pfau, Jan Hendrik 020240
Leibniz University Hannover, Hannover, Germany

Pfeiffer, Oliver 020141
University of Applied Science Cologne, Cologne, Germany

Pfeiffer, Oliver 020140
University of Applied Sciences Cologne, Cologne, Germany

Philipp, Daniel 020215, 020231
Fraunhofer ISE, Freiburg, Germany

Pierro, Marco 020489, 020494
Eurac Research, Bolzano, Italy

Pieters, Bart E. 020180
FZJ, Jülich, Germany

Pieterse, Marco 020495
Chemconserve, Bussum, The Netherlands

Pietralunga, Silvia Maria 020066
CNR-IFN, Milan, Italy

Pietsch, Veith 020331
Aquila Capital, Hamburg, Germany
Pilat, Eric 020311
CEA / INES, Le Bourget-du-Lac, France
Pilat, Eric 020317
CEA INES, Le Bourget-du-Lac, France
Pillai, Akhildev 020558
Becquerel Institute, Brussels, Belgium
Pinheiro, Philippe 020457
Luxembourg Institute of Science and Technology, Esch-sur-Alzette, Luxembourg
Pinho Almeida, Marcelo 020348
University of São Paulo, São Paulo, Brazil
Pinto, Cristina Leyre 020497
CENER, Sarriguren, Spain
Pinto, Luciana 020092
UFRJ, Rio de Janeiro, Brazil
Pitaval, Sébastien 020244
SOLAÏS, Valbonne, France
Pitz-Paal, Robert 020237, 020331
DLR, Cologne, Germany
Plakhotnyuk, Maksym 020039
ATLANT 3D, Taastrup, Denmark
Platero Gaona, Carlos A. 020332
UPM, Madrid, Spain
Plaza, Caroline 020543, 020564, 020573
Becquerel Institute France, Lyon, France
Polacchi, Cristina 020509, 020513
Eurac Research, Bolzano, Italy
Polo, Jaime 020300
CENER, Sarriguren, Spain
Polo, Jesús 020297
CIEMAT, Madrid, Spain
Polverini, Davide 020181
Directorate General for Internal Market, Industry, Entrepreneurship and SMEs, Brussels, Belgium
Polverini, Davide 020497
European Comission, Brussels, Belgium
Pongthanacharoenkul, Nattapark 020230
Kiwa PI Berlin, Berlin, Germany
Poortmans, Jef 020064
Hasselt Unversity, Genk, Belgium
Popescu, Lacramioara 020068
ISC Konstanz, Konstanz, Germany
Pospischil, Maximilian 020225
Highline Technologies, Freiburg, Germany

Poulsen, Peter B. 020039
DTU, Copenhagen, Denmark
Poulsen, Peter B. 020250, 020265, 020267, 020376, 020451
DTU, Roskilde, Denmark
Poulsen, Peter Behrensdorff 020028, 020306, 020346
DTU, Roskilde, Denmark
Pourshafi, Pouya 020121, 020125, 020137
AESOLAR, Koenigsbrunn, Germany
Pozza, Cristian 020551
Eurac Research, Bolzano, Italy
Prakash, Jai 020429
NISE, Gurugram, India
Prando, Davide 020485, 020489
Edyna, Bolzano, Italy
Prasad, Manjunath 020225
ISC Konstanz, Konstanz, Germany
Pravettoni, Mauro 020402
Technology Innovation Institute, Abu Dhabi, United Arab Emirates
Preis, Pirmin 020003
ISC Konstanz, Konstanz, Germany
Preu, Ralf 020475
Fraunhofer ISE, Freiburg, Germany
Preuschoff, Jonas 020101
HTW, Berlin, Germany
Protti, Alexander Aguilar 020140
Fraunhofer ISE, Freiburg, Germany
Protti, Alexander 020137
Fraunhofer ISE, Freiburg, Germany
Provost, Marion 020116
IPVF, Palaiseau, France
Puel, Jean Baptiste 020062
IPVF, Palaiseau, France
Puertas López, Antonio Manuel 020100
University of Almeria, Almeria, Spain
Puttock, Claire 020367
Nextracker, Fremont, United States of America

Queste, Samuel 020068
Marie and Louis Pasteur University, Besançon, France
Quiroz, Mónica 020328
Qualifying Photovoltaics, Madrid, Spain

R. Ledesma, Javier 020363
UPM, Madrid, Spain

Rabanal Arabach, Jorge 020183
University of Antofagasta, Antofagasta, Chile

Rabanal-Arabach, Jorge 020129, 020342, 020417, 020422
University of Antofagasta, Antofagasta, Chile

Rabiei, Hossein 020063
ISFH, Emmerthal, Germany

Rachdi, Lazhar 020035, 020068
ISC Konstanz, Konstanz, Germany

Radzevicius, Aurimas 020225
Valoe Cells, Vilnius, Lithuania

Rafiee, Hossein 020539
Frankfurt University of Applied Sciences, Frankfurt am Main, Germany

Raginskis, Justinas 020380
Kaunas University of Technology, Kaunas, Lithuania

Raievska, Oleksandra 020117, 020149
HI ERN, Erlangen, Germany

Rajan, S. Prithivi 020262
LuciSun, Villers-la-Ville, Belgium

Rajkiewicz, Katarzyna 020551
NAPE, Warsaw, Poland

Rakotoniaina, Jean Patrice 020311
CEA / INES, Le Bourget-du-Lac, France

Ramachandran Nair, Jishnu 020233
Fraunhofer CSP, Halle, Germany

Ramesh, Santhosh 020389
imec, Genk, Belgium

Ramírez Ledesma, Javier 020535
UPM, Madrid, Spain

Ramirez, S. 020396
PV Lighthouse, Coledale, Australia

Rampino, Stefano 020087
National Research Council, Parma, Italy

Ramspeck, Klaus 020050
halm elektronik, Frankfurt am Main, Germany

Ranisch, Tadeus 020101
HTW, Berlin, Germany

Ranta, Samuli 020286, 020400
TUAS, Turku, Finland

Ranta, Samuli 020298, 020398
Turku University of Applied Sciences, Turku, Finland

Raposo, Mauro 020565
University of Évora, Évora, Portugal

Ratnagiri, Abhinav 020367
Nextracker, Fremont, United States of America

Raugewitz, Annika 020063, 020114
ISFH, Emmerthal, Germany

Raval, Mehul 020005, 020222, 020463
RCT Solutions, Konstanz, Germany

Razanajao, Aina 020244
SOLAÏS, Valbonne, France

Razi, Umair 020085
IREC, Barcelona, Spain

Recart, Federico 020097
UPV/EHU, Bilbao, Spain

Redondo Cuevas, Marta 020332
UPM, Madrid, Spain

Redondo, Juan Manuel 020209
UPM, Madrid, Spain

Rehan, Muhammad 020112
KIER, Daejeon, South Korea

Rehman, Anees ur 020111, 020164
Hohai University, Changzhou, China

Reichart, Hannah 020167, 020232
University of Applied Sciences Cologne, Cologne, Germany

Reichel, Christian 020123, 020137, 020140
Fraunhofer ISE, Freiburg, Germany

Reichle, Julian 020005, 020222, 020463
RCT Solutions, Konstanz, Germany

Reinders, Angele 020253
TU Eindhoven, Eindhoven, The Netherlands

Reindl, Thomas 020263
SERIS, Singapore, Singapore

Reis, Luiz Filipe 020530
Casa dos Ventos, Fortaleza, Brazil

Rémondeau, Paul 020251
EPFL, Neuchâtel, Switzerland

Renard, Charles 020058
CNRS, Palaiseau, France

Rende, Fedele 020255
ACCA Software, Cosenza, Italy

Rennhofer, Marcus 020180, 020281, 020318, 020334, 020347, 020430
AIT, Vienna, Austria

Rentsch, Jochen 020475
Fraunhofer ISE, Freiburg, Germany

Rerat, Michel 020060
IPREM, Pau, France

Reshef, Liad 020379
Agricultural Research Organization, Rishon LeZion, Israel

Revol, Inès 020074
LAAS-CNRS, Toulouse, France

Reyal, Jean-Pierre 020303
SemperStyl, Eragny, France

Riaño, Sandra 020197, 020358
TECNALIA, Derio, Spain

Richards, Bryce S. 020272
KIT, Karlsruhe, Germany

Riechelman, Stefan 020181
PTB, Braunschweig, Germany

Riechelmann, Stefan 020177, 020199, 020211
PTB, Braunschweig, Germany

Riedel-Lyngskær, Nicholas 020451
DTU, Roskilde, Denmark

Rienäcker, Michael 020063
ISFH, Emmerthal, Germany

Rindert, Sören 020230
Kiwa PI Berlin, Berlin, Germany

Ríos Moral, Lucía 020501
UCM, Madrid, Spain

Ríos-Ledesma, Felipe 020446
UPM, Madrid, Spain

Ripke, Melanie 020006
ISFH, Emmerthal, Germany

Riva, Roland 020495
CEA, Le Bourget-du-Lac, France

Rivas Rodríguez, José Manuel 020326
Enertis Applus+, Madrid, Spain

Robledo, Jesús 020262
LuciSun, Villers-la-Ville, Belgium

Rodríguez Lucas, Delia 020407
EkiLabs, Boston, United States of America

Rodríguez Plaza, José Luis 020508
Autonomous University of Madrid, Madrid, Spain

Rodríguez Rodríguez, Araceli 020501
UCM, Madrid, Spain

Rodríguez Salazar, David Leonardo 020441
District University of Bogotá, Bogotá, Colombia

Rodríguez, Araceli 020508
UCM, Madrid, Spain

Rodríguez, Diego Julián 020526
Francisco José de Caldas District University, Bogota, Colombia

Rodríguez, Isabel 020257
IMDEA Nanoscience, Madrid, Spain

Rodriguez, Sonia Maria 020289
UPV/EHU, Leioa, Spain

Rodríguez, Velia 020097
UPV/EHU, Bilbao, Spain

Rodríguez-Conde, Sofía 020326
Enertis Applus+, Madrid, Spain

Rodríguez-Gallegos, Carlos D. 020149, 020150
SERIS, Singapore, Singapore

Rodríguez-Romero, Sebastián 020342, 020417, 020422
University of Antofagasta, Antofagasta, Chile

Rodziewicz, Hanna 020498
Gdansk University of Technology, Gdansk, Poland

Römer, Udo 020006, 020063
ISFH, Emmerthal, Germany

Röver, Ingo 020225
LuxChemTech, Freiberg, Germany

Rojas, Christian A. 020422
Federico Santa María Technical University, Valparaíso, Chile

Rojas-Henríquez, Katalina 020129
University of Antofagasta, Antofagasta, Chile

Román, Eduardo 020139
Tecnalia, Donostia - San Sebastián, Spain

Romeo, Alessandro 020057, 020089, 020093
University of Verona, Verona, Italy

Romer, Pascal 020231
Fraunhofer ISE, Freiburg, Germany

Roodt, Roelof 020185
Nelson Mandela University, Port Elizabeth, South Africa

Roosloot, Nathan 020169
Institute for Energy Technology, Kjeller, Norway

Rosca, Victor 020030
TNO, Petten, The Netherlands

Rosen, Isaac 020225
Copprint, Jerusalem, Israel

Rosenfeld, Lavi 020379
Agricultural Research Organization, Rishon LeZion, Israel

Rosina, Konstantin 020241
Solargis, Bratislava, Slovakia

Rossa, Carlos 020432, 020434
Sunveon, Madrid, Spain

Rouffie, Brice 020068
SEGTON Advanced Technology, Versailles, France

Roulleau, Lea 020303
CSTB, Marne-la-Vallée, France

Rousset, Jean 020116
EDF, Palaiseau, France

Roy, Shantanu 020519
CSTEP, Bengaluru, India

Rudolph, Dominik 020003, 020068
ISC Konstanz, Konstanz, Germany

Rudzikas, Matas 020380
The Applied Research Institute for Prospective Technologies, Vilnius, Lithuania

Rüther, Ricardo 020377
Solar Energy Research Laboratory Fotovoltaica/ UFSC, Florianópolis, Brazil

Rüther, Ricardo 020548
UFSC, Florianopolis, Brazil

Ruf, Manuel 020455
Robert Bosch, Stuttgart, Germany

Ruiz Donoso, Elena 020331
DLR, Almería, Spain

S. Sousa, Graciana 020090
Federal University of Rio de Janeiro, Rio de Janeiro, Brazil

Safarian, Jafar 020011
NTNU, Trondheim, Norway

Sah, Dheeraj 020039
Aarhus University, Aarhus, Denmark

Sahin, Hasret 020479
LUT University, Lappeenranta, Finland

Saito, Kimihiko 020106
Tokyo City University, Setagaya, Japan

Salem, Mohammad 020428
Australian University, Kuwait City, Kuwait

Salerno, Giorgia 020077
University of Milano-Bicocca, Milan, Italy

Salis, Fabio 020541
Iberdrola, Rome, Italy

Salvador, Antonio 020358
MAGTEL, Córdoba, Spain

Sample, Tony 020213
European Commission JRC, Ispra, Italy

Samuolienė, Giedrė 020380
The Lithuanian Research Centre for Agriculture and Forestry, Kaunas, Lithuania

San José, Luis Javier 020209, 020453
UPM, Madrid, Spain

Sánchez de León Peque, Miguel 020243
ieco.io, Vigo, Spain

Sanchez Garcia, Alfredo 020270
SINTEF, Trondheim, Norway

Sanchez, Hugo 020056, 020158, 020284
Anhalt University of Applied Sciences, Köthen, Germany

Sanchez, Jesus 020437
UPV/EHU, Vitoria-Gasteiz, Spain

Sanchez, Laura 020437
UPV/EHU, Leioa, Spain

Sánchez, Yudania 020085
IREC, Barcelona, Spain

Sanchez-Friera, Paula 020412, 020513, 020521
Solkeys, Gijón, Spain

Sanchez-Ruiz, Alain 020437
UPV/EHU, Vitoria-Gasteiz, Spain

Sansavini, Giovanni 020296
ETH, Zurich, Switzerland

Sansoni, Paola 020066
CNR-INO, Florence, Italy

Santamaría Fernández, Susanna 020249
TECNALIA, Derio, Spain

Santamaría-Sancho, Juan 020363
UPM, Madrid, Spain

Santos, Jose Domingo 020197, 020198, 020358
TECNALIA, Derio, Spain

Santos, Rodrigo 020530
Casa dos Ventos, Fortaleza, Brazil

Sanz Martinez, Asier 020546
Tecnalia, Bilbao, Spain

Sanz, Asier 020514
Tecnalia, BRTA, Derio, Spain

Sanz, Asier 020197
TECNALIA, Derio, Spain

Sanz-Cuadrado, Cristina 020575
UPM, Madrid, Spain

Sanz-Saiz, Carlos 020297
CIEMAT, Madrid, Spain

Sarafijanovic-Djukic, Natasa 020204
FFHS, Regensdorf, Switzerland

Saretti, Angelica 020301
Polytechnic University of Bari, Bari, Italy

Sarkadi, Monika 020569
ISC Konstanz, Konstanz, Germany

Sauer, Thomas 020140
EXXERGY, Gräfelfing, Germany

Saura, Juan Antonio 020506
University of Murcia, Murcia, Spain

Savisalo, Tuukka 020225
Valoe, Mikkeli, Finland

Saw, Min Hsian 020402
Technology Innovation Institute, Abu Dhabi, United Arab Emirates

Saxena, Anmol Ratan 020429
NIT, Delhi, India

Sayed, Abdullah Abu 020180, 020230
Kiwa PI Berlin, Berlin, Germany

Scaltrito, Luciano 020079
Polytechnic University of Turin, Turin, Italy

Scerri, Kenneth 020334
University of Malta, Msida, Malta

Schading, Steve 020443
University of Agder, Grimstad, Norway

Schäfer, Aysim 020388
Next2Sun Technology, Dillingen, Germany

Schäfer, Sebastian 020539
Frankfurt University of Applied Sciences, Frankfurt am Main, Germany

Schenk, Paul 020192
Fraunhofer CSP, Halle, Germany

Schermer, John 020067
Radboud University, Nijmegen, The Netherlands

Scherret, Jacqueline 020255
A-Null Development, Vienna, Austria

Schifferegger, Raffael 020162
OFI, Vienna, Austria

Schimanke, Sabrina 020006
ISFH, Emmerthal, Germany

Schirmer, Yoko 020101
HTW, Berlin, Germany

Schläger, Christian 020240
Leibniz University Hannover, Hannover, Germany

Schlatmann, Rutger 020101
HTW, Berlin, Germany

Schmidt Davidsen, Rasmus 020037, 020104
Aarhus University, Aarhus, Denmark

Schnaus, Dominik 020237
TUM, Garching, Germany

Schneider, Andreas 020129, 020183
University of Applied Sciences Gelsenkirchen, Gelsenkirchen, Germany

Schneider, Astrid 020255
TU Wien, Vienna, Austria

Schneider, Friedrich 020482
LPKF SolarQuipment, Suhl, Germany

Schneider, Marc Gabriel 020522
University of Applied Science Cologne, Cologne, Germany

Schneiderlöchner, Eric 020033
VON ARDENNE, Dresden, Germany

Schnierer, Branislav 020262
Solargis, Bratislava, Slovakia

Schönau, Maximilian 020361
Coburg University of Applied Sciences, Coburg, Germany

Schönau, Maximilian 020544
smartblue, Munich, Germany

Schönheits, Markus 020468, 020470
bifa Umweltinstitut, Augsburg, Germany

Schranz, Christian 020255
TU Wien, Vienna, Austria

Schrempf, Michael 020199
PTB, Braunschweig, Germany

Schrijvers, Patrick 020390
MARIN, Wageningen, The Netherlands

Schröter, Nick 020142
Fraunhofer CSP, Halle, Germany

Schubert, Martin C. 020475
Fraunhofer ISE, Freiburg, Germany

Schubnel, Baptiste 020238
CSEM, Neuchâtel, Switzerland

Schüler, Marc Andre 020388
Next2Sun Technology, Dillingen, Germany

Schüler, Marc Andre 020411
Next2Sun, Dillingen, Germany

Schueler, Nadine 020015
Freiberger Instruments, Freiberg, Germany

Schulte-Huxel, Henning 020008, 020260
ISFH, Emmerthal, Germany

Schultz, Christof 020101
HTW, Berlin, Germany

Schulz, Philip 020060
IPVF, Palaiseau, France

Schulze, Achim 020361
Rosenheim Technical University of Applied Sciences, Rosenheim, Germany

Schulze, Patricia S.C. 020475
Fraunhofer ISE, Freiburg, Germany

Schwenke, Almut 020495
SGL Battery Solutions, Meitingen, Germany

Sciuto, Marcello 020010
Enel Green Power, Catania, Italy

Scognamiglio, Alessandra 020541
ENEA, Naples, Italy

Scognamiglio, Alessandra 020378
ENEA, Portici, Italy

Sedaghat, Ahmad 020428
Australian University, Kuwait City, Kuwait

Seiffert, Christoph 020169
Institute for Energy Technology, Kjeller, Norway

Seiffert, Daniela 020008
centrotherm international, Blaubeuren, Germany

Seitz, Matthias 020468
bifa Umweltinstitut, Augsburg, Germany

Selj, Josefine H. 020169
Institute for Energy Technology, Kjeller, Norway

Senno, Maximiliano Alejandro 020226
University of Valencia, Paterna, Spain

Senturk, Bilge 020556
ODTU GUNAM, Ankara, Türkiye

Setien, Eneko 020198
TECNALIA, Derio, Spain

Šetkus, Arūnas 020157
Center for Physical Sciences and Technology (FTMC), Vilnius, Lithuania

Shaaban, Ahmed 020402
Technology Innovation Institute, Abu Dhabi, United Arab Emirates

Shah, Syed Fawad Ali 020112
KENTECH, Naju-Si, South Korea

Shanmugam, Raphael 020218, 020220
ISC Konstanz, Konstanz, Germany

Sharma, Rajesh Kumar 020071, 020081
SVNIT, Surat, India

Sharma, Sushma 020563
SRM University, Sonipat, India

Shen, Xinyi 020226
University of Oxford, Oxford, United Kingdom

Shen, Zhenjue 020001
YIST, Jiangyin, China

Shin, Donghyeop 020112
KIER, Daejeon, South Korea

Shin, Woo Gyun 020324, 020357
KIER, Daejeon, South Korea

Shin, Woo-gyun 020561
KIER, Daejeon, South Korea

Shirai, Yasuhiro 020115
NIMS, Tsukuba, Japan

Shirazi, Elham 020544
University of Twente, Enschede, The Netherlands

Shishavan, Amir Asgharzadeh 020367
Nextracker, Fremont, United States of America

Shishido, Hirotaka 020106
Tokyo City University, Setagaya, Japan

Shochet, Ofer 020225
Copprint, Jerusalem, Israel

Shyong, Yung-Jen 020163
ITRI, Hsinchu, Taiwan

Sicot, Lionel 020217
CEA / INES, Le Bourget-du-Lac, France

Sidler, Anika 020226
School of Life Sciences FHNW, Muttenz, Switzerland

Siebert, Michael 020206
ISFH, Emmerthal, Germany

Siefer, Gerald 020246
Fraunhofer ISE, Freiburg, Germany

Sierra, Daniel 020491
UPM, Madrid, Spain

Sigounis, Anna-Maria 020248, 020249
Concordia University, Montreal, Canada

Søiland, Anne-Karin 020495
ReSiTec, Kristiansand, Norway

Silva, José A. 020304, 020409, 020420
University of Évora, Évora, Portugal

Silva, José 020403
University of Évora, Évora, Portugal

Silvestre, Santiago 020301
UPC, Barcelona, Spain

Simeunovic, Jelena 020238
CSEM, Neuchâtel, Switzerland

Simón-Allué, Raquel 020127, 020414, 020517
ENDEF, Zaragoza, Spain

Singh, Ravi 020571
DNV, Arnhem, The Netherlands

Sinha, Amish Kumar 020463
RCT Solutions, Konstanz, Germany

Sinopoli, Alessandro 020042
QEERI, Doha, Qatar

Sivaramakrishnan Radhakrishnan, Hariharsudan 020064
Hasselt Unversity, Genk, Belgium

Sivaramakrishnan, Hariharsudan 020225
IMEC, Genk, Belgium

Snaith, Henry 020226
University of Oxford, Oxford, United Kingdom

Søndenå, Rune 020503
Institute for Energy Technology, Kjeller, Norway

Sobajima, Yasushi 020131
Gifu University, Gifu, Japan

Soler Toledo, Denet 020509
University of Antofagasta, Antofagasta, Chile

Solomon, Asfaw A. 020479
LUT University, Lappeenranta, Finland

Solórzano, Jorge 020328
Qualifying Photovoltaics, Madrid, Spain

Sondoqah, Mousa 020316
Becquerel Institute, Bolzano, Italy

Sondoqah, Mousa 020261
Eurac Research, Bolzano, Italy

Song, Hee-eun 020045
KIER, Daejeon, South Korea

Spagnolo, Sofia 020462, 020466
RSE, Milan, Italy

Spataru, Sergiu V. 020265, 020267, 020283, 020376, 020451
DTU, Roskilde, Denmark

Spataru, Sergiu Viorel 020346
DTU, Roskilde, Denmark

Spera, Fabian 020411
Next2Sun, Dillingen, Germany

Spihola, Jan 020355
DiSUN Deutsche Solarservice, Werder, Germany

Sraisth, 020005, 020222
RCT Solutions, Konstanz, Germany

Sraisth, Sraisth 020463
RCT Solutions, Konstanz, Germany

Staňková, Tereza 020107
Czech Technical University, Prague, Czech Republic

Steckenreiter, Verena 020063
ISFH, Emmerthal, Germany

Stegemann, Bert 020309
Berlin University of Applied Sciences, Berlin, Germany

Stegemann, Bert 020101
HTW, Berlin, Germany

Stellbogen, Dirk 020312
ZSW, Stuttgart, Germany

Stensborg, Jan F. 020250
Stensborg, Roskilde, Denmark

Stensborg, Jan 020306
Stensborg, Roskilde, Denmark

Stieldorf, Karin 020255
TU Wien, Vienna, Austria

Stierstorfer, Johannes 020225
WIP - Renewable Energies, Munich, Germany

Stierstorfer, Johannes 020551
WIP Renewable Energies, Munich, Germany

Stivanello, Juan José 020226
Eurac Research, Bolzano, Italy

Stoicescu, Liviu 020198
Solarzentrum Stuttgart, Stuttgart, Germany

Stowhas-Villa, Alejandro 020422
Federico Santa María Technical University, Valparaiso, Chile

Stoyanova Lyubenova, Teodora 020173
European Commission JRC, Ispra, Italy

Sträter, Hendrik 020211
PTB, Braunschweig, Germany

Strey, Jessica 020063, 020114
ISFH, Emmerthal, Germany

Strömberg, Rich 020472
University of Alaska, Fairbanks, United States of America

Stroyuk, Oleksander 020185
HI ERN, Erlangen, Germany

Stroyuk, Oleksandr 020117, 020149, 020150
HI ERN, Erlangen, Germany

Suárez Sánchez, Sergio 020326
Enertis Applus+, Madrid, Spain

Subasi, Dilara Maria 020475
Fraunhofer ISE, Freiburg, Germany

Sudbury, Ben A. 020396
PV Lighthouse, Coledale, Australia

Suemitsu, Issei 020484
Hitachi, Kokubunji, Japan

Suhonen, Riikka 020423
VTT Technical Research Centre of Finland, Oulu, Finland

Sulca, Kabir Paúl 020191, 020205
University of Valladolid, Valladolid, Spain

Svatos, Jan 020250
DTU, Roskilde, Denmark

Sylla, David 020063
ISFH, Emmerthal, Germany

Syre Wiig, Marie 020340
IFE, Kjeller, Norway

Szarek, Magda 020298, 020398
University of Turku, Turku, Finland

Taghipour Kani, Ghaem 020335, 020374
Amirkabir University of Technology, Tehran, Iran

Takahashi, Kanji 020106
Tokyo City University, Setagaya, Japan

Talvi, Micke 020528
Tampere University, Tampere, Finland

Tanahashi, Tadanori 020436
AIST, Koriyama, Japan

Tang, Kai 020011
SINTEF, Trondheim, Norway

Tang, Torben IPU P/S, Virum, Denmark	020028
Tang, Torben IPU, Virum, Denmark	020037
Tayebjee, Murad J. Y. UNSW, Sydney, Australia	020065
Taylor, Nigel European Commission JRC, Ispra, Italy	020210
Tellez Rodriguez, Eduardo Kiwa PI Berlin, Berlin, Germany	020230
Teppe, Andreas RCT Solutions, Konstanz, Germany	020005
Terheiden, Barbara University of Konstanz, Constance, Germany	020031
Terrados, Cristian University of Valladolid, Valladolid, Spain	020205
Thakur, Dhruv Singh SVNIT, Surat, India	020071, 020081
Theocharides, Spyros Univers, Courbevoie, France	020371
Thomas, Jean Ciel et Terre, Lille, France	020169
Thorning, Jacob K. DTU, Roskilde, Denmark	020267, 020283
Thorsteinsson, Sune DTU, Copenhagen, Denmark	020039
Thorsteinsson, Sune DTU, Lyngby, Denmark	020037
Thorsteinsson, Sune DTU, Roskilde, Denmark	020028, 020249, 020250, 020265, 020306, 020477
Timofte, Tudor ISC Konstanz, Konstanz, Germany	020218, 020221
Ting, San-Yu ITRI, Hsinchu, Taiwan	020161, 020163
Tissier, Corentin CSEM, Neuchâtel, Switzerland	020238
Tönies, Alexandra University of Applied Sciences Cologne, Cologne, Germany	020523
Tomšič, Špela University of Ljubljana, Ljubljana, Slovenia	020047
Tong, Yongfeng QEERI, Doha, Qatar	020108, 020109
Topič, Marko University of Ljubljana, Ljubljana, Slovenia	020047, 020269, 020319
Torabi, Narges University of Verona, Verona, Italy	020089

Torelly, Guilherme 020092
PUC-Rio, Rio de Janeiro, Brazil

Torre, Gorka 020437
UPV/EHU, Leioa, Spain

Torres Aguilar, Moira Itzel 020214
CentraleSupélec, Gif-sur-Yvette, France

Torres Aguilar, Moira Itzel 020406
CNRS, Gif-sur-Yvette, France

Torres Silva, Nicole 020546
ATAMOSTEC, Santiago, Chile

Torres, Oscar 020110
National University of Colombia, Bogotá, Colombia

Tosi, Irene 020037
IPU, Virum, Denmark

Tran Caliste, Thu Nhi 020546
European Synchrotron Radiation Facility (ESRF), Grenoble, France

Treberspurg, Christoph 020255
Treberspurg und Partner Ziviltechniker, Vienna, Austria

Treberspurg, Martin 020255
Treberspurg und Partner Ziviltechniker, Vienna, Austria

Trefzer, Aaron 020135
Fraunhofer ISE, Freiburg, Germany

Trifiletti, Vanira 020087
University of Milano-Bicocca, Milan, Italy

Trigo-Gonzalez, Mauricio 020342, 020422
University of Antofagasta, Antofagasta, Chile

Tsai, Min-An 020053, 020083, 020161, 020163
ITRI, Hsinchu, Taiwan

Tsanakas, Ioannis (John) A. 020262
CEA / INES, Le Bourget-du-Lac, France

Tsanakas, Ioannis (John) A. 020544
CEA, Le Bourget-du-Lac, France

Tsanakas, Ioannis (John) 020546
CEA / INES, Le Bourget-du-Lac, France

Tsanakas, Ioannis (John) 020317
CEA INES, Le Bourget-du-Lac, France

Tsanakas, Ioannis (John) 020513, 020521
CEA, Le Bourget-du-Lac, France

Tsanakas, Ioannis 020217, 020338
CEA / INES, Le Bourget-du-Lac, France

Tsanakas, Ioannis 020500
CEA, Le Bourget-du-Lac, France

Tsanakas, John A. 020311
CEA / INES, Le Bourget-du-Lac, France

Tseberlidis, Giorgio 020093
University of Milano Bicocca, Milan, Italy

Tseberlidis, Giorgio University of Milano-Bicocca, Milan, Italy	020087
Tsoi, Konstantin ODTÜ-GÜNAM, Ankara, Türkiye	020113
Tsombou, Francois M. Fujairah Research Centre, Fujairah, United Arab Emirates	020402
Tsuno, Yuki AIST, Koriyama, Japan	020436
Tsunoda, Jun Hitachi, Kokubunji, Japan	020484
Tsunoda, Jun Hitachi, Tokyo, Japan	020186
Tulinski, Lona ZHAW, Winterthur, Switzerland	020385
Tune, Daniel ISC Konstanz, Konstanz, Germany	020220, 020221, 020225
Turcu, Mircea ISFH, Emmerthal, Germany	020063
Turek, Marko Fraunhofer CSP, Halle (Saale), Germany	020004, 020052
Ueda, Yuzuru Tokyo University of Science, Tokyo, Japan	020320, 020525
Ujvari, Gusztav AIT, Vienna, Austria	020318, 020430
Ulbikaitė, Vaidvilė Applied Research Institute for Prospective Technologies, Vilnius, Lithuania	020157
Ulbikas, Juras Protechnology, Vilnius, Lithuania	020225
Ulyashin, Alexander G. SINTEF, Oslo, Norway	020011
Unsur, Veysel ODTÜ-GÜNAM, Ankara, Türkiye	020020
Urban, Harald TU Wien, Vienna, Austria	020255
Useni, Yannick University of Lubumbashi, Lubumbashi, Congo (DRC)	020393
Uzuner, Bahri Eren ODTÜ-GÜNAM, Ankara, Türkiye	020113
Väisänen, Kaisa-Leena VTT Technical Research Centre of Finland, Oulu, Finland	020423
Vaicikauskas, Viktoras Center for Physical Sciences and Technology (FTMC), Vilnius, Lithuania	020157

Valaski, Rogério 020090
National Institute of Metrology Quality and Technology, Rio de Janeiro, Brazil

Valencia, Felipe 020342, 020546
AtamosTec, Santiago, Chile

Vallerotto, Guido 020209, 020246, 020257
UPM, Madrid, Spain

van Aken, Bas B. 020405
TNO, Petten, The Netherlands

van der Heide, Arvid 020472
imec, Genk, Belgium

van der Zee, Friso F. 020405
Wageningen University and Research, Wageningen, The Netherlands

Van Dyck, Rik 020225
IMEC, Genk, Belgium

van Dyk, E. Ernest 020193, 020416
Nelson Mandela University, Port Elizabeth, South Africa

van Dyk, Ernest E. 020344
Nelson Mandela University, Port Elizabeth, South Africa

Van Overstraeten, Julien 020543
Becquerel Institute France, Lyon, France

Van Overstraeten, Julien 020252
Becquerel Institute, Brussels, Belgium

vanBaal, Rene 020492
Belectric, Kolitzheim, Germany

Vanhanen, Tuomas 020225
Valoe, Mikkeli, Finland

Vargas, Renzo 020348
University of São Paulo, São Paulo, Brazil

Varney, Valérie 020522
University of Applied Science Cologne, Cologne, Germany

Varney, Valérie 020523
University of Applied Sciences Cologne, Cologne, Germany

vas Dyk, Ernest 020185
Nelson Mandela University, Port Elizabeth, South Africa

Vasconcelos, Letícia 020530
Casa dos Ventos, Fortaleza, Brazil

Vavilkin, Tatjana 020302
Soltech, Genk, Belgium

Vázquez Adán, Alejandra 020501
UCM, Madrid, Spain

Vázquez, A. 020508
UCM, Madrid, Spain

Veas, Christian 020136, 020234
PCCL, Leoben, Austria

Vecino, Fernando Román 020346
DTU, Roskilde, Denmark
Veerman, Sebastian 020035
ISC Konstanz, Konstanz, Germany
Vega de Seoane, José Maria 020252
Becquerel Institute Spain, San Sebastian, Spain
Vega de Seoane, Jose 020546
Becquerel Institute, Brussels, Belgium
Vega-Herrera, Jorge 020342
University of Antofagasta, Antofagasta, Chile
Vehus, Tore Sandnes 020443
University of Agder, Grimstad, Norway
Veirman, Jordi 020203, 020226, 020254
Eurac Research, Bolzano, Italy
Velasco, Angel 020367
Nextracker, Fremont, United States of America
Veludo, Jorge 020317
Galp Energia, Lisbon, Portugal
Veneri, Alessandro 020093
University of Verona, Verona, Italy
Vergura, Silvano 020301
Polytechnic University of Bari, Bari, Italy
Verlinden, Pierre 020001
YIST, Jiangyin, China
Vermang, Bart 020064
Hasselt Unversity, Genk, Belgium
Vernay, Christophe 020244
SOLAÏS, Valbonne, France
Vero, Giuseppe 020301
Polytechnic University of Bari, Bari, Italy
Veronese, Elisa 020513
Eurac Research, Bolzano, Italy
Veurman, Welmoed 020063
ISFH, Emmerthal, Germany
Viani, Lucas 020326
Enertis Applus+, Madrid, Spain
Vicente-Laiglesia, Pablo 020181
European Climate, Infrastructure and Environment
Executive Agency, Brussels, Belgium
Vidal de Oliveira, Aline 020377
Solar Energy Research Laboratory Fotovoltaica/ UFSC,
Florianópolis, Brazil
Vidal, Beatriz Muñoz 020414
IaSol, Zaragoza, Spain
Vidal-Fuentes, Pedro 020094
IREC, Barcelona, Spain

Videla-Magnata, Natalia 020129
Universidad de Antofagasta, Antofagasta, Chile

Videla-Magnata, Natalia 020417
University of Antofagasta, Antofagasta, Chile

Vilches, Anna Morales 020388
Next2Sun Technology, Dillingen, Germany

Villalonga Palou, Joan Tomás 020432, 020434
Sunveon, Madrid, Spain

Villén, Raúl 020127, 020414, 020517
ENDEF, Zaragoza, Spain

Villodas, Aritz 020198
TECNALIA, Derio, Spain

Vincent, Laetitia 020058
CNRS, Palaiseau, France

Vincent, Robin 020196
PVsyst, Geneva, Switzerland

Viorel Spataru, Sergiu 020191
DTU, Roskilde, Denmark

Viriyaroj, Bergpob 020298
Aalto University, Espoo, Finland

Viti, Valeria 020541
Legance, Milan, Italy

Vitoshkin, Helena 020379
Agricultural Research Organization, Rishon LeZion, Israel

Vögeli, Pascal 020385
ZHAW, Winterthur, Switzerland

Vogt, Malte R. 020515
TU Delft, Delft, The Netherlands

Vogt, Thomas 020482
DLR, Oldenburg, Germany

Vollbrecht, Joachim 020063, 020114
ISFH, Emmerthal, Germany

Voltan, Alessandro 020010
Applied Materials, Treviso, Italy

von Friedeburg, Christoph 020557
CF Energy Research-Consulting-Operation, Berlin, Germany

Voronko, Yuliya 020162, 020249
OFI, Vienna, Austria

Vorster, Frederik J. 020193, 020344, 020416
Nelson Mandela University, Port Elizabeth, South Africa

Vorster, Frederik 020185
Nelson Mandela University, Port Elizabeth, South Africa

Vuillon, Laurent 020338
CNRS, Chambery, France

Vulic, Natasa 020296
Univesity of Applied Arts and Sciences Northwestern Switzerland, Muttenz, Switzerland

Vumbugwa, Monphias 020185, 020193, 020344
Nelson Mandela University, Port Elizabeth, South Africa

Waibel, Christoph 020511
Flemish Institute for Technological Research (VITO), Genk, Belgium

Wakabayashi, Ryo 020484
Hitachi, Kokubunji, Japan

Wakazono, Kouzen 020131
Gifu University, Gifu, Japan

Wallner, Gernot M. 020227
University of Linz, Linz, Austria

Walpita, Harsha 020169
University of Oslo, Kjeller, Norway

Walsh, Yoselyn 020520
Costa Rica Institute of Technology, Cartago, Costa Rica

Wambach, Karsten 020468, 020470
bifa Umweltinstitut, Augsburg, Germany

Wang, Chia-Chen 020549
ITRI, Hsinchu, Taiwan

Wang, Shuo 020286, 020400
TUAS, Turku, Finland

Wang, Tzuya 020549
ITRI, Hsinchu, Taiwan

Wang, Xiaolin 020381
Mälardalen University, Västerås, Sweden

Wannenwetsch, Jann 020312
EnBW, Karlsruhe, Germany

Wargocki, Pawel 020551
DTU, Roskilde, Denmark

Waschl, Alfred 020255
buildingSMART, Vienna, Austria

Weber, Thomas 020180, 020230
Kiwa PI Berlin, Berlin, Germany

Weeber, Arthur W. 020515
TU Delft, Delft, The Netherlands

Wei, Wenpeng 020484
Hitachi, Kokubunji, Japan

Weihs, Philipp 020281
BOKU, Vienna, Austria

Weinrich, Frank 020177
PTB, Braunschweig, Germany

Weiß, Marius 020361
Coburg University of Applied Sciences, Coburg, Germany

Wellens, Christine Fraunhofer ISE, Freiburg, Germany	020135
Whyatt, Duncan Lancaster University, Lancaster, United Kingdom	020394
Wienands, Karl ISC Konstanz, Konstanz, Germany	020218, 020220, 020221
Wiesenfarth, Maike Fraunhofer ISE, Freiburg, Germany	020246
Wietler, Tobias ISFH, Emmerthal, Germany	020063
Wilbert, Stefan DLR, Almería, Spain	020235, 020237, 020239, 020331
Willers, Guido Fraunhofer CSP, Halle, Germany	020201
Wilson, Helen R. Fraunhofer ISE, Freiburg, Germany	020249
Winter, Renate ISFH, Emmerthal, Germany	020063
Winter, Stefan PTB, Braunschweig, Germany	020177, 020181
Wirtz, Wiebke ISFH, Emmerthal, Germany	020260
Witkowska, Agnieszka Gdansk University of Technology, Gdansk, Poland	020498
Wittmer, Bruno PVsyst, Geneva, Switzerland	020196
Wolf, Andreas Fraunhofer ISE, Freiburg, Germany	020031
Wong, Craig Kiwa PI Berlin, Berlin, Germany	020230
Wu, Li-Guo TSEC, Hsinchu, Taiwan	020021
Wu, Yu TNO, Petten, The Netherlands	020030
Wyss, Philippe CSEM, Neuchâtel, Switzerland	020068
Xiong, Weizhen Tokyo University of Science, Tokyo, Japan	020320
Xu, Jiahui YIST, Jiangyin, China	020001
Xu, Wenhao TÜV Rheinland, Shanghai, China	020144, 020208
Xu, Xiaoqi SERIS, Singapore, Singapore	020263

Xu, Yu 020263
SERIS, Singapore, Singapore
Xuereb, Steven 020180, 020230
Kiwa PI Berlin, Berlin, Germany

Yadav, Shivendra 020071, 020081
SVNIT, Surat, India
Yamaguchi, Yosuke 020484
Hitachi, Kokubunji, Japan
Yanagida, Masatoshi 020115
NIMS, Tsukuba, Japan
Yanar, T. Meriç 020027
Kalyon PV, Ankara, Türkiye
Yang, Donggeon 020323
K-water, Daejeon, South Korea
Yang, Hyoung-Kyu 020449
KETI, Wonmi-gu, South Korea
Yde, Leif 020250, 020306
Stensborg, Roskilde, Denmark
Ye, JiaYi 020102
SERIS, Singapore, Singapore
Yerci, Selcuk 020113
ODTÜ-GÜNAM, Ankara, Türkiye
Ylikunnari, Mari 020423
VTT Technical Research Centre of Finland, Oulu, Finland
Ylinen, Marko 020444
Satakunta University of Applied Sciences, Pori, Finland
Ylipaino, Juho 020444, 020445, 020554
TUAS, Tampere, Finland
Yılmaz, Büşra 020521
Kameleon Solar, Roosendaal, The Netherlands
Yordadov, Georgi 020389
imec, Diepenbeek, Belgium
Younes, Kareem 020487
Khalifa University, Abu Dhabi, United Arab Emirates
Yu, Cheng-Yeh 020021, 020053
TSEC, Hsinchu, Taiwan
Yu, Shusen 020406
Ecole Polytechnique, Palaiseau, France
Yuan, Xiao 020001
YIST, Jiangyin, China
Yun, Jae Ho 020112
KENTECH, Naju-si, South Korea

Zaimi, Mhammed 020171
University of Chouaib Doukkali, El Jadida, Morocco

Zanatta Britto, João Victor 020025
PUCRS, Porto Alegre, Brazil
Zanesco, Izete 020023, 020025
PUCRS, Porto Alegre, Brazil
Zaror, Yasmin 020225
WIP - Renewable Energies, Munich, Germany
Zarzalejo, Luis F. 020237, 020331
CIEMAT, Madrid, Spain
Zekri, Atef 020146
QEERI, Doha, Qatar
Zerafa, Steve 020334
PIXAM, Msida, Malta
Zhang, Geng 020001
Jolywood (ShanXi) Solar Technology, Taiyuan, China
Zhang, Jingwei 020111
Hohai University, Changzhou, China
Zhang, Kai 020233
FZJ, Jülich, Germany
Zhang, Wenjing 020001
YIST, Jiangyin, China
Zhang, Wuai 020101
HZB, Berlin, Germany
Zhang, Yating 020144, 020208
TÜV Rheinland, Shanghai, China
Zhou, Qilin 020102
SERIS, Singapore, Singapore
Zhu, Junjie 020017
Institute for Energy Technology, Kjeller, Norway
Ziaullah, Abdul Wahab 020278, 020291
QEERI, Doha, Qatar
Zilles, Roberto 020154, 020348
University of São Paulo, São Paulo, Brazil
Zimmermann, Iwan 020116
IPVF, Palaiseau, France
Zubillaga, Oihana 020139
Tecnalia, Donostia - San Sebastián, Spain
Zugasti, Eugenia 020334
CENER, Pamplona, Spain
Zugasti, Eugenia 020300
CENER, Sarriguren, Spain
Zwahlen, Theo 020369
BFH, Burgdorf, Switzerland

KEYWORDS OF EU PVSEC 2025 PROCEEDINGS PAPERS

42nd European Photovoltaic Solar Energy Conference and Exhibition (EU PVSEC 2025)

Bilbao, Spain
22-26 September 2025

Volume 6 of 6

ISBN: 979-8-3313-2987-7

Printed from e-media with permission by:

Curran Associates, Inc.
57 Morehouse Lane
Red Hook, NY 12571

Some format issues inherent in the e-media version may also appear in this print version.

WIP – Renewable Energies
Sylvensteinstr. 2
81369 Munchen
Germany

Phone: +49 89 72012735
Fax: +49 89 72012791

wip@wip-munich.de

Additional copies of this publication are available from:

Curran Associates, Inc.
57 Morehouse Lane
Red Hook, NY 12571 USA
Phone: 845-758-0400
Fax: 845-758-2633
Email: curran@proceedings.com
Web: www.proceedings.com

42nd European Photovoltaic Solar Energy Conference and Exhibition

Proceedings of the International Conference

22 September – 26 September 2025

Edited by:

C. DEL CAÑIZO
Solar Energy Institute
UPM
Spain

R. KENNY
European Commission
Joint Research Centre
Italy

J. BERGMILLER
WIP Renewable Energies
Germany

J. DE GREGORIO
WIP Renewable Energies
Germany

Edition Team:

B. Yildiz
L. Großhans
A. Michaelsen
U.E. Birgi
WIP Renewable Energies
Germany

Photos at:

Coordination of the Technical Programme:

European Commission Joint Research Centre
Via E. Fermi 1
21020 Ispra (VA)
Italy

Institutional Support:

European Commission

Institutional PV Industry Cooperation:

SolarPower Europe

ESMC – European Solar Manufacturing Council

Supporting Organisations:

AUSTRALIAN PV INSTITUTE

ASOM – Alliance for Solar Mobility

BASQUE ENERGY CLUSTER

BILBAO CONVENTION BUREAU

EASE – European Association for Storage of Energy

ETIP PV – European Technology & Innovation Platform PV

GÜNDER – Turkish Solar Energy Society

IEA PVPS - IEA Photovoltaic Power Systems Programme

INSTITUTO SOLAR DE ENERGÍA SOLAR

LDES – Long Duration Energy Storage Council

NSEFI – National Solar Energy federation of India

NUS /SERIS – National University of Singapore / Solar Energy Research Institute of Singapore

UPM - Polytechnic University of Madrid

Supporting Associations:

EERA – European Energy Research Aliance

EREF – European Renewable Energies Federation

EUREC – The Association of European Renewable Energy Research Centres

VDMA Photovoltaic Equipment

Local Support:
ENTE VASCO DE LA ENERGÍA
EUH – University of the Basque Country

EU PVSEC 2025 realised by:

WIP Renewable Energies
Sylvensteinstr. 2, 81369 Munich, Germany
Tel: +49 89 720 12 735, Fax: +49 89 720 12 791
Email: pv.conference@wip-munich.de
www.eupvsec.org
www.wip-munich.de

Proceedings produced and published by:

WIP Renewable Energies
Sylvensteinstr. 2, 81369 Munich, Germany
Tel: +49 89 720 12 735, Fax: +49 89 720 12 791
Email: pv.conference@wip-munich.de
www.eupvsec.org
www.wip-munich.de

42nd EUROPEAN PHOTOVOLTAIC SOLAR ENERGY CONFERENCE AND EXHIBITION
22 SEPTEMBER – 26 SEPTEMBER 2025

EU PVSEC 2025 COMMITTEES

INTERNATIONAL SCIENTIFIC ADVISORY COMMITTEE (ISAC)

Chair

P. Szymanski, European Commission Joint Research Centre, Director of Energy, Transport and Climate, Petten, The Netherlands

Committee Members

V. Bermúdez Benito, Founder & Principal Consultant, Berbetin, Antibes, France
G.C. Eder, OFI, Vienna, Austria
P. Frankl, Head of the Renewable Energy Division, International Energy Agency, France
M. Getsiou, European Commission, DG RTD, Brussels, Belgium
S.W. Glunz, Head of Division Photovoltaics - Research, Fraunhofer ISE, Freiburg, Germany
N.M. Haegel, Director of the National Center for Photovoltaics, NREL, Golden, USA
R. Kenny, European Commission Joint Research Centre, Directorate for Energy and Transport and Climate, Ispra, Italy
S. Nowak, Managing Director of NET Nowak Energy & Technology, St. Ursen, Switzerland
R. Schlatmann, Chairman of ETIP PV, Head of the Solar Energy Division at Helmholtz-Zentrum Berlin, Germany
W.C. Sinke, TNO Energy Transition, The Netherlands
M. Topič, Head of Laboratory of Photovoltaics and Optoelectronics of the University of Ljubljana, Slovenia
P. Verlinden, Director at Amrock, Visiting Professor at Sun Yat-Sen University, Guangzhou, China
E. Voroshazi, Head of PV module process laboratory, CEA, Le Bourget-du-Lac, France
J. Bergmiller, Managing Director Events & Knowledge Transfer, WIP Renewable Energies, Munich, Germany
J. de Gregorio, Head of Unit, Scientific Services and Cooperation, WIP Renewable Energies, Munich, Germany

CONFERENCE EXECUTIVE COMMITTEE

Conference General Chair

C. del Cañizo, UPM, Madrid, Spain

Technical Programme Chair

R. Kenny, European Commission Joint Research Centre, Directorate for Energy and Transport and Climate, Ispra, Italy

Committee Members

W.C. Sinke, Program Development Manager, TNO Energy Transition, The Netherlands
S. Nowak, Managing Director of NET Nowak Energy & Technology, St. Ursen, Switzerland
M. Topič, Head of Laboratory of Photovoltaics and Optoelectronics of the University of Ljubljana, Slovenia
V. Bermúdez Benito, BERBETIN, France
E. Voroshazi, Head of PV Module Process Laboratory, CEA, Le Bourget-Du-Lac France
H. Ossenbrink, Former European Commission Joint Research Centre, Germany
J. Bergmiller, Managing Director Events & Knowledge Transfer, WIP Renewable Energies, Munich, Germany
J. de Gregorio, Head of Unit, Scientific Services and Cooperation, WIP Renewable Energies, Munich, Germany

2025 SCIENTIFIC COMMITTEE

Programme Technical Chair

R. Kenny, European Commission, Joint Research Centre, Italy

Topic Chairs

Topic 1: Silicon Materials and Cells
F. Schindler, Fraunhofer ISE, Germany

Topic 2: Thin Films and New Concepts
I. Gordon, imec, Belgium

Topic 3: Photovoltaic Modules and BoS Components
T. Barnes, NREL, USA

Topic 4: PV Systems Engineering, Integrated/Applied PV
A.M. Gracia Amillo, FUNDACIÓN CENER, Spain

Topic 5: PV in the Energy Transition
C. Agraffeil, CEA / INES, France

Topic Organisers and Paper Review Experts

Topic 1: Silicon Materials and Cells

F. Schindler, Fraunhofer ISE, Germany
C. Fischer, Wacker Chemie, Germany
G. Hahn, University of Konstanz, Germany
K. Ding, Forschungszentrum Jülich, Germany
P. Roca i Cabarrocas, CNRS-LPICM, France
A. W. Weeber, TNO Energy Transition, The Netherlands
D. Muñoz, CEA / INES, France
S. W. Glunz, Fraunhofer ISE, Germany
K. Bothe, ISFH, Germany
M. Topic, University of Ljubljana, Slovenia
P. Fath, RCT-Solutions, Germany
S. Peters, Hanwha Q CELLS, Germany

M.P. Bellmann, SINTEF, Norway
A. Ciesla, UNSW, Australia
C. Hagendorf, Freiberg Instruments, Germany
X. Yu, Zhejiang University, China
J.S. Lee, KIER, South Korea
R. Brendel, ISFH, Germany
T. Dullweber, ISFH, Germany
J. Horzel, Fraunhofer ISE, Germany
W. Nemeth, NREL, United States of America
R. Turan, METU, Türkiye
F. Menchini, ENEA, Italy
W. Favre, CEA, France

J. Meier, Meier Technologies, Switzerland
J. Schmidt, ISFH, Germany
M. Wright, University of Oxford, United Kingdom
J. Zhao, CSEM, Switzerland
A. Morisset, CSEM, Switzerland
A. Richter, Fraunhofer ISE, Germany
J. Linke, ISC Konstanz, Germany
B. Geerligs, TNO Energy Transition, The Netherlands
S. Dubois, CEA, France
M. Hermle, Fraunhofer ISE, Germany
B. Terheiden, University of Konstanz, Germany
P. Delli Veneri, ENEA, Italy
T. Matsui, AIST, Japan
Y. Ohshita, Toyota Technological Institute, Japan
E. Bruhat, HOLOSOLIS, France
A. Augusto, Dalarna University, Sweden
F. Ferrazza, ENI S.p.A., Italy
A. Otaegi, UPV/EHU, Spain
M.C. Schubert, Fraunhofer ISE, Germany
H. Duman, KalyonPV, Türkiye
N. Usami, Nagoya University, Japan
Y. Zhu, UNSW, Australia
D. Brunner, RENA Technologies, Germany
A. Danel, CEA, France
C. Gerardi, 3Sun, Italy
H.J. Nonnenmacher, Meyer Burger, Germany
P. Verlinden, AMROCK, Australia
Q. Wang, Wang, Qi, China
W. Zhang, Zhang, Weiming, China
Y. Chen, Trina Solar Energy, China
E. Krassowski, CE Cell Engineering, Germany
M. Foti, 3Sun, Italy
D.L. Bätzner, Meyer Burger Research, Switzerland

Topic 2: Thin Films and New Concepts
I. Gordon, imec, Belgium
J.C. Goldschmidt, Marburg University, Germany
F. Schoofs, Oxford PV, United Kingdom
N. Kyranaki, Hasselt University, Belgium
S. Veenstra, TNO Energy Transition, The Netherlands
T. Aernouts, imec, Belgium
A.N. Tiwari, SOLTIWA, Switzerland
G. Siefer, Fraunhofer ISE, Germany
M. Edoff, Uppsala University, Sweden
A. Martí Vega, UPM, Spain
J. Poortmans, imec, Belgium
I. Ramiro, UPM, Spain
T. Magorian Friedlmeier, ZSW, Germany

S. Albrecht, HZB, Germany
S. Berson, CEA, France
P. Carroy, CEA, France
C. Case, Oxford PV, United Kingdom
G. Coletti, FuturaSun, Italy
S. De Wolf, KAUST, Saudi Arabia
U.W. Paetzold, KIT, Germany
H. Sivaramakrishnan Radhakrisnan, imec, Belgium
P. Schulze, Fraunhofer ISE, Germany
L. Wang, Technology Innovation Institute, United Arab Emirates
Y. Smirnov, Applied Materials, United States of America
B. Stannowski, HZB, Germany
F. Fertig, Hanwha Q CELLS, Germany
L. Lancellotti, ENEA, Italy
S. Cros, CEA, France
S. Hayase, The University of Electro-Communications, Japan
S. Huang, Macquarie University, Australia
M. Khenkin, HZB, Germany
C. Lin, National Taiwan University, Taiwan
M.S.H. Norton, University of Cyprus, Cyprus
P. Pistor, Pablo de Olavide University, Spain
W. Tress, Zurich University of Applied Sciences, Switzerland
A. Aguirre, imec, Belgium
D. Lan, UNSW Sydney, China
M. Saliba, University of Stuttgart, Germany
P. Manshanden, TNO Energy Transition, The Netherlands
L. Vesce, University of Rome II, Italy
I. Dogan, TNO Solliance, The Netherlands
Y. Kuang, imec, Belgium
M. Al Katrib, IPVF, France
M.I. Hossain, QEERI, Qatar
W.H. Chiu, Chang Gung University, Taiwan
C. Chen, Ming Chi University of Technology, Taiwan
C. Fell, CSIRO Energy Technology, Australia
G. Brammertz, imec, Belgium
T. Dalibor, Avancis, Germany
S. Ishizuka, AIST, Japan
A. Redinger, University of Luxembourg, Luxembourg
A. Romeo, University of Verona, Italy
V. Sittinger, Fraunhofer IST, Germany
M. Theelen, TNO/Solliance, The Netherlands
G. Timò, RSE, Italy
A. Kanevce, ZSW, Germany
A. Pérez-Rodríguez, IREC, Spain
R. Gutzler, ZSW, Germany
W. Witte, ZSW, Germany
T. Nishimura, Tokyo Institute of Technology, Japan
C. Qian, University of New South Wales, Australia
J.P. Connolly, CentraleSupelec, France
J.P. Kleider, CNRS/GeePs, France
I. Konovalov, University of Applied Sciences Jena, Germany
Y. Okada, University of Tokyo, Japan
M. Rusu, HZB, Germany
H. Meddeb, DLR, Germany
E. Saucedo, Universitat Politècnica de Catalunya (UPC), Spain
P. Vidal-Fuentes, FUNDACIÓ INSTITUT DE RECERCA EN ENERGIA DE CATALUNYA, Spain
C. Malerba, ENEA, Italy
C. Becker, HZB, Germany
D. Kuciauskas, NREL, United States of America
M. Ochoa, University of Cantabria, Spain
T. Tayagaki, AIST, Japan
S. Wasmer, WAVELABS Solar Metrology Systems, Germany
S. Zandi, UNSW, Australia
C. Messmer, University of Freiburg, Germany
J.B. Puel, Institut Photovoltaïque d'Ile de France (IPVF), France
S. Ternes, University of Rome II, Italy

Topic 3: Photovoltaic Modules and BoS Components
V. Bermúdez Benito, BERBETIN, France
R. Preu, Fraunhofer ISE, Germany
R. Gottschalg, Fraunhofer CSP, Germany
T. Barnes, NREL, United States of America
G. Friesen, SUPSI, Switzerland
G. Bardizza, TÜV Rheinland Solar, Italy

V. Barth, CEA, France
A. Faes, CSEM, Switzerland
A. Lennon, Sundrive Solar, Australia
M. Mittag, Fraunhofer ISE, Germany
M.A. Muñoz-García, UPM, Spain
H. Nagel, Fraunhofer ISE, Germany
S. Pietralunga, CNR, Italy
T. Timofte, ISC Konstanz, Germany

S. Feldbacher, PCCL, Austria
A. Halm, ISC Konstanz, Germany
H. Hanifi, AESOLAR, Germany
E. Warren, NREL, United States of America
S. Zhang, Trina Solar Energy, China
X. Zhen, Canadian Solar, China
G. Beaucarne, Dow Silicones Belgium, Belgium
T. Bejat, CEA, France
C. Camus, LayTec, Germany
U. Jahn, Fraunhofer CSP, Germany
G. Oreski, PCCL, Austria
M. Pander, Fraunhofer CSP, Germany
T. Sample, European Commission JRC, Italy
A. Morlier, imo-imomec, Belgium
C. Barretta, PCCL, Austria
P. Gebhardt, Fraunhofer ISE, Germany
C. Sen, UNSW, Australia
O. Arriaga Arruti, CSEM, Switzerland
X. Gu, NIST, United States of America
C. Xiao, Chinese Academy of Sciences, United States of America
R. Aninat, TNO/Solliance, The Netherlands
S. Mitterhofer, NIST, United States of America
B. Hoex, UNSW, Australia
E. Özkalay, SUPSI, Switzerland
M. Bokalič, University of Ljubljana, Slovenia
S. Bordihn, ISFH, Germany
M. Despeisse, CSEM, Switzerland
J. Govaerts, imec, Belgium
J. Lopez-Garcia, STS-Certified, Spain
M. Pravettoni, Technology Innovation Institute, United Arab Emirates
T. Stoyanova Lyubenova, Joint Research Centre, Italy
C. Ulbrich, HZB, Germany
J. Moereke, Avancis, Germany
Y.S. Long, ITRI, Taiwan
D. Pavanello, European Commission JRC, Italy
A.K. Vidal de Oliveira, UFSC, Brazil
J. Bengoechea, CENER, Spain
M. Ernst, ANU, Australia
H. Ellis, European Commission JRC, Italy
B. Mihaylov, European Commission JRC, Italy
G. Chowdhury, 3E, Belgium
B. Aissa, QEERI - Qatar Environment and Energy Research Institute, Qatar

Topic 4: PV Systems Engineering, Integrated/Applied PV
A. Gracia Amillo, CENER, Spain
W.G.J.H.M. van Sark, Utrecht University, The Netherlands
K. Lappalainen, Tampere University, Finland
J.M. Almeida Serra, University of Lisbon, Portugal
I. Tsanakas, CEA, France
C. Buerhop-Lutz, HI ERN, Germany
D. Moser, Becquerel Institute Italia, Italy
F. Frontini, SUPSI, Switzerland
G.C. Eder, OFI, Austria
A. Scognamiglio, ENEA, Italy
A. Chatzipanagi, European Commission JRC, Italy
I. Antón Hernández, UPM, Spain
R.M.E. Valckenborg, TNO, The Netherlands
T. Reindl, SERIS, Singapore
J.R. Gonzalez, European Space Agency, The Netherlands
G. Mütter, Gerhard Mütter e.U., Austria
T. Merdzhanova, Forschungszentrum Jülich, Germany

V. Lara-Fanego, Solargis, Spain
A. Louwen, Eurac Research, Italy
A. Martinez Fernandez, European Commission JRC, Italy
T. Oozeki, AIST, Japan
J. Remund, Meteotest, Switzerland
M. Sengupta, NREL, United States of America
M. Zehner, Rosenheim Technical University of Applied Sciences, Germany
B. Nouri, German Aerospace Center, Spain
S. Poddar, UNSW, Australia
D. Bachour, HBKU/ Qatar Foundation, Qatar
J. Yang, NREL, United States of America
S. Bouguerra, imo-imomec, Belgium
C. Alonso-Tristán, UBU, Spain
M. Carbone, ENEL Green Power, Italy
M. Dennenmoser, BayWa r.e. Solar Projects GmbH, Germany
C.W. Hansen, Sandia National Laboratories, United States of America
A. Neubert, DNV Maritime Software GmbH, Germany
D. Berrian, Belectric, Germany
M. Oliosi, PVsyst, Switzerland
J. Moschner, KU Leuven / EnergyVille, Belgium
C. Bucher, BUAS, Switzerland
B. Wittmer, PVsyst SA, Switzerland
M. Bolen, SB Energy, United States of America
D. Daßler, Fraunhofer CSP, Germany
R. Einhaus, ZSW, Germany
P. Hacke, NREL, United States of America
A. Heimsath, Fraunhofer ISE, Germany
J. Lin, PV Guider, Taiwan
A. Migan-Dubois, GeePs, France
M. Rinio, University of Karlstad, Sweden
J.S. Stein, Sandia National Laboratories, United States of America
D. Stellbogen, ZSW, Germany
M. Theristis, Sandia National Laboratories, United States of America
A. Virtuani, CSEM, Switzerland
A. Driesse, PV Performance Labs, Germany
M. Øgaard, IFE, Norway
A. Nobre, SERIS, Singapore
T. Trupke, UNSW, Australia
C. Cornaro, University of Rome II, Italy
G. A. dos Reis Benatto, DTU, Denmark
S. Malik, Fraunhofer CSP, Germany
S. Lindig, Univers SAS, France
M.M. Nygård, Institute for Energy Technology, Norway
P. Alonso Gomez, BayWa r.e., Germany
Y. Assoa, CEA, France
P. Bonomo, SUPSI, Switzerland
V. D'Ambrosio, University of Naples Federico II, Italy
E. Román Medina, Tecnalia, Spain
L.H. Slooff, TNO Energy Transition, The Netherlands
S. Villa, TNO, The Netherlands
M. La Rosa, Glass to Power, Italy
T. Del Caño, Onyx Solar Energy, Spain
X. Zhihao, AIST, Japan
P. Sharif, ODTU-GUNAM, Türkiye
K. Umeda, TAISEI CORPORATION, Japan
S. Boddaert, CSTB, France
N. Lysgaard Andersen, DTU, Denmark
K. Meyer, ISFH, Germany
T. Biel, NET Nowak Energy & Technology, Switzerland
F. Colucci, ENEA, Italy
A. Pascaris, NREL, United States of America
C. Dupraz, INRAE, France
C. Alonso-García, CIEMAT, Spain
A. Lefort, BayWa, Germany
H.N. Riise, IFE, Norway
M.A. Schüler, Next2Sun Technology GmbH, Germany
P.J. Pérez-Higueras, University of Jaén, Spain
K. Oda, Agritree,

M. Berwind, Fraunhofer ISE, Germany
M. Dörenkämper, TNO, The Netherlands
M. Heinrich, Fraunhofer ISE, Germany
B. Newman, Lightyear, The Netherlands
A. Reinders, Eindhoven University of Technology, The Netherlands
T. Tanahashi, AIST, Japan
J. Leloux, LuciSun, Belgium
E. Shirazi, University of Twente, The Netherlands
K. Araki, University of Miyazaki, Japan
K. Nishioka, University of Miyazaki, Japan
R. Campesato, CESI, Italy
V. Khorenko, Azur Space, Germany
G. Kakoulaki, European Commission Joint Research Centre, Italy
H. Toyota, JAXA, Japan
P. Garcia-Linares, UPM, Spain
I. Weiss, Weiss, Ingrid, Germany
A. Hensel, Fraunhofer ISE, Germany
J.S. da Fernandes, Hochschule Offenburg, Germany
Y. Ueda, Tokyo University of Science, Japan
J. Braid, Sandia National Laboratories, United States of America

Topic 5: PV in the Energy Transition
J. Stierstorfer, WIP Renewable Energies, Germany
R. Pestana, R&D Nester, Portugal
P.J. Alet, CSEM, Switzerland
C. Agraffeil, CEA, France
K. WAMBACH, Wambach-Consulting, Germany
C. del Cañizo, UPM, Spain
L. Großhans, WIP Renewable Energies, Germany
M. Getsiou, European Commission DG RTD, Belgium
S. Nowak, NET Nowak Energy & Technology, Switzerland
C. Breyer, LUT University, Finland
I. Kaizuka, RTS Corporation, Japan
G. Masson, Becquerel Institute, Belgium
P. Baliozian, VDMA, Germany
L. Großhans, WIP Renewable Energies, Germany
C. Candelise, Bocconi University, Italy
S. Caneva, WIP Renewable Energies, Germany

G. Barchi, Eurac Research, Italy
R. Bründlinger, AIT, Austria
V. Efthymiou, University of Cyprus, Cyprus
M. Centeno Brito, University of Lisbon, Portugal
F. Carigiet, ZHAW, Switzerland
B. Gaiddon, HESPUL, France
F.Z. Ouchani, Green Energy Park, Morocco
M. Rennhofer, AIT, Austria
G. Adinolfi, ENEA, Italy
W. Schaffer, Salzburg Netz, Austria
A. Haber, e-control, Austria
G. Heilscher, Technische Hochschule Ulm, Germany
A. Anctil, Michigan State University, United States of America
S. Arancón, Plug and Play, Spain
S. Capaccioli, ETA - Florence Renewable Energies, Italy
V. Fthenakis, Columbia University, United States of America
G. Heath, NREL, United States of America
K. Komoto, Mizuho Research & Technologies, Ltd., Japan
W. Palitzsch, LuxChemtech, Germany
S. Ovaitt, NREL, United States of America
M. de Wild-Scholten, SmartGreenScans, The Netherlands
S. Herceg, Fraunhofer ISE, Germany
C. Polacchi, Eurac Research, Italy
N. Espinosa, Universidad de Murcia, Spain
E. Drahi, TotalEnergies OneTech, France
S. Guastella, RSE, Italy

H. Ossenbrink, Band Gap, Germany
D. Polverini, European Commission DG GROW, Belgium
N. Taylor, European Commission JRC, Italy
K.A. Weiß, Fraunhofer ISE, Germany
I. Kafedjiska, Helmholtz Zentrum Berlin, Germany
P. Malbranche, Solar Action, France
S. De Iuliis, ENEA, Italy
T. Haarberg, BNW-Energy, Norway
A. Nayfeh, Khalifa University, United Arab Emirates
E. Vartiainen, Fortum Renewables Oy, Finland
E. Veronese, Eurac Research, Italy
P. Sanchez-Friera, Solkeys, Spain
N. Cherradi, Desert Technologies, Saudi Arabia
S. Nold, Fraunhofer ISE, Germany
H.J.J. Yu, CEA, France
M. Beck, U.S. Department of Energy, United States of America
M. Woodhouse, NREL, United States of America
A.B. Cristóbal, UPM, Spain
G. Ruggieri, Insubria University, Italy
S. Tay, NUS, Singapore

Awards Coordinators

Student Awards Coordinator
A.H.M. Smets, Delft University of Technology, The Netherlands

Student Awards Committee
R. Kenny, EU PVSEC Technical Programme Chair, Italy
C. del Canizo, Conference Chair, UPM, Spain
E. Voroshazi, CEA, France
J. Poortmans, imec, Belgium
P.J. Alet, CSEM, Switzerland
S. Caneva, WIP Renewable Energies, Germany
A. Romeo, University of Verona, Italy
G. Friesen, SUPSI, Switzerland
F. Schindler, Fraunhofer ISE, Germany
J.C. Goldchmidt, Marburg University, Germany
D. Moser, Becquerel Institute, Italy
K. Ding, FZJ, Germany
W.C. Sinke, TNO Energy Transition, The Netherlands
M. Topic, University of Ljubljana, Slovenia
R. Schlatman, HZB, Germany
S. Glunz, Fraunhofer ISE, Germany
A.M. Vega, UPM, Spain
I. Kaizuka, RTS, Japan
P.D. Veneri, ENEA, Italy
J. Bengoechea, CENER, Spain

Poster Awards Coordinator
P. Malbranche, Solar Action, France

Poster Awards Committee
R. Kenny, European Commission JRC, Italy
C. del Canizo, UPM, Spain
W. van Sark, Utrecht University, The Netherlands
I. Tsanakas, CEA INES, France
L. Miranda, Oxford PV, United Kingdom
D. Munoz, CEA INES, France
I. Gordon, imec, Belgium
E. Roman, Tecnalia, Spain
G. Eder, OFI, Austria
I. Antón, UPM, Spain
S. Veenstra, TNO, The Netherlands
J.M. Almeida Serra, University of Lisbon, Portugal
T. Magorian Friedlmeier, ZSW, Germany
J. Stierstorfer, WIP Renewable Energies, Germany

G. Kakoulaki, European Commission JRC, Italy
T. Barnes, NREL, USA
T. Merdzhanova, Forschungszentrum Jülich, Germany

Highlights Committee
C. del Cañizo, UPM, Madrid, Spain
R. Kenny, European Commission Joint Research Centre, Directorate for Energy and Transport and Climate, Ispra, Italy
W.C. Sinke, TNO Energy Transition, The Netherlands
S. Nowak, Managing Director of NET Nowak Energy & Technology, St. Ursen, Switzerland
M. Topič, Head of Laboratory of Photovoltaics and Optoelectronics of the University of Ljubljana, Slovenia
V. Bermúdez Benito, BERBETIN, France
E. Voroshazi, Head of PV Module Process Laboratory, CEA, Le Bourget-Du-Lac France
H. Ossenbrink, Band Gap, Germany
J. Bergmiller, Managing Director Events & Knowledge Transfer, WIP Renewable Energies, Munich, Germany
J. de Gregorio, Head of Unit, Scientific Services and Cooperation, WIP Renewable Energies, Munich, Germany
S. Leanza, Marketing and PR Manager, WIP Renewable Energies, Munich, Germany
B. Yildiz, Project Manager Events & Knowledge Transfer, WIP Renewable Energies, Munich, Germany
F. Schindler, Fraunhofer ISE, Freiburg, Germany
I. Gordon, imec, Leuven, Belgium
T. Barnes, NREL, Evergreen, USA
A.M. Gracia Amillo, FUNDACION CENER, Sarriguren, Spain
C. Agraffeil, CEA / INES, Le Bourget-du-Lac, France

SUBJECT INDEX

Topic Code	**Session Type**	**Day Codes**
1 Silicon Materials and Cells	P = Plenary Session	A = Monday, 22 September 2025
2 Thin-Films and New Concepts	O = Oral Session	B = Tuesday, 23 September 2025
3 Photovoltaic Modules	V = Visual Session	C = Wednesday, 24 September 2025
4 Photovoltaic Systems		D = Thursday, 25 September 2025
5 Photovoltaics in the Energy Transition		E = Friday, 26 September 2025

e.g. 1AO.4 ⇒ 1= Silicon Materials and Cells, A=Monday, O=Oral session, 4=Session 4

FOREWORD

The European Photovoltaic Solar Energy Conference and Exhibition (EU PVSEC) stands as the World's leading and most renowned forum for PV research and development and the biggest conference on PV solar energy. In 2025, celebrating its 42nd edition, the EU PVSEC was the essential meeting and exchanging point for global PV experts from research, development, and industry.

Held from 22–26 September 2025 in Bilbao, Spain, the EU PVSEC 2025 was a resounding success, showcasing a wide range of cutting-edge research results. Bringing together both the Conference and the Exhibition, this edition attracted more than 1600 participants from 61 countries who contributed over 1000 presentations across various fields of science and technology. The event provided an essential platform for the exchange of knowledge and ideas on photovoltaic research, innovations, and applications. In the exhibition area 51 companies from all parts of the world welcomed visitors and presented their products and services.

Conference Highlights

The EU PVSEC covered a broad range of topics with an extensive programme that offers an opportunity for workers from across the entire field of photovoltaics to share their findings, as well as an opportunity for multidisciplinary learning. Rapid advances in materials, designs, and manufacturing processes reflect the accelerating expansion of the global PV market. The programme was arranged into 5 topics as follows:

- Silicon Materials and Cells;
- Thin Films and New Concepts;
- Photovoltaic Modules and Balance of System Components;
- PV Systems Engineering, Integrated/Applied PV;
- PV in the Energy Transition.

Communicating the key messages from the conference, not only to participants, but also to other researchers, key stakeholders, policy makers and the general public was an important added value. We thank the Highlights Committee, composed of selected members of the Scientific Committee, as well as the Session Chairs, for providing a comprehensive summary of the findings and state of the art research that were delivered during this year's event. Some key highlights are listed below, while further details may be found in the dedicated highlights presentation in the annex of these proceedings.

Cross-cutting themes:

- Demonstrated the versatility of solar technologies, spanning traditional and emerging application areas.
- Sustainability and circularity remain central, with research focused on reducing material use, such as replacing silver with copper, and advancing end-of-life management of modules.
- Ensuring long-term stability and predictable energy yield is equally essential, with many examples of studies on degradation mechanisms and efforts to elucidate their root-causes, such as in the case of UVID.
- The role of artificial intelligence across the PV value chain is rapidly expanding, from design to operations and maintenance, including among many others drone applications.

Latest Solar Innovations in Materials, Cells, Modules and PV Systems:

While silicon solar cells remain the cornerstone of PV technology, perovskite solar cells continue to stand out as the leading complementary technology to silicon, both as standalone devices and in tandem configurations. Research efforts are increasingly focused on enhancing stability, understanding degradation mechanisms, improving durability and scalability, and ensuring full industrial compatibility.

Many companies presented impressive results on industrial-size single-junction perovskite modules as well as perovskite-based tandem modules, and several new efficiency records were announced during the event. The rapid pace of innovation in cell and module architecture underscores the need for accelerated and more robust testing and qualification methodologies. Both the industry and the research community are moving swiftly to assess and improve reliability in this fast-evolving PV landscape.

A major focus in module research remains the optimisation of materials and packaging to ensure long lifetimes and predictable energy yields from high-efficiency cells. In parallel, many innovative advances in the operation and maintenance (O&M) of PV systems were presented and discussed.

Applications, Grid Integration and Storage

"PV can be deployed everywhere": from space applications to agrivoltaics, PV noise barriers, building-integrated photovoltaics (BIPV), floating PV systems, and even vehicles. Among these, agrivoltaics is gaining momentum as a promising dual land use approach, offering economic benefits for farmers while increasing resilience to climate change.

Flexibility solutions, particularly through battery storage, were recognised in many technical presentations as essential to accommodate higher PV penetration levels and to reduce energy curtailment. At the same time, strengthening grid infrastructure and enhancing grid management capabilities remain critical to enable the next phase of large-scale PV integration.

Photovoltaics in the Energy Transition

Options for re-establishing competitive module manufacturing in Europe were extensively analysed, including detailed policy recommendations for industrial support and market growth. Currently, a mismatch persists between global PV module installation rates and production rates, resulting in growing inventories and sharply reduced prices.

Finally, inclusiveness, diversity, citizen participation, awareness, education, and social engagement were

underlined as vital dimensions of the sector's long-term sustainability and innovation capacity.

EU PVSEC 2025 Proceedings

Selection for inclusion in the conference was made by the Scientific Committee's paper review experts and topic organisers (see the listing on pages 010002-001-005), to whom we express our sincere gratitude for their comprehensive review work and overall contribution to the success of the conference.

The EU PVSEC 2025 Proceedings contain the full papers covering most of the highlights described above and more. The Proceedings provide a comprehensive overview of the PV solar sector, its current status and future prospects in science, research, innovation, development and deployment extending to 3,750 pages. In addition to the 299 submitted papers, the proceedings include 101 presentations (slides) shown during the plenary and oral presentations as well as 176 poster files of the visual presentations. In total this amounts to 576 publications.

The Conference Proceedings are published as downloadable files and are also fully accessible online. A DOI code (Digital Object Identifier) has been assigned to each paper. This ensures unequivocal and permanent identification and full citability. The EU PVSEC 2025 papers can be viewed and downloaded in a full free open access from the EU PVSEC's Proceedings website https://userarea.eupvsec.org/proceedings.

The proceedings of the EU PVSEC 2025 strengthen the commitment to providing quick and open access to high quality scientific results. This is a powerful source for targeted and quick information search and retrieval, enabling you to search by topic, keywords, paper title, DOI, author, or organization.

We are confident that these Proceedings will play an important role in providing a comprehensive overview of the current actors and activities in the global PV sector and that they will disseminate information on the state-of-the-art of technologies and applications. This can generate further research, add momentum to innovation and promote interest in PV worldwide.

We would like to cordially thank all authors and participants of the EU PVSEC 2025 for their contributions and look forward to welcoming you in Rotterdam, The Netherlands from 14 – 18 September 2026 at the EU PVSEC 2026, the 43rd European Photovoltaic Solar Energy Conference and Exhibition

The Editors

TABLE OF CONTENTS OF EU PVSEC 2025 PROCEEDINGS PAPERS

Visual SESSION 1CV.2 Si Solar Cells | Characterisation & Modelling of Silicon Cells and Their Building Blocks

[1] Anhalt University of Applied Sciences, Köthen, Germany; [2] Fraunhofer CSP, Halle, Germany

Oral SESSION 2AO.2 Advances in Chalcogenide Devices

2AO.2.3 A New Method for Sb-doped CdSeTe/CdTe Devices with Superior Stability 020057
Elisa Artegiani[1], Mariyam Mukhtar[1], Alessandro Romeo[1]
[1] *University of Verona, Verona, Italy*

Oral SESSION 2AO.3 III-V Based Devices | Tandem and Perovskite Solar Cells

2AO.3.3 Micro-Crystal GaAs Array Sub-Cells for Si Tandem Solar Cells 020058
James Patrick Connolly[1], Ahmed Nejim[2], Alexandre Jaffré[1], José Alvarez[1], Jean-Paul Kleider[1], Denis Mencaraglia[1], Laurie Dentz[3], Géraldine Hallais[3], Frederic Hamouda[3], Laetitia Vincent[3], Daniel Bouchier[3], Charles Renard[3]
[1] *CNRS, Gif-sur-Yvette, France;* [2] *SILVACO, St. Ives, United Kingdom;* [3] *CNRS, Palaiseau, France*

2AO.3.5 Multiscale Models for Perovskite Optimisation 020060
Philippe Baranek[1], James Patrick Connolly[2], Antoine Gissler[1], Philip Schulz[3], Michel Rerat[4], Roberto Dovesi[5]
[1] *EDF R&D, Palaiseau, France;* [2] *CNRS, Gif-sur-Yvette, France;* [3] *IPVF, Palaiseau, France;* [4] *IPREM, Pau, France;* [5] *Academy of Sciences of Turin, Torino, Italy*

2AO.3.6 Modelling Recovery in Perovskite Solar Cells under Light and Dark to Address Stability Challenges 020062
Guillem Álvarez-Pérez[1], Jean Baptiste Puel[1], Jean François Guillemoles [1]
[1] *IPVF, Palaiseau, France*

Oral SESSION 2BO.10 Advanced Modelling and Characterisation of Perovskite Solar Cells

2BO.10.2 On Perimeter Losses in Perovskite Top- and Poly-Si-Passivated Silicon Bottom Cells – Do Small Area Tandems Reveal the Full Efficiency Potential? 020063
Felix Haase[1], Lukas Brockmann[1], Annika Raugewitz[1], Verena Steckenreiter[1], Verena Barnscheidt[1], Roland Clausing[1], Sara Baumann[1], Joachim Vollbrecht[1], Welmoed Veurman[1], Johannes Löhr[1], Dongyang Liu[1], Mircea Turcu[1], Lasse Nasebandt[1], Udo Römer[1], David Sylla[1], Jessica Strey[1], Martha Löhning[1], Larissa Mettner[1], Renate Winter[1], Anja Christ[1], Heike Kohlenberg[1], Cornelia Marquardt[1], Emanuel Brueckner[1], Hossein Rabiei[1], Michael Rienäcker[1], Sarah Kajari-Schröder[1], Tobias Wietler[1], Robby Peibst[1]
[1] *ISFH, Emmerthal, Germany*

2BO.10.5 In-depth Characterization and Simulation Approach for the Understanding of In- and Outdoor Degradation of Perovskite Solar Cells 020064
Jonathan Parion[1], Amit Kumar Harit[1], Elias Peraticos[2], Vasiliki Paraskeva[2], Maria Hadjipanayi[2], Aranzazu Aguirre[1], Filip Duerinckx[1], Hariharsudan

Sivaramakrishnan Radhakrishnan[1], Jef Poortmans[1], Johan Lauwaert[3], Bart Vermang[1]
[1] *Hasselt Unversity, Genk, Belgium;* [2] *University of Cyprus, Nicosia, Cyprus;* [3] *Ghent University, Ghent, Belgium*

Oral SESSION 2BO.8 Advanced Conversion Devices

2BO.8.1 Singlet Fission Route for >30% Efficient Solar Cells: Silicon Cell Requirements 020065
Shona McNab[1], Alex J. Baldacchino[1], Pheobe Pearce[1], Alvin Mo[1], Alison Ciesla[1], Bram Hoex[1], Nicholas J. Ekins-Daukes[1], Murad J. Y. Tayebjee[1], Michael P. Nielsen[1]
[1] *UNSW, Sydney, Australia*

2BO.8.5 Performance of a 4-Terminals Spectral Splitting Asymmetric Solar Concentrator in Diffuse Sunlight: a Numerical Study 020066
Floriana Morabito[1], Daniela Fontani[2], Paola Sansoni[2], Mehdi Ahmadi[3], Salvatore Lombardo[3], Andrea Farina[1], Silvia Maria Pietralunga[1]
[1] *CNR-IFN, Milan, Italy;* [2] *CNR-INO, Florence, Italy;* [3] *CNR-IMM, Catania, Italy*

2BO.8.6 GaAs for Thermophotonics: From Thin-Film Solar Cells to Highly Efficient LEDs 020067
Natasha Gruginskie[1], Peter Mulder[1], Gerard Bauhuis[1], Jani Oksanen[2], John Schermer[1]
[1] *Radboud University, Nijmegen, The Netherlands;* [2] *Aalto University, Espoo, Finland*

Visual SESSION 2BV.1 New Materials, Devices and Conversion Concepts | New Modelling and Characterisation Techniques

2BV.1.4 Low-Energy Electron Multiplication on Nanostructured Solar Cells: a Novel Route to Overcome Si-PV Efficiency Limits 020068
Mikaël Hosatte[1], Brice Rouffie[1], Zbigniew T. Kuznicki[1], Frédéric Milesi[2], Bertrand Paviet-Salomon[3], Audrey Morisset[3], Philippe Wyss[3], Lejo Joseph Koduvelikulathu[4], Lazhar Rachdi[4], Lacramioara Popescu[4], Dominik Rudolph[4], Marek Basta[5], Andrzej Miszczuk[5], Martyna Majak[5], Beata Basta[5], Samuel Queste[6]
[1] *SEGTON Advanced Technology, Versailles, France;* [2] *CEA, Grenoble, France;* [3] *CSEM, Neuchâtel, Switzerland;* [4] *ISC Konstanz, Konstanz, Germany;* [5] *Roltec, Poznań, Poland;* [6] *Marie and Louis Pasteur University, Besançon, France*

2BV.1.5 Tailoring CBTSSe Solar Cells for Indoor Photovoltaic Applications 020069
Hitarth Narsi Patel[1], Bindu Pamula[1], Deepak Joshi[1], Vivek Garg[1]
[1] *SVNIT, Surat, India*

2BV.1.6 Theoretical Insights through DFT into $AgBiS_2$ Thin Films Absorber for Photovoltaic Applications 020071
Dhruv Singh Thakur[1], Rajesh Kumar Sharma[1], Nithin Chatterji[1], Vivek Garg[1], Shivendra Yadav[1]
[1] *SVNIT, Surat, India*

Visual SESSION 2BV.2 Compound and Organic Semiconductors

Visual SESSION 2CV.3 Perovskite-based Tandems and Multijunctions

Gerardo Gordillo[1], Oscar Torres[1], Julian Peña-Bermudez[2]
[1] National University of Colombia, Bogotá, Colombia; [2] University of the Caribbean, Santo Domingo, Dominican Republic

2CV.3.71 Comparative Analysis and Efficiency Optimization of Sulfur-based Chalcogenide Perovskites ($MgHfS_3$, $CaZrS_3$, $BaZrS_3$) via Interface Engineering for High-Performance Solar Cells 020111
Anees ur Rehman[1], Kung Ding[1], Jingwei Zhang[1], Xiang Chen[1]
[1] Hohai University, Changzhou, China

2CV.3.72 Development of Inorganic Perovskite $CsPbI_3$ with Heterojunction Engineering at the Buried Interface for Enhanced Stability and Performance 020112
Syed Fawad Ali Shah[1], Hyeonwook Park[1], Muhammad Rehan[2], Donghyeop Shin[2], Kihwan Kim[2], Jae Ho Yun[3]
[1] KENTECH, Naju-Si, South Korea; [2] KIER, Daejeon, South Korea; [3] KENTECH, Naju-si, South Korea

Oral SESSION 2DO.6 Industrially Scalable Processes to Manufacture Perovskite Solar Cells and Modules

2DO.6.2 Eliminating P2 Scribes: A New Interconnection Design for Efficient Perovskite Solar Modules Under Indoor Lighting 020113
Bahri Eren Uzuner[1], Konstantin Tsoi[1], Gorkem Gunbas[1], Selcuk Yerci[1]
[1] ODTÜ-GÜNAM, Ankara, Türkiye

2DO.6.5 Evaporated Self Assembled Monolayer (SAM) Hole Transport Layers for Scalable Perovskite Solar Cells 020114
Joachim Vollbrecht[1], Verena Barnscheidt[1], Roland Clausing[1], Johannes Löhr[1], Larissa Mettner[1], Adam Neuba[2], Annika Raugewitz[1], Jessica Strey[1], Robby Peibst[1]
[1] ISFH, Emmerthal, Germany; [2] Paderborn University, Paderborn, Germany

Oral SESSION 2DO.7 Insights Into the Stability of Perovskite Solar Cells and Modules

2DO.7.1 Outdoor Performance and Degradation Analysis of Inverted Perovskite Solar Cells 020115
Makoto Konagai[1], Hayato Okawa[1], Ryousuke Ishikawa[1], Masatoshi Yanagida[2], Yasuhiro Shirai[2]
[1] Tokyo City University, Setagaya, Japan; [2] NIMS, Tsukuba, Japan

Oral SESSION 2DO.8 Multiple Aspects of Perovskite PV Research

2DO.8.2 Strategies for Quasi-2D Perovskite Integration in p-i-n Solar Cells 020116
Anna Capitaine[1], Hugo Le Bossenec[1], Marion Provost[1], Alexandra Levtchenko[1], Daniel Ory[2], Jean Rousset[2], Iwan Zimmermann[1], Anyssa Derj[1],

Mirella Al Katrib[1]
[1] IPVF, Palaiseau, France; [2] EDF R&D, Palaiseau, France

2DO.8.3 Innovative Approach to Bismuth-Antimony-Iodide Double Perovskite PV Absorbers via Anion Exchange and Solide-State Reactions 020117
Oleksandr Stroyuk[1], *Oleksandra Raievska*[1], *Sachin Kinge*[2], *Jens Hauch*[1], *Christoph J. Brabec*[1]
[1] HI ERN, Erlangen, Germany; [2] Toyota Motors Europe, Brussels, Belgium

Visual SESSION 3AV.1 PV Module Design and Manufacturing

3AV.1.1 Investigating the 3-Dimensional Structure of Metallic Filler Particles in Electrically Conductive Adhesives 020119
Stephan Grosser[1], *Alexander Müller*[1], *Robert Göckeritz*[1], *Tobias Nitsche*[2], *Daniel Buckland*[2], *Giuseppe Galbiati*[2], *Bengt Jaeckel*[1]
[1] Fraunhofer CSP, Halle, Germany; [2] Henkel, Düsseldorf, Germany

3AV.1.6 Investigation on Different Bypass Diodes for Shade Resistant PV-Modules 020121
Jens Froebel[1], *Matthias Pander*[1], *Bengt Jaeckel*[1], *Andreas Maixner*[2], *Pouya Pourshafi*[2], *Afshin Bakhtiari*[2], *Hamed Hanifi*[2]
[1] Fraunhofer CSP, Halle, Germany; [2] AESOLAR, Koenigsbrunn, Germany

3AV.1.7 Optimization of Infrared Soldering Process to Reduce the Temperature Inhomogeneity in Silicon Solar Cells Using Finite Element Methods 020123
Daniel Christopher Joseph[1], *Angela De Rose*[1], *Christian Reichel*[1], *Andreas J. Beinert*[1], *Holger Neuhaus*[1]
[1] Fraunhofer ISE, Freiburg, Germany

3AV.1.10 Performance Evaluation of a New Design Photovoltaic Module with Reduced Self-Shading 020125
Pouya Pourshafi[1], *Andreas Maixner*[1], *Hamed Hanifi*[1]
[1] AESOLAR, Königsbrunn, Germany

3AV.1.11 Materials Assessment for PV-T Modules Thermal Performance Improvement 020127
Lucía Cano[1], *Raquel Simón-Allué*[1], *Raúl Villén*[1], *Yolanda Lara*[1], *Isabel Guedea*[1]
[1] ENDEF, Zaragoza, Spain

3AV.1.12 Evaluating Repair Techiniques for c-Si PV Modules: Spot-Welding 020129
Jorge Rabanal-Arabach[1], *Sonia Beltran-Condori*[1], *Natalia Videla-Magnata*[1], *Katalina Rojas-Henríquez*[1], *Andreas Schneider*[2], *Edward Fuentealba-Vidal*[1]
[1] University of Antofagasta, Antofagasta, Chile; [2] University of Applied Sciences Gelsenkirchen, Gelsenkirchen, Germany

3AV.1.13 Thermally Conductive Filler Particle Mixed Silicone Layer to Provide Heat Dissipation Functionality to c-Si Solar Cell Modules without Encapsulants 020131
Yasushi Sobajima[1], *Kouzen Wakazono*[1], *Keisuke Ohdaira*[2]
[1] Gifu University, Gifu, Japan; [2] JAIST, Ishikawa, Japan

3AV.1.16 Ultrasonic Characterization of Ethylene-Vinyl Acetate in Glass-Glass-Modules 020132
Christopher Bruce Konu[1], *Rico Meier*[1]
[1] HTW Berlin, Berlin, Germany

Visual SESSION 3AV.2 PV Module Durability and Reliability

Nathan Roosloot[1], Harsha Walpita[2], Christoph Seiffert[1], Jean Thomas[3], Maarten Dörenkämper[4], Minne M. de Jong[4], Josefine H. Selj[1], Gaute Otnes[1]
[1] Institute for Energy Technology, Kjeller, Norway; [2] University of Oslo, Kjeller, Norway; [3] Ciel et Terre, Lille, France; [4] TNO, Eindhoven, The Netherlands

Visual SESSION 3AV.3 PV Modules Characterisation and Performances Assessment

3AV.3.1 A New Method for Comprehensive Power Rating and Performance Analysis of PERC Modules based on Half-Cut Cell Technology 020171
Khadija El Ainaoui[1], Mhammed Zaimi[2], Imane Flouchi[1], Said Elhamaoui[1], Yasmine El mrabet[1], Abdellatif Ghennioui[1], El Mahdi Assaid[2]
[1] Green Energy Park, Benguerir, Morocco; [2] University of Chouaib Doukkali, El Jadida, Morocco

3AV.3.2 Energy Rating Analysis of Heterojunction PV Modules 020173
Teodora Stoyanova Lyubenova[1], Ewan D. Dunlop[1]
[1] European Commission JRC, Ispra, Italy

3AV.3.3 Trend of Temperature Coefficients of c-Si Module Technologies from the past 15 Years 020175
Bengt Jaeckel[1], Matthias Pander[1]
[1] Fraunhofer CSP, Halle, Germany

3AV.3.6 Angle of Incidence Measurements on Bifacial PV Modules 020177
Frank Weinrich[1], Stefan Riechelmann[1], Stefan Winter[1]
[1] PTB, Braunschweig, Germany

3AV.3.8 Plug & Play IV Curve Tracer for PV Modules 020179
Adrian Jäggi[1], Christof Bucher[1], Matthias Burri[1]
[1] BFH, Burgdorf, Switzerland

3AV.3.9 Seasonal and Location-Dependent Temperature Coefficients for Thin-Film PV Modules: Enhancing Yield Prediction Accuracy 020180
Thomas Weber[1], Abdullah Abu Sayed[1], Benjamin Lippke[1], Steven Xuereb[1], Marcus Rennhofer[2], Bart E. Pieters[3]
[1] Kiwa PI Berlin, Berlin, Germany; [2] AIT, Vienna, Austria; [3] FZJ, Jülich, Germany

3AV.3.10 Standardisation Methods for Bifacial Energy Yield Estimation and PV Module Long-Term Performance Degradation Estimation: Potential Policy Implications 020181
Jaione Bengoechea[1], Ana Maria Gracia Amillo[1], Stefan Riechelmann[2], Stefan Winter[2], Giorgio Bardizza[3], Christos Monokroussos[4], Davide Polverini[5], Pablo Vicente-Laiglesia[6], Maria Getsiou[7]
[1] CENER, Sarriguren, Spain; [2] PTB, Braunschweig, Germany; [3] TÜV Rheinland Italia, Milan, Italy; [4] TÜV Rheinland, Shanghai, China; [5] Directorate General for Internal Market, Industry, Entrepreneurship and SMEs, Brussels, Belgium; [6] European Climate, Infrastructure and Environment Executive Agency, Brussels, Belgium; [7] Directorate General for Research and Innovation, Brussels, Belgium

3AV.3.11 Shaalke: Development of a MATLAB Software Tool for Advanced Statistical Outdoor Data Evaluation 020183

Cristian Terrados[1], Eva de la Viuda[1], Kabir Paul Sulca[1], Julian Anaya[1], Miguel Ángel González[1], Oscar Martínez[1]
[1] *University of Valladolid, Valladolid, Spain*

3BO.11.6 Luminescence Measurements of PV Modules with a Cost-Effective and Small-Sized Hood-Based Tool under Daylight Conditions 020206
Marc Köntges[1], Michael Siebert[1], Dieter Lorenz[2], Bernd Kuhrmann[2], Michael Fuß[2]
[1] *ISFH, Emmerthal, Germany;* [2] *MBJ Solutions, Ahrensburg, Germany*

Oral SESSION 3BO.12 Characterisation and Energy Rating of PV Modules

3BO.12.1 Developing a New I-V Translation Methodology in Accordance with IEC 60891:2021 Correction Procedure 1 and 2 020208
Wenhao Xu[1], Yating Zhang[1], Mengdi Liu[1], Christos Monokroussos[1], Werner Herrmann[2], Giorgio Bardizza[2], Harald Müllejans[3]
[1] *TÜV Rheinland, Shanghai, China;* [2] *TÜV Rheinland Solar, Cologne, Germany;* [3] *European Commission JRC, Ispra, Italy*

3BO.12.2 Characterization of Vehicle Integrated Photovoltaic Modules 020209
Ricardo Moruno[1], Francisco José Martín[1], Juan Manuel Redondo[1], Javier Malo[1], Luis Javier San José[1], Guido Vallerotto[1], Steve Askins[1], Rubén Núñez[1], César Domínguez[1], Ignacio Antón[1], Rebeca Herrero[1]
[1] *UPM, Madrid, Spain*

3BO.12.4 Estimating the Energy Yield of Bifacial Photovoltaics with the JRC's Photovoltaic Geographic Information System 020210
Nigel Taylor[1], Teodora Lyubenova[1], Lavanya Malarkannan[2], Nikos Alexandris[1], Alexandros Falangas[3], Robert Kenny[1], Ewan D. Dunlop[1], Blago Mihaylov[1]
[1] *European Commission JRC, Ispra, Italy;* [2] *National Physical Laboratory, Teddington, United Kingdom;* [3] *TRASIS International, Brussels, Belgium*

3BO.12.5 An Update on Energy Rating Amendments – Integration of Bifacial Modules 020211
Stefan Riechelmann[1], Hendrik Sträter[1], Ana Maria Gracia Amillo[2], Sophie Pelland[3], Anton Driesse[4]
[1] *PTB, Braunschweig, Germany;* [2] *CENER, Pamplona, Spain;* [3] *Natural Resources Canada, Varennes, Canada;* [4] *PV Performance Labs, Freiburg, Germany*

Oral SESSION 3BO.14 Characterisation and Outdoor Monitoring of Perovskite-based PV Modules

3BO.14.1 Outdoor Measurements of Perovskite Modules 020213
Hanna Ellis[1], Harald Müllejans[1], Ewan D. Dunlop[1], Tony Sample[1]
[1] *European Commission JRC, Ispra, Italy*

Oral SESSION 3BO.15 Outdoor Performances and Degradation Analysis of PV Modules

Nikolina Pervan[1], Jutta Geier[1], Christian Veas[1], Gernot Oreski[1]
[1] PCCL, Leoben, Austria

Oral SESSION 4AO.7 Solar Resource Assessment

4AO.7.4 Potential of Decimeter-Resolution Ground Albedo Data for Bifacial Photovoltaics 020235
Niklas Blum[1], Bijan Nouri[1], Yann Fabel[1], Stefan Wilbert[1]
[1] DLR, Almeria, Spain

4AO.7.5 Method for the Determination of Spectral Responsivity of Digital Solar Irradiance Sensors 020236
David Hinken[1], Sebastian Denke[1], Karsten Bothe[1], Rolf Brendel[1]
[1] ISFH, Emmerthal, Germany

Oral SESSION 4AO.8 Solar Irradiance Forecasting

4AO.8.2 Cutting-Edge Generative AI for Intra-Hour Solar Forecasting 020237
Yann Fabel[1], Dominik Schnaus[2], Bijan Nouri[1], Stefan Wilbert[1], Niklas Blum[1], Luis F. Zarzalejo[3], Julia Kowalski[4], Robert Pitz-Paal[5]
[1] DLR, Almeria, Spain; [2] TUM, Garching, Germany; [3] CIEMAT, Madrid, Spain; [4] RWTH, Aachen, Germany; [5] DLR, Cologne, Germany

4AO.8.4 Integrating Satellite Imagery and GNNs for Improving Day-Ahead Solar Irradiance Forecasting 020238
Baptiste Schubnel[1], Jelena Simeunovic[1], Corentin Tissier[1], Pierre-Jean Alet[1], Rafael E. Carrillo[1]
[1] CSEM, Neuchâtel, Switzerland

4AO.8.5 Enhancing Intra-Hour Solar Irradiance Forecasting for Solar Applications: A Blended Model of Satellite, Sky Imager and Persistence 020239
Bijan Nouri[1], Jorge Lezaca[2], Yann Fabel[1], Annette Hammer[2], Niklas Blum[1], Stefan Wilbert[1]
[1] DLR, Almeria, Spain; [2] DLR, Oldenburg, Germany

Oral SESSION 4AO.9 Irradiance for PV Design | Shading and Glare Mitigation

4AO.9.1 Reflective Properties of Urban Materials and Their Impact on PV Yield 020240
Christian Schläger[1], Dennis Bredemeier[1], Arne Dittrich[2], Jan Hendrik Pfau[1], Philip Kühne[1], Rolf Brendel[2]
[1] Leibniz University Hannover, Hannover, Germany; [2] ISFH, Emmerthal, Germany

4AO.9.3 Understanding Short-Term PV Power Variability Based on Solargis Time Series Data and Simulations 020241
Martin Opatovsky[1], Marta Pelfort Ojer[1], Juraj Betak[1], Konstantin Rosina[1]
[1] Solargis, Bratislava, Slovakia

4AO.9.5 Accelerating Photovoltaic System Simulations via Statistical Data Aggregation 020243

Adrián Blanco Aguiar[1], Brais González Rodríguez[2], María Martínez-Barbeito[1], Miguel Sánchez de León Peque[1]
[1] ieco.io, Vigo, Spain; [2] University of Vigo, Vigo, Spain

4AO.9.6 Addressing Glare Problematics for Photovoltaic Projects in the Immediate Proximity of Roads and Railways through the Use of Accurate Digital Surface Models 020244
Christophe Vernay[1], John Coutel[1], Aina Razanajao[1], Sébastien Pitaval[1]
[1] SOLAÏS, Valbonne, France

Plenary SESSION 4AP.1 PV Everywhere

4AP.1.3 Micro-Concentrator Photovoltaics for Deep Space Missions: Overcoming LILT Challenges with High-Specific-Power Solar Arrays 020246
Guido Vallerotto[1], Anderson Bermudez-Garcia[2], Gerald Siefer[3], Maike Wiesenfarth[3], Almudena Garcia-Sanchez[1], Ignacio Antón[1], Carsten Baur[4], Pier Luigi Coz[4], César Domínguez[1]
[1] UPM, Madrid, Spain; [2] Thales Alenia Space, Cannes, France; [3] Fraunhofer ISE, Freiburg, Germany; [4] European Space Agency, Noordwijk, The Netherlands

Oral SESSION 4BO.16 Color in Photovoltaics

4BO.16.1 Experimental Investigation of Colored BIPV/T Systems for Wood-Framed Roofs 020248
Anna-Maria Sigounis[1], Andreas Athienitis[1]
[1] Concordia University, Montreal, Canada

4BO.16.3 How to Perform Accurate Colour Measurements for BIPV Module Glass Covers: an IEA PVPS Task 15 Round-Robin Measurement Campaign 020249
Markus Babin[1], Gabriele C. Eder[2], Thomas Friesen[3], Martina Pelle[4], Gabriella Gonnella[5], Fabrizio Leonforte[6], Yuliya Voronko[2], Helen R. Wilson[7], Sune Thorsteinsson[1], Laura Maturi[4], Niccolò Aste[6], Claudio Del Pero[6], Janne Halme[8], Jun-Tae Kim[9], Susanna Santamaría Fernández[10], Anna-Maria Sigounis[11], Hua Ge[11], Gabi Friesen[12], Francesco Frontini[12]
[1] DTU, Roskilde, Denmark; [2] OFI, Vienna, Austria; [3] Megasol Energie, Deitingen, Switzerland; [4] Eurac Research, Bolzano, Italy; [5] Eurac research, Bolzano, Italy; [6] Polytechnic University of Milan, Milan, Italy; [7] Fraunhofer ISE, Freiburg, Germany; [8] Aalto University, Espoo, Finland; [9] Kongju National University, Chungnam, South Korea; [10] TECNALIA, Derio, Spain; [11] Concordia University, Montreal, Canada; [12] SUPSI, Mendrisio, Switzerland

4BO.16.6 Predicting Light Scatter in Structural Colored BIPV Modules and Textured Glass Using Radiance 020250
Nanna Lysgaard Andersen[1], Markus Babin[1], Jan Svatos[1], Karlis Petersons[2], Leif Yde[2], Jan F. Stensborg[2], Catarina G. Ferreira[3], Ananta Paul[3], Jani Lamminaho[3], Joel D. Cox[3], Morten Madsen[3], Peter B. Poulsen[1], Sune Thorsteinsson[1]
[1] DTU, Roskilde, Denmark; [2] Stensborg, Roskilde, Denmark; [3] SDU Climate Cluster, Odense, Denmark

Oral SESSION 4BO.17 Performance of PV on/in Buildings

4BO.17.1 Modeling Partial Shading at the Cell Level on Photovoltaic Modules 020251

Jean-Paul Calin[1], Jacques Levrat[2], Antonin Faes[2], Fahradin Mujovi[2], Paul Rémondeau[3], Kléber Nicolet-dit-Félix[3], Bénédicte Bonnet-Eymard[2], Didier Dalmazzone[1], Aïcha Hessler-Wyser[3], Christophe Ballif[3]

[1] ENSTA Paris, Palaiseau, France; [2] CSEM, Neuchâtel, Switzerland; [3] EPFL, Neuchâtel, Switzerland

4BO.17.2 Market Potential of Building-Integrated Photovoltaics: a Granular Analysis of the European Building Stock 020252

Juan Ignacio Martinez[1], Julien Van Overstraeten[2], Philippe Macé[2], José Maria Vega de Seoane[1], Elina Bosch[2], Mélodie de l'Epine[3]

[1] Becquerel Institute España, San Sebastian, Spain; [2] Becquerel Institute, Brussels, Belgium; [3] Becquerel Institute France, Lyon, France

4BO.17.3 Photovoltaics in the Built Environment – an Overview of Timely Topics for Research and Development 020253

Francesco Frontini[1], Angele Reinders[2]

[1] SUPSI, Mendrisio, Switzerland; [2] TU Eindhoven, Eindhoven, The Netherlands

4BO.17.5 Advancing BIPV: Shingled HJT Technology for High-Efficiency and Aesthetic Solar Integration 020254

Gabriella Gonnella[1], Alvaro De Gruijter[1], Jordi Veirman[1], Martina Pelle[1], Laura Maturi[1], David Moser[2], Luis Fialho[1]

[1] Eurac Research, Bolzano, Italy; [2] Bequerel Institute Italy, Trento, Italy

4BO.17.6 PV-Planning and Simulation, Daylight Simulation and Energy-Certificate Calculation based on an Open-BIM-Building-Model 020255

Astrid Schneider[1], Karin Stieldorf[1], Christian Schranz[1], Harald Urban[1], Alfred Waschl[2], Markus Feichtner[3], Fedele Rende[4], Andrea Aiello[4], Martin Hauer[5], Kurt Battisti[6], Markus Dörn[6], Jacqueline Scherret[6], Martin Treberspurg[7], Christoph Treberspurg[7]

[1] TU Wien, Vienna, Austria; [2] buildingSMART, Vienna, Austria; [3] Sonnenkraft Energie, St. Veit/Glan, Austria; [4] ACCA Software, Cosenza, Italy; [5] Bartenbach, Vienna, Austria; [6] A-Null Development, Vienna, Austria; [7] Treberspurg und Partner Ziviltechniker, Vienna, Austria

Oral SESSION 4BO.5 PV-Products for Buildings

4BO.5.1 Fabrication of a Novel Semi-Translucent BIPV Module Providing High Power Density and Active Daylight Management 020257

Almudena Garcia-Sanchez[1], Guido Vallerotto[1], Jaime J. Hernández[2], Alejandro García-Cañas[2], Steve Askins[1], Ignacio Antón[1], Isabel Rodríguez[2], César Domínguez[1]

[1] UPM, Madrid, Spain; [2] IMDEA Nanoscience, Madrid, Spain

4BO.5.3 A Comparative Study of Photovoltaic Shading Devices for Net Zero Energy Buildings across French Climates 020259

Visual SESSION 4BV.4 BIPV

Visual SESSION 4CV.1 Advances in Operation, Performance and Maintenance of PV Systems

Oral SESSION 4DO.1 PV Tracking and Simulation

Oral SESSION 4DO.2 Agrivoltaic Technologies

4DO.5.4 Development and Evaluation of Agrivoltaic System in Olive Groves based on a Novel Smart Tracking Algorithm 020392

Ildefonso Muñoz[1], Irati Amatriain[1], Gregorio Olivares[1], Gillen Abrego[2], Eusebio Gainza[2], Iñaki Cornago[1]

[1] CENER, Sarriguren, Spain; [2] ALLOTARRA, Allo, Spain

4DO.5.5 Adoption and Optimisation Analysis of Agrivoltaic Systems for Horticultural Production and Energy Autonomy in Lubumbashi/DR Congo 020393

Eddie Bilitu[1], Shu-Ngwa Asaa[2], Sara Bouguerra[3], Nikoleta Kyranaki[3], Ismail Kaaya[3], Yannick Useni[4], Michael Daenen[3]

[1] Hasselt University, Hasselt, Belgium; [2] imo-imomec, Genk, Belgium; [3] imec, Genk, Belgium; [4] University of Lubumbashi, Lubumbashi, Congo (DRC)

Visual SESSION 4DV.1 Agrivoltaics Approaches, Experiences, Results | Integrated and Innovative PV Applications

4DV.1.5 Maximizing Economic Performance of Agrivoltaic Systems through Module Array Design 020394

Habeel Alam[1], Jenny Nelson[2], Alona Armstrong[1], Duncan Whyatt[1], Nauman Butt[3]

[1] Lancaster University, Lancaster, United Kingdom; [2] Imperial College London, London, United Kingdom; [3] Lahore University of Management Sciences, Lahore, Pakistan

4DV.1.7 Bifacial and Mismatch Factors of Agri-Photovoltaics Systems 020396

Keith R. McIntosh[1], Solomon Freer[1], Bastien J. J. Ardissone[1], S. Ramirez[1], Ben A. Sudbury[1], Malcolm D. Abbott[1]

[1] PV Lighthouse, Coledale, Australia

4DV.1.10 Performance Analysis of Agrivoltaic System Configurations in Nordic Conditions 020398

Magda Szarek[1], Sami Jouttijärvi[1], Lauri Karttunen[1], Samuli Ranta[2], Kati Miettunen[1]

[1] University of Turku, Turku, Finland; [2] TUAS, Turku, Finland

4DV.1.11 Irradiance Management in Agrivoltaic Systems with Varying Designs Across Latitudes: Toward Finland's First Significant Demonstration 020400

Shuo Wang[1], Soroush Moradi Zavie Kord[2], Hugo E. Huerta[1], Antti Lajunen[2], Samuli Ranta[1]

[1] TUAS, Turku, Finland; [2] University of Helsinki, Helsinki, Finland

4DV.1.12 An Innovative Agrivoltaic System for Desert Climates with Anti-Soiling, Irradiance Control, and Water Management 020402

Sagarika Kumar[1], Min Hsian Saw[1], Ahmed Shaaban[1], Kamil Jaworczak[1], Nursulu Kuzhagaliyeva[1], Carlos G. Parrilla[2], Francois M. Tsombou[2], Fouad Lamghari[2], Mauro Pravettoni[1]

[1] Technology Innovation Institute, Abu Dhabi, United Arab Emirates; [2] Fujairah Research Centre, Fujairah, United Arab Emirates

4DV.1.15 Review of Sensor Technologies for Monitoring Agrivoltaic Systems 020403

Sara Pereira[1], José A. Silva[1], Luís Fialho[2], Pedro Horta[1]

[1] University of Évora, Évora, Portugal; [2] Eurac Research, Bolzano, Italy

Visual SESSION 4DV.4 PV System Engineering

[1] *Luxembourg Institute of Science and Technology, Esch-sur-Alzette, Luxembourg;* [2] *University of Lisbon, Lisbon, Portugal*

4EO.2.6 Optimizing Angular Performance of Curved VIPV Modules 020459
Francisco José Martín[1], *Rebeca Herrero*[1], *Ignacio Antón*[1]
[1] *UPM, Madrid, Spain*

Oral SESSION 5CO.4 Life Cycle Assessment of Silicon and Perovskite-based Cells and Modules

5CO.4.1 Towards Low-Impact Triple-Junction Perovskite/Silicon Tandem Modules: LCA of Precursor Materials to Describe the Influence of Background Data Sources 020461
Alejandra Galarza[1], *Sebastian Nold*[2], *Lars Oberbeck*[3]
[1] *IPVF, Palaiseau, France;* [2] *Fraunhofer ISE, Freiburg, Germany;* [3] *TotalEnergies OneTech, Paris, France*

5CO.4.3 Sustainability Assessment of Perovskite/Silicon Tandem Solar Modules: from Laboratory Scale to Industrial Implementation 020462
Elisabetta Brivio[1], *Andrea Danelli*[1], *Sofia Spagnolo*[1], *Pierpaolo Girardi*[1]
[1] *RSE, Milan, Italy*

5CO.4.4 LCA Learning Curve for Crystalline Silicon Solar Technologies based on Technology Improvements 020463
Julian Reichle[1], *Moritz Fath*[1], *Sraisth*[1], *Amish Kumar Sinha*[1], *Mehul Raval*[1], *Wolfgang Jooss*[1], *Peter Fath*[1], *Gourab Das*[1]
[1] *RCT Solutions, Konstanz, Germany*

Oral SESSION 5CO.5 Life Cycle Assessment of New PV Applications and Recycling

5CO.5.1 Optimizing AgriPV: A Comprehensive Assessment Framework for Sustainable Energy and Agriculture 020464
Ana Patrícia Lopes[1], *Bruno Barrionuevo* [2], *Daniel P. Albuquerque*[3], *Diogo Cordeiro*[4], *Cláudia Fernandes*[3], *Athanasios T. Balafoutis* [2], *Rui Castro*[1]
[1] *University of Lisbon, Lisbon, Portugal;* [2] *CERTH, Athens, Greece;* [3] *Centre for New Energy Technologies, Sacavém, Portugal;* [4] *EDP, Lisbon, Portugal*

5CO.5.2 Environmental Sustainability Assessment of Agrivoltaic Systems: a Life Cycle Approach 020466
Maria Anna Cusenza[1], *Andrea Danelli*[1], *Pierpaolo Girardi*[1], *Sofia Spagnolo*[1]
[1] *RSE, Milan, Italy*

5CO.5.4 Closing the Circle: Integrating the Circular Footprint Formula into Photovoltaic System Life Cycle Assessment 020467
Alexis Barrou[1], *Selin Kandiyoti-Eskenazi*[1], *Jacques Levrat*[1], *Bertrand Paviet-Salomon*[1], *Christophe Ballif*[1]
[1] *CSEM, Neuchâtel, Switzerland*

5CO.5.6 Environmental Benefits of Silicon Kerf Secondary Products in Pilot Processes over Conventional Production of Equivalent Products with Primary Raw Materials in China and Europe 020468
René Peche[1], Matthias Seitz[1], Markus Schönheits[1], Karsten Wambach[1]
[1] bifa Umweltinstitut, Augsburg, Germany

Oral SESSION 5CO.6 PV Recycling and Circularity

5CO.6.4 Quantification of Technical Recyclability of PV Modules for Different Recycling Scenarios 020470
Matthias Hämmer[1], Kerstin Baumann[1], Karsten Wambach[1], Markus Schönheits[1]
[1] bifa Umweltinstitut, Augsburg, Germany

5CO.6.5 IEC Technical Report 63525 on the Reuse of PV Modules: Final Result 020472
Arvid van der Heide[1], Serge Noels[2], Jan Clyncke[2], Rich Strömberg[3]
[1] imec, Genk, Belgium; [2] PV CYCLE, Brussels, Belgium; [3] University of Alaska, Fairbanks, United States of America

Plenary SESSION 5CP.1 Si PV Manufacturing: Pushing the Limits of Performance

5CP.1.4 Business Model Optimization for European Solar PV: A Study on Costs and Commercial Strategies 020474
Ian Kenchington[1], Philippe Macé[1], Gaëtan Masson[1], Joris Libal[2]
[1] Becquerel Institute, Brussels, Belgium; [2] ISC Konstanz, Konstanz, Germany

Plenary SESSION 5CP.2 Perovskite – Silicon Tandems: Towards Commercialisation | PV Stability in the Field

5CP.2.3 Total Cost of Ownership, LCA and LCOE Analysis of Perovskite-Silicon Tandems Compared to Single Junction Crystalline Silicon PV Technologies 020475
Baljeet Singh Goraya[1], Dilara Maria Subasi[1], Peter Henri Brailovsky[1], Henning Nagel[1], Patricia S.C. Schulze[1], Martin C. Schubert[1], Jochen Rentsch[1], Martin Hermle[1], Ralf Preu[1], Sebastian Nold[1]
[1] Fraunhofer ISE, Freiburg, Germany

Oral SESSION 5DO.11 The Road to Massive PV Deployment

5DO.11.1 Integration of Solar PV in a Norwegian Energy System, Navigating the Trade-offs between Land Use and Solar Power Production 020476
Petry Kristine Nøttum Haaland[1], Ole-Morten Midtgård[1], Magnus Korpås[1]
[1] NTNU, Trondheim, Norway

Oral SESSION 5DO.18 PV Recycling and Material Demand

Visual SESSION 5DV.2 Life Cycle Analysis and PV Recycling | Citizens Participation and Awareness

Sponsors

Author Index

Keyword Index

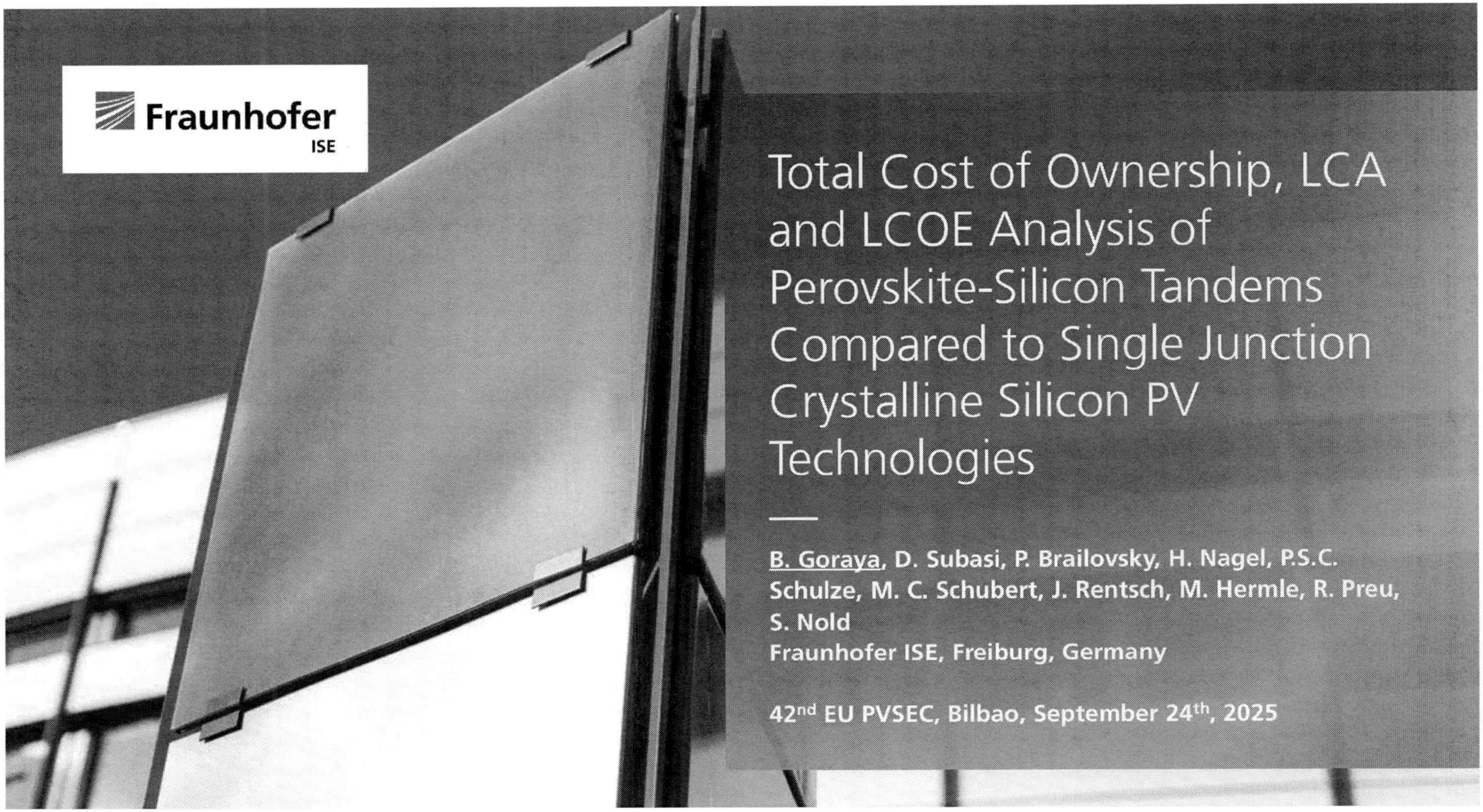
Fraunhofer
ISE
Total Cost of Ownership, LCA and LCOE Analysis of Perovskite-Silicon Tandems Compared to Single Junction Crystalline Silicon PV Technologies
B. Goraya, D. Subasi, P. Brailovsky, H. Nagel, P.S.C. Schulze, M. C. Schubert, J. Rentsch, M. Hermle, R. Preu, S. Nold
Fraunhofer ISE, Freiburg, Germany
42nd EU PVSEC, Bilbao, September 24th, 2025

TCO, LCA and LCOE Analysis of Pero-Si Tandems vs. SJ c-Si PV Technologies

Key Questions

1. **What are the production costs, carbon footprint and electricity costs of Perovskite-Silicon tandems compared to single junction crystalline-Silicon technologies?**
2. **What to focus on for making Perovskite-Silicon tandems economically and environmentally competitive?**

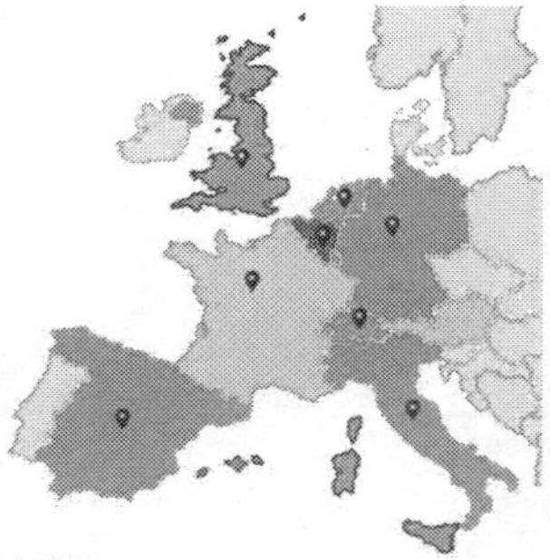

EU project VIPERLAB:
FULLY CONNECTED VIRTUAL AND PHYSICAL PEROVSKITE PHOTOVOLTAICS LAB

Duration: May 2021 to Nov 2024

https://www.viperlab.eu/

Fraunhofer ISE

Total Cost of Ownership (TCO) of Pero-Si Tandems vs. SJ c-Si PV Technologies

Methodology for Cost Modelling

Production cost assessment for single process steps and TCO for process routes [1].

Equipment and process data for state-of-the-art technology required.

→ **Data acquisition for industrial production equipment is crucial for assessment!**

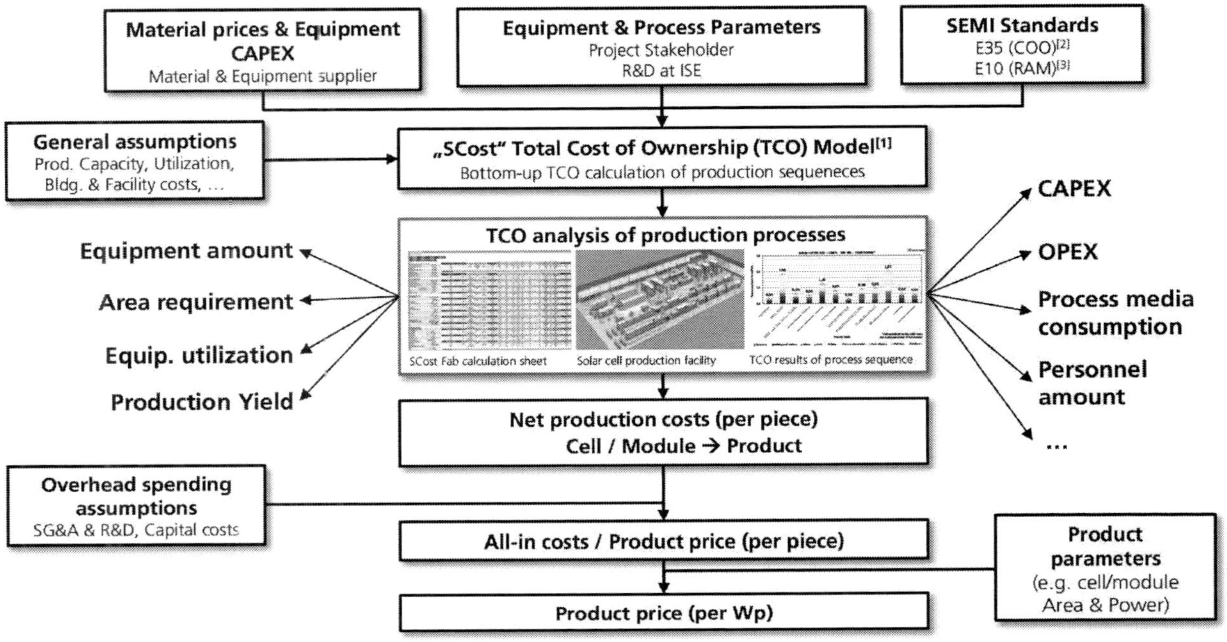

[1] https://www.ise.fraunhofer.de/en/business-areas/photovoltaics-production-technology-and-transfer/technology-assessment-and-transfer.html
[2] Guide to Calculate Cost of Ownership (COO) Metrics for Semiconductor Manufacturing Equipment, SEMI E35-0618.
[3] Specification for Definition and Measurement of Equipment Reliability, Availability, and Maintainability (RAM) and Utilization, SEMI E10-0814E.

Fraunhofer ISE

Total Cost of Ownership (TCO) of Pero-Si Tandems vs. SJ c-Si PV Technologies

Analysed Technologies and Key Inputs for Modelling

4 technologies evaluated for cell (n-Cz 130µm M10 wafer) and module (72 cell glass-glass) production:

- **2 single junction crystalline-Silicon based:**
- **2 fully textured 2-Terminal tandems:**

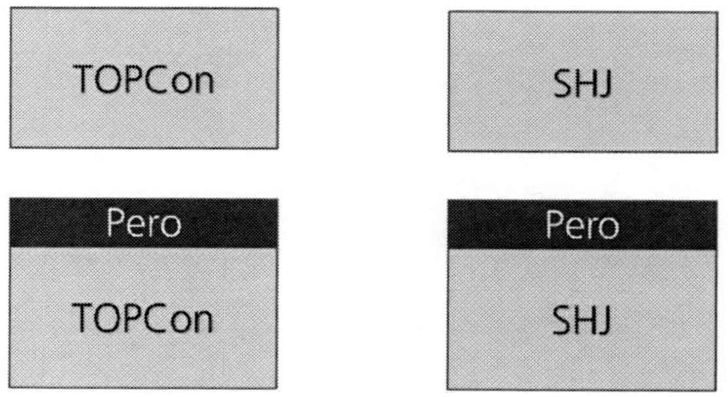

Location: Green field production site in Eastern Europe.
Annual output: Same number of modules produced per year (5.2 to 6.4 GWp/a)
n-Cz 130 µm M10 wafer price: 19 €ct/wafer[1]

1: OPIS avg. wafer price 2024

Fraunhofer ISE

Total Cost of Ownership (TCO) of Pero-Si Tandems vs. SJ c-Si PV Technologies

Analysed Cell Production Sequences

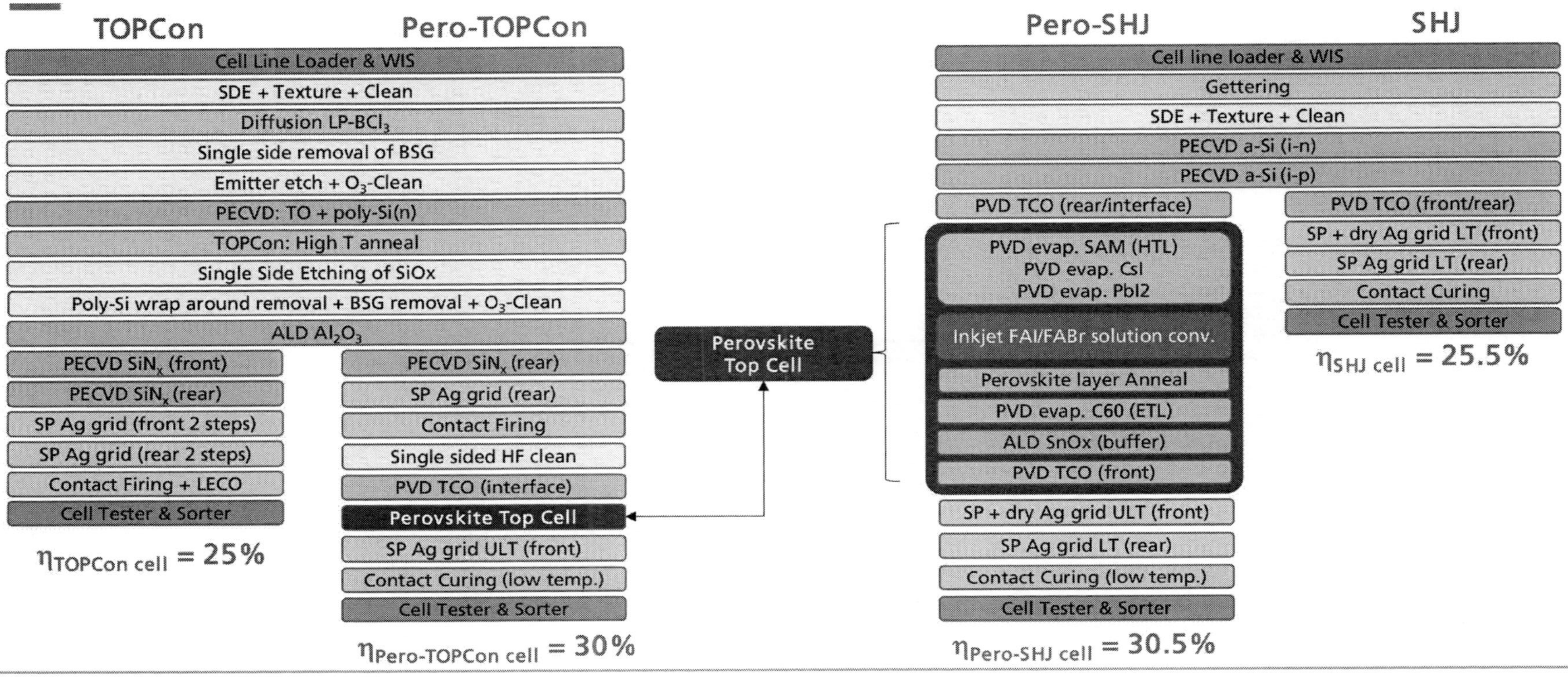

Fraunhofer ISE

Total Cost of Ownership (TCO) of Pero-Si Tandems vs. SJ c-Si PV Technologies

Perovskite Top Cell Material Prices

Very high prices for perovskite materials currently used in research.

Perovskite Materials	Researched price for low volume orders	Price with 50% reduction	Price with 90% reduction	Unit
C60	**41,400**	**20,700**	**4,140**	€/kg
FAI	1,167	584	117	
FABr	1,460	730	146	
SAM 2-PACz	**470,000**	**235,000**	**47,000**	
CsI	**13,600**	**6800**	**1,360**	
PbI2	**3,500**	**1750**	**350**	

PbI_2, CsI, SAM 2-PACz and **C60** have the **largest material cost share**, based on their specific consumptions, of the perovskite top cell.

- Low volume orders based on ISE orders, internet research and from contacting material suppliers.
- Not shown here are the solvents like butanol and ethanol which are bulk materials and will not be impacted by scaling.

Fraunhofer ISE

Total Cost of Ownership (TCO) of Pero-Si Tandems vs. SJ c-Si PV Technologies

Analysed Technologies

4 technologies evaluated for cell (n-Cz 130µm M10 wafer) and module (72 cell glass-glass) production:

- **2 single junction crystalline-Silicon based:**
- **2 fully textured 2-Terminal tandems:**

2 further scenarios for non-optimized tandems with:

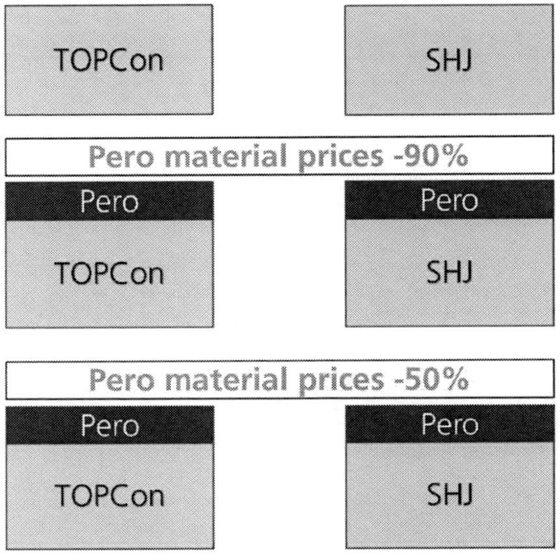

Fraunhofer ISE

Total Cost of Ownership (TCO) of Pero-Si Tandems vs. SJ c-Si PV Technologies

Analysed Module Production Sequence

72 cell Glass-Glass module
2 mm Glass loader1
Lay-up POE1
Combined tabber stringer + Auto bussing
Lay-up Cells / POE2 / 2mm Glass2
Module Lamination
Edge trimming and Framing
Junction box mounting + seal
Curing line
Module Flasher & Sorter
Labelling & Packaging

→ Butyl edge sealant for Pero-Silicon tandem module instead of silicone for SJs

Materials (e.g. glass, POE, Al-frame, etc.) **account for ~80%** of module production costs for the single junction modules.

Butyl edge sealant for tandems increases module production costs by **~20%** vs. single junction modules.

Cell-type	Eta cell	Eta module / P_{mpp} (72 cells/mod)
TOPCon	25.0 %	23.0 % / 593 Wp
Pero-TOPCon	30.0 %	27.3 % / 705 Wp
SHJ	25.5 %	23.4 % / 605 Wp
Pero-SHJ	30.5 %	27.8 % / 717 Wp

- Module dimensions: 2278 x 1134 mm
- CTM (power loss) considered as -0.21% & -1.11% absolute for the SJ and tandems respectively.

Fraunhofer ISE

Total Cost of Ownership (TCO) of Pero-Si Tandems vs. SJ c-Si PV Technologies

All-in Module Cost Comparison for all Technologies

All-in-module costs (Wp) for:

- Pero-TOPCon tandems vs. TOPCon: + 5% to + 42%
- Pero-SHJ tandems vs. SHJ: -0.1% to +34%

Pero-Si tandems can provide competitive all-in module costs to established & mature SJ technologies.

Focus on reducing perovskite material prices!

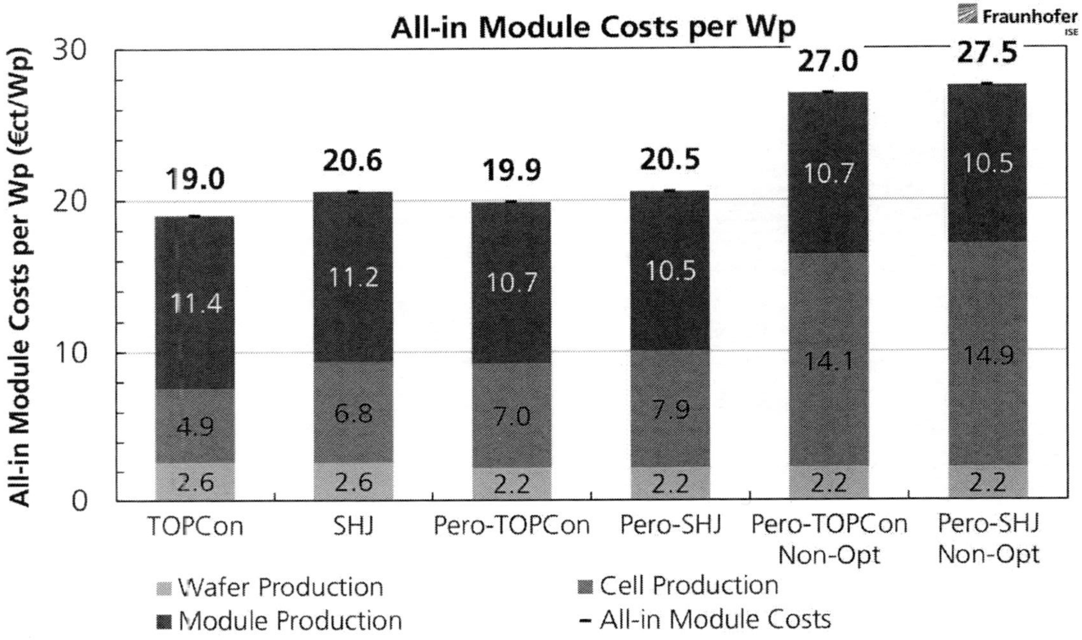

Note: All-in Module costs include SG&A / R&D costs and cost of capital on top of production costs.
Module efficiency: TOPCon - 23%, SHJ - 23.4%, Pero-TOPCon - 27.3%, Pero-SHJ - 27.8%

Fraunhofer ISE

LCOE Analysis of Pero-Si Tandems vs. SJ c-Si PV Technologies

General Assumptions and Key Inputs

LCOE evaluation for:

- 10 kWp residential rooftop system
- Location: Southern Germany (GHI: 1300 kWh/m^2a)
- Assumed same annual specific PV energy yield for:
  - TOPCon and Pero-TOPCon of 1256 kWh/kWp/a
  - SHJ and Pero-SHJ of 1268 kWh/kWp/a

For TOPCon, SHJ, Pero-TOPCon and Pero-SHJ:

- Degradation rate (1st year/2nd year on): 1 / 0.5 %/year
- System life: 30 years

For non-optimized Pero-Si tandems:

- Degradation rate (1st year/2nd year on): 1 / 1 %/year
- System life: 20 years

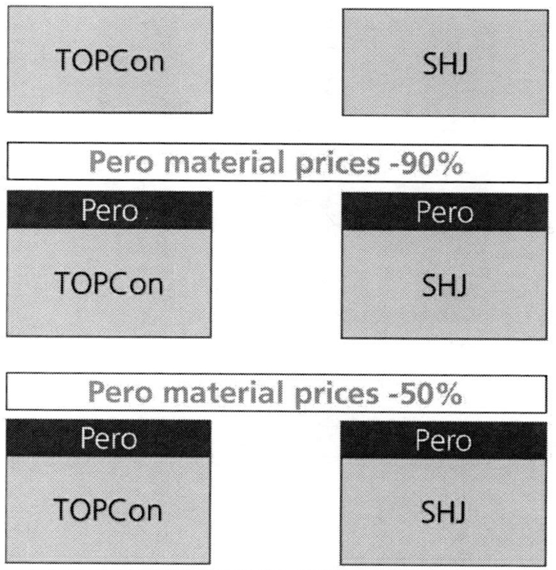

Fraunhofer ISE

LCOE Analysis of Pero-Si Tandems vs. SJ c-Si PV Technologies

Nominal LCOE for Residential Rooftop Systems

LCOE Results

- Pero-Si tandems can provide lower LCOE than the SJ counterparts.
- Non-optimized Pero-Si tandems show substantially higher LCOE than SJ counterparts.

Low perovskite material prices, high reliability and stability are key for Pero-Si tandems to provide a competitive LCOE!

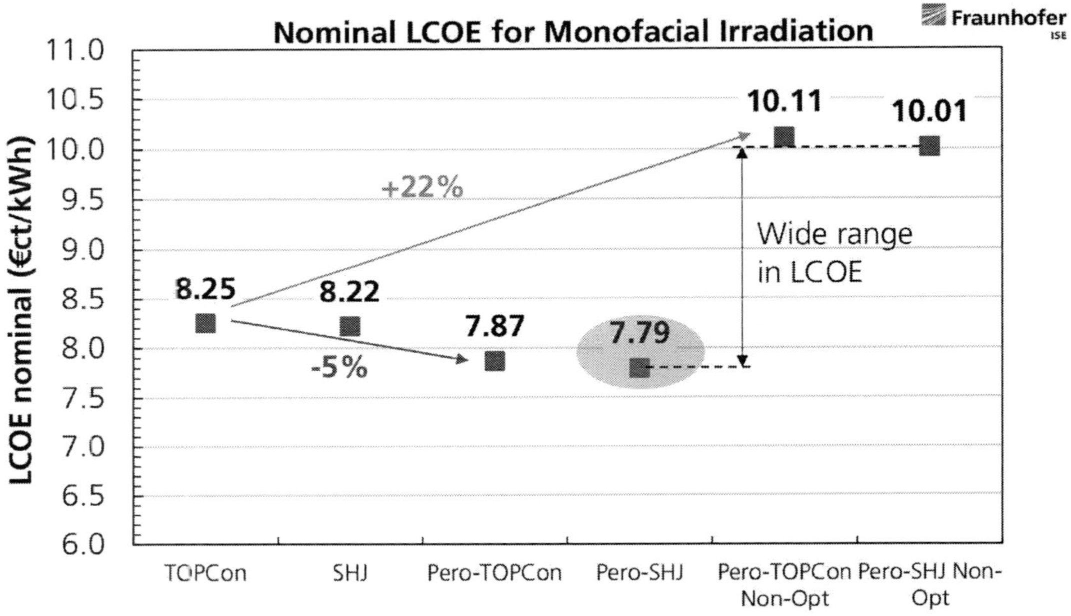

LCOE parameters: System size: 10 kWp (pitched roof); GHI: 1300 kWh/m²a; Degradation (1st year/2nd year on): 1/(0.5/1) %/a; Temp. coeff.: -0.27/-0.32 %/K; System life: 30/20 years; WACC: 5%
BOS costs: Inverter 10 €ct/Wp; Area proportional BOS costs: 103 €/m²; Power proportional BOS costs: 22 €ct/Wp; Soft BOS costs: 23 €ct/Wp;
Annual costs: 1 €ct/Wp; Margin: 15% on total PV system costs.

Fraunhofer ISE

LCOE Analysis of Pero-Si Tandems vs. SJ c-Si PV Technologies

LCOE Residential Rooftop – Sensitivity Analysis

Iso-LCOE curves for all assessed technologies.

To achieve the same LCOE:

~2% higher cell efficiency required for Pero-Si tandems compared to SJ technologies.

For the non-optimized Pero-Si tandems, a **cell efficiency gain of >10%** required.

Focus on reducing perovskite material prices, improving reliability and stability of Pero-Si tandems!

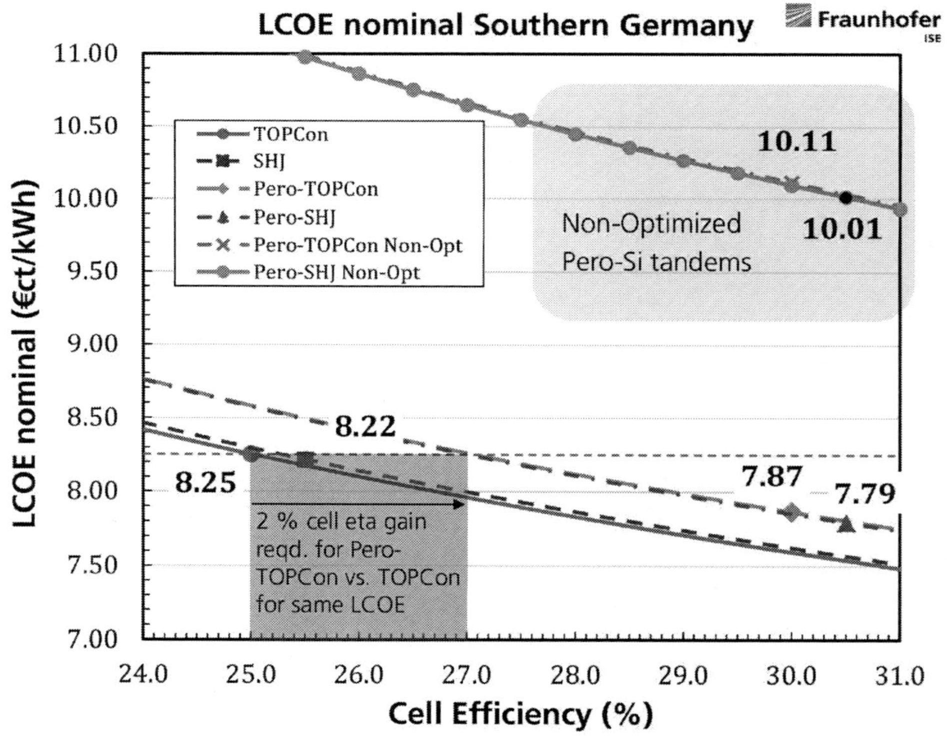

LCOE parameters: System size: 10 kWp (pitched roof); GHI: 1300 kWh/m²a; Degradation (1st year/2nd year on): 1/(0.5/1) %/a; Temp. coeff.: -0.27 / -0.32 %/K; System life: 30/20 years; WACC: 5%
BOS costs: Inverter 10 €ct/Wp; Area proportional BOS costs: 103 €/m²; Power proportional BOS costs: 22 €ct/Wp; Soft BOS costs: 23 €ct/Wp; Annual costs: 1 €ct/Wp; Margin: 15% on total PV system costs.

Fraunhofer ISE

Life Cycle Assessment (LCA) of Pero-Si Tandems vs. SJ c-Si PV Technologies

General Assumptions and Key Inputs

Focus on Carbon Footprint in g CO_2-eq/kWh or the Global Warming Potential (GWP)

- Residential rooftop system, functional unit 1 kWh
- Wafers are assumed to be supplied from China.
- Cells and modules are assumed to be produced in Germany.
- Proxy consumables are used for materials not available in the Life Cycle Inventory.

For TOPCon, SHJ, Pero-TOPCon and Pero-SHJ:

- Degradation rate (1st year/2nd year on): 1 / 0.5 %/year
- System life: 30 years

For non-optimized Pero-Si tandems:

- Degradation rate (1st year/2nd year on): 1 / 1 %/year
- System life: 20 years

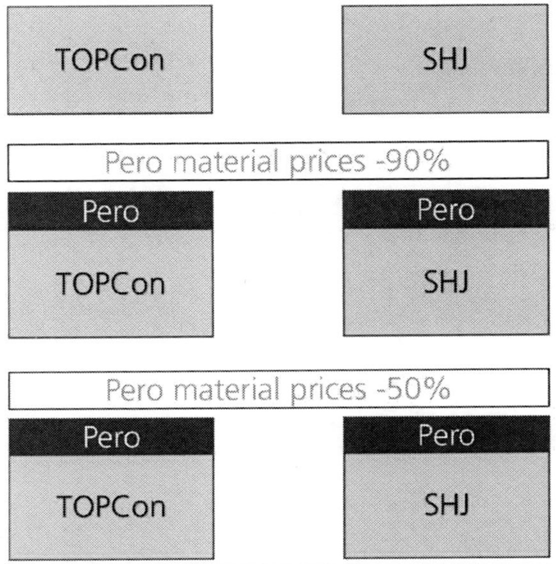

Climate change within Environmental Footprint 3.0 impact assessment method, the Ecoinvent 3.11 database, allocation cut-off by classification used and the LCA Software SimaPro.

Fraunhofer ISE

Life Cycle Assessment (LCA) of Pero-Si Tandems vs. SJ c-Si PV Technologies

Carbon Footprint or Global Warming Potential (GWP) Assessment

Pero-Si tandems show **lower GWP** than the SJ counterparts.

Non-optimized Pero-Si tandems show **substantially higher GWP** than SJ counterparts.

Perovskite materials and perovskite top cell production only **contributes ~1%** to the GWP of Pero-Si tandems.

Focus on improving reliability and stability of tandems!

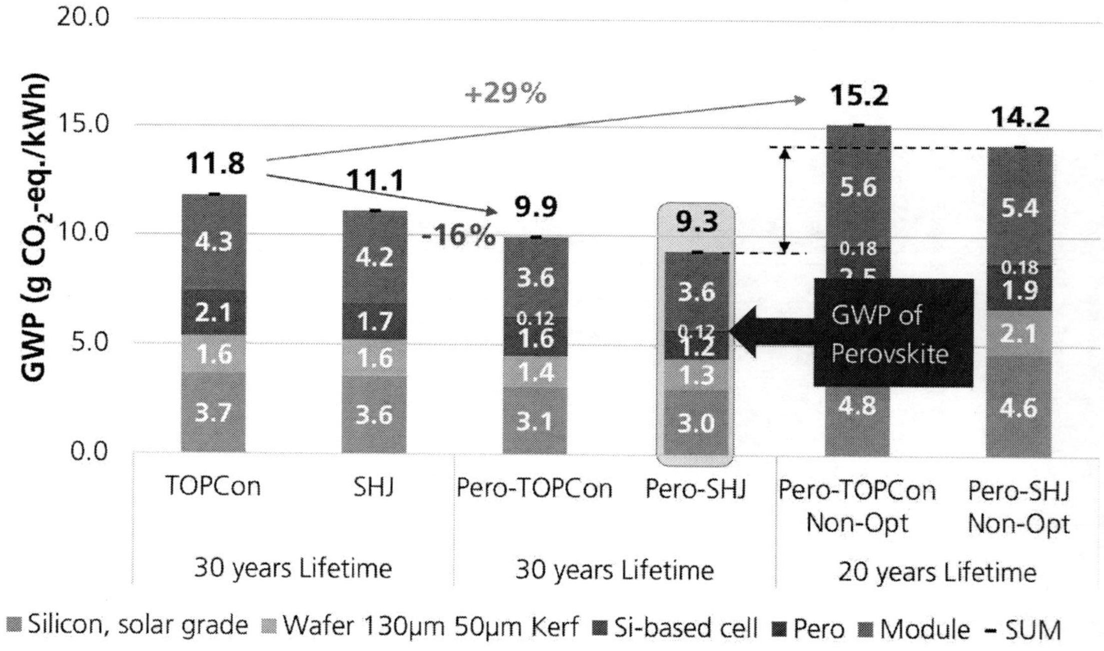

14

Climate change within Environmental Footprint 3.0 impact assessment method, the Ecoinvent 3.11 database, allocation cut-off by classification used and the LCA Software SimaPro.

A.A. Khan et al, Environmental Profile of Scalable Perovskite Silicon Tandem vs. Silicon Heterojunction Technology, tandemPV workshop 2023, Fraunhofer Lighthouse project MaNiTU.

Fraunhofer ISE

TCO, LCA and LCOE Analysis of Pero-Si Tandems vs. SJ c-Si PV Technologies

Summary & Takeaways

TCO analysis shows that **Pero-Si tandems can provide competitive all-in module costs** to established & mature single junction technologies.

- **Focus on reducing perovskite material prices!**

LCOE analysis shows that **~2% higher cell efficiency required for Pero-Si tandems** (-90% perovskite material price, -0.5%/a degradation rate & 30-year lifetime) compared to single junction technologies to achieve the same LCOE.

- **Focus on reducing perovskite material prices and improving reliability and stability!**

LCA shows **that Pero-Si tandems can provide the lowest carbon footprint / GWP** from all assessed technologies.

- **Focus on improving reliability and stability!**

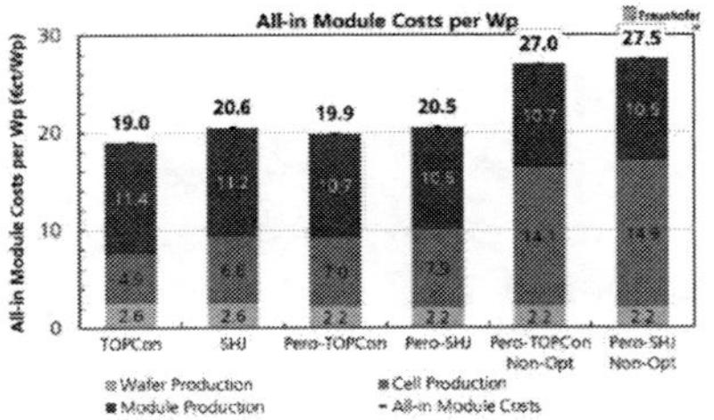

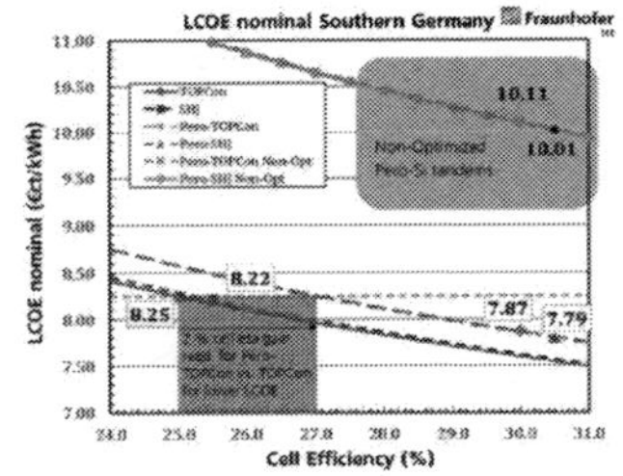

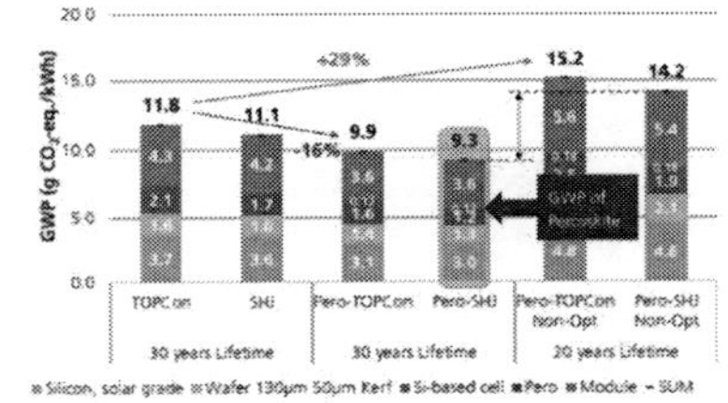

Fraunhofer ISE

Thank You for Your Attention!

Contact

Baljeet Singh Goraya
Techno-Economic and Ecological Analyses
baljeet.singh.goraya@ise.fraunhofer.de

Fraunhofer ISE
Heidenhofstrasse 2
79110 Freiburg, Germany
www.ise.fraunhofer.de

Fraunhofer ISE

VIPERLAB
FULLY CONNECTED VIRTUAL AND PHYSICAL PEROVSKITE PHOTOVOLTAICS LAB

This project has received funding from the European Union's Horizon 2020 research and innovation programme under grant agreement N°101006715.

Link to Fraunhofer ISE contributions of the 42nd EU PVSEC:
https://ise.link/eupvsec2025
available as of 26.09.2025

42nd European Photovoltaic Solar Energy Conference and Exhibition

This presentation was selected by the Sc. Committee of the EU PVSEC 2025 for submission of a full paper to one of the EU PVSEC's collaborating peer-reviewed journals.

INTEGRATION OF SOLAR PV IN A NORWEGIAN ENERGY SYSTEM, NAVIGATING THE TRADE-OFFS BETWEEN LAND USE AND SOLAR POWER PRODUCTION

Petry Kristine Nøttum Haaland, Ole-Morten Midtgård, Magnus Korpås
Department of Electric Energy, Norwegian University of Science and Technology (NTNU),
O. S. Bragstads Plass 2E, 7034 Trondheim
petry.k.n.haaland@ntnu.no

ABSTRACT: In recent years, the expansion of renewable energy sources (RES) has accelerated, with solar photovoltaic (PV) poised to play a central role in future energy systems. However, this growth has led to rising tensions over land use conflicts, along with growing concerns about biodiversity loss and environmental degradation. This study assesses land use requirements across various renewable energy scenarios for Norway, highlighting trade-offs between spatial demands and system configurations. Results show a wide range of land use needs, from 18.43 to 5149 km^2, depending on the scenario and metric applied. Our findings emphasize the importance of consistent land use metrics and the integration of socio-economic factors in energy planning. As RES deployment intensifies, strategic planning is essential to protect ecosystems and maintain public support, both critical for achieving climate targets.
Keywords: Land use requirements, RES, Solar PV, Socio-economics

1 INTRODUCTION

Achieving a climate-neutral economy increasingly depends on the large-scale deployment of renewable energy sources (RES) [1]. Currently, the electricity and heating sectors account for roughly 30% of global greenhouse gas (GHG) emissions. This share is expected to rise due to ongoing electrification across sectors [2], making the integration of RES a critical strategy for emission reduction [3]. Among the available technologies, solar power has seen particularly rapid growth, with forecasts indicating continued strong expansion in the coming years [4].

Several studies have explored long-term planning for power systems [5]–[8]. Yet most optimization models tend to prioritize techno-economic parameters. This narrow focus overlooks key practical constraints, such as land availability, which becomes increasingly relevant as RES deployment scales up [5]. While solar and wind energy are renewable and abundant, the land required for their infrastructure is limited. Consequently, solutions derived from energy system models may not always be viable when spatial limitations are taken into account. As the energy transition will require greater capacity, land-use constraints may challenge the feasibility of proposed configurations [9]–[11].

The rapid expansion of RES has also led to growing concerns about land use, particularly regarding the development of previously undisturbed natural areas. These concerns include potential impacts on biodiversity and ecosystem integrity [12], [13]. To ensure that ecological, recreational, and societal interests are respected, land use must be carefully considered in the planning and implementation of RES infrastructure.

This paper investigates the potential role of solar photovoltaic (PV) in Norway's future energy system, with a particular focus on the trade-offs between land use and increased RES integration. Norway is currently in the early stages of deploying utility-scale PV systems [14]. With a projected power deficit by 2027 and rising electricity demand driven by widespread electrification, expanding generation capacity is becoming increasingly urgent [15]. Solar energy could play a key role in meeting this demand, but its spatial implications must be thoroughly assessed to ensure sustainable integration into the national energy system.

The primary contributions of this paper are as follows: A detailed evaluation of Norway's future power system and potential decarbonization pathways, emphasizing land use considerations and the integration of solar PV technologies. It further explores the trade-offs between land use and RES deployment by analyzing multiple scenarios with varying restrictions for RES integration. Although the analysis is focused on Norway, the insights are relevant to broader contexts facing similar challenges.

The remainder of the paper is structured as follows: Section 2 describes the methodology, including key inputs and assumptions. Section 3 presents the results and discusses the findings, while Section 4 offers concluding remarks.

2 METHODOLOGY

2.1 Model design

A detailed case study of the North European power system is carried out to analyze the trade-offs between land use and the integration of RES. The modeled system consists of six interconnected regions. Regions 1 through 5 represent Norway's electricity system, divided according to its different price zones (NO1–NO5). Region 6, referred to as the Continent, is a simplified representation of the broader North European grid. It aggregates data from Denmark, the United Kingdom, Germany, Belgium, the Netherlands, and Sweden to account for cross-border electricity exchanges between Norway and its neighboring countries. The energy system model is adapted from the framework presented in [16], with modifications made to suit the specific scope and objectives of this analysis.

The analysis is conducted using the GenX modeling framework, an open-source tool designed for optimizing long-term investments in electricity generation, storage, transmission infrastructure, and demand-side technologies to meet a projected electricity demand [17]. GenX formulates the problem as a constrained linear or mixed-integer linear optimization, enabling the identification of cost-effective investment portfolios and operational strategies. The framework operates deterministically and is typically used for capacity expansion planning for a specified future year, based on the optimization formulation in Equation 1.

The GenX model's objective function integrates multiple cost components to reflect the economic considera-

10.4229/EUPVSEC2025/5DO.11.1
020476-001

tions involved in power system planning. The first term captures fixed annual expenditures, encompassing both capital investments and fixed operation and maintenance (O&M) costs. The second and third terms represent variable costs linked to electricity generation and fuel usage. The fourth component introduces penalties for unmet demand and reserve shortages, ensuring system reliability is prioritized. The fifth term accounts for startup costs associated with technologies requiring unit commitment modeling, calculated by multiplying the startup cost by the number of startup events for each generator cluster at each time step. Finally, the model includes costs associated with transmission infrastructure expansion.

In addition to these cost terms, GenX enforces a set of constraints to ensure realistic system behavior. These include technology-specific constraints such as capacity limits, operational bounds, and resource availability, as well as system-wide constraints like reserve requirements, hourly energy balance, and compliance with CO_2 emissions caps. The model also incorporates unit commitment constraints, startup and shutdown dynamics, and storage cycling behavior.

$$\min \sum_{z \in Z} \sum_{g \in G} \left(C_{g,z}^{\text{Inv}} \cdot A_{g,z} \cdot \delta_{g,z}^{\text{Inv}} + C_{g,z}^{\text{FixOM}} \cdot \Delta_{g,z} \right)$$
$$+ \sum_{z \in Z} \sum_{t \in T} \sum_{g \in G} \left(G_{g,z}^{\text{VarOM}} + G_{g,z}^{\text{Fuel}} \right) \cdot \phi_{g,t,z}$$
$$+ \sum_{z \in Z} \sum_{t \in T} \left(C_s^{\text{VarOM}} \cdot \phi_{g,t,z} + C_s^{\text{VarOM}} \cdot \phi_{s,t,z} \right)$$
$$+ \sum_{z \in Z} \sum_{t \in T} \left(C^{\text{curt}} \cdot \gamma_{t,z}^e + C^R \cdot \gamma_{t,z}^r \right)$$
$$+ \sum_{z \in Z} \sum_{t \in T} \sum_{g \in G} \left(\Pi_{g,z}^{\text{START}} + \epsilon_{g,t,} \right)$$
$$+ \sum_{l \in L} \pi_l^{\text{TCAP}} \cdot \Delta \phi_l^{\max} \tag{1}$$

To solve the optimization problem, a detailed configuration of the North European power system is required, including assumptions about generation technologies, demand profiles, and energy storage options. The following section outlines the data inputs and modeling assumptions used in setting up the system.

2.2 Input data and assumptions

The simulations are grounded in projected costs and assumptions for the year 2040. A brownfield optimization strategy is employed, utilizing existing generation assets as documented in [18]. No additional capacity is permitted for hydropower or run-of-river technologies. Furthermore, consistent with the expected coal phase-out, new coal-fired power investments are excluded from the model [19].

Hydropower scheduling is optimized over a one-year horizon, incorporating historical inflow patterns, power-to-energy conversion ratios, reservoir limitations, and minimum storage thresholds. Norwegian inflow data are sourced from [20], while continental data are derived from [21]. Due to the absence of detailed hourly inflow data for run-of-river systems, their inflows are assumed to mirror those of reservoir-based hydropower. Given the relatively minor contribution of run-of-river generation to total output, this simplification is not expected to significantly influence the results. Investment cost estimates for hydropower are taken from [22].

To reflect the variability of RES, hourly capacity factors are extracted from [23]. After analyzing weather data spanning 2007–2019, the year 2013 is selected as representative and used as the benchmark. Nuclear power maintenance is modeled as a flexible resource, with hourly availability data sourced from [21]. Other generation technologies are modeled with fixed capacity factors.

Fuel prices and corresponding CO_2 emissions are based on data from [24] and [25]. Bioenergy is treated as carbon-neutral, following the assumptions outlined in [26]. Technical specifications for all generation technologies are drawn from [27]. Investment, fixed, and O&M costs are aligned with the EU Reference Scenario 2020 [27], and annuity calculations assume a 5% discount rate. To streamline computation, power plants are grouped into clusters with similar characteristics.

Transmission capacities between regions are compiled from ENTSOG and ENTSO-E Ten-Year Network Development Plans (TYNDPs). Hourly electricity demand profiles are derived from historical data [18], scaled using projections from [28] and [29]. Norway's annual demand is set at 199 TWh, while the total demand for Northern Europe is 1708 TWh. Inter-annual demand fluctuations are captured using average variations from 2015 to 2021. The value of lost load is assumed to be 10,000$/MWh.

The model further incorporates two energy storage technologies, lithium-ion batteries with a 4-hour discharge duration and pumped hydro storage (PHS) for seasonal balancing. This enables an evaluation of how different storage solutions affect land use. Battery cost assumptions are based on [30], while PHS costs are sourced from [31]. Details on the model setup, along with comprehensive input data, are available in [32].

2.3 Description of cases

To quantify the role of solar power in Norway's future energy system and examine the trade-offs between land use and increased RES development, four different cases are investigated. The cases are categorized as the following. Case 1: No additional investments allowed in emitting thermal power generation, case 2: No additional investments allowed in emitting thermal and onshore wind power generation, case 3: No additional investments allowed in emitting thermal, onshore, and offshore wind power generation, and case 4: No additional investments allowed in emitting thermal, onshore, and ground-mounted PV power generation. The different cases are displayed in Table I.

Investments are allowed in both the Norwegian and Northern European energy systems, subject to the same investment constraints in each region.

Table I: RES investment options for the different cases.

Case	Onshore wind	Offshore wind	Solar PV Utility	Solar PV Roof
1	X	X	X	X
2		X	X	X
3			X	X
4		X		X

No cases allow for investments in emitting thermal power capacity.
Abbreviations:
Solar PV Utility: Utility-scale ground-mounted PV,
Solar PV Roof.: Roof-mounted PV.

Each case is initially run with a CO_2 cap at 90% of 1990 emission levels, in alignment with the objectives of the European Union [33].

2.4 Land use requirements in energy system modeling

Landscape assessment traditionally lacks standardized units and remains partly subjective. As highlighted in [12], perceptions of landscape impact are inherently personal, shaped by individual experiences and biases. In literature there is currently a large range of estimates and boundary levels for calculation of land use requirements, with land-use information collected either from official documentation, calculated using geometrical rules, or manual drawings [34]. Given the critical role of land use in planning low-carbon energy systems, there is a growing need for methodological consistency [34].

Although exact quantification of land use impacts is complex, researchers have approached the issue using both quantitative and qualitative indicators. Quantitative metrics typically measure the physical area affected, which may include the directly occupied space, required spacing, buffer zones, and areas influenced by noise or visual intrusion [12]. Qualitative metrics, on the other hand, capture public attitudes and aesthetic responses to landscape changes, offering insights into the social dimensions of energy infrastructure [12]. This duality emphasizes the importance of a holistic framework that integrates physical land use assessments with public perception studies [12]. A widely adopted quantitative classification distinguishes between direct and total land use requirements [12].

Direct land use refers to the actual footprint of energy infrastructure, encompassing elements such as access roads, spacing between panels or turbines, and other installations designed to mitigate operational effects. Total land use, by contrast, includes broader considerations such as visual and acoustic impacts, as well as the overall environmental footprint. These additional factors contribute to significant variability in land use estimates across studies and regions, largely due to differing interpretations of indirect impacts [12].

In this study, land use requirements are estimated by calculating the mean values derived from an extensive review of existing literature. The analysis focuses on onshore wind and solar PV technologies, given their anticipated prominence in future energy systems [35]. Although bioenergy could entail substantial land demands due to the large areas required for cultivation and infrastructure [36], our model excludes new bioenergy investments due to their high capital costs. Consequently, bioenergy-related land use is not considered in this assessment.

Offshore wind is assigned a land use value of zero, as it does not occupy terrestrial space. However, it is acknowledged that offshore installations can affect surrounding marine ecosystems and coastal areas [36]. Similarly, rooftop PV systems are assumed to have zero land use requirements, as they utilize pre-existing built environments. The specific land use values applied in this study are summarized in Table II.

3 RESULTS AND DISCUSSION

In the following section, we examine the trade-offs associated with land use requirements under varying restrictions on the deployment of RES, with a particular emphasis on the role of solar PV in shaping Norway's future energy system. We analyze land use implications across the different cases, highlighting the balance between minimizing land footprint and enabling RES expansion.

Table II: Direct and total land use requirements for different RES ([12], [34], [37]–[49]).

RES	Direct (m^2/MW)	Total (m^2/MW)
Onshore wind	3570	212 778
Utility-scale PV	11 045	30 682

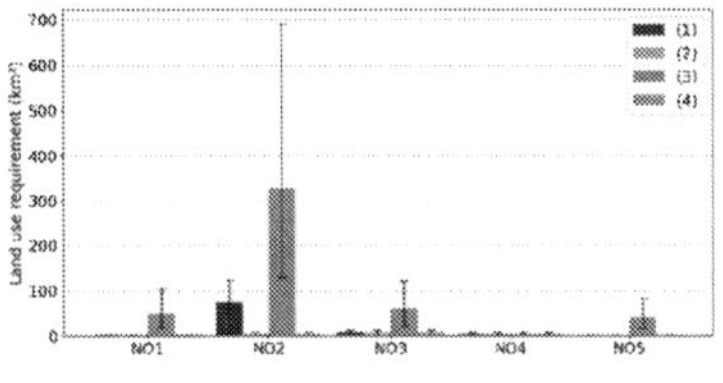

(a) Direct land use requirements.

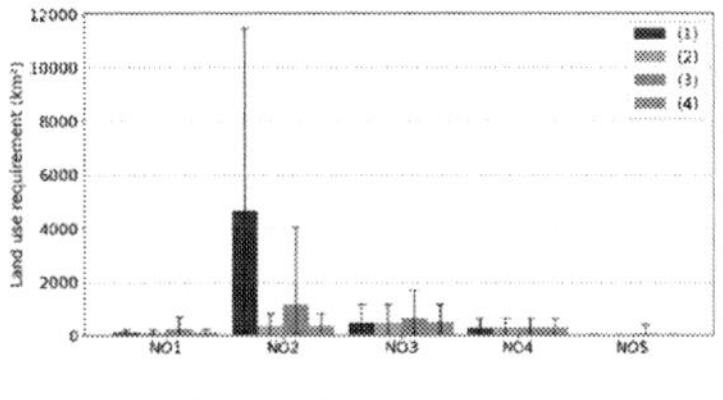

(b) Total land use requirements.

Figure 1: Land use requirements for the different cases in Norway, divided into each price zone. In the figure, (1) - (4) corresponds to case 1 - 4.

Fig. 1 highlights the substantial differences in both direct and total land use requirements across the various modeled scenarios. Case 3 emerges as the most land-intensive in terms of direct land use, primarily due to extensive deployment of ground-mounted PV systems, which dominate the energy mix in the absence of wind capacity. The PV investments are mostly concentrated in NO2, where solar irradiance is comparatively higher. Conversely, NO4 does not feature any PV installations, as prolonged periods of low solar availability during winter make solar energy less viable. Although NO4 experiences extended daylight in summer (the midnight sun), this seasonal peak in solar generation does not align with Norway's electricity demand, which is highest in winter [50]. This misalignment underscores a temporal disconnect between solar energy production and consumption patterns.

In contrast, scenarios that incorporate wind energy generally exhibit lower direct land use. This is largely attributed to wind power's higher capacity factor and the relatively small physical footprint of individual turbines. However, assessing land use based solely on turbine foundations can underestimate the broader spatial impact of wind energy. Adequate spacing between turbines and the associated grid infrastructure contribute to a larger total land footprint and can influence surrounding ecosystems [12]. These broader impacts are evident in Fig. 1b, where total land use requirements increase significantly, especially in onshore wind scenarios.

10.4229/EUPVSEC2025/5DO.11.1

As illustrated in Fig. 1b, case 1 now shows the highest total land use. Despite lower installed capacities in case 1, the need for greater spacing and supporting infrastructure substantially raises the overall land demand.

Error bars in Fig. 1 reflect the significant uncertainty in land use requirement literature, discussed in Section 2.4.

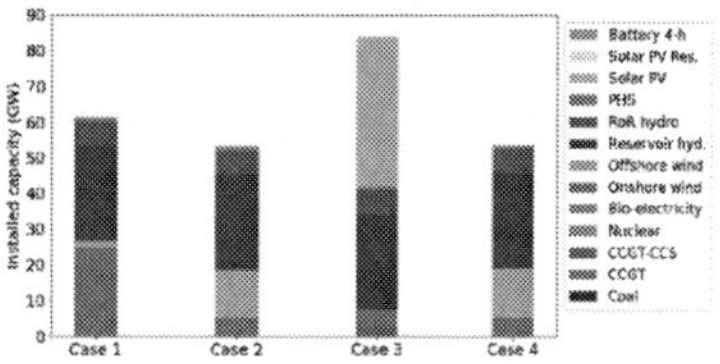

Figure 2: Total installed capacity in Norway for the different cases (in GW). 'Solar PV' refers to ground-mounted photovoltaic systems, while 'Solar PV Res.' denotes residential roof-mounted photovoltaic systems.

Fig. 2 displays the total installed capacity across the different scenarios analyzed. Each case involves a significant expansion of RES, largely driven by anticipated reductions in technology costs by 2040. Case 3, which excludes wind power investments, shows the highest installed capacity overall, with ground-mounted PV systems comprising 89% of the total. This heavy reliance on solar PV is primarily due to its low capital cost, but also reflects the need to offset its lower capacity factor and seasonal generation variability compared to wind. As a result, despite its large installed capacity, case 3 delivers the lowest renewable electricity output due to less efficient capacity utilization. Across all scenarios, no new nuclear capacity is added, reflecting the assumption of prohibitively high capital costs for nuclear projects.

Initially, the model favors onshore wind due to its cost-effectiveness and favorable wind conditions. In scenarios where onshore wind is excluded (cases 2–4), the system compensates by shifting toward more expensive offshore wind or by increasing PV deployment. As shown in Fig. 3, these adjustments lead to higher total system costs and increased average energy prices.

In cases 2 and 4, the absence of onshore wind leads to a greater reliance on offshore wind, which carries higher investment costs. In case 3, the system compensates for limited solar availability by installing additional PV capacity. However, due to the daily fluctuations in solar output, this scenario also requires supplementary investments in carbon capture and storage (CCS) and increased use of natural gas to maintain system reliability and flexibility. These factors contribute to higher overall costs, in addition to increased emissions.

Based on our results, direct land use requirements across the modeled cases range from 0.006% to 0.16% of Norway's total land area [51]. When total land use is considered, these estimates increase markedly, reaching between 0.4% and 1.69%. It is important to note that these calculations do not exclude areas unsuitable for development, such as mountainous regions or ice-covered terrain, implying that the actual land footprint could be even greater. Additionally, the projected rise in electrification across all energy sectors is expected to further amplify land use demands [2].

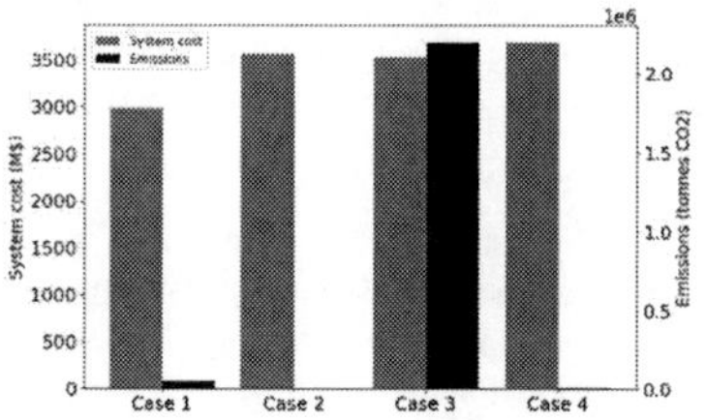

(a) Total system costs (left axis, in M\$) and total emissions (right axis, in tonnes CO_2), for Norway.

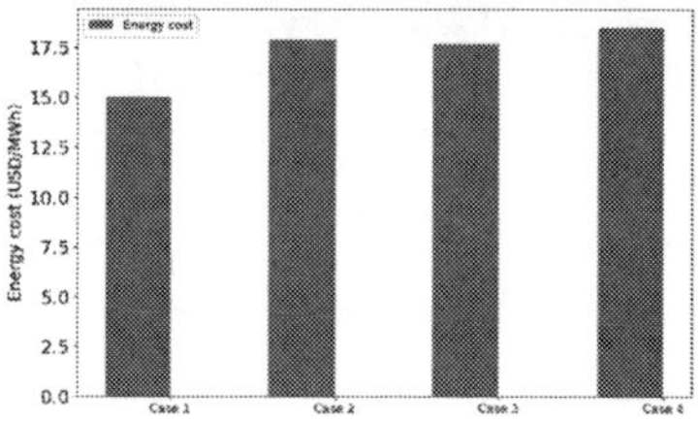

(b) Average energy cost per MWh, for Norway.

Figure 3: Total system costs, energy costs and total emissions for Norway.

These results underscore the significant variability in land use outcomes depending on the selected renewable energy deployment strategy and highlight the spatial implications of transitioning to a power system with 90% renewable energy. However, due to the considerable uncertainty and variation in current land use methodologies these percentages could vary, depending on the specific assumptions and calculation methods applied.

4 CONCLUSION

This study explores how solar power could shape Norway's future energy system, focusing on the balance between land use and renewable energy deployment. Depending on the scenario, meeting climate goals may require between 18.43 and 5149 km^2 of land, up to 1.69% of Norway's total area.

Transitioning to a low-emission system will inevitably impact land use. While different renewable energy strategies can reduce spatial demands, they often involve trade-offs. However, all RES development carry some degree of environmental consequences. To protect ecosystems, and minimize environmental degradation, this must be carefully evaluated and assessed.

Future research should examine land use impacts at the local level and include offshore wind in comparative analyses. Integrating socio-economic factors into energy models will also be essential to fully understand the societal effects of the energy transition.

AI DECLARATION

In preparing this work, we used Copilot to assist with language refinement and to generate initial code for figure plotting. All content produced with the help of this tool was carefully reviewed and revised by us, and we take full responsibility for the final version of the publication.

10.4229/EUPVSEC2025/5DO.11.1
020476-004

REFERENCES

[1] K. Calvin et al., "IPCC, 2023: Climate change 2023: Synthesis report. contribution of working groups i, II and III to the sixth assessment report of the intergovernmental panel on climate change [core writing team, h. lee and j. romero (eds.)]. IPCC, geneva, switzerland." edition: First. [Online]. Available: https://www.ipcc.ch/report/ar6/syr/

[2] I. B. Boa Morte, O. d. Q. F. Araújo, C. R. V. Morgado, and J. L. de Medeiros, "Electrification and decarbonization: a critical review of interconnected sectors, policies, and sustainable development goals," *Energy Storage and Saving*, vol. 2, no. 4, pp. 615–630, Dec. 2023. [Online]. Available: https://www.sciencedirect.com/science/article/pii/S2772683523000456

[3] M. Ge, J. Friedrich, and L. Vigna, "4 charts explain greenhouse gas emissions by countries and sectors." [Online]. Available: https://www.wri.org/insights/4-charts-explain-greenhouse-gas-emissions-countries-and-sectors

[4] International Energy agency, "Solar PV – Analysis." [Online]. Available: https://www.iea.org/reports/solar-pv

[5] Y.-k. Chen, J. G. Kirkerud, and T. F. Bolkesjø, "Balancing GHG mitigation and land-use conflicts: Alternative northern european energy system scenarios," *Applied Energy*, vol. 310, p. 118557. [Online]. Available: https://www.sciencedirect.com/science/article/pii/S0306261922000435

[6] M. Victoria, E. Zeyen, and T. Brown, "Speed of technological transformations required in europe to achieve different climate goals," *Joule*, vol. 6, no. 5, pp. 1066–1086. [Online]. Available: https://www.sciencedirect.com/science/article/pii/S2542435122001830

[7] A. Grubler, C. Wilson, N. Bento, B. Boza-Kiss, V. Krey, D. L. McCollum, N. D. Rao, K. Riahi, J. Rogelj, S. De Stercke, J. Cullen, S. Frank, O. Fricko, F. Guo, M. Gidden, P. Havlík, D. Huppmann, G. Kiesewetter, P. Rafaj, W. Schoepp, and H. Valin, "A low energy demand scenario for meeting the 1.5 °c target and sustainable development goals without negative emission technologies," *Nature Energy*, vol. 3, no. 6, pp. 515–527, number: 6 Publisher: Nature Publishing Group. [Online]. Available: https://www.nature.com/articles/s41560-018-0172-6

[8] G. Luderer, Z. Vrontisi, C. Bertram, O. Y. Edelenbosch, R. C. Pietzcker, J. Rogelj, H. S. De Boer, L. Drouet, J. Emmerling, O. Fricko, S. Fujimori, P. Havlík, G. Iyer, K. Keramidas, A. Kitous, M. Pehl, V. Krey, K. Riahi, B. Saveyn, M. Tavoni, D. P. Van Vuuren, and E. Kriegler, "Residual fossil CO2 emissions in 1.5–2 °c pathways," *Nature Climate Change*, vol. 8, no. 7, pp. 626–633, number: 7 Publisher: Nature Publishing Group. [Online]. Available: https://www.nature.com/articles/s41558-018-0198-6

[9] L. Späth, "Large-scale photovoltaics? yes please, but not like this! insights on different perspectives underlying the trade-off between land use and renewable electricity development," *Energy Policy*, vol. 122, pp. 429–437. [Online]. Available: https://www.sciencedirect.com/science/article/pii/S0301421518304762

[10] M. Koelman, T. Hartmann, and T. Spit, "Land use conflicts in the energy transition: Dutch dilemmas," *TeMA - Journal of Land Use, Mobility and Environment*, vol. 11, no. 3, pp. 273–284. [Online]. Available: http://www.serena.unina.it/index.php/tema/article/view/5830

[11] P. Scherhaufer, S. Höltinger, B. Salak, T. Schauppenlehner, and J. Schmidt, "Patterns of acceptance and non-acceptance within energy landscapes: A case study on wind energy expansion in austria," *Energy Policy*, vol. 109, pp. 863–870. [Online]. Available: https://www.sciencedirect.com/science/article/pii/S0301421517303488

[12] R. Ioannidis and D. Koutsoyiannis, "A review of land use, visibility and public perception of renewable energy in the context of landscape impact," *Applied Energy*, vol. 276, p. 115367. [Online]. Available: https://www.sciencedirect.com/science/article/pii/S0306261920308795

[13] V. Kati, C. Kassara, Z. Vrontisi, and A. Moustakas, "The biodiversity-wind energy-land use nexus in a global biodiversity hotspot," *Science of The Total Environment*, vol. 768, p. 144471, May 2021. [Online]. Available: https://www.sciencedirect.com/science/article/pii/S0048969720380025

[14] Energeia, "Solkraftverk i norge." [Online]. Available: https://www.energeia.no/solkraft-i-norge-perspektivnotat

[15] Statnett. Statnetts kortsiktige markedsanalyse. [Online]. Available: https://www.statnett.no/om-statnett/nyheter-og-pressemeldinger/nyhetsarkiv-2022/kortsiktig-markedsanalyse-okende-forbruk-gir-kraftunderskudd-fra-2027/

[16] P. K. N. Haaland, V. Aubin, and M. Korpås, "Quantifying energy-related carbon emissions of low-emission neighborhoods: A comparison of different approaches [unpublished manuscript]," 2025.

[17] J. D. Jenkins and N. A. Sepulveda, "Enhanced decision support for a changing electricity landscape: The GenX configurable electricity resource capacity expansion model."

[18] Power Statistics. Power statistics. [Online]. Available: https://www.entsoe.eu/data/power-stats/

[19] World Economic Forum. G7 countries agree phaseout for unabated coal power, and other top energy stories. [Online]. Available: https://www.weforum.org/agenda/2024/05/energy-news-g7-coal-phaseout-renewables-batteries/

[20] Hydrologiske data - NVE. [Online]. Available: https://www.nve.no/vann-og-vassdrag/hydrologiske-data/

[21] M. Korpås, L. Warland, J. Tande, and K. Uhlen, "Tradewind D3.2 Grid modelling and power system data," 2007.

[22] M. Jafari, M. Korpås, and A. Botterud, "Power system decarbonization: Impacts of energy storage duration and interannual renewables variability," *Renewable Energy*, vol. 156, pp. 1171–1185. [Online]. Available: https://www.sciencedirect.com/science/article/pii/S0960148120306820

[23] Renewables.ninja. Renewables.ninja. [Online]. Available: https://www.renewables.ninja/

[24] ENTSO-E and ENTSOG. ENTSO-e and ENTSOG TYNDP 2024 draft scenarios report. [Online]. Available: https://2024.entsos-tyndp-scenarios.eu/

[25] Our World in Data. Carbon dioxide emissions factors. [Online]. Available: https://ourworldindata.org/grapher/carbon-dioxide-emissions-factor

[26] M. Karmellos, D. Kopidou, and D. Diakoulaki, "A decomposition analysis of the driving factors of CO2 (carbon dioxide) emissions from the power sector in the european union countries," *Energy*, vol. 94, pp. 680–692. [Online]. Available: https://www.sciencedirect.com/science/article/pii/S0360544215015406

[27] European Commision. EU reference scenario 2020 - european commission. [Online]. Available: https://energy.ec.europa.eu/data-and-analysis/energy-modelling/eu-reference-scenario-2020_en

[28] ENTSO-E. Major trends reshaping the power sector — ENTSO-e vision on market design and system operation towards 2030. [Online]. Available: https://vision2030.entsoe.eu/major-trends-reshaping-the-power-sector/

[29] Entso-e and entsog tyndp 2024 draft scenarios report. Accessed: 2024-10-09. [Online]. Available: https://2024.entsos-tyndp-scenarios.eu/

[30] W. Cole and A. Karmakar, "Cost projections for utility-scale battery storage: 2023 update," *Renewable Energy*.

[31] J. P. Deane, B. P. Ó Gallachóir, and E. J. McKeogh, "Techno-economic review of existing and new pumped hydro energy storage plant," *Renewable and Sustainable Energy Reviews*, vol. 14, no. 4, pp. 1293–1302, May 2010. [Online]. Available: https://www.sciencedirect.com/science/article/pii/S1364032109002779

[32] P. Haaland, "Integration-of-solar-PV-in-a-Norwegian-energy-system," Jun. 2025, original-date: 2025-06-06T08:53:00Z. [Online]. Available: https://github.com/pkhaaland/Integration-of-solar-PV-in-a-Norwegian-energy-system

[33] European Commision, "Climate strategies & targets - European Commission." [Online]. Available: https://climate.ec.europa.eu/eu-action/climate-strategies-targets_en

[34] O. Turkovska, K. Gruber, M. Klingler, C. Klöckl, L. Ramirez Camargo, P. Regner, S. Wehrle, and J. Schmidt, "Methodological and reporting inconsistencies in land-use requirements misguide future renewable energy planning," *One Earth*, vol. 7, no. 10, pp. 1741–

1759. [Online]. Available: https://www.sciencedirect.com/science/article/pii/S2590332224004755
[35] International Energy Agency, "World Energy Outlook – Topics." [Online]. Available: https://www.iea.org/topics/world-energy-outlook
[36] J. K. Nøland, J. Auxepaules, A. Rousset, B. Perney, and G. Falletti, "Spatial energy density of large-scale electricity generation from power sources worldwide," *Scientific Reports*, vol. 12, no. 1, p. 21280, Dec. 2022, publisher: Nature Publishing Group. [Online]. Available: https://www.nature.com/articles/s41598-022-25341-9
[37] P. Denholm, P. Brown, W. Cole, T. Mai, B. Sergi, M. Brown, P. Jadun, J. Ho, J. Mayernik, C. McMillan, and R. Sreenath, "Examining supply-side options to achieve 100% clean electricity by 2035." [Online]. Available: https://www.osti.gov/biblio/1885591
[38] J. E. Diffendorfer, B. Sergi, A. Lopez, T. Williams, M. Gleason, Z. Ancona, and W. Cole, "The interplay of future solar energy, land cover change, and their projected impacts on natural lands and croplands in the US," *Science of The Total Environment*, vol. 947, p. 173872. [Online]. Available: https://www.sciencedirect.com/science/article/pii/S0048969724040208
[39] M. Bolinger and G. Bolinger, "Land requirements for utility-scale PV: An empirical update on power and energy density," *IEEE Journal of Photovoltaics*, vol. 12, no. 2, pp. 589–594. [Online]. Available: https://ieeexplore.ieee.org/document/9676427/
[40] C. de Castro, M. Mediavilla, L. J. Miguel, and F. Frechoso, "Global solar electric potential: A review of their technical and sustainable limits," *Renewable and Sustainable Energy Reviews*, vol. 28, pp. 824–835, Dec. 2013. [Online]. Available: https://www.sciencedirect.com/science/article/pii/S1364032113005807
[41] N. Martín-Chivelet, "Photovoltaic potential and land-use estimation methodology," *Energy*, vol. 94, pp. 233–242, Jan. 2016. [Online]. Available: https://www.sciencedirect.com/science/article/pii/S0360544215014863
[42] S. Ong, C. Campbell, P. Denholm, R. Margolis, and G. Heath, "Land-use requirements for solar power plants in the united states," pp. NREL/TP–6A20–56 290, 1 086 349. [Online]. Available: http://www.osti.gov/servlets/purl/1086349/
[43] P. Denholm, M. Hand, M. Jackson, and S. Ong, "Land use requirements of modern wind power plants in the united states." [Online]. Available: https://www.osti.gov/biblio/964608
[44] J. van Zalk and P. Behrens, "The spatial extent of renewable and non-renewable power generation: A review and meta-analysis of power densities and their application in the u.s." *Energy Policy*, vol. 123, pp. 83–91. [Online]. Available: https://www.sciencedirect.com/science/article/pii/S0301421518305512
[45] P. Saunders, *Land Use Requirements of Solar and Wind Power Generation: Understanding a Decade of Academic Research*.
[46] M. S. Kenawi, R. D. Hedger, K. T. Alfredsen, B. K. Sandercock, M. Korpås, and T. H. Bakken, "Land efficiency of renewable energy in Norway: A synthesis of footprint and production density," *Renewable Energy*, vol. 252, p. 123514, 2025. [Online]. Available: https://www.sciencedirect.com/science/article/pii/S0960148125011760
[47] NVE, "Direkte påvirket areal - NVE." [Online]. Available: https://www.nve.no/energi/energisystem/vindkraft-paa-land/arealbruk-for-vindkraftverk/direkte-paavirket-areal/
[48] U. R. Fritsche, G. Berndes, A. L. Cowie, V. H. Dale, K. L. Kline, F. X. Johnson, H. Langeveld, N. Sharma, H. Watson, and J. Woods, "Energy and land use," *Work. Pap. Glob. L. Outlook*, pp. 14–15, 2017.
[49] A. M. Trainor, R. I. McDonald, and J. Fargione, "Energy sprawl is the largest driver of land use change in united states," *PLOS ONE*, vol. 11, no. 9, p. e0162269, publisher: Public Library of Science. [Online]. Available: https://journals.plos.org/plosone/article?id=10.1371/journal.pone.0162269
[50] J. O. G. Tande and K. Vogstad, "(PDF) OPERATIONAL IMPLICATIONS OF WIND POWER IN A HYDRO BASED POWER SYSTEM." [Online]. Available: https://www.researchgate.net/publication/234165681_OPERATIONAL_IMPLICATIONS_OF_WIND_POWER_IN_A_HYDRO_BASED_POWER_SYSTEM
[51] Country Reports, "Norway geography, maps, climate, environment and terrain from Norway | - CountryReports." [Online]. Available: https://www.countryreports.org/country/Norway/geography.htm

10.4229/EUPVSEC2025/5DO.11.1

Evaluating the impact of photovoltaics for lifecycle global warming potential of buildings according to EN 15978 - a Danish Case Study

Sune Thorsteinsson, Markus Babin, Nanna Lysgaard Andersen, Gisele A. dos Reis Benatto
Technical University of Denmark, Institute of Electrical and Photonics Engineering, 4000 Roskilde, Denmark

ABSTRACT: The EU energy performance of buildings directive (EPBD) has recently been updated to tighten energy performance regulations and is demanding solar solutions on all buildings, to be fully implemented by 2030 through national building codes. However, article 7 also states that life cycle global warming potential (GWP) must be calculated (according to EN 15978) with a reference study period of 50 years, and that national limit values on life cycle GWP must be introduced by 2030. Denmark has since 2023 enforced this methodology with national adaptions and parameters.

This work evaluates the impact of PV on the GWP of buildings following Danish rules, using collected environmental product declarations of PV system components. The results show, that for almost all cases the addition of a PV system increases the GWP of buildings, owing to a combination of a high GWP load of PV materials compared to standard roofing materials, decreasing emission factors (based on political ambitions of climate neutrality), and high impact of component replacement.

Tying the GWP benefits of PV to political ambitions of renewable energy generation decreases the value of PV in countries with high political ambitions and does not appropriately consider buildings as an active part of the energy system. Therefore article 7 in part counteracts the stated intentions of the EPBD and the authors recommend that PV should be excluded from the GWP assessment of buildings.

Keywords: Global warming assessments, Building-integrated photovoltaics, Building attached photovoltaics, sustainability of construction works, Energy performance directive.

1 INTRODUCTION

The European Union has strong aims of energy independence and high ambitions to reach climate goals. Different directives have been agreed on as a means to reach this goal, including several solar strategies. These directives provide an overall framework that is implemented via national legislation in the member states. In particular, the energy performance of buildings directive (EPBD) [1] has recently been updated, tightening energy regulations and in essence making buildings a significant part of the energy system, and demanding solar solutions on all buildings, fully implemented by 2030. However, one aspect not yet analyzed in detail by the PV community is article 7 (and Annex III), demanding that life cycle global warming potential (GWP) must be calculated (according to EN 15978) for all buildings with a reference study period of 50 years. In conjunction, national limit values on life cycle GWP must be introduced in member states and enforced from 2028 onwards. Tracking of the GWP of buildings is an important means to lower the CO_2 emissions from the construction sector, where the emissions are significant [1].

While life cycle assessment (LCA) of PV products and electricity production is well established – including recently updated data [2-5] – few scientific works have addressed the impact of building added (BA) and building integrated (BI) -PV on the life cycle GWP of buildings.
The LCA analysis of PV commonly provides emissions in the range of approximately 16-38 g/kWh for a central European location (GTI of 1331 kWh/m^2) and concludes that the highest contributor to the global warming potential is associated cell production and underlying upstream processes [5] and the associated emissions are strongly dependent on the electricity mix at the place of production. Grinham et al [6] have conducted building LCA analysis according to EN 15978 and concluded that the carbon balance for PV is strongly dependent on future scenarios assumed for the carbon load of the grid.

EN 15978:2011 [7] challenges BAPV and in particular BIPV as the GWP load of PV materials per m^2 is a factor of 5-15 times higher than that of e.g. common roofing materials. This is in combination with the so-called emission factors used to convert produced energy into global warming potential – typically based on expected future grid emissions.

This work collects environmental product declarations (EPDs) for BAPV and BIPV elements as well as inverters and mounting systems, and uses this data to calculate their impact on the GWP of buildings. It further analyzes how the Danish emission factors are derived, and the potential implications for the BAPV and BIPV market.

2 METHODOLOGY

2.1 The EN 15978 and derived Danish implementation.

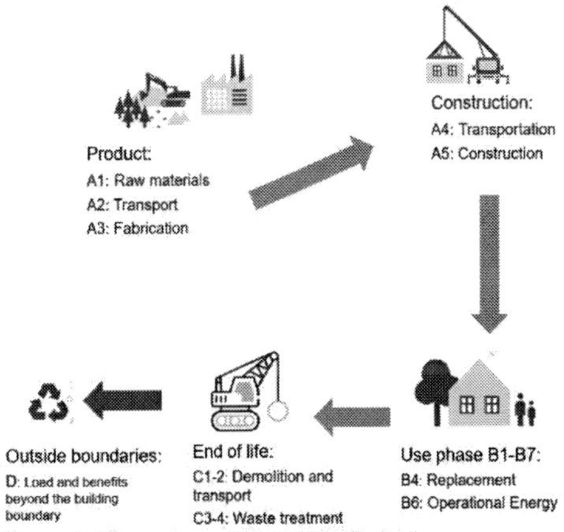

Figure 1: Illustration of the EN15978:2011

EN 15978:2011 divides the buildings life cycle into modules A1-3 (raw material extraction and fabrication), modules A4-5 (construction and transportation), modules

B1-7, covering the "Use" stage, modules C1-4, containing end of life, and module D, gathering all benefits and loads beyond the system boundaries. For compliance with the GWP limit values, only modules A to C can be used. These principles are illustrated in Figure 1.

For the Danish 2025 regulation [8], modules A1-3 (raw material extraction and fabrication), B4 (replacement), B6 (operational energy), C3 (waste processing), and C4 (disposal) are to be included in the assessment – considering a reference study period of 50 years. After summation and normalization by the floor area and consideration period, the total GWP must be below the limit values of 4-8 kg CO_2 eq/(m^2 (floor area)*year), depending on building type, with exceptions for special and agricultural buildings. Separate limits are enforced on modules A4-5 (construction and transportation), based on construction product specific Danish parameters, and any contributions to module D must be declared.

B4 (replacement) is calculated as the sum of modules A1-3 and C3-4, multiplied by the number of replacements needed, rounded up to the nearest integer. Based on the product lifetime stated in a national table – 30 years for PV – one full replacement is needed to reach the reference study period.

The GWP for B6 (only operational energy used for heating and ventilation) is the on-site consumed (or produced electricity), multiplied by an emission factor for a given year, which is published in the Danish building code, shown in Figure 2 [9].

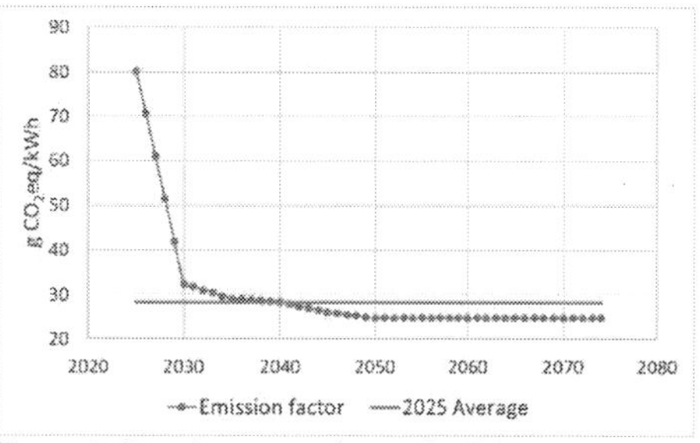

Figure 2: Danish emission factors for 2025

According to the Danish rules [8], only the part of the PV system that contributes to the energy performance compliance of a building up of max 13.2 kWh/(m^2*year) is included in the calculation (with no distinction of ground mounted, BA- or BIPV). Within the energy performance compliance, all PV energy can be assigned to module B6, lowering the GWP of the building. Any energy exceeding this limit, however, cannot be included, and can be considered "outside the energy frame". For BIPV solutions, PV surfaces not part of the energy frame can be counted as cover glass (not specified in further detail), and inverters and stands[1] are to be included for the energy frame part.

In the original Danish implementation, the full GWP of a BIPV system had to be included, but only up to 13.2 kWh/(m^2*year) could be used for CO_2 displacement in B6. This meant that only 5-15 % of the PV energy could be used to reduce GWP – in practice excluding any BIPV cladding solution. Therefore, this deviation from the EN 15978 standard was introduced, which is also suggested in the updated proposal for the standard.

The data for the GWP assessment can be obtained either from valid EPDs, which is a third party authorized LCA analysis of construction products, or (in the Danish case) from so-called generic data [10]. This generic data is provided for construction products, determined if there is more than 5 EPDs available as the 75 % quartile + 10 % (accounting for modules A-C). For product categories without EPDs it can be derived from the German ÖKOBAUDAT database [11] with an added 10 % margin to promote use of product-specific EPDs [12].

2.2 EPD collection and comparison

EPDs are collected for PV panels, inverters and mounting systems. In the EPDs no differentiation between BIPV and BIPV are made.

The functional unit for inverters is 1 kWh interpreted as the load pr kWh allocated to the inverting functionality of a model plant. With the power rating of the inverter, the converted energy (and lifetime), the load of the inverter can be converted to pr W_{ac}.

For the GWP load calculations a plant DC to AC ratio of 1.3 is assumed. To enable comparison of the GWP loads, inverters loads are converted to pr square meter, using a specific area yield of 200 W/m^2 corresponding to a nominal rated AC power of 154 W_{ac}/m^2.

The PV energy per m^2 is calculated using the performance ratio method, assuming an annual insolation (H) of 1000 kWh/m^2, a performance ratio (PR) of 80% and a degradation rate (d) of 0.5% p.a., these numbers correspond to typical parameters for horizontally mounted PV installations in Denmark. With the product-dependent specific area yield (Y) [Wp/m^2] and assuming system replacement after 25 years, the average annual energy (E_{avg}) are calculated as:

$$E_{avg} = \frac{H}{G_{stc}} * Pr * Y * \frac{1}{25}\sum_{1}^{25}(1-d)^i$$

The degradation-averaged emission factor is calculated as follows:

$$\epsilon_{avg} = \frac{1}{50}\left(\sum_{1}^{25}\epsilon_i(1-d)^i + \sum_{26}^{50}\epsilon_i(1-d)^{i-25}\right)$$

Here, ϵ_i is the emission factor for year i in g(CO_2eq)/kWh. Consequently, the GWP reduction from PV produced electricity is:

$$B6_{GWP,PV} = 50 * \epsilon_{avg} * E_{avg}$$

Based on ϵ_{avg}, the GWP per m2 PV area ($GWP_{PV_{area}}$) for where the PV is providing a neutral GWP contribution, can be calculated as:

$$\epsilon_{avg} = GWP_{system,pr\,KWh} = \frac{2 * GWP_{system,area}}{E_{avg} * 50}$$

$$GWP_{PV_{area}} = \epsilon_{avg} * E_{avg} * 25 - GWP_{inv} - GWP_{mounting}$$

For calculating the PV system GWP load, data from the panel specific EPDs is combined with the average load of the inverters and mounting systems corresponding to 1 m^2 PV. For the BIPV systems the mounting system is omitted as at least 3 of the BIPV systems are roof systems where the panels are directly mounted on the roof battens.

The lifetime of all the inverters is stated in the EPDs

[1] In the legislative text "stands" (and not mounting systems) are used not further detailed providing a minor for cut-off limits (e.g. module clamps).

to be 25 years and the lifetime of the mounting systems is assumed to be at least 50 years, therefore a total of 2 inverters and 1 mounting system is used to reach the 50 years.

3 RESULTS

3.1 EPD results

The load for the Danish included phases (A1-3 and C3-4) for the four categories are shown in Figure 3 and the corresponding numbers displayed in Table 1. EPDs for PV panels included both US, European and Asian manufactures and EPDs for inverters were found in the power range from 6-330 kW with 8/9 in the 50-330 kW range.

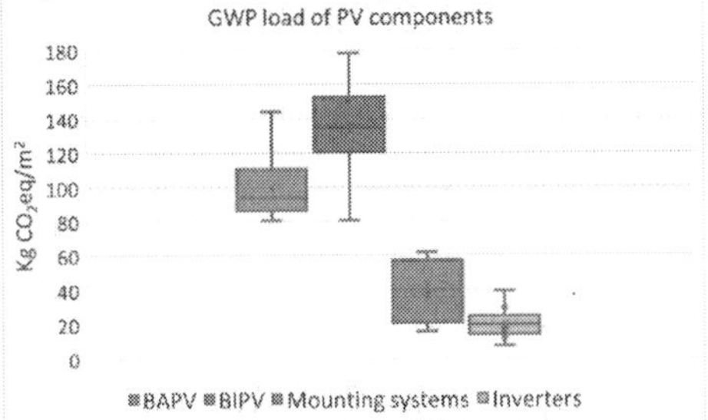

Figure 3: Statistics on collected EPDs

Table 1: EPD statistics (for the BIPV system sum and share the mounting system is excluded).

	BAPV	BIPV	Mounting	Inverter
Average (kg CO_2eq/m^2)	100,0	139,0	39,0	20,0
Samples	10	7	4	9
Min (kg CO_2eq/m^2)	80,5	80,5	16,0	7,6
Max (kg CO_2eq/m^2)	144,0	178,2	61,0	39,3
Average system sum (kg CO_2eq/m^2)	159,0	159,0		
Relative Share	63%	87%	25%	13%

Further a comparison of loads of commonly used building materials (data sourced from Ökobaudat [11]) to PV materials are made in Figure 4.

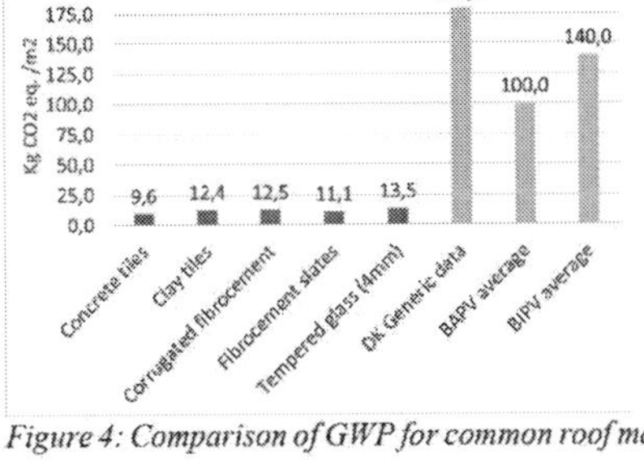

Figure 4: Comparison of GWP for common roof materials.

In summary, the following observations can be made:

- PV materials have a 5-15 times high GWP load compared to commonly used roofing materials.
- No significant dependency of place of production was identified for the PV modules.
- The PV panels are the main contributor to the GWP load, however the inverter and mounting system have non-negligible shares.
- Within each category there is some variability which is subject to further investigation. For the inverters no correlation with nameplate rating were found, however this is to be revisited when more inverter EPDs in a more widespread power range are available. One EPD for a power optimizer was found with a GWP load of 30 g/W corresponding to a load of 5.6 kg/m² using 200 Wp/m² and a sizing factor of 1.

3.2 GWP impact on the building of the PV system

In Figure 5 the CO2 balance for 1 m² is seen over the consideration period together with the expected annual energy production for the average BAPV solution. As expected, the PV deployment has a high carbon intensity and the energy production is used to displace CO_2 during its operation. In year 26 the entire PV plant is replaced, except for the mounting structure. The CO_2 reduction is steep in the beginning and flattens towards the end of the consideration period due to the decreasing emission factors. While the first plant almost entirely displaces its embedded CO_2, the second plant only displaces approximately 80% of its embedded CO_2.

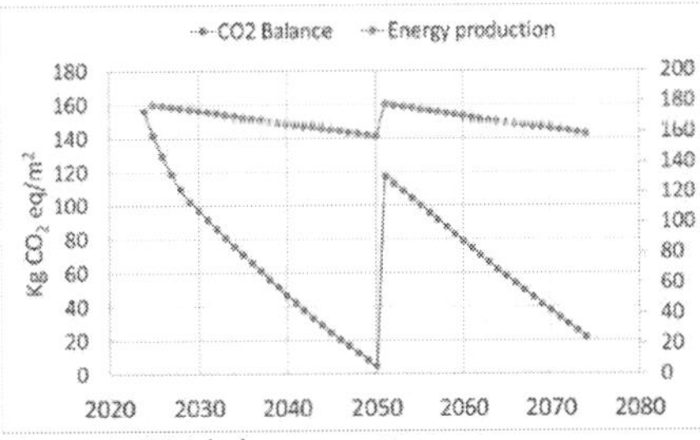

Figure 5: CO2 balance over time.

In Figure 6 the imbedded CO_2 together with the displaced CO_2 is shown for the average and extremes of the BAPV and BIPV systems using the average values of inverters and mounting systems (latter only for BAPV). Values are GWP/(m²PV*year), which are the Danish units used. As can be seen almost all PV systems increase the GWP of the building. Only the lowest GWP BAPV system is lowering the GWP with negligible amounts. What can also be observed is that the materials savings (here clay tiles) from the displaced roof material for BIPV systems are not significant.

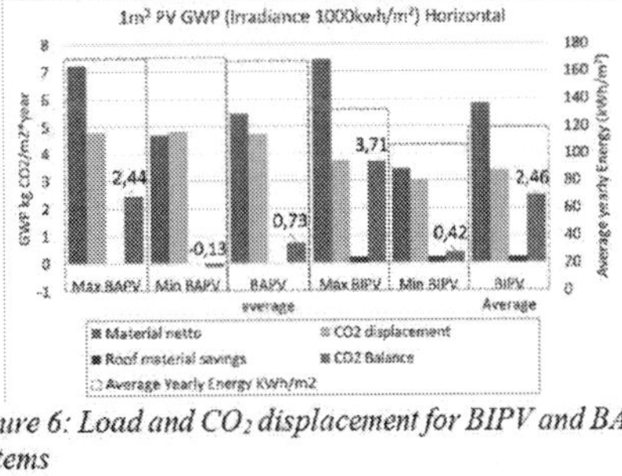

Figure 6: Load and CO_2 displacement for BIPV and BAPV systems

10.4229/EUPVSEC2025/5DO.11.3

The CO_2 balance final impact on the building GWP calculation depends on the building design, but assuming flat roof with a roof area equal to the useful floor area up to 13.2 kWh/m2 can be included, depending on the building energy performance calculation. For this case, the shown balance will enter the final contribution with approximately 8 % weight for BAPV systems and 11 % for the BIPV systems. Despite the small final impact, a contribution of up to ~0,25 kg CO2 pr m2 pr year corresponds to 6-7% of the lowest GWP limit for buildings, this impact is with some significance, requiring GWP savings on other building parts.

In Figure 7 the lines represent the limits where the PV systems have a neutral influence on the GWP calculation of the buildings where sensitivity analysis is performed for various insolation values using average values for mounting systems and inverters. Dotted lines represent the extrema for mounting and inverters for the 1000 kWh/m2 base case.

As can be seen, neutral GWP contributions are reached at around 80 kg CO_2/m^2 for efficiencies above 22,5 % for the 1000 kWh/year base case, with most of the products being far from these limits. What can also be seen is careful choice of inverter and mounting system can facilitate a positive contribution.

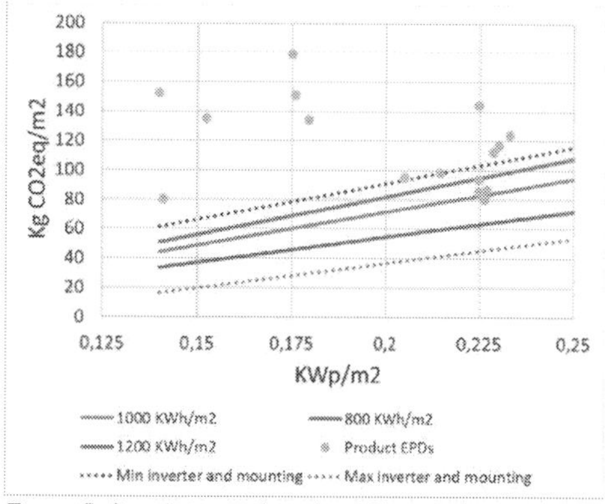

Figure 7: Sensitivity analysis for CO2 contribution

3.3 Emission factors

Prior to discussing the findings it is required to investigate the assumptions behind the emission factors for the Danish case which are shown in Figure 2. Inspecting the emission factors, it can be seen that the 2025 value is around 80 g CO_2/kWh and during the 5 first years fairly rapidly decreases to 30 g CO_2/kWh and from there on over 20 years is reduced to approximately 25 g CO_2/kWh. Based on [9] these numbers are derived from the expected electricity mix needed in the Danish grid to comply with the political aim of 70 % reduction in 2030 and carbon neutrality in 2050 using the national energy agency's forecast from 2022. This forecast (Figure 8) predicts an almost 4-fold increase in electricity production (whereof around 2/3 is expected to be used for P2X). This need is roughly covered by 75 % wind energy and 20 % solar energy and the remaining 5 % covering biomass-based generation and import of electricity.

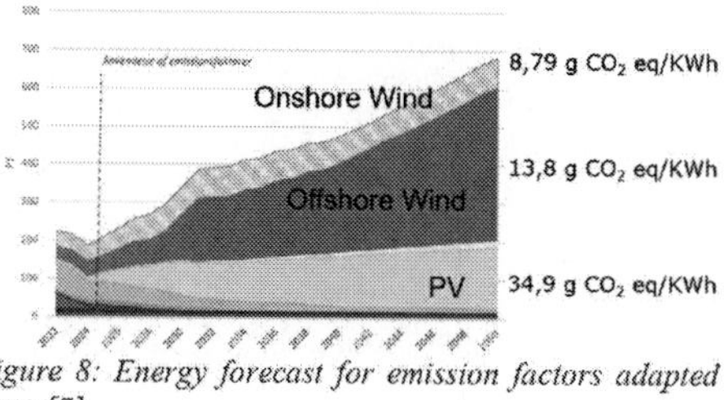

Figure 8: Energy forecast for emission factors adapted from [7].

PV on roof tops are excluded in these calculations, however only as a marginal share in Figure 10 (yellow patterned area). For biomass, only emissions related to processing and transportation are included as biomass is per EU definition sustainable.

In essence, the expected deployment of renewable energy is used to lower the value of the CO_2 displacement on buildings, and at the same time PV on buildings is contributing to lowering the grid emissions. This results in a circular relationship, negatively affecting the CO_2 displacement potential for buildings with marginalization to what exceeds the expected annual additions in renewable energy generation.

4 DISCUSSION

Overall these findings show that the addition of PV generally increases the building GWP according to Danish rules and insolation conditions - for certain products to an extend where compliance to the national GWP limits will require GWP savings elsewhere in the building design. The presented data assumes 2025 deployment, and with the decreasing emission factors later deployment will make the GWP increase even higher.

Denmark already has fairly low emissions from the grid and is especially via the rules in force expected to have so in the future. This results in a disincentive for PV on buildings, as CO_2 displacement is insufficient to compensate for the embedded GWP. In countries with higher emission factors the opposite may be true, with high CO_2 displacement by PV installations allowing the use more carbon-heavy construction products, while still staying within the limits.

Both cases are contradictory to the intentions of the EPBD, where solar PV on buildings is advocated, with buildings being expected to be a significant part of the energy system. The authors acknowledge the importance of a less carbon intensive construction sector, however the way PV is expected to be accounted for in the calculations is not desirable.

Furthermore, calculating the emission factors based on the expected deployment of renewable energy, including solar PV, is not desirable, as solar PV on buildings in most countries also contributes to lowering the emission factors. This results in a circular relationship, which can lead to undesirable effects. Further high political ambitions for carbon neutrality will decrease the GWP benefits, if all EU countries follow the Danish methods.

As has been the case for the past and will be the case in the future, the embodied emissions from the PV and other renewable sources will decrease. Therefore, the emission factors are expected to be updated based on more recent energy projections and LCA data and as the GWP

10.4229/EUPVSEC2025/5DO.11.3

benefit of PV scales with the difference between the embodied CO_2 emissions from the PV plant and the expected grid emissions, the time differences between the EPD and the emission factors publication dates becomes one of the most deciding factors. EPDs have in general a validity of 5 years.

All in all, with a fairly rapidly changing energy system developing towards electrification, the Danish implementation of EN 15978 seems to be an uncertain and volatile method for including PV in the GWP assessment of buildings, and therefore the method is not suitable and counteracts the intentions in the EPBD and associated policies. The challenges described for PV calls for a holistic assessment where PV on buildings are also regarded as a part of the energy system and not marginalized and compared to expected expansion of renewable energy as in the Danish case.

Based on the above, the authors do not see a feasible long-term solution for incorporating PV in a non-circular desirable manner via the EN 15978 standard. While the authors acknowledge that PV has to account for its embedded carbon, including them via the GWP of buildings as per the current methodology does not result in the desirable outcome.

A consensus should be found between the PV community and the construction sector to find a more appropriate method for assessing the GWP impact of PV on buildings. As such, IEA PVPS Task 15 activity A2 is working on expanding this analysis to other countries.

5 CONCLUSION

This study used valid environmental product declarations to assess the global warming potential of PV in buildings following Danish rules derived from EN 15978. The analysis shows that when both inverters and mounting systems are included, the addition of a BA- and BIPV system increases the global warming potential of a building. The increase is caused by a combination of approximately 10 times high load compared to commonly used roofing materials, the need for replacement of the PV system and especially the rapid decreasing emission factors calculated based on expected renewable energy deployment to reach political goals.

The method marginalizes PV, is volatile and uncertain, and therefore is not suitable for this assessment in the authors' opinion. It is debatable whether PV should be excluded from this assessment and assessed via other better suited methods, such as the upcoming Ecodesign rules.

6 ACKNOWLEDGEMENTS

This work was funded by EUDP as part of the "IEA PVPS Task 15 Phase 3" project under grant 134243-534202.

7 REFERENCES

[1] European Union **Directive (EU) 2024/1275 of the European Parliament and of the Council of 24 April 2024 on the energy performance of buildings 2024, https://eur-lex.europa.eu/legal-content/EN/TXT/?uri=OJ:L_202401275&pk_keyword=Energy&pk_content=Directive Last visited 1601-2025**

[2] Müller, A., Friedrich, L., Reichel, C., Herceg, S., Mittag, M., & Neuhaus, D. H. (2021). A comparative life cycle assessment of silicon PV modules: Impact of module design, manufacturing location and inventory. Solar Energy Materials and Solar Cells, 230, 111277. https://doi.org/10.1016/j.solmat.2021.111277

[3] Stucki, M., Götz, M., de Wild-Scholten, M., Frischknecht, R. IEA PVPS Task 12 2023. Fact sheet: Environmental Life Cycle Assessment of Electricity from PV Systems 2023 update. https://iea-pvps.org/wp-content/uploads/2024/05/Task-12-Fact-Sheet-v2-1.pdf

[4] Fares, Hafsa & Lobaccaro, Gabriele & Nouha, Gazbour & Nygaard Rasmussen, Freja & Chèze, David & Pierrès, Nolwenn & Wurtz, Etienne. (2025). A methodology for assessing environmental impact of building integrated PV in low carbon footprint electricity generation context. Energy and Buildings. 329. 115219. 10.1016/j.enbuild.2024.115219.

[5] Khan, A.A., Reichel, C., Molina, P., Friedrich, L., Subasi, D.M., Neuhaus, H., *et al.* (2024) Global Warming Potential of Photovoltaics with State-of-the Art Silicon Solar Cells: Influence of Electricity Mix, Installation Location and Lifetime. *Solar Energy Materials and Solar Cells*, 269, Article 112724. https://doi.org/10.1016/j.solmat.2024.112724

[6] Jonathan Grinham, Henning Fjeldheim, Bin Yan, Tor Dokka Helge, Kristian Edwards, Tine Hegli, Ali Malkawi, Zero-carbon balance: The case of HouseZero, Building and Environment, Volume 207, Part B, 2022, 108511, https://doi.org/10.1016/j.buildenv.2021.108511.

[7] Sustainability of construction works – Assessment of environmental performance of buildings – Calculation method : DS/EN 15978:2011

[8] https://www.bygningsreglementet.dk/tekniske-bestemmelser/11/krav/

[9] Mathilde Sørensen Nilsson, Linda Høibye og Steffen Enersen Maagaard, Emissionsfaktorer El, fjernvarme og ledningsgas 2025-2075, Artelia 2023 https://www.sbst.dk/Media/638282171394687135/Emissionsfaktorer%20for%20el%20fjernvarme%20og%20ledningsgas%20for%202025-2075.pdf (visited Jan 17th 2025)

[10] Social og Bolig styrelsen 2025, Danish Generic data, https://www.bygningsreglementet.dk/media/1o1nnozd/tabel-7-2025.xlsx (visited August 14th 2025)

[11] https://www.oekobaudat.de/en.html (visited August 14th 2025)

[12] Kragh, J., & Birgisdottir, H. (2023). *Udvikling af dansk generisk LCA-data*. (1 udg.) Institut for Byggeri, By og Miljø (BUILD), Aalborg Universitet. BUILD Rapport Bind 2023 Nr. 16

DTU

Evaluating the impact of photovoltaics for lifecycle global warming potential of buildings according to EN 15978 - a Danish Case Study

Sune Thorsteinsson, Nanna L. Andersen, Markus Babin, Gisele A. dos Reis Benatto
Technical University of Denmark, Department of Electrical and Photonics Engineering, 4000 Roskilde, Denmark
sunth@dtu.dk

DTU

Content

1. Motivation
2. Introduction to EN15978(:2011)
3. Collected EPD data
4. Danish Case study
5. Immediate conclusions
6. Discussion

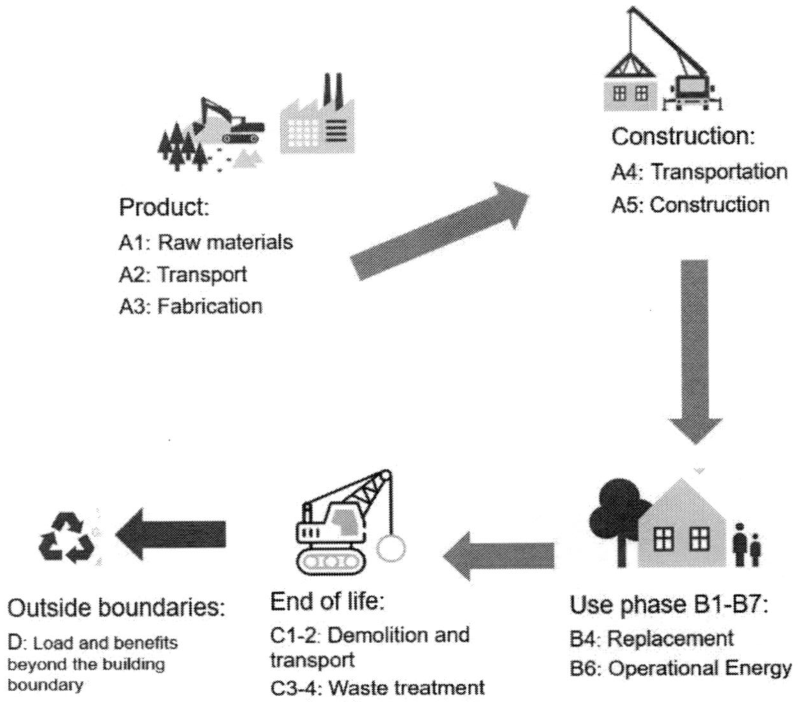

DTU

Motivation

The newly agreed Energy performance directive for Buildings in EU (EPDB), demands:

- All (new) buildings to be solar ready
- Implemented in National buildings codes

However, what is overlooked in the PV-industry:

- EPD article 7.2 and Annex III:
  - Whole life Carbon via EN15978
  - Consideration period 50 years

- Whole life carbon (WLC) of buildings provides significant CO_2 emissions

Overview of **whole life carbon** regulations and initiatives across Europe

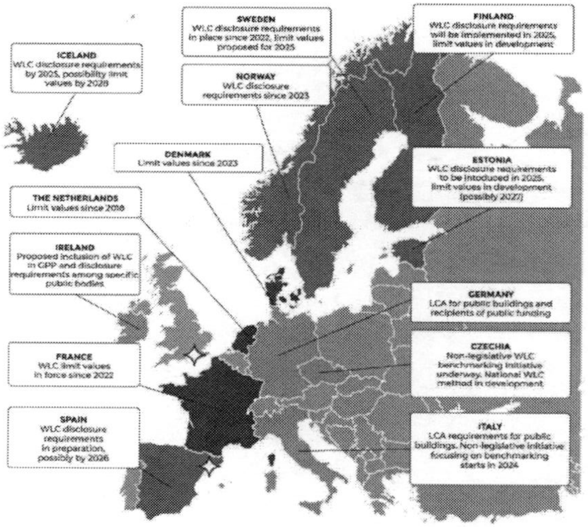

- WLC regulation with limit values in force
- WLC disclosure requirements in force
- WLC legislation (disclosure/limit values) proposed
- Other non-legislative requirements in place or preparing for WLC measurement and benchmarking

BPIE (Buildings Performance Institute Europe) (2025). Defining a common vision for climate neutral buildings: a comprehensive and harmonised framework for whole-life carbon measurement across Europe. https://www.bpie.eu/publication/defining-a-common-vision-for-climate-neutral-buildings-a-comprehensive-and-harmonised-framework-for-whole-life-carbon-measurement-across-europe/

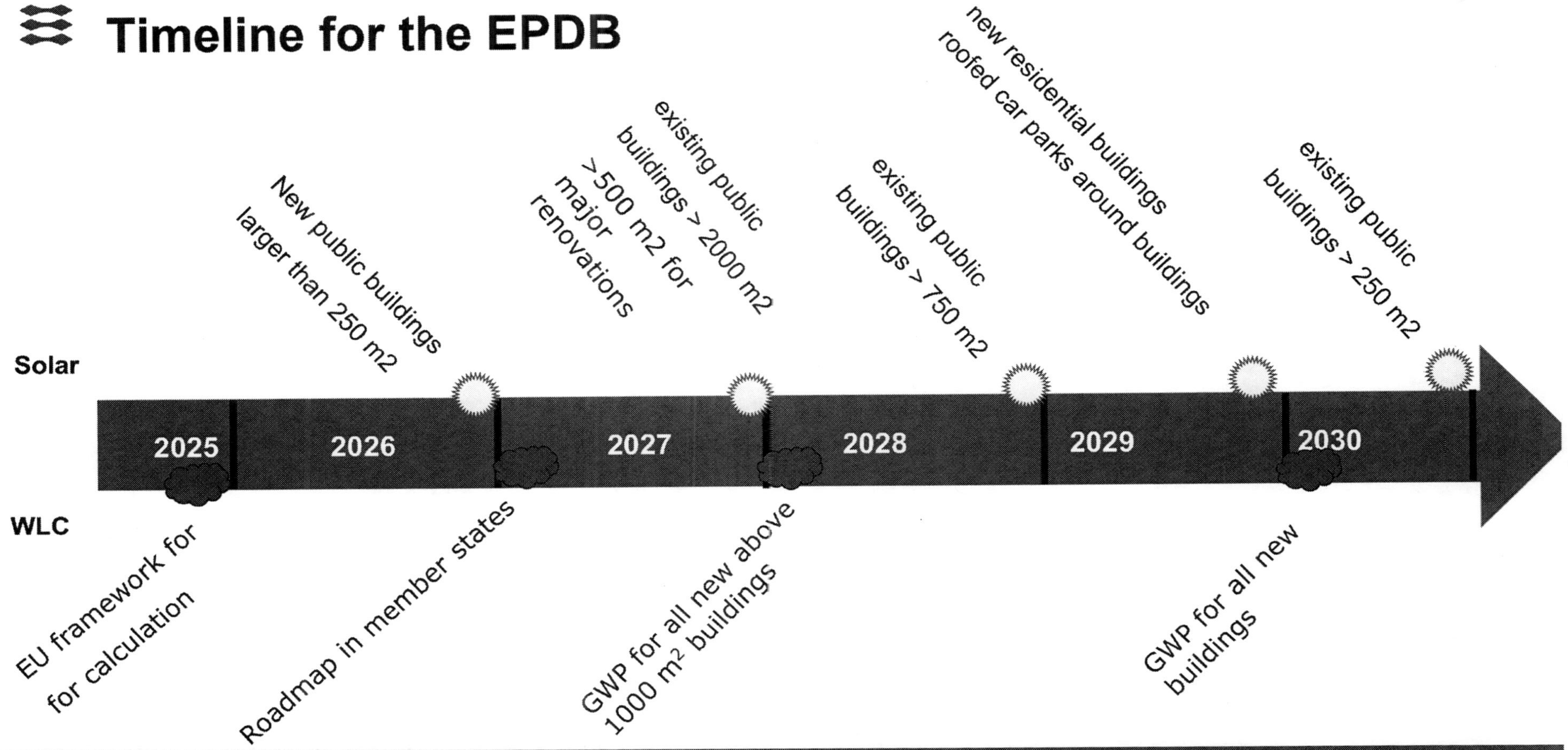
DTU
Timeline for the EPDB
Solar
WLC
2025
2026
2027
2028
2029
2030
New public buildings
larger than 250 m2
existing public
buildings > 2000 m2
>500 m2 for
major
renovations
existing public
buildings > 750 m2
new residential buildings
roofed car parks around buildings
existing public
buildings > 250 m2
EU framework for
for calculation
Roadmap in member states
GWP for all new above
1000 m2 buildings
GWP for all new
buildings
Date
DTU
Title
4

DTU

Few facts on PV and GWP

- **PVs have 10-15 times higher CO_2 load than most roofs**
  - Important to use the PV energy for CO_2 displacement
    - Data collected from:
      - Environmental product declarations (EPDs)
      - Ökobaudat
- **Around ~2/3 of the GWP load is from cell production (C-Si)**
  - Similar load for buildings and other applications

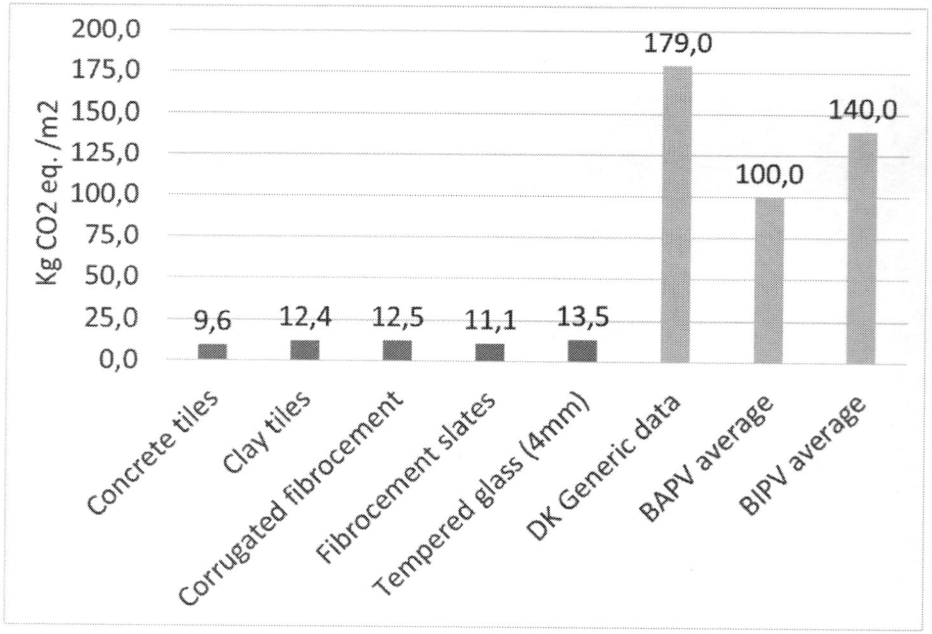

DTU

EN 15978(:2011) Sustainability of construction works

- **Calculate the Whole life LCA of Buildings**
  - Cradle to Grave approach
  - Sums **all** the loads and benefits of all modules

NB direct implementation of EN 15978:2011

- BIPV -full load of PV system
- Only displace CO_2 from operational energy (smaller fraction)

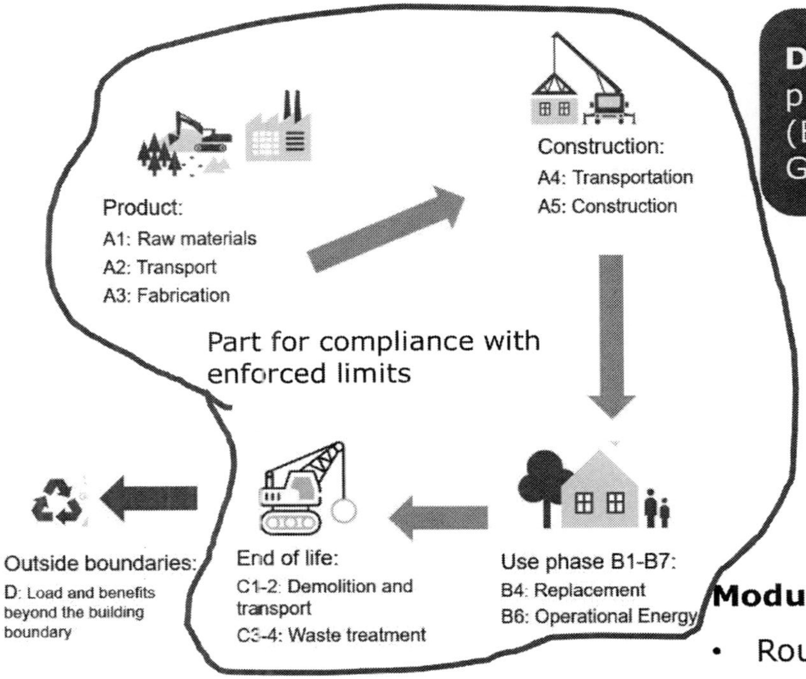

Data: Environmental product declarations (EPDs) or national Generic Data

Module B:

- Rounded up replacements
- Loads from only operational energy substitute with "Most likely impacts"

DTU

Danish Implementation

- Implementation
  - Follows EN15978, include
    - Significant impact phases included
    - Reference study period 50 years
  - **Danish Limits 4-8 kg CO_2 eq/(m^2 (floor area)*year)**

  - **Include PV if part of energy performance compliance (up to 13.2) kWh/(m^2*year)**
    - Include inverters and "stands"
    - **BIPV roofing:**
    - PV exceeding energy performance compliance, use "cover glass"
  - GWP load of operational energy - use published emission factors

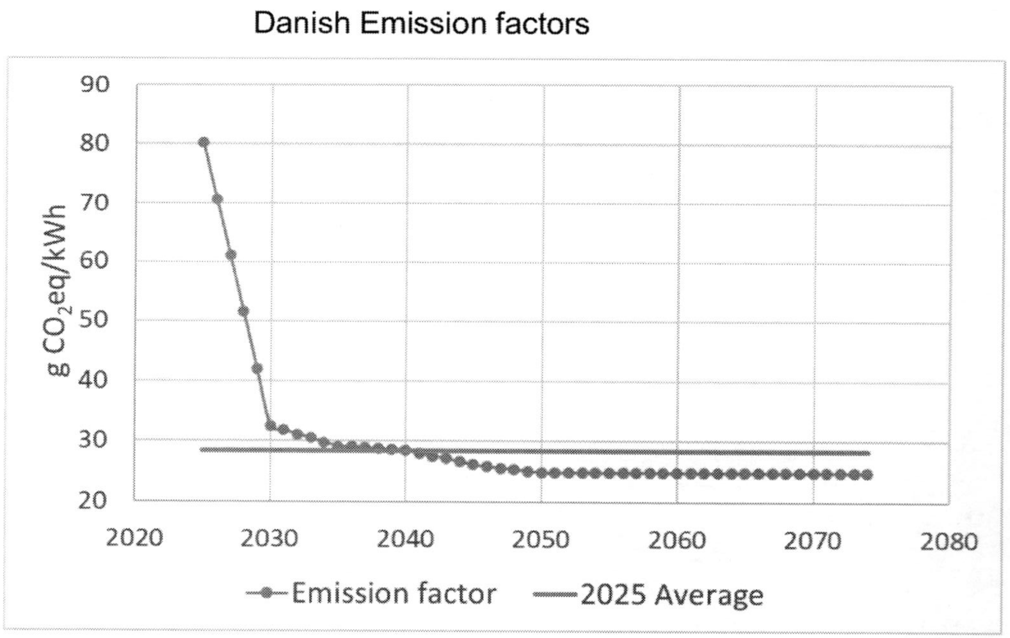

DTU

Collected EPDs

Methods:

1. Collected Environmental product declarations (EPDs) for:

- BAPV panels (10)
- BIPV panels (7)
- Inverters (9) (6kW-300 kW)
- Mounting systems for roofs (4)

2. Summed for the included Danish phases

➢ Panels largest contributors
➢ Inverters and mounting structures contributes

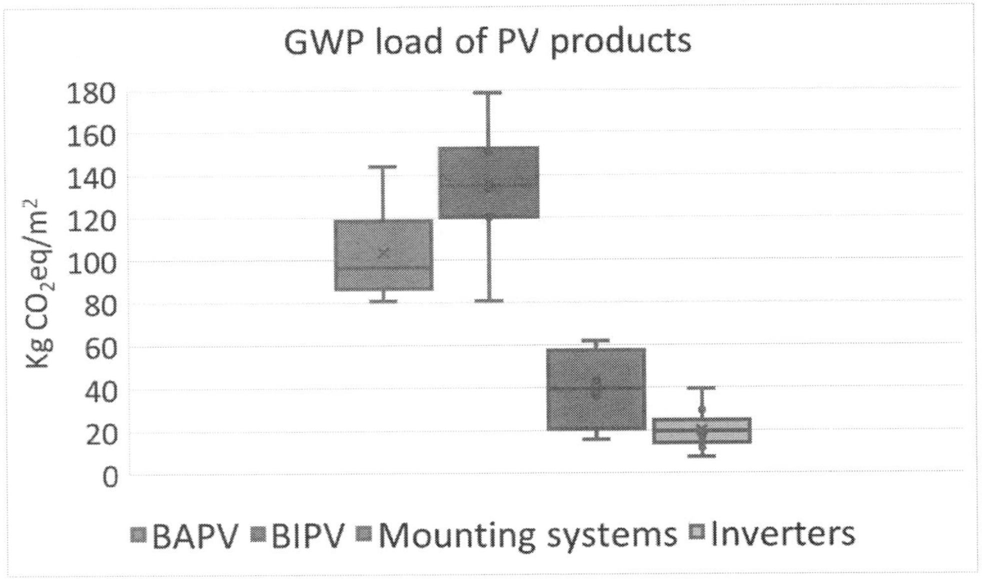

	BAPV	BIPV	Mounting	Inverter
Average system (kg CO_2eq/m^2)	159,0	159,0		
Relative Share	63%	87%	25%	13%

Inverters converted from WP to m^2 assuming 20% module efficiency
And DC AC ratio of 1.3
Mounting systems excluded from BIPV

DTU

Danish Case study

Example calculation:

- Calculated the impact of 1m² PV (Danish rules, 2025 deployment)
- CO_2 balance vs time (Average BAPV)
- Replacement after 25 years
  - First plant almost neutral
  - Second plant adds CO2 to the building
    - Energy estimations based on PR method

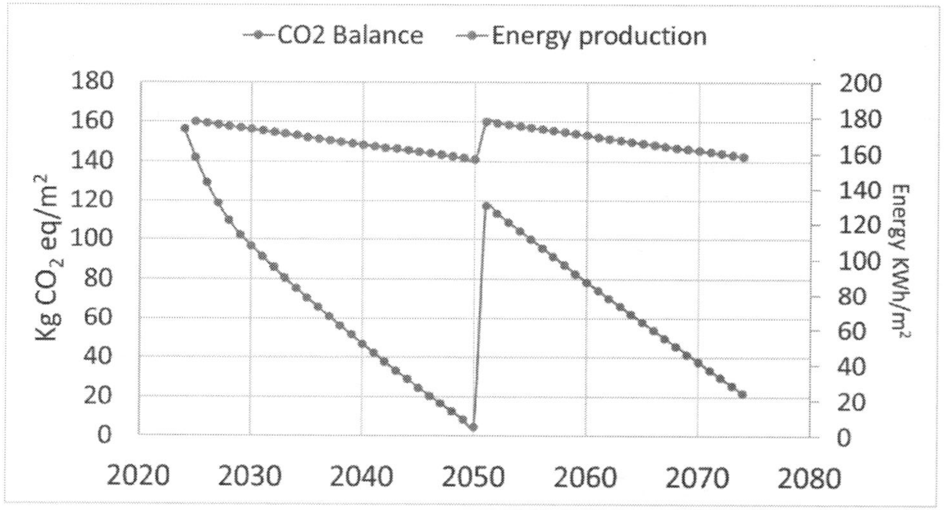

Assumptions (Typical Danish conditions)	
GHI	1000 kWh/m2
Pr	0,8
Degradation	0,5 % P.a
DC to AC Ratio	1,3
Lifetime panels and inverters	25 years
Lifetime Mounting	50 years

Performance ratio based method

$$E_{year,n} = \frac{H}{G_{stc}} * Pr * Y * (1-d)^i$$

CO_2 displacement

$$GWP(t)_{year,n} = \sum GWP_{EPD} - \sum_{0}^{n} E_{year,i}\epsilon_i$$

DTU

Danish Case study

Methods:

1. Collected Environmental product declarations (EPDs) for:

2. Calculated the GWP impact acc to Danish law:

Findings:

- Almost all PV products increases the GWP of the building!!
- For BIPV, Material savings not significant

- Contribution to final building GWP (depends on building)
  - But can be significant

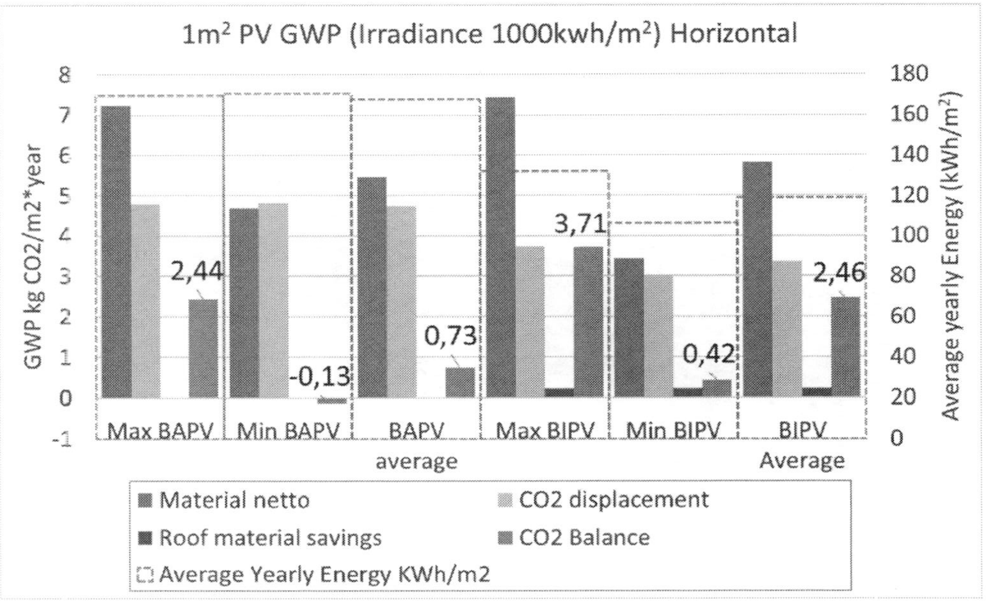

Danish Limits 4-8 kg CO_2 eq/(m^2 (floorarea)*year)

DTU

Danish Case study – Emission factors

- Based on the national energy agency's forecast on national electricity mix from 2022

- **Forecast made to achieve political ambitions**
  - Carbon neutrality in 2050
  - 70% reduction in 2030
  - 4 fold increase in electricity production towards 2050
  - Biomass combustion excluded

  …

  Most~ covered by Wind and (Land based) PV

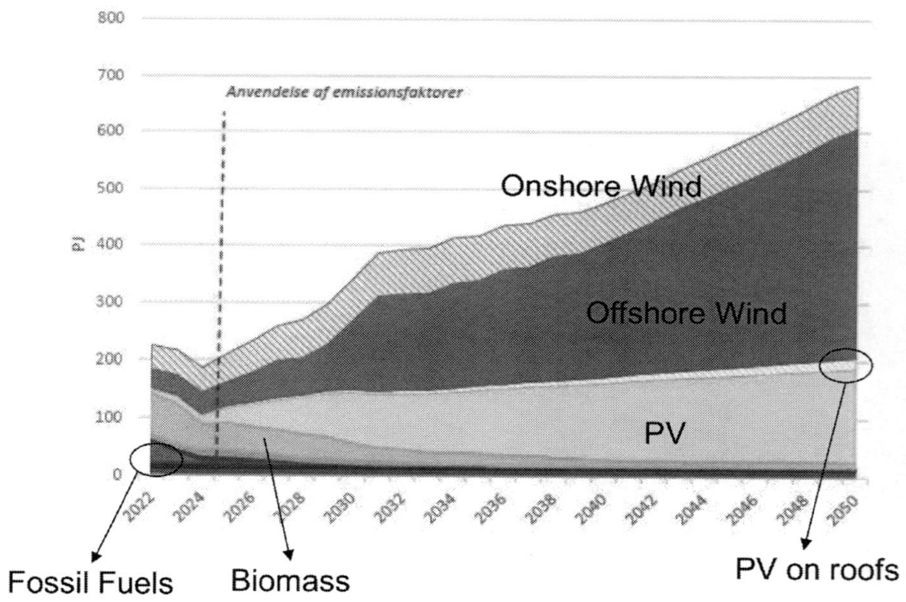

DTU

Danish Case study – Emission factors

- Derived based on the national energy agencies forecast on national electricity mix in 2022

Findings

- Emission factors reduced with expected deployment of Renewable Energy (RE) incl PV
- CO_2 displacement for PV on buildings is **Circular** and **Marginal**:
  - PV on buildings contributes to lower grid emissions
  - Displacement for PV
    - What exceeds expected deployment of RE
- High political RE ambitions – low benefits of PV on buildings

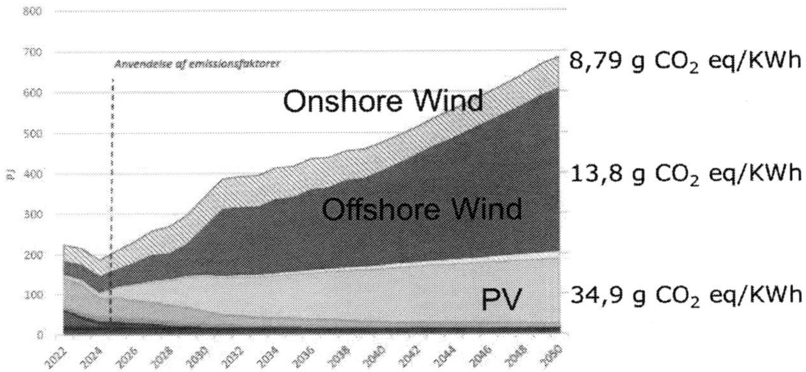

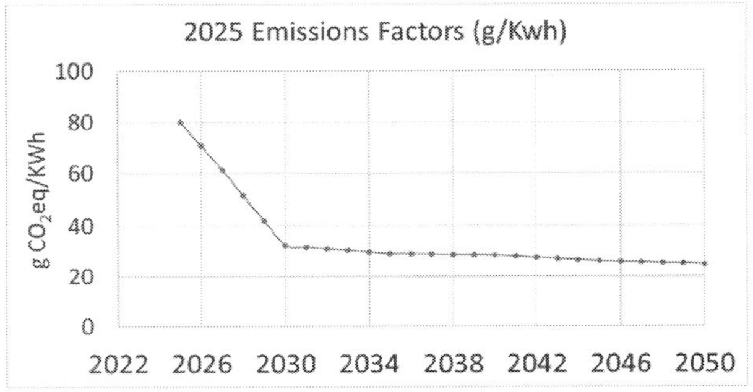

https://www.sbst.dk/Media/638282171394687135/Emissionsfaktorer%20for%20el%20fjernvarme%20og%20ledningsgas%20for%202025-2075.pdf

DTU

Conclusions

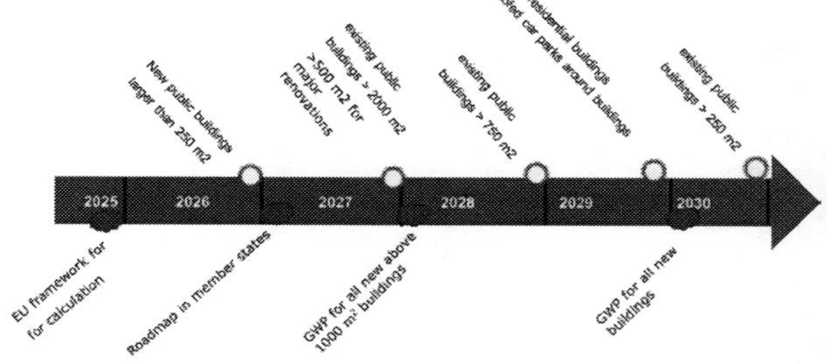

- GWP calculations required for all buildings in whole EU
- PV on buildings increases GWP in Danish implementation
- Benefits of PV **inversely** linked to political ambitions
- High emission factors (in other countries) facilitates use of carbon heavy materials
- BIPV challenge: Only a minor fraction of a BIPV installation can displace CO_2 despite full GWP load acc. To EN15978:2011
- **Overall Danish implementation not desirable for PV on buildings and against the intentions of the EPBD.**

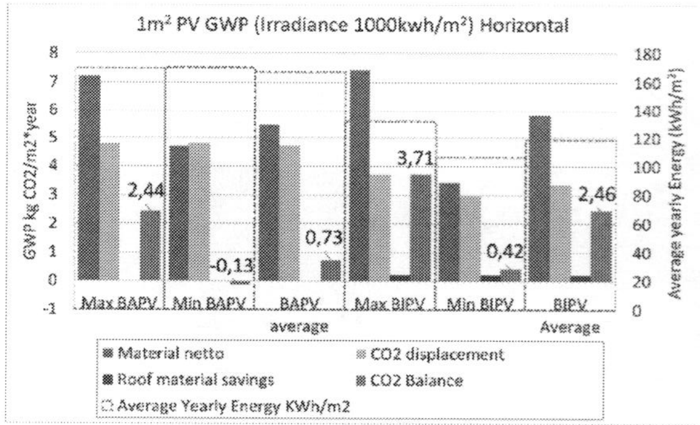

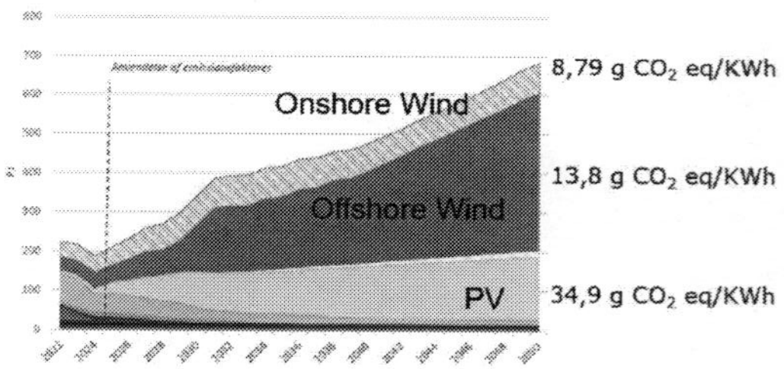

DTU

Maybe time for Reflection

- The Authors personally don't find this method long term sustainable!
- Time to step back and go beyond various standards with sector focus
  - evaluate these methods for PV in a holistic setting

https://nbi.ku.dk/english/www/niels/bohr/koebenhavnerfo-tolkningen/

.... Similar to Bohr, Heisenberg and Pauli
100 years ago Discussed Quantum Mechanics

DTU

Discussion

Is there here a flaw in the EPDB directive?

Should PV be excluded in the GWP assessment of buildings?

Is it better ECO-design framework for the environmental footprint of PV?

Is it at all desirable that Building LCA benefits for PV is tied to the national grid emissions (and ambitions for RE deployment)

IEA PVPS TASK 15 A2, is working on this:

"BIPV in the environmental labelling"

Join if you can contribute

Visit 5DV.2.1 today @ 10:30.

"Expected deployment of renewable energy among PV is used to decrease the benefit of PV on buildings"

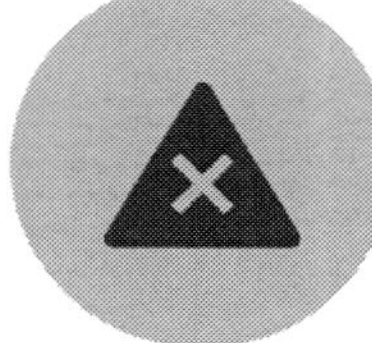

DTU

sunth@dtu.dk

Thank you

Date DTU Title 16

DTU

Module B

Relevant for PV:

- **B4: Replacement**
  - Rounded up number of replacements to reach consideration period 50 Years:
    - EG: PV lifetime of 30 years
      - » Full load of one replacement (not 2/3 replacement)
- **B6: Energy**
  - Only include operational energy (both on side produced and imported)
    - Operational energy for building operation (heat, ventilation etc.)
    - **Not energy from occupants** (Cooking, washing etc.)
  - … and to CO2 equivalents

"The net environmental benefits and/or loads of energy…. By calculating the substituted impacts … from the most likely corresponding energy supply based on current average technology and practice" (EN15978:2011)

Use phase B1-B7:

B1: Use

B2: Maintenance

B3: Reparation

B4: Replacement

B5: Renovation

B6: Operational Energy

B7: Operational water use

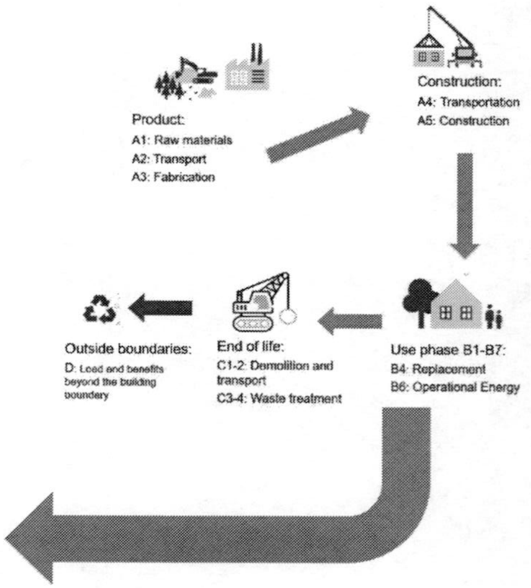

DTU

LCA requirements for PV in a danish context

"Sensitivity analysis"

- "Required" GWP/m^2 as a function of efficiency.
  - PV to have zero GWP influence
  - Product EPDs as Datapoints.

Results

- Requirements ~80 kg CO2/m2 for the base case if installed efficiency is 22.5%
- Only one product fulfills that
- Choice of inverter and mounting system is important
- For 2026 deployment its "worse"

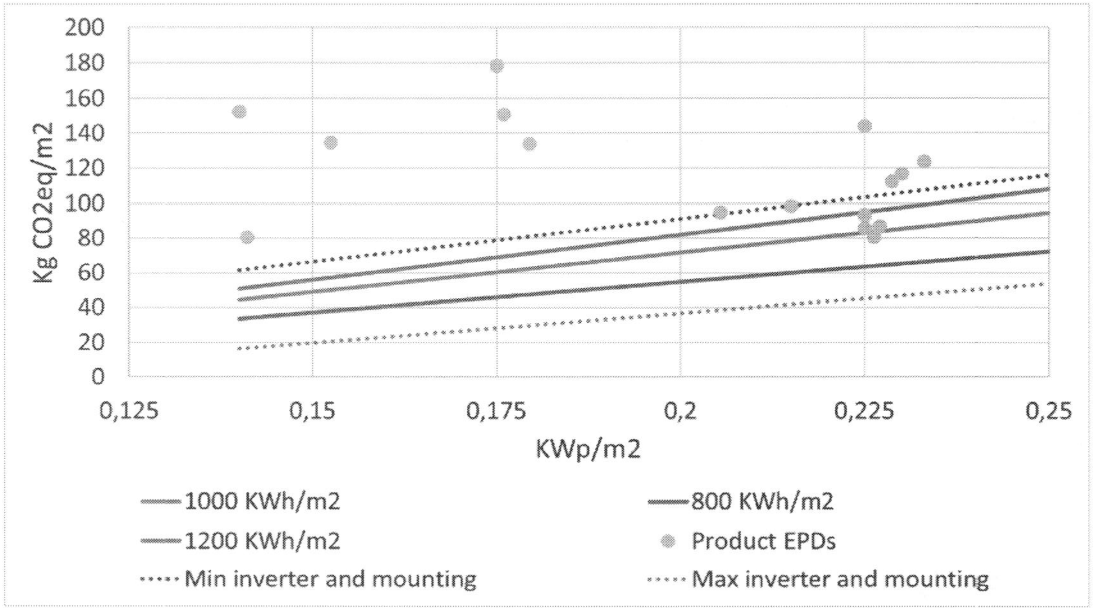

DTU

EN 15978(:2011) Sustainability of construction works

- **Get rid of text, center figure and add text on the phases where relevant**
- **Calculate the Whole life LCA of Buildings**
  - Cradle to Grave approach
  - Sums **all** the loads and benefits of all materials, processes and utilities used for the building construction and operation
  - **Data:** Environmental product declarations or national Generic Data In a cloud
  - **Operational phase (Module B) Higlightthe NB statement**
    - Rounded up replacements
    - Loads from only operational energy substitute with “Most likely impacts”
- Only Phases A-C to be used for compliance with limits

NB direct implementation of 15978:2011

➢ BIPV -full load of PV system

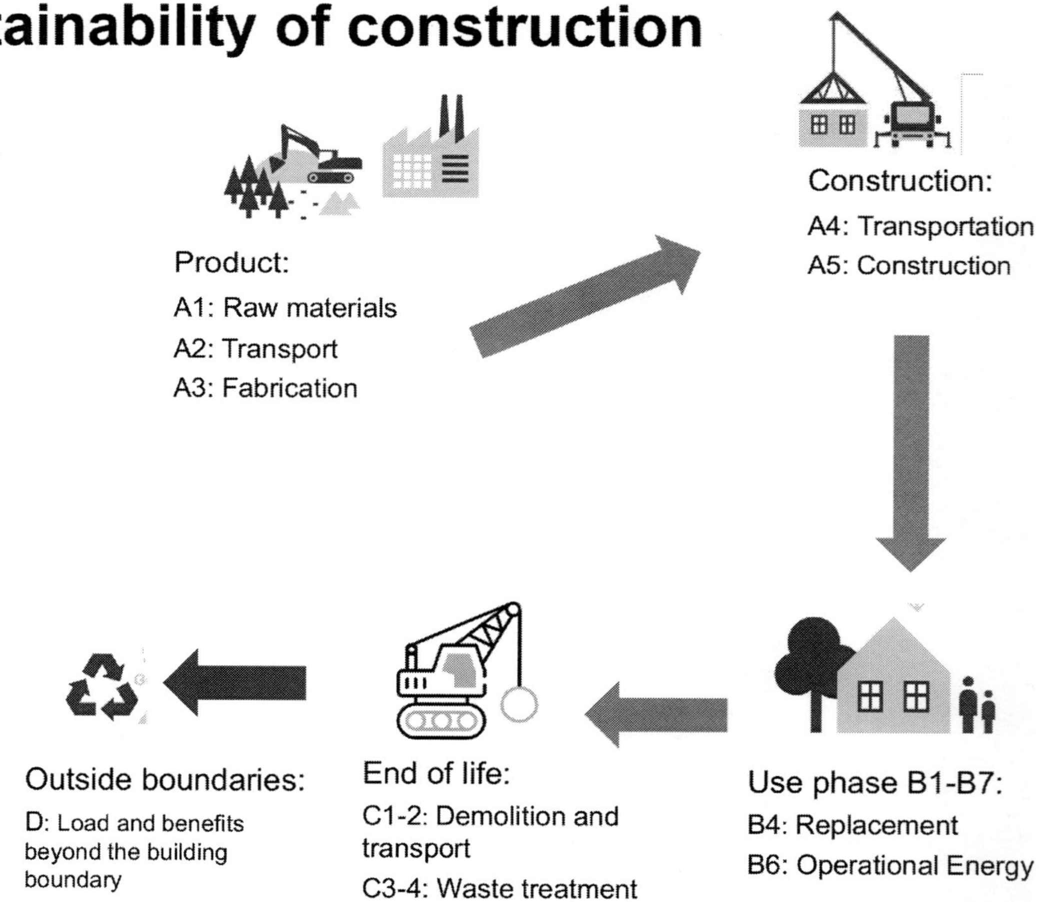

42nd European Photovoltaic Solar Energy Conference and Exhibition

This presentation was selected by the Sc. Committee of the EU PVSEC 2025 for submission of a full paper to one of the EU PVSEC's collaborating peer-reviewed journals.

ENERGY RETURN ON INVESTMENT TRENDS OF SOLAR PV IN THE ENERGY TRANSITION

Hasret Sahin[1], A.A. Solomon[1,2], Christian Breyer[1]
[1] School of Energy Systems, LUT University, Lappeenranta, Finland
[2] School of Technology and Innovations, University of Vaasa, Finland
Corresponding author: Hasret Sahin, hasret.sahin@lut.fi

ABSTRACT: Solar photovoltaics (PV) is expected to play a central role in the global energy transition, yet its long-term energy requirements for its installations and operations are often underestimated. This study examines the evolution of energy return on investment (EROI) for solar PV systems between 2015 and 2050 across nine world regions. The analysis uses a dynamic modelling framework that combines life cycle assessment with cost-optimised system modelling, considering both utility-scale and prosumer-scale systems under five transition pathways. These include three rapid transition scenarios aiming for 100% renewable energy by 2035, 2040, and 2050, and two International Energy Agency scenarios that reflect more conservative policy projections. The findings show that under accelerated transitions, utility-scale PV achieves consistent improvements, with most regions converging to EROI values between 30 and 45 by mid-century. The highest outcomes are recorded in the Middle East and Africa, supported by large-scale adoption of single-axis tracking technologies. Prosumer-scale PV systems improve more gradually but still approach an EROI of 30 in most regions. By contrast, conservative scenarios deliver more uneven results, with strong performance in high-resource regions such as the Middle East but much weaker progress elsewhere. These findings highlight that the scale and configuration of solar PV deployment are decisive in shaping long-term energy returns.
Keywords: Solar photovoltaics; EROI; life cycle impact assessment; energy transition.

1 INTRODUCTION

The accelerated deployment of renewable energy (RE) technologies entails considerable embedded energy requirements, which are frequently underrepresented in feasibility assessments [1] [2] [3] [4]. This issue is particularly salient for solar photovoltaics (PV), given their anticipated central role in future electricity generation [5]. As a widely applied metric, physical energy return on investment (EROI), defined as the ratio of usable energy output to the cumulative energy inputs across the entire lifecycle, enables a detailed evaluation of the performance of RE systems [6] [7] [8]. However, reported physical EROI values for solar PV systems vary considerably, influenced by differences in technology type, methodological choices, geographic conditions, and reliance on outdated data [4] [9] [10]. In addition, most existing studies do not account for energy learning rates (ELRs), standardise energy quality across primary sources, and incorporate dynamic systemwide interactions [4] [11] [12].

To address this gap, the present study investigates the dynamic evolution of solar PV EROI trends by using the LUT Energy System Transition Model (LUT-ESTM) [13] [14] with LUT standing for Lappeenranta-Lahti University of Technology. This study briefly introduces the LUT-EROI model for application at technology level. The analysis applies five energy transition (ET) pathways, three LUT-Best Policy Scenarios (LUT-BPS) and two International Energy Agency (IEA) scenarios [15], across nine regions. By integrating life cycle assessment (LCA) with cost-optimised energy system modelling and employing cumulative energy demand (CED) as a key impact indicator, the study provides a comprehensive evaluation of how the EROI of only solar PV systems develops between 2015 and 2050 under contrasting the ET conditions.

2 MATERIALS AND METHOD

This study evaluates the energy requirements of solar PV systems and the evolution of their EROI across nine regions within a systemwide, full sector energy modelling framework. Notably, most technology-level analyses of solar PV EROI are conducted in isolation from the broader power system, which limits the ability to capture the effects of capacity expansion, solar PV deployment dynamics, and system-level interactions with sufficient accuracy [16] [17]. Accordingly, this study analyses systemwide EROI trends for solar PV systems under five transition scenarios introduced by Aghahosseini et al. [15]. These include three LUT-BPS, which examine the effects of accelerated transition timelines (2035, 2040, and 2050), and two IEA scenarios re-simulated within the LUT-ESTM for consistency [14] [15]. The assessment spans nine global regions to capture geographical heterogeneity, with full scenario descriptions and results available in Aghahosseini et al. [15].

2.1 Summary of the energy transition scenarios

The LUT-ESTM is a cost-optimisation model that resolves hourly energy flows across a full year [13] [14]. It is designed to capture near- and medium-term transition pathways towards 100% RE systems, while incorporating external constraints for long-term objectives. The model is applicable at national, regional, and global scales, with an emphasis on RE integration and sector coupling [13] [15].

Within this framework, five scenarios are assessed. The three LUT-BPS scenarios aim to achieve a 100% RE system by 2035, 2040, and 2050, minimising the role of fossil fuels and nuclear power while maintaining cost-effectiveness [15]. For comparison, two IEA scenarios are included: the IEA Sustainable Development Scenario (IEA-SDS), which reflects a Paris Agreement–aligned pathway with expanded roles for nuclear power and carbon capture and sequestration, and the IEA Stated Policy Scenario (IEA-STEPS), which represents a business-as-usual scenario based on current policy commitments [15] [18] [19].

The reason for selecting five different scenarios is the clear treatment of technology switching and replacement, which is a decisive factor in shaping the pace of solar PV systems expansion [4].

2.2 Quantification of energy use for solar PV systems

Energy use is quantified through CED, a standard LCA indicator that captures both direct and indirect inputs [20]. However, differences in system boundaries, data quality, and regional specificity often limit comparability [8] [21] [22]. An additional challenge is the lack of harmonised methods for accounting for qualitative differences among primary energy sources [12], which reduces the robustness of CED-based assessments. Addressing these issues requires a transparent, systemwide framework capable of tracing cascading energy flows. Such an approach involves the development of consistent life cycle inventories, rigorous system-level analysis, and the integration of technical and financial assumptions into energy modelling tools in line with their operational principles.

In this study, CED values are derived from the ecoinvent v3.7.1 database and converted from primary energy equivalent ($MJ_{pe\text{-}eq}$) to an electricity-equivalent basis (MJ_{el}) using standardised conversion factors, following the approaches of Solomon et al. [12] and Sahin et al. [4] [9]. To provide a more detailed representation, structural energy use (construction and decommissioning) is expressed per unit of capacity (MJ_{el}/kW), while operational energy use is expressed per unit of electricity generated (MJ_{el}/kWh), with full load hours treated as part of the operational phase. All PV-related CED values are reorganised by lifecycle stage and adjusted for technological improvements and ELRs at five-year intervals [4] [11] as well as considering technology shifts in the current and future markets. The reference CED value is estimated which decline by 52% in 2050 compared to 2015 level [4] as illustrated in Figure 1.

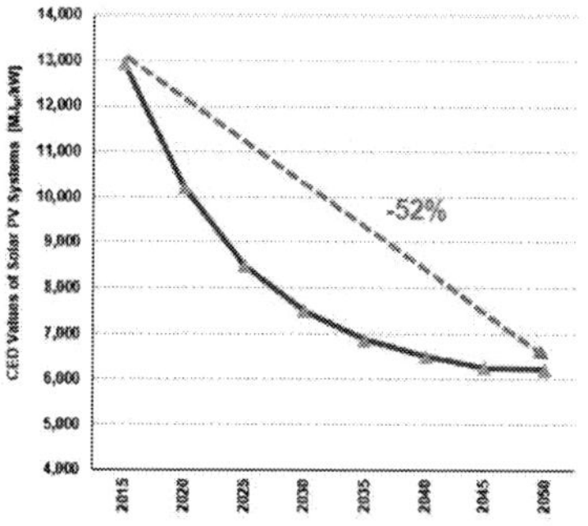

Figure 1: Changes in the CED values of solar PV systems over the years, considering ELRs values [4] [11]. The red line represents the CED values of solar PV systems (MJ_{el}/kW).

Transmission and distribution are excluded, as their contribution to CED is negligible and does not affect EROI estimates. The comprehensive CED database employed in this study is documented in Sahin et al. [17], while the systemwide EROI methodology is detailed in the studies of Solomon et al. [5] and Sahin et al. [4].

2.3 Technology level LUT-EROI model

The physical EROI is defined as the ratio of usable energy output to the total energy invested across a technology's lifecycle. The LUT-EROI framework extends this concept to a systemwide perspective, allowing the integration of power-to-X technologies and establishing a link between technology-specific and system-level results. In this study, the LUT-EROI methodology of Sahin et al. [4] is followed, but the calculation scope is adjusted from systemwide to technology level.

After conversion of CED values from $MJ_{pe\text{-}eq}$ to MJ_{el}, structural CED values are expressed as $E_{capacity}$ (MJ_{el}/kW), representing construction and decommissioning phases, while operational CED values are denoted as $E_{operation}$ (MJ_{el}/kWh) (see Equation 1). Note that $E_{operation}$ only contains yearly upstream fuel supply chain energy requirements for producing the necessary fuels (excluding their intrinsic energy content) and consumables used in operation. For natural gas and oil, dynamic decline functions from Delannoy et al. [23] are applied, expressed in MJ_{el}/kWh, whereas coal is modelled with a fixed exponential decay rate following Sgouridis et al. [24]. For other fuels, upstream energy requirements are taken directly from the ecoinvent database and adjusted to align with this study's modelling assumptions. In the next step, $E_{operation}$ is adjusted to a lifetime perspective by accounting for variations in full load hours. Within a systemwide energy framework, technologies do not operate at their maximum rated load but instead function alongside other technologies, reflecting the integrated operating conditions of the system. Accordingly, for each solar PV system type (fixed-tilted, single-axis, and prosumer-based), the respective full load hours (FLH) and lifetimes are applied to determine the final operational values. These are then combined with $E_{capacity}$ to estimate the total lifecycle energy investment for each solar PV system type. In Equation 1, $E_{inv_{t,n}}$ represents the total lifecycle energy investment for technology, t, where n is the capacity unit (expressed in kW). LT_t states the lifetime of the technology.

$$E_{inv_{t,n}} = E_{capacity} + \left(E_{operation} \cdot FLH \cdot LT_t\right) \qquad \text{(Eq.1)}$$

Once $E_{inv_{t,n}}$ is calculated for all solar PV system types, it is normalised by the respective technology lifetime to obtain annual energy investments. This step is necessary because (i) CED values vary over time with ELRs, which is assumed to 14% [11] and (ii) the energy requirements for new solar PV system installations and decommissioning activities also change over time. In Equation 2, the annual electricity generation term ($ES_{t,year}$) is represented as gross generation, since estimating net output for solar PV systems would require location-specific grid loss data, which differs widely across regions. Technology-specific EROI ($EROI_{t,year}$) is calculated using $Capacity_t$, which represents the cumulative installed capacity of each solar PV systems. This is derived by combining the energy investments of newly installed and decommissioned units with the previous year's capacity. In doing so, the method generates dynamic CED values over time and provides more reliable estimates than approaches that assume constant values, particularly for solar PV systems.

$$\mathrm{EROI}_{t,year} = \frac{\mathrm{ES}_{t,year}}{\sum_{n=1}^{N_t} \frac{E_{inv_{t,n}}}{\mathrm{LT}_t} \cdot \mathrm{Capacity}_t} \quad \text{(Eq.2)}$$

Technology-specific solar PV systems' EROI values are assessed at five-year intervals for the period 2015–2050. Further methodological details regarding the systemwide EROI are available in Sahin et al. [4].

3 RESULTS AND DISCUSSION

This section begins with a concise overview of solar PV growth across nine regions under five scenarios, drawing on the study of Aghahosseini et al. [15]. It then provides analysis about the EROI trends of solar PV systems per regions. The analysis considers only grid-connected PV capacities and does not include storage options or off-grid systems.

3.1 Regional perspectives on Solar PV expansion during the energy transition

Solar PV deployment rises steeply across all regions under the LUT-BPS scenarios, in sharp contrast to the modest growth projected by the IEA pathways. By 2050, total installed capacity reaches 52.9 TW in LUT-BPS2035 and 58 TW in both LUT-BPS2040 and LUT-BPS2050, while the IEA-SDS and IEA-STEPS cases reach only 10.9 TW and 7.7 TW, respectively. Utility-scale PV systems dominate in every scenario, though their technological composition differs. In the LUT-BPS scenarios, single-axis tracking systems provide around 61% of the total capacity by 2050, with fixed-tilted systems contributing 20–22%. In the IEA scenarios, the balance shifts, with fixed-tilted systems accounting for 94% in the IEA-SDS and 67% in IEA-STEPS. Trackers play a secondary role, appearing only in the IEA-SDS where they reach 20% of the capacity mix. Prosumers-scale solar PV are most prominent in the LUT-BPS2035, reaching 19% due to the shorter ET period favouring distributed uptake, while their shares fall to 17% in other LUT-BPSs and drop further under the IEA scenarios, to 6% in the IEA-SDS and 13% in the IEA-STEPS.

Europe and Eurasia show a distinct pattern, relying heavily on fixed-tilted and prosumer systems. By 2050, fixed-tilted systems represent 7–10% of regional capacity under the LUT-BPS scenarios, with prosumers contributing about 2%. Single-axis trackers remain absent altogether. Under the IEA scenarios, fixed-tilted deployment falls to 6% in Europe and is negligible in Eurasia, while prosumers stagnate at very low levels. In Middle East and North Africa (MENA), Sub-Saharan Africa (SSA), Southeast Asia (SE-Asia), and the South Asian Association for Regional Cooperation (SAARC), the dominant role of utility-scale PV capacity is reinforced. LUT-BPS results show single-axis tracking system rising to 4–9% of capacity by 2050, though fixed-tilted systems remain relevant only in SAARC (8%). In the IEA scenarios, the only significant uptake of tracking system appears in MENA under the IEA-STEPS, reaching 20%. Instead, SAARC records higher fixed-tilted shares, with both IEA-SDS and IEA-STEPS reaching 15%. Prosumer-scale implementation remains minor across all four regions, never exceeding 1–2%. South America (S-Am) represents a clear outlier: by 2050, single-axis tracking PV accounts for just 2-3% in the LUT-BPS, and a comparable share of fixed-tilted systems in the IEA scenarios. The growth in the prosumers remain limited to about 1% in the LUT-BPS and negligible under the IEA scenarios.

The most dynamic growth is concentrated in Northeast Asia (NE-Asia) and North America (N-Am), which stands out as the most single-axis tracking-intensive regions under the LUT-BPS scenarios. By 2050, single-axis tracking PV system accounts for more than 20% of global PV capacity in N-Am and 22% in NE-Asia. Prosumer-scale system is also more important in these regions, contributing 3-8%, while fixed-tilted systems decline to residual levels (2% or less). In the IEA scenarios, the pattern reverses: fixed-tilted systems account for 15-35% of total capacity, while single-axis tracking systems fall to negligible levels. Prosumer-scale deployment is only visible in NE-Asia, where it stabilises at a modest 7–8%.

3.2 Technology-specific EROI trends of solar PV across regions

The assessment of EROI for utility-scale PV systems provides critical insights into how technology deployment patterns shape long-term energy returns. Since utility-scale installations dominate solar PV capacity across all scenarios, their performance strongly influences regional and global outcomes. The following results examine EROI developments across nine regions under both LUT-BPS and IEA scenarios, highlighting the role of technology composition, particularly the balance between single-axis tracking and fixed-tilted systems in driving efficiency gains and regional disparities.

3.2.1 EROI trends of utility-scale PV system across nine major regions

The evolution of EROI in utility-scale PV systems mirrors the dynamics of large-scale solar expansion during the ET. Under the LUT-BPS scenarios, most regions show steady improvements, with values clustering in the 30-45 range by 2050, though Europe and Eurasia advance more slowly. By contrast, the IEA scenarios reveal a more uneven picture: MENA and SSA retain comparatively high returns above 40 and 34, while Europe, Eurasia, and NE-Asia remain below 30, underscoring the regional disparities that emerge under more conservative ET pathways.

The EROI trends of utility-scale PV systems is strongly shaped by the balance between single-axis tracking and fixed-tilted capacity expansion. Under the LUT-BPSs, the rapid growth of single-axis tracking, accounting for more than 60% of total capacity by 2050, drives significant efficiency gains and higher EROI outcomes across most regions. Table I provides the technology-level EROI estimates of utility-scale PV systems for each region under the LUT-BPSs. By mid-century, MENA and SSA record the highest values at 46 and 43, respectively, supported by large-scale deployment of tracking systems in high-resource areas. S-Am and N-Am also benefit from substantial single-axis tracking adoption, reaching values around 40, while SE-Asia and SAARC exceed 37 and NE-Asia approaches 35. Europe and Eurasia, where fixed-tilted systems remain more dominant and tracking penetration is limited, achieve lower results, stabilising around 31. Across the LUT-BPS2035, LUT-BPS2040, and LUT-BPS2050, the differences lie mainly in the timing of solar PV deployment directly associated with ET time horizon, but all converge toward similar levels by 2050, illustrating how single-axis tracking-led expansion underpins higher energy returns.

Table I: Utility-scale PV system EROI values in 2050 across nine regions for LUT-BPS scenarios.

Regions / EROI value	BPS2035	BPS2040	BPS2050
Europe	25.2	28.4	30.7
Eurasia	25.8	28.9	30.6
MENA	38.6	44.3	45.7
SSA	39.2	41.8	43.4
SAARC	33.3	35.6	37.2
NE-Asia	29.1	32.3	34.8
SE-Asia	33.3	35.9	37.2
N-Am	33.4	37.3	39.8
S-Am	33.8	38.9	40.4

Table II reports the EROI estimates for utility-scale PV systems across all regions under the IEA-SDS and IEA-STEPS scenarios. The technology mix shifts toward fixed-tilted systems, constraining overall EROI growth. Despite maintaining high values in MENA (41) and SSA (34) due to enormous harvestable solar energy resource, other regions record weaker performances compared to the LUT-BPS scenarios. Europe is most affected, falling below 20 by 2050, while Eurasia remains only slightly above 21. NE-Asia also declines relative to the LUT-BPS scenarios, with values of 28 in the IEA-SDS and 25 in the IEA-STEPS. S-Am and N-Am achieve more modest improvements, stabilising around 33, reflecting their limited reliance on tracking systems under these pathways.

Table II: Utility-scale PV system EROI values in 2050 across nine regions for IEA scenarios.

Regions / EROI value	SDS	STEPS
Europe	19.2	17.5
Eurasia	22.0	21.3
MENA	41.1	41.4
SSA	34.7	34.3
SAARC	31.9	33.3
NE-Asia	27.9	24.6
SE-Asia	25.5	25.3
N-Am	32.3	32.6
S-Am	33.5	32.5

In summary, the LUT-BPSs highlight how large-scale adoption of single-axis tracking systems enables most regions to converge between 30 and 45 by 2050, reinforcing the role of technology choice in shaping long-term EROI trends. In contrast, the IEA scenarios, dominated by fixed-tilted deployment, produce uneven results, with only MENA and SSA achieving high returns, while Europe, Eurasia, and NE-Asia lag behind.

3.2.2 EROI trends of prosumer-scale PV system across nine major regions

The EROI trends of prosumer-scale PV systems is closely linked to the growth of utility-scale PV installations. In the LUT-BPSs, values rise steadily and largely converge, with most regions approaching or surpassing 30 by 2050, independent of whether the ET is fast-tracked or gradual. The IEA scenarios, however, display more uneven developments: Europe and SE-Asia achieve the highest improvements, reaching above 40 and 30 respectively, whereas Eurasia and S-Am remain constrained in the 20-25 range, reflecting wider disparities.

In the LUT-BPS2035, rapid early improvements are most evident in resource-rich regions. By 2050, MENA, SSA, and SAARC exceed an EROI of 30, while SE-Asia, NE-Asia, N-Am, and S-Am converge near this benchmark. Eurasia reaches 28, whereas Europe lags behind, remaining at 25. The other LUT-BPS scenarios yield broadly similar outcomes, as the relatively modest expansion of prosumer-scale capacity has only a minor effect on technology-level EROI results. LUT-BPS2040 follows the same trend but with slower progress, illustrating that the difference lies primarily in timing of ET. LUT-BPS2050 represents the most gradual pathway, yet by mid-century the regional pattern remains consistent, with SSA and MENA leading, most other regions clustering around 30, and Europe stabilising at the lower bound of 25. Table III summarises the technology-level EROI estimates of prosumer-scale PV systems for each region under the LUT-BPSs, while the corresponding results for the IEA scenarios are presented in Table IV.

Table III: Prosumer-scale PV systems EROI values in 2050 across nine major regions for LUT-BPSs.

Regions / EROI value	BPS2035	BPS2040	BPS2050
Europe	25.0	25.0	25.0
Eurasia	28.0	28.1	29.2
MENA	34.7	34.7	36.3
SSA	33.6	33.6	35.4
SAARC	33.8	33.8	35.5
NE-Asia	27.0	27.0	28.1
SE-Asia	29.2	29.2	30.3
N-Am	28.6	25.3	27.1
S-Am	25.3	28.6	30.5

Table IV: Prosumer-scale PV systems EROI values in 2050 across nine major regions for IEA scenarios.

Regions / EROI value	SDS	STEPS
Europe	44.0	44.0
Eurasia	25.7	25.7
MENA	32.6	32.6
SSA	33.2	33.2
SAARC	32.1	32.1
NE-Asia	29.5	29.5
SE-Asia	34.6	34.6
N-Am	32.6	32.6
S-Am	26.1	26.1

10.4229/EUPVSEC2025/5DO.11.4

The IEA-SDS case reveals sharper contrasts across regions. Europe performs exceptionally well, reaching an EROI of 44 by 2050 and surpassing all LUT-BPS outcomes. SE-Asia also exceeds 30, while NE-Asia remains close to this level. N-Am crosses 30, S-Am stabilises between 25 and 30, and Eurasia shows only limited progress. The IEA-STEPS scenario reinforces this divergence: Europe again records values above 40, SE-Asia remains strong, SSA and MENA approach 30, and Eurasia stays below 25. The relatively high EROI results in the IEA scenarios are linked to the decommissioning of prosumer-scale PV systems, which lowers the overall energy requirements of this technology compared with the LUT-BPS cases. At the same time, capacity expansion and improvements in system efficiency emerge as the main drivers of prosumer-scale EROI across all scenarios.

Taken together, the LUT-BPS scenarios indicate a steady convergence of regional EROI values towards 30 by 2050, while the IEA scenarios highlight a more uneven pattern, with Europe and SE-Asia achieving rapid advances and Eurasia and South America lagging behind.

4 CONCLUSIONS

This study examines the long-term evolution of the energy return on investment (EROI) of solar photovoltaics (PV) across nine global regions by applying the LUT-EROI framework in conjunction with the LUT Energy System Transition Model. Through the integration of life cycle assessment, dynamic cumulative energy demand data, and cost-optimised transition pathways, the analysis provides a novel systemwide perspective that captures the effects of technology composition, energy learning rates, and scenario design on technology-level EROI trends. Furthermore, the consistent assessment of both utility- and prosumer-scale PV within accelerated LUT Best Policy Scenarios (LUT-BPS) and International Energy Agency (IEA) scenarios represents a significant methodological advancement over previous static or technology-isolated investigations.

Key findings highlight that:

- Utility-scale PV systems achieve the highest EROI improvements in regions with large-scale adoption of single-axis tracking, converging between 30 and 45 by 2050 under the LUT-BPSs.
- Prosumer-scale PV systems show slower but steady improvements, with most regions approaching an EROI of 30 by 2050, though Europe achieves exceptionally high values above 40 in the IEA pathways. This is mainly due to the reducing overall energy needs compared with the LUT-BPS cases.
- Scenario design shapes the technology-level EROI outcomes. The accelerated ETs favour convergence and higher long-term returns, while conservative pathways produce uneven patterns, with weaker results in Eurasia and South America.
- Solar PV technology mix is the decisive factor. The dominance of fixed-tilted systems in IEA scenarios constrains EROI growth, whereas widespread adoption of single-axis tracking systems in LUT-BPS pathways underpins stronger performance.

Overall, the results demonstrate that ambitious and technology-optimised transition strategies not only enable rapid defossilisation but also improve the energy efficiency of the transition itself, strengthening the case for accelerated deployment of different solar PV system technologies.

In terms of limitations, the spatial aggregation may obscure regional variations in resource availability and system performance, potentially affecting EROI outcomes of solar PV systems. The life cycle inventories from the ecoinvent may not fully capture the solar PV supply chain, and reliance on a single database for cumulative energy demand (CED) values could lead to overestimation. Systemwide EROI results are further shaped by global supply chain dependencies, such as intercontinental transport of PV components, and by the exclusion of emerging solar PV technologies. Recycling processes, as well as transmission and distribution networks, are also omitted due to limited data or their marginal contribution to overall CED.

5 ACKNOWLEDGEMENTS

The authors gratefully acknowledge the public financing of the Academy of Finland for the biophysical limits of the energy transition project (317681).

6 REFERENCES

[1] M. M. Vanegas Cantarero, "Of renewable energy, energy democracy, and sustainable development: A roadmap to accelerate the energy transition in developing countries," 2020, *Elsevier Ltd.* doi: 10.1016/j.erss.2020.101716.

[2] I. Gunnarsdottir, B. Davidsdottir, E. Worrell, and S. Sigurgeirsdottir, "Review of indicators for sustainable energy development," 2020, *Elsevier Ltd.* doi: 10.1016/j.rser.2020.110294.

[3] H. Neofytou, A. Nikas, and H. Doukas, "Sustainable energy transition readiness: A multicriteria assessment index," *Renewable and Sustainable Energy Reviews*, vol. 131, 2020, doi: 10.1016/j.rser.2020.109988.

[4] H. Sahin, A. A. Solomon, A. Aghahosseini, and C. Breyer, "Systemwide energy return on investment in a sustainable transition towards net zero power systems," *Nat Commun*, vol. 15, no. 1, p. 208, 2024, doi: 10.1038/s41467-023-44232-9.

[5] A. A. Solomon, H. Sahin, and C. Breyer, "The pitfall in designing future electrical power systems without considering energy return on investment in planning," *Appl Energy*, vol. 369, p. 123570, 2024, doi: 10.1016/j.apenergy.2024.123570.

[6] D. J. Murphy and C. A. S. Hall, "Year in review—EROI or energy return on (energy) invested," *Ann N Y Acad Sci*, vol. 1185, no. 1, pp. 102–118, 2010, doi: 10.1111/j.1749-6632.2009.05282.x.

[7] C. A. S. Hall, J. G. Lambert, and S. B. Balogh, "EROI of different fuels and the implications for society," *Energy Policy*, vol. 64, pp. 141–152, 2014, doi: 10.1016/j.enpol.2013.05.049.

[8] D. J. Murphy, M. Raugei, M. Carbajales-Dale, and B. Rubio Estrada, "Energy Return on Investment of Major Energy Carriers: Review and Harmonization," *Sustainability*, vol. 14, no. 12, p. 7098, 2022, doi: 10.3390/su14127098.

[9] H. Sahin, A. A. Solomon, A. Aghahosseini, and C. Breyer, "The impact of spatial representation in energy transition modelling on systemwide energy return on investment," *IET Renewable Power Generation*, vol. 18, no. 14, pp. 2706–2722, 2024, doi: 10.1049/rpg2.13117.

[10] H. Sahin, A. A. Solomon, A. Aghahosseini, and C. Breyer, "Uneven Distribution of Natural Resources Impacts on Systemwide Energy Return on Investment ," *(submitted)*, 2025.

[11] M. Görig and C. Breyer, "Energy Learning Curves of PV Systems," *Environ Prog Sustain Energy*, vol. 35, no. 3, pp. 914–923, 2016, doi: 10.1002/ep.12340.

[12] A. A. Solomon, N. B. Manjong, and C. Breyer, "The necessity to standardise primary energy quality in achieving a meaningful quantification of related indicators," *Smart Energy*, vol. 12, p. 100115, 2023, doi: 10.1016/j.segy.2023.100115.

[13] D. Bogdanov *et al.*, "Costs and benefits of highly ambitious energy transition pathways for Europe," *Energy*, vol. 336, p. 138477, 2025, doi: 10.1016/j.energy.2025.138477.

[14] D. Bogdanov *et al.*, "Low-cost renewable electricity as the key driver of the global energy transition towards sustainability," *Energy*, vol. 227, p. 120467, 2021, doi: 10.1016/j.energy.2021.120467.

[15] A. Aghahosseini *et al.*, "More renewable energy leads to a faster transition at lower cost as revealed by comparative analysis of global energy transition scenarios," *(submitted)*, 2025.

[16] Z. Zhou and M. Carbajales-Dale, "Assessing the photovoltaic technology landscape: Efficiency and energy return on investment (EROI)," *Energy Environ Sci*, vol. 11, no. 3, pp. 603–608, 2018, doi: 10.1039/c7ee01806a.

[17] H. Sahin, A. A. Solomon, A. Aghahosseini, and C. Breyer, "Systemwide energy return on investment in a sustainable transition towards net zero power systems (Supplementary Dataset - CED Database.xlsx).," 2024, *Figshare*. doi: 10.6084/m9.figshare.24602349.

[18] IEA, "World Energy Outlook 2021," Paris, 2021. https://www.iea.org/reports/world-energy-outlook-2021

[19] A. Aghahosseini *et al.*, "Energy system transition pathways to meet the global electricity demand for ambitious climate targets and cost competitiveness," *Appl Energy*, vol. 331, p. 120401, 2023, doi: 10.1016/j.apenergy.2022.120401.

[20] M. A. J. Huijbregts *et al.*, "Is Cumulative Fossil Energy Demand a Useful Indicator for the Environmental Performance of Products?," *Environ Sci Technol*, vol. 40, no. 3, pp. 641–648, 2006, doi: 10.1021/es051689g.

[21] R. Frischknecht, F. Wyss, S. Büsser Knöpfel, T. Lützkendorf, and M. Balouktsi, "Cumulative energy demand in LCA: the energy harvested approach," *Int J Life Cycle Assess*, vol. 20, no. 7, pp. 957–969, 2015, doi: 10.1007/s11367-015-0897-4.

[22] D. J. Murphy, M. Carbajales-Dale, and D. Moeller, "Comparing apples to apples: Why the net energy analysis community needs to adopt the life-cycle analysis framework," *Energies*, vol. 9, no. 11, pp. 1–16, 2016, doi: 10.3390/en9110917.

[23] L. Delannoy, P. Y. Longaretti, D. J. Murphy, and E. Prados, "Peak oil and the low-carbon energy transition: A net-energy perspective," *Appl Energy*, vol. 304, p. 117843, 2021, doi: 10.1016/j.apenergy.2021.117843.

[24] S. Sgouridis, D. Csala, and U. Bardi, "The sower's way: quantifying the narrowing net-energy pathways to a global energy transition," *Environmental Research Letters*, vol. 11, no. 9, p. 094009, 2016, doi: 10.1088/1748-9326/11/9/094009.

42nd EU PVSEC, 2025, Bilbao, Spain

Unveiling the evolutionary energy performance of solar PV systems through systemwide EROI perspective

Hasret Sahin, A.A. Solomon, Christian Breyer

LUT University, Lappeenranta, Finland

LUT University

Table of Contents

LUT University

Overview and Motivation
Materials and Methods
- LUT Energy System Transition Model (LUT-ESTM)
- Energy Transition Scenarios
- Systemwide LUT-EROI model

Results
- Synopsis of Energy Modelling Results
- Regional EROI Patterns of Solar PV Systems
- The Storage Trade-off: Batteries and Solar PV EROI

Conclusions
Limitations

More information ► hasret.sahin@lut.fi

Overview and Motivation

LUT University

Regional energy system transitions

- Showing regional asymmetries as shaped by strategies and regulations.
- Massive energy requirements are necessary and changing depending on the region.
- Solar PV systems and batteries are central to future power systems, yet their EROI interactions remain underexplored.

Existing energy return on investment (EROI) studies

- Focus mainly on static, technology-level analyses.
- Show wide divergence in solar PV systems EROI values due to location, technology, and boundary definitions.
- Rarely capture dynamic, systemwide effects such as energy learning rates and storage integration.

This research aims to:

- Develop a dynamic framework for assessing solar PV systems and with/without battery options EROI at both technology and system level.
- Analyse five transition scenarios across nine global regions using the LUT Energy System Transition Model (LUT-ESTM).
- Provide insights into systemwide EROI trends at the technology level (2015–2050) under varying pathways, enhancing the robustness of energy transition planning.

More information ► hasret.sahin@lut.fi

Table of Contents

LUT University

More information ► hasret.sahin@lut.fi

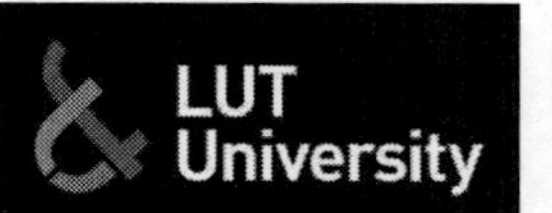

LUT Energy System Transition Model (LUT-ESTM)

LUT University

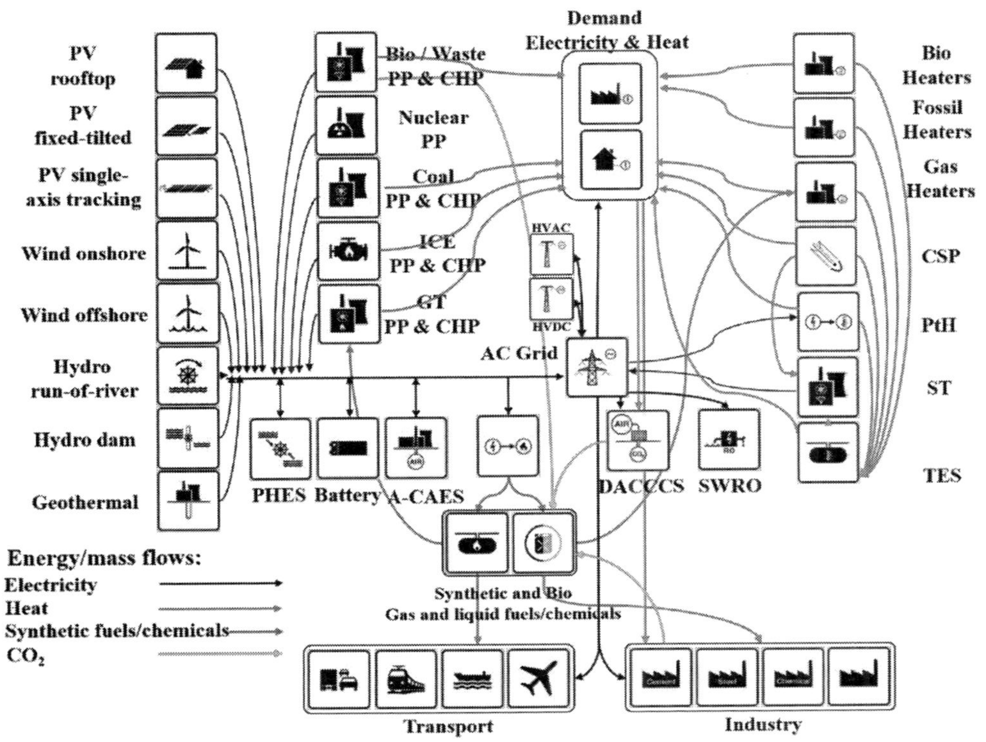

Figure 1. Mapping of technologies and connections within LUT-ESTM.

- Technology-oriented, bottom-up cost-optimisation model.
- Covers ~170 energy technologies.
- Operates with full hourly resolution over an entire year.
- Structured at country, regional, and global levels.
- Uses 5-year time steps to capture transition dynamics and their changes.
- Identifies short- and medium-term pathways guided by long-term targets.
- Minimises system costs while ensuring technology feasibility (Bogdanov et al., 2025; 2021).

References:

Bogdanov, D., Ram, M., Satymov, R., Lopez, G., Mensah, T., Sadovskaia, K., & Breyer, C. (2025). Costs and benefits of highly ambitious energy transition pathways for Europe. Energy, 138477.

Bogdanov, D., Ram, M., Aghahosseini, A., Gulagi, A., Oyewo, A. S., Child, M., ... & Breyer, C. (2021). Low-cost renewable electricity as the key driver of the global energy transition towards sustainability. Energy, 227, 120467.

5

Unveiling the evolutionary energy performance of solar PV systems through systemwide EROI perspective

More information ► hasret.sahin@lut.fi

Energy Transition Scenarios

LUT University

- Energy transition scenarios are divided into two groups (Aghahosseini et al., 2025) .

Group 1: LUT – Best Policy Scenarios (BPS) (optimisation-based).

LUT-BPS2035: Achieving a 100% renewable energy (RE) system by the year 2035.

LUT-BPS2040: Achieving a 100% RE system by the year 2040.

LUT-BPS2050: Achieving a 100% RE system by the year 2050.

- Fossil & nuclear phased out at end-of-life, no new build.
- Cost-optimal RE, wind repowering, full storage mix.
- Integration of power-to-X (PtX) systems.

Group 2: IEA Reference (re-simulated in LUT-ESTM).

Stated Policies Scenario (IEA-STEPS): benchmark, business-as-usual; fossil & nuclear retained.

Sustainable Development Scenario (IEA-SDS): Paris-aligned; coal & oil decline, nuclear & carbon capture and storage (CCS) expand, RE ~60% capacity by 2050.

- IEA outputs (capacity, demand, CO_2 costs) retained; LUT-ESTM supplies load/resource profiles.
- IEA-NZE (Net-Zero by 2050) could not be used due to intransparency and lack of accessible data.

Reference: Aghahosseini A, Solomon AA, Bardi U, Creutzig F, Hoekstra A, Jacobson MZ, et al. (2025). More renewable energy leads to a faster transition at lower cost as revealed by comparative analysis of global energy transition scenarios (under review).

More information ► hasret.sahin@lut.fi

Systemwide LUT-EROI model

LUT University

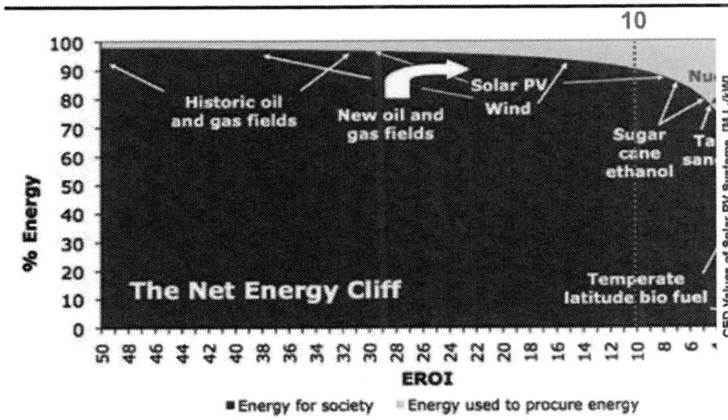

Figure 2. Net Energy Cliff in EROI (Murphy et al., 2010) .

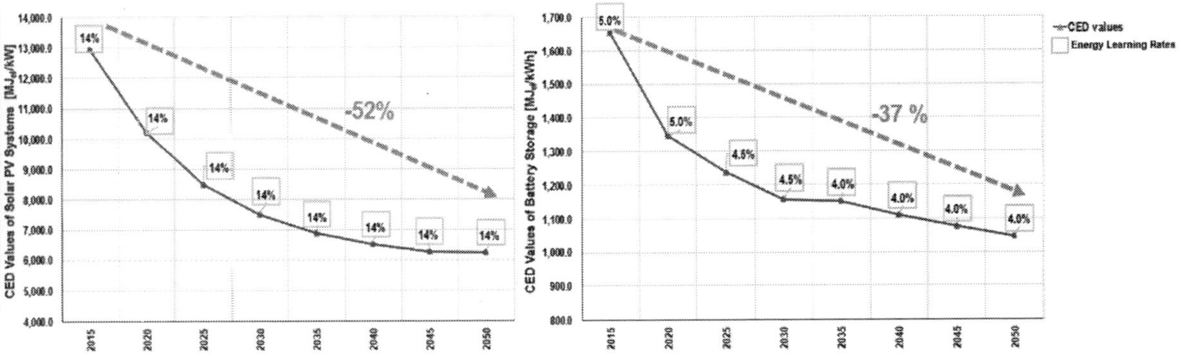

Figure 3. Changes in the CED values of solar PV systems (left) and of battery storage (right) over the years, considering ELR values (Sahin et al., 2024).

- **EROI measures the ratio of usable energy gained vs. energy invested.**
- **The minimum EROI threshold for the society (Critical minimum: ~10)**
  - **Below this, too much energy is reinvested into the system itself.**
  - **Leaves insufficient surplus energy for essential societal functions.**
- **EROI ≈ 10–20: sustainable but limited societal growth.**
- **EROI > 20: enabled industrial growth and high living standards.**

References:

Murphy, D. J., & Hall, C. A. (2010). Year in review—EROI or energy return on (energy) invested. Annals of the new york academy of sciences, 1185(1), 102-118.

Sahin, H., Solomon, A. A., Aghahosseini, A., & Breyer, C. (2024). Systemwide energy return on investment in a sustainable transition towards net zero power systems. Nature Communications, 15(1), 208.

Unveiling the evolutionary energy performance of solar PV systems through systemwide EROI perspective

More information ▶ hasret.sahin@lut.fi

Systemwide LUT-EROI model

LUT University

EROI

$$EROI = \frac{E_{out}}{E_{inv}} = \frac{E_{an} \cdot LT}{E_{inv}} = \frac{E_{an}}{(E_{inv}/LT)} \quad \text{Eq. 1}$$

Systemwide EROI

$$EROI_{syst,year} = \frac{ES_{year}}{\sum_t \frac{(\sum_{n=1}^{N_t} E_{inv_{t,n}} \cdot Capacity_t)}{LT_t}} \quad \text{Eq. 2}$$

Invested energy through

$$E_{inv_{t,n}} = E_{capacity} + (E_{operation} \cdot FLH \cdot LT_t) \quad \text{Eq. 3}$$

E_{inv}: Total energy required to deliver that energy of a system and/or an energy source through a lifetime.

E_{out}: Total usable energy (final electricity generation).

E_{an}: Annual electricity generation.

$EROI_{syst,year}$: Annual systemwide approach of EROI.

ES_{year}: Annual net energy generation feeding to the transmission network

$E_{inv_{t,n}}$: The invested energy per unit of kW capacity for a specific technology.

$E_{capacity}$: The adapted CED value per kW

$E_{operation}$: The adapted operation CED value per kWh

N_t: The maximum capacity of the technology.

t : time
n : is the capacity unit (kW or kWh)
LT : lifetime of a technology
FLH : full load hour of a technology
LT_t : the lifetime of a technology

- **Systemwide EROI based on a unified system-level analysis.**
- **Assesses system changes over defined time periods.**
- **Treats the entire energy system as one entity.**
- **Avoids reliance on individual technology-level EROI values (Sahin et al, 2024; Solomon et al., 2024).**

References:

Sahin, H., Solomon, A. A., Aghahosseini, A., & Breyer, C. (2024). Systemwide energy return on investment in a sustainable transition towards net zero power systems. Nature Communications, 15(1), 208.

Solomon, A. A., Sahin, H., & Breyer, C. (2024). The pitfall in designing future electrical power systems without considering energy return on investment in planning. Applied Energy, 369, 123570.

Unveiling the evolutionary energy performance of solar PV systems through systemwide EROI perspective

More information ▶ hasret.sahin@lut.fi

Systemwide LUT-EROI Model

LUT University

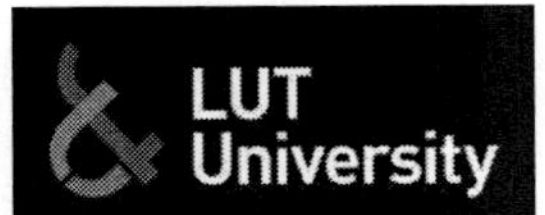

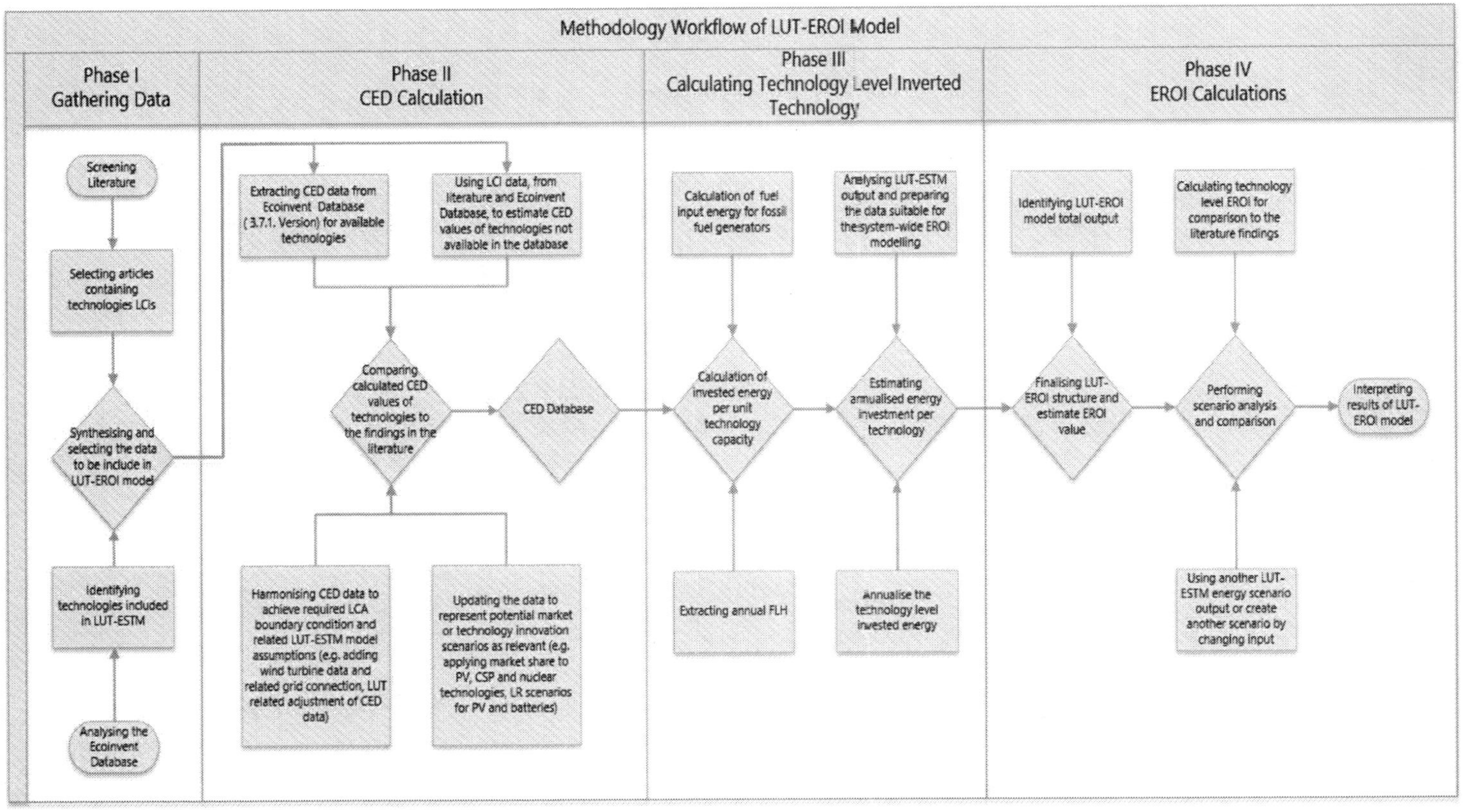

Figure 4. The methodology of systemwide LUT-EROI model (Sahin et al., 2024).

Reference: Sahin, H., Solomon, A. A., Aghahosseini, A., & Breyer, C. (2024). Systemwide energy return on investment in a sustainable transition towards net zero power systems. Nature Communications, 15(1), 208.

Unveiling the evolutionary energy performance of solar PV systems through systemwide EROI perspective

More information ► hasret.sahin@lut.fi

Table of Contents

Overview and Motivation

Materials and Methods

- LUT Energy System Transition Model (LUT-ESTM)
- Energy Transition Scenarios
- Systemwide LUT-EROI model

Results

- Synopsis of Energy Modelling Results
- Regional EROI Patterns of Solar PV Systems
- The Storage Trade-off: Batteries and Solar PV EROI

Conclusions

Limitations

More information ► hasret.sahin@lut.fi

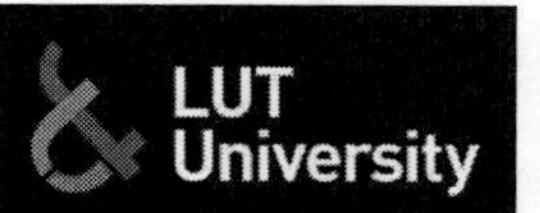

Synopsis of Energy Modelling Results

LUT University

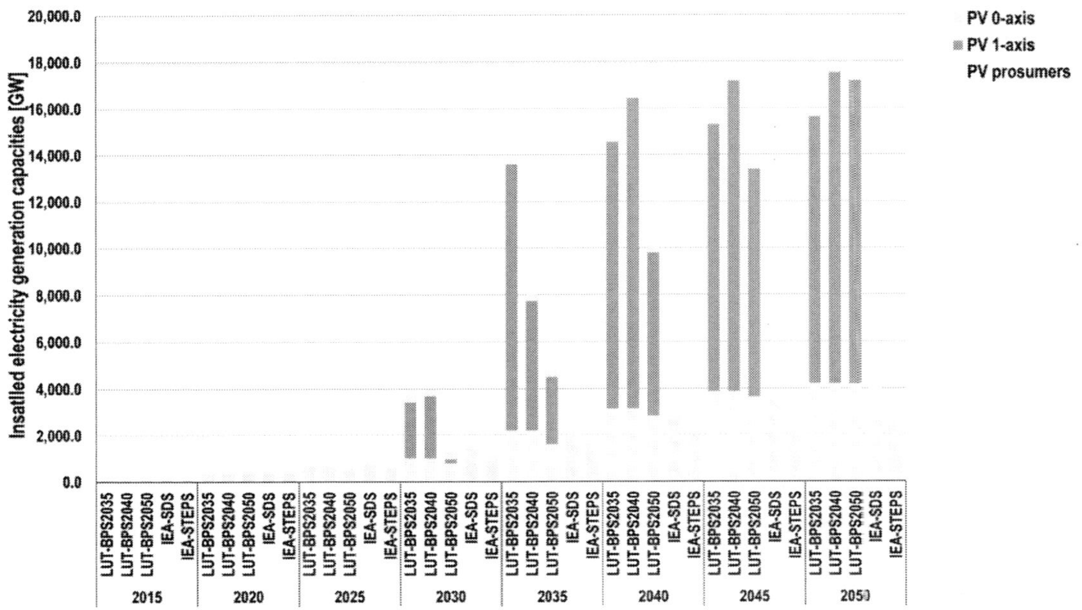

Figure 5. Installed capacity of solar PV systems of Northeast Asia.

Solar PV systems

Single-axis solar PV (1-axis):

- Largest capacity expansion. Strongest growth in Northeast Asia (NE-Asia), Southeast Asia (SE-Asia) and North America (N-Am).

Fixed-tilted solar PV (0-axis) :

- Moderate expansion. Notable growth in South Asia and Europe.

Prosumer-scale solar PV:

- Plays only a minor role in most regions. Clear increase in NE-Asia and Europe.

The LUT-BPS scenarios promote prosumer PV more strongly than the IEA scenarios (Aghahosseini et al., 2025).

Battery storage growth closely parallels solar PV capacity expansion.

Reference: Aghahosseini A, Solomon AA, Bardi U, Creutzig F, Hoekstra A, Jacobson MZ, et al. (2025). More renewable energy leads to a faster transition at lower cost as revealed by comparative analysis of global energy transition scenarios (under review).

More information ► hasret.sahin@lut.fi

Regional EROI Patterns of Solar PV Systems
Utility-scale Solar PV System

LUT University

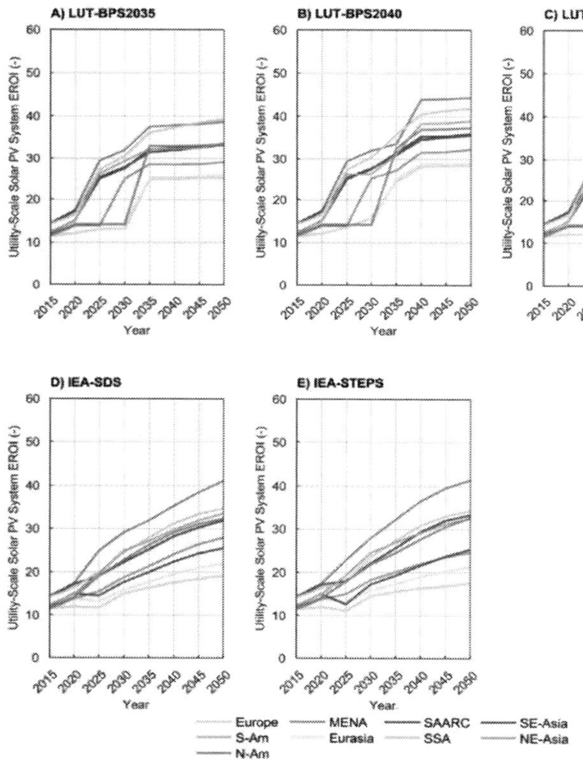

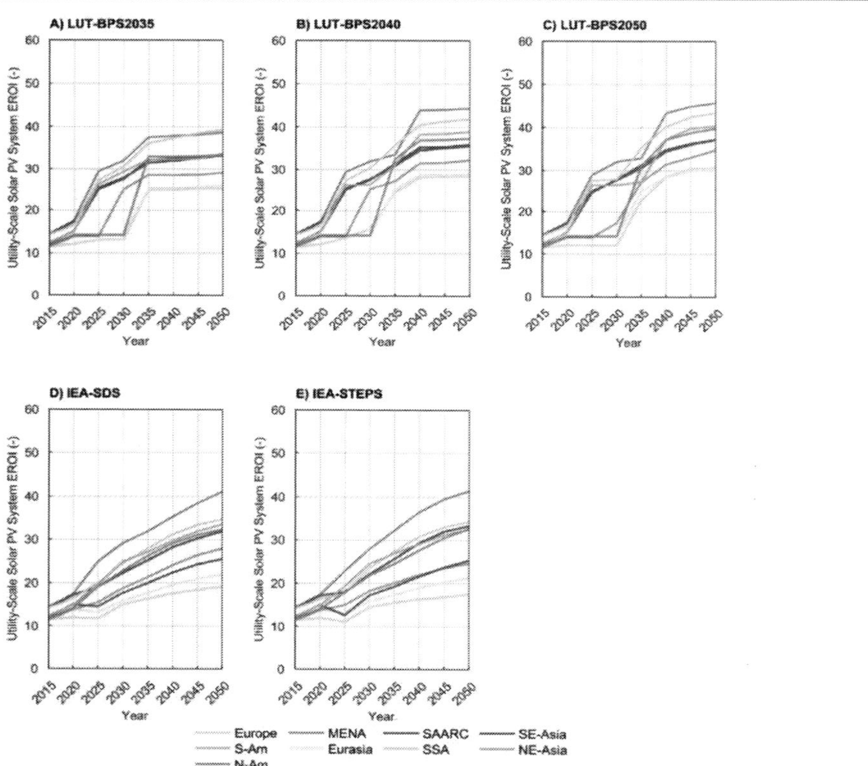

Figure 6. The regional EROI trends for solar PV utility system for nine regions.

<u>Sub-Saharan Africa (SSA) and Middle East and North Africa (MENA):</u>

- LUT-BPS: strongest global performers, exceeding 40 by 2050 (except LUT-BPS2035).
- IEA: MENA remains strong above 40, SSA stabilises around 35.

<u>South America (S-Am), N-Am and SAARC:</u>

- LUT-BPS: values in the range of 30–40 by 2050.
- IEA: more moderate, between 25 and 35.
- SAARC: 30–35 under the LUT-BPS, slightly above 30 under the IEA.

<u>NE-Asia and SE-Asia:</u>

- LUT-BPS: both exceed 30, with SE-Asia higher than NE-Asia (25–35 range).
- IEA: both converge, stabilising between 20 and 25.

<u>Europe and Eurasia:</u>

- IEA: slow progress, EROI at 15–20 by 2050.
- LUT-BPS: faster increase, reaching 25–30.

Reference: Sahin, H., Solomon, A.A., Aghahosseini, A., Breyer, C., (2026) Unveiling the evolutionary energy performance of solar photovoltaic systems through systemwide EROI perspective.

Unveiling the evolutionary energy performance of solar PV systems through systemwide EROI perspective

More information ► hasret.sahin@lut.fi

Regional EROI Patterns of Solar PV Systems

Prosumer-scale Solar PV Systems

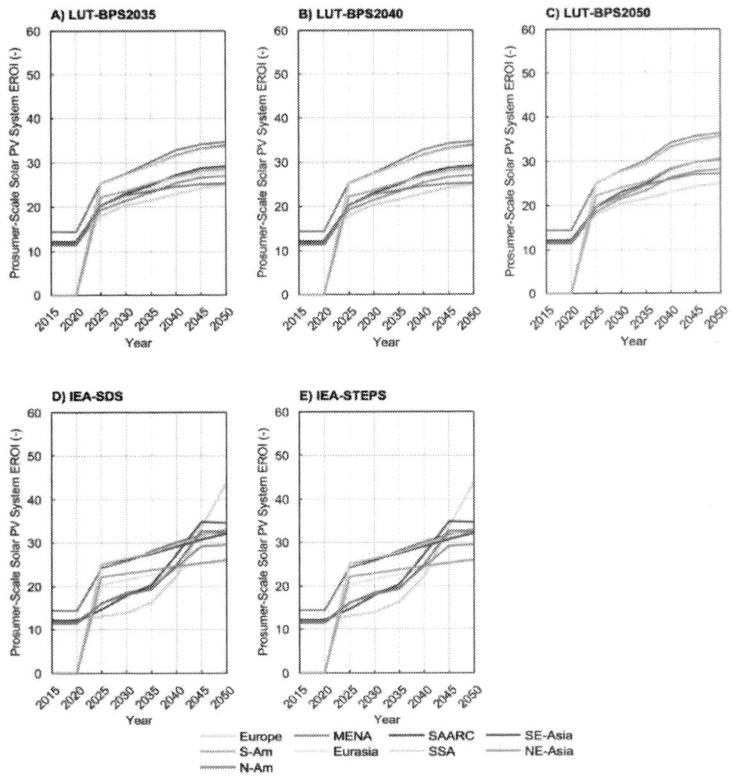

Figure 7. The regional EROI trends for solar PV prosumer system for nine regions.

SSA and MENA:

- LUT-BPS: strongest performers, exceeding 30 by 2050.
- IEA: values remain close to 30.

NE-Asia and SE-Asia:

- LUT-BPS: reach around 30 by 2050.
- IEA: SE-Asia exceeds 30, NE-Asia Asia stays near 30.

Europe:

- LUT-BPS: moderate growth to 20–25 by 2050.
- IEA: strong improvement, reaching 44 by 2050.

Eurasia:

- LUT-BPS: rises close to 30 by 2050.
- IEA: limited progress, staying between 20–25.

S-Am and N-Am:

- LUT-BPS: both reach around 30 by 2050.
- IEA: S-Am stabilises at 25–30, N-Am rises above 30.

Reference: Sahin, H., Solomon, A.A., Aghahosseini, A., Breyer, C., (2026) Unveiling the evolutionary energy performance of solar photovoltaic systems through systemwide EROI perspective.

Unveiling the evolutionary energy performance of solar PV systems through systemwide EROI perspective

More information ► hasret.sahin@lut.fi

Regional EROI Patterns of Solar PV Systems

Utility-scale Solar PV System with Grid-scale Battery Storage

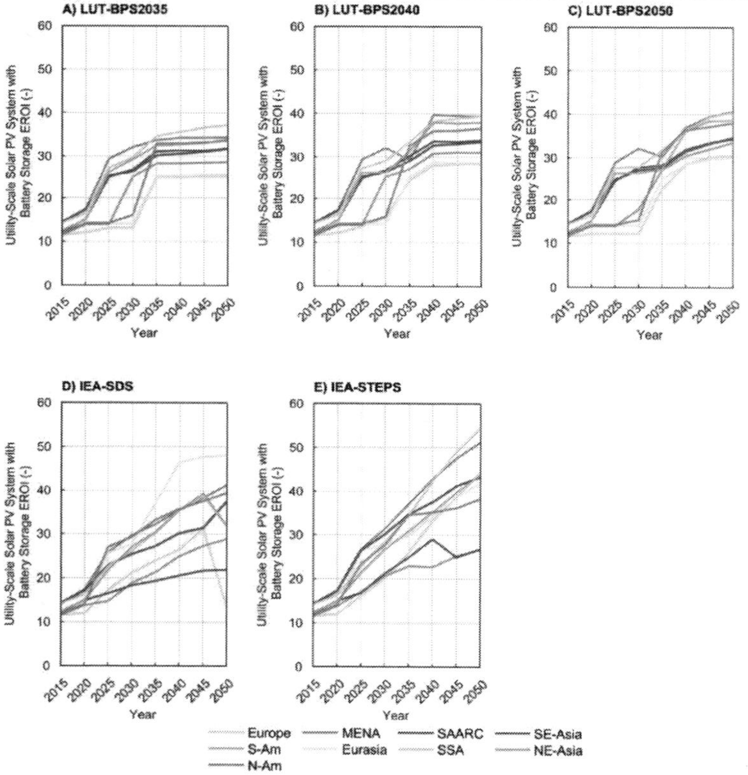

Figure 8. The regional EROI trends for solar PV utility system with complementary battery storage for nine regions.

MENA,SSA and SAARC:

- LUT-BPS: SSA and MENA above 40, SAARC around 35 by 2050.
- IEA: SSA peaks at 54 (IEA-STEPS), all three converge near 40 (IEA-SDS).

S-Am and N-Am:

- LUT-BPS: steady growth, reaching mid-30s to 40 by 2050.
- IEA: stabilise around 30.

NE-Asia and Southeast Asia:

- LUT-BPS: strong rise to 40–45 by 2050.
- IEA: remain moderate, 20–30.

Europe:

- LUT-BPS: lowest values, ~25 (LUT-BPS2030), modest rise to 30 (BPS2040).
- IEA: declines further, dropping to 14 by 2050.

Eurasia:

- LUT-BPS: slow progress, ~30 by 2050.
- IEA: stronger in SDS, reaching 48 by 2050.

Reference: Sahin, H., Solomon, A.A., Aghahosseini, A., Breyer, C., (2026) Unveiling the evolutionary energy performance of solar photovoltaic systems through systemwide EROI perspective.

14 Unveiling the evolutionary energy performance of solar PV systems through systemwide EROI perspective

More information ▶ hasret.sahin@lut.fi

Regional EROI Patterns of Solar PV Systems

Prosumer-scale Solar PV System with Prosumer-scale Battery Storage

LUT University

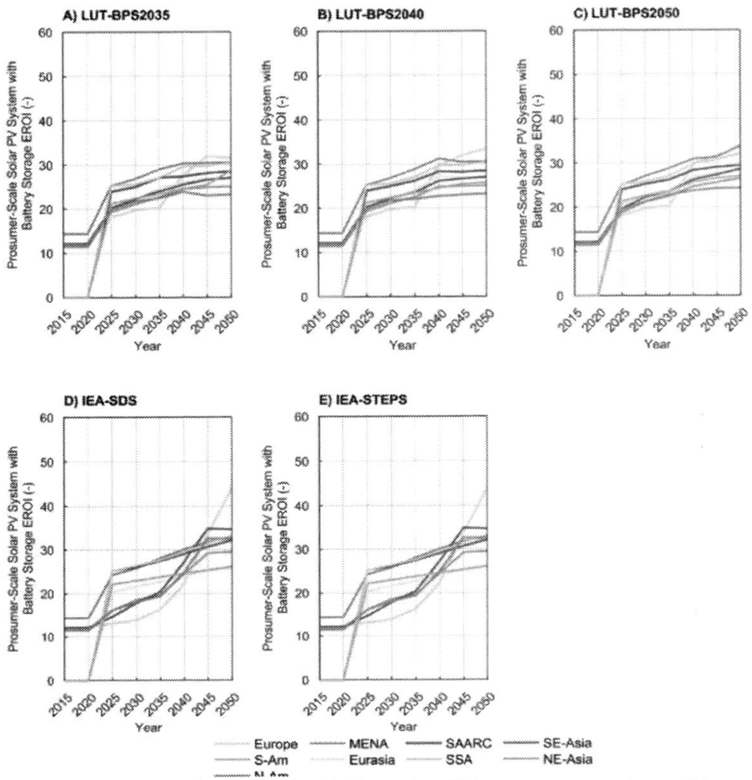

Figure 9. The regional EROI trends for solar PV prosumer system with complementary battery storage for nine regions.

Europe, MENA, SSA and SAARC:

- LUT-BPS: reach 30–35 by 2050, among the highest globally.
- IEA: MENA, SSA, SAARC stay near 30; Europe rises sharply after 2035 to ~45 by 2050.

S-Am and N-Am:

- Both grow steadily under all scenarios.
- By 2050: North America >30 in IEA, ~25 in LUT-BPS

NE-Asia and Southeast Asia:

- LUT-BPS: converge at ~30 by 2050.
- IEA: SE Asia rises to nearly 35, NE Asia remains closer to 30

Eurasia:

- Stable across scenarios.
- Slightly below 30 by 2050.

Reference: Sahin, H., Solomon, A.A., Aghahosseini, A., Breyer, C., (2026) Unveiling the evolutionary energy performance of solar photovoltaic systems through systemwide EROI perspective.

15

Unveiling the evolutionary energy performance of solar PV systems through systemwide EROI perspective

More information ► hasret.sahin@lut.fi

Table of Contents

LUT University

More information ► hasret.sahin@lut.fi

Conclusions

LUT University

- **Systemwide EROI is shaped** more by system design than technology performance, **this highlights the** need for system-level assessment.
- **Solar PV is the cornerstone of future energy systems, with** utility-scale PV achieving the highest returns, **while prosumer PV supports decentralisation.**
- **Battery integration** lowers EROI **but is essential for flexibility and stability.**
- Limiting the energy transition period **has** little effect on technology-level EROI **but leads to a significant** decrease at the system level.
- LUT-BPS scenarios: **faster short-term gains, more diversification, but** lower overall EROI **due to high prosumer battery use.**
- IEA scenarios: **slower early growth, but** higher long-term EROIs **from utility-scale focus and lower battery demand.**

More information ► hasret.sahin@lut.fi

Table of Contents

LUT University

Overview and Motivation

Materials and Methods

- » LUT Energy System Transition Model (LUT-ESTM)
- » Energy Transition Scenarios
- » Systemwide LUT-EROI model

Results

- » Synopsis of energy modelling results
- » Regional EROI Patterns of Solar PV Systems
- » The Storage Trade-off: Batteries and Solar PV EROI

Conclusions

Limitations

Unveiling the evolutionary energy performance of solar PV systems through systemwide EROI perspective

More information ► hasret.sahin@lut.fi

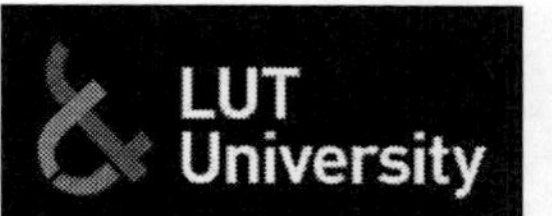

Limitations

LUT University

- Aggregation in spatial representation may obscure regional differences in resource availability and system performance, potentially influencing EROI outcomes.
- The life cycle inventories for solar PV systems in ecoinvent may not fully capture the entire supply chain.
- Extracted CED values from only one database might result in overestimation of CED values compared to reality.
- Systemwide EROI results are further affected by complex international supply chain dependencies, such as the transport of PV components across continents, and by the absence of advanced technologies such as tunnel oxide passivated contact or perovskite PV panels, which are not yet included.
- Recycling of materials and waste is excluded from CED estimates due to the absence of detailed process data.
- Transmission and distribution networks are also omitted, as their contribution to overall CED is considered marginal.

More information ► hasret.sahin@lut.fi

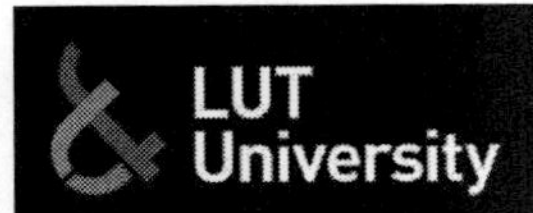

Thank you for your attention!
LUT University
Hasret Sahin, M.Sc., PhD.
Project Researcher
LUT University, Solar Economy Lab Research Group
hasret.sahin@lut.fi

References

LUT University

- Aghahosseini A, Solomon AA, Bardi U, Creutzig F, Hoekstra A, Jacobson MZ, et al. (2025). More renewable energy leads to a faster transition at lower cost as revealed by comparative analysis of global energy transition scenarios (under review).
- Bogdanov, D., Ram, M., Aghahosseini, A., Gulagi, A., Oyewo, A. S., Child, M., ... & Breyer, C. (2021). Low-cost renewable electricity as the key driver of the global energy transition towards sustainability. Energy, 227, 120467. https://doi.org/10.1016/j.energy.2021.120467
- Bogdanov, Breyer et al., 2021. Full energy sector transition towards 100% renewable energy supply: integrating power, heat, transport and industry sectors including desalination, Applied Energy, 283, 116273. https://doi.org/10.1016/j.apenergy.2020.116273
- Murphy, D. J., & Hall, C. A. (2010). Year in review—EROI or energy return on (energy) invested. Annals of the new york academy of sciences, 1185(1), 102-118. https://doi.org/10.1111/j.1749-6632.2009.05282.x
- Sahin, H., Solomon, A. A., Aghahosseini, A., & Breyer, C. (2024). Systemwide energy return on investment in a sustainable transition towards net zero power systems. Nature Communications, 15(1), 208. https://doi.org/10.1038/s41467-023-44232-9
- Sahin, H., Solomon, A.A., Aghahosseini, A., Breyer, C., (2026) Unveiling the evolutionary energy performance of solar photovoltaic systems through systemwide EROI perspective.
- Solomon, A. A., Sahin, H., & Breyer, C. (2024). The pitfall in designing future electrical power systems without considering energy return on investment in planning. Applied Energy, 369, 123570. https://doi.org/10.1016/j.apenergy.2024.123570

More information ► hasret.sahin@lut.fi

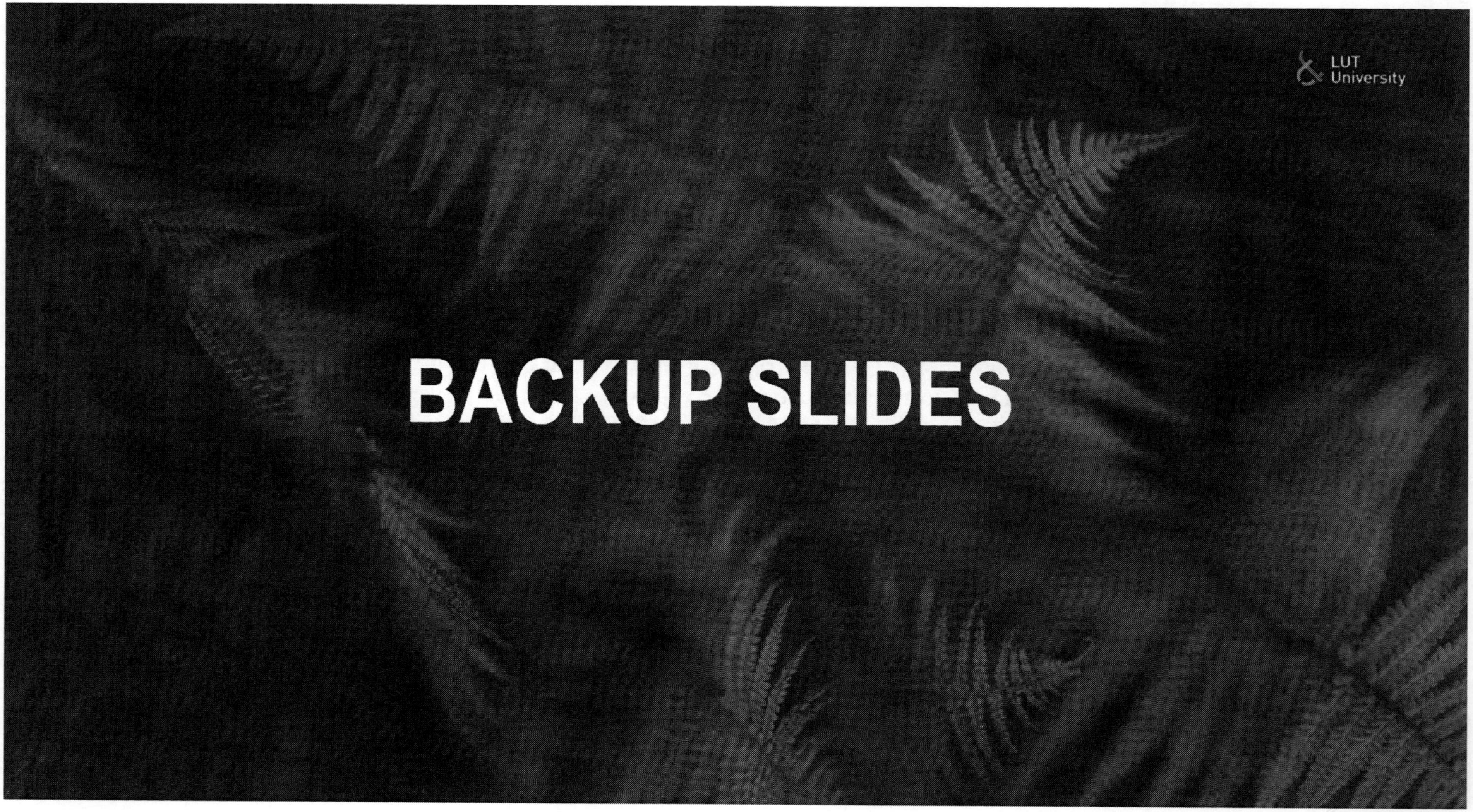
LUT
University
BACKUP SLIDES

CED Value Modifications

LUT University

Solar PV technologies

- PV module performance has continuously increased; at the same time, the solar PV industry has improved material requirements for the balance of the systems. These combined enhancements have resulted in decreases in cumulative energy demand (CED).
- CED values were recalculated using an average energy learning rate (ELR) of 14% until 2030, following the estimate of Görig and Breyer (2016).
- Note that the CED values in the ecoinvent database report CED values in conventional primary energy units without accounting for energy quality differences of natural energy resources, so standardisation to "joules" with appropriate "conversion factors" is needed to harmonise all energy inputs to the quality level of electricity (Solomon et al., 2024).
- The modified CED values are reorganised considering the global annual production of solar PV technologies, and reference CED values are founded for solar PV systems.
- All CED values are presented as MJ_{el}/kW.

Table 1. Reference CED values for solar PV system from 2015 to 2050.

	Reference CED values for solar PV systems (MJ_{el}/kW) (Sahin et al., 2024)
2015	12,939
2020	10,204
2025	8478
2030	7504
2035	6865
2040	6505
2045	6265
2050	6229

References:

Görig, M., & Breyer, C. (2016). Energy Learning Curves of PV Systems. Environmental Progress & Sustainable Energy, 35(3), 914–923. https://doi.org/10.1002/ep.12340.

Sahin, H., Solomon, A. A., Aghahosseini, A., & Breyer, C. (2024). Systemwide energy return on investment in a sustainable transition towards net zero power systems. Nature Communications, 15(1), 208.

Solomon, A. A., Sahin, H., & Breyer, C. (2024). The pitfall in designing future electrical power systems without considering energy return on investment in planning. Applied Energy, 369, 123570.

Unveiling the evolutionary energy performance of solar PV systems through systemwide EROI perspective

More information ► hasret.sahin@lut.fi

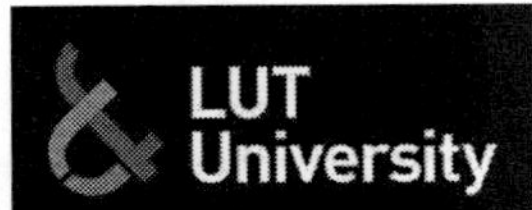

CED Value Modifications

LUT University

Battery storage technologies

- Utility-scale battery and prosumer-scale battery LCIs are derived and adjusted based on the future capacities reported by Xu et al. (2020), while ELR values are taken from Hsieh et al. (2019). In the ecoinvent v3.7.1 LCA database, no data exists for specific battery systems.
- Based on literature reviews and capacity considerations, the CED values for utility-scale and prosumer-scale battery storage are assumed to be the same.

Table 2. ELR implementation on battery storage CED value.

Implementation of ELR on CED values of battery storage (Sahin et al., 2024)	Reference CED values for battery systems (MJ_{el}/kWh)	ELR (%) (Hsieh et al., 2019)
CED values obtained from the literature	**1654**	N/A
2015	1654	5.0%
2020	1346	5.0%
2025	1237	4.5%
2030	1157	4.5%
2035	1152	4.0%
2040	1110	4.0%
2045	1075	4.0%
2050	1046	4.0%

References:

Hsieh, I. Y. L., Pan, M. S., Chiang, Y. M., & Green, W. H. (2019). Learning only buys you so much: Practical limits on battery price reduction. Applied Energy, 239(January), 218–224. https://doi.org/10.1016/j.apenergy.2019.01.138.

Sahin, H., Solomon, A. A., Aghahosseini, A., & Breyer, C. (2024). Systemwide energy return on investment in a sustainable transition towards net zero power systems. Nature Communications, 15(1), 208.

Xu, C., Dai, Q., Gaines, L. et al. Future material demand for automotive lithium-based batteries. Commun Mater 1, 99 (2020). doi.org/10.1038/s43246-020-0009.

Unveiling the evolutionary energy performance of solar PV systems through systemwide EROI perspective

More information ► hasret.sahin@lut.fi

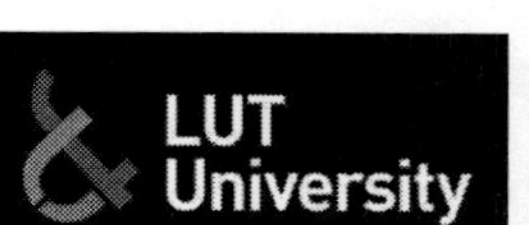

References

LUT University

- Görig, M., & Breyer, C. (2016). Energy Learning Curves of PV Systems. Environmental Progress & Sustainable Energy, 35(3), 914–923. https://doi.org/10.1002/ep.12340
- Hsieh, I. Y. L., Pan, M. S., Chiang, Y. M., & Green, W. H. (2019). Learning only buys you so much: Practical limits on battery price reduction. Applied Energy, 239(January), 218–224. https://doi.org/10.1016/j.apenergy.2019.01.138 .
- Sahin, H., Solomon, A. A., Aghahosseini, A., & Breyer, C. (2024). Systemwide energy return on investment in a sustainable transition towards net zero power systems. Nature Communications, 15(1), 208. https://doi.org/10.1038/s41467-023-44232-9
- Solomon, A. A., Sahin, H., & Breyer, C. (2024). The pitfall in designing future electrical power systems without considering energy return on investment in planning. Applied Energy, 369, 123570. https://doi.org/10.1016/j.apenergy.2024.123570
- Xu, C., Dai, Q., Gaines, L. et al. Future material demand for automotive lithium-based batteries. Commun Mater 1, 99 (2020). https://doi.org/10.1038/s43246-020-00095-x

More information ► hasret.sahin@lut.fi

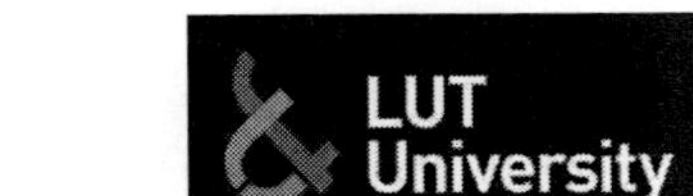

DNV

WHEN TRUST MATTERS
GreenPowerMonitor
a DNV company

Projections of PV Power Potential Worldwide: an Update Using CMIP6 Global Climate Models

Pau Mercade Ruiz[1], Gerardo Guerra[1], Gaetana Anamiati[1], Lars Landberg[2]
[1]GreenPowerMonitor a DNV Company
[2]DNV Denmark

25 September 2025

Contents

- Objective
- PV power model
- Modelling challenges
- Data specifications
- Results
- Conclusions

Objective

Project PV power production into the future and assess the impact of climate change on future PV power production

Motivation

- World share of electricity production from solar is increasing.
- Electricity production from solar is susceptible to changing climate conditions.

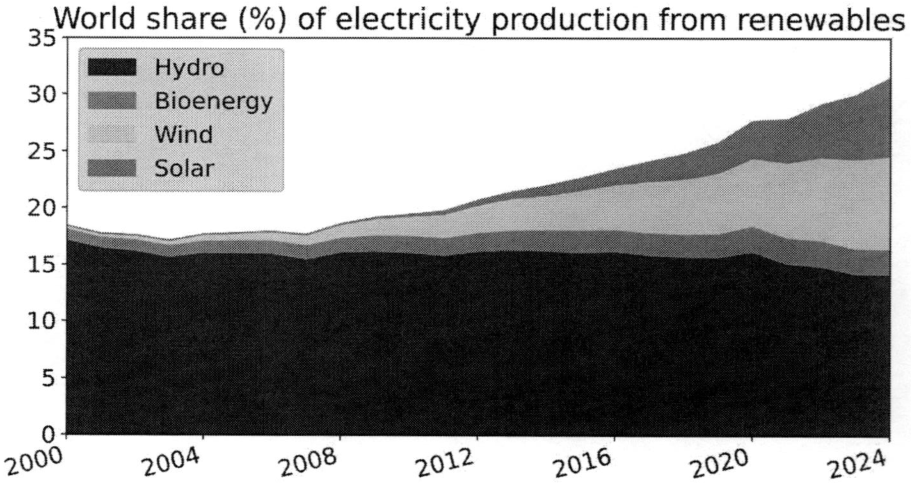

Ember - Yearly Electricity Data (2025).
Data retrieved from:
https://ember-energy.org/data/yearly-electricity-data/

DNV

PV power model

1. PV Power Potential (PVP) is defined as the ratio of PV power produced by the PV system to its nominal power.

2. PVP can be modelled as a linear combination of solar irradiance, the product (*) irradiance * irradiance, irradiance * air temperature, and irradiance * wind speed.

3. Future irradiance, air temperature and wind speed can be modelled using Global Climate Models (GCMs).

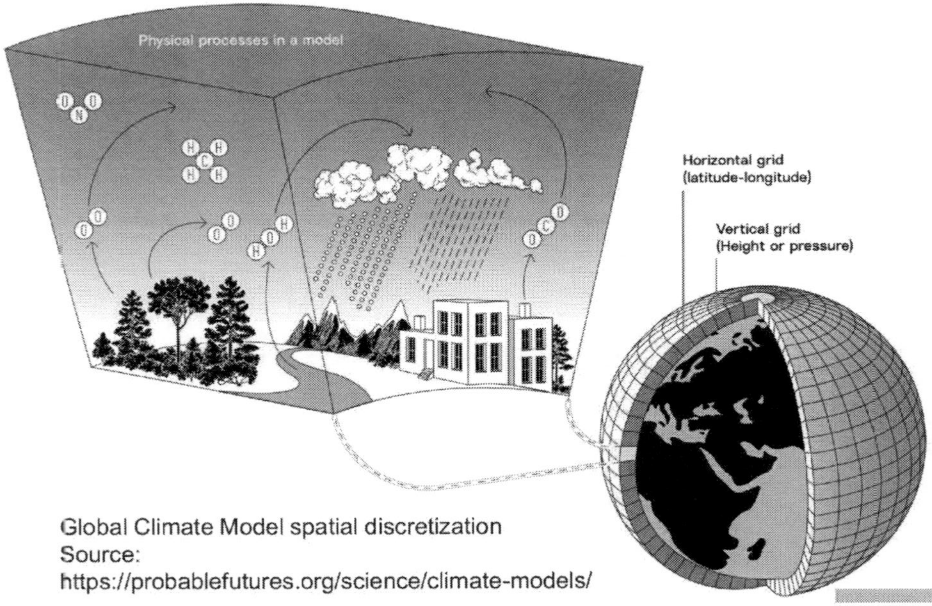

Global Climate Model spatial discretization
Source:
https://probablefutures.org/science/climate-models/

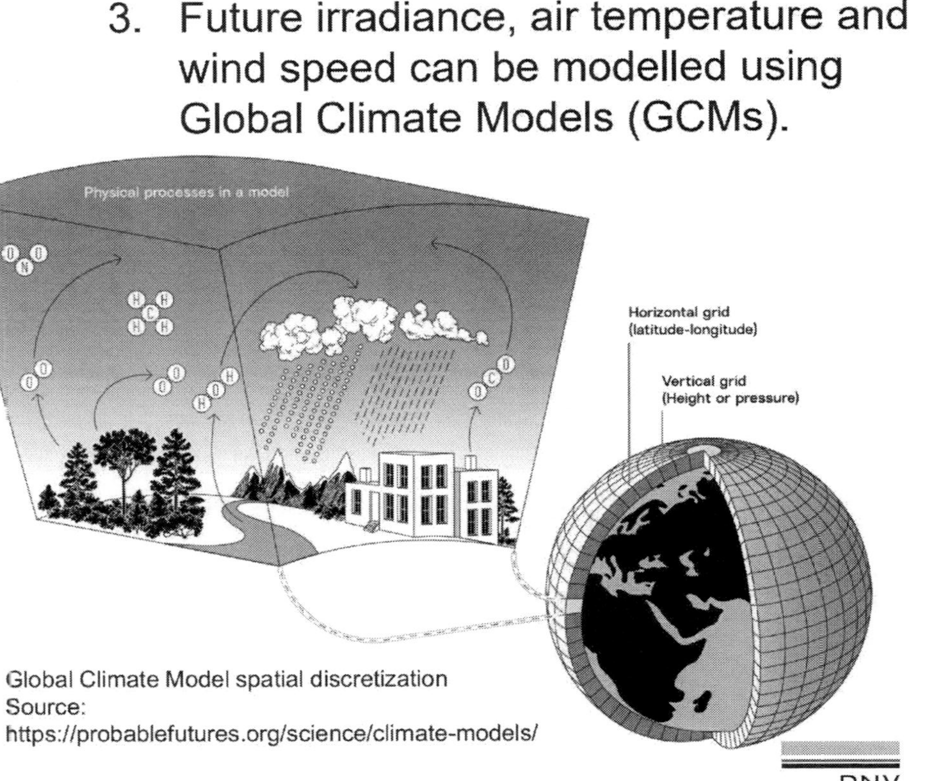

Climate modelling challenges

- Global Climate Models (GCMs) are computationally expensive to run.
- The Coupled Model Intercomparison Project Phase 6 (CMIP6) is a global climate modelling project coordinated by the World Climate Research Programme (WRCP).
- It involves numerous international modelling groups who run simulations of past, present, and future climates using different GCMs to better understand climate change and improve GCMs.
- Large amounts of data have been generated from these climate modelling endeavors, which are then archived and made available to researchers worldwide through the Earth System Grid Federation (ESGF).

PV power potential modelling challenges

- PV Power Potential (PVP) model is nonlinear and meant for instantaneous evaluation.
- PVP model is nonlinear and thus it may render inaccurate results when using daily and monthly Global Climate Model (GCM) data.
- However, daily and monthly GCM data are readily available and computationally inexpensive to handle.
- A method to generate hourly data is developed based on modulating historical hourly data to prescribed monthly GCM data.

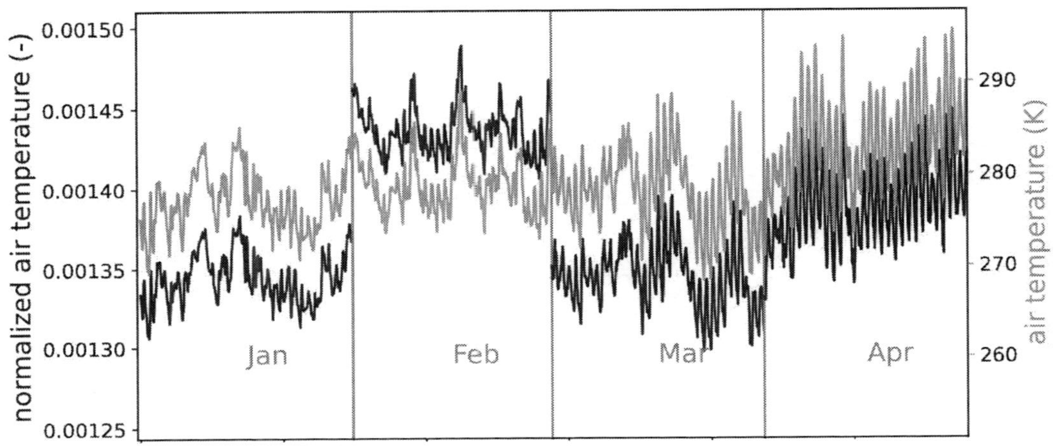

DNV

Data specifications

- Monthly Global Climate Model (GCM)-simulated solar irradiance, air temperature and wind speed.
  - Data retrieved from the Coupled Model Intercomparison Project Phase 6 (CMIP6) database for the historical and SSP5-8.5 experiments.
  - Ensemble consisting of 10 different GCMs.
- Hourly reanalysis solar irradiance, air temperature and wind speed.
  - Data retrieved from the European Centre for Medium-Range Weather Forecasts (ECMRWF) Reanalysis v5 (ERA5) dataset.
- Quantile Delta Mapping (QDM) performed on CMIP6 projections based on historical ERA5 data.

Results period 2061-2090 vs historical 1991-2020

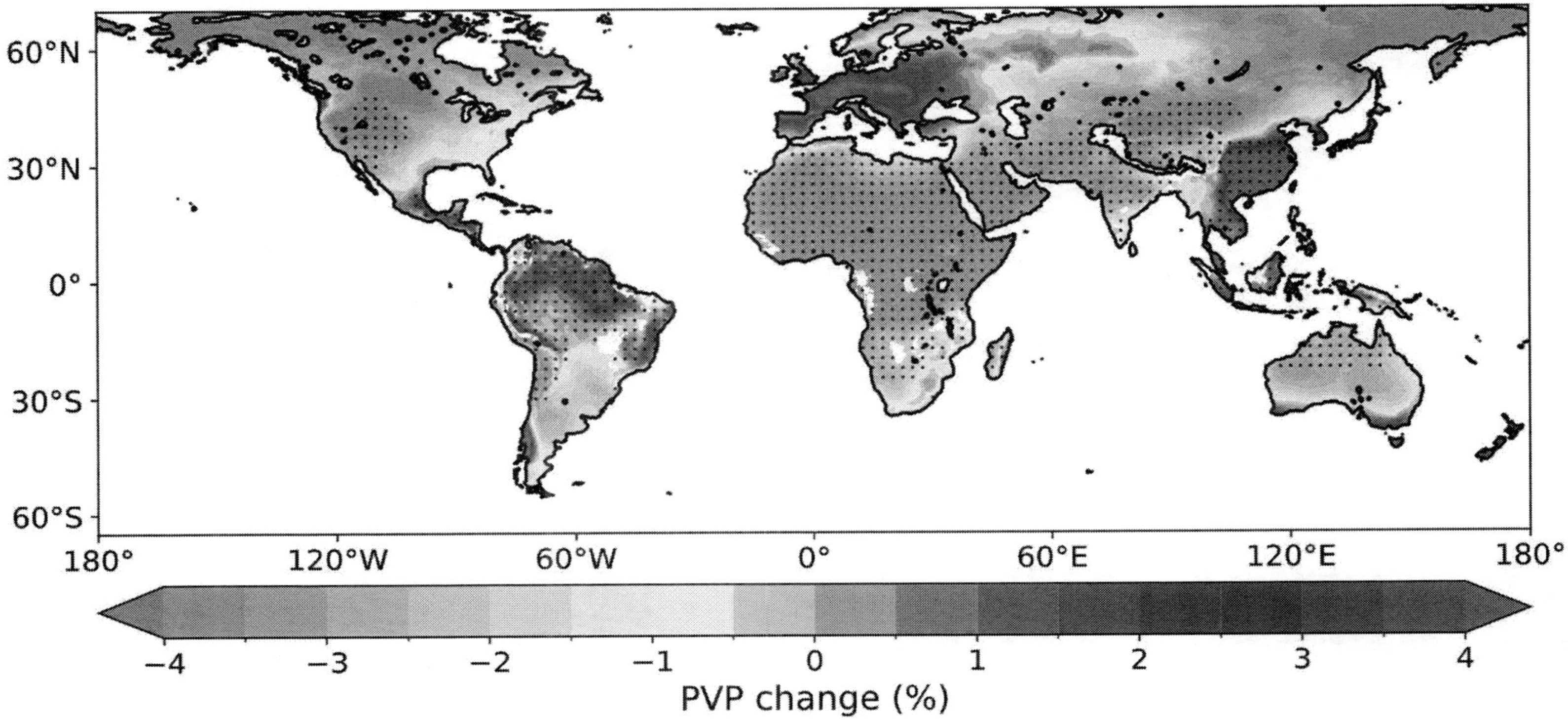

Results period 2061-2090 vs historical 1991-2020

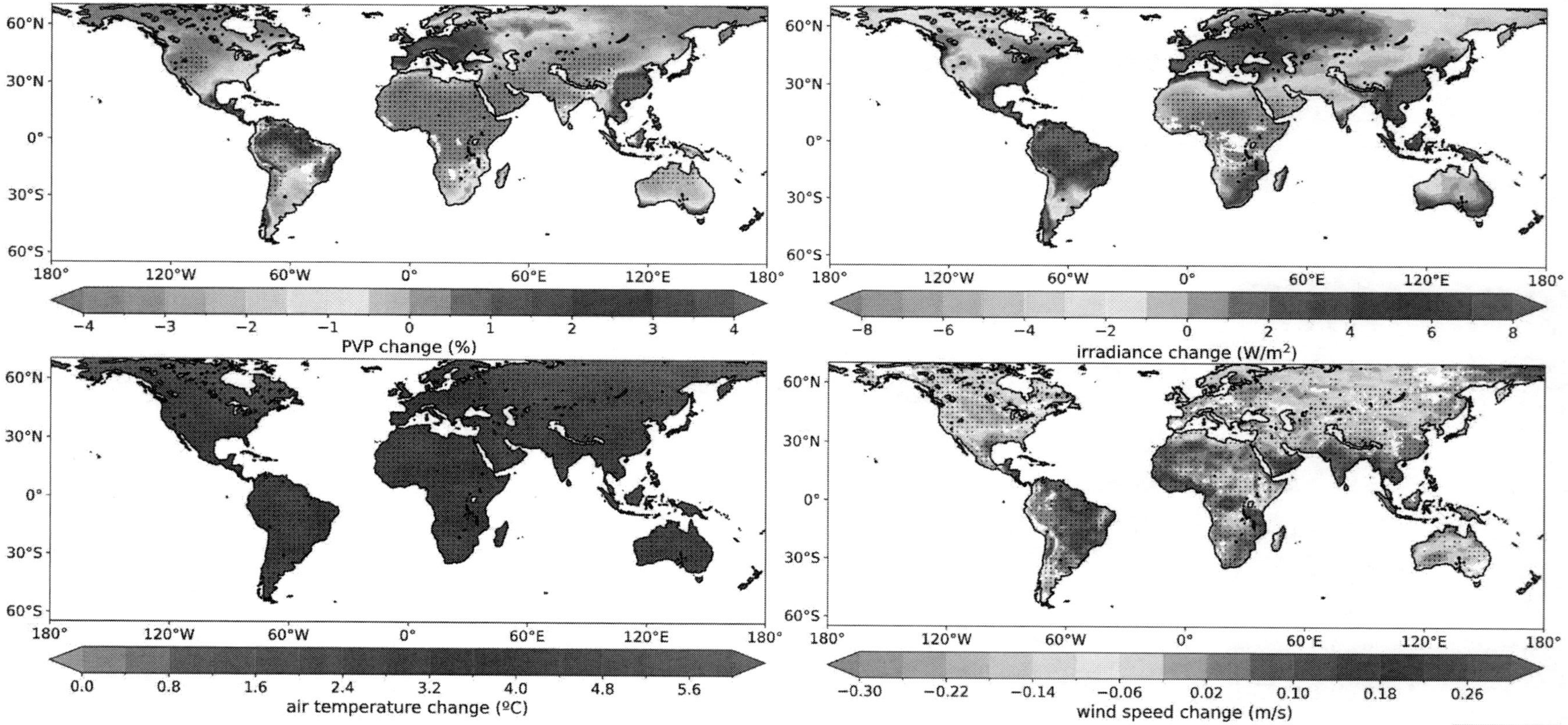

Results period 2061-2090 vs historical 1991-2020

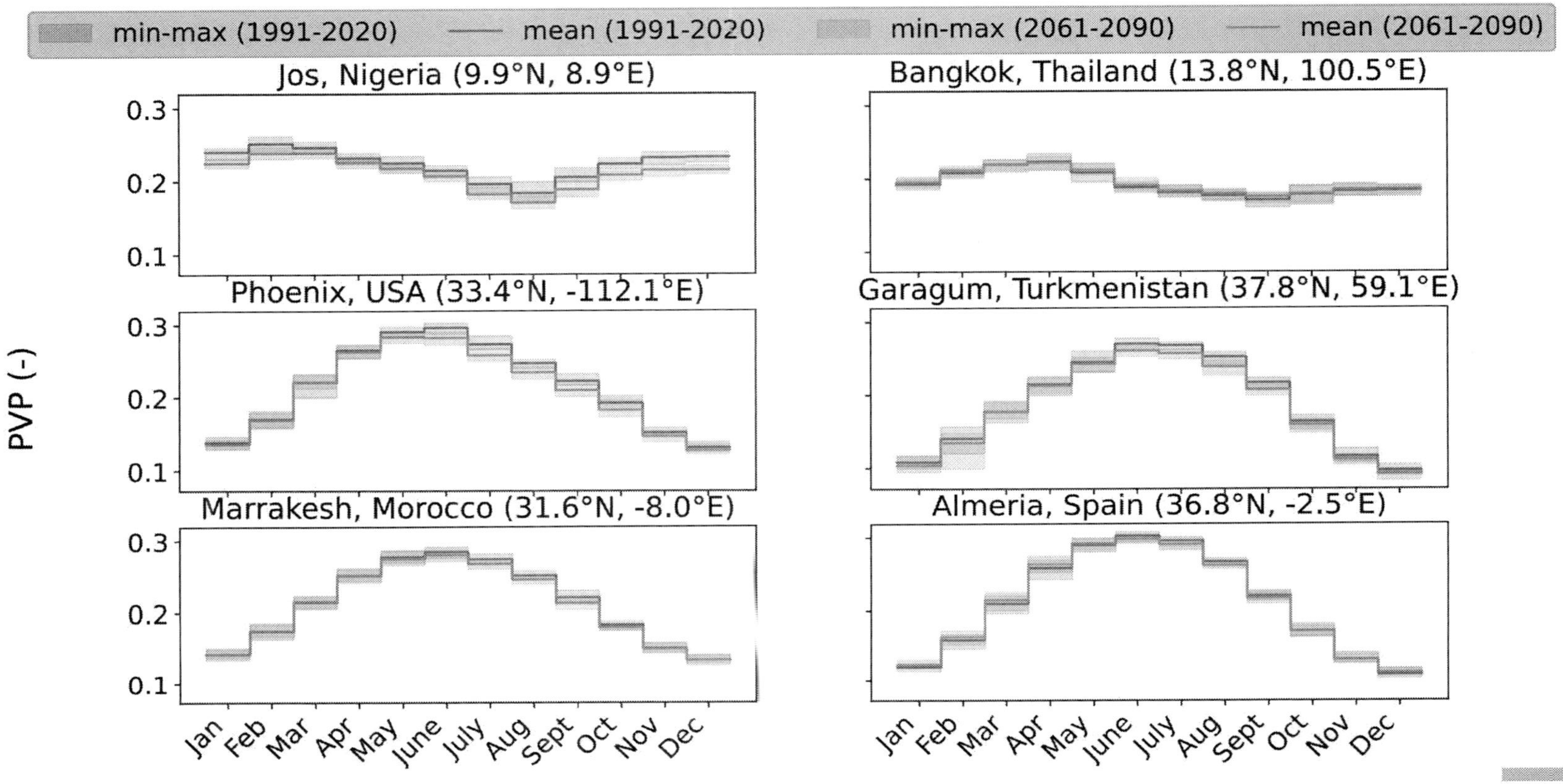

DNV

Results period 2061-2090 vs historical 1991-2020

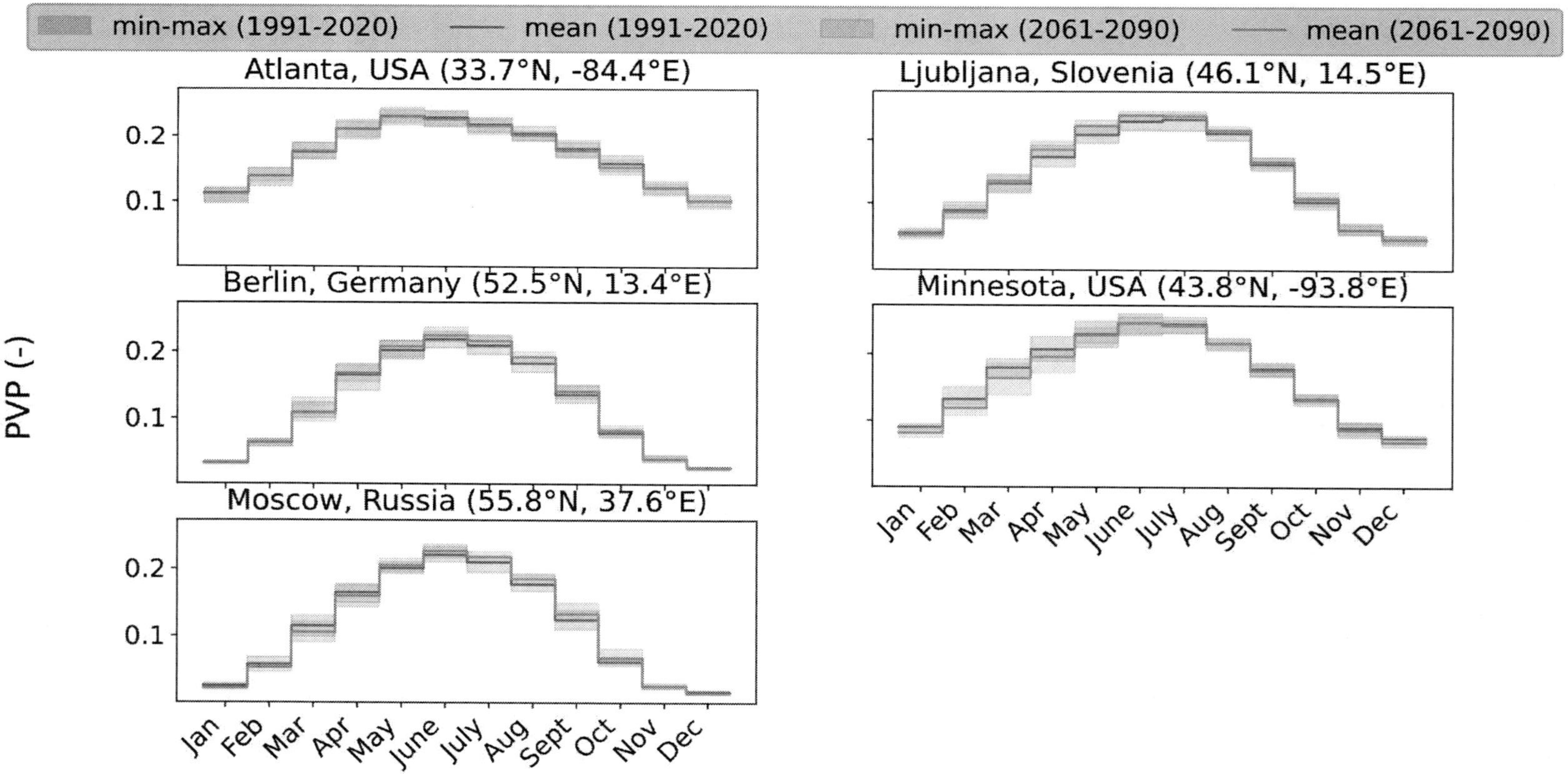

DNV

Conclusions

- A method has been developed to enable hourly-resolution climate-dependent nonlinear models be evaluated using monthly Global Climate Model (GCM) data.
- The method has been used to project PVP into the future to study the impact of climate change on the future PVP.
- The results show no major changes in future PVP assuming the worst-case high-emissions scenario.
- Climate modelling has its limitations and should be considered when interpreting these results.
- There are other aspects of PV systems not considered in this study, such as PV efficiency and reliability, that might be more greatly impacted by climate change.

WHEN TRUST MATTERS

www.dnv.com

DNV

42nd European Photovoltaic Solar Energy Conference and Exhibition

This presentation was selected by the Sc. Committee of the EU PVSEC 2025 for submission of a full paper to one of the EU PVSEC's collaborating peer-reviewed journals.

THE COST OF OWNERSHIP AND MINIMUM SUSTAINABLE PRICE OF POLO BJ CELLS PRODUCED IN GERMANY

Gomez Trillos, Juan Camilo [1]; Buddana, Viswa Harinath [1]; Papantoni, Veatriki [1]; Min, Byungsul [2]; Junge, Sebastian [2]; Kähler, Jan-Dirk [3]; Schneider, Friedrich [4]; Brendel, Rolf [2]; Vogt, Thomas [1]

1 DLR Institute of Networked Energy Systems, Carl-von-Ossietzky-Straße 15, 26129 Oldenburg, Germany
2 Institute for Solar Energy Research Hamelin (ISFH), Am Ohrberg 1, 31860 Emmerthal, Germany
3 Centrotherm International AG, Württemberger Str. 31, 89143 Blaubeuren, Germany
4 LPKF SolarQuipment GmbH

ABSTRACT: This study analyses the Cost of Ownership (CoO) and the Minimum Sustainable Price (MSP) of producing POLO BJ solar cells in a 5 GWp/a production facility in Germany compared to a facility with equal output but producing cells of the PERC concept. Assuming that the POLO BJ concept can achieve a cell efficiency of 24.2% in industrial production, the estimated CoO is 5.79 ¢/Wp, whereas the MSP is 7.16 ¢/Wp. These were found lower than for PERC, assumed with an efficiency of 23.1%, which resulted in a CoO of 6.31¢/Wp and a MSP of 7.75 ¢/Wp, respectively. The higher superior efficiency of POLO BJ also results in lower Levelized Cost of Electricity (LCOE) of between 3.02 and 3.32 ¢/kWh, depending on the module type, which is 0.14 ¢/kWh less than for systems fitted with PERC cells. Overall, this study suggests that POLO BJ solar cells are a cost-effective alternative to PERC cells.

Keywords: Cost of Ownership, Minimum Sustainable Price, Levelized Cost of Electricity, POLO BJ, PERC

1 INTRODUCTION

The global photovoltaic (PV) industry is currently experiencing a rapid growth. Annual installations reached 447 GWp in 2023 and global cumulative installed capacity of approximately 1.6 TWp by the same year [1].

China is currently dominating the PV supply chain, accounting for 92% of polysilicon production, 98% of wafer production and 84.6% of module production [2, 3]. Despite significant growth in PV deployment, Europe's PV manufacturing sector only represents 4% of polysilicon production and an estimate of 2.3 GWp*a-1 cell production capacity [4]. In addition, Germany has the largest share of the EU market, but domestic manufacturing remains modest, with an estimated 1.8 GWP*a^{-1} module manufacturing capacity [4, 5].

Besides the market situation, new technological developments in the field are emerging. The Aluminium Back Surface Field (Al-BSF), standard of the industry until 2013, was succeeded by the Passivated Emitter and Rear Cell (PERC) concept. Predicted physical limitations of the PERC concept at an efficiency of around 24% urged the industry to find new alternatives [6]. Recently, the Tunnel Oxide Passivated Contact (TOPCon) concept has become the incumbent cell type in the market, making use - in contrast to Al-BSF and PERC – of n-type silicon. However, other possibilities are the subject of research, which might have potential towards commercialization.

As a possible alternative, we investigate the p-type back junction (BJ) solar cell featuring n+-type passivating poly-Si on oxide (POLO) rear contacts. With a similar process flow as the well-known PERC concept, the POLO BJ concept could be produced by PERC production lines with minor modifications. POLO BJ has a leaner process flow compared to the current mainstream TOPCon concept, because it has fewer processing steps, including the absence of the boron diffusion. In addition, the POLO BJ cell concept allows up to 50 % less Ag consumption compared to TOPCon, as it uses Al metallization on the front side instead. Finally, further innovations are possible, such as an upgrade to the POLO IBC (interdigitated back contact) concept with only one additional laser process step or an Ag-free metallization by replacing the Ag rear contact with Al. Although the POLO BJ concept has demonstrated high efficiencies of up to 24.2% in practice, it has not undergone commercial production so far [7].

Some previous publications have addressed the manufacturing costs of photovoltaic cells; however, they focus on heterojunction solar cells [8], PERC cells [9, 10] or TOPCon cells [11, 12]. As the manufacturing costs of POLO BJ in Europe have not yet been assessed, this publication fills this research gap by performing a bottom-up cost analysis of the production of POLO BJ cells considering a production capacity of 5 GWp*a-1 in Germany.

2 METHODOLOGY

The main metrics assessed in this analysis were the Cost of Ownership (CoO), and the Minimum Sustainable Price (MSP) of POLO BJ cells. Two alternative manufacturing sequences using either a wet chemical etching process (POLO BJ-W) or laser ablation (POLO BJ-L) for single-side SiO_2 removal were assessed for POLO BJ, as shown in Figure 1. All these calculations were contrasted against the production of PERC cells under similar assumptions.

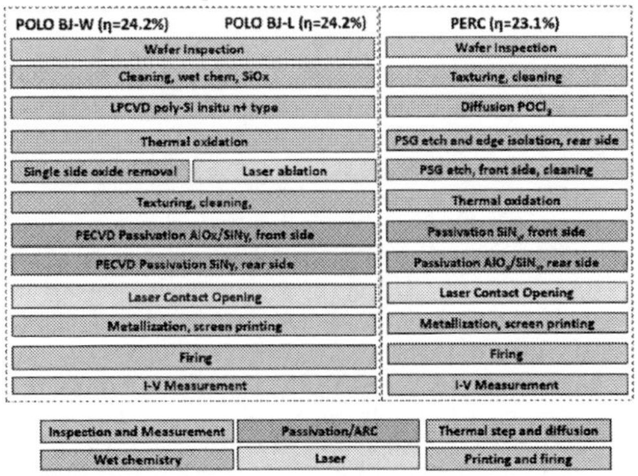

Figure 1. Comparison of the assumed production sequence for POLO BJ using wet-chemistry (POLO BJ-W), POLO BJ using laser-ablation (POLO BJ-L) and PERC. Source:

Own figure.

Additionally, assuming that these cells are integrated into modules and PV systems, the Levelized Cost of Electricity (LCOE) of electricity produced with POLO BJ cells was also estimated.

A production capacity of 5 GWp*a^{-1} of POLO BJ PV cells was assumed as the basis for the following calculations. For the calculation, a power conversion efficiency of 24.2% was assumed as the baseline for POLO BJ cells [7]. The wafer format assumed for the production of POLO was M12/G12.

For a fair comparison of the production of POLO BJ cells against PERC cells, the production of the latter concept was assumed with the same output (5 GWp*a^{-1}) and wafer format (M12/G12). For PERC, a maximum efficiency of 23.1% was assumed, in line with the maximum efficiency reported for spot prices in the market [13]. The same geographical scope for the production (Germany), same base prices of chemicals and tool costs were assumed for PERC, with differences only in the process steps required for cell production and the resulting power conversion efficiency.

2.1 Cost of Ownership

The Cost of Ownership (CoO) methodology was used to estimate the cost of producing POLO BJ cells. A Microsoft Excel® template, adapted from a SEMI and VDMA template, was used to calculate the costs step-by-step for the entire production sequence [14, 15]. Factors like capital costs of tools, throughput, footprint, chemical and gas consumption, electricity consumption and labour costs were considered in the analysis for each of the analysed alternatives.

2.2 Minimum Sustainable Price

To obtain comparable results against market prices, the Minimum Sustainable Price (MSP) was also calculated, considering capital costs, operational expenditures and taxes. The approach followed in this study was previously described by Powell et al. 2015 [16]. The calculations assumed 12.5% of operative expenditures including sales, administration, research and development, 3 months of net working capital, 7-year depreciation time for tools and 20-year depreciation time for facilities, and 8% nominal weighted average cost of capital (WACC)

2.3 Levelized Cost of Electricity

The Levelized Cost of Electricity (LCOE) was calculated for utility-scale PV plants using POLO BJ and PERC cells, considering monofacial (glass-backsheet) and bifacial modules (glass-glass). The module production costs and final prices were not accounted in a bottom-up way, but considered by applying a mark-up factor to the total material cost of the modules. Additional cost items for system integration, such as inverters, racking, and installation costs were also considered. Installation locations in Germany and Spain, with different irradiance conditions were considered in the analysis. Temperature corrections, cell-to-module (CTM) losses, and geometrical losses in modules were also assumed. Moreover, a performance ratio of 0.86 and a system lifetime of 25 years for modules and 15 years for inverters was also considered. Finally, a nominal Weighted Average Cost of Capital (WACC) of 5% and an operational expenditure (OPEX) of 1% CAPEX*a^{-1} were also assumed in the LCOE calculation.

3 RESULTS

The following section summarizes the main results of the analyses carried out in this study, starting by the CoO and MSP, which reflect the cell producer perspective, and moving on to the LCOE, reflecting the final electricity consumer perspective.

3.1. CoO and MSP of POLO BJ and PERC cells

The results summarized in Figure 2 reveal that the CoO of POLO BJ cells are lower compared to PERC cells. The CoO value obtained for PERC cells considering local cell production were 6.31 ¢*Wp^{-1}. Furthermore, the CoO obtained for POLO BJ-W and POLO BJ-L were 5.98 and 5.79 ¢*Wp^{-1}, respectively. Therefore, this translates to a reduction of 5.3% in the CoO of POLO BJ-W compared to PERC and a higher reduction of 8.3% when the POLO BJ-L sequence is considered. The lower costs associated with POLO BJ-L compared to POLO BJ-W can be attributed to the use of a laser process for a one-side SiO2 removal, which reduces chemical and electricity consumption, in addition to the capital costs due to slightly higher throughput of the laser tools.

A similar trend can be found for the MSP, also shown in Figure 2, revealing that POLO BJ-L cells can achieve the lowest value among the considered alternatives, at 7.16 ¢*Wp^{-1}, followed closely by POLO BJ-W cells with an MSP of 7.38 ¢*Wp^{-1} and finally by PERC cells with an MSP of 7.75 ¢*Wp^{-1}. Therefore, the POLO BJ allows a reduction of between 4.7% and 7.6% compared to the PERC alternative. In contrast to the CoO calculations, the MSP calculation considers operating expenses, income tax and capital costs not included in the CoO but also necessary for a financially sustainable operation of a company, which add between 1.37 and 1.44 ¢*Wp^{-1} to the overall CoO, representing a significant 18.6-19.2% of the total MSP in each of the cases considered.

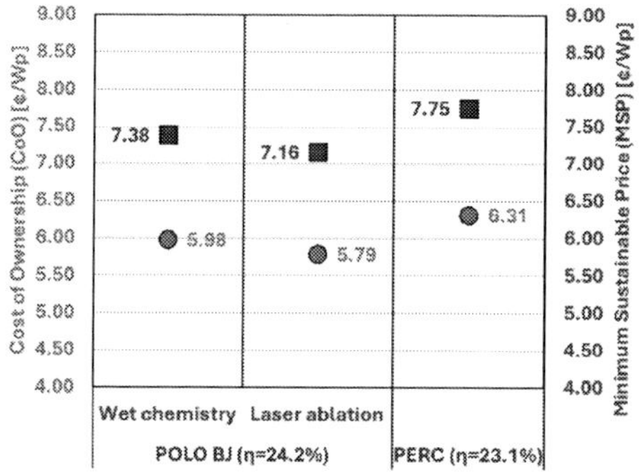

Figure 2. Cost of Ownership (CoO) and Minimum Sustainable Price (MSP) for the POLO BJ-W (Wet chemistry), POLO BJ-L (Laser ablation) and PERC cells. Source: Own figure.

3.2 LCOE of Systems with POLO BJ and PERC cells

Figure 3 presents the results of the LCOE for 5 MWp

utility scale PV systems using modules fitted with POLO BJ-W, POLO BJ-L, and PERC cells in both monofacial and bifacial configurations. According to the results, bifacial glass-glass modules generally result in a lower LCOE compared to monofacial glass-backsheet modules, despite being more expensive to produce. In short, the higher cost incurred to be assumed in the production of these modules types is offset by the additional electricity output due to rear capture of reflected solar irradiance.

The comparison of LCOE results for two selected locations - Germany and Spain - reveals a lower LCOE in Spain due to the higher irradiance, which is representative of Southern European Conditions. In

Germany, the LCOE for systems using monofacial glass-backsheet modules with PERC cells was calculated at 5.19 ¢*kWh^{-1}. If higher-efficiency POLO BJ-W cells are considered instead, this value decreases to 5.00 ¢*kWh^{-1}, and further drops to 4.98 ¢*kWh^{-1} when using POLO BJ-L cells. As for the results in Spain, the LCOE values for systems with monofacial modules containing PERC, POLO BJ-W, and POLO BJ-L cells are 3.46, 3.34, and 3.32 ¢*kWh^{-1}, respectively.

The use of bifacial modules decreases further the costs, achieving LCOE values of 4.78, 4.60, and 4.58 ¢*kWh^{-1} for PERC-based, POLO BJ-W-based, and POLO BJ-L-based modules, respectively. When the conditions in Spain are considered, the LCOE values decrease further to 3.16, 3.04, and 3.02 ¢*kWh^{-1} for systems making use of PERC-based modules, POLO BJ-W cells, and POLO BJ-L cells. Overall, the use of POLO BJ cells instead of PERC cells can lead to a reduction in LCOE of up to 0.20 in Germany or up to 0.14 ¢*kWh^{-1} in Spain. These findings suggest that POLO BJ cells offer a more economically viable option for PV systems, particularly when used in bifacial configurations.

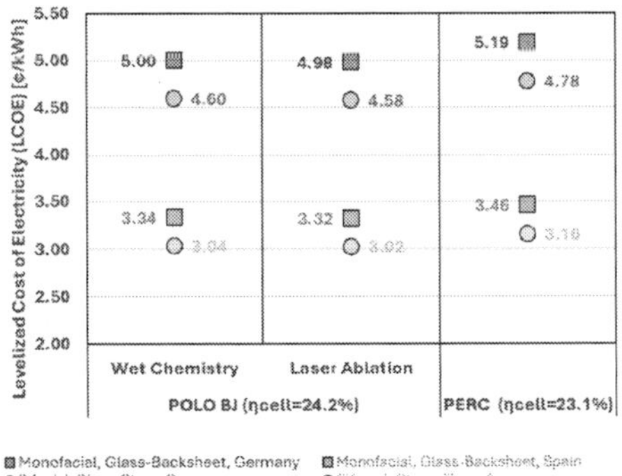

Figure 3. Comparison of the levelized cost of electricity (LCOE) for systems using monofacial glass -backsheet modules and bifacial glass-glass modules built with POLO BJ-W (η_{cell}=24.2%), POLO BJ-L (η_{cell}=24.2%) and PERC cells (η_{cell}=23.1%). Values for Germany and Spain are presented for comparison.

4 DISCUSSION

4.1 Comparison against other studies

Although comparing the results of this study to other publications' results is challenging due to variations in assumptions, production sequences, and calculation methods, some comparisons against other studies were made. To start with this, a study by Kafle et al. 2021 reported "all-in cell" production costs of 11.9 cents per watt-peak (¢*Wp^{-1}) for bi-PERC cells and between 12.9-13.2 ¢*Wp^{-1} for TOPCon cells [12]. In contrast, this study found minimum selling price (MSP) values of 7.75 ¢*Wp^{-1} for PERC and 7.16-7.38 ¢*Wp^{-1} for POLO BJ cells. These differences can be attributed to various factors, including production capacity, labour costs, CAPEX, and wafer prices.

Another study by Chang et al. 2022 predicted production costs ranging from 10 to 18 ¢*Wp^{-1} by 2025 for PERC cells with a module efficiency of 22.9-25% [10]. The median cost distribution for PERC modules produced in Italy was estimated at 15 ¢*Wp^{-1}, which is higher than the costs found in this study for monofacial and bifacial glass-backsheet PERC modules (12.66 ¢*Wp^{-1} and 15.29 ¢*Wp^{-1}, respectively) [10]. The results for POLO BJ-W and POLO BJ-L cells fell within a range of 11.84-14.57 ¢*Wp^{-1}.

A recent study by Nold et al. (2024) reported an average MSP of 12.8 ¢Wp-1 for fully locally produced TOPCon cell manufacturing in Europe [11]. When considering only wafer-to-cell conversion, an MSP of 5.2 ¢*Wp^{-1} was found, which is comparable to the MSP of 5.43 ¢*Wp^{-1} calculated for POLO BJ-L cells after subtracting wafer costs in our study. Therefore, our results are approximately 4.4% higher than those reported by Nold et al. 2024. This difference can be attributed to variations in overhead, financing, and profit values, as well as equipment and factory depreciation costs.

4.2. Comparison against market prices

The LCOE for PV electricity at utility-scale was reported by IRENA to be 4.4 ¢*kWh^{-1} in 2023, with a range of 3.1-11.0 ¢*kWh^{-1}. Specifically, in Germany, the LCOE was estimated at 6.3 ¢*kWh^{-1}, being higher than the results obtained in this study, ranging from 4.58 to 5.19 ¢*kWh^{-1} [17].

Regarding prices of cells and modules, PV Infolink's latest data shows that 23.1% PERC cells in M12 format are priced at 3.7 ¢*Wp^{-1}, while high, low, and average prices for PERC cells in M10 format are reported at 8.5, 3.5, and 3.6 ¢*Wp^{-1}, respectively, mainly based on Chinese production [13]. The estimated Minimum Selling Price (MSP) results in this study are therefore on the upper side of this range when considering local production, which in turn is affected by higher electricity prices and labour costs.

4.3. Limitations

Main limitations of this study include the sole focus on cell production and a simplified approach for module production rather than a bottom-up method. In addition, silicon wafer was considered as market-supplied, but integrated production of poly-silicon, wafers and modules can also have synergies not accounted here. To provide a more comprehensive understanding, future studies should consider the production of polysilicon, wafers, cells, and modules within an integrated supply chain framework.

In addition, other advanced concepts like POLO Interdigitated Back Contact (IBC) with a higher efficiency potential were not considered within this study. Finally, with the growing market share of the n-type silicon based technology TOPCon, a comparative analysis between POLO-based technologies and TOPCon is necessary to

10.4229/EUPVSEC2025/5DO.11.6

provide a fair assessment of their relative merits. This comparison should be based on common assumptions to ensure comparability and provide a clearer understanding of the strengths and weaknesses of each technology.

5 CONCLUSIONS

This study examined the Cost of Ownership and Minimum Sustainable Price of POLO BJ cells assumed with an efficiency of 24.2% and produced using a wet-chemistry and laser-ablation processes in comparison with PERC cells assumed with an efficiency of 23.1%.

The Cost of Ownership (CoO) for POLO BJ cells produced using the wet-chemistry and laser-ablation processes were estimated at 5.98 and 5.79 ¢*Wp^{-1}, respectively, which is lower than the CoO for PERC cells at 6.31 ¢*Wp^{-1}. In the same line, the Minimum Sustainable Price (MSP) for POLO BJ cells was calculated to be lower than that of PERC cells, at 7.38 ¢*Wp^{-1} and 7.16 ¢*Wp^{-1}, respectively, compared to 7.75 ¢*Wp^{-1} for PERC cells.

The impact on the final electricity cost of systems using POLO BJ and PERC was also assessed by means of the levelized cost of electricity (LCOE) cells. The LCOE for monofacial glass-backsheet modules built with POLO BJ cells via laser ablation was calculated to be 3.32 ¢*kWh^{-1} in southern European conditions, while bifacial glass-glass modules had an LCOE of 3.02 ¢*kWh^{-1}. Overall, results CoO, MSP and LCOE show cost advantages of the POLO BJ concept compared to the established PERC concept.

6 ACKNOWLEDGEMENTS

This work was financially supported by the German Federal Ministry for Economic Affairs and Energy (BMWE) under funding code number 03EE1150B (APOLON).

7 REFERENCES

[1] SolarPower Europe, *Global Market Outlook for Solar Power 2024-2028.* [Online]. Available: https://api.solarpowereurope.org/uploads/Global_Market_Outlook_for_Solar_Power_2024_a083b6dcd5.pdf (accessed: Jul. 9 2025).

[2] G. Masson, M. de l'Epine, and I. Kaizuka, *Trends in Photovoltaic Applications 2024.* [Online]. Available: https://iea-pvps.org/wp-content/uploads/2024/10/IEA-PVPS-Task-1-Trends-Report-2024.pdf (accessed: Jul. 11 2025).

[3] International Energy Agency, *Special Report on Solar PV Gloval Supply Chains.* [Online]. Available: https://iea.blob.core.windows.net/assets/d2ee601d-6b1a-4cd2-a0e8-db02dc64332c/SpecialReportonSolarPVGlobalSupplyChains.pdf (accessed: Jul. 9 2025).

[4] Sinovoltaics Group Limited, *Europe Solar Supply Chain Map - Edition 1 - 2025.* [Online]. Available: https://sinovoltaics.com/ (accessed: Jul. 11 2025).

[5] EnergyTrend, *European Solar Industry: Capacity, Challenges, and Future Prospects.* [Online]. Available: https://www.energytrend.com/news/20240510-46909.html

[6] B. Min *et al.,* "A Roadmap Toward 24% Efficient PERC Solar Cells in Industrial Mass Production," *IEEE J. Photovoltaics*, vol. 7, no. 6, pp. 1541–1550, 2017, doi:10.1109/JPHOTOV.2017.2749007.

[7] B. Min *et al.,* "24.2% efficient POLO back junction solar cell with an AlO x /SiN y dielectric stack from an industrial-scale direct plasma-enhanced chemical vapor deposition system," *Progress in Photovoltaics*, vol. 33, no. 1, pp. 236–244, 2025, doi: 10.1002/pip.3828.

[8] A. Louwen, W. van Sark, R. Schropp, and A. Faaij, "A cost roadmap for silicon heterojunction solar cells," *Solar Energy Materials and Solar Cells*, vol. 147, pp. 295–314, 2016, doi: 10.1016/j.solmat.2015.12.026.

[9] N. L. Chang *et al.,* "A techno-economic analysis method for guiding research and investment directions for c-Si photovoltaics and its application to Al-BSF, PERC, LDSE and advanced hydrogenation," *Sustainable Energy Fuels*, vol. 2, no. 5, pp. 1007–1019, 2018, doi: 10.1039/C8SE00047F.

[10] N. L. Chang, M. Dehghanimadvar, and R. Egan, "The cost of risk mitigation—Diversifying the global solar PV supply chain," *Joule*, vol. 6, no. 12, pp. 2686–2688, 2022, doi: 10.1016/j.joule.2022.12.003.

[11] S. Nold *et al.,* "Comparative Global PV Manufacturing Cost and Sustainable Pricing Assessment: China, Southeast Asia, India, USA, and Europe," EU-PVSEC2024 - Vienna. Accessed: Jul. 14 2025. [Online]. Available: https://userarea.eupvsec.org/proceedings/EU-PVSEC-2024/5EO.3.2/

[12] B. Kafle, B. S. Goraya, S. Mack, F. Feldmann, S. Nold, and J. Rentsch, "TOPCon – Technology options for cost efficient industrial manufacturing," *Solar Energy Materials and Solar Cells*, vol. 227, p. 111100, 2021, doi: 10.1016/j.solmat.2021.111100.

[13] InfoLink, *Spot Price.* [Online]. Available: https://www.infolink-group.com/spot-price/ (accessed: Jul. 11 2025).

[14] VDMA, *Total Cost of Ownership (TCO).* [Online]. Available: https://www.vdma.eu/viewer/-/v2article/render/46841813 (accessed: Jul. 9 2025).

[15] S. Raithel, J. Amano, D. Bouldin, F. Wessendorf, and F. Buenting, *Total Cost of Ownership in PV Manufacturing Guide.* [Online]. Available: https://www.vdma.eu/documents/34570/16191053/PV_CoO-Guide.pdf/5fd20ced-7e43-2405-1192-1fea710bc7c9?t=1644490641814?filename=PV_CoO-Guide.pdf (accessed: 08.082025).

[16] D. M. Powell, R. Fu, K. Horowitz, P. A. Basore, M. Woodhouse, and T. Buonassisi, "The capital intensity of photovoltaics manufacturing: barrier to scale and opportunity for innovation," *Energy Environ. Sci.*, vol. 8, no. 12, pp. 3395–3408, 2015, doi: 10.1039/C5EE01509J.

[17] International Renewable Energy Agency, *Renewable Power Generation Costs in 2023.* [Online]. Available: https://www.irena.org/-/media/Files/IRENA/Agency/Publication/2024/Sep/IRENA_Renewable_power_generation_costs_in_2023.pdf (accessed: Jul. 11 2025).

THE COST OF OWNERSHIP AND MINIMUM SUSTAINABLE PRICE OF POLO BJ CELLS PRODUCED IN GERMANY

Gomez Trillos, Juan Camilo[1]; Buddana, Viswa Harinath[1]; Papantoni,Veatriki[1]; Min, Byungsul[2]; Junge, Sebastian[2]; Kähler, Jan-Dirk[3]; Schneider, Friedrich[4]; Brendel, Rolf[2]; Vogt, Thomas[1]

[1] DLR, Oldenburg, Germany; [2] ISFH, Hamelin, Germany; [3] Centrotherm International, Hannover, Germany; [4] LPKF SolarQuipment, Suhl, Germany

DLR

1

Introduction

APOLON – Investor-oriented development of POLO technology for a PV production in Germany and Europe

- Goal: Strengthen European PV manufacturing competitiveness
- Focus : Polysilicon on oxide (POLO BJ & IBC) technologies
- Key assessments: Cost of Ownership (CoO), Minimum Sustainable Price (MSP), Levelized Cost of Electricity (LCOE)
- Benchmark (POLO) vs. PERC technology

Funded by : BMWE

Federal Ministry for Economic Affairs and Energy

Project Partners: **ISFH, DLR, Centrotherm, LPKF**

China's Dominance in Global PV Supply Chains

- **Why China so dominant?**
  - Cheaper electricity and labour costs
  - Large-scale factories → lower production costs
  - Heavy investment in new technologies (n-type TOPCon, HJT)
- **What this means for Europe?**
  - Global prices are set from China → increased entry barriers and difficulties for new EU manufacturers
  - Strong reliance on China → supply and competitiveness risks, similar to Europe's past challenges with fossil fuel dependence.

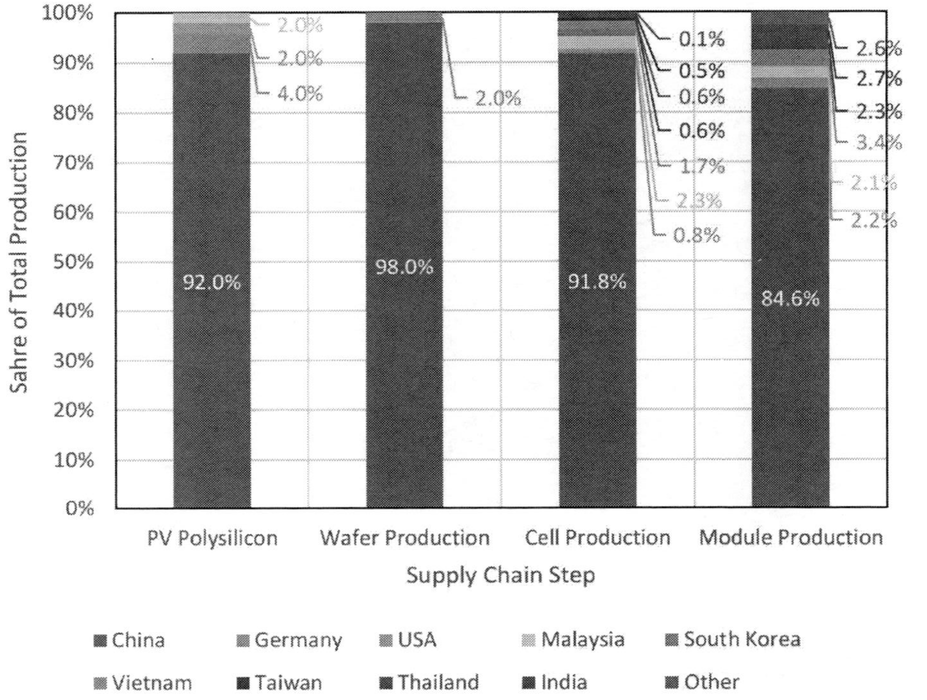

Source: Masson, G.; l'Epine, M.; Kaizuka, I.; Trends in Photovoltaic Applications 2024

PV Cell Price Trend (2023-2025)

DLR

- **Drivers of decline:**
  - Large-scale **overcapacity in China** (>500 GW cell capacity)
  - Rapid **Shift to n-type** technologies (TOPCon, HJT) improving efficiency
  - **Economies of scale** in production and supply chains
- **Implications for Europe:**
  - Local production costs: ~$0.20 - 0.25/W → nearly double import prices
  - Policy measures are necessary to compensate the price gap and support European PV competitiveness

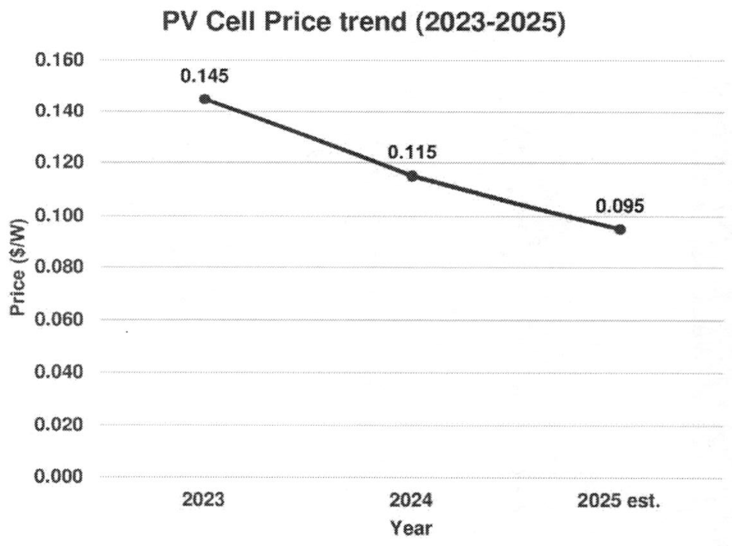

Source: Fall 2024 Solar Industry Update; Winter 2025 Solar Industry Update; PV spot price

Key Cost Metrics

Cost of Ownership (CoO)

- **Definition:** Manufacturing cost per watt (¢/Wp)
- **Covers:** Materials, energy, labor, consumables, depreciation, yield losses, overheads
- **Tells us:** How much it costs the factory to produce 1 W of cell capacity?

Minimum Sustainable Price (MSP)

- **Definition:** Lowest selling price per watt (¢/Wp) that ensures financial sustainability
- **Covers:** CoO + financing (WACC), SG&A, taxes, profit margin
- **Tells us:** The price floor at which the factory can stay profitable long term

Levelized Cost of Electricity (LCOE)

- **Definition:** Average lifetime cost of electricity per kWh produced
- **Covers:** System CAPEX (modules + BOS), O&M, discount rate, lifetime generation
- **Tells us:** How much one kilowatt-hour of electricity costs over the system's lifetime?

Considered Cell Concepts and Production Sequences

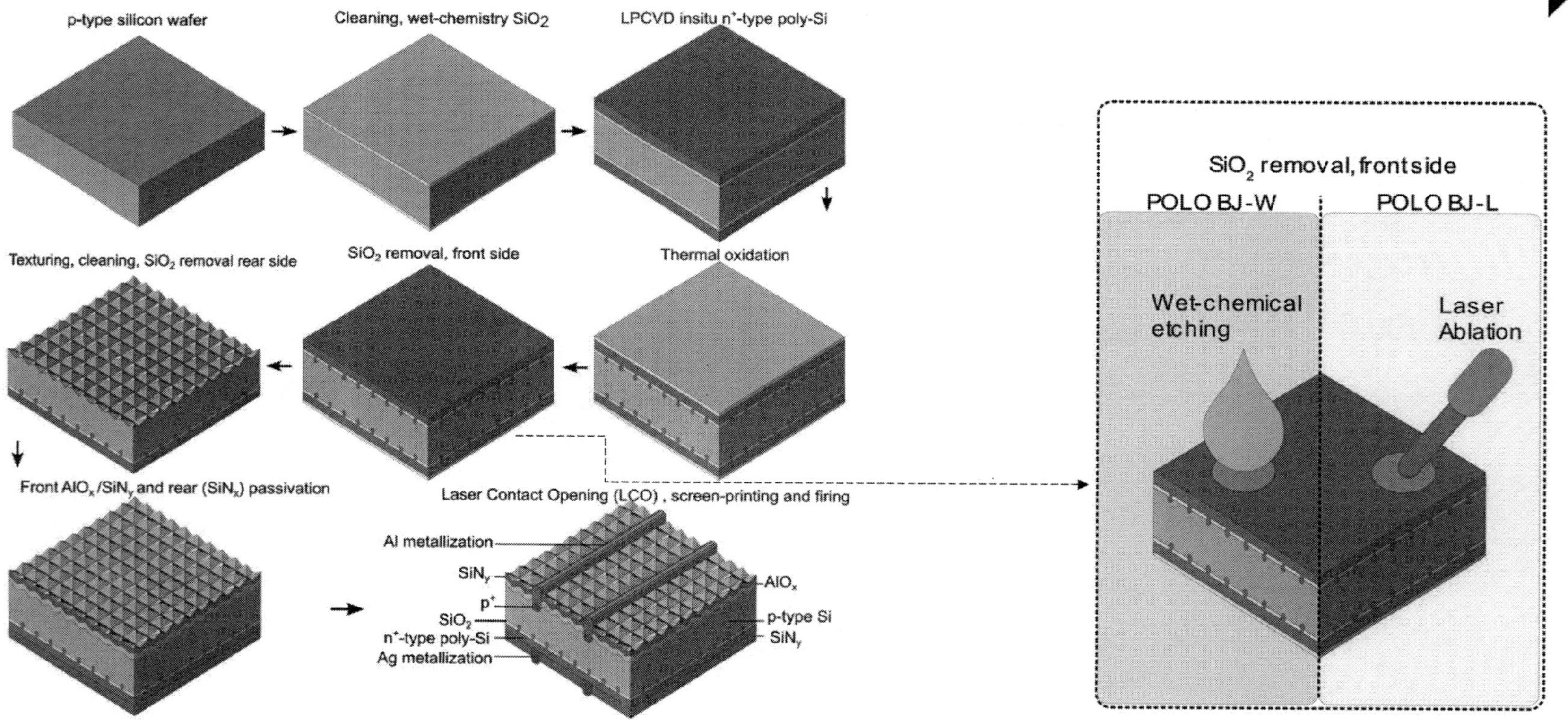

Source: Gomez Trillos, J.C. et al; 2025; The Cost of Ownership and Minimum Sustainable Price of POLO BJ Cells produced in Germany. [Manuscript submitted for publication]

Cost of Ownership (CoO)

- 'POLO BJ-Laser' achieves lower CoO than 'POLO BJ-Wet' chemistry, mainly due to reduced chemical usage.
- CoO for POLO BJ (η_{cell}=24.2%) is 8.2% lower than that of PERC (η_{cell}=23.1%), therefore highlighting the economic benefits of POLO BJ.
- Dominant cost factors:
  1. Materials & consumables
  2. Wafers
  3. Labour
  4. Utilities

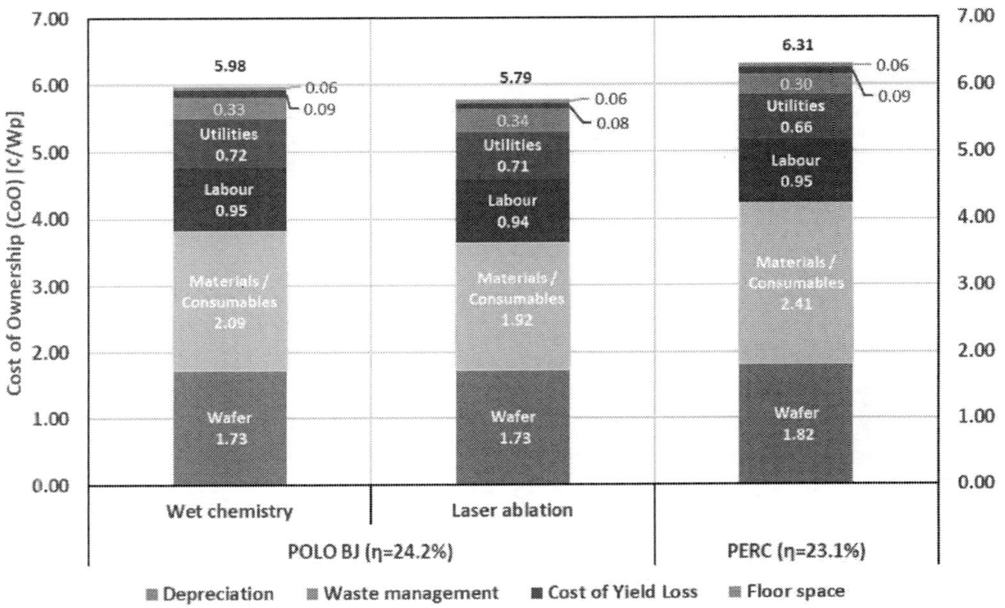

Source: Gomez Trillos, J.C. et al; 2025; The Cost of Ownership and Minimum Sustainable Price of POLO BJ Cells produced in Germany. [Manuscript submitted for publication]

7

Minimum Sustainable Price (MSP)

- MSP of POLO BJ is up to 7.6% lower than PERC (24.2% vs 23.1% effeiciency)
- MSP per Wp driven by higher material costs for PERC and subsequently by the lower efficiency assumption made for this type of cell.
- MSP for POLO BJ is within the range of spot market price range for TOPCon (3.8-11.0 USD ct/Wp, August 2025)

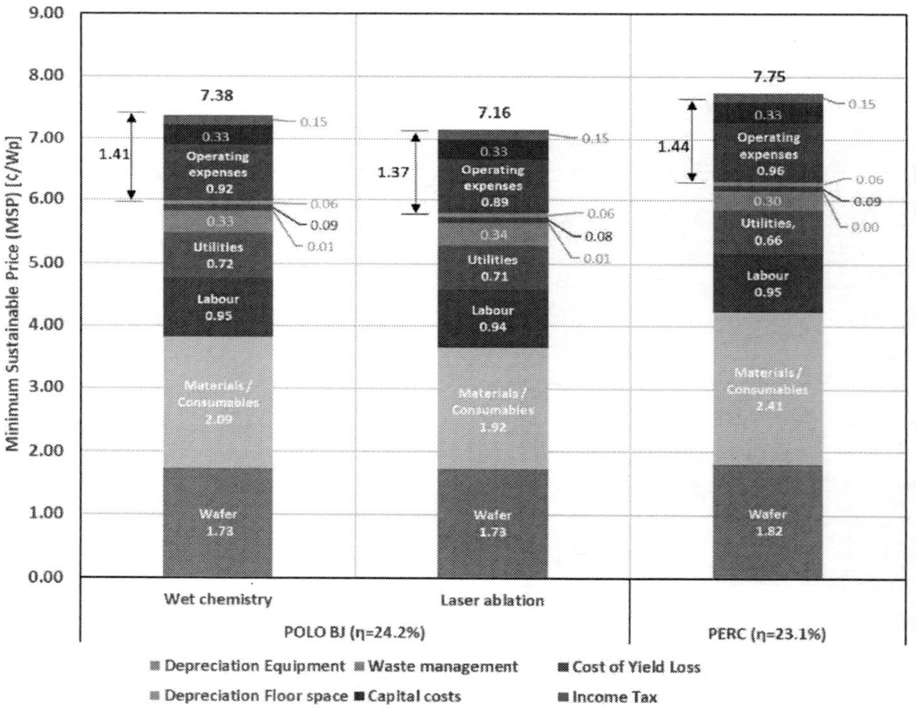

Source: Gomez Trillos, J.C. et al; 2025; The Cost of Ownership and Minimum Sustainable Price of POLO BJ Cells produced in Germany. [Manuscript submitted for publication]

9

Levelized Cost of Electricity (LCOE)

- LCOE(bifacial) < LCOE (monofacial) due to higher electricity yield and despite higher module costs.
- LCOE (Germany) > LCOE (Spain) due to the higher solar resources in Spain.
- LCOE of POLO BJ is up to 0.14 ¢/kWh lower than PERC (Southern Europe, bifacial systems).
- LCOE of POLO BJ is competitive in both Germany and Southern Europe, aligning with reported global values

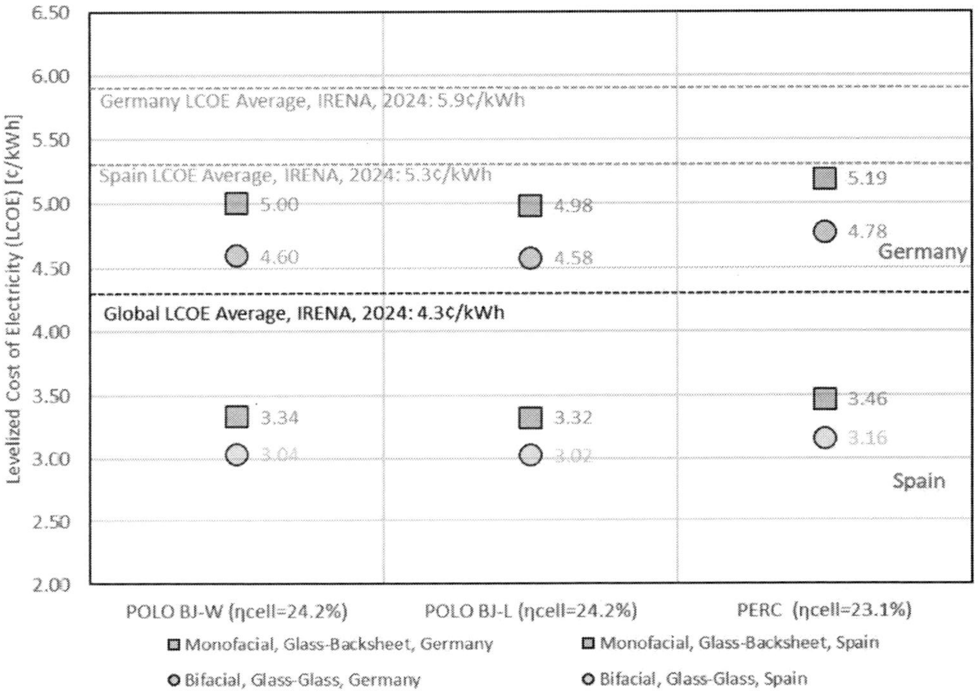

Source: Gomez Trillos, J.C. et al; 2025; The Cost of Ownership and Minimum Sustainable Price of POLO BJ Cells produced in Germany. [Manuscript submitted for publication]

For Global and Germany'y LCOE average: IRENA; 2025; Renewable Power Generation Costs 2024. International Renewable Energy Agency, Abu Dhabi.

Pathways for the Reduction of the MSP

Considering a base MSP for POLO BJ – laser cells

- 0.24 ¢/Wp less MSP if efficiency = 25%.
- 0.76 ¢/Wp less MSP for upscaling the plant to 30GWp
- 0.32 ¢/Wp reduction in MSP by lowering Ag from 9 mg/Wp to 6 mg/Wp
- 0.20 c/Wp reduction in MSP through lower WACC (Weighted Average Cost of Capital) and income tax
- All these possibilities combined lead to a reduction of 1.52 ¢/Wp (21.2%$_{rel}$)

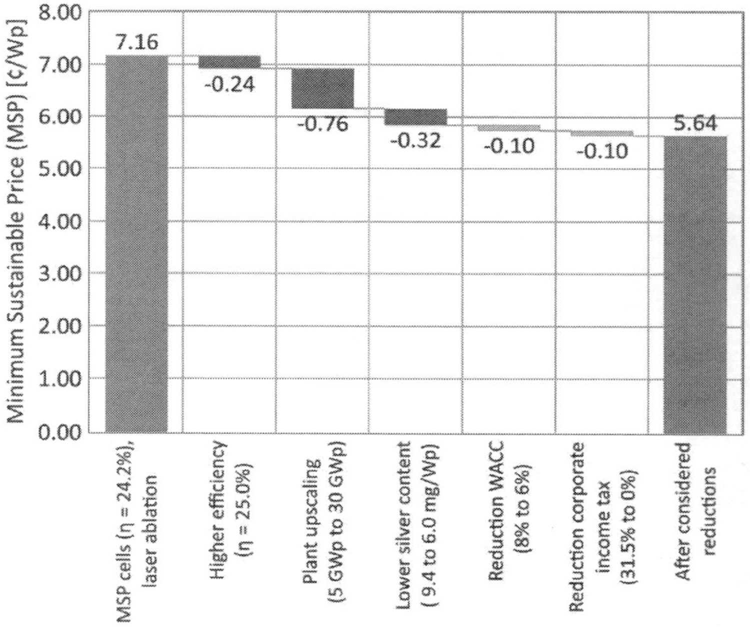

Source: Gomez Trillos, J.C. et al; 2025; The Cost of Ownership and Minimum Sustainable Price of POLO BJ Cells produced in Germany. [Manuscript submitted for publication]

Conclusion

Key Takeaways

- **Cost Advantage**
  → **POLO BJ** shows clear economic gains over PERC:
  - Up to 8% lower **CoO**
  - Up to 7–8% lower **MSP**
  - Competitive with **current TOPCon market prices**
- **Efficiency and LCOE**
  → 24.2% efficiency assumed (vs 23.1% for PERC)
  → LCOE analysis: POLO BJ delivers **lower electricity costs**, especially in high-irradiance regions
- **Upscaling Potential**
  → Combined improvements (efficiency, scaling, silver reduction, financing) can reduce
  - MSP ↓ >20% → ~5.6 ¢/Wp
  - 30 GW scaling + silver savings + 25% eff. + financing
- **European Relevance**
  → Local production still >30% costlier than China
  → Needs policy support & innovation to close gap

Impressum

DLR

Topic:	**The Cost of Ownership and Minimum Sustainable Price of POLO BJ Cells produced in Germany**
Date:	2025-09-22
Author:	Gomez Trillos, Juan Camilo; Buddana, Viswa Harinath; Papantoni,Veatriki; Min, Byungsul; Junge, Sebastian; Kähler, Jan-Dirk; Schneider, Friedrich; Brendel, Rolf; Vogt, Thomas
Institute:	DLR Institute of Networked Energy Systems (Oldenburg)
Credits:	All figures „DLR (CC BY-NC-ND 3.0)“, unless otherwise stated

Annex

DLR

14

Methodology to Calculate CoO

Plant output	GWp/a

General inputs

Prices	*Unit*
Cell Efficiency	%
Cell area/format	cm^2
Wafers price	$/piece
Material	$/kg
Utilities	$/kWh
Consumables	$/piece
Labour	$/a*FTE
Floor space	$\$/a*m^2$
Waste disposal	$\$/m^3$
Depreciation time	a

Inputs step i

Item	*Unit*
Throughput tool	piece/h
Tool number	-
Productive time	h/a
Material	kg/wafer
Tool price	$
Tool footprint	m^2
Utilities	kW
Consumables	piece/a
Waste volume	m^3/h
Labour	FTE/shift
Yield loss	%

Results step i

CoO process i	USD
CoO per cell i	USD/piece
CoO per power unit i	USD/Wp
CoO per area unit i	USD/m^2

Aggregated results sequence

CoO	USD
CoO	USD/piece
CoO	USD/Wp
CoO	USD/m^2

Iterative process to calculate MSP

Methodology to Calculate MSP

$$B_{Gross\ income,t} = B_t - C_{var,t} - D_{facility,t} + D_{tools,t}$$

$$C_{var,t} = C_{mat,t} + C_{utilities,t} + C_{waste,t} + C_{labour,t} + C_{yield\ loss,t}$$

$$B_{Operating\ income,t} = B_{Gross\ income,t} - C_{OPEX,t}$$

$$C_{OPEX} = f_{OPEX} * B_t$$

$$C_{tax,t} = B_{Operating\ income,t} * f_{income\ tax,t}$$

$$R_{cash\ flow,0} = C_{Investment,t} + \Delta NWC$$

$$R_{cash\ flow,t} = B_{Operating\ income,t} - C_{tax,t} + D_{facility,t} + D_{tools,t} + \Delta NWC + C_{Investment,t} + B_{salvage,t}$$

$$R_{NPV} = R_{cash\ flow,0} + \sum_{t=1}^{T} \frac{IR_{cash\ flow,t}}{(1+i)^t}$$

$$R_{NPV} = 0$$

$$B_t = B_1 \quad \forall t > 0$$

$$C_{var,t} = C_{var,1} \quad \forall t > 0$$

$$C_{OPEX,t} = C_{OPEX,1} \quad \forall t > 0$$

$$C_{tax,t} = C_{tax,1} \quad \forall t > 0$$

September 25, 2025
EUPVSEC 2025, 5DO.14.3

HITACHI

Empirical Analysis of Zero-Shot Cross-Frequency Forecasting for Missing Data Prediction in Real-time PV Management

Issei Suemitsu*, Toru Kono, Ryo Wakabayashi,
Jun Tsunoda, Yosuke Yamaguchi, Wenpeng Wei
Research & Development Group, Hitachi, Ltd.

Background

HITACHI

Rapid expansion of renewable energy has made energy systems more diverse and complex.

- EMS must control heterogeneous devices with different sampling cycles in real-time.
- Data must be observed at higher frequencies.
- Packet loss or sensor errors leads to frequent missing data.

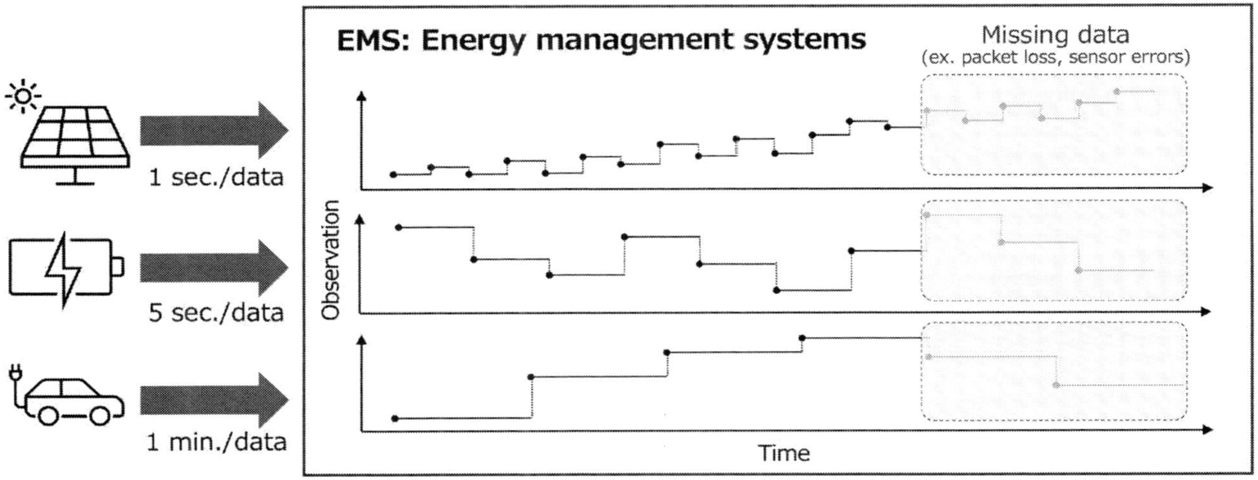

Conventional methods: Rule-based

HITACHI

Rule-based method, like Last-Observation-Carried-Forward (LOCF) rule, is popular to handle missing data in existing EMS.

- LOCF simply copies the last observed value for each missing point.
- Fast and easy to implement, but often fails to capture sudden fluctuations.
- Leads to inaccurate forecasting and potential grid instability.

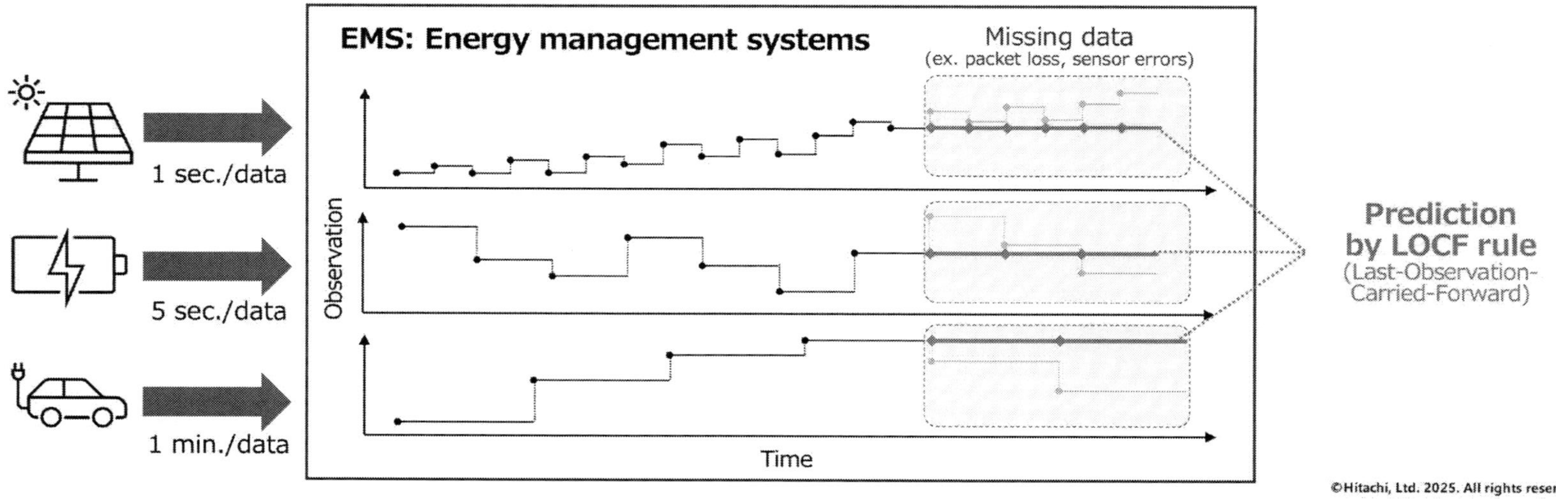

Conventional methods: Machine learning

HITACHI

ML methods can predict missing values with much higher accuracy, but requires separate models for each device and resolution.

- Leading High data collection and model maintenance costs
- Difficult to scale for large and diverse EMS environments

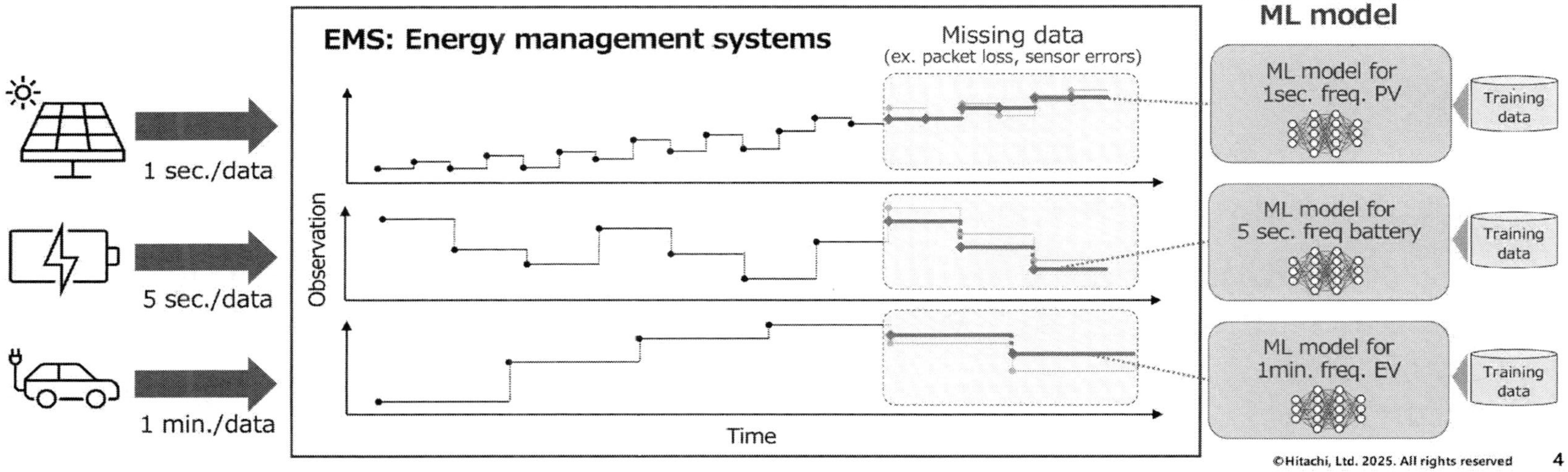

Motivation

HITACHI

Time Series Foundation Models (TSFM) show the significant potential for prediction against unseen targets (zero-shot forecasting).

- Trained on a large dataset with various series to predict unseen ones without retraining.
- But generalization ability to unseen time resolutions is not well validated.
- **Our study addresses this gap with empirical analysis.**

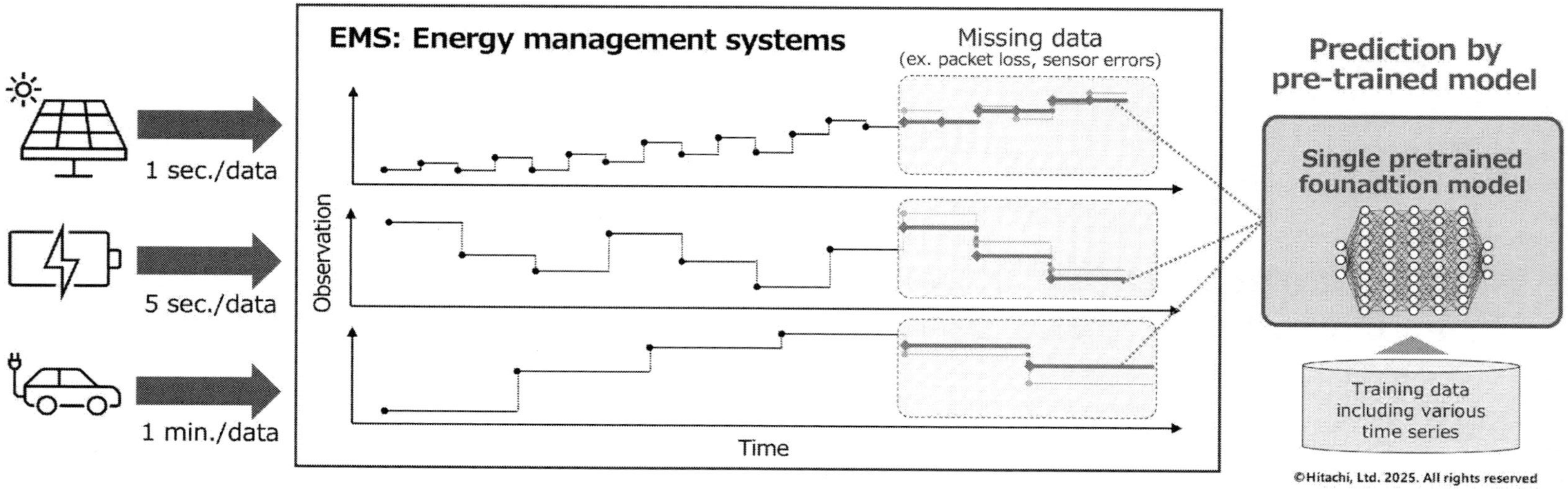

 5

Problem Definition

HITACHI

Zero-Shot Cross-Frequency Forecasting

- Train on time-series dataset including diverse devices and time resolutions
- Evaluate forecasting accuracies at unseen devices and resolutions without retraining
- Research question: which model architectures can generalize across frequencies?

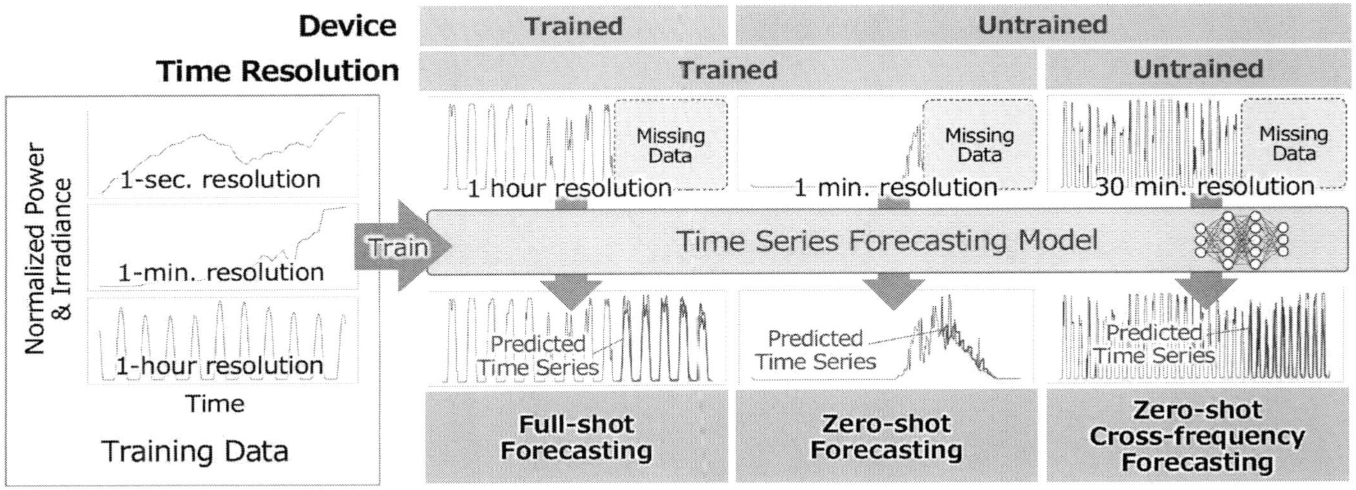

Research Objectives

HITACHI

① Construct a large multi-resolution PV & irradiance dataset

② Benchmark SoTA forecasting models in zero-shot cross-frequency

③ Propose a resolution-aware model using Mixture-of-Experts (MoE)

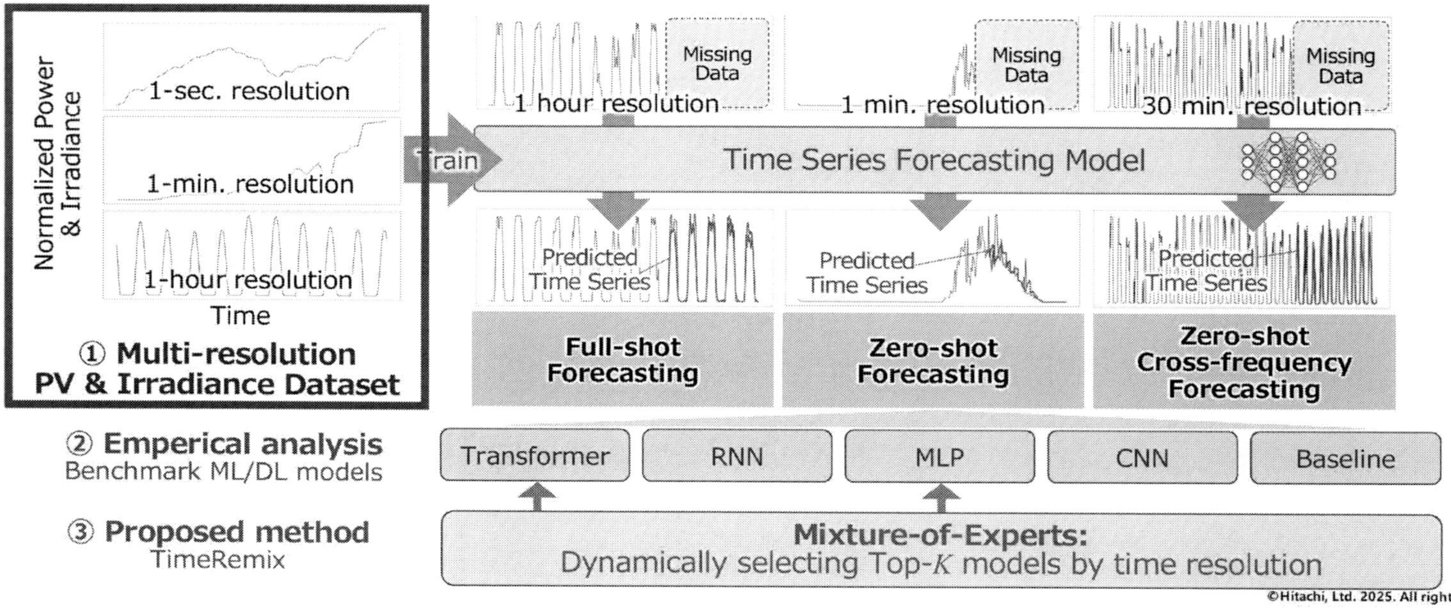

① Multi-resolution PV and irradiance data

HITACHI

100+ million data points with multiple time-resolutions, integrating 4 public PV & irradiance datasets

- Train: 1 sec, 1 min, 1 hour resolution times series from 3 datasets.
- Zero-shot test: 5 sec – 1 hour resolution (Resampled from Monash dataset)

Table 1: PV and irradiance dataset. Total observations: 174,661,306. * indicates resampled data.

Dataset	Resolution	Series	Length	Observation	Usage
Oahu Solar Measurement Grid [21]	1 second	6	10,321,203	61,927,218	Train/Test
PSML [22]	1 minute	66	1,573,565	103,855,290	Train/Test
DKASC, Alice Springs [23]	1 hour*	21	69,386	1,457,106	Train/Test
Monash Solar Power Dataset [24]	5 second*	1	5,840,017	5,840,017	Test
	30 second*	1	973,337	973,337	Test
	1 minute*	1	486,669	486,669	Test
	5 minute*	1	97,334	97,334	Test
	30 minute*	1	16,223	16,223	Test
	1 hour*	1	8,112	8,112	Test

② Benchmark Setting

HITACHI

Autoregression forecasting task

- **Input**:
  recent T=120 observations of the targets & covariates
- **Output**: next S=24 step forecast
- Models trained to minimize **Mean Squared Error (MSE) loss**

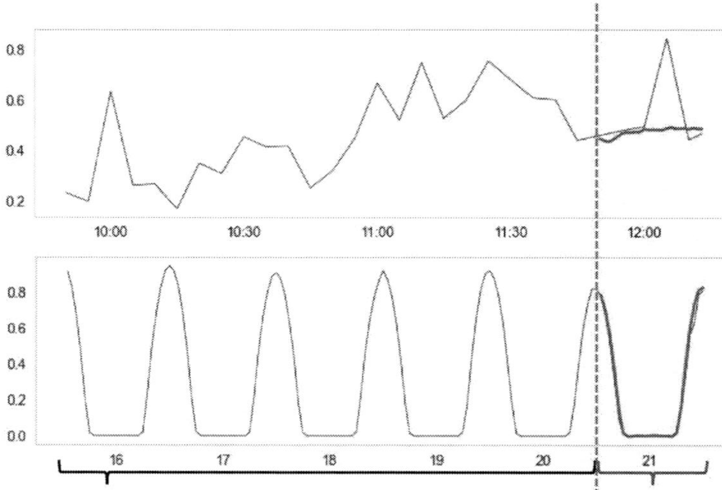

1 min. resolution
(PSML)

1 hour resolution
(DKASC, Alice Springs)

Input:
recent T=120 observed targets & covariates

Output:
next S=24 step forecast of targets

$X^i_{1:T}$ =

- Y^i_t: Normalized target timeseries ([0.416, 0.415, 0.413, ...])
- Z^i_t: 11 past covariates
  10 time-stamp features
  (month, day, hour, min., sec. converted with sin & cos)
  + **time resolution** τ^i (1 ~ 3600 sec.)

y^i_1	⋯	$y^i_T)$
$\sin(month^i_1)$	⋯	$\sin(month^i_T)$
$\cos(month^i_1)$	⋯	$\cos(month^i_T)$
⋮	⋯	⋮
$\cos(second^i_1)$	⋯	$\cos(second^i_T)$
$\tau^i/3600$	⋯	$\tau^i/3600$

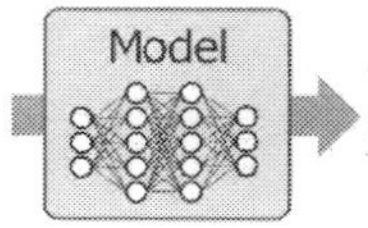

$\hat{Y}^i_{T+1:T+S}$

y^i_{T+1}	⋯	y^i_{T+S}

② Benchmarked Models

Transformer:

1. **iTransformer**: Encoder-only Series-wise token
2. **PatchTST**: Encoder-only, Patch-wise token
3. **Timer**: Decoder-only, Patch-wise token

Recurrent Neural Network (RNN):

4. **LSTM**: An RNN with gating mechanisms
5. **S-Mamba**: Selective state-space mechanism

Multi-Layer Perceptron (MLP):

6. **TSMixer**: Mixing across multiple channels
7. **TimeMixer**: Multiscale mixing architecture

Convolutional Neural Network (CNN):

8. **TCN**: Causal convolution and skip connections

Baselines:

9. **LOCF**: A simple rule-based method.
10. **Moirai-MoE**: A SoTA pretrained TSFM using MoE (without retraining)

Models #1~9 are trained under same conditions
(3 layers with 512 hidden units, 20% dropout,
100,000 training steps, AdamW with 0.0001 learning rate.)

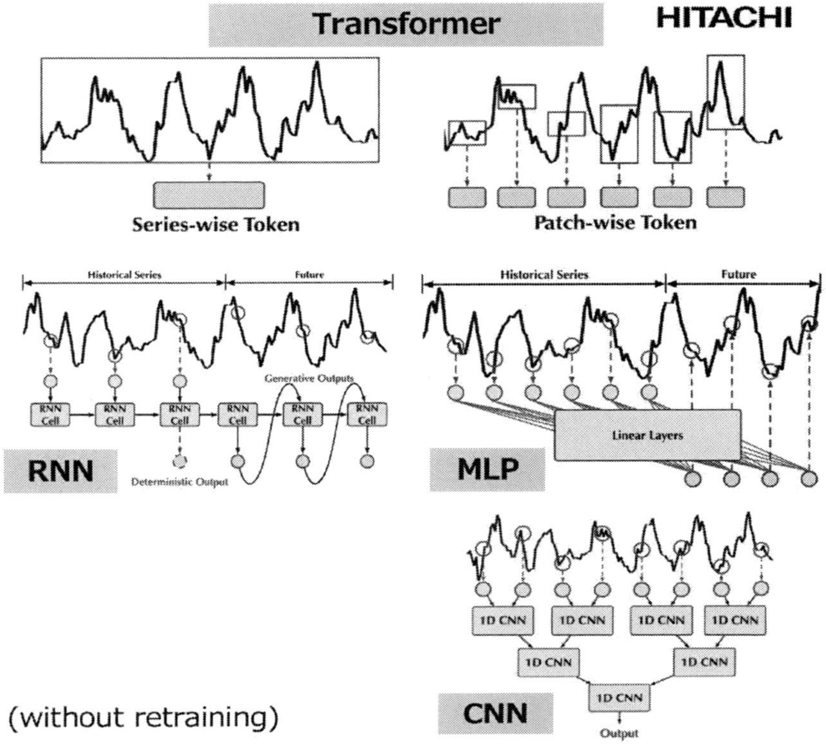

Figures: Wang, Y., Wu, H., Dong, J., Liu, Y., Long, M., & Wang, J. (2024). Deep Time Series Models: A Comprehensive Survey and Benchmark. http://arxiv.org/abs/2407.13278

② Benchmark Results: Zero-Shot Forecasting

HITACHI

Prediction accuracies were influenced by model architectures and time resolutions.

- Transformers show high accuracies at high-frequencies (5–30 sec)
- RNNs & MLPs performed better at lower frequencies (1 min–1 hour)

Zero-shot cross-frequency forecasting performance
(RMSE: Smaller is better)

1st 2nd 3rd
Untrained

Algorithm	Monash, Solar Power Dataset [24]					
	5 sec.	30 sec.	1 min.	5 min.	30 min.	1 hour
iTransformer	0.0175	0.0635	0.0855	0.1683	0.4268	0.1260
PatchTST	0.0178	0.0631	0.0849	0.1529	0.3882	0.1359
Timer	0.0204	0.0685	0.0899	0.1497	0.4335	0.1291
LSTM	0.0479	0.2855	0.0887	0.1238	0.2349	0.1585
S-Mamba	0.0255	0.0639	0.0836	0.1940	0.4298	0.1388
TSMixer	0.1328	0.1035	0.0830	0.1196	0.3423	0.1353
TimeMixer	0.0334	0.0713	0.0845	0.1535	0.4320	0.1291
TCN	0.0535	0.0998	0.1127	0.1780	0.6076	0.1308
LOCF (Naïve seasonal)	0.0229	0.0652	0.0995	0.1121	0.4576	0.5017
Moirai-MoE	0.1029	0.1436	0.1759	0.2127	0.3684	0.1918

③ Proposed method: TimeRemix

HITACHI

Time Resolution-aware Mixture-of-Experts Forecaster

Adaptively combining multiple expert models specialized for a particular resolution.

- Sparse MoE architecture:
  - **Experts** (iTransformer, PatchTST, LSTM, TSMixer, TimeMixer) selected for performances at specific time resolutions.
  - **Gating network** dynamically activates only the top K=2 experts for each input series.
  - Final prediction is the weighted-average of selected experts' outputs.

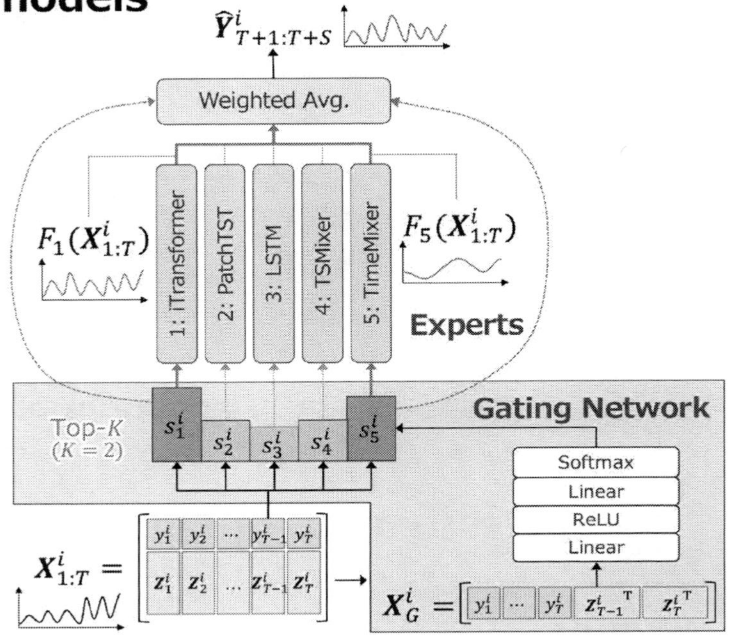

③ Effectiveness of TimeRemix: Accuracy

HITACHI

Robust zero-shot cross-frequency forecasting ability across all resolutions

Zero-shot cross-frequency forecasting performance (RMSE: Smaller is better)

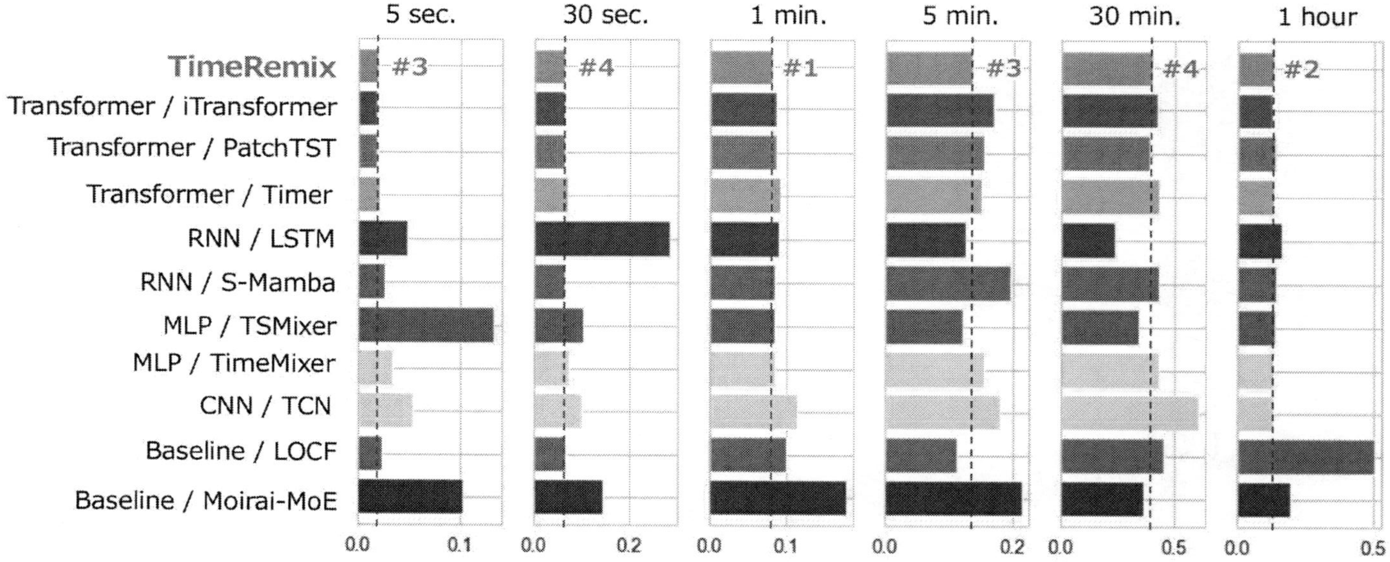

③ Effectiveness of TimeRemix: Efficiency

HITACHI

Balances predictive accuracy with computational efficiency, since only a few experts are activated at once.

- Demonstrates superior generalization capability obtained by sparse MoE.

Aggregated zero-shot forecasting accuracy by geometric mean of the RMSEs

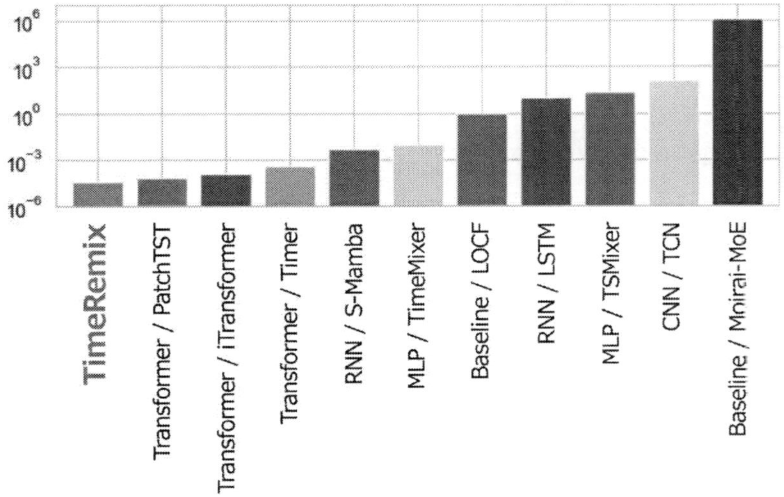

Inference time
[sec./sample]

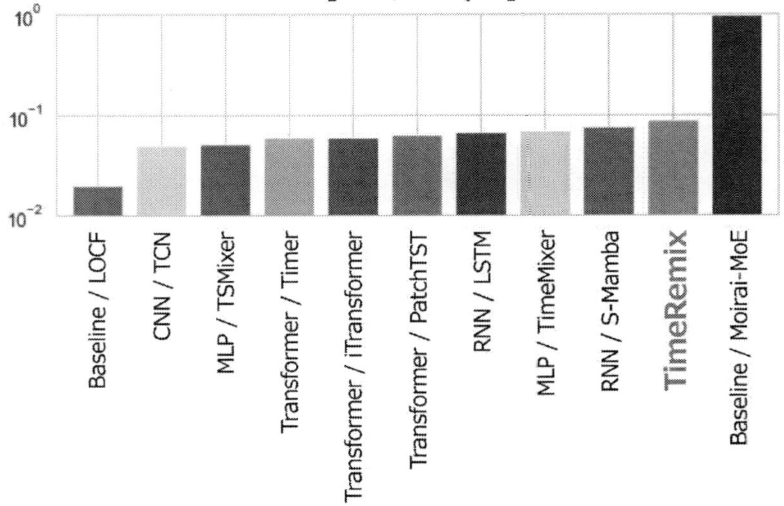

③ Expert selection results

HITACHI

Gating network changes expert selection by time resolution.

- At second-level resolutions, Transformers were selected more often.
- At minute-to-hour resolutions, LSTM and MLPs became dominant.

Average gating weights of experts in zero-shot forecasting
(Higher weight means more frequent expert selection)

	5 sec.	30 sec.	1min.	5 min.	30 min.	1hour
iTransformer	0.709	0.680	0.632	0.554	0.653	0.565
PatchTST	0.170	0.159	0.107	0.021	0.004	0.081
LSTM	0.068	0.104	0.186	0.288	0.125	0.004
TSMixer	0.003	0.000	0.006	0.000	0.051	0.065
TimeMixer	0.050	0.057	0.069	0.137	0.167	0.285

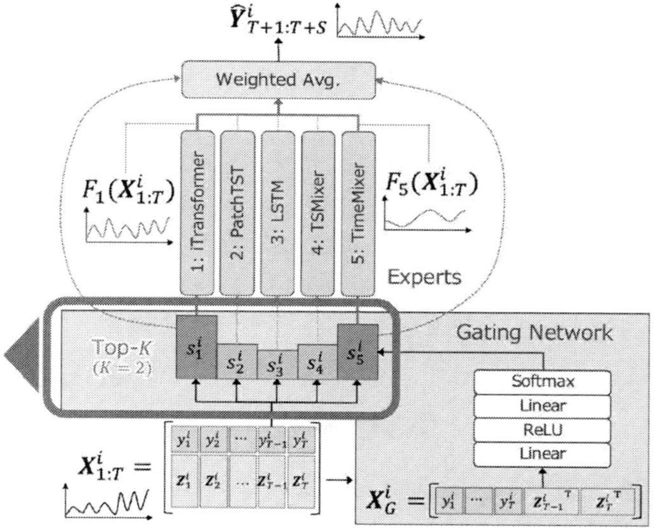

HITACHI

③ Expert selection results

Trend of expert selection matches the benchmark results.

TimeRemix learned to assign appropriate experts according to time resolution.

Average gating weights of experts in zero-shot forecasting

	5 sec.	30 sec.	1min.	5 min.	30 min.	1hour
iTransformer	0.709	0.680	0.632	0.554	0.653	0.565
PatchTST	0.170	0.159	0.107	0.021	0.004	0.081
LSTM	0.068	0.104	0.186	0.288	0.125	0.004
TSMixer	0.003	0.000	0.006	0.000	0.051	0.065
TimeMixer	0.050	0.057	0.069	0.137	0.167	0.285

Zero-shot prediction results of single models (RMSE)

Algorithm	Monash, Solar Power Dataset					
	5 sec.	30 sec.	1 min.	5min.	30 min.	1 hour
iTransformer	**0.0175**	**0.0635**	0.0855	0.1683	0.4268	**0.1260**
PatchTST	**0.0178**	**0.0631**	0.0849	0.1529	0.3882	0.1359
LSTM	0.0479	0.2855	0.0887	**0.1238**	**0.2349**	0.1585
TSMixer	0.1328	0.1035	**0.0830**	**0.1196**	**0.3423**	0.1353
TimeMixer	0.0334	0.0713	**0.0845**	0.1535	0.4320	**0.1291**

③ Visualization of Forecasted Time Series

HITACHI

TimeRemix aligns with the best-performing model at each resolution

- Behaves like Transformer at high frequency, like MLP at low frequency

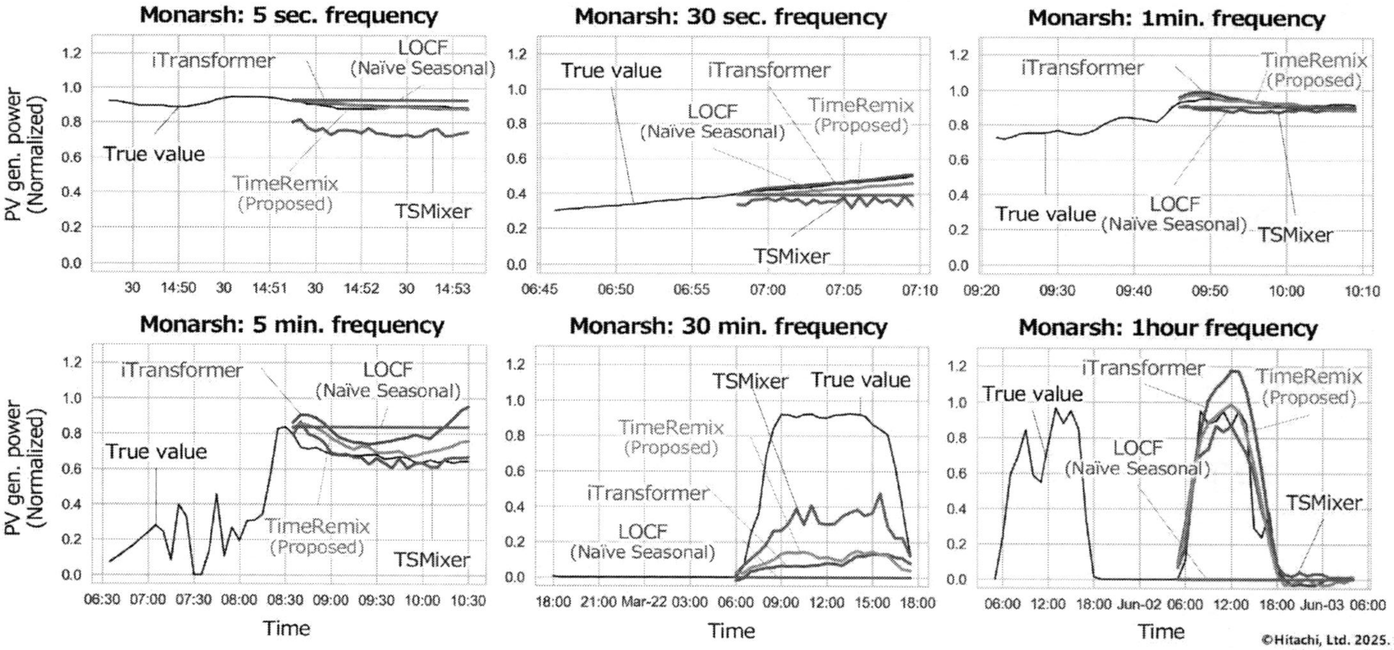

Conclusion

HITACHI

- Built a large multi-resolution dataset (>100M points)
- Benchmarked 10 forecasting methods
- Proposed TimeRemix, achieved robust zero-shot cross-frequency forecasting
- But challenges remain. (e.f. 30 mins forecast is much worse than 1hour)
- Future work: fully resolution-invariant forecasting architectures

Monash Solar Power Dataset (Zero-shot prediction)

30 min. frequency | 1hour frequency

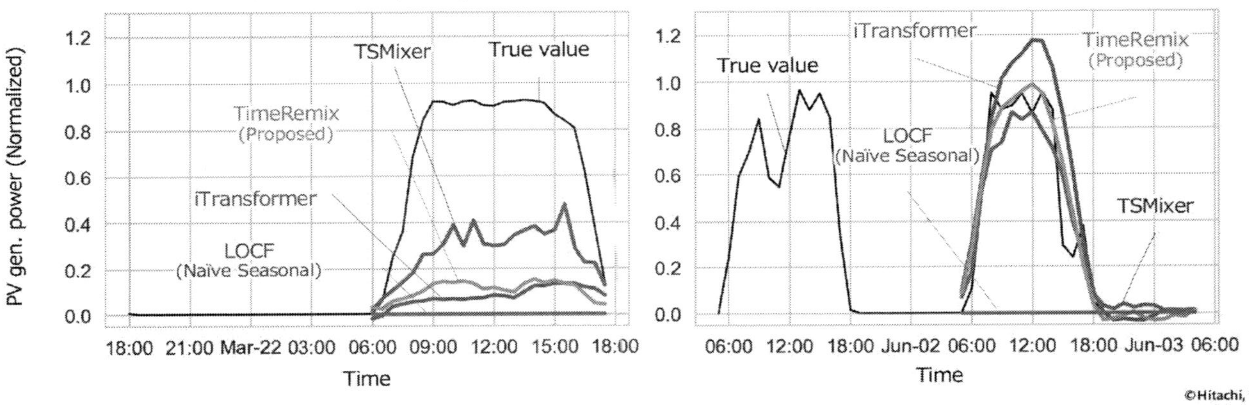

Acknowledgments

HITACHI

Thanks public dataset providers:

- "Oahu Solar Measurement Grid (1-Year Archive): 1-Second Solar Irradiance; Oahu, Hawaii (Data)" at http://dx.doi.org/10.5439/1052451, reference number NREL Report No. DA-5500-56506,

- "PSML: A Multi-scale Time-series Dataset for Machine Learning in Decarbonized Energy Grids (Dataset)" at https://doi.org/10.5281/zenodo.5130611, reference number Version 0.2,

- "Desert Knowledge Australia Centre. 19/06/2024. Download Data. Alice Springs" at https://dkasolarcentre.com.au/download, reference number 19/06/2024,

- "Solar Power Dataset (4 Seconds Observations)" in Monash Time Series Forecasting Repository at https://doi.org/10.5281/zenodo.3992664, reference number Version 2.

Thank you for your attention.

HITACHI

Cotact: Issei Suemitsu,
Research & Development Group, Hitachi, Ltd.,
1-280 Higashi-Koigakubo, Kokubunji, Tokyo 185-8601, Japan,
Email Address: issei.suemitsu.rj@hitachi.com

① Details of dataset

HITACHI

Dataset	Training period	Validation period	Test period
Oahu Solar Measurement Grid (1 sec. resolution)	**3 months** 2011-07-01 06:00:00 - 2011-10-01-05:59:59	**24 days** 2011-10-01 06:00:00 - 2011-10-25 05:59:59	**7 days** 2011-10-25 06:00:00 - 2011-10-31 20:00:00
PSML (1 min. resolution)	**2 years** 2018-01-01 06:00:00 - 2020-01-01 05:59:00	**10 months** 2020-01-01 06:00:00 - 2020-10-01 05:59:00	**2 months** 2020-10-01 06:00:00 - 2020-12-31 23:59:00
DKACS, Alice Spring* (1 hour resolution)	**6 years** 2016-10-01 00:00:00 - 2022-09-30 23:00:00	**1 year** 2022-10-01 00:00:00 - 2023-09-30 23:00:00	**11 months** 2023-10-01 00:00:00 - 2024-01-31 23:00:00
Monarsh, Solar Power Dataset*	-	-	**11 months** 2019-11-01 00:00:00 - 2020-10-03 23:00:00

* Data from the southern hemisphere has been adjusted by adding 180 days to align with northern hemisphere seasons.

② Benchmarked Models: #1-3

HITACHI

Transformer:

1. **iTransformer**: An encoder-only Transformer, tokenizes the entire time series
2. **PatchTST**: An encoder-only Transformer-based model using patch-wise tokens
3. **Timer**: A decoder-only Transformer-based model using patch-wise tokens

Tokenization

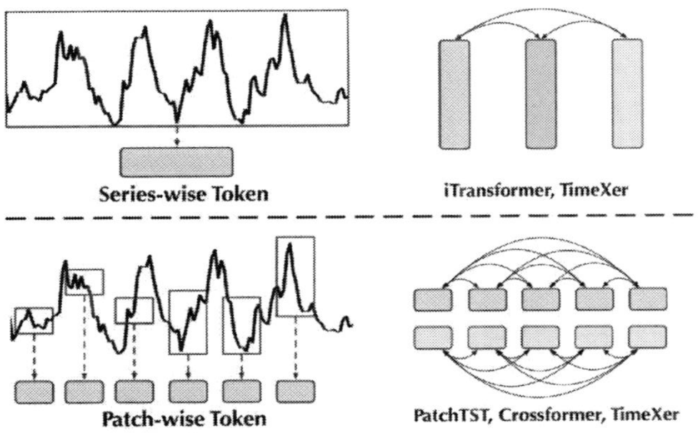

Wang, Y., Wu, H., Dong, J., Liu, Y., Long, M., & Wang, J. (2024). Deep Time Series Models: A Comprehensive Survey and Benchmark. http://arxiv.org/abs/2407.13278

Encoder and Decoder

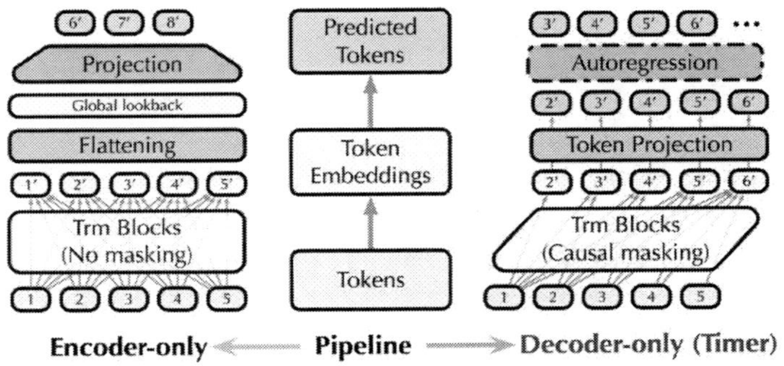

Liu, Y., Zhang, H., Li, C., Huang, X., Wang, J., & Long, M. (2024). Timer: Transformers for Time Series Analysis at Scale. http://arxiv.org/abs/2402.02368

② Benchmarked Models: #4-7

HITACHI

Recurrent Neural Network (RNN):

4. **LSTM (Long short-term memory)**: An RNN with gating mechanisms

5. **S-Mamba**: A Mabma-based method using a selective state-space mechanism

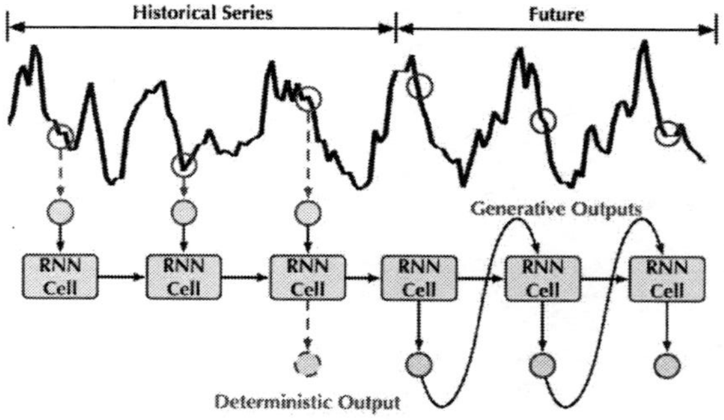

Multi-Layer Perceptron (MLP):

6. **TSMixer**: A MLP-based method mixing time series across multiple channels.

7. **TimeMixer**: A MLP-based method with multiscale mixing architecture

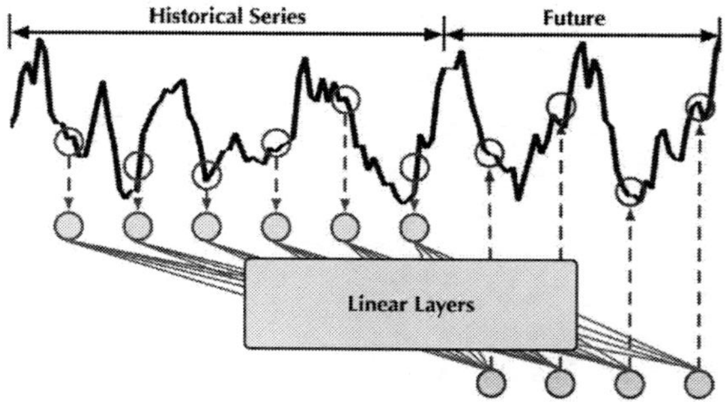

Wang, Y., Wu, H., Dong, J., Liu, Y., Long, M., & Wang, J. (2024).
Deep Time Series Models: A Comprehensive Survey and Benchmark, http://arxiv.org/abs/2407.13278

② Benchmarked Models: #8-10

HITACHI

Convolutional Neural Network (CNN):

8. **TCN**: A DNN model using causal convolution and skip connections

Baselines:

9. **LOCF**: A naive baseline substituting the most recent received value for every future point.
10. **Moirai-MoE**: A SoTA pretrained TSFM with a sparse MoE within the Transformer architecture.

CNN

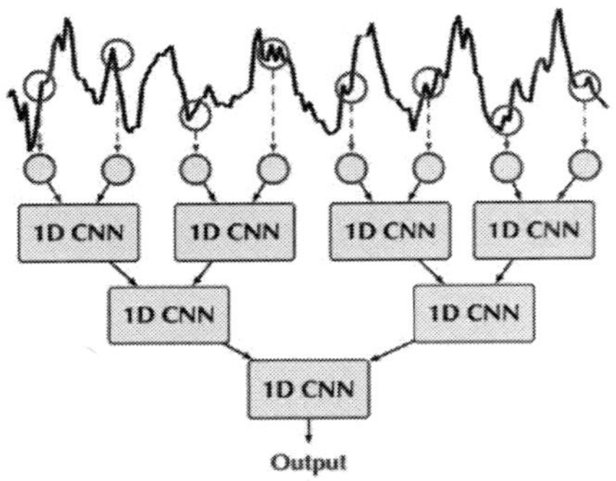

Wang, Y., Wu, H., Dong, J., Liu, Y., Long, M., & Wang, J. (2024). Deep Time Series Models: A Comprehensive Survey and Benchmark, http://arxiv.org/abs/2407.13278

Moirai-MoE

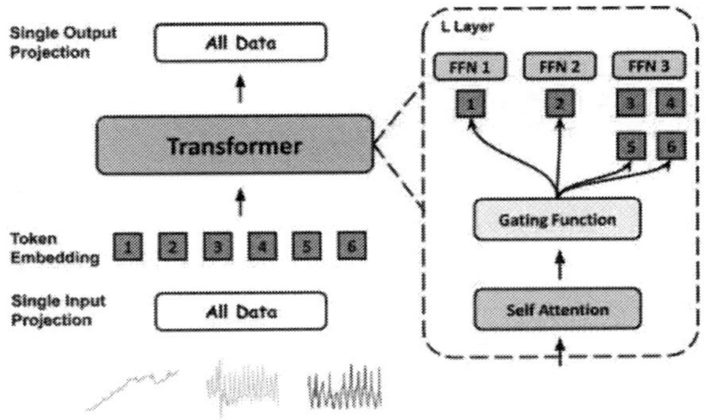

Liu, X., Liu, J., Woo, G., Aksu, T., Liang, Y., Zimmermann, R., Liu, C., Savarese, S., Xiong, C., & Sahoo, D. (2024). Moirai-MoE: Empowering Time Series Foundation Models with Sparse Mixture of Experts. http://arxiv.org/abs/2410.10469

② Benchmark Results: Full-Shot Forecasting

HITACHI

Forecasting at trained datasets and resolutions

- Transformers performed best at high-frequency (1 sec.)
- MLPs were better at low-frequency (1 hour)
- LOCF worked for 1 sec, but failed otherwise.

Full-shot forecasting performance

RMSE (Smaller is better)

1st 2nd 3rd

Algorithm	Oahu Solar Measurement Grid [21] (1 sec.)	PSML [22] (1 min.)	DKASC, Alice Springs [23] (1 hour)	Inference time [sec./sample]
iTransformer	0.0124	0.0458	0.0733	0.0600
PatchTST	0.0123	0.0476	0.0895	0.0638
Timer	0.0151	0.0499	0.0788	0.0593
LSTM	0.0319	0.0475	0.0725	0.0676
S-Mamba	0.0136	0.0460	0.0792	0.0767
TSMixer	0.0183	0.0411	0.0752	0.0520
TimeMixer	0.0179	0.0459	0.0788	0.0686
TCN	0.0294	0.0648	0.0834	0.0494
LOCF (Naïve seasonal)	0.0083	0.0508	0.3977	0.0197
Moirai-MoE	0.2419	0.0583	0.1225	0.9768
TimeRemix (Ours)	0.0146 (#4)	0.0412 (#2)	0.0749 (#3)	0.0892 (#10)

② Full-Shot Results: Visualization

HITACHI

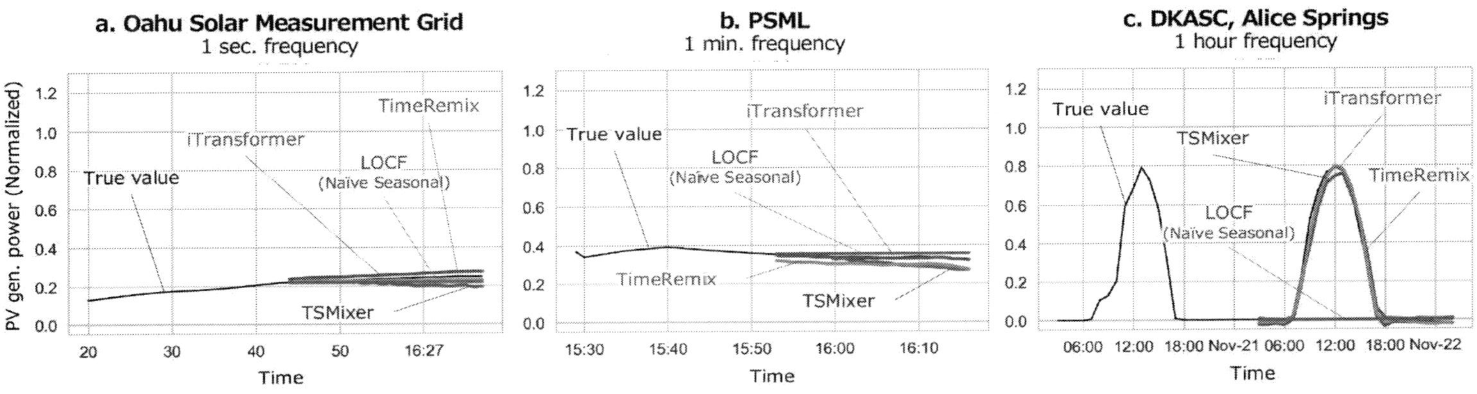

③ Load Balancing Loss

HITACHI

- Sparse gating can cause An **auxiliary load balancing loss** is introduced to mitigate the load imbalance, where some experts are overused while others are underutilized.
- Minimizing the load balancing loss **encourages the gating network to select a diverse set of experts** and provide training opportunities to all experts.

$$\mathcal{L}_{\text{Load}} = M \sum_{m=1}^{M} D_m P_m,$$

$$D_m = \frac{1}{N_{\mathcal{B}}} \sum_{\mathbf{X} \in \mathcal{B}} \mathbb{1} \left\{ \underset{m' \in \mathcal{M}}{\operatorname{argmax}} \, G(\mathbf{X})_{m'} = m \right\},$$

$$P_m = \frac{1}{N_{\mathcal{B}}} \sum_{\mathbf{X} \in \mathcal{B}} G(\mathbf{X})_m,$$

$G(\boldsymbol{X})_m$: the gate value of m-th expert

D_m: the fraction to activate expert m

P_m: the proportion of the gating probability allocated to expert m

$\mathbb{1}$: the indicator function that returns 1 if the condition is true and 0 otherwise.

$$\mathcal{L}_{\text{MoE}} = \mathcal{L}_{\text{MSE}} + \lambda \, \mathcal{L}_{\text{Load}},$$

Total loss function: $\lambda = 10^{-5}$

③ Effectiveness of TimeRemix

HITACHI

Robust zero-shot forecasting across all resolutions

- TimeRemix is competitive with each single model by adapting to each time resolution.

Zero-shot cross-frequency forecasting performance
(RMSE: Smaller is better)

1st 2nd 3rd
Untrained

Algorithm	Monash, Solar Power Dataset [24]					
	5 sec.	30 sec.	1 min.	5 min.	30 min.	1 hour
iTransformer	0.0175	0.0635	0.0855	0.1683	0.4268	0.1260
PatchTST	0.0178	0.0631	0.0849	0.1529	0.3882	0.1359
Timer	0.0204	0.0685	0.0899	0.1497	0.4335	0.1291
LSTM	0.0479	0.2855	0.0887	0.1238	0.2349	0.1585
S-Mamba	0.0255	0.0639	0.0836	0.1940	0.4298	0.1388
TSMixer	0.1328	0.1035	0.0830	0.1196	0.3423	0.1353
TimeMixer	0.0334	0.0713	0.0845	0.1535	0.4320	0.1291
TCN	0.0535	0.0998	0.1127	0.1780	0.6076	0.1308
LOCF (Naïve seasonal)	0.0229	0.0652	0.0995	0.1121	0.4576	0.5017
Moirai-MoE	0.1029	0.1436	0.1759	0.2127	0.3684	0.1918
TimeRemix (Ours)	0.0194 (#3)	0.0647 (#4)	0.0800 (#1)	0.1345 (#3)	0.4030 (#4)	0.1291 (#2)

EU PVSEC
European Photovoltaic Solar Energy
Conference and Exhibition

From PV potential to Grid Impact: An Estimation of the Future PV Penetration in South-Tyrolean Electricity Grid

eurac research — Azim Heydari, Enrico Dalla Maria, David Moser, **Grazia Barchi**

edyna — Davide Prando, Alessandro Donadello

Outline

- ❑ Motivation
- ❑ Objectives
- ❑ PV potential assessment
- ❑ Grid impact assessment
- ❑ Conclusion & reflection

Context and Motivation

- Achieve the energy and climate targets at regional, national and European level

- Significant increase of PV installations in 2022

P.A. Bolzano

- PV plant installed in 2022 → 1597 (+209%)
- PV power installed in 2022 → 30.2 MW (+209%)
- PV production in 2022 → 304 GWh

Source: INFotovoltaico – statistiche trimestrali GSE dati al 31/12/2022

Objectives

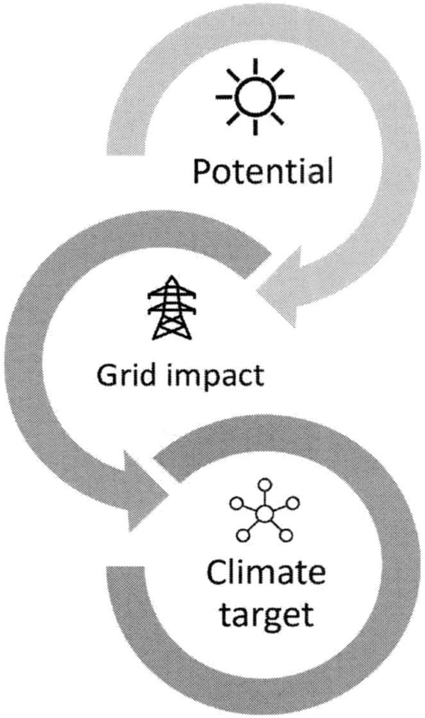

Identify the PV potential aggregated at primary substation level

Evaluate the capacity of the electricity grid to host the identified PV penetration

Comparison of the PV potential, grid hosting capacity and regional climate targets in 2030 and 2040

PV potential assessment – methodology I

Step 1: Identify Primary Substations	• Voronoi Polygons to limit area of the primary substations
Step 2: Detect rooftop	• Identify rooftop within each primary substation area
Step 3: Optimize selection Criteria	• Exclude buildings with insufficient rooftop space
Step 4: Estimate PV potential	• Calculate the rooftop solar PV potential for each primary substation

QGIS

PV potential assessment – results I

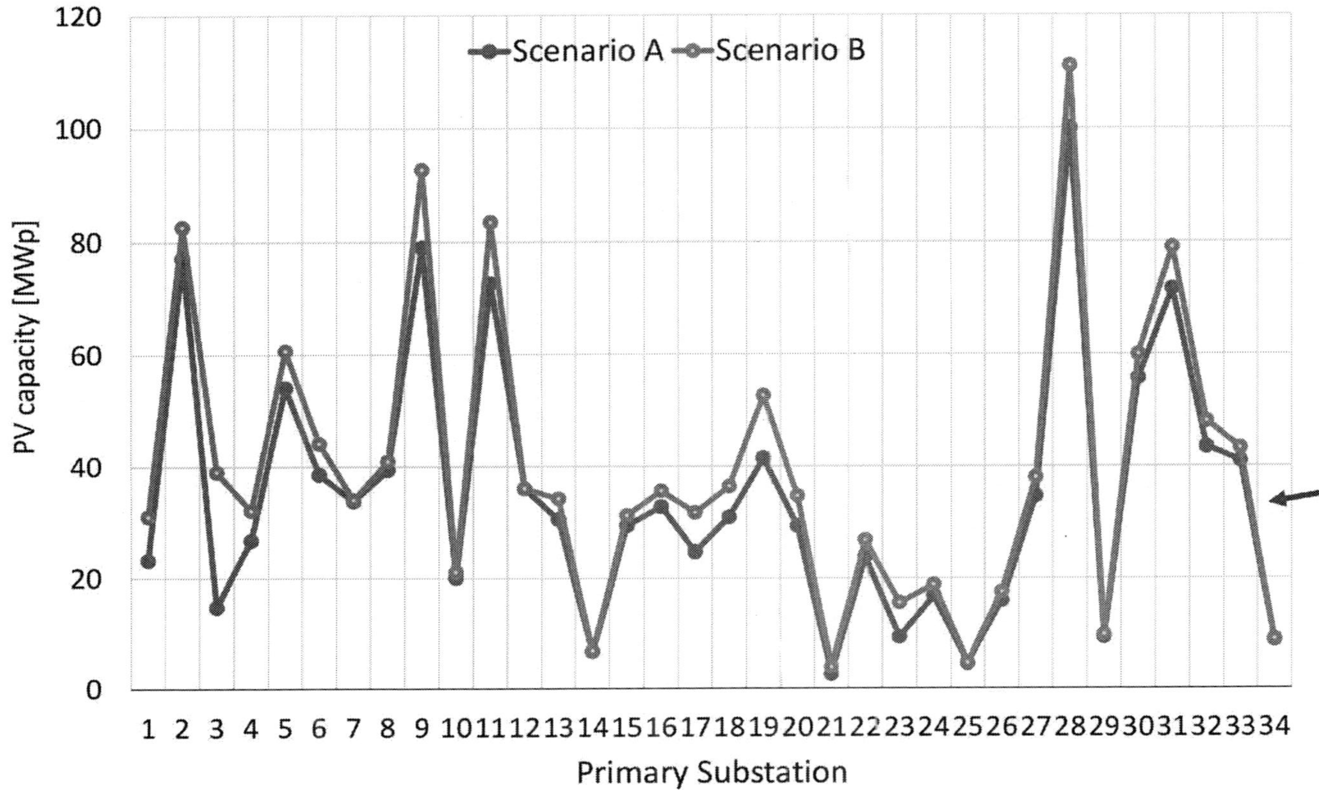

- **Scenario A**: roof-top PV potential for residential buildings
- **Scenario B**: roof-top PV potential for residential +commercial +industrial buildings

~ 39 MWp

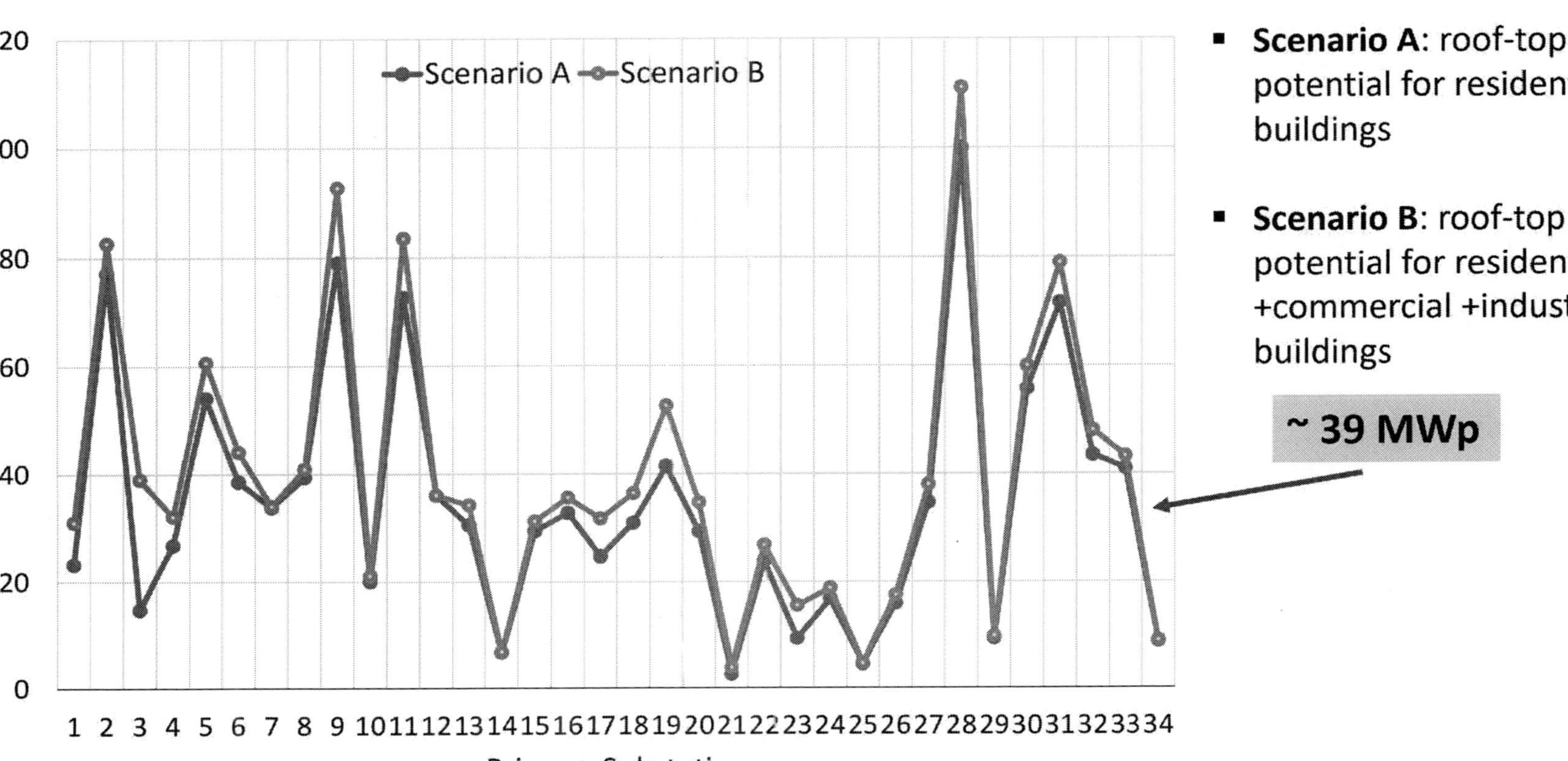

...but what about the grid?

Hosting capacity definition

The *amount of PV that can be integrated into a given distribution network keeping its performance within an acceptable range and without modification of the existing power grid infrastructure*

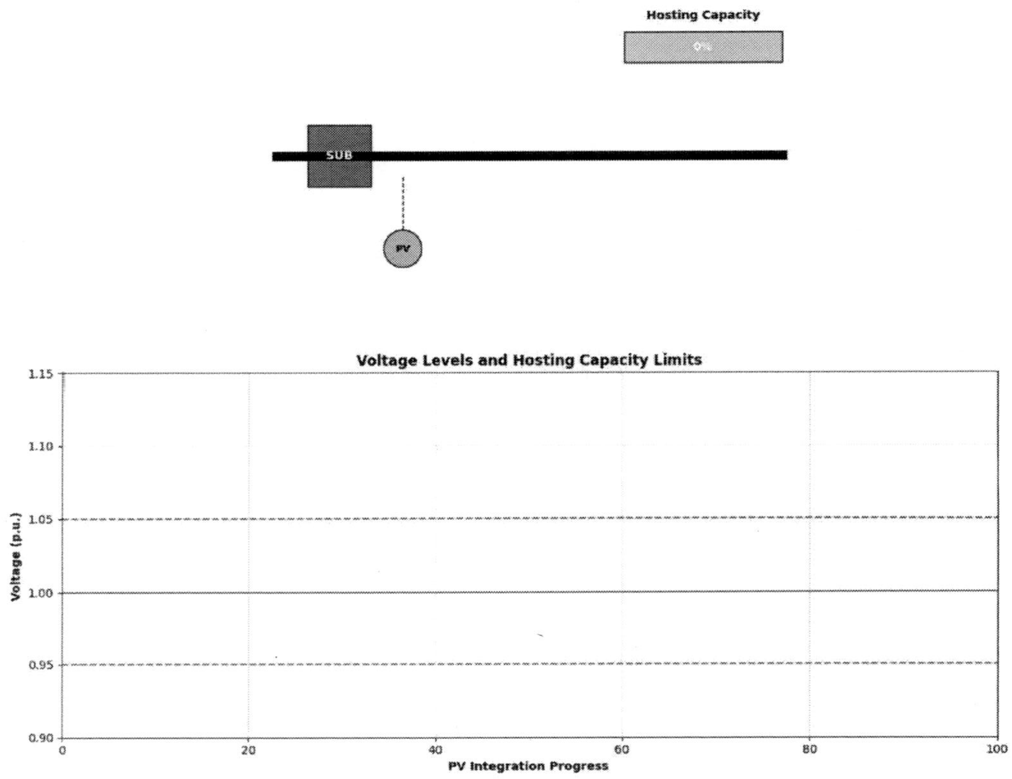

Hosting capacity methodology

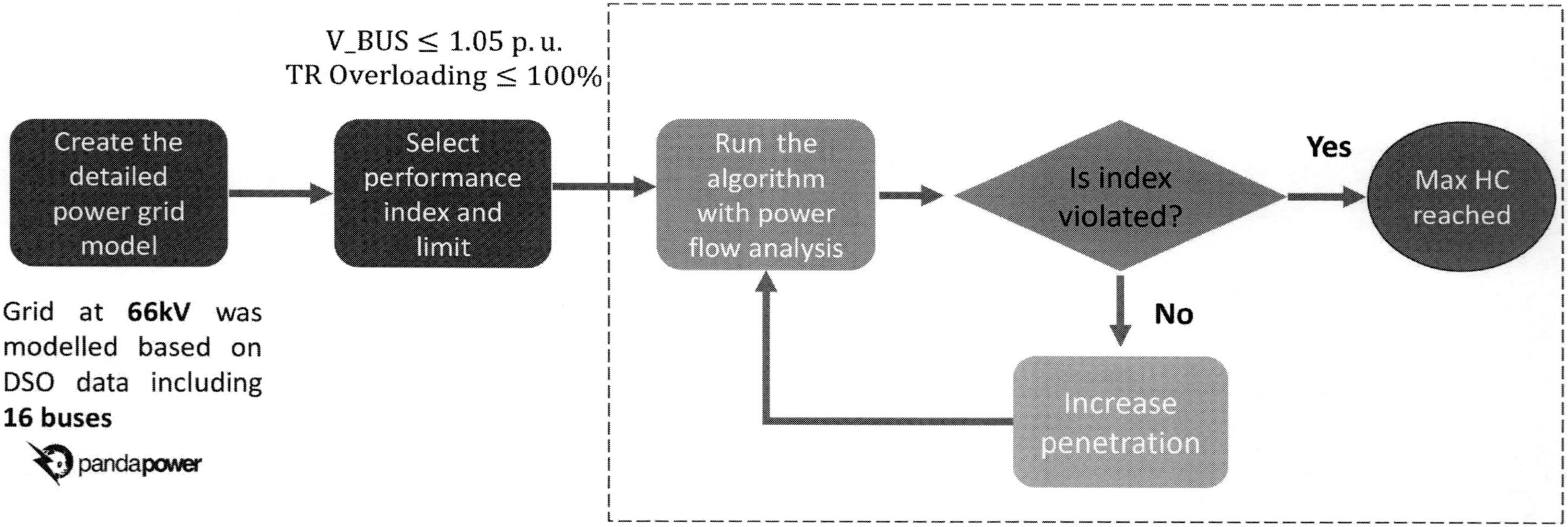

Grid at **66kV** was modelled based on DSO data including **16 buses**

pandapower

Monte-Carlo Iteration

PV power normally distributed → $\mathcal{N}(\mu_{PV}, \sigma_{PV})$

PV placement uniformly distributed → $\mathcal{U}\ (b1, b_N)$

PV HC results: PV maximum capacity @ 66kV

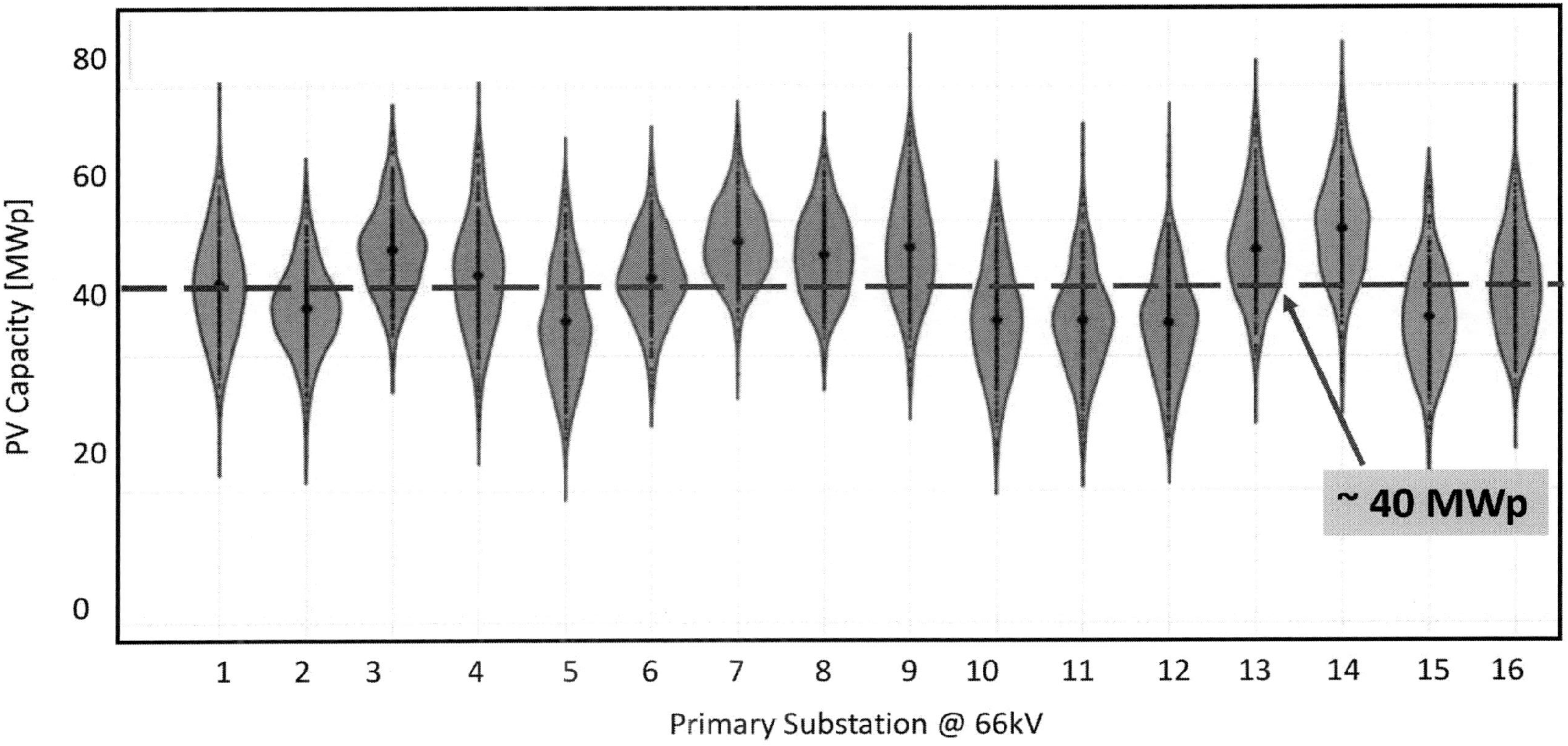

PV HC with respect to the Klimaplan targets

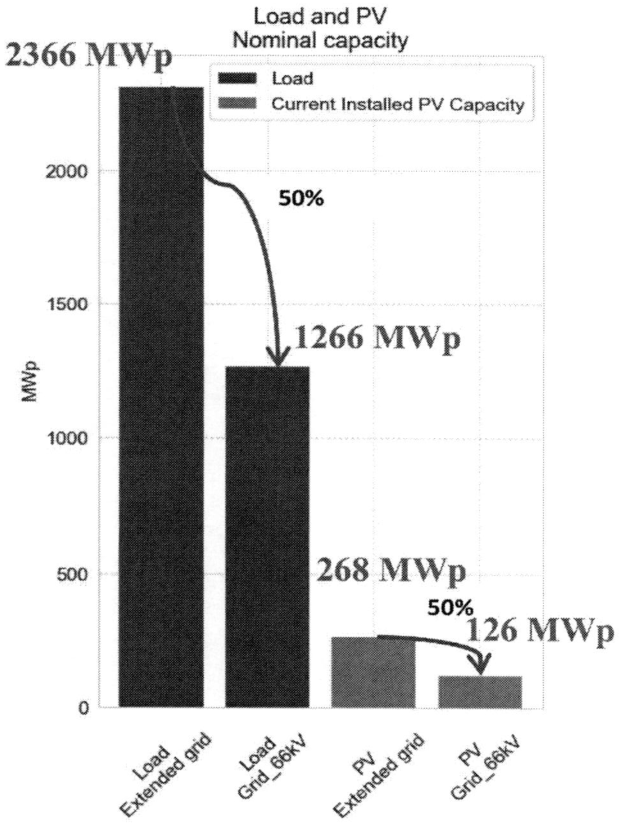

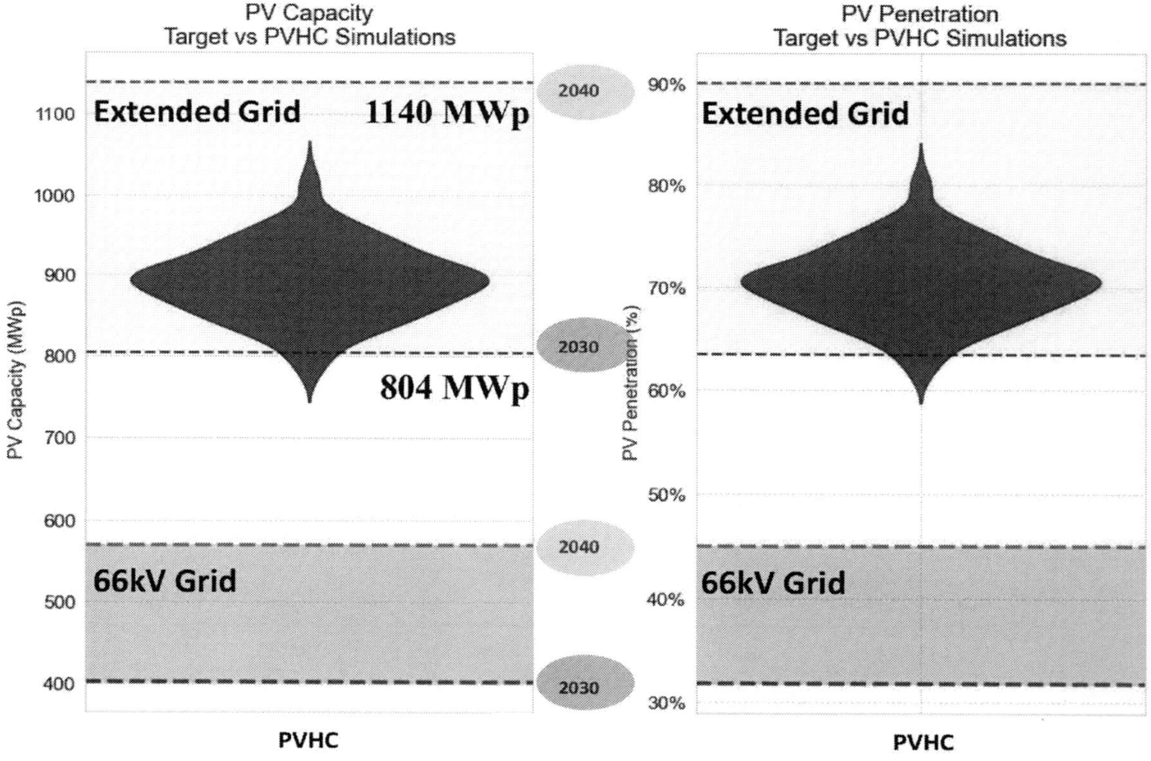

What about considering time-variability?

We used real 15 min load data measured at a primary cabin level provided by an Italian DSO

Actually, in the control zone there is 10 MW of distributed PV capacity, we studied the case in which the **2030 target of 25 MW** will be reached compared with no PV case

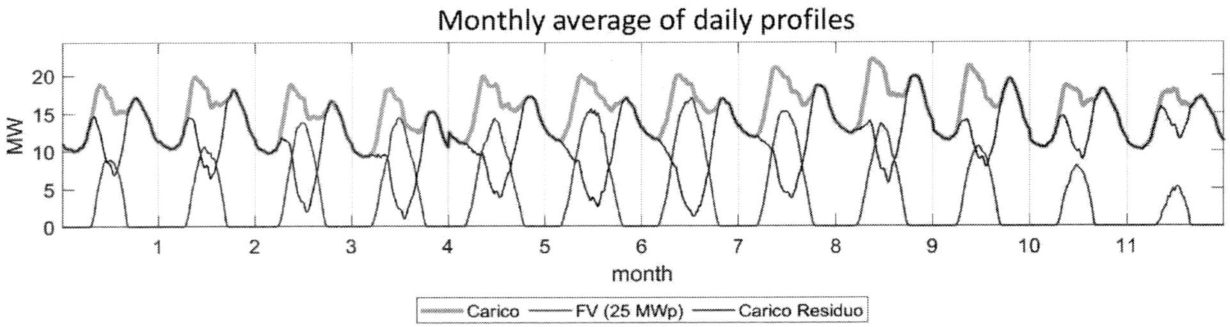

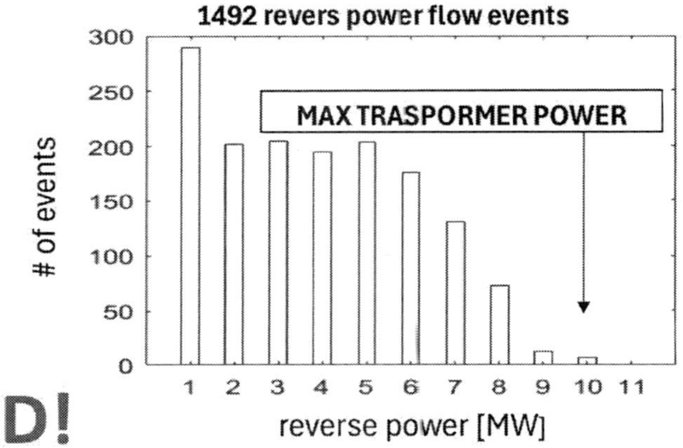

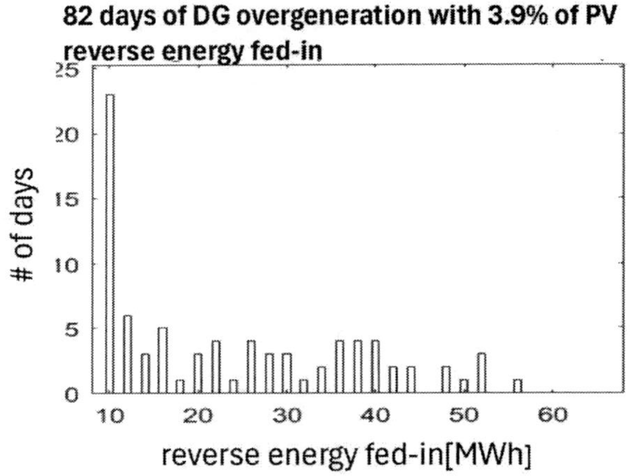

TO BE MITIGATED!

Conclusion & reflection

- An estimation of PV potential of the South-Tyrol region on rooftop and a possible local grid impact has been presented
- The mean PV HC is around 900 MWp, close to the 2030 klimaplan installation targets (804 MWp).
- However, the current HC analysis is limited by neglecting the time-variable nature of PV and load → time-series 2030 simulations reveal reverse power flow
- Limitation in the steady-state assessment of potential and HC and mitigation solution required!

Thank you!

e-mail: grazia.barchi@eurac.edu

NOI Spa - NOI TechPark Bolzano

ASSESSING THE ECONOMIC VALUE FOR GRID OPERATORS OF QUANTIFIED SMOOTHING EFFECTS FROM PV SYSTEMS WITH VARYING ORIENTATIONS

Johan Lindahl
Becquerel Sweden AB
Staffansvägen 14, 74142 Knivsta, Sweden, johan@becquerelsweden.se

ABSTRACT: As the number of solar photovoltaic (PV) installations grows rapidly, accurate registry data and efficient use of existing grid capacity are increasingly critical for stable and cost-effective distribution grid operation, as well as for enabling further PV deployment without unnecessary physical grid reinforcement. This study employs an innovative remote sensing method that combines aerial imagery, machine learning, and Light Detection and Ranging (LiDAR) data to identify, validate, and simulate PV power generation. The method can detect discrepancies between grid operator registries and actual PV installations and quantify the orientation-based smoothing effects that arise when distributed PV systems have varying azimuths and tilt angles. By accounting for these effects, it can free up significant existing capacity in low-voltage distribution grids, reducing the need for costly reinforcements. Application of the method in three Swedish low-voltage grids demonstrated tangible economic benefits, with planned investments of 400,000 (~€36k) and 1.5 million SEK (~€136k) avoided. The study evaluates the value creation of inventory-based PV mapping and PV orientation smoothing effect analysis from the perspective of grid operators, highlighting the method's potential as a cost-effective, data-driven tool for grid planning, investment prioritization, and integration of distributed PV power generation.
Keywords: Photovoltaics, Grid capacity, Economic value assessment, Remote sensing, Orientation smoothing effect

1 INTRODUCTION

Solar power is expanding at a rapid pace both globally and in Sweden. In 2024, photovoltaics (PV) accounted for 75% of all newly installed power generation capacity worldwide, with a preliminary addition of 600 GW [1]. In the European Union, solar now represents 14% of electricity generation [1], of which about half is distributed PV systems connected to a grid connection point where also consumption takes place. This fast and decentralized growth is fundamentally challenging electricity distribution grids [2] which in northern Europe have traditionally been designed to handle peak demand occurring during cold winter days. In areas with high PV penetration, the most critical loading hours for distribution grids now occur during sunny summer days rather than during winter peaks, marking a paradigm shift in grid planning.

A key challenge for grid operators lies in the lack of detailed information about the grid connected PV systems. Typically, Distributed System Operators (DSOs) only have access to basic data such as the property address and the installed capacity of modules and/or inverters. Missing information includes the azimuth and tilt of the PV systems [3], whether installations consist of multiple orientations, and the total actual PV generation profiles as DSOs only measure the power injected to the grid. In the absence of more detailed information, DSOs face challenges in accurately estimating PV power injected into the grid [4], [5], and it is therefore praxis among DSOs in Sweden (and many more European countries) to assume that all PV systems can produce their maximum power — usually the rated power of the inverters — simultaneously and that no electricity is self-consumed. These assumptions tend to overestimate grid stress, leading to unnecessary and costly reinforcements.

In practice, this scenario cannot occur, since distributed PV systems are typically rooftop-mounted and therefore follow the underlying roof geometry [3]. As a result, their orientations and tilt angles vary considerably [6], producing asynchronous generation patterns and giving rise to a natural 'smoothing effect,' here defined as the PV Orientation Smoothing Effect (POSE).

To address this information gap, an AI-based remote sensing and PV power simulation model package, called *Alfrödull*, has been developed. By combining aerial imagery with Light Detection and Ranging (LiDAR) data, this method can identify more than 95% of all PV systems in a given area [7], [8] and estimate their azimuth and tilt with an accuracy of ±3° in 95% of cases [6]. These parameters are then used to simulate the hourly electricity generation of individual PV systems with high spatial and temporal resolution. Validation against measured data from 40 reference systems shows strong agreement, with coefficients of determination (R^2) in the range 0.83–0.96 [9].

A crucial outcome of this approach is the ability to quantify the POSE, i.e., the reduction in aggregated PV power peaks due to differences in PV system orientations. By simulating the generated power from all PV systems connected to a distribution grid over several years of historical weather data (2017–2024), this smoothing effect has been systematically quantified and analyzed in three Swedish grids, down at the level of individual substations, in a parallel technical study [10].

Building on these results, the present study investigates the value creation of the remote sensing generated data and the economic implications of the quantified POSE analysis from a DSO perspective.

Traditionally, increasing the acceptance limit [11] for PV systems in distribution grids requires physical grid reinforcement, with associated costs determined by the scope and capacity of the grid. If the power lines cannot handle the increased load, they may need to be replaced or upgraded, costing between €10k and €100k per kilometer (in Sweden), depending on whether they are overhead lines or underground cables. Additionally, transformers may require upgrades, which can range from €10k to €500k.

2 DATA

Alfrödull scans were applied to the most recent aerial imagery of three Swedish low voltage grids — June 2024 for Falun (FLN), and May 2024 for Karlshamn (KHN) and

Fagersta (FGA) — covering their respective grid areas. The scans identified 2015 PV systems within FLN, 327 within KHN and 256 within FGA. Of those it turned out that 80, 1 and 28, respectively, were off-grid systems not connected to the distribution grid.

For all grid-connected PV systems in these grids, PV power generation was simulated at 30-minute resolution and subsequently aggregated at the substation level. The POSE was then calculated for each substation as the difference between the maximum aggregated PV output observed over the 2017–2024 period and the sum of the rated AC capacities of the connected inverters, following the methodology described in detail in [10].

3 METHODOLOGY

To assess the perceived value of the *Alfrödull* method from a DSO perspective, two semi-structured interviews were conducted. The first took place with the Head of Grid Market, Oscar Willén, at the Swedish DSO Falu Elnät, and the second with the Head of the Grid Business Area, Benjamin Gacanin, together with the Business Developer, Felix Kjellvåg, at Karlshamn Energi. Full interview transcripts (in Swedish) are available in this research project report [12].

The objective of the interviews was to collect qualitative insights regarding the benefits of improved knowledge about existing solar PV capacity, the potential to avoid or postpone costly grid reinforcements, and the requirements and expectations for a method such as *Alfrödull* to be applicable in routine grid planning.

3 RESULTS AND DISCUSSION

3.1 Detection of Discrepancies in PV Registries

An unexpected value of the *Alfrödull* method, first identified in [7] and confirmed in this study, is its ability to detect discrepancies between PV systems identified through remote sensing and those registered by DSOs.

Once applied to a grid area, *Alfrödull* generates a dataset of PV system polygons that can be compared with the DSO's administrative registry, which is based on notifications submitted by installers or property owners. Both PV databases contain errors, but by aligning them — using property identifiers as a linking key — missing or incorrect entries can be identified, thereby improving overall data quality. Figure 1 illustrates this overlap using a Venn diagram of actual PV installations within the scanned grid areas. Such reconciliation is a necessary first step toward constructing a complete and connected database that can be used to simulate PV generation and quantify the PV orientation smoothing effects.

Because *Alfrödull* relies exclusively on remote sensing data sources, such as aerial orthophotos, LiDAR data and geospatial data from the Swedish Land Survey, it can detect PV modules that are absent from the DSO's registry. Discrepancies may occur when systems are installed without formal notification, when registration processes are incomplete, or when installations are off-grid applications. Conversely, *Alfrödull* may also identify systems inconsistencies in reported system size, for example when the observed module area does not match the registered capacity.

Although effective, *Alfrödull* does not capture every system. Certain types, such as vertically mounted PV arrays or building-integrated PV (BIPV) systems, remain undetectable in aerial imagery. Even conventional rooftop installations can be overlooked if, for instance, they are heavily shaded at the time of imaging [7]. Nonetheless, the machine-learning-based recognition method achieves an identification accuracy of about 95% [7]. This is supported by the results shown in Figure 1, where 96.7% of all 2,489 grid-connected PV systems in the three scanned grids were correctly identified.

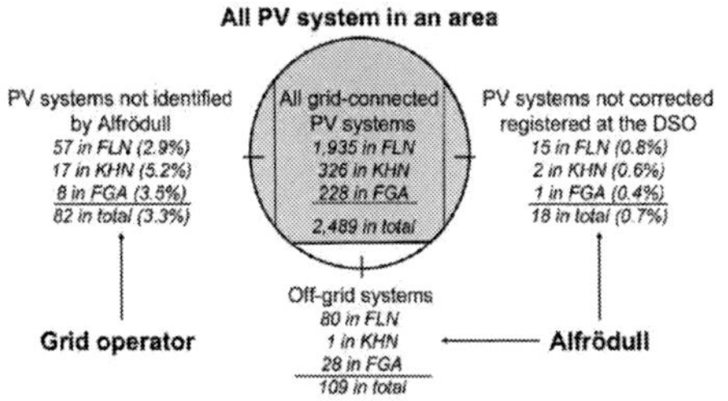

Figure 1. Venn diagram over the results of the inventory scans of three distribution grids.

Cross-checks against DSO registries showed that 79 systems in FLN, one in KHN and 28 in FGA were mounted on buildings without grid connection and were therefore correctly absent from the registries, as Figure 1 shows. The registries, in turn, listed 82 grid-connected systems commissioned before the aerial surveys that *Alfrödull* failed to detect. Conversely, *Alfrödull* identified 18 PV systems across the three grids on grid-connected buildings without corresponding completion reports in the DSO registries, despite the installations being visible in imagery for at least nine months.

In addition, 51 systems in FLN, 35 in KHN and 7 in FGA showed significant discrepancies between observed module area, adjusted using tilt derived from LiDAR data [6], and the registered capacity. Karlshamn Energi followed up on these 35 cases in KHN and confirmed after contact with the system owners that 27 systems indeed had an incorrectly registered size. The causes varied and in some cases included: (1) incorrect information provided at the time of registration by the installer, (2) main fuse capacity had mistakenly been recorded as PV capacity, (3) systems that had been expanded after the initial registration without this being reported, since no change in subscription or fuse rating was required, and (4) in a few instances battery capacity had erroneously been added to PV capacity in the registry.

Both DSOs highlighted in the interviews that the independent inventory added clear value, primarily by identifying missing or incorrectly registered systems. Karlshamn Energi emphasized the benefit of verifying suspected anomalies and proactively contacting customers to correct errors, while Falu Elnät valued the improved overview of actual installed capacity and the reduced uncertainty in grid planning. Although, according to the interviews, the discrepancies in their registry had limited direct economic impact for the DSOs, they noted that errors could lead to missed compensation for customers and pose safety risks for maintenance personnel, as unregistered systems may cause unanticipated reverse power flow.

The findings indicate that remote sensing can serve as a useful tool for improving PV registry quality, which is important for grid planning, load calculations, and future investments. The analysis also highlighted deficiencies in existing routines, which the two DSOs reported intending to address.

3.2 Value of Freed Grid Capacity through POSE

The interviews with two Swedish DSOs highlighted how detailed analyses of orientation-based smoothing effects can inform grid planning and investment decisions in areas with high PV penetration. Both Karlshamn Energi and Falu Elnät confirmed that the rapid increase in PV installations has created local capacity challenges, leading in some cases to concrete investments in grid lines or new substations. For example, Karlshamn Energi had planned a new substation at an estimated cost of approximately 1.5 million SEK (~€136k), while Falu Elnät had implemented minor reinforcements but emphasized that most investments are primarily guided by the age of certain parts of their grid and technical condition rather than PV-induced capacity limits.

Across the three studied grids in [13], POSE, i.e., the overestimation of injected PV power relative to rated AC capacity, ranged from 8.7% in KHN to 11.5–11.8% in FLN and FGA. Maximum POSE at individual substations reached up to 20–24% of rated AC power, highlighting that local effects can substantially exceed grid-average values [13].

Representatives from both DSOs acknowledged the value of the remote-sensing-generated data and the POSE analyses, where Figure 2 illustrates the quantified orientation-based smoothing effects in the FGA grid, serving as an example of the analysis conducted and the type of data delivered to the three DSOs.

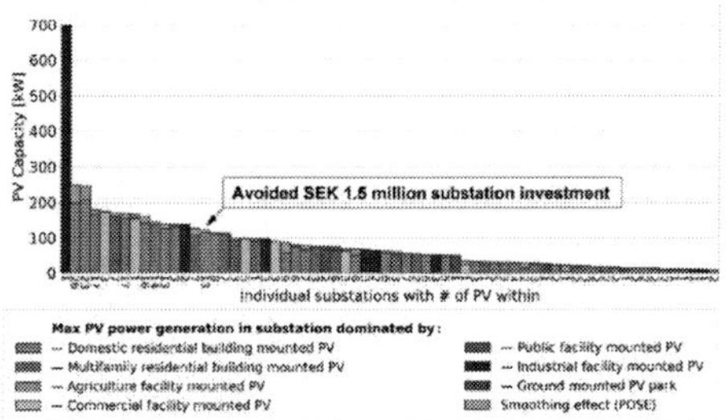

Figure 2. Registered PV capacity at all 91 transformer substations in the FGA grid with at least one PV installation as of May 2024. Each bar represents one substation, with the bar height showing the total rated AC capacity of all connected PV systems—corresponding to the capacity the grid operator assumes could be fed into the grid simultaneously. Bar colors indicate the market segment contributing the largest share of capacity at each substation, while the orange segment denotes the POSE in each substation. Numbers below the bars show the number of PV installations per substation. The arrow points to the substation where Karlshamn Energi had planned a new transformer investment.

The detailed capacity assessments generated by *Alfrödull* were in the interviews described as an important, evidence-based complement to previous methods. Karlshamn Energi reported that the POSE analysis allowed several pending PV customers to be connected without constructing the planned substation, yielding a savings of 1.5 million SEK (~€136k). Similarly, Falu Elnät postponed a planned cable reinforcement costing 400,000 SEK (~€36k) after the POSE analyses indicated more available capacity than previously assumed [10]. Beyond these specific cases, the analyses provide a valuable tool for evaluating other substations as additional PV installations will be installed.

The remote-sensing generated PV power generation data and POSE analysis were particularly appreciated by the two DSOs in early stages of the connection process, enabling faster and more accurate responses to customers while improving the prioritization of grid interventions. For example, Karlshamn Energi used the detailed analyses of interconnected substations to adjust low-voltage grid breakpoints, optimizing capacity utilization without new investments. Falu Elnät emphasized the importance of considering alternative costs, including preserving residual value in existing components, avoiding displacement effects, and limiting increased grid losses.

3.3 Knowledge Gain among the DSOs

Both DSOs also reported a knowledge gain from the analyses. Karlshamn Energi highlighted that some planned investments could have been avoided and that certain customer connections had previously been rejected unnecessarily. This prompted follow-up with customers and internal process improvements, particularly regarding their pre-notifications and post-connection verification. Both interviewees concluded that existing calculation models did not always reflect actual PV power generation, emphasizing the need for data-driven, installation-specific approaches.

3.4 Regulation, Incentives and Governance

The interviewees further noted that current Swedish and EU regulation and incentive structures largely favor traditional physical grid expansion rather than digitalization or innovative, flexible solutions, which complicates the adoption of methods that could optimize existing infrastructure and delay or avoid costly investments. Karlshamn Energi emphasized that economic incentives for data-driven decision-making, increased digitalization, and smarter grid use are currently limited, although these solutions are crucial for handling electrification and future capacity needs cost-effectively. Falu Elnät shared similar views, noting that their historical financial margins allowed testing new technologies despite regulatory uncertainties and unclear guidance on evaluating alternative technologies.

Both DSOs agreed that upcoming EU requirements for greater flexibility and efficient use of existing infrastructure will drive future development. Strategic use of already collected data, particularly at the substation level, was identified as critical. Forecasts for local power generation, such as PV, were highlighted as an important tool for integrating flexibility solutions in operational management, with remote sensing data generated by *Alfrödull* serving as a concrete example of how such data can be leveraged effectively.

Municipal ownership was described as a strength in promoting innovation, sustainability, and long-term capacity planning. Karlshamn Energi noted that their municipal board provides clear strategic goals related to sustainable development and proactive capacity planning, supporting initiatives such as digitalization and flexible grid agreements. Falu Elnät similarly reported that municipal ownership encourages innovation and a broader, long-term perspective, fostering investments that benefit the municipality. Even when objectives such as

10.4229/EUPVSEC2025/5DO.14.5

capacity utilization or innovation are not formally stated in ownership directives, they are actively discussed and prioritized in strategic planning.

4 CONCLUSIONS

This study demonstrates the potential of combining remote sensing and high-resolution PV simulation to optimize grid capacity, guide investment decisions, and facilitate the integration of distributed PV generation, offering a cost-effective and scalable tool for modern distribution grid management.

The *Alfrödull* method enables accurate identification of installed PV systems, detection of discrepancies in DSO registries, and quantification of orientation-based smoothing effects. By accounting for smoothing effects, substantial existing grid capacity can be unlocked, reducing the need for costly physical grid reinforcements, as evidenced by avoided investments of 400,000 SEK (~€36k) and 1.5 million SEK (~€136k) in the participating grids.

Interviews with two Swedish DSOs revealed that the method provides both tangible economic benefits and valuable operational insights, supporting data-driven grid planning, prioritization of grid interventions, and faster customer connections. Moreover, the analyses contribute to improved registry accuracy, reducing risks associated with unregistered or incorrectly registered PV systems.

The study also highlights institutional and regulatory factors affecting the adoption of data-driven solutions. While current incentives and frameworks often favor traditional physical grid expansions, municipal ownership and emerging EU requirements for greater flexibility present opportunities for innovative approaches.

5 ACKNOWLEDGEMENTS

The author gratefully acknowledges financial support from the Swedish Energy Agency (Project number P2024-02998). The Agency had no role in the study's design, execution, or interpretation.

The author also sincerely thanks Oscar Willén at Falu Elnät, and Benjamin Gacanin and Felix Kjellvåg at Karlshamn Energi, for their support in scanning their respective grids, granting permission to publish the general results, and participating in the interviews.

4 REFERENCES

[1] IEA PVPS task 1 *et al.*, "Trends in Photovoltaic Applications — 2024," 2024.

[2] R. Gupta *et al.*, "Spatial analysis of distribution grid capacity and costs to enable massive deployment of PV, electric mobility and electric heating," *Appl Energy*, vol. 287, no. October 2020, p. 116504, 2021, doi: 10.1016/j.apenergy.2021.116504.

[3] S. Killinger *et al.*, "On the search for representative characteristics of PV systems: Data collection and analysis of PV system azimuth, tilt, capacity, yield and shading," *Solar Energy*, vol. 173, no. August, pp. 1087–1106, 2018, doi: 10.1016/j.solener.2018.08.051.

[4] Å. L. Sørensen, J. Hole, D. Bjerkehagen, and H. T. Walnum, "From customers to prosumers: PV systems impact on residential load profiles , peak power , and coincidence," in *CIRED 2025 Conference*, 2025, pp. 1–5.

[5] T. Landelius, S. Andersson, and R. Abrahamsson, "System Imbalance from Solar Energy Trading," in *Proceedings ot the 8th Solar Integration Workshop*, 2018, pp. 1–18.

[6] D. Lingfors, R. Johansson, and J. Lindahl, "Deriving the orientation of existing solar energy systems from LiDAR data at scale," *Solar Energy*, vol. 291, no. 113344, 2025, doi: 10.1016/j.solener.2025.113344.

[7] J. Lindahl, R. Johansson, and D. Lingfors, "Mapping of decentralised photovoltaic and solar thermal systems by remote sensing aerial imagery and deep machine learning for statistic generation," *Energy and AI*, vol. 14, p. 100300, 2023, doi: 10.1016/j.egyai.2023.100300.

[8] Å. Frimane, R. Johansson, J. Munkhammar, D. Lingfors, and J. Lindahl, "Identifying small decentralized solar systems in aerial images using deep learning," *Solar Energy*, vol. 262, 2023, doi: 10.1016/j.solener.2023.111822.

[9] G. Öhgren, L. Molin, M. Lindh, D. Lingfors, and J. Lindahl, "Remote sensing compatible snow loss modelling for PV power simulations," *Solar Energy*, vol. Unpublishe, 2025.

[10] J. Widén, G. Öhgren, E. Lindvall, D. Lingfors, and J. Lindahl, "Quantifying distributed PV orientation smoothing effects and their impact on electricity grid performance," *Manuscript*.

[11] M. H. J. Bollen and S. K. Rönnberg, "Hosting capacity of the power grid for renewable electricity production and new large consumption equipment," *Energies (Basel)*, vol. 10, no. 9, 2017, doi: 10.3390/en10091325.

[12] J. Lindahl, "Alfrödull — Frigörande av nätkapacitet för solceller genom fjärranalys — Slutrapport P2024-02998," 2025.

[13] J. Widén, G. Öhgren, E. Lindvall, D. Lingfors, and J. Lindahl, "Quantifying distributed PV orientation smoothing effects and their impact on electricity grid performance," *Manuscript*.

COST AND RELIABILITY OF 24/7 CARBON FREE ELECTRICITY FROM PV – EVALUATION OF OVERNIGHT SOLAR-PLUS-STORAGE IN ABU DHABI

Harry Apostoleris[1], Kareem Younes[2], Matteo Chiesa[2,3]
[1] EPRI
[2] Khalifa University, Abu Dhabi, UAE
[3] UiT The Arctic University of Norway, Tromso, NO
HApostoleris@EPRI.com

ABSTRACT: This manuscript considers the deployment of PV with battery energy storage systems (PV+BESS) as a resource for 24/7 carbon-free energy (24/7 CFE). Its analysis is based on a real upcoming project in Abu Dhabi that was announced earlier this year to combine 5.2GW of PV with 19GWh of lithium iron phosphate (LFP) batteries to create a "round the clock" solar power station that functions as a 1GW baseload generator suitable for supplying data centers or other large continuous loads that require on-demand power [1]. Using this project as a guide, we study the potential of PV+BESS 24/7 CFE resources from both a cost and reliability perspective, including an estimated cost breakdown and LCOE assessment of the announced plant design based on recent market developments and survey of global PV and BESS projects; availability analysis of 24/7 solar based on a simple dispatch algorithm to assess its suitability as a true baseload generator; and discussion of the implications of real-world 24/7 solar for energy system planning and energy storage requirements to support deep decarbonization. The technoeconomic study finds that a total project cost of 6bnUSD, as reported for the facility planned in Abu Dhabi, can be explained by recent changes in the LFP battery and stationary storage market, leading to total levelized cost of electricity in the range of 60-80USD/MWh, with 97% availability as a baseload resource, with exact cost depending on specific assumptions about systems configuration, load and performance. We consider the cost impact of incorporating peaking gas-fired capacity to back up PV+BESS, as is planned at the Abu Dhabi facility [2]. Through this study we demonstrate how changing battery economics are rapidly shifting Li-ion technology towards longer-duration storage applications, enabling higher cost-effective penetration of PV in national energy systems.
Keywords: energy storage, clean firm power, hybrid power plants, data center energy supply

1 BACKGROUND

1.1 Solar Energy in the UAE

Despite its status a major oil-exporting country, the United Arab Emirates (UAE) has become a global leader in utility-scale solar energy deployment, consistently setting records for scale and low cost in utility-scale PV systems. As analyzed in previous work [3-5], PV projects in the UAE have pushed the limits of economic feasibility based on a combination of low hardware cost, with bulk imports from leading equipment manufacturers (increasing dominated by Chinese vendors); low labor costs strongly tied to the South Asian labor market; and a favorable financing environment with low-rate financing available to projects backed by large state-connected entities. Prices achieved under aggressive PPA auctions (e.g. the first solar PPA at less than <3c/kWh achieved in Dubai in 2017) have often been "ahead of their time," raising questions as to their viability before seeing these prices replicated across the world as global markets "catch up" to the trends being anticipated by aggressive local bids. Recent announcements in the hybrid solar+storage space continue this trend of leading on renewable energy costs, and are illustrative to understand shape of global energy storage market, strategic approaches to energy storage deployment & prospects for further solar energy deployment around the world.

1.2 Energy for AI growth

The UAE has ambitious goals for artificial intelligence, aiming to become a global leader in hosting AI data centers. Global challenges in energy sector resulting from the emergence of new electrical demand from AI (recently on display in the US and elsewhere) have included stress on the energy hardware supply chain – e.g. spiking prices and extended wait times for gas turbines; costs of grid and generation capacity upgrades which have led to rising consumer prices as the cost of building new capacity to serve AI are passed on to ratepayers; and grid stability challenges due to unique and highly variable load profile of AI data centers. In response to this, solutions have been proposed including increasing the flexibility of AI data center loads, as is being explored in EPRI's "DCFlex" initiative [6], or simply to partly or fully insulate data center from the grid through the use of on-site storage for demand smoothing, or generating the needed energy fully on site. On-site or dedicated data center power supply presents a natural use case for "clean firm" power, or 24/7 CFE, where a combination of renewables and energy storage replaces conventional power station. The most recently launched renewable energy project in Abu Dhabi offers an example of how carbon-free or newly carbon-free energy can be supplied to data centers or other large loads from dedicated renewable+storage hybrid facilities.

2 ABU DHABI'S "ROUND THE CLOCK" SOLAR ENERGY PROJECT – COST ANALYSIS

2.1 Description of the plant

The planned "round the clock" solar power plant has been described as part of the country's AI strategy, indicating its intent to be used to power AI data centers. The facility will consist of 5.2GW PV and 19GWh BESS supplying 1GW baseload power to the grid [7]. The plant is part of a total investment of 10bnUSD package for PV+BESS, and open-cycle gas turbine plant providing backup power, and grid connection and upgrades; 6bnUSD of this has been allocated to the PV+BESS component as shown in Table 1 [8]

While the price tag for this project seems low relative to global expectations, recent developments in global

10.4229/EUPVSEC2025/5DO.14.6

markets for PV and particularly batteries offer justification for what, for some, are surprising numbers.

Table I: Total investment in clean firm power supply for AI in Abu Dhabi

	Capacity	Cost ($)
PV +BESS	5.2GW/19GWh	5.2bn
OCGT	1GW	1.35bn
Transmission upgrades		2.5bn

2.2 Market developments: PV

Utility-scale PV in the Gulf region saw falling capex pre-2020, followed by a plateau post-covid at ~600USD/kW. Pure PV PPA prices around 1.5c/kWh have been the norm and are now the expectation for new-build solar in much of the region (Figure 1). Some savings in opex have reported, largely due to the emergence of robotic cleaning as a means to reduce the labor intensiveness of combatting the rapid soiling of modules that occurs in the dusty desert climate of the Gulf.

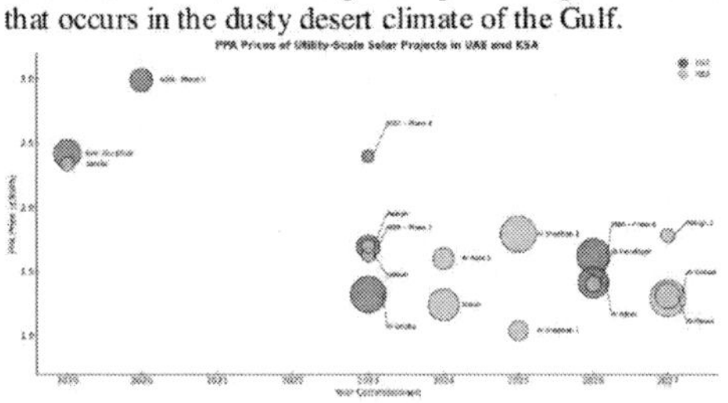

Figure 1: PPA Prices for utility-scale solar in the UAE and Saudi Arabia

Table II: Current costs in Gulf region for utility scale PV & battery systems

	Cost	Cost ($)
PV	600USD/kW	5.2bn
BESS [9]	90USD/kWh	1.35bn
BESS Construction	240USD/kW	

2.3 Market developments: Batteries

More significant changes have occurred in this decade in the Li-ion battery market, comparable to what occurred in the PV module market in the previous decade, where a combination of industrial scaling and extreme price pressure brought both market prices and production costs dramatically lower. In the case of batteries, much of the growth driving industrial learning has been in the EV industry, where lithium-iron-phosphate (LFP) technology has become dominant. In addition, a mandate in China that utility-scale PV installations include energy storage drove stationary storage product development by Chinese firms. Battery cell prices of 60USD/kWh reported in 2024 [10], with further price drops are expected over next 1-2 years, with. These falling costs have been reflected in recent BESS projects in region, particularly in Saudi Arabia where BESS costs of just over 90USD/kWh$_{usable}$ have been confirmed.

2.4 Overnight and levelized cost assessment

Overall, the past several years have seen core technology cost decreases, particularly in energy storage, coupled with overall inflation & high financing costs. Taking this into consideration, the reported capex for the PV+BESS project is consistent with the current global market and local factors. In Figure 2 we show a modeled cost and LCOE breakdown, based on the values first used in [3] with adjustments to technology costs that have changed in the intervening years.

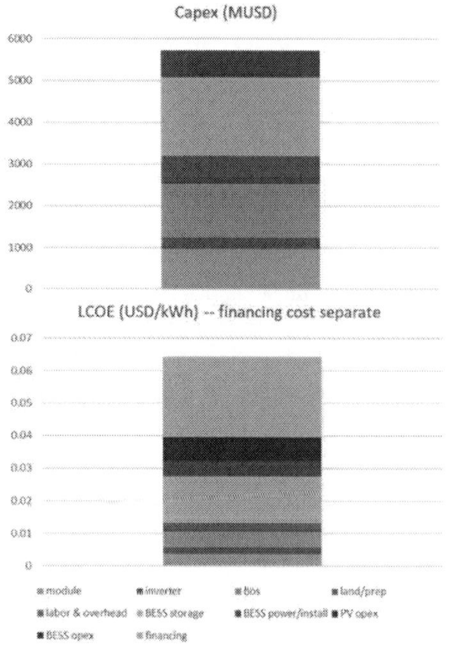

Figure 2: Capex and LCOE estimated breakdown for 24-7 PV+BESS providing 1GW baseload power

3 PERFORMANCE AS A BASELOAD RESOURCE

To assess the performance of the proposed plant as a baseload power resource, we implemented a simple dispatch algorithm where energy generated from solar

1. is dispatched to meet demand
2. After meeting demand, is fed to battery
3. if battery is full, curtailed
4. If demand exceeds solar generation, energy is dispatched from storage
5. if net demand exceeds dispatchable energy from storage, energy shortage is recorded

In Figure 3 we compare the summer day performance of the plant to a rainy or cloudy period with lower solar generation in the winter. Periods of low energy production are seen to challenge system availability as a baseload resource, as the battery is not charged sufficiently during the day to supply a full 1GW at night. These periods reduce the total annual availability to ~97%, which necessitates the inclusion of the gas turbine backup system in order to serve as a true "firm" resource.

10.4229/EUPVSEC2025/5DO.14.6

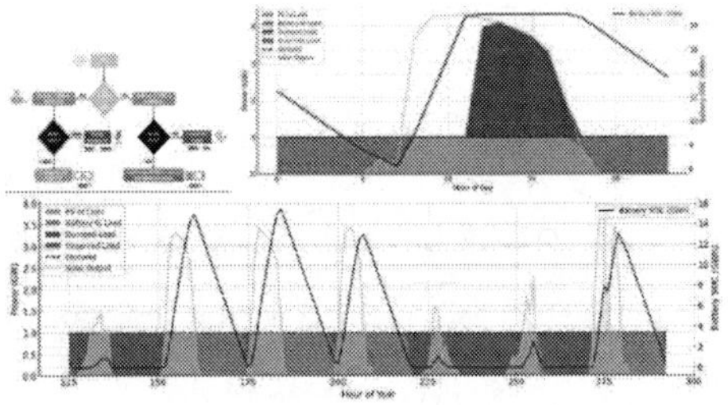

Figure 3: Simple dispatch algorithm (top left) applied on a summer day (top right) and a cloudy winter week (bottom)

4 STRATEGIC ENERGY PLANNING – CLIMBING THE ENRGY STORAGE LADDER

The previous section illustrated how 24-hour energy can be provided from a hybrid PV+BESS system with a fossil fuel backup. However, baseload availability is not necessary for an energy system in transition. Rather, storage can be deployed progressively to address the challenges that arise from higher and higher renewable penetrations in the energy system. In Figure 4 we visualize energy storage requirements as a "ladder" of different storage durations addressing different challenges that arise at different levels of solar adoption [Table 3], highlighting a strategic approach of building storage to meet immediate needs. The falling cost of storage offers an argument in favor of this approach, whereby additional storage hours can be added at lower cost in future years as the need arises. The calculated LCOE for different storage durations at current costs is plotted in Figure 5.

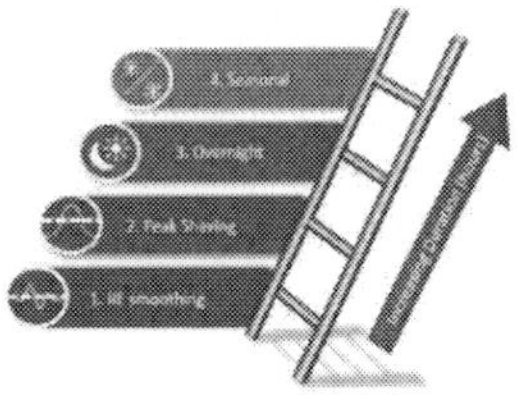

Figure 4: Strategic energy storage deployment, "climbing the ladder" of different use cases as renewable penetration increases

Table III: Use cases for different storage durations in energy systems

Function	Duration
RE smoothing	~1hr
Ramp rate management, peak shaving	~4hr
Overnight storage, island operation	~24hr
Multiday-seasonal storage	days-months

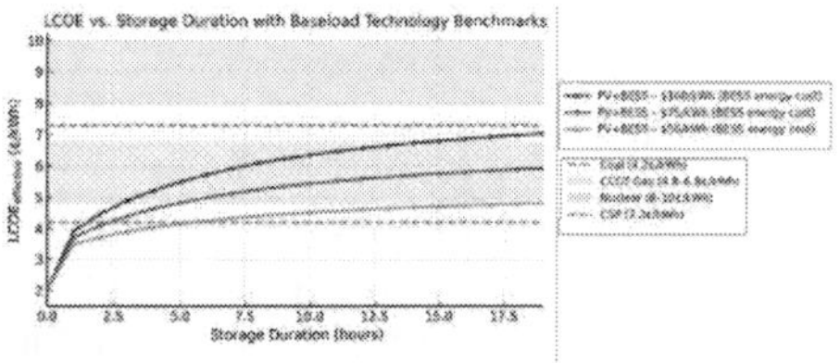

Figure 5: calculated LCOE for PV+BESS at varying storage durations

6 CONCLUSIONS

In this study we have looked at the economics and performance of PV+BESS systems as baseload generation resource. These economics are rapidly evolving due to major changes occurring in battery market, driven by EV adoption, internal policies in China and industrial learning curve previously observed for PV modules. Nominal clean-firm PV+BESS (clean firm) systems appear to be approaching viability in the most favorable markets; however, true firm power requires conventional (e.g. gas turbine) backup for resilience through low-sun periods. More generally we note that "clean-firm" may not always be the most useful concept to guide near-term energy system planning under highly dynamic market conditions; expected future price reductions favor strategic approach to energy storage deployment to maximize the rate of PV adoption, where storage systems are built with the duration necessary to integrate existing PV generation, and longer duration systems are added in the future at lower cost to integrate future PV. Finally we note that, while the energy storage cost revolution that will drive next wave of PV adoption appears to be underway, reliability remains an open question, on which long-term success of PV will depend.

REFERENCES

[1] Masdar, "UAE President witnesses launch of world's first 24/7 Solar PV, Battery Storage gigascale project to be built in Abu Dhabi," 14 Jan 2025. [Online]. Available: https://masdar.ae/en/news/newsroom/uae-president-witnesses-launch-of-worlds-first-24-7-solar-pv-battery-storage.

[2] J. Benny, "Taqa and Ewec to develop 1GW gas turbine plant in Abu Dhabi to support tech push," *The National*, pp. https://www.thenationalnews.com/business/energy/2025/04/03/taqa-and-ewec-to-develop-1gw-gas-turbine-plant-in-abu-dhabi-to-support-tech-push/, 3 April 2025.

[3] Apostoleris, H., Sgouridis, S., Stefancich, M., & Chiesa, M. (2018). Evaluating the factors that led to low-priced solar electricity projects in the Middle East. Nature Energy, 3(12), 1109-1114.

[4] H. Apostoleris and M. Chiesa, "The role of financing in realizing ultra-low solar electricity prices in the Middle East," 2019 IEEE 46th Photovoltaic Specialists Conference (PVSC), Chicago, IL, USA, 2019, pp. 0595-0600, doi: 10.1109/PVSC40753.2019.8980633.

[5] Apostoleris, H., Al Ghaferi, A., & Chiesa, M. (2021). What is going on with Middle Eastern solar prices, and what does it mean for the rest of us?. *Progress in Photovoltaics: Research and Applications*, *29*(6), 638-648.

[6] EPRI -- Homepage | DCFlex [https://dcflex.epri.com/]

[7] MEED | Abu Dhabi moves ahead with AI power plants (2024) https://www.meed.com/abu-dhabi-moves-ahead-with-ai-power-plants
[8] Gulf Construction Online: Taqa, Ewec, Masdar in deal to develop $9.8bn energy projects https://gulfconstructiononline.com/ArticleTA/432157
[9] SEC receives Bids for 1,000 MW Battery Energy Storage System Projects - SaudiGulf Projects https://www.saudigulfprojects.com/2025/04/sec-receives-bids-for-1000-mw-battery-energy-storage-system-projects/
[10] Where are EV battery prices headed in 2025 and beyond? | S&P Global https://www.spglobal.com/automotive-insights/en/blogs/2025/01/where-are-ev-battery-prices-headed-in-2025-and-beyond

10.4229/EUPVSEC2025/5DO.14.6

EPRI

Cost and reliability of 24/7 Carbon Free Electricity from PV

Evaluation of overnight solar-plus-storage in Abu Dhabi

Harry Apostoleris, EPRI Gulf
Kareem Younes, Khalifa University
Matteo Chiesa, Khalifa University

www.epri.com

Introduction to the authors and the UAE

- **Harry Apostoleris** – EPRI Gulf
  - Gulf region office of EPRI focusing on utility-sector research for GCC countries (Saudia Arabia, UAE, Qatar, Bahrain, Kuwait, Oman)
  - 13 years in UAE -- CPV → PV module & system economics → energy system planning
  - Previously Dubai Electricity & Water Authority (DEWA) R&D Center, Masdar Institute
- UAE has consistently set records for scale and low cost in international utility-scale PV, pushes limits of economic feasibility with combination of
  - Low hardware cost
  - Low labor cost
  - Favorable financing environment
  - Involvement of major state-backed entities
  - E.g. first <3c/kWh PPA for solar (2017), now ~1.5c/kWh typical

EPRI

Introduction to the authors and the UAE

- **Harry Apostoleris** – EPRI Gulf
  - Gulf region office of EPRI focusing on utility-sector research for GCC countries (Saudia Arabia, UAE, Qatar, Bahrain, Kuwait, Oman)
  - 13 years in UAE -- CPV → PV module & system economics → energy system planning
  - Previously Dubai Electricity & Water Authority (DEWA) R&D Center, Masdar Institute
- UAE has consistently set records for scale and low cost in internation utility-scale PV, pushes limits of economic feasibility with combination of
  - Low hardware cost
  - Low labor cost
  - Favorable financing environment
  - Involvement of major state-backed entities
  - E.g. first <3c/kWh PPA for solar (2017), now ~1.5c/kWh typical

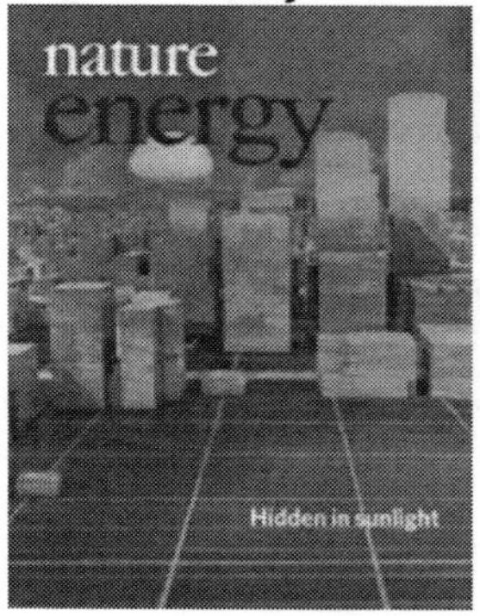

Apostoleris et al., *Nature Energy* 2018

Matteo Chiesa
(Khalifa University)

Kareem Younes
(Khalifa University)

- Recent announcements in solar + storage are illustrative to understand shape of global energy storage market, strategic approaches to energy storage deployment & prospects for further solar energy deployment around the world

EPRI

Background – AI boom and grid impacts

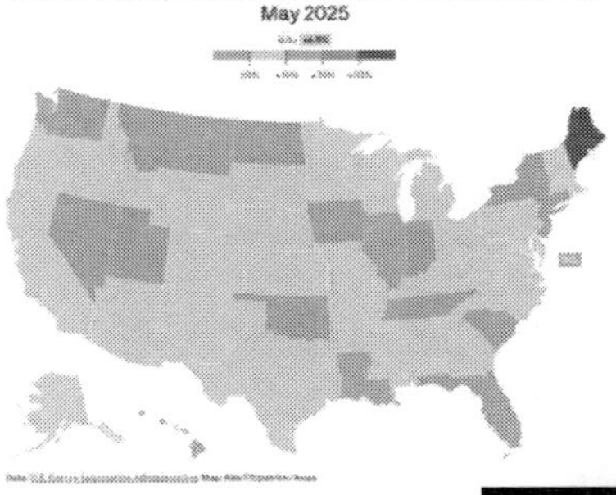

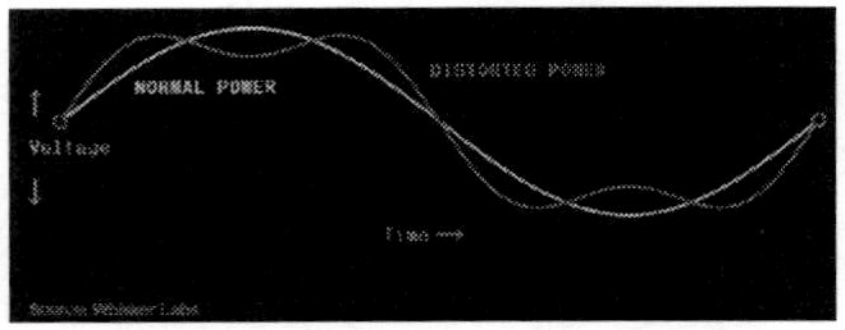

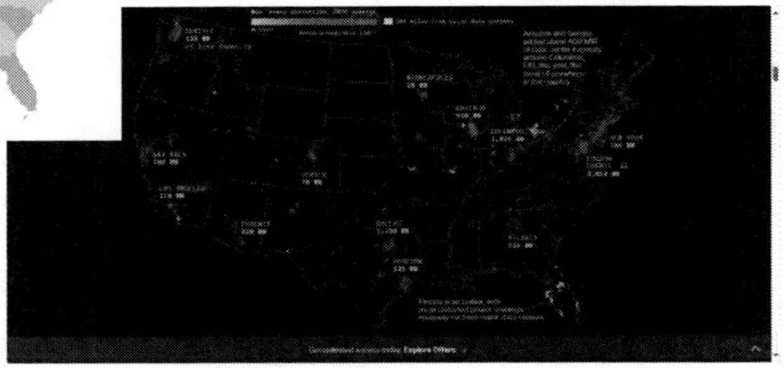

- UAE has ambitious goals for AI/data centers
- Global challenges in energy sector (e.g. in US)
  - Supply/demand impacts
  - Equipment supply chain – e.g. gas turbines
  - costs of grid/capacity upgrades – rising consumer prices
  - Grid stability challenges due to unique load of AI data centers
- Approaches
  - Grid upgrades to manage new load types
  - Data centers as a source of flexibility? [EPRI DC flex]
  - Partly or fully insulate data center from grid (on site storage for smoothing, or fully on site energy production
    - "Clean firm" power where solar+storage replaces conventional power station
  - Abu Dhabi project is on grid, but lessons are applicable to on-site power generation as well

EPRI

Description of the project

- 5.2GW PV, 19GWh BESS, 1GW baseload supply to grid
- Described as part of AI strategy [MEED | Abu Dhabi moves ahead with AI power plants]
- 6bnUSD investment in plant, total 10bnUSD package for PV+BESS, OCGT backup plant, grid connection/enhancements
- Very low price tag – but so was 2017 PV.....

Component	Capacity	Cost
PV+BESS	5.2GW/19GWh	$6bn
OCGT	1GW	$1.35bn
Grid enhancement		$2.5bn

https://gulfconstructiononline.com/ArticleTA/432157

Masdar, EWEC launch world-biggest 24/7 solar PV and battery project in Abu Dhabi

By Andy Colthorpe

January 15, 2025

Middle East, Africa & Middle East | Connected Technologies, Grid Scale | Technology, Business, Policy

LinkedIn | Twitter | Reddit | Facebook | Email

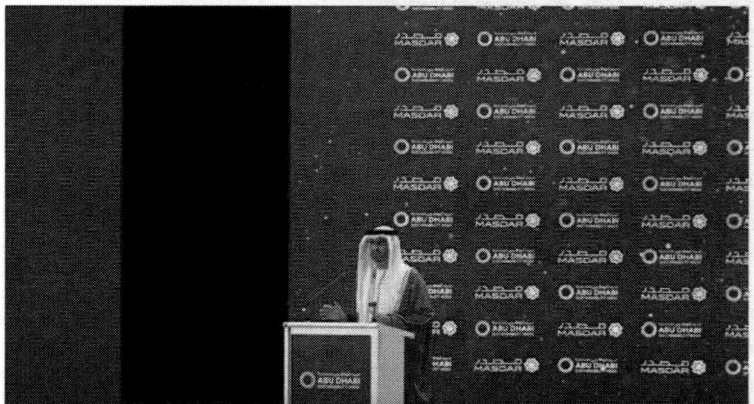

Dr Sultan Al Jaber, UAE Minister of Industry and Advanced Technology and chairman of Masdar gave a speech outlining the need for solutions to meet rapidly growing energy demand from applications including generative AI. Image: Masdar

Masdar, EWEC world-biggest solar-battery project in Abu Dhabi- Energy-Storage.News

EPRI

Market developments – PV systems

- Falling Capex throughout region pre-2020, plateau post-covid ~600USD/kW
  - "Pure" PV PPA prices around 1.5c/kWh – aggressive pricing but consistent with regional expectations
- Some savings in opex reported due to robotic cleaning

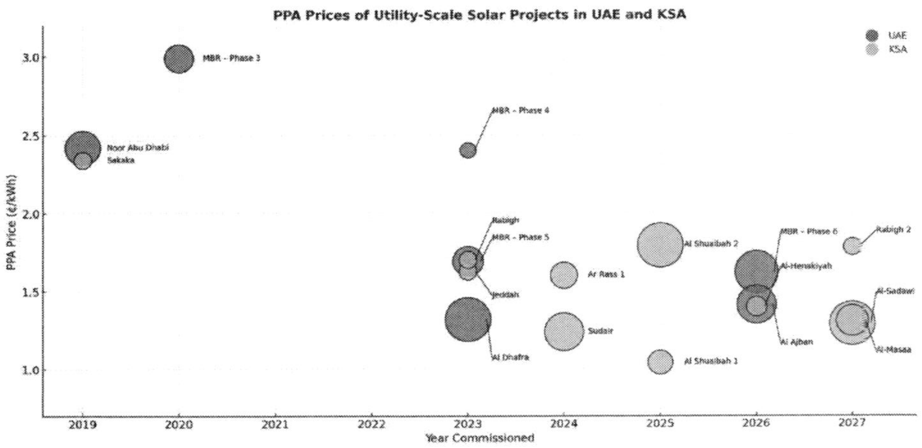

Component	Capacity	Unit cost	Source
PV	5.2GW	$600/kW	UAE/KSA

Market developments – BESS

- Major changes in this decade –comparable to module market changes in previous decade
- EV industry drives Li-ion (specifically LFP) manufacturing
- Storage mandate for PV installations drove stationary storage product development by Chinese firms
- Further price drop expected over next 1-2 years
- 2024 – 60USD/kWh battery cell costs [Where are EV battery prices headed in 2025 and beyond? | S&P Global]
- Reflected in recent BESS projects in region (Saudi Arabia)

EPRI 2023

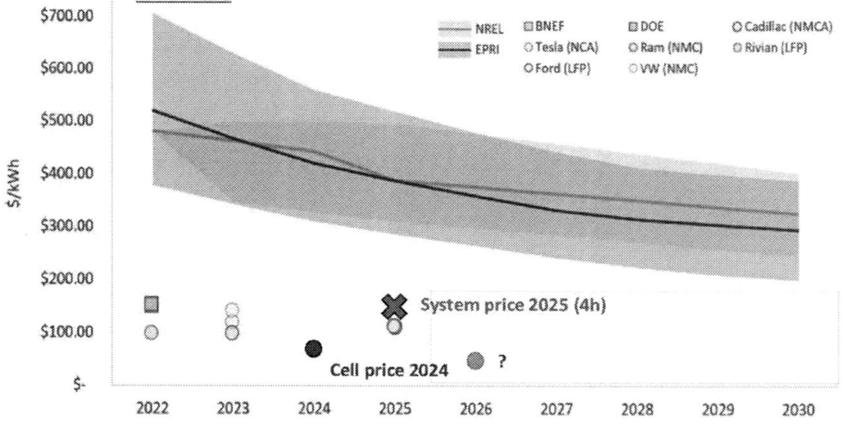

Component	Capacity	Unit cost	Source
PV	5.2GW	$600/kW	UAE/KSA
BESS energy	19GWh	$90/kWh	KSA
BESS power	2.5GW	$240/kW	KSA

SEC receives Bids for 1,000 MW Battery Energy Storage System Projects - SaudiGulf Projects

System & levelized electricity cost assessment

- Core technology cost decreases coupled w/ overall inflation & high financing costs
- Reported capex reflects current global market & local factors

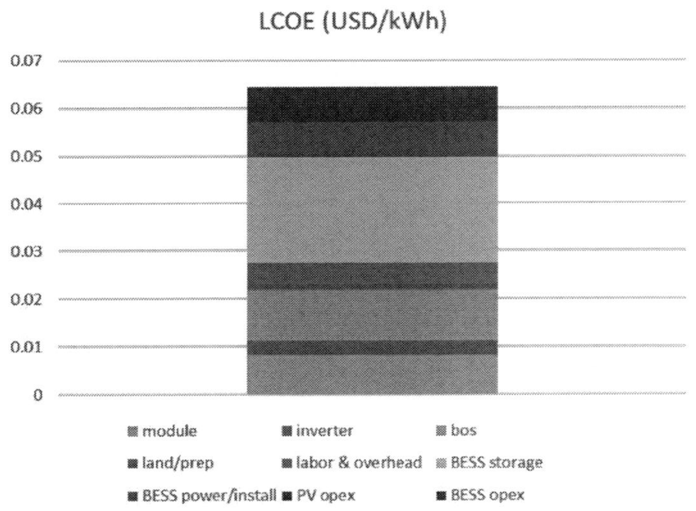

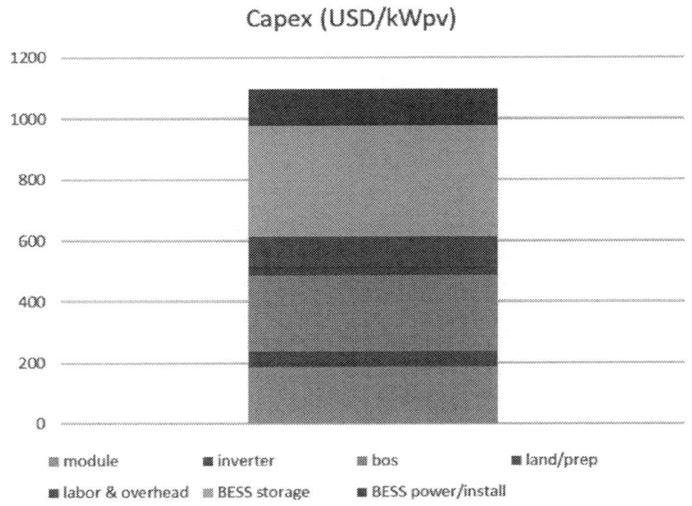

System & levelized electricity cost assessment

- Core technology cost decreases coupled w/ overall inflation & high financing costs
- Reported capex reflects current global market & local factors

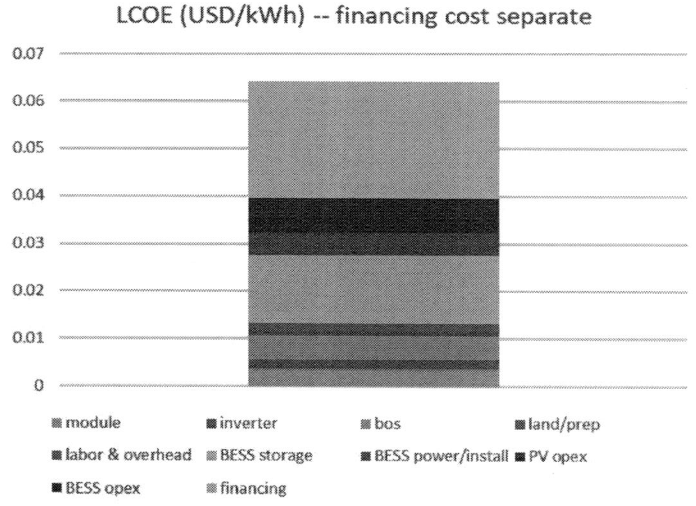

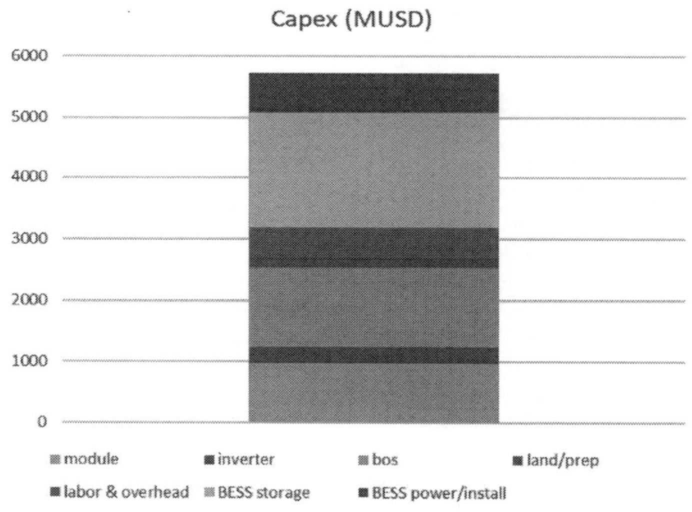

Availability as a baseload energy resource – model

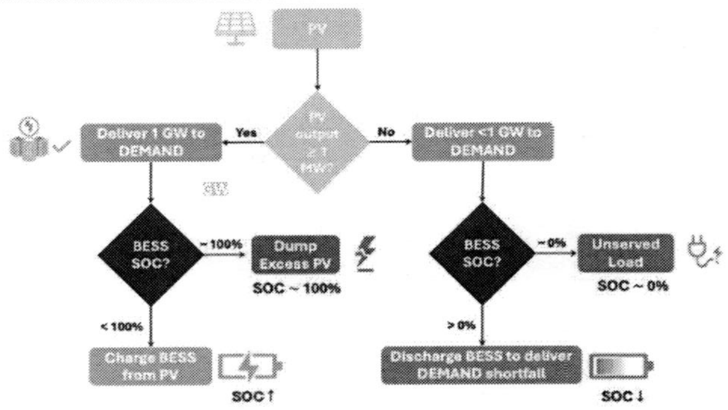

- Simple dispatch algorithm implemented where energy generated from solar
  - 1. is dispatched to meet demand
  - 2. After meeting demand, is fed to battery
  - 3. if battery is full, curtailed
  - 4. If demand exceeds solar generation, energy is dispatched from storage
  - 5. if net demand exceed dispatchable energy from storage, energy shortage is recorded
- Summer day performance:

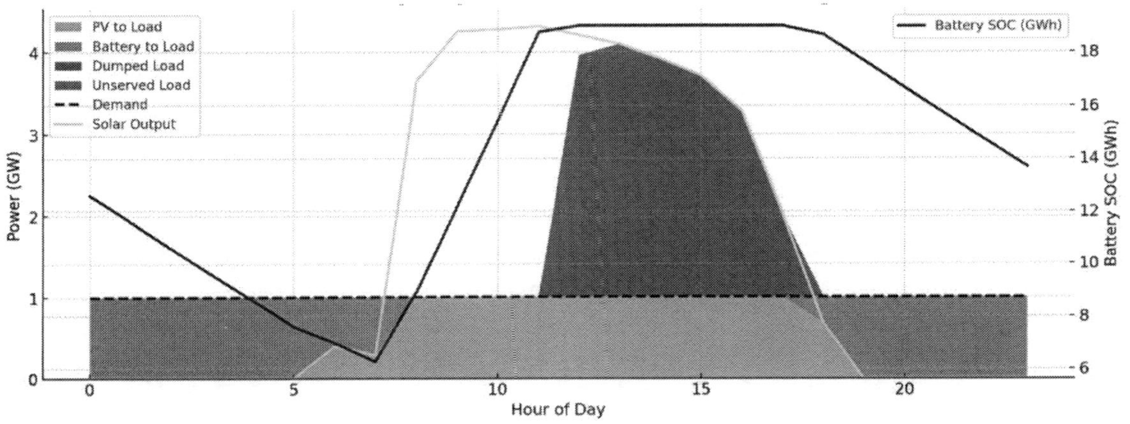

EPRI

Availability as a baseload energy resource – results

- Rainy/cloudy periods (or in general periods of lower solar generation) challenge system availability as a baseload resource
- Red areas indicate periods of unserved load (where battery is not charged sufficiently to supply full 1GW at night)
  - Total annual availability ~97%
- This is what necessitates the inclusion of the gas turbine backup system in order to serve as a baseload resources
  - At current pricing, increases LCOE by ~1.5c/kWh

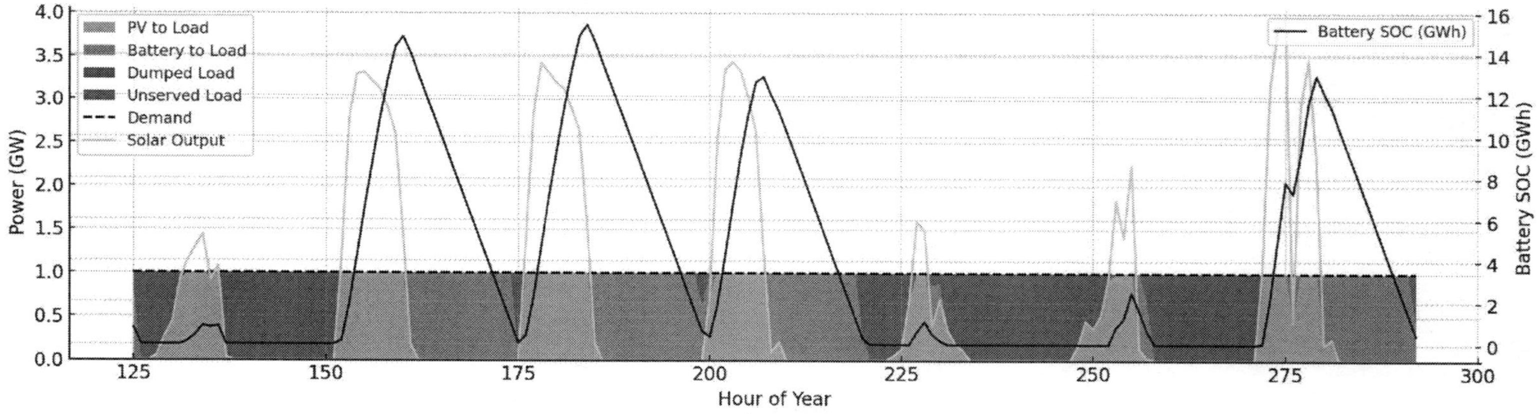

EPRI

Strategic energy storage planning – climbing the "ladder"

- However, baseload availability is not necessary for an energy system in transition
- Visualizing energy storage requirements as a "ladder" of different storage durations addressing different challenges that arise at different levels of solar adoption highlights strategic approach of building storage to meet immediate needs
- Falling cost of storage argues in favor of this approach (add needed storage capacity in future when it is cheaper)

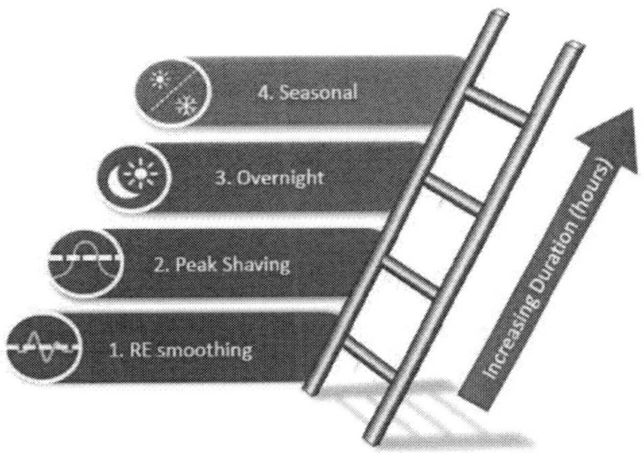

	Function	Duration	Description	Impact on energy system
1	RE & Transient smoothing/Black start/ Primary reserve	<1h	Energy storage under 1-hour duration for smoothing of solar output, frequency regulation & black start	Reduce spinning reserve requirement/ peaker use to balance RE & transient fluctuations
2	Ramp rate management/peak shaving/energy trading	1-4h	1-to-4-hour energy storage for peak shaving and ramp rate management for solar	Avoid peaker operation in normal conditions
3	Overnight storage/Island operation	4-16h	Medium duration or overnight energy storage in non-solar hours	Avoid Combined Cycle plant operation for normal overnight generation
4	Multi-day/seasonal energy shifting	Days-Months	Large-scale seasonal energy storage for balancing seasonal variation in solar output (summer vs winter production)	Avoid nearly all combined cycle plant use; stored energy can provide emergency backup

EPRI

Strategic energy storage planning – climbing the "ladder"

- However, baseload availability is not necessary for an energy system in transition
- Visualizing energy storage requirements as a "ladder" of different storage durations addressing different challenges that arise at different levels of solar adoption highlights strategic approach of building storage to meet immediate needs
- Falling cost of storage argues in favor of this approach (add needed storage capacity in future when it is cheaper)

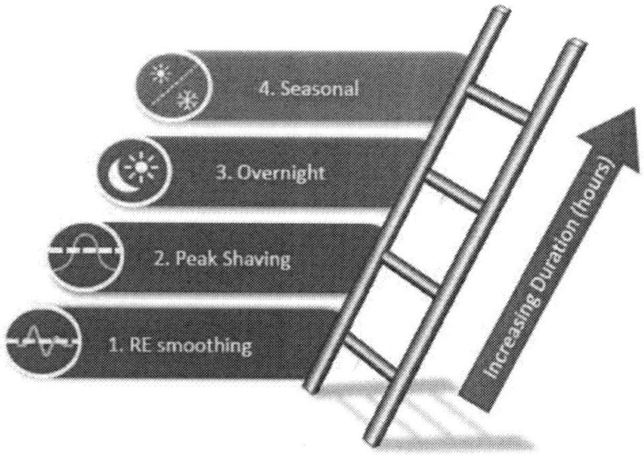

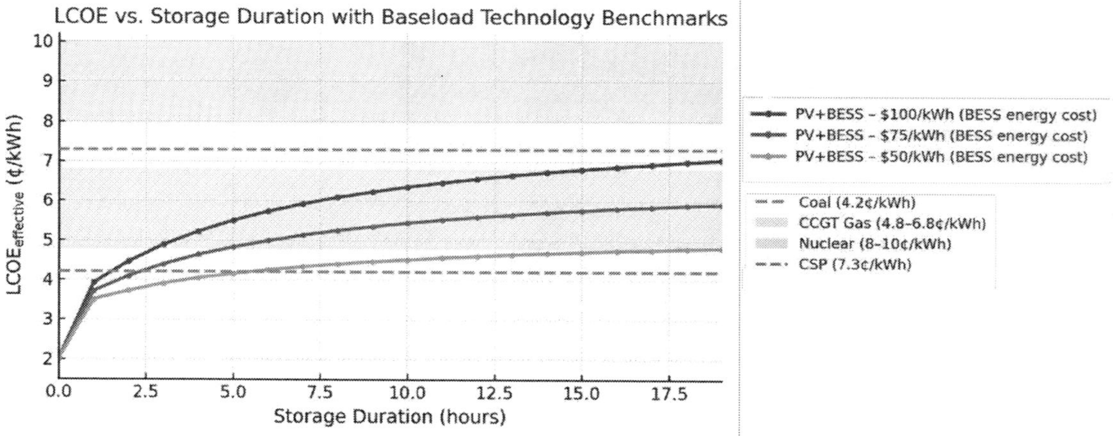

EPRI

Conclusions

- Major changes occurring in battery market, driven by EV adoption, internal policies in China and industrial learning curve previously observed for PV modules
- Nominal clean-firm PV+BESS (clean firm) systems are already achievable at viable cost in most favorable markets; true firm power requires conventional e.g. gas turbine backup for resilience through low-sun periods
- Clean-firm may not be the most useful concept to guide near-term energy system planning under highly dynamic market conditions
- Expected future price reductions favor strategic approach to energy storage deployment to maximize the rate of PV adoption, where storage systems are built with the duration necessary to integrate existing PV generation, and longer duration systems are added in the future at lower cost to integrate future PV
- **Storage cost revolution that will drive next wave of PV adoption appears to be underway – but reliability remains an open question, on which long-term success of PV will depend**

Energy Systems Research @EPRI: More Information

Sign up for the ESCA Newsletter
bit.ly/escanewsletter

See all public research on our website: esca.epri.com

EPRI's Energy Systems and Climate Analysis Group regularly posts public research, news, and events on our website, and newsletter.

Website **Newsletter**

Link Tree: bit.ly/m/epriesca

For questions or more information, please contact eea@epri.com

EPRI

eurac
research

Mitigating the grid impact of solar DG by a VPP firm generation strategy

Marco Pierro & Grazia Barchi(EURAC)
Alessandro Donadello & Davide Prando (Edyna)

Motivations

Distributed PV generation has a number of impacts on the distribution/transmission grid, including:

1. **Faster provision in unit commitment** due to increased load ramps (increasing the "duck curve")
2. **Congestions on transformers** on secondary/primary substations and **cables overload** due to overproduction and thus saturation of hosting capacity at distribution level;
3. **Needs to limit solar generation, zero (or negative) energy prices**; **increase of stop/restart** dispatchable generation units, due to overproduction at the transmission grid level;
4. **Needs of additional reserves** due to the increased variability in residual load.

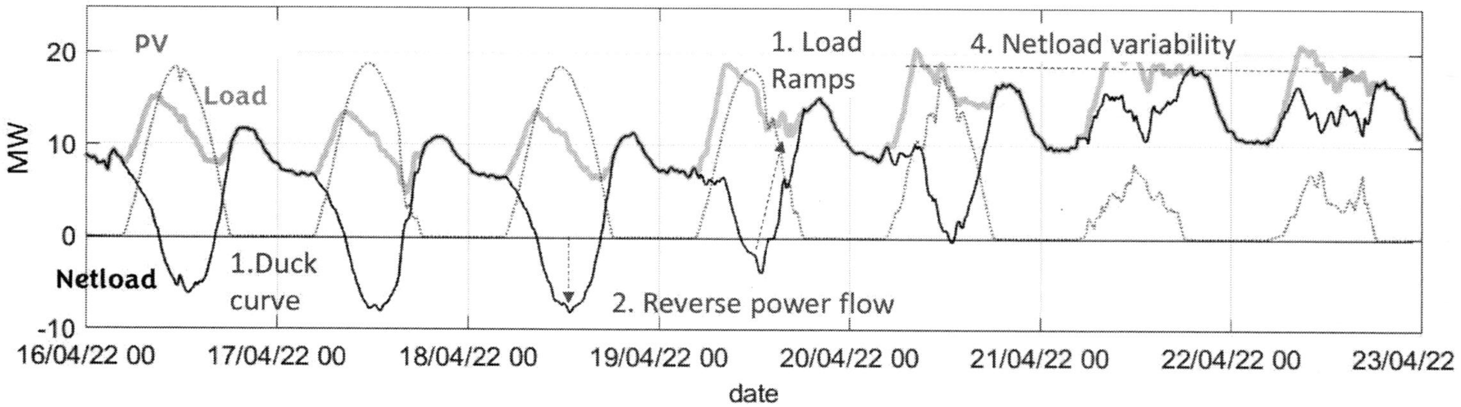

Motivations

Available space in the Dutch grid for large-scale commercial users.

High PV installation rate and uncontrolled feed-in, leading to significant congestions and rising costs to balance the grid.

Negative electricity prices Vs renewables share in the Netherlands

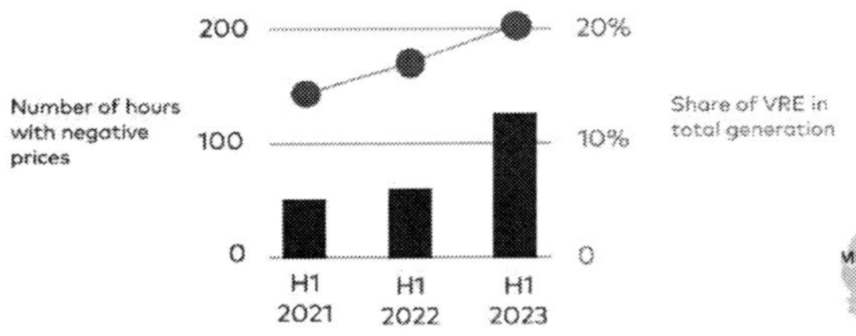

Source: IEA Electricity Market Report

Feed-in capacity

Source: IEA, Fitch Solutions

Actually, these issues start to appear on macro scale

Dutch power grid has **already reached its hosting capacity** for commercial users in many areas

Inequitable access to distributed energy resources due to grid infrastructure limits in California

Anna M. Brockway, Jennifer Conde & Duncan Callaway

Nature Energy **6**, 892–903 (2021) | Cite this article

https://www.gridx.ai/blog/the-netherlands-conundrum-low-grid-capacity-high-feed-in

Aim

The aim of this work is to propose a firm PV strategy to mitigate reverse power flows and netload ramps due to high solar DG and thus increase hosting capacity at primary/secondary station levels

DSOs consider solar DG in the control zone (pertaining to a secondary/primary substation) as produced by a Virtual Power Plant and place batteries (BESS) near the substation

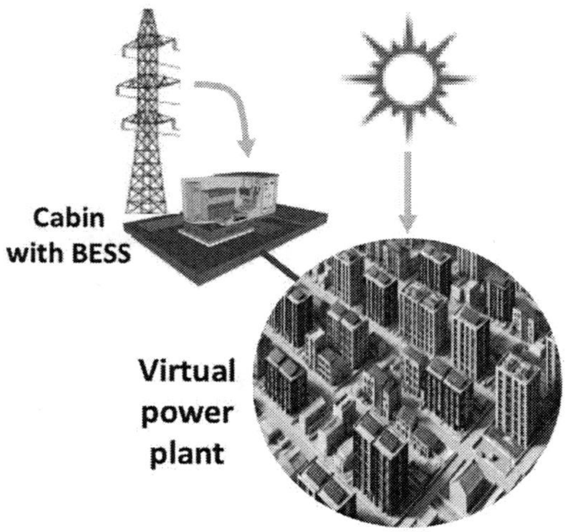

During the daylight batteries absorb from the grid the fraction of the solar DG exceeding a predefined baseload target

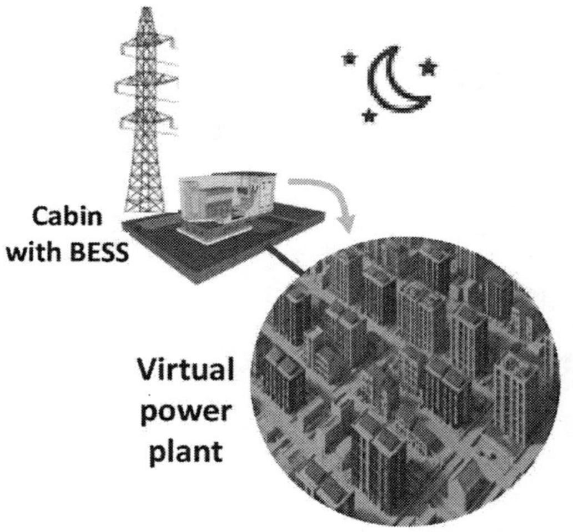

During the night batteries provides the baseload target as much is possible

Firm PV-based strategy

With this strategy

1) It would be possible to **redistribute some of the PV DG** (self-consumed or in excess) during the hours of less or no solar generation.

2) Distributed PV & Grid batteries **ensures a baseload round the clock** decreasing the consumption of the control zone without altering its profile

thus

it reduces load ramps, revers power flow and possible congestions at transformer level.

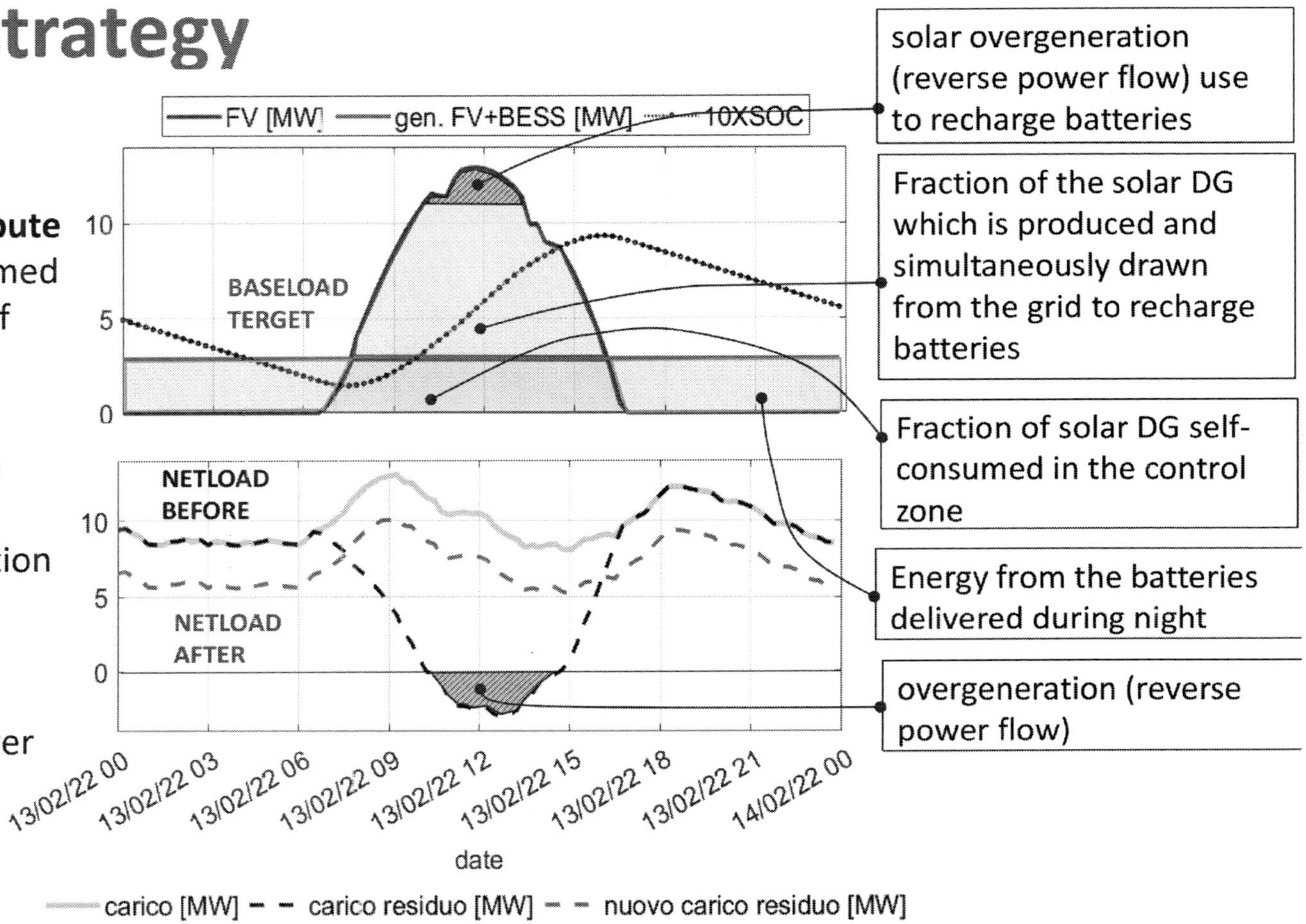

Distribute PV generation impact on distribution grid

We used real 15 min load data measured at a primary cabin level provided by an Italian DSO

Actually, in the control zone there is 10 MW of distributed PV capacity, we studied the case in which the **2030 target of 25 MW** will be reached compared with no PV case

In the control zone will be:

- About **1500 revers power flow events** with a max power of **10 MW** from MV/HV
- About **80 days of revers flow** with a max revers energy of **60 MWh per day**

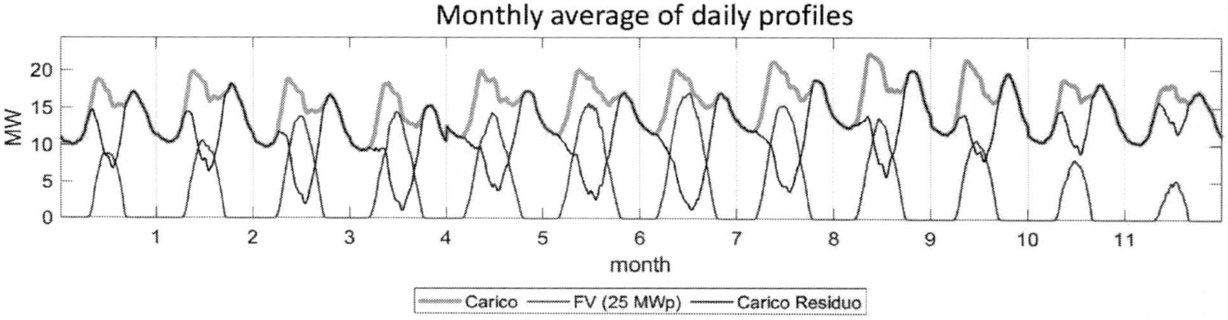

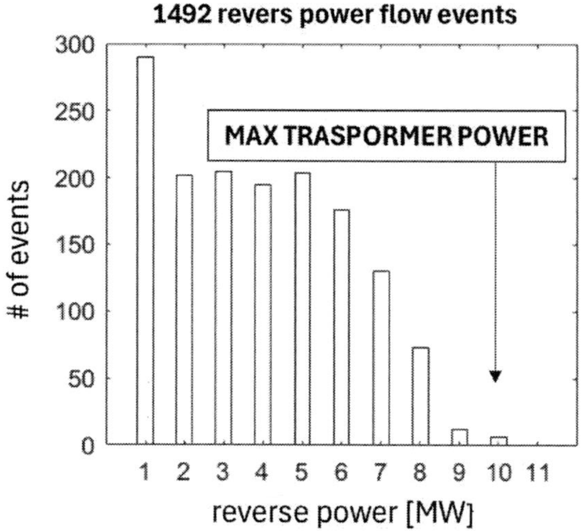

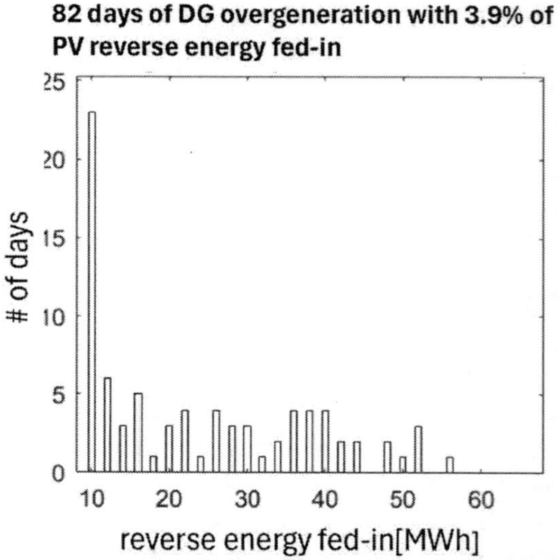

Distribute PV generation impact on distribution grid

Ramps on different time scales involve different types of reserves.

Compared to the scenario without PV generation the one with 25 MWp installed **increases ramps on all time scales** especially on the 4-hour one since on clear days less power commitment is required in the middle hours of the day

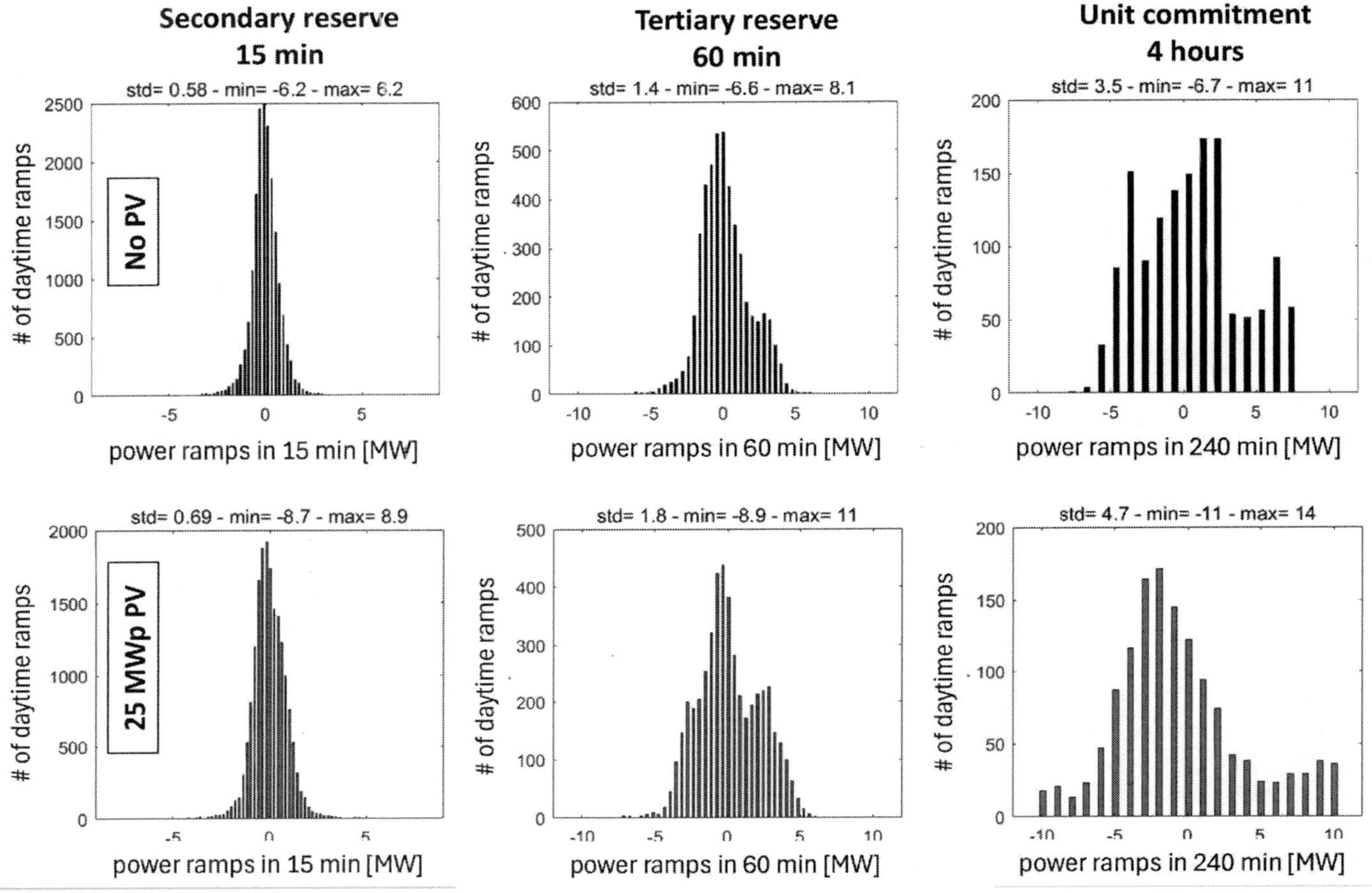

System size

Battery should be able:

- To store the max daily revers energy (60 kWh in this case)
- To fully discarge during nigh and to be recharged with the energy exceeding the baseload target during the next day
- To be not fully regarged during the day otherwise overgeneration power not stored could give rise to reverse power flows

The **baseload level** (set monthly) must:

- be high enough to minimize the energy that needs to be stored
- be not too high to ensure baseload solar production for a large number of hours (76% of the annual hours in this case)

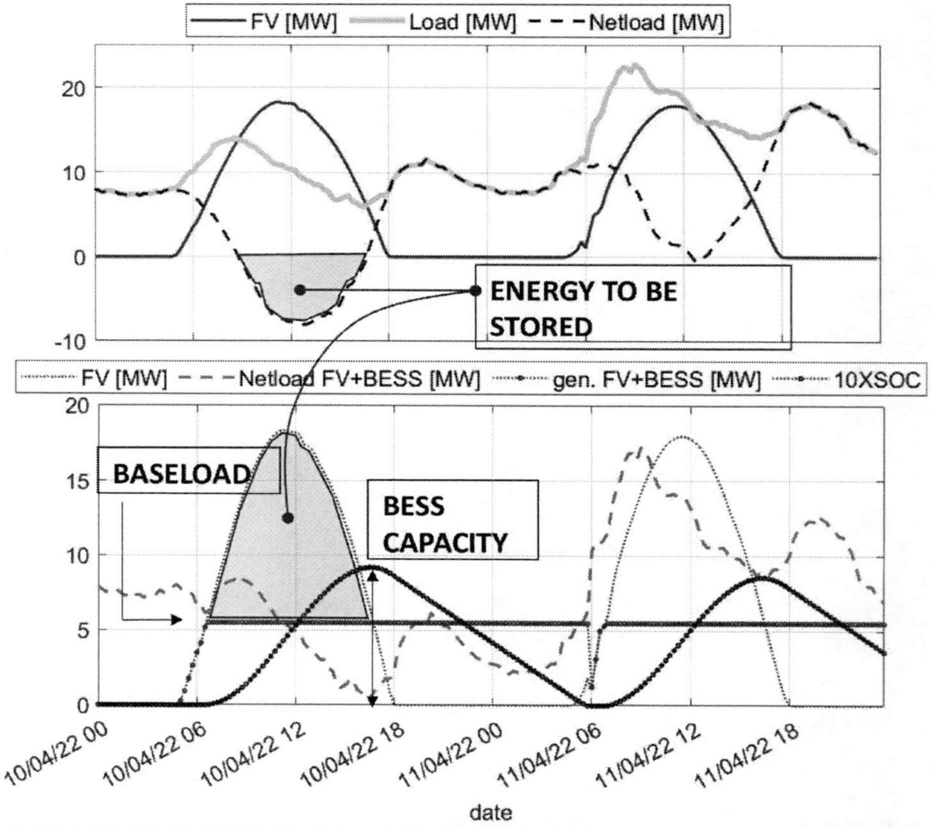

Results

Through a not trivial optimization process, monthly baseload levels and battery capacity were assessed.

- The load levels range from a minimum of **1.2 MW in December** to a **maximum of 7.6 MW in July**.
- The minimum battery capacity is **82 MWh (3.3 MWh/MWp)** with 20.5 MW of power.

Monthly average of daily profiles

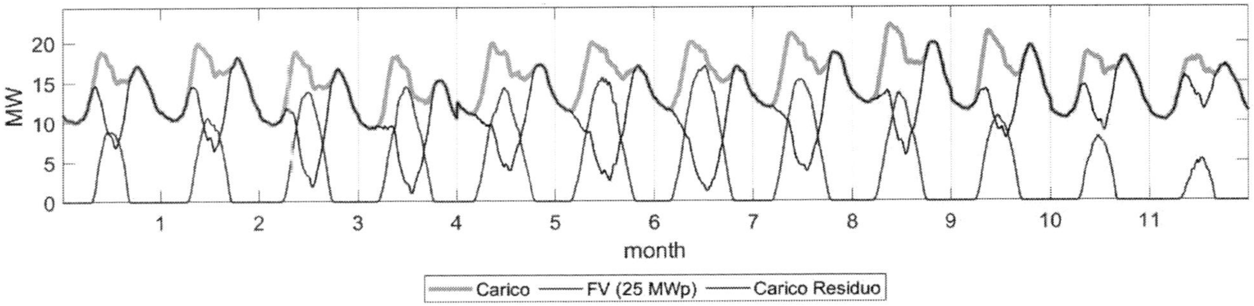

PV DG is transformed in a much more smoothed generation round the clock

Netload profile is much more similar to the load one but rescale

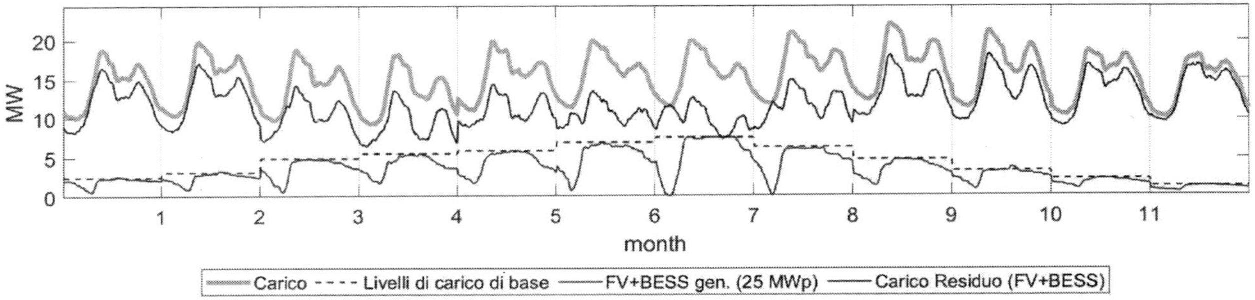

Results

The **number of reverse power flows** is reduced by **96%** and the **maximum reverse power by 33%** from 10 MW to 3 MW

The **generated solar energy fed into the transmission grid** is reduced **from about 4% to less than 0.05%.** Thus, all PV energy generated remains in the control zone

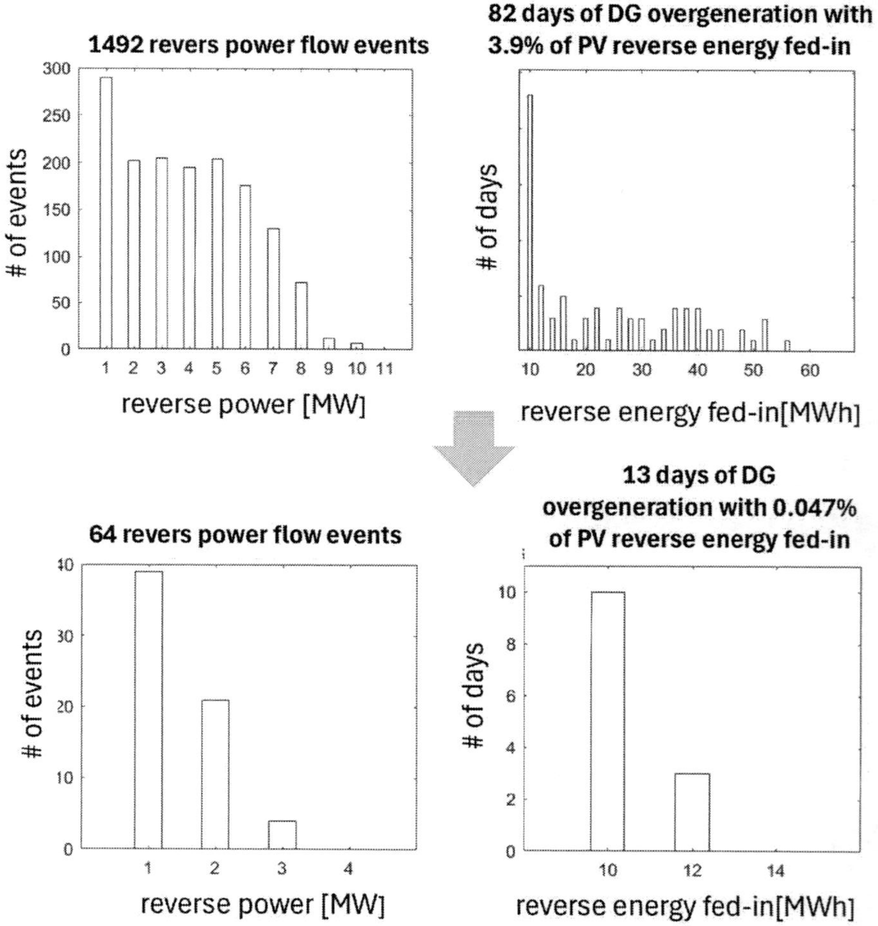

Results

The distribution of ramps is **practically restored** to the levels found in the absence of solar generation.

Ramps could be **further lowered with the use of PV power forecasting**, which would anticipate events and smooth out battery charging and discharging.

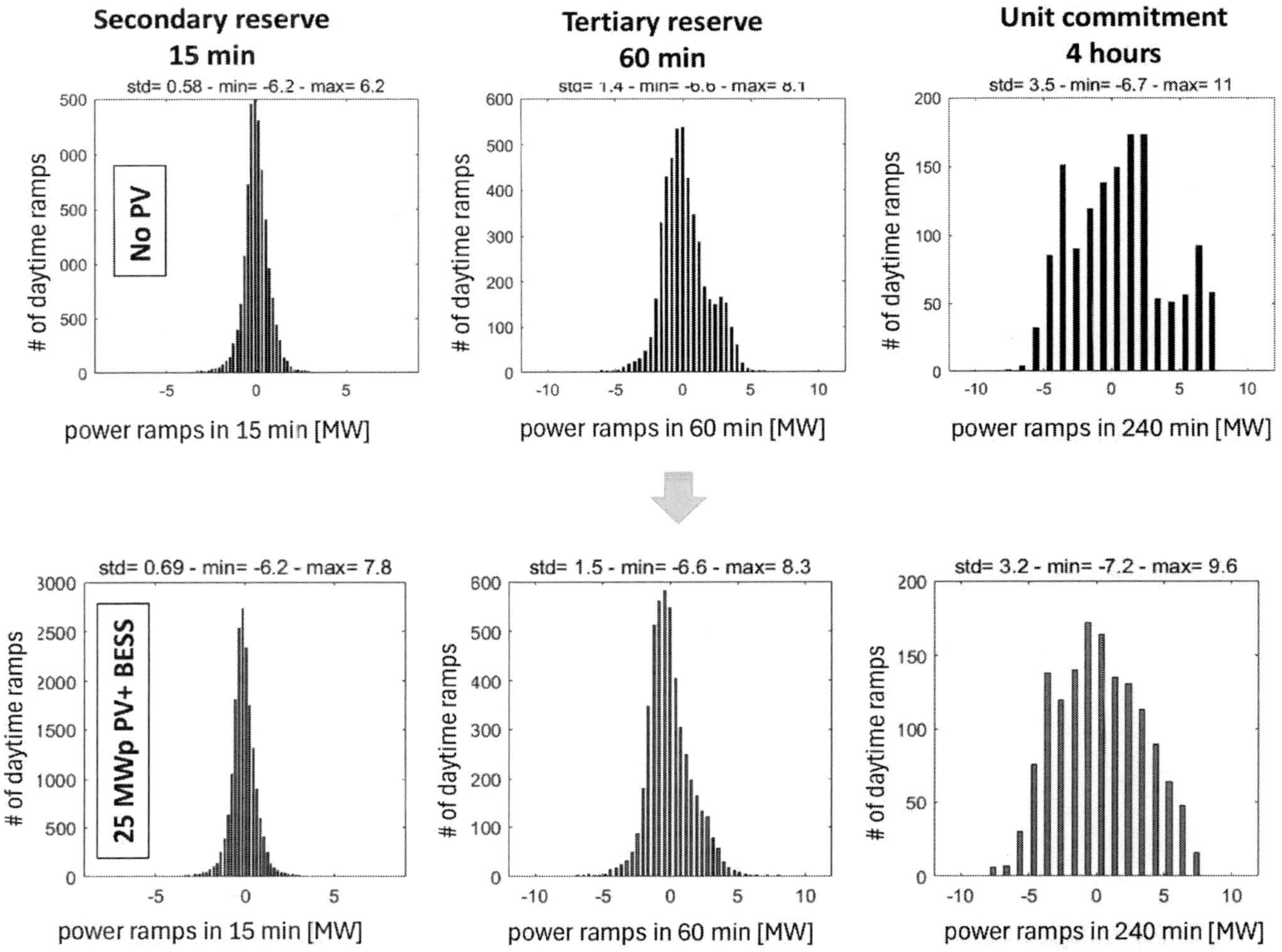

Conclusions

1. This strategy allows:

- To **restore grid hosting capacity** when transformers are no more able to dispatch the PV DG peaks reverse feed-in;
- **To reduce the flexibility requirements of the transmission grid** by decreasing ramps at all time scales and restoring a residual load profile very similar to the electrical demand in the absence of distributed solar generation;
- **To provide flexibility services to the grid** through batteries: synthetic inertia (ultra fast reserve), frequency and voltage regulation etc.

2. **The strategy increases solar self-production in the control area** by locally increasing the fraction of demand covered by solar: in this case with 25 MW of PV installed it would increase from 20 % to 25 %.

3. **DG's self-generation is no longer an economic loss for Utilities but a gain**. The Utilities could buy some of the self-consumption and energy fed into the grid during the day (at low prices) and then resell this energy at night (at high prices).

Thank you for your attention

Marco Pierro

Marco.pierro@eurac.edu

www.eurac.edu

eurac research

QUANTIFYING THE GAP: RULE-BASED VS. SMART ENERGY MANAGEMENT OF RESIDENTIAL PV SELF-CONSUMPTION WITH STORAGE

Carolina Crespo, Rodrigo Amaro e Silva, Miguel Centeno Brito
University of Lisbon, Faculty of Sciences, Instituto Dom Luiz, Lisboa, Portugal
Faculdade de Ciências da Universidade de Lisboa, Campo Grande Edifício C1, Piso 1, 1749-016 Lisboa

ABSTRACT: The growing adoption of residential photovoltaic (PV) and battery systems has led to an increasing interest in energy management strategies that optimize performance and maximize savings. These range from simple rule-based methods to advanced optimization and machine learning approaches. Among them, self-consumption maximization (SCM) stands out as a practical, low-cost, rule-based strategy requiring no external infrastructure or forecasting.

This work assesses the adequacy of SCM for residential PV and battery systems within collective self-consumption schemes. SCM performance is benchmarked against a MILP model with perfect foresight to quantify the gap between SCM and the theoretical optimum. A case study in Portugal shows that SCM achieves results within 1-7% of optimality, even for dynamic tariffs. Achieving optimality would correspond to maximum cost savings of €5 per household per month, when compared to SCM. Given the modest potential gains, the limits imposed by forecast uncertainty on practical performance, and the higher costs of implementing more complex methods, SCM is likely the most cost-effective solution for most residential applications, particularly in sunny climates like Portugal.

Keywords: Battery Energy Management, Home Energy Management System, Battery Energy Storage System, Residential PV, Collective Self-consumption

1 INTRODUCTION AND MOTIVATION

In recent years, the adoption of distributed photovoltaics (PV) has grown rapidly, often accompanied by the deployment of distributed energy storage, typically in the form of batteries. Batteries enable end-users to (i) store surplus PV generation for later self-consumption and (ii) shift demand in time by charging from the grid during low-price periods and discharging to cover consumption during high-price periods.

This evolution has fueled significant research interest in energy management strategies, which govern battery charging and discharging and, in some cases, the operation of controllable loads such as washing machines or HVAC systems. Proposed methods span from classical optimization techniques to the increasingly popular machine learning approaches [1]. However, deploying these advanced strategies in real-world systems entails costs for hardware, software, forecasting services (informing the expected load and generation), and, potentially, cloud-based infrastructure. For such approaches to deliver tangible benefits, the resulting savings must outweigh these expenses.

In contrast, many real-world PV-battery systems rely on simpler, rule-based approaches, most notably self-consumption maximization (SCM) [2]. SCM requires no external infrastructure and uses only instantaneous load and PV generation data to determine whether to charge or discharge the battery. Specifically, the battery charges during PV surplus (if not full) and discharges during load deficits (if sufficiently charged).

Many studies claiming improvements over baseline energy management strategies face a common issue: the lack of standardization in baseline definitions hinders comparability and the consistency of performance assessments. Beaudin and Zareipour highlighted this issue in 2015 [3], urging the adoption of common baselines, but more recent literature has yet to address this. Moreover, Azuatalam et al. [2] compared seven energy management strategies, including rule-based, classical optimization, and machine learning approaches, and found that simple rule-based methods such as SCM can achieve near-optimal results, especially under real-world conditions where forecast uncertainty degrades the performance of more complex methods, but does not affect SCM.

The objective of this work is to assess the suitability of SCM for energy management of distributed PV and battery systems, focusing on residential collective self-consumption schemes.

2 MEASURING THE POTENTIAL FOR INTELLIGENCE

Beyond the lack of standardized baselines, much of the literature on energy management strategies fails to quantify how distant the achieved performance is from the theoretical optimum. This work addresses this by explicitly measuring the performance difference between SCM and the optimal solution, providing a clear assessment of SCM's adequacy and the potential value of adopting more advanced strategies.

To this end, we introduce the Potential for Intelligence (PFI), defined in Eq. 1, as a metric to evaluate both the effectiveness of SCM and the remaining room for improvement. Installing a PV-battery system managed solely by a charge controller performing SCM delivers certain cost-saving benefits. However, in theory, an ideal energy management strategy with perfect foresight could further maximize these savings. PFI quantifies the gap between the outcome of SCM and this theoretical optimum, normalized by the maximum achievable savings compared to a scenario without a PV-battery system (illustrated in **Figure 1**).

$$PFI = \frac{c_{\text{SCM}} - c_{\text{optimal}}}{c_{\text{no system}} - c_{\text{optimal}}} \quad (1)$$

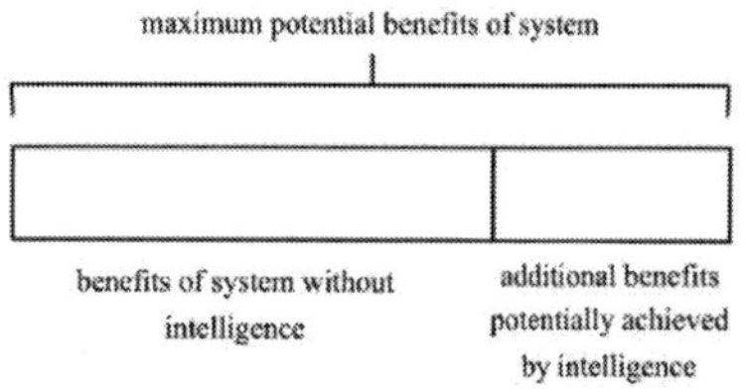

Figure 1: Of the total potential benefits of installing a PV-battery system, part can be achieved with a simple charge controller and SCM, while additional benefits require more sophisticated energy management strategies.

3 CASE STUDY DESCRIPTION

We apply the PFI metric to a case study involving a collective self-consumption scheme in Portugal, comprising 18 households. The analysis uses one full year of real energy consumption data alongside PV generation profiles obtained from PVGIS [4]. A sensitivity analysis was also conducted by testing different combinations of tariff schemes and installed PV and battery capacities.

Two tariff schemes were tested:

- **Dual tariff**: Electricity prices are €0.24/kWh between 9:00 and 22:00 (peak period) and €0.15/kWh during off-peak hours;
- **Dynamic tariff**: Prices vary hourly, following the fluctuations of the Iberian wholesale electricity market.

In both scenarios, surplus generation can be sold to the grid at a constant value of €0.045/kWh.

4 RESULTS AND DISCUSSION

The results are presented in **Figure 2**, which shows PFI heatmaps for different combinations of battery storage capacity and installed PV capacity. In most scenarios, SCM is found to perform well, with generally low PFI values. Even in scenarios with the highest remaining potential for improvement, the additional cost savings achievable with advanced energy management strategies are modest—approximately €5 per household per month, as shown in **Figure 3**.

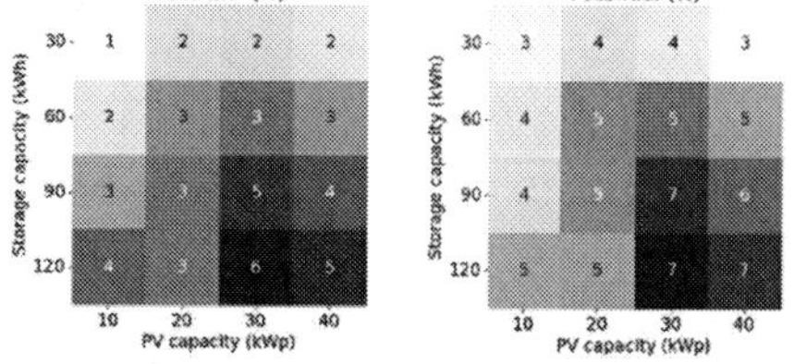

(a) Dual tariff **(b)** Dynamic tariff

Figure 2: Heatmaps of PFI (%) for the case study, showing results under dual and dynamic tariffs across combinations of varying storage and PV installed capacities.

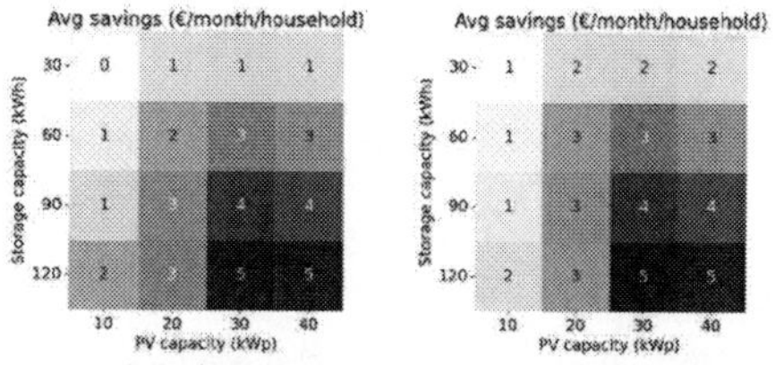

(a) Dual tariff **(b)** Dynamic tariff

Figure 3: Heatmaps of average potential monthly savings per household for the case study achieved by an optimization with perfect foresight, when compared with SCM. Results are shown for a dual and a dynamic tariff, across combinations of varying storage and PV.

Two factors explain the robust performance of SCM in this context: abundant solar resource and favorable tariff alignment. This can be observed in **Figure 4**, which shows the energy management determined by SCM over three consecutive days for one of the scenarios.

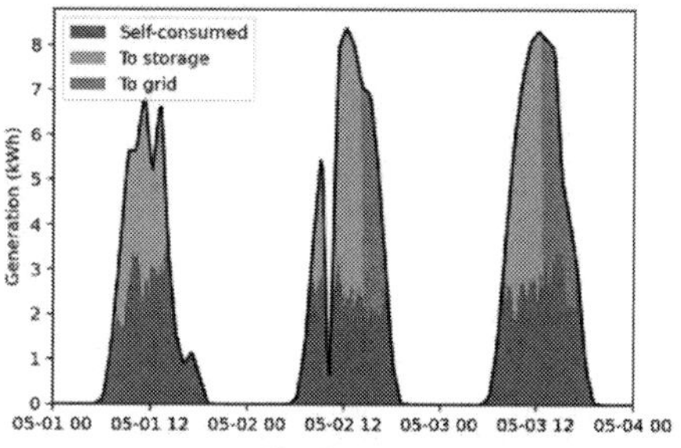

(a) PV generation

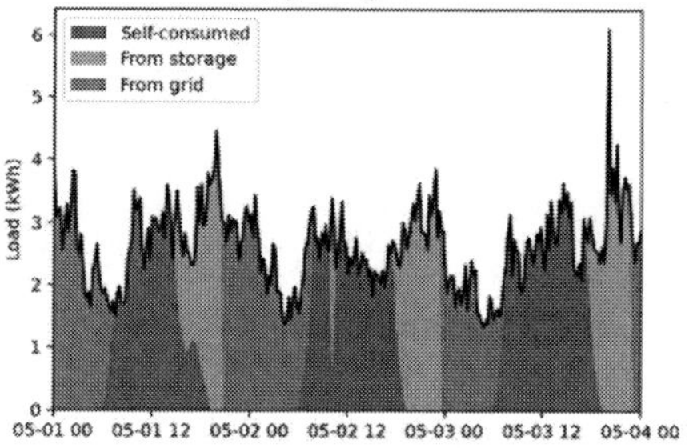

(b) Energy consumption

Figure 4: Energy management determined by SCM over a 3-day period. Figure 4a shows PV generation and its use, while Figure 4b shows the collective energy consumption and its source, in kWh over 15-minute periods.

The second and third days exhibit high solar production. SCM prioritizes immediate self-consumption and stores the surplus generation. Once the battery is full, surplus generation is injected into the grid. In the evening, the stored energy covers consumption, and by the time the battery is depleted, it is nearly midnight, when electricity prices are at their lowest. In such scenarios, SCM effectively minimizes energy costs, leaving little room for improvement through more advanced strategies.

In contrast, on days with lower solar generation, such as the first day shown in **Figure 4**, the surplus is insufficient to fully charge the battery, resulting in earlier reliance on grid energy during peak price periods. In these cases, price arbitrage – charging the battery with low-cost grid energy for later use – becomes critical for cost savings beyond what SCM can provide. It is in these situations that a smart strategy can outperform SCM. However, such days are relatively infrequent in Mediterranean climates. Additionally, hybrid approaches combining SCM with minimal forecasting and pre-set charging schedules could offer a cost-effective alternative to fully intelligent, high-cost solutions.

It is worth emphasizing that the optimal results reported here represent a theoretical upper bound, obtained under the assumption of perfect foresight. In reality, forecast errors inevitably lead to suboptimal decisions, preventing even advanced control strategies from fully realizing the theoretical potential. When these limitations are combined with the additional costs of forecasting services, cloud infrastructure, and more complex hardware, the economic advantage of intelligent energy management over simple rule-based control can be marginal. In contrast, SCM offers a robust, low-cost solution that is inherently resilient to uncertainty.

Future work could extend this analysis to other climates, assessing SCM's effectiveness under varying solar resource availability. An exploration of the impact of aggregation or diverse residential consumption patterns would also be valuable to generalize these findings.

5 ACKNOWLEDGEMENTS

This work is supported by the Portuguese Fundação para a Ciência e Tecnologia, FCT, I.P./MCTES through national funds (PIDDAC): UID/50019/2025 and LA/P/0068/2020 (https://doi.org/10.54499/LA/P/0068/2020), as well as the FCT Studentship UI/BD/154674/2023, and Project ATE: Aliança para a Transição Energética financed by IAPMEI - Agência para a Competitividade e Inovação, I. P.

6 REFERENCES

[1] Leitao, J., Gil, P., Ribeiro, B., & Cardoso, A. (2020). A survey on home energy management. *IEEE Access, 8,* 5699–5722. https://doi.org/10.1109/ACCESS.2019.2963502

[2] Azuatalam, D., Paridari, K., Ma, Y., Förstl, M., Chapman, A. C., & Verbič, G. (2019). Energy management of small-scale PV-battery systems: A systematic review considering practical implementation, computational requirements, quality of input data and battery degradation. Renewable and Sustainable Energy Reviews, 112, 555–570. https://doi.org/10.1016/j.rser.2019.06.007

[3] Beaudin, M., & Zareipour, H. (2015). Home energy management systems: A review of modelling and complexity. *Renewable and Sustainable Energy Reviews, 45,* 318–335. https://doi.org/10.1016/j.rser.2015.01.046

[4] Huld, T., Müller, R., & Gambardella, A. (2012). A new solar radiation database for estimating PV performance in Europe and Africa. *Solar Energy, 86*(6), 1803–1815. https://doi.org/10.1016/j.solener.2012.03.006

42nd European Photovoltaic Solar Energy Conference and Exhibition

This presentation was selected by the Sc. Committee of the EU PVSEC 2025 for submission of a full paper to one of the EU PVSEC's collaborating peer-reviewed journals.

SOLUTIONS FOR OPTIMIZING SHARED PV INSTALLATIONS AT RENEWABLE ENERGY COMMUNITIES DRIVEN BY CITIZENS

Ana B. Cristóbal*[a,b] (0000-0002-4314-6160), Sergio Morales[a], Daniel Sierra[a], Laura Palomino[b], Luis Narvarte (0000-0002-6289-7605)[b].

a) Escuela Técnica Superior de Ingeniería de Sistemas Informáticos, Universidad Politécnica de Madrid, C/Alan Turing s/n, 28031 Madrid, Spain

b) Instituto de Energía Solar, Universidad Politécnica de Madrid, C/Nikola Tesla s/n, 28031 Madrid, Spain.

anabelen.cristobal@upm.es, sergio.morales.gonzalez@alumnos.upm.es, daniel.sierra@alumnos.upm.es, laura.palomino@upm.es, luis.narvarte@upm.es

ABSTRACT: The rapid emergence of Renewable Energy Communities (RECs) across Europe highlights the potential of citizen-led initiatives to accelerate the transition toward decentralized and sustainable energy systems. However, their effective operation requires digital tools capable of providing real-time data on consumption and production—resources often limited to company-driven projects with proprietary platforms. This work presents the design and implementation of an open, modular framework that empowers communities to autonomously monitor and manage shared photovoltaic installations. The system integrates low-cost Shelly EM devices, configured through the MQTT protocol, with a Docker-based backend deployed on AWS and a flexible data model supporting both public and private resources. Core functionalities include real-time visualization, hierarchical user roles, and integration with national data sources such as Spain's REData API. By lowering technical and administrative barriers, the platform strengthens citizen participation, enhances decision-making on energy allocation and surpluses, and offers a scalable digital infrastructure aligned with the original vision of community-driven renewable energy.
Keywords: Renewable Energy Communities (REC), IoT-based Energy Monitoring, MQTT Protocol, Citizen Participation, Dockerized Architecture

1 INTRODUCTION

Historically, the energy system has been dominated by large corporations, heavily dependent on fossil fuels and centralized distribution. However, technological advances, regulatory changes, the European energy crisis, and growing social commitment to sustainability have paved the way for the emergence of energy communities. European legislation distinguishes between two types: Citizen Energy Communities (CEC), defined in Directive (EU) 2019/944, and Renewable Energy Communities (REC), defined in Directive (EU) 2018/2001. While both frameworks coexist, in practice, the concept of REC has become the prevailing reference.

These communities can engage in a wide range of activities, including the production, consumption, sharing, storage, and sale of renewable energy, as well as initiatives for energy efficiency, sustainable mobility, and environmental awareness. Beyond reducing carbon footprints and energy costs, they foster social cohesion and empower citizens by directly involving them in energy management and decision-making.

According to the EC, there are more than 9,000 RECs in the EU, involving more than 1.5 million citizens in early 2024 [1]. Schwanitz estimated 10,540 initiatives involving more than 2 million people, an installed renewable capacity ranging from 7.2–9.9 GW and investments made 6.2–11.3 billion € for 30 EU countries [2]. Spain serves as a relevant example: 659 REC initiatives were registered by the end of 2024 [3] - twice as many as in 2023.

Despite their rapid growth, energy communities still face major challenges [4], particularly regarding digitalization. The effective management of collective self-consumption requires accurate, real-time data on both generation and demand; without it, participants cannot fully optimize the use of locally produced renewable energy or make informed decisions on how to valorize surpluses and define allocation coefficients. In Spain, for example, DSOs allow adjustments of allocation shares from community installations up to four times per year, but most users remain unable to take informed decisions beyond fixed distributions typically based on their initial investment.

Many communities promoted by energy companies benefit from proprietary digital platforms that streamline these processes, but this model contrasts with the original vision of Renewable Energy Communities (RECs) as citizen-led initiatives aimed at empowering local actors. For grassroots projects, open-access digital tools are still lacking, limiting their ability to autonomously register, monitor, and manage energy flows, and ultimately hindering their potential for self-governance and scalability.

In this work, we present a digital framework designed to support citizen-led RECs in managing shared photovoltaic installations. The proposed solution combines open-access monitoring and data management tools to provide real-time insights on consumption and generation, enable more flexible allocation strategies, and facilitate collective decision-making. By lowering technical and administrative barriers, this approach aims to strengthen citizen participation, improve the economic performance of community energy projects, and contribute to the broader transition toward decentralized and sustainable energy systems.

2 TECHNICAL FRAMEWORK

2.1 Monitoring Demand

Electricity users are entitled to access the readings recorded by their smart meters. This information can be obtained either by physically inspecting the meter or through the application or website usually provided by the energy retailer, which connects to the distributor's metering infrastructure. As illustrated in Figure 1, daily consumption data are aggregated into three established periods (peak, flat, and off-peak), as well as the overall historical consumption profile.

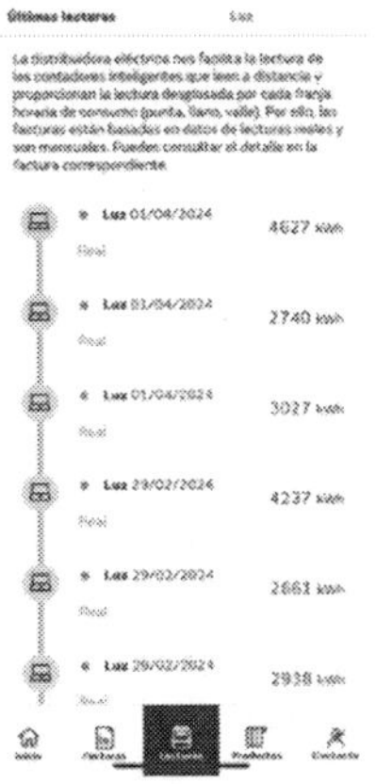

Figure 1: Example of consumption data displayed by the regulated market retailer of the Naturgy group.

This approach presents two major limitations. First, implementing a data integration or extraction process individually for each retailer is unfeasible, particularly given that Spain has more than 400 energy retailers, each with its own interpretation of data access rights. Second, the aggregated data provided do not enable real-time consumption monitoring.

It is therefore logical that consumption data should be accessed directly from the distributor, which owns the smart meters and bears responsibility for providing such access. Since there are only five distribution companies in Spain, developing integrations with them may appear more manageable.

Figure 2 illustrates the access interface of Unión Fenosa Distribución. In practice, the application requires approximately two minutes to establish a connection before displaying real-time demand data. Although the system allows scheduled queries, these are limited to 30-minute intervals and cannot provide continuous real-time monitoring.

Figure 2: Data access through the distributor's application:

(a) user access panel; (b) real-time demand; (c) scheduled queries interface.

Attempts to develop external APIs capable of continuous calls to distributor systems have been blocked, as such activity is deemed potentially hazardous. In response, the five main electricity distributors in Spain created DATADIS, a centralized database designed to provide secure access to consumption data. As shown in Figure 3, DATADIS allows users to extract data from any smart meter, and also permits access to third-party data upon prior authorization.

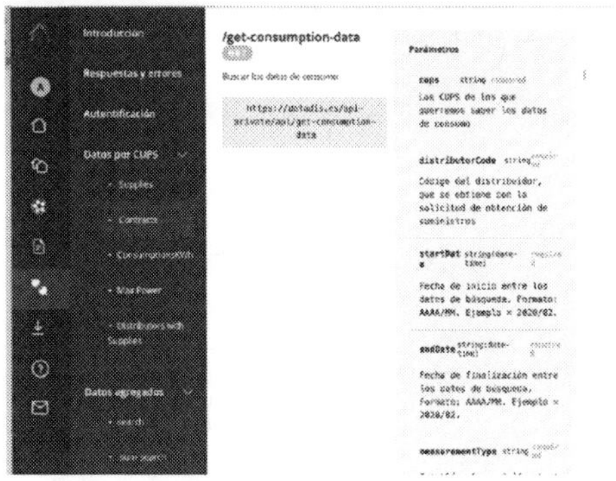

Figure 3: Overview of the DATADIS API platform.

2.2 Monitoring Production

Most distributed generation sources produce direct current (DC), which requires conversion to alternating current (AC) for domestic use. This task is performed by the inverter, which also provides the most relevant point for monitoring production. Inverters typically employ the Modbus protocol over TCP/IP or serial ports. Although robust, Modbus requires a dedicated server to query the inverter periodically and transmit data to users, which is impractical for non-expert citizens.

An alternative approach is to expose port 502 for remote Modbus access. However, because manufacturers implement Modbus differently, no universal solution exists. Moreover, configuring firewall exceptions requires technical expertise, rendering this option inaccessible for most communities.

A more viable solution is the deployment of universal electrical measurement devices capable of integrating with existing meters and inverters, while remaining non-intrusive. These devices should connect to an open-access platform, allowing all community members to monitor real-time energy flows.

2.2.1 Open Hardware

An initial attempt considered a custom ESP32-based device. While cost-effective, this solution remains a DIY approach, requiring technical knowledge beyond the capacity of most citizens. Consequently, commercially available alternatives were explored.

One promising option is the Shelly EM, a compact device that measures current, voltage, and other electrical parameters. It connects via Wi-Fi and can be operated remotely. Crucially, it supports the MQTT protocol, enabling integration with user-defined servers rather than relying solely on the manufacturer's cloud infrastructure. This flexibility, together with comprehensive documentation and backward compatibility, positioned the Shelly EM as the preferred choice for this study. Citizens can directly purchase and configure the device to connect with the **renew-net.com** open framework developed here.

2.2.2 Open Software

Currently, no open-source platform provides real-time visualization of energy community behaviour connected to IoT devices. Therefore, this study proposes the creation of such a platform.

Table I: Functional and Non-Functional Requirements of the Open Platform

ID	Name	Type	Description
RQF01	MQTT Connection with Shelly EM	Functional	Connectivity with Shelly EM meters via MQTT must be supported.
RQF02	MQTT to Database Proxy	Functional	Telemetry data must be stored in a persistent database.
RQF03	Configurable Graph	Functional	Users must be able to visualize data via configurable graphs.
RQF04	Hierarchical Roles	Functional	User roles with specific permissions must be defined.
RQF05	Sensor Integration	Functional	Users must select which sensors connect to the server.
RQNF01	Concurrency in MQTT Agent	Non-Functional	The system must ensure atomicity and resource exclusivity.
RQNF02	UX/UI Design	Non-Functional	The interface must be minimalist and user-friendly.
RQNF03	System Performance	Non-Functional	Responses must occur in <1s for up to 100 concurrent users.
RQNF05	Secure Sessions	Non-Functional	Sessions must expire after 1 hour; registration requires admin approval.
RQNF06	Secure Backend Requests	Non-Functional	Backend must use JWT authentication; no unauthenticated routes permitted.

3.2 General Architecture

The high-level architecture of the system is hosted on Amazon Web Services (AWS). The infrastructure is containerized using Docker, which ensures modularity, portability, and ease of deployment. Docker containers also enable scalability, allowing the system to adapt to higher loads when required.

- **Backend Container (Node.js + Express):** Provides REST APIs and serves the frontend application.
- **MSSQL Container (Database):** Manages relational data, including authentication, roles, and community resources.
- **MQTT Broker Container:** Handles telemetry ingestion, normalization, and database insertion.

While SQL Server supports structured data management effectively, telemetry data may be better served by migrating to a **NoSQL model** (e.g., MongoDB, Cassandra) or adopting **cloud-native time-series databases** such as Amazon Timestream or Azure Time Series Insights.

This modular, containerized design facilitates maintainability, supports scalability, and lays the foundation for real-time, citizen-driven monitoring of energy communities.

Currently, the entire system runs on a single EC2 virtual machine (1 vCPU, 4 GB RAM), which is sufficient for a pool of fewer than 100 users. The choice of containerization reflects the system's long-term goal of being continuously developed and extended, with Docker ensuring simplicity for collaborative work and future enhancements.

3 IMPLEMENTATION

3.1 Shelly EM Connection in the User's Internal Network.

The Shelly EM device can be connected to one or two current clamps (50A), depending on whether the user has an individual PV installation. Collective energy communities behave as users without self-consumption, therefore requiring only one clamp. Figure 4 illustrates the general connection scheme.

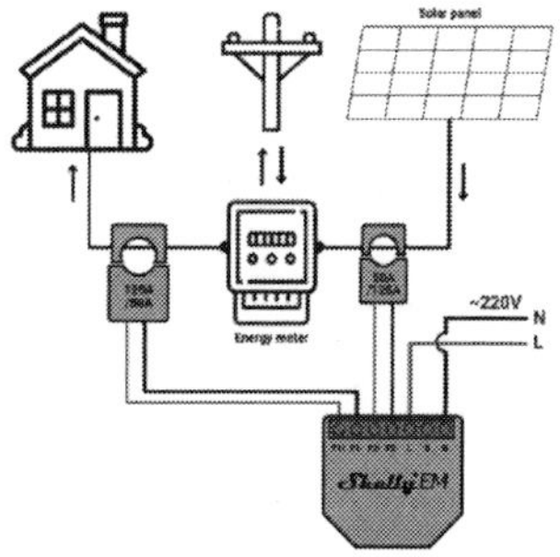

Figure 4: General connection scheme of Shelly EM devices (reproduced with permission from Shelly Spain).

Once the hardware is installed, the device must be paired with the Shelly mobile application (available on iOS and Android). The app requires the creation of a "room," which may represent an entire household or a single room. This design allows users to organize and manage multiple Shelly devices efficiently—up to 40 devices for non-premium users. Within the chosen room, the Shelly EM associated with consumption and/or production is added. If correctly installed, the application displays the detected energy flows in real time (Figure 5).

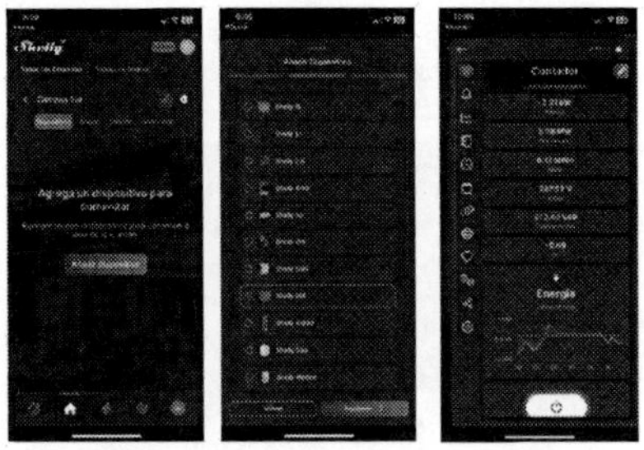

Figure 5: Process of linking a Shelly EM device to the Shelly mobile application.

3.2 Data and Resource Modelling (Business Logic)

The backend data model follows a decoupled design in which the primary entities are roles, devices, and resources, linked to users. The resources are the central elements of the system, shared across authorized users. Each resource has an optional owner_id field; when absent, the resource is considered public and accessible to all users (e.g., the national electricity price monitor).

Currently, three resource types are implemented:

- Electricity Price Monitor: Public resource displaying hourly electricity prices via the official REData API (National Grid Operator). Since data are fetched in real time from the API, no dedicated backend table is required (Figure 6).

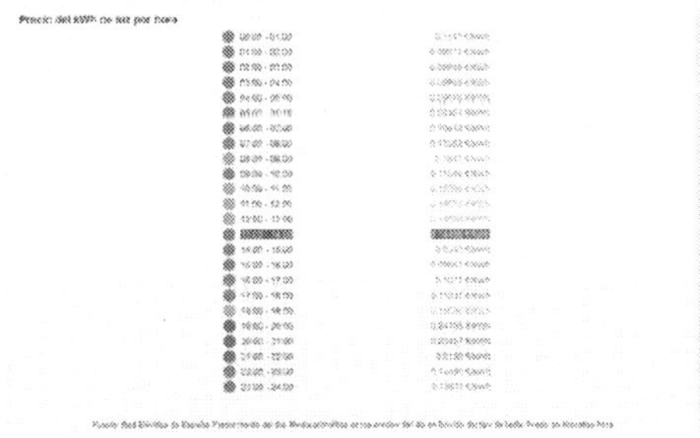

Figure 6: Hourly electricity price data provided by Red Eléctrica (REData API).

- Shelly EM Monitor: Private resource representing telemetry collected by Shelly EM sensors. Data are stored in the em_telemetry database table, aggregated over time, and presented to users as hourly graphs (Figure 7).

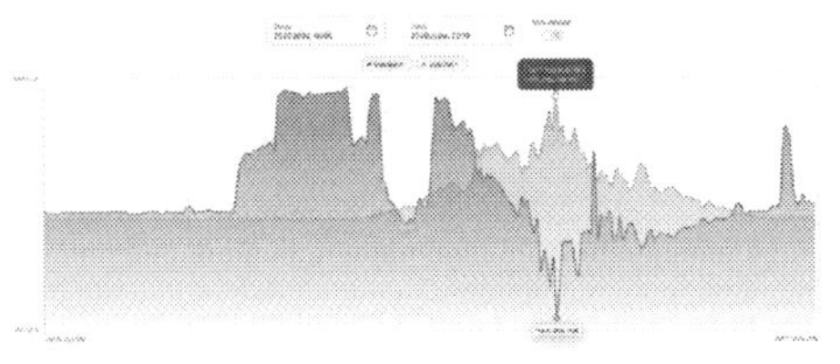

Figure 7: Monitoring resource displaying Shelly EM device telemetry data.

- Energy Community Resource: A collaborative resource with internal hierarchy. Two user roles are defined: administrators and regular members. Administrators can view all consumption and production data, while regular users only see their own. Aggregate community graphs are available to all participants. The database includes two dedicated tables to manage participants and their devices. Figures 8 and 9 show the community dashboard, including aggregated consumption/production, individual user balances, and hypothetical scenarios for collective PV installations.

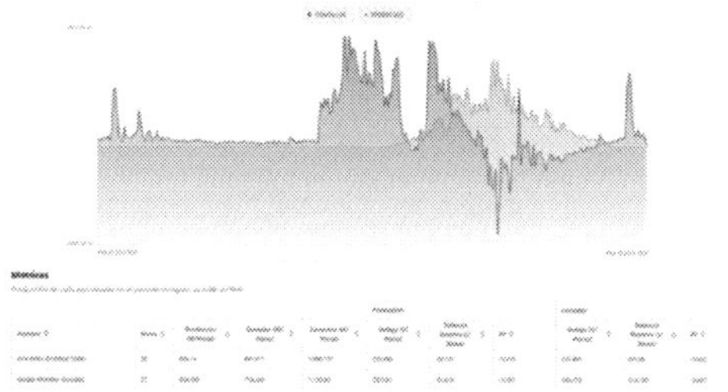

Figure 8: Example of the energy community dashboard from the administrator's perspective.

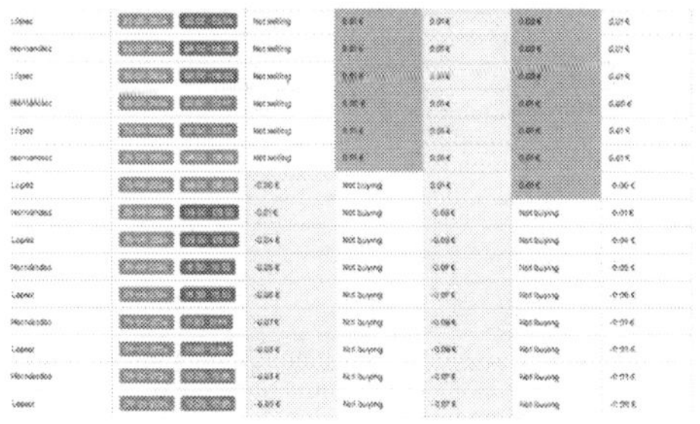

Figure 9: Energy community dashboard showing aggregated data, user balances, and hypothetical collective PV scenarios.

3.3 MQTT Broker Integration

Communication between devices and the platform relies on the MQTT (Message Queuing Telemetry Transport) protocol, widely adopted in IoT for its lightweight, publish–subscribe architecture. In this model, devices (clients) publish telemetry to specific topics, while other clients subscribe to those topics. A central broker manages message distribution, ensuring delivery to authorized subscribers.

In the proposed system, the broker also stores telemetry in the database, making it the central interface between IoT devices and the backend. MQTT was selected not only because it is an industry standard but also because Shelly EM devices support it exclusively.

3.4 Connecting a Shelly EM to the Telemetry Server

The integration of a Shelly EM with the telemetry server involves two main steps:

Step 1: Connect the device to the server. The user connects to the Shelly EM's default Wi-Fi network, which follows

10.4229/EUPVSEC2025/5DO.15.3

the SSID format: shelly<MODEL>-XXXXXXXXXXXX. Credentials must be provided to authorize telemetry publication (Figure 10).

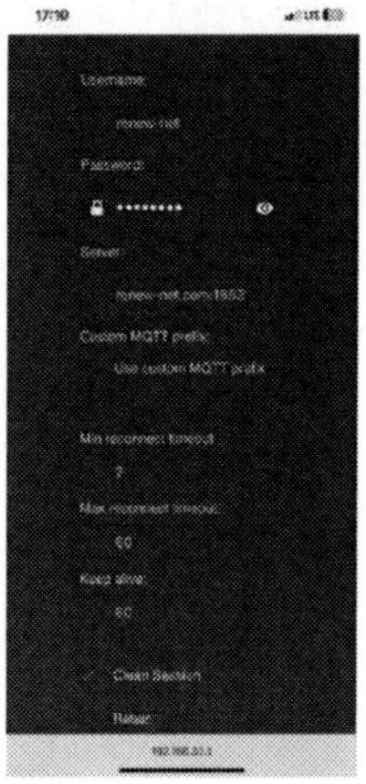

Figure 10. Shelly EM configuration interface for enabling MQTT and connecting to the telemetry server.

Step 2: Integrate the device into the application. Within the platform https://renew-net.com, users register their device under "My Devices" by entering the name, description, and unique identifier, which can be extracted from the Wi-Fi SSID. After this step, telemetry data are transmitted and visualized in the user account (Figure 11).

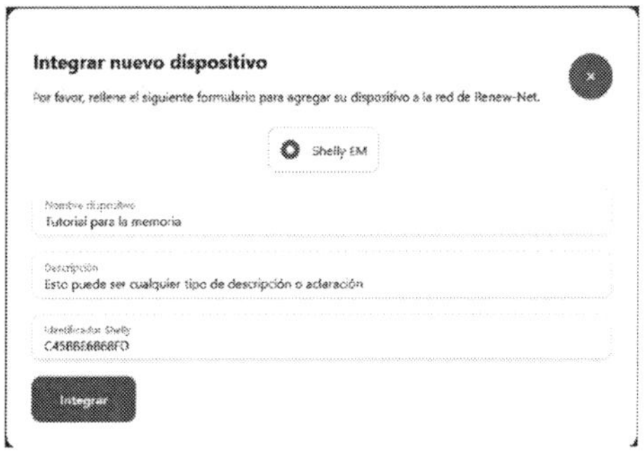

Figure 11. Device integration process within the renew-net.com application.

4 CONCLUSIONS

This work has presented the design and implementation of a modular, open platform aimed at enabling citizen-led energy communities in Spain to monitor both demand and production in real time. The system integrates low-cost hardware (Shelly EM devices) with an MQTT-based communication layer, a Dockerized backend infrastructure deployed on AWS, and a flexible data model that supports individual and collective resources.

The proposed solution addresses key barriers that energy communities currently face: the difficulty of accessing real-time consumption data through retailers or distributors, the lack of universal monitoring tools for production, and the absence of open platforms tailored to community needs. By combining commercial IoT devices with an open software architecture, the system offers an affordable and scalable approach that empowers citizens to actively participate in energy management.

Three main contributions can be highlighted:

1. **Practical integration of hardware and software**: The Shelly EM devices, when reconfigured to operate with MQTT, provide a universal and accessible entry point for collecting real-time telemetry.
2. **Modular and scalable architecture**: The use of Docker containers and AWS resources ensures that the system can evolve, scale, and be maintained collaboratively.
3. **Community-oriented data model**: The introduction of role-based access and shared resources allows for both individual monitoring and collective visualization within energy communities.

The results demonstrate that it is technically feasible for communities to deploy their own open, interoperable monitoring infrastructure without relying exclusively on proprietary or distributor-controlled systems.

Future work will focus on enhancing the scalability of the platform by integrating non-relational databases optimized for time-series telemetry, improving the user interface for broader accessibility, and exploring regulatory pathways that would allow community energy trading at the local level.

5 ACKNOWLEDGEMENTS

This research has been funded by the project "FOREVERPV-CM: For an Environmentally Friendly Photovoltaic Technology" (TEC2024/ECO72), granted by the Comunidad de Madrid.

6 REFERENCES

[1] Interreg Danube Region. (2024) Recent Survey Highlights Potential of Energy Communities in the EU. https://interreg-danube.eu/projects/nrgcom/news/recent-survey-highlights-potential-of-energy-communities-in-the-eu

[2] Schwanitz, V.J., et al., Statistical evidence for the contribution of citizen-led initiatives and projects to the energy transition in Europe. Scientific Reports, 2023. **13**: p. 1342.

[3] ECODES. (2024). Observatorio de comunidades energéticas. https://ecodes.org/biblioteca/documento?v=1&id=643-observatorio-de-comunidades-energeticas&descarga-documento=1&h=5160f5c50cd9e7fc57a8d9236a9640094015a7c59b22d1aa450f648c39166087

[4] European Commission, *Barriers and drivers report*. 2024, Energy Communities Repository. https://circabc.europa.eu/ui/group/8f5f9424-a7ef-4dbf-b914-1af1d12ff5d2/library/22055ff9-1f49-41f8-a321-cbf20ca3d316/details

42nd European Photovoltaic Solar Energy Conference and Exhibition

This presentation was selected by the Sc. Committee of the EU PVSEC 2025 for submission of a full paper to one of the EU PVSEC's collaborating peer-reviewed journals.

ENHANCED VALUE OF GRID-CONNECTED PV WITH BATTERY STORAGE IN A NEGATIVE PRICE ENVIRONMENT

Djaber Berrian, Gaurang Chhapia, Rene vanBaal, Johannes Linder
Belectric Holding GmbH, Wadenbrunner Str. 10, 97509 Kolitzheim, e-mail: djaber.berrian@belectric.com

ABSTRACT: In recent years, the global installed PV system capacity has reached record levels, especially in the EU. This has led to more frequent negative prices due to overproduction. Consequently, utility-scale PV systems are often curtailed during these periods, reducing their value and attractiveness. Our study quantifies the value loss of PV systems during high negative price hours and explores solutions to enhance PV asset value by integrating battery storage. According to our models, PV systems can lose up to 11% of annual production due to negative price hours, while batteries can increase their production by up to 7% under these negative hours. Combining PV with battery storage shows greater resilience to negative price fluctuations, with almost no change in net energy production (PV + battery) during negative price hours.

Keywords: photovoltaic systems; negative electricity prices; battery energy storage systems; energy curtailment; economic valuation; grid flexibility; hybrid energy systems

1 INTRODUCTION

The deployment of photovoltaic (PV) systems has accelerated recently, with an additional 1 terawatt (TW) added between 2022 and 2024, bringing the global total to 2 TW. However, this rapid growth has led to challenges, particularly for grid-connected PV systems, as the number of hours with negative electricity prices has surged, reaching 457 hours in Germany and over 500 hours in Nordic countries [1]. This devalues PV assets and makes them less attractive investments. This study explores methods to increase PV system value by integrating them with battery energy storage systems (BESS) to enhance resilience against negative prices. We examine two market scenarios: low and high negative price environments and assess the benefits of co-locating PV with BESS.

It is widely recognized in literature that integrating a high proportion of renewable energy into the grid will eventually necessitate battery energy storage systems to stabilize the grid against the intermittent nature of these sources [2]. However, BESS can offer various grid services and financial advantages. Therefore, a thorough analysis of PV production and its net value in a negative price environment, as well as the extent to which BESS can enhance the PV net value in negative price environment, remain largely unquantified. This study employs advanced, bankable tools like PVsyst and COSMOS, utilizing 15–20-year price curves to simulate the intricate dynamics of a grid-connected hybrid PV + BESS system operating in a merchant market with access to day-ahead (DA) markets, automatic Frequency Restoration Reserve (aFRR), and Frequency Containment Reserve (FCR). Using these modeling tools, we will examine the extent to which PV value diminishes in negative price environments and how it interacts with BESS. The multiservice optimization approach also enables us to identify the market in which BESS is most productive under varying low and high negative price conditions.

2 METHODOLOGY AND KEY MATERIALS

We have modeled a hybrid PV + BESS plant in Germany based the summarized tools in Figure 1. PVsyst is known for its accuracy [3], it is used to model the energy production of a fixed-tilt bifacial n-type PV plant. We have used the price forecast for energy storage from Aurora research [4]. The energy production and prices curves are then used in COSMOS [5] to model the dispatch of PV + BESS system. COSMOS Uses a multiple linear solver with constraints for dispatching a battery between day-ahead, intraday, and FCR and aFRR markets to optimize battery usage and maximize profits.

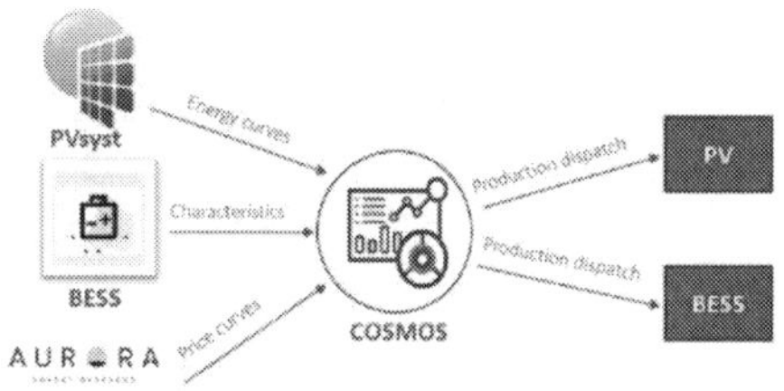

Figure 1 The structure of the modeling tool, inputs and outputs for

In our study we assume PV has priority over BESS, i.e BESS will work around PV production. BESS will deliver at times when PV production does not meet the grid capacity. We considered a 2-hour battery (45MW) with 1.5 cycles per day, and max yearly cycles of 547.5 cycles, and DoD 95%. The round-trip efficiency of BESS is assumed to be 82% including auxiliary losses. The battery and PV module yearly degradation are shown in Figure 2 and 3 respectively. The project is located in Germany and project lifetime is assumed to be 15 years from 2026 to 2040 for BESS and 20 years for PV. After 15 years only PV is assumed to be in operation, while BESS has reached the end of life.

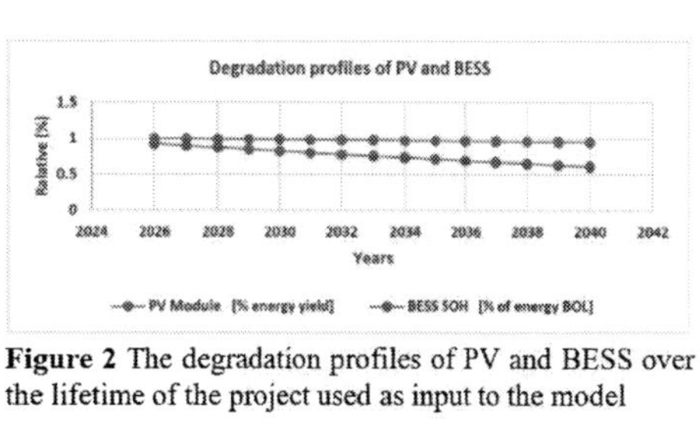

Figure 2 The degradation profiles of PV and BESS over the lifetime of the project used as input to the model

As can be seen in Figure 2, compared to PV modules, BESS degrades much faster than PV modules, after 15 years BESS will have a remaining capacity of 60%, whereas PV modules can deliver 94% of the initial specific energy yield. To assess the impact of negative

10.4229/EUPVSEC2025/5DO.15.4

price curves on the value of PV systems and determine how effectively BESS can enhance PV resilience against these curves, we examined two scenarios. Scenario 1 (S1) spans 15 years with a low frequency of negative price hours, while Scenario 2 (S2) covers 15 years with a high frequency of negative price hours. Negative hours are recorded in the day-ahead market. For instance, the yearly count of negative prices, as reported by Aurora research, is shown in Figure 3.

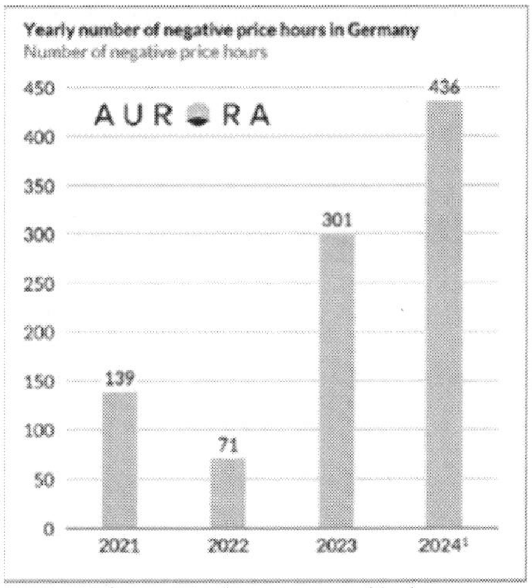

Figure 3 The negative hours measured in day

3 RESULTS & DISCUSSION

We simulated the energy production of PV and BESS over a 15-year period under both low and high negative price environments. The graph in Figure 4 illustrates the relative changes between (S1) and (S2). Over the 15 years, a clear trend emerges: PV production experiences a devaluation ranging from approximately -4% to -11%, while BESS production shows an improvement varying from around 4% to 7%, depending on the year. These results signify the fact that the energy or value lost for PV can be restored or gained again through BESS.

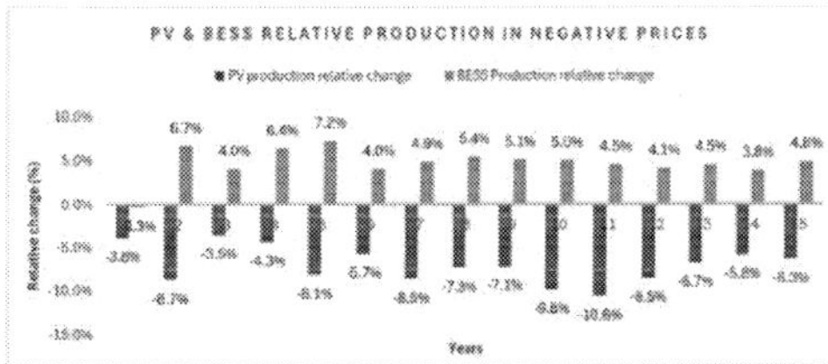

Figure 4 The relative change in energy produced by PV and BESS under high negative price environment

The decline in energy production from PV systems is primarily due to curtailment during periods of negative prices. When there is an oversupply of energy in the market, prices can drop significantly, even becoming negative in recent years. During these times, asset owners reduce PV production. The plot in Figure 5 illustrates the simulation of PV energy curtailed in both low and high negative price environments. As shown, more PV energy is lost (curtailed) in a high negative price environment compared to a low negative price environment. This explains the loss in PV production seen previously in Figure 4

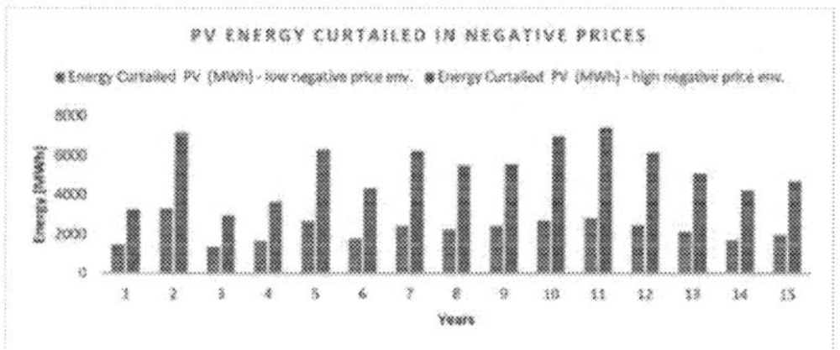

Figure 5 PV curtailed energy under high and low negative price environment

On the contrary, BESS has shown increased production in markets with high negative prices (Figure 4). We modeled and analyzed production across different markets to understand BESS behavior in both low and high negative price environments.

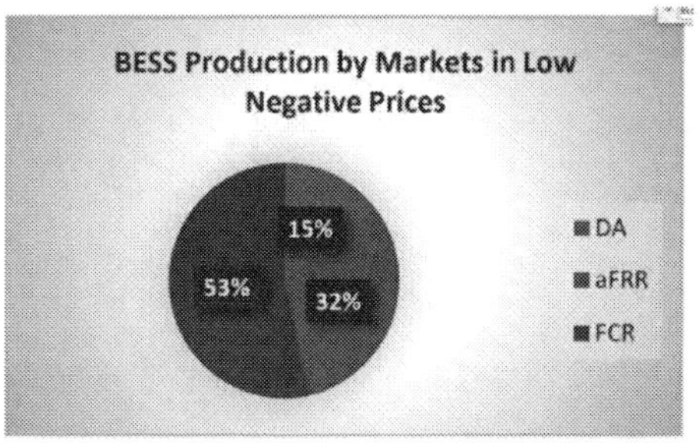

(a)

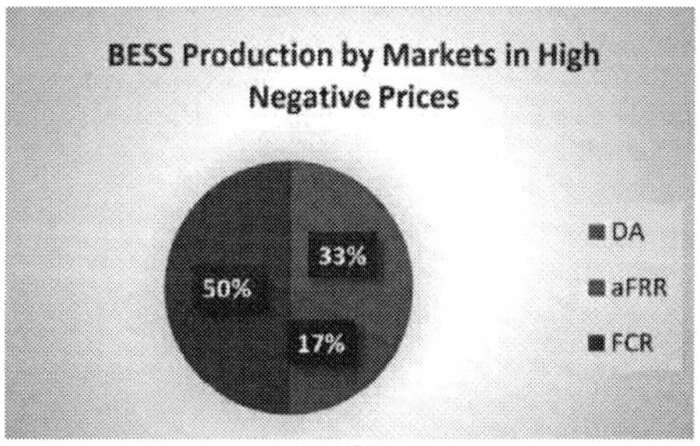

(b)

Figure 6 The distribution of BESS production per market over the project lifetime. (a) Low scenario, (b) high scenario.

The pie charts in Figure 6 summarize the relative production over 15 years across various markets (DA, aFRR, FCR) for both scenarios, S1 (a) and S2 (b). As can be seen, in a low negative price environment, BESS primarily operates in the FCR and aFRR markets, with the day-ahead (DA) market being secondary. However, in a high negative pric environment, BESS prioritizes the DA market over aFRR. This shift occurs because BESS can capitalize on negative prices in the DA market by charging during negative price hours and discharging during positive price hours, thus maximizing profits. In the full abstract, we will explore the techno-economic implications of these behaviors and determine whether the revenue patterns align with the energy production trends of PV and BESS.

Finally, while earlier results indicated that PV systems lose value during periods of high negative prices, an interesting finding emerged when we examined the total production of PV and BESS (hybrid) in both low and high negative price environments. We discovered that the total production remains nearly unchanged, with only a 0.01% relative difference. This suggests that integrating BESS with PV enhances the robustness and resilience of PV systems against negative prices.

4 CONCLUSIONS

The analysis of energy output under varying price scenarios reveals contrasting impacts on PV and BESS systems. Under high-negative-price conditions, PV energy output experiences a notable decline - up to 11% - primarily due to increased curtailment. However, this effect diminishes over time and becomes negligible, reflecting the evolving market dynamics and system adaptations. In contrast, BESS energy output significantly increases under the same conditions. This surge is largely driven by enhanced participation in day-ahead and intraday markets, where BESS capitalizes on price volatility. These findings highlight the complementary role of BESS in mitigating curtailment losses and enhancing system flexibility in a high-renewable, price-volatile environment. The economic analysis reveals that integrating a BESS with a PV plant significantly enhances its financial performance under negative electricity price conditions. While standalone PV systems experience a decline in Net Present Value (NPV) due to curtailment and reduced market revenues; the addition of BESS not only mitigates these losses but also unlocks substantial economic gains. The hybrid system consistently outperforms the standalone PV configuration across scenarios, demonstrating both reduced downside risk and increased upside potential. Moreover, while PV revenues tend to decline under prolonged negative price conditions, BESS revenues improve markedly, driven by active participation in day-ahead and intraday markets. Over time, as market conditions stabilize and negative price events become less frequent, the economic gap narrows. These findings underscore the strategic importance of designing storage-ready PV systems, either through initial integration or future retrofitting, to maintain and enhance asset value in evolving electricity markets.

5 References

[1] Magazine, P. V. " Europe posts negative power prices for 2024 as renewables rise" PV Magazine (2025).

[2] T, Teh, Jiashen, and Ching-Ming Lai. "Reliability impacts of the dynamic thermal rating and battery energy storage systems on wind-integrated power networks." Sustainable Energy, Grids and Networks 20 (2019): 100268

[3] Nussbaumer, Hartmut, et al. "Accuracy of simulated data for bifacial systems with varying tilt angles and share of diffuse radiation." Solar Energy 197 (2020): 6-21.

[4] Aurora Energy Research. Chronos for Batteries. https://auroraer.com/software/chronos, 2025. Accessed July 21, 2025

[5] Clean Horizon, "Energy storage & Price forecast " https://www.cleanhorizon.com/about/, accessed 01.2025.

10.4229/EUPVSEC2025/5DO.15.4

BELECTRIC® MEMBER OF ELEVION GROUP

Enhanced Value of Grid-Connected PV **with Battery Storage in a Negative Price Environment**

42nd EU PVSEC Conference, Bilbao

D. Berrian, G. Chhapia, R. VanBaal, J. Linder

September 25th, 2025

Content

01 Motivation
02 Methodology
03 Results & Discussion
04 Conclusions

Motivation

Motivation

The Solar PV Paradox: Growth & Cannibalisation

"It took the solar PV industry **68 years** to reach **1 TW** of installed capacity - from 1954-2022. It has taken only **2 years** to reach **the next TW (2022-2024)**"
Global Solar Council and SolarPower Europe

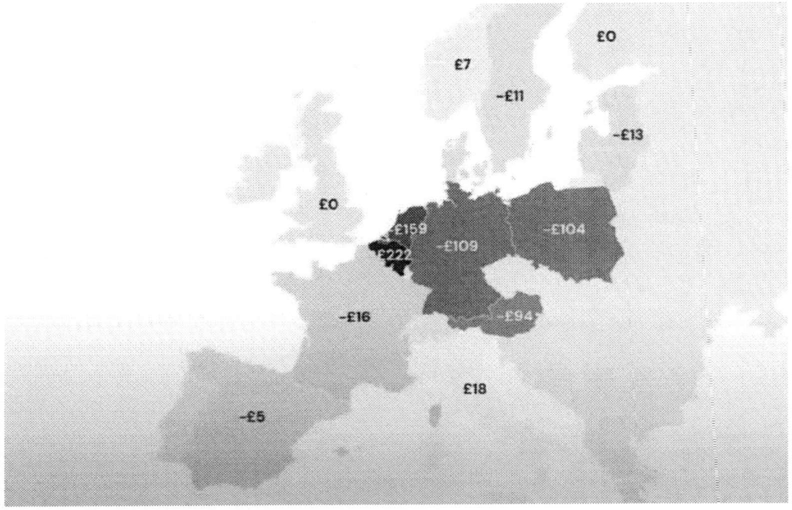

Day-ahead prices 27.04.2025 at 11am April 2025
Source: Nord Pool, OMIE, Iberian Electricity Market Operat

Several EU countries face the challenge of increasing frequency of negative electricity hours

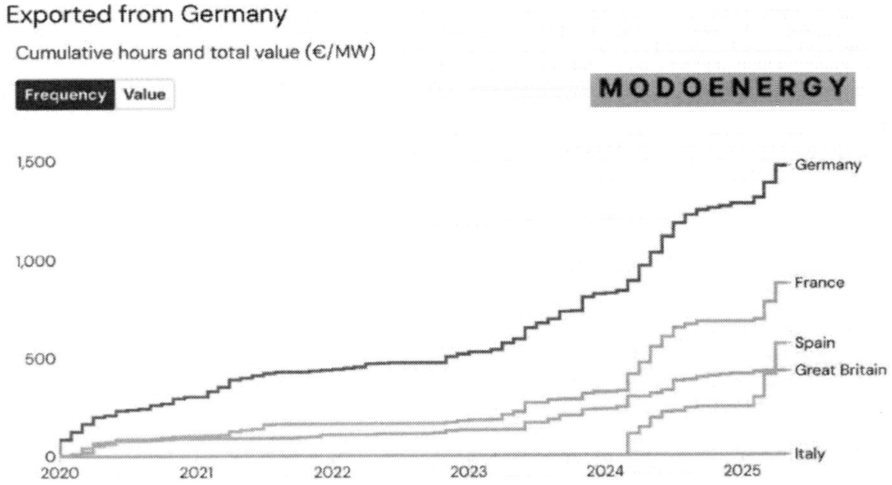

Verband Deutscher Maschinen- und Anlagenbau. International technology roadmap for photovoltaic, 2023. URL https://www.vdma.org/international-technology-roadmap-photovoltaic.

Motivation
The Solar PV Paradox: Growth & Cannibalisation

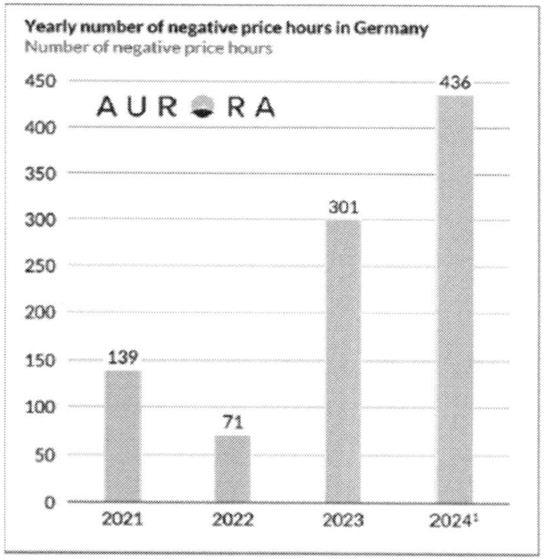

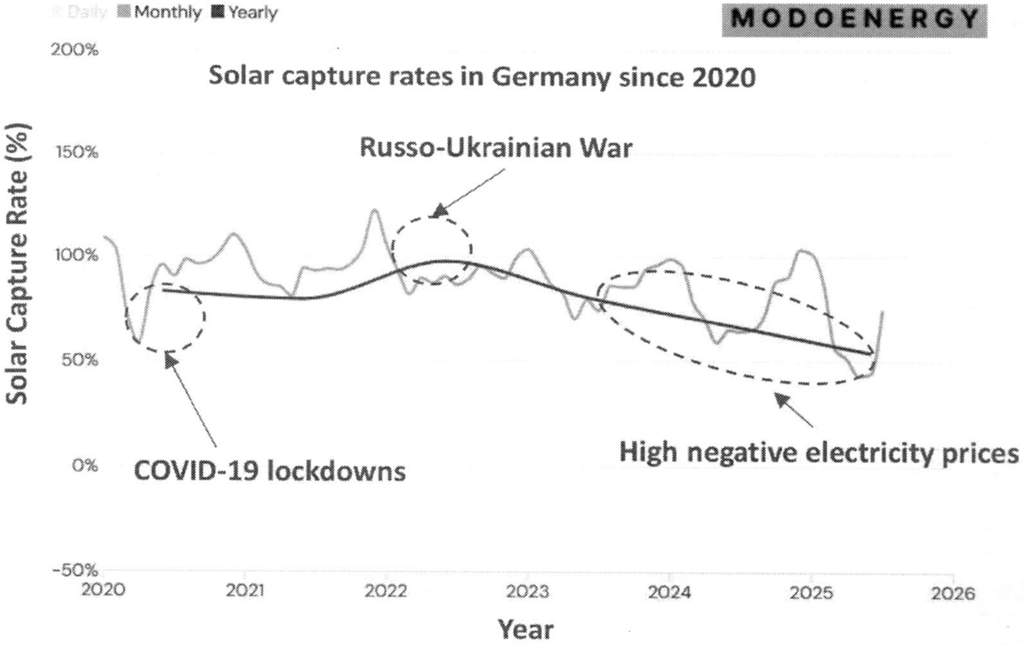

1. What behaviour do PV and BESS exhibit under high negative electricity prices?
2. How can BESS enhance the value of PV assets during periods of negative electricity prices?

Methodology

Methodology
Site Description

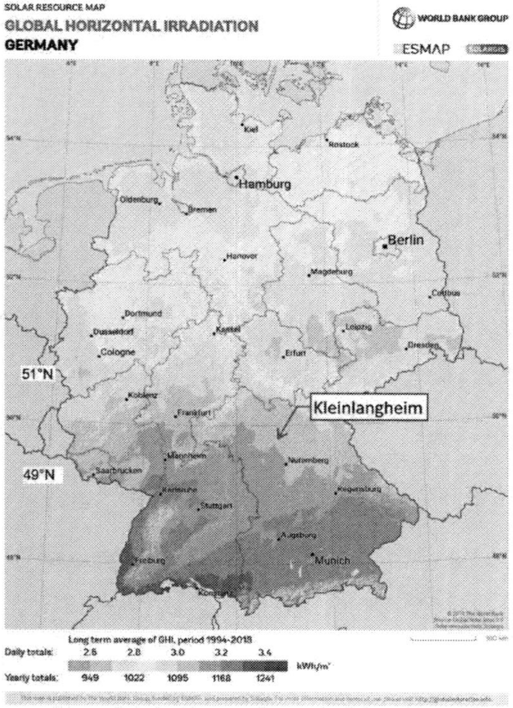

Bifacial Solar Trackers + Battery Energy Storage (BESS)

- 60 MWp PV with 1.2 DC/AC ratio, 2m RS, 50MW BESS, 50 MW Grid
- PV lifetime 30 years, BESS lifetime 15 years, 2H, 1.5 Cycle/day
- BESS + PV Sharing the same grid connection. Focus Front of the Meter applicaiton

BELECTRIC® | MEMBER OF ELEVION GROUP

Methodology
Modeling & Simulation

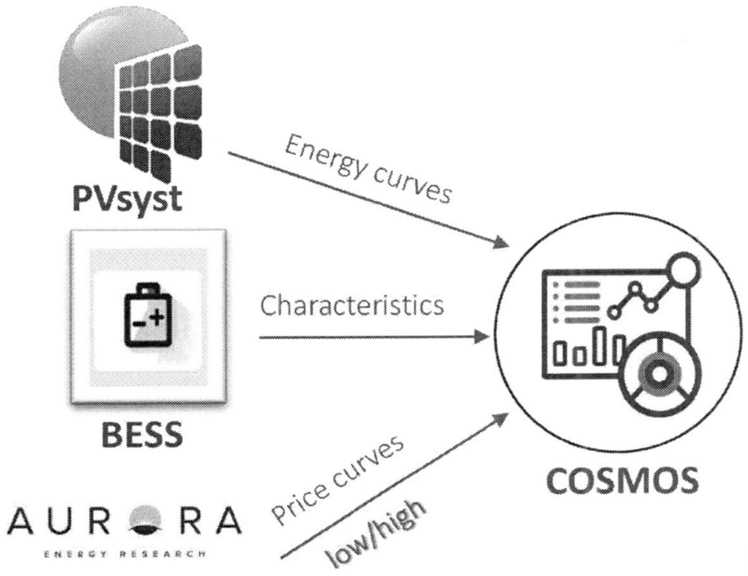

[1] Clean Horizon. Major Upgrade to Clean Horizon's COSMOS Tool. https://www. cleanhorizon.com/news/major-upgrade-to-clean-horizons-cosmos-tool/, 2025. Accessed July 21, 2025.
[2] Mermoud, André, and Bruno Wittmer. "PVSYST user's manual." Switzerland, January (2014).
[3] Aurora Energy Research. Chronos for Batteries. https://auroraer.com/software/chronos, 2025. Accessed July 21, 2025.

Methodology
Modeling & Simulation

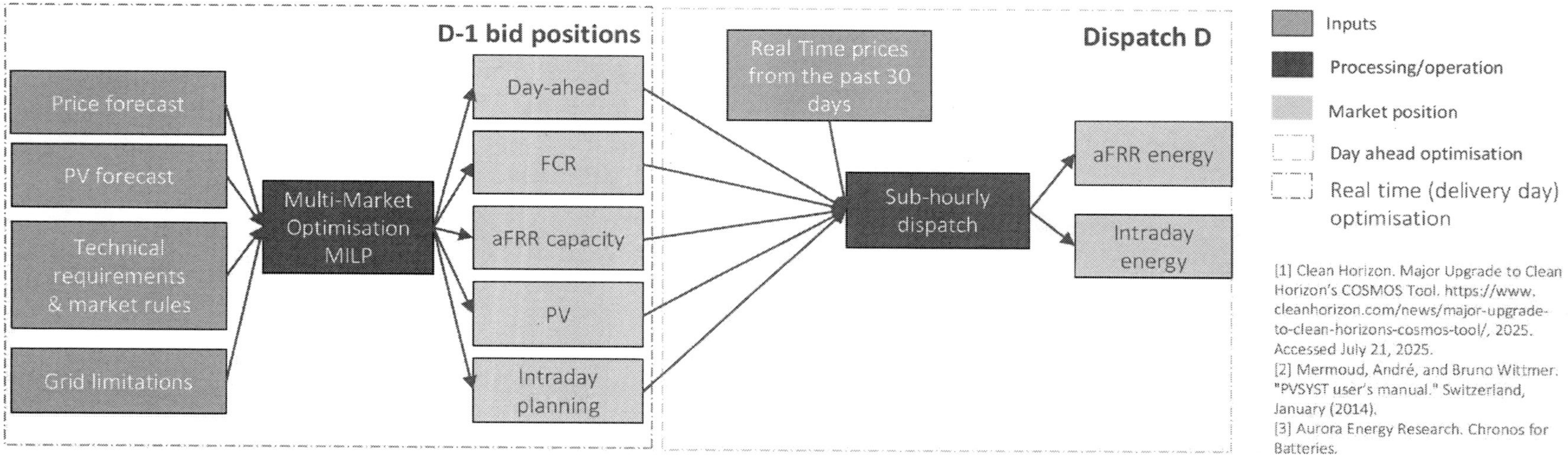

1. Perfect foresight for d-1 (based on forward looking price curves)
2. Imperfect foresight for real-time energy prices: aFRR energy, intraday (based on historical data)
3. PV generation was given priority over BESS for feeding electricity into the grid.
4. BESS can charge from the grid (grey storage)

[1] Clean Horizon. Major Upgrade to Clean Horizon's COSMOS Tool. https://www.cleanhorizon.com/news/major-upgrade-to-clean-horizons-cosmos-tool/, 2025. Accessed July 21, 2025.
[2] Mermoud, André, and Bruno Wittmer. "PVSYST user's manual." Switzerland, January (2014).
[3] Aurora Energy Research. Chronos for Batteries. https://auroraer.com/software/chronos, 2025. Accessed July 21, 2025.
[4] Rachel Locquet. Unlocking bess revenues in europe's key markets. PVTech Magazine, 2025. Published by Clean Horizon, accessed via PVTech.

Methodology
Modeling & Simulation

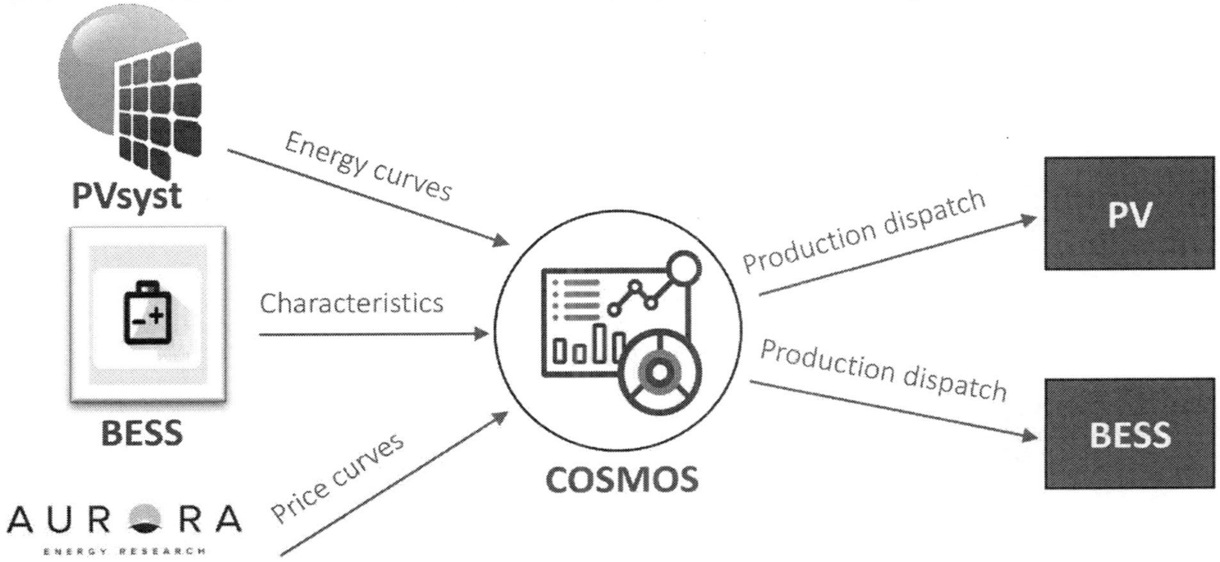

GERMAN BATTERY REVENUE STACK

1. Perfect foresight for d-1 (based on forward looking price curves)
2. Imperfect foresight for real-time energy prices: aFRR energy, intraday (based on historical data)
3. PV generation was given priority over BESS for feeding electricity into the grid.
4. BESS can charge from the grid (grey storage)

[1] Mermoud, André, and Bruno Wittmer. "PVSYST user's manual." Switzerland, January (2014).
[2] Aurora Energy Research. Chronos for Batteries. https://auroraer.com/software/chronos, 2025. Accessed July 21, 2025.
[4] Clean Horizon. Major Upgrade to Clean Horizon's COSMOS Tool. https://www.cleanhorizon.com/news/major-upgrade-to-clean-horizons-cosmos-tool/, 2025. Accessed July 21, 2025.
[5] Rachel Locquet. Unlocking bess revenues in europe's key markets. PVTech Magazine, 2025. Published by Clean Horizon, accessed via PVTech.

Results & Discussion

BELECTRIC

Results & Discussion
Behaviour of PV Assets During Periods of Negative Electricity Prices

PV energy sold under low vs high scenario

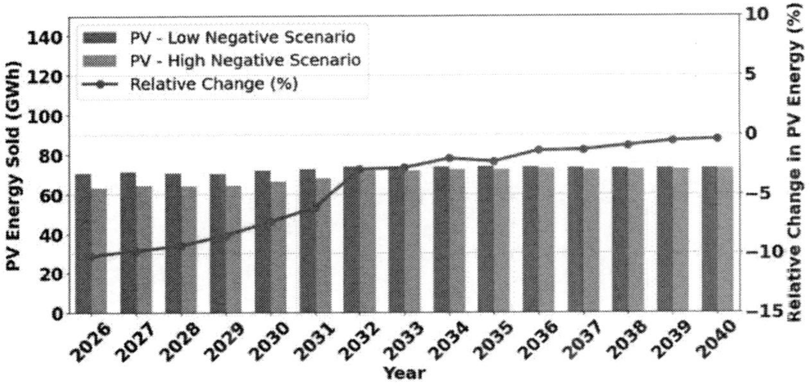

PV energy curtailed under low vs high scenario

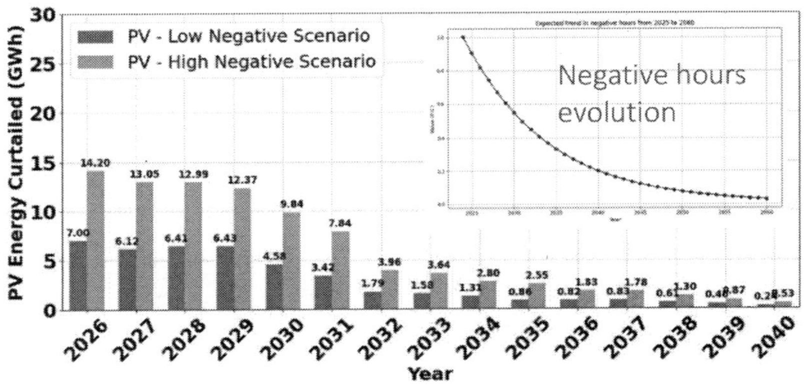

- PV energy sold drops under high negative electricity price scenario
- Largest production drop in first 5 years
- Curtailment drives production decline
- Curtailment gap between high and low scenarios becomes negligible after 10 years

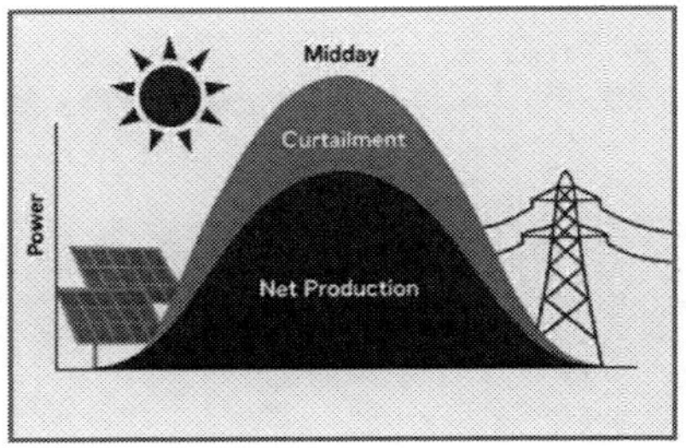

BELECTRIC® | MEMBER OF ELEVION GROUP

Results & Discussion
Behaviour of BESS Assets During Periods of Negative Electricity Prices

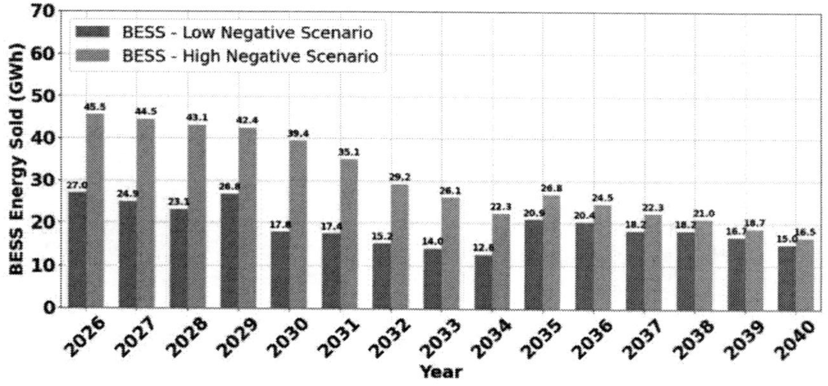

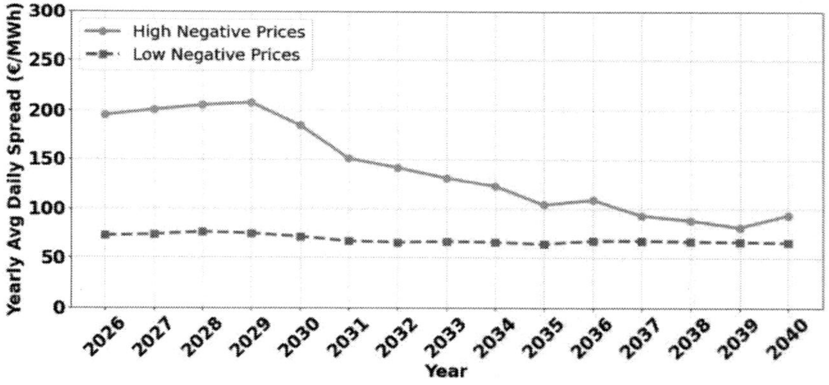

- BESS output declines with aging, possibly market depth
- BESS has higher output under high negative price scenario
- Day-ahead spreads are much larger in high scenario, compared to low scenario
- Frequent negative prices widen spreads, boosting BESS output

BELECTRIC® MEMBER OF ELEVION GROUP

Results & Discussion
Less Curtailment or Additional Revenue Streams?

PV + BESS (Curtailment vs Revenues) High neg. scenario

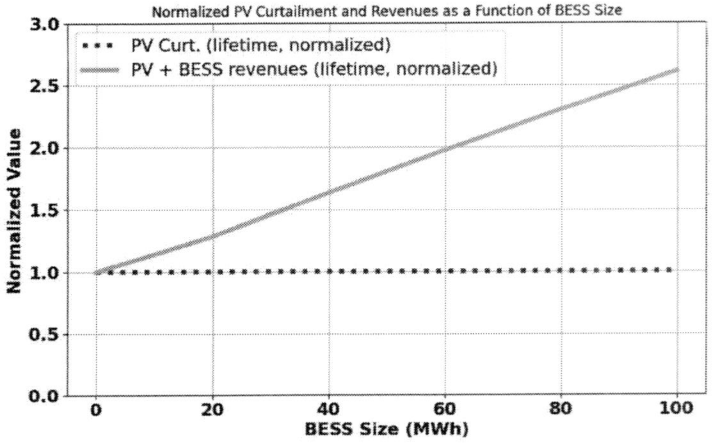

- BESS doesn't cut PV curtailment! <u>(Grey Storage)</u>
- Larger BESS capacity boosts lifetime revenues of the hybrid system (PV + Battery)
- The BESS improves the value of the PV asset by additional revenue stream through day ahead market

BESS energy production in day-ahead – Low Negative Scenario

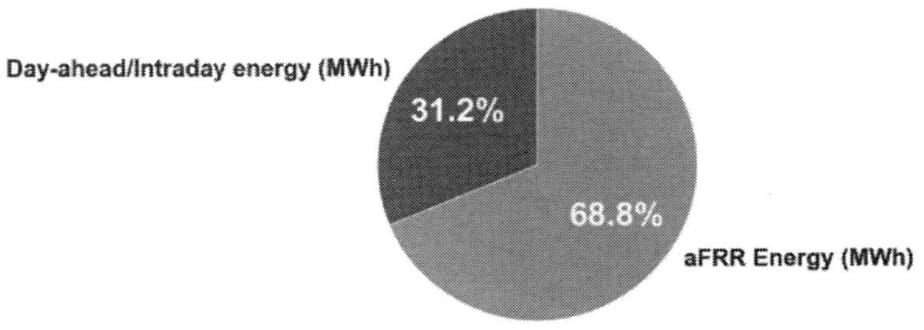

BESS energy production in day-ahead – High Negative Scenario

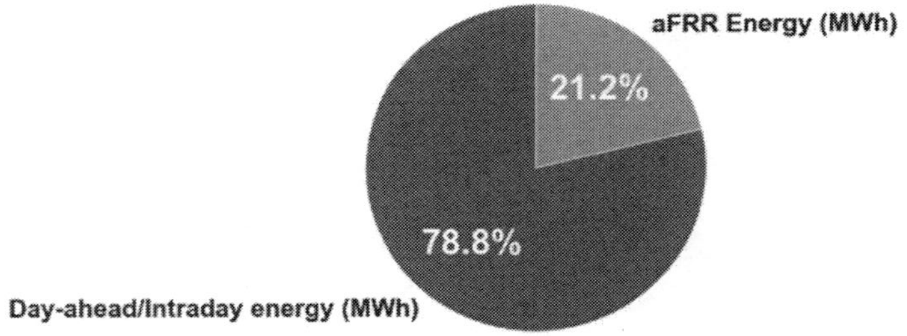

BELECTRIC® | MEMBER OF ELEVION GROUP

Results & Discussion

Robustness of PV economics with BESS Integration

Setup

- AC coupled Lithium Ion Battery
- 2h System, 1.5 cycles per day
- Market entry Jan 2027
- BESS Lifetime 15 years
- PV lifetime 30 years
- BESS to grid ratio, 1:1

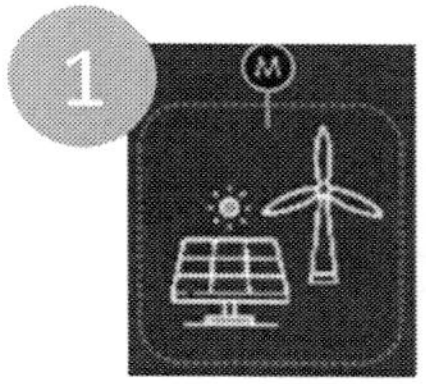

PV – High Negative Scenario

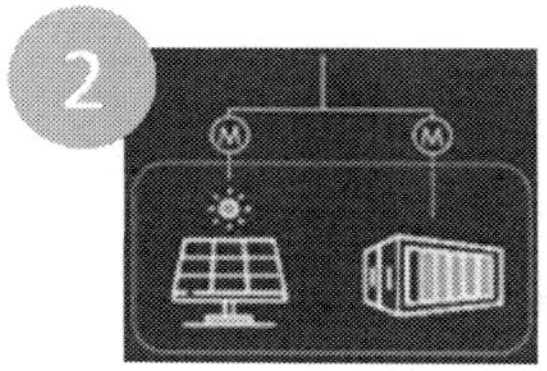

Hybrid – Low Negative Scenario

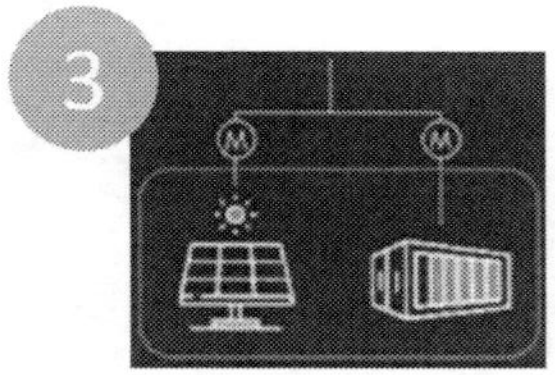

Hybrid – High Negative Scenario

- PV asset value is vulnerable to negative prices
- Retrofitting PV with BESS on the same grid connection enhances project economics

Conclusions

Conclusions
Summary of key takeaways

- **PV value** declines under **negative electricity prices**, while **BESS benefits** from them
- **BESS boosts** PV value **not by reducing curtailment** (grey storage), but by **adding day-ahead trading**
- **Retrofitting** BESS to PV assets on the same grid connection **improves project economics**
- Recommendation to developers, investors: **develop/design** PV projects to be **battery-ready**

Thank you for your attention!

Dr. Djaber Berrian
Innovation & System Design

For any questions
djaber.berrian@belectric.com

BELECTRIC

Together, let's
take the chance
BELECTRIC GmbH
Wadenbrunner Str. 10
97509 Kolitzheim
T +49 9385 548-9000
F +49 9385 548-9040
info@belectric.com
www.belectric.com

TOR VERGATA
UNIVERSITY OF ROME

Infinity, a small-scale prototype for firm-PV generation

Federico Andreozzi

University of Rome Tor Vergata
Department of Enterprise Engineering

ROME TECHNOPOLE INNOVATION ECOSYSTEM

25 September 2025 42nd European Photovoltaic Solar Energy Conference and Exhibition Bilbao Exhibition Center

ESTER

TOR VERGATA
UNIVERSITY OF ROME

Agenda

- What is firm PV generation
- Firm PV for Tor Vergata – Simulation study
- The IN.FI.NI.TY. Prototype
- Experimental parameters
- Results
- Conclusions & future work

ROME TECHNOPOLE INNOVATION ECOSYSTEM

25 September 2025 42nd European Photovoltaic Solar Energy Conference and Exhibition Bilbao Exhibition Center

ESTER

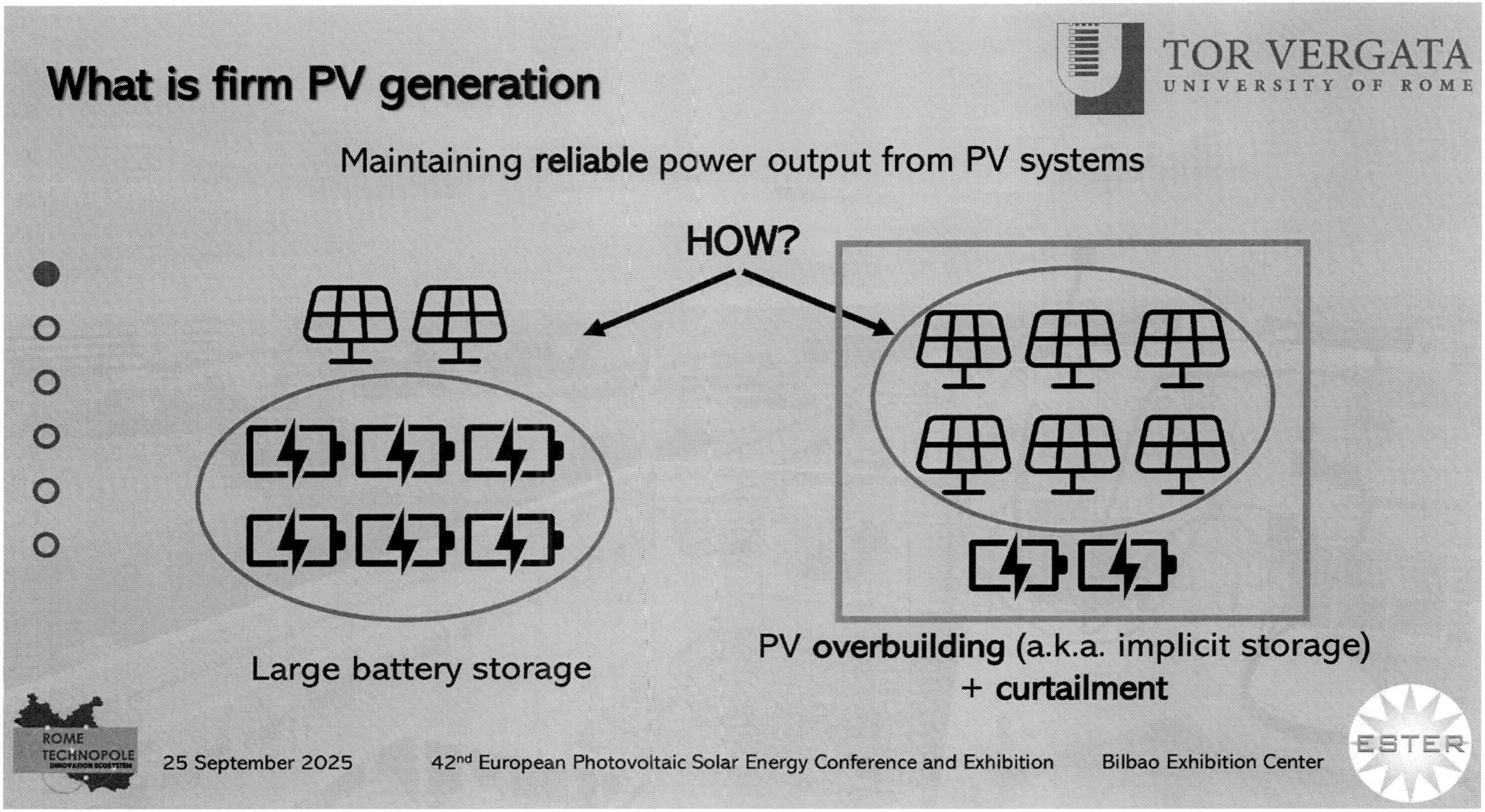
What is firm PV generation
TOR VERGATA
UNIVERSITY OF ROME
Maintaining reliable power output from PV systems
HOW?
Large battery storage
PV overbuilding (a.k.a. implicit storage)
+ curtailment
ROME TECHNOPOLE
25 September 2025
42nd European Photovoltaic Solar Energy Conference and Exhibition
Bilbao Exhibition Center
ESTER

Firm-PV for Tor Vergata – Simulation study

TOR VERGATA
UNIVERSITY OF ROME

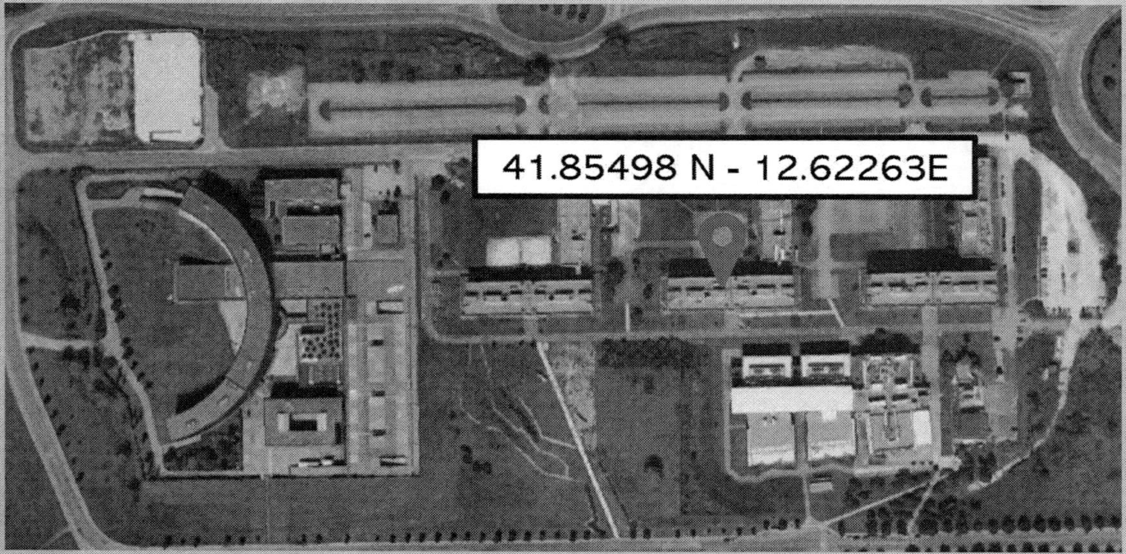

Objective:

Finding the amount of **PV oversizing** and **battery storage** that **minimizes the LCOE** of a PV plant serving the **Engineering Macro-Area** of Tor Vergata University for increasing Self Production **(SP)**.

ROME TECHNOPOLE INNOVATION ECOSYSTEM

25 September 2025 42nd European Photovoltaic Solar Energy Conference and Exhibition Bilbao Exhibition Center

ESTER

Firm-PV for Tor Vergata – Simulation study

TOR VERGATA
UNIVERSITY OF ROME

SP (%)	Installed capacity				Curt. (%)	LCOE (€/MWh)			
	PV (MWp)	BESS (MWh)	OVS[1]	NDY[2]		2023	2030	2040	2050
65	2.3	2.6	1.4	0.25	24	111.9	85.0	80.0	75.0
80	3.0	4.6	1.5	0.44	27	129.7	91.5	84.3	77.1
90	4.3	6.8	2	0.61	45	159.5	107.6	97.7	87.8
100	9.8	16.5	3.9	1.55	72	317.2	207.5	186.1	164.6

[1] Oversizing
[2] Number of days of electrical demand stored

Bovesecchi, G., Andreozzi, F., Petitta, M., Pierro, M., Perez, R., & Cornaro, C. (2025). Flexible photovoltaic generation strategy for Rome Technopole. *Energy Conversion and Management: X*, *27*, 101204. https://doi.org/10.1016/J.ECMX.2025.101204

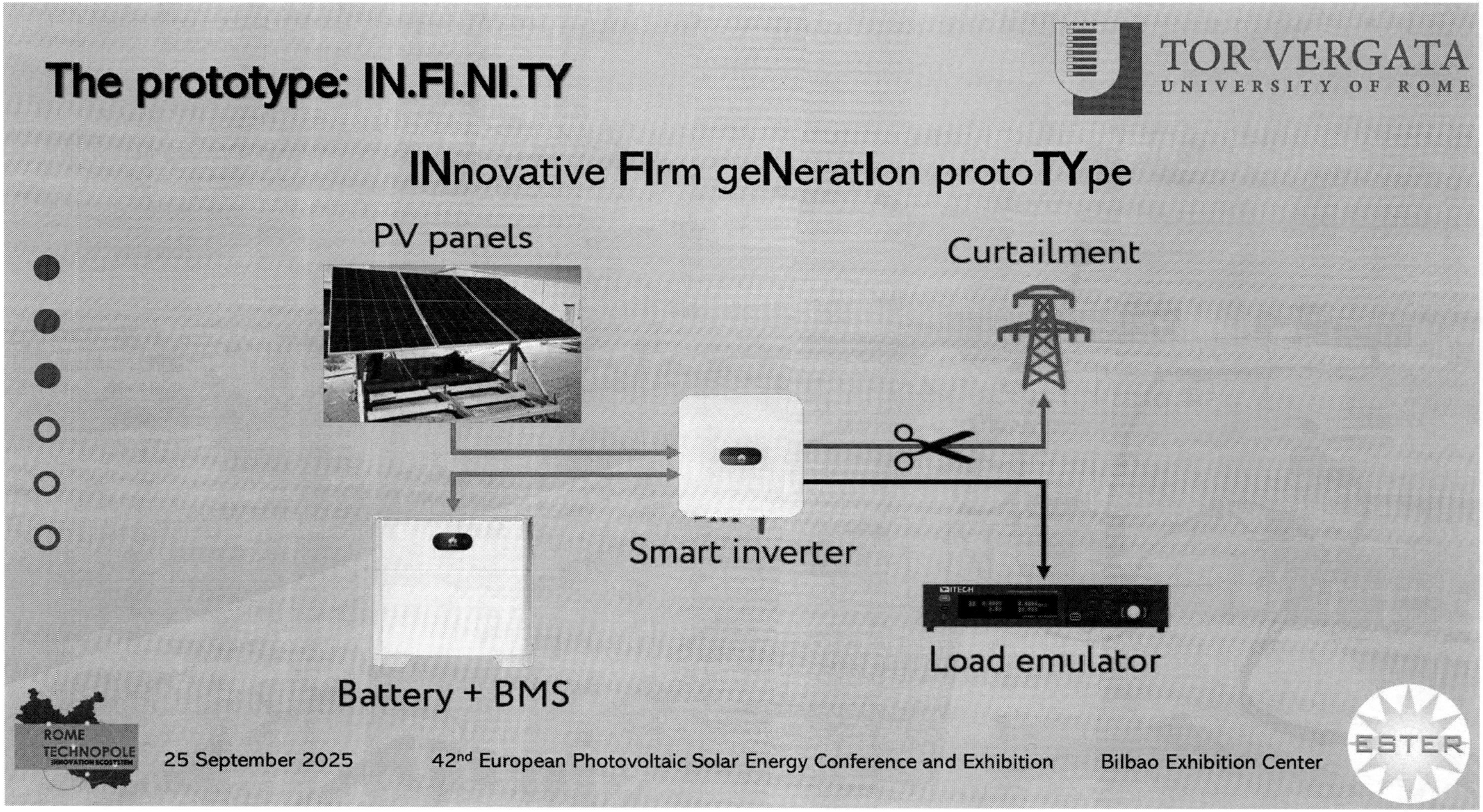
The prototype: IN.FI.NI.TY
TOR VERGATA
UNIVERSITY OF ROME
INnovative FIrm geNeratIon protoTYpe
PV panels
Curtailment
Smart inverter
Battery + BMS
Load emulator
ROME
TECHNOPOLE
25 September 2025
42nd European Photovoltaic Solar Energy Conference and Exhibition
Bilbao Exhibition Center
ESTER

The prototype: IN.FI.NI.TY

TOR VERGATA
UNIVERSITY OF ROME

PV panels

3x 605-W bifacial modules from JA Solar.

Total peak power: **1815 W**.

South-oriented at **30°** tilt angle.

The prototype: IN.FI.NI.TY

TOR VERGATA
UNIVERSITY OF ROME

Battery + BMS

Huawei LUNA2000-5KW-CO

Battery capacity: **5 kWh**.

The Battery Management System (**BMS**) and the inverter manage **power flows to and from the battery**.

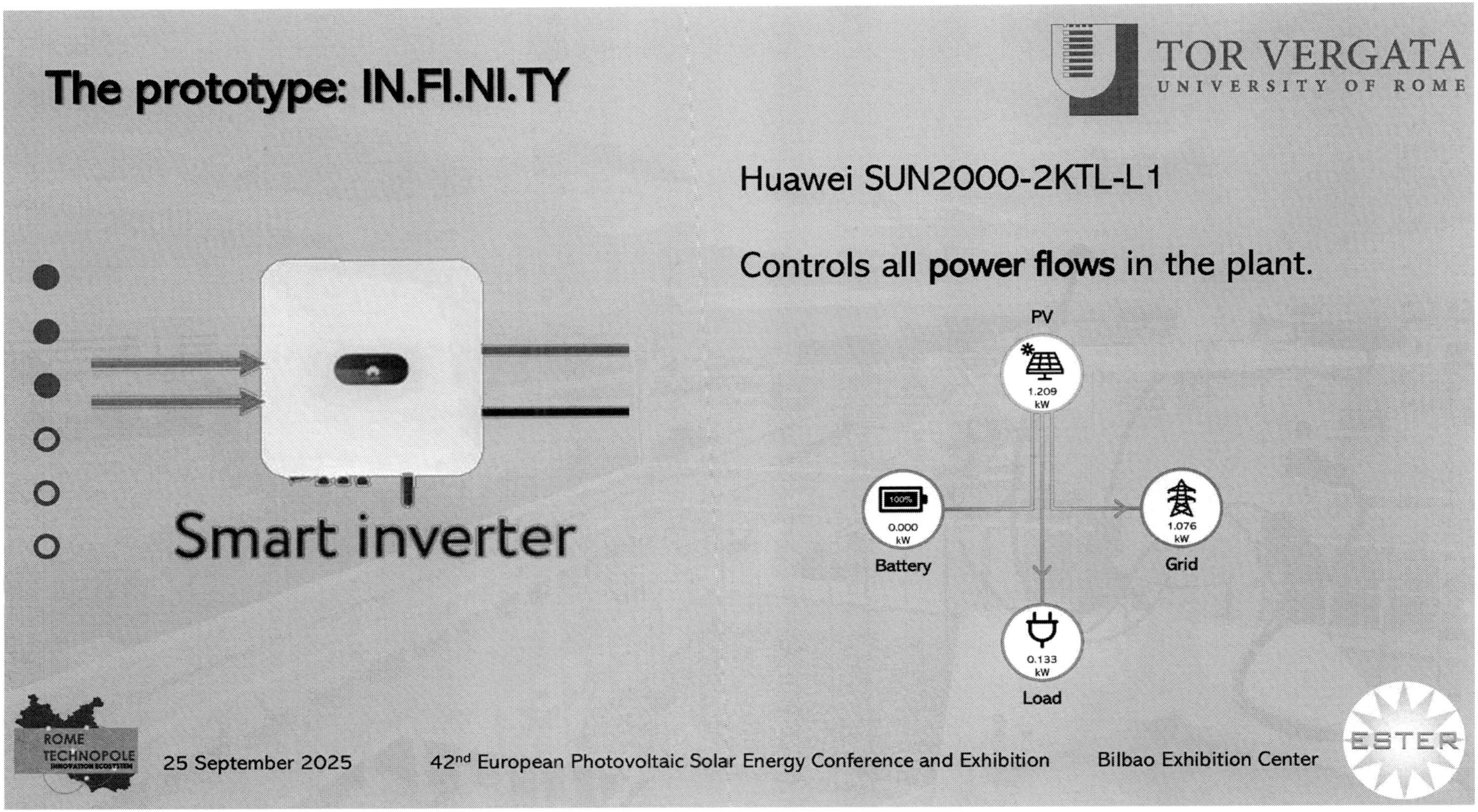
TOR VERGATA
UNIVERSITY OF ROME
The prototype: IN.FI.NI.TY
Smart inverter
Huawei SUN2000-2KTL-L1
Controls all power flows in the plant.
PV
1.209 kW
Battery
100%
0.000 kW
Grid
1.076 kW
Load
0.133 kW
ROME TECHNOPOLE
25 September 2025
42nd European Photovoltaic Solar Energy Conference and Exhibition
Bilbao Exhibition Center
ESTER

The prototype: IN.FI.NI.TY

Load emulator

ITech IT-M3323

Provides **controllable DC power load**.

Power request value **updated live** via MatLab.

Connected to the inverter via a **AC/DC converter**.

The prototype: IN.FI.NI.TY

TOR VERGATA
UNIVERSITY OF ROME

Curtailment

Grid connection to simulate **curtailment** and **residual load**.

Smart power sensor measures **energy to and from the grid** (curtailment and residual load).

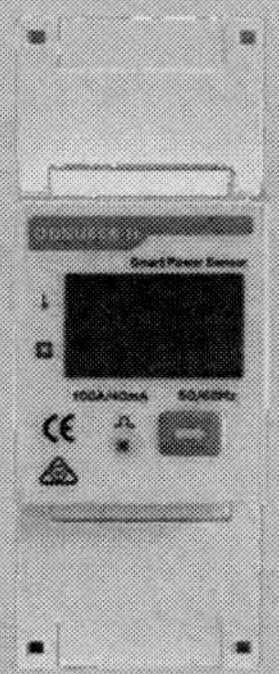

ROME TECHNOPOLE

25 September 2025 42nd European Photovoltaic Solar Energy Conference and Exhibition Bilbao Exhibition Center

ESTER

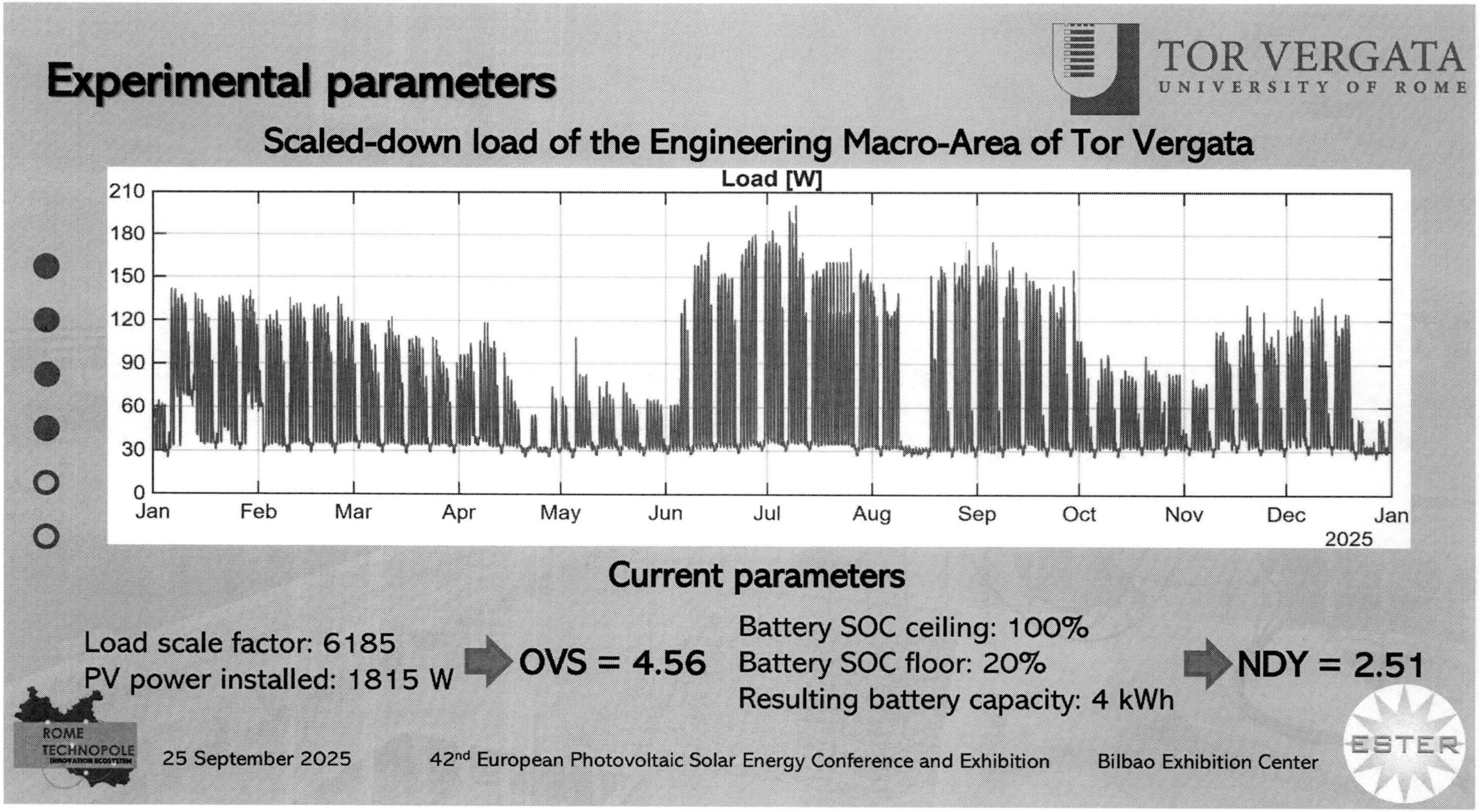
Experimental parameters
TOR VERGATA
UNIVERSITY OF ROME
Scaled-down load of the Engineering Macro-Area of Tor Vergata
Load [W]
210
180
150
120
90
60
30
0
Jan
Feb
Mar
Apr
May
Jun
Jul
Aug
Sep
Oct
Nov
Dec
Jan
2025
Current parameters
Load scale factor: 6185
PV power installed: 1815 W
OVS = 4.56
Battery SOC ceiling: 100%
Battery SOC floor: 20%
Resulting battery capacity: 4 kWh
NDY = 2.51
ROME
TECHNOPOLE
25 September 2025
42nd European Photovoltaic Solar Energy Conference and Exhibition
Bilbao Exhibition Center
ESTER

Experimental parameters

TOR VERGATA
UNIVERSITY OF ROME

Scaled-down load of the Engineering Macro-Area of Tor Vergata

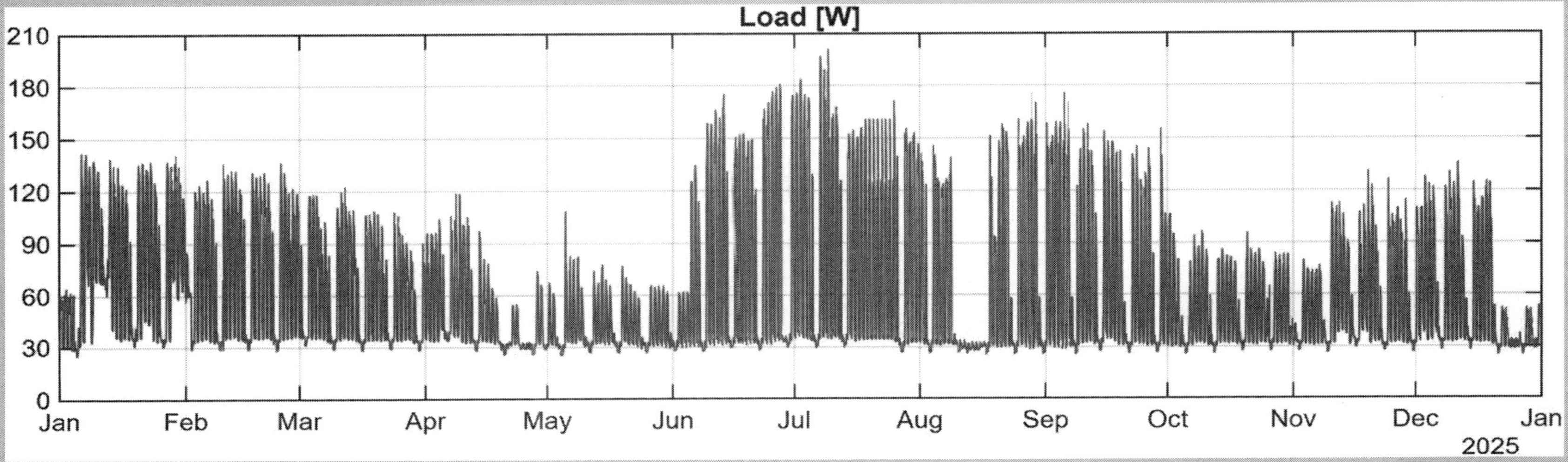

Expected results

OVS = 4.56 → SP = 100%

NDY = 2.51 → Curt. = 78%

ROME TECHNOPOLE

25 September 2025 42nd European Photovoltaic Solar Energy Conference and Exhibition Bilbao Exhibition Center

ESTER

Results

TOR VERGATA
UNIVERSITY OF ROME

Power flows for a **high-irradiance** day and for a **low-irradiance** one

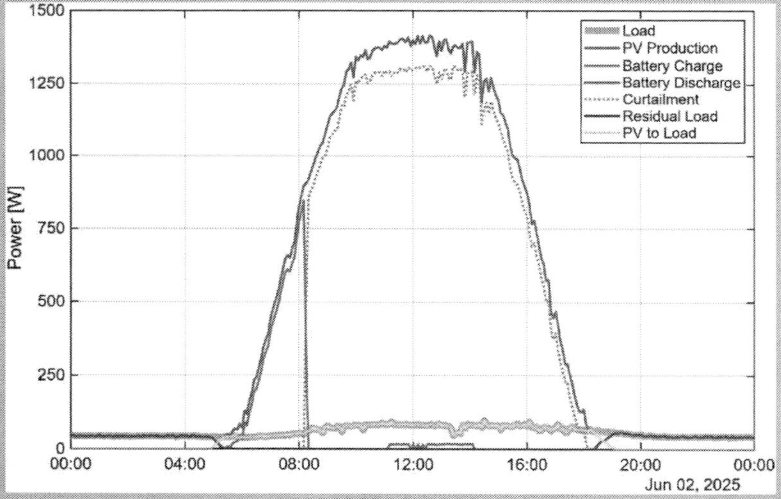

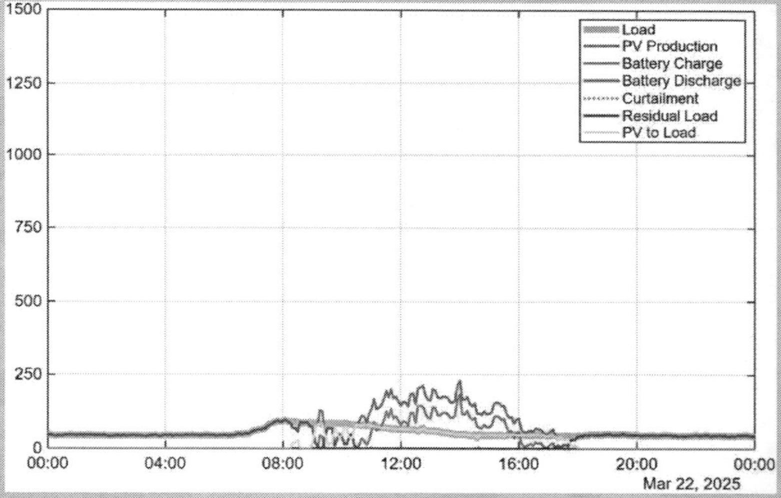

ROME TECHNOPOLE INNOVATION ECOSYSTEM

ESTER

Results

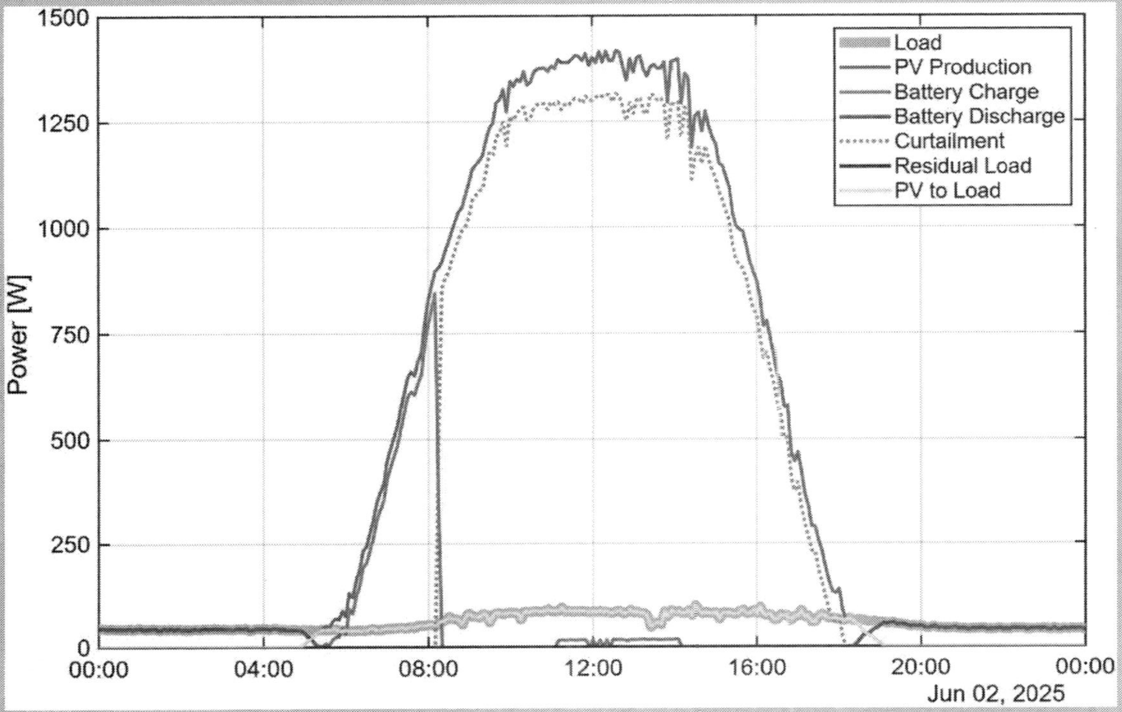

High-irradiance day (02 June 2025)

- > 1400 W peak power generation (11.9 kWh total)
- Battery fully charged at 8:00
- 83.4% curtailment
- Load during the day covered entirely by PV.

TOR VERGATA
UNIVERSITY OF ROME

Results

Low-irradiance day
(22 March 2025)

- < 250 W peak power generation (1.03 kWh total).
- **Battery** only charged from **70 to 76%.**
- **No curtailment.**
- **Load** during the day covered **mostly by PV.**

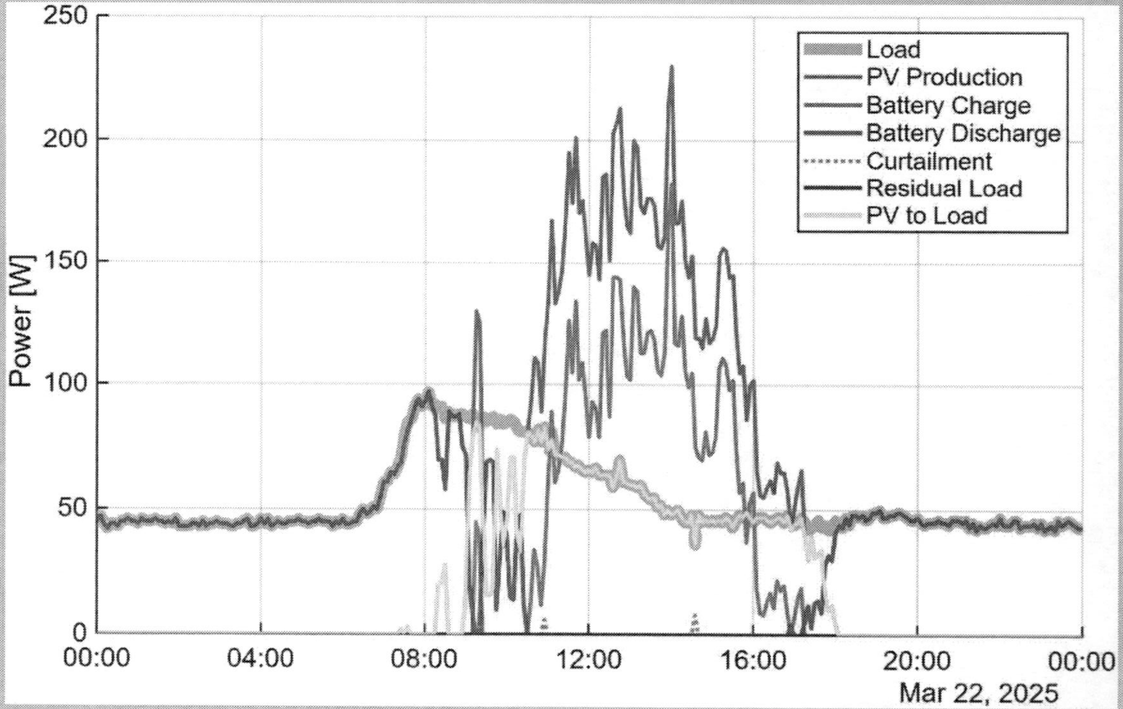

ROME TECHNOPOLE

25 September 2025 42nd European Photovoltaic Solar Energy Conference and Exhibition Bilbao Exhibition Center

ESTER

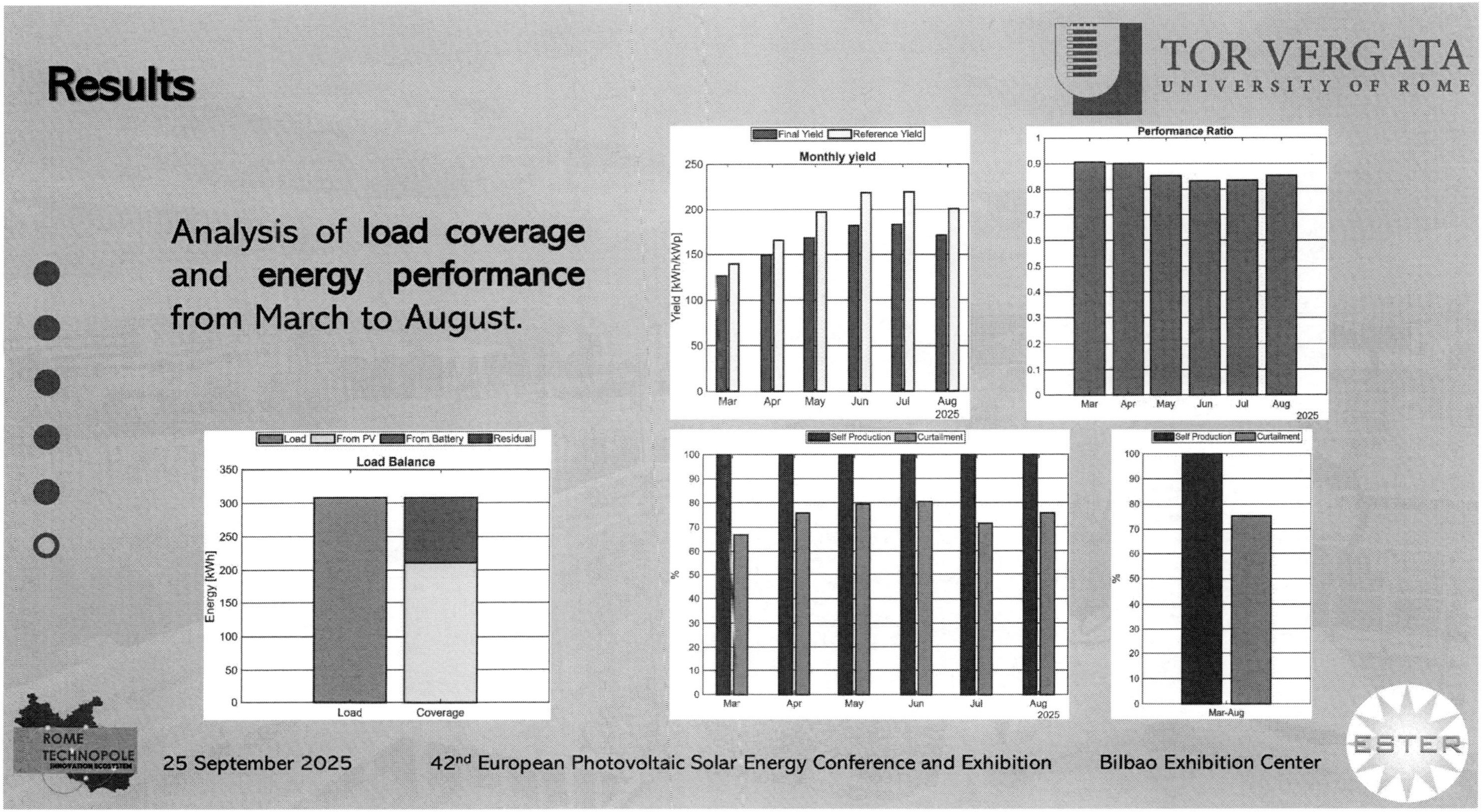
Results
TOR VERGATA
UNIVERSITY OF ROME
Analysis of load coverage and energy performance from March to August.
Final Yield
Reference Yield
Monthly yield
Yield [kWh/kWp]
Mar Apr May Jun Jul Aug
2025
Performance Ratio
Mar Apr May Jun Jul Aug
2025
Load
From PV
From Battery
Residual
Load Balance
Energy [kWh]
Load
Coverage
Self Production
Curtailment
%
Mar Apr May Jun Jul Aug
2025
Self Production
Curtailment
%
Mar-Aug
ROME TECHNOPOLE
25 September 2025
42nd European Photovoltaic Solar Energy Conference and Exhibition
Bilbao Exhibition Center
ESTER

Results

TOR VERGATA
UNIVERSITY OF ROME

PV performance

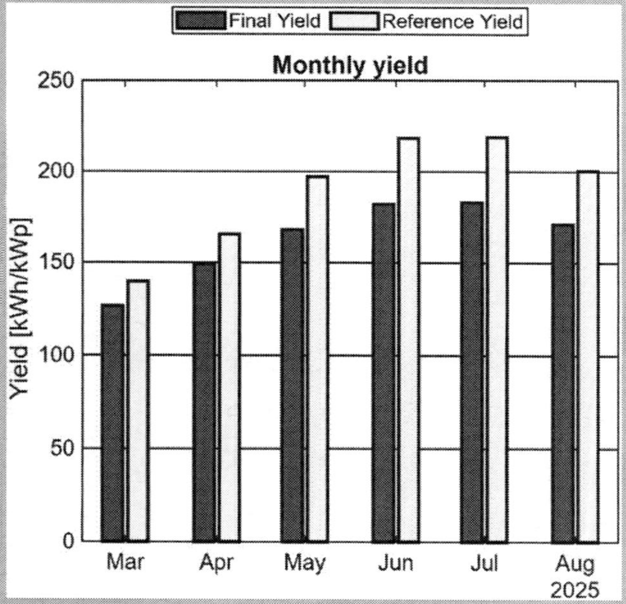

Yield ranging between **126.6 kWh/kWp** (March) and **183.1 kWh/kWp** (July).

PR between 0.8 and 0.9, peaking at **0.91** in March.

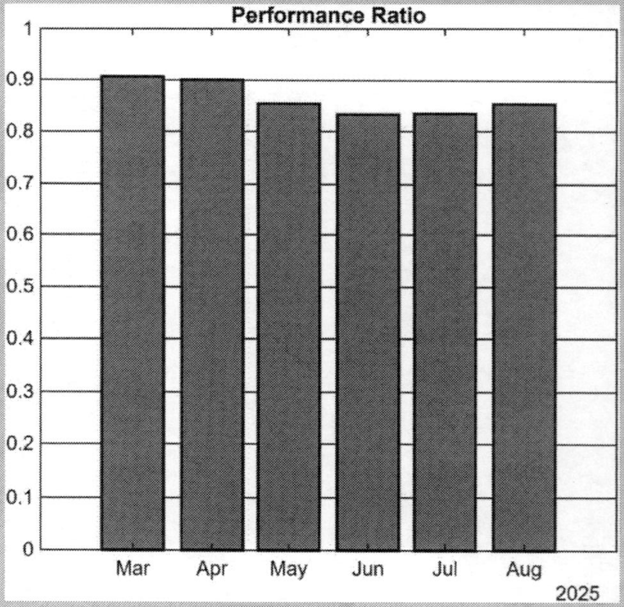

ROME TECHNOPOLE INNOVATION ECOSYSTEM

25 September 2025 42nd European Photovoltaic Solar Energy Conference and Exhibition Bilbao Exhibition Center

ESTER

Results

TOR VERGATA
UNIVERSITY OF ROME

Load coverage

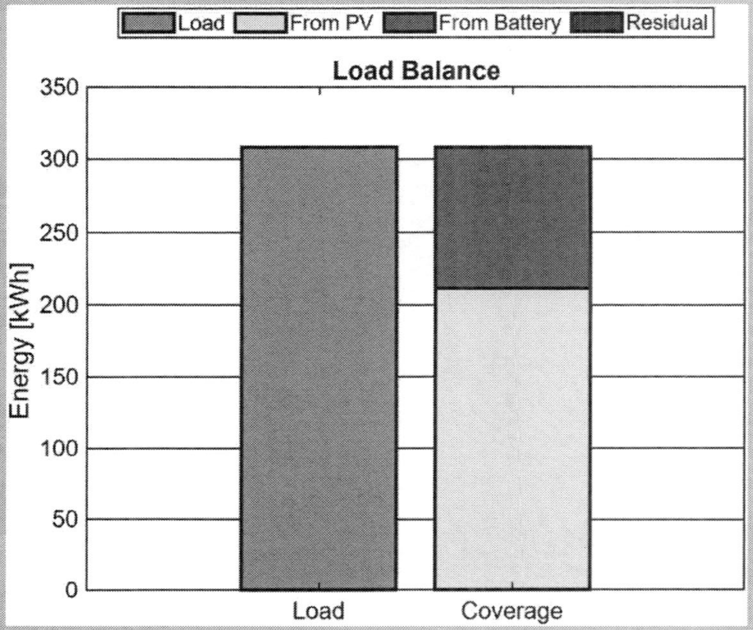

Load **fully covered** by the **PV+BESS** combination.

No grid support needed at any point.

Results

TOR VERGATA
UNIVERSITY OF ROME

Plant percentage indicators

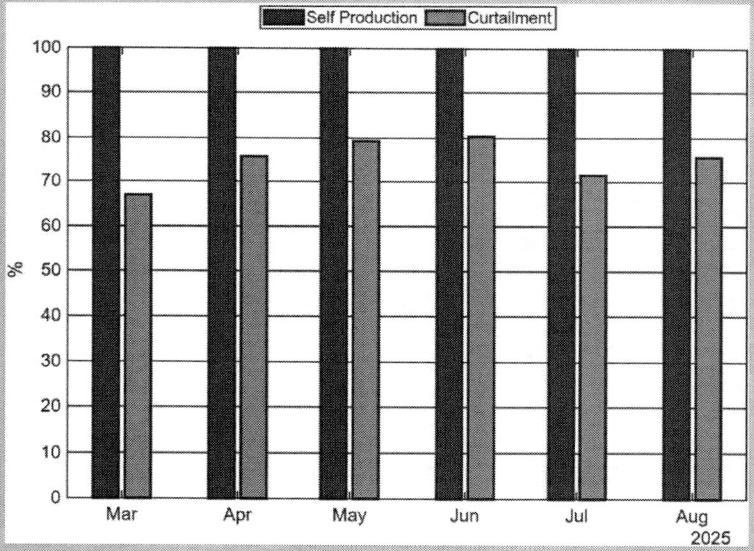

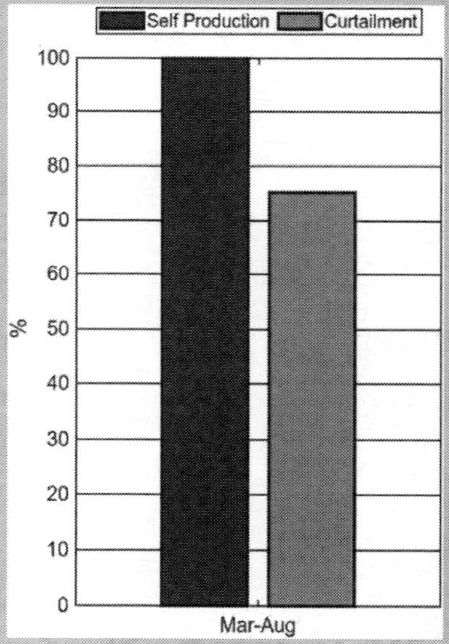

Self production stable at **100%** every month.

Curtailment peaked at **80.4% in June**, averaging at **75.3%** for the whole period.

ROME TECHNOPOLE

25 September 2025 42nd European Photovoltaic Solar Energy Conference and Exhibition Bilbao Exhibition Center

ESTER

Results

TOR VERGATA
UNIVERSITY OF ROME

Analysis of the battery's State Of Charge (SOC)

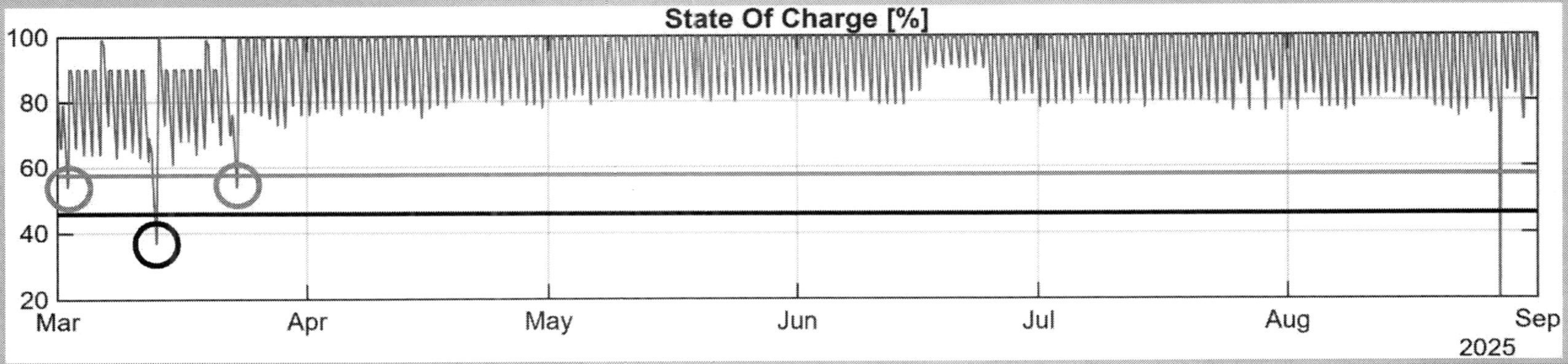

The battery **fully depleted** its charge only **once** (27-Aug).

This was due to a **communication error** that required inverter reset.

Lowering target SP to 99.5% reduces NDY to 1.76 (2.8 kWh – 100% to 44%).

SOC only went below 44% twice (13-Mar, 27-Aug).

Matching the simulation SP target (100% ± 1.5%) brings NDY down to 1.3 (2.1 kWh – 100% to 58%).

SOC only went below 58% four times (02-Mar, 13-Mar, 23-Mar, 27-Aug)

TOR VERGATA
UNIVERSITY OF ROME

Conclusions & future work

- The prototype was able to meet the electrical demand for the whole period, achieving the expected **100% Self Production**.
- Even on **low-irradiance days**, the **load was mostly covered** by the oversized PV during daylight hours.
- Average **curtailment** was **in line with expectations** (75.3% vs. 78%).
- **Battery capacity could be reduced** by 30-50 % without significantly hindering Self Production.

What's next?

- Testing during the **winter period**, when **less sunlight** is expected.
- **LCOE analysis** once enough data is available.
- Testing of **different load profiles**.
- **Upscaling** to a larger plant size.

ROME TECHNOPOLE INNOVATION ECOSYSTEM

25 September 2025 42nd European Photovoltaic Solar Energy Conference and Exhibition Bilbao Exhibition Center

ESTER

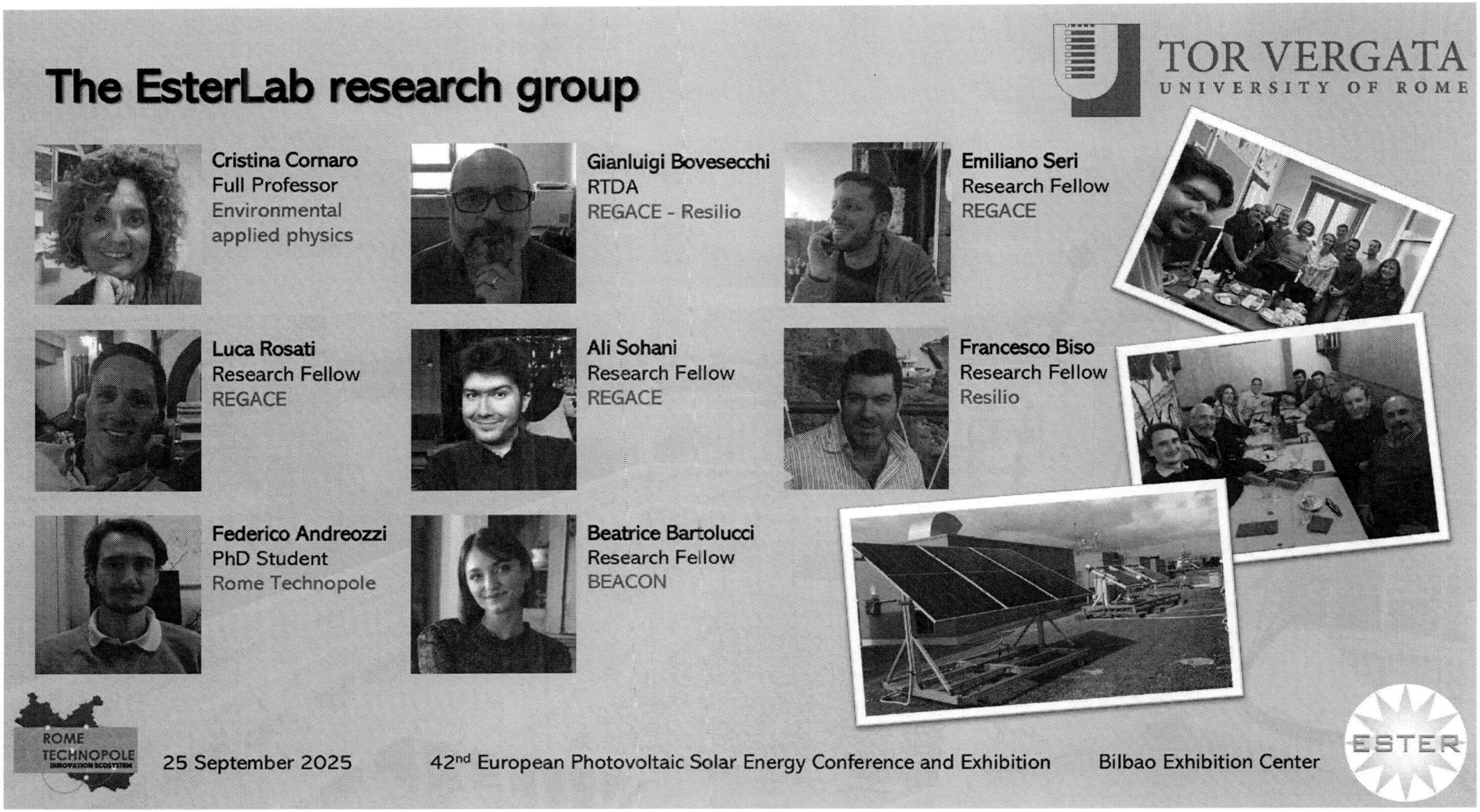
The EsterLab research group
TOR VERGATA
UNIVERSITY OF ROME
Cristina Cornaro
Full Professor
Environmental applied physics
Gianluigi Bovesecchi
RTDA
REGACE - Resilio
Emiliano Seri
Research Fellow
REGACE
Luca Rosati
Research Fellow
REGACE
Ali Sohani
Research Fellow
REGACE
Francesco Biso
Research Fellow
Resilio
Federico Andreozzi
PhD Student
Rome Technopole
Beatrice Bartolucci
Research Fellow
BEACON
ROME TECHNOPOLE
25 September 2025
42nd European Photovoltaic Solar Energy Conference and Exhibition
Bilbao Exhibition Center
ESTER

ROME
TECHNOPOLE
INNOVATION ECOSYSTEM
TOR VERGATA
UNIVERSITY OF ROME
ESTER
Thank you!
My contact:
federico.andreozzi@uniroma2.it
Follow us on Instagram:
@esterlab.unitov
Visit our website:
www.ester.uniroma2.it
ESTERLAB.UNITOV

42nd European Photovoltaic Solar Energy Conference and Exhibition

This presentation was selected by the Sc. Committee of the EU PVSEC 2025 for submission of a full paper to one of the EU PVSEC's collaborating peer-reviewed journals.

ECO-EFFICIENT PROCESSING AND REFINING ROUTES FOR SECONDARY RAW MATERIALS FROM SILICON INGOT AND WAFER MANUFACTURING

Martin Bellmann*[1], Berhane Darsene Dimd[1], Anne-Karin Søiland[2], Arne Dahle[3], C. Landaas[4], Victorien Iwaszko[5], Rene Peche[6], Wolfram Palitzsch[7], Philippe Lenain[8], Iratxe de Meatza[9], Theodora Kyratsi[10], Liu Huiping[11], Emanuele Milani[12], Guy Chichignoud[13], Stefan Fischer[14], Almut Schwenke[15], Eirik Nordboe[16], Marco Pieterse[17], Roland Riva[18]

[1]SINTEF, Trondheim Norway, [2]ReSiTec AS, Kristiansand Norway, [3]NorSun, Oslo Norway, [4]Northern Silicon, Meråker Norway, [5]ROSI Solar, Saint-Martin-d'Hères France, [6]bifa Umweltinstitut GmbH, Augsburg Germany, [7]LuxChemtech GmbH, Freiberg Germany, [8]benkei, Lyon France, [9]CIDETEC, San Sebastian Spain, [10]University of Cyprus, Nicosia Cyprus, [11]GRÄNGES, Finspång Sweden, [12]Marelli Europe SPA, Venaria Reala Italy, [13]Institut Polytechnique De Grenobl, Grenoble France, [14]SGL Carbon GmbH, Meitingen Germany, [15]SGL Battery Solutions, Meitingen Germany, [16]Fiven Norge AS, Lillesand Norway, [17]Chemconserve, Bussum The Netherlands, [18]Commissariat à l'énergie atomique et aux énergies alternatives, Le Bourget-du-Lac France

ABSTRACT: In the ICARUS project, 18 European partners collaborate to develop and scale innovative technologies for recovering and refining secondary raw materials from silicon photovoltaic (PV) ingot and wafer manufacturing. The production of PV modules generates significant quantities of waste, particularly silicon kerf, graphite, and silica residues. ICARUS aims to transform these waste streams into high-value secondary materials suitable for reintegration into the PV value chain and other industrial applications. Four industrial pilot-scale processes were developed, targeting the purification and reuse of these materials. Results from the pilots demonstrate both the technical feasibility and economic potential of substituting these recovered materials for virgin and critical raw materials. This work provides a viable pathway toward a more resource-efficient and circular PV manufacturing industry.
Keywords: Photovoltaics, Silicon, Silicon Kerf, Silica, Recycling, Circularity

1 INTRODUCTION

Global deployment of photovoltaic (PV) technology continues to accelerate, driven by declining module costs and net-zero emission targets. Alongside this growth, the silicon PV value chain generates substantial production wastes during ingot manufacturing and wafering. These include silicon kerf losses from wafering, as well as silica and graphite components from crystallization furnaces. A significant proportion of these wastes is either disposed of in landfills or diverted into low-value applications. Such practices not only result in the loss of potentially valuable materials but also conflict with sustainability and circular economy principles.

In general the literature demonstrates clear progress in recovering high-purity products from silicon kerf [1], silica waste [2], and graphite [3]. However, current methods generally yield secondary materials with limited recovery efficiency and insufficient quality for high-value reuse. In addition, significant recycling techniques are not yet scalable to industrial level due to their complexity and multi-stage approach. The ICARUS project addresses this challenge by developing and scaling industrially relevant routes for the recovery, refinement, and reintegration of secondary raw materials from ingot and wafer manufacturing.

The ICARUS project is a collaborative effort between 18 EU (European Union) partners. The work focuses on developing targeted technological solutions to refine and reuse silicon kerf, graphite, and silica wastes from PV manufacturing. Four industrial pilot technologies have been designed and tested at pilot scale to assess improved recycling processes, with the potential to outperform existing methods. The main goal is the production of high-purity, high-value secondary raw materials, thereby addressing the quality limitations often encountered in current recycling approaches. By 2027, the project aims to enable large-scale resource recovery, with projected capacities of 3.5 million tons of silicon kerf, 700 thousand tons of silica, and 480 thousand tons of graphite, demonstrating both scalability and economic viability. The work in ICARUS contributes directly to sustainability and circular economy goals by transforming waste into reusable raw materials, reducing environmental impacts, and improving the overall efficiency of the silicon PV value chain.

2 METHODOLOGY

This section provides a brief overview of the ICARUS project and PV waste volume estimates and characterization. It also discusses the four pilot-scale recycling technologies developed for silicon kerf, graphite, and silica.

2.1 Overview of ICARUS

The ICARUS project is organized into six work packages (WPs). WP1 addreses logistics, treatment, quality, quantity, and sourcing of silicon PV production waste. WP2 develops industrial routes for collecting and pre-treating silicon, silica, and graphite. WP3 reintroduces these wastes into silicon production, while WP4 focuses on controlled conditioning of purified silicon. WP5 upgrades a lab-scale reactor to semi-industrial scale for converting silicon waste into valuable materials. Finally, WP6 drives market uptake by demonstrating high-end prototypes that utilize recovered silicon, silica, and graphite.

2.2 Waste volume estimates and characterization

PV ingot manufacturing generates significant waste. To assess the potential of recycling pathways, it is essential to estimate waste volumes and characterize materials. Volume estimates provide context for the scale of the challenge, while characterization supports evaluation of technical feasibility and processing needs. In this work, silicon kerf waste was estimated using factors such as annual PV installations, the ratio of production to installations, crystalline PV production volumes, and the cell-to-wafer ratio. Estimates of crucible and pot scrap waste assumed multi-batch ingot pulling with M10 and G12 wafer dimensions, while graphite waste was estimated at 100 tons per gigawatt of PV capacity, as reported by [4].

The characterization of waste materials and produced silicon was carried out using several analytical techniques. Inductively Coupled Plasma Mass Spectrometry (ICP-MS) was applied to detect metallic and non-metallic impurities at trace levels, while LECO analysis was used to quantify carbon and oxygen contents. X-ray Diffraction (XRD) was employed to determine crystallographic structure and phase composition, and Scanning Electron Microscopy (SEM) was used to examine surface morphology. Together, these techniques assess chemical purity and morphology, ensuring recycled materials meet quality standards for high-performance applications.

2.3 Pilot technologies

The four industrial pilot technologies which are the core of the ICARUS project are:

- Pilot A: Collects and processes silicon kerf cake, graphite, and silica waste according to defined standards, delivering the material either to end-user groups for final applications or to other pilots for further refining.
- Pilot B: Aims to produce silicon with higher quality and at a lower cost than conventional metallurgical silicon processes. This pilot uses secondary materials such as graphite, silica, and silicon kerf in a pilot-scale submerged arc furnace (SAF).
- Pilot C: Scales up the annual controlled conditioning of silicon, based on material received from Pilot A to a capacity of 500 tons per year, aiming to improve the quality of granular silicon for PV applications.
- Pilot D: Will scale up a small-scale reactor to a semi-industrial level, targeting a capacity of 50–70 tons per year. The process is based on the reaction of free silicon in the kerf with a sodium hydroxide solution under controlled temperature and pressure conditions, producing hydrogen, sodium silicates, and reaction heat.

3 RESULT AND DISCUSSION

This section reports the key findings from waste volume estimates and material characterization, along with results from the four pilot projects, with emphasis on Pilot B.

3.1 Waste volume estimates and characterization result

The estimation of silicon kerf waste accounts for losses from wafering as well as cropping, squaring, chamfering, and grinding operations. Figure 1 shows the estimated global cumulative kerf generation from 2018 to 2027, indicating that annual volumes could reach about 700 kMT by 2027. Similarly, Figure 2 presents projected cumulative silica and graphite wastes from 2023 to 2027. Overall, these estimates highlight the substantial volumes of waste generated in ingot and wafer manufacturing. Although typically treated as waste, these materials represent a valuable opportunity for recycling and reintegration into the PV value chain and other applications.

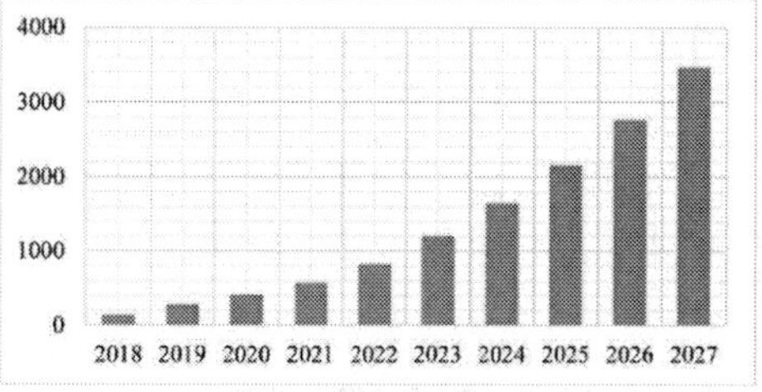

Figure 1: Cummulative silicon kerf waste in kMT.

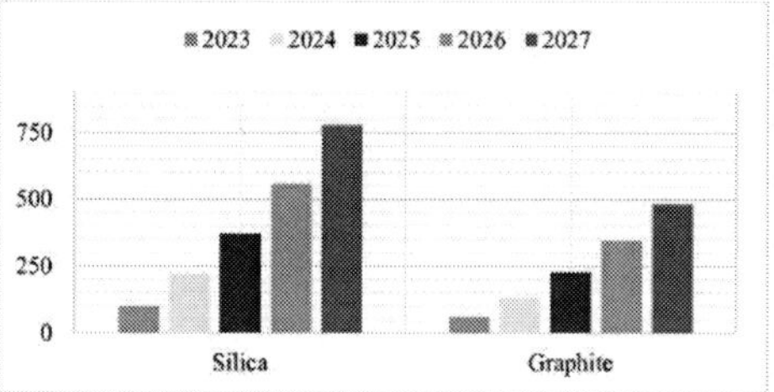

Figure 2: Cummulative silica and graphite waste in ton.

Impurity analysis of silicon kerf samples from different sources was conducted using ICP-MS. The results show that the main dopant impurities are boron, gallium, and phosphorus, with concentrations varying across samples. The main metallic impurities include aluminum, calcium, iron, and nickel. LECO analysis indicated carbon concentrations of 1–2 wt.% and oxygen content of 4–5 wt.% in most samples. SEM and XRD analyses revealed irregular morphologies, with the kerf consisting mainly of crystalline silicon and an amorphous phase.

LECO analysis of five graphite powder samples revealed significantly higher ash content compared to a virgin reference sample. ICP-MS analysis of the ash identified silicon, cobalt, and calcium as the main impurities. XRD results showed the presence of graphite 2H, SiC, and crystalline SiO2 phases, while SEM revealed multiple phases with distinct morphologies across different regions of the samples. Similar characterization was carried out on silica waste samples, which were found to consist mainly of amorphous silica and crystalline cristobalite, with calcium identified as the primary impurity.

3.2 Results from the pilots

The ICARUS project aims to transform silicon kerf, graphite, and silica waste into high-value secondary raw materials by developing and scaling four pilot technologies for efficient recycling. This section presents their results, with a more focus on Pilot B, chosen as the most representative of the overall processing chain, while summarizing key outcomes from the other pilots.

Pilot A: Industrial-scale processing routes for silicon kerf waste have been established at Technology Readiness Level (TRL) 7. A continuous drying system has been successfully commissioned as an alternative to the existing batch drying process for silicon kerf filter cake. This system achieves moisture levels of less than 1 wt%. Additionally, an industrial-scale post treatment process has been developed for material intended for use into lithium-ion batteries and thermoelectric modules. A

10.4229/EUPVSEC2025/5DO.18.1

pretreatment process has also been implemented to significantly reduce contaminants such as aluminum, nickel, and iron. For the silica waste, a processing route has been developed and a pilot line established, targeting raw material specification suitable for production of high purity silicon carbide.

Pilot B: This pilot aimed to reintroduce silicon kerf, graphite, and silica waste into the silicon value chain through carbothermic reduction. Two experimental campaigns were carried out in a pilot-scale SAF. The process began with the collection and pretreatment of raw materials, followed by agglomeration into self-reducing briquettes. Three types of briquettes were made, Type A (pure quartz and carbon black with binder and water), Type B (pot scrap, carbon black, binder, and water), and Type C (silicon kerf with binder and water). These briquettes were then subjected to pilot-scale carbothermic reduction in the SAF to produce silicon, which was subsequently analyzed to determine its purity. The two experimental campaigns which were run over a period of three days and three nights consisted of two experiments, totaling four experiments. These are:

- EXP 1: Type A briquettes and quartz lumps as charge.
- EXP 2: Type A briquettes, quartz lumps, and pot scrap lumps as charge.
- EXP 3: Type B briquettes and pot scrap lumps as charge.
- EXP 4: Type B and Type C briquettes and pot scrap lumps as charge.

Across two SAF campaigns, a total of 92 kg of silicon was produced through twelve tapping operations. In the first campaign (EXP 1 and EXP 2), 60 kg of silicon was obtained, while the second campaign (EXP 3 and EXP 4) yielded 32 kg. ICP-MS analysis of six samples from each tap (Tables I) confirmed that the produced silicon met metallurgical-grade purity requirements [5], with the second campaign achieving slightly higher purity than the first.

Table I: Purity of the tapped silicon measured by ICP-MS.

Sample	Purity (%)	
	Campaign 1	Campaign 2
1	97.87	98.43
2	98.27	98.16
3	98.47	98.01
4	98.39	98.47
5	98.34	98.78
6	98.79	98.05

Detailed ICP-MS analysis of Campaign 1 samples showed phosphorus as the dominant dopant, slightly above metallurgical-grade thresholds, while boron and gallium remained within limits. Aluminum exceeded the threshold in early tappings but stabilized later, iron was acceptable in half of the tappings, and titanium consistently exceeded limits; other metals were within range, confirming overall suitability for metallurgical-grade silicon. In Campaign 2, phosphorus and boron levels decreased, gallium increased, and aluminum and iron were well controlled, though calcium, titanium, chromium, and nickel exceeded thresholds. Despite these variations, it can be concluded that the produced silicon in this campaign met metallurgical-grade standards, an encouraging result given that 70% of the feedstock came from recycled pot scrap and kerf.

Pilot C: A combined system for powder feeding, melting, solidification, and granulation has been developed and commissioned. The powder feeding unit has a capacity of 500 tons per year, while the melting and granulation units handle 50 tons per year. The process successfully demonstrated the production of recycled silicon at a flow rate of 1 kg/h, achieving 4N purity.

Pilot D: A chemical conversion process for silicon waste has been scaled up to 87 tons per year, producing waterglass and green hydrogen for diverse market applications. End-of-life PV panels and semiconductor industry residues were also shown to be valuable alternative sources for material recovery.

4 CONCLUSIONS

This study through the ICARUS project highlights the substantial volumes of silicon kerf, silica, and graphite waste generated during ingot and wafer manufacturing and demonstrates their huge potential as valuable secondary raw materials. Detailed characterization of these wastes confirmed the suitability of these wastes as substitutes for virgin materials, while the successful implementation of four pilot technologies within the ICARUS project validated the technical feasibility of their recovery and reuse. Together, these results provide a strong foundation for integrating recycling into the PV value chain, advancing both sustainability and circular economy objectives in the PV industry.

5 ACKNOWLEDGEMENT

This work is part of ICARUS project funded by Horizon 2020 research and innovation programme under grant agreement No 958365.

6 REFERENCES

[1] Li, J., Lin, Y., Wang, F., Shi, J., Sun, J., Ban, B., Liu, G. and Chen, J., 2021. Progress in recovery and recycling of kerf loss silicon waste in photovoltaic industry. Separation and Purification Technology, 254, p.117581. https://doi.org/10.1016/j.seppur.2020.117581.

[2] Yang, S., Han, S., Chen, J., Wei, K. and Ma, W., 2024. A sustainable mineral process for silicon and quartz recovery from quartz crucible waste ash via electrical separation. Minerals Engineering, 216, p.108887. https://doi.org/10.1016/j.mineng.2024.108887.

[3] Zhang, Y., Z. Chen, K. Xie, X. Chen, Y. Hu, and W. Ma. Purification of Waste Graphite from Crucibles Used in Photovoltaic Crystallization by an Alkali-Acid Method. Metals 2023, 13, 1180. 2023. https://doi.org/10.3390/met13071180.

[4] Brailovsky, P., Baumann, K., Held, M., Briem, A.K., Wambach, K., Gervais, E., Herceg, S., Mertvoy, B., Nold, S. and Rentsch, J., 2023. Insights into circular material and waste flows from c-Si PV industry. EPJ Photovoltaics, 14, p.5. https://doi.org/10.1051/epjpv/2022029.

[5] Metallurgical-Grade Silicon (MGS) - WikiChip. https://en.wikichip.org/wiki/metallurgical-grade_silicon#google_vignette.

ECO-EFFICIENT PROCESSING AND REFINING ROUTES FOR SECONDARY RAW MATERIALS FROM SILICON INGOT AND WAFER MANUFACTURING

M.P. BELLMANN*[1], B.D. DIMD [1] , A.K SØILAND [2], ET AL.
[1] SINTEF, NORWAY AND [2]RESITEC, NORWAY

ICARUS ICARUS ICARUS 1

Content

1. Why recycling matters
2. ICARUS project
3. Pilot technologies
4. Results
5. Discussion & Outlook

Why recycling matters

- PV deployment is accelerating → huge silicon demand
- Ingot & wafer production generates large waste streams: kerf, crucible, and pot scrap and graphite.
- Current practice: landfill, low-value uses, and not industrial scale.
- Need for scalable, high value and circular recycling solutions: **ICARUS Project**

ICARUS project

- H2020 project with 18 EU partners.
- Goal: Recover, refine, reintegrate PV waste.
- Focus: Silicon kerf, Graphite, Silica.
- Develop 4 scalable pilot technologies (Pilot A-D).

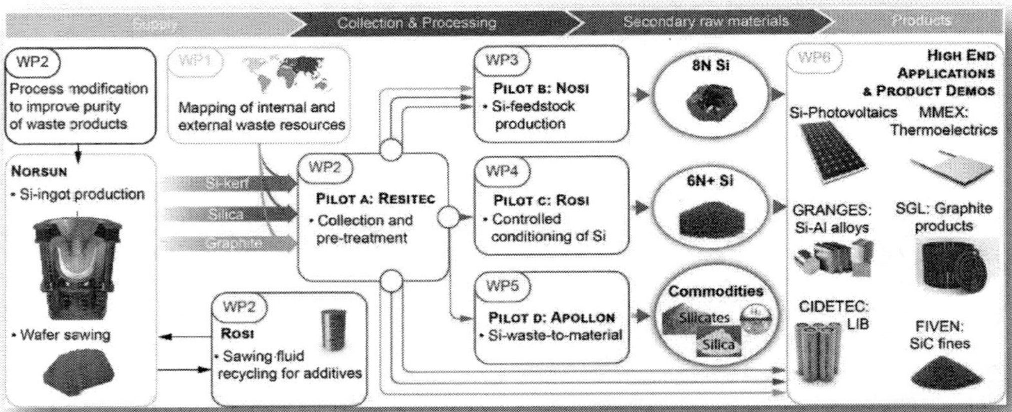

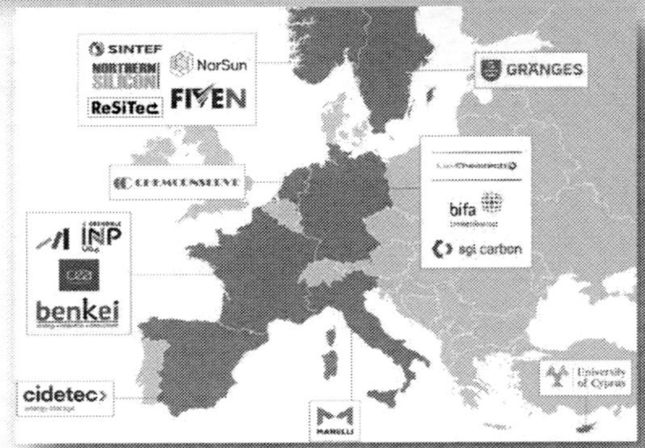

Pilot technologies: Pilot A

Collects and processes silicon kerf cake, graphite, and silica waste according to defined standards.

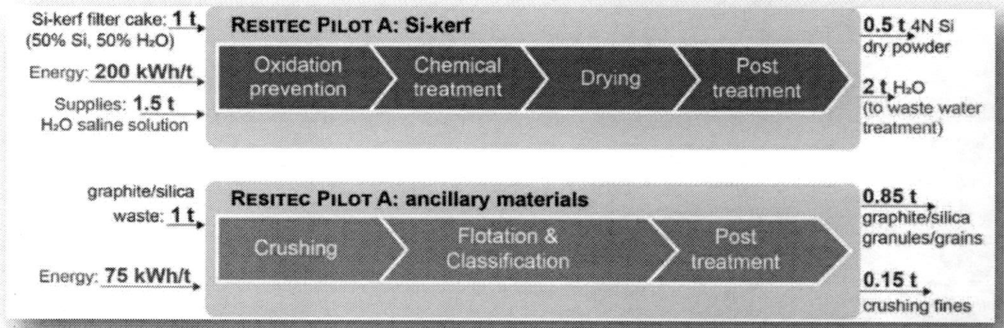

Pilot technologies: Pilot B

Silicon production via carbothermic reduction in SAF using waste materials

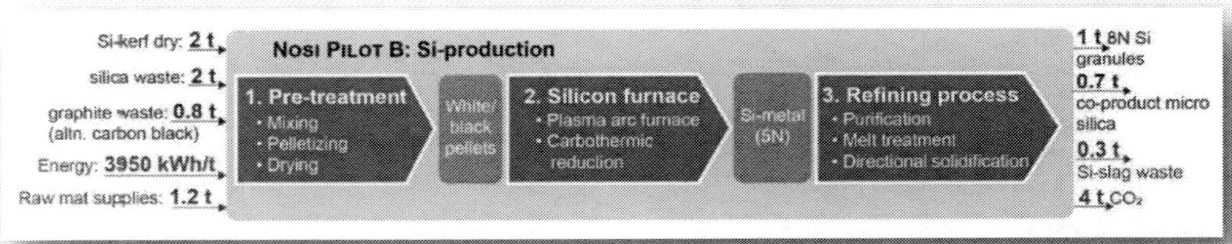

ICARUS ICARUS ICARUS 6

Pilot technologies: Pilot C

Scales up the granulation & conditioning of silicon, based on material from PilotA.

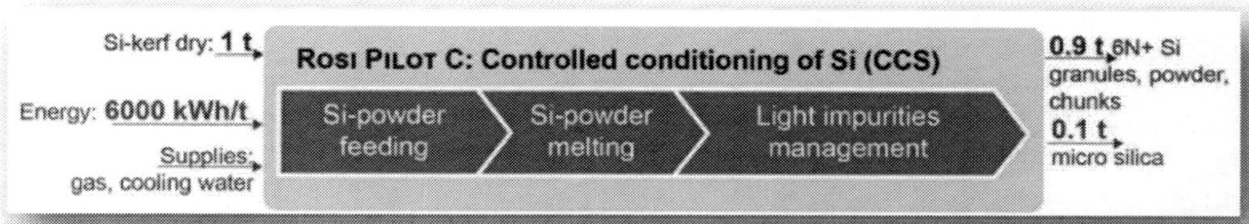

Pilot technologies: Pilot D

Scales up a reactor using a controlled reaction of free silicon in kerf with sodium hydroxide solution under controlled temperature and pressure conditions.

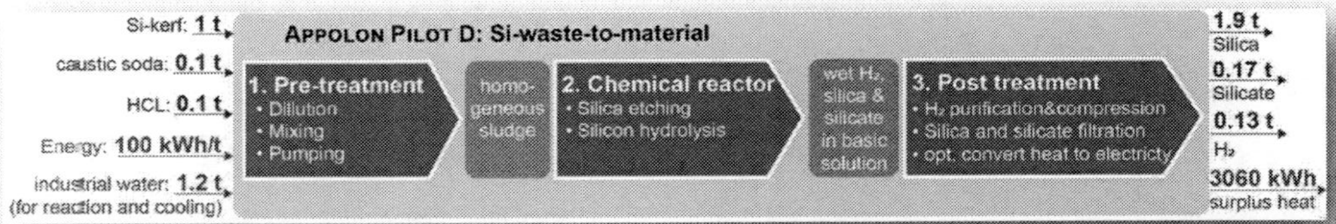

Results

Volume

Characterization

Pilot results

Results

Volume

Characterization

Pilot results

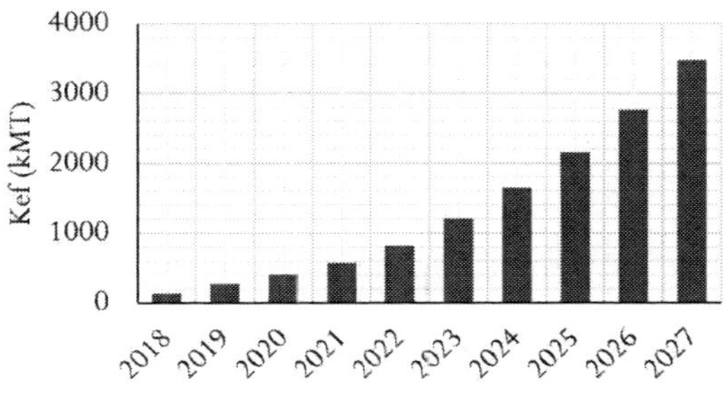

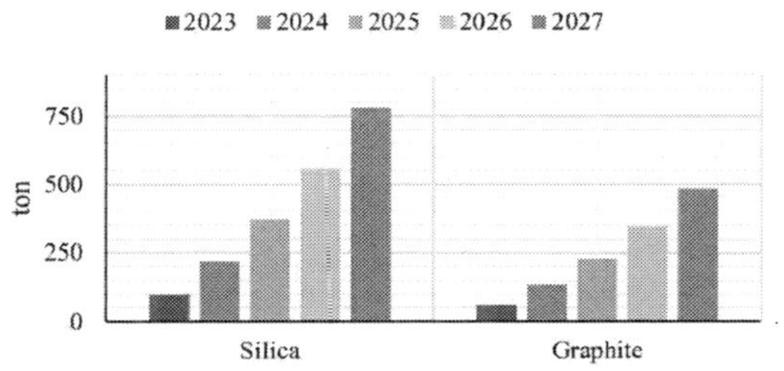

- Substantial volumes of waste are generated each year.
- With appropriate collection, purification, and processing strategies, there is strong potential to recycle and reintegrate these materials into the PV value chain.

Results

Volume

Characterization

Pilot results

Material	Characterization summary
Kerf	Impurities: B, Ga, P; Al, Ca, Fe, Ni C: 1-2 wt.% and O: 4-5 wt.% Phases: Crystalline + amorphous
Graphite	High ash vs virgin graphite Impurities: Si, Co, Ca Phases: Graphite 2H, SiC, SiO_2
Silica	Mainly amorphous silica + cristobalite Primary impurity: Ca

With proper pretreatment, these waste materials can substitute a significant share of virgin raw materials in PV ingot manufacturing.

Results

Volume

Characterization

Pilot A

- TRL 7 industrial-scale routes for kerf & silica waste developed.
- Continuous drying system → <1 wt% moisture.
- Pretreatment process that removes Al, Ni, Fe contaminants.
- Post-treatment process that enables use in Li-ion batteries & thermoelectric modules.

Results

Volume

Characterization

Pilot B

- Reintroduce silicon kerf, graphite, and silica waste via carbothermic reduction in SAF.
- Agglomeration of waste into self-reducing briquettes.
- Three types of briquettes: Type A[1], Type B[2], and Type C[3].
- Two campaigns with 4 experiments:
  - EXP 1: Type A briquettes and quartz lumps.
  - EXP 2: Type A briquettes, quartz lumps, and pot scrap lumps.
  - EXP 3: Type B briquettes and pot scrap lumps.
  - EXP 4: Type B and Type C briquettes and pot scrap lumps.

[1] *Type A: pure quartz and carbon black with binder and water*

[2] *Type B: pot scrap, carbon black, binder, and water*

[3] *Type C: silicon kerf with binder and water*

Results

Volume

Characterization

Pilot B

- Produced a total of 92 kg silicon.
  - 60 kg in Campaign 1 (EXP 1 & 2)
  - 32 kg in Campaign 2 (EXP 3 & 4)
- ICP-MS analysis confirmed metallurgical-grade purity.

Sample	Purity	
	Camp. 1	Camp. 2
1	97.87	98.43
2	98.27	98.16
3	98.47	98.01
4	98.39	98.47
5	98.34	98.78
6	98.79	98.05

Results

Volume

Characterization

Pilot C

- Integrated system for powder feeding, melting, solidification & granulation commissioned.
- Achieved 4N purity recycled silicon.
- Significant reduction in carbon & oxygen impurities.

Results

Volume

Characterization

Pilot D

- Chemical conversion process for silicon waste scaled to 87 t/year.
- Produces waterglass and green hydrogen for multiple markets.
- Demonstrated alternative feedstocks: EoL PV panels & semiconductor waste.

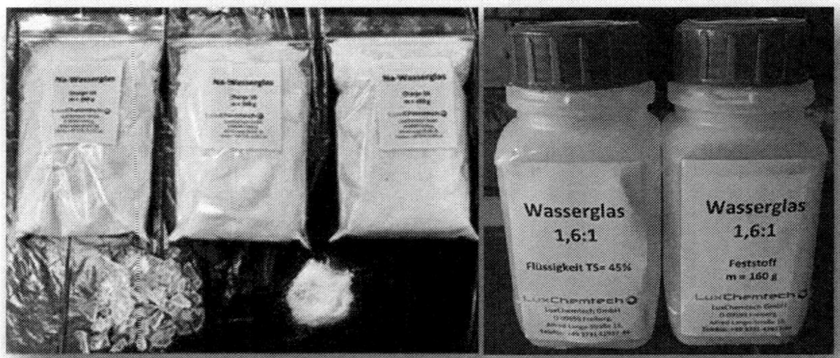

Discussion & Outlook

1. Pilot results prove feasibility of recycling kerf, silica, and graphite.
2. Recovered materials meet standards for PV and other industries.
3. Reduces reliance on virgin inputs ⟶ supports circular economy.
4. Next step:
   - Optimize recycling processes to control impurities.
   - Address operational inconsistencies between experiments.
   - Consider broad applications.

Thank you!! Questions?

martin.bellmann@sintef.no
berhane.dimd@sintef.no

42nd European Photovoltaic Solar Energy Conference and Exhibition

This presentation was selected by the Sc. Committee of the EU PVSEC 2025 for submission of a full paper to one of the EU PVSEC's collaborating peer-reviewed journals.

NEW THERMOMECHANICAL TESTS TO ASSESS THE RECYCLABILITY INDEX OF PHOTOVOLTAIC MODULES

Cristina L. Pinto[1], Asier Murillo[1], Ana María Gracia[1], Felice Alfieri[2], Nieves Espinosa[3], Davide Polverini[4]

[1]National Renewable Energy Centre (CENER), Spain
[2]Viegand Maagøe A/S, København, Denmark
[3]University of Murcia, Spain
[4] European Commission, DG Internal Market, Industry, Entrepreneurship and SMEs, Brussels, Belgium
cpinto@cener.com

ABSTRACT: In the context of the increasing efforts to enhance the sustainability of photovoltaic (PV) technologies, recyclability has emerged as a critical aspect to address within the circular economy framework and EU regulatory directives. This study focuses on new thermomechanical tests developed to address the recyclability of PV modules. Specifically, new thermomechanical techniques have been designed to evaluate the dismantlability of PV modules, focusing on two critical processes: the removal of the aluminium frame and the separation of the PV laminate (back-sheet + encapsulant + solar cell) from the glass substrate(s) (or both substrates in the case of glass-glass modules). For the frame removal test, the required maximum force was measured to assess the dismantling efficiency. The separation of the PV laminate was achieved using a thermomechanical technique, ensuring precision, measurability and repeatability of the process. These techniques were applied to a set of 18 modules, comprising two units of nine distinct models representing various PV technologies.
Keywords: PV Recyclability index, aluminium frame removal, delamination, thermomechanical test

1 INTRODUCTION

The accelerated deployment of PV technology plays a crucial role in securing energy supply and combating climate change. However, this growth also leads to a significant increase in end-of-life PV module waste, with projections estimating between 78 and 200 million tons of industrial waste by 2050, representing a loss of approximately $80 billion in recoverable materials [1]. To address this challenge, the European Climate, Infrastructure and Environment Executive Agency (CINEA) launched an initiative to develop a standardised recyclability index for PV modules and PV inverters based on previous research findings [2]. This effort aimed to reduce waste generation, resource consumption, and environmental impacts.

Table I: Scoring parameters and aggregation of the recyclability index for PV modules

Type of parameters	N		Parameter	Aggregation
Service-related parameters	1		Technology identification	5%
	2		Dismantling of the information and conditions for access	10%
	3	3.1	Disclosure of material composition	10%
		3.2	Disclosure of the presence and location of Critical, Strategic and Environmental Relevant materials	10%
Dismantling-related parameters	6	6.2	Removability of the encapsulant after a heating process: peel-off test	15%
		6.3	Removability of the encapsulant from the glass after a heating process: hot knife test	15%
		6.4	Removability of the frame	15%
Material-based parameters	7		Level of concentration of hazardous substances and other substances affecting the recycling process	15%
	8		Selection of materials based on recyclability complexity	10%
	9		Combination of materials used / homogeneity	10%

This initiative focuses on developing and validating recyclability scoring systems for PV modules and PV inverters, ensuring they are cost-effective, rapid, and accessible for manufacturers and market surveillance bodies. Key aspects include identifying priority parts based on material relevance and recyclability, defining critical recycling parameters (service-related, dismantling-related, and material-based), establishing scoring criteria, and developing recyclability scores for PV products (

Table *I*). Introducing this recyclability index could represent a significant step toward fostering sustainability in the PV industry, particularly by promoting design-for-recycling principles.

The current study focuses on the technical evaluation of the dismantling processes for PV modules as part of the broader recyclability assessment, which covers the following parameters:

- 6.2. Removability of the encapsulant (delamination) after heating for glass-backsheet modules.
- 6.3 Removability of the encapsulant (delamination) after a heating process for glass-glass modules.
- 6.4 Removability (dismantling) of the frame.

The research activity presented in this paper is part of the overall initiative to develop the aforementioned recyclability index, with a specific focus on the development of thermomechanical testing for the assessment of the frame and encapsulant-cell laminate removability. Another paper, also submitted to EUPVSEC 2025 (5CO.6.3), elaborates in more detail on the architecture and general methodological approach of the recyclability index for PV modules, as well as on the policy implications.

By focusing on the dismantling phase, we isolate some of the key recycling-related aspects, such as design, providing critical data for the calibration of the recyclability index. Specifically, we designed and tested customised thermomechanical techniques developed to measure the dismantling-related parameters for the systematic evaluation of the dismantlability and recyclability of PV modules at the moment of placing them on the market. For this work, two main steps are going to be taken:

1. Removal of Aluminium Frames: Measuring the maximum force required for frame dismantling.
2. Separation of PV Laminates from Glass Substrates: Utilising a thermomechanical-based blade and measuring the force decrease between two temperatures needed to efficiently separate the PV laminate from glass substrate on glass-backsheet modules, and the force needed to separate both glasses from glass-glass PV modules, minimising material degradation.

2 METHODOLOGY AND MATERIALS

This section includes the specifications of the PV models used and the description of the various tests developed to assess, quantitatively, the dismantlability of PV modules to reach and separate, when possible, their main components.

2.1 Tested PV modules

The photovoltaic (PV) module models were selected to represent a wide variety of systems currently installed. Two units of each model were used to perform the tests. Table II provides the list of the 9 selected PV module models, supported by a reasoning for the selection of specific technologies/models.

Table II. List of PV models with their specifications

Product ID	Technology	Power (W)	Module type - Bifaciality
Model 1	mc-Si, n-BC	420	Monofacial
Model 2	mc-Si, non-encapsulant	550	Glass-glass
Model 3	Si, HJT	450	Monofacial
Model 4	mc-Si, PERC Shingled	430	Monofacial
Model 5	mc-Si, TOPCon	525	Glass-glass
Model 6	mc-Si, p-BC	610	Monofacial
Model 7	mc-Si, n-TOPCon, half cut	600	Glass-glass
Model 8	mc-Si, i-TOPCon	605	Glass-glass
Model 9	Thin-film	400	Glass-glass

The selection of PV models across a spectrum of established, emerging, and niche technologies, ranging from PERC and TOPCon to IBC, HJT, thin-film, and recyclable designs, ensures a comprehensive representation of the current PV module market and potential new designs. It not only reflects the dominant technologies in deployment today but also anticipates future trends, enabling a robust evaluation of recyclability that aligns with the evolving landscape of photovoltaic innovation.

2.2 PV module frame removal process

This section describes the experimental procedure used to dismantle the aluminium frames from commercial and newly manufactured PV modules. The process was designed to quantify the mechanical resistance of frame detachment and to study the structural characteristics of the frame, analysing the potential failure modes during dismantling under the condition that the module's glass should remain intact. Maintaining the integrity of the glass is critical, as breakage would compromise subsequent recycling processes

Each PV model unit was tested individually using a custom-designed rectangular test bench (Figure 1). This bench is equipped with lateral pressure units that can be repositioned along sliding rails to accommodate varying module sizes and ensure precise application of force. Each piston is fitted with a load cell at its end, and all load cells are connected to a central measurement device that records the sum of the forces applied by all pistons during the test. As a result, the maximum total detachment force exerted on the frame is captured and recorded as a single value.

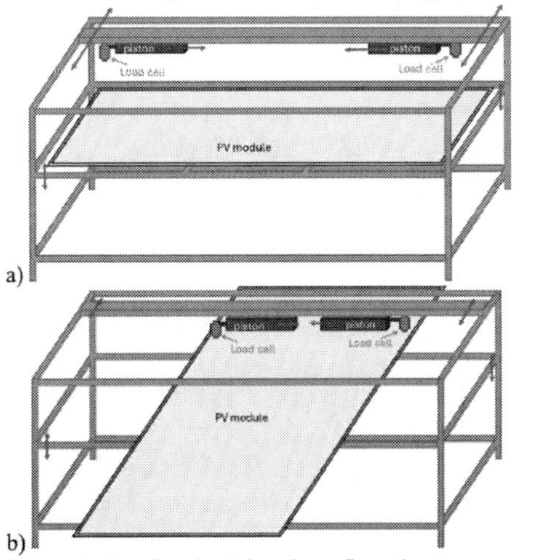

Figure 1. Test bench. a) bench configuration to remove short frames (denoted A-B); b) bench configuration to remove long frames (denoted 1-2)

The test procedure consists of five distinct steps aimed at removing both the long and short sides of the aluminium frame while maintaining the integrity of the glass. The complete methodology is described in [3].

The maximum total force recorded in each of the five steps is stored, and from these five values, an average detachment force is calculated. This average is then used

to evaluate the recyclability performance of the PV module within the proposed index framework.
The scoring system for parameter 6.4 is defined as follows (Table III):

Table III. Scoring system of parameter 6.4

Force	Score
The glass has been broken in the process	1 point
$F > 14710\ N$	3 points
$9807\ N < F \leq 14710\ N$	4 points
$F \leq\ 9807\ N$	5 points

2.3 Delamination of glass-backsheet PV modules

The delamination tests were carried out using the same custom-built rectangular test bench employed for the frame removal procedure. However, in this configuration, the pneumatic pistons are not used. Instead, the setup is adapted with additional components specifically designed for thermal-mechanical delamination of PV modules.

The bench is equipped with a hot plate capable of reaching temperatures between 50 °C and 200 °C, which allows precise thermal conditioning of the module section to be tested.

A motorised horizontal arm is mounted on the bench, whose movement speed can be precisely adjusted. Attached to this arm is a load cell, which records the force applied during the delamination process. Fixed to the arm is a 10.00 cm wide steel blade, used to initiate and propagate the separation between the front glass and the laminate.

This configuration allows controlled, quantifiable and repeatable delamination testing by combining thermal softening of the encapsulant with mechanical cutting, while simultaneously recording the force required to perform the operation. Unlike shredding or crushing techniques—which destroy the module structure and mask design differences—this method allows assessment of how specific design choices affect dismantling performance. This is essential for this study, which aims to incentivise manufacturers to adopt more sustainable and circular design strategies for PV modules.

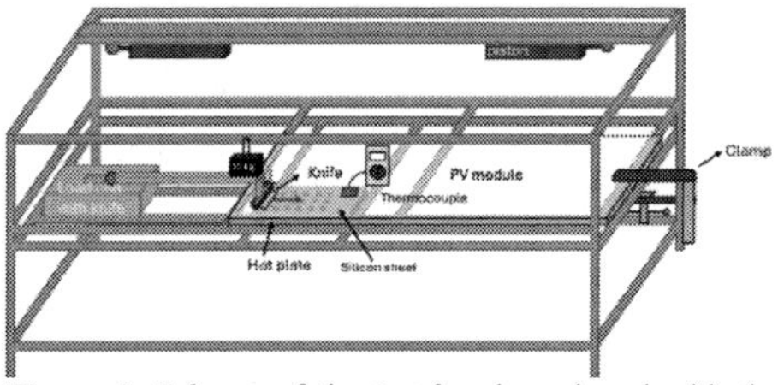

Figure 2. Scheme of the test bench equipped with the delamination test.

The delamination process is conducted at $T_1 = 70°C$ and $T_2 = 150°C$. The selected temperatures were chosen based on the thermochemical properties of the encapsulant materials. According to calorimetric analyses, the melting point of the most common encapsulants—EVA, POE, and TPO—lies within the range of 70–90 °C (although this may vary depending on the specific composition of the encapsulant). Therefore, a temperature of 70 °C was selected to remain below the melting point while still representing a temperature that can realistically be reached by a PV module in normal working conditions. The second temperature chosen was 150 °C, as it is well above the melting point and far beyond the working temperatures that PV modules would normally experience. This approach allows for the analysis of the reduction in the force required for delamination between the two temperature conditions.

In order to account for possible local variations in adhesion strength across the PV module surface and to address the possible inhomogeneity of the adhesion force of the encapsulant to the glass in various regions of the module derived from the manufacturing process, each delamination test is performed in three predefined zones (Figure 3):

Zone A: Upper-left corner (or one corner)
Zone B: Centre of the module
Zone C: Lower-right corner (or the opposite corner to Zone A)

The complete methodology is described in [3].

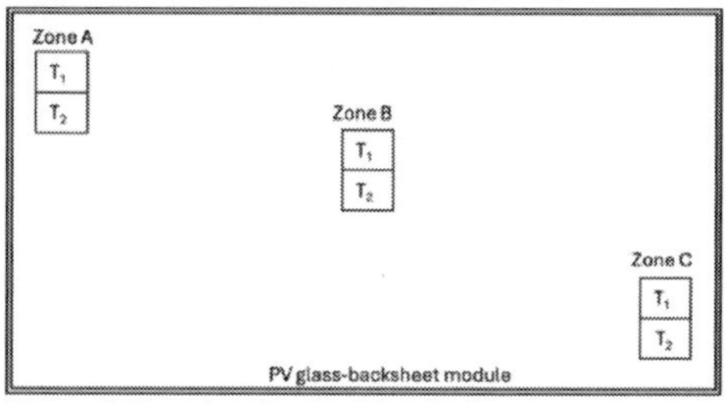

Figure 3. Locations for the delamination test.

Before the delamination procedure begins, the perimeter of each selected zone (A, B, and C) is carefully cut using a precision cutter with sufficient depth to reach the glass interface, ensuring that the entire laminate stack is fully separated along the border of the test area. Then the blade is manually positioned, and its movement is activated at a slow speed of 50 mm/min. Once the blade has penetrated between the glass and the remaining layers, the testing speed is set to 150 mm/min. The test width corresponds to the blade width: 10 cm. The total test length is 11 cm, although only 7.00 cm of constant force is considered for calculating the average force in N/mm, following the details defined in the standard peel-off test (IEC 61730-2). The decrease in the average delamination force will be a key criterion for assessing the recyclability of modules.

$$Force\ Reduction\ (\%) = \left(\frac{F_{T_1} - F_{T_2}}{F_{T_1}}\right) \times 100$$

Each module is evaluated based on the average percentage reduction across all three zones. The scoring system is defined as follows (Table IV):

Table IV. Scoring system of parameter 6.2

Force Reduction (%)	Score
< 30%	1 points
30% – 60%	3 points
> 60%	5 points

This scoring approach reflects the ability of the encapsulant and module design to facilitate separation at elevated temperatures. It rewards products that can be delaminated more easily under thermal conditions, thus promoting design strategies aligned with high-efficiency

10.4229/EUPVSEC2025/5DO.18.2

and low-contamination recycling processes.

2.4 Delamination of glass-glass PV modules

In contrast to glass-backsheet modules, glass-glass configuration makes it impossible to perform the delamination process; nevertheless, with a thin knife, it is feasible to enter between the two glasses and separate them.

The test is conducted on the same rectangular testing bench used in earlier tests. The test equipment consists of a motorised cutting device equipped with a load cell to monitor the applied force. A metal blade of 25.00 cm is mounted on the adjustable arm.

Before testing, the glass-glass modules are heated to a temperature of 160°C. This thermal conditioning ensures that the encapsulant becomes sufficiently softened to facilitate separation without damaging the structural integrity of the glass layers. A thermocouple is attached directly to the module to monitor the surface temperature. Once the target temperature is reached, the separation test begins. The blade is inserted between the two glass layers at a module corner while moving at a reduced speed of 50 mm/min, ensuring controlled and precise insertion. Once the blade tip has entered the module, the load cell is reset to zero, and the speed is increased to 150 mm/min. From this point, the test proceeds automatically, with the blade progressing deeper into the module structure until it enters 11.00 cm inside the module (Figure 4).

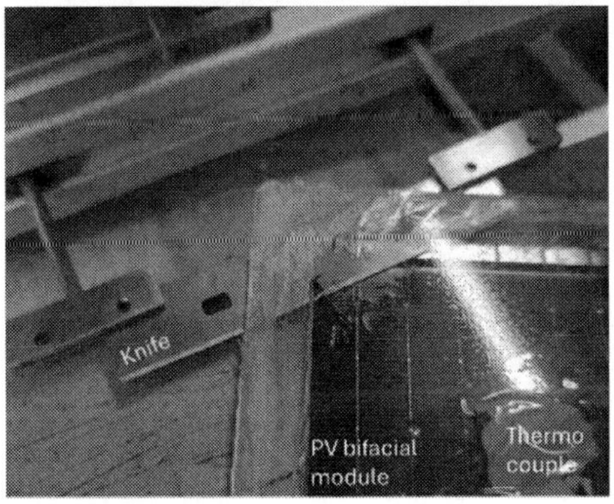

Figure 4. Photo of the glass-glass PV delamination test with a hot knife.

As the blade advances diagonally from the corner, the resistance gradually increases due to the enlarging interface area, resulting in a linear upward trend in the force profile. Thus, the slope of the force curve (in N/mm^2) is the main metric used in glass-glass modules; therefore, a mean value between the results obtained from the four corners will be the main result of this test. The scoring system is defined as follows (**Table *V***)

Table V. Scoring system of parameter 6.3

Slope of Force Curve (N/mm^2)	Score
< 5 N/mm^2	5 points
5 – 15 N/mm^2 included	3 points
> 15 N/mm^2	1 points

Lower slope values indicate a softer and more easily separable encapsulant at the test temperature, and thus better recyclability potential. Conversely, higher slope values suggest stronger adhesion or less responsive encapsulants, which hinder separation and may result in glass contamination during recycling.

Take into account that the slicing direction significantly affects the measured force gradient; all modules must be positioned in a standardised orientation, such that the blade enters perpendicularly to the corner diagonal. This standardisation ensures the comparability of results across different samples

3 RESULTS AND DISCUSSION

The PV dismantling test encompasses the PV module aluminium frame removal test and the delamination of the modules, using a different technique for glass-backsheet and glass-glass devices, as explained above.

3.1 Aluminium frame removal test results

Starting from the frame removal test, 9 PV module models were tested, performing two tests per side, distinguishing between the long-side frames (Frame 1–2) and the short-side frames (Frame A–B). For each side, two tests were conducted per module, both applying pressure near the corners, and the average of the two measurements was considered. The force is expressed in Kgf, which is approximately equal to 9.8 N.

The results are depicted in Figure 5.

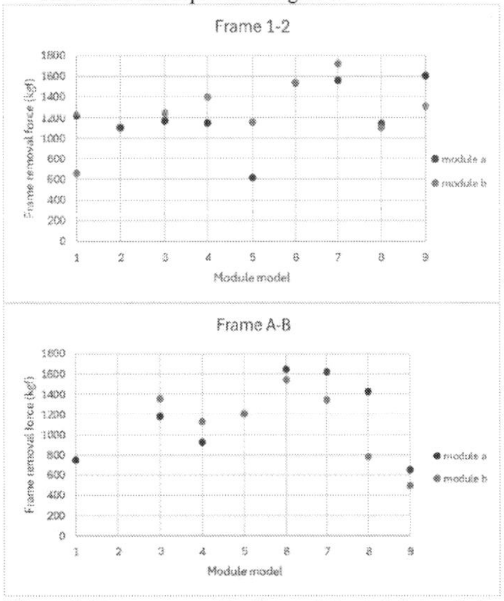

Figure 5. Frame removal test by module models 1 to 9, for the two devices tested per module type (a and b). top) test carried out between Frames 1-2, bottom) test carried out between Frames A-B.

The distribution of the recorded forces reveals a broad variability. The required forces span a range from below 800 kgf to values exceeding 1400 kgf. Despite being the same model from the same manufacturer, some intra-model variation is evident. For instance, in model 5, the removal force for Frame 1–2 varied from around 600 kgf to approximately 1200 kgf. Similar discrepancies appear in other models and for Frame A–B as well. For Model module 2, only one device was tested (module a) since the module glass and cells shattered while removing the Frame 1-2, therefore it was decided not to test the second device (module b). Similarly, for Model 1, unit b was damaged while changing the test bench configuration between frame removal and frame A-B could not be tested.

3.2 Delamination of glass-backsheet modules

Delamination tests were conducted on three types of PV modules: shingled, HJT (with multi-busbar contacts), and BC (with rear-side contacts only). These technologies enable the evaluation of differences in delamination resistance attributable to the various contact configurations.

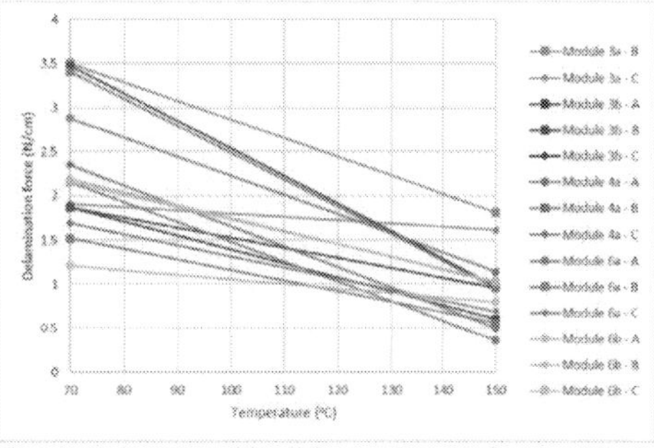

Figure 6. Results of the delamination of glass-backsheet modules

According to the results depicted in Figure ***6***, significant discrepancies were observed in the delamination results between the two units of each PV module tested, and even between different zones of the same module (same colour in the graph). These variations are primarily attributed to the high sensitivity of the delamination process to the precise positioning and orientation of the blade during testing. Factors such as whether the blade crosses a single cell, multiple cells, or areas without cells, as well as the direction of delamination relative to the busbars, can have a major influence on the measured force. In particular, delamination performed perpendicular to the busbars may cause the blade to snag or encounter increased resistance, resulting in higher force values. Nevertheless, there is a clear tendency for the delamination force to decrease with increasing temperature, with a pronounced reduction from 70 °C to 150 °C. A more detailed discussion of the results is described in the recyclability index testing report [3].

3.3 Delamination of glass-glass modules

Following the methodology described above, the results of glass-glass modules are presented in Figure 7.

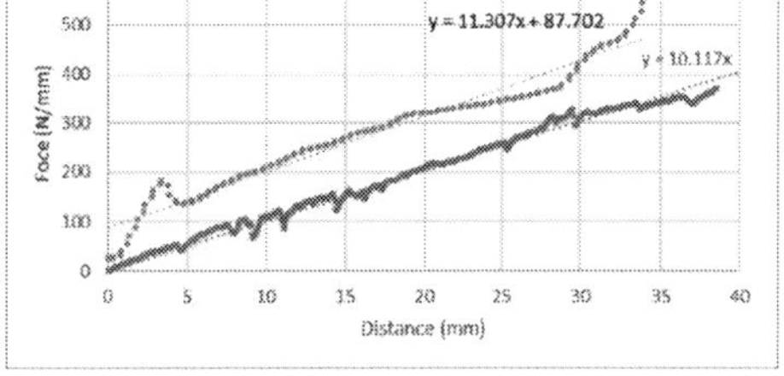

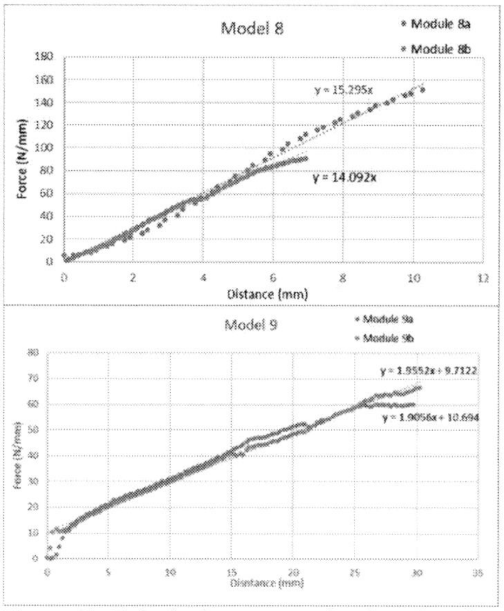

Figure 7. Delamination test results for glass-glass modules.

The delamination tests on the three glass-glass models reveal clear differences in behaviour. For Model 7, both units exhibit a similar trend, with comparable slopes of 10.12 N/mm² and 11.31 N/mm². Model 8 also shows consistent behaviour between units, with values of 15.30 N/mm² and 14.09 N/mm², although it should be noted that for unit 8a the penetration depth was limited to 10 mm due to positioning constraints, whereas a penetration of 110 mm would be required for a fully representative value. In contrast, the thin-film modules (Model 9) require significantly lower delamination forces, as expected from the absence of c-Si cells, with values of 1.91 N/mm² and 1.96 N/mm² for the two units tested.

3.4 Recyclability index of the PV nodules

In the following section, the recyclability index results are presented, focusing specifically on parameter 6 – dismantling-related parameters. To contextualise the results, the performance of the tested models is compared against a fictitious 'ideal module,' which is assumed to reach the maximum possible score for dismantling-related parameters. This comparison highlights the gap between current industrial designs and the best-case scenario, providing valuable insights into how different design choices influence recyclability.

The results are presented in **Figure 8**. The dismantling-related parameters reveal significant variability among the tested modules when compared to the fictitious ideal module. Frame removability shows relatively high values for most modules, with several reaching 0.75, close to the maximum score, although some designs (e.g., Model 2 and Model 6) display lower values, reflecting the fact that Model 2 did not pass the test as the glass got broken during the process, and potential difficulties in separating the aluminium frame for Module 6. In terms of delamination, glass–backsheet configurations generally achieve higher scores than glass–glass designs. Notably, Modules 7 and 8 exhibit measurable scores for glass–glass delamination, but these remain well below the ideal benchmark. On the contrary, Model 9 got the maximum punctuation in the glass-glass delamination process. The comparison with the virtual ideal module underscores the existing gap between current module designs and the maximum recyclability potential, especially in delamination processes. These findings emphasise that, while progress has been made in simplifying frame removal, further innovations are required in encapsulant and laminate design to significantly improve recyclability performance.

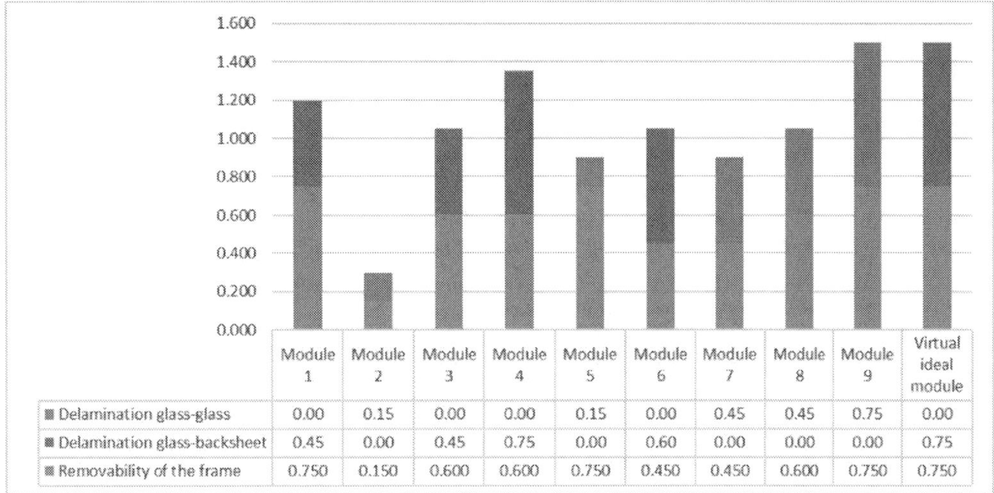

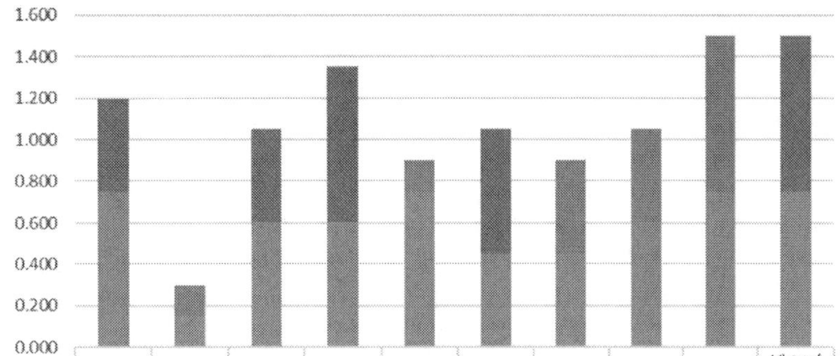

	Module 1	Module 2	Module 3	Module 4	Module 5	Module 6	Module 7	Module 8	Module 9	Virtual ideal module
Delamination glass-glass	0.00	0.15	0.00	0.00	0.15	0.00	0.45	0.45	0.75	0.00
Delamination glass-backsheet	0.45	0.00	0.45	0.75	0.00	0.60	0.00	0.00	0.00	0.75
Removability of the frame	0.750	0.150	0.600	0.600	0.750	0.450	0.450	0.600	0.750	0.750

Figure 8. Recyclability index of the PV modules, based only on the dismantling-related parameters.

4 CONCLUSIONS

This work presents the development and application of a novel 3-in-1 thermomechanical testing bench designed to assess dismantling-related parameters within the recyclability index for photovoltaic modules. The equipment enables a systematic and repeatable evaluation of three critical tests: the removal of aluminium frames, the delamination of glass–backsheet modules, and the delamination of glass–glass modules.

The results obtained across a representative set of PV technologies demonstrate that frame removal is generally less challenging than delamination, with several modules approaching the maximum score for this parameter. However, a considerable disparity was observed in the forces required to remove the aluminium frames. This variability is strongly influenced by multiple design aspects, such as the geometry of the profiles and the type of sealing materials (e.g., silicones) employed.

In contrast, delamination processes remain the main bottleneck. The delamination tests on glass-backsheet modules showed notable dispersion, largely due to the sensitivity of the results to the positioning of the blade, which strongly affects the measured force. The comparison with a fictitious ideal module highlights the significant design gap that still exists between current commercial products and the recyclability potential envisioned under circular economy principles.

These tests also represent the first application of this dismantling methodology, and their results have been instrumental in redefining and refining the overall procedure. The discrepancies observed, especially in delamination measurements, have provided valuable insights that allowed us to describe the methodology more precisely and establish clearer testing protocols, thereby reducing uncertainty and enhancing reproducibility for future evaluations.

Overall, the findings underline the importance of integrating design-for-recycling principles into PV module development. Improvements in encapsulant formulations, laminate configurations, and frame assembly strategies will be key to facilitating efficient dismantling, thereby supporting the broader objective of establishing a standardised recyclability index for PV products. This study provides a technical foundation that can guide both manufacturers and policymakers toward more sustainable photovoltaic systems.

REFERENCES

[1] IRENA, M. M. Aman, and K. H. Solangi, *End-Of-Life Management: Solar Photovoltaic Panels. International Renewable Energy Agency and the International Energy Agency Photovoltaic Power Systems*, vol. 47, no. 5. 2018. [Online]. Available: https://www.osti.gov/servlets/purl/1561525/%0
[2] Viegand Maagøe, Universidad de Murcia, and CENER, "Development of a recyclability index for photovoltaic products," 2025. https://www.pv-recyclability-index.eu/
[3] Viegand Maagøe, Universidad de Murcia, and CENER, "Technical support for the development of a recyclability index for photovoltaic products : Testing , calibration and validation," 2025. [Online]. Available: https://www.pv-recyclability-index.eu/documents/

SYNTHESIS AND ANALYSIS OF POLYANILINE PROPERTIES WITH VARIOUS COUNTERIONS FOR SILVER RECOVERY FROM TECHNOLOGICAL SOLUTIONS AFTER SILICON PV CELLS LEACHING

Hanna Rodziewicz[1], Anna Kuczyńska-Łażewska*,[1], Agnieszka Witkowska[2]
1 Gdansk University of Technology, Faculty of Chemistry
2 Gdansk University of Technology, Faculty of Applied Physics and Mathematics, Institute of Nanotechnology and Materials Engineering
ul. Narutowicza 11/12 80-233 Gdańsk, Poland
anna.lazewska@pg.edu.pl

ABSTRACT: In the presented work a one-step synthesis of polyaniline using four different organic acids and a hydrochloric acid solution was described. Polyaniline is a conductive polymer, so can be used for hydrometallurgical recovery of silver ions. Possible applications of the PAni/Ag composite were analysied. Fourier-transform infrared spectroscopy, UV-Vis spectroscopy and thermogravimetric analysis were carried out to evaluate the composition and structure of the synthesized materials. In addition, pH and specific conductivity were measured. The obtained spectra confirmed the presence of key functional groups, bonds and energy transitions for the analyzed substances. The specific conductivity values for all samples confirmed the ability of the materials to conduct electricity. The use of five different acids at the polymerization stage resulted in slightly different structures between the materials. The materials were placed in a solution of $AgNO_3$ to investigate the possibility of silver ions recovery on the polymer structure. The samples were subjected to X-ray spectroscopy and tested on the scanning electron microscope with Energy-dispersive X-ray spectroscopy, which made it possible to analyze the structure of the polymer and check for the presence of silver. In the future, the samples can be used for hydrometallurgical recovery of silver, and it will be examined how different counter-ions affect the efficiency of such a process and the final percentage of metal obtained.
Keywords: polyaniline, composites, silver recovery

1 INTRODUCTION

Composite materials are currently being applied on a wide scale across various scientific and engineering disciplines. Continuous efforts are directed toward the development of novel combinations of well-characterized components. In numerous reports, the fabrication of nanocomposites containing, among others, polyaniline and silver nanoparticles has been described. Owing to its advantageous properties, particularly electrical conductivity, polyaniline is frequently employed as a key element of such composites.

One of the applications reported in the literature involves the preparation of a material coated with silver, polyaniline, and aminated graphene oxide. This material was found to exhibit shielding effectiveness against electromagnetic interference across a broad frequency range. It was further demonstrated that the efficiency of the obtained fabrics remained high regardless of the frequency band. In addition, the composite containing silver, polyaniline, and aminated graphene oxide exhibited the highest antibacterial activity—97% against *Escherichia coli* and 99% against *Staphylococcus aureus*. Such results suggest that these materials may represent a breakthrough, as their shielding capacity against electromagnetic radiation can be utilized for the protection of human health [1]. A polyaniline/tungsten (V) phosphate/silver nanocomposite was subsequently employed for the fabrication of a selective membrane targeting hazardous heavy metal ions [2]. Selectivity studies indicated that the membrane responded to lead ions even at very low concentrations, down to 10^{-7} M. Another polyaniline-based composite, incorporating silver and gold nanoparticles, was synthesized with the aim of forming a buffer layer in polymer photovoltaic cells [3]. High electrical conductivity and optical transparency (76–81%) were obtained in the resulting composites. Impedance spectroscopy measurements confirmed that charge transport was improved in solar cells containing nanocomposites with equal proportions of silver and gold. Enhanced light absorption by the active layer was also observed, and plasmonic coupling between the nanoparticles was suggested to further broaden the absorption range, thereby increasing device efficiency. These findings indicate that such a material may in the future replace the polymer blends currently used in polymer solar cells.

Current approaches to photovoltaic panel recycling are primarily focused on the separation of individual components. The efficiency of such processes is typically evaluated by the quantity and purity of the recovered element. Subsequently, the separated components are often directed to appropriate processing facilities and reintroduced into the production cycle through applications in various industrial sectors.

The application of conducting polymers may enable the recovery of elements such as silver from PV cells. The deposition of silver particles onto a conductive material results in the formation of a composite that can be further utilized. This approach eliminates the need for the direct separation of silver from photovoltaic cells, which is otherwise a complex and costly multi-stage process. Given that potential applications of polyaniline–silver composites are already documented, the recovery of silver using this polymer appears particularly promising. The resulting material could serve as a foundation for novel industrial solutions.

2 MATERIALS AND METHODS

2.1 Synthesis of Polyaniline

The initial syntheses were carried out according to

the procedure described by J. Laska and J. Widlarz. The process commenced with the preparation of an acid solution. Since the aim was to obtain polyaniline containing different counterions in its structure, the following five acids were employed: hydrochloric acid (HCl), 4-toluenesulfonic acid (TSA), 4-sulfanilic acid (SAA), sulfonobenzoic acid (SBA), polyphosphoric acid (PPA). Solutions of 0.02 mol concentration were prepared, and the flasks containing these solutions were placed in an ice bath. Upon cooling, 4.6 mol of aniline was added to each flask. While the reaction mixtures were cooling and the substances combining, a 0.066 mol solution of ammonium persulfate was prepared. After mixing the acid solution with aniline, five portions of 10 ml of the oxidant solution were added at 10-minute intervals in order to control the course of the reaction. The flasks were then left for approximately 5 hours. Once the synthesis was complete, the mixtures were filtered, washed with distilled water, and left to dry. Each synthesis, with the exception of TSA, was carried out twice to assess reproducibility. All used compounds were pure analitycal grade (Merck, Germany).

2.2 Fourier Transform Infrared Spectroscopy (FTIR)

Fourier transform infrared spectroscopy enables the analysis of a given substance in terms of its organic functional groups and hydrogen bonds. For solid-state samples, the material must be finely ground and mixed with a substance such as KBr, which exhibits low infrared absorption. Measurements were performed using a Thermo Scientific Nicolet iS50 FT-IR spectrometer (Thermo Scientific, USA).

2.3 Ultraviolet-Visible Spectroscopy (UV-Vis)

This analysis enables the determination of a wide range of compounds, including aromatic hydrocarbons, aldehydes, ketones, acids, amines, and rare earth elements, with particular sensitivity to conjugated bonds and aromatic groups. Sample preparation began with thorough grinding of the investigated material with barium sulfate (VI) in a mortar. The mixture was subsequently placed in a measurement cuvette and analyzed. Measurements were conducted using a Perkin Elmer Lambda 365+ UV/Vis spectrophotometer (PerkinElmer, USA).

2.4 Thermogravimetric Analysis (TG)

The resulting thermogram represents the change in sample mass (ordinate axis) as a function of either time or temperature (abscissa axis). The measurements were carried out using a Netzsch TG 209F3 thermogravimetric analyzer (NETZSCH, Germany).

2.5 Specific Conductivity Measurements

Conductometric studies were performed by dissolving 10 mg of polyaniline in 30 ml of dimethyl sulfoxide (DMSO). Conductivity was measured by immersing an electrode in the solution and recording the values on a conductometer. Both the electrode and the conductometer were manufactured by Elmetron, specifically models ECF-1 and CX-461, respectively (Elmetron, Poland).

2.6 pH measurement

The pH of the samples was determined by dispersing 10 mg of polyaniline in 20 ml of distilled water. The electrode was then immersed in the suspension, and the pH value was recorded. The analysis was performed using a Mettler Toledo pH meter (Mettler Toledo, Switzerland)

2.7 Silver recovery

In preliminary experiments, silver was recovered from a standardized solution prepared from 100 ppm silver nitrate ($AgNO_3$) and water. The samples were immersed in the solution, filtered, and the resulting powder was subjected to further analyses.

2.8 Synchrotron radiation-based investigation

With the support of the National Synchrotron Radiation Centre SOLARIS in Kraków, spectroscopic measurements were carried out for polyaniline samples as well as for polyaniline–silver composites at PIRX line. Metallic indium was used as a sample carrier, since it was crucial to obtain information on the carbon–nitrogen bonds, which can confirm the oxidation state of the polymer achieved during synthesis. During the experiment, high-quality near-edge soft X-ray absorption spectra were collected for most of the samples, mainly in the partial fluorescence yield (PFY) mode and also in the total electron yield (TEY) mode for samples with chloride counterions in the temperature of liquid nitrogen (around 80 K).

3 RESULTS AND DISCUSSION

3.1 Thermogravimetric

The thermogravimetric curves obtained for PAni Cl1 and PAni Cl2 differ markedly from one another (Fig. 1). The first significant mass losses for PAni Cl1 were observed already at around 80 °C. The peak at this temperature may suggest the presence of benzene or cyclohexane. At this stage, water loss from the analyzed sample undoubtedly also began. The decrease observed at 200 °C (Fig. 1) indicates polymer chain degradation, which continues until the end of the process, as reflected by the non-uniform shape of the curve [4]. In the case of PAni Cl2, the first slight mass loss occurs around 100 °C and corresponds to water evaporation from the analyzed material. Subsequently, starting at approximately 300 °C (Fig. 1), polymer degradation begins and persists up to 700 °C. The most pronounced mass loss for the first sample, recorded at 80 °C, suggests that a substantial fraction of the substrates remained unreacted during polymerization. Consequently, the small amount of polymer that formed likely exhibited an unstable structure. This explains why polymer chain degradation commenced at a lower temperature than expected.

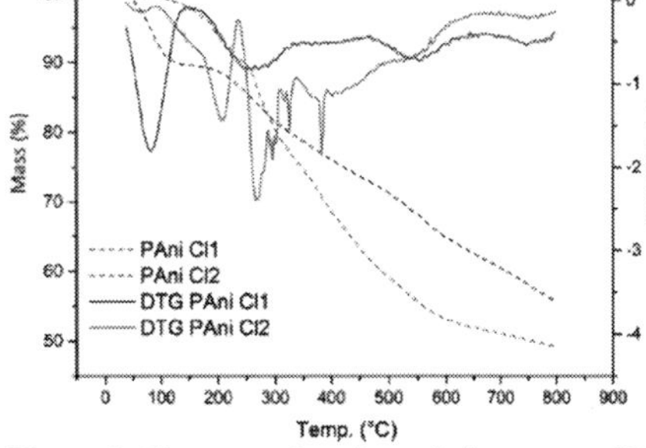

Figure 1: Thermogravimetric analysis curves – PAni Cl1, PAni Cl2

The comparison of curves obtained for PAni SAA1 and PAni SAA2 is presented in Figure 2. For both substances, the course of mass loss with increasing temperature is very similar. In the range of 90–100 °C, the first small band appears, indicating water evaporation. Subsequently, at approximately 250 °C (Fig. 2), polymer chain degradation begins [4]. A significant difference between the curves of the two samples is observed in the range of 300–350 °C (Fig. 5). At this point, PAni SAA2 exhibits a peak corresponding to as much as 45% mass loss, whereas PAni SAA1 does not display such a pronounced decrease. This difference may result from the presence of a greater amount of unreacted SAA in the synthesis of PAni SAA2. The peak may be attributed to the degradation of 4-sulfanilic acid, whose boiling point is 337 °C. Polymer degradation ends in the temperature range of 600–650 °C.

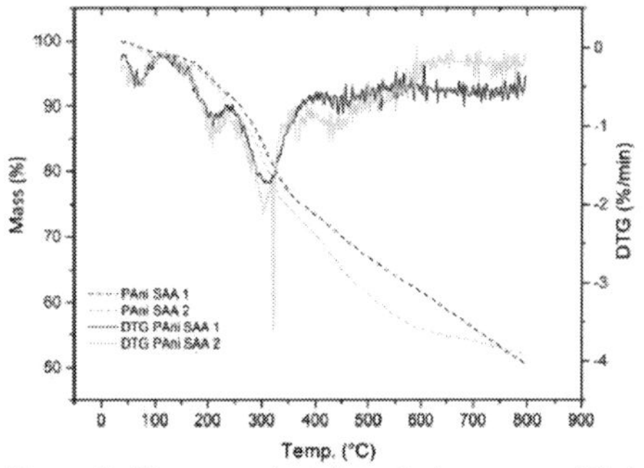

Figure 2: Thermogravimetric analysis curves – PAni SAA1, PAni SAA2

The curves for PAni SBA1 and PAni SBA2 exhibit identical profiles and overlap with each other (Fig. 3). At the beginning, as in other cases, a slight water loss is visible, followed by a peak at 200 °C. This peak can most likely be associated with the degradation of unreacted SBA acid. Subsequently, at approximately 300 °C (Fig. 3), polymer degradation begins and continues until reaching 600 °C [4].

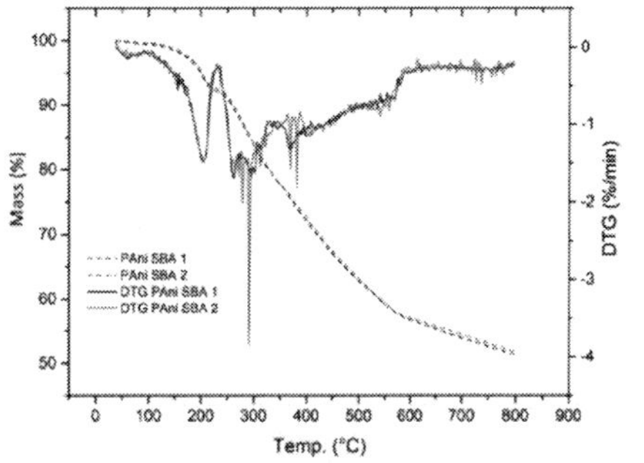

Figure 3: Thermogravimetric analysis curves – PAni SBA1, PAni SBA2

A comparison of all curves on a single plot reveals many similarities among the samples (Fig. 4). Against this background, PAni Cl1 stands out most distinctly, which can be attributed to unsuccessful synthesis. Apart from this exception, the remaining materials demonstrate good thermal stability.

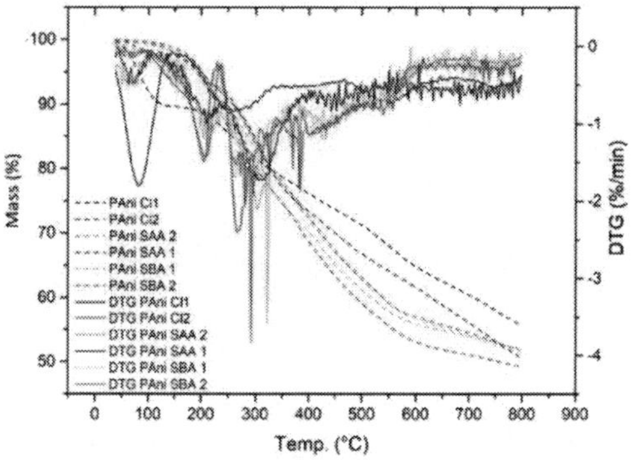

Figure 4: Thermogravimetric analysis curves – comparison of all substances

3.2 FTIR

The spectra obtained from Fourier transform infrared spectroscopy revealed that the individual spectra of the samples did not exhibit significant differences in most cases (Fig. 5). Several characteristic peaks were consistently observed, beginning with a broad band in the region of 3450–3230 cm⁻¹, attributed to N–H stretching vibrations (Jiang & Cui, 2006), indicative of amine groups. In this range, O–H stretching vibrations could also be identified. The peak at 1564 cm^{-1} corresponds to the stretching vibrations of C=N and C=C bonds within the quinoid ring of polyaniline. Furthermore, bands between 1450–1610 cm^{-1} (Fig. 5) confirm the presence of C=C stretching vibrations, consistent with the aromatic nature of the substance. The band at 1283 cm^{-1} may be ascribed to C=N stretching vibrations, characteristic of amines or amine-containing functional groups. Additional C–H stretching vibrations were observed around 830 cm^{-1} (Fig. 5), corresponding to aliphatic structures and present in all spectra. A distinct band at 1050 cm^{-1} (Fig. 5), observed only in spectrum SAA1, is assigned to S=O stretching vibrations. Moreover, bands near 690 cm^{-1}, detected for SAA1 and SBA1, are associated with S–O stretching vibrations [5]. These two bands confirm the presence of sulfonic groups attached to the aromatic rings in the SAA1 and SBA1 samples. Minor differences in the 1000–1300 cm^{-1} region may result from variations in oxidation state or protonation of the polyaniline salts. Additionally, differences in spectral stability could be linked to variations in conjugated system stability.

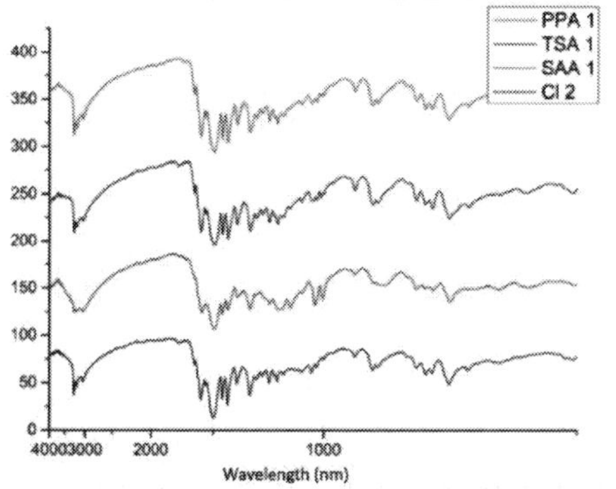

Figure 5: FTIR spectra for PAni PPA1, PAni TSA1,

10.4229/EUPVSEC2025/5DV.2.4

PAni SAA1, PAni Cl2

3.2 UV-Vis

The comparison of spectra for all materials (Figs. 6-7) shows that they are highly similar, with no significant differences suggesting alternative electronic transitions. A peak around 260 nm (Fig. 6) is consistently observed across spectra, corresponding to $\pi \rightarrow \pi^*$ transitions. This transition reflects electron excitation from lower-energy multiple bonds to higher energy states due to strong absorption at 260 nm, confirming the presence of benzene structures [6]. Another absorption maximum appears around 430 nm (Fig. 6), associated with $n \rightarrow \pi^*$ transitions [4], characteristic of aniline. These maxima suggest that the studied substances possess potential for electrical conductivity. The absence of a distinct band in the 800–1000 nm range, typically indicative of polyaniline, may result from short polymer chain length and the presence of impurities in the samples.

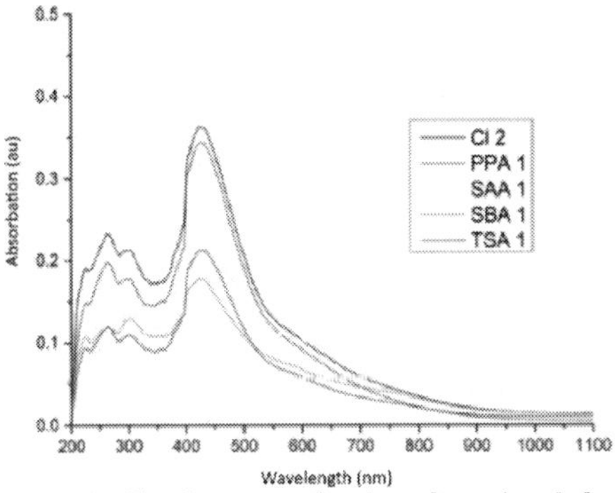

Figure 6: Absorbance as a function of wavelength for PAni PPA1, PAni TSA1, PAni SAA1, PAni Cl2

In the absorption versus energy spectrum, a band with a peak at approximately 2.8 eV is observed (Fig. 7). The pronounced absorption at this energy level corresponds to the transition of benzene rings into their quinoid form [6]. In practice, this indicates the formation of two carbonyl groups within the rings. Another absorption band exhibits a maximum at around 4.7 eV (Fig. 7), which suggests the excitation of benzene rings as a result of protonation of amino groups. The entire band is broad and inhomogeneous; however, as in the case of the previous spectrum, this effect can be attributed to the presence of impurities.

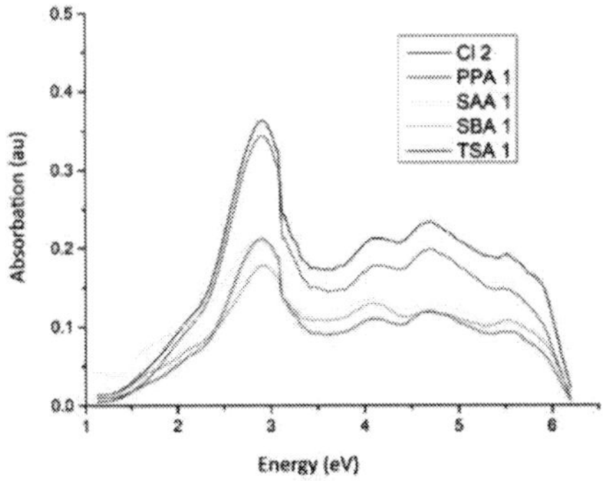

Figure 7: Absorbance as a function of energy for PAni PPA1, PAni TSA1, PAni SAA1, PAni Cl2.

3.4 Conductivity

The conductivity of undoped polyaniline at room temperature is approximately 0.5 µS/cm [7,8]. The analyzed samples exhibited higher conductivities (Table I), confirming the influence of incorporated counterions on enhanced conductivity. The conductivity values of the materials did not differ by orders of magnitude and remained comparable. Despite minor variations, the highest conductivity was observed for PAni Cl2 and PAni SAA1, whereas the lowest was recorded for PAni Cl1 (likely due to unsuccessful synthesis, as confirmed by TG analysis) and PAni SBA2.

3.5 pH measurement

The obtained pH values were generally consistent across samples, except for PAni Cl1 (where polymerization was unsuccessful). The substances exhibited pH values between 5 and 6 (Table I), indicating weakly acidic properties. The reduced pH is attributed to the incorporation of acidic groups into the polymer structure. The lowest pH value was recorded for PAni PPA2, likely due to the stronger acidity of PPA compared to the other acids. Conversely, the highest pH was observed for PAni SBA1.

Table I: Conductivity [µS/cm] and pH values.

Sample	Conductivity	pH
PAni Cl1	8.45	3.90
PAni Cl2	10.95	5.10
PAni SAA1	10.90	5.70
PAni SAA2	10.65	5.68
PAni SBA1	8.75	5.72
PAni SBA2	8.48	5.50
PAni PPA1	10.05	5.27
PAni PPA2	9.20	4.98
PAni TSA1	10.40	5.65

3.6 Synchrotron radiation-based investigation

The results will enable the investigation of the local structure (chemical coordination and electronic state) of the main elements constituting the polymer structure, such as N (K-edge: 409.9 eV), C (K-edge: 284.5 eV), and O (K-edge: 543.1 eV). Measurements of all samples were carried out at 80 K, as the samples proved to be unstable. In the TEY mode, only conductive samples were measured and analyzed. Unexpectedly, most of the samples were non-conductive, which made it impossible to collect TEY spectra for samples with P or S counterions.

Figure 8 presents the spectrum obtained during the analysis of measurements performed at the PIRX beamline. The spectra correspond to repeated measurements of the nitrogen K-edge in the PANI Cl2 sample. Distinct peaks at 399 eV and 402.8 eV are observed, confirming the emeraldine salt structure of polyaniline [9].

10.4229/EUPVSEC2025/5DV.2.4

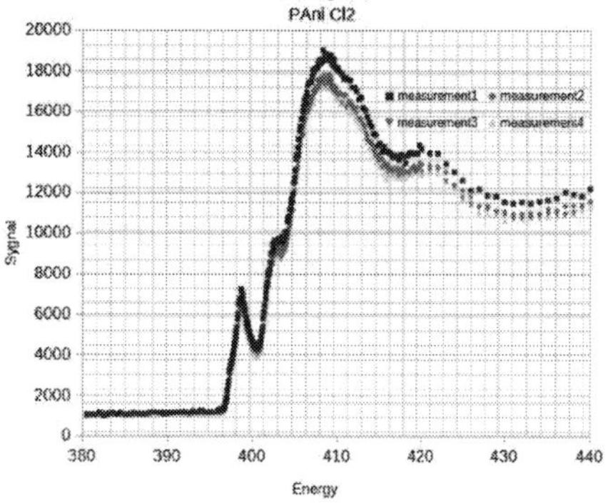

Figure 8: Nitrogen K egde XANES spectra for PAni Cl2

The signal originating from the recovered material, i.e., Ag ions, was very weak. The lines observed in the range of 360–400 eV were inconclusive regarding their possible origin from the silver M45 edges. The most probable explanation for this type of signal in this range is reflection from a chromium mirror.

4 CONCLUSION

The conducted studies demonstrated that the obtained polyaniline samples exhibit distinct properties depending on the acid used for doping. Thermogravimetric analysis confirmed generally good thermal stability of the materials, with PAni Cl1 standing out due to unsuccessful synthesis and the presence of unreacted substrates. FTIR spectroscopy revealed characteristic bands corresponding to N–H, C=N, C=C, and C–H vibrations, while sulfonic acid-doped samples additionally showed signals confirming the presence of sulfonic groups attached to aromatic rings. UV-Vis spectra displayed consistent absorption bands related to $\pi \rightarrow \pi^*$ and $n \rightarrow \pi^*$ transitions, typical of aniline and benzene structures, confirming the potential of the studied substances for electrical conductivity.

Electrical conductivity measurements further demonstrated the significant influence of counterions on material properties, with the highest values recorded for PAni Cl2 and PAni SAA1, and the lowest for PAni Cl1 and PAni SBA2. At the same time, pH measurements (typically within the 5–6 range) confirmed the weakly acidic nature of polyaniline, resulting from the incorporation of acidic groups into the polymer structure.

Synchrotron radiation-based investigations enabled detailed analysis of the local structure of key elements forming the polymer backbone, including N, C, and O. The results confirmed the presence of the emeraldine salt form in the PAni Cl2 sample. However, difficulties were encountered in collecting TEY spectra for samples containing P and S counterions due to their low conductivity. The signal attributed to the recovered silver ions proved to be very weak, while the observed lines in the 360–400 eV range were inconclusive and most likely originated from chromium mirror reflection.

Overall, the obtained results indicate that the synthesized materials exhibit favorable physicochemical properties and can be considered promising candidates for studies on the hydrometallurgical recovery of silver from silicon photovoltaic cells.

5 ACKNOWLEDGMENTS

Research at the National Synchrotron Radiation Centre SOLARIS is supported by the Ministry of Science and Higher Education , Poland, under contract no. 1/SOL/2021/2. This research was founded from the 233004 grant and performed with assist of Marcin Zając from NSRC SOLARIS.

Participation in EUPVESC 2025 is made possible through the PROM project funded by NAVA.

6 REFERENCES

[1] Akram, S., Aziz, H., Imran, A., Javid, A., Nosheen, A., Ashraf, M., Xue, Z., & Raza, M. (2023). Fabrication of silver/polyaniline/aminated graphene oxide coated textiles for electromagnetic interference shielding application within the different bands of frequency. Synthetic Metals, 298, 117440. https://doi.org/10.1016/j.synthmet.2023.117440

[2] Khan, A., Asiri, A. M., Rub, M. A., Azum, N., Khan, A. A. P., Khan, S. B., Rahman, M. M., & Khan, I. (2013). Synthesis, characterization of silver nanoparticle embedded polyaniline tungstophosphate-nanocomposite cation exchanger and its application for heavy metal selective membrane. Composites Part B: Engineering, 45(1), 1486–1492. https://doi.org/10.1016/j.compositesb.2012.09.023

[3] Babaei, Z., Rezaei, B., Pisheh, M. K., & Afshar-Taromi, F. (2020). In situ synthesis of gold/silver nanoparticles and polyaniline as buffer layer in polymer solar cells. Materials Chemistry and Physics, 248. https://doi.org/10.1016/j.matchemphys.2020.122879

[4] Ramalingam, R. J., Al-Lohedan, H., & T., R. (2016). Synthesis, surface and textural characterization of ag doped polyaniline-SiO2(Pan-Ag/RHA) nanocompositesderivedfrom biomass materials. Digest Journal of Nanomaterials and Biostructures, 11, 731–740.

[5] Chu, J., Li, X., Li, Q., Ma, J., Wu, B., Wang, X., Zhang, R., Gong, M., & Xiong, S. (2020). Hydrothermal synthesis of PANI nanowires for high-performance supercapacitor. High Performance Polymers, 32(3), 258–267. https://doi.org/10.1177/0954008319856664

[6] Padmapriya, S., Seshadri, H., Jaidev, K. J., Venkatachalam, S., Kumar, D., & Pal, S. (2017). Storage and evolution of hydrogen in acidic medium by polyaniline. International Journal of Energy Research, 42, 1196–1209. https://doi.org/10.1002/er.3920

[7] Catedral, M. D., Tapia, A. K. G., Sarmago, R. V, Tamayo, J. P., & Del Rosario, E. J. (2004). Effect of Dopant Ions on the Electrical Conductivity and Microstructure of Polyaniline (Emeraldine Salt) (T. 16, Numer 2).

[8] Chaudhari, H. K., & Kelkar, D. S. (1997). Investigation of Structure and Electrical Conductivity in Doped Polyaniline. W Polymer International (T. 42).
[9] Izumi, C. M. S., Constantino, V. R. L., Ferreira, A. M. C., & Temperini, M. L. A. (2006). Spectroscopic characterization of polyaniline doped with transition metal salts. Synthetic Metals, 156(9–10), 654–663. "https://doi.org/10.1016/j.synthmet.2005.12.023"

COMPARATIVE LCA ANALYSIS OF DELAMINATION METHODS FOR PHOTOVOLTAIC MODULES MADE OF CDTE

Anna Kuczyńska-Łażewska
Faculty of Chemistry, Gdansk University of Technology
Narutowicza 11/12, Gdansk PL-80-233, Poland

ABSTRACT: A key step in the recycling of photovoltaic modules is the delamination process, which can be carried out by thermal, chemical or mechanical methods. An analysis of the literature reveals a paucity of life-cycle analyses taking into account the different recycling processes for thin-film modules (CdTe), the completion of which is necessary to fully understand the issue.

The project included an assessment of the environmental impact of various delamination processes (thermal and chemical methods) of modules made with CdTe thin-film technology. In order to collect the data needed for the LCA analysis, experiments were carried out to determine the energy consumption, emissions and potentially harmful waste generated during the delamination process. The LCA analysis conducted on the collected primary data was compared with the analysis for secondary data based on scientific literature.

The data obtained during the project will provide a broader view of the recycling process and enable the identification of environmentally sensitive areas.

Keywords: photovoltaic module; recycling; CdTe; LCA

1 INTRODUCTION

Thin film photovoltaic cells encompass cells composed of:

• Amorphous silicon with an efficiency of 4-8% - a-Si,
• Tandem, a blend of amorphous and microcrystalline silicon with a yield of 9.8% - a-Si and μc-Si,
• Cadmium telluride with an efficiency of 11% - CdTe,
• Copper indium gallium disulfide/diselenide with an efficiency of 12% - CI(G)S [1].

Technologies related to renewable energy sources that are based on rare metals may have a negative environmental impact, despite the apparent benefits due to the rising demand for these raw materials. Hence, it's crucial to analyze environmental aspects of these processes. We need to monitor production, recycling processes and available new technologies that are developed to optimize the consumption of valuable raw materials. The estimated energy recovery time for CdTe modules is approximately 1 year [2]. However, this duration depends on the quantity of available raw materials and there is an environmental cost connected to that.

As the production technology of photovoltaic modules has advanced, so have the methods for material recovery from these processes. Consequently, with the introduction of new cells in the market, recycling techniques have been devised to reclaim the materials used in the manufacturing process and reintegrate them into the production cycle. When compared with traditional methods like incineration or fine grinding, the recycling process of CdTe-based modules is decidedly less environmentally intrusive, with the exception of the space required for the installation [3].

After technological review of available technologies, the environmental impact of known solutions was analyzed. Standard First Solar (FS) method significantly mitigates the adverse effects of used thin-film CdTe modules, for instance, by lowering the overall energy demand from 81 MJ/m^2 to 12 MJ/m^2 [3]. Moreover, it can decrease the detrimental environmental impact of this kind of module by approximately 10% in areas such as general energy demand, acidification, eutrophication, global warming, and photochemical ozone depletion [3].

The one of the newest and most complex life cycle assessment (LCA) was performed by Ravikumar et al. on 2020 [4] taking into consideration main First Solar technology and all other options available at that point in time (Figure 1).

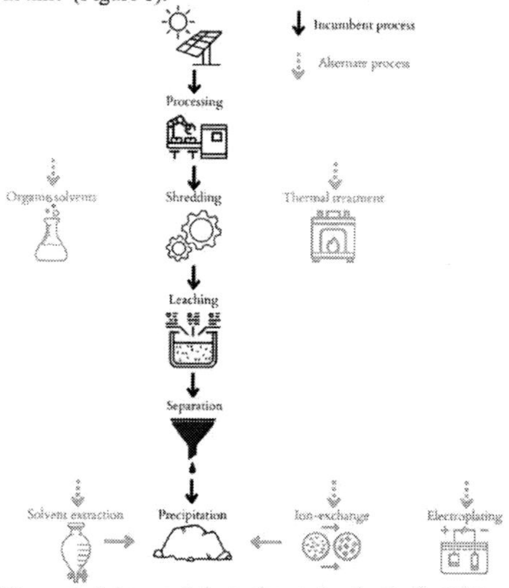

Figure 1: Scheme of alternative technologies in CdTe modules recycling (based on [4])

Four alternative delamination techniques: thermal delamination, organic solvent dissolution, bath sonification and probe sonification with two alternative methods of cadmium extraction: Cd ion-exchange resin and solvent extraction as well as tellurium precipitation. In total eight different combinations were analyzed. [4]

From the presented results they conclude that the lowest impacts are connected with First Solar technology. The thermal delamination+ leaching+ precipitation of unrefined semiconductor material (USM) process may be the competition, especially taking into account that the only difference is with the delamination process. Changing mechanical delamination to the thermal process seems to be a good alternative if we look from the environmental point of view. It does not bring as high energy consumption as it may seem but gives the benefit of better recovered glass

10.4229/EUPVSEC2025/5DV.2.7

quality. Another alternative is mechanical delamination+ leaching+ icon exchange+ precipitation which gives an alternative to the recovery process by use of ion exchange columns. This technology is on the laboratory scale stage and may be a good alternative to USM precipitation and the opportunity of getting recovered materials of higher purity.

2 METHODOLOGY

The data for analysis came from secondary sources, publications based on data provided by companies involved in the recycling of photovoltaic modules and other electronic devices, and data collected as a result of laboratory tests. The list of secondary sources for the data used in the analysis can be found in Table I.

The LCA analysis was performed using the ReCiPe, Endpoint Egalitarian method in the SimaPro 7.1 program, using databases from the program itself.

2.1 Boundary conditions

The analysis was based on the following assumptions:

• The functional unit of analysis is 1 m^2 of a module (series 4 FirstSolar, US) weighing 16.667 kg.

• The recycling plant is located in the USA and serves most of the country in a centralized recycling system.

2.2 LCI for CdTe module recycling

Despite the many recycling methods described above, there are not many publications containing accurate data on the conditions and quantities of substances used. A review of existing LCA analyses for photovoltaic module recycling has identified three methods for separating the semiconductor from the glass and the same number of methods for recovering the semiconductor for which LCI data are available. All six are described in Table I.

Table I: CdTe panel recycling methods analyzed in part one

Name	Acronym	Source for LCI
Thermal delamination, leaching, and precipitation	TL	[2], [4]–[6]
Thermal delamination, leaching, organic solvent	TR	[2], [4]–[6]
Theraml delamination, leaching, ion exchange column and precipitation	TK	[2], [4]–[6]
Mechanical grinding, leaching, and precipitation	ML	[2], [4]–[16]
Solvent extraction, leaching, and precipitation	RL	[4], [6], [8], [10]
Thermal delamination, leaching, and precipitation	TL	[4], [6], [8], [10], [13]

3 RESULTS AND DISCUSSION

3.1 Literature review

Part one of the research was based on the use of secondary data from literature sources. There was the preferable scenario, pessimistic scenario, and a normalized one took into account while collecting data. At first three different approaches to the recovery process were analyzed (Table I – TL, TR, TK) and for the second part three different approaches to delamination were analyzed (Table I – ML, RL, TL). Example of results for single process is shown at Figure 2.

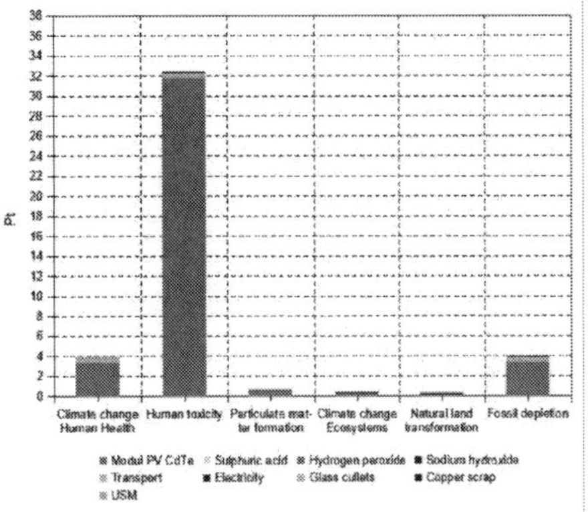

Figure 2. Selected results of LCA for TL recycling method after normalization and weighing.

Although the analysis (Fig. 2) indicates that the photovoltaic module is the input with the largest share in the final result of each analysis, it will not be discussed further, due to its identical presence in each of the methods. This means that it has no ultimate impact on the differences between the results for the subsequent recycling methods. The second input with the largest share in the analysis result varies depending on the method analyzed and the scenario considered.

For the ML method in the scenario containing normalized values, the input with the largest total contribution was transport, while for the other two scenarios, both optimistic and pessimistic, this input was electricity. The same situation was true for the TL method. In the analysis of the RL method, solvent (o-dichlorobenzene) was the second input with the highest influence in the total impact. For the scenario chosen as the most likely, its presence significantly increased the results for this method. The same is true for optimistic scenarios. For the pessimistic scenario, the input with the largest total share was electricity, because of the assumption the additional heating will be needed.

This means that the areas where improvement should be made according to the CdTe recycling process are efficiency of the energy use and the solvent substitution to the environmentally safe option. Also, the important seams are the PV waste collecting system which can be a big factor in the environmental impact of the recycling technology. In this work we will focus only on on-site technology process optimization.

The most sensitive and noteworthy risk points are human health and fossil fuel consumption and in these categories the uncertainty analysis was performed using Monte Carlo method with 1000 iterations.

Comparisons of the TL, TR, and TK recycling methods for all three scenarios were presented in Figure 3. The TR method had the biggest environmental impact, significantly higher than TK and TL method. The TL method achieved the lowest results and is the best option in terms of environmental impact, but it is not a big significant benefit in comparison to TK method.

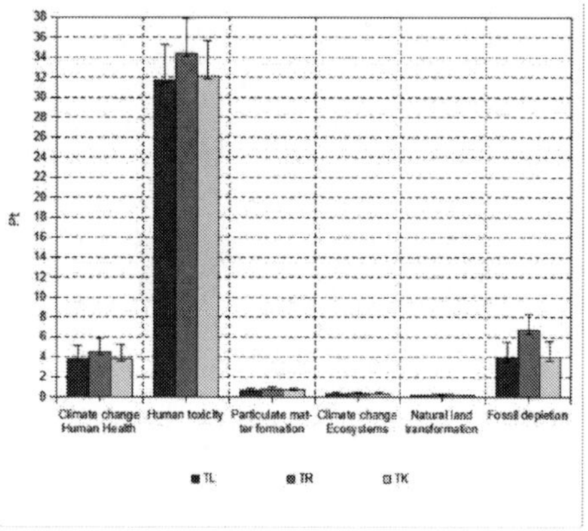

Figure 3. Selected results of LCA for different recycling methods (TL, TR, TK) after normalization and weighing.

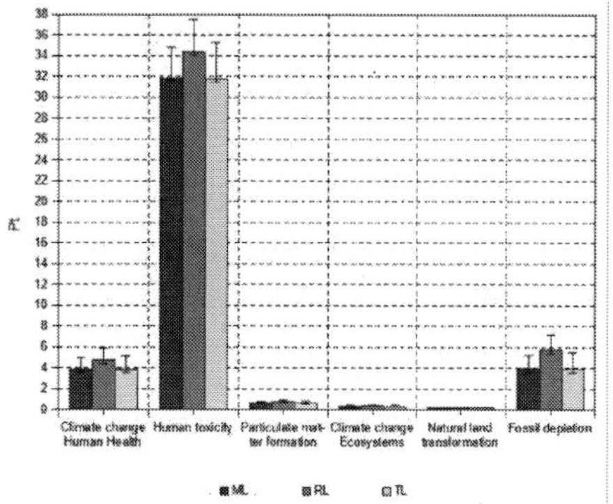

Figure 4. Selected results of LCA for different delamination methods (ML, RL, TL) after normalization and weighing.

The comparison results for the normalized values of the ML, RL, and TL methods indicate that in all six impact categories, the TL method consistently scores the lowest number of points (40.7 pt total) and is therefore the most environmentally friendly. The ML method came in second place. The differences in the results for both methods are small (Fig. 4.). In the Human Toxicity category, the difference between the two methods was only 0.3%. Similarly small differences between the results can be seen in the comparison of the most optimistic scenarios. In this comparison, but for pessimistic scenario the ML process must be identified as the most environmentally friendly process.

3.2 Experimental data

Primary data for the thermal delamination were collected during thermal decomposition of 5x5 cm CdTe module fragment in the tube furnace with air flow in different temperatures (400, 500, 600 °C). The emissions were collected to the Tedlar bags and analyzed using gas chromatography with thermal conductivity and flame ionization detector (GC-TCD+FID). The main groups of emissions were selected: hydrocarbons, aldehydes and ketones, acidic acid and polycyclic aromatic hydrocarbons (PAHs). The ratios in general gas mixture were determined and taken as a input to the LCA. And the energy consumption during each 3h process was measured.

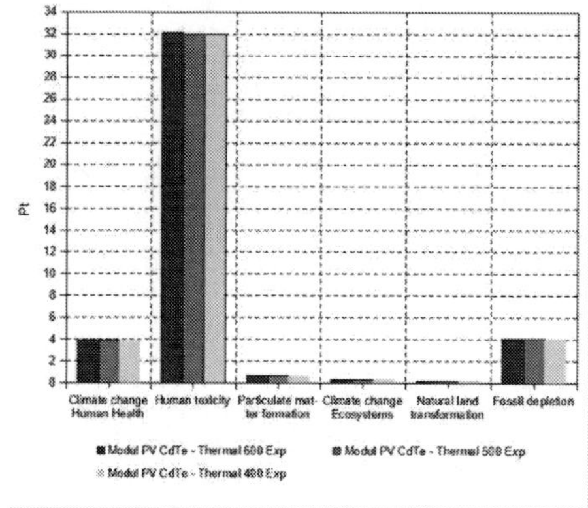

Figure 5. Selected results of LCA for thermal delamination method in different temperatures (400, 500, 600 °C) after normalization and weighing.

From the results (Fig. 5) we can conclude that with this equipment and size there is no significant difference with fossil fuel depletion connected to energy consumption. However, the temperature has a big impact on the gas emissions and the ratio between each faction and in connection with Human Toxicity.

Primary data for chemical delamination were collected during solvent bath of the 5x5 cm CdTe module fragment in different temperatures (25, 40, 60 °C). The electric power consumption, the evaporation rate and amount of solvent used were noted.

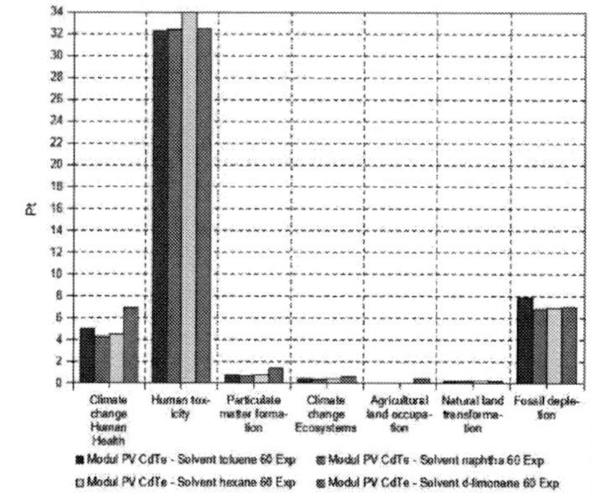

Figure 6. Selected results of LCA for chemical delamination method with different solvents (toluene, hexane, naphtha, d-limonene) at 60 °C after normalization and weighing.

From the obtained results (Fig. 6) the biggest difference is connected to the solvent type and not the temperature. Only for the hexane the evaporation rate was significant and greatly impacted the solvent consumption and the emissions, therefore also impacted the Human Toxicity. From the analysis we can conclude that naphtha and d-limonene have the lowest environmental impact were d-limonene has bigger share in the Climate Change than naphtha what may seem surprising. Even d-limonene seemed like an environmentally friendly option due to the production from citrus peels, the LCA results show that may not be the best option.

4 CONCLUSIONS

Based on a review of the literature the recycling process based on leaching and precipitation should be considered the most environmentally friendly. In addition to that it was found that the thermal delamination method has the least impact on the environment.

Therefore, it was recommended to collect more accurate data sets for the TL method for further comparative analyses. These data should include, in particular, emissions related to the thermal delamination process, because although the use of appropriate filters and scrubbers is assumed, it would be good to take into account their absence in a pessimistic scenario. In addition, the data on electricity consumption provided in the inputs for the TL method came from a process conducted in the laboratory conditions. For a larger scale of the process, this input may vary significantly, and research on this topic should be conducted.

Based on the recommendation during experimental part of data collecting focused was made on the impact of temperature in thermal delamination. Mainly on the gaseous emissions and energy consumption. There was not heat recovery conducted during the experiment, but it may be possible according to high caloric value of the EVA.

During the chemical delamination experiment the focus was on the solvent as a key factor. Most important was the type of the solvent, because it determined the source of the solvent and also the number of emissions to the atmosphere. Depending on the boiling point and how volatile the solvent was, the amount used was different what impacted the LCA.

From the results the conclusion may be made that from an environmental perspective, energy consumption is not a major concern. The crucial aspect is the temperature of the process. In the case of chemical delamination, it increases emissions and the amount of solvent used. During thermal delamination temperature plays a significant role because of the influence on the composition of waste gases.

5 ACKNOWLEDGMENTS

This publication is the result of research project No. 2023/07/X/ST4/00996 founded by The Polish National Science Centre (NCN). Author also would like to acknowledge Alicja Krawiecka (Eng. student) and Bartłomiej Malinowski (M.Sc. student) for participating in the research.

6 REFERENCES

[1] A. Paiano, "Photovoltaic waste assessment in Italy," *Renew. Sustain. Energy Rev.*, vol. 41, pp. 99–112, 2015, doi: 10.1016/j.rser.2014.07.208.

[2] W. Berger, F.-G. Simon, K. Weimann, and E. A. Alsema, "A novel approach for the recycling of thin film photovoltaic modules," *Resour. Conserv. Recycl.*, vol. 54, no. 10, pp. 711–718, 2010, doi: 10.1016/j.resconrec.2009.12.001.

[3] J. Tao and S. Yu, "Review on feasible recycling pathways and technologies of solar photovoltaic modules," *Sol. Energy Mater. Sol. Cells*, vol. 141, pp. 108–124, 2015, doi: 10.1016/j.solmat.2015.05.005.

[4] D. Ravikumar *et al.*, "Environmentally improved CdTe photovoltaic recycling through novel technologies and facility location strategies," *Prog. Photovoltaics Res. Appl.*, vol. 28, no. 9, pp. 887–898, 2020, doi: 10.1002/pip.3279.

[5] P. Sinha, M. Cossette, and J.-F. Ménard, "END-OF-LIFE CDTE PV RECYCLING WITH SEMICONDUCTOR REFINING," in *27th European Photovoltaic Solar Energy Conference and Exhibition*, 2012, pp. 4653–4656, doi: 10.4229/27thEUPVSEC2012-6CV.4.9.

[6] D. T. Ravikumar, P. Sinha, and M. Tao, "An Anticipatory-Lifecycle Approach Towards Increasing the Environmental Gains from Photovoltaic Systems Through Improved Manufacturing and Recycling," no. December, 2016.

[7] M. Held and R. Ilg, "Update of environmental indicators and energy payback time of CdTe PV systems in Europe," *Prog. Photovoltaics Res. Appl.*, vol. 19, no. 5, pp. 614–626, Aug. 2011, doi: 10.1002/PIP.1068.

[8] M. Raugei, M. Isasa, and P. F. Palmer, "Potential Cd emissions from end-of-life CdTe PV," *Int. J. Life Cycle Assess.*, vol. 17, no. 2, pp. 192–198, Feb. 2012, doi: 10.1007/S11367-011-0348-9/FIGURES/2.

[9] V. M. Fthenakis and H. C. Kim, "CdTe photovoltaics: Life cycle environmental profile and comparisons," *Thin Solid Films*, vol. 515, no. 15, pp. 5961–5963, May 2007, doi: 10.1016/J.TSF.2006.12.138.

[10] V. M. Fthenakis, P. Duby, W. Wang, C. Graves, and A. Belova, "Recycling of CdTe Photovoltaic Modules: Recovery of Cadmium and Tellurium," *21st Eur. Photovolt. Sol. energy Conf.*, pp. 2539–2541, 2006

[11] M. Held, "Life cycle assessment of CdTe module recycling," in *24th European Photovoltaic Solar Energy Conference*, 2009, pp. 2370–2375.

[12] P. Sinha, "Life cycle materials and water management for CdTe photovoltaics," *Sol. Energy Mater. Sol. Cells*, vol. 119, pp. 271–275, 2013, doi: 10.1016/j.solmat.2013.08.022.

[13] T. Maani, I. Celik, M. J. Heben, R. J. Ellingson, and D. Apul, "Environmental impacts of recycling crystalline silicon (c-SI) and cadmium telluride (CDTE) solar panels," *Sci. Total Environ.*, vol. 735, p. 138827, 2020, doi: 10.1016/j.scitotenv.2020.138827.

[14] G. Giacchetta, M. Leporini, and B. Marchetti, "Evaluation of the environmental benefits of new high value process for the management of the end of life of thin film photovoltaic modules," *J. Clean. Prod.*, vol. 51, pp. 214–224, 2013, doi: 10.1016/j.jclepro.2013.01.022.

[15] V. Fthenakis *et al.*, "Life Cycle Inventories and Life Cycle Assessments of Photovoltaic Systems," 2011. Accessed: Sep. 22, 2025.

[16] D. Ravikumar, P. Sinha, T. P. Seager, and M. P. Fraser, "An anticipatory approach to quantify energetics of recycling CdTe photovoltaic systems," *Prog. Photovoltaics Res. Appl.*, vol. 24, no. 5, pp. 735–746, May 2016, doi: 10.1002/PIP.2711.

Design for Repair of PV modules: A meaningful or crazy idea?

Gernot Oreski[1], Sonja Feldbacher[1], Anika Gassner[2], Gabriele Eder[2], Ioannis Tsanakas[3], Timea Bejat[3]

[1] Polymer Competetence Center Leoben, Austria
[2] OFI Austrian Research Institute for Chemistry and Technology, Austria
[3] Univ. Grenoble Alpes, CEA, Liten, Campus Ines, 73375 Le Bourget du Lac, France

PCCL
Polymer Competence Center Leoben

PV module design

- Standard PV module design: The current PV module design and packaging concept, with interconnected solar cells in between two transparent polymer films, a frontglass and a backsheet or backglass was developed over 40 years ago
- Design for Repair: Potential to extend the functional lifespan of modules, reduce waste, and enhance sustainability in the solar energy sector
- Current state: No comprehensive strategies addressing "Design for Repair" or the "Right for Repair" have been published for PV modules

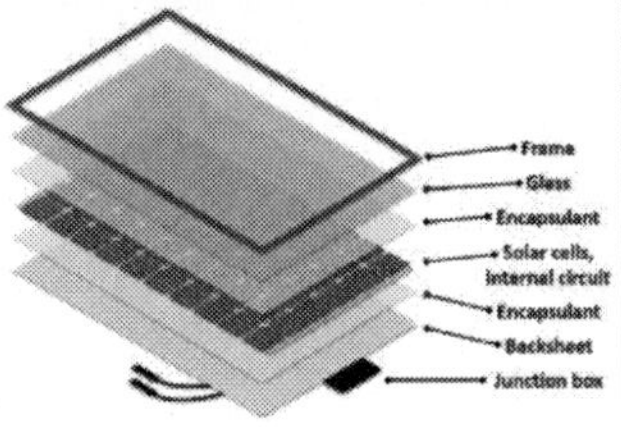

Figure 1: Most common configurations of PV modules for crystalline silicon cells https://doi.org/10.1016/j.rser.2022.112160

Durability-Repairability Paradox

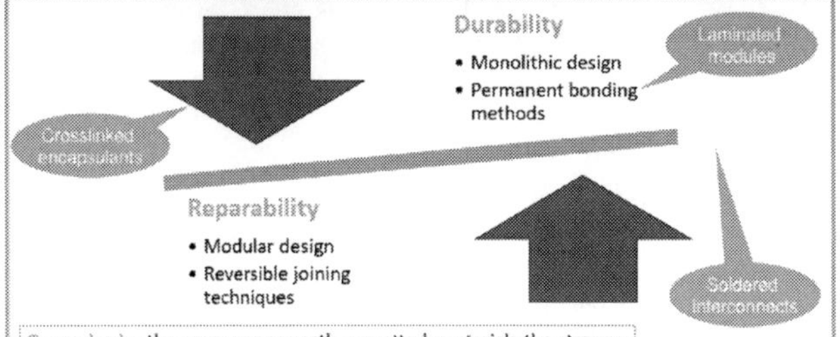

General rule: the more permanently you attach materials the stronger and more durable it is, but the more difficult it is to repair and replace.

Objectives and Methodology

Main objective: To explore opportunities & challenges of Design for Repair (DfR) in PV modules through literature and market survey

Literature survey on repair-oriented PV research → Market scan of start-ups → Identification of enabling technologies

Results

A few research groups and start-ups are working on new PV designs and module materials

Focus is on improving recyclability of modules and components

Many of these innovations also enable easier repair

Reversible adhesives for frames and junction boxes

Approach:

- **Modification** of existing silicone adhesive system by addition of functional fillers to the formulation to thermally trigger debonding of the adhesive connection after service life
- **Functional fillers** expand upon reaching a temperature threshold and facilitate debonding by overcoming the maximum strength of the adhesive joint

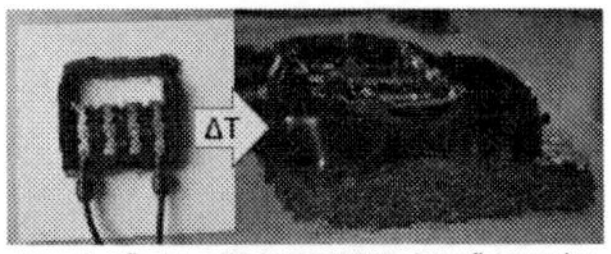

Figure 2: Adhesive connection containing thermally expanding fillers before (left) and after (right) thermally triggering the expansion;. **Wanghofer et al., 2023;** https://doi.org/10.1016/j.ijadhadh.2023.103454

Benefit

- Enables removal of damaged frames or junction boxes **without harming the PV module**

Challenges

- **Prevent expansion** under normal operating conditions
- **Ensure** reliable functional **triggering** throughout the entire lifetime

Self healing polymer layers (for electrically conductive adhesives, encapsulants)

Approach:

- Introduction of **thermally responsive self healing polymers** based on reversible polymer networks that exploit daily temperature changes to repair micro-defects

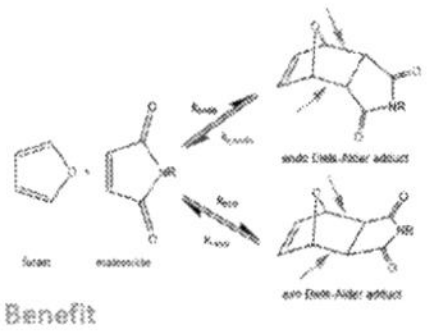

Figure 3: Reversible Diels–Alder (DA) reactions between maleimide and furan derivatives, forming Diels–Alder adducts. Reversible Diels–Alder bonds are indicated by red arrows. **Ehrhardt et al., 2020** http://dx.doi.org/10.3390/polym12112543

Benefit

- **Extending reliability** could be achieved if self-healing repairs microcracks/ delamination while maintaining adhesion and conductivity under thermal and mechanical stress

Challenges

- **Long-term stability:** Organic DA networks may degrade under 25+ years of outdoor exposure
- **Material compatibility:** Potential issues with other PV module materials or additives (e.g., fillers, crosslinkers, conductive particles)
- **Processing & performance trade-offs:** Dynamic networks may reduce mechanical strength and increase creep

Modular designs

Approach:

- **Encapsulant free module design:** Glass–glass construction sealed using a double edge-seal (e.g. N.I.C.E. Module Technology, Biosphere Solar)
- New concepts using liquid encapsulation (Biosphere Solar)

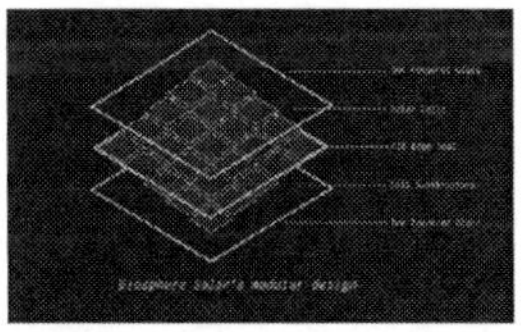

Figure 4: PV module concept without encapsulation. ©Biosphere Solar https://www.biosphere.solar

Benefit

- **Modular design** allowing for the replacement of individual components such as solar cells without damaging the entire unit
- **Absence** of traditional encapsulants may eliminate common degradation issues such as yellowing and delamination

Challenges

- **Performance:** Reflective losses due to lack of optical coupling between glass and cell
- **Long-term stability:** Butyl based edge seals provide excellent barrier to water vapor but not oxygen

What about thermoplastic encapsulants? They should be separable?

CONCLUSIONS AND OUTLOOK

- No comprehensive strategies addressing "Design for Repair" or the "Right for Repair" have been published for PV modules
- Emerging Design for Repair Concepts: Current research explores reversible adhesives, self-healing materials, and encapsulant-free designs to enable easier repair and cell replacement in PV modules
- Low TRL Challenges: Most proposed approaches remain at low technology readiness levels and lack validation for long-term durability and reliability
- Future Outlook: Demonstrating robustness and performance is critical for advancing repair-friendly PV designs toward market adoption

- This work was done within the Austrian research project ReNewPV and as part of the IEA-PVPS Task 13 Subtask 1.2 "Performance and Reliability of Second Life PV"
- The final report of this activity will be published until the end of 2025 and can be downloaded for free from this website: https://iea-pvps.org/research-tasks/reliability-and-performance-of-pv-systems/

Not really, it is more complicated

ORCID ID
Polymer Competence Center Leoben GmbH (PCCL), Saurauqasse 1, 8700 Leoben, Austria
Corresponding Author: Gernot.oreski@pccl.at

cea ofi IEA PVPS ReNewPV

Follow my LinkedIn Account for PV Encapsulation Mythbusters! Starting in Autumn 2025

020500002

ADVANCING SOLAR ENERGY SUSTAINABILITY: TACKLING PHOTOVOLTAIC CELL UPCYCLING THROUGH METAL RECOVERY

Vázquez Adán, A.[1], López Cuéllar, J.M.[1], Ríos Moral, L.[1], Caballero L.J.[2], Dasilva-Villanueva N.[2], Fuertes Marrón D.[2], del Cañizo, C.[2], Díez Alcántara, E.[1], Rodríguez Rodríguez A.[1]
[1]Departamento de Ingeniería Química y de Materiales, Fac. Ciencias Químicas, Universidad Complutense de Madrid, Avenida Complutense (28040), Madrid, Spain.
[2]Instituto de Energía Solar, ETSI Telecomunicación, Universidad Politécnica de Madrid, Avenida Complutense 40 (28040), Madrid, Spain.

ABSTRACT: The rapid growth of photovoltaic (PV) installations around the world has led to a significant accumulation of PV end-of-life (EoL) cells. This paper aims to study the recycling process for these cells to recover valuable metals like silver and aluminium, as well as the silicon wafer while maintaining its quality to be reused. Two alternative routes were considered: a basic etching, with KOH/ethanol/water mixtures, and nitric acid leaching followed by electrolysis. The etching experiments enabled the physical separation of the contacts; however, rigorous control of the variables is important to minimize silicon loss. Silver and aluminium etched contacts could be separated thereof in a sieving process due to their difference in average size. Leaching experiments were performed with various nitric acid concentrations, with 3M as reference value. In this case, the silver contacts were extracted and transferred to the solution and subsequently recovered as native silver by means of electrodeposition. Usually, after delamination and encapsulant removal, the cells of an EoL PV-module are completely fragmented. Therefore, depending on the size of the fragments, one strategy may be more effective than another.
Keywords: Recycling, Solar Cells, Silicon, Metal Recovery

1 INTRODUCTION

Solar photovoltaic (PV) energy has a crucial role in the global effort to achieve decarbonization, becoming a priority for governments, businesses and society in general, with many entities aiming to be carbon neutral by 2050, with the aim of limiting global temperature rise to 1.5 ºC [1]. The integration of solar energy, particularly through optimized PV systems, offers a viable solution to reduce CO_2 emissions, replacing traditional energy sources [2]. In this sense, according to the International Energy Agency [3], the cumulative global PV capacity reached 2.2 TW in 2024 (1.9 TW according to IRENA [4]), and the evolution of annual PV installations achieved a maximum growth of 554 GW, in 2024 (566 GW according to ITRPV, 2024 results [5]). ITRPV predictions [5] indicate that installed capacity is expected to increase to 63.4 TW in 2050 in a zero-greenhouse gas emission scenario.

However, due to the estimated lifetime of a PV module being between 25 to 30 years, the exponential growth of installations is generating a progressive accumulation of waste. This mainly affects devices, installed from the 1990s to the 2000s, crystalline silicon wafer based.

Even though it is true that solar PV can produce net zero-emission electricity for 25-30 years, the total environmental impact during the entire life cycle, including the manufacturing and waste management phases, must be considered. The former contributes to the total carbon footprint of the module, as it consumes water and raw materials, and the purification of silicon is energy intensive (according to the literature [6] approximately 40% of the overall costs associated with module manufacturing can be attributed to wafer production). Additionally, a fraction of off-specs solar cells is rejected during the manufacturing process without becoming part of a module, adding up to the waste.

Considering the number of discarded cells and the current accumulated capacity of photovoltaic waste, the purpose of this research is to study possible paths for the recycling process of these cells with the aim of recovering the metals (mainly silver and aluminium), as well as the silicon wafer, while maintaining its quality to be reused. Two possible ways have been explored: a basic etching and an acid leaching followed by electrolysis, minimizing the environmental impact and contributing to effective recycling strategies. Usually, after delamination and encapsulant removal, the cells of an EoL panel are totally fragmented into small pieces. So, depending on the size of the fragments one strategy will be more adequate than the other.

Basic etching and acid leaching plus electrodeposition emerge as a critical innovation within this framework, offering several advantages. In the first case, it is possible to recover high purity metal contacts and to reuse the basic solution for several cycles. In the second case, by applying an electric current, silver ions in solution are reduced to metallic silver at the cathode. This process not only ensures a high-efficiency recovery, but also eliminates the need for additional purification steps, making it highly scalable for industrial applications. In addition, this study has identified optimal operating conditions for electrodeposition, including current density and electrode material, to maximize recovery rates and minimize energy consumption. On the other hand, in literature, other alternatives, such as selective adsorption, have also employed to selectively recover metals from CIGS cells leachates [7]. Figure 1 displays the complete recycling process of EoL solar modules, in which both processes would follow, just after the previous removal of backsheet and encapsulants.

This research presents a novel integration of chemical and electrochemical techniques that overcome the limitations of traditional metal recovery methods. The proposed methodologies minimize the generation of secondary waste and the consumption of chemical reagents and enables the extraction of silver with high purity.

2 EXPERIMENTAL PROCEDURES

Several chemical routes were explored, with different types of solar cells. In this paper, basic etching and acid leaching experiments were done on Al-BSF cells with SiN_x Antireflection Coating (ARC) manufactured in the nineties, and on more recent PERC solar cells. Some results are highlighted in this section; more details can be found in [8].

10.4229/EUPVSEC2025/5DV.2.10

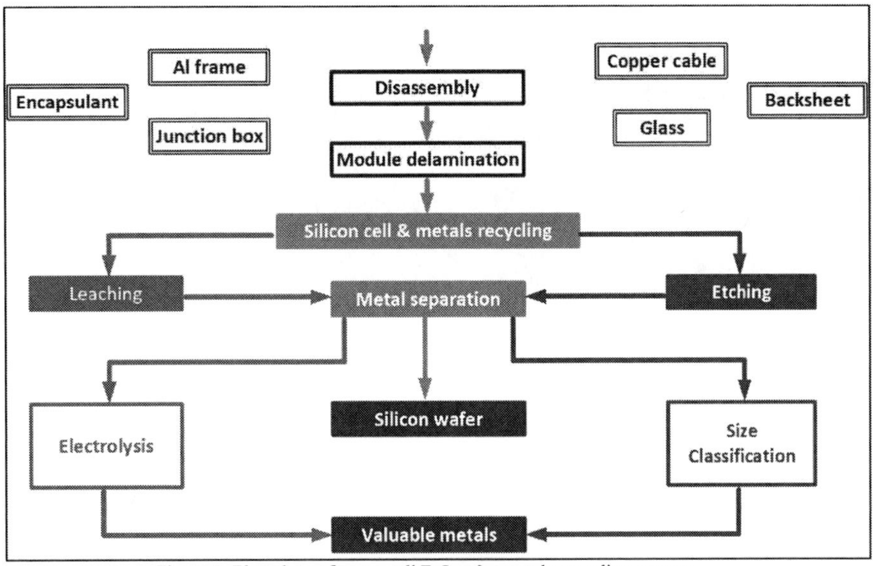

Figure 1. Flowchart of an overall EoL solar panels recycling process

2.1 Basic etching

The alkaline route is based on the physical separation of the metal contacts by etching the silicon layer immediately below, using aqueous KOH solutions, with ethanol added as a surfactant, facilitating the release of hydrogen bubbles generated in the process. Different compositions and different operational conditions (varying temperature, with or without stirring), were tested, while keeping the solution-to-solid ratio constant. Several analytical techniques were used to characterise the solid and liquid fractions resulting from the process: the solid fraction was examined by scanning electron microscopy (SEM) and X-ray fluorescence (XRF), while the liquid fraction was analysed using inductively coupled plasma (ICP) spectroscopy. This combination of techniques allowed to assess the purity of the metal contacts and the silicon wafer, as well as to quantify the transfer of solid material to the liquid phase during the etching process.

At the end of etching process, the silicon wafers were washed with distilled water and dried. Afterwards, the organics were cleaned with an RCA-1 treatment (5:1:1 v/v mixture of 27% ammonia (NH_3), 30% hydrogen peroxide (H_2O_2) and deionised water), and the ARC was removed with 2% HF.

2.2 Acid leaching + electrodeposition

Acid leaching was carried out by digestion of solar cell fragments with nitric acid solutions, being 3 M the acid concentration of reference.

The recovery of metals from the acid leaching processes was carried out by precipitation to recover silver in the form of silver chloride and by electrodeposition to recover silver in native form.

3 RESULTS AND DISCUSSION

3.1.Basic etching

As indicated, the etching experiments were developed with KOH/ethanol/water mixtures in all cases.

It is important to point out that as the concentration of potassium hydroxide increases, the etching time decreases and the loss of silicon from the wafer increases. This indicates that a rigorous control of the variables (concentration, time, temperature) is necessary. In the absence of ethanol, the process gives rise to foams that make the retrieval of the metallic contacts difficult. On the other hand, the incorporation of mechanical agitation has been shown to enhance the process, leading to a substantial reduction in etching time and reducing the loss of silicon. In this study, the potential reutilization of the etching solution for several etching cycles was examined. It was observed that agitation helped the reuse of the basic solution one or two additional cycles until the formation of very fine silica powder, which inhibits the etching process. The use of an etching solution of 35% KOH, and 5% ethanol at 65°C, with a solid/liquid ratio of 15 g/L, has been found effective to completely demetallize an Al-BSF cell fragment in less than 40 min. Additionally, the etching solution could be reused up to three etching cycles.

Concerning PERC cells, the best results were attained through the utilization of a basic solution composed of 25% KOH and 5% ethanol. These conditions facilitated the complete cell demetallization at a temperature of 65°C in less than 25 minutes. Figure 2 shows an example of demetallized Al-BSF (a) and PERC (b) cell.

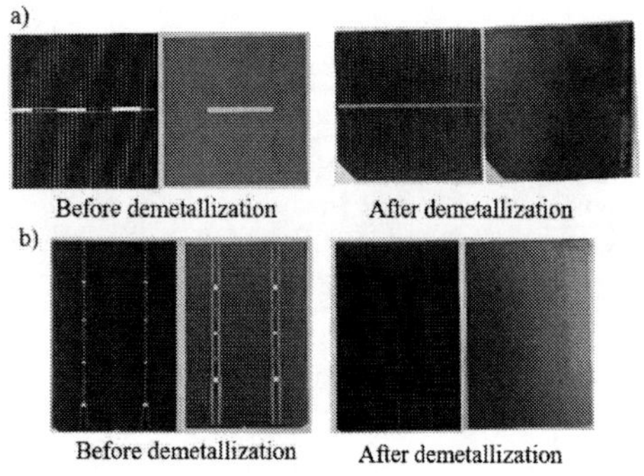

Figure 2. a) BSF cell before and after demetallization, b) PERC cell before and after demetallization.

Following the etching tests, the recuperation of the metal species in solid phase was conducted physically by filtration. The samples were then dried and sieved to separate aluminium from silver.

For this purpose, a granulometric analysis of the resulting metals was carried out to ensure an effective sieving process. In the case of Al-BSF cells it was possible to effectively separate silver and aluminium particles due to their different size and morphology, which was not the case of PERC cells.

After the etching process, a thorough cleaning of the contactless wafers was carried out in order to elucidate if these wafer fragments would be suitable for the fabrication of new devices. This is usually carried out by analysing the minority charge carrier lifetime of the wafers. As a quick reference, if this value exceeds 100 µs at an injection level of 10^{15} cm^{-3}, the silicon substrate could result in an efficient solar cell (η>20%) [6].

3.2. Acid leaching + electrodeposition.

When the size of the delaminated cell fragments is not large enough to efficiently separate the contacts after the etching step, the recovery of silver through acid leaching followed by electrodeposition has proved to be an efficient method yielding high purity silver. Regarding acid leaching efficiency, the use of nitric acid as a leaching agent has been demonstrated to facilitate the effective dissolution of silver. This reagent demonstrated high efficiency in isolating silver with a minimal impact on the structural integrity of the silicon wafer. In addition, analysis of the solid residue (demetallized solar cell fragment) revealed a complete metal elimination.

Electrodeposition was selected as a convenient recovery method, eliminating the need for subsequent silver purifying processes. The process was studied employing silver synthetic solutions in three distinct stages. Initially, the material of the cathode was selected, with stainless steel cathode as the most suitable option, as compared to copper, which suffered from lixiviation, thereby contaminating the medium. The study of the circulating current density as a function of applied voltage (in the range of 0.8 to 3.2 V) showed an increased recovery of silver with increasing current. Boron-Doped Diamond (BDD), Mixed Metal Oxide (MMO) and carbon filter were studied as anodes. Among them, BDD emerged as the most suitable option. The filter carbon process is rapid but causes iron leaching due to nitric acid capillarity. The MMO anode performance is too slow because of Oxygen Evolution Reaction (OER), and oxygen formation. In turn, BDD offers a moderate rate without these drawbacks. Finally, the effect of the initial metal composition was investigated, by preparing synthetic solutions with an initial silver concentration ranging from 5 to 1000 ppm. The results of this study indicated that the process was effective in terms of selective silver recovery, even at the highest silver concentrations.

The results obtained with synthetic solutions were then extended to lixiviates from real solar cells. Figure 3 shows a drastic decrease in silver concentration in the solution over processing time, while the concentrations of other metals, such as silicon and aluminium, remained constant, indicating a selective removal of silver into the solid phase.

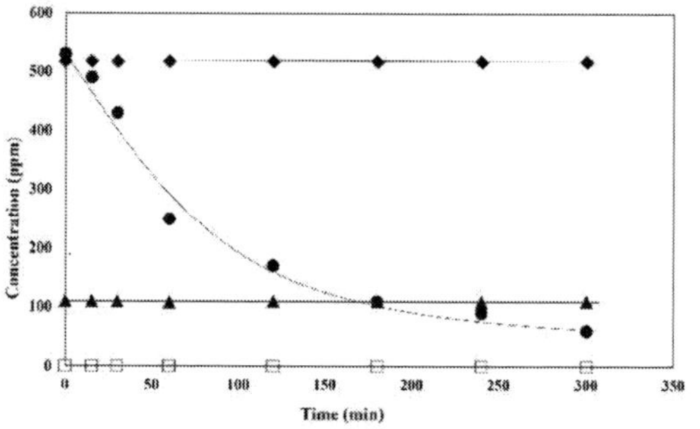

Figure 3. Concentrations of different metals, silver (●), copper (□), aluminium (▲) and silicon (◆) from real cell leachates as a function of processing time.

4 CONCLUSIONS

In summary, the KOH/ethanol/water etching process effectively demetallizes silicon wafers and recovers metallic contacts in solid phase. Careful control of KOH concentration, temperature, ethanol addition, and agitation is necessary to optimize etching rates, minimize silicon loss, and allow solution reuse. In this process, ethanol prevents foaming, and agitation improves efficiency. Demetallized Si-wafers must be cleaned and their minority carrier lifetime assessed to determine their reusability as substrates for new device fabrication. Recovered contacts can be efficiently separated by sieving due to the large difference between silver and aluminium particle sizes, and granulometric analysis can be used to ensure accuracy.

Stainless steel is a suitable cathode for silver recovery by electrodeposition after acidic etching of cell fragments. High current densities improve silver recovery, BDD offered the best balance as anode compared to carbon felt or MMO. Tests using real solar cells leachates demonstrated full silver recovery, confirming electrodeposition as an effective and selective method for the recovery of high-purity silver from PV-waste.

5 ACKNOWLEDGEMENTS

Grants No. TED2021-129624B-C41/C42 funded by the Spanish International Research Agency MCIN/AEI/10.13039/501100011033 and by “NextGenerationEU”/PRTR.

Grant No. PID2023-148369OB-C41 funded by the Spanish International Research Agency MCIN/AEI/10.13039/501100011033 and by “NextGenerationEU”/FEDER.

Grant No. TEC-2024ECO-72 funded by the

Directorate-General for Research and Technological Innovation of the Community of Madrid (Spain)

6 REFERENCES

[1] R. Basnet *et al.*, Sol. Energy Mater. Sol. Cells 292 (2025) 113816.
[2] IM. Peters *et al.*, Cradle-to-cradle recycling in terawatt photovoltaics: A vision of perpetual utility, Joule (2024).
[3] International Energy Agency, *Snapshot of Global PV Markets 2025 Task 1 Strategic PV Analysis & Outreach*, 2025.
[4] International Renewable Energy Agency, *Renewable Capacity Statistics 2025*, 2025.
[5] VDMA, *International Technology Roadmap for Photovoltaics: 2024 results*, 2025.
[6] J. Hofstetter *et al.*, Prog. Photov. 24 (2016) 122.
[7] V. Ramos *et al.*, Surfaces 8 (2025) 59.
[8] M. Tierno *et al.*, Solar Energy 274 (2024) 112533.

Sustainability strategies for optimising the use phase of photovoltaics: an overview from a Life Cycle perspective

Gamarra, A. R.*, Lechón, Y., Garraín, D.
Research Center on Energy, Environment and Technology (Ciemat). Av. Complutense, 40. 28040. Madrid.
anarosa.gamarra@ciemat.es, yolanda.lechon@ciemat.es, daniel.garrain@ciemat.es

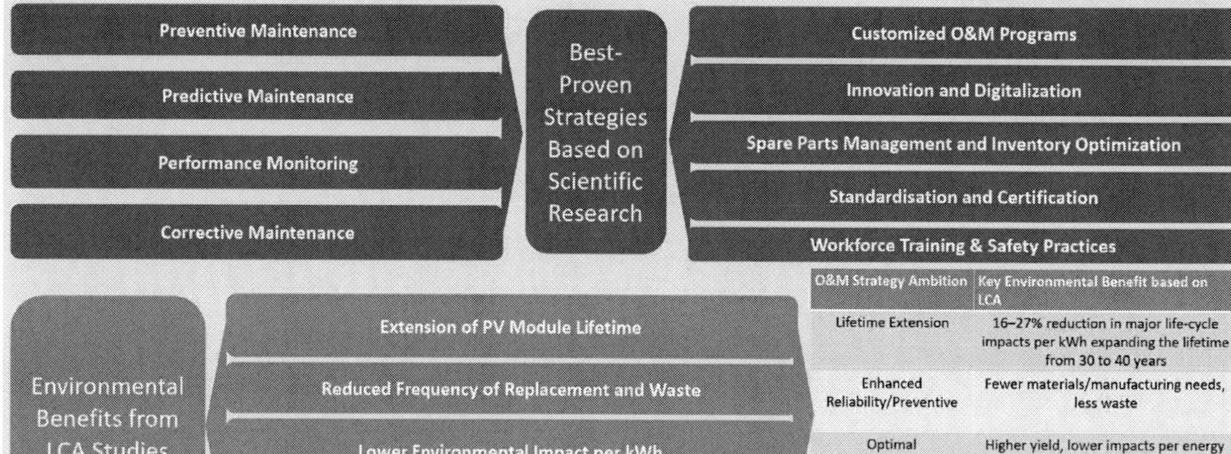

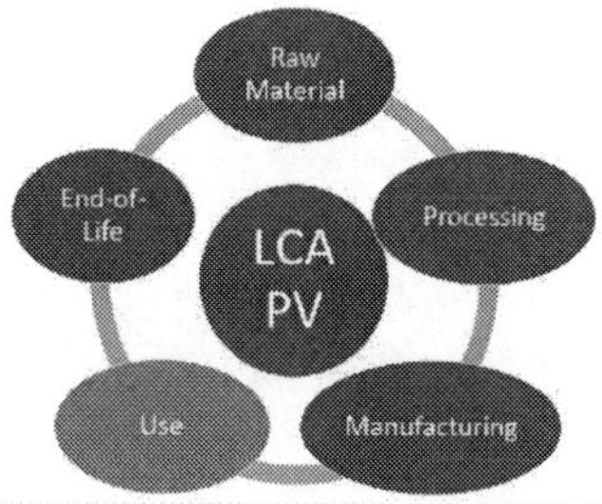

Introduction and methods

- The use phase, encompassing operational and performance factors, influences overall sustainability across different PV technologies.
- The Life Cycle Assessment (LCA) and the Life Cycle Costing analysis of photovoltaic (PV) systems have become essential to understanding their environmental impacts throughout their entire lifespan.
- The aim of this paper is to provide an up-to-date overview of the LCA/LCC of PV, focusing on the strategies for optimising the O&M phase, by reviewing the most recent literature and expected outcomes on the subject.
- The analysis of more than 25 scientific papers and grey literature reporting LCA and LCC of sustainability strategies undertaken in the O&M stage of PV published recently from 2022 allows to: 1) identify the best strategies proposed in the literature; and 2) identify which are the environmental and economic benefits associated along the life cycle of PV, and 3) to know which and how the benefits have been analysis by LCA and LCC and quantified.

Results

Best-Proven Strategies Based on Scientific Research

- Preventive Maintenance
- Predictive Maintenance
- Performance Monitoring
- Corrective Maintenance
- Customized O&M Programs
- Innovation and Digitalization
- Spare Parts Management and Inventory Optimization
- Standardisation and Certification
- Workforce Training & Safety Practices

Environmental Benefits from LCA Studies

- Extension of PV Module Lifetime
- Reduced Frequency of Replacement and Waste
- Lower Environmental Impact per kWh
- Support of Recycling and Resource Efficiency

O&M Strategy Ambition	Key Environmental Benefit based on LCA
Lifetime Extension	16–27% reduction in major life-cycle impacts per kWh expanding the lifetime from 30 to 40 years
Enhanced Reliability/Preventive	Fewer materials/manufacturing needs, less waste
Optimal Cleaning/Diagnostics	Higher yield, lower impacts per energy unit
Digital Predictive/Drones/AI	Early issue detection, enabling longer asset use
Recycling-Focused Planning	Greater resource efficiency, less landfill waste

Cost Component	Description	Share LCC
Initial Cost	Solar panels, inverters, installation, mechanical & civil works	26%
Operation & Maintenance	Manpower, panel cleaning, regular inspections, system monitoring	63%
Failure Cost	Minor repairs, parts replacement (especially inverters and balance-of-system components)	11%

Economic Benefits from LCC Studies

- Significant Share of Life Cycle Cost
- Reduced Failure Costs
- Optimized Inspection and Cleaning
- Improved Operational Efficiency
- Longer Lifetime, Better Payback
- Asset and Inventory Optimization
- Support for Circular Economy

O&M Strategy Ambition	Key Economic Benefit based on LCC
Planned Maintenance	Reduces costs by 12-40%; extends asset life
Predictive Maintenance	Further savings beyond preventive (~8–12%)
Reactive/Corrective Maintenance	Up to 3-5 times more costly than planned
Performance Monitoring	Minimizes downtime and repair costs
Cleaning Management	Enhances yield, reduces degradation costs

Conclusions and ongoing developments

- The most scientifically validated and effective strategy is a combination of digital, data-driven predictive maintenance and robust performance monitoring, tailored to site-specific conditions. This maximizes reliability, minimizes both operating costs and downtime, and supports long-term profitability and sustainability in PV systems.
- LCAs confirm that the best O&M strategies—particularly those that extend service life, improve performance, and support recycling—substantially enhance the environmental profile of PV systems and help realize their sustainability potential.
- LCC studies consistently demonstrate that robust O&M strategies—especially those emphasizing reliability, preventive actions, and efficient resource allocation—can significantly reduce the lifetime costs and maximize the economic value of PV installations. In essence, shifting from reactive to planned and predictive maintenance, coupled with digital monitoring and proactive cleaning, produces the greatest measurable reductions in PV lifecycle cost.

ONGOING RESEARCH: **SOLARIS PROJECT** will provide an updated comprehensive assessment and quantification and comparison of benefits for sustainability by conducting the LCA, LCC and Socioeconomically Extended Input-Output Analysis (SEMRIO) of several solutions in a range of use-cases encountered (ground-mounted small- and utility-scale PVs, rooftop, floating PVs, AgriPV).

- Two groups of solutions:
  - Digital: Accurate weather and power generation forecasting; Energy trading tool for optimised energy selling and prolonged battery energy storage system BESS lifetime PV asset management software, relying on automated monitoring and inspection data gathering, for accurate fault detection, identification, predictive maintenance and decision-support to the operator.
  - Physical: Strategies against soiling for PV system increased performance and lower cleaning costs; Wind load sensing for adapted self-protection; Novel impedance sensing device for continuous, accurate and preventive fault detection and location & Novel inverter prototype for prolonged components lifetime and reconfiguration; Automated multi-imagery and high-resolution PV inspection using drones for fault location.

Acknowledgements

We thank the Solaris Project. This research is funded by the European Union under grant agreement no.101146377. Views and opinions expressed are however those of the author(s) only and do not Necessarily reflect those of the European Union or CINEA. Neither the European Union nor the granting authority can be held responsible for them.

References

A detailed list of reference can be found in the link (QR)

ENERGY SYSTEMS ANALYSIS UNIT

SOLARIS

42nd European Photovoltaic Solar Energy Conference and Exhibition
Bilbao (SPAIN). September, 2025

EU PVSEC

Recycling end-of-life PV modules

Pulsed lasers, light flashes and hot knives

Per-Anders Hansen*, Rune Søndenå
Institute for Energy Technology
Corresponding author: per-anders.hansen@ife.no

INTRODUCTION

The stream of discarded PV modules has previously been fairly small, but is rapidly increasing. It is expected that by 2050, 5-7 Mtons of discarded PV modules will have to be handled each year globally [1]. Still, there is no established method to recycle PV modules today. A major challenge is that neither old nor current PV modules were designed with recycling in mind. Separating a module back into its material components is difficult. Doing so in a way that preserves the various materials for further recycling while also being economically viable, even more so.

In this work, we have investigated three different method to separate the glass pane from the rest (metals, silicon and various polymers and laminate adhesives). The aim is to in one way or another sever the polymer bonding everything onto the glass, while at the same time keeping the glass intact in one piece.

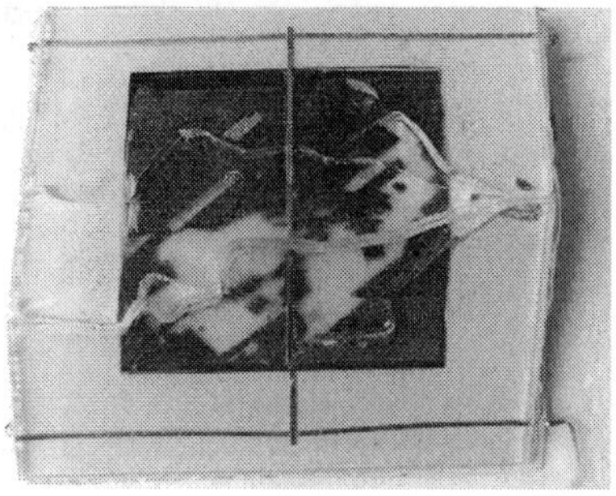

Mini-module after repeated Xe flashing, showing loose wafer fragments.

Hot knife

A simple, electrically heated knife edge being pushed along the glass surface.

+ Simple and inexpensive
- Creates toxic fumes
- Hard work when done by hand

The electrically heated hot knife, used to separate the back sheet, cells and metals from the glass pane.

Flash lamp

Optically heating the silicon wafer beyond the charring temperature of the cell/polymer interface.

+ Does not (intentionally) heat the whole device
+ No fumes created
+ Cell was separated on both sides, resulting in a loose wafer
- Requires very expensive power / battery packs
- Metal was stuck on glass
- Did not separate the areas between and around cells, where only the white backsheet was visible

Pulsed laser

A more advanced form of Xe flash lamps, but bringing a spot above the interface charring temperature within the duration of a single laser pulse. Lasering was carried out by SYLSTAD AS and VDlaser AS.

+ No* fumes (some smell present)
+ Can shear the glass/metal and white glass/backsheet areas
- Only shears the irradiated side, as the while wafer isn't heated
• Exact mechanism depends on laser type and laser parameters

TOPCon lifetimes from different oxide routes and annealing

Conclusions

This work was carried out by hand. All three methods will benefit from proper automation and optimization. The hot knife resulted in relatively clean glass and a backsheet containing everything else. However, the two optical methods had major advantages by being fume-free*. The non-glass components are sent to further processing.

REFERENCES

[1] (2016) End-of-Life Management: Solar Photovoltaic Panels. I.R.E.A.a.I.E.A.P.P. Systems IRENA and IEA-PVPS.

Hyperspectral Imaging for Advanced Material Identification and Quantification of Processed PV Materials

Authors

L. Neumaier[1*], M. De Biasio[1], A. Gassner[2,3], G.C. Eder[2]

[1] SAL, Silicon Austria Labs GmbH, Villach, Austria
[2] OFI, Austrian Research Institute for Chemistry and Technology, Vienna, Austria
[3] TU Wien, Institute of Materials Science and Technology, Vienna, Austria
*Lukas.neumaier@silicon-austria.com; M:+43 664 88200146

This work was carried out as part of the Austrian project "PVReValue - Holistic Recycling of Photovoltaic Modules" (FFG No. 897767), which is funded by the Federal Ministry for Climate Action, Environment, Energy, Mobility, Innovation and Technology BMK as part of the Circular Economy - Energy and Environmental Technology Call 2022 and handled by the Austrian Research Promotion Agency (FFG).

Abstract

An advanced, layer-by-layer separation and recycling process for end-of-life (EoL) photovoltaic (PV) modules is developed, aiming for a material recovery rate of over 95% by weight. The workflow covers input characterization, component separation, fraction processing, and output analysis. Key recyclable groups are (i) front glass, (ii) metals/semiconductors (Si), and (iii) backsheet plastics. The main challenge is removing the crosslinked EVA encapsulant. Near-infrared hyperspectral imaging (HSI) is integrated for non-destructive material identification, detecting residual encapsulant on glass, solar cells, and backsheets. Machine-learning-based spectral analysis enables real-time classification and higher material purity. Early results confirm accurate material mapping in mixed streams, supporting scalable recycling and advancing a circular PV economy.

Keywords: recycling, circular economy, hyperspectral imaging, material classification, non-destructive analysis

APPROACH

PV recycling: Structured process under development to achieve >95 wt% recovery from EoL PV modules.

- **Multi-step workflow**
  (i) Input characterization, (ii) layer-by-layer component separation (waterjet cutting or milling), (iii) further processing of fractions, (iv) output characterization, (v) recycling of refined output fractions
- **Precise separation of main fractions**
  Glass, backsheet (+ residues of encapsulant), and solar cells + metallic connectors + wires with encapsulant

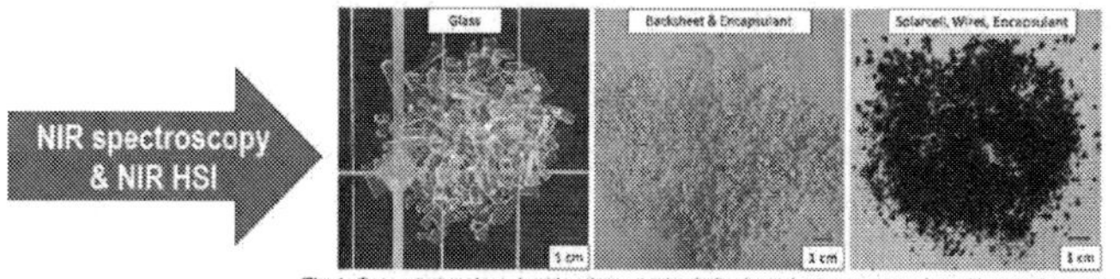

Fig.1: Separated and crushed fractions obtained after layer-by-layer separation with waterjet cutting

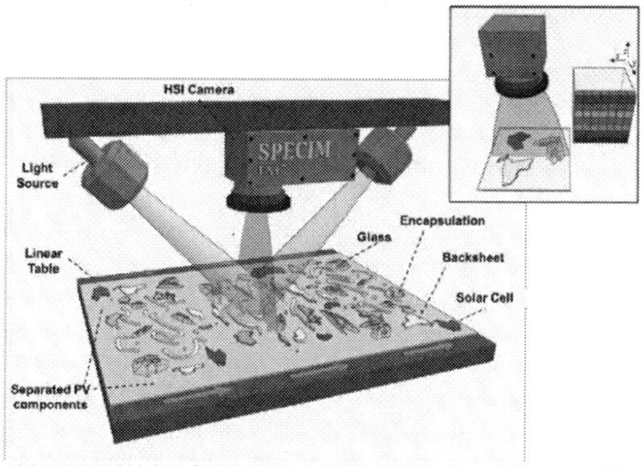

Fig.2: HSI setup to measure different components of PV materials after the separation process of EoL modules; *Insert*: spatial scanning via HSI

RESULTS

NIR spectroscopy & NIR hyper spectral imaging

- Rapid, non-destructive **material identification** of EoL PV modules and fractions
- Detection of **contaminants/residues** to ensure high-quality recovery
- Quantification of **material composition** in mixed fractions

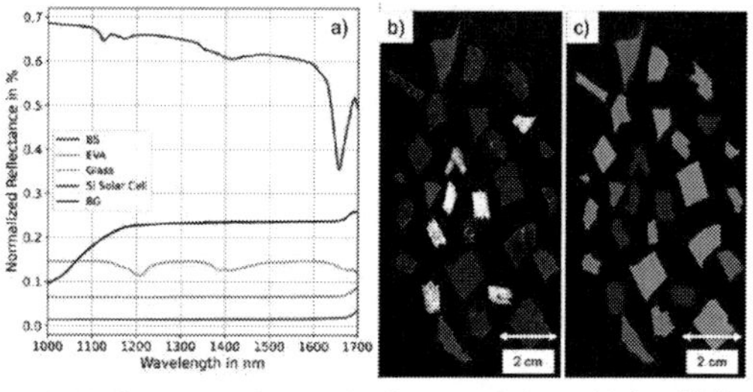

Fig.3.: (a) Reference spectra by class; (b) False-color sample image; (c) Color-coded HSI classification result of PV components

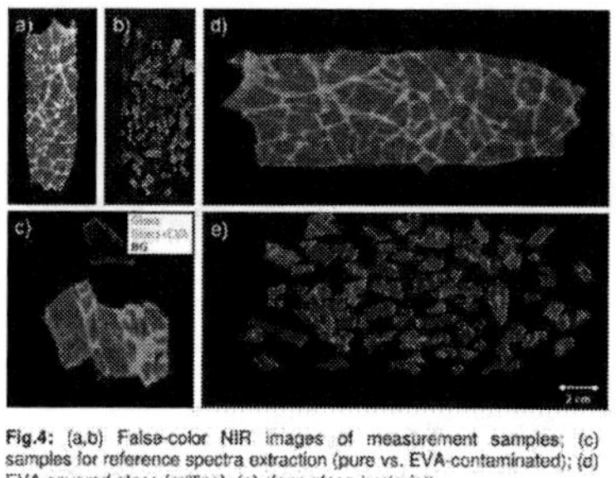

Fig.4: (a,b) False-color NIR images of measurement samples; (c) samples for reference spectra extraction (pure vs. EVA-contaminated); (d) EVA-covered glass (milling); (e) clean glass (waterjet).

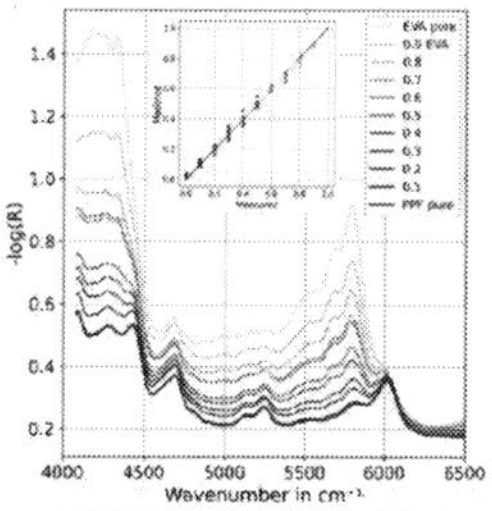

Fig.5: NIR analysis of EVA–PET mix: reflectance spectra by ratio; *insert:* predicted vs. measured EVA content

SUMMARY

NIR spectroscopy and HSI were utilized for identifying and quantifying PV recycling fractions.

- HSI detects **EVA residues, classifies materials** in real time, and **improves separation accuracy**.
- **Waterjet cutting delivers cleaner** glass and separated backsheet layers than **milling**.
- **Flake sorter integration** could **enhance precision** for fine, transparent fractions (e.g., PET).

Future Work

Initial tests **confirm feasibility**, but **further optimization is needed** for complex material mixtures and small grain sizes (e.g.: adaption of detection algorithms).

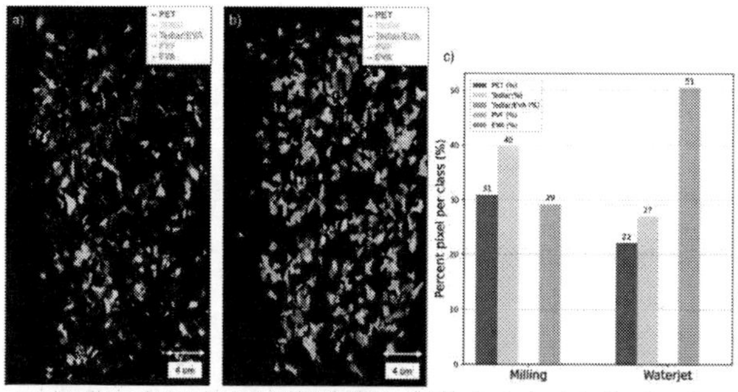

Fig.6: Classification of PET, Tedlar, Tedlar/EVA, PVF, EVA in rough BS fraction (1–4.3 mm): (a) milling, (b) waterjet, (c) Comparison of material type distribution (percent pixel per material class) after milling and waterjet cutting

EU PVSEC 2025
22.-26.09.2025
Bilbao Exhibition Center

PVReValue

Bundesministerium Klimaschutz, Umwelt, Energie, Mobilität, Innovation und Technologie
FFG
Kreislaufwirtschaft & Produktionstechnologien
im Rahmen von open4innovation

Silicon Austria Labs GmbH
Sandgasse 34, 8010 Graz, Austria
www.silicon-austria-labs.com
contact@silicon-austria.com

SOCIAL LCA OF PEROVSKITES: INITIAL FINDINGS AND PATHS FOR IMPROVEMENT

Anna Barguès[1], Philippe Macé[2], Melodie de l'Epine[1], Damien Gautier[2]
[1]Becquerel Institute France, Lyon (France) [2]Becquerel Institute, Brussels (Belgium)
Rue Praetere 2, 1000 Brussels, Belgium. +32 493 451 720

ABSTRACT: Social Life Cycle Assessments (S-LCAs) evaluate the social impacts of products across their life cycle, from manufacturing to end-of-life. They consider aspects such as working conditions, human rights, gender equity, health and safety, and community engagement [1]. While Environmental LCAs (E-LCAs) are well-established with clear methods, databases like Ecoinvent and GaBi, and standardized frameworks such as ISO 14040 and ISO 14044, S-LCAs remain less mature due to the complex and context-specific nature of social issues. Limited data availability and regional differences further complicate evaluations [2]. In the photovoltaic sector, S-LCAs are still rare, as most studies focus on environmental aspects such as carbon emissions and resource use. Yet social impacts are critical for ensuring fair labour conditions and ethical supply chains. Although UNEP guidelines provide a foundation, further efforts are needed to refine methods and develop standardized indicators for meaningful assessments [3]. This publication presents preliminary results of the social assessment of an innovative silicon/perovskite tandem module. The study identifies key social impacts, explores alternative material provenance or processing sites, and highlights routes to reduce negative impacts. Conducted within the NEXUS project, it contributes to Europe's clean energy transition by supporting eco-designed, sustainable, and socially responsible PV production.
Keywords: Perovskites, social risks, value chain.

1 INTRODUCTION

The large-scale deployment of perovskite–silicon tandem (PST) photovoltaics offers significant potential for efficiency improvements and cost reductions, positioning these technologies as a key driver in the global transition to low-carbon energy. However, the rapid industrialization of PST modules also raises critical questions regarding the social impacts associated with their supply chains. From raw material extraction and processing to manufacturing and end-of-life management, each stage carries potential social risks, including labor conditions, community impacts, and equitable resource access.

To address these concerns, the NEXUS project conducted a comprehensive Social Life Cycle with two primary objectives: first, to systematically identify and quantify social risks across the PST value chain; and second, to evaluate opportunities for improvement through responsible sourcing, process optimization, and circular economy strategies, ensuring socially sustainable deployment alongside technological advancement.

2. METHODOLOGICAL APPROACH

UNEP Guidelines for Social Life Cycle Assessment of Products and Organizations, with the overarching aim of evaluating the social impacts associated with manufacturing PST technologies to ensure a responsible and sustainable energy transition.

The assessment was conducted in OpenLCA 2.2 using the PSILCA v3 database as the primary data source, which provides coverage of over 70 qualitative and quantitative social indicators organized into 25 subcategories across four stakeholder groups: workers, value chain actors, local communities, and society.

Given the complexity of analyzing all available indicators, a participatory approach was adopted to refine the scope, using a Best-Worst Scaling (BWS) survey administered to project partners. This method allowed experts to identify and prioritize the most relevant indicators while ensuring that all stakeholder categories were represented.

Through this process, the initial long list was reduced to eight key indicators: goods produced by forced labor and fatal accidents (workers), anti-competitive behavior and public sector corruption (value chain actors), indigenous rights and sanitation coverage (local communities), and illiteracy and education expenditures (society).

The system boundary for the analysis was cradle-to-cradle, encompassing raw material extraction, manufacturing, use, and end-of-life, with both baseline and optimized PST module configurations considered.

Following inventory compilation, the impact assessment phase applied PSILCA's risk characterization method, which assigns risk levels (from no risk to very high risk) to each indicator, translating them into numerical factors expressed in Medium Risk Hours per USD of output.

The interpretation phase consolidated results, highlighted key risks and opportunities, and provided

3. MAIN ASSUMPTIONS

The study focuses exclusively on the manufacturing phase of perovskite-silicon tandem photovoltaic modules, comparing a baseline and an optimized architecture. Both configurations share the same overall design, consisting of a perovskite thin-film top cell combined with a silicon heterojunction (SHJ) bottom cell in a two-terminal (2T) tandem structure. The module assembly and Balance of System (BOS) are identical in both cases.

The optimized configuration introduces several improvements at the cell level. Silicon wafers are sourced from Norway instead of China, reducing the social and environmental risks linked to supply. Wafer cleaning processes have been modified to use less water and solvents, lowering resource intensity. Cell metallization is performed using the advanced Electrically Conductive Adhesive (ECA) technique, which also allows a 40% reduction in silver consumption compared to the traditional multi-wire brazing approach. For the transparent conductive oxide (TCO) layer, aluminum zinc oxide (AZO) is adopted in place of the commonly used indium tin oxide (ITO), avoiding the reliance on indium. Finally, the deposition of the perovskite layer is carried out with a solvent-free evaporated process, replacing conventional solvent-based techniques and further reducing potential risks associated with hazardous materials.

4. RESULTS

The S-LCA focuses on the manufacturing phase of the baseline and optimized PST PV modules, with results expressed in medium-risk hours per 1 m² of module. This unit reflects the estimated working hours under medium social risk conditions associated with producing 1 m² of module.

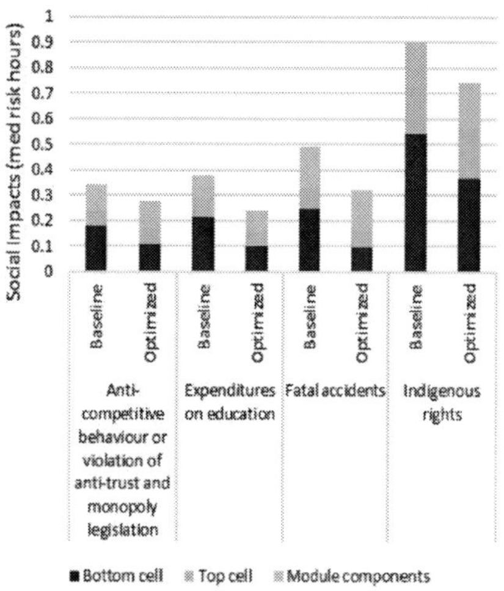

Figure 1: Social impacts of module manufacturing of Baseline and Optimized scenarios for the selected indicators

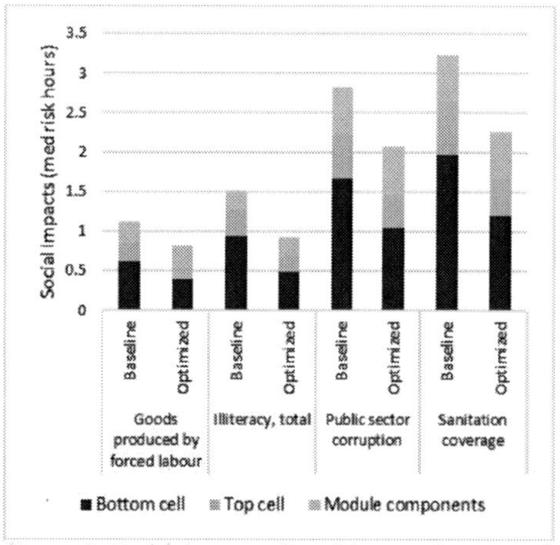

Figure 2: Social impacts of module manufacturing of Baseline and Optimized scenarios for the selected indicators

Table I: Social impact difference to produce baseline or optimized configurations

Social indicators	Reduction in impact (optimized vs. baseline)
Anti-competitive behavior or violation of anti-trust and monopoly legislation	-20%
Expenditure on education	-36%
Fatal accidents	-35%
Goods produced by forced labor	-27%
Illiteracy	-39%
Indigenous rights	-18%
Public sector corruption	-27%
Sanitation coverage	-30%

The largest contribution to social impacts comes from the silicon heterojunction (SHJ) bottom cell, since it represents the bulk of materials and costs.

A significant reduction in impacts is achieved in the optimized configuration thanks to changes in wafer production. Moving wafer manufacturing from China to Norway lowers risks across indicators due to stricter labor protections, better gender equality, higher health and safety standards, and a cleaner energy mix (mainly hydropower instead of coal) [4][5].

The perovskite top cell shows smaller but still meaningful improvements. The optimized design replaces traditional busbar brazing with Electrically Conductive Adhesives (ECA) and reduces silver use by 40%. Since silver mining is often linked to unsafe working conditions and community risks, this reduction directly lowers the social footprint of the module. In both baseline and optimized cases, the indicator with the largest weight is sanitation coverage, reflecting limited access to safe sanitation in some producing countries, which strongly drives overall social risk.

5. CONCLUSIONS

Key Findings: This study applied a Social Life Cycle Assessment to evaluate the potential social risks associated with the manufacturing of perovskite-silicon tandem photovoltaic modules. Results highlight that the silicon heterojunction bottom cell represents the largest contributor to overall social risks, emphasizing its central role in shaping the sustainability profile of these technologies. Nevertheless, the optimized configuration, featuring wafers sourced from Norway, reduced silver consumption through advanced metallization techniques, and solvent-free deposition processes, demonstrated clear improvements compared to the baseline, confirming the potential of targeted technological and sourcing strategies to mitigate social impacts.

Limitations: Despite providing valuable insights, the study is subject to limitations that must be acknowledged when interpreting results. A significant source of uncertainty arises from the reliance on secondary datasets and country-level averages, which may fail to capture local conditions or rapidly evolving supply chains. In particular, the lack of primary, industry-scale data for perovskite technologies introduces variability, as many inventory flows had to be modeled using proxy data not fully adapted to novel PV materials. Assumptions regarding sourcing locations, process configurations, and market dynamics further shape outcomes and can influence the magnitude of reported risks. These uncertainties underscore the need for caution in extrapolating results too broadly.

Paths for Improvement: Looking forward, several avenues for improvement emerge. Developing more accurate and geographically resolved datasets will be essential for refining S-LCA in the context of emerging PV technologies. Equally important is the adaptation of social indicators to the realities of globalized and fast-changing supply chains, ensuring assessments remain relevant and actionable. Strengthening methodological frameworks will reduce uncertainty and enhance robustness, while integrating S-LCA insights into sourcing strategies and policy development can help build more transparent and socially responsible supply chains. Ultimately, embedding social considerations into material choices and technology design will ensure that the PV sector contributes not only to climate goals but also to broader objectives of equity, transparency, and human rights.

6. ACKNOWLEDGEMENTS AND FUNDING

The work described has received funding as part of the NEXUS project from the European Union's Horizon Europe research and innovation program under grant agreement N° °101075330.

7. REFERENCES

[1] K. Maister, C. Di Noi, A. Ciroth, and M. Srocka, "PSILCA v.3 Database documentation," 2020.

[2] A. M. R. O. Chabrawi, J. M. de Andrade, C. M. L. Ugaya, and M. Traverso, "Towards reliable primary data collection and harmonized set of indicators in S-LCA on the stakeholder worker," International Journal of Life Cycle Assessment, pp. 1–19, Nov. 2024, doi: 10.1007/S11367-024-02400-Z/TABLES/8.

[3] Catherine. Benoît and Bernard. Mazijn, Guidelines for social life cycle assessment of products. United Nations Environment Programme, 2009.

[4] "Gender Gap Norway - Gender Equality - Red Yellow Blue The Gender Gap in Norway: A Comprehensive Analysis (RYB). (n.d.). from https://redyellowblue.org/data/no/gender-gap-norway/," 2025.

[5] "Electricity production - Norwegian Energy. (n.d.). from https://energifaktanorge.no/en/norsk-energiforsyning/kraftproduksjon/".

10.4229/EUPVSEC2025/5DV.2.29

42nd European Photovoltaic Solar Energy Conference and Exhibition

LIFE CYCLE ANALYSIS IN PHOTOVOLTAIC RECYCLING STRATEGIES: CHEMICAL AND THERMOMECHANICAL PROCESSES

J.A. Saura, N.Espinosa

University of Murcia, UM, Spain

1 INTRODUCTION

Solar photovoltaic energy is growing rapidly, surpassing 1 TW of installed capacity in 2021. This growth leads to an increase in waste, which could reach 60–78 million tons by 2050. To promote the circular economy, it is necessary to develop sustainable recycling strategies.[1]

2 GOAL

To compare two methods for recycling end-of-life photovoltaic modules: pyrolysis, which recovers high-purity materials, and thermomechanical processes, which require less energy. The analysis is performed using a Life Cycle Assessment (LCA).

3 METHODOLOGY

The functional unit of the study is 1,000 kg of end-of-life photovoltaic modules. OpenLCA software (v2.4) is used with the Ecoinvent database (v3.11), applying a Consequential LCA (CLCA) approach. Environmental impacts are assessed according to the EF 3.1 methodology, including climate change, toxicity, and eutrophication, among others.[2]

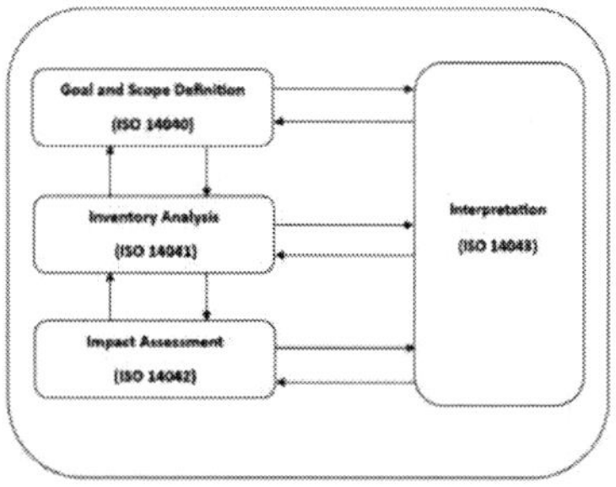

4 RESULTS

Pyrolysis offers greater material recovery, achieving silicon purity of 6–7N and high metal recovery rates, although it requires greater energy consumption and generates ionizing radiation impacts. Thermomechanical processes, on the other hand, consume less energy and have lower toxicity and radiation impacts, but produce lower purity materials. Both processes show net environmental benefits compared to the production of virgin raw materials.[3],[4],[5]

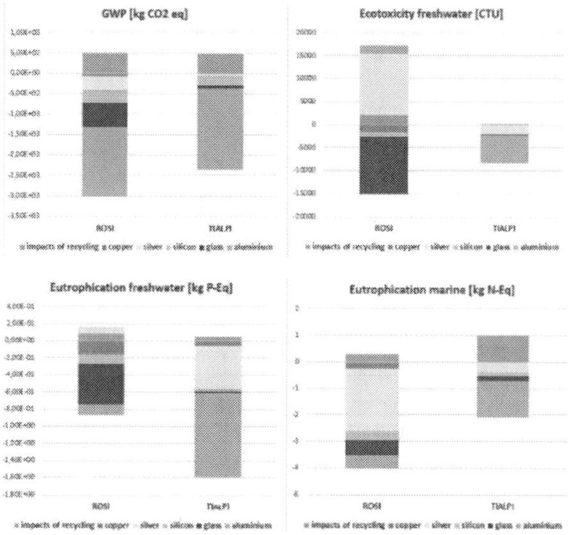

5 CONCLUSION

Both methods are sustainable, with distinct advantages. Pyrolysis is more suitable when seeking to maximize the quality and purity of materials, while thermomechanical recycling is more energy-efficient and better at reducing certain environmental impacts. The optimal choice will depend on the context: industry may prioritize purity, while public policies will tend to favor reducing overall impacts.

REFERENCES

[1] Sim, Y., Tay, A., Tay, Y. B., et al. (2025). Open challenges and opportunities in photovoltaic recycling. Nature Rev. Electr. Eng.
[2] Hauschild, M. Z., & Rosenbaum, R. K. (2018). Life Cycle Assessment: Theory and Practice. Springer.
[3] Fan, H. (2021). Life cycle assessment of an innovative recycling treatment for crystalline silicon PV modules. TU Eindhoven.
[4] Ardente, F., Latunussa, C., & Blengini, G. (2019). Resource efficient recovery of metals from PV panel recycling. Waste Management, 91, 156–167.
[5] Mazzi, A., Barbiero, C., Miserocchi, F., et al. (2024). Life cycle assessment of Al-C[illegible]ing from photovoltaic waste. Resour. Conserv. Recycl., 211, 107885.

020506-001

CONTACT

ja.sauragarcia@um.es
nieves.espinosa@um.es

THE LANDSCAPE OF PV RECYCLING: CHALLENGES TO MAKE PV AN EXAMPLE OF CIRCULAR ECONOMY

del Cañizo C., Fuertes Marrón D.
Instituto de Energía Solar, ETSI Telecomunicación, Universidad Politécnica de Madrid,
Avenida Complutense 40 (28040), Madrid, Spain.

ABSTRACT: The recycling of PV modules has emerged as a topic of enormous relevance, driven by the urgent need to manage the decommissioning of millions of modules expected over the coming decades. The development of universal, effective, scalable, and environmentally responsible recycling pathways (either up- or down-cycling) for PV modules requires a holistic understanding of technological diversity, process engineering, regulatory support, and economic models. This paper offers a set of reflections on key questions that help outline the landscape of photovoltaic recycling. By identifying core issues and emerging trends, it aims to contribute to a clearer understanding of the opportunities and obstacles that lie ahead in the transition toward a circular solar economy.

Keywords: Recycling, PV Waste, Silicon, Circularity

1 INTRODUCTION

The recycling of photovoltaic (PV) modules has emerged as a topic of enormous relevance, driven by the urgent need to manage the decommissioning of millions of modules expected over the coming decades. As solar energy deployment accelerates globally, the end-of-life management of PV systems becomes a critical challenge for both environmental sustainability and resource recovery.

This concern has sparked a vast amount of research and development (R&D) activity aimed at supporting industrial initiatives in PV recycling. A clear upward trend can be exemplified by a quick survey of the scientific literature indexed in the Web of Science under the search terms "Photovoltaic" AND "Recycling": 562 papers were published between 2000 and 2020, while the period from 2021 to 2025 saw a significant increase to 980 publications. Notably, 16 articles including the term "review" in the title were just published in 2024 and 2025, underscoring the intensifying interest and complexity of the field [1-16].

A critical reading of these reviews highlights the difficulty in grasping and systematically organizing the diversity of source materials to be recycled, the wide range of process conditions, and the varying levels of technological maturity. These challenges reflect the multifaceted nature of PV recycling, which spans materials science, mechanical and chemical engineering, environmental policy, and industrial scalability.

This paper offers a set of reflections on key questions that help outline the landscape of photovoltaic recycling. By identifying core issues and emerging trends, it aims to contribute to a clearer understanding of the opportunities and obstacles that lie ahead in the transition toward a circular solar economy.

2 UPDATING ESTIMATIONS ON PV WASTE

To illustrate the huge amounts of PV waste to be handled in the next decades, the projections published in 2016 by IRENA/IEA PVPS are frequently referenced: between 1.7 and 8 million tonnes were expected to be decommissioned in 2030, and between 60 and 70 million tonnes in 2050 [17]. It has to be noted that these figures built up on an estimation of a cumulative PV capacity reaching 1632 GW in 2030, 4512 GW in 2050, while the 2000 GW landmark was already surpassed in 2024, and the annual installed capacities have been in the range of the hundreds GW since then [18].

This growth of PV installed capacity above expectations demands a continuous update of waste estimations. In Figure 1 we compare 2016 IRENA estimations with our own calculations. We have considered the projections in annual installed capacity until 2050 of the ambitious yet plausible "Verlinden scenario" presented in [19], which foresees a cumulative capacity in 2030 in the range of 7000 GW, and in 2050 of 71000 GW. We followed the methodology developed by researchers from CIEMAT [20]-[22] to model the generation of PV waste, for which two different Weibull distributions are proposed, one "Regular loss" representative of what is expected from conventional PV technology according to field experience, and another "Early loss", which introduces a corrected shape factor to take into account potential module failure during the early life stages.

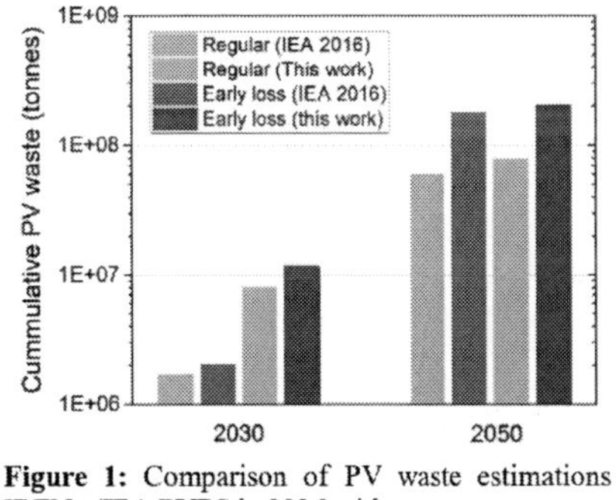

Figure 1: Comparison of PV waste estimations from IRENA/IEA PVPS in 2026 with our own.

It is clear how the increased deployment of photovoltaic capacity will cause the amount of PV waste to skyrocket well above the 2016 estimates. We are now talking about 2 to 12 million tonnes in 2030 (higher than initial estimates but in the same order of magnitude), and between 177 and 205 million tonnes in 2050 (approximately triple the initial estimates).

Additionally, we have included the initial loss of PV modules due to breakage during transport an installation, that neither the Regular nor the Early loss scenarios capture, which is of increasing importance along with the size of the new plants. We assume this additional loss to be in the range of 1% of the number of installed modules,

10.4229/EUPVSEC2025/5DV.2.31

according to the testimony of several EPC contractors that have been contacted. We show in Figure 2 how this additional source of losses sum up to the previous estimations.

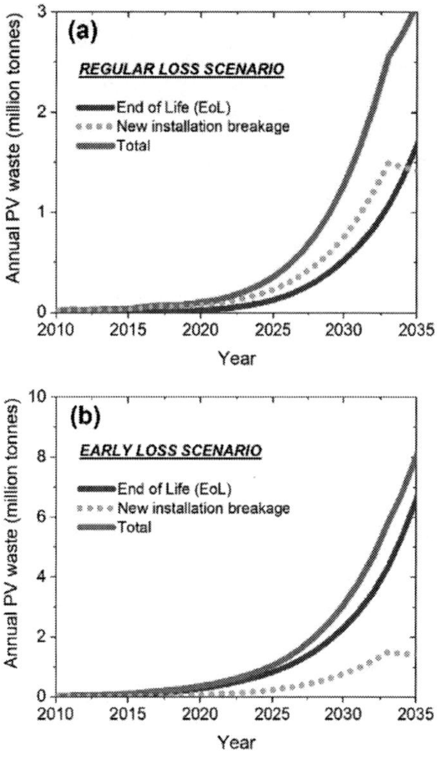

Figure 2: PV waste estimations when considering that 1% of PV modules break during installation and transport. (a) Regular loss scenario. (b) Early loss scenario.

The reduction of the PV waste due to the breakage during installation from 2033 on derives from the stabilisation of annual installed capacity according to the Verlinden scenario, which translates into a gradual reduction in terms of mass due to technological improvements.

Note that the installation breakage can be a concern in practical terms (mainly in the short term for the Regular loss scenario), as the large volume of broken new modules, even surpassing that of the old ones reaching their end-of-life, will arrive at the same time to the recycling plants. This will pose the relevant challenge of handling the technological differences between the old and the new modules, being the latter larger, with different metal contact schemes, and having glass-to-glass encapsulation, lower amounts of silver, etc.

3 RECYCLING METHODS

Figure 3 sketches the steps of a generic recycling process. There exists a wide variety of methods (mechanical, thermal, chemical, electrical, and combinations of them) to separate the components and recover the materials, which have been experimentally tested. The transition from laboratory-scale to industrial implementation requires a careful evaluation of several critical dimensions.

Among these, the *universality* of a given recycling pathway stands out as a major challenge due to the technological evolution among PV modules of different generations [23]: PV modules differ significantly in their construction, encompassing various configurations such as glass-backsheet and glass-glass architectures, the diversity in cell technologies—ranging from traditional aluminum back surface field (Al-BSF) cells to more advanced passivated emitter and rear cells (PERC) and tunnel oxide passivated contact (TOPCon) cells—, the transition from the universally used ethylene-vinyl acetate (EVA) encapsulant to other alternative ones such as polyolefin elastomer (POE), or similarly the variation in backsheet compositions including polyvinyl fluoride (PVF), polyvinylidene fluoride (PVDF), and polyethylene terephthalate (PET). Each variety requires tailored chemical or thermal treatments for effective separation and recovery.

Scalability is another critical issue. While many recycling techniques have demonstrated promising results at the laboratory level, scaling these processes to industrial capacities introduces new challenges. These include the need for robust automation, consistent feedstock quality, and economic viability under fluctuating market conditions. The transition often demands significant capital investment and process optimization to ensure throughput, reliability, and compliance with environmental regulations.

Environmental impact remains a central concern in evaluating recycling strategies. Some processes rely on toxic chemicals or generate hazardous emissions, including volatile organic compounds and acidic gases. The use of solvents, high-temperature treatments, and mechanical shredding must be assessed not only for their effectiveness but also for their ecological footprint. Life cycle assessments (LCAs) are essential tools to quantify these impacts and guide the development of cleaner, safer alternatives [24][25].

Cost is a decisive factor in the feasibility of PV recycling. Expenses arise from labor, energy consumption, chemical reagents, equipment maintenance, and logistics. Without sufficient economic incentives or regulatory frameworks, many recycling operations will struggle to achieve profitability. One promising approach to address this issue is the implementation of Extended Producer Responsibility (EPR), which shifts the financial burden of end-of-life management to manufacturers. Additionally, optimizing logistics—such as centralized module collection systems and minimum viable plant sizes—can improve economies of scale and reduce operational costs.

4 REINJECTION OF PV MATERIALS IN THE PRODUCTIVE SECTOR

The recovery of materials from end-of-life PV modules opens opportunities across several industrial sectors. Recycled metals, such as aluminum, copper, and silver, benefit from well-established markets, as metal recycling is already deeply integrated into global supply chains and industrial practices. In contrast, glass presents greater challenges, particularly in meeting the quality requirements of float or tempered glass industries, which

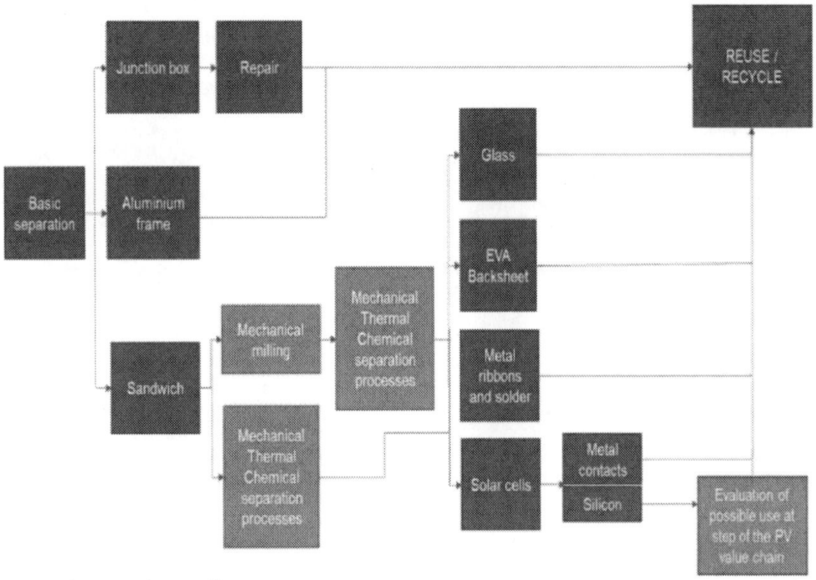

Figure 3: Steps in a generic recycling process.

demand specific physical and compositional properties. Polymers, including encapsulants and backsheets, are more difficult to valorize due to degradation and contamination; however, their calorific value offers potential for use as alternative energy sources through controlled thermal recovery processes. Silicon, depending on its purity but also on its resulting morphology (as powder, granulate or small/medium wafer pieces) after recovery, can serve diverse applications—from low-grade uses as an additive in construction materials or metallurgy, to high-purity feedstock for new solar cells, batteries or electronic devices [26] [27].

4.1 Downcycling or upcycling

The design of a recycling route should have in mind the achievable quality of the recovered materials, which will determine whether a "downcycling" or an "upcycling" approach can be followed to reinject them in the productive sector. By downcycling we refer to the conversion of the waste materials into new ones of lower intrinsic quality and reduced functionality with respect to their original application, while upcycling means that the original quality of the material is maintained or even improved after recovery.

Downcycling presents a practical advantage due to its relative simplicity, which translates into lower processing costs and easier implementation at scale. This approach typically involves less demanding separation and/or purification steps, making it attractive for early-stage or cost-sensitive operations. However, the reduction in quality and functionality can diminish the original value of the recovered materials and limit their appeal in secondary markets. In contrast, upcycling enables their reuse in high-performance applications, but it generally requires more complex and costly processes, often involving high energy input or hazardous chemicals, which may lead to increased environmental impacts.

4.2 Benefits of full circularity

The benefits that may come with a full circularity are exemplified in Table I by the new power capacity that could be served by the direct re-injection of the recovered silicon and silver in the PV-value chain from end-of-life PV modules, in case their quality is maintained. For these rough estimations, silicon is considered to be 3.5% of the total module mass, and silver 0.06%. For the new capacity, it is assumed that 2 g/W of silicon and 10 mg/W of silver are needed.

Table I: Cumulative power capacity that could be served by the usage of recycled silicon and silver by the solar industry from now on to year 2030 and 2050, depending on the scenario (Regular loss or Early loss) and considering the initial breakage during installation and transport.

	PV power (GW) covered by the recovered silicon	PV power (GW) covered by the recovered silver
	Accumulated up to 2030	
Regular loss	101	461
Early loss	271	1239
	Accumulated up to 2050	
Regular loss	3588	16404
Early loss	8113	37089

Even if these numbers are just taken as a starting point, as they do not incorporate the dynamism with which technological innovations are changing the configuration of the module, they show that at the short term (2030) between 1%-4% of the total power could be covered by recycled silicon, going to 5-11% in 2050. In the case of silver, the fractions move from 7-18% in 2030 to 23-52% in 2050.

10.4229/EUPVSEC2025/5DV.2.31

5 CONCLUSIONS

The vertiginous growth of the installed PV capacity draws a scenario in which millions of modules will have to be decommissioned when they reach their end-of-life. The prospects of how much PV waste we will have to manage should be continuously updated, as the reality in the deployment of PV plants surpasses the expectations.

The development of universal, effective, scalable, and environmentally responsible recycling pathways for PV modules requires a holistic understanding of technological diversity, process engineering, regulatory support, and economic models.

The choice between downcycling and upcycling of recovered materials involves a trade-off between economic feasibility and material value preservation, with implications for both sustainability and industrial viability.

Addressing these interconnected challenges is essential for building a fully sustainable and circular photovoltaic industry.

5 ACKNOWLEDGEMENTS

The financial support from the Spanish International Research Agency MCIN/AEI/10.13039/501100011033 through the RESLIENS (TED2021-129624B-C41) and MORE-N (PID2023-148369OB-C41) projects is greatly acknowledged, together with that of the Directorate-General for Research and Technological Innovation of the Community of Madrid through Grant No. TEC-2024ECO-72.

6 REFERENCES

[1] E. Gerold *et al.*, Advancements and Challenges in Photovoltaic Cell Recycling: A Comprehensive Review, Sustainability 16 (2024) 2542.

[2] PH. Chen *et al.*, Comprehensive Review of Crystalline Silicon Solar Panel Recycling: From Historical Context to Advanced Techniques, Sustainability 16 (2024) 60.

[3] YR. Maghraby *et al.*, Towards sustainability via recycling solar photovoltaic Panels, A review, Solar Energy 285 (2025) 113805.

[4] S. Song *et al.*, Water treatment methods in heavy metals removal during photovoltaic modules recycling: a review, Resour. Conserv. Recycl., 208 (2024) 107701.

[5] S. Rout *et al.*, Unlocking silver from end-of-life photovoltaic panels: A concise review, Renew. Sust. Energ. Rev. 210 (2025) 115205.

[6] R. Vinayagamoorthi, Recycling of end of life photovoltaic solar panels and recovery of valuable components: A comprehensive review and experimental validation, J. Environm. Chemical Engineering 12 (2024) 111715.

[7] R. Sanathi, A technical review of crystalline silicon photovoltaic module recycling, Solar Energy 281 (2024) 112869.

[8] M. Martínez, Technological Advancement in Solar Photovoltaic Recycling: A Review, Minerals 14 (2024) 638.

[9] S. Preet, A comprehensive review on the recycling technology of silicon based photovoltaic solar panels: Challenges and future outlook, J. Clean Prod. 12 (2024) 141661.

[10] AA. Vucinic, Recycling of photovoltaic cells – A review, Detritus 27 (2024) 47-65.

[11] M. Akhter, Sustainable Strategies for Crystalline Solar Cell Recycling: A Review on Recycling Techniques, Companies, and Environmental Impact Analysis, Sustainability 16 (2024) 5785.

[12] N. Mukwevho, Methodological approaches for resource recovery from end-of-life panels of different generations of photovoltaic technologies - A review, Renew. Sust. Energ. Rev. 207 (2025) 114980.

[13] A. Babaei, A Review of Photovoltaic Waste Management from a Sustainable Perspective, Electricity 5 (2024) 734-750.

[14] A. Ghaherami, Delamination Techniques of Waste Solar Panels: A Review, Clean Technol. 6 (2024) 280-298.

[15] ZA. Biyouki, Solar Photovoltaics Value Chain and End-of-Life Management Practices: A Systematic Literature Review, Sustainibility 16 (2024) 7038.

[16] MKH. Rabaia, Enabling the circular economy of solar PV through the 10Rs of sustainability: Critical review, conceptualization, barriers, and role in achieving SDGs, Sustainability 11 (2024) 100106.

[17] IRENA/IEA PVPS, EoL Management: Solar PV panels (2016).

[18] IEA Global Energy Review (2025).

[19] NM. Haegel *et al.*, Photovoltaics at multi-terawatt scale: Waiting is not an option, Science 380 (2023) 39-42.

[20] JD. Santos *et al.*, Projection of the photovoltaic waste in Spain until 2050, Journal of Cleaner Production 196 (2018) 1613-1628.

[21] JD. Santos *et al.*, Update of the projection of the photovoltaic waste in Spain until 2050, European Photovoltaic Solar Energy Conference (2019).

[22] MB. Nieto-Morone *et al.*, State and prospects of photovoltaic module waste generation in China, USA, and selected countries in Europe and South America, Sustainable Energy Fuels 7 (2023) 2163.

[23] International Technology Roadmap Photovoltaic 15th Edition (2024).

[24] Mao *et al.*, Overview of life cycle assessment of recycling end-of-life photovoltaic panels: A case study of crystalline silicon photovoltaic panels, J. Cleaner Prod. 434 (2024) 140320.

[25] IEA PVPS, Advances in Photovoltaic Module Recycling (2024).

[26] IM. Peters *et al.*, Cradle-to-cradle recycling in terawatt photovoltaics: A vision of perpetual utility, Joule (2024).

[27] R. Deng *et al.*, Recent progress in silicon photovoltaic module recycling processes, Resources, Conservation & Recycling 187 (2022) 106612.

RECOVERY OF METAL CONTACTS AND REUTILIZATION OF SILICON SUBSTRATES FROM RECYCLED SOLAR CELLS

Dasilva-Villanueva N.[1], Fuertes Marrón D.[1], Caballero L.J.[1], Rodríguez A.[2], Díez E.[2], Vázquez, A.[2], Muñoz J.A.[2], Braña A.F.[3], Rodríguez Plaza J.L.[4], Cánovas E.[5], Menghini M.[5], Antoine C.[5], del Cañizo C.[1]
[1]Instituto de Energía Solar, ETSI Telecomunicación, Universidad Politécnica de Madrid, Avenida Complutense 40 (28040), Madrid, Spain.
[2]Departamento de Ingeniería Química y de Materiales, Universidad Complutense de Madrid, Spain
[3]Grupo de Electrónica y Semiconductores, Departamento de Física Aplicada, Universidad Autónoma de Madrid (28049), Madrid, Spain
[4]Laboratorio de Crecimiento de Cristales, Departamento de Física de Materiales, Universidad Autónoma de Madrid (28049), Madrid, Spain
[5]Instituto Madrileño de Estudios Avanzados (IMDEA) Nanociencia (28049), Madrid, Spain

ABSTRACT: As the installed capacity of photovoltaic (PV) systems increases, so does the need to address the accumulation of waste from decommissioned modules, a challenge that requires the development of cost-effective and efficient recycling strategies. This work presents the main results in the research carried out within the RESILIENS project (funded by the Spanish National Research Agency) to develop a cost-effective and environmentally meaningful technological recycling process for silicon solar cells, that allows the recovery of precious metals and the reutilization of silicon substrates. On the one hand, three methods were evaluated for metal recovery: (i) acid leaching, for which 3 M HNO_3 was found to be the most effective, and an organic acidic medium, with Fe^{3+} as an oxidant and Cl^- to avoid Fe precipitation, was also explored; (ii) alkaline etching with KOH/ethanol/water, that allowed the separation of metal contacts and the removal of anti-reflection coatings with minimal silicon loss; and (iii) acidophilic and halotolerant bacteria, that effectively performed the bioleaching. On the other hand, p-type monocrystalline ingots with suitable electrical properties were obtained from the Czochralski growth of fragments of old boron-doped multicrystalline silicon wafers. Phosphorus gettering treatments were applied to p-type recrystallized wafers, achieving lifetimes in excess of 250 μs. Cells fabricated on recrystallised silicon showed only 5.2 % relative lower efficiency than reference ones, attributable to processing, not to the material quality. Conversion to n-type silicon was demonstrated when phosphorus emitters were present in the recrystallized material, Conversion to n-type silicon was demonstrated when phosphorus emitters were present, although challenges due to excessive doping were identified. The RESILIENS project has contributed to the reduction of the environmental footprint associated with solar photovoltaic energy, supporting the transformation of PV technology into a true example of circular economy.
Keywords: Recycling, Solar Cells, Silicon, Metal Recovery

1 INTRODUCTION

The recent and immediate record-breaking new PV installations will translate, with a time lag equivalent to the present useful life of the PV-modules of 25-30 years, into equally large amounts of PV-components waiting for disposal. Forecasts in this respect reveal that up to ten million tons of PV components will need recycling by 2030, a figure that goes up to the hundreds of million tons of accumulated weight by 2050 globally [1].

The existing infrastructures designed for PV-module recycling have been conceived to date for the recovery of massive (and passive) elements, like glass and aluminum frames, which are easily removable from old modules and reutilized for new products with minimal marginal costs associated. Approximately 74% of the total weight of a typical crystalline silicon (c-Si) PV module is contributed by the glass cover, while only a 3% is contributed by silicon (the actual solar cells), 1% by copper (electric connectors), and around 0.13% by silver (cell contact lines) and other metals (mostly tin and lead from contact pastes) [2]. These proportions adhere to the current normative, however, the social demand for a sustainable industrial production will shortly translate into more demanding requirements for clean energy technologies, PV in particular.

This reality urgently calls for the design and adoption of affordable and effective strategies for recycling and reutilization of all PV components, and particularly of those most energy-demanding in their manufacturing and thus responsible for the largest quote of environmental impact: the solar cells. To address this challenge, four institutions (IES-UPM, UCM, UAM, and IMDEA-Nano) have joined efforts in the research project RESILIENS, which explores an efficient approach to recycle the components of high intrinsic value in the PV module, specifically ultrapure silicon and precious metals, opening the door for the reutilization of such components into the manufacturing of new commercial products.

The approach of this work covers both the exploration of several chemical routes for the recovery of metal contacts (while preserving as much as possible the silicon substrates) and the recrystallization of old p-type wafers into monocrystalline substrates to reinject them in the PV value chain.

2 RECOVERY OF METAL CONTACTS

Several chemical routes were explored, based on alkaline etching, acidic leaching and bioleaching, respectively. Starting experiments were done on BSF solar cells with TiO_2 anti-reflection coating (ARC) manufactured in the eighties, and then to SiN_x ARC ones manufactured in the nighties. More recent PERC solar cells have also been processed. Some results are highlighted in this section, more details can be found in [3] and [4].

2.1 Alkaline route

The alkaline route is based on the physical separation of the metal contacts by etching the silicon layer immediately below, using aqueous KOH solutions, to which ethanol is added to act as a surfactant, facilitating the release of the hydrogen bubbles generated in the process. Different compositions and different operational conditions (varying temperature, with or without stirring), were tested, while keeping the solution-to-solid ratio constant. Several analytical techniques were used to characterise the solid and liquid fractions resulting from the process: the solid fraction was examined by scanning electron microscopy (SEM) and X-ray fluorescence (XRF), while the liquid fraction was analysed using inductively coupled plasma (ICP) spectroscopy. This combination of techniques allowed to assess the purity of the metal contacts and the silicon wafer, as well as to quantify the transfer of solid material to the liquid phase during the etching process.

For the samples with TiO_2 ARC, the front and back contacts (mainly Ag, determined by EDX measurements performed after detaching) were physically detached so that it was possible to recover them intact as solids. The underlying back side of the cell (mainly the aluminium-BSF layer), along with the antireflective coating and a tiny amount of Ag remnants were dissolved in the solution.

For the samples with SiN_x ARC, a two-step process was designed. The first one physically detached the Al layer from the back side and consisted of a solution of KOH and water. The second was intended to separate the metallic Ag contacts, and EtOH was added to the solution. Afterwards, Ag contacts were separated from Al contacts by sieving due to their difference in size. In contrast, for PERC cells, the alkaline etch was performed in a single step because these cells lacked the rear full Al layer. At the end of etching process, both the fragments and the silicon wafers themselves were washed with distilled water and dried. Afterwards, the organics were cleaned with an RCA-1 treatment (5:1:1 v/v mixture of 27% ammonia (NH_3), 30% hydrogen peroxide (H_2O_2) and deionised water), and the ARC was removed with 2% HF. The results of the two-step process for cells from five different manufacturers is shown in Table I.

Table I: Summary of the results obtained for the two-step etching processes optimized for solar cells coming from five different manufacturers.

St	Variables	Cell 1	Cell 2	Cell 3	Cell 4	Cell 5
1	[KOH] (% v/v)	5	5	5	5	25
	[EtOH] (% v/v)	0	0	0	0	5
	T(°C)	35	40	40	50	65
	t (min)	15	14	15	15	15
	Mass loss (%)	13,4	12,7	13,6	10,9	3,0
	Si loss (%)	0,2	11,2	12,2	9,9	1,3
	Ag (%)	0	0	0	0	1,6
	Al (%)	13,2	1,5	1,5	1,0	0
2	[KOH] (% v/v)	30	30	30	25	-
	[EtOH] (% v/v)	5	5	5	5	-
	T(°C)	65	70	70	65	-
	t (min)	12	16	20	15	-
	Mass loss (%)	6,3	6,4	2,7	2,4	-
	Si loss (%)	4,6	5,6	1,6	1,7	-
	Ag (%)	17,	0,8	1,1	0,7	-
	Al (%)	0	0	0	0	-

2.2 Acidic route

Acid leaching was carried out by digestion of solar cell fragments with nitric acid solutions, 3 M being the most suitable acid concentration. Acidic organic leaching was also tested, using Fe^{3+} as oxidant and a complexing agent (Cl^-) to avoid iron precipitation.

The recovery of metals from the acid leaching processes was carried out by precipitation to recover silver in the form of silver chloride and by electrodeposition tests to recover silver in native form.

2.3 Bioleaching route

An alternative procedure to demetallize the solar cells by means of microorganisms was also tested. Studies have been carried out using Acidithiobacillus ferrooxidans and Acidihalobacter prosperus as active agents. These microorganisms oxidize Fe^{2+}, generating Fe^{3+} which, in the presence of Al, causes its solubilization as Al^{3+} by a redox reaction. It has been observed that the ARC protects the metals against the action of these microorganisms, though.

3 RECRYSTALLIZATION OF Si FRAGMENTS

Regarding the reutilization of decommissioned Si substrates, the strategy has been to validate their reinjection at the crystallization step, using them as polysilicon feedstock. In the absence of sufficient quantities of demetalised silicon in our project, fragments of p-type multicrystalline wafers manufactured in the 2000s were used as a starting material for the growth of small Cz ingots. In some cases, conventional phosphorus emitters were diffused thermally in supersaturation conditions so that the starting material contained phosphorus and boron. Wafers were sliced from those ingots, and their optoelectronic properties were measured, mainly focusing on transport parameters, such as carrier lifetime and mobility.

3.1 Wafers grown from p-type multicrystalline material

During the crystallization process the dopant concentration along the ingot is expected to increase, due to the liquid-solid segregation coefficient of boron in silicon. This behavior is confirmed through 4-point probe resistivity measurements on wafers cut along the ingot, with resistivity values of recrystallized wafers ranging from 0.9 to 0.7 Ω·cm, whose evolution along the ingot is in good agreement with Scheil's model [5].

In order to determine the feasibility of processing new solar cells from the recrystallized wafers, the carrier lifetime was used as a metric [6]. Inductively-coupled photoconductance decay measurements yield carrier lifetime values between 5 and 45 μs at an injection level of 10^{15} cm^{-3}, values that increase up to several hundreds of microseconds after performing a phosphorus diffusion gettering (PDG) process to get rid of possible contaminants introduced during the recrystallization stage. Carrier lifetime measurements of the multicrystalline wafers before recrystallization, alongside the monocrystalline samples before and after the PDG are presented in Fig. 1. They show the efficacy of the gettering process for the elimination of spurious contaminants introduced during the recrystallization process, and with that the validation of recycled Si for the manufacturing of high-efficiency solar cells.

The minority carrier mobility of the recrystallized substrates is also analyzed. Through Time-of-flight measurements in a Haynes-Shockley setup, average electron mobility values in the range of 1000 $cm^2V^{-1}s^{-1}$ are obtained.

THz time domain spectroscopy (THz-TDS) measurements were made to interrogate in the AC limit the values of doping and mobility [7]. The measured samples provided Drude-like fingerprints in the frequency resolved complex conductivity. Fit to the data provided hole mobilities of approximately 400 $cm^2V^{-1}s^{-1}$, and doping in the range of 2×10^{16} cm^{-3}. The evolution of the doping content along the ingot was in good agreement with Scheil's model, validating the 4-probe measurement estimated in the DC limit.

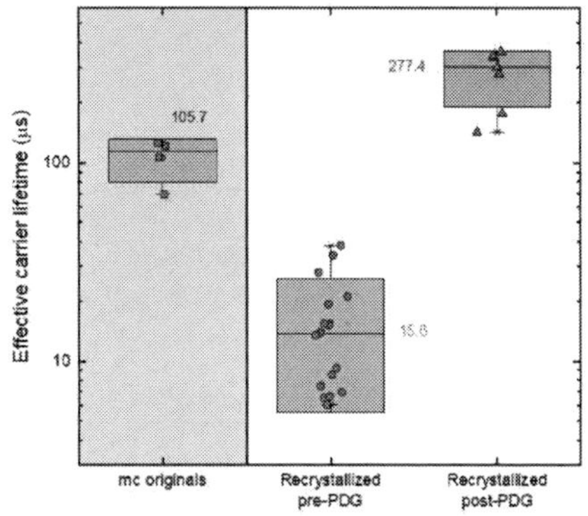

Figure 1: Effective carrier lifetime at an injection level $\Delta n = 10^{15}$ cm^{-3} for the original multicrystalline wafers (grey) and the monocrystalline recrystallized wafers before (blue) and after (red) a P-diffusion gettering. Average values can be found in text.

3.2 Wafers grown from p-type multicrystalline material with diffused phosphorus emitters

In this case, after wafer cutting the hot probe indicated the wafers where n-type all along the ingot. Very low resistivities were measured with the four-point measurement, which corresponds to a distribution according to the Scheil equation of an initial phosphorus concentration of the order of 10^{18} cm^{-3} (see Fig. 2).

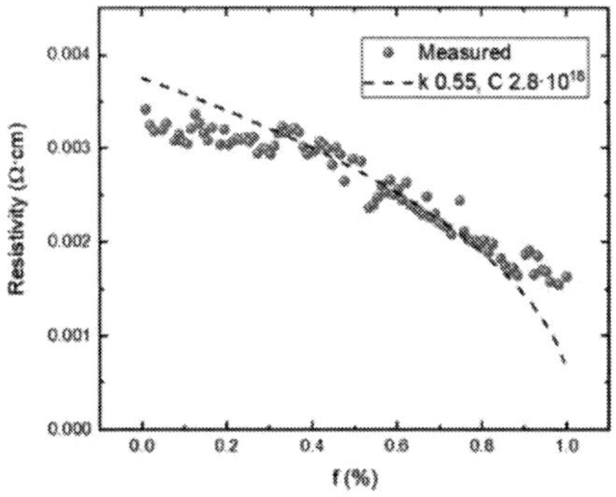

Figure 2: Resistivity measurement on wafers cut across the n-type compensated ingot, with estimation of the initial phosphorus concentration. f stands for the solidified fraction of the ingot.

Different hypotheses have been evaluated to explain why the phosphorus concentration in the material is much higher than expected. The two most plausible ones are the following. Firstly, we have to take into account that the phosphorus emitter has diffused on both sides of the wafer, so that the amount of n-type dopant is double what it would be in a conventional cell. Secondly, the diffusion under supersaturation conditions implies the incorporation of electrically inactive phosphorus [8], which dissolves in the molten silicon and occupies substitutional positions in the grown ingot, where it is electrically active and therefore contributes to the electrical properties of the substrates.

3.3 Solar cells on recrystallized silicon wafers

Conventional P-diffused emitter, Al-BSF solar cells were manufactured on some of the p-type recrystallized wafers, as well as on one of the original multicrystalline wafers and one demetallized substrate fragment. Further detail on the manufacturing of the solar cells can be found elsewhere [6].

Our findings suggest that the primary performance constraints observed in devices fabricated on recrystallized material and demetallized wafer fragments are not ascribed to material quality deterioration eventually incurred during the recovery and reuse phases of the silicon substrates. Rather, they stem from pitfalls encountered during cell manufacturing, notably highlighted by subpar BSF performance discerned in QE assessments and inadequate edge definition in the photolithography stage for front contact provisioning.

4 CONCLUSIONS

Three methods have been evaluated in the framework of the RESILIENS project for metal recovery from end-of-life silicon solar cells: alkaline etching, acidic leaching and bioleaching. Leaching with 3 M HNO_3 was the most effective acidic route, and a HALO medium with Fe^{3+} and Cl- was explored to avoid precipitation. In parallel, acidophilic and halotolerant bacteria were used for bioleaching. Alkaline etching with KOH/ethanol/water allowed the separation of metal contacts and the removal of ARC with minimal silicon loss. This strategy was optimised by design of experiments, and a selective sequence has been proposed to separate aluminium and silver.

The RESILIENS project has also proved that the recrystallization of silicon is feasible and that the distribution of dopants follows the expected behavior. In the case of using p-type silicon as starting material, resistivities and interstitial oxygen concentrations are within the expected values. The initial carrier lifetime values are modest, but after a gettering process they are within acceptable values for the fabrication of high efficiency solar cells, consistently exceeding 100 µs and reaching in the best cases more than 350 µs in some cases. In the case of using p-type silicon with n-type diffused emitters as starting material, n-type compensated wafers with a very high phosphorus concentration are obtained, possibly derived from the presence of electrically inactive phosphorus in the emitters diffused under supersaturation conditions.

The steps undertaken in the RESILIENS project towards the recycling of silicon solar cells support the idea that routes for the recovery and reutilization of their most valuable elements are technologically viable, and its establishment would lead the PV industry as a good example of circular economy.

10.4229/EUPVSEC2025/5DV.2.32

5 ACKNOWLEDGEMENTS

We acknowledge Dr. Nikolay Abrosimov from Leibniz-Institut für Kristallzüchtung for crystal growth. Financial support from Grants No. TED2021-129624B funded by the Spanish International Research Agency MCIN/AEI/10.13039/501100011033 and by "NextGenerationEU"/PRTR is also acknowledged.

6 REFERENCES

[1] C. del Cañizo, D. Fuertes, "The landscape of PV recycling: challenges to make PV an example of circular economy, this conference.
[2] IM. Peters *et al.*, Cradle-to-cradle recycling in terawatt photovoltaics: A vision of perpetual utility, Joule (2024).
[3] M. Tierno *et al.*, Solar Energy 274 (2024) 112533.
[4] A. Vázquez *et al.*, Advancing solar energy sustainability: tackling PV cell upcycling through metal recovery, this conference.
[5] E. Scheil, Int. J. Mat. Research 34 (1942) 70.
[6] J. Hofstetter *et al.*, Prog. Photov. 24 (2016) 122.
[7] R. Ulbricht *et al.*, Rev. Mod. Phys. 89 (2017) 29901.
[8] H. Wagner *et al.*, J. Appl. Phys. 119 (2016) 185704.

Critical Review of Environmental LCA Methods and Their Representation of Current PV Market

Cristina Polacchi[1a], Atse Louwen[1b], Sandra Gallmetzer[1c], Luis André Pereira Fialho[2d], Denet Soler Toledo[2e]

[1]Eurac Research, Institute for Renewable Energy, Bolzano, Italy
[2]Centro de Desarrollo Energético CDEA-UA, Universidad de Antofagasta - Campus Coloso, Antofagasta, Chile
[a]cristina.polacchi@eurac.edu; [b]atse.lowen@gmail.com; [c]sandra.gallmetzer@eurac.edu; [d]luis.fialho@eurac.edu; [e]denet.soler@uantof.cl

Introduction

- The aim of this study is to evaluate existing **methods and inventories** used for environmental lifecycle assessments (E-LCA) of photovoltaic (PV) systems, in particular towards identifying gaps to perform **location-specific studies,** considering all the phases from manufacturing to operation and maintenance (O&M), to end-of-life operations.
- The **Atacama Desert in Chile** was chosen as a **case study**, since the study is part of the **CACTUS project**, which aims to enhance collaboration between European and Latin American countries in the field of PV development.
- The case study was also selected due to a **lack of representativeness** of studies in **desert contexts**.

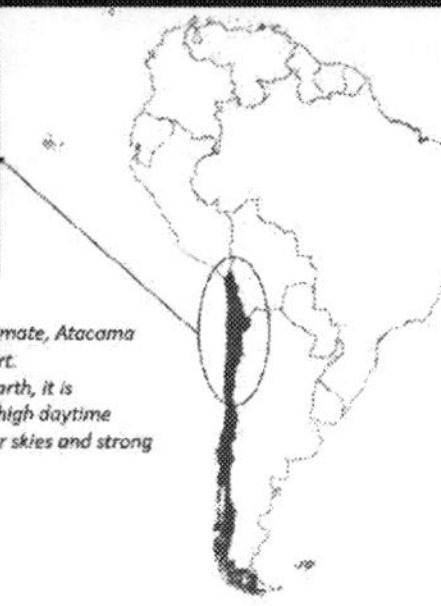

Atacama Desert climate:
While Chile has a very variegate climate, Atacama Desert is considered as a cold desert.
Being one of the driest places on earth, it is characterized by very low rainfall, high daytime temperatures and cold nights, clear skies and strong solar radiation.

ENVIRONMENTAL LCA HOTSPOTS PER LIFECYCLE STAGE: ATACAMA DESERT CASE STUDY

Manufacturing and system design

- The majority of LCA studies are focused on PV technologies (Al-BSF, PERC) that are **non representative of the current market** (PERC, SHJ, TOPCon)
- Only a few LCA studies adequately address the **Balance of System (BOS).**
- **Regionalization** of manufacturing processes in LCA studies is most often performed by only changing the **energy mix** of the country desired, in the manufacturing processes, without considering a **PV system design tailored** to the specific climatic conditions.

In *Table 1*, the **stress factors** affecting the operating conditions and the resulting **design requirements** of a PV system in the Atacama Desert are summarized

Table 1. *Summary of Atacama desert conditions that have an influence on PV design manufacturing requirements*

	Atacama desert conditions
Köppen-Geiger classification	• Arid Cold Desert (BWk) [1]
PV stress factors	• Accelerated wear • High UV • Saline and corrosive soil • Limited water resources [2]
PV system design	• UV resistant encapsulant (PO over EVA) and backsheet • High anti-reflective coated glass • Hydrophobic or anti-soiling coatings to reduce particle adhesion • Compatibility with ad-hoc cleaning processes • High temperature resistant BOS components [3]

O&M

- **O&M is highly site-specific**, even in desert climates with similar characteristics (hot desert (BWh), foggy desert (BWn), cold desert (BWk)).
- Specific **degradation mechanisms** occurs depending on installation location climatic conditions: the **environmental impact** is depending on the climatic stress factors.
- **O&M phase** is often neglected in LCA studies, while it can be almost **as important as the PV design phase** in LCA, especially in remote areas (e.g., desert regions) due to transport operations and faster components replacement [2].
- **Water cleaning** remains the most adequate process, equipped with water **mitigation systems to reduce water stress,** due to limited water resources of the area (e.g., recirculation and filtering, adaptive cleaning based on monitoring soiling ratio)

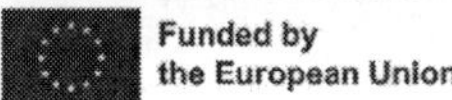

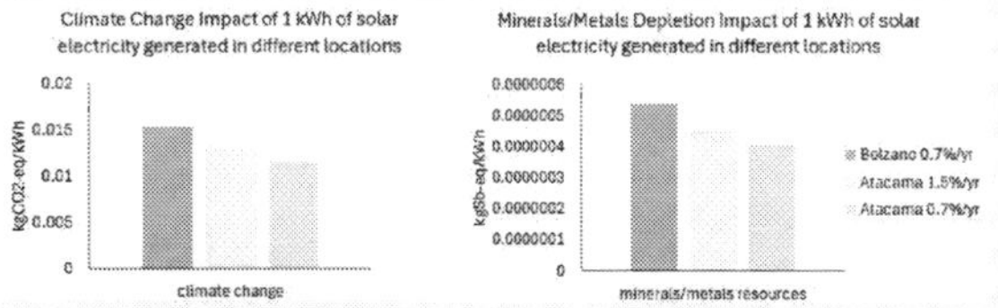

Figure 1. Cradle-to-gate Environmental impact results of 1 kWh of solar electricity, installed in different regions, reflecting the difference of results with different linear annual degradation rates assumed

End-of-life

- Different **LCA modelling methods** make LCA results difficult to compare:
  - **End-of-life approach**: evaluating the benefit from the avoided burdens thanks to the recycling;
  - **Cut-off approach**: using economic allocation to attribute the impact of the recycled co-products.
- LCA are not always reflecting the differences in **legislative requirements of different countries,** related to PV waste management and recycling processes. A summary of legislative requirements is presented for EU and Chile in *Table 2.*

Table 2. *Comparison of legislative framework for PV waste management between Europe and Chile*

	Europe	Chile
Law	WEEE Directive [4]	REP Law (20.920) [5]
Timeline	2003 first version 2012 new version 2014 PV included in the scope	2016 passed 2023 in force
Type of waste	Electrical and electronic equipment	General waste, including electric and electronic equipment
Producer responsibility	Yes: producers must deliver PV waste to an authorised centre	Yes: producers must deliver PV waste to an authorised centre
Quantitative collection target	85% of panels recovered and 80% prepared for reuse and recycled	Not specified

Conclusions and next steps

- **LCA inventories** reflecting **up-to-date market** situation and **geographical context, adequately including O&M and end-of-life stages,** are crucial to perform reliable and accurate LCA studies.
- **Social aspects**, addressing the significant lack of methodology harmonization and available inventories, will be discussed as a next step within CACTUS project.
- For future studies it would be beneficial to provide location specific **LCA guidelines** for **other regions of the world** with different climatic conditions.
- **Environmental Product Declarations (EPDs)** can be used as a future reliable source for LCA inventories and benchmark for results comparison.
- Ad-hoc lifecycle frameworks to **include circularity aspects** in lifecycle assessment and embrace the circular economy perspective needs to be improved.

References

[1] J. H. Schween, D. Hoffmeister, U. Löhnert, Filling the observational gap in the Atacama Desert with a new network of climate stations, Global and Planetary Change, Volume 184, 2020, 103034, ISSN 0921-8181, https://doi.org/10.1016/j.gloplacha.2019.103034.
[2] D. Soler, L. Rigamonti, N. Gazbour, E. Fuentealba, Environmental performance of a 1 MW photovoltaic plant in the Atacama Desert: A life cycle assessment study, Solar Energy, Volume 292, 2025, 113454, ISSN 0038-092X, https://doi.org/10.1016/j.solener.2025.113454.
[3] M. Mehdi, N. Ammari, A. A. Merrouni, S. Elhamaoui, M. Dahmani, Innovative design and field performance evaluation of a desert-adapted PV module for enhanced solar energy harvesting and reliability in harsh arid environments, Applied Energy, Volume 366, 2024, 123359, ISSN 0306-2619, https://doi.org/10.1016/j.apenergy.2024.123359.
[4] Directive 2012/19/EU of the European Parliament and of the Council of 4 July 2012 on waste electrical and electronic equipment (WEEE)
[5] Ley N°20.920 "REP": "Marco para la Gestión de Residuos, la Responsabilidad Extendida del Productor y Fomento al Reciclaje"

Enhanced Solar Photovoltaic Performance Through Improved Research Infrastructure for Adapted Climate Conditions — cactus-pv.eu

Funded by the European Union

This project has received funding from the European Union's Horizon Europe research and innovation programme under grant agreement No. 101132182.

A MULTI-MODAL MACHINE LEARNING FRAMEWORK FOR IMPROVED HEALTH ASSESSMENT OF END-OF-LIFE PV MODULES

Berhane Darsene Dimd*[1], Martin Bellmann[1], and Christine Klos[2]
[1]Department of Sustainable Energy Technology, SINTEF Industry, Alfred Getz Vei 2, Trondheim, 7034, Norway
[2]Buhck Re.Energy GmbH & Co. KG, Liebigstraße 46 22133 Hamburg, Germany

ABSTRACT: The rapid increase in photovoltaic (PV) installations worldwide has raised growing concerns about the management of end-of-life (EOL) PV modules, with waste volumes projected to rise significantly in the coming decades. Robust and accurate health assessment of EOL PV modules is essential to enable their reuse as second-life products and to optimize recycling processes. Several studies have explored machine learning (ML) methods for assessing PV module health using current-voltage (IV) data and electroluminescence (EL) imaging. While successful, most of these techniques have been applied to single data sources, either EL images for crack detection or IV curves for failure classification. Such approaches fail to use the full potential of integrating multiple characterization methods. This paper proposes a conceptual framework for combining diverse data sources, such as EL images and IV curves, using ML approaches for EOL PV module health assessment at waste management facilities. It integrates both EL images and IV curves and uses the correlations between visual and electrical data to provide a more robust and reliable assessment of module health. This can identify degradation patterns and performance issues with better accuracy than single-data approaches, ultimately improving the sorting of EOL PV modules for reuse or recycling. The proposed framework can support circular economy objectives and sustainability in PV systems by reducing environmental impact and improving management of growing EOL module volumes.

Keywords: PV module, End-of-life PV, Machine learning, EL imaging, IV data, Circular economy

1 INTRODUCTION

The rapid global expansion of PV systems has driven installed capacity beyond 1.4 TW as of 2023, with further growth anticipated [1]. As PV modules near the end of their operational lifetimes, effective waste management has become imperative. A 2016 report by the International Renewable Energy Agency (IRENA) and the International Energy Agency Photovoltaic Power Systems (IEA-PVPS) projects that PV waste could reach 1.7 million tons by 2030 and 60 million tons by 2050 under standard failure scenarios, with worst-case scenarios seeing these figures increase to 8 million and 78 million tons, respectively [2]. This increasing wave of decommissioned PV modules underscores the urgent need for sustainable strategies to handle end-of-life (EOL) PV modules. Current PV waste management strategies focus on recycling materials and extending module lifespans through reuse. The principle of reuse, in particular, supports the circular economy by conserving resources and reducing energy intensive processing. However, second-life applications for decommissioned modules face challenges related to performance, safety, and financial viability [3]. This work focuses on the former, the performance aspect of EOL PV modules. Accurate and reliable health assessments are important for determining whether EOL modules are suitable for reuse or must be directed to recycling.

Manual inspections using IV curve testing and EL imaging are commonly used to evaluate module health condition. While effective, these techniques require specialized equipment, and demand a high level of human expertise, raising concerns about scalability as EOL PV volume increases. Machine learning (ML) based health assessments offer promising solution for automating and streamlining EOL module health monitoring. These methods can rapidly identify defects and performance issues and can process large volumes. Research in this domain remains in development, but findings suggest these approaches can improve decision-making and improve waste management efficiency. This shift toward automated health assessment could prove essential for handling the expected rise in EOL PV modules. This work focuses on evaluating ML-based techniques for PV module health assessment and proposing a conceptual framework of multi-modal ML approach to improve the accuracy and robustness of health assessments at waste management facilities.

Existing ML-based approaches predominantly analyze single data sources, such as EL imaging for crack detection or IV curves for classifying failure modes; however, each method alone provides only a partial view on the condition of EOL PV modules. In contrast, the multi-modal machine learning approach proposed in this work integrates both EL images and IV curves, using the correlations between visual and electrical data to provide a more robust and reliable assessment of module health. This multi-modal model can identify degradation patterns and performance issues with better accuracy than single-data approaches, ultimately improving the sorting of EOL modules for reuse or recycling in waste management facilities.

2 METHODLOGY

Health assessment of EOL PV modules is essential for determining their suitability for reuse or recycling. This section explores common defects in EOL PV modules and the detection methods used to identify them. It also reviews existing ML techniques for PV module health assessment, followed by a discussion of the proposed multi-modal ML approach.

2.1 Common defects and their detection

PV modules experience various defects over their operational lifetime, which can impact their performance. The most common defects include cell cracks, delamination, potential-induced degradation (PID), bypass diode failure, and hot spots. These defects vary in severity, ranging from minor defects (e.g., soiling and frame deformation) to moderate defects (e.g., snail trails and back sheet issues) and major defects (e.g., hotspots and cell cracks). Their detection methods also differ, including visual inspection (e.g., glass breakage and delamination), IV characterization (e.g., mismatches and degradation), and EL imaging (e.g., microcracks).

2.2 Existing ML approaches

Several studies in the literature have explored ML methods for assessing the health of PV modules using IV curve data and EL imaging. Authors in [4] used ML models for PV fault classification based on IV curves, employing convolutional neural networks (CNNs) to identify faults caused by soiling and cell cracks, achieving 96% accuracy on real-world test data. Similarly, authors in [5] implemented ML algorithms to classify PV module conditions into eight categories using IV curve data. On the other hand, authors in [6], [7] employed EL images for the automated detection and classification of defects in PV modules. In both approaches, a CNN is used as the base model. In summary, ML-based PV module health assessment relying solely on IV characterization or EL imaging has inherent limitations. IV curves lack spatial resolution, while EL imaging does not provide direct performance information. A multi-modal ML approach integrating both methods can improve health assessment by using their complementary advantages.

2.3 The proposed approach

The proposed multi-modal ML approach in this work integrates both EL images and IV curve data, using correlations between visual and electrical data to provide a comprehensive and reliable assessment of EOL PV module health. By combining these complementary data sources, the model improves the detection of degradation patterns and performance issues with better accuracy than single-data approaches. This improved health assessment method allows more effective sorting of EOL modules for reuse or recycling, contributing to a more efficient and sustainable EoL PV waste management process. The overall workflow of the proposed approach is shown in this Figure 1.

The proposed framework provides an end-to-end pipeline for assessing the health of EoL PV modules using EL imaging and IV characterization. The overall workflow consists of image processing (segmentation and data augmentation), feature extraction, classification, evaluation, and module-level decision making.

a) Image processing: EL images of entire PV modules are segmented into individual solar cell images. This allows cell-level defect detection and ensures that the classification model operates on consistent input regions. Since the dataset typically exhibits strong class imbalance, with certain defect categories (e.g., critical defects) underrepresented, image augmentation techniques including random rotation, zooming, and horizontal/vertical flipping are applied to increase their representation and improve classifier robustness.
b) Feature extraction: For each cell image, high-level features are extracted using a pre-trained convolutional neural networks (ResNet50, EfficientNetB0, MobileNetV2, and others). The classification head is removed, and the output of the final pooling layer is used to generate a feature vector. Each vector is paired with its ground-truth defect label for supervised learning.
c) Classification: The extracted features and labels are divided into training and testing sets using stratified sampling. A Support Vector Machine (SVM) is trained on the training data.
d) Model evaluation: The trained model is evaluated on the held-out test set. The performance is evaluated using standard classification metrics and the confusion matrix, which emphasizes the per-class classification accuracy.
e) Module-level decision: Following cell-level classification, results are aggregated to determine the condition of the entire module. A set of predefined decision rules is applied, which take into account the number and severity of defective cells. These rules are combined with information from IV characterization, which directly reflects the module's electrical performance. The combined assessment is used to determine whether a given module is suitable for second-life applications or should be directed to recycling pathways.

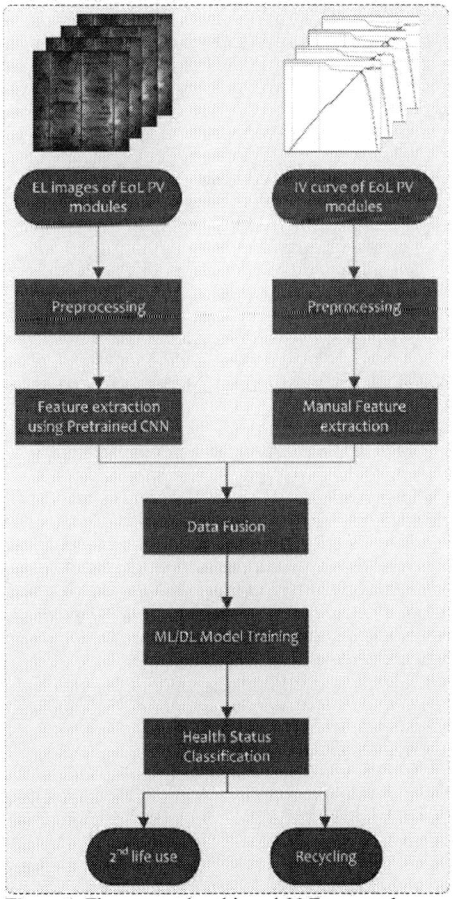

Figure 1: The proposed multi-modal ML approach.

3 PRELIMINARY RESULTS AND DISCUSSION

In this preliminary study, a total of 1200 cell-level EL images were used to evaluate the effectiveness of the proposed approach. The dataset was divided into 80% for training and 20% for testing. Within the training data, five-fold cross-validation was used to optimize model performance and reduce the risk of overfitting. Feature representations were extracted using five different CNN backbones: ResNet50, EfficientNetB0, DenseNet121, MobileNetV2, and InceptionV3. These features were then used to train a SVM classifier. Model performance was assessed in terms of the F1-score, the harmonic mean of precision and recall, which provides a balanced evaluation across classes and is particularly suitable in the presence of class imbalance.

Figure 2 presents the summary of the performance of the five backbone–SVM models based on the F1-score for three classes. As it can be seen from the result, all architectures showed consistently high performance especially for the major and normal defect classes. In contrast, all struggled on classifying the minor defect class. Among the tested backbones, EfficientNetB0 showed has the best performance, achieving an average score of 0.97 across all classes. These findings suggest that while defect detection is highly reliable for major and normal classes, classification of minor defects remains a challenge.

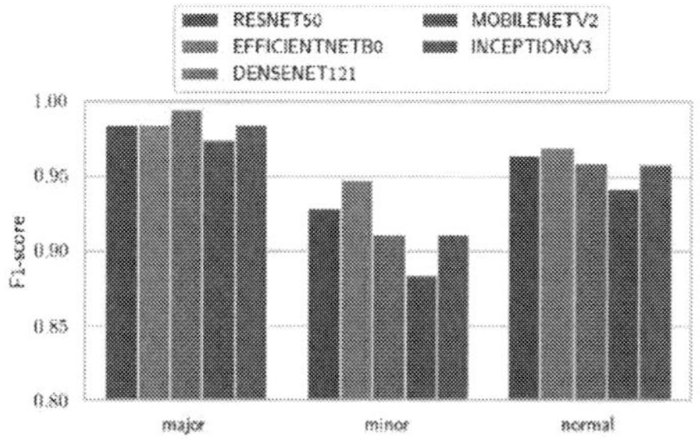

Figure 2: F1-score of the five models on the test data.

The confusion matrix (Figure 3) and t-SNE visualization (Figure 4) further support the above F1-score results for EfficientNetB0. The major class is clearly separable, achieving near-perfect classification with only 3 misclassifications. The normal class also performs well, though it is confused with the minor class. Overall, the results confirm that EfficientNetB0 provides robust and balanced performance.

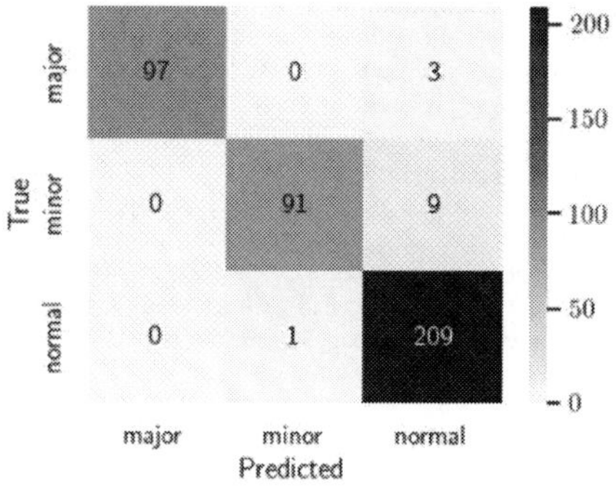

Figure 3: Confusion matix result for EfficientNetB0.

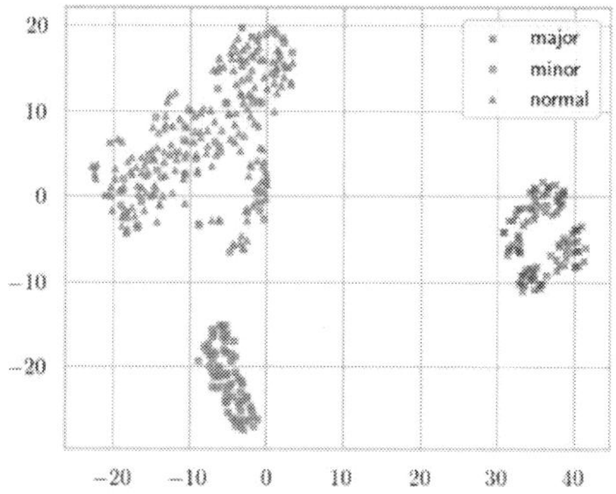

Figure 4: t-SNE result for EfficientNetB0.

4 CONCLUSION

The preliminary results indicate that a multi-modal ML approach gives promising improvements in EOL PV module health assessment, though several challenges remain. Limited availability of standardized datasets combining IV curves and EL images limits robust model training and validation. Moreover, fusing heterogeneous data and ensuring model generalization across diverse environmental conditions, degradation modes, and PV technologies add further complexity. Nevertheless, with the rapid growth of EOL PV modules, this approach has important implications for sustainable waste management. Reliable health assessment can facilitate reuse of functional modules and reduce premature disposal. At scale, such methods support more efficient PV waste processing, yielding both economic and environmental benefits.

5 ACKNOWLEDGEMENT

This work is part of the QUASAR project funded by the European Union's Horizon Europe research and innovation programme under grant agreement number 101122298.

7 REFERENCES

[1] "Solar energy." Accessed: Jan. 28, 2025. Solar energy
[2] "End-of-life management Solar Photovoltaic Panels." Accessed: Jan. 28, 2025. End-of-life management

Solar Photovoltaic Panels.
[3] "Re-use of pv modules: progress in standardisation and learnings from a real case study – trust pv." Accessed: Jan. 28, 2025. RE-USE OF PV MODULES: PROGRESS IN STANDARDISATION AND LEARNINGS FROM A REAL CASE STUDY – TRUST PV.
[4] M. W. Hopwood, J. S. Stein, J. L. Braid, and H. P. Seigneur, "Physics-Based Method for Generating Fully Synthetic IV Curve Training Datasets for Machine Learning Classification of PV Failures," Energies, vol. 15, no. 14, Art. no. 14, Jan. 2022. https://doi.org/10.3390/en15145085.
[5] B. Li, C. Delpha, A. Migan-Dubois, and D. Diallo, "Fault diagnosis of photovoltaic panels using full I–V characteristics and machine learning techniques," Energy Conversion and Management, vol. 248, p. 114785, Nov. 2021. https://doi.org/10.1016/j.enconman.2021.114785
[6] W. Tang, Q. Yang, K. Xiong, and W. Yan, "Deep learning based automatic defect identification of photovoltaic module using electroluminescence images," Solar Energy, vol. 201, pp. 453–460, May 2020. https://doi.org/10.1016/j.solener.2020.03.049.
[7] D. Korkmaz and H. Acikgoz, "An efficient fault classification method in solar photovoltaic modules using transfer learning and multi-scale convolutional neural network," Engineering Applications of Artificial Intelligence, vol. 113, p. 104959, Aug. 2022. https://doi.org/10.1016/j.engappai.2022.104959.

10.4229/EUPVSEC2025/5DV.2.35

REMOTE FEASIBILITY ASSESSMENT OF PV PANEL REPAIRS AND REPLACEMENTS FROM A LIFE CYCLE PERSPECTIVE USING IRT AND HDR IMAGERY FROM UAV

Christoph Waibel[1,2], Pieter-Jan Baeck[1], Elias Hafidi[3]
[1]Flemish Institute for Technological Research (VITO), Boeretang 200, 2400 Mol, Belgium
[2]EnergyVille, Thor Park 8310, 3600 Genk, Belgium
[3]Inflights BV, Cantersteen 12, 1000 Brussels, Belgium
christoph.waibel@vito.be

This paper investigates the life cycle impact and carbon payback time (CPBT) of PV panel repairs and replacements in ground mounted farms. Using UAV captured RGB and IRT images, multiclass classification models are used to identify different anomaly types. Following, the parametric embodied impact calculator for PV panels, ACACIA, is used to assess CPBT from repair and replacement interventions in different scenarios. As case study, faulty panels in Spain, Bilbao, and Belgium, Brussels, are investigated. Results suggest that PV replacements need about 6 years to reach carbon break even. However, if sub components of a panel can be repaired, such as the backsheet or the junction box, CBPT can be down to 0.03 years. It suggests that full PV panel replacements need to be evaluated with the remaining operation time of the PV farm, especially towards its end of planned service time. Ideally, a 2nd life of a replaced PV panel should be foreseen, or partial repairs of sub components enforced, thus ensuring an environmentally beneficial repair and replacement.
Keywords: Remote Sensing, Life Cycle Assessment, Fault Detection, Computer Vision, Repair

1 INTRODUCTION

Ground-mounted PV plants consist of arrays of interlinked panels that can be damaged by various environmental factors. When damage occurs, an assessment is made to evaluate risks (e.g., fire or electrical hazards) and power loss, guiding decisions on whether to replace, isolate, or leave the panels in place. UAV-based remote inspection thereby has become an efficient and cost-effective method for anomaly detection. Captured images include high definition range (HDR) in RGB, infrared thermal (IRT) or Photoluminescence (PIL), and they should be used complementarily for the detection of various anomalies [1].

More recently, computer vision (CV) and deep learning (DL) techniques have been successfully implemented to automatically detect various defect types, using multiclass classification algorithms [2]. For the training of such classification models, large datasets are required, where images are labelled with their certain defect type, or as non-defect. Various large open datasets exist for different image types, ranging from RGB, IRT, PIL, and more [3], which eases developing own classification models.

However, in case a malfunctioning panel is detected, the question still remains on the exact intervention to partake: repair, replace, or keep. Especially in from the perspective of the environmental impact that a PV panel has, a context-dependent assessment is necessary to ensure a potential PV replacement contributes positively.

2 METHODOLOGY

In this paper, we propose a workflow where (i) unmanned aerial vehicles (UAV) equipped with RGB and IRT cameras are used to capture images of ground mounted PV farms, where (ii) these images are then used to autonomously detect various defect types and anomalies using multiclass classification algorithms trained on open datasets, and subsequently (iii) the embodied impact of different interventions are assessed, including repair of the panel or complete replacement, using the open source parametric embodied impact configurator of PV panels called ACACIA [4] (see **Figure 1**).

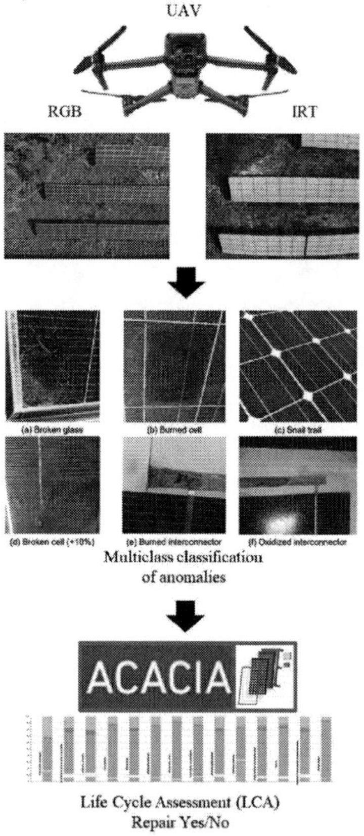

Figure 1: Proposed Workflow from UAV image capture to anomaly classification and LCA calculation for repairs.

10.4229/EUPVSEC2025/5DV.2.36

The scientific novelty of this paper lies in the remote and autonomous quantification of the environmental impact of potential repairs, depending on the damage type (or affected panel component). This adds crucial information for making environmentally and economically conscious decisions on which interventions to take for the damaged panels. This first and easy to obtain estimation using UAV and defect classification combined with embodied impact calculations is important as it might influence the decision to employ a repair & replacement team on-site.

In the following, the methodology is further outlined in 2.1 Remote Sensing, 2.2 Defect Detection with Computer Vision, 2.3 Life Cycle Assessment using ACACIA.

2.1 Remote Sensing

Drones (i.e. UAV) are now commonly used for remote anomaly detection on PV farms [1]. Various imaging techniques are used, with the most popular and accessible techniques being visual (i.e., RGB) and infrared thermal (IRT) imaging. These can capture different defects and should be used complementarily. Using RGB images, surface related issues can be easily spotted, including glass and frame breakage, delamination, browning/yellowing, snail trails, or soiling. Using IRT, on the other hand, reveals hot spots on solar cells or entire panels, on cables, and junction boxes (**Table I**). It is thereby important to note that defects at different layers and components of a PV panel can be detected using different sensing techniques (**Figure 2**).

Table I: Overview of considered failure types detectable with RGB and IRT at each PV layer. Table adapted after Chen et al. (2025) [3] and Friesen et al. (2025) [5].

PV component	Failure modes	Imaging techniques
Frame, Front Cover	Breakage	RGB
Encapsulant	Yellowing, Delamination	RGB
Solar cells	Cracking, Hotspot	RGB, IRT
Backsheet	Delamination, Cracking	RGB
Junction box, connector	Breakage, poor sealing, hot	RGB, IRT

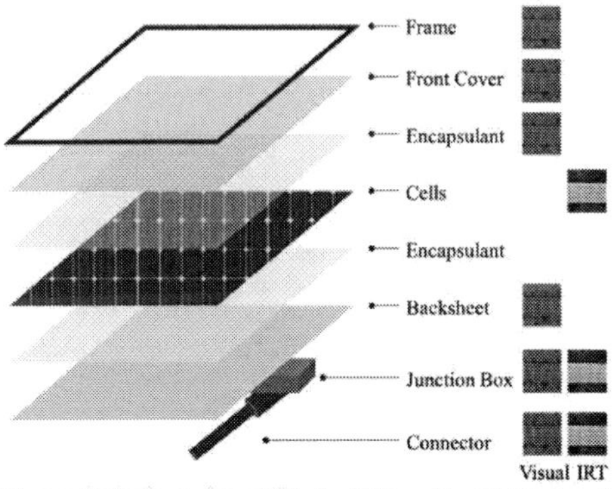

Figure 2: Defects detectable by IRT and/or RGB at each PV layer. Image modified after Chen et al. (2025) [3]

2.2 Defect Detection with Computer Vision

Common PV failure types are listed and described in the IEA technical report by Köntges et al. 2014 [6] and Friesen et al. 2025 [5], and it becomes apparent that many can be detected using vision based approaches. Using Computer vision (CV) and more recently deep learning (DL) models, such failures and defects can be recognized for autonomously using images of the panel to be inspected as input to the model [2]. Thereby, Convolutional Neural Networks (CNN) are employed and existing work has demonstrated their reliable and effective utilization to predict different faults using RGB and IRT images. Therefore, for this study, we assume a reliable classification from our input images and keep a demonstration for our own DL implementation for future work.

2.3 Life Cycle Assessment using ACACIA

In order to improve the cost efficiency and reliability of PV systems, it is crucial to obtain an understanding of common failures over the life time of a system [7]. Furthermore, from an environmental perspective, it is essential to ensure a proper end-of-life procedure of panels, and it has been shown that common monocrystalline and polycrystalline PV panels can be recycled to a high degree, regaining most of the materials [8].

Nevertheless, a major challenge remains in repairing defect PV panels. This is due to their design with laminated layers bond together (**Figure 2**). However, a major contribution to the environmental impact of a PV panel is from the solar cells. It is therefore of interest to identify the defect component in a panel and if possible conduct a repair maintaining the most environmentally intensive parts if those are undamaged.

In the workflow of this paper, we use an open-source browser-implemented life cycle assessment (LCA) configurator called ACACIA [4]. It offers a break-down of various PV panel components with configurable parts as shown in **Figure 2**.

3 CASE STUDY

We calculate the environmental impact, more specifically the global warming potential (GWP) and the resulting carbon payback time (CPBT), for following scenarios.

a) **Full PV replacement:** Any failure type requires full PV replacement
b) **Replacing junction box only:** Junction box and connectors can be replaced, anything else requires panel replacement.
c) **Replacing PET backsheet:** Junction box and connectors, backsheets, frame and front cover can be replaced, but defects in encapsulant and solar cells require panel replacement
d) **Replacing frame:** Same assumptions as c)
e) **Replacing front cover:** Same assumptions as c)

To test our workflow, we consider two PV farms, one in Belgium, Brussels, and one in Spain, Bilbao. Grid carbon emissions are obtained from ElectricityMaps [9] for the year 2024 (**Figure 3**). As lifetime of the PV farms and the panels, we assume 30 years. Annual electricity yield is calculated using PVGIS [10]. We further assume monocrystalline solar cells with an aluminum frame,

10.4229/EUPVSEC2025/5DV.2.36

tempered glass front cover, ethylene vinyl acetate (EVA) encapsulant, and polyethylene terephthalate (PET) backsheet. We also assume that the PV farms have a string layout with panels of 500 Wp with bypass diodes, such that faulty panels would not lead to a failure of the entire string.

While a comprehensive list of common failures and their associate risks, as well as appropriate response measures, are given in the technical reports from the IEA [5,6], they do not provide a quantification of failure occurrence. Therefore, since it is not clear, which failure type occurs how often, we list the environmental impact for each scenario, separately.

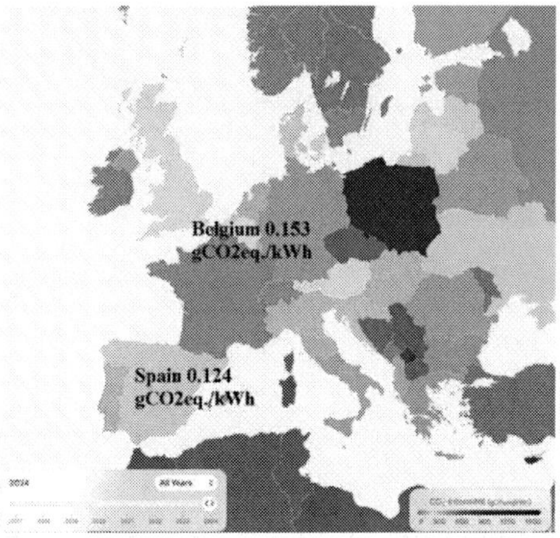

Figure 3: Grid carbon intensities for 2024 in Belgium and Spain. Image modified after ElectricityMaps [9]

4 RESULTS

Assuming a 35° South orientation for PV panels in both locations, Bilbao and Brussels, we can calculate the annual yield of a 500 Wp monocrystalline panel of 1.95 m² as follows: 659.86 kWh per year in Bilbao, or 338.39 kWh/m² per year, and 582.40 kWh per year in Belgium, Brussels, or 298.67 kWh/m² per year.

Considering the grid carbon intensities of both locations for 2024 (124 gCO_2eq/kWh in Spain and 153 gCO_2eq/kWh in Belgium), it translates to 42 $kgCO_2eq/m^2$ carbon abatement per year in Spain, Bilbao, and 45.7 $kgCO_2/m^2$ carbon abatement per year in Belgium, Brussels of a new PV panel.

The GWP of the configured PV panel for each component is shown in **Figure 4** and it sums to 266 $kgCO_2eq/m^2$ total GWP. It means that the CBPT of a new panel is 6.3 years in Spain, Bilbao, and 5.8 years in Belgium, Brussels. Following the same calculation, we show CBPT for all scenarios a) to e) in **Figure 5**.

The results show that for all other scenarios, where we assume a repair of a defect panel by replacing only subcomponents of a panel, the CBPT is significantly reduced. Replacing the frame of a panel shows a CBPT of about 0.5 years, replacing the front cover has a CBPT of about 0.3 years, and replacing the backsheet or the junction box even has a CBPT of 0.1 years or less.

The differences between Spain and Belgium are marginal despite the higher yield possible in Spain. This is caused by lower grid intensities in Spain.

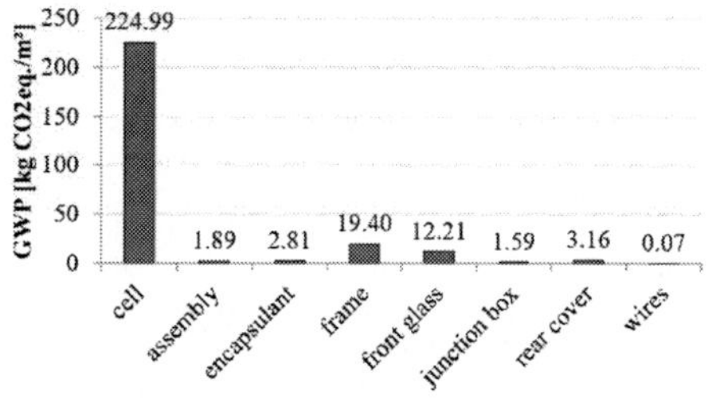

Figure 4: Global warming potential (GWP) per component of a monocrystalline PV panel using RER (European) data from ACACIA (Galimshina et al. 2024 [4]). Sum is 266.1 $kgCO_2eq./m^2$

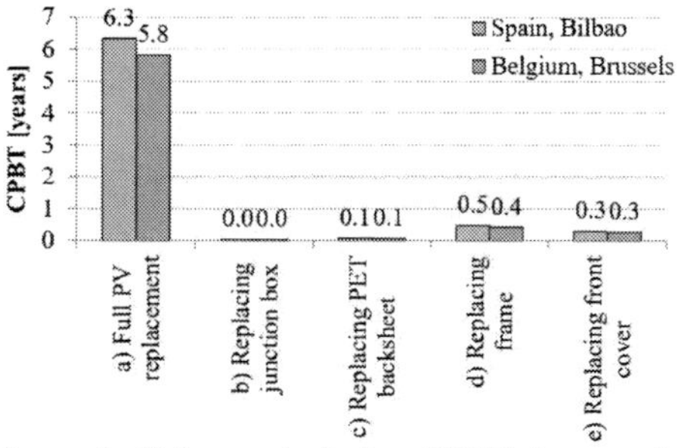

Figure 5: Carbon payback time (CPBT) in years for different repair / replacement scenarios.

5 DISCUSSION AND CONCLUSION

Using both RGB and IRT images in remote PV assessment complements the detectable fault types as they provide complementary information. With UAVs, a first estimation of the reparability of faulty PV panels can thus be done efficiently and effectively. With a following embodied environmental impact assessment, decisions can thus be made on the most economical and ecological interventions, whether be it repairing the faulty panel, replacing it, or leaving it in place. The workflow is a viable and efficient option for remote diagnostics of PV farms.

However, IRT and RGB images are evidently not able to detect all defects, and equipping UAVs with additional cameras and sensors, such as with daylight photoluminescence (PIL), should be considered [11,12]. Regarding the utilization of DL and CV models for the automatic detection of fault using images as inputs, large databases for established cell technologies (mono- and polycrystalline) are widespread, but newer cell technologies may likely need further development and model training [12,13].

With respect to the CBPT of PV panel replacements and component repairs, it is evident that the solar cell has the highest impact. Thus, it would be beneficial if only the damaged layers of a panel could be replaced and repaired while avoiding the replacement of the most carbon intensive components. Further research should investigate the feasibility of PV panel architectures with easier separability of the layers, and few related work is

10.4229/EUPVSEC2025/5DV.2.36

existing in the literature [14]. That way, frame, front cover, or backsheets, which all have minor impacts but are commonly involved in PV defects, could be more easily repaired, thus significantly reducing the environmental impact of interventions.

In conclusion, using the proposed workflow in this paper, from remote assessment of PV panel defects with UAVs, over autonomous defect classification using CV and DL, to an LCA assessment of different repair and replacement interventions, founded and informed decisions can be made, balancing between cost and environmental impact.

ACKNOWLEDGEMENT

This work has been funded by the European Union under Grant Agreement No 101138374. Views and opinions expressed are however those of the author(s) only and do not necessarily reflect those of the European Union or the European Health and Digital Executive Agency (HADEA). Neither the European Union nor the granting authority can be held responsible for them.

REFERENCES

[1] I. Høiaas, K. Grujic, A.G. Imenes, I. Burud, E. Olsen, N. Belbachir. "Inspection and condition monitoring of large-scale photovoltaic power plants: A review of imaging technologies". Renewable and Sustainable Energy Reviews 161 (2022) 112353.

[2] K. Masita et al. "Deep learning in defects detection of PV modules: A review." Solar Energy Advances (2025): 100090.

[3] X. Chen, B. Li, J.L. Braid, B. Byford, D.J. Colvin, A. Glaws, N. Jost, B. Pierce, S. Rabade, M. Springer, A. Jain. "Open data sets for assessing photovoltaic system reliability". Applied Energy 395 (2025) 126132.

[4] Galimshina, Alina, et al. "High-resolution parametric embodied impact configurator for PV and BIPV systems." Renewable Energy 236 (2024): 121404. https://acacia.arch.ethz.ch

[5] G. Friesen et al. "IEA-PVPS T13-30:2025: Photovoltaic Failure Fact Sheets (PVFS)". IEA Technical Report Task 13: Reliability and Performance of Photovoltaic Systems, International Energy Agency (2025).

[6] M. Köntges et al. "Performance and Reliability of Photovoltaic Systems". IEA Technical Report Subtask 3.2: Review of Failures of Photovoltaic Modules, International Energy Agency (2014).

[7] K.A. Weiß et al. "IEA-PVPS T13-16:2021: Service Life Estimation for Photovoltaic Modules". IEA PVPS Task 13: Reliability Performance, Operation and Reliability of Photovoltaic Systems, International Energy Agency (2014).

[8] G. Ansanelli et al. "A life cycle assessment of a recovery process from end-of-life photovoltaic panels." Applied Energy 290 (2021): 116727.

[9] ElectricityMaps, https://app.electricitymaps.com, website accessed [21.09.2025]

[10] PVGIS. https://pvgis.com/ , website accessed [21.09.2025]

[11] J.W. Weber et al. "Daylight photoluminescence imaging of photovoltaic systems using inverter-based switching". Prog Photovolt Res Appl. 2024;32:643–651.

[11] B. Doll et al. "Photoluminescence for Defect Detection on Full-Sized Photovoltaic Modules". IEEE Journal of Photovoltaics, Vol. 11, No. 6, November 2021

[12] M. Köntges et al. "IEA-PVPS T13-30:2025: Degradation and Failure Modes in New Photovoltaic Cell and Module Technologies". IEA Technical Report Task 13: Reliability and Performance of Photovoltaic Systems, Sandia National Laboratories.

[13] M. Aghaei et al. "Autonomous Intelligent Monitoring of Photovoltaic Systems: An In-Depth Multidisciplinary Review". Progress in Photovoltaics: Research and Applications, 2025; 33:381–409

[14] A. Majdi et al. "Fundamental study related to the development of modular solar panel for improved durability and repairability." IET Renewable Power Generation 15.7 (2021): 1382-1396.

Remote Feasibility Assessment of PV Panel Repairs and Replacements from a Life Cycle Perspective using IRT and HDR Imagery from UAV

SOLMATE
https://www.solmate-project.eu/

Christoph Waibel[1,2], Pieter-Jan Beeck[1], Elias Hafidi[3]
[1]Flemish Institute for Technological Research (VITO), Boeretang 200, 2400 Mol, Belgium christoph.waibel@vito.be
[2]EnergyVille, Thor Park 8310, 3600 Genk, Belgium
[3]Inflights BV, Cenforsteen 12, 1000 Brussels, Belgium

Abstract

This paper investigates the life cycle impact and carbon payback time (CPBT) of PV panel repairs and replacements in ground mounted farms. Using UAV captured RGB and IRT images, multiclass classification models are used to identify different anomaly types. Following, the parametric embodied impact calculator for PV panels, ACACIA, is used to assess CPBT from repair and replacement interventions in different scenarios. As case study, faulty panels in Spain, Bilbao, and Belgium, Brussels, are investigated. Results suggest that PV replacements need about 6 years to reach carbon break even. However, if sub components of a panel can be repaired, such as the backsheet or the junction box, CBPT can be down to 0.03 years. It suggests that full PV panel replacements need to be evaluated with the remaining operation time of the PV farm, especially towards its end of planned service time. Ideally, a 2nd life of a replaced PV panel should be foreseen, or partial repairs of sub components enforced, thus ensuring an environmentally beneficial repair and replacement.

Keywords: *Remote Sensing, Life Cycle Assessment, Fault Detection, Computer Vision, Repair*

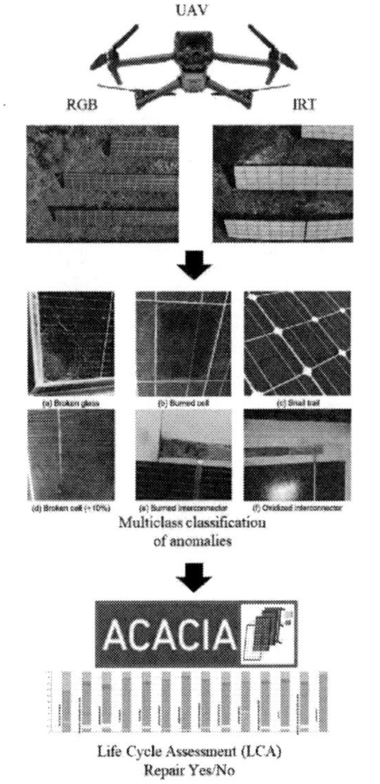

Figure 1: Proposed Workflow from UAV image capture to anomaly classification and LCA calculation for repairs.

Acknowledgement

This work has been funded by the European Union under Grant Agreement No 101138374. Views and opinions expressed are however those of the author(s) only and do not necessarily reflect those of the European Union or the European Health and Digital Executive Agency (HADEA). Neither the European Union nor the granting authority can be held responsible for them.

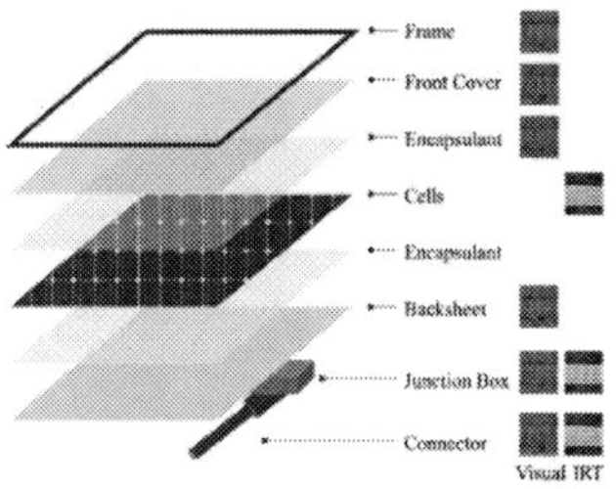

Figure 2: Defects detectable by IRT and/or RGB at each PV layer. Image modified after Chen et al. (2025) [3]

Table I: Overview of considered failure types detectable with RGB and IRT at each PV layer. Table adapted after Chen et al. (2025) [3] and Friesen et al. (2025) [5].

PV component	Failure modes	Imaging techniques
Frame, Front Cover	Breakage	RGB
Encapsulant	Yellowing, Delamination	RGB
Solar cells	Cracking, Hotspot	RGB, IRT
Backsheet	Delamination, Cracking	RGB
Junction box, connector	Breakage, poor sealing, hot	RGB, IRT

Scenarios

a) **Full PV replacement:** Any failure type requires full PV replacement
b) **Replacing junction box only:** Junction box and connectors can be replaced, anything else requires panel replacement.
c) **Replacing PET backsheet:** Junction box and connectors, backsheets, frame and front cover can be replaced, but defects in encapsulant and solar cells require panel replacement
d) **Replacing frame:** Same assumptions as c)
e) **Replacing front cover:** Same assumptions as c)

Calculated for Spain, Bilbao, and Belgium, Brussels, on 35° South tilt, with a 500 Wp panel of 1.95m².

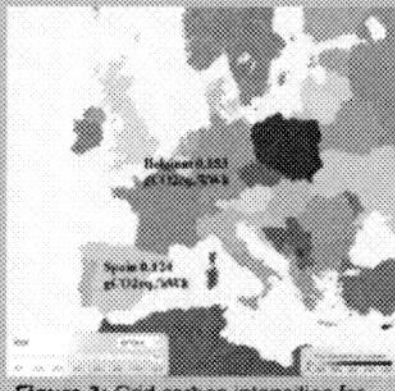

Figure 3: Grid carbon intensities for 2024 in Belgium and Spain. Image modified after app.electricitymaps.com

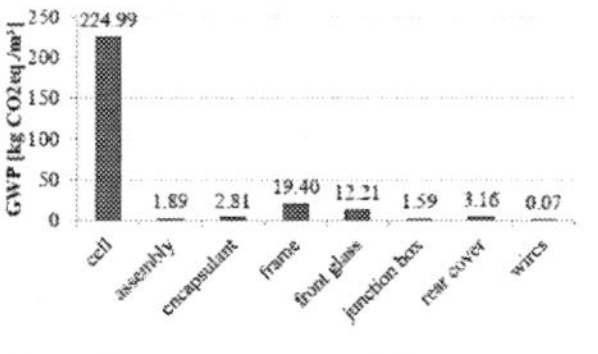

Figure 4: Global warming potential (GWP) per component of a monocrystalline PV panel using RER (European) data from ACACIA (Galimshina et al. 2024 [4]). Sum is 266.1 kgCO2eq./m²

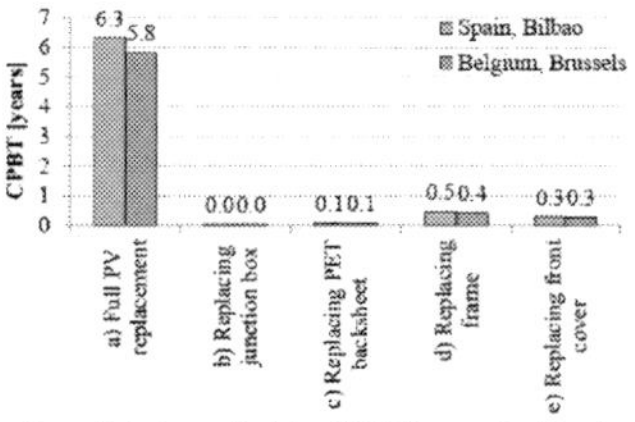

Figure 5: Carbon payback time (CPBT) in years for different repair / replacement scenarios.

Results & Conclusion

- Carbon payback times (CBPT) are significantly lower when only repairing the damaged components in a a panel and not replacing the entire panel.
- The highest environmental impact stem from the solar cells. Other components have a marginal global warming potential (GWP)
- Infrared thermal (IRT) and visual (RGB) images provide complementary information and should both be used in remote fault detection
- Additional sensors and image techniques, such as daylight photoluminescence should be considered to detect further defect types
- Novel PV panel designs with easier separability of layers should be considered
- Novel cell technologies will require retraining of the classification algorithms
- Overall, the proposed workflow is an efficient approach towards a first estimate for PV panel repairs, balancing between environmental and economic considerations

REFERENCES
[1] I. Høiaas, K. Grujic, A.G. Imenes, I. Burud, E. Olsen, N. Belbachir. "Inspection and condition monitoring of large-scale photovoltaic power plants: A review of imaging technologies". Renewable and Sustainable Energy Reviews 161 (2022) 112353.
[2] K. Masita et al. "Deep learning in defects detection of PV modules: A review." Solar Energy Advances (2025): 100090.
[3] X. Chen, B. Li, J.L. Braid, B. Byford, D.J. Colvin, A. Glaws, N. Jost, B. Pierce, S. Rabade, M. Springer, A. Jain. "Open data sets for assessing photovoltaic system reliability". Applied Energy 395 (2025) 126132.
[4] Galimshina, Alina, et al. "High-resolution parametric embodied impact configurator for PV and BIPV systems." Renewable Energy 236 (2024): 121404. https://acacia.arch.ethz.ch
[5] G. Friesen et al. "IEA-PVPS T13-30:2025: Photovoltaic Failure Fact Sheets (PVFS)". IEA Technical Report Task 13: Reliability and Performance of Photovoltaic Systems, International Energy Agency (2025).
[6] M. Köntges et al. "Performance and Reliability of Photovoltaic Systems". IEA Technical Report Subtask 3.2: Review of Failures of Photovoltaic Modules, International Energy Agency (2014).
[7] K.A. Weiß et al. "IEA-PVPS T13-16:2021: Service Life Estimation for Photovoltaic Modules". IEA PVPS Task 13: Reliability Performance, Operation and Reliability of Photovoltaic Systems, International Energy Agency (2014).
[8] G. Ansanelli et al. "A life cycle assessment of a recovery process from end-of-life photovoltaic panels." Applied Energy 290 (2021): 116727.
[9] ElectricityMaps, https://app.electricitymaps.com, website accessed [21.09.2025]
[10] PVGIS, https://pvgis.com/ , website accessed [21.09.2025]
[11] J.W. Weber et al. "Daylight photoluminescence imaging of photovoltaic systems using inverter-based switching". Prog Photovolt Res Appl. 2024;32:643–651.
[11] B. Doll et al. "Photoluminescence for Defect Detection on Full-Sized Photovoltaic Modules". IEEE Journal of Photovoltaics, Vol. 11, No. 6, November 2021
[12] M. Köntges et al. "IEA-PVPS T13-30:2025: Degradation and Failure Modes in New Photovoltaic Cell and Module Technologies". IEA Technical Report Task 13: Reliability and Performance of Photovoltaic Systems, Sandia National Laboratories.
[13] M. Aghaei et al. "Autonomous Intelligent Monitoring of Photovoltaic Systems: An In-Depth Multidisciplinary Review". Progress in Photovoltaics: Research and Applications, 2025; 33:381–409
[14] A. Majdi et al. "Fundamental study related to the development of modular solar panel for improved durability and repairability." IET Renewable Power Generation 15.7 (2021): 1382-1396.

Funded by the European Union

vito.be

ETIP Photovoltaics

Enabling Innovation Through ESG: A Roadmap for the European PV

Sustainability as a competitive advantage for Europe

Abeer Ali Khan[1*], Paula Sánchez-Friera[2], Sebastien Lizin[3], Samira Jama Aden[4], Pinar Derin-Gure[5], Jan Clyncke[6], John (Ioannis) A. Tsanakas[7], Marcello Passaro[8], Perine Louise Fleury[9], Cristina Polacchi[10], Veronese Elisa[10]

[1]First Solar Recycling GmbH, Germany, [2] Solkeys, Gijón, Spain, [3] Hasselt University, Belgium, [4] Helmholtz-Zentrum Berlin, Germany, [5] Middle East Technical University, Ankara, Turkiye, [6] PV CYCLE a.i.s.b.l., Belgium, [7] CEA, Liten, Univ. Grenoble Alpes, Campus INES, 73375 Le Bourget du Lac, France, [8] Sunzest Solar, Netherlands, [9] Biosphere Solar B.V., Netherlands, [10] Eurac Research, Italy

* e-mail: AbeerAli.Khan@FirstSolar.com

CONTEXT

Integrating ESG principles across the PV life cycle is essential. EU initiatives (e.g EUPI-PV and 2024 SRIA) stress sustainability in manufacturing, deployment, and recycling, addressing emissions, sourcing, equity, and circularity. Yet advancing further requires inclusive engagement, fair labor, and just transition measures, supported by robust metrics and governance to **boost innovation** and **ensure a resilient transition, and strengthen Europe's competitiveness and energy sovereignty**.

METHODOLOGICAL FRAMEWORK

This research examines the PV industry across its three life cycles -manufacturing, installation and operation, and end-of-life -assessing ESG impacts and priority areas. It draws on EU projects, expert insights, research, and policy to identify lessons learned and position ESG as a driver of innovation and EU competitiveness.

STRATEGIC RECOMMENDATIONS

For Policymakers

- Embed verifiable ESG criteria in solar-related regulations and funding
- Strengthen traceability and harmonize standards
- Support design for circularity beyond recycling
- Ensure policies are open to innovation in technology and system design

For Industry and Companies

- Adopt standardized ESG reporting and promote harmonization
- Innovate in sustainable manufacturing circular operations and maintenance (O&M) and supply chains
- Promote fair labor, diversity, equity, and inclusion
- Create community engagement plans

For Researchers and Technology Developers

- Advance interdisciplinary ESG research
- Focus on decarbonization, circularity, and critical and strategic material recovery
- Support innovation in deployment models
- Design PV to be resilient and durable in variable climatic conditions

	Environmental Aspects	Social Aspects	Governance Aspects
Manufacturing	**Outcome:** •PV manufacturing is the **largest contributor to lifecycle emissions**, due to energy-intensive processes. •**Critical and strategic raw materials** are required in PV manufacturing (e.g., silver, indium) **Solution:** •**Decarbonizing** manufacturing •**Credible** ecodesign solutions with **improving material and energy** use efficiency	**Outcome:** •**Labor conditions** vary geographically, with documented risks of forced labor. •**Gender gaps** persist, and **Social Acceptance** is limited due to negative externalities. **Solution:** •Ensure **stakeholder engagement** •Expand **job training programs** •**Zero tolerance** to state-sponsored forced labor	**Outcome:** •Variability in ESG standards, reporting and gaps in global supply chain **transparency**. **Solution:** • Responsible sourcing in line with **UN Guiding Principles on Business and Human Rights** •**Enhancing verifiability** of ESG reported information
Installation and Operation	**Outcome:** •**Land use conflicts** for ground-mounted PV systems and **water consumption**, mainly for panel cleaning in arid regions. **Solution:** •Responsibly developed ground-mounted systems, **Agrivoltaics, floating PV, IPV and BIPV** represent promising strategies to optimize land use •**Dry cleaning** technologies and **self-cleaning** coatings.	**Outcome:** •PV supports local **job creation**, yet equitable access to training and quality employment remains uneven. •PV expands **energy access but** has high upfront costs. •Lack of **public acceptance** of PV solutions **Solution:** •**Transparent** planning and fair benefit-sharing •Innovative financing mechanisms •Proactive **community and stakeholder engagement.**	**Outcome:** •Deployment governance must ensure **responsible project siting** through effective environmental permitting •Inclusive **stakeholder consultation**, and the fostering of public-private partnerships. **Solution:** •Implement **best practices throughout the life cycle** of a solar project (from development to decommissioning)
End-of-Life	**Outcome:** •Current recycling technologies recover **bulk materials**. •Recovery of valuable materials like silicon and silver remains limited due to **lack of policy framework**. **Solution:** •Policy initiatives and research into **design-for-circularity and promote high value recycling** are key to **scaling** sustainable end-of-life management.	**Outcome:** •Recycling sector growth offers new **employment opportunities**. **Solution:** •Occupational **health and safety standards** to be enforced •**Public acceptance** of end-of-life initiatives. •**Training and education** throughout the value chain.	**Outcome:** •Regulatory frameworks mandate recycling, but **global harmonization is lacking** **Solution:** •Strengthening and harmonizing **standards for recycling** and circular economy policies. •**Streamline cross-boundary transportation** of PV waste destined for recycling.

Funded by the European Union, under the Horizon Europe programme, Grant agreement number 101075398. Views and opinions expressed are however those of the author(s) only and do not necessarily reflect those of the European Union or European Climate, Infrastructure and Environment Executive Agency. Neither the European Union nor the granting authority can be held responsible for them.

https://ekioceanproject.com/

EU PVSEC 2025

A NOVEL TOOL FOR THE IDENTIFICATION OF SUSTAINABLE LOCATIONS OF MARINE FLOATING PHOTOVOLTAIC PLANTS

Gotzon Mandiola[1,2], Ibon Galparsoro[1], Iratxe Menchaca[1], María Jesús Belzunce[1], Iñigo Mendikoa[3], Juan Bald[1], Asier Sanz[3]*

[1] AZTI, Marine Research Division, Basque Research and Technology Alliance (BRTA), Herrera Kaia Portualdea z/g, 20110, Pasaia, Spain.
[2] University of the Basque Country (UPV/EHU), Plentzia, Bizkaia, Spain.
[3] Tecnalia, Basque Research and Technology Alliance (BRTA), Edificio 700, 48160, Derio, Bizkaia, Spain.

*Speaker
For more details, contact gmandiola@azti.es

INTRODUCTION

- Offshore floating photovoltaic (FPV) energy can help to diversify the renewable energy production capacity.
- The novel development status of this technology poses uncertainty regarding its potential environmental impacts.
- Blue economy maritime activities should be sustainable and must comply with the 'Do No Significant Harm' (DNSH) principles.

OBJECTIVES

- Investigate the environmental risk associated with the FPV technologies in the marine environment.
- Identify suitable locations for FPV deployment in Europe, developing a Bayesian Network (BN) model.
- Integrate the BN model into a decision-making tool.

Study area

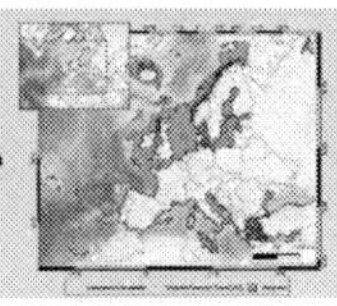

METHODS

1. Identification of **environmental risk** associated with FPV technologies → Systematic Literature Review.
2. Capture **expert knowledge** of environmental risk associated with FPV technologies → Delphi method.
3. Develop and implement a BN model to **identify suitable locations** considering technical, activities and environmental assessment.
4. Integrate the model into **VAPEM tool** for user-friendly applicability (https://aztidata.es/vapem/).

RESULTS

Systematic Literature Review

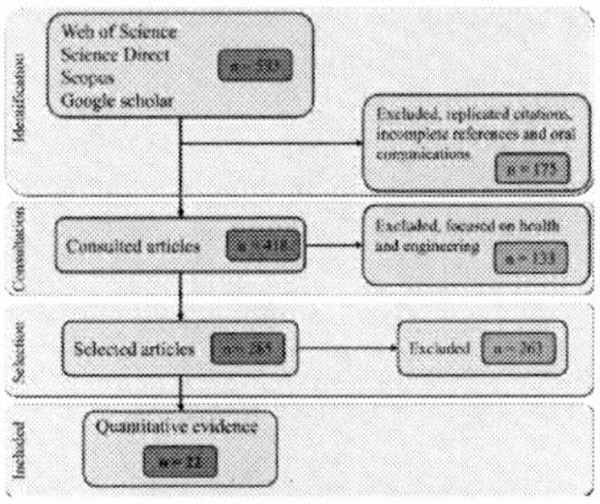

Expert knowledge (Delphi method)

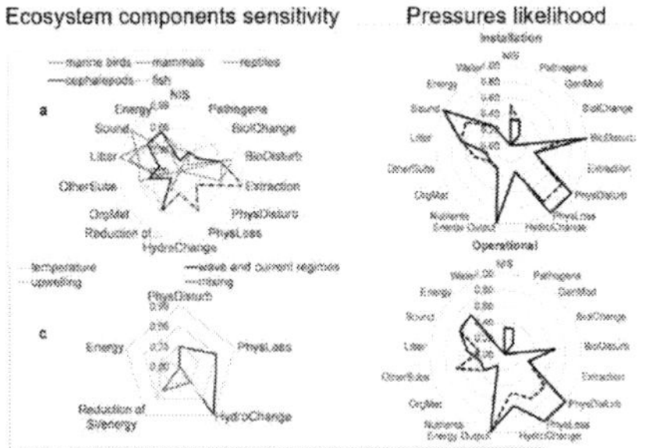

Bayesian Network modeling

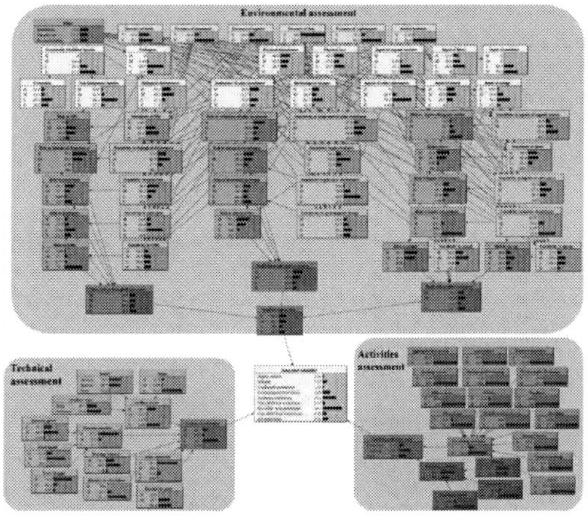

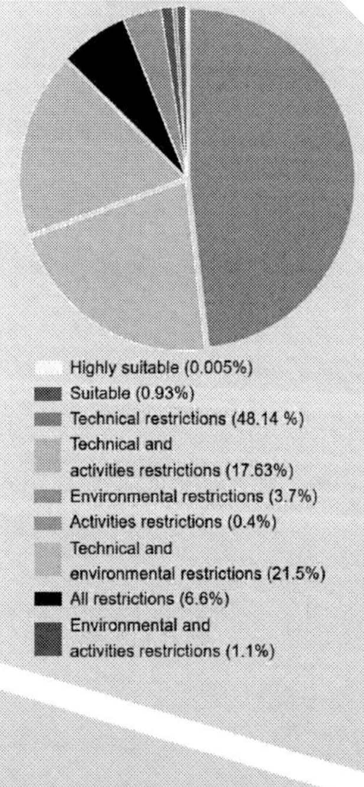

Integrated suitability

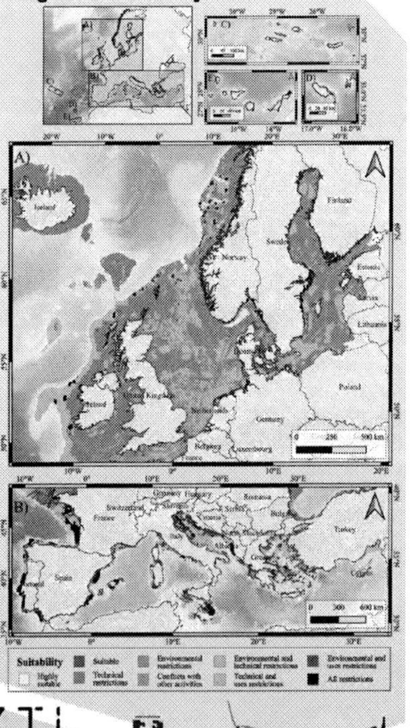

CONCLUSION

- A total of 154 km2 are highly suitable for offshore FPV.
- A total of 27,279 km2 are suitable for offshore FPV.
- The main limitation for offshore FPV development are related to technical restrictions.
- Useful results for industry, researchers, policy and decision-makers.

VAPEM

Ecological assessment and maritime spatial planning tool

https://aztidata.es/vapem/

Project founded by the Department of Economic Development, Sustainability and Environment of the Basque Government.

Research founded by: EKIOCEAN

tecnalia MEMBER OF BASQUE RESEARCH & TECHNOLOGY ALLIANCE
AZTI MEMBER OF BASQUE RESEARCH & TECHNOLOGY ALLIANCE
POLYMAT
ITSAS-REM
bcam basque center for applied mathematics
BASQUENERGY CLUSTER

LIFE CYCLE ASSESSMENT OF A SILICON-HETEROJUNCTION-BASED PV SYSTEM

Arthur W. Weeber, Shashank Bhardwaj, Olindo Isabella, Malte R. Vogt
PVMD group Delft University of Technology
Mekelweg 4, 2628 CD Delft, The Netherlands

ABSTRACT: This paper presents a Life Cycle Analysis (LCA) of a silicon-heterojunction-based PV rooftop system produced and installed in the Netherlands in 2024. A prospective LCA (pLCA) for 2035 was carried out assuming different future scenarios (Integrated Assessment Models and Shared Socioeconomic Pathways). Future material consumption and efficiencies were taken from the ITRPV 2024. Material and energy input data were taken from the EcoInvent database and the LCA was performed using Brightway2.0. Since data from EcoInvent do not correspond to current technology we have adjusted these data. For example, in the database of EcoInvent wafer thickness and kerf loss are outdated and have been scaled down: wafer thickness from 270 to 120 µm and kerf loss from 180 to 55 µm. PECVD input data are based on TU Delft lab results and scaled to M10 wafer size. Metallization input data are based on the ITRPV 2024 data and other process parameters are taken from literature. Recycling and disposal are not included. For the 2024 reference rooftop system with performance ratio (*PR*) of 0.75, the Global Warming Potential (GWP1000) is 22 g CO_2-eq/kWh, which is lower than results presented in literature. For the 2035-SSP2-REMIND scenario the GWP1000 is 6.9 g CO_2-eq/kWh. With *PR*=0.85 the GWP1000 values will be respectively 19.4 and 6.1 g CO_2-eq/kWh.
Keywords: LCA, pLCA, Silicon, Heterojunction, PV system

1 INTRODUCTION

The progress made in efficiency, cost reduction and increase in production volume is huge and beyond expectation of many organizations. Nowadays the cumulative installed PV capacity is over 2 TWp [1] and expected to grow to about 75 TWp in 2050 [2]. With this enormous market size, the environmental impact profile and sustainability of PV is becoming more important. A life cycle analysis (LCA) can be used to quantify a set of environmental impact factors.

For an accurate LCA you need recent input parameters for material and energy consumption. These input parameters are hard to get mainly because of proprietary reasons. Furthermore, most PV LCA studies have not been carried on the current high-efficiency Si PV technologies such as TOPCon and silicon heterojunction (SHJ) technology, but on PERC technology [3, 4], which is currently being phased out (or, is almost phased out).

In this study, we provide an LCA for a 22 m² rooftop PV system based on SHJ PV technology and using material input data from the ITRPV 2024 [5] and using the electricity mix of the Netherlands. Data from ITRPV 2024 will also be used for prospective LCAs (pLCAs) for 2035. The pLCAs for 2035 were done assuming different future scenarios involving Integrated Assessment Models (IAMs) and Shared Socioeconomic Pathways (SSPs) [6].

Recycling and disposal are not included in this study.

2 APPROACH AND METHODOLOGY

2.1 Rooftop PV system

The LCAs and pLCAs are based on a SHJ technology-based rooftop system. The module size is 2 m² consisting of 56 M10 SHJ solar cell and the system consists of 11 modules (22 m²). More accurately, the parameters are scaled to these sizes. As already stated: recycling and disposal are not included in this study.

The modules are assumed to be monofacial.

2.2 Input parameters and LCA software

For the input parameters the EcoInvent 3.9.1 database was used [7]. Since several input parameters are relatively old, some key parameters were scaled down. The ITRPV 2024 was used to obtain more recent data and for future data for the pLCA 2035. The wafer thickness and kerf losses were scaled down to 120 µm and 55 µm respectively for the 2024 reference, and to 100 µm and 40 µm for the 2035 scenarios. The Ag consumption was adjusted down to 4 g/cm² (front and rear) for 2024 and to 2 g/cm² for 2035. The calculations were scaled to M10 wafer size with which the Ag consumption would correspond to 140 mg/cell for 2024 and 80 mg/cell for 2035. The cell and module efficiencies are based on lab results of Zhao *et al.* [8] and on data from the ITRPV 2024.

Details about adjusted parameters can be found in Table I.

Table I: Adjusted input parameters for LCA 2024 and pLCA 2035

Input	LCA 2024	pLCA 2035
Cell thickness[5]	120 µm	100 µm
Kerf loss[5]	55 µm	40 µm
Ag consumption[5]	140 mg/cell	80 mg/cell
η_{cell}	24.2%[7]	26.6% [5]
η_{module}	22.2%[based on [7]]	24.4%[5]
Lifetime[5]	30 yrs	40 yrs
Degradation rate[5]	2% first year 0.6% next years	1% first year 0.5% next years

The consumption of precursor gases to deposit the amorphous layers is based on lab processing of Zhao *et al.* [8] and scaled to M10 wafers. For the other heterojunction specific layers data from Louwen [10] were used. For the standard processing, and the module and system components data from a IEA PVPS T12 report [3] were used.

Brightspace 2.0 [9] software was used for the LCA and pLCA. For the impact assessment the ReCiPe 2016 model [11] was applied using the so-called midpoint indicators. The assessment was done for all 18 LCA impact categories. The focus of discussion in this paper is on the Global Warming Potential (GPW1000). The LCA results of the other impact categories / indicators can be found in the appendix.

10.4229/EUPVSEC2025/5DV.2.43

The electricity mix of the Netherlands in 2024 was assumed for the energy input parameter, meaning manufacturing is assumed to be in the Netherlands.

2.3 Scenarios prospective LCA

To determine potential future environmental impact parameters pLCA involving SSP IAMs REMIND (Regional Model of Investment and Development) and IMAGE (Integrated Model to Assess the Global Environment) were used [13]. The scenarios applied in this study are:

- 2035 SSP1 REMIND: Sustainable pathway in which economic growth is balanced with social equity and environmental goals.
- 2035 SSP2 REMIND: A pathway including incremental policy changes and technological improvements to address climate issues.
- 2035 SSP2 IMAGE: A pathway including incremental policy changes and technological improvements to address climate issues, but less strict than REMIND.
- 2035 SSP5: Pathway in which rapid economic growth is key and fossil fuel based, and resulting in climate change that needs to be mitigated (and therefore not meeting the Paris agreements).

From the descriptions it can be seen that the first one (2035 SSP2 REMIND) is the most sustainable one and the last one (SSP5) is not sustainable at all.

2.4 Energy output PV system

To calculate the energy output of the system the following simple equation is used:

$$E = I_{\text{irrad}} \cdot LT \cdot \eta_{\text{mod}} \cdot A \cdot PR \cdot DR$$

In which E is the energy generated, I_{irrad} the annual irradiation level per m^2 (kWh/m^2/yr), LT is the lifetime of the module (years), η_{mod} the module efficiency, A the area (m^2), PR the performance ratio and DR the degradation level.

For I_{irrad} we took 1000 kWh/m^2/yr which corresponds the Global Horizontal Irradiance in the Netherlands (a conservative number with respect to optimal orientation). The performance ratio PR is assumed to be 0.75. For the module efficiency η_{mod}, system area A, etc. we refer to previous paragraphs.

2.5 Sensitivity analysis *PR* and energy consumption for SoG Si and wafering

In this paragraph we show the sensitivity of the 2024 results on *PR* and on the energy consumption for production Solar Grade Si (SoG Si) and wafering.

As already stated PR=0.75 was used to determine the energy output of the PV system, which is a conservative number with respect to optimal orientation in the Netherlands. PR=0.85 was also used to show the impact of a more optimistic performance assumption and the LCA results with this current value will also be presented.

For the production of SoG Si and wafering EcoInvent contains data that are about 10 years old. In that period the cumulative installation capacity has grown with a factor of 16, meaning 2^4! The processing of SoG Si and wafering has certainly improved and will use less energy than 10 years ago. If we assume a learning rate of 5% it will mean that the energy consumption has decreased with a factor of 0.95^4=0.73. Of course this a simplified assumption because the wafer thickness and kerf losses have been reduced during that period and also saving material consumption and energy. In our sensitivity analysis we evaluated an improved process for SoG Si production and wafering (all processes up to and including wafering) assuming a reduction in energy consumption of 20-70%.

3 RESULTS AND DISCUSSION

3.1 LCA GWP1000

The GWP1000 (Climate Change) for our reference (2024) rooftop system with 22.2% module efficiency is 22 g CO_2-eq/kWh and is lower than values presented in literature. Fig. 1 shows a comparison with results from Louwen [10] and Barrou [13]. Both studies resulted in about 35 g CO_2-eq/kWh, also for SHJ-based PV systems.

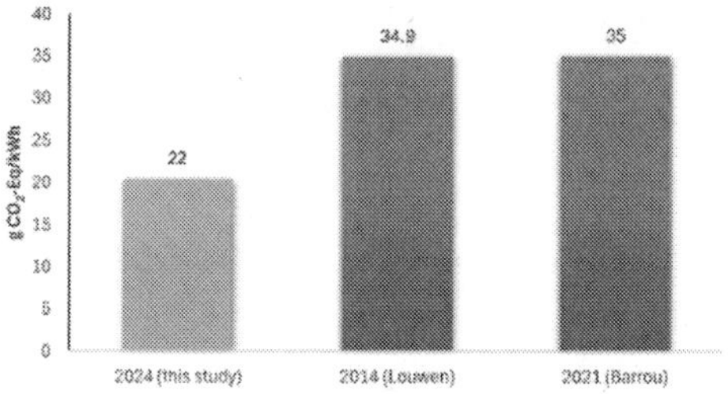

Figure 1: GWP results of our study on an SHJ-based system compared to results of Louwen and Barrou.

However, this comparison needs some more discussion about the parameters used. The main differences are described below. Louwen used an irradiation level of 1700 kWh/m^2 and Barrou 1391 kWh/m^2. Also different wafer thickness were used in both studies, 180 µm and 170 µm respectively. For the kerf losses it was 130 µm and 85 µm respectively. The same holds for η_{mod}, which were 18.4% and 21.8% respectively. In both cases a lifetime of 30 years and PR=0.75 were used, the same values as in our study. Another difference is the electricity mix used for determining the energy consumption. Louwen used the average European electricity mix of 2014 (UCTE, 531 g CO_2-eq/kWh) and Barrou assumed for production of cells, modules and systems and for the end-of-life processing the European electricity mix (2020, 418 g CO_2-eq/kWh), and for SoG Si and wafer production the Chinese electricity mix (2020, 1023 g CO_2-eq/kWh). Material transport and end-of-life measures were included by Barrou as well. We used the electricity mix of (and full production in) the Netherlands (2024, 370 g CO_2-eq/kWh), which has a lower carbon footprint than the ones used by Louwen and Barrou. It looks like comparing apples with pears, but we have performed some simple linear scaling on these parameters (irradiation level, efficiency and electricity mix on the total GWP1000, and for SoG Si and wafering on the part from raw SiO_2 material up to and including wafering) with respect to the Louwen study. Using this linear scaling on the GWP determined by Louwen (34.9 g CO_2-eq/kWh) to conditions and parameters used in our study (electricity mix 370 g CO_2-eq/kWh, 1000 kWh/m^2/yr, 22.4% efficiency, 120 µm wafer thickness, 55 µm kerf loss), we estimate a GWP of Louwen corresponding to 28-29 g CO_2-eq/kWh. With a more detailed analysis than this linear scaling and doing it for more parameters, the results might be even closer to each other.

In his 2014 study, Louwen [10] also performed a prospective LCA for 2020. He assumed for 2020 50 µm kerf free wafers, 23.5% module efficiency and progress on many other parameters. The GWP of that study resulted in a value of 21 g CO_2-eq/kWh, in the same range as our result.

A recent IEA PVPS Task 12 study on PERC showed a GWP of 26 g CO_2-eq/kWh for a system installed in Northern Italy (1361 kWh/m^2/yr). Module manufacturing was assumed to be in China with a wafer thickness of 170 µm and $\eta_{mod.}$=21.2%. End of life and transportation were included in this study. The higher irradiation level will increase the energy output compared to our study, but the lower efficiency will slightly decrease it. However, the module manufacturing in China and the thicker wafers will increase the CO_2 emission compared to our study. A first estimate shows that these effects will more or less compensate each other keeping the GWP of this PERC technology in the same range as of our study.

3.2 pLCA GWP1000 for 2035

Fig. 2 shows the pLCA GWP1000 results 2035 compared to the current 2024 result. The 2035-SSP2-REMIND results in the lowest expected GWP1000 due to the incremental policy changes (more renewable energy in the energy mix) and technology improvements. It results in a significant decrease to 6.9 g CO2-eq/kWh. The reduction for the 2035-SSP5 scenario is the lowest because that scenario is still fossil fuel based.

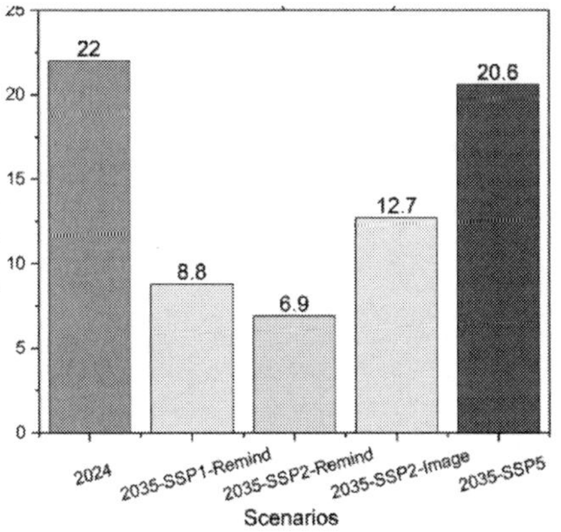

Figure 2: GWP1000 for SHJ-based rooftop system and the pLCA GWP1000 results for 2035.

Fig. 3 shows the share of the individual components / manufacturing steps for a module for 2024 and the 2035 results. In general module manufacturing step represents the largest fraction in GWP1000. Again the 2035-SSP2-REMIND shows the lowest GWP.

3.3 Ecotoxicity

Fig. 4 shows the impact on ecotoxicity potential for freshwater and marine for the LCA 2024 reference and pLCA 2035 SSP1 and SSP2 scenarios. The impact factors for the 2035 scenarios are significantly lower than for the 2024 reference, but do hardly differ from each other. In case of the implementation of policy changes on ecotoxicity for future scenarios the impact would be different for the different scenarios.

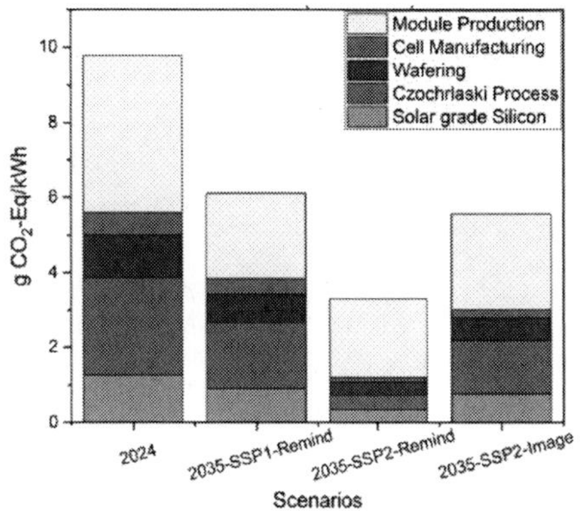

Figure 3: GPW1000 results of individual module components for pLCA 2035 compared to the 2024 reference.

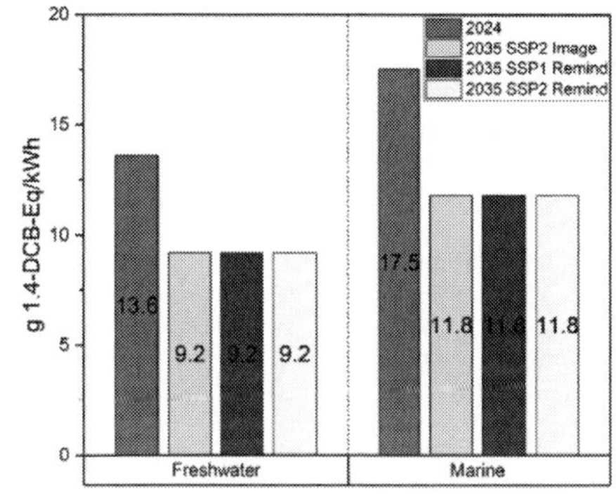

Figure 4: Ecotoxicity potential for fresh water and marine of a SHJ-based PV system for 2024 and pLCA for 2035.

3.4 Sensitivity analysis on *PR* and energy consumption for SoG Si production and wafering.

Fig. 5 shows the sensitivity analysis of the GWP1000 on *PR* for the 2024 reference and the 2035 SSP1 and SSP2 scenarios. Since the *PR* directly scales with the energy output of the system, the GWP1000 will also directly scale with *PR*. In fig. 5 the results for *PR*=0.75 and *PR*=0.85 are shown. The lowest GW1000 is for the 2035-SSP2-REMIND scenario with a value of 6.1 g CO_2-eq/kWh.

Fig. 6 shows the potential change in GWP1000 in case it is assumed that process development for SoG Si production and wafering has been improved (which is certainly the case but to the best of our knowledge not yet quantified in literature). The impact on GWP1000 for reducing the electricity consumption for SoG Si and wafering to 20-30% seems to have a minor impact on the overall GWP1000. Only the one of 70% shows a clear impact while this 70% corresponds to a learning rate of about 5%. So, it might be a realistic assumption.

3.5 Other LCA impact parameters

The LCA and pLCA results for all studied mid-point impact categories / indicators can be found in the appendix. The results of the other indicators show a similar trend as the ecotoxicity potential but will not be discussed further.

10.4229/EUPVSEC2025/5DV.2.43
020515-003

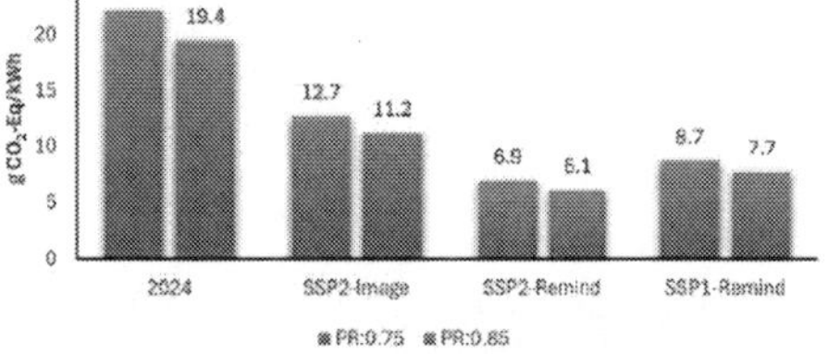

Figure 5: Sensitivity of *PR* on GWP1000 for the 2024 reference and 2035 SSP1 and SSP2 scenarios.

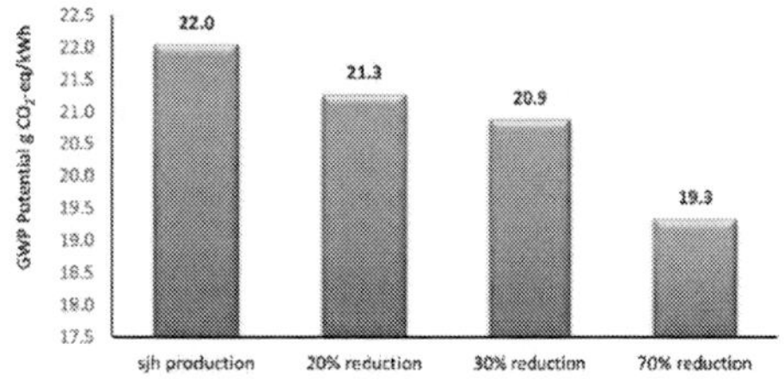

Figure 6: Sensitivity of the reduction of electricity consumption of SoG Si production and wafering on GWP1000 of the 2024 reference.

4 CONCLUSION

In our study the GWP1000 of a rooftop PV system based on SHJ PV technology, and produced and installed in 2024, is 22 g CO_2-eq/kWh. It is assumed that the system is produced in the Netherlands (Dutch electricity mix) and has an annual in-plane irradiation of 1000 kWh/m^2/yr (Global Horizontal Irradiance in the Netherlands). Direct comparison with other studies is difficult because differences in production location (electricity mix, CO_2 emissions), irradiation levels during operation and module efficiency (kWh generation), etc. A first more detailed comparison shows that the GWP of our study is lower than the one from other studies on SHJ based PV technology. However, it seems to be in the same range as the results of an IEA PVPS Task 12 study on a PERC system in Northern Italy.

For pLCAs with different future scenarios and assuming *PR*=0.85, the GWP1000 can decline to about 6 g CO_2-eq/kWh (2035 SSP2 REMIND). Since input data on SoG Si and wafering for our reference PV system are from 2014, introducing a learning rate for electricity consumption for these process steps will further reduce the GWP1000 indicator.

5 REFERENCES

[1] A. Jäger-Waldau, EPJ Photovolt. 16 (2025) 22

[2] N. Haegel *et al.*, Science 380 (2023) 6640

[3] A. Danelli *et al.* IEA PVPS T12, https://doi.org/10.69766/EEMP5995

[4] A. Müller *et al*, SolMat 230 (2021) 111277

[5] ITRPV 15th edition Results 2023, May 2024 vdma.org

[6] R. Sacchi *et al.*, Renew. Sustain. Energy Rev. 160 (2022) 112311,

[7] EcoInvent, https://ecoinvent.org/

[8] Y. Zhao *et al.* SolMat 258 (2023) 112413

[9] Brightspace, https://docs.brightspace.dev/en/latest/

[10] A. Louwen, PhD thesis Utrecht University 2016 and A. Louwen *et al.* Prog. Photovolt.: Res. Appl. 23 (2015) 1406 (thesis and paper show slightly different results)

[11] M. Huijbregts *et al.*, Int. J. Life Cycle Assess., 22 (2017) 138

[12] Premise, Introduction to premise 2024 https://premise.readthedocs.io/en/latest/introduction.html

[13] A. Barrou, MSc thesis EPFL 2022, https://infoscience.epfl.ch/handle/20.500.14299/198917

APPENDIX

Table A1: Environmental impact assessment for an SHJ-based PV rooftop system produced and installed in the Netherlands. Data for the LCA 2024 and for pLCA 2035-SSSP REMIND are presented.

Indicator	Unit/kWh	SHJ 2024 reference	2035 SSP2-REMIND
Climate Change GWP1000	kg CO_2-eq	2.20E-02	6.9E-03
Terrestrial acidification potential (TAP)	kg 1.4-DCB-eq	9.0E-05	3.4E-05
Freshwater ecotoxicity potential (FETP)	kg 1.4-DCB-eq	1.4E-02	9.2E-03
Marine ecotoxicity potential (METP)	kg 1.4-DCB-eq	1.7E-02	1.2E-02
Terrestrial ecotoxicity potential (TETP)	kg 1.4-DCB-eq	1.1E-01	9.2E-02
Fossil fuel potential (FFP)	kg oil-eq	5.6E-03	1.7E-03
Freshwater eutrophication potential (FEP)	kg P-eq	2.5E-05	1.3E-05
Marine eutrophication potential (FEP)	kg N-eq	1.2E-06	5.6E-07
Human toxicity potential (HTPc)	kg 1.4-DCB-eq	3.5E-03	2.3E-03
Human toxicity potential (HTPnc)	kg 1.4-DCB-eq	1.7E-01	1.1E-01
Ionizing radiation potential (IRP)	kg ^{60}Co-eq	2.4E-03	9.3E-04
Agricultural land occupation (LOP)	m^2 crop-eq	1.6E-03	1.0E-03
Surplus ore potential (SOP)	kg Cu-eq	1.0E-03	7.0E-04
Ozone depletion potential (ODPinfinite)	kg CFC-11-eq	9.5E-09	3.5E-09
Particulate matter formation potential (PMFP)	kg PM2.5-eq	4.3E-05	1.2E-05
Photochemical oxidant formation: human health (HOFP)	kg NO_x-eq	6.8E-05	2.5E-05
Photochemical oxidant formation: terrestrial ecosystems (EOFP)	kg NO_x-eq	7.1E-05	2.7E-05
Water consumption potential	m^3	3.5E-04	2.1E-04

Life Cycle Assessment of a Silicon Heterojunction based PV System

Arthur W. Weeber*, Shashank Bhardwaj, Olindo Isabella, Malte R. Vogt

Photovoltaic Materials and Devices Laboratory, Delft University of Technology, The Netherlands (*Contact: a.w.weeber@tudelft.nl)

1. Motivation

- Environmental impact profile and sustainability of PV are becoming more important
- Old input data for LCA are generally used because actual data material and energy consumption are hard to get (proprietary reasons)
- Hardly any recent papers on LCA SHJ technology
- Prospective LCA studies hardly available

2. Approach – Method

- Input parameters from EcoInvent[1] v3.9.1 used
- Input data scaled down to more recent values, and based on ITRPV 2024[2] and recent lab results by Zhao *et al.*[3]
- Prospective LCA (pLCA) for 2035 based on projections by ITRPV 2024[2]
- Future energy scenarios applied involving Integrated Assessments Models (IAMs) IMAGE and REMIND and Shared Socioeconomics Pathways (SSPs):
  - 2035 SSP1 REMIND: Sustainable pathway in which economic growth is balanced with social equity and environmental goals
  - 2035 SSP2 REMIND: Pathway including incremental policy changes and technological improvements to address climate changes
  - 2035 SSP2 IMAGE: as SSP2 REMIND but less strict
  - 2035 SSP5: Pathway with rapid economic growth and not meeting Paris Agreements
- Brightway2.0[4] software used to perform LCAs and pLCAs
- Focus on carbon footprint GWP1000 (global warming potential)
- Sensitivity analysis based on performance ratio and on energy consumption up to and including wafer process
- System size: rooftop, 22 m^2

3. Input data

- Input parameters scaled to M10 processing and based on Zhao *et al.*, ITRPV 2024 (see table 1), Louen *et al.*[5] and IEA PVPS T12 report[6]. System components based on this IEA PVPS report[6].
- Electricity mix of / manufacturing in the Netherlands
- Energy output PV system based on simple calculations and in-plane irradiation of 1000 kWh/m^2 (GHI in the Netherlands), so conservative
- Performance ratio PR=0.75, also conservative

Table 1: Input data LCA 2024 and pLCA 2035

Input	Data 2024	Data 2035
Cell thickness[2]	120 μm	100 μm
Ag consumption[2]	140 mg/cell	80 mg/cell
η_{cell}	24.2%[3]	26.6%[2]
η_{module}	22.2% based on [3]	24.4%[2]
Lifetime[2]	30 years	40 years
Annual degradation rate[2]	2% first year, 0.6% remaining	1% first year, 0.5% remaining

4. Results LCA

- GWP1000 for 2024: 22 g CO_2-eq/kWh
- Comparison literature (see Fig. 1):
  - ~35 g CO_2-eq/kWh (also PR=0.75, 30 yrs lifetime) by:
    - Louwen *et al.* 1700 kWh/m^2 in-plane irradiation, η_{mod}=18.4%, 180 μm wafer[5]
    - Barrou, 1391 kWh/m^2 in-plane irradiation, η_{mod}=21.8%, 170 μm wafer[6]
  - ~26 g CO_2-eq/kWh for PERC in IEA PVPS T12 report on a plant in Italy with 1368 kWh/m^2 [7]

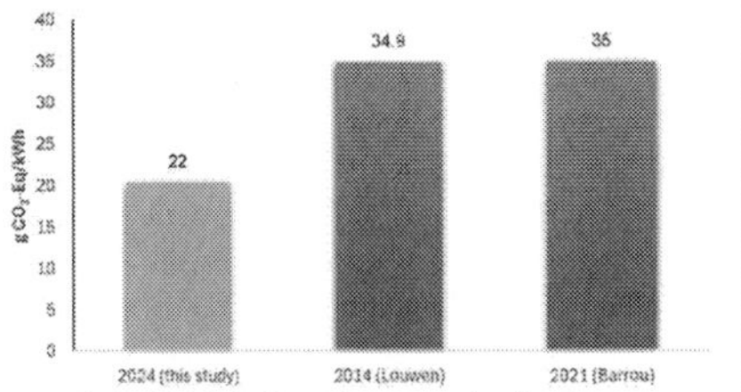

Fig 1. LCA result this study compared to literature

5. Results pLCA 2035

- Depending on the future scenario the GWP1000 could be reduced to 6.9 g CO_2-eq/kWh in 2035 (Fig. 2)
- Module production is largest fraction, especially for 2035 SSP2 REMIND (Fig. 3, only the module)

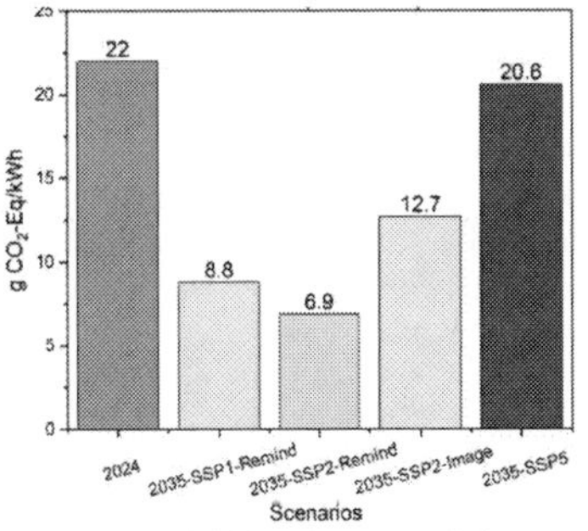

Fig 2. GWP1000 for rooftop system 2024 and pLCA result for 2035

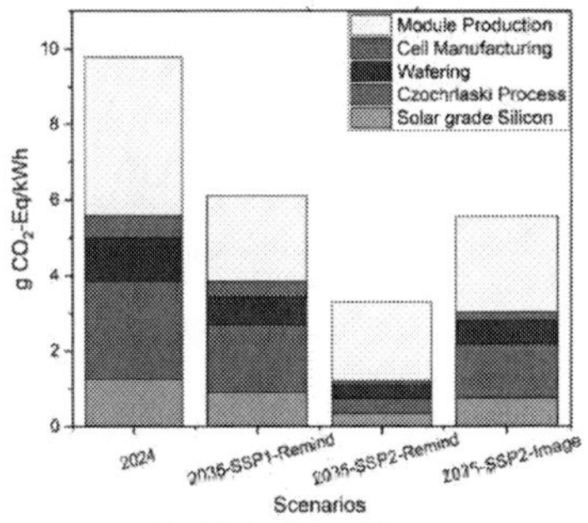

Fig 3. GWP1000 for SHJ module components for 2024 and for pLCA 2035

6. Sensitivity results to PR and Si wafer

- GWP1000 scales directly with PR (Fig. 4)
- With 2035 SSP2 scenario GWP1000 could be reduced to 6.1 g CO_2-eq/kWh
- 2035 SSP5 not shown, but scales in the same way (about 18 g-CO_2-eq/kWh for PR=0.85)
- EcoInvent parameters for Si are based on data from 10 years ago. Lower energy consumption for SoG Si production and wafers expected.
- Fig. 5 shows impact on GWP1000 for 20-70% reduction in energy consumption from raw SiO_2 material up to and including wafering (2024 results)

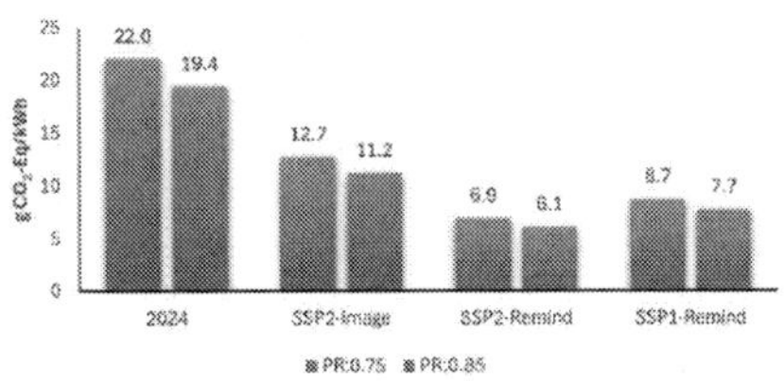

Fig 4. Sensitivity of PR on GWP1000 for 2024 and 2035

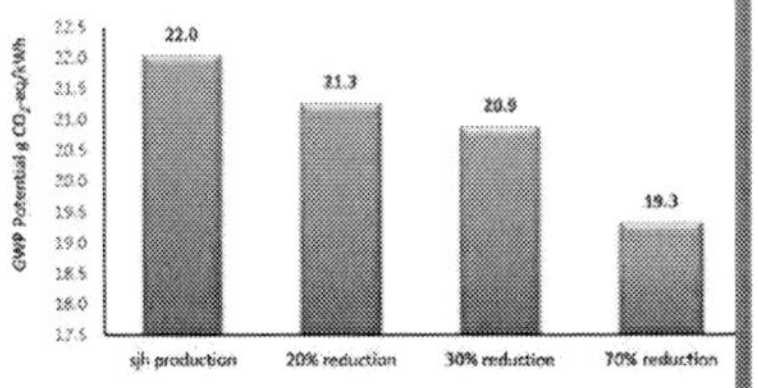

Fig 5. Sensitivity of reduction energy consumption for all production steps up to and including wafering (from SiO_2 -> wafer, 2024 results)

7. Conclusion

- The carbon footprint GWP1000 for SHJ-technology-based rooftop systems is about 22 g CO_2-eq/kWh as determined by using more recent data for processing and material consumption.
- Depending on future scenarios it can potentially be reduced to 6.9 g CO_2-eq/kWh and with assuming PR=0.85 even to about 6 g CO_2-eq/kWh in 2035.
- The carbon footprint GWP1000 for current SHJ technology from this study is significantly lower than data from literature, but in the same range as recent results on PERC technology. Note that this is despite this study assuming the lowest annual irradiation of 1000 kWh/m^2 due to being focused on the Netherlands.
- Assuming higher cell and module efficiencies for the future will reduce the carbon footprint GWP1000 to even lower values.

[1] https://ecoinvent.org/
[2] International Technology Roadmap PV ITRPV May 2024 - 2023 Results, vdma.org
[3] Zhao *et al.* SolMat doi:10.1016/j.solmat.2023.112413
[4] https://docs.brightway.dev/en/latest/
[5] Louwen *et al.* Progr. Photovolt. Res. Appl. doi:10.1002/pip.2540
[6] Barrou, MSc thesis EPFL 2022, https://infoscience.epfl.ch/handle/20.500.14299/198917
[7] A. Danelli et al. , IEA PVPS T12 , 2024, https://doi.org/10.69766/EEMP5995

PVMD TU Delft

REUSE, REDESIGN AND RECOVERY OF RESIDENTIAL SOLAR INSTALLATIONS COMPONENTS

Author(s): Y. Lara[1]*, R. Villén[1], R. Simón-Allué[1], G. Brun[1], I. Guedea[1]
Company / Institute(s): [1]ENDEF
Address(es): *yolanda.lara@endef.com

ABSTRACT: MUTABLE project is an industrial research initiative focused on applying circular economy principles in residential photovoltaic (PV) and photovoltaic-thermal (PVT or hybrid) installations. The overarching goal of MUTABLE is to define and develop an integral circularity strategy applicable to small self-consumption solar installations. This includes photovoltaic and hybrid installations, as well as complementary energy systems such as heat pumps, recovery devices, and storage systems. The project is structured around three interconnected pillars: reuse, redesign, and recovery, with the aim of defining methodologies to identify the most suitable route for each component of a solar installation and to determine maintenance needs to extend their lifespan.

Key activities within the project involve the disassembly and reassembly of photovoltaic, solar hybrid, and complementary installations, followed by monitoring their performance before and after these processes to validate operation and quantify reuse percentages.

This initiative is expected to provide valuable knowledge to develop new products, processes, and services with a reduced environmental footprint, ultimately increasing efficiency in solar residential energy use and minimizing waste generation. **Keywords:** Photovoltaics, Hybrid photovoltaic-thermal (PVT) collectors, circularity, second-life, circular economy, sustainability.

1 INTRODUCTION

Solar PV installations increased a 33% in 2024 over 2023, reaching a 2.2 TW cumulative installed solar PV capacity. It is estimated that by 2029, annual global solar installations may reach 930 GW [1]. Projected PV-related waste volumes are projected between 1.7 and 60 million tonnes, by 2030 and 2050, respectively [2]. This waste can be increased by material losses and damages during logistics stages, such as packaging, transportation, and storage [3]. The development of a circular mindset among the PV value chain is, therefore, critical to secure the availability of secondary raw materials and to prevent, delay, or mitigate environmental damage [4].

Europe adopted the Circular Economy Action Plan [5] seeking to include initiatives throughout the entire product life cycle, focusing on how products are designed and promoting circular economy processes.

To move to circular-based economy, both PV reuse and recycling need to be assessed. Current PV panel designs do not facilitate materials separation, leading these panels to low-value recycling or landfills. Similarly, current business models rarely allow for product maintenance, refurbishing, take-back, or recycling. PV reuse assessment is yet to be explored. There is a lack of reliable data on module degradation, yearly aging, as well as on business cases for reuse [4]. A survey among 3996 households in Flanders (Belgium) shown that PV reuse is considered interesting among younger, highly educated, migrant and less risk-averse customers segments [6].

Regarding PV recycling, the 2012/19/EU11 European Directive [7] requires the processing of photovoltaic panels at the end of their useful life (EOL) and establishes measures aimed at protecting the environment and human health by preventing or reducing the adverse impacts of the generation and management of waste electrical and electronic equipment (WEEE). Partly due to the implementation of this directive, associations such as PVCycle, carry out processes to separate the raw materials from photovoltaic panels during recycling.

MUTABLE project represents a significant leap in scientific innovation within the solar energy residential sector, particularly in its pioneering approach to circular economy principles.

- Integral Circularity Strategy: MUTABLE systematically focuses on reuse, redesign, and recovery as interconnected pillars, providing a holistic framework for extending the lifecycle of solar components. This shift from linear to circular processes is fundamental to increasing the sustainability of solar residential installations.
- Methodology for Component Routing: The project is developing specific methodologies to identify the "best route" for each individual component within a solar residential installation. This granular approach to material flow, considering direct reuse, redesign, or recovery, offers a framework for decision-making that optimizes resource utilization and minimizes waste.
- Redesign for Enhanced Reusability: The project's focus on redesigning hybrid panels (water and air) is highly innovative. By addressing inherent design flaws (e.g., hydraulic circuit breakage in water hybrid panels) and integrating recycled/second-life materials, MUTABLE directly contributes to increasing the reusability and prolonging the lifespan of these complex components. This includes the exploration of Building Integrated Photovoltaics (BIPV) for air hybrid systems, aiming to reduce material consumption by integrating panels directly into building envelopes.
- Best Practices Guide and Material Categorization: The creation of a formal "Best Practices Guide" for disassembly and assembly, specifically aimed at material recovery and reuse, is a significant practical innovation.

The primary aim of the MUTABLE project is to establish and implement a comprehensive circularity strategy within the solar energy residential sector, encompassing the entire lifecycle of solar installations and associated energy systems. This strategic approach is designed to be transversal, integrating circular economy principles. The project's global objective is broken down into four main outcomes:

- Increase reuse rate: by identifying the current reuse rate of materials and equipment across different types of solar residential installations, and characterizing improvement areas.

10.4229/EUPVSEC2025/5DV.2.44
020517-001

- Redesign hybrid solar panels: by identifying specific redesign needs for both water and air hybrid solar panels, as well as their associated installations, to enhance the reuse rate of their components.
- Assessing recovery paths: by defining the most appropriate recovery processes for materials that cannot be directly reused or redesigned.
- Develop a Methodology & Best Practices Guide: by designing a robust methodology for identifying the optimal path for each component of a solar installation to improve its sustainability, alongside creating a guide of best practices that applies across all company workstreams to ensure the highest levels of circularity in installations and equipment.

The work comprises the disassembly and assembly of four solar installations (one PV- and three PVT-based), as well as their ancillary systems, to define characterizing methodologies for the different elements. The disassembly and assembly processes will be documented and the newly assembled installations will be monitored to compare their performance after the disassembly and reassembly process.

2 METHODOLOGY & DEVELOPMENT

2.1 Analysis and planning.

As first step, comprehensive analysis of different solar PV and PVT installations was conducted, examining both their assembly and operational aspects to identify potential routes for reuse, recycling, and recovery of materials.

Four installation typologies were defined according to their components (see **Table I**). Each of these typologies was assessed separately. A manual for dismantling each one of the installations was prepared, to maximize components recovery, as well as a manual for reassembling the installations, taking into account the observations made during the dismantling process. These processes were applied in each one of the installations, allowing to iterate and refine the manuals.

This led to the development and continuous updating of a "Best Practices Guide" for disassembly and assembly, specifically designed to maximize material recovery and reuse. This guide represents a significant improvement, as no formal protocol for material recovery existed within the company prior to this project.

Table I: Installation typologies

Typology	Components	Connections
PVT water panels, type A	Hybrid panels	Electrical
	Inverters	
	Structures	Hydraulic
	Ancillary hydraulics	
PVT water panels, type B	Hybrid panels	Electrical
	Inverters	
	Structures	Hydraulic
	Ancillary hydraulics	
Photovoltaic panels	Hybrid panels	Electrical
	Inverters	
	Structures	
PVT air panels	Hybrid panels	Electrical
	Inverters	
	Structures	Pneumatic
	Ancillary pneumatics	

A methodology to classify the materials during disassembly was designed and tested. Two sticker-based methods were proposed: one based on colour codes and another combining shapes and colours. After practical application, the colour-code-only method (Method 1) was identified as the most efficient due to its simplicity and ease of use in the field, and it will be adopted for future phases.

Table II: Classification method 1

Item	Meaning
●	Good condition. Reuse directly
●	To be reviewed. Reuse or Redesign
●	Poor condition. Recycling or Recovery

By applying this method, three main routes were chosen for all the components assessed (Reuse, Redesign, Recycling). It is worth to say that a percentage of materials from each of the four disassembled installations were sent to recycling, due to different wearing conditions, installation age and in-the-field issues found during both dismantling and installing.

2.2 Disassembly, classification, and assembly of Installations.

Four types of solar installations were successfully disassembled, classified and re-assembled (if possible) in different locations, including water hybrid panels (Type A and Type B), simple photovoltaic panels, and air hybrid panels, along with their auxiliary components. From now on, the processes followed by each one of the installations is detailed.

2.2.1. Photovoltaic-thermal water panels, type A.

Figure 1: PVT water, type A. Initial installation.

This installation consists of 25 glazed PVT-water panels, south orientation, 45° tilt (**Figure 1**). During the disassembly process, the major part of the wiring as well as the structures (**Figure 2** d)) were classified to be reused. Nevertheless, the PV laminates, hydraulic connections, and insulating materials (see **Figure 2** a), b), c)) were found to be severely damaged, making them unsuitable for reuse, and were classified for recycling or potential recovery routes.

10.4229/EUPVSEC2025/5DV.2.44
020517-002

a) PVT panels b) Removed conducts

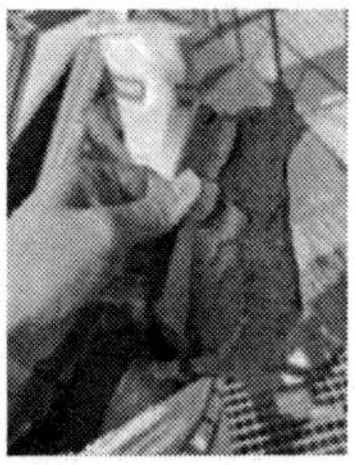

c) Insulating material d) Structures

Figure 2: PVT water, type A. Dissassembly.

2.2.2. Photovoltaic-thermal water panels, type B.

This second installation, **Figure 3**, comprises 8 PVT-water-based unglazed panels distributed in two benches, 30° tilt, south orientation, as well as an ancillary heat pump and inertia tanks.

Figure 3: PVT water, type B. Initial installation.

During disassembly, PVT panels and structures were classified to be directly reused (**Figure 4** a) and d)). Piping insulation was found in good condition, thus retained, and auxiliary hydraulic elements (heat pump, tanks) were carefully removed, with the working fluid recovered (**Figure 4** c)). Electrical components, wiring, and internal probes were also disassembled. Key elements like electrical panels, water tanks, and expansion vessels were categorized as directly reusable, while hydraulic circuits (**Figure 4** b)) and wiring required further review.

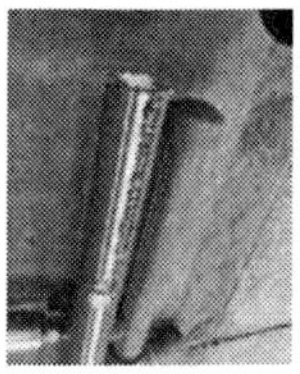

a) PVT panels b) Retired conducts

c) Water+glicol recovery d) Structures

Figure 4: PVT water, type B. Dissassembly.

For the newly assembled installation, PVT panels, structures, inverters, hydraulic components and most of the pipes have been directly reused. Due to space restrictions, only 4 panels have been installed (**Figure 5**), while the rest have been stored. Also, the heat pump has been reused, adapting the hydraulic circuits to the new location. Those hydraulic circuits were kept as long as possible during the disassembly process in order to maximize their use during the reassembly.

Figure 5: PVT water, type B. Final installation.

2.2.3. Photovoltaic panels.

The photovoltaic installation has 4 half-cell panels, 320Wp each, **Figure 6**.

Figure 6: Photovoltaic panels. Initial installation.

Panels (**Figure 7** a)), structures (**Figure 7** b)), conduits and trays were classified as reusable, emphasizing the need for careful planning due to varying dimensions in new installations. Cabling and conduits (**Figure 7** c)) were disassembled, with MC4 connectors marked for functional review prior to be reused.

10.4229/EUPVSEC2025/5DV.2.44

a) PV panels b) Structures

c) Wiring

Figure 7: Photovoltaic panels. Dissassembly.

The major part of the components (panels, inverter, wiring and trays) have been reused in the new installation. As the new installation is coplanar, former structures have been stored for later use.

Figure 8: Photovoltaic panels. Final installation.

2.2.4. Photovoltaic-thermal air panels.

Air-based hybrid panels consist of 5 PVT panels with 45° tilt, facing south, with a 5° west deviation, together with a fan for air circulation and ancillary ducts, **Figure 9**.

Figure 9: PVT air panels. Initial installation.

The disassembly process involved both exterior (cabling, conduits, probes, panels, structures, **Figure 10**) and interior (control system, inverter, fan…) components. Some cables showed damage from weather exposure and were marked for review.

a) Panels, wiring, ducts. Front view b) Panels, wiring, ducts. Rear view

Figure 10: PVT air panels. Dissassembly.

In the reassembled installation, **Figure 11**, the mounting system had to be modified, including concrete blocks for the structures. One of the most delicate aspects was the connection between panels, that was carefully reinstalled, and has been pointed out as one of the redesign needs to be taken into account.

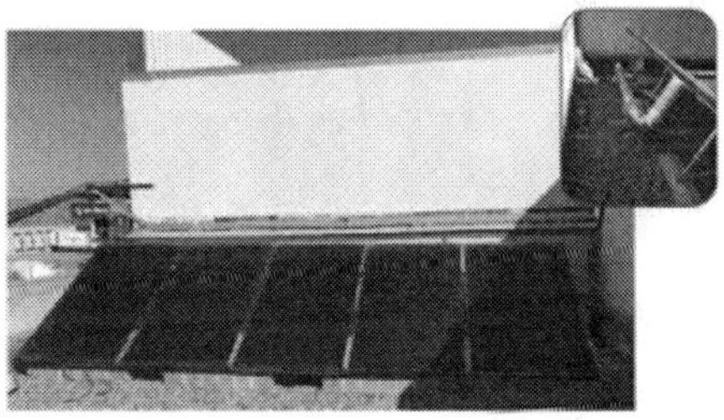

Figure 11: PVT air panels. Final installation.

All disassembled materials were catalogued, classified, and assigned to specific routes (reuse, review, or recovery) according to the newly defined methodology. Three of the four installation types were successfully reassembled at new locations using the reused materials.

2.3 Assessment of Redesign needs and Reuse rate.

Crucial redesign needs were identified for both water and air hybrid panels during the works.

For water hybrid panels type B (**Figure 12**), the primary redesign focus identified is to prevent hydraulic circuit breakage, both within the panel and at external connections. Solutions involve reducing the number of internal conduits/unions and minimizing external connections (e.g., through a single inlet/outlet design and larger panel sizes). Research has begun on larger glass-glass PV laminates and a redesigned thermal absorber to optimize heat transfer and robustness.

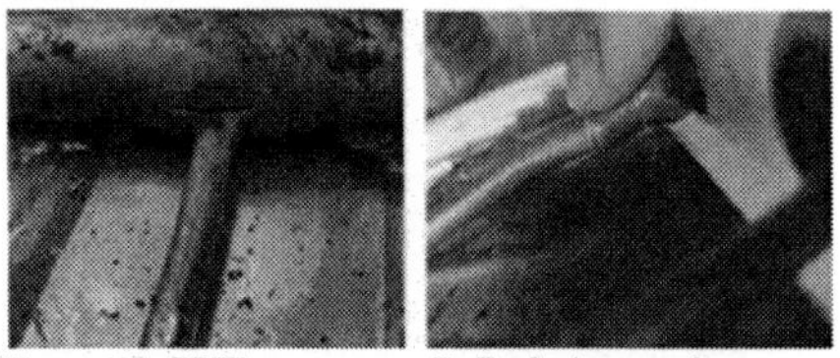

Figure 12: PVT water, type B. Redesign needs.

10.4229/EUPVSEC2025/5DV.2.44

For air hybrid panels, critical elements identified for redesign include the air inlet filter, inter-panel connections, air outlet tube fixation, and the sealing of electrical wiring. Additionally, a global redesign effort has commenced for a new PVT air system concept integrated into inclined building roofs (BIPV), aiming to reduce material usage and expand applicability.

a) Inlet filter b) Inter-panel connections

Figure 13: PVT air panels. Redesign needs.

Regarding the reuse route it is worth mentioning that the dismantling, classifying and storing processes for the large amount of material moved required a higher available workspace than expected (**Figure 14**), as many elements were installed in compact spaces.

Figure 14: Overview of components stored during classification process.

An estimated overall reuse rate of 30% of the material was achieved through the new processes defined in the project. The reuse rate varied significantly depending on both, component type and the specific requirements of the new assembly locations. For instance, plumbing elements from the PVT water type B installation, demonstrated a high reuse rate of approximately 70%. Components such as wiring, can be reused in their majority, although need to go through electrical safety and working tests prior to their reutilization. As mentioned before, for all the installations assessed there is always a percentage of the disassembled material that goes into recycling.

4 CONCLUSIONS

The experimental work described comprises the disassembly and assembly of photovoltaics, photovoltaic-thermal solar installations, as well as ancillary systems, together with the definition of methodologies to assign paths for the different elements (to be reused, redesigned or recycled). The main conclusions obtained from the work are summarized below.

- A methodology for material categorization, easy to use in the field, was designed and tested.
- Four types of solar installations were successfully disassembled, and all disassembled materials were assigned to Reuse, Redesign or Recovery routes.
- A "Best Practices Guide" for assembly and disassembly processes, designed to maximize material recovery and reuse, has been developed.
- Crucial redesign needs were identified for both water and air hybrid panels.
- Three of the four installation types were successfully reassembled at new locations using the reused materials, achieving an overall reuse rate of 30%.

As further work, the main immediate steps are focused on assessing the identified redesign needs as well as evaluation the performance of the three second-life installations.

5 ACKNOWLEDGEMENTS

This work was undertaken in the framework of MUTABLE project, funded by FEDER/Gobierno de Aragón/Project EC-35-2024.

6 REFERENCES

[1]. SolarPower Europe (2025): Global Market Outlook for Solar Power 2025-2029
[2]. IRENA. End-of-Life Management: Solar Photovoltaic Panels International Renewable Energy Agency. 2016.
[3]. Iseri, F. et al; A Circular Economy Systems Engineering Framework for Waste Management of Photovoltaic Panels; Ind. Eng. Chem. Res. 2025, 64, 14986−14997
[4]. Franco, M.A.; Groesser, S.N. A Systematic Literature Review of the Solar Photovoltaic Value Chain for a Circular Economy. Sustainability 2021, 13, 9615. https://doi.org/10.3390/su13179615
[5]. COMMUNICATION FROM THE COMMISSION TO THE EUROPEAN PARLIAMENT, THE COUNCIL, THE EUROPEAN ECONOMIC AND SOCIAL COMMITTEE AND THE COMMITTEE OF THE REGIONS A new Circular Economy Action Plan For a cleaner and more competitive Europe
[6]. Van Opstal, W.; Smeets, A.; When do circular business models resolve barriers to residential solar PV adoption? Evidence from survey data in Flanders; Energy Policy 182 (2023) 113761
[7]. DIRECTIVE 2012/19/EU OF THE EUROPEAN PARLIAMENT AND OF THE COUNCIL of 4 July 2012 on waste electrical and electronic equipment (WEEE)

42nd European Photovoltaic Solar Energy Conference and Exhibition

EU PVSEC 2025

Reuse, redesign and recovery of residential solar installations components

Y. Lara[1*], R. Villén[1], R. Simón-Allué[1], G. Brun[1], I. Guedea[1]
[1]ENDEF
*Corresponding author: yolanda.lara@endef.com

The goal of MUTABLE is to define and develop an integral circularity strategy applicable to small self-consumption solar installations. This includes photovoltaic and hybrid installations, as well as complementary energy systems such as heat pumps, recovery devices, and storage systems. The primary aim of is to establish and implement a comprehensive circularity strategy within the solar energy residential sector, encompassing the entire lifecycle of solar installations and associated energy systems.

Approach & classification methodology

Increase reuse rate

Identify the current reuse rate of materials and equipment across different types of solar residential installations, and characterize improvement areas.

Redesign hybrid solar panels

Identify specific redesign needs for both water and air hybrid solar panels, as well as their associated installations, to enhance the reuse rate of their components.

Assessing recovery paths

Define the most appropriate recovery processes for materials that cannot be directly reused or redesigned

Typology	Components	Connections
PVT water panels, type A	Hybrid panels	Electrical
	Inverters	
	Structures	Hydraulic
	Ancillary hydraulics	
PVT water panels, type B	Hybrid panels	Electrical
	Inverters	
	Structures	Hydraulic
	Ancillary hydraulics	
Photovoltaic panels	PV Panels	Electrical
	Inverters	
	Structures	
PVT air panels	Hybrid panels	Electrical
	Inverters	
	Structures	Neumatic
	Ancillary neumatics	

Four typologies were defined according to their components. Each typology was dismantled independently.

Methodology & Best Practices Guide

- Good condition – Reuse directly
- To be reviewed – Reuse or Redesign
- Poor condition – Recycling or Recovery

A **methodology** (color-coded, sticker-based) to classify the components while dismantling was developed. Easy to use and non-invasive to the components or the workers, to be used in roofs while working.

Best Practices Guide for disassembly and assembly installations to be able to reuse the most of material were prepared

Main routes were chosen for the all the components. For all the installations, part of the materials were sent to recycling. Reuse ratio varies depending on both, type of components and new locations. Components such as wiring, able to be reused, needs to pass electrical safety and working tests prior to reuse.

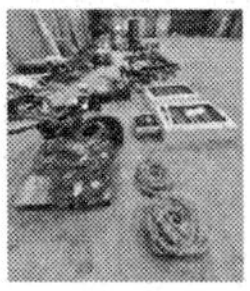

Results and discussion

PV panels

Figure 1. Photovoltaic panels. Initial installation

Figure 2. Disassembly

Figure 3. Photovoltaic panels. Final installation

Panels, inverter, wiring and canalizations reused.
The new installation is coplanar, former structures stored for later use.

Main routes

REUSE – REDESIGN – RECOVERY

PVT water, type A

Figure 4. PVT water, type A. Initial installation

Figure 5. Disassembly

Panels, insulating material and ducts were very damaged.
Recycling route, no reassembly.

Main routes

REUSE – REDESIGN – RECOVERY

PVT water, type B

Figure 6. PVT water, type B Initial installation

Figure 7. Disassembly

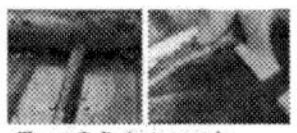

Figure 8. Redesign needs

Panels, structures, inverters, hydraulic components and most of the pipes reused.
Only 4 out of 8 panels mounted due to space limitation.

Welding points between joints and reducing number of conduits identified as main redesign needs.

Figure 9. PVT water, type B. Final installation

Main routes

REUSE – REDESIGN – RECOVERY

PVT air

Figure 10. PVT air panels. Initial installation

Figure 11. Disassembly

Figure 12. Redesign needs

Panels, structures, inverter, air ducts and fan reused.

Air filters and junctions between panels identified as main redesign needs.

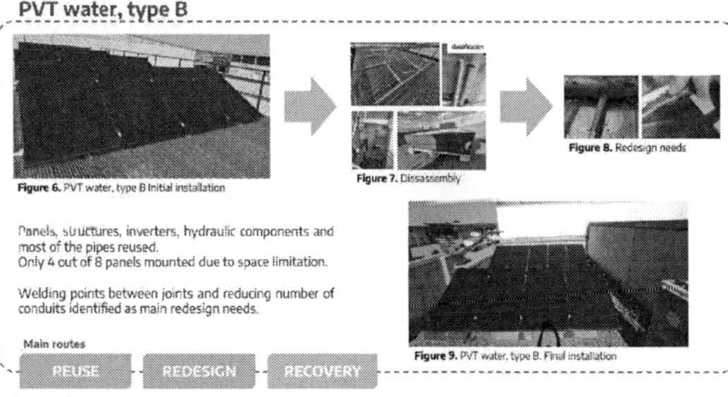

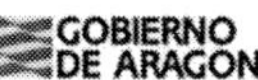

Figure 13. PVT air panels. Final installation

Main routes

REUSE – REDESIGN – RECOVERY

Conclusions

1. A **methodology for material categorization**, easy to use in the field, was designed and tested.
2. **Four types of solar installations were successfully disassembled,** and all disassembled materials were assigned to Reuse, Redesign or Recovery routes.
3. A **"Best Practices Guide"** for assembly and disassembly processes, designed to maximize material recovery and reuse, has been developed.
4. Crucial redesign needs were identified for both water and air hybrid panels
5. Three of the four installation types were **successfully reassembled at new locations** using the reused materials, achieving an **overall reuse rate of 30%.**

ENDEF website MUTABLE
Cofinanciado por la Unión Europea 020518-001
Ministerio de Hacienda Fondos Europeos
Gobierno de Aragón
Funded by: FEDER/Gobierno de Aragón/Project EC-35-2024

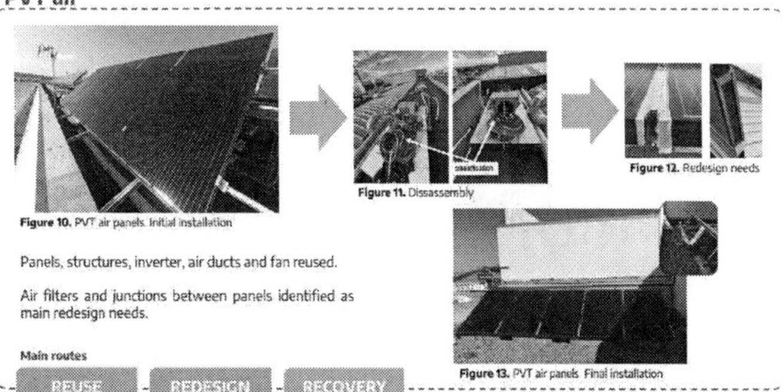

CSTEP

Rooftop Solar Explorer: Mapping the Rooftop Solar Potential of 100+ Cities in India

Shantanu Roy, Saptak Ghosh, and Mahesh Kalshetty
Center for Study of Science, Technology and Policy (CSTEP), Bengaluru, India
Contact: shantanu@cstep.in

EU PVSEC 2025
42nd European Photovoltaic Solar Energy Conference and Exhibition

CSTEP

Introduction

In alignment with India's flagship rooftop solar scheme—PM Surya Ghar: Muft Bijli Yojana—aiming to solarise 10 million households, a potential assessment exercise is essential to accelerate rooftop solar adoption. It enables the accurate estimation of optimal system size, techno-economic viability, and shadow-free rooftop areas. By allowing easy visualisation of installations and identifying high-potential roofs and regions, it supports informed decision making, demand aggregation, and greater consumer awareness.

We undertook this assessment to deliver rooftop-level solar potential insights through an intuitive and user-friendly digital platform—the Rooftop Solar Explorer (RTSE) tool. The tool is designed to visualise shadow-free areas and estimate optimal system size, along with potential financial savings over a 25-year period.

CSTEP

Objectives

- To develop a user-friendly platform that estimates rooftop solar potential, optimal system size, and long-term savings
- To build a scalable, replicable, and automated model for rooftop solar mapping using high-resolution aerial imagery
- To support the large-scale implementation of PM Surya Ghar: Muft Bijli Yojana
- To assist government agencies, electricity utilities, and developers in identifying high-potential rooftops and ensuring efficient demand aggregation
- To contribute to India's renewable energy goals of 500 GW by 2030 and net-zero emission target by 2070 through decentralised solar deployment

CSTEP

Methodology

The foundation of the Rooftop Solar Explorer (RTSE) tool lies in aerial data collection and preprocessing. The process begins with capturing raw aerial data, which are then transformed into precise geospatial layers enabling rooftop-level solar analysis.

1. True Ortho Imagery:

- High-resolution aerial imagery captured using drones/satellites
- Ensures accurate rooftop (50 cm × 50 cm grids) outlines
- AI/ML algorithms applied for automated rooftop digitisation

2. Digital Surface Modelling:

- Captures rooftop heights, slopes, and surrounding areas
- Used for shading analysis using ArcGIS hill-shade approach and solar potential mapping

3. 3D Point Cloud:

- 3D model generation and visualisation

4. Solar Radiation and System Sizing

- Data sourced from the National Solar Radiation Database (NSRDB) by the National Renewable Energy Laboratory (NREL) are used to compute grid-wise annual global horizontal irradiance (GHI)
- Panels placed in portrait/landscape layouts to optimise the capacity utilisation factor (CUF) and match demand

4. Development of RTSE tool:

- All datasets integrated into the RTSE platform
- Provides automated rooftop identification, shadow-free solar potential, optimal system sizing, and long-term financial savings

CSTEP

Methodology

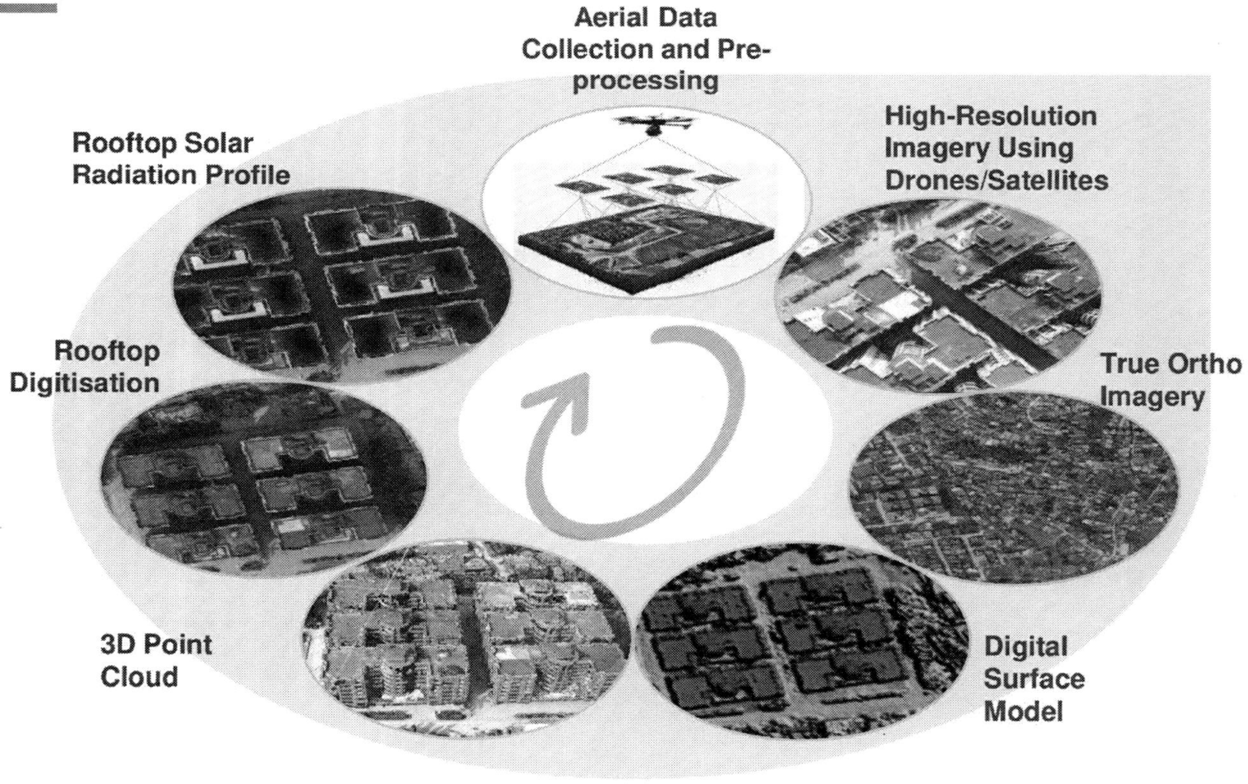

www.cstep.in

5

CSTEP

Results

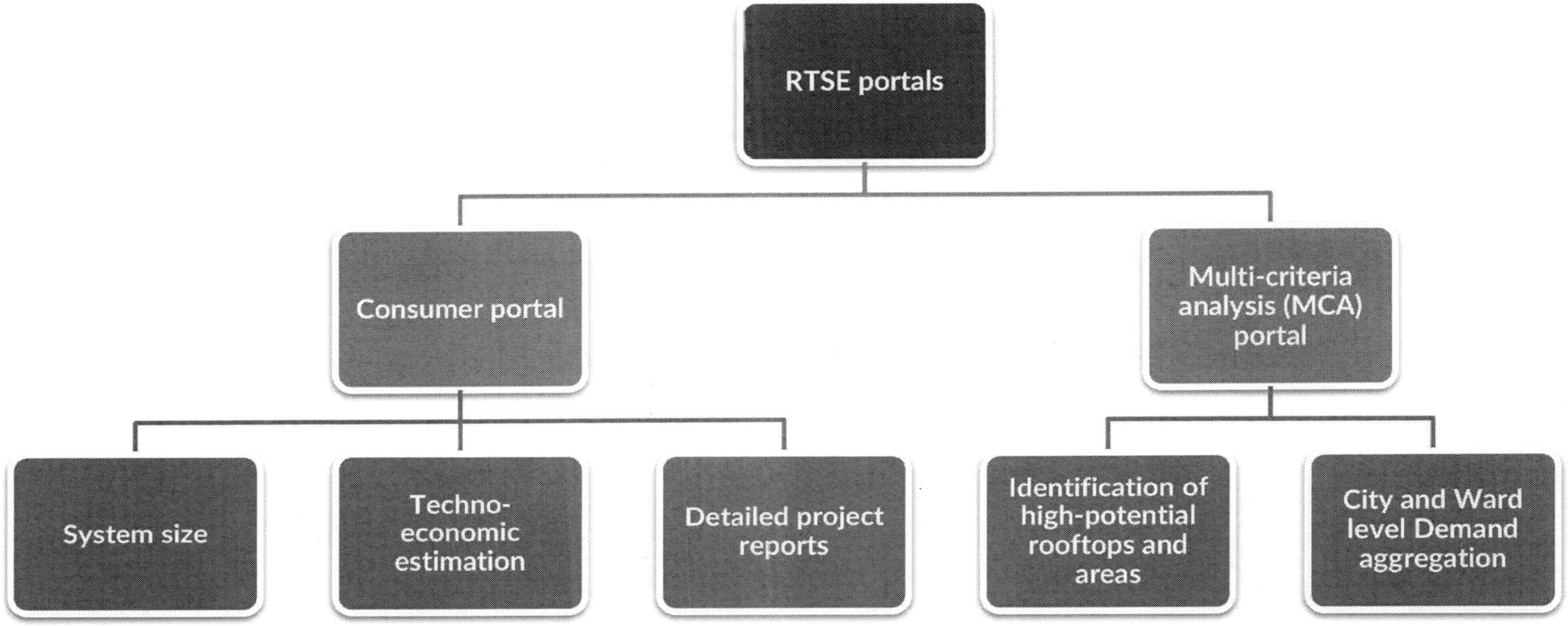

www.cstep.in

CSTEP

RTSE (Consumer Portal)

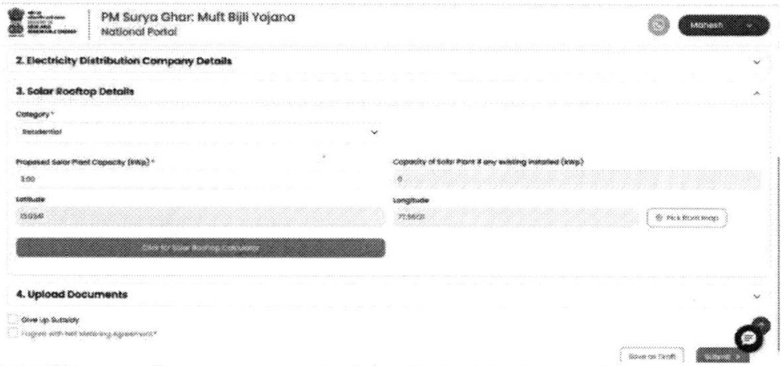

RTSE on Government of India's National Portal for Rooftop Solar

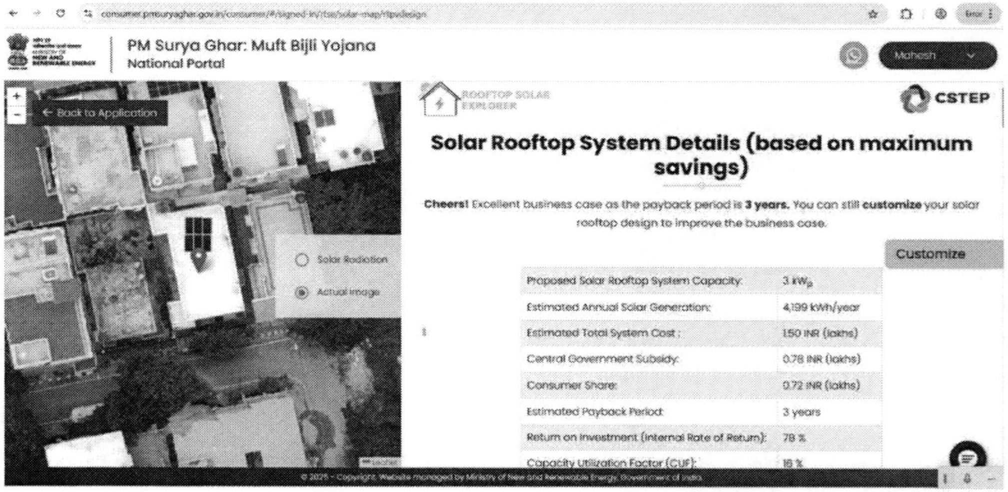

Information on the optimal system size, along with techno-economic details, based on available shadow-free rooftop area, the consumer's electricity consumption profile, and state-specific energy tariff, is provided and can be further customised

CSTEP

RTSE (MCA Portal)

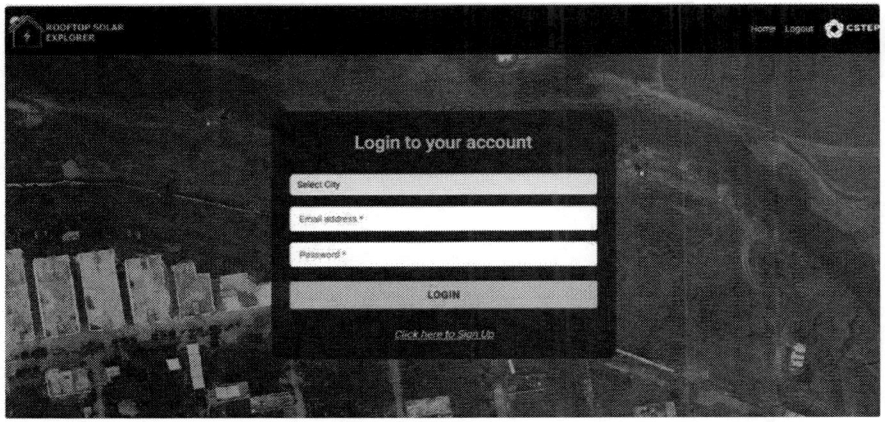

Select a city and enter credentials

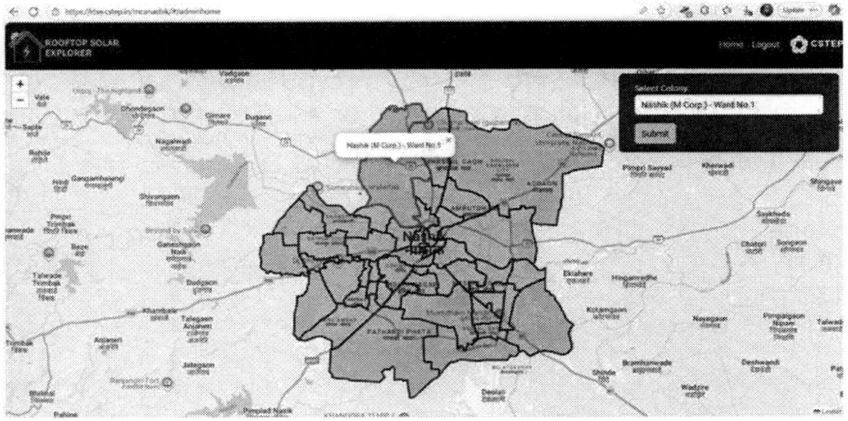

Select a ward within the city

CSTEP

RTSE (MCA Portal)

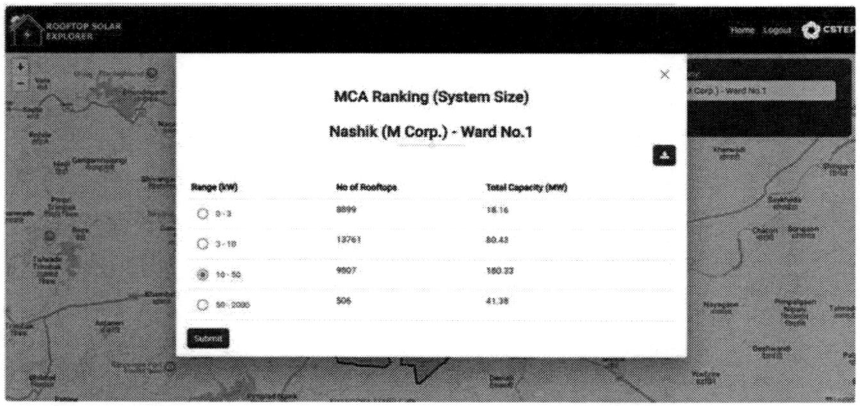

Different system size ranges in the ward will be shown

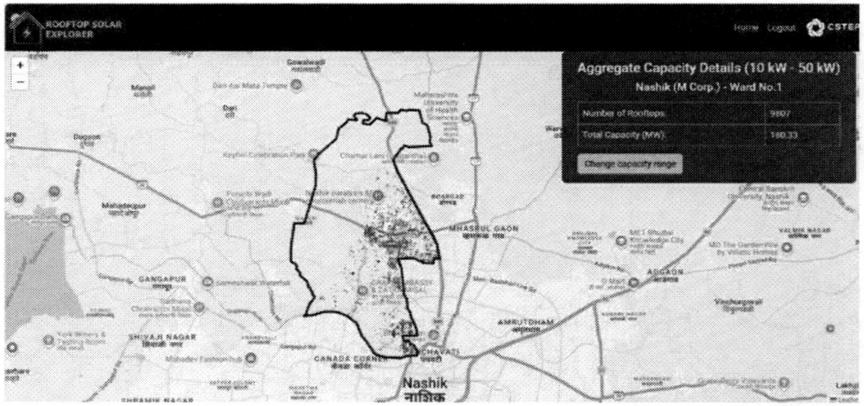

Choose any range to obtain a detailed view, with the option to further evaluate individual roofs

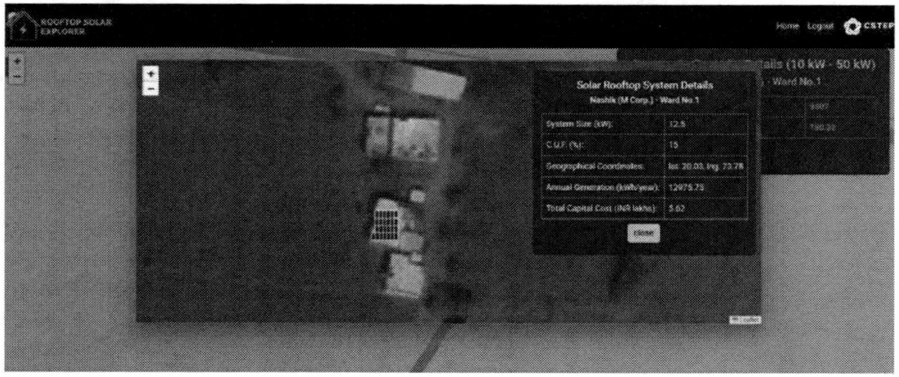

Systems details for a selected roof

CSTEP

Conclusion

- RTSE: First-of-its-kind geospatial rooftop solar potential assessment tool in India
- Piloted in 2020 in Bengaluru and then expanded to multiple cities across India
- Currently operational in 100+ cities in India
- Integrated into the Government of India's National Portal for Rooftop Solar (https://pmsuryaghar.gov.in/)
- Fully automated, scalable, and user-centric
- Optimal system sizing based on available shadow-free area and the consumer's electricity consumption
- Accessed by over 200,000 users
- Empowering consumers and accelerating adoption
- Providing policy and planning support
- Identification of high-potential rooftops for demand aggregation at the city/state level

Way Forward:

Expand to India's rural regions and other developing nations

Integrate advanced AI/ML for improved accuracy

Develop RTSE as a global model for rooftop solar adoption

www.cstep.in

CSTEP

Media Coverage and Recognition

- Shortlisted as an ‘Innovator’ in the Asia-Pacific region for 2025 Energy Heroes Awards organised by Sustainable Energy for ALL (SEforALL): https://www.seforall.org/news/announcing-the-2025-energy-heroes-award-shortlist
- RTSE presentation hosted on the official website of the Ministry of New and Renewable Energy, Government of India: https://solarrooftop.pmsuryaghar.gov.in/notification/160_notification.pdf
- Featured as a pioneering solution in rooftop solar adoption by The India Climate Collaborative (ICC): https://indiaclimatecollaborative.org/blog/voices-from-india-s-climate-ecosystem
- RTSE has received extensive coverage through state launch events in Madhya Pradesh, Chhattisgarh, Kerala, and Karnataka

CSTEP

References

https://saga-gis.sourceforge.io/saga_tool_doc/9.4.1/ta_lighting_2.html

https://www.researchgate.net/publication/2539232_The_solar_radiation_model_for_Open_source_GIS_Implementation_and_applications

https://developer.nrel.gov/docs/solar/nsrdb/suny-india-data-download/

https://developer.nrel.gov/docs/solar/nsrdb/meteosat-download/

https://developer.nrel.gov/docs/solar/nsrdb/himawari-download/

www.cstep.in

CSTEP

THANK YOU

www.cstep.in

42nd European Photovoltaic Solar Energy Conference and Exhibition

PROMISE

INTERACTIVE LEARNING FOR PV SYSTEMS: A BOARD GAME-BASED TEACHING STRATEGY FOR OPERATIONS AND MAINTENANCE

Melodie de L'Epine[1], Yoselyn Walsh[2], Carlos Meza[3], Brian Azzopardi[4,5,6,7]

[1]ICARES Consulting (Becquerel Institute), Belgium [2]Costa Rica Institute of Technology, Cartago, Costa Rica, [3]Anhalt University of Applied Sciences, Koethen, Germany, [4] The Foundation for Innovation and Research – Malta, [5] The University of Malta, [6] The Malta College of Arts, Science and Technology, [7] Azzopardi and Associates, Malta. Corresponding author: carlos.meza@hs-anhalt.de

Challenge in PV education

- The global demand for skilled professionals in solar energy is rising.
- Traditional theoretical education often fails to prepare students for the complex, real-world challenges of Photovoltaic (PV) system operation and maintenance (O&M).

Learning objectives

- Understand the balance between initial investment and long-term costs.
- Identify common operational risks (e.g., weather, soiling) and their impact on performance.
- Learn the value of preventive strategies like insurance and system protection.
- Practice budgeting for operational expenses and strategic investments.

Work description and goals

- Apply gamification to support foundational and practical operation and maintenance skills.
- Developed two educational board games, SolarTycoon and a second case-study focused game, to simulate the technical and financial aspects of running a solar energy business.
- This study details the design, implementation, and reception of the games during an international training event for higher education students.

Methodology

Needs assessment
Surveys with educators & stakeholders

Platform development
Scenario simulations & multiplayer features

Content creation
Real-world PV challenges

Pilot testing
Across academia and industry

Impact evaluation
Mixed methods

Continuous Improvement
Iterative feedback integration

Board Games:

a) Facilitator-Guided Game

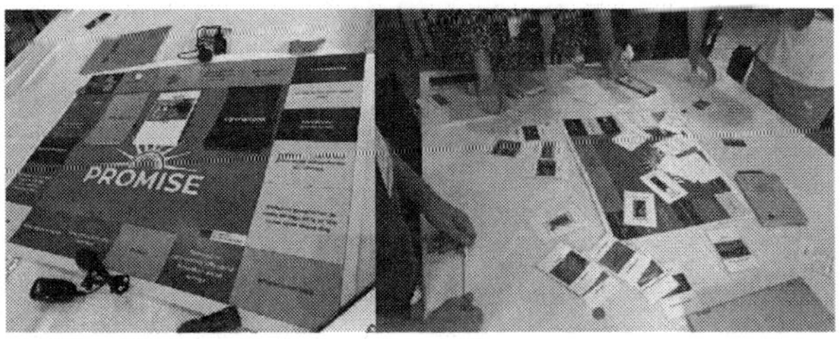

In-depth diagnostic and O&M tasks
Discussion-based, real-time decisions
Tested in 2025 and 2023

b) Solar Tycoon

Tycoon gameplay: manage PV systems
Deal with equipment, weather events, and finance
Tested 2025

Preliminary results

↑ Engagement and motivation
↑ Knowledge retention (pre-post tests)
↑ Collaboration and problem-solving
Learners appreciated immersive, visual formats

Satisfaction survey

To what extent do you agree with the following statement: "The game was engaging and kept my attention."?

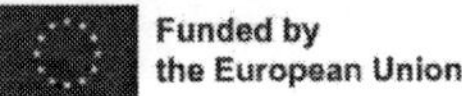

Future work

- Scale platform to more learners and contexts
- Add AI-based personalization
- Multilingual & region-specific localization
- Embed into curricula and training programs

Acknowledgments

Partly funded by the European Union under Grant 101079469 PROMISE "Photovoltaics Reliability Operations and Maintenance Innovative Solutions for Energy Alliance" project, under Grant 101075747 and UK Research and Innovation (UKRI) TRANSIT "TRANSITion to sustainable future through training and education" project, European Union, Xjenza Malta under Grant REP-2023-061 RoOPFEVs "Robust Optimization Framework for PVs and EVs Integration at Low Voltage Network" project.

Industrial Design Students in Costa Rican Institute of Technology for volunteer in the creation of Solar Tycoon

Follow our Journey
@Promise
PvPromise.eu
info@pvpromise.eu

FOUNDATION FOR INNOVATION AND RESEARCH - MALTA
AUSTRIAN INSTITUTE OF TECHNOLOGY
cea
CENER
HOCHSCHULE ANHALT University of Applied Sciences
BECQUEREL INSTITUTE
PIXAM
TEC | Tecnológico de Costa Rica

Funded by the European Union

This project has received funding from the European Union's Horizon Europe, Widening Participation and Spreading Excellence action, under grant agreement n°101079469.

ETIP Photovoltaics 42nd European Photovoltaic Solar Energy Conference and Exhibition
SolarHub

Gender Diversity in Photovoltaics: Experiences and Support Mechanisms

Pinar Derin-Güre*, Chiara Busto, Rita Ebner, Hande Eryilmaz, Perine Fleury, Nikoletta Fodor, Ivan Gordon, Eren Cihan Gülsoy, Ulrike Jahn, Delfina Munoz, Ezgi Pehlivanlı, Paula Sánchez-Friera, Ioannis Tsanakas, Busra Yilmaz.

Context

The PV sector remains highly gendered. Women and gender-diverse individuals are severely underrepresented in technical and leadership roles, hindering both innovation and a just energy transition. This study moves beyond numbers to explore lived experiences, identifying key barriers and support mechanisms, using a qualitative analysis techniques.

WHAT ABOUT YOU?

The Research Gap

Existing literature often focuses on quantitative gaps. This is the first qualitative study in PV to investigate the lived experiences of professionals from under- represented gender groups to identify the nuanced barriers they face and the support mechanisms that truly foster inclusion and advancement.

Methodology

This study adopts a qualitative research design based on **semi-structured interviews** with a diverse group of professionals from across the European PV sector. We use the snowball technique for interviews.

Participants: Diverse professionals across the European PV sector. (14 interviews completed, 35 planned).

Analysis: Thematic analysis of career pathways and workplace culture.

Interview Outcomes

Work–life balance remains a challenge for women in PV, who often face disproportionate care burdens, frequent travel, and burnout, mitigated mainly through supportive partners and outcome-focused work styles. Gender gaps persist in pay and promotion, with wage differences of up to 30%, slower advancement, and barriers in salary negotiation that can fuel imposter syndrome. Interviewees recommended solutions such as transparent pay structures, mentorship, flexible work policies, gender quotas, and recognition of diverse leadership styles.

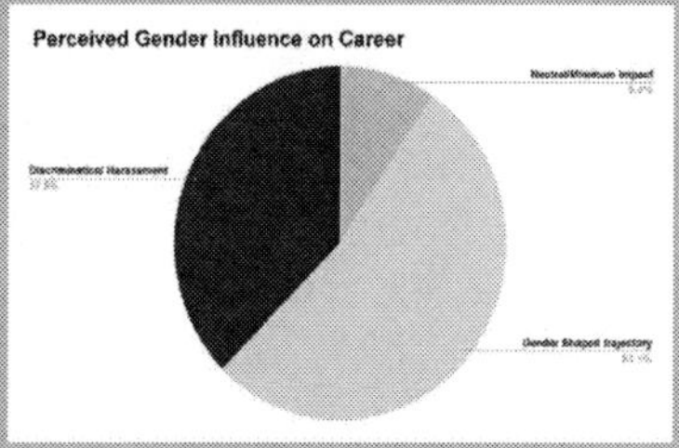

Pay & Promotion

Theme	Examples
Wage gap	Up to 30% difference (interview 14)
Promotion bias	Women told they need more "experience" while men promoted sooner
Negotiation gap	Women negotiate less often, or seen as "aggressive" when they do
Positive discrimination & Tokenism	Women (accused of) being chosen for roles to "tick boxes" → imposter syndrome

Work-Life Balance

Theme	Finding
Family care Burden	Mothers disproportionately responsible, career sacrifices
Travel demands	Difficult for mothers, easier for single/unmarried women
Burnout	Women with kids often 'exhausted, depleted'
Coping strategies	Simplifying personal life, relying on partner, focusing on results not hours

Recommendations for Change

Level	Recommendation
Organisational	Transparent pay scales; mentorship; (non-gendered) parental leave; flexible hours
Cultural	Shift away from gender stereotypes; recognition of diverse leadership styles
Policy	Quotas; accountability in promotions; visibility for women experts
Personal advice (to newcomers)	"Negotiate early"; "find mentors/sponsors"; "don't be afraid to leave toxic workplaces"

Barriers and Support factors

Hindrances	Supports
Lack of role models, stereotypes, cultural conditioning	Mentorship, female professors, supportive colleagues
Male-dominated networks & decision-making	Growing diversity policies
Bias in assigning roles (pastoral vs technical)	Visibility of women leaders
Structural issues (pay opacity, hiring bias)	Flexible work arrangements, EU-funded equity pushes

Visibility and Leadership

Dimension	Findings
Conference invitations	Most women invited (esp. recently) but often tokenised or often the same small group
Leadership roles	~40% hold significant leadership roles but are still sidelined
Overall visibility	Technical leadership remains male dominated

POLICY RECOMMENDATIONS

Policy Area	Industry	Research
Leadership & Representation	Gender diversity targets in leadership; transparent promotions; equal pay; visibility in decision-making through gendered data.	Gender balance in conference speakers, panels, awards; track and report gender-disaggregated data.
Workplace Culture	Zero-tolerance harassment policies; unconscious bias training; value diverse leadership styles.	Supportive environments; standardized recognition systems to reduce bias.
Work-Life Balance	Flexible work models; equal parental leave; childcare support.	Recognize caregiving-related career breaks in evaluations; improve parental leave and support systems.
Career Support / Mentorship	Structured mentorship programs; women-focused networks; retraining and reskilling opportunities.	Formal mentorship networks; negotiation and leadership training; funding for women-led projects.
Long-Term Change	Partnerships with education systems; outreach to schools to promote PV careers.	Outreach to schools/universities; highlight female role models; cross-sector partnerships for inclusivity.

Funded by the European Union, under the Horizon Europe programme, Grant agreement number 101086110. Views and opinions expressed are, however, those of the author(s) only and do not necessarily reflect those of the European Union or European Climate, Infrastructure and Environment Executive Agency. Neither the European Union nor the granting authority can be held responsible for them.

*Corresponding Author. Email: pderin@metu.edu.tr

ODTÜ METU
ODTÜ GÜNAM

ADVANCED MACHINE-LEARNING-BASED ANALYSIS OF CRITICS AND THE SILENT MAJORITY REGARDING THE ENERGY TRANSITION AND PHOTOVOLTAICS ON TIKTOK

WHAT ALGORITHMIC APPROACHES ARE SUITABLE FOR SENTIMENT ANALYSIS AND STANCE DETECTION OF PUBLISHED VIDEO CONTENT AND COMMENTS?

Marc Schneider, Jannik Achenbach, Janek Gehrlein, Anne Maren Feldhof, Eva-Maria Grommes, Valérie Varney,
University of Applied Sciences Cologne
Faculty of Process Engineering, Energy and Mechanical Systems
Cologne Innovation and Transfer Lab
marc_gabriel.schneider@smail.th-koeln.de

Abstract—In this research project, several approaches of natural language processing are outlined to perform opining mining on the social media platform TikTok. The goal is to analyse the views of critics and the silent majority regarding the energy transition and photovoltaics. First, a dataset containing published TikTok videos with the hashtag #Energiewende, #Solarenergie and #Photovoltaik is created. After filtering out irrelevant content using an Ensemble Classifier model made up of a Random Forest and Support Vector Machine, the entities of the dataset undergo a sentiment analysis as well as a stance detection. Finally, the machine learning results are evaluated, revealing that there are slightly more videos in favour of the energy transition and photovoltaics. The engagement on the other hand is higher for neutral and negative videos. At last, the most used nouns by the critics are gathered and visualized with the aid of a word cloud. Although the word cloud does not show the context, in which the words are used, each word can be reviewed intuitively to gain a better idea of what aspects of the energy transition and photovoltaics are the most relevant to critics.

Keywords—machine learning, natural language processing, sentiment analysis, stance detection, ET, PV, TikTok, opinion mining

1 Introduction

With the human society facing the global warming crisis, transitioning from fossil fuels to renewable energies, a process called energy transition (ET), is a frequently discussed issue. In particular, photovoltaics (PV) play a central role in this transition and are increasingly debated in public discourse [1]. Especially social media platforms such as TikTok offer a place where political discourse takes place. This makes TikTok and social media in general an important aspect to consider when analysing the public's opinion toward the ET and PV [2]. However, due to the large amount of content available on TikTok today, machine learning (ML) is an essential tool to process and analyse the given data. A rapidly developing field within ML is natural language processing (NLP), which allows computers to understand and generate human language [3]. This study investigates different algorithmic approaches for sentiment analysis and stance detection. The underlying research question is to determine what approaches are suitable for on social media published videos and comments.

There are different ML models used in NLP including Logistic Regression (LR), Random Forests (RF) and Support Vector Machines (SVM) [4].

Additionally, multiple deep learning (DL) approaches, so called transformer models, are emerging. These models are expected to better understand natural language and more complex texts [3, 4]. One very popular model out of this field is called BERT [4, 5]. BERT stands for Bidirectional Encoder Representations from Transformers and was introduced in 2019. Because of its architecture, BERT can be easily adapted to different tasks such as sequence classification or sentiment analysis. The model can be fine-tuned by adding an additional output layer specialized to the performing tasks. As a result, BERT can create state-of-the-art ML models for NLP [5].

Using an approach based on ML and NLP, the goal of this research is to detect the sentiment, stance, and subjectively relevant topics of critics as well as the silent majority (SM) regarding the ET and PV. Furthermore, different technical approaches for these tasks are investigated and compared.

The SM refers to a large group of people within a population who do not publicly express their opinions, beliefs, or political preferences due to a lack of interest, fear of backlash, or a desire to avoid conflict. However, they can still have a significant influence on elections or policy decisions, which makes it crucial for political strategy, market research as well as social analysis to understand the group's sentiment [6]. In this paper, it is assumed that the SM's opinion on the

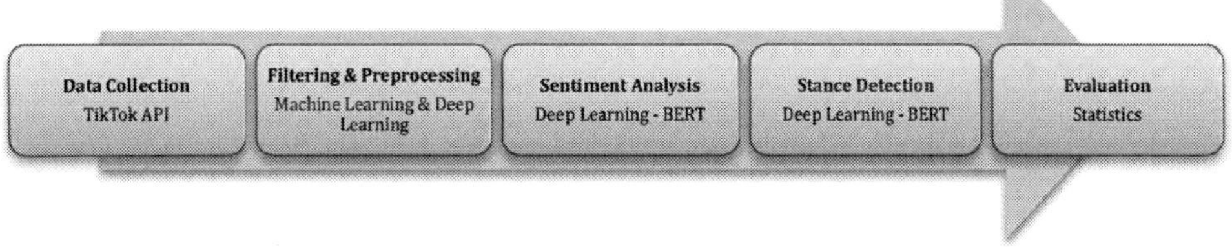

Figure 1: Software Pipeline

10.4229/EUPVSEC2025/5DV.2.61
020522-001

given subject cannot be reduced to being merely *positive, neutral,* or *negative*. Nevertheless, the group does hold an opinion, although it remains underrepresented in political discourse.

2 Machine learning pipeline

In this project, a pipeline was developed, that can also be applied to other subjects. The pipeline includes the steps data collection, filtering and preprocessing, and sentiment as well as stance prediction using ML models. The final step consists of evaluating and visualizing the results.

2.1 Data collection

To collect public data related to the ET and PV on TikTok, the official TikTok API was used [7]. It allows the user to create a dataset, made up of all the videos using a certain hashtag. In this project, all videos using #Energiewende (#energytransition), #Solarenergie (#solarenergy) and #Photovoltaik (#photovoltaics) (case-insensitive) in their video description were gathered leading to an initial dataset of 19274 entities. All entities have the following entries: *username, video_description, view_count, like_count, comment_count, share_count, create_time, video_id* and *voice_to_text*, the latter being only available for those videos, that have the appropriate option turned on. To extract the remaining *voice_to_text-files*, the respective videos were downloaded manually and then Google Speech Recognition was performed on those videos [8]. Additionally, the comments of all videos, that were labelled as relevant, were gathered using the entries *comment_username, video_id, comment_id, parent_comment_id,* and *creation_time*. The aspect of relevance as well as data filtering is explained in the next chapter.

2.2 Filtering and preprocessing

Filtering the dataset is a crucial step to ensure that its content aligns with the given topic. The content includes all videos tagged with *#Energiewende, #Solarenergie* and *#Photovoltaik* and contains both relevant content and irrelevant entries, such as spam, advertisements, or unrelated material. Since manual reviewing is impractical at the given scale, an automated ML approach was employed to classify videos into relevant and irrelevant classes.

The results confirm that traditional models like RF and SVM, when combined in an ensemble, can outperform transformer-based models like BERT in filtering tasks, possibly due to the limited size of the fine-tuning dataset and the overfitting risk in deep models.

2.2.1 Approach

Four primary classifiers were used: LR, RF, SVM and BERT. LR was chosen due to its simplicity, RF was used as it is another model suitable for text classification [4]. SVM, being a very popular model, was also picked and finally, BERT was chosen, given its promising performance [4, 5]. Furthermore, an Ensemble Classifier was developed, that combines LR, RF and SVM to predict together and therefore could improve the performance.

Data preprocessing involved tokenizing and normalizing the text in the *voice_to_text*-column as well as removing stop words and special characters. For traditional models such as LR, RF, and SVM, TF-IDF-vectorization was used to generate numerical representations of the texts. BERT was fine-tuned on the dataset over five epochs, leveraging its pre-trained embeddings for deep semantic understanding.

Feature engineering played a significant role in improving the models' performance by adding a manually designed keyword matching score in addition to TF-IDF-vectorization. This binary feature detected, whether specific keywords such as "energy", "climate", "heating policy", "wind", "nuclear", "coal", "electricity", or "sun" appeared in the respective video transcript. If at least one keyword was detected, the score was set to 1. Otherwise, it was set to 0. This feature, along with TF-IDF, was included in all models except BERT, which operated directly on embeddings. All models were trained and tested on a manually labelled dataset of 200 annotated entities, with an 80:20 training-validation split. Hyperparameter optimization using Grid Search was performed for the traditional models, while BERT was fine-tuned with a batch size of 16 over five epochs. After being trained, the models were evaluated using standard metrics including accuracy, precision, recall, and F1-score, to ensure a comprehensive assessment of their performance [4].

2.2.2 Results

The evaluation results of the optimized models are summarized below in Table 1:

Table 1: Accuracies of selected algorithms

Model	LR	RF	SVM	BERT	Ensemble Classifier
Accuracy	0.64	0.88	0.88	0.82	0.88
Precision (relevant)	0.69	0.91	0.91	0.79	0.91
Recall (relevant)	0.82	0.91	0.91	1	0.91
F1-Score (relevant)	0.75	0.91	0.91	0.88	0.91
Precision (irrelevant)	0.43	0.82	0.82	1	0.82
Recall (irrelevant)	0.27	0.82	0.82	0.45	0.82
F1-Score (irrelevant)	0.33	0.82	0.82	0.62	0.82

The results reveal key observations: LR achieved the lowest accuracy of 0.64 compared to the other models, possibly due to its simplicity [4]. Therefore, it was rejected for further use. RF, SVM, and the Ensemble Classifier, which combines predictions from LR, RF, and SVM, produced the best result for accuracy achieving a score of 88%, while also performing well regarding the other scores. The fine-tuned BERT model attained an accuracy of 0.82, while also excelling in precision for the irrelevant data, but underperforming in recall. This limited its overall effectiveness. The Ensemble Classifier was chosen for the final filtering, cropping down the dataset to 6715 entities, making up approximately 35% of the original dataset.

2.3 Sentiment Analysis

Sentiment analysis has become an essential tool for understanding public opinion on various topics [9]. By analysing text sequences, it predicts the underlying emotion without specifying a target or topic [10].

$$Sentiment(T) = \{Positive, Neutral, Negative\} \quad (1)$$

Sentiment analysis enables organizations and governments to assess attitudes toward specific topics, or policies, although being limited to only detecting the emotional tone of a text [11].

In this project, sentiment analysis was performed on videos as well as their comments. It focused on the transcribed text from the *voice_to_text* entries to uncover the emotional tone of the content and understand the communication culture on TikTok.

2.3.1 Approach

The sentiment analysis utilized the *german-sentiment-bert model* [12]. It is a fine-tuned BERT model that was trained on 1.834 million German-language samples from diverse sources, including Twitter, Facebook, and hotel reviews, making it very suitable for analysing social media content [12]. As a result, a general sentiment classification model specialized on German text was developed. The model takes text sequences as an input and predicts the sentiment class, being either *positive*, *neutral* or *negative*.

To evaluate the model's performance on the obtained dataset, 100 entities were manually assigned one of the three classes introduced above. The initial accuracy of the model was 61%. However, since the model was trained primarily on shorter text samples, whereas the dataset included many longer *voice_to_text* entries, there were still improvements to be made [12].

To address this issue, a Sliding Window Technique was implemented, meaning that long texts were divided into overlapping segments, each receiving an individual sentiment prediction [13]. The sentiment of the original text was then determined by the most frequently predicted sentiment class of the segments. It is a rather simple approach, expected not to claim much computational resources, while still considering the text's context thanks to the overlapping of half a segment length. To find the optimal segment length, a parameter optimization was performed, in which different text lengths were tested by calculating the respective model accuracy.

2.3.2 Results

Table 2 shows the results of the parameter optimization. Using this technique, the model's performance improved from an accuracy score of 61% to 67% (Table 2). This improvement demonstrates the effectiveness of segment-based analysis when encountering longer texts.

Table 2: Accuracy over segment lengths

Length	Accuracy
10	0.36
50	0.49
100	0.56
150	0.57
200	0.66
250	0.66
300	0.65
350	0.67
400	0.65
450	0.66
512	0.65

Table 3 displays the classification report of the sentiment analysis, showing different scores for each one of the three sentiment classes. The sentiment analysis model demonstrates consistent performance for the *negative*-class, achieving precision, recall, and F1-scores of 0.71. For the *positive* class, the model achieved a high precision score of 86%, indicating reliable predictions, but a lower recall score of 61% suggests some under-detection of *positive* sentiment. The neutral-class performed the weakest, with a precision of 55% and an F1-score of 61%, indicating difficulties in distinguishing *neutral* sentiment from other classes.

Table 3: Classification report sentiment analysis

	Precision	Re-call	F1-Score	Sup-port
positive	0.86	0.61	0.72	31
neutral	0.55	0.68	0.61	38
negative	0.71	0.71	0.71	31

2.4 Stance detection

Stance detection is a crucial task in NLP that aims to identify the position or attitude expressed in a text toward a specific target. Unlike sentiment analysis, which focuses solely on the emotional tone, stance detection determines whether the author supports, opposes, or remains *neutral* towards a given subject [14]. This means that stance detection differs from sentiment analysis in that it requires understanding the context and relationship between the text and the target. For instance, a *positive* sentiment of written content may not necessarily indicate support for the related topic [10, 14].

$$Stance(T, U|G) = \{Favour, Against, Neutral\} \quad (2)$$

Given the context of this research, the target G represents the ET and PV. The other model inputs are the text (T) or the user (U).

2.4.1 Approach

For model training, 100 entities were manually labelled regarding their stance towards the ET and PV, the three classes being *favour*, *neutral* or *against*. For the stance detection the *bert-base-german-cased* was chosen as the underlying architecture due to its robust performance in German sequence classification tasks [15].

The model itself is already an adapted BERT model for generating text embeddings of German-language contents. Therefore, the next step was to fine-tune the

model by adding an additional output layer to classify texts into the three stance categories.
Since the model has a maximum sequence length of 512 words [15], the Sliding Window Technique, introduced in chapter 2.3.1, was used once again. Furthermore, the texts were split into shorter sequences of 256 words, to multiply the amount of labelled data for training. Based on the hypothesis that the stance of a text equals the stance of every one of its sequences, the sequences were then labelled according to the stance of their root *voice_to_text* entry. This hypothesis was later to be proven or rejected.
The labelled and enhanced dataset was split into training and testing sets, with 80% of the data used for training and 20% used for testing. The model was trained over three epochs using the Hugging Face Trainer API [16]. Since the labelling of 100 randomly selected videos led to class imbalance, oversampling was employed to compensate for this effect. To balance the three stance classes, random entries from the minority classes in the training set were duplicated until all classes contained an equal number of samples. The test set was not augmented and thus remained untouched, ensuring a fair evaluation of the model's performance. This approach helped stabilize the training process and ensured that the model did not become biased towards the majority class [17].

2.4.2 Results
Table 4 displays the classification report of the stance detection.

Table 4: Classification stance detection

	Precision	Recall	F1-score	Sup-port
favour	0.75	0.81	0.78	22
neutral	0.85	0.66	0.75	18
against	0.82	0.87	0.84	32

The stance classification model demonstrates strong performance, made evident by the high precision, recall, and F1-scores across all three stance categories, especially the *favour*- and *against*-classes. The overall accuracy of the model was 81%. The model performed slightly worse regarding the *favouring*-class, which may be correlated to the fact that only very few videos in the dataset express a *positive* sentiment. Overall, the results indicate a high effectiveness of the model in accurately identifying stances. Therefore, the hypothesis from above has been proven, in that it is indeed a reliable way to multiply the training data without manual work and without impairing the results.

2.5 Comments
In this chapter, the as *relevant* categorized videos' comments are analysed. Because of their hierarchical structure, each comment has a *parent_comment_id*. A comment is either associated directly with the video itself (first-layer comment) or linked to the *comment_id* of another comment, in which case it represents a response (second-layer comment). Two different approaches were examined to maximize the performance of sentiment analysis and stance detection on this data. To measure the performance of each approach, 60 comments were manually assigned a sentiment and stance class.
For the sentiment analysis, the model, introduced in chapter 2.3, was used again and achieved an accuracy of 64%. For stance detection, a different approach to the one, presented in chapter 2.4, was tested. This approach takes the predicted stance of the parent comment as well as the predicted sentiment of the comment itself to generate its stance class. This rule-based algorithm adopts the parent stance, if the sentiment is *positive* or *neutral* and takes the opposite stance, if the sentiment is *negative*. For a *neutral* parent stance, the comment stance equals the corresponding predicted sentiment.
The expectation, that this approach would lead to a higher accuracy was proven wrong. It achieved an accuracy score of 51%, whereas directly using the trained stance model, presented in chapter 2.4, led to a score of 62%. A reason for achieving a lower accuracy could be the suboptimal performance of the sentiment analysis, meaning a higher accuracy of the model used for sentiment analysis could lead to a higher accuracy with the approach presented above.

3 Evaluation
After the pipeline (Fig. 1, p.1) was run through, every *relevant* video entity as well as their corresponding comments had received a predicted sentiment and stance class. That data could then be evaluated.
At first the distribution of sentiment and stance classes over all entities was analysed:

Table 5: Sentiment distribution along videos and comments

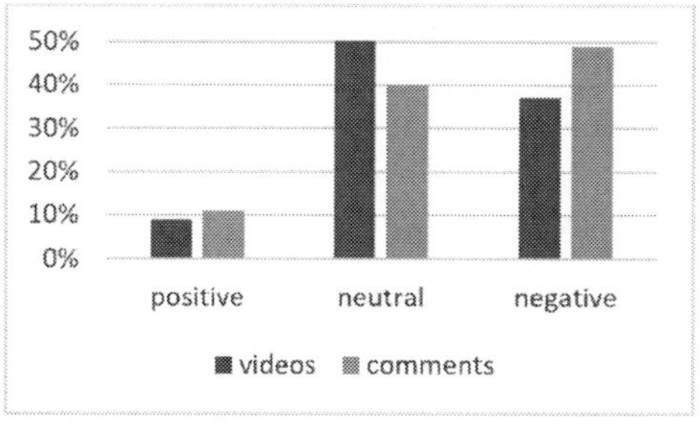

For the *positive*-class, both the videos and comments have almost similar scores with a difference of 2%. There were more *neutral* videos than comments, having received scores of 54% and 40%, respectively. On the other hand, the *negative*-labelled comments' score of 49% surpassed the videos' score of 37%.

Table 6: Stance distribution along videos and comments

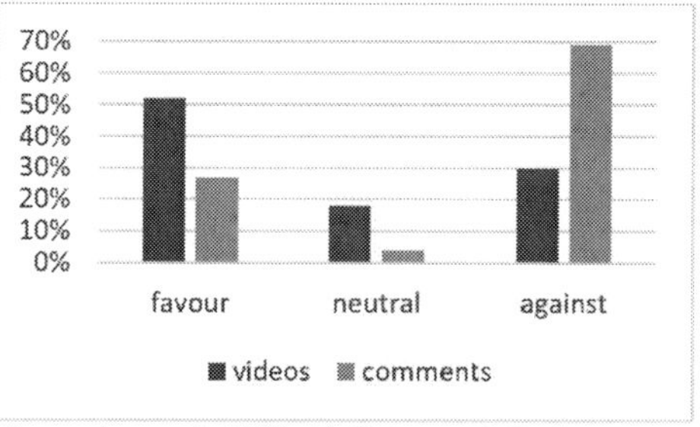

The results seen in Table 6 indicate a polarized stance distribution for both videos and comments, as only 18% and 4% of the *relevant* content was labelled *neutral*. While roughly half of the videos are in *favour* of the ET and PV, the stance distribution of the

10.4229/EUPVSEC2025/5DV.2.61
020522-004

evaluated comments leans strongly towards the *against*-class.
When comparing Table 5 to Table 6, one can observe that the content that was labelled *negative* or *against*, respectively, is very similar in frequency between both sentiment and stance distribution. However, the content with a *neutral* sentiment has shifted over to the *favour*-class regarding the stance. This suggests that content in *favour* of the ET and PV tends to be expressed with a more *neutral* sentiment compared to the content labelled as *against*. Furthermore, it was observed that 944 videos (making up 14% of all videos) received a *negative* sentiment but a *favour* stance. Additionally, 2249 videos (33% of all videos) received a *neutral* sentiment and *favour* stance. These two observations highlight the difference between sentiment and stance once again and underline the importance of considering them separately, as stated in literature [16, 15].
To infer the stance of the SM towards the ET and PV, the mean engagement statistics of the videos were analysed. The results are shown in Table 7. Since the SM typically refrains from expressing opinions through comments, it is assumed that their stance is most accurately reflected through passive engagement metrics such as view and like counts. Users who engage with content by viewing or liking without commenting may represent this group. Their behaviour thus provides an indirect but meaningful signal of general public opinion.

Table 7: Mean engagement statistics over stance

Mean / Stance	Views	Likes	Comments	Shares
favour	10601	215	29	15
neutral	14363	215	18	35
against	12210	504	45	86

The mean engagement statistics over all stance classes of all videos show that videos with a *negative* stance receive by far the most likes, comments, and shares, while neutral videos are the most viewed. These observations suggest that the SM's stance lies somewhere between *neutral* and *against*.
Since the user engagement is not evenly distributed over all videos on social media, the ten most liked videos using with *#Energiewende, #Solarenergie* and *#Photovoltaik* were investigated separately, as they are assumed to be highly representative of the public's opinion. Regarding the stance, nine of those videos are labelled *against* and the one remaining is labelled as *neutral*. In terms of sentiment, seven of them are *negative* and three as *neutral*. These observations support the statement from above, that the SM is opposing the idea of transitioning to renewable energy sources using photovoltaics.
To gain a better understanding of what topics are relevant for the critics of the ET and PV, a word cloud was generated, containing the most frequently occurring words in *against*-classified content, though only the nouns were considered. The word cloud reveals that the most popular noun used by critics is *energy*, closely followed by *climate*, *gas*, *heating*, *price*, and *Federal*. Other commonly used words include *state, economic,* and *policy*. While the context, in which these words were used, is hardly accessible, each word can be manually reviewed and analysed. That way, it is still possible to gain an idea of what the critics could have meant when using these words.

4 Limitations

To better understanding the topics, that are of high importance for different groups of people on social media, the topic modelling could be further elaborated. A common technique, used for this task, is the Latent Dirichlet Allocation (LDA) [18]. In addition, although the developed software pipelines achieve respectable accuracy across the different submodules, they are still far from perfect. This needs to be kept in mind when interpreting the sentiment and stance detection results.

5 Conclusion

During the first step of the pipeline, the TikTok API proved to be a competent tool for collecting a large amount of published data to obtain a dataset. In the second part of the pipeline Filtering & preprocessing, several algorithms containing machine learning and DL classifiers were investigated and compared. Contrary to expectations, the DL model BERT, that promised great performance in understanding complex natural human language [4], was not able to achieve the best results compared to the other applied models. The presented Ensemble Classifier containing a RF and SVM model performed the best with an accuracy of 88%. However, that does not mean this behaviour will occur every time, it just shows that precisely engineered machine learning models can also outperform DL models, which have a higher grade of automatization.
Moving on to sentiment analysis, the goal was to implement a pre-trained BERT model, that can precisely detect the sentiment of a text. The model *german-sentiment-bert* achieved a good baseline accuracy of 61%, that could be further improved to 67% using the Sliding Window Technique. This proved sequence-based analysis of complex natural language to work accurately.
For the stance detection, another fine-tuned BERT model called *bert-base-german-cased* was introduced. To create a classification model, an additional output layer was added. The model achieved an accuracy of 81% on the test dataset, which can be considered a solid result for this task [10]. Finally, the results as well as the engagement regarding the stance and sentiment classes were analysed, revealing key insights on critics and the SM towards the ET and PV on TikTok.
The evaluation of publicly available TikTok content on ET and PV shows that the majority of videos have a *neutral* sentiment, followed by a *negative* one. However, a shift becomes apparent when examining the stance detection results. In this case, the *favour* class has the highest percentage, followed by the *against* class. This suggests that most videos supporting ET and PV adopt a more neutral tone and sentiment compared to those in the *against* class. A closer manual analysis confirms this: while 14% of all published videos have a *negative* sentiment combined with a *favour* stance, 33% of all videos show a neutral sentiment combined with a *favour* stance. These statistics indicate that most of the in-*favour* videos use a neutral or *negative* tone, which may reflect frustration while still supporting the topic.
The results of sentiment analysis and stance detection for the comments suggest a different interpretation. While sentiment analysis shows a considerable number of comments using a neutral tone, with the

10.4229/EUPVSEC2025/5DV.2.61

majority being *negative*, stance detection reveals a strong shift towards the *against* class. Around 69% of all comments were labeled as *against*, highlighting a strongly *negative* attitude towards ET and PV among the audience. To gain insights into the topics most important to the critics, the most frequently used nouns in the videos and comments labeled with an *against* stance were analyzed. Although this approach has a clear limitation, since the context in which these words are used is missing, it still provides a first impression of which topics might matter most to this group of users. Among the most frequently used nouns were, for example, *climate, gas, heating, price,* and *Federal,* indicating that the critics are dissatisfied with government actions related to heating, gas heating systems and associated costs, which may be connected to a transition toward renewable energy.

6 Acknowledgements

The study is part of the project MPower, which is funded by the German Federal Ministry of Research, Technology and Space (BMFTR). The authors thank their colleagues and students for their important contributions and discussions.

7 References

[1] I. Heras-Saizarbitoria, E. Cilleruelo, und I. Zamanillo, „Public acceptance of renewables and the media: an analysis of the Spanish PV solar experience“, Renew. Sustain. Energy Rev., Bd. 15, Nr. 9, S. 4685–4696, Dez. 2011, doi: 10.1016/j.rser.2011.07.083.

[2] D. Amangeldi, A. Usmanova, und P. Shamoi, „Understanding Environmental Posts: Sentiment and Emotion Analysis of Social Media Data“, IEEE Access, Bd. 12, S. 33504–33523, 2024, doi: 10.1109/ACCESS.2024.3371585.

[3] K. R. Chowdhary, „Natural Language Processing“, in Fundamentals of Artificial Intelligence, K. R. Chowdhary, Hrsg., New Delhi: Springer India, 2020, S. 603–649. doi: 10.1007/978-81-322-3972-7_19.

[4] Y. Mao, Q. Liu, und Y. Zhang, „Sentiment analysis methods, applications, and challenges: A systematic literature review“, J. King Saud Univ. - Comput. Inf. Sci., Bd. 36, Nr. 4, S. 102048, Apr. 2024, doi: 10.1016/j.jksuci.2024.102048.

[5] J. Devlin, M.-W. Chang, K. Lee, und K. Toutanova, „BERT: Pre-training of Deep Bidirectional Transformers for Language Understanding“, 24. Mai 2019, arXiv: arXiv:1810.04805. doi: 10.48550/arXiv.1810.04805.

[6] „Silent Majority - ECPS“. Zugegriffen: 8. August 2025. [Online]. Verfügbar unter: https://www.populismstudies.org/Vocabulary/silent-majority/

[7] „Research API | TikTok for Developers“. Zugegriffen: 8. August 2025. [Online]. Verfügbar unter: https://developers.tiktok.com/products/research-api

[8] SpeechRecognition: Library for performing speech recognition, with support for several engines and APIs, online and offline. Python. Zugegriffen: 8. August 2025. Verfügbar unter: https://github.com/Uberi/speech_recognition#readme

[9] Z. Drus und H. Khalid, „Sentiment Analysis in Social Media and Its Application: Systematic Literature Review“, Procedia Comput. Sci., Bd. 161, S. 707–714, Jan. 2019, doi: 10.1016/j.procs.2019.11.174.

[10] A. ALDayel und W. Magdy, „Stance detection on social media: State of the art and trends“, Inf. Process. Manag., Bd. 58, Nr. 4, S. 102597, Juli 2021, doi: 10.1016/j.ipm.2021.102597.

[11] M. Wankhade, A. C. S. Rao, und C. Kulkarni, „A survey on sentiment analysis methods, applications, and challenges“, Artif. Intell. Rev., Bd. 55, Nr. 7, S. 5731–5780, Okt. 2022, doi: 10.1007/s10462-022-10144-1.

[12] O. Guhr, A.-K. Schumann, F. Bahrmann, und H. J. Böhme, „Training a Broad-Coverage German Sentiment Classification Model for Dialog Systems“, in Proceedings of the Twelfth Language Resources and Evaluation Conference, N. Calzolari, F. Béchet, P. Blache, K. Choukri, C. Cieri, T. Declerck, S. Goggi, H. Isahara, B. Maegaard, J. Mariani, H. Mazo, A. Moreno, J. Odijk, und S. Piperidis, Hrsg., Marseille, France: European Language Resources Association, Mai 2020, S. 1627–1632. Zugegriffen: 8. August 2025. [Online]. Verfügbar unter: https://aclanthology.org/2020.lrec-1.202/

[13] T. G. Dietterich, „Machine Learning for Sequential Data: A Review“, in Structural, Syntactic, and Statistical Pattern Recognition, T. Caelli, A. Amin, R. P. W. Duin, D. de Ridder, und M. Kamel, Hrsg., Berlin, Heidelberg: Springer, 2002, S. 15–30. doi: 10.1007/3-540-70659-3_2.

[14] S. E. Bestvater und B. L. Monroe, „Sentiment is Not Stance: Target-Aware Opinion Classification for Political Text Analysis“, Polit. Anal., Bd. 31, Nr. 2, S. 235–256, Apr. 2023, doi: 10.1017/pan.2022.10.

[15] „google-bert/bert-base-german-cased · Hugging Face“. Zugegriffen: 8. August 2025. [Online]. Verfügbar unter: https://huggingface.co/google-bert/bert-base-german-cased

[16] „Trainer“. Zugegriffen: 8. August 2025. [Online]. Verfügbar unter: https://huggingface.co/docs/transformers/main_classes/trainer

[17] R. Mohammed, J. Rawashdeh, und M. Abdullah, „Machine Learning with Oversampling and Undersampling Techniques: Overview Study and Experimental Results“, in 2020 11th International Conference on Information and Communication Systems (ICICS), Apr. 2020, S. 243–248. doi: 10.1109/ICICS49469.2020.239556.

[18] I. Vayansky und S. A. P. Kumar, „A review of topic modeling methods“, Inf. Syst., Bd. 94, S. 101582, Dez. 2020, doi: 10.1016/j.is.2020.101582.

THE ROLE OF TARGET GROUPS AND GATEKEEPERS IN THE DEPLOYMENT OF MORE SUSTAINABLE PHOTOVOLTAIC SYSTEMS: A PARTICIPATORY APPROACH

Alexandra Tönies, Larissa Müller, Eva-Maria Grommes, Valérie Varney
University of Applied Sciences Cologne
Alexandra.toenies@th-koeln.de

ABSTRACT: In the challenge of supporting a sustainable energy transition, societal innovation is a powerful tool for enabling new technologies to reach their full potential. With the goal of designing effective action strategies, this paper argues for the relevance of participatory target group structuration in motivational approaches based on green purchase behavior research. Building on insights from environmental and marketing psychology, limitations of one-size-fits-all strategies are highlighted, and a workshop format designed for collaborative target group identification is introduced. In a use case on promoting more sustainable photovoltaic modules, researchers and practitioners jointly participated in the format, combining brainstorming and touchpoint mapping, in order to identify and prioritize relevant target groups. The workshop proved effective in structuring target groups for transdisciplinary cooperation, while also underlining the challenges of well-adapted stakeholder involvement. Findings revealed a focus on Business-to-Business dynamics for the present case, shaped by the gatekeeping role of organizational actors in the photovoltaic market. Since existing green purchase behavior models center mostly on individual consumers, the study concludes that further research on motivational factors in B2B contexts is essential for developing effective and context-specific strategies.
Keywords: Environmental Psychology, Green Purchase Behavior, Sustainable Energy Transition, Target Group Identification, Organizational Factors

1 INTRODUCTION

An impactful, sustainable energy transition requires not only technical innovations, but also the societal innovations that enable them to realize their full potential. Environmental psychology plays a significant role in identifying the most powerful factors that facilitate such a transition. Green Purchase Behavior research for example investigates the motivational factors involved in sustainable decision making concerning purchase situations. Especially given the at times higher costs of sustainable alternatives, the understanding of behavior drivers here is crucial. Some well-known influencing factors are attitudes, subjective norms, and perceived behavioral control, integrated in the famous theory of planned behavior introduced by Ajzen from 1985 [1], one of the best empirically researched and further developed models in environmental psychology. This model proposes attitudes, subjective norms, and perceived behavioral control as interdependent motivational factors, influencing behavioral intention, which then directly influences the behavior itself. However, while the model has been refined and enriched with more detail since its first introduction, and many more alterations as well as new models have been derived, green purchase behavior research suggests that there is a gap to be addressed in order to tackle universal societal challenges like climate change. Not every public and not every context is the same, with each of them providing different individual, social, and structural dynamics, which is why participatory target group analysis should play a central role in designing effective action strategies. This paper investigates this issue by introducing a workshop-based target group identification method that facilitates inter- and transdisciplinary collaboration, while remaining flexible and time-efficient. As part of the Green Solar Modules project, focused on the development and deployment of more sustainable photovoltaic modules, the workshop goal in the use case was to better understand relevant motivational dynamics in the field of photovoltaics for the stakeholders of this project specifically.

Research in environmental and marketing psychology shows that one-size-fits-all approaches do not achieve effective behavior change [2], [3], [4]. This is already evident in green purchase behavior models, mostly developed with private customers in mind, hereafter referred to as Business-to-Consumer (B2C). Research here highlights how motivational factors vary by country [4], product type [4], and between private and professional purchasing contexts [2]. Depending on the cultural background, local norms, regulations, and values might differ, for example, [5], [6]. Comparing different product types, such as fashion, food, and photovoltaic (PV), varying argument types have been found most important, ranging from peer perception and social norms [7], over health concerns [8], to financial incentives [9]. Concerning private and professional purchasing contexts, automatic spill-over effects from one context to the other have not been supported. Furthermore, empirical research has found unique motivational factors for organizations, such as supplier responsiveness, green compliance, corporate social responsibility [2], or perceived structural pressures [10]. When aiming for green purchase behavior, the necessity thus becomes clear to establish awareness of the context and potential target groups, as a base for all motivational strategies.

Despite this, target group identification is rarely addressed in PV adoption research. This may be due, in part, to the more advanced state of B2C green purchase behavior, compared to Business-to-Business (B2B), which shapes dominant approaches automatically. Another barrier, however, is the lack of standardized and easy-to-use identification methods. In marketing psychology, this typically involves the steps of segmentation – dividing populations into groups with similar, purchase-relevant traits – and positioning, which prioritizes the most promising segments for tailored outreach [11]. However, scientific literature offers no standard methodology for this [12]. Best practice examples use participatory workshops, but these are often lengthy, individualized, and poorly documented [13], making them impractical for most projects without a marketing specialization.

Equally important, inter- and transdisciplinary

10.4229/EUPVSEC2025/5DV.2.62

collaborations are increasingly seen as essential for addressing the complexity of the energy transition, as they promise solutions with a more holistic understanding [14], which are therefore more effective [15]. At the same time, logistical and methodological challenges are typically inherent to these settings, given that they bring together stakeholders with different schedules, institutional backgrounds, and perspectives. For target group identification to be feasible and impactful in such contexts, tools must be resource-efficient, flexible, and accessible. The approach introduced by this paper – a participatory workshop design drawing from user experience and marketing research – responds directly to these constraints.

In response to the increasing prominence of inter- and transdisciplinary energy transition projects, this paper focuses on participatory collaboration as a means of developing target group insights. Since motivational strategies depend fundamentally on this context-sensitive knowledge, leveraging the rich perspectives of interdisciplinary teams is essential. Participatory research supports this notion, emphasizing that collective creativity can produce outcomes that exceed those of any single stakeholder [16].

2 METHODOLOGY

For the purpose of this study, a compact participatory workshop design was developed to support inter- and transdisciplinary collaboration. To enable efficient and inclusive target group identification, elements from user experience research were combined with participatory principles. The workshop was designed with the goal of remaining adaptable and time-efficient while enabling the identification of relevant target groups. This was considered crucial as to best support the integration of the various stake- and knowledge-holders in the project, with different localizations and schedules. The participants were representatives of the project partners in PV sales and interested project members with experience in PV sales. Both practitioners and researchers were included to ensure a mix of market expertise and academic perspectives.

The workshop was conducted remotely during a time frame of two hours and divided into the following parts: Introduction, Collective Brainstorming, Touchpoint Maps, and Closure and Feedback (Fig.1). For effective collaboration, an online workspace for drawing and mind mapping was used and a moderator guided through the format.

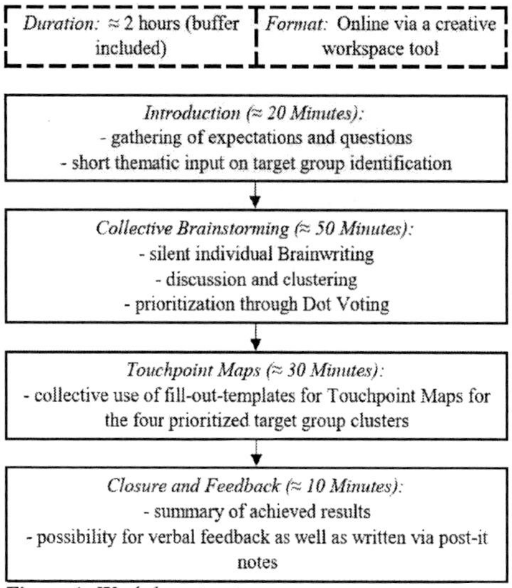

Figure 1: Workshop structure

Given the participants' diverse expertise backgrounds, a thematic introduction on target group work and its practical relevance, as well as the workshop goals, was essential to establish a shared conceptual foundation. To this end, questions and expectations were first collected, followed by a brief input on the topic of target group analysis. The input relied heavily on real life examples and recognizable case studies in order to make the approach tangible for non-specialists.

During the Collective Brainstorming part, various target group types from the perspective of the participants were silently collected (brainwriting), guided by the categories of current, potential and excluded target groups. Following, the gathered groups were discussed, clustered, and finally prioritized. While the discussion and clustering invited verbal exchange, the prioritization took place via a timed dot-voting. The four most important target group clusters were then transferred to the next step in the workshop, the Touchpoint Maps.

To identify relevant interaction dynamics for future intervention strategies concerning the prioritized target groups, touchpoint maps were adapted from user experience research for this stage. Such maps enable the participants to identify existing (or likely) points of contact with customer groups or stakeholders in a group setting, producing richer results. Templates of touchpoint maps structured through a timeline provided visual guidance to the participants, to be filled out based on their experience.

For the Closure and Feedback section, a brief overview of the achieved results was given, and next steps were briefly described. Feedback on the workshop was collected for the further development of such tools.

Despite a flexible appointment search via an online appointment scheduling tool, not everyone was able to attend the workshop in real time, which is why the results of another participant were subsequently integrated via written communication. This ensured that all voices were at least partially represented, and that the results reflected the input of all intended stakeholders.

To strengthen the reliability of the outcomes as a basis for future action strategies, the workshop results were later reviewed by the project coordination. This additional strategic evaluation validated the findings, pointing to an effective workshop conduction.

3 RESULTS

The workshop results show that large-scale buyers, like engineering, procurement, and construction companies (EPCs) or distributors, module manufacturers, standardization bodies, investors, and (solar) installers, in their function as decision-makers for the end-consumer, are perceived as the most important target groups (Fig. 2). Furthermore, the written retrospective integration also showed small-scale commercials and the public buildings sector as important target groups. In total, 22 current and potential target groups have been listed, which have subsequently been organized into a visual system of interactions, with the most important groups highlighted (Fig. 3).

The participatory workshop revealed a focus on B2B dynamics. Even if modules were ultimately meant for private use, B2B groups functioned as distributors.

The Touchpoint Maps segment of the workshop focused therefore on large-scale buyers, module manufacturers, standardization bodies, and investors as the most important target groups. Large-scale buyers and module manufacturers were addressed together, as their touchpoints were perceived by the participants to be very similar. As the results of the touchpoint maps were collected for future reference during the creation of action strategies and are not the subject of this paper, they will not be described in detail.

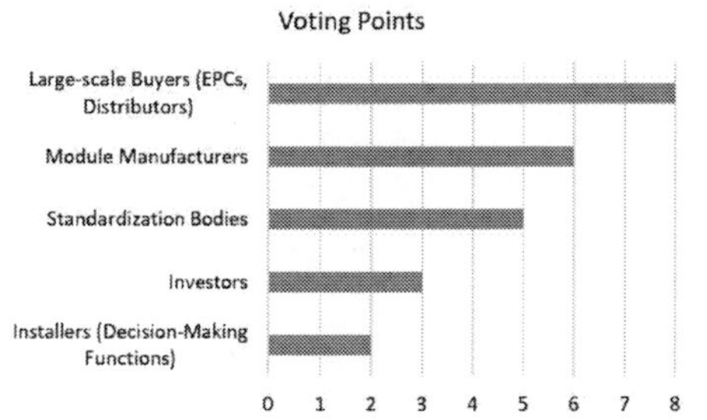

Figure 2: The perceived importance of identified target group clusters for the project. EPCs = Engineering, Procurement, and Construction companies

4 DISCUSSION

Based on the workshop results, a need to further develop purchase behavior research in the B2B sector is highlighted. With organizational actors occupying an in-between role, they function as gatekeepers to individual customers, influencing selection, as well as perception. They are hereby in a position to consciously and subconsciously limit the perceived options of choice for consumers and guide information flow as well as decision-making [17].

The term gatekeeper is used here as introduced by Kurt Lewin in 1947, who coined this concept when investigating food habits and household decision-making

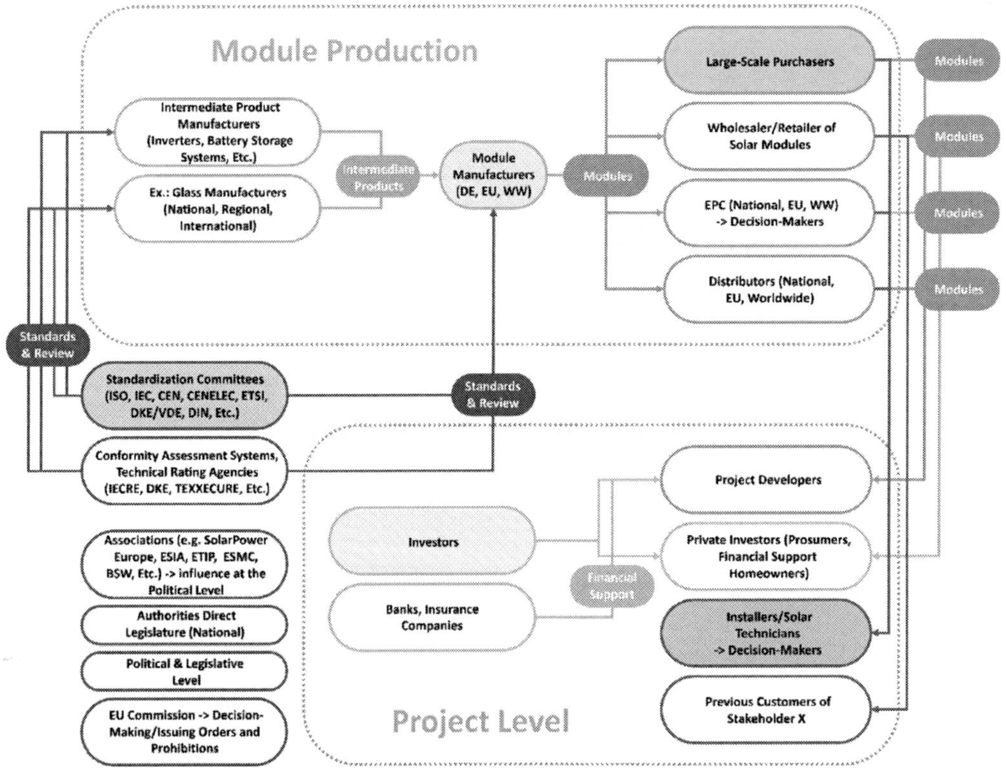

Figure 3: Structuration of the identified target groups on the PV market

10.4229/EUPVSEC2025/5DV.2.62
020523-003

[17]. Thereby, information flow does not occur automatically but is shaped through metaphorical gates it must pass through, with certain individuals or mechanisms acting as gatekeepers that can regulate, filter, or block this flow. At its core, gatekeeper theory postulates that the transmission of information is shaped by actors or processes that control what enters, what is delayed, and what is excluded, thereby influencing collective outcomes [18]. Gatekeepers do therefore not necessarily have to want to manipulate outcomes, but given the structural dependencies present, they will do so nonetheless. The model has since been extended from household decision making to various domains, including communication, journalism, and organizational studies [19].

If the goal is to foster the wider adoption of more sustainable solar panels, rather than only addressing private customers, the gatekeeper roles must therefore also be addressed. Such advancements would prove beneficial for supporting more systemic angles in environmental psychology as well. The individualization of responsibility for sustainable development is typically criticized in environmental psychology and calls for alternative solutions on a bigger scale [20]. Targeting B2B dynamics would contribute here, given the system of interactions on the photovoltaic market and resulting potential multiplier positions of gatekeepers (also see Fig. 3). To this date, such research remains mostly general and tends to focus on economic factors most instead of the likewise integration of psychological, contextual, and organizational variables. Given the empirical rejection of the homo economicus, such a focus would be incomplete and needs to be elaborated [21], [22]. Seeing that organizations are entities made up of human individuals and the empirical evidence for their potential for irrational decision-making, there is no reason why they should be treated differently [23]. Drawing on insights from B2C literature – where variations in motivational factors across countries, product types, and use contexts have been observed – the paper argues for a more nuanced development in B2B research as well.

Using target group analysis as the basis for effective motivational strategies is widely the norm in marketing and communication science, but typically overlooked in motivational research on green purchase behavior. Given the structure of the PV market and the insights gained through this workshop, this will be key in facilitating more sustainable buying behavior. In order to foster a citizen-centered energy transition, action initiatives must be strategically developed, with careful consideration given to the target groups of engagement and their specific needs.

The created workshop design itself received positive feedback and produced valuable results, which were also supported in a further validation by the project coordination, speaking to its effectiveness. By documenting the applied structure in sufficient detail to be reproduced, practical orientation for more targeted investigations in pursuit of creating powerful action strategies has been provided. While the workshop produced valuable results, such as the discovery and prioritization of relevant target groups, as well as the identification of meaningful points of contact, future approaches must consider certain constraints. The fact that an additional strategic evaluation was deemed necessary might suggest that not all relevant parties were involved in the workshop itself. This highlights the importance of careful evaluation of stakeholder involvement in participatory work [24].

Furthermore, this reflects a common dynamic in transdisciplinary work, where tangible results are often needed early on to encourage participation down the line. Initial differences in professional and experiential backgrounds require bridging efforts before meaningful collaboration can emerge. In such cases, a workshop like this can serve as a foot-in-the-door approach, laying the groundwork for deeper cooperation.

As demonstrated in the current study, for the goal of fostering the adoption of more sustainable energy systems, a participatory approach through collaborative, creative formats is not only useful with citizens, but also in inter- or transdisciplinary project settings. Thus, effective levers of action for the specific context become more visible. Functioning as an exploratory basis, the results of the current use case should further be validated across different green purchasing scenarios [4] and project structures.

4 REFERENCES

[1] I. Ajzen, 'From Intentions to Actions: A Theory of Planned Behavior', in *Action Control*, J. Kuhl and J. Beckmann, Eds, Berlin, Heidelberg: Springer Berlin Heidelberg, 1985, pp. 11–39. doi: 10.1007/978-3-642-69746-3_2.

[2] N. B. Bommenahalli Veerabhadrappa, S. Fernandes, and R. Panda, 'A review of green purchase with reference to individual consumers and organizational consumers: A TCCM approach', *Clean. Responsible Consum.*, vol. 8, p. 100097, Mar. 2023, doi: 10.1016/j.clrc.2022.100097.

[3] Y. Du and P. H. Kim, 'One size does not fit all: Strategy configurations, complex environments, and new venture performance in emerging economies', *J. Bus. Res.*, vol. 124, pp. 272–285, Jan. 2021, doi: 10.1016/j.jbusres.2020.11.059.

[4] X. Zhang and F. Dong, 'Why Do Consumers Make Green Purchase Decisions? Insights from a Systematic Review', *Int. J. Environ. Res. Public. Health*, vol. 17, no. 18, p. 6607, Sept. 2020, doi: 10.3390/ijerph17186607.

[5] A. Biswas and M. Roy, 'Green products: an exploratory study on the consumer behaviour in emerging economies of the East', *J. Clean. Prod.*, vol. 87, pp. 463–468, Jan. 2015, doi: 10.1016/j.jclepro.2014.09.075.

[6] B. Kumar, A. K. Manrai, and L. A. Manrai, 'Purchasing behaviour for environmentally sustainable products: A conceptual framework and empirical study', *J. Retail. Consum. Serv.*, vol. 34, pp. 1–9, Jan. 2017, doi: 10.1016/j.jretconser.2016.09.004.

[7] K. Peattie, 'Green Consumption: Behavior and Norms', *Annu. Rev. Environ. Resour.*, vol. 35, no. 1, pp. 195–228, Nov. 2010, doi: 10.1146/annurev-environ-032609-094328.

[8] R. S. Hughner, P. McDonagh, A. Prothero, C. J. Shultz, and J. Stanton, 'Who are organic food consumers? A compilation and review of why people purchase organic food', *J. Consum. Behav.*, vol. 6, no. 2–3, pp. 94–110, Mar. 2007, doi: 10.1002/cb.210.

[9] W. Poortinga, L. Steg, and C. Vlek, 'Values, Environmental Concern, and Environmental Behavior: A Study into Household Energy Use', *Environ. Behav.*, vol. 36, no. 1, pp. 70–93, Jan. 2004, doi: 10.1177/0013916503251466.

[10] X. Yu, Y. Tao, D. Wang, and M. M. Yang, 'Disengaging pro-environmental values in B2B green buying decisions: Evidence from a conjoint experiment', *Ind. Mark. Manag.*, vol. 105, pp. 240–252, Aug. 2022, doi: 10.1016/j.indmarman.2022.05.020.

[11] M. R. Czinkota, M. Kotabe, D. Vrontis, and S. M. R. Shams, *Marketing Management: Past, Present and Future.* in Springer Texts in Business and Economics. Cham: Springer International Publishing, 2021. doi: 10.1007/978-3-030-66916-4.

[12] R. Basu, W. M. Lim, A. Kumar, and S. Kumar, 'Marketing analytics: The bridge between customer psychology and marketing decision-making', *Psychol. Mark.*, vol. 40, no. 12, pp. 2588–2611, Dec. 2023, doi: 10.1002/mar.21908.

[13] J. K. Saint Clair, 'Consumer Identity: A Comprehensive Review and Integration of Contemporary Research', in *The Cambridge Handbook of Consumer Psychology*, 2nd edn, C. Lamberton, D. D. Rucker, and S. A. Spiller, Eds, Cambridge University Press, 2023, pp. 179–227. doi: 10.1017/9781009243957.009.

[14] H. Sanoff, *Participatory Environmental Design*. 2018.

[15] J. Bergold and S. Thomas, 'Partizipative Forschung', in *Handbuch qualitative Forschung in der Psychologie*, Springer, 2010, pp. 333–344. [Online]. Available: https://link.springer.com/content/pdf/10.1007/978-3-531-92052-8.pdf

[16] E. B.-N. Sanders and P. J. Stappers, 'Co-creation and the new landscapes of design', *Co-Des.*, vol. 4, no. 1, pp. 5–18, 2008.

[17] K. Lewin, 'Frontiers in Group Dynamics: Concept, Method and Reality in Social Science; Social Equilibria and Social Change', *Hum. Relat.*, vol. 1, no. 1, pp. 5–41, June 1947, doi: 10.1177/001872674700100103.

[18] K. Barzilai-Nahon, 'Toward a theory of network gatekeeping: A framework for exploring information control', *J. Am. Soc. Inf. Sci. Technol.*, vol. 59, no. 9, pp. 1493–1512, July 2008, doi: 10.1002/asi.20857.

[19] P. J. Shoemaker and T. Vos, *Gatekeeping Theory*, 0 edn. Routledge, 2009. doi: 10.4324/9780203931653.

[20] S. N. Jorgenson, J. C. Stephens, and B. White, 'Environmental education in transition: A critical review of recent research on climate change and energy education', *J. Environ. Educ.*, vol. 50, no. 3, pp. 160–171, May 2019, doi: 10.1080/00958964.2019.1604478.

[21] D. Ariely, *Predictably irrational: the hidden forces that shape our decisions*, 1st ed. New York, NY: Harper, 2008.

[22] A. Tversky and D. Kahneman, 'Judgment under Uncertainty: Heuristics and Biases: Biases in judgments reveal some heuristics of thinking under uncertainty.', *Science*, vol. 185, no. 4157, pp. 1124–1131, Sept. 1974, doi: 10.1126/science.185.4157.1124.

[23] H. R. Arkes and C. Blumer, 'The psychology of sunk cost', *Organ. Behav. Hum. Decis. Process.*, vol. 35, no. 1, pp. 124–140, Feb. 1985, doi: 10.1016/0749-5978(85)90049-4.

[24] P. Jones, 'Contexts of Co-creation: Designing with System Stakeholders', in *Systemic Design: Theory, Methods, and Practice*, P. Jones and K. Kijima, Eds, Tokyo: Springer Japan, 2018, pp. 3–52. doi: 10.1007/978-4-431-55639-8_1.

The Role of Target Groups and Gatekeepers in the Deployment of More Sustainable Photovoltaic Systems: A Participatory Approach

Alexandra Tönies, Larissa Müller, Valérie Varney

University of Applied Sciences Cologne

One Size-Fits-All Approaches and Target Group Analysis in Green Purchase Behaviour

- Achieving a sustainable energy transition requires more than technological advancement; it depends on societal innovation to ensure these technologies can be widely adopted. Green purchase behavior research focuses on factors influencing such purchase decisions.
- Empirical research shows different motivational factors for different contexts, which is important for designing effective action strategies [1], [2]. However, while target group analysis is typically encountered in marketing or communication science, it is not typically mentioned in green purchase behavior research.
- The majority of empirically investigated models in green behaviour research is focused on individual end consumers (e.g. Theory of Planned Behaviour), likely further shaping the nature of action strategies.

Cultural Context

- Motivational factors differ by country and cultural background [1].
- Local norms, regulations, and values are examples shaping purchasing decisions in green energy [3], [4].

Product Context

- Drivers of purchase behaviour vary by type of product [1].
- Product-specific attributes such as cost, durability, and performance perception influence decision-making for example as well as their respective target audiences, societal perceptions and surrounding ecosystems [5], [6], [7].

Private or Professional Context

- Green behaviour in private life does not automatically spill over into professional contexts. Empirical evidence shows partly distinct motivational drivers in private vs. workplace contexts [2]. Structural pressures can for example shape professional decisions [8].
- Organizations can neither solely be treated through a homo oeconomicus lense [9], as they are made up of people and demonstrate irrational decision fallacies as well (e.g. sunk cost fallacy) [10].

But How Does This Translate to Practical Interventions?

- Despite theory, practical methods for target group identification are lacking in PV adoption research.
- Marketing psychology suggests segmentation and positioning, but scientific literature does not mention a standardized methodology.
- Participatory workshops as best practice examples are promising but time-consuming, highly individualized, and vaguely documented.

An Adaptable Workshop Design for Participatory Target Group Identification

- A participatory remote workshop was developed for target group identification in the PV sector, involving sales partners and project members.
- The Structure consisted of three main parts (see also Figure 1):
  - Thematic introduction to establish a shared foundation with real-life examples and case studies.
  - Brainwriting/brainstorming to collect, cluster, and prioritize current, potential, and excluded target groups.
  - Touchpoint maps to identify points of contact with the four priority groups.
- Flexible participation was enabled, with absent participants contributing retrospectively via written communication.
- An additional strategic validation by the project coordination was requested, which confirmed the workshop results and at the same time highlights the importance of carefully evaluating stakeholder involvement.
- Considering typical transdisciplinary challenges in co-creation, the workshop can also function as a foot-in-the-door approach, bridging different professional backgrounds and building a basis for more meaningful collaboration.

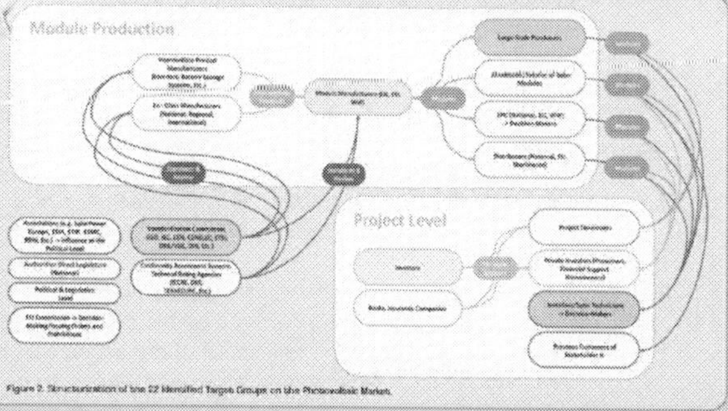

Figure 2: Structurization of the 22 Identified Target Groups on the Photovoltaic Market.

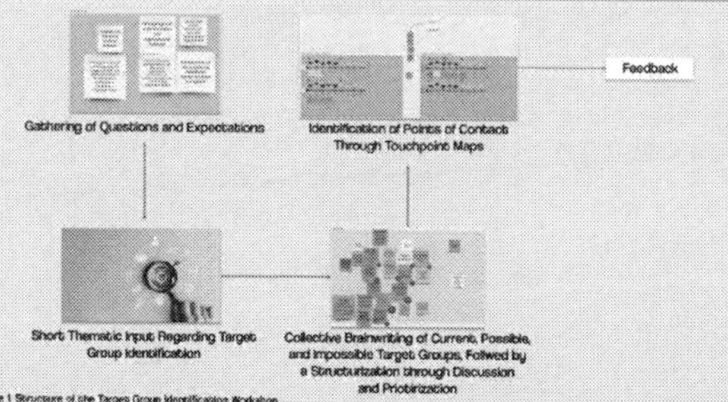

Figure 1 Structure of the Target Group Identification Workshop

Workshop Results & Conclusions

- 22 target groups were identified and organized into a visual interaction system, with the 5 prioritized groups highlighted (see Figure 2).
- Primary groups identified: large-scale buyers, module manufacturers, standardization bodies, investors, and installers.
- Additional groups (retrospective inclusion): small-scale commercials and public buildings.
- Results revealed the central role of B2B dynamics, showing that organizational players functioning as gatekeepers are decisive for citizens' perceptions, information flows, and ultimate purchasing decisions.
- Findings support the need for expanded B2B research on green purchase behaviour, complementing B2C insights and at the same time addressing critiques in environmental psychology about overemphasizing individual responsibility by targeting systemic dynamics and enabling multiplier effects.

Literature:

[1] X. Zhang and F. Dong, 'Why Do Consumers Make Green Purchase Decisions? Insights from a Systematic Review', Int. J. Environ. Res. Public. Health, vol. 17, no. 18, p. 6607, Sep. 2020, doi: 10.3390/ijerph17186607.
[2] N. B. Bommenahalli Veerabhadrappa, S. Fernandes, and R. Panda, 'A review of green purchase with reference to individual consumers and organizational consumers: A TCCM approach', Clean. Responsible Consum., vol. 8, p. 100097, Mar. 2023, doi: 10.1016/j.clrc.2022.100097.
[3] A. Biswas and M. Roy, 'Green products: an exploratory study on the consumer behaviour in emerging economies of the East', J. Clean. Prod., vol. 87, pp. 463–468, Jan. 2015, doi: 10.1016/j.jclepro.2014.09.075.
[4] S. Kumar, A. K. Manrai, and L. A. Manrai, 'Purchasing behaviour for environmentally sustainable products: A conceptual framework and empirical study', J. Retail. Consum. Serv., vol. 34, pp. 9–1, Jan. 2017, doi: 10.1016/j.jretconser.2016.09.004.
[5] R. S. Hughner, P. McDonagh, A. Prothero, C. J. Shultz, and J. Stanton, 'Who are organic food consumers? A compilation and review of why people purchase organic food', J. Consum. Behav., vol. 6, no. 3–2, pp. 110–94, Mar. 2007, doi: 10.1002/cb.210.
[6] W. Poortinga, L. Steg, and C. Vlek, 'Values, Environmental Concern, and Environmental Behavior: A Study into Household Energy Use', Environ. Behav., vol. 36, no. 1, pp. 93–70, Jan. 2004, doi: 0013916503251466/10.1177.
[7] K. Peattie, 'Green Consumption: Behavior and Norms', Annu. Rev. Environ. Resour., vol. 35, no. 1, pp. 228–195, Nov. 2010, doi: 10.1146/annurev-environ-094328-032609.
[8] X. Yu, Y. Tao, D. Wang, and M. M. Yang, 'Disengaging pro environmental values in B2B green buying decisions: Evidence from a conjoint experiment', Ind. Mark. Manag., vol. 105, pp. 252–240, Aug. 2022, doi: 10.1016/j.indmarman.2022.05.020.
[9] A. Tversky and D. Kahneman, 'Judgment under Uncertainty: Heuristics and Biases: Biases in judgments reveal some heuristics of thinking under uncertainty.', Science, vol. 185, no. 4157, pp. 1131–1124, Sep. 1974, doi: 10.1126/science.185.4157.1124.
[10] H. R. Arkes and C. Blumer, 'The psychology of sunk cost', Organ. Behav. Hum. Decis. Process., vol. 35, no. 1, pp. 140–124, Feb. 1985, doi: 4-90049(85)6978-0749/10.1016.

Technology Arts Sciences TH Köln

Subtopic 5.6: Societal Challenges; Citizens' Participation, Awareness

42nd European Photovoltaic Solar Energy Conference and Exhibition

This presentation was selected by the Sc. Committee of the EU PVSEC 2025 for submission of a full paper to one of the EU PVSEC's collaborating peer-reviewed journals.

POLYNOMIAL SURFACE MODEL-BASED BALANCING MARKET BID PLANNING AND EVALUATION FOR MULTI-SITE PV PLANTS

Jindan Cui[1], Xue Fang[1], Takashi Oozeki[2], Yuzuru Ueda[1]
[1]Tokyo University of Science, Japan, [2]National Institute of Advanced Industrial Science and Technology (AIST), Japan
cui_jindan@rs.tus.ac.jp

ABSTRACT: The Seventh Basic Energy Plan sets an ambitious target of expanding solar power generation beyond the current 7%, highlighting a strong national commitment to renewable energy. However, the large-scale deployment of photovoltaics (PV) faces two critical challenges: the inherent uncertainty of power generation due to weather variability, and the decline in profitability associated with daytime price drops under high renewable energy penetration. This study explores the creation of new value for PV systems through the provision of reserve power to address these challenges. Accurate management of prediction errors is essential to unlock this value and improve dispatchability. Building on our previous work, we applied kernel density estimation to model the probability distribution of historical prediction errors and constructed a polynomial surface model that incorporates PV-predicted values and the clearness index as features, with cumulative probability serving as the error threshold. In this study, the model is extended to multiple sites to demonstrate its general applicability and to evaluate the smoothing effect of aggregated prediction errors. The results show that aggregating PV reserve power can effectively reduce imbalances in balancing market operations, underscoring its potential to support the sustainable, large-scale integration of PV into the power grid.
Keywords: multi-site PV plant, polynomial surface, reserve power, headroom setting, balancing market bid planning

1 INTRODUCTION

The Seventh Basic Energy Plan released in December 2024, sets an ambitious goal to significantly increase solar power generation, beyond the current target of 7%. This signals a strong commitment to expanding the use of solar energy in Japan over the next few decades. However, the main challenge facing solar power as it strives to become a major source of electricity is the unpredictability of power generation due to weather fluctuations. The potential influx of renewable energy into the electricity market could also threaten to the profitability of solar power generation. If electricity prices plummet during the day, as a result of increased renewable energy supply, the business of generating solar power generation may become unsustainable, leading to a slower expansion of solar systems.

To overcome these challenges, this study investigates the creation of a new value for PV systems in the form of reserve power. Accurate management of prediction errors is essential for unlocking this value and enabling PV systems to provide both stable power supply and dispatch capacity. Over the past several years, we have explored various approaches to this problem, including a statistical model (quantile regression), a machine learning model (Support Vector Machine, SVM), a hybrid of the two [1], feature importance analysis using Random Forest (RF), multiple-initial-time modeling [2], and rare-event risk analysis of extreme prediction errors [3]. These studies have consistently highlighted the importance of accurately setting error-absorption headroom to mitigate the risks associated with prediction errors.

Building on this foundation, the present study develops a reserve-setting method that enhances error absorption capability and reduces imbalance events in the balancing market, particularly in contexts where individual PV plants face difficulty participating effectively. In Ref. [4], we employed a statistical approach based on kernel density estimation of historical prediction error distributions, followed by the construction of a polynomial surface model using cumulative probability as the error threshold, with PV-predicted values and the clearness index as explanatory variables. In this study, we extend this approach by validating the polynomial surface model across multiple sites. Furthermore, we investigate the smoothing effect of aggregated prediction errors, demonstrating that multi-site deployment can further reduce imbalances and improve the operational value of PV reserve power in balancing markets.

2 METHODOLOGIES

2.1 Approach

In this study, we applied the optimal polynomial surface model (Model 1 in Ref. [4]) to secure sufficient headroom for absorbing day-ahead prediction errors when six individual PV power plants provide reserve power to the balancing market without relying on batteries or intraday procurement. This approach was used to validate the model's applicability in practical market operations.

In day-ahead planning, it is essential to manage prediction errors of PV power plants—variable power sources—in order to formulate effective bidding strategies based on predicted power generation. To address this, we employed models that estimate the distribution of prediction errors using historical data, and then set error-absorption headroom according to the required cumulative probability. The headroom was determined as a function of two explanatory variables: predicted power generation and clearness index, an indicator of weather conditions.

2.2 Single site

The procedure for the building of a model is as follows:

Initially, at each site, the historical PV prediction errors are obtained in Eq. (1).

$$e(i,t) = P_f(i,t) - P_m(i,t), t \in \{19, 20, \cdots, 30\} \quad (1)$$

where P_f and P_m represent the predicted and measured PV power generation from the historical records, respectively; The subscript i denotes the site location; and t represents the 30-min time steps in accordance with market

10.4229/EUPVSEC2025/5DV.3.1
020525-001

conventions. Only PV generation between 09:00 and 15:00 (bidding slots 19–30) was considered. Both the predicted and measured PV power generation values were normalized by the installed capacity.

Then, sample sets R_n of error e were created corresponding to P_n, where P_n represents a 0.01 kW unit of P_f. For each sample set R_n, outliers exceeding 1.5 times the interquartile range were excluded. The probability distribution and probability density function (PDF), denoted as $\hat{f}_h(e)$, were then estimated using kernel density estimation. A normal (Gaussian) kernel function with 0 mean and unit variance was employed.

$$(P_n, e) \in R_n, n \in \{0,\ 0.01,\ 0.02, 0.03,\ \cdots\cdots\} \tag{2}$$

$$\hat{f}_h(e) = \frac{1}{mh}\sum_{j=1}^{m} K\left(\frac{e - e_j}{h}\right) \tag{3}$$

where e_j denotes a random error sample obtained from the estimated probability distribution, m is the total number of samples, and $K(\cdot)$ representes the kernel smoothing function. In this study, we employed the Gaussian (normal) kernel, with h denoting the bandwidth parameter [4].

Second, for each set R_n the cumulative distribution function (CDF), $\hat{F}_h(e)$, was estimated using kernel density estimation. Based on $\hat{F}_h(e)$, the error threshold e_{th} corresponding to a cumulative probability μ was identified for each R_n.

$$\hat{F}_h(e) = \int_{-\infty}^{e_{\max}} \hat{f}_h(e)de \tag{4}$$

$$e_{th} = \hat{F}_h^{-1}(\mu) \tag{5}$$

Third, the prediction error H_e in each sample set closest to e_{th} was identified, and the corresponding original predicted value, $P_{f,orig}$ and CI were retrieved. The CI was then calculated as follows.

$$CI(i,t) = \frac{H_g(i,t)}{H_O(i,t)} \tag{6}$$

where H_O and H_g represnt the extraterrestrial horizontal irradiance and global horizontal irradiance, respectively. CI ranges from 0 to 1, with lower values indicating overcast or rainy conditions, and values approaching 1 correspond to clear-sky conditions.

Fourth, a bivariate polynomial surface for cumulative probability μ was created using predicted PV generation P_f and CI as explanatory variables. Both predicted and measured CI values were considered in this analysis. The P_f variable was modeled as a quadratic term, while CI was treated as a linear term. The planned values were then updated using Eq. (8).

$$H_e^{\mu} = f_{py}(P_f, {P_f}^2, CI) \tag{7}$$

$$P_{rev}(t) = P_f(t) - H_e^{\mu}(t) \tag{8}$$

Fifth, measured data from the test period were used to evaluate imbalance. The main objective of this research was to develop planned market values that prevent shortages. The number of negative imbalance event, $ImbC^-$, was calculated using Eq. (9). In addition, the amounts of shortage (negative) and surplus (positive) were calculated and evaluated based on the deviation from the planned values, as defined in Eqs. (10)–(12).

$$ImbC^- = \sum_t t,\ if\ P_m(t) < P_{rev}(t) \tag{9}$$

$$ImbA^- = \sum_t P_{rev}(t) - P_m(t),\ if\ P_m(t) < P_{rev}(t) \tag{10}$$

$$ImbA^+ = \sum_t P_m(t) - P_{rev}(t),\ if\ P_m(t) \geq P_{rev}(t) \tag{11}$$

$$ImbA = ImbA^- + ImbA^+ \tag{12}$$

where $ImbC^-$, $ImbA^+$, $ImbA^-$, and $ImbA$ represent the number of negative imbalance events, positive imbalance amount [kW・30min], negative imbalance amount [kW・30min], overall imbalance amount, respectively, with time spots defined as 12 intervals per day. The bid count ($BidC$) and bid amount ($BidA$) are defined in Eqs. (13) and (14), respectively.

$$BidC = \sum_t t,\ if\ P_{rev}(t) > 0 \tag{13}$$

$$BidA = \sum_t P_{rev}(t),\ if\ P_{rev}(t) > 0 \tag{14}$$

2.3 Multiple sites

The six locations are integrated to generate planned values and evaluate imbalances. For multi-site integration, the mean values of each feature, normalized by the PV capacity at each site, were first computed as follows:

$$\bar{P}_f(t) = \frac{1}{N}\sum_i^N \frac{P_f(i,t)}{P_{AS}(i)} \tag{15}$$

$$\bar{P}_m(t) = \frac{1}{N}\sum_i^N \frac{P_m(i,t)}{P_{AS}(i)} \tag{16}$$

$$\bar{H}_g(t) = \frac{1}{N}\sum_i^N H_g(i,t) \tag{17}$$

$$\bar{H}_O(t) = \frac{1}{N}\sum_i^N H_O(i,t) \tag{18}$$

where P_{AS} denotes the installed PV capacity per site and N represents the total number of sites. Subsequently, the aggregated prediction errors and clearness index were derived using Eqs. (1) and (6), the same procedure described in Section 2.2 was applied. The evaluation indicators were also computed using Eqs.(9)–(14), in addition, imbalances were evaluated on a monthly basis..

3 SIMULATION AND RESULTS

3.1 Datasets

We used the one-hour grid point value meso-scale model (GPV-MSM) forecast meteorological data [5] to predict PV power P_f by interpolating to 30-min intervals, and one-min meteorological observation data [6] to estimate PV power as measured data P_m, which were then accumulated into 30-minute values for each site. The

10.4229/EUPVSEC2025/5DV.3.1
020525-002

meteorological values considered in this study included solar radiation, outdoor air temperature and wind speed. The initial value of the GPV-MSM was assumed to be 12:00 JST (03:00 UTC) on the previous day to satisfy the balance market bid (planned value) at 15:00.

PV power was calculated using the Erbs and Perez models [4], assuming an installation tilt angle of 20° and a south-facing tilt azimuth. The analysis period spanned from September 1, 2019, to August 31, 2022, focusing on data between 09:00 and 15:00 each day. The model was trained using a two-year period (September 2019 to August 2021), and its performance was evaluated over a subsequent one-year test period (September 2021 to August 2022). Six sites were selected for multi-site analysis: Utsunomiya, Choshi, Kofu, Maebashi, Tateno, and Tokyo. In this study, the headroom setting model was established by normalizing the values with respect to PV capacity, assuming a PV capacity of 1 kW.

3.2 Results and discussions

Figure 1 presents the polynomial surfaces for each location. The surfaces based on measured CI values of the explanatory variables ($\mu = 1.0$) are shown on the left, while those based on predicted CI values are shown in the middle ($\mu = 1.0$) and on the right ($\mu = 0.95$). In the measured CI model, the data points closely approximate a plane, whereas in the predicted CI model, they form a quadratic surface. This behavior reflects the correlation between CI values and prediction errors. For Kofu and Maebashi, the predicted CI model exhibits slightly different surface characteristics compared to other locations, with smaller errors observed where the correlation between the explanatory variables is stronger.

Figure 2 illustrates the polynomial surfaces representing different cumulative probabilities in the integration of multiple locations. As the cumulative probability μ increases, prediction errors decrease, the surface flattens, and the variation in prediction error with respect to the explanatory variables narrows.

Figures 3 and 4 show the standard deviation of historical errors. The error distribution and standard deviation at each individual location are approximately 0.13, whereas the deviation after integration is reduced to 0.08, indicating a smoothing effect. Table I summarizes the number of imbalance events, the imbalance amounts, the number of possible bids, and the bid amounts for each location and after integration. The predicted CI model notably reduces the frequency of negative imbalance events compared with the measured CI model. Out of 4380 spots per year (12 × 365), the average number of negative imbalances per location under the predicted CI model is 242, but this is reduced to 102 after integration—less than half. Due to missing data, the number of bids ($BidC$) for Maebashi, Tateno, and Tokyo is slightly reduced, although nearly all spots are still bid upon. Regarding the bid amount ($BidA$), Kofu yields the largest potential bid individually; however, after integrating six sites, the total bid amount is slightly reduced due to the smoothing effect.

Figure 5 presents the number and amount of negative imbalances, as well as the potential bids, for the integrated system using the predicted CI model. As the cumulative probability μ increases, the number of bids remains unchanged, while the potential bid amount decreases from 1872.5 kW ($\mu = 0.5$) to 1187.5 kW ($\mu = 1.0$). Concurrently, the number of negative imbalance events declines markedly from 1836 per year to 106.

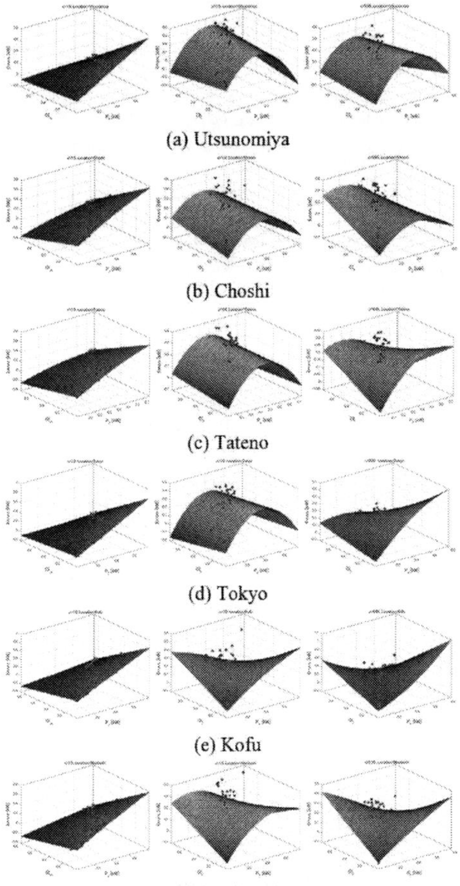

(a) Utsunomiya

(b) Choshi

(c) Tateno

(d) Tokyo

(e) Kofu

(f) Maebashi

Figure 1: Polynomial surfaces of single site

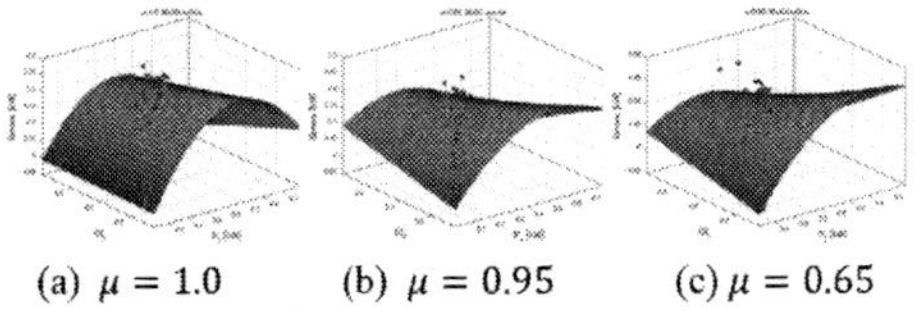

(a) $\mu = 1.0$ (b) $\mu = 0.95$ (c) $\mu = 0.65$

Figure 2: Polynomial surfaces of multi-site integration

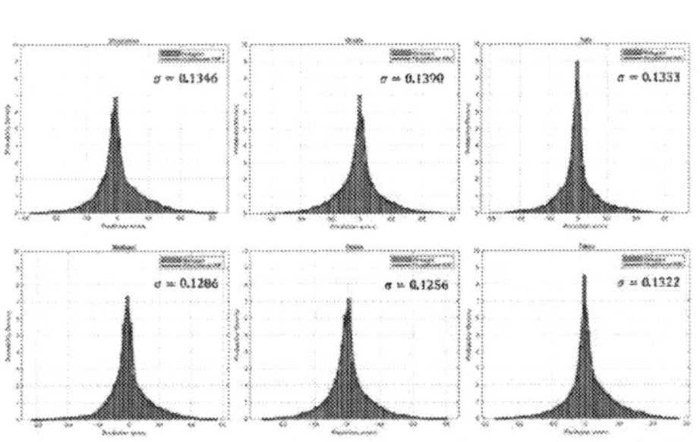

Figure 3: Frequency distribution and PDF of historical errors at each location

Figure 6 shows the average monthly headroom and available bid amounts. The smallest percentage of headroom relative to PV generation predictions is observed in April (30.2%), and the largest in September (45.6%). The black line indicates measured PV generation, while the monthly averages confirm that headroom settings successfully absorbed prediction errors across all months. On a spot-by-spot basis, the maximum number of negative imbalance events was 22 in January, 0 in July, September, and December, and within 11 in all other months (noting that a maximum of 12 reserve power spots could be offered per day).

Table II provides a comparison with several previously implemented models. Approaches based on importance analysis or different initial times reduced shortages by approximately half when prediction values were directly applied to planning. In contrast, the polynomial surface model reduced negative imbalance events to 281 events. Furthermore, when multiple locations were integrated under the same model, the number of negative imbalances was further reduced to 106 events—less than half the single-location result.

4 CONCLUSIONS

In this study, we employed a model that estimates the error threshold corresponding to a given cumulative probability by fitting a polynomial surface to the historical distribution of prediction errors at a single site. This threshold was then used to define the headroom required to absorb prediction errors. We extended this approach by validating the polynomial surface model across multiple sites and further evaluating its applicability in capturing the smoothing effect of site integration.

The standard deviation of prediction errors at individual sites was 0.1322, which decreased to 0.0839 after integrating six sites. Moreover, the number of negative imbalance events was reduced to 106 through multi-site integration. These significant reductions in error variability and imbalance events demonstrate the potential of PV power generation to provide balancing capacity.

ACKNOWLEDGEMENTS
This study was supported by NEDO "Demonstration study of photovoltaic power generation technology to create flexibility."

REFERENCES

[1] J. Cui, B. Jie, X. Fang, T. Oozeki and Y. Ueda, "Absorption of PV Power Prediction Errors with Headroom Control by Statistical, Machine Learning and Combined Models," IEEJ Transactions on Power and Energy (TEEE B), Vol.19 No.2, Dec. 2023. DOI: 10.1002/tee.23966

[2] J. Cui, X. Fang, T. Oozeki and Y. Ueda, "Absorption of PV Power Prediction Errors with Headroom Control by variable importance-considering SVR model with different initial values," 40th European Photovoltaic Solar Energy Conference and Exhibition (EU PVSEC), Lisbon, Portugal, Sept. 2023.

[3] J. Cui, X. Fang, T. Oozeki and Yuzuru Ueda, "Day-ahead Planning and Shortfall Risk Assessment in the Balancing Market for Sola power Plant," Journal of Japan Solar Energy System, Vol.51, No.5 (289), Sept. 2025. DOI:10.24632/jses.51.5_1 (in Japanes)

[4] J. Cui, X. Fang, T. Oozeki and Y. Ueda, "Development of Error Absorption Headroom Setting Algorithm using Polynomial Surfaces to Create Reserve Power in PV Power Plants," IEEJ Transactions on Power and

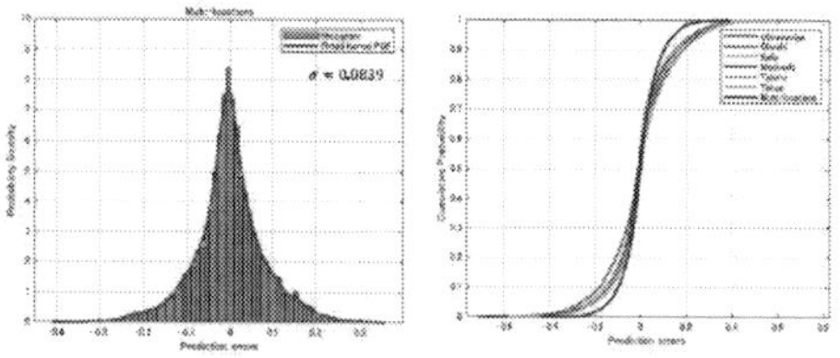

Figure 4: Frequency distribution and PDF of historical errors in multi-site integration

Table I: Imbalance evaluation ($\mu = 1.0$)

Predicted CI	Utsunomiya	Choshi	Kofu	Maebashi	Tateno	Tokyo	Integration
$ImbC^-$	222	237	229	246	281	238	106
	5.1%	5.4%	5.2%	5.6%	6.4%	5.4%	2.4%
$ImbA$	1002.8	1001.3	829.7	889.7	889.5	937.9	736.1
$BidC$	4380	4380	4380	4372	4379	4379	4370
$BidA$	952	961	1282	1085	1010	928	1188
Measured CI	**Utsunomiya**	**Choshi**	**Kofu**	**Maebashi**	**Tateno**	**Tokyo**	**Integration**
$ImbC^-$	952	1725	1912	1562	1583	1355	415
	21.7%	39.4%	43.7%	35.7%	36.1%	30.9%	9.5%
$ImbA$	518.3	536.2	436.1	440.0	466.9	450.3	476.8
$BidC$	4380	4380	4380	4372	4379	4379	4370
$BidA$	1568	1690	1917	1759	1640	1616	1474

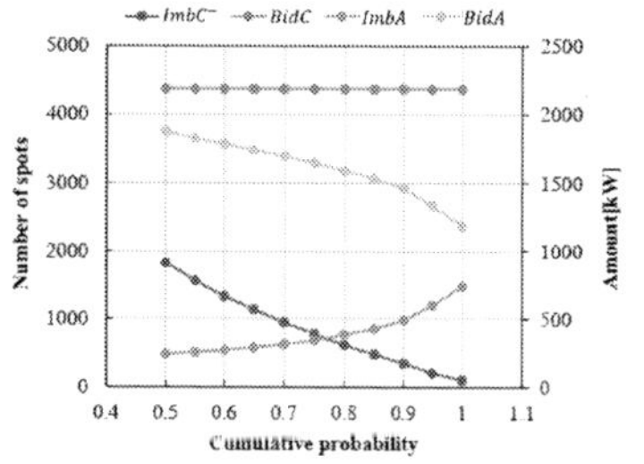

Figure 5: Evaluation results for multi-site integration (predicted CI model)

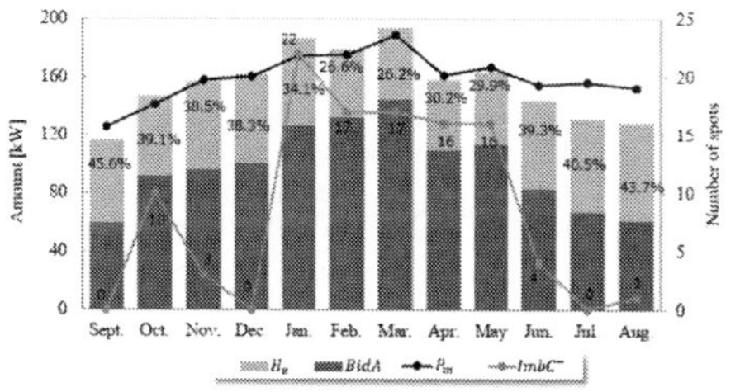

Figure 6: Monthly headroom (predicted CI model)

Table II: Comparison with different models (Tateno)

	Physical	SVR without importance	SVR with importance	SVR with importance	Polynomial surface	Polynomial surface (multi-site)
	The most recent initial values			8 different initial values	The most recent initial values	
$ImbC^-$	2570	2329	2154	1456	281	106
$ImbA$	514	500	500	604	890	736
$ImbA^+$	150	240	248	442	866	732
$ImbA^-$	364	260	252	162	23	4

Energy (TEEE B), Vol.20 No.12, July. 2025. DOI: 10.1002/tee.70086

[5] Japan Meteorological Business Support Center, "Grid Point Value Data from the Meso-Scale Model (MSM)." https://www.jmbsc.or.jp/jp/online/file/f-online10200.html.

[6] Japan Meteorological Agency, "Weather Services." https://www.jma.go.jp/jma/index.html.

INTEGRATION OF SOLAR ENERGY INTO ELECTRIC MOBILITY INFRASTRUCTURE

D.J. Rodriguez, J.F. Pantoja and J. Hernandez
Francisco José de Caldas District University
djrodriguezp@udistrital.edu.co

ABSTRACT: The transition to sustainable mobility requires comprehensive solutions that combine renewable energy sources, such as solar energy, with innovative urban planning strategies. Solar energy has established itself as one of the most promising technologies to drive this transformation, thanks to its ability to generate clean, decentralized, and low-environmental-impact electricity. In the context of electric mobility, solar-powered charging stations represent a strategic alternative to reduce dependence on the conventional electricity grid while optimizing the use of urban space. This integration not only responds to the growing energy demand of modern cities but also strengthens the resilience of electrical systems by leveraging local and sustainable resources. Furthermore, the incorporation of geolocation methodologies—such as cluster analysis, segmentation, and spatial correlation—is an essential tool for efficiently reorganizing the territory and planning electric charging infrastructure. These techniques make it possible to identify patterns in energy demand, identify areas of high solar irradiation, and locate urban areas with the highest density of electric vehicles. This facilitates strategic planning that ensures the proper allocation of resources to regions with the greatest potential impact in terms of energy efficiency, coverage, and sustainability.

Keywords: sustainable mobility, Solar energy, Electric vehicle charging infrastructure, Urban planning.

1 INTRODUCTION

The transition to sustainable mobility requires comprehensive solutions that combine renewable energy sources, such as solar energy, with urban planning strategies. Solar energy is emerging as one of the most promising technologies to drive this transformation, thanks to its ability to generate clean and decentralized electricity. In the context of electric mobility, solar-powered charging stations offer an opportunity to reduce dependence on the conventional electricity grid, limiting its impact on it, while maximizing the efficient use of urban space. This integration not only responds to the growing energy demands of modern cities but also strengthens the resilience of electrical systems through the use of local and sustainable resources.

In countries like Colombia, the accelerated incorporation of charging stations faces barriers associated with the reliability and capacity of the distribution network, [1]. Official reports show that, in 2023, the SAIDI (average interruption duration) exceeded the regulatory targets projected by CREG, while the SAIFI (interruption frequency) increased compared to previous years, although it remained close to the objectives, demonstrating that service continuity remains a challenge in several local distribution systems. These conditions, combined with episodes of system stress due to climate events such as El Niño and charging capacity restrictions in urban networks for new loads (such as fast EV charging), make connecting charging infrastructure complex without complementary measures.

The transition to sustainable mobility requires comprehensive solutions that combine renewable sources with urban planning and grid management. In this context, solar photovoltaic energy is consolidating as an ideal technology for supplying clean and decentralized electricity, reducing grid dependence and the environmental impact of transportation. In the context of electric mobility, charging stations powered (fully or partially) by on-site generation provide a strategic alternative for diversifying supply and cushioning peak demand in distribution circuits, [2].

Furthermore, the incorporation of geolocation methodologies such as cluster analysis, spatial correlation, and Voronoi zones offers a rigorous framework for organizing the territory and optimizing charging infrastructure. These tools make it possible to identify demand patterns, assess accessibility, and superimpose the available solar potential over each service area. The unit of analysis shifts from the city as a whole to each Voronoi polygon associated with a station, where investments can be prioritized based on expected load, grid constraints, and local irradiance, [3].

Faced with the reality of imperfect continuity indices and grids with limited capacity to absorb charging peaks, the integration of on-site photovoltaics at charging stations becomes a key enabler. By supplying part of the energy locally, the net power demanded from the feeder is reduced, transformer overloads are alleviated, and the risk of voltage dips during critical hours is limited. This approach is consistent with evidence on hosting capacity in urban grids: without management measures (local generation, storage, smart charging), the widespread use of EVs can strain the operating margins of the distribution network.

Overlaying irradiance maps (IDEAM/Global Solar Atlas, or simulations validated with PVsyst) on Voronoi polygons allows for the quantification of annual and seasonal solar resources for each service area. PV fields are then sized to cover target fractions of demand (e.g., 30–60% of energy), and peak demand reductions are estimated using diurnal generation profiles. This cross-layering converts Voronoi zones into energy planning units, prioritizing polygons with high EV density and higher GHI for the deployment of solar rooftops, PV canopies, and near-station PV micro-plants. (For Bogotá, recent public planning underscores that achieving adoption goals requires timely and strategic investments in charging infrastructure, which is further enhanced by local generation contributions), [4].

On-site generation is most effective when integrated with storage (batteries) and smart charging strategies (power management, scheduling, and pricing), and ideally with V2G schemes where regulations allow. This technical package makes it possible to smooth demand at transformers, cover peaks with local power, and continue operating during short interruptions (station island mode or microgrid). Station standardization and interoperability, a framework already promoted at the regulatory level, reduces friction for users and facilitates operational coordination at the city/country level.

In short, the integration of charging infrastructure and solar radiation is not an optional extra, but a co-dependent design: Voronoi polygons allow for the alignment of demand and resources, on-site PV mitigates the chargeability of the local grid, and smart storage/charging increases resilience. All of this is especially pertinent in Colombia, where service quality still shows room for improvement, climate cycles can stress the system, and the EV/charger ratio highlights the need to accelerate deployment with technical solutions that free up grid capacity.

2 METHODOLOGY

The methodology employed in this research was based on a comprehensive approach combining geospatial analysis, statistical modeling, and energy infrastructure assessment techniques. First, data on solar radiation, vehicle density, and mobility patterns were collected and processed from official and collaborative sources. These data were integrated into a geographic information system (GIS), enabling clustering, territorial segmentation, and spatial correlation analyses to identify optimal areas for installing solar charging stations for electric vehicles.

To project the growth of the electric vehicle (EV) fleet in Colombia, data were collected from the Colombia Open Data platform, which offers official information on vehicle sales and registrations. Additionally, sector reports from Fenalco and ANDI, as well as statistics from the International Energy Agency (IEA), were used to compare national trends with the international landscape. These data sets cover the period from 2015 to 2023, including the evolution of pure electric vehicles (BEVs), electric hybrids (HEVs), and plug-in hybrids (PHEVs). The consolidation of these sources allowed not only to analyze the historical dynamics of the market, but also to establish the basis for the construction of a polynomial regression model that projects EV growth in the country toward 2030.

In parallel, georeferenced data related to the location of existing charging stations and road infrastructure were collected, primarily using the OpenStreetMap and Electromaps platforms. This information allowed the analysis to integrate the spatial distribution of charging infrastructure across the country, as well as its concentration in strategic urban areas such as Bogotá, Medellín, and Cali. Using geographic information systems (GIS) tools, analysis layers were generated that facilitated the identification of charging station accessibility, coverage, and density patterns. These inputs were essential for assessing the correlation between the location of charging points and the potential demand for electric vehicles, providing technical criteria for planning new stations and optimizing their distribution.

For the analysis of solar radiation conditions, official databases from IDEAM and the Global Solar Atlas were used, complemented by historical irradiance series obtained using PVsyst software. These sources provided average global horizontal irradiance (GHI) values ranging from 3.5 to 6.0 kWh/m²/day, depending on the region analyzed. The data were processed to generate monthly and hourly radiation profiles, which allowed for a more accurate estimate of the photovoltaic potential available to power the charging infrastructure. Simulations were performed using PVsyst that integrated solar module efficiency parameters, system losses, and local climatic conditions, generating realistic scenarios to evaluate the energy contribution of solar stations in different cities across the country.

Planning the electric charging infrastructure in Colombia required the integration of solar radiation data, electric vehicle records, and the georeferenced location of existing charging stations. Based on this information, spatial analysis tools within a GIS environment were used, allowing the territory to be segmented into zones of influence around each station. To achieve this, the Voronoi diagram method was applied, with the goal of assigning exclusive service areas to each charging point, ensuring more equitable coverage and reducing infrastructure redundancies. This approach revealed inequalities in current distribution, especially in cities like Bogotá, where the concentration of stations in the north creates accessibility gaps in peripheral areas.

Spatial segmentation using Voronoi was key to assessing the correlation between vehicle density, charging demand, and solar radiation potential. In areas with a high concentration of electric vehicles, such as Chapinero and Suba, the polygons associated with each station had a higher user density, indicating the need to strengthen the infrastructure in these areas. This analysis also allowed for the identification of strategic areas for network expansion, prioritizing regions with high levels of solar irradiation and the availability of urban space suitable for the installation of photovoltaic systems. In this way, Voronoi zones become planning units that combine accessibility criteria, energy demand, and solar resources, facilitating more robust and sustainable decision-making.

Finally, a proposal was made to reinforce the electrical grid in the identified critical areas by integrating distributed photovoltaic systems and lithium-ion battery storage. These solutions would reduce overload at conventional grid nodes and improve the system's resilience to peak demand. By locating solar panels in Voronoi industrial estates with the highest user density, a hybrid model is created that combines existing infrastructure with local clean generation sources. This not only increases the autonomy of the charging stations but also contributes to the country's energy transition by optimally utilizing the solar resources available in each region.

3 RESULTS

3.1 Adoption of electric vehicles in Colombia.

Electric mobility is becoming established as a fundamental pillar in the search for a sustainable future with lower GHG emissions. The adoption of EVs in recent years has grown exponentially, driven by innovations, advances, and technological developments in batteries and charging stations, driven by responsible government policies committed to environmental protection, [5].

In the analysis of EV adoption in Colombia, information was collected from the Open Data Colombia platform, which provides official information on EV sales in Colombia. This information allows to identify trends in

10.4229/EUPVSEC2025/5DV.3.2
020526-002

the Colombian market, analyze its evolution and evaluate the impact of government policies on EV adoption. In addition, the information available in OpenStreetMap was used to analyze the location and distribution of charging stations distributed throughout the national territory. These collaborative data sources allow a geospatial visualization of the charging infrastructure, identifying concentration patterns in strategic mobility areas in urban areas, [6], [7].

The data analyzed corresponds to EVs sold in Colombia with some degree of electrification, that is, BEV, HEV or PHEV. Within this group, EVs represent a significant part of the market. Figure 1 shows the distribution of EVs and hybrids sold in Colombia, classified according to fuel type. Hybrid vehicles represent 88.3% of the total, indicating that the majority of buyers opt for this type of vehicle. This suggests that, although the Colombian market is moving towards electrification, the current preference is more inclined towards hybrid solutions that allow a more gradual transition to electric mobility.

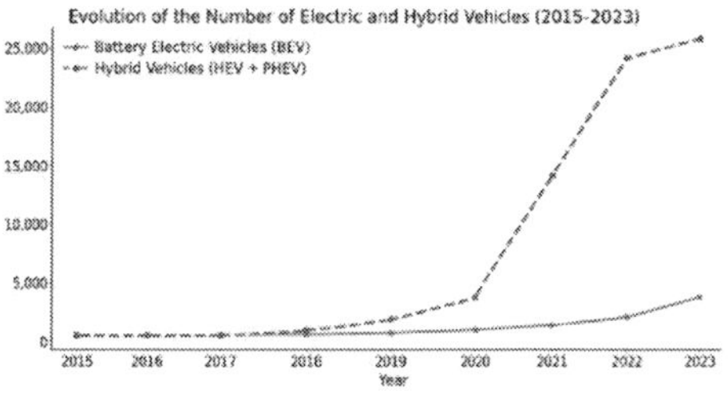

Figure 1: Distribution of EVs and hybrids by 2023. Source: Own elaboration.

Furthermore, analyzing the 2015 period, the number of EVs increased more than 30-fold, and by 2023, the growth was more than 250-fold, a significant increase in EVs. For every EV, there were approximately 7.6 hybrids. The trend indicates rapid progress toward sustainable mobility, with a clear current market preference for hybrid vehicles, possibly due to their lower cost, greater range, or more favorable support infrastructure. Click or tap here to enter text.

The temporal evolution of EV sales has been constant, with a notable increase in registrations starting in 2020. The departments with the highest sales levels are Bogotá D.C., Antioquia, Cundinamarca, and Valle del Cauca, due to a combination of factors, such as the economic capacity of the population, local incentive policies, and the charging infrastructure available in these regions. Figure 2 shows the distribution by department of EVs sold in Colombia as of January 2022, according to the joint report by Fenalco and ANDI. The departments with the highest number of EV registrations are Bogotá, representing 79.8%, Antioquia with 13.1%, Cundinamarca with 4%, and Valle del Cauca with 4%, reflecting a growing interest in zero-emission electric mobility, with the city of Bogotá leading the way.

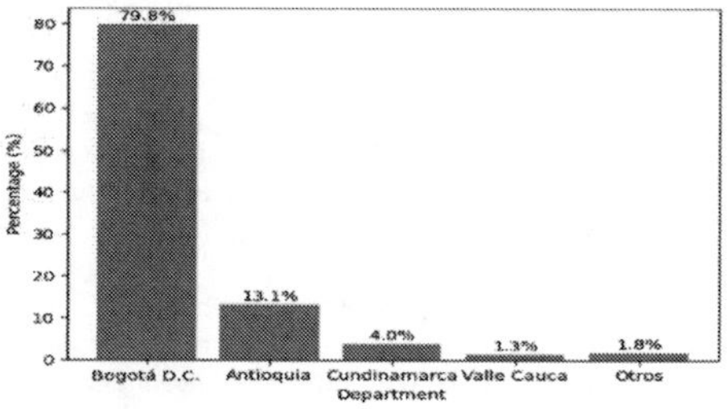

Figure 2: EVs by department in Colombia, as of February 2022. Source: Own elaboration.

Figure 3 shows the temporal evolution of EV registrations in Colombia between 2010 and 2022. During the period between 2010 and 2017, the number of annual registrations remained relatively low and stable, with fewer than 500 units per year. Since 2018, sustained growth in EV registrations has been evident, with particularly marked increases between 2020 and 2022. This accelerated increase can be attributed to multiple factors, such as the expansion of charging infrastructure, the implementation of government incentives, and greater environmental awareness among users. Law 1964 of 2019 played a key role by establishing benefits such as exemption from peak and plate charges, discounts on SOAT (Social Attention Tax) and technical-mechanical inspections, among other incentives aimed at encouraging the adoption of this technology.

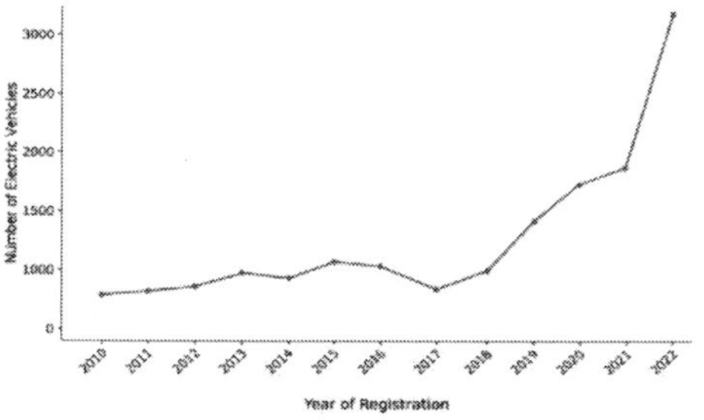

Figure 3: Temporal evolution of EVs in Colombia. Source: Transport Minister.

In 2022, the number of registrations exceeded 3,000 units. Specifically, between January and June of that year, 1,891 EVs were registered, with a monthly average of 315 registrations. This figure represents considerable progress compared to the goal established in the National Development Plan, which projected 6,000 EVs by the end of the government's term. Together, these data reflect a structural shift toward the electrification of the Colombian vehicle fleet, [8], [9].

3.2 Projection of its growth in Colombia.

The growth observed in EV sales in recent years reflects a significant shift towards the electrification of the vehicle fleet in Colombia. This recent boost suggests that the EV market in the country is in an expansion phase with projections of sustained growth in the short and medium term. Below, one of the possible methodologies to estimate the projection of EVs in Colombia until 2030 is presented. Based on the evolution shown in Figure 3, a trend is identified that can be modeled with a second-order polynomial regression, represented in equation (1).

$$\hat{y} = \beta_0 + \beta_1 x + \beta_2 x^2 \qquad (1)$$

With estimated values of $\beta_0, \beta_1, \beta_2$ using the least squares method, the model allows projecting EV sales in Colombia for the period 2023–2030, showing a trend of sustained growth in the adoption of Evs, [10].

The estimated coefficients of the second-order polynomial regression model are shown in equation (2):

$$\beta_0 = 126151352{,}33,\ \beta_1 = 125330{,}73,\ \beta_2 = 31{,}13 \qquad (2)$$

Therefore, the equation of the fitted model is shown in equation (3).

$$\hat{y} = 126151352{,}33 + 125330{,}73x + 31{,}13x^2 \qquad (3)$$

where, x represents the year and y^ the projected quantity of EVs, with coefficient of determination $R^2 \approx 0.872$, which indicates that approximately 87.2% of the variability in the historical VE data is explained by the 2nd-order polynomial regression model, a fairly adequate fit for projection purposes.

The accelerated growth of the EV market in Colombia has been driven by a combination of government incentives, environmental awareness among users, and technological innovations in these technologies. Recent statistics show a sustained increase in EV and hybrid sales, reflecting a progressive structural transformation in the country's mobility. This growth has been accompanied by the gradual expansion of charging infrastructure, which still presents coverage and capacity challenges.

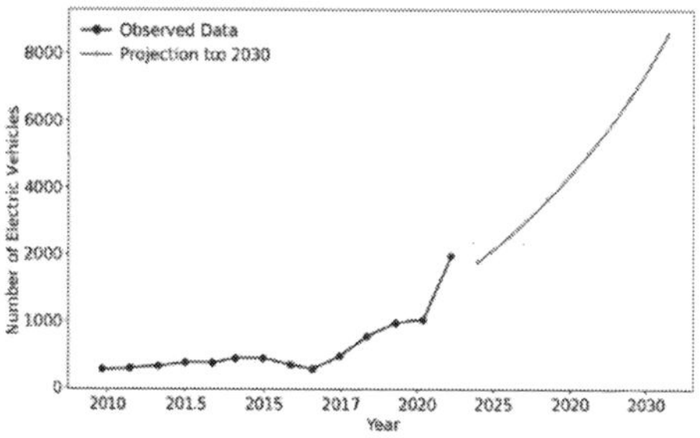

Figure 4: EV Projection to 2030 in Colombia. Source: Own elaboration.

Figure 4 shows the projection made with the model in equation (3), which indicates an accelerated and sustained trend through 2030. Based on historical data from 2010 to 2022, it is estimated that by 2030 the number of EVs registered in the country could exceed 8,900 vehicles, a growth that represents an approximate increase of 185% in 7 years, a significant expansion in the adoption of EVs in Colombia. The trend suggests that Colombia is moving towards a more widespread adoption of EVs, maintaining an accelerated growth rate. The boom in sales reflects a clear transition towards sustainable mobility.

3.3 Charging infrastructure for electric vehicles.

This trend goes hand in hand with the charging infrastructure, represented in Figure 5, where Bogotá leads with 80 charging stations, well above others and followed by cities such as Medellín and Cali. The Ministry of Mines and Energy, through its public policy, promotes electric mobility in Colombia. Through Resolution 40123 of 2024, users will be able to charge their EVs nationwide, without restrictions on access and payment. It seeks to facilitate access to charging stations and requires users to be informed about charging prices and other associated costs. In this context, it is evident that Colombia faces great challenges in the transition to electric mobility, with the lack of charging infrastructure being one of the main research and development topics to achieve the transformation of the conventional vehicle fleet to electric.

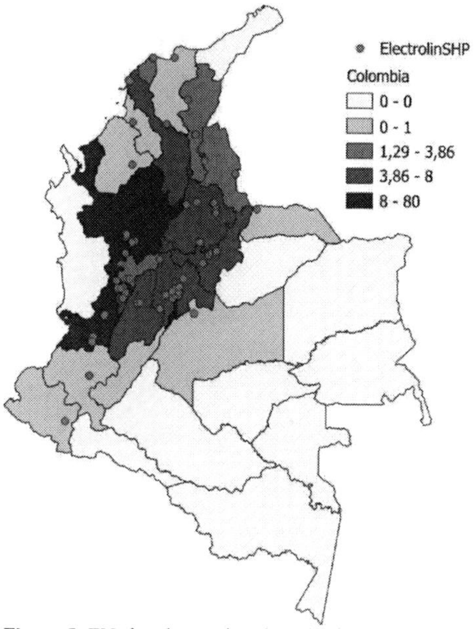

Figure 5: EV charging stations in Colombia by February 2024. Source: Own elaboration.

In Colombia, cities such as Bogotá, Medellín, and Cali already have public EV charging stations, driven by companies such as Celsia, Enel-Codensa, and Terpel, which have invested in infrastructure, including fast chargers. However, development has been limited. Carlos Ghosn, former CEO of Renault-Nissan, points out that the slow adoption of EVs is partly due to insufficient charging infrastructure and a lack of integration with urban planning. In 2020, the country had nearly 3,000 EVs, 47 charging stations, and 114 connectors, significant but insufficient figures given the growing demand. Although the NTC 2050 regulation governs technical aspects of charging systems, there are still no clear guidelines on their location, expansion, and strategic planning. This limits progress toward mass and sustainable electric mobility in the country, [11], [12], [13].

The 2018–2022 National Development Plan set a target of 6,600 registered EVs, which was surpassed with 8,128 units at the end of the period. By 2024, Colombia will have approximately 202 charging stations and 475 connectors, although Electromaps reports 311 charging points, mainly in Bogotá, Medellín, and Cali. The vehicle fleet exceeds 10,000 EVs, and according to the International Energy Agency, there should be at least 1,000 chargers, which shows a deficit of more than 50%. This gap limits the achievement of the goal of net-zero emissions by 2050. The lack of infrastructure can generate range anxiety in users, suggesting a rapid and planned expansion of charging stations in the country [14].

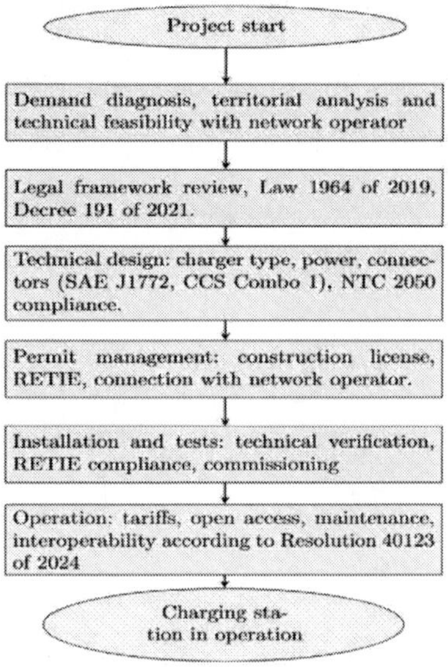

Figure 6: Projection and installation of an EV charging station in Colombia.Source: Prepared by the authors.

The installation of an EV charging station in Colombia requires compliance with a comprehensive process, structured under a legal and technical framework, which establishes clear guidelines to guarantee the safety, efficiency, and interoperability of the infrastructure. From a legal perspective, laws such as 1964 of 2019, decrees such as 191 of 2021, and MinEnergía resolutions (such as 40123 of 2024) define incentives, obligations, and conditions for access and interoperability. In parallel, the technical framework is supported by standards such as NTC 2050, SAE J1772, and resolutions 40405 and 40223, which regulate electrical aspects, connector types, and charging levels. The correct application of these frameworks allows for the design, licensing, installation, and operation of charging stations under safety, quality, and sustainability criteria. Figure 6 shows the process of installing a charging station, looking at the legislation, regulations and decrees established by local and national governments.

3.4 Solar radiation conditions in Colombia.

Colombia, due to its privileged location in the tropics and its geographic diversity, has abundant solar resources distributed relatively evenly throughout the year. Unlike countries with distinct seasons, its proximity to the equator allows solar radiation to vary less seasonally, although factors such as cloud cover, precipitation, and altitude significantly influence each region.

The regions with the highest average solar radiation are the Caribbean Coast, the Eastern Plains, and southwestern areas (Valle del Cauca, Huila, and Tolima), where daily averages reach 5.0 to 6.0 kWh/m²/day. In contrast, regions of the Andean region, particularly in areas with high cloud cover such as Antioquia, Nariño, and Cundinamarca, show more moderate levels, ranging from 3.5 to 4.5 kWh/m²/day.

Figure 7: Colombia solar radiation map. Source: IDEAM

Colombia has one of the highest solar potentials in Latin America, with a national average of nearly 4.5 kWh/m²/day. This represents a significant opportunity for the development of solar photovoltaic and thermal energy projects, contributing to the country's energy transition. Regional variability and the presence of areas with high cloud cover require a design adapted to local conditions, integrating storage and energy systems hybrids where necessary.

In the particular case of Bogotá, located at an altitude of 2,640 meters above sea level and with approximate coordinates of 4.7°N, 74.1°W, it presents a solar radiation pattern characterized by moderate values due to its tropical latitude and the influence of its high altitude. The city receives an average of between 3.5 and 4.5 kWh/m²/day of global horizontal irradiance (GHI), with seasonal variations marked by the rainy and dry seasons.

The solar radiation pattern in Bogotá (see Figure 8) is influenced by the bimodal rainfall cycle (typically in April-May and October-November), which causes decreased radiation levels due to cloudiness. In contrast, the months of December-March and July-August typically experience higher levels of solar radiation.

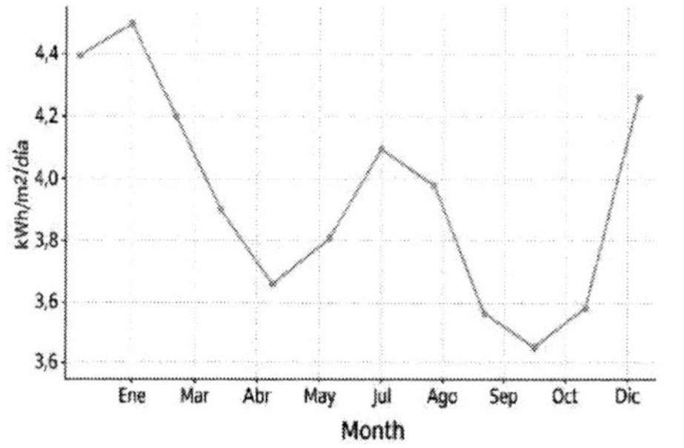

Figure 8: Bogotá—Monthly average daily global horizontal irradiance (GHI) ($kWh \cdot m^{-2} \cdot day^{-1}$). Author's

calculations using representative climatological values. Sources: IDEAM – NASA.

The Moran index (see Figure 9) was used to evaluate the spatial distribution of demand and infrastructure using the city of Bogotá, Colombia, as a case study. Positive autocorrelation patterns were revealed in high-density traffic areas such as Suba and Chapinero. Furthermore, tools such as Voronoi diagrams were presented to divide the territory into optimal coverage regions around existing charging stations, maximizing access and minimizing operating costs. For example, it was indicated that stations in the north of Bogotá have more efficient coverage, while peripheral areas show uneven distribution.

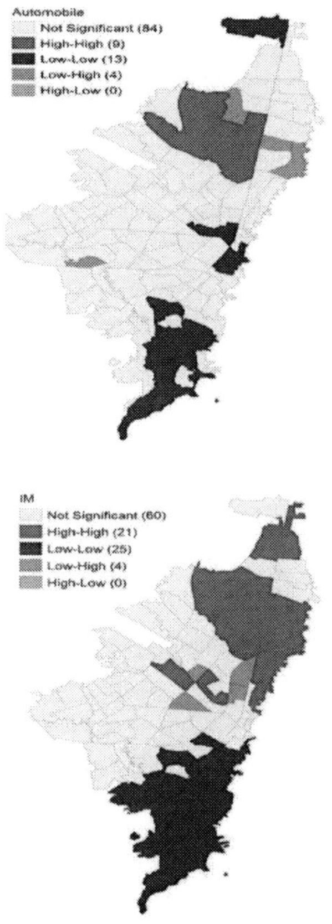

Figure 9: Spatial correlation index (Moran's Index) number of cars and mobility. Source: Own elaboration.

The planning of electric charging stations in urban areas was also analyzed using Voronoi zone segmentation, addressing key issues of accessibility, grid saturation, and sustainability. These zones divide the territory based on proximity to energy generating points, such as existing charging stations, allowing for maximizing coverage and minimizing infrastructure redundancies. This approach is particularly useful in cities like Bogotá, where the uneven distribution of energy resources and electric charging demand requires efficient solutions. This model demonstrated that the strategic relocation of stations in areas with high vehicle density, such as Chapinero and Usaquén, could increase grid coverage by 20% without significantly increasing operating costs.

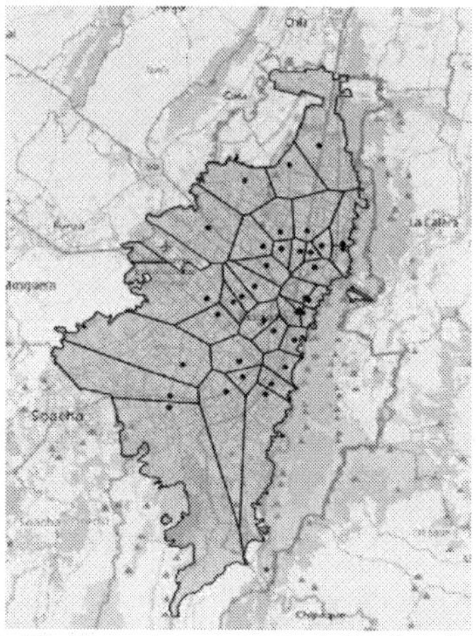

Figure 10: Voronoi zone segmentation based on EV charging stations and their area of influence. Source: Own elaboration.

The analysis of Voronoi polygons (see Figure 10) generated from the location of charging stations revealed marked heterogeneity in service coverage. In cities like Bogotá, polygons associated with stations located in central areas had small areas of influence due to the high density of charging points, while in peripheral areas, large polygons were identified, reflecting gaps in the existing infrastructure. This disparity highlights the need for more balanced planning, prioritizing the installation of new stations in areas with low coverage to improve equity in access to electric mobility.

Furthermore, the results showed that the polygons with the highest vehicle density coincided with the areas with the highest levels of saturation in the charging network. For example, in towns such as Chapinero and Usaquén, the Voronoi polygons concentrate the highest proportion of registered electric vehicles, placing significant pressure on the available infrastructure. This finding highlights the importance of using spatial segmentation not only as a visualization tool but also as a technical criterion for prioritizing investments and planning station expansion based on actual demand.

Finally, by integrating solar radiation data into the spatial analysis, polygons with high potential for the incorporation of supporting photovoltaic systems were identified. These results suggest that installing solar panels at stations strategically located within the most demanding polygons could reduce dependence on the conventional grid and increase local energy resilience. In this sense, Voronoi zones are established as a powerful tool not only for segmenting charging station coverage but also for guiding the transition toward a more sustainable, decentralized, and renewable-based electric mobility model.

4 CONCLUSIONS

The use of Voronoi zones allowed for the establishment of an analytical framework in which each charging station is directly associated with a catchment area determined by spatial proximity. This approach not only revealed the uneven coverage of infrastructure across urban areas but also provided a basis for superimposing other critical variables, such as solar radiation and electric vehicle density. In this way, each polygon became a planning unit that allows for the simultaneous assessment of charging demand and solar resource availability.

By integrating solar radiation maps obtained from IDEAM, the Global Solar Atlas, and PVsyst simulations within Voronoi polygons, it was possible to identify areas with a high correlation between energy demand and photovoltaic potential. For example, areas such as northern Bogotá showed polygons with high vehicle density and, at the same time, radiation levels close to 4.5 kWh/m²/day, making them prime candidates for reinforcement with distributed solar systems. In contrast, peripheral areas with low radiation and lower vehicle density require other types of support strategies, such as storage or grid interconnection.

This integrated analysis allows for a shift from purely spatial planning to a more robust energy model, where charging infrastructure is complemented by local renewable electricity generation. The incorporation of photovoltaic systems in strategic industrial parks not only reduces pressure on the conventional grid but also increases station autonomy and improves resilience to peak demand. In this way, the combination of spatial segmentation and solar resource assessment becomes a key tool for guiding investment decisions, maximizing coverage, reducing operating costs, and enhancing the sustainability of the electric mobility system in Colombia.

REFENCIAS

[1] J. Martínez-Gómez and V. S. Espinoza, "Challenges and Opportunities for Electric Vehicle Charging Stations in Latin America," *World Electric Vehicle Journal 2024, Vol. 15, Page 583*, vol. 15, no. 12, p. 583, Dec. 2024, doi: 10.3390/WEVJ15120583.

[2] T. Khatib and L. Sabri, "Grid Impact Assessment of Centralized and Decentralized Photovoltaic-Based Distribution Generation: A Case Study of Power Distribution Network with High Renewable Energy Penetration," *Math Probl Eng*, vol. 2021, no. 1, p. 5430089, Jan. 2021, doi: 10.1155/2021/5430089.

[3] S. Boonprong, N. Punturasan, P. Varnakovida, and W. Prechathamwong, "Towards Sustainable Urban Mobility: Voronoi-Based Spatial Analysis of EV Charging Stations in Bangkok," *Sustainability 2024, Vol. 16, Page 4729*, vol. 16, no. 11, p. 4729, Jun. 2024, doi: 10.3390/SU16114729.

[4] N. A. Díaz Meza, "An interactive tool for visualization and prediction of solar radiation and photovoltaic generation in Colombia," 2021, *Universidad de los Andes*. Accessed: Sep. 09, 2025. [Online]. Available: https://hdl.handle.net/1992/53603

[5] F. Kogan, "Remote sensing land surface changes: The 1981-2020 intensive global warming," *Remote Sensing Land Surface Changes: The 1981-2020 Intensive Global Warming*, pp. 1–462, Feb. 2023, doi: 10.1007/978-3-030-96810-6/COVER.

[6] IDECA, "Transporte - Temáticas - Datos Abiertos Bogotá." Accessed: Sep. 11, 2025. [Online]. Available: https://datosabiertos.bogota.gov.co/group/transporte?organization=sdm

[7] OpenStreetMap, "OpenStreetMap." Accessed: Sep. 11, 2025. [Online]. Available: https://www.openstreetmap.org./#map=5/4.63/-74.30

[8] C. Xue, H. Zhou, Q. Wu, X. Wu, X. X.- Sustainability, and undefined 2021, "Impact of incentive policies and other socio-economic factors on electric vehicle market share: A panel data analysis from the 20 countries," *mdpi.comC Xue, H Zhou, Q Wu, X Wu, X XuSustainability, 2021•mdpi.com*, Accessed: Sep. 11, 2025. [Online]. Available: https://www.mdpi.com/2071-1050/13/5/2928

[9] K. S. Giraldo Florez and D. A. Moreno Gomez, "Estrategias para impulsar la demanda y oferta de vehículos eléctricos en Bogotá en los estratos sociales 4, 5 y 6 para mejorar la calidad del aire," Jul. 07, 2023. Accessed: Sep. 11, 2025. [Online]. Available: http://hdl.handle.net/10726/5211

[10] M. Islamovic and T. Lind Supervisor Trudy-Ann Stone Karlskrona, "Development of a new forecasting equation simulating EV sales globally A combination approach," 2021, Accessed: Sep. 11, 2025. [Online]. Available: www.bth.se/mba

[11] I. Avellaneda Bolívar, Y. N. Cárdenas Zipa, and J. C. Rodríguez Sanguino, "Estrategias para impulsar el desarrollo de los sistemas de carga de vehículos eléctricos en Colombia.," Nov. 06, 2024, *Universidad Ean*. Accessed: Sep. 11, 2025. [Online]. Available: http://hdl.handle.net/10882/14149

[12] C. Blum, C. Correa Escaf, J. F. Charry, A. Luis, O. Rodriguez, and S. Aparicio, "Socios del Proceso: E2050 Colombia 2 Estrategia Climática de Largo Plazo de Colombia para Cumplir con el Acuerdo de París (E2050) REPÚBLICA DE COLOMBIA Presidente de la República: Iván Duque Márquez Ministerio de Relaciones Exteriores Ministra de Relaciones Exteriores", Accessed: Sep. 11, 2025. [Online]. Available: www.cambioclimatico.gov.co;

[13] I. Avellaneda Bolívar, Y. N. Cárdenas Zipa, and J. C. Rodríguez Sanguino, "Estrategias para impulsar el desarrollo de los sistemas de carga de vehículos eléctricos en Colombia.," Nov. 06, 2024, *Universidad Ean*. Accessed: Sep. 11, 2025. [Online]. Available: http://hdl.handle.net/10882/14149

[14] La República, "'Hay un déficit de 40% de puntos de carga para el parque automotor de vehículos eléctricos.'" Accessed: Sep. 11, 2025. [Online]. Available: https://www.larepublica.co/empresas/hay-un-deficit-de-40-de-puntos-de-carga-para-vehiculos-electricos-3541949

Integration of Solar Energy into Electric Mobility Infrastructure

Diego J. Rodriguez [1] Jaime F. Pantoja [1] Johann A. Hernandez [1]
[1]Universidad Distrital Francisco José de Caldas
Facultad de Ingenieria
Bogota - Colombia

Motivation

- The shift toward sustainable mobility demands integrated solutions that merge renewable energy, especially solar, with advanced urban planning.
- Solar-powered charging stations reduce dependence on traditional grids, generate clean and decentralized electricity, and bolster urban energy resilience.
- Geolocation tools such as clustering and spatial analysis enable identification of high-demand areas, optimal solar irradiation zones, and regions with dense electric-vehicle use, ensuring efficient resource allocation and sustainable infrastructure planning.
- Combining solar generation with smart grid strategies supports peak-demand management and enhances the reliability of urban energy systems.
- This holistic approach accelerates the decarbonization of transport and strengthens cities' ability to adapt to future growth and climate challenges.

Methodology

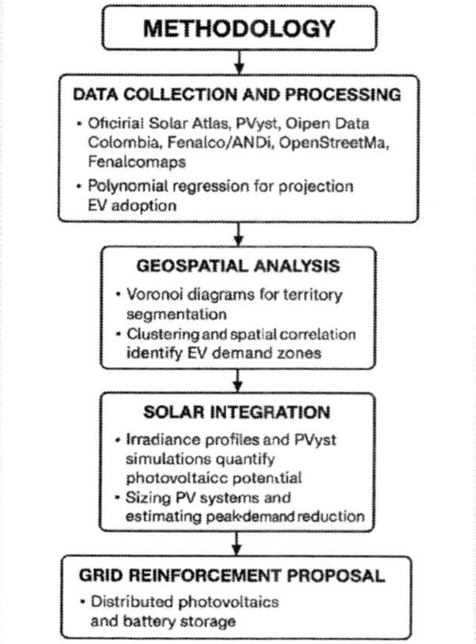
METHODOLOGY
DATA COLLECTION AND PROCESSING
• Oficirial Solar Atlas, PVyst, Oipen Data Colombia, Fenalco/ANDi, OpenStreetMa, Fenalcomaps
• Polynomial regression for projection EV adoption
GEOSPATIAL ANALYSIS
• Voronoi diagrams for territory segmentation
• Clustering and spatial correlation identify EV demand zones
SOLAR INTEGRATION
• Irradiance profiles and PVyst simulations quantify photovoltaicc potential
• Sizing PV systems and estimating peakdemand reduction
GRID REINFORCEMENT PROPOSAL
• Distributed photovoltaics and battery storage

Voronoi Zones and Their Application to Electric Mobility

Solar Potential and Voronoi-Based Planning

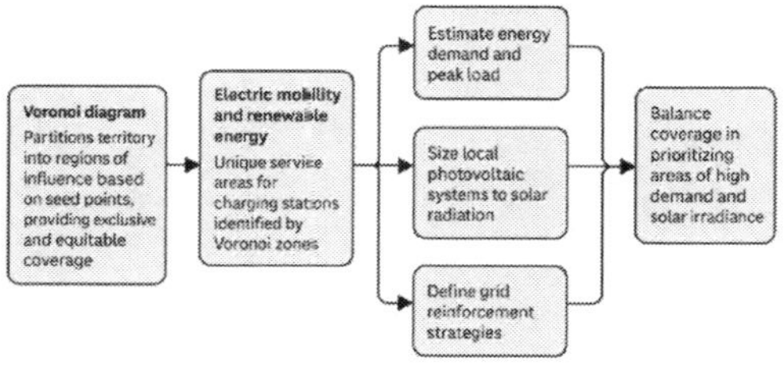
Voronoi diagram
Partitions territory into regions of influence based on seed points, providing exclusive and equitable coverage
Electric mobility and renewable energy
Unique service areas for charging stations identified by Voronoi zones
Estimate energy demand and peak load
Size local photovoltaic systems to solar radiation
Define grid reinforcement strategies
Balance coverage in prioritizing areas of high demand and solar irradiance

Projected EV Expansion (2030)

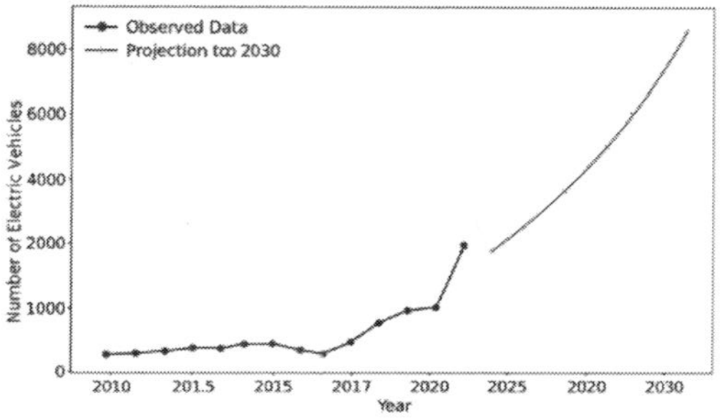
Observed Data
Projection to 2030
Number of Electric Vehicles
Year
0
1000
2000
4000
6000
8000
2010
2015
2017
2020
2025
2030

Figure 1. Observed electric vehicle (EV) registrations in Colombia (2010–2023) and second-order polynomial regression projection through 2030, showing an estimated growth exceeding 8,900 units by the end of the decade.

Based on 2010–2023 data and a second-order polynomial regression ($R^2 \approx 0.87$), Colombia's electric vehicle (EV) fleet could exceed 8,900 units by 2030—about 185% above 2023 levels. This growth, driven by incentives, battery and charging innovations, and rising environmental awareness, underscores the need for well-planned charging networks supported by local renewable energy.

Optimizing Charging Infrastructure with Voronoi and Solar Data

Bogota

Figure 2. Solar radiation Colombia map.

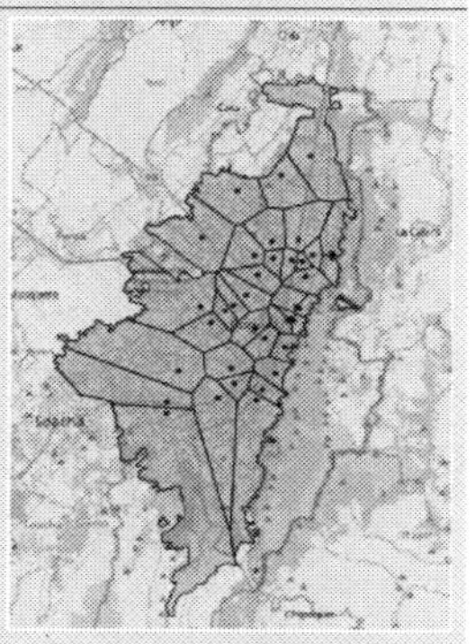

Figure 3. Voronoi Bogotá Zones.

Conclusions

- The combination of **Voronoi zones** with solar irradiance and electric vehicle (EV) density data enabled precise definition of service areas for each charging station, optimizing location and reducing infrastructure redundancies.
- Overlaying solar radiation maps with energy demand revealed that regions such as northern Bogotá have high potential for integrating distributed photovoltaic generation, fostering a more autonomous and resilient charging network.
- The integration of **photovoltaic systems and energy storage** into charging stations decreases dependence on the conventional grid, mitigates transformer overloads, and improves service continuity, particularly in urban networks with limited capacity.
- This approach provides a strategic tool to guide investments, maximize EV charging coverage, and accelerate the transition toward a more **sustainable and decentralized electric mobility** model in Colombia.

References

[1] J. Martinez-Gómez and V. S. Espinoza, "Challenges and Opportunities for Electric Vehicle Charging Stations in Latin America," World Electric Vehicle Journal 2024, Vol. 15, Page 583, vol. 15, no. 12, p. 583, Dec. 2024, doi: 10.3390/WEVJ15120583.

[2] Y. Khetib and L. Sabri, "Grid Impact Assessment of Centralized and Decentralized Photovoltaic-Based Distribution Generation: A Case Study of Power Distribution Network with High Renewable Energy Penetration," Math Probl Eng, vol. 2021, no. 1, p. 5430089, Jan. 2021, doi: 10.1155/2021/5430089.

[3] S. Boonprong, N. Punnasasan, P. Varnakovida, and W. Prechathamwong, "Towards Sustainable Urban Mobility: Voronoi-Based Spatial Analysis of EV Charging Stations in Bangkok," Sustainability 2024, Vol. 16, Page 4729, vol. 16, no. 11, p. 4729, Jun. 2024, doi: 10.3390/SU16114729.

[4] N. A. Diaz Meza, "An interactive tool for visualization and prediction of solar radiation and photovoltaic generation in Colombia," 2021, Universidad de los Andes. Accessed: Sep. 09, 2025. [Online]. Available: https://hdl.handle.net/1992/53603

[5] F. Kogan, "Remote sensing land surface changes: The 1981-2020 intensive global warming," Remote Sensing Land Surface Changes: The 1981-2020 Intensive Global Warming, pp. 1–462, Feb. 2022, doi: 10.1007/978-3-030-96810-6/COVER.

ESTIMATING PHOTOVOLTAIC POWER RAMP RATES USING SINGLE POINT IRRADIANCE MEASUREMENT

Micke Talvi[1], Jan Kleissl[2] and Kari Lappalainen[1]
[1]Tampere University, Electrical Engineering, P.O. Box 692, FI-33101 Tampere, Finland
[2]University of California, San Diego, Center for Energy Research and Department of Mechanical and Aerospace Engineering, CA 92093-0411, United States
micke.talvi@tuni.fi, jkleissl@ucsd.edu, kari.lappalainen@tuni.fi

ABSTRACT: Generation power of photovoltaic (PV) power plants can fluctuate drastically. In this paper, it is studied how accurately different PV power modeling methods that can be executed using single point irradiance measurement estimate the PV power ramp rates (RR). 4 PV power modeling methods are compared to each other and to the measured generation power of a PV power plant. The investigation is done with 4 PV power plant sizes. The main quantities investigated are the highest observed power RRs and the distribution of the power RRs. The study is based on measured irradiance and PV power. It was found that there can be significant differences among the PV power modeling methods, and in contrast to the measured PV power when the variability of PV power was considered. Based on the results, the R2021 method performed the best, and the M2011 method performed the worst.
Keywords: Photovoltaic power, Power fluctuations, Photovoltaic power modeling, Irradiance fluctuations

1 INTRODUCTION

International Energy Agency has estimated the share of global electricity produced with variable renewable energy power plants to be 30% in 2030. Solar power alone would generate roughly 20% of the global electricity in 2030 [1]. One downside of solar photovoltaic (PV) power is that the power generation of PV power plants can fluctuate drastically. The highest observed ramp rate (RR) caused by irradiance variability for a 48 MW PV power plant was 176 %/min in [2]. These power fluctuations should be mitigated, as with the significantly increasing share of PV power in the power grids, the power fluctuations are likely to cause issues. Some solutions to this are increasing the amount of regulative power in the power grids and implementing stricter grid rules. For example, Puerto Rico has set an RR limit of 10 %/min [3]. The RR limit is a threshold that the output powers of power plants may not exceed. However, the PV power fluctuations easily exceed the commonly applied RR limits.

When studying the amount of regulative power needed for mitigation of the PV power fluctuations, accurate PV power modeling methods are necessary if measured PV power data cannot be acquired. Highly accurate PV power modeling methods exist, but they often require comprehensive climate measurements to be executed, which are generally not available in the studied PV power plant locations. Modeling methods that take timeseries measurements at a single point can produce PV power that is usually sufficiently accurate to project daily or annual generation. However, when considering the highest observed power RRs and the variability of PV power, the PV power modeled with simple methods may differ significantly from the real produced PV power.

For instance, in [4], where the PV power was simulated using the PV modeling method proposed in [5] (referred to as M2011 method), the highest observed upward and downward power RRs were found to be significantly smaller compared to those of the real produced PV power. In [6], a wavelet variability model (WVM) was proposed for PV power modeling. The WVM method was found to compare well against the other simulation methods of the time. In [6] it was also found that a moving average method for PV power modeling was found to underestimate the highest power RRs. In [7], a cloud advection model (referred to as R2021 method) was proposed for PV power modeling. The R2021 method was tested against 2 other methods (the M2011 and WVM methods), and the R2021 method was found to perform well against the methods. However, the highest power RRs during short timescales were not presented in sufficient detail to clearly see the differences and the accuracies of the methods.

As the PV power fluctuations can be extremely fast, the use of high temporal resolution of power data would be necessary when conducting a study involving PV power variability. The fastest PV power fluctuations may not be detected if the sampling frequency is lower than 1 Hz [8]. Thereby, this study uses a high temporal resolution of PV power and irradiance data to precisely investigate the PV power variability.

In this study, various PV power modeling methods are compared considering the variability of PV power. The aim of this study is to investigate how well the PV power modeling methods model power variability and spatial smoothing of actual PV power plants. We studied how power modeled with various methods correspond to the measured power of different size PV power plants when PV power variability is considered. The PV power modeling methods of this study were chosen to be methods that model PV power smoothing using only a single point irradiance measurement. The study is conducted using 1 s temporal resolution for the measured irradiance and PV power.

2 DATA AND METHODS

2.1 Data

This study is based on power and plane of array (POA) irradiance measurements from the 48 MW Copper Mountain Solar 1 PV Plant at Boulder City, Nevada (35.78° N, 115.00° W). The PV power plant is composed of fixed-tilt thin-film CdTe PV modules which are manufactured by First Solar [9]. The POA irradiance was measured using a reference cell. The PV modules and the reference cell are facing south, and their tilt angle is 25°. The main parameter values used for the simulations are presented in Table I. The typical cloud speed and the

Table I. Parameter values used for the simulations.

Plant area 0.5 MW	12478 m^2
Plant area 6 MW	160104 m^2
Plant area 10 MW	268354 m^2
Plant area 20 MW	544788 m^2
Typical cloud speed	23 m/s [10]
Typical movement direction of cloud shadows	49.5° (north-east-ward) [10]
Normal operating cell temperature (NOCT)	45 °C [9]
Temperature coefficient of power, β	-0.25 %/°C [9]

movement direction of the cloud shadows determined in [10] are from the same PV power plant location. Hourly temperature data of North Las Vegas was used to calculate the temperature correction for the modeled PV powers. North Las Vegas was chosen, as it was the closest location to the Copper Mountain PV power plant with sufficient temperature data. The temperature data was provided by CustomWeather, Inc [11]. The period investigated consists of 4 months: March, April, May, and June 2012. The temporal resolution of the power and irradiance data was 1 s.

The PV power plant was artificially regulated during 33 days of the studied period. These short regulation periods included multiple extremely fast upward and downward power ramps and maintaining power at a certain level which would have significantly affected the results. Thereby, these 33 days were excluded from the study. Thus, a total of 89 days were used for the study.

2.2 PV power modeling

The investigation was done using 4 different PV power plant sizes: 0.5, 6, 10 and 20 MW. For each PV power plant size, a section of the Copper Mountain 1 PV Plant with that nominal power was selected and its power was modeled based on irradiance and temperature measurements. The area of each modeled PV power plant was determined based on the PV array area of the corresponding section of the Copper Mountain 1 PV Plant. The shapes of the studied PV power plants were kept close to a square. Figs. 1 and 2 present satellite photographs of the Copper Mountain 1 PV Plant showing the studied sections of the plant [12].

4 PV power modeling methods that can be executed with a single point irradiance measurement were used for the study. The results of the methods were compared among each other and against the measured PV power. The chosen methods were the R2021 method [7], the M2011 method [5], the average irradiance method (AIM) that is used for example in [13], and the WVM method [6]. The WVM method was executed using the WVM model in the pvlib library [14].

After the smoothed irradiances were calculated for the 4 methods, the effect of temperature on power production was taken into account. First, the average temperature of the PV modules T_{PVM} was calculated using the equation of [15] which can estimate the T_{PVM} using ambient temperature T_{amb} and smoothed POA irradiance G_{S} as

$$T_{\mathrm{PVM}} = T_{\mathrm{amb}} + (NOCT - 20)\frac{G_{\mathrm{S}}}{800}. \quad (1)$$

Once the T_{PVM} was calculated, the generated PV power P_{PV} of each method was calculated using an equation [16] that takes into account the effect of the T_{PVM} on P_{PV} as

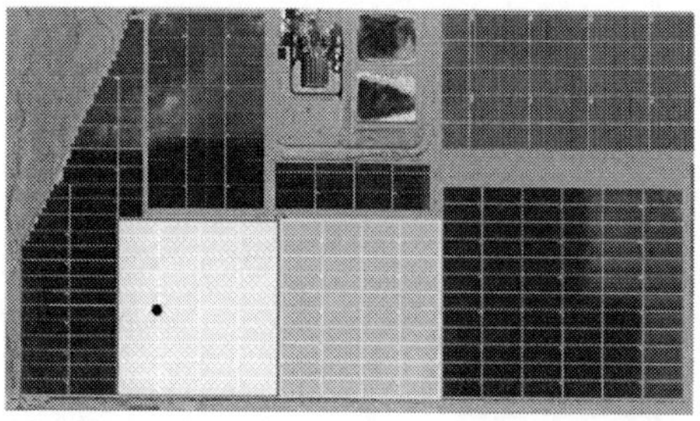

Figure 1: Satellite photograph of the Copper Mountain Solar 1 PV Plant [12]. The imaginary 10 MW and 20 MW PV power plants are indicated with red and yellow rectangles, respectively. The black dot indicates the location of the reference cell.

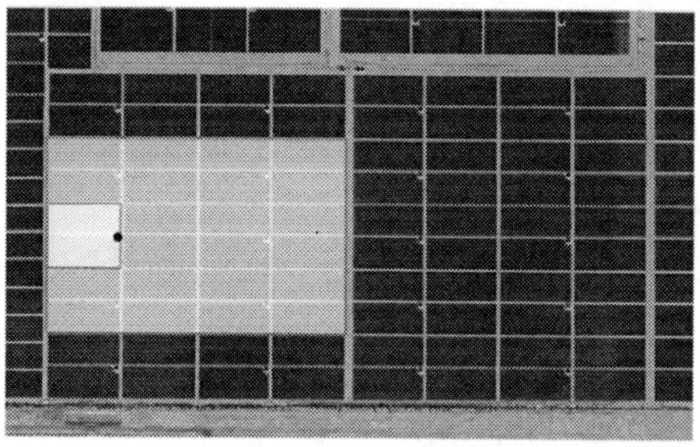

Figure 2: Satellite photograph of a part of the Copper Mountain Solar 1 PV Plant [12]. The imaginary 0.5 MW and 6 MW PV power plants are indicated with blue and green rectangles, respectively. The black dot indicates the location of the reference cell.

$$P_{\mathrm{PV}} = \frac{P_{\mathrm{nom,PV}}}{G_{\mathrm{STC}}} G_{\mathrm{S}}[1 - \beta(T_{\mathrm{PVM}} - T_{\mathrm{STC}})], \quad (2)$$

where $P_{\mathrm{nom,PV}}$ is the nominal power of the PV power plant, G_{STC} is the irradiance in standard test conditions (STC), β is the temperature coefficient of power, and T_{STC} is the temperature in STC. The main quantities that were investigated in this paper are the highest observed power RRs and the distribution of the power RRs.

3 RESULTS AND DISCUSSION

3.1 Example

Fig. 3 presents an example of the behavior of the measured POA irradiance and the modeled and measured PV powers of the 0.5 MW PV power plant during a highly fluctuating period. The figure shows that all the PV powers modeled with different methods follow the measured PV power and irradiance closely, but their lines are smoother. The PV power modeled with the M2011 method seems to be significantly smoother than the other lines. Moreover, the small upward ramps in irradiance roughly at 13:46:10, 13:47:05 and 13:48:45 seem to be nearly neglected with the M2011 method. Fig. 3 shows that the measured PV power had sharp power ramps that were often faster than those of the measured irradiance. These sharp ramps in measured PV power were caused by the combined effect of changing environmental conditions and the operation of the inverter including maximum power point tracking (MPPT).

10.4229/EUPVSEC2025/5DV.3.3

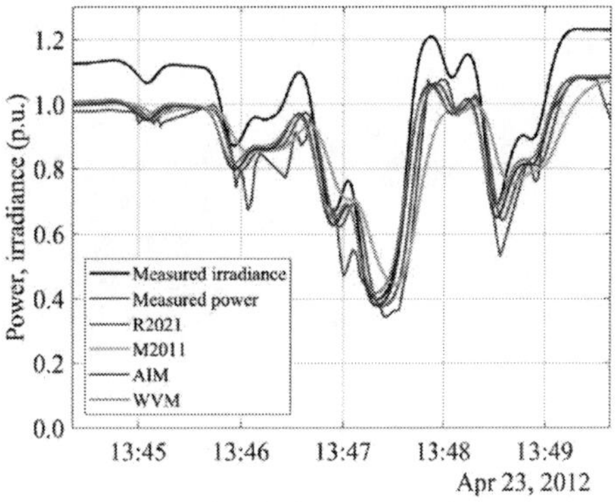

Figure 3: Example of the measured irradiance, the measured PV power and the modeled PV powers during a highly fluctuating period for the 0.5 MW PV power plant.

Table II: Highest observed upward and downward irradiance RRs during 1 s for the measured single point irradiance and the smoothed irradiances for the 0.5 MW and 6 MW PV power plants.

	0.5 MW		6 MW	
	Up	Down	Up	Down
Measured irradiance (%/min)	444.1	468.7	444.1	468.7
R2021 (%/min)	424.7	446.2	284.3	287.0
M2011 (%/min)	261.6	260.0	39.4	36.1
AIM (%/min)	409.0	429.1	219.8	216.7
WVM (%/min)	372.5	391.9	266.0	277.2

3.2 Smoothed irradiances

Table II presents the highest observed upward and downward irradiance RRs during 1 s for the measured and smoothed irradiances for the 0.5 MW and 6 MW PV power plants. The R2021 method performed best among the modeling methods when the highest irradiance RRs are considered. The M2011 performed the worst among the methods, and its highest irradiance RRs were significantly lower than those of the other methods or the measured irradiance.

Figs. 4 and 5 present the shares of time when the irradiance RRs for the measured and smoothed irradiances of the 0.5 MW and 6 MW PV power plants exceeded certain RR magnitudes as a function of that magnitude. Figs. 4 and 5 show that the R2021, AIM and WVM methods yielded quite similar results among each other and compared to the measured irradiance. With the M2011 method, the RR magnitudes higher than 5 %/min were slightly more infrequent compared to the other methods for the 0.5 MW PV power plant, but there was a significant difference when considering the results of the 6 MW PV power plant. It seems that a clear performance difference emerges between the M2011 method and the other methods already at a PV power plant size of 6 MW when the variability of the smoothed irradiance is considered.

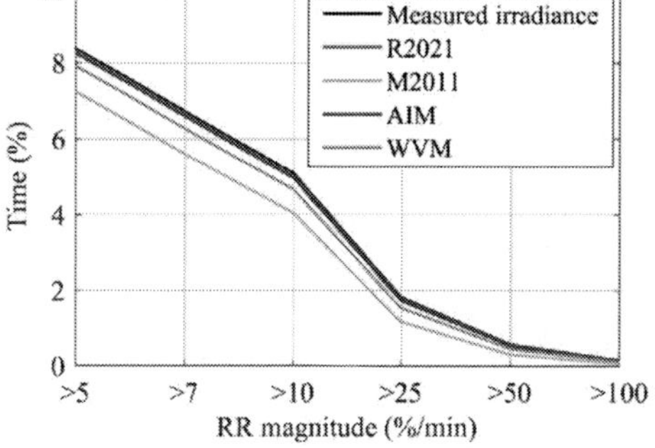

Figure 4: Share of the time when the RRs of the measured and smoothed irradiances of the 0.5 MW PW power plant exceeded certain RR magnitude as a function of the RR magnitude exceeded.

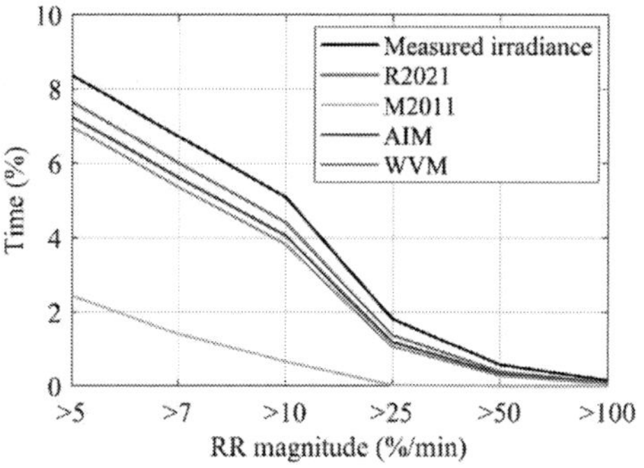

Figure 5: Share of the time when the RRs of the measured and smoothed irradiances of the 6 MW PW power plant exceeded certain RR magnitude as a function of the RR magnitude exceeded.

3.3 Modeled PV powers

Table III presents the highest observed upward and downward power RRs for the 0.5 MW, 6 MW, 10 MW and 20 MW PV power plants with the measured and modeled PV powers. The highest power RRs of the measured PV power of the 10 MW PV power plant are well in line with the highest power RRs recorded for a 9.5 MW PV power plant in [17] (300 %/min). The highest observed upward and downward power RRs of the measured PV power were significantly higher than those recorded with the modeled PV powers especially for small PV power plant sizes. In general, the difference in the highest observed power RRs of the measured and modeled PV powers decreased as the size of the PV power plant increased. The R2021 method achieved the closest values to the measured PV power for PV power plant sizes of 0.5 MW, 6 MW and 10 MW. For the 20 MW PV power plant, the WVM method achieved the closest values to the measured PV power. The M2011 method differed most from the measured PV power, and the relative difference increased significantly as the size of the PV power increased.

It is interesting how small the errors were between the highest observed RRs of the WVM method and the measured PV power for the 20 MW PV power plant. In general, the highest observed RRs yielded with the modeled PV powers were quite different from the measured PV power. This is reasonable as the fastest

10.4229/EUPVSEC2025/5DV.3.3

Table III: Highest observed upward and downward power RRs during 1 s for the 0.5 MW, 6 MW, 10 MW and 20 MW PV power plants with the measured and modeled PV powers.

	0.5 MW		6 MW		10 MW		20 MW	
	Up	Down	Up	Down	Up	Down	Up	Down
Measured power (%/min)	1196.5	1369.1	416.8	340.0	280.5	251.1	200.4	223.9
R2021 (%/min)	372.7	395.6	250.4	254.0	228.7	231.5	140.4	142.7
M2011 (%/min)	235.1	225.5	37.0	30.4	21.7	19.3	11.6	9.8
AIM (%/min)	360.0	378.5	194.6	193.3	160.1	159.3	104.5	106.0
WVM (%/min)	329.9	346.9	234.1	245.0	214.5	223.8	179.1	185.7

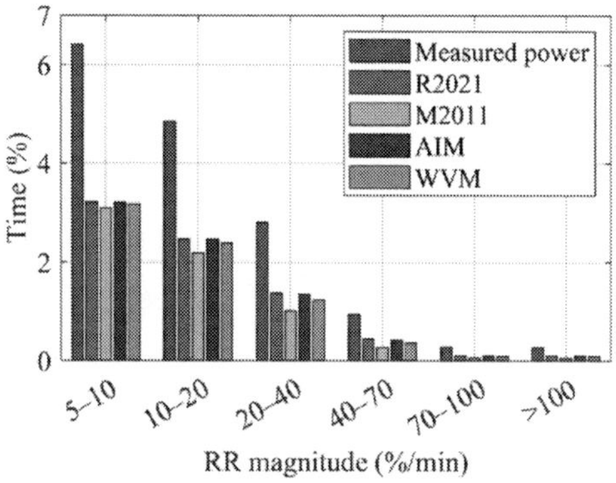

Figure 6: Distribution of the power RRs that exceeded 5 %/min during 1 s time windows for the measured and modeled PV power of the 0.5 MW PV power plant.

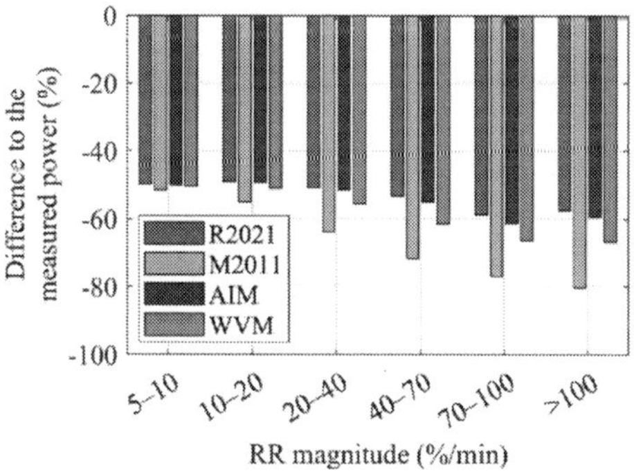

Figure 7: Differences in the power RR distributions of the modeled PV power and the measured PV power of the 0.5 MW PV power plant.

power fluctuations of the measured PV power are extreme occasions, and it is very challenging to model them reliably using only single point irradiance measurements.

When comparing the highest RRs of the measured irradiance and the measured PV power of the 0.5 MW PV power plant, those of the measured PV power were more extreme than those of the measured irradiance. The highest observed irradiance RRs during 1 s in [17] and [18] were 3840 %/min and 4230 %/min, respectively, which are significantly larger than the one recorded in this study. In [17], the highest observed irradiance RR during 10 s was 408 %/min. In this study, the highest observed upward and downward RRs during 10 s for the measured irradiance were 378.6 %/min and 393.0 %/min, respectively. These values are well in line with the corresponding value of [17] (408 %/min). For the measured PV power of the 0.5 MW PV power plant, the highest observed power RRs during 10 s were 474.0 %/min and 456.8 %/min, respectively for the upward and downward RRs. When comparing the highest irradiance RRs observed in this study and in [17] and [18], the PV power plant location may have caused the major difference in the values — the locations of the PV power plants studied in [17] and [18] may produce extreme irradiance transitions depending on the highest cloud optical depth, highest speed of cloud formation, and/or highest cloud speed at the site.

However, there may be also other factors considering the highest irradiance RRs observed between these studies. One factor could be the different irradiance measurement and data collection devices. The use of reference cells for measuring irradiance might not enable capturing the fastest irradiance transitions in contrast to the pyranometers used in [18]. The sampling rate used for the irradiance measurements is likely to affect the variability of the recorded irradiance as well. In [19], a sampling rate of 0.1 s was used for the irradiance measurements, and the highest observed upward and downward irradiance RRs during 1 s were 22296 %/min and 19554 %/min, respectively. These values are significantly larger than the corresponding ones of [17] and [18] which both had a sampling rate of 1 s for the irradiance measurements.

The reason why the highest RRs of the measured PV power were extreme in contrast to the measured irradiance, is that the operation of the inverter, especially the MPPT algorithm, may have escalated some of the fastest power ramps. This effect was the strongest with the 0.5 MW PV power plant, as it had only 1 inverter, whereas the studied larger PV power plants had multiple inverters. An example of the fast power ramps that are likely caused by the inverter can be seen in Fig. 3 roughly at 13:45 and 13:46. However, the highest observed power RRs of the 0.5 MW PV power plant are in line with the fastest observed power RRs of the 0.143 MW and 0.958 MW PV power plants studied in [17] (1980 %/min and 600 %/min, respectively).

Figs. 6, 8, 9 and 10 present the distributions of the power RRs that exceeded 5 %/min during 1 s time windows for the measured and modeled PV powers of the 0.5 MW, 6 MW, 10 MW and 20 MW PV power plants, respectively. Figs. 7 and 11 present the differences in the power RR distributions of the modeled and measured PV power for the 0.5 MW and 20 MW PV power plants, respectively. Fig. 6 shows that the measured PV power had significantly more power RRs that exceeded the RR magnitude level of 5 %/min compared to the modeled PV powers for the 0.5 MW PV power plant. One reason that caused this difference can be explained by the shadows of

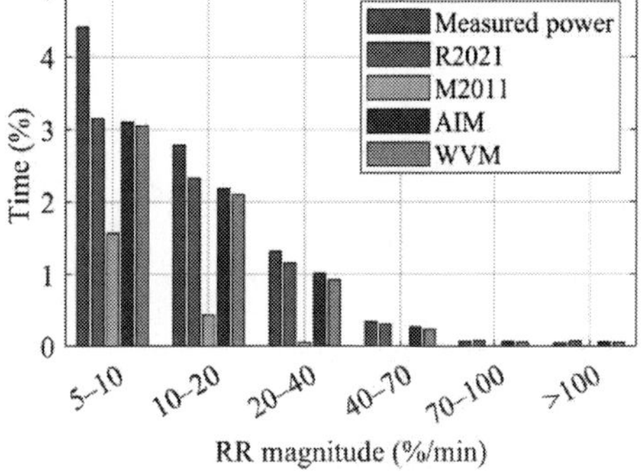

Figure 8: Distribution of the power RRs that exceeded 5 %/min during 1 s time windows for the measured and modeled PV power of the 6 MW PV power plant.

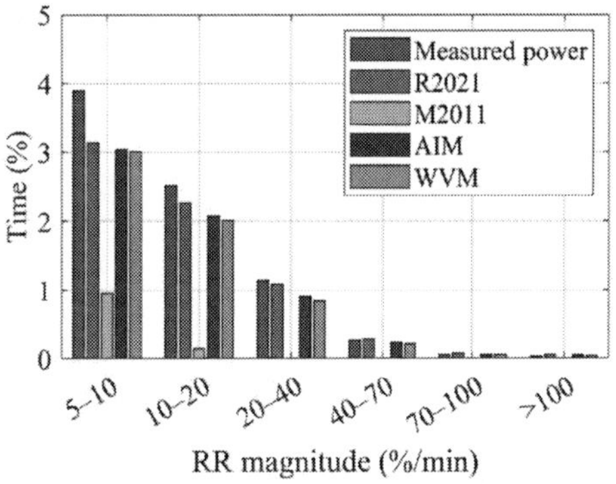

Figure 9: Distribution of the power RRs that exceeded 5 %/min during 1 s time windows for the measured and modeled PV power of the 10 MW PV power plant.

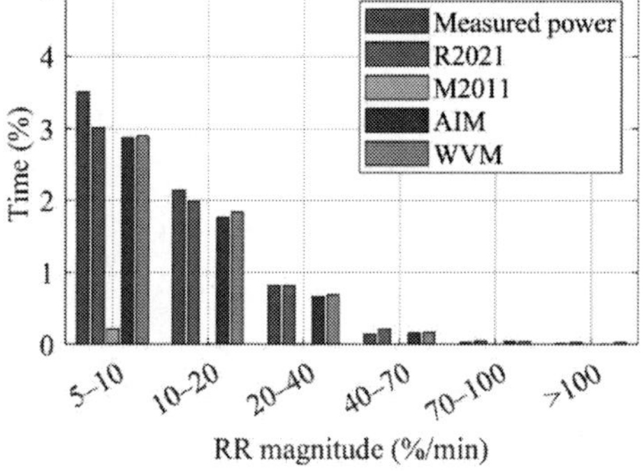

Figure 10: Distribution of the power RRs that exceeded 5 %/min during 1 s time windows for the measured and modeled PV power of the 20 MW PV power plant.

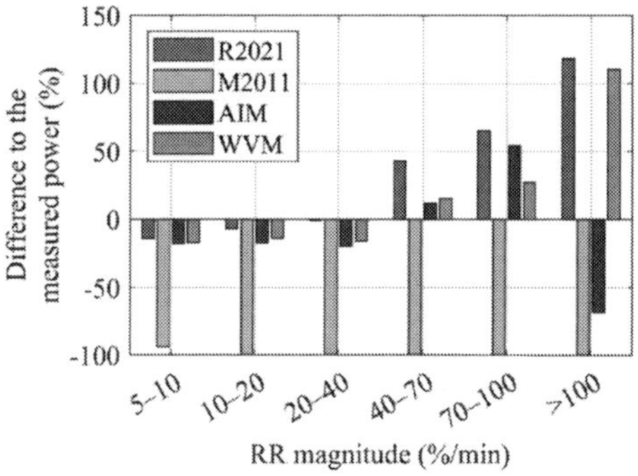

Figure 11: Differences in the power RR distributions of the modeled PV power and the measured PV power of the 20 MW PV power plant.

small clouds that covered the PV power plant partially but did not cover the reference cell. The shadows of small clouds can cause significant power fluctuations for a small PV power plant, but for a larger PV power plant, their effect is not as strong. The power RR distributions for the modeled PV powers of the 0.5 MW PV power plant were similar to each other. Considering Figs. 6 and 7, the values of the M2011 method were smaller in contrast to the other methods, and the difference to the other methods gradually increased with increasing RR magnitude.

Figs. 8 and 9 show that the distributions of the power RRs of the R2021, AIM and WVM methods were quite similar with those of the measured PV power for the 6 MW and 10 MW PV power plants. The distributions of the methods were also very similar to each other. The reason why the total amounts of power RRs that exceeded the RR magnitude of 5 %/min were lower for the 6 MW and 10 MW PV power plants than for the 0.5 MW PV power plant is that the PV power fluctuations become smoother with increasing PV power plant size [5]. This effect can be seen also when comparing the results of the 20 MW PV power plant (Fig. 10) to the results of the smaller PV power plants. The M2011 method differed clearly from the other methods. Considering the results of Figs. 8 and 9, the R2021 method yielded the closest results to the measured PV power. The R2021, AIM and WVM methods slightly overestimated the amount of power RRs above the RR magnitude of 70 %/min with the 6 MW and 10 MW PV power plants. An interesting finding is that even the RR distributions of the R2021, AIM and WVM methods did not change that much between the 6 MW and 10 MW PV power plants, the RR distribution of the M2011 method changed significantly.

Figs. 10 and 11 show that the R2021, AIM and WVM methods modeled the measured PV power of the 20 MW PV power plant quite accurately when the RR magnitude was smaller than 70 %/min. With larger RR magnitudes, the relative difference to the RR distribution of the measured PV power started to increase with the R2021, AIM and WVM methods. The R2021 method performed best for RR magnitudes below 40 %/min, the AIM method performed best for RR range from 40 to 70 %/min and the WVM method performed best for RR magnitudes above 70 %/min. The RR distribution of the M2011 method was far off the RR distribution of the measured PV power.

Considering all the results presented, the M2011 performed the worst among the methods studied. With the 0.5 MW PV power plant, the results of the M2011 method were similar to the results of the other methods to some extent. However, for the larger PV power plants, the difference between the M2011 method and the other methods grew significantly. It seems that the smoothed irradiance produced with the M2011 is oversmoothed. Oversmoothing of the measured irradiance can be seen also in Fig. 3. Oversmoothing of the irradiance using the M2011 method was suspected also in [4]. The M2011 method may perform better when long-term variability of

PV power is considered, as stated in [7]. It can be concluded that the M2011 method should not be used to model PV power when the short-term variability and the highest RRs of PV power are of importance, for example in studies of smoothing PV power fluctuations by energy storage systems.

Considering all results, overall the R2021 method performed the best. However, the WVM method performed slightly better than the R2021 method when considering the RR magnitudes larger than 70 %/min with the 10 MW and 20 MW PV power plants. This means that the WVM method might be the best one among these methods to estimate the highest power RRs of large-scale PV power plants. The AIM method yielded surprisingly accurate results in contrast to the other methods and measured PV power, even though the AIM method is fundamentally the simplest and the easiest to implement among the studied methods. This means that the AIM method is a solid choice when simplicity and low computing time are the desired features.

All methods except for M2011 depend on the cloud speed. Neglecting cloud formation and dissipation, PV power ramps are caused by the translation of cloud shadows across the PV plant area (or vice versa). If the cloud is large enough, this movement transitions the PV plant from a completely unshaded to a completely shaded condition with the time between the states derived from the ratio of PV plant length in the direction of cloud motion (x) divided by the cloud speed (v). The ramp rate is then given by RR = $(P_{\text{clear}} - P_{\text{cloudy}})\ v\ /\ x$, where P_{cloudy} mostly depends on the optical depth of the cloud. This equation shows that the RR is directly proportional to the cloud speed. In this study for simplicity a constant cloud speed of v = 23 m / s is used. However, in the real world cloud speeds vary with atmospheric wind speeds [20]. Therefore, especially extreme RRs are expected to occur under conditions of extreme cloud speeds. Therefore, in this paper the modeled maximum RRs are likely underestimated as a result of the constant cloud speed assumption.

The days excluded from the study due to power management / curtailment may have contained periods during which the measured irradiance or the measured PV powers could have fluctuated with higher RRs than those reported. It should be noted that actual PV power plants are likely to yield higher power RRs than the ones reported here because of power management.

4 CONCLUSIONS

This paper estimated PV power variability using PV power modeling methods that can be executed using single point irradiance measurement. The study was executed using the measured irradiance and PV power data of 1 s temporal resolution, thus creating an accurate basis for studying PV power variability. The study period consisted of 89 days. The highest observed power RRs, distributions of the RRs by the RR magnitude and power graphs of the methods were analyzed.

It was found that there can be significant differences between the measured and the modeled PV powers when the highest observed RRs and the RR distributions are considered. Moreover, there can be a significant difference between the different PV power modeling methods. It was found that the R2021 method performed best among the studied methods. The M2011 method performed the worst. The results of this study are valuable for future research into mitigation of PV power variability as well as for planning and sizing of PV power plants and their energy storage systems.

ACKNOWLEDGMENTS

M. Talvi was funded by KAUTE foundation and Business Finland (grant number 1191/31/2022) and K. Lappalainen was funded by the Research Council of Finland (funding decision 348701).

REFERENCES

[1] International Energy Agency, 2024. Available online: https://www.iea.org/reports/renewables-2024 (accessed on 23.8.2025).

[2] K. Lappalainen, J. Kleissl, Proceedings of the 40th European Photovoltaic Solar Energy Conference and Exhibition, Vol. I (2023) 020522. https://doi.org/10.4229/EUPVSEC2023/5DV.2.6.

[3] V. Gevorgian, S. Booth, National Renewable Energy Laboratory Technical Report (2013), NREL/TP-5D00-57089.

[4] M. Talvi, K. Lappalainen, Proceedings of the 41st European Photovoltaic Solar Energy Conference and Exhibition, Vol. I (2024) 020510. https://doi.org/10.4229/EUPVSEC2024/5DV.2.4.

[5] J. Marcos, L. Marroyo, E. Lorenzo, D. Alvira, E. Izco, Progress in Photovoltaics: Research and Applications 19 (2011) 505. https://doi.org/10.1002/pip.1063.

[6] M. Lave, J. Kleissl, J. S. Stein, IEEE Transactions on Sustainable Energy 4 (2013) 501. https://doi.org/10.1109/TSTE.2012.2205716.

[7] J. Ranalli, E.E.M. Peerlings, Journal of Renewable and Sustainable Energy 13 (2021) 033704. https://doi.org/10.1063/5.0050428.

[8] D. Torres Lobera, A. Mäki, J. Huusari, K. Lappalainen, T. Suntio, S. Valkealahti, International Journal of Photoenergy 2013 (2013) 837310. https://doi.org/10.1155/2013/837310.

[9] First Solar FS Series 2 PV Module. Available online: https://www.firstsolar.com/Resources/Downloads (accessed on 26.8.2025).

[10] J.L. Bosch, J. Kleissl, Solar Energy 95 (2013) 13. https://doi.org/10.1016/j.solener.2013.05.027.

[11] CustomWeather, Inc. https://customweather.com/. (accessed on 22.5.2025).

[12] Google Earth (2025) https://earth.google.com/web/ (accessed on 24.8.2025).

[13] K. Lappalainen, J. Kleissl, Journal of Renewable and Sustainable Energy 12 (2020) 043502. https://doi.org/10.1063/5.0007550.

[14] K. Anderson, C. Hansen, W. Holmgren, A. Jensen, M. Mikofski, A. Driesse, Journal of Open Source Software 8 (2023) 5994, https://doi.org/10.21105/joss.05994.

[15] R.P. Kenny, E.D. Dunlop, H.A. Ossenbrink, H. Müllejans, Progress in Photovoltaics: Research and Applications 14 (2006) 155. https://doi.org/10.1002/pip.658.

[16] E. Skoplaki, J.A. Palyvos, Solar Energy 83 (2009) 614. https://doi.org/10.1016/j.solener.2008.10.008.

[17] J. Marcos, L. Marroyo, E. Lorenzo, D. Alvira, E. Izco, Progress in Photovoltaic Research and Applications 19 (2011) 218. https://doi.org/10.1002/pip.1016.
[18] T. Tomson, Solar Energy 84 (2010) 318. http://dx.doi.org/10.1016/j.solener.2009.11.013.
[19] K. Lappalainen, S. Valkealahti, Solar Energy 112 (2015) 55. https://doi.org/10.1016/j.solener.2014.11.018.
[20] M. Lave, J. Kleissl, Solar Energy 91 (2013) 11. https://doi.org/10.1016/j.solener.2013.01.023.

Tampere University

UC San Diego

ESTIMATING PHOTOVOLTAIC POWER RAMP RATES USING SINGLE POINT IRRADIANCE MEASUREMENT

Micke Talvi and Kari Lappalainen — **Tampere University, Electrical Engineering**
Jan Kleissl — **University of California, San Diego**

Data and methods

- Single point irradiance measurements were used to simulate produced photovoltaic (PV) power. The temperature correction was considered.
- 4 PV power modeling methods were compared:
  - Method proposed by Ranalli and Peerlings 2021 ("R2021")
  - Method proposed by Marcos et al. 2011 ("M2011")
  - Average irradiance method (AIM)
  - Method proposed by Lave et al. 2013 (wavelet variability model, WVM)
- Measured PV power of 48 MW Copper Mountain Solar 1 PV Plant at Boulder City, Nevada
- Simulation period of 4 months: March–June of 2012 (89 days)
- Measurements of PV power productions and plane of array irradiance with a 1 s time resolution

Table I: *Parameter values used for the simulations.*

Typical cloud speed	23 m/s
Typical movement direction of cloud shadows	49.5° (north-east-ward)
Normal operating cell temperature	45 °C
Temperature coefficient of power	−0.25 %/°C

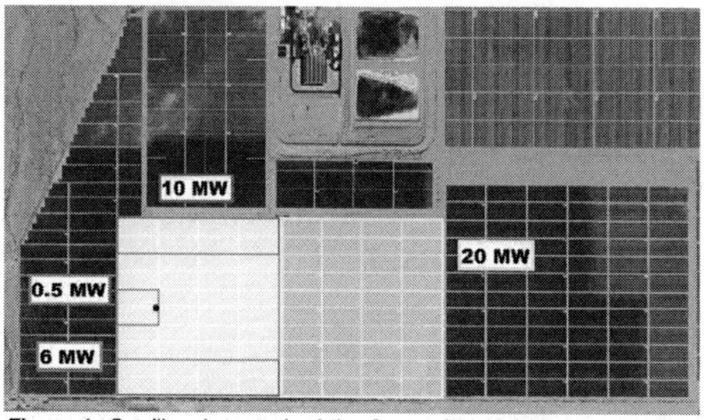

Figure 1: *Satellite photograph of the Copper Mountain Solar 1 PV Plant indicating the imaginary PV power plants and their nominal powers with rectangles. The black dot indicates the location of the irradiance measurement.*

Results

- The main quantities investigated were the highest observed power ramp rates (RR) and the distribution of the power RRs.
- The measured PV power had periods during which it was regulated, these days were excluded. The sharp ramps in measured power were caused by changing conditions and operation of the inverter (Fig. 2).
- The smoothed irradiance produced with the M2011 method is oversmoothed (Fig. 2).

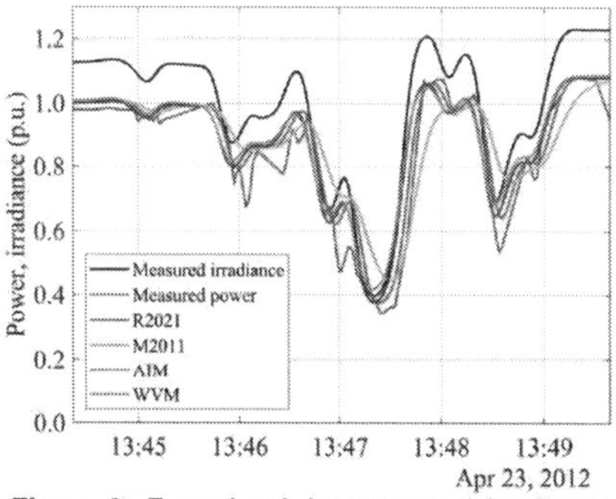

Figure 2: *Example of the measured irradiance, the measured PV power and the modeled PV powers during a highly fluctuating period for the 0.5 MW PV power plant.*

- On overall, the R2021 method performed best. The WVM method might be better than the R2021 method when larger PV power plants are considered.
- The M2011 method performed worst. The AIM method yielded surprisingly accurate results, even though it is fundamentally simple and very easy to implement.

Table II: *The highest observed upward and downward power RRs during 1 s for the 0.5 MW, 6 MW, 10 MW and 20 MW PV power plants with the measured and modeled PV powers.*

	0.5 MW		6 MW		10 MW		20 MW	
	Up	Down	Up	Down	Up	Down	Up	Down
Measured power (%/min)	1196.5	1369.1	416.8	340.0	280.5	251.1	200.4	223.9
R2021 (%/min)	372.7	395.6	250.4	254.0	228.7	231.5	140.4	142.7
M2011 (%/min)	235.1	225.5	37.0	30.4	21.7	19.3	11.8	9.8
AIM (%/min)	360.0	370.5	194.6	193.3	160.1	159.3	104.5	106.0
WVM (%/min)	329.9	346.9	234.1	245.0	214.5	223.8	179.1	185.7

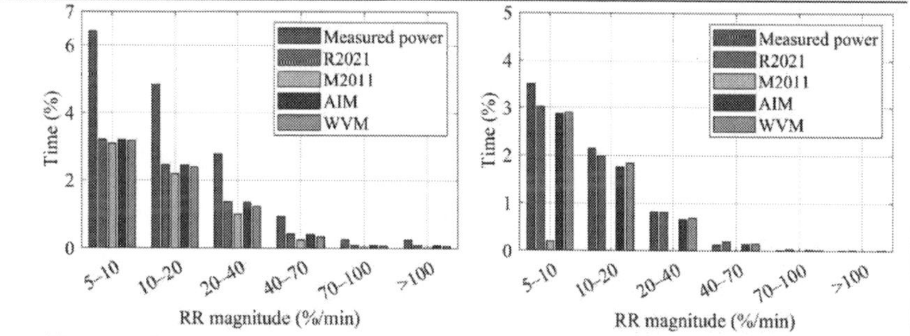

Figure 3: *Distributions of the power RRs that exceeded 5 %/min during 1 s time windows for the measured and modeled PV power of the 0.5 MW (left) and 20 MW (right) PV power plants.*

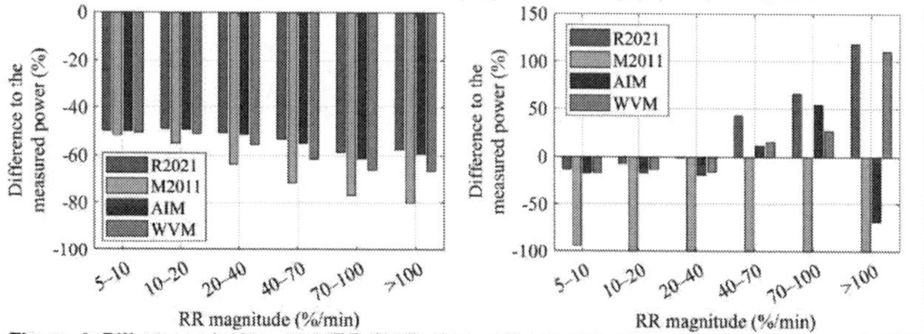

Figure 4: *Differences in the power RR distributions of the modeled PV power and the measured PV power of the 0.5 MW (left) and 20 MW (right) PV power plants.*

Conclusions

- There can be significant differences among the PV power modeling methods, and in contrast to the measured PV power, when the variability of PV power is considered.
- The R2021 method performed the best, and the M2011 method performed the worst.

Related journal articles

- M. Talvi, T. Roinila, K. Lappalainen, Energies 16 (2023) 4313. https://doi.org/10.3390/en16114313.
- K. Lappalainen, S. Valkealahti, Renewable Energy 196 (2022) 1366–1375. https://doi.org/10.1016/j.renene.2022.07.069.

Contact information

- M.Sc. Micke Talvi
- Doctoral Researcher
- Tampere University, Finland
- **micke.talvi@tuni.fi**

OPTIMIZING HYBRID WIND-SOLAR PLANTS IN BRAZIL: ADDRESSING CURTAILMENT AND CONSTRAINED-OFF CHALLENGES

Letícia Vasconcelos[1, a)], *Luiz Reis*[1, b)], *Lúcio Paiva*[1, c)], *Luis Castro*[1, d)] *and Rodrigo Santos*[1, e)]

[1]*Casa dos Ventos Energias Renováveis*

[a)]*leticia. bezerra@casadosventos. com. br*

[b)]*luiz. reis@casadosventos. com. br*

[c)]*lucio. paiva@casadosventos. com. br*

[d)]*guilherme. castro@casadosventos. com. br*

[e)]*rodrigo. raimundo@casadosventos. com. br*

Hybrid wind-solar plants in Brazil offer significant advantages due to resource complementarity and shared infrastructure. However, their operation faces two key power generation restrictions. The first is curtailment, an internal power reduction to respect contracted transmission limits when combined output is high, typically affecting the solar plant. The second, constrained-off, is a less predictable reduction imposed by the National Electric System Operator (ONS) due to systemic grid constraints, severely impacting the project's economic viability and revenue predictability. This article presents a methodology to analyze the combined impact of curtailment and constrained-off on the optimal sizing of a solar plant in a hybrid complex. Through a case study of a new photovoltaic plant being added to an existing wind farm, we calculate and compare the resulting generation losses across different installed capacity scenarios to support decision-making.

Keywords: hybrid power plants, curtailment, constrained-off, sizing optimization, grid integration

1 INTRODUCTION

1.1 The Context of Brazil's Energy Transition

Brazil is in a decisive phase of its energy transition, seeking to diversify its electricity matrix beyond traditional sources. In this scenario, the expansion of power generation from unconventional renewable sources has gained significant prominence. The first large-scale wind farms were implemented around 2007, followed by the first large solar photovoltaic plants in mid-2015. This expansion has been driven by the abundance of these resources in the country and the need to increase the security and sustainability of the energy supply. In 2024, according to [1], wind and solar sources accounted for 14.1% and 9.3% of the internal electricity supply, respectively.

The growing penetration of these renewable sources, however, introduces significant challenges for the operation of the National Interconnected System (SIN). The SIN is a complex and massive transmission grid, according to [2], with over 174,000 kilometers of transmission lines and substations with a combined capacity of over 414 GVA in 2024. For reference, the sections connecting Porto Alegre and Manaus are equivalent to interconnecting Lisbon, Portugal, and Stockholm, Sweden, as shown in Figure 1, which was extracted from [3].

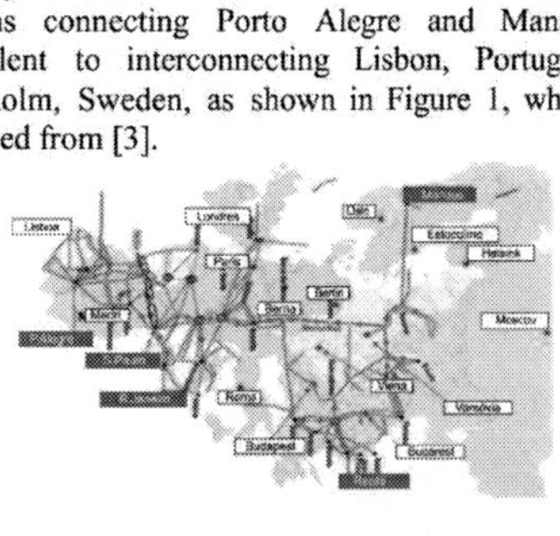

Figure 1: Brazil-Europe Comparison. Source: [3]

Operating an electrical system on this scale is inherently complex, requiring continuous effort to ensure reliability and continuity. In the context of the urgent transition to a cleaner energy matrix, this complexity is heightened by the intermittency of wind and solar sources and the uncontrollability of Micro and Mini Distributed Generation (MMDG) plants. The growth of MMDG is reshaping grid behavior, with daytime solar production leading to a high supply of generation. This shifts the net demand peak to the early evening, a new challenge that, without proper management, can lead to systemic constraints such as constrained-off during peak generation hours. Given this context, the electricity sector has sought solutions that maximize the economic efficiency of generation and transmission assets. This is where the association of different generation sources in the same project becomes a strategic alternative.

1.2 The Rise of Hybrid Wind-Solar Power Plants

In Brazil, energy generation projects that exploit more than one source, such as wind and solar, were only regulated in 2021 through Normative Resolution (REN) 954/2021, [4], established by the National Electric Energy Agency (ANEEL). This resolution defined four ways to associate power plants with different generation sources that share the same connection point in the SIN.

Among these modalities, the possibility of connecting a new plant to an existing one stands out, allowing the sharing of the transmission system usage contract. In this case, the Transmission System Usage Amount (MUST) must be defined between the total installed power of the largest plant and the sum of the installed power of both plants. This enables the addition of a new plant with a fraction of the installed power of the existing one, without the need to contract additional transmission capacity.

Given this regulatory scenario, the association between wind and solar plants has become an attractive

10.4229/EUPVSEC2025/5DV.3.6

business model, especially in regions with good resource complementarity. Since wind generation occurs predominantly at night, adding a smaller solar plant to an existing wind farm brings significant advantages compared to operating only the wind plant.

Among the main benefits are: optimized energy delivery to the grid, reduced uncertainties, and lower modulation costs for flat energy supply ; financial gains from sharing transmission system usage contracts and common infrastructure ; and more efficient use of the transmission system, which reduces operational costs.

1.3 The Problem: Generation Constraints

The variability of wind and solar resources can lead to situations where combined generation exceeds the capacity of the substation and the contracted transmission limits. To avoid surpassing these limits, it becomes necessary to reduce the generation of one of the sources, a process known as curtailment. Typically, solar plants are more affected, as interrupting wind turbines is more complex. A high curtailment rate is undesirable, as it directly impacts solar energy production. Thus, the optimal sizing of the solar plant requires rigorous analysis to minimize power reductions and uncertainties.

Additionally, the growth of MMGD has changed the electrical system's demand profile in recent years. Previously, the system experienced a rapid increase in demand between 2 PM and 4 PM. However, with the high penetration of MMGD , this period now shows a demand valley. Peak demand, however, still occurs after 6 PM, a factor that has contributed to the increase in constrained-off events, as highlighted in [5].

According to ANEEL Normative Resolutions REN 1030/2022 and REN 1073/2022 [6], [7], constrained-off is defined as the forced reduction of generation from centrally dispatched wind plants or wind plant clusters included in the scheduling by the National Electric System Operator (ONS) due to external factors unrelated to the plants. These events occur for three main reasons: external unavailability, when essential transmission equipment, such as transmission lines, transformers, and circuit breakers, are out of operation; compliance with electrical reliability requirements, when the system cannot operate normally due to technical limitations of equipment or transmission lines; and energy-related reasons, when generation must be reduced due to low system demand.

The ONS is responsible for notifying plants about the need of power reductions. In cases of constrained-off due to unavailability or reliability, the reduction affects plants located in the interference region. For energy-related constrained-off, priority is given to constrained-off where the economic impact on consumers is minimized. Since there are no well-defined regulatory criteria for selecting which plants will have their generation reduced, constrained-off is a much less predictable event than curtailment.

1.4 Objective of the Study

Given this scenario, new associations of solar plants with wind farms that already face constrained-off make the sizing of the solar plant even more challenging. The solar plant will be subject to two types of generation restriction: curtailment, applied to photovoltaic generation when the total power exceeds the MUST, and constrained-off, imposed by the ONS. In view of this, the article addresses the optimization of a solar plant in a hybrid complex, presenting a case study with different scenarios of installed solar power to analyze how curtailment and constrained-off impact the decision on the size of the solar plant.

2 METODOLOGY

2.1 Case Study Description

The objective of this study is to analyze the impact of grid operational constraints, such as curtailment and constrained-off events, on the performance of a large-scale hybrid wind-solar power plant. The base case consists of a wind plant with an installed capacity of 817 MW associated with a solar photovoltaic (PV) power plant.

To determine the optimal configuration of the solar component, its installed alternating current (AC) capacity is parameterized, varying from 50 MW to 500 MW in 50 MW increments. For each capacity level, the analysis explores different inverter loading scenarios by evaluating a DC/AC ratio ranging from 1.052 to 1.333. This approach allows for an investigation into how both the injection capacity (MWac) and the PV array sizing (MWp) influence the technical and financial outcomes under operational constraint conditions.

2.2 Data Source

The generation assets analyzed are pre-operational projects. Consequently, the electricity generation time series for the wind source was obtained through computational simulations based on references [8] and [9], which provided hourly production estimates. The solar time series was generated using the PVsyst software. To simulate the impact of operational constraints, historical constrained-off data from an existing hybrid wind-solar plant already in operation within the SIN was used. This data was collected directly from the ONS open data portal. The selection of this reference asset was based on its systemic proximity to the project under analysis, with its connection point located in the fourth electrical neighborhood of the target substation, which indicates a network relevance and a similar technical behavior.

The data used for the simulation covers a full one-year period, from September 1, 2024, to August 31, 2025. The analysis methodology does not forecast future changes in the constrained-off profile. The dataset did not require any handling of missing data, as no gaps were identified within the analyzed period.

2.3 Simulation and Analysis Process

The simulation process was designed to quantify two distinct layers of generation constraints: constrained-off, a physical limitation imposed by the grid, and curtailment, a contractual restriction. The methodology applies a historical constraint profile from a reference plant to the potential generation of the hybrid project under analysis.

2.3.1 Step 1: Determining the Grid Export Factor

Considering that constrained-off represents the grid's inability to export generated energy, the first step is to derive a "Grid Export Factor" from the reference plant's data. This factor normalizes the grid's export capacity relative to the reference asset's installed capacity. To prevent the factor from being skewed by non-grid-related outages (e.g., scheduled maintenance), it is calculated exclusively for time intervals where constrained-off events were recorded.

A single, unified Grid Export Factor (*ref_hybrid_export_factor*) is calculated for all periods. This factor is defined as the ratio of the total actual generation (wind + solar) from the reference plant to the total installed capacity of the reference complex. This ensures that the factor consistently represents the overall grid's export capability, regardless of the time of day.

2.3.2 Step 2: Simulating Constrained-off on the Target Project

This unified export factor is then transferred to the project under analysis to estimate the dynamic power injection limit (*estimated_grid_limit_kW*) at the target substation. The application of this factor is conditional on the target plant's operational state to correctly scale the limit.

During periods with solar generation: The limit is calculated by multiplying the *ref_hybrid_export_factor* by the total installed capacity of the target hybrid complex (wind + solar).

During periods without solar generation: The limit is calculated by multiplying the same *ref_hybrid_export_factor* by the installed capacity of only the wind component of the target plant.

The hybrid plant's generation after this grid constraint (*hybrid_production_after_cof_kW*) is defined as the minimum value between its potential generation (*hybrid_potential_kW*) and the estimated grid limit. The amount of energy not injected due to this constraint is quantified as constrained-off (*coff_kW*).

2.3.3 Step 3: Pro-rata Allocation of Constrained-off

Once the total constrained-off amount (*coff_kW*) is determined, it is allocated between the wind and solar sources. The allocation follows the principle of equal treatment for sources of the same priority, as detailed in [10]. Since wind and solar sources share the same hierarchical priority in restriction-based dispatch, the cut is proportionally distributed based on the potential generation of each technology at the moment of the constraint, as shown in the equations below:

$$\text{wind\_ratio} = \frac{\text{wind\_potential\_kW}}{\text{hybrid\_potential\_kW}}$$

$$\text{solar\_ratio} = \frac{\text{solar\_potential\_kW}}{\text{hybrid\_potential\_kW}}$$

$$\text{coff\_wind\_kW} = \text{coff\_kW} \times \text{wind\_ratio}$$

$$\text{coff\_solar\_kW} = \text{coff\_kW} \times \text{solar\_ratio}$$

The final generation of each source after constrained-off is the difference between its potential generation and the allocated cut.

2.3.4 Step 4: Applying the Contractual Limit (MUST)

The total plant generation, already adjusted for constrained-off (*hybrid_production_after_cof_kW*), is then subjected to the contracted transmission system usage limit (MUST), which for this study corresponds to the installed capacity of the wind component (817 MW).

The surplus amount, defined as curtailment (*curtailment_kW*), is entirely allocated to the solar component of the hybrid complex, which is a premise of the project's business model.

The methodology used is summarized in the following flowchart.

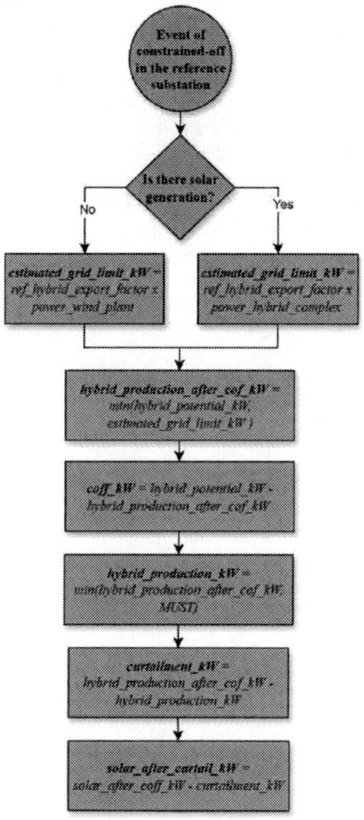

Figure 2: Flowchart of the constrained-off and curtailment calculation process

2.4 Analysis Metrics

Based on the calculated results for constrained-off, affecting both wind and solar sources, and for curtailment, applied exclusively to the solar generation, the following metrics are calculated to analyze and compare the scenarios:

$$\text{solar\_coff\_loss} = \frac{\text{coff\_solar\_kW}}{\text{solar\_potential\_kW}}$$

$$\text{wind\_coff\_loss} = \frac{\text{coff\_wind\_kW}}{\text{wind\_potential\_kW}}$$

$$\text{solar\_curtail\_loss} = \frac{\text{curtailment\_kW}}{\text{solar\_after\_coff\_kW}}$$

$$\text{solar\_total\_loss} = \frac{\text{curtailment\_kW} + \text{coff\_solar\_kW}}{\text{solar\_potential\_kW}}$$

$$\text{hybrid\_coff\_loss} = \frac{\text{coff\_kW}}{\text{hybrid\_potential\_kW}}$$

$$\text{hybrid\_total\_loss} = \frac{\text{coff\_kW} + \text{curtailment\_kW}}{\text{hybrid\_potential\_kW}}$$

3 RESULTS

3.1 Profile and Seasonality of Constrained-Off

10.4229/EUPVSEC2025/5DV.3.6

The analysis of historical data demonstrates that, despite the inherent uncertainty regarding future constrained-off levels for a plant at a specific point in the system, it is possible to identify clear patterns of days, times, and months with the highest curtailments. This occurs because constrained-off events for energy-related and reliability reasons are driven by surpluses of renewable generation, which coincide with the overlap between high wind production and the onset of solar production. Additionally, the lack of controllability of MMDG plants, which cannot be curtailed by the grid operator, also contributes to the high percentage of curtailment that solar energy experiences. Figure 3 illustrates the daily constrained-off profiles for the reference substation of this study, compared to the generation of the respective energy sources.

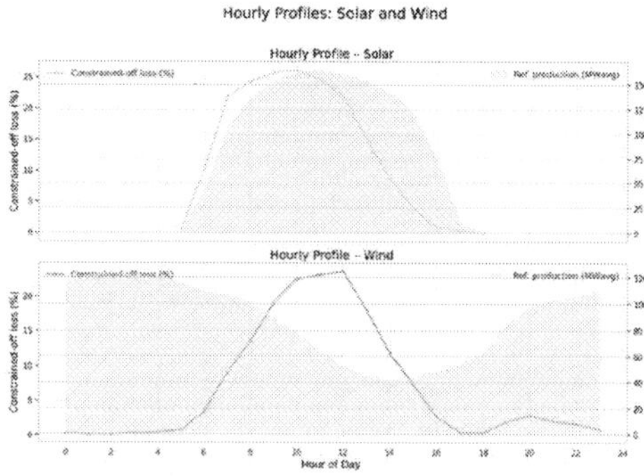

Figure 3: Hourly constrained-off profiles and potential solar and wind power generation of the reference hybrid plant.

The distribution of curtailments throughout the week can be explained by the consumption profile. Energy demand tends to be lower on weekends due to reduced consumption in factories and commercial units, which generates a surplus of generation and can lead to more constrained-off events for energy-related reasons. Figure 4 presents the hourly constrained-off profiles for each day of the week for the reference hybrid plant.

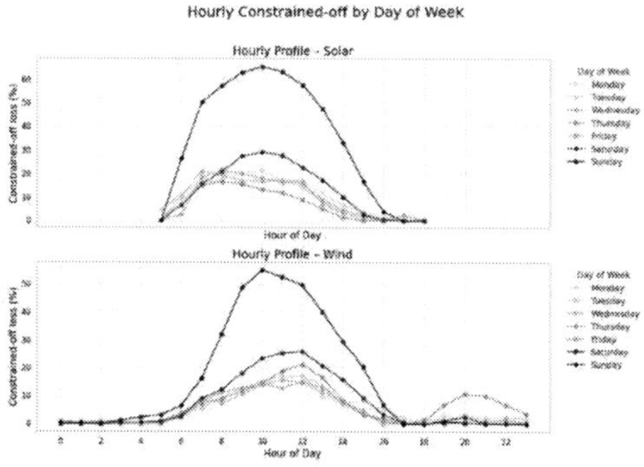

Figure 4: Hourly profiles of constrained-off for each day of the week of the reference hybrid plant.

The analysis of the monthly profile, presented in Figure 5, corroborates the conclusions from figures 3 and 4. It shows that the largest volumes of constrained-off occur in the months with high production, confirming that generation surpluses are the main cause of losses. This correlation between peaks in generation and peaks in operational restriction is consistent with the hourly dynamics already identified.

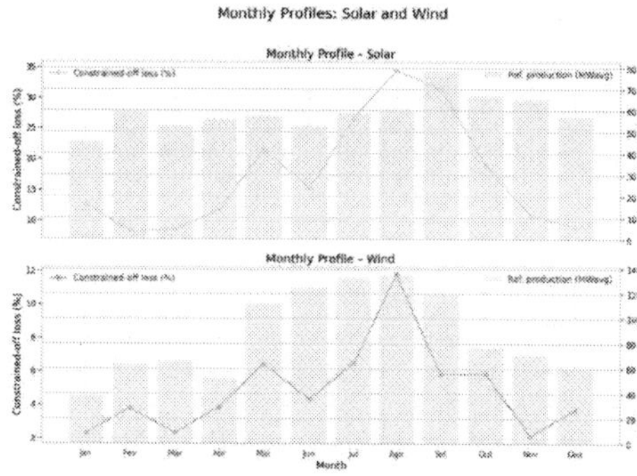

Figure 5: Monthly profiles of constrained-off and potential generation of solar and wind energy.

3.2 Quantitative Loss Analysis

The correlation between constrained-off events and moments of high generation is crucial for understanding the results presented. Given that curtailment events also occur during these peak generation periods, the overlap of both restrictions requires an integrated analysis. Evaluating losses in isolation, whether due to curtailment or constrained-off, can underestimate or distort the total loss profile, as one event can impact the other.

To demonstrate this effect, two simulations were conducted, both with a 200 MWac solar plant and the same DC/AC ratio. The first considered only curtailment events, assuming the absence of constrained-off. The second included the occurrence of both effects. Figure 6 illustrates the hourly and monthly loss profiles for each scenario. When comparing the curves, it is observed that the constrained-off loss in the second scenario absorbs a significant portion of the loss that, in the first scenario, would be categorized as curtailment in an isolated evaluation.

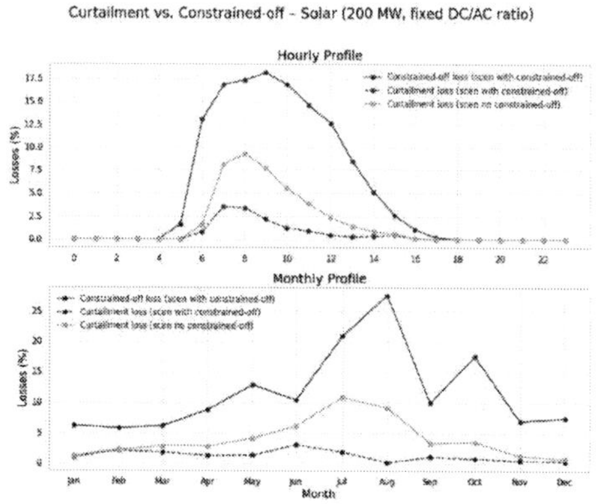

Figure 6: Comparison of loss profiles in a scenario that includes only curtailment versus a scenario that considers both events.

10.4229/EUPVSEC2025/5DV.3.6

4 DISCUSSION

4.1 Analysis of Results

The two types of generation restrictions, curtailment and constrained-off, behave in distinct ways due to their natures. Curtailment is a direct function of the plant's installed capacity in relation to its internal and contractual export capacities. On the other hand, constrained-off is a function of the regional or national grid state, imposed by the ONS due to external factors.

The result of this dynamic is evidenced in Figure 7, which presents the relationship between the installed capacity of the solar plant and the percentage of losses. The bottom curve, "Curtailment only," which considers only curtailment losses, shows an almost linear growth as solar capacity increases, reflecting the saturation of the internal export limit. In contrast, the top curve, "Effective total loss," which includes the effect of constrained-off, shows a less pronounced total loss growth. This highlights the main implication of the study: the resilience of larger-scale projects to constrained-off. Although they lose more energy in absolute terms due to this restriction, the percentage loss does not increase proportionally, making the risk more manageable compared to smaller projects.

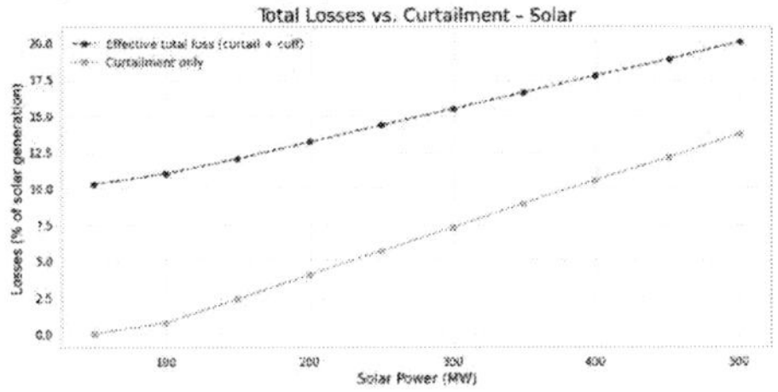

Figure 7: Comparison of losses in scenarios that include only curtailment versus scenarios that consider both events.

As expected, the total solar loss, which considers both curtailment and constrained-off, varies directly with the DC/AC ratio, as illustrated in Figure 8. The behavior of the curve for each DC/AC ratio is consistent, indicating that scenarios with higher photovoltaic panel overloads result in greater losses. This is due to a higher DC/AC ratio increasing the total generation of the hybrid complex, causing more curtailment or constrained-off events. The slope of the curves in the figure demonstrates that the increase in losses is more pronounced at higher solar capacities, confirming the need for a careful analysis when sizing the project.

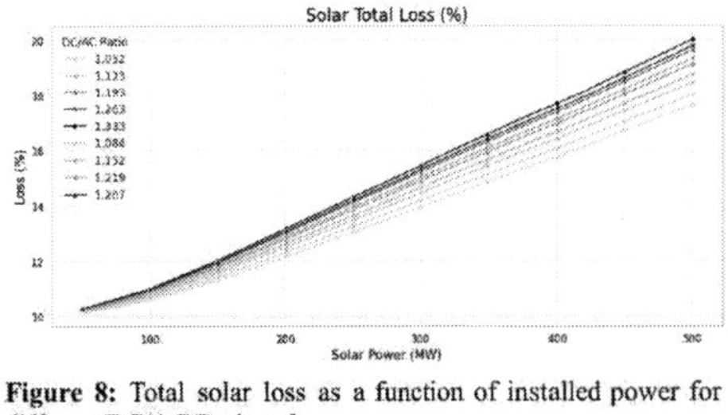

Figure 8: Total solar loss as a function of installed power for different DC/AC Ratio values.

Another crucial point for decision-making is the impact of increased constrained-off on the wind project, as detailed in Figure 9. Given that the *estimated_grid_limit_kW* depends on the total installed capacity of the hybrid complex, scenarios with higher solar capacity will result in a greater curtailment limit. This curtailment, when necessary, is apportioned between the two sources based on their potential generation at that moment. Although the increase in solar capacity may, in some cases, lead to more constrained-off events that affect the wind project, the percentage impact on wind production is minimal. It is even possible, in some cases, for the wind project to benefit if the increase in the *estimated_grid_limit_kW* is greater than the increment in photovoltaic generation, resulting in more headroom for wind energy export.

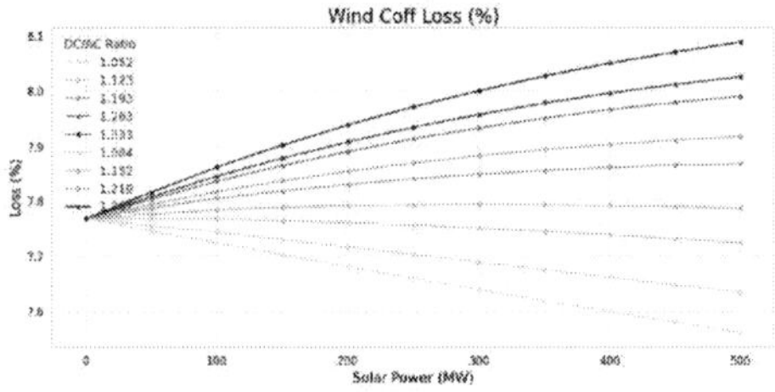

Figure 9: Wind constrained-off loss as a function of solar scale for different DC/AC Ratio values.

4.2 Implication for Investors

Figure 10 illustrates the impact of constrained-off on the economic viability of different solar project configurations, expressing the percentage difference in LCOE relative to a scenario that considers only curtailment. As expected, the LCOE is always higher when constrained-off is included, as the revenue loss from grid restrictions reduces the project's competitiveness. However, the analysis demonstrates that the increase in LCOE is less pronounced as the installed capacity of the solar plant grows. This trend suggests that, in scenarios with constrained-off risk, the ideal configuration points to larger solar capacities. This is due to the fact that larger-scale projects are able to dilute the losses caused by this effect more effectively, reducing the percentage impact on LCOE and making them more resilient to grid restrictions.

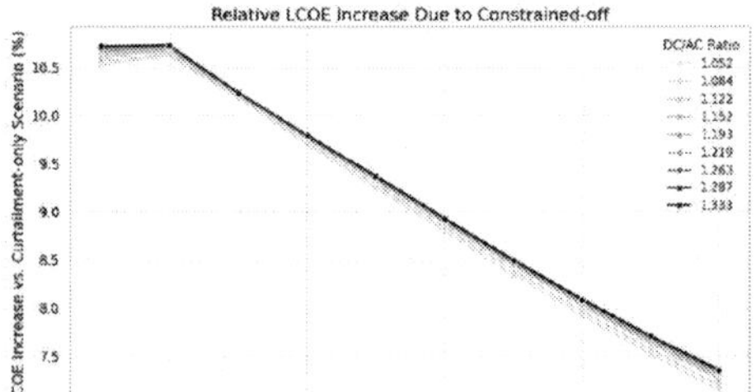

Figure 10: Percentage difference in LCOE between scenarios that consider only curtailment and scenarios that include the effects of constrained-off.

As constrained-off events often happen during the same periods, a portion of the energy that would have been lost to curtailment is instead attributed to constrained-off. This analysis underscores the importance of treating constrained-off as a key variable in the sizing and design phase, rather than merely a discount factor in a Power Purchase Agreement (PPA).

5 CONCLUSION

In a scenario with increasing grid operational restrictions, this study aimed to analyze the impact of total losses, comprising curtailment and constrained-off, on the optimal sizing of a solar plant associated with a wind farm. The results demonstrated that an isolated evaluation of each type of restriction can lead to erroneous conclusions, highlighting the importance of a methodology that integrates both effects for an accurate analysis.

The main contribution of this work is the clear demonstration that curtailment is intrinsically sensitive to project scale, growing as the installed solar capacity increases. In contrast, constrained-off losses are a function of the regional/national grid state and do not depend on the project scale to the same extent. Although larger-scale projects lose more energy in absolute terms due to constrained-off, the percentage impact on the total project is less pronounced, making larger projects more resilient and economically viable under these conditions.

For future work, it is suggested that the proposed methodology be applied to other regions of Brazil to verify how the constrained-off dynamic behaves in different subsystems of the electrical grid. Furthermore, the research can be enhanced by incorporating predictive models for constrained-off, aiming for greater analytical precision. Another important step would be to analyze the impact of energy storage solutions (batteries) to mitigate the effects of curtailment and constrained-off, thereby optimizing energy delivery and project profitability.

6 REFERENCES

[1] Empresa de Pesquisa Energética. (2025). *National energy balance 2025: Base year 2024*. Rio de Janeiro: EPE. Retrieved from https://www.epe.gov.br/sites-pt/publicacoes-dados-abertos/publicacoes/PublicacoesArquivos/publicacao-885/topico-771/Relat%C3%B3rio%20Final_BEN%202025.pdf

[2] Operador Nacional do Sistema Elétrico. (2024, December 27). *PARPEL Magazine* [2024 issue]. Rio de Janeiro: ONS. Retrieved from https://www.ons.org.br/AcervoDigitalDocumentosEPublicacoes/Revista%20PARPEL%20_2024_VF_27.12.24.pdf

[3] Oliveira, F. J. A. de (Ed.). (2020). *Energy operation planning in Brazil's National Interconnected System: Concepts, mathematical modeling, generation and load forecasting* [Portuguese: O planejamento da operação energética no Sistema Interligado Nacional: conceitos, modelagem matemática, previsão de geração e carga]. São Paulo: Artliber. Retrieved from https://www.ons.org.br/AcervoDigitalDocumentosEPublicacoes/O%20Planejamento%20da%20Operacao%20Energ%C3%A9tica%20no%20Sistema%20Interligado%20Nacional%20conceitos,%20modelagem%20matem%C3%A1tica,%20previs%C3%A3o%20de%20gera%C3%A7%C3%A3o%20e%20carga.pdf

[4] Agência Nacional de Energia Elétrica. (2021, November 30). *Normative Resolution No. 954/2021: Regulation of hybrid and associated power plants*. Brasília, DF: ANEEL. Retrieved from https://www2.aneel.gov.br/cedoc/ren2021954.html

[5] Operador Nacional do Sistema Elétrico. (2024, February). *Revista PARPEL* [Issue 2023-3]. Rio de Janeiro: ONS. Retrieved from https://www.ons.org.br/AcervoDigitalDocumentosEPublicacoes/Revista%20PARPEL%202023-3-Fev24%20VF.pdf

[6] Agência Nacional de Energia Elétrica. (2022, July 26). *Normative Resolution No. 1,030/2022: Consolidation of regulatory acts related to demand response, ancillary services, generation restrictions, and energy settlement mechanisms*. Brasília, DF: ANEEL. Retrieved from https://www2.aneel.gov.br/cedoc/ren20221030.pdf

[7] Agência Nacional de Energia Elétrica. (2023, September 12). *Normative Resolution No. 1,073/2023: Amendment to Normative Resolution No. 1,030/2022 regarding procedures for constrained-off of wind power plants*. Brasília, DF: ANEEL. https://www2.aneel.gov.br/cedoc/ren20231073.pdf

[8] Caldas, J., Delmiro, T., & Ferrer, V. (2022). *Time series energy calculation for wind power projects*. In *Proceedings of Brasil Windpower 2022*.

[9] Lazar, M., & Oliveira, D. (2022). *Long-term analysis and annual energy forecast for different wind measurement periods*. In *Proceedings of Brasil Windpower 2022*.

[10] Operador Nacional do Sistema Elétrico. (2019, August). *Submodule 26.2: Criteria for classification of power plants' operation modality* (Revision 2019.08, effective September 4, 2019). Rio de Janeiro: ONS. Retrieved from https://www.ons.org.br/ProcedimentosDeRede/Módulo%2026/Submódulo%2026.2/Submódulo%2026.2%202019.08.pdf

10.4229/EUPVSEC2025/5DV.3.6

Optimizing Hybrid Wind-Solar Plants in Brazil: Addressing Curtailment and Constrained-off Challenges

cdv desenvolvimento

Letícia Vasconcelos, Luiz Reis, Lúcio Paiva, Luis Castro and Rodrigo Santos

CdV Desenvolvimento

The overlap with curtailment reveals that constrained-off is a key variable in the design phase, not just a loss factor to be applied in the final feasibility analysis.

Abstract & Introduction

Brazil's energy transition presents challenges for grid operation. Hybrid wind-solar projects offer advantages but face two generation constraints: **curtailment** (internal limitation) and **constrained-off** (grid-imposed restriction). This work proposes a methodology to analyze the combined impact of both losses on the optimal sizing of solar projects associated with wind plants.

Methodology

Data Source: Historical constrained-off data from September 2024 to August 2025 of an operating hybrid plant in the SIN.

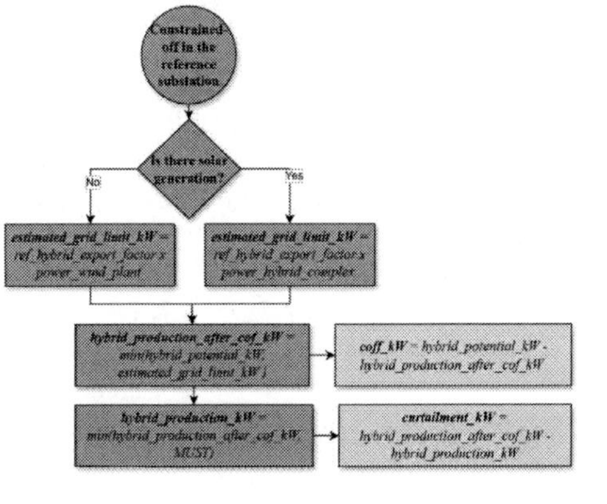

Figure 1: Flowchart of the constrained-off and curtailment calculation process.

Simulation: Comparing two scenarios:

1) Curtailment only.
2) Curtailment + constrained-off.

Analysis: Evaluating percentage losses and the impact on LCOE (Levelized Cost of Energy) for different solar power capacities and DC/AC ratios.

Loss Profiles: Daily and Monthly

Data analysis reveals that constrained-off losses are highest during peak generation periods when high wind and solar production overlap.

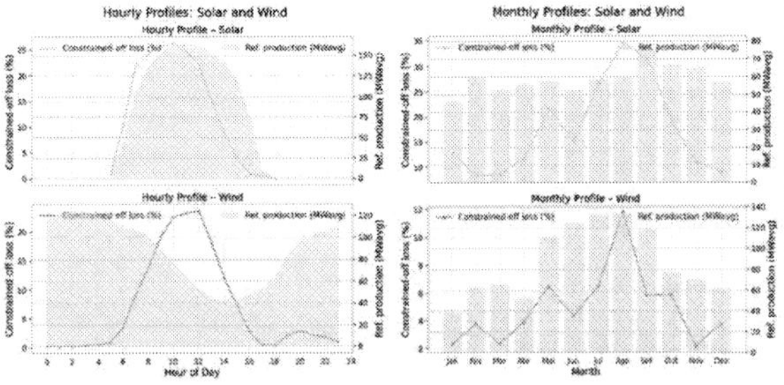

(a) (b)

Figure 2: profiles of constrained-off losses and potential solar and wind power generation for the reference hybrid power plant. (a) Hourly; (b) Monthly.

Impact Analysis

Loss overlap shows that constrained-off absorbs a significant portion of what would be lost to curtailment alone. The resilience of larger projects to constrained-off is a key factor.

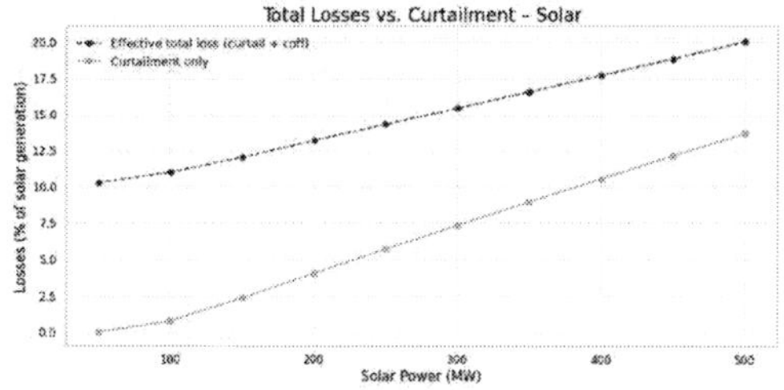

Figure 3: Comparison of losses in scenarios that include only curtailment versus scenarios that consider both events.

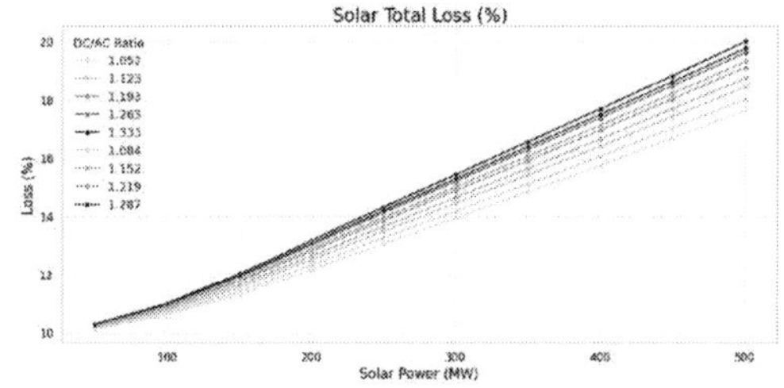

Figure 4: Total solar loss as a function of solar scale for different DC/AC ratio values.

Financial Implications

Constrained-off increases LCOE, but larger solar projects are more efficient at diluting this percentage loss.

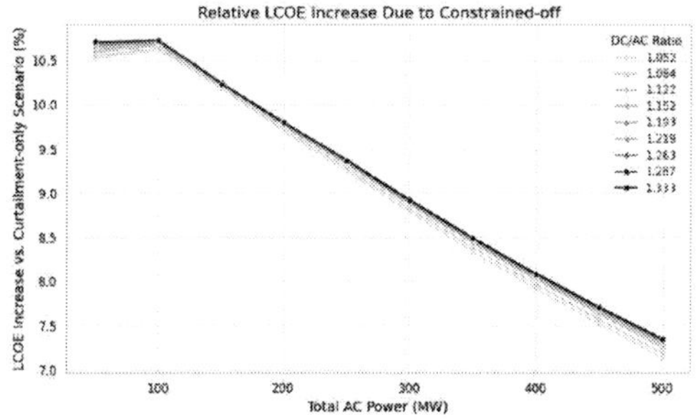

Figure 5: Percentage difference in LCOE between scenarios that consider only curtailment and scenarios that include the effects of constrained-off.

Conclusion and future work

- Isolated loss evaluation for curtailment or constrained-off is insufficient.
- For the site analyzed, larger-scale solar projects associated with wind plants demonstrate greater resilience to constrained-off, making them more attractive.
- Next steps: Predictive models, application in other Brazilian regions and analysis of storage solutions (batteries).

COMPARING APPROACHES FOR ESTIMATING RESIDENTIAL PV SYSTEM ORIENTATIONS

Johan Lindahl[a], Joakim Munkhammar[b] and Gustav Öhgren[a]
[a]Becquerel Sweden AB, Staffansvägen 14, SE-74142 Knivsta, Sweden, johan.lindahl@becquerelsweden.se
[b]Department of Civil and Industrial Engineering, Uppsala University, SE-751 21 Uppsala, Sweden, joakim.munkhammar@angstrom.uu.se

ABSTRACT: Accurate knowledge of photovoltaic (PV) system orientations—tilt and azimuth—is crucial for forecasting generation, assessing self-consumption, and managing distributed solar power. Yet, orientation data are often missing or unreliable in PV databases. This study compares three approaches for determining the orientation of residential PV systems in Sweden: (i) self-reported values from the national capital subsidy program, (ii) statistical orientation distributions based on PV penetration, and (iii) a LiDAR-based method using aerial imagery and linear regression. Validation was performed against a manually derived ground truth dataset of 104 PV polygons across three municipalities. Self-reported orientations proved highly inaccurate, primarily because the application form allowed only a single entry for a system's azimuth and tilt and lacked clear guidance on azimuth conventions, compounded by imprecise or careless estimations from applicants. In contrast, the LiDAR-based method closely matched the ground truth, with R^2 values of 0.96 for azimuth and 0.82 for tilt and captured the diversity of real-world orientations more accurately than the statistical model. These results demonstrate that LiDAR-based remote sensing provides a reliable, scalable, and high-accuracy approach for determining PV system orientations, supporting improved generation forecasts, grid operation planning, and the integration of distributed solar power at high penetration levels.
Keywords: Photovoltaics, Orientation methods, Azimuth, Tilt, Remote Sensing

1 INTRODUCTION

Solar power is growing rapidly worldwide. In 2024, photovoltaic (PV) systems made up 75% of all newly installed power generation capacity globally, adding an estimated 600 GW [1]. Within the European Union, solar now accounts for 14% of total electricity generation, of which about half is distributed PV systems [1].

Integrating large shares of PV power into the power grid is challenging due to weather variability [2], which affects system stability and requires effective management [3], [4]. As distributed PV adoption grows, accurately forecasting both generation and self-consumption [5] at local and regional levels becomes crucial for optimizing grid operation and energy management [6], [7].

The orientation, i.e., tilt and azimuth, of a PV system highly influences the PV power output profile. Although installed capacity is often reported in PV databases, tilt and azimuth are most often not reported [8]. For instance, a global study by Killinger et al. [9] found that among 14.8% of the world's installed PV capacity analyzed (as of 2017), tilt and azimuth data were available for only 1.7%.

To address this gap, several approaches have been proposed: (1) collect the azimuth and tilt through manual self-reporting — usually connect to different subsidy schemes, (2) assuming optimal tilt and azimuth for maximum power generation at each location [10], [11], (3) estimating a single representative orientation by minimizing discrepancies between simulated and observed regional PV power output [7], (4) using statistical models based on existing PV system orientations [12] or rooftop solar potential [13], (5) applying machine learning or parameterization models to infer orientation from reported PV generation [14], (6) employing remote sensing techniques, such as aerial image analysis combined with 3D building data [15] or calibrating tilt based on nearby systems in non-profit PV databases [16] and (7) using LiDAR data and linear regression to estimate the orientation [17], [18], [19], [20].

This study presents a novel comparison of three of these approaches that has been applied in Sweden for assessing the orientation of PV systems. The first approach evaluates orientation data reported by PV system owners or installers to the Swedish direct capital subsidy program registry [21], [22]. The second approach applies to the model by Ramadhani et al. [13], which estimates statistical orientation distributions based on PV penetration levels. The third approach leverages the method developed by Lingfors et al. [17], which uses Light Detection and Ranging (LiDAR) data to derive tilt and azimuth angles of solar energy systems.

The aim of this study is to evaluate and compare the three distinct approaches for assessing the orientation of residential PV systems, focusing on their accuracy and practical applicability.

2 DATA

2.1 Data from the Swedish Capital Subsidy Program

In mid-2009, a subsidy program was launched in Sweden in which actors could apply for direct capital support for PV installations [21]. The scheme remained in place until 2021, though it was revised several times — for example, lowering support levels in response to declining technology prices and rising market demand [22].

Applications for the capital subsidy had to include project location, applicant details (e.g., address and contact information), planned start and completion dates, and a project description. Moreover, the description needed to specify the type of PV system, whether it would be grid-connected, the estimated total rated power of the modules (kW), and the planned installation site. In the application form, applicants could also enter the azimuth and tilt of the system in two dedicated fields, following the exact instruction in Swedish directly translated to:

"Orientation – azimuth and tilt must be specified as degree values, with azimuth ranging from 0–360 and tilt from 0–90."

This information was recorded and stored in the subsidy program database by the Swedish Energy Agency. Although many applications omitted orientation data, a considerable share did include it. In this study, those entries represent approach (1) described in the introduction

— i.e., the collection of azimuth and tilt through manual self-reporting.

In this study, azimuth is defined such that −90° corresponds to East, 0° to South, and 90° to West and consequently the azimuth data from the direct capital subsidy database was recalculated to match this definition.

3 METHODOLOGY

3.1 Manually Created Ground Truth Dataset

To create a ground truth dataset, residential PV systems first need to be located. For this purpose, the *Alfrödull* [23] remote sensing pipeline was applied to the latest aerial orthophotos from the Swedish Land Survey to identify residential PV installations within the Swedish municipalities of Fagersta (May 2024), Falun (June 2024) and Karlshamn (May 2024).

In the first step of the *Alfrödull* pipeline, a Convolutional Neural Network (CNN) deep-learning model, developed in [24], is used to detect PV systems in aerial imagery across the target area. When applied in Sweden, the CNN algorithm has been shown to accurately identify over 95% of all existing solar energy systems at the municipal level [24].

In the second step, polygons of the identified PV systems are generated, either manually or preferably using the U-net segmentation method described in [25]. These polygons provide the coordinates and orthographic (top-down) area of each PV module cluster. This enables the extraction of LiDAR data for the rooftops hosting the PV systems, which is then used to calculate tilt and azimuth, as further described in section 3.2 and in detail in [17]. A residential PV system containing two PV polygons, generated using the above-mentioned remote sensing pipeline, is illustrated in Figure 1.

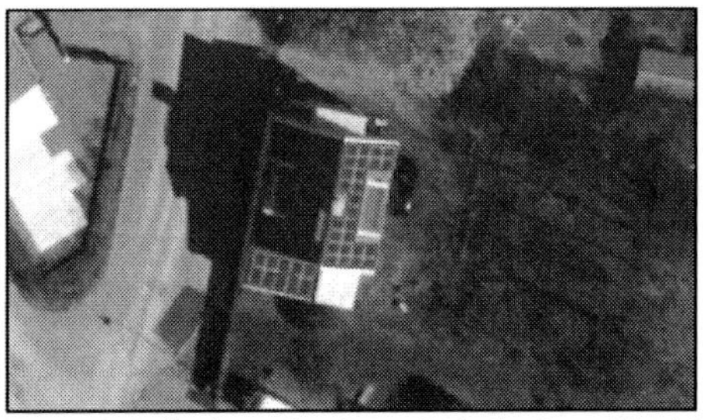

Figure 1. Orthophoto showing a single-family residential house with two distinct clusters of PV modules, each outlined by blue polygons. © Lantmäteriet, 2024. The dark red line indicates the azimuth measurement performed in QGIS for the polygon marked with a bright red cross.

Two different methodologies were applied to manually determine the orientation of the generated residential PV polygons in the ground truth dataset. Azimuth was obtained through manual measurements in QGIS using the "Azimuth Measurement" plugin, as illustrated in Figure 1. Tilt was determined by extracting Google Street View images of the building containing the PV polygon, selecting views taken at an estimated ~85–95° angle relative to the measured azimuth of the polygon, i.e. close to perpendicular. An online angle measurement tool was then applied to these images, as illustrated in Figure 2.

Figure 2. Google Street View image taken approximately perpendicular to the PV polygon marked with a red cross in Figure 1. Image © Google, 2024. The overlay illustrates the online angle measurement tool and the manually derived tilt of the PV system.

The manual derivation of both azimuth and tilt angles is subject to uncertainties. Firstly, the Swedish orthophotos are not orthorectified orthophotos — i.e., they are projected relative to terrain without accounting for building heights — which means that some buildings appear tilted or skewed. Moreover, it is not always possible to obtain Google Street View images that are perfectly perpendicular to the roof being measured. Both factors contribute to slightly distorted measurements. In addition, there is the risk of human error when performing measurements based solely on screenshotted street view images. Overall, the authors estimate that the accuracy of manual tilt and azimuth determinations for the manual ground truth is within ±3° for both angles.

While manually derived azimuths could be collected for all 4,817 residential PV polygons across the three municipalities, only 1,012 of these had a corresponding subsidy application, and just 249 of those applications included both tilt and azimuth values provided by the applicant. The availability of Google Street View images taken close to perpendicular to the polygons' azimuth further reduced our dataset to 104 polygons.

When analyzing the database of the Swedish subsidy scheme, a major drawback was identified: applicants could only enter a single azimuth and tilt value in the submission form. For PV systems consisting of multiple clusters of modules with different orientations, this restriction inevitably introduces errors in the reported orientation. For example, in Figure 1, the marked southernmost smaller PV polygon has a tilt of approximately 8° and an azimuth of 13°, whereas the adjacent larger polygon has a tilt of 45° and an azimuth of −79°. The applicant for this system reported a tilt of 45° and an azimuth of −90°, which reasonably represents the larger polygon but completely misrepresents the smaller one. To assess how widespread this application form and database design limitation was, the authors classified systems with more than one polygon into *primary* and *secondary polygons*, assigning the *primary* status to the cluster whose tilt and azimuth values were closest to the established ground truth. In the example of Figure 1, the larger east-facing polygon was designated as the *primary polygon*, while the smaller southernmost polygon was considered secondary. If two polygons are installed on the same roof facet, both are assigned as *primary* or *secondary*.

3.2 The LiDAR Data and Linear Regression Method

As demonstrated by Lingfors et al. [17], the tilt and azimuth of a solar energy system can be derived from

LiDAR point cloud data. Since Swedish orthophotos are not orthorectified orthophotos PV polygons may be spatially misaligned. To overcome this, Lingfors et al. [17] developed and described in detail an orthorectification procedure to align PV polygons with the LiDAR data.

The results in [17] showed that for most PV polygons detected by the *Alfrödull* remote sensing pipeline in municipal scans, the available Swedish LiDAR data contained a sufficient number of points to enable reliable orientation estimation. However, in cases where LiDAR data could not be used with confidence, a set of special cases and rules was defined to assign a plausible and realistic orientation. These include:

1. **Insufficient LiDAR points** → no regression performed; tilt fixed at 26°[1], azimuth set to the southernmost long edge the polygon.
2. **Ground-mounted systems (>2 m from buildings)** → tilt set to 30°, azimuth set to the southernmost long edge of the polygon, panels assumed to be 0.75 m above ground.
3. **Vertical systems** (not identifiable from aerial images) → added manually with tilt 90°, azimuth set to the southernmost long edge of the polygon.
4. **Flat-roof systems (tilt <5°)** → tilt adjusted to 10°[2], azimuth set to the southernmost long edge of the polygon.
5. **Flat-roof systems oriented east–west** → treated as bi-directional by splitting the PV polygon. Tilt adjusted to 10°, two different azimuths set based on the southernmost long edge of the polygon with 180° difference.
6. **Unrealistically high tilts from LiDAR** (caused by outdated or misleading data) → treated as in case 1.

These special cases are also relevant for some of the PV systems included in this study.

In [17], the method was evaluated on 3,500 Swedish solar energy systems using a manually derived ground truth azimuth dataset, following the same procedure described in Section 3.1. For 91–95% of the systems, the model accurately estimated the azimuth within the stated uncertainty margin of ±3° [17].

3.3 The Statistical Model Based on PV Penetration

The Ramadhani et al model [13], can be used to estimate the distribution of residential PV tilt and azimuth angles based on penetration level — defined in this study as the number of residential PV systems divided by the total number of residential buildings. Flat roofs (0° in tilt) are first excluded, and then the tilt and azimuth distributions of non-zero tilt roofs are estimated according to the stochastic variables:

$$\mathbb{X}_{Tilt} \sim \mathcal{N}[\mu(x), \sigma(x)],$$

for tilt and:

$$\mathbb{X}_{Azimuth} \sim \mathcal{U}[-180(x), 180(x)],$$

for azimuth. Here $x \in [0, 1]$ is the penetration level defined as the number of roofs with PV installations divided by total amount of roofs. In [13], the parameters were determined to be $\mu(x) = -0.078x + 26.295$ and $\sigma(x) = 0.028x + 6.429$. The complete Ramadhani et al model is then based on using these distributions with an addition of a degenerate distribution at zero for the tilt distribution for the flat roofs, see [13], [26] for more detailed information.

It should be mentioned that the model settings were determined in [13] based on a PV model with the hypothesis of best-roofs-first (in terms of yearly solar energy yield) for PV installations.

In this study the Ramadhani statistical model is tested on the three municipalities of Knivsta, Uppvidinge and Falun and compared to a model which fits normal distributions to both tilt and azimuth using the Matlab function "fitdist". According to a remote sensing-based study on PV penetration levels [27] Knivsta reached a residential penetration level of $x = 0.0375$ in 2023, while Uppvidinge reported $x = 0.0231$ in 2022 and Falun $x = 0.0232$ in 2020.

To assess the goodness-of-fit between the produced distributions of the model and the distribution of the observations, the Kolmogorov-Smirnov (K-S) test statistic was used. Formally, the K-S test statistic $K \in [0, 1]$ is based on the maximum deviation between two distributions [28]:

$$K = \max_x |F_1(x) - F_1(x)|,$$

where F_1 and F_2 are cumulative density functions (CDFs) of the probability distributions to be tested. The K-S test statistic is a negatively oriented score such that lower values mean higher goodness-of-fit.

3.4 Model evaluation

The accuracy of two methods, the LiDAR-based method and database-derived parameters, in estimating tilt and azimuth of PV systems was evaluated using the metrics shown in Table 1.

Table 1. Evaluation metrics and their definitions.

Evaluation metric	Definition
Coefficient of determination	$R^2 = 1 - \frac{\sum_{i=1}^{n}(y_i - x_i)^2}{\sum_{i=1}^{n}(y_i - \bar{x})^2}$
Root Mean Square Error	$RMSE = \sqrt{\frac{1}{n}\sum_{i=1}^{n}(y_i - x_i)^2}$
Mean Absolute Error	$MAE = \frac{1}{n}\sum_{i=1}^{n}\lvert y_i - x_i\rvert$

In the evaluation metric formulas presented in Table 1, y_i represents the estimated value of a datapoint, x_i the corresponded measured value, $\bar{x}$ the overall mean of the measured values, n the number of observations. The variables thus refer to either tilt or azimuth.

[1]Based on a sample of 100 PV systems with correctly identified azimuths, the mean tilt was 26°, which appears to be the most common roof inclination for single-family houses in Sweden [17], confirmed in Figure 4 in this study.

[2]The prevailing practice in Sweden for PV installations on large commercial and industrial (C&I) flat roofs is to mount the modules in rows with a tilt of 10° [29].

4. RESULTS AND DISCUSSION

4.1 Comparing Manual Self-Reporting and the LiDAR based Method with the Manually Created Ground Truth Dataset

As described in Section 3.1, a complete-case total data set of 104 PV system polygons in the three municipalities could be created for which applicants for the Swedish capital subsidy program had filled in both azimuth and tilt estimations, and for which it also was possible to manually derive both azimuth and tilt values from the orthophotos and Google Street view images, respectively. In addition, the LiDAR data and linear regression method of [17] could also generate both azimuth and tilt values based on either the sufficient LiDAR data or the six special cases specified in section 3.2.

When comparing the results of the three methods it became evident that many applicants for the capital subsidy used inconsistent definitions. The application form instructs that azimuth values should range from 0° to 360°, and when azimuth data from the subsidy database was analyzed, the authors concluded that different applicants appear to have used either of the two conventions:

- Clockwise from North (0°–360°): East = 90°, South = 180°, West = 270°, North = 0°.
- Clockwise from South (0°–360°): East = 270°, South = 0°, West = 90°, North = 180°.

To enable a more fair comparison of the methods, the authors therefore adopted for each PV system a generous interpretation of which of the two azimuth convention the applicant likely have used — to bring them as close as possible to the ground truth — and then recalculated that value to the definition used in this study, i.e., that −90° corresponds to the East, 0° to the South, and 90° to the West.

Figure 3 shows the distribution of azimuth angles for each PV polygon derived by the three methods (after the generous interpretation modification of the subsidy scheme data) while Figure 4 presents the corresponding distribution of tilt angles.

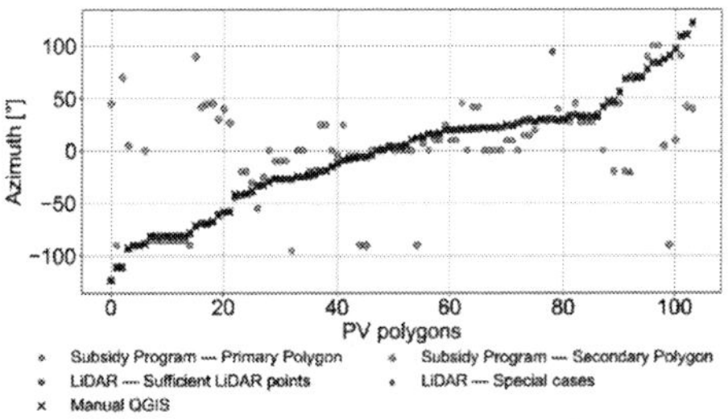

Figure 3. Distribution of azimuth angles derived by three different methods for each PV polygon. Yellow markers show values reported in the Swedish direct capital subsidy program (circles = *primary polygons*, squares = *secondary polygons*). Orange markers represent results from the LiDAR-based method (circles = sufficient LiDAR points, triangles = special-case estimations). Black crosses indicate manually measured azimuth angles from QGIS.

As shown in Figure 3, there is a strong correlation between the manually derived ground truth and the LiDAR-based methodology for azimuth angles: only 2 out of 104 PV polygons (1.9%) differed by more than ±3°. In contrast, applications submitted under the capital subsidy program showed much poorer accuracy, with 86 polygons (82.7%) deviating by more than ±3° from the ground truth. Not only were errors more frequent in the self-reported data, but the magnitude of the deviations was also often substantial, as seen in Figure 3.

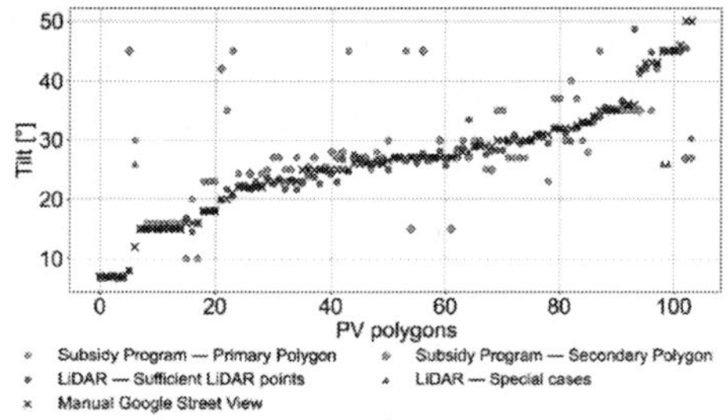

Figure 4. Distribution of tilt angles derived by three different methods for each PV polygon. Yellow markers show values reported in the Swedish direct capital subsidy program (circles = *primary polygons*, squares = *secondary polygons*). Orange markers represent results from the LiDAR-based method (circles = sufficient LiDAR points, triangles = special-case estimations). Black crosses indicate manually measured tilts from Google Street View.

Figure 4 shows a similar pattern for tilt angles. Here too, the LiDAR-based method aligns closely with the ground truth: only 7 out of 104 PV polygons (6.7%) differed by more than ±3°. By comparison, 35 polygons (33.7%) from the subsidy database deviated by more than ±3°. Again, the self-reported data show both more errors and larger discrepancies.

Furthermore, the accuracy of the subsidy database and the LiDAR-based method in estimating tilt and azimuth as compared to the ground truth dataset is summarized in and Table 2 (azimuth) Table 3 (tilt), showing R^2, MAE, and RMSE.

Table 2. Accuracy of the LiDAR-based method and the self-reporting method of the Swedish subsidy database as compared to the manually derived ground truth dataset in estimating azimuth, illustrated by R^2, MAE, and RMSE.

Case / Method	R^2	MAE [°]	RMSE [°]
LiDAR	0.96	2.17	10.82
Database	0.06	31.38	52.55

Table 3. Accuracy of the LiDAR-based method and the self-reporting method of the Swedish subsidy database as compared to the manually derived ground truth dataset in estimating tilt, illustrated by R^2, MAE, and RMSE.

Case / Method	R^2	MAE [°]	RMSE [°]
LiDAR	0.82	1.49	3.91
Database	0.30	4.21	7.76

When interpreting the results in Tables 2 and 3, it should be noted that the ground truth dataset is not absolute, as the manual measurements of azimuth and tilt angles are subject to uncertainties, estimated by the authors to be within ±3°. Nevertheless, the trends observed in Figures 3 and 4 are corroborated by the statistical measures presented in Tables 2 and 3. The LiDAR-based method demonstrates superior accuracy compared to the database-derived values. For instance, considering R^2, the LiDAR-based method achieves 0.96 for azimuth and 0.82 for tilt, whereas the database-derived parameters yield 0.3 and 0.06, respectively.

As mentioned earlier, a major source of discrepancy in both tilt and azimuth between the direct capital subsidy data and the ground truth or LiDAR-based method is that applicants could only enter a single value for each parameter in the submission form. Figures 3 and 4 show, however, that this limitation does not fully explain the deviations: 21 *primary* polygons differed by more than ±10° in azimuth, and 6 by more than ±10° in tilt. When accuracy was assessed using only the *primary polygon* values (as defined in Section 3.1), the results were R^2, MAE, and RMSE values of 0.57, 3.27°, and 5.73° for tilt, and 0.81, 13.92° and 20.14° for azimuth. Even under this favorable assumption, the database accuracy remains substantially lower than that of the LiDAR-based method, most likely because applicants were imprecise or careless when estimating roof orientations.

For the LiDAR-based method, 3 of the 104 polygons could not be reliably assessed due to insufficient LiDAR points (special case 1). In these cases, a fixed tilt of 26° was assigned and the azimuth was set perpendicular to the southernmost long edge of the polygon. This simplification introduced substantial errors, including one case where the southernmost edge did not align with the module cluster's lower boundary, leading to an azimuth offset of –90°. The second major azimuth error came from a non-special-case polygon that deviated by +64°, properly due to noise in the LiDAR data. All three special-case polygons also appeared among the seven polygons with tilt deviations greater than ±3°, with actual errors of –19°, –19°, and +14°. The remaining four non-special-case polygons showed tilt deviations of –19.7°, –4.6°, +5.5°, and +12.7°.

Overall, the LiDAR-based method demonstrated a stronger fit for azimuth than for tilt, as indicated by the higher R^2 value. At the same time, higher MAE and RMSE for azimuth suggest that occasional large errors can occur, as seen in the two polygons with –90° and +64° deviations.

4.2 Comparing the Statistical Model and the LiDAR based Method

The formal K–S test statistics for the agreement between modeled and observed distributions are presented in Table 4 for both the Ramadhani et al. model and the fitted normal distributions, separately for tilt and azimuth. For tilt, the K–S statistics are similar for the two models, indicating comparable performance. In contrast, for azimuth there is a pronounced difference: the Ramadhani et al. model departs much more strongly from the observed distribution than the fitted normal model. Keeping in mind that the K-S test statistic score is a negatively oriented score, the normal distribution model outperforms the Ramadhani model for the azimuth angle distribution estimation.

Table 4. Kolmogorov-Smirnov test statistics for Ramadhani model / normal distribution.

Variable	Knivsta	Falun	Uppvidinge
Tilt	0.19/0.16	0.14/0.22	0.19/0.15
Azimuth	0.49/0.07	0.50/0.07	0.46/0.06

This comparison is not entirely a fair comparison from a modelling and general perspective, since the normal distribution models were in fact trained on the data sets given, and not another data set and generalized as instructed for the Ramadhani model case. However, the mean value for the fitted normal distributions ranged from 3.87 to 4.48 and the standard deviation from 52.17 to 61.83, which shows a close universal fit to these distributions for these data sets, albeit both for Swedish towns and for similar low penetration levels. A proposal could be that the distribution of the azimuth is in fact universal regardless of penetration level and, based on the mean value of this data, that μ=4.263 and σ=52.335 are suggested parameters for this distribution. Investigating the universality of this proposition is left for future work.

It should also be mentioned that while the Ramadhani model as a statistical method is testable on the distributions of orientations of an aggregate of buildings in this study, it lacks the detailed system-to-system comparison features that are inherent to the self-reporting and LiDAR-based methods, such as the results in Section 4.1.

Moreover, since the majority of applications in the direct capital subsidy scheme lack reported orientation values, a direct comparison of general distributions is also not feasible.

However, as the LiDAR-based method generates both azimuth and tilt angles for all polygons of all PV systems within a scanned area, it enables a comparison of the overall distribution of orientations. Figure 5 presents such a comparison of the azimuth distributions obtained from the Ramadhani statistical model [13] and the LiDAR-based method [17] for all actual residential PV systems in the three Swedish municipalities of Knivsta, Uppvidinge and Falun in 2022.

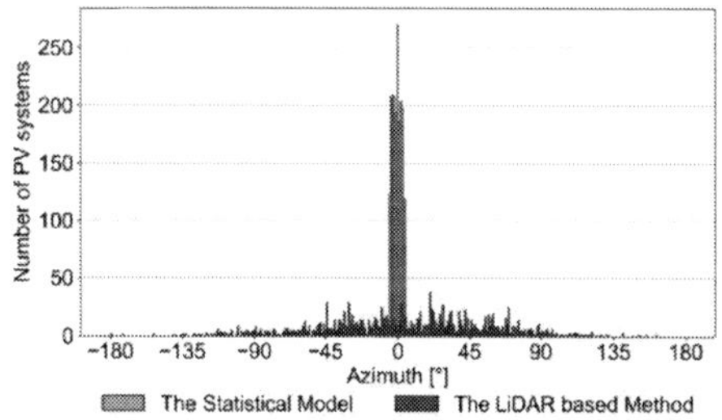

Figure 5. Histograms of the azimuth distribution from random samples using the Ramadhani et al. [13] model, which estimates orientation based on PV penetration levels, and the Lingfors et al. [17] method, which derives tilt and azimuth angles using LiDAR data, for 1922 actual residential PV systems in three Swedish municipalities in 2022.

As shown in Figure 5, the Ramadhani statistical model — assuminh that the "best" roofs are utilized first — produces a much narrower distribution of azimuth angles than the LiDAR-based method, which explain the high K-S test statistic values. While this result was expected from the probability distribution fit estimates, the difference is substantial in system azimuth orientation diversity. The LiDAR-based method is highly accurate in deriving azimuth angles for PV polygons, both in our dataset (where it produced only 2 erroneous azimuths out of 104 polygons) and in previous work [17], which demonstrated accurate azimuth estimation within a ±3° uncertainty margin for 91–95% of systems in these three municipalities. We therefore conclude that the assumption underlying the statistical model — that PV systems are installed on the best-oriented residential roofs — does not reflect reality and leads to erroneous estimates of the actual orientation distribution of residential PV systems.

5 CONCLUSIONS

This study compared three approaches for assessing the orientation of residential PV systems in Sweden: (i) self-reported values from the national capital subsidy program [21], (ii) statistical orientation distributions based on PV penetration levels [13], and (iii) a LiDAR data and linear regression method [17].

The results demonstrate that self-reported values are highly unreliable. During the analyses, two major design flaws were identified in the application form of the Swedish direct capital subsidy scheme. Firstly, the form provided only a single field for azimuth and tilt angles. In practice, many PV systems consist of multiple clusters of modules installed with different orientations. Restricting applicants to one entry per system has therefore proven to be a significant flaw, leading to substantial errors in capturing the true orientation of PV systems. Second, the instructions for reporting azimuth angles were insufficient. It became evident that applicants had used at least two different conventions — where an azimuth of 0° was taken to represent either north or south.

Since it is impossible to know which azimuth convention was applied in each individual case without a ground truth for comparison, the entire subsidy database becomes unreliable for analyzing azimuth data in isolation. Combined with the restriction of allowing only one orientation value per system, these design flaws render the Swedish capital subsidy program database practically unusable for orientation statistics. This serves as an important lesson for the design of future self-reporting systems.

However, because a ground truth was established in this study, it was possible to filter out these form-related issues and assess the accuracy of the self-reporting method. The results show that substantial errors arise not only from database design, but also from imprecise or careless estimations by applicants.

By contrast, the LiDAR-based approach [17] showed strong agreement with the manually derived ground truth, for both tilt and azimuth. Although occasional large errors occurred in special cases with insufficient LiDAR data or noise, overall performance was far superior to the database values. This suggests that LiDAR offers a robust and scalable means to derive system-level orientations at high accuracy.

The statistical model by Ramadhani et al. [13] provided some insight into aggregate distributions but failed to capture the diversity of real-world orientations. Its underlying assumption — that PV installations preferentially occupy the "best" roofs — led to a much narrower azimuth distribution than observed with LiDAR and it is concluded that the statistical approach cannot substitute for detailed system-level information.

In conclusion, LiDAR-based methods currently provide the most accurate and comprehensive option for determining PV system orientations at scale, while self-reported databases and statistical models are of limited reliability. For researchers and actors such as grid operators and aggregators, the adoption of remote sensing approaches based on LiDAR-derived system orientations will be essential for improving PV generation forecasts, enabling more effective network planning, and supporting the transition to high shares of distributed solar power.

6 ACKNOWLEDGEMENTS

The author gratefully acknowledges financial support from the Swedish Energy Agency (Project number P2023-00440). The Agency had no role in the study's design, execution, or interpretation.

7 REFERENCES

[1] IEA PVPS task 1 *et al.*, "Trends in Photovoltaic Applications — 2024," 2024.

[2] R. Luthander, D. Lingfors, and J. Widén, "Large-scale integration of photovoltaic power in a distribution grid using power curtailment and energy storage," *Solar Energy*, vol. 155, pp. 1319–1325, 2017, doi: 10.1016/j.solener.2017.07.083.

[3] N. Etherden and M. H. J. Bollen, "Increasing the hosting capacity of distribution networks by curtailment of renewable energy resources," in *Proceedings ot the 2011 IEEE PES Trondheim PowerTech*, IEEE, 2011, pp. 1–7. doi: 10.1109/PTC.2011.6019292.

[4] G. Barchi, M. Pierro, and D. Moser, "The impact of photovoltaic power estimation modeling on distribution grid voltages," in *2021 IEEE International Conference on Environment and Electrical Engineering and 2021 IEEE Industrial and Commercial Power Systems Europe (EEEIC / I&CPS Europe)*, 2021, pp. 1–6.

[5] R. Luthander, J. Widén, D. Nilsson, and J. Palm, "Photovoltaic self-consumption in buildings: A review," *Appl Energy*, vol. 142, pp. 80–94, 2015, doi: 10.1016/j.apenergy.2014.12.028.

[6] M. Pierro *et al.*, "Photovoltaic generation forecast for power transmission scheduling: A real case study," *Solar Energy*, vol. 174, no. October, pp. 976–990, 2018, doi: 10.1016/j.solener.2018.09.054.

[7] M. Pierro *et al.*, "Impact of PV / Wind Forecast Accuracy and National Transmission Grid Reinforcement on the Italian Electric System," 2022.

[8] Å. L. Sørensen, J. Hole, D. Bjerkehagen, and H. T. Walnum, "From customers to prosumers: PV systems impact on residential load profiles, peak power, and coincidence," in *CIRED 2025 Conference*, 2025, pp. 1–5.

[9] S. Killinger *et al.*, "On the search for representative characteristics of PV systems: Data collection and analysis of PV system azimuth, tilt, capacity, yield and shading," *Solar Energy*, vol. 173, no. August, pp. 1087–1106, 2018, doi: 10.1016/j.solener.2018.08.051.

[10] E. Hartvigsson, M. Odenberger, P. Chen, and E. Nyholm, "Estimating national and local low-voltage grid capacity for residential solar photovoltaic in Sweden, UK and Germany," *Renew Energy*, vol. 171, pp. 915–926, 2021, doi: 10.1016/j.renene.2021.02.073.

[11] D. Lingfors and J. Widén, "Development and

validation of a wide-area model of hourly aggregate solar power generation," *Energy*, vol. 102, pp. 559–566, 2016, doi: 10.1016/j.energy.2016.02.085.

[12] Y. M. Saint-Drenan, G. H. Good, M. Braun, and T. Freisinger, "Analysis of the uncertainty in the estimates of regional PV power generation evaluated with the upscaling method," *Solar Energy*, vol. 135, pp. 536–550, 2016.

[13] U. H. Ramadhani, D. Lingfors, J. Munkhammar, and J. Widén, "On the properties of residential rooftop azimuth and tilt uncertainties for photovoltaic power generation modeling and hosting capacity analysis," *Solar Energy Advances*, vol. 3, no. February, p. 100036, 2023, doi: 10.1016/j.seja.2023.100036.

[14] S. Killinger, N. Engerer, and B. Müller, "QCPV: A quality control algorithm for distributed photovoltaic array power output," *Solar Energy*, vol. 143, pp. 120–131, 2017.

[15] K. Mayer *et al.*, "3D-PV-Locator: Large-scale detection of rooftop-mounted photovoltaic systems in 3D," *Appl Energy*, vol. 310, no. December 2021, p. 118469, 2022, doi: 10.1016/j.apenergy.2021.118469.

[16] G. Kasmi, L. Dubus, P. Blanc, and Y. M. Saint-Drenan, "Towards unsupervised assessment with open-source data of the accuracy of deep learning-based distributed PV mapping," in *CEUR Workshop Proceedings*, 2022.

[17] D. Lingfors, R. Johansson, and J. Lindahl, "Deriving the orientation of existing solar energy systems from LiDAR data at scale," *Solar Energy*, vol. 291, no. 113344, 2025, doi: 10.1016/j.solener.2025.113344.

[18] J. Martín-Jiménez, S. Del Pozo, M. Sánchez-Aparicio, and S. Lagüela, "Multi-scale roof characterization from LiDAR data and aerial orthoimagery: Automatic computation of building photovoltaic capacity," *Autom Constr*, vol. 109, no. September 2019, p. 102965, 2020, doi: 10.1016/j.autcon.2019.102965.

[19] B. Tian, R. C. G. M. Loonen, R. Valckenborg, and J. L. M. Hensen, "A fully automated urban PV parameterization framework for improved estimation of energy production profiles," 2025. doi: https://doi.org/10.48550/arXiv.2505.19876.

[20] D. Lingfors, J. Bright, N. Engerer, J. Ahlberg, S. Killinger, and J. Widén, "Comparing the capability of low- and high-resolution LiDAR data with application to solar resource assessment, roof type classification and shading analysis," *Appl Energy*, vol. 205, no. June, pp. 1216–1230, 2017, doi: 10.1016/j.apenergy.2017.08.045.

[21] Sveriges Riksdag, *Svensk författningssamling — Förordning (2009:689) om statligt stöd till solceller*. Sweden, 2009.

[22] H. Rydehell, B. Lantz, I. Mignon, and J. Lindahl, "The impact of solar PV subsidies on investment over time — the case of Sweden," *Energy Econ*, vol. 133, no. April, p. 107552, 2024, doi: 10.1016/j.eneco.2024.107552.

[23] L. Molin, S. Ericson, D. Lingfors, J. Munkhammar, and J. Lindahl, "Validation of a PV generation model for simulation of wide area aggregated distributed PV power generation that takes individual systems location and orientation into account," in *40th European Photovoltaic Solar Energy Conference and Exhibition (EUPVSEC)*, 2023, pp. 020527–001. doi: http://dx.doi.org/10.4229/EUPVSEC2023/5DV.2.10.

[24] J. Lindahl, R. Johansson, and D. Lingfors, "Mapping of decentralised photovoltaic and solar thermal systems by remote sensing aerial imagery and deep machine learning for statistic generation," *Energy and AI*, vol. 14, p. 100300, 2023, doi: 10.1016/j.egyai.2023.100300.

[25] Å. Frimane, R. Johansson, J. Munkhammar, D. Lingfors, and J. Lindahl, "Identifying small decentralized solar systems in aerial images using deep learning," *Solar Energy*, vol. 262, 2023, doi: 10.1016/j.solener.2023.111822.

[26] U. H. Ramadhani, F. Johari, O. Lindberg, and J. Munkhammar, "A city-level assessment of residential PV hosting capacity for low-voltage distribution systems considering rooftop data and uncertainties," *Appl Energy*, vol. 371, no. February, p. 123715, 2024, doi: 10.1016/j.apenergy.2024.123715.

[27] E. Ekstrand and F. Hermodsson, "Assessing Rooftop Solar Energy Adoption — The remaining potential across market segments and the impact of socio-economic factors," Master Thesis, Uppsala University, 2024.

[28] W. J. Conover, *Practical Nonparametric Statistics*, Third Edit. New York: John Wiley & Sons, 1999.

[29] S. Liljeroth, "A techno-economic study of commercial and industrial PV systems in Sweden," Master Thesis, Uppsala University, 2025.

42nd European Photovoltaic Solar Energy Conference and Exhibition

Comparing Approaches for Estimating Residential PV system Orientations

Johan Lindahl[a], Joakim Munkhammar[b], Gustav Öhgren[a]
[a]Becquerel Sweden AB, Sweden, johan@becquerelsweden.se
[b]Department of Civil and Industrial Engineering, Sweden, joakim.munkhammar@angstrom.uu.se

Introduction

Solar power is expanding rapidly, with PV now the dominant source of new global power capacity. However, integrating distributed PV into electricity grids requires accurate data on system orientation (tilt and azimuth), which strongly affects generation profiles but is rarely reported. To address this discrepancy, we compare three approaches for estimating PV orientations in Sweden against a manually created ground-truth dataset.

A Manually Created Ground-truth Dataset

To build a ground-truth dataset:

- Residential PV systems were identified using the Alfrödull remote sensing pipeline [1], applied to aerial orthophotos in three Swedish municipalities.
- Manual orientation measurements (see images) were used for validation, with an estimated measurement error of ±3° for both tilt and azimuth.
- Out of 4,817 detected PV polygons, only 104 had both matching subsidy applications that included tilt and azimuth values and suitable Google Street View coverage close to perpendicular to the polygon.

Orthophoto showing a single-family residential house with two distinct clusters of PV modules, each outlined by blue polygons. © Lantmäteriet, 2024. The dark red line indicates the azimuth measurement performed in QGIS for the polygon marked with a bright red cross.

Google Street View image taken approximately perpendicular to the PV polygon marked with a red cross in Figure 1. Image © Google, 2024. The overlay illustrates the online angle measurement tool and the manually derived tilt of the PV system.

(2) The LiDAR Data and Linear Regression Method

Following Lingfors et al. [2], PV tilt and azimuth can be derived from LiDAR point cloud data:

- For most systems, LiDAR points allow reliable orientation estimates.
- When LiDAR data are insufficient, pre-defined rules are applied: fixed tilts and azimuth aligned with the polygon's southernmost long edge are used for ground-mounted, flat-roof, vertical, or misaligned PV systems.

Orthophoto showing a single-family residential house with two distinct clusters of PV modules. © Lantmäteriet, 2024. Building footprint polygons are outlined in yellow, and the two PV polygons are shown in red.

LiDAR point clouds corresponding to the two buildings. Points within the building footprint polygons are shown in yellow, while points within the PV system polygons (in red) are shown in dark blue and framed in dark blue rectangle to illustrate the final derived orientation.

(1) Data from the Swedish Capital Subsidy Program

Sweden's capital subsidy program for PV ran from 2009–2021:

- Applicants were required to provide project details, including rated capacity and location; tilt and azimuth could be entered optionally.
- Optional orientation values were entered manually in the application form and stored in the national database.
- The subsidy application form only allowed single azimuth and tilt values, causing errors for multi-cluster systems. Multi-polygon systems were classified into primary and secondary polygons, with the primary chosen as closest to the ground truth.

(3) The Statistical Model Based on PV Penetration

The Ramadhani et al. model [3]:

- Predicts PV tilt and azimuth based on penetration level, defined as the number of residential PV systems divided by the total number of residential buildings:
- The model assumes PV is installed on "best" roofs first, i.e., those with highest annual solar yield.
- The model was tested in three municipalities — Knivsta, Uppvidinge, and Falun — where residential PV penetration levels were 3.75% (2023), 2.31% (2022), and 2.32% (2020), respectively.

Results

The LiDAR-based method demonstrated substantially higher accuracy than the self-reported subsidy database in estimating both tilt and azimuth. For tilt, the LiDAR-based method achieved an R^2 of 0.82 with a mean absolute error (MAE) of 1.49° and a root mean square error (RMSE) of 3.91°, compared to the database values of 0.30, 4.21°, and 7.67°, respectively. For azimuth, the LiDAR demonstrated an accuracy of R^2 of 0.96, MAE of 2.17°, and RMSE of 10.82°, whereas the database values were at 0.06, 31.38°, and 52.55°.

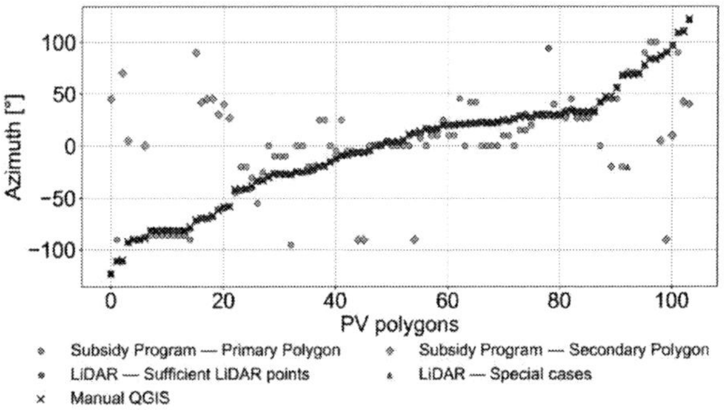

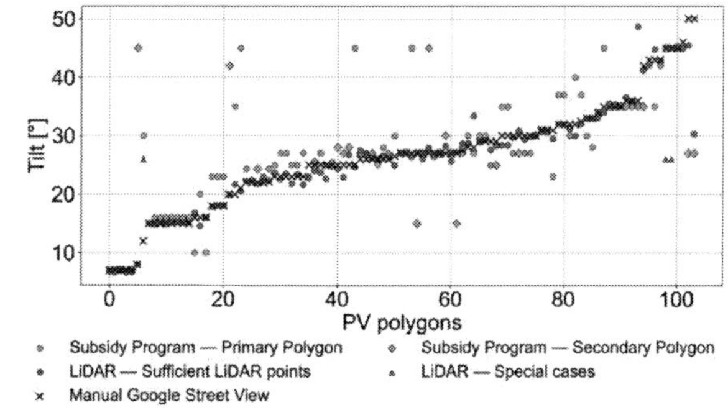

Distribution of azimuth and tilt angles derived from the Swedish capital subsidy database and the LiDAR-based method, compared with manually created ground truth.

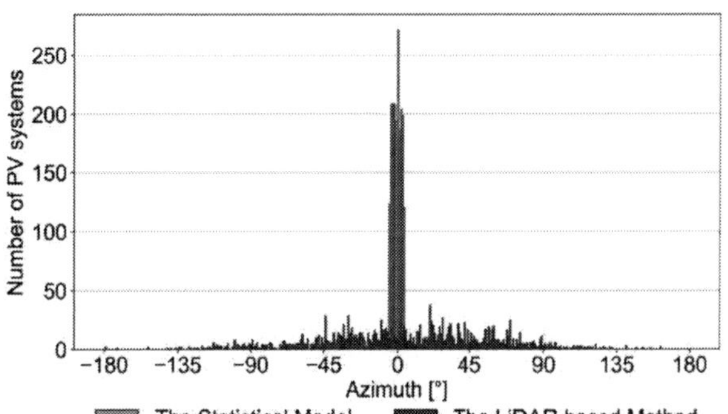

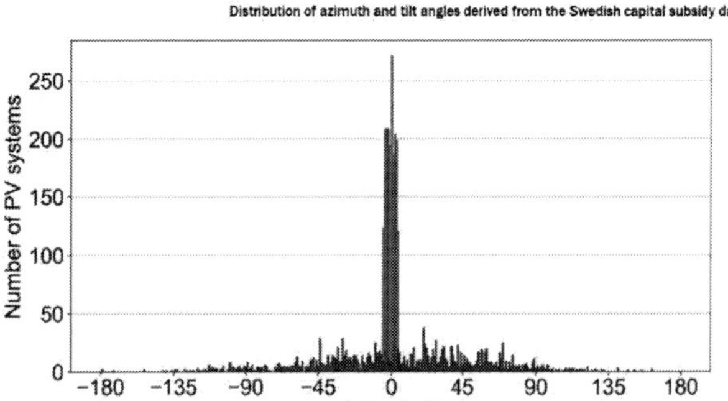

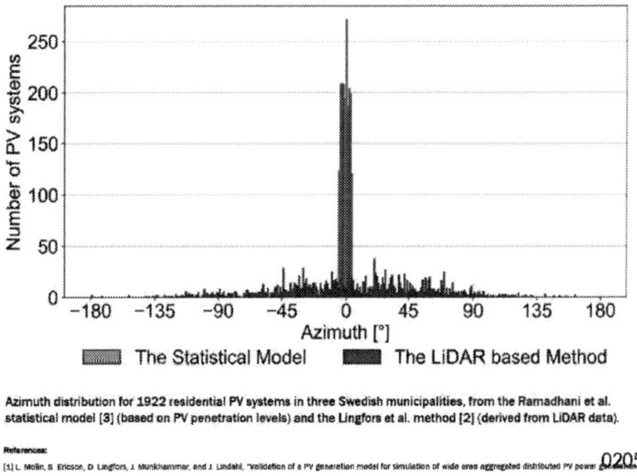

Azimuth distribution for 1922 residential PV systems in three Swedish municipalities, from the Ramadhani et al. statistical model [3] (based on PV penetration levels) and the Lingfors et al. method [2] (derived from LiDAR data).

Conclusions

This study compared three approaches for determining residential PV system orientations in Sweden.

- Self-reported data were found to be highly unreliable due to:
  - Only one azimuth respective tilt entry allowed per system, which fails for multi-cluster PV installations.
  - Inconsistent azimuth conventions where 0° was interpreted as either North or South by applicants.
  - Additional errors from imprecise applicant estimates of their roof orientation.
- The statistical model, which assumes PV systems are installed on the "best" roofs first, produced a much narrower azimuth distribution than what is observed in reality.
- The LiDAR-based method showed strong agreement with the manually derived ground truth, achieving high accuracy for both azimuth and tilt.

This study demonstrates that the LiDAR-based method developed in [2] is a robust, scalable, and reliable approach for obtaining PV system-level orientation data.

References:
[1] L. Molin, S. Ericson, D. Lingfors, J. Munkhammar, and J. Lindahl, "Validation of a PV generation model for simulation of wide area aggregated distributed PV power generation that takes individual systems location and orientation into account," in 40th European Photovoltaic Solar Energy Conference and Exhibition (EUPVSEC), 2023, pp. 020527-001.
[2] D. Lingfors, R. Johansson, and J. Lindahl, "Deriving the orientation of existing solar energy systems from LiDAR data at scale," Solar Energy, vol. 291, no. 113344, 2025
[3] U. H. Ramadhani, D. Lingfors, J. Munkhammar, and J. Widén, "On the properties of residential rooftop azimuth and tilt uncertainties for photovoltaic power generation modeling and hosting capacity analysis," Solar Energy Advances, vol. 3, no. February, p. 100036, 2023

ADVANCED ENERGY MANAGEMENT SYSTEM FOR SOLAR-PLUS-STORAGE SYSTEMS

Marangis Demetris[1], Herodotou Panayiotis[1], Livera Andreas[1], Makrides George[1], Georghiou George E.[1]
University of Cyprus, 2109 Nicosia, Cyprus
[1]PHAETHON Centre of Excellence for Intelligent, Efficient and Sustainable Energy Solutions,
2109 Nicosia, Cyprus
*Corresponding authors: Demetris Marangis (marangis.demetris@ucy.ac.cy)

ABSTRACT: A major challenge in the energy transition is the effective integration of renewable energy sources into the electrical grid, while optimizing power flow and reducing costs through advanced energy management system (EMS) controllers. Although recent advancements have improved EMS controllers, significant gaps remain in their validation under dynamic conditions, such as fluctuating loads and storage constraints. This study addresses these challenges by developing an optimized controller using linear programming, that minimizes costs and optimizes power flow among the grid, photovoltaic (PV) modules and battery storage. The proposed model utilizes historical load data from the University of Cyprus nanogrid, which features a 40 kWp PV system and a 50-kWh battery, and is benchmarked against a reference rule-based controller across various prediction horizons and operational scenarios. The results demonstrated that the advanced controller consistently reduces grid dependence and operational expenses, with the day ahead prediction horizon yielding mean daily savings of €6.90/kWh. Furthermore, in scenarios with sudden drops in PV output (such as during curtailment events), the advanced controller achieved cost savings of up to €24.04/kWh compared to the rule-based alternative, demonstrating its superior performance.
Keywords: controller, energy management system, energy storage, optimization, photovoltaic.

1 INTRODUCTION

Reducing dependence on fossil fuels is crucial for addressing global warming. Transitioning to renewable energy sources (RES), such as photovoltaic (PV) systems, provides a sustainable solution and is vital for building a greener future. RES promote a more decentralized approach to electricity generation, play a key role in reducing greenhouse gas emissions, and help mitigate the environmental impacts associated with conventional energy production [1].

Integrating a high share of RES into the energy mix presents significant challenges due to their intermittent and unpredictable nature. These technical obstacles can adversely affect the reliability and power quality of the utility grid [2], [3]. Moreover, the daily and seasonal variability of PV power generation leads to pronounced imbalances between energy supply and demand, increasing overall grid instability [4]. Consequently, the introduction of energy storage technologies is crucial for maintaining a consistent supply of renewable energy and for bridging the gap between fluctuating demand and supply. Integrating battery energy storage systems (BESS) provides an effective means of enhancing the stability, reliability, and flexibility of the utility grid [5], [6]. Specifically, combining BESS with PV systems allows surplus energy to be stored for later use during periods of low solar generation (e.g., evenings or cloudy days). This integration not only helps to smooth out fluctuations in power output but also supports grid stability and increases the overall share of renewable energy within grid networks [7], [8].

To optimize the integration of PV and storage systems within modern grid networks, the development and deployment of advanced Energy Management System (EMS) controllers are crucial. These sophisticated EMS controllers enable the creation of optimal charging and discharging schedules for BESS, thereby increasing the utilization of renewable energy through demand-side management while simultaneously reducing operational costs [9], [10].

Researchers have explored numerous EMS strategies, including load shifting, integrating energy storage for peak shaving, and applying advanced algorithms such as genetic algorithms, Extreme Learning Machine (ELM), k-means clustering, and Support Vector Regression (SVR) to reduce costs [8,9]. In this domain, Babu et al. [11] employed a multi-objective genetic algorithm, that utilized forecasted solar PV and wind generation data, to optimize grid and battery power usage in a 2.5 MW microgrid. This method enabled efficient renewable energy integration and economically optimal operation under both fixed and dynamic tariff conditions. Similarly, in [12], an EMS controller based on the modified grey wolf optimizer was developed for PV-based microgrids, achieving cost reductions of 23.34% on sunny days and 45.55% on cloudy days compared to a mixed linear programming approach.

Although advanced EMS controllers have already been developed, they often lack validation under dynamic optimization conditions that consider storage constraints, fluctuating load demands, and variable electricity pricing. Addressing this gap is a critical industrial requirement, particularly for nanogrid and microgrid operations, where analyzing historical load data across various seasons is essential. The proposed work tackles this challenge by developing an advanced EMS controller based on the revised simplex method (i.e., a linear programming algorithm). The proposed solution enhances grid flexibility by promoting cost-effective strategies for renewable integration and optimizing battery operation. The controller considers various parameters and constraints, including dynamic grid pricing, varying load demands, and upper and lower limits on the battery's state of charge (SOC).

2 METHODOLOGY

The approach followed to design the EMS controllers consisted of the following steps: (a) experimental setup and data acquisition (b) development of the rule-based and advanced EMS controllers (c) development of forecasting algorithms, (d) performance evaluation and validation of EMS controllers and (e) test scenarios.

10.4229/EUPVSEC2025/5DV.3.8

2.1 Experimental setup and data acquisition

The first step included the acquisition of load data from the nanogrid of the University of Cyprus. Historical load data (at hourly intervals) were collected over a yearly period (01/06/2019-01/06/2020). During this evaluation period, the average hourly load was 14.3 kWh, with a peak load of 105.11 kWh. The nanogrid included a 40 kWp PV system and a battery with a usable capacity of 50 kWh. Dynamic time-of-use electricity prices were incorporated to simulate realistic fluctuations in energy costs. These prices were based on Cyprus's electricity tariffs [13], and were adjusted to reflect current rates. Extremely high load data were identified from 29/04/2020 to 01/06/2020, which were not representative of the seasonal behavior of the nanogrid, and were excluded from the analysis.

2.2 Development of the rule-based and advanced EMS controllers

The two controllers were developed during this stage: a rule-based controller and an advanced EMS controller. The rule-based controller operates as a state machine, using predefined rules to manage the battery's charging and discharging behavior. When PV production exceeds load demand, the surplus energy is used to charge the battery. During peak demand periods in the evening, the battery discharges stored energy to supply the load.

The advanced EMS controller is designed to optimize power flow among the grid, the PV system, and the battery, with the objective of minimizing costs using a linear programming-based algorithm, known as the revised simplex method [14]. This method is chosen for its efficiency and robustness in solving large-scale linear programming problems, which align well with the mathematical formulations of EMS. Its reliable convergence and computational efficiency make it a widely adopted approach in energy system optimization applications [15], [16].

PV system, load, and battery data were used as inputs to the model. The optimization problem is described below (Eq. 1):

$$\min \sum_{t=1}^{N} C_{grid,t} \times P_{grid,t} \quad (1)$$

where $C_{grid,t}$ represents the electricity price at a given time t, N denotes the total number of hourly intervals in a day, $P_{grid,t}$ is the energy drawn from the grid at time t, occurring when the combined supply from the PV system and the battery is insufficient to meet the demand.

Various constraints were used to control the state of charge (SOC) limits, as well as the battery's discharging rate and power flow from the grid ($P_{grid,t}$ $P_{curtail,t}$). Specifically, the battery's lower and upper SOC limits were set at 20% and 100%, respectively, to prolong battery lifespan and improve grid frequency regulation [17], [18]. A round-trip efficiency of 96% was assumed, accounting for typical conversion and charging losses that usually range between 1% and 5% per cycle. The complete set of equations defining these constraints for the optimization problem is provided below (Eq. 2-7).

$$C_{bat} \geq SOC_i \geq 0.2 \times C_{bat} \quad (2)$$

$$P_{\max charge} \geq P_{bat,t} \geq -P_{\max discharge} \quad (3)$$

$$SOC_t = SOC_{t-1} + \eta_{bat} \times P_{bat,t} \quad (4)$$

$$P_{load,t} - P_{PV,t} + P_{bat,t} = P_{grid,t} + P_{curtail,t} \quad (5)$$

$$P_{grid,t} \geq 0 \quad (6)$$

$$0 \leq P_{curtail,t} \leq P_{PV,t} \quad (7)$$

where $P_{curtail,t}$ represents the surplus energy fed back into the grid at time t in times of excess supply, C_{bat} is the maximum battery capacity, SOC_t and SOC_{t-1} is the state of charge of the battery at time t and t-1 respectively, $P_{max\,charge}$ and $P_{max\,discharge}$ represent the maximum charging and discharging power that can be drawn from the battery at each time t (in this case it is 25 kWh), $P_{bat,t}$ represents the power flow from the battery (positive is discharging, negative is charging), η_{bat} is the charging and discharging efficiency, $P_{load,t}$ is the load power at time t, and P_{PV} is the PV generated power at time t.

The algorithm iteratively updates the parameters until the objective function converges to a value within a minimum tolerance close to zero. The optimization variable is the battery power flow (i.e., $P_{bat,t}$), which represents the rate of charging or discharging of the battery at each time step. The developed EMS controller adjusts this variable to determine the optimal daily charging and discharging schedule, with the goal of minimizing the total electricity cost.

2.3 Development of forecasting algorithms

To simulate real-life applications, PV generation and load were forecasted using machine learning algorithms. In this paper, the extreme Gradient Boosting method (XGBoost) [19] method and the linear regression (LR) [20] were employed, both of which have demonstrated high accuracy in forecasting tasks [21], [22]. Each algorithm was applied to forecast PV generation and load over different prediction horizons (i.e., 2, 12 and 24 hours ahead corresponding to forecasts at time t+2, t+12 and t+24). For each horizon and forecast data (PV or load), the better-performing algorithm was selected as input for the advanced EMS controller.

The forecasting algorithms used as inputs the PV and load data from one week and one day prior to the current measurement, as well as the most recent measurement (at time t) before the forecast. The dataset was divided into 70% for training (01/06/2019-19/01/2020) and 30% for testing (20/01/2020-29/04/2020).

2.4 Performance evaluation and validation of EMS controllers

The accuracy of the forecasting algorithms across different test cases was evaluated using the normalized Root Mean Square Error (nRMSE). For PV forecasting, the error was normalized by the nominal capacity of the PV plant (i.e., 40 kWp), while for load forecasting, normalization was based on the maximum hourly load value of 105 kWh. The formula for the nRMSE metric can be found in [23].

The performance of the optimization model was also benchmarked against the rule-based controller using the daily energy cost and daily cost savings as evaluation metrics. Eq. 8-9 below detail the calculations used for each metric.

$$Daily\ energy\ cost = \frac{\sum_{t=1}^{N} E_{grid,hour} \times C_{grid,t}}{\sum_{t=1}^{N} E_{load,hour}} \quad (8)$$

$$Daily\ cost\ savings = \frac{C_{O,day} - C_{RB,day}}{\sum_{t=1}^{N} E_{load,hour}} \quad (9)$$

where $E_{grid,hour}$ is the hourly energy imported by the grid, N is the number of hours in each day (i.e., 24), $E_{load,hour}$ is the hourly energy demanded by the microgrid, $C_{O,day}$ and $C_{RB,day}$ represent the daily price costs of the advanced EMS controller and the rule-based controller.

2.5 Test scenarios

Two different test scenarios were considered in this study. The first scenario simulated real-life applications

10.4229/EUPVSEC2025/5DV.3.8

and it included the optimization of the EMS controller using forecasted data and the tuning of the rule-based controller using actual data. The assessment was conducted over the test set period.

In the second scenario, a curtailment event was introduced during midday hours (12:00 to 14:00) on a randomly selected day in each of the four seasons (spring, summer, autumn, and winter). In this scenario, the developed controller was optimized based on data that did not include the curtailment event, in contrast with the reference rule-based controller, which accounted for this event. This scenario was designed to assess the algorithm's effectiveness in responding to unforeseen curtailment events and to evaluate its robustness in managing sudden fluctuations in PV generation.

For each scenario, the effectiveness of the EMS controllers was evaluated across various prediction horizons: (i) 2 hours ahead, (ii) 12 hours ahead, and (iii) 24 hours ahead – day ahead. The different prediction horizons were used to further optimize and evaluate the ability of the advanced EMS controller to reduce operational costs.

3 RESULTS

3.1 Accuracy of forecasting algorithms

The PV generation forecasting algorithms were developed using a sequential 70:30% train and test set approach. Both algorithms (i.e., the XGBoost and LR) were employed to forecast PV generation 2, 12 and 24 hours ahead and the results are summarized in Fig. 1. The XGBoost algorithm achieved the lowest error of 8.93% at 2 hours ahead prediction horizon, compared to 9.71% achieved by the LR. In contrast, the LR outperformed slightly the XGBoost algorithm when forecasting 12 hours and day ahead.

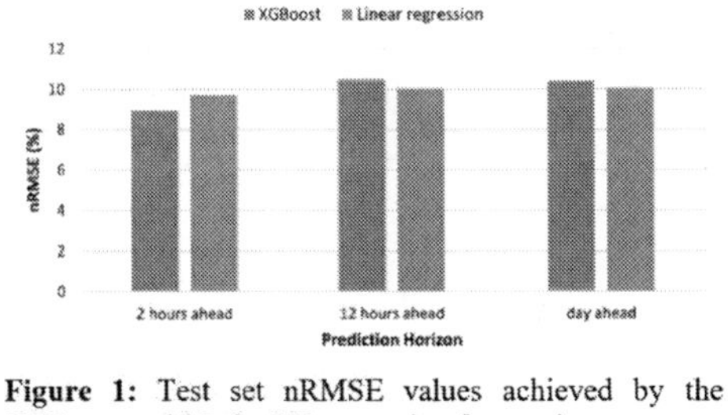

Figure 1: Test set nRMSE values achieved by the XGBoost and LR for PV generation forecasting.

Fig. 2 shows the results obtained by the XGBoost and LR for load forecasting across the different prediction horizons. The XGBoost outperformed LR for 2 and 12 hours ahead prediction horizons, while the LR has shown better accuracy for the day ahead prediction horizon.

It is worth noting that the accuracy of both models decreased when forecasting longer prediction horizons. In addition, both algorithms have consistently shown low forecast errors across all prediction horizons, indicating their robustness and suitability for forecasting applications.

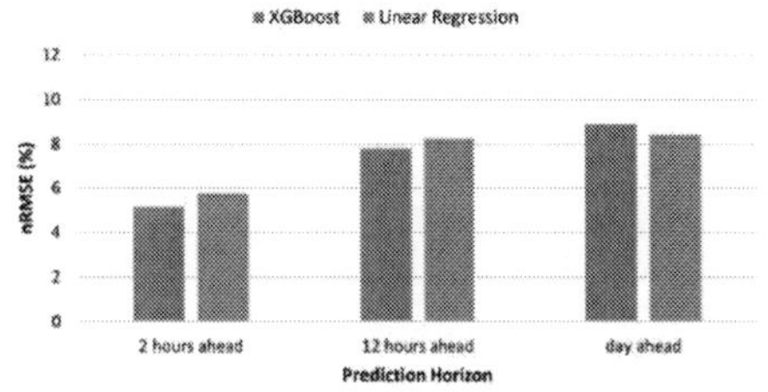

Figure 2: Test set nRMSE values achieved by the XGBoost and LR for load forecasting.

Overall, the XGBoost algorithm demonstrated superior accuracy for 2 hours ahead forecasts, while for day ahead forecasts, the LR method yielded better accuracy (see Table I). Therefore, a combination of both algorithms is proposed to achieve the lowest forecasting error.

Table I: Best performing algorithm for each prediction horizon and forecast data.

Prediction horizon	PV	Load
2 hours ahead	XGBoost	XGBoost
12 hours ahead	LR	XGBoost
day ahead	LR	LR

3.2 Scenario 1 – Real-life conditions

The first scenario simulated real-life applications and it included the optimization of the EMS controller using forecasted data and the tuning of the rule-based controller using actual data.

The performance of the EMS controllers was evaluated based on the mean daily energy cost over the test set period, with the results across different prediction horizons illustrated in Fig. 3. The advanced EMS controller with the day ahead prediction horizon achieved the best performance, yielding a mean daily energy cost of €41.28/kWh. This corresponds to a cost reduction of €6.90/kWh compared to the rule-based controller, which achieved a mean daily energy cost of €48.18/kWh. In contrast, the advanced EMS controller was less cost effective at shorter prediction horizons; for the 2 hours horizons, the mean daily energy costs increased to €94.74/kWh, while at the 12 hours ahead horizon, it rose to €54.44/kWh.

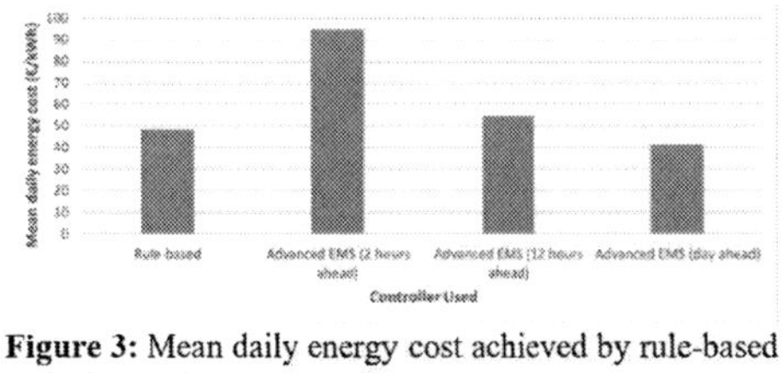

Figure 3: Mean daily energy cost achieved by rule-based and advanced EMS controllers.

To further analyze the controllers' behavior, Fig. 4 presents the comparison of power flows and the battery's SOC over a day ahead prediction horizon. The results show that the advanced EMS controller effectively manages the battery SOC, allowing for nearly autonomous operation with no grid imports during the observed day.

This strategy maximizes cost savings and reduces dependence on the grid. In contrast, the rule-based controller charged the battery during high-price periods and utilized the PV generated power less efficiently, leading to higher grid costs.

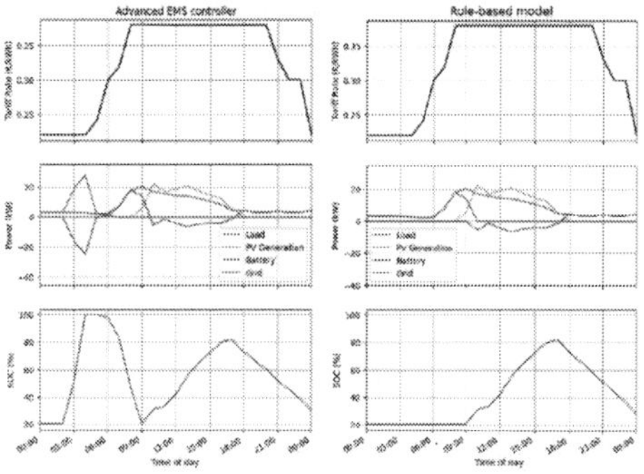

Figure 4: Hourly tariff rates (top), power flow between load, PV, battery and grid (middle) and SOC of the battery during a day for the rule-based (right) and advanced EMS controllers (left).

Fig. 5 illustrates the daily energy costs (€/kWh) achieved by the rule-based controller (orange) and the advanced EMS controller (blue) over the test set period. The advanced EMS controller consistently yields lower daily energy costs compared to the rule-based controller. The cost difference between the two controllers is most pronounced during periods of high load and relatively low PV production (i.e., December - February). During such periods, the advanced EMS controller achieved significant savings when compared to the rule-based controller. Conversely, the difference was noticeably smaller in March and April, when the PV generation was significantly higher than the load demand. The results indicate that in cases of positive net load (PV > load), both the advanced EMS controller and rule-based controller performed relatively well, whereas in cases of negative net load (PV < load), the advanced EMS controller outperforms the rule-based controller.

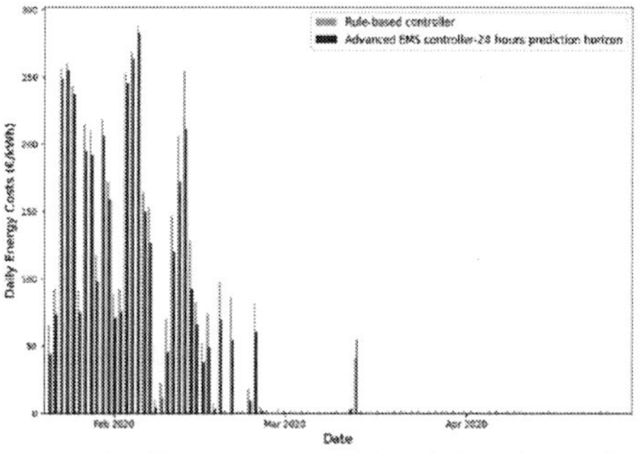

Figure 5: Daily energy costs of the rule-based controller (orange) and advanced EMS controller (blue) over test set period.

Fig. 6 presents the daily energy cost savings (€/kWh) achieved by the advanced EMS controller relative to a rule-based controller over the test set period. The mean daily savings were €6.90/kWh, highlighting the substantial cost efficiency improvement delivered by the advanced EMS controller. The most significant cost reductions were observed in mid-February, with daily energy cost savings reaching up to €45/kWh. Notably, the advanced EMS controller demonstrated significant savings under high demand conditions (e.g., January and February), whereas less savings were observed during low demand conditions (e.g., March and April). This adaptability underscores its potential to enhance operational performance and reduce costs in demand-intensive environments, such as the University of Cyprus nanogrid.

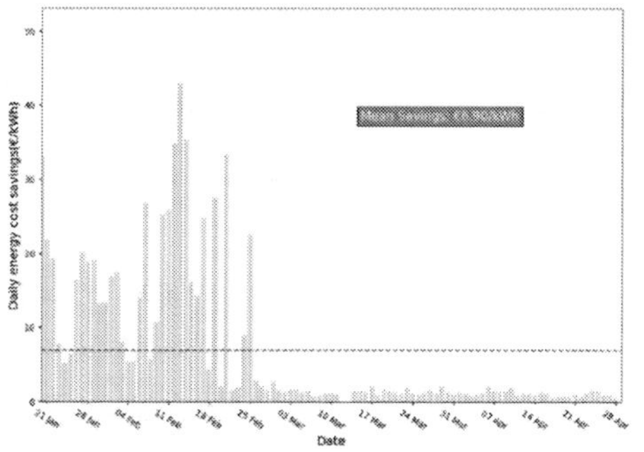

Figure 6: Daily energy cost savings achieved by the advanced EMS controller when compared to the rule-based model over the yearly period.

3.3 Scenario 2 – Curtailment event

In this scenario, a curtailment event was introduced during midday hours (12:00 to 14:00) on a randomly selected day in each of the four seasons (spring, summer, autumn, and winter). Fig. 7 illustrates the daily energy cost savings achieved by both the rule-based and advanced EMS controllers across various prediction horizons and different seasons, during an unexpected curtailment event.

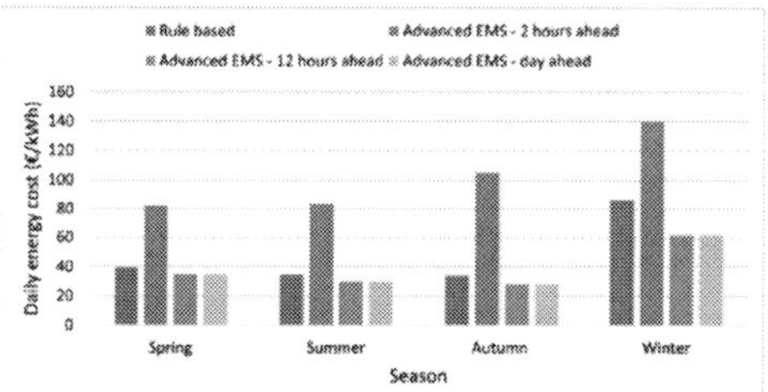

Figure 7: Daily energy cost of the two controllers over the four seasons and across various prediction horizons during a random curtailment event.

The results highlight clear differences in performance and cost efficiency between the two controllers. Specifically, the advanced EMS controller with 2 hours ahead prediction horizon showed limited robustness to abrupt changes in PV output, leading to higher daily energy costs ranging from €82/kWh to €140/kWh. In contrast, the advanced EMS controller for 12 and 24 hours ahead exhibited greater resilience, delivering superior performance (daily energy costs ranging from €28.51/kWh to €62.21/kWh). Finally, the rule-based controller achieved significant lower costs when compared to the 2 hours ahead horizon. The 12 hours ahead and day ahead prediction horizon achieved equal daily energy cost savings between €4.75/kWh and €24.04/kWh. The seasonal analysis showed that the highest savings occurred in winter, which is characterized by high energy demand and low PV generation.

Overall, the 12 hours and day ahead prediction horizons consistently provided the most reliable and cost-effective results across all seasons, highlighting the developed EMS controller's capability to balance forecast accuracy with operational flexibility. In contrast, the advanced EMS controller with the 2 hours ahead prediction horizon limited adaptability to sudden PV output fluctuations significantly undermined its performance.

4 CONCLUSION

To increase the share of RES in the grid, it is essential to integrate EMS controllers to optimize power flow between systems, reduce costs, and enhance overall system reliability. Despite recent advancements in EMS development, a major challenge remains the lack of validation of these algorithms' robustness under dynamic conditions, including storage limitations, fluctuating load demand, and variable electricity pricing.

In this paper, an advanced EMS controller based on linear programming was developed and evaluated using various prediction horizons and across different seasons. Additionally, the controller's robustness was tested in scenarios involving unexpected curtailment events. Its performance was also compared against a rule-based controller. Both controllers were tested using historical data from the University of Cyprus nanogrid system, incorporating a 40 kWp PV plant and a 50 kWh battery.

The results demonstrated that the advanced EMS controller with the day ahead prediction horizon effectively manages power flows, particularly during periods of high energy demand, reducing reliance on the grid and achieving mean cost savings of €6.90/kWh. When curtailment events were introduced, the 12 hours and day ahead prediction horizons achieved the best performance, with cost savings ranging from €4.75/kWh to €24.04/kWh.

Future work will focus on comparing the proposed approach with other optimization algorithms, improving the accuracy and robustness of forecasting models, and conducting further benchmarking in commercial and industrial settings to evaluate the generalizability and performance of the EMS controller.

5 ACKNOWLEDGMENTS

This work was funded by the EMS4PVBEV project. The EMS4PVBEV project is financed by the Recovery and Resilience Facility of the NextGenerationEU instrument through the Cyprus Research and Innovation Foundation (ENTERPRISES/ENERGY/1123/0011).

6 REFERENCES

[1] M. Adham, S. Keene, and R. B. Bass, "Distributed Energy Resources: A Systematic Literature Review," Energy Reports, vol. 13, pp. 1980–1999, 2025, doi: 10.1016/j.egyr.2025.01.026.

[2] A. Q. Al-Shetwi, M. A. Hannan, K. P. Jern, M. Mansur, and T. M. I. Mahlia, "Grid-connected renewable energy sources: Review of the recent integration requirements and control methods," J Clean Prod, vol. 253, p. 119831, 2020, doi: 10.1016/j.jclepro.2019.119831.

[3] H. Jafarizadeh, E. Yamini, S. M. Zolfaghari, F. Esmaeilion, M. E. H. Assad, and M. Soltani, "Navigating challenges in large-scale renewable energy storage: Barriers, solutions, and innovations," Energy Reports, vol. 12, pp. 2179–2192, 2024, doi: 10.1016/j.egyr.2024.08.019.

[4] S. D. Ahmed, F. S. M. Al-Ismail, M. Shafiullah, F. A. Al-Sulaiman, and I. M. El-Amin, "Grid integration challenges of wind energy: A review," Ieee Access, vol. 8, pp. 10857–10878, 2020, doi: 10.1109/ACCESS.2020.2964896.

[5] A. H. Nebey, "Recent advancement in demand side energy management system for optimal energy utilization," Energy Reports, vol. 11, pp. 5422–5435, 2024, doi: 10.1016/j.egyr.2024.05.028.

[6] A. Azarhooshang, D. Sedighizadeh, and M. Sedighizadeh, "Two-stage stochastic operation considering day-ahead and real-time scheduling of microgrids with high renewable energy sources and electric vehicles based on multi-layer energy management system," Electric Power Systems Research, vol. 201, p. 107527, 2021, doi: 10.1016/j.epsr.2021.107527.

[7] M. Hasan and H. Serra Altinoluk, "Current and future prospective for battery controllers of solar PV integrated battery energy storage systems," Front Energy Res, vol. 11, p. 1139255, 2023, doi: 10.3389/fenrg.2023.1139255.

[8] A. Jain and S. Bhullar, "Design and performance analysis of solar PV-battery energy storage system integration with three-phase grid," J Power Sources, vol. 640, p. 236486, 2025, doi: 10.1016/j.jpowsour.2025.236486.

[9] M. Darwish, S. Ioannou, A. Janbey, H. Amreiz, and C. C. Marouchos, "Review of battery management systems," in 2021 International Conference on Electrical, Computer, Communications and Mechatronics Engineering (ICECCME), IEEE, 2021, pp. 1–6. doi: 10.1109/ICECCME52200.2021.9590884.

[10] H. Abouobaida, L. de Oliveira-Assis, E. P. P. Soares-Ramos, H. Mahmoudi, J. M. Guerrero, and M. Jamil, "Energy management and control strategy of DC microgrid based hybrid storage system," Simul Model Pract Theory, vol. 124, p. 102726, 2023, doi: 10.1016/j.simpat.2023.102726.

[11] V. V. Babu, J. P. Roselyn, and P. Sundaravadivel, "Multi-objective genetic algorithm based energy management system considering optimal utilization of grid and degradation of battery storage in microgrid," Energy Reports, vol. 9, pp. 5992–6005, 2023, doi: 10.1016/j.egyr.2023.05.067.

[12] A. Kumar, M. Alaraj, M. Rizwan, and U. Nangia, "Novel AI based energy management system for smart grid with RES integration," IEEE Access, vol. 9, pp. 162530–162542, 2021, doi: 10.1109/ACCESS.2021.3131502.

[13] V. Venizelou, G. Makrides, V. Efthymiou, and G. E. Georghiou, "Residential consumption responsiveness under time-varying pricing," in 2018 IEEE International Energy Conference (ENERGYCON), IEEE, 2018, pp. 1–6. doi: 10.1109/ENERGYCON.2018.8398735.

[14] Q. Huangfu and J. A. J. Hall, "Novel update techniques for the revised simplex method," Comput Optim Appl, vol. 60, no. 3, pp. 587–608, 2015, doi: 10.1007/s10589-014-9689-1.

[15] M. Mohammadi, Y. Noorollahi, B. Mohammadi-ivatloo, M. Hosseinzadeh, H. Yousefi, and S. T. Khorasani, "Optimal management of energy hubs and smart energy hubs–A review," Renewable and Sustainable Energy Reviews, vol. 89, pp. 33–50, 2018, doi:

10.1016/j.rser.2018.02.035.
[16] L. Olatomiwa, S. Mekhilef, M. S. Ismail, and M. Moghavvemi, "Energy management strategies in hybrid renewable energy systems: A review," Renewable and Sustainable Energy Reviews, vol. 62, pp. 821–835, 2016, doi: 10.1016/j.rser.2016.05.040.
[17] S.-M. Cho, J.-C. Kim, and S.-Y. Yun, "Optimum State-of-Charge Operating Range for Frequency Regulation of Energy Storage Systems Using a Master–Slave Parallel Genetic Algorithm," Electronics (Basel), vol. 9, no. 8, p. 1298, 2020, doi: 10.3390/electronics9081298.
[18] M. Darwish, S. Ioannou, A. Janbey, H. Amreiz, and C. C. Marouchos, "Review of battery management systems," in 2021 International Conference on Electrical, Computer, Communications and Mechatronics Engineering (ICECCME), IEEE, 2021, pp. 1–6. doi: 10.1109/ICECCME52200.2021.9590884.
[19] T. Chen and C. Guestrin, "Xgboost: A scalable tree boosting system," in Proceedings of the 22nd acm sigkdd international conference on knowledge discovery and data mining, 2016, pp. 785–794. doi: 10.1016/j.eswa.2025.129449.
[20] G. James, D. Witten, T. Hastie, R. Tibshirani, and J. Taylor, "Linear regression," in An introduction to statistical learning: With applications in python, Springer, 2023, pp. 69–134. doi: 10.1007/978-1-0716-1418-1_3.
[21] D.-J. Bae, B.-S. Kwon, and K.-B. Song, "XGBoost-based day-ahead load forecasting algorithm considering behind-the-meter solar PV generation," Energies (Basel), vol. 15, no. 1, p. 128, 2021, doi: 10.3390/en15010128.
[22] M. AlShafeey and C. Csáki, "Evaluating neural network and linear regression photovoltaic power forecasting models based on different input methods," Energy Reports, vol. 7, pp. 7601–7614, 2021, doi: 10.1016/j.egyr.2021.10.125.
[23] S. Theocharides, G. Makrides, G. E. Georghiou, and A. Kyprianou, "Machine learning algorithms for photovoltaic system power output prediction," in 2018 IEEE International Energy Conference (ENERGYCON), 2018, pp. 1–6. doi: 10.1109/ENERGYCON.2018.8398737.

AN OPEN VIRTUAL POWER PLANT FOR RENEWABLE ENERGY COMMUNITIES - STRATEGIES FOR CENTRALIZED BATTERIES

Rita Hogan Almeida, Luis Miguel Carrasco, Javier Ramírez Ledesma, Javier Martín Rueda, Ana Belén Cristóbal, Laura Palomino, Kiane Alves e Silva, Luis Narvarte
Instituto de Energía Solar, Universidad Politécnica de Madrid, Spain
rita.hogan@upm.es

ABSTRACT: An open Virtual Power Plant designed for rural Renewable Energy Communities (REC) is presented, considering centralized batteries associated with photovoltaic (PV) generators. To evaluate different possibilities of battery allocation among self-consumers, three strategies have been considered: i) priority-based distribution, ii) fixed proportional distribution, and iii) variable proportional distribution. The model has been applied to a real REC located in the Calatayud Region (Spain), composed of 22 end-users. Results show that the variable proportional distribution achieves the best performance in terms of self-consumption and self-sufficiency, while the priority-based distribution presents the lowest indicators. The analysis confirms the relevance of centralized batteries to increase local use of solar and stored energy, although some strategies are not possible under current legislation.
Keywords: Energy Communities, Photovoltaics, Storage, Virtual Power Plants

1 INTRODUCTION

A virtual power plant (VPP) combines distributed energy resources (DER) with advance management systems to, for example, balance generation and consumption [1]. A renewable energy community (REC) consists of end-users (individuals, households, businesses, local authorities) that collaborate to generate and manage renewable energy, typically using self-consumption photovoltaic (PV) systems sized based on self-consumption rate (SCR) and self-sufficiency rate (SSR) [2]. Merging VPP and REC means building a VPP that integrates DER, end-users and advance management systems to control electricity generation and consumption.

In the current state-of-the-art, there are a huge variety of VPPs [3], but there is no specialized version for REC. Accordingly, we are developing an open VPP tailored specifically for rural and distributed REC, using existing components to interoperate with inverters, batteries and manageable devices, developing data management systems and specialized local optimization algorithms, as well as different strategies (algorithms to maximize SCR and SSR and local energy resilience).

Particularly, this paper describes three preliminary strategies for centralized batteries associated with PV generators for collective self-consumption: i) priority-based distribution, supplying energy by predefined sequence; ii) fixed proportional distribution, based on total fixed shares; and iii) variable proportional distribution, based on hourly consumption shares.

In the priority-based distribution, end-users are ranked according to a predetermined priority order; in the fixed proportional distribution, all end-users are assigned a fixed percentage of available energy; and in the variable proportional distribution the allocation of available energy is done on an hourly basis according to the end-users' demand profiles.

In the three strategies, the final objective of the model is to know the use of energy from the PV plant and the centralized battery to reduce costs and enhance the use of solar and stored energy, while minimizing surpluses that go outside the self-consumer network.

The model is then applied to a case-study: a small village in Calatayud Region, Spain

2 MODEL AND STRATEGIES DESCRIPTION

This section provides a detailed overview of the strategies, beginning with the main inputs and outputs, followed by an in-depth explanation of the three distinct strategies.

2.1 Inputs

The model considers the following inputs:

- PV peak power
- Hourly PV production (8760 values)
- Hourly consumption for each end user (8760 values per user)
- Battery storage capacity
- Minimum depth of discharge
- Maximum depth of charge

2.2 Outputs

The following hourly outputs are obtained:

- PV energy consumed directly by end-users (E_{PV})
- PV energy used to charge the battery (E_{bat})
- Battery state of charge
- Unmet energy demand (this is, energy not covered by PV or battery)

By summing the previous values, monthly and annual values are used to better understand the VPP network performance. In addition to the aggregated data, the following annual values are calculated:

- Self-consumption rate (SCR)
- Self-sufficiency rate (SSR)

The SCR reflects the proportion of PV-generated energy that is directly consumed by the load or through stored energy, as opposed to being exported to the grid. Similarly, the SSR measures the extent to which the total energy demand is met by self-generated energy from the PV and storage systems. These metrics are defined as follows [4]:

$$SCR = \frac{E_{PV} + E_{bat}}{E_{PV\_available}} . 100 \quad [\%] \tag{1}$$

10.4229/EUPVSEC2025/5DV.3.9

$$SSR = \frac{E_{PV} + E_{bat}}{E_{load}}.100 \quad [\%] \qquad (2)$$

where E_{PV} and E_{bat} correspond to the self-consumed energy from PV and battery, respectively, $E_{PV\_available}$ is the available PV energy and E_{load} refers to the total energy demand of all self-consumers.

A high SCR indicates efficient local energy use, minimizing reliance on grid exports. A higher SSR indicates greater self-sufficiency, reducing the system's dependence on the grid.

2.3 Scenarios

Three allocation scenarios are considered (a detailed explanation is presented in the next sections):

- **Priority-based distribution:** PV and battery-stored energies are supplied to end-users according to a predefined sequence of priority.
- **Fixed proportional distribution:** PV energy and battery-stored energy are allocated based on each end-user's predetermined share of total energy usage.
- **Variable proportional distribution:** PV energy and battery-stored energy are allocated based on each end-user's predetermined share of hourly energy usage.

2.3.1 Priority-based distribution

Initially, end-users are ranked according to a predetermined priority order.

Thereafter, the following criteria are applicable for each hour:

1. Surplus PV production: If PV energy generation exceeds the total consumption of all end-users, their energy needs are fully met by PV. Any excess energy is then directed to charge the battery, or exported to the national grid if battery is completely charged.
2. Insufficient PV production: If PV generation falls short of total demand, the system attempts to discharge the battery to cover the deficit. If the battery cannot supply enough energy, some demand remains unmet.
   In this case, PV energy is first allocated to the highest-priority users. Then, battery is used to supply the next group in the priority order. Lower-priority users may experience partial or complete energy shortfalls.

2.3.2 Proportional distribution

In the fixed proportional distribution, end-users are firstly assigned a fixed and uniform allocation of available energy.

On the other hand, in the variable proportional distribution, end-users are initially allocated available energy on an hourly basis according to their demand profile.

In the two proportional distribution scenarios, the following conditions shall apply on an hourly basis:

1. Surplus PV production: If PV energy available for each end-user exceeds its individual consumption, energy needs are fully met by PV. Any excess energy is then directed to charge the battery, or exported to the national grid if battery is completely charged.
2. Partial sufficiency of assigned PV shares: When the allocated PV energy is sufficient for some users but not for all, two cases appear:
   a. If an end-user's assigned PV share is sufficient: They consume their portion of PV energy. Any remaining PV energy after all allocations is used to charge the battery.
   b. If an end-user's assigned PV share is insufficient: The battery is discharged considering the shares to supplement the shortfall (if stored energy is available).
3. Insufficient PV production: If PV generation falls short for all end-users (for example during night-time), the system attempts to discharge the battery considering the shares. This is, if allocated energy in the battery for each end-user is enough, demand for this end-user is fulfilled, if not some demand remains unmet.

The difference between fixed and variable proportional distributions lies in the fact that the former applies a constant percentage throughout the year, while the latter assigns an hourly percentage to each self-consumer based on their previous annual energy consumption profile.

3 CASE-STUDY DESCRIPTION

A REC made up of a static south-oriented 68 kWp PV generator installed at 25° inclination, a 370 kWh battery capacity, and with 22 self-consumers has been used to validate the strategies developed. From the 22 end-users, 17 are individual households and 5 belong to a cultural association. This system, apart from the battery, represents a real installation in a small village in Calatayud Region, Spain.

Based on a previous simulation of the PV system in SISIFO [5], annual PV energy production is 1,530 kWh/kWp.

The battery capacity is determined based on the average daily energy demand. Operational limits are defined such that the minimum and maximum state of charge correspond to 20% and 80% of the total battery capacity, respectively. Real consumption data of the 22 self-consumers are available and used as input. Annual energy consumption per end-user is presented in Figure 1, in which one (number 18, representing a cultural association) stands out due to its high consumption.

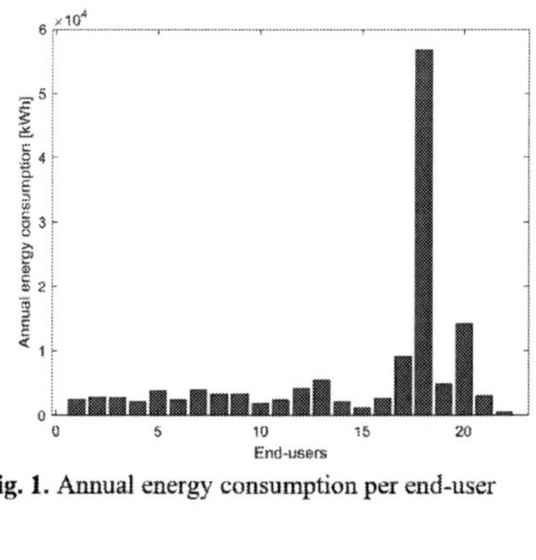

Fig. 1. Annual energy consumption per end-user

Annual consumption is 135 MWh, and Figure 2 shows the monthly distribution of the total consumption (as the sum of the 22 end-users).

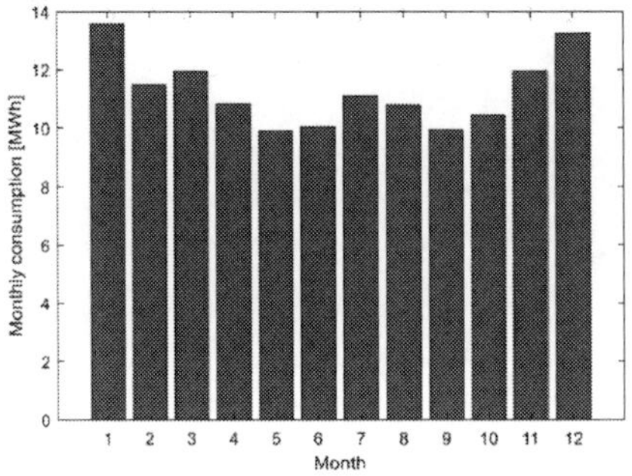

Fig. 2. Monthly distribution of the total consumption

4 RESULTS

This work presents a VPP made up of a PV plant, a centralized battery and different self-consumers.

For presentation clarity, the different scenarios will be enumerated as follows:

- Scenario 1: Priority-based distribution
- Scenario 2: Fixed proportional distribution
- Scenario 3: Variable proportional distribution

The PV energy produced by the PV generator is 104,070 kWh (obviously the same for three scenarios). Table I shows the annual outputs obtained in terms of PV energy used, and Table II the unmet energy demand. As expected, PV used reaches its maximum in scenario 3 (90,596 kWh), while the lowest value is obtained in scenario 1 (78,215 kWh). PV energy consumed directly is equal in scenarios 1 and 3 in total, However, this equal total does not reflect uniform consumption across individual end-users—each user consumes PV energy differently depending on the scenario.

Table I: PV energy used for the 3 scenarios under study

Scenario	1	2	3
PV energy consumed directly [kWh]	57,101	32,631	57,101
PV energy used to charge the battery [kWh]	21,114	51,895	33,495

Table II: Unmet energy demand for the 3 scenarios under study

Scenario	1	2	3
Unmet energy demand [kWh]	57,009	50,699	44,628

Unmet energy demand is 42% in the first scenario, 37% in the second one, and 33% in the third scenario.

Table III includes the two rates considered for the 3 scenarios: as expected, lowest values are always obtained in scenario 1 and highest ones in scenario 3.

Table III: SCR and SSR for the 3 scenarios under study

Scenario	1	2	3
SCR [%]	75%	81%	87%
SSR [%]	58%	63%	67%

In no-batteries scenarios equivalent to these ones, SCR and SSR are obviously lower. Particularly, SCR in scenario 1 and 3 would be 55% and SSR 42%. For scenario 2, SCR 31% and SSR 24%.

5 CONCLUSIONS AND FUTURE WORK

This work presented a VPP made up of a PV generator, a centralized battery and different self-consumers/end-users.

Three allocation scenarios had been considered: priority-based distribution, fixed proportional distribution and variable proportional distribution.

The application of the different scenarios to a particular village showed the expected results: scenario 3 (variable proportional distribution) is the one who presents higher values of both self-consumption and self-sufficient rates, with values of 87% and 67% respectively. Although, this scenario, as well as the first one, is not possible in some countries due to current legislation.

The next phase in the development of this VPP will involve the following steps:

- Modelling of a new variable proportional distribution: by feature dynamic, real-time management of power distribution based on current PV production, battery state-of-charge, demand and usage patterns, and grid energy prices.
- Modeling of grid interconnection: by integrating mechanisms for simulating energy exchange with the national grid, including bidirectional power flows, grid constraints, and regulatory frameworks.
- Integration of economic constraints: by incorporating parameters such as electricity tariffs, market price dynamics, and battery costs.
- Inclusion of electric vehicles [6]: to extend the system modeling framework to account for electric vehicles as dynamic assets, considering their charging behavior, and mobility patterns.
- Migration to python and open-source deployment: with the goal of enhance scalability, maintainability, and fostering community collaboration through open-source.

6 ACKNOWLEDGEMENTS

JALON: Funded by the European Union. Views and opinions expressed are however those of the author(s) only and do not necessarily reflect those of the European Union or CINEA. Neither the European Union nor the granting authority can be held responsible for them.

7 REFERENCES

[1] N. Naval, J. M. Yusta, Virtual power plant models and electricity markets - A review, Renewable and Sustainable Energy Reviews, Volume 149, 2021, 111393, https://doi.org/10.1016/j.rser.2021.111393.

[2] European Union. Directive (EU) 2018/2001 of the European Parliament and of the Council on the Promotion of the Use of Energy from Renewable Sources; European Union: Brussels, Belgium, 2018.

[3] M. Esfahani, A. Alizadeh, B. Cao, I. Kamwa, M. Xu, Bridging theory and practice: A comprehensive review of virtual power plant technologies and their real-world applications, Renewable and Sustainable Energy Reviews, Volume 222, 2025, 115929, https://doi.org/10.1016/j.rser.2025.115929

[4] R. Luthander, J. Widén, D. Nilsson, J. Palm, Photovoltaic self-consumption in buildings: A review, Applied Energy, Volume 142, 2015, Pages 80-94, https://doi.org/10.1016/j.apenergy.2014.12.028

[5] Universidad Politécnica de Madrid, "SISIFO: An online simulator of PV systems," 2025, v3.3. Accessed: Jul. 31, 2025. [Online]. Available: https://www.sisifo.info

[6] C. Sanz-Cuadrado, L. Narvarte, A. B, Cristóbal, Energy Valorization Strategies in Rural Renewable Energy Communities: A Path to Social Revitalization and Sustainable Development. Energies 2025, 18, 2561. https://doi.org/10.3390/en18102561

VALIDATION OF A MULTISTRATEGY ENERGY MANAGEMENT SYSTEM FOR BATTERY IN PV PLANTS

Celena Lorenzo[a], Laura Barrutia[a], Luis Narvarte[a], Jesús Heras[b], Carlos Awadallah[b]
[a]Instituto de Energía Solar - Universidad Politécnica de Madrid, 28031 Madrid, Spain
[b]Wattkraft España, 28046, Madrid, Spain

c.lorenzon@upm.es

ABSTRACT: The integration of Li-ion batteries with photovoltaic (PV) plants is crucial for enhancing grid stability and maximizing renewable energy utilization. However, advanced Energy Management Systems (EMS) are required to optimize battery operation for both performance-oriented and regulation-oriented services. This paper presents the preliminary validation of a smart EMS for a grid-connected PV-battery system, tested at the UPM facilities. The EMS implements five control strategies: Time-of-Use arbitrage, Peak Shaving, Maximization of Self-Consumption, Frequency Regulation, and Capacity Market participation. Preliminary results demonstrate accurate power tracking (RMSE < 0.25 kW) and rapid response times (<650 ms) for the first three strategies, confirming the system's readiness for grid services. While current performance is suitable for capacity markets, faster response times are needed for ancillary services. Future work will integrate an AI-based market predictor to enable dynamic strategy selection and improve economic returns.

Keywords: Li-ion batteries, Energy Management System (EMS), photovoltaic systems, grid services

1 INTRODUCTION

The mitigation of climatic change and the depletion of fossil fuels are leading to a very fast energy transition, where electrification is playing a key role [1]. Electrification goes hand in hand with the large-scale deployment of renewable energy. However, the increasing penetration rates of intermittent energy sources (mainly wind and solar) are putting at risk the stability of the electric grids [2]. A recent example was the blackout that affected the interconnected electrical grid of Spain and Portugal on April 28, 2025, where the lack of sufficient operational energy reserves for frequency regulation was one of the key causes that led to the grid's collapse [3].

The integration of energy storage systems is one of the most powerful tools for strengthening the power grid. In particular, the use of Li-ion batteries integrated with PV systems is one of the solutions to this problem to receive more attention [4], [5], [6]. Although a lot has already been done [7][2], [8], [9] , advanced Energy Management Systems (EMS) are necessary for better optimization of the system performance and of the energy trading of PV plants.

Furthermore, one of the main barriers to the massive deployment of Li-ion batteries is still their high cost [10]. Control strategies that improve the performance of the PV plant will increase its economic revenue. In addition, control strategies related to grid regulation (i.e. frequency regulation, contingency market, capacity market…) have a great economical potential, as the grid operators pay considerable amounts just for availability [11]. To amortize the initial investment cost of the battery in a reasonably short period of time, it is necessary to combine both types of strategies (performance-oriented and regulation-oriented).

This paper presents the preliminary results for the validation of a smart EMS system for the integration of batteries in PV plants. This validation is taking place with an outdoor demonstrator at the UPM facilities. The smart EMS will be able to integrate different control strategies, attending to different objectives. Some of these strategies are already commercially available (for example, the Maximization of Self-Consumption) and others are more innovative (for example, Grid-Ancillary Services). There will be two operation modes: manual (where a certain control strategy is selected) and automatic (where the EMS itself will be able to decide which one of the control strategies is more convenient, depending on several external factors like the market prices for different services).

2 METHODOLOGY

2.1 Objectives and validation planning

This work is part of a European research project called PVOP [12], that aims at the innovative digitalization of the PV sector. One of the central lines of work is related to the control of PV plants to optimize their performance. The main objectives of this line of work are:

- To develop and demonstrate technical solutions for the control of PV plants to maximize their performance.
- To optimize the energy trading of PV plants with batteries.

For achieving these objectives, the smart EMS for a Li-ion battery will be implemented in two phases:

1. An alpha version is being currently developed, integrated and validated in an outdoor demonstrator at the UPM facilities. This demonstrator is composed of a Li-ion battery (model LUNA 97kWh/100kW), powered by a 16 kW_p PV generator and connected to the electric grid (although capable of stand-alone operation), according to Figure 1:

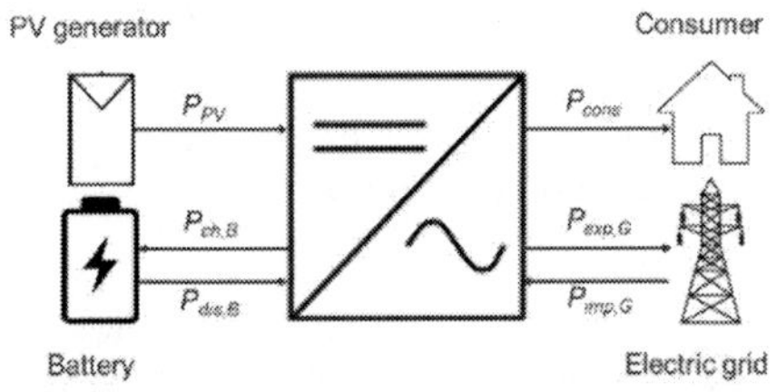

Figure 1: Schematic of the demonstrator at the UPM facilities.

2. Using the lessons learnt during the alpha version validation, a beta version will be implemented and validated in a real PV power plant, under real operation conditions.

This paper presents the preliminary results for the validation of the alpha version, including some of the control strategies that will be implemented in the smart EMS.

2.2 Control strategies

There are five different control strategies that will be implemented in the smart EMS: three of them are performance-oriented (TOU, PS and MSC) and two, regulation-oriented (FR and CM). They are described in Table I:

Table I: Battery control strategies to be implemented in the smart EMS.

Operating modes	**Revenue Generation**	**Return on Investment**
Time of Use (TOU) Arbitrage	TOU arbitrage involves charging the battery during off-peak hours when electricity prices are low and discharging during peak hours when prices are high. This process allows the BESS to capitalize on price differentials by buying low and selling high	Consistently leveraging daily market fluctuations generates regular income, contributing to the overall revenue stack and shortening the payback period.
Peak Shaving (PS)	Peak shaving reduces the demand charges on electricity bills by lowering the peak demand during high-consumption periods. By discharging the battery during peak times, businesses can avoid the highest tariff rates associated with their peak usage.	A significant reduction in demand charges, which can constitute a large portion of industrial and commercial electricity bills, directly improves net income. This cost-saving measure adds to the revenue stack, accelerating the return on investment. This operation mode can avoid Grid reconstruction (AGR).
Maximization of Self-Consumption (MSC)	This mode ensures that energy generated by a PV system is used as much as possible on-site rather than being exported to the grid at lower rates. The BESS stores excess solar energy during the day for use during the night or periods of low generation.	Maximizing self-consumption reduces dependency on grid electricity, leading to substantial savings on energy bills. These savings contribute to the revenue stack, resulting in a faster recovery of the BESS investment.
Frequency Regulation (FR) and Ancillary Services	Providing grid services such as frequency regulation, voltage support, and spinning reserve can generate additional income. Utilities and grid operators often pay for these ancillary services to maintain grid stability and reliability.	Participating in these markets provides a steady revenue stream, adding to the revenue stack and ensuring a quicker payback period.
Capacity Market (CM)	Capacity markets allow BESS owners to receive payments for being available to supply energy during high-demand periods, ensuring sufficient capacity for grid stability.	By participating in these markets, the BESS earns additional income simply by being available, which adds to the revenue stack and contributes to faster investment recovery.

The three performace-oriented strategies (TOU, PS and MSC) have already been validated for two different consumption profiles (during two complete days for each profile). These profiles were simulated in order to be representative of a typical residential and industrial consumptions. The real PV production of the PV generator was scaled-up in order to be of a similar magnitude as the consumption.

The FR and CM strategies do not require of a specific control validation: it is only necessary to assure that the battery can deliver/absorb a certain amount of energy (with high accuracy) in a short period of time (as demanded by the grid operator). Both metrics (accuracy when following a power setpoint and response time) have been characterized during the validation of the three other strategies.

3 RESULTS

3.1 Time of Use (TOU)

The objective of this strategy is to set a charge and a discharge period for the next day, depending on the electricity prices announced by the grid operator. When the prices are lower, the battery will charge from the grid; when the prices are higher, it will sell the electricity to the grid. For the validation of this strategy, the PV energy was directly self-consumed by the university.

Figure 2 presents the power profiles (commands sent to the battery, loads consumption, PV inverters active power, charge and discharge battery power and energy at the Point of Injection -POI-) for a complete day with the TOU control implemented. It can be observed that the battery is charged between 13-15h (when electricity prices were lower) and discharged between 21-23h (when electricity prices were higher).

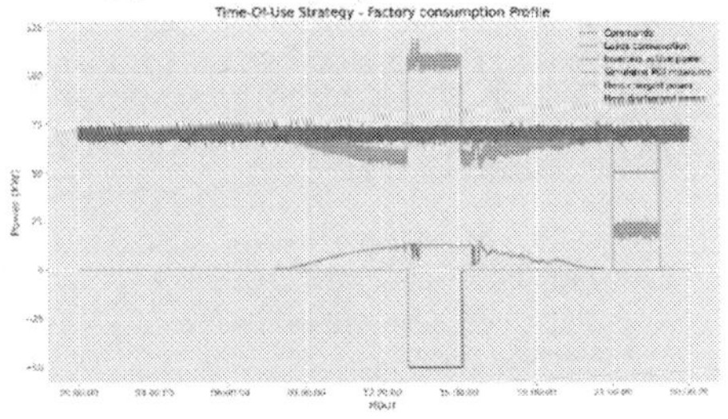

Figure 2: Power profiles during the validation of the TOU control strategy.

The KPIs obtained during the TOU validation are the following:

- RMSE ($P_{SetPoint;Battery}$ - $P_{measured,Battery}$) < **0.25 kW**
- $t_{transition}$ < **600 ms**
- $\frac{\text{Energy trade during TOU hours}}{\text{Total energy trade}} = \mathbf{100\%}$

3.2 Peak Shaving (PS)

The objective of this strategy is to use the battery to stop the system from going over the contracted power limit. This happens when consumption is too high and the avilable PV power isn't enough.

Figure 3 presents the power profiles (commands sent to the battery, loads consumption, PV inverters active power, charge and discharge battery power) for a complete day with the PS control implemented. It can be observed that the battery is charged with the PV surplus and discharged when the loads consumption exceeds the PS threshold. The result is that the POI measures exceed this threshold but very briefly. Actually, when calculating the total energy consumed for every 15-minutes period (which is the period that the grid operator considers for detecting an excess in consumption), the grid limitation was always respected.

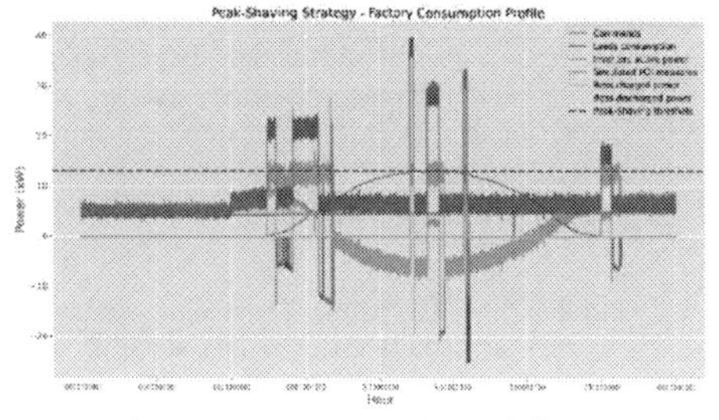

Figure 3: Power profiles during the validation of the PS control strategy.

The KPIs obtained during the PS validation are the following:

- RMSE ($P_{SetPoint;Battery}$ - $P_{measured,Battery}$) < **0.2 kW**
- $t_{transition}$ < **500 ms**
- $\int_{t1}^{t2} P_{imp/exp,G} \leq P_{max,G} \times 15min$: **100%**

3.3 Maximization of Self-Consumption (MSC)

The objective of this strategy is to use the battery for storing PV energy when it exceeds the loads consumption, and discharging when the consumption exceeds the PV production. This way, the PV self-consumtpion is maximized.

Figure 4 presents the power profiles (commands sent to the battery, loads consumption, PV inverters active power, charge and discharge battery power) for a complete day with the MSC control implemented. It can be observed that the battery is charged when the PV production is high (during the central hours of the day) and discharged when the PV production decreases in the morning and in the evening. This way, the excess of PV energy at midday is later used for covering the evening consumption. In consequence, less PV energy is sold to the grid, and less electricity is bought from it. This does not only represent an economic advantage, but also avoids the congestion of the transmission electric lines.

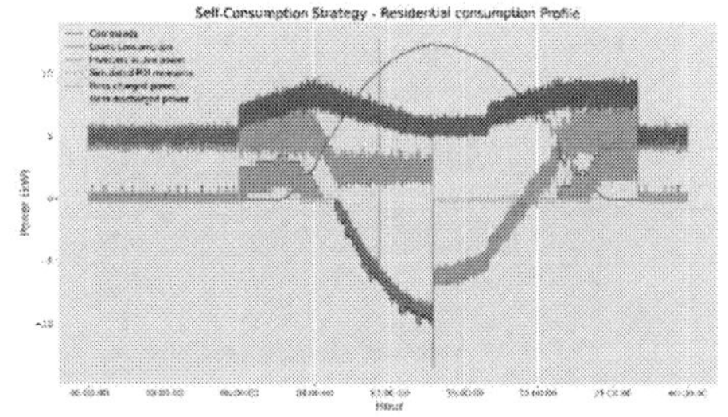

Figure 4: Power profiles during the validation of the MSC control strategy.

The KPIs obtained during the PS validation are the following:

- RMSE ($P_{SetPoint;Battery}$ - $P_{measured,Battery}$) < **0.25 kW**
- $t_{transition}$ < **650 ms**
- $Self - Consumption\ Rate = 82 - 100\%$

10.4229/EUPVSEC2025/5DV.3.11

4 CONLUSIONS

-The three control strategies -TOU, PS and MSC- have been correctly implemented. The different control logics have fulfilled their objectives: charging/discharging when indicated depending on the electricity market prices (TOU), avoiding that the energy at the Point of Injection exceeds a certain power limit (PS) and maximizing the PV self-consumption for reducing the PV surplus sold to the grid (MSC).

-The EMS fulfils the power commands with good accuracy: the mean RMSE is lower than 0.25kW, while the power commands range between 5-100kW.

-Response times are sufficient for normal FR and CM, where batteries need to be able to act in 2-3s [8].

-Response times might be insufficient for contingency markets, which are part of Ancillary Services, where batteries need to be able to act in 200-300ms [13].

The next step is to integrate these three control strategies into a single smart EMS, that will decide which one is the most convenient at every moment (mainly from an economic point of view, although degradation will also be considered). This smart EMS will also consider possible revenues from participating in Capacity Markets. However, the response times still need to be lowered before considering participating in the FR and Ancillary Services markets. This implies both hardware and software improvements.

Finally, an AI-based electricity market predictor will be integrated into the smart EMS. This way, the electricity prices will be estimated for longer periods than one day, potentially improving the battery management.

REFERENCES

[1] IEA, "World Energy Outlook 2023," 2023. [Online]. Available: www.iea.org/terms

[2] IRENA, "Renewable Power Generation Costs in 2022", 2023. [Online]. Available: www.irena.org

[3] Red Eléctrica, "Incidente en el Sistema Eléctrico Peninsular Espanol el 18 de junio de 2025". [Online]. Available: chrome-extension://efaidnbmnnnibpcajpcglclefindmkaj/https://d1n1o4zeyfu21r.cloudfront.net/WEB_Incidente_SistemaElectricoPeninsularEspanol_18junio2025.pdf

[4] H. C. Hesse, M. Schimpe, D. Kucevic, and A. Jossen, "Lithium-ion battery storage for the grid - A review of stationary battery storage system design tailored for applications in modern power grids", *Energies,* vol. 10, no. 12, 2017, doi: 10.3390/en10122107.

[5] C. A. Hill, M. C. Such, D. Chen, J. Gonzalez, and W. M. K. Grady, "Battery energy storage for enabling integration of distributed solar power generation," *IEEE Trans Smart Grid*, vol. 3, no. 2, pp. 850–857, 2012, doi: 10.1109/TSG.2012.2190113.

[6] P. Ferreira Torres *et al.*, "Energy Storage as a Transmission Asset—Assessing the Multiple Uses of a Utility-Scale Battery Energy Storage System in Brazil," *Energies (Basel)*, vol. 18, no. 4, Feb. 2025, doi: 10.3390/en18040902.

[7] M. Pinho Almeida, A. R. Arrifano Manito, G. Figueiredo Pinto Filho, and R. Zilles, "Optimization tool for operating isolated diesel-photovoltaic-battery hybrid power systems using day-ahead power forecasts," *Journal of Renewable and Sustainable Energy*, vol. 15, no. 4, Jul. 2023, doi: 10.1063/5.0156371.

[8] Y. Shi, B. Xu, D. Wang, and B. Zhang, "Using Battery Storage for Peak Shaving and Frequency Regulation: Joint Optimization for Superlinear Gains," *IEEE Transactions on Power Systems*, vol. PP, Feb. 2017, doi: 10.1109/TPWRS.2017.2749512.

[9] S. Tibude, G. Goyal, A. Ranjan, and S. Bodkhe, *Advanced Energy Management Strategies for Hybrid Energy Storage Systems in Electric Vehicles: A Comprehensive Review*. 2025. doi: 10.1109/ICPC2T63847.2025.10958756.

[10] O. Schmidt, S. Melchior, A. Hawkes, and I. Staffell, "Projecting the Future Levelized Cost of Electricity Storage Technologies," *Joule*, vol. 3, no. 1, pp. 81–100, Jan. 2019, doi: 10.1016/j.joule.2018.12.008.

[11] AEMO, "Ancillary Services Market Report. Australian Energy Market Operator." Available: https://www.aemo.com.au/energy-systems/electricity/national-electricity-market-nem/system-operations/ancillary-services

[12] "PVOP Project: Digitalization of Photovoltaic Systems. Horizon Europe Programme." Available: https://pvop.eu/

[13] ENTSO-E, "Market Report 2023", Available: https://www.entsoe.eu/about/

PHOTOVOLTAIC HOSTING CAPACITY IN NORDIC DISTRIBUTION GRIDS

Lauri Aaltonen and Kari Lappalainen
Tampere University, Electrical Engineering Unit, P. O. Box 692, FI-33101 Tampere, Finland
lauri.aaltonen.tuni.fi, kari.lappalainen@tuni.fi

ABSTRACT: Due to the ongoing energy transition, distribution grids are experiencing a rapid change. Centralized power production is being replaced by variable, distributed electricity production such as wind and solar power. Many consumers have been installing photovoltaic (PV) power production at their premises. The variability of PV generation and its impact on grid performance poses challenges. Understanding these challenges is crucial for optimizing PV system integration. This research aims to investigate the factors affecting PV hosting capacity in Nordic distribution grids using real measurement data for PV modules as well as real Finnish distribution grid data. The findings will prove insights on different types of low voltage grids in Finland and compare them.
Keywords: hosting capacity, energy transition, photovoltaic power production, distribution grid

1 INTRODUCTION

Photovoltaic (PV) installations are on the rise in Europe but also in Nordic countries such as Finland. According to the Energy Authority of Finland, grid-connected PV production capacity rose over 300 MW during the year 2023 [1]. In the neighboring country, Sweden, the amount was even higher, around 1600 MW [2]. A large portion of the installed PV production is micro production, i.e., it is connected to the low voltage (LV) distribution grid. Also, electric vehicles are increasing in popularity for newly registered cars.

The components in electrical grids can have a lifetime of even many decades which means that many sections of the grids were designed a long time ago with only consumption customers in mind. A high penetration of distributed generation such as PV may create issues in the grids that the distribution system operators (DSOs) need to solve. Some of these solutions, like grid reinforcements, can be costly and time consuming. In the end, the grid customers are the ones paying for it via subscription fees.

When the PV penetration increases enough in the grid, some grid constraint will be exceeded. Hosting capacity (HC) is defined as the maximum amount of new distributed generation or load that the grid can handle before any of the selected constraints are exceeded. Reverse power flow results in overvoltage, instead of undervoltage as in forward power flow. Similarly, also the thermal limits, e.g., line ampacity or transformer loading, can be exceeded. Other factors that limit the HC can be unbalance issues if the PV installations are single phase. Power quality can also be an issue with cloud movements causing rapid voltage changes as well as grid connected inverter injecting harmonic currents. According to a literature review by Fatima et al. [3] the most pronounced limiting constraint used in PV HC studies was voltage violations, followed by ampacity and unbalance. According to [4] in LV grids those were power quality and feeder threshold limits. In Nordic grids unbalance is not generally an issue since most LV customers have three phase connections to the grid.

Generally, DSOs have solved the issues with classical grid reinforcement measures. For example, if line section ampacity is a limiting factor or the customer voltage is out of bounds, changing the size of the cabling changes the impedance and therefore mitigates the severe load flow case.

Many studies of PV hosting capacity have been done for low voltage grids [5–6]. Unfortunately, most of the studies used a test grid instead of a real grid. Few studies [7–8] have been done using real grid values, but those studies usually focused on a single grid type, and none have been done for Nordic distribution grids.

This paper studies PV HC in three real Nordic LV distribution grids. The next chapter focuses on data and methods of this study. The 10 second interval PV production data is formed from power plant measurements, sun position and aerial imagery. Grid data is collected from a DSO. The customer load data from hourly energy meter readings is utilized. Chapter 3 presents and discusses the results from the grids based on the time-based simulations from summer months of 2024. Finally, in Chapter 4 some concluding remarks are made. The results of this study are applicable for distribution grids in the Nordic countries, since they share similar grid structure, climate, electricity market etc.

2 DATA AND METHODS

2.1 Data

The data used in this study is from four summer months in 2024: May, June, July and August. As the goal is to study PV hosting capacity, the nighttime hours, 18:00–06:00 EEST, were omitted from the data.

This study uses LV grid data from one of the Finnish DSOs, Tampereen Energia Sähköverkko Oy. This data includes grid component information, topology and customer load profiles. Load profiles are on a 1-hour measurement interval.

The data used to model PV power production is from Tampere University Solar PV Power Station Research Plant [9] that is in the same area as the DSO. The solar data used was in 10-second intervals. Backsheet temperature of a PV module was measured with a National Instruments Pt100 thermocouple. Global and diffuse horizontal irradiances were recorded with Kipp & Zonen CMP22 and CMP21 pyranometers, respectively.

2.2 Modelling of PV power production

PV power production was modelled using the irradiance measurements and the module backsheet temperature measurement. The diffuse irradiance is measured with a pyranometer (CMP21) that has a shading ring to block the direct irradiation. To calculate the irradiance that a PV module with an arbitrary tilt and orientation receives the direct irradiance needs to be known. Direct irradiance G_{direct} can be calculated by subtracting the diffuse

10.4229/EUPVSEC2025/5DV.3.14

irradiation $G_{diffuse}$ from the global one G_{global}, i.e., $G_{direct} = G_{global} - G_{diffuse}$.

Since all the production is assumed to be installed at rooftops, the roof orientation and tilt play a central role when determining the unique production profile for each rooftop. To know the irradiance that the PV modules receive, one must know the installation tilt and azimuth angles as well as the position of the Sun in addition to the irradiance.

The position of the Sun, i.e., the zenith and azimuth angles, were calculated for every timestamp using the algorithm of [10]. The algorithm takes GPS-coordinates and timestamps as inputs. It does not consider other things impacting the local observed sun position such as air pressure among other things. The position of the Sun was calculated for a single GPS-point selected in central Tampere area as all the studied grids for the study were nearby. The resulting estimate of the Sun elevation from the horizon, in the city of Tampere for one day is presented in Fig. 1. and azimuth in Fig. 2.

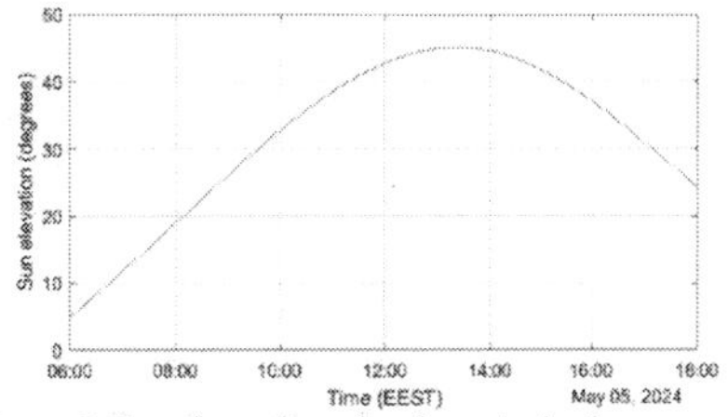

Figure 1: Local sun elevation from the horizon as a function of time for May 5th, 2024.

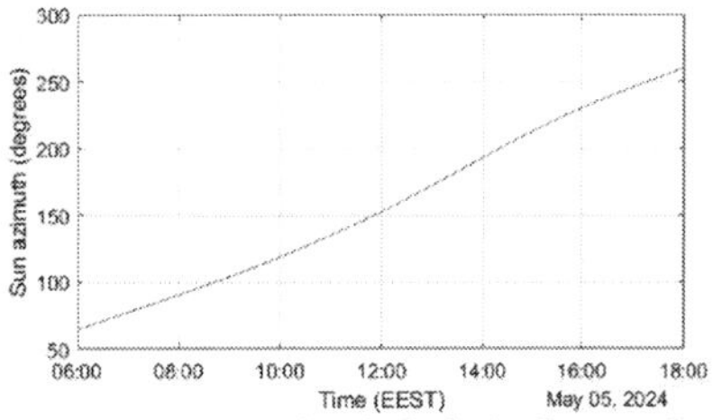

Figure 2: Local sun azimuth clockwise from north as a function of time for May 5th, 2024.

As the tilt and azimuth angle of a PV module are known, as well as Sun position in the sky for every timestep, the direct irradiation arriving at the module can be calculated as

$$G_{\text{Direct, module}} = \cos(\text{AOI})\, G_{\text{Direct}}, \quad (2)$$

where AOI is the angle-of-incidence meaning the angle between the sunrays and the normal of the module. The total irradiance of the module is therefore

$$G_{\text{Module}} = G_{\text{Direct, module}} + G_{\text{Diffuse, module}}. \quad (3)$$

This means that even if the position of the Sun goes behind the module, i.e., Eq. (2) goes to zero, the module will still receive some diffuse irradiation and produce some, although small, power. In this study the measured diffuse horizontal irradiance was used as $G_{\text{Diffuse, module}}$, i.e., $G_{\text{Diffuse, module}} = G_{\text{Diffuse}}$.

As the PV plant size increases, i.e., the plant is utilizing a larger land area, the irradiance fluctuations become smoother. A spatial irradiance method proposed in [11] was used to smooth out the irradiance measurement. The spatial irradiance G_S was calculated as

$$G_s(t) = \frac{G_{\text{Module}}(t)}{\left(\frac{\sqrt{A_{\text{PV}}}}{2\pi \cdot 0.0204 \cdot A_{\text{PV}}^{-0.4997}}\right)s + 1}, \quad (4)$$

where A_{PV} is the area in hectares that is occupied by the PV plant and s is the Laplace-variable.

The generated PV power was obtained using an equation [12] that takes the PV module temperature into account, as temperature greatly affects the current–voltage characteristics of the PV modules. The generated power of the PV plant is

$$P_{\text{Gen, PV}} = \frac{P_{\text{nom}}}{G_{\text{STC}}} G_S[1 - \beta(T_{\text{PVM}} - T_{\text{STC}})], \quad (5)$$

where P_{nom} is the nominal power of the PV system, G_{STC} is the irradiance in standard test conditions (STC), β is the temperature coefficient estimated to be 0.0045 1/°C based on average value from [11], T_{STC} is the temperature in the STC and T_{PVM} is the PV module temperature measured from the backsheet.

In this study, PV power production for the roofs of flat roofed buildings and the south-facing roofs of gabled buildings was formed using Eqs. (1–5) and an aerial image tool [13] illustrated in Fig. 3 along with its production curve in Fig. 4.

Figure 3: PV plant size selection example using the aerial image tool [13] for a tilted roof of a detached house.

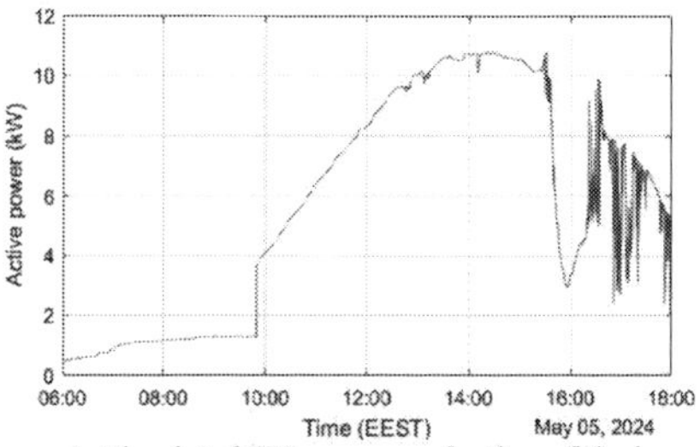

Figure 4: Simulated PV power production of the house in Fig. 4 for May 5th, 2024.

As can be seen from Figs. 3–4, the roof azimuth

deviates 26 degrees from South to West. This means that the peak production happening during the solar noon at approximately 13:15 in Fig. 1 is shifted in the production figure to the right, to around 14:00. The sudden boost in production just before 10:00 is due to the Sun moving from the backside and side of the panel to the front of the panel, geographically. This can be verified by inspecting Fig. 2. The evening of that day was cloudy so that can be seen as the high variation of power at the end of the production curve.

Although the PV power plant is operating at unity power factor, the possible inverter filter might produce reactive power to the grid. The produced reactive power was modelled as

$$Q_{\text{Gen, PV}} = d_0 + d_1 P_{\text{Gen, PV}}, \tag{6}$$

where d_0 and d_1 are coefficients determined to be 0.072 and 0.034, respectively. [14]

For houses with a tilted roof, a 45° tilt angle was assumed for the installation of PV modules and the whole south facing roof area was assumed to be utilized. For flat roofed houses, a tilt angle of 45° was assumed with a row spacing of 1.5 m to prevent self-shading during the peak hours. Self-shading effect was not considered, as it does not typically occur at the highest production hours. P_{nom} was calculated by multiplying the area occupied by the modules by a typical PV power density of 200 W/m². Only the habited houses were utilized, i.e., no sheds or garages were considered. If the orientation of a gabled house deviated over 80° degrees from South, i.e., it was not very suitable for a PV installation, it was omitted.

2.3 Low voltage grids

Three example low voltage grids were chosen: rural, suburban and urban. The rural grid, presented in Fig. 5, was a countryside grid comprising mostly of overhead lines with some of the consumer connection lines being cabled connections. The area had mostly farms and summer cottages as customers. The suburban grid, in Fig. 6, was chosen from the outskirts of Tampere city with a mix of detached houses and townhouse complexes. The urban grid, shown in Fig. 7., included several big apartment buildings, a small store, a bar and a few detached houses. The urban grid was fully underground cabled and the suburban one was mostly underground cabled with a small exception of the northernmost feeder having a relatively short amount of overhead line.

The suburban grid features the highest amount of connection points while the urban and rural ones have clearly fewer. A connection point may have one or more customers: a connection point of a detached house has typically one customer, but an apartment building can have several. For example, a connection point with main fuses of 3x320 A may have several 3x25 A fused customers who are all metered individually. These customers of each connection point are summed together to form the grid connection point power. As the customers are LV customers, only their hourly active power consumption is measured. For the study, all customers were assumed to have a 0.95 power factor. Grid data, e.g., cable lengths and types, were fetched from the same system that the DSO uses to design and document the grids, network information system (NIS).

2.4 Hosting capacity determination

The factors that were used to determine the hosting

Figure 5: Topology of the rural grid.

Figure 6: Topology of the suburban grid.

Figure 7: Topology of the urban grid.

capacity were transformer rating, line continuous ampacity and customer connection point under-/overvoltage. The transformer rating and line ampacities were collected from the NIS.

The customer voltages need to be within agreed limits that vary between regions and countries. USA uses the ANSI-standard which defines the limits as ±5% from the nominal. Germany has set a +3% limit for overvoltage on top of the European one [15] which sets limits to be ±10%. [3] For this study, the European standard was applied.

PV penetration was increased in increments and simulations in Matlab-Simulink were performed. The increment steps were the roofs, which were selected to adopt PV production at a random order.

There are many ways to define HC. For this study the HC is defined with transformer rating as a reference. This means that HC is the maximum amount of PV penetration that the grid can handle without breaking the constraints presented by nominal active power of the PV in the grid compared to the nominal apparent power of the distribution transformer.

3 RESULTS AND DISCUSSION

The simulations were performed in Matlab-Simulink environment. The maximum and minimum voltages that each customer experienced during the 4 months simulation time were saved. Fig. 8. presents the extreme customer voltages for all three grids as a function of PV penetration.

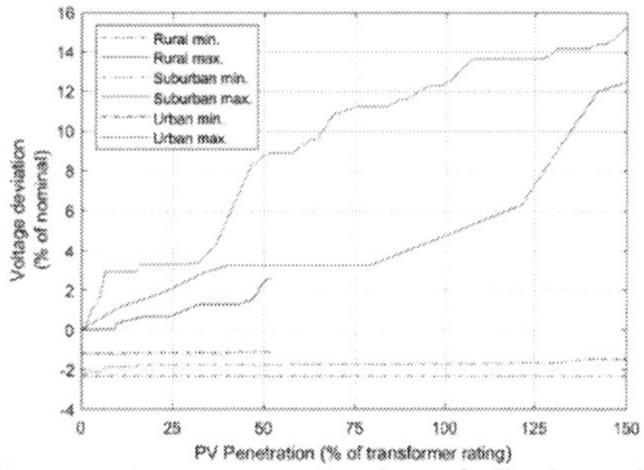

Figure 8: Customer extreme voltages for the three grids as a function of PV penetration in the grid.

The suburban grid has most roofs, so it has many smaller PV penetration increments. The rural grid has low number of customers but a weaker grid and less consumption as many of the summer cottages are used only for a few days a year, resulting in bigger impact on every added PV plant to the grid. The urban grid maximum customer voltage did not exceed the set limit even when all the available roof space was used.

The recorded maximum line ampacities for the grids are presented in Fig. 9 as a function of the PV penetration. The urban grid seems to be heavily loaded, and the PV penetration increments do hardly any harm. The relative maximum currents in the suburban and rural grid increased rapidly with large steps. For the suburban grid, not every added PV system contributed to the highest observed current but only a few.

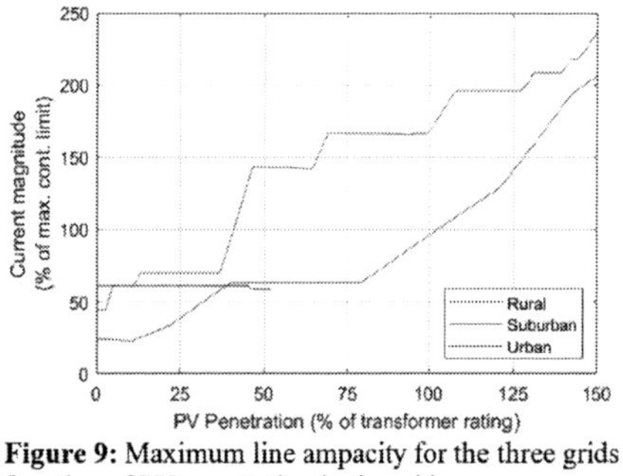

Figure 9: Maximum line ampacity for the three grids as a function of PV penetration in the grid.

The highest transformer loading is presented in Fig. 10 as a function of the PV penetration. The urban grid transformer experienced benefit from high PV penetration. This means that the time of the highest consumption occurred when there was significant amount of PV production and the consumption was much larger than the PV production. For the suburban and rural grids, the transformer loading stayed the same or lowered slightly before the increasing PV penetration started to make it higher.

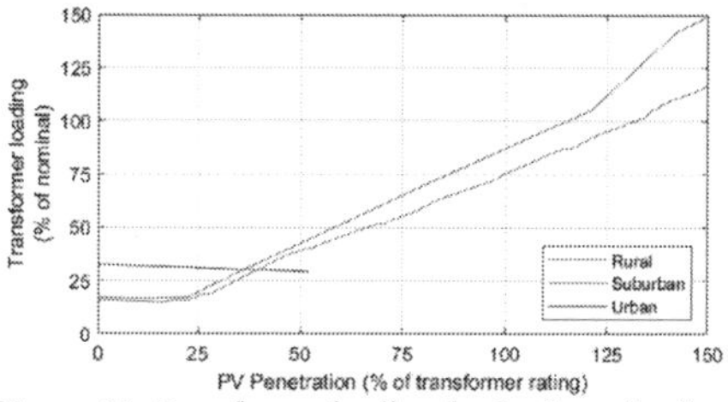

Figure 10: Transformer loading for the three distribution transformers as a function of PV penetration in the grid.

The hosting capacity results are gathered to Table I. The rural grid HC was 102.59% and suburban grid 41.04%. Both had the same limiting factor: line ampacity.

Depending on the voltage profile along the medium voltage feeder, which was not considered in the study, a different limit could be used. The results would have changed if a 5% overvoltage limit had been used. The urban grid did not reach that limit either. The rural grid would still have had the same limiting factor. For the suburban grid, the overvoltage would have become the limiting factor and the HC would have decreased slightly below 40%.

Table I: Hosting capacity with the transformer rating as a reference and the HC limiting factor.

	HC	Limiting factor
Rural	102.59 %	Line ampacity
Suburban	41.04 %	Line ampacity
Urban	-	-

There are only few previous studies made with a time series method for real life LV grids. In real Brazilian LV grids the HC was 38.2% of transformer rating [16]. For a residential LV grid in Zürich, Switzerland HC was determined to be 43% when comparing PV production to the load energy of the grid [17]. A Danish study using real LV grid data from a DSO and 24-hour field measurements found the HC to be 40% of the customer PVs [18].

A study [19] made with example LV grids using Monte Carlo method indicates that the rural HC will be reached at a lower penetration rate than for the urban and intermediate types. A study in Australia [20] using a suburban radial LV grid indicates PV HC to be 35% of the transformer rating. This is closely in line with the results obtained with the Finnish grid in this study. For an urban grid, an earlier study [21] focusing on a part of a real grid in Perth, Australia indicates that the HC will be around 31.9%. For the urban grid in this study, any violations of the factors limiting the HC were not achieved due to insufficient roof space available.

There are several factors in the methodology used that have caused some level of inaccuracy in the results. The sun position used in the study is slightly inaccurate due to the earth rotation speed variance, atmospheric conditions etc. but most importantly the actual GPS coordinates are

10.4229/EUPVSEC2025/5DV.3.14

slightly different for every house. Also, elevation from sea level plays a role in sun observation.

The PV power modeling holds some simplifications and assumptions. The module temperature in tilted roof installations could be slightly higher than the test plant measured module temperature used due to the hot roof being more near and air not flowing as freely. The diffuse irradiation will be slightly different with different installations. For example, flat roofs will have a lower diffuse component due to the nearby panel rows blocking the hemisphere seen by the module. In addition, self-shading and shading from nearby structures were not included in the study.

The customer's consumption was known only from the hourly energy meter readings. For future, a more detailed consumption profile should be studied.

4 CONCLUSIONS

This paper studied photovoltaic hosting capacity in Nordic distribution grids. Three different low voltage grids were chosen: rural, suburban and urban. A time-based simulation was performed in Matlab/Simulink for four summer months of 2024.

The data for grid components and hourly customer consumption was received from a local DSO Tampereen Energia Sähköverkko Oy. The PV production was considered for the roofs of flat roofed buildings and the south-facing roofs of gabled buildings. The roof size, tilt and orientation were considered individually using aerial imagery. Irradiance and PV module temperature measurements were used together with sun position and the unique roof data to form individual production profiles with a 10 second resolution.

The HC was the lowest for the suburban grid with line ampacity as a limiting factor. The rural grid experienced the same situation with a higher HC. The increasing PV penetration caused the urban grid transformer to be under less load. The customer voltages were increased in the urban grid but only to a relatively low level compared to the limit.

There were small uncertainties in the study related to PV production formulation, mainly due to shading not considered. As the time passes and new energy meters get installed, the study should be revised using consumption data with a higher temporal resolution.

ACKNOWLEDGEMENTS

This work used grid and customer data of Tampereen Energia Sähköverkko Oy. L. Aaltonen was funded by Tampereen Energia Sähköverkko Oy and K. Lappalainen was funded by the Research Council of Finland (funding decision 348701).

REFERENCES

[1] Energy Authority of Finland. Available online (accessed on 11.9.2025): https://energiavirasto.fi/en/-/solar-power-production-capacity-rose-to-1-000-megawatts.

[2] IEA. Available online (accessed on 11.9.2025), https://iea-pvps.org/national_survey/national-survey-report-of-pv-power-applications-in-sweden-2023-2.

[3] S. Fatima, V. Püvi, M. Lehtonen, Energies 13 (2020) 4756. https://doi.org/10.3390/en13184756.

[4] W. Martin, Y. Stauffer, C. Ballif, A. Hutter, P.J. Alet, 2018 IEEE PES Innovative Smart Grid Technologies Conference Europe (2018) 1–6. https://doi.org/10.1109/ISGTEurope.2018.8571427.

[5] B. Navarro, M. Navarro, 2017 IEEE PES Innovative Smart Grid Technologies Conference Europe (2017) 1–6. https://doi.org/10.1109/ISGTEurope.2017.8260210.

[6] M.-T. Do, A. Bruyere, B. Francois, IEEE Manchester PowerTech (2017) 1–6. https://doi.org/10.1109/PTC.2017.7981041.

[7] M. Bartecka, G. Barchi, J. Paska, Energies 13 (2020) 2524. https://doi.org/10.3390/en13102524.

[8] D. Schwanz, S. Ronnberg, M. Bollen, IEEE Manchester PowerTech (2017) 1–6. https://doi.org/10.1109/PTC.2017.7981274.

[9] D. Torres Lobera, A. Mäki, J. Huusari, K. Lappalainen, T. Suntio, S. Valkealahti, International Journal of Photoenergy 2013 (2013) 837310. https://doi.org/10.1155/2013/837310.

[10] M. Blanco, K. Milidonis, A. Bonanos, Solar Energy 212 (2020), 339–341. https://doi.org/10.1016/j.solener.2020.10.084.

[11] J. Marcos, L. Marroyo, E. Lorenzo, D. Alvira, E. Ezco, Progress in Photovoltaics: Research and Applications 19 (2011) 505. https://doi.org/10.1002/pip.1063.

[12] E. Skoplaki, J.A. Palyvos, Solar Energy 83 (2009) 614. https://doi.org/10.1016/j.solener.2008.10.008.

[13] Tampere city map service. Available online (accessed on 4.9.2025): https://kartat.tampere.fi/oskari/.

[14] A. Woyte, V. Van Thong, R. Belmans, J. Nils, IEEE Transaction on Energy Conversion 21 (2006) 202–209. https://doi.org/10.1109/TEC.2005.845454.

[15] Finnish Standards, SFS-EN 50160: Voltage characteristics of electricity supplied by public electricity networks (2022).

[16] R. Torquato, D. Salles, C. Oriente Pereira, P.C.M. Meira, W. Freitas, IEEE Transactions on Power Delivery 33 (2018) 1002–1012. https://doi.org/10.1109/TPWRD.2018.2798707.

[17] M.J. Weisshaupt, B. Schlatter, P. Korba, E. Kaffe, F. Kienzle, IFAC-PapersOnLine 49 (2016), 336–341. https://doi.org/10.1016/j.ifacol.2016.10.714.

[18] J. Hu, M. Marinelli, M. Coppo, A. Zecchino, H.W. Bindner, Electric Power Systems Research 131 (2016) 267–274. https://doi.org/10.1016/j.epsr.2015.10.025.

[19] A. Arshad, M. Lindner, M. Lehtonen, Energies 10 (2017) 1702. https://doi.org/10.3390/en10111702.

[20] M.M. Rahman, A. Arefi, G.M. Shafiullah, S. Hettiwatte, International Journal of Electrical Power & Energy Systems 99 (2018) 11–27. https://doi.org/10.1016/j.ijepes.2017.12.034.

[21] X. Su, M.A.S. Masoum, P.J. Wolfs, IEEE Transactions on Sustainable Energy 5 (2014) 967–977. https://doi.org/10.1109/TSTE.2014.2313862.

42nd European Photovoltaic Solar Energy Conference and Exhibition

Tampere University | TAMPEREEN ENERGIA SÄHKÖVERKKO | DSII Doctoral School of Industry Innovations

PHOTOVOLTAIC HOSTING CAPACITY IN NORDIC DISTRIBUTION GRIDS

Lauri Aaltonen and Kari Lappalainen — **Tampere University, Electrical Engineering**

Data and methods

- Data from the solar PV power research plant of Tampere University
  - Module temperature
  - Global horizontal irradiance (GHI)
  - Diffuse horizontal irradiance (DHI)
  - Four summer months (May–August 2024) with a 10 second resolution
- Grid data from the local DSO (Tampereen Energia Sähköverkko Oy)
  - Grid information, e.g., line lengths, line types, topology
  - Customer hourly consumption data from summer months of 2024
- Identification of hosting capacity (HC)
  - Criteria for HC used was continuous ampacity and voltage violation (± 10%).
  - PV plants were inserted to the grid randomly, roof-by-roof, to cover the south-facing roof areas.
  - PV penetration was expressed with respect to the nominal transformer power.
- Simulation model
  - Simulations were performed using Matlab/Simulink.
  - PV power production was modelled based on measured temperature and irradiances.
  - The house orientation, south-facing roof area and roof type (tilted/flat) were considered individually for every roof.

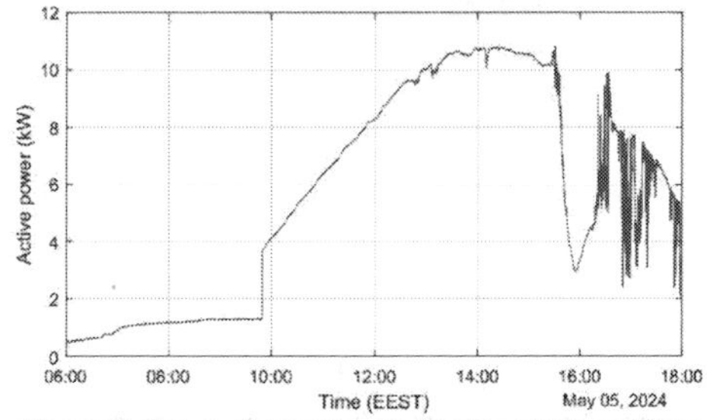

Figure 1: One roof area selected for the study and its modelled active PV power production for May 5th 2024.

Results

- Three examples of different kind of low voltage grids were chosen for the study
  - Rural, Suburban and Urban
- Rural grid
  - Mostly farms and summer cottages
  - Overhead lines and underground cables
  - Number of connection points: 16
  - Number of roofs with PV: 16
  - HC: 102.59%
  - Limiting factor: Line ampacity
- Suburban grid
  - Mix of detached houses and townhouses
  - Underground cables
  - Number of connection points: 59
  - Number of roofs with PV: 73
  - HC: 41.04%
  - Limiting factor: Line ampacity
- Urban grid
  - Mix of detached houses, apartment buildings, a supermarket and a local pub.
  - Underground cables
  - Number of connection points: 16
  - Number of roofs with PV: 16
  - HC: No limit achieved
- Future considerations
  - Façade installations
  - In rural grids, the utilization of near by space such as cropland
  - Secondary batteries may be utilized along the PV installations.

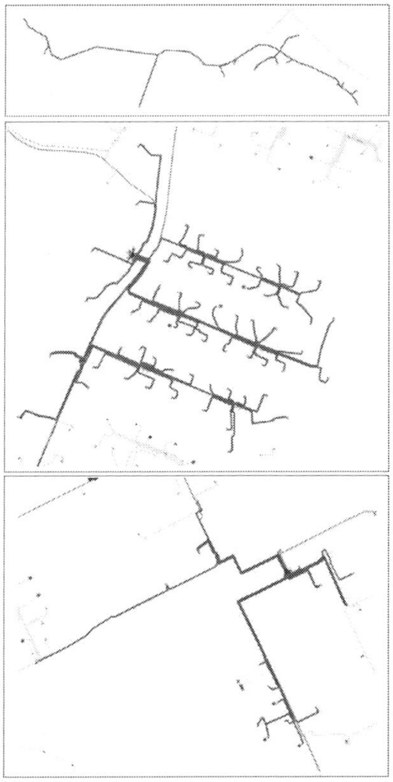

Figure 2: Low voltage grids studied: Rural (top), Suburban (middle) and Urban (bottom) highlighted in bold red.

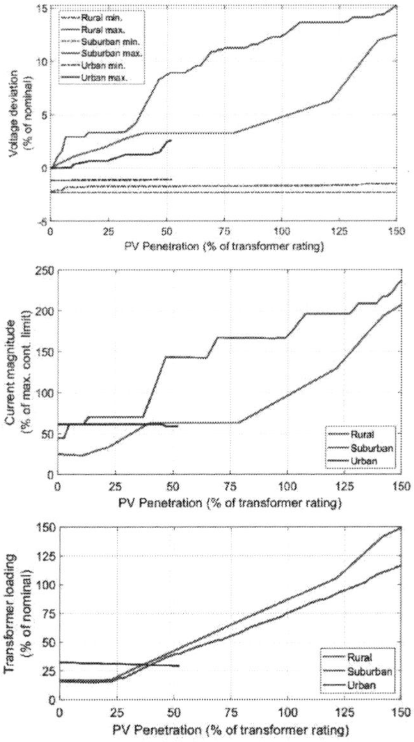

Figure 3: The customer voltage minimum and maximum (top), the maximum line loading (middle) and the maximum transformer loading (bottom) as a function of PV penetration.

Conclusions

- Line ampacity was the limiting factor for rural and suburban grids.
- Limits of hosting capacity are hard to achieve in urban grids due to the high power consumption compared to the available roof area.

Related journal article

- D. Torres Lobera, et. al., International Journal of Photoenergy (2013) 837310. https://doi.org/10.1155/2013/837310

Contact information

- Lauri Aaltonen
- Researcher
- Tampere University, Finland
- **lauri.aaltonen@tuni.fi**

MAXIMIZING MARKET VALUE IN SOLAR POWER PLANTS USING BATTERY STORAGE SYSTEMS

Hossein Rafiee[1], Rasoul Manochehrian[1], Dr. Sebastian Schäfer[1]
[1]Frankfurt University of Applied Sciences, Faculty of Computer Science and Engineering
Nibelungenplatz 1, 60318 Frankfurt am Main, Germany
Corresponding author: hossein.rafiee@stud.fra-uas.de

ABSTRACT: The more an electricity market is supplied by solar power, the lower the electricity price will be in times of high sun irradiation. For instance, in Germany prices at noon on sunny days are often close to zero. Therefore, the performance of a solar power plant should not be evaluated by its electricity output alone. In fact, the market value of electricity generation is more important since power plant operators seek to maximize their profits.
Battery storage can increase the market value by unbundling the timing of generation from the timing of sales. The success of this strategy mainly depends on three variables: the cost of the solar power plant, the cost of the battery system, and the electricity market conditions, particularly price levels and volatility. These variables are highly dynamic in the context of energy transition.
In this paper, we simulate a realistic solar power plant in Mainz using PVsyst program with adjustable plant capacity. We then develop an algorithm to increase the market value of solar electricity using battery storage. Based on mentioned variables, we calculate the optimal ratio of solar generation to battery capacity, enabling operators to select the most suitable configuration respective market conditions.
Keywords: Market Value, Solar Power Plant, PV Systems, Storage System, Optimal Capacity of Battery Storage

1 INTRODUCTION

The rising need for energy and international desire to reduce carbon emissions and apprehensions over climate change drive the expansion of renewable energy [1]. The two most popular types of renewable energy are solar and wind, a trend which is likely to be sustained in future energy systems [2]. The share of these variable renewable energy sources in power generation has been increasing rapidly. This trend has been mainly supported by government policies and further boosted by falling costs, as technologies improved and production expanded. Today, renewables can already compete with conventional energy sources in terms of generation cost [3]. They have almost negligible marginal costs. Consequently, their revenue depends on the covariance of market price developments and weather patterns [4, 5].

In order to measure and describe variations in renewable energy generation, a framework known as "Energy Quality" was most recently emerged [6]. While energy quality addresses the technical challenges associated with power fluctuations and grid stability. This article focuses on the economic dimension of renewable integration—specifically the concept of "market value."

The full integration of wind and solar power into electricity markets can be challenging. This is mainly because of two key reasons: on the one hand, their output depends on weather conditions, on the other hand, they have almost no cost for producing extra electricity. As a result, when wind and solar energy are available, they can offer electricity with low marginal cost, which lowers the overall electricity price. This leads to lower earnings for these same producers, a situation known as "self-cannibalization," first introduced in 1991 [7]. More recent studies confirm this effect, showing that the market value of wind and solar energy decreases as their output increases, especially when their production patterns do not match electricity demand. [8]. Thus, as more variable renewable energy is used, concerns about the need for flexibility and the volatility of electricity prices are increasing [9].

In [10] authors have analyzed the factors that can affect the market value. [11] aims at optimizing PV power plants, including components arrangements within the installation site, the inverter topology, cables, PV modules, the number of inverters, PV module tilt angle and shading effect result in increasing energy injected to the grid. In [12] the focus is on developing a better understanding of how the market value interacts with penetration and how policies and prices affect the market value. In this paper, we focus on improving the revenue (market value) of a PV power plant. The idea is to find better times to sell electricity production instead of increasing energy injected into the grid (E-g).

2 BATTERY STORAGE

2.1 Role and Cost Trends

When solar energy continues to expand its share in electricity generation, the role of energy storage technologies becomes increasingly important. Among various options, lithium-ion batteries are one possibility.

Lithium-ion batteries have become a major player in the energy sector, especially as storage technologies gain importance in balancing renewable generation. In the first half of 2024, global energy storage installations reached 64.9 GWh, marking a 93.8% year-on-year increase. Besides, the global battery technology market was valued at USD 213.36 billion in 2024 and is projected to grow from USD 252.13 billion in 2025 to around USD 431.65 billion by 2030 [13,14,15].

One of the key reasons for this rapid adoption is the continuous decline in battery prices. Between 2007 and 2014, lithium-ion prices dropped by roughly 14%, followed by annual reductions of 6–9% in the years that followed. Much of this progress has been driven by innovation in the automotive sector and the large-scale production of batteries for consumer electronics [13].

This steady cost reduction opens up new opportunities for the power sector. However, despite the lower investment costs, battery systems still require a combination of technical and economic benefits to justify deployment. Stacking multiple value streams is often necessary to make battery storage financially viable in utility-scale applications [13].

The Levelized Cost of Electricity (LCOE) is commonly used to compare power plants that have different cost structures and generation profiles. It is calculated by dividing the present value of total life time cost of building and running a plant by the discounted total lifetime energy production. This makes it possible to fairly compare different technologies, even if they vary in size, investment costs, or operational lifespans [16].

$$LCOE = \frac{\text{Total Life Cycle Cost}}{\text{Total Lifetime Energy Production}} \quad (1)$$

One of the biggest challenges in increasing the share of renewables in electricity generation is dealing with their variable output. Among the available solutions, cost-effective energy storage remains a key requirement. For any storage system, the Levelized Cost of Electricity Storage (LCOES) is a useful metric that reflects the minimum average price per kilowatt-hour that would be needed for the system to recover its total lifetime costs [13]. This value helps investors understand whether a storage installation is financially viable under specific market conditions.

2.2 Market Value

In order to determine the revenues of the feed-in electricity in the market, the market value concept has been introduced. The average revenue earned per unit of energy is defined as the 'market value' or 'absolute market value' of renewables [10]. The mathematical representation is given as follows:

$$MV_{abs} = \frac{\sum_{h=1}^{n} p_h \times f_h}{f_m} \quad (2)$$

Where,
MV_{abs}: absolute market value
h: hour
n: number of hours in respective month
m: month
p: electricity market price
f: feed-in/generation of renewable plant

The absolute market value compared to LCOE indicate how far renewables will be able to pay for themselves at regular electricity markets. However, even if renewables can pay for themselves in conventional energy markets on average, this may not result in high deployment rates without support due to the greater risks associated with investing in RE, as demonstrated by Tietjen et al. [17] and Bunn and Yusupov [18]. They contend that the risk-return profile of renewables gets progressively less appealing over time as the merit order impact lowers market income. Their participation in balancing markets and other market segments could be a solution (see for example [19]).

The market value of variable renewable energy sources (VRES), such as wind and solar, can be assessed by comparing the price they receive in the electricity market to the average market price over the same period. This comparison is expressed through a metric known as the value factor.

The value factor is calculated as the ratio between the generation-weighted average electricity price (based on the hourly output of the renewable source) and the time-weighted average market price, which already includes the contribution of the source under examination. In other words, it reflects how well the timing of renewable electricity generation aligns with higher or lower market prices. Alternative definitions exist, such as comparing to an average price that excludes the source itself or excludes all renewables, but these rely on non-observable counterfactual prices. Therefore, the comparison with the observed average market price is the practical and most widely applied definition.

$$VF = \frac{MV}{\bar{p}} \quad (3)$$

Where,
VF: is the Value Factor
$\bar{p}$: is the average wholesale day-ahead price

A value factor above 1 means that the energy is mostly generated during high-price hours while a value below 1 indicates that the generation occurs when electricity prices are lower on average [20].

This metric is essential for evaluating the economic competitiveness of renewables, especially as their share in the energy mix increases and their market value becomes more sensitive to the timing of production.

The variability of renewable generation influences its market value in two main ways, commonly referred to as the correlation effect and the merit-order effect [20].

The correlation effect occurs when the generation profile of a renewable source aligns positively with periods of high electricity prices, typically driven by high demand or external factors. In such cases, the renewable source benefits from selling electricity at a higher-than-average price.

On the other hand, the merit-order effect becomes relevant when the installed capacity of renewables is large enough to influence market prices. During hours with high wind or solar output, the supply of electricity from renewables shifts the residual load curve to the left, pushing down the market-clearing price. As more renewable capacity is added, the resulting downward pressure on prices becomes stronger, thereby reducing the market value of additional renewable output [20]. This effect is particularly pronounced in capacity-constrained thermal systems. However, it should be noted that this effect only applies in the short and medium term, since, in the long run, an adaptation of the power plant mix will cancel the merit-order effect.

At the core of the merit-order effect lies the structure of short-term electricity supply [20]:

Firstly, generation section technologies have different variable and fixed cost structures which lead to a supply curve that increases with quantity.

Secondly, the cost of storage and the lack of sufficient installed capacity limit the ability to shift surplus renewable generation to periods of higher market value.

As mentioned, in contrast to MV, the Levelized Cost of Electricity (LCOE) represents the average cost per unit of electricity produced, calculated based on all expenses over the lifetime of the asset [21]. While this definition aligns well with dispatchable generators, a slight adjustment is needed for variable renewable sources like wind and solar. For these technologies, LCOE is more accurately calculated by dividing total costs by the actual energy output, not the theoretical potential before curtailment. As a result, the LCOE for wind and solar tends to rise at high penetration levels, where curtailment becomes more frequent.

Each generation of technology has its own value factor, shaped by its production profile, variability and how well it aligns with electricity demand and market prices. Technologies that consistently deliver power during high-price hours tend to have higher market values while those producing during low-demand periods may receive lower prices. As a result, each technology fits into a different role within the system and contributes optimally to a different share of total generation.

At high levels of VRE penetration, curtailment becomes a major factor, especially in systems lacking flexibility. Without sufficient storage or transmission capacity, excess renewable generation during low-demand periods cannot be absorbed, which leads to a drop in market value. In contrast, when the system includes additional flexibility options—such as battery storage, hydrogen storage, or enhanced grid interconnection—market value can be maintained or even improved. This highlights the importance of coordinating storage investment with the expansion of renewable generation.

3 METHODOLOGIES

3.1 PVsyst Modelling

In this paper, we employed PVsyst to calculate the electricity injected into the grid by a photovoltaic power plant. The hourly PV generation profile of the power plant was simulated using PVsyst. Additionally, hourly day-ahead electricity market prices for Germany (year 2024) were obtained from Enerdata [22]. A specific geographical location was defined for the simulation: Mainz; a city near Frankfurt, one of Europe's major economic hubs. Mainz is a promising candidate for the installation of a solar power plant due to its proximity to Frankfurt and its comparatively lower land costs.

We then used Meteonorm data and incorporated important location-specific parameters into PVsyst, such as irradiation, temperature and system orientation.

A 750-kW solar power plant was considered in this study. Although the plant size is set to 750 kW, the impact of system size will be neutralized in later stages of the analysis, as the focus shifts to relative economic indicators, such as the change in market value relative to the change in LCOE (ΔMV / ΔLCOE).

The selected PV module and inverter used in the system design are shown below. PVsyst automatically suggests suitable inverter power based on the I-V curve of the selected module. Following this, we selected the most appropriate inverter and PVsyst generated a complete system configuration including the number of inverters, strings and modules in series.

The main output of PVsyst is the hourly electricity production over a full year, representing the energy that can be injected into the grid.

After simulating energy production in PVsyst and calculating the generated electricity, we determine the average market value of a certain year which represents the average revenue per unit of energy. This metric is then used to optimize the dispatch strategy with the goal of maximizing revenue. A key observation is that the point of maximum energy injection into the grid does not necessarily coincide with the point of maximum market value. This discrepancy arises due to variations in hourly electricity prices in the day-ahead market. Since battery storage allows energy injections to be shifted to higher-priced hours, different battery sizes result in variations in both produced and injected energy. Therefore, maximizing grid injection does not always maximize market value.

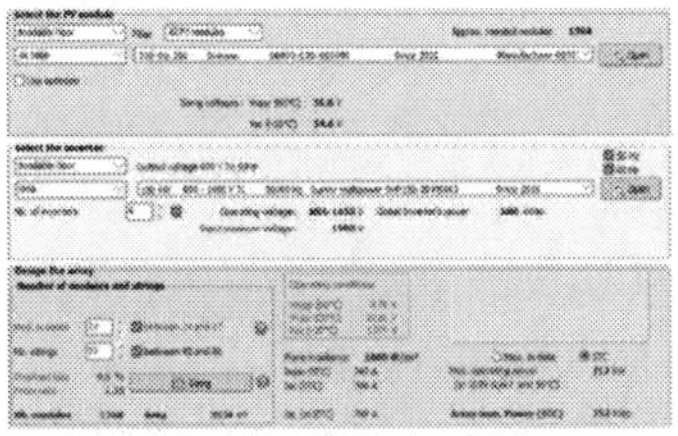

Figure 1: PV module and inverter in the system

Table I: Calculated optimum tilt for 6 meters pitch

	Tilt=20	Tilt=21	Tilt=22	Tilt=23
Eg (Kwh/year)	823065.6	823626.6	823935.3	823940.3
MV (Cent/Kwh)	3.4973	3.49650	3.4957	3.4948
Eg x MV (€/year)	28785.07	28798.1	28802.31	28795.07
Area (m2)	8100	8100	8100	8100
Price for area (€/year)	2430	2430	2430	2430
Total (€/year)	26355.07	26368.1	26372.31	26365.07

If we use PVsyst's optimization tools, the software provides the optimal pitch and tilt angle that maximizes the annual energy yield injected into the grid. Based on the selected optimum configuration, we then calculate the following parameters:

Market value (MV) of the electricity generated, Injected energy into the grid (E-g), Required land area for the power plant, estimated land cost, Ground Coverage Ratio (GCR)

The ground coverage ratio (GCR) is defined as the ratio between the active PV area and the total ground area occupied by the same PV system:

$$GCR = \frac{Area_{PV}}{Area_{Ground}} \quad (4)$$

In many real-world scenarios, the available ground area is constrained, such as in rooftop systems or when the PV system must be installed on a plot of land with limited area. So, if we decrease the pitch, we can install more rows of panels within the same area which increases the active PV surface and consequently the GCR. The lower the pitch, the more sheds can be fitted on a given plot of land.

Since we consider a regular, shed-based PV layout, the GCR can be approximated by the ratio of the module length to the pitch distance. However, we have to also consider mutual shading. Mutual shading occurs when one row of panels casts a shadow on the adjacent row, especially during low solar angles. This trade-off between compactness (high GCR) and shading losses must be carefully evaluated in the optimization process.

To better illustrate this issue, the following table presents the results for different tilt angles. In this analysis, the land cost is assumed to be €0.30 per square meter per year.

By comparing the "Total" row in the results table, the optimal combination is identified: a tilt angle of 22 degrees with a row spacing (pitch) of 6 meters.

While other combinations could also be considered, our choice corresponds to the investor's optimum, which makes it the appropriate reference point for the following analysis.

3.2 Dispatch Strategy

We model a battery storage system to increase the market value by storing energy when the price is low and inject it into the grid when the price is high. While this part is very straightforward, there are also several disadvantages to a battery which need to be considered: first of all, its investment cost. We start by considering variable Levelized Cost of Electricity (LCOE) for the power plant and a variable surcharge for the battery, then generalizing the specific values by using relative values. For simplicity, we ignore inverter consumption and assume a battery efficiency of 97%.

In the next step, we develop an algorithm to manage battery storage and electricity dispatch with the objective of maximizing the market value — without the assumption of an unrealistic perfect foresight.

This strategy is based on day-ahead market data and aims to make use of limited and realistic forecasts, as typically available in actual electricity markets.

To define this strategy, we impose the following constraints on the charging and discharging behavior of the battery:

Lower Price Threshold:

This threshold determines when the system should store energy instead of injecting it into the grid. It is calculated as

((mean (S1)-min(S1))/2) +min(S1)

Where,

S1: represents the vector of hourly electricity prices for each day. If the price at a given hour is below this limit, and battery capacity is available, the energy will be stored rather than sold.

Upper Price Threshold:

Energy stored in the battery will only be discharged to the grid when the electricity price reaches the daily maximum. In this way, we ensure that stored energy is utilized at the most economically favorable time of day.

These thresholds are designed to reflect realistic operational conditions, assuming that market participants have access to day-ahead electricity price forecasts, as is commonly the case in most European markets. Thus, the strategy relies on limited foresight (one-day lookahead), making it applicable to real-world systems.

This approach allows for improved utilization of the battery by exploiting daily price fluctuations, without relying on hypothetical or unrealistic assumptions about long-term market behavior. The resulting control logic can be easily implemented and adapted to other systems with similar data availability.

3.3 Optimization Approach

The primary objective of this study is to identify the optimal combination of a solar power plant and battery storage system at which the rate of increase in market value closely matches the rate of increase in the Levelized Cost of Electricity (LCOE) induced by expanding battery capacity.

This condition, where the ratio between the relatives change leading to the optimum where the relative increase

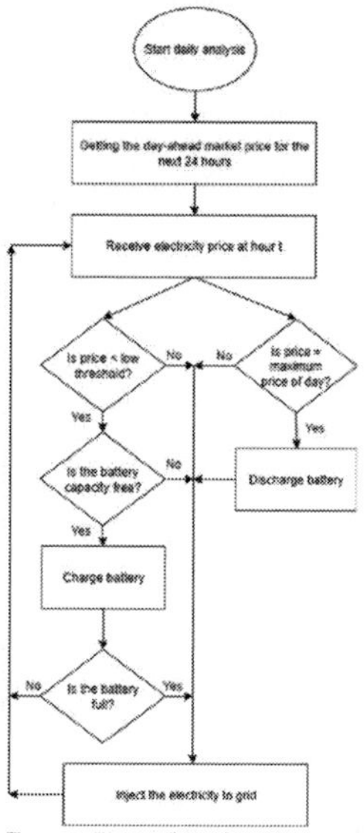

Figure 2: Battery dispatch logic based on day-ahead prices and battery state

of the market value is equal to the relative increase in LCOE approaches one, indicates that each unit of additional market value is offset by an equal increase in cost. These points mark the economically optimal configuration of the system.

To reach this point, we conduct a systematic analysis by varying two key input parameters: battery price and battery size, both expressed in relation to the PV power plant.

The analysis begins with a baseline scenario featuring a battery price of 0.1 cents per kWh and a battery size equivalent to 1% of the total installed PV capacity. These values are then incrementally increased to cover the entire solution space, and for each case, the corresponding market value, LCOE, and their ratio are calculated and evaluated. By expressing both parameters as percentages, we eliminate the dependency on absolute system size. This allows the results to remain scalable and applicable across different PV plant capacities, irrespective of their specific dimensions in the PVsyst model.

The approach ensures that the findings are generalizable and can inform decision-making for a broad range of system scales and investment conditions.

4 RESULTS

The results clearly show that as the relative battery capacity increases compared to the installed PV capacity, the ratio of market value to LCOE gradually approaches unity, particularly at lower battery price levels. Conversely, at higher battery prices, the optimal ratio can only be achieved with smaller storage capacities, since the economic benefit of additional storage decreases relative to its cost. This highlights the dual dependence of economic viability on both battery size and battery price, and the importance of identifying a balanced configuration under different cost scenarios.

In simpler terms, when the ratio between market value and LCOE reaches around 1, any extra benefit from storing and shifting energy is balanced out by the extra cost of adding the battery. This creates a point where the system reaches economic balance — where including the battery neither improves nor worsens the overall cost-effectiveness.

Moreover, the results indicate that once the battery capacity becomes large enough to cover all the storable energy of a given day, further capacity increases no longer change the amount of energy sold during peak-price hours. From this point onward, the market value reaches its ceiling and remains constant ($\Delta MV = 0$). This saturation effect repeats across all battery price levels, since MV is determined by market prices and dispatched electricity (E-grid) rather than battery cost.

This balance is especially important in electricity markets with fluctuating prices or high solar shares, where the role of batteries is not to increase production, but to make the timing of energy injections smarter and more profitable. For project developers and investors, identifying this point helps ensure that battery systems are not only technically useful, but also financially reasonable.

This relationship is visually confirmed in Figure 3, which presents a 3D plot mapping battery price, battery size (as a percentage of PV capacity), and the resulting market value-to-LCOE ratio.

In this visualization, red points represent scenarios where the ratio is approximately equal to 1, marking optimal combinations where the economic value gained matches the cost incurred.

Conversely, the surrounding blue region illustrates a wide range of non-optimal configurations, where the ratio diverges substantially from unity. These are either scenarios in which the battery is too expensive to justify economically, or too small to contribute meaningfully to market value optimization.

To highlight the critical configurations more clearly, Figure 4 presents a two-dimensional plot of battery price versus battery capacity. Red points indicate the cases where the market value to LCOE ratio is close to unity. The concentration of these points along a narrow diagonal zone emphasizes that the economic optimum is confined to a small and well-defined region. Within this region, the balance between cost and value of battery integration is achieved, and even small changes in battery pricing have a strong impact on the outcome.

This focused representation reveals a level of detail that was not easily detectable in the broader 3D plot, where the critical region appeared only as a thin strip. By isolating the relevant configurations, the figure makes it evident that the system is highly sensitive to modest changes in price or capacity. Such sensitivity means that even small adjustments can quickly shift the system from an optimal to a non-optimal configuration, underscoring the importance of precise sizing in real-world applications. Moreover, it should be noted that the optimum itself is not static but will evolve over time as market conditions and technology parameters change.

These results also reinforce the earlier observation that the optimal balance between cost and value is achieved only at specific combinations of battery price and capacity. Beyond this point, increasing the battery capacity does not lead to significant additional gains and will even reduce the overall economic efficiency of the system.

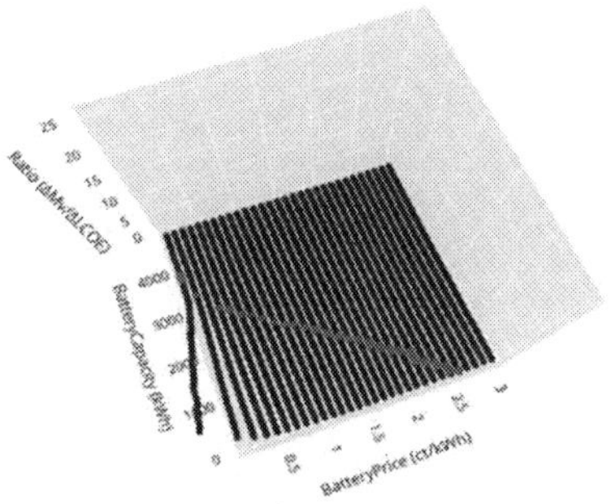

Figure 3: Market value to LCOE (ratio) across battery prices and capacities

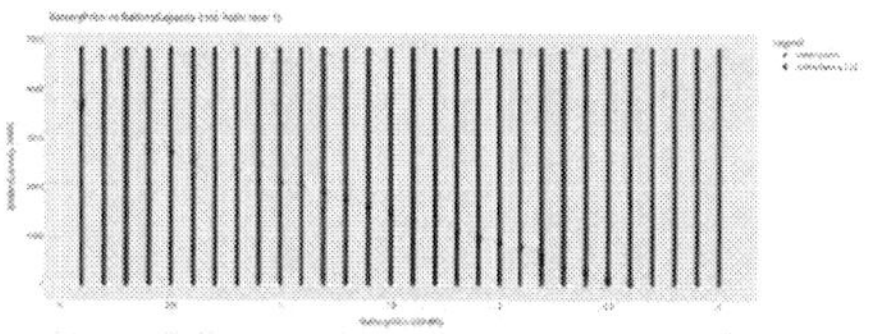

Figure 4: Battery price vs. battery capacity, red points mark ratio ≈ 1

Overall, the figure complements the quantitative analysis by offering a clear graphical representation of the economic optimum for battery integration. It visually demonstrates the limited and sensitive nature of the feasible zone and highlights the importance of careful sizing and realistic pricing to achieve viable outcomes for renewable energy projects, without relying on assumptions of perfect foresight.

5 CONCLUSIONS

While renewable energy generation inherently faces challenges such as uncertainty and intermittency, our analysis demonstrates that the economic outcome depends not only on the presence of storage but also on its careful sizing and operation. Simply adding a battery is not sufficient; rather, the way it is dimensioned and managed makes a decisive difference in financial performance.

Previous studies have primarily focused on integrating battery storage with solar power plants to mitigate periods of low solar availability [2,11,13], often emphasizing the technical role of storage rather than its economic implications. While such approaches have typically emphasized energy production alone, they often neglect the impact of day-ahead market prices and the associated fluctuations in market value.

In contrast, this study shows that the financial benefit of battery integration crucially depends on the interplay between battery price and battery size, with each price level corresponding to a specific capacity that maximizes profitability. By modeling battery behavior (charging and discharging) based on price thresholds rather than generation patterns alone, this research presents a more realistic and economically grounded approach for managing storage dispatch.

10.4229/EUPVSEC2025/5DV.3.16
020539-005

A key contribution of this research is the introduction of hourly price-based optimization for battery charging and discharging. This dynamic scheduling approach ensures that energy is stored and sold during the most profitable hours, which directly increases the market value of the system. This methodology sets the study apart from earlier work by explicitly linking technical storage behavior to economic indicators.

Additionally, the analysis of the ratio between market value increase and LCOE increase provides a practical and scalable method for identifying the optimal battery size for any solar plant and cost condition. This approach does not rely on unrealistic assumptions of perfect foresight and is applicable across different project sizes and market environments.

These findings offer a valuable framework for more informed and economically sound decision-making by investors, system designers, and plant operators, highlighting how optimized storage integration can significantly improve the financial viability of solar projects.

6 REFERENCES

[1] Wennersten, R., Q. Sun, and H. Li, The future potential for Carbon Capture and Storage in climate change mitigation–an overview from perspectives of technology, economy and risk. Journal of cleaner production, 2015. 103: p. 724-736.

[2] Wang, W., B. Yuan, Q. Sun, and R. Wennersten, Application of energy storage in integrated energy systems—A solution to fluctuation and uncertainty of renewable energy. Journal of Energy Storage, 2022. 52: p. 104812.

[3] Jansen, M., et al., Offshore wind competitiveness in mature markets without subsidy. Nature Energy, 2020. 5(8): p. 614-622.

[4] Sensfuß, F., M. Ragwitz, and M. Genoese, The merit-order effect: A detailed analysis of the price effect of renewable electricity generation on spot market prices in Germany. Energy policy, 2008. 36(8): p. 3086-3094.

[5] Würzburg, K., X. Labandeira, and P. Linares, Renewable generation and electricity prices: Taking stock and new evidence for Germany and Austria. Energy Economics, 2013. 40: p. S159-S171.

[6] Zhang, X.-P. and Z. Yan, Energy quality: A definition. IEEE Open Access Journal of Power and Energy, 2020. 7: p. 430-440.

[7] Grudd, M. Value of variable sources on power systems. in IEE Proceedings C (Generation, Transmission and Distribution). 1991. IET.

[8] Hirth, L. and A. Radebach, The market value of wind and solar power: an analytical approach. 2016.

[9] Shimomura, M., et al., Beyond the merit order effect: Impact of the rapid expansion of renewable energy on electricity market price. Renewable and Sustainable Energy Reviews, 2024. 189: p. 114037.

[10] Winkler, J., M. Pudlik, M. Ragwitz, and B. Pfluger, the market value of renewable electricity–Which factors really matter? Applied energy, 2016. 184: p. 464-481.

[11] Zidane, T.E.K., et al., Grid-connected Solar PV power plants optimization: A review. IEEE Access, 2023. 11: p. 79588-79608.

[12] Hirth, L., The market value of variable renewables: The effect of solar wind power variability on their relative price. Energy economics, 2013. 38: p. 218-236.

[13] Arteaga, J. and H. Zareipour, A price-maker/price-taker model for the operation of battery storage systems in electricity markets. IEEE Transactions on Smart Grid, 2019. 10(6): p. 6912-6920.

[14] Global energy storage market: H1 2024 installation figures, Robin Song

[15] Markets and markets – Battery technology market size, share and trend.

[16] Foster, J., L. Wagner, and A. Bratanova, LCOE models: A comparison of the theoretical frameworks and key assumptions. Energy Economics and Management Group Working Papers, 2014. 4.

[17] Tietjen, O., M. Pahle, and S. Fuss, Investment risks in power generation: A comparison of fossil fuel and renewable energy dominated markets. Energy Economics, 2016. 58: p. 174-185.

[18] Bunn, D. and T. Yusupov, The progressive inefficiency of replacing renewable obligation certificates with contracts-for-differences in the UK electricity market. Energy Policy, 2015. 82: p. 298-309.

[19] Fernandes, C., P. Frías, and J. Reneses, Participation of intermittent renewable generators in balancing mechanisms: A closer look into the Spanish market design. Renewable Energy, 2016. 89: p. 305-316.

[20] Hirth, L., The market value of variable renewables. 2012.

[21] Brown, T. and L. Reichenberg, Decreasing market value of variable renewables can be avoided by policy action. Energy Economics, 2021. 100: p. 105354.

[22] Enerdata. Global Energy & CO_2 Data. Available at: https://yearbook.enerdata.net

42nd European Photovoltaic Solar Energy Conference and Exhibition

EU PVSEC

Maximizing Market Value in Solar Power Plants Using Battery Storage Systems

Hossein Rafiee, Rasoul Manochehrian, Dr. Sebastian Schäfer
Frankfurt University of Applied Sciences, Faculty of Computer Science and Engineering

FRANKFURT UNIVERSITY OF APPLIED SCIENCES

Introduction

Background
The rapid growth of renewable energy especially solar PV, is crucial to reduce carbon emissions and combat climate change. The battery storage of a PV power plant can increase the market value by unbundling the timing of generation from the timing of sale.

Problem
However, solar power has very low marginal costs and depends on weather conditions. When PV capacity increases, it pushes electricity prices down during sunny hours resulting in reducing the revenues of PV producers. This effect is known as self-cannibalization; The market value of wind and solar energy decreases when their output increases, especially when their production patterns do not match electricity demand [1].

Objective
This study aims to improve the economic performance (market value) of PV power plants by shifting their electricity output to the hours with higher market prices using an optimal battery storage system instead of only increasing total energy production [2].

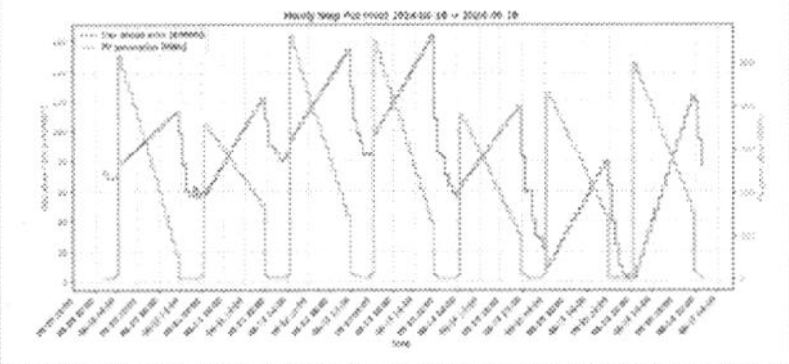

Battery Storage

Role
As PV penetration rises, storage becomes essential for smoothing variability and time-shifting energy to higher-price hours that causes mitigating self-cannibalization.
Nowadays, Lithium-ion is the most practical option for short-to-medium duration applications due to maturity, scalability and efficiency.

Trends
In the first half of 2024, global energy storage installations reached 64.9 GWh, marking a 93.8% year-on-year increase. Li-ion has the majority share.
The global battery technology market was valued at USD 213.36 billion in 2024 and is projected to grow from USD 252.13 billion in 2025 to around USD 431.65 billion by 2030 [3].

Economics
Falling costs has opened new opportunities but stacking revenue streams (arbitrage + ancillary services) is often required. We benchmark economics with LCOE for generation and LCOE_S for storage to compare technologies consistently [4].

$$\mathrm{LCOE} = \frac{\text{Total Life Cycle Cost}}{\text{Total Lifetime Energy Production}}$$

$$\mathrm{LCOE\_S} = \frac{\text{Total Lifetime Cost of Storage}}{\text{Total Lifetime Discarged Energy}}$$

Market Value & Value Factor

Concept
The market value (MV) is the average revenue per kWh that a technology earns [5]:

$$\mathrm{MV_{abs}} = \frac{\sum_{h=1}^{n} P_h \times f_h}{f_m}$$

The value factor (VF) compares MV to the average market price:

$$VF = \frac{MV}{\bar{p}}$$

VF > 1 → generation matches high-price hours
VF < 1 → generation during low-price hours (self-cannibalization risk)

Effects
Correlation effect: When renewable output aligns with high prices → MV ↑

Merit-order effect: High renewable output shifts supply curve → lowers market prices → MV ↓

Challenges
As VRE penetration grows, curtailment increases, which raises LCOE and reduces MV.
Storage and grid flexibility are key to maintain MV at high penetration levels.

Methodology

PVsyst Modeling

Hourly PV generation for a 750 kW plant was simulated in PVsyst using Meteonorm weather data for Mainz (near Frankfurt).

PVsyst provided annual hourly electricity output, which we combined with hourly day-ahead market prices (Germany, 2024).

We varied tilt and pitch to maximize energy yield (Eg) and calculated market value (MV), required land area, land cost, and ground coverage ratio (GCR).

The tilt that results in the highest Eg is not necessarily the one with the highest MV.

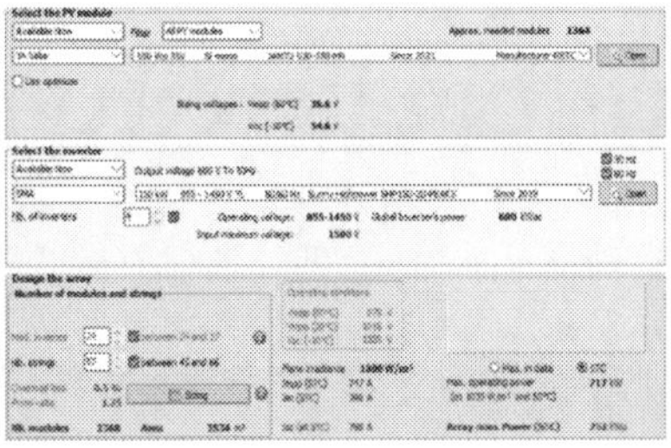

	Tilt=20	Tilt=21	Tilt=22	Tilt=23
Eg (Kwh/year)	823065.6	823626.6	823935.3	823940.3
MV (Cent/Kwh)	3.4973	3.49650	3.4957	3.4948
Eg x MV (€/year)	28785.07	28798.1	28802.31	28795.07
Area (m2)	8100	8100	8100	8100
Price for area (€ /year)	2430	2430	2430	2430
Total (€/year)	26355.07	26368.1	26372.31	26365.07

Dispatch Strategy

A battery storage system was added to shift energy from low-price hours to the daily peak-price hour.

Thresholds are calculated daily from day-ahead prices:
Lower threshold = ((mean(S1)-min(S1))/2)+min(S1)
Upper threshold = max(S1)

The control algorithm only uses 1-day foresight to reflect real market conditions.

Logic:
If price < lower → charge (if capacity free)
If price = daily max → discharge
Otherwise inject directly to grid

Optimization Approach

Goal
Finding the **economic balance point**
Where battery size-price is:

$$\frac{\Delta \mathrm{MV}}{\Delta \mathrm{LCOE}} \approx 1$$

This means the added revenue matches the added cost.

We varied battery size (1–644% of PV capacity) and battery price (0.1–3 cent/kWh), calculated MV, LCOE and their ratio for every scenario.

Once battery capacity exceeds the storable daily energy, market value saturates (ΔMV = 0) and no further benefit is achieved.

Using relative values makes results scalable and system-size independent.

Results

Across scenarios, increasing battery capacity tends to move the market-value-to-LCOE ratio toward unity at lower battery prices, while higher prices shift the optimum to smaller capacities as marginal cost overtakes marginal value.

A clear saturation appears once capacity can cover the day's storable energy: market value plateaus and additional capacity no longer increases revenue.

The economically attractive solutions form a narrow band; small deviations in price or size quickly push the system off-optimal, highlighting the need for precise sizing.

These patterns are consistent under the one-day-ahead dispatch used here.

The left plot maps the full design space; the right zoom reveals the narrow optimum band where PV + battery configurations are near economic balance (red = near-neutral, blue = off-optimal). The band is highly sensitive to battery price and size, and once daily storable energy is covered, market value saturates—larger batteries add no further revenue.

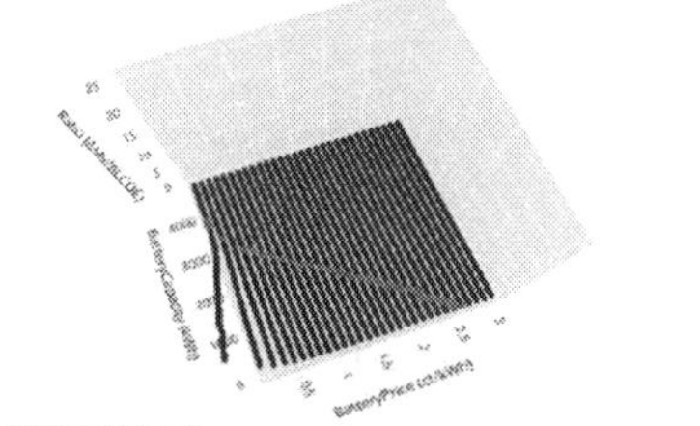

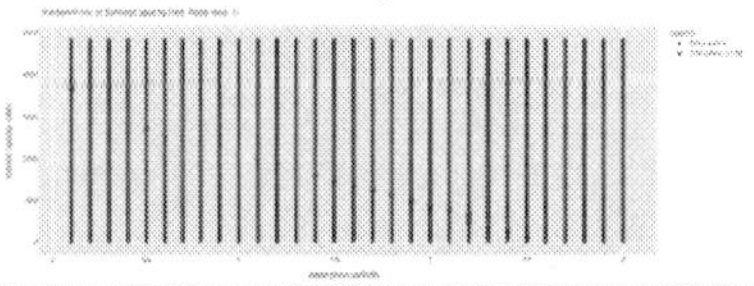

Conclusions

Optimized storage adds value not by increasing energy, but by shifting timing: price-based, day-ahead dispatch (with one-day foresight) is financially decisive.

Our results show a narrow, price-sensitive band where PV + battery reaches economic balance (MV rises in step with LCOE). Beyond the daily storable-energy point, market value saturates and larger batteries no longer improve revenues.

This price-driven control (rather than generation-only scheduling) links storage behavior directly to market value and avoids unrealistic perfect foresight. The ΔMV vs ΔLCOE perspective provides a practical, scalable way to size batteries across projects and cost conditions.

Implication: precise sizing and price-aware dispatch are essential; at higher battery prices, smaller capacities are favored, while lower prices can justify larger storage, always within the narrow band where added value matches added cost.

Acknowledgements

Data: Enerdata (2024) day-ahead prices; Meteonorm weather inputs.

Simulations with PVsyst; data processing and analysis in Python.

No external funding; no conflicts of interest.

Travel support was provided by Frankfurt University of Applied Sciences.

References

[1] Hirth, L. and A. Radebach, The market value of wind and solar power: an analytical approach. 2016
[2] SMARD (Bundesnetzagentur), Day-ahead market prices (DE-LU bidding zone), 2024-01–2024-12; accessed 18 Sep 2025.
[3] Global energy storage market: H1 2024 installation figures, Robin Song
[4] Brown, T. and L. Reichenberg, Decreasing market value of variable renewables can be avoided by policy action. Energy Economics, 2021. 100: p. 105354.
[5] Winkler, J., M. Pudlik, M. Ragwitz, and B. Pfluger, The market value of renewable electricity–Which factors really matter? Applied energy, 2016. 184: p. 464-481

Contact Information

Hossein Rafiee — hossein.rafiee@stud.fra-uas.de
Rasoul Manochehrian — rasoul.manochehrian@stud.fra-uas.de
Dr. Sebastian Schäfer — sebastian.schaefer@fb2.fra-uas.de

ROAD TO ECOLOGICAL TRANSITION: THE ITALIAN PERSPECTIVE OF THE AGRIVOLTAICS DEVELOPMENT

Alessandra Scognamiglio, Celeste Mellone and Giulia Guidetti, Valeria Viti, Lorenzo Massaro and Cesare Gatti, Fabio Salis
AIAS and ENEA, Green Horse Legal Advisory, PedersoliGattai, Iberdrola Renovables Italia
presidente@associazioneitalianagrivoltaicosostenibile.com; celeste.mellone@greenhorseadvisory.com; giulia.guidetti@greenhorseadvisory.com; vviti@pglex.it; lmassaro@pglex.it; cgatti@pglex.it; fsalis@iberdrola.it

ABSTRACT: This paper has been jointly prepared by the authors, as experts, researchers and players of the renewable energy sector and in their quality of members of AIAS (Italian Association for Sustainable Agrivoltaic), as the most relevant association in Italy for the development of a sustainable way of doing agrivoltaics.
As Agri-PV represents nowadays the most sustainable way to combine the agricultural land use and the renewable energy production, a multidisciplinary and cross-sectoral approach is necessary to demonstrate its value, avoiding any type of misconception about land use and making the Agri-PV social accepted.
For that purpose, energy-law experts, together with policymakers and researchers, can together validate the operational feasibility of Agri-PV to gain public and institutional support. On one hand, the technical support is crucial for implementing technical innovations to the plant and, on the other hand, the role of legal experts is necessary for clearly understanding the regulatory framework in the context of which the industry stakeholders operate. Awareness of the values of Agri-PV needs to be preserved, along with the need to achieve European targets, and requires a correct interpretation of the regulations and an evolving vision of the renewable energy market.
In the ecological transition context, a multi-sectoral approach deriving from associations between professionals and players in the energy, environment and agricultural sectors, can certainly support the correct development of Agri-PV in Italy.
Keywords: cooperation, innovation, cross-lateral approach, energy transition, agrivoltaic.

1 INTRODUCTION

Dealing with daily and global challenges regarding the energy transition has made real the necessity to improve and implement innovative solutions in order to ensure energy security, environmental sustainability, and food production. As Agri-Photovoltaics (Agri-PV) can combine the renewable energy production with the agricultural land use, they can represent the best solution to these interconnected challenges. Italy has recently implemented a detailed legal and regulatory framework to regulate the way of developing Agri-PV, by introducing certain principles that can be emulate by other EU member states. This paper will be focused on Italy's legal advancements in Agri-PV and its practical challenges and criticalities and on the crucial support that the associations together with the renewable energy sector experts may give to implement the proper approach and way of doing Agri-PV in Italy.

2 ITALIAN LEGAL FRAMEWORK: AGRI-PV FUNDAMENTALS

The development of Agri-PV in Italy became real and regulated following the adoption in June 2022 by MASE – Ministry of Environment and Energy Security jointly with CREA – Council for agricultural research and for the analysis of agricultural economy and GSE – Operator for energy services, of the national guidelines on Agri-PV (the "**Italian Guidelines**"), that have the purpose to establish the essential requirements necessary to define a plant as Agri-PV. Italian Guidelines are not binding in nature, but merely provide guidance in the Agri-PV sector.

Based on the objective requirements listed under the Italian Guidelines (*e.g.* thresholds of minimum occupied agricultural surface and electrical producibility; panels minimum height, depending on the agricultural activity carried out; implementation of monitoring system), a distinction between the standard Agri-PV technology – on one side – and the advanced one – on the other side - has been defined in order to make the latter eligible for certain advantages. In general terms, (i) the standard Agri-PV is a PV system that adopts solutions to preserve the continuity of agricultural and pastoral cultivation activities at the installation site; (ii) the advanced Agri-PV is a PV system that, in accordance with the provisions of article 65, paragraph 1-*quater* and 1-*quinquies*, of Decree-Law No. 1/2012, adopts innovative integrative solutions with assembly of the modules elevated from the ground, also providing for the rotation of the modules themselves, in any case in such a way as not to compromise the continuity of agricultural and pastoral cultivation activities, also possibly allowing the application of digital and precision agriculture tools; moreover, it provides for the simultaneous implementation of monitoring systems to verify the impact of the photovoltaic installation on crops, water savings, agricultural productivity for different types of crops, continuity of the activities of the farms involved, recovery of soil fertility, microclimate, and resilience to climate change.

Only advanced Agri-PV are eligible to receive incentives tariffs and PNRR capital grants, according to the Ministerial Decree No. 436/2023, that supports the construction and operation in Italy of new agrivoltaic plants for a total capacity of 1.04 GW and an electricity production of at least 1300 GWh/year (the "**Agrivoltaic Decree**"). Eligible Agri-PV may access such public incentives through direct access (i.e. direct application to a register, in case of Agri-PV having a nominal power capacity lower than 1 MW) or through the participation to public auctions (for Agri-PV higher than 1 MW).

Agrivoltaic Decree – together with its operating rules – set precise criteria for accessing the tariff incentives on the energy production and the PNRR capital grants up to 40% of the eligible costs related to the development and

10.4229/EUPVSEC2025/5DV.3.31
020541-001

construction phase. As deeper detailed in the following section, the most practical criteria to be investigated regards the subjective requirements of the beneficiaries, that shall be – or shall have a strict contractual relationship with – agricultural companies or entrepreneurs. Otherwise, from the technical standpoint, most of the support to the implementation of Agri-PV eligible for the Agrivoltaic Decree is granted by the operating rules (that firmly establish the definition of PLV – *Produzione Lorda Vendibile*, as a benchmark to measure the effective agricultural production and the surface dedicated to the agricultural activity) and technical guidelines that have been *medio tempore* enacted (*e.g.* CREA-GSE guidelines on the monitoring systems; CEI-PAS 82-93, setting the technical rules on Agri-PV (CEI - Italian Electrotechnical Committee); UNI/PdR 148/2023 aimed at providing the reference practice for realizing Agri-PV (Italian Standards Organization - UNI).

3 CURRENT REGULATORY FRAMEWORK – WHERE WE ARE

3.1 Prohibition to install PV systems on agricultural lands

Before delving into the most recent authorization procedure updates, it is crucial to summarize the recent prohibition of installing traditional PV systems on agricultural lands, even if they are considered suitable for RES plants installation in accordance with the current legal framework in Italy (cfr. Legislative Decree No. 199/2021). Such prohibition has been introduced by Italian Government through the Law Decree No. 63/2024 (subsequently converted into Law No. 101/2024 – the "**Agricultural Decree**") in order to avoid the agricultural soil consumption, exclusively allowing the installation of Agri-PV on agricultural lands. Even if this type of prohibition slows down the energy transition process, it may be considered coherent with the needs of safeguarding the agricultural landscape and its value. Nonetheless, the relevant strict application is causing several critical between RES operators and requires an innovative approach that makes real and usable the harmonization between the renewable energy production with agricultural activities, delivering environmental and socio-economic benefits. This is the primary challenge that the legislator shall understand and deal with in ensuring – through the adoption of a specific legislation – the sustainable transformation of the landscape.

Indeed, a prudent a more literal interpretation of the prohibition at hand requires that advanced Agri-PV are exclusively allowed on agricultural areas, without taking in consideration that the continuity of agricultural activity can be ensured also through the installation of standard Agri-PV as well. This is the main reason why the Agricultural Decree has been challenged before the Italian Constitutional Court, that is going to rule on the constitutional lawfulness of such strict prohibition.

3.2 The new RES Code

In order to summarize and encompass all the national regulation that came across over the years in the renewable energy sector, the Italian legislator has recently enacted the Legislative Decree No. 190/2024 (the "**RES Code**"), aimed at simplifying and regulate the authorization regimes for the construction and operation of RES plants, by envisaging three main administrative procedures that RES projects undergo, based on power, type, location. The construction of new RES plants, repowering and revamping interventions are now efficiently summarized in sole and comprehensive code, that regulates the different developments of RES project and the technical modifications of RES plants in operation, by envisaging different authorization regimes (i.e. free building activity, PAS – *Procedura Abilitativa Semplificata* and AU – *Autorizzazione Unica*). From the authorization perspective, relevant updates and administrative simplifications have been introduced by the RES Code in relation to Agri-PV:

- Agri-PV $\geq$ 12 MW in agricultural areas shall demonstrate the "compatibility and integration with agricultural activity" to qualify for certain authorization regimes;
- RES Code includes Agri-PV within the list of cases where ordinary thresholds are adjusted;
- Agri-PV up to 5 MW may undergo to free building activity (with no need of starting any authorization procedures) if certain pre-requirements are met and they are located on suitable areas, in accordance with the law.

Landscape constraints remain strongly safeguarded even where Agri-PV are allowed and this contributes to make the coexistence of agricultural and landscape values with renewable energy production effective.

Nonetheless, the effective application of such simplified procedure and the way to ensure the continuity of agricultural activity shows practical issues that need to be addressed to the public authority. In detail, such practical issues are currently managed on a case-by-case basis, depending on the access of Agri-PV to the public incentives under the Agrivoltaic Decree or on the standard development of Agri-PV in order to avoid the general ban of installation of photovoltaic system on agricultural lands.

4 THE EVOLVING REGULATION OF AGRI-PV: LEGAL INSTRUMENTS AND ORGANISATIONAL MODELS

The regulation of the relationship between agricultural operators and electricity operators remains in an evolving state, as the legislator has not yet enacted a definitive and comprehensive set of rules.

Against this background of regulatory uncertainty, it is particularly important to frame the matter from two complementary perspectives, each one highlighting different aspects of the interaction between the parties.

The first perspective concerns the rights which must necessarily be held by both operators to validly and effectively carry out their respective activities.

The second perspective is not underpinned by a fixed and predetermined framework of rules, but instead develops in practice through contractual negotiations, sectoral guidelines and the gradual emergence of best practices. It is therefore characterised by a degree of flexibility, requiring careful case-by-case assessment to balance agricultural productivity with energy generation objectives.

In conclusion, while the definitive regulatory discipline has yet to crystallise, the dual focus on such perspectives provides a useful analytical framework for understanding and structuring the complex relationship between agricultural and electricity operators, as will be illustrated in the following sections.

4.1 Rights required for the exercise of agricultural and energy activities

As mentioned above, the structure of Agro-PV projects requires, as a preliminary step, careful consideration of the co-existence of two entities whose interests are distinct yet necessarily convergent.

On the one hand, the agricultural entrepreneur, whose primary concern lies in maintaining and, where possible, enhancing farming activities. On the other hand, there is the energy operator, whose focus is directed towards the construction and long-term management of the photovoltaic installation.

As of today, the legal system does not lay down a comprehensive set of provisions specifically governing the relationship between these two parties. Accordingly, reference must first be made to the general categories of civil law and to the legal instruments capable of ensuring:

- the lawful availability of land for the development of the project and,
- the continued exercise of agricultural activities on the same site.

In the case of ground-mounted photovoltaic plants, the widespread use of surface rights (Articles 952 et seq. of the Italian Civil Code) became established as the most appropriate legal instrument, given the specific and limited needs of such projects.

However, the scope of surface rights is expressly limited by Article 956 of the Italian Civil Code, which excludes their extension to cultivation rights. This limitation acquires particular significance in the context of Agri-PV projects, where the coexistence of agricultural and energy activities is of the essence and where the surface rights alone cannot adequately regulate the continuity of farming on the same land.

It therefore becomes necessary to identify alternative or complementary legal instruments capable of reconciling both dimensions. In the context of Agri-PV, surface rights, taken alone, do not ensure the exercise of agricultural activity. Yet the latter constitutes not only an essential and qualifying element for the lawfulness of the intervention itself, but also a requirement for access to the incentives established by the legislator.

This context has therefore given rise to the widespread need to identify and implement alternative or complementary legal instruments capable of integrating the agricultural dimension with the production of electricity.

The main solutions identified in both legal doctrine and practice include:

(i) the right of usufruct (Article 981 of the Italian Civil Code): which grants the holder the full enjoyment of the land and the right to collect its fruits, thereby ensuring the continuation of cultivation;

(ii) the loan for use agreement (Article 1803 of the Italian Civil Code): which secures the use of the land for agricultural purposes without transferring ownership, while maintaining flexibility in the allocation of rights; and

(iii) the rural land lease agreement (Articles 1628 et seq. of the Italian Civil Code and Law No. 203/1982): expressly designed to govern the management and cultivation of agricultural land and therefore particularly suited to contexts in which agricultural activity must be safeguarded.

Even in situations where both agricultural and energy activities are entrusted to a single special purpose vehicle (SPV), the entity must still be vested with the appropriate legal rights.

4.2 Flexible models of cooperation between agricultural and energy operators

The absence of codified provisions leaves room for flexible arrangements and case-specific solutions, often developed through contractual practice, administrative guidelines, and the gradual consolidation of sectoral best practices.

In general terms, as set forth by the Italian Guidelines, the following subjects are entitled to obtain authorisation for Agri-PV projects, identified as follows:

(i) **Agricultural enterprises**, whether individual or associated, which implement Agri-PV projects with the aim of reducing production costs through the utilisation of their own agricultural land; and

(ii) **Temporary associations of enterprises**, composed of energy sector operators together with one or more agricultural enterprises, which, by virtue of a specific agreement, make available their land for the construction of the Agri-PV projects.

In both scenarios, the regulatory framework requires that the agricultural activity will continue to be carried out, maintaining the centrality of farming as the qualifying element of such projects.

On the other hand, with reference to access to the incentives set forth by the Agrivoltaic Decree the related GSE operating rules, the framework of subjective eligibility requirements is set out in a binding and detailed manner. In particular, the following categories are entitled to apply for incentives:

(i) **Agricultural entrepreneurs**: this category includes agricultural entrepreneurs in the form of natural persons or companies, agricultural cooperatives, agricultural companies governed by Legislative Decree No. 99/2004, consortia composed of several entrepreneurs or agricultural companies, as well as cooperatives and their consortia engaged in the activities referred to in Article 2135 of the Civil Code. All these entities are expressly classified as "agricultural operators" for the purposes of the decree and are, as such, eligible for incentives; and

(ii) **Temporary associations of companies (ATI)**: these are also eligible provided that they include at least one of the above-mentioned agricultural operators. Where the ATI takes the form of a separate legal entity, compliance with the eligibility requirements is verified with reference to that entity. In any event, at least one member of the ATI must meet the subjective requirements set out in Article 4(1)(a) of the decree, and at least one member must qualify as a "producer" within the meaning of Appendix A to the GSE Operating Rules.

In light of the foregoing, it clearly emerges that the regulatory framework for Agri-PV is characterised by significant gaps and by the absence of a uniform and comprehensive set of provisions capable of governing all relevant profiles. As a result, while certain parameters are prescribed in a binding and detailed manner (notably with respect to access to incentives), other aspects are merely outlined through non-binding guidelines or left entirely to contractual and notarial practice. Accordingly, the definition of the most appropriate legal structure for each project cannot be resolved through the application of a single model. Rather, it necessarily requires a case-by-case assessment, tailored to the specific needs of the parties involved, to ensure both the continuity of agricultural activity and the bankability and long-term stability of the energy investment.

4.3 The development perspective

The lack of a sole model to adhere to and the need to implement the contractual relationship on a case-by-case basis, contributes to increase the uncertainty among the RES operators. Indeed, the partnership between energy operators and agricultural stakeholders is currently developing within a regulatory environment that, although politically and institutionally supportive of agrivoltaics, remains heavily influenced by agrarian legal structures designed for a different economic context, no longer suited to the multifunctional use of agricultural land enabled by agrivoltaic systems. Rather than promoting true contractual freedom, the system often requires parties to negotiate in derogation of rigid norms, creating legal uncertainty and operational risks. The challenge lies in introducing new contractual models specifically designed for agrivoltaics, capable of reconciling the need for flexible and modern agreements with compliance obligations related to agricultural qualification, land availability, and the respect of both the agronomic plan and the continuity of agricultural activity throughout the system's operational life. These models should ideally be officially recognized by competent authorities to ensure legal certainty and facilitate implementation. A constructive dialogue between the agricultural and energy sectors, supported by legal and technical expertise, could foster the evolution of contractual practices toward more modern standards, without compromising the autonomy of the parties.

4.4 Practical issue: transferability of Agri-PV projects under the Agrivoltaic Decree

A further issue concerns the admissibility of transferring Agri-PV projects or replacing the beneficiary operator after the award of incentives. This question has become increasingly relevant in practice, as several operators admitted to the Agrivoltaic Decree call for tenders, have raised doubts regarding the extent to which changes in project ownership or operator substitution may be lawfully carried out.

The GSE operating rules provide that any subjective or objective change occurring after the competitive procedure, upon entry into operation, or during the incentive period must be duly notified in accordance with the prescribed procedures. The same rules further specify that all eligibility requirements must continue to be met throughout the duration of the incentive scheme.

Neither the Agrivoltaic Decree nor the GSE operating rules, however, expressly regulate the admissibility of transfers of projects or changes in the beneficiary operator. As a result, there is no interpretative certainty on this issue. In this regulatory vacuum, it appears reasonable to consider, by analogy, the principles set out in the Legislative Decree No. 36/2023 (Public Procurement Code) regarding subjective changes.

Nonetheless, the actual compatibility of those principles with the specific features of PNRR measures and Agri-PV projects remains to be assessed.

Under public procurement law, Article 119 of Legislative Decree No. 36/2023 lays down the principle of the non-transferability of agreements, subject to the specific derogations provided in Article 120. These derogations allow a change of contractor in cases of corporate restructuring, insolvency, or succession *mortis causa*, provided that the incoming operator satisfies the original selection criteria, that no substantial amendments are made to the contract, and that no attempt at circumvention is evident. Administrative case law (Council of State, No. 1370/2013; No. 3819/2015; TAR Sicily, No. 2881/2019; Council of State, No. 6216/2019) has gone further, extending the principle to successful tenderers who had not yet signed a contract, to safeguard freedom of corporate reorganisation.

Two main principles emerge:

(i) **Principle of substantial continuity of the operator**: to avoid circumvention, the contracting authority must verify the legal basis for the proposed takeover, the subjective suitability of the incoming operator, and the continuing compliance of the outgoing operator with the initial requirements; and

(ii) **Limits on "additional" changes**: a distinct issue arises in respect of replacing members of a temporary association of companies (ATI). The new Public Contracts Code no longer treats such changes as automatically prohibited. They may be admissible provided that the conditions laid down in the legislation are satisfied (see Articles 68, 94, 95, 97(2), and 100), and that no alteration is made to the financial offer. In this regard, the Campania Regional Administrative Court, in its judgment No. 5211/2024, confirmed the admissibility of subjective changes within an ATI, provided that these served to ensure the consortium's operational capacity and did not introduce elements detrimental to transparency or competition.

5 THE MULTIDISCIPLINARY APPROACH

The potential positive impact of Agri-PV and its relevant proper installation can be better addressed by means of a joint professional approach. Associations between professionals and players in the energy, environment and agricultural sectors, in a common effort, can certainly support to define an appropriate policy frameworks and a common strategy for Agri-PV as well as to reach the targets of the European Green Deal.

With the concrete support of AIAS as well as of the researchers' approach, it is possible to reach an integration of Agri-PV into the landscape - that remains a significant barrier to their implementation - and to overcome the practical criticalities that RES operators and legal experts are daily facing.

In detail, energy-law experts, together with policymakers and researchers can play a key-role to explain to the renewable energy industry the concrete advantages deriving from the combination and synergy of agricultural activity and renewable energy production:

- Energy-law experts play a crucial role in shaping and interpreting Agri-PV policy and legal framework, by helping to balance the interests of the agriculture and energy sectors. As noted above, energy-law experts can help reduce

uncertainty and attract investment to the Agri-PV sector. Moreover, they can influence policy developments that support the broader objectives of the European Green Deal, such as climate neutrality by 2050.
- Technical experts and researchers have the responsibility to collaborate with institutions and other market participants by offering agronomic data and innovative solutions, in order to allow a sustainable transformation of the agricultural landscape. Indeed, it is not uncommon for public authorities responsible for protecting the landscape values to mistakenly focus on land consumption, without considering that agrivoltaic systems are inherently designed to preserve agricultural land use and implement appropriate mitigation measures. This achievement can be made possible through public-private partnerships, able to play a key-role in establishing necessary unified regulations.
- Developers' aim is to ensure the most competitive solutions, which do not raise energy costs for consumers and for the development of Agri-PV. The simplification of administrative regimes and grid connection procedures is necessary to achieve such renewables goals. From the development perspective, it is crucial to establish a clear regulatory framework that financially supports advanced, experimental agrivoltaics technologies, allowing them to mature and reach their full value and potential.

5 CONCLUDING REMARKS

The foregoing analysis demonstrates that the existing legal framework applicable to Agri-PV projects remains fragmented and, to a significant extent, undeveloped. While certain profiles are governed by binding provisions of positive law, others are merely outlined in soft-law instruments or are left to be structured through contractual autonomy and notarial practice.

In such a context, the simplified administrative procedures cannot clearly explain their concrete *favor* to Agri-PV development, as the single public bodies involved may act in a different way – basing on the different interpretation and application they may give to the legislative framework – and no uniform legal model can be regarded as dispositive or capable of universal application.

More broadly, the considerations set out in this paper support a general principle: the regulation of Agri-PV projects should be directed towards ensuring a genuine balance between the primacy of agricultural activity and the long-term sustainability of energy production.

Such balance is more effectively achieved through flexible and cooperative model legal structures than through rigid or exclusionary regulatory prescriptions. Indeed, notwithstanding the entry into force of several legal prescriptions, it is clear they do not sufficiently cover all the sub-fields connected to the agricultural sector. As experts of renewable energy sectors, we learnt that a pragmatic and tailor-made approach may fill the lack of a proper regulation and may be more capable to meet the needs of all the parties involved during the development phase as well as during the negotiation among private and public parties.

Conversely, an excessively prescriptive approach would risk either degenerating into speculative exploitation of agricultural land, or, at the other extreme, paralysing the development of a sector which, by its very design, has the potential to contribute decisively to the twin objectives of ecological transition and rural development.

42nd European Photovoltaic Solar Energy Conference and Exhibition

42nd European Photovoltaic Solar Energy Conference and Exhibition

Road to ecological transition: the Italian perspective of the agrivoltaics development

RESEARCH PERSPECTIVE

The effective integration of agrivoltaic systems requires ongoing research to ensure a sustainable transformation of the landscape and demonstrate social acceptance. This calls for innovative regulatory and technical solutions that highlight their tangible value to the public. Such integration relies on a cohesive, transdisciplinary vision that combines diverse perspectives and shares experimental and technical results.

Alessandra Scognamiglio, Senior Researcher and Coordinator task force Sustainable Agrivoltaics at ENEA

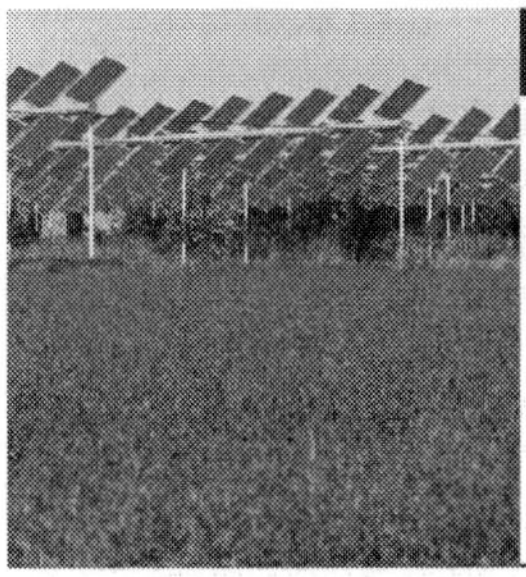

ASSOCIATION PERSPECTIVE

Associations are crucial in advancing agrivoltaics by uniting institutions, trade associations and companies, supporting EU and State Members in shaping policy frameworks and a common strategy. This collaboration is essential to enhance regulations, align partnerships with the RES market, and advance the energy transition in line with European Green Deal objectives.

Alessandra Scognamiglio, President of AIAS

LEGAL PERSPECTIVE

Italy has introduced a dedicated regulation for agrivoltaic systems, recognizing their key role in the energy transition. Recent legal updates aim to accelerate their deployment, highlighting the synergy between renewable energy development and agricultural land use. This collaboration between RES developers, stakeholders and agricultural partners requires specific legal regulation through ad hoc contractual forms, designed to balance and integrate the distinct needs of both the renewable energy and agricultural sectors. In view of the PNRR and FER X incentives, it is essential that the contractual regulations set out a framework that will stand the test of time.

Celeste Mellone, Partner and Co-head of Regulatory at Green Horse Legal Advisory
Valeria Viti, Partner at PedersoliGattai
Giulia Guidetti, Senior Associate at Green Horse Legal Advisory
Lorenzo Massaro, Senior Associate at PedersoliGattai
Cesare Gatti, Associate at PedersoliGattai

DEVELOPMENT PERSPECTIVE

The partnership between energy operators and agricultural stakeholders is growing within a regulatory framework still shaped by outdated agrarian laws, unsuited to the multifunctional use of land enabled by agrivoltaics. A constructive dialogue, supported by legal and technical expertise, is essential to modernize contractual practices while preserving party autonomy and ensuring legal protection for both sides.

Fabio Salis, Regulatory and Public Affairs Manager at Iberdrola Renovables Italia

GREEN HORSE | PedersoliGattai | Iberdrola | ENEA | AIAS Associazione Italiana Agrivoltaico Sostenibile

Green Horse Advisory Website | PerdersoliGattai Website | Iberdrola Website | Enea Website | AIAS Website

020542-001

POTENTIAL OF AGRIVOLTAICS IN THE EU UNDER DIFFERENT REGULATION SCENARIOS

Julien Van Overstraeten[1], Caroline Plaza[2], Philippe Macé[1], Elina Bosch[1], Mélodie de l'Épine[2]
[1]Becquerel Institute, Brussels (Belgium) [2]Becquerel Institute France, Lyon (France)
Rue Praetere 2, 1000 Brussels, Belgium. +32 493 451 720

ABSTRACT: The use of agricultural land for photovoltaic (PV) deployment has raised concerns, as rising installation rates intensify competition between food and energy production. To address this, several countries have introduced restrictions on PV use in agriculture. Agrivoltaics (AgriPV) offer a promising alternative by enabling the dual use of land for food cultivation and renewable electricity generation. Estimates of the technical potential vary widely: the Joint Research Centre of the European Commission calculated 944 GWp for 1% of the Utilized Agricultural Area (UAA) in the EU [1], while Danish researchers estimated up to 51 TWp if the entire UAA were used [2]. Unlike studies focused on maximum potential, this work evaluates a more restricted AgriPV potential, explicitly shaped by regulations designed to safeguard agricultural activity and food security. The analysis estimates a "minimal" potential by systematically excluding unsuitable land and applying regulatory constraints such as crop suitability, yield preservation, and ground coverage ratios. Even under the most stringent scenarios, the remaining potential remains significant, corresponding to 34% of the REPowerEU 2030 solar target. These results show that AgriPV can make a meaningful contribution to Europe's decarbonisation strategy without undermining agricultural production.*Keywords: Agrivoltaics, Technical potential, Regulatory constraints, Land use.*

1 INTRODUCTION

Photovoltaic installations on agricultural land have long been explored as a means to expand renewable energy production. Traditionally, such projects often replaced agricultural activities, but rising PV adoption has intensified competition for land, prompting some countries to impose restrictions. Agrivoltaics offers a promising alternative by enabling dual land use, combining food production with electricity generation. Beyond energy, AgriPV systems can protect crops and livestock from extreme weather while providing additional income for farmers.

Studies have estimated significant technical potential in Europe, with figures ranging from 51 TWp across the continent to 944 GWp if just 1% of agricultural land were utilized [1][2]. These figures highlight the transformative role agrivoltaics could play in achieving renewable energy targets while safeguarding food systems.

However, realizing this potential requires overcoming barriers such as technological adaptation for different crop types, alignment with agricultural practices, and the establishment of clear regulatory frameworks. Despite growing interest, concerns from farmers' organizations and the public highlight the need for robust governance to balance renewable energy goals with food security and responsible land use.

2. METHODOLOGICAL APPROACH

The assessment of the agrivoltaics market potential in this work follows a multi-step approach, divided into two main sections. The first section focuses on estimating the current technical potential for agrivoltaics, starting from the area in the European Union actively used for agricultural activities, known as the Utilized Agricultural Area. This excludes idle lands and wooded areas and represents the Gross Technical Potential. To refine this estimate and obtain a Realistic Technical Potential, several exclusions were applied, including protected agricultural and landscape areas, prohibitive terrains such as steep or flood-prone lands, and High Nature Value farmland important for biodiversity and traditional farming practices.

Then, economic considerations were incorporated to determine the Economic Technical Potential. Surfaces deemed unprofitable due to low PV yield or difficult synergy with crops were excluded, as were areas incompatible with agrivoltaic systems, such as energy crops or tree plantations, either due to physical constraints or intrinsic opposition to dual-use systems. Initially expressed in millions of hectares, these areas are later converted into potential installed capacity in GWp during the market potential analysis.

The second section evaluates the specific market potential through scenario-based modeling. Using the diffusion of innovations framework, an S-shaped curve is applied to project the annual Total Addressable Market (TAM) for agrivoltaics from 2024 to 2100, with the Economic Technical Potential defining the maximum achievable capacity by 2100.

To account for regulatory constraints and the need to maintain agricultural productivity, three scenarios were designed to estimate the Serviceable Addressable Market (SAM), reflecting variations in ground coverage limits, yield preservation, and other restrictions.

Table I: Summary of scenarios considered for the SAM assessment

	Loose regulation scenario	Medium regulation scenario	Strict regulation scenario
Prioritization of degraded soil	No	Yes	Yes
Selection of crops	No	No	Yes
Average density	0,60 MWp/ha	0,57 MWp/ha	0,54 MWp/ha

Although not considered here, a further step could define the Serviceable Obtainable Market (SOM) by integrating additional political, social, supply chain, and economic constraints, providing a more realistic projection of agrivoltaics deployment potential.

3. RESULTS

3.1. Technical potential for AgriPV in Europe

The gross technical potential for agrivoltaics in Europe accounts for over 155 million ha. Through exclusion of land that is either protected, under high nature value farming recognition, or subject to adverse terrain conditions, a realistic technical potential of just under 78 million ha is calculated. Finally, taking into out areas subject to insufficient irradiation conditions or intrinsically incompatible with agrivoltaics, an economic technical potential of 76,6 million ha is obtained.

3.2. Specific market potential for AgriPV in Europe

The total addressable market, here taken as equivalent to the economic technical potential of 76,6 million of ha, represents a very significant surface area, which will likely not be entirely exploited by agrivoltaics. Instead, the serviceable addressable market (SAM) assessment provides a more realistic vision of the evolution of the area that could be exploited by agrivoltaics.

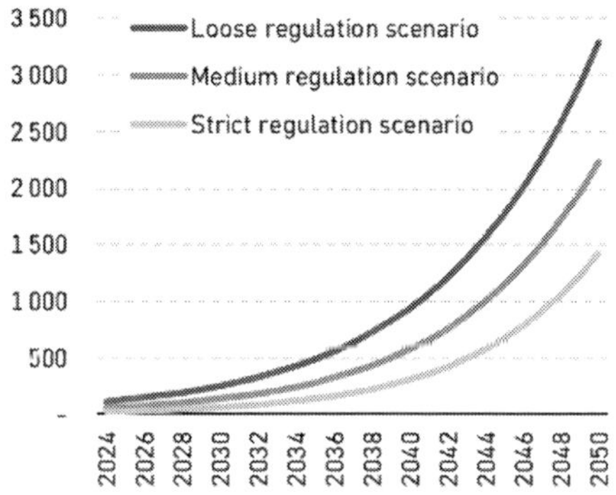

Figure 1: Cumulative serviceable addressable European agriPV market, in GWp

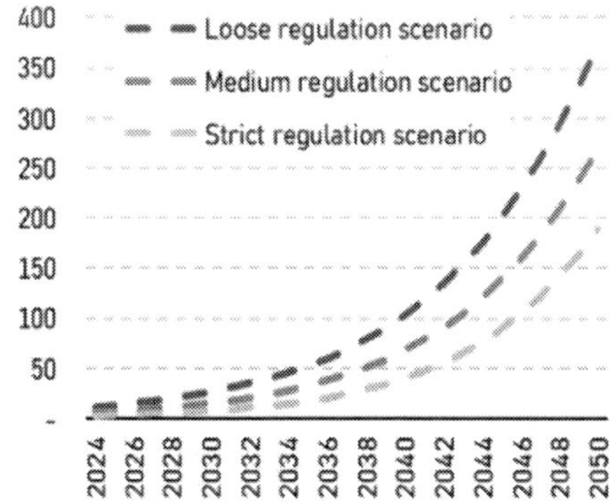

Figure 2: Annual serviceable addressable European agriPV market, in GWp

The serviceable addressable market assessment provides a realistic outlook on the potential deployment of agrivoltaics in Europe, taking into account regulatory constraints that safeguard agricultural activity and food security. Figure 1 and Figure 2 illustrate the evolution of cumulative and annual SAM up to 2050, expressed in GWp. While initial deployment progresses slowly, growth accelerates toward the middle of the century, positioning agrivoltaics as a key contributor to PV deployment in Europe, where competition for land limits the availability of large, non-agricultural sites for ground-mounted PV plants.

By 2050, the cumulative SAM reaches approximately 3,000 GWp under loose regulation, slightly above 2,000 GWp under medium regulation, and around 1,400 GWp under strict regulation. The corresponding annual SAM peaks at 377 GWp, 272 GWp, and 193 GWp, respectively. Despite the limitations inherent in the stricter scenario, agrivoltaics could still cover up to 34% of the EU's 2030 solar target of 750 GWDC (600 GWAC) under REPowerEU [3].

These scenarios highlight the decisive role of regulation in shaping AgriPV's development. While larger, high-density projects may accelerate progress toward PV targets, smaller-scale installations designed with strong synergies between energy generation and agricultural activity may provide a more sustainable pathway. The balance between these approaches will depend on the regulatory framework, which will ultimately determine how agrivoltaics can support both renewable energy expansion and the continuity of European agriculture.

Table II: Summary of serviceable addressable market (SAM) results for AgriPV in Europe [GWp]

	2050		
Regulation scenario	Loose	Medium	Strict
Cumulative	3289	2232	1424
Annual	377,3	272,1	193,1

4 CONCLUSIONS

Unlike studies focused on estimating maximum technical potential, this work evaluates a more restricted agrivoltaics potential, explicitly shaped by regulations aimed at preserving agricultural activity and safeguarding food security. Even under the most stringent regulatory scenarios, the remaining potential proves substantial, corresponding to 34% of the REPowerEU 2030 solar target and thus capable of covering a significant share of Europe's future energy demand. This highlights that agrivoltaics can make a meaningful contribution to decarbonization strategies without compromising agricultural production.

Nonetheless, regulatory uncertainty remains a central challenge for the sector. Overly strict land-use policies could unnecessarily constrain deployment and delay the achievement of renewable energy targets, while excessively loose frameworks risk encouraging "alibi agriculture," where the agricultural function becomes secondary to energy generation. Both extremes threaten the credibility and long-term sustainability of the concept.

To unlock agrivoltaics' full potential, coordinated policy support is required, along with transparent and robust regulatory frameworks that align energy and agricultural priorities. Furthermore, building awareness within markets and among stakeholders—farmers, energy developers, policymakers, and the public—will be critical to foster acceptance and encourage models that deliver both food and energy security. In this way, agrivoltaics can evolve from a niche concept into a cornerstone of Europe's sustainable energy transition.

5 REFERENCES

[1] A. Chatzipanagi, N. Taylor and A. Jaeger-Waldau, "Overview of the potential and challenges for Agri-Photovoltaics in the European Union," Publications Office of the European Union, Luxembourg, 2023.
[2] K. A. K. Niazi and M. Victoria, "Comparative analysis of photovoltaic configurations for agrivoltaic systems in Europe," Progress in Photovoltaics: Research and Applications, vol. 31, no. 11, pp. 1101-1113, 2023.
[3] B. Meban, "Landmark EU Solar Strategy: SolarPower Europe Response", SolarPowerEurope. www.solarpowereurope.org/press-releases/landmark-eu-solar-strategy-solar-power-europe-response. 2022.

6 ACKNOWLEDGMENT AND FUNDING

The work described has received funding as part of the SEAMLESS-PV project from the European Union's Horizon Europe research and innovation program under grant agreement N° 101096126.

SMART ENERGY SYSTEM INTEGRATION OF PHOTOVOLTAIC: FROM STRATEGIC AND RESEARCH INNOVATION AGENDA TO EU FUNDED PROJECTS

Grazia BARCHI[1], Maximilian SCHÖNAU[2], Pierre-Jean ALET[3], Venizelos EFTHYMIOU[4], Gofran CHOWDHURY[5], Marion PERRIN[6], Elham SHIRAZI[7], Ioannis (John) A. TSANAKAS[8]

[1] EURAC Research - Institute for Renewable Energy, Italy, grazia.barchi@eurac.edu
[2] smartblue AG / Coburg University of Applied Sciences, Dept. of Electrical Engineering and Computer Sciences, Germany, maximilian.schoenau@smartblue.de
[3]CSEM, Switzerland, pierre-jean.alet@csem.ch
[4] EPL Technology Frontiers Ltd, Cyprus, venizelos@epltechfront.com
[5]3E, Belgium, gofran.chowdhury@3e.eu
[6]Energy Pool, France, marion.perrin@energy-pool.eu
[7]Faculty of Engineering Technology, University of Twente, Enschede, The Netherlands, e.shirazi@utwente.nl
[8]CEA-INES, France, venizelos@epltechfront.com

ABSTRACT: The EU has set an ambitious target to reach climate neutrality by 2050, with a rapidly rising share of PV and wind generation reshaping the energy system in terms of planning and operation. A high penetration of PV systems requires advanced monitoring and control systems and techniques, as well as technology that provides system stability and minimises congestion during peak production hours. In this context, Challenge 4 of the Strategic Research and Innovation Agenda (SRIA), developed within ETIP-PV, is dedicated to "Smart Energy System Integration of Photovoltaics for Large-Scale Deployment and High Penetration". Despite the Challenge identified six roadmaps, a systematic and scalable synthesis of the thematic evolution and strategic relevance of grid integration PV challenges, solutions, and evolutions remains limited in relation to EU-funded projects. This paper introduces an LLM-based methodology for analyzing a decade of EU-funded projects data, mapped to the Challeng 4 SRIA roadmap, and extracting indicators to reveal trends, dominant themes, and gaps. The framework provides a reproducible methodology to possibly guide research directions, funding priorities, and policy development.

Keywords: Photovoltaic, Smart Energy System, Digitalization, Large Language Model, Artificial Intelligence

1 INTRODUCTION

The cumulative installed solar photovoltaic (PV) capacity in the EU reached 338 GW in 2024, representing a significant increase from the 16 GW in 2009 when the Renewable Energy Directive was first introduced [1]. The European Solar Energy Strategy foresees 600 GW of PV deployment overall across European countries by 2030 [2]. The increase of PV is mainly due to lower production and installation costs, as well as the support of policy frameworks, where PV is becoming one of the technology drivers for the European energy transition.

In 2024, the International Energy Agency (IEA) reported that global investments in solar PV exceeded those for all other sources of electricity generation combined, highlighting the central role of PV in the ongoing energy transition [3].

The European Union's climate neutrality target by 2050 requires a rapid increase in the integration of renewable energy sources into the energy system, particularly wind and solar systems, which are expected to cover at least 50% of energy demand.

This transition brings significant challenges for grid integration in the energy system, as renewables are inherently variable and unpredictable. In particular, the system operation and planning procedure will evolve to properly address local voltage stability issues, regional congestion risks, and the complexities of cross-border power exchanges. Advanced solutions require real-time control, predictive monitoring, demand-side flexibility, and the deployment of new technologies, such as grid-forming inverters and energy storage systems, to ensure reliable and resilient grid performance as renewable energy sources become more dominant.

To overcome such present and future limitations as well as to increase PV deployment further and boost efficiency, the European Technology and Innovation Platform for Photovoltaics (ETIP-PV) has recently updated the Strategic Research and Innovation Agenda (SRIA) on PV [4] to identify, among other priorities, the five most crucial challenges that should be addressed in the coming years as priority, to establish reasonable targets for 2035. In this multifaceted scenario, Challenge 4 on "Smart Energy System Integration of Photovoltaics for Large-Scale Deployment and High Penetration" aims to enhance and develop seamless energy systems capable of better utilizing and optimizing the amount of available PV energy alongside other renewable energy sources, in order to meet the expectation of both users and stakeholders in terms of lower costs, higher remuneration and overall higher efficiency.

Over the past decade, numerous EU-funded projects have contributed to advancing PV innovation, integration, and sustainability through technical development, socio-economic impact, and policy alignment, forming a rich yet complex landscape of strategic efforts. Despite the volume and diversity of these projects, a systematic and scalable analysis of their thematic evolution and strategic relevance remains limited.

This paper introduces a methodology based on large language models (LLMs) to analyze and synthesize insights from ten years of EU project data on PV system topics related to the Challenge 4 SRIA (SRIA-Ch4) priorities. Considering the semantic abilities of LLMs, we aimed to extract key values and indicators that reveal trends, dominant themes, and contribution distribution within the SRIA-Ch4 areas. The approach enables us to capture a snapshot of project trends and identify relevant topics that may inform future research directions, funding priorities, and policy frameworks.

10.4229/EUPVSEC2025/5DV.3.37

Our analysis contributes to the field of AI-assisted research synthesis and provides a replicable framework for strategic intelligence in energy innovation.
In this way, the findings are expected to support stakeholders, including researchers, policymakers, and industry actors, in navigating the evolving landscape of PV energy system integration with greater clarity and foresight.

2 METHODOLOGY

LLM models of OpenAI [5] were used to analyze EU PV project data related to the SRIA priorities. LLMs have shown promising results for conducting literature reviews, especially for screening smaller texts [6], [7]. OpenAI's models have also proven to have satisfactory accuracy when applied to problems within the photovoltaic domain [8], [9].
Before going into the detail of the methodology, we summarize in Table 1 the correspondence between the specific six roadmap in SRIA-Ch4 [4] and what we refer to as "roadmap topic".

For the specific meaning and objectives of each roadmap item, we refer readers to the SRIA-Ch4.

Table 1: Mapping of roadmaps identified in Challenge 4 of the SRIA and the selected and used roadmap topics

Roadmap SRIA-Ch4	Roadmap Topic
R1: More intelligence in distributed control	Distributed control intelligence
R2: Improved efficiencies by integration of PV-systems in DC-networks	PV integration in DC Networks
R3: Hybrid systems including demand flexibility (PV + storage + batteries + green hydrogen/fuel cells or gas turbines etc)	Hybrid RES Systems with Demand flexibility
R4: Aggregated energy and VPPs	Aggregation and Market participation
R5: Interoperability in communication and operation of RES smart grids	Interoperability in Smart Grids
R6: Digitalization of PV systems	Digitalization of PV systems

2.1 Using LLMs for the Analyzation of EU funded Projects

All projects funded by the EU under the Horizon framework program for research and innovation from 2014 to 2027, publicly available [10], [11] were downloaded, imported and analyzed by their project titles and objectives. The dataset consists of 52,848 research projects, most of which are unrelated to PV. Thus, the projects were preprocessed with a smaller system prompt and *GPT4o-mini* [12], to filter projects, that do not relate to the PV domain. This resulted in 474 projects that are relevant to the SRIA on PV.

A more detailed system prompt and *GPT5* [13] were employed to implement a second, stricter filter and a deeper analysis. The model was instructed to assign a percentage w_{pt} indicating how much of the project p aligns with each of the roadmap topics t (including the category "other" to attribute the percentages that did not match the roadmap).

GPT5 was able to reliably return percentages that summed up to 1 across all topics. To avoid inconsistencies that smaller models may introduce (e.g., percentages not summing exactly to 1), we recommend first having the model assign each topic to a simple scale and, second, converting these scores to percentages through normalization of the simple scores.

The second filtering by *GPT5* resulted in 255 projects, with varying levels of alignment with the evaluated roadmaps.

The estimated relevance R_t of every topic was calculated by the average of these percentages over the number of projects n_p:

$$R_t = \frac{1}{n_p} \cdot \sum_p w_{pt} \tag{1}$$

By multiplying the percentages by the project funding F_p, the funding for the strategic topics F_t was estimated:

$$F_t = \sum_p w_{pt} \cdot F_p \tag{2}$$

The project's duration in every year Δt_{py} divided by the total project duration Δt_p was utilized, to get an estimation of the budget for every strategic roadmap topic of the SRIA-Ch4 over the last years F_{ty}:

$$F_{ty} = \sum_p w_{pt} \cdot F_p \cdot \frac{\Delta t_{py}}{\Delta t_p} \tag{3}$$

Figure 1 illustrates the methodology's outline. The system prompts are in Appendix A1 and A2. As a user prompt, the project title and objective were given.

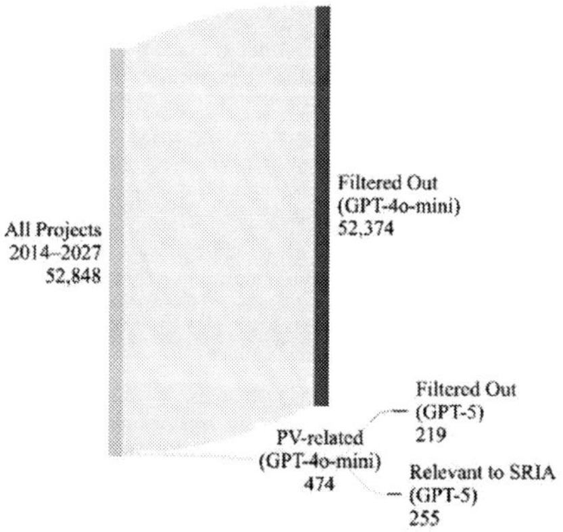

Figure 1: Outline of the project screening

This is not a rigorous quantitative method. It is a heuristic proxy constrained by the limited information contained in the project's objective and the subjectivity of topic taxonomies as well as the uncertainty inherent to the LLM-based classification. The results should therefore be read as indicative, comparative trends, useful for assessing the relative salience of topics across the portfolio, rather than as exact, auditable allocations at the level of individual projects.

2.2 Validation

The filtering of the *GPT4o-mini* model and the analysis of *GPT5* were manually labelled for a subset of 100 and 50 projects, respectively. For the validation of the filtering, the test dataset was randomly sampled of 50 predicted positives (projects that are part of the PV domain) and 50 predicted negatives (projects that do not relate to PV).

Coincidentally, the validation yielded 3 false positives and 3 false negatives. This proves that the filtering process is very reliable, with accuracy, precision, specificity, and recall of 94% each. None of the incorrectly classified samples had PV as their primary focus; misclassifications occurred only in borderline cases.

The share of the project attributable to the individual strategic topics returned by *GPT5* w_p were manually labelled for a test subset of 50 projects. Comparing *GPT5*'s outputs with these annotations yielded a mean absolute error of 9 percentage points and a root mean squared error of 15 percentage points on average over all categories. This indicates a significant discrepancy between the prediction and manual label, highlighting the subjective and qualitative nature of the labels. Thus, an evaluation strategy emphasizing agreement within relative ranking, rather than exact equality was adopted by calculating the spearman correlation [14]. With a spearman correlation of 50 % on average over all categories, the correlation of the ranking of the projects seems adequate for comparative analyses.

3 RESULTS ON EU-PROJECT DISTRIBUTION

Based on the methodology and analysis described in Section 2, we found that 255 projects were classified as relevant to the SRIA-Ch4 and the strategic roadmaps. Table 2 displays the difference between the estimated relevance of the topics, Eq (1), and the distribution, when it is scaled by the funding, Eq. (2). Larger differences between these values could indicate topics that were more prominent in the project summaries but had less funding on average. **Error! Reference source not found.** displays the funding share by strategic topic over time, Eq. (3). The values are normalized, and they are grouped by four periods, i.e. before 2019, 2020-2022, 2023-2025 and beyond 2025. It is interesting to see how the roadmap topics distribution changes from before 2019 till 2025.

Table 2: Comparison between the estimated relevance and the estimated funding share of strategic topics.

Strategic Topic	Estimated Relevance	Estimated Funding Share
Aggregation & Market Participation	19 %	21 %
Hybrid RES Systems with Demand Flexibility	17 %	21 %
Interoperability in Smart Grids	17 %	21 %
Digitalization of PV Systems	25 %	19 %
Distributed Control Intelligence	18 %	16 %
PV Integration in DC Networks	3 %	2 %

We can appreciate that in the first three bars, there is a higher distribution of funded projects in the topic of *Aggregation & Market Participation*. This is not surprising, as the topic is broad and covers not only projects more focused on PV but also energy systems and smart grids in general. Moving from left to right, we can notice no significant changes in the Hybrid RES and Distributed Control Intelligence topics, which on average remain almost the same, while the Digitalization of PV Systems and PV Integration in DC Networks show some variation. This trend is reasonable and aligns with, on one hand, the growing relevance of digitalization, especially with the advent of AI, and, on the other hand, the increase in distributed energy resources that naturally operate on DC. Along with PV, this drives the evolution of fully supplied DC networks.

Figure 3 shows the distribution of the normalized estimated relevance across roadmap topics. The first four topics resulted in similar slices. *Digitalization of PV Systems* seems to be a common topic, accounting for 25% of the share. *Aggregation & Market Participation*, *Hybrid RES Systems with Demand Flexibility*, *Interoperability in Smart Grids* and *Distributed Control Intelligence* accounted for roughly one-fifth each. The topic *Distributed Control Intelligence* was mentioned a bit less, with only

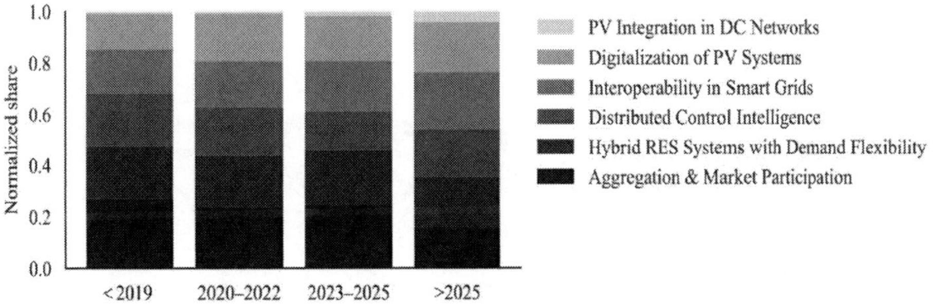

Figure 2: Estimated share of funded budget by strategic topic over time.

10.4229/EUPVSEC2025/5DV.3.37

16 % percent. *PV Integration in DC Networks* represents only a small fraction.

This figure results complementary with respect to Figure 2. Indeed, if from one side we report the distribution based on the total budget allocated to the specific topics on the other side (Fig. 3) we report the normalized value based on the number of funded projects. The results do not change too much, but they are also not the same and this lead to the consideration that different budget has been allocated to different number of projects by suggesting that some of them require possible an higher investment due possible to different reasons: infrastructure requirements, starting technology readiness level, number of partners to be involved and so on.

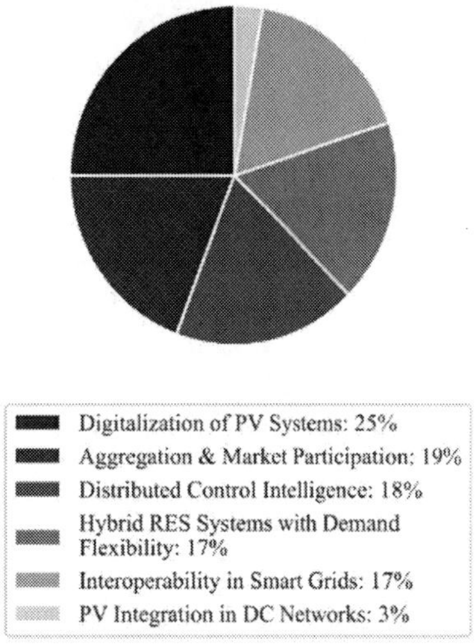

Figure 3: Estimated distribution of the projects alignment to the strategic topics.

Error! Reference source not found. displays the sum of the estimated funding of all strategic topics over time. The trajectory from 2018 to 2025 demonstrates an increase with a peak in 2024 at nearly €125 million. This upward trend reflects a period of intensified investment, potentially linked to strategic research initiatives or policy shifts. The slight decline projected for 2025 is mainly related to the fact that we have only a partial view based on the project funded by under the Horizon Europe in the first phases, so limited to the ones reported in the public database from CORDIS. A general consideration that we can assess, but as more a qualitative than a quantitative comment is that while the annual installation of PV increased over 4-fold from 2018 to 2023 [15], the estimated funding into the strategic topics based on the proposed methodology seems to have increased only 2-fold in this timeframe.

4 QUERING PROJECTS FOR SPECIFIC TOPICS

LLMs can be used for topic-centric retrieval - i.e., to ask when a specific technique first appears in EU proposals and how it evolves thereafter. As an example, we queried the data for drone-based fault detection in PV modules. Using the prompt provided in Appendix A3, we acquired all projects related to drone-based monitoring, which were summarized by *GPT5* to:

EU support for drone-based PV inspection first appears in Horizon 2020 proposals in the mid-2010s. EASY PV (2016–2018) explicitly deployed RPAS to capture thermal imagery of PV plants, georeferenced with high-accuracy GNSS/RTK to pinpoint defective modules—marking the entry of drone thermography into EU-funded O&M workflows. In parallel, CDRONE (2016) explored an autonomous inspection-and-cleaning concept for large-scale solar, positioning aeronautical robotics as a lever to cut O&M costs. Together, these feasibility- and implementation-oriented projects show early EU interest focused on proving that aerial imaging could be made precise, safe, and economically relevant for utility PV.

Under Horizon Europe, the theme matures from proofs of concept to integrated asset-management toolchains. PROMISE (2022–2025) built a Malta-based reliability platform that includes satellite and drone vision for data collection and modeling, embedding UAV imagery within broader reliability science and capacity building. SOLARIS (2024–2028) goes further, specifying automated multi-spectral PV inspection using drones for early fault detection and linking these inspections to forecasting, preventive maintenance, and trading via an AI-driven asset-management suite. In short, drone inspection entered EU proposals in 2015–2016 with thermographic RPAS pilots and, by 2022–2024, evolved into multi-sensor, automated, and AI-integrated inspection pipelines at fleet scale.

Functionality-centric retrieval with LLMs enables the tracing of when concrete techniques first appear in the proposals and how they evolve. In future, this method can be developed further to yield reproducible evidence to inform about specific funding priorities.

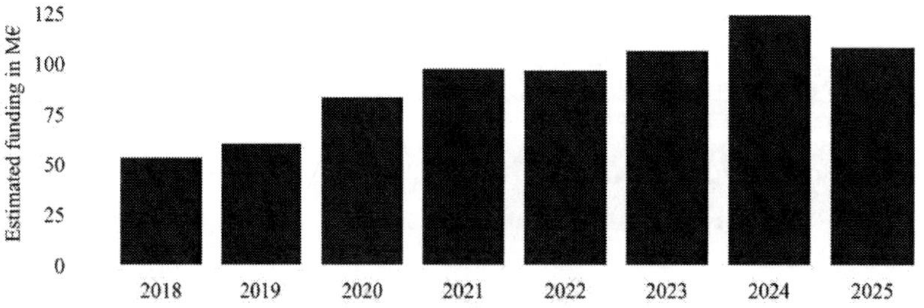

Figure 4: Estimated funding into all strategic topics over time.

10.4229/EUPVSEC2025/5DV.3.37

5 CONCLUSIONS

A LLM-based pipeline to map Horizon 2020 and Horizon Europe programme to ETIP-PV's SRIA-ch4 was presented in this study. From 52,848 records, a two-stage process yielded 255 PV-relevant projects with graded alignments across the six roadmap topics. Validation shows LLMs are suited for high-volume triage and thematic synthesis.

To strengthen the analysis of EU fund allocation, rejected proposals (if made publicly available) could be included alongside funded ones in future works, enabling a comparative assessment that identifies the factors for funding success.

Subsequent work may also analyze the remaining 99 % of the funded projects more detailed. Especially the share of renewable energies related to so-called conventional energy projects of the EU could be of public interest.

In future, LLMs may be utilized to increase the transparency of bureaucratic processes. Future infrastructure enabled by LLMs could provide a queryable view of how EU funds are allocated.

ACKNOWLEDGEMENT

Special thanks to Sander Schubert and Joseph Jachmann for their support with this work.

REFERENCES

[1] A. Jaeger-Waldau, "PV Status Report 2010," JRC Publications Repository. Accessed: Sep. 12, 2025. [Online]. Available: https://publications.jrc.ec.europa.eu/repository/handle/JRC59708

[2] European Parliament, "EU Solar Energy Strategy | Legislative Train Schedule," European Parliament. Accessed: Sep. 16, 2025. [Online]. Available: https://www.europarl.europa.eu/legislative-train/package-repowereu-plan/file-eu-solar-strategy

[3] "Overview and key findings – World Energy Investment 2024 – Analysis," IEA. Accessed: Sep. 12, 2025. [Online]. Available: https://www.iea.org/reports/world-energy-investment-2024/overview-and-key-findings

[4] ETIP PV, "Strategic Research and Innovation Agenda on Photovoltaics, Update." Accessed: Sep. 16, 2025. [Online]. Available: https://media.etip-pv.eu/filer_public/f5/8b/f58b06d7-60fa-457a-8562-80eb71fa667c/etip_pv_-_sria_report_update-_august24.pdf

[5] "OpenAI Platform." Accessed: Feb. 06, 2025. [Online]. Available: https://platform.openai.com

[6] J.-L. Lieberum *et al.*, "Large language models for conducting systematic reviews: on the rise, but not yet ready for use—a scoping review," *Journal of Clinical Epidemiology*, vol. 181, p. 111746, 2025, doi: https://doi.org/10.1016/j.jclinepi.2025.111746.

[7] M. Mostafapour, J. H. Fortier, K. Pacheco, H. Murray, and G. Garber, "Evaluating Literature Reviews Conducted by Humans Versus ChatGPT: Comparative Study," *JMIR AI*, vol. 3, p. e56537, Aug. 2024, doi: 10.2196/56537.

[8] M. Schönau *et al.*, "Predicting the Shading of Photovoltaic Systems Using Machine Learning," *PV-Symposium Proc*, vol. 2, Aug. 2025, doi: 10.52825/pv-symposium.v2i.2636.

[9] M. Schönau *et al.*, "String outages in photovoltaic plants," *Renewable Energies*, vol. 3, no. 1, Jan. 2025, doi: 10.1177/27533735251347879.

[10] Publications Office, "CORDIS - EU research projects under Horizon 2020 (2014-2020)." Publications Office of the European Union, 2015. doi: 10.2906/112117098108/12.

[11] Publications Office, "CORDIS - EU research projects under HORIZON EUROPE (2021-2027)." Publications Office, Jul. 25, 2022. doi: 10.2906/112117098108/20.

[12] "GPT-4o mini: advancing cost-efficient intelligence." Accessed: Aug. 20, 2025. [Online]. Available: https://openai.com/index/gpt-4o-mini-advancing-cost-efficient-intelligence/

[13] "Introducing GPT-5." Accessed: Aug. 20, 2025. [Online]. Available: https://openai.com/index/introducing-gpt-5/

[14] C. Spearman, "The Proof and Measurement of Association between Two Things," *The American Journal of Psychology*, vol. 15, no. 1, p. 72, Jan. 1904, doi: 10.2307/1412159.

[15] IEA, "Photovoltaic Power Systems Programme Task Updates 2024." Accessed: Aug. 27, 2025. [Online]. Available: https://iea-pvps.org/annual-reports/iea-pvps-task-updates-2024/

APPENDIX

A1 Prompt for the Filtering Process

Below the prompt that was provided to *gpt-4o-mini-2024-07-18* for the filtering of the research projects, using the models default configuration. Line breaks and white spaces were adapted to increase readability.

```
You are a senior research scientist working
for the European Commission at ETIP PV in
the working group Digital PV, Grid and
Storage.

TASK: Assess the alignment of the research
projects to the Strategic Research and
Innovation Agenda (SRIA).

Strategic Roadmap:
Distributed Control Intelligence,
PV Integration in DC Networks,
Hybrid RES Systems with Demand Flexibility,
Aggregation & Market Participation,
Interoperability in Smart Grids,
Digitalization of PV Systems

CRITICAL RULES:
- Return a JSON Object according to this
Schema:
{"type":"json_schema","json_schema":{"name"
:"SRIA_Alignment_Evaluation","schema":{"typ
e":"object","properties":{"Is_aligned":{"ty
pe":"boolean","description":"True if the
project aligns with the
SRIA"}},"required":["Is_aligned"],"addition
alProperties":false},"strict":true}}

- Return False for projects that do not
relate to the PV domain.
- You will be penalized for incorrect
classifications or wrong JSON format.
```

A2 Prompt for the Evaluation Process

Below is the prompt that was provided to *gpt-5-2025-08-07* for the analysis of the filtered research projects, using the models default configuration:

```
You are a senior research scientist working for the European Commission at ETIP PV in the working group Digital PV, Grid and Storage.

TASK: Assess the alignment of the research projects to the Strategic Research and Innovation Agenda (SRIA).

Decide based on the following criteria:

Technological Focus:
 Smart Inverters
 Grid-forming Inverters
 DC Networks / Microgrids
 Hybrid Systems (PV + Wind + Hydro + Storage)
 Virtual Power Plants (VPPs)
 Forecasting Tools
 Digital Twins
 Artificial Intelligence (AI) for PV
 Edge AI & Big Data
 IoT in Energy Systems

Key Performance Indicators (KPIs):
 Forecasting Accuracy
 Grid Support Capabilities
 Energy Efficiency Gains
 LCOE (Levelized Cost of Energy) Reduction
 Interoperability Standards
 AI-based Predictive Maintenance

Enabling Technologies:
 Energy Storage (Batteries, Green Hydrogen)
 Vehicle-to-Grid (V2G)
 Smart Grids
 Cybersecurity for DER
 Sensor Integration
 Wireless Power Transmission

Core Themes:
 Smart Energy Systems
 Photovoltaics (PV)
 Energy System Integration
 Renewable Energy Sources (RES)
 Decarbonization
 Energy Transition
 Distributed Energy Resources (DER)

For each strategic roadmap in the SRIA for the field Digital PV, Grid, and Storage, evaluate the given project and assign a percentage (0-100) indicating how much of the project aligns with that specific roadmap. Also include a value for <OTHER>, which is the percentage of the project that does not fit into any of the strategic roadmap categories. The sum of all percentages (including <OTHER>) must equal exactly 100 %.

Strategic Roadmap:
Distributed Control Intelligence,
PV Integration in DC Networks,
Hybrid RES Systems with Demand Flexibility,
Aggregation & Market Participation,
Interoperability in Smart Grids,
Digitalization of PV Systems

CRITICAL RULES:
- Return a JSON Object according to this Schema:
```



```
{"type":"json_schema","json_schema":{"name":"SRIA_Alignment_Evaluation","schema":{"type":"object","properties":{"reasoning":{"type":"string","description":"Short reasoning for the percentages"},"alignment_scores":{"type":"object","properties":{"Distributed Control Intelligence":{"type":"number"},"PV Integration in DC Networks":{"type":"number"},"Hybrid RES Systems with Demand Flexibility":{"type":"number"},"Aggregation & Market Participation":{"type":"number"},"Interoperability in Smart Grids":{"type":"number"},"Digitalization of PV Systems":{"type":"number"},"<OTHER>":{"type":"number"}},"additionalProperties":false,"required":["Distributed Control Intelligence","PV Integration in DC Networks", "Hybrid RES Systems with Demand Flexibility", "Aggregation & Market Participation", "Interoperability in Smart Grids", "Digitalization of PV Systems","<OTHER>"]},"Is_aligned":{"type":"boolean","description":"True if the project aligns with SRIA"}},"required":["reasoning","alignment_scores","Is_aligned"],"additionalProperties":false},"strict":true}}
```



```
- Return zeros for projects that do not relate to the PV domain.
- You will be penalized for incorrect classifications or wrong JSON format.
```

A3 Prompt for Quering the Drone-Based Monitoring

Below is the prompt that was provided to *gpt-5-2025-08-07* for querying the filtered research projects for drone based-monitoring, using the models default configuration:

```
You are a senior research scientist working for the European Commission at ETIP PV in the working group Digital PV, Grid and Storage.

TASK: Decide if the given project contributes to drone-based PV fault detection using heat signatures.

Return True, if the project mentions drones/UAVs/UAS for PV inspection, if it uses thermal / infrared imaging, thermography, or heat signature analysis or if it clearly enables
these.

CRITICAL RULES:
- Return a JSON Object according to this Schema: { "type": "json_schema", "json_schema": { "name": "Drone_Monitoring_Evaluation", "schema": { "type": "object", "properties": { "reasoning": { "type": "string", "description": "Short reasoning for the decision", }, "Is_aligned": { "type": "boolean", "description": "True if the project contributes to drone-based PV fault detection.", }, }, "required": ["reasoning", "Is_aligned"], "additionalProperties": False, }, "strict": True, }, }

- You will be penalized for incorrect classifications or wrong JSON format.
```

10.4229/EUPVSEC2025/5DV.3.37

SMART ENERGY SYSTEM INTEGRATION OF PHOTOVOLTAIC: FROM STRATEGIC AND RESEARCH INNOVATION AGENDA TO EU FUNDED PROJECTS

Grazia BARCHI[1], Maximilian SCHÖNAU[2], Pierre-Jean ALET[3], Venizelos EFTHYMIOU[4], Gofran CHOWDHURY[5], Marion PERRIN[6], Elham SHIRAZI[7], Ioannis (John) A. TSANAKAS[8]

[1]EURAC Research - Institute for Renewable Energy, Italy; [2]smartblue AG / Coburg University of Applied Sciences, Dept. of Electrical Engineering and Computer Sciences, Germany; [3]CSEM, Switzerland; [4]EPL Technology Frontiers Ltd, Cyprus; [5]3E, Belgium; [6]Energy Pool, France; [7]Faculty of Engineering Technology, University of Twente, Enschede, The Netherlands; [8]CEA-INES, France

INTRODUCTION

- The ETIP-PV has recently updated its Strategic Research and Innovation Agenda (SRIA) to address the most crucial challenges for photovoltaic (PV) deployment and efficiency by 2035. Considering that the most of PV installation will be integrated into the energy system, Challenge 4 focuses on the **"Smart Energy System Integration of Photovoltaics for Large-Scale Deployment and High Penetration."**
- The aims of the paper are:
  - ➢ to present a methodology based on large language models (LLMs) to analyze and synthesize insights from almost ten years of funded EU project data on PV system topics related to Challenge 4 of the SRIA (SRIA-Ch4);
  - ➢ to extract key values and indicators that reveal trends, dominant themes in the selected EU funded project;
  - ➢ to support stakeholders in navigating the evolving PV energy system integration past, present and future trend.

Roadmap SRIA-Ch4	Roadmap Topic
R1: More intelligence in distributed control	Distributed control intelligence
R2: Improved efficiencies by integration of PV-systems in DC-networks	PV Integration in DC Networks
R3: Hybrid systems including demand flexibility (PV + storage + batteries + green hydrogen/fuel cells or gas turbines)	Hybrid RES Systems with Demand Flexibility
R4: Aggregated energy and VPPs	Aggregation and Market participation
R5: Interoperability in communication and operation of RES smart grids	Interoperability in Smart Grids
R6: Digitalization of PV systems	Digitalization of PV Systems

METHODOLOGY

- Scope & data: Objectives of 52,848 Horizon 2020 and Horizon Europe projects from 2014–2027.
- Two-stage screening:
  - ✓ Stage 1: GPT-4o-mini filters to PV domain → 474 candidates
  - ✓ Stage 2: GPT-5 assigns share of each project to 6 SRIA-Ch4 roadmap topics
- Result: 255 relevant projects with graded alignment across the 6 topics.

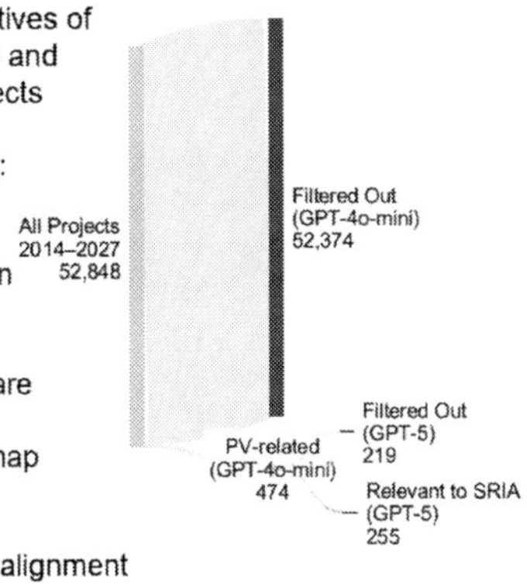

- Validation resulted in high accuracy of the filtering process, and acceptable accuracy for the topic shares for comparative analyses
- LLMs enables the tracing of when concrete techniques first appear in the proposals and how they evolve

LLMs can increase the knowledge of EU funded project

```
You are a senior research scientist [...]
Assess the alignment of the research
projects to the Strategic Research and
Innovation Agenda (SRIA) [...]
```

GPT5

RESULTS ON EU FUNDED PROJECTS

- The barplot shows the funding share by strategic topic over time. The values are normalized, and moving from left to right we can appreciate that:

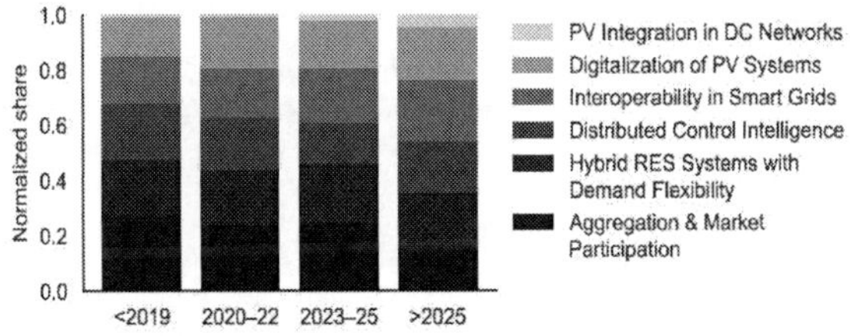

- higher distribution of the *Aggregation & Market Participation* topic in the past years;
- no significant changes in the *Hybrid RES* and *Distributed Control Intelligence* topics;
- *Digitalization of PV Systems and PV Integration in DC Networks* show increase demonstrating the up-to-date relevance of DC grid and AI in the near future.

- LLMs can be used for specific topic-centric retrieval - i.e., to ask when drone-based monitoring, was funded by the EU:

There were 4 projects related to drone-based monitoring:

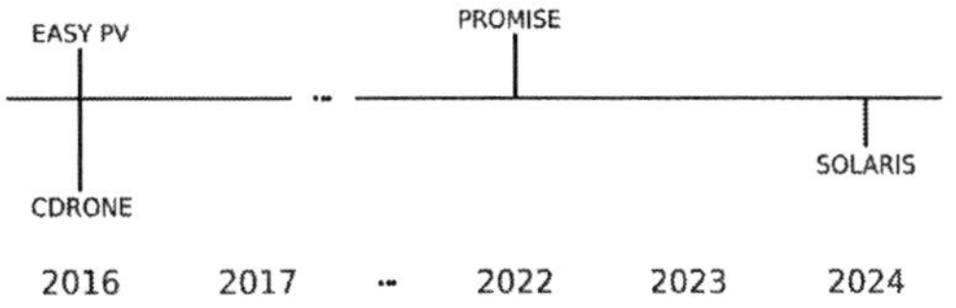

- *EASY PV (2016–2018): Drone-based thermal imaging*
- *CDRONE (2016): Drone inspection-and-cleaning concept*
- *PROMISE (2022–2025): Integrating satellite and drone data into asset modeling*
- *SOLARIS (2024–2028): Automated multi-spectral drone inspections linked to AI-driven asset management*

Summary: An LLM-based methodology maps a decade of EU-funded PV projects to ETIP-PV's Strategic Research and Innovation Agenda, revealing trends, gaps, and possible funding priorities of the EU.

FOSTERING COLLABORATION OF RESEARCH INFRASTRUCTURES AND STAKEHOLDERS IN EUROPE AND LATIN AMERICA TOWARDS CLIMATE-RESILIENT PV SYSTEMS: THE CACTUS PROJECT

Ioannis (John) A. Tsanakas[1*], Delfina Muñoz[1], Romain Couderc[1], Aitor Marzo[2], Asier Sanz Martinez[3], Atse Louwen[4], David Moser[4], Felipe Valencia[5], Nicole Torres Silva[5], Luis Alejandro Cardenas Garcia[6], Fernando Augusto Herrera Leon[6], Thu Nhi Tran Caliste[7], Mark R. Johnson[8], Sarah Essam T. Mohammed[9], Jose V. de Seoane[10]

[1] CEA, Liten, Univ. Grenoble Alpes, Campus INES, Le Bourget du Lac, France
[2] Universidad de Granada, Granada, Spain
[3] Tecnalia, Bilbao, Spain
[4] Eurac Research, Institute for Renewable Energy, Bolzano, Italy
5 ATAMOSTEC, Santiago, Chile
[6] Universidad Nacional de Colombia (UNAL), Bogota, Colombia
[7] European Synchrotron Radiation Facility (ESRF), Grenoble, France
[8] Institut Laue-Langevin (ILL), Grenoble, France
[9] EU SOLARIS, Almeria, Spain
[10] Becquerel Institute, Brussels, Belgium

*corresponding author : ioannis.tsanakas@cea.fr

ABSTRACT: The CACTUS project is an international initiative fostering collaboration between European (EU) and Latin American and Caribbean (LAC) research infrastructures (RIs) to enhance photovoltaic (PV) performance, reliability, and sustainability across diverse climatic conditions. Many high solar potential regions, such as LAC, lack dedicated research facilities for long-term PV performance evaluation, while European RIs require broader climate validation. CACTUS bridges this gap by integrating world-class RIs, expertise, and standardized methodologies for testing PV systems under real-world environmental stressors. The project employs a multidisciplinary approach that combines experimental field studies, advanced material characterization, and predictive modeling. Key areas of research include degradation mechanisms in extreme climates, harmonization of testing protocols, and development of predictive maintenance strategies. Leveraging state-of-the-art facilities such as ESFRI landmarks (ILL & ESRF) and EU-SOLARIS, CACTUS also explores novel PV materials and architectures, ensuring the transferability of research outcomes across global PV markets. Recent activities have focused on field studies in the Atacama Desert, where researchers are evaluating soiling measurement methodologies to assess dust accumulation and its impact on PV performance. Additionally, synchrotron-aided characterization techniques are being explored to analyze PV degradation mechanisms at the microscopic level. These early results provide promising insights into climate-specific PV behavior. The project's structured two-year implementation plan includes RI optimization, collaborative field studies, methodology standardization, and knowledge dissemination. By fostering international cooperation, CACTUS aims to deliver transformative advancements in climate-resilient solar energy deployment, enhancing durability, efficiency, and sustainability in the global PV sector.

Keywords: *PV systems; EU-LAC collaboration; research infrastructures; climate-specific PV O&M.*

1 INTRODUCTION: CONTEXT and AIM

The performance and long-term viability of photovoltaic (PV) technology are highly dependent on environmental conditions, yet current research and testing infrastructures are often limited in their ability to assess PV systems under diverse climatic stressors. Many regions with high solar potential, such as Latin America and the Caribbean (LAC), lack dedicated research facilities for long-term performance analysis. Conversely, European research infrastructures (RIs) have developed extensive methodologies but require broader climate validation. Addressing these gaps necessitates an international and interdisciplinary approach.

The CACTUS project emerges as a response to this need, fostering a bi-regional collaboration between Europe (EU) and LAC. The initiative brings together world-class RIs, scientific expertise, and technological capabilities to develop a sustainable ecosystem for PV research. This collaboration enables the exchange of methodologies, data, and best practices to improve the performance, reliability, and sustainability of PV technologies across different environmental conditions (Fig. 1). By building on existing RIs and establishing new synergies, CACTUS will provide tools to facilitate the deployment of solar energy in an efficient and climate-resilient manner.

The primary objective of CACTUS is to advance the scientific understanding of PV systems' long-term behavior in different climates by improving testing infrastructures and developing standardized methodologies. This effort is crucial for optimizing PV performance, enhancing system bankability, and ensuring widespread social acceptance of solar technologies.

10.4229/EUPVSEC2025/5DV.3.38

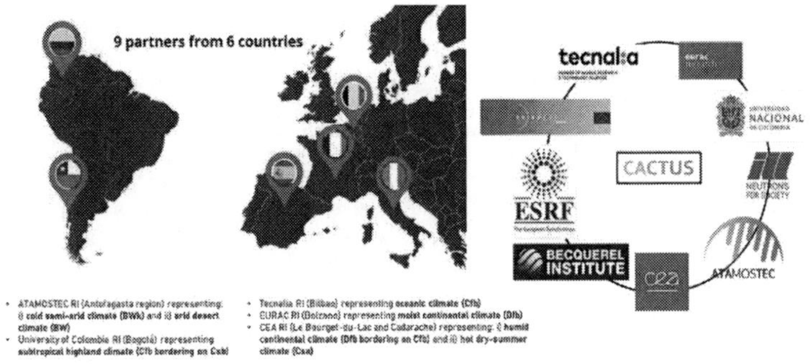

Figure 1: Geographic distribution of RIs involved in CACTUS and their respective climate zones per Köppen classification

2 APPROACH

CACTUS employs an integrative methodology combining experimental field studies, advanced material characterization, and predictive modeling. The project's six work packages (WPs) encompass a comprehensive approach, addressing RI enhancement, knowledge exchange, sustainability assessment, and policy integration (Fig. 2).

A core aspect of CACTUS is the development and enhancement of both indoor and outdoor RIs across diverse geographic locations. This enables the study of degradation mechanisms under real-world conditions such as extreme heat, high humidity, sand abrasion, and UV exposure. The project leverages world-class facilities, including ESFRI landmarks (ILL & ESRF) and EU-SOLARIS, alongside premier PV research institutions in both EU and LAC.

Beyond physical infrastructure, CACTUS aims to standardize testing protocols and data-sharing methodologies. The project will establish common frameworks for PV module degradation analysis, operational reliability assessment, and predictive maintenance strategies. This harmonization of methodologies across regions will provide robust, transferrable knowledge applicable to different PV markets. A significant scientific contribution of CACTUS lies in its exploration of novel PV materials and architectures. By characterizing performance in diverse climatic settings, the project will provide critical data to refine material selection for emerging PV technologies, such as tandem solar cells and bifacial modules. The research outcomes will feed into industry standards and best practices for PV design and deployment. Additionally, CACTUS incorporates sustainability and circular economy principles by conducting comprehensive life-cycle assessments (LCA). These assessments will evaluate the environmental footprint of PV technologies throughout their operational lifespan, providing essential data for policymakers and stakeholders.

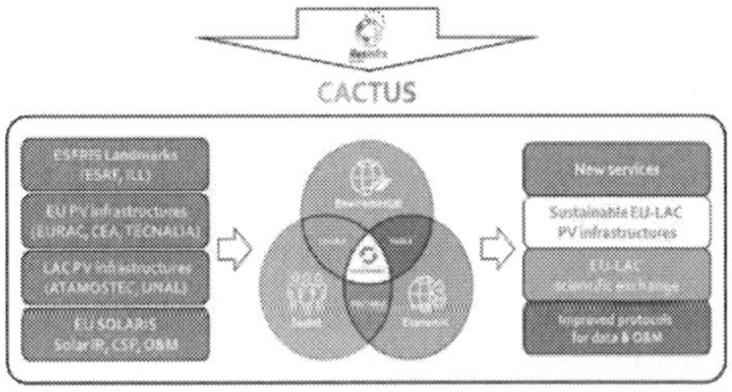

Figure 2: Conceptual framework of CACTUS, illustrating the interconnection between RIs, under the social-environmental-economic nexus for PV deployment.

The collaborative structure of CACTUS is pivotal to its innovation potential. By fostering exchanges between EU and LAC researchers, the project promotes skill development, knowledge transfer, and long-term partnerships. Workshops, training programs, and joint research campaigns will ensure the dissemination of best practices and accelerate innovation in PV performance optimization.

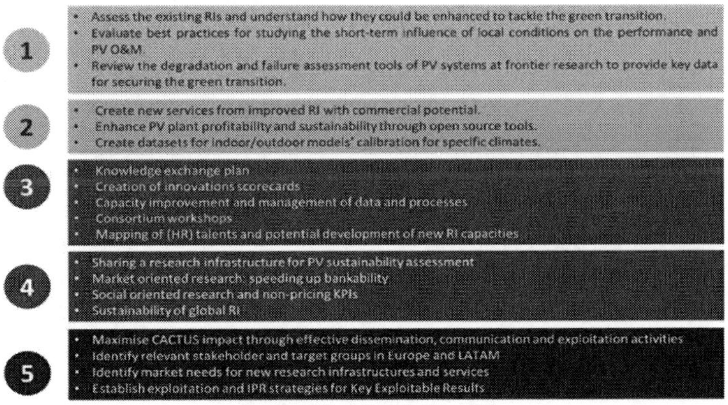

Figure 3: Outline of CACTUS activities.

10.4229/EUPVSEC2025/5DV.3.38

3 MILESTONES and ONGOING WORK

CACTUS is expected to generate a wealth of collaborative scientific and technological outcomes towards climate-resilient PV, from design/component level to operational PV system scale (Fig. 4). One key outcome is the creation of a high-quality, long-term dataset on PV performance and degradation under real-world conditions. This dataset will serve as a foundation for developing more accurate reliability models, failure detection algorithms, and predictive maintenance strategies. Another critical result will be the establishment of guidelines, recommendations and best practices for testing, monitoring and maintenance of PV systems in diverse climatic stress profiles and different applications. These protocols will be shared both among the participating RIs and to interested PV stakeholders, facilitating greater alignment between EU and LAC research methodologies, improving the transferability of results across regions and setting the groundwork for future updates in existing (e.g. IEC) standards.

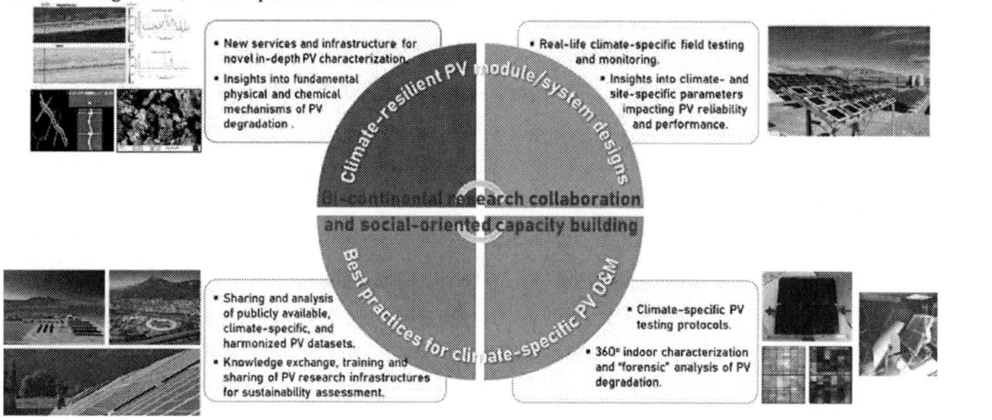

Figure 4: Ongoing collaborative research activities in CACTUS.

The implementation plan for CACTUS is structured over a two-year period, with key milestones including:

- Optimization and interconnection of RIs to facilitate high-quality PV performance monitoring.
- Execution of collaborative field studies and laboratory-based assessments to validate degradation models.
- Development and publication of standardized methodologies for climate-specific PV evaluation.
- Knowledge dissemination through international conferences, technical workshops, and training sessions.
- Delivery of policy recommendations based on sustainability assessments and techno-economic analyses.

By strengthening collaboration between research infrastructures in different climate zones, CACTUS is set to provide transformative insights that will enhance the durability, efficiency, and sustainability of PV systems.

Currently, there are two major activities carried out by CACTUS partners, the preliminary outcomes of which are summarized in Fig. 5 and 6. In Atacama desert, an activity led by ATAMOSTEC focuses on the intercomparison of soiling measurement methodologies, in order to:

- Evaluate and compare methodologies to measure dust accumulation and assess soiling losses on PV modules in the Atacama Desert.
- Validate soiling measurement methodologies using the advanced PSDA (Atacama Solar Platform) infrastructure.
- Generate results that can be extrapolated to other regions with similar climatic conditions.

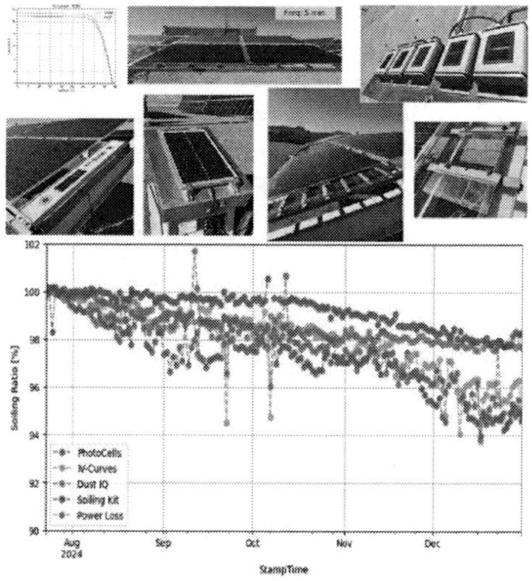

Figure 5: Overview of the employed infrastructure and preliminary results of the ongoing intercomparison of soiling measurement methodologies in Atacama Desert. The activity is led by ATAMOSTEC, involves all CACTUS partners' expertise and will carry on for at least 15 months, to shed light into seasonal, annual climate-specific effects.

Further, ESRF experts, along with CEA and ILL researchers are working on exploring and employing ESRF's unique Synchrotron-aided characterization techniques, as potential future services for advanced characterization and analysis of PV degradation mechanisms at microscopic scale. Results, so far, are very promising, suggesting that we can study in-depth not only the native state PV modules at solar cell and sub-cell level, but also to assess and distinguish degradation patterns over time, under the influence of different climatic profiles.

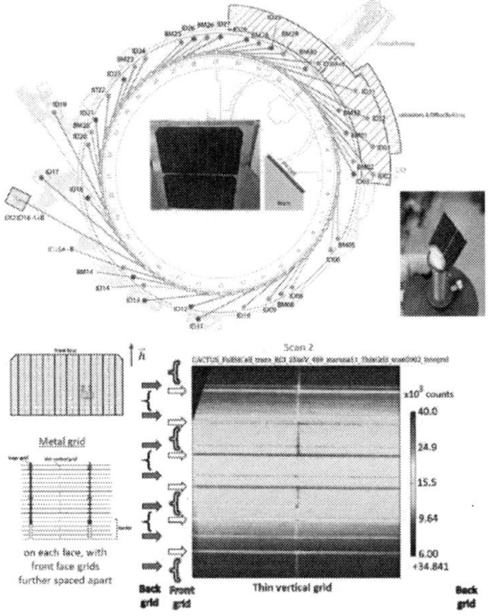

Figure 6: Overview of the employed infrastructure and preliminary results of the ongoing activity led by ESRF, for advanced characterization and analysis of PV degradation mechanisms at microscopic scale, employing ESRF's unique Synchrotron-aided testing methods.

The CACTUS project is strategically designed to bridge the critical gap between photovoltaic research advancements and industrial market requirements. A comprehensive stakeholder survey was conducted to align the project's objectives with practical needs, identifying paramount industry concerns such as long-term reliability across diverse climatic conditions, the accurate prediction of real-world performance, and establishing climate-specific bankability assurances. Prominent technical challenges include ultraviolet-induced degradation in desert environments, humidity-driven corrosion in tropical zones, and mechanical stress from snow and ice loading in alpine climates. To evaluate the project's capacity to address these needs, a systematic analysis of its research infrastructures was undertaken. A SWOT analysis of the project's testing capabilities (Fig. 7) confirmed the strategic strength of its geographically distributed facilities, which provide unparalleled environmental exposure. However, the analysis also revealed significant capability gaps within the project's scope, particularly in testing resilience to hail and high-wind impacts, a shortage of predictive maintenance tools, and the need for more affordable access mechanisms for small and medium-sized enterprises. In direct response to these industry-identified needs and infrastructural insights, the project has developed novel, climate-adaptive testing protocols.

Methodologies like the Desert Label and STROKE testing are already addressing market demand by providing more relevant and accelerated reliability assessments, thereby enabling manufacturers to develop more robust products and allowing investors to make better-informed financial decisions based on validated, climate-specific performance data.

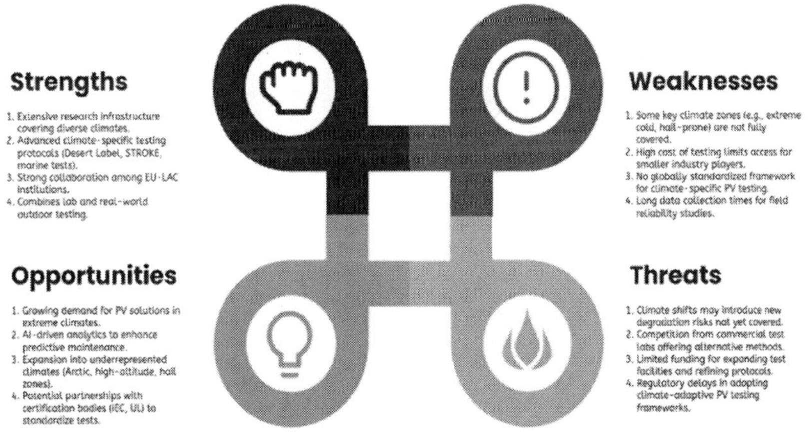

Figure 7: Overview of the employed infrastructure and preliminary results of the ongoing activity led by ESRF, for advanced characterization and analysis of PV degradation mechanisms at microscopic scale, employing ESRF's unique Synchrotron-aided testing methods.

4 CONCLUSIONS - OUTLOOK

The CACTUS project has established a unique bi-regional collaboration between Europe and Latin America & the Caribbean, addressing one of the most pressing challenges in photovoltaic (PV) deployment: the lack of climate-representative infrastructures and standardized methodologies for long-term performance evaluation. By interconnecting world-class research facilities, harmonizing testing approaches, and fostering interdisciplinary knowledge exchange, CACTUS provides the foundation for advancing PV reliability studies across diverse climatic conditions. Early results from ongoing activities—such as the intercomparison of soiling methodologies in the Atacama Desert and synchrotron-aided degradation analysis at ESRF—demonstrate the project's capacity to generate high-quality data and innovative characterization methods, both of which are critical for bridging the gap between laboratory studies and field-relevant insights.

The project highlights that climate-specific stressors—including soiling, humidity-driven corrosion, UV degradation, and thermal cycling—require tailored testing and mitigation strategies. CACTUS directly responds to these needs by developing adaptive testing protocols, sustainability assessments, and techno-economic frameworks to ensure PV systems' durability, bankability, and social acceptance in different regions. Looking forward, key priorities include:

- expanding climate-tailored reliability assessments to encompass additional stress factors (e.g. hail, wind, and snow loads),
- integrating advanced predictive maintenance tools with real-time field data, and
- strengthening accessibility of testing infrastructures for industry stakeholders, particularly SMEs.

By aligning scientific research with market and policy needs, CACTUS not only advances the state-of-the-art in PV testing but also lays the groundwork for future updates of international standards and guidelines. Ultimately, the project is expected to deliver a lasting impact by enabling climate-resilient PV deployment, supporting the global energy transition with reliable, sustainable, and regionally adapted solar technologies.

ACKNOWLEDGEMENTS

This work has been carried out in the framework of the Horizon Europe CACTUS project. CACTUS project has received funding from the European Union's Horizon Europe research and innovation programme under grant agreement No. 101132182.

Fostering collaboration of research infrastructures and stakeholders in Europe and Latin America towards climate-resilient PV systems: the CACTUS project

Ioannis (John) A. Tsanakas[1], Delfina Muñoz[1], Romain Couderc[1], Aitor Marzo[2], Asier Sanz Martinez[3], Atse Louwen[4], David Moser[4], Felipe Valencia[5], Nicole Torres Silva[5], Luis Alejandro Cardenas Garcia[6], Fernando Augusto Herrera Leon[6], Thu Nhi Tran Caliste[7], Mark R. Johnson[8], Sarah Essam T. Mohammed[9], Jose V. de Seoane[10]

[1] **CEA**, Univ. Grenoble Alpes, Campus INES, Le Bourget-du-Lac, France; [2] **Universidad de Granada, Granada**, Spain; [3] **Tecnalia**, Bilbao, Spain; [4] **Eurac Research**, Instit. for Renewable Energy, Bolzano, Italy; [5] **ATAMOSTEC**, Santiago, Chile; [6] **Universidad Nacional de Colombia**, Bogota, Colombia; [7] **European Synchrotron Radiation Facility**, Grenoble, France; [8] **Institut Laue-Langevin**, Grenoble, France; [9] **EU SOLARIS**, Almeria, Spain; [10] **Becquerel Institute**, Brussels, Belgium

Project Coordinator and Corresponding Author: **Ioannis (John) A. Tsanakas** ioannis.tsanakas@cea.fr

Context

Solar photovoltaic (PV) technologies are expanding rapidly worldwide, but their long-term performance depends heavily on climatic conditions. Many regions with high solar potential (e.g., Latin America) lack dedicated testing facilities, while European infrastructures need broader climate validation.

CACTUS bridges this gap by fostering collaboration between European and Latin American research infrastructures (RIs) to develop reliable, bankable, and climate-resilient PV solutions.

Mission

The objectives/mission of CACTUS project are multifold:

- Build a **bi-regional ecosystem** of complementary RIs between EU & LAC.
- Develop **standardized testing protocols** for PV under **diverse climates**.
- Advance knowledge on **PV degradation mechanisms in extreme conditions**.
- Provide tools for industry, policymakers, and investors to **increase PV system bankability, sustainability, and acceptance**.
- Contribute to the green energy transition by ensuring PV reliability worldwide.

Research Infrastructures

CACTUS integrates unique infrastructures across diverse climates:

- Atacama Desert Solar Platform (Chile) – desert/high-irradiance testing.
- CEA-INES (France) – advanced climate chambers & accelerated stress tests.
- Universidad Nacional de Colombia – tropical climate outdoor monitoring.
- EURAC (Italy) – Alpine tests, electroluminescence, and PV-storage integration.
- TECNALIA (Spain) – smart grid & outdoor PV testing facilities.

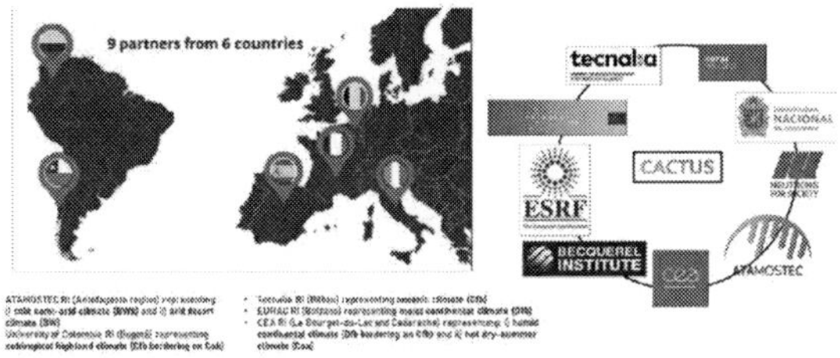

Example outcomes – Early insights

Climate-specific testing and reliability activities

☐ An ongoing 15+ month soiling measurement campaign in the Atacama Desert, led by ATAMOSTEC, is providing **the first intercomparison of soiling testing methodologies under extreme high-irradiance and low-humidity conditions**. This study aims to validate measurement techniques and quantify soiling losses, with **results applicable to other arid regions worldwide**.

☐ Preliminary synchrotron-aided analyses conducted by ESRF and ILL, in collaboration with CEA, are **revealing micro-scale degradation mechanisms in PV modules**. These high-resolution techniques offer unprecedented insights into material behavior under climatic stressors, enabling **deeper understanding of failure modes such as encapsulant degradation, corrosion, and cell-level defects**.

Strengths

1. Extensive research infrastructure covering diverse climates.
2. Advanced climate-specific testing protocols (Desert Label, STROKE, marine tests).
3. Strong collaboration among EU–LAC institutions.
4. Combines lab and real-world outdoor testing.

Weaknesses

1. Some key climate zones (e.g., extreme cold, hail-prone) are not fully covered.
2. High cost of testing limits access for smaller industry players.
3. No globally standardized framework for climate-specific PV testing.
4. Long data collection times for field reliability studies.

Opportunities

1. Growing demand for PV solutions in extreme climates.
2. AI-driven analytics to enhance predictive maintenance.
3. Expansion into underrepresented climates (Arctic, high-altitude, hail zones).
4. Potential partnerships with certification bodies (IEC, UL) to standardize tests.

Threats

1. Climate shifts may introduce new degradation risks not yet covered.
2. Competition from commercial test labs offering alternative methods.
3. Limited funding for expanding test facilities and refining protocols.
4. Regulatory delays in adopting climate-adaptive PV testing frameworks.

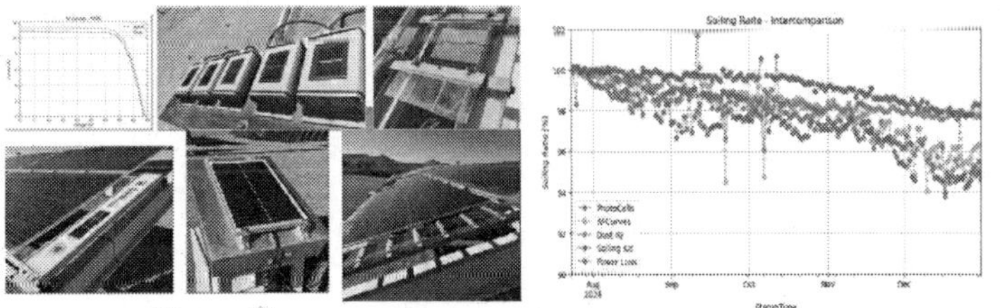

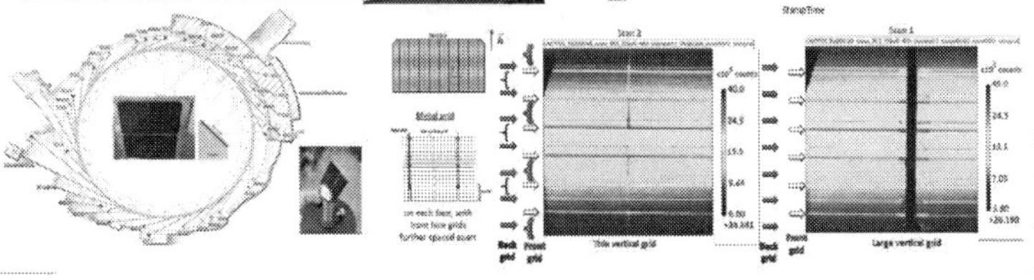

Bridging Research and Industry/Market Needs

☐ **Stakeholder Needs:** A CACTUS survey identified top concerns: reliability in diverse climates, real-world performance, and climate-specific bankability. Key issues include desert UV degradation, tropical humidity corrosion, and alpine snow mechanical stress.

☐ **Research Infrastructures:** A SWOT analysis confirmed the strength of CACTUS's distributed facilities but highlighted gaps in testing for hail/wind, predictive maintenance tools, and more affordable access for smaller players.

☐ **Novel Testing Protocols Development:** New climate-adaptive protocols like the Desert Label and STROKE testing are already addressing industry demand for more relevant and accelerated reliability assessments.

Impact and Outlook

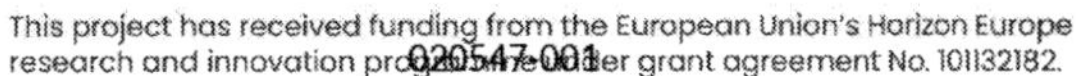

- ☑ Providing guidelines and best practices for climate-specific PV testing and O&M.
- ☑ Supporting updates to international standards (IEC)
- ☑ Strengthening EU–LAC scientific cooperation.
- ☑ Ensuring durable, efficient, and sustainable deployment of PV.

Funded by the European Union — This project has received funding from the European Union's Horizon Europe research and innovation programme under grant agreement No. 101132182.

PHOTOVOLTAIC SOLAR ENERGY INTEGRATION IN THE BASIC EDUCATION CURRICULA IN BRAZIL

Amanda Mendes Ferreira Gomes[1], Daniel Odilio dos Santos[1], Aline Cristiane Pan[2], Ricardo Rüther[1]
[1]Universidade Federal de Santa Catarina, Fotovoltaica/UFSC Laboratory, Florianópolis, Brazil
[2]Universidade Federal do Rio Grande do Sul, Engenharia de Gestão de Energia, Tramandaí, Brazil
E-mail: amandamendesfg@gmail.com, daniel.odilio@gmail.com, aline.pan@ufrgs.br, ricardo.ruther@ufsc.br

ABSTRACT: This study examines the integration of photovoltaic (PV) solar energy into Brazil's National Common Curricular Base (BNCC) to assess how early education can contribute to preparing future professionals for the renewable energy (RE) sector. With global PV capacity reaching record levels, the sector faces a growing demand for skilled workers in installation, maintenance, system design, and policy development. Education is a key driver to address this need, yet significant gaps persist in aligning school curricula with labor market demands. Using BNCC as a reference, the research analyzes competencies across the school levels. Findings reveal that PV-related content begins as early as the second year of elementary school with topics such as the Sun, light, heat, and recycling. In middle school, the curriculum expands to cover energy sources, thermal machines, the greenhouse effect, and electricity use. High school introduces more abstract competencies, including socio-environmental impacts, RE alternatives, and digital applications. However, advanced topics such as legislation, green hydrogen, and storage technologies remain absent. The study concludes that while the BNCC provides a valuable framework, curricular reforms are required to incorporate RE and practical applications. Finally, expanding PV education early supports the energy transition despite challenges.

Keywords: photovoltaic, education, school.

1 INTRODUCTION

In 2024, the power sector experienced an unprecedented expansion of renewable energy (RE) capacity, increasing by 18% with a record-breaking addition of 741 GW. Photovoltaic (PV) energy was the primary driver, contributing 602 GW, followed by wind energy, which contributed 117 GW. Other RE sources, whether for power, heat, or transport fuels, added only marginally to the global supply. This remarkable growth underscores the urgent need to address rising electricity demand, driven by population and economic growth, through continued investments in RE. In 2024, Global investment in RE amounted to $728 billion, representing an 8% increase compared to 2023. This pace of growth was significantly slower than in previous years, when investments expanded by 19% in 2023 and 23% in 2022. The primary factor behind this deceleration was the marked reduction in wind power financing [1]. As of August 2025, Brazil's installed PV capacity had surpassed 59 GW, constituting 23.5% of the country's electricity mix. This capacity is distributed between 70% distributed generation (DG) and 30% centralized generation, a different scenario from the rest of the world [2].

This growth in the RE market reinforces the pressing need for highly qualified professionals to respond to the sector's demands [1]. This trend has significantly impacted the PV energy sector, propelling its accelerated growth and driving an increasing demand for specialized expertise in installation, operation, maintenance, and system design. In response to this growing demand, educational institutions worldwide are integrating curricula centered on RE, with a particular focus on PV [3]. This involves comprehensively restructuring existing educational curricula, integrating novel technical courses, and providing students with theoretical knowledge and practical skills. This knowledge should be integrated into the foundational education of students from the earliest stages of their academic careers, ideally beginning in elementary school [4]. Despite this, studies have demonstrated that school curricula lack a significant focus on RE and Education for Sustainable Development (ESD), resulting in low levels of knowledge and awareness among students [5], [6], [7]. Furthermore, studies have revealed a discrepancy between the number of courses available and industry demand [8]. This highlights a critical shortage of qualified professionals, particularly in developing countries, and a misalignment between educational curricula and the sector's specific needs [9], [10].

Brazil's recently proposed Basic Education (BE) curriculum introduces innovative concepts and pedagogical approaches, formally established through the National Common Curricular Base (BNCC, in Portuguese Base Nacional Comum Curricular) [11]. **Figure 1** shows the BE model in Brazil.

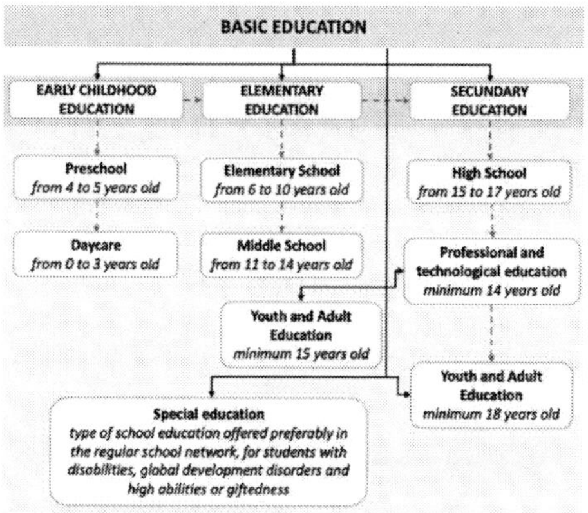

Figure 1. General diagram of the structure of Brazilian education and its divisions. Adapted from [12].

This document outlines the essential learnings to be addressed in Brazilian schools from Early Childhood Education to High School. BE encompasses general competencies and has three stages: early childhood, elementary and secondary education. It aims to ensure the right to learning and the full development of all students, promoting equality in the educational system, contributing to comprehensive education, and constructing a fairer, democratic, and inclusive society [11].

Considering this scenario, this study evaluates the implementation of the teaching of subjects and specific knowledge necessary for developing and stimulating professionals focused on PV energy in the future in basic education (elementary, middle, and high school education), using the BNCC as a basis. The innovation of this work is in the analysis of the curricula and evaluation of the training of elementary, middle, and high school students to ensure they are prepared to meet the challenges of the PV energy sector in the future. Additionally, it will examine the Brazilian government's primary initiatives to achieve this objective, which are closely related to the Sustainable Development Goals (SDGs) proposed for the 2030 Agenda, particularly quality education (SDG 4), gender equality (SDG 5), affordable and clean energy (SDG 7), decent work and economic growth (SDG 8), and climate action (SDG 13) [13].

2 PROFESSIONAL AND EDUCATIONAL SCENARIO IN BRAZIL AND THE WORLD

Globally, the solar PV sector is poised for significant job growth, with projections indicating the creation of up to 40 million energy sector jobs by 2050, including 18 million in RE - a threefold increase from current levels. The PV sector's growth catalyzes job creation, both directly within the industry (upstream) and indirectly in related fields such as manufacturing, construction, and logistics (downstream) [14]. The distribution of these jobs is expected to be as follows: 55% in Asia, 14% in Europe, and 13% in the Americas. In the European Union, employment is projected to reach 530,000 by 2026 and double by 2030, contingent on the efficacy of industrial strategies and workforce development. The PV energy sector in Brazil employs approximately 214,000 professionals, including both direct and indirect jobs, a figure propelled by large-scale projects and the expanding adoption of distributed generation (DG) systems [15]. Projections indicate that the number of jobs in this sector will reach 554,000 by 2030, 966,000 by 2034, and 1.4 million by 2038 [16].

Given this scenario, training new professionals has become an urgent priority. The education of professionals commences at an early stage in BE, preceding higher education. Environmental and RE education can shape individuals' perceptions of the world and influence how they treat and manage it. It serves as both a process and a tool to empower participation and learning across all age groups, particularly among young people, utilizing a bidirectional communication paradigm that flows from educators to learners and vice versa [17]. Integrating RE education into school curricula has been demonstrated to foster critical thinking skills and empower students to become environmentally conscious citizens capable of making informed decisions regarding energy consumption and conservation in their daily lives. This integration underscores the environmental issues and consequences of using non-RE sources [18]. The subject of energy, more specifically RE sources, is included in the educational curricula in several countries [19].

The BNCC advocates for a teaching model emphasizing student autonomy and an active, participatory process, including research, collaboration, and knowledge sharing. Students are encouraged to engage in investigative processes during the final years of elementary education and throughout high school. Consequently, the teaching of natural sciences aims to develop several key skills: observing the world and formulating questions, analyzing needs, identifying problems, proposing hypotheses, developing explanations and models, and constructing evidence-based arguments. Furthermore, students must enhance their knowledge by gradually incorporating scientific principles. Studies highlight the importance of these skills in developing citizens who are capable of solving problems and making informed decisions [20].

Figure 2 illustrates the general competencies at the elementary and high education established by the BNCC.

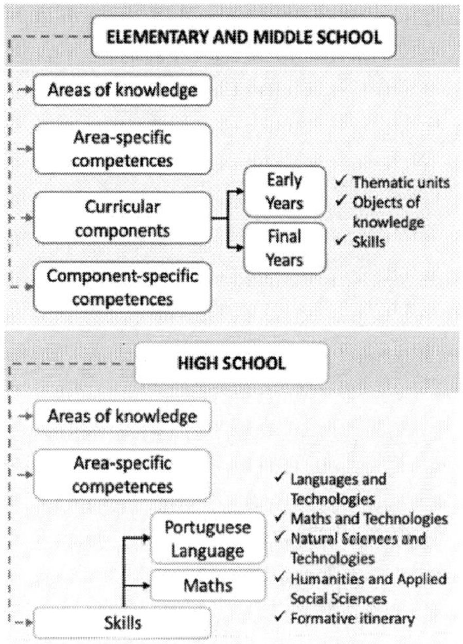

Figure 2. Diagram of the general competencies at the elementary and high school schools established by BNCC. Adapted from [21].

The elementary is organized into five areas of knowledge: Languages (Portuguese, Art, Physical Education, English – only for middle school), Maths, Natural Sciences, Human Sciences (Geography and History), and Religious Education. The sub-areas are designated as "component-specific competencies," which facilitate horizontal articulation between the areas, encompassing all curricular components and facilitating vertical articulation between the years. In contrast, high school education is structured into four areas of knowledge: Languages and Technologies (Portuguese language, Art, Physical Education, English language), Mathematics and Technologies, Natural Sciences and their Technologies (Biology, Physics and Chemistry), Human and Applied Social Sciences (History, Geography, Sociology and Philosophy). Furthermore, the recent amendments to the LDB, as a consequence of Law No. 13,415/2017, indicate a diversified and flexible model for high school education, including different formative itineraries [21]. Formative itineraries may be structured in several ways, focusing on one area of knowledge, technical and professional training, or mobilizing competencies and skills from different areas to create integrated itineraries [11].

Recent research emphasizes the necessity for educational institutions to implement curricula encompassing diverse topics, including PV, energy efficiency, and electric vehicles. Additionally, it should address broader issues such as energy, biodiversity, the environment, globalization, industrialization, and the impact of human beings on climate change [22]. These curricula should be integrated into the existing curricula and complemented by practical activities contributing to students' overall education and development. However, implementing such a plan poses several challenges, including the need for teacher training and the development of effective educational policies [23]. Furthermore, teachers need to be adequately equipped with the requisite knowledge and skills to effectively integrate these topics into their teaching [24].

3 MATERIALS AND METHODS

This study employs the BNCC as the foundation for a critical analysis of the subjects proposed for each year of primary and secondary education. It examines the subjects and their stated objectives, establishing direct connections with the knowledge and skills required of RE professionals, with particular emphasis on PV. **Figure 3** presents the materials and methods used in this article.

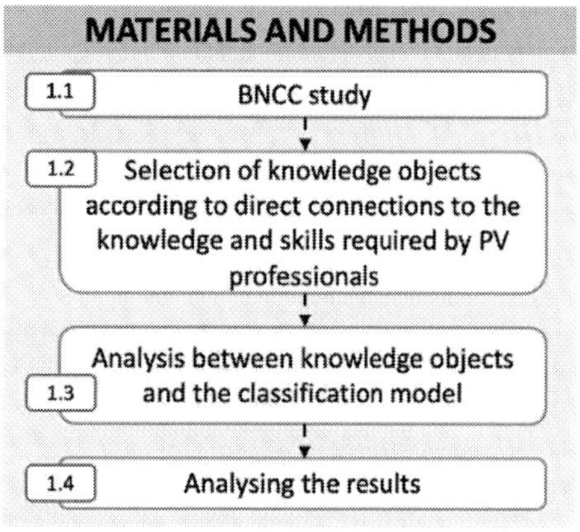

Figure 3. Materials and methods used in this article.

Table 1 illustrates the rationale for imparting the competencies and their interrelationships with PV energy. For each competency code, there are subjects associated with PV energy. The principal subjects of PV energy have been classified into seven categories: PV energy fundamentals and basic projects, Installation, O&M and commissioning, materials and chemical engineering, environmental impact, architectural integration, legislation, and additional topics. The PV sector may comprise a range of related areas, including sales, logistics, finance, accounting, law, and the infrastructure and health support sectors, which are not included in this work.

Table 1: Classification of the different areas of knowledge and competence

1 INDEX – SUBJECT	SPECIFIC SUBJECT	2 INDEX
1 – PV energy fundamentals and basic projects	PV energy fundamentals	1.1
	Optimizing the orientation of PV modules and using solar resources	1.2
	Calculating the site's PV energy potential	1.3
	Location planning for PV system installations	1.4
	Support for simulations and modelling	1.5
	Fundamentals of electricity and circuits	1.6
	Electrical equipment and components	1.7
2 – Installation, O&M and commissioning	Installation and O&M practices	2.1
	Training and certification of technicians	2.2
	Fault diagnosis	2.3
3 – Materials and chemical engineering	Development of PV materials	3.1
	Manufacturing processes	3.2
4 – Environmental impact	Life cycle assessment	4.1
	Impact on local ecosystems	4.2
	Reduction of carbon emissions	4.3
	Sustainability and recycling	4.4
5 – Architectural integration	Aesthetics and functionality	5.1
	Energy efficiency	5.2
6 – Legislation	Government incentives	6.1
	Safety regulations	6.2
	Energy market and tariffs	6.3
	R&D	6.4
7 – Adicional topics	BESS	7.1
	Electromobility	7.2
	Green hydrogen	7.3
	Fair energy transition	7.4

4 RESULTS AND DISCUSSIONS

Table 2 presents the knowledge objectives related to PV subjects in elementary and middle school curricula. The BNCC introduces the teaching of PV energy as early as the second year of elementary school science. For instance, one of the learning objectives is to compare the effects of solar radiation (heating and reflection) on various types of surfaces, such as water, sand, soil, dark, light, and metallic surfaces. The "Matter and energy" and "Earth and Universe" thematic unit of 8th-grade science presents specific topics related to energy sources and types, energy transformation, calculating electricity consumption, electrical circuits, and the conscious use of electricity. The units include EF08CI01, EF08CI02, EF08CI03, EF08CI04, EF08CI05, EF08CI06, EF08CI13, EF08CI15 and EF08CI16. For example, the code EF08CI01 focuses on identifying and classifying different sources (RE and non-RE) and types of energy used in homes, communities, or cities. The code EF08CI06 is specifically designed to discuss and evaluate electricity generation plants and their impacts.

Table 2: Knowledge objectives on PV-related subjects in elementary and middle school curricula

YEAR	THEMATIC UNITS	CODE - KNOWLEDGE OBJECTS

2° YEAR	Earth and Universe	EF02CI07 – The Sun moving in the sky EF02CI08 – The Sun as a source of light and heat
3° YEAR	Matter and energy	EF03CI02 – Effects of light on materials and Hearing and visual health
	Earth and Universe	EF03CI07 – Characteristics of the Earth EF03CI08 – Observing the sky EF03CI10 - Land uses
4° YEAR	Earth and Universe	EF04CI09 – Cardinal points
5° YEAR	Matter and energy	EF05CI01 – Physical properties of materials EF05CI05 – Recycling
	Earth and Universe	EF05CI11 – Earth's rotational movement
6° YEAR	Earth and Universe	EF06CI14 – Earth's shape, structure and movements
7° YEAR	Matter and energy	EF07CI05 – History of fuels and thermal machines
	Earth and Universe	EF07CI13 – Greenhouse effect EF07CI14 – Ozone layer
8° YEAR	Matter and energy	EF08CI01 – Sources and types of energy EF08CI02 – Energy transformation EF08CI03 – Classify residential electrical equipment EF08CI04 – Calculating electricity consumption EF08CI05 – Electrical circuits EF08CI06 – Conscious use of electricity
	Earth and Universe	EF08CI13/EF08CI15 – The Sun, Earth and Moon system EF08CI16 – Climate
9° YEAR	Matter and energy	EF09CI04 – The structure of matter EF09CI06 – Radiation and its applications

In high school, as show on **Table 3**, students are introduced to more abstract concepts, including non-technical aspects of RE and PV energies. The code EM13CNT309 of the Specific Competencies and Skills requires the analysis of socio-environmental, political, and economic issues related to the world's current dependence on non-RE resources. It also requires a discussion on the need to introduce alternative and new energy and materials technologies, including a comparison of different types of engines and production processes for new materials.

Table 3: Knowledge objectives on PV-related subjects in high school curricula

COMPETENCE	KNOWLEDGE OBJECTS
SPECIFIC COMPETENCE 1	EM13CNT101, EM13CNT103, EM13CNT106, and EM13CNT107 – Analyze natural phenomena and technological processes, based on the interactions and relationships between matter and energy, to propose individual and collective actions that improve production processes, minimize socio-environmental impacts and improve living conditions at local, regional and global levels.
SPECIFIC COMPETENCE 3	EM13CNT302, EM13CNT303, EM13CNT307, EM13CNT308, EM13CNT309, and EM13CNT310 – Investigate problem situations and evaluate applications of scientific and technological knowledge and their implications in the world, using procedures and languages specific to the natural sciences, to propose solutions that consider local, regional and/or global demands, and communicate their findings and conclusions to a variety of audiences, in a variety of contexts and through different media and Digital Information and Communication Technologies (TDIC).

4.1 Analyses of Basic Education Competencies

Table 4, **Table 5**, and **Table 6** present a detailed analysis of each competence, focusing on its application in the context of elementary, middle, and high schools, respectively. Each competence is assigned a code (base on **Table 1**) provides a detailed account of the codes pertinent to the competency analyses. A review of the competencies reveals numerous subjects already encompassed within the BNCC following its new revision. The syllabus includes a diverse range of technical subjects. Notably, the elementary school competencies covered are the initial ones, mainly within the first five indexes. The first four indexes are the subject of intensive study in the second year. From the 3° year onwards, there is an integration with elements related to the environment, such as conservation, life cycles, and recycling. The more advanced indexes, such as legislation and other areas of knowledge, have not yet been introduced to students.

Table 4: Analysis of competencies of elementary school

BNCC CODE	ANALYSIS OF COMPETENCIES
	SCIENCES – 2° YEAR
EF02CI07	1.1, 1.2, 1.4, 1.5, 1.6, 5.1
EF02CI08	1.1, 1.2, 1.5, 1.6, 4.1, 4.3 and 4.4
	SCIENCES – 3° YEAR
EF03CI02	1.1, 1.2, 1.5, 3.1, 5.1 and 5.2
EF03CI07	4.2, 4.3, 5.1, and 5.2
EF03CI08	1.1, 1.2, 1.3, 1.5 and 5.2
EF03CI10	1.1, 1.3, 1.4, 1.5, 2.1, 2.2, 4.2, 4.3, and 5.2
	SCIENCES – 4° YEAR
EF04CI09	1.1, 1.2, 1.3, 1.5, 1.6, 5.1, and 5.2
	SCIENCES – 5° YEAR
EF05CI01	1.1, 1.5, 1.6, 2.3, 3.1, 3.2, and 5.1
EF05CI05	2.1, 4.1, 4.2, 4.3, 4.4, 5.2, and 6.1
EF05CI11	1.1, 1.2, 1.3, 1.4, 1.5, 1.6, 5.1

As students progress through middle school, it becomes evident that the subjects are increasingly interconnected, both with one another and with the real world. The competencies encompass a greater degree of dialogue and critical thinking about various subjects, including thermal machines, RE in general, the ozone layer, and the environment. The suggestions for the competencies are continually developed through dialogue to propose solutions to the problems presented. The incorporation of the items in index 7 has yet to be openly discussed, yet they represent a significant number of the currently known solutions to the problems studied by the students. In 8° year, there are nine competencies related to the subject. Conversely, the 9° year is focused on material properties, an essential area for the development and improvement of one of the main elements of the PV system: the PV module.

Table 5: Analysis of competencies of middle school

CODE	ANALYSIS OF COMPETENCIES
SCIENCES – 6° YEAR	
EF06CI14	1.2, 1.3, 1.5, 1.6, 5.1, and 5.2
SCIENCES – 7° YEAR	
EF07CI05	4.1, 4.2, 4.3, 4.4, 6.1, 6.3, 7.2, and 7.3
EF07CI13	4.1, 4.2, 4.3, 4.4, 6.1, 6.3, 7.1, 7.2, and 7.3
EF07CI14	4.1, 4.2, 4.3, 4.4, 5.2, 6.1, 6.3, 7.1, 7.2, and 7.3
SCIENCES – 8° YEAR	
EF08CI01	1.1, 1.3, 4.1, 4.2, 4.3, 5.2, 6.1, 7.1, 7.2, and 7.3
EF08CI02	1.1, 1.6, 1.7, 2.1, 2.2, 2.3, and 5.2
EF08CI03	1.1, 1.6, 5.2, 6.1, 7.1, and 7.2
EF08CI04	1.1, 1.6, 5.2, 6.1, 7.1, and 7.2
EF08CI05	1.1, 4.3, 4.4, 5.2, 6.1, 6.3, 7.1, 7.2, and 7.3
EF08CI06	4.2, 4.3, 4.4, 6.1, 6.2, 6.3, 7.1, 7.2, and 7.3
EF08CI13	1.1, 1.2, 1.3, 1.5, 1.6, 5.1, and 5.2
EF08CI15	1.1, 1.2, 1.3, 1.5, 1.6, 2.1, 3.1, and 3.2
EF08CI16	4.1, 4.2, 4.3, 4.4, 5.1, 5.2, 6.1, 6.3, 7.1, 7.2, 7.3, and 7.4
SCIENCES – 9° YEAR	
EF09CI04	1.1, 1.3, 3.1, and 3.2
EF09CI06	1.1, 1.3, 3.1, and 3.2

Notably, the elementary school competencies covered are the initial ones, mainly within the first five indexes. The first four indexes are the subject of intensive study in the second year. From the 3° year onwards, there is an integration with elements related to the environment, such as conservation, life cycles, and recycling. The more advanced indexes, such as legislation and other areas of knowledge, have not yet been introduced to students.

Table 6: Analysis of competencies of high school

GENERAL COMPETENCIES OF HIGH SCHOOL	
NATURE SCIENCES AND THEIR TECHNOLOGIES IN HIGH SCHOOL: SPECIFIC COMPETENCES AND SKILLS	
CODE BNCC	**CODE**
SPECIFIC COMPETENCE 1	
EM13CNT101	1.1, 3.1, 3.2, 4.1, 4.2, 4.3, 4.4, 7.1, 7.2, 7.3, and 7.4
EM13CNT103	1.1, 1.3, 1.6, 4.2, 4.3, 5.2, and 6.1
EM13CNT106	1.1, 1.7, 4.1, 4.2, 4.3, 4.4, 5.2, 6.1, 6.2, 6.3, 7.1, 7.2, 7.3, and 7.4
EM13CNT107	1.1, 1.6, 2.1, 7.1, 7.2, and 7.3
SPECIFIC COMPETENCE 3	
EM13CNT302	6.1, 6.2, 6.3, and 6.4
EM13CNT303	6.1, 6.2, 6.3, and 6.4
EM13CNT307	3.1, 3.2, and 4.2
EM13CNT308	6.1 and 6.4
EM13CNT309	4.1, 4.2, 4.3, 4.4, 6.1, 6.2, 6.3, 6.4, 7.1, 7.2, and 7.3
EM13CNT310	4.2, 6.1, 6.3, and 6.4

At the high school level, the competencies become more comprehensive, encompassing a range of analytical, evaluative, interpretative, and investigative tasks. A more extensive analysis of applications and connections with the wider world is proposed, necessitating a deeper level of reflection and critical thinking than at the middle school level. Furthermore, the indications are linked to digital devices and applications.

5 CONCLUSIONS

The findings of this study reveal both gaps and opportunities that call for targeted strategies to better align the education sector with the current and future demands on PV market. In particular, they highlight structural shortcomings that limit the capacity of the existing system to prepare professionals adequately for this field.

A review of the relevant literature, combined with an analysis of government-proposed curricula, indicates that the current educational framework requires substantial improvement. Despite the BNCC's recommendations, many basic and technical education programs still fail to incorporate essential content related to PV energy. The omission of topics such as emerging technologies and practical applications restricts students' ability to acquire the knowledge and competencies necessary to pursue careers in the sector.

6 ACKNOWLEDGMENT

This work was conducted during a scholarship supported by the International Cooperation Program PROBRAL fostering a collaborative exchange between TH Köln-University of Applied Sciences and the Universidade Federal de Santa Catarina (UFSC). The partnership was financed by Capes – Brazilian Federal Agency for Support and Evaluation of Graduate Education within the Ministry of Education of Brazil and the German Academic Exchange Service (DAAD). A.M.F.G acknowledges CAPES (Coordenação de Aperfeiçoamento de Pessoal de Nível Superior) for a Ph.D scholarship. D.O.S acknowledges CNPq (Conselho Nacional de Desenvolvimento Científico e Tecnológico.) for a Ph.D scholarship.

7 REFERENCES

[1] REN21, "Renewables 2025 Global Status Report: Global overview," Paris, 2025.

[2] ABSOLAR, "Energia Solar Fotovoltaica no Brasil - Infográfico ABSOLAR," 2025. [Online]. Available: https://www.absolar.org.br/mercado/infografico/

[3] P. Jennings, "New directions in renewable energy education," *Renewable Energy*, vol. 34, no. 2, pp. 435–439, Feb. 2009, doi: 10.1016/j.renene.2008.05.005.

[4] P. Rillero, A. Koerner, A. K. Daragmeh, and K. Soykal, "Active Learning Methodologies in a Solar Power, Middle-Grade Curriculum for Palestinian Schools," *Int J Env Sci Ed*, vol. 16, no. 2, Feb. 2020, doi: 10.29333/ijese/7814.

[5] L. Agirreazkuenaga and P. M. Martinez, "Secondary students' perception, positioning and insight on education for sustainability," *International Research in Geographical and Environmental Education*, vol. 30, no. 3, pp. 218–237, Jul. 2021, doi: 10.1080/10382046.2021.1877952.

[6] E. Çakirlar Altuntaş and S. L. Turan, "Awareness of

secondary school students about renewable energy sources," *Renewable Energy*, vol. 116, pp. 741–748, Feb. 2018, doi: 10.1016/j.renene.2017.09.034.
[7] F. Hoque, R. M. Yasin, and K. Sopian, "Revisiting Education for Sustainable Development: Methods to Inspire Secondary School Students toward Renewable Energy," *Sustainability*, vol. 14, no. 14, p. 8296, Jul. 2022, doi: 10.3390/su14148296.
[8] L. R. do Nascimento, M. Braga, R. A. Campos, H. F. Naspolini, and R. Rüther, "Performance assessment of solar photovoltaic technologies under different climatic conditions in Brazil," *Renewable Energy*, vol. 146, pp. 1070–1082, Feb. 2020, doi: 10.1016/j.renene.2019.06.160.
[9] D. Kimuli, R. Nabaterega, N. Banadda, I. Kabenge, A. Ekwamu, and P. Nampala, "Advanced Education and Training Programs to Support Renewable Energy Investment in Africa," *International Journal of Education and Practice*, vol. 5, no. 1, pp. 8–15, 2017, doi: 10.18488/journal.61/2017.5.1/61.1.8.15.
[10] H. Lucas, S. Pinnington, and L. F. Cabeza, "Education and training gaps in the renewable energy sector," *Solar Energy*, vol. 173, pp. 449–455, Oct. 2018, doi: 10.1016/j.solener.2018.07.061.
[11] Brasil, "Base Nacional Comum Curricular: Educação é a base," MEC, Brasília, 2018.
[12] Brasil, "Conheça a história da educação brasileira." Accessed: Jul. 03, 2024. [Online]. Available: http://portal.mec.gov.br/pet/33771-institucional/83591-conheca-a-evolucao-da-educacao-brasileira
[13] UN, "Transformando Nosso Mundo: A Agenda 2030 para o Desenvolvimento Sustentável," 2015.
[14] A. F. Almarshoud and E. Adam, "A transition toward localizing the value chain of photovoltaic energy in Saudi Arabia," *Clean Techn Environ Policy*, vol. 23, no. 7, pp. 2049–2059, Sep. 2021, doi: 10.1007/s10098-021-02102-2.
[15] IRENA, "Renewable energy statistics 2024," International Renewable Energy Agency, Abu Dhabi, 2024.
[16] D. G. für I. Z. (GIZ) G. GIZ, "A mão de obra na cadeia produtiva do setor solar brasileiro," 2023.
[17] H. R. Hungerford and T. L. Volk, "Changing Learner Behavior Through Environmental Education," *The Journal of Environmental Education*, vol. 21, no. 3, pp. 8–21, Mar. 1990, doi: 10.1080/00958964.1990.10753743.
[18] M. K. A. Sulaiman, L. Halim, N. Mohamad Arsad, and R. Mohamad Yasin, "Exploring Challenges for Integrating Solar PV Technology in Secondary Schools' Education," in *Proceedings of the 2nd International Conference on Social Sciences, ICONESS 2023, 22-23 July 2023, Purwokerto, Central Java, Indonesia*, Purwokerto, Indonesia: EAI, 2023. doi: 10.4108/eai.22-7-2023.2335096.
[19] R. Corina, T. Ovidiu, A. Iulia, M. Cristina, and A. Ştefan, "A critical review of the photovoltaic effect teaching in high-school," *Rom. Rep. Phys.*, vol. 76, no. 1, pp. 901–901, Mar. 2024, doi: 10.59277/RomRepPhys.2024.76.901.
[20] A. R. Da Conceição and E. C. Fireman, "Controvérsias sociocientíficas e o ensino por investigação: uma estratégia didática para auxiliar no desenvolvimento de habilidades propostas pela Base Nacional Comum Curricular," *#Tear*, vol. 9, no. 2, Dec. 2020, doi: 10.35819/tear.v9.n2.a4308.
[21] Brasil, "Lei Nº 13.415, de 16 de Fevereiro de 2017," 2017.
[22] A. T. E. D. Oliveira, A. A. Sobreira, H. F. D. Costa, J. D. S. Ferreira, and C. A. S. Perez, "A energia solar fotovoltaica: transformação, evolução, aspectos ambientais e abordagens na sala de aula," *RSD*, vol. 11, no. 9, p. e25811932533, Jul. 2022, doi: 10.33448/rsd-v11i9.32533.
[23] L. F. A. Cordeiro and M. A. G. Fernandes, "Perspectivas da energia fotovoltaica na capacitação de professores para desenvolvimento de uma educação ambiental," *Environmental Scientiae*, vol. 3, no. 2, pp. 60–68, Jan. 2022, doi: 10.6008/CBPC2674-6492.2021.002.0006.
[24] M. F. Ferreira, M. A. V. Freitas, N. F. Da Silva, A. F. Da Silva, and L. R. L. D. Paz, "Insertion of Photovoltaic Solar Systems in Technological Education Institutions in Brazil: Teacher Perceptions Concerning Contributions towards Sustainable Development," *Sustainability*, vol. 12, no. 4, p. 1292, Feb. 2020, doi: 10.3390/su12041292.

PHOTOVOLTAIC DEVELOPMENT AND LANDSCAPE CONFLICTS IN TAIWAN: STATUS AND RESOLUTIONS

WANG TZU-YA, WANG CHIA-CHEN/
Industrial Technology Research Institute
DianaWang@itri.org.tw, molly.wang@itri.org.tw

ABSTRACT: The turbulent international situation in recent years has triggered a global fossil fuel supply crisis, leading to a rise in renewable energy; and solar photovoltaics (solar PV) accounts for over half of the current worldwide renewable energy production. Aiming to achieve its 2050 Net zero Emissions goals, Taiwan is actively promoting the development of solar PV and other renewable energy sources. Although solar PV causes fewer environmental issues than traditional power generation methods and related impact can usually be mitigated through proper measures, the public may still have reservations about the installations' impact on local landscapes, environment, and ecosystem since the solar panels are usually set up near living zones. This study complied relevant past literature and categorized them into impacts on the visual landscape, environment, and habitats for discussion.

Looking back on Taiwan's development of solar PV, there were several incidents in which the public expressed concerns related to landscape, environment, and ecosystem issues. There was much controversy and conflict surrounding the installation sites as well. This study looked at the three most controversial cases in Taiwan and realized the importance of communicating with the public. Taiwan has introduced the *Directions for the Landscape and Ecological Environment Assessment of Ground-Mounted Photovoltaic Systems* (設置地面型太陽光電設施景觀及生態環境審定原則) for the solar PV operators' reference to reduce the impact on landscape and environment when setting up solar power facilities and a lot of sites are designed as per *The Directions*. Yet we discovered that when compared with similar regulations or policy in other countries, Taiwan's *Directions* do not include guidelines and instructions on how to communicate with the locals as well as how the implementations can be adjusted according to local conditions. In the future, our government should review and refine these aspects to improve the overall domestic solar PV installation environment and reduce the pertinent impacts on landscape, environment, and ecosystems.

Keywords: Solar PV, Landscape, Renewable Energy Policy

1 INTRODUCTION

A global fossil fuel crisis has been set off by recent regional wars and the COVID-19 pandemic. This significantly affected the global supply chain and energy industry, highlighting the importance of renewable energy, especially solar PV[1]. As the pandemic gradually slowed down in 2023, the growth of worldwide solar PV cumulative capacity hit a record high of 1,552.3 GW. The annual new installed capacity increased by nearly 50% and solar PV development continues to take up a major role in the global renewable energy industry[2].

Located in East Asia and on the west side of the Pacific, Taiwan has an area of 35,980 m^2[3] and is the 38th largest island in the world. About 70% of this island is mountain terrain. The average temperature is 23.5℃, the average global solar radiation (Rs) accumulates to 5,287.2 MJ/m^2 per year, and the average sunshine hours reach 1,732 days/year [4]. The population is around 23,278,642 people, Gross domestic product (GDP) is about USD 791.61 billion, and GDP per capita is approximately USD 34,050[5]. By the end of 2023, Taiwan's solar PV installed capacity reached 12.42GW[6].

As more countries respond to the 2050 net-zero declaration, Taiwan also announced our 2050 Net zero Emissions goals in 2021. The government later released *Taiwan's Pathway to Net zero Emissions in 2050 and Strategy Details*[7], *The 12 Key Strategies*[8], and *Net zero Emissions Pathway 2023-2026 Outline Plan*[9]. Renewable energy thus became a key player in Taiwan's transition to Net zero Emissions by 2050. In 2009, the Legislative Yuan adopted the Renewable Energy Development Act which serves as the basis for renewable energy development in Taiwan. The Act was amended in 2019 to optimize the regulatory environment for launching renewable energy policies and speed up the development of renewable energy. According to the Ministry of Economic Affairs (MOEA), the objectives for Taiwan's energy transition are to "promote green energy, increase natural gas, reduce coal-fired power, achieve nuclear-free". In the category of "promote green energy", the MOEA projects that by 2025, 20% of the total power generated should come from renewable energy sources [10], solar PV installed capacity should reach 20 GW, wind power at 5.6 GW, hydropower at 2 GW, and biomass energy at 800 MW. Taiwan launched a series of promotion plans since 2016 to gradually achieve the goal of 20% renewable energy[10] and set the target of 20 GW solar PV installation capacity in 2025.

Although renewable energy can strongly support the sustainable development of energy, the rapid increase of solar PV installed capacity has led to issues caused by inappropriate site selections or development projects that occur without sufficient planning beforehand. These incidents bring on conflicts between solar PV, landscape, and the environment, not only hindering the installation of solar PV in Taiwan, many countries are also facing similar issues[11], [12], [13]. Therefore, in addition to exploring the potential impacts of solar PV development on the landscape and environment in Taiwan, this study will also explain the *Directions for the Landscape and Ecological Environment Assessment of Ground-Mounted Photovoltaic Systems* which was released to solve the conflicts between solar PV and landscapes and explore how solar panels affect the surrounding ecological environment. What kind of countermeasures can Taiwan come up with? And what other regulations or examples abroad can be used as references?

2 THE POTENTIAL IMPACTS OF SOLAR PV DEVELOPMENT ON THE LANDSCAPE

Solar PV can reduce greenhouse gas emissions, reactivate degraded land, improve air and water quality, and strengthen the energy autonomy of a nation. It also contributes to sustainable development and therefore generally receives more support from the public[14]. It should be noted that renewable energy generation facilities still have some impact on the surrounding environment. While the impact caused by solar PV is usually lesser and may be minimized through appropriate mitigation measures[14], the setting of solar panels could still impact the surrounding landscape. In this study, a "landscape" is defined according to the European Landscape Convention: "The landscape is part of the land, as perceived by local people or visitors, which evolves through time as a result of being acted upon by natural forces and human beings[15]." In other words, the landscape is associated with the emotional relationship between people and the land. According to relative literature, types of impact on the landscape caused by solar panels can be categorized into Visual, Environmental, and Habitat impact.

2.1 Visual Impacts

Although society is very accepting of solar PV, the energy conversion efficiency of solar power is not as high as traditional power-generating methods and requires more land. Site selection often clashes with local land use and natural landscape [19], and the subjective visual impact is one of the main reasons why the public objects to setting up renewable energy equipment such as solar panel [19], [25]. The visual impact caused by solar panels mainly depends on subjective preferences, and these preferences may be affected by life experience, culture, age, and education level[19], [20], [26]. Past studies[20] usually use the term "Unity" to describe the degree of coherence and harmony of the visual elements and present the level of visual impact. However, it is difficult to quantify the visual impact caused by solar panels[14]. Many past research[14] [16], [17], [18], [20] pointed out that solar panels could cause visual impact on the surrounding landscape. Impact factors mentioned in most literature include visual aesthetics impact, color, fractality, and visibility.

2.1.1 Visual aesthetics impact

The impact of visual aesthetics is defined in literature as changes in landscapes caused by development, resulting in changes in our subjective and objective perceptions of the environment[16]. In other words, the landscape created by solar panels and the surrounding environment affects visual experience. If solar panels are set up in a natural environment, their visual impact increases; contrarily, if the solar panels are integrated into modern buildings, they may have a positive aesthetic impact[18]. Some studies[14] mentioned that California has established regulations that state large areas of land cannot be used as solar PV sites. The regulation takes the potential recreation value of the land into consideration as well as the possible visual impact and impacts on the ecosystem and habitats. However, the setup of solar panels can replace a portion of the mining industry and transform large highland forests into recreational areas. Therefore, even if solar panels have some impact on visual aesthetics, it also frees up visual landscapes[14].

There is a study[16] points out that visual impact is one of the main landscape impact factors to consider when installing solar PV sites. The objective indicators of visual aesthetic impact include visibility, color, and fractality[16], [21]. This paper went through related literature[18], [20], [22], [27] and summarized the objective indicators that affect visual aesthetics as follows:

2.1.1.1 Color

Literature[21] indicates that there is a contrasting relationship between the surface color of solar panels and the color of surrounding landscapes (e.g., vegetation, soil, sky, etc.). There is a research[20] also mentions that color is considered an important objective factor in the perception of aesthetics in many studies. The paper on the aesthetic impact of solar panels concludes that solar panels cause an aesthetic impact since they change the landscape. Furthermore, adjacent colors affect our perception of a particular color, and the color of the solar panels often does not blend in with the surrounding buildings or environments. Especially in rural areas, the color of the solar panels strongly stands out from the color scheme of the natural landscape, making it more likely to cause negative visual experiences[20]. Fernandez-Jimenez et al. also listed color as one of the indexes when selecting new site locations. They converted the colors of the planned installation area grid into variables and then standardized the variables so that the values of all grids are between 0 and 1. The numeral values of all grids under various conditions were then compared. Solar panels installed in grids with values closer to 0 would have less visual impact. If the value is 0, then observers onsite or pedestrians barely notice the solar PV equipment[27].

2.1.1.2 Fractality

Fractality refers to the overall profile of the solar panels[21]. Usually when designing the deployment of solar panels, the objective is to spread out to the largest area possible within the limited plot of land to maximize generation capacity and reduce installation costs[16]; yet the visual relationship between the solar panels and the surrounding landscape is often overlooked during the designing process, and the arrangement, layout, and shape of the panels may affect the visual experience of pedestrians and viewers. Measures to address this issue include employing Building-integrated photovoltaics (BIPV) and increasing patterns in the grid to further integrate the panels with the surrounding landscape as well as adjusting the space porosity within the module layout to complement the surrounding landscape. Major design parameters that affect the porosity are the azimuth angle, angle of inclination, and density. Flexible designing for solar PV landscapes formed by large areas of land use and landscape transformation can reduce the impact of large-scale ground-mounted solar PV systems on the landscape and increase ecosystem protection potential[16]. If we want to let the equipment blend in with the surrounding landscape, it may be necessary to cut down a certain degree of generation efficiency to allow better integration of the panels and the surrounding landscape[22].

2.1.1.3 Visibility

In the paper by Kapetanakis et al., impact caused by Visibility is considered the most important. The impact, or how obvious the facility is, depends on the total area covered by solar PV. When installing solar PV, either hide them around buildings or roads or set them up in a place where people can see them[18]. While operators are usually more inclined to hide the panels to avoid affecting the visual scene, it should be noted that when the visibility of solar PV is low, the public would have less of a positive impression of the facility. Thus, experts normally suggest integrating solar PV with buildings, a method that also increases the panels' installation capacity and shading properties. Furthermore, the correct site selection can also reduce the visual impact of large solar PV sites[18]. Relevant study[22] analyzed the proportion of solar PV facilities with visible by the edges and launched obscuring measures such as planting hedges or orchards around them. This reduces the visibility of solar PV facilities and increases the growing space for plants and animals. Some sites will set up observation decks for visitors and promote the deck as a local attraction to enhance the positive impression of solar PV[22].

2.1.2 Other factors

In addition to visual impacts, relevant literatures[16], [20], [28] also mention other visual influence factors caused by solar PV, including objective factors such as shape and size, density, contrast, and regularity. These are mainly controlled by the distance between solar panels and have a great impact in urban[20]. Integration, which is similar to Visibility, is divided into Non-integration, Partial Integration, and Integration in the research. The difference is that the term is usually used when discussing integration with buildings[20], [28]. There is also a study[16]that assess relevant landscape factors based on landscape sensitivity. The factors include terrain, patches, particles, and landscape characteristics. Highly intense, diverse, and unique terrains as well as complex, rugged, and irregular plots have higher landscape sensitivity and are more likely to see landscape conflicts at renewable energy installation sites[16].

2.2 Environmental Impact

Solar PV may also cause microclimate impact during the power generation process. We compiled the environmental impact factors frequently mentioned in relevant literature, namely temperature, glare, noise, electromagnetic fields, waste, and emissions, as follows:

2.2.1 Temperature

The principle of solar PV power generation is that the solar PV modules absorb solar radiation and then directly convert it into electricity[23]. Chiabrando et al. pointed out that the modules may reach 70°C during the power generation process, resulting in a temperature increase in the surrounding air[19] and may affect the soil carbon cycle[24] as well as plant productivity and organic mass decomposition rates. However, we can significantly reduce the module overheating problem by setting up ventilation equipment and thus avoid power generation efficiency decrease due to overheated module components. To summarize, the temperature of the modules may increase during power generation, but under normal weather conditions, this would only cause a slight effect on the surrounding microclimate[19].

2.2.2 Glare

Glare is a visual stimulus caused by uncontrolled brightness. Excessive light and reflected sunlight could cause short-term photophobia[27], yet it is still relatively difficult to eliminate the glare effects of solar PV [19], [20]. Currently, the negative glare effects caused by solar PV can be mitigated by computer simulations or Anti-Reflection Coating (ARC) materials[20].

Yet past study[20] also mentions that while existing computer software can use the DEM (Digital Elevation Model) and GIS (Geographic Information System) to simulate glare in specific situations and predict the path and direction of reflected beams, there are still disparities between the simulations and the actual situations. Moreover, so far there is no literature that provides glare indexes for such special situations, nor are there any standard values for reference. Nevertheless, the simulation results can still be used as a reference during the designing stage to alleviate glare problems that may occur after the solar panels are set. There are also many types of ARC materials that are being developed, such as nanostructure materials with composites of silicon, silicon dioxide, titanium oxide, zirconium oxide, zinc oxide, cobalt oxide, stannic oxide, carbon, and GaN, as well as ARCs with metal ions that can reduce the glare effect on viewers[20].

2.2.3 Noise

According to previous studies[18], solar PV sites generate less noise than general building activities and diesel generator units[18], [29] as the lack of significant operating components and mechanical vibrations in the solar PV system allows it to operate quietly. The only sources of noise in these systems are the transformers and booster stations. Since solar panels mainly generate power during the day, any possible noise impact is usually limited to the daytime and causes less interference to the residents during nighttime or silent hours. Effective soundproofing and noise control measures are set up during construction to reduce potential noise impact on the locals. In summary, the operation process of solar PV is quiet. Noise mitigation measures should be implemented during construction to ensure the lowest impact on local communities[18].

2.2.4 Electromagnetic field

Currently, there are no study indicates that solar PV sites have higher electromagnetic waves, however, there may be higher electromagnetic waves during the transition from low to medium or high voltage during electricity transmission. As a result, some medium- and high-voltage cables are buried underground to reduce their magnetic field. The setup of the facilities should also comply with local standards to assure the public[17].

2.2.5 Waste and emissions

Solar PV generates less waste and emissions than traditional power generation methods. Greenhouse gas and $PM_{2.5}$ emissions, in particular, are significantly reduced[16], [29]. Notwithstanding, the production process of solar panels can still produce gas and may cause pollution if not handled properly.[19] Furthermore, the processing of decommissioned solar panels also requires special care. Panel materials such as metals, silicon, glass, and plastic may contaminate the soil if handled improperly[19]. There are also a study[18] mentions that if a solar panel catches fire during operation, certain chemicals could be released into and pollute the atmosphere. Hence, it is crucial to have emergency responding actions and disaster prevention measures in place for material storage, operations, and maintenance to avoid the negative effects of waste and emissions[18].

2.2.6 Other factors

10.4229/EUPVSEC2025/5DV.3.41

Other environmental impacts solar PV may generate include soil erosion during construction and impact on water quality, historical landscapes, surface runoff, surface albedo, and surface roughness. As solar panels are static power generating facilities, most impacts occur during the manufacturing and construction phases, for example, wastewater produced during manufacturing. However, the severity of the impact still requires more supporting research[19], [29]. In terms of surface runoff effects, changes in land use and land cover or the panels installed on hill slopes could double or even triple soil penetration, runoff ratio, and evapotranspiration; thus, proper protection of water and land resources and the deployment of monitoring facilities are necessary during the construction of solar PV, especially when setting up facilities on hill slopes[14]. In general, the operation of solar panels does not have a significant impact on the environment.

2.3 Habitat Impacts

This section compiled the impacts of solar PV on the ecosystem that are discussed more frequently in previous literature. Topics covered include land occupation, land use and land cover effects, the impact on birds and wildlife, habitat fragmentation, and soil erosion.

2.3.1 Land occupation

Solar PV is a renewable energy power source that requires a large area of land. Although some solar panels are mounted on the roof and thus avoid the land use issue, the setup of other solar panels still needs land. If the site is set on degraded land, it can not only avoid additional land use or land cover changes but also support land activation in the area. It could even increase the supply of the local ecosystem, such as stabilizing soil and having carbon sequestration properties[30]. Research[16] has also shown that cutting down the required land area and increasing power density decreases not only land occupation but also the visual impact[16].

2.3.2 Land use and land cover

The installation of solar panels changes the land use and land cover of an area. Depending on the site selection, different types of land use and land cover create different degrees of impact. For example, a site located on arable land could disrupt the local agricultural production landscape and ecosystem. It could also destroy the rich soil and lead to conflicts with the locals who have an emotional connection with the land[18]. However, in terms of land use intensity, if a solar PV installation has a lifespan of 30 years, the land of each unit generation capacity does not change with time; but for mines that supply coal to coal-fired power plants, the surface soil would require decades to recover. Solar PV has the advantage that as the equipment lifespan increases, the land occupied per unit generation capacity gradually decreases[29]. Past studies[29] indicate that the land occupied by solar PV can recover more quickly and the land use intensity is significantly less than that of coal-fired power plants. The impact on local land use and land cover is also notably less[17], [29].

2.3.3 Birds risk and wildlife

Birds and wildlife are often crucial factors in the review for solar PV installation permits, yet studies on the correlations between this new technology and the surrounding ecosystem are relatively few. Since solar PV sites are usually encircled by fences that keep wildlife from entering, this could disrupt the hiding places, migratory routes, and food supply of local wildlife. In some overseas cases, operators even use herbicide to clean up the site area, which impacts wildlife habitats as well[29], [30].

A previous study in South Africa[31] looked at the abundance of invertebrate colonies in the solar PV site area, power supply area, and the surrounding ranch area. Results showed no significant differences, indicating solar PV facilities have little impact on invertebrate animal colonies[31]. Another study in the UK[32] also compared bird monitoring results of a solar PV site with control sites ranging from 6 to 280m away from the site. Findings indicated that the average number of bird species on the solar PV project site was 15.2 species, which is higher than the control areas (12.8 species). The site also had a higher total number of birds (averaging 47.8 birds). This concludes that the solar PV site has a higher bird diversity and their behavior onsite is not much different from other locations[32].

Some research[18] [29] suggests that customized studies and analyses of the surrounding wildlife and ecosystem should be conducted during the development phase and ecologically sensitive areas or natural reserves should be avoided to reduce the impact of solar PV installations on the surrounding environment[18] [29].Nevertheless, there are not many related studies and more research and confirmation will be needed to determine the impact of solar PV on birds and wildlife and subsequent countermeasures.

2.3.4 Habitat fragmentation

The installed solar panels could cause the vegetation beneath them to degrade or disappear, especially on farmland sites, the panels are more likely to affect the growth of local plants. The project site could also affect the local animal habitat as well as the growth pattern of flora and fauna[19]. Habitat loss and fragmentation are considered major threats to biodiversity, and the layout of solar PV facilities could affect the distribution of species and alter the biological corridor[19].

Nevertheless, studies[32] have shown that local biodiversity can be improved when solar PV sites implement site management measures. These measures include seeding various species at one location, limiting herbicide use, conducting protective grazing or mowing, and managing the edges of wildlife habitats. These actions expand the diversity of plants, especially wildflowers, and consequently boost the diversity of other species. The increasing number of butterflies and bees can pollinate and benefit the surrounding farmlands or orchards and give the neighboring landscape beautiful flowers[32], [33].

2.3.5 Soil erosion

Land preparation work for the solar PV project site includes removing existing vegetation, evening out the surface, and compacting the soil[17]. When farmlands or forests are converted for solar PV use, the soil penetration rate and evapotranspiration volume will be affected[29] and, without relevant protection measures, could lead to soil erosion and even increase the possibility of floods, especially for solar PV sites set on hill slopes.[17] Proactive monitoring and related research are necessary to protect local hydrology and soil resources[17], [29].

2.3.6 Other factors

10.4229/EUPVSEC2025/5DV.3.41

The above-mentioned ecological effects aside, the installment of solar PV will change the use of land yet the impact on land modification and soil quality is milder and more neutral compared to conventional power generation systems. Actual impacts will require continuous observation through research.[29] In terms of soil quality impact mitigation measures, the study[18] proposes that the impact can be reduced by avoiding ecologically sensitive areas and restoring affected plants and animals around the project site. Changes in land use and land cover can also lead to the degradation of plants and loss of habitats, both of which affect the local ecosystem.[29] As described in 3.4, the setup of solar PV could cause some degree of habitat loss and fragmentation and thus disturb the migration or food foraging of certain species. As a result, the study also highlights the importance of habitat management and recommends avoiding sensitive areas when setting up the site, especially for large-scale sites[17], [18]. Nonetheless, the study[29] also suggests that more research is needed to observe and confirm the actual impact since solar PV show a lesser impact on ecosystems and habitat loss compared to conventional power generation methods. Furthermore, the construction process may cause surface disturbances. Although most of these effects are temporary, permanent damage could occur if appropriate mitigation measures are not taken. For that reason, an appropriate site selection should avoid ecologically sensitive areas and valuable historic and natural beauty areas to minimize impact[18].

3 CASES OF CONFLICT BETWEEN SOLAR PV INSTALLATIONS AND LANDSCAPE IN TAIWAN

As Taiwan begin to aggressively develop solar PV, the process generated many conflicts between the solar PV sites and local landscape, environment, and ecology. While the conflicts delayed the progress of related cases, they have also made the community more aware of these issues. This chapter will discuss the cases from the perspectives of visual, environmental, and ecological impacts.

3.1 Case of Visual Impact

According to past studies[14], [16], [17], [18], [20], the visual impacts caused by solar PV include visual conflicts and not blending in with the surrounding landscapes. The most controversial case of visual impact in Taiwan happened at a solar PV site in Pingtung in Southern Taiwan. This site is located on the slopes along Highway where leads to Kenting, a popular tourist destination. When the operators were setting up the solar panels, they removed the original vegetation on the slopes to prepare the land. Most of the removed plants were white popinac trees, which is a foreign species. Although the operators had conducted visual landscape simulation analysis before construction and continuously rolled out landscape engineering projects according to their development plan, the construction continued for over a year and the visitors going to and from Kenting filed complaints to the local government for this eyesore along the road. This action garnered much attention from the public. In this case, we see that solar PV sites set on the slopes of the roadside are more likely to conflict with the surrounding landscape as they are highly visible due to their location. This affects the travelers' visual aesthetics, causing a negative impression among the public and consequently toward solar PV.

3.2 Case of Environmental Impact

There are many studies[14], [17], [18] indicate that solar PV may cause issues such as light pollution and noise in the environment. Although no studies have clearly shown that solar PV are harmful to humans, the Taiwanese public is still skeptical about setting up solar panels. For example, during the construction phase of a solar PV site in Tainan City, the public severely protested because of concerns about the environment. This solar PV project site is situated close to a residential community, and during the construction period, residents have protested multiple times against the possible light pollution, low-frequency noise, and hot island effect. The local government later executed noise tests onsite after the construction was completed and found all to be within regulatory standards (maximum outside noise value at 53.6 dB), yet the public protested fiercely during the construction process. This project was eventually completed; however, we recommend that in the future, the operators, local government, and public should communicate better to minimize these conflicts and protect the rights of the public.

3.3 Case of Habitat Impact

Previous studies[14], [16], [17], [19] have shown that the impacts of solar PV on the ecological environment can destroy animal habitats and endanger certain species.[29], [30] However, operators are usually inclined to select a land area of a certain size for ground-mounted PV system setups due to setup cost and size. Taiwan has limited land and a dense population, and our flat plains are nearly fully developed. In recent years, local operators have turned to hill slopes or coastlines for solar panel setups. However Taiwan's unique geographic location has created a rich biodiversity and cultivated many indigenous species, and the slopes that are potential solar PV sites are the main living areas of endangered animals. A solar PV project site located on the slopes in Miaoli County is an example. Since the development area overlaps with the habitat of protected wildlife, the administration process review and operations have attracted much attention from environmental protection groups and the local public. This slope area is the habitat of endangered animals such as pangolins, crab-eating mongooses, and leopard cats, as a result, the operators invited ecologists to serve as advisors during the initial stage of development to reduce the impact on the ecosystem. The operators also promised to avoid highly sensitive zones, minimize construction areas, and carry out ecological compensation and thus received permission from the government[34]. To further protect the environment and ecosystem, the operators installed automatic cameras after the site started operations and even successfully captured images of wildlife including masked palm civets and leopard cats. Yet despite these measures, the Leopard Cat Association of Taiwan was still skeptical of the installation of this solar PV facility and pointed out that the biggest issue is site selection[35] as the facility is in an area where leopard cats frequent and the forest form of the area is intact. Even with ecological compensation measures afterward, it is still difficult to restore the functionality of the original habitat. The Association also suggested that local briefings should be held in areas with major ecological disputes and the operators should communicate clearly with residents to reduce the opposition[35].

4 HOW DOES TAIWAN RESOLVE THE

CONFLICTS BETWEEN SOLAR PV DEVELOPMENT AND LANDSCAPE?

Densely populated and with limited land resources, Taiwan only has a few suitable areas for renewable energy, and the power generation conversion efficiency of solar PV is relatively lower and requires larger areas of land[19]. Even though solar PV is a type of low-degree development, has multiple uses for the same piece of land, and the development process is strictly regulated by law, the public is still skeptical of solar PV in terms of visual, environmental, and habitat and landscape impacts. In response, Energy Administration, the MOEA, introduced the *Directions for the Landscape and Ecological Environment Assessment of Ground-Mounted Photovoltaic Systems*[36] for solar PV operators and relevant management agencies to use as a reference when designing the landscape and conducting reviews to decrease the impact solar PV setups could have on the surrounding landscape, habitats, and environments.

4.1 Newly established *Directions for the Landscape and Ecological Environment Assessment of Ground-Mounted Photovoltaic Systems*

To maintain the overall landscape of our country while promoting solar PV, the Energy Administration established the *Directions for the Landscape and Ecological Environment Assessment of Ground-Mounted Photovoltaic Systems* according to the resolution of the Ponds and Hydro Facilities Policies Environmental Evaluation meeting session called by the Executive Yuan on March 30, 2018. *The Directions* were announced on May 1, 2018, after the contents of the Directions were discussed in two cross-department expert meetings.

The Directions mainly targets large-scale ground-mounted solar PV sites (only those with a scale of 2 MW are regulated) to balance solar PV development and landscape and ecological environment protection. Furthermore, Class I environmentally sensitive areas are avoided according to the *Regulations for Examination Operations of Non-urban Development* (非都市土地開發審議作業規範). The overall content of *The Directions* mainly focuses on matters related to landscape and ecological aspects so that solar PV operators have guidelines for the initial stage of site selection and planning as well as the later construction and operation phases to reduce the impact of solar PV on the environment and landscape as much as possible.

For landscape's aspect, the content includes local contour lines should be taken into consideration when planning solar sites, panel module design should be adjusted accordingly to fit local characteristics, avoid elevated setups for cables, remove unnecessary lighting equipment, and maintain the original site landform.

For ecological aspect, since the establishment of the solar PV site could affect the surrounding ecological environment, operators are required by law to carry out suitable greening measures with indigenous species as the primary vegetation choice to avoid damaging the local indigenous ecosystem.

The construction and operation phases of solar PV are also regulated. During the construction phase, the site authorities can request the operator to conduct ecological surveys and implement environmental, safety, and health protection measures for planning and construction. After the facilities begin operations, regulations state that when maintaining the solar PV facilities, cleaning agents are prohibited to avoid polluting the water quality and ecological environment of the surrounding farmlands.

4.2 Revising the *Directions for the Landscape and Ecological Environment Assessment of Ground-Mounted Photovoltaic Systems*

The number of solar PV installations in Taiwan continues to grow annually as local sites rapidly expand, and the public's concerns about the noise, glare, and landscape ecology issues caused by solar PV have increased as well. To decrease the public's apprehension, the Energy Administration reviewed the appropriate distance between solar PV and settlements at the end of 2023 and revised *The Directions*. The Energy Administration commissioned a research team to launch tests at the solar PV sites. *The Directions* were decided based on the glare simulation and noise measurement reports as well as the conclusions of the discussion meetings attended by the Ministry of Agriculture, the Ministry of the Interior, the PVGSA, and the Taiwan Photovoltaic Industry Association on September 7 and October 17, 2023.

According to the results of the glare simulation, when the distance between the solar PV site and settlements exceeds 15 m, the glare impact on humans caused by solar panels is greatly reduced, and when paired with a hedge fence setup, the glare effect can be eliminated. To ensure that the glare caused by solar panels will not affect the settlements, the Administration took public opinions and the *Regulations for Examination Operations of Non-urban Development* into consideration and added *Article 6* in the revised version of *The Directions*. The new regulation mandates that ground-mounted solar PV installments that reach 2 MW should be set up in accordance with The Directions and comply with *Subsection 1* or *2* according to the installment model.

Article 6, Subparagraph 1 of *The Directions* regulates compound fishery and electricity symbiosis models. Fishery and electricity symbiosis models are usually large-scale installments and located close to farming villages and thus need to be regulated. Furthermore, according to *The Regulations for Examining the Application of Structuring Farming Facilities on Agricultural Land* (申請農業用地作農業設施容許使用審查辦法), solar PV facilities should not exceed 40% of the located farm-use land area. Since the installation has already reserved space for flexible retractions, there are only regulations on the adjunct boundary to settlements with over 50 households to avoid the solar PV landscape from affecting the residents.

Article 6, Subparagraph 2 regulates non-compound models. As non-compound models are usually large-scale setups that could easily cause land use conflicts with their neighbors, borders that are non-adjacent to settlements are also required to retract 15m and more or retract 10m and have hedge fences over 1.5m tall. Regarding the form of the hedge fences, fences irrelevant to agricultural operations are not allowed to be set up on farm-use land, therefore, the hedge fences should be installed with a transparent mesh without a fixed base to allow for other uses of the land in the future. In addition, the hedge fences are required to be set at least 5m from the site boundaries to reduce the visual pressure and protect the safety of road users as well as enhance overall landscape aesthetics. Indigenous climbing plants are preferred for the hedges to protect local biodiversity.

In addition to introducing *Subparagraph 1 and 2* to *The Directions* based on the glare simulation results,

Subparagraph 3 was also added based on the noise measurement results. Since the results show that the noise levels can only fall below the Class 2 standards stated in *The Noise Control Standards* when they are over 20m away from the unit substations, *Subparagraph 3* stipulated that the unit substation and converter, which are the main noise sources of solar PV sites, should be placed at 20m from settlements, and the noise measured around the site should be lower than the residential-use Class 2 daytime standard (57 dB). If the noise level exceeds the standard, soundproofing facilities must be added to avoid any noise disturbing the surrounding environment.

5 ANALYSIS AND DISCUSSION ON SOLAR PV AND LANDSCAPE CONFLICT COUNTERMEASURES

There are many solar PV developments in Taiwan have encountered landscape, ecological, and environmental conflicts, but these issues are not exclusive to Taiwan. Other countries are also experiencing many challenges in terms of balancing solar PV development and ecological environment protection. The International Union for Conservation of Nature and Natural Resource (IUCN) released the "Mitigating biodiversity impacts associated with solar and wind energy development: Guidelines for project developers" in February 2021[37] to help solar PV and wind power operators understand the potential risks these installations could have on the ecosystem, habitats, and communities. It also suggests a series of evaluation structures and methods which include four principles: Avoidance, Minimizations, Restoration, and Offset. For example, the sites should avoid sensitive zones, avoid construction during certain seasons or periods, and use as much surface soil and indigenous plants as possible to recover the ecosystem.

In addition to guidance from international organizations, countries have also formulated regulations or guidelines for solar PV and other renewable energy operators to reduce the impact on the surrounding ecological environment. For example, the city of Lingewaard[38] in the Netherlands launched a series of energy installation plans to achieve its 2050 net-zero goals and formulated relevant self-government ordinances as well. Solar energy parks were set up since roof-mounted solar panels could not satisfy the current energy demand. These sites not only increase renewable energy production volume but also prevent land fragmentation issues. If other farming areas wish to set up solar panels, the project must be proposed and widely supported by the locals, and approved sites are required to give back to the local community. The solar energy parks are also required to blend in with the existing landscape. The existing landscape elements, vegetation types, historical buildings, and openness of the space should all be taken into consideration. If we use the dike zone as an example, the facility and surrounding landscape are integrated by using indigenous plants to shape the riverbank, building windbreaks, setting up recreational routes, and planting natural herbs to beautify the sides of the ditches.

South Korea, like Taiwan, has many mountains and less plain areas, and thus many solar panels are installed on mountain slopes. To avoid slope disasters caused by solar PV setups, the sites must be evaluated and reviewed as many environment-related regulations. Moreover, different regions also have pertinent regulations to prevent setting solar PV sites too close to settlements or scenic areas. For example, Yeongju City introduced *The Standards for the Permission of Solar Power Generation Facilities Development* (발전시설의개발행위허가기준, Bal Jeon Si Seol Ui Gae Bal Haeng Wi Heo Ga Gi Jun)[39] which stipulates that solar PV sites should be 1,000m away from tourist areas, 500m away from communities with more than 10 households and roads, 300m away from communities with 5-10 households, and must not be installed in national cultural properties or protected scenic areas. Yet, to increase renewable energy setups, *The Site Selection Standards*, announced by the South Korean Ministry of Trade, Industry, and Energy Resources in February 2023, stated that the maximum isolation distance for solar PV facilities set in residential areas is 100m. If it is a residential area with more than 10 people, a briefing meeting needs to be held and the project can only go forward with the consent of two-thirds of the residents. There are also local incentives for relaxing or abolishing the isolation distance limit for renewable energy power generation facilities, such as weighted incentives for Korean renewable energy certificates.

Japan has *The Environmental Impact Assessment Act* (環境影響評価法) which included solar PV into the environmental assessment recognition criteria on March 5, 2019. It stipulates that a Class-1 business environmental assessment should be conducted if the site reaches more than 40 MW, and 30-40 MW sites should undergo a Class-2 business environmental assessment (whether the environmental assessment is required should be decided case by case). In addition, there are also *The Regulations on the Prevention of Sediment Disasters Act* (土砂災害警戒区域等における土砂災害防止対策の推進に関する法律, Dosya saigai keikai kuiki nado ni okeru dosya saigai bousi taisaku no suisin ni kan suru houritu) and *The Forest Act* (森林法, Sinrinhou) that restrict development in sediment disaster monitoring areas, steep slopes, and forests. Many local governments also have self-government ordinances to protect the surrounding landscape and ecological environments from being affected by solar PV developments. Examples include Hyōgo Prefecture's *Solar Power Generating Facilities and Local Environment Coordination Act* (太陽光発電施設等と地域環境との調和に関する条例, Taiyoukou hatuden sisetu nado to tiiki kankyou to no tyouwa ni kan suru zyourei)[40]. It listed out the factors that should be considered during the planning and setup stages, such as solar power generation facilities installed on sloped areas that are visible from main roads and urban areas must be located at sites with a 30-degree or lower angle of inclination. It also states that development areas of 5,000 m^2 should maintain good communications with stakeholders such as adjacent land owners or lessees, adjoining building owners and lessees, local neighborhood committee residents, and personnel designated by the mayor of the city/village; and the operators must submit their business plan to the local government at least 60 days before the construction commences. The Japanese Ministry of Environment introduced *The Guidance on the Solar Power Generation Environment* (太陽光発電の環境配慮ガイドライン, Taiyoukou hatuden no kankyou hairyo gaidorain) in 2020. *The Guidance* is a reference for operators setting up solar PV in regions that do not have specific regulations on landscape environments. According to the Guidance, during the designing phase, operators should consider the environmental impacts of the installation, including land stability, sewage discharge, noise, glare, dust and vibration caused by construction, landscape, wildlife and ecosystem, and the possibility of interacting with nature, to lessen the public's doubts.

Energy Administration, Ministry of Economic Affairs, R.O.C introduced the *Directions for the Landscape and Ecological Environment Assessment of Ground-Mounted Photovoltaic Systems* in 2018 to provide guidance on the protection of landscapes and ecosystems for large-scale sites and reduce the impact of solar PV development on surrounding areas. In 2023, The Principle was revised and protection provisions regarding hedge fences and the distance between solar PV sites and settlements were added. Compared with the relevant regulations and guidelines of other countries, Taiwan's Central Government is not only spearheading solar PV developments and setting pertinent administrative guidance but also has launched regulations and standards for different models with clear target groups and concrete numbers to protect the surrounding environment. Nevertheless, if we wish to decrease the public's concerns about solar PV installments, in future revisions of relevant regulations, legislative authorities could consider the suggestions from the Leopard Cat Association of Taiwan concerning the case on the Miaoli hillside site and the developments done in protected wildlife habitats as well as the importance of public communication as highlighted in the self-government ordinances in the Netherlands, South Korea, and Japan. The new regulations can also stipulate the proportion of people who consent to the matter. Furthermore, since *The Directions* are a guidance introduced by the Central Government and set for large-scale sites, regional governments should also set up their self-government ordinances or guidelines according to their respective landscape features and conditions. This can further protect the important natural resources of the area and make the public more accepting of solar PV.

6 CONCLUSION

As countries move towards their sustainable net zero goals, the importance of renewable energy is rising. Nonetheless, the public is still skeptical of the increasing solar PV installments and concerned about the landscape, environmental, and ecological impacts caused by the facilities owing to their proximity to cities, rural areas, and settlements. Visual impact issues can be effectively reduced with landscape visual and color analyses and additional hedge fences. In terms of environment, solar PV have a smaller impact on the environment compared to traditional power-generating facilities, and most of these impacts can be significantly lessened with measures such as deploying ventilation facilities, ARC, or sound-proofing devices. As for the land area requirement for solar PV installations, although some panels can be mounted on rooftops, some panels are still set on the ground, thus giving the impression that solar PV takes up a larger land area than traditional power generation facilities. However, traditional power generating facilities require large areas of land and the coal mine environments are difficult to restore. Ground-mounted solar PV systems are usually set on degraded land and consequently increase land use rate, and after a 20- to 30-year installation period, solar PV does not cause as much negative damage to the site land in terms of land use and occupation. If the solar PV site avoids sensitive areas during the planning stage and later deploys site management measures, research[32] shows that the bird diversity at the site is actually higher. This demonstrates that with the proper protection measures and thoughtful site selection, solar PV can help protect vulnerable habitats[41].

Solar PV installations in Taiwan have generated much public concern regarding landscape, environment, and ecological aspects. We found that lack of communication with the locals is the main cause of their concern. *The Directions for the Landscape and Ecological Environment Assessment of Ground-Mounted Photovoltaic Systems* was introduced by the Taiwanese government to lessen the impact on landscape and ecological environment caused by solar PV facilities in Taiwan and serve as a reference for solar PV operators in the areas of landscape and ecological environment protection. Many sites have followed *The Directions*' guidance and designed setups that blend in with local landscape features while protecting the ecosystem. Examples include the Taixi Offshore Island Emerging Industrial Zone in Yunlin (**Figure 1**) and the solar PV site in Chiayi's salt field (**Figure 2**). Still, although Taiwan's central government has introduced clear administrative guidelines on the distance between the sites and residential buildings as well as the planning and design of the setups, when compared with the regulations in other countries, Taiwan still lacks regulations and guidelines for communication with the local public as well as the flexibility for adjustments according to regional characteristics. If we are to improve Taiwan's overall solar PV environment and achieve our renewable energy development goals of 2025, 2030, and 2050, we would work harder in these areas. Hopefully, the conflicts between solar PV and landscape, environment, and habitats can be reduced through relevant research.

Figure 1: Aerial view of the solar PV site at the Taixi Offshore Island Emerging Industrial Zone in Yunlin[42]

Figure 2: Aerial view of the solar PV site in a salt field in Chiayi[43]

7 REFERENCE

[1] H. H. Pourasl, R. V. Barenji, and V. M. Khojastehnezhad, "Solar energy status in the world: A comprehensive review," Energy Reports, vol. 10. Elsevier Ltd, pp. 3474–3493, Nov. 01, 2023. doi: 10.1016/j.egyr.2023.10.022.

[2] International Energy Agency, "Renewables 2023 — Analysis and forecast to 2028," Jan. 2024.
[3] Central Intelligence Agency, "Taiwan-Country Summary." Accessed: Feb. 06, 2024. [Online]. Available: https://www.cia.gov/the-world-factbook/countries/taiwan/summaries
[4] TAIWAN CENTRAL WEATHER BUREAU, "CLIMATOLOGICAL DATA ANNUAL REPORT PART I–SURFACE DATA," 2022.
[5] International Monetary Fund, "Taiwan Province of China Datasets." Accessed: Feb. 06, 2024. [Online]. Available: https://www.imf.org/external/datamapper/profile/TWN
[6] Bureau of Energy, "Renewable Energy Generation Capacity," energy statistics monthly report.
[7] National Development Council et al., "General Introduction on the Taiwan 2050 Net Zero Emission Pathway and Strategy," Mar. 2022.
[8] Ministry of Economic Affairs, "12 Key Strategies." Accessed: Feb. 16, 2024. [Online]. Available: https://www.ndc.gov.tw/Content_List.aspx?n=733396F648BE2845
[9] Environmental Protection Administration, Executive Yuan, "Net-Zero Emissions Pathway 2023-2026 Outline Plan," Jan. 2023.
[10] Ministry of Economic Affairs, Renewable Energy Development Act. Taiwan, 2019.
[11] R. Ioannidis and D. Koutsoyiannis, "A review of land use, visibility and public perception of renewable energy in the context of landscape impact," Appl Energy, vol. 276, Oct. 2020, doi: 10.1016/j.apenergy.2020.115367.
[12] J. Cousse, "Still in love with solar energy? Installation size, affect, and the social acceptance of renewable energy technologies," Renewable and Sustainable Energy Reviews, vol. 145, Jul. 2021, doi: 10.1016/j.rser.2021.111107.
[13] L. Späth, "Large-scale photovoltaics? Yes please, but not like this! Insights on different perspectives underlying the trade-off between land use and renewable electricity development," Energy Policy, vol. 122, pp. 429–437, Nov. 2018, doi: 10.1016/j.enpol.2018.07.029.
[14] D. Turney and V. Fthenakis, "Environmental impacts from the installation and operation of large-scale solar power plants," Renewable and Sustainable Energy Reviews, vol. 15, no. 6. Elsevier Ltd, pp. 3261–3270, 2011. doi: 10.1016/j.rser.2011.04.023.
[15] Council of Europe, Council of Europe Landscape Convention. European Treaty Series, 2004, pp. 2–3.
[16] A. Scognamiglio, "'Photovoltaic landscapes': Design and assessment. A critical review for a new transdisciplinary design vision," Renewable and Sustainable Energy Reviews, vol. 55. Elsevier Ltd, pp. 629–661, Mar. 01, 2016. doi: 10.1016/j.rser.2015.10.072.
[17] A. Dhar, M. A. Naeth, P. D. Jennings, and M. Gamal El-Din, "Perspectives on environmental impacts and a land reclamation strategy for solar and wind energy systems," Science of the Total Environment, vol. 718. Elsevier B.V., May 20, 2020. doi: 10.1016/j.scitotenv.2019.134602.
[18] T. Tsoutsos, N. Frantzeskaki, and V. Gekas, "Environmental impacts from the solar energy technologies," Energy Policy, vol. 33, no. 3, pp. 289–296, Feb. 2005, doi: 10.1016/S0301-4215(03)00241-6.
[19] R. Chiabrando, E. Fabrizio, and G. Garnero, "The territorial and landscape impacts of photovoltaic systems: Definition of impacts and assessment of the glare risk," Renewable and Sustainable Energy Reviews, vol. 13, no. 9, pp. 2441–2451, Dec. 2009. doi: 10.1016/j.rser.2009.06.008.
[20] N. Sánchez-Pantoja, R. Vidal, and M. C. Pastor, "Aesthetic impact of solar energy systems," Renewable and Sustainable Energy Reviews, vol. 98. Elsevier Ltd, pp. 227–238, Dec. 01, 2018. doi: 10.1016/j.rser.2018.09.021.
[21] I. A. Kapetanakis, D. Kolokotsa, and E. A. Maria, "Parametric analysis and assessment of the photovoltaics' landscape integration: Technical and legal aspects," Renew Energy, vol. 67, pp. 207–214, 2014, doi: 10.1016/j.renene.2013.11.043.
[22] D. Oudes and S. Stremke, "Next generation solar power plants? A comparative analysis of frontrunner solar landscapes in Europe," Renewable and Sustainable Energy Reviews, vol. 145, Jul. 2021, doi: 10.1016/j.rser.2021.111101.
[23] M. Zeman, "Introduction to photovoltaic solar energy," Delft University of Technology, vol. 2, no. 6, 2003.
[24] A. Armstrong, S. Waldron, J. Whitaker, and N. J. Ostle, "Wind farm and solar park effects on plant-soil carbon cycling: Uncertain impacts of changes in ground-level microclimate," Glob Chang Biol, vol. 20, no. 6, pp. 1699–1706, 2014, doi: 10.1111/gcb.12437.
[25] X. Pang, U. Mörtberg, and N. Brown, "Energy models from a strategic environmental assessment perspective in an EU context - What is missing concerning renewables?," Renewable and Sustainable Energy Reviews, vol. 33, pp. 353–362, May 2014. doi: 10.1016/j.rser.2014.02.005.
[26] V. Bertsch, M. Hall, C. Weinhardt, and W. Fichtner, "Public acceptance and preferences related to renewable energy and grid expansion policy: Empirical insights for Germany," Energy, vol. 114, pp. 465–477, Nov. 2016, doi: 10.1016/j.energy.2016.08.022.
[27] L. A. Fernandez-Jimenez et al., "Site selection for new PV power plants based on their observability," Renew Energy, vol. 78, pp. 7–15, Jun. 2015, doi: 10.1016/j.renene.2014.12.063.
[28] S. Naspetti, S. Mandolesi, and R. Zanoli, "Using visual Q sorting to determine the impact of photovoltaic applications on the landscape," Land use policy, vol. 57, pp. 564–573, Nov. 2016, doi: 10.1016/j.landusepol.2016.06.021.
[29] D. Turney and V. Fthenakis, "Environmental impacts from the installation and operation of large-scale solar power plants," Renewable and Sustainable Energy Reviews, vol. 15, no. 6. Elsevier Ltd, pp. 3261–3270, 2011. doi: 10.1016/j.rser.2011.04.023.
[30] R. R. Hernandez et al., "Environmental impacts of utility-scale solar energy," Renewable and Sustainable Energy Reviews, vol. 29, pp. 766–779, 2014. doi: 10.1016/j.rser.2013.08.041.
[31] C. Jeal, V. Perold, C. L. Seymour, S. Ralston-Paton, and P. G. Ryan, "Utility-scale solar energy facilities – Effects on invertebrates in an arid environment," J Arid Environ, vol. 168, pp. 1–8, Sep. 2019, doi: 10.1016/j.jaridenv.2019.05.008.
[32] B. Hannah Montag, D. Guy Parker, T. Clarkson, and H. Montag, THE EFFECTS OF SOLAR FARMS ON LOCAL BIODIVERSITY: A COMPARATIVE STUDY.
[33] H. Blaydes, S. Potts, D. Whyatt, and A. Armstrong, "On-site floral resources and surrounding landscape characteristics impact pollinator biodiversity on solar parks," in EGU General Assembly Conference Abstracts, 2022, pp. EGU22-2180.

[34] Miaoli County Government, "Creating A Solar PV Site That Exists In Harmony With The Natural Environment, Miaoli County Government Hopes For 'Win-Win-Win' Solution For The Zhusen Solar Photovoltaic Site" Accessed: Mar. 18, 2024. [Online]. Available: https://www.miaoli.gov.tw/News_Content2.aspx?n=285&s=498443

[35] Leopard Cat Association of Taiwan, "Why Is Zhusen Solar Photovoltaic Site So Important? The Association Supervisor Clarifies The Context Of The Disputes And Case." Accessed: Mar. 18, 2024. [Online]. Available: https://www.twlcat.org/2022/06/2613/

[36] Bureau of Energy, MOEA, Principles for Landscape and Ecological Environment Assessments for Ground-mounted Solar Photovoltaic Facility Installation. Taiwan, 2023. Accessed: Feb. 19, 2024. [Online]. Available: https://www.moeaea.gov.tw/ECW/populace/Law/Content.aspx?menu_id=15558

[37] L. van B. J. N. C. F. C. W. D. P. N. C. G. Bennun, "Mitigating biodiversity impacts associated with solar and wind energy development," Gland, Cambridge, 2021. Accessed: Jun. 27, 2024. [Online]. Available: https://portals.iucn.org/library/node/49283

[38] Gemeenteblad van Lingewaard, "Beleidsregel van de gemeenteraad van de gemeente Lingewaard houdende regels omtrent Beleidskader zonne-energie," Lingewaard, Jan. 2020. Accessed: Jun. 25, 2024. [Online]. Available: https://zoek.officielebekendmakingen.nl/gmb-2020-14308.html#extrainformatie

[39] 여의도멋쟁이, "영주시 태양광 조례 - 발전시설의 개발행위 허가기준 [출처] 영주시 태양광 조례 - 발전시설의 개발행위 허가기준|작성자 여의도멋쟁이." Accessed: Jun. 27, 2024. [Online]. Available: https://blog.naver.com/PostView.naver?blogId=eovoice&logNo=222193682327&parentCategoryNo=&categoryNo=130&viewDate=&isShowPopularPosts=true&from=search

[40] 兵庫県庁, 太陽光発電施設等と地域環境との調和に関する条例. 日本, 2018. Accessed: Jun. 27, 2024. [Online]. Available: https://web.pref.hyogo.lg.jp/ks29/taiyoukoujourei.html

[41] SEIA, "Climate, Conservation, Community: Moving the Land Use Conversation from Conflict to Solution." Accessed: Mar. 25, 2024. [Online]. Available: https://www.seia.org/blog/climate-conservation-community-moving-land-use-conversation-conflict-solution

[42] Vena Energy, "Yunlin Emerging Power Plant." Accessed: Jun. 27, 2024. [Online]. Available: https://venaenergy.tw/project/e2/

[43] Vena Energy, "Chiayi Yizhu Power Plant." Accessed: Jun. 27, 2024. [Online]. Available: https://venaenergy.tw/project/mingus/

10.4229/EUPVSEC2025/5DV.3.41

Photovoltaic Development and Landscape Conflicts in Taiwan: Status and Resolutions

ITRI
Industrial Technology Research Institute

WANG, TZU-YA (DianaWang@itri.org.tw), WANG, CHIA-CHEN / Industrial Technology Research Institute (ITRI)

1 Introduction

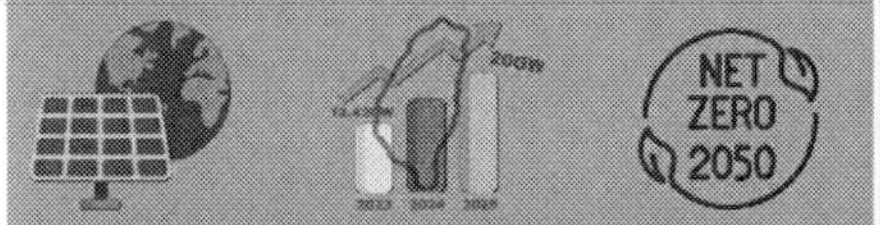

1,1552.3GW | 2025 PV goals | Emissions goals

BUT IMPACT

Landscape | Environment | Habitat

Literature review: Identify the landscape-related issues solar PV installations may encounter.

Case study: The situation of solar PV and landscape conflicts with Taiwan's cases.

Solution analysis: With forming the *Directions for the Landscape and Ecological Environment Assessment of Ground-Mounted Photovoltaic Systems.*

2 The Potential Impacts of Solar PV on the Landscape

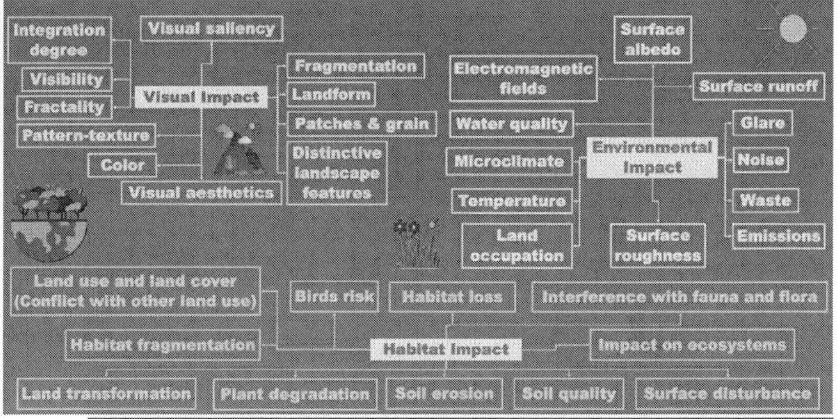

3 Cases of Conflict Between Solar PV and Landscape in Taiwan

Case of Visual Impact

A solar PV site in Pingtung

- The operators removed the original vegetation on the slopes to prepare the land.
- Located on the slopes along Highway leading to a popular tourist destination that affect the travelers' visual aesthetics.

(Source: https://sdgs.udn.com/sdgs/story/123880/7602490)

Case of Environmental Impact

A solar PV site in Tainan

- Close to a community, and residents protested against the possible light pollution, noise, and hot island effect.
- The noise tests onsite was within regulatory standards.
- Operators should communicate with the stakeholders better to minimize conflicts.

Case of Habitat Impact

A solar PV site in Miaoli

- With limited land and a dense population, recently, operators have turned to slopes.
- The area is the habitat of endangered animals such as leopard cats.
- An ecological association suggested that these areas should held local briefings.

(Source: https://conservation.forest.gov.tw/0002225)

4 How Does Taiwan Resolve the Conflicts Between Solar PV Development and Landscape?

Taiwan Ministry of Economic Affairs established *Directions for the Landscape and Ecological Environment Assessment of Ground-Mounted Photovoltaic Systems*

With cross-department expert meetings 2 times + Discussion meeting 1 time → May 1, 2018 announced

1. Targeting large-scale ground-mounted solar PV (**2MW ↑**).
2. Important regulations:
   1) Avoiding Class I environmentally sensitive areas.
   2) Considering local contour lines and maintaining the original site landform.
   3) Carrying out suitable greening with indigenous species as the primary.
   4) Requesting to conduct ecological surveys.
   5) Prohibiting cleaning agents.

With glare simulation + noise measurement + Discussion meetings 2 times → November 22, 2023 Revised

Continue to use the important previous version related to landscape and ecology.

Adding maintaining a certain distance between solar PV & buildings:

1) Fishery and electricity symbiosis models:

2) Non-compound models:

= Greening fence

glare simulation + noise measurement + Discussion meetings 3 times → March 31, 2025 Revised

Continue to use the previous version related to landscape and ecology, **but not limited to 2 MW.**

Modify the distance between solar PV & buildings:

1) 2ha ↑ : 20m or 15m+Greening fence
2) 2ha ↓ : 20m
3) Inverter: 20m

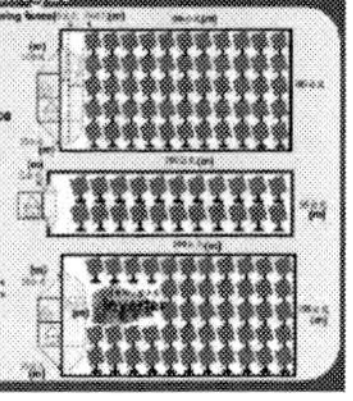

5 Discussion

Landscape conflict between solar PV cases in Taiwan, and overseas examples for reference.

Impact Category	Cases in Taiwan	Overseas examples for reference	Future suggestions
Visual	Site in Pingtung which is next to Highway	1. Lingewaard City, the Netherlands: take into account the existing landscape elements to integrate the facilities with the local landscape during the planning stage. And in farming areas must be supported by the locals. 2. Hyōgo Prefecture: Install the facility on the main road slope area, the slope angle must be less than 30°, and retained a percentage of green space.	1. Visual landscape simulation analysis should be carried out and pertinent response solutions should be proposed. 2. Communicate with the locals before development and obtain local government support.
Environment	Site in Tainan which is closed to a community	Refer to the self government ordinances of Japan and South Korea: It should be explained to the local public before development and the consent of residents should be obtained. 1. Hyōgo Prefecture, Japan: *Solar Power Generating Facilities and Local Environment Coordination Act* (太陽光発電施設等と地域環境との調和に関する条例) 2. Yeongju City, South Korea: The Standards for the Permission of Solar Power Generation Facilities Development (발전시설의개발행위허가기준)	1. Prior to planning, the operator, government, and residents need to communicate better. 2. Energy-related authorities should promote correct information related to solar photovoltaics more actively.
Habitat	Site in Miaoli which near the habitat of endangered animals	According to *the Guidance on the Solar Power Generation Environment released*(太陽光発電の環境配慮ガイドライン) by Japan's Ministry of Environment, the operator should learn more about the local habitat and wildlife lifestyle through literature studies, interviews, field surveys, and other methods before development.	1. Avoid Class 1 sensitive areas protected by law. 2. The operator should start ecological monitoring before development and carry out conservation work in the surrounding area.

Reference

1. D. Turney and V. Fthenakis, "Environmental impacts from the installation and operation of large-scale solar power plants," Renewable and Sustainable Energy Reviews, vol. 15, no. 6. Elsevier Ltd, pp. 3261–3270, 2011. doi: 10.1016/j.rser.2011.04.023.
2. Council of Europe, Council of Europe Landscape Convention. European Treaty Series, 2004, pp. 2–3.
3. A. Scognamiglio, "'Photovoltaic landscapes': Design and assessment. A critical review for a new transdisciplinary design vision," Renewable and Sustainable Energy Reviews, vol. 55. Elsevier Ltd, pp. 629–661, Mar. 01, 2016. doi: 10.1016/j.rser.2015.10.072.
4. A. Dhar, M. A. Naeth, P. D. Jennings, and M. Gamal El-Din, "Perspectives on environmental impacts and a land reclamation strategy for solar and wind energy systems," Science of the Total Environment, vol. 718. Elsevier B.V., May 20, 2020. doi: 10.1016/j.scitotenv.2019.134602.
5. T. Tsoutsos, N. Frantzeskaki, and V. Gekas, "Environmental impacts from the solar energy technologies," Energy Policy, vol. 33, no. 3, pp. 289–296, Feb. 2005, doi: 10.1016/S0301-4215(03)00241-6.
6. R. Chiabrando, E. Fabrizio, and G. Garnero, "The territorial and landscape impacts of photovoltaic systems: Definition of impacts and assessment of the glare risk," Renewable and Sustainable Energy Reviews, vol. 13, no. 9, pp. 2441–2451, Dec. 2009, doi: 10.1016/j.rser.2009.06.008.
7. N. Sánchez-Pantoja, R. Vidal, and M. C. Pastor, "Aesthetic impact of solar energy systems," Renewable and Sustainable Energy Reviews, vol. 98. Elsevier Ltd, pp. 227–238, Dec. 01, 2018. doi: 10.1016/j.rser.2018.09.021.
8. I. A. Kapetanakis, D. Kolokotsa, and E. A. Maria, "Parametric analysis and assessment of the photovoltaics' landscape integration: Technical and legal aspects," Renew Energy, vol. 67, pp. 207–214, 2014, doi: 10.1016/j.renene.2013.11.043.
9. D. Oudes and S. Stremke, "Next generation solar power plants? A comparative analysis of frontrunner solar landscapes in Europe," Renewable and Sustainable Energy Reviews, vol. 145, Jul. 2021, doi: 10.1016/j.rser.2021.111101.
10. M. Zeman, "Introduction to photovoltaic solar energy," Delft University of Technology, vol. 2, no. 6, 2003.
11. A. Armstrong, S. Waldron, J. Whitaker, and N. J. Ostle, "Wind farm and solar park effects on plant-soil carbon cycling: Uncertain impacts of changes in ground-level microclimate," Glob Chang Biol, vol. 20, no. 6, pp. 1699–1706, 2014, doi: 10.1111/gcb.12437.
12. Gemeenteblad van Lingewaard, "Beleidsregel van de gemeenteraad van de gemeente Lingewaard houdende regels omtrent Beleidskader zonne-energie," Lingewaard, Jan. 2020. Accessed: Jun. 25, 2024. [Online]. Available: https://zoek.officielebekendmakingen.nl/gmb-2020-14308.html#extrainformatie

Acknowledgments

The work was supported by the Energy Administration, Ministry of Economic Affairs, Taiwan, through financial funding as well as administrative and technical guidance.

6 Conclusion

Solar PV installation ↑

- **Visual Impact Solution** → 1. landscape visual and color analyses 2. Adding hedge fences
- **Environmental Impact Solution** → 1. Deploying ARC, ventilation, or sound-proofing devices 2. setting on degraded land and increase land use rate
- **Habitat Impact Solution** → Avoiding sensitive areas and deploying site management measures an help protect vulnerable habitats.

Taiwan has Revised the *Directions for the Landscape and Ecological Environment Assessment of Ground-Mounted Photovoltaic Systems* → designing with local landscape and protecting the ecosystem & maintaining distance from buildings

Taiwan lacks of:
1. The regulations for communication with the local.
2. The flexibility for adjustments according to region.

BREEZE PROJECT: ADVANCING PV IMPLEMENTATION IN BUILDING RENOVATIONS

Duygu Celik*[1], Johannes Stierstorfer[1], Claire Morin[2], Thomas Garabetian[2], Cristian Pozza[3], Francesco Babich[3], Akshit Gupta[3], Giobertti Raul Morantes Quintana[3], Laura Maturi[3], Ulrich Oberegger Filippi[3], Daniele Antonucci[3], Pawel Wargocki[4], Andrei Vladimir Litiu[5], Nicolandrea Calabrese[6], Giovanni Murano[6], Francesca Caffari[6], Jerzy Kwiatkowski[7], Katarzyna Rajkiewicz[7], Olivier Greslou[8], Dominique Caccavelli[8]

[1]WIP Renewable Energies, [2]Solar Power Europe, [3]EURAC Research, [4]Technical University of Denmark, [5]EPB Center, [6]ENEA - Italian National Agency for New Technologies, Energy and Sustainable Economic Development, [7]NAPE - National Energy Conservation Agency, [8]CSTB - Scientific and Technical Centre for Building

WIP Renewable Energies, Sylvenstein Strasse 2, Munich, Germany (*duygu.celik@wip-munich.de)

ABSTRACT

BREEZE (Building Renovation Efforts for Zero Emission Buildings) aims to accelerate the integration of solar photovoltaic (PV) systems into new and renovated buildings across EU Member States in line with the Energy Performance of Buildings Directive (EPBD). The project supports national implementation of the Solar Mandate by addressing key technical, financial, and regulatory barriers to large-scale PV deployment.

BREEZE focuses on the effective use of rooftop PV, building-integrated photovoltaics (BIPV), and balcony PV to improve building energy performance while maintaining architectural quality. By developing standardized tools and practical frameworks, the project promotes cost-effective PV integration in renovation projects and strengthens the link between energy efficiency and on-site renewable generation.

Pilot activities in Poland, Italy, and France will test PV deployment strategies under different building types, climates, and regulatory conditions, generating insights applicable across the EU. In parallel, BREEZE advances energy performance assessment methods to ensure compliance with EPBD targets and Indoor Environmental Quality (IEQ) standards.

Through capacity-building activities, policy guidance, and best practice development, the project equips policymakers, designers, and industry professionals with the knowledge and tools needed to support a coordinated, sustainable, and scalable approach to solar energy integration in Europe's building sector.

Keywords: Building Renovation, Energy Performance of Buildings Directive (EPBD), Building-Integrated Photovoltaics (BIPV), Solar Mandate

1 AIM AND APPROACH

BREEZE project aims to optimize the implementation of the Energy Performance of Buildings Directive (EPBD)[1] with a focus on supporting the Solar Mandate, which requires the integration of solar photovoltaic (PV) systems in new and renovated buildings across EU Member States (MSs). The project aims to identify, address, and overcome key technical, financial, and regulatory barriers that hinder the deployment of solar PV technologies in the building sector, thereby facilitating the large-scale integration of renewable energy solutions into Europe's building stock.

BREEZE follows a multi-phase, data-driven methodology designed to generate actionable results at both technical and policy level. The approach starts with identifying Member States' needs and challenges regarding Solar Mandate implementation, followed by the development of analytical frameworks, indicators, and best practices to assess PV potential and deployment scenarios. Pilot activities in Poland, France, and Italy will test these methodologies, while capacity-building and stakeholder engagement will ensure the long-term adoption of project outcomes.

Project's PV-specific objectives include supporting the Solar Mandate[2] implementation at national level and promoting the integration of PV and BIPV (Building Integrated Photovoltaics) into renovation projects. Through this, BREEZE will help Member States align renovation practices with EU sustainability goals by developing cost-optimal renovation scenarios and regulatory guidelines for effective PV adoption.

2 SCIENTIFIC INNOVATION AND RELEVANCE

The scientific innovation of BREEZE lies in its approach to quantify and contextualize the potential of solar PV integration within the broader framework of building energy performance. The project combines technical analysis, geographic data, and economic

[1] https://commission.europa.eu/news-and-media/news/focus-energy-efficiency-buildings-2020-02-17_en

[2] https://energy.ec.europa.eu/topics/energy-efficiency/energy-performance-buildings/energy-performance-buildings-directive/solar-energy-buildings_en

modelling to estimate the potential for solar deployment across different building types and European climates, offering policymakers a comprehensive understanding of how the Solar Mandate can be effectively implemented.

An important focus is the development of a data-driven decision-support framework that integrates solar PV potential into building performance assessment methodologies. This framework will include parameters such as local irradiation, building typology, grid connection, energy consumption patterns, and investment costs. By introducing key performance indicators (KPIs) for solar PV and BIPV integration, the framework aims to enable a transparent evaluation of energy, economic, and environmental benefits, tailored to national contexts. These insights will directly inform future policy development and investment strategies related to building decarbonization.

In parallel, BREEZE will place a strong emphasis on BIPV systems, which merge architectural functionality with on-site renewable generation. The project will assess BIPV's potential to improve energy self-sufficiency, reduce electricity demand, and contribute to long-term sustainability goals, while preserving aesthetic and structural integrity. The results will support the creation of performance benchmarks and deployment scenarios for BIPV systems that reflect different climatic, technical, and socio-economic conditions.

3 SOLAR PV DEPLOYMENT AND RENOVATION FRAMEWORK

Building on its base, BREEZE is developing a comprehensive framework for solar PV deployment within building renovation strategies, and linking technical potential, economic feasibility, and policy applicability. The framework aims to demonstrate how solar PV can be systematically integrated into building retrofit processes. This approach ultimately will help Member States and industry actors meet the goals of the Energy Performance of Buildings Directive (EPBD) while accelerating the shift toward a greener building stock.

At its core, this framework connects energy efficiency improvements with solar energy generation. BREEZE will produce detailed renovation case studies that explore PV integration under a wide range of conditions, including different building types (residential, commercial, and public), architectural forms, climatic zones, and energy consumption profiles. These studies will assess both traditional rooftop PV systems and building-integrated photovoltaic (BIPV) applications, as well as façade and balcony-mounted PV, providing a full picture of how solar technologies can be adapted to urban and rural contexts.

The renovation scenarios will consider future energy needs such as the electrification of transport and heating through electric vehicles (EVs) and heat pumps, recognizing the increasing role of self-consumption and demand-side management in modern buildings. Each scenario will be assessed in terms of cost-effectiveness, energy yield, grid interaction, and occupant comfort, using performance indicators consistent with EPBD requirements and Indoor Environmental Quality (IEQ) standards.

These case studies will not only quantify PV potential but will also provide guidance for decision-makers on how to identify cost-optimal renovation pathways. By combining energy performance simulations with local solar resource data and economic modeling, BREEZE will show how the integration of solar PV can lower energy demand, reduce operating costs, and improve building resilience. The results will feed directly into national and regional planning instruments, providing concrete evidence for policymakers and investors.

An important outcome of this work will be the development of best practice guidelines to help Member States implement the Solar Mandate at national level. These guidelines will include a combination of regulatory, technical, and procedural recommendations. Regulatory best practices will focus on adapting building codes and permitting rules to facilitate solar installations during renovation, ensuring that PV systems, including BIPV, are considered from the design phase. The guidance will also address technical standards, safety requirements, and architectural integration, helping to align innovation with practical implementation.

In addition, BREEZE will compile country specific best practices based on lessons from the project's pilot regions (Poland, Italy, and France) and other EU experiences that its project partners have. These examples will cover construction permits, grid connection procedures, and inter-agency coordination, offering real insights into how permitting and administrative processes can be simplified to support the broader uptake of solar technologies.

To support on-the-ground implementation, the framework will include practical reference materials for professionals, such as rooftop PV installation examples, user-friendly checklists, and design guidelines tailored for renovation projects. These resources are intended for a broad range of stakeholders such as installers, engineers, architects, and building owners, helping ensure safe, efficient, and compliant PV integration. Special attention will be given to BIPV applications, providing recommendations on component selection, mounting solutions, and maintenance practices that maintain both energy performance and visual quality.

By combining technical baseline with policy relevance, the PV deployment and renovation framework will serve as a bridge between high-level solar policy objectives and practical implementation at building level. It aims to make PV integration in renovation projects both achievable and scalable, equipping European Member States with the knowledge, methods, and examples needed to turn the Solar Mandate into real, visible progress across Europe's building sector.

4 EXPECTED IMPACTS

BREEZE will have a practical impact on how Member States plan and implement the Solar Mandate under the Energy Performance of Buildings Directive (EPBD). The project will provide clear tools, data, and guidelines to help national and local authorities integrate solar PV systems in both new constructions and renovation projects. These materials will demonstrate how combining energy efficiency measures with solar generation can reduce energy use, cut emissions, and improve the overall performance of buildings in a realistic and cost-effective way.

By analysing data from various building types, climates, and socio-economic contexts, BREEZE will give policymakers a comprehensive understanding of where and how solar PV can deliver the greatest benefits. This will support the preparation of national Solar Mandate implementation plans that reflect local conditions, such as sunlight availability, grid capacity, electricity prices, and the existing building stock, while ensuring consistency with EU energy and climate targets. The pilot projects in Poland, Italy, and France will play a key role in testing these methods under real conditions, producing lessons that can be transferred to other Member States.

Beyond the policy level, BREEZE will also help the construction and renovation sectors adopt solar technologies more informed. Through applied case studies, the project will illustrate how rooftop, façade, and building-integrated PV systems can enhance energy performance, increase self-consumption, and reduce pressure on electricity networks. The tools developed will assist architects, engineers, and building owners in selecting and designing PV systems that match their technical needs and financial possibilities.

5 LONG-TERM OUTLOOK AND CONCLUSIONS

In addition to its technical and analytical contributions, BREEZE places strong emphasis on training and knowledge sharing. The project will engage national authorities, local governments, and industry professionals through workshops, practical guides, and policy dialogues. These activities will ensure that the knowledge and experience gained within BREEZE can be distributed and applied well beyond the project's lifetime. By creating a shared understanding among regulators, installers, and designers, BREEZE will help bridge the gap between policy and on-the-ground implementation.

In the longer term, BREEZE aims to make solar energy integration a standard element of building renovation across Europe. The project's work on harmonized regulations, simplified permitting, and well-documented best practices will remove key barriers that currently slow down PV deployment. Its emphasis on cost-effective and scalable renovation solutions will help Member States meet their EPBD targets while reducing reliance on fossil fuels and improving building resilience.

Ultimately, BREEZE contributes to a more consistent approach to solar deployment in the European building stock. By linking technical knowledge with practical policy tools, it will support the creation of national strategies that are realistic, flexible, and aligned with EU objectives. In doing so, the project will not only increase the integration of solar PV systems but also help make Europe's buildings cleaner and more efficient for the energy transition towards a climate-neutral future.

6 ACKNOLWEDGEMENTS

This project is funded by the European Union, in the frame of LIFE Programme. Views and opinions expressed are however those of the authors only and do not necessarily reflect those of the European Union. Neither the European Union nor the granting authority can be held responsible for them.

INTEGRATING ENERGY POLICY INTO SPATIAL PLANNING FRAMEWORKS: A STUDY OF TAIWAN'S APPROACH

Tzu Han Hung
Industrial Technology Research Institute (ITRI)
14F.-1, No.248, Sec. 3, Nanjing E. Rd., Songshan Dist., Taipei City 105403, Taiwan, R.O.C.

ABSTRACT: Taiwan faces the dual challenges of limited land availability and the urgent need to transition to renewable energy in pursuit of its 2050 net-zero carbon emissions target. This study explores how Taiwan can effectively integrate energy policy—particularly solar power development—into its spatial planning system. Despite recent legal advances, such as the 2016 Spatial Planning Act and the subsequent National Spatial Plan (2018), existing mechanisms still fall short in resolving land use conflicts between energy infrastructure and other sectoral priorities. Current energy-related spatial plans often lack specific siting criteria or actionable implementation strategies, especially at the local level. To address this policy gap, the study reviews solar development governance models from four high-density countries—Japan, India, South Korea, and the Netherlands—each demonstrating successful integration of spatial and energy planning. Comparative insights reveal key strategies: Japan emphasizes community-driven implementation within a hierarchical planning system; India promotes state-level autonomy supported by central energy goals; South Korea demonstrates close policy alignment across planning levels; and the Netherlands exemplifies integration through a robust permitting and environmental planning system. The paper argues that Taiwan should establish a more effective framework that enables cross-sectoral coordination, clarifies site selection principles, strengthens local government participation, and encourages multifunctional land use such as agrivoltaics. It highlights the opportunity presented by Taiwan's upcoming revision of county and municipal spatial plans, as well as the development of the Solar Power Land Use White Paper, to embed spatial considerations more concretely into renewable energy strategies. Ultimately, the study concludes that a successful integration model must include clear spatial guidance, legal mechanisms for coordination, adaptive policy tools, and stakeholder engagement processes. These recommendations serve not only to improve Taiwan's internal planning coherence but also to contribute to global knowledge on renewable energy integration in densely populated, land-constrained contexts.
Keywords: Spatial Planning Integration, Renewable Energy Policy, Solar PV

1 INTRODUCTION

Taiwan, an island nation situated on the western edge of the Pacific Ocean, faces unique challenges in land resource management. Its territory of 36,197 square kilometers accommodates approximately 23 million people, resulting in a population density of 640 people per square kilometer. Beyond meeting residential needs, Taiwan must balance industrial development—particularly in the technology-intensive sector with major players such as TSMC and Vanguard International Semiconductor—while addressing food security, climate change adaptation, and disaster prevention concerns. Through the implementation of the Spatial Planning Act of 2016 and the subsequent approval of the National Spatial Plan (2018) [1] and 18 municipal/county spatial plans (2021), Taiwan has established a comprehensive spatial planning and management framework. This framework progressively integrates various sectoral development plans, including housing, commercial, agricultural, energy, water resources, and disaster management policies, coordinating them at the policy level to foster harmonious development with minimal conflicts.

In alignment with global net-zero carbon emissions initiatives, Taiwan enacted the Renewable Energy Development Act in 2009 and established subsequent subsidiary regulations to promote energy security and green economy objectives. Under this legislation, the Ministry of Economic Affairs (MOEA) set an ambitious target of 20GW solar power generation by 2025, initially planning for 3GW from rooftop installations and 17GW from ground-mounted systems [2]. Recent implementation assessments have led to adjusted targets of 8GW for rooftop installations and 12GW for ground-mounted systems. These policy directives are being incorporated into the forthcoming White Paper on Land Use for Renewable Energy Development: Solar Power, which aims to integrate with national and local spatial plans to ensure comprehensive energy development considerations, establish appropriate site selection criteria and planning design principles, and mitigate intersectoral conflicts and coordination challenges with local development objectives.

The brief two-year period between the implementation of the Spatial Planning Act and the approval of the National Spatial Plan has limited the effective integration of various sectoral development proposals into spatial planning. The energy policy component of the National Spatial Plan, for instance, merely references the 2025 power generation targets without providing substantive guidance on development locations or suitable installation types. Moreover, it fails to grant local governments sufficient autonomy in implementation. The current National Spatial Plan also lacks effective mechanisms to resolve conflicts when locations designated by different sectoral policies overlap, particularly in establishing development priorities or facilitating composite development opportunities.

This paper examines countries that, like Taiwan, successfully manage solar power facility generation despite limited land resources and high population density, specifically focusing on Japan, India, South Korea, and the Netherlands. Through analysis of their spatial and sectoral planning systems, particularly examining how different levels of spatial planning interface with sectoral plans, this study aims to understand how these nations optimize solar power development within constrained territories. These insights will inform Taiwan's strategy to achieve its policy objectives while contributing to the global initiative toward 2050 net-zero carbon emissions.

2 SPATIAL PLANNING AND LAND USE CONTROL MEASURES FOR SOLAR ENERGY POLICY

2.1 Sectoral spatial plans in the spatial planning system

Taiwan's current spatial planning and land use control legislation is based on the Regional Planning Act. The planning and management framework follows a top-down hierarchy: National Spatial Development Strategy, Regional Plans, County/Municipal Comprehensive Development Plans, and Urban Plans. Although the National Spatial Development Strategy exists at the highest level, it lacks legal effectiveness and thus holds no substantive spatial planning and control authority. Consequently, within Taiwan's overall planning system, the Regional Plan serves as the highest-level statutory spatial plan, providing spatial planning guidance and control authority to municipalities and counties. Most sectoral plans—such as tourism development, technical industry introduction, and agricultural policy implementation—are generally implemented according to relevant control regulations after their policy plans receive Executive Yuan approval, rather than being integrated into spatial planning. This excludes town building plans, large-scale industrial park development, and urban plan expansion and renewal projects.

Following the Ministry of the Interior's announcement of the revised National Regional Plan on May 16, 2017, a "Regional Sectoral Plan" chapter was added to incorporate policy and plan contents approved by the Executive Yuan. However, this addition still lacks site selection principles and fails to identify development scopes, making it difficult for local governments to guide appropriate land use and balance conflicts between different sectoral policies.

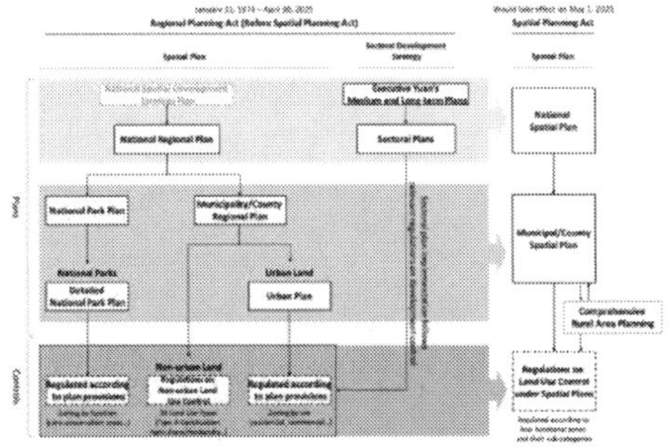

Figure 1: Spatial Planning System in Taiwan

In response to climate change and the needs for environmental conservation and cultural asset preservation, while promoting reasonable resource and industrial allocation and strengthening national land integration management mechanisms, Taiwan initiated a series of legal framework operations after enacting the Spatial Planning Act in 2016. This initiative aims to establish comprehensive legal management and a new national spatial planning system by May 2025. The system will encompass planning and management from mountains to oceans, urban to rural areas, and national parks to general development areas, integrating existing systems including national park plans, urban plans, and various Executive Yuan-approved sectoral policy plans to construct a more comprehensive and balanced development framework.

Given the extensive planning scope and broad policy content, spatial planning will be implemented at three levels. First, the central government (Ministry of the Interior) announced and implemented the National Spatial Plan in 2018, establishing unified principles for designating land functional zones. Land classification is based on carrying capacity, conservation sensitivity, and disaster potential, while also presenting overall policy development goals. Following this national guidance, local governments develop county/municipal spatial plans, considering local conditions to fine-tune land functional zone designations and establish suitable development directions and specific implementation measures [3]. At the town, township, and district levels, comprehensive rural area planning is developed under county/municipal spatial plan guidance. This planning responds to local settlement conditions and development context, as well as local industry needs, to formulate future development visions and spatial configurations. These local-level plans, in turn, inform and may lead to adjustments in the county/municipal spatial plans and enable the development of distinctive land use control measures that reflect local conditions, thereby facilitating autonomous planning and governance.

To prevent conflicts between ministerial policies, Articles 9 and 10 of the Spatial Planning Act mandate that national and county/municipal spatial plans must integrate the policies, goals, current development status, future potential capacity, and locations of various sectors. Article 4 of the Spatial Planning Act Enforcement Rules specifies that sectoral spatial plans must include, at minimum, development strategies and locations for policy plans. According to the County/Municipal Spatial Plan Planning Manual published by the Ministry of the Interior, development strategies must address policy implementation issue analysis, response methods, and related public facility or construction planning. Development locations should consider plans and locations already approved by the Executive Yuan, central ministries, and local governments. These plans should provide supply-demand gap analysis and response measures for different sectoral policy items, including housing, industry, transportation, sewerage facilities, long-term care facilities, medical care, energy, water, and other important public facilities.[3]

As shown in Table I, sectoral plans in the National Spatial Plan can be categorized into four types:

(1) "Facility Construction Plans" - such as fishing port development, specific industrial park expansion plans, and railway underground projects in specific areas, which have clear development sites and scales, representing areas of active government investment and construction.
(2) "Development Guidance Areas" - plans that primarily involve government incentives and guidance for private enterprise investment, without clearly defined policy boundaries, requiring coordination with other laws, subsidies, or related supporting measures for implementation.
(3) "Legal and Operational Mechanism Revisions" and
(4) "Subsidy and Guidance Measures" - both categories represent government administrative planning with no spatial planning content.

This classification reveals that only the first category

of sectoral plans fully complies with the guidance of the Spatial Planning Act, its Enforcement Rules, and the Spatial Planning Manual by providing specific development scale and location details. The second type of sectoral plans, which guide industrial development, typically have development targets but lack specific site locations. With modifications, these could comply with relevant regulations. The third and fourth types of sectoral plans, having no spatial planning elements, cannot fulfill the regulatory requirements.

Table I: Classification of Public Facilities Plans in Taiwan's National Spatial Plan

Subsector	Responsible Authority	Plan Types A	B	C	D
Sewerage	National Land Management Agency	✓		✓	✓
Environmental Protection	Ministry of Environment				✓
Long-term Care Facilities	Ministry of Health and Welfare (MOHW)			✓	✓
Medical Facilities	MOHW			✓	
Education	Ministry of Education			✓	✓
Energy	Bureau of Energy	✓	✓	✓	✓
Water	Water Resources Agency	✓			

Plan Types:
A: Facility Construction Plans
B: Development Guidance Areas
C: Legal and Operational Mechanism Revisions
D: Subsidy and Guidance Measures

Among the sectoral plans classified in the National Spatial Plan, only three sectors fall under the "Development Guidance Areas" type: manufacturing, mining and soil/stone extraction, and energy facilities. The manufacturing sector plan involves site inventory and supporting measure development based on the "White Paper on Industrial Land Use," which guides industries toward suitable locations. For mining and soil/stone extraction, the sector plan is based on the mineral resource distribution inventory conducted by the Bureau of Mines, Ministry of Economic Affairs. After local governments complete these sectoral plans identifying suitable mining locations, the land use controls in spatial planning will be adjusted to accommodate the development areas specified in the sectoral plans.

The energy facilities sector plan is more complex, encompassing multiple energy types including traditional nuclear, thermal, and hydroelectric power facilities, as well as various renewable energy sources. This diversity makes it challenging for the National Spatial Plan to designate specific development locations due to the varying requirements for site selection and planning across different energy types. For instance, some counties have implemented stricter land use control measures and developed energy conservation and alternative energy programs in response to existing nuclear and thermal power facilities within their jurisdictions. In terms of alternative energy development, counties are currently prioritizing solar and wind power deployment, working to identify potential development locations and installation types.

The solar power development guidance in the National Spatial Plan follows the "Two-Year Solar Power Promotion Plan" [2], prioritizing rooftop installations on public buildings, factories, agricultural facilities, and other structures. For ground-mounted solar power installations, the six counties and cities shown in Table II are located in Taiwan's southwestern region, which receives more sunlight than other areas and possesses more undeveloped and underutilized land. These areas include idle salt industry lands, severe land subsidence areas, water bodies, sealed landfills, and contaminated lands, which are designated as priority development areas. However, the spatial plan does not provide comprehensive location guidelines or planning design principles, limiting the sector plan's effectiveness in implementing spatial planning guidance functions.

The salt industry lands serve as an illustrative example. Taiwan's southwestern coast contains numerous areas previously designated for salt production, some of which are adjacent to settlements or near migratory bird habitats. Not all these areas are suitable for renewable energy facility development. However, due to the lack of clear guidance in the National Spatial Plan, there is no framework to guide developers toward suitable locations or formulate response strategies for local ecological and social issues.

As demonstrated by the ground-mounted solar development guidance in the counties shown in Table II, the absence of suitable location guidance and clear development directions in the National Spatial Plan has led to varying approaches among counties. Some jurisdictions, like Changhua County, cannot delineate locations suitable for solar power development. Other counties largely adhere to the areas specified in the National Spatial Plan, such as garbage landfills and contaminated lands, as designated areas for ground-mounted solar power installations.

Table II: Development Guidance for Ground-mounted Solar Power in Six Southwestern Counties' Spatial Plans

City / County	Designated Development Sites
Changhua County	1. Agriculturally unsuitable areas 2. Aquavoltaic zones
Yunlin County	1. Agriculturally unsuitable areas 2. Aquavoltaic zones 3. Offshore industrial zones
Chiayi County	1. Coastal public salt industry lands 2. Public landfills 3. Agriculturally unsuitable areas 4. Aquavoltaic zones
Tainan City	1. Salt industry lands 2. Closed or rehabilitating landfills 3. General lands (urban agricultural zones / non-urban lands) 4. Agriculturally unsuitable areas 5. Aquavoltaic zones
Kaohsiung City	1. Agriculturally unsuitable areas 2. Aquavoltaic zones
Pingtung County	Revitalization of severe land subsidence areas

2.2 Functional Zones and Land Use Control Measures

Following the National Spatial Plan's guidance, marine and terrestrial areas are divided into different functional zones based on conservation, utilization, and management needs, as well as land use patterns and resource conditions. These zones include:

10.4229/EUPVSEC2025/5DV.3.43

- National Conservation Areas (protecting terrestrial and marine ecological resources)
- Marine Resource Areas
- Agricultural Development Areas (focusing on maintaining agricultural, forestry, and fishery production)
- Urban-Rural Development Areas (for population concentration and diverse uses such as commercial and industrial activities)

Within these four functional zones, further detailed classifications are made based on environmental conditions and development carrying capacity. [4]

As shown in Figure 2, draft functional zone maps for six counties in southwestern Taiwan are currently under review pending approval. Analysis of the draft zoning results reveals four distinct zones:

(1) From Changhua County to northern Tainan City: This region shows concentrated agricultural production, with land primarily classified as Type 1 Agri. Development Areas. It emphasizes preserving agricultural production functions and maintaining food crop capabilities, mainly permitting uses related to agricultural production, processing, storage, and marketing.

(2) Eastern mountainous areas of the six counties: These are primarily designated as Type 1 and Type 2 National Conservation Areas, prioritizing ecological and natural resource conservation. In areas with steep slopes and environmentally sensitive resources, only public facilities or other essential life-supporting functions are permitted. In forest and hillside areas with lower environmental sensitivity, moderate flexibility in land use is permitted, such as tourism and recreation facilities. Areas on hillsides used for fruit trees, tea plantations, and other agricultural purposes are designated as Type 3 Agricultural Development Areas to support hillside agricultural development.

(3) Western coastal areas of Tainan City and Kaohsiung City: This region serves as the main population concentration area, with land designated as Type 1 Urban-Rural Development Areas to support urban functions and industrial-commercial development.

(4) Areas between urban areas and hillsides: These are designated as Type 2 Agricultural Development Areas, allowing diverse agricultural use and partial conversion to non-agricultural uses. [5], [6], [7], [8], [9], [10]

According to the draft Regulations for Land Use Controls in National Spatial Plans released for public review in late April 2024, land use controls will be implemented based on functional zone classifications and the development goals established in local governments' spatial plans. For example:

- In Agricultural Development Areas, aquavoltaic development is primarily regulated as "aquaculture facilities," with solar installations classified as auxiliary facilities and thus exempted from spatial planning authority approval.
- In Urban-Rural Development Areas, ground-mounted solar installations require written approval from spatial planning authorities to prevent adverse impacts on rural settlements.
- For developments exceeding certain scale thresholds, solar facilities must undergo public participation procedures, including public exhibitions and hearings, before obtaining approval from the spatial planning review committee.

Article 23 of the Spatial Planning Act authorizes local governments to establish their own control measures based on the local development context. These measures, specified in the Land Use Guidelines chapter of county/municipal spatial plans, take precedence once approved by the Ministry of the Interior.

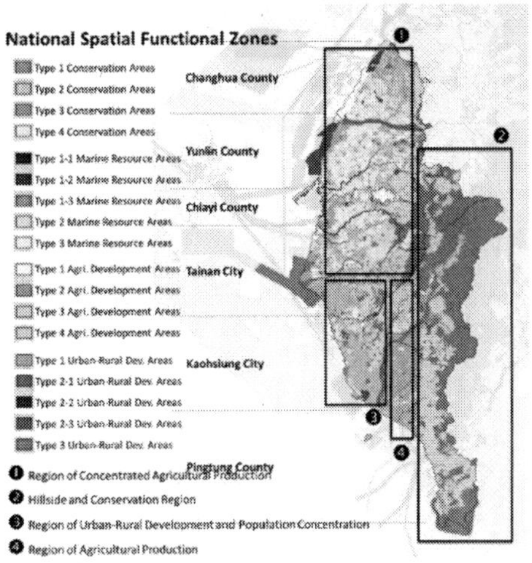

Figure 2: Draft Map of National Spatial Functional Zones for Six Counties in Southwestern Taiwan

3 SOLAR ENERGY DEVELOPMENT POLICY

3.1 Solar Energy Types and Distribution

In response to the global emphasis on energy conservation and renewable energy transition toward net-zero emissions, Taiwan has progressively developed relevant policies. The implementation of the Renewable Energy Development Act and its subsidiary regulations in 2009 aimed to achieve energy security, green economy, and environmental sustainability goals. To promote solar power development, the Executive Yuan approved the "Two-Year Solar Power Promotion Plan" in 2016, focusing on both rooftop and ground-mounted installations. The plan prioritizes rooftop installations sequentially on public buildings, factories, agricultural facilities, and other buildings, while targeting ground-mounted facilities in idle salt industry lands, Class 1 groundwater management zones where groundwater extraction for irrigation is not feasible, water bodies, and closed landfills. [2]

To expand solar power policy implementation, the Renewable Energy Development Act was partially amended in 2019, adopting the principle of "reduce coal, increase gas, phase out nuclear, expand green energy" as its long-term direction. The amendment stipulates that by 2025, renewable energy capacity should reach 29GW, with solar power accounting for 20GW, approximately 70% of the total renewable energy capacity. The Plan for Achieving 6.5GW Solar Power Target, released in the same year, emphasized three main pillars: requiring industrial park development projects to install solar power systems and major electricity users to fulfill environmental sustainability commitments as part of their corporate social responsibilities; establishing joint central-local government guidelines to expedite development review and dispute resolution; and promoting the integration of solar development with farming, animal husbandry, and aquaculture facilities, emphasizing multiple-use principles to address concerns about solar power encroaching on agricultural land.

Following these policy implementation principles, the current solar power development distribution in Taiwan is shown in Table III. Nearly 3,000 hectares of development area is located in Type 2 Agricultural Development Areas, designated for agricultural production and diversified development. Approximately 70% consists of green energy facilities integrated with agricultural operations, primarily focusing on aquavoltaic systems. The remaining 30% comprises ground-mounted solar power installations. Under future National Spatial Plan controls, only developments exceeding certain scale thresholds will granted with use permits.

Table III: Distribution of Solar Power Installations by National Spatial Functional Zone Classification in Taiwan

National Functional Zone & Zone Type		Area (Hectares)	Percentage of Total Area
National Conservation Area	Type 1	4.621	0.07%
	Type 2	40.255	0.61%
	Type 4	72.881	1.10%
Agricultural Development Area	Type 1	2,139.660	32.41%
	Type 2	2,984.546	45.21%
	Type 3	11.324	2.90%
	Type 4	0.060	0.00%
	Type 5	12.348	0.19%
Urban-Rural Development Area	Type 1	167.220	2.53%
	Type 2-1	53.366	0.81%
	Type 2-2	932.322	14.12%
	Type 2-3	3.545	0.05%
Total		6,602.148	100.00%

The second highest concentration of solar power development is in Type 1 Agricultural Development Areas, which encompass prime agricultural environments, including special agricultural areas designated under the Regional Plan Act and aquaculture production zones established by the Ministry of Agriculture. Our analysis indicates that approximately 30% of existing solar installation sites will be classified as Type 1 Agricultural Development Areas under the new system. Among these, around 75% are agricultural green energy facilities—solar power systems integrated with agricultural operations—which comply with agricultural land use controls under the new system, as they are categorized as agricultural facilities.

3.2 Taiwan Solar Energy Development White Paper

The Ministry of Economic Affairs initiated planning for the "White Paper on Land Use for Renewable Energy Development: Solar Power" in late 2022. Throughout 2023, the ministry conducted 47 expert and scholar interviews and organized five large-scale public engagement events. Through these activities, the ministry aimed to communicate energy policy visions while gathering stakeholder concerns and improvement suggestions to refine renewable energy land planning goals and development strategies.

The white paper establishes short-term goals of achieving 31GW installation capacity by 2030 and long-term goals of reaching 40-80GW cumulative solar power generation by 2050. The implementation framework consists of three main approaches:

(1) Establishing mutually beneficial partnerships between central and local governments, emphasizing central-level framework development to guide local autonomous planning.
(2) Scale-differentiated energy governance, developing site selection, development, and supervision measures for large-scale special zones, while providing subsidy and guidance measures for small-scale community-based autonomous energy development.
(3) Renewable energy development with local co-prosperity, proposing mechanisms for solar power development to benefit local neighborhood development and strengthen community participation.

The policy programs and implementation strategies are shown in Table IV. Based on their nature, the implementation measures fall into four categories: spatial planning, legal and operational mechanism construction, guidance or subsidy measures, and local support and compensation programs. Among these, legal regulations and local support are the primary policy promotion methods, with the Administration of Energy developing regulations for solar power site selection, development standards, design specifications, and public rights protection to implement energy and industrial development that can prosper alongside local communities.

Table IV: Policy Implementation Strategies in the White Paper on Land Use for Renewable Energy Development: Solar Power

Strategies	Implementation A	B	C	D
Application Streamlining		✓		
Technical Standards		✓		
Subsidy Programs			✓	
Aquavoltaic Zones	✓			
Demonstration Zones	✓	✓		
Community Energy		✓		✓
Environmental Compensation	✓	✓		
Local Transparency				✓
Public Participation		✓		✓
Indigenous Rights		✓		✓
Local Service Stations				✓
Compensation Schemes			✓	✓
Local Authority Coordination		✓		

Implementation:
A: Spatial Planning
B: Legal & Mechanism Improvement
C: Subsidy & Guidance
D: Local Support & Compensation

As shown in Table IV, the spatial planning category includes promoting aquavoltaic zones, establishing environmental compensation mechanisms and operation management regulations, and developing site selection principles for national demonstration zones. This category also emphasizes the construction of development review and operation management systems for large-scale projects. The mechanism prioritizes national and public lands and Taiwan Sugar Corporation's lands for large-scale developments while encouraging local autonomous development for small-scale projects. These smaller projects continue to focus on integrated PV installations combined with agriculture, along with community-based rooftop solar power systems.

Overall, while the white paper has established a comprehensive social communication framework and identified key action items, it has not yet specified implementation procedures for individual policies, evaluated program feasibility, or conducted spatial mapping. Furthermore, it does not fully meet the requirements for sectoral plans as specified in Articles 4 and 6 of the Spatial Planning Act Enforcement Rules, and additional research is needed to determine how to align these elements in the future.

4 METHODOLOGY

4.1 Review of Recent Studies

Recent academic research addressing both spatial planning and energy development has primarily focused on three areas: energy development strategies across different cities, integrated planning for spatial and energy systems, and the roles of central and local governments in multi-level governance. These studies provide valuable theoretical and practical insights for this research.

Asarpota and Nadin (2020) developed an assessment framework through a literature review and policy analysis to evaluate the relationship between energy planning and spatial planning in Hong Kong, Auckland, Oslo, and Vancouver. Their analysis compared transportation and accessibility, urban patterns, energy grid structure, and infrastructure systems including drainage and waste management. The study revealed that none of these cities had effectively incorporated nergy infrastructure planning and supply efficiency considerations into their spatial structure and urban patterns [11].

In the same year, Stoeglehner examined the implementation of integrated spatial and energy planning in Austria's Styria province. Using quantitative analysis, the study evaluated the balance between renewable energy generation potential and CO2 emissions to identify areas both requiring and suitable for energy plan implementation. Through talent development and government subsidy programs, the province supported local governments in implementing these strategies. The results demonstrated Styria's successful implementation of integrated spatial and energy planning strategies, emphasizing the crucial role and responsibilities of local governments in the process [12].

Drawing on both literature review and case studies, Dobravec, Matak, Sakulin, and Krajačić (2021) examined the mechanisms and impacts of decentralized central-local governance in Austria's local government energy and climate policy implementation. Through interviews and policy analysis, they identified key challenges and opportunities facing local governments in policy development and implementation. Their findings indicated that while local governments have significant potential in energy and climate policy implementation, they require stronger coordination in decentralized governance, including increased funding, human resources, technical support, and improved vertical and horizontal communication [13].

De Laurentis and Pearson (2021) investigated how Italy and England adapted their policy planning to promote renewable energy, examining various government departments, governance methods, and infrastructure arrangements. Their comparative case study analyzed conditions in three Italian regions (Apulia, Tuscany, and Sardinia) and two UK autonomous territories (Wales and Scotland). Through interviews and literature analysis, they gathered policy formulation data and statistics from these regions to compare approaches and outcomes. Their research demonstrated that social structure, economic conditions, and infrastructure configuration significantly influence energy policy implementation in regional energy transitions [14].

4.2 Analytical Approach to Taiwan's Spatial-Energy Policy Integration

While recent research on spatial planning and energy policy provides valuable theoretical and practical insights, some aspects are not directly applicable to Taiwan's context. Most studies focus on countries with relatively mature energy development systems, whereas Taiwan faces the distinct challenge of enhancing renewable energy development within limited land area. Furthermore, Taiwan is currently transforming its spatial planning system. To achieve policy goals during this transition period and effectively integrate energy and spatial planning systems, it is essential to analyze policy planning mechanisms and hierarchical governance frameworks to identify a development path suitable for Taiwan.

This study will employ methods including literature review, comparative research, case study, and policy analysis. First, it will systematically collect and analyze relevant domestic and international literature to examine how different countries with similar land conditions manage their spatial planning policies, controls, and energy policy implementation and support measures. Second, by comparing Taiwan's approach with other countries' spatial planning and energy policies, it will identify applicable successful experiences and conduct an in-depth analysis of specific implementation cases to extract key feasible strategies and policy recommendations. Finally, applying these case studies to Taiwan's context, along with the integrated application of the aforementioned research methods, will enable this study to thoroughly analyze Taiwan's current challenges and opportunities. Through analyzing the relationship between spatial planning and energy policy, we will propose specific recommendations to strengthen coordination between these two policy systems and facilitate smooth policy implementation.

5 CASE STUDY AND DISCUSSION

Taiwan's 2018 National Spatial Plan lacks clear spatial guidance for solar power development, which has hindered local governments from identifying appropriate development areas and has led to conflicts in sectoral policy implementation. The energy authority should leverage the upcoming comprehensive five-year review of county/municipal spatial plans to address this issue. Before the finalization of spatial plan changes in 2028, they should translate the current White Paper on Land Use for Renewable Energy Development: Solar Power into concrete spatial terms, developing site selection principles and land use guidance that can be integrated into spatial plans. Concurrently, they should align with spatial planning authorities' timeline for comprehensive rural area planning, providing energy development recommendations to facilitate the systematic implementation of energy policy goals across different scales.

This study examines countries that, like Taiwan, have achieved higher solar power development capacity despite high population density, aiming to construct an appropriate spatial guidance framework. By analyzing how these countries integrate their spatial planning and energy policies, we can derive insights for Taiwan's improvement. The study focuses on four countries: Japan, India, South Korea, and the Netherlands, examining each country's spatial planning framework, energy sector planning system, and methods of integrating spatial planning with energy promotion policies.

5.1 Japan

Japan has a population density of approximately 333 people per square kilometer, ranking 27th globally. Despite its dense population and limited land resources, Japan's solar power development reached 78GW by 2022, ranking third worldwide. To understand its national spatial planning framework and methods of integrating spatial planning with energy policies, we analyze its national spatial planning system, central energy planning guidance, and local decentralized governance to identify lessons for improving Taiwan's integration of spatial and sectoral plans.

5.1.1 Spatial Planning Framework

Japan released its revised National Spatial Plan in July 2023 under the National Spatial Planning Act [15]. The plan addresses national challenges including accelerated population decline leading to local development crises, climate disaster risks, and changing international conditions. In response to these challenges, Japan established the vision of "National Spatial Strategy: Harnessing Regional Strengths for a New Era" and formulated comprehensive, long-term development directions.

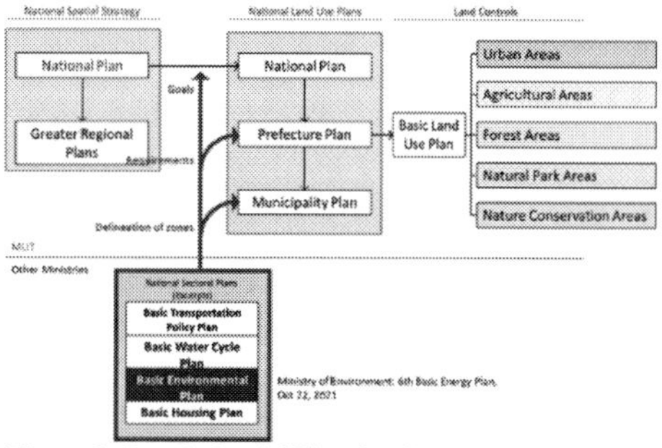

Figure 3: Japan's Spatial Planning System

As shown in Figure 3, Japan's spatial planning framework follows a hierarchical structure from planning to implementation control. At the central level, the Ministry of Land, Infrastructure, Transport and Tourism develops the National Spatial Strategy, dividing the country into eight major living spheres and collaborating with local governments to formulate eight greater regional plans with specific policy implementation goals. At the prefecture level, following national and regional development visions, local spatial strategies are developed. These strategies classify land into five categories based on location, environmental resources, and social, economic, and cultural needs, establishing land use guidance principles for each category. At the municipality level, local authorities propose specific land use control measures based on prefecture guidance, implementing the spatial planning framework through substantive controls [15], [16], [17].

5.1.2 Energy Sector Planning

To achieve its 2050 carbon neutrality goal, Japan's Ministry of Economy, Trade and Industry approved the "6th Basic Energy Plan" in October 2021. This plan outlines future energy development directions, policy implementation methods, integration requirements with other plans, and measures to address energy supply-demand structure issues. For renewable energy promotion, the Basic Energy Plan emphasizes "communities" as the primary implementation unit, focusing on mutual prosperity between energy businesses and communities. It designates "Energy Development Promotion Zones" based on community needs to provide flexible land use control measures. Considering the Fukushima nuclear disaster and tsunami experiences, the plan integrates with the Basic Disaster Management Plan, positioning renewable energies as alternative energy sources during disasters to ensure stable energy supply during evacuation and disaster relief [18].

At the prefecture level, policy planning focuses on two main pillars: energy and disaster management, through the "Plan for Implementing Global Warming Countermeasures" and "Regional Disaster Management Plan" respectively. The former emphasizes both energy conservation and generation, addressing low-carbon materials, recycling and circular use, diverse energy resource development and investment, improved energy storage applications, and value-added directions for multi-functional developments. These include combining agriculture with renewable energy development and incorporating renewable energy into urban public facilities. The disaster management plans vary by region according to prevalent disaster types. For example, in areas prone to storms and floods, plans emphasize stable energy supply strategies during disasters, including coastal wind turbine utilization and solar power development in hillside rural areas, while focusing on connecting energy storage facilities with evacuation centers.

At the municipality level, implementation is the primary focus. For global warming countermeasures, municipalities establish specific subsidy requirements for residents and local businesses developing energy projects, while also inventorying public infrastructure and introducing new construction projects, such as solar-powered parking lots and expanded special zones for energy businesses. Disaster management plans focus on inventorying evacuation sites and examining overall energy use and storage to ensure effective utilization during disasters [19].

5.1.3 Spatial Planning and Energy Sector Integration

Central-level plans in Japan establish only future development directions and overall national goals. The spatial plans outline development visions for the country and its eight living spheres without specifying detailed plans or land controls. Similarly, energy and disaster management plans highlight future development visions, policy programs, and related regulations, explicitly designating municipalities as the main implementation bodies and empowering local governments to determine

10.4229/EUPVSEC2025/5DV.3.43

appropriate planning programs.

At the prefecture level, land use plans clearly establish land classifications and usage guidance for each category. Controls specified in energy plans and disaster management measures for different land categories are incorporated into land use plans, which establish permitted and conditional installation requirements. For example, land use plans specify that renewable energy promotion zones are designated for renewable energy development, and projects involving agricultural land must obtain land use conversion permits under the Cropland Act. At the municipality level, land use plans must clearly define land use controls and building management requirements for each land parcel. Reviews must be conducted to determine locations for future energy facilities and evacuation sites in disaster prevention plans, ensuring development plan feasibility and enabling contextual adjustments based on each village's development needs.

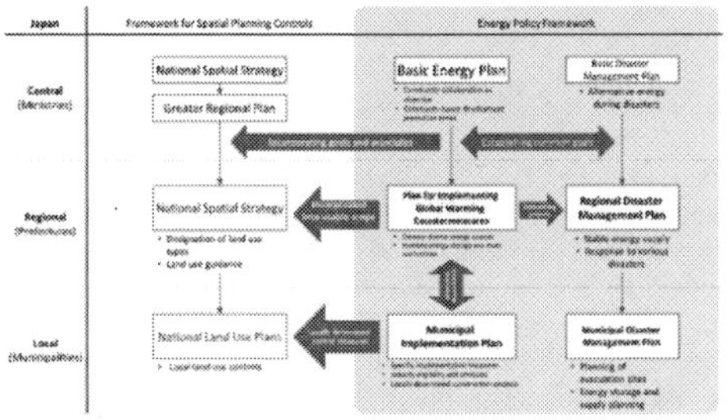

Figure 4: Japan's Spatial–Energy Policy Integration

5.2 India

India has a population density of approximately 431 people per square kilometer, ranking 26th globally. Despite its limited development space, India achieved a solar power installation capacity of 63.19GW by 2022, ranking fourth worldwide. This study analyzes India's comprehensive national plans and basic energy plans to examine its policy integration approaches and identify effective strategies for Taiwan's spatial and sectoral planning coordination.

5.2.1 Spatial Planning Framework

India, as a federal system, designates the National Land Use Planning Commission of the federal government to coordinate national land use planning and development strategies through comprehensive plans spanning decades. These plans, reviewed every five years, cover economics, finance, employment, education, agriculture, and other sectors. During the implementation of the 12th Five-Year Plan (2012-2017), the Indian federal government established the National Institution for Transforming India (NITI Aayog) to replace the commission in 2015. This restructuring transformed India's development strategies and governance methods, establishing a committee led by the Prime Minister with department heads as members to promote state cooperation and develop national development priorities collaboratively. The new institution focuses on providing consultation, conducting surveys, and offering guidance for collaboration, no longer drafting national five-year comprehensive plans but allowing state governments to formulate their own spatial planning approaches.

Currently, spatial planning in India is managed by state governments through Development Plans (DP), which are updated every 10 years. These plans encompass two main components: regulation formulation and developable area identification. The former includes detailed land use controls, building management rules, building design specifications, and urban design guidelines. The latter divides land into functional zones based on location and environmental sensitivity levels to balance orderly development and ecological protection. For areas where the government intends to introduce specific development, Special Plan Development zones (SPD zones) are designated to clearly identify areas requiring future attention.

Following the development plan visions proposed by state governments, cities within their jurisdiction are divided into multiple districts, with each district governed by specific Town Planning Schemes (TPS) established by municipal governments. For example, in Gujarat state, 33 cities have proposed town planning schemes for 222 districts. As of 2023, 80 schemes have received formal approval, while the remaining schemes are in the review and hearing stages. Each district's town planning scheme must clearly delineate road patterns, designate open spaces, and establish reasonable distribution of industry and public facilities. These plans must comply with their respective state government's development plan controls and enable developers to apply for required development permits, promoting orderly development of India's national space [20], [21].

5.2.2 Energy Sector Planning

India's energy sector planning began in 2008 with the National Action Plan on Climate Change (NAPCC) proposed by the Ministry of Environment, Forest and Climate Change. This plan launched several ambitious initiatives, including the Jawaharlal Nehru National Solar Mission (JNNSM) proposed in 2010 by the Ministry of New and Renewable Energy (MNRE). The mission initially aimed to achieve 20GW of solar power generation by 2022. Due to strong electricity demand across the country, particularly in off-grid areas, both rooftop and ground-mounted solar power zones achieved remarkable results. Consequently, in 2015, the mission target was revised to 100GW by 2022, allocating 40GW for rooftop installations and 60GW for medium and large-scale ground-mounted solar power zones. The mission also aimed to promote the widespread application of solar technology to reduce fossil fuel dependence and address global climate change challenges [22].

To implement the National Solar Mission, MNRE collaborates with two state-owned enterprises: the Indian Renewable Energy Development Agency Limited (IREDA) and the Solar Energy Corporation of India (SECI). IREDA manages renewable energy development financing and preferential loans, providing financial support for solar power development, while SECI focuses on solar power technology development and increasing its application scope, including constructing large-scale solar zones and promoting off-grid solar street lights in rural communities.

Considering the disparity between urban and rural development, with uneven distribution of off-grid and grid-connected areas and some rural communities lacking power resources, the National Solar Mission promotes both off-grid and grid-connected solar power facilities. Since 2014, off-grid solar power development has prioritized installing solar-powered street lights in areas with less than 50% grid coverage. Additionally, solar-powered lighting and irrigation pump facilities are installed in rural areas, along with home lighting systems and student study lamps for households still using coal, improving rural areas' quality of life and production conditions.

For grid-connected areas, solar power development is guided and promoted through various policy initiatives including:

- The Solar Park Scheme, which focuses on establishing large-scale ground-mounted solar power parks to increase generation through concentrated installation.
- The Viability Gap Funding Scheme (VGF Scheme), which provides federal government subsidies to reduce initial installation costs, attracting more small and medium enterprises to invest and participate.
- The Central Public Sector Undertakings (CPSU) Scheme, which encourages central public agencies to invest in solar power facility installation, expanding commercial applications and enhancing technology application diversity.
- The Canal Bank & Canal Top Scheme, which installs solar panels above waterways, conserving terrestrial land while increasing national solar power generation and enhancing its economic viability and market competitiveness [23].

The Solar Park Scheme exemplifies this approach. The federal government's MNRE coordinates with state governments to review and designate locations for large-scale park development projects, with state governments managing implementation details, including development scope, scale, and arrangement patterns. State governments also determine whether to collaborate with MNRE and SECI for bidding and developer selection, ensuring selected developers can access IREDA financing support. A unique feature of this scheme is "landowner shareholding," which invites original landowners to participate as investors. In a system similar to rights conversion in urban renewal, landowners can use their land as share capital. This approach contributes to the local economy while reducing community resistance to solar power facilities.

5.2.3 Spatial Planning and Energy Sector Integration

India's central-level spatial planning provides policy consultation and survey services without explicit control and planning guidance. Planning principles, legal regulations, and development goals are established at the state level, with implementation details delegated to individual cities. This ensures plans align with local conditions, visions, and development needs while enabling concrete implementation controls.

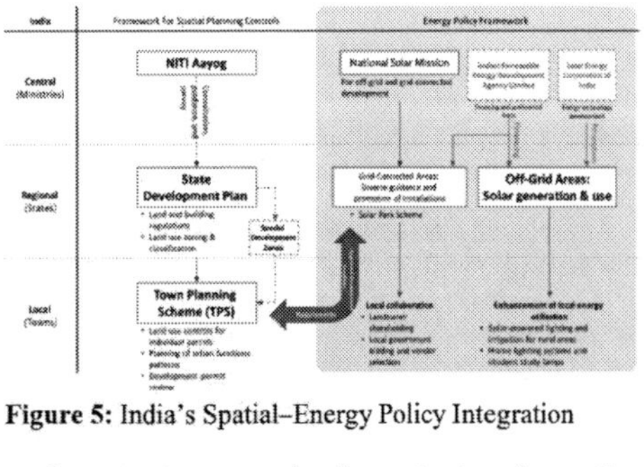

Figure 5: India's Spatial–Energy Policy Integration

In contrast, energy planning maintains clear policy guidance and responsibility division at the central level. The National Solar Mission specifies future development goals and sub-plan scopes for both off-grid and grid-connected projects. While state governments propose specific implementation plans for various sub-plans, it is the city governments that review solar project applications to verify compliance with Town Planning Scheme (TPS) controls, thereby achieving integration between spatial planning and energy sectors.

5.3 South Korea

South Korea has a population density of approximately 516 people per square kilometer, ranking 20th globally. Despite limited development space, its solar power installation capacity reached 22GW by 2022, ranking eighth worldwide. This study analyzes South Korea's comprehensive national spatial plans and basic energy plans to examine its integration of spatial and energy policies, seeking insights for Taiwan's policy integration.

5.3.1 Spatial Planning Framework

South Korea's spatial planning framework is based on two regulations: the Framework Act on The National Land and the National Land Planning and Utilization Act. Under these laws, the central government, special autonomous cities, and provincial governments develop Comprehensive Plans, while city and county governments prepare City/County Management Plans and District Unit Planning. These plans propose specific development programs and implementation measures based on their respective Comprehensive Plans and land use control laws [24].

The Fifth National Comprehensive Plan (2020-2040), proposed by the South Korean central government in 2019, aims to address domestic population decline, which has necessitated adjustments to industrial transformation strategies, living needs, and sustainable development approaches. The plan places "people" at its core, establishing land development visions and proposing multiple development management strategies, including:

- Promoting distinctive and decentralized regional development.
- Strengthening cross-administrative district solidarity and cooperation.
- Revitalizing regional industrial innovation.
- Promoting culture and tourism.
- Building safe and livable environments.
- Constructing efficient infrastructure and smart national land management systems.

Regarding energy development, the plan proposes three major goals and policy strategies for local governments to implement in their spatial planning:

(1) Promote energy-saving green buildings and gradually strengthen requirements for zero-energy buildings.
(2) Enhance self-sufficiency capabilities in specific development zones, such as industrial parks and designated development areas, achieving the zones' energy generation and consumption goals through expanded energy storage facilities and distribution.
(3) Construct low-energy consumption urban patterns by integrating energy facilities, spatial distribution of urban activities, and transportation systems to transition toward energy-efficient urban spatial structures.

At the local government level, special autonomous

10.4229/EUPVSEC2025/5DV.3.43

cities and provincial governments develop local development plans following the central government's comprehensive planning goals. For example, in the Fifth National Comprehensive Plan, Jeju Island is designated to develop with the vision of "Carbon Free Island Jeju." Subsequently, the Jeju Special Self-Governing Province government drafted the Third Jeju Free International City Comprehensive Plan (2022-2031) in 2022, providing detailed implementation strategies for this vision:

- Urban structure: Enhance smart management and information systems to strengthen smart infrastructure construction, creating comfortable and safe living environments.
- Industrial development: Create diverse development and multi-functional island living by introducing and developing agriculture, forestry, livestock, marine, tourism, and logistics industries, while upgrading industries and combining them with technology to enhance productivity and innovation.
- Tourism: Establish management regulations for natural landscape resources and improve international accessibility and community amenities and services to develop tourist potential.

These comprehensive plans, approved by autonomous cities and provincial governments, identify developable regions and authorize cities and counties within their jurisdiction to propose specific development locations, project procedures, and compliance requirements based on local conditions. For example, Seogwipo City within Jeju's jurisdiction developed its management plan following Jeju's Fifth Comprehensive Plan. The plan divides the city into five areas: residential, commercial, industrial, green, and special management areas. Different land use control measures are established for each category to ensure land use rationality and implementation of visions from the higher-level plan. Additionally, considering the higher-level plan's emphasis on tourism and its implications for livable environments, local quality of life, and culture, Seogwipo City's management plan requires public participation mechanisms for all development projects and coordinates with local residents on landscape requirements to balance urban development and environmental quality.

5.3.2 Energy Sector Planning

South Korea's current national energy policy follows the Third Basic Energy Plan developed by the Ministry of Trade, Industry and Energy (MOTIE) in 2019. This plan is reviewed and updated every five years to address the latest developments and challenges in the energy sector, and work has already begun on formulating the Fourth Basic Energy Plan. The Third Basic Energy Plan [25] aims to improve energy use efficiency and strengthen electricity demand management across industrial, transportation, and building sectors to rationalize energy pricing. To achieve these goals, the plan promotes electric vehicle adoption, energy storage system (ESS) installation, and development of both large-scale ground-mounted solar power zones and small-scale distributed generation facilities at the community level to increase energy industry flexibility and grid stability, while encouraging public participation in energy development to achieve overall green transformation of the energy structure.

To implement the Basic Energy Plan's goals, Korea Electric Power Corporation (KEPCO) drafted Korea's Tenth Basic Power Supply and Demand Plan in 2023, which was approved by MOTIE to establish timeline and phase goals for the next 15 years. The plan, reviewed every two years to adjust energy source proportions, aims to gradually reduce nuclear energy's share while increasing renewable energy power supply to meet future energy demands and respond more flexibly to climate change challenges.

Following guidance from the Basic Energy Plan and Basic Power Supply and Demand Plan, each special autonomous city and provincial government must develop its own "local energy plan." Currently, 17 local energy plans have been completed and are updated every five years, following the Basic Energy Plan's review frequency. For example, Jeju Island's local energy plan sets a development goal of achieving 1.5GW within five years and establishes three local development principles:

(1) Ensure local communities share in the economic benefits of renewable energy development.
(2) Integrate energy storage system (ESS) deployment with electric vehicle infrastructure and transportation networks.
(3) Improve public acceptance of solar power and other renewable energy projects through resident collaboration and engagement.

Through top-down guidance on energy infrastructure planning, with each special autonomous city and provincial government autonomously proposing suitable local implementation measures, South Korea is achieving a more sustainable, low-carbon, and democratic energy transition.

5.3.3 Spatial Planning and Energy Sector Integration

At the central government level, South Korea's spatial and energy plans present only overall national development goals and evaluable development directions. For example, spatial plans indicate goals of combining low-carbon energy with rural joint development, while energy basic plans respond by suggesting rural communities can achieve spatial planning goals through electric vehicle promotion, expanded energy storage facilities, or distributed small power plant installation.

At the special autonomous city and provincial government level, Jeju Island provides an illustrative example. Its comprehensive spatial planning coordinates electric vehicle infrastructure with transportation network planning, integrating energy storage facilities while inventorying urban road networks and related public facility distribution. The spatial plan establishes building controls and landscape regulations, authorizing local authorities for review while specifying review criteria. This approach constructs locally self-governed mechanisms to guide public-private partnerships, including subsidy mechanisms for businesses installing energy management facilities, methods for managing industrial energy demand, requirements for landscape and buffer distances, and regulations for solar power equipment in new buildings.

At the city and county level, governments propose specific implementation methods for higher-level plans according to each jurisdiction's management plan. Seogwipo City in Jeju Island demonstrates this through several approaches:

- Establishing site selection principles for energy facilities, identifying suitable locations for hybrid facilities and agricultural land eligible for conversion to energy facilities to delineate areas for future development.
- Developing landscape agreements with local residents

to ensure development projects align with local landscape planning.

- Evaluating key construction projects and industries desired by local communities, such as establishing an energy research base in the eastern area and a smart grid certification center to support local renewable energy development.
- Expanding its smart grid outward from the research base, integrating tourism hotspots to create green tourism routes, and gradually incorporating populated areas into the smart grid region.

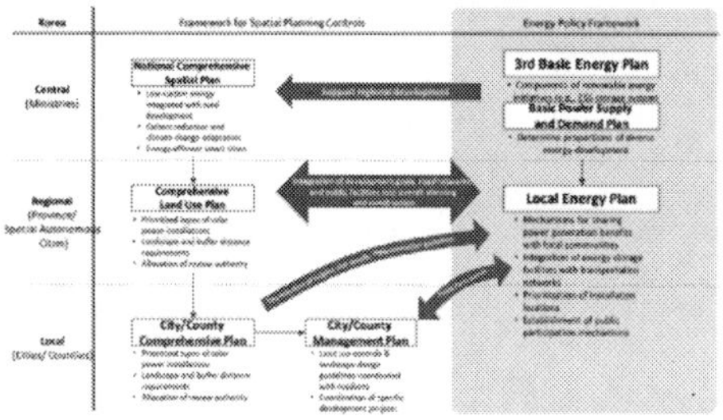

Figure 6: South Korea's Spatial–Energy Policy Integration

5.4 The Netherlands

The Netherlands has a population density of approximately 423 people per square kilometer, ranking 24th globally. Despite limited development space, its solar power installation capacity reached 18.85GW by 2022, ranking 13th worldwide. This study analyzes the Netherlands' comprehensive national plans and basic energy plans to examine its integration of spatial planning and energy policies to inform Taiwan's approach to policy integration.

5.4.1 Spatial Planning Framework

The Netherlands' spatial planning system has recently undergone major reform through the Environment and Planning Act (Omgevingswet), which was amended in 2023 and implemented on January 1, 2024. This amendment marks a shift from top-down central guidance toward collaborative planning between different levels of government. As many laws and supporting regulations are still being established, the regulatory transition period is expected to continue until 2030, when the new planning and control mechanism will be fully implemented.

Under the 2024 Environment and Planning Act, two central-level ministries—the Ministry of Infrastructure and Water Management and the Ministry of Interior and Kingdom Relations—collaborate with provincial governments to develop environmental visions (Omgevingsvisie), establishing long-term environmental management goals to guide sustainable development. For specific areas or cross-sectoral priorities, such as water resource conservation or air quality improvement zones, programs (Programma) are developed to establish implementation strategies and goals. Cities under Dutch provinces then develop their environmental plans (Omgevingsplan) based on national and provincial guidelines, detailing local building management, land use regulations, and urban design requirements.

This planning system enables all levels of government to establish detailed regulations and effectively control land development rights. This planning system establishes a hierarchy from broad environmental vision goals, through specific program actions, to detailed environmental plan requirements, ensuring consistency and effectiveness in spatial development and environmental management. All land use activities, including logging, building facade modifications, or solar panel installations on buildings and in courtyards, must follow environmental permit (Omgevingsvergunning) procedures and obtain approval from municipal governments. The permit system verifies whether proposed activities comply with environmental plans for specific areas, examining potential impacts on endangered species habitats, effects on birds and mammals, and compliance with building and landscape regulations. Municipal governments evaluate these impacts and issue time-limited environmental permits. For solar power facilities, environmental permits are typically valid for 15-20 years, depending on installation location and type. Upon expiration, compliance with updated regulations must be verified for renewal or extension. Through this system, the Netherlands achieves coordinated and efficient planning and development review while ensuring proper protection of natural and human environments.

5.4.2 Energy Sector Planning

The Netherlands' energy and climate policy framework has recently undergone comprehensive updates and consolidation to address global climate change challenges and promote national energy transition. Energy policy implementation is guided by two primary national agreements: the Energy Agreement (Energieakkoord) and the Climate Agreement (Klimaatakkoord). The former focuses on improving energy efficiency, increasing renewable energy adoption, and creating green economy employment opportunities, while the latter establishes specific goals and pathways for reducing greenhouse gas emissions. In 2023, the Ministry of Economic Affairs and Climate Policy developed the "National Energy System Plan" (Nationaal Plan Energiesysteem, NPE) based on these agreements to establish its energy development vision and long-term goals. This led to the National Regional Energy Strategy Program (Nationaal Programma Regionale Energiestrategie, NP RES), which guides regions in developing localized Regional Energy Strategy (RES) plans to achieve national energy and climate goals [27].

The National Energy System Plan (NPE) focuses on achieving energy transition while ensuring energy supply security and sustainability, promoting economic growth and technological innovation, and improving energy system flexibility and efficiency. It emphasizes cross-sector cooperation mechanisms, incorporating government, business, and civil society participation. By employing multiple communication channels to gain insights into diverse perspectives, it aims to build consensus and advance energy transition. The National Regional Energy Strategy Program (NP RES) coordinates regional energy strategy plans (RES) across the country, ensuring local actions align with national goals while encouraging regions to leverage their unique resources and conditions to develop renewable energy and improve energy efficiency.

Recognizing that addressing climate change and energy transition challenges requires more than individual local government action, Regional Energy Strategies (RES) connect provincial and municipal governments to effectively integrate local resources and address regional

10.4229/EUPVSEC2025/5DV.3.43

challenges, thereby enhancing energy efficiency and renewable energy expansion. Social equity and economic sustainability must be considered to ensure the transition neither creates social division nor places undue economic burden on specific groups. Each regional strategy undergoes updates every five years to reflect local circumstances, including technological advances, policy changes, and current development conditions, ensuring the strategies remain timely and context-appropriate.

5.4.3 Spatial Planning and Energy Sector Integration

The Netherlands' Environmental Vision (Omgevingsvisie) and National Regional Energy Strategy Program (NP RES) share aligned development goals of achieving sustainable energy transition and addressing climate change challenges while emphasizing cross-sector cooperation and local participation. The Netherlands' Environmental Vision (Omgevingsvisie) and National Regional Energy Strategy Program (NP RES) share aligned development goals of achieving sustainable energy transition and addressing climate change challenges while emphasizing cross-sector cooperation and local participation.

The National Regional Energy Strategy Program and local Regional Energy Strategies (RES) interface closely with local Environmental Plans (Omgevingsplan) regarding solar power development regulations. These strategy plans emphasize renewable energy, particularly solar power's role in the Dutch energy system, establishing development goals and implementation measures. Local Environmental Plans provide specific development regulations for solar power, including suitable locations, scale restrictions, design requirements, and ecological impact considerations. These regulations ensure solar power development meets both energy transition needs and maintains regional environmental quality, ecological conservation, and landscape character. Additionally, Environmental Plans highlight the importance of public participation, which it requires for larger-scale solar power developments to ensure broad social support and acceptance.

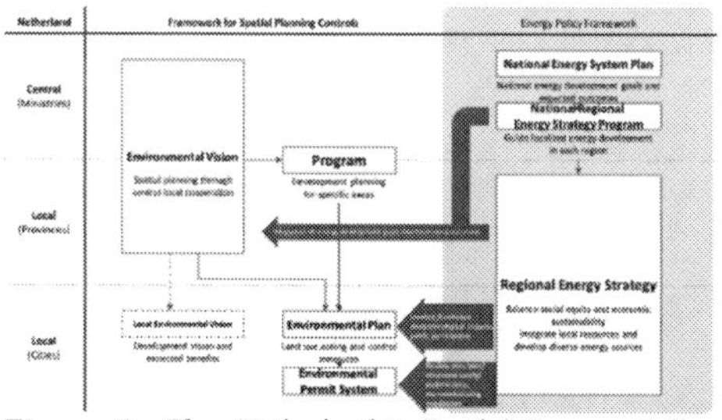

Figure 7: The Netherlands' Spatial–Energy Policy Integration

The Environmental Permit (Omgevingsvergunning) system provides crucial oversight during development, ensuring solar facilities comply with local Environmental Plan requirements. These permits govern the entire project lifecycle from construction through operation, maintenance, and eventual dismantling and site restoration, including safety standards for electrical and structural systems. Developers must conduct regular maintenance and monitoring to ensure long-term operational safety and efficiency while minimizing environmental impacts. The permits also stipulate dismantling and restoration requirements, ensuring sites can return to their original state or remain suitable for alternative uses, maintaining sustainable land use practices.

6 DISCUSSION

Taiwan faces challenges similar to those of Japan, India, South Korea, and the Netherlands, including limited spatial resources, high population density, and urgent needs to address climate change and energy transition. Analysis of these countries provides practical models for integrating spatial planning and energy policies that can inform Taiwan's national land and energy policy development.

Japan's spatial planning framework most closely resembles Taiwan's. Taiwan can learn from Japan's layered spatial governance and community-led model, particularly how community participation plays a key role in energy development plans. For Taiwan, this suggests that when advancing renewable energy policies, especially solar and wind power, efforts should focus on strengthening local government and community leadership and participation. This approach ensures energy development plans meet both national net-zero carbon emission goals and gain local support, while reflecting specific local development needs and conditions, making it more feasible to implement the policies.

Japan's spatial planning framework most closely resembles Taiwan's. Taiwan can learn from Japan's layered spatial governance and community-led model, particularly how community participation plays a key role in energy development plans. For Taiwan, this suggests that when advancing renewable energy policies, especially solar and wind power, efforts should focus on strengthening local government and community leadership and participation. This approach ensures energy development plans meet both national net-zero carbon emission goals and gain local support, while reflecting specific local development needs and conditions, making the policies more feasible to implement.

India's approach is distinctive in highlighting state governments' crucial role in spatial and energy planning within a federal system, particularly in their proactive promotion of solar power development and implementation of landowner shareholding, which helps reduce public resistance to solar power installations. India's planning and energy policy integration process suggests approaches for Taiwan to enhance local government autonomy and responsibility, encouraging regions to formulate and implement spatial planning and energy transition strategies based on their specific characteristics and conditions. Simultaneously, county/municipal governments should maintain consistency with national policy goals to ensure energy targets are effectively implemented.

South Korea's experience demonstrates close coordination between national comprehensive spatial planning and basic energy plans, particularly in improving energy efficiency and promoting renewable energy use, with both aspects responding to and aligning with each other at the planning stage. For Taiwan, this emphasizes that energy policy and spatial planning have the potential for further alignment, particularly in incorporating energy efficiency and renewable energy development goals into spatial planning. This alignment enables clear policy

10.4229/EUPVSEC2025/5DV.3.43

directions and related controls to be proposed during spatial plan formulation, promoting policy integration across land use, buildings, and industries.

The Netherlands offers a distinct approach, with nationally controlled land development rights and mandatory government environmental permits for all development projects. Through its Environment and Planning Act, the Netherlands establishes sustainable development as the foundation of national planning, emphasizing both public participation and local government responsibilities in plan formulation. In this system, central and provincial governments propose development goals and frameworks, while cities establish specific environmental plans including land use, landscape, and urban design requirements. At the development stage, the environmental permit system interfaces with energy sector plans, ensuring energy development complies with land regulations. Taiwan can learn from this approach that cross-departmental collaboration and public participation mechanisms during the planning stage can strengthen the harmony and inclusiveness of national and energy plans, reducing stakeholder concerns about and resistance to energy development.

7 CONCLUSION

In practice, Taiwan's spatial planning and energy policies often show inconsistencies, particularly in renewable energy policy implementation. Questions arise about whether sustainable development should prioritize land conservation and agricultural use, or whether energy transition should take precedence. Recent years have seen pronounced disputes between solar power development and spatial planning, primarily because solar power, as a relatively mature renewable energy technology domestically, is mostly installed in terrestrial areas. This easily provokes discussions about impacts on surrounding areas, including potential ecological effects, community landscape issues, and preservation of agricultural production environments. These conflicts indicate insufficient integration between spatial planning and energy policies, affecting both energy transition progress and the ability of central and local spatial plans to provide effective guidance, making it difficult to balance local development visions with centrally determined directions and capacity allocation.

Currently, Taiwan is working to integrate various sectoral plans—including housing, commercial, agricultural, energy, water resources, and disaster management policies—through the 2016 Spatial Planning Act, National Spatial Plan, and county/municipal spatial plans to create a harmonious development environment with minimal conflicts. However, these efforts require further strengthening, particularly in effectively integrating energy policies with spatial planning.

In this context, the publication of the White Paper on Land Use for Renewable Energy Development: Solar Power presents Taiwan with an opportunity to integrate energy planning with municipal and county spatial plans, which are scheduled for review and update in 2026. The White Paper systematically addresses energy and spatial plan integration issues by providing clear site selection principles and development guidance, ensuring energy development plans meet both national energy transition goals and local spatial planning needs. For example, while former salt production lands may be suitable for solar power development in principle, areas containing bird habitats and foraging zones should be excluded for environmental conservation and ecological preservation. Coastal windbreak forests should be protected to prevent impacts on inland microclimates. Depending on local conditions, developments must either maintain appropriate buffer distances from nearby communities to preserve rural landscapes, or establish close cooperation with adjacent settlements and contribute a portion of power industry revenue to local development. If this white paper effectively fulfills its integration function, Taiwan can promote consistency between spatial planning and energy policies during its energy transition while building a foundation for achieving its 2050 net-zero carbon emissions goal through robust planning and implementation.

Analysis of Japan, India, South Korea, and the Netherlands provides valuable insights for effectively integrating spatial planning and energy policies. These countries demonstrate the importance of layered governance at central and local levels, enhanced community participation channels and intensity, and cross-departmental collaboration in promoting spatial and energy integration. Notably, strengthening public participation and local government leadership facilitates smoother implementation of energy plans. Additionally, case studies show that domestic technological innovation can improve energy efficiency and diversify renewable energy installation options, enabling more choices in multi-functional solar power facilities. For example, semi-transparent solar modules can better integrate with agricultural facilities, while smaller modules can reduce building form restrictions. Beyond technology, establishing clear policy and planning goals remains crucial for achieving energy transition and sustainable development.

Integrating these key factors, Taiwan can pursue effective energy policy implementation through the following adjustments to policy support measures:

(1) Strengthen policy consistency and cross-departmental collaboration: Ensure effective integration between energy plans and spatial planning through establishing cross-departmental collaboration mechanisms, promoting information sharing and policy coordination across departments.
(2) Strengthen local government and community participation: Grant local governments greater decision-making authority in energy plan formulation and implementation, and encourage community engagement in energy plan discussion, planning, and execution to enhance acceptance and implementation effectiveness.
(3) Promote technological innovation and policy flexibility: Encourage technological innovation, particularly in improving energy efficiency and renewable energy utilization, while maintaining policy flexibility to respond to rapid changes in energy markets and climate conditions.
(4) Strengthen public participation and social acceptance: Enhance public understanding and support for energy policy and spatial planning integration through effective communication mechanisms, ensuring transparency and fairness in policy formulation and implementation.

Beyond these general policy adjustments, to effectively address Taiwan's challenges in integrating spatial planning and energy policies, the following

10.4229/EUPVSEC2025/5DV.3.43

regulatory principles should be incorporated into the White Paper on Land Use for Renewable Energy Development and spatial sector plans, drawing from international development strategies and key success factors. These should serve as central-level guidelines, while local spatial plans and township/district rural area comprehensive planning should lead implementation:

(1) The spatial plan for the energy sector, which guides local spatial plans, should highlight local development conditions and community needs: Municipal and county governments can adjust energy development strategies according to local conditions while complying with the total capacity goals and site selection principles established in the central-level spatial plan. This ensures flexibility and innovation in energy policy implementation. Furthermore, under Article 17 of the Spatial Planning Act, sectoral authorities may consult with spatial planning authorities of the same level during policy planning. When agencies face conflicts over site selection in spatial planning, they may coordinate through the Ministry of Interior. By utilizing public participation procedures specified in spatial plans and legally required project review processes, the government can successfully integrate policy implementation across different sectors.

(2) Propose site selection principles: Drawing from international experience, when promoting renewable energy, particularly the technologically mature solar and wind power, the balance between ecological protection and land use must be considered. Site selection should prioritize previously developed or less ecologically sensitive areas, actively promoting multi-functional facilities that integrate energy installations with existing buildings or agricultural operations to minimize environmental impacts.

(3) Establish comprehensive monitoring and evaluation mechanisms: Regularly review the progress and effectiveness of energy policy and spatial planning integration, and adjust policy strategies and supporting measures—including subsidies, penalties, and guidance—based on actual conditions. This ensures continued policy adaptability and effectiveness, enabling timely responses to technological progress, market changes, and evolving social needs.

In conclusion, as Taiwan faces the challenges of integrating spatial and energy systems in a new era, it should learn from international development processes and successful experiences, adopting systematic yet flexible strategies that allow for innovation. This requires continuous adjustment of policy directions, strengthening of institutional and regulatory frameworks, and promotion of active participation across social sectors to achieve harmonious development of spatial and energy systems, working together toward a greener and more sustainable future.

8 REFERENCE

[1] Ministry of the Interior, Taiwan. (2018). "National Spatial Plan."

[2] Ministry of Economic Affairs, Taiwan. (2017). "Two-Year Solar power Promotion Plan (revised version)" .

[3] Ministry of the Interior. (2019), Taiwan. "Manual for Municipal and County Spatial planning" .

[4] Ministry of the Interior, Taiwan. (2023). "Operational Manual for National Spatial Planning: Functional Zoning, Sub-classification, and Land Use Delineation" .

[5] Yunlin County Government, Taiwan. (2021). "Yunlin County Spatial Plan" .

[6] Kaohsiung City Government, Taiwan. (2021). "Kaohsiung City Spatial Plan" .

[7] 2021. Tainan City Government, Taiwan. (2021). "Tainan City Spatial Plan" .

[8] Chiayi County Government, Taiwan. (2021). "Chiayi County Spatial Plan" .

[9] Changhua County Government, Taiwan. (2021). "Changhua County Spatial Plan" .

[10]Pingtung County Government, Taiwan. (2021). "Pingtung County Spatial Plan" .

[11]K. Asarpota and V. Nadin, "Energy Strategies, the Urban Dimension, and Spatial Planning," Energies (Basel), vol. 13, no. 14, 2020.

[12]G. Stoeglehner, "Integrated spatial and energy planning: a means to reach sustainable development goals," Evolutionary and Institutional Economics Review, vol. 17, no. 2, pp. 473–486, Jul. 2020, doi: 10.1007/s40844-020-00160-7.

[13]V. Dobravec, N. Matak, C. Sakulin, and G. Krajačić, "Multilevel governance energy planning and policy: a view on local energy initiatives," Energy Sustain Soc, vol. 11, no. 1, Dec. 2021, doi: 10.1186/s13705-020-00277-y

[14]C. De Laurentis and P. J. G. Pearson, "Policy-relevant insights for regional renewable energy deployment," Energy Sustain Soc, vol. 11, no. 1, Dec. 2021, doi: 10.1186/s13705-021-00295-4.

[15]Ministry of Land, Infrastructure, Transport and Tourism, Japan. (2023). "National Spatial Strategy (National Plan)".

[16]Ministry of Land, Infrastructure, Transport and Tourism, Japan. (2023). "Sixth National Land Use Plan (National Plan)".

[17]Ministry of Land, Infrastructure, Transport and Tourism, Japan. (2016). "Greater Regional Plan for the Tohoku Region—From Earthquake Reconstruction to Independent Development".

[18]Ministry of Economy, Trade and Industry, Japan (2021). "Sixth Basic Energy Plan".

[19]Niigata City Government, Japan. (2023). "Niigata Citys' Regional Plan for National Resilience (revised)".

[20]G. of G. Urban Development and Urban Housing Department, Comprehensive General Development Control Regulations-2017. 2017.

[21]S. Ballaney, "Town Planning Mechanism in Gujarat, India," 2008.

[22]F. and C. C. Ministry of Environment, "National Action Plan on Climate Change (NAPCC)," 2021. [Online]. Available: https://dst.gov.in/climate-change-programme

[23]Ministry of New and Renewable Energy, "Off-grid and Decentralised Solar PV Applications Program Phase 3 Guidelines and Amendments," 2018.

[24]S. Choo, Spatial Planning System. Korea Research Institute for Human Settlements, 2013.

[25]I. and E. Ministry of Trade, "The 3rd Basic Energy Plan-A New Energy Paradigm for the Future," 2019.

[26]K. Changhoon, "Status and Evaluation of Regional Energy Plans - Centered on Guidelines," 2019.
[27]Ministry of Economic Affairs and Climate Policy. (2023). "National energy system plan. Netherlands".

10.4229/EUPVSEC2025/5DV.3.43
020552-015

Integrating Energy Policy into Spatial Planning Frameworks: A Study of Taiwan's Approach

Tzu Han Hung
Industrial Technology Research Institute

ITRI Industrial Technology Research Institute

ABSTRACT

How can land-scarce regions balance development needs with ambitious renewable energy goals for a sustainable future?

Taiwan, an island of 36,197 km² with a population of 23 million and density of 640/km², faces competing demands for housing, high-tech industry, food security, climate adaptation, and disaster prevention. The 2016 Spatial Planning Act, the National Spatial Plan (2018), and 18 municipal plans (2021) established a framework to integrate sectoral policies, yet challenges remain. Energy policy, for example, sets a 20GW solar target by 2025 (revised to 8GW rooftop, 12GW ground-mounted) under the Renewable Energy Development Act (2009), but national planning offers limited spatial guidance, weak local autonomy, and insufficient mechanisms to coordinate overlapping land uses.

To address this gap, this article compares four land-constrained countries with higher solar deployment—**Japan, India, South Korea, and the Netherlands**. By analyzing how their spatial planning systems align with sectoral policies, it identifies governance and planning approaches that guide solar development within limited territory. The study aims to provide lessons for Taiwan to strengthen land–energy integration, resolve policy conflicts, and achieve its net-zero 2050 goals.

INTRODUCTION

Taiwan enacted the Spatial Planning Act in 2016, launching a new system to be fully applied by 2025. The framework operates at three levels: the National Spatial Plan (2018) sets broad zoning principles; municipal/county plans adapt them locally; and township plans reflect settlement and industry needs with community-based controls. While the law requires integration of sectoral policies, energy planning remains difficult, as diverse facility types—nuclear, thermal, hydro, and multiple renewables—make it hard to designate suitable zones or guide capacity.

For solar PV, the only clear rule is that composite systems combining agriculture or aquaculture with PV are widely permitted, resulting in most installations being placed in farmland, particularly fishpond-based aquavoltaics. Ground-mounted PV, by contrast, is mainly limited to already developed areas or low-value lands such as idle salt fields, subsidence zones, reclaimed landfills, and contaminated sites. This distribution reflects the current lack of precise spatial guidance and planning principles for renewable energy under the spatial planning system.

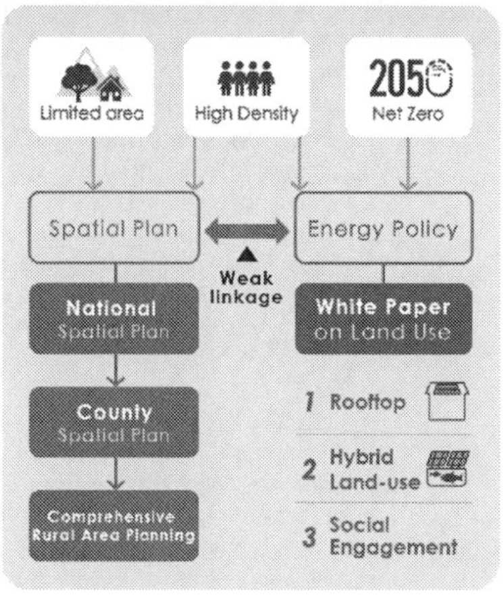

CASE STUDY & DISCUSSION

Taiwan's 2018 National Spatial Plan lacks clear solar siting guidance, limiting local governments and causing policy conflicts. The energy authority should use the 2028 spatial plan review to turn the Solar Land Use White Paper into concrete site selection and land use principles, aligning with rural planning to better implement energy goals. This study compares four land-scarce, high-density countries—Japan, India, South Korea, and the Netherlands—that achieved higher solar capacity. By analyzing how they integrate spatial and energy planning, it seeks to provide a framework for Taiwan to strengthen guidance, align sectoral policies, and advance renewable development.

	Taiwan	Japan	India	South Korea	The Netherlands
Population Density & Solar Capacity	640/km² world 17th; 9.7GW world 17th	333/km² world 27th; 78GW world 3rd	431/km² world 26th; 63.19GW world 4th	516/km² world 20th; 22GW world 8th	423/km² world 24th; 18.85GW world 13th
	• Use the Solar White Paper to guide energy policy with ongoing social dialogue. • Not yet integrated with sectoral spatial strategies in spatial plan.	• Guide energy policy via National Basic Energy Plan with disaster integration. • Embed targets in National Spatial Plan, locals set zoning and controls.	• National solar mission to guide off-grid and grid-connected development. • Spatial planning defines local permitted grid-connected zones and review rules.	• Integrate energy plan with national spatial planning to guide local growth. • Municipal scale: plan energy with public facilities, stressing local participation and siting rules.	• Embed energy goals in the National Environmental Vision. • Local plans, shaped by citizen participation, set overall development and review rules.

Spatial Planning and Energy Sector Integration

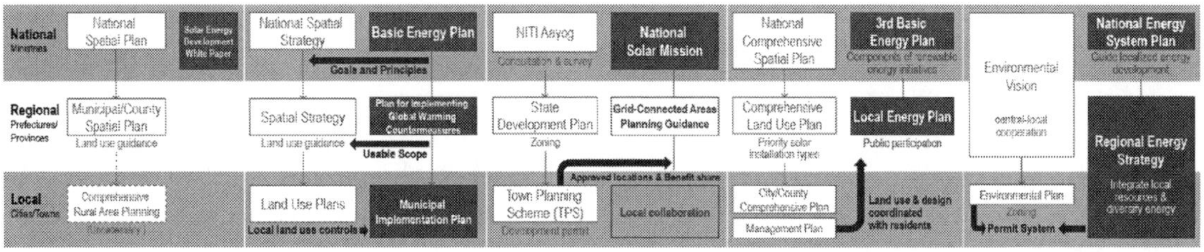

	Taiwan	Japan	India	South Korea	The Netherlands
Insights from Cases	Taiwan draws on four countries' models of spatial–energy integration to guide its policy planning.	Taiwan's spatial framework aligns most with Japan's, where layered governance and community-led models can guide stronger **local participation**.	India's state-level, localized model emphasizes **benefit-sharing with people**, reducing negative perceptions of solar power.	South Korea shows close **coordination between land and energy planning**, integrating at the policy stage to prevent future conflicts.	Unlike others, the Netherlands requires national approval for development, **emphasizing public participation to align with local planning**.

CONCLUSION

To bridge Taiwan's land–energy planning gap, the White Paper and spatial plans should adopt other countries' strategies in the following principles:

1. **Local spatial plans should align energy development with community needs and local characteristics.**
   - Localized, community-driven
   - Social dialogue & coordination
2. **Local plans should define siting principles for energy development.**
   - Landscape preservation
   - Ecological sensitivity
3. **Central–local governments should coordinate robust monitoring and evaluation mechanisms.**

REFERENCES

- Taiwan Government Reports. (2018–2023). National Spatial Plan; White Paper on Land Use for Renewable Energy Development: Solar Power; Municipal spatial plans; Approved project lists.
- Japan (MLIT & METI). (2015, 2021). National Spatial Strategy; 6th Strategic Energy Plan.
- India (GoI & MNRE). (2008, 2010). National Action Plan on Climate Change; Jawaharlal Nehru National Solar Mission.
- South Korea (MOLIT, MOTIE & KEPCO). (2019–2020). 5th Comprehensive National Territorial Plan; 3rd National Energy Master Plan; 10th Basic Power Supply Plan.
- Netherlands Government. (2019–2020). National Spatial Strategy (NOVI); National Energy and Climate Plan (NECP).

ACKNOWLEDGMENTS This work was supported by the Energy Administration, Ministry of Economic Affairs, Taiwan.

itri537353@itri.org.tw
14F.-1, No.2, Nanjing E. Rd., Songshan Dist., Taipei City 105403, Taiwan, R.O.C.

Presented at EU PVSEC 2025

UTILIZATION OF SMALL-SCALE SOLAR POWER PRODUCTION IN FINNISH GRID-BALANCING MARKETS THROUGH A VIRTUAL POWER PLANT

Eino Kujansivu[1,2], Aleksi Ojala[1], Juho Ylipaino[2,3], Juha Koskela[2]
[1] Solarigo Systems Oy, Pirkkala, Finland
[2] Tampere University, Tampere, Finland
[3] Tampere University of Applied Sciences, Tampere, Finland
eino.kujansivu@solarigo.fi, aleksi.ojala@solarigo.fi, juho.ylipaino@tuni.fi, juha.j.koskela@tuni.fi

ABSTRACT: This study analyses the techno-economic feasibility of small-scale solar photovoltaic (PV) systems (<1 MWp) in Finnish reserve markets through a virtual power plant (VPP) framework. The focus of this study is on the Frequency Containment Reserve for Disturbances (FCR-D) down, which requires rapid response to over-frequency events. In this study, high-resolution production data from one PV portfolio is analysed together with 0.1-second frequency measurements to assess both technical suitability and revenue potential. The results show that aggregated small-scale solar PV systems can actively contribute to grid stability while offering notable financial benefits for solar producers. Compared to pure day-ahead trading, aggregated PV portfolios can offer reserve capacity and generate additional revenues of 5-10 % or 4-6 €/MWh during high output periods, with only marginal energy curtailment.
Keywords: Photovoltaic systems, virtual power plant, power system balancing, demand response, reserve markets

1 INTRODUCTION

The ongoing transition from traditional synchronous generators to renewable, inverter-based sources, such as solar PV, brings challenges to grid stability and power system operations [1]. Solar and wind power are characterized by variability, weather dependency, and a lack of inherent rotational inertia [1], [2]. These factors can contribute to power fluctuations and periods of overproduction during high-output periods increasing the need for fast-acting reserves and renewable energy curtailment [1]. In Finland, the demand for fast-acting, downward regulatory reserves, particularly FCR-D down, has increased rapidly in recent years [3].

As the share of distributed generation (DG), including solar PV, continues to grow, its role in supporting system stability becomes increasingly important [4]. Beyond supplying energy, DG units are expected to provide flexibility, balancing, and ancillary services, thereby complementing traditional large-scale generators in maintaining the reliability of the main grid [5].

By aggregation, distributed energy resources (DER) can actively participate in reserve markets thereby providing both transient and long-term grid services [2], [6]. Aggregation can be enabled through a virtual power plant (VPP) framework, where for example geographically distributed solar PV units can be pooled into a unified cloud-based resource [6]. This enables them to meet the needed minimum market entry constraints [6]. By participating in these markets, aggregated PV can contribute to grid balancing and reduce reliance on conventional flexibility sources. This in turn helps mitigate frequency deviations and supports the integration of higher shares of renewable energy sources (RES).

In addition to technical benefits, integrating into these markets also creates new revenue opportunities for DER owners. In Finland, the average electricity price has decreased each year since 2023, settling at a considerably lower level compared with the price peaks of 2022 [7]. Moreover, price fluctuations have intensified alongside growth in RES production. It has also been argued that the average electricity price in the Finnish day-ahead market will decrease significantly by 2030 as the share of RES increases [8].

For solar PV in particular, this implies lower attainable market values. Because solar PV generation is concentrated during specific hours of the day, additional capacity tends to coincide with existing production peaks. This oversupply lowers market prices during those hours, leading to the so-called cannibalization effect. It has been studied that adding 1 GW of solar capacity to the Finnish grid reduces attainable revenues from solar PV by around 5%, while 2 GW and 3 GW reduce them by approximately 8% and 12%, respectively [9].

As investments in RES are mostly driven by the return rate of the investment, which is largely determined by electricity market prices, these effects have major implications for project viability [8]. Even modest revenue reductions may prevent projects from reaching a final investment decision. This further underlines the importance of diversifying revenue streams, for instance through participation in reserve markets and/or long-term power purchase agreements.

This study focuses on analysing the potential FCR-D down revenues for small-scale solar PV aggregated in different portfolio configurations. The analysis is based on one real-world PV portfolio (VPP1) as well as scaled scenarios with multiplied installed capacities. The objective is to evaluate the extent to which aggregated PV can reliably contribute to FCR-D and how different portfolio sizes impact achievable revenues. By examining these scenarios, the study provides insights into the economic viability of pure PV-based participation in FCR-D. Participation in these markets offers a potential hedge against declining day-ahead revenues and market cannibalization, creating opportunities to stabilize long-term returns on investment.

The study provides new knowledge on techno-economic feasibility of aggregated small-scale PV systems in Finnish reserve markets. To the best of the authors' knowledge, there are no prior studies on the issue. The paper is structured as follows: section 2 describes the methodology and data , section 3 presents the main results, section 4 discusses their implications, and in the end section 5 concludes the paper.

2 METHODOLOGY

This study applies a quantitative approach to evaluate the revenue potential of aggregated small-scale PV systems in the Finnish FCR-D down market. The analysis focuses on the month of June 2025, chosen due to its high solar irradiance and peak PV production conditions in Finland. This period provides a representative case for assessing PV-based participation in reserve markets during times of maximum technical feasibility.

To maintain clarity, the analysis excludes acquisition and operational costs of the virtual power plant (VPP), such as platform management fees. All results are presented on a net-of-tax basis. Reported revenues therefore reflect only the relative improvement obtained from reserve markets in addition to day-ahead trading. It is further assumed that the portfolios participate in reserve markets in all hours where technical feasibility is met.

2.1 Data Collection

An existing PV portfolio was selected as the empirical data for the study. Portfolio VPP1 comprised 16 PV units owned by Solarigo Systems Oy, with a total installed power of 4.9 MWp / 4 MVA. Measured power data with 15-second and 1-hour resolution was obtained for the whole portfolio. To assess scalability, additional scenarios were created by scaling the measured power data of VPP1 by factors of 3 and 6 thus creating VPP2 (14.6 MWp / 12 MVA) and VPP3 (29.2 MWp / 24 MVA).

In addition, data from Fingrid (Finnish TSO) and ENTSO-E transparency platforms were used in the analysis [7], [10]. Fingrids data accounted for 0.1 second frequency data metered across different substations in Finland and FCR-D down hourly market prices. Finnish day-ahead prices were gathered from ENTSO-E.

2.2 Market Requirements

When participating in hourly FCR-D markets, each unit must define a maintained reserve power level, i.e. the minimum power that can be guaranteed for the entire bidding period [11]. For generation in down-regulation reserves, this corresponds to the lowest instantaneous active power within the hour. The maintained power must be equal to or greater than the offered bid to the market, since the full offered capacity may be activated in the worst-case scenario.

Due to the variability of solar PV, short cloud passages can significantly reduce intra-hour power, making the hourly minimum output often considerably lower than the hourly average. In this study, the hourly power offered to FCR-D was determined to be the VPPs lowest forecasted instantaneous power gathered from 15-second data $P_{min,h}$. Due to minimum market entry constraints, the $P_{min,h}$ needs to be equal or greater than 1 MW:

$$P_{min,h}(t) \geq 1MW$$

2.3 Calculation of Down-Regulated Energy

For FCR-D down, down-regulation is directly linked to frequency deviations above the normal operating band. When system frequency rises above 50.1 Hz, down-regulation begins, increasing linearly until full activation at 50.5 Hz [12]. To calculate the energy regulated during a one-second interval, a C_s coefficient was introduced. The coefficient accounts for full and minimal activation (50,5 Hz corresponds to C_s = 1, 50,1 Hz to C_s = 0) and is constrained to lie within the interval [0,1]. The coefficient was defined as a normalized function of grid frequency f:

$$C_s(t_2) = \frac{f(t_2) - 50.1\text{Hz}}{50.5\text{Hz} - 50.1\text{Hz}}, \quad C_s(t_2) \in [0,1] \quad (1)$$

- C_s = 1: full activation at $f \geq 50.5$ Hz
- C_s = 0: minimal activation at $f \leq 50.1$ Hz
- $C_s \in [0,1]$: partial activation, linearly scaled between 50.1 and 50.5 Hz

To calculate the average activation level of down-regulation over one hour, the one-second coefficients are aggregated into an hourly coefficient C_h. This represents the mean share of offered capacity that was activated during hour t:

$$C_h(t) = \frac{1}{3600} \sum_{t_2=1}^{3600} C_s(t_2) \quad (2)$$

To calculate the amount of down-regulated energy during hour t, the hourly activation coefficient is multiplied by the offered minimum power:

$$E_{reg,h}(t) = C_h(t) \cdot P_{min,h}(t) \quad (3)$$

2.4 Calculation of Financial Revenues

To quantify the economic impact of FCR-D participation, three revenue streams were calculated: day-ahead market revenues, day-ahead losses caused by down-regulation, and FCR-D market revenues. These were combined to evaluate both absolute income levels and the relative improvement compared with pure day-ahead trading. The following equations define the main steps of the calculation.

To calculate the loss of day-ahead market revenue L_{DA} caused by down-regulation, the day-ahead price is multiplied by the curtailed energy during hour t:

$$L_{DA}(t) = A_{DA}(t) \cdot E_{req}(t) \quad (4)$$

To calculate the revenue R_{DA} from the day-ahead market during hour t, the average day-ahead price A_{DA} is multiplied by the produced energy E_{PV}:

$$R_{DA}(t) = A_{DA}(t) \cdot E_{PV}(t) \quad (5)$$

To calculate the revenue from participation in the FCR-D reserve market R_{RM}, the hourly FCR-D market price A_{RM} is multiplied by the offered minimum power $P_{min,h}$:

$$R_{RM}(t) = A_{RM}(t) \cdot P_{min,h}(t) \quad (6)$$

To compare the baseline revenue with the revenue including down-regulation, three measures are defined. The baseline revenue per unit of production was obtained by dividing the day-ahead revenue by the produced energy. The revenue including regulation per unit of production was calculated by subtracting the day-ahead revenue loss and adding the FCR-D revenue. Finally, the additional revenue share was determined by comparing the revenue including regulation to the baseline revenue.

3 RESULTS

This section presents the main findings of the study regarding both the technical activation behaviour of the

10.4229/EUPVSEC2025/5DV.3.60

FCR-D down product and its economic implications for aggregated PV portfolios. The analysis focuses on two aspects: (3.1) the frequency deviations that determine when down-regulation is triggered, and (3.2) the resulting revenue effects for different portfolio sizes. By combining high-resolution frequency measurements with detailed PV production data, the results highlight how often activations occur, how much energy is curtailed, and what additional revenues can be obtained through market participation

3.1 Analysis of Frequency Deviations and Down Regulation

The month of June 2025 was analysed to capture high solar irradiance and frequent PV generation. Frequency deviations above 50.1 Hz occurred almost daily, although their total duration was relatively short. Over the observation period, the system frequency exceeded 50.1 Hz for 18,887 seconds (0.73% of all seconds). Despite the limited total duration, the number of individual exceedance events was high: on average 28.6 events occurred each day, with a mean duration of 22.5 seconds per event (Table I).

These findings indicate that although the total time over 50,1 Hz remains minimal, reserve activations take place relatively frequently. Consequently, the FCR-D down market represents a low-utilization but high-activation product.

Table I: Summary of findings from frequency analysis (June 2025).

Indicator	Result
Duration of frequency over 50,1 Hz (s)	18887 s
Duration of frequency over 50,1 Hz (%)	0.73%
Total amount of exceedance events	858
Average amount of daily exceedance events	28.6
Average duration of exceedance event	22.54 s

Figure I further illustrate that activations occurred almost daily throughout the month. This underlines the recurrent nature of frequency exceedances, even though their durations varied strongly from day to day. From the perspective of PV portfolios, this means that down-regulation events are a regular feature of system operation.

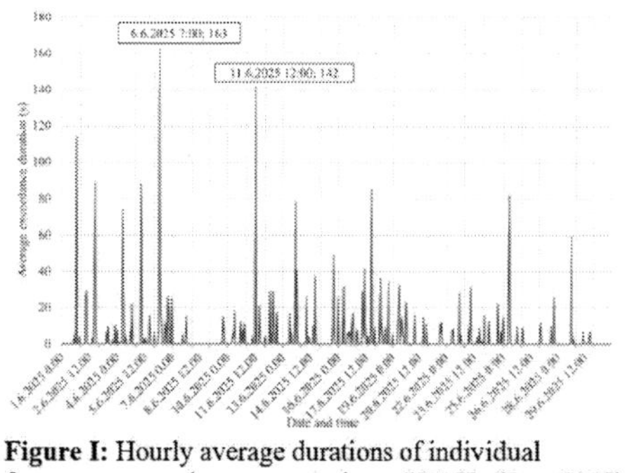

Figure I: Hourly average durations of individual frequency exceedance events above 50.1 Hz (June 2025).

Figure II illustrates the hourly distribution of PV generation (bars) and the total duration of frequency exceedances above 50.1 Hz (line) during June 2025. The results show that frequency deviations are not evenly distributed across the day. Instead, they tend to coincide with the midday hours when PV production is highest.

Interestingly, during the hours between 14:00 and 17:00, when PV output is near its maximum, the frequency exceedances are minimal. This suggests that system frequency stabilises during the very peak generation hours, while activation events cluster more strongly in the morning and late afternoon periods. For PV operators, this pattern implies that the highest production hours may be less exposed to down-regulation, further reducing the effective curtailment risk.

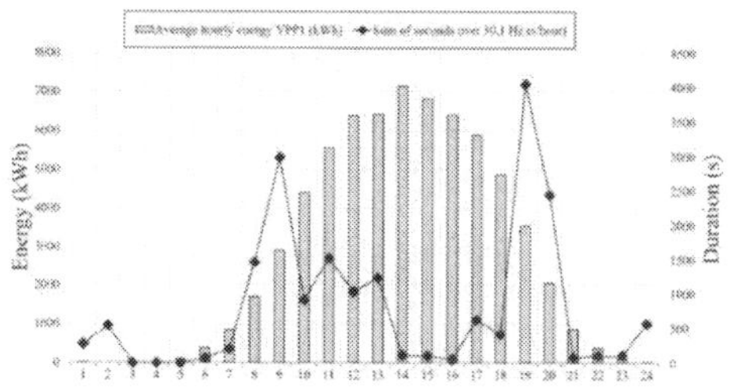

Figure II: Hourly averages of produced energy from VPP1 (bars) and total duration with grid frequency >50.1 Hz (brown line).

Figure III presents the hourly averages of down-regulated energy (bars, left axis) together with the activation coefficient C_h (line, right axis) for June 2025. The results demonstrate that down-regulated energy volumes remain very small, with noticeable curtailment occurring only during a few isolated hours. In these hours, PV production and the corresponding activation coefficient peaks, indicating that system frequency exceeded the 50.1 Hz threshold more persistently.

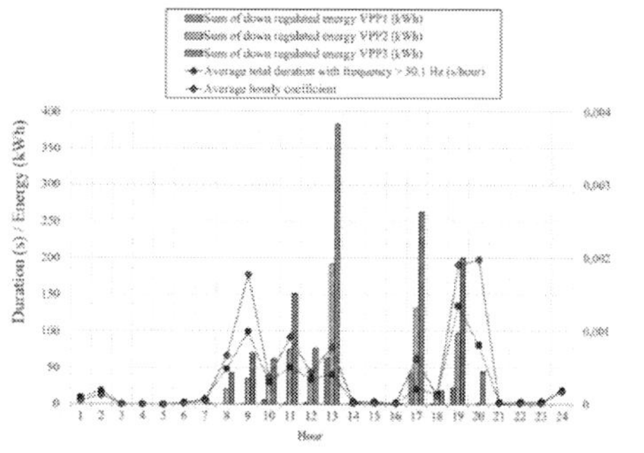

Figure III: Hourly sums of down-regulated energy (bars, left axis), average duration with grid frequency >50.1 Hz (blue line, left axis), and average hourly down regulation coefficient (green line, right axis).

3.2 Financial Implications

In the FCR-D down market, curtailed generation during activation events is not compensated. Consequently, energy losses must be accounted for in the revenue assessment. Table II illustrates, that across all portfolio sizes, curtailed energy represented less than

10.4229/EUPVSEC2025/5DV.3.60

0.05% of total production, confirming that energy losses are economically insignificant.

At the same time, participation in the reserve market increased revenues by 5–10% during June 2025 compared with day-ahead trading alone. Larger portfolios benefited disproportionately, as they met the 1 MW minimum bidding requirement more consistently and could allocate a higher share of generation to the market.

Table II: Summary of Financial Implications from FCR-D Down Participation in all Scenarios (June 2025).

Indicator	VPP1	VPP2	VPP3
Power plant capacity (MVA)	4	12	24
Allocations:			
Total generation (MWh)	667.9	2003.8	4007.6
Energy offered to FCR-D market (MWh)	209.8	927.7	1982.7
Offered share to FCR-D market (%)	31.4	46.3	49.5
Down-regulated energy (MWh)	0.14	0.64	1.32
Share of down-regulated energy (%)	0.02	0.03	0.03
Gross revenues:			
Day-ahead revenue (€)	15 900	47 700	95 300
FCR-D revenue (€)	1 100	4 600	9 700
Day-ahead losses (€)	-11	-35	-71
Revenue efficiency:			
Day-ahead (€/MWh)	59.1	59.1	59.1
Total (€/MWh)	63.0	64.7	65.1
Revenue increase (%)	6.6	9.5	10.1

Figure IV further illustrates that the smaller portfolios failed to meet the 1 MW minimum bid requirement more often, lowering available revenues. Larger portfolios could allocate bids in lower production hours. Moreover, the hourly revenue pattern closely follows the typical solar production profile, with revenues peaking around midday and vanishing during night-time hours. This shows that the financial potential of FCR-D down participation is strongly coupled with the normal generation profile of PV.

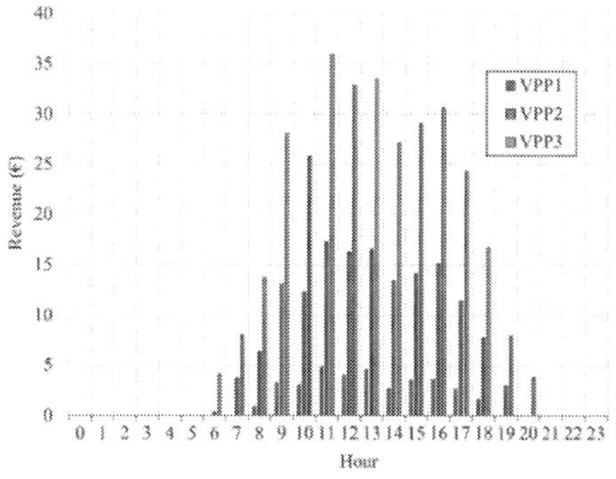

Figure IV: Hourly averages of additional gain (€) from FCR-D participation.

Figure V illustrates that revenues per offered capacity were largely similar across portfolios during active hours, indicating that the marginal value of each MWh in FCR-D down is independent of system size. The decisive factor is the ability to consistently cross the market entry threshold.

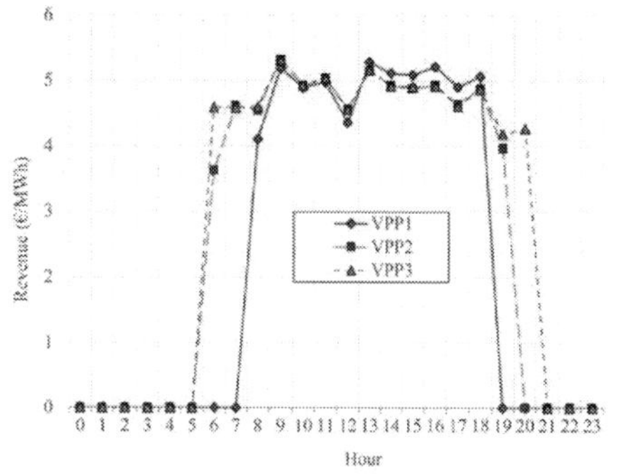

Figure V: Hourly averages of additional revenue (€/MWh) from FCR-D participation normalized to total capacity (lines, left axis).

4 DISCUSSION

This study assessed the techno-economic feasibility of aggregating small-scale PV portfolios for participation in the Finnish FCR-D down market. The findings indicate that while even modest portfolios can technically qualify, the economic benefits scale disproportionately with aggregated capacity. VPP1 (~5 MWp) generated only marginal additional revenues, whereas VPP3 (~30 MWp) achieved a significantly higher improvement in portfolio profitability. These results underline that aggregation is not only a prerequisite for market entry but also the key driver of economic viability.

From a technical perspective, down-regulation energy losses were found to be negligible compared with total PV production. However, activations occurred on average 29 times a day, which may place additional operational stress on components despite the small amount of curtailed energy.

Defining the available bidding capacity remains crucial for PV-only portfolios. The hourly minimum output often falls well below the hourly mean, requiring conservative bidding strategies to avoid non-compliance. High-resolution 15-second data revealed substantial intra-hour variability, underlining the need for accurate forecasting methods and robust VPP management. In practice, this could involve pyranometer-based irradiance forecasting.

It should also be emphasized that the analysis was limited to June 2025, representing conditions most favourable for PV-based reserve participation. The results therefore provide illustrative insights rather than annual averages. Extending the analysis to other months and seasonal regimes is essential for capturing the full potential. Furthermore, it should be emphasized that the revenues showcased in this study are not guaranteed in the long term. The total demand for FCR-D down is limited, and if the total reserve capacity offered increases substantially, clearing prices may decrease. This could lead to a cannibalization effect similar to that observed in

10.4229/EUPVSEC2025/5DV.3.60
020554-004

electricity markets, where additional capacity reduces the market value of its own production. Therefore, while the present analysis demonstrates clear short-term benefits, the long-term revenues of PV participation in reserves will also depend on market development and the balance between supply and demand.

5 CONCLUSION

This study demonstrates that aggregated small-scale PV systems can provide both technical and economic value in the Finnish FCR-D down market. While individual units cannot meet the 1 MW entry requirement, aggregated portfolios are able to participate effectively. The results indicate that during peak production months, portfolio revenues can increase by 5–10% or 4-6 €/MWh compared with day-ahead trading alone, with curtailed energy losses remaining insignificant.

The findings therefore suggest that VPP-based aggregation offers a viable pathway for integrating distributed PV into reserve markets. Participation can provide an additional and stable revenue stream for PV owners, helping to mitigate the effects of declining day-ahead prices and market cannibalisation. At the same time, it supports the reliability of the Nordic power system by offering fast-acting reserves in periods of over frequency.

Overall, while small-scale PV alone cannot deliver balancing capacity, aggregated portfolios can contribute meaningfully to system flexibility. The results underline that market design enabling distributed resources to participate is crucial for both the profitability of future PV investments and the stability of the evolving energy system.

Future research should extend the temporal scope to cover different seasons and longer time frames in order to capture annual dynamics more accurately. Another important direction is to investigate hybrid VPP concepts that combine solar PV with battery energy storage systems, thereby increasing reliability and market participation hours. Moreover, while this paper concentrated on FCR-D down, other reserve products such as aFRR and mFRR represent promising markets for aggregated PV portfolios and deserve dedicated analysis.

6 DECLARATION OF GENERATIVE AI AND AI-ASSISTED TECHNOLOGIES IN THE WRITING PROCESS

During the preparation of this work the authors used ChatGPT-5 to improve readability and language. After using this tool, the authors reviewed and edited the content as needed and take full responsibility for the content of the publication.

7 REFERENCES

[1] N. Riaz, S. Repo, and A. Lindfors. "Evaluating the Self-Balancing Potential of Rooftop Photovoltaic Systems and its Impact on the Net Demand Profile," in *2023 IEEE PES Innovative Smart Grid Technologies Europe (ISGT EUROPE)*. IEEE, 2023, pp. 1-6. doi: 10.1109/ISGTEurope56742.2023.10287534.

[2] R. Sharma and M. Karimi-Ghartemani, "Addressing Abrupt PV Disturbances, and Mitigating Net Load Profile's Ramp and Peak Demands, Using Distributed Storage Devices," in Energies, vol. 13, no. 5, p. 1024, Feb. 2020.

[3] Fingrid Oyj, "Reserve Market Day 2025," publication, 2025. Accessed Sept. 6, 2025. [Online]. Available:https://www.fingrid.fi/globalassets/dokumentit/en/electricity-market/reserves/reservimarkkinapaiva-2025-eng.pdf

[4] R. Nida, L. Peltonen, A. Hilden, S. Repo and P. Järventausta, "Frequency response of a microgrid under the influence of enhanced spatial and orientational smoothing of photovoltaic output." in IET Conference Proceedings CP823. Vol. 2023. No. 6. Stevenage, UK: The Institution of Engineering and Technology, 2023. pp. 3734-3738. doi: https://doi.org/10.1049/icp.2023.0738

[5] Fingrid Oyj, " Johtokatu – tiekartta vihreään sähköjärjestelmään," publication, 2017. Accessed Sept. 7, 2025. [Online]. Available: https://www.fingrid.fi/globalassets/dokumentit/fi/sahkomarkkinat/kehityshankkeet/fingrid-tiekartta-vihreaan-sahkojarjestelmaan-2017-web.pdf

[6] V. Lopes, J. Alves, J. Teixeira, R. Faia, L. Gomes, Z. Vale and P. Salomé, "Enhancing Energy Systems Efficiency through Virtual Power Plants: considerations for the Portuguese case." *2024 IEEE 22nd Mediterranean Electrotechnical Conference (MELECON)*. IEEE, 2024, pp. 1072-1077. doi: 10.1109/MELECON56669.2024.10608732.

[7] ENTSO-E, Day-ahead prices, [Online]. Available: https://transparency.entsoe.eu/dashboard/show

[8] P. Hasanpori Divshali, N. Riaz, A. Kulmala and S. Repo, "Day-ahead electricity market estimation of finland in 2030," in *26th International Conference and Exhibition on Electricity Distribution, CIRED 2021: Online*. Institution of Engineering and Technology IET, 2021. pp 3075-3079. doi: https://doi.org/10.1049/icp.2021.2113

[9] A. Junkala, "The Impact of Cannibalization on Profitability of Utility Scale Solar Power in Finland," Aalto University publication, 2025. Available: https://aaltodoc.aalto.fi/server/api/core/bitstreams/ceae462e-b502-4a49-a4b6-3a4a12e5e9db/content

[10] Fingrid Oyj, avoin data, [Online]. Available: https://data.fingrid.fi/

[11] Fingrid Oyj, "Liite 1: Ehdot ja edellytykset taajuuden vakautusreservin (FCR) toimittajalle." Accessed: Sept. 7, 2025. Available: https://www.fingrid.fi/sahkomarkkinat/reservit/reservituotteet-ja-markkinoille-osallistuminen/fcr-taajuusohjattu-kaytto--ja-hairioreservi/

[12] Fingrid Oyj, "Liite 2 Taajuuden vakautusreservien (FCR) teknisten vaatimuksien todentaminen ja hyväksyttämisprosessi." Accessed: Sept. 7, 2025. Available: https://www.fingrid.fi/sahkomarkkinat/reservit/reservituotteet-ja-markkinoille-osallistuminen/fcr-taajuusohjattu-kaytto--ja-hairioreservi/

SOLARIGO Tampere University Tampere University of Applied Sciences

Utilization of Small-Scale Solar Power Production in Finnish Grid-Balancing Markets Through a Virtual Power Plant

Eino Kujansivu[1,2], Aleksi Ojala[1], Juho Ylipaino[2,3] and Juha Koskela[2]

[1] Solarigo Systems Oy, Pirkkala, Finland

[2] Tampere University, Tampere, Finland

[3] Tampere University of Applied Sciences, Tampere, Finland

Introduction

The ongoing energy transition from traditional synchronous generators to renewable, inverter-based sources, such as photovoltaic (PV) systems, creates new challenges for grid stability and increases the need for balancing resources. One important solution is participation in reserve markets, where flexible assets help maintain system frequency. The Nordic Frequency Containment Reserve for Disturbances, down-regulation (FCR-D down) is a reserve product that activates when system frequency rises above 50.1 Hz. To participate, units must meet a minimum bid size of 1 MW, which small-scale PV systems cannot reach individually. Recent advances in aggregation through virtual power plants (VPPs) allow distributed PV systems to be combined into larger cloud-based units, enabling market access. This creates an opportunity for PV operators to gain additional revenues while contributing to grid stability. This study evaluates the potential revenues from FCR-D down in June 2025 (Finland) for small-scale solar PV combined in different aggregated system configurations. June was chosen as it represents high solar irradiance and strong PV production in Finland.

Eino Kujansivu
eino.kujansivu@solarigo.fi
Project Engineer, MSc student
Solarigo Systems Oy,
Tampere University

Tampere, Finland

Methodology

Data and Scenarios

The analysis is based on measured solar PV production data and high-resolution system frequency records, combined with market price data. Three virtual power plants (VPP1–VPP3) are used as case studies, and together they represent aggregated systems of different sizes. This allows us to examine how aggregation level affects market eligibility and revenue potential.

Measured data:
PV production from VPP1, consisting of 16 small-scale systems (4.9 MWp / 4 MVA) with 15-second and 1-hour resolution for June 2025 (Finland).

Frequency data:
0.1-second resolution frequency measurements from substations across Finland from Fingrid. The data was averaged out to a one-second interval.

Market data:
Hourly FCR-D down prices from Fingrid and day-ahead prices from ENTSO-E.

Scaled aggregated scenarios:
Two larger virtual power plants created from the VPP1 dataset:

VPP2 → 14.6 MWp / 12 MVA
VPP3 → 29.2 MWp / 24 MVA

Market Requirements and Assumptions

- In hourly FCR-D markets, each unit must define a maintained reserve power level ($P_{min,h}$) i.e. the lowest active power that can be guaranteed during the bidding hour.
- To qualify for market entry, the maintained power must be at least 1 MW: $P_{min,h}(t) \geq 1\text{MW}$
- Activation is triggered when frequency rises above 50.1 Hz and increases linearly until full down-regulation at 50.5 Hz.
- The analysis excludes VPP purchase and operational costs (e.g., platform fees).
- All values are net-of-tax, and results reflect only the relative revenue increase compared to day-ahead markets.
- Participation is assumed in all hours that are technically feasible for the system.

Calculations

1. Regulation coefficient, C_s
To calculate the energy regulated during a one-second interval, a C_s coefficient was introduced. The coefficient was defined as a normalized function of grid frequency f:

$$C_s(t_2) = \frac{f(t_2) - 50.1\text{Hz}}{50.5\text{Hz} - 50.1\text{Hz}}, \quad C_s(t_2) \in [0,1]$$

- $C_s = 1$: full activation at $f \geq 50.5$ Hz
- $C_s = 0$: minimal activation at $f \leq 50.1$ Hz
- $C_s \in [0,1]$: partial activation, linearly scaled between 50.1 and 50.5 Hz

2. Hourly coefficient, C_h
To calculate the average activation level of down-regulation over one hour, the one-second coefficients are aggregated into an hourly coefficient C_h. This represents the mean share of offered capacity that was activated during hour t:

$$C_h(t) = \frac{1}{3600} \sum_{t_2=1}^{3600} C_s(t_2)$$

3. Down-regulated energy, E_{reg}
To calculate the amount of down-regulated energy during hour t, the hourly activation coefficient is multiplied by the offered minimum power:

$$E_{reg,h}(t) = C_h(t) \cdot P_{min,h}(t)$$

4. Day-ahead market revenue, R_{DA}
To calculate the revenue R_{DA} from the day-ahead market during hour t, the average day-ahead price A_{DA} is multiplied by the produced energy E_{PV}:

$$R_{DA}(t) = A_{DA}(t) \cdot E_{PV}(t)$$

5. Day-ahead revenue loss, L_{DA}
To calculate the loss of day-ahead market revenue L_{DA} caused by down-regulation, the day-ahead price is multiplied by the curtailed energy during hour t:

$$L_{DA}(t) = A_{DA}(t) \cdot E_{req}(t)$$

6. FCR-D revenue, R_{RM}
To calculate the revenue from participation in the FCR-D reserve market R_{RM}, the hourly FCR-D market price A_{RM} is multiplied by the offered minimum power $P_{\min,h}$:

$$R_{RM}(t) = A_{RM}(t) \cdot P_{min,h}(t)$$

7. Revenue comparison
To compare the baseline revenue with the revenue including down-regulation, three measures are defined. The baseline revenue per unit of production was obtained by dividing the day-ahead revenue by the produced energy. The revenue including regulation per unit of production was calculated by subtracting the day-ahead revenue loss and adding the FCR-D revenue. Finally, the additional revenue share was determined by comparing the revenue including regulation to the baseline revenue:

Key results

- Frequency deviations >50.1 Hz occurred only 0.73% of the time → confirms FCR-D down is low utilization product.
- Deviations happened almost daily (858 times in June, ~29 times/day), with an average duration of ~23 seconds.
- Larger aggregated systems (VPP2–VPP3) met the 1 MW requirement more often, enabling more hours of market eligibility.
- Down-regulated energy was minimal (0.02–0.03% of generation), even though frequency exceeded 50.1 Hz frequently.
- Additional revenues increased with aggregation: up to +10% compared to day-ahead trading alone.

Table 1 summarizes generation, revenues, and revenue efficiency for the three aggregated systems in June of 2025 (VPP1–VPP3)

Indicator	VPP1	VPP2	VPP3
Power plant capacity (MVA)	4 MVA	12 MVA	24 MVA
Allocations:			
Total generation (MWh)	667.9 MWh	2003.8 MWh	4007.6 MWh
Energy offered to FCR-D (MWh)	209.8 MWh	927.7 MWh	1982.7 MWh
Offered share to FCR-D (%)	31.4%	46.3%	49.5%
Down regulated energy (MWh)	0.14 MWh	0.64 MWh	1.32 MWh
Share of down-regulated energy (%)	0.02%	0.03%	0.03%
Gross revenues:			
Day-ahead revenue (€)	15 900 €	47 700 €	95 300 €
FCR-D revenue (€)	1 100 €	4 600 €	9 700 €
Day-ahead losses (€)	-11 €	-35 €	-71 €
Revenue efficiency:			
Day-ahead (€/MWh)	59.1 €/MWh	59.1 €/MWh	59.1 €/MWh
Total (€/MWh)	63.0 €/MWh	64.7 €/MWh	65.1 €/MWh
Revenue increase (%)	6.6%	9.5%	10.1%

Discussion

- **Aggregation is essential:** Small PV systems cannot meet the 1 MW market entry limit alone. Larger aggregated systems enable more hours of FCR-D participation.
- **Economic benefits are moderate but positive:** In June, participation in FCR-D down increased revenues by 5–10% compared to day-ahead trading, while down-regulation losses stayed minimal.
- **Market saturation and cannibalization risks:** As more PV and other flexible capacity enters reserve markets, increased supply may reduce prices and erode long-term profitability.
- **Low activated energy eases integration with contracts:** Minimal down-regulation makes participation compatible with many solar PPAs and guarantee-of-origin frameworks without risking production guarantees.
- **Accurate forecasting and communication are critical:** Reliable high-resolution data is needed for conservative bidding. Pyranometers can improve irradiance forecasts, while local frequency measurements reduce communication needs.

Conclusions

- **PV participation in FCR-D down increases profitability:** Aggregation enables market entry and provides moderate but positive additional revenues.
- **FCR-D down is characterized by frequent but low-volume activations:** Although the total curtailed energy is minimal, activations are frequent and fast, which may stress equipment.

Further details are available in the conference publication.

MARKET UPTAKE ROLE OF COLORED PV: A STAKEHOLDER-CENTRIC ANALYSIS OF FACILITATING AND RESTRAINING FORCES

Bilge Senturk*, Pinar Derin-Gure*,**, Gunes Kurtulus*
* ODTU GUNAM, Middle East Technical University Center for Solar Energy Research and Applications, Ankara, Türkiye
** METU, Middle East Technical University Departmant of Economics, Ankara, Türkiye
bilge.senturk@odtugunam.org, pderin@metu.edu.tr, gunes.kurtulus@odtugunam.org

ABSTRACT: This study examines the market uptake of colored photovoltaic (PV) technologies developed for building-integrated photovoltaics (BIPV), with the aim of elucidating the driving and restraining forces that shape their acceptance across diverse stakeholder groups. Semi-structured interviews were conducted, the qualitative data were thematically coded, and subsequently analyzed through force field analysis (FFA), thereby enabling a systematic comparison of facilitating and constraining dynamics. The findings indicate that restraining forces presently outweigh facilitating ones. Primary among the barriers are high upfront costs, protracted payback periods, and regulatory uncertainties. In contrast, architects' emphasis on aesthetic integration, the visibility afforded by public pilot projects, and the environmental benefits of adoption emerge as salient facilitating factors. Government incentives are revealed to play a dual role: acting as a powerful enabler when present, yet becoming a formidable barrier when absent. Overall, the results suggest that while structural and financial impediments continue to constrain short-term commercialization, the active involvement of architects, combined with targeted policy frameworks, financial incentives, and awareness-raising strategies, can recalibrate the balance in favor of facilitating forces. In the long term, colored PV may thus evolve beyond a technological novelty to become a transformative paradigm that fuses architectural aesthetics with sustainable energy transitions in the built environment.
Keywords: Building-integrated photovoltaics, Colored photovoltaics, Market uptake, Stakeholder analysis, Force-field analysis, Semi-structured interviews, Türkiye

1 INTRODUCTION

In the development of BIPV technology, the redesign of the building envelope as a multifunctional element has come to the forefront. Photovoltaic modules replace building components such as roofs, façades, skylights, and windows, thereby generating electricity while also providing additional benefits such as thermal insulation and daylight control. This multifunctionality enables the creation of a building material that, beyond its role as an energy technology, also supports architectural aesthetics and sustainability. However, it is emphasized that BIPV solutions still face constraints such as high initial costs and maintenance challenges; therefore, access to and widespread adoption of the technology largely depend on further cost reductions [1,2].

In recent years, colored PV applications, a prominent type of BIPV, have been developed particularly to enhance integration into dense urban fabrics and protected historical buildings. Colored PVs make it possible to camouflage photovoltaic cells with unique colors and patterns. Indeed, the ability to obtain various shades such as blue, green, yellow, and orange by altering the thickness of anti-reflective coatings, the application of semi-transparent and diverse color variations with thin-film, OPV, and DSSC-based modules, as well as the incorporation of distinctive patterns through digital printing, ceramic, or mineral coatings on the front glass surface, can be cited as examples of this technological diversity [3]. Market forecasts indicate that colored PVs are largely shaped by aesthetic compatibility and social acceptance. Conventional PVs (black and dark blue) create visual incompatibility in urban contexts and therefore face limited adoption, whereas colored solutions align with architectural aesthetics and are more widely accepted, particularly in public and office buildings [4,5]. Therefore, colored PV technologies gain value in the context of architectural integrity and acceptance, and it is suggested that the market will initially develop in prestigious public and commercial buildings and, over time, become standardized and widespread in the residential sector [6,7,8]. Although coloring processes lead to losses in electrical efficiency, their ability to preserve architectural integrity while enhancing market acceptance renders these solutions a strategic option in line with the nearly zero-energy building target.

The importance of stakeholder analysis in understanding market processes for innovative applications such as colored PV lies in revealing their societal functions beyond being merely technical innovations. In this respect, it is argued that technological performance should be assessed in conjunction with users' needs, aesthetic perceptions, cultural values, and institutional regulations [9]. Indeed, interviews conducted with different actors make visible the barriers and opportunities that standard individuals may not perceive, thereby overcoming preconceptions and contributing to the development of a more realistic roadmap for the market [10,11]. Therefore, interviews can be considered a key methodological tool in such research for understanding market acceptance dynamics, comprehensively assessing the barriers and opportunities related to the technology, and developing more feasible policy and design recommendations. Examining both the barriers limiting the diffusion of BIPV technologies and the driving dynamics aimed at overcoming them is an important step for market acceptance research. In this study, force field analysis, a managerial analysis tool [12] based on stakeholder interviews, will be applied to understand the adoption and architectural integration of the technology.

Stakeholder analysis research on colored PV solutions has found very limited coverage in the literature. In particular, field studies employing qualitative methods on color preferences and perceptions regarding the use of colored PV remain scarce. Among the prominent studies in the literature, Hille et al. [5], in their survey-based empirical research conducted with 408 homeowners in Switzerland, demonstrated that the color of the modules and the degree of integration with the building are decisive factors in user preferences. The same study also revealed that a large proportion of participants, despite higher costs, showed a tendency toward aesthetically compatible and colored PV solutions. In a more recent study [13] conducted in China, two different methods were employed. The first was an online survey supported with photographs, and the second consisted of face-to-face interviews in which colored modules were shown to participants. Through these methods, different building types and color compatibility scenarios were evaluated, and the results revealed that colored modules significantly enhance integration, particularly in urban areas and historical buildings.

Aqel [10], examining the application of colored PV in municipal buildings in Sweden, conducted interviews with 17 solar energy experts from different cities and revealed the decisive role of architects and municipalities in the dissemination of this technology. Similarly, in their study on the colored PV market in Denmark, Klysner et al. [11] clarified the barriers (e.g., efficiency loss, installation difficulties, lack of knowledge) and opportunities (e.g., aesthetic compatibility, biomimetic solutions) to the diffusion of colored panels through qualitative interviews with manufacturers, installers, building owners, municipal officials, and architects. In conclusion, the limited number of studies conducted on colored PV demonstrate that such technologies are shaped by cultural and perceptual dimensions such as aesthetic compatibility, architectural integrity, and user perception. Nevertheless, the fact that the literature has not yet been sufficiently examined through in-depth qualitative analyses clearly indicates the need for interdisciplinary research on this subject.

In this study, the stakeholder analysis to be conducted for colored PV technologies is expected to provide a significant scientific contribution by offering a unique framework for the integration of this innovative technology into current market dynamics and for enhancing its social acceptance. Understanding stakeholders' aesthetic expectations, levels of technological trust, and the opportunities and challenges they may encounter in the BIPV market reveals the critical factors influencing the widespread adoption of colored PVs. Finally, the analysis carried out within the scope of this study demonstrates that BIPV technologies can be associated with green business models in the context of Türkiye and contributes to the debates on green growth and sustainable development.

2 METHODOLOGY

2.1. Aim and Approach

For this purpose, information was first gathered from different stakeholders through semi-structured interviews based on themes appropriate for force field analysis, then coded into data, and finally analyzed using the force field method.

2.2 Semi-Structured Interviews

In line with the aim of the study, a total of 13 interviews were conducted. While most of the interviewees consisted of architects, all participants were experts/experienced in the field of solar energy technology (Table 1). In this way, it becomes possible to highlight the driving and restraining factors that need to be taken into account for the diffusion and development of the market.

Table 1. Stakeholder List

ID	Stakeholder Category	Sub-Category	Experience Duration (Years)
1	Public	Ministry of Energy and Natural Resources	10
2	Public	Ministry of Environment, Urbanization and Climate Change	19
3	Academia	Architecture	42
4	Academia	Architecture	25
5	Academia	Electric Electronical Engineer	20
6	Private	Architecture	38
7	Private	Architecture	23
8	Private	Architecture	21
9	Private	Glass Manufacturing	16
10	Private	Panel Manufacturing	8
11	Private	Panel Mounting/ Installing	12
12	NGO	Solar Energy Association	15
13	NGO	Solar Energy Association	16

During the final review of the coded data obtained from the interviews, 15 key factors (Figure 1) were identified under four main themes (aesthetic and social acceptance, policy and institutional framework, financial dynamics, and technical capacity), and the force field analysis method was applied to the driving and restraining factors.

2.3 Force Field Analysis: Comparison of Facilitating and Restraining Stakeholders

Force field analysis, developed by Kurt Lewin [14], systematically reveals the interaction of opposing forces that shape the adoption processes of innovative technologies. In the adoption of BIPV, the most common facilitating stakeholders are typically architects, contractors, governments, investors, and manufacturers [15,16,17,18], while the restraining stakeholders are generally identified as building owners and individual users [15,19].

The FFA process consists of four steps. First, each stakeholder's comments on the technology (for example, glass manufacturers' emphasis on technical requirements, architects' aesthetic concerns, and users' perceptions of comfort) were extracted as open codes. Second, these codes were then combined and transformed into higher-level themes (e.g., "Aesthetic and architectural integration," "Uncertainty in energy policies"). In the third stage, each factor was scored within a range of -5 to +5 according to its degree of importance and direction of influence (Figure 1). In other words, scoring was carried out by considering how frequently a factor was emphasized by stakeholders and to what extent it influenced their decisions [20]. A factor with a high total score is regarded as both a more critical determinant compared to others and one that needs to be addressed strategically. For instance, if "high costs and long payback periods" received one of the highest total scores, this should be understood as the strongest restraining force in the commercialization of colored PV. Finally, the interaction of the factors was interpreted in terms of how they were strengthened or weakened within the same context. The graphic design is based on Lewin's [14] classical force field model. On one side are the facilitating forces, and on the other side are the restraining forces. In the diagram (Figure 1), the length of the arrows or the total score of a factor visually reflects its relative importance. Thus, rather than direct causality between factors, the graphic illustrates the balance (which side is more dominant) and highlights which forces stand out.

3. RESULTS

The force field analysis conducted in this study comparatively reveals the driving and restraining forces shaping the diffusion of colored PV technologies in Türkiye.

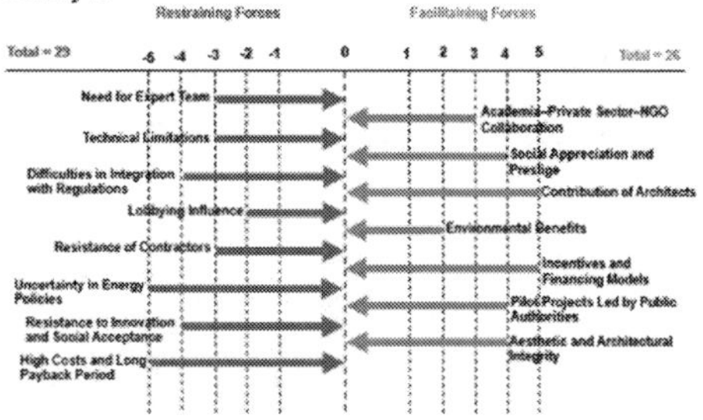

Figure 1. Force Field Diagram

The findings indicate that, at present, restraining forces are more dominant than facilitating dynamics, and therefore the potential for large-scale adoption remains limited in the short term. In particular, high initial costs and uncertainties regarding energy policies emerge as the most critical barriers. By contrast, architects' strong interest in aesthetic integration and the visibility that public demonstration projects can create are among the key facilitating factors. The analysis also points to the dual nature of certain forces. For instance, when public support exists through incentives and policy instruments, it functions as a strong driving dynamic, whereas in its absence it becomes a significant barrier. However, uncertainties in energy policies and difficulties in regulatory integration materialize this dual nature in favor of restraining forces.

Moreover, these forces are also seen to interact with one another. For instance, increasing public awareness of environmental benefits both weakens a restraining factor such as low acceptance levels and simultaneously becomes a supportive force for concerns over aesthetics and sustainability. Therefore, targeted policies, financial incentives, and awareness-raising strategies are of critical importance for shifting the balance.

4. CONCLUSION

In the diffusion of colored PV technology, both driving and significant restraining dynamics are observed to coexist. Beyond the need for incentives and appropriate financing models in the face of high costs, factors such as architects' interest in aesthetic integration, the active involvement of glass manufacturers in the process, and the visibility created by public pilot projects stand out as key elements facilitating the adoption of the technology. In addition, the alignment of colored PVs with sustainability policies and their potential to enhance building value provide a strong basis of legitimacy in terms of social acceptance and prestige effects. Nevertheless, the lack of public incentives, difficulties in regulatory integration, and uncertainties in energy policies are among the main constraints hindering the widespread diffusion of the technology.

On the other hand, the continued dominance of restraining forces particularly high costs and long payback periods creates a lack of social acceptance at the user level, while raising public awareness and making applications that integrate with aesthetic values more visible can enhance acceptance. In this context, activating incentive mechanisms, developing creative financing models, and promoting experience sharing through exemplary projects in public buildings are of critical importance. In this way, the impact of restraining factors can be weakened, facilitating forces can become more visible, and ultimately the path can be opened for colored PV technology to become a more viable option in the context of Türkiye.

References

[1] Biyik, E., Araz, M., Hepbasli, A., Shahrestani, M., Yao, R., Shao, L., Essah, E., Oliveira, A. C., del Cano, T., Rice, E., Lechon, J. L.Andrade, L., Mendes, A. & Atlı, Y. B. (2017). A key review of building integrated photovoltaic (BIPV) systems. Engineering science and technology, an international journal, 20(3), 833-858.
[2] Lu, L., & Law, K. M. (2013). Overall energy performance of semi-transparent single-glazed photovoltaic (PV) window for a typical office in Hong Kong. Renewable energy, 49, 250-254.
[3] Eder, G., Peharz, G., Trattnig, R., Bonomo, P., Saretta, E., Frontini, F., Polo Lopez, C. S., Wilson, H. R., Eisenlohr, J., Chivelet, N. M.,Karlsson, S., Jakica, N. & Zanelli, A. (2019). Coloured bipv: Market, research and development. https://www.diva-portal.org/smash/get/diva2:1305998/FULLTEXT01.pdf
[4] Hardy, D., Kerrouche, A, Roaf, S. C. and Richards, B.S. (2013). Improving the aesthetics of photovoltaics through use of coloured encapsulants. In: PLEA2013 - 29th Conference, Sustainable Architecture for a Renewable Future, Munich, Germany, 10-12 September 2013, Munich, Germany.
[5] Hille, S. L., Curtius, H. C., & Wüstenhagen, R. (2018). Red is the new blue–The role of color, building integration and country-of-origin in homeowners'preferences for residential photovoltaics. Energy and Buildings, 162, 21-31.
[6] Lim, J.W., Kim, G., Shin, M., Yun, S.J. (2017). Colored a-Si: H transparent solar cells employing ultrathin transparent multi-layered electrodes. Sol. Energy Mater. Sol. Cells, 163, 164–169.
[7] Wang, M., Peng, J., Li, N., Yang, H., Wang, C., Li, X. & Lu, T. (2016) Comparison of energy performance between PV double skin facades and PV insulating glass units. Appl. Energy, 194, 148–160.
[8] Peharz, G., Berger, K., Kubicek, B., Aichinger, M., Grobbauer, M., Gratzer, J., Nemitz, W., Großschädl, B., Auer, C. & Prietl, C. (2017). Application of plasmonic coloring for making building integrated PV modules comprising of green solar cells. Renew. Energy, 109, 542–550.
[9] Müggenburg, H., Tillmans, A., Schweizer-Ries, P., Raabe, T., & Adelmann, P. (2012). Social acceptance of PicoPV systems as a means of rural electrification—A socio-technical case study in Ethiopia. Energy for Sustainable Development, 16(1), 90-97.

[10] Aqel, S. (2021). Application of Colored Solar Panels on Municipal Buildings in Sweden: The Multiple Benefits for an Innovative Renewable Society.
[11] Klysner, N. F., Lenau, T. A., & Lakhtakia, A. (2021, March). Building-integrated photo-voltaics: market challenges and bioinspired solutions. In Bioinspiration, Biomimetics, and Bioreplication XI 11586, pp. 32-47.
[12] Taleb, H. M., & Pitts, A. C. (2009). The potential to exploit use of building-integrated photovoltaics in countries of the Gulf Cooperation Council. Renewable Energy, 34(4), 1092-1099.
[13] Zhou, A., Thomaschke, R., Wessels, A., Glunz, S., Speck, T., & Kiesel, A. (2024). (Not) in my city: An explorative study on social acceptance of photovoltaic installations on buildings. Technology in Society, 79, 102725.
[14] Lewin K. (1951). Field Theory in Social Science. Harper Row, London.
[15] Curtius, H. C. (2018). The adoption of building-integrated photovoltaics: barriers and facilitators. Renewable Energy, 126, 783-790.
[16] Yap, A. B. K., Goh, K. C., Seow, T. W., & Goh, H. H. (2015, May). Stakeholder Roles in Building Integrated Photovoltaic (BIPV) Implementation. In InCIEC 2014: Proceedings of the International Civil and Infrastructure Engineering Conference 2014 (pp. 951-961). Singapore: Springer Singapore.
[17] Chang, R., Cao, Y., Lu, Y., & Shabunko, V. (2019). Should BIPV technologies be empowered by innovation policy mix to facilitate energy transitions?-Revealing stakeholders' different perspectives using Q methodology. Energy Policy, 129, 307-318.
[18] Tabakovic, M., Fechner, H., Van Sark, W., Louwen, A., Georghiou, G., Makrides, G., ... & Betz, S. (2017). Status and outlook for building integrated photovoltaics (BIPV) in relation to educational needs in the BIPV sector. Energy Procedia, 111, 993-999.
[19] Wu, J. H. (2023). A holistic exploration on the development of Innovation Ecosystems: A Dutch case study on Building Integrated PhotoVoltaics (Master Thesis). Eindhoven University of Technology.
[20] Pavloudakis, F., Spanidis, P. M., & Roumpos, C. (2023). Using force field analysis for examining and managing stakeholders' perceptions of mining projects. Materials Proceedings, 15(1), 5.

10.4229/EUPVSEC2025/5DV.3.65
020556-004

42nd European Photovoltaic Solar Energy Conference and Exhibition

CF ENERGY
Research-Consulting-Operation GmbH

Rooftop PV on Apartment Buildings: Business Models and Experiences

Christoph v. Friedeburg cvfriede@cf-energy.eu www.cf-energy.eu

Abstract Apartment building roofs offer several GW of PV capacity. But business models must be **usable for laypeople, ideally without extensive hardware, and characterized by intuitive quantities.** Shown are case studies with real consumption data series.

Motivation More than **77% of Germany's citizens live in cities** (1). Globally, 57% of the global population lived in cities in 2021 (2). Accordingly, substantial measures to curb carbon emissions must be continued in urban areas, which includes the energy sector. Clean energy deployment in proximity to consumption also mitigates the need for costly transmission grid upgrades.
In the city of Berlin, the **estimated PV potential is 6.5 – 10 GW.** About 75% of that is on the roofs of multi-family homes (3). Using the rough estimate of 1000 kWh/kWp for PV in Germany (4), 6.5 GW can yield **6.5 TWh of clean energy** from rooftops. 2024 saw an addition of 101 MWp of PV, and a new total of 381 MWp (5). In 2024, almost 60 % of Germany' s electric power generation was from clean power, with the rest still coming from fossil sources (6). **Tapping the rooftop potential is a critical step to reach climate targets.**

Situation and Approach While single-family homes can use an easy self-consumption business model, and large buildings offer economies of scale, **smaller to medium apt. buildings** (2 - 50 units) are facing a difficult situation, with less roof space, and involving owners, tenants, and investors. In Berlin, Germany, on average each building has 2.6 apartments (7). Business models exist (8), but only 2022/23 has new legislation removed some key hurdles (9). Models must be **financially acceptable and usable for laypeople.** System owners must **maximise the self-consumption rate R_{SC}** to achieve acceptable economics, i.e. sell PV el. in-house for higher prices than they receive from feed-in tariffs; whereas the **autarky rate A** determines the savings for the end users who replace external electricity with cheaper solar. Studies recommend R_{SC} of 25-35% depending on system size and external electricity prices (e.g. 10,11). System capacities in relation to in-house consumption is of relevance.
Key quantities: Total electricity consumption in building=C; PV production W_T (inverter data); W_F fed to grid (meter data); self-consumption (in the building) $W_{SC}=W_T-W_F$; self-consumption rate $R_{SC}=W_{SC}/W_T$; $A=W_{SC}/C$

Case 1: Consumption in bldg systems

Framework: Apt. bldg owned by Owners Association (OA). System 8.8 kWp; no battery storage, no smart meters

Business model:
- OC members are system owners **and** el. consumers
- easy allocation of external el. purchase savings and FIT income acc. to OC member's bldg. shares
- building system consumption (elevators, garage, lighting…)
- C = 6,15 MWh/a
- April '23 – March '24

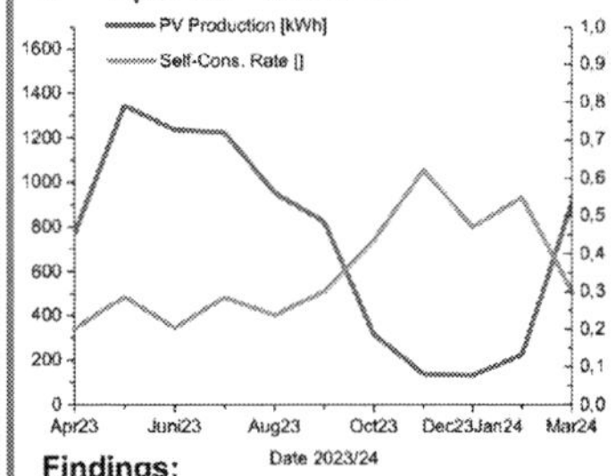

Findings:
- R_{SC}: annual avg. 29%
- **A:** annual avg. 36,3%
- low during spring/summer - more daytime excess PV electricity
- higher in winter, but much lower production figures during that period

Case 2: Case 1 upgrade, connection of bldg systems bus with EV charging stations in garage

Business model:
- like Case 1 + electricity sold by OA to charge pot. users (mostly OA members)
- C = 11213,1 MWh/a, thereof assumed C_{EV} 5 MWh for EV charging, rest C_B for bldg
- May'24-April'25

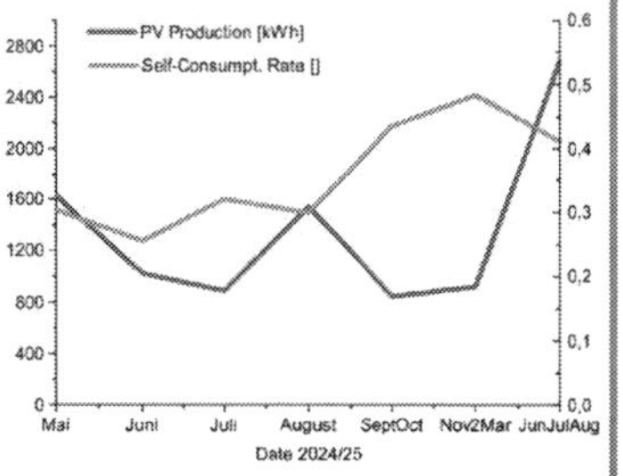

Findings:
- R_{SC}: annual avg. increased to 35%
- **A:** dropped to 21,3% based on C
- (A based on C_B raised to 38,9%)
- again lower in spring/summer
- Measure worked, but effect lower-than-hoped

Comparison of autarky rates in relation to PV production per consumption

Framework: Six apt. bldgs. with mixed owner and tenant occupancy. Systems between 8.8 and 99.8 kWp, no battery storage.

Business models:

P1, 2: see Cases 1, 2 (light blue, purple)

P3: (yellow) collective-net-metered system (no smart meters) operated by CF Energy, electricity sold to apts and for bldg. systems, data from launch April 24-Dec24. **A=0.49, R_{SC}=0.27**

P4-7: system operated by cooperative BuergerEnergie Berlin (12), electricity sales managed by energy provider EWS (13).

P4 (dark blue) el. used for bldg. systems only

P5,6,7 for bldg. systems and apts. Usage data for CY2024 courtesy of BEB, EWS

Shown is autarky rate A in relation to ratio W_T/C

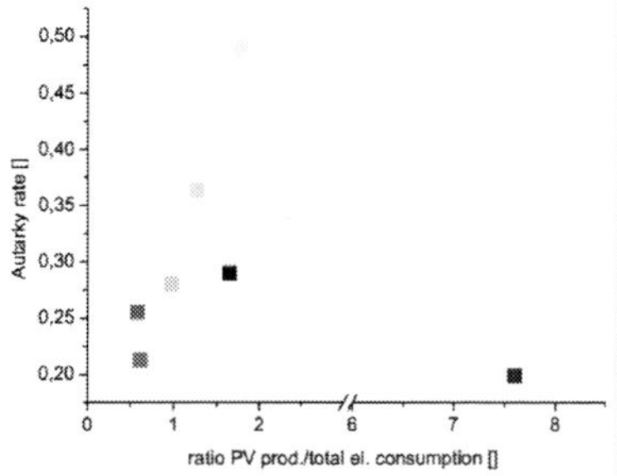

Findings:
- For projects considered, A up to 49% achievable w/o battery storage
- W_T/C ratios of 0.5-2 seem advisable from autarky rate viepoint

Conclusions Simple business models for small apt bldgs have been tested over different seasons or a full year. They have been shown in terms of self-consumption rates to be economically feasible, even without battery storage, smart meters or systematic demand-side management. Increasing the number of users increases profitability, demand-side management and battery storage offer further potential for profitability.

References **(1)** Turulski (2023) Grad der Urbanisierung in Deutschland bis 2021, statista.com **(2)** Urban population set to increase by almost 700 million by 2030 (acc. 15/06/23), destatis.de **(3)** Bergner J. et al. (2019) Das Berliner Solarpotential, HTW Berlin **(4)** regional-photovoltaik.de and Global Solar Atlas (acc16092025) **(5)** SolarCity Berlin – monitoring report 2024 (2025) **(6)** PR Nr.091: Stromerzeugung 2024 (2025), Stat. Bundesamt **(7)** Gebäude- und Wohnungsbestand in Deutschland (2014), Statistische Ämter des Bundes und der Länder **(8)** e.g. Neue Geschäftsmodelle, Bundesverband Solarwirtschaft e.V., solarwirtschaft.de, acc15/06/23 **(9)** e.g. Das neue Erneuerbare-Energien-Gesetz 2023, Energieagentur Niedersachsen, acc.16/06/23 **(10)** D. Ritter et al. (2021) Wirtschaftlichkeit von Photovoltaik-Dachanlagen, Umweltbundesamt 2021 **(11)** Fina et al. (2018) Wirtschaftlichkeitsbewertung und Methoden zur optimalen Dimensionierung von PV-Anlagen und Speichersystemen in Mehrparteienhäusern, 15. Symp. Energieinnovation **(12)** BürgerEnergie Berlin www.buerger-energie-berlin.de **(13)** EWS www.ews-schoenau.de

EU PVSEC
5 DV.3.66 22.-26.9.2025

TECHNO-ECONOMIC MODELLING OF INDUSTRIAL-SCALE SINGLE-JUNCTION PEROVSKITE MODULE MANUFACTURING

Ian Kenchington, Anna Bargues, Philippe Macé, Melodie de l'Épine, Gaëtan Masson, Akhildev Pillai
Becquerel Institute
Rue Praetere 2, 1000 Brussels, Belgium. +32 493 451 720

ABSTRACT:
As the PV industry expands to meet Net-Zero targets, it is entering the multi-terawatt era. Perovskite solar cells (PSCs) are widely viewed as the next technological leap. Competitiveness in Europe requires assessing the economic viability of large-area, solvent-free manufacturing, not just efficiency. This study applies a bottom-up techno-economic model that integrates materials, utilities, labour, and equipment at each process step to estimate factory-gate costs of vacuum thermal evaporation-based perovskite, using a GW-scale baseline and sensitivity analysis.

Results show that vacuum thermal evaporation, while solvent-free, is the costliest deposition step owing to high CAPEX and significant material losses, indicating a need for yield-improvement and recovery strategies. Beyond deposition, structural layup steps (e.g., glass and framing) are major cost drivers, amplified by labour-intensive handling and logistics mark-ups linked to extra-EU imports. Frameless or lightweight foil designs could lower material expenditures, though trade-offs in handling and performance should be studied. Sensitivity results highlight the dominance of equipment depreciation, pointing to automation and scale-up as key levers.

Overall, the findings prioritise R&D on process efficiency, material utilisation, automation, and design innovation to support EU-based industrial deployment of PSCs.

Keywords: Perovskites, vacuum thermal evaporation, techno-economic model, manufacturing.

1. INTRODUCTION

The rapid expansion of PV highlights both the promise of perovskite solar cells and the need to industrialise them sustainably in Europe. While PSCs combine high efficiency with low-temperature, scalable processing, deployment is constrained by stability, yield, and manufacturability, and by Europe's reliance on imported PV value chains. In this study, manufacturing using solvent-free, evaporation-based production routes are studies for better compatibility with the EU's manufacturing goals.

This study, conducted within the framework of the VALHALLA project, quantifies the step-by-step factory-gate costs of PSCs. The objectives are to identify the main cost drivers (labour, depreciation, materials, and yield), and to assess their implications for life-cycle costs. The analysis seeks to inform design decisions, guide R&D priorities on yueld and material utilization, and support eco-design and future EU industrial deployment.

2. METHODOLOGICAL APPROACH

The study applies a bottom-up techno-economic model developed by Becquerel Institute. This model is modular in design; allocating equipment, materials, consumables, and utilities to finite 'steps' to enable an analysis on specific sections of the productive flow.

The productive steps have been set to depict the layup and manufacturing of perovskite based in vacuum thermal evaporation, as set within this study's scope.

The specific process flow is described below. For analysis purposes, all Laser steps are analysed as one:

1. Substrate cleaning and layup
2. TCO sputtering
3. Laser P1
4. HTL evaporation
5. Perovskite evaporation
6. Organic ETL evaporation
7. Inorganic ETL ALD
8. Laser P2
9. Rear-electrode evaporation
10. Laser P3
11. ALD encapsulation
12. Back layup
13. Framing

The data inputs used combine insights from the VALHALLA project, partner consultations on OPEX and scheduling, literature review, vendor information, and expert judgement. A GW-scale baseline is used, with a sensitivity analysis on consumable prices, process and location-based variables. Outputs include factory-gate cost breakdowns by step, and a prioritised set of levers for cost reduction.

For the simulation, a 1GW manufacturing line is simulated to run on a three 8-hour shift per day basis, 5 days a week. The line is set to run at 85% availability, 92% performance and 9% quality yield for an overall equipment efficiency of 77%. **Table I** describes other general investment and operational cost inputs.

3. RESULTS

3.1. Stack and processs overview

For material choice, this analysis focuses in one of the main stacks studied in the VALHALLA project. **Table II** describes all materials used in the stack for the studied module design, depicting their role and application process –sputter, evaporation, ALD, or layup for materials that do not require granular deposition. To enable the objective of solvent-free manufacturing, the absorber ($FAMAPbI_3$) is applied via vacuum thermal evaporation.

10.4229/EUPVSEC2025/5DV.3.67

Table I: Main assumptions

Energy	
Electricity cost	0,10 €/kWh
Labour	
Operator	54,9 k€/FTE
Engineer	103,9 k€/FTE
CAPEX	
Equipment	109 M€
Total consumption	20,4 MW
Depreciation	5 years

Table II: Stack description and application process

Material	Process	Role in Stack
Glass 2mm	Layup	*Front Layer*
ITO	Sputter	*Fr. Electrode*
MeO-2PACz	Evaporation	*SAM HTL*
FAMAPbI3	Evaporation	*Perovskite*
C60	Evaporation	*Organic ETL*
SnO2	ALD	*Inorganic ETL*
Cu	Evaporation	*Back Electrode*
Al2O3	ALD	*Encapsulation*
EVA	Layup	*Rear Layer*
Polybutadine	Layup	*Rear Layer*
Glass 2mm	Layup	*Rear Layer*
Al frame	Layup	*Framing*

3.2. Process cost breakdown

The full costs for the studied stack is 17,5 €cents per Wp, where 13,7 €ct come from defined process steps. The remainder is attributed to costs not related to production, such as overheads, R&D and sales. **Figure 1** provides a breakdown of those costs by each productive step.

Materials covers all net material utilization at their respective step. Utilities consider electricity and water per machine step. Labour represents the cost of the operator requirements per process. Maintenance and equipment items are proportional to each step's CAPEX. Material losses are specific to each material and its application, deposition or layup.

From the coating steps, perovskite evaporation has the highest cost at 1,5 €ct/Wp (**Figure 1**), mainly driven by materials and yield losses. This is followed by bottom contact evaporation, placing all evaporation stages at a relatively expensive position compared with sputtering and ALD. At the boundaries of the process, front layup and framing stand out as major costs, the latter adding high labour intensity. A further look into the components of these steps may explain the main cost drivers.

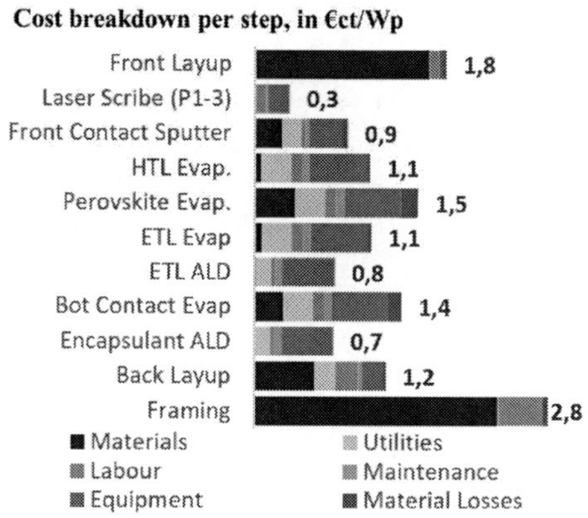

Figure 1: Manufacturing cost breakdown, per productive step

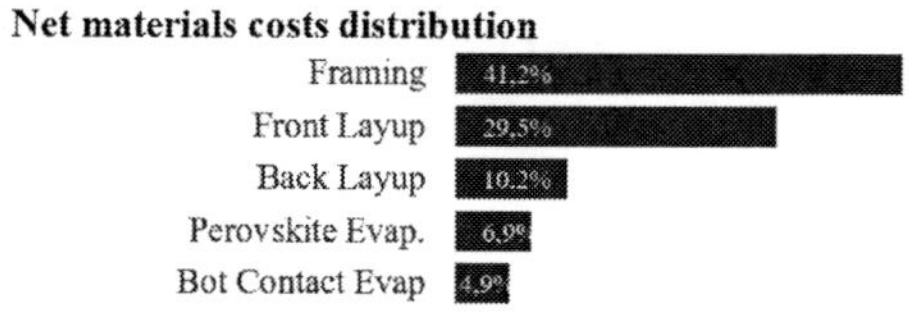

Figure 2: Top 5 net-material using steps, in € step materials/€ total materials

Regarding net materials distribution, framing stands as the most expensive, followed by front layup. Their costs are driven by bulky inputs with high logistics mark-ups, as they are normally procured from outside the EU.

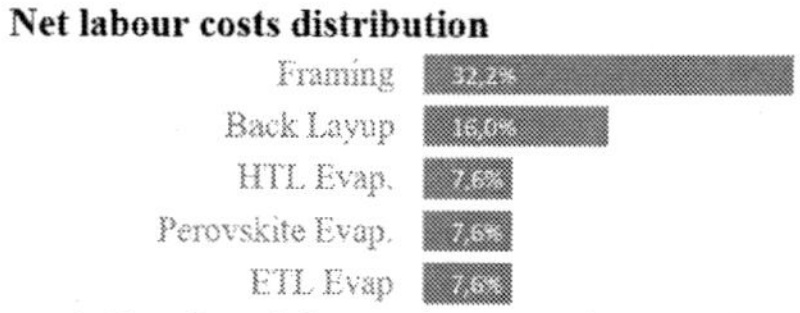

Figure 3: Top 5 net labour using steps, in € step labour/€ total labour

Upon analysing labour requirements, the framing step again dominates, followed by back layup and evaporation steps, also requiring significant operator time. This is due to these steps' need for manual precision in assembly and coating.

10.4229/EUPVSEC2025/5DV.3.67

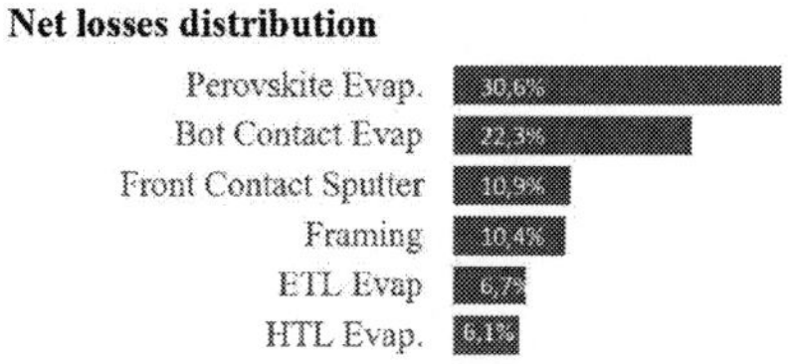

Figure 4: Top 6 net losses steps, in € step losses/€ total losses

On the net losses front, evaporation stands out as the steps concentrating the largest material losses with their low process yields, while front contact sputtering concentrates part of the inefficiencies.

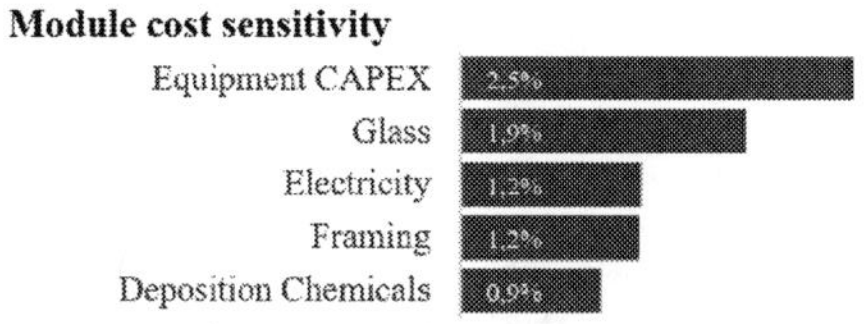

Figure 5: Sensitivity analysis results, in Total Costs variation from a 10% variation on each input

A sensitivity analysis is performed by varying by 10% several OPEX and CAPEX input variables; **Figure 5** displays the results from the top 5 most sensitive among such inputs.

The model is most sensitive to the equipment CAPEX, shifting costs by more than 2% upon a 10% variation. Glass follows closely, reflecting its heavy baseline share. Electricity and other consumables have smaller but still visible effects. These results underline the importance of equipment standardization for large scale manufacturing, and supply-chain optimization for reducing factory-gate costs.

4. CONCLUSIONS

As perovskite developments become increasingly promising regarding their performance and stability, a clear pathway towards mass manufacturing must be set. In this study, a bottom-up theoretical approach was taken to identify the main challenges that mature, GW-scale, solvent-free, and large-sized perovskite modules manufacturing, is set to present. Below are listed the main issues found.

Vacuum thermal evaporation:

EU-based perovskite manufacturing can perform as a solvent-free method under vacuum thermal evaporation, but it becomes the costliest deposition step due to its high CAPEX and significant material use.

Process efficiency and yield losses:

High material losses across all evaporation steps highlight the need for yield improvement and/or residue recovery strategies. Here, perovskite evaporation concentrates over almost a third (30,6%) of all lost materials, followed by copper losses (22,3%), also an evaporation step.

High costs on structural materials:

Framing and glass are major cost drivers, not related to deposition but to layup process steps. Their high reliance on manual processing increases costs and points towards the need for automation, but this is greatly amplified by logistics and import dependence as these must be sourced from ex-EU countries, facing high shipping and import duties.

Structure design alternatives:

Complementary to the above statement, design choices (frameless or lightweight foil structures) can reduce material costs by dropping glass or aluminium from the bill of materials altogether, but this may affect in-process handling or module performance.

Early CAPEX estimates:

Equipment weighs heavy on costs. Nonetheless, as there is little to no evidence of installed GW-capable facilities, some extrapolation was used to estimate the final CAPEX figures. Learning effects from large-scale deployment may reduce these costs over time.

5. ACKNOWLEDGEMENTS AND FUNDING

The work described has received funding as part of the VALHALLA project from the European Union's Horizon Europe research and innovation program under grant agreement N° 101082176.

6. REFERENCES

[1] J. Cordell, M. Woodhouse and E. Warren, "Technoeconomic analysis of perovskite/silicon tandem solar modules," *Joule,* 2025.

[2] N. Chang, B. Newman and R. Egan, "Future cost projections for photovoltaic module manufacturing using a bottom-up cost and uncertainty model," *Solar Energy Materials and Solar Cells,* vol. 237, April 2022.

[3] M. Dehghanimadvar, R. Egan and N. Chang, "Economic assessment of local solar module assembly in a global market," *Cell Reports Physical Science,* vol. 3, no. 2, 16 February 2022.

[4] T. Abzieher, D. T. Moore, M. Roß, S. Albrecht, J. Silvia, H. Tan and e. a. Quentin Jeangros, "Vapor phase deposition of perovskite photovoltaics: short track to commercialization?," *Energy & Environmental Science,* vol. 17, pp. 1645-1663, 2024.

DECARBONIZING SOLAR PV: EVALUATING THE ROLE OF CRITICAL MINERAL SUPPLY CHAINS

Engin Deniz, Prof. Dr. Melih Soner Çeliktaş*
*Ege University, İzmir, Türkiye

The rapid growth of solar photovoltaics (PV) needed for global climate goals has intensified focus on the upstream critical mineral supply chains enabling this technology. This paper synthesizes recent findings on the greenhouse gas (GHG) emissions associated with key minerals used in PV systems – notably silicon, copper, lithium, and cobalt – and the strategies to decarbonize these supply chains. Life-cycle assessments and supply-chain analyses reveal that mining, processing, and refining of these minerals can contribute significantly to the embodied emissions of PV installations, with hotspots in energy-intensive stages like polysilicon refining, copper smelting, and battery metal production. Emissions vary widely by region depending on the energy mix and production practices, highlighting opportunities for supply chain optimization. We discuss mitigation options including renewable-powered mineral processing, electrification of mining equipment, energy efficiency, recycling, and alternative materials, alongside emerging policy frameworks (e.g. EU Critical Raw Materials Act, international due diligence regimes) aimed at aligning mineral supply chains with climate targets. The literature indicates that a combination of technological improvements and policy interventions could substantially reduce upstream emissions (by ~30–40% in many cases) and enhance supply security. Ensuring the sustainability of critical mineral supply chains is imperative for PV to deliver on its promise of truly clean energy.
Keywords: Solar PV; Critical minerals; Supply chain emissions; Life-cycle assessment; Decarbonization.

1 INTRODUCTION

Solar photovoltaic (PV) power is a cornerstone of global decarbonization, with deployment expected to quadruple by 2030 [1]. While PV generates electricity with negligible operational emissions, the upstream supply chains of critical minerals present significant sustainability challenges [2,3]. Modern PV systems rely on high-purity silicon for cells, copper and silver for conductive components, aluminum for frames, and, in storage applications, lithium, cobalt, and nickel. The production of these materials is energy intensive and generates substantial greenhouse gas (GHG) emissions [4,5]. Reducing embodied emissions is therefore essential to preserve PV's net climate benefits [1,2].

Beyond carbon impacts, extraction and processing raise environmental and social concerns. Over 70% of global cobalt originates in the Democratic Republic of Congo, where artisanal mining is associated with hazardous conditions and child labor [6]. Lithium brine extraction in Chile's Atacama Desert consumes about 90% of withdrawn water, stressing fragile ecosystems and indigenous livelihoods [7]. Polysilicon production in Xinjiang, which supplies nearly 45% of global output, relies on coal-based electricity and has been linked to forced labor [1,8]. These cases illustrate the risk of perpetuating environmental injustice in the pursuit of low-carbon energy. As Mulvaney (2024) argues, it is unjust to compromise public health and ecosystems in resource-producing regions to enable decarbonization elsewhere [9].

Together, these challenges highlight the need for a systematic assessment of how mineral supply chains affect PV's decarbonization potential. This paper evaluates the role of critical mineral supply chains in shaping the sustainability of PV by synthesizing evidence from life cycle assessments (LCAs), multi-regional input–output (MRIO) studies, and scenario analyses. It identifies major emission hotspots, compares regional and technological differences, and assesses mitigation strategies. This paper contributes by consolidating evidence across LCA, MRIO, and scenario studies into a unified framework. Unlike previous studies that focus on single minerals or stages, this approach provides a new comparative perspective across materials and regions, and identifies where interventions in supply chains have the highest leverage for decarbonization.

2 LITERATURE REVIEW AND METHODOLOGY

By integrating these strands of evidence, the analysis goes beyond individual case studies to provide a comparative assessment that links technical emission factors with policy and governance contexts. Evidence is drawn from life cycle assessments (LCAs), multi-regional input–output (MRIO) models, simulation studies, and institutional reports. Process-based LCAs provide cradle-to-gate emission factors for PV materials. Reported life-cycle intensities of PV electricity are typically 20–50 g CO_2/kWh, compared with more than 400 g CO_2/kWh for coal power [1,2]. Most emissions arise from upstream production of silicon, copper, aluminum, lithium, and cobalt [4,5].

MRIO and optimization models capture indirect emissions embedded in trade flows. Maeno et al. (2025) show that rerouting Japanese imports of iron and copper from coal-intensive suppliers to lower-carbon producers such as Canada could reduce embodied emissions by up to 40% [10]. Cui et al. (2025) demonstrate that reshoring or diversifying PV manufacturing significantly alters both carbon intensity and costs[2]. Simulation and material flow studies add insights on mineral demand and supply risks. Güz and Murakami (2025) emphasize the importance of integrating economic, environmental, and policy parameters when modelling flows of lithium, cobalt, nickel, and copper[11].

A few processes dominate embodied emissions. Polysilicon production accounts for 70–80% of module energy demand; coal-based production in Xinjiang emits roughly three times more CO_2 than production in Europe with hydro or nuclear power [1,2].
Copper refining and smelting are also energy intensive. Refining in Canada with hydropower results in far lower emissions than in Kazakhstan or Mongolia, where coal dominates [10]. Aluminum smelting shows similar contrasts, with coal-based production in China among the most carbon-intensive worldwide [1]. Lithium and cobalt refining add further emissions, especially in fossil-fuel-

based processes; spodumene roasting and brine conversion are energy demanding, and cobalt refining in China compounds the footprint [5,6,7].

2.1 Scope and Limitations

The review covers studies from 2000 to 2025, with scenarios extending to 2050. Minerals considered are silicon, copper, lithium, cobalt, and aluminum, with regional focus on China, the European Union, North America, Africa, and Latin America. The study synthesizes published analyses and institutional reports rather than generating new emission inventories. Limitations include incomplete disclosure of industrial data, variation in LCA methods, and uncertainty in MRIO assumptions. These are addressed by triangulating multiple sources and reporting ranges where possible.

3 RESULTS AND DISCUSSION

3.1 Emission Hotspots and Regional Variability

Embodied emissions in PV supply chains depend primarily on the energy intensity of refining and processing and the carbon profile of the electricity used. Fig. 1 summarizes upstream greenhouse gas (GHG) intensities for key minerals used in PV technologies, showing both average values and reported ranges.

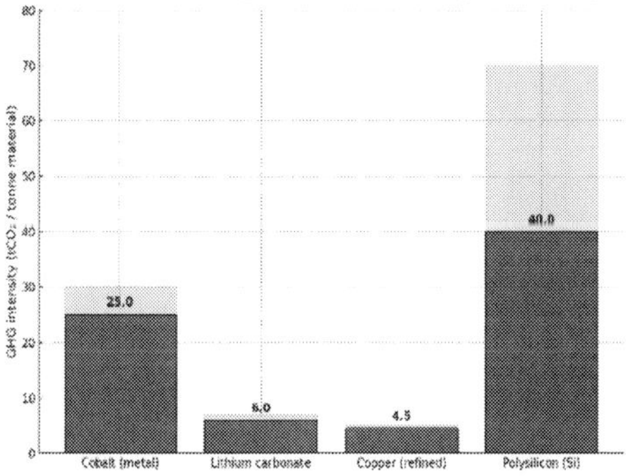

Figure 1: Upstream GHG emissions of key PV minerals (average and range). Data: IEA [1].

Beyond these averages, substantial regional and technological variability exists. Fig. 2 highlights this for polysilicon, lithium, and nickel. Polysilicon production dominates module manufacturing energy demand: coal-based production in Xinjiang emits nearly three times more CO_2 than hydropower- or nuclear-based production in Europe [1,2]. Comparable contrasts exist for copper and aluminum. Copper refined in Canada with hydropower has far lower emissions than copper from coal-dependent Kazakhstan or Mongolia [10]. Aluminum smelting in China, where coal dominates the power mix, remains among the most carbon-intensive globally [1]. Lithium and cobalt refining add further embodied emissions, as spodumene roasting, brine conversion, and cobalt processing are highly energy-intensive and often powered by fossil fuels [5,6,7].

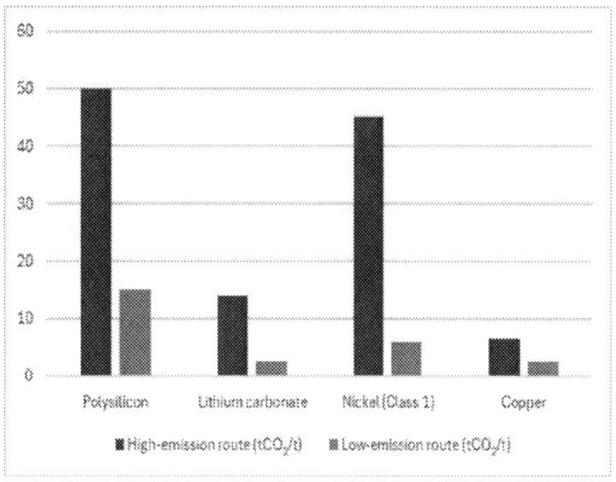

Figure 2: Regional and technological variability in emissions intensity of polysilicon, lithium, and nickel. Data: IEA [1], Maeno et al. [10].

3.2 Supply Chain Scenarios and Trade-Offs

Scenario-based analyses highlight how different supply chain configurations influence both emissions and system resilience. Localising PV manufacturing in Europe, where cleaner electricity mixes are available, yields modest but meaningful reductions in global supply chain emissions while supporting employment and reducing reliance on China [2]. Conversely, abrupt protectionist measures, such as eliminating imports from China without sufficient domestic capacity, may raise emissions as production shifts to coal-based regions. Evidence suggests that balanced diversification is the most effective approach: distributing production geographically to exploit low-carbon energy while maintaining open trade to preserve efficiency [10,3]. In parallel, technological advances have reduced the carbon intensity of PV production. Efficiency gains in wafer slicing, cell processing, and partial decarbonization of electricity halved module-level emission intensity between 2011 and 2021, although absolute emissions rose due to the rapid expansion of global production [1].

Geographic concentration of supply also introduces systemic risks. More than 80% of polysilicon and wafers are produced in China, linking global module availability to a single dominant supplier [1,2]. Over 70% of cobalt originates in the Democratic Republic of Congo, where governance challenges and artisanal mining raise both ethical and security concerns [6]. Lithium production in Chile's Atacama Desert is vulnerable to ecological limits and water scarcity [7]. The Global Critical Minerals Outlook projects that under current policies, supply from existing and announced projects may meet only 70% of copper demand and 60% of lithium demand by 2035 [3]. Addressing these risks requires investment in new, low-carbon mining and refining capacity, supported by streamlined permitting and robust environmental standards.

10.4229/EUPVSEC2025/5DV.3.73
020559-002

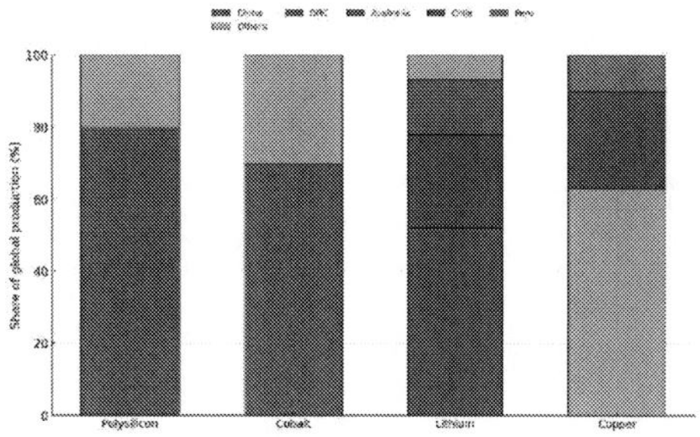

Figure 3: Geographic concentration of PV-critical mineral supply (polysilicon, cobalt, lithium, copper). Data: IEA [3], European Commission [15].

PV supply chain emissions and risks are determined by production geography, process energy sources, and market concentration. Cleaner electricity inputs, technological innovation, recycling, and diversification of suppliers can reduce embodied emissions while simultaneously strengthening resilience. These measures are essential for ensuring that the rapid scale-up of PV deployment proceeds in alignment with global climate targets.

3.3 Mitigation Strategies for Decarbonizing Mineral Supply Chains

Decarbonizing the mineral supply chains that underpin photovoltaic technologies requires a combination of technological, operational, and structural measures. The literature identifies three broad areas of intervention: the integration of clean energy and efficiency improvements in mining and refining, the reconfiguration of supply chains through low-carbon sourcing and recycling, and technological innovation in processes and materials.

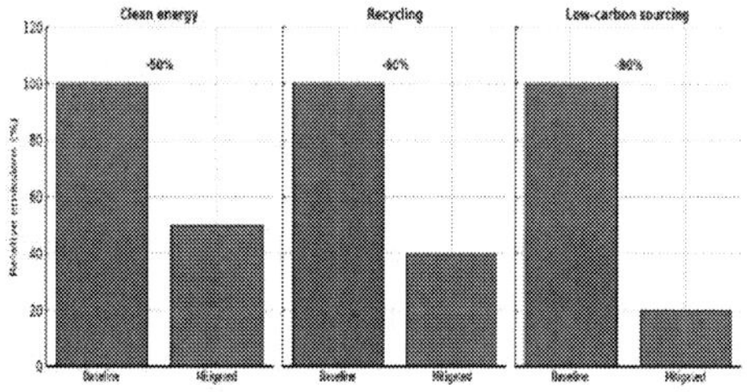

Figure 4: Mitigation strategies to decarbonize PV mineral supply chains (clean energy integration, recycling, low-carbon sourcing). Data: IEA [3], Islami et al. [5].

A principal pathway to reduce emissions is the replacement of fossil energy with renewable electricity in mining and refining. The deployment of on-site solar and wind systems, as well as the use of clean power for electro-refining and smelting, has already been adopted in a number of large-scale operations. These measures directly reduce Scope 1 and 2 emissions and can also lower operating costs in the long term, given the falling cost of renewable energy [1]. Complementary measures include the use of advanced grinding mills, heat recovery systems in smelters, and the application of digital optimization tools to improve energy efficiency. Increasingly, electrification of mining fleets is also being pursued, with battery-electric and hydrogen-powered haul trucks offering the potential to eliminate diesel combustion if coupled with low-carbon electricity [5]. Taken together, renewable integration and efficiency improvements substantially reduce the baseline energy intensity of mineral production.

The geographical location and energy mix of mineral production are decisive factors in determining embodied emissions. Procuring materials such as aluminum and copper from regions powered by hydroelectric or nuclear energy, and avoiding imports from coal-intensive suppliers, can significantly lower supply chain emissions. Multi-regional input–output modelling suggests that such re-routing of imports could reduce embodied emissions by up to 40% for major importing economies [10]. Increasing transparency and traceability through certificates of origin and digital tracking systems supports this transition by enabling verification of carbon footprints [12]. In parallel, diversification strategies that expand domestic refining capacity or establish new supply partnerships in regions with cleaner energy mixes enhance both sustainability and security of supply.

Recycling represents another essential strategy for long-term decarbonization. Secondary production of metals such as aluminum and copper requires 70–90% less energy than primary extraction, and recycling of end-of-life photovoltaic modules and batteries can return significant quantities of silicon, silver, lithium, cobalt, and nickel to the supply chain. Projections suggest that by 2040 secondary materials could meet more than 20% of the cumulative demand for aluminum, copper, and silicon in the PV sector, and as much as 70% of silver demand, provided supportive policy frameworks are in place [3]. Although recycling technologies and collection systems are still developing, their future contribution to reducing emissions and resource pressures is expected to be substantial. Recent advances include environmentally benign methods such as subcritical water delamination [22] and enzymatic delamination [23], both of which demonstrate high recovery potential for crystalline silicon PV modules without the use of hazardous solvents.

Technological innovation also provides important opportunities to reduce emissions. Low-carbon process innovations such as the use of hydrogen in high-temperature metallurgy, the deployment of carbon capture and storage at refining plants, and the development of direct lithium extraction methods are being tested and could significantly reduce both energy consumption and process emissions [7]. At the same time, advances in photovoltaic and battery technologies are reducing dependence on the most emission-intensive or socially problematic minerals. In the PV sector, manufacturers are increasingly substituting silver with copper-based metallization, while in the battery sector the adoption of cobalt-free chemistries such as lithium iron phosphate reduces both emissions and supply risks associated with cobalt mining in the Democratic Republic of Congo. Emerging materials such as perovskite solar cells may further lower the energy and mineral intensity of PV production if stability and scalability challenges can be resolved.

These mitigation strategies are not mutually exclusive but complementary. The combination of clean energy integration, efficiency improvements, low-carbon sourcing, recycling, and innovation offers a realistic pathway to substantially reduce embodied emissions in photovoltaic supply chains while at the same time improving resilience and sustainability. Current modelling suggests that if implemented in parallel, these measures could reduce the carbon footprint of PV-related mineral production by one third to one half within the next two decades, compared to a continuation of current practices [1,2,10].

3.4 Policy implications and governance

Decarbonizing mineral supply chains for photovoltaics is not only a technical challenge but also a matter of governance. The achievement of global climate goals, including the 1.5 °C target of the Paris Agreement, depends on decarbonizing industrial supply chains in parallel with energy generation [13,14].

International accords such as the Paris Agreement [13] and the Glasgow Climate Pact [14] have expanded the focus of climate policy to include industrial emissions. Regional initiatives follow this trend. The European Union's Critical Raw Materials Act sets binding targets for domestic extraction (10%), processing (40%), and recycling (15%) of annual consumption, while requiring diversification of imports so that no more than 65% originates from a single country [15]. These provisions are coupled with strict environmental and social standards, effectively linking supply security with sustainability. Since exporters to Europe must comply with these requirements, the CRMA is expected to shape global production practices [3].

Responsible sourcing is increasingly codified in law. The EU Battery Regulation requires companies to calculate and disclose the carbon footprint of batteries and comply with OECD due diligence guidelines [12]. In the United States, enforcement actions restrict imports of polysilicon and related products linked to forced labor in Xinjiang, as documented in official labor investigations [8]. Traceability initiatives such as the Global Battery Alliance's Battery Passport are emerging to verify origin and sustainability metrics [17]. Trade measures are also evolving: the EU Carbon Border Adjustment Mechanism internalizes carbon costs for imports in energy-intensive sectors [18], while the Minerals Security Partnership coordinates cross-country investment in sustainable mining [19]. Incentives complement regulation: the U.S. Inflation Reduction Act provides tax credits for critical minerals processed domestically or in free-trade countries [20], and carbon pricing in Canada makes low-carbon metallurgy more competitive [21].

The policy landscape is developing rapidly, reflecting the recognition that mineral supply chains are central to the energy transition [3,17]. Concerns remain, however, that strict regulation could slow project development or raise costs, creating bottlenecks in mineral availability [3]. Policymakers therefore need to balance carrots and sticks: providing incentives for investment while enforcing sustainability standards. International coordination will be essential to avoid fragmentation or carbon leakage [10,2]. The emerging consensus is that critical minerals governance must integrate security and sustainability, ensuring that clean energy technologies are supported by clean and resilient supply chains [3, 15].

4 SUMMARY AND CONCLUSIONS

The decarbonization of solar PV must extend beyond electricity generation to the mineral supply chains that underpin the technology. Rising demand for silicon, copper, lithium, and cobalt could significantly increase upstream emissions if left unchecked, partially offsetting PV's climate benefits [1,2]. Scenario studies indicate that powering mining and refining with renewable energy, improving process efficiencies, and shifting to low-carbon suppliers can reduce embodied emissions by 30–40% in the near term [10,5]. In the longer run, scaling recycling of PV modules and batteries could meet a substantial share of demand, while material innovations such as low-silver cell designs or cobalt-free batteries further lessen dependence on high-impact inputs [3,6].

Achieving these gains requires stronger commitments from both industry and policymakers. Manufacturers can lead by disclosing upstream emissions and adopting Scope 3 reduction targets, while governments can align climate and resource policies through carbon pricing, recycling mandates, and critical minerals strategies [12,13]. Such measures move beyond incremental efficiency gains and address the systemic drivers of supply chain emissions. International cooperation on standards, transparency, and responsible mining practices will be essential to ensure security of supply without sacrificing environmental or social integrity.

Ultimately, reducing the upstream footprint of mineral supply chains is indispensable if PV is to remain one of the lowest-carbon energy sources. By combining clean energy inputs, circular material flows, and robust governance reforms, the PV industry can expand while enhancing resilience and equity. Only with sustainable and just supply chains can solar power fully deliver on its promise as the backbone of a net-zero future [3,2]. The novelty of this work lies in its integration of diverse methods into a coherent assessment of PV mineral supply chains. The synthesis offers new insights into priority areas for action, highlighting leverage points such as renewable-powered refining, diversified sourcing, and circular material flows. These results provide the PV community and policymakers with a consolidated framework for guiding sustainable supply chain strategies.

References

[1] International Energy Agency (IEA), Solar PV Global Supply Chains, Paris, 2022. Available at: https://www.iea.org/reports/solar-pv-global-supply-chains

[2] Cui, H. et al., Policy-driven transformation of global solar PV supply chains and resulting impacts, Nature Communications, Vol. 14, No. 61979, 2025. https://doi.org/10.1038/s41467-025-61979-5

[3] International Energy Agency (IEA), Global Critical Minerals Outlook 2025, Paris, 2025. Available at: https://www.iea.org/reports/global-critical-minerals-outlook-2025

[4] Ramírez-Márquez, C., Posadas-Paredes, T., and Ponce-Ortega, J. M., From Resource Abundance to Responsible Scarcity: Rethinking Natural Resource Utilization in the Age of Hyper-Consumption, Resources, Vol. 14, No. 8, p. 118, 2025. https://doi.org/10.3390/resources14080118

[5] Islami, M. S., Urmee, T., Lund, C., Bahri, P. A., and Anisuzzaman, M., Decarbonisation strategies for critical mineral supply chain: State-of-the-art in mining and refining industries, Renewable & Sustainable Energy Reviews, Vol. 218, 115811, 2025. https://doi.org/10.1016/j.rser.2025.115811

[6] Baumann-Pauly, D., Why cobalt mining in the DRC needs urgent attention, Council on Foreign Relations Blog, 2020. Available at: https://www.cfr.org/blog/why-cobalt-mining-drc-needs-urgent-attention

[7] Cambero, F., Lithium mining is slowly sinking Chile's Atacama salt flat, study shows, Reuters, 2024. Available at: https://www.reuters.com/sustainability/land-use-biodiversity/lithium-mining-is-slowly-sinking-chiles-atacama-salt-flat-study-shows-2024-08-22/

[8] U.S. Department of Labor (DOL), ILAB: Solar supply chain "forced labor" storyboard, Washington, DC, 2023. Available at: https://www.dol.gov/agencies/ilab/reports/child-labor/list-of-goods/supply-chains/solar

[9] Mulvaney, D., Embodied energy injustice and the political ecology of solar power, Energy Research & Social Science, Vol. 115, 103607, 2024. https://doi.org/10.1016/j.erss.2024.103607

[10] Maeno, T., Tokito, S., Yokoi, R., and Kagawa, S., Global supply chain restructuring for low-carbon procurement of minerals, Resources, Environment and Sustainability, Vol. 20, 100215, 2025. https://doi.org/10.1016/j.resenv.2025.100215

[11] Güz, Ş. and Murakami, S., A systematic literature review of simulation models for flows, markets, and sustainability of critical energy transition minerals, Resources, Conservation and Recycling Advances, Vol. 27, 200271, 2025. https://doi.org/10.1016/j.rcradv.2025.200271

[12] OECD, Responsible mineral supply chains, Paris, 2023. Available at: https://www.oecd.org/en/topics/sub-issues/due-diligence-guidance-for-responsible-business-conduct/responsible-mineral-supply-chains.html

[13] UNFCCC, Paris Agreement, Bonn, 2015. Available at: https://unfccc.int/process-and-meetings/the-paris-agreement

[14] UNFCCC, Glasgow Climate Pact, Bonn, 2021. Available at: https://unfccc.int/process-and-meetings/conferences/glasgow-climate-change-conference-october-november-2021/outcomes-of-the-glasgow-climate-change-conference

[15] European Commission, Critical Raw Materials Act, Brussels, 2023. Available at: https://single-market-economy.ec.europa.eu/sectors/raw-materials/areas-specific-interest/critical-raw-materials/critical-raw-materials-act_en

[16] European Parliament, Regulation (EU) 2023/1542 concerning batteries and waste batteries, Brussels, 2023.

[17] OECD, Global Battery Alliance: Battery Passport initiative, Paris, 2023. Available at: https://www.globalbattery.org/battery-passport/

[18] European Commission, Carbon Border Adjustment Mechanism (CBAM), Brussels, 2023. Available at: https://taxation-customs.ec.europa.eu/carbon-border-adjustment-mechanism_en

[19] U.S. Department of State, Minerals Security Partnership, Washington, DC, 2022. Available at: https://www.state.gov/minerals-security-partnership/

[20] U.S. Congress, Inflation Reduction Act, Washington, DC, 2022. Available at: https://www.congress.gov/bill/117th-congress/house-bill/5376

[21] Government of Canada, Carbon pricing framework, Ottawa, 2023. Available at: https://www.canada.ca/en/services/environment/weather/climatechange/climate-plan/carbon-pollution-pricing.html

[22] A. Birtürk, M.S. Çeliktaş, Subcritical water delamination: A promising path to efficient recycling of critical minerals, Journal of Cleaner Production, Vol. 469, 143147, 2024. https://doi.org/10.1016/j.jclepro.2024.143147

[23] S.C. Karagöz, T.K. Gündoğdu, H. Sarıaltın, M.S. Çeliktaş, A novel enzymatic delamination method for sustainable recycling of crystalline silicon photovoltaic (c-Si PV) modules, Separation and Purification Technology 361 (2025) 131373. https://doi.org/10.1016/j.seppur.2024.131373

EU PVSEC 2025
42nd European Photovoltaic Solar Energy Conference and Exhibition

DECARBONIZING SOLAR PV: EVALUATING THE ROLE OF CRITICAL MINERAL SUPPLY CHAINS

Engin Deniz, Prof. Dr. Melih Soner Çeliktaş*

*Ege University, İzmir, Türkiye

INTRODUCTION

Solar PV is central to global decarbonization, with capacity expected to quadruple by 2030. While PV electricity is nearly emission-free in operation, upstream supply chains of critical minerals present significant sustainability challenges. High-purity silicon, copper, lithium, and cobalt are energy-intensive to mine and refine, generating substantial greenhouse gas emissions that risk offsetting PV's climate benefits. Regional practices also raise environmental and social concerns, from child labor in cobalt mining to water stress in lithium brine extraction and coal-based polysilicon production in Xinjiang. Addressing these upstream impacts is essential for PV to remain a truly sustainable technology.

METHODOLOGY

This study synthesizes findings from life cycle assessments (LCA), multi-regional input–output (MRIO) models, simulation studies, and institutional reports. LCAs quantify cradle-to-gate emission factors for PV-critical minerals, while MRIO captures indirect emissions embodied in international trade flows. Simulation and material flow models are used to explore future demand and supply risks, while scenario analysis evaluates the effects of decarbonization measures such as renewable-powered refining, electrification of mining fleets, and recycling. This mixed-methods approach enables identification of emission hotspots, comparison of regional and technological differences, and assessment of mitigation strategies under alternative supply chain futures, with results reported as ranges to reflect uncertainty.

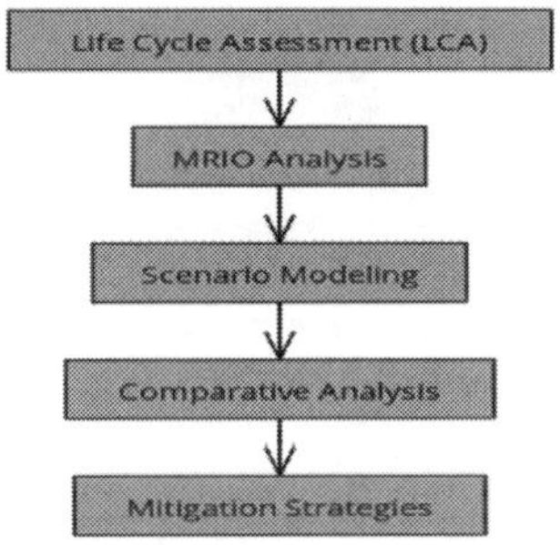

Figure 1: Analytical framework (LCA + MRIO + scenarios ⟶ comparative analysis ⟶ mitigation)

RESULTS

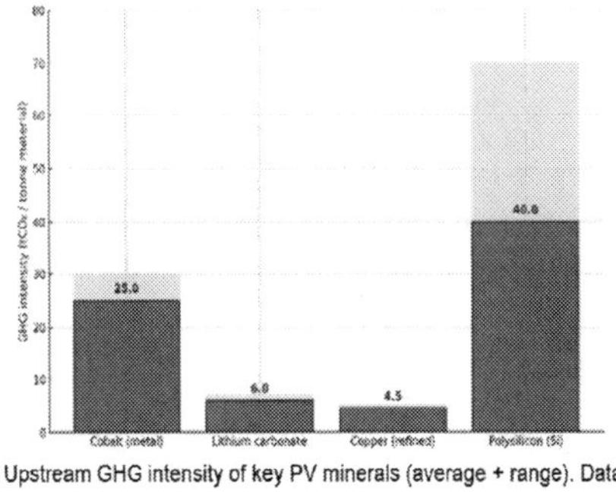

Figure 2: Upstream GHG intensity of key PV minerals (average + range). Data: IEA [1]

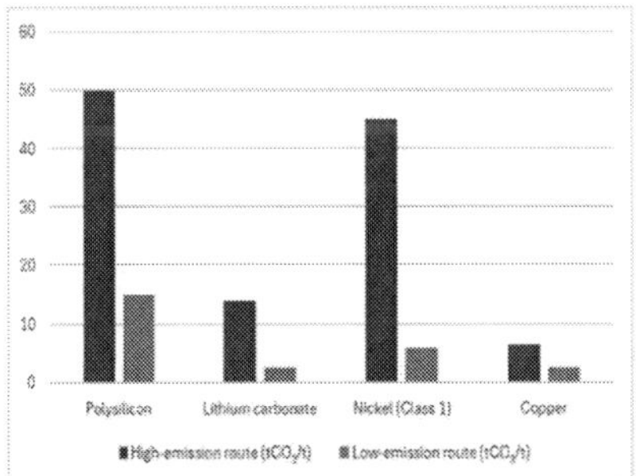

Figure 3: Regional variability in emissions intensity for polysilicon, lithium, nickel. Data: IEA [2].

RESULTS CONT.

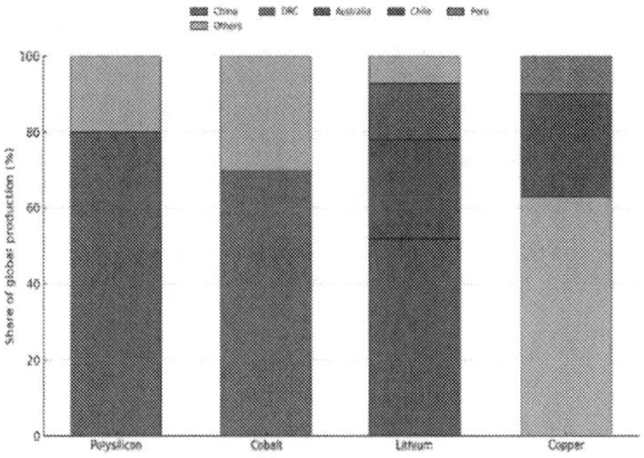

Figure 4: Geographic concentration of PV-critical mineral supply. Data: IEA [2].

MITIGATION STRATEGIES

- Renewable-powered refining can cut emissions by ~50%.
- Recycling reduces energy use by 70–90%.
- Electrified mining fleets eliminate diesel combustion.
- Substitution and material efficiency ease pressure on critical minerals.

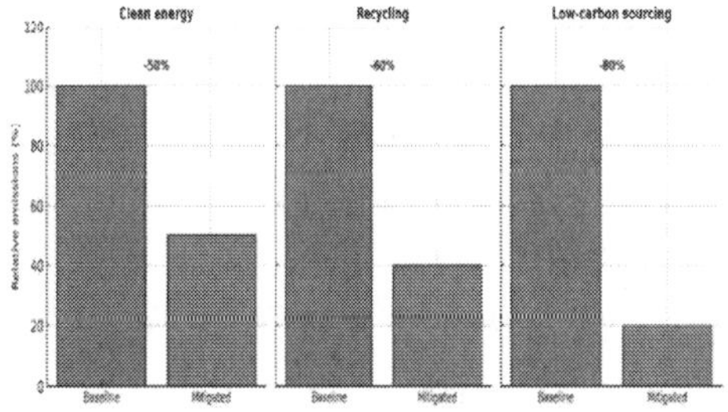

Figure 5: Mitigation strategies for upstream decarbonization (clean energy, recycling, low-carbon sourcing). Sources: IEA [2]

POLICY IMPLICATIONS

- EU Critical Raw Materials Act (CRMA): requires that at least 40% of strategic mineral processing capacity be located in the EU by 2030.
- Paris Agreement: links the decarbonization of mineral supply chains to global climate targets, reinforcing the need to cut upstream emissions.
- EU Carbon Border Adjustment Mechanism (CBAM): will place a carbon price on imported materials, increasing the competitiveness of low-emission supply routes.

CONCLUSIONS

- Critical minerals are major emission hotspots in the solar PV supply chain.
- Mitigation strategies can reduce embodied emissions by 30–40%, particularly through renewable-powered refining and recycling.
- Combining policy, technology, and recycling is essential to build resilient and low-carbon supply chains for solar PV.

REFERENCES

[1] International Energy Agency (IEA). Solar PV Global Supply Chains. Paris: IEA, 2022.

[2] International Energy Agency (IEA). Global Critical Minerals Outlook 2025. Paris: IEA, 2025.

[3] Cui, H. et al. Nature Communications, 2025 — analysis of PV supply-chain decarbonization and regional shifts.

[4] European Commission. Proposal for a Regulation on Critical Raw Materials (CRMA), COM(2023) 160 final, 2023.

[5] United Nations (UNFCCC). Paris Agreement, 2015.

A FINANCIAL MODEL FOR THE DEPLOYMENT OF KOREAN FARM-BASED PHOTOVOLTAIC SYSTEM

*Hye-mi Hwang, Seok-whan Ko , Woo-gyun Shin, Young Chul Ju, Jin-Seok Lee
Renewable Energy System Laboratory, Korea Institute of Energy Research, Rep. of Korea
presenting author (hyemi@kier.re.kr)

Abstract

With the increasing emphasis on the importance of photovoltaic (PV) deployment for achieving carbon neutrality by 2050, the expansion of PV systems in rural areas is expected to grow in Korea. As rural households in Korea represent economically vulnerable regions due to declining agricultural income caused by an aging population, the deployment of farm-based photovoltaic systems is expected to generate additional non-agricultural income (from solar power generation), thereby contributing to increased household income. However, current government-supported rural PV programs often require substantial upfront investment from participants, limiting access for many farming households.

To address this limitation, this study proposes a project financing model aimed at revitalizing rural PV deployment, based on a previously developed lightweight rooftop photovoltaic system. The proposed model is designed to enable broad participation among farmers while ensuring economic feasibility. This study establishes standardized deployment units for farm-based photovoltaic systems applicable to individual farmhouses, storage facilities, and livestock barns. A rental-based structure is proposed to ensure revenue generation for each deployment unit based on system capacity. Furthermore, the proposed financial model is applied to these standardized units to analyze its economic feasibility from both the farmers' and project developers' perspectives.

Rural Solar PV Financing Model Design

Target characteristics

- Aging workforce
- Capital shortage from income decline
- Farmland/forest-based site

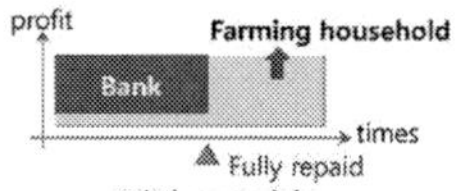

<Existing model>

<Proposed model>

Financing structure

- Social economy organization- based model
- PV equipment rental → short maturity profile
- Easy to recycle & re-use facilities

Standard PV installation unit

- Set rental units : 3 kW, 9 kW
- Considering marginal cost changes & farm size
- Stable marginal cost at 100kW; reduced under 100kW
- 99 kW standard unit finalized (subsidized unit 30kW)

Standard rental unit	
Residential	3 kW
Cattle shed/ Warehouse	9 kW

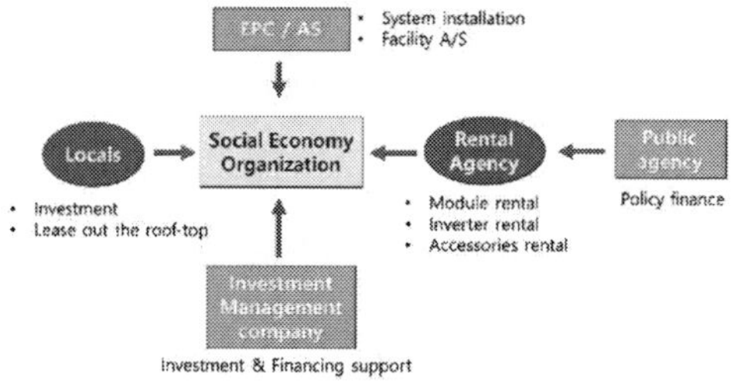

< Rural PV : Finance & Deployment Structure >

Financial Model Economic Analysis

Return Analysis for Rental Providers

- Rental agency deploys PV to 20% of Farms (99kW/30kW)
- **Full Net Income Distribution : Equity IRR 3.29%**
- Case : 20-Year Rental
- 50% Leverage (3% interest, 20-year Amortization)
  : Equity IRR 4.23%

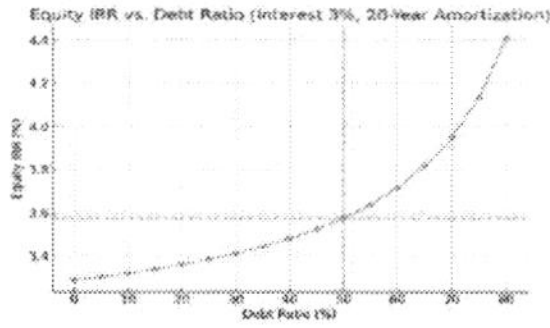

Key Risk Analysis

- Key Risk
  : Rental termination, unpaid rental fees, Equipment failure
- If 5% of rentals are terminated after 1year
  → IRR drops by 0.4%
- Managing cost risks
  (1) cost-related risks reflected in rental fees
  (2) covered by insurance

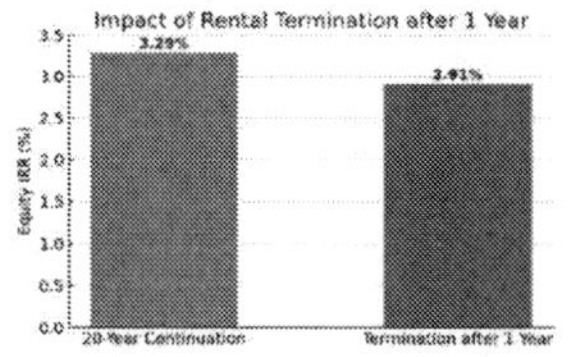

Economic Analysis of Rural PV Financing Model

- Assumption
  : Capacity Factor 14%, REC+SMP 135 KRW/kWh
- Economic Feasibility Secured for 99kW/30kW

Item	Standard (99kW)	subsidized (30kW)
NPV	KRW 25.6 million	KRW 51.6 million
IRR	16.7%	9.3%
Pay back period	6 years	8 years
B/C	1.4	1.6

Sensitivity Analysis of Rural PV Model

- 0.5% Increase in Capacity Factor → 2~ 3% Increase in IRR
- 5 KRW Increase in Electricity sales price →2~3% Increase in IRR

C.F(%)	14.5	15	15.5	16	16.5
IRR(%)	16.5	19.1	21.6	24	26.4
NPV (KRW billion)	23.9	30.3	36.7	43.1	49.4
PBP(year)	5	4	4	4	3

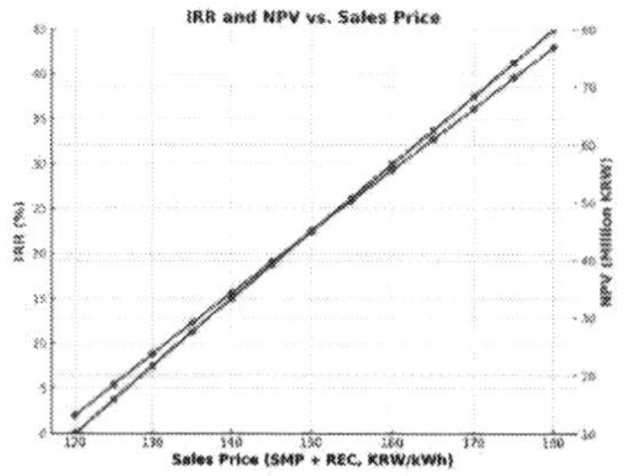

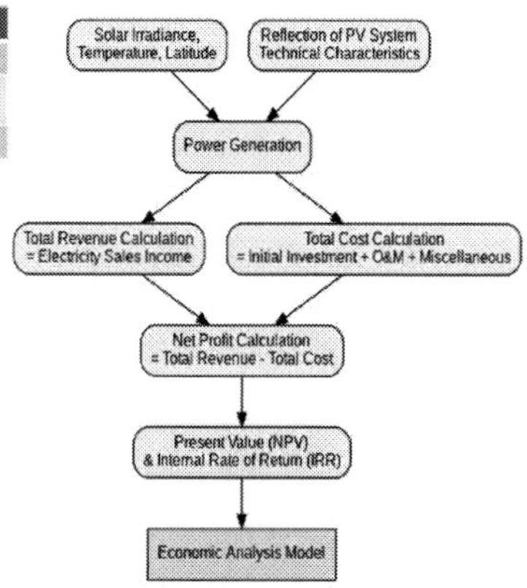

Conclusions

- **Development of Deployment Model and Profit Structure** for Farmer-Led Rural PV Dissemination → Proposal of **Social Economy Enterprise and Rental Operator Structure**
- **Customized Deployment Framework** reflecting target regions and farm household characteristics, with **risk analysis-basid rental fee setting and operation plan**
- **Economic feasibility achievable** for both rental operators and social enterproses **without goverment support** under the proposed model

PHOTOVOLTAIC ENERGY PRODUCTION IN TWO UNIVERSITY CAMPUSES: A COMPARATIVE STUDY

Aarón Ortiz-Peña,[1] Mahamadou Abdou-Tankari[2], Andrés Honrubia-Escribano[1], Emilio Gómez-Lázaro[1]
[1]Renewable Energy Research Institute, and Department of Electrical, Electronic, Automatic and Communications Engineering, ETSII-AB, University of Castilla-La Mancha (UCLM) Albacete, Spain
Aaron.ortiz@uclm.es Andres.honrubia@uclm.es Emilio.gomez@uclm.es
[2]CERTES Laboratory, University Paris-Est Creteil (UPEC), 94010 Creteil, France
Mahamadou.abdou-tankari@u-pec.fr

ABSTRACT: The transition to renewable energy is vital to reduce dependence on fossil fuels and curb greenhouse gas emissions. Universities, as energy-intensive institutions with diverse activities, offer a particularly suitable context for photovoltaic system deployment. This study evaluates two operational PV installations at the University of Castilla-La Mancha, located on the Albacete and Toledo campuses, using hourly monitoring data from October 2024 to February 2025. At Albacete, all electricity produced was consumed, as demand consistently exceeded generation, with demand peaks of 2 MWh compared with maximum PV output of 400 kWh. In Toledo, demand surpassed 800 kWh, while PV generation reached 200 kWh. Average demand coverage was 8.2% in Toledo and 7.9% in Albacete, shaped by consumption profiles and the limitations of zero-injection systems. Generation patterns revealed broader, more centred curves at Albacete due to dual module orientations, while Toledo showed a skewed profile from west-facing modules. Economically, savings amounted to 26,600 € at Albacete and 14,600 € at Toledo, with results confirming that both PV generation and electricity prices determine financial benefits. Overall, the study demonstrates the capacity of PV systems in universities to lower electricity costs and grid dependence, while stressing the importance of analyses based on real operational data.
Keywords: Electricity demand coverage, solar pv systems in buildings, public buildings, real monitoring data

1 INTRODUCTION

The growing demand for renewable energy stems from both the need to reduce dependence on non-renewable sources and the urgency to mitigate their environmental impact [1]. Electricity generation from fossil fuels remains associated with high CO_2 emissions, in contrast with European energy efficiency plans that set ambitious targets for reducing greenhouse gas emissions by 2050 [2]. This energy transition is further conditioned by the increasing demand for electricity [3], as well as the sharp rise in energy prices in recent years, particularly following the war in Ukraine [4]. This context has reinforced the importance of reducing consumption from the external distribution grid, especially in the building sector, which accounts for around 40% of electricity demand and approximately 35% of CO_2 emissions [5].

Within this sector, universities represent a distinct group of large-scale buildings with high energy consumption, due to the wide variety of activities they host, ranging from teaching and administrative management to research, the latter being the most energy-intensive [6]. Added to this are significant cooling requirements during warmer periods, which further highlight the need for efficiency measures and renewable energy systems. However, such strategies are often not prioritised in these institutions, as energy costs are not directly borne by users [7]. Among the renewable technologies implemented in university environments, solar photovoltaic (PV) energy is the most widespread, as it can exploit available surfaces such as rooftops, façades and car parks without interfering with daily activities [8]. Numerous studies have assessed its feasibility through simulation-based approaches, analysing demand coverage and payback periods in universities across different countries [9–11]. Although some works report experiences of real-world installations [12,13], the majority of analyses remain based on estimated radiation and generation data, without incorporating measured values.

The literature review therefore reveals several limitations: a predominance of feasibility assessments over evaluations based on real operational data, a scarcity of comparative studies between installations under similar conditions, and a lack of detailed analyses considering aspects such as seasonal variability, performance across different types of days, or the influence of system design. These gaps justify the need for research that rigorously compares PV systems in real operation, in order to provide more accurate and useful results for future implementations. The literature review highlights several limitations. The gaps identified in the research are:

- Predominance of simulation studies over real operational data.
- Lack of comparative analyses between PV systems with measured data.
- Limited focus on system design and architectural integration.
- Efficiency often assessed with simulated rather than measured indicators.
- Seasonal variability and daily load patterns rarely addressed.

The objectives of this study are:

- Compare two PV installations at UCLM (Toledo and Albacete).
- Analyse operational performance using real data.
- Identify maximum generation values and demand coverage.
- Evaluate economic savings from solar PV generation.

2 CASE STUDY

The University of Castilla-La Mancha (UCLM) is a public higher education institution in Spain, with

10.4229/EUPVSEC2025/5DV.3.75

campuses spread across several cities, including Albacete and Toledo. This study focuses on these two campuses due to their contrasting architectural and climatic characteristics.

The Albacete campus (38.99° N, 1.86° W) is a modern, purpose-built site in the south-east of the city, hosting faculties such as Industrial Engineering, Medicine, and Computer Science. Its contemporary infrastructure, laboratories, and well-planned layout make it representative of university buildings in a continental Mediterranean climate. In contrast, the Toledo campus (39.86° N, 4.03° W), located along the River Tagus, occupies a refurbished historical site combining 19th-century industrial structures with modern educational buildings. It hosts faculties including Architecture, Environmental Sciences, and Humanities, providing a unique setting to examine energy efficiency in heritage and mixed-use university buildings.

In 2024, both campuses implemented solar PV systems to reduce reliance on the external grid and lower electricity costs, building on earlier measures taken in 2022 in response to rising energy prices [14]. The Albacete PV installation has a total capacity of 637.42 kWp, comprising 1,099 modules rated at 580 Wp, mainly distributed across the rooftops of biomedical sciences buildings. The Toledo campus installed a 339.35 kWp system with 617 modules rated at 550 Wp, spread over several rooftops across the campus.

The climatic differences between the locations are also notable: Toledo lies in climate zone C4, with mild winters and hot summers, whereas Albacete is classified as D3, with colder winters and moderately severe summers. These contrasts provide a valuable context for comparing the performance of PV systems under different environmental and architectural conditions.

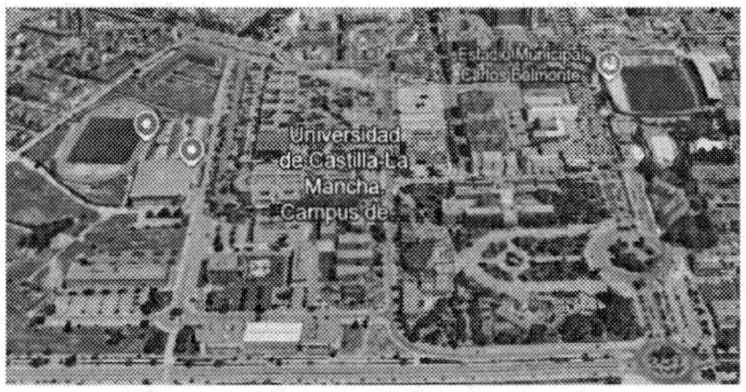

Figure 1. Albacete University Campus.

Figure 2. Toledo University Campus.

3 METHODOLOGY

3.1 General methodology

This study presents a detailed analysis of the hourly energy generation in both campuses under investigation, alongside the total electrical energy demand. To this end, during the study period, which spans from October 2024 to February 2025, data were monitored on an hourly basis. Subsequently, the data were processed and analysed using the Matlab [14] software to identify null values or any values that did not correspond to reality. Following this procedure, the various results were obtained. Figure 3 illustrates the methodology applied in this study, encompassing data monitoring, preprocessing, and analysis.

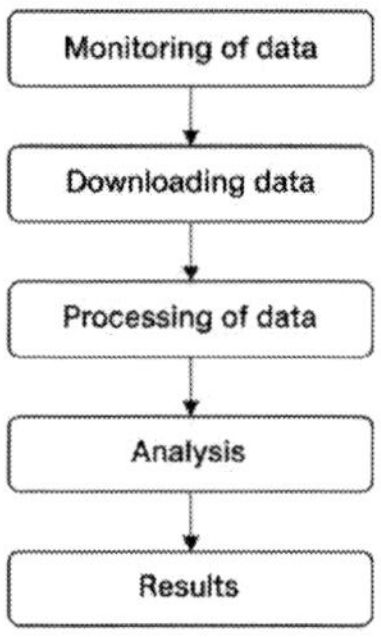

Figure 3. Applied methodology.

3.2 Equations

For this study, several equations were employed to analyse energy generation and consumption. A key indicator is the PV demand coverage, calculated as follows, Equation 1:

$$D.coverage\ (\%) = \frac{E_{PV}\ (kWh)}{Total\ consumption\ (kWh)} * 100 \quad (1)$$

Where E_{PV} represents the energy generated by the solar PV system during the considered period, compared to the total campus consumption.
Another important parameter is the average solar PV generation, which allows for defining hourly generation patterns, Equation 2:

$$E_{mean} = \frac{\sum_{i=1}^{d} E_{ch}\ (kWh)}{d} \quad (2)$$

Where E_{mean} is the energy generated in a specific hour and ddd is the number of days considered for the average.
The monthly economic savings from solar PV generation are estimated using, Equation 3:

$$Monthly\ savings\ (€) = EF_m * EP_m \quad (3)$$

Where EF_m is the energy generated in the month and EP_m is the average electricity price during that period.

4 RESULTS

This section presents the various results obtained from the data analysis. At the Albacete campus, all the energy generated is consumed, as the electricity demand exceeds generation, with recorded demand values reaching up to 2

MWh, while PV generation peaks at around 400 kWh. At the Toledo campus, electricity demand exceeds 800 kWh, compared with a generation of approximately 200 kWh. Figure 4 illustrates the monthly solar PV generation for both campuses under study. It can be observed that the highest consumption for both campuses occurs in February. Although the installed capacity at the Albacete campus is 1.9 times greater than that of Toledo, generation in Albacete during this month was 2.2 times higher than in Toledo, owing to climatic conditions. The increase in electricity consumption in February may be attributed to several factors, such as weather conditions or greater use of the facilities.

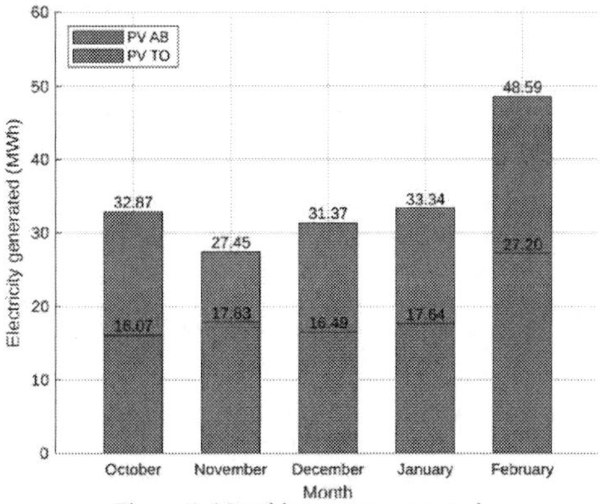

Figure 4. Monthly energy generated.

Figure 5 illustrates the daily demand coverage achieved by both generation systems, calculated on the basis of Equation 1. For the Toledo campus, demand coverage values range from 1% to 17%, while for the Albacete campus they vary between 2% and 15%. The fact that Albacete can reach higher daily coverage values is primarily due to its greater overall electricity demand. Nevertheless, it should also be noted that the effective coverage at this campus is constrained by the presence of zero-injection systems, which prevent surplus electricity from being fed into other parts of the network. As a result, the level of demand coverage is not solely indicative of higher PV generation; rather, it is strongly influenced by the interaction between generation and the specific consumption profile of each campus. In total terms, the average demand coverage during the study period was 8.2% for Toledo and 7.9% for Albacete, highlighting the relatively balanced performance of both systems despite their differences in size and configuration.

Figure 6 presents the average generation profiles for the two campuses under study. At Albacete, the maximum peak occurs between 12:00 and 13:00 hours, with values reaching approximately 200 kWh. In contrast, the Toledo installation records its maximum peak slightly later, at 13:00 hours, with generation approaching 120 kWh. When comparing the shapes of the generation curves, it becomes evident that the Albacete installation produces electricity over a broader time range than Toledo. This wider curve is the result of the system's design, which incorporates PV modules with both positive and negative azimuths, allowing it to capture solar radiation across different orientations and providing a more balanced, centred profile. Conversely, the curve for the Toledo installation shows a pronounced rightward skew. This asymmetry is explained by the fact that most of its modules have a positive azimuth, oriented between south and west, which leads to higher generation levels when the sun shifts towards the western horizon in the afternoon.

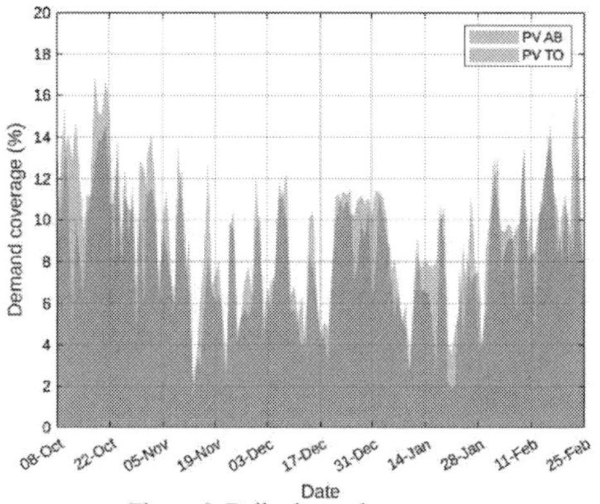

Figure 5. Daily demand coverage.

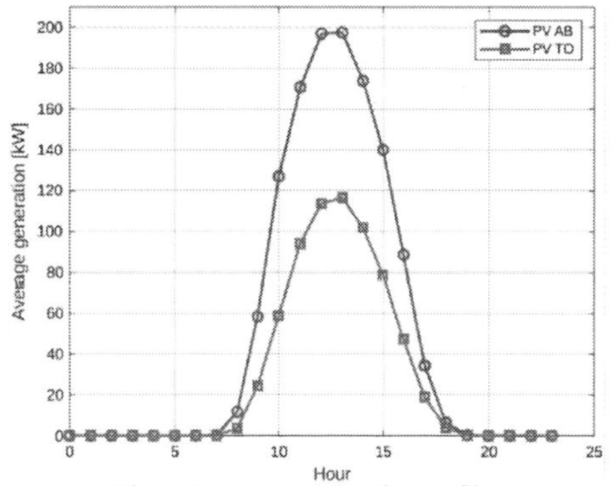

Figure 6. Average generation profile.

Solar PV generation leads to a reduction in the electricity bill, as it decreases the demand for power from the external grid. Figure 7 presents the monthly savings achieved through renewable generation, alongside the average hourly electricity price. The latter is calculated on the basis of the final hourly tariff applied to the university, which is derived from the market price plus additional coefficients that increase the final value above the wholesale market rate. When comparing these savings with Figure 4, which displays total monthly generation, it becomes evident that the month with the highest generation does not necessarily correspond to the month with the greatest financial savings. For instance, in December and January, both campuses generated significant amounts of renewable electricity; however, savings were higher in December. This is explained by the higher electricity price in December, 0.18 €/kWh, compared with January 0.15 €/kWh. Thus, the price of electricity is a determining factor in identifying which months yield the greatest reductions in the electricity bill. The month with the largest savings is February, which also corresponds to the highest level of generation. In this case, the amount of electricity generated was sufficiently high to offset the relatively lower price of 0.15 €/kWh. This confirms that financial savings depend on a dual effect: both the volume

10.4229/EUPVSEC2025/5DV.3.75

of electricity generated and the prevailing electricity price. In total, during the study period, the Albacete campus achieved savings of approximately 26,600 €, while the Toledo campus recorded savings of about 14,600 €.

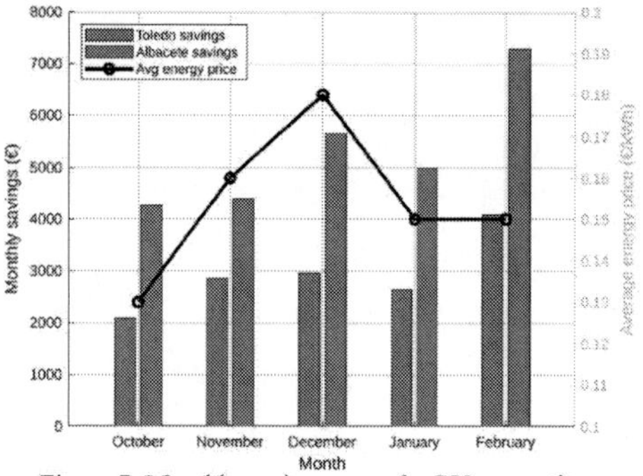

Figure 7. Monthly savings per solar PV generation.

5 CONCLUSIONS

This study compared two PV installations at the Albacete and Toledo campuses of the University of Castilla-La Mancha using real operational data. Both systems reduced demand from the external grid, with performance influenced by system design, consumption patterns and climatic conditions. At Albacete, all generated electricity was consumed, as demand exceeded PV output. Its installed capacity is 1.9 times greater than Toledo's, and generation in peak months was up to 2.2 times higher. Its wider, balanced generation curve, due to modules with both positive and negative azimuths, contrasted with Toledo's narrower, right-skewed profile caused by west-oriented modules. Average demand coverage reached 8.2% at Toledo and 7.9% at Albacete, shaped not only by generation but also by consumption levels and zero-injection system constraints. Thus, demand coverage is not solely an indicator of PV output.

Economically, savings depended on both generation and electricity prices. Although generation peaked in January, higher tariffs in December led to greater savings that month, while February achieved the largest overall savings due to much higher output despite lower prices. Over the study period, Albacete saved about 26,600 € and Toledo 14,600 €.

Overall, solar PV systems in universities show significant potential to cut costs and reduce reliance on the grid, while this work highlights the value of real operational data for accurate evaluation and planning of future installations.

6 ACKNOWLEDGMENT

This research was partially funded by the State Research Agency (Agencia Estatal de Investigación, AEI); by the European Regional Development Fund (Fondo Europeo de Desarrollo Regional, FEDER) through project PID2021-126082OB-C21; and by the Council of Communities of Castilla- La Mancha (Junta de Comunidades de Castilla-La Mancha, JCCM) through project SBPLY/23/180225/000226.

7 REFERENCES

[1] Yu, C., Moslehpour, M., Tran, T. K., Trung, L. M., Ou, J. P., & Tien, N. H. (2023). Impact of non-renewable energy and natural resources on economic recovery: Empirical evidence from selected developing economies. *Resources policy*, *80*, 103221.

[2] Colmenar-Santos, A., Muñoz-Gómez, A. M., Rosales-Asensio, E., & López-Rey, Á. (2019). Electric vehicle charging strategy to support renewable energy sources in Europe 2050 low-carbon scenario. *Energy*, *183*, 61-74.

[3] Karipoğlu, F., & Denizli, O. (2025). Towards renewable energy islands in Türkiye: Potential and challenges. *Renewable and Sustainable Energy Reviews*, *211*, 115324.

[4] Kaur, C., Siddiki, J., & Singh, P. (2024). The asymmetric impact of input prices, the Russia-Ukraine war and domestic policy changes on wholesale electricity prices in India: A quantile autoregressive distributed lag analysis. *Energy Economics*, *132*, 107428.

[5] Pérez-Lombard, L., Ortiz, J., & Pout, C. (2008). A review on buildings energy consumption information. Energy and buildings, 40(3), 394-398.

[6] Ortiz-Peña, A., Honrubia-Escribano, A., Gallego-Giner, I., Galán, Á., & Gómez-Lázaro, E. (2025). Analysis and impact of electrical energy consumption in the academic sector. A case study of the university of Castilla-La Mancha. *Energy Conversion and Management: X*, 100894.

[7] de Souza Silva, J. L., de Melo, K. B., dos Santos, K. V., Sakô, E. Y., da Silva, M. K., Moreira, H. S., ... & Villalva, M. G. (2022). Case study of photovoltaic power plants in a model of sustainable university in Brazil. *Renewable Energy*, *196*, 247-260.

[8] Hasapis, D., Savvakis, N., Tsoutsos, T., Kalaitzakis, K., Psychis, S., & Nikolaidis, N. P. (2017). Design of large scale prosuming in Universities: The solar energy vision of the TUC campus. *Energy and Buildings*, *141*, 39-55.

[9] Kalkan, N., Bercin, K., Cangul, O., Morales, M. G., Saleem, M. M. K. M., Marji, I., ... & Tsigkogianni, E. (2011). A renewable energy solution for Highfield Campus of University of Southampton. *Renewable and sustainable energy reviews*, *15*(6), 2940-2959.

[10] Hasapis, D., Savvakis, N., Tsoutsos, T., Kalaitzakis, K., Psychis, S., & Nikolaidis, N. P. (2017). Design of large scale prosuming in Universities: The solar energy vision of the TUC campus. *Energy and Buildings*, *141*, 39-55.

[11] Ahmed, A., Nadeem, T. B., Naqvi, A. A., Siddiqui, M. A., Khan, M. H., Zahid, M. S. B., & Ammar, S. M. (2022). Investigation of PV utilizability on university buildings: A case study of Karachi, Pakistan. *Renewable Energy*, *195*, 238-251.

[12] Allouhi, A., Saadani, R., Kousksou, T., Saidur, R., Jamil, A., & Rahmoune, M. (2016). Grid-connected PV systems installed on institutional buildings: Technology comparison, energy

analysis and economic performance. *Energy and Buildings*, *130*, 188-201.

[13] Obeng, M., Gyamfi, S., Derkyi, N. S., Kabo-bah, A. T., & Peprah, F. (2020). Technical and economic feasibility of a 50 MW grid-connected solar PV at UENR Nsoatre Campus. *Journal of Cleaner Production*, *247*, 119159.

[14] MathWorks. (2024). *MATLAB (Version R2024b) [Computer software]*. Natick, MA: The MathWorks, Inc. https://www.mathworks.com.

DRIVING GLOBAL LEADERSHIP IN THE SOLAR PV MODULE VALUE CHAIN: THE ROLE OF EARLY ADOPTION AND IMPLEMENTATION OF IEC STANDARDS

Deepti[1], Saurabh Kumar[2], Sushma Sharma[1], Gaurav Kumar[3]
[1]Faculty of Management and Commerce, SRM University, Delhi-NCR, Sonepat, Haryana, India
[2]PTB Braunshweig, Germany
[3]MERI College of Engineering and Technology, Bahadurgarh, Haryana, India

ABSTRACT: This paper will explore the relationship between early adoption of IEC standards, their implementation and a country's leadership in the solar PV module value chain. It will analyse economic and geo-economic trends in PV module manufacturing, the role of standards adoption and implementation in driving innovation and reliability, and how this correlates with cost reductions and production growth in these countries. The study will highlight countries that have demonstrated consistent adoption and implementation of IEC standards, their manufacturing output, and the impact on global competitiveness in the solar PV industry. The research will delve into the role of conformity assessment bodies like testing and calibration laboratories in Germany, China, India and Vietnam. These bodies play a pivotal role in implementation of standards, contributing to product quality, safety, and performance consistency. The study will examine how these technical frameworks support the solar PV ecosystem by fostering trust in components and systems, enabling seamless integration into global supply chains, and enhancing the credibility of manufacturers in the global market.
Keywords: Photovoltaic (PV), IEC Standards, Adoption vs. Implementation, Exports, Quality Infrastructure

1 INTRODUCTION

Photovoltaic technologies have given new means of providing electrical energy to the Global economy. The narrative of solar PV industry is shifting even beyond so called unending energy source available from the Sun. Factors like absence of continuous transportation like for conventional fuels, allure of lesser carbon emissions, phasing out of old coal-based plants are incentivising countries to push for development of domestic solar PV industry. For the development of solar PV industry, both supply-push policies and demand-pull policies are being tried by the authorities. [1] [2] Policies like production linked incentives and even local content requirement to attract local production for domestic demand are also being tried. [3] Rather than looking in silos, the impact of economic or market policies or focus on R&D activities, this paper has attempted approach to look at the solar PV industry trade outcomes of past few decades in selected countries and correlate them with quality infrastructure of these same countries with technical specifications acceptable at the Global level.

Standards formulated at the International Electrotechnical Commission (IEC) level are considered the most accepted technical norms at the Global level. Its membership is open to all the countries and participation activities are coordinated through their national standards body serving the role of national committee to the IEC. Other international standardisation organisations like ISO, ITU, Codex are also formulating standards in other different areas of the economy. Within the electrotechnical sector as well, there exists various areas of standardisation for which the structure of organising works into different technical committees (or even sub-committee or working groups) exists. Member countries can opt for participating or observer membership in their interest areas.

In this work, the role of both adoption and implementation of IEC standards on the export competitiveness for solar PV module value chain will be analysed. For the implementation aspects, the role of metrology and conformity assessment bodies are also studied in the context of establishing leadership in the solar PV module sector. Four countries, namely Germany, China, India and Vietnam, have been studied where policymakers are maintaining continuity in terms of policies for promotion of the solar PV industry.

2 METHODOLOGIES

2.1 Adoption of standards

The technical committee TC 82 at the level of IEC is formulating international standards in the area of solar PV technologies. Some of the major IEC Standards in this field are IEC 61215 (earlier 61646), IEC 61730, IEC TS 62804, IEC 62716, IEC TS 63342, IEC 60904 series, IEC 62446. Adoption of these standards at the national level through stakeholder consultation may serve as the first step to create awareness and push for their implementation. Aspects like test methods for design qualification and type approval, construction requirements, measurement of potential-induced degradation-delamination, ammonia corrosion resistance, light induced degradation at elevated temperatures are covered in these documents. Even though solar PV technologies are evolving rapidly and direct one-to-one specifications for latest technologies may not be addressed, some horizontal baseline criteria for evaluating outcomes still exist. A simpler evolution chart of solar PV technologies starting from monocrystalline to perovskite and tandem is given at Figure 1. More detailed mapping of different technologies since 1976 along with efficiency is also being maintained by NREL. [4] [5] For the innovation, patent filing statistics analysed in various studies reveals that after 2000; inventors from USA, Germany and China are among the leaders. However, after 2005, surge in new solar PV patent families from China was observed followed with subsequent rise in new solar PV patent families from Germany. But within a span of few years, these new patent numbers from USA and Germany decreased and China took the leadership position in the new solar PV patenting. [6]

10.4229/EUPVSEC2025/5DV.3.86

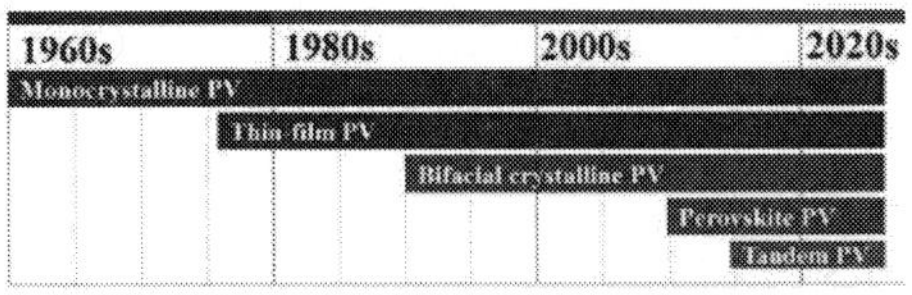

Figure 1: Solar PV technologies over the years

If we look at national level standardisation efforts, all the four countries taken in this study have technical committees comprising national level stakeholders. In Germany (DE) it is DKE/K 373 [7], in China (CN) it is SAC/TC 90 [8], in India (IN) it is BIS/ETD 28 [9] and in Vietnam (VN) it is TCVN/TC/E8 [10]. Except Vietnam, the other three countries are also represented as participating members in the work of IEC TC 82 with the right to vote and involved in formulation, review and revision of standards. [11] Standards formulated at the level of IEC TC 82 are getting adopted as national standards by the national level technical committees in all the four countries. The information comparing year of publication of important IEC Standards in the area of solar PV with year of adoption in these countries is given at Table I gathered from the official website of those organisations.

As can be seen from the Table I, Germany is regularly adopting IEC standards in the area of solar PV as national standards. This adoption is also more often earlier as compared to other countries. India is also adopting these standards and delay gaps seen during the 1990s, 2000s are gradually decreasing. The same adoption process is comparatively very less in China. In the case of Vietnam it is even lesser prior to 2020.

2.2 Export of Commodities

Trade flow measurements among national economies happen on the basis of HSN codes which are presently harmonised till 6 digits level. HSN 854140 was in operation till 2021 with description as Photosensitive semiconductor devices, incl. PV cells whether or not assembled in modules or made up into panels; light emitting diodes (excluding PV generators). Afterwards, four distinct categorisation was done bringing out clearer demarcation by codes HSN 854142 meant for PV cells not assembled in modules or made up into panels and HSN 854143 meant for PV cells assembled in modules or made up into panels.

From the ITC trade map data [12], it is observed that under HSN 854140 in terms of US Dollars, in 2003 Germany had exports of 0.8 billion, China 0.3 billion, India 46 million and Vietnam just 3 thousand. In 2023, these amount values combined with HSN 854142 and 854143 changed to 0.5 billion for Germany, 1.5 billion for India, 8 billion for Vietnam and 43 billion for China. Year 2003 was a pivotal year which marked the beginning of rising patent filings, increased production and exports.

Table I: Adoption of IEC standards for solar PV in Germany, China, India and Vietnam

Sr No	IEC Standards/ Documents	Adoption year			
		DE	CN	IN	VN
1	61215-1:2016	2017	N/A	2019	2017
2	61215-1:2021	2022	N/A	2023	N/A
3	61215-1-1:2016	2018	N/A	2019	2017
4	61215-1-1:2021	2022	N/A	2023	2025
5	61215-1-2:2016	2017	N/A	2019	2020
6	61215-1-2:2021	2023	N/A	2023	N/A
7	61215-1-3:2016	2017	N/A	2019	2020
8	61215-1-3:2021	2023	N/A	2023	N/A
9	61215-1-4:2016	2017	N/A	2019	2020
10	61215-1-4:2021	2023	N/A	2023	N/A
11	61215-2:2016	2019	N/A	2019	2017
12	61215-2:2021	2022	N/A	2023	N/A
13	61646:1996	1998	2002	N/A	N/A
14	61646:2008	2009	N/A	2014	2015
15	61730-1:2004	2007	2006	2010	N/A
16	61730-1:2016	2018	N/A	2019	2018
17	61730-1:2023	N/A	N/A	2025	N/A
18	61730-2:2004	2007	N/A	2010	N/A
19	61730-2:2016	2018	N/A	2019	2018
20	61730-2:2023	N/A	N/A	2025	N/A
21	TS 62804-1:2015	2017	N/A	2019	N/A
22	TS 62804-1:2025	N/A	N/A	N/A	N/A
23	TS 62804-1-1: 2020	N/A	N/A	N/A	N/A
24	TS 62804-2:2022	N/A	N/A	N/A	N/A
25	62716:2013	2014	2023	2018	N/A
26	TS 63342:2022	N/A	N/A	N/A	N/A
27	60904-1:1987	1995	1996	1989	N/A
28	60904-1:2006	2007	N/A	2010	2020
29	60904-1:2020	2023	N/A	2024	N/A
30	60904-1-1:2017	2018	N/A	2020	2020
31	TS 60904-1-2: 2019	2022	N/A	2020	N/A
32	TS 60904-1-2: 2024	N/A	N/A	N/A	N/A
33	60904-2:1989	1995	1996	1993	N/A
34	60904-2:2007	2008	N/A	2013	N/A
35	60904-2:2015	2015	N/A	2018	2020
36	60904-2:2023	2024	N/A	2025	N/A
37	60904-3:1989	1995	1996	1998	N/A
38	60904-3:2008	2009	N/A	2013	N/A
39	60904-3:2016	2017	N/A	2018	N/A
40	60904-3:2019	2020	N/A	2020	2020
41	60904-4:2009	2010	N/A	2014	N/A
42	60904-4:2019	2021	N/A	2024	2020
43	60904-5:1993	1996	1997	2010	N/A
44	60904-5:2011	2011	N/A	2014	2020
45	60904-7:1995	N/A	N/A	N/A	N/A
46	60904-7:1998	1998	2006	N/A	N/A
47	60904-7:2008	2009	N/A	2013	N/A
48	60904-7:2019	2021	N/A	2023	2020
49	60904-8:1995	N/A	N/A	N/A	N/A
50	60904-8:1998	1998	2002	2010	N/A
51	60904-8:2014	2015	N/A	2018	2020
52	60904-8-1:2017	2018	2020	2020	2020
53	60904-9:1995	N/A	2006	N/A	N/A
54	60904-9:2007	2008	N/A	2010	2020
55	60904-9:2020	2024	N/A	2023	N/A
56	60904-10:1998	1998	2012	N/A	N/A
57	60904-10:2009	2010	N/A	2014	2020
58	60904-10:2020	2022	N/A	2023	N/A
59	60904-13:2018	2019	N/A	2020	N/A
60	TR 60904-14: 2020	N/A	N/A	2023	N/A
61	62446-1:2016	2016	N/A	N/A	2017
62	62446-2:2020	2021	N/A	2023	N/A
63	62446-3:2017	2018	N/A	2020	N/A
64	TS 63126:2020	2022	2024	2023	N/A

10.4229/EUPVSEC2025/5DV.3.86
020563-002

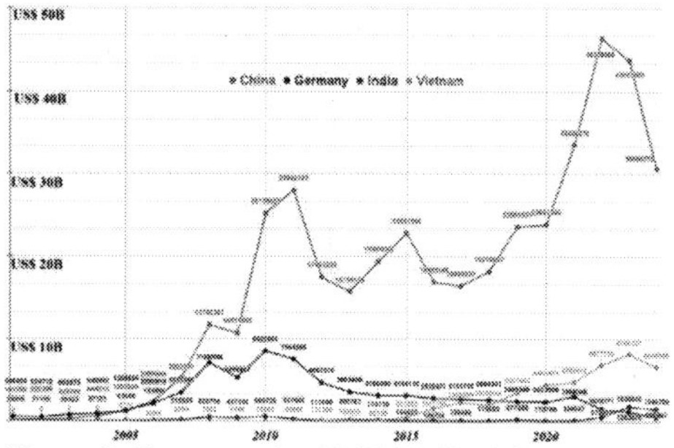

Figure 2: Exports under HSN 854140 (after 2021 - 854142 and 854143) from 2001 to 2024

2.3 Quality infrastructure for implementation

Implementation of technical specifications in any economy starts from the basic foundation of metrology providing traceable, consistent measurement services through a downstream network upto conformity assessment services like testing and certification bodies, which often runs via accreditation bodies.

Germany had the basic foundation of metrology services for the solar PV sector in its economy much earlier starting in 1986. [13] [14] China started these metrology services in its economy in 2006. [15] In India, the primary cell calibration facility has been established in 2024. [16] whereas Vietnam doesn't have any such service provider in its own domestic economy and relies on collaboration with other economies. [17]

In the downstream network of quality infrastructure services, data related to IAF and ILAC based certifications and reports is not publicly available. Another alternative multilateral mechanism in place, i.e. the IECEE conformity assessment system run by IEC itself is utilised to arrive at a measurable outcome of downstream services emanating from the quality infrastructure setup. Present figures of IECEE recognised certification bodies (NCBs) and test laboratories (CBTLs) in the solar PV sector as well as number of standards in the recognition scope are given in Table II. [18]

Table II: Number of IECEE recognised multilateral arrangement NCBs and CBTLs

	NCBs (Number of standards including year versions)	CBTLs (Number of Standards including year versions)
DE	5 (120)	5 (57)
CN	2 (28)	30 (398)
IN	0	6 (73)
VN	0	0

Going one step further, the number of IECEE certificates issued to factory locations in these four countries were also looked into to get perspective on implementation of Standards. Statistics of year wise such certificates issued are given in Figure 3.

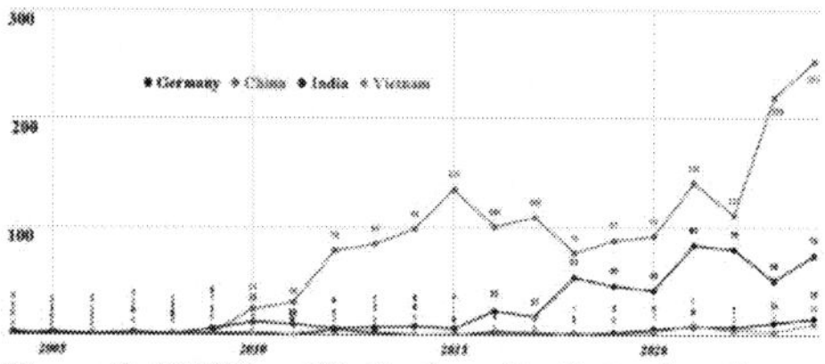

Figure 3: IECEE certificates issued to factory locations from 2004 to 2024

3 RESULTS

Information obtained from the methodologies, competitiveness in the Global market for potential future leadership in the solar PV sector was analysed.

3.1 Role of early adoption

Notional adoption of IEC standards giving them the status of national standards is found to have no positive correlation with competitiveness in the Global market. China and Vietnam have much larger scale of exports even without formal adoption of IEC standards at their respective national committee level.

3.2 Role of implementation

At the time when solar PV sector exports were insignificant, Germany had the basic foundation of metrology services in its economy. This may explain its better export competitiveness at the nascent stage in early 2000s. Later on, China started metrology services at the national level at the right time when the solar PV sector saw an initial spurt in 2006. Downstream services of multilateral certification saw rise in 2010 after exports started rising in 2008. In India, the exports growth has remained subdued despite the faster response in adoption of Standards after 2010s and scalability potential due to rising domestic demand. This may be explained by a combination of absence of metrology services in its economy as well as absence of multilateral certification bodies with local presence. In Vietnam, exports started rising in 2016 followed by an increase in issued certifications after 2019. Though not leading the exports, Vietnam has surpassed both India and Germany by a large margin despite the absence of both metrology services and multilateral recognised certification bodies in its country.

4 ADDITIONAL FACTORS

4.1 The results from the role of adoption and implementation of IEC standards are unable to be uniformly applied in all four countries. Additional policy factors by these countries may also be playing a part in these outcomes impacting each other.

4.2 Both supply-side push and demand-side pulls also need a deeper look with possible intertwining outcome results. In Europe, policies initiated in 2008 and 2009 could have aided in driving up exports from other countries while the domestic industry might not have been in a position to scale up to the level of pulls created from the demand-side. [19]

10.4229/EUPVSEC2025/5DV.3.86
020563-003

4.3 Starting from 2016, In India as well, similar demand-side pull policies were seen into effect which was also supplemented with supply-side pushes like local content requirements and production linked incentives. [20] However, the export competitiveness has not seen the results as compared to Vietnam despite a comparatively higher number of IECEE certificates issued to factories. The study combining more external factors with verifiable data still remains an opportunity for the future.

5 CONCLUSIONS

5.1 There emerges two models when it comes to standards for consideration of policymakers in making their decisions. One is the VIKAS model, where one actively pursues Validation of Knowledge to Advance Standards. It can be Indigenous knowledge and one shouldn't hesitate even if it's international knowledge. Countries are seen achieving competitiveness with direct use of IEC standards by their industries. Another is the GHULAM model, where Growth remains Hindered Under Loaned Adopted Manak/Standards. Notional adoption just conferring the national status without active implementation serves no purpose in driving competitiveness of the industry.

5.2 Quality of preparedness in terms of basic foundation of quality infrastructure in terms of metrology also emerges as a key aspect for seizing any demand-side pulls seen in the Global market. This basic foundation also needs to be built with downstream conformity assessment bodies providing services to the industry with multilateral acceptance.

6 ACKNOWLEDGMENTS

This research has been supported with sponsorship by the Physikalisch-Technische Bundesanstalt (PTB), International Cooperation Division, Germany.

7 REFERENCES

[1] Daoyuan Wen *et al.*, "Development of solar photovoltaic industry and market in China, Germany, Japan and the United States of America using incentive policies", *Energy Exploration & Exploitation*, Volume 39, Issue 5, December 2020, doi:10.1177/0144598720979256

[2] Alejandro Nuñez-Jimenez *et al.*, "Beyond innovation and deployment: Modeling the impact of technology-push and demand-pull policies in Germany's solar policy mix", *Research Policy*, Volume 51, Issue 10, December 2022, doi: 10.1016/j.respol.2022.104585

[3] Narendra Shiradkar *et al.*, "Recent developments in solar manufacturing in India", *Solar Compass*, Volume 1, May 2022, 100009, doi: 10.1016/j.solcom.2022.100009

[4] National Renewable Energy Laboratory, Best research-cell efficiency Chart, Washington, DC, NREL, [Online] Accessed: 01 September 2025

[5] Zhenguo Li *et al.*, "Prospects of Photovoltaic Technology", *Engineering*, Volume 21, February 2024, doi: 10.1016/j.eng.2022.07.008

[6] Pia Andres, "Adapting to Competition: Solar PV Innovation in Europe and the Impact of the 'China Shock'", *Environmental & Resource Economics*, Volume 87, Issue 12, October 2024, doi: 10.1007/s10640-024-00904-8

[7] DKE/K 373, Accessed: 01 September 2025 [Online] https://www.din.de/en/getting-involved/standards-committees/dke/publications

[8] SAC/TC 90, Accessed: 01 September 2025 [Online] https://std.samr.gov.cn/search/orgDetailView?data_id=CFF3396241D07764E05397BE0A0A1558

[9] BIS/ETD 28, Accessed: 01 September 2025 [Online] https://www.services.bis.gov.in/php/BIS_2.0/dgdashboard/Published_Standards

[10] TCVN/TC/E8, Accessed: 01 September 2025 [Online] http://tracuu.tcvn.vn/sdomain/front/tieu-chuan-viet-nam

[11] IEC/TC 92, Accessed: 01 September 2025 [Online] https://www.iec.ch/dyn/www/f?p=103:29:206618903840223::::FSP_ORG_ID,FSP_LANG_ID:1276,25

[12] ITC Trade Map, Accessed: 01 September 2025 [Online] https://www.trademap.org/

[13] J. Metzdorf *et al.*, "Absolute indoor calibration of large area solar cells", *5th European Symposium on Photovoltaic Generators in Space*, Proceeding Pages 397-401, November 1986

[14] S. Winter et al., "Primary Reference Cell Calibration at the PTB based on an improved DSR facility", *16th European Photovoltaic Solar Energy Conference*, March 2000, doi: 10.4324/9781315074405

[15] Institute of Electrical Engineering, Chinese Academy of Sciences, Accessed: 01 September 2025 [Online] http://english.iee.cas.cn/ns/es/201404/t20140422_119823.html

[16] Prathap Pathi *et al.*, "India's PV Quality Infrastructure Boost for Calibrating Solar Cells", *Akshay Urja*, Volume 15, Issue 3, April 2025

[17] Wolff Carl *et al.*, "The global dimension of the energy transition", *tm - Technisches Messen*, Volume 92, Pages 413-423, August 2025, doi: 10.1515/teme-2025-0041.

[18] IECEE certificates, Accessed: 01 September 2025 [Online] https://certificates.iecee.org/#/search

[19] Ole Langniß *et al.*, "Advanced mechanisms for the promotion of renewable energy—Models for the future evolution of the German Renewable Energy Act", *Energy Policy*, Volume 37, Issue 4, April 2009, doi: 10.1016/j.enpol.2008.11.007

[20] Malti Goel, "Solar rooftop in India: Policies, challenges and outlook", *Green Energy & Environment*, Volume 1, Issue 2, July 2016 doi: 10.1016/j.gee.2016.08.003

42nd European Photovoltaic Solar Energy Conference and Exhibition

This presentation was selected by the Sc. Committee of the EU PVSEC 2025 for submission of a full paper to one of the EU PVSEC's collaborating peer-reviewed journals.

SOCIAL HOUSING AND ENERGY COMMUNITIES: BALANCING AFFORDABILITY AND PROFITABILITY IN MULTI-APARTMENT BUILDINGS.

Elina Bosch1, Caroline Plaza2, Melodie De L'Epine2, Gaëtan Masson1
1 Becquerel Institute, Brussels, Belgium;
2 Becquerel Institute France, Lyon, France

ABSTRACT: Energy poverty remains a major challenge in the European Union, disproportionately affecting residents of social housing. At the same time, declining photovoltaic (PV) costs and new EU legislation on renewable energy communities create opportunities for energy sharing schemes that can reduce bills and improve access to clean energy. Yet, translating this potential into practice is particularly complex in multi-apartment social housing. This paper identifies and categorises the barriers to PV-based energy sharing in this context, drawing on a literature review and empirical evidence from three demonstration sites of the ProLight project in Spain, Portugal, and Italy. The analysis highlights the central role of fair benefit allocation and scope definition, the constraints of limited roof space, and the challenges of high tenant turnover, arrears risk, and low administrative literacy. In addition, fragmented decision rights, split incentives, and procurement and state-aid rules create further institutional hurdles. The findings underline that energy sharing can only succeed when accompanied by tailored business models, trusted intermediaries, and supportive regulatory frameworks. Coupling energy sharing with refurbishment strategies, subsidies, and co-creation processes can enhance both fairness and feasibility, positioning social housing as a critical driver of an inclusive energy transition.
Keywords: solar photovoltaics, energy sharing, business models, social housing, energy poverty

1 INTRODUCTION

Energy poverty remains a persistent challenge across the European Union (EU). Estimates from the Joint Research Centre (JRC) suggest that between 8% and 16% of the EU population can be classified as energy poor, with the precise figure depending on the methodology used [1]. The issue is complex and multi-dimensional: it can manifest as low absolute energy expenditure, a disproportionately high share of household income spent on energy, inability to maintain adequate indoor warmth, or arrears on utility bills. While only a small fraction of EU citizens meet all these conditions simultaneously, almost 40% of households are energy poor according to at least one indicator.

At the same time, photovoltaic (PV) technology has become increasingly affordable, creating new opportunities to expand access to clean energy [2]. The EU has also introduced a supportive regulatory framework through the Clean Energy for All Europeans package, which includes Article 2 of the Electricity Directive (EU) 2019/944 and Article 22 of the Renewable Energy Directive (RED II). These legislative measures laid the foundation for and promote the establishment of joint self-consumption schemes, citizen energy communities (CECs) and renewable energy communities (RECs), allowing households, businesses, and public organisations to share locally generated electricity Importantly, the RED II explicitly requires Member States to ensure that participation in renewable energy communities is open to all consumers, including low-income and vulnerable households [3].

The integration of PV within energy-sharing schemes is therefore increasingly recognised as a promising strategy to alleviate energy poverty. Evidence suggests that households are willing to engage: for example, one recent study reported that 91.3% of respondents (in two Italian social housing neighbourhoods) would be willing to invest in or request shared PV systems from their landlords [4]. Such initiatives can improve access to affordable, sustainable electricity, reducing both costs and vulnerability for disadvantaged groups.

However, translating this potential into practice is far from straightforward. Multiple barriers—technical, social, regulatory, administrative, governance, and financial—continue to hinder the development and scaling of energy sharing initiatives. Against this backdrop, this study explores social housing and energy communities, focusing on how to balance affordability and profitability in multi-apartment buildings, with the aim of identifying viable pathways to address energy poverty while ensuring long-term sustainability.

2 METHODS

2.1 Approach to barrier identification and categorization

Our analysis aims at developing a clearer understanding of the barriers specific to social housing in the context of energy sharing schemes.

To this end, we conduct a literature review of academic papers and policy reports that explicitly address this topic, as well as publications presenting relevant case studies.

In parallel, we draw on empirical insights from the demonstration districts of the ProLight project, which provide practical evidence on how energy-sharing schemes are being implemented in multi-apartment social housing.

Identified barriers are contextualised in relation to the specific features of social housing, including the socio-economic profile of residents, governance and ownership structures, and the prevalence of energy poverty. For each barrier, it is further indicated whether it is most relevant during the setup phase, the operational phase, or across both stages of implementation.

2.2 ProLight demonstration sites

In the frame of the ProLight project, there are three demonstration sites which are related to social housing and energy sharing schemes. These demonstration sites are at different stage of energy-sharing scheme implementation (running phase, setting-up phase, feasibility assessment phase).

First, the Guernica TEK demonstration site in Spain which is a running energy community based on 200 solar panels located on the local San Fidel school. Electricity is shared with 150 homes, shops and public buildings.

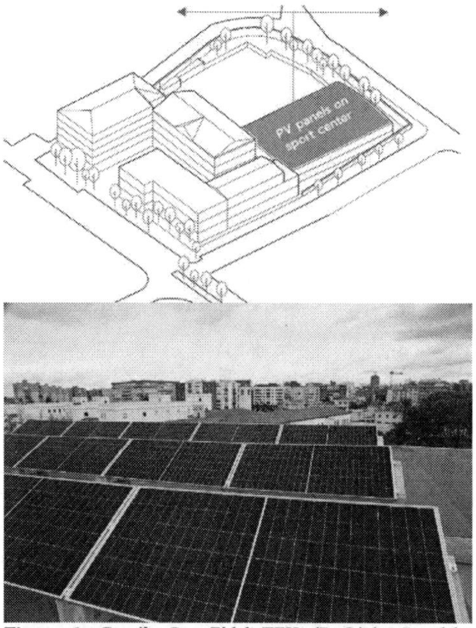

Figure 1: Gernika-San Fidel TEK (ProLight Spanish demonstration site)

Second, the Matosinhos demonstration site in Portugal where an energy sharing scheme is being set up in a recently refurbished social housing multi-apartment building. The energy sharing scheme will be based on a 200 kWp solar photovoltaic system located on the roof. Electricity will be shared with the residents as well as with a few local shops located on the ground floor of the building.

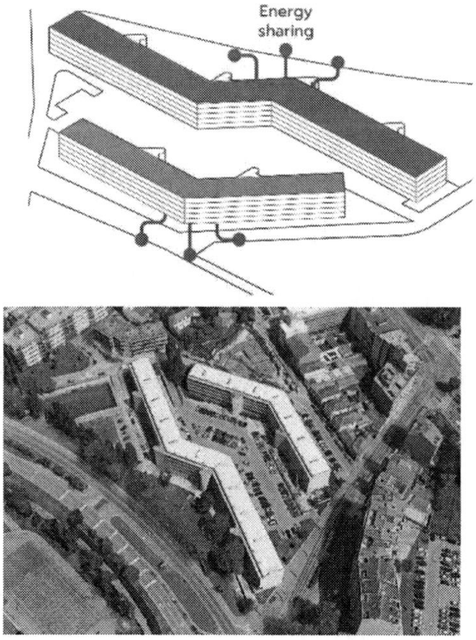

Figure 2: Matosinhos (ProLight Portuguese demonstration site)

Third, the Urbana New Living demonstration site in Italy. The establishment of an energy community is being considered in this recently refurbished social housing multi-apartment building. The building currently has a rooftop PV installation but which only covers the common electricity loads (corridors, elevators, ...).

Figure 3: Urbana New Living (ProLight Italian demonstration site)

2.2 Recommendations for model definition

For the different identified challenges, recommendations with regards to model definition are provided. In particular, model definition recommendations resonate with Business Model Canvas components such as cost structure, ownership, benefit and revenue distribution, ... The Business Model Canvas was selected because it is a widely used and flexible tool that facilitates the structured analysis of value creation, stakeholder roles, and financial flows, making it particularly suitable for innovations at the intersection of technology, governance, and social objectives.

3 BARRIERS AND RECOMMENDATIONS WITH REGARDS TO MODEL DEFINITION

3.1 Barriers related to (PV-based) energy sharing scheme

Benefit allocation design (most relevant in setup phase): Establishing fair distribution keys is a central issue. While this applies broadly, the need for equitable allocation mechanisms is heightened in social housing, where affordability constraints mean that even small imbalances can have strong distributional consequences [4]. As seen in the examples of demonstration sites in ProLight, a certain diversity of socio-economic profiles as well as energy consumption profiles can be observed in a social housing building. In the Italian demonstration site, the social housing includes around half of 'affordable rents", around 15% of "social rent", the rest being sold units. In the Portuguese demonstration sites, the ground-floor of the social housing building, includes a few shops which can contribute positively to the overall energy sharing scheme profitability through the presence of complementary consumption patterns, but needs to be an attention point to avoid concentrating the energy saving benefits on a few profiles only.

Energy-sharing scope selection (most relevant in setup phase): Whether on-site produced electricity should cover only the common load (corridors, elevators, …) or also extend to the individual housing units' consumption directly shapes both fairness and feasibility. Indeed cost minimization and self-consumption maximization goals may conflict. For example, with a common load scope, the savings for each self-consumed kWh will typically be higher with savings on most electricity price components including taxes and network fees. On the contrary, if the scope extends to individual unit's load, each self-consumed kWh will allow savings on the commodity component of electricity price and in some case partially on network fees with taxes still being applicable.

Allocation and billing complexity (relevant in both setup and operational phase): Complex metering arrangements and the use of algorithms to manage sharing keys create higher onboarding and follow-up needs in social housing compared to private dwellings [4] [5] [6]. The example of the energy community demonstration site in Spain in ProLight has shown how the presence of an external private utility can play a key role in facilitating administrative, legal and financial procedures.

3.2 Barriers related to multi-apartment setting

Physical constraints (most relevant in setup phase): The limited roof surface relative to the number of dwellings restricts the scale of PV that can be installed. This is a general challenge in multi-apartment buildings, but in social housing the higher dwelling density exacerbates the limitation [6].

3.3 Barriers related to socio-economic setting

CAPEX and access to finance (most relevant in setup phase): Access to upfront investment is often more difficult in social housing, where both providers and tenants face tighter financial constraints and limited borrowing capacity [9] [10].

Tenant rotation and arrears risk (most relevant in operational phase): High participant turnover and the risk of non-payment are more salient in social housing than in private housing, directly affecting revenue stability and long-term viability [13]. This is particularly relevant for private social housing units, where the economic benefit of implementing an energy sharing scheme may not be immediately obvious to the owner. However, by lowering tenants' energy bills, such schemes can reduce the risk of rent arrears and thereby improve payment stability.

Awareness, trust, and administrative literacy (relevant in both setup and operational phase): Language barriers and low energy literacy levels increase onboarding and communication challenges in social housing, requiring additional support measures throughout the lifecycle of the project [1] [2] [3]. The example of the Italian demonstration site in ProLight project has shown that the presence of a local intermediary (i.e. a local social manager) is essential to build trust and enhances outreach activities towards local citizens. In general, across all demonstration site in ProLight, the implementation of energy sharing schemes (or other energy saving measures) are systematically accompanied with end-user information sharing, engagement and co-creation activities which can take various forms of communication and dissemination action such as workshops, door-to-door communication, …

3.4 Barriers related to social housing setting.

Fragmented decision rights (most relevant in setup phase): Multiple actors—housing companies, facility managers, tenant committees—hold decision-making power. This fragmentation often delays or complicates project development [7] [8].

Split-incentive / landlord–tenant dilemma (most relevant in setup phase): This barrier is especially acute in social housing because the social housing sector remains fundamentally tenant-based [11]. While mass giveaways (UK, Ireland, Romania, …) did significantly shift housing into owner-occupancy, those practices have been mostly phased out. Moreover, regulated rent regimes typically prevent the recovery of capital expenditures through tenants' energy bills, decoupling investment incentives from user benefits [8].

Procurement and state-aid constraints (most relevant in setup phase): In publicly owned or managed housing, strict procurement rules and state-aid considerations create additional delays and limit flexibility. These rules are designed to ensure transparency and fairness, but in practice they can create lengthy administrative processes and restrict the ability to experiment with innovative financing models. In particular, they can make it more difficult to mobilise alternative sources of support, such as sponsorships or donations, which could otherwise help reduce upfront investment needs [7].

3.5 Barriers related to energy poverty context

Reliance on pre-existing energy efficiency measures (most relevant in setup phase): Energy sharing typically becomes viable only after refurbishment or retrofitting, as inefficient building envelopes undermine both the economic case and comfort outcomes. This dependency is especially relevant in social housing, where building stock is often older and poorly insulated [14] [15].

Challenges in benefit quantification (most relevant in operational phase): If analysis focuses only on monetary savings, the true social benefits are underestimated. In social housing, affordability constraints often lead to energy under-consumption (e.g. not heating), meaning that savings appear low despite major improvements in comfort and well-being [1].

4 CONCLUSIONS

This study has shown that while photovoltaic-based energy sharing holds significant potential to alleviate energy poverty in social housing, its implementation faces a complex set of interrelated barriers. These range from technical and physical constraints, such as limited roof space and metering complexity, to socio-economic and institutional challenges, including limited investment capacity, tenant turnover, arrears risk, and fragmented decision rights. Importantly, the social housing context amplifies these challenges: affordability constraints heighten the distributional consequences of benefit allocation, administrative literacy gaps demand stronger engagement and support measures, and strict procurement and state-aid rules limit flexibility in financing.

10.4229/EUPVSEC2025/5EO.1.1

Despite these obstacles, the analysis of the ProLight demonstration sites illustrates that energy sharing in social housing can be made viable when barriers are explicitly addressed in the design of business models. Careful definition of benefit allocation keys and scope, transparent billing arrangements, and the involvement of trusted intermediaries are essential for building trust and ensuring equity. Likewise, coupling energy sharing with refurbishment strategies, mobilising targeted subsidies and grants, and fostering cooperative governance arrangements can enhance both feasibility and long-term sustainability.

A better understanding of the barriers is also critical for shaping replication strategies, ensuring that lessons from the ProLight demonstration sites can be transferred to other contexts. Already at this stage, many insights have been gained regarding both technical and social aspects, while within a year, by the end of the project, more quantitative evidence will become available. These forthcoming results will further inform business model orientations, supporting the definition of viable pathways to scale up PV-based energy sharing in social housing.

Overall, PV-based energy sharing should not be viewed as a stand-alone solution but rather as part of a broader strategy to reduce energy poverty in multi-apartment buildings. By embedding such schemes within supportive regulatory frameworks and ensuring that social and economic safeguards are prioritised, they can deliver not only economic savings but also improved comfort, well-being, and social cohesion. In this way, social housing can become a key driver of an inclusive and just energy transition in Europe.

5 REFERENCES

[1] S. a. D. I. MAIER, «Who is "energy poor" in the EU,» 2024.

[2] IEA PVPS Task 1, «Trends in PV Applications 2024,» 2024.

[3] European Parliament and the Council , «Directive (EU) 2018/2001 of the European Parliament and of the Council of 11 December 2018 on the promotion of the use of energy from renewable sources,» 2024.

[4] L. Marchi, L. Felicioni, F. Sabatini et L. Errante, «Exploring Energy Literacy in Italian Social Housing: A Survey of Inhabitants Preparing the Ground for Climate Transition,» Sustainability , 2023.

[5] M. R. P. S. M. A. A. L. B. F. M. Federico Gianaroli, «Development of dynamic sharing keys: Algorithms supporting management of renewable energy community and collective self consumption,» Energy and Buildings, vol. 311, 2024.

[6] I. a. E. E. A. D.-G. f. E. F. B. L.-E. K. M. C. e. a. European Climate, «Report on energy sharing,» Publications Office of the European Union, 2025.

[7] V. M. G. P. M. M. D. Casalicchio, «Renewable Energy Communities: Business Models of Multi-family Housing Buildings,» Smart and Sustainable Planning for Cities and Regions, p. 261–276, 23 March 2021.

[8] M. K. E. N. F. S. R. M. Fritz Braeuer, «Optimal system design for energy communities in multi-family buildings: the case of the German Tenant Electricity Law,,» Applied Energy, vol. 305, 2022.

[9] J. a. D. Q. Arnould, «Energy communities in the EU: Opportunities and barriers to financing,» Amsterdam, 2022.

[10] J. a. D. Q. Arnould, « Energy Communities in the EU: Fulfilling consumer rights and protections,» Amsterdam, 2022.

[11] G. S. H. P. D. F. F. C. A. D. V. N. C. C. M.-B. I. a. U. A. Koukoufikis, «Energy Communities and Energy Poverty,» Publications Office of the European Union, Luxembourg, 2023.

[12] Housing Europe, «Alleviating energy poverty in social and privately-owned homes from 2020 until today,» [En ligne]. Available: https://www.housingeurope.eu/alleviating-energy-poverty-in-social-and-privately-owned-homes-from-2020-until-today/. [Accès le September 2025].

[13] F. G. R. Hanke, «The struggle of energy communities to enhance energy justice: insights from 113 German cases,» Energ Sustain Soc, vol. 13, n° %116, 2023.

[14] L. Marchi, L. Felicioni, F. Sabatini et L. Errante, «Exploring Energy Literacy in Italian Social Housing: A Survey of Inhabitants Preparing the Ground for Climate Transition,» Sustainability , vol. 15, 2023.

[15] E. F. I. S. T. D. A. Y. J. B. G. A. L. R. B. O.-S. S. P. B. M. A. B. Directorate-General for Energy, «Study on mapping of regulatory frameworks and barriers for individual and collective renewables self-consumption in EU Member States,» Publications Office of the European Union, 2024.

[16] B. R. A. R. Aravind Poshnath, «Adoption of Renewable Energy Systems in common properties of multi-owned buildings: Introduction of 'Energy Entitlement',» Energy Policy, vol. 174, 2023.

[17] OECD, «Social Housing: A Key Part of Past and Future Housing Policy,» 2020.

[18] L. B. P. E. M. Castellazzi, «Overcoming the split incentive barrier in the building sectors: unlocking the energy efficiency potential in the rental & multifamily sectors,» Publications Office of the European Union, Luxembourg, 2017.

[19] P. McManamon, «Toward Building Energy Reduction Through Solar Energy Systems Retrofit Options: An Equest Model,» Journal of Applied Engineering Sciences, 2018.

[20] U. Madushika, T. Ramachandra, G. Karunasena et Udakara, «Energy Retrofitting Technologies of Buildings: A Review-Based Assessment,» Energies, 2023.

6 ACKNOWLEDGMENT AND FUNDING

The work described has received funding as part of the PROLIGHT project from the European Union's Horizon Europe research and innovation program under grant agreement N° 101079902.

STUDY FOR AN AGRIVOLTAIC BASED RURAL ENERGY COMMUNITY IN ALENTEJO PORTUGAL

José A. Silva[1], Joana Correia[1], Sara Pereira[1], Vasco Cabecinha[2], Dorivaldo Duarte[1], Henrique Fava[1], João Barroso[1], Mauro Raposo[1], Luís Fialho[3], Afonso Cavaco[1], Pedro Horta[1]
[1]Renewable Energies Chair, Universidade de Évora, Polo da Mitra, Edifício Ário Lobo de Azevedo, 7000-083 Nossa Senhora de Tourega, Portugal
[2] Faculdade de Ciências e Tecnologia, Universidade Nova de Lisboa, 2829-516 Caparica, Portugal
[3]Eurac Research-Institute for Renewable Energy, 39100 Bolzano, Italy

ABSTRACT: We present a study for the creation of a rural renewable energy community (REC) based on an agrivoltaic (or AgriPV) plant in the Portuguese region of Alentejo. The REC includes an AgriPV power plant with two different configurations, overhead and interspatial with a total capacity of 175 kW, located at the university campus in Nossa Senhora de Tourega. The community encloses the university campus and the neighbouring village of Valverde. The daily energy production profiles of two AgriPV plant configurations are analysed, for a winter and a summer day. These profiles are compared with the consumption profiles of the university campus, and an average household in Évora, and the strategies to maximize the energy community self-consumption are discussed. The main difficulties and advantages of managing agricultural activities and selling agricultural products in the energy community are also examined.
Keywords: agrivoltaics, sensors, monitoring, microclimate, soil

1 INTRODUCTION

In recent years, the installation of PV capacity has been growing steadily, reaching 597 GW in 2024 [1]. This growth has been particularly steep in Portugal, where the installed capacity increased 5-fold in four years, reaching 5.7 GW last year [2]. The main driver for this growth has been the deployment of large-scale photovoltaic power plants, the spread of which is triggering protests from various local stakeholders, raising issues as land-use competition and landscape impact.

Recently, agrivoltaics has emerged as an effective strategy to tackle these issues by proposing the integration of energy and agriculture production in the same area, thus mitigating the competition for land use, and lessening the impacts on the landscape when compared to conventional PV plants.

Renewable Energy Communities (RECs) are local groups of citizens, companies and public authorities that cooperate in production, management and consumption of energy. RECs are a way to empower citizens and promote engagement in renewable energy projects and allow them to access lower electricity prices. The European Union introduced the concept of renewable energy communities in the Clean Energy for all Europeans, and considers REC as way to enable citizen driven actions that can boost energy decarbonization [3].

The expected increase in the installation of AgriPV systems will promote distributed electricity production in rural areas, where frequently electric grid access is limited. Integrating agrivoltaic systems in RECs appears as an interesting solution to use efficiently the PV energy produced, and foster REC in rural areas, promoting decarbonization and sustainable development in these environments.

Moreover, energy poverty remains a challenge in Portugal, with 15.7% of the population in 2024 reporting that they could not afford to keep their home adequately warm, levels that rise above 30% among those at risk of poverty [4]. This situation is particularly significant in Alentejo region due to low incomes, ageing population, and extreme summer heat [5]. So, the development of RECs in Alentejo can have a significant impact on the population's living standard. Furthermore, due to the high solar potential available in the region, as well as its large agricultural area, AgriPV is particularly promising.

In this article, we present a study for the creation of a REC coupling the campus from Universidade de Évora with the neighbouring village of Valverde, considering an AgriPV plant as the main source of renewable energy.

2 METHODS

Our study started by analysing the consumption profiles of the Universidade de Évora's campus, Pólo da Mitra, and of the village of Valverde. Next, the energy production profiles for the agrivoltaic plant, to be installed on the university's campus, were estimated using the PVsyst 8.0.13 software [6], and compared with the consumption profiles. Strategies for increasing energy self-consumption in the community are then discussed.

Finally, the integration of agricultural activities in the REC, as well as distributing agricultural products among the REC's members, is discussed.

2.1 Valverde Renewable Energy Community

Valverde is a small village in Évora municipality, with approximately 150 inhabitants and an area of 0.132 km2. The university campus, *Pólo da Mitra*, is located at a distance of approximate 1 km, making viable, according to Portuguese legislation, the creation of a renewable energy community between these two sites [7].

In Figure 1 a map a of the Renewable Energy Community analysed is presented.

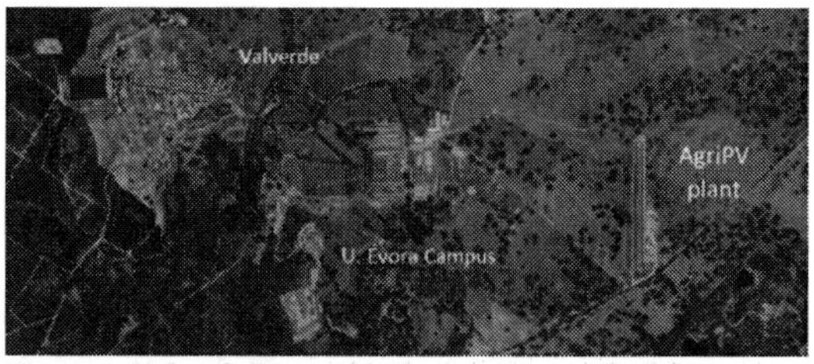

Figure 1: Valverde Renewable Energy Community [8].

2.1 Energy load profiles

<u>Valverde Village</u>

The rural community of Valverde is mainly composed of households and a few small businesses (i.e., restaurants

10.4229/EUPVSEC2025/5EO.1.2

and cafés). So, the energy demand for this community is mainly determined households' consumption. To determine the average daily energy consumption profile for a Valverde household, it was assumed that this profile is similar to consumption profile obtained by Gouveia et al for the municipality of Évora in 2014 [9]. The daily energy consumption profiles of a household in Évora, for a winter day, a summer day and the annual average are shown in Figure 2.

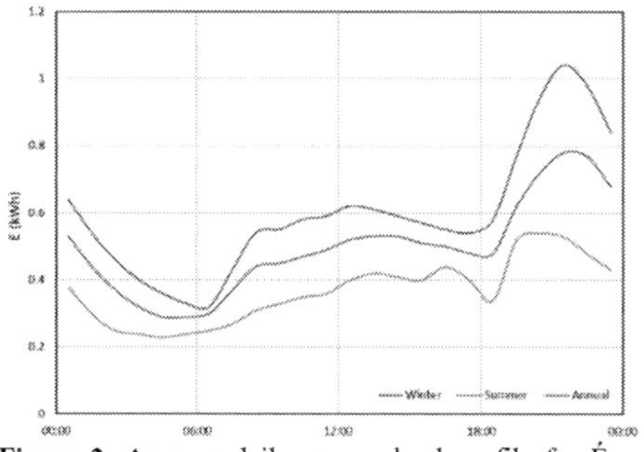

Figure 2: Average daily energy load profile for Évora municipality (adapted from [9])

It can be observed that in all three cases, the peak of energy demand occurs after 18:00, and this peak in winter is approximately twice as high as the summer peak. A second consumption peak can be observed during the morning, and similarly to the evening, the morning peak is also twice as high in winter as in summer.

Pólo da Mitra university campus

The university campus is composed of three main buildings that account for most of the energy load, two dedicated to education and research activities, and one Veterinary Hospital. There also some infrastructures that support research and education with smaller energy loads. In Figure 3, the daily energy loads of the university campus, for a day in summer and a day in winter in 2023 are presented.

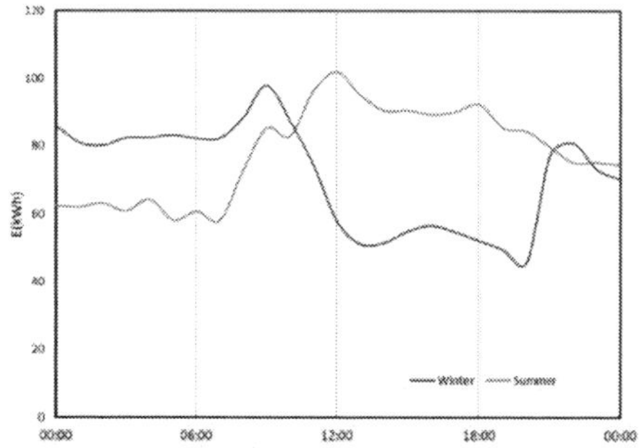

Figure 3: Average daily energy load profile for Pólo da Mitra university campus.

It can be observed that the load profiles are very distinct between winter, where the highest consumption is observed during morning and evening, and summer, where the highest load is observed during the afternoon, suggesting that climatization is the most significant energy consumption in the campus. Nonetheless, the maximum daily consumption for both days is similar (~100 kWh). Also, as expected, unlike the energy load for households. The daily energy load profile of the university is mostly concentrated in sunny hours, thus more aligned with the typical production of PV.

2.2 Agrivoltaic power plant

The agrivoltaic system considered in this study includes two different configurations, one overhead and one interspatial. The characteristics of the two configurations considered are the following:

Overhead system:

- Bifacial monocrystalline silicon modules
- Capacity: 70.8 kWp
- Orientation: North-South, 30° or (-45°,45°)
- Height from the ground: 4 m
- Interrow distance: 4.5 m
- Ground coverage ratio: 35%
- Area: 1200 m^2 + control area
- Type of crops: Intensive

Interspatial system:

- Bifacial monocrystalline silicon module
- Capacity: 103.8 kWp
- Orientation: North-South; 90°
- Height from the ground: 0.5 m
- Modules/row: 2 × 22
- Interrow distance: 8 m
- Area for agricultural use: ~ 90%
- Area: 1700 m^2 + control area
- Type of crops: Extensive

The energy production of these agrivoltaic systems was estimated by performing computer simulations with PVsyst [6]. In the case of the overhead configuration, two scenarios were considered: one with a fixed tilt angle θ=30°, which is approximately the optimal angle for the site, and another considering a tracking path between -45° and 45°.

3 RESULTS AND DISCUSSION

3.1 AgriPV energy production

Overhead configuration

The specific energy production obtained for the two overhead AgriPV systems were the following:

Overhead system (θ=30°): 1412 kWh/(kWp·year)

Overhead system (-45 °<θ<=45°): 1748 kWh/(kWp·year)

As expected, the system with sun tracking has a significantly higher energy production, with a relative gain of 24% compared to the fixed one. However, it must be mentioned that, in an agrivoltaic system, the sun tracker path often needs to consider the radiation needs of the plants, rather than just maximising the energy yield [10].

In figures 4 and 5 are presented the energy production annual profiles for the overhead configuration, respectively fixed and with tracking.

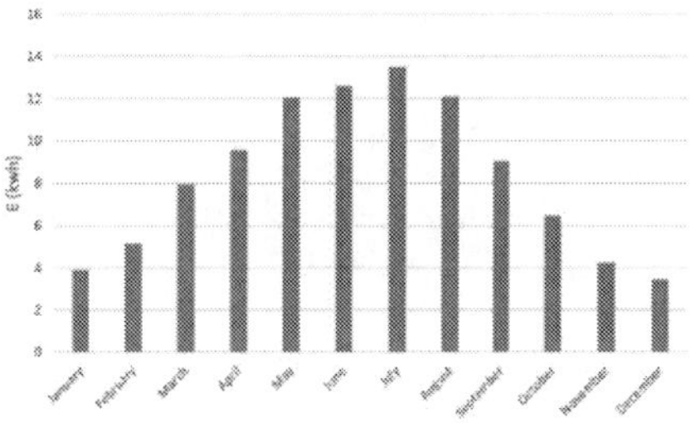

Figure 4: Annual energy production profile for the AgriPV plant with overhead configuration, θ=30º.

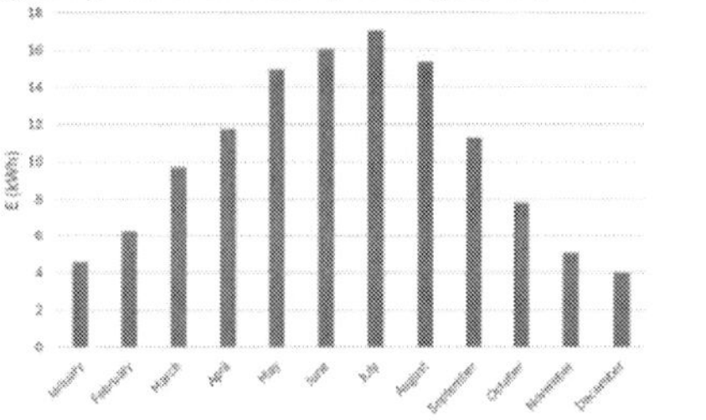

Figure 5: Annual energy production profile for the AgriPV plant with overhead configuration, -45º < θ < 45.

It can be observed that despite the significant difference in energy yield, the two AgriPV systems have similar annual energy production profiles, with a significantly higher energy production in summer than in winter. In fact, for the fixed system, the ratio between the maximum monthly production attained in July and the minimum monthly production attained in December is 3.9, while for the overhead system with tracking, it is 4.3.

In figures 6 and 7, the daily energy production profiles for the overhead AgriPV system with a fixed axis for a winter and a summer day are presented.

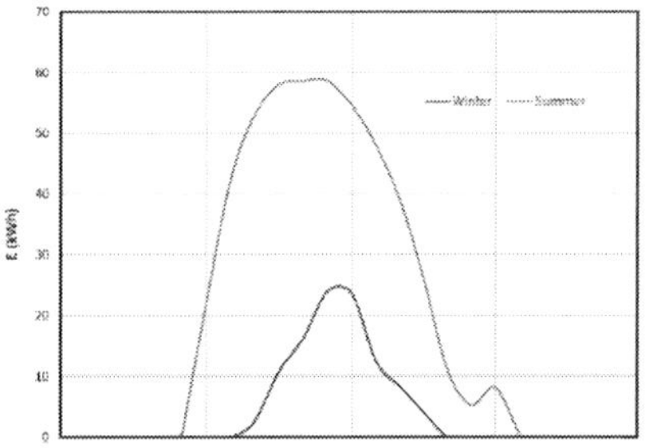

Figure 6: Daily energy production profile for winter and summer, for the AgriPV plant with overhead configuration, θ=30º.

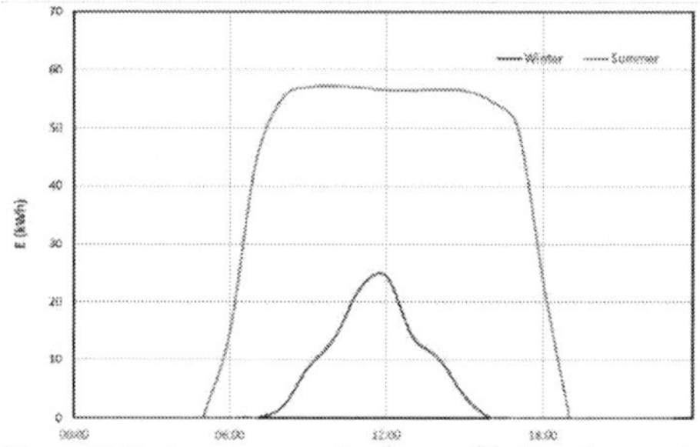

Figure 7: Daily energy production profile for winter and summer, for the AgriPV plant with overhead configuration, -45º < θ < 45.

It can be observed that, as expected, both the production peak and production hours are lower in the winter than in summer. Nevertheless, for the tracker system, a large production plateau is observed in the summer daily profile, contributing to the higher summer energy production of this system when compared to the fixed one.

Interspatial configuration

The specific energy production obtained for the AgriPV interspatial system was 673 kWh/(kWp·year), which is approximately half of the value obtained for the overhead fixed system. This feature is mainly due to the non-optimal tilt angle (40%) and near shading (20%) due to the trees that surround the installation site.

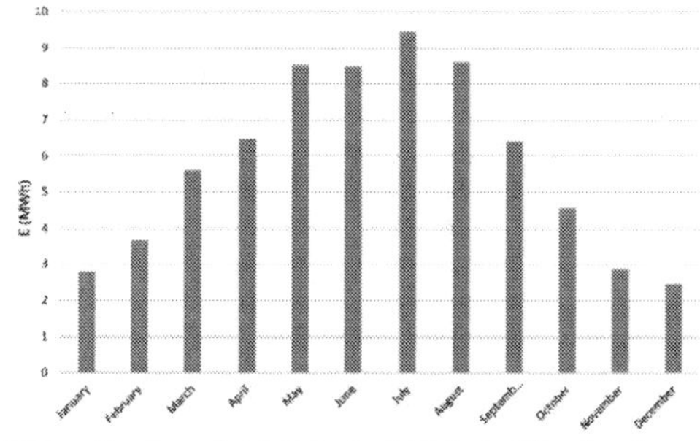

Figure 8: Annual energy production profile for the AgriPV plant with interspatial configuration.

Similar to what was observed for the two overhead systems analysed, there is a significant imbalance between summer and winter energy production for the AgriPV interspatial system (Figure 8). For this system, the ratio between the maximum monthly production, attained in July, and the minimum reached in December was 3.9.

In Figure 9 the daily energy production profile for the interspatial AgriPV plant for summer and winter is presented.

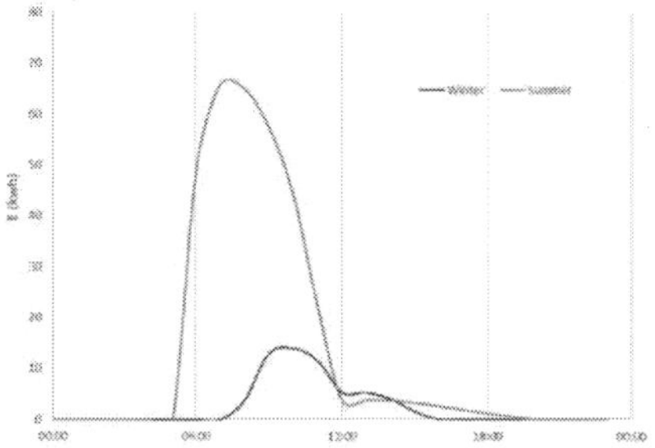

Figure 9: Daily energy production profile for winter and summer, for the AgriPV plant with interspatial configuration.

It can be observed that for both winter and summer, the daily energy production profile has a peak in the morning. Moreover, it can be observed that the near-shading of the surrounding trees impacts production in the afternoon. This effect is particularly significant in the summer.

3.2 Comparison energy load with energy production

When comparing the AgriPV plant energy production profiles, both daily and annual, it can be concluded that the production of the AgriPV does not fit well with the average energy demand for a typical Évora household. In fact, the energy production for the three AgriPV systems is significantly higher in summer, while the energy consumption is higher in winter. Also, the daily energy load peaks in the evening, when the production from the AgriPV systems is very low or zero. Still, the AgriPV production can supply the households' morning energy needs. Moreover, to maximise self-consumption of the AgriPV plant and improve the economic viability of the renewable energy community, the AgriPV plant installed power should consider the summer consumption.

3.3 Integrating agricultural activities in RECs

The successful integration of an AgriPV project in a renewable energy community strongly depends on the existence of a compromise between maximising energy and agricultural production. This must start with a clear definition of the main objectives of the renewable energy community by its members. Next, making a choice of compatible crops and plant configurations is crucial. Moreover, frequently the radiation needs of the crops require that the PV systems are not in the optimal position for energy production, thus limiting the energy yield of the AgriPV system.

In terms of the community organisation, the agricultural activities can either be developed in a cooperative way by the REC members (i.e., small farmers) or by farming enterprises. In any case, the REC members should have the possibility to access to the agricultural products at a lower price.

4 CONCLUSIONS

AgriPV and RECs are two innovative concepts that already play a key role in boosting PV deployment and energy decarbonization. The joint use of the two concepts has great synergistic potential.

Ensuring energy self-consumption within the REC can help to make AgriPV projects viable and boost PV energy production locally.

Besides electricity production and distribution, RECs members must have the possibility to participate in agricultural production and have access to food goods at reduced prices.

To improve the profitability of the agrivoltaic plant and the economic success of the REC, the sizing of the plant must be made, with the view of maximising the energy self-consumption rate, so in the case of the Valverde renewable energy, based on summer consumption

REC members must plan together the design and operation plan of the AgriPV plant to achieve their common goals.

5 ACKNOWLEDGEMENTS

This research was supported by the Alliance for the Energy Transition (56) co-financed by the European Union through the Recovery and Resilience Plan (PRR).

6 REFERENCES

[1] SolarPower Europe, "Global Market Outlook for Solar Power 2025-2029," 2025.

[2] Direção Geral de Energia e Geologia (DGEG), "Estatísticas rápidas das renováveis - junho de 2025".

[3] Directorate General for Energy - European Commission, "Clean Energy for all Europeans Package," 2019.

[4] Instituto Nacional de Estatítica (INE), "Press Release World Energy Efficiency Day," 2025. [Online]. Available: https://www.ine.pt/ngt_server/attachfileu.jsp?look_parent Boui=715631147&att_display=n&att download=y.

[5] S. Peralta, B. P. Carvalho, J. Fanha and M. Fonseca, "Portugal, Balanço Social 2024. Nova School of Business and Economics,," 2025.

[6] PVsyst 8.0.13 Photovoltaic Software, Webgenève., [Online]. Available: https://www.pvsyst.com/.

[7] Diário da Républica (Portugal), vol. 10/22, pp. 3-185, 14 01 2022.

[8] Adapted from Google Earth, [Online]. Available: https://earth.google.com/.

[9] J. P. Gouveia, J. Seixas and A. Mestre, "Daily electricity consumption profiles from smart meters - Proxies of behavior for space heating and cooling," Energy, vol. 141, pp. 108-122, 2017.

[10] D. Fumey et al., "Dynamic agrivoltaics, climate protection for grapevine driven by artificial intelligence," in Proceedings 22nd GiESCO International Meeting, 2023.

UNIVERSIDADE DE ÉVORA

SOL4R

Study for an agrivoltaic based rural energy community in Alentejo Portugal

J. A. Silva[1], J. Correia[1], S. Pereira[1], V. Cabecinha[2], D. Duarte[1], H. Fava[1], J. Barroso[1], M. Raposo[1], L. Fialho[3], A. Cavaco[1], P. Horta[1]

[1] Solar4R, Universidade de Évora, Portugal
[2] Faculdade de Ciências e Tecnologia, Universidade Nova de Lisboa, Portugal
[3] Eurac Research - Institute for Renewable Energy, Italy

UNIVERSIDADE DE ÉVORA

Outline

- Motivation & context
- Case study: Valverde AgriPV-REC
  - Compare energy production and load profiles
  - Maximize self-consumption in the REC
  - Integrating agricultural activities in RECs
- Conclusions & Future work

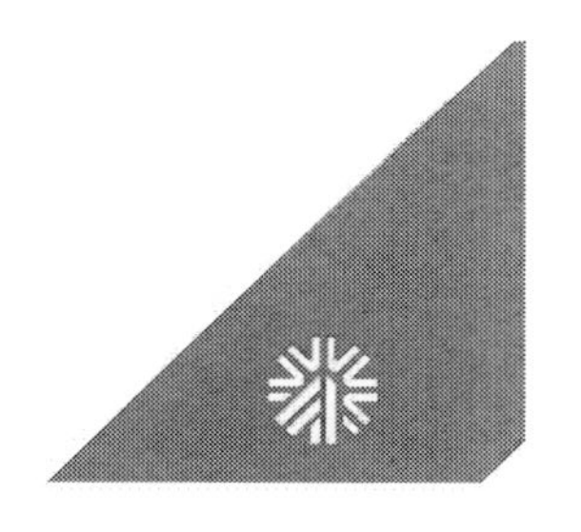

Motivation & context

UNIVERSIDADE DE ÉVORA

AgriPV & RECs

- RECs can address the problem of limited grid access in rural areas.
- AgriPV plants can boost the deployment of PV capacity and the creation of RECs in rural areas
- REC members can have a role in the energy and agricultural production, and access electricity and food at reduced prices

Source: Enel Green Power

Case study: Valverde AgriPV-REC

UNIVERSIDADE DE ÉVORA

Location: Évora, Portugal

AgriPV plant
(38°31'51"N 8°00'14"W)

Case study: Valverde AgriPV-REC

UNIVERSIDADE DE ÉVORA

AgriPV plant - Overhead system

- Bifacial c-Si modules; 70.8 kWp
- North-South, 30º or (-45º, 45º)
- Height from the ground: 4 m
- Interrow distance: 4.5 m
- Ground coverage ratio: 35%
- Intensive crops (ex: lettuce, potatoes)
- Area: 1200 m^2

Source: AgriSolar Clearinghouse

Case study: Valverde AgriPV-REC

UNIVERSIDADE DE ÉVORA

AgriPV plant - Interspatial system

- Bifacial c-Si modules; 103.8 kWp
- North-South; 90°
- Height from the ground: 0.5 m
- Modules/row: 2 × 22
- Interrow distance: 8 m
- Area for agricultural use: ~ 90%
- Extensive crops: (Ex: forage cereals)
- Total area: 1700 m^2

Source: Next2Sun

Case study: Valverde AgriPV-REC

UNIVERSIDADE DE ÉVORA

Energy production – Overhead system, N-S

θ=30º

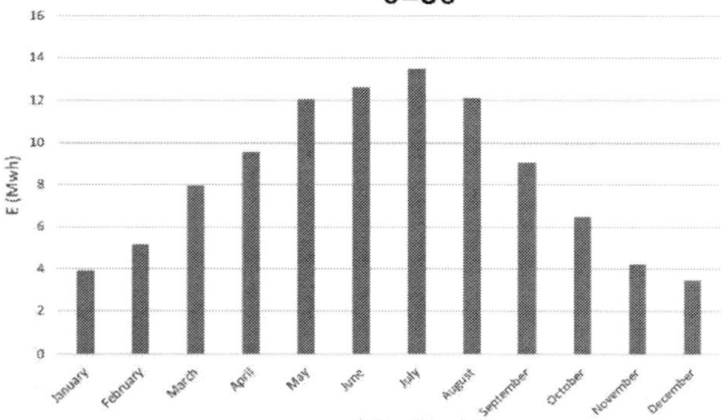

-45º<Θ<45º

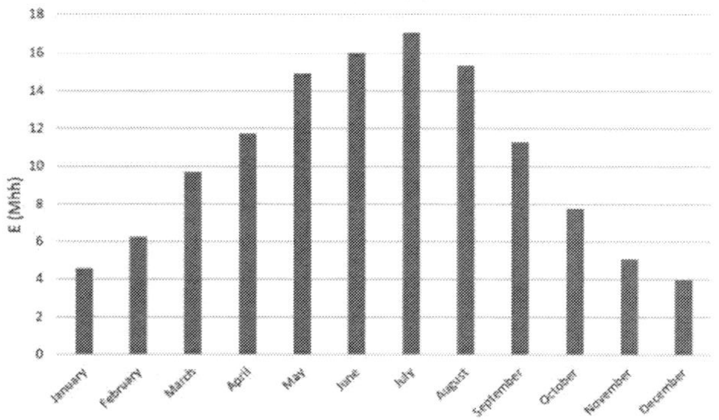

Annual profile

- Significant diferences between summer and winter production:
  - θ=30º: $Month_{max}/Month_{min} = 3.9$
  - -45º<θ<45º $Month_{max}/Month_{min} = 4.3$

Case study: Valverde AgriPV-REC

UNIVERSIDADE DE ÉVORA

Energy production – Overhead system, N-S

θ=30º

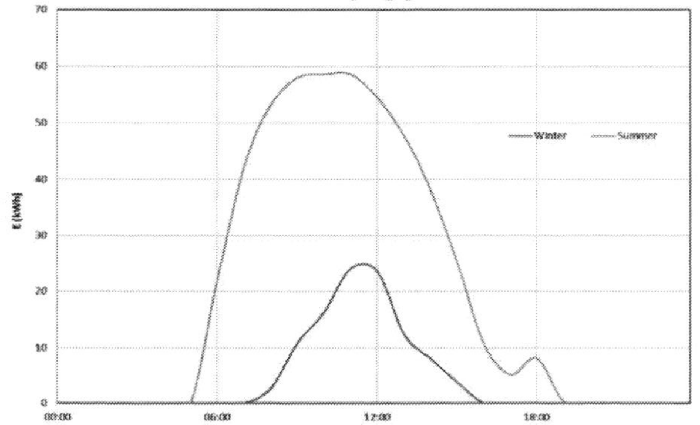

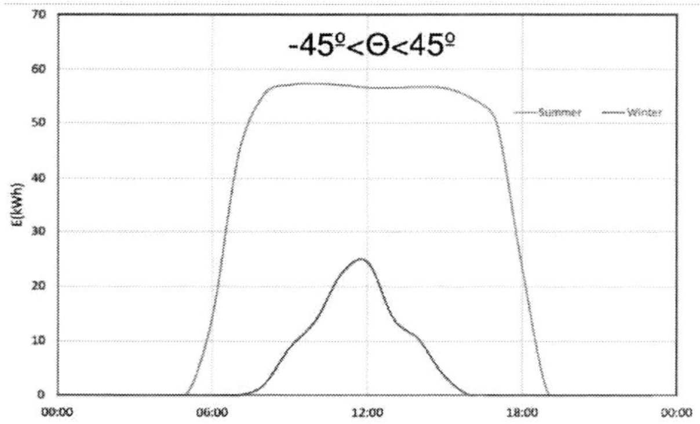

<u>Annual profile</u>

- Significant diferences between summer and winter production:
  - θ=30º: $Month_{max}/Month_{min}$ = 3.9
  - -45º<θ<45º $Month_{max}/Month_{min}$ = 4.3

<u>Daily profile</u>

- Large production plateau in summer for system with tracking
- Specific production:
  - θ=30º: 1412 kWh/kWp
  - -45º<θ<45º: 1748 kWh/kWp **+ 24%**

→ But sometimes tracking mode most be adapted to the crops needs

Case study: Valverde AgriPV-REC

UNIVERSIDADE DE ÉVORA

Energy production – Interspatial system, N-S 90°

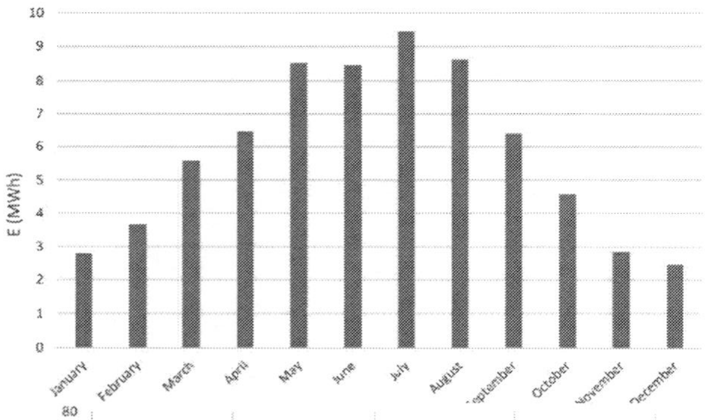

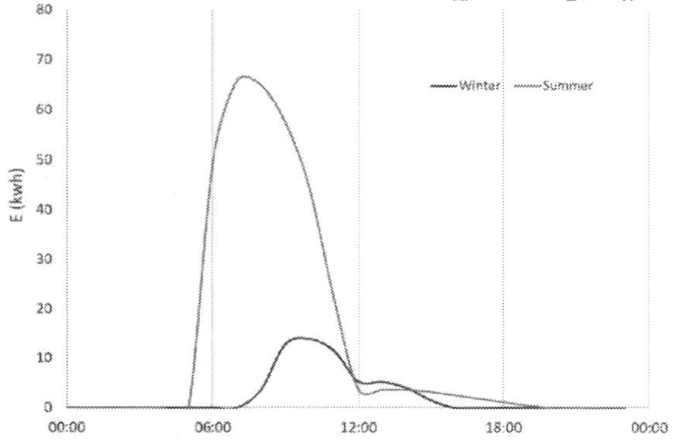

Annual profile

- $Month_{max}/Month_{min} = 3.9$

Daily profile

- Production peaks in the morning both in summer and winter
- Specific production:
  - 673 kWh/kWp ~ ½ Overhead system fixed
- Significant losses due to the tilt angle (~40%) and near shadings (~20%)

Case study: Valverde AgriPV-REC

UNIVERSIDADE DE ÉVORA

Energy load profiles

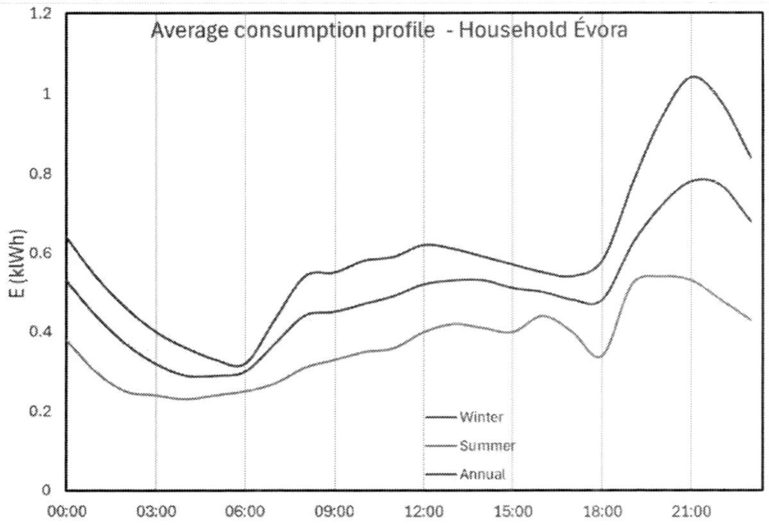

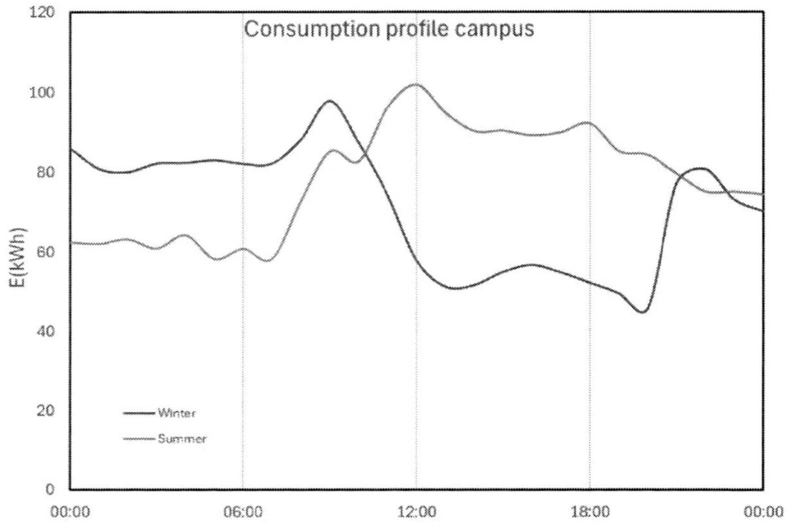

- Largest consumption after 18:00
- Winter peak ~ 2× summer peak
- AgriPV production can adapt to morning consumption

- Very distinct winter and summer consumption profiles
- Similar consumption maximum in winter and summer
- Can partially complement household consumption

Source: J. P. Goveia et al., Energy 141 (2017) 108 - 122

Case study: Valverde AgriPV-REC

UNIVERSIDADE DE ÉVORA

Compatibility between energy supply and demand

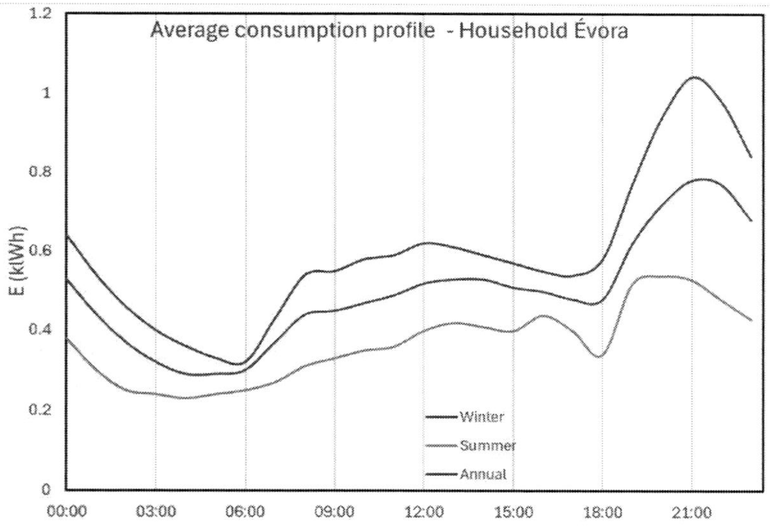

- The AgriPV plant energy production profiles (daily and annual) do not fit well the average energy demand for a typical Évora's household
- PV production can supply the morning energy needs (morning peak)
- To maximize self-consumption PV installed power should take in account summer consumption

Source: J. P. Goveia et al., Energy 141 (2017) 108 - 122

Case study: Valverde AgriPV-REC

UNIVERSIDADE DE ÉVORA

Agricultural production

- In an AgriPV project, there must be a compromise between maximizing energy and agricultural production
  → Not always easy!
- The choice of compatible crops and plant configurations is crucial
- Agricultural activities can either be developed in a cooperative way by the REC members or by farming enterprises.
- In any case, REC members should have access to the agricultural products at lower a price

UNIVERSIDADE DE ÉVORA

Conclusions

- AgriPV and RECs will play a key role in energy decarbonization. The joint use of the two concepts has great synergistic potential.
- Ensuring energy self-consumption within the REC improves viability of AgriPV projects and boosts PV energy production locally
- Besides electricity production and distribution, RECs members can participate in crops growing and access food at reduced prices
- AgriPV plants must be planned to maximize the self-consumption rate → based on summer consumption
- REC members must plan together the design and operation plan of the AgriPV plant to achieve their common goals

UNIVERSIDADE DE ÉVORA

Future work

- The AgriPV plant will allow for the identification of the best options in terms of crops, PV layouts, and tracking modes.
- Engage local farmers and populations in our AgriPV project namely by involving them in the choice of crops and agriculture practices
- Support the creation of future AgriPV-REC promoted by citizens, farmers associations, companies and local authorities

UNIVERSIDADE DE ÉVORA

Also at this conference:

4DV.1.15 S. Pereira et al., Review of Sensor Technologies for Monitoring Agrivoltaic Systems

4DV.1.25 J. dos Santos et al., Agrivoltaic – Study of potential in Portugal

UNIVERSIDADE
DE ÉVORA

SOL4R

Thank you !

jose.silva@uevora.pt

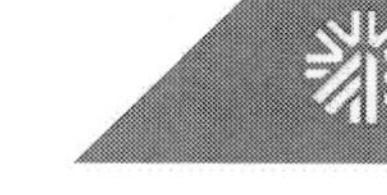

CHALLENGES AND LESSONS LEARNED IN THE IMPLEMENTATION OF A REGIONAL-SCALE PV ENERGY COMMUNITY IN SPAIN

L. M. Carrasco, R. H. Almeida, Kiane Alves e Silva, L. Narvarte
Instituto de Energía Solar, Universidad Politécnica de Madrid
luismiguel.carrasco@upm.es

ABSTRACT: This article presents the experience accumulated over two and a half years in the design, creation, and implementation of a large-scale regional renewable energy community in a rural area covering 2,500 km² in northern Spain. The implementation of this energy community has faced numerous barriers and challenges, including those stemming from rural depopulation and aging, legal limitations in the establishment of energy communities, technological innovation, and financing issues. The main barriers encountered and the lessons learned by this experience are listed and described, grouped into five categories, with the aim of sharing them to contribute to the creation of a new paradigm in the implementation of bottom-up initiatives with real local impact.
Keywords: Energy Community, Lessons Learned, PV self-consumption

1 INTRODUCTION

The European Commission launched in 2022 the REPowerEU [1] plan to responde to the hardships and global energy market disruption caused by Russia's invasion of Ukraine. The plan aims both to end the EU's dependence on Russian fossil fuels, and tackling the climate crisis through energy savings, diversification of energy supplies, and accelerated roll-out of renewable energy to replace fossil fuels in homes, industry and power generation.

One of the REPowerEU's proposals for achieving its objectives was the development of energy communities (EC). The aim was to establish at least one energy community in each municipality with a population of over 10,000 by 2025 [2]. This would mean that, by this year, around 90,000 energy communities should have been established across Europe. There is no updated information about the number of ECs in Europe, but this figure was set at 9,000 in early 2024 [3] [4], which is far from the goal set out in the plan.

While there is much that could be speculated about the causes of this gap, all the evidence suggests that the lack of a paradigm for implementing CEs is hindering the development of these initiatives [5]. The difficulty in creating such communities, whether renewable [6] or citizen-based [7] as defined by European Directives, lies in the absence of well-established, well-tested and widely accepted EC models, as already evidenced by some authors [8] [9] [10].

Since 2022, a new experience of innovative EC has been developed in Spain, creating a large-scale Renewable Energy Community (REC) in the Calatayud County (Aragon region), with the support of the LIFE European Commission programme [11], which aims to bring a new approach to facilitate the emergence and growth of citizen-led energy community projects throughout Europe.

This article discusses the creation of this REC and the challenges it faced to become an instrument of social innovation that contributes to solving local social needs in depopulated rural regions. The document analyses the lessons learned during the implementation of this REC over a period of two and a half years, from technical, economic, legal, administrative and organisational perspectives. The aim of this work is to contribute to the establishment of a future paradigm for the expansion of RECs throughout Europe.

2 A LARGE-SCALE REGIONAL RENEWABLE ENERGY COMMUNITY

2.1 Goals of the REC.

Comunidad de Energías Renovables de la Comarca de Calatayud (CERCA) [12], as was named this REC, was created in a bottom-up approach to tackle the social challenges of a depopulated rural area of around 2,500 km² in the north of Spain. This region is composed of 67 municipalities and a total population of around 36,000 people. The population of the area has shrunk by almost 60% over the past 80 years. This has resulted in an ageing population who are concerned about the future of their villages. In fact, depopulated rural areas are, in general, characterized by:

- Low population density,
- Migration process to cities,
- Ageing population,
- Lack of basic services (education, health, communications, etc.),
- Poor organizational structures to implement local initiatives.

CERCA was created with the aim of contributing to the fight against the phenomenon of depopulation and its consequences. The innovative character of the regional REC compared to other possible solutions, such as the creation of multiple local RECs in the various villages of the region, lies in the fact that, for this initiative to have a real local impact, it must maximise the economic, environmental and social benefits for its members.

Therefore, the benefits of creating a single regional-scale REC instead of multiple local RECs are:

- It creates "community" since the REC joints regional actors for a common purpose.
- It maximizes regional impact. A regional REC has the capacity to reach all the municipalities in the area, including those too small to establish their own local REC.
- Resource optimization. Centralized management consolidates expertise across technical, economic, fiscal, and administrative processes in renewable project deployment.
- Economies of scale. Centralized procurement of PV components and installation services results in more competitive prices than if the projects were implemented independently.

CERCA was established with the goal of integrating 5,000 people (around 13.5% of the total population) and

75 businesses and industries in the region into the energy community. Initially, CERCA's activity focuses on developing of photovoltaic self-consumption projects, which are financed by the users (prosumers) themselves. In order to maximise the impact of this PV energy in the area, CERCA has been set up as an electricity retailer, compensating for the lack of regulation surrounding energy communities in Spain. This enables CERCA to monetise the surplus electricity fed into the grid, as well as supply, aggregate and store energy.

Figure 1: 116 kWp PV generator in Maluenda, installed on the roof of a winery, supplying energy for the winery itself and 23 homes in the municipality

2.2 Achievements of CERCA.

As of August 2025, CERCA had 150 members and had developed 18 projects in 15 villages in the region (one of which is shown in Figure 1). These projects had a total nominal PV power of 825 kWp and directly benefited more than 500 people. The users themselves financed these projects entirely, amounting to €760,000. They will recover 21% VAT and 40% subsidy from the IDAE's IMPLEMENTA programme [13]. Additionally, CERCA supplies electricity to 180 consumption points with a total supply power of 850 kW.

3 CHALLENGES, BARRIERS AND LESSONS LEARNED

To implement the regional REC, CERCA developed from the outset a methodology based on fostering engagement, awareness, and skills within the region, with the aim of overcoming the challenges inherent in introducing such an innovative model in a decentralized, depopulated, and aging rural environment. In addition to this challenge, CERCA has had to overcome several other obstacles, including the absence of REC regulation in Spain, administrative barriers to the legalisation and activation of PV self-consumption systems, the lack of established technical criteria for designing such systems, and the shortage of technical qualifications in the region.

The main barriers and challenges overcome by CERCA are detailed below, along with the lessons learned. These are categorised as follows: organisational, financial, technical, legal and administrative.

3.1 Organizational aspects

Don't start from scratch, make a clear proposal. When CERCA started the process of creating a REC, one of the main roles of the local promoter group was to establish a clear proposal of the type of REC that they wanted to convey to the targeted residents, associations, businesses, companies and town councils.

There are many possibilities for RECs, and one of them must be chosen. They can be small (on a village scale) or large (on a regional scale); with little citizen participation or, on the contrary, trying to promote it; limited to PV self-consumption or with the ambition to offer all the services that the European Directive grants to RECs; and they can be cooperatives, foundations, associations, private companies, etc. It must also have a spirit that motivates the creation of the REC. This spirit is what drives the promoter group and must be passed on to potential participants. A spirit that is rooted in the need it seeks to address.

The CERCA promoter group suffered from a reality in the Calatayud region that is common to other regions of rural Spain: the lack of a future for its villages caused by population decline and, in general, institutional neglect. The motivation for building a REC was so that its villages could have a future. And this is the spirit of CERCA: a REC whose impact is to contribute to the future of the villages of the Calatayud region and reverse the trend toward depopulation.

- **LESSON 1:** Difficulty in developing bottom-up initiatives when starting from scratch. If the promoter group does not establish a clear REC proposal, the discussion on said proposal will be transferred to the potential participants, generating noise, producing confusion and delaying the process with endless discussions. This discussion should take place within the promoter group. If there are differing sensitivities within this group, they should be resolved before going out to plant the idea.

A structure based exclusively on volunteers is the main threat to the sustainability of a REC. While the REC's promoter group must be composed of local citizens mobilized around a clearly perceived need, the management and operation phase of the REC cannot rely solely on volunteer work. The scale of the REC, the technical complexity of managing PV systems, and the responsibility for managing relatively large volumes of micro-investments require a professional and well-compensated structure to sustain and provide the REC with the necessary stability.

- **LESSON 2**: The misidentification of real participation processes with volunteerism causes serious problems in the medium term. By definition, volunteers have limited time and capacity. They have an important role to play, namely, maintaining the spirit that gave birth to the REC and maintaining it throughout its existence. But they often resist coexisting with a professional structure that is necessary when the REC enters its phase of maturity, consolidation, and growth. Achieving this transition to coexistence between volunteers and professionals is a challenge for the sustainability of the REC.

Communicating the REC proposal established by the promoter group among residents, associations, businesses, companies and town councils takes much longer than initially imagined. It requires interviews with mayors prior to the multiple visits to each village. The initial visits serve only to introduce the idea. The idea is discussed by the interlocutors in the villages, and questions arise, necessitating revisits.

This process, which seeks real participation through the appropriation of the idea by the final recipients, is long, requires a lot of time in the territory and a lot of dedication from a specialized team.

- **LESSON 3**: The seeding phase takes much longer than initially imagined. A REC that aspires to truly engage its members must build awareness and commitment by spreading the word, spreading the REC spirit, and explaining the proposal in detail. This isn't done from a remote office; it requires numerous visits and a significant amount of time spent on the ground. This requires forming a professional local team to execute these actions and ensure a constant presence in the area. The financial means must be secured to maintain this local team for a longer period than previously planned.

Real participation of residents requires the involvement of municipal representatives. CERCA's experience of developing projects in Calatayud's villages has shown that citizens' trust can only be gained if their mayor's trust is first secured. Cooperation between mayors and council secretaries is mandatory for developing community projects in small villages.

Contrary to popular belief, politics has a greater influence in rural areas than in urban ones. If the mayor is not consulted when a project is initiated in a village, they will resist it and become an obstacle. Therefore, it is essential to obtain the mayor's approval before visiting a village to raise awareness, but this is not easy due to their workload, lack of resources, and the large number of invitations they receive to events. Consequently, invitations from the REC get lost among the many other messages they receive.

The CERCA experience shows that after a year of visiting the villages with no apparent results, the turning point came with a call from the Calatayud Region government itself to all its mayors and town secretaries for three workshops in which the mayors were explained the design and the economic impact that CERCA could have on their town councils and their residents, all the legal aspects were explained to the secretaries and the technical aspects were explained to the town council technicians. The call was a success; all the mayors were familiar with the CERCA project thanks to the hard work of the previous year, and the support of the Calatayud Region government gave them the confidence to join the project. After the workshops, the mayors and secretaries addressed the CERCA representatives, saying, "Come and introduce CERCA to my neighbours!".

- **LESSON 4**: Need of institutional support, mainly from Municipalities. In rural environments, real participation of residents in a REC requires the involvement of mayors.
- **LESSON 5**: In order to publicise the REC, it is necessary to have the collaboration of the supra-local institution that brings together all the municipalities in the region, so that it can convene them. This will encourage the mayors to attend and ensure high trust.

Lack of skills in depopulated rural areas. The region has been found to have a general lack of knowledge about energy and how the electricity sector works. This is not just a feature of rural societies; it also occurs in urban ones.There is also a notable lack of digitalisation among the population in the Calatayud region, which makes it difficult to sign contracts online, disseminate information through digital media or implement PV production monitoring systems.

- **LESSON 6**: Training in general technical aspects related to energy, as well as finding creative solutions to the lack of digitalisation in rural areas, must be prioritised.

3.2 Financial aspects

Grants do not respect the timeframes needed for real participation. CERCA has benefited from the IMPLEMENTA programme, a public aid scheme run by Spanish government through the IDAE agency and designed to subsidise PV installations within the RECs. Thanks to the appeal of subsidies when it comes to making investment decisions, this aid has accelerated the implementation of projects. However, the programme's implementation period was only 14 months, a timeframe incompatible with the participatory processes required by any initiative aiming for real citizen participation, which require a longer timescale.

Furthermore, CERCA has exploited the collective nature of RECs by aggregating demand through collective PV self-consumption. This has enabled installation costs to be reduced by up to 50%. For instance, while an individual 3 kWp PV system might cost around €1,500/kWp, that cost can drop to approximately €700/kWp in a jointly managed 60 kWp facility. This allows for more efficient use of public money in the form of subsidies, limiting it to its catalytic effect: taking as an example, the IMPLEMENTA programme subsidy, 40% of this reduced cost, would amount to around €280/kWp, just 18.7% of the individual system cost.

- **LESSON 7**: Public grants are a lever to promote RECs among the population, but the deadlines established by these grants do not match with the time needed for the awareness and engagement of the people for a real participation.
- **LESSON 8**: The ideal PV configuration is to group participants through collective self-consumption systems to achieve economies of scale and to increase the power to raise community awareness. Aggregation effect not only reduce costs but to use efficiently public funding as a catalyst mechanism.

Need of appropriate financial schemes. Even with a 40% grant and a 21% VAT refund on the remaining cost, these public supports were only accessible after project execution. Because CERCA was a newly created entity, banks were unwilling to finance neither the grant nor the VAT. Citizens had to front 100% of the investment and wait over two years for reimbursement, with no interest. This up-front burden effectively excluded low-income households from participating and reduced the participation in general. However, this experience also demonstrated the willingness of a large portion of the citizens of the Calatayud region to invest in private equity.

- **LESSON 9**: Innovative financing schemes are needed to reduce the financial risks of RECs while supporting them in project development.

Real participation in a REC, which translates into micro-investments, requires a significant amount of time spent in the territory. The creation and financing of collective projects by citizens both require a constant presence in the territory. Participatory activities involving engagement, awareness and skills, the organisation of collective initiatives and their continuous monitoring, as well as the region's lack of digitalisation, mean it is essential to be close to citizens. This situation requires personnel with highly specialised communication and interpersonal skills to be present in villages at weekends and public holidays – when villages are most populated –, building bonds of trust.

- **LESSON 10**: Projects financed by capital contributions from the users themselves requires a very strong presence in the territory and social skills.

3.3 Technical aspects.

Sizing PV systems for self-consumption. CERCA has sized PV systems with a self-consumption rate of at least 0.5, based on each user's historical consumption. However, users have different priorities and have generally requested more PV power than our calculations have suggested.

- **LESSON 11**: Sizing tools that enable to make decisions based on various criteria, not just technical or economic one, are needed.

Assuring quality in self-consumption PV systems. The profitability of micro-investments in PV systems depends on their continued performance for at least 25 years. This is only achieved if both the components and the system are of very high quality. The quality of PV systems is not a question of price but of ensuring good quality components and good practices in the installation phase.

It is widely known that this is achieved through the application of rigorous technical specifications and quality control testing to ensure compliance. However, these technical specifications are very rarely included in the contract with the installer, especially if the PV systems are relatively small.

- **LESSON 12**: To ensure the quality and lifetime of PV systems for at least 25 years, a set of technical specifications must be included in installation contracts and installers must be required to comply with them.

Maximise the local impact of renewable energy generation projects. PV surpluses are becoming increasingly cheaper on the electricity market because Spain's electricity production supply is saturated during peak hours. This causes electricity prices to fall below zero, resulting in the so-called 'duck curve', as shown in Figure 2. In order to reverse this situation and maximise the local impact of energy generated by RECs, it is necessary to implement storage systems and demand management strategies that enable generation to be matched with demand.

- **LESSON 13**: There is a need of advance management systems to balance generation and consumption in RECs integrating energy storage systems and demand management strategies.

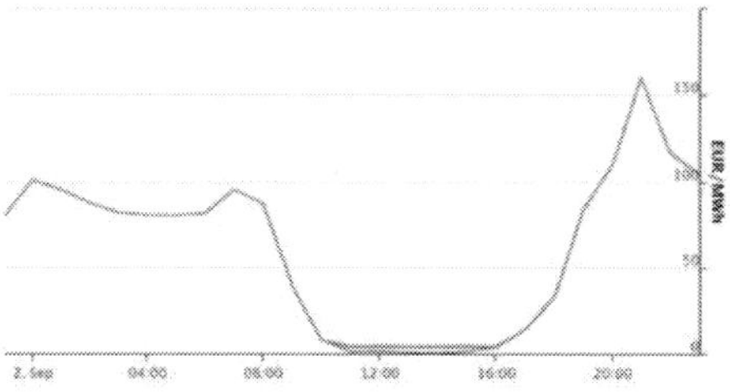

Figure 2: "Duck curve" that shows the evolution of the market price of electricity (€/MWh) in Spain and Portugal on 2 September 2025. At midday, the price is almost €0 (*source: OMIE* [14]).

Involving local installers as a driver for the project. CERCA's ambition is to collaborate with the region's communities to secure their future. This requires boosting regional economic activity, including that of local electricians and SMEs. To maximise local impact, CERCA involves local installers in the installation of its PV systems. These installers can also become REC representatives, which would benefit both themselves and REC. Local installers are trusted by some local councils, for whom they provide maintenance services.

- **LESSON 14**: Local engineers and PV installers must be involved in the REC projects and benefit from training in technical specifications and other issues. They can become representatives of the REC by proposing new projects that will benefit themselves and the energy community.

3.4 Legal aspects

Need of a REC's regulation adapted to rural communities. As a REC, CERCA's objectives are to provide its members with economic, environmental and social benefits through the production, consumption, trading, aggregation and storage of energy. However, Spain still has no regulations that permit RECs to carry out all these activities.

- **LESSON 15**: The failure to transpose the European directive into Spanish law prevents a REC from carrying out the activities envisaged in the EU legislation. No proper management of surpluses can be achieved within the self-consumption law. RECs must become electricity retailers to this end.

Self-consumption optimization. Collective PV self-consumption in Spain is carried out by assigning static distribution coefficients to consumers, regulated by law in Royal Decree 244/2019 [15]. This static distribution causes that some of the generated energy is fed into the grid instead of being used by other prosumers, preventing that energy from having a local impact throughout the year.

- **LESSON 16**: National regulation should be updated to allow for the implementation of dynamic distribution coefficients in collective PV self-consumption. This measure would maximize self-consumption rates in collective initiatives, increasing the local impact of RECs.

3.5 Administrative aspects

The development of collective PV self-consumption projects is a complex process due to the numerous requirements and regulations set by different competent bodies that must be met, as well as the interaction of a wide variety of actors involved in commissioning a self-consumption facility. This process involves everything from the initial design to the final activation of self-consumption by the utility and the effective application in the prosumer's electricity bill. However, the phase involving activation with the utility company takes the longest. This activation procedure has the following phases:

1. Having a connection point to the electricity distribution grid. If this does not exist, it will be necessary to request an electricity supply access point. This procedure can take up to a year.
2. Obtaining access and connection permits. The experience in Aragon with the electricity utility

operating in the region is that this procedure takes a few weeks unless the utility requires in its connection conditions the reinforcement of the distribution grid. In this case, the procedure can take many months and can be very costly.

3. Signing the technical access contract with the distributor. For this procedure, the utility has a maximum legal deadline of 5 months.
4. Obtaining approval from the utility after inspection of the connection to the electricity distribution grid. The time between the request for an inspection and the inspector's visit to the installation varies greatly and can take more than 1 month. In addition, we have found inconsistencies in the internal technical criteria of the utility, which makes these times much longer.
5. Activation of self-consumption with the electricity retailer. This procedure, which is carried out between the electricity retailer and the electricity company, has a very variable execution time, which can be up to 2 months.

Based on its experience with the 18 installations carried out to date, CERCA estimates that the average total activation time for self-consumption is approximately 12 months. This situation has been confirmed by other authors [16] and discourages project participants, as well as having a very negative impact on the return on investment for prosumers. Prosumers see their installations idle for months, without access to the economic and environmental benefits to which they have contributed.

- **LESSON 17**: The lead times for obtaining permits and legalising shared self-consumption systems are very long, several months or even a year in some cases. Simplified procedures with shorter response times are needed.

4 ABOUT THE STANDARIZATION OF LARGE-SCALE RECs IN RURAL AREAS

The previous barriers encountered and lessons learned raise the question of whether a standard could be formulated for the implementation of these energy communities. To answer this question, we must consider the maturity degree of these initiatives, bearing in mind that they are complex, since they involve technical, social, economic and legal aspects, among others.

Apart from the aforementioned problem of the war in Ukraine and the resulting difficulties in Europe's energy supply, the world is in the midst of an energy paradigm crisis due two main reasons. The first is the combination of climate change and the depletion of fossil fuels. Secondly, the emergence and falling cost of electricity generation technologies that do not require centralisation for efficient production (i.e. renewable energies) has opened the door to distributed electricity generation, as opposed to the old model of centralised production involving large thermal, nuclear and hydroelectric power stations.

The emergence of these renewable technologies has made it possible to propose a new, decentralised paradigm in which electricity can be produced where it is consumed using renewable technology.

Within this paradigm, various models are being developed, including distributed PV systems for self-consumption, large-scale PV plants, wind farms with or without integrated storage, and renewable energy communities. There are also different promotional and management models: some are government- or traditional electricity company-led (top-down), while others are led by civil society initiatives (bottom-up). The energy transition process promoted by Europe is an example of this alternative, top-down paradigm. The REC is one of the main examples of an energy transition designed in bottom-up way.

We are therefore still in the early stages of the emergence of multiple energy models, none of which have become established, nor has a new stable paradigm yet been formed. In this scenario, the only option is to share attractive experiences that contribute to the establishment of a prevailing model.

For this reason, we do not consider the lessons learned presented in this document to be universal. Therefore, they may not be applicable in other regions of Europe. The realities and challenges faced by rural communities vary widely, and what works in one place may not work in another.

These lessons do not represent a standard model that can be replicated with guaranteed success. Our aim is to share our experience of designing, establishing and implementing the large-scale regional renewable energy community of Calatayud, including the positive aspects and, above all, the things that should be avoided. We share this experience with the intention and responsibility of contributing to the development of a model for the new paradigm.

5 CONCLUSIONS

This document outlines the main barriers encountered and sets out 16 key lessons learned during the two-and-a-half-year design, creation and implementation process of the Calatayud Region's Regional Renewable Energy Community (CERCA).

These experiences have been categorised as organisational, financial, technical, legal and administrative, and the barriers encountered and lessons learned in each case have been defined.

The aim of this document is to share these lessons and thereby contribute to the creation of the model for the new REC paradigm.

6 ACKNOWLEDGEMENTS

This work has been possible thanks to the Project Joining Actors for LOcal development of New large-scale regional energy communities (LIFE21-CET-ENERCOM-JALON), under grant agreement 101076395. Funded by the European Union. Views and opinions expressed are, however, those of the author(s) only and do not necessarily reflect those of the European Union or CINEA. Neither the European Union nor the granting authority can be held responsible for them.

7 REFERENCES

[1] E. Commission., «REPowerEU: Joint European action for more affordable, secure and sustainable energy,» 2022.

[2] E. Comission, «https://ec.europa.eu/commission/presscorner/detail/en/ip_22_3131,» 18 May 2022. [On line]. Available: https://ec.europa.eu/commission/presscorner/detail/en/ip_22_3131. [Last access: 20 June 2025].

[3] L. Arfini, «EU now has 9,000+ "energy communities": smart, decentralised, flexible generation and consumption,» 13 November 2023. [On line]. Available: https://energypost.eu/eu-now-has-9000-energy-communities-smart-decentralised-flexible-generation-and-consumption/. [Last access: 20 June 2025].

[4] I. D. Region, «Recent Survey Highlights Potential of Energy Communities in the EU,» 2024.

[5] E. Commission, «Barriers and drivers report. 2024, Energy Communities Repository.».

[6] «Directive (EU) 2018/2001 on the promotion of the use of energy from renewable sources, as amended by Directive (EU) 2023/2413,» 2023. [On line]. Available: http://data.europa.eu/eli/dir/2018/2001/oj. [Last access: 20 June 2025].

[7] «Directive (EU) 2023/2413 of the European Parliament and of the Council of 18 October 2023 amending Directive (EU) 2018/2001 as regards the promotion of energy from renewable sources,» 2023. [On line]. Available: http://data.europa.eu/eli/dir/2023/2413/oj. [Last access: 20 June 2025].

[8] L. Gruber, U. Bachhiesl y S. Wogrin, «The current state of research on energy communities,» *Elektrotech. Inftech.*, nº 138, p. 515–524, 2021.

[9] M. Koltunov, S. Pezzutto, A. Bisello, G. Lettner, A. Hiesl, W. van Sark, A. Louwen y E. Wilczynski, «Mapping of Energy Communities in Europe: Status Quo and Review of Existing Classifications,» *Sustainability*, nº 15, 2023.

[10] L. Peeters, L. F. López y C. Trompoukis, «Addressing the gaps in understanding and assessing energy communities,» *Energy Research & Social Science*, vol. 127, 2025.

[11] «LIFE21-CET-ENERCOM-JALON,» 2022. [On line]. Available: https://ec.europa.eu/info/funding-tenders/opportunities/portal/screen/opportunities/projects-details/43252405/101076395/LIFE2027.

[12] CERCA, «cercaenergia.com,» [On line]. Available: https://cercaenergia.com/. [Last access: September 2025].

[13] Instituto para La Diversificación y Ahorro de la Energía (IDAE), *Programa de Incentivos a proyectos piloto singulares de comunidades energéticas (Programa CE Implementa)*, Orden TED/1446/2021, de 22 de diciembre de 2021 del Ministerio para la Transición Ecológica y el Reto Demográfico.

[14] OMIE, «Operador de mercado eléctrico,» [On line]. Available: https://www.omie.es/. [Last access: 02 09 2025].

[15] Ministerio para la Transición Ecológica, *Real Decreto 244/2019, de 5 de abril, por el que se regulan las condiciones administrativas, técnicas y económicas del autoconsumo de energía eléctrica.*, 2019, p. 35674 to 35719.

[16] Greenpeace España (colaboration with Alianza por el Autoconsumo), «Autoconsumo en España, diagnóstico, retos y propuestas,» 2023.

Introduction

INSTITUTO DE ENERGÍA SOLAR

Systems transition theory

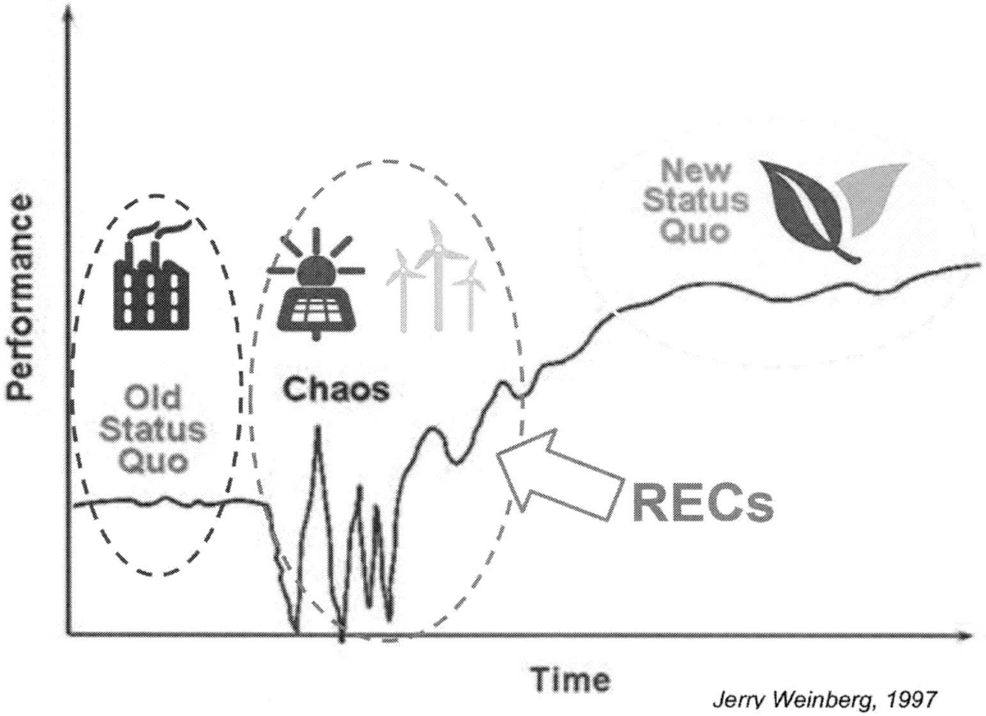

Jerry Weinberg, 1997

POLITÉCNICA

EU PVSEC 2025

CHALLENGES AND LESSONS LEARNED IN THE IMPLEMENTATION OF A REGIONAL-SCALE PV ENERGY COMMUNITY IN SPAIN

L. M. Carrasco, R. H. Almeida, Kiane Alves e Silva, L. Narvarte

Instituto de Energía Solar, Universidad Politécnica de Madrid, Madrid (SPAIN)

INSTITUTO DE ENERGÍA SOLAR

POLITÉCNICA

Introduction

INSTITUTO DE ENERGÍA SOLAR

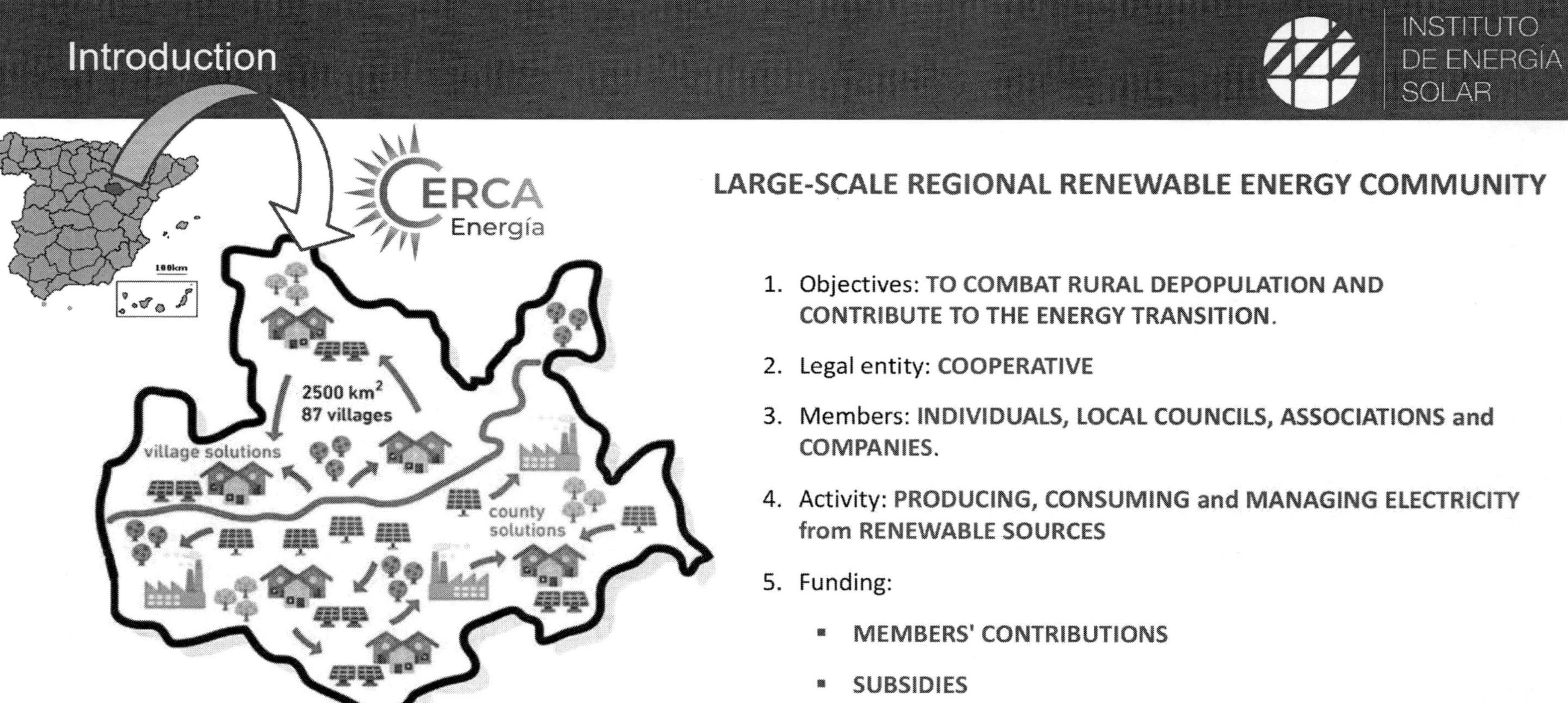

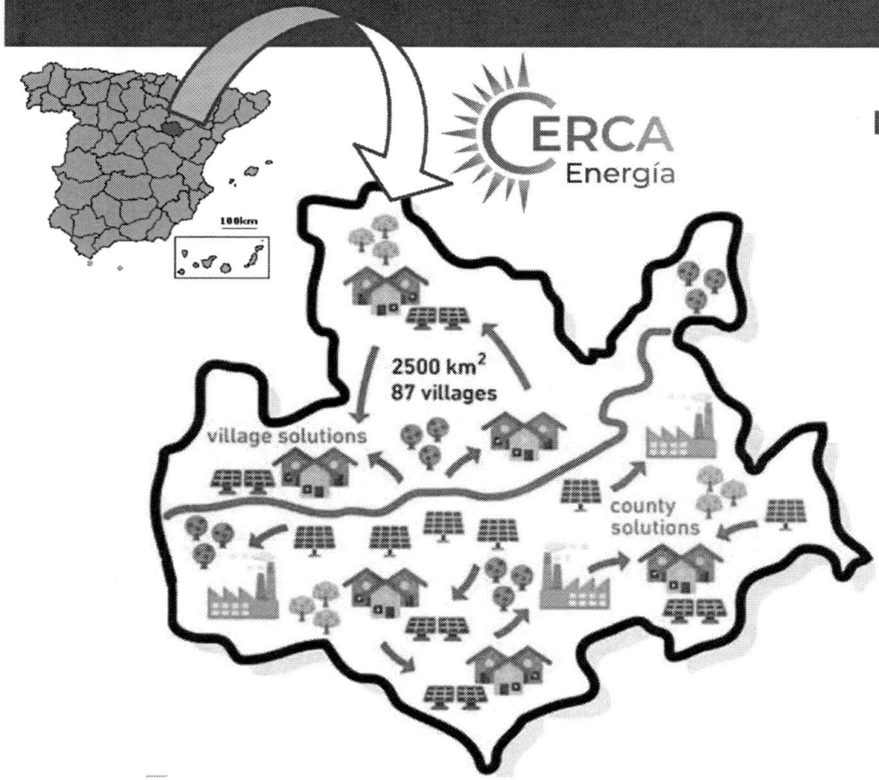

LARGE-SCALE REGIONAL RENEWABLE ENERGY COMMUNITY

1. Objectives: TO COMBAT RURAL DEPOPULATION AND CONTRIBUTE TO THE ENERGY TRANSITION.
2. Legal entity: COOPERATIVE
3. Members: INDIVIDUALS, LOCAL COUNCILS, ASSOCIATIONS and COMPANIES.
4. Activity: PRODUCING, CONSUMING and MANAGING ELECTRICITY from RENEWABLE SOURCES
5. Funding:
   - MEMBERS' CONTRIBUTIONS
   - SUBSIDIES

POLITÉCNICA

JALON

Funded by the European Union

3

Introduction

INSTITUTO DE ENERGÍA SOLAR

METHODOLOGY

- AWARNESS, ENGAGEMENT and SKILLS CAMPAIGN
- PARTICIPATION MODELS
- WORKSHOPS FOR REGIONAL KEY ACTORS
- LOCAL INSTALLERS
- PV QUALITY SPECIFICATIONS
- 1st PHASE FUNDING:
  - 40% PUBLIC GRANT
  - 60% PARTICIPANTS' EQUITY
  - TRANSPARENCY

4

Introduction

INSTITUTO DE ENERGÍA SOLAR

ACHIEVEMENTS

- **150 members**
- **18 projects** in **15 villages** (**825 kWp**)
- **500 beneficiaries**
- **€760,000** invested by participants.

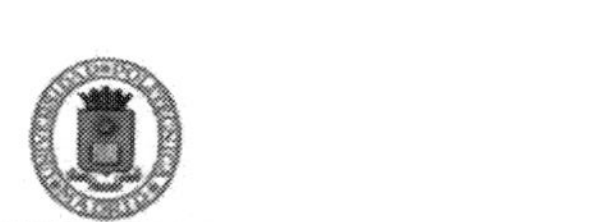

POLITÉCNICA

Barriers and lessons learned

INSTITUTO DE ENERGÍA SOLAR

BARRIERS

1. **Organizational**
2. **Financial**
3. **Technical**
4. **Legal**
5. **Administrative**

LESSONS LEARNED

POLITÉCNICA

Barriers and lessons learned

INSTITUTO DE ENERGÍA SOLAR

1. Organizational aspects

LESSON 1

Difficulty in developing bottom-up initiatives when starting from scratch. Don't start from scratch.

LESSON 2

The scale of the REC requires technical skills and responsible management. A structure based exclusively on volunteers is a threat to the sustainability of a REC.

LESSON 3

The seeding phase takes much longer than initially imagined. Communicating the REC proposal in the region requires a lot of time in the territory.

LESSON 4

Citizens' trust can only be gained if their mayor's trust is first secured. Need of institutional support, mainly from Municipalities.

POLITÉCNICA

Barriers and lessons learned

INSTITUTO DE ENERGÍA SOLAR

1. Organizational aspects

LESSON 5

Difficulties when trying to contact the mayors. Need of collaboration of the supra-local institution that unites all the municipalities in the region.

LESSON 6

Lack of skills on energy and poor digital culture. Training in these areas is necessary.

POLITÉCNICA

Barriers and lessons learned

INSTITUTO DE ENERGÍA SOLAR

2. Financial aspects

LESSON 7

Grants do not respect the timeframes needed for real participation.

LESSON 8

Grouping participants together through collective self-consumption systems creates economies of scale and increases the ability to raise community awareness.

LESSON 9

Innovative financing schemes are needed to reduce the financial risks of RECs while supporting them in project development.

LESSON 10

The creation and financing of collective projects by citizens both require a constant presence in the territory.

POLITÉCNICA

Barriers and lessons learned

INSTITUTO DE ENERGÍA SOLAR

3. Technical aspects

LESSON 11

Sizing tools for PV systems that enable to make decisions based on various criteria, not just technical or economic one, are needed.

LESSON 12

Technical specifications must be included in installation contracts and installers must be required to comply with them.

LESSON 13

To achieve real local impact, shared energy must be increased integrating energy storage systems and demand management strategies.

LESSON 14

Local installers must be involved in the REC projects and benefit from training in technical specifications.

POLITÉCNICA

Barriers and lessons learned

INSTITUTO DE ENERGÍA SOLAR

4. Legal aspects

LESSON 15

No proper management of energy surpluses can be achieved within the current Spanish self-consumption law. RECs must become electricity retailers to this end.

LESSON 16

National regulation should be updated to allow for the implementation of dynamic distribution coefficients in collective PV self-consumption.

5. Administrative aspects

LESSON 17

Lead times for obtaining permits and activating collective self-consumption systems are very long. Simplified procedures with shorter response times are required.

POLITÉCNICA

Conclusion

INSTITUTO DE ENERGÍA SOLAR

This new knowledge aims to contribute to the establishment of the new paradigm in the setting up of RECs.

POLITÉCNICA

Conclusions

INSTITUTO DE ENERGÍA SOLAR

https://jalon-ce.eu/

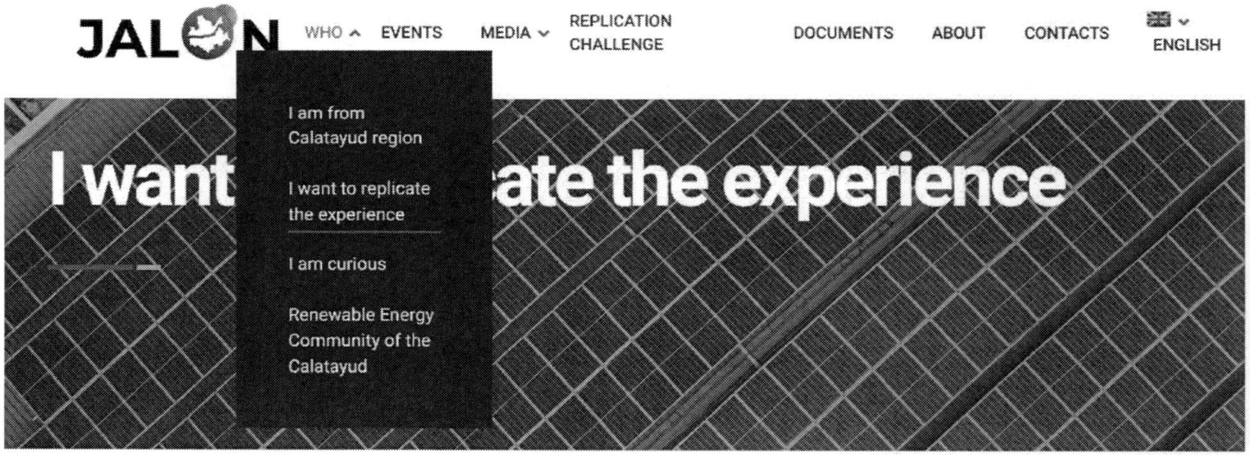

Guide Regional Energy Community Standard Model

POLITÉCNICA

Thank you for your attention

INSTITUTO DE ENERGÍA SOLAR

Dr. Luis Miguel Carrasco

luismiguel.carrasco@upm.es

Happy to take your questions

Funded by the European Union

Funded by the European Union. Views and opinions expressed are however those of the author(s) only and do not necessarily reflect those of the European Union or CINEA. Neither the European Union nor the granting authority can be held responsible for them.

POLITÉCNICA

KONSOLE WORKSHOP: A MODEL FOR RENEWABLE ENERGY EDUCATION AND CAREER DEVELOPMENT

Jayaprasad Arumughan, Monika Sarkadi, Radovan Kopecek, Florian Buchholz, Kristian Peter
International Solar Energy research Center, Rudolf-Diesel Strasse 15, D-78467 Konstanz, Germany.
konsole@isc-konstanz.de

ABSTRACT: KonSoLe (German: *Konstanzer Solare Lernwerkstatt*, translated as *Constance Solar Student Workshop*) at the International Solar Energy Research Center (ISC) Konstanz was developed to provide school students and young learners with a structured introduction to solar photovoltaic (PV) technology and sustainability. The program integrates short theory sessions, age-specific practical activities such as assembling simple solar devices or mini-modules, guided laboratory tours, and interactive exercises on energy consumption and climate impact. This blended approach allows participants to link scientific concepts with hands-on experience while fostering awareness of renewable energy in the context of social and ecological sustainability. Workshop evaluation combined short quizzes on theoretical and laboratory content with structured questionnaires administered immediately after the sessions. Responses were recorded anonymously using Likert scales and supplemented by open-ended feedback. The outcomes show consistently high levels of engagement, with over 85% of participants reporting increased knowledge and nearly 70% highlighting the practical module fabrication as a key learning element. Interest in renewable energy as a study and career field was reinforced, and more than half of respondents indicated that they could imagine pursuing a technical career path. Viewed through selected dimensions of Social Cognitive Career Theory (SCCT), the results suggest that the workshop strengthened self-efficacy, shaped positive career outcome expectations, and stimulated interest development. Younger participants in particular expressed openness to renewable energy careers, while older learners with established vocational orientations responded more variably. Across groups, social impact and innovation were cited as main perceived benefits, although limited job opportunities were identified as a concern. Overall, KonSoLe demonstrates the potential of practice-oriented interventions to enhance knowledge transfer and encourage sustainability-focused career intentions.
Keywords: Solar photovoltaic technology, Education for Sustainable Development (ESD), PV- career orientation, Social Cognitive Career Theory (SCCT)

1 INTRODUCTION

The transition to renewable energy depends not only on technological innovation but also on building a skilled and inclusive workforce. While engineering and policy measures aim to reduce greenhouse-gas emissions, social dimensions such as distributional fairness and meaningful participation determine whether energy transitions are equitable and effective. At the same time, energy poverty (the lack of reliable access to electricity in many rural areas of the Global South) highlights the need for actionable, locally adapted solutions. Decentralized photovoltaic systems frequently offer faster, more cost-effective, and context-sensitive routes to electrification than centralized grid expansion, and they can generate direct social benefits for education, health and livelihoods.

Education and capacity building are therefore central to ensuring that decentralized solar technologies are adopted in ways that are both technically sound and socially just. The International Solar Energy Research Center (ISC) Konstanz, founded in 2005, has developed a range of academic and professional training activities to bridge research, industry and public engagement. In 2017, the International Solar Energy Research Center (ISC) Konstanz launched the *Konstanzer Solare Lernwerkstatt* (KonSoLe, translated as *Constance Solar Student Workshop*), an outreach program that combines short lectures, hands-on module fabrication, laboratory visits, and group work to introduce students and local citizens to photovoltaic technology, sustainability, and renewable-energy careers. The feedback from the program indicates high engagement and effective knowledge transfer, and points to both opportunities and gaps in career guidance.

This paper examines the KonSoLe workshop as a practical model for renewable-energy education and career development. Using Social Cognitive Career Theory (SCCT) as an analytical frame, we assess how hands-on learning, role modelling by professionals, and reflective activities influence self-efficacy, outcome expectations and interest in PV careers. The paper presents participant feedback, interprets these findings in light of SCCT, and discusses implications for scaling similar educational programs and for policy makers seeking to strengthen workforce pipelines for the energy transition [1,2,3].

2 THE WORKSHOP PROGRAM

2.1 Program Structure

The KonSoLe workshop is a unique blend of Science, Technology, Engineering, and Mathematics (STEM) education and Education for sustainable Development (ESD). STEM education is an approach to learning and teaching the core subjects of STEM by integrating them and applying them to real-world problems. Its goal is to develop students' critical thinking, problem-solving, and creative skills, preparing them for future careers in a technology-driven world.

On the other hand, ESD is an educational approach that empowers individuals to take informed, responsible actions for a sustainable future. It integrates knowledge, skills, values, and attitudes related to environmental integrity, economic viability, and social justice into all forms of education. ESD also promotes competencies like critical thinking and collaborative decision-making to address global challenges such as climate change, inequality, and resource depletion.

The workshops are delivered in two parallel streams tailored to age and school grade: one for students through grade 7 (up to 13 years) and the other for students from

10.4229/EUPVSEC2025/5EO.1.5

grade 8 onward (14+ years). Each workshop begins with a concise, 30 minute theoretical introduction to solar energy covering basic photovoltaic principles with emphasis on crystalline-silicon technology, typical domestic applications such as rooftop and balcony systems, the role of balance of system (BOS) components, and the contribution of solar power to carbon-neutral goals. Participants learn the operation of a solar cell, key BOS elements, and the climate relevance of decentralized PV systems.

The theory block is followed by an age-appropriate practical session. Younger students construct simple, safe solar devices that demonstrate immediate cause–effect (for example, a small solar fan assembled from an upcycled glass bottle). Older students assemble mini solar modules from industry-standard components: soldering cells into strings, laminating a prototype module, and configuring outputs for USB charging. Materials provided for module fabrication include crystalline silicon cells, tabbing wire, EVA sheets, back-sheets and glass plates. Soldering and assembly are carried out by participants under instructor supervision, and the finished modules are taken home.

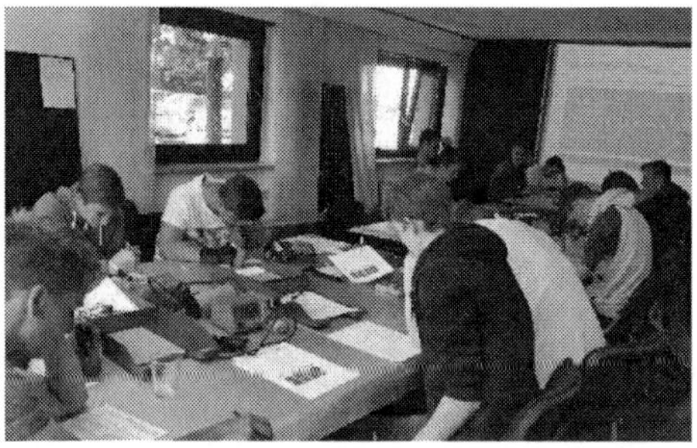

Figure 1: Students participating in the hands-on session

As appropriate for participant level, assembled modules are characterized using IV-curve measurements and imaging techniques such as electroluminescence (EL) and photoluminescence (PL) to introduce basic testing and quality concepts. Modules may be paired with a DC–DC converter or small storage device to provide stable USB power for practical demonstrations, including smartphone charging.

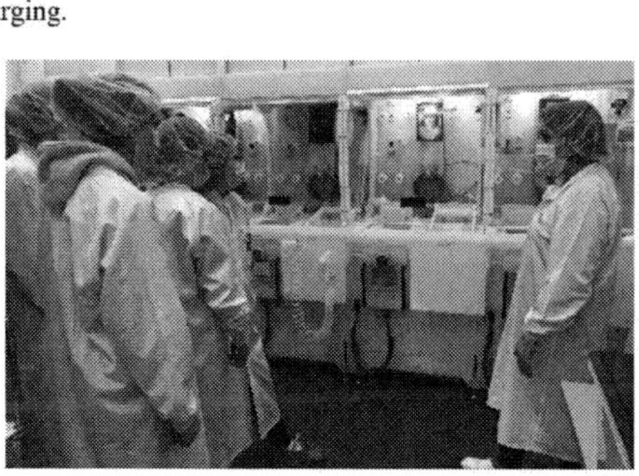

Figure 2: Participants visiting the solar cell fabrication cleanroom.

All participants undertake a laboratory visit to observe cell and module processing and to see key characterization equipment (for example, IV tracers and EL imaging) in operation, and to view the institute's operational PV installations. Prior to the lab tour participants receive brief safety instructions; cleanroom entry requires protective coats and gloves (figure 2). Cleanroom access is limited to six participants at a time, so larger groups rotate in subgroups.

The third segment is devoted to interactive ESD-Methods (Education for Sustainable Development, also known as Global Education) and is aimed to place PV technology in a social-ecological frame. This perspective has proved to be an effective incentive for students with less affinity for technical subjects. The methods used are include an illustrated presentation with interactive exercises: a game analyzing the distribution of the Earth´s population compared to the distribution of energy consumption, leading to an overall insight on Earth overload, energy poverty and the outstanding climate (in)justice. These concepts are discussed in the group and the role of PV as one important solution for these global challenges is highlighted. Students are encouraged to inspect their own lifestyles through a CO_2-footprint calculation, connecting local choices to global impacts. Depending on the age – they are encouraged to explore their handprint potential for more transformative action: one of these being a future career in the field of renewable energies. The typical workshop group consists of 12–16 students.

Figure 3: Interactive session on sustainability

The workshop concludes with a structured feedback questionnaire assessing engagement, perceived knowledge gain and career interest. Participants receive brief wrap-up materials, certificates and take-home items as appropriate, for example a solar propeller or a USB module charger fabricated by the participants.

3 EVALUATION APPROACH AND FEEDBACK INSTRUMENTS

3.1 Evaluation Methods

To evaluate the success and participant involvement in the KonSoLe workshops, we administered a short structured questionnaire at the end of the workshop. Responses were collected anonymously on a five-point Likert scale (1 = strongly disagree to 5 = strongly agree), without personal identifiers. For analysis, responses were grouped into three categories: *fully agree*, *agree*, and *not agree*. The questionnaire covered multiple dimensions, including program engagement, perceived knowledge gain, prior knowledge of solar energy, interest in further study, ease of completing the practical task (e.g., assembling a solar propeller or mini-module), technical career aspirations, concern about climate change, and willingness to contribute to a sustainable future. Open-ended fields invited participants to provide additional comments and suggestions.

3.2 Evaluation Outcomes

The feedback indicates exceptionally high levels of engagement and knowledge transfer. Specifically, 88.7% fully agreed that the program was engaging, and 87.5% fully agreed that they gained new knowledge. In contrast, the statement "New to Topic" garnered only 30.4% full agreement, with 32.4% not agreeing, which implies that many participants already had some familiarity with the subject matter. Interest in solar and renewable energy was robust (45.7% fully agree and 41.1% agree), and the practical, hands-on component, solar module fabrication, was well received (69.4% fully agree). Regarding career interests, 54.5% fully agreed on the potential for a technical career, although 21.7% did not agree, indicating an opportunity for enhanced career guidance. Additionally, concerns about climate change (68.7% fully agree) and commitment to sustainability (71.4% fully agree) were prominent. Overall, these preliminary results demonstrate that the KonSoLe workshop effectively engages participants, imparts valuable knowledge, and fosters a strong commitment to sustainability, while also highlighting areas for further refinement in addressing varied levels of prior knowledge and career guidance.

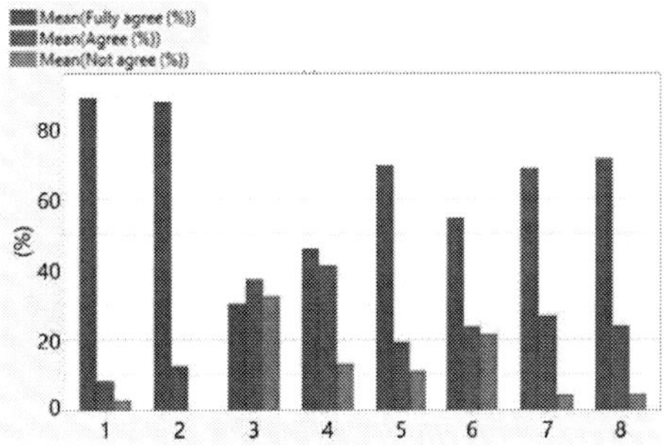

Figure 4: Student engagement and learning outcomes in renewable energy from the KonSoLe Workshop. The graph summarizes responses to eight statements: 1) The program was very engaging, 2) I gained substantial new knowledge, 3) I am already familiar with the topic, 4) I would like to learn more about solar or renewable energy, 5) I could build the solar module with ease, 6) I could imagine pursuing a technical career, 7) I am concerned about climate change and its ecological and social impacts, and 8) I am committed to promoting a sustainable future.

3.3 Evaluation of the Results Using SCCT

Viewed through the lens of SCCT, our evaluation highlights several relevant dimensions, even though the study does not probe the theory in depth. The questionnaire items were designed to address key career-related aspects: confidence in skills and knowledge (self-efficacy), expected benefits of a career in renewable energy (outcome expectations), interest in further learning, career intentions, and external influences such as school, policy, and perceived job market conditions.

Participants reported increased confidence in their skills and knowledge. Responses regarding outcome expectations revealed that a majority considered a career in renewable energy to be rewarding, with particular emphasis on social impact and technological innovation. Most participants indicated that their interest in renewable energy increased after the workshop, with hands-on activities and teamwork identified as the most engaging components. Many expressed that they could envision pursuing a career in the renewable energy sector. Younger students appeared more open to this possibility, whereas participants from vocational training backgrounds showed mixed responses, as many already had firmly defined career goals. A large share expressed interest in further training, internships, or mentorship opportunities in renewable energy. The most frequently cited challenge was the perception of limited job opportunities. Follow-up feedback, collected indirectly through schoolteachers, suggested that several former participants had already chosen career paths within the renewable energy sector; however, due to data protection regulations, systematic tracking was not possible, and such responses were obtained only on a voluntary basis.

4. SUMMARY

This paper presents the design, implementation, and evaluation of the KonSoLe workshop, an educational program aimed at introducing young learners to solar photovoltaic (PV) technology and renewable energy careers. The workshop combines lectures, laboratory visits, and hands-on activities, giving participants both theoretical understanding and practical experience. Many students who attended the KonSoLe workshop later returned to ISC for their bachelor's or master's theses, and a few went on to join ISC as engineers or scientists. To assess its impact, two evaluation tools were employed: a structured feedback questionnaire developed by the project team and an additional survey based on selected principles of SCCT.

The results show consistently high levels of engagement, increased knowledge, and strong interest in renewable energy. Participants reported greater confidence in their skills (self-efficacy), positive expectations about career opportunities, and motivation to explore further learning and training. While younger students were particularly open to renewable energy careers, participants with existing vocational training showed more mixed responses, highlighting the importance of targeted career guidance at an early age. Social impact and innovation were perceived as the most rewarding aspects of the sector, although limited job opportunities were cited as a challenge.

Overall, the findings demonstrate that the KonSoLe workshop effectively combines education with career orientation, fostering knowledge, motivation, and commitment to sustainability. The approach highlights the potential of hands-on, practice-oriented learning formats to inspire the next generation of renewable energy professionals.

Future development of the KonSoLe workshop should place stronger emphasis on career guidance by linking participants to study pathways, apprenticeships, and local job opportunities in the renewable sector. Expanding follow-up opportunities such as mentoring or internships, while tailoring activities to different knowledge levels, will help sustain motivation and ensure long-term impact.

With careful scaling and ongoing evaluation, KonSoLe can serve as a replicable model for renewable energy education that not only builds knowledge but also guides students toward meaningful career pathways.

4.1 References

[1] Bandura, A. 1986. Social foundations of Thought and Action: A social Congnitive Theory. Engelwood Cliffs, NJ: Prentice-Hall.

[2] Lent, R. W., Brown, S. D., & Hackett, G. (1994). Toward a unifying social cognitive theory of career and academic interest, choice, and performance. Journal of Vocational Behavior,*45*(1),79–122. https://doi.org/10.1006/jvbe.1994.1027

[3] Lent, R. W., Brown, S. D., & Hackett, G. (2000). Contextual supports and barriers to career choice: A social cognitive analysis. *Journal of Counseling Psychology, 47*(1), 36–49. https://doi.org/10.1037/0022-0167.47.1.36

10.4229/EUPVSEC2025/5EO.1.5
020569-004

A SNAPSHOT OF GLOBAL PV MARKETS – 2024

Gaëtan Masson[1], Melodie de l'Epine[2], Arnulf Jäger Waldau[3],
Izumi Kaizuka[4], Amelia Oller Westerberg[5], Jose Donoso[6]
[1] IEA PVPS Task 1, Brussels, Belgium; [2] IEA PVPS Task 1, Lyon, France;
[3] European Commission JRC, Ispra, Italy; [4] RTS Corporation, Tokyo, Japan;
[5] Becquerel Sweden, Knivsta, Sweden; [6] UNEF, Madrid, Spain

ABSTRACT: The objective of this paper is to propose a reliable and accurate perspective on key markets and policies related to PV development in 2024 and previously. It aims at offering a clear analysis of how PV markets have developed in 2024, with updated numbers, along with an analysis of the policies behind the development. In this paper are displayed and analyzed survey results for the calendar year 2024 concerning PV markets and policies, as well as other key issues. An increasing number of national markets experienced notable growth in 2024 with impacts on policy development. Figures show that over 601 GW of PV systems have been installed in the world last year. Consequently, cumulative capacity crossed the 2.3 TW mark in 2024.

Keywords: Photovoltaic (PV), Market, IEA PVPS

1 INTRODUCTION

This Trends paper gives information on the development of PV power applications in the PVPS member and non-member countries and is largely based on the information provided by IEA PVPS countries in addition to Becquerel Sweden and the European Union through its European Commission. The report includes information on national market developments at the end of the former year, in this case, 2024. The International Energy Agency – Photovoltaic Power System Programme (IEA PVPS)'s Task 1 is responsible for strategy and outreach within the IEA PVPS program. This includes policy, market and industry analysis. A key deliverable of Task 1 is the annual Snapshot of Global PV Markets publication, together with the annual flagship report Trends in PV Application.

The objective of the series of annual Snapshot and Trends reports — which have been published since 1992 (Trends) [1] and 2013 (Snapshot) [2] — is to present and interpret developments in both the PV systems and components being used in the PV power systems market and the changing applications for these products within that market. These trends are analyzed in the context of the business, policy and non-technical environment in the reporting countries.

2 THE GLOBAL PV INSTALLED CAPACITY

This paper presents the latest survey results for the calendar year 2024 concerning PV markets and policies, as well as other key issues. An increasing number of national markets experienced notable growth in 2024, and that impacted policy choices. The capacity figures given are nominal DC peak power (Wp) under standard test conditions (i.e. 1 000 W irradiance, air mass 1.5 light spectrum and 25 °C device temperature) for consistency reasons. As not all countries report DC peak power (Wp) for solar PV systems, instead reporting AC power, these capacity figures are converted to Wp DC.

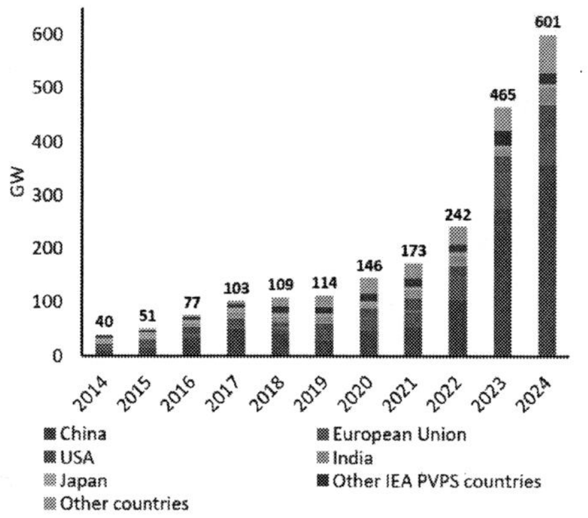

Figure 1: Evolution of annual PV installations (GW-DC)

While the final figures for 2024 could slightly continue to be refined in the future, nearly final figures show that around 601 GW of PV systems have been installed in the world last year. Some important trends observed are as follows.

The global PV market grew to around 601 GW in 2024, compared to around 465 GW in 2023. This represents a year-on-year growth of approximately 30%.

Asia scored the first place again in 2024 with China (357 GW[1]) and India (32 GW) leading the way. With around 47 GW deployed this year, the market in USA grew nearly 35%, after an already high 2023 (35 GW).

The market in EU grew significantly to around 66 GW. The top countries are Germany with (17 GW) and Spain with (8.7 GW) installed in 2024, followed by Italy (6.7 GW), France (6 GW) and Poland (4.2 GW).

[1] China's National Energy Administration (NEA) publishes in AC and Becquerel Institute applies a conversion ratio from AC to DC. A range of values is often provided to account for uncertainty in AC/DC conversion ratios, with regards to new utility scale capacity in China, where the minimal annual volume considers official China reporting and the maximal annual volume considers a further 42 GW that *could* have been installed considering the uncertainty surrounding official conversion ratios from AC to DC of Utility scale systems. If no range is specified, compiled data refers to the **higher** totals with Official China reporting values.

10.4229/EUPVSEC2025/5EO.3.1

Preliminary numbers show that installations in the Middle East and Africa regions amounted to around 8.7 GW last year.

Fast development was observed once again in Latin America, with around 14.3 GW installed in Brazil, and 2.1 GW in Chile.

Drivers for PV development include record-breaking competitiveness levels and development of distributed PV.

Annual installed capacity largely surpassed the 500 GW threshold reached for the first time in 2024, while total cumulative installed capacity in the world reached at least 2.3 TW.

3 MARKET DEVELOPMENT

In 2024, the PV market saw an important growth for the fifth year in a row after 2019's limited growth. Globally, the trend is upwards by exceeding the 601 GW annual installed capacity as expressed in Fig. 1.

Asia remains the leader of the global PV market. Next to China (357 GW), India and Japan remain a relevant presence in the global market with respectively 32 GW and 5.6 GW installed.

In other parts of Asia, the market observed steady growth in Thailand (3 GW) and decrease in South Korea (2.5 GW). Pakistan showed a massive increase with 18 GW installed in the last year. Australia installed 5.3 GW in 2024, a highest level since 2021.

In the Americas, the USA market grew from the previous year by approximately 35% (47 GW), on the other hand Brazil installed at least 14.3 GW in 2024 (it maintained the growth rate of the previous year, and cumulative capacity reached 52 GW). PV installations in Chile almost doubled in 2024 reaching a cumulative installed capacity of 11.3 GW while installations in Mexico were at a higher level (2.1 GW) compared to 2023. The market in Canada remained at a low level in 2024 with 321 MW installed compared to the record level seen in 2021 (2.0 GW).

In the European Union, Germany has gained back the leading position with nearly 17 GW installed in this period, surpassing Spain. In 2024, Spain (8.7 GW), Italy (6.7 GW), France (6 GW) and Poland (4.2 GW) can be mentioned as leading countries as well. The Netherlands added over 3.4 GW and Greece 2.6 GW while seven, countries added more than 1 GW namely Austria, Portugal, Hungary, and Ireland.

New development occurred in Africa (Egypt, South Africa) and in the Middle East (UAE, Saudi Arabia) which led to GW-scale cumulative installation levels: 8.7 GW in South Africa, 7.6 GW in the UAE, 4.7 GW in Egypt, and 6.6 GW in Saudi Arabia, for instance. Israel installed 0.9 GW in 2024.

In 2024, thirty-six countries passed the GW mark concerning annual installed PV capacity. Fifty-eight countries reached at least 1 GW cumulatively in 2024. China alone represented 1.1 TW. Germany, which used to lead the rankings for years, lost its leading position in 2015 and now ranks fourth (100 GW). The USA are second (225 GW) and India is third (124 GW). With close to 398 GW of total capacity, Europe is now significantly behind Asia, leading with at least 1.4 TW, with much more to come in the coming years.

4 GRID-CONNECTED CENTRALIZED AND DISTRIBUTED

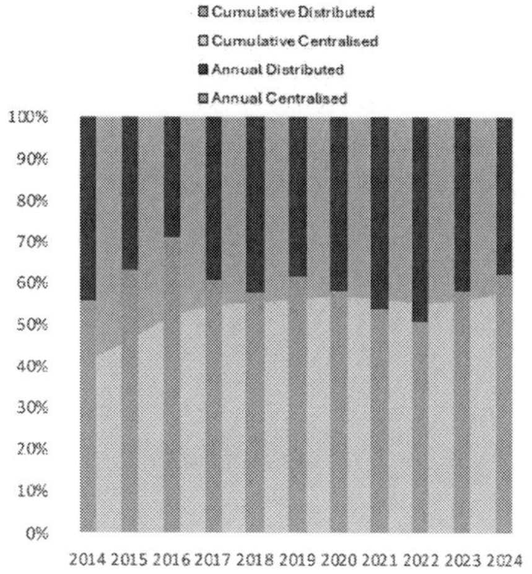

Figure 2: Segmentation of PV installation 2014-2024

Regarding the share of distributed and centralized installations at the global level, the trend has changed several times over the years.

Before 2013, most new PV installations were distributed systems, i.e. mainly installed on rooftops.

However, in more recent years, the market has seen a strong development of grid connected centralized installations. This changing trend is because centralized PV has evolved faster in terms of cost, and most of the major PV development in emerging PV markets are coming from utility-scale PV. The success of utility-scale installations is attributed to the fact that installation time and cost per Wp are lower than for distributed PV plants.

In the last years, tenders have driven PV development and continued to be granted in many countries in the world with extremely competitive prices, well below 20 USD/MWh in the sunniest places. One of the key trends of 2024 is the further development of utility-scale plants without financial incentives. Such development is mostly independent of policy decisions, which makes its potential virtually unlimited.

10.4229/EUPVSEC2025/5EO.3.1

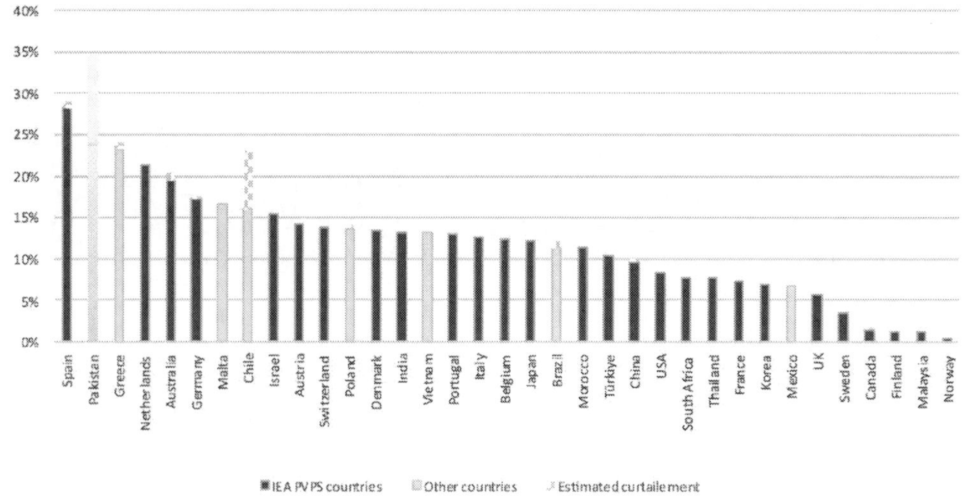

Figure 3: National PV penetration in % of the final electricity demand based on 2024 capacities.
Note: the electricity production from PV per country in this report is an estimate of what the minimal theoretical production should be the following year, when all the PV systems installed at the end of the year have generated electricity for one year. For this reason, the PV penetration rates here are an estimate and are likely to differ from official PV production and penetration numbers in many countries - they should be considered as indicative, providing a reliable estimation for comparison between countries and do not replace official data.

Distributed PV market share, after suffering from a small decline in 2019, has gradually increased, reaching an even higher level in 2024 than in 2017.

The market has also continued to diversify in 2024. While floating PV (FPV) adds to utility-scale, BIPV complements BAPV in the built environment, although it remains a niche. Other emerging segments such as agricultural PV (APV) or PV integrated in vehicles (VIPV) are showing the potential for further diversification of PV components, but their current levels of development remain limited. Dual use of land and surfaces is an option deeply investigated around the world.

At the local level, the region with the highest share of grid-connected centralized installations was Europe until 2011 which was holding 80% of the utility-scale system installed globally. Starting from 2012, American and Asian countries share started to grow and by the end of 2013 Asia became the main region for utility-scale projects.

5 ELECTRICITY PRODUCTION

The electricity production from PV per country as shown in Fig. 3 estimates what the PV production could be, based on the cumulative PV capacity at the end of 2024 (close to optimum siting, orientation and average weather conditions). These numbers, which are not based on actual measurements, should therefore be considered as indicative, aiming at comparing different situations in different countries rather than official data. In several countries, the PV contribution to the final electricity demand has passed the 5% mark with Spain in the first place with more than 25%. Greece and Pakistan tie at second with nearly 23%, and Netherlands, Chile, Australia and Germany follow. In total, PV contribution amounts to more than 8% of the electricity demand in the world.

6 CONCLUSIONS

This brief overview of the situation of the PV market and its deployment shows that in 2024 the annual PV market reached at least 601 GW worldwide and the cumulative installed capacity represented over 2.3 TW. The global PV market is, more than ever, dominated by a few leading countries even if many new PV markets are developing on all continents, at different paces. Although, slowed by supply chain issues and regulation changes in some countries, solar PV has continued its relentless progression overall in 2024. Production capacities have significantly increased in 2024, in particular, upstream (polysilicon and wafer). China remains the main manufacturing hub worldwide, by far. Larger wafers and larger modules continue their dominance on the market, with 182 mm and 210 mm wafers established as the new standards, and 166 mm disappearing.

7 REFERENCES

[1] IEA PVPS, TRENDS 2024 In Photovoltaic application, https://iea-pvps.org/trends_reports/trends/
[2] IEA PVPS, 2024 Snapshot of Global PV Markets, https://iea-pvps.org/snapshot-reports/snapshot-2023

42nd European Photovoltaic Solar Energy Conference and Exhibition

This presentation was selected by the Sc. Committee of the EU PVSEC 2025 for submission of a full paper to one of the EU PVSEC's collaborating peer-reviewed journals.

EXPLORING THE REVENUE POTENTIAL OF PHOTOVOLTAIC SYSTEMS PARTICIPATING IN FREQUENCY CONTAINMENT RESERVE

Emil Petkovski, Theo Bosma, Marcel Eijgelaar, Ravi Singh
Group Research and Development, DNV
Utrechtseweg 310, 6812 AR Arnhem, The Netherlands
emil.petkovski@dnv.com

ABSTRACT: This paper investigates the financial prospects of photovoltaic (PV) systems without battery storage providing frequency containment reserve (FCR) services by operating with a dedicated active power reserve. Using operational data from a 49.5 MWp PV system in the Netherlands the potential revenue from FCR provision was compared against earnings in the day-ahead (DA) electricity market, over the period of January 1st to October 31st 2024. The analysis indicated that in 136 out of 304 days, average FCR prices exceeded DA market prices, during the 12:00–16:00 interval, relevant for PV systems. Moreover, actively providing FCR services would have been possible and profitable on 71 of these days, generating an additional revenue of €53,661, corresponding to an 11.34% increase compared to selling energy exclusively on the DA market for those days. Overall, incorporating FCR into the operational strategy resulted in a revenue boost of approximately 2.87% over the entire 10-month study period. These findings highlight the potential economic benefits for PV systems without battery storage actively participating in frequency regulation.
Keywords: photovoltaics, frequency containment reserve, ancillary services, power reserve, solar power

1 INTRODUCTION

The total cumulative installed photovoltaic (PV) system capacity at the end of 2024 is estimated at 2.25 TW, of which 602 GW were added in the last year alone [1]. This rapid expansion confirms that solar power will remain central in addressing global energy demand while reducing greenhouse gas emissions. However, as PV integration accelerates, updated grid regulations increasingly impose additional requirements on these systems, such as frequency driven active power curtailment. This can be achieved using traditional hill-climbing methods such as the Perturb and Observe (P&O) by imposing an upper limit for the produced power, so that further maximum power point (MPP) tracking is disabled once this point is reached. Moreover, there are multiple constant power generation (CPG) strategies which also enable reduced power operation, without providing the knowledge of the MPP and the available power reserve at any given moment [2, 3].

Still, achieving full participation in frequency regulation of PV systems without costly battery storage, would require maintaining a dedicated active power reserve to be used during underfrequency events. Multiple flexible power point (FPP) tracking algorithms have been presented in literature to achieve this goal. [4, 5] are based on curve fitting techniques, while in [6, 7] neural network have been trained to perform an estimation of the maximum power and require as input the measurement of solar radiation and PV cell temperature. [8, 9] present an FPP tracking algorithm based on a single diode model, requiring only the measurement of PV cell temperature. Such model-based algorithms must be periodically updated to reflect PV aging and other degradation factors. [10] presents an update strategy by switching to the P&O algorithm in intervals when the system is targeting maximum power production.

Practical demonstrations also exist. For instance, in [11] the National Renewable Energy Laboratory (NREL) demonstrated that a 300 MW PV plant, equipped with an advanced power plant controller (PPC), can provide multiple frequency response functions by maintaining a 30 MW active power reserve. This was achieved by having one of the 80 inverters comprising the PV plant perform MPP while the others operate at a reduced power point.

Finally, [12] shows that storage-less PV systems equipped with strategy agnostic FPP trackers can reliably provide frequency containment reserve (FCR) and automatic frequency restoration reserve services, by combining dynamic modeling with a statistical assessment of forecast errors to meet stringent transmission system operator (TSO) availability requirements.

Nonetheless, it is important to highlight that there is currently no FPP tracking algorithm implemented on a commercially available solar converter or PPC. The reason is twofold. Firstly, FPP trackers are more complicated from a technical point of view than existing CPG strategies which enable simple power curtailment. Secondly, if a PV system is operating with an active power reserve, then by definition it is sacrificing potential revenue. Solar inverter manufacturers will prioritize the development of FPP trackers if there are specific grid requirements mandating full PV participation in frequency regulation, or if there are economic benefits for PV systems doing so.

[13] demonstrated that integrating PV systems into primary frequency regulation can significantly lower the operating costs of power systems. The work also showed that by having PV participate in ancillary services the power system can accommodate more PV energy, which should in turn improve PV profitability, however this improvement is not quantified.

The following paper investigates the potential for revenue of PV systems operating with an active power reserve to provide FCR services in the Netherlands. The aim and approach of this research are presented in section 2. In section 3, multiple constraints are defined to ensure that the PV system complies with the requirements of the FCR service. The results and conclusions are presented in sections 4 and 5, respectively.

2 AIM AND APPROACH

This research has investigated the economic viability of PV systems operating with an active power reserve to provide FCR services in the Netherlands. To that end, the potential revenue of a PV system on the DA market was compared to that of the FCR market.

The DA and FCR market prices for the Netherlands were sourced from the transparency platform of the European Network of Transmission System Operators for Electricity (ENTSO-e) for the interval from January 1st until October 31st 2024. Moreover, the field data of a PV system in the Netherlands with an installed DC capacity of 49.45 MWp and AC capacity of 35.6 MW at point of connection was utilized.

The FCR market prices were quoted with a unit of [€/MW/ISP] where ISP stands for Imbalance Settlement period and lasts for 15 minutes. Therefore, the values were multiplied by 4 to reflect the revenue earned per MW for 1 hour [€/MW/h]. In contrast, the DA market prices are expressed directly with the unit of [€/MWh].

Currently, the FCR market is operated jointly by the Austrian, Belgian, Czech, Danish, Dutch, French, German, Slovenian, and Swiss TSOs. Bidding opens seven days before delivery (D-7 at 11:00 CET), with closure on the day before delivery (D-1 at 08:00 CET). Once the bids of all TSOs are collected, they are sent to a common optimization algorithm [14]. The market stipulates a minimum bid of 1 MW, with the same resolution [15].

Activation of FCR begins as soon as possible but no later than 2 seconds after a frequency deviation; and rises at least linearly. The activation speed is 30 s for the full allocated volume. These requirements could be easily met by PV or any converter-based resource, owing to their fast dynamic response. The FCR market is organized in six 4-hour blocks throughout a 24-hour interval. The block of interest for PV systems would be from 12:00 to 16:00 hours, therefore it is the only time block considered in this analysis.

The starting assumption of this research was that in the intervals of the day when there is abundant production of PV power, the price of electricity on the DA market will be very low (even negative). Moreover, the value of FCR in the same intervals should be relatively high because the share of electricity production of traditional sources would be low, and PV systems do not provide FCR.

Figure 1 presents the DA and FCR prices in the Netherlands in the interval of 12 to 16 o'clock for every day from January 1st until October 31st. It can be observed that the electricity price drops in the spring and summer months. Moreover, the figure shows that in the same months the price of FCR is generally higher. Note that, for better visualization, the y-axis of Figure 1 is limited to a lower value of -25, however there are multiple days for which the DA market price is far lower than this value.

Once the average DA and FCR market prices were compared over this 10-month interval it was identified that for 136 out of 304 days the average prices of FCR are higher, for the 4-hour interval of interest. The next step is to assess the actual PV production during these periods, in order to determine the amount of active power the system could maintain in reserve, for FCR participation.

3 CONSTRAINTS

Since FCR is defined as a symmetric service, any participating PV system must be capable of both increasing and decreasing its output by the nominated power reserve (P_R). Hence, the **first power constraint** is that the value of the selected power reserve must be smaller or equal to half of the maximum available power (P_{MAP}) that the PV system can sustain throughout the selected 4-hour interval, as expressed in Equation 1.

$$P_{MAP} - 2 \cdot P_R \geq 0 \qquad (1)$$

Modern PV systems in the Netherlands commonly use string or multistring inverters. Therefore, by selectively disconnecting strings, the output power of the systems can be adjusted in steps of a few kilowatts. Nonetheless, in order to implement power as a function of frequency droop control, a more continuous change of the output power would be required which can be achieved using the aforementioned FPP trackers. These trackers cannot accurately operate at very low irradiation (less than 100 W/m^2) due to the changes in the I-V characteristic of the PV modules. Therefore, a **second power constraint** has been added that the P_{MAP} of the PV system must be higher than 6 MW, This roughly construes to an irradiation of 120 W/m^2, considering that the installed power of the PV system is 49.45 MW.

The **third power constraint** is that the reserve bids must be submitted in multiples of 1 MW. For example, if P_{MAP} is 21 MW for a certain 4-hour interval, according to the first condition, the amount of power kept in reserve can be 10.5 MW, however the third condition will limit P_R to

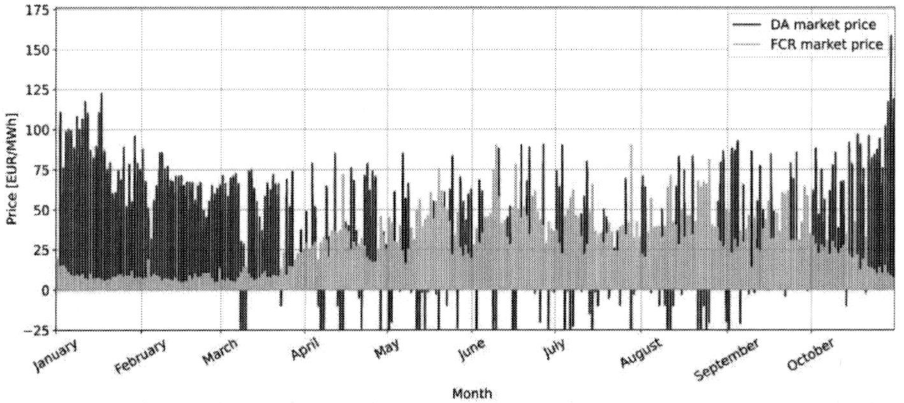

Figure 1: DA and FCR market price in the Netherlands in the interval of 12:00 to 16:00 hours for every day from 1st of January until 31st of October

10 MW.

A PV system without battery storage will opt to maintain an active power reserve only if in the selected 4-hour block the average price per MW of the FCR service (FCR_p) is higher than the DA market price (DA_p) per MWh (Equation 2). Moreover, when the DA market prices are negative, a modern PV system is capable of curtailing its production down to zero. However, a PV system providing FCR would have to operate with the selected power reserve, in order to maintain the symmetrical provision requirement of FCR. This means that during negative DA prices the average price of FCR must be higher than the negative value of the DA market price, for that 4-hour interval.

$$FCR_p > DA_p,\ if\ DA_p \geq 0 \qquad FCR_p > -DA_p,\quad if\ DA_p < 0 \qquad (2)$$

Therefore, a price constraint is formed dictating that the average value of the FCR price during the 4-hour interval of interest must be higher than the absolute value of the DA price, as shown in Equation 3.

$$FCR_p > |DA_p| \qquad (3)$$

Only days which meet this price constraint and the 3 aforementioned power constraints have been considered in this research.

4 RESULTS

For the purpose of this study, it is assumed that the PV system has perfect foresight of the DA and FCR market prices, as well as a perfect forecast of its power production. The goal is to evaluate whether the total revenue made in a year can be increased by participating in the FCR and DA markets as opposed to just participating in the DA market.

In the first case, it is considered that the PV system earns revenue solely by participating in the DA market ($DA_{revenue}$). This revenue is calculated as the sum of the product of the available PV production ($P_{available}$) and the day ahead prices, calculated for every minute of PV data. It is equal to zero when the DA price is negative because the PV system would cease production, as shown in Equation 4.

$$DA_{revenue} = \sum DA_p \cdot P_{available},\ if\ DA_p \geq 0 \qquad DA_{revenue} = 0,\quad if\ DA_p < 0 \qquad (4)$$

In the second case, it is considered that the PV system utilizes its reserve in the interval of 12 to 16 o'clock to earn a revenue providing FCR ($FCR_{revenue}$), equal to the sum of the product of FCR price and P_R, as shown in Equation 5. Of course, during negative DA market prices this will result in a loss (FCR_{cost}). The net revenue (FCR_{net}) is their difference.

$$FCR_{revenue} = \sum FCR_p \cdot P_R \qquad FCR_{cost} = \sum DA_p \cdot P_R,\ if\ DA_p < 0 \qquad FCR_{net} = FCR_{revenue} - FCR_{cost} \qquad (5)$$

At the same time, the system continues to participate on the DA market with the remaining power which is $P_{available}$ minus P_R. This results in a reduced revenue on the DA market ($DA_{reduced}$). For all hours outside the 4 hour interval $DA_{reduced}$ is equal to $DA_{revenue}$, as shown in Equation 6.

$$DA_{reduced} = \sum DA_p \cdot (P_{available} - P_R),\ if\ DA_p \geq 0 \qquad DA_{reduced} = 0,\ if\ DA_p < 0 \qquad (6)$$

The overall increase of revenue (RI) of the PV system is calculated according to Equation 7.

$$RI = FCR_{net} + DA_{reduced} - DA_{revenue} \qquad (7)$$

Figure 2 shows the minute and minimum hourly production of the PV system on April 12th 2024. For this day, the maximum production available throughout the 4-hour interval is 18.668 MW, therefore $P_R = 9$ MW.

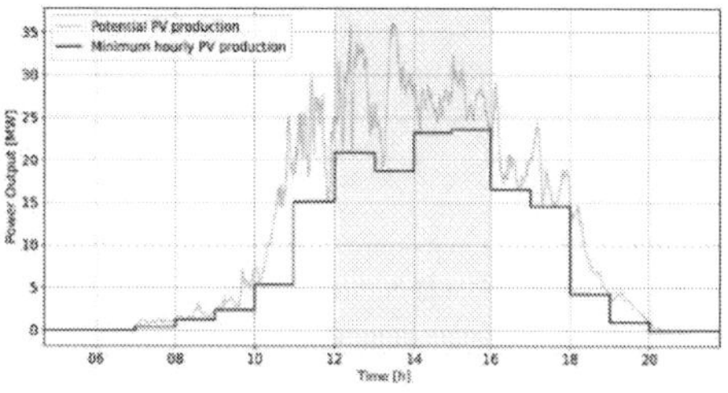

Figure 2: Comparison of minute and minimum hourly PV production values for April 12th 2024

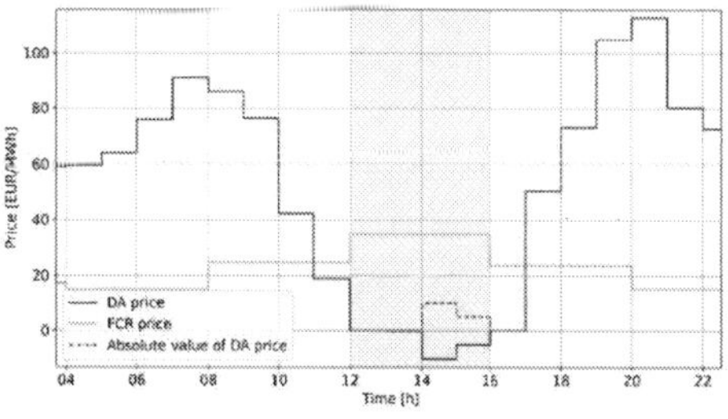

Figure 3: Comparison of the DA market electricity price, its absolute value and the price of FCR for April 12th 2024

The results for the day are shown in Table I. Notably, $DA_{reduced}$ is equal to $DA_{revenue}$ because the DA prices during the 12:00 to 16:00 hours are zero or negative, as shown in Figure 3, which means a PV system would be curtailed if it was not providing FCR. The revenue earned on the FCR market is equal to €1,251. However, by participating in FCR the PV system must produce the 9 MW of P_R also during the period of 14:00 to 16:00 hours, in which the price of electricity on the DA market is negative, thus incurring an FCR_{cost} of €136. Therefore, the revenue for this day has been increased by €1,115, which is a 32,6 % increase with respect to simply participating in the DA market.

Table I: Economic outlook for April 12th 2024

Metric	Value [€]
$DA_{revenue}$	3,420.6
$DA_{reduced}$	3,420.6
$FCR_{revenue}$	1,251.4
FCR_{cost}	-136.4
FCR_{net}	1,115
RI	1,115

The same analysis has been performed over the entire period from January 1st to October 31st 2024 and the results are presented in Table II.

When the power and price constraints are considered, 71 days have been identified in which providing FCR would be profitable for the PV system. The revenue for the 71 days has been increased by €53,661 which is an increase of 11.34%. Equally interesting is that the PV system only sacrificed a revenue of €12,005 on the DA market to earn €65,666 on the FCR market. Therefore, the main conclusion is that it is financially justified for PV systems to participate in FCR in certain intervals, however opportunities might be limited, since only 71 days met the necessary criteria. When multiplying the available PV production by the DA market prices for the entire observed 10-month interval it was calculated that the total revenue of the PV system for this period equals €1,869,207. Relative to this figure, the revenue increase for the PV system participating in FCR is equal to 2.87%. Nevertheless, there could be even more favorable conditions for FCR participation in countries with many more clear and sunny days than the Netherlands. Furthermore, if the FCR service is redefined in 1-hour instead of 4-hour time slots, there would be more hours in a year in which it would be favorable for PV to participate.

Table II: Economic outlook for the entire observed 10-month period

Metric	Value [€]
$DA_{revenue}$	473,377
$DA_{reduced}$	461,372
$FCR_{revenue}$	77,659
FCR_{cost}	-11,993
FCR_{net}	65,666
RI	53,661

This analysis, however, has relied on the assumption of perfect day-ahead forecasting of PV production, which enables the precise estimation of the active power that can be reserved. However, the irradiance falling on a PV system can rapidly change due to the passage of a dense cloud, resulting in a proportionally large change in the output power. In reality, forecasting PV production one day in advance is accurate in estimating energy production over longer, hourly periods, but cannot exactly predict the timing of such dips in production, nor their severity.

This limited accuracy is acceptable for the DA electricity market, however the FCR service demands the highest degree of confidence that the allocated capacity will be available throughout the selected time interval.

The extended version of this paper will address this limitation by considering 1 Hz irradiance and PV panel data from three locations in the Netherlands. The goal is to show how aggregating PV production at different locations can reduce the variability of the combined power output and increase the amount of power reserve that can be reliably provided for FCR.

5 CONCLUSION

This research assessed the economic viability of PV systems operating with an active power reserve to provide FCR services in the Netherlands. The analysis used minute-resolution production data from a 49.45 MWp PV plant and FCR and DA market prices covering the period from January 1st to October 31st, 2024.

It was found that on 136 out of 304 days, the average FCR prices exceeded DA prices during the 12:00–16:00 interval, which is particularly relevant for PV systems. Based on the PV production data, 71 days were identified where providing FCR would have been profitable. During these intervals, the PV system could have earned an additional €53,661, representing an 11.34% increase compared to supplying its energy solely to the DA market on those days. This additional revenue stream corresponds to an overall increase of 2.87% in total DA market earnings over the 10-month period. Equally interesting is that the PV system sacrificed only €12,005 on the DA market to earn €65,666 from FCR participation. Therefore, the results indicate that it is financially justified for PV systems to participate in FCR provision, albeit opportunities might be limited, since only 71 days met the necessary criteria. Finally, regions with higher solar irradiance and more sunny days then the Netherlands should offer even more favorable conditions. Redefining FCR provision from 4-hour to 1-hour time blocks would also increase the number of profitable hours in a year, for PV systems.

6 REFERENCES

[1] "Renewables 2025 Global status report: Global Overview", Available online: https://www.ren21.net/wp-content/uploads/2019/05/25-1395_GO_2025_Full_Report_13opt.pdf

[2] A. Sangwongwanich, Y. Yang, F. Blaabjerg and H. Wang, "Benchmarking of constant power generation strategies for single-phase grid-connected Photovoltaic systems," 2016 IEEE Applied Power Electronics Conference and Exposition (APEC), Long Beach, CA, USA, 2016, pp. 370-377, doi: 10.1109/APEC.2016.7467899.

[3] H. D. Tafti et al., "Extended Functionalities of Photovoltaic Systems With Flexible Power Point Tracking: Recent Advances," in IEEE Transactions on Power Electronics, vol. 35, no. 9, pp. 9342-9356, Sept. 2020, doi: 10.1109/TPEL.2020.2970447.

[4] E. I. Batzelis, G. E. Kampitsis and S. A. Papathanassiou, "Power Reserves Control for PV Systems With Real-Time MPP Estimation via Curve Fitting," in IEEE Transactions on Sustainable Energy, vol. 8, no. 3, pp. 1269-1280, July 2017, doi: 10.1109/TSTE.2017.2674693.

[5] E. I. Batzelis, S. A. Papathanassiou and B. C. Pal, "PV System Control to Provide Active Power Reserves Under Partial Shading Conditions," in IEEE Transactions on Power Electronics, vol. 33, no. 11, pp. 9163-9175, Nov. 2018, doi: 10.1109/TPEL.2018.2823426.

[6] J. M. Gomez and P. K. Shanmugam, "Flexible power point tracking using a neural network for power reserve control in a Grid-Connected PV system,"

Energies, vol. 15, no. 21, p. 8234, Nov. 2022, doi: 10.3390/en15218234.
[7] P. Verma, T. Kaur, and R. Kaur, "Power control strategy of an integrated PV system for active power reserve under dynamic operating conditions," Sustainable Energy Technologies and Assessments, vol. 45, p. 101066, Feb. 2021, doi: 10.1016/j.seta.2021.101066.
[8] L. Cristaldi, M. Faifer, C. Laurano, R. Ottoboni, E. Petkovski and S. Toscani, "Power Generation Control Algorithm for the Participation of Photovoltaic Panels in Network Stability," in IEEE Transactions on Instrumentation and Measurement, vol. 72, pp. 1-9, 2023, Art no. 9000809, doi: 10.1109/TIM.2023.3238745
[9] L. Cristaldi, M. Faifer, C. Laurano, E. Petkovski, F. Ponci, I. Sowa et al, "Model-Based algorithm for flexible power point tracking for photovoltaic participation in primary frequency regulation," Energies, vol. 17, no. 9, p. 2049, Apr. 2024, doi: 10.3390/en17092049.
[10] L. Cristaldi, M. Faifer, C. Laurano, E. Petkovski, S. Toscani and R. Ottoboni, "Parameters Update Strategy for Model-Based MPPT for PV Systems," 2024 IEEE International Instrumentation and Measurement Technology Conference (I2MTC), Glasgow, United Kingdom, 2024, pp. 1-5, doi: 10.1109/I2MTC60896.2024.10560743.
[11] C. Loutan, P. Klauer, S. Chowdhury, S. Hall, M. Morjaria, V. Chadliev et al., "Demonstration of essential reliability services by a 300-MW solar photovoltaic power plant," Mar. 2017. doi: 10.2172/1349211.
[12] C. Konstantinopoulos, I. Avramiotis-Falireas, S. Bolognani, D. Groß, A. Chacko and G. Hug, "Reliability assessment of PV units in primary and secondary frequency control ancillary services," 2019 16th International Conference on the European Energy Market (EEM), Ljubljana, Slovenia, 2019, pp. 1-6, doi: 10.1109/EEM.2019.8916279.
[13] X. Fang, J. Tan, H. Yuan, S. Yin and J. Wang, "Providing Ancillary Services with Photovoltaic Generation in Multi- Timescale Grid Operation," 2020 52nd North American Power Symposium (NAPS), Tempe, AZ, USA, 2021, pp. 1-5, doi: 10.1109/NAPS50074.2021.9449700.
[14] ENTSO-E, "Frequency Containment Reserves (FCR)," Network Codes – Electricity Balancing. [Online]. Available: https://www.entsoe.eu/network_codes/eb/fcr/. [Accessed: Jul. 31, 2025].
[15] TenneT TSO B.V., "FCR Manual for BSPs: Requirements and Procedures for Supply of FCR," Version 3.3, SOP-SYS FCR HB, Arnhem, The Netherlands, Mar. 17, 2022. [Online]. Available:https://netztransparenz.tennet.eu/fileadmin/user_upload/SO_NL/Handboek_FCR_voor_BSPs_-_EN_version.pdf [Accessed: Jul. 4, 2025].

DNV

WHEN TRUST MATTERS

Exploring the Revenue Potential of Photovoltaic Systems Participating in Frequency Containment Reserve

Emil Petkovski, Theo Bosma, Marcel Eijgelaar and Ravi Singh
emil.petkovski@dnv.com

26 September 2025

EU PVSEC 2025
42nd European Photovoltaic Solar Energy Conference and Exhibition

Introduction

- As the integration of PV systems accelerates, updated grid regulations increasingly impose additional requirements on these systems, such as active power curtailment during overfrequency events
- However, full participation of PV systems without battery storage in frequency regulation will require operating with an active power reserve
- Various flexible power point (FPP) tracking algorithms that enable such operation have been presented in literature. However, commercially available solutions are lacking due to technical and economic challenges

Introduction

- As the integration of PV systems accelerates, updated grid regulations increasingly impose additional requirements on these systems, such as active power curtailment during overfrequency events
- However, full participation of PV systems without battery storage in frequency regulation will require operating with an active power reserve
- Various flexible power point (FPP) tracking algorithms that enable such operation have been presented in literature. However, commercially available solutions are lacking due to technical and economic challenges
- Solar inverter manufacturers will prioritize the development of FPP trackers if there are specific grid requirements mandating full PV participation in frequency regulation, or if there are economic benefits for PV systems doing so
- **This research has investigated the economic viability of PV systems operating with an active power reserve to provide frequency containment reserve (FCR) services in the Netherlands**

Introduction II

- The potential revenue of a PV system participating on the day ahead (DA) and FCR markets was compared
- The DA and FCR market prices were downloaded for the Netherlands in the interval of January 1st to October 31st, 2024, from the ENTSO-e website
- The FCR service in the Netherlands is organized in 6 four-hour blocks throughout a 24-hour interval. The block of interest for PV systems, considered in this analysis, is **from 12 to 16 hours**
- The production data of a PV system in the Netherlands with an installed DC capacity of 49.5 MWp and an AC capacity of 35.6 MW at the point of connection was utilized

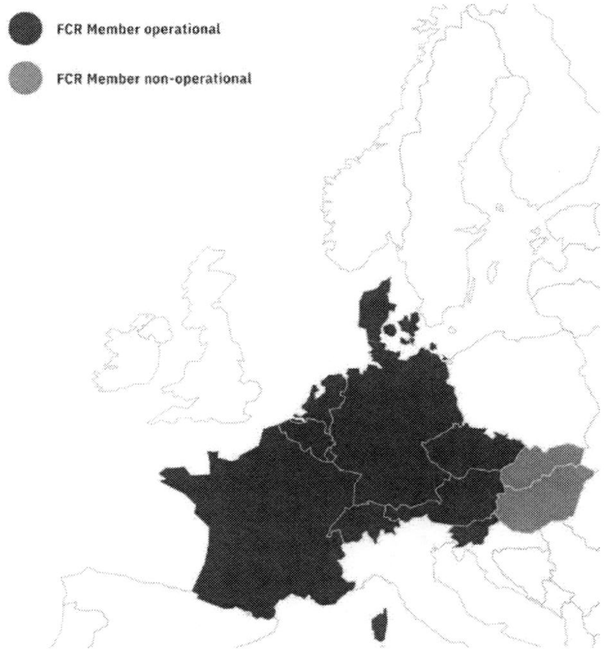

Initial assumption

- In periods of the day when there is abundant PV production, the price of electricity on the DA market will be very low (even negative). However, the price of FCR in the same intervals would be relatively high because the share of electricity production by traditional sources would be low, and PV systems do not provide FCR
- Once the average DA and FCR prices were compared over the 4-hour interval it was identified that for **136 out of 305 days the FCR prices are higher**

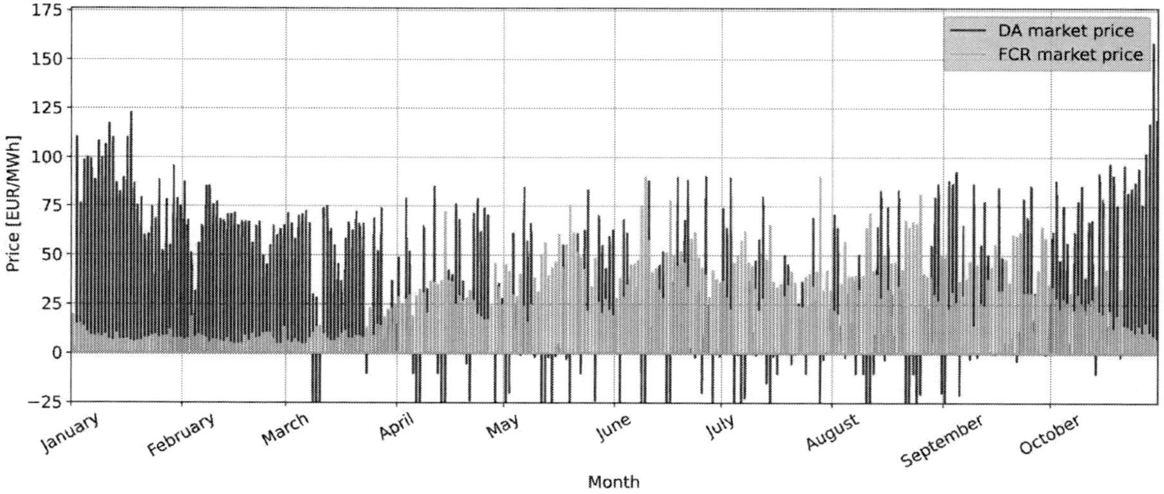

Initial assumption II

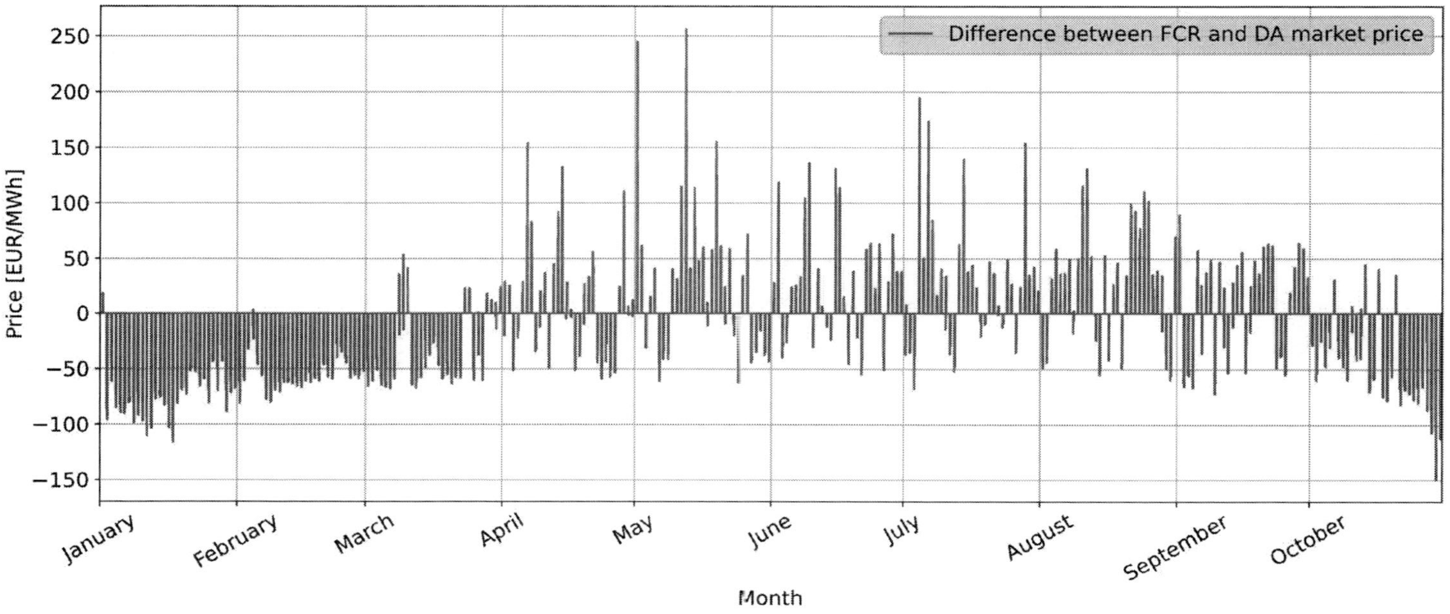

EUPVSEC

DNV

Economic Metrics

- It is assumed that the **PV system has perfect foresight of the DA and FCR market prices, and perfect forecast of its power production**
- **The goal is to show whether the total revenue made in a year can be increased by participating in the FCR and DA market as opposed to just participating in the DA market**
- In the first case, it is considered that the PV system earns revenue solely by participating in the DA market ($DA_{revenue}$)
- This revenue is calculated as the sum of the product of the available PV production ($P_{available}$) and the day ahead prices (DA_p), calculated for every minute of PV data

$$DA_{revenue} = \sum DA_p \cdot P_{available}\,, \qquad if\ DA_p \geq 0$$

$$DA_{revenue} = 0, \qquad if\ DA_p < 0$$

Economic Metrics II

- In the second case, it is considered that the PV system utilizes its reserve in the interval of 12 to 16 hours to earn a revenue providing FCR ($FCR_{revenue}$), equal to the sum of the product of FCR price (FC_p) and P_R. Of course, during negative DA market prices this will result in a loss (FCR_{cost})

$$FCR_{revenue} = \sum FCR_p \cdot P_R$$

$$FCR_{cost} = \sum DA_p \cdot P_R\,, \qquad if\ DA_p < 0$$

$$FCR_{net} = FCR_{revenue} - FCR_{cost}$$

- Moreover, the system still participates in the DA market with the remaining power which is $P_{available}$ minus P_R. This will result in a reduced revenue on the DA market ($DA_{reduced}$)

$$DA_{reduced} = \sum DA_p \cdot (P_{available} - P_R)\,, \qquad if\ DA_p \geq 0$$

$$DA_{reduced} = 0, \qquad if\ DA_p < 0$$

- The overall increase of revenue (RI) of the PV system is calculated as:

$$RI = FCR_{net} + DA_{reduced} - DA_{revenue}$$

EUPVSEC

DNV

Results: 12 April 2024

- The figure on the left shows the minute and minimum hourly production of the PV system on 12 April 2024. The maximum available production throughout the 4-hour interval is **18.7 MW**, therefore $\mathbf{P_R = 9\ MW}$
- The figure on the right shows the electricity price on the DA and FCR markets

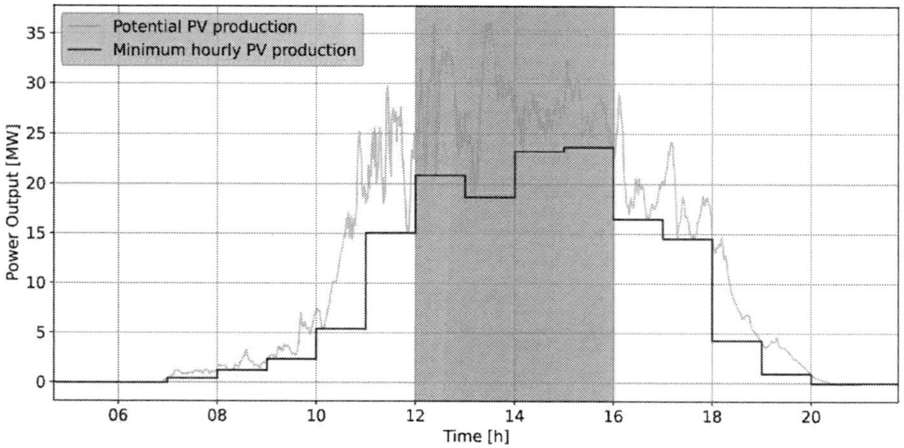

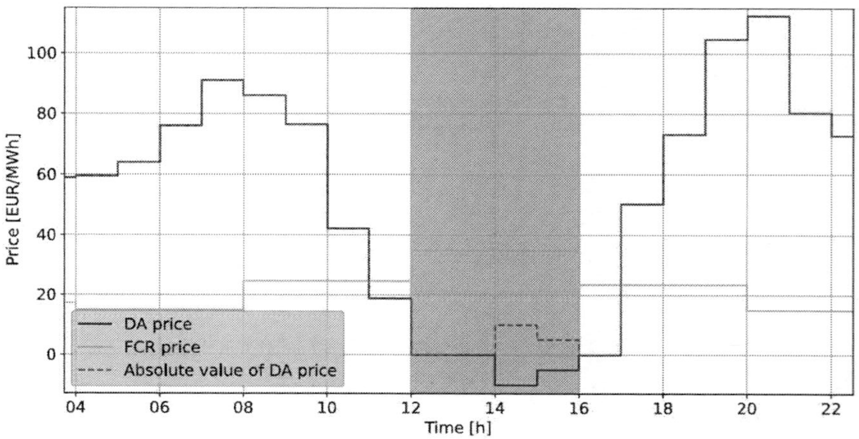

Results II: 12 April 2024

- Notably, $DA_{reduced}$ is equal to $DA_{revenue}$ because the DA prices during the 12 to 16 hours are zero or negative which means a PV system would be curtailed if it wasn't providing FCR
- The revenue for this day has been increased by **1,115 EUR, or 32,6%**

Time interval	**12.04.2024**
$DA_{revenue}$ [EUR]	3,420.6
$DA_{reduced}$ [EUR]	3,420.6
$FCR_{revenue}$ [EUR]	1,251.4
FCR_{cost} [EUR]	-136.4
FCR_{net} [EUR]	1,115
RI [EUR]	1,115

Results: 10-month analysis

- The analysis has been performed on the entire period from 1 January to 31 October 2024. When the power and price constraints are taken into account, **71 days have been identified** in which providing FCR would be profitable for the PV system
- The **revenue for the 71 days has been increased by 53,661 EUR which is an increase of 11.34%.** Therefore, it is financially justified for PV systems to participate in FCR in certain intervals, but opportunities might be limited
- The total revenue made by the PV system on the DA market over the 10-month interval equals 1,869,207 EUR. Relative to this figure, the **revenue increase for the PV system participating in FCR is equal to 2.87%**

Time interval	**01.01.2024 – 31.10.2024**
$DA_{revenue}$ [EUR]	473,377
$DA_{reduced}$ [EUR]	461,372
$FCR_{revenue}$ [EUR]	77,659
FCR_{cost} [EUR]	-11,993
FCR_{net} [EUR]	65,666
RI [EUR]	**53,661**

Conclusion & extended analysis

- It was financially justified for the analyzed PV system to provide FCR for 71 out of the 305 considered days
- The revenue for those days has been increased by 53,661 EUR which is an increase of 11.34%, or 2.87 % when compared to the total revenue earned on the DA market during the 10-month period
- Results could be much better for countries with more sunny days in a year and more stable irradiance profiles than the Netherlands
- Redefining FCR provision from 4-hour to 1-hour time blocks would also increase the number of profitable hours in a year, for PV systems
- The extended paper considered 1 Hz resolution irradiance and PV panel temperature data from three locations in the Netherlands. The results demonstrated the potential of spatial aggregation to enhance the reliability of PV systems in providing FCR services, enabling a portfolio of PV plants to participate more frequently and offer a higher guaranteed power reserve

EUPVSEC

DNV

Thank you for your attention!

emil.petkovski@dnv.com

EUPVSEC

DNV

Appendix

EUPVSEC

DNV

Constraints

- The **first power constraint** is that the value of the selected power reserve must be smaller or equal to half of the maximum available power (P_{MAP}) sustained throughout the 4-hour interval

$$P_{MAP} - 2 \cdot P_R \geq 0$$

- The **second power constraint** dictates that the P_{MAP} of the PV system must be higher than 6 MW, which roughly construes to an irradiance of 120 W/m^2

$$P_{MAP} \geq 6\ MW$$

- The **third power constraint** is that the power reserve must be traded in blocks of 1 MW

Constraints II

- **A price constraint** is introduced, dictating that the average value of the FCR price during the 4-hour interval of interest must be higher than the absolute value of the DA price

$$FCR\ price > DA\ price, \qquad if\ DA\ price \geq 0$$
$$FCR\ price > -(DA\ price), \qquad if\ DA\ price < 0$$

Which can be more coherently summarized as:

$$FCR\ price > |DA\ price|$$

- **Only days which meet all these constraints have been considered in the analysis!**

Results: 3 August 2024

- The figure on the left shows the minute and minimum hourly production of the PV system on 3 August 2024. The maximum available production throughout the 4-hour interval is **13.2 MW**, therefore $\mathbf{P_R = 6\ MW}$
- The figure on the right shows the electricity price on the DA and FCR markets

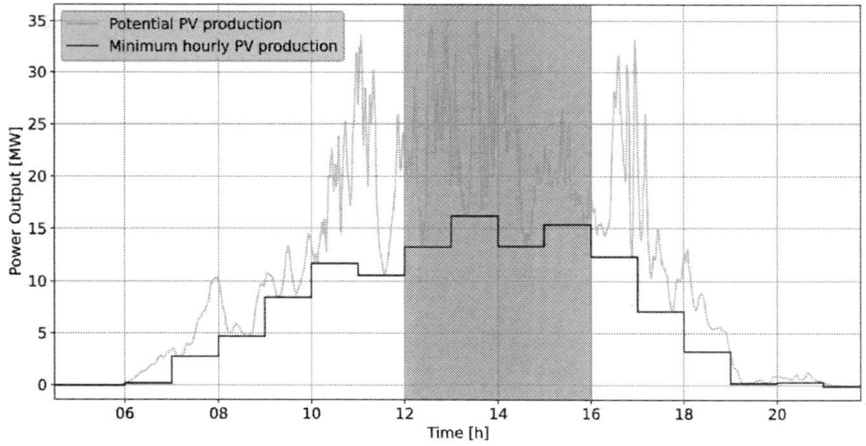

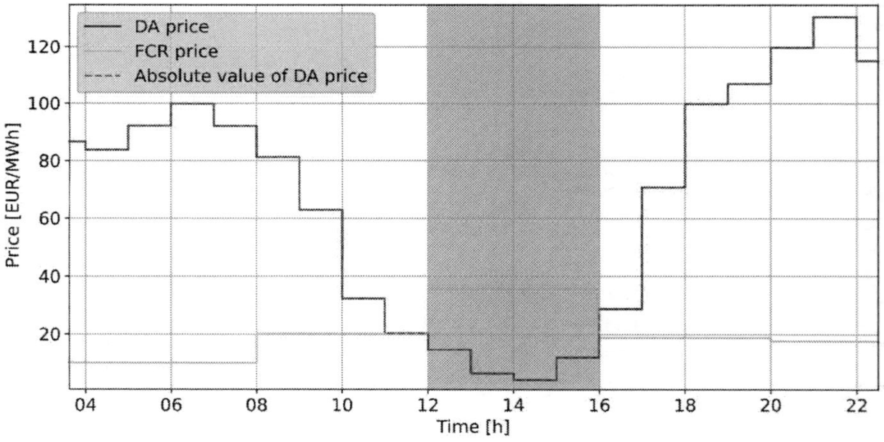

EUPVSEC

DNV

Results II: 3 August 2024

- Notably, $DA_{reduced}$ is lower than $DA_{revenue}$ because the DA prices are higher than zero. Of course, the DA price is still lower than the FCR price, otherwise the day wouldn't be of interest
- The revenue for this day has been increased **by 628.4 EUR, or 10,27%**

Time interval	**03.08.2024**
$DA_{revenue}$ [EUR]	6,121.3
$DA_{reduced}$ [EUR]	5,898.2
$FCR_{revenue}$ [EUR]	851.5
FCR_{cost} [EUR]	0
FCR_{net} [EUR]	851.5
RI [EUR]	628.4

Results: 10-month interval & Pmax > 8 MW

- When the new power constraint is considered, **56 days have been identified** in which providing FCR would be profitable for the PV system.
- The **revenue for the 56 days has been increased by 48,587 EUR which is an increase of 12%.**
- Relative to the 1,869,207 EUR figure, the **revenue increase for the PV system participating in FCR is equal to 2.6%**.

Time interval	**01.01.2024 – 31.10.2024**
$DA_{revenue}$ [EUR]	405,038
$DA_{reduced}$ [EUR]	394,457
$FCR_{revenue}$ [EUR]	70,205
FCR_{cost} [EUR]	-11,036
FCR_{net} [EUR]	59,169
RI [EUR]	**48,587**

REVENUES AT RISK AND MITIGATION STRATEGIES FOR SOLAR PV PLANTS IN TIMES OF NEGATIVE ELECTRICITY PRICES

Philippe Macé[1], Elina Bosch[1], Caroline Plaza[2], David Moser[3] Gaëtan Masson[1]
[1]Becquerel Institute
[2]Becquerel Institute France
[3]Becquerel Institute Italia
p.mace@becquerelinstitute.org

ABSTRACT: The European PV market is entering a new phase as negative electricity prices increasingly overlap with midday solar generation, shifting market risk back to producers. With subsidy-free business models and corporate PPAs expanding while traditional support schemes contract, project revenues and financing conditions are becoming more constrained. Mitigation strategies can help manage these challenges, though their effectiveness varies. Options such as revenue-oriented system design and PV–storage integration can reduce exposure to low or negative prices, but they typically involve cost trade-offs and uncertain returns, often requiring multiple revenue streams to ensure profitability. Beyond enhancing competitiveness, these measures are becoming critical for project feasibility. By supporting financing, securing grid access, and strengthening debt service resilience, they can determine whether PV projects are viable at all. As European electricity markets evolve, the capacity to implement effective mitigation strategies will be central to sustaining the growth and resilience of solar deployment.
Keywords: solar PV, negative prices, mitigation strategies, competitiveness, risk

1 INTRODUCTION

In many European countries, an increasing occurrence of very low and negative prices on electricity markets has been observed in recent years. In 2024, the number of negative day-ahead price hours reached 4838, which marked a 98% year-on-year growth. Researchers have shown that it is correlated with the increasing penetration of renewable energy, such as wind and solar photovoltaics. This correlation implies that the occurrence of low and negative prices typically happens in times of high PV production (in comparison to electricity demand level) [1] [2] [3] [4] [5].

At the same time, PV producers face higher market exposure.

In the case of unsubsidized photovoltaic (PV), projects depend partially or totally on wholesale market revenues (merchant or PPA-backed assets). Such projects are common in countries with little to no guaranteed remuneration schemes, (e.g., Spain, Belgium) but also in other countries where such schemes are in place as with increased competitiveness of solar PV and the higher electricity prices on the European market in 2022 / early 2023 PV developers have been encouraged to investigate unsubsidized options. In February 2024, 40% of utility-scale PV additions in Germany were unsubsidized (outside of the national EEG scheme) with business models predominantly based on Power Purchase Agreements but also on merchant PV [7]. In France, as per a report published in November 2024 by the energy regulation commission, close to 20% of the PV electricity generation came from unsubsidized PV [5].

Higher market exposure is also observed for subsidized PV as policy markers are increasingly shifting the risk to producers. In Great Britain, since the fourth Contract for Difference (CfD) Allocation Round (AR) which opened at the end of 2021, the CfD contracts foresee that no payment is issued in case of negative day-ahead price [10]. In France, under the feed-in premium ("complément de rémunération"), PV producer do not receive any remuneration during periods of negative prices, but, beyond a certain threshold of annual negative price hours, they will receive a specific "negative price premium" provided they stopped all production (and injection) during these hours. [5] In Germany, since 2016, if negative prices occur for a period longer than 6 consecutive hours, no market premium is paid during the negative price episode. However, the feed-in premium contract duration is extended by the number of hours during which the market premium was lost. Recent regulatory change in early 2025 reduced the negative price episode duration as of which no market premium is received 1 hour in 2027 [11]. These examples show that there is a common trend to reshape support mechanisms conditions to optimize the allocation of public funding and reduce the burden of negative prices in order to incentivize PV producers to adapt and react upon electricity market signals.

These two parallel trends of increasing occurrence of negative prices and increasing exposure of PV producers to electricity market trends impact profitability at different PV project steps. During project development and planning, this renders revenue modelling more complex and increases uncertainty. Before construction and installation, this deteriorates financing conditions with some banks relucant or not willing to finance merchant PV projects and less attractive gearing ratio being imposed (from 70:30 to 50:50). Eventually during the operation phase of PV project, this puts revenues at risk. In Belgium the solar capture rate has decreased from 92%in 2023 to 56% in 2024 [4].

This study aims at quantifying this impact and investigating different mitigation strategies.

2 METHODS

2.1 Input data

Hourly PV production was obtained from PVGIS. Capital and operational expenditures (CAPEX and OPEX) were derived from industry watch reports and targeted surveys. Hourly day-ahead electricity prices were generated through a prospective scenario-based approach, explicitly exploring different trajectories to capture the uncertainty surrounding long-term trends in negative prices over the next 20–30 years. While negative prices are expected to act as corrective market signals, leading to gradual self-balancing, the timing and pace of this adjustment remain highly uncertain. Finally, project revenues were computed by matching hourly PV production with hourly electricity prices on a one-to-one basis.

2.3 Output

Main profitability indicators are used such as the Net Present Value Equity (NPVe), the Internal Return Rate Equity (IRRe) as well as the Debt Service Coverage Ratio allowing to measure availability of cash flows to cover debt obligations.

3 PROFITS AT RISK

3.1 Quantification of the profitability at risk

Under the assumed assumptions found in Table I, it can be seen in Figure 1A, 1B and 1C, how the decreasing solar capture rate under a merchant PV business model combined with deteriorated conditions (gearing ratios shifting towards lower shares of debt) lead to deteriorated profitability indicators such as NPV equity and IRR equity. With a 65% solar capture rate and the least attractive gearing ratio the break-even of the project is almost not reached under the considered assumptions.

Table I: Key assumptions for the profitability at risk assessment

Yield [kWh/kWp]	1171 (South Germany)
CAPEX [€/Wp]	0.54
OPEX [€/kWp]	19
Lifetime [years]	30
Degradation rates	1%/0.4%
Installed capacity [MW]	10
Interest rate	4%
Cost of equity	10%
Share of debt	50%-70%
Business model	Merchant

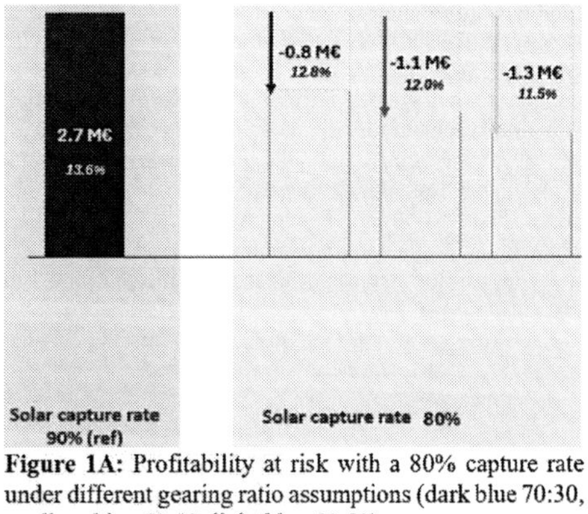

Figure 1A: Profitability at risk with a 80% capture rate under different gearing ratio assumptions (dark blue 70:30, medium blue 60:40, light blue 50:50).

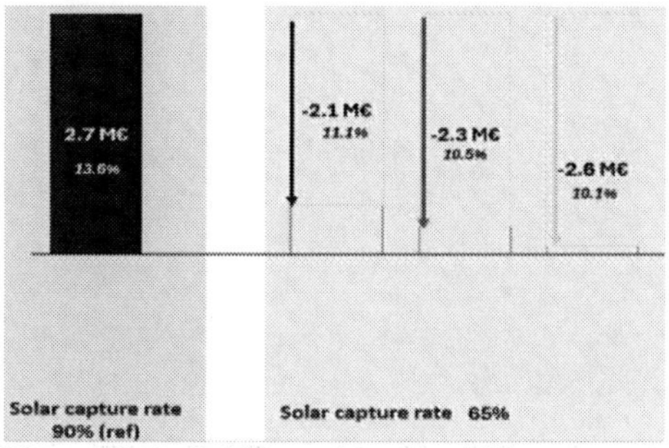

Figure 1B: Profitability at risk with a 65% capture rate under different gearing ratio assumptions (dark blue 70:30, medium blue 60:40, light blue 50:50).

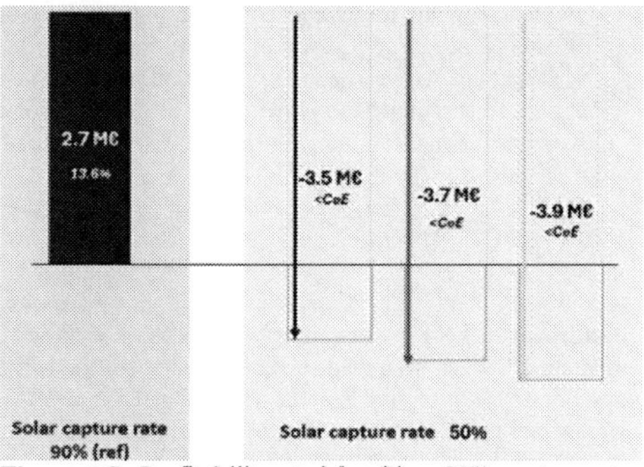

Figure 1C: Profitability at risk with a 50% capture rate under different gearing ratio assumptions (dark blue 70:30, medium blue 60:40, light blue 50:50).

4 MITIGATION STRATEGIES RESULTS

The investigated mitigation strategies include (a) alternative PV designs as well as (b) the addition of battery storage.

3.2 Alternative PV designs

3.2.1 Comparison based on lifetime based profitability indicators.

The considered alternative designs which are compared to a conventional south-oriented and optimally tilted ground-mounted PV (S_O) are (i) a Vertical PV system oriented East and West (V_EW), (ii) a ground-mounted PV plant mixing East- and West-oriented, tilted PV panels with a 50° tilt (EW_50°) and (iii) a ground-mounted PV plant with a one-axis tracker (sun-tracking strategy) (Trac.). These different PV designs are characterised by differences in terms of CAPEX, OPEX, yield, and weighted average selling price (WASP) as shown in Table II.

Table II: Key assumptions for the different considered PV designs

	S_O	V_EW | EW_50° | Trac.
Yield [kWh/kWp]	1171	1174 | 935 | 1324
CAPEX [€/Wp]	0.54	0.61 | 0.53 | 0.58
OPEX [€/kWp]	19	20.4 | 18.5 | 20
WASP* [€/MWh]	55.6	65.9 | 59.4 | 62.8
Lifetime [years]		30
Degradation rates		1%/0.4%
Installed capacity [MW]		10
Interest rate		4%
Cost of equity		10%
Share of debt		60%

** Calculated with 2024-2025 German Day-Ahead Prices*

As shown in Figure 2, under the considered assumptions, alternative design (i) shows an interest in terms of NPV improvement compared to the South Optimal reference starting with 5 to 10 years of negative prices. It requires 10 to 15 years of negative prices to reach a NPV higher by 10% or more compared to the reference South Optimal system.

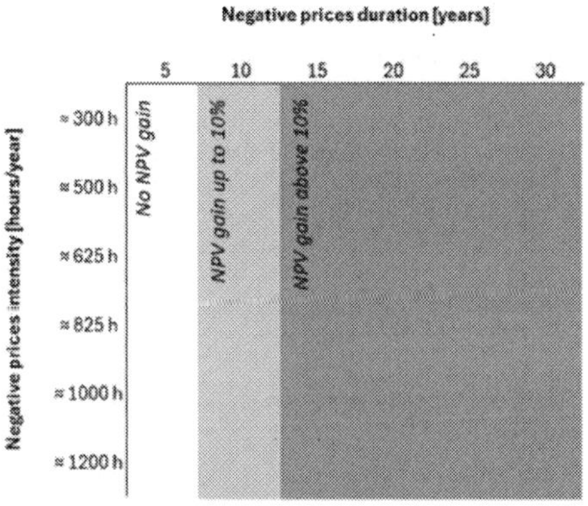

Figure 2: NPV comparison between the South Optimal and the vertical East-West PV design.

As shown in Figure 3, under the considered assumptions, for alternative design (ii) the lower yield is never compensated by the higher average selling price and lower CAPEX/OPEX.

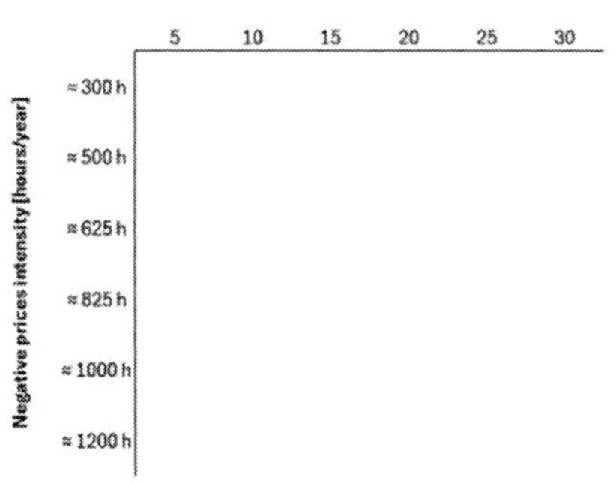

Figure 3: NPV comparison between the South Optimal and the tilted East-West PV design.

As shown in Figure 4, under the considered assumptions, for alternative design (iii) there is a clear advantage of the presence of the tracker as the additional costs are compensated by the additional production and higher average selling price. When looking whether the additional costs are compensated by the higher average selling price only (i.e., not taking into account the higer yeild from the sun tracking), there is an interest in terms of NPV improvement compared to the South Optimal reference starting with 5 to 10 years of moderately frequent (300h-900h per year) negative prices. It requires either higher frequency of negative prices (<900h per year) or longer periods of negative prices (10 to 15 years) to reach a NPV higher by 10% or more compared to the reference South Optimal system.

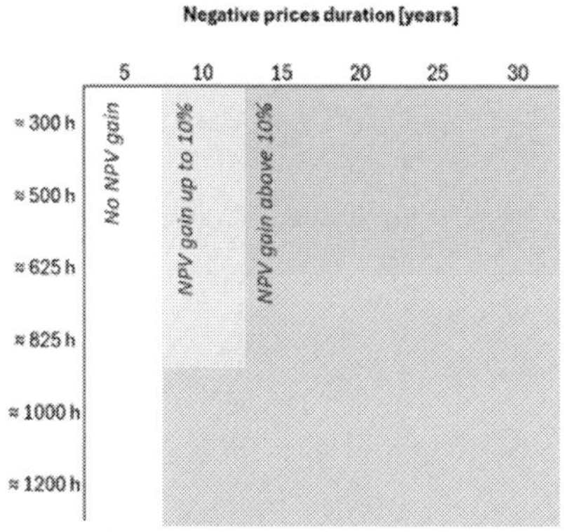

Figure 4: NPV comparison between the South Optimal and the PV system with one-axis tracker.

It can be added that whether similar results would be obtained in other countries would have to be investigated under country specific conditions. Although it is expected that the alternative designs would lead similar advantages in terms of weighted average selling price, some national conditions such as the irradiation conditions or the electricity prices patterns would influence results.

3.2.2 Comparison based on monthly indicators

In markets with negative prices, projects can face monthly cash gaps that certain indicators, including annual financial metrics, can hide but which are critical to consider as it can have an impact on the project's robustness with regards to solvency.

Focusing on the vertical East-West alternative design, when looking at a monthly time scale, the advantages can be also be appreciated in terms of average monthly value from generated electricity (Figure 5), monthly cash flow available for Debt Service (Figure 6) and Debt Service Coverage Ratio (Figure 7). Looking at this later indicator, it can be seen how selecting a vertical East-West alternative design can be an efficient mitigation strategy for the PV project to withstand periods of stress, by safeguarding monthly debt service coverage ratios (DSCR).

10.4229/EUPVSEC2025/5EO.3.3

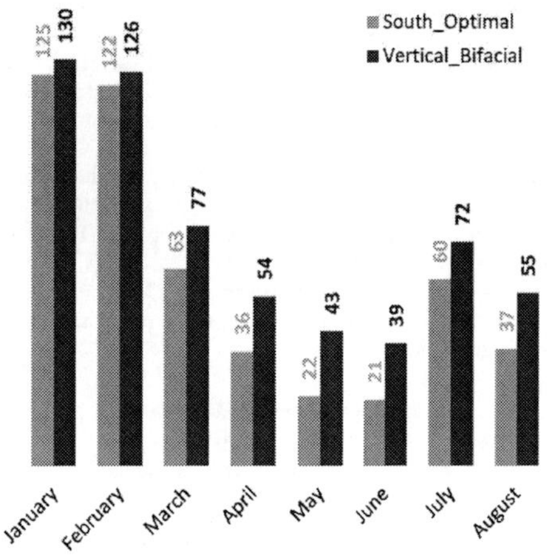

Figure 5: Average monthly value from generated electricity in €/MWh (based on 2025 Day-Ahead prices)

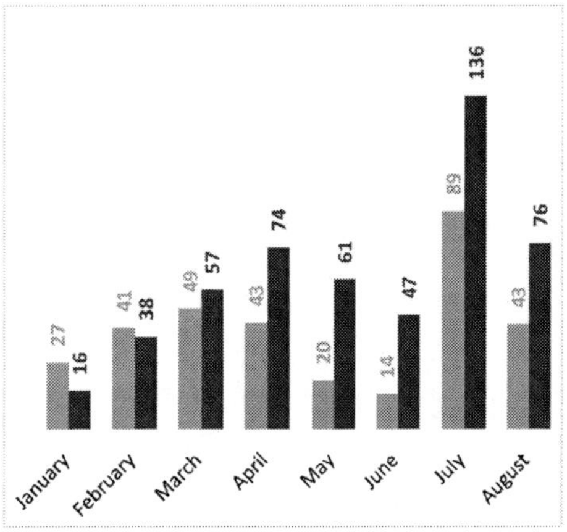

Figure 6: Monthly Cash Flow Available for Debt Service in thousand euros (based on 2025 Day-Ahead prices)

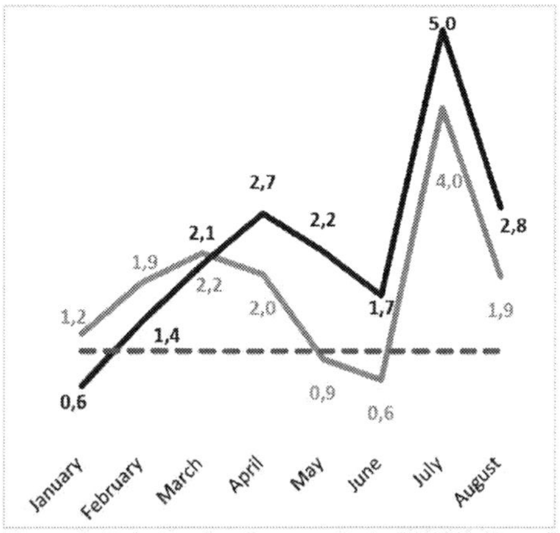

Figure 7: Debt Service Coverage Ratio (DSCR) (the red dotted line corresponds to the threshold of DSCR=1)

3.2.3 Addition of storage

The second studied mitigation strategy is the addition of a storage system. The main techno-economic assumptions can be found in Table III.

Table III: Key assumptions for the addition of storage mitigation strategy

Yield [kWh/kWp]	1171 (South Germany)
CAPEX PV [€/Wp]	0.54
CAPEX BESS [€/kWh]	350
OPEX PV [€/kWp]	19
OPEX BESS [€/kWh.yr]	5.25
Lifetime [years]	15
Degradation rates	1%/0.4%
Installed capacity PV [MW]	10
Installed capacity BESS [MWh]	14
Interest rate	4%
Cost of equity	10%
Share of debt	60%
Business model PV	Merchant (+ charging the battery)
Business model BESS	Arbitrage (charging from PV)

As shown in Figure 8, the addition of a storage system shifts part of the production to higher-value hours. This allows to increase the average selling price of produced PV electricity from 56 €/MWh in the South Optimal case without storage to 79 €/MWh. Specifically, the electricity which is produced by the PV system, then stored, then injected into the grid has an average weighted value of 125 €/MWh.

Nevertheless, for the considered business model, where the battery system's revenue are solely based on arbitrage using PV electricity only, the additional revenues do not compensate the additional costs, worsening the business case overall. For the addition of storage to be a relevant mitigation strategy for PV against negative prices, it is important to unlock higher revenue for the battery. For example, the arbitrage model can be either extended by also allowing charging from the grid (while giving priority to charging from the PV system) or decoupled by only charging from the grid to fully leverage the occurrence of negative prices. Moreover, revenue stacking by capturing revenues from grid services also contributes to consolidate the battery system business case. Eventually, for this mitigation strategy as well, having sufficient long and pronounced (i.e., high price spreads) negative prices episodes, remains an important prerequisite for the profitability of BESS which based at least part of their revenues from arbitrage business models.

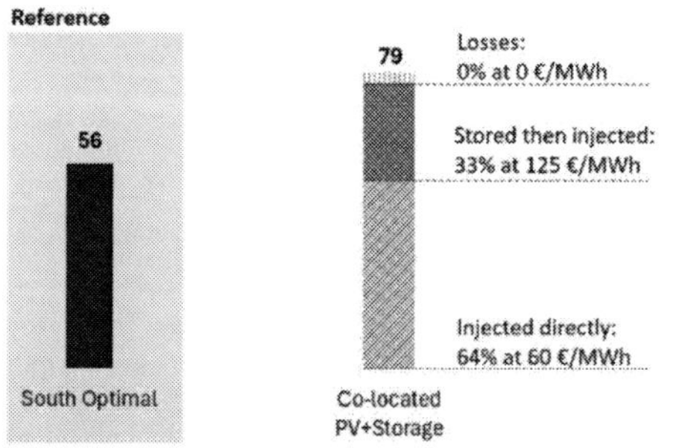

Figure 8: Weighted average electricity valuation in €/MWh (based on 2024-2025 Day-Ahead prices)

10.4229/EUPVSEC2025/5EO.3.3

5 CONCLUSIONS

The European PV market is undergoing rapid transformation as market conditions evolve. Rising occurrences of negative electricity prices increasingly coincide with midday solar output, shifting market risk back to producers in an environment where subsidy-free business models, merchant PV, and corporate PPAs are expanding, while traditional support schemes are tightening. These dynamics directly affect project profitability through reduced revenues and more restrictive financing conditions, requiring careful consideration of mitigation strategies.

A range of measures exists, though their efficiency varies widely. Adjustments in PV system design can improve revenue resilience by prioritizing value capture over maximum generation, albeit at the cost of higher investment or operational expenses and potential reductions in annual output—an approach that only proves beneficial if negative price trends persist. Similarly, pairing PV with storage enables producers to shift electricity to higher-priced hours and thus raise its value. However, the economics of battery storage remain challenging, as investment costs are not always offset by arbitrage revenues alone, necessitating stacked revenue streams to secure profitability.

Importantly, these mitigation measures can play a decisive role beyond enhancing competitiveness. By enabling access to financing, securing grid connection, or improving solvency and debt serviceability, they can determine whether projects are viable at all. As such, the capacity to integrate effective mitigation strategies is becoming a critical factor not only for profitability but also for the feasibility and resilience of PV deployment in Europe's changing market landscape.

6 REFERENCES

[1] Market Observatory for Energy of the European Commission, «Quarterly report on European electricity markets,» 2024.
[2] Brian Publicover, «Europe posts record negative power prices for 2024 as renewables rise,» PV Magazine, 21 January 2025.
[3] Bundesnetzagentur, «Bundesnetzagentur ver¬öf¬fent¬licht Da¬ten zum Strom¬markt 2024,» 3 January 2025. [En ligne].
[4] CREG, «Étude sur l'impact de l'intégration des énergies renouvelables sur le fonctionnement des marchés de l'électricité à court terme,» 2024.
[5] CRE, «Analyse de la CRE sur le phénomène de prix de l'électricité négatifs et recommandations relatives aux dispositifs de soutien aux énergies renouvelables,» 2024.
[6] S. Enkhardt, «https://www.pv-magazine.de/2024/03/21/photovoltaik-anlagen-ohne-eeg-foerderungen-machen-im-februar-40-prozent-des-zubaus-aus/,» PV Magazine Deutschland, 21 March 2024.
[7] Renewable Exchange, «Negative Prices in 2024: Is the Sun Setting On the CfD?,» 16 January 2025. [En ligne]. Available: https://renewable.exchange/blog/negative-prices-in-2024-is-the-sun-setting-on-the-cfd/.
[8] FFE, «Negative Strompreise – Wie viele Anlagen erneuerbarer Energien fahren durch?,» 21 October 2024. [En ligne]. Available: https://www.ffe.de/veroeffentlichungen/negative-strompreise-wie-viele-anlagen-erneuerbarer-energien-fahren-durch/.

10.4229/EUPVSEC2025/5EO.3.3

42nd European Photovoltaic Solar Energy Conference and Exhibition

This presentation was selected by the Sc. Committee of the EU PVSEC 2025 for submission of a full paper to one of the EU PVSEC's collaborating peer-reviewed journals.

A COMMODITY TODAY, INCOMPATIBLE TOMORROW: THE PARADOX OF PV?

Bert Herteleer[1], Gernot Oreski[2], Silvana Ovaitt[3], Ulrike Jahn[4],
Ralph Gottschalg[4], Ian Marius Peters[5], Gabriele Friesen[1], Mauro Caccivio[1]
[1]SUPSI, Switzerland, [2]PCCL, Austria, [3] NREL, USA [4] Fraunhofer CSP, Germany [5] HI ERN, Germany
bert.herteleer@supsi.ch

ABSTRACT: Since the year 2000, the PV industry has seen a thousand-fold increase in deployments to over 2 TW by 2024, while module prices have dropped more than 98%. During this time, the perception has grown of PV modules as commodities. However, when PV modules have to be replaced beyond available spares, owners are confronted with the challenge that modules compatible with the existing modules and mounting systems are not available at scale. When PV modules must be sourced on the market, the second paradox of PV emerges: module warranties have lengthened and strengthened, while variations in the bill of materials have increased, yet testing durations and scopes have not scaled accordingly. The findings underscore the urgent need for industry-wide standardisation, increased transparency and trust-but-verify mentality, extended qualification protocols, and strategies to mitigate the operational and economic risks associated with PV module obsolescence.

Keywords: reliability, technological evolution, module testing for lifetime, material qualification, transparency, repowering

1 Introduction

The PV industry and PV modules have experienced spectacular growth and cost declines over the past decades, with deployments growing a thousand-fold from 1-2 GWp in 2000 to over 2 TWp by 2024, with costs dropping 98% over the same time, thanks to widespread learning and innovation, and economies of scale, and translating lab champion cells to production lines in 2.5 to 3 years [1]. Particularly in the past decade, the rate of technology change and innovation within the PV module industry has accelerated, moving from 1.6 m^2 and ~300 Wp Al-BSF mono-facial modules to 2-3 m^2 500-700 Wp PERC/TOPCon/HJT bifacial modules [1].

The intense competition and cost pressures have seen Original Equipment Manufacturers (OEMs) pre-qualifying suppliers, allowing OEMs to host reverse auctions to reduce costs, as well as use functionally "identical" materials from different suppliers, whose formulations often vary from each other. Consequently, variations in the Bill of Materials (BOM) such as differences in adhesives, encapsulants, and backsheets, are possible within one series of modules, even with "live" BOM updates during production [2], or documented in utility-scale PV farms [3], leading to different degradation and failure modes within the same PV systems.

At some point during the technical lifetime of a PV power plant, modules must be replaced due to a variety of reasons. These can include Extreme Weather Events (EWEs) such as hurricanes or snow events [4], to floods [5], hail and lightning [6], poor O&M practices or poor siting [7], and module failures (quality and reliability), including aggressive degradation [8]. While still nascent, repowering of PV systems is starting, where PV systems may see modules replaced (reskinning) all the way to deep re-engineering of the full power plant, with causes ranging from technical to economical [9].

Depending on the spare parts management strategy established in the development phase, spare modules will be readily available, or the CAPEX-saving reduction in spares sees the need to procure modules on the market. Given the rapid technological development, it is then impossible to procure replacement modules at scale whose physical and electrical characteristics are directly compatible with the existing Balance-of-System (BOS).

Even new, more efficient PV modules obtained **for free** would still carry a significant cost for a farm, as much of the engineering, design and installation work would have to be repeated, to accommodate the modules with different characteristics and match these with the mounting equipment and inverters in use. Thus, the **commodity-incompatibility paradox of PV modules**: these are treated price-wise as a commodity, yet the need for PV modules to be compatible physically and electrically to ensure long-term reliable and safe operation with maximum possible yield makes them outdated shortly after they are installed.

This paper aims to shed light on the implications of these practices, including the challenges posed by accelerated material innovation, the lack of long-term reliability data, and the systemic obstacles to effective lifecycle management.

2 Background and historical overview

Between 1954 and 1985, the PV industry experimented widely with various designs, cell technologies, encapsulants, and front cover solutions [10]. The USA-funded Block Buys I-V between 1975 and 1985 stimulated the industry to address weak points while providing the guaranteed revenue needed for the manufacturing of the modules. In this period, most manufacturers converged on a common design: strings of series-connected crystalline silicon solar cells integrated into a multilayer encapsulant composite and supported by a robust frame. This architecture proved durable in the field and has remained largely unchanged since, with minor tweaks over time.

The Block Buys also had a fundamental impact on testing and qualification methodologies, developed by the Jet Propulsion Laboratory (JPL). These tests informed subsequent IEC 61215 qualification tests, particularly the accelerated test designs that inform current Module Qualification Test (MQT) protocols [11] of IEC 61215 and IEC TS 63397. Already in 2009, Osterwald and McMahon identified an important issue that has not yet been resolved until today:

"A serious flaw with identifying a test report as a certification is that the product quality requirements normally enforced by an outside agency are missing. A manufacturer is free to make changes to a module, such as changing the supplier of the encapsulation material, and still claim that the module is "certified." It is not difficult to imagine scenarios in which such manufacturing changes could adversely affect the lifetime of a PV module." [11]

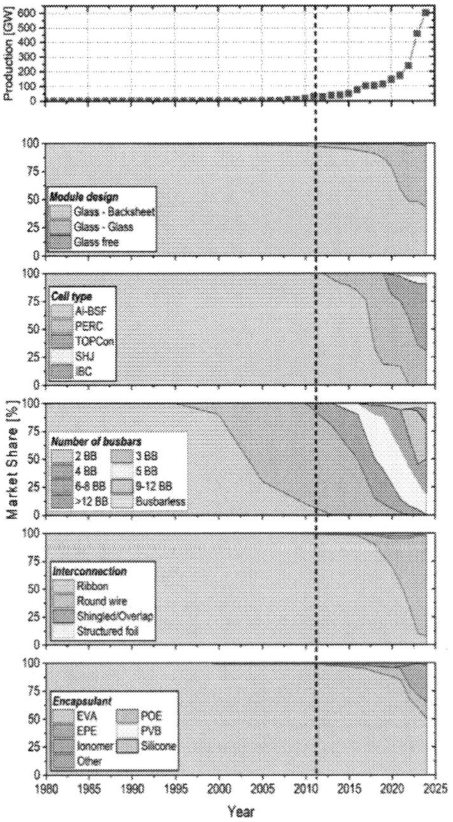

Figure 1: Yearly PV module production and market shares for different module designs and Bill of Materials between 1980 and 2024. Data compiled from IEA PVPS Snapshot Reports, ITRPV Reports, Fraunhofer ISE PV Reports, and verified against annual reports of top module manufacturers.

Similarly, PV module manufacturers were known to overstate their nominal power by 6-7%, which, when combined with Light Induced Degradation (LID) of ~3%, resulted in real-life performance of -10% versus nameplate in 2005 [10]. Figure 1 shows the evolution of commercially successful c-Si PV modules and key BOM components over time. (By definition, this therefore excludes experimentation and small batches by manufacturers that did not achieve lasting success.) These charts were reconstructed by combining data reported in the literature with interpolation to fill in missing years. This analysis focuses on crystalline silicon PV cell architectures (Al-BSF, PERC, TOPCon, SHJ, IBC), module design variants (glass–glass, glass–backsheet, lightweight glass-free), encapsulant materials, interconnect types (round wire, ribbon), and busbar configurations.

The historical analysis of photovoltaic (PV) production and shipments between 1980 and 2024 reveals a clear inflection point in the industrial growth trajectory. From 1980 through 2000, global PV production expanded slowly from 0.01 GWp to 0.3 GWp per year, with cumulative shipments below 2 GWp, reflecting a niche market supported mainly by off-grid systems and early demonstration projects. During the subsequent decade (2001–2010), growth accelerated under the influence of feed-in tariff policies in Europe and Japan, raising annual production to 20 GWp and cumulative shipments to approximately 41 GWp by 2010. The true industrial turning point occurred in the period 2010–2012, when annual production exceeded 20 GWp and cumulative shipments crossed the 100 GWp threshold, marking the transition from early market expansion to large-scale industrialization. This inflection coincides with the entry and rapid rise of Chinese manufacturing and steep cost reductions, as steps of the strategy to establish PV as a mainstream energy technology.

Figure 2 illustrates the exponential growth of PV installations worldwide over the past 25 years, achieving a thousand-fold increase from 2 GWp in 2000 to 2.2 TWp in 2024, while experiencing similarly spectacular cost declines of 98% or more, with spot prices for Tier-1 c-Si modules reaching 0.1 $/W in 2024. Even the period 2010-2024 saw cost declines of 90% or more in $/W terms for PV modules.

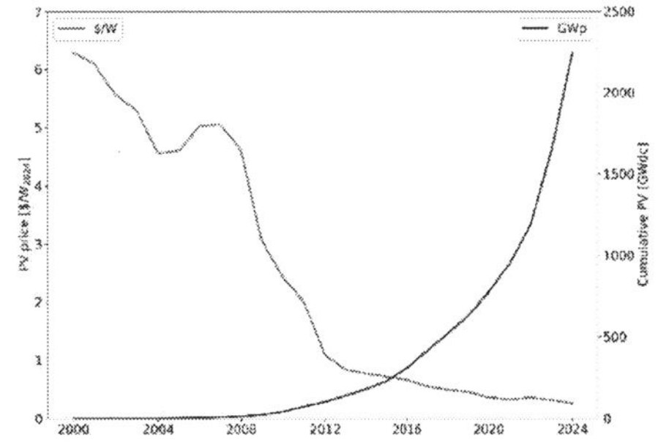

Figure 2: Cumulative worldwide deployments 2000-2024, with module prices in 2024 $/W. Price data from [12], installation data from [13].

From Figure 1 and Figure 2, together with the rapid increase of maximum commercially available module power between 2018 (~350 Wp) and 2022 (~650 Wp) documented by [1], the **first paradox of PV** becomes evident: PV modules are treated price-wise as a commodity, yet the need for PV modules to be compatible physically and electrically to ensure long-term reliable and safe operation with maximum possible yield makes them outdated as soon as they are installed.

The consequences of this paradox are manyfold, with most of the risk residing with asset owners. To further lower costs, PV systems typically are highly optimised for the chosen PV module and inverter combination, together with the mounting solution (fixed or single-axis tracking). This combination drives system design, including string

lengths, and the length and width of arrays, as well as inter-row distances. Asset owners usually have between 0.1% and 3% of modules as spares, with 0.5% the most prevalent, to use for expected and reasonable module failures. If, for whatever reason more than the available spare modules need to be replaced within the technical lifetime of the power plant, the asset owner and the O&M provider are confronted with a serious challenge: finding compatible spares, with the same or very similar BOM *at scale* is next to impossible, once more than two years have passed, as module manufacturers continuously implement technology and process changes to their production lines.
A PV module failure is defined here as the most stringent combination of an effect or issue that poses a safety risk, or that the power output of the module(s) is so low due to performance loss that reliable operation of the solar plant is not possible. For the latter, this means that the current and/or voltage of the modules has declined enough that inverters are unable to operate within their designed DC input range, or unable to meet grid performance standard requirements.

Industry experience compiled by IEA PVPS Task 13 shows that many early-life failure modes take at least one to three years to be identified from their first deployment at scale, while (slightly) slower yet important degradation modes such as PID can be reported by year 3 and 4 of operation [14]. Even in moderate climates, module failures by year 10-12 of operation have also damaged inverters due to repeated insulation resistance issues [15]. In times of exponential deployment, 2-5 years equates to 50-70% of worldwide cumulative installations, with currently more than 1.4 TWp less than 5 years old.

When comparing the PV industry to other industries, some challenges and peculiarities can be identified. The PV industry's rapid technological evolution and cost-reduction efforts have prioritized innovation over long-term material qualification, where new module designs, e.g., "big floppy modules" [16] are put on the market and deployed faster than they can be tested by independent third parties. Compounding this issue, the PV industry operates in large-scale yet unique production batches (100 MW to 5 GWp), with rapid iteration and technological advancement [1] ensuring that specific module designs and configurations are not replicated.

Using cumulative doublings from reaching 1 GWp cumulative installations since the year 2000 as an indicator for maturity, an outside look of the industry would yield the black dotted curve of Figure 3. The (semi-) viable moment for each technology can then be indicated, while the "birth" of the technology occurs when 1 GWp/y of installations is reached. An outside view of the industry misses the contributions of the different technologies over time, where until 2012, there was only Al-BSF being produced and sold at GW-scale. From 2012 onwards, PERC rapidly gained market share due to its efficiency and cost benefits. The growth of TOPCon has been nothing short of spectacular, with cumulative deployments surpassing Al-BSF in 4 to 5 years. By contrast, back contact (IBC) and heterojunction (HJT) technologies have scaled slower than PERC and TOPCon, due to more complex processing steps, higher production quality requirements and commensurate manufacturing costs.

A key benefit for the industry has been that technology and manufacturing learnings are transferable for c-Si technologies, and that many of the cell technologies share common processes and machines, whereby transitioning from lab to fab could happen within 1-3 years [1]. Nevertheless, this still required enormous investments over the past years, with top Chinese manufacturers building ingot, cell, wafer and module fabs at 5 GW to 25 GW scales, repeating this effort over multiple years. These high investments to scale rapidly while defending or gaining market share during intense price wars have affected the financial stability of many manufacturers, with the Chinese government taking steps to reduce overcapacity [17].

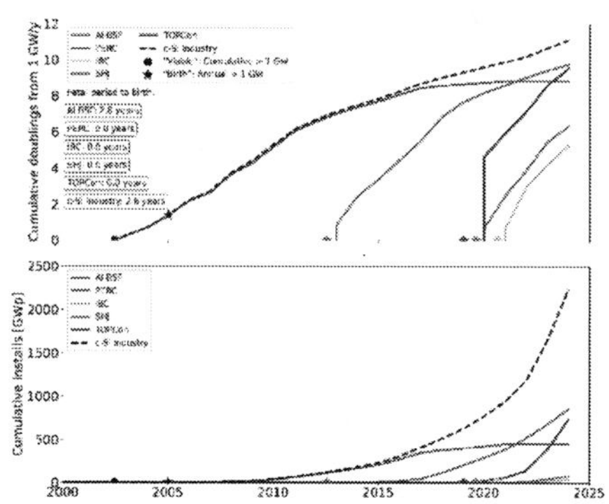

Figure 3: Worldwide cumulative doublings by c-Si cell technology and cumulative GWp deployments.

The actions of the leading Chinese manufacturers regarding changes to module warranty durations, both for workmanship (10 to 25 years, depending on the company) and STC power loss over time (from -0.5%/year to -0.3%/y, from 25 years to 30 years or more), suggest that they are confident that these new module technologies are better made, and will suffer lower degradation rates compared to previous generations. While module manufacturers have increased automation and with-it improved quality control of the manufacturing process, design and material choices such as variations in encapsulant recipes, or glass thickness and treatments, still represent potential avenues for unknown, or faster-than-expected failure modes. Recent examples with glass-glass modules have seen spontaneous glass breakage occur [16], while BOM variations such as different EVA recipes of modules within utility-scale farms result in different degradation modes and speeds [18].

The very rapid growth of new cell technologies in the past decade, combined with the introduction of larger module sizes and variations in BOM components, thus leave the industry with potential risks, where the impact can be in the multi-GW range. Compared to the mature 20+ years of Al-BSF learning and deployment period to reach ~0.45 TW, PERC and TOPCon are TW-scale toddlers, where long-term (10 years or more) outdoor reliability data is non-existent. Already, new failure modes such as UV-induced degradation (UVID) have emerged for PERC and TOPCon, with the manufacturing process also appearing to play a role, more than only the cell technology [19].

3 Main challenges

3.1 Module warranties

PV module manufacturers typically provide limited warranties on their products:

- A workmanship warranty, covering manufacturing defects. These are currently in the range of 10-15 years, with some manufacturers offering 25 years.
- An STC power warranty, often called a degradation warranty. Here, the power output of PV modules is guaranteed for 25 to 30 years, with guaranteed end-of-warranty values ranging between 87% and 80%, expressed as an initial power loss of 1% to 3% in the first year, and subsequent 0.3% to 0.5% power loss per year.

Most module manufacturers appear to use the reliability and failure model of Vázquez and Rey-Stolle [20], where they assume that 1% of modules will fail over the warranty period. They have three parameters to optimise for power warranties: the duration of the warranty, the guaranteed power or equivalent annual degradation rate, and the associated percentage of modules that will fail over the warranty period. For this, they typically set aside 1% of PV module revenues as liabilities on their balance sheet when modules are sold and use warranty claims data and forecasting models to determine which portion of the liability will be used in the current year, and the remainder for future years. As module costs have dropped significantly over the years, current practice for warranty liability budgeting is to use the average price of PV modules over the past two years. Hence, while PV module shipments by the leading manufacturers have shown an exponential trend, the monetary impact on their balance sheet has been much less severe.

Some manufacturers self-insure for module warranties and carry this liability on their balance sheet, whereas others take out insurance against warranty claims. Importantly, standard warranty documents from manufacturers mention that they decide on the solution, if a warranty claim is valid:

- Replacement modules, to make up for the power underperformance;
- A cash equivalent using current spot prices; or,
- Repairing PV modules.

Replacement modules are provided by the manufacturer from available modules, and therefore provide zero guarantee to owners that replacement modules will be compatible (physically and electrically) with the purchased PV modules.

The exponential decline in PV module prices while sales have grown exponentially (Figure 2) has been a boon for module manufacturers, as the monetary liability has declined with module prices. Conversely, all PV systems built during this period of exponential cost declines have owners who stand to lose much, if the performance is (much) less than expected during the warranty period, and particularly if the useful lifespan is shortened.

3.2 Tests of PV modules

A major challenge accompanying the accelerated innovation cycles in PV module technology is the mismatch between the pace of material and design changes and the long service lifetimes expected from PV systems. While the introduction of novel materials and components has enabled cost reductions and performance gains, modules are now being deployed at the gigawatt scale without sufficient long-term reliability data, particularly from outdoor field testing [21]. This has led to the emergence of unexpected failure modes only a few years after deployment, including potential-induced degradation (PID) [22], backsheet chalking and cracking [23], light- and elevated-temperature-induced degradation (LeTID) [24], ultraviolet-induced degradation (UVID) [25], cell corrosion [26] and low-stress glass fracture. Many of these issues were not detected by the standardized single stress accelerated tests commonly applied at the time, highlighting the need for more representative qualification protocols.

Consequently, new accelerated testing approaches increasingly employ combinations or sequences of stressors that better capture real-world conditions and enable earlier identification of degradation modes linked to new module materials and architectures [21].

A further complication is the lack of transparency in the bill of materials (BOM). Externally, modules may appear identical, yet employ different encapsulants, backsheets, or other polymeric components, with variations not only across manufacturers but also within product lines over time. Polymers are particularly problematic, as their performance depends strongly on stabilizer and additive formulations, which are often proprietary and subject to change. Additives also govern material interactions, which are key drivers of degradation. For example, polyamide (PA)-based backsheets exhibit markedly different cracking behaviour depending on the type of EVA encapsulant employed [27]. Such interactions make it difficult to predict module reliability based on individual component properties alone [28].

The consequences of this variability are already evident at the system level. Field studies have documented cases where modules installed in the same PV park but with different BOMs showed divergent degradation pathways, resulting in heterogeneous degradation patterns and performance losses across the site. In more severe cases material incompatibilities have led to insulation issues followed by inverter shutdowns, which were triggered by the unexpected module behaviour [29].

3.3 Repowering and replacement challenges

The decision to repower or replace comes after either a specific fault or underproduction has been identified in the system (reliability-driven repowering), or economic gains are desired and have been evaluated by a technical team. A main consideration upon doing the feasibility evaluation of repowering, is the availability of spare parts and compatibility dilemmas.

As a first step to determining if repowering is needed, whether for reliability or economic reasons, requires knowledge of the health of the system. This can be assessed by perceived underperformance in the SCADA daily data production. After removing simple yet common causes like offline inverters, stuck trackers, and soiling, if the degradation of the system is pervasive it might signal to a bigger underperformance issue. Ground-teams might be sent to identify some of these issues and do visual inspections of the array, with thermal imaging a second easily accessible technique. In cases where the reason of power loss is not clear, third parties and consultants are often involved, and beyond data and visual inspection they might involve drone-aerial inspections. Electrical measurements by qualified electricians in the inverter as well as module level can also detect any ground faults, or specific module underperformance. If power loss is due to a couple outlier modules or a section, owners might opt for replacement or repair of that section by either using the spares, or purchasing similar modules in the resale market.

The format of PV modules (width and size) has changed considerably over the last decade, posing physical challenges to adapt the racking solution to the new module type. Furthermore, the change in area and efficiency mean power output and voltages will also vary, and might not match the rest of the strings or inverter requirements. Inversely, inverters' end of life, whether planned or premature, can kick into gear repowering and replacement decisions, as new inverters have also changed from 600 V to 1000 V and even now 1500 V input requirements, with very few legacy options available. DC-DC optimizers can offer partial relief from this re-engineering challenge, albeit at relatively high cost, and recent findings indicating that their use at scale may be less of panacea than expected [30].

For PV systems impacted by Extreme Weather Events (EWEs), repowering options become highly situation-specific, as the nature of the damage can vary, from a portion of the system (e.g., a tornado cutting through a wind farm, or hail damage), to wholescale damage due to flooding, hurricanes, or typhoons [7]. Nevertheless, on the technical side, in-depth analyses are typically required, which may have to extend beyond the path of visible damage, for example by doing on-site electroluminescence (EL) [31] or photoluminescence (PL) inspections.

If the asset owner, together with the insurer, deems the asset worthy of being restored to its pre-damaged state, the question then arises as to how this can be achieved. In practice, severely damaged modules or inverter sections will be restored with new PV modules, as physically and electrically compatible modules are unavailable at scale: the first paradox of PV rearing its head again.

4 Reliability and testing

When comparing the PV industry to other industries, some challenges and peculiarities can be identified. The PV industry's rapid technological evolution and cost-reduction efforts have prioritized innovation over long-term material qualification, where new cell technologies (e.g. high efficiency solar cell technologies like TOPCon or SHJ) or new module designs are put on the market and deployed faster than they can be tested by independent third parties. Consequently, unanticipated failure modes such as spontaneous glass fracture and UV-induced degradation (UVID) cell degradation have emerged.

The lack of standardisation for PV modules contrasts sharply with other industries, where spare parts with consistent specifications remain available for years or decades.

Hence, the **second paradox of PV** emerges: Increased warranty durations, more product and BOM variations, while testing is reduced in time and cost. This interacts directly with the first paradox of PV, as the low margins for PV module manufacturers and the commodity-like perception decrease the appetite for more stringent product qualification tests by manufacturers, or product quality testing and verification by customers and wholesale distributors.

5 Solutions and recommendations

5.1 Transparency

Even though the PV industry and its stakeholders have more data and more transparency than other industries, significant improvements can still be made.
While manufacturers are loath to lose their competitive advantage by sharing the ingredients to their winning recipe, the lack of information on the BOMs impacts knowledge generation on the link between materials and degradation and failure modes.

As annual PV module deployments have risen sixfold to 600 GWp since 2017-2018, the speed and duration of accelerated tests has not shortened, nor have research groups and companies specialised in reliability testing of PV modules scaled accordingly. Furthermore, the need for in-depth data and insights on material-specific and multi-material interactions has grown.

Improved and faster information flows between manufacturers, laboratories and research groups, and field data from commercially deployed systems are needed. Multiple possible solutions are possible that satisfy the competing needs and requirements of manufacturers and asset owners. These can range from dual reporting of module failures, once to the module manufacturer for warranty claims and information, and on the other to a trusted third party, whether this is the government of a country, or a multi-country institute or organisation.

5.2 Reliability

With PV moving firmly into the TW era, its importance to the safe and reliable operation of electrical grids grows too. In the short term, the performance of newly deployed PV systems is likely going to be as expected; the risk to asset owners, investors, and electrical grids may materialise much later. For long-term investors such as pension funds, the longevity and performance of the asset is crucial: they stand to lose most if the lifetime of the asset is years shorter than expected. The larger challenge is with investors with much shorter investment horizons: a PV farm may change hands multiple times over its lifetime. One of the technical challenges for the due diligence phase for the soon-to-be owner is the estimation of Remaining Useful Life (RUL), which requires a deep understanding of PV system performance and degradation, combined with the use of historical performance data and the judicious use of additional tests, such as drone-based IR, EL or PL. Here, non-destructive testing methods that can detect the BOM of PV modules may generate valuable complementary information for the RUL model of the power plant, which then informs the financial model.

This still requires fundamental science to be done, where weathering of materials is tested in outdoor conditions as well as accelerated tests. Acceleration factors for module qualification testing from IEC 61215 have been based on practical considerations, cost, and time. However, practical evidence from the industry shows that tests from IEC 61215 are deemed to not be stringent enough, with testing companies advertising 2 times or 3 times IEC [61215] as being a better indicator of module reliability.

10.4229/EUPVSEC2025/5EP.1.3

Here, the development of physics and chemistry-based acceleration factors is still a much-needed work in progress, which can be informed by approaches used in the car and roofing material industries.

5.3 Maturity and financial viability
Whether module manufacturers are prudent in extending warranty durations and guaranteeing higher rated performance over the warranty duration is yet to be seen. Module warranty claims may be much higher in the future than historical rates: not necessarily because the product is fundamentally different, rather that improved metrology of PV systems combined with machine learning or AI permit under-performance to be more rapidly and accurately determined. For module manufacturers operating for years on razor-thin or even negative margins, even a small change in warranty claims rates can have devastating impacts. The Chinese government, together with module manufacturers have been expressing concern over the consequences of the price wars on the viability of the PV module value chain [17], yet the potential impact of warranty claims is not yet publicly mentioned.

5.4 Increased standardisation
Increasing standardisation of shapes and sizes of PV modules has been a bottom-up process, driven by manufacturers aiming to optimise for volume usage within shipping containers [32]. Consortia of the largest module manufacturers have been created, with the aim of adhering to the same physical dimensions [33]. Compared to the rapid changes in physical dimensions in the past decade [1], this evolution marks as a respite for industry stakeholders. The risk that arises from further standardisation is that it continues the cycle of the first paradox of PV: more (physical) standardisation allows modules to be more easily interchangeable and replaceable, further supporting the view of modules as commodities. Moreover, if sizes do stabilise for the coming years or even decades, the advent of AI and robotics has the potential to reduce labour costs for installation, O&M, as well as removal or replacement. Surprisingly, *more* commoditisation of PV *whilst* remaining standardised may prove to be a possible way out of the first paradox of PV. Nevertheless, module reliability is a key factor for the survival of the industry and investors.

6 Conclusions

Despite the outside or whole-of-industry view that PV modules are a commodity, a deeper look shows that modules are not interchangeable between brands, nor are modules replaceable one-for-one with newer designs. This first paradox of PV is strongly linked to the second paradox of PV, where module warranties have become longer and more stringent, yet testing has not adapted accordingly. In practice, PV modules are obsolete within a few years of installation, with spares at scale unavailable. The potential risks for asset owners are large, as any event over the system lifetime where module damages or failures exceeds the available spare stock of modules leads to costly or sub-optimal solutions, such as partial or rolling repowering of the power plant. In such cases, financial returns can suffer a strong hit.

While sophisticated investors and stakeholders perform detailed due diligence on PV system suppliers, their view is still constrained to the tests they perform, while others such as rooftop PV system owners, purchase a product with the hope of good performance. Solutions such as a Production or Performance (quality) Border Adjustment Mechanism with mandatory testing with public-facing results, or similar forms of public data sharing can further drive manufacturers to ensure quality and reliability of products, and help maintain trust in PV as a durable cornerstone technology for a low-emissions economy. Here, "trust but verify" is a motto that must be applied widely, with the benefit that increased testing and transparency can root out unreliable products, manufacturers and suppliers. While the potential for PV to scale to TW-level installations per year exists, this rests on the need for PV systems and their components to be reliable for decades, while being exposed to the elements and potentially stronger storms.

One surprising (partial) way out of the PV as a commodity paradox is to lean in even more, by standardising and freezing module dimensions. This would allow modules to be more easily replaceable when inevitable failures occur. Addressing the second paradox of PV with increased warranty durations and more stringent terms while testing has not adapted accordingly will be a challenge that must be addressed head-on. The key to the survival of manufacturers, investors and customers alike though, is that module reliability and quality can be maintained, more transparency and testing implemented, while scaling further and potentially decreasing even more in price.

ACKNOWLEDGEMENTS
This paper was done within the IEA PVPS Task 13.

This report is supported by the Swiss Federal Office of Energy (SFOE) under the contract no. SI/502398-01.
The work in IEA PVPS Task 13 is supported by the Austrian Research Agency (FFG) under contract no. FO999908094.
This work is supported by the German Federal Ministry for Economic Affairs and Energy (BMWE) under contract no. 03EE1120B.
This work was authored [in part] by the National Renewable Energy Laboratory for the U.S. Department of Energy (DOE) under Contract No. DE-AC36-08GO28308. Funding provided by the U.S. Department of Energy's Office of Energy Efficiency and Renewable Energy (EERE) under Solar Energy Technologies Office (SETO) Agreement 52184. The views expressed in the article do not necessarily represent the views of the DOE or the U.S. Government. The U.S. Government retains and the publisher, by accepting the article for publication, acknowledges that the U.S. Government retains a nonexclusive, paid-up, irrevocable, worldwide license to publish or reproduce the published form of this work, or allow others to do so, for U.S. Government purposes.

REFERENCES

[1] Y. Chen, D. Chen, P. P. Altermatt, S. Zhang, L. Wang, X. Zhang, J. Xu, Z. eng, H. Shen and P. J. Verlinden, "Technology evolution of the photovoltaic industry: Learning from history and recent progress," *Prog Photovolt Res Appl.*, vol. 31, no. 12, pp. 1194-1204, 2023.

[2] R. J. Gómez, E. Jiménez, D. Sanz, C. Sandoval, J. Cuaresma, J. C. Vázquez, S. Rodríguez-Conde, H. Silva and V. Parra, "Bifacial Modules for Large Scale PV Plants: Lessons Learned and Current Limitations from a Factory/Manufacturing Inspection Outlook," in *EU PVSEC*, 2020.

[3] C. Buerhop-Lutz, O. Stroyuk, T. Pickel, T. Winkler, J. Haugh and I. M. Peters, "PV modules and their backsheets - A case study of a Multi-MW PV power station," *Solar Energy Materials and Solar Cells,* vol. 231, p. 111295, 2021.

[4] N. D. Jackson and T. Gunda, "Evaluation of extreme weather impacts on utility-scale photovoltaic plant performance in the United States," *Applied Energy,* vol. 302, p. 117508, 2021.

[5] "Reliability and safety issues observed in flood affected PV power plants and strategies to mitigate the damage in future," in *46th IEEE PVSC*, 2019.

[6] D. C. Jordan, K. Perry, R. White and C. Deline, "Extreme Weather and PV Performance," *IEEE Journal of Photovoltaics,* vol. 13, no. 6, pp. 830-835, 2023.

[7] U. Jahn, B. Herteleer, C. Tjengdrawira, I. Tsanakas, M. Richter, G. Dickeson and A. Astigarraga, "Guidelines for Operation and Maintenance of Photovoltaic Power Plants in Different Climates," IEA PVPS, 2022.

[8] M. Köntges, S. Kurtz, C. Packard, U. Jahn, K. A. Berger, K. Kato, T. Friesen and H. Liu, "Review of Failures of Photovoltaic Modules," IEA PVPS, 2014.

[9] S. Ovaitt, H. Mirletz, B. Mirletz and M. Prilliman, "Repowering PV Systems Demystified: Terms, Motives, Economics and Impacts," in *53rd IEEE PVSC*, 2025.

[10] M. A. Green, "Silicon Photovoltaic Modules: A Brief History of the First 50 Years," *Prog. Photovolt: Res. Appl.,* vol. 13, pp. 447-455, 2005.

[11] C. R. Osterwald and T. J. McMahon, "History of accelerated and qualification testing of terrestrial photovoltaic modules: A literature review," *Prog. Photovolt: Res. Appl.,* vol. 17, pp. 11-33, 2009.

[12] IRENA (2025); Nemet (2009); Farmer and Lafond (2016), ""Solar photovoltaic module price" [dataset]," 2025.

[13] G. Masson, A. Van Rechem, M. de l'Epine and A. Jäger-Waldau, "Snapshot of Global PV Markets 2025," April 2025. [Online]. Available: https://iea-pvps.org/snapshot-reports/snapshot-2025/. [Accessed 25 Aug 2025].

[14] M. Köntges, G. Oreski, U. Jahn, M. Herz, P. Hacke and K.-A. Weiss, "Assessment of Photovoltaic Module Failures in the Field," IEA PVPS Task 13, 2017.

[15] M. Libra, D. Mrázek, I. Tyukhov, L. Severová, V. Poulek, J. Mach, T. Šubrt, V. Beránek, R. Svoboda and J. Sedláček, "Reduced real lifetime of PV panels – Economic consequences," *Solar Energy,* vol. 259, pp. 229-234, 2023.

[16] E. C. Palmiotti, M. Springer, J. Zuboy, T. J. Silverman, J. L. Braid, D. C. Jordan, S. Rabade and T. M. Barnes, "Growing Panes: Investigating the PV Technology Trends Behind Frequent Early Failures in Modern Glass–Glass Modules," *IEEE Journal of Photovoltaics,* vol. 15, no. 2, pp. 297-308, 2025.

[17] "China moves to curb solar overcapacity, stabilize pricing," PV Magazine, 7 July 2025. [Online]. Available: https://www.pv-magazine.com/2025/07/07/china-moves-to-curb-solar-overcapacity-stabilize-pricing/. [Accessed 19 September 2025].

[18] C. Buerhop, O. Stroyuk, O. Mashkov, A. Barabash, J. Hauch and I. Peters, "Polymer encapsulation impact on potential-induced degradation in PV modules revealed by a multi-modal field study," *Solar Energy Materials and Solar Cells,* vol. 277, p. 113111, 2024.

[19] F. Thome, P. Meßmer, S. Mack, E. Schnabel, F. Schindler, W. Kwapil and M. Schubert, "UV-Induced Degradation of Industrial PERC, TOPCon, and HJT Solar Cells: The Next Big Reliability Challenge?," *Solar RRL,* vol. 8, no. 23, p. 2400628, 2024.

[20] "Photovoltaic Module Reliability Model Based on Field Degradation Studies," *Prog. Photovolt: Res. Appl.,* vol. 16, no. 5, pp. 419-433, 2008.

[21] G. Oreski, J. S. Stein, G. C. Eder, K. Berger, L. Bruckman, R. French, J. Vedde and K.-A. Weiß, "Motivation, benefits, and challenges for new photovoltaic material & module developments," *Progress in Energy,* vol. 4, no. 3, p. 032003, 2022.

[22] V. Naumann, D. Lausch, S. Großer, M. Werner, S. Swatek, C. Hagendorf and J. Bagdahn, "Microstructural Analysis of Crystal Defects Leading to Potential-Induced Degradation (PID) of Si Solar Cells," *Energy Procedia,* vol. 33, pp. 76-83, 2013.

[23] Moffitt, S. L., S. Uličná, S.-S. Jhang, P.-C. Pan, M. Owen-Bellini, P. Hacke, M. D. Kempe, J. Tracy, K. R. Choudhury, L. T. Schelhas and X. Gu, "PVDF-based backsheet cracking: Mapping in situ phase evolution by X-ray scattering," *Solar Energy Materials and Solar Cells,* vol. 282, p. 113355, 2025.

[24] "New insights on LeTID/BO-LID in p-type mono-crystalline silicon," *Solar Energy Materials and Solar Cells,* vol. 226, p. 111085, 2021.

[25] M. U. Khan, C. Sen, M. Pollard, T. Huang, M. Gao, R. Lv, Y. Yu, X. Wu, H. Wang, X. Wang and B. Hoex, "UV-induced degradation in TOPCon solar cells: Hydrogen dynamics and impact of UV wavelength," *Solar Energy Materials and Solar Cells,* vol. 294, p. 113895, 2026.

[26] C. Sen, H. Wang, M. U. Khan, J. Fu, X. Wu, X. Wang and B. Hoex, "Buyer aware: Three new failure modes in TOPCon modules absent from PERC technology," *Solar Energy Materials and Solar Cells,* vol. 272, p. 112877, 2024.

[27] R. Heidrich, M. Lüdemann, A. Mordvinkin and R. Gottschalg, "Diffusion of UV Additives in Ethylene-Vinyl Acetate Copolymer Encapsulants and the Impact on Polymer Reliability," *EEE Journal of Photovoltaics,* vol. 14, no. 1, pp. 131-139, 2024.

[28] G. C. Eder, Y. Voronko, G. Oreski, Mühleisen, M. Knausz, A. Omazic, A. Rainer, C. Hirschl and H. Sonnleitner, "Error analysis of aged modules with cracked polyamide backsheets," *Solar Energy Materials and Solar Cells,* vol. 203, p. 110194, 2019.

[29] C. Buerhop-Lutz, T. Pickel, O. Stroyuk, J. Hauch and I. M. Peters, "Insulation resistance in relation to distribution of backsheet types in strings and inverters," *Solar Energy Materials and Solar Cells,* vol. 246, p. 111913, 2022.

[30] C. Bucher, J. Wandel and D. Joss, "Life Expectancy of PV Inverters and Optimizers in Residential PV Systems," in *WCPEC-8*, Milan, 2022.

[31] W. Hobbs, "Storms and Other Events: Experiences with Cell Cracks," in *PV Reliability Workshop*, Lakewood, 2020.

[32] Trina Solar, "The Trina Solar Vertex Module White Paper," May 2020. [Online]. Available: https://solar-media.s3.amazonaws.com/assets/DIGITAL%20SERIES%202020/SSFDigital20/Vertex%20by%20Trina%20Solar/Vertex%20White%20Paper.pdf. [Accessed 24 September 2025].

[33] Trina Solar, "Trina Solar partners with five other PV manufacturers to launch 700W+ Photovoltaic Open Innovation Ecological Alliance," December 2023. [Online]. Available: https://www.trinasolar.com/eu-en/resources/newsroom/eu-trina-solar-partners-five-other-pv-manufacturers-launch-700w-photovoltaic-open. [Accessed 24 September 2025].

[34] H. Inano, Y. Akemoto and K. Asakura, "Impact of silicon and other contaminants on the melting process in photovoltaic glass recycling," *Journal of Non-Crystalline Solids,* vol. 666, p. 123724, October 2025.

42nd European Photovoltaic Solar Energy Conference and Exhibition

This presentation was selected by the Sc. Committee of the EU PVSEC 2025 for submission of a full paper to one of the EU PVSEC's collaborating peer-reviewed journals.

RENEWABLE ENERGY COMMUNITIES AND CITIZEN PARTICIPATION IN TECHNOLOGICAL AND SOCIAL INNOVATIONS

Cristina Sanz-Cuadrado, Kiane Alves e Silva, Luis Narvarte, Ana B. Cristóbal
Instituto de Energía Solar, Universidad Politécnica de Madrid
C/Alan Turing s/n, 28031 Madrid, Spain
cristina.sanzc@upm.es; kiane.asilva@alumnos.upm.es; luis.narvarte@upm.es; anabelen.cristobal@upm.es

ABSTRACT: Citizen engagement represents a crucial concern in innovation processes. Reaching high commitment and active levels for participatory actions is still challenging. This research seeks to illustrate the crucial role citizens have played in fostering both technological and social innovations within the low-carbon energy sector, particularly in the photovoltaic sector by analyzing the levels of participation defined by Arnstein's classification. To achieve this objective, this work examines real-world experiences that exemplify effective citizen engagement in innovation processes. Firstly, a comprehensive overview of the role citizens played in deploying technical innovations in the energy sector is described. It illustrates how these innovations have been enhanced through collaboration with citizens or have emerged directly from their involvement, combining original material with a thorough bibliographic review. Additionally, the paper delves into the levels of engagement observed in Energy Communities (ECs), one of the most significant social innovations. By exploring and analyzing 34 ECs, it becomes evident that the transition from passive to active citizen-led innovations remains a challenge. However, some inspirational examples are shown. By positioning citizens as vital agents of change, this exploration underscores their importance in the transition to sustainable energy systems and aims to inspire others to follow the described cases.
Keywords: technological innovation, social innovation, photovoltaic, citizen participation, energy communities

1 INTRODUCTION

To respond to the challenges of the climate change, innovation is one of the key responses, especially in the development of solutions to mitigate its impacts. Traditionally, innovation has been driven by a "triple helix" model [1], [2], consisting of the collaboration between industry, government, and academia. However, in the last decade, the role of citizens has been recognized as crucial in innovation ecosystems [3], [4], [5], [6], [7], [8], [9], [10] particularly in addressing the climate change [11], [12], [13]. With this new paradigm, known as the "quadruple helix" model, innovation move beyond centered innovations to citizen-centered processes, acknowledging citizens as both end-users and integral members of democratic systems. Such a responsible approach to development involves navigating Arnstein's Ladder of Citizen Participation [15].

Social acceptance of renewable energy is a key factor in the deployment of renewable energy technologies [15], [16], [17]. Since the introduction of its concept in 2006 [18], it has been studied in the energy transition planning, reporting the role of citizens as end-users in the literature [19], [20], [21].

However, the lack of meaningful citizen participation, where the highest levels of Arnstein's ladder, is observed in many initiatives that often adopt a paternalistic approach or a tokenistic strategy. Chilvers et al. [22] analyzed 257 public engagement initiatives in low-carbon energy revealing that most citizen participation efforts remain confined to the lower rungs of Arnstein's Ladder and are often institutionally driven rather than citizen-led. This underscores the gap in achieving deeper and transformative engagement.

The definition of social innovation in the energy transition came in 2018. It addresses the social and community well-being in innovations related to the low-carbon transition [23]. In this regard, the literature points to a growing trend developing mechanisms that empower citizens to co-design the energy transition and design citizen-driven business models [24], [25], [26].

In relation to this trend towards social innovations in the energy transition, the concept of energy communities (ECs) [27], [28] has also emerged as an innovative approach that involves citizens in the reconfiguration of energy systems [29] [28]. These collective initiatives represent citizen-driven energy actions to advance the energy transition [30], [31]. However, the idea of communities of energy [32] has existed for decades, empowering citizens as drivers of change and allowing them to take an active role in innovation in several ways. The novelty of the concept of ECs resides in its capacity to undertake a range of activities and its role in promoting real social impact by encouraging active and meaningful citizen participation.

Through this work, we aim to honor the anonymous contributions of countless citizens who have played a pivotal role in advancing science and technology, especially in the photovoltaic (PV) sector. By bringing to light stories that may have been overlooked, we seek to inspire the PV scientific and technological community to adopt diverse participatory methodologies to their own technical innovations' deployment. At the same time, we want to highlight a paradox: even in social innovations closely tied to this field, such as the fancy ECs, the urgency to capitalize on opportunities often overshadows the very essence of community involvement. Ironically, this leads to the promotion of so-called social innovations with minimal genuine community participation.

The paper is organized as follows, firstly, the state-of-the-art section reviews two cases where citizen participation was instrumental in driving technological innovation process in the PV sector during the last decades of the 20th century.

After this brief review, the paper explores the development of ECs, one of the most dynamic social innovation processes in the European energy sector. This section will examine the level of engagement of participants in those innovative initiatives aligning with Arnstein's levels of engagement. This is addressed through a comprehensive literature review, where we identified 34 ECs across Europe.

2 STATE-OF-THE-ART

In 1986, researchers developed projects utilizing Solar Home Systems (SHSs) [33] in Sierra del Segura, Spain. SHSs are one of the earliest examples of direct collaboration between citizens and researchers in the development of PV innovations. In this project, the value of the researcher-citizen partnerships is highlighted. This experience continued into the early 1990s in countries such as Algeria, Bolivia, Mexico, and Sri Lanka [34] [35], [36], [37] [38], [39]. Through innovative citizen science methodologies developed by researchers, they successfully established self-consumption standards for rural electrification tailored to different family typologies. This approach ensured "social acceptability" by focusing on practical solutions that resonated with local communities. Interestingly, even residents with little or no literacy participated actively by recording their household energy use through meters installed by the research team.

After the success of SHSs, the advantages of collaboration between researchers and end-users became evident in the deployment of PV water pumping systems, largely due to their decentralized nature. In 2002, the involvement of more than 1,300 household from two regions of Morocco resulted in the participation of 20,000 people in the recording of their daily water consumption habits [40]. These collaborations were essential to tailor the water pumps to local needs. Researchers developed and implemented a methodology [41] for introducing technological innovations in social groups, drawing on General Systems Theory [42] and the concepts of "hardware," "software," and "orgware". In this framework, the perceived needs of end-users play a crucial role, as evidenced by findings reported 12 years after the systems were installed [43].

A standout example of public involvement in PV research is the "Counting the Sun" program [44], which represents one of the first citizen science projects in this area. This project collaborated with the Dutch Public Authorities and engaged 5,000 household with PV installations. It consisted of an awareness campaign on domestic PV systems performance. Participants provided data in a citizen science initiative. Some challenges were faced since the accuracy of the citizen science data is a critical issue [45].

The potential collaboration of engaging citizens within the PV sector is recognized in GRECO project [46]. Participants collaborated in the identification and access to some of the oldest PV installations worldwide to develop studies on the aging and repair of PV modules.

Another successful project is MASLOWATEN [47] which demonstrated the cooperation of farmers and irrigation communities with researchers to create different mechanisms for PV irrigation demonstrators [48]. This example shows the implication of farmers in the design process that led to the creation of ad-hoc technical solutions.

Some other examples of citizen collaboration with researchers can be found in the literature.

3 ENERGY COMMUNITIES

Moving from technical innovations to social innovations this research aims to analyze current citizen participation in ECs, one of the latest mechanisms of social innovations that has recently gained greater notoriety and interest. According to the European Federation of Citizen Energy Cooperatives, there are currently 1,900 European energy cooperatives and around 1,250,000 citizens participating [30]. Furthermore, the European Commission estimated that by 2030 EC will hold 17% of wind and 21% of solar capacity [49].

3.1 Methodology

Although citizen participation is the hallmark of ECs, how citizens organize and take action within these communities can vary significantly and should be categorized into distinct types. A literature review of 34 ECs was conducted using Harzing's Publish or Perish application that includes Google Scholar and Scopus databases. Three search axes have been included in relation to the topic, the application and the scope. The keywords used for the research were: citizen science, social motivation, energy community, renewable energy, lessons learned, case study and state of the art.

After the bibliographic research, the ECs were categorized on three parameters. (a) Community membership (residential households, commercial businesses, industrial facilities, municipal entities, or specific groups based on geographical locations, such as islands). (b) Energy power range: Range 1 (0-500 kW), Range 2 (501-1,000 kW), Range 3 (1,001-10,000 kW), Range 4 (10,001-100,000 kW), and Range 5 (>100,001 kW). (c) Business model: Group 1 (neighborhood associations), Group 2 (municipal initiatives), Group 3 (regional cooperatives), and Group 4 (national and international cooperatives).

Each group has been analyzed according to these categorizations focusing on citizen participation level. This analysis aims to identify the categories in which participants demonstrate the highest levels of engagement and to understand the mechanisms that drive this involvement. The level of citizen participation has been adapted from Arnstein's theory to align with the explanations presented in the GRECO Practical Guide on Open Science [50], which categorizes engagement into six levels, from direct participation in the decision-making and operational processes of the EC, to limited engagement where information flows primarily from the community to its members and complete absence of citizen participation or engagement efforts. Fig. 1 summaries and illustrates the six levels defined in the GRECO.

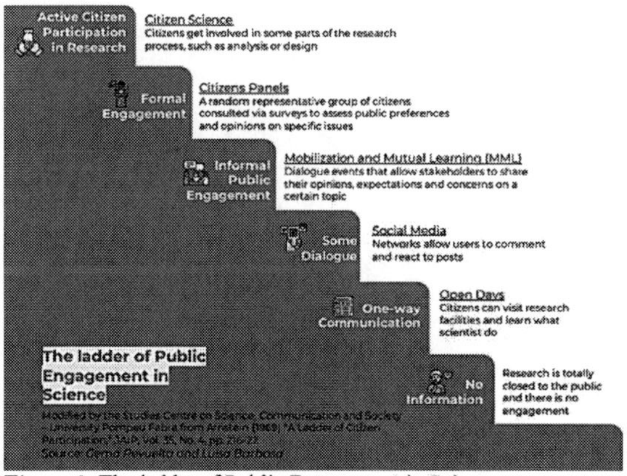

Figure 1: The ladder of Public Engagement in Science defined in GRECO [50].

3.2 Results

Regarding the 34 ECs analyzed and classified following the GRECO Practical Guide on Open Science, 32.4% of the cases achieve the highest level of citizen participation: Active Citizen Involvement (Fig. 2).

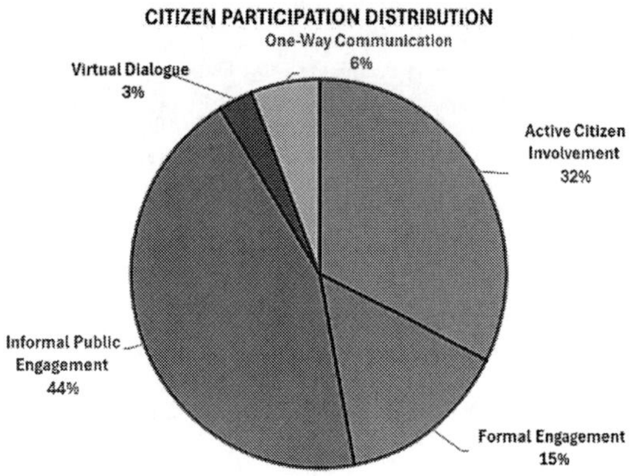

Figure 2: Distribution of citizen participation across the 34 ECs analyzed.

In the following, those ECs that reach the highest level of engagement (Active Citizen Involvement) are analyzed according to the three parameters that have been defined previously: community membership, range power and business model.

In terms of community membership, 36.4% of actively participating ECs are island-based projects, followed by 27.3% of residential ECs (Fig. 3).

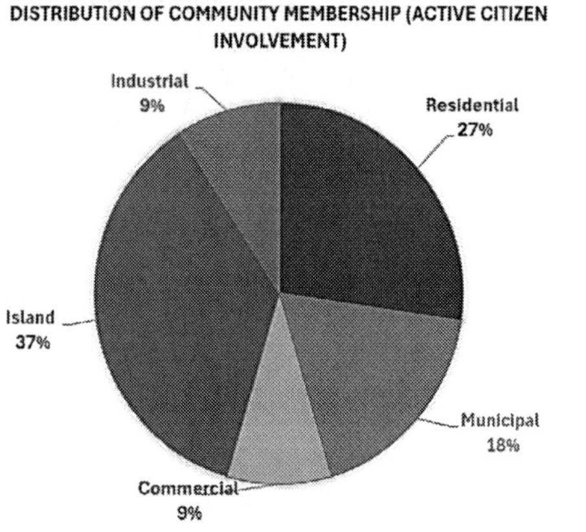

Figure 3: Distribution of ECs regarding community membership classification (Active Citizen Involvement)

Regarding the power range (Fig. 4), most of the ECs with active participation have power ranges below 500kW, corresponding to Group 1 (54.5%). In addition, it is observed that none of the ECs with installed power above 100,000kW have Active Citizen Involvement.

Finally, the predominant business model in the ECs with active participation corresponds to neighborhood associations (63.6%), which are included in Group 1 (see Fig. 5). As it was observed in the case of range power, national and international cooperatives do not reach the highest levels of citizen participation.

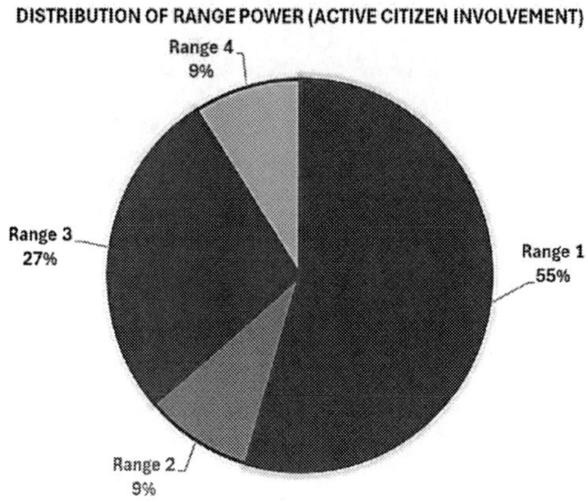

Figure 4: Distribution of ECs regarding range power classification (Active Citizen Involvement)

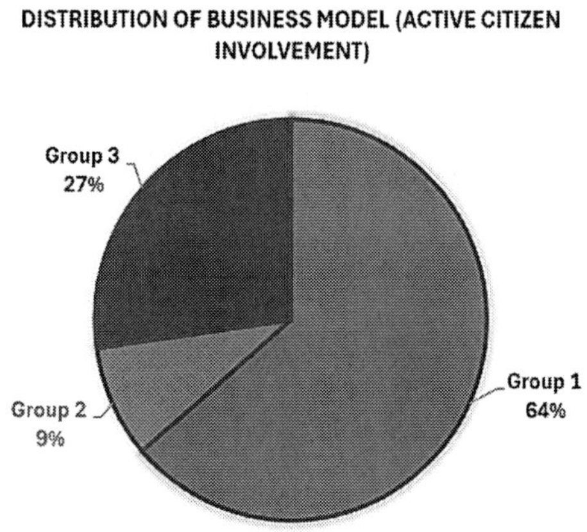

Figure 5: Distribution of ECs regarding business model classification (Active Citizen Involvement)

4 CONCLUSIONS

4.1 Key lessons learned

This study demonstrates how citizens can move beyond traditional surveys and opinion polls—while still acknowledging their complementary role—toward fostering responsible innovations that better meet societal needs. Public engagement plays a key role in achieving meaningful citizen collaboration in driving technical and social innovations.

In this regard, some key lessons can be drawn from our research.

- Researchers must maintain direct involvement to build trust and foster meaningful collaboration.
- Researchers must develop activities aligned within a framework of real, sustained partnership.

- Researchers must carefully design their activities, considering factors such as methodology, language barriers, and ways to measure participant satisfaction.
- Researchers must ensure compliance with relevant legislation and ethical guidelines, particularly when handling personal data.
- Researchers must address the challenge posed by citizen science activities, especially regarding the accuracy and reliability of data collected by non-expert participants.

4.2 Participation in Energy Communities

Social innovations, such as ECs, effectively promote citizen engagement by aligning technical solutions with social needs. Our analysis underscores the importance of smaller initiatives (neighborhood and municipal projects), which enable participation in a more personal way. This aligns with some successful examples such as CERCA in Spain [51] and the Feldheim community in Germany [52]. Small-scale initiatives prioritize social needs than economic benefits, providing a wide sense of belonging to the community.

In contrast, national and international ECs demonstrated to be more impersonal, and participation is often driven to obtain economic profits.

To conclude, these collective community-driven EC definitively pave the way for citizen science in a broad sense. ECs redefine citizens' traditional roles as mere end-users by transforming them into local micro-investors—through mechanisms such as loans or participation accounts.

ACKNOWLEDGEMENT

This project has received funding from the European Union's Horizon 2020 research and innovation programme under grant agreement No 101036418.

5 REFERENCES

[1] H. Etzkowitz, "Innovation in Innovation: The Triple Helix of University-Industry-Government Relations," *http://dx.doi.org/10.1177/05390184030423002*, vol. 42, no. 3, pp. 293–337, Sep. 2003, doi: 10.1177/05390184030423002.

[2] H. Etzkowitz and L. Leydesdorff, "The dynamics of innovation: from National Systems and 'Mode 2' to a Triple Helix of university–industry–government relations," *Res Policy*, vol. 29, no. 2, pp. 109–123, Feb. 2000, doi: 10.1016/S0048-7333(99)00055-4.

[3] "Why researchers should resolve to engage in 2017," *Nature*, vol. 541, no. 7635, pp. 5–5, Jan. 2017, doi: 10.1038/541005a.

[4] European Commission and D.-G. for R. and Innovation, *Re-finding industry – Defining innovation*. Publications Office, 2018. doi: doi/10.2777/927953.

[5] P. O. of the E. Union, "Outreach to newcomers and societal engagement in industrial technologies : reports of the Horizon 2020 Advisory Group on nanotechnologies, advanced materials, biotechnology, and advanced manufacturing and processing (NMBP).," Dec. 2018, doi: 10.2777/810639.

[6] European Commission, *LAB – FAB – APP — Investing in the European future we want*. Publications Office, 2017. doi: doi/10.2777/477357.

[7] C. Vélot, "Scientists and Civil Society Must Move Together toward a New Science," *Front Public Health*, vol. 4, May 2016, doi: 10.3389/fpubh.2016.00096.

[8] E. Pain, "To be a responsible researcher, reach out and listen," *Science (1979)*, Jan. 2017, doi: 10.1126/science.caredit.a1700006.

[9] B. K. Sovacool, "What are we doing here? Analyzing fifteen years of energy scholarship and proposing a social science research agenda," *Energy Res Soc Sci*, vol. 1, pp. 1–29, Mar. 2014, doi: 10.1016/j.erss.2014.02.003.

[10] European Commission, "Open innovation, open science, open to the world – A vision for Europe," Publications Office, 2015. doi: doi/10.2777/061652.

[11] EUROPEAN COMMISSION, "COM(2016)763 - Accelerating Clean Energy Innovation - EU monitor," Brussels. Accessed: Jul. 11, 2024. [Online]. Available: https://www.eumonitor.eu/9353000/1/j9vvik7m1c3gyxp/vk9u7wddoazh

[12] World Energy Council, "World Energy Scenarios- Composing energy futures to 2050," 2013, Accessed: Jul. 11, 2024. [Online]. Available: https://www.worldenergy.org/assets/downloads/World-Energy-Scenarios_Composing-energy-futures-to-2050_Full-report1.pdf

[13] Y. Cabannes, "Contributions of Participatory Budgeting to climate change adaptation and mitigation. Current local practices around the world & lessons from the field," 2020.

[14] S. R. Arnstein, "A Ladder Of Citizen Participation," *J Am Inst Plann*, vol. 35, no. 4, pp. 216–224, 1969, doi: 10.1080/01944366908977225.

[15] B. K. Sovacool and P. Lakshmi Ratan, "Conceptualizing the acceptance of wind and solar electricity," *Renewable and Sustainable Energy Reviews*, vol. 16, no. 7, pp. 5268–5279, Sep. 2012, doi: 10.1016/j.rser.2012.04.048.

[16] P. Zhai and E. D. Williams, "Analyzing consumer acceptance of photovoltaics (PV) using fuzzy logic model," *Renew Energy*, vol. 41, pp. 350–357, May 2012, doi: 10.1016/j.renene.2011.11.041.

[17] K. Buhr and V. Wibeck, "Communication approaches for carbon capture and storage: Underlying assumptions of limited versus extensive public engagement," *Energy Res Soc Sci*, vol. 3, pp. 5–12, Sep. 2014, doi: 10.1016/j.erss.2014.05.004.

[18] R. Wüstenhagen, M. Wolsink, and M. J. Bürer, "Social acceptance of renewable energy innovation: An introduction to the concept," *Energy Policy*, vol. 35, no. 5, pp. 2683–2691, May 2007, doi: 10.1016/j.enpol.2006.12.001.

[19] T. Sharpton, T. Lawrence, and M. Hall, "Drivers and barriers to public acceptance of future energy sources and grid expansion in the United States,"

Renewable and Sustainable Energy Reviews, vol. 126, p. 109826, Jul. 2020, doi: 10.1016/j.rser.2020.109826.

[20] M. Sarrica, S. Brondi, P. Cottone, and B. M. Mazzara, "One, no one, one hundred thousand energy transitions in Europe: The quest for a cultural approach," *Energy Res Soc Sci*, vol. 13, pp. 1–14, Mar. 2016, doi: 10.1016/j.erss.2015.12.019.

[21] B. K. Sovacool, "Rejecting renewables: The socio-technical impediments to renewable electricity in the United States," *Energy Policy*, vol. 37, no. 11, pp. 4500–4513, Nov. 2009, doi: 10.1016/j.enpol.2009.05.073.

[22] J. Chilvers, R. Bellamy, H. Pallett, and T. Hargreaves, "A systemic approach to mapping participation with low-carbon energy transitions," *Nature Energy 2021 6:3*, vol. 6, no. 3, pp. 250–259, Mar. 2021, doi: 10.1038/s41560-020-00762-w.

[23] T. Hoppe and G. De Vries, "Social Innovation and the Energy Transition," *Sustainability*, vol. 11, no. 1, p. 141, Dec. 2018, doi: 10.3390/su11010141.

[24] T. Höfer and R. Madlener, "A participatory stakeholder process for evaluating sustainable energy transition scenarios," *Energy Policy*, vol. 139, p. 111277, Apr. 2020, doi: 10.1016/j.enpol.2020.111277.

[25] B. Lennon, N. P. Dunphy, and E. Sanvicente, "Community acceptability and the energy transition: a citizens' perspective," *Energy Sustain Soc*, vol. 9, no. 1, p. 35, Dec. 2019, doi: 10.1186/s13705-019-0218-z.

[26] A. Ambrose, "Walking with Energy: Challenging energy invisibility and connecting citizens with energy futures through participatory research," *Futures*, vol. 117, p. 102528, Mar. 2020, doi: 10.1016/j.futures.2020.102528.

[27] European Union, *DIRECTIVES DIRECTIVE (EU) 2018/2001 OF THE EUROPEAN PARLIAMENT AND OF THE COUNCIL of 11 December 2018 on the promotion of the use of energy from renewable sources (recast) (Text with EEA relevance)*. 2018. Accessed: Jan. 29, 2024. [Online]. Available: https://eur-lex.europa.eu/legal-content/EN/TXT/PDF/?uri=CELEX:32018L2001

[28] M. European Union, "Directive (EU) 2019/944 of the European Parliament and of the Council of 5 June 2019 on common rules for the internal market for electricity and amending Directive 2012/27/EU," *Off. J. Eur. Union*, vol. 158, pp. 125–199, 2019.

[29] E. Commission and D.-G. for Energy, *Clean energy for all Europeans*. Publications Office, 2019. doi: https://data.europa.eu/doi/10.2833/9937.

[30] "REScoop." Accessed: Oct. 06, 2023. [Online]. Available: https://www.rescoop.eu/

[31] European Comission, "Energy communities." Accessed: Oct. 09, 2023. [Online]. Available: https://energy.ec.europa.eu/topics/markets-and-consumers/energy-communities_en

[32] E. Atutxa, I. Zubero, and I. Calvo-Sotomayor, "Scalability of Low Carbon Energy Communities in Spain: An Empiric Approach from the Renewed Commons Paradigm," *Energies 2020, Vol. 13, Page 5045*, vol. 13, no. 19, p. 5045, Sep. 2020, doi: 10.3390/EN13195045.

[33] E. Lorenzo, A. Krezinger, and M. Montero, "Consumo en Viviendas Rurales Fotovoltaicas Españolas," *Mundo Electrónico* , vol. 168, pp. 109–115, 1986.

[34] J. Aguilera and E. Lorenzo, "PV rural electrification in the Bolivian altiplane," in *1st World Renewable Energy Congress* , 1989, pp. 241–245.

[35] B. Yaici, S. Labd, and E. Lorenzo, "PV Electrification of a Village in a hot-arid area of Algeria," in *Proceedings 10th European Photovoltaic Solar Energy Conference and Exhibition*, Lisbon, 1991, pp. 1105–1106.

[36] J. M. Huacuz and J. Agredano, "Beyond the grid: photovoltaic electrification in rural Mexico," *Progress in Photovoltaics: Research and Applications*, vol. 6, no. 5, pp. 379–395, Sep. 1998, doi: 10.1002/(SICI)1099-159X(1998090)6:5<379::AID-PIP238>3.0.CO;2-Z.

[37] J. M. Huacuz and A. M. Martínez, "Renewable energy rural electrification: Sustainability aspects of the Mexican programme in practice," *Nat Resour Forum*, vol. 19, no. 3, pp. 223–231, Aug. 1995, doi: 10.1111/j.1477-8947.1995.tb00612.x.

[38] L. Gunaratne, "Solar Photovoltaics in Sri Lanka: a Short History," *Progress in Photovoltaics: Research and Applications* , vol. 2, pp. 307–316, 1994.

[39] L. Gunaratne, "Using the principles of marketing for commercial dissemination of solar PV in Sri Lanka," . *Energy for Sustainable Development* , vol. 2, no. 4, pp. 41–45, 1995.

[40] L. Navarte, E. Lorenzo, and M. Aandam, "Patrones de consumo de agua en sistemas rurales de bombeo fotovoltaico," *Era Solar*, vol. 109, pp. 20–29, 2002.

[41] L. Navarte, E. Lonrezo, and M. Aandam, "Lessons from a PV Pumping Programme in South Morocco," *Prog. Photovolt: Res. Appl.*, vol. 13, pp. 261–270, 2005.

[42] E. Rogers, *Diffusion of Innovations*. The Free Press, 1983.

[43] L. Navarte and E. Lorenzo, "Sustainability of PV water pumping programmes: 12-years of successful experience," *Prog. Photovolt: Res. Appl*, vol. 18, pp. 291–298, 2010.

[44] W. G. J. H. M. van Sark *et al.*, "'Counting the Sun' – a Dutch Public Awareness Campaign on PV Performance," in *29th European Photovoltaic Solar Energy Conference and Exhibition*, 2014, pp. 4161–4164. doi: 10.4229/EUPVSEC20142014-7AV.6.72.

[45] O. Tsafarakis *et al.*, "Three years experience in a Dutch public awareness campaign on photovoltaic system performance," *IET Renewable Power Generation*, vol. 11, no. 10, pp. 1229–1233, Aug. 2017, doi: 10.1049/iet-rpg.2016.1037.

[46] "GRECO- Putting Open Science into action in an engineering project - Greco Project." Accessed: Oct. 29, 2024. [Online]. Available: https://www.greco-project.eu/

[47] "MASLOWATEN: Market uptake of an innovative irrigation Solution based on low water-energy consumption." European Project 640771. Accessed: Jul. 11, 2024. [Online]. Available: https://cordis.europa.eu/project/id/640771

[48] R. H. Almeida *et al.*, "Development and Test of Solutions to Enlarge the Power of PV Irrigation and Application to a 140 kW PV-Diesel Representative Case," *Energies 2018, Vol. 11, Page 3538*, vol. 11, no. 12, p. 3538, Dec. 2018, doi: 10.3390/EN11123538.

[49] European Commission; Directorate-General for Energy, *COMMISSION STAFF WORKING DOCUMENT IMPACT ASSESSMENT Accompanying the document Proposal for a Directive of the European Parliament and of the Council on the promotion of the use of energy from renewable sources (recast)*. 2016.

[50] L. Barbosa, E. Albiñana, C. Cañizo, A. Cristóbal, and G. Revuelta, "Practical guide on Open Science for researchers," 2021, doi: 10.5281/zenodo.3968115.

[51] "CERCA Energia | Comunidad de Energías Renovables de la Comarca de Calatayud." Accessed: May 05, 2025. [Online]. Available: https://cercaenergia.com/

[52] J. Young and M. Brans, "Analysis of factors affecting a shift in a local energy system towards 100% renewable energy community," *J Clean Prod*, vol. 169, pp. 117–124, Dec. 2017, doi: 10.1016/J.JCLEPRO.2017.08.023.

42nd European Photovoltaic Solar Energy Conference and Exhibition

Renewable Energy Communities and Citizen Participation in Technological and Social Innovations

Cristina Sanz-Cuadrado*, Kiane Alves e Silva, Luis Narvarte, Ana B. Cristóbal

Instituto de Energía Solar, Universidad Politécnica de Madrid, Madrid (SPAIN)

INSTITUTO DE ENERGÍA SOLAR

POLITÉCNICA

INSTITUTO
DE ENERGÍA
SOLAR

Image generated by Artificial Intelligence using Canva's AI Image Generator

POLITÉCNICA

Innovation: classic model vs. responsible paradigm

INSTITUTO DE ENERGÍA SOLAR

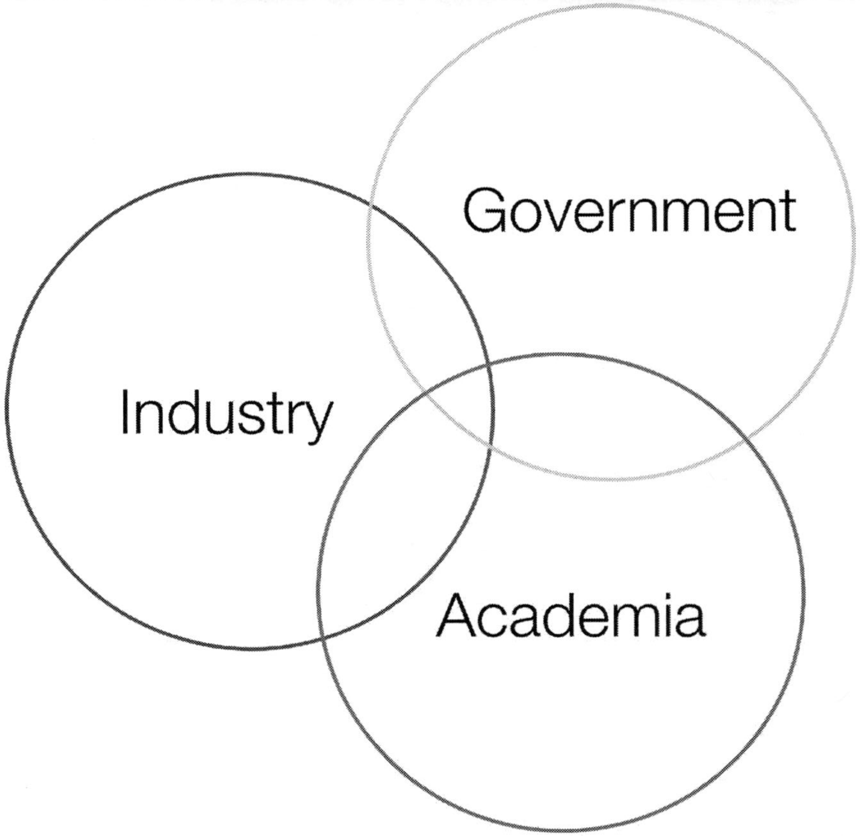

POLITÉCNICA

Innovation: classic model vs. responsible paradigm

INSTITUTO DE ENERGÍA SOLAR

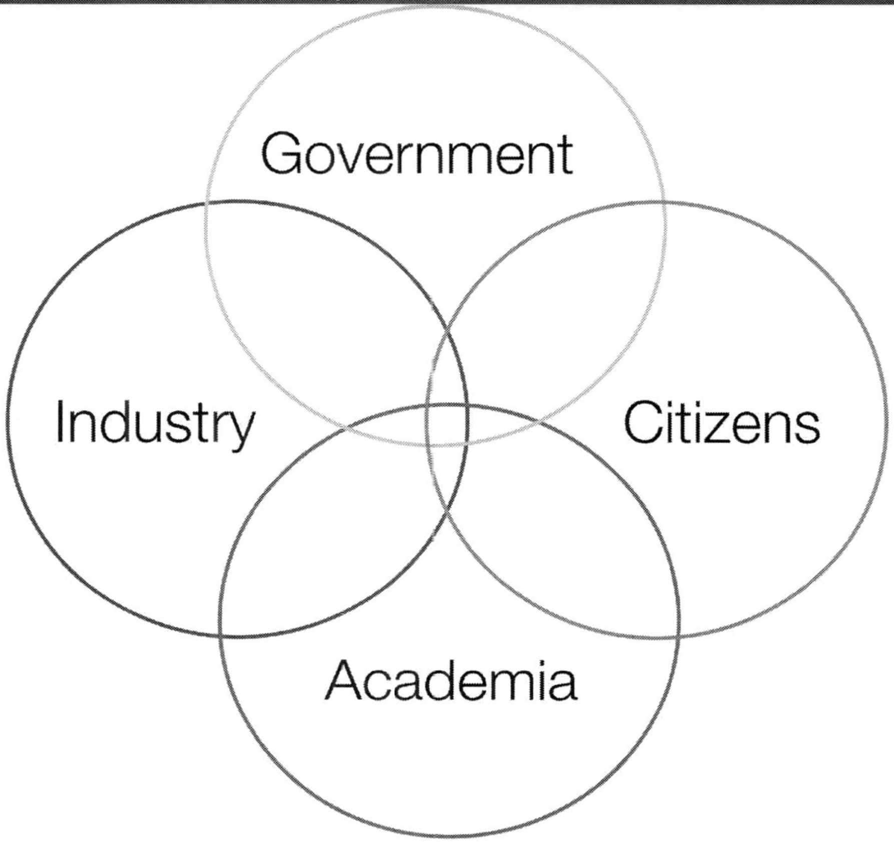

- Social acceptance
- Behavioral change
- Implementation of new technologies and policies successfully

POLITÉCNICA

Objectives

INSTITUTO DE ENERGÍA SOLAR

- To unveil initiatives where citizens play a decisive role in driving technological and social innovations within the low-carbon energy sector
- Review several cases where citizen participation has been instrumental in technological innovation processes
- Energy Communities: Are ECs mechanisms for authentic citizen-led initiatives, or are they merely repurposing citizens as passive consumers under a new guise?

POLITÉCNICA

Solar Home Systems

INSTITUTO DE ENERGÍA SOLAR

- Rural electrification in the 1980s
- Sierra del Segura (Andalusia, Spain)
- Replication: Bolivia, Brazil, Mexico, Algeria, Sri Lanka…
- Citizen participation:
  - Listening to the real needs of citizens
  - Definition of a standard for technical specifications for SHSs based on the needs
  - Citizen science: coping the "symbols" of the counter due to illiteracy

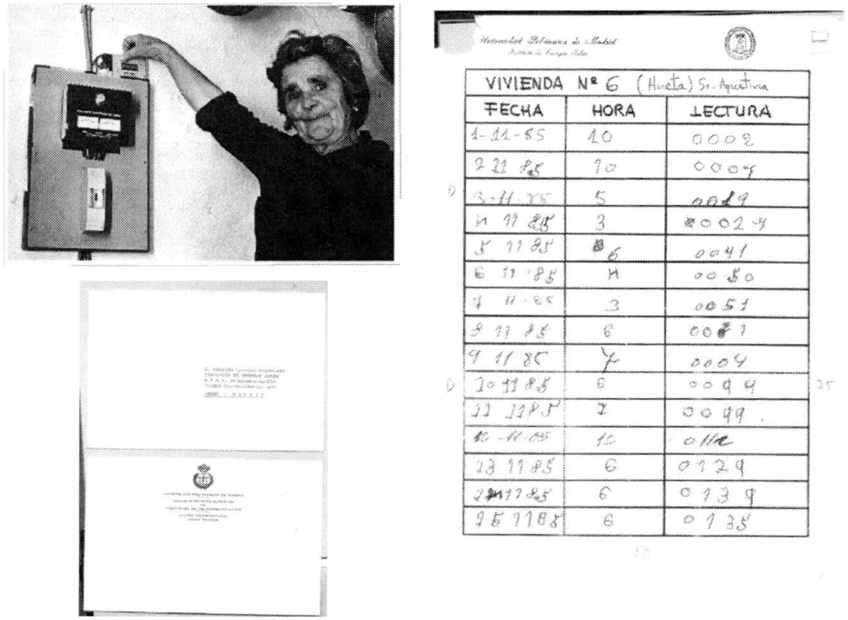

Figure 1. Details of the data recorded by the villagers in 1985 and the pre-addressed envelope to where they sent the data sheets. (Woman picture taken from [54])

Solar Home Systems

INSTITUTO DE ENERGÍA SOLAR

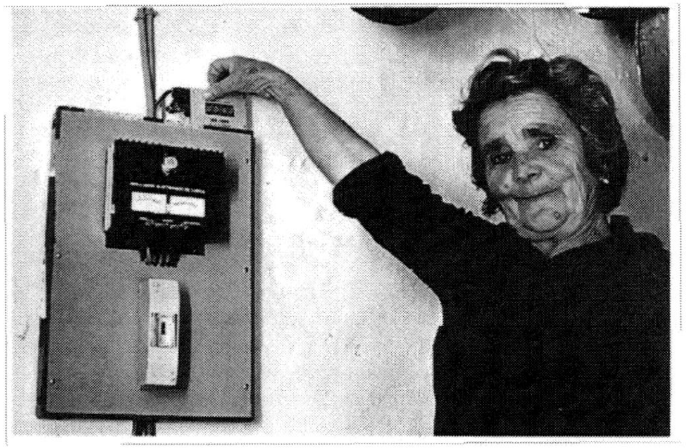

Universidad Politécnica de Madrid
Instituto de Energía Solar

VIVIENDA Nº 6 (Hueta) Sr. Agustina		
FECHA	HORA	LECTURA
1-11-85	10	0002
2 11 85	10	0004
3-11-85	5	0019
4 11 85	3	0027
5 11 85	6	0041
6 11 85	4	0050
7 11-85	3	0051
8 11 85	6	0071
9 11 85	7	0004
10 11 85	6	0094
11 11 85	7	0099.
12-11-85	12	0112
13 11 85	6	0129
14 11 85	6	0139
15 11 85	6	0135

POLITÉCNICA

Solar Home Systems

INSTITUTO DE ENERGÍA SOLAR

	5 11 85	6	0041
	6 11 '85	H	0050
	7 11 - 85	3	0051
	8 11 85	6	0081
	9 11 85	7	0004
D	10 11 85	6	0094
	11 11 85	7	0099 .
	12 - 11 - 85	11	011[illegible]

75

PV water pumping systems

INSTITUTO DE ENERGÍA SOLAR

- 2002 – Morocco
- 1,300 households -> 20,000 people participating
- Replication: Algeria, Tunisia
- Methodology: according to users needs -> Citizen collaborations were essential for tailoring the water pumps to local needs

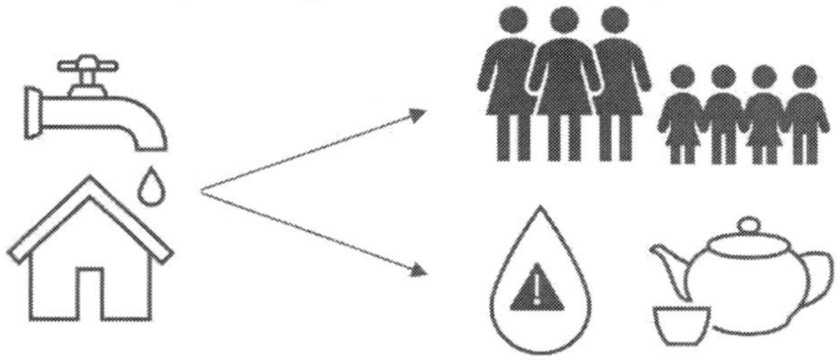

- Technological innovations: minimizing the level of innovation to be accepted by users

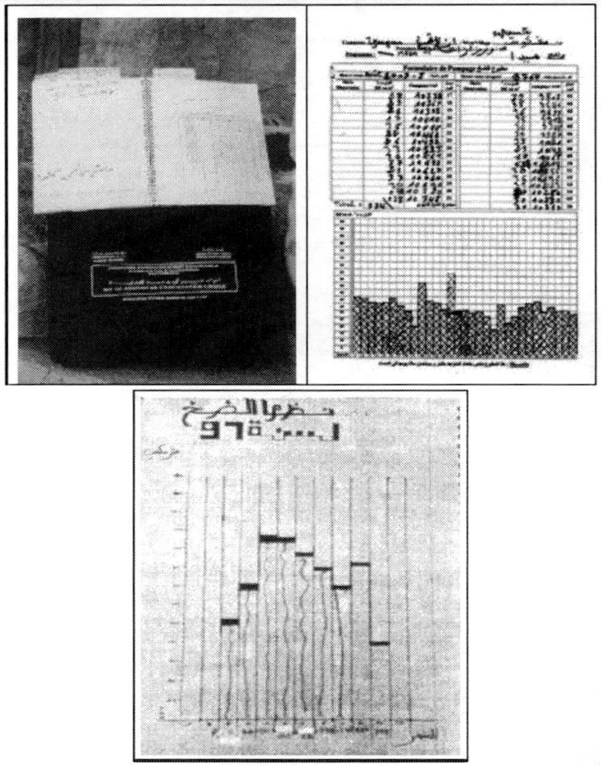

Figure 7. a) Register of water meter figures in each house; b) sketch of the total daily consumption in Iferd [95]; c) register and sketch of the monthly pumped water volume in Iferd

POLITÉCNICA

Energy Communities

INSTITUTO DE ENERGÍA SOLAR

- Collective participation in the energy system
- Idea of communities of energy: existed for decades
  - Empowering citizens as drivers of change
- Analysis of 34 Energy Communities across Europe
- Parameters of classification:
  - Community membership
  - Energy power range
  - Business model
  - Public Engagement in Science (GRECO)

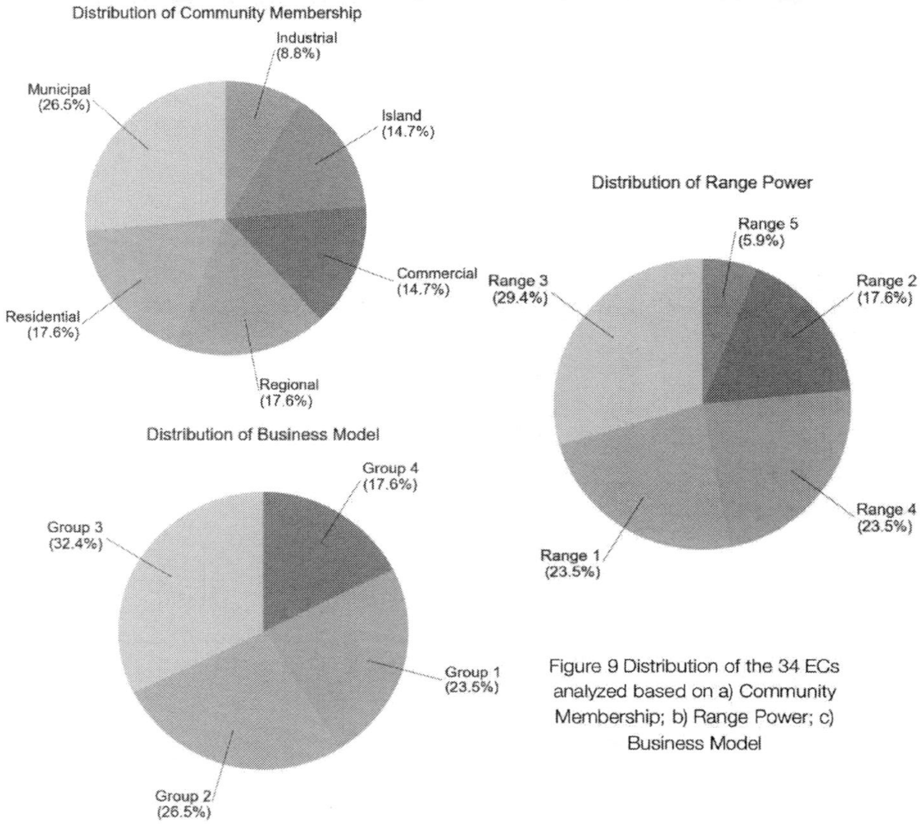

Figure 9 Distribution of the 34 ECs analyzed based on a) Community Membership; b) Range Power; c) Business Model

POLITÉCNICA

Energy Communities

INSTITUTO DE ENERGÍA SOLAR

- Classification based on the ladder of Public Engagement in Science (GRECO)

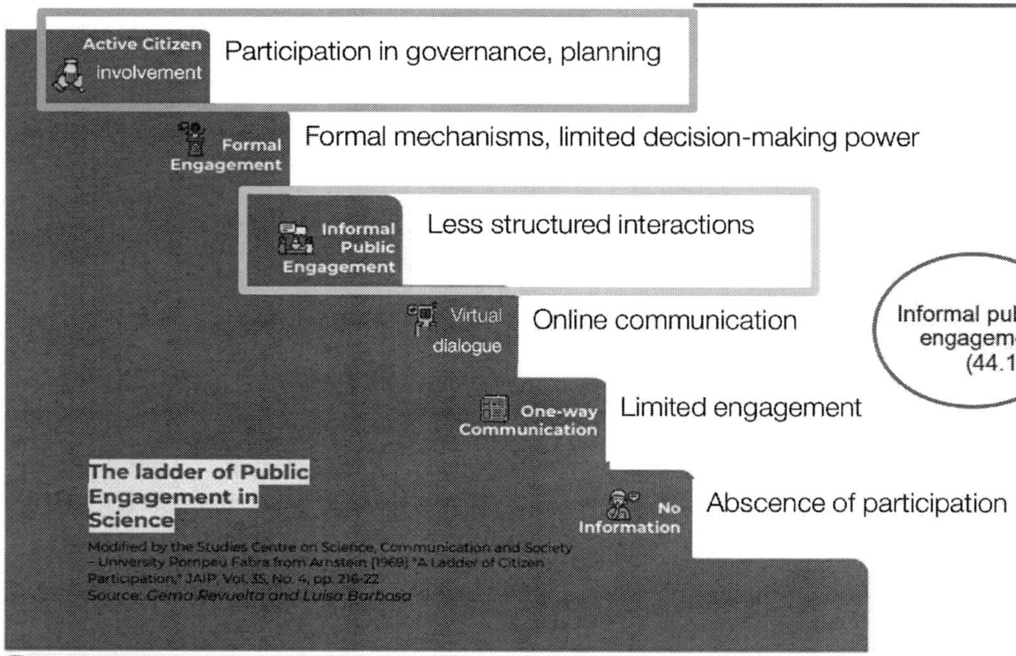

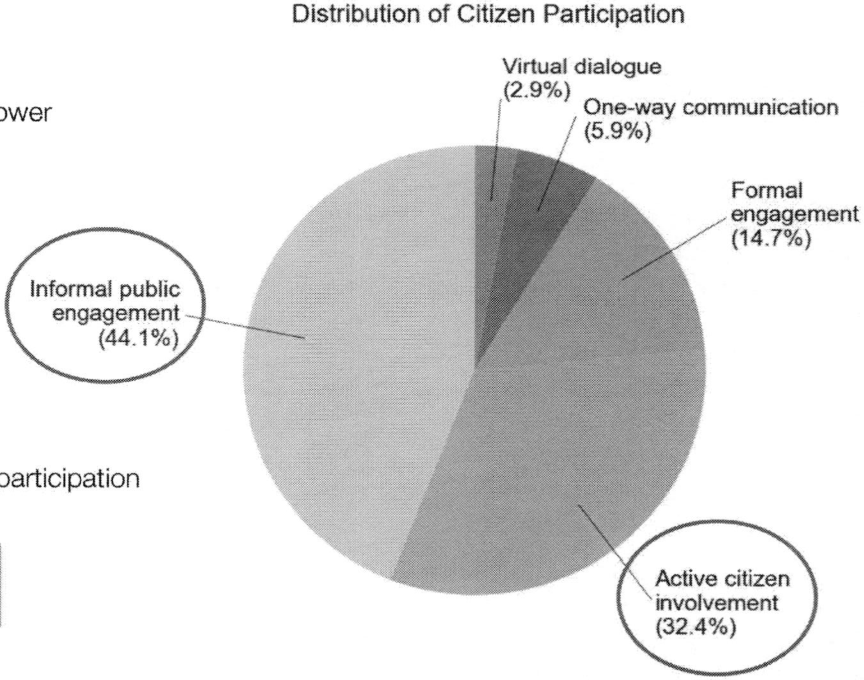

Figure 8 Distribution of Citizen Participation in the ECs analyzed

Energy Communities – Active citizen involvement

INSTITUTO DE ENERGÍA SOLAR

- Community membership
  - residential households
  - commercial businesses
  - industrial facilities
  - municipal entities
  - specific groups based on geographical locations (island-based or regional).

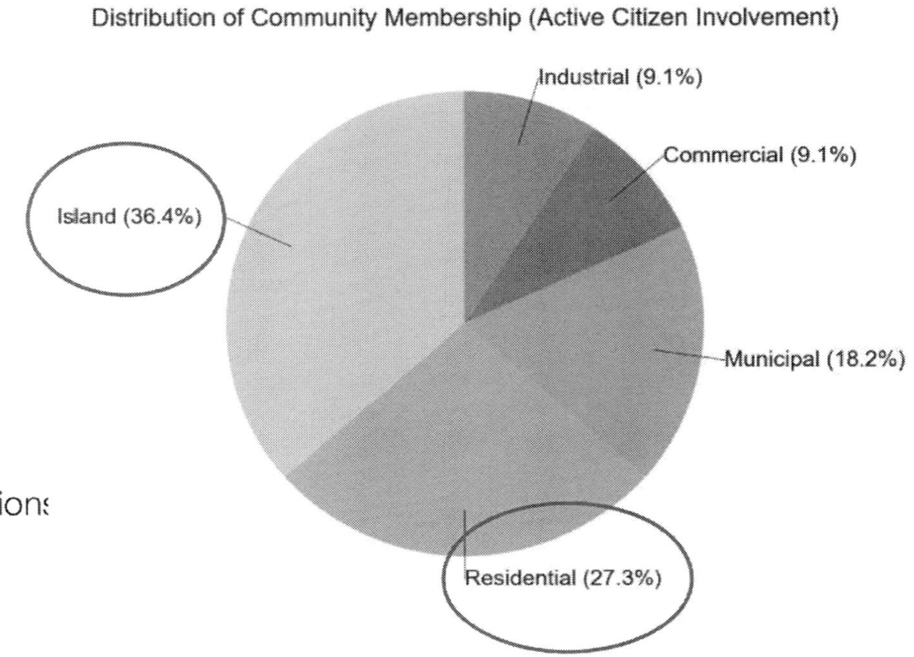

Figure 10 Distribution of the category "Community Membership" in those initiatives that achieved Active Citizen Involvement level

POLITÉCNICA

Energy Communities – Active citizen involvement

INSTITUTO DE ENERGÍA SOLAR

- Energy power range
  - Range 1: 0-500 kW
  - Range 2: 501-1,000 kW
  - Range 3: 1,001-10,000 kW
  - Range 4: 10,001-100,000 kW
  - Range 5: > 100,001 kW

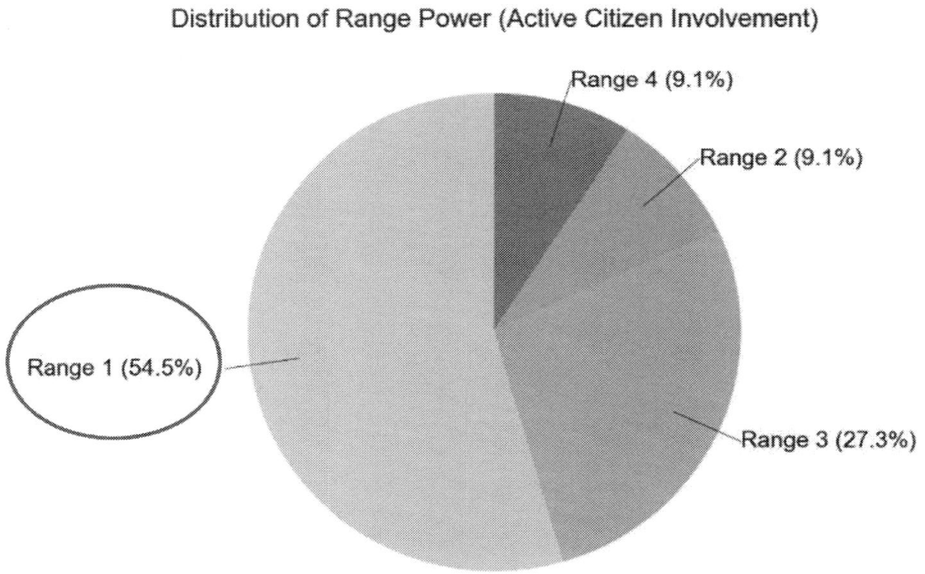

Figure 11 Distribution of the category "Range Power" in those initiatives that achieved Active Citizen Involvement level.

POLITÉCNICA

Energy Communities – Active citizen involvement

INSTITUTO DE ENERGÍA SOLAR

- Business model
  - Group 1 - neighborhood associations
  - Group 2 - municipal initiatives
  - Group 3 - regional cooperatives
  - Group 4 - national and international cooperatives

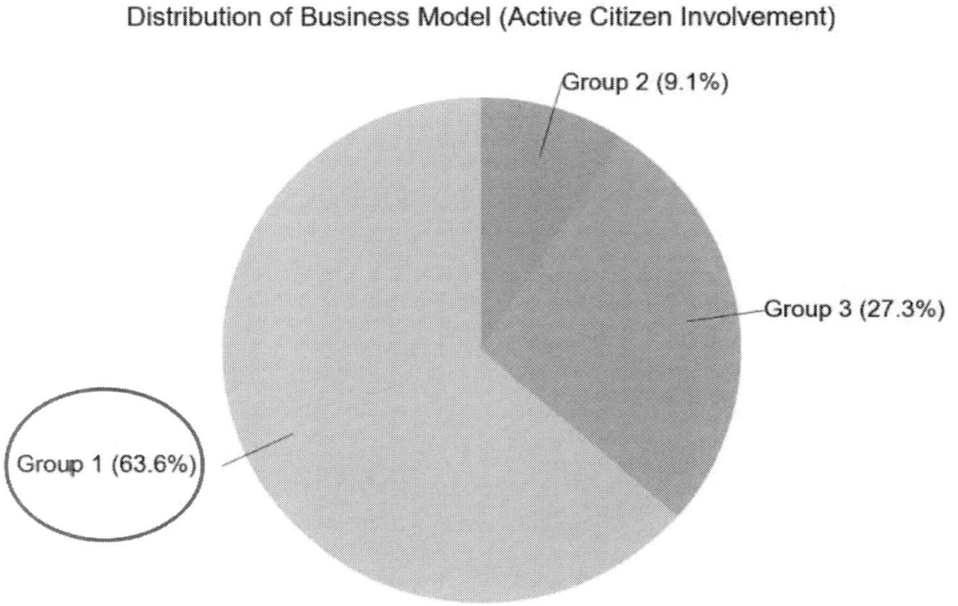

Figure 12 Distribution of the category "Business Model" in those initiatives that achieved Active Citizen Involvement level

POLITÉCNICA

Energy Communities – Active citizen involvement

INSTITUTO DE ENERGÍA SOLAR

- Observations
  - Residential households
  - Small systems (<500 kW)
  - Neighborhood associations

- Conclusions
  - **Redefinition of citizens' traditional roles** as mere participants and self-consumers.
  - Drivers: not simply providing cheap energy but also **to foster the social value** behind it
  - Models **to pave the way for citizen science** in a broad sense

Key lessons learned

INSTITUTO DE ENERGÍA SOLAR

1. **Maintaining direct involvement** in the process:
   - to build trust and foster meaningful collaboration

2. **Collaboration** activities:
   - real, sustained partnership framework

3. **Planning** is a critical aspect:
   - design, methodology, language barriers, ways to measure participant satisfaction

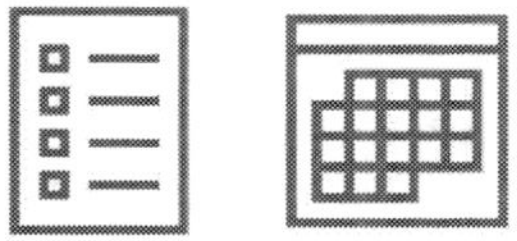

4. **Ethical considerations** are equally important in public participation:
   - relevant legislation and ethical guidelines, particularly when handling personal data

5. **Critical challenge of citizen science activities:**
   - regarding the accuracy and reliability of data collected by non-expert participants

POLITÉCNICA

INSTITUTO DE ENERGÍA SOLAR

We can continue to deliver tools, or we can finally start listening to those who hold the instruction manual

The **FUTURE** isn't a puzzle to be solved alone: it's a story to be written **TOGETHER**.

Image generated by Artificial Intelligence using Canva's AI Image Generator

POLITÉCNICA

INSTITUTO DE ENERGÍA SOLAR

Cristina Sanz-Cuadrado cristina.sanzc@upm.es

Thank you for your attention

Happy to take your questions

We gratefully acknowledge the support of these institutions:

AURORA

For more information, read our paper: "Citizen Engagement for Social and Technological Innovation in Sustainable Energy Systems" in Advanced Energy and Sustainability Research

POLITÉCNICA

INSTITUTO
DE ENERGÍA
SOLAR

Innovation in photovoltaics since 1979

EU PVSEC
22 — 26
September
BEC —
Bilbao Exhibition Centre
Bilbao —
Spain
EU
PVSEC
2025
42nd European
Photovoltaic Solar Energy
Conference and Exhibition

030001-001

Conference Highlights

Robert Kenny

European Commission Joint Research Centre

EU PVSEC Technical Programme Chair

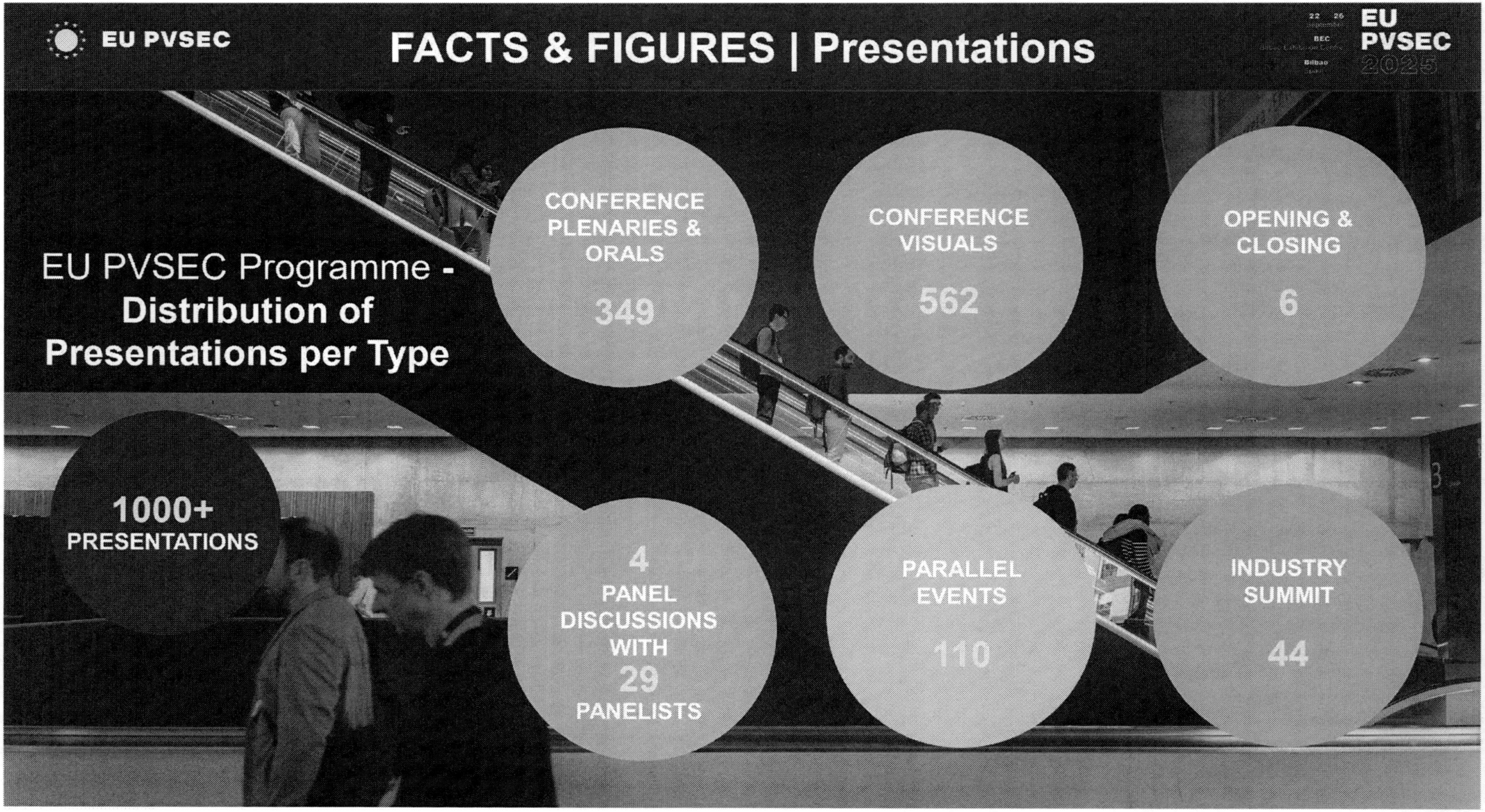
EU PVSEC
FACTS & FIGURES | Presentations
22 26
BEC
Bilbao
EU
PVSEC
2025
EU PVSEC Programme - Distribution of Presentations per Type
CONFERENCE PLENARIES & ORALS
349
CONFERENCE VISUALS
562
OPENING & CLOSING
6
1000+
PRESENTATIONS
4
PANEL DISCUSSIONS WITH
29
PANELISTS
PARALLEL EVENTS
110
INDUSTRY SUMMIT
44

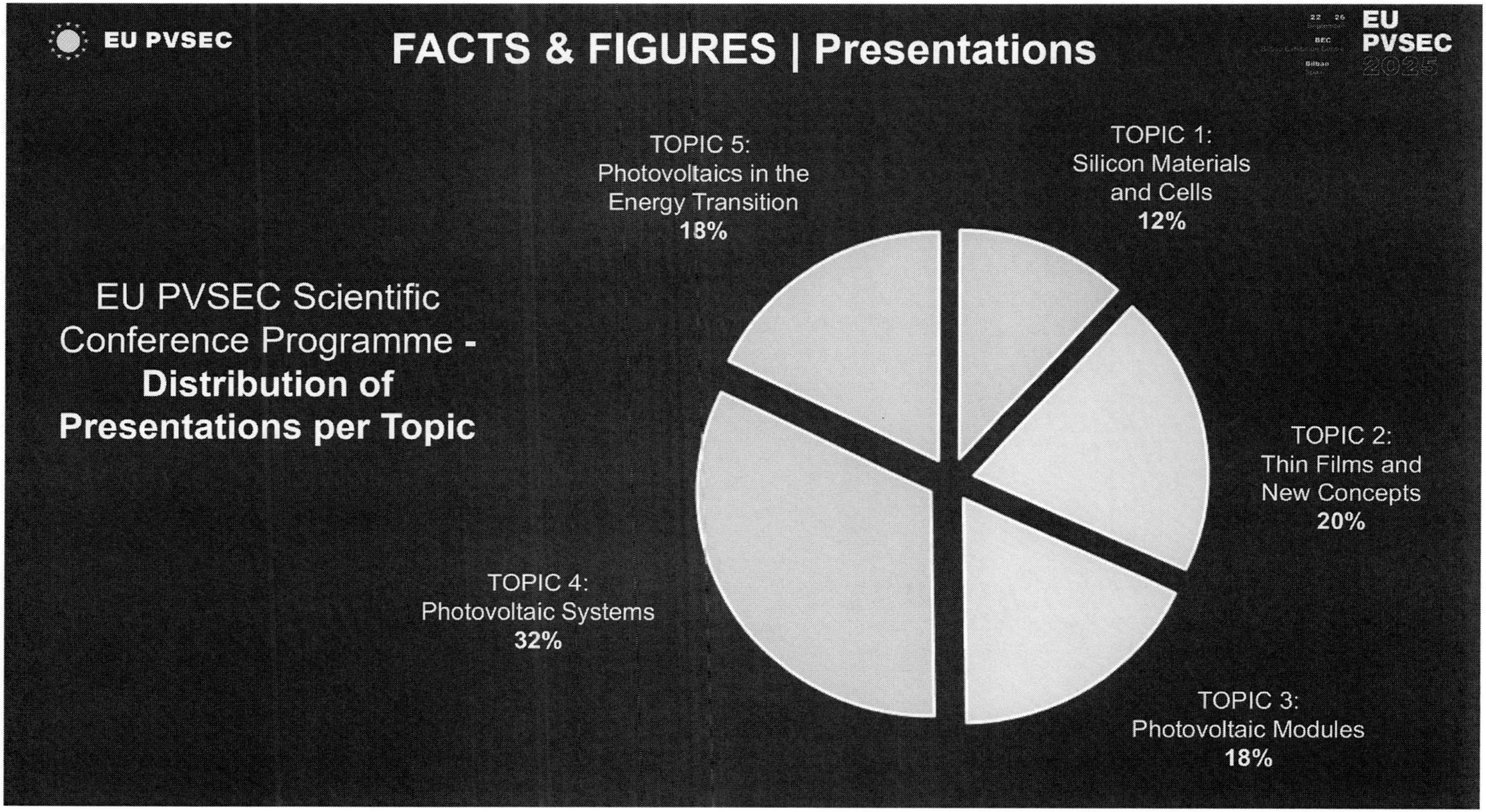
EU PVSEC
FACTS & FIGURES | Presentations
22 26
BEC
Bilbao
EU
PVSEC
2025
EU PVSEC Scientific Conference Programme - Distribution of Presentations per Topic
TOPIC 5:
Photovoltaics in the Energy Transition
18%
TOPIC 1:
Silicon Materials and Cells
12%
TOPIC 2:
Thin Films and New Concepts
20%
TOPIC 4:
Photovoltaic Systems
32%
TOPIC 3:
Photovoltaic Modules
18%

EU PVSEC

FACTS & FIGURES | Participants

EU PVSEC 2025

Participants by Countries
Top 10

No	Country	Participants
1	Germany	310
2	Spain	270
3	France	108
4	Italy	90
5	The Netherlands	76
6	South Korea	67
7	Switzerland	62
8	Japan	55
9	Belgium	44
10	Norway	35

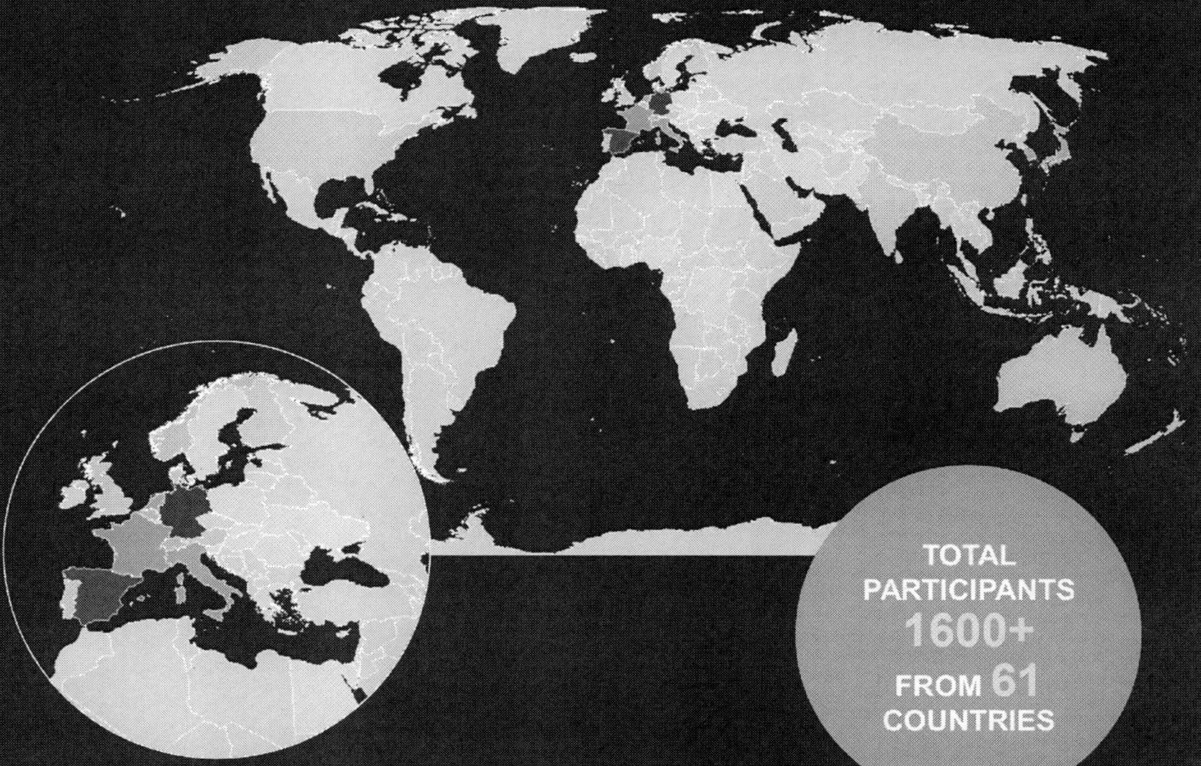

TOTAL PARTICIPANTS 1600+ FROM 61 COUNTRIES

Plenary Session "PV Everywhere"
OPENING
Monday, 22 Sept. 2025
Becquerel Prize Ceremony
Welcome Messages
Jon DE GREGORIO
Moderated Panel Discussion "Solar in Turbulent Times: Global Dynamics and the Way Forward"
Key Note Speech "The Dual Face of Global Solar Growth"
EU PVSEC 2025
www.eupvsec.org
Bilbao Exhibition Centre
Torsten BRAMMER

EU PVSEC

PANEL DISCUSSIONS

22 – 26 BEC Bilbao

EU PVSEC 2025

BO.13 Reliability and Bankability in PV
"The rapid developments of PV technology require increased attention to be paid to reliability testing."

CO.7 Challenges and Opportunities of PV up to 2030
"PV Technology is already reliable and cost effective, and even though improvements are welcome, key blockages are storage and grid strengthening. AI and robotics are essential to meet the scale of developments needed."

DO.13 Scalability and Manufacturability Prospects in Europe for New Technologies
"The prospects for reaching the 30GW target for PV module manufacturing in Europe were discussed and policy measures proposed."

EU PVSEC

22 26 BEC Bilbao EU PVSEC 2025

CONFERENCE

KEY MESSAGES

Cross-cutting themes emerged throughout the programme, showcasing how solar technologies can be applied everywhere, from traditional to emerging fields.

- Sustainability and circularity remain central, with research focused on reducing material use, such as replacing silver with copper, and advancing end-of-life management of modules.
- Ensuring long-term stability and predictable energy yield is equally essential, with studies of degradation mechanisms such as UVID carried out.
- The role of AI across the PV value chain is rapidly expanding, from design to operations and maintenance, including drone applications.

EU PVSEC

EU PVSEC 2025

CONFERENCE

TOPIC 1: SILICON MATERIALS AND CELLS

Enhancements in IV measurement procedures

- Michael Rauer, Fraunhofer ISE: 1AO.4.5 *Universal Contacting Approaches for the Characterization of Solar Cells*
- Shuai Nie, UNSW: 1AO.4.6 *Contact-Free J-V: a Simple Technique for Universal State-of-the-Art Solar Cells*

Replacement of critical by sustainable materials:

- Reduced Ag consumpion e.g. by replacing by Cu (plating)
- In-free SHJ solar cells and Pero-Si tandems

EU PVSEC

22 26 SEP BEC Bilbao

EU PVSEC 2025

CONFERENCE

TOPIC 1: SILICON MATERIALS AND CELLS

Great advance in understanding of UV induced degradation and Hydrogen related degradation

- Excellent PLENARY by Bram Hoex (presenting for Muhammad Umair Khan), UNSW: 1CP.3.5 *Understanding the Root Cause of UV-Induced Degradation in TOPCon and PERC Solar Cells*

Further high quality orals:

- Christina Hollemann, ISFH: 1AO.4.2 *Mitigating UV-Induced Degradation: Impact of PECVD and PEALD AlOx Layers Deposited in a Tube-Type Direct Plasma-Enhanced Chemical Vapor Deposition System*
- Hugo Lajoie, CEA: 1AO.4.3 *New Insights on UV-Induced Degradation of SHJ Solar Cells*
- Byungsul Min, ISFH: 1BO.3.6 *UV Stable Passivation Stack with Plasma-Enhanced Atomic Layer Deposition of Aluminum Oxide from an Industrial Tube-Type Direct Plasma-Enhanced Chemical Vapor Deposition System*
- Wolfram Kwapil, Fraunhofer ISE: 1AO.5.6 *Impact of Illumination on Solar Cell Properties: Insights into Atomic Hydrogen Release*

EU PVSEC

22 – 26 September

BEC

Bilbao

EU PVSEC 2025

CONFERENCE

TOPIC 1: SILICON MATERIALS AND CELLS

Advances in TOPCon and SHJ technology → Pushing the Limits of Performance

- Fantastic keynote lecture (PLENARY) on heterojunction solar cells by Dr. Guangtao Yang, Trina: 1CP.1.1 *Silicon Surface and Interface Study for >27% Efficient SHJ Solar Cell*
  - Deep insight into technological aspects eg. influence of rear side polishing on cell performance
  - Very high efficiencies for both-sides contacted HJT > 27%
  - Issues with CAPEX, sustainibility (Ag, In)
  - Pero-Si tandem cells on large area and modules

Late News Presentation on 27.8% efficient back contact silicon solar cells by Hua Wu, Longhi: 1DO.9.1 *Hybrid Interdigitated Back Contact Silicon Solar Cells with Superior Efficiency*

Late News Presentation as TOPCon for Bottom Solar Cells in Pero-Si Tandem devices by Jana Polzin-Isabelle Polzin, Fraunhofer ISE: 1DO.9.3 *Silicon Solar Cells – From High Efficiency Single-junction to Bottom Cells in Two-Terminal Perovskite-Silicon Tandem Devices*

EU PVSEC

EU PVSEC 2025

CONFERENCE

TOPIC 1: SILICON MATERIALS AND CELLS

Further high quality orals:

- Hua Wu, Longhi: 1DO.9.1 *Hybrid Interdigitated Back Contact Silicon Solar Cells with Superior Efficiency*
- Daming Chen, Trina: 1AO.5.1 *Large Area i-TOPCon Solar Cells with 25.9% Record Efficiency*
- Maysa Sarsour, UNSW: 1AO.6.1 *Evaluating Silicon Heterojunction Solar Cell Stability under Industrial Illuminated Hydrogenation Conditions*

Bottom cell optimization for Pero-Si tandems

EU PVSEC

22 26 September BEC Bilbao

EU PVSEC 2025

CONFERENCE

TOPIC 2: THIN FILMS AND NEW CONCEPTS

A lot of focus on the long-term stability improvement and upscaling of tandem devices based on a variety of materials (hence not only pero-Si).

Many companies (e.g. Hanwha Q-cells, Oxford PV, Microquanta Seminconductor, Jinko Solar, Longi, etc. non-exhaustive list) presented impressive results on industrial size single-junction pero modules and pero-based tandem modules. A highlight here was the plenary talk from Hanwha Q-cells showing a record large area (M10) pilot-scale Pk/Si tandem cell of 28.6% efficiency.

EU PVSEC

EU PVSEC 2025

CONFERENCE

TOPIC 2: THIN FILMS AND NEW CONCEPTS

In the field of pero-Si tandems, there is clearly more focus on improving the stability of the tandem devices than before with many contributions doing in-depth investigations into the different degradation mechanisms that can occur in pero-Si tandems.

In this respect, 2DO9.5 presented a consensus statement about reliability testing of perovskite-based tandems that is endorsed by specialists worldwide from both industry and research and presents a kind of minimum that should be done in terms of testing and reporting concerning the stability and lifetime of perovskite-based tandem devices.

More and more advanced characterization methods for perovskite and perovskite - silicon tandem solar cells are being used, hyperspectral imaging methods identify non-uniformities by layer for processing development.

EU PVSEC

EU PVSEC 2025

CONFERENCE

TOPIC 2: THIN FILMS AND NEW CONCEPTS

Another clear trend is that pero-TOPCon cells are nearing the same record efficiencies as pero-Heterojunction cells. A highlight talk here was the certified 34.22% efficiency perovskite/ topcon tandem solar cell(1cm2) by Jinko Solar 2CO2.1

Another highlight was the 30.5% triple junction pero/pero/silicon cell by EPFL (2CO2.3)

In the field of perovskite single junction devices, 2DO.7.3 showed perovskite devices with remarkable reliability, withstanding 4 years of outdoor exposure. The degradation mechanism is attributed to the diurnal behaviour, also verified and replicated with indoor experiments.

2AO3.6 investigated experimental degradation and recovery of perovskite solar cells, improving the comprehension of instability's dynamics, to extend the lifetime of devices.

EU PVSEC

EU PVSEC 2025

CONFERENCE

TOPIC 2: THIN FILMS AND NEW CONCEPTS

In the field of compound semiconductors, there were many presentations on alternative materials for perovskite in tandems. In this way, first monolithic $(AgCu)(InGa)Se_2$ on Si tandem cells were demonstrated as well as 16.1% semitransparent Ag doped $Cu(InGa)S_2$ sulfide top cells.

An exciting highlight in this field was 2BO8.2 in which UPC Barcelona achieved 18% efficiency under indoor lighting for kesterite solar cells with alkali doping

EU PVSEC

22 26

BEC

EU PVSEC 2025

Bilbao

CONFERENCE

TOPIC 3: PHOTOVOLTAIC MODULES

"Reliable packaging to Maximize the energy yield from high efficiency cells"

big theme: Optimizing module materials and packaging for long lifetime and predictable energy yield from high efficiency cells. The industry and research community are moving quickly to assess and improve reliability.

- Understanding, accelerated testing, and mitigating UV-ID in n-type cells and modules
- How do you develop accelerated tests for constantly changing BOMs - new encapsulants, new metallization, thinner glass, and high efficiency cells

EU PVSEC

EU PVSEC 2025

CONFERENCE

TOPIC 3: PHOTOVOLTAIC MODULES

- Degradation and metastability in packaged perovskite tandems - understanding energy yield and realistic degradation rates
- Characterization out of the lab and into the field and factory - accurate outdoor performance, online quality control measurements for encapsulant cross linking
- Reducing silver content and metallization temperatures - reliability of low temperature and low silver metallization
- Developing glass qualification requirements to minimize breakage

EU PVSEC

EU PVSEC 2025

CONFERENCE

TOPIC 4: PHOTOVOLTAIC SYSTEMS

Advances in O&M of PV systems

(4CV.1) focuses on fault detection, cleaning optimization, soiling (and snow 4CO.8), UAV for autonomous monitoring and digital twin.

Data driven and AI based O&M (4CO.9) including a medicine-like workflow in Autonomous multi-AI agent system for health monitoring: a fully automated O&M pipeline with field robotics (4CO.9.4 D. Moser, EURAC)

PV Everywhere from space to agricultural applications like integration in vineyards (Mo, Opening plenary) and many other **integrated options** as we have seen throughout the week. On Thursday (4DO.4) agriPV, noise barriers and floating integrated systems. AgriPV technologies (4DO.2), BIPV

PV needs solar energy. **Solar resource and forecasting** (Mo, 4AO.7-9 & Tu 4BV.3). Shortly IEA PVPS T16 will publish minute irradiance data, some including GT over 220 stations worldwide with. Same format and quality controlled. (*Worldwide solar radiation measurement database with quality-control added value*, Anne Forstinger CSP Services, 4AO.7.1)

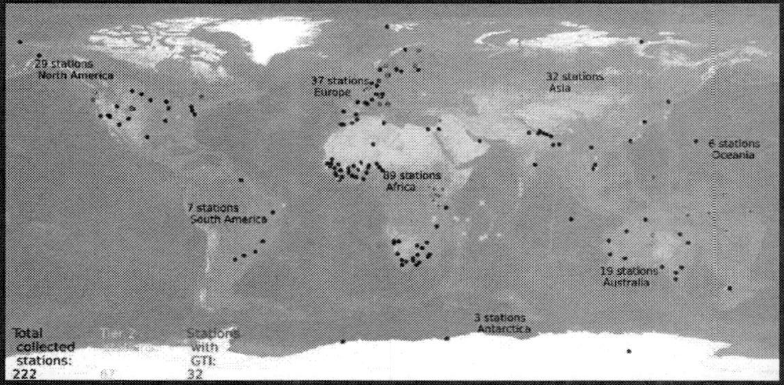

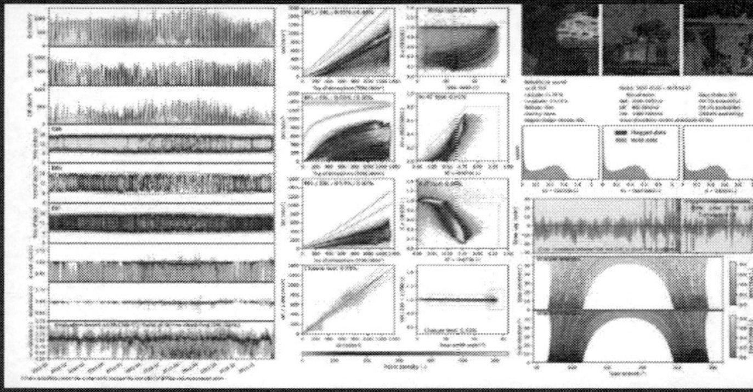

(4BV.3). Poster winner 4BV.3.12 *Advancing Very Short-Term Solar Irradiance Forecasting in Africa: A Low-Cost Sky Imaging and Machine Learning-Based Approach*, implications for PV deployment and grid integration (Martin Ansong, KIT). Runner-up 4BV.3.25 *Evaluating the Suitability of Köppen-Geiger Climate Classifications for Photovoltaic Systems: Micro-climate Analysis and Risk Assessment Maps,* with worldwide distribution of humidity related risk assessment for PV performance (Pavan Kumar Panda, Anhalt University of Applied Sciences).

Integrated PV

BIPV (4BO.16) examples of coloured modules (which was main topic of the poster session along with fire concerns of BIPV, 4BV.4), lightweight solutions (4BO.5) and modelling partial shading effects 4BO.17.1, *Modelling partial shading at the cell level on PV modules,* Jean-Paul Calin, ENSTA) and 4BO.17.3, *Comparing the energy yield and degradation rates of smart PV modules compared to conventional PV system designs in shaded urban scenario's,* Youri Blom, TU DELF.

AgriPV 4DO.2 the room was fully packed showing the interest in the topic. 5 talks were on new ways of sharing light (2 spectral splitting before the PV conversion, 2 semitransparent PV modules both c-Si and CdTe, 1 on downshifting encapsulate) + 1 new AgrivPV like application with Algae instead of crops.

4DO.4 also included AgriPV and **Others types of integration like noise barriers and floating.** In addition to performance other aspects like (*Hydrological and ecological effects on floating PV,* Konstantin Ilgen, FHO ISe) have been highlighted this week

4DO4.2

BOS and tracking systems (4DO.1) focused on backtracking strategies and terrains with complex topography.

4DO.1.4

CONFERENCE

TOPIC 4: PHOTOVOLTAIC SYSTEMS

Reliability of PV systems

Several presentations focused long-term monitored degradation, failure modes and degradation modes identification techniques (non-destructive, aerial images, AI-based)

4BO.6.1 *Three decades, three climates: insights and lessons on PV reliability*. Good BOM offer very high reliability in power production, with 30-35 years old modules showing 0.24% degradation rate per year.

4BO.6.3 *Non-destructive detection of water ingress in solar modules using NIR spectroscopy* (Oleksandr Mashkow HI ERN) proved near-infrared absorption (NIRA) technique to detect water ingress in modules in the field, which correlated with the module degradation.

4BO.7.2 *Robust PV performance loss rate calculation for high latitudes* (Lauri Karttunen, Meteo Inst Helsinki) and 4BO.7. 3 *Detailed analysis of degradation rates of operating PV assets in tropical climate conditions* (Xioaqi Xu, Seris Singapore) Performance loss rates reported for high latitudes and tropics based on solid data sets. PLR in the tropics -1.4%/year

4DO.3.6 PV system design and assessment highlighted how inverter safety issues are extremely important and how more research about inverter safety and reliability is needed.

EU PVSEC

EU PVSEC 2025

CONFERENCE

TOPIC 5: PHOTOVOLTAICS IN THE ENERGY TRANSITION

Main topics of interest :

- Flexibility
- Artificial intelligence
- EoL management

EU PVSEC

22 26 September BEC Bilbao EU PVSEC 2025

CONFERENCE

TOPIC 5: PHOTOVOLTAICS IN THE ENERGY TRANSITION

5.1 Grid Integration and Flexibility Enablers (2 sessions)

- Smoothing effect related to different orientations of PV systems in a given area allows 10 to 15% additional hosting capacity of the distribution grid compared to the conservative calculation that consists in summing the AC power. Such accurate calculation enabled by high resolution large area images and LIDAR and induces therefore very low costs.

5.2 Sustainability of PV (4 sessions)

- New inventories LCI and LCA for emerging technologies even though lack of data for perovskites, LCA showing a way for low environmental Impacts with technology improvement and localisation. / Technological improvements will contribute to the reduction of environmental Impact / Grid Efficiency has an Impact on the environmental Footprint.
- Manufacturing optimization / Reuse & recycling: results from the perspective of economic performance – would it convince manufacturer to consider it if economic benefit ?
- EoL Management /recycling -> emerging field attracting lots of activities / mainly EU projects (EVERPV / ICARUS / QASAR) – highlight on polymer, interesting question came up and to be debated for the next decade: is it worth it to consider polymer (EVA/ backsheet) recycling ?
- Major progress in methodology and indicators to assess sustainable design & circularity and improve transparency recyclability index, technical recyclability, digital passport)

EU PVSEC

22 26 BEC Bilbao EU PVSEC 2025

CONFERENCE

TOPIC 5: PHOTOVOLTAICS IN THE ENERGY TRANSITION

5.3 Scenarios for Renewables, Policy, Global Challenges (1 session)

- wide scope of contributions on the way to massive, medium- to long-term PV deployment -> should not be taken for granted despite positive projections since there can be limiting factors such as public acceptance / regulatory restrictions and effect of climate change

5.4 Costs, Economics, Finance and Markets (1 session)

- Annual installed capacity over 400 GWp / total cumulative installed capacity worldwide over 2.1 TWp / Clear mismatch between PV module installations rate worldwide and PV module production rate leading to bunch of inventories and drastically reduced prices.

5.6 Societal Challenges; Citizens' Participation, Awareness (1 session)

- data and analysis in gender aspects are emerging in PV! (poster session) + Highlight on innovation in education! On example that targets students & skilled workers -> mobile Lab for advanced experimental training PV-related to bring skills and characterization tools everywhere.

PARALLEL
EVENTS

Diversity
Prejudice
Change
Avoid Blind Spots
Job Loss?
Integration
Creativity
Internal Friction

EU PVSEC

22 26 BEC Bilbao

EU PVSEC 2025

PARALLEL EVENTS

- Perovskite Innovation Roundtable: Driving EU Leadership in Perovskite Innovation
- Women in PV presents: Leading with Inclusion – Embracing the 6 Traits of Inclusive Leadership
- Unlocking the Potential of Integrated Photovoltaic Systems - European R&D Approach
- Why Do PV Plants Perform Lower than Expected? (Estimating losses by backtracking algorithms in undulating terrain & Analysis of the loss chain and identification of deviations from initial expectations)
- PV Made in the EU: How Do Companies Die and How Can They Thrive?

22 — 26
September
BEC —
ilbao Exhibition Centre
Bilbao — Spain
EU
PVSEC
2025
EXHIBITION
FORUM
INDUSTRY
SUMMIT

The road to a
sustainable future

EU PVSEC

EU PVSEC 2025

INDUSTRY SUMMIT

Industry Summit Opening (session I)

Session Title: Solar PV production in Europe - the way forward

Moderators: Begoña Molinete, Walburga Hemetsberger

Key Takeaway:

This session discussed the state of play of European manufacturing projects and whether there is enough European support. It was clear that political support is further lacking – only 3 Member States have developed schemes to support European manufacturing. While the Net Zero Industry Act is helpful to diversify supplies, it will not particularly support European manufacturing.

All panellists agreed that apart from further policy support (financing, derisking) collaboration is the way forward.

EU PVSEC

EU PVSEC 2025

INDUSTRY SUMMIT

Session II
Session Title: International corporations in the light of changing geopolitics
Moderators: Radovan Kopecek, Puzant Baliozian

Key takeaway:
EU machine builders are still supporting mostly Indian but also US and EU projects with their technology and expertise. The major arguments for choosing EU tech are quality, training, support and low OPEX.

Session III
Session Title: PV Systems: How do we get the produced electricity in Europe into the grid?
Moderators: Catarina Augusto, Peter Fath

Key Takeaway:
Hybrid PV + storage systems (co-located or distributed) are essential for integrating PV into electricity grids. Storage adds flexibility and stabilizes the grid, making it a cornerstone of resilient energy systems; while the technology is mature, scalable and bankable revenue models remain the key gap for widespread deployment.

LIST OF EXHIBITORS
(in alphabetical order)

Company name	Country
2nd Cycle FlexCo	Austria
9-Tech	Italy
Avalon ST / Pasan	Switzerland
BASQUENERGY Cluster	Spain
Becquerel Institute	Belgium
ECOPROGETTI	Italy
EKIENERGY	Spain
ESMC Pavilion	Belgium
Eternal Sun I WAVELABS	The Netherlands
EU PVSEC Startup Pavilion	
European Commission JRC	Italy
exateq	Germany
FLUXiM AG	Switzerland
G2V Optics	Canada
GALEA	Spain
halm elektronik	Germany
HighLine Technology	Germany
IEA PVPS	
Innovations in Optics, Inc.	United States of America
ISC Konstanz	Germany
LAB14	Germany
MBJ Solutions	Germany
Mondragon Assembly	Spain
Nagase Chemtex America	United States of America
NEO Messtechnik Holding	Austria
ODTÜ GÜNAM	Türkiye
Phoenixolar	China
PSE Instruments	Germany
PVsyst	Switzerland
RCT Future	Germany
RCT Solutions	Germany
RENA	Germany
ReNewPV-CA21148 / 5GSOLAR	Estonia
SALD B.V.	The Netherlands

SCIPRIOS	Germany
SEMILAB	Hungary
SINGULUS TECHNOLOGIES	Germany
Sinton Instruments	United States of America
SOLAR MATERIALS	Germany
SolarNL	The Netherlands
Soli Tek R&D	Lithuania
TAMURA ELSOLD	Germany
TECNALIA	Spain
The Netherlands Pavilion	The Netherlands
TNO	The Netherlands
University of the Basque Country	Spain
Vector Energy	Spain
VON ARDENNE	Germany
WCPEC-9	South Korea
WIP Renewable Energies	Germany
ZSW	Germany

We thank the EU PVSEC 2025 Sponsors

Platinum

MONDRAGON ASSEMBLY

Gold

ENERGIAREN EUSKAL ERAKUNDEA
ENTE VASCO DE LA ENERGÍA

G2V
ENGINEER THE SUN

halm.

RCT solutions

Silver

Sinton instruments

Bronze

AESOLAR

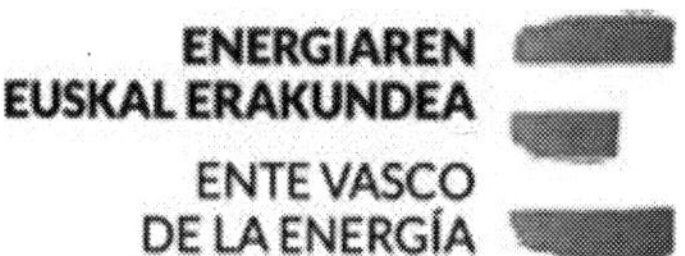

AUTHORS OF EU PVSEC 2025 PROCEEDINGS PAPERS

A. dos Reis Benatto, Gisele DTU, Roskilde, Denmark	020028, 020037, 020039, 020191, 020265, 020376, 020477
Aaltonen, Lauri Tampere University, Tampere, Finland	020537
Abad Alcaraz, Verónica University of Almería, La Cañada de San Urbano, Spain	020336
Abbott, Malcolm D. PV Lighthouse, Coledale, Australia	020396
Abbotto, Alessandro University of Milano-Bicocca, Milan, Italy	020077
Abdallah, Amir A. QEERI, Doha, Qatar	020146, 020166
Abdel Nour, Christine EDF R&D, Moret Loing Orvanne, France	020188
Abdelrahim, Mohamed QEERI, Doha, Qatar	020166
Abdou-Tankari, Mahamadou Paris-East Créteil University, Créteil, France	020562
Abrego, Gillen ALLOTARRA, Allo, Spain	020392
Acciarri, Maurizio University of Milano-Bicocca, Milan, Italy	020087
Acevedo Devoto, M. Ignacia ISC Konstanz, Konstanz, Germany	020220
Achenbach, Jannik University of Applied Science Cologne, Cologne, Germany	020522
Acinas, Victor Applied Materials, Dublin, Ireland	020019
Adachi, Satoru NIED, Shinjo, Japan	020436
Aden, Samira HZB, Berlin, Germany	020513
Adinolfi Borea, Riccardo University of Bologna, Bologna, Italy	020314
Adnan Hameed, Mohammed Martin-Luther-University Halle-Wittenberg, Halle, Germany	020156
Adothu, Baloji DEWA, Dubai, United Arab Emirates	020229
Aghaei, Mohammadreza NTNU, Aalesund, Norway	020335, 020356
Aghaei, Mohammadreza NTNU, Ålesund, Norway	020374, 020375

Aghamohammadi, Amirhossain Amirkabir University of Technology, Tehran, Iran	020356
Aguirre, Aranzazu Hasselt Unversity, Genk, Belgium	020064
Ahmadi, Mehdi CNR-IMM, Catania, Italy	020066
Aiello, Andrea ACCA Software, Cosenza, Italy	020255
Aimé, Jérémie CEA / INES, Le Bourget-du-Lac, France	020217, 020311
Aissa, Brahim QEERI, Doha, Qatar	020042, 020075, 020108, 020109, 020146, 020147
Aizpurua, Jon Tecnalia, Donostia - San Sebastián, Spain	020139
Akbayrak, Serdar Necmettin Erbakan University, Konya, Türkiye	020020
Akram, M. Waqar Hohai University, Changzhou, China	020164
Al Katrib, Mirella IPVF, Palaiseau, France	020116
Alam, Habeel Lancaster University, Lancaster, United Kingdom	020394
Alberts, Vivian DEWA, Dubai, United Arab Emirates	020229
Albuquerque, Daniel P. Centre for New Energy Technologies, Sacavém, Portugal	020464
Alet, Pierre-Jean CSEM, Neuchâtel, Switzerland	020238, 020544
Alexandris, Nikos European Commission JRC, Ispra, Italy	020210
Alfieri, Felice Viegand Maagøe, Copenhagen, Denmark	020497
Ali, Adnan QEERI, Doha, Qatar	020147
Allen, Vince SunDrive Solar, Kurnell, Australia	020048
Alloji, Esma Necmettin Erbakan University, Konya, Türkiye	020020
Almeida Silva, José University of Évora, Évora, Portugal	020565
Almuneau, Guilhem LAAS-CNRS, Toulouse, France	020074
Alonso, Ricardo TECNALIA, Derio, Spain	020197, 020198, 020353, 020358
Alonso-Montesinos, Joaquín University of Almeria, Almeria, Spain	020100

Alonso-Montesinos, Joaquín 020336
University of Almería, La Cañada de San Urbano, Spain

Álvarez Hervás, José Domingo 020336
University of Almería, La Cañada de San Urbano, Spain

Alvarez, José 020040, 020058
CNRS, Gif-sur-Yvette, France

Álvarez, Marta 020300
CENER, Sarriguren, Spain

Álvarez-Pérez, Guillem 020062
IPVF, Palaiseau, France

Alvaro Høye, Ingar 020443
Solkraft Sør, Øyslebø, Norway

Alves e Silva, Kiane 020439, 020535, 020567, 020575
UPM, Madrid, Spain

Amaro e Silva, Rodrigo 020490
University of Lisbon, Lisbon, Portugal

Amatriain, Irati 020392
CENER, Sarriguren, Spain

Anamiati, Gaetana 020448, 020481
GreenPowerMonitor a DNV company, Barcelona, Spain

Anaya, Julian 020191, 020205
University of Valladolid, Valladolid, Spain

Ancillao, Andrea 020079
Polytechnic University of Turin, Turin, Italy

Anderlini, Alessandro 020155
Coveme, Gorizia, Italy

Andersen, Nanna L. 020250
DTU, Roskilde, Denmark

Andersen, Nanna Lysgaard 020306
DTU, Roskilde, Denmark

Andrade-Arvizu, Jacob 020094
IREC, Barcelona, Spain

Andreozzi, Federico 020494
University of Rome Tor Vergata, Rome, Italy

Anefnaf, Ikram 020093
University of Verona, Verona, Italy

Ansong, Martin 020272
KIT, Eggenstein-Leopoldshafen, Germany

Antognini, Luca 020196
PVsyst, Geneva, Switzerland

Antoine, C. 020508
IMDEA Nanoscience Institute, Madrid, Spain

Antón, Ignacio 020209, 020246, 020257, 020453, 020459
UPM, Madrid, Spain

Antonucci, Daniele 020551
Eurac Research, Bolzano, Italy

Apostoleris, Harry 020487
EPRI, Dubai, United Arab Emirates

Arakawa, Hayato 020436
NIED, Shinjo, Japan

Aranguren, Gerardo 020289, 020353
UPV/EHU, Bilbao, Spain

Arbaretaz, Sebastien 020317
CEA INES, Le Bourget-du-Lac, France

Ardissone, Bastien J. J. 020396
PV Lighthouse, Coledale, Australia

Arduino, Daniele 020079
Polytechnic University of Turin, Turin, Italy

Ariolli, Daniela Maria Godinho 020325
BayWa r.e, Rome, Italy

Ariza Camacho, Maria Jesus 020100
University of Almeria, Almería, Spain

Armstrong, Alona 020394
Lancaster University, Lancaster, United Kingdom

Arribat, Mathieu 020074
LAAS-CNRS, Toulouse, France

Arrizabalaga, Igor 020139
Tecnalia, Donostia - San Sebastián, Spain

Artegiani, Elisa 020057, 020089, 020093
University of Verona, Verona, Italy

Arumughan, Jayaprasad 020569
ISC Konstanz, Konstanz, Germany

Asaa, Shu-Ngwa 020393
imo-imomec, Genk, Belgium

Ascencio-Vásquez, Julián 020371
Univers, Courbevoie, France

Askins, Steve 020209, 020257
UPM, Madrid, Spain

Assaid, El Mahdi 020171
University of Chouaib Doukkali, El Jadida, Morocco

Aste, Niccolò 020249
Polytechnic University of Milan, Milan, Italy

Astigarraga, Alexander 020226
Eurac Research, Bolzano, Italy

Athienitis, Andreas 020248
Concordia University, Montreal, Canada

Aurrekoetxea, Olaia 020302
TECNALIA, Saint Sebastian, Spain

Awadallah, Carlos 020536
Wattkraft, Madrid, Spain

Azkona, Nekane 020055, 020097, 020153, 020287
UPV/EHU, Bilbao, Spain

Azzopardi, Brian 020318, 020334, 020520
FIR, Birkirkara, Malta
Azzopardi, Carmel 020334
FIR, Birkirkara, Malta

Babich, Francesco 020551
Eurac Research, Bolzano, Italy
Babics, Maxime 020217
CEA / INES, Le Bourget-du-Lac, France
Babin, Markus 020249, 020250, 020306, 020477
DTU, Roskilde, Denmark
Bachour, Dunia A. 020275, 020278
QEERI, Doha, Qatar
Bachour, Dunia 020291
QEERI, Doha, Qatar
Baderiya, Naman 020390
MARIN, Wageningen, The Netherlands
Badosa Franch, Jordi 020214
Polytechnic Institute of Paris, Palaiseau, France
Baeck, Pieter-Jan 020511
Flemish Institute for Technological Research (VITO), Genk, Belgium
Bai, Jianbo 020164
Hohai University, Changzhou, China
Bailache, Simon 020303
CSTB, Marne-la-Vallée, France
Bakhtiari, Afshin 020121
AESOLAR, Koenigsbrunn, Germany
Balafoutis, Athanasios T. 020464
CERTH, Athens, Greece
Bald, Juan 020514
AZTI, PASAIA, Spain
Baldacchino, Alex J. 020065
UNSW, Sydney, Australia
Baležentienė, Skirmantė 020380
The Applied Research Institute for Prospective Technologies, Vilnius, Lithuania
Baležentis, Algirdas 020380
The Applied Research Institute for Prospective Technologies, Vilnius, Lithuania
Ballif, Christophe 020467
CSEM, Neuchâtel, Switzerland
Ballif, Christophe 020251
EPFL, Neuchâtel, Switzerland
Bandaru, Narendra 020039, 020043, 020104
Aarhus University, Aarhus, Denmark

Bang, Ole 020043
Technical University of Denmark, Copenhagen, Denmark

Barakel, Damien 020188
Toulon University, Marseille, France

Baraket, Mira 020039
ATLANT 3D, Taastrup, Denmark

Baranek, Philippe 020060
EDF R&D, Palaiseau, France

Barchi, Grazia 020485, 020489, 020544
Eurac Research, Bolzano, Italy

Bardizza, Giorgio 020181
TÜV Rheinland Italia, Milan, Italy

Bardizza, Giorgio 020208
TÜV Rheinland Solar, Cologne, Germany

Bardizza, Giorgio 020144
TÜV Rheinland, Cologne, Germany

Barguès, Anna 020505
Becquerel Institute France, Lyon, France

Barguès, Anna 020558
Becquerel Institute, Brussels, Belgium

Barnscheidt, Verena 020063, 020114
ISFH, Emmerthal, Germany

Barretta, Chiara 020325
PCCL, Leoben, Austria

Barrionuevo, Bruno 020464
CERTH, Athens, Greece

Barroso, João 020565
University of Évora, Évora, Portugal

Barrou, Alexis 020467
CSEM, Neuchâtel, Switzerland

Barrutia, Laura 020446, 020536
UPM, Madrid, Spain

Barth, Vincent 020134
CEA / INES, Le Bourget-du-Lac, France

Barth, Vincent 020019
CEA, Le Bourget-du-Lac, France

Barth, Vincent 020226
CEA/ INES, Le Bourget-du-Lac, France

Bartholomäus, Martin 020346
DTU, Roskilde, Denmark

Bartolo, Brian 020334
FIR, Birkirkara, Malta

Basta, Beata 020068
Roltec, Poznań, Poland

Basta, Marek 020068
Roltec, Poznań, Poland

Battisti, Kurt 020255
A-Null Development, Vienna, Austria

Bauhuis, Gerard 020067
Radboud University, Nijmegen, The Netherlands

Baumann, Kerstin 020470
bifa Umweltinstitut, Augsburg, Germany

Baumann, Sara 020063
ISFH, Emmerthal, Germany

Baumann, Ulrike 020006
ISFH, Emmerthal, Germany

Baur, Carsten 020246
European Space Agency, Noordwijk, The Netherlands

Beaucarne, Guy 020384
Dow Silicones Belgium, Seneffe, Belgium

Becker, Carl 020331
DLR, Almería, Spain

Behrensdorff Poulsen, Peter 020037
DTU, Lyngby, Denmark

Beinert, Andreas J. 020123
Fraunhofer ISE, Freiburg, Germany

Bejat, Timea 020225, 020500
CEA, Le Bourget-du-Lac, France

Belawadi, Aditya Girish 020231
Fraunhofer ISE, Freiburg, Germany

Belferkous, Brahim Anis 020325
PCCL, Leoben, Austria

Bellmann, Martin 020495, 020510
SINTEF, Trondheim, Norway

Bellvert, Eduard 020139
Tecnalia, Donostia - San Sebastián, Spain

Beltran-Condori, Sonia 020129, 020417
University of Antofagasta, Antofagasta, Chile

Belzunce, María Jesús 020514
AZTI, PASAIA, Spain

Bendix, Peter 020388
Next2Sun Technology, Dillingen, Germany

Bengoechea, Jaione 020181, 020300
CENER, Sarriguren, Spain

Bermudez Benito, Veronica 020146
QEERI, Doha, Qatar

Bermudez-Garcia, Anderson 020246
Thales Alenia Space, Cannes, France

Berrian, Djaber 020492
Belectric, Kolitzheim, Germany

Berson, Solenn 020134
CEA / INES, Le Bourget-du-Lac, France

Besson, Pierre 020373
INES, Le Bourget-du-Lac, France
Betak, Juraj 020241
Solargis, Bratislava, Slovakia
Bettucci, Ottavia 020077
University of Milano-Bicocca, Milan, Italy
Bhardwaj, Shashank 020515
TU Delft, Delft, The Netherlands
Bhatnagar, Shrey 020367
Nextracker, Fremont, United States of America
Biard, Yves 020303
SemperStyl, Eragny, France
Bieber, Lisa-Marie 020195
Fraunhofer ISE, Freiburg, Germany
Bilitu, Eddie 020393
Hasselt University, Hasselt, Belgium
Binani, Ashish 020225
TNO, Petten, The Netherlands
Binetti, Simona 020093
University of Milano Bicocca, Milan, Italy
Binetti, Simona 020087
University of Milano-Bicocca, Milan, Italy
Blakesley, James 020293
National Physical Laboratory, Teddington, United Kingdom
Blanc, Philippe 020291
MINES Paris, Nice, France
Blanco Aguiar, Adrián 020243
ieco.io, Vigo, Spain
Blieske, Ulf 020141
University of Applied Science Cologne, Cologne, Germany
Blieske, Ulf 020140
University of Applied Sciences Cologne, Cologne, Germany
Blstak Catlosova, Katarina 020274
Solargis, Bratislava, Slovakia
Blum, Niklas 020235, 020237, 020239
DLR, Almería, Spain
Boccardi, Roberto 020039
DTU, Copenhagen, Denmark
Boccardi, Roberto 020037
DTU, Lyngby, Denmark
Boccardi, Roberto 020028
DTU, Roskilde, Denmark
Boddaert, Simon 020302, 020303
CSTB, Marne-la-Vallée, France
Bokalič, Matevž 020047, 020319
University of Ljubljana, Ljubljana, Slovenia

Bolink, Henk J. 020226
University of Valencia, Paterna, Spain
Bonal, Victor 020085
UAM, Madrid, Spain
Bonnet, Martin 020141
University of Applied Science Cologne, Cologne, Germany
Bonnet-Eymard, Bénédicte 020251
CSEM, Neuchâtel, Switzerland
Borgers, Tom 020225
IMEC, Genk, Belgium
Borgna, Luciano 020369
BFH, Burgdorf, Switzerland
Borie, Benjamin 020039
ATLANT 3D, Taastrup, Denmark
Borowski, Peter 020307
Avancis, Munich, Germany
Borriello, Aniello 020378
ENEA, Portici, Italy
Borzi, Giovanni 020019
Enginsoft, Padua, Italy
Bosch, Elina 020252, 020543, 020564, 020573
Becquerel Institute, Brussels, Belgium
Bosma, Theo 020571
DNV, Arnhem, The Netherlands
Bothe, Karsten 020236
ISFH, Emmerthal, Germany
Bou-Nassif, Liliane 020338
CETHIL, Villeurbanne, France
Bouchier, Daniel 020058
CNRS, Palaiseau, France
Bouguerra, Sara 020156, 020294, 020389, 020393
imec, Genk, Belgium
Bourdin, Vincent 020406
CNRS, Paris, France
Bourgeois, Antoine 020102
SERIS, Singapore, Singapore
Bovesecchi, Gianluigi 020494
University of Rome Tor Vergata, Rome, Italy
Brabec, Christoph J. 020117
HI ERN, Erlangen, Germany
Bradford, David Roy 020077
Newcastle University, Newcastle upon Tyne, United Kingdom
Brailovsky, Peter Henri 020475
Fraunhofer ISE, Freiburg, Germany
Braña, Alejandro F. 020508
Autonomous University of Madrid, Madrid, Spain

Brandstätter, Andreas Lenzing Plastics, Lenzing, Austria	020227
Braun, Christian Luxembourg Institute of Science and Technology, Esch-sur-Alzette, Luxembourg	020457
Brecl, Kristijan University of Ljubljana, Ljubljana, Slovenia	020269, 020319
Bredemeier, Dennis Leibniz University Hannover, Hannover, Germany	020240
Breitenbücher, Marian Highline Technologies, Freiburg, Germany	020225
Brendel, Rolf ISFH, Emmerthal, Germany	020006, 020008, 020236, 020240, 020260, 020482
Brendstrup Møller, Clara Bolette DTU, Roskilde, Denmark	020028
Bretzel, Tamara Fraunhofer ISE, Freiburg, Germany	020195
Breyer, Christian LUT University, Lappeenranta, Finland	020479
Brito, Miguel University of Lisbon, Lisbon, Portugal	020457
Brivio, Elisabetta RSE, Milan, Italy	020462
Brockmann, Lukas ISFH, Emmerthal, Germany	020063
Brodnicke, Linda ETH, Zurich, Switzerland	020296
Brueckner, Emanuel ISFH, Emmerthal, Germany	020063
Bründlinger, Roland AIT, Vienna, Austria	020369
Brun, Gonzalo ENDEF, Zaragoza, Spain	020414, 020517
Bruno, Maddalena Fraunhofer ISE, Freiburg, Germany	020452
Buceta, Alicia CENER, Sarriguren, Spain	020300
Bucher, Christof BFH, Burgdorf, Switzerland	020179, 020322, 020359, 020369, 020386
Buchholz, Florian ISC Konstanz, Konstanz, Germany	020035, 020225, 020569
Buchmann, Johanna Berlin University of Applied Sciences, Berlin, Germany	020309
Buck, Thomas ISC Konstanz, Konstanz, Germany	020033

Buckland, Daniel 020119, 020218
Henkel, Düsseldorf, Germany
Buddana, Viswa Harinath 020482
DLR, Oldenburg, Germany
Bühlmann, Gian-Luca 020385
ZHAW, Winterthur, Switzerland
Buerhop, Claudia 020149, 020150, 020377
HI ERN, Erlangen, Germany
Buerhop-Lutz, Claudia 020185, 020230
HI ERN, Erlangen, Germany
Burgers, Antonius R. 020405
TNO, Petten, The Netherlands
Burri, Matthias 020179
BFH, Burgdorf, Switzerland
Busto, Chiara 020521
Eni, Novara, Italy
Butrichi, Fabio 020087
University of Milano-Bicocca, Milan, Italy
Butt, Nauman 020394
Lahore University of Management Sciences, Lahore, Pakistan

C. Tavares, Fabiele 020090
Federal University of Rio de Janeiro, Duque de Caxias, Brazil
Cabal, Raphael 020034
University Grenoble Alpes, Le Bourget-du-Lac, France
Caballero, Luis Jaime 020501, 020508
UPM, Madrid, Spain
Caballero, Raquel 020094
CSIC, Madrid, Spain
Caballero, Raquel 020085
IO-CSIC, Madrid, Spain
Cabecinha, Vasco 020565
Nova University Lisbon, Lisbon, Portugal
Cabello, Fatima 020085
IO-CSIC, Madrid, Spain
Caçapietra Pires da Silva, Lucas Teixeira 020025
PUCRS, Porto Alegre, Brazil
Caccavelli, Dominique 020551
CSTB, Bussy-Saint Georges, France
Caccivio, Mauro 020204, 020574
SUPSI, Mendrisio, Switzerland
Caffari, Francesca 020551
ENEA, Ispra, Italy
Calabrese, Nicolandrea 020551
ENEA, Ispra, Italy

Calin, Jean-Paul 020251
ENSTA Paris, Palaiseau, France

Çalışkan Arslan, Meriç 020006, 020135
Kalyon PV, Ankara, Türkiye

Caluori, Philip 020455
Virtual Vehicle, Graz, Austria

Camara, Assa 020274
Solargis, Bratislava, Slovakia

Cambarau, Werther 020139
Tecnalia, Donostia-San Sebastián, Spain

Campana, Pietro Elia 020381
Mälardalen University, Västerås, Sweden

Campos Guzman, Laura 020331
DLR, Almería, Spain

Cancro, Carmine 020378
ENEA, Naples, Italy

Canesse, Auriane 020196
PVsyst, Geneva, Switzerland

Cañizo, Carlos 020097
IES-UPM, Madrid, Spain

Cano, Francisco J. 020139
Tecnalia, Donostia - San Sebastián, Spain

Cano, Lucía 020127
ENDEF, Zaragoza, Spain

Cánovas, Enrique 020508
IMDEA Nanoscience Institute, Madrid, Spain

Cao, Han 020263
SERIS, Singapore, Singapore

Capitaine, Anna 020116
IPVF, Palaiseau, France

Cappelle, Jan 020329, 020351
KU Leuven, Ghent, Belgium

Capron, Guillaume 020217
CEA / INES, Le Bourget-du-Lac, France

Carballo López, José Antonio 020336
University of Almería, La Cañada de San Urbano, Spain

Cardenas, Luis Alejandro 020339, 020546
National University of Colombia, Bogotá, Colombia

Carmo, Paulo 020304, 020420
University of Évora, Évora, Portugal

Carrasco, Luis Miguel 020439, 020535, 020567
UPM, Madrid, Spain

Carrillo Mejía, Luis 020279
District University of Bogotá, Bogotá, Colombia

Carrillo, Rafael E. 020238
CSEM, Neuchâtel, Switzerland

Carroy, Perrine 020226
CEA/ INES, Le Bourget-du-Lac, France
Carstens, Justus 020003
ISC Konstanz, Konstanz, Germany
Cartenì, Fabrizio 020378
University of Naples Federico II, Naples, Italy
Casappa, Michele 020087
National Research Council, Parma, Italy
Casasola Paesa, Marta 020389
Hasselt University, Diepenbeek, Belgium
Castilla Nieto, María del Mar 020336
University of Almería, La Cañada de San Urbano, Spain
Castillo Patton, Daniel Jason 020326
Enertis Applus+, Madrid, Spain
Castro, Luis Guilherme 020530
Casa dos Ventos, Fortaleza, Brazil
Castro, Rui 020464
University of Lisbon, Lisbon, Portugal
Castro-Gallardo, Fernando 020417, 020422
University of Antofagasta, Antofagasta, Chile
Cavaco, Afonso 020304, 020565
University of Évora, Évora, Portugal
Cebecauer, Tomas 020274
Solargis, Bratislava, Slovakia
Çekerek, Gamze 020006
Kalyon PV, Ankara, Türkiye
Celik, Duygu 020551
WIP Renewable Energies, Munich, Germany
Çeliktaş, Melih Soner 020559
Ege University, İzmir, Türkiye
Centazzo, Massimo 020006
EnPV, Karlsruhe, Germany
Centeno Brito, Miguel 020421, 020490
University of Lisbon, Lisbon, Portugal
Cereceda, Eneko 020055, 020097, 020153, 020287
UPV/EHU, Bilbao, Spain
Ceretti, Mattia 020204
SUPSI, Mendrisio, Switzerland
Cesar, I. 020405
TNO, Petten, The Netherlands
Ceuppens, Ignas 020302
BUILD`UP, Aarschot, Belgium
Chatterji, Nithin 020071
SVNIT, Surat, India
Chen, Daniel 020048
SunDrive Solar, Kurnell, Australia

Chen, Syh-Homg 020161
ITRI, Hsinchu, Taiwan

Chen, Xiang 020111
Hohai University, Changzhou, China

Cheung, Kak Pong 020313
Kiel University of Applied Sciences, Kiel, Germany

Chhapia, Gaurang 020492
Belectric, Kolitzheim, Germany

Chiba, Takahiro 020436
Hokkaido University of Science, Sapporo, Japan

Chichignoud, Guy 020495
13Institut Polytechnique De Grenoble, Grenoble, France

Chicote, Beatriz 020289
Mondragon University, Arrasate-Mondragon, Spain

Chiesa, Matteo 020487
Khalifa University, Abu Dhabi, United Arab Emirates

Chini de Freitas, Felipe 020023
PUCRS, Porto Alegre, Brazil

Cho, Yunae 020045
KIER, Daejeon, South Korea

Choi, Kwan Bum 020102
SERIS, Singapore, Singapore

Chouder, Aissa 020301
University of M'sila, M'sila, Algeria

Chowdhury, Gofran 020276, 020544
3E, Brussels, Belgium

Christ, Anja 020063
ISFH, Emmerthal, Germany

Chrkavy, Daniel 020262
Solargis, Bratislava, Slovakia

Chueh, Wei-Lo 020021
TSEC, Hsinchu, Taiwan

Ciesla, Alison 020065
UNSW, Sydney, Australia

Cirimele, Vincenzo 020314
University of Bologna, Bologna, Italy

Clausing, Roland 020063, 020114
ISFH, Emmerthal, Germany

Clochard, Laurent 020031
Nines Photovoltaics, Dublin, Germany

Clochard, Laurent 020007
Nines Photovoltaics, Dublin, Ireland

Clyncke, Jan 020472, 020513
PV CYCLE, Brussels, Belgium

Coşkun, Özlem 020006, 020027, 020225
Kalyon PV, Ankara, Türkiye

Colberts, Fallon 020389
Zuyd University, Heerlen, The Netherlands

Colin, Hervé 020217, 020262
CEA / INES, Le Bourget-du-Lac, France

Collin, Stéphane 020074
C2N, Palaiseau, France

Colwell, Jack 020048
SunDrive Solar, Kurnell, Australia

Comak, Mertcan 020003
ISC Konstanz, Konstanz, Germany

Connolly, James Patrick 020058, 020060
CNRS, Gif-sur-Yvette, France

Cordeiro, Diogo 020464
EDP, Lisbon, Portugal

Cornago, Iñaki 020392
CENER, Sarriguren, Spain

Cornaro, Cristina 020494
University of Rome Tor Vergata, Rome, Italy

Correa, Guillermo 020412
Gonvarri MS R&D, Corvera - Asturias, Spain

Correia, Joana 020565
University of Évora, Évora, Portugal

Couderc, Romain 020217, 020311, 020546
CEA / INES, Le Bourget-du-Lac, France

Coutel, John 020244
SOLAÏS, Valbonne, France

Cowan, Don 020230
Kiwa PI Berlin, Hudson, United States of America

Cox, Joel D. 020250
SDU Climate Cluster, Odense, Denmark

Cox, Joel D 020306
SDU Climate Cluster, Odense, Denmark

Coz, Pier Luigi 020246
European Space Agency, Noordwijk, The Netherlands

Crespo, Carolina 020490
University of Lisbon, Lisbon, Portugal

Cristiane Pan, Aline 020548
UFRGS, Tramandaí, Brazil

Cristóbal, Ana Belén 020491, 020535, 020575
UPM, Madrid, Spain

Crozier McCleland, Jacqueline 020185, 020344
Nelson Mandela University, Port Elizabeth, South Africa

Cuadra, Juan Manuel 020318
CENER, Sarigurren, Spain

Cui, Jindan 020320, 020525
Tokyo University of Science, Tokyo, Japan

Culot, Dominique 020384
Dow Silicones Belgium, Seneffe, Belgium
Curon, Jonathan 020384
Dow Silicones Belgium, Seneffe, Belgium
Cusenza, Maria Anna 020466
RSE, Milan, Italy

D. Pinto, Luciana 020090
Federal University of Rio de Janeiro, Rio de Janeiro, Brazil
Daenen, Michael 020156, 020389, 020393
imec, Genk, Belgium
Dagla, Anastasia 020276
3E, Brussels, Belgium
Dahle, Arne 020225, 020495
Norsun, Oslo, Norway
Dahlioui, Dounia 020443
University of Agder, Grimstad, Norway
Dalibor, Thomas 020307
Avancis, Munich, Germany
Dalla Maria, Enrico 020485
Eurac Research, Bolzano, Italy
Dalla Torre, Francesco 020010
Applied Materials, Treviso, Italy
Dalmazzone, Didier 020251
ENSTA Paris, Palaiseau, France
Damon, Keanu 020382
7SecondSolar, Cape Town, South Africa
Danelli, Andrea 020462, 020466
RSE, Milan, Italy
Darsene Dimd, Berhane 020270
SINTEF, Trondheim, Norway
Das, Gourab 020005, 020222, 020463
RCT Solutions, Konstanz, Germany
Dasilva-Villanueva, Nerea 020014, 020501, 020508
UPM, Madrid, Spain
Daßler, David 020313
Fraunhofer CSP, Halle, Germany
Daßler, David 020355
Fraunhofer IMWS, Halle, Germany
Daume, Darwin 020361
pvnode, Rosenheim, Germany
Davidsen, Rasmus Schmidt 020028, 020039, 020043
Aarhus University, Aarhus, Denmark
De Almeida, Laura 020074
LAAS-CNRS, Toulouse, France

De Biasio, Martin 020504
Silicon Austria Labs, Villach, Austria

De Blasi, Mariam 020378
Enel Green Power, Pisa, Italy

de Graaf, Gertjan J. 020405
TNO, Petten, The Netherlands

de Groot, Koen M. 020405
TNO, Petten, The Netherlands

De Gruijter, Alvaro 020254
Eurac Research, Bolzano, Italy

de Jong, Minne M. 020169, 020425
TNO, Eindhoven, The Netherlands

De Jong, Richard 020156, 020294, 020389
imec, Genk, Belgium

de l`Epine, Mélodie 020252, 020505, 020543, 020564
Becquerel Institute France, Lyon, France

de l`Epine, Melodie 020225, 020334, 020520, 020558
Becquerel Institute, Brussels, Belgium

de l`Epine, Melodie 020570
IEA PVPS Task 1, Lyon, France

de la Casa Higueras, Juan 020269
University of Jaén, Jaén, Spain

de la Viuda, Eva 020205
University of Valladolid, Valladolid, Spain

de Meatza, Iratxe 020495
CIDETEC, San Sebastián, Spain

De Rose, Angela 020123
Fraunhofer ISE, Freiburg, Germany

De Rose, Jonas 020010
Fraunhofer ISE, Freiburg, Germany

Debastiani Benato, Betina 020019
AMIRES, Prague, Czech Republic

Deepti, 020563
SRM University, Sonipat, India

Del Campo, Valeria 020311
Federico Santa María Technical University, Valparaiso, Chile

del Cañizo, Carlos 020014, 020501, 020507, 020508
UPM, Madrid, Spain

Del Pero, Claudio 020249
Polytechnic University of Milan, Milan, Italy

Del Pozo, Alberto 020197, 020198
TECNALIA, Derio, Spain

del Prado Santamaria, Rodrigo 020191, 020376
DTU, Roskilde, Denmark

del Ser, Javier 020358
UPV/EHU, Bilbao, Spain

Delgado-Sanchez, Jose Maria 020089
University of Seville, Seville, Spain

Delli Veneri, Paola 020378
ENEA, Naples, Italy

Denafas, Julius 020225, 020353
Solitek, Vilnius, Lithuania

Deniz, Engin 020559
Ege University, İzmir, Türkiye

Denke, Sebastian 020236
ISFH, Emmerthal, Germany

Dentz, Laurie 020058
CNRS, Palaiseau, France

Derin Gure, Pinar 020513, 020521, 020556
ODTU GUNAM, Ankara, Türkiye

Derj, Anyssa 020116
IPVF, Palaiseau, France

Dessì, Alessio 020077
CNR-ICCOM, Sesto Fiorentino, Italy

Devenson, Jan 020157
Center for Physical Sciences and Technology (FTMC), Vilnius, Lithuania

Dhimish, Mahmoud 020346, 020376
DTU, Roskilde, Denmark

Di Matteo, Alfredo 020010
Enel Green Power, Catania, Italy

Diab, Mohanad 020203
Eurac Research, Bolzano, Italy

Diano, Marcello 020378
M2M Engineering, Naples, Italy

Diaz, Roberto 020300
Notio Association, Toledo, Spain

Díaz, Sara 020365, 020366
CENER, Sarriguren, Spain

Dietrich, Andreas 020355
DiSUN Deutsche Solarservice, Werder, Germany

Díez Alcántara, Eduardo 020501
UCM, Madrid, Spain

Díez, Eduardo 020508
UCM, Madrid, Spain

Dimd, Berhane Darsene 020495, 020510
SINTEF, Trondheim, Norway

Ding, Kaining 020233
FZJ, Jülich, Germany

Ding, Kung 020111
Hohai University, Changzhou, China

Dittmann, Sebastian 020318
Anhalt University of Applied Sciences, Köthen, Germany

Dittrich, Arne ISFH, Emmerthal, Germany	020240
Dizier, Antoine INES, Le Bourget-du-Lac, France	020373
Djeukeu, Ivanol Jaurece halm elektronik, Frankfurt am Main, Germany	020050
Dobreva, Petja University of Namibia, Windhoek, Namibia	020193
Dörenkämper, Maarten TNO, Eindhoven, The Netherlands	020169
Dörn, Markus A-Null Development, Vienna, Austria	020255
Doi, Minh Thong CEA INES, Le Bourget-du-Lac, France	020317
Domínguez, César UPM, Madrid, Spain	020209, 020246, 020257
Donadello, Alessandro Edyna, Bolzano, Italy	020485, 020489
Donėlienė, Jolanta Applied Research Institute for Prospective Technologies, Vilnius, Lithuania	020157
Donoso, José UNEF, Madrid, Spain	020570
Doppler, Christian Virtual Vehicle, Graz, Austria	020455
dos Reis, Givaldo University of São Paulo, São Paulo, Brazil	020348
dos Santos, Jeremias University of Évora, Évora, Portugal	020409
Doucet, Jean-Baptiste LAAS-CNRS, Toulouse, France	020074
Dovesi, Roberto Academy of Sciences of Turin, Torino, Italy	020060
Driesse, Anton PV Performance Labs, Freiburg, Germany	020211, 020293, 020452
Duarte, Dorivaldo University of Evora, Évora, Portugal	020418, 020565
Dubois, Sebastien University Grenoble Alpes, Le Bourget-du-Lac, France	020034
Dubravskij, Piotr Applied Research Institute for Prospective Technologies, Vilnius, Lithuania	020157
Dubravskij, Piotr Modern E-Technologies, Vilnius, Lithuania	020380
Duerinckx, Filip Hasselt Unversity, Genk, Belgium	020064, 020225

Düz, Cansel 020135
Kalyon PV, Ankara, Türkiye

Dullweber, Thorsten 020006, 020007, 020008, 020225
ISFH, Emmerthal, Germany

Dunlop, Ewan D. 020173, 020210, 020213
European Commission JRC, Ispra, Italy

Dupon, Olivier 020294
imec, Genk, Belgium

Dupuis, Julien 020188
EDF R&D, Moret Loing Orvanne, France

Dutykh, Denys 020338
Khalifa University, Abu Dhabi, United Arab Emirates

Duzellier, Sophie 020073
University of Toulouse, Toulouse, France

Dypvik Sødahl, Elin 020340
IFE, Kjeller, Norway

Ebert, Matthias 020426
Fraunhofer CSP, Halle, Germany

Ebert, Matthias 020355
Fraunhofer IMWS, Halle, Germany

Ebner, Rita 020318, 020334, 020521
AIT, Vienna, Austria

Echeverria, Oihane 020139
Tecnalia, Donostia - San Sebastián, Spain

Eder, Gabriele C. 020160, 020162, 020249, 020500, 020504
OFI, Vienna, Austria

Eelma, Tonis 020302
IBS, Tartu, Estonia

Efthymiou, Venizelos 020544
EPL Technology Frontiers, Dhali, Cyprus

Egan, Renate 020048
UNSW, Sydney, Australia

Egido, Miguel-Ángel 020407
UPM, Madrid, Spain

Eidtmann, Maximilian 020385
ZHAW, Winterthur, Switzerland

Eijgelaar, Marcel 020571
DNV, Arnhem, The Netherlands

Eikelboom, Erik 020225
Futurasun, Citadella, Italy

Einhaus, Roland 020312
ZSW, Stuttgart, Germany

Eisenacher, Matthias 020141
University of Applied Science Cologne, Cologne, Germany

Eiternick, Stefan 020004, 020052
Fraunhofer CSP, Halle (Saale), Germany
Ekins-Daukes, Nicholas J. 020065
UNSW, Sydney, Australia
El Ainaoui, Khadija 020171
Green Energy Park, Benguerir, Morocco
El mrabet, Yasmine 020171
Green Energy Park, Benguerir, Morocco
Elgaili, Mohamed 020166
QEERI, Doha, Qatar
Elhamaoui, Said 020171
Green Energy Park, Benguerir, Morocco
Ellis, Hanna 020213
European Commission JRC, Ispra, Italy
Engelen, Tine 020389
Hasselt University, Diepenbeek, Belgium
Erber, Alexander 020386
BFH, Burgdorf, Switzerland
Eryılmaz, Hande 020521
ODTÜ-GÜNAM, Ankara, Türkiye
Escudero, Ana 020414
IaSol, Zaragoza, Spain
Esmailifar, Seyyed Majid 020335, 020356, 020374, 020375
Amirkabir University of Technology, Tehran, Iran
Espinosa, Nieves 020497, 020506
University of Murcia, Murcia, Spain
Essam T. Mohammed, Sarah 020546
EU SOLARIS, Almeria, Spain
Esteras, Miguel 020358
TECNALIA, Derio, Spain
Eyhorn, Steffen 020369
Fraunhofer ISE, Freiburg, Germany

Fabel, Yann 020235, 020237, 020239
DLR, Almería, Spain
Fabris, Francesca 020225
Futurasun, Citadella, Italy
Faes, Antonin 020251
CSEM, Neuchâtel, Switzerland
Falangas, Alexandros 020210
TRASIS International, Brussels, Belgium
Fang, Xue 020525
Tokyo University of Science, Tokyo, Japan
Fano, Vanesa 020055, 020097, 020153, 020287
UPV/EHU, Bilbao, Spain

Farhat, Mohammad 020428
Australian University, Kuwait City, Kuwait

Farina, Andrea 020066
CNR-IFN, Milan, Italy

Farrias-Basulto, Guillermo 020101
HZB, Berlin, Germany

Fath, Moritz 020463
RCT Solutions, Konstanz, Germany

Fath, Peter 020005, 020463
RCT Solutions, Konstanz, Germany

Fava, Henrique 020565
University of Évora, Évora, Portugal

Feichtner, Markus 020255
Sonnenkraft Energie, St. Veit/Glan, Austria

Feichtner, Markus 020160
Sonnenkraft Energy, St. Veit/Glan, Austria

Feldbacher, Sonja 020136, 020500
PCCL, Leoben, Austria

Feldhof, Anne Maren 020522
University of Applied Science Cologne, Cologne, Germany

Fernandes, Cláudia 020464
Centre for New Energy Technologies, Sacavém, Portugal

Fernández Solas, Álvaro 020331
DLR, Almería, Spain

Ferrando, Jorge 020226
University of Valencia, Paterna, Spain

Ferreira, Catarina G. 020250
SDU Climate Cluster, Odense, Denmark

Ferreira, Catarina 020306
SDU Climate Cluster, Odense, Denmark

Ferrero, Sergio 020079
Polytechnic University of Turin, Turin, Italy

Feuerherdt, Niels 020309
Berlin University of Applied Sciences, Berlin, Germany

Fialho, Luis 020203, 020254, 020261, 020304, 020403, 020409, 020418, 020420, 020565
Eurac Research, Bolzano, Italy

Figueroa, Andrés 020339
National University of Colombia, Bogotá, Colombia

Fischer, Stefan 020495
SGL Carbon, Meitingen, Germany

Fleischanderl, Martin 020136
voestalpine Stahl, Linz, Austria

Fleury, Perine 020513, 020521
Biosphere Solar, Delft, The Netherlands

Flouchi, Imane 020171
Green Energy Park, Benguerir, Morocco

Fodor, Nikoletta 020521
SolarPower Europe, Brussels, Belgium

Fontani, Daniela 020066
CNR-INO, Florence, Italy

Forster, Jacob 020135
Fraunhofer ISE, Freiburg, Germany

Forstinger, Anne 020331
CSP Services, Cologne, Germany

Franch, Jordi Badosa 020406
Ecole Polytechnique, Palaiseau, France

Franchi, Daniele 020077
CNR-ICCOM, Sesto Fiorentino, Italy

Franquet, Erwin 020259, 020428
Côte d`Azur University, Nice, France

Frasson, Nicola 020019
Applied Materials, San Biagio di Callalta, Italy

Freer, Solomon 020396
PV Lighthouse, Coledale, Australia

Freitag, Marina 020077
Newcastle University, Newcastle upon Tyne, United Kingdom

Freund, Timo 020312
EnBW, Karlsruhe, Germany

Friansyah, Rizal 020376
DTU, Roskilde, Denmark

Friesen, Gabi 020160, 020249, 020574
SUPSI, Mendrisio, Switzerland

Friesen, Thomas 020249
Megasol Energie, Deitingen, Switzerland

Fritz Muñoz, Benjamín 020099
UPV, Valencia, Spain

Froebel, Jens 020121, 020142, 020192, 020223
Fraunhofer CSP, Halle, Germany

Frontini, Francesco 020249, 020253
SUPSI, Mendrisio, Switzerland

Fuentealba-Vidal, Edward 020129, 020311, 020342, 020417, 020422
University of Antofagasta, Antofagasta, Chile

Füreder-Kitzmüller, Friedrich 020136
voestalpine Stahl, Linz, Austria

Fuertes Marrón, David 020014, 020501, 020507, 020508
UPM, Madrid, Spain

Fuertes, David 020097
IES-UPM, Madrid, Spain

Furnari, Alessandro 020010
Enel Green Power, Catania, Italy

Fuß, Michael 020206
MBJ Solutions, Ahrensburg, Germany

Gabor, Andrew M. 020166
BrightSpot Automation, Boulder, United States of America

Gaete, Martin 020311
University of Antofagasta, Antofagasta, Chile

Gafert, Michael 020369
AIT, Vienna, Austria

Gageot, Tristan 020040
CEA / INES, Le Bourget-du-Lac, France

Gainza, Eusebio 020392
ALLOTARRA, Allo, Spain

Galarza, Alejandra 020461
IPVF, Palaiseau, France

Galbiati, Giuseppe 020119, 020218
Henkel, Düsseldorf, Germany

Galdikas, Algirdas 020157
Applied Research Institute for Prospective Technologies, Vilnius, Lithuania

Galiana, Beatriz 020085
Charles III University of Madrid, Madrid, Spain

Galiazzo, Marco 020019
Applied Materials, San Biagio di Callalta, Italy

Gall, Stefan 020101
HZB, Berlin, Germany

Gallmetzer, Sandra 020261, 020509
Eurac Research, Bolzano, Italy

Galparsoro, Ibon 020514
AZTI, PASAIA, Spain

Gamarra, Ana Rosa 020502
CIEMAT, Madrid, Spain

Ganter, Alissa 020296
ETH, Zurich, Switzerland

Gaona García, Elvis Eduardo 020279
District University of Bogotá, Bogotá, Colombia

Garabetian, Thomas 020551
SolarPower Europe, Brussels, Belgium

García Campos, Enrique 020336
University of Almería, La Cañada de San Urbano, Spain

García, Fernando 020326
UC3M, Madrid, Spain

García, Sonia 020139
Tecnalia, Donostia - San Sebastián, Spain

García-Cañas, Alejandro 020257
IMDEA Nanoscience, Madrid, Spain

García-Salinas, María José 020100
University of Almeria, Almería, Spain

Garcia-Sanchez, Almudena 020246, 020257
UPM, Madrid, Spain
Garg, Vivek 020069, 020071, 020081
SVNIT, Surat, India
Garraín, Daniel 020502
CIEMAT, Madrid, Spain
Gasse, Hugues 020073
University of Toulouse, Toulouse, France
Gassner, Anika 020160, 020162, 020500, 020504
OFI, Vienna, Austria
Gatti, Cesare 020541
PedersoliGattai, Milan, Italy
Gattu, Apoorva 020003
ISC Konstanz, Konstanz, Germany
Gautier, Damien 020505
Becquerel Institute, Brussels, Belgium
Gauvin, Xavier 020302
Bouygues Construction, Saint-Quentin-en-Yvelines, France
Ge, Hua 020249
Concordia University, Montreal, Canada
Gebhardt, Paul 020195
Fraunhofer ISE, Freiburg, Germany
Geerligs, L. J. 020030
TNO, Petten, The Netherlands
Gehrlein, Janek 020522
University of Applied Science Cologne, Cologne, Germany
Geier, Jutta 020234
PCCL, Leoben, Austria
Geml, Fabian 020031
University of Konstanz, Constance, Germany
Genovese, Maria 020378
Enel Green Power, Pisa, Italy
Georghiou, George E. 020534
University of Cyprus, Nicosia, Cyprus
Germani, Simone 020302
CEI, Milan, Italy
Getsiou, Maria 020181
Directorate General for Research and Innovation, Brussels, Belgium
Geymayer, Lukas 020136
voestalpine Stahl, Linz, Austria
Ghahremani, Amirreza 020335, 020374
Amirkabir University of Technology, Tehran, Iran
Ghennioui, Abdellatif 020171
Green Energy Park, Benguerir, Morocco
Ghosh, Saptak 020519
CSTEP, Bengaluru, India

Girardi, Pierpaolo — 020462, 020466
RSE, Milan, Italy

Giroux-Julien, Stephanie — 020338
CNRS, Villeurbanne, France

Gissler, Antoine — 020060
EDF R&D, Palaiseau, France

Göckeritz, Robert — 020119
Fraunhofer CSP, Halle, Germany

Gohil, Hardik — 020222
RCT Solutions, Konstanz, Germany

Gomes de Venuto, Vitor — 020025
PUCRS, Porto Alegre, Brazil

Gomez Trillos, Juan Camilo — 020482
DLR, Oldenburg, Germany

Gomez-Lazaro, Emilio — 020562
University of Castilla-La Mancha, Albacete, Spain

Gonnella, Gabriella — 020249, 020254
Eurac research, Bolzano, Italy

González Pérez, Sara — 020151
ULL, San Cristóbal de La Laguna, Spain

González Rodríguez, Brais — 020243
University of Vigo, Vigo, Spain

González, Miguel Ángel — 020205
University of Valladolid, Valladolid, Spain

González-Díaz, Benjamín — 020151
ULL, San Cristóbal de La Laguna, Spain

Goraya, Baljeet Singh — 020475
Fraunhofer ISE, Freiburg, Germany

Gordillo, Gerardo — 020110
National University of Colombia, Bogotá, Colombia

Gordon, Ivan — 020521
imec, Genk, Belgium

Gottschalg, Ralph — 020158
Anhalt University of Applied Sciences, Köthen, Germany

Gottschalg, Ralph — 020056, 020201, 020229, 020233, 020284, 020574
Fraunhofer CSP, Halle, Germany

Govaerts, Jonathan — 020019
imec, Genk, Belgium

Gracia Amillo, Ana María — 020211
CENER, Pamplona, Spain

Gracia Amillo, Ana María — 020318
CENER, Sarigurren, Spain

Gracia Amillo, Ana María — 020181, 020365, 020366, 020497
CENER, Sarriguren, Spain

Gregory, Geoffrey — 020006
EnPV, Karlsruhe, Germany

Greslou, Olivier 020551
CSTB, Bussy-Saint Georges, France

Grommes, Eva-Maria 020522, 020523
University of Applied Science Cologne, Cologne, Germany

Grosser, Stephan 020119, 020142, 020218
Fraunhofer CSP, Halle, Germany

Grünsteidl, Stefan 020307
Avancis, Munich, Germany

Gruginskie, Natasha 020067
Radboud University, Nijmegen, The Netherlands

Guedea, Isabel 020127, 020517
ENDEF, Zaragoza, Spain

Gülsoy, Eren Cihan 020521
METU, Ankara, Türkiye

Gümüs Çiftci, Burcu 020027
Kalyon PV, Ankara, Türkiye

Guerra, Gerardo 020448, 020481
GreenPowerMonitor a DNV company, Barcelona, Spain

Guidetti, Giulia 020541
Green Horse Advisory, Milan, Italy

Guillemoles, Jean François 020062
IPVF, Palaiseau, France

Guillevin, Nicolas 020225
TNO, Petten, The Netherlands

Gunbas, Gorkem 020113
ODTÜ-GÜNAM, Ankara, Türkiye

Gupta, Akshit 020551
Eurac Research, Bolzano, Italy

Gutierrez, Jose Ruben 020055, 020097, 020153, 020287
UPV/EHU, Bilbao, Spain

Gutjahr, Astrid 020030
TNO, Petten, The Netherlands

Haaland, Petry Kristine Nøttum 020476
NTNU, Trondheim, Norway

Haase, Felix 020063
ISFH, Emmerthal, Germany

Hadiwidjaja, Stella 020102
SERIS, Singapore, Singapore

Hadjipanayi, Maria 020064
University of Cyprus, Nicosia, Cyprus

Haedrich, Ingrid 020195, 020231
Fraunhofer ISE, Freiburg, Germany

Hämmer, Matthias 020470
bifa Umweltinstitut, Augsburg, Germany

Hafidi, Elias 020511
Inflights BV, Brussels, Belgium
Hagemann, Elizabeth M. 020416
Nelson Mandela University, Port Elizabeth, South Africa
Hallais, Géraldine 020058
CNRS, Palaiseau, France
Halle, Lasse 020359
BFH, Burgdorf, Switzerland
Hallensleben, Carina 020220
TAMURA-ELSOLD, Ilsenburg, Germany
Halm, Andreas 020218, 020220, 020221
ISC Konstanz, Konstanz, Germany
Halme, Janne 020249
Aalto University, Espoo, Finland
Hamada, Toshiyuki 020190
Osaka Electro-Communication University, Osaka, Japan
Hammer, Annette 020239
DLR, Oldenburg, Germany
Hamouda, Frederic 020058
CNRS, Palaiseau, France
Hanifi, Hamed 020121, 020125, 020137, 020223
AESOLAR, Koenigsbrunn, Germany
Hansen, Per-Anders 020017, 020503
Institute for Energy Technology, Kjeller, Norway
Harit, Amit Kumar 020064
Hasselt Unversity, Genk, Belgium
Harrison, Samuel 020225
CEA, Le Bourget-du-Lac, France
Hashem, Ahmad 020056, 020201
Anhalt University of Applied Sciences, Köthen, Germany
Hategan, Sergiu Mihai 020283
West University of Timisoara, Timisoara, Romania
Hauch, Jens 020117, 020149, 020150
HI ERN, Erlangen, Germany
Hauer, Martin 020255
Bartenbach, Vienna, Austria
Haverkamp, Helge 020008
centrotherm international, Blaubeuren, Germany
Hee Lee, Sang 020045
KIER, Daejeon, South Korea
Heidrich, Robert 020233
Fraunhofer CSP, Halle, Germany
Heikkinen, Kyösti 020423
VTT Technical Research Centre of Finland, Oulu, Finland
Heiser, Moritz 020230
Kiwa PI Berlin, Berlin, Germany

Helbig, Matthias ISC Konstanz, Konstanz, Germany	020220
Helten, David CSP Services, Cologne, Germany	020331
Hennig, Carsten saferay holding, Berlin, Germany	020313, 020355
Hennig, Patrick Kiel University of Applied Sciences, Kiel, Germany	020313
Heras, Jesús Wattkraft, Madrid, Spain	020536
Hermle, Martin Fraunhofer ISE, Freiburg, Germany	020475
Hernández Mora, Johann Alexander District University of Bogotá, Bogotá, Colombia	020279, 020441
Hernández, Jaime J. IMDEA Nanoscience, Madrid, Spain	020257
Hernández, Johann Francisco José de Caldas District University, Bogota, Colombia	020526
Herodotou, Panayiotis University of Cyprus, Nicosia, Cyprus	020534
Herrera Leon, Fernando Augusto National University of Colombia, Bogotá, Colombia	020339, 020546
Herrero, Leire Tecnalia, Donostia - San Sebastián, Spain	020139
Herrero, Rebeca UPM, Madrid, Spain	020209, 020453, 020459
Herrmann, Werner TÜV Rheinland Solar, Cologne, Germany	020208
Herteleer, Bert KU Leuven, Ghent, Belgium	020329, 020351
Herteleer, Bert SUPSI, Mendrisio, Switzerland	020574
Hessler-Wyser, Aïcha EPFL, Neuchâtel, Switzerland	020251
Heydari, Azim Eurac Research, Bolzano, Italy	020485
Hinken, David ISFH, Emmerthal, Germany	020236
Hladys, Bertrand CEA, Grenoble, France	020010
Hoex, Bram UNSW, Sydney, Australia	020065
Hofer, Leo BFH, Burgdorf, Switzerland	020322
Hoffmann, Erik EnPV, Karlsruhe, Germany	020006

Hogan Almeida, Rita — 020535, 020567
UPM, Madrid, Spain

Hollemann, Christina — 020008
ISFH, Emmerthal, Germany

Holovský, Jakub — 020107
Czech Technical University, Prague, Czech Republic

Honrubia-Escribano, Andrés — 020562
University of Castilla-La Mancha, Albacete, Spain

Hopp, Tobias — 020384
Sunman Energy, Frankfurt, Germany

Horn, Jonas — 020050
halm elektronik, Frankfurt am Main, Germany

Horta, Pedro — 020304, 020403, 020409, 020418, 020420, 020565
University of Évora, Évora, Portugal

Hosatte, Mikaël — 020068
SEGTON Advanced Technology, Versailles, France

Hoß, Jan — 020004, 020035
ISC Konstanz, Konstanz, Germany

Hossain, Mohammad Istiaque — 020042, 020075, 020108, 020109, 020146, 020147
QEERI, Doha, Qatar

Hou, Yi — 020102
SERIS, Singapore, Singapore

Hsiao, Pei-Chieh — 020048
UNSW, Sydney, Australia

Hsieh, Cho Fan — 020083, 020161, 020163
ITRI, Hsinchu, Taiwan

Hu, Shuaifeng — 020226
University of Oxford, Oxford, United Kingdom

Huang, Chris — 020048
SunDrive Solar, Kurnell, Australia

Huang, Gan — 020272
KIT, Eggenstein-Leopoldshafen, Germany

Huang, Lu-Jan — 020425
TNO, Leiden, The Netherlands

Huang, Tzu-Yen — 020096
National Synchrotron Radiation Research Center, Hsinchu, Taiwan

Hügi, Matthias — 020322
BFH, Burgdorf, Switzerland

Huemer, Martin — 020227
University of Linz, Linz, Austria

Huerta, Hugo E. — 020286, 020400
TUAS, Turku, Finland

Hüttl, Bernd — 020361
Coburg University of Applied Sciences, Coburg, Germany

Hulik Jansova, Marketa 020274
Solargis, Bratislava, Slovakia

Hung, Tzu Han 020552
ITRI, Taipei City, Taiwan

Hutterer-Tik, Thomas 020347
Watt Analytics, Vienna, Austria

Hwang, Hye-Mi 020324, 020357, 020561
KIER, Daejeon, South Korea

Iglesias, Unai 020139
Tecnalia, Donostia - San Sebastián, Spain

Ikeda, Kazuaki 020436
AIST, Koriyama, Japan

Infante, Paulo 020420
University of Évora, Évora, Portugal

Isabella, Olindo 020515
TU Delft, Delft, The Netherlands

Ishikawa, Ryousuke 020106, 020115
Tokyo City University, Setagaya, Japan

Iwaszko, Victorien 020495
ROSI Solar, Saint-Martin-d'Hères, France

Izquierdo-Roca, Victor 020094
IREC, Barcelona, Spain

J. N. Soares, Guillermo 020090
Federal University of Rio de Janeiro, Duque de Caxias, Brazil

Jacob, Julieu 020302
METABUILD, Berlin, Germany

Jacobs, Ayesha 020382
Zutari, Cape Town, South Africa

Jaeckel, Bengt 020056, 020119, 020121, 020140, 020142, 020175, 020192, 020201, 020223, 020229
Fraunhofer CSP, Halle, Germany

Jäger Waldau, Arnulf 020570
European Commission, Rome, Italy

Jäger, Philip 020006
ISFH, Emmerthal, Germany

Jäggi, Adrian 020179
BFH, Burgdorf, Switzerland

Järventausta, Pertti 020445
Tampere University, Tampere, Finland

Jaffré, Alexandre 020058
CNRS, Gif-sur-Yvette, France

Jahn, Ulrike 020521, 020574
Fraunhofer CSP, Halle, Germany

Jahn, Ulrike — 020355
Fraunhofer IMWS, Halle, Germany

Jahreis, Sophia — 020142, 020192
Fraunhofer CSP, Halle, Germany

Jakomin, Roberto — 020090
Federal University of Rio de Janeiro, Duque de Caxias, Brazil

Jakubik, Martin — 020274
Solargis, Bratislava, Slovakia

Jakuza, Paola — 020089
University of Padova, Padova, Italy

Jalkh, Judy — 020455
Virtual Vehicle, Graz, Austria

Jandl, Ralf — 020204
FFHS, Zurich, Switzerland

Jankovec, Marko — 020197
University of Ljubljana, Ljubljana, Slovenia

Jaworczak, Kamil — 020402
Technology Innovation Institute, Abu Dhabi, United Arab Emirates

Jensen, Adam R. — 020267
DTU, Kongens Lyngby, Denmark

Jeong, Jungi — 020323
K-water, Daejeon, South Korea

Jeong, Kyung Taek — 020045
KIER, Daejeon, South Korea

Jeong, Minsoo — 020045
KIER, Daejeon, South Korea

Jeronimo, Pedro — 020010
CEA, Grenoble, France

Jiang, Zonghan — 020158, 020201
Anhalt University of Applied Sciences, Köthen, Germany

Jimenez, Maria — 020302
Onyx Solar, Avila, Spain

Jimeno, Juan Carlos — 020055, 020097, 020153, 020287, 020289, 020353
UPV/EHU, Bilbao, Spain

Jo, Hyunsik — 020323
K-water, Daejeon, South Korea

Job, Enzo — 020231
Fraunhofer ISE, Freiburg, Germany

Johnson, Mark Robert — 020546
Institut Laue-Langevin (ILL), Grenoble, France

Joo, Dongmyoung — 020449
KETI, Wonmi-gu, South Korea

Jooss, Wolfgang — 020005, 020222, 020463
RCT Solutions, Konstanz, Germany

Joseph, Daniel Christopher 020123
Fraunhofer ISE, Freiburg, Germany

Joshi, Deepak 020069, 020081
SVNIT, Surat, India

Joss, David 020359, 020369, 020386
BFH, Burgdorf, Switzerland

Jouini, Anis 020034
ECM Technologies, Grenoble, France

Jouttijärvi, Sami 020286, 020298, 020398
University of Turku, Turku, Finland

Joziak, Roman 020230
Kiwa PI Berlin, Berlin, Germany

Ju, Young-Chul 020324, 020357, 020561
KIER, Daejeon, South Korea

Jugo, Josu 020437
UPV/EHU, Leioa, Spain

Junge, Sebastian 020008, 020482
ISFH, Emmerthal, Germany

Kaaya, Ismail 020156, 020294, 020389, 020393
imec, Genk, Belgium

Kähler, Jan-Dirk 020482
Centrotherm International, Blaubeuren, Germany

Kahraman, Mert 020027
Kalyon PV, Ankara, Türkiye

Kainz, Konrad 020430
AIT, Vienna, Austria

Kaiser, Martin 020215
Fraunhofer ISE, Freiburg, Germany

Kaizuka, Izumi 020570
RTS Corporation, Tokyo, Japan

Kajari-Schröder, Sarah 020063
ISFH, Emmerthal, Germany

Kallioharju, Kari 020444, 020445
TUAS, Tampere, Finland

Kalliojärvi, Heidi 020194
Tampere University, Tampere, Finland

Kalshetty, Mahesh 020519
CSTEP, Bengaluru, India

Kaltenbach, Thomas 020195
Fraunhofer ISE, Freiburg, Germany

Kamphues, Joshua 020031
University of Konstanz, Constance, Germany

Kandiyoti-Eskenazi, Selin 020467
CSEM, Neuchâtel, Switzerland

Kang, Min Gu 020045
KIER, Daejeon, South Korea

Kapetanovic, Viktor 020367
Nextracker, Fremont, United States of America

Karhu, Juha 020286
Finnish Meteorological Institute, Helsinki, Finland

Kari, Thøger 020191, 020376
DTU, Roskilde, Denmark

Karimy, Hedayatullah 020052
Fraunhofer CSP, Halle (Saale), Germany

Karttunen, Lauri 020298, 020398
University of Turku, Turku, Finland

Kasper, Ruth 020167, 020232
University of Applied Sciences Cologne, Cologne, Germany

Katouli, Tannaz 020195
Fraunhofer ISE, Freiburg, Germany

Kaufmann, Kai 020355
DENKweit, Halle, Germany

Kawabata, Rudy 020092
PUC-Rio, Rio de Janeiro, Brazil

Kemp, Linda 020390
MARIN, Wageningen, The Netherlands

Kenchington, Ian 020225, 020474, 020558
Becquerel Institute, Brussels, Belgium

Kenny, Robert 020210
European Commission JRC, Ispra, Italy

Khan, Abeer Ali 020513
First Solar, Mainz, Germany

Khosravi, Arash 020381
Mälardalen University, Västerås, Sweden

Kikkert, Benjamin W. J. 020405
TNO, Petten, The Netherlands

Kilickaya, Seda 020020
ODTÜ-GÜNAM, Ankara, Türkiye

Kim, Jin-Hong 020449
KETI, Wonmi-gu, South Korea

Kim, Jun-Tae 020249
Kongju National University, Chungnam, South Korea

Kim, Kihwan 020112
KIER, Daejeon, South Korea

Kim, Seok Won 020449
KETI, Wonmi-gu, South Korea

Kim, Yong-Jin 020045
KIER, Daejeon, South Korea

Kinge, Sachin 020117
Toyota Motors Europe, Brussels, Belgium

Kitamura, Ibuki 020190
Osaka Electro-Communication University, Osaka, Japan

Kitzberger, Gregor 020136
voestalpine Stahl, Linz, Austria

Kivambe, Maulid 020166
QEERI, Doha, Qatar

Kizukuri, Rihoko 020220
TAMURA-ELSOLD, Ilsenburg, Germany

Kladas, Anastasios 020329, 020351
KU Leuven, Ghent, Belgium

Kleider, Jean-Paul 020040, 020058
CNRS, Gif-sur-Yvette, France

Kleissl, Jan 020528
University of California, San Diego, United States of America

Klengel, Robert 020355
Fraunhofer IMWS, Halle, Germany

Klenk, Markus 020385
ZHAW, Winterthur, Switzerland

Klos, Christine 020510
Buhck Re.Energy, Hamburg, Norway

Kluska, Sven 020019
Fraunhofer ISE, Freiburg, Germany

Klute, Carola 020355
Fraunhofer IMWS, Halle, Germany

Knausdorf, Christian 020361
Coburg University of Applied Sciences, Coburg, Germany

Ko, Seok-whan 020561
KIER, Daejeon, South Korea

Ko, Suk Whan 020324, 020357
KIER, Daejeon, South Korea

Koc, Timurhan 020376
DTU, Roskilde, Denmark

Koduvelikulathu, Lejo Joseph 020035, 020068
ISC Konstanz, Konstanz, Germany

Koduvelikulathu, Lejo 020003
ISC Konstanz, Konstanz, Germany

Köntges, Marc 020206
ISFH, Emmerthal, Germany

Koepge, Ringo 020142, 020192
Fraunhofer CSP, Halle, Germany

Koester, Lukas 020203, 020261, 020325
Eurac Research, Bolzano, Italy

Kohlenberg, Heike 020063
ISFH, Emmerthal, Germany

Kohno, Tohru 020186
Hitachi, Tokyo, Japan

Kolahi, Mohammad 020356, 020375
University of Isfahan, Isfahan, Iran
Konagai, Makoto 020106, 020115
Tokyo City University, Setagaya, Japan
Kono, Toru 020484
Hitachi, Kokubunji, Japan
Konu, Christopher Bruce 020132
HTW Berlin, Berlin, Germany
Kopecek, Radovan 020569
ISC Konstanz, Konstanz, Germany
Kopp, Nils 020220
TAMURA-ELSOLD, Ilsenburg, Germany
Korkmaz Arslan, Melisa 020020
ODTÜ-GÜNAM, Ankara, Türkiye
Korpås, Magnus 020476
NTNU, Trondheim, Norway
Kortetmäki, Aki 020444, 020445
TUAS, Tampere, Finland
Koskela, Juha 020444, 020445, 020554
Tampere University, Tampere, Finland
Kossen, Eric J. 020030
TNO, Petten, The Netherlands
Kowalski, Julia 020237
RWTH, Aachen, Germany
Kräling, Ulli 020215
Fraunhofer ISE, Freiburg, Germany
Kraft, Thomas M. 020423
VTT Technical Research Centre of Finland, Oulu, Finland
Krainer, Diana Maria 020430
AIT, Vienna, Austria
Krasilnikov, Inga 020379
Tel Aviv University, Tel Aviv, Israel
Krever Lopes, Bruno 020023
PUCRS, Porto Alegre, Brazil
Kribus, Abraham 020379
Tel Aviv University, Tel Aviv, Israel
Krishnan, Sasikumar 020361
Coburg University of Applied Sciences, Coburg, Germany
Kroon, Jan 020225
TNO, Petten, The Netherlands
Kuan, Ta-Ming 020021, 020053
TSEC, Hsinchu, Taiwan
Kubicek, Bernhard 020281, 020318, 020334, 020347, 020430
AIT, Vienna, Austria
Kucuk, E. Busra 020030
TNO, Petten, The Netherlands

Kuczyńska-Łażewska, Anna 020498, 020499
Gdansk University of Technology, Gdansk, Poland

Kühne, Philip 020240
Leibniz University Hannover, Hannover, Germany

Kuhrmann, Bernd 020206
MBJ Solutions, Ahrensburg, Germany

Kujansivu, Eino 020554
Solarigo Systems, Pirkkala, Finland

Kumar, Gaurav 020563
MERI College of Engineering and Technology, Bahadurgarh, India

Kumar, Sagarika 020402
Technology Innovation Institute, Abu Dhabi, United Arab Emirates

Kumar, Saurabh 020563
PTB, Braunshweig, Germany

Kuo, Cheng-Wen 020021, 020053
TSEC, Hsinchu, Taiwan

Kurtulus, Gunes 020556
ODTU GUNAM, Ankara, Türkiye

Kuruganti, Vaibhav V. 020033
ISC Konstanz, Konstanz, Germany

Kurz, Hannes 020136
voestalpine Stahl, Linz, Austria

Kusch, Alexander 020361
Coburg University of Applied Sciences, Coburg, Germany

Kuzhagaliyeva, Nursulu 020402
Technology Innovation Institute, Abu Dhabi, United Arab Emirates

Kuznicki, Zbigniew T. 020013, 020068
SEGTON Advanced Technology, Versailles, France

Kwiatkowski, Jerzy 020551
NAPE, Warsaw, Poland

Kyranaki, Nikoleta 020156
Hasselt University, Genk, Belgium

Kyranaki, Nikoleta 020393
Hasselt University, Hasselt, Belgium

Kyranaki, Nikoleta 020294
imec, Genk, Belgium

Kyratsi, Theodora 020495
University of Cyprus, Nicosia, Cyprus

L. Andersen, Nanna 020477
DTU, Roskilde, Denmark

L. Souza, Patrícia 020090
Federal University of Rio de Janeiro, Rio de Janeiro, Brazil

Lachowicz, Agata 020039
CSEM, Neuchâtel, Switzerland

Lahr, Simon 020388
Next2Sun Technology, Dillingen, Germany

Lahr, Simon 020411
Next2Sun, Dillingen, Germany

Lajunen, Antti 020400
University of Helsinki, Helsinki, Finland

Lambertz, Andreas 020233
FZJ, Jülich, Germany

Lamblot, Hervé 020302
Sunstyle, Paris, France

Lamghari, Fouad 020402
Fujairah Research Centre, Fujairah, United Arab Emirates

Lamminaho, Jani 020250, 020306
SDU Climate Cluster, Odense, Denmark

Landaas, Christian 020495
Northern Silicon, Meråker, Norway

Landberg, Lars 020448
DNV Denmark, Hellerup, Denmark

Landberg, Lars 020481
DNV Denmark, Hellerup, Spain

Landes, Dieter 020361
Coburg University of Applied Sciences, Coburg, Germany

Landová, Lucie 020107
Czech Technical University, Prague, Czech Republic

Lansade, David 020073
University of Toulouse, Toulouse, France

Lappalainen, Kari 020194, 020528, 020537
Tampere University, Tampere, Finland

Lara, Yolanda 020127, 020414, 020517
ENDEF, Zaragoza, Spain

Larionova, Yevgeniya 020006, 020007, 020225
ISFH, Emmerthal, Germany

Låstad, Jonas 020011
NTNU, Trondheim, Norway

Laurens-Berge, Clarisse 020034
University Grenoble Alpes, Le Bourget-du-Lac, France

Laurikėnas, Paulius 020353
Solitek, Vilnius, Lithuania

Lauwaert, Johan 020064
Ghent University, Ghent, Belgium

Lazaro-Castrillon, Luna 020085
IO-CSIC, Madrid, Spain

Le Bossenec, Hugo 020116
IPVF, Palaiseau, France

Le Brun, Anton 020096
Australian Nuclear Science and Technology Organisation, Lucas Heights, Australia

Lechón, Yolanda 020502
CIEMAT, Madrid, Spain

Ledesma, Javier R. 020337
UPM, Madrid, Spain

Ledesma, Javier 020446
UPM, Madrid, Spain

Lee, Chun-Wei 020021
TSEC, Hsinchu, Taiwan

Lee, Hyunju 020046
Meiji University, Kanagawa, Japan

Lee, Jieun 020323
K-water, Daejeon, South Korea

Lee, Jin-Seok 020324, 020357, 020561
KIER, Daejeon, South Korea

Legarrea, Aritz 020365
CENER, Sarriguren, Spain

Lelievre, Jean-Francois 020373
INES, Le Bourget-du-Lac, France

Lelong, Benoit 020373
Cythelia Energy, La Motte-Servolex, France

Leloux, Jonathan 020262
LuciSun, Villers-la-Ville, Belgium

Lenain, Philippe 020495
benkei, Lyon, France

Lennon, Alison 020048
UNSW, Sydney, Australia

Lenz, Markus 020226
School of Life Sciences FHNW, Muttenz, Switzerland

Lenzmann, Frank 020019
TNO Energy Transition, Petten, The Netherlands

Leone, Sander 020405
Novar, Rotterdam, The Netherlands

Leonforte, Fabrizio 020249
Polytechnic University of Milan, Milan, Italy

Leopold, Ulrich 020457
Luxembourg Institute of Science and Technology, Esch-sur-Alzette, Luxembourg

Levrat, Jacques 020251, 020467
CSEM, Neuchâtel, Switzerland

Levtchenko, Alexandra 020116
IPVF, Palaiseau, France

Lewandowski, Simon 020073
University of Toulouse, Toulouse, France

Leza, Baurin 020412
Gonvarri MS R&D, Corvera - Asturias, Spain

Lezaca, Jorge 020239
DLR, Oldenburg, Germany

Li, Xinyang 020222
RCT Solutions, Konstanz, Germany

Li, Yung-Chih 020021
TSEC, Hsinchu, Taiwan

Li, Yuxuan 020001
East China University of Science and Technology, Shanghai, China

Libal, Joris 020218, 020474
ISC Konstanz, Konstanz, Germany

Lichtenberger, Janine 020430
AIT, Vienna, Austria

Lițiu, Andrei Vladimir 020551
EPB Center, Rotterdam, The Netherlands

Lin, Shih-Chieh 020021
TSEC, Hsinchu, Taiwan

Lindahl, Johan 020486, 020532
Becquerel Sweden, Knivsta, Sweden

Linder, Johannes 020492
Belectric, Kolitzheim, Germany

Lindfors, Anders 020286
Finnish Meteorological Institute, Helsinki, Finland

Lindig, Sascha 020371
Univers, Courbevoie, France

Linke, Jonathan 020004, 020035, 020225
ISC Konstanz, Konstanz, Germany

Linß, Volker 020033
VON ARDENNE, Dresden, Germany

Lipovšek, Benjamin 020047
University of Ljubljana, Ljubljana, Slovenia

Lippke, Benjamin 020180, 020230
Kiwa PI Berlin, Berlin, Germany

List-Kratochvil, Emil 020101
HZB, Berlin, Germany

Litrico, Grazia 020010
Enel Green Power, Catania, Italy

Liu, Cui 020001
East China University of Science and Technology, Shanghai, China

Liu, Dongyang 020063
ISFH, Emmerthal, Germany

Liu, Han-Chang 020350
ITRI, Tainan, Taiwan

Liu, Huiping 020495
GRÄNGES, Finspång, Sweden

Liu, Mengdi 020144, 020208
TÜV Rheinland, Shanghai, China

Liu, Yung-Tsung 020053, 020083
ITRI, Hsinchu, Taiwan

Livera, Andreas 020534
University of Cyprus, Nicosia, Cyprus

Lizin, Sebastien 020513, 020521
UHasselt, Hasselt, Belgium

Llarena, María Elena 020151
ITER, Granadilla de Abona, Spain

Loeckenhoff, Ruediger F. 020416
AZUR SPACE Solar Power, Heilbronn, Germany

Löhning, Martha 020063
ISFH, Emmerthal, Germany

Löhr, Johannes 020063, 020114
ISFH, Emmerthal, Germany

Lokhat, Ismaël 020262
Cythelia Energy, La Motte-Servolex, France

Lokhat, Ismael 020373
Trace Software, Saint-Romain-de-Colbosc, France

Lombardo, Salvatore 020066
CNR-IMM, Catania, Italy

Long, Yean-San 020053, 020083
ITRI, Hsinchu, Taiwan

Longo, Giulia 020099
UPV, Valencia, Spain

Lopes Gomes, Carlos Javier 020432, 020434
Sunveon, Madrid, Spain

Lopes, Ana Patrícia 020464
University of Lisbon, Lisbon, Portugal

López Cuéllar, Juan Manuel 020501
UCM, Madrid, Spain

López Dalmau, Daniel 020432, 020434
Sunveon, Madrid, Spain

López, Nuria 020451
DTU, Roskilde, Denmark

Lorenz, Dieter 020206
MBJ Solutions, Ahrensburg, Germany

Lorenzo Pigueiras, Eduardo 020363
UPM, Madrid, Spain

Lorenzo, Celena 020337, 020536
UPM, Madrid, Spain

Lorenzo, Eduardo 020439, 020446
UPM, Madrid, Spain

Lossen, Jan — 020003, 020035
ISC Konstanz, Konstanz, Germany

Louwen, Atse — 020203, 020226, 020261, 020509, 020546
Eurac Research, Bolzano, Italy

Louwen, Atse — 020316
RISE, Boras, Sweden

Lu, Huan-Wu — 020161
ITRI, Hsinchu, Taiwan

Lu, Matthew — 020230
Kiwa PI Berlin, Shanghai, China

Lucea, Aingeru — 020197, 020198
TECNALIA, Derio, Spain

Lüdemann, Marius — 020233
Fraunhofer CSP, Halle, Germany

Luís, Margarida — 020421
University of Lisbon, Lisbon, Portugal

Lustoza de Souza, Patricia — 020092
UFRJ, Rio de Janeiro, Brazil

Ly, Moussa — 020023, 020025
PUCRS, Porto Alegre, Brazil

Lyubenova, Teodora — 020210
European Commission JRC, Ispra, Italy

M. Bazilio, Willian — 020092
PUC-Rio, Rio de Janeiro, Brazil

M. S. Kawabata, Rudy — 020090
Pontifical Catholic University of Rio de Janeiro, Rio de Janeiro, Brazil

M. Torelly, Guilherme — 020090
Pontifical Catholic University of Rio de Janeiro, Rio de Janeiro, Brazil

Ma Lu, Silvia — 020381
Mälardalen University, Västerås, Sweden

Ma, Xiang — 020011
SINTEF, Oslo, Norway

Macé, Philippe — 020225, 020252, 020474, 020505, 020543, 020558, 020573
Becquerel Institute, Brussels, Belgium

Mack, Sebastian — 020031
Fraunhofer ISE, Freiburg, Germany

Madsen, Morten — 020250, 020306
SDU Climate Cluster, Odense, Denmark

Mahmood, Aysha — 020265, 020376
DTU, Roskilde, Denmark

Maixner, Andreas — 020121, 020125, 020137, 020223
AESOLAR, Koenigsbrunn, Germany

Maiz, Alexander 020437
UPV/EHU, Vitoria-Gasteiz, Spain

Majak, Martyna 020068
Roltec, Poznań, Poland

Makrides, George 020534
University of Cyprus, Nicosia, Cyprus

Malarkannan, Lavanya 020210
National Physical Laboratory, Teddington, United Kingdom

Malcorps, Philippe 020276
3E, Brussels, Belgium

Malik, Stephanie 020313
Fraunhofer CSP, Halle, Germany

Malik, Stephanie 020355
Fraunhofer IMWS, Halle, Germany

Maliutina, Kristina 020141
University of Applied Science Cologne, Cologne, Germany

Malo, Javier 020209
UPM, Madrid, Spain

Mancini, Simone 020425
TNO, Eindhoven, The Netherlands

Mandiola, Gotzon 020514
AZTI, PASAIA, Spain

Manganiello, Patrizio 020389
Hasselt University, Diepenbeek, Belgium

Manganiello, Patrizio 020294
imec, Genk, Belgium

Manito, Alex 020348
University of São Paulo, São Paulo, Brazil

Manochehrian, Rasoul 020539
Frankfurt University of Applied Sciences, Frankfurt am Main, Germany

Manzolini, Giampaolo 020261
Polytechnic University of Milan, Milan, Italy

Maqsood, Ayman 020101
HZB, Berlin, Germany

Marangis, Demetris 020534
University of Cyprus, Nicosia, Cyprus

Marcos-Castro, Ana 020297
CIEMAT, Madrid, Spain

Marechal, Philippe 020217
CEA / INES, Le Bourget-du-Lac, France

Marí Soucase, Bernabé 020099
UPV, Valencia, Spain

Markert, Jochen 020231
Fraunhofer ISE, Freiburg, Germany

Marquardt, Cornelia 020063
ISFH, Emmerthal, Germany

Marteau, Baptiste 020034
ECM Technologies, Grenoble, France
Martín Rueda, Javier 020535
UPM, Madrid, Spain
Martín, Francisco José 020459
UPM, Madrid, Spain
Martín, Francisco 020209
UPM, Madrid, Spain
Martín-Chivelet, Nuria 020297
CIEMAT, Madrid, Spain
Martín-Rueda, Javier 020337, 020363
UPM, Madrid, Spain
Martínez González, Mario 020326
Enertis Applus+, Madrid, Spain
Martinez, Juan Ignacio 020252
Becquerel Institute Spain, San Sebastian, Spain
Martinez, Oscar 020191, 020205
University of Valladolid, Valladolid, Spain
Martínez-Barbeito, María 020243
ieco.io, Vigo, Spain
Maruyama, Rodrigo P. 020154, 020348
University of São Paulo, São Paulo, Brazil
Marzo, Aitor 020311, 020546
University of Granada, Granada, Spain
Mashkov, Oleksandr 020149, 020150, 020377
HI ERN, Erlangen, Germany
Massaro, Lorenzo 020541
PedersoliGattai, Milan, Italy
Masson, Gaëtan 020474, 020558, 020564, 020573
Becquerel Institute, Brussels, Belgium
Masson, Gaëtan 020570
IEA PVPS Task 1, Brussels, Belgium
Mateos, Yeray 020055, 020153
UPV/EHU, Bilbao, Spain
Maturi, Laura 020249, 020254, 020551
Eurac Research, Bolzano, Italy
Mayer-Ullmann, Philipp 020430
AIT, Vienna, Austria
Mazzoleni, Stefano 020378
University of Naples Federico II, Naples, Italy
McIntosh, Keith R. 020396
PV Lighthouse, Coledale, Australia
McNab, Shona 020065
UNSW, Sydney, Australia
Meereboer, Martijn 020225
Energyra, Westknollendam, The Netherlands

Meier, Rico 020132
HTW Berlin, Berlin, Germany
Meixner, Michael 020050
halm elektronik, Frankfurt am Main, Germany
Mekhaldi, Bouchra 020406
Ecole Polytechnique, Palaiseau, France
Melges de Andrade, Adnei 020154
University of São Paulo, São Paulo, Brazil
Melino, Francesco 020314
University of Bologna, Bologna, Italy
Mellone, Celeste 020541
Green Horse Advisory, Rome, Italy
Menard, Lionel 020291
MINES Paris, Nice, France
Mencaraglia, Denis 020058
CNRS, Gif-sur-Yvette, France
Menchaca, Iratxe 020514
AZTI, PASAIA, Spain
Mendes Ferreira Gomes, Amanda 020548
UFSC, Florianopolis, Brazil
Mendikoa, Iñigo 020514
Tecnalia, BRTA, Derio, Spain
Meneghini, Matteo 020089
University of Padova, Padova, Italy
Ménézo, Christophe 020317
LOCIE, Le Bourget-du-Lac, France
Menghini, Mariela 020508
IMDEA Nanoscience Institute, Madrid, Spain
Mercade Ruiz, Pau 020448, 020481
GreenPowerMonitor a DNV company, Barcelona, Spain
Merino, Amanda 020040
CEA / INES, Le Bourget-du-Lac, France
Merino, José Manuel 020085
UAM, Madrid, Spain
Mermoud, André 020196
PVsyst, Geneva, Switzerland
Merodio, Pablo 020337
UPM, Madrid, Spain
Mertens, Jan 020389
imec, Genk, Belgium
Mertens, Verena 020006, 020008
ISFH, Emmerthal, Germany
Meßmer, Marius 020031
Fraunhofer ISE, Freiburg, Germany
Messmer, Tobias 020218, 020221, 020225
ISC Konstanz, Konstanz, Germany

Messner, Christian 020369
AIT, Vienna, Austria

Mettner, Larissa 020063, 020114
ISFH, Emmerthal, Germany

Meusel, Manuel 020052
Fraunhofer CSP, Halle (Saale), Germany

Meyer, Kevin 020260
ISFH, Emmerthal, Germany

Meza, Carlos 020318, 020334, 020426, 020520
Anhalt University of Applied Sciences, Köthen, Germany

Mezzasalma, Frédéric 020217
CEA / INES, Le Bourget-du-Lac, France

Micha, Daniel 020092
CEFET/RJ, Petrópolis, Brazil

Michael, Poland 020193
Nelson Mandela University, Port Elizabeth, South Africa

Miclea, Paul-Tiberiu 020233
Fraunhofer CSP, Halle, Germany

Midtgård, Ole-Morten 020476
NTNU, Trondheim, Norway

Miettunen, Kati 020286, 020298, 020398
University of Turku, Turku, Finland

Migan-Dubois, Anne 020406
CNRS, Gif-sur-Yvette, France

Mignonac, Alexandre 020217
CEA / INES, Le Bourget-du-Lac, France

Mignonac, Alexandre 020334
CEA, Cadarache, France

Mignonac, Alexandre 020318
CEA, Saint-Paul-Lez-Durance, France

Miguel Laborda, María 020414
IaSol, Zaragoza, Spain

Mihailetchi, Valentin Dan 020033
ISC Konstanz, Konstanz, Germany

Mihailetchi, Valentin 020225
ISC Konstanz, Konstanz, Germany

Mihaylov, Blago 020210
European Commission JRC, Ispra, Italy

Milani, Emanuele 020495
Marelli Europe, Venaria Reala, Italy

Milesi, Frédéric 020068
CEA, Grenoble, France

Min, Byungsul 020008, 020482
ISFH, Emmerthal, Germany

Mirandona López, Haritz 020432, 020434
Sunveon, Madrid, Spain

Miró-Llorente, Marta 020094
IREC, Barcelona, Spain

Misra, Prashant 020429
NISE, Gurugram, India

Miszczuk, Andrzej 020068
Roltec, Poznań, Poland

Mittag, Max 020137
Fraunhofer ISE, Freiburg, Germany

Mittal, Ankit 020318
AIT, Vienna, Austria

Mittelman, Gur 020379
Afeka Tel-Aviv Academic College of Engineering, Tel Aviv, Israel

Mizushima, Io 020028
IPU P/S, Virum, Denmark

Mizushima, Io 020037
IPU, Virum, Denmark

Mngomezulu, Ndumiso 020344
PVinsight, Port Elizabeth, South Africa

Mo, Alvin 020065
UNSW, Sydney, Australia

Mockeviciute-Azzopardi, Austeja 020334
FIR, Birkirkara, Malta

Moe Nygård, Magnus 020340
IFE, Kjeller, Norway

Moehlecke, Adriano 020023, 020025
PUCRS, Porto Alegre, Brazil

Mohammadi, Mohammad Hossein 020037, 020104
Aarhus University, Aarhus, Denmark

Mollier, Stéphane 020262
CEA / INES, Le Bourget-du-Lac, France

Moltke, Asbjørn 020043
Technical University of Denmark, Copenhagen, Denmark

Mondaca-Cuevas, Gino 020422
University of Antofagasta, Antofagasta, Chile

Monokroussos, Christos 020181
TÜV Rheinland Shanghai, Shanghai, China

Monokroussos, Christos 020144, 020208
TÜV Rheinland, Shanghai, China

Monteiro Martins, Filipa 020317
Galp Energia, Lisbon, Portugal

Montes, Carlos 020151
ITER, Granadilla de Abona, Spain

Montoya, Josefa 020311
University of Antofagasta, Antofagasta, Chile

Morabito, Floriana 020066
CNR-IFN, Milan, Italy

Moradi Sizkouhi, Amirmohammad 020356, 020375
Concordia University, Montreal, Canada

Moradi Zavie Kord, Soroush 020400
University of Helsinki, Helsinki, Finland

Morales, Sergio 020491
UPM, Madrid, Spain

Morantes Quintana, Giobertti Raul 020551
Eurac Research, Bolzano, Italy

Mordvinkin, Anton 020233
Fraunhofer CSP, Halle, Germany

Moreda, Guillermo P. 020407
UPM, Madrid, Spain

Morin, Claire 020551
SolarPower Europe, Brussels, Belgium

Morisset, Audrey 020068
CSEM, Neuchâtel, Switzerland

Morlier, Arnaud 020156
Hasselt University, Genk, Belgium

Morlier, Arnaud 020294, 020389
imec, Genk, Belgium

Mortazavifar, Leila 020056, 020158, 020201, 020284
Anhalt University of Applied Sciences, Köthen, Germany

Moruno, Ricardo 020209, 020453
UPM, Madrid, Spain

Mosel, Frank 020015
PVA TePla, Wettenberg, Germany

Moser, David 020573
Becquerel Institute Italy, Trento, Italy

Moser, David 020316
Becquerel Institute, Bolzano, Italy

Moser, David 020254
Bequerel Institute, Trento, Italy

Moser, David 020203, 020226, 020261, 020325, 020485, 020489, 020546
Eurac Research, Bolzano, Italy

Mouhoubi, Felicia 020134
CEA / INES, Le Bourget-du-Lac, France

Müllejans, Harald 020208, 020213
European Commission JRC, Ispra, Italy

Müller, Alexander 020119
Fraunhofer CSP, Halle, Germany

Müller, Larissa 020523
University of Applied Sciences Cologne, Cologne, Germany

Mugica, Maikel 020139
Tecnalia, Donostia - San Sebastián, Spain

Mujovi, Fahradin 020251
CSEM, Neuchâtel, Switzerland

Mukherjee, Srijani 020338
CEA / INES, Le Bourget-du-Lac, France
Mukhtar, Mariyam 020057
University of Verona, Verona, Italy
Mulder, Peter 020067
Radboud University, Nijmegen, The Netherlands
Muller, Matthew 020314
NREL, Denver, United States of America
Munkhammar, Joakim 020532
Uppsala University, Uppsala, Sweden
Muñoz Cerón, Emilio 020269
University of Jaén, Jaén, Spain
Muñoz, Delfina 020040, 020311, 020546
CEA / INES, Le Bourget-du-Lac, France
Muñoz, Delfina 020521
CEA, Le Bourget-du-Lac, France
Muñoz, Delfina 020226
CEA/ INES, Le Bourget-du-Lac, France
Muñoz, Ildefonso 020365, 020366, 020392
CENER, Sarriguren, Spain
Muñoz, Jesús Ángel 020508
UCM, Madrid, Spain
Muñoz García, Miguel-Ángel 020407
UPM, Madrid, Spain
Murano, Giovanni 020551
ENEA, Ispra, Italy
Murillo, Asier 020497
CENER, Sarriguren, Spain
Musembi, Robinson J. 020272
University of Nairobi, Nairobi, Kenya

Nabipouor, Mohammad 020426
Anhalt University of Applied Sciences, Köthen, Germany
Nagel, Henning 020475
Fraunhofer ISE, Freiburg, Germany
Nakamura, Kyotaro 020046
Toyota Technological Institute, Nagoya, Japan
Nanno, Ikuo 020190
Nanno Energy Research Center, Yamaguchi, Japan
Nargelienė, Viktorija 020157
Center for Physical Sciences and Technology (FTMC), Vilnius, Lithuania
Narsi Patel, Hitarth 020069
SVNIT, Surat, India
Narvarte, Luis 020337, 020446, 020491, 020535, 020536, 020567, 020575
UPM, Madrid, Spain

Nascimento, Lucas 020377
Solar Energy Research Laboratory Fotovoltaica/ UFSC, Florianópolis, Brazil

Nasebandt, Lasse 020063
ISFH, Emmerthal, Germany

Nasser, Hisham 020226
ODTÜ-GÜNAM, Ankara, Türkiye

Naveiro, José Manuel 020414
ENDEF, Zaragoza, Spain

Nazififard, Mohammad 020259, 020428
Côte d'Azur University, Nice, France

Nejim, Ahmed 020058
SILVACO, St. Ives, United Kingdom

Nel, Paul 020382
7SecondSolar, Cape Town, South Africa

Nelson, Jenny 020394
Imperial College London, London, United Kingdom

Neuba, Adam 020114
Paderborn University, Paderborn, Germany

Neuber, Viola 020031
Fraunhofer ISE, Freiburg, Germany

Neuhaus, Holger 020123, 020140
Fraunhofer ISE, Freiburg, Germany

Neumaier, Lukas 020504
Silicon Austria Labs, Villach, Austria

Neussl, Vassilissa 020318, 020430
AIT, Vienna, Austria

Neykova, Neda 020107
Czech Technical University, Prague, Czech Republic

Nezhad, Mahyar 020230
Kiwa PI Berlin, Hudson, United States of America

Nguyen, Viet Xuan 020008
centrotherm international, Blaubeuren, Germany

Nicolet-dit-Félix, Kléber 020251
EPFL, Neuchâtel, Switzerland

Nicot-Senneville, Zoltan 020102
SERIS, Singapore, Singapore

Nielsen, Michael P. 020065
UNSW, Sydney, Australia

Nissen, Hauke 020313
Wattmanufactur, Galmsbüll, Germany

Nitsche, Tobias 020119, 020218
Henkel, Düsseldorf, Germany

Nobre, André M. 020263
PV Doctor, Singapore, Singapore

Noels, Serge 020472
PV CYCLE, Brussels, Belgium

Noh, Yong-Su 020449
KETI, Wonmi-gu, South Korea
Nold, Sebastian 020461
Fraunhofer ISE, Freiburg, France
Nold, Sebastian 020475
Fraunhofer ISE, Freiburg, Germany
Nordboe, Eirik 020495
Fiven Norge, Lillesand, Norway
Norde Santos, Fernanda 020331
DLR, Almería, Spain
Nouri, Bijan 020235, 020237, 020239
DLR, Almería, Spain
Nova, David 020339
National University of Colombia, Bogotá, Colombia
Núñez, Rubén 020209, 020453
UPM, Madrid, Spain
Núñez-Osorio, Alessia 020100
University of Almeria, Almeria, Spain
Nurmesjärvi, Antti 020423
VTT Technical Research Centre of Finland, Oulu, Finland
Nussbaumer, Hartmut 020385
ZHAW, Winterthur, Switzerland
Nyang'onda, Thomas N. 020272
University of Nairobi, Nairobi, Kenya

Obeidavi, Sahereh 020361
Coburg University of Applied Sciences, Coburg, Germany
Oberbeck, Lars 020461
TotalEnergies OneTech, Paris, France
Oberegger Filippi, Ulrich 020551
Eurac Research, Bolzano, Italy
Ocaña, Luis Manuel 020151
ITER, Granadilla de Abona, Spain
Ockert, Ajka 020312
EnBW, Karlsruhe, Germany
Odilio dos Santos, Daniel 020548
UFSC, Florianopolis, Brazil
Öhgren, Gustav 020532
Becquerel Sweden, Knivsta, Sweden
Öttl, Christian 020347
Watt Analytics, Vienna, Austria
Öz, Aksel Kaan 020135
Fraunhofer ISE, Freiburg, Germany
Özden, Talat 020226
ODTÜ-GÜNAM, Ankara, Türkiye

Özkalay, Ebrar 020160, 020204
SUPSI, Mendrisio, Switzerland

Ogura, Atsushi 020046
Meiji University, Kanagawa, Japan

Ohdaira, Keisuke 020131
JAIST, Ishikawa, Japan

Ohshita, Yoshio 020046
Toyota Technological Institute, Nagoya, Japan

Ojala, Aleksi 020554
Solarigo Systems, Pirkkala, Finland

Okawa, Hayato 020115
Tokyo City University, Setagaya, Japan

Okel, Lars A. G. 020030
TNO, Petten, The Netherlands

Oksanen, Jani 020067
Aalto University, Espoo, Finland

Oliosi, Michele 020196
PVsyst, Geneva, Switzerland

Olivares, Douglas 020311
University of Antofagasta, Antofagasta, Chile

Olivares, Gregorio 020365, 020366, 020392
CENER, Sarriguren, Spain

Oliveira Santos, João Victor 020188
EDF R&D, Moret Loing Orvanne, France

Oliveira, Helena 020420
University of Évora, Évora, Portugal

Oller Westerberg, Amelia 020570
Becquerel Sweden, Knivsta, Sweden

Ollo, Olatz 020139
Tecnalia, Donostia - San Sebastián, Spain

Oozeki, Takashi 020436, 020525
AIST, Koriyama, Japan

Opatovsky, Martin 020241, 020262
Solargis, Bratislava, Slovakia

Oreski, Gernot 020136, 020234, 020325, 020500, 020574
PCCL, Leoben, Austria

Ortega, Eneko 020055, 020153, 020287, 020353
UPV/EHU, Bilbao, Spain

Ortega, Eneko 020289, 020437
UPV/EHU, Leioa, Spain

Ortega, Pascal 020214
University of French Polynesia, Faa'a, French Polynesia

Ortiz-Pena, Aaron 020562
University of Castilla-La Mancha, Albacete, Spain

Ory, Daniel 020188
EDF R&D, Palaiseau, France

Ory, Daniel EDF, Palaiseau, France	020116
Osman, Alaa ISFH, Emmerthal, Germany	020006
Osuna, Jose Antonio MAGTEL, Córdoba, Spain	020358
Osvald, Oliver Solargis, Bratislava, Slovakia	020274
Otaegi, Aloña UPV/EHU, Bilbao, Spain	020055, 020097, 020153, 020287
Otnes, Gaute Institute for Energy Technology, Kjeller, Norway	020169
Otto, Nicolas HTW, Berlin, Germany	020101
Otto, William MARIN, Wageningen, The Netherlands	020390
Ou, Chao-Wei National Chin-Yi University of Technology, Taichung, Taiwan	020350
Ovaitt, Silvana NREL, Denver, United States of America	020314
Ovaitt, Silvana NREL, Golden, United States of America	020574
Oviedo Hernandez, Guillermo BayWa r.e, Rome, Italy	020325
Ozer, Shay Agricultural Research Organization, Rishon LeZion, Israel	020379
P. Pires, Maurício Federal University of Rio de Janeiro, Rio de Janeiro, Brazil	020090
Pabiou, Herve CETHIL, Villeurbanne, France	020338
Pabst, Elena ZSW, Stuttgart, Germany	020312
Paiva, Lúcio Casa dos Ventos, Fortaleza, Brazil	020530
Palais, Olivier Toulon University, Marseille, France	020188
Palitzsch, Wolfram LuxChemTech, Freiberg, Germany	020225, 020495
Palomino, Laura UPM, Madrid, Spain	020491, 020535
Pamir Aly, Shahzada DEWA, Dubai, United Arab Emirates	020229
Pamula, Bindu SVNIT, Surat, India	020069

Panda, Pavan Kumar 020284
Anhalt University of Applied Sciences, Köthen, Germany

Pandar, Matthias 020229
Fraunhofer CSP, Halle, Germany

Pander, Matthias 020121, 020142, 020175, 020192, 020218, 020223, 020232
Fraunhofer CSP, Halle, Germany

Panduri, Fabio 020322
BFH, Burgdorf, Switzerland

Pantoja, Jaime 020526
Francisco José de Caldas District University, Bogota, Colombia

Papantoni, Veatriki 020482
DLR, Oldenburg, Germany

Paraficz, Danuta 020204
FFHS, Zurich, Switzerland

Paraskeva, Vasiliki 020064
University of Cyprus, Nicosia, Cyprus

Pardo, Eduardo 020414
Tecnova, Almeira, Spain

Parfeniukas, Karolis 020039
ATLANT 3D, Taastrup, Denmark

Parion, Jonathan 020064
Hasselt Unversity, Genk, Belgium

Park, Hyeonwook 020112
KENTECH, Naju-Si, South Korea

Parmar, Richa 020429
NISE, Gurugram, India

Parra, Johan 020406
Ecole Polytechnique, Palaiseau, France

Parra, Johan 020214
Polytechnic Institute of Paris, Palaiseau, France

Parrilla, Carlos G. 020402
Fujairah Research Centre, Fujairah, United Arab Emirates

Pascual Gallego, Valero 020407
UPM, Madrid, Spain

Pasquier, Mathis 020451
DTU, Roskilde, Denmark

Passaro, Marcello 020513
Sunzest Solar, Rotterdam, The Netherlands

Patel, Dharm 020355
Fraunhofer IMWS, Halle, Germany

Paul, Ananta 020250, 020306
SDU Climate Cluster, Odense, Denmark

Paulescu, Marius 020283
West University of Timisoara, Timisoara, Romania

Paviet-Salomon, Bertrand 020068, 020467
CSEM, Neuchâtel, Switzerland

Payno, David 020085, 020094
UAM, Madrid, Spain

Pearce, Pheobe 020065
UNSW, Sydney, Australia

Peche, René 020468, 020495
bifa Umweltinstitut, Augsburg, Germany

Pehlivanli, Ezgi 020521
METU, Ankara, Türkiye

Peibst, Robby 020006, 020063, 020114
ISFH, Emmerthal, Germany

Pelfort Ojer, Marta 020241
Solargis, Bratislava, Slovakia

Pelland, Sophie 020211
Natural Resources Canada, Varennes, Canada

Pelle, Martina 020249, 020254
Eurac Research, Bolzano, Italy

Peña-Bermudez, Julian 020110
University of the Caribbean, Santo Domingo, Dominican Republic

Peng, Cheng-Yu 020350
National Chin-Yi University of Technology, Taichung, Taiwan

Pera, David 020457
Luxembourg Institute of Science and Technology, Esch-sur-Alzette, Luxembourg

Perani, Martina 020204
FFHS, Zurich, Switzerland

Peraticos, Elias 020064
University of Cyprus, Nicosia, Cyprus

Pereda, Ainhoa 020198, 020358
TECNALIA, Derio, Spain

Pereira Fialho, Luis Andre 020509
Eurac Research, Bolzano, Italy

Pereira, Sara 020403, 020418, 020565
University of Évora, Évora, Portugal

Pérez García, Manuel 020336
University of Almería, La Cañada de San Urbano, Spain

Pérez, Ernesto 020339
National University of Colombia, Bogotá, Colombia

Pérez, Jairo 020412
Gonvarri AgroTech, Corvera - Asturias, Spain

Pérez, Jorge 020412
Gonvarri AgroTech, Corvera - Asturias, Spain

Pérez, Luis 020412
Gonvarri MS R&D, Corvera - Asturias, Spain

Perez, Richard 020494
University at Albany, Albany, United States of America

Perez-Astudillo, Daniel 020275, 020278, 020291
QEERI, Doha, Qatar

Pérez-García, Manuel 020100
University of Almeria, Almería, Spain

Pérez-Rodríguez, Alejandro 020085, 020094
IREC, Barcelona, Spain

Pernas, Tomás 020412
Gonvarri AgroTech, Corvera - Asturias, Spain

Pernau, Thomas 020008
centrotherm international, Blaubeuren, Germany

Perrin, Marion 020544
Energy Pool, Le Bourget-du-Lac, France

Pervan, Nikolina 020136, 020234
PCCL, Leoben, Austria

Peter Amalathas, Amalraj 020107
University of Jaffna, Jaffna, Sri Lanka

Peter, Kristian 020569
ISC Konstanz, Konstanz, Germany

Peters, Ian Marius 020230, 020263
Forschungszentrum Jülich, Erlangen, Germany

Peters, Ian Marius 020149, 020150, 020377, 020574
HI ERN, Erlangen, Germany

Petersons, Karlis 020250, 020306
Stensborg, Roskilde, Denmark

Petkovski, Emil 020571
DNV, Arnhem, The Netherlands

Petzschmann, Jonas 020312
ZSW, Stuttgart, Germany

Pfau, Jan Hendrik 020240
Leibniz University Hannover, Hannover, Germany

Pfeiffer, Oliver 020141
University of Applied Science Cologne, Cologne, Germany

Pfeiffer, Oliver 020140
University of Applied Sciences Cologne, Cologne, Germany

Philipp, Daniel 020215, 020231
Fraunhofer ISE, Freiburg, Germany

Pierro, Marco 020489, 020494
Eurac Research, Bolzano, Italy

Pieters, Bart E. 020180
FZJ, Jülich, Germany

Pieterse, Marco 020495
Chemconserve, Bussum, The Netherlands

Pietralunga, Silvia Maria 020066
CNR-IFN, Milan, Italy

Pietsch, Veith 020331
Aquila Capital, Hamburg, Germany
Pilat, Eric 020311
CEA / INES, Le Bourget-du-Lac, France
Pilat, Eric 020317
CEA INES, Le Bourget-du-Lac, France
Pillai, Akhildev 020558
Becquerel Institute, Brussels, Belgium
Pinheiro, Philippe 020457
Luxembourg Institute of Science and Technology, Esch-sur-Alzette, Luxembourg
Pinho Almeida, Marcelo 020348
University of São Paulo, São Paulo, Brazil
Pinto, Cristina Leyre 020497
CENER, Sarriguren, Spain
Pinto, Luciana 020092
UFRJ, Rio de Janeiro, Brazil
Pitaval, Sébastien 020244
SOLAÏS, Valbonne, France
Pitz-Paal, Robert 020237, 020331
DLR, Cologne, Germany
Plakhotnyuk, Maksym 020039
ATLANT 3D, Taastrup, Denmark
Platero Gaona, Carlos A. 020332
UPM, Madrid, Spain
Plaza, Caroline 020543, 020564, 020573
Becquerel Institute France, Lyon, France
Polacchi, Cristina 020509, 020513
Eurac Research, Bolzano, Italy
Polo, Jaime 020300
CENER, Sarriguren, Spain
Polo, Jesús 020297
CIEMAT, Madrid, Spain
Polverini, Davide 020181
Directorate General for Internal Market, Industry, Entrepreneurship and SMEs, Brussels, Belgium
Polverini, Davide 020497
European Comission, Brussels, Belgium
Pongthanacharoenkul, Nattapark 020230
Kiwa PI Berlin, Berlin, Germany
Poortmans, Jef 020064
Hasselt Unversity, Genk, Belgium
Popescu, Lacramioara 020068
ISC Konstanz, Konstanz, Germany
Pospischil, Maximilian 020225
Highline Technologies, Freiburg, Germany

Poulsen, Peter B. 020039
DTU, Copenhagen, Denmark

Poulsen, Peter B. 020250, 020265, 020267, 020376, 020451
DTU, Roskilde, Denmark

Poulsen, Peter Behrensdorff 020028, 020306, 020346
DTU, Roskilde, Denmark

Pourshafi, Pouya 020121, 020125, 020137
AESOLAR, Koenigsbrunn, Germany

Pozza, Cristian 020551
Eurac Research, Bolzano, Italy

Prakash, Jai 020429
NISE, Gurugram, India

Prando, Davide 020485, 020489
Edyna, Bolzano, Italy

Prasad, Manjunath 020225
ISC Konstanz, Konstanz, Germany

Pravettoni, Mauro 020402
Technology Innovation Institute, Abu Dhabi, United Arab Emirates

Preis, Pirmin 020003
ISC Konstanz, Konstanz, Germany

Preu, Ralf 020475
Fraunhofer ISE, Freiburg, Germany

Preuschoff, Jonas 020101
HTW, Berlin, Germany

Protti, Alexander Aguilar 020140
Fraunhofer ISE, Freiburg, Germany

Protti, Alexander 020137
Fraunhofer ISE, Freiburg, Germany

Provost, Marion 020116
IPVF, Palaiseau, France

Puel, Jean Baptiste 020062
IPVF, Palaiseau, France

Puertas López, Antonio Manuel 020100
University of Almeria, Almeria, Spain

Puttock, Claire 020367
Nextracker, Fremont, United States of America

Queste, Samuel 020068
Marie and Louis Pasteur University, Besançon, France

Quiroz, Mónica 020328
Qualifying Photovoltaics, Madrid, Spain

R. Ledesma, Javier 020363
UPM, Madrid, Spain

Rabanal Arabach, Jorge — 020183
University of Antofagasta, Antofagasta, Chile

Rabanal-Arabach, Jorge — 020129, 020342, 020417, 020422
University of Antofagasta, Antofagasta, Chile

Rabiei, Hossein — 020063
ISFH, Emmerthal, Germany

Rachdi, Lazhar — 020035, 020068
ISC Konstanz, Konstanz, Germany

Radzevicius, Aurimas — 020225
Valoe Cells, Vilnius, Lithuania

Rafiee, Hossein — 020539
Frankfurt University of Applied Sciences, Frankfurt am Main, Germany

Raginskis, Justinas — 020380
Kaunas University of Technology, Kaunas, Lithuania

Raievska, Oleksandra — 020117, 020149
HI ERN, Erlangen, Germany

Rajan, S. Prithivi — 020262
LuciSun, Villers-la-Ville, Belgium

Rajkiewicz, Katarzyna — 020551
NAPE, Warsaw, Poland

Rakotoniaina, Jean Patrice — 020311
CEA / INES, Le Bourget-du-Lac, France

Ramachandran Nair, Jishnu — 020233
Fraunhofer CSP, Halle, Germany

Ramesh, Santhosh — 020389
imec, Genk, Belgium

Ramírez Ledesma, Javier — 020535
UPM, Madrid, Spain

Ramirez, S. — 020396
PV Lighthouse, Coledale, Australia

Rampino, Stefano — 020087
National Research Council, Parma, Italy

Ramspeck, Klaus — 020050
halm elektronik, Frankfurt am Main, Germany

Ranisch, Tadeus — 020101
HTW, Berlin, Germany

Ranta, Samuli — 020286, 020400
TUAS, Turku, Finland

Ranta, Samuli — 020298, 020398
Turku University of Applied Sciences, Turku, Finland

Raposo, Mauro — 020565
University of Évora, Évora, Portugal

Ratnagiri, Abhinav — 020367
Nextracker, Fremont, United States of America

Raugewitz, Annika — 020063, 020114
ISFH, Emmerthal, Germany

Raval, Mehul 020005, 020222, 020463
RCT Solutions, Konstanz, Germany

Razanajao, Aina 020244
SOLAÏS, Valbonne, France

Razi, Umair 020085
IREC, Barcelona, Spain

Recart, Federico 020097
UPV/EHU, Bilbao, Spain

Redondo Cuevas, Marta 020332
UPM, Madrid, Spain

Redondo, Juan Manuel 020209
UPM, Madrid, Spain

Rehan, Muhammad 020112
KIER, Daejeon, South Korea

Rehman, Anees ur 020111, 020164
Hohai University, Changzhou, China

Reichart, Hannah 020167, 020232
University of Applied Sciences Cologne, Cologne, Germany

Reichel, Christian 020123, 020137, 020140
Fraunhofer ISE, Freiburg, Germany

Reichle, Julian 020005, 020222, 020463
RCT Solutions, Konstanz, Germany

Reinders, Angele 020253
TU Eindhoven, Eindhoven, The Netherlands

Reindl, Thomas 020263
SERIS, Singapore, Singapore

Reis, Luiz Filipe 020530
Casa dos Ventos, Fortaleza, Brazil

Rémondeau, Paul 020251
EPFL, Neuchâtel, Switzerland

Renard, Charles 020058
CNRS, Palaiseau, France

Rende, Fedele 020255
ACCA Software, Cosenza, Italy

Rennhofer, Marcus 020180, 020281, 020318, 020334, 020347, 020430
AIT, Vienna, Austria

Rentsch, Jochen 020475
Fraunhofer ISE, Freiburg, Germany

Rerat, Michel 020060
IPREM, Pau, France

Reshef, Liad 020379
Agricultural Research Organization, Rishon LeZion, Israel

Revol, Inès 020074
LAAS-CNRS, Toulouse, France

Reyal, Jean-Pierre 020303
SemperStyl, Eragny, France

Riaño, Sandra 020197, 020358
TECNALIA, Derio, Spain
Richards, Bryce S. 020272
KIT, Karlsruhe, Germany
Riechelman, Stefan 020181
PTB, Braunschweig, Germany
Riechelmann, Stefan 020177, 020199, 020211
PTB, Braunschweig, Germany
Riedel-Lyngskær, Nicholas 020451
DTU, Roskilde, Denmark
Rienäcker, Michael 020063
ISFH, Emmerthal, Germany
Rindert, Sören 020230
Kiwa PI Berlin, Berlin, Germany
Ríos Moral, Lucía 020501
UCM, Madrid, Spain
Ríos-Ledesma, Felipe 020446
UPM, Madrid, Spain
Ripke, Melanie 020006
ISFH, Emmerthal, Germany
Riva, Roland 020495
CEA, Le Bourget-du-Lac, France
Rivas Rodríguez, José Manuel 020326
Enertis Applus+, Madrid, Spain
Robledo, Jesús 020262
LuciSun, Villers-la-Ville, Belgium
Rodríguez Lucas, Delia 020407
EkiLabs, Boston, United States of America
Rodríguez Plaza, José Luis 020508
Autonomous University of Madrid, Madrid, Spain
Rodríguez Rodríguez, Araceli 020501
UCM, Madrid, Spain
Rodríguez Salazar, David Leonardo 020441
District University of Bogotá, Bogotá, Colombia
Rodríguez, Araceli 020508
UCM, Madrid, Spain
Rodríguez, Diego Julián 020526
Francisco José de Caldas District University, Bogota, Colombia
Rodríguez, Isabel 020257
IMDEA Nanoscience, Madrid, Spain
Rodriguez, Sonia Maria 020289
UPV/EHU, Leioa, Spain
Rodríguez, Velia 020097
UPV/EHU, Bilbao, Spain
Rodríguez-Conde, Sofía 020326
Enertis Applus+, Madrid, Spain

Rodríguez-Gallegos, Carlos D. 020149, 020150
SERIS, Singapore, Singapore

Rodríguez-Romero, Sebastián 020342, 020417, 020422
University of Antofagasta, Antofagasta, Chile

Rodziewicz, Hanna 020498
Gdansk University of Technology, Gdansk, Poland

Römer, Udo 020006, 020063
ISFH, Emmerthal, Germany

Röver, Ingo 020225
LuxChemTech, Freiberg, Germany

Rojas, Christian A. 020422
Federico Santa María Technical University, Valparaíso, Chile

Rojas-Henríquez, Katalina 020129
University of Antofagasta, Antofagasta, Chile

Román, Eduardo 020139
Tecnalia, Donostia - San Sebastián, Spain

Romeo, Alessandro 020057, 020089, 020093
University of Verona, Verona, Italy

Romer, Pascal 020231
Fraunhofer ISE, Freiburg, Germany

Roodt, Roelof 020185
Nelson Mandela University, Port Elizabeth, South Africa

Roosloot, Nathan 020169
Institute for Energy Technology, Kjeller, Norway

Rosca, Victor 020030
TNO, Petten, The Netherlands

Rosen, Isaac 020225
Copprint, Jerusalem, Israel

Rosenfeld, Lavi 020379
Agricultural Research Organization, Rishon LeZion, Israel

Rosina, Konstantin 020241
Solargis, Bratislava, Slovakia

Rossa, Carlos 020432, 020434
Sunveon, Madrid, Spain

Rouffie, Brice 020068
SEGTON Advanced Technology, Versailles, France

Roulleau, Lea 020303
CSTB, Marne-la-Vallée, France

Rousset, Jean 020116
EDF, Palaiseau, France

Roy, Shantanu 020519
CSTEP, Bengaluru, India

Rudolph, Dominik 020003, 020068
ISC Konstanz, Konstanz, Germany

Rudzikas, Matas 020380
The Applied Research Institute for Prospective Technologies, Vilnius, Lithuania

Rüther, Ricardo 020377
Solar Energy Research Laboratory Fotovoltaica/ UFSC, Florianópolis, Brazil

Rüther, Ricardo 020548
UFSC, Florianopolis, Brazil

Ruf, Manuel 020455
Robert Bosch, Stuttgart, Germany

Ruiz Donoso, Elena 020331
DLR, Almería, Spain

S. Sousa, Graciana 020090
Federal University of Rio de Janeiro, Rio de Janeiro, Brazil

Safarian, Jafar 020011
NTNU, Trondheim, Norway

Sah, Dheeraj 020039
Aarhus University, Aarhus, Denmark

Sahin, Hasret 020479
LUT University, Lappeenranta, Finland

Saito, Kimihiko 020106
Tokyo City University, Setagaya, Japan

Salem, Mohammad 020428
Australian University, Kuwait City, Kuwait

Salerno, Giorgia 020077
University of Milano-Bicocca, Milan, Italy

Salis, Fabio 020541
Iberdrola, Rome, Italy

Salvador, Antonio 020358
MAGTEL, Córdoba, Spain

Sample, Tony 020213
European Commission JRC, Ispra, Italy

Samuolienė, Giedrė 020380
The Lithuanian Research Centre for Agriculture and Forestry, Kaunas, Lithuania

San José, Luis Javier 020209, 020453
UPM, Madrid, Spain

Sánchez de León Peque, Miguel 020243
ieco.io, Vigo, Spain

Sanchez Garcia, Alfredo 020270
SINTEF, Trondheim, Norway

Sanchez, Hugo 020056, 020158, 020284
Anhalt University of Applied Sciences, Köthen, Germany

Sanchez, Jesus 020437
UPV/EHU, Vitoria-Gasteiz, Spain

Sanchez, Laura 020437
UPV/EHU, Leioa, Spain
Sánchez, Yudania 020085
IREC, Barcelona, Spain
Sanchez-Friera, Paula 020412, 020513, 020521
Solkeys, Gijón, Spain
Sanchez-Ruiz, Alain 020437
UPV/EHU, Vitoria-Gasteiz, Spain
Sansavini, Giovanni 020296
ETH, Zurich, Switzerland
Sansoni, Paola 020066
CNR-INO, Florence, Italy
Santamaría Fernández, Susanna 020249
TECNALIA, Derio, Spain
Santamaría-Sancho, Juan 020363
UPM, Madrid, Spain
Santos, Jose Domingo 020197, 020198, 020358
TECNALIA, Derio, Spain
Santos, Rodrigo 020530
Casa dos Ventos, Fortaleza, Brazil
Sanz Martinez, Asier 020546
Tecnalia, Bilbao, Spain
Sanz, Asier 020514
Tecnalia, BRTA, Derio, Spain
Sanz, Asier 020197
TECNALIA, Derio, Spain
Sanz-Cuadrado, Cristina 020575
UPM, Madrid, Spain
Sanz-Saiz, Carlos 020297
CIEMAT, Madrid, Spain
Sarafijanovic-Djukic, Natasa 020204
FFHS, Regensdorf, Switzerland
Saretti, Angelica 020301
Polytechnic University of Bari, Bari, Italy
Sarkadi, Monika 020569
ISC Konstanz, Konstanz, Germany
Sauer, Thomas 020140
EXXERGY, Gräfelfing, Germany
Saura, Juan Antonio 020506
University of Murcia, Murcia, Spain
Savisalo, Tuukka 020225
Valoe, Mikkeli, Finland
Saw, Min Hsian 020402
Technology Innovation Institute, Abu Dhabi, United Arab Emirates
Saxena, Anmol Ratan 020429
NIT, Delhi, India

Sayed, Abdullah Abu 020180, 020230
Kiwa PI Berlin, Berlin, Germany

Scaltrito, Luciano 020079
Polytechnic University of Turin, Turin, Italy

Scerri, Kenneth 020334
University of Malta, Msida, Malta

Schading, Steve 020443
University of Agder, Grimstad, Norway

Schäfer, Aysim 020388
Next2Sun Technology, Dillingen, Germany

Schäfer, Sebastian 020539
Frankfurt University of Applied Sciences, Frankfurt am Main, Germany

Schenk, Paul 020192
Fraunhofer CSP, Halle, Germany

Schermer, John 020067
Radboud University, Nijmegen, The Netherlands

Scherret, Jacqueline 020255
A-Null Development, Vienna, Austria

Schifferegger, Raffael 020162
OFI, Vienna, Austria

Schimanke, Sabrina 020006
ISFH, Emmerthal, Germany

Schirmer, Yoko 020101
HTW, Berlin, Germany

Schläger, Christian 020240
Leibniz University Hannover, Hannover, Germany

Schlatmann, Rutger 020101
HTW, Berlin, Germany

Schmidt Davidsen, Rasmus 020037, 020104
Aarhus University, Aarhus, Denmark

Schnaus, Dominik 020237
TUM, Garching, Germany

Schneider, Andreas 020129, 020183
University of Applied Sciences Gelsenkirchen, Gelsenkirchen, Germany

Schneider, Astrid 020255
TU Wien, Vienna, Austria

Schneider, Friedrich 020482
LPKF SolarQuipment, Suhl, Germany

Schneider, Marc Gabriel 020522
University of Applied Science Cologne, Cologne, Germany

Schneiderlöchner, Eric 020033
VON ARDENNE, Dresden, Germany

Schnierer, Branislav 020262
Solargis, Bratislava, Slovakia

Schönau, Maximilian 020361
Coburg University of Applied Sciences, Coburg, Germany

Schönau, Maximilian 020544
smartblue, Munich, Germany

Schönheits, Markus 020468, 020470
bifa Umweltinstitut, Augsburg, Germany

Schranz, Christian 020255
TU Wien, Vienna, Austria

Schrempf, Michael 020199
PTB, Braunschweig, Germany

Schrijvers, Patrick 020390
MARIN, Wageningen, The Netherlands

Schröter, Nick 020142
Fraunhofer CSP, Halle, Germany

Schubert, Martin C. 020475
Fraunhofer ISE, Freiburg, Germany

Schubnel, Baptiste 020238
CSEM, Neuchâtel, Switzerland

Schüler, Marc Andre 020388
Next2Sun Technology, Dillingen, Germany

Schüler, Marc Andre 020411
Next2Sun, Dillingen, Germany

Schueler, Nadine 020015
Freiberger Instruments, Freiberg, Germany

Schulte-Huxel, Henning 020008, 020260
ISFH, Emmerthal, Germany

Schultz, Christof 020101
HTW, Berlin, Germany

Schulz, Philip 020060
IPVF, Palaiseau, France

Schulze, Achim 020361
Rosenheim Technical University of Applied Sciences, Rosenheim, Germany

Schulze, Patricia S.C. 020475
Fraunhofer ISE, Freiburg, Germany

Schwenke, Almut 020495
SGL Battery Solutions, Meitingen, Germany

Sciuto, Marcello 020010
Enel Green Power, Catania, Italy

Scognamiglio, Alessandra 020541
ENEA, Naples, Italy

Scognamiglio, Alessandra 020378
ENEA, Portici, Italy

Sedaghat, Ahmad 020428
Australian University, Kuwait City, Kuwait

Seiffert, Christoph 020169
Institute for Energy Technology, Kjeller, Norway

Seiffert, Daniela 020008
centrotherm international, Blaubeuren, Germany

Seitz, Matthias 020468
bifa Umweltinstitut, Augsburg, Germany

Selj, Josefine H. 020169
Institute for Energy Technology, Kjeller, Norway

Senno, Maximiliano Alejandro 020226
University of Valencia, Paterna, Spain

Senturk, Bilge 020556
ODTU GUNAM, Ankara, Türkiye

Setien, Eneko 020198
TECNALIA, Derio, Spain

Šetkus, Arūnas 020157
Center for Physical Sciences and Technology (FTMC), Vilnius, Lithuania

Shaaban, Ahmed 020402
Technology Innovation Institute, Abu Dhabi, United Arab Emirates

Shah, Syed Fawad Ali 020112
KENTECH, Naju-Si, South Korea

Shanmugam, Raphael 020218, 020220
ISC Konstanz, Konstanz, Germany

Sharma, Rajesh Kumar 020071, 020081
SVNIT, Surat, India

Sharma, Sushma 020563
SRM University, Sonipat, India

Shen, Xinyi 020226
University of Oxford, Oxford, United Kingdom

Shen, Zhenjue 020001
YIST, Jiangyin, China

Shin, Donghyeop 020112
KIER, Daejeon, South Korea

Shin, Woo Gyun 020324, 020357
KIER, Daejeon, South Korea

Shin, Woo-gyun 020561
KIER, Daejeon, South Korea

Shirai, Yasuhiro 020115
NIMS, Tsukuba, Japan

Shirazi, Elham 020544
University of Twente, Enschede, The Netherlands

Shishavan, Amir Asgharzadeh 020367
Nextracker, Fremont, United States of America

Shishido, Hirotaka 020106
Tokyo City University, Setagaya, Japan

Shochet, Ofer 020225
Copprint, Jerusalem, Israel

Shyong, Yung-Jen 020163
ITRI, Hsinchu, Taiwan

Sicot, Lionel 020217
CEA / INES, Le Bourget-du-Lac, France

Sidler, Anika 020226
School of Life Sciences FHNW, Muttenz, Switzerland

Siebert, Michael 020206
ISFH, Emmerthal, Germany

Siefer, Gerald 020246
Fraunhofer ISE, Freiburg, Germany

Sierra, Daniel 020491
UPM, Madrid, Spain

Sigounis, Anna-Maria 020248, 020249
Concordia University, Montreal, Canada

Søiland, Anne-Karin 020495
ReSiTec, Kristiansand, Norway

Silva, José A. 020304, 020409, 020420
University of Évora, Évora, Portugal

Silva, José 020403
University of Évora, Évora, Portugal

Silvestre, Santiago 020301
UPC, Barcelona, Spain

Simeunovic, Jelena 020238
CSEM, Neuchâtel, Switzerland

Simón-Allué, Raquel 020127, 020414, 020517
ENDEF, Zaragoza, Spain

Singh, Ravi 020571
DNV, Arnhem, The Netherlands

Sinha, Amish Kumar 020463
RCT Solutions, Konstanz, Germany

Sinopoli, Alessandro 020042
QEERI, Doha, Qatar

Sivaramakrishnan Radhakrishnan, Hariharsudan 020064
Hasselt Unversity, Genk, Belgium

Sivaramakrishnan, Hariharsudan 020225
IMEC, Genk, Belgium

Snaith, Henry 020226
University of Oxford, Oxford, United Kingdom

Søndenå, Rune 020503
Institute for Energy Technology, Kjeller, Norway

Sobajima, Yasushi 020131
Gifu University, Gifu, Japan

Soler Toledo, Denet 020509
University of Antofagasta, Antofagasta, Chile

Solomon, Asfaw A. 020479
LUT University, Lappeenranta, Finland

Solórzano, Jorge 020328
Qualifying Photovoltaics, Madrid, Spain

Sondoqah, Mousa 020316
Becquerel Institute, Bolzano, Italy

Sondoqah, Mousa 020261
Eurac Research, Bolzano, Italy

Song, Hee-eun 020045
KIER, Daejeon, South Korea

Spagnolo, Sofia 020462, 020466
RSE, Milan, Italy

Spataru, Sergiu V. 020265, 020267, 020283, 020376, 020451
DTU, Roskilde, Denmark

Spataru, Sergiu Viorel 020346
DTU, Roskilde, Denmark

Spera, Fabian 020411
Next2Sun, Dillingen, Germany

Spihola, Jan 020355
DiSUN Deutsche Solarservice, Werder, Germany

Sraisth, 020005, 020222
RCT Solutions, Konstanz, Germany

Sraisth, Sraisth 020463
RCT Solutions, Konstanz, Germany

Staňková, Tereza 020107
Czech Technical University, Prague, Czech Republic

Steckenreiter, Verena 020063
ISFH, Emmerthal, Germany

Stegemann, Bert 020309
Berlin University of Applied Sciences, Berlin, Germany

Stegemann, Bert 020101
HTW, Berlin, Germany

Stellbogen, Dirk 020312
ZSW, Stuttgart, Germany

Stensborg, Jan F. 020250
Stensborg, Roskilde, Denmark

Stensborg, Jan 020306
Stensborg, Roskilde, Denmark

Stieldorf, Karin 020255
TU Wien, Vienna, Austria

Stierstorfer, Johannes 020225
WIP - Renewable Energies, Munich, Germany

Stierstorfer, Johannes 020551
WIP Renewable Energies, Munich, Germany

Stivanello, Juan José 020226
Eurac Research, Bolzano, Italy

Stoicescu, Liviu 020198
Solarzentrum Stuttgart, Stuttgart, Germany

Stowhas-Villa, Alejandro 020422
Federico Santa María Technical University, Valparaiso, Chile

Stoyanova Lyubenova, Teodora 020173
European Commission JRC, Ispra, Italy

Sträter, Hendrik 020211
PTB, Braunschweig, Germany

Strey, Jessica 020063, 020114
ISFH, Emmerthal, Germany

Strömberg, Rich 020472
University of Alaska, Fairbanks, United States of America

Stroyuk, Oleksander 020185
HI ERN, Erlangen, Germany

Stroyuk, Oleksandr 020117, 020149, 020150
HI ERN, Erlangen, Germany

Suárez Sánchez, Sergio 020326
Enertis Applus+, Madrid, Spain

Subasi, Dilara Maria 020475
Fraunhofer ISE, Freiburg, Germany

Sudbury, Ben A. 020396
PV Lighthouse, Coledale, Australia

Suemitsu, Issei 020484
Hitachi, Kokubunji, Japan

Suhonen, Riikka 020423
VTT Technical Research Centre of Finland, Oulu, Finland

Sulca, Kabir Paúl 020191, 020205
University of Valladolid, Valladolid, Spain

Svatos, Jan 020250
DTU, Roskilde, Denmark

Sylla, David 020063
ISFH, Emmerthal, Germany

Syre Wiig, Marie 020340
IFE, Kjeller, Norway

Szarek, Magda 020298, 020398
University of Turku, Turku, Finland

Taghipour Kani, Ghaem 020335, 020374
Amirkabir University of Technology, Tehran, Iran

Takahashi, Kanji 020106
Tokyo City University, Setagaya, Japan

Talvi, Micke 020528
Tampere University, Tampere, Finland

Tanahashi, Tadanori 020436
AIST, Koriyama, Japan

Tang, Kai 020011
SINTEF, Trondheim, Norway

Tang, Torben 020028
IPU P/S, Virum, Denmark

Tang, Torben 020037
IPU, Virum, Denmark

Tayebjee, Murad J. Y. 020065
UNSW, Sydney, Australia

Taylor, Nigel 020210
European Commission JRC, Ispra, Italy

Tellez Rodriguez, Eduardo 020230
Kiwa PI Berlin, Berlin, Germany

Teppe, Andreas 020005
RCT Solutions, Konstanz, Germany

Terheiden, Barbara 020031
University of Konstanz, Constance, Germany

Terrados, Cristian 020205
University of Valladolid, Valladolid, Spain

Thakur, Dhruv Singh 020071, 020081
SVNIT, Surat, India

Theocharides, Spyros 020371
Univers, Courbevoie, France

Thomas, Jean 020169
Ciel et Terre, Lille, France

Thorning, Jacob K. 020267, 020283
DTU, Roskilde, Denmark

Thorsteinsson, Sune 020039
DTU, Copenhagen, Denmark

Thorsteinsson, Sune 020037
DTU, Lyngby, Denmark

Thorsteinsson, Sune 020028, 020249, 020250, 020265, 020306, 020477
DTU, Roskilde, Denmark

Timofte, Tudor 020218, 020221
ISC Konstanz, Konstanz, Germany

Ting, San-Yu 020161, 020163
ITRI, Hsinchu, Taiwan

Tissier, Corentin 020238
CSEM, Neuchâtel, Switzerland

Tönies, Alexandra 020523
University of Applied Sciences Cologne, Cologne, Germany

Tomšič, Špela 020047
University of Ljubljana, Ljubljana, Slovenia

Tong, Yongfeng 020108, 020109
QEERI, Doha, Qatar

Topič, Marko 020047, 020269, 020319
University of Ljubljana, Ljubljana, Slovenia

Torabi, Narges 020089
University of Verona, Verona, Italy

Torelly, Guilherme 020092
PUC-Rio, Rio de Janeiro, Brazil

Torre, Gorka 020437
UPV/EHU, Leioa, Spain

Torres Aguilar, Moira Itzel 020214
CentraleSupélec, Gif-sur-Yvette, France

Torres Aguilar, Moira Itzel 020406
CNRS, Gif-sur-Yvette, France

Torres Silva, Nicole 020546
ATAMOSTEC, Santiago, Chile

Torres, Oscar 020110
National University of Colombia, Bogotá, Colombia

Tosi, Irene 020037
IPU, Virum, Denmark

Tran Caliste, Thu Nhi 020546
European Synchrotron Radiation Facility (ESRF), Grenoble, France

Treberspurg, Christoph 020255
Treberspurg und Partner Ziviltechniker, Vienna, Austria

Treberspurg, Martin 020255
Treberspurg und Partner Ziviltechniker, Vienna, Austria

Trefzer, Aaron 020135
Fraunhofer ISE, Freiburg, Germany

Trifiletti, Vanira 020087
University of Milano-Bicocca, Milan, Italy

Trigo-Gonzalez, Mauricio 020342, 020422
University of Antofagasta, Antofagasta, Chile

Tsai, Min-An 020053, 020083, 020161, 020163
ITRI, Hsinchu, Taiwan

Tsanakas, Ioannis (John) A. 020262
CEA / INES, Le Bourget-du-Lac, France

Tsanakas, Ioannis (John) A. 020544
CEA, Le Bourget-du-Lac, France

Tsanakas, Ioannis (John) 020546
CEA / INES, Le Bourget-du-Lac, France

Tsanakas, Ioannis (John) 020317
CEA INES, Le Bourget-du-Lac, France

Tsanakas, Ioannis (John) 020513, 020521
CEA, Le Bourget-du-Lac, France

Tsanakas, Ioannis 020217, 020338
CEA / INES, Le Bourget-du-Lac, France

Tsanakas, Ioannis 020500
CEA, Le Bourget-du-Lac, France

Tsanakas, John A. 020311
CEA / INES, Le Bourget-du-Lac, France

Tseberlidis, Giorgio 020093
University of Milano Bicocca, Milan, Italy

Tseberlidis, Giorgio 020087
University of Milano-Bicocca, Milan, Italy

Tsoi, Konstantin 020113
ODTÜ-GÜNAM, Ankara, Türkiye

Tsombou, Francois M. 020402
Fujairah Research Centre, Fujairah, United Arab Emirates

Tsuno, Yuki 020436
AIST, Koriyama, Japan

Tsunoda, Jun 020484
Hitachi, Kokubunji, Japan

Tsunoda, Jun 020186
Hitachi, Tokyo, Japan

Tulinski, Lona 020385
ZHAW, Winterthur, Switzerland

Tune, Daniel 020220, 020221, 020225
ISC Konstanz, Konstanz, Germany

Turcu, Mircea 020063
ISFH, Emmerthal, Germany

Turek, Marko 020004, 020052
Fraunhofer CSP, Halle (Saale), Germany

Ueda, Yuzuru 020320, 020525
Tokyo University of Science, Tokyo, Japan

Ujvari, Gusztav 020318, 020430
AIT, Vienna, Austria

Ulbikaitė, Vaidvilė 020157
Applied Research Institute for Prospective Technologies, Vilnius, Lithuania

Ulbikas, Juras 020225
Protechnology, Vilnius, Lithuania

Ulyashin, Alexander G. 020011
SINTEF, Oslo, Norway

Unsur, Veysel 020020
ODTÜ-GÜNAM, Ankara, Türkiye

Urban, Harald 020255
TU Wien, Vienna, Austria

Useni, Yannick 020393
University of Lubumbashi, Lubumbashi, Congo (DRC)

Uzuner, Bahri Eren 020113
ODTÜ-GÜNAM, Ankara, Türkiye

Väisänen, Kaisa-Leena 020423
VTT Technical Research Centre of Finland, Oulu, Finland

Vaicikauskas, Viktoras 020157
Center for Physical Sciences and Technology (FTMC), Vilnius, Lithuania

Valaski, Rogério National Institute of Metrology Quality and Technology, Rio de Janeiro, Brazil	020090
Valencia, Felipe AtamosTec, Santiago, Chile	020342, 020546
Vallerotto, Guido UPM, Madrid, Spain	020209, 020246, 020257
van Aken, Bas B. TNO, Petten, The Netherlands	020405
van der Heide, Arvid imec, Genk, Belgium	020472
van der Zee, Friso F. Wageningen University and Research, Wageningen, The Netherlands	020405
Van Dyck, Rik IMEC, Genk, Belgium	020225
van Dyk, E. Ernest Nelson Mandela University, Port Elizabeth, South Africa	020193, 020416
van Dyk, Ernest E. Nelson Mandela University, Port Elizabeth, South Africa	020344
Van Overstraeten, Julien Becquerel Institute France, Lyon, France	020543
Van Overstraeten, Julien Becquerel Institute, Brussels, Belgium	020252
vanBaal, Rene Belectric, Kolitzheim, Germany	020492
Vanhanen, Tuomas Valoe, Mikkeli, Finland	020225
Vargas, Renzo University of São Paulo, São Paulo, Brazil	020348
Varney, Valérie University of Applied Science Cologne, Cologne, Germany	020522
Varney, Valérie University of Applied Sciences Cologne, Cologne, Germany	020523
vas Dyk, Ernest Nelson Mandela University, Port Elizabeth, South Africa	020185
Vasconcelos, Letícia Casa dos Ventos, Fortaleza, Brazil	020530
Vavilkin, Tatjana Soltech, Genk, Belgium	020302
Vázquez Adán, Alejandra UCM, Madrid, Spain	020501
Vázquez, A. UCM, Madrid, Spain	020508
Veas, Christian PCCL, Leoben, Austria	020136, 020234

Vecino, Fernando Román 020346
DTU, Roskilde, Denmark
Veerman, Sebastian 020035
ISC Konstanz, Konstanz, Germany
Vega de Seoane, José Maria 020252
Becquerel Institute Spain, San Sebastian, Spain
Vega de Seoane, Jose 020546
Becquerel Institute, Brussels, Belgium
Vega-Herrera, Jorge 020342
University of Antofagasta, Antofagasta, Chile
Vehus, Tore Sandnes 020443
University of Agder, Grimstad, Norway
Veirman, Jordi 020203, 020226, 020254
Eurac Research, Bolzano, Italy
Velasco, Angel 020367
Nextracker, Fremont, United States of America
Veludo, Jorge 020317
Galp Energia, Lisbon, Portugal
Veneri, Alessandro 020093
University of Verona, Verona, Italy
Vergura, Silvano 020301
Polytechnic University of Bari, Bari, Italy
Verlinden, Pierre 020001
YIST, Jiangyin, China
Vermang, Bart 020064
Hasselt Unversity, Genk, Belgium
Vernay, Christophe 020244
SOLAÏS, Valbonne, France
Vero, Giuseppe 020301
Polytechnic University of Bari, Bari, Italy
Veronese, Elisa 020513
Eurac Research, Bolzano, Italy
Veurman, Welmoed 020063
ISFH, Emmerthal, Germany
Viani, Lucas 020326
Enertis Applus+, Madrid, Spain
Vicente-Laiglesia, Pablo 020181
European Climate, Infrastructure and Environment
Executive Agency, Brussels, Belgium
Vidal de Oliveira, Aline 020377
Solar Energy Research Laboratory Fotovoltaica/ UFSC,
Florianópolis, Brazil
Vidal, Beatriz Muñoz 020414
IaSol, Zaragoza, Spain
Vidal-Fuentes, Pedro 020094
IREC, Barcelona, Spain

Videla-Magnata, Natalia 020129
Universidad de Antofagasta, Antofagasta, Chile

Videla-Magnata, Natalia 020417
University of Antofagasta, Antofagasta, Chile

Vilches, Anna Morales 020388
Next2Sun Technology, Dillingen, Germany

Villalonga Palou, Joan Tomás 020432, 020434
Sunveon, Madrid, Spain

Villén, Raúl 020127, 020414, 020517
ENDEF, Zaragoza, Spain

Villodas, Aritz 020198
TECNALIA, Derio, Spain

Vincent, Laetitia 020058
CNRS, Palaiseau, France

Vincent, Robin 020196
PVsyst, Geneva, Switzerland

Viorel Spataru, Sergiu 020191
DTU, Roskilde, Denmark

Viriyaroj, Bergpob 020298
Aalto University, Espoo, Finland

Viti, Valeria 020541
Legance, Milan, Italy

Vitoshkin, Helena 020379
Agricultural Research Organization, Rishon LeZion, Israel

Vögeli, Pascal 020385
ZHAW, Winterthur, Switzerland

Vogt, Malte R. 020515
TU Delft, Delft, The Netherlands

Vogt, Thomas 020482
DLR, Oldenburg, Germany

Vollbrecht, Joachim 020063, 020114
ISFH, Emmerthal, Germany

Voltan, Alessandro 020010
Applied Materials, Treviso, Italy

von Friedeburg, Christoph 020557
CF Energy Research-Consulting-Operation, Berlin, Germany

Voronko, Yuliya 020162, 020249
OFI, Vienna, Austria

Vorster, Frederik J. 020193, 020344, 020416
Nelson Mandela University, Port Elizabeth, South Africa

Vorster, Frederik 020185
Nelson Mandela University, Port Elizabeth, South Africa

Vuillon, Laurent 020338
CNRS, Chambery, France

Vulic, Natasa 020296
Univesity of Applied Arts and Sciences Northwestern Switzerland, Muttenz, Switzerland

Vumbugwa, Monphias 020185, 020193, 020344
Nelson Mandela University, Port Elizabeth, South Africa

Waibel, Christoph 020511
Flemish Institute for Technological Research (VITO), Genk, Belgium

Wakabayashi, Ryo 020484
Hitachi, Kokubunji, Japan

Wakazono, Kouzen 020131
Gifu University, Gifu, Japan

Wallner, Gernot M. 020227
University of Linz, Linz, Austria

Walpita, Harsha 020169
University of Oslo, Kjeller, Norway

Walsh, Yoselyn 020520
Costa Rica Institute of Technology, Cartago, Costa Rica

Wambach, Karsten 020468, 020470
bifa Umweltinstitut, Augsburg, Germany

Wang, Chia-Chen 020549
ITRI, Hsinchu, Taiwan

Wang, Shuo 020286, 020400
TUAS, Turku, Finland

Wang, Tzuya 020549
ITRI, Hsinchu, Taiwan

Wang, Xiaolin 020381
Mälardalen University, Västerås, Sweden

Wannenwetsch, Jann 020312
EnBW, Karlsruhe, Germany

Wargocki, Pawel 020551
DTU, Roskilde, Denmark

Waschl, Alfred 020255
buildingSMART, Vienna, Austria

Weber, Thomas 020180, 020230
Kiwa PI Berlin, Berlin, Germany

Weeber, Arthur W. 020515
TU Delft, Delft, The Netherlands

Wei, Wenpeng 020484
Hitachi, Kokubunji, Japan

Weihs, Philipp 020281
BOKU, Vienna, Austria

Weinrich, Frank 020177
PTB, Braunschweig, Germany

Weiß, Marius 020361
Coburg University of Applied Sciences, Coburg, Germany

Wellens, Christine 020135
Fraunhofer ISE, Freiburg, Germany

Whyatt, Duncan 020394
Lancaster University, Lancaster, United Kingdom

Wienands, Karl 020218, 020220, 020221
ISC Konstanz, Konstanz, Germany

Wiesenfarth, Maike 020246
Fraunhofer ISE, Freiburg, Germany

Wietler, Tobias 020063
ISFH, Emmerthal, Germany

Wilbert, Stefan 020235, 020237, 020239, 020331
DLR, Almeria, Spain

Willers, Guido 020201
Fraunhofer CSP, Halle, Germany

Wilson, Helen R. 020249
Fraunhofer ISE, Freiburg, Germany

Winter, Renate 020063
ISFH, Emmerthal, Germany

Winter, Stefan 020177, 020181
PTB, Braunschweig, Germany

Wirtz, Wiebke 020260
ISFH, Emmerthal, Germany

Witkowska, Agnieszka 020498
Gdansk University of Technology, Gdansk, Poland

Wittmer, Bruno 020196
PVsyst, Geneva, Switzerland

Wolf, Andreas 020031
Fraunhofer ISE, Freiburg, Germany

Wong, Craig 020230
Kiwa PI Berlin, Berlin, Germany

Wu, Li-Guo 020021
TSEC, Hsinchu, Taiwan

Wu, Yu 020030
TNO, Petten, The Netherlands

Wyss, Philippe 020068
CSEM, Neuchâtel, Switzerland

Xiong, Weizhen 020320
Tokyo University of Science, Tokyo, Japan

Xu, Jiahui 020001
YIST, Jiangyin, China

Xu, Wenhao 020144, 020208
TÜV Rheinland, Shanghai, China

Xu, Xiaoqi 020263
SERIS, Singapore, Singapore

Xu, Yu 020263
SERIS, Singapore, Singapore

Xuereb, Steven 020180, 020230
Kiwa PI Berlin, Berlin, Germany

Yadav, Shivendra 020071, 020081
SVNIT, Surat, India

Yamaguchi, Yosuke 020484
Hitachi, Kokubunji, Japan

Yanagida, Masatoshi 020115
NIMS, Tsukuba, Japan

Yanar, T. Meriç 020027
Kalyon PV, Ankara, Türkiye

Yang, Donggeon 020323
K-water, Daejeon, South Korea

Yang, Hyoung-Kyu 020449
KETI, Wonmi-gu, South Korea

Yde, Leif 020250, 020306
Stensborg, Roskilde, Denmark

Ye, JiaYi 020102
SERIS, Singapore, Singapore

Yerci, Selcuk 020113
ODTÜ-GÜNAM, Ankara, Türkiye

Ylikunnari, Mari 020423
VTT Technical Research Centre of Finland, Oulu, Finland

Ylinen, Marko 020444
Satakunta University of Applied Sciences, Pori, Finland

Ylipaino, Juho 020444, 020445, 020554
TUAS, Tampere, Finland

Yılmaz, Büşra 020521
Kameleon Solar, Roosendaal, The Netherlands

Yordadov, Georgi 020389
imec, Diepenbeek, Belgium

Younes, Kareem 020487
Khalifa University, Abu Dhabi, United Arab Emirates

Yu, Cheng-Yeh 020021, 020053
TSEC, Hsinchu, Taiwan

Yu, Shusen 020406
Ecole Polytechnique, Palaiseau, France

Yuan, Xiao 020001
YIST, Jiangyin, China

Yun, Jae Ho 020112
KENTECH, Naju-si, South Korea

Zaimi, Mhammed 020171
University of Chouaib Doukkali, El Jadida, Morocco

Zanatta Britto, João Victor 020025
PUCRS, Porto Alegre, Brazil
Zanesco, Izete 020023, 020025
PUCRS, Porto Alegre, Brazil
Zaror, Yasmin 020225
WIP - Renewable Energies, Munich, Germany
Zarzalejo, Luis F. 020237, 020331
CIEMAT, Madrid, Spain
Zekri, Atef 020146
QEERI, Doha, Qatar
Zerafa, Steve 020334
PIXAM, Msida, Malta
Zhang, Geng 020001
Jolywood (ShanXi) Solar Technology, Taiyuan, China
Zhang, Jingwei 020111
Hohai University, Changzhou, China
Zhang, Kai 020233
FZJ, Jülich, Germany
Zhang, Wenjing 020001
YIST, Jiangyin, China
Zhang, Wuai 020101
HZB, Berlin, Germany
Zhang, Yating 020144, 020208
TÜV Rheinland, Shanghai, China
Zhou, Qilin 020102
SERIS, Singapore, Singapore
Zhu, Junjie 020017
Institute for Energy Technology, Kjeller, Norway
Ziaullah, Abdul Wahab 020278, 020291
QEERI, Doha, Qatar
Zilles, Roberto 020154, 020348
University of São Paulo, São Paulo, Brazil
Zimmermann, Iwan 020116
IPVF, Palaiseau, France
Zubillaga, Oihana 020139
Tecnalia, Donostia - San Sebastián, Spain
Zugasti, Eugenia 020334
CENER, Pamplona, Spain
Zugasti, Eugenia 020300
CENER, Sarriguren, Spain
Zwahlen, Theo 020369
BFH, Burgdorf, Switzerland

KEYWORDS OF EU PVSEC 2025 PROCEEDINGS PAPERS